BECKETT®

THE #1 AUTHORITY ON COLLECTIBLES

BASEBALL CARD PRICE GUIDE

NUMBER 31

THE HOBBY'S MOST RELIABLE AND RELIED UPON SOURCE™

Edited By Brian Fleischer with the staff of
BECKETT BASEBALL
Founder & Advisor: Dr. James Beckett III

Manufactured in the United States of America
Published by Beckett Media LLC

Beckett Media LLC
4635 McEwen Dr.
Dallas, TX 75244

265 S. Anita Drive, Suite 120
Orange, CA 92868

www.beckett.com

First Printing
ISBN 1-930692-77-3

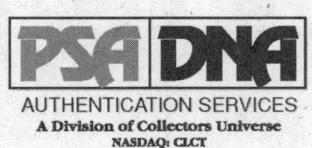

CONTENTS

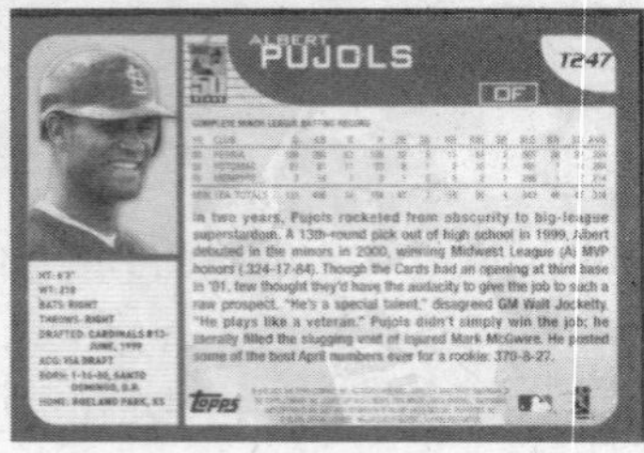

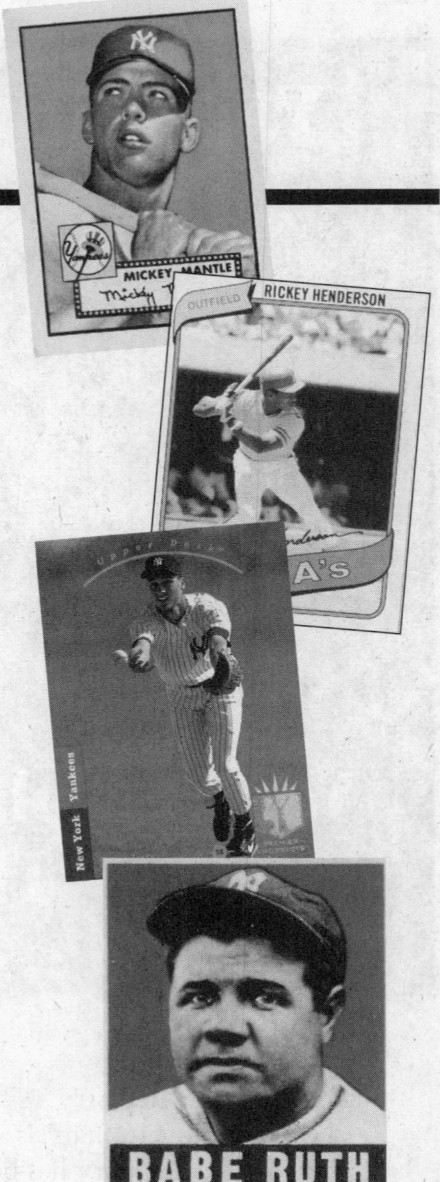

About the Author

Based in Dallas, Beckett Media LP, an Apprise Media company, is the leading publisher of sports and specialty market collectible products in the U.S. Beckett operates Beckett.com and is the premier publisher of monthly sports and entertainment collectibles magazines. Beckett, the number one authority on collectibles, currently publishes 18 magazines with a combined circulation of more than 1.1 million.

The growth of Beckett Media's sports magazines, *Beckett Baseball*, *Beckett Sports Card Monthly, Beckett Basketball*, *Beckett Football* and *Beckett Hockey,* is another indication of the unprecedented popularity of sports cards. Founded in 1984 by Dr. James Beckett, Beckett sports magazines contain the most extensive and accepted monthly Price Guide, collectible superstar covers, colorful feature articles, the Hot List, tips for beginners, Readers write letters to and responses from the editors, information on errors and varieties, autograph collecting tips and profiles of the sport's Hottest stars. Published every other month, *Beckett Baseball* is the hobby's largest baseball periodical.

The *Beckett Almanac of Baseball Cards & Collectibles* is the best annual guide available to the exciting world of baseball cards and collectibles. Read it and use it, and may your enjoyment and your card collection increase in the coming months and years.

HOW TO USE AND CONDITION GUIDE

Isn't it great? Every year this book gets bigger and better with all the new sets coming out. But even more exciting is that every year there are more attractive choices and, subsequently, more interest in the cards we love so much. This edition has been enhanced and expanded from the previous edition. The cards you collect–who appears on them, what they look like, where they are from, and (most important to most of you) what their current values are–are enumerated within. Many of the features contained in the other Beckett Price Guides have been incorporated into this volume since condition grading, terminology, and many other aspects of collecting are common to the card hobby in general. We hope you find the book both interesting and useful in your collecting pursuits.

The *Beckett Baseball Card Price Guide* has been successful where other attempts have failed because it is complete, current, and valid. This Price Guide contains not just one, but two prices by condition for all the basketball cards listed. These account for most of the baseball cards in existence. The prices were added to the card lists just prior to printing and reflect not the author's opinions or desires, but the going retail prices for each card based on the active market (sports memorabilia conventions and shows, sports card shops, mail-order catalogs, local club meetings, auction results, and other firsthand reports of actual realized prices).

What is the best price guide available on the market today? Of course card sellers will prefer the price guide with the highest prices, while card buyers will naturally prefer the one with the lowest prices. Accuracy, however, is the true test. Use the price guide used by more collectors and dealers than all the others combined because it's not the lowest and not the highest – but the most accurate guide, and is produced with integrity.

To facilitate your use of this book, read the complete introductory section on the following pages before going to the pricing pages. Every collectible field has its own terminology; we've tried to capture most of these terms and definitions in our glossary. Please read carefully the section on grading and the condition of your cards, as you will not be able to determine which price column is appropriate for a given card without first knowing its condition.

HOW TO COLLECT

Each collection is personal and reflects the individuality of its owner. There are no set rules on how to collect cards. Since card collecting is a hobby or leisure pastime, what you collect, how much you collect, and how much time and money you spend collecting are entirely up to you. The funds you have available for collecting and your own personal taste should determine how you collect.

It is impossible to collect every card ever produced. Therefore, beginners as well as intermediate and advanced collectors usually specialize in some way. One of the reasons this hobby is popular is that individual collectors can define and tailor their collecting methods to match their own tastes.

Many collectors select complete sets from particular years, acquire only certain players, some collectors are only interested in the first cards or Rookie Cards of certain players, and others collect cards by team.

Remember, this is a hobby so pick a style of collecting that appeals to you.

DETERMINING VALUE

Why are some cards more valuable than others? Obviously, the economic laws of supply and demand are applicable to card collecting just as they are to any other field where a commodity is bought, sold or traded in a free, unregulated market.

Supply (the number of cards avail-

GLOSSARY/LEGEND

Our glossary defines terms most frequently used in the card collecting hobby. Many of these terms are common to other types of sports memorabilia collecting. Some terms may have several meanings depending on the use and context.

Cabinet Card – Popular and highly valuable photographs on thick card stock produced in the 19th and early 20th century.

Checklist – A list of the cards contained in a particular set. The list is always in numerical order if the cards are numbered. Some unnumbered sets are artificially numbered in alphabetical order or by team.

CL – Checklist card. A card that lists, in order, the cards and players in the set or series.

CO – Coach.

Common Card – The typical card of any set. It has no premium value accruing from the subject matter, numerical scarcity, popular demand, or anomaly.

Convention – A gathering of sealers and collectors at a single location of the purpose of buying, selling and trading sports memorabilia items. Conventions are open to the public and sometimes feature autograph guests, door prizes, contests, or seminars. They are frequently referred to as "shows."

COR – Corrected.

continued on page 8.

BASEBALL CARD EXCHANGE

21686 E. Lincoln Highway Unit C • Lynwood, IL 60411
CALL US: (708) 753-1040 • FAX (708) 753-1046
EMAIL US: BBCEXCHANGE@SPRINTMAIL.COM

Over the past 15 years, we have become the leading buyer of vintage unopened material. We are extremely aggresive in buying pre-1990 unopened material from all sports in any quantity!!

We would now like to offer the same:
• Courtesy • Professionalism • Knowledge

IN BUYING YOUR VINTAGE SPORTSCARDS

We are aggressively looking to purchase your pre-1975:
• Complete Sets • Partial Sets • Group Lots • Single Cards
• Graded or Ungraded • Any Condition • Topps, Bowman, Leaf, Fleer, etc.
• Tobacco Cards • Caramel Cards • Goudey, Playball, Diamond Stars, etc.

So when you are ready to sell your collection, please call and you will see how we have earned our reputation for being honest, friendly and fair! We have the funds available for any size collection and will come to your location to purchase your cards!

VISIT US AT
WWW.BBCEXCHANGE.COM

able on the market) is less than the total number of cards originally produced since attrition diminishes that original quantity. Each year a percentage of cards is typically thrown away, destroyed or otherwise lost to collectors. This percentage is much, much smaller today than it was in the past because more and more people have become increasingly aware of the value of their cards.

For those who collect only Mint condition cards, the supply of older cards can be quite small indeed. Until recently, collectors were not so conscious of the need to preserve the condition of their cards. For this reason, it is difficult to know exactly how many 1953 Topps are currently available, Mint or otherwise. It is generally accepted that there are fewer 1953 Topps available than 1963, 1973 or 1983 Topps cards. If demand were equal for each of these sets, the law of supply and demand would increase the price for the least available sets. Demand, however, is never equal for all sets, so price correlations can be complicated. The demand for a card is influenced by many factors. These include: (1) the age of the card; (2) the number of cards printed; (3) the player(s) portrayed on the card; (4) the attractiveness and popularity of the set; and (5) the physical condition of the card.

In general, (1) the older the card, (2) the fewer the number of the cards printed, (3) the more famous, popular and talented the player, (4) the more attractive and popular the set, and (5) the better the condition of the card, the higher the value of the card will be. There are exceptions to all but one of these factors: the condition of the card. Given two cards similar in all respects except condition, the one in the best condition will always be valued higher.

While those guidelines help to establish the value of a card, the countless exceptions and peculiarities make any simple, direct mathematical formula to determine card values impossible.

REGIONAL VARIATION

Since the market varies from region to region, card prices of local players may be higher. This is known as a regional premium. How significant the premium is and if there is any premium at all depends on the local popularity of the team and the player.

The largest regional premiums usually do not apply to superstars, who often are so well-known nationwide that the prices of their key cards are too high for local dealers to realize a premium.

Lesser stars often command the strongest premiums. Their popularity is concentrated in their home region, creating local demand that greatly exceeds overall demand.

Regional premiums can apply to popular retired players and sometimes can be found in the areas where the players grew up or starred in college.

A regional discount is the converse of a regional premium. Regional discounts occur when a player has been so popular in his region for so long that local collectors and dealers have accumulated quantities of his key cards. The abundant supply may make the cards available in that area at the lowest prices anywhere.

SET PRICES

A somewhat paradoxical situation exists in the price of a complete set vs. the combined cost of the individual cards in the set. In nearly every case, the sum of the prices for the individual cards is higher than the cost for the complete set. This is prevalent especially in the cards of the last few years. The reasons for this apparent anomaly stem from the habits of collectors and from the carrying costs to dealers. Today, each card in a set normally is produced in the same quantity as all other cards in its set.

Many collectors pick up only stars, superstars and particular teams. As a result, the dealer is left with a shortage of certain player cards and an abundance of others. He therefore incurs an expense in simply "carrying" these less desirable cards in stock. On the other hand, if he sells a complete set,

GLOSSARY/LEGEND

Continued from page 14

Dealer – A person who engages in the buying, selling and trading sports collectibles or supplies. A dealer may also be a collector, but as a dealer, his main goal it to earn a profit.

Die-Cut – A card with part of its stock partial cut, allowing one or more parts to be folded or removed. After removal or appropriate folding, the remaining part of the card can frequently be made to stand up.

DK – Diamond King.

DP – Draft pick or Double print. A double print is a card that was printed in double the quantity compared to other cards in the same series.

ERR – Error card. A card with erroneous information, spelling or depiction on either side of the card. Most errors are not corrected by the manufacturer.

High Number – The cards in the last series of a set in a year in which such high-numbered cards were printed or distributed in significantly less amounts than the lower numbered cards. Not all years have high numbers in terms of this definition.

HOF – Hall of Fame or a card that pictures of Hall of Famer (HOFer).

IA – In action.

Insert – A card or any other sports collectible contained and sold in the same package along with a card or cards from a major set. An insert card may or may not be numbered in the same sequence as the major set. Many times the inserts are randomly inserted in packs.

continued on page 10

he gets rid of large numbers of cards at one time. For this reason, he generally is willing to receive less money for a complete set. By doing this, he recovers all of his costs and also makes a profit.

The disparity between the price of the complete set and the sum of the individual cards also has been influenced by the fact that some of the major manufacturers now are pre-collating card sets. Since "pulling" individual cards from the sets involves a specific type of labor (and cost), the singles or star card market is not affected significantly by pre-collation.

Set prices also do not include rare card varieties, unless specifically stated. Of course, the prices for sets do include one example of each type for the given set, but this is the least expensive variety.

CONDITION GUIDE

The value of your card is dependent on the condition or "grade" of your card. Prices in this issue reflect the highest raw condition (i.e. not professionally graded by a third party) of the card most commonly found at shows, shops, on the internet, and right out of the pack for brand new releases. This generally means Near Mint-Mint condition for modern era cards. Space constraints prevent a complete guide to grading your card from being printed here. However, please see Beckett.com for specific information on how to assess the condition or grade of your card. Use the following chart as a guide to estimate the value of your cards in a variety of conditions using the prices found in this issue.

GENERAL CARD FLAWS

CENTERING

Current centering terminology uses numbers representing the percentage of border on either side of the main design. Obviously, centering is diminished in importance for borderless cards.

Slightly Off-Center (60/40)

A slightly off-center card is one that upon close inspection is found to have one border bigger than the opposite border. This degree once was offensive to only purists, but now some hobbyists try to avoid cards that are anything other than perfectly centered.

Off-Center (70/30)

An off-center card has one border that is noticeably more than twice as wide as the opposite border.

Badly Off-Center (80/20 or worse)

A badly off-center card has virtually no border on one side of the card.

Miscut

A miscut card actually shows part of the adjacent card in its larger border and consequently a corresponding amount of its card is cut off.

CORNER WEAR

Corner wear is the most scrutinized grading criteria in the hobby.

Corner with a slight touch of wear

The corner still is sharp, but there is a slight touch of wear showing. On a dark-bordered card, this shows as a dot of white.

Fuzzy corner

The corner still comes to a point, but the point has just begun to fray. A slightly "dinged" corner is considered the same as a fuzzy corner.

Slightly rounded corner

The fraying of the corner has increased to where there is only a hint of a point. Mild layering may be evident. A "dinged" corner is considered the same as a slightly rounded corner.

Rounded corner

The point is completely gone. Some layering is noticeable.

Badly rounded corner

The corner is completely round and rough. Severe layering is evident.

CREASES

A third common defect is the crease. The degree of creasing in a card is

GLOSSARY/LEGEND

Continued from page 16

JSY – Jersey.

Major Set – A set produced by a national manufacturer of cards.

Multi-Player Card – A single card depicting two or more players.

Parallel – A card that is similar in design to its counterpart from a basic set, but offers a distinguishing quality.

(RC) – Rookie Logo Card. These cards feature the official MLBPA Rookie Logo. However, the player depicted on the card has already had a Rookie Card(s) issued in a previous year.

RC – Rookie Card.

Redemption – A program established by multiple card manufacturers that allows collectors to main in a special card (usually a random insert) in return for special cards, sets, or other prizes not available through conventional channels.

Refractor – A card that features a design element that enhances its color or appearance by deflecting light.

ROY – Rookie of the Year.

Series – The entire set of cards issued by a particular manufacturer in a particular year. Within a particular set, a series can refer to a group of consecutively numbered cards printed at the same time.

Set – One of each of the entire run of cards of the same type produced by a particular manufacturer during a single year.

Skip-Numbered – A set that has many unissued card numbers between the lowest and highest number in the set. A major

continued on page 12

ATTENTION READERS:

YOUR 2009 MAGAZINE RELEASE SCHEDULE...

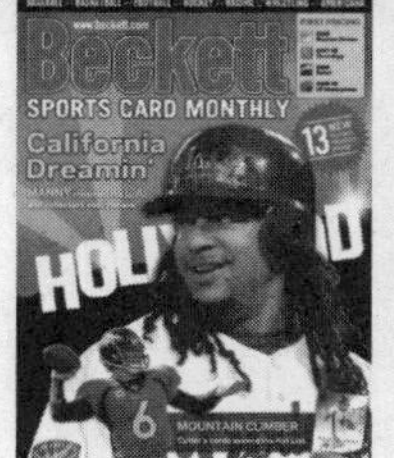

BECKETT SPORTS CARD MONTHLY

Cover	On Newsstands
January	December 10, 2008
February	January 14, 2009
March	February 11, 2009
April	March 11, 2009
May	April 15, 2009
June	May 13, 2009
July	June 10, 2009
August	July 15, 2009
September	August 12, 2009
October	September 16, 2009
November	October 14, 2009
December	November 11, 2009
Jan. 2010	December 9, 2009

8 Issues Per Year

BECKETT BASEBALL

Cover	On Newsstands
Dec/Jan	November 26, 2008
February	January 28, 2009
April	March 25, 2009
May	April 29, 2009
June	May 27, 2009
July	June 24, 2009
Aug/Sept	July 29, 2009
Oct/Nov	September 30, 2009
Dec/Jan	November 25, 2009

8 Issues Per Year

BECKETT FOOTBALL

Cover	On Newsstands
January	December 10, 2008
February	January 28, 2009
March/April	February 25, 2009
May/June	April 29, 2009
July/August	June 24, 2009
September	August 26, 2009
October	September 30, 2009
Nov/Dec	October 28, 2009
January	December 30, 2009

6 Issues Per Year

BECKETT BASKETBALL

Cover	On Newsstands
Jan/Feb	December 24, 2008
Mar/Apr	February 25, 2009
May/Jun	April 29, 2009
Jul/Aug	June 24, 2009
Sep/Oct	August 26, 2009
Nov/Dec	October 28, 2009
Jan/Feb	December 30, 2009

6 Issues Per Year

BECKETT HOCKEY

Cover	On Newsstands
January	December 10, 2008
Feb/Mar	January 28, 2009
Apr/May	March 25, 2009
Jun/Jul	May 27, 2009
Aug/Sep	July 29, 2009
Oct/Nov	September 30, 2009
Dec/Jan	November 25, 2009

For more information, visit www.beckett.com

difficult to show in a drawing or picture. On giving the specific condition of an expensive card for sale, the seller should note any creases additionally. Creases can be categorized as to severity according to the following scale.

Light Crease
A light crease is a crease that is barely noticeable upon close inspection. In fact, when cards are in plastic sheets or holders, a light crease may not be seen (until the card is taken out of the holder). A light crease on the front is much more serious than a light crease on the card back only.
Medium Crease
A medium crease is noticeable when held and studied at arm's length by the naked eye, but does not overly detract from the appearance of the card. It is an obvious crease, but not one that breaks the picture surface of the card.
Heavy Crease: A heavy crease is one that has torn or broken through the card's picture surface, e.g., puts a tear in the photo surface.

ALTERATIONS

Deceptive Trimming
This occurs when someone alters the card in order (1) to shave off edge wear, (2) to improve the sharpness of the corners, or (3) to improve centering – obviously their objective is to falsely increase the perceived value of the card to an unsuspecting buyer. The shrinkage usually is evident only if the trimmed card is compared to an adjacent full-sized card or if the trimmed card is itself measured.

Obvious Trimming
Obvious trimming is noticeable and unfortunate. It is usually performed by non-collectors who give no thought to the present or future value of their cards.

Deceptively Retouched Borders
This occurs when the borders (especially on those cards with dark borders) are touched up on the edges and corners with magic marker or crayons of appropriate color in order to make the card appear to be Mint.

MISCELLANEOUS CARD FLAWS

The following are common minor flaws that, depending on severity, lower a card's condition by one to four grades and often render it no better than Excellent-Mint: bubbles (lumps in surface), gum and wax stains, diamond cutting (slanted borders), notching, off-centered backs, paper wrinkles, scratched-off cartoons or puzzles on back, rubber band marks, scratches, surface impressions and warping.

The following are common serious flaws that, depending on severity, lower a card's condition at least four grades and often render it no better than Good: chemical or sun fading, erasure marks, mildew, miscutting (severe off-centering), holes, bleached or retouched borders, tape marks, tears, trimming, water or coffee stains and writing.

GRADES

Pristine
Centering: 50/50 all around on front. 60/40 or better on back.
Corners: Perfect to the naked eye and Mint under magnification.
Edges: Perfect to the naked eye and virtually free of flaws under magnification.
Surface: No print spots. Flawless color, devoid of registration or focus imperfections. Perfect gloss, devoid of scratches and metallic print lines.

Gem Mint (GemMt)
Centering: 50/50 one way, 55/45 the other on front. 60/40 or better on back
Corners: Mint to the naked eye, but slight imperfections allowed under magnification.
Edges: Virtually Mint to the naked eye. A speck of wear is allowed under intense scrutiny.
Surface: A few extremely minor print spots, detectable only under intense scrutiny. Deep color, devoid of registration or focus imperfections. Perfect gloss,

GLOSSARY/LEGEND
Continued from page 18

set in which only a few numbers were not printed is not considered to be skip-numbered.

SP – Single or Short Print. A short print is a card that was printed in less quantity compared to the other cards in the same series.

TP – Triple print. A card that was printed in triple the quantity compared to the other cards in the same series.

UER – Uncorrected error.

VAR – Variation card. One of two or more cards from the same series, with the same card number, that differ from one and other in some way. This sometimes occurs when the manufacture notices an error in one or more of the cards, corrects the mistake, and then resumes the printing process. In some cases, on of the variations may be relatively scarce.

*** –** Used to denote multi-sport set or an announced print run of a particular card.

devoid of scratches and metallic print lines

Mint (Mt)
Centering: 55/45 both ways on front. 70/30 or better on back.
Corners: Mint upon close inspection. A speck of wear is allowed under intense scrutiny.
Edges: Virtually Mint to the naked eye. Unobtrusive specks of chipping on the borders are allowed.
Surface: A handful of printing specks or one minor spot. Very minor focus or color imperfections. Clean gloss with one or two tiny scratches barely noticeable to the naked eye. One faint, unobtrusive metallic print line is allowed.

Near Mint/Mint (NrMt-Mt)
Centering: 60/40 both ways or better on front. 80/20 or better on back.
Corners: Sharp to the naked eye, but slight imperfections allowed under close examination.
Edges: Relatively smooth borders. Specks of chipping visible to the naked eye are allowed.
Surface: A few minor print spots. Very minor color or focus imperfections. Solid gloss with very minor scratches detectable only upon close inspection. Or a subtle metallic print line.

Near Mint (NrMt)
Centering: 65/35 both ways or better on front. 90/10 or better on back. Very slight diamond cutting is allowed.
Corners: Very minor wear on two or three corners is allowed.
Edges: Slight roughness, minor chipping or very minor notching is allowed.
Surface: A few noticeable print spots or minor speckling is allowed. Minor color or focus imperfections. Very minor border discoloration. A very minor wax stain on back. Solid gloss with a few minor scratches detectable upon close inspection. A few metallic print lines.

Excellent Mint (ExMt)
Centering: 70/30 both ways or better on front. 95/5 or better on back. Slight diamond cutting is allowed.
Corners: Fuzzy corners, but free of dings and fraying.
Edges: Moderate roughness, moderate chipping or minor notching is allowed.
Surface: Noticeable print spots. Minor color or focus imperfections. Minor border discoloration and color or focus imperfections. Minor wax stains or extremely subtle ink marks. Relatively solid gloss with minor scratches, but devoid of scuffing. Noticeable metallic print lines.

Excellent (Ex)
Centering: 75/25 both ways or better on front. 95/5 or better on back. Slight diamond cutting is allowed.
Corners: Four fuzzy corners, a touch of notching or a minor ding is allowed.
Edges: Noticeable roughness - but no layering. Very slight notching or noticeable chipping is allowed.
Surface: Noticeable print spots. Minor color or focus imperfections. Minor border discoloration. Minor wax stains or very light ink mark. Some gloss lost from surface with minor scratches, but devoid of scuffing.

Very Good/Excellent (VgEx)
Centering: 80/20 both ways or better on front. 100/0 or better on back. Moderate diamond cutting is allowed.
Corners: Slight notching or layering, or moderate dings are allowed.
Edges: Readily chipped or notched and/or slightly layered.
Surface: Heavy print spots. Hairline creases. Moderate color or focus imperfections. Moderate border discoloration. Moderate wax stains. Very light ink mark or tape stain. A good deal of gloss lost from surface. Very minor scuffing or an extremely subtle tear in the form of a touch of broken surface paper.

Very Good (Vg)
Centering: 85/15 both ways or better on front. 100/0 or better on back. Moderate diamond cutting is allowed.
Corners: Slightly rounded or noticeably notched corners with slight layering is allowed.
Edges: Heavy notching, moderate layering or heavy chipping is allowed.
Surface: Heavy print spots. Very minor creases. Noticeable color or focus imperfections. Noticeable border discoloration. Noticeable wax stains. Light ink mark or tape stain. Very little surface gloss. Minor scuffing or a very minor tear.

Good (G)
Centering: 90/10 both ways or better on front. 100/0 or offcut on back. Noticeable diamond cutting is allowed.
Corners: Noticeably rounded or heavily notched corners with moderate layering.
Edges: Severely chipped, notched or layered.
Surface: Severe print spots. Noticeable creases. Noticeable color or focus imperfections. Noticeable border discoloration. Heavy wax stains. Moderate ink mark or tape stain. A surface devoid of gloss. Noticeable scuffing or a noticeable tear.

Poor (P)
Centering: 100/0 or offcut on front or back. Heavy diamond cutting is allowed.
Corners: Heavily rounded or heavily notched with noticeable layering.
Edges: Destructive chipping, notching or layering.
Surface: Severe print spots. Heavy creases. Severe color or focus imperfections. Heavy border discoloration. Severe stains. No original gloss. Heavy scuffing or a severe tear.

MODERN MARKETPLACE

BY DAVID LEE AND JON GOLD

Collectors like choices, and when it comes to buying their favorite cards and products, today's hobby provides more buying options than ever.

Most collectors have experienced buying from hobby shops, retail stores and Internet auction sites and storefronts. Positive and negative experiences can be experienced from each. The important thing is to figure out what fits you best. Over the next few pages we will examine the pros and cons of buying from the hobby's three main avenues.

INTERNET

PROS +

GREAT PRICES +

Everyone loves a great deal, and if you're looking to score good prices on boxes and singles, your best bet is the Internet. With such a wide selection of product for sale from dealers and collectors across the country (and sometimes other countries), prices are generally going to be lower.

Internet auction sites like eBay can be a great place to upgrade your better cards.

"Ninety-eight and a half percent of my collection was obtained through the Internet," says collector Peter L. (a.k.a. jaderock on the Beckett.com Message Boards) from San Francisco.

Condition always plays a factor in price, and there is usually a broader spectrum of cards in various conditions to choose from. So, if your standards aren't too high, you can find low prices on great cards. A recent eBay search revealed various ungraded 1963 Topps Pete Rose Rookie Cards ($1,000 high book value) that sold for as low as $227 in somewhat poor condition to as high as $710 in excellent condition. Of course, there's the roadblock of not being able to inspect the card first-hand, which can also greatly affect price.

Many times, dealers and distributors will sell boxes of cards on sites like BeckettMarketplace.com and eBay. Depending on the popularity of the product and how long it's been on the market, you can find some great deals.

WIDER SELECTION +

"You basically can find whatever you want on the Internet," says Dayton Grissam of Lynchburg, Ohio. If you're looking for a particular card, it's just a matter of time before a copy pops up on the web. A recent search pulled up 2,291 Ken Griffey Jr. items for sale in eBay's sports cards category. More than 64,300 Griffey items were found on BeckettMarketplace.com at the same time.

With so many jersey cards produced these days, the Internet allows collectors to pick and choose which swatches they want for a lot of jersey cards. The two-color patch doesn't do enough for you? Just hold out for a sweet four-color patch, or better yet, a logo patch.

FAST AND EASY +

How many times have you jumped on the Internet and stumbled across cards from a new product that you didn't even know was out yet? It happens every month. That's how quickly the Internet market works.

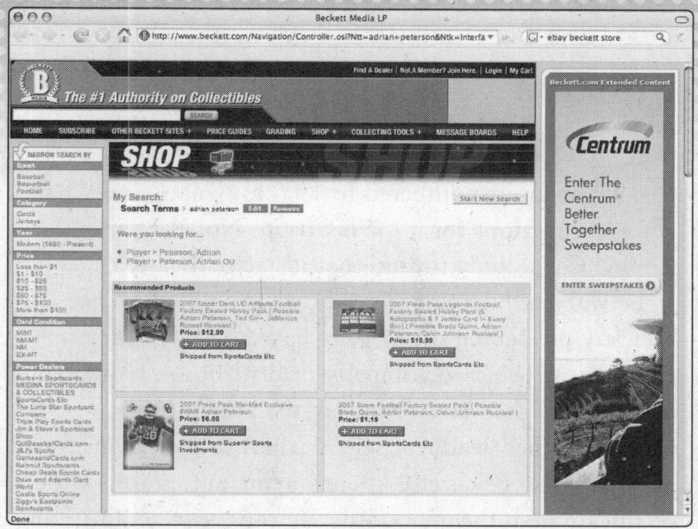

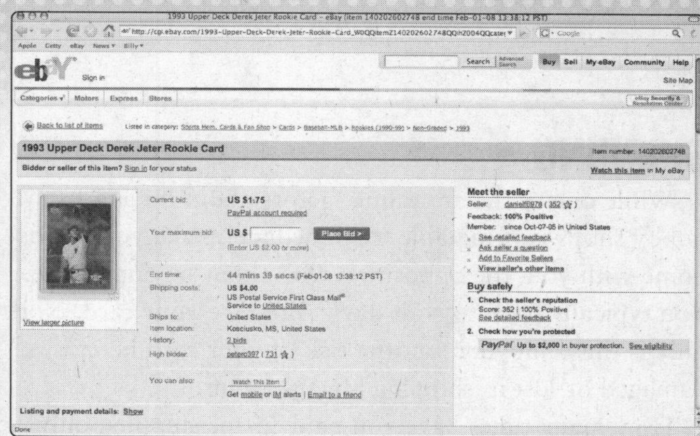

Online marketplaces like BeckettMarketplace.com and eBay have changed the hobby forever.

Cards you need can be yours with just a few clicks. Need those last few base cards to complete your set? Buy 'em all from one dealer on BeckettMarketplace.com. Don't want to mess with piecing together a Topps Chrome set? Buy one already completed. Third-party transaction services like PayPal make it easy to pay for your item.

ABILITY TO FIND RARE CARDS +

Let's face it: Card companies would never be able to make the rare cards that they do if collectors weren't able to buy and sell over the Internet. Cards numbered to 50 or 10 or 5 would probably never be seen if it weren't for the web. Say you pull a triple autograph of Alex Rodriguez, Albert Pujols and Ryan Howard. Would you be able to get the money you want for that card if there was no Internet?

COLLECTOR-TO-COLLECTOR +

"Auction sites allow collector-to-collector interaction. That normally means the lowest price," says Jay Z. of Pittsburgh, Pa. Collectors are free to buy, sell and trade via auction sites and collector communities. The Internet essentially turns every collector into a dealer. It's great to find fellow collectors who collect the same thing you do. The collector-to-collector interaction can mean bargain prices on some cards, but inflated prices on other cards that receive frenzied bidding.

CONS -

OFF-SITE -

One of the main fundamental flaws with buying online is not being able to inspect the item in person. This creates a lot of problems, but most importantly, you run the risk of getting a damaged card. Sure, that Mickey Mantle Rookie Card looks fine on your screen, but when you get it, you find a 1-inch crease and a pen mark on the back. Some sellers will use a sample scan of a card instead of the actual card you receive. This usually happens with cheaper, higher-volume cards.

Be careful when buying ungraded vintage cards online. Scans sometimes don't accurately reflect the true condition of the card.

The fact is, scans can be deceiving, or worse yet, doctored to make the card look better. Older computer screens also can render an inaccurate image. A good way to keep this from happening to you is to stick to buying graded cards, especially vintage. Still, nothing beats being able to hold and inspect the card yourself.

SHIPPING –

While one of the appealing factors about buying from hobby shops is being able to immediately take your cards home with you, the opposite is true about buying online. You typically have to wait days to receive your card. Not only is this annoying, but the risk of your card being damaged or lost in shipping always looms.

How many times have you paid $5 for shipping only to receive your card in a top loader and a regular envelope? While auction sites like eBay have tried to crack down on sellers overcharging for shipping, you still need to check the shipping costs and methods before you buy.

BUYING COMPETITION –

Competition is usually a good thing. After all, that is how card values increase. But when you're on the buying end, competition is nothing more than a roadblock to getting your cards. Nearly every collector knows the feeling of losing the high bid on a card with 30 seconds left. This is especially annoying when the card you're trying to buy is rare and probably won't pop up again for months.

Buying competition is at its peak on the hottest cards, and the Internet is the prime way for collectors to jump on the hottest cards. This results in higher prices for you and the increased likelihood that you'll miss out on the card you want.

SELLER ANONYMITY –

One of the biggest complaints collectors have when buying online is not knowing who they are buying from. Buying from a faceless seller hundreds of miles away is always risky. You just never know when someone is trying to scam you.

"You have to do your research when buying online," says Scott Smith of Kissimmee, Fla. "When it comes to eBay, reading feedback is a must."

Pay attention to the title and description of the card or item you're buying. Some sellers will call any card picturing a rookie a Rookie Card, even when it's obviously a parallel or insert numbered to 10. How many times have you seen auctions for a "1968 Topps Nolan Ryan Rookie Card" only to find that it's actually a reprint?

Be wary of buying pre-sell boxes. Some sellers are honestly pre-selling their boxes based on what they expect from the card company or distributor. However, occasionally they do not receive the amount they ordered. Other deadbeat sellers will just take your money and run. Also be careful about buying autographs with a certificate of authenticity. Anyone can write a COA, but that doesn't make the autograph real. Look for COA's from legitimate authentication and autograph companies, such as PSA/DNA, Steiner, James Spence Authentication, UDA and Tri-Star.

Although fake patches have become less of a problem over the last few years, they still exist. Some sellers will replace ordinary jersey swatches with prime patch pieces. While there's no easy way to avoid this, stick with cards that you know were intended to have patches. Ask the seller for close-up scans of the card so that you can inspect the patch area for any signs of tampering.

HOBBY SHOPS/ SHOWS

PROS +

CUSTOMER SERVICE +

Nothing beats the hobby shop experience. One of the main reasons most people collect cards today is because they have (or had) a local hobby shop to go to. Whether you're looking for a particular product, picking up some supplies or just talking hobby, good customer service from your dealer and being able to interact with fellow collectors is invaluable.

"You get to talk to people with the same interests as yourself and brag about or show off your collections and hear about the big pulls out of the new products," says collector Alan Risa of Orangeburg, S.C.

Any good dealer will help you look for cards you need, even if this means searching the Internet and other shops for you. Many dealers keep boxes of duplicate cards from base sets and inserts for collectors to look through. This is helpful when completing base sets or looking for your favorite players.

"I have established a good relationship with several card shops in my area," says collector Michael Snyder of Charlestown, R.I. "They know the product and go out of their way to make sure you have a positive experience. They usually crack a few boxes of a product and can show you what comes in the box. One of my favorite card shops keeps an eye out for my favorite players and teams and cuts me a really good break on the price."

TRUSTWORTHY DEALERS +

The key here is to get to know your local dealers and develop a relationship with the ones you find you can trust. Those you can trust will always give you a fair price. You also don't have to worry about them selling you mixed-up packs from boxes that the big pulls have already been removed from. The risk of running into a dealer you don't know is greater at collectible shows.

IN-SHOP INCENTIVES/ PROMOTIONS +

Many hobby shops offer incentives and promotions, such as giveaways, contests and free products. One of the most frequently used is a weekly buying incentive in which shops hand out tickets to customers who spend a certain amount. At the end of the week, prizes and gift certificates are given away.

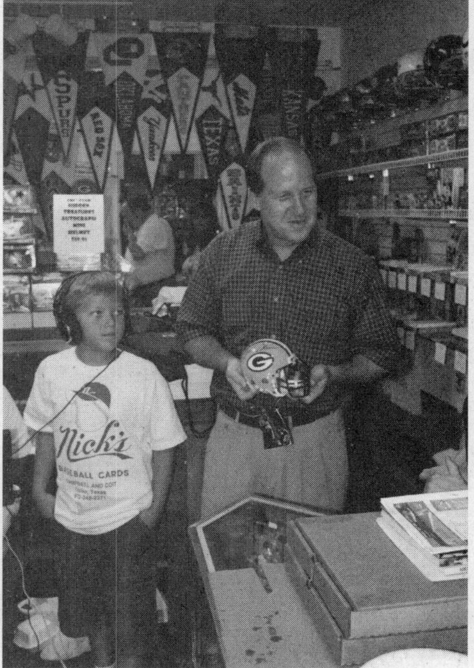

League promotions, like the NFL Player of Day, the MLB/Upper Deck Player of the Month, the NBA Hobby Shop Makeover, and card company promotions, like Topps Turn Back the Clock, have given collectors more reasons to visit their local hobby shops. Recently, Upper Deck began working with 200 hobby shops around the country to form its new redemption center program in which collectors submitted their redemption cards through the shops. More than three years ago, the major professional sports leagues, along with the card companies and other industry leaders, formed National Trading Card Day in which free cards were given away at shops around the country. The MLB still promotes the event, which takes place in the spring.

ABILITY TO INSPECT CARDS +

It's funny how the benefits of buying in-person from hobby shops are directly opposite of the disadvantages of buying from the Internet. A prime example is being able to inspect the cards first-hand at shops and shows. If you throw down $150 for that Alex Rodriguez Rookie Card, at least you were able to examine the card's condition to see if it meets your standards. You can feel comfortable with your decision. Card shows provide more opportunities to do this, since you can often find multiple copies of the card you're looking for.

Another great advantage is being able to buy boxes and packs from just about every current product on the market. Just ask your dealer when they are expecting a new product. Many dealers also keep boxes and packs of past products. Some great deals can be found with these.

CONS -

GENERALLY HIGHER PRICES -

Your dealer has to keep his shop running, and that means paying taxes and bills. Unfortunately, that usually translates into higher prices. While most dealers' prices may not be unfair, it's tough to shell out $40 on a card you can get for $25 online. But remember, they are called dealers. While some prices may be a little more than you're willing to pay, a lot of shop owners are willing to cut you a deal on multiple cards or trades.

SMALLER SELECTION -

With so many different products produced these days, and so many cards being produced in low quantities, it's tough for dealers to maintain an inventory of current cards that collectors are looking for. However, good dealers know their customers, and will try to keep an inventory tailored to their customers.

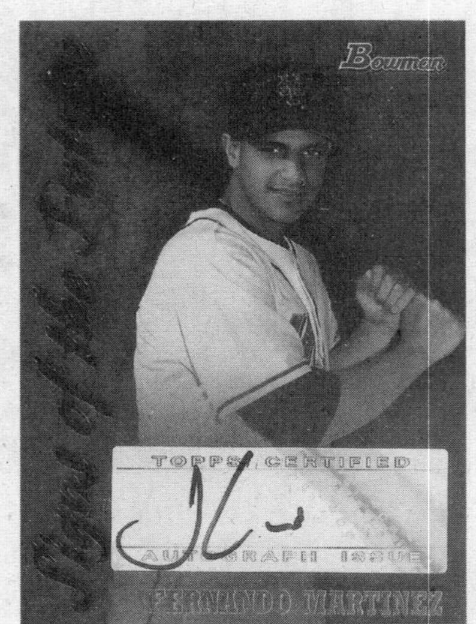

2007 Bowman Signs of the Future autograph exclusives were retail-only.

RETAIL

PROS +

CHEAPER PRODUCTS +

It's a fact: Most retail-only releases carry a lower SRP than their hobby-exclusive counterparts. Because retail outlets such as Target and Wal-Mart demand more impulse-purchase opportunities for their broader customer base, most retail products fall in the $1.99 to $2.99 pack range.

So, where as 2008 Topps Opening Day, for example, can be had for about a buck a pack at retail, the hobby version, 2008 Topps Series One, carries a $2 SRP in hobby shops.

By and large, most of the contents of those varied packs — with the possible exception of a few exclusive inserts on either side — are the same. But the odds of pulling those contents are typically much longer at retail.

"With retail, the biggest advantage is obviously the price," says collector Jeremy Lund. "But the biggest disadvantage is the long shot."

RETAIL EXCLUSIVES +

A relatively recent phenomenon, the inclusion of retail-exclusive inserts has served to liven up the retail-shopping experience and provide collectors the kind of bang for their buck — albeit on a smaller scale — that used to be the hobby's exclusive domain.

Most manufacturers have experimented with the idea; and most have experienced success. Bowman has produced two distinct exclusives for Target and Wal-Mart. Topps produced Target-exclusive Mickey Mantle Relic cards in 2006 and 2007.

It is a fact: Collectors are actively seeking these retail-exclusive cards—either in person at the store or online—

just as they would any other short-printed cards.

READILY AVAILABLE LOCATIONS +

As the number of neighborhood hobby shops — once the bread and butter of any collector's existence — has continued to dwindle over the last decade, larger retail outlets continue to pop up all over the country on seemingly every street corner.

And most are equipped with a self-contained sports cards section full of variety.

Simply, finding a hobby shop in your zip code these days is a whole lot more difficult than it used to be. But locating a Target or a Wal-Mart or a Kmart or any other mass merchant can be as easy as opening your eyes.

What collectors lose in customer service and the sense of community afforded by hobby shops is often offset by the ease of use in finding a store that sells cards in the first place.

"[Chain stores] do an unbelievable amount of sales in hobby boxes," says Tim Franz of Excell Marketing, a major retail card distributor that handles Target, among other accounts. "There is a demand for product. For some, especially in rural areas, we are the hobby shop."

CONS -

PACK SEARCHING -

Pack searching stinks. Pack searchers stink. But it comes with the territory of buying sports cards at retail. When there's no one to mind the inventory (at least no one to strictly monitor every pack that's purchased like in a hobby shop) the buyer must beware. And most collectors are.

Obviously, not everyone is a pack searcher and not every pack has been searched. But the fact remains that the unsavory practice is a lot more apt to happen at retail than in your local hobby shop.

"I don't touch retail packs due to searching," says Beckett.com Message Board member panthergoergefan. "I have seen at least three offenders [in my area]. One guy had a scale on him and was weighing the packs at Target."

Adds Excell Marketing's Franz: "Obviously, a great concern that retailers have is shrinkage. We're concerned about stuff being stolen as things escalate in price."

TOUGHER ODDS -

As noted earlier, the trade-off for being able to readily find more affordable products at retail is that the goodies inside those products are usually a lot harder to come by. Take virtually any product you can think of that has a hobby/retail split and what you'll typically find are dramatically different odds. For example, most products that offer three or four "hits" per box at hobby will usually provide one such hit at retail.

As with just about any hobby, the bottom line is to be well informed. If you know what you're getting into before you get into it, you greatly reduce the potential for disappointment.

NO CUSTOMER SERVICE/CAMARADERIE -

One of the greatest joys of a local hobby shop isn't *just* the inventory. It's the sense of belonging and companionship you get with that inventory that keeps the people coming back. As the theme song from famed television series Cheers so eloquently pointed out: "Sometimes you want to go where everybody knows your name."

At your local hobby shop, it's likely that everyone does know your name. On the flipside, it's difficult to imagine the manager at Wal-Mart greeting you as you walk in the door and telling you that he set aside a few boxes of the new product for you.

There's an inherent warmth at most hobby shops—one based upon years of personal exchanges—that you just can't get at a store that sells razors and dog food along with your favorite football cards.

David Lee is editor of Beckett Football *and* Beckett Sports Card Monthly. *Jon Gold is a reporter for the* Las Vegas Review-Journal.

2001 Absolute Memorabilia

The 2001 Playoff Absolute Memorabilia set was issued in one series totally 200 cards. The set features color action player photos highlighted on metalized film board with the 50 rookie cards infused with a swatch of game-worn/used bat and jersey. The following cards were available via mail exchange cards (of which expired on June 1st, 2003): 151 - Bud Smith, 154 - Josh Beckett, 161 Ben Sheets, 164 - Carlos Garcia, 169 - Donaldo Mendez, 171 Jackson Melian, 173 Adrian Hernandez, 186 - C.C. Sabathia, 188 - Adam Pettyjohn, 193 - Alfonso Soriano, 196 - Billy Sylvester and 200 - Matt White.

COMP.SET w/o SP's (150)	15.00	40.00
COMMON CARD (1-150)	.30	.75
COMMON RPM (151-200)	3.00	8.00
1 Alex Rodriguez	1.25	3.00
2 Barry Bonds	2.00	5.00
3 Cal Ripken	2.50	6.00
4 Chipper Jones	.75	2.00
5 Derek Jeter	2.00	5.00
6 Troy Glaus	.30	.75
7 Frank Thomas	.75	2.00
8 Greg Maddux	1.25	3.00
9 Ivan Rodriguez	.50	1.25
10 Jeff Bagwell	.50	1.25
11 Ryan Dempster	.30	.75
12 Todd Helton	.50	1.25
13 Ken Griffey Jr.	1.25	3.00
14 Manny Ramirez Sox	.50	1.25
15 Mark McGwire	2.00	5.00
16 Mike Piazza	1.25	3.00
17 Nomar Garciaparra	1.25	3.00
18 Pedro Martinez	.50	1.25
19 Randy Johnson	.75	2.00
20 Rick Ankiel	.30	.75
21 Rickey Henderson	.75	2.00
22 Roger Clemens	1.50	4.00
23 Sammy Sosa	.75	2.00
24 Tony Gwynn	1.00	2.50
25 Vladimir Guerrero	.75	2.00
26 Kazuhiro Sasaki	.30	.75
27 Roberto Alomar	.50	1.25
28 Barry Zito	.50	1.25
29 Pat Burrell	.30	.75
30 Harold Baines	.30	.75
31 Carlos Delgado	.30	.75
32 J.D. Drew	.30	.75
33 Jim Edmonds	.30	.75
34 Darin Erstad	.30	.75
35 Jason Giambi	.30	.75
36 Tom Glavine	.50	1.25
37 Juan Gonzalez	.30	.75
38 Mark Grace	.50	1.25
39 Shawn Green	.30	.75
40 Tim Hudson	.30	.75
41 Andruw Jones	.50	1.25
42 David Justice	.30	.75
43 Jeff Kent	.30	.75
44 Barry Larkin	.50	1.25
45 Rafael Furcal	.30	.75
46 Mike Mussina	.50	1.25
47 Hideo Nomo	.75	2.00
48 Rafael Palmeiro	.50	1.25
49 Adam Piatt	.30	.75
50 Scott Rolen	.50	1.25
51 Gary Sheffield	.30	.75
52 Bernie Williams	.50	1.25
53 Bob Abreu	.30	.75
54 Edgardo Alfonzo	.30	.75
55 Edgar Renteria	.30	.75
56 Phil Nevin	.30	.75
57 Craig Biggio	.50	1.25
58 Andres Galarraga	.30	.75
59 Edgar Martinez	.50	1.25
60 Fred McGriff	.50	1.25
61 Magglio Ordonez	.30	.75
62 Jim Thome	.50	1.25
63 Matt Williams	.30	.75
64 Kerry Wood	.30	.75
65 Moises Alou	.30	.75
66 Brady Anderson	.30	.75
67 Garret Anderson	.30	.75
68 Russell Branyan	.30	.75
69 Tony Batista	.30	.75
70 Vernon Wells	.30	.75
71 Carlos Beltran	.30	.75
72 Adrian Beltre	.30	.75
73 Kris Benson	.30	.75
74 Lance Berkman	.30	.75
75 Kevin Brown	.30	.75
76 Dee Brown	.30	.75
77 Jeromy Burnitz	.30	.75
78 Timo Perez	.30	.75
79 Sean Casey	.30	.75
80 Luis Castillo	.30	.75
81 Eric Chavez	.30	.75
82 Jeff Cirillo	.30	.75
83 Bartolo Colon	.30	.75
84 David Cone	.30	.75
85 Freddy Garcia	.30	.75
86 Johnny Damon	.50	1.25
87 Ray Durham	.30	.75
88 Jermaine Dye	.30	.75
89 Juan Encarnacion	.30	.75
90 Terrence Long	.30	.75
91 Carl Everett	.30	.75
92 Steve Finley	.30	.75
93 Cliff Floyd	.30	.75
94 Brad Fullmer	.30	.75
95 Brian Giles	.30	.75
96 Luis Gonzalez	.30	.75
97 Rusty Greer	.30	.75
98 Jeffrey Hammonds	.30	.75
99 Mike Hampton	.30	.75
100 Orlando Hernandez	.30	.75
101 Richard Hidalgo	.30	.75
102 Geoff Jenkins	.30	.75
103 Jacque Jones	.30	.75
104 Brian Jordan	.30	.75
105 Gabe Kapler	.30	.75
106 Eric Karros	.30	.75
107 Jason Kendall	.30	.75
108 Adam Kennedy	.30	.75
109 Deion Sanders	.50	1.25
110 Ryan Klesko	.30	.75
111 Chuck Knoblauch	.30	.75
112 Paul Konerko	.30	.75
113 Carlos Lee	.30	.75
114 Kenny Lofton	.30	.75
115 Javy Lopez	.30	.75
116 Tino Martinez	.50	1.25
117 Ruben Mateo	.30	.75
118 Kevin Millwood	.30	.75
119 Jimmy Rollins	.30	.75
120 Raul Mondesi	.30	.75
121 Trot Nixon	.30	.75
122 John Olerud	.30	.75
123 Paul O' Neill	.50	1.25
124 Chan Ho Park	.30	.75
125 Andy Pettitte	.50	1.25
126 Jorge Posada	.50	1.25
127 Mark Quinn	.30	.75
128 Aramis Ramirez	.30	.75
129 Mariano Rivera	.75	2.00
130 Tim Salmon	.50	1.25
131 Curf Schilling	.30	.75
132 Richie Sexson	.30	.75
133 John Smoltz	.50	1.25
134 J.T. Snow	.30	.75
135 Jay Payton	.30	.75
136 Shannon Stewart	.30	.75
137 B.J. Surhoff	.30	.75
138 Mike Sweeney	.30	.75
139 Fernando Tatis	.30	.75
140 Miguel Tejada	.30	.75
141 Jason Varitek	.75	2.00
142 Greg Vaughn	.30	.75
143 Mo Vaughn	.30	.75
144 Robin Ventura	.30	.75
145 Jose Vidro	.30	.75
146 Omar Vizquel	.50	1.25
147 Larry Walker	.30	.75
148 David Wells	.30	.75
149 Rondell White	.30	.75
150 Preston Wilson	.30	.75
151 Bud Smith RPM RC	3.00	8.00
152 Cory Aldridge RPM RC	3.00	8.00
153 Wilmy Caceres RPM RC	3.00	8.00
154 Josh Beckett RPM	4.00	10.00
155 Wilson Betemit RPM RC	4.00	10.00
156 Jason Michaels RPM RC	3.00	8.00
157 Albert Pujols RPM RC	90.00	150.00
158 Andres Torres RPM RC	3.00	8.00
159 Jack Wilson RPM RC	4.00	10.00
160 Alex Escobar RPM	3.00	8.00
161 Ben Sheets RPM	4.00	10.00
162 Rafael Soriano RPM RC	3.00	8.00
163 Nate Frese RPM RC	3.00	8.00
164 Carlos Garcia RPM	3.00	8.00
165 Brandon Larson RPM RC	3.00	8.00
166 Alexis Gomez RPM RC	3.00	8.00
167 Jason Hart RPM	3.00	8.00
168 Nick Johnson RPM	3.00	8.00
169 Donaldo Mendez RPM	3.00	8.00
170 Christian Parker RPM RC	3.00	8.00
171 Jackson Melian RPM	3.00	8.00
172 Jack Cust RPM	3.00	8.00
173 Adrian Hernandez RPM	3.00	8.00
174 Joe Crede RPM	4.00	10.00
175 Jose Mieses RPM RC	3.00	8.00
176 Roy Oswalt RPM	4.00	10.00
177 Eric Munson RPM	3.00	8.00
178 Xavier Nady RPM	3.00	8.00
179 Horacio Ramirez RPM RC	4.00	10.00
180 Abraham Nunez RPM	3.00	8.00
181 Jose Ortiz RPM	3.00	8.00
182 Jeremy Owens RPM RC	3.00	8.00
183 Claudio Vargas RPM RC	3.00	8.00
184 Marcus Giles RPM	3.00	8.00
185 Aubrey Huff RPM	3.00	8.00
186 C.C. Sabathia RPM	3.00	8.00
187 Adam Dunn RPM	4.00	10.00
188 Adam Pettyjohn RPM	3.00	8.00
189 Elpidio Guzman RPM RC	3.00	8.00
190 Jay Gibbons RPM RC	4.00	10.00
191 Wilkin Ruan RPM RC	3.00	8.00
192 Tsuyoshi Shinjo RPM RC	4.00	10.00
193 Alfonso Soriano RPM	4.00	10.00
194 Corey Patterson RPM	3.00	8.00
195 Ichiro Suzuki RPM RC	40.00	80.00
196 Billy Sylvester RPM	3.00	8.00
197 Juan Uribe RPM RC	4.00	10.00
198 Johnny Estrada RPM RC	4.00	10.00
199 Carlos Valderrama RPM RC	3.00	8.00
200 Matt White RPM	3.00	8.00

2001 Absolute Memorabilia Ball Hoggs

Randomly inserted in packs, this 46 card set features color action player photos with swatches of game-used baseballs embedded in the cards. Each card was sequentially numbered and the print runs are listed after the players' names in the checklist below. The first 25 of each card are spotlighted with a holo-foil stamp and labeled "Boss Hoggs." Exchange cards were seeded into packs for the following players: Jeff Bagwell, Darin Erstad, Chipper Jones, Magglio Ordonez, Cal Ripken and Alex Rodriguez. The deadline to redeem the cards was June 1st, 2003.

BH1 Vladimir Guerrero/75	10.00	25.00
BH2 Troy Glaus/75	6.00	15.00
BH3 Tony Gwynn/75	10.00	25.00
BH4 Cal Ripken/175	20.00	50.00
BH5 Todd Helton/75	10.00	25.00
BH6 Jacque Jones/125	6.00	15.00
BH7 Shawn Green/100	6.00	15.00
BH8 Ichiro Suzuki/50	60.00	120.00
BH9 Scott Rolen/100	10.00	25.00
BH10 Roger Clemens/75	10.00	25.00
BH11 Ken Griffey Jr./25		
BH14 Sammy Sosa/75	10.00	25.00
BH15 J.D. Drew/50	6.00	15.00
BH16 Barry Bonds/75	15.00	40.00
BH17 Pat Burrell/75	6.00	15.00
BH18 Mark McGwire/75	40.00	80.00
BH19 Mike Piazza/50	10.00	25.00
BH20 Magglio Ordonez/125	6.00	15.00
BH21 Miguel Tejada/75	6.00	15.00
BH22 Albert Pujols/75	125.00	200.00
BH23 Derek Jeter/50	20.00	50.00
BH24 Johnny Damon/125	10.00	25.00
BH25 Mike Sweeney/75	6.00	15.00
BH26 Ben Grieve/125	6.00	15.00
BH27 Jeff Kent/75	6.00	15.00
BH28 Andres Galarraga/75	6.00	15.00
BH29 Richie Sexson/25		
BH30 J.Encarnacion/125	6.00	15.00
BH31 Ruben Mateo/75	6.00	15.00
BH33 Manny Ramirez Sox/75	10.00	25.00
BH35 Ivan Rodriguez/75	10.00	25.00
BH36 Darin Erstad/125	6.00	15.00
BH37 Carlos Delgado/100	6.00	15.00
BH38 Jeff Bagwell/125	10.00	25.00
BH39 Jermaine Dye/75	6.00	15.00
BH40 Jose Ortiz/50	6.00	15.00
BH41 Gary Sheffield/75	6.00	15.00
BH42 Eric Chavez/125	6.00	15.00
BH43 Mark Grace/75	10.00	25.00
BH44 Rafael Palmeiro/125	10.00	25.00
BH45 Tsuyoshi Shinjo/75	10.00	25.00
BH46 Terrence Long/75	6.00	15.00
BH47 Carlos Delgado/25		
BH48 Frank Thomas/75	10.00	25.00
BH49 Chipper Jones/25		
BH50 Jason Giambi/75	6.00	15.00

2001 Absolute Memorabilia Boss Hoggs

Randomly inserted in packs, this 50-card set is a parallel version of the regular insert set with a holo-foil stamp and labeled "Boss Hoggs." Each card features a patch of a game-used baseball. This set is the first 25 of each card printed in the regular insert set. The following cards are autographed: 1/2/3/5/10/22/32/34/41/49. Exchange cards (with a redemption deadline of June 1st, 2003) were issued in packs for Jeff Bagwell, Darin Erstad, Chipper Jones, Magglio Ordonez, Cal Ripken and Alex Rodriguez. The Chipper and A-Rod cards were intended to be redeemed for autograph cards, the others were all for non-autographed cards.

AU CL: 1-3/5/10/22/32/34/41/49.

2001 Absolute Memorabilia Home Opener Souvenirs

Randomly inserted in packs at the rate of one per box, this 50-card set features color photos of top performers showcased on conventional board with foil featuring a swatch of an authentic game-used base embedded in the cards. Only 400 serially numbered sets were produced.

OD1 Barry Bonds	10.00	25.00
OD2 Cal Ripken	15.00	40.00
OD3 Pedro Martinez	4.00	10.00
OD4 Troy Glaus	3.00	8.00
OD5 Frank Thomas	4.00	10.00
OD6 Alex Rodriguez	6.00	15.00
OD7 Ivan Rodriguez	4.00	10.00
OD8 Jeff Bagwell	4.00	10.00
OD9 Mark McGwire	15.00	40.00
OD10 Todd Helton	4.00	10.00
OD11 Gary Sheffield	3.00	8.00
OD12 Manny Ramirez Sox	4.00	10.00
OD13 Mike Piazza	6.00	15.00
OD14 Sammy Sosa	4.00	10.00
OD15 Preston Wilson	3.00	8.00
OD16 Tony Gwynn	6.00	15.00
OD17 Vladimir Guerrero	4.00	10.00
OD18 Carlos Delgado	3.00	8.00
OD19 Roberto Alomar	4.00	10.00
OD20 Todd Helton	4.00	10.00
OD21 Albert Pujols UER	30.00	60.00
Base shows a DiamondBacks logo		
Dbacks did not play Cards opening day		
OD22 Jason Giambi	3.00	8.00
OD23 Sammy Sosa	4.00	10.00
OD24 Ken Griffey Jr.	6.00	15.00
OD25 Darin Erstad	3.00	8.00
OD26 Mark McGwire	15.00	40.00
OD27 Carlos Delgado	3.00	8.00
OD28 Juan Gonzalez	3.00	8.00
OD29 Mike Sweeney	3.00	8.00
OD30 Alex Rodriguez	6.00	15.00
OD31 Roger Clemens	6.00	15.00
OD32 Tsuyoshi Shinjo	4.00	10.00
OD33 Ben Grieve	3.00	8.00
OD34 Jeff Kent	3.00	8.00
OD35 Vladimir Guerrero	4.00	10.00
OD36 Shawn Green	3.00	8.00
OD37 Rafael Palmeiro	4.00	10.00
OD38 Tony Gwynn	6.00	15.00
OD39 Scott Rolen	4.00	10.00
OD40 Ken Griffey Jr.	6.00	15.00
OD41 Albert Pujols	30.00	60.00
OD42 Barry Bonds	10.00	25.00
OD43 Mark Grace	4.00	10.00
OD44 Bernie Williams	4.00	10.00
OD45 Frank Thomas	4.00	10.00
OD46 Jermaine Dye	3.00	8.00
OD47 Mike Piazza	6.00	15.00
OD48 Chipper Jones	4.00	10.00
OD49 Richie Sexson	3.00	8.00
OD50 Magglio Ordonez	3.00	8.00

2001 Absolute Memorabilia Home Opener Souvenirs Autographs

Randomly inserted in packs, this ten-card set features autographed action color photos of top players with a swatch of a game-used baseball and/or base embedded in the card. Only 25 serially numbered sets were produced but the cards are actually serial numbered out of 400 (whereby the first 25 of each card were signed by players participating in this program). No pricing is provided due to market scarcity. Exchange cards, with a redemption deadline of June 1st, 2003, were seeded into packs for Troy Glaus, Cal Ripken and Alex Rodriguez.

OD2 Cal Ripken
OD4 Troy Glaus
OD6 Alex Rodriguez
OD16 Tony Gwynn
OD17 Vladimir Guerrero
OD19 Roberto Alomar
OD21 Albert Pujols
OD28 Juan Gonzalez
OD31 Roger Clemens
OD37 Rafael Palmeiro

2001 Absolute Memorabilia Home Opener Souvenirs Double

Randomly inserted in packs, this 50-card set is parallel to the regular insert set with two swatches of game-used bases embedded in the card. Only 200 serially numbered sets were produced.

*DOUBLE: .6X TO 1.5X BASIC SOUV.

2001 Absolute Memorabilia Home Opener Souvenirs Triple

Randomly inserted in packs, this 50-card set is parallel to the regular insert set with three swatches of game-used bases embedded in the card. Only 75 serially numbered sets were produced.

*TRIPLE: 1.25X TO 3X BASIC SOUV.

2001 Absolute Memorabilia Signing Bonus Baseballs

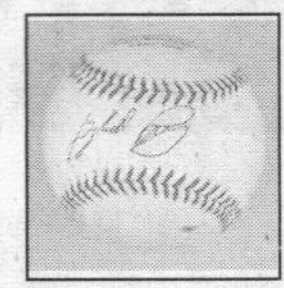

Randomly inserted one per box, this set features baseballs signed by a select group of stellar performers. The players' names are listed below in alphabetical order with the sequential numbering of the quantity signed following the names.

1 Al Oliver/500	10.00	25.00
2 Andre Dawson/550	10.00	25.00
3 Barry Bonds/25		
4 Bill Madlock/524	10.00	25.00
5 Bill Mazeroski/25		
6 Billy Williams/325	10.00	25.00
7 Bob Feller/550	10.00	25.00
8 Bob Gibson/25		
9 Bobby Doerr/300	10.00	25.00
10 Bobby Richardson/500	15.00	40.00
11 Boog Powell/500	10.00	25.00
12 Brian Jordan/25		
13 Bucky Dent/500	10.00	25.00
14 Charles Johnson/25		
15 Chipper Jones/25		
16 Clete Boyer/500	10.00	25.00
17 Dale Murphy/25		
18 Dave Concepcion/500	10.00	25.00
19 Dave Kingman/500	10.00	25.00
20 Don Larsen/200	10.00	25.00
21 Don Newcombe/500	10.00	25.00
22 Don Zimmer/500	10.00	25.00
23 Duke Snider/25		
24 Earl Weaver/300	10.00	25.00
25 Enos Slaughter/525	15.00	40.00
26 Fergie Jenkins/1000	10.00	25.00
27 Frank Howard/500	10.00	25.00
28 Frank Robinson/25		
29 Frank Thomas/25		
30 Gary Carter/200	10.00	25.00
31 Gaylord Perry/1000	10.00	25.00
32 George Foster/500	10.00	25.00
33 George Kell/300	10.00	25.00
34 Goose Gossage/500	10.00	25.00
35 Greg Maddux/25		
36 Hank Aaron/25		
37 Hank Bauer/500	10.00	25.00
38 Harmon Killebrew/200	20.00	50.00
39 Henry Rodriguez/400	10.00	25.00
40 Herb Score/500	10.00	25.00
41 Hoyt Wilhelm/500	15.00	40.00
42 J.D. Drew/25		
43 Javy Lopez/25		
44 Jim Edmonds/25		
45 Jim Palmer/500	10.00	25.00
46 Joe Pepitone/500	10.00	25.00
47 Johnny Bench/25		
48 Johnny Podres/500	10.00	25.00
49 Juan Marichal/485	10.00	25.00
50 Kirby Puckett/25		
51 Larry Doby/300	15.00	40.00
52 Lou Brock/25		
53 Luis Tiant/500	10.00	25.00
54 Magglio Ordonez/200	10.00	25.00
55 Manny Ramirez Sox/25		
56 Maury Wills/500	10.00	25.00
57 Mike Schmidt/25		
58 Minnie Minoso/1000	10.00	25.00
59 Monte Irvin/500	15.00	40.00
60 Moose Skowron/500	10.00	25.00
61 Nolan Ryan/25		
62 Ozzie Smith/25		
63 Phil Rizzuto/25		
64 Ralph Kiner/100	20.00	50.00
65 Randy Johnson/25		
66 Red Schoendienst/500	10.00	25.00
67 Reggie Jackson/25		
68 Rickey Henderson/25		
69 Robin Roberts/500	15.00	40.00
70 Roger Clemens/25		
71 Rollie Fingers/575	10.00	25.00
72 Ryne Sandberg/25		
73 Sean Casey/25		
74 Stan Musial/25		
75 Steve Carlton/25		
76 Steve Garvey/1000	10.00	25.00
77 Todd Helton/25		
78 Tom Glavine/25		
79 Tom Seaver/25		
80 Tommy John/1000	10.00	25.00
81 Tony Gwynn/25		
82 Tony Perez/400	10.00	25.00
83 Wade Boggs/25		
84 Warren Spahn/500	40.00	80.00
85 Whitey Ford/25		
86 Willie Mays/25		
87 Willie McCovey/25		
88 Willie Stargell/25		
89 Yogi Berra/25		

2001 Absolute Memorabilia Tools of the Trade

Randomly inserted in packs, this 50-card set features action color player images with game-worn/used jerseys, batting gloves, bats, and hats embedded in the cards. The cards with swatches of batting gloves were serially numbered to 50, with hats to 100, with bats to 100, and with jerseys to 300. Exchange cards with a redemption deadline of June 1st, 2003 were seeded into packs for the following cards: Roberto Alomar Bat, Roberto Alomar Glove, Jeff Bagwell Bat, Darin Erstad Bat, Troy Glaus Bat, Troy Glaus Hat, Troy Glaus Jsy, Tom Glavine Hat, Shawn Green Bat, Tony Gwynn Glove, David Justice Bat, Greg Maddux Hat, Kazuhiro Sasaki Jsy and Larry Walker Jsy.

TT1 Vladimir Guerrero Jsy	6.00	15.00
TT2 Troy Glaus Jsy	4.00	10.00
TT3 Tony Gwynn Jsy	10.00	25.00
TT4 Todd Helton Jsy	6.00	15.00
TT5 Scott Rolen Jsy	6.00	15.00
TT6 Roger Clemens Jsy	15.00	40.00
TT7 Pedro Martinez Jsy	6.00	15.00
TT8 Richie Sexson Jsy	4.00	10.00
TT9 Magglio Ordonez Jsy	4.00	10.00
TT10 Ben Grieve Jsy	4.00	10.00
TT11 Jeff Bagwell Jsy	6.00	15.00
TT12 Edgar Martinez Jsy	6.00	15.00
TT13 Greg Maddux Jsy	10.00	25.00
TT14 Larry Walker Jsy	4.00	10.00
TT15 Frank Thomas Jsy	6.00	15.00
TT16 Edgardo Alfonzo Jsy	4.00	10.00
TT17 Cal Ripken Jsy	20.00	50.00
TT18 Jose Vidro Jsy	4.00	10.00
TT19 Andruw Jones Jsy	6.00	15.00
TT20 Kaz Sasaki Jsy	4.00	10.00
TT21 Barry Bonds Bat	30.00	80.00
TT22 Juan Gonzalez Bat	10.00	25.00
TT23 Andruw Jones Bat	15.00	40.00
TT24 Cal Ripken Bat	40.00	100.00
TT25 Greg Maddux Bat	15.00	40.00
TT26 Manny Ramirez Sox Bat	15.00	40.00
TT27 Roberto Alomar Bat	15.00	40.00
TT28 Shawn Green Bat	10.00	25.00
TT29 Edgardo Alfonzo Bat	10.00	25.00
TT30 Rafael Palmeiro Bat	15.00	40.00
TT31 Hideo Nomo Bat	75.00	150.00
TT32 A. Galarraga Bat	10.00	25.00
TT33 Todd Helton Bat	15.00	40.00
TT34 Darin Erstad Bat	10.00	25.00
TT35 Ivan Rodriguez Bat	15.00	40.00
TT36 Sean Casey Bat	10.00	25.00
TT37 V. Guerrero Bat	15.00	40.00
TT38 David Justice Bat	10.00	25.00
TT39 Troy Glaus Bat	10.00	25.00
TT40 Jeff Bagwell Bat		
TT41 Barry Bonds Glove	75.00	150.00
TT42 Cal Ripken Glove	100.00	200.00
TT43 Rob Alomar Glove	15.00	40.00
TT44 Sean Casey Glove	10.00	25.00
TT45 Tony Gwynn Glove		
TT46 Bernie Williams Hat	15.00	40.00
TT47 Barry Zito Hat	15.00	40.00
TT48 Greg Maddux Hat		
TT49 Tom Glavine Hat	15.00	40.00
TT50 Troy Glaus Hat	10.00	25.00

2001 Absolute Memorabilia Tools of the Trade Autographs

Randomly inserted in packs, this 10-card set is an autographed partial parallel version of the regular insert set. Only 25 serially numbered sets were produced. Due to market scarcity, no pricing is provided. An exchange card with a redemption deadline of June 1st, 2003 was placed into packs for the Troy Glaus Bat card.

TT1 Vladimir Guerrero Jsy
TT3 Tony Gwynn Jsy
TT5 Scott Rolen Jsy
TT6 Roger Clemens Jsy
TT17 Cal Ripken Bat
TT22 Juan Gonzalez Bat
TT32 Andres Galarraga Bat
TT33 Todd Helton Bat
TT35 Ivan Rodriguez Bat
TT39 Troy Glaus Bat

2002 Absolute Memorabilia

This 200 card standard-size set was issued in August, 2002. The set was released in a big box which contained two nine pack mini-boxes as well as a "Signing Bonus" framed piece. The first 150 cards of this set featured veterans while the final cards feature rookies and prospects with a stated print run of 1000 serial numbered sets.

COMP.SET w/o SP's (150)	15.00	40.00
COMMON CARD (1-150)	.30	.75
COMMON CARD (151-200)	2.00	5.00
1 David Eckstein	.30	.75
2 Darin Erstad	.30	.75
3 Troy Glaus	.30	.75
4 Garret Anderson	.30	.75
5 Tim Salmon	.50	1.25
6 Curt Schilling	.30	.75

7 Randy Johnson .75 2.00
8 Luis Gonzalez .30 .75
9 Mark Grace .50 1.25
10 Tom Glavine .50 1.25
11 Greg Maddux 1.25 3.00
12 Chipper Jones .75 2.00
13 Gary Sheffield .30 .75
14 John Smoltz .50 1.25
15 Andruw Jones .50 1.25
16 Wilson Betemit .30 .75
17 Tony Batista .30 .75
18 Javier Vazquez .30 .75
19 Scott Erickson .30 .75
20 Josh Towers .30 .75
21 Pedro Martinez .50 1.25
22 Johnny Damon Sox .50 1.25
23 Manny Ramirez .50 1.25
24 Rickey Henderson .75 2.00
25 Trot Nixon .30 .75
26 Nomar Garciaparra 1.25 3.00
27 Juan Cruz .30 .75
28 Kerry Wood .30 .75
29 Fred McGriff .50 1.25
30 Moises Alou .30 .75
31 Sammy Sosa .75 2.00
32 Corey Patterson .30 .75
33 Mark Buehrle .30 .75
34 Keith Foulke .30 .75
35 Frank Thomas .75 2.00
36 Kenny Lofton .30 .75
37 Magglio Ordonez .30 .75
38 Barry Larkin .50 1.25
39 Ken Griffey Jr. 1.25 3.00
40 Adam Dunn .30 .75
41 Juan Encarnacion .30 .75
42 Sean Casey .30 .75
43 Bartolo Colon .30 .75
44 C.C. Sabathia .30 .75
45 Travis Fryman .30 .75
46 Jim Thome .50 1.25
47 Omar Vizquel .50 1.25
48 Ellis Burks .30 .75
49 Russell Branyan .30 .75
50 Mike Hampton .30 .75
51 Todd Helton .50 1.25
52 Jose Ortiz .30 .75
53 Juan Uribe .30 .75
54 Juan Pierre .30 .75
55 Larry Walker .30 .75
56 Mike Rivera .30 .75
57 Robert Fick .30 .75
58 Bobby Higginson .30 .75
59 Josh Beckett .30 .75
60 Richard Hidalgo .30 .75
61 Cliff Floyd .30 .75
62 Mike Lowell .30 .75
63 Roy Oswalt .30 .75
64 Morgan Ensberg .30 .75
65 Jeff Bagwell .50 1.25
66 Craig Biggio .50 1.25
67 Lance Berkman .30 .75
68 Carlos Beltran .30 .75
69 Mike Sweeney .30 .75
70 Neifi Perez .30 .75
71 Kevin Brown .30 .75
72 Hideo Nomo .75 2.00
73 Paul Lo Duca .30 .75
74 Adrian Beltre .30 .75
75 Shawn Green .30 .75
76 Eric Karros .30 .75
77 Brad Radke .30 .75
78 Corey Koskie .30 .75
79 Doug Mientkiewicz .30 .75
80 Torii Hunter .30 .75
81 Jacque Jones .30 .75
82 Ben Sheets .30 .75
83 Richie Sexson .30 .75
84 Geoff Jenkins .30 .75
85 Tony Armas Jr. .30 .75
86 Michael Barrett .30 .75
87 Jose Vidro .30 .75
88 Vladimir Guerrero .75 2.00
89 Roger Clemens 1.50 4.00
90 Derek Jeter 2.00 5.00
91 Bernie Williams .50 1.25
92 Jason Giambi .30 .75
93 Jorge Posada .50 1.25
94 Mike Mussina .50 1.25
95 Andy Pettitte .50 1.25
96 Nick Johnson .30 .75
97 Alfonso Soriano .30 .75
98 Shawn Estes .30 .75
99 Al Leiter .30 .75
100 Mike Piazza 1.25 3.00
101 Roberto Alomar .50 1.25
102 Mo Vaughn .30 .75
103 Jeromy Burnitz .30 .75
104 Tim Hudson .30 .75
105 Barry Zito .30 .75
106 Mark Mulder .30 .75
107 Eric Chavez .30 .75
108 Miguel Tejada .30 .75
109 Carlos Pena .30 .75
110 Jermaine Dye .30 .75
111 Mike Lieberthal .30 .75
112 Scott Rolen .50 1.25
113 Pat Burrell .30 .75
114 Brandon Duckworth .30 .75
115 Bobby Abreu .30 .75
116 Jason Kendall .30 .75
117 Aramis Ramirez .30 .75
118 Brian Giles .30 .75
119 Pokey Reese .30 .75
120 Phil Nevin .30 .75
121 Ryan Klesko .30 .75
122 Jeremy Giambi .30 .75
123 Trevor Hoffman .30 .75
124 Barry Bonds 2.00 5.00
125 Rich Aurilia .30 .75
126 Jeff Kent .30 .75
127 Tsuyoshi Shinjo .30 .75
128 Ichiro Suzuki 1.50 4.00
129 Edgar Martinez .50 1.25
130 Freddy Garcia .30 .75
131 Bret Boone .30 .75
132 Matt Morris .30 .75
133 Tino Martinez .50 1.25
134 Albert Pujols 1.50 4.00
135 J.D. Drew .30 .75
136 Jim Edmonds .30 .75
137 Gabe Kapler .30 .75
138 Paul Wilson .30 .75
139 Ben Grieve .30 .75
140 Wade Miller .30 .75
141 Chan Ho Park .30 .75
142 Alex Rodriguez 1.25 3.00
143 Rafael Palmeiro .50 1.25
144 Juan Gonzalez .30 .75
145 Ivan Rodriguez .50 1.25
146 Carlos Delgado .30 .75
147 Jose Cruz Jr. .30 .75
148 Shannon Stewart .30 .75
149 Raul Mondesi .30 .75
150 Vernon Wells .30 .75
151 So Taguchi RP RC 3.00 8.00
152 Kazuhisa Ishii RP RC 3.00 8.00
153 Hank Blalock RP 3.00 8.00
154 Sean Burroughs RP 2.00 5.00
155 Geronimo Gil RP 2.00 5.00
156 Jon Rauch RP 2.00 5.00
157 Fernando Rodney RP 2.00 5.00
158 Miguel Asencio RP RC 2.00 5.00
159 Franklyn German RP RC 2.00 5.00
160 Luis Ugueto RP RC 2.00 5.00
161 Jorge Sosa RP RC 3.00 8.00
162 Felix Escalona RP RC 2.00 5.00
163 Colby Lewis RP 2.00 5.00
164 Mark Teixeira RP 3.00 8.00
165 Mark Prior RP 3.00 8.00
166 Francis Beltran RP RC 2.00 5.00
167 Joe Thurston RP 2.00 5.00
168 Earl Snyder RP RC 2.00 5.00
169 Takahito Nomura RP RC 2.00 5.00
170 Bill Hall RP 2.00 5.00
171 Marlon Byrd RP 2.00 5.00
172 Dave Williams RP 2.00 5.00
173 Yorvit Torrealba RP 2.00 5.00
174 Brandon Backe RP RC 3.00 8.00
175 Jorge De La Rosa RP RC 2.00 5.00
176 Brian Mallette RP RC 2.00 5.00
177 Rodrigo Rosario RP RC 2.00 5.00
178 Anderson Machado RP RC 2.00 5.00
179 Jorge Padilla RP RC 2.00 5.00
180 Allan Simpson RP RC 2.00 5.00
181 Doug Devore RP RC 2.00 5.00
182 Steve Bechler RP RC 2.00 5.00
183 Raul Chavez RP RC 2.00 5.00
184 Tom Shearn RP RC 2.00 5.00
185 Ben Howard RP RC 2.00 5.00
186 Chris Baker RP RC 2.00 5.00
187 Travis Hughes RP RC 2.00 5.00
188 Kevin Mench RP 2.00 5.00
189 Drew Henson RP 2.00 5.00
190 Mike Moriarty RP RC 2.00 5.00
191 Corey Thurman RP RC 2.00 5.00
192 Bobby Hill RP 2.00 5.00
193 Steve Kent RP RC 2.00 5.00
194 Satoru Komiyama RP RC 2.00 5.00
195 Jason Lane RP 2.00 5.00
196 Angel Berroa RP 2.00 5.00
197 Brandon Puffer RP RC 2.00 5.00
198 Brian Fitzgerald RP RC 2.00 5.00
199 Rene Reyes RP RC 2.00 5.00
200 Hee Seop Choi RP 2.00 5.00
NNO Mark Prior Promo

2002 Absolute Memorabilia Spectrum

Randomly inserted into packs, this is a parallel to the basic set. The veteran cards (1-150) were issued to a stated print run of 100 serial numbered sets while the rookies and prospects were issued to a stated print run of 50 serial numbered sets.

*SPECTRUM 1-150: 2.5X TO 6X BASIC
72 Hideo Nomo 5.00 12.00
151 So Taguchi RP 4.00 10.00
152 Kazuhisa Ishii RP 4.00 10.00
153 Hank Blalock RP 4.00 10.00
154 Sean Burroughs RP 3.00 8.00
155 Geronimo Gil RP 3.00 8.00
156 Jon Rauch RP 3.00 8.00
157 Fernando Rodney RP 3.00 8.00
158 Miguel Asencio RP 3.00 8.00
159 Franklyn German RP 3.00 8.00
160 Luis Ugueto RP 3.00 8.00
161 Jorge Sosa RP 4.00 10.00
162 Felix Escalona RP 3.00 8.00
163 Colby Lewis RP 3.00 8.00
164 Mark Teixeira RP 6.00 15.00
165 Mark Prior RP 4.00 10.00
166 Francis Beltran RP 3.00 8.00
167 Joe Thurston RP 3.00 8.00
168 Earl Snyder RP 3.00 8.00
169 Takahito Nomura RP 6.00 15.00
170 Bill Hall RP 3.00 8.00
171 Marlon Byrd RP 3.00 8.00
172 Dave Williams RP 3.00 8.00
173 Yorvit Torrealba RP 3.00 8.00
174 Brandon Backe RP 4.00 10.00
175 Jorge De La Rosa RP 4.00 10.00
176 Brian Mallette RP 3.00 8.00
177 Rodrigo Rosario RP 3.00 8.00
178 Anderson Machado RP 3.00 8.00
179 Jorge Padilla RP 3.00 8.00
180 Allan Simpson RP 3.00 8.00
181 Doug Devore RP 3.00 8.00
182 Steve Bechler RP 3.00 8.00
183 Raul Chavez RP 3.00 8.00
184 Tom Shearn RP 3.00 8.00
185 Ben Howard RP 3.00 8.00
186 Chris Baker RP 3.00 8.00
187 Travis Hughes RP 3.00 8.00
188 Kevin Mench RP 3.00 8.00
189 Drew Henson RP 3.00 8.00
190 Mike Moriarty RP 3.00 8.00
191 Corey Thurman RP 3.00 8.00
192 Bobby Hill RP 3.00 8.00
193 Steve Kent RP 3.00 8.00
194 Satoru Komiyama RP 3.00 8.00
195 Jason Lane RP 3.00 8.00
196 Angel Berroa RP 3.00 8.00
197 Brandon Puffer RP 3.00 8.00
198 Brian Fitzgerald RP 3.00 8.00
199 Rene Reyes RP 3.00 8.00
200 Hee Seop Choi RP 3.00 8.00

2002 Absolute Memorabilia Absolutely Ink

Inserted into packs at stated odds of one in 22 hobby and one in 36 retail, these 59 cards feature a mix of active player and retired superstars who signed cards for this set. Many players were printed to shorter supply and we have notated that information next to their name in our checklist. Cards with a stated print run of 50 or fewer are not priced due to market scarcity.

GOLD RANDOM INSERTS IN PACKS
GOLD PRINT RUN 25 SERIAL #'d SETS
NO GOLD PRICING DUE TO SCARCITY
1 Adrian Beltre 6.00 15.00
2 Alex Rodriguez SP/50 * 60.00 120.00
3 Ben Sheets 6.00 15.00
4 Bernie Williams SP/25 *
5 Bobby Doerr 6.00 15.00
6 Blaine Neal 4.00 10.00
7 Carlos Beltran 6.00 15.00
8 Carlos Pena 4.00 10.00
10 Corey Patterson SP/150 * 6.00 15.00
11 Curt Schilling SP/15 *
12 Dave Parker 6.00 15.00
13 David Justice SP/65 * 10.00 25.00
14 Don Mattingly SP/75 * 40.00 80.00
15 Duaner Sanchez 4.00 10.00
16 Eric Chavez SP/100 * 6.00 15.00
17 Freddy Garcia SP/200 * 6.00 15.00
18 Gary Carter SP/150 * 6.00 15.00
19 Gary Sheffield SP/25 *
20 George Brett SP/25 *
21 Greg Maddux SP/25 *
22 Ivan Rodriguez SP/50 * 20.00 50.00
23 J.D. Drew SP/100 * 6.00 15.00
24 Jack Cust 4.00 10.00
25 Jason Michaels 4.00 10.00
26 Jermaine Dye SP/125 * 6.00 15.00
27 Jim Palmer SP/150 * 6.00 15.00
28 Jose Vidro 4.00 10.00
29 Josh Towers 4.00 10.00
30 Kerry Wood SP/50 * 15.00 40.00
31 Kirby Puckett SP/50 * 50.00 100.00
32 Luis Gonzalez SP/75 * 10.00 25.00
33 Luis Rivera 4.00 10.00
34 Manny Ramirez SP/50 * 20.00 50.00
35 Marcus Giles 6.00 15.00
36 Mark Prior SP/100 * 10.00 25.00
37 Mark Teixeira SP/100 * 15.00 40.00
38 Marlon Byrd SP/250 * 6.00 15.00
39 Matt Ginter 4.00 10.00
40 Moises Alou SP/150 * 6.00 15.00
41 Nate Frese 4.00 10.00
42 Nick Johnson 6.00 15.00
43 Nomar Garciaparra SP/15 *
44 Pablo Ozuna 4.00 10.00
45 Paul Lo Duca SP/200 * 6.00 15.00
46 Richie Sexson 6.00 15.00
47 Roberto Alomar SP/100 * 10.00 25.00
48 Roy Oswalt SP/300 * 6.00 15.00
49 Ryan Klesko SP/75 * 10.00 25.00
50 Sean Casey SP/125 * 6.00 15.00
51 Shannon Stewart 6.00 15.00
52 So Taguchi 6.00 15.00
53 Terrence Long 4.00 10.00
54 Timo Perez 4.00 10.00
55 Todd Helton SP/25 *
56 Tony Gwynn SP/50 * 40.00 80.00
57 Troy Glaus SP/300 * 10.00 25.00
58 Vladimir Guerrero SP/225 * 15.00 40.00
59 Wade Miller 4.00 10.00
60 Wilson Betemit 4.00 10.00

2002 Absolute Memorabilia Absolutely Ink Numbers

This is a parallel to the Absolutely Ink insert set. Each card can be identified as they were issued to that player's print uniform number. If a player signed 25 or fewer or these cards, there is no pricing due to market scarcity.

1 Adrian Beltre/29 12.50 30.00
2 Alex Rodriguez/3
3 Ben Sheets/15
5 Bobby Doerr/1
7 Carlos Beltran/15
8 Carlos Pena/15
10 Corey Patterson/20
12 Dave Parker/39 10.00 25.00
13 David Justice/23
14 Don Mattingly/23
16 Eric Chavez/3
17 Freddy Garcia/34 12.50 30.00
18 Gary Carter/8
19 Gary Sheffield/10
20 George Brett/5
21 Greg Maddux/31 60.00 120.00
22 Ivan Rodriguez/7
23 J.D. Drew/7
24 Jack Cust/67 6.00 15.00
25 Jason Michaels/22
26 Jermaine Dye/24
27 Jim Palmer/22
28 Jose Vidro/3
29 Josh Towers/35 8.00 20.00
30 Kerry Wood/34 20.00 50.00
31 Kirby Puckett/34 60.00 120.00
32 Luis Gonzalez/20
33 Luis Rivera/60 6.00 15.00
34 Manny Ramirez/24
35 Marcus Giles/22
36 Mark Prior/22
40 Moises Alou/18
42 Nick Johnson/36 12.50 30.00
43 Nomar Garciaparra/5
44 Pablo Ozuna/3
45 Paul Lo Duca/16
46 Richie Sexson/11
47 Roberto Alomar/12
48 Roy Oswalt/44 10.00 25.00
49 Ryan Klesko/30 12.50 30.00
50 Sean Casey/21
51 Shannon Stewart/24
52 So Taguchi/99 10.00 25.00
53 Terrence Long/12
54 Timo Perez/6
56 Tony Gwynn/19
57 Troy Glaus/25
58 Vladimir Guerrero/27 30.00 60.00
59 Wade Miller/52 6.00 15.00
60 Wilson Betemit/24

2002 Absolute Memorabilia Signing Bonus

Inserted into "full" boxes at one per box and with a SRP of $40 per frame, these 313 items was highlighted by a signature of the featured player. These frame have all different stated print runs and we have notated that information in our checklist next to their names. Frames with a print run of 25 or less are not priced due to market scarcity.

1 Bob Abreu Gray-N/53 15.00 40.00
2 Bob Abreu Stripe-N/53 15.00 40.00
3 Grover Alexander Gray/1
4 Rob Alomar Gray-N/12
5 Rob Alomar Gray-N/100 15.00 40.00
6 Rob Alomar Stripe-N/100 15.00 40.00
7 Moises Alou Blue-L/250 10.00 25.00
8 Moises Alou Blue-N/18
9 Moises Alou Gray-N/18
10 Moises Alou Stripe-L/250 10.00 25.00
11 Moises Alou Stripe-N/18
12 Jeff Bagwell Gray-N/5
13 Jeff Bagwell Red-N/5
14 Jeff Bagwell Stripe-N/5
15 Jeff Bagwell White-N/5
16 Carlos Beltran Black-N/15
17 Carlos Beltran Blue-N/50 15.00 40.00
18 Carlos Beltran Gray-N/50 15.00 40.00
19 Carlos Beltran White-N/15
20 Adrian Beltre Blue-N/150 10.00 25.00
21 Adrian Beltre Gray-N/150 10.00 25.00
22 Adrian Beltre White-N/29 20.00 50.00
23 Lance Berkman Gray-N/17
24 Lance Berkman Red-N/17
25 Lance Berkman Stripe-N/17
26 Lance Berkman White-N/17
27 Angel Berroa Black-N/100 8.00 20.00
28 Angel Berroa Blue-N/100 8.00 20.00
29 Angel Berroa Gray-N/50 10.00 25.00
30 Angel Berroa White-N/4
31 Wilson Betemit Gray-N/250 6.00 15.00
32 Wilson Betemit White-N/250 6.00 15.00
33 Craig Biggio Gray-N/7
34 Craig Biggio Red-N/7
35 Craig Biggio Stripe-N/7
36 Craig Biggio White-N/7
37 Hank Blalock Blue-N/12
38 Hank Blalock Gray-N/50 15.00 40.00
39 Hank Blalock White-N/100 12.50 30.00
40 George Brett Blue-N/5
41 George Brett Gray-N/5
42 George Brett White-N/5
43 Lou Brock Gray-N/100 15.00 40.00
44 Lou Brock White-N/200 12.50 30.00
45 Kevin Brown Blue-N/27 20.00 50.00
46 Kevin Brown Gray-N/150 10.00 25.00
47 Kevin Brown White-N/100 12.50 30.00
48 Mark Buehrle Black-N/200 12.50 30.00
49 Mark Buehrle Gray-N/200 12.50 30.00
50 Mark Buehrle Stripe-N/56 30.00 60.00
51 Sean Burroughs Blue-N/21
52 Sean Burroughs Gray-N/21
53 Sean Burroughs White-N/21
54 Marlon Byrd Gray-N/61 10.00 25.00
55 Marlon Byrd Stripe-N/61 10.00 25.00
56 Steve Carlton Gray-N/100 12.50 30.00
57 Steve Carlton Stripe-N/150 10.00 25.00
58 Sean Casey Gray-N/21
59 Sean Casey Stripe-L/100 12.50 30.00
60 Sean Casey Stripe-N/21
61 Eric Chavez Gray-N/25
62 Eric Chavez Green-N/3
63 Eric Chavez White-N/28 20.00 50.00
64 Roger Clemens Gray-N/10
65 Roger Clemens Stripe-N/10
66 Ty Cobb Gray/6
67 Eddie Collins Gray/1
68 Juan Cruz Blue-L/51 10.00 25.00
69 Juan Cruz Blue-N/51 10.00 25.00
70 Juan Cruz Gray-N/51 10.00 25.00
71 Juan Cruz Stripe-L/51 10.00 25.00
72 Juan Cruz Stripe-N/51 10.00 25.00
73 J.D. Drew Gray-N/100 12.50 30.00
74 J.D. Drew White-N/7
75 Bran Duckworth Gray-N/56 10.00 25.00
76 B.Duckworth Stripe-N/150 6.00 15.00
77 Adam Dunn Gray-N/10
78 Adam Dunn Stripe-L/10
79 Adam Dunn Stripe-N/44 30.00 60.00
80 Jermaine Dye Gray-N/250 10.00 25.00
81 Jermaine Dye Green-N/100 12.50 30.00
82 Jermaine Dye White-N/100 12.50 30.00
83 Morg Ensberg Gray-N/100 12.50 30.00
84 Morg Ensberg Red-N/100 12.50 30.00
85 Morg Ensberg Stripe-N/100 12.50 30.00
86 Morg Ensberg White-N/100 12.50 30.00
87 Darin Erstad Gray-N/5
88 Darin Erstad White-N/17
89 Cliff Floyd Gray-N/200 10.00 25.00
90 Cliff Floyd Stripe-N/200 10.00 25.00
91 Jimmie Foxx Gray/1
92 Freddy Garcia Blue-N/34 20.00 50.00
93 Freddy Garcia Gray-N/34 20.00 50.00
94 Freddy Garcia White-N/125 10.00 25.00
95 Nomar Garciaparra Gray-N/5
96 Nomar Garciaparra White-N/5
97 Troy Glaus Gray-N/50 30.00 60.00
98 Troy Glaus White-N/100 15.00 40.00
99 Tom Glavine Gray-N/25
100 Tom Glavine White-N/200 20.00 50.00
101 Luis Gonzalez Black-N/20
102 Luis Gonzalez Gray-N/125 10.00 25.00
103 Luis Gonzalez Purple-N/125 10.00 25.00
104 Luis Gonzalez Stripe-N/125 10.00 25.00
105 Hank Greenberg Gray/1
106 Vlad Guerrero Gray-N/27 60.00 120.00
107 V.Guerrero Stripe-N/150 40.00 80.00
108 Tony Gwynn Blue-N/19
109 Tony Gwynn Gray-N/19
110 Tony Gwynn White-N/19
111 Rich Hidalgo Gray-N/100 8.00 20.00
112 Rich Hidalgo Red-N/135 6.00 15.00
113 Rich Hidalgo Stripe-N/15
114 Rich Hidalgo White-N/150 6.00 15.00
115 Rogers Hornsby Gray/1
116 Tim Hudson Gray-N/50 30.00 60.00
117 Tim Hudson Green-N/100 15.00 40.00
118 Tim Hudson White-N/15
119 Kazuhisa Ishii Blue-N/17
120 Kazuhisa Ishii Gray-N/17
121 Kazuhisa Ishii White-N/17
122 Reg Jackson Gray-N/44 40.00 80.00
123 Reg Jackson Stripe-N/44 50.00 100.00
124 Nick Johnson Gray-N/200 10.00 25.00
125 Nick Johnson Stripe-N/200 10.00 25.00
126 Walter Johnson Gray/4
127 Andruw Jones Gray-N/75 30.00 60.00
128 Andruw Jones White-N/25
129 Chipper Jones Gray-N/10
130 Chipper Jones White-N/10
131 Al Kaline Gray-N/6
132 Al Kaline White-L/250 20.00 50.00
133 Al Kaline White-N/6
134 Gabe Kapler Blue-N/125 10.00 25.00
135 Gabe Kapler Gray-N/18
136 Gabe Kapler White-N/175 10.00 25.00
137 Ryan Klesko Blue-N/30 20.00 50.00
138 Ryan Klesko Gray-N/30 20.00 50.00
139 Ryan Klesko White-N/30 20.00 50.00
140 Nap Lajoie Gray/1
141 Jason Lane Gray-N/100 12.50 30.00
142 Jason Lane Red-N/100 12.50 30.00
143 Jason Lane Stripe-N/100 12.50 30.00
144 Jason Lane White-N/100 12.50 30.00
145 Barry Larkin Gray-N/50 30.00 60.00
146 Barry Larkin Stripe-L/100 15.00 40.00
147 Barry Larkin Stripe-N/11
148 Paul LoDuca Blue-N/16
149 Paul LoDuca Gray-N/16
150 Paul LoDuca White-N/50 15.00 40.00
151 Fred Lynn Gray-N/250 10.00 25.00
152 Fred Lynn White-N/150 10.00 25.00
153 Connie Mack Gray/2
154 Greg Maddux Gray-N/31 100.00 200.00
155 Greg Maddux White-N/31 100.00 200.00
156 Roger Maris Gray/3
157 Edgar Martinez Blue-N/150 20.00 50.00
158 Edgar Martinez Gray-N/150 20.00 50.00
159 Edgar Martinez White-N/11
160 Pedro Martinez Gray-N/5
161 P.Martinez White-N/45 60.00 120.00
162 Don Mattingly Gray-N/100 60.00 120.00
163 D.Mattingly Stripe-N/100 60.00 120.00
164 Will McCovey Gray-N/190 12.50 30.00
165 Will McCovey White-N/250 12.50 30.00
166 Wade Miller Gray-N/150 6.00 15.00
167 Wade Miller Stripe-N/250 6.00 15.00
168 Wade Miller Red-N/52 10.00 25.00
169 Wade Miller White-N/52 10.00 25.00
170 Paul Molitor Blue-N/75 15.00 40.00
171 Paul Molitor Gray-N/100 12.50 30.00
172 Paul Molitor White-N/125 10.00 25.00
173 Mark Mulder Gray-N/20
174 Mark Mulder Green-N/20
175 Mark Mulder White-N/40 15.00 40.00
176 Mike Mussina Gray-N/5
177 Mike Mussina Stripe-N/5
178 Jose Ortiz Gray-N/125 6.00 15.00
179 Jose Ortiz Purple-N/125 6.00 15.00
180 Jose Ortiz Stripe-L/125 6.00 15.00
181 Jose Ortiz Stripe-N/125 6.00 15.00
182 Roy Oswalt Gray-N/44 15.00 40.00
183 Roy Oswalt Red-N/44 15.00 40.00
184 Roy Oswalt Stripe-N/100 12.50 30.00
185 Roy Oswalt White-N/100 12.50 30.00
186 Mel Ott Gray/3
187 Rafael Palmeiro Blue-N/25
188 Rafael Palmeiro Gray-N/25
189 Rafael Palmeiro White-N/25
190 Jim Palmer Gray-N/250 10.00 25.00
191 Jim Palmer White-N/150 10.00 25.00
192 Dave Parker Black-N/150 12.50 30.00
193 Dave Parker White-N/150 12.50 30.00
194 Cor Patterson Blue-L/250 10.00 25.00
195 Cor Patterson Blue-N/20
196 Cor Patterson Gray-N/250 10.00 25.00
197 Cor Patterson Stripe-L/250 10.00 25.00
198 Cor Patterson Stripe-N/250 2.00 5.00
199 Carlos Pena Gray-N/19
200 Carlos Pena Green-N/250 6.00 15.00
201 Carlos Pena White-N/150 6.00 15.00
202 Tony Perez Gray-N/24
203 Tony Perez Stripe-L/250 10.00 25.00
204 Tony Perez Stripe-N/24
205 Juan Pierre Gray-N/75 15.00 40.00
206 Juan Pierre Purple-N/75 10.00 25.00
207 Juan Pierre White-L/75 10.00 25.00
208 Juan Pierre White-N/75 10.00 25.00
209 Mark Prior Blue-L/75 15.00 40.00
210 Mark Prior Blue-N/125 12.50 30.00
211 Mark Prior Gray-N/75 15.00 40.00
212 Mark Prior Stripe-L/50 15.00 40.00
213 Mark Prior Stripe-N/22
214 Kirby Puckett Blue-N/34 60.00 120.00
215 Kirby Puckett Gray-N/34
216 Kirby Puckett Stripe-N/34 60.00 120.00
217 Albert Pujols Gray-N/5
218 Albert Pujols White-N/100 150.00 250.00
219 Aram Ramirez Black-N/125 10.00 25.00
220 Aram Ramirez Gray-N/50 15.00 40.00
221 Aram Ramirez White-N/16
222 Manny Ramirez Gray-N/24
223 Manny Ramirez White-N/5
224 Phil Rizzuto Gray-N/250 40.00 80.00
225 Phil Rizzuto Stripe-N/10
226 B.Robinson Gray-N/250 12.50 30.00
227 B.Robinson White-N/150 40.00 80.00
227A Brooks Robinson ERR White-N/150
Card says in print it was signed by Jim Palmer
228 Jackie Robinson Gray/3
229 Alex Rodriguez Blue-N/3
230 Alex Rodriguez Gray-N/15
231 Alex Rodriguez White-N/15
232 Ivan Rodriguez Blue-N/7
233 Ivan Rodriguez Gray-N/7
234 Ivan Rodriguez White-N/7
235 Scott Rolen Gray-N/17
236 Scott Rolen Stripe-N/17
237 Babe Ruth Gray/8
238 N.Ryan Angel Gray-N/30 125.00 250.00
239 N.Ryan Angel White-N/30 125.00 250.00
240 N.Ryan Astro Gray-N/34 125.00 250.00
241 N.Ryan Astro White-N/34 125.00 250.00
242 N.Ryan Rgr Blue-N/34 125.00 250.00
243 N.Ryan Rgr Gray-N/34 125.00 250.00
244 N.Ryan Rgr White-N/34 125.00 250.00
245 C.C. Sabathia Blue-N/15
246 C.C. Sabathia Gray-N/10
247 C.C. Sabathia White-N/10
248 Ryne Sandberg Blue-L/50 75.00 150.00
249 Ryne Sandberg Blue-N/23
250 Ryne Sandberg Gray-N/23
251 R.Sandberg Stripe-L/50 75.00 150.00
252 Ryne Sandberg Stripe-N/23
253 Curt Schilling Black-N/10
254 Curt Schilling Gray-N/10
255 Curt Schilling Purple-N/10
256 Curt Schilling Stripe-N/5
257 Mike Schmidt Gray-N/100 60.00 120.00
258 M.Schmidt Stripe-N/100 60.00 120.00
259 Richie Sexson Blue-N/100 12.50 30.00
260 Richie Sexson Gray-N/100 12.50 30.00
261 Richie Sexson White-N/100 12.50 30.00
262 Ben Sheets Blue-N/150 10.00 25.00
263 Ben Sheets Gray-N/100 12.50 30.00
264 Ben Sheets White-N/100 12.50 30.00
265 Gary Sheffield Gray-N/11
266 Gary Sheffield White-N/11
267 George Sisler Gray/3
268 Alfonso Soriano Gray-N/12
269 A.Soriano Stripe-N/100 15.00 40.00
270 Tris Speaker Gray/1
271 Shan Stewart Blue-N/150 10.00 25.00
272 Shan Stewart Gray-N/100 8.00 20.00
273 Shan Stewart White-N/24
274 Mike Sweeney Black-N/100 12.50 30.00
275 Mike Sweeney Blue-N/100 12.50 30.00
276 Mike Sweeney Gray-N/100 12.50 30.00
277 Mike Sweeney White-N/100 12.50 30.00
278 So Taguchi Gray-N/99 20.00 50.00
279 So Taguchi White-N/99 20.00 50.00
280 Mark Teixeira Blue-N/100 20.00 50.00
281 Mark Teixeira Gray-N/23
282 Mark Teixeira White-N/100 20.00 50.00
283 Miguel Tejada Gray-N/50 30.00 60.00
284 Miguel Tejada Green-N/4
285 Miguel Tejada White-N/40 30.00 60.00
286 Frank Thomas Black-N/35 60.00 120.00
287 Frank Thomas Gray-N/10
288 Frank Thomas White-N/10
289 Juan Uribe Gray-N/25
290 Juan Uribe Purple-N/25
291 Juan Uribe White-L/4
292 Juan Uribe White-N/4
293 Jav Vazquez Gray-N/125 10.00 25.00
294 Jav Vazquez Stripe-N/125 10.00 25.00
295 Jose Vidro Gray-N/150 6.00 15.00
296 Jose Vidro Gray-N/150 6.00 15.00
297 Honus Wagner Gray/11
298 Bernie Williams Gray-N/15
299 Bernie Williams Stripe-N/15
300 Ted Williams Gray/1
301 Hack Wilson Gray/1
302 Dave Winfield Gray-N/25
303 Dave Winfield Stripe-N/25
304 Kerry Wood Blue-L/34 40.00 80.00
305 Kerry Wood Blue-N/34 40.00 80.00
306 Kerry Wood Gray-N/34 40.00 80.00
307 Kerry Wood Stripe-L/34 40.00 80.00
308 Kerry Wood Stripe-N/34 40.00 80.00
309 Cy Young Gray/2
310 Barry Zito Gray-N/25
311 Barry Zito Green-N/25
312 Barry Zito White-N/50 30.00 60.00

2002 Absolute Memorabilia Signing Bonus Entry Cards

Issued one per pack, these 20 cards are "contest" cards which when sent in enabled collectors to win various items relating to the featured player.

1 Chipper Jones
2 Mark Prior
3 Adam Dunn

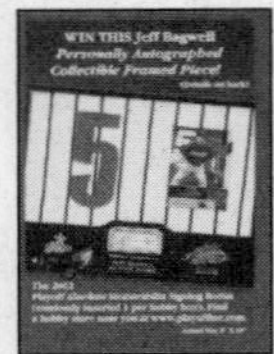

5 Kazuhisa Ishii
6 Vladimir Guerrero
7 Greg Maddux
8 Nomar Garciaparra
10 Ryne Sandberg
11 Jeff Bagwell
12 Paul Molitor
13 George Brett
14 Kirby Puckett
16 Reggie Jackson
17 Roger Clemens
18 Tony Gwynn
19 Albert Pujols
20 Alex Rodriguez
DM Don Mattingly
LB Lance Berkman
PM Pedro Martinez

2002 Absolute Memorabilia Team Quads

Inserted into hobby packs at a stated rate of one in 18, these cards feature four players from 20 of the 30 different major league teams.

*GOLD: .75X TO 2X BASIC QUADS
*SPECTRUM: .6X TO 1.5X BASIC QUADS
SPECTRUM ODDS 1:36 HOBBY

Card	Low	High
1 Troy Glaus	2.00	5.00
Darin Erstad		
Garret Anderson		
Troy Percival		
2 Curt Schilling	2.00	5.00
Randy Johnson		
Luis Gonzalez		
Mark Grace		
3 Chipper Jones	3.00	8.00
Andruw Jones		
Greg Maddux		
Tom Glavine		
4 Nomar Garciaparra	3.00	8.00
Manny Ramirez		
Trot Nixon		
Pedro Martinez		
5 Kerry Wood	2.00	5.00
Sammy Sosa		
Fred McGriff		
Moises Alou		
6 Frank Thomas	2.00	5.00
Magglio Ordonez		
Mark Buehrle		
Kenny Lofton		
7 Ken Griffey Jr.	3.00	8.00
Barry Larkin		
Adam Dunn		
Sean Casey		
8 C.C Sabathia	2.00	5.00
Jim Thome		
Bartolo Colon		
Russell Branyan		
9 Todd Helton	2.00	5.00
Larry Walker		
Juan Pierre		
Mike Hampton		
10 Jeff Bagwell	2.00	5.00
Craig Biggio		
Lance Berkman		
Richard Hidalgo		
11 Shawn Green	2.00	5.00
Adrian Beltre		
Hideo Nomo		
Paul Lo Duca		
12 Mike Piazza	3.00	8.00
Roberto Alomar		
Mo Vaughn		
Roger Cedeno		
13 Roger Clemens	5.00	12.00
Derek Jeter		
Jason Giambi		
Mike Mussina		
14 Barry Zito	2.00	5.00
Tim Hudson		
Eric Chavez		
Miguel Tejada		
15 Pat Burrell	2.00	5.00
Scott Rolen		
Bobby Abreu		
Marlon Byrd		
16 Bernie Williams	2.00	5.00
Jorge Posada		
Alfonso Soriano		
Andy Pettitte		
17 Barry Bonds	4.00	10.00
Rich Aurilia		
Tsuyoshi Shinjo		
Jeff Kent		
18 Ichiro Suzuki	4.00	10.00
Kazuhiro Sasaki		
Bret Boone		
Edgar Martinez		
19 Albert Pujols	4.00	10.00
J.D. Drew		
Jim Edmonds		
Tino Martinez		
20 Alex Rodriguez	3.00	8.00
Ivan Rodriguez		
Juan Gonzalez		
Rafael Palmeiro		

2002 Absolute Memorabilia Team Quads Materials

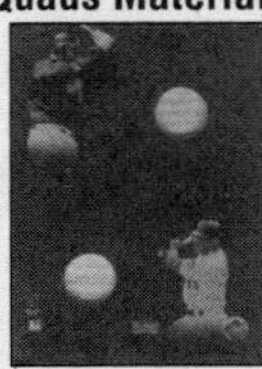

Randomly inserted into packs, these 19 cards parallel the Team Quads insert set. Each card be identified by both the four pieces of memorabilia on the card as well as having a stated print run of 100 serial numbered sets. Please note that card number 7 does not exist.

GOLD PRINT RUN 25 SERIAL #'d SETS
NO GOLD PRICING DUE TO SCARCITY

Card	Low	High
1 Troy Glaus Jsy	10.00	25.00
Darin Erstad Jsy		
Garret Anderson Jsy		
Troy Percival Jsy		
2 Curt Schilling Jsy	15.00	40.00
Randy Johnson Jsy		
Luis Gonzalez Jsy		
Mark Grace Jsy		
3 Chipper Jones Jsy	20.00	50.00
Andruw Jones Jsy		
Greg Maddux Jsy		
Tom Glavine Jsy		
4 Nomar Garciaparra Jsy	20.00	50.00
Manny Ramirez Jsy		
Pedro Martinez Jsy		
Trot Nixon Bat		
5 Kerry Wood Base	15.00	40.00
Sammy Sosa Base		
Fred McGriff Base		
Moises Alou Base		
6 Frank Thomas Jsy	15.00	40.00
Magglio Ordonez Jsy		
Mark Buehrle Jsy		
Kenny Lofton Bat		
8 C.C Sabathia Jsy	15.00	40.00
Jim Thome Jsy		
Bartolo Colon Jsy		
Russell Branyan Jsy		
9 Todd Helton Jsy	15.00	40.00
Larry Walker Jsy		
Juan Pierre Jsy		
Mike Hampton Jsy		
10 Jeff Bagwell Jsy	15.00	40.00
Craig Biggio Jsy		
Lance Berkman Jsy		
Richard Hidalgo Pants		
11 Shawn Green Jsy	30.00	60.00
Adrian Beltre Jsy		
Hideo Nomo Jsy		
Paul Lo Duca Jsy		
12 Mike Piazza Jsy	15.00	40.00
Roberto Alomar Shoe		
Mo Vaughn Bat		
Roger Cedeno Bat		
13 Roger Clemens Base	40.00	80.00
Derek Jeter Ball		
Jason Giambi Ball		
Mike Mussina Ball		
14 Barry Zito Jsy	10.00	25.00
Tim Hudson Jsy		
Eric Chavez Bat		
Miguel Tejada Jsy		
15 Pat Burrell Jsy	15.00	40.00
Scott Rolen Jsy		
Bobby Abreu Jsy		
Marlon Byrd Jsy		
16 Bernie Williams Jsy	15.00	40.00
Jorge Posada Jsy		
Alfonso Soriano Bat		
Andy Pettitte Jsy		
17 Barry Bonds Ball	20.00	50.00
Rich Aurilia Base		
Tsuyoshi Shinjo Base		
Jeff Kent Base		
18 Ichiro Deck Deck	40.00	80.00
Kazuhiro Sasaki Deck		
Edgar Martinez Base		
Bret Boone Base		
19 Albert Pujols Ball	30.00	60.00
J.D. Drew Base		
Jim Edmonds Base		
Tino Martinez Base		
20 Alex Rodriguez Jsy	15.00	40.00
Ivan Rodriguez Jsy		
Juan Gonzalez Jsy		
Rafael Palmeiro Jsy		

2002 Absolute Memorabilia Team Tandems

Inserted into hobby packs at stated odds of one in 12 hobby and one in 36 retail packs, these 40 cards feature two stars who are also teammates.

*GOLD: .75X TO 2X BASIC TANDEMS
GOLD ODDS 1:72 HOBBY, 1:216 RETAIL
*SPECTRUM: .6X TO 1.5X BASIC TANDEMS
SPECTRUM ODDS 1:36 HOBBY

Card	Low	High
1 Troy Glaus	1.25	3.00
Darin Erstad		
2 Curt Schilling	2.00	5.00
Randy Johnson		
3 Chipper Jones	2.00	5.00
Andruw Jones		
4 Greg Maddux	3.00	8.00
Tom Glavine		
5 Nomar Garciaparra	3.00	8.00
Manny Ramirez		
6 Pedro Martinez	1.25	3.00
Trot Nixon		
7 Kerry Wood	2.00	5.00
Sammy Sosa		
8 Frank Thomas	2.00	5.00
Magglio Ordonez		
9 Ken Griffey Jr.	3.00	8.00
Barry Larkin		
10 C.C Sabathia	1.25	3.00
Jim Thome		
11 Todd Helton	1.25	3.00
Larry Walker		
12 Bobby Higginson	1.25	3.00
Shane Halter		
13 Cliff Floyd	1.25	3.00
Brad Penny		
14 Jeff Bagwell	1.25	3.00
Craig Biggio		
15 Shawn Green	1.25	3.00
Adrian Beltre		
16 Ben Sheets	1.25	3.00
Richie Sexson		
17 Vladimir Guerrero	2.00	5.00
Jose Vidro		
18 Mike Piazza	3.00	8.00
Roberto Alomar		
19 Roger Clemens	4.00	10.00
Mike Mussina		
20 Derek Jeter	5.00	12.00
Jason Giambi		
21 Barry Zito	1.25	3.00
Tim Hudson		
22 Eric Chavez	1.25	3.00
Miguel Tejada		
23 Pat Burrell	1.25	3.00
Scott Rolen		
24 Brian Giles	1.25	3.00
Aramis Ramirez		
25 Ryan Klesko	1.25	3.00
Phil Nevin		
26 Barry Bonds	4.00	10.00
Rich Aurilia		
27 Ichiro Suzuki	4.00	10.00
Kazuhiro Sasaki		
28 Albert Pujols	4.00	10.00
J.D. Drew		
29 Alex Rodriguez	3.00	8.00
Ivan Rodriguez		
30 Carlos Delgado	1.25	3.00
Shannon Stewart		
31 Mo Vaughn	1.25	3.00
Roger Cedeno		
32 Carlos Beltran	1.25	3.00
Mike Sweeney		
33 Edgar Martinez	1.25	3.00
Bret Boone		
34 Juan Gonzalez	1.25	3.00
Rafael Palmeiro		
35 Johnny Damon	2.00	5.00
Rickey Henderson		
36 Sean Casey	1.25	3.00
Adam Dunn		
37 Jeff Kent	1.25	3.00
Tsuyoshi Shinjo		
38 Lance Berkman	1.25	3.00
Richard Hidalgo		
39 So Taguchi	1.25	3.00
Tino Martinez		
40 Hideo Nomo	1.25	3.00
Kazuhisa Ishii		

2002 Absolute Memorabilia Team Tandems Materials

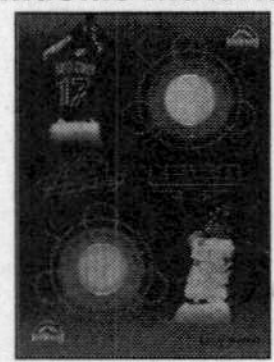

Inserted into hobby packs at a stated rate of one in 33 hobby and one in 164 retail, these 40 cards form a complete parallel to the Team Tandem insert set. These cards feature two pieces of memorabilia on each card. According to the manufacturer a few cards were printed in shorter supply and we have notated the announced print runs next to the card in our checklist. It was believed shortly after release that card 27 was not produced. Copies of the card eventually did surface but it's generally accepted to be one of the shortest cards in the set with a rumored print run of 100 copies.

Card	Low	High
1 Troy Glaus Jsy	4.00	10.00
Darin Erstad Bat		
2 Curt Schilling Jsy	6.00	15.00
Randy Johnson Jsy		
3 Chipper Jones Bat	6.00	15.00
Andruw Jones Bat		
4 Greg Maddux Jsy	10.00	25.00
Tom Glavine Jsy		
5 Nomar Garciaparra Bat	10.00	25.00
Manny Ramirez Bat SP/200 *		
6 Pedro Martinez Jsy	8.00	20.00
Trot Nixon Bat SP/200 *		
7 Kerry Wood Base	8.00	20.00
Sammy Sosa Base SP/250 *		
8 Frank Thomas Bat	6.00	15.00
Magglio Ordonez Bat		
9 Ken Griffey Jr. Base	6.00	15.00
Barry Larkin Base		
10 C.C Sabathia Jsy	8.00	20.00
Jim Thome Bat SP/225 *		
11 Todd Helton Bat	6.00	15.00
Larry Walker Bat		
12 Bobby Higginson Bat	4.00	10.00
Shane Halter Bat		
13 Cliff Floyd Bat	4.00	10.00
Brad Penny Jsy		
14 Jeff Bagwell Bat	6.00	15.00
Craig Biggio Bat		
15 Shawn Green Bat	4.00	10.00
Adrian Beltre Bat		
16 Ben Sheets Jsy	4.00	10.00
Richie Sexson Bat		
17 Vladimir Guerrero Bat	6.00	15.00
Jose Vidro Bat		
18 Mike Piazza Bat	8.00	20.00
Roberto Alomar Bat SP/250 *		
19 Roger Clemens Fld Glv	50.00	100.00
Mike Mussina Fld Glv SP/50 *		
20 Derek Jeter Base	12.50	30.00
Jason Giambi Base SP/200 *		
21 Barry Zito Jsy	6.00	15.00
Tim Hudson Shoe SP/200 *		
22 Eric Chavez Bat	6.00	15.00
Miguel Tejada Bat SP/200 *		
23 Pat Burrell Bat	6.00	15.00
Scott Rolen Bat		
24 Brian Giles Bat	4.00	10.00
Aramis Ramirez Bat		
25 Ryan Klesko Bat	6.00	15.00
Phil Nevin Jsy SP/250 *		
26 Barry Bonds Base	8.00	20.00
Rich Aurilia Base		
27 Ichiro Suzuki Deck		
Kazuhiro Sasaki Deck SP		
28 Albert Pujols Base	8.00	20.00
J.D. Drew Base SP/150 *		
29 Alex Rodriguez Bat	8.00	20.00
Ivan Rodriguez Bat		
30 Carlos Delgado Bat	4.00	10.00
Shannon Stewart Bat		
31 Mo Vaughn Bat	4.00	10.00
Roger Cedeno Bat		
32 Carlos Beltran Bat	4.00	10.00
Mike Sweeney Bat		
33 Edgar Martinez Bat	6.00	15.00
Bret Boone Bat		
34 Juan Gonzalez Bat	6.00	15.00
Rafael Palmeiro Bat		
35 Johnny Damon Bat	6.00	15.00
Rickey Henderson Bat		
36 Sean Casey Bat	6.00	15.00
Adam Dunn Shoe SP/100 *		
37 Jeff Kent Bat	6.00	15.00
Tsuyoshi Shinjo Bat SP/250 *		
38 Lance Berkman Bat	4.00	10.00
Richard Hidalgo Bat		
39 So Taguchi Bat	8.00	20.00
Tino Martinez Bat SP/100 *		
40 Hideo Nomo Jsy	15.00	40.00
Kazuhisa Ishii Jsy SP/50 *		

2002 Absolute Memorabilia Team Tandems Materials Gold

Randomly inserted into packs, this is a parallel to the Team Tandem insert set. Each card has gold foil and was issued to a stated print run of 50 serial numbered sets.

Card	Low	High
1 Troy Glaus Jsy	10.00	25.00
Darin Erstad Jsy		
2 Curt Schilling Jsy	15.00	40.00
Randy Johnson Jsy		
3 Chipper Jones Jsy	15.00	40.00
Andruw Jones Jsy		
4 Greg Maddux Jsy	25.00	60.00
Tom Glavine Jsy		
5 Nomar Garciaparra Jsy	20.00	50.00
Manny Ramirez Jsy		
6 Pedro Martinez Jsy	15.00	40.00
Trot Nixon Bat		
7 Kerry Wood Base	15.00	40.00
Sammy Sosa Ball		
8 Frank Thomas Jsy	15.00	40.00
Magglio Ordonez Jsy		
9 Ken Griffey Jr. Base	15.00	40.00
Barry Larkin Base		
10 C.C Sabathia Jsy	15.00	40.00
Jim Thome Jsy		
11 Todd Helton Jsy	15.00	40.00
Larry Walker Jsy		
12 Bobby Higginson Bat	10.00	25.00
Shane Halter Bat		
13 Cliff Floyd Jsy	10.00	25.00
Brad Penny Jsy		
14 Jeff Bagwell Jsy	15.00	40.00
Craig Biggio Jsy		
15 Shawn Green Jsy	10.00	25.00
Adrian Beltre Jsy		
16 Ben Sheets Jsy	10.00	25.00
Richie Sexson Jsy		
17 Vladimir Guerrero Jsy	15.00	40.00
Jose Vidro Jsy		
18 Mike Piazza Jsy	15.00	40.00
Roberto Alomar Shoe		
19 Roger Clemens Jsy	50.00	120.00
Mike Mussina Shoe		
20 Derek Jeter Ball	25.00	60.00
Jason Giambi Ball		
21 Barry Zito Jsy	12.50	30.00
Tim Hudson Jsy		
22 Eric Chavez Bat	12.50	30.00
Miguel Tejada Jsy		
23 Pat Burrell Jsy	15.00	40.00
Scott Rolen Jsy		
24 Brian Giles Jsy	10.00	25.00
Aramis Ramirez Jsy		
25 Ryan Klesko Fld Glv	12.50	30.00
Phil Nevin Jsy		
26 Barry Bonds Ball	20.00	50.00
Rich Aurilia Base		
27 Ichiro Suzuki Ball	50.00	100.00
Kazuhiro Sasaki Deck		
28 Albert Pujols Ball	15.00	40.00
J.D. Drew Base		
29 Alex Rodriguez Jsy	20.00	50.00
Ivan Rodriguez Jsy		
30 Carlos Delgado Jsy	10.00	25.00
Shannon Stewart Jsy		
31 Mo Vaughn Bat	10.00	25.00
Roger Cedeno Bat		
32 Carlos Beltran Jsy	10.00	25.00
Mike Sweeney Jsy		
33 Edgar Martinez Jsy	15.00	40.00
Bret Boone Jsy		
34 Juan Gonzalez Jsy	15.00	40.00
Rafael Palmeiro Jsy		
35 Johnny Damon Bat	15.00	40.00
Rickey Henderson Bat		
36 Sean Casey Jsy	10.00	25.00
Adam Dunn Hat		
37 Jeff Kent Jsy	12.50	30.00
Tsuyoshi Shinjo Bat		
38 Lance Berkman Jsy	10.00	25.00
Richard Hidalgo Pants		
39 So Taguchi Jsy	12.50	30.00
Tino Martinez Bat		
40 Hideo Nomo Jsy		
Kazuhisa Ishii Jsy		

2002 Absolute Memorabilia Tools of the Trade

Issued in hobby packs at stated odds of one in nine hobby and one in 24 retail, these 95 cards feature many of the leading players in the game.

*GOLD: .75X TO 2X BASIC TOOLS
GOLD ODDS 1:45 HOBBY, 1:144 RETAIL

Card	Low	High
1 Mike Mussina	1.50	4.00
2 Rickey Henderson	2.50	6.00
3 Raul Mondesi	1.00	2.50
4 Nomar Garciaparra	4.00	10.00
5 Randy Johnson	2.50	6.00
6 Roger Clemens	5.00	12.00
7 Shawn Green	1.00	2.50
8 Todd Helton	1.50	4.00
9 Aramis Ramirez	1.00	2.50
10 Barry Larkin	1.50	4.00
11 Byung-Hyun Kim	1.00	2.50
12 C.C. Sabathia	1.00	2.50
13 Curt Schilling	1.00	2.50
14 Darin Erstad	1.00	2.50
15 Eric Karros	1.00	2.50
16 Freddy Garcia	1.00	2.50
17 Greg Maddux	4.00	10.00
18 Jason Kendall	1.00	2.50
19 Jim Thome	1.50	4.00
20 Juan Gonzalez	1.00	2.50
21 Kazuhiro Sasaki	1.00	2.50
22 Kerry Wood	1.00	2.50
23 Luis Gonzalez	1.00	2.50
24 Mark Mulder	1.00	2.50
25 Rich Aurilia	1.00	2.50
26 Ray Durham	1.00	2.50
27 Ben Grieve	1.00	2.50
28 Bret Boone	1.00	2.50
29 Edgar Martinez	1.50	4.00
30 Ivan Rodriguez	1.50	4.00
31 Jorge Posada	1.50	4.00
32 Mike Piazza	4.00	10.00
33 Pat Burrell	1.00	2.50
34 Robin Ventura	1.00	2.50
35 Trot Nixon	1.00	2.50
36 Adrian Beltre	1.00	2.50
37 Bernie Williams	1.50	4.00
38 Bobby Abreu	1.00	2.50
39 Carlos Delgado	1.00	2.50
40 Craig Biggio	1.50	4.00
41 Garret Anderson	1.00	2.50
42 Jermaine Dye	1.00	2.50
43 Johnny Damon Sox	1.00	2.50
44 Tim Salmon	1.50	4.00
45 Tino Martinez	1.50	4.00
46 Fred McGriff	1.50	4.00
47 Gary Sheffield	1.00	2.50
48 Adam Dunn	1.00	2.50
49 Joe Mays	1.00	2.50
50 Kenny Lofton	1.00	2.50
51 Josh Beckett	1.00	2.50
52 Bud Smith	1.00	2.50
53 Johnny Estrada	1.00	2.50
54 Charles Johnson	1.00	2.50
55 Craig Wilson	1.00	2.50
56 Terrence Long	1.00	2.50
57 Andy Pettitte	1.50	4.00
58 Brian Giles	1.00	2.50
59 Juan Pierre	1.00	2.50
60 Cliff Floyd	1.00	2.50
61 Ivan Rodriguez	1.50	4.00
62 Andruw Jones	1.50	4.00
63 Lance Berkman	1.00	2.50
64 Mark Buehrle	1.00	2.50
65 Miguel Tejada	1.00	2.50
66 Wade Miller	1.00	2.50
67 Johnny Estrada	1.00	2.50
68 Tsuyoshi Shinjo	1.00	2.50
69 Scott Rolen	1.50	4.00
70 Roberto Alomar	1.50	4.00
71 Mark Grace	1.50	4.00
72 Larry Walker	1.00	2.50
73 Jim Edmonds	1.00	2.50
74 Jeff Kent	1.00	2.50
75 Frank Thomas	2.50	6.00
76 Carlos Beltran	1.00	2.50
77 Barry Zito	1.00	2.50
78 Alex Rodriguez	4.00	10.00
79 Troy Glaus	1.00	2.50
80 Ryan Klesko	1.00	2.50
81 Tom Glavine	1.50	4.00
82 Ben Sheets	1.00	2.50
83 Manny Ramirez	1.50	4.00
84 Shannon Stewart	1.00	2.50
85 Vladimir Guerrero	2.50	6.00
86 Chipper Jones	2.50	6.00
87 Jeff Bagwell	1.50	4.00
88 Richie Sexson	1.00	2.50
89 Sean Casey	1.00	2.50
90 Tim Hudson	1.00	2.50
91 J.D. Drew	1.00	2.50
92 Ivan Rodriguez	1.50	4.00
93 Magglio Ordonez	1.00	2.50
94 John Buck	1.00	2.50
95 Paul Lo Duca	1.00	2.50

2002 Absolute Memorabilia Tools of the Trade Materials

Randomly inserted into packs, this is a parallel to the Tools of the Trade insert set. Each card features a game worn piece(or pieces) of the featued player. Cards in this set were printed to all sorts of different print runs which we have notated.

1-32 PRINT RUN 300 SERIAL #'d SETS
33-47 PRINT RUN 250 SERIAL #'d SETS
48-55 PRINT RUN 150 SERIAL #'d SETS
56-61 PRINT RUN 125 SERIAL #'d SETS
62-66 PRINT RUN 50 SERIAL #'d SETS
67 PRINT RUN 100 SERIAL #'d CARDS
68-82 PRINT RUN 200 SERIAL #'d SETS
83-87 PRINT RUN 75 SERIAL #'d SETS
88-95 PRINT RUN 50 SERIAL #'d SETS

Card	Low	High
1 Mike Mussina Jsy	4.00	10.00
2 Rickey Henderson Jsy	4.00	10.00
3 Raul Mondesi Jsy	3.00	8.00
4 Nomar Garciaparra Jsy	6.00	15.00
5 Randy Johnson Jsy	4.00	10.00
6 Roger Clemens Jsy	6.00	15.00
7 Shawn Green Jsy	3.00	8.00
8 Todd Helton Jsy	4.00	10.00
9 Aramis Ramirez Jsy	3.00	8.00
10 Barry Larkin Jsy	4.00	10.00
11 Byung-Hyun Kim Jsy	4.00	10.00
12 C.C. Sabathia Jsy	3.00	8.00
13 Curt Schilling Jsy	3.00	8.00
14 Darin Erstad Jsy	3.00	8.00
15 Eric Karros Jsy	3.00	8.00
16 Freddy Garcia Jsy	3.00	8.00
17 Greg Maddux Jsy	6.00	15.00
18 Jason Kendall Jsy	3.00	8.00
19 Jim Thome Jsy	4.00	10.00
20 Juan Gonzalez Jsy	3.00	8.00
21 Kazuhiro Sasaki Jsy	3.00	8.00
22 Kerry Wood Jsy	3.00	8.00
23 Luis Gonzalez Jsy	3.00	8.00
24 Mark Mulder Jsy	3.00	8.00
25 Rich Aurilia Jsy	3.00	8.00
26 Ray Durham Jsy	3.00	8.00
27 Ben Grieve Jsy	3.00	8.00
28 Bret Boone Jsy	3.00	8.00
29 Edgar Martinez Jsy	4.00	10.00
30 Ivan Rodriguez Jsy	4.00	10.00
31 Jorge Posada Jsy	4.00	10.00
32 Mike Piazza Jsy	6.00	15.00
33 Pat Burrell Bat	3.00	8.00
34 Robin Ventura Bat	3.00	8.00
35 Trot Nixon Bat	3.00	8.00
36 Adrian Beltre Bat	3.00	8.00
37 Bernie Williams Bat	4.00	10.00
38 Bobby Abreu Bat	3.00	8.00
39 Carlos Delgado Bat	3.00	8.00
40 Craig Biggio Bat	4.00	10.00
41 Garret Anderson Bat	3.00	8.00
42 Jermaine Dye Bat	3.00	8.00
43 Johnny Damon Sox Bat	4.00	10.00
44 Tim Salmon Bat	4.00	10.00
45 Tino Martinez Bat	4.00	10.00
46 Fred McGriff Bat	4.00	10.00
47 Gary Sheffield Bat	3.00	8.00
48 Adam Dunn Shoe	4.00	10.00
49 Joe Mays Shoe	4.00	10.00
50 Kenny Lofton Shoe	6.00	15.00
51 Josh Beckett Shoe	4.00	10.00
52 Bud Smith Shoe	4.00	10.00
53 Johnny Estrada Shin	4.00	10.00
54 Charles Johnson Shin	4.00	10.00
55 Craig Wilson Shin	4.00	10.00
56 Terrence Long Fld Glv	4.00	10.00
57 Andy Pettitte Fld Glv	6.00	15.00
58 Brian Giles Fld Glv	6.00	15.00
59 Juan Pierre Fld Glv	4.00	10.00
60 Cliff Floyd Fld Glv	4.00	10.00
61 Ivan Rodriguez Fld Glv	10.00	25.00
62 Andruw Jones Hat	10.00	25.00
63 Lance Berkman Hat	6.00	15.00
64 Mark Buehrle Hat	6.00	15.00
65 Miguel Tejada Hat	6.00	15.00
66 Wade Miller Hat	6.00	15.00
67 Johnny Estrada Mask	4.00	10.00
68 Tsuyoshi Shinjo Bat-Shoe	6.00	15.00
69 Scott Rolen Jsy-Bat	8.00	20.00
70 Roberto Alomar Bat-Shoe	8.00	20.00
71 Mark Grace Jsy-Fld Glv	6.00	15.00
72 Larry Walker Jsy-Bat	6.00	15.00
73 Jim Edmonds Jsy-Bat	6.00	15.00
74 Jeff Kent Jsy-Bat	6.00	15.00
75 Frank Thomas Jsy-Bat	8.00	20.00
76 Carlos Beltran Jsy-Bat	6.00	15.00

77 Barry Zito Jsy-Shoe 6.00 15.00
78 Alex Rodriguez Jsy-Bat 10.00 25.00
79 Troy Glaus Jsy-Jsy 6.00 15.00
80 Ryan Klesko Bat-Fld Glv 6.00 15.00
81 Tom Glavine Jsy-Shoe 8.00 20.00
82 Ben Sheets Jsy-Bat 6.00 15.00
83 Manny Ramirez 15.00 40.00
Jsy-Fld Glv-Shoe
84 Shannon Stewart 8.00 20.00
Jsy-Bat-Hat
85 Vladimir Guerrero 20.00 50.00
Jsy-Bat-Fld Glv
86 Chipper Jones 20.00 50.00
Jsy-Bat-Fld Glv
87 Jeff Bagwell 15.00 40.00
Jsy-Bat-Hat
88 Richie Sexson 15.00 40.00
Jsy-Bat-Shoe-Btg Glv
89 Sean Casey 15.00 40.00
Jsy-Bat-Shoe-Hat
90 Tim Hudson 15.00 40.00
Jsy-Hat-Shoe-Fld Glv
91 J.D. Drew 15.00 40.00
Jsy-Bat-Hat-Shoe
92 Ivan Rodriguez 15.00 40.00
Fld Glv-Chest-Jsy-Mask
93 Magglio Ordonez 15.00 40.00
Jsy-Shoe-Hat-Btg Glv
94 John Buck 10.00 25.00
Fld Glv-Chest-Shin-Mask
95 Paul Lo Duca 15.00 40.00
Jsy-Chest-Shin-Mask

2003 Absolute Memorabilia

This 208-card set was issued in two separate series. The primary Absolute Memorabilia product - containing cards 1-200 from the basic set - was released in July, 2003. The cards were issued in six card packs with an approximate SRP of $7.50 which came 18 packs to a box and 16 boxes to a case. The first 150 cards feature veterans while the final 50 cards feature a mix of rookies and veterans. Those cards were issued to a stated print run of 1500 serial numbered sets. Cards 201-208 were randomly seeded into packs of DLP Rookies and Traded issued in December, 2003. Each card was serial-numbered to 1000 copies.

COMP.LO SET w/o SP's (150) 15.00 40.00
COMMON CARD (1-150) .30 .75
COMMON CARD (151-208) 1.50 4.00
1 Nomar Garciaparra 1.25 3.00
2 Barry Bonds 2.00 5.00
3 Greg Maddux 1.25 3.00
4 Roger Clemens 1.50 4.00
5 Derek Jeter 2.00 5.00
6 Alex Rodriguez 1.25 3.00
7 Chipper Jones .75 2.00
8 Sammy Sosa .75 2.00
9 Alfonso Soriano .30 .75
10 Albert Pujols 1.50 4.00
11 Adam Dunn .30 .75
12 Tom Glavine .50 1.25
13 Pedro Martinez .50 1.25
14 Jim Thome .50 1.25
15 Hideo Nomo .75 2.00
16 Roberto Alomar .50 1.25
17 Barry Zito .30 .75
18 Troy Glaus .30 .75
19 Kerry Wood .30 .75
20 Magglio Ordonez .30 .75
21 Todd Helton .50 1.25
22 Craig Biggio .50 1.25
23 Roy Oswalt .30 .75
24 Torii Hunter .30 .75
25 Miguel Tejada .30 .75
26 Tsuyoshi Shinjo .30 .75
27 Scott Rolen .50 1.25
28 Rafael Palmeiro .50 1.25
29 Victor Martinez .50 1.25
30 Hank Blalock .30 .75
31 Jason Lane .30 .75
32 Junior Spivey .30 .75
33 Gary Sheffield .30 .75
34 Corey Patterson .30 .75
35 Corky Miller .30 .75
36 Brian Tallet .30 .75
37 Cliff Lee .30 .75
38 Jason Jennings .30 .75
39 Kirk Saarloos .30 .75
40 Wade Miller .30 .75
41 Angel Berroa .30 .75
42 Mike Sweeney .30 .75
43 Paul Lo Duca .30 .75
44 A.J. Pierzynski .30 .75
45 Drew Henson .30 .75
46 Eric Chavez .30 .75
47 Tim Hudson .30 .75
48 Aramis Ramirez .30 .75
49 Jack Wilson .30 .75
50 Ryan Klesko .30 .75
51 Antonio Perez .30 .75
52 Dewon Brazelton .30 .75
53 Mark Teixeira .50 1.25
54 Eric Hinske .30 .75
55 Freddy Sanchez .30 .75
56 Mike Rivera .30 .75
57 Alfredo Amezaga .30 .75
58 Cliff Floyd .30 .75
59 Brandon Larson .30 .75
60 Richard Hidalgo .30 .75
61 Cesar Izturis .30 .75
62 Richie Sexson .30 .75
63 Michael Cuddyer .30 .75
64 Javier Vazquez .30 .75
65 Brandon Claussen .30 .75
66 Carlos Rivera .30 .75
67 Vernon Wells .30 .75
68 Kenny Lofton .30 .75
69 Aubrey Huff .30 .75
70 Adam LaRoche .30 .75
71 Jeff Baker .30 .75
72 Jose Castillo .30 .75
73 Joe Borchard .30 .75
74 Walter Young .30 .75
75 Jose Morban .30 .75
76 Vinnie Chulk .30 .75
77 Christian Parker .30 .75
78 Mike Piazza 1.25 3.00
79 Ichiro Suzuki 1.50 4.00
80 Kazuhisa Ishii .30 .75
81 Rickey Henderson .75 2.00
82 Ken Griffey Jr. 1.25 3.00
83 Jason Giambi .30 .75
84 Randy Johnson .75 2.00
85 Curt Schilling .30 .75
86 Manny Ramirez .50 1.25
87 Barry Larkin .50 1.25
88 Jeff Bagwell .50 1.25
89 Vladimir Guerrero .75 2.00
90 Mike Mussina .50 1.25
91 Juan Gonzalez .30 .75
92 Andruw Jones .50 1.25
93 Frank Thomas .75 2.00
94 Sean Casey .30 .75
95 Josh Beckett .30 .75
96 Lance Berkman .30 .75
97 Shawn Green .30 .75
98 Bernie Williams .50 1.25
99 Pat Burrell .30 .75
100 Edgar Martinez .50 1.25
101 Ivan Rodriguez .50 1.25
102 Jeremy Guthrie .30 .75
103 Alexis Rios .40 1.00
104 Nic Jackson .30 .75
105 Jason Anderson .30 .75
106 Travis Chapman .30 .75
107 Mac Suzuki .30 .75
108 Toby Hall .30 .75
109 Mark Prior .50 1.25
110 So Taguchi .30 .75
111 Marlon Byrd .30 .75
112 Garret Anderson .30 .75
113 Luis Gonzalez .30 .75
114 Jay Gibbons .30 .75
115 Mark Buehrle .30 .75
116 Wily Mo Pena .30 .75
117 C.C. Sabathia .30 .75
118 Ricardo Rodriguez .30 .75
119 Robert Fick .30 .75
120 Rodrigo Rosario .30 .75
121 Alexis Gomez .30 .75
122 Carlos Beltran .30 .75
123 Joe Thurston .30 .75
124 Ben Sheets .30 .75
125 Jose Vidro .30 .75
126 Nick Johnson .30 .75
127 Mark Mulder .30 .75
128 Bobby Abreu .30 .75
129 Brian Giles .30 .75
130 Brian Lawrence .30 .75
131 Jeff Kent .30 .75
132 Chris Snelling .30 .75
133 Kevin Mench .30 .75
134 Carlos Delgado .30 .75
135 Orlando Hudson .30 .75
136 Juan Cruz .30 .75
137 Jim Edmonds .30 .75
138 Geronimo Gil .30 .75
139 Joe Crede .30 .75
140 Wilson Valdez .30 .75
141 Runelvys Hernandez .30 .75
142 Nick Neugebauer .30 .75
143 Takahito Nomura .30 .75
144 Andres Galarraga .30 .75
145 Mark Grace .50 1.25
146 Brandon Duckworth .30 .75
147 Oliver Perez .30 .75
148 Xavier Nady .30 .75
149 Rafael Soriano .30 .75
150 Ben Kozlowski .30 .75
151 Pr. Redman ROO RC 1.50 4.00
152 Craig Brazell ROO RC 1.50 4.00
153 Nook Logan ROO RC 2.00 5.00
154 Greg Aquino ROO RC 1.50 4.00
155 Matt Kata ROO RC 1.50 4.00
156 Ian Ferguson ROO RC 1.50 4.00
157 C.Wang ROO RC 8.00 20.00
158 Beau Kemp ROO RC 1.50 4.00
159 Alej. Machado ROO RC 1.50 4.00
160 Mi. Hessman ROO RC 1.50 4.00
161 Fran. Rosario ROO RC 1.50 4.00
162 Pedro Liriano ROO 1.50 4.00
163 Rich Fischer ROO RC 1.50 4.00
164 Franklin Perez ROO RC 1.50 4.00
165 Oscar Villarreal ROO RC 1.50 4.00
166 Arnie Munoz ROO RC 1.50 4.00
167 Tim Olson ROO RC 1.50 4.00
168 Jose Contreras ROO RC 2.00 5.00
169 Fran. Cruceta ROO RC 1.50 4.00
170 Jer. Bonderman ROO RC 3.00 8.00
171 Jeremy Griffiths ROO RC 1.50 4.00
172 John Webb ROO 1.50 4.00
173 Phil Seibel ROO RC 1.50 4.00
174 Aaron Looper ROO RC 1.50 4.00
175 Brian Stokes ROO RC 1.50 4.00
176 G.Quiroz ROO RC 1.50 4.00
177 Fern. Cabrera ROO RC 1.50 4.00
178 Josh Hall ROO RC 1.50 4.00
179 D. Markwell ROO RC 1.50 4.00
180 Andrew Brown ROO RC 2.00 5.00
181 Doug Waechter ROO RC 2.00 5.00
182 Felix Sanchez ROO RC 1.50 4.00
183 Gerardo Garcia ROO 1.50 4.00
184 Matt Bruback ROO RC 1.50 4.00
185 Mi. Hernandez ROO RC 1.50 4.00
186 Rett Johnson ROO RC 1.50 4.00
187 Ryan Cameron ROO RC 1.50 4.00
188 Rob Hammock ROO RC 1.50 4.00
189 Clint Barmes ROO RC 1.25 3.00
190 Brandon Webb ROO RC 3.00 8.00
191 Jon Leicester ROO RC 1.50 4.00
192 Shane Bazzell ROO RC 1.50 4.00
193 Joe Valentine ROO RC 1.50 4.00
194 Josh Stewart ROO RC 1.50 4.00
195 Pete LaForest ROO RC 1.50 4.00
196 Shane Victorino ROO RC 2.50 6.00
197 Terrmel Sledge ROO RC 1.50 4.00
198 Lew Ford ROO RC 2.00 5.00
199 T.Wellemeyer ROO RC 1.50 4.00
200 Hideki Matsui ROO RC 4.00 10.00
201 Adam Loewen ROO RC 2.00 5.00
202 Ramon Nivar ROO RC 1.50 4.00
203 Dan Haren ROO RC 2.50 6.00
204 Dontrelle Willis ROO 2.00 5.00
205 Chad Gaudin ROO RC 1.50 4.00
206 Rickie Weeks ROO RC 3.00 8.00
207 Ryan Wagner ROO RC 1.50 4.00
208 Delmon Young ROO RC 5.00 12.00

2003 Absolute Memorabilia Spectrum

*SPECTRUM 1-150: 2.5X TO 6X BASIC
*SPECTRUM 151-208: .6X TO 1.5X BASIC
1-200 RANDOM INSERTS IN PACKS
201-208 RANDOM IN DLP R/T PACKS
STATED PRINT RUN 100 SERIAL #'d SETS
157 Chien-Ming Wang ROO 30.00 60.00
190 Brandon Webb ROO 5.00 12.00
200 Hideki Matsui ROO 6.00 15.00
201 Adam Loewen ROO 3.00 8.00
206 Rickie Weeks ROO 5.00 12.00
208 Delmon Young ROO 8.00 20.00

2003 Absolute Memorabilia Absolutely Ink

Inserted at a stated rate of one in 552, these 40 cards feature authentic autographs from a mix of established major leaguers and some of the best prospects. Due to market scarcity, no pricing is provided for these cards.

STATED ODDS 1:552
NO PRICING DUE TO SCARCITY
1 Vladimir Guerrero
2 Adam Dunn
3 Roy Oswalt
4 Victor Martinez
5 Edgar Martinez
6 Eric Hinske
7 Adam Johnson
8 Jose Vidro
9 Jeff Baker
10 Jeremy Guthrie
11 Wily Mo Pena
12 Toby Hall
13 Bobby Abreu
14 Fernando Rodney
15 Doug Nickle
16 Rodrigo Rosario
17 Brandon Claussen
18 Jermaine Dye
19 Rafael Soriano
20 Dee Brown
21 Donaldo Mendez
22 Mark Prior
23 Joe Borchard
24 Brian Lawrence
25 Nick Neugebauer
26 Doug Davis
27 Tim Hudson
28 Christian Parker
29 Barry Larkin
30 Drew Henson
31 Mike Maroth
32 Corey Patterson
33 Jeremy Giambi
34 Cliff Bartosh
35 Tom Glavine
36 Mark Teixeira
37 Jack Wilson
38 Roberto Alomar
39 Barry Zito
40 Troy Glaus

2003 Absolute Memorabilia Absolutely Ink Blue

RANDOM INSERTS IN PACKS
PRINT RUNS B/WN 10-25 COPIES PER
NO PRICING DUE TO SCARCITY
1 Vladimir Guerrero/25
2 Adam Dunn/10
3 Roy Oswalt/25
4 Victor Martinez/10
5 Edgar Martinez/25
6 Eric Hinske/25
7 Adam Johnson/15
8 Jose Vidro/25
9 Jeff Baker/25
10 Jeremy Guthrie/25
11 Wily Mo Pena/15
12 Toby Hall/15
13 Bobby Abreu/25
14 Fernando Rodney/15
15 Doug Nickle/15
16 Rodrigo Rosario/25
17 Brandon Claussen/15
18 Jermaine Dye/25
19 Rafael Soriano/15
20 Dee Brown/15
21 Donaldo Mendez/15
22 Mark Prior/10
23 Joe Borchard/10
24 Brian Lawrence/15
25 Nick Neugebauer/15
26 Doug Davis/15
27 Tim Hudson/10
28 Christian Parker/15
29 Barry Larkin/10
30 Drew Henson/10
31 Mike Maroth/15
32 Corey Patterson/10
33 Jeremy Giambi/25
34 Cliff Bartosh/15
35 Tom Glavine/10
36 Mark Teixeira/10
37 Jack Wilson/15
38 Roberto Alomar/10
39 Barry Zito/10
40 Troy Glaus/10

2003 Absolute Memorabilia Absolutely Ink Gold

RANDOM INSERTS IN PACKS
PRINT RUNS B/WN 5-10 COPIES PER
NO PRICING DUE TO SCARCITY
1 Vladimir Guerrero/10
2 Adam Dunn/5
3 Roy Oswalt/10
4 Victor Martinez/5
5 Edgar Martinez/10
6 Eric Hinske/10
7 Adam Johnson/10
8 Jose Vidro/10
9 Jeff Baker/10
10 Jeremy Guthrie/10
11 Wily Mo Pena/10
12 Toby Hall/10
13 Bobby Abreu/10
14 Fernando Rodney/10
15 Doug Nickle/10
16 Rodrigo Rosario/10
17 Brandon Claussen/10
18 Jermaine Dye/10
19 Rafael Soriano/10
20 Dee Brown/10
21 Donaldo Mendez/10
22 Mark Prior/5
23 Joe Borchard/5
24 Brian Lawrence/10
25 Nick Neugebauer/10
26 Doug Davis/10
27 Tim Hudson/5
28 Christian Parker/10
29 Barry Larkin/5
30 Drew Henson/5
31 Mike Maroth/10
32 Corey Patterson/5
33 Jeremy Giambi/10
34 Cliff Bartosh/10
35 Tom Glavine/5
36 Mark Teixeira/5
37 Jack Wilson/10
38 Roberto Alomar/5
39 Barry Zito/5
40 Troy Glaus/5

2003 Absolute Memorabilia Atlantic City National

Collectors attending the 2003 Atlantic City National who opened Donruss Product while at their corporate booth were able to receive these specially produced cards. These cards parallel the regular Playoff Absolute Memorabilia set but have a special Atlantic City National embossing on the front and were printed to a stated print run of five serial numbers which is visible on the back. Due to market scarcity, no pricing is provided for these cards.

STATED PRINT RUN 5 SERIAL #'d SETS
NO PRICING DUE TO SCARCITY

2003 Absolute Memorabilia Glass Plaques

Inserted at the stated rate of one per sealed box, these 273 cards feature etched-glass collectibles with an autograph and/or a piece of game-used memorabilia. We have identified what comes with the card along with the stated print run in our checklist. Please note that for plaques with stated print runs of 25 or fewer no pricing is provided due to market scarcity.

1 Roberto Alomar AU/25
2 Roberto Alomar AU-Jsy/25
3 Roberto Alomar Bat-Jsy/100 15.00 40.00
4 Roberto Alomar Jsy/150 10.00 25.00
5 Jeff Bagwell AU/15
6 Jeff Bagwell AU-Jsy/10
7 Jeff Bagwell Bat-Jsy/100 15.00 40.00
8 Jeff Bagwell Jsy/150
9 Ernie Banks AU/15
10 Ernie Banks AU-Jsy/10
11 Ernie Banks Bat-Jsy/25
12 Ernie Banks Jsy/150 10.00 25.00
13 Lance Berkman AU/25
14 Lance Berkman AU-Jsy/25
15 Lance Berkman Bat-Jsy/100 10.00 25.00
16 Lance Berkman Jsy/150 6.00 15.00
17 Yogi Berra AU/25
18 Yogi Berra AU-Jsy/25
19 Yogi Berra Bat-Jsy/150
20 Yogi Berra Jsy/150
21 Barry Bonds Ball-Base/50 60.00 120.00
22 Barry Bonds Ball-Base/100 50.00 100.00
23 Barry Bonds Base/200 40.00 80.00
24 George Brett AU/15
25 George Brett AU-Jsy/10
26 George Brett Bat-Jsy/50 100.00 200.00
27 George Brett Jsy/200 40.00 80.00
28 Pat Burrell AU/25
29 Pat Burrell AU-Jsy/10
30 Pat Burrell Bat-Jsy/100 10.00 25.00
31 Pat Burrell Jsy/150 6.00 15.00
32 Steve Carlton AU/50 20.00 50.00
33 Steve Carlton AU-Jsy/25
34 Steve Carlton Bat-Jsy/100
35 Steve Carlton Jsy/150 6.00 15.00
36 R.Clemens Sox AU/15
37 R.Clemens Sox AU-Jsy/25
38 R.Clemens Sox Fld Glv-Jsy/50 100.00 200.00
39 R.Clemens Sox Jsy/150 40.00 80.00
40 R.Clemens Yanks AU/15
41 R.Clemens Yanks AU-Jsy/10
42 Clemens Yanks Glv-Jsy/50 100.00 200.00
43 R.Clemens Yanks Jsy/200 40.00 80.00
44 Roberto Clemente Bat-Jsy/50
45 Roberto Clemente Bat-Jsy/150
46 Roberto Clemente Jsy/200
47 Jose Contreras AU/25
48 Jose Contreras AU-Jsy/25
49 Jose Contreras Jsy-Jsy/100 15.00 40.00
50 Jose Contreras Jsy/150
51 Adam Dunn AU/25
52 Adam Dunn AU-Jsy/25
53 Adam Dunn Bat-Jsy/100 10.00 25.00
54 Adam Dunn Jsy/150 6.00 15.00
55 Bob Feller AU/50 15.00 40.00
56 Bob Feller AU-Jsy/25
57 Bob Feller Jsy-Jsy/50 15.00 40.00
58 Bob Feller Jsy/100 6.00 15.00
59 N.Garciaparra Bat-Jsy/100 40.00 80.00
60 N.Garciaparra Jsy/200 30.00 60.00
61 Jason Giambi Bat-Jsy/100 10.00 25.00
62 Jason Giambi Jsy/150 6.00 15.00
63 Troy Glaus AU/25
64 Troy Glaus AU-Jsy/25
65 Troy Glaus Bat-Jsy/100
66 Troy Glaus Jsy/150 6.00 15.00
67 Juan Gonzalez AU/15
68 Juan Gonzalez AU-Jsy/10
69 Juan Gonzalez Bat-Jsy/100
70 Juan Gonzalez Jsy/150
71 Luis Gonzalez AU/25
72 Luis Gonzalez AU-Jsy/25
73 Luis Gonzalez Bat-Jsy/100 10.00 25.00
74 Luis Gonzalez Jsy/150 6.00 15.00
75 Mark Grace AU/50 60.00 120.00
76 Mark Grace AU-Jsy/25
77 Mark Grace Bat-Jsy/100
78 Mark Grace Jsy/150 10.00 25.00
79 Shawn Green AU/15
80 Shawn Green AU-Jsy/10
81 Shawn Green Bat-Jsy/100 10.00 25.00
82 Shawn Green Jsy/150 6.00 15.00
83 Ken Griffey Jr. Ball-Base/50
84 Ken Griffey Jr. Ball-Base/100
85 Ken Griffey Jr. Base/200
86 Vladimir Guerrero AU/25
87 Vladimir Guerrero AU-Jsy/25
88 Vladimir Guerrero Bat-Jsy/100 15.00 40.00
89 Vladimir Guerrero Jsy/150
90 Tony Gwynn AU/15
91 Tony Gwynn AU-Jsy/10
92 Tony Gwynn Bat-Jsy/150
93 Tony Gwynn Jsy/200
94 Todd Helton AU/25
95 Todd Helton AU-Jsy/25
96 Todd Helton Bat-Jsy/100
97 Todd Helton Jsy/150
98 R.Henderson AU/15
99 R.Henderson AU-Jsy/10
100 R.Henderson Bat-Jsy/100 15.00 40.00
101 R.Henderson Jsy/200 10.00 25.00
102 Tim Hudson AU/50 30.00 60.00
103 Tim Hudson AU-Jsy/25
104 Tim Hudson Hat-Jsy/100 10.00 25.00
105 Tim Hudson Jsy/150 6.00 15.00
106 Torii Hunter AU/50 20.00 50.00
107 Torii Hunter AU-Jsy/25
108 Torii Hunter Hat-Jsy/100 10.00 25.00
109 Torii Hunter Jsy/150
110 Kazuhisa Ishii AU/15
111 Kazuhisa Ishii AU-Jsy/10
112 Kazuhisa Ishii Bat-Jsy/100 10.00 25.00
113 Kazuhisa Ishii Jsy/200 6.00 15.00
114 Derek Jeter Ball-Base/50
115 Derek Jeter Ball-Base/150
116 Derek Jeter Base/200
117 Randy Johnson AU/15
118 Randy Johnson AU-Jsy/10
119 Randy Johnson Bat -Jsy/100 15.00 40.00
120 Randy Johnson Jsy/150 10.00 25.00
121 Andruw Jones AU/25
122 Andruw Jones AU-Jsy/25
123 Andruw Jones Bat-Jsy/100
124 Andruw Jones Jsy/150 10.00 25.00
125 Chipper Jones AU/15
126 Chipper Jones AU-Jsy/10
127 Chipper Jones Bat-Jsy/100 15.00 40.00
128 Chipper Jones Jsy/150 10.00 25.00
129 Al Kaline AU/50
130 Al Kaline AU-Jsy/25
131 Al Kaline Bat-Jsy/100 15.00 40.00
132 Al Kaline Jsy/150 10.00 25.00
133 Barry Larkin AU/50 30.00 60.00
134 Barry Larkin AU-Jsy/25
135 Barry Larkin Bat-Jsy/100 15.00 40.00
136 Barry Larkin Jsy/150 10.00 25.00
137 Greg Maddux AU/15
138 Greg Maddux AU-Jsy/10
139 Greg Maddux Bat -Jsy/100 30.00 60.00
140 Greg Maddux Jsy/200 20.00 50.00
141 Pedro Martinez AU/10
142 Pedro Martinez AU-Jsy/10
143 Pedro Martinez Bat-Jsy/100 15.00 40.00
144 Pedro Martinez Jsy/150 10.00 25.00
145 H.Matsui Ball-Base/50 50.00 100.00
146 H.Matsui Ball-Base/150 30.00 60.00
147 H.Matsui Base/200 15.00 40.00
148 Don Mattingly AU/25
149 Don Mattingly AU-Jsy/25
150 Don Mattingly Bat-Jsy/100
151 Don Mattingly Jsy/200
152 Mark Mulder AU/50 20.00 50.00
153 Mark Mulder AU-Jsy/25
154 Mark Mulder Jsy/150 6.00 15.00
155 Mark Mulder Jsy-Jsy/100 10.00 25.00
156 Stan Musial AU/15
157 Stan Musial AU-Jsy/10
158 Stan Musial Bat-Jsy/150
159 Stan Musial Jsy/200
160 Hideo Nomo AU/15
161 Hideo Nomo AU-Jsy/10
162 Hideo Nomo Bat-Jsy/50 60.00 120.00
163 Hideo Nomo Bat-Jsy/100 15.00 40.00
164 Hideo Nomo Jsy/200 10.00 25.00
165 Magglio Ordonez AU/50 20.00 50.00
166 Magglio Ordonez AU-Jsy/25
167 M.Ordonez Bat-Jsy/100 10.00 25.00
168 Magglio Ordonez Jsy/150 6.00 15.00
169 Roy Oswalt AU/50 20.00 50.00
170 Roy Oswalt AU-Jsy/25
171 Roy Oswalt Bat-Jsy/100 10.00 25.00
172 Roy Oswalt Jsy/150 6.00 15.00
173 Rafael Palmeiro AU/25
174 Rafael Palmeiro AU-Jsy/25
175 Rafael Palmeiro Bat-Jsy/100 15.00 40.00
176 Rafael Palmeiro Jsy/150 10.00 25.00
177 Mike Piazza AU/15
178 Mike Piazza AU-Jsy/10
179 Mike Piazza Bat-Jsy/50 50.00 100.00
180 Mike Piazza Bat-Jsy/100 30.00 60.00
181 Mike Piazza Jsy/200 20.00 50.00
182 Mark Prior AU/25
183 Mark Prior AU-Jsy/25
184 Mark Prior Bat-Jsy/100 15.00 40.00
185 Mark Prior Jsy/150 10.00 25.00
186 Albert Pujols AU/25
187 Albert Pujols AU-Jsy/25
188 Albert Pujols Bat-Jsy/150 50.00 100.00
189 Albert Pujols Jsy/150 40.00 80.00
190 Manny Ramirez AU/15
191 Manny Ramirez AU-Jsy/10
192 Manny Ramirez Bat-Jsy/100 15.00 40.00
193 Manny Ramirez Jsy/150 10.00 25.00
194 Cal Ripken AU/15
195 Cal Ripken AU-Jsy/10
196 Cal Ripken Bat-Jsy/150 60.00 120.00
197 Cal Ripken Jsy/200 50.00 100.00
198 Frank Robinson AU/50 30.00 60.00
199 Frank Robinson AU-Jsy/25
200 Frank Robinson Bat-Jsy/100 15.00 40.00
201 Frank Robinson Jsy/150 10.00 25.00
202 Alex Rodriguez AU/15
203 Alex Rodriguez AU-Jsy/25
204 Alex Rodriguez Bat-Jsy/100
205 Alex Rodriguez Jsy/200
206 N.Ryan Angels AU/15
207 N.Ryan Angels AU-Jsy/25
208 N.Ryan Angels Jacket-Jsy/150
209 N.Ryan Angels Jsy/200 50.00 100.00
210 N.Ryan Astros AU/15
211 N.Ryan Astros AU-Jsy/25
212 N.Ryan Astros Fld Glv-Jsy/25
213 N.Ryan Astros Jsy/200 50.00 100.00
214 N.Ryan Astros Jsy-Jsy/100 60.00 120.00
215 N.Ryan Rgr AU/15
216 N.Ryan Rgr AU-Jsy/10
217 N.Ryan Rgr Fld Glv-Jsy/25
218 N.Ryan Rgr Jsy/200 50.00 100.00
219 N.Ryan Rgr Jsy-Jsy/100 60.00 120.00
220 R.Sandberg AU/15
221 R.Sandberg AU-Jsy/10
222 R.Sandberg Bat-Jsy G/50 75.00 150.00
223 R.Sandberg Bat-Jsy S/50 75.00 150.00
224 R.Sandberg Jsy/200 40.00 80.00
225 Curt Schilling AU/25
226 Curt Schilling AU-Jsy/25
227 Curt Schilling Fld Glv-Jsy/50
228 Curt Schilling Jsy/150 6.00 15.00
229 Mike Schmidt AU/25
230 Mike Schmidt AU-Jsy/25
231 Mike Schmidt Bat-Jsy/100 50.00 100.00
232 Mike Schmidt Jsy/200 40.00 80.00
233 Ozzie Smith AU/15
234 Ozzie Smith AU-Jsy/10
235 Ozzie Smith Bat-Jsy/100 50.00 100.00
236 Ozzie Smith Jsy/150 40.00 80.00
237 A.Soriano AU/15
238 A.Soriano AU-Jsy/10
239 A.Soriano Bat-Jsy/150 10.00 25.00
240 A.Soriano Jsy/150 6.00 15.00
241 Sammy Sosa Bat-Jsy/150 15.00 40.00
242 Sammy Sosa Jsy/200 10.00 25.00
243 Junior Spivey AU/50
244 Junior Spivey AU-Jsy/25
245 Junior Spivey Bat-Jsy/100 10.00 25.00
246 Junior Spivey Jsy/150 6.00 15.00
247 I.Suzuki Ball-Base/50 60.00 120.00
248 I.Suzuki Ball-Base/150 50.00 100.00
249 I.Suzuki Base/200 30.00 60.00
250 Mark Teixeira AU/50
251 Mark Teixeira AU-Jsy/25
252 Mark Teixeira Bat-Jsy/100 15.00 40.00
253 Mark Teixeira Jsy/150 10.00 25.00
254 Miguel Tejada AU/50 30.00 60.00
255 Miguel Tejada AU-Jsy/25
256 Miguel Tejada Bat-Jsy/100 10.00 25.00
257 Miguel Tejada Jsy/150 6.00 15.00
258 Frank Thomas AU/25
259 Frank Thomas AU-Jsy/25
260 Frank Thomas Bat-Jsy/100 15.00 40.00
261 Frank Thomas Jsy/150 10.00 25.00
262 Bernie Williams AU/15
263 Bernie Williams AU-Jsy/10
264 Bernie Williams Bat-Jsy/100 15.00 40.00

265 Bernie Williams Jsy/150 10.00 25.00
266 Kerry Wood AU/50 30.00 60.00
267 Kerry Wood AU-Jsy/25
268 Kerry Wood Bat-Jsy/100 10.00 25.00
269 Kerry Wood Jsy/150 6.00 15.00
270 Barry Zito AU/50 20.00 50.00
271 Barry Zito AU-Jsy/25
272 Barry Zito Hat-Jsy/100 10.00 25.00
273 Barry Zito Jsy/150 6.00 15.00

2003 Absolute Memorabilia Player Collection

*PLAY.COLL: .75X TO 2X PRESTIGE PC
STATED PRINT RUN 75 SERIAL #'d SETS
SEE 2003 PRESTIGE PLAY.COLL FOR PRICING
SPECTRUM PRINT RUN 25 SERIAL #'d SETS
NO SPECTRUM PRICING DUE TO SCARCITY
RANDOM INSERTS IN PACKS

2003 Absolute Memorabilia Portraits Promos

STATED ODDS ONE PER BOX
1 Vladimir Guerrero 1.00 2.50
2 Luis Gonzalez .40 1.00
3 Andruw Jones .60 1.50
4 Manny Ramirez .60 1.50
5 Derek Jeter 2.50 6.00
6 Eric Hinske .40 1.00
7 Curt Schilling .40 1.00
8 Adam Dunn .40 1.00
9 Jason Jennings .40 1.00
10 Mike Piazza 1.50 4.00
11 Jason Giambi .40 1.00
12 Jeff Bagwell .60 1.50
13 Rickey Henderson 1.00 2.50
14 Randy Johnson 1.00 2.50
15 Roger Clemens 2.00 5.00
16 Troy Glaus .40 1.00
17 Hideo Nomo 1.00 2.50
18 Joe Borchard .40 1.00
19 Torii Hunter .40 1.00
20 Lance Berkman .40 1.00
21 Todd Helton .60 1.50
22 Mike Mussina .40 1.00
23 Vernon Wells .40 1.00
24 Pat Burrell .40 1.00
25 Ichiro Suzuki 2.00 5.00
26 Shawn Green .40 1.00
27 Frank Thomas 1.00 2.50
28 Barry Zito .40 1.00
29 Barry Bonds 2.50 6.00
30 Ken Griffey Jr. 1.50 4.00
31 Albert Pujols 2.00 5.00
32 Roberto Alomar .60 1.50
33 Barry Larkin .60 1.50
34 Tony Gwynn 1.25 3.00
35 Chipper Jones 1.00 2.50
36 Pedro Martinez .60 1.50
37 Juan Gonzalez .40 1.00
38 Greg Maddux 1.50 4.00
39 Tim Hudson .40 1.00
40 Sammy Sosa 1.00 2.50
41 Victor Martinez .60 1.50
42 Mark Buehrle .40 1.00
43 Austin Kearns .40 1.00
44 Kerry Wood .40 1.00
45 Nomar Garciaparra 1.50 4.00
46 Alfonso Soriano .40 1.00
47 Mark Prior .60 1.50
48 Richie Sexson .40 1.00
49 Mark Teixeira .60 1.50
50 Craig Biggio .60 1.50
51 Rafael Palmeiro .60 1.50
52 Carlos Beltran .40 1.00
53 Bernie Williams .60 1.50
54 Eric Chavez .40 1.00
55 Paul Konerko .40 1.00
56 Nolan Ryan 2.50 6.00
57 Mark Mulder .40 1.00
58 Miguel Tejada .40 1.00
59 Roy Oswalt .40 1.00
60 Jim Edmonds .40 1.00
61 Ryan Klesko .40 1.00
62 Cal Ripken 3.00 8.00
63 Josh Beckett .40 1.00
64 Kazuhisa Ishii .40 1.00
65 Alex Rodriguez 1.50 4.00
66 Mike Sweeney .40 1.00
67 C.C. Sabathia .40 1.00
68 Jose Vidro .40 1.00
69 Magglio Ordonez .40 1.00
70 Carlos Delgado .40 1.00
71 Jorge Posada .60 1.50
72 Bobby Abreu .40 1.00

2003 Absolute Memorabilia Rookie Materials Jersey Number

Randomly inserted into packs, these 15 cards feature not only game-worn jersey swatches but were printed to a stated print run which matched the player's jersey number. For cards with a print run of 25 or fewer, no pricing is provided due to market scarcity.

RANDOM INSERTS IN PACKS
PRINT RUNS B/WN 5-51 COPIES PER
NO PRICING ON QTY OF 25 OR LESS
1 Stan Musial Jsy/6
2 Yogi Berra Jsy/35 20.00 50.00
3 Vladimir Guerrero Jsy/27 20.00 50.00
4 Randy Johnson Jsy/51 20.00 50.00
5 Andruw Jones Jsy/25
6 Jeff Kent Jsy/11
7 Nomar Garciaparra Jsy/5
8 Hideo Nomo Jsy/16
9 Ivan Rodriguez Jsy/7
10 Alfonso Soriano Jsy/33 20.00 50.00
11 Scott Rolen Jsy/17
12 Juan Gonzalez Jsy/19
13 Rafael Palmeiro Bat/25
14 Mike Schmidt Bat/20
15 Cal Ripken Bat/8

2003 Absolute Memorabilia Rookie Materials Season

Randomly inserted into packs, these 15 cards feature not only game-worn jersey swatches but were printed to a stated print run which matched the player's debut season.

RANDOM INSERTS IN PACKS
PRINT RUNS B/WN 42-101 COPIES PER
1 Stan Musial Jsy/42 60.00 120.00
2 Yogi Berra Jsy/47 30.00 60.00
3 Vladimir Guerrero Jsy/97 10.00 25.00
4 Randy Johnson Jsy/89 10.00 25.00
5 Andruw Jones Jsy/96 10.00 25.00
6 Jeff Kent Jsy/92 6.00 15.00
8 Hideo Nomo Jsy/95 15.00 40.00
9 Ivan Rodriguez Jsy/91 10.00 25.00
10 Alfonso Soriano Jsy/101 6.00 15.00
11 Scott Rolen Jsy/96 10.00 25.00
12 Juan Gonzalez Jsy/89 6.00 15.00
13 Rafael Palmeiro Bat/86 10.00 25.00
14 Mike Schmidt Bat/73 30.00 60.00
15 Cal Ripken Bat/82 40.00 80.00

2003 Absolute Memorabilia Signing Bonus

Randomly inserted into packs, these 10 cards feature authentic autographs of baseball legends. Each of these cards were issued to a stated print run of 15 serial numbered sets and no pricing is provided due to market scarcity.

STATED PRINT RUN 15 SERIAL #'d SETS
BLUE PRINT RUN 10 SERIAL #'d SETS
GOLD PRINT RUN 5 SERIAL #'d SETS
RANDOM INSERTS IN PACKS
NO PRICING DUE TO SCARCITY
1 Nolan Ryan
2 Cal Ripken
3 Don Mattingly
4 Kirby Puckett
5 Tony Gwynn
6 Ozzie Smith
7 Mike Schmidt
8 Reggie Jackson
9 Yogi Berra
10 Stan Musial

2003 Absolute Memorabilia Spectrum Signatures

Randomly inserted into packs, these cards not only parallel the basic Playoff Absolute Memorabilia set but also were signed by the featured player. Cards 201-208 were randomly seeded into packs of DLP

Rookies and Traded. Quantities of each card range from 5-304 copies per. Please note that we have put the stated print run next to the player's name in our checklist. If 25 or fewer of a card was signed, there is no pricing due to market scarcity.

3 Greg Maddux/10
4 Roger Clemens/15
6 Alex Rodriguez/15
7 Chipper Jones/10
9 Alfonso Soriano/15
10 Albert Pujols/10
11 Adam Dunn/15
12 Tom Glavine/25
13 Pedro Martinez/5
14 Jim Thome/10
15 Hideo Nomo/5
16 Roberto Alomar/15
17 Barry Zito/25
18 Troy Glaus/10
19 Kerry Wood/15
20 Magglio Ordonez/25
21 Todd Helton/10
22 Craig Biggio/10
23 Roy Oswalt/25
24 Torii Hunter/25
25 Miquel Tejada/25
27 Scott Rolen/10
28 Rafael Palmeiro/10
29 Victor Martinez/100 15.00 40.00
30 Hank Blalock/50 10.00 25.00
31 Jason Lane/50
32 Junior Spivey/50 6.00 15.00
33 Gary Sheffield/10
34 Corey Patterson/50 6.00 15.00
35 Corky Miller/100
36 Brian Tallet/100
37 Cliff Lee/100
38 Jason Jennings/100
39 Kirk Saarloos/100
40 Wade Miller/50 6.00 15.00
41 Angel Berroa/100 6.00 15.00
42 Mike Sweeney/50 10.00 25.00
43 Paul Lo Duca/50 10.00 25.00
44 A.J. Pierzynski/100 10.00 25.00
45 Drew Henson/50 6.00 15.00
46 Eric Chavez/10
47 Tim Hudson/50 15.00 40.00
48 Aramis Ramirez/10
49 Jack Wilson/25
50 Ryan Klesko/25
51 Antonio Perez/25
52 Dewon Brazelton/50 6.00 15.00
53 Mark Teixeira/50 15.00 40.00
54 Eric Hinske/100 6.00 15.00
55 Freddy Sanchez/100 6.00 15.00
56 Mike Rivera/25
57 Alfredo Amezaga/100 6.00 15.00
58 Cliff Floyd/25
59 Brandon Larson/100
60 Richard Hidalgo/100 6.00 15.00
61 Cesar Izturis/25
62 Richie Sexson/25
63 Michael Cuddyer/100 6.00 15.00
64 Javier Vazquez/25
65 Brandon Claussen/25
66 Carlos Rivera/100
67 Vernon Wells/25
68 Kenny Lofton/50 15.00 40.00
69 Aubrey Huff/100 10.00 25.00
70 Adam LaRoche/100 6.00 15.00
71 Jeff Baker/100 6.00 15.00
72 Jose Castillo/100 6.00 15.00
73 Joe Borchard/100 6.00 15.00
74 Walter Young/100 6.00 15.00
75 Jose Morban/100
76 Vinnie Chulk/100 6.00 15.00
77 Christian Parker/25
78 Mike Piazza/5
80 Kazuhisa Ishii/25
81 Rickey Henderson/5
85 Curt Schilling/10
86 Manny Ramirez/10
87 Barry Larkin/50 40.00 80.00
88 Jeff Bagwell/5
89 Vladimir Guerrero/50 20.00 50.00
90 Mike Mussina/10
91 Juan Gonzalez/5
92 Andruw Jones/25
94 Sean Casey/10
95 Josh Beckett/100 15.00 40.00
96 Lance Berkman/25
97 Shawn Green/25
98 Bernie Williams/10
99 Pat Burrell/10
100 Edgar Martinez/50 20.00 50.00
101 Ivan Rodriguez/5
102 Jeremy Guthrie/100 6.00 15.00
103 Alexis Rios/100 10.00 25.00
104 Nic Jackson/100 6.00 15.00
105 Jason Anderson/100
106 Travis Chapman/100 6.00 15.00
107 Mac Suzuki/304 10.00 25.00
108 Toby Hall/25
109 Mark Prior/50 12.50 30.00
110 So Taguchi/25
111 Marlon Byrd/100 6.00 15.00
112 Garret Anderson/10
113 Luis Gonzalez/10
114 Jay Gibbons/100 6.00 15.00
115 Mark Buehrle/25
116 Wily Mo Pena/25
117 C.C. Sabathia/25
118 Ricardo Rodriguez/100 6.00 15.00
119 Robert Fick/100 6.00 15.00
120 Rodrigo Rosario/25
121 Alexis Gomez/100 6.00 15.00
122 Carlos Beltran/25
123 Joe Thurston/100
124 Ben Sheets/50 10.00 25.00
125 Jose Vidro/25
126 Nick Johnson/50 10.00 25.00
127 Mark Mulder/50 10.00 25.00
128 Bobby Abreu/25
129 Brian Giles/10
130 Brian Lawrence/25
132 Chris Snelling/100 6.00 15.00
133 Kevin Mench/100 10.00 25.00
135 Orlando Hudson/50 6.00 15.00
136 Juan Cruz/100
138 Geronimo Gil/25
139 Joe Crede/100 6.00 15.00
140 Wilson Valdez/25
141 Runelvys Hernandez/100 6.00 15.00
142 Nick Neugebauer/25
143 Takahito Nomura/47 10.00 25.00
144 Andres Galarraga/25
145 Mark Grace/25
146 Brandon Duckworth/25
147 Oliver Perez/50 10.00 25.00
148 Xavier Nady/100 6.00 15.00
149 Rafael Soriano/25
150 Ben Kozlowski/100 6.00 15.00
151 Prentice Redman ROO/250 4.00 10.00
152 Craig Brazell ROO/250 4.00 10.00
153 Nook Logan ROO/250 6.00 15.00
154 Greg Aquino ROO/250 4.00 10.00
155 Matt Kata ROO/250 4.00 10.00
156 Ian Ferguson ROO/250 4.00 10.00
157 Chien Wang ROO/250 125.00 250.00
158 Beau Kemp ROO/250 4.00 10.00
159 Alej Machado ROO/250 4.00 10.00
160 Mike Hessman ROO/250 4.00 10.00
161 Franc Rosario ROO/250 4.00 10.00
162 Pedro Liriano ROO/250 4.00 10.00
163 Rich Fischer ROO/250 4.00 10.00
164 Franklin Perez ROO/250
165 Oscar Villarreal ROO/250 4.00 10.00
166 Arnie Munoz ROO/250 4.00 10.00
167 Tim Olson ROO/250 4.00 10.00
168 Jose Contreras ROO/250 8.00 20.00
169 Franc Cruceta ROO/250 4.00 10.00
170 J.Bonderman ROO/250 20.00 50.00
171 Jeremy Griffiths ROO/250 4.00 10.00
172 John Webb ROO/250
173 Phil Seibel ROO/250
174 Aaron Looper ROO/250 4.00 10.00
175 Brian Stokes ROO/250 4.00 10.00
176 Guillermo Quiroz ROO/250 4.00 10.00
177 Fernando Cabrera ROO/250 4.00 10.00
178 Josh Hall ROO/250 4.00 10.00
179 Diego Markwell ROO/250 4.00 10.00
180 Andrew Brown ROO/250 6.00 15.00
181 Doug Waechter ROO/250 6.00 15.00
182 Felix Sanchez ROO/250 4.00 10.00
183 Gerardo Garcia ROO/250
184 Matt Bruback ROO/250 4.00 10.00
185 Michel Hernandez ROO/250
186 Rett Johnson ROO/250 4.00 10.00
187 Ryan Cameron ROO/250 4.00 10.00
188 Rob Hammock ROO/250 4.00 10.00
189 Clint Barmes ROO/250 6.00 15.00
190 Brandon Webb ROO/250 30.00 60.00
191 Jon Leicester ROO/250 4.00 10.00
192 Shane Bazzell ROO/250 4.00 10.00
193 Joe Valentine ROO/250 4.00 10.00
194 Josh Stewart ROO/250
195 Pete LaForest ROO/250 4.00 10.00
196 Shane Victorino ROO/250 15.00 40.00
197 Termel Sledge ROO/250 4.00 10.00
198 Lew Ford ROO/250 6.00 15.00
199 Todd Wellemeyer ROO/250 4.00 10.00
201 Adam Loewen ROO/100 10.00 25.00
202 Ramon Nivar ROO/100 4.00 10.00
203 Dan Haren ROO/100 10.00 25.00
204 Dontrelle Willis ROO/25
205 Chad Gaudin ROO/50 6.00 15.00
206 Rickie Weeks ROO/25
207 Ryan Wagner ROO/100 4.00 10.00
208 Delmon Young ROO/25

2003 Absolute Memorabilia Team Tandems

STATED ODDS 1:48
*SPECTRUM: 1.25X TO 3X BASIC
SPECTRUM RANDOM INSERTS IN PACKS
SPECTRUM PRINT RUN 100 #'d SETS
1 Sammy Sosa 2.00 5.00
Mark Prior
2 Vladimir Guerrero 2.00 5.00
Jose Vidro
3 Bernie Williams 2.00 5.00
Alfonso Soriano
4 Mike Sweeney 1.25 3.00
Carlos Beltran
5 Magglio Ordonez 1.25 3.00
Paul Konerko
6 Adam Dunn 1.25 3.00
Austin Kearns
7 Randy Johnson 2.00 5.00
Curt Schilling
8 Hideo Nomo 2.00 5.00
Kazuhisa Ishii
9 Pat Burrell 1.25 3.00
Bobby Abreu
10 Todd Helton 2.00 5.00
Larry Walker

2003 Absolute Memorabilia Team Tandems Materials

1-7/10 PRINT RUN 100 SERIAL #'d SETS
8-9 PRINT RUN 40 SERIAL #'d SETS
SPECTRUM 1-7/10 PRINT RUN 25 #'d SETS
SPECTRUM 8-9 PRINT RUN 10 #'d SETS
NO SPECTRUM PRICING DUE TO SCARCITY
RANDOM INSERTS IN PACKS
ALL FEATURE DUAL JERSEY SWATCHES
1 Sammy Sosa 10.00 25.00
Mark Prior
2 Vladimir Guerrero 10.00 25.00
Jose Vidro
3 Bernie Williams 10.00 25.00
Alfonso Soriano
4 Mike Sweeney 6.00 15.00
Carlos Beltran
5 Magglio Ordonez 6.00 15.00
Paul Konerko
6 Adam Dunn 6.00 15.00
Austin Kearns
7 Randy Johnson 10.00 25.00
Curt Schilling
8 Hideo Nomo 20.00 50.00
Kazuhisa Ishii/40
9 Pat Burrell 10.00 25.00
Bobby Abreu/40
10 Todd Helton 10.00 25.00
Larry Walker

2003 Absolute Memorabilia Team Trios

STATED ODDS 1:88
*SPECTRUM: 1X TO 2.5X BASIC
SPECTRUM RANDOM INSERTS IN PACKS
SPECTRUM PRINT RUN 50 SERIAL #'d SETS
1 Greg Maddux 6.00 15.00
Chipper Jones
Andruw Jones
2 Sammy Sosa 4.00 10.00
Mark Prior
Kerry Wood
3 Pedro Martinez 6.00 15.00
Nomar Garciaparra
Manny Ramirez
4 Jason Giambi 6.00 15.00
Alfonso Soriano
Roger Clemens
5 Alex Rodriguez 6.00 15.00
Rafael Palmeiro
Mark Teixeira
6 Mike Piazza 6.00 15.00
Roberto Alomar
Tsuyoshi Shinjo
7 Jeff Bagwell 4.00 10.00
Craig Biggio
Lance Berkman
8 Troy Glaus 4.00 10.00
Garret Anderson
Troy Percival
9 Miguel Tejada 4.00 10.00
Eric Chavez
Barry Zito
10 Luis Gonzalez 4.00 10.00
Randy Johnson
Curt Schilling

2003 Absolute Memorabilia Team Trios Materials

1-2/4-5/7/9-10 PRINT RUN 100 #'d SETS
3/6/8 PRINT RUNS B/WN 40-50 COPIES PER
SPECTRUM 1-2/4-5/7/9-10 PRINT 25 #'d SETS
SPECTRUM 3/6/8 PRINT RUN 10 #'d SETS
NO SPECTRUM PRICING DUE TO SCARCITY
RANDOM INSERTS IN PACKS
ALL FEATURE THREE JERSEY SWATCHES
1 Greg Maddux 15.00 40.00
Chipper Jones
Andruw Jones
2 Sammy Sosa 15.00 40.00
Mark Prior
Kerry Wood
3 Pedro Martinez 40.00 80.00
Nomar Garciaparra
Manny Ramirez/50
4 Jason Giambi 20.00 50.00
Alfonso Soriano
Roger Clemens
5 Alex Rodriguez 15.00 40.00
Rafael Palmeiro
Mark Teixeira
6 Mike Piazza 30.00 60.00
Roberto Alomar
Tsuyoshi Shinjo/40
7 Jeff Bagwell 15.00 40.00
Craig Biggio
Lance Berkman
8 Troy Glaus 15.00 40.00
Garret Anderson
Troy Percival/40
9 Miguel Tejada 15.00 40.00
Eric Chavez
Barry Zito
10 Luis Gonzalez 15.00 40.00
Randy Johnson
Curt Schilling

2003 Absolute Memorabilia Tools of the Trade

STATED ODDS 1:5
*SPECTRUM: 1X TO 2.5X BASIC
SPECTRUM RANDOM INSERTS IN PACKS
SPECTRUM PRINT RUN 100 #'d SETS
1 Sammy Sosa 1.50 4.00
2 Nomar Garciaparra 2.50 6.00
3 Andruw Jones 1.00 2.50
4 Troy Glaus .60 1.50
5 Greg Maddux 2.50 6.00
6 Rickey Henderson 1.50 4.00
7 Alex Rodriguez 2.50 6.00
8 Manny Ramirez 1.00 2.50
9 Lance Berkman .60 1.50
10 Roger Clemens 3.00 8.00
11 Ivan Rodriguez 1.00 2.50
12 Kazuhisa Ishii .60 1.50
13 Alfonso Soriano .60 1.50
14 Austin Kearns .60 1.50
15 Mike Piazza 2.50 6.00
16 Curt Schilling .60 1.50
17 Jeff Bagwell 1.00 2.50
18 Todd Helton 1.00 2.50
19 Randy Johnson 1.50 4.00
20 Vladimir Guerrero 1.50 4.00
21 Kerry Wood .60 1.50
22 Rafael Palmeiro 1.00 2.50
23 Roy Oswalt .60 1.50
24 Chipper Jones 1.50 4.00
25 Pat Burrell .60 1.50
26 Jason Giambi .60 1.50
27 Pedro Martinez 1.00 2.50
28 Roberto Alomar 1.00 2.50
29 Shawn Green .60 1.50
30 Adam Dunn .60 1.50
31 Juan Gonzalez .60 1.50
32 Mark Prior 1.00 2.50
33 Hideo Nomo 1.50 4.00
34 Torii Hunter .60 1.50
35 Mark Teixeira 1.00 2.50
36 Craig Biggio 1.00 2.50
37 Rafael Palmeiro 1.00 2.50
38 Jeff Bagwell 1.00 2.50
39 Albert Pujols 3.00 8.00
40 Richie Sexson .60 1.50
41 Alex Rodriguez 2.50 6.00
42 Carlos Delgado .60 1.50
43 Frank Thomas 1.50 4.00
44 Sammy Sosa 1.50 4.00
45 Marlon Byrd .60 1.50
46 Mark Prior 1.00 2.50
47 Adrian Beltre .60 1.50
48 Tom Glavine 1.00 2.50
49 So Taguchi .60 1.50
50 Jeff Bagwell 1.00 2.50
51 Mike Sweeney .60 1.50
52 Luis Gonzalez .60 1.50
53 Chipper Jones 1.50 4.00
54 Jason Giambi .60 1.50
55 Miguel Tejada .60 1.50
56 Todd Helton 1.00 2.50
57 Andruw Jones 1.00 2.50
58 Mike Piazza 2.50 6.00
59 Manny Ramirez 1.00 2.50
60 Randy Johnson 1.50 4.00
61 Carlos Beltran .60 1.50
62 Victor Martinez 1.00 2.50
63 Orlando Hudson .60 1.50
64 Jeff Kent .60 1.50
65 Greg Maddux 2.50 6.00
66 Garret Anderson .60 1.50
67 Joe Thurston .60 1.50
68 Mark Teixeira 1.00 2.50
69 Kazuhisa Ishii .60 1.50
70 Austin Kearns .60 1.50
71 Pat Burrell .60 1.50
72 Joe Borchard .60 1.50
73 Josh Phelps .60 1.50
74 Travis Hafner .60 1.50
75 So Taguchi .60 1.50
76 Victor Martinez 1.00 2.50
77 Paul Lo Duca .60 1.50
78 Bernie Williams 1.00 2.50
79 Josh Phelps .60 1.50
80 Marlon Byrd .60 1.50
81 Manny Ramirez 1.00 2.50
82 Jason Giambi .60 1.50
83 Jeff Bagwell 1.00 2.50
84 Sammy Sosa 1.50 4.00
85 Josh Phelps .60 1.50
86 Tim Hudson .60 1.50
87 Randy Johnson 1.50 4.00
88 Troy Glaus .60 1.50

89 Joe Thurston .60 1.50
90 Miguel Tejada .60 1.50
91 Adam Dunn .60 1.50
92 Magglio Ordonez .60 1.50
93 Mike Sweeney .60 1.50
94 Andruw Jones 1.00 2.50
95 Carlos Beltran .60 1.50
96 Joe Borchard .60 1.50
97 Austin Kearns .60 1.50
98 Richie Sexson .60 1.50
99 Mark Prior 1.00 2.50
100 Mark Teixeira 1.00 2.50
101 Ryan Klesko .60 1.50
102 Jason Jennings .60 1.50
103 Travis Hafner .60 1.50
104 Mark Buehrle .60 1.50
105 Eric Hinske .60 1.50
106 Rafael Palmeiro 1.00 2.50
107 Roy Oswalt .60 1.50
108 Kerry Wood .60 1.50
109 Brian Giles .60 1.50
110 Ivan Rodriguez 1.00 2.50

2003 Absolute Memorabilia Tools of the Trade Materials

1-74 PRINT RUNS B/WN 40-250 COPIES PER
75-90 PRINT RUNS B/WN 50-125 COPIES PER
91-97 PRINT RUN 100 SERIAL #'d SETS
98-104 PRINT RUN 50 SERIAL #'d SETS
105-110 PRINT RUN 50 SERIAL #'d SETS
RANDOM INSERTS IN PACKS
1 Sammy Sosa Jsy/250 4.00 10.00
2 Nomar Garciaparra Jsy/250 6.00 15.00
3 Andruw Jones Jsy/250 4.00 10.00
4 Troy Glaus Jsy/250 3.00 8.00
5 Greg Maddux Jsy/250 4.00 10.00
6 Rickey Henderson Jsy/40 10.00 25.00
7 Alex Rodriguez Jsy/250 6.00 15.00
8 Manny Ramirez Jsy/250 4.00 10.00
9 Lance Berkman Jsy/250 3.00 8.00
10 Roger Clemens Jsy/250 6.00 15.00
11 Ivan Rodriguez Jsy/250 4.00 10.00
12 Kazuhisa Ishii Jsy/40 6.00 15.00
13 Alfonso Soriano Jsy/250 3.00 8.00
14 Austin Kearns Jsy/250 3.00 8.00
15 Mike Piazza Jsy/250 4.00 10.00
16 Curt Schilling Jsy/250 3.00 8.00
17 Jeff Bagwell Jsy/250 4.00 10.00
18 Todd Helton Jsy/250 4.00 10.00
19 Randy Johnson Jsy/250 4.00 10.00
20 Vladimir Guerrero Jsy/250 4.00 10.00
21 Kerry Wood Jsy/250 3.00 8.00
22 Rafael Palmeiro Jsy/250 4.00 10.00
23 Roy Oswalt Jsy/250 3.00 8.00
24 Chipper Jones Jsy/250 4.00 10.00
25 Pat Burrell Jsy/40 6.00 15.00
26 Jason Giambi Jsy/250 3.00 8.00
27 Pedro Martinez Jsy/250 4.00 10.00
28 Roberto Alomar Jsy/40 10.00 25.00
29 Shawn Green Jsy/250 3.00 8.00
30 Adam Dunn Jsy/250 3.00 8.00
31 Juan Gonzalez Jsy/40 6.00 15.00
32 Mark Prior Jsy/250 4.00 10.00
33 Hideo Nomo Jsy/250 6.00 15.00
34 Torii Hunter Jsy/250 3.00 8.00
35 Mark Teixeira Jsy/250 4.00 10.00
36 Craig Biggio Pants/250 4.00 10.00
37 Rafael Palmeiro Pants/250 4.00 10.00
38 Jeff Bagwell Pants/250 4.00 10.00
39 Albert Pujols Jsy/200 6.00 15.00
40 Richie Sexson Pants/250 3.00 8.00
41 Alex Rodriguez Bat/250 6.00 15.00
42 Carlos Delgado Bat/250 3.00 8.00
43 Frank Thomas Bat/75 6.00 15.00
44 Sammy Sosa Bat/250 4.00 10.00
45 Marlon Byrd Bat/250 3.00 8.00
46 Mark Prior Bat/250 4.00 10.00
47 Adrian Beltre Bat/250 3.00 8.00
48 Tom Glavine Bat/250 4.00 10.00
49 So Taguchi Bat/250 3.00 8.00
50 Jeff Bagwell Bat/250 4.00 10.00
51 Mike Sweeney Bat/250 3.00 8.00
52 Luis Gonzalez Bat/250 3.00 8.00
53 Chipper Jones Bat/100 6.00 15.00
54 Jason Giambi Bat/250 3.00 8.00
55 Miguel Tejada Bat/250 3.00 8.00
56 Todd Helton Bat/250 4.00 10.00
57 Andruw Jones Bat/250 4.00 10.00
58 Mike Piazza Bat/250 4.00 10.00
59 Manny Ramirez Bat/250 4.00 10.00
60 Randy Johnson Bat/250 4.00 10.00
61 Carlos Beltran Bat/250 3.00 8.00
62 Victor Martinez Bat/250 4.00 10.00
63 Orlando Hudson Bat/250 3.00 8.00
64 Jeff Kent Bat/250 3.00 8.00
65 Greg Maddux Bat/250 4.00 10.00
66 Garret Anderson Bat/150 3.00 8.00
67 Joe Thurston Bat/250 3.00 8.00
68 Mark Teixeira Bat/250 4.00 10.00
69 Kazuhisa Ishii Bat/250 3.00 8.00
70 Austin Kearns Bat/250 3.00 8.00
71 Pat Burrell Bat/100 4.00 10.00
72 Joe Borchard Bat/250 3.00 8.00
73 Josh Phelps Bat/250 3.00 8.00
74 Travis Hafner Bat/250 3.00 8.00
75 So Taguchi Shoe/125 4.00 10.00
76 Victor Martinez Fld Glv/125 6.00 15.00
77 Paul Lo Duca Shoe/125 4.00 10.00
78 Bernie Williams Shoe/125 6.00 15.00
79 Josh Phelps Shoe/125 4.00 10.00
80 Marlon Byrd Fld Glv/125 4.00 10.00
81 Manny Ramirez Hat/100 6.00 15.00
82 Jason Giambi Hat/125 3.00 8.00
83 Jeff Bagwell Hat/50
84 Sammy Sosa Shoe/125 6.00 15.00
85 Josh Phelps Hat/125 4.00 10.00
86 Tim Hudson Hat/125 4.00 10.00
87 Randy Johnson Hat/125
88 Troy Glaus Btg Glv/125 4.00 10.00
89 Joe Thurston Fld Glv/125 4.00 10.00
90 Miguel Tejada Hat/125 4.00 10.00
91 Adam Dunn Btg Glv-Fld Glv/100 6.00 15.00
92 Magglio Ordonez Btg Glv-Hat/100 6.00 15.00
93 Mike Sweeney Btg Glv-Fld Glv/100 6.00 15.00
94 Andruw Jones Btg-Glv-Hat/100 10.00 25.00
95 Carlos Beltran Hat-Shoe/100 6.00 15.00
96 Joe Borchard Fld Glv-Shoe/100 6.00 15.00
97 Austin Kearns Hat-Shoe/100 6.00 15.00
98 Richie Sexson 10.00 25.00
Btg Glv-Fld Glv-Hat/50
99 Mark Prior 15.00 40.00
Fld Glv-Hat-Shoe/50
100 Mark Teixeira 15.00 40.00
Fld Glv-Hat-Shoe/50
101 Ryan Klesko 10.00 25.00
Btg Glv-Hat-Shoe/50
102 Jason Jennings
Btg Glv-Hat-Shoe/50
103 Travis Hafner 10.00 25.00
Btg Glv-Fld Glv-Shoe/50
104 Mark Buehrle 10.00 25.00
Btg Glv-Fld Glv-Hat/50
105 Eric Hinske 10.00 25.00
Btg Glv-Fld Glv-Hat-Shoe/50
106 Rafael Palmeiro 30.00 60.00
Btg Glv-Fld Glv-Hat-Shoe/50
107 Roy Oswalt 15.00 40.00
Btg Glv-Fld Glv-Hat-Shoe/50
108 Kerry Wood 15.00 40.00
Btg Glv-Fld Glv-Hat-Shoe/50
109 Brian Giles 15.00 40.00
Btg Glv-Fld Glv-Hat-Shoe/50
110 Ivan Rodriguez 30.00 60.00
Btg Glv-Fld Glv-Hat-Shoe/50

2003 Absolute Memorabilia Tools of the Trade Materials Spectrum

*SPECTRUM p/r 40-50: 1.25X TO 3X BASIC
PRINT RUNS B/WN 10-50 COPIES PER
NO PRICING ON QTY OF 25 OR LESS

2003 Absolute Memorabilia Total Bases

STATED ODDS 1:16
1 Albert Pujols 3.00 8.00
2 Nomar Garciaparra 2.50 6.00
3 Jason Giambi .60 1.50
4 Miguel Tejada .60 1.50
5 Rafael Palmeiro 1.00 2.50
6 Sammy Sosa 1.50 4.00
7 Pat Burrell .60 1.50
8 Lance Berkman .60 1.50
9 Bernie Williams 1.00 2.50
10 Jim Thome 1.00 2.50
11 Carlos Beltran .60 1.50
12 Eric Chavez .60 1.50
13 Alex Rodriguez 2.50 6.00
14 Magglio Ordonez .60 1.50
15 Brian Giles .60 1.50
16 Alfonso Soriano .60 1.50
17 Shawn Green .60 1.50
18 Vladimir Guerrero 1.50 4.00
19 Garret Anderson .60 1.50
20 Todd Helton 1.00 2.50
21 Barry Bonds 4.00 10.00
22 Jeff Kent .60 1.50
23 Torii Hunter .60 1.50
24 Ichiro Suzuki 3.00 8.00
25 Derek Jeter 4.00 10.00
26 Chipper Jones 1.50 4.00
27 Jeff Bagwell 1.00 2.50
28 Mike Piazza 2.50 6.00
29 Rickey Henderson 1.50 4.00
30 Ken Griffey Jr. 2.50 6.00

2003 Absolute Memorabilia Total Bases Materials 1B

RANDOM INSERTS IN PACKS
PRINT RUNS B/WN 28-165 COPIES PER
1 Albert Pujols/109 8.00 20.00
2 Nomar Garciaparra/112 8.00 20.00
3 Jason Giambi/100 4.00 10.00
4 Miguel Tejada/140 4.00 10.00
5 Rafael Palmeiro/58 10.00 25.00
6 Sammy Sosa/90 6.00 15.00
7 Pat Burrell/87 4.00 10.00
8 Lance Berkman/90 4.00 10.00
9 Bernie Williams/146 4.00 10.00
10 Jim Thome/73 6.00 15.00
11 Carlos Beltran/94 4.00 10.00
12 Eric Chavez/92 4.00 10.00
13 Alex Rodriguez/101 8.00 20.00
14 Magglio Ordonez/103 4.00 10.00
15 Brian Giles/68 4.00 10.00
16 Alfonso Soriano/117 4.00 10.00
17 Shawn Green/92 4.00 10.00
18 Vladimir Guerrero/128 4.00 10.00
19 Garret Anderson/107 4.00 10.00
20 Todd Helton/109 6.00 15.00
21 Barry Bonds/70 12.50 30.00
22 Jeff Kent/114 4.00 10.00
23 Torii Hunter/92 4.00 10.00
24 Ichiro Suzuki/165 15.00 40.00
25 Derek Jeter/147 15.00 40.00
26 Chipper Jones/117 6.00 15.00
27 Jeff Bagwell/100 6.00 15.00
28 Mike Piazza/76
29 Rickey Henderson/28 15.00 40.00
30 Ken Griffey Jr./36

2003 Absolute Memorabilia Total Bases Materials 2B

RANDOM INSERTS IN PACKS
PRINT RUNS B/WN 6-56 COPIES PER
NO PRICING ON QTY OF 25 OR LESS
1 Albert Pujols/40 20.00 50.00
2 Nomar Garciaparra/56 15.00 40.00
3 Jason Giambi/34
4 Miguel Tejada/30
5 Rafael Palmeiro/34
6 Sammy Sosa/19
7 Pat Burrell/39 6.00 15.00
8 Lance Berkman/35 10.00 25.00
9 Bernie Williams/37
10 Jim Thome/19
11 Carlos Beltran/44 6.00 15.00
12 Eric Chavez/31
13 Alex Rodriguez/27 30.00 80.00
14 Magglio Ordonez/47 6.00 15.00
15 Brian Giles/37
16 Alfonso Soriano/51 6.00 15.00
17 Shawn Green/31 10.00 25.00
18 Vladimir Guerrero/37 10.00 25.00
19 Garret Anderson/56 6.00 15.00
20 Todd Helton/39 10.00 25.00
21 Barry Bonds/31 25.00 60.00
22 Jeff Kent/42 6.00 15.00
23 Torii Hunter/37 6.00 15.00
24 Ichiro Suzuki/27
25 Derek Jeter/26 30.00 80.00
26 Chipper Jones/35 15.00 40.00
27 Jeff Bagwell/33 15.00 40.00
28 Mike Piazza/23
29 Rickey Henderson/6
30 Ken Griffey Jr./8

2003 Absolute Memorabilia Total Bases Materials 3B

RANDOM INSERTS IN PACKS
PRINT RUNS B/WN 1-8 COPIES PER
NO PRICING DUE TO SCARCITY

2003 Absolute Memorabilia Total Bases Materials HR

RANDOM INSERTS IN PACKS
PRINT RUNS B/WN 5-57 COPIES PER
NO PRICING ON QTY OF 25 OR LESS
1 Albert Pujols/34 25.00 60.00
2 Nomar Garciaparra/24
3 Jason Giambi/41 6.00 15.00
4 Miguel Tejada/34 10.00 25.00
5 Rafael Palmeiro/43 10.00 25.00
6 Sammy Sosa/49 10.00 25.00
7 Pat Burrell/37 6.00 15.00
8 Lance Berkman/42 6.00 15.00
9 Bernie Williams/19
10 Jim Thome/52 10.00 25.00
11 Carlos Beltran/29 10.00 25.00
12 Eric Chavez/34 10.00 25.00
13 Alex Rodriguez/57 15.00 40.00
14 Magglio Ordonez/38 6.00 15.00
15 Brian Giles/38 6.00 15.00
16 Alfonso Soriano/39 6.00 15.00
17 Shawn Green/42 6.00 15.00
18 Vladimir Guerrero/39 10.00 25.00
19 Garret Anderson/29 10.00 25.00
20 Todd Helton/30
21 Barry Bonds/46 20.00 50.00
22 Jeff Kent/37 6.00 15.00
23 Torii Hunter/29 10.00 25.00
24 Ichiro Suzuki/8
25 Derek Jeter/18
26 Chipper Jones/26 15.00 40.00
27 Jeff Bagwell/31 15.00 40.00
28 Mike Piazza/33 20.00 50.00
29 Rickey Henderson/5
30 Ken Griffey Jr./8

2004 Absolute Memorabilia

This 250-card set was released in June, 2004. The set was issued in four-card packs with an $35 SRP which came six packs to a box and 12 boxes to a case. The first 200 cards of the set feature veterans while the final 50 cards in the set feature Rookie Cards printed to various print runs. Cards numbered 1-200 were issued to a stated print run of 1349 serial numbered sets. The final 50 cards were randomly inserted into packs.

COMMON ACTIVE (1-200) .75 2.00
COMMON RETIRED (1-200) .75 2.00
1-200 PRINT RUN 1349 SERIAL #'d SETS
COMMON CARD (201-250) 1.50 4.00
COMMON AU (201-250) 3.00 8.00
201-250 RANDOM INSERTS IN PACKS
201-250 NON AU PRINT RUNS 1000 #'d PER
201-250 AU PRINTS B/WN 500-700 #'d PER
1 Troy Glaus .75 2.00
2 Garret Anderson .75 2.00
3 Tim Salmon .75 2.00
4 Bartolo Colon .75 2.00
5 Troy Percival .75 2.00
6 Nolan Ryan Angels 3.00 8.00
7 Vladimir Guerrero 1.25 3.00
8 Richie Sexson .75 2.00
9 Shea Hillenbrand .75 2.00
10 Luis Gonzalez .75 2.00
11 Brandon Webb .75 2.00
12 Randy Johnson 1.25 3.00
13 Robby Hammock .75 2.00
14 Edgar Gonzalez .75 2.00
15 Roberto Alomar .75 2.00
16 Andruw Jones .75 2.00
17 Chipper Jones 1.25 3.00
18 Dale Murphy .75 2.00
19 Rafael Furcal .75 2.00
20 J.D. Drew .75 2.00
21 Bubba Nelson .75 2.00
22 Julio Franco .75 2.00
23 Adam LaRoche .75 2.00
24 Michael Hessman .75 2.00
25 Warren Spahn .75 2.00
26 Jay Gibbons .75 2.00
27 Cal Ripken 5.00 12.00
28 Miguel Tejada .75 2.00
29 Adam Loewen .75 2.00
30 Rafael Palmeiro .75 2.00
31 Javy Lopez .75 2.00
32 Luis Matos .75 2.00
33 Jason Varitek 1.25 3.00
34 Carl Yastrzemski 2.00 5.00
35 Manny Ramirez .75 2.00
36 Trot Nixon .75 2.00
37 Curt Schilling .75 2.00
38 Pedro Martinez .75 2.00
39 Nomar Garciaparra 2.00 5.00
40 Luis Tiant .75 2.00
41 Kevin Youkilis .75 2.00
42 Michel Hernandez .75 2.00
43 Sammy Sosa 1.25 3.00
44 Greg Maddux 2.00 5.00
45 Kerry Wood .75 2.00
46 Mark Prior .75 2.00
47 Ernie Banks 1.25 3.00
48 Aramis Ramirez .75 2.00
49 Brendan Harris .75 2.00
50 Todd Wellemeyer .75 2.00
51 Frank Thomas 1.25 3.00
52 Magglio Ordonez .75 2.00
53 Carlos Lee .75 2.00
54 Joe Crede .75 2.00
55 Joe Borchard .75 2.00
56 Mark Buehrle .75 2.00
57 Sean Casey .75 2.00
58 Adam Dunn .75 2.00
59 Austin Kearns .75 2.00
60 Ken Griffey Jr. 2.00 5.00
61 Barry Larkin .75 2.00
62 Ryan Wagner .75 2.00
63 Jody Gerut .75 2.00
64 Jeremy Guthrie .75 2.00
65 Travis Hafner .75 2.00
66 Brian Tallet .75 2.00
67 Todd Helton .75 2.00
68 Preston Wilson .75 2.00
69 Jeff Baker .75 2.00
70 Clint Barmes .75 2.00
71 Joe Kennedy .75 2.00
72 Jack Morris .75 2.00
73 George Kell .75 2.00
74 Preston Larrison .75 2.00
75 Dmitri Young .75 2.00
76 Ivan Rodriguez .75 2.00
77 Dontrelle Willis .75 2.00
78 Josh Beckett .75 2.00
79 Miguel Cabrera .75 2.00
80 Mike Lowell .75 2.00
81 Luis Castillo .75 2.00
82 Juan Pierre .75 2.00
83 Jeff Bagwell .75 2.00
84 Jeff Kent .75 2.00
85 Craig Biggio .75 2.00
86 Lance Berkman .75 2.00
87 Andy Pettitte .75 2.00
88 Roy Oswalt .75 2.00
89 Chris Burke .75 2.00
90 Jason Lane .75 2.00
91 Roger Clemens 2.50 6.00
92 Mike Sweeney .75 2.00
93 Carlos Beltran .75 2.00
94 Angel Berroa .75 2.00
95 Juan Gonzalez .75 2.00
96 Ken Harvey .75 2.00
97 Byron Gettis .75 2.00
98 Alexis Gomez .75 2.00
99 Ian Ferguson .75 2.00
100 Duke Snider .75 2.00
101 Shawn Green .75 2.00
102 Hideo Nomo 1.25 3.00
103 Kazuhisa Ishii .75 2.00
104 Edwin Jackson .75 2.00
105 Fred McGriff .75 2.00
106 Hong-Chih Kou .75 2.00
107 Don Sutton .75 2.00
108 Rickey Henderson 1.25 3.00
109 Cesar Izturis .75 2.00
110 Robin Ventura .75 2.00
111 Paul Lo Duca .75 2.00
112 Rickie Weeks .75 2.00
113 Scott Podsednik .75 2.00
114 Junior Spivey .75 2.00
115 Lyle Overbay .75 2.00
116 Tony Oliva .75 2.00
117 Jacque Jones .75 2.00
118 Shannon Stewart .75 2.00
119 Torii Hunter .75 2.00
120 Johan Santana 1.25 3.00
121 J.D. Durbin .75 2.00
122 Jason Kubel .75 2.00
123 Michael Cuddyer .75 2.00
124 Nick Johnson .75 2.00
125 Jose Vidro .75 2.00
126 Orlando Cabrera .75 2.00
127 Zach Day .75 2.00
128 Mike Piazza 2.00 5.00
129 Tom Glavine .75 2.00
130 Jae Weong Seo .75 2.00
131 Gary Carter .75 2.00
132 Phil Seibel .75 2.00
133 Edwin Almonte .75 2.00
134 Aaron Boone .75 2.00
135 Kenny Lofton .75 2.00
136 Don Mattingly 2.50 6.00
137 Jason Giambi .75 2.00
138 Alex Rodriguez Yanks 2.00 5.00
139 Jorge Posada .75 2.00
140 Bernie Williams .75 2.00
141 Hideki Matsui 2.00 5.00
142 Mike Mussina .75 2.00
143 Mariano Rivera 1.25 3.00
144 Gary Sheffield .75 2.00
145 Derek Jeter 2.50 6.00
146 Chien-Ming Wang 3.00 8.00
147 Javier Vazquez .75 2.00
148 Jose Contreras .75 2.00
149 Whitey Ford .75 2.00
150 Kevin Brown .75 2.00
151 Eric Chavez .75 2.00
152 Barry Zito .75 2.00
153 Mark Mulder .75 2.00
154 Tim Hudson .75 2.00
155 Rich Harden .75 2.00
156 Eric Byrnes .75 2.00
157 Jim Thome .75 2.00
158 Bobby Abreu .75 2.00
159 Marlon Byrd .75 2.00
160 Lenny Dykstra .75 2.00
161 Steve Carlton .75 2.00
162 Ryan Howard 4.00 10.00
163 Bobby Hill .75 2.00
164 Jose Castillo .75 2.00
165 Jay Payton .75 2.00
166 Ryan Klesko .75 2.00
167 Brian Giles .75 2.00
168 Henri Stanley .75 2.00
169 Jason Schmidt .75 2.00
170 Jerome Williams .75 2.00
171 J.T. Snow .75 2.00
172 Bret Boone .75 2.00
173 Edgar Martinez .75 2.00
174 Ichiro Suzuki 2.50 6.00
175 Jamie Moyer .75 2.00
176 Rich Aurilia .75 2.00
177 Chris Snelling .75 2.00
178 Scott Rolen .75 2.00
179 Albert Pujols 2.50 6.00
180 Jim Edmonds .75 2.00
181 Stan Musial 2.00 5.00
182 Dan Haren .75 2.00
183 Red Schoendienst .75 2.00
184 Aubrey Huff .75 2.00
185 Delmon Young .75 2.00
186 Rocco Baldelli .75 2.00
187 Dewon Brazelton .75 2.00
188 Mark Teixeira .75 2.00
189 Hank Blalock .75 2.00
190 Nolan Ryan Rgr 3.00 8.00
191 Alfonso Soriano .75 2.00
192 Michael Young .75 2.00
193 Vernon Wells .75 2.00
194 Roy Halladay .75 2.00
195 Carlos Delgado .75 2.00
196 Dustin McGowan .75 2.00
197 Josh Phelps .75 2.00
198 Alexis Rios .75 2.00
199 Eric Hinske .75 2.00
200 Josh Towers .75 2.00
201 Kazuo Matsui/1000 RC 2.00 5.00
202 Fernando Nieve AU/500 RC 3.00 8.00
203 Mike Rouse/1000 RC 1.50 4.00
204 Dennis Sarfate AU/500 RC 3.00 8.00
205 Josh Labandeira AU/500 RC 3.00 8.00
206 Chris Oxspring AU/500 RC 3.00 8.00
207 Alfredo Simon/1000 RC 1.50 4.00
208 Cory Sullivan AU/500 RC 3.00 8.00
209 Ruddy Yan AU/500 3.00 8.00
210 Jason Bartlett AU/500 RC 4.00 10.00
211 Akinori Otsuka/1000 RC 1.50 4.00
212 Lincoln Holdzkom/1000 RC 1.50 4.00
213 Justin Leone/1000 RC 2.00 5.00
214 Jorge Sequea AU/500 RC 3.00 8.00
215 John Gall/1000 RC 2.00 5.00
216 Jerome Gamble/1000 RC 1.50 4.00
217 Tim Bittner AU/500 RC 3.00 8.00
218 Ronny Cedeno AU/500 RC 6.00 15.00
219 Justin Hampson/1000 RC 1.50 4.00
220 Ryan Wing AU/500 RC 3.00 8.00
221 Mariano Gomez AU/500 RC 3.00 8.00
222 Carlos Vasquez/1000 RC 1.50 4.00
223 Casey Daigle AU/500 RC 3.00 8.00
224 Renyel Pinto AU/500 RC 3.00 8.00
225 Chris Shelton AU/500 RC 10.00 25.00
226 Mike Gosling AU/700 RC 3.00 8.00
227 Aarom Baldiris AU/700 RC 3.00 8.00
228 Ramon Ramirez AU/700 RC 3.00 8.00
229 Roberto Novoa AU/500 RC 3.00 8.00
230 Sean Henn AU/500 RC 3.00 8.00
231 Jamie Brown AU/500 RC 3.00 8.00
232 Nick Regilio AU/500 RC 3.00 8.00
233 Dave Crouthers AU/700 RC 3.00 8.00
234 Greg Dobbs AU/500 RC 3.00 8.00
235 Angel Chavez AU/500 RC 3.00 8.00
236 Willy Taveras AU/500 RC 8.00 20.00
237 Justin Knoedler AU/500 RC 3.00 8.00
238 Ian Snell AU/700 RC 6.00 15.00
239 Jason Frasor AU/500 RC 3.00 8.00
240 Jerry Gil AU/500 RC 3.00 8.00
241 Carlos Hines AU/500 RC 3.00 8.00
242 Ivan Ochoa AU/500 RC 3.00 8.00
243 Jose Capellan AU/700 RC 3.00 8.00
244 Onil Joseph AU/700 RC 3.00 8.00
245 Hector Gimenez AU/700 RC 3.00 8.00
246 Shawn Hill AU/700 RC 3.00 8.00
247 Freddy Guzman AU/700 RC 3.00 8.00
248 Graham Koonce AU/500 3.00 8.00
249 Ronald Belisario AU/500 RC 3.00 8.00
250 Merkin Valdez AU/700 RC 4.00 10.00

2004 Absolute Memorabilia Retail

*RETAIL 1-200: .1X TO .25X BASIC
1-200 ISSUED IN RETAIL PACKS
RETAIL CARDS ARE NOT SERIAL #'d

2004 Absolute Memorabilia Spectrum Gold

*GOLD 1-200: 1.5X TO 4X BASIC ACTIVE
*GOLD 1-200: 1.5X TO 4X BASIC RETIRED
*GOLD 201-250: .6X TO 1.5X BASIC
*GOLD 201-250: .3X TO .8X BASIC AU
RANDOM INSERTS IN PACKS
STATED PRINT RUN 50 SERIAL #'d SETS

2004 Absolute Memorabilia Spectrum Platinum

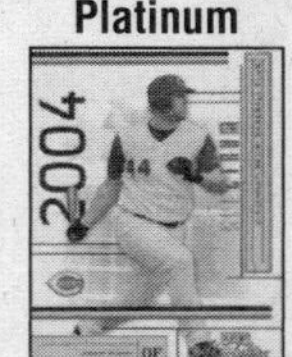

RANDOM INSERTS IN PACKS
STATED PRINT RUN 1 SERIAL #'d SET
NO PRICING DUE TO SCARCITY

2004 Absolute Memorabilia Spectrum Silver

*SILVER 1-200: 1X TO 2.5X BASIC ACTIVE
*SILVER 1-200: 1X TO 2.5X BASIC RETIRED
*SILVER 201-250: .4X TO 1X BASIC
*SILVER 201-250: .2X TO .5X BASIC AU

RANDOM INSERTS IN PACKS
STATED PRINT RUN 100 SERIAL #'d SETS

2004 Absolute Memorabilia Signature Spectrum Gold

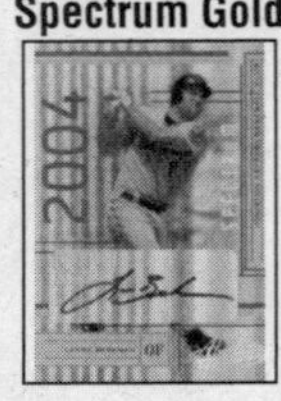

RANDOM INSERTS IN PACKS
PRINT RUNS B/WN 1-100 COPIES PER
NO PRICING ON QTY OF 10 OR LESS
1 Troy Glaus/15 30.00 60.00
2 Garret Anderson/100 6.00 15.00
6 Nolan Ryan Angels/10
7 Vladimir Guerrero/25 30.00 60.00
8 Richie Sexson/15 15.00 40.00
9 Shea Hillenbrand/100 6.00 15.00
11 Brandon Webb/100 4.00 10.00
12 Randy Johnson/1
15 Roberto Alomar/25 20.00 50.00
16 Andruw Jones/5
17 Chipper Jones/5
18 Dale Murphy/100 10.00 25.00
19 Rafael Furcal/100 6.00 15.00
22 Julio Franco/25 12.50 30.00
23 Adam LaRoche/100 4.00 10.00
25 Warren Spahn/5
26 Jay Gibbons/100 4.00 10.00
27 Cal Ripken/1
29 Adam Loewen/100 4.00 10.00
30 Rafael Palmeiro/1
32 Luis Matos/50 5.00 12.00
33 Jason Varitek/25 30.00 60.00
34 Carl Yastrzemski/1
35 Manny Ramirez/1
36 Trot Nixon/100 6.00 15.00
37 Curt Schilling/1
40 Luis Tiant/50 8.00 20.00
41 Kevin Youkilis/25 8.00 20.00
43 Sammy Sosa/5
45 Kerry Wood/25 20.00 50.00
46 Mark Prior/100 10.00 25.00
47 Ernie Banks/100 20.00 50.00
48 Aramis Ramirez/5
51 Frank Thomas/5
52 Magglio Ordonez/100 6.00 15.00
53 Carlos Lee/100 6.00 15.00
54 Joe Crede/50 8.00 20.00
56 Mark Buehrle/10
57 Sean Casey/1
58 Adam Dunn/5
59 Austin Kearns/100 4.00 10.00
61 Barry Larkin/25 20.00 50.00
62 Ryan Wagner/50 5.00 12.00
63 Jody Gerut/100 4.00 10.00
64 Jeremy Guthrie/25 8.00 20.00
65 Travis Hafner/25 8.00 20.00
67 Todd Helton/5
68 Preston Wilson/100 6.00 15.00
69 Jeff Baker/25 8.00 20.00
72 Jack Morris/100
73 George Kell/100 6.00 15.00
77 Dontrelle Willis/10
78 Josh Beckett/5
79 Miguel Cabrera/100 10.00 25.00
80 Mike Lowell/1
81 Luis Castillo/25 8.00 20.00
83 Jeff Bagwell/25 40.00 80.00
85 Craig Biggio/5
86 Lance Berkman/5
87 Andy Pettitte/25 30.00 60.00
88 Roy Oswalt/10
93 Carlos Beltran/100 6.00 15.00
94 Angel Berroa/100 4.00 10.00
95 Juan Gonzalez/10
100 Duke Snider/100 10.00 25.00
101 Shawn Green/1
102 Hideo Nomo/1
103 Kazuhisa Ishii/5
104 Edwin Jackson/50 5.00 12.00
105 Fred McGriff/1
106 Hong-Chih Kou/25 40.00 80.00
107 Don Sutton/25 12.50 30.00
108 Rickey Henderson/5
110 Robin Ventura/10
111 Paul Lo Duca/5
112 Rickie Weeks/24 12.50 30.00
113 Scott Podsednik/100 10.00 25.00
114 Junior Spivey/10
115 Lyle Overbay/10
116 Tony Oliva/50 8.00 20.00
117 Jacque Jones/100 6.00 15.00
118 Shannon Stewart/5
119 Torii Hunter/100 6.00 15.00
120 Johan Santana/10
124 Nick Johnson/5
125 Jose Vidro/10
126 Orlando Cabrera/10
128 Mike Piazza/1
130 Jae Weong Seo/100 6.00 15.00
131 Gary Carter/100 6.00 15.00
136 Don Mattingly/100 30.00 60.00
138 Alex Rodriguez/1
139 Jorge Posada/25 20.00 50.00
140 Bernie Williams/5
142 Mike Mussina/1
143 Mariano Rivera/1
144 Gary Sheffield/25 20.00 50.00
146 Chien-Ming Wang/25 125.00 200.00
147 Javier Vazquez/5
148 Jose Contreras/5
149 Whitey Ford/5
151 Eric Chavez/1
152 Barry Zito/1
153 Mark Mulder/100 6.00 15.00
154 Tim Hudson/5
155 Rich Harden/50 8.00 20.00
158 Bobby Abreu/5
159 Marlon Byrd/100 4.00 10.00
160 Lenny Dykstra/100 6.00 15.00
161 Steve Carlton/50 8.00 20.00
164 Jose Castillo/50 5.00 12.00
165 Jay Payton/100 4.00 10.00
166 Ryan Klesko/5
170 Jerome Williams/50 5.00 12.00
171 J.T. Snow/10
173 Edgar Martinez/5
175 Jamie Moyer/5
176 Rich Aurilia/5
178 Scott Rolen/50 12.50 30.00
179 Albert Pujols/1
180 Jim Edmonds/10
181 Stan Musial/100 30.00 60.00
182 Dan Haren/25 8.00 20.00
183 Red Schoendienst/100 6.00 15.00
184 Aubrey Huff/100 6.00 15.00
185 Delmon Young/100 10.00 25.00
186 Rocco Baldelli/5
187 Dewon Brazelton/25 8.00 20.00
188 Mark Teixeira/50 12.50 30.00
189 Hank Blalock/25 12.50 30.00
190 Nolan Ryan Rgr/10
192 Michael Young/100 10.00 25.00
193 Vernon Wells/10
194 Roy Halladay/25 12.50 30.00
197 Josh Phelps/5
198 Alexis Rios/50 8.00 20.00
199 Eric Hinske/1
202 Fernando Nieve/100 6.00 15.00
205 Josh Labandeira/100 4.00 10.00
206 Chris Oxspring/100 4.00 10.00
208 Cory Sullivan/100 4.00 10.00
209 Ruddy Yan/100 4.00 10.00
210 Jason Bartlett/100 6.00 15.00
212 Lincoln Holdzkom/100 4.00 10.00
213 Justin Leone/100 6.00 15.00
214 Jorge Sequea/100 4.00 10.00
217 Tim Bittner/100 4.00 10.00
219 Justin Hampson/100 4.00 10.00
220 Ryan Wing/100 4.00 10.00
221 Mariano Gomez/100 4.00 10.00
222 Carlos Vasquez/100 6.00 15.00
224 Renyel Pinto/100 5.00 12.00
225 Chris Shelton/100 10.00 25.00
226 Mike Gosling/10
227 Aarom Baldiris/10
228 Ramon Ramirez/10
230 Sean Henn/100 4.00 10.00
232 Nick Regilio/100 4.00 10.00
233 Dave Crouthers/10
234 Greg Dobbs/50 6.00 15.00
235 Angel Chavez/100 4.00 10.00
238 Ian Snell/10
242 Ivan Ochoa/100 4.00 10.00
243 Jose Capellan/10
244 Onil Joseph/10
245 Hector Gimenez/10
246 Shawn Hill/10
247 Freddy Guzman/10
248 Graham Koonce/100 4.00 10.00
250 Merkin Valdez/10

2004 Absolute Memorabilia Signature Spectrum Platinum

RANDOM INSERTS IN PACKS
STATED PRINT RUN 1 SERIAL #'d SET
NO PRICING DUE TO SCARCITY

2004 Absolute Memorabilia Signature Spectrum Silver

RANDOM INSERTS IN PACKS
PRINT RUNS B/WN 1-250 COPIES PER
NO PRICING ON QTY OF 14 OR LESS
1 Troy Glaus/34 15.00 40.00
2 Garret Anderson/100 6.00 15.00
6 Nolan Ryan Angels/25 75.00 150.00
7 Vladimir Guerrero/100 12.50 30.00
8 Richie Sexson/34 10.00 25.00
9 Shea Hillenbrand/100 6.00 15.00
11 Brandon Webb/100 4.00 10.00
12 Randy Johnson/1
13 Robby Hammock/250 4.00 10.00
14 Edgar Gonzalez/104 4.00 10.00
15 Roberto Alomar/32 15.00 40.00
16 Andruw Jones/50 12.50 30.00
17 Chipper Jones/10
18 Dale Murphy/100 10.00 25.00
19 Rafael Furcal/100 6.00 15.00
21 Bubba Nelson/250 4.00 10.00
22 Julio Franco/100 6.00 15.00
23 Adam LaRoche/100 4.00 10.00
24 Michael Hessman/250 4.00 10.00
25 Warren Spahn/10
26 Jay Gibbons/100 4.00 10.00
27 Cal Ripken/5
29 Adam Loewen/100 4.00 10.00
30 Rafael Palmeiro/5
32 Luis Matos/100 4.00 10.00
33 Jason Varitek/50 15.00 40.00
34 Carl Yastrzemski/5
35 Manny Ramirez/5
36 Trot Nixon/100 6.00 15.00
37 Curt Schilling/5
40 Luis Tiant/100 6.00 15.00
41 Kevin Youkilis/25 6.00 15.00
42 Michael Hernandez/190 4.00 10.00
43 Sammy Sosa/21 50.00 100.00
45 Kerry Wood/50 12.50 30.00
46 Mark Prior/100 8.00 20.00
47 Ernie Banks/100 20.00 50.00
48 Aramis Ramirez/50 8.00 20.00
49 Brendan Harris/250 4.00 10.00
50 Todd Wellemeyer/250 4.00 10.00
51 Frank Thomas/50 15.00 40.00
52 Magglio Ordonez/100 6.00 15.00
53 Carlos Lee/100 6.00 15.00
54 Joe Crede/100 6.00 15.00
55 Joe Borchard/250 4.00 10.00
56 Mark Buehrle/10
57 Sean Casey/50 8.00 20.00
58 Adam Dunn/100 10.00 25.00
59 Austin Kearns/100 4.00 10.00
61 Barry Larkin/50 12.50 30.00
62 Ryan Wagner/100 4.00 10.00
63 Jody Gerut/100 4.00 10.00
64 Jeremy Guthrie/50 5.00 12.00
65 Travis Hafner/50 5.00 12.00
66 Brian Tallet/250 4.00 10.00
67 Todd Helton/10
68 Preston Wilson/100 6.00 15.00
69 Jeff Baker/50 5.00 12.00
70 Clint Barmes/250 6.00 15.00
71 Joe Kennedy/250 4.00 10.00
72 Jack Morris/96
73 George Kell/100 6.00 15.00
74 Preston Larrison/250 4.00 10.00
77 Dontrelle Willis/100 10.00 25.00
78 Josh Beckett/25 15.00 40.00
79 Miguel Cabrera/100 10.00 25.00
80 Mike Lowell/25 10.00 25.00
81 Luis Castillo/50 5.00 12.00
83 Jeff Bagwell/50 30.00 60.00
85 Craig Biggio/50 8.00 20.00
86 Lance Berkman/25 15.00 40.00
87 Andy Pettitte/25 20.00 50.00
88 Roy Oswalt/25 10.00 25.00
89 Chris Burke/250 6.00 15.00
90 Jason Lane/231 6.00 15.00
93 Carlos Beltran/100 6.00 15.00
94 Angel Berroa/100 4.00 10.00
95 Juan Gonzalez/25 10.00 25.00
96 Ken Harvey/200 4.00 10.00
97 Byron Gettis/250 4.00 10.00
98 Alexis Gomez/250 4.00 10.00
99 Ian Ferguson/104 4.00 10.00
100 Duke Snider/100 10.00 25.00
101 Shawn Green/1
102 Hideo Nomo/1
103 Kazuhisa Ishii/25 10.00 25.00
104 Edwin Jackson/100 4.00 10.00
105 Fred McGriff/50 30.00 60.00
106 Hong-Chih Kou/50 20.00 50.00
107 Don Sutton/100 6.00 15.00
108 Rickey Henderson/10
109 Cesar Izturis/101 4.00 10.00
110 Robin Ventura/25 10.00 25.00
111 Paul Lo Duca/50 8.00 20.00
112 Rickie Weeks/21 10.00 25.00
113 Scott Podsednik/100 10.00 25.00
114 Junior Spivey/89 4.00 10.00
115 Lyle Overbay/89 4.00 10.00
116 Tony Oliva/72 6.00 15.00
117 Jacque Jones/100 6.00 15.00
118 Shannon Stewart/100 6.00 15.00
119 Torii Hunter/100 6.00 15.00
120 Johan Santana/50 12.50 30.00
121 J.D. Durbin/250 4.00 10.00
122 Jason Kubel/250 4.00 10.00
123 Michael Cuddyer/225 4.00 10.00
124 Nick Johnson/25 10.00 25.00
125 Jose Vidro/25 6.00 15.00
126 Orlando Cabrera/25 10.00 25.00
127 Zach Day/100 4.00 10.00
128 Mike Piazza/5
130 Jae Weong Seo/100 6.00 15.00
131 Gary Carter/100 6.00 15.00
132 Phil Seibel/177 4.00 10.00
133 Edwin Almonte/250 4.00 10.00
136 Don Mattingly/100 30.00 60.00
138 Alex Rodriguez/1
139 Jorge Posada/50 12.50 30.00
140 Bernie Williams/10
142 Mike Mussina/1
143 Mariano Rivera/5
144 Gary Sheffield/100 10.00 25.00
146 Chien-Ming Wang/50 75.00 150.00
147 Javier Vazquez/25 10.00 25.00
148 Jose Contreras/25 10.00 25.00
149 Whitey Ford/50 12.50 30.00
151 Eric Chavez/50 8.00 20.00
152 Barry Zito/1
153 Mark Mulder/100 6.00 15.00
154 Tim Hudson/50 12.50 30.00
155 Rich Harden/100 6.00 15.00
156 Eric Byrnes/250 4.00 10.00
158 Bobby Abreu/10
159 Marlon Byrd/100 4.00 10.00
160 Lenny Dykstra/100 6.00 15.00
161 Steve Carlton/100 6.00 15.00
162 Ryan Howard/250 30.00 60.00
163 Bobby Hill/250 4.00 10.00
164 Jose Castillo/100 4.00 10.00
165 Jay Payton/100 4.00 10.00
168 Henri Stanley/112 4.00 10.00
170 Jerome Williams/100 4.00 10.00
171 J.T. Snow/89 6.00 15.00
173 Edgar Martinez/50 12.50 30.00
175 Jamie Moyer/19 15.00 40.00
176 Rich Aurilia/25 6.00 15.00
177 Chris Snelling/177 4.00 10.00
178 Scott Rolen/100 10.00 25.00
179 Albert Pujols/5
180 Jim Edmonds/50 12.50 30.00
181 Stan Musial/100 30.00 60.00
182 Dan Haren/200 4.00 10.00
183 Red Schoendienst/100 6.00 15.00
184 Aubrey Huff/100 6.00 15.00
185 Delmon Young/100 10.00 25.00
186 Rocco Baldelli/50 8.00 20.00
187 Dewon Brazelton/50 5.00 12.00
188 Mark Teixeira/100 10.00 25.00
189 Hank Blalock/50 8.00 20.00
190 Nolan Ryan Rgr/25 75.00 150.00
192 Michael Young/100 10.00 25.00
193 Vernon Wells/14
194 Roy Halladay/50 8.00 20.00
196 Dustin McGowan/250 4.00 10.00
197 Josh Phelps/25 6.00 15.00
198 Alexis Rios/100 6.00 15.00
199 Eric Hinske/5
200 Josh Towers/158 4.00 10.00
202 Fernando Nieve/250 5.00 12.00
203 Mike Rouse/100 4.00 10.00
204 Dennis Sarfate/100 4.00 10.00
205 Josh Labandeira/250 4.00 10.00
206 Chris Oxspring/250 4.00 10.00
207 Alfredo Simon/100 4.00 10.00
208 Cory Sullivan/250 4.00 10.00
209 Ruddy Yan/250 4.00 10.00
210 Jason Bartlett/250 6.00 15.00
211 Akinori Otsuka/100 12.50 30.00
212 Lincoln Holdzkom/250 4.00 10.00
213 Justin Leone/250 6.00 15.00
214 Jorge Sequea/250 4.00 10.00
215 John Gall/50 8.00 20.00
217 Tim Bittner/250 4.00 10.00
219 Justin Hampson/250 4.00 10.00
220 Ryan Wing/250 4.00 10.00
221 Mariano Gomez/250 4.00 10.00
222 Carlos Vasquez/250 6.00 15.00
223 Casey Daigle/150 4.00 10.00
224 Renyel Pinto/250 5.00 12.00
229 Roberto Novoa/225 5.00 12.00
230 Sean Henn/250 4.00 10.00
231 Jamie Brown/200 4.00 10.00
232 Nick Regilio/250 4.00 10.00
234 Greg Dobbs/250 4.00 10.00
235 Angel Chavez/250 4.00 10.00
237 Justin Knoedler/225 4.00 10.00
239 Jason Frasor/225 4.00 10.00
240 Jerry Gil/225 4.00 10.00
241 Carlos Hines/225 4.00 10.00
242 Ivan Ochoa/250 4.00 10.00
248 Graham Koonce/250 4.00 10.00
249 Ronald Belisario/225 4.00 10.00

2004 Absolute Memorabilia Absolutely Ink

PRINT RUNS B/WN 1-100 COPIES PER
NO PRICING ON QTY OF 10 OR LESS
*SPECTRUM p/r 25: .75X TO 2Xp/r 100
*SPECTRUM p/r 25: .6X TO 1.5X p/r 50
*SPECTRUM p/r 25: .5X TO 1.2X p/r 25
SPECTRUM PRINTS B/WN 1-25 COPIES PER
NO SPECT.PRICING ON QTY OF 10 OR LESS
RANDOM INSERTS IN PACKS
1 Adam Dunn/100 10.00 25.00
2 Al Kaline/100 20.00 50.00
3 Alan Trammell/100 6.00 15.00
4 Albert Pujols/5
5 Alex Rodriguez Rgr/1
6 Andre Dawson Cubs/100 6.00 15.00
7 Andre Dawson Expos/100 6.00 15.00
8 Andruw Jones/50 12.50 30.00
9 Angel Berroa/50 5.00 12.00
10 Aramis Ramirez/50 8.00 20.00
11 Aubrey Huff/100 6.00 15.00
12 Austin Kearns/100 4.00 10.00
13 Barry Larkin/50 12.50 30.00
14 Barry Zito/5
15 Bernie Williams/5
16 Bert Blyleven/100 6.00 15.00
17 Billy Williams/100 6.00 15.00
18 Bo Jackson/5
19 Bob Feller/100 10.00 25.00
20 Bob Gibson/25 20.00 50.00
21 Bobby Doerr/100 6.00 15.00
22 Brandon Webb/100 10.00 25.00
23 Brett Myers/50 8.00 20.00
24 Brooks Robinson/100 10.00 25.00
25 Cal Ripken/5
26 Carl Yastrzemski/5
27 Carlos Beltran/100 6.00 15.00
28 Carlos Lee/100 6.00 15.00
29 Carlton Fisk/10
30 Chipper Jones/5
31 Craig Biggio/50 8.00 20.00
32 Curt Schilling/5
33 Dale Murphy/100 10.00 25.00
34 Darryl Strawberry/100 6.00 15.00
35 Dave Concepcion/50 8.00 20.00
36 Dave Parker/50 8.00 20.00
37 Deion Sanders/10
38 Don Mattingly/100 30.00 60.00
39 Dontrelle Willis/100 10.00 25.00
40 Duke Snider/100 10.00 25.00
41 Dwight Gooden/100 6.00 15.00
42 Edgar Martinez/50 12.50 30.00
43 Eric Chavez/50 8.00 20.00
44 Ernie Banks/100 20.00 50.00
45 Fergie Jenkins/100 6.00 15.00
46 Frank Robinson/100 10.00 25.00
47 Frank Thomas/25 30.00 60.00
48 Fred Lynn/50 5.00 12.00
49 Fred McGriff/25 40.00 80.00
50 Garret Anderson/100 6.00 15.00
51 Gary Carter Expos/100 6.00 15.00
52 Gary Carter Mets/100 6.00 15.00
53 Gary Sheffield/50 12.50 30.00
54 Gaylord Perry/100 6.00 15.00
55 George Brett/5
57 Hank Blalock/100 6.00 15.00
58 Harold Baines/50 8.00 20.00
59 Hideo Nomo/1
62 Jacque Jones/100 6.00 15.00
63 Jae Weong Seo/100 6.00 15.00
64 Jamie Moyer/25 12.50 30.00
65 Jason Varitek/50 20.00 50.00
66 Jay Gibbons/50 5.00 12.00
67 Jim Edmonds/25 20.00 50.00
68 Jim Palmer/100 10.00 25.00
69 Jim Rice/50 8.00 20.00
70 Joe Carter/5
71 Johan Santana/50 12.50 30.00
72 Jorge Posada/50 12.50 30.00
73 Josh Beckett/25 20.00 50.00
74 Juan Gonzalez/25 12.50 30.00
75 Keith Hernandez/100 6.00 15.00
76 Kirby Puckett/25 50.00 100.00
77 Luis Tiant/100 6.00 15.00
78 Magglio Ordonez/100 6.00 15.00
79 Manny Ramirez/1
80 Mariano Rivera/1
81 Mark Grace/25 30.00 60.00
82 Mark Mulder/100 6.00 15.00
83 Mark Prior/100 10.00 25.00
84 Mark Teixeira/100 10.00 25.00
85 Marty Marion/100 6.00 15.00
86 Mike Lowell/25 12.50 30.00
87 Mike Mussina/1
88 Mike Piazza/5
89 Nick Johnson/10
90 Nolan Ryan/25 75.00 150.00
91 Orel Hershiser/100 15.00 40.00
92 Orlando Cepeda/100 6.00 15.00
95 Paul O'Neill/5
96 Pedro Martinez/1
97 Phil Niekro/100 6.00 15.00
98 Rafael Palmeiro/5
99 Ralph Kiner/100 10.00 25.00
100 Randy Johnson/5
101 Red Schoendienst/100 6.00 15.00
102 Rickey Henderson/10
103 Robin Roberts/50 8.00 20.00
104 Robin Ventura/100 6.00 15.00
105 Robin Yount/5
106 Rocco Baldelli/25 12.50 30.00
108 Ryne Sandberg/10
109 Sammy Sosa/21 50.00 100.00
110 Sean Casey/23 12.50 30.00
111 Shannon Stewart/50 5.00 12.00
112 Shawn Green/10
113 Stan Musial/100 30.00 60.00
114 Steve Carlton/50 8.00 20.00
115 Steve Garvey/100 6.00 15.00
116 Todd Helton/10
117 Tommy John/100 6.00 15.00
118 Tony Gwynn/25 40.00 80.00
119 Tony Oliva/100 6.00 15.00
120 Torii Hunter/100 6.00 15.00
121 Trot Nixon/50 8.00 20.00
122 Troy Glaus/50 12.50 30.00
123 Vernon Wells/25 12.50 30.00
124 Vladimir Guerrero/100 15.00 40.00
125 Will Clark/100 10.00 25.00

2004 Absolute Memorabilia Absolutely Ink Material

PRINT RUNS B/WN 5-100 COPIES PER
NO PRICING ON QTY OF 14 OR LESS
*PRIME p/r 25: .5X TO 1.2X BASIC p/r 25
PRIME PRINT RUNS B/WN 1-25 COPIES PER
NO PRIME PRICING ON QTY OF 5 OR LESS
RANDOM INSERTS IN PACKS
ADD 20% FOR NOTATED AUTOGRAPHS
1 Adam Dunn Jsy/100 12.50 30.00
2 Al Kaline Pants/50 30.00 60.00
3 Alan Trammell Jsy/100 12.50 30.00
4 Albert Pujols Jsy/5
5 Alex Rodriguez Rgr Jsy/5
6 Andre Dawson Cubs Jsy/100 8.00 20.00
7 Andre Dawson Expos Jsy/100 8.00 20.00
8 Andruw Jones Jsy/10
9 Angel Berroa Jsy/100 6.00 15.00
11 Aubrey Huff Jsy/100 8.00 20.00
12 Austin Kearns Jsy/100 6.00 15.00
13 Barry Larkin Jsy/10
14 Barry Zito Jsy/5
15 Bernie Williams Jsy/5
16 Bert Blyleven Jsy/100 8.00 20.00
17 Billy Williams Jsy/100 12.50 30.00
18 Bo Jackson Jsy/10
19 Bob Feller Jsy/100 12.50 30.00
20 Bob Gibson Jsy/7
21 Bobby Doerr Jsy/100 8.00 20.00
22 Brandon Webb Jsy/50 15.00 40.00
23 Brett Myers Jsy/100 8.00 20.00
24 Brooks Robinson Jsy/100 12.50 30.00
25 Cal Ripken Jsy/5
26 Carl Yastrzemski Jsy/5
27 Carlos Beltran Jsy/100 8.00 20.00
28 Carlos Lee Jsy/100 8.00 20.00
29 Carlton Fisk Jsy/5
30 Chipper Jones Jsy/5
31 Craig Biggio Jsy/10
32 Curt Schilling Jsy/5
33 Dale Murphy Jsy/100 12.50 30.00
34 Darryl Strawberry Jsy/100 8.00 20.00
35 Dave Concepcion Jsy/50 10.00 25.00
36 Dave Parker Jsy/100 8.00 20.00
37 Deion Sanders Jsy/7
38 Don Mattingly Jsy/50 50.00 100.00
39 Dontrelle Willis Jsy/20 20.00 50.00
41 Dwight Gooden Jsy/60 10.00 25.00
42 Edgar Martinez Jsy/100 20.00 50.00
43 Eric Chavez Jsy/10
44 Ernie Banks Jsy/50 30.00 60.00
45 Fergie Jenkins Pants/100 8.00 20.00
46 Frank Robinson Jsy/50 15.00 40.00
47 Frank Thomas Jsy/5
48 Fred Lynn Jsy/100 6.00 15.00
49 Fred McGriff Jsy/20 40.00 80.00
50 Garret Anderson Jsy/100 8.00 20.00
51 Gary Carter Expos Jsy/100 8.00 20.00
52 Gary Carter Mets Jacket/100 8.00 20.00
53 Gary Sheffield Jsy/100 12.50 30.00
54 Gaylord Perry Jsy/100 8.00 20.00
55 George Brett Jsy/5
57 Hank Blalock Jsy/100 8.00 20.00
58 Harold Baines Jsy/100 8.00 20.00
59 Hideo Nomo Jsy/5
62 Jacque Jones Jsy/5
63 Jae Weong Seo Jsy/100 6.00 15.00
64 Jamie Moyer Jsy/100 8.00 20.00
65 Jason Varitek Jsy/100 20.00 50.00
66 Jay Gibbons Jsy/100 6.00 15.00
67 Jim Edmonds Jsy/5
68 Jim Palmer Jsy/100 12.50 30.00
69 Jim Rice Jsy/100 8.00 20.00
70 Joe Carter Jsy/50 10.00 25.00
71 Johan Santana Jsy/100 12.50 30.00
72 Jorge Posada Jsy/15 30.00 60.00
73 Josh Beckett Jsy/5
74 Juan Gonzalez Jsy/10
75 Keith Hernandez Jsy/100 8.00 20.00
76 Kirby Puckett Jsy/5
77 Luis Tiant Jsy/100 8.00 20.00
78 Magglio Ordonez Jsy/10
79 Manny Ramirez Jsy/5
80 Mariano Rivera Jsy/14
81 Mark Grace Jsy/10
82 Mark Mulder Jsy/20 12.50 30.00
83 Mark Prior Jsy/5
84 Mark Teixeira Jsy/10
85 Marty Marion Jsy/100 8.00 20.00
86 Mike Lowell Jsy/60 10.00 25.00
87 Mike Mussina Jsy/5
88 Mike Piazza Jsy/5
89 Nick Johnson Jsy/5
90 Nolan Ryan Jsy/10
92 Orlando Cepeda Bat/65 10.00 25.00
95 Paul O'Neill Bat/10
96 Pedro Martinez Jsy/5
97 Phil Niekro Jsy/25 12.50 30.00
98 Rafael Palmeiro Jsy/5
99 Ralph Kiner Bat/100 12.50 30.00
100 Randy Johnson Jsy/5
101 Red Schoendienst Jsy/60 10.00 25.00
102 Rickey Henderson Jsy/5
103 Robin Roberts Hat/50 10.00 25.00
104 Robin Ventura Jsy/65 15.00 40.00
105 Robin Yount Jsy/5
106 Rocco Baldelli Jsy/10
108 Ryne Sandberg Jsy/5
109 Sammy Sosa Jsy/10
110 Sean Casey Jsy/75 8.00 20.00
111 Shannon Stewart Jsy/100 6.00 15.00
112 Shawn Green Jsy/5
113 Stan Musial Jsy/5
114 Steve Carlton Jsy/50 10.00 25.00
115 Steve Garvey Bat/100 12.50 30.00
116 Todd Helton Jsy/5
117 Tommy John Jsy/100 8.00 20.00
118 Tony Gwynn Jsy/5
119 Tony Oliva Jsy/100 8.00 20.00
120 Torii Hunter Jsy/50 10.00 25.00
121 Trot Nixon Jsy/100 8.00 20.00
122 Troy Glaus Jsy/10
123 Vernon Wells Jsy/10
124 Vladimir Guerrero Jsy/55 30.00 60.00
125 Will Clark Jsy/100 12.50 30.00

2004 Absolute Memorabilia Absolutely Ink Combo Material

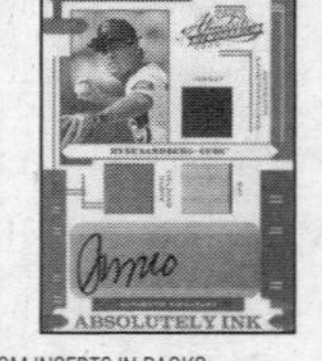

*COMBO p/r 100: .5X TO 1.2X p/r 100
*COMBO p/r 50-65: .6X TO 1.5X p/r 75-100
*COMBO p/r 50-65: .5X TO 1.2X p/r 50-65
*COMBO p/r 25: .75X TO 2X p/r 100
PRINT RUNS B/WN 1-100 COPIES PER
NO PRICING ON QTY OF 10 OR LESS
PRIME PRINT RUNS B/WN 1-5 COPIES PER
NO PRIME PRICING DUE TO SCARCITY
RANDOM INSERTS IN PACKS
43 E.Chavez Bat-Jsy/15 15.00 40.00
74 J.Gonzalez Bat-Jsy/15 15.00 40.00

2004 Absolute Memorabilia Absolutely Ink Triple Material

RANDOM INSERTS IN PACKS
PRINT RUNS B/WN 1-10 COPIES PER
PRIME PRINT RUNS B/WN 1-5 COPIES PER
RANDOM INSERTS IN PACKS
NO PRICING DUE TO SCARCITY

2004 Absolute Memorabilia Fans of the Game

RANDOM INSERTS IN RETAIL PACKS
251 Landon Donovan .75 2.00
252 Jennie Finch 2.00 5.00
253 Bonnie Blair .75 2.00
254 Dan Jansen .75 2.00
255 Kerri Strug 1.25 3.00

2004 Absolute Memorabilia Fans of the Game Autographs

RANDOM INSERTS IN RETAIL PACKS
SP PRINT RUNS PROVIDED BY DONRUSS
SP'S ARE NOT SERIAL-NUMBERED
251 Landon Donovan 15.00 40.00
252 Jennie Finch 90.00 150.00
253 Bonnie Blair SP/250 15.00 40.00
254 Dan Jansen SP/250 10.00 25.00
255 Kerri Strug SP/250 20.00 50.00

2004 Absolute Memorabilia Marks of Fame

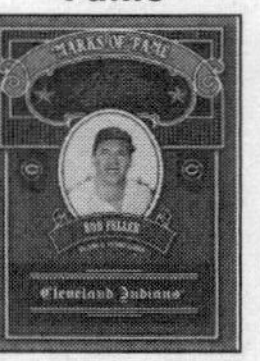

STATED PRINT RUN 100 SERIAL #'d SETS
*SPECTRUM: .75X TO 2X BASIC
SPECTRUM PRINT RUN 25 SERIAL #'d SETS
RANDOM INSERTS IN PACKS
1 Nolan Ryan 8.00 20.00
2 Ernie Banks 3.00 8.00
3 Bob Feller 2.00 5.00
4 Duke Snider 3.00 8.00
5 Sammy Sosa 3.00 8.00
6 Whitey Ford 3.00 8.00
7 Steve Carlton 2.00 5.00
8 Tony Gwynn 4.00 10.00
9 Jim Bunning 2.00 5.00
10 Stan Musial 5.00 12.00
11 Cal Ripken 15.00 40.00
12 George Brett 8.00 20.00
13 Gary Carter 2.00 5.00
14 Jim Palmer 2.00 5.00
15 Gaylord Perry 2.00 5.00

2004 Absolute Memorabilia Marks of Fame Signature

PRINT RUNS B/WN 10-100 COPIES PER
NO PRICING ON QTY OF 10 OR LESS
*SPECTRUM p/r 25: .6X TO 1.5X p/r 100
*SPECTRUM p/r 25: .5X TO 1.2X p/r 50
SPECTRUM PRINTS B/WN 1-25 COPIES PER
NO SPECT.PRICING ON QTY OF 10 OR LESS
RANDOM INSERTS IN PACKS
1 Nolan Ryan/50 75.00 150.00
2 Ernie Banks/50 20.00 50.00
3 Bob Feller/100 10.00 25.00
4 Duke Snider/100 10.00 25.00
5 Sammy Sosa/21 50.00 100.00
6 Whitey Ford/25 20.00 50.00
7 Steve Carlton/100 6.00 15.00
8 Tony Gwynn/25 40.00 80.00
9 Jim Bunning/100 10.00 25.00
10 Stan Musial/50 30.00 60.00
11 Cal Ripken/10
12 George Brett/25 60.00 120.00
13 Gary Carter/100 6.00 15.00
14 Jim Palmer/50 8.00 20.00
15 Gaylord Perry/100 6.00 15.00

2004 Absolute Memorabilia Signature Club

RANDOM INSERTS IN PACKS
PRINT RUNS B/WN 5-50 COPIES PER
NO PRICING ON QTY OF 5 OR LESS
1 Sammy Sosa Bat/5
2 Gary Sheffield Bat/50 15.00 40.00
3 Vladimir Guerrero Bat/5
4 Will Clark Bat/50 15.00 40.00
5 Ernie Banks Bat/50 30.00 60.00

2004 Absolute Memorabilia Signature Material

PRINT RUNS B/WN 25-50 COPIES PER
PRIME PRINT RUN 5 SERIAL #'d SETS
NO PRIME PRICING DUE TO SCARCITY
*COMBO: .5X TO 1.2X BASIC
COMBO PRINTS B/WN 25-50 COPIES PER
COMBO PRIME PRINT 5 SERIAL #'d SETS
NO COMBO PRIME PRICE DUE SCARCITY
RANDOM INSERTS IN PACKS
2 Gary Carter Jsy/50 10.00 25.00
3 Dale Murphy Jsy/50 15.00 40.00
4 Don Mattingly Jsy/25 60.00 120.00
5 Stan Musial Jsy/25 60.00 120.00

2004 Absolute Memorabilia Team Quad

STATED PRINT RUN 100 SERIAL #'d SETS
*SPECTRUM: 1X TO 2.5X BASIC
SPECTRUM PRINT RUN 25 SERIAL #'d SETS
RANDOM INSERTS IN PACKS
1 Craig Biggio 3.00 8.00
Lance Berkman
Jeff Kent
Jeff Bagwell
2 Nomar Garciaparra 5.00 12.00
Manny Ramirez
Pedro Martinez
Trot Nixon
3 Paul Konerko 3.00 8.00
Carlos Lee
Magglio Ordonez
Frank Thomas
4 John Smoltz 3.00 8.00
Chipper Jones
Andruw Jones
Rafael Furcal
5 Garret Anderson 2.00 5.00
Troy Percival
Troy Glaus
Darin Erstad
6 Steve Finley 3.00 8.00
Brandon Webb
Randy Johnson
Luis Gonzalez
7 Paul Lo Duca 3.00 8.00
Hideo Nomo
Shawn Green
Kazuhisa Ishii
8 Larry Walker 3.00 8.00
Todd Helton
Jason Jennings
Preston Wilson
9 A.J. Burnett 3.00 8.00
Dontrelle Willis
Brad Penny
Josh Beckett
10 Jose Reyes 5.00 12.00
Jae Weong Seo
Tom Glavine
Mike Piazza
11 Bernie Williams 8.00 20.00
Derek Jeter
Jason Giambi
Alfonso Soriano
12 Rich Harden 2.00 5.00
Tim Hudson
Barry Zito
Mark Mulder
13 Kevin Millwood 3.00 8.00
Marlon Byrd
Jim Thome
Bobby Abreu
14 Edgar Renteria 6.00 15.00
Jim Edmonds
Albert Pujols
Scott Rolen
15 Roger Clemens 6.00 15.00
Andy Pettitte
Wade Miller
Roy Oswalt

2004 Absolute Memorabilia Team Quad Material

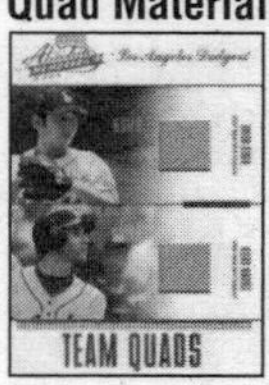

STATED PRINT RUN 100 SERIAL #'d SETS
PRIME PRINT RUN 5 SERIAL #'d SETS
NO PRIME PRICING DUE TO SCARCITY
RANDOM INSERTS IN PACKS
ALL HAVE 4 JSY SWATCHES UNLESS NOTED
CARD 15 IS BAT-BAT-JSY-JSY
1 Jeff Kent 10.00 25.00
Lance Berkman
Craig Biggio
Jeff Bagwell
2 Nomar Garciaparra 15.00 40.00
Manny Ramirez
Pedro Martinez
Trot Nixon
3 Paul Konerko 10.00 25.00
Carlos Lee
Magglio Ordonez
Frank Thomas
4 John Smoltz 10.00 25.00
Chipper Jones
Andruw Jones
Rafael Furcal
5 Garret Anderson 6.00 15.00
Troy Percival
Troy Glaus
Darin Erstad
6 Steve Finley 10.00 25.00
Brandon Webb
Randy Johnson
Luis Gonzalez
7 Paul Lo Duca 10.00 25.00
Hideo Nomo
Shawn Green
Kazuhisa Ishii
8 Larry Walker 10.00 25.00
Todd Helton
Jason Jennings
Preston Wilson
9 A.J. Burnett 10.00 25.00
Dontrelle Willis
Brad Penny
Josh Beckett
10 Jose Reyes 10.00 25.00
Jae Weong Seo
Tom Glavine
Mike Piazza
11 Bernie Williams 15.00 40.00
Derek Jeter
Jason Giambi
Alfonso Soriano
12 Rich Harden 6.00 15.00
Tim Hudson
Barry Zito
Mark Mulder
13 Kevin Millwood 10.00 25.00
Marlon Byrd
Jim Thome
Bobby Abreu
14 Edgar Renteria 15.00 40.00
Jim Edmonds
Albert Pujols
Scott Rolen
15 Roger Clemens Bat 15.00 40.00
Andy Pettitte Bat
Wade Miller Jsy
Roy Oswalt Jsy

2004 Absolute Memorabilia Team Tandem

STATED PRINT RUN 250 SERIAL #'d SETS
*SPECTRUM: 2X TO 5X BASIC
SPECTRUM PRINT RUN 25 SERIAL #'d SETS
RANDOM INSERTS IN PACKS
1 Vladimir Guerrero 1.50 4.00
Reggie Jackson
2 Dale Murphy 1.50 4.00
Chipper Jones
3 Gary Carter 2.00 5.00
Mike Piazza
4 Miguel Tejada 5.00 12.00
Cal Ripken
5 Gary Sheffield 2.50 6.00
Derek Jeter
6 Curt Schilling 1.50 4.00
Pedro Martinez
7 Roger Clemens 2.50 6.00
Andy Pettitte
8 Mike Sweeney 3.00 8.00
George Brett
9 Kazuhisa Ishii 1.50 4.00
Hideo Nomo
10 Austin Kearns 1.00 2.50
Adam Dunn
11 Miguel Cabrera 1.50 4.00
Dontrelle Willis
12 Don Mattingly 3.00 8.00
Derek Jeter
13 Barry Zito 1.00 2.50
Eric Chavez
14 Jim Thome 2.50 6.00
Mike Schmidt
15 Albert Pujols 2.50 6.00
Stan Musial
16 Nolan Ryan 4.00 10.00
Alex Rodriguez
17 Kerry Wood 1.50 4.00
Mark Prior
18 Rafael Palmeiro 1.50 4.00
Jay Gibbons
19 Nomar Garciaparra 2.00 5.00
Manny Ramirez
20 Ivan Rodriguez 2.00 5.00
Mike Piazza

2004 Absolute Memorabilia Team Tandem Material

STATED PRINT RUN 250 SERIAL #'d SETS
PRIME PRINT RUN 5 SERIAL #'d SETS
NO PRIME PRICING DUE TO SCARCITY
RANDOM INSERTS IN PACKS
1 Reggie Jackson Bat 4.00 10.00
Vladimir Guerrero Bat
2 Chipper Jones Jsy 4.00 10.00
Dale Murphy Jsy
3 Gary Carter Jsy 4.00 10.00
Mike Piazza Jsy
4 Miguel Tejada Bat 10.00 25.00
Cal Ripken Bat
5 Derek Jeter Bat 10.00 25.00
Gary Sheffield Bat
6 Curt Schilling Bat 4.00 10.00
Pedro Martinez Bat
7 Roger Clemens Bat 6.00 15.00
Andy Pettitte Bat
8 Mike Sweeney Jsy 6.00 15.00
George Brett Jsy
9 Kazuhisa Ishii Jsy 4.00 10.00
Hideo Nomo Jsy
10 Austin Kearns Jsy 3.00 8.00
Adam Dunn Jsy
11 Dontrelle Willis Jsy 4.00 10.00
Miguel Cabrera Jsy
12 Don Mattingly Jsy 15.00 40.00
Derek Jeter Jsy
13 Barry Zito Jsy 3.00 8.00
Eric Chavez Jsy
14 Jim Thome Jsy 8.00 20.00
Mike Schmidt Jsy
15 Albert Pujols Jsy 15.00 40.00
Stan Musial Jsy
16 Nolan Ryan Jsy 12.50 30.00
Alex Rodriguez Jsy
17 Mark Prior Jsy 6.00 15.00
Kerry Wood Jsy
18 Rafael Palmeiro Jsy 4.00 10.00
Jay Gibbons Jsy
19 Nomar Garciaparra Jsy 6.00 15.00
Manny Ramirez Jsy
20 Ivan Rodriguez Jsy 4.00 10.00
Mike Piazza Jsy

2004 Absolute Memorabilia Team Trio

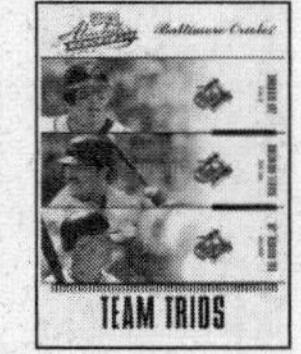

STATED PRINT RUN 100 SERIAL #'d SETS
*SPECTRUM: 1X TO 2.5X BASIC
SPECTRUM PRINT RUN 25 SERIAL #'d SETS
RANDOM INSERTS IN PACKS
1 Kerry Wood 3.00 8.00
Mark Prior
Sammy Sosa
2 Hank Blalock 5.00 12.00
Mark Teixeira
Alex Rodriguez
3 Vernon Wells 2.00 5.00
Roy Halladay
Carlos Delgado
4 Mike Mussina 3.00 8.00
Jorge Posada
Mariano Rivera
5 Shannon Stewart 2.00 5.00
Torii Hunter
Jacque Jones
6 Carlos Beltran 2.00 5.00
Mike Sweeney
Angel Berroa
7 Dontrelle Willis 3.00 8.00
Miguel Cabrera
Josh Beckett
8 Jeff Bagwell 3.00 8.00
Craig Biggio
Lance Berkman
9 Nomar Garciaparra 5.00 12.00
Pedro Martinez
Manny Ramirez
10 Shawn Green 3.00 8.00
Kazuhisa Ishii
Hideo Nomo
11 Mark Mulder 2.00 5.00
Barry Zito
Tim Hudson
12 Jim Edmonds 6.00 15.00
Scott Rolen
Albert Pujols
13 Cal Ripken 10.00 25.00
Jay Gibbons
Rafael Palmeiro
14 Sammy Sosa 6.00 15.00
Mark Grace
Ryne Sandberg
15 Nolan Ryan 10.00 25.00
Roger Clemens
Randy Johnson

2004 Absolute Memorabilia Team Trio Material

STATED PRINT RUN 100 SERIAL #'d SETS
CARD 15 PRINT RUN 25 SERIAL #'d CARDS
PRIME PRINT RUN 5 SERIAL #'d SETS
NO PRIME PRICING DUE TO SCARCITY
RANDOM INSERTS IN PACKS
ALL HAVE 3 JSY SWATCHES UNLESS NOTED
CARD 15 HAS FIELD GLOVE SWATCHES
1 Sammy Sosa 6.00 15.00
Mark Prior
Kerry Wood
2 Hank Blalock 6.00 15.00
Mark Teixeira
Alex Rodriguez
3 Vernon Wells 4.00 10.00
Roy Halladay
Carlos Delgado
4 Mike Mussina 12.50 30.00
Jorge Posada
Mariano Rivera
5 Shannon Stewart 4.00 10.00
Jacque Jones
Torii Hunter
6 Carlos Beltran 4.00 10.00
Mike Sweeney
Angel Berroa
7 Dontrelle Willis 6.00 15.00
Miguel Cabrera
Josh Beckett
8 Jeff Bagwell 6.00 15.00
Craig Biggio
Lance Berkman
9 Nomar Garciaparra 10.00 25.00
Pedro Martinez
Manny Ramirez
10 Shawn Green 6.00 15.00
Kazuhisa Ishii
Hideo Nomo
11 Mark Mulder 4.00 10.00
Barry Zito
Tim Hudson
12 Jim Edmonds 10.00 25.00
Scott Rolen
Albert Pujols
13 Cal Ripken 20.00 50.00
Jay Gibbons
Rafael Palmeiro
14 Sammy Sosa 15.00 40.00
Mark Grace
Ryne Sandberg
15 Roger Clemens Fld Glv 50.00 100.00
Nolan Ryan Fld Glv
Randy Johnson Fld Glv/25

2004 Absolute Memorabilia Tools of the Trade Blue

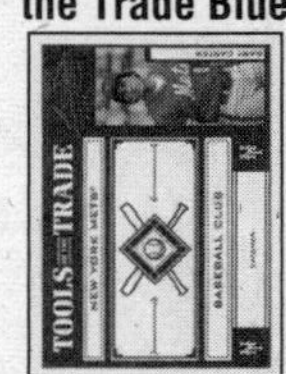

STATED PRINT RUN 250 SERIAL #'d SETS
BLACK PRINT RUN 1 SERIAL #'d SET
NO BLACK PRICING DUE TO SCARCITY
BLACK SPECTRUM PRINT RUN 1 #'d SET
NO BLACK SPEC.PRICING DUE SCARCITY
*BLUE SPEC: .75X TO 2X BASIC
BLUE SPECTRUM PRINT RUN 125 #'d SETS
*GREEN: .6X TO 1.5X BASIC
GREEN PRINT RUN 150 SERIAL #'d SETS
*GREEN SPEC: 1.5X TO 4X BASIC
GREEN SPECTRUM PRINT RUN 50 #'d SETS
*RED: .5X TO 1.2X BASIC
RED PRINT RUN 200 SERIAL #'d SETS
*RED SPECTRUM: 1X TO 2.5X BASIC
RED SPECTRUM PRINT RUN 100 #'d SETS
RANDOM INSERTS IN PACKS
1 Adam Dunn H 1.00 2.50
2 Adam Dunn A 1.00 2.50
3 Alan Trammell 1.00 2.50
4 Albert Pujols H 2.50 6.00
5 Albert Pujols A 2.50 6.00
6 Alex Rodriguez M's 2.00 5.00
7 Alex Rodriguez Rgr H 2.00 5.00
8 Alex Rodriguez Rgr Alt 2.00 5.00
9 Alfonso Soriano 1.00 2.50
10 Andre Dawson 1.00 2.50
11 Andruw Jones H 1.50 4.00
12 Andruw Jones A 1.50 4.00
13 Andy Pettitte H 1.50 4.00
14 Andy Pettitte A 1.50 4.00
15 Angel Berroa 1.00 2.50
16 Aubrey Huff 1.00 2.50
17 Austin Kearns 1.00 2.50
18 Barry Zito Alt 1.00 2.50
19 Barry Zito A 1.00 2.50
20 Bernie Williams 1.50 4.00
21 Bobby Abreu 1.00 2.50
22 Brandon Webb 1.00 2.50
23 Cal Ripken H 5.00 12.00
24 Cal Ripken A 5.00 12.00
25 Cal Ripken Alt 5.00 12.00
26 Carlos Beltran 1.00 2.50
27 Carlos Delgado H 1.00 2.50
28 Carlos Delgado A 1.00 2.50
29 Carlos Lee 1.00 2.50
30 Chipper Jones H 1.50 4.00
31 Chipper Jones A 1.50 4.00
32 Craig Biggio H 1.00 2.50
33 Craig Biggio A 1.00 2.50
34 Curt Schilling D'backs 1.00 2.50
35 Curt Schilling Phils 1.00 2.50
36 Dale Murphy H 1.50 4.00
37 Dale Murphy A 1.50 4.00
38 Darryl Strawberry 1.00 2.50
39 Derek Jeter H 2.50 6.00
40 Derek Jeter A 2.50 6.00
41 Don Mattingly H 2.50 6.00
42 Don Mattingly A 2.50 6.00
43 Dontrelle Willis H 1.50 4.00
44 Dontrelle Willis A 1.50 4.00
45 Dwight Gooden 1.00 2.50
46 Edgar Martinez 1.50 4.00
47 Eric Chavez 1.00 2.50
48 Frank Thomas A 1.50 4.00
49 Frank Thomas Alt 1.50 4.00
50 Garret Anderson 1.00 2.50
51 Gary Carter 1.00 2.50
52 Gary Sheffield 1.00 2.50
53 George Brett H 2.50 6.00
54 George Brett A 2.50 6.00
55 Greg Maddux 2.00 5.00
56 Hank Blalock 1.00 2.50
57 Hideo Nomo 1.50 4.00
58 Ivan Rodriguez Marlins 1.50 4.00
59 Ivan Rodriguez Rgr 1.50 4.00
60 Jacque Jones 1.00 2.50
61 Jae Weong Seo 1.00 2.50
62 Jason Giambi Yanks 1.00 2.50
63 Jason Giambi A's 1.00 2.50
64 Javy Lopez 1.00 2.50
65 Jay Gibbons 1.00 2.50
66 Jeff Bagwell A 1.50 4.00
67 Jeff Bagwell Alt 1.50 4.00
68 Jeff Kent 1.00 2.50
69 Jim Edmonds 1.00 2.50
70 Jim Thome 1.50 4.00
71 Jorge Posada 1.50 4.00
72 Jose Canseco 1.50 4.00
73 Jose Reyes 1.00 2.50
74 Josh Beckett 1.00 2.50
75 Juan Gonzalez 1.00 2.50
76 Kazuhisa Ishii 1.00 2.50
77 Kerry Wood H 1.00 2.50
78 Kerry Wood Alt 1.00 2.50
79 Kirby Puckett 1.50 4.00
80 Lance Berkman 1.00 2.50
81 Lou Brock 1.50 4.00
82 Luis Castillo 1.00 2.50
83 Luis Gonzalez 1.00 2.50
84 Magglio Ordonez 1.00 2.50
85 Manny Ramirez Sox 1.50 4.00
86 Manny Ramirez Indians 1.50 4.00
87 Marcus Giles 1.00 2.50
88 Mark Grace 1.50 4.00
89 Mark Mulder 1.00 2.50
90 Mark Prior H 1.50 4.00
91 Mark Prior A 1.50 4.00
92 Mark Teixeira 1.50 4.00
93 Marlon Byrd 1.00 2.50
94 Miguel Cabrera 1.50 4.00
95 Miguel Tejada 1.00 2.50
96 Mike Lowell 1.00 2.50
97 Mike Mussina O's 1.50 4.00
98 Mike Mussina Yanks 1.50 4.00
99 Mike Piazza Marlins 2.00 5.00
100 Mike Piazza Dodgers 2.00 5.00
101 Mike Piazza Mets 2.00 5.00
102 Mike Schmidt H 2.50 6.00
103 Mike Schmidt A 2.50 6.00
104 Mike Sweeney 1.00 2.50
105 Nick Johnson 1.00 2.50
106 Nolan Ryan Angels 4.00 10.00
107 Nolan Ryan Astros 4.00 10.00
108 Nolan Ryan Rangers 4.00 10.00
109 Nomar Garciaparra H 2.00 5.00
110 Nomar Garciaparra A 2.00 5.00
111 Pat Burrell 1.00 2.50
112 Paul Lo Duca 1.00 2.50
113 Pedro Martinez Sox 1.50 4.00
114 Pedro Martinez Expos 1.50 4.00
115 Preston Wilson 1.00 2.50
116 Rafael Palmeiro O's 1.50 4.00
117 Rafael Palmeiro Rgr 1.50 4.00
118 Randy Johnson D'backs 1.50 4.00
119 Randy Johnson M's 1.50 4.00
120 Richie Sexson 1.00 2.50
121 Rickey Henderson A's 1.50 4.00
122 Rickey Henderson Padres 1.50 4.00
123 Rickey Henderson M's 1.50 4.00
124 Roberto Alomar 1.50 4.00
125 Rocco Baldelli 1.00 2.50
126 Rod Carew 1.50 4.00
127 Roger Clemens Sox 2.50 6.00
128 Roger Clemens Yanks 2.50 6.00
129 Roy Halladay 1.00 2.50
130 Roy Oswalt 1.00 2.50
131 Ryne Sandberg 2.50 6.00
132 Sammy Sosa H 1.50 4.00
133 Sammy Sosa A 1.50 4.00
134 Sammy Sosa Sox 1.50 4.00
135 Scott Rolen 1.50 4.00
136 Shawn Green 1.00 2.50

137 Steve Carlton 1.50 4.00
138 Tim Hudson 1.00 2.50
139 Todd Helton H 1.50 4.00
140 Todd Helton A 1.50 4.00
141 Tom Glavine Braves 1.50 4.00
142 Tom Glavine Mets 1.50 4.00
143 Tony Gwynn A 2.00 5.00
144 Tony Gwynn Alt 2.00 5.00
145 Torii Hunter 1.00 2.50
146 Trot Nixon 1.00 2.50
147 Troy Glaus 1.00 2.50
148 Vernon Wells 1.00 2.50
149 Vladimir Guerrero 1.50 4.00
150 Will Clark 1.50 4.00

2004 Absolute Memorabilia Tools of the Trade Signature Blue Spectrum

PRINT RUNS B/WN 1-100 COPIES PER
NO PRICING ON QTY OF 10 OR LESS
BLACK PRINT RUN 1 SERIAL #'d SET
NO BLACK PRICING DUE TO SCARCITY
GREEN PRINT RUN B/WN 1-10 COPIES PER
NO GREEN PRICING DUE TO SCARCITY
*RED p/r 50: .5X TO 1.2X BLUE p/r 100
*RED p/r 25: .6X TO 1.5X BLUE p/r 100
*RED p/r 23-25: .5X TO 1.2X BLUE p/r 50
*RED p/r 25: .4X TO 1X BLUE p/r 25
RED PRINT RUNS B/WN 1-50 COPIES PER
NO RED PRICING ON QTY OF 11 OR LESS
RANDOM INSERTS IN PACKS
1 Adam Dunn H/10
2 Adam Dunn A/10
3 Alan Trammell/100 6.00 15.00
4 Albert Pujols H/1
5 Albert Pujols A/1
10 Andre Dawson/100 6.00 15.00
11 Andruw Jones H/1
12 Andruw Jones A/1
13 Andy Pettitte H/1
14 Andy Pettitte A/1
15 Angel Berroa/100 4.00 10.00
16 Aubrey Huff/100 6.00 15.00
17 Austin Kearns/100 4.00 10.00
18 Barry Zito Alt/1
19 Barry Zito A/1
20 Bernie Williams/1
22 Brandon Webb/100 4.00 10.00
23 Cal Ripken H/8
24 Cal Ripken A/8
25 Cal Ripken Alt/8
26 Carlos Beltran/100 6.00 15.00
29 Carlos Lee/100 6.00 15.00
30 Chipper Jones H/10
31 Chipper Jones A/10
32 Craig Biggio H/1
33 Craig Biggio A/1
34 Curt Schilling D'backs/1
35 Curt Schilling Phils/1
36 Dale Murphy H/50 15.00 40.00
37 Dale Murphy A/50 15.00 40.00
38 Darryl Strawberry/50 10.00 25.00
41 Don Mattingly H/50 40.00 80.00
42 Don Mattingly A/50 40.00 80.00
43 Dontrelle Willis H/25 20.00 50.00
44 Dontrelle Willis A/25 20.00 50.00
45 Dwight Gooden/50 10.00 25.00
46 Edgar Martinez/25 20.00 50.00
47 Eric Chavez/1
48 Frank Thomas A/25 30.00 60.00
49 Frank Thomas Alt/25 30.00 60.00
50 Garret Anderson/100 6.00 15.00
51 Gary Carter/100 6.00 15.00
52 Gary Sheffield/10
53 George Brett H/5
54 George Brett A/5
56 Hank Blalock/10
57 Hideo Nomo/1
60 Jacque Jones/50 10.00 25.00
61 Jae Weong Seo/25 12.50 30.00
65 Jay Gibbons/50 6.00 15.00
66 Jeff Bagwell A/5
67 Jeff Bagwell Alt/5
69 Jim Edmonds/25 20.00 50.00
71 Jorge Posada/25 20.00 50.00
73 Jose Reyes/25 12.50 30.00
74 Josh Beckett/5
75 Juan Gonzalez/20 12.50 30.00
76 Kazuhisa Ishii/5
77 Kerry Wood H/25 20.00 50.00
78 Kerry Wood Alt/25 20.00 50.00
79 Kirby Puckett/10
80 Lance Berkman/10
81 Lou Brock/100 10.00 25.00
82 Luis Castillo/10
84 Magglio Ordonez/50 10.00 25.00
85 Manny Ramirez Sox/1
86 Manny Ramirez Indians/1
87 Marcus Giles/50 10.00 25.00
88 Mark Grace/25 20.00 50.00
89 Mark Mulder/100 6.00 15.00
90 Mark Prior H/50 12.50 30.00
91 Mark Prior A/50 12.50 30.00
92 Mark Teixeira/50 15.00 40.00
93 Marlon Byrd/50 6.00 15.00
94 Miguel Cabrera/100 10.00 25.00
96 Mike Lowell/1
99 Mike Piazza Marlins/5
100 Mike Piazza Dodgers/5
101 Mike Piazza Mets/5
102 Mike Schmidt H/25 50.00 100.00
103 Mike Schmidt A/25 50.00 100.00
105 Nick Johnson/1
106 Nolan Ryan Angels/25 75.00 150.00
107 Nolan Ryan Astros/25 75.00 150.00
108 Nolan Ryan Rangers/25 75.00 150.00
112 Paul Lo Duca/50 10.00 25.00
115 Preston Wilson/100 6.00 15.00
116 Rafael Palmeiro O's/1
117 Rafael Palmeiro Rgr/1
118 Randy Johnson D'backs/1
119 Randy Johnson M's/1
121 Rickey Henderson A's/10
122 Rickey Henderson Padres/5
123 Rickey Henderson M's/5
124 Roberto Alomar/10
125 Rocco Baldelli/10
126 Rod Carew/10
129 Roy Halladay/25 12.50 30.00
130 Roy Oswalt/25 12.50 30.00
131 Ryne Sandberg/5
132 Sammy Sosa H/5
133 Sammy Sosa A/5
134 Sammy Sosa Sox/5
135 Scott Rolen/50 15.00 40.00
136 Shawn Green/1
137 Steve Carlton/50 10.00 25.00
138 Tim Hudson/10
139 Todd Helton H/1
140 Todd Helton A/1
141 Tom Glavine Braves/10
142 Tom Glavine Mets/10
143 Tony Gwynn A/25 40.00 80.00
144 Tony Gwynn Alt/25 40.00 80.00
145 Torii Hunter/50 10.00 25.00
146 Trot Nixon/25 12.50 30.00
147 Troy Glaus/1
148 Vernon Wells/10
149 Vladimir Guerrero/25 30.00 60.00
150 Will Clark/50 15.00 40.00

2004 Absolute Memorabilia Tools of the Trade Material Combo

PRINT RUNS B/WN 25-250 COPIES PER
SINGLE PRINT RUNS B/WN 1-5 COPIES PER
NO SINGLE PRICING DUE TO SCARCITY
SINGLE PS PRINT RUN 1 SERIAL #'d SET
NO SINGLE PS PRICING DUE TO SCARCITY
*COMBO PS p/r 25: 1.5X TO 4X COM.p/r 250
*COMBO PS p/r 25: 1X TO 2.5X COM.p/r 100
COMBO PS PRINT RUNS B/WN 1-25 PER
NO COMBO PS PRICING ON 10 OR LESS
*TRIO p/r 100: .6X TO 1.5X COMBO p/r 250
*TRIO p/r 100: .5X TO 1.2X COMBO p/r 100
*TRIO p/r 50: 1X TO 2.5X COMBO p/r 250
*TRIO p/r 50: .6X TO 1.5X COMBO p/r 100
*TRIO p/r 25: 1.5X TO 4X COMBO p/r 250
*TRIO p/r 25: .75X TO 2X COMBO p/r 100
TRIO PRINT RUNS B/WN 5-100 COPIES PER
NO TRIO PRICING ON QTY OF 10 OR LESS
TRIO PS PRINT RUNS B/WN 1-10 PER
NO TRIO PS PRICING DUE TO SCARCITY
*QUAD p/r 50: 1.5X TO 4X COMBO p/r 250
*QUAD p/r 50: 1.25X TO 3X COMBO p/r 100
*QUAD p/r 50: .6X TO 1.5X COMBO p/r 25
*QUAD p/r 25: 2X TO 5X COMBO p/r 250
*QUAD p/r 25: 1X TO 2.5X COMBO p/r 100
QUAD PRINT RUNS B/WN 1-50 COPIES PER
NO QUAD PRICING ON QTY OF 10 OR LESS
QUAD PS PRINT RUNS B/WN 1-10 PER
NO QUAD PS PRICING DUE TO SCARCITY
*FIVE p/r 25: 2.5X TO 6X COMBO p/r 250
*FIVE p/r 25: 2X TO 5X COMBO p/r 100
*FIVE p/r 25: .75X TO 2X COMBO p/r 25
FIVE PRINT RUNS B/WN 10-25 COPIES PER
NO FIVE PRICING ON QTY OF 10 OR LESS
FIVE PS PRINT RUNS B/WN 1-5 COPIES PER
NO FIVE PS PRICING DUE TO SCARCITY
*SIX p/r 25: 3X TO 8X COMBO p/r 250
*SIX p/r 25: 2.5X TO 6X COMBO p/r 100
SIX PRINT RUNS B/WN 5-25 COPIES PER
NO SIX PRICING ON QTY OF 5 OR LESS
SIX PS PRINT RUNS B/WN 1-5 COPIES PER
NO SIX PS PRICING DUE TO SCARCITY
RANDOM INSERTS IN PACKS
1 A.Dunn H Bat-Jsy/250 2.50 6.00
2 A.Dunn A Bat-Jsy/250 2.50 6.00
3 A.Trammell Bat-Jsy/250 2.50 6.00
4 A.Pujols H Bat-Jsy/250 8.00 20.00
5 A.Pujols A Bat-Jsy/250 8.00 20.00
6 A.Rod M's Bat-Jsy/250 4.00 10.00
7 A.Rod Rgr H Bat-Jsy/250 4.00 10.00
8 A.Rod Rgr Alt Bat-Jsy/250 4.00 10.00
9 A.Soriano Bat-Jsy/100 3.00 8.00
10 A.Dawson Bat-Jsy/250 2.50 6.00
11 A.Jones H Bat-Jsy/100 4.00 10.00
12 A.Jones A Bat-Jsy/250 3.00 8.00
13 A.Pettitte H Bat-Jsy/100 4.00 10.00
14 A.Pettitte A Bat-Jsy/100 4.00 10.00
15 A.Berroa Bat-Jsy/250 2.00 5.00
16 A.Huff Bat-Jsy/250 2.50 6.00
17 A.Kearns Bat-Jsy/250 2.00 5.00
18 B.Zito Alt Bat-Jsy/250 2.50 6.00
19 B.Zito A Bat-Jsy/250 2.50 6.00
20 B.Williams Bat-Jsy/250 3.00 8.00
21 B.Abreu Bat-Jsy/250 2.50 6.00
22 B.Webb Bat-Jsy/250 2.00 5.00
23 C.Ripken H Bat-Jsy/250 12.50 30.00
24 C.Ripken A Bat-Jsy/250 12.50 30.00
25 C.Ripken Alt Bat-Jsy/250 12.50 30.00
26 C.Beltran Bat-Jsy/250 2.50 6.00
27 C.Delgado H Bat-Jsy/250 2.50 6.00
28 C.Delgado A Bat-Jsy/250 2.50 6.00
29 C.Lee Bat-Jsy/250 2.50 6.00
30 C.Jones H Bat-Jsy/250 4.00 10.00
31 C.Jones A Bat-Jsy/250 4.00 10.00
32 C.Biggio H Bat-Jsy/250 2.50 6.00
33 C.Biggio A Bat-Jsy/100 3.00 8.00
34 C.Schill D'backs Bat-Jsy/250 2.50 6.00
35 C.Schill Phils Bat-Jsy/250 2.50 6.00
36 D.Murphy H Bat-Jsy/250 3.00 8.00
37 D.Murphy A Bat-Jsy/100 4.00 10.00
38 D.Strawberry Bat-Jsy/250 2.50 6.00
39 D.Jeter H Bat-Jsy/100 15.00 40.00
40 D.Jeter A Bat-Jsy/100 15.00 40.00
41 D.Mattingly H Bat-Jsy/100 10.00 25.00
42 D.Mattingly A Bat-Jsy/100 10.00 25.00
43 D.Willis H Bat-Jsy/250 3.00 8.00
44 D.Willis A Bat-Jsy/250 3.00 8.00
45 D.Gooden Bat-Jsy/250 2.50 6.00
46 E.Martinez Bat-Jsy/250 3.00 8.00
47 E.Chavez Bat-Jsy/250 2.50 6.00
48 F.Thomas A Bat-Jsy/250 4.00 10.00
49 F.Thomas Alt Bat-Jsy/250 4.00 10.00
50 G.Anderson Bat-Jsy/250 2.50 6.00
51 G.Carter Bat-Jsy/250 2.50 6.00
52 G.Sheffield Bat-Jsy/250 2.50 6.00
53 G.Brett H Bat-Jsy/250 8.00 20.00
54 G.Brett A Bat-Jsy/250 8.00 20.00
55 G.Maddux Bat-Jsy/250 5.00 12.00
56 H.Blalock Bat-Jsy/250 2.50 6.00
57 H.Nomo Bat-Jsy/250 5.00 12.00
58 I.Rod Marlins Bat-Jsy/250 3.00 8.00
59 I.Rod Rgr Bat-Jsy/250 3.00 8.00
60 J.Jones Bat-Jsy/250 2.50 6.00
62 J.Giambi Yanks Bat-Jsy/250 2.50 6.00
63 J.Giambi A's Bat-Jsy/250 2.50 6.00
64 J.Lopez Bat-Jsy/250 2.50 6.00
65 J.Gibbons Bat-Jsy/250 2.00 5.00
66 J.Bagwell A Bat-Jsy/250 3.00 8.00
67 J.Bagwell Alt Bat-Jsy/250 3.00 8.00
68 J.Kent Bat-Jsy/250 2.50 6.00
69 J.Edmonds Bat-Jsy/250 2.50 6.00
70 J.Thome Bat-Jsy/250 3.00 8.00
71 J.Posada Bat-Jsy/250 3.00 8.00
72 J.Canseco Bat-Jsy/250 3.00 8.00
73 J.Reyes Bat-Jsy/250 2.50 6.00
74 J.Beckett Bat-Jsy/250 2.50 6.00
75 J.Gonzalez Bat-Jsy/250 2.50 6.00
76 K.Ishii Bat-Jsy/250 2.50 6.00
77 K.Wood H Bat-Jsy/250 2.50 6.00
78 K.Wood Alt Bat-Jsy/250 2.50 6.00
79 K.Puckett Bat-Jsy/250 6.00 15.00
80 L.Berkman Bat-Jsy/250 2.50 6.00
81 L.Brock Bat-Jsy/250 3.00 8.00
82 L.Castillo Bat-Jsy/250 2.00 5.00
83 L.Gonzalez Bat-Jsy/250 2.50 6.00
84 M.Ordonez Bat-Jsy/250 2.50 6.00
85 M.Ramirez Sox Bat-Jsy/250 3.00 8.00
86 M.Ram Indians Bat-Jsy/250 3.00 8.00
87 M.Giles Bat-Jsy/25 6.00 15.00
88 M.Grace Bat-Jsy/250 3.00 8.00
89 M.Mulder Bat-Jsy/250 2.50 6.00
90 M.Prior H Bat-Jsy/250 3.00 8.00
91 M.Prior A Bat-Jsy/250 3.00 8.00
92 M.Teixeira Bat-Jsy/250 3.00 8.00
93 M.Byrd Bat-Jsy/250 2.00 5.00
94 M.Cabrera Bat-Jsy/250 3.00 8.00
95 M.Tejada Bat-Jsy/250 2.50 6.00
96 M.Lowell Bat-Jsy/250 2.50 6.00
97 M.Muss O's Jsy-Pants/250 3.00 8.00
98 M.Muss Yanks Jsy-Jsy/250 3.00 8.00
99 M.Piazza Marlins Bat-Jsy/250 5.00 12.00
100 M.Piaz Dodgers Bat-Jsy/250 5.00 12.00
101 M.Piazza Mets Bat-Jsy/250 5.00 12.00
102 M.Schmidt H Bat-Jsy/100 10.00 25.00
103 M.Schmidt A Bat-Jsy/100 10.00 25.00
104 M.Sweeney Bat-Jsy/250 2.50 6.00
105 N.Johnson Bat-Jsy/250 2.50 6.00
106 N.Ryan Angels Jkt-Jsy/250 10.00 25.00
107 N.Ryan Astros Jkt-Jsy/250 10.00 25.00
108 N.Ryan Rgr Jsy-Pants/250 10.00 25.00
109 N.Garciaparra H Bat-Jsy/250 5.00 12.00
110 N.Garciaparra A Bat-Jsy/250 5.00 12.00
111 P.Burrell Bat-Jsy/250 2.50 6.00
112 P.Lo Duca Bat-Jsy/250 2.50 6.00
113 P.Martinez Sox Bat-Jsy/250 3.00 8.00
114 P.Mart Expos Bat-Jsy/250 3.00 8.00
115 P.Wilson Bat-Jsy/250 2.50 6.00
116 R.Palmeiro O's Bat-Jsy/250 3.00 8.00
117 R.Palmeiro Rgr Bat-Jsy/250 3.00 8.00
118 R.John D'backs Bat-Jsy/250 4.00 10.00
119 R.Johnson M's Bat-Jsy/250 4.00 10.00
120 R.Sexson Bat-Jsy/250 2.50 6.00
121 R.Hend A's Bat-Jsy/250 4.00 10.00
122 R.Hend Padres Bat-Jsy/250 4.00 10.00
123 R.Hend M's Bat-Jsy/250 4.00 10.00
124 R.Alomar Bat-Jsy/250 3.00 8.00
125 R.Baldelli Bat-Jsy/250 2.50 6.00
126 R.Carew Bat-Jsy/250 3.00 8.00
127 R.Clemens Sox Bat-Jsy/250 6.00 15.00
128 R.Clem Yanks Bat-Jsy/250 6.00 15.00
129 R.Halladay Jsy-Jsy/250 2.50 6.00
130 R.Oswalt Bat-Jsy/250 2.50 6.00
131 R.Sandberg Bat-Jsy/250 6.00 15.00
132 S.Sosa H Bat-Jsy/250 4.00 10.00
133 S.Sosa A Bat-Jsy/250 4.00 10.00
134 S.Sosa Sox Bat-Jsy/250 4.00 10.00
135 S.Rolen Bat-Jsy/250 3.00 8.00
136 S.Green Bat-Jsy/250 2.50 6.00
137 S.Carlton Bat-Jsy/250 2.50 6.00
138 T.Hudson Bat-Jsy/250 2.50 6.00
139 T.Helton H Bat-Jsy/250 3.00 8.00
140 T.Helton A Bat-Jsy/250 3.00 8.00
141 T.Glav Braves Bat-Jsy/250 3.00 8.00
142 T.Glav Mets Bat-Jsy/250 3.00 8.00
143 T.Gwynn A Bat-Jsy/250 6.00 15.00
144 T.Gwynn Alt Bat-Jsy/250 6.00 15.00
145 T.Hunter Bat-Jsy/250 2.50 6.00
146 T.Nixon Bat-Jsy/250 2.50 6.00
147 T.Glaus Bat-Jsy/250 2.50 6.00
148 V.Wells Bat-Jsy/250 2.50 6.00
149 V.Guerrero Bat-Jsy/250 4.00 10.00
150 W.Clark Bat-Jsy/250 3.00 8.00

2004 Absolute Memorabilia Tools of the Trade Material Signature Single

PRINT RUNS B/WN 1-50 COPIES PER
NO PRICING ON QTY OF 11 OR LESS
SINGLE PS PRINT RUNS B/WN 1-5 PER
NO SINGLE PS PRICING DUE TO SCARCITY
*COMBO p/r 25: .5X TO 1.2X SINGLE p/r 50
COMBO PRINT RUNS B/WN 1-25 PER
NO COMBO PRICES ON QTY OF 10 OR LESS
COMBO PS PRINT RUNS B/WN 1-5 PER

NO COMBO PS PRICING DUE TO SCARCITY
TRIO PRINT RUNS B/WN 1-10 COPIES PER
NO TRIO PRICING DUE TO SCARCITY
TRIO PS PRINT RUNS B/WN 1-5 PER
NO TRIO PS PRICING DUE TO SCARCITY
QUAD PRINT RUNS B/WN 1-10 COPIES PER
NO QUAD PRICING DUE TO SCARCITY
QUAD PS PRINT RUNS B/WN 1-5 PER
NO QUAD PS PRICING DUE TO SCARCITY
RANDOM INSERTS IN PACKS
1 Adam Dunn H Jsy/25 20.00 50.00
2 Adam Dunn A Jsy/25 20.00 50.00
3 Alan Trammell Jsy/25 20.00 50.00
4 Albert Pujols H Jsy/5
5 Albert Pujols A Jsy/5
6 Alex Rodriguez M's Jsy/5
7 Alex Rodriguez Rgr H Jsy/5
8 Alex Rodriguez Rgr Alt Jsy/5
10 Andre Dawson Jsy/25 12.50 30.00
11 Andruw Jones H Jsy/5
12 Andruw Jones A Jsy/5
15 Angel Berroa Jsy/50 6.00 15.00
16 Aubrey Huff Jsy/1
17 Austin Kearns Jsy/28 10.00 25.00
18 Barry Zito Alt Jsy/1
19 Barry Zito A Jsy/1
20 Bernie Williams Jsy/5
21 Bobby Abreu Jsy/25 12.50 30.00
22 Brandon Webb Jsy/25 10.00 25.00
23 Cal Ripken H Jsy/8
24 Cal Ripken A Pants/8
25 Cal Ripken Alt Jsy/8
26 Carlos Beltran Jsy/15 15.00 40.00
29 Carlos Lee Jsy/25 12.50 30.00
30 Chipper Jones H Jsy/10
31 Chipper Jones A Jsy/10
32 Craig Biggio A Jsy/7
33 Craig Biggio A Jsy/7
34 Curt Schilling D'backs Jsy/1
35 Curt Schilling Phils Jsy/1
36 Dale Murphy H Jsy/25 20.00 50.00
37 Dale Murphy A Jsy/25 20.00 50.00
38 Darryl Strawberry Jsy/39 10.00 25.00
41 Don Mattingly H Jsy/5
42 Don Mattingly A Jsy/5
43 Dontrelle Willis H Jsy/25 20.00 50.00
44 Dontrelle Willis A Jsy/25 20.00 50.00
45 Dwight Gooden Jsy/16 15.00 40.00
46 Edgar Martinez Jsy/11
47 Eric Chavez Jsy/3
48 Frank Thomas A Jsy/5
49 Frank Thomas Alt Jsy/5
50 Garret Anderson Jsy/16 15.00 40.00
51 Gary Carter Jsy/8
52 Gary Sheffield Jsy/11
53 George Brett H Jsy/5
54 George Brett A Jsy/5
55 Greg Maddux Jsy/1
56 Hank Blalock Jsy/9
57 Hideo Nomo Jsy/1
60 Jacque Jones Jsy/1
61 Jae Weong Seo Jsy/25 10.00 25.00
65 Jay Gibbons Jsy/5
66 Jeff Bagwell A Jsy/5
67 Jeff Bagwell Alt Jsy/5
69 Jim Edmonds Jsy/5
71 Jorge Posada Jsy/20 20.00 50.00
72 Jose Canseco Jsy/5
74 Josh Beckett Jsy/21 20.00 50.00
75 Juan Gonzalez Jsy/5
76 Kazuhisa Ishii Jsy/5
79 Kirby Puckett Jsy/5
80 Lance Berkman Jsy/5
81 Lou Brock Jsy/5
82 Luis Castillo Jsy/25 10.00 25.00
84 Magglio Ordonez Jsy/5
85 Manny Ramirez Sox Jsy/5
86 Manny Ramirez Indians Jsy/5
88 Mark Grace Jsy/5
89 Mark Mulder Jsy/20 12.50 30.00
90 Mark Prior H Jsy/10
91 Mark Prior A Jsy/10
92 Mark Teixeira Jsy/10
93 Marlon Byrd Jsy/29 10.00 25.00
94 Miguel Cabrera Jsy/20 20.00 50.00
96 Mike Lowell Jsy/19 15.00 40.00
97 Mike Mussina O's Jsy/5
98 Mike Mussina Yanks Jsy/5
99 Mike Piazza Marlins Jsy/1
100 Mike Piazza Dodgers Jsy/1
101 Mike Piazza Mets Jsy/1
106 Nolan Ryan Angels Jsy/5
107 Nolan Ryan Astros Jsy/5
108 Nolan Ryan Rgr Jsy/5
112 Paul Lo Duca Jsy/50 10.00 25.00
113 Pedro Martinez Sox Jsy/1
114 Pedro Martinez Expos Jsy/1
115 Preston Wilson Jsy/44 10.00 25.00
116 Rafael Palmeiro O's Jsy/5
117 Rafael Palmeiro Rgr Jsy/5
118 Randy Johnson D'backs Jsy/1
119 Randy Johnson M's Jsy/1
120 Richie Sexson Jsy/11
125 Rocco Baldelli Jsy/25 12.50 30.00
126 Rod Carew Jsy/10
129 Roy Halladay Jsy/32 12.50 30.00
130 Roy Oswalt Jsy/10
131 Ryne Sandberg Jsy/5
132 Sammy Sosa H Jsy/1
133 Sammy Sosa A Jsy/1
134 Sammy Sosa Sox Jsy/1
137 Steve Carlton Jsy/25 12.50 30.00
138 Tim Hudson Jsy/5
139 Todd Helton H Jsy/5
140 Todd Helton A Jsy/5
141 Tom Glavine Braves Jsy/5
142 Tom Glavine Mets Jsy/5
143 Tony Gwynn A Jsy/10
144 Tony Gwynn Alt Jsy/10
145 Torii Hunter Jsy/25 12.50 30.00
146 Trot Nixon Jsy/25 12.50 30.00
147 Troy Glaus Jsy/5
148 Vernon Wells Jsy/10
149 Vladimir Guerrero Jsy/5
150 Will Clark Jsy/10

2005 Absolute Memorabilia

This 100-card set was released in June, 2005. The set was issued in four-pack boxes which came 18 to a case. Cards numbered 1 through 95 feature active veterans while cards numbered 96 through 100 feature Rookie Cards. An 100-card update set was released in December, 2005. That update set was the final product released by Donruss/Leaf/Playoff to fulfill their contract with MLB and MLBPA which began in 2001.

COMMON CARD (1-200) .40 1.00
1 Andruw Jones .60 1.50
2 B.J. Upton .40 1.00
3 Jim Edmonds .40 1.00
4 Johan Santana 1.00 2.50
5 Jeff Bagwell .60 1.50
6 Derek Jeter
7 Eric Chavez
8 Albert Pujols 2.00 5.00
9 Craig Biggio .60 1.50
10 Hank Blalock .40 1.00
11 Chipper Jones 1.00 2.50
12 Jacque Jones .40 1.00
13 Alfonso Soriano .40 1.00
14 Carl Crawford .40 1.00
15 Ben Sheets .40 1.00
16 Garret Anderson .40 1.00
17 Luis Gonzalez .40 1.00
18 Andy Pettitte .60 1.50
19 Miguel Tejada .40 1.00
20 Carlos Delgado .40 1.00
21 Austin Kearns .40 1.00
22 Adrian Beltre .40 1.00
23 Rafael Palmeiro .60 1.50
24 Greg Maddux 1.50 4.00
25 Jason Bay .40 1.00
26 Jason Varitek 1.00 2.50
27 David Ortiz 1.00 2.50
28 Dontrelle Willis .40 1.00
29 Adam Dunn .40 1.00
30 Carlos Lee .40 1.00
31 Manny Ramirez .60 1.50
32 Rocco Baldelli .40 1.00
33 Jeff Kent .40 1.00
34 Jake Peavy .60 1.50
35 Vernon Wells .40 1.00
36 Ichiro Suzuki 2.00 5.00
37 C.C. Sabathia .40 1.00
38 Hideki Matsui 1.50 4.00
39 Gary Sheffield .40 1.00
40 Paul Lo Duca .40 1.00
41 Vladimir Guerrero 1.00 2.50
42 Omar Vizquel .60 1.50
43 Lance Berkman .40 1.00
44 Shawn Green .40 1.00
45 Josh Beckett .40 1.00
46 Barry Zito .40 1.00
47 Roger Clemens 1.50 4.00
48 Sean Casey .40 1.00
49 Edgar Renteria .40 1.00
50 Mark Teixeira .60 1.50
51 Frank Thomas 1.00 2.50
52 Khalil Greene .60 1.50
53 Bobby Abreu .40 1.00
54 Rafael Furcal .40 1.00
55 Jose Vidro .40 1.00
56 Nomar Garciaparra 1.00 2.50
57 Melvin Mora .40 1.00
58 Trot Nixon .40 1.00
59 Magglio Ordonez .40 1.00
60 Michael Young .40 1.00
61 Richie Sexson .40 1.00
62 Alex Rodriguez 1.50 4.00
63 Tim Hudson .40 1.00
64 Todd Helton .60 1.50
65 Mike Lowell .40 1.00
66 Mark Mulder .40 1.00
67 Sammy Sosa 1.00 2.50
68 Mark Prior .60 1.50
69 Shannon Stewart .40 1.00
70 Miguel Cabrera .60 1.50
71 Troy Glaus .40 1.00
72 Scott Rolen .60 1.50
73 Ken Griffey Jr. 1.50 4.00
74 Mike Piazza 1.00 2.50
75 Roy Halladay .40 1.00
76 Larry Walker .60 1.50
77 Kerry Wood .40 1.00
78 Mike Mussina .60 1.50
79 Curt Schilling .60 1.50
80 Rich Harden .40 1.00
81 Victor Martinez .40 1.00
82 Roy Oswalt .40 1.00
83 Pedro Martinez .60 1.50
84 Tom Glavine .60 1.50
85 Randy Johnson 1.00 2.50
86 Ivan Rodriguez .60 1.50
87 Carlos Beltran .40 1.00
88 Torii Hunter .40 1.00
89 Hideo Nomo 1.00 2.50
90 Jim Thome .60 1.50
91 Aramis Ramirez .40 1.00
92 J.D. Drew .40 1.00
93 Javy Lopez .40 1.00
94 David Wright 1.50 4.00
95 Bobby Crosby .40 1.00
96 Jeff Niemann RC 1.00 2.50
97 Yuniesky Betancourt RC 1.50 4.00
98 Tadahito Iguchi RC 1.50 4.00
99 Phil Humber RC 1.00 2.50
100 Justin Verlander RC 2.00 5.00
101 Al Kaline 1.25 3.00
102 Albert Pujols 2.00 5.00
103 Alex Rodriguez 1.50 4.00
104 Andruw Jones .60 1.50
105 Aubrey Huff .40 1.00
106 Barry Zito .40 1.00
107 Ben Sheets .40 1.00
108 Chipper Jones 1.00 2.50
109 Curt Schilling .60 1.50
110 Dale Murphy .75 2.00
111 David Dellucci .40 1.00
112 David Ortiz 1.00 2.50
113 Dennis Eckersley .50 1.25
114 Derek Jeter 2.00 5.00
115 Don Mattingly 2.50 6.00
116 Don Sutton .50 1.25
117 Dontrelle Willis .40 1.00
118 Duke Snider .75 2.00
119 Edgar Renteria .40 1.00
120 Fergie Jenkins .50 1.25
121 Frank Robinson .50 1.25
122 Frank Thomas 1.00 2.50
123 Garret Anderson .40 1.00
124 Gary Sheffield .40 1.00
125 Greg Maddux 1.50 4.00
126 Hideki Matsui 1.50 4.00
127 Hideo Nomo 1.00 2.50
128 Ichiro Suzuki 2.00 5.00
129 Jamie Moyer .40 1.00
130 Jason Varitek 1.00 2.50
131 Jeff Bagwell .60 1.50
132 Stephen Drew RC 4.00 10.00
133 Jeff Niemann 1.00 2.50
134 Jeremy Bonderman .40 1.00
135 Jim Bunning .50 1.25
136 Jim Leyritz .40 1.00
137 Jim Thome .60 1.50
138 Johan Santana 1.00 2.50
139 John Kruk .50 1.25
140 Johnny Podres .50 1.25
141 Jose Guillen .40 1.00
142 Justin Verlander 2.00 5.00
143 Keiichi Yabu RC .40 1.00
144 Keith Foulke .60 1.50
145 Keith Hernandez .50 1.25
146 Ken Griffey Jr. 1.50 4.00
147 Kent Hrbek .50 1.25
148 Anthony Lerew .40 1.00
149 Larry Walker .60 1.50
150 Lew Ford .40 1.00
151 Lou Brock .75 2.00
152 Luis Aparicio .50 1.25
153 Luis Tiant .50 1.25
154 Manny Ramirez .60 1.50
155 Mark Mulder .40 1.00
156 Mark Prior .60 1.50
157 Mark Teixeira .60 1.50
158 Marty Marion .50 1.25
159 Miguel Cabrera .60 1.50
160 Miguel Tejada .40 1.00
161 Mike Lieberthal .40 1.00
162 Mike Piazza 1.00 2.50
163 Minnie Minoso .50 1.25
164 Monte Irvin .50 1.25
165 Morgan Ensberg .40 1.00
166 Nolan Ryan 3.00 8.00
167 Octavio Dotel .40 1.00
168 Omar Vizquel .60 1.50
169 Ozzie Smith 2.00 5.00
170 Pedro Martinez .60 1.50
171 Phil Humber 1.00 2.50
172 Phil Rizzuto .75 2.00
173 Prince Fielder RC 2.00 5.00
174 Ralph Kiner .75 2.00
175 Randy Johnson 1.00 2.50
176 Red Schoendienst .50 1.25
177 Rich Gossage .50 1.25
178 Rick Dempsey .40 1.00
179 Rickie Weeks .40 1.00
180 Robin Roberts .50 1.25
181 Rod Carew .75 2.00
182 Roger Clemens 1.50 4.00
183 Rollie Fingers .50 1.25
184 Ron Guidry .50 1.25
185 Ron Santo .75 2.00
186 Russ Ortiz .40 1.00
187 Ryne Sandberg 2.50 6.00
188 Sammy Sosa 1.00 2.50
189 Scott Rolen .60 1.50
190 Stan Musial 2.00 5.00
191 Steve Carlton .50 1.25
192 Steve Garvey .50 1.25
193 Steve Stone .50 1.25
194 Tim Salmon .60 1.50
195 Todd Helton .60 1.50
196 Todd Walker .40 1.00
197 Tom Gordon .40 1.00
198 Trot Nixon .40 1.00
199 Troy Percival .40 1.00
200 Vladimir Guerrero 1.00 2.50

2005 Absolute Memorabilia Retail

*RETAIL: .12X TO .3X BASIC
ISSUED ONLY IN RETAIL PACKS
RETAIL CARDS LACK FOIL FRONTS

2005 Absolute Memorabilia Spectrum Gold

*GOLD p/r 50: 1.25X TO 3X BASIC
*GOLD p/r 50: 1.25X TO 3X BASIC RC
*GOLD p/r 25: 1.5X TO 4X BASIC
RANDOM INSERTS IN PACKS
PRINT RUNS B/WN 10-50 COPIES PER
NO PRICING ON QTY OF 10
NO RC YR PRICING ON QTY OF 25
132 Stephen Drew/50 20.00 50.00

2005 Absolute Memorabilia Spectrum Platinum

RANDOM INSERTS IN PACKS
STATED PRINT RUN 1 SERIAL #'d SET
NO PRICING DUE TO SCARCITY

2005 Absolute Memorabilia Spectrum Silver

*SILVER p/r 100-150: 1X TO 2.5X BASIC
*SILVER p/r 100-150 : 1X TO 2.5X BASIC RC
RANDOM INSERTS IN PACKS
1-100 PRINT RUN 100 SERIAL #'d SETS
101-200 PRINT RUN 150 SERIAL #'d SETS
132 Stephen Drew/150 12.50 30.00

2005 Absolute Memorabilia Autograph Spectrum Gold

*GOLD p/r 41-50: .5X TO 1.2X SILV p/r 74-150
*GOLD p/r 41-50: .4X TO 1X SILV p/r 40-64
*GOLD p/r 21-34: .6X TO 1.5X SILV p/r 74-150
*GOLD p/r 21-34: .5X TO 1.2X SILV p/r 40-64
*GOLD p/r 21-34: .4X TO 1X SILV p/r 22-34
OVERALL AU-GU ODDS ONE PER PACK
PRINT RUNS B/WN 1-50 COPIES PER
NO PRICING ON QTY OF 14 OR LESS
120 Fergie Jenkins/50 8.00 20.00
122 Frank Thomas/25 20.00 50.00
131 Jeff Bagwell/27 20.00 50.00

2005 Absolute Memorabilia Autograph Spectrum Platinum

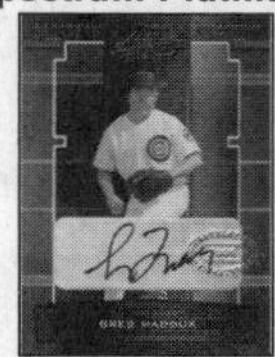

OVERALL AU-GU ODDS ONE PER PACK
STATED PRINT RUN 1 SERIAL #'d SET
NO PRICING DUE TO SCARCITY

2005 Absolute Memorabilia Autograph Spectrum Silver

OVERALL AU-GU ODDS ONE PER PACK
PRINT RUNS B/WN 1-150 COPIES PER
NO PRICING ON QTY OF 13 OR LESS
101 Al Kaline/150 12.50 30.00
102 Albert Pujols/9
104 Andruw Jones/4
106 Barry Zito/74 6.00 15.00
107 Ben Sheets/93 6.00 15.00
109 Curt Schilling/5
110 Dale Murphy/10
111 David Dellucci/150 6.00 15.00
113 Dennis Eckersley/100 6.00 15.00
115 Don Mattingly/22 40.00 80.00
116 Don Sutton/137 6.00 15.00
117 Dontrelle Willis/4
118 Duke Snider/50 12.50 30.00
119 Edgar Renteria/148 6.00 15.00
120 Fergie Jenkins/10
121 Frank Robinson/150 10.00 25.00
122 Frank Thomas/13
123 Garret Anderson/64 8.00 20.00
124 Gary Sheffield/100 10.00 25.00
125 Greg Maddux/50 50.00 100.00
127 Hideo Nomo/5
129 Jamie Moyer/150 6.00 15.00
131 Jeff Bagwell/1
133 Jeff Niemann/150 6.00 15.00
134 Jeremy Bonderman/43 8.00 20.00
135 Jim Bunning/150 10.00 25.00
136 Jim Leyritz/99 4.00 10.00
138 Johan Santana/40 15.00 40.00
140 Johnny Podres/150 6.00 15.00
141 Jose Guillen/145 4.00 10.00
142 Justin Verlander/150 15.00 40.00
143 Keiichi Yabu/150 6.00 15.00
144 Keith Foulke/150 10.00 25.00
145 Keith Hernandez/149 6.00 15.00
147 Kent Hrbek/98 6.00 15.00
150 Lew Ford/150 4.00 10.00
151 Lou Brock/126 10.00 25.00
152 Luis Aparicio/110 6.00 15.00
153 Luis Tiant/147 6.00 15.00
154 Manny Ramirez/34 30.00 60.00
155 Mark Mulder/150 6.00 15.00
156 Mark Prior/10
157 Mark Teixeira/91 10.00 25.00
158 Marty Marion/150 6.00 15.00
159 Miguel Cabrera/146 10.00 25.00
161 Mike Lieberthal/150 6.00 15.00
162 Mike Piazza/3
163 Minnie Minoso/150 6.00 15.00
164 Monte Irvin/150 6.00 15.00
166 Nolan Ryan/50 40.00 80.00
167 Octavio Dotel/150 4.00 10.00
168 Omar Vizquel/150 10.00 25.00
169 Ozzie Smith/50 20.00 50.00
171 Phil Humber/108 6.00 15.00
172 Phil Rizzuto/109 10.00 25.00
173 Prince Fielder/45 50.00 100.00
174 Ralph Kiner/150 10.00 25.00
176 Red Schoendienst/150 6.00 15.00
177 Rich Gossage/150 6.00 15.00
178 Rick Dempsey/104 4.00 10.00
179 Rickie Weeks/148 6.00 15.00
180 Robin Roberts/148 6.00 15.00
181 Rod Carew/150 10.00 25.00
182 Roger Clemens/10
183 Rollie Fingers/120 6.00 15.00
184 Ron Guidry/150 10.00 25.00
185 Ron Santo/142 10.00 25.00
186 Russ Ortiz/150 4.00 10.00
187 Ryne Sandberg/150 20.00 50.00
188 Sammy Sosa/15 50.00 100.00
189 Scott Rolen/87 10.00 25.00
190 Stan Musial/150 30.00 60.00
191 Steve Carlton/100 6.00 15.00
192 Steve Garvey/144 6.00 15.00
193 Steve Stone/150 6.00 15.00
194 Tim Salmon/147 6.00 15.00
195 Todd Helton/5
196 Todd Walker/150 4.00 10.00
197 Tom Gordon/150 4.00 10.00
198 Trot Nixon/43 8.00 20.00
199 Troy Percival/144 6.00 15.00

2005 Absolute Memorabilia Absolutely Ink

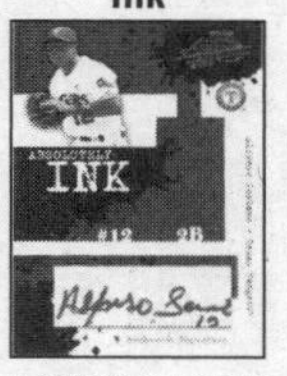

OVERALL AU-GU ODDS ONE PER PACK
PRINT RUNS B/WN 1-150 COPIES PER
NO PRICING ON QTY OF 14 OR LESS
101 Al Kaline/150 12.50 30.00
102 Alan Trammell/1
103 Alfonso Soriano/67 6.00 15.00
104 Barry Larkin/12
105 Ben Sheets/150 6.00 15.00
106 Bill Madlock/1
107 Bobby Doerr/1
109 Cal Ripken/25 75.00 150.00
110 Dale Murphy/8
111 Dennis Eckersley/150 6.00 15.00
112 Don Sutton/150 6.00 15.00
113 Duke Snider/150 10.00 25.00
114 Fergie Jenkins/100 6.00 15.00
115 Frank Thomas/50 20.00 50.00
116 Gary Sheffield/25 15.00 40.00
117 Gaylord Perry/100 6.00 15.00
118 Jacque Jones/100 6.00 15.00
119 Jae Weong Seo/100 6.00 15.00
120 Jeremy Bonderman/100 6.00 15.00
121 Jim Rice/14
122 Joe Torre/25 15.00 40.00
123 Johan Santana/1
124 Juan Gonzalez/10
125 Junior Spivey/75 4.00 10.00
126 Luis Aparicio/150 6.00 15.00
127 Magglio Ordonez/100 6.00 15.00
128 Mark Grace/1
129 Michael Young/75 6.00 15.00
130 Mike Schmidt/17 40.00 80.00
131 Morgan Ensberg/51 8.00 20.00
132 Orlando Cabrera/100 6.00 15.00
133 Paul Konerko/100 10.00 25.00
134 Rollie Fingers/100 6.00 15.00
135 Roy Oswalt/100 6.00 15.00
136 Scott Rolen/27 15.00 40.00
137 Sean Casey/63 8.00 20.00
138 Tom Seaver/12
139 Torii Hunter/100 6.00 15.00
140 Wade Boggs/50 12.50 30.00

2005 Absolute Memorabilia Absolutely Ink Spectrum

*SPEC p/r 74: .4X TO 1X INK p/r 67-150
*SPEC p/r 39-50: .5X TO 1.2X INK p/r 67-150
*SPEC p/r 25-34: .6X TO 1.5X INK p/r 67-150
*SPEC p/r 25-34: .5X TO 1.2X INK p/r 50-63
*SPEC p/r 16-19: .75X TO 2X INK p/r 67-150
OVERALL AU-GU ODDS ONE PER PACK
PRINT RUNS B/WN 1-74 COPIES PER
NO PRICING ON QTY OF 14 OR LESS
109 Cal Ripken/25 75.00 150.00

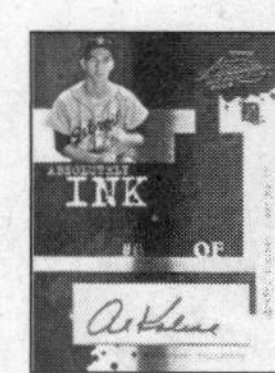

2005 Absolute Memorabilia Absolutely Ink Swatch Single

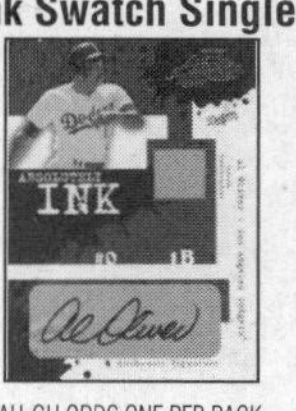

OVERALL AU-GU ODDS ONE PER PACK
PRINT RUNS B/WN 1-50 COPIES PER
NO PRICING ON QTY OF 10 OR LESS
1 Rafael Furcal Jsy/50 10.00 25.00
2 Shawn Green Jsy/5
3 Dale Murphy Jsy/50 15.00 40.00
4 Duke Snider Pants/25 20.00 50.00
5 Bill Madlock Bat/50 10.00 25.00
6 J.T. Snow Jsy/5
7 Bobby Crosby Jsy/50 10.00 25.00
8 Cal Ripken Jsy/25 75.00 150.00
9 Hank Blalock Jsy/25 12.50 30.00
10 Vernon Wells Jsy/50 10.00 25.00
11 Lyle Overbay Jsy/50 6.00 15.00
12 Melvin Mora Jsy/5
13 Omar Vizquel Jsy/50 15.00 40.00
14 Ernie Banks Jsy/10
15 Ben Sheets Jsy/25 12.50 30.00
16 Aramis Ramirez Jsy/25 12.50 30.00
17 Todd Helton Jsy/5
18 Travis Hafner Jsy/50 10.00 25.00
19 Mike Lowell Jsy/25 8.00 20.00
20 Frank Robinson Bat/50 15.00 40.00
21 Josh Beckett Jsy/10
22 Juan Gonzalez Jsy/50 10.00 25.00
24 Manny Ramirez Jsy/5
25 Jim Edmonds Jsy/10
26 Dave Concepcion Jsy/1
27 Darryl Strawberry Jsy/50 10.00 25.00
28 Alexis Rios Bat/50 10.00 25.00
30 Magglio Ordonez Jsy/50 10.00 25.00
31 Jay Gibbons Jsy/50 6.00 15.00
32 Steve Carlton Jsy/25 12.50 30.00
34 Kerry Wood Jsy/25 20.00 50.00
35 Dontrelle Willis Jsy/15 30.00 60.00
36 Eric Chavez Jsy/25 12.50 30.00
37 Keith Hernandez Jsy/50 10.00 25.00
38 Carlos Zambrano Jsy/50 10.00 25.00
39 Brett Myers Jsy/50 6.00 15.00
40 Rich Harden Jsy/50 10.00 25.00
41 Danny Kolb Jsy/50 6.00 15.00
42 Mark Prior Jsy/25 15.00 40.00
43 Joey Gathright Jsy/25 8.00 20.00
44 David Cone Jsy/50 10.00 25.00
45 Carlos Lee Jsy/50 10.00 25.00
46 Deion Sanders Jsy/5
47 Jack Morris Jsy/50 10.00 25.00
48 Torii Hunter Jsy/50 10.00 25.00
49 Garret Anderson Jsy/50 10.00 25.00
50 Craig Biggio Jsy/10
51 Dave Parker Bat/50 10.00 25.00
52 C.C. Sabathia Jsy/50 10.00 25.00
53 Dennis Eckersley A's Jsy/50 10.00 25.00
54 Barry Larkin Jsy/25 20.00 50.00
55 Brandon Webb Pants/50 12.50 30.00
56 Sean Casey Jsy/50 10.00 25.00
57 Johan Santana Jsy/50 20.00 50.00
58 Miguel Cabrera Jsy/50 15.00 40.00
59 Bert Blyleven Jsy/50 6.00 15.00
60 Casey Kotchman Jsy/50 10.00 25.00
61 Dwight Gooden Jsy/50 10.00 25.00
62 Milton Bradley Jsy/50 6.00 15.00
63 John Kruk Jsy/50 15.00 40.00
64 Michael Young Jsy/50 10.00 25.00
65 Mike Mussina Jsy/5
66 Robin Ventura Jsy/50 10.00 25.00
67 Tim Hudson Jsy/25 20.00 50.00
68 Will Clark Bat/50 15.00 40.00
69 Lew Ford Jsy/50 6.00 15.00
70 Jody Gerut Jsy/50 6.00 15.00
71 Don Sutton Jsy/50 6.00 15.00
72 B.J. Upton Bat/25 12.50 30.00
73 Austin Kearns Jsy/50 6.00 15.00
74 Rollie Fingers Jsy/5
75 Barry Zito Jsy/10
76 Lee Smith Jsy/5
77 Ryan Wagner Jsy/50 6.00 15.00
78 Jermaine Dye Jsy/50 10.00 25.00
79 Scott Rolen Jsy/10
80 Al Oliver Jsy/50 10.00 25.00
81 Angel Berroa Pants/50 6.00 15.00
82 Edgar Renteria Jsy/50 10.00 25.00
83 Dennis Eckersley Sox Jsy/25 12.50 30.00
84 Roy Oswalt Jsy/50 10.00 25.00
85 David Ortiz Jsy/5
86 Dave Righetti Jsy/50 10.00 25.00
87 Aubrey Huff Jsy/25 12.50 30.00
88 Chipper Jones Jsy/10
89 Jose Vidro Jsy/50 6.00 15.00
90 Harold Baines Jsy/50 10.00 25.00
92 Mark Mulder Jsy/10
93 Ken Harvey Jsy/50 6.00 15.00
94 Orel Hershiser Jsy/10
95 Jason Bay Jsy/50 10.00 25.00
96 Dwight Evans Jsy/50 15.00 40.00
97 Luis Tiant Pants/50 6.00 15.00
98 Ron Santo Bat/50 15.00 40.00
99 Brian Roberts Jsy/50 10.00 25.00
100 Marty Marion Jsy/50 10.00 25.00
101 Al Kaline Bat/50 15.00 40.00
102 Alan Trammell Jsy/63 10.00 25.00
103 Alfonso Soriano Bat/100 8.00 20.00
104 Barry Larkin Bat/50 12.50 30.00
105 Ben Sheets Jsy/40 10.00 25.00
106 Bill Madlock Bat/150 8.00 20.00
107 Bobby Doerr Pants/82 8.00 20.00
108 Brandon Webb Pants/46 12.50 30.00
109 Cal Ripken Jsy/50 60.00 120.00
110 Dale Murphy Jsy/50 15.00 40.00
111 Dennis Eckersley Jsy/150 8.00 20.00
112 Don Sutton Jsy/10
114 Fergie Jenkins Pants/55 10.00 25.00
115 Frank Thomas Bat/50 30.00 60.00
116 Gary Sheffield Fld Glv/150 12.50 30.00
117 Gaylord Perry Jsy/150 8.00 20.00
118 Jacque Jones Bat/45 10.00 25.00
119 Jae Weong Seo Jsy/1
120 Jeremy Bonderman Jsy/15 15.00 40.00
121 Jim Rice Jsy/95 8.00 20.00
122 Joe Torre Jsy/1
123 Johan Santana Jsy/118 15.00 40.00
124 Juan Gonzalez Jsy/75 8.00 20.00
125 Junior Spivey Jsy/75 5.00 12.00
126 Luis Aparicio Bat/10
127 Magglio Ordonez Bat/150 8.00 20.00
128 Mark Grace Fld Glv/150 8.00 20.00
129 Michael Young Jsy/10
130 Mike Schmidt Sock/75 30.00 60.00
132 Orlando Cabrera Jsy/45 10.00 25.00
133 Paul Konerko Bat/34 20.00 50.00
134 Rollie Fingers Jsy/1
135 Roy Oswalt Bat/44 10.00 25.00
136 Scott Rolen Jsy/150 12.50 30.00
137 Sean Casey Jsy/10
138 Tom Seaver Hat/150 15.00 40.00
139 Torii Hunter Jsy/1
140 Wade Boggs Bat/150 12.50 30.00

2005 Absolute Memorabilia Absolutely Ink Swatch Single Spectrum

*SPEC p/r 36-50: .5X TO 1.2X SNG p/r 75-150
*SPEC p/r 36-50: .4X TO 1X SNG p/r 40-63
*SPEC p/r 25: .6X TO 1.5X SNG p/r 75-150
*SPEC p/r 25: .5X TO 1.2X SNG p/r 40-63
*SPEC p/r 15-17: .75X TO 2X SNG p/r 75-150
*SPEC p/r 15-17: .6X TO 1.5X SNG p/r 40-63
*SPEC p/r 15-17: .5X TO 1.2X SNG p/r 25-34
OVERALL AU-GU ODDS ONE PER PACK
PRINT RUNS B/WN 1-50 COPIES PER
NO PRICING ON QTY OF 13 OR LESS
23 Mark Teixeira Jsy/25 20.00 50.00
92 Mark Mulder Jsy/25 12.50 30.00
109 Cal Ripken Jsy/25 75.00 150.00

2005 Absolute Memorabilia Absolutely Ink Swatch Single Spectrum Prime

*PRIMEp/r70-100: .5X TO 1.2X SNGp/r75-150
*PRIME p/r 70-100: .4X TO 1X SNG p/r 40-63
*PRIME p/r 20-35: .75X TO 2X SNG p/r 75-150
*PRIME p/r 20-35: .4X TO 1X SNG p/r 15
OVERALL AU-GU ODDS ONE PER PACK
PRINT RUNS B/WN 1-100 COPIES PER
NO PRICING ON QTY OF 10 OR LESS
112 Don Sutton Jsy/100 8.00 20.00
119 Jae Weong Seo Jsy/45 12.50 30.00
122 Joe Torre Jsy/70 12.50 30.00
126 Luis Aparicio Jsy/25 15.00 40.00
134 Rollie Fingers Jsy/25 15.00 40.00

2005 Absolute Memorabilia Absolutely Ink Swatch Double

*DBL p/r 70-100: .4X TO 1X SNG p/r 75-150
*DBL p/r 50: .5X TO 1.2X SNG p/r 75-150
*DBL p/r 50: .4X TO 1X SNG p/r 40-63
*DBL p/r 20-30: .6X TO 1.5X SNG p/r 75-150
*DBL p/r 20-30: .5X TO 1.2X SNG p/r 40-63
*DBL p/r 20-30: .4X TO 1X SNG p/r 25-34
*DBL p/r 15-18: .75X TO 2X SNG p/r 75-150
*DBL p/r 15-18: .6X TO 1.5X SNG p/r 40-63
*DBL p/r 15-18: .5X TO 1.2X SNG p/r 25-34
OVERALL AU-GU ODDS ONE PER PACK
PRINT RUNS B/WN 1-100 COPIES PER
NO PRICING ON QTY OF 10 OR LESS
23 Mark Teixeira Fld Glv-Jsy/50 15.00 40.00
92 Mark Mulder Jsy-Jsy/20 12.50 30.00
122 Joe Torre B-J/70 12.50 30.00
129 Michael Young B-J/25 12.50 30.00
137 Sean Casey J-SH/100 8.00 20.00

2005 Absolute Memorabilia Absolutely Ink Swatch Double Spectrum

*SPEC p/r 40-50: .5X TO 1.2X SNG p/r 75-150
*SPEC p/r 40-50: .4X TO 1X SNG p/r 40-63
*SPEC p/r 20-30: .6X TO 1.5X SNG p/r 75-150
*SPEC p/r 20-30: .5X TO 1.2X SNG p/r 40-63
*SPEC p/r 15: .75X TO 2X SNG p/r 75-150
*SPEC p/r 15: .6X TO 1.5X SNG p/r 40-63
OVERALL AU-GU ODDS ONE PER PACK
PRINT RUNS B/WN 1-50 COPIES PER
NO PRICING ON QTY OF 10 OR LESS
122 Joe Torre B-J/15 30.00 60.00
129 Michael Young B-J/25 12.50 30.00
137 Sean Casey J-SH/50 10.00 25.00

2005 Absolute Memorabilia Absolutely Ink Swatch Double Spectrum Prime

*PRIME p/r 50: .6X TO 1.5X SNG p/r 75-150
*PRIME p/r 25: .75X TO 2X SNG p/r 75-150
*PRIME p/r 25: .6X TO 1.5X SNG p/r 40-63
*PRIME p/r 15: 1X TO 2.5X SNG p/r 75-150
OVERALL AU-GU ODDS ONE PER PACK
PRINT RUNS B/WN 1-50 COPIES PER
NO PRICING ON QTY OF 10 OR LESS
134 Rollie Fingers J-J/25 15.00 40.00

2005 Absolute Memorabilia Absolutely Ink Swatch Triple

*TRIP p/r 75: .4X TO 1X SNG p/r 40-63
*TRIP p/r 50: .6X TO 1.5X SNG p/r 75-150
*TRIP p/r 50: .5X TO 1.2X SNG p/r 40-63
*TRIP p/r 25: .75X TO 2X SNG p/r 75-150
*TRIP p/r 25: .6X TO 1.5X SNG p/r 40-63
*TRIP p/r 25: .5X TO 1.2X SNG p/r 25-34
*TRIP p/r 15: .75X TO 2X SNG p/r 40-63
OVERALL AU-GU ODDS ONE PER PACK
PRINT RUNS B/WN 1-75 COPIES PER
NO PRICING ON QTY OF 10 OR LESS
8 Cal Ripken Bat-Jsy-Pants/25 90.00 180.00
23 Mark Teixeira Bat-Hat-Jsy/75 15.00 40.00
126 Luis Aparicio B-J-P/15 20.00 50.00
129 Michael Young B-J-J/25 15.00 40.00

2005 Absolute Memorabilia Absolutely Ink Swatch Triple Spectrum

*SPEC p/r 25: .75X TO 2X SNG p/r 75-150
*SPEC p/r 25: .6X TO 1.5X SNG p/r 40-63
OVERALL AU-GU ODDS ONE PER PACK
PRINT RUNS B/WN 1-25 COPIES PER
NO PRICING ON QTY OF 10 OR LESS
23 Mark Teixeira Bat-Hat-Jsy/25 30.00 60.00
129 Michael Young B-J-J/25 15.00 40.00

2005 Absolute Memorabilia Absolutely Ink Swatch Triple Spectrum Prime

*PRIME p/r 25: 1X TO 2.5X SNG p/r 75-150
*PRIME p/r 15: 1X TO 2.5X SNG p/r 40-63
OVERALL AU-GU ODDS ONE PER PACK
PRINT RUNS B/WN 1-25 COPIES PER
NO PRICING ON QTY OF 10 OR LESS

2005 Absolute Memorabilia Heroes

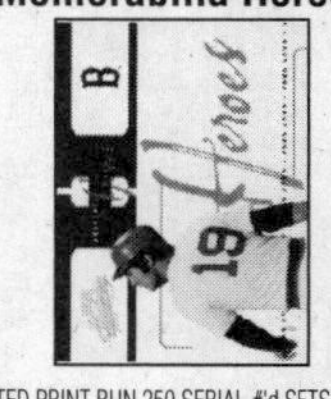

STATED PRINT RUN 250 SERIAL #'d SETS
*SPEC 1-50: 1X TO 2.5X BASIC
*SPEC 51-70: .75X TO 2X BASIC
SPEC 1-50 PRINT RUN 50 #'d SETS
SPEC 51-70 PRINT RUN 100 #'d SETS
*REV.SPEC: 1.5X TO 4X BASIC
REVERSE SPEC.PRINT RUN 25 #'d SETS
RANDOM INSERTS IN PACKS
1 Billy Martin 1.00 2.50
2 Rickey Henderson 1.00 2.50
3 Alan Trammell .75 2.00
4 Lenny Dykstra .75 2.00
5 Jeff Bagwell 1.00 2.50
6 Steve Garvey .75 2.00
7 Catfish Hunter 1.00 2.50
8 Cal Ripken 5.00 12.00
9 Reggie Jackson 1.00 2.50
10 Gary Sheffield .75 2.00
11 Edgar Martinez 1.00 2.50
12 Roberto Alomar 1.00 2.50
13 Luis Tiant .75 2.00
14 Jim Rice .75 2.00
15 Carlos Beltran .75 2.00
16 Hideo Nomo 1.25 3.00
17 Mark Grace .75 2.00
18 Joe Cronin .75 2.00
19 Tony Gwynn 2.00 5.00
20 Bo Jackson 1.50 4.00
21 Roger Clemens Sox 2.00 5.00
22 Roger Clemens Yanks 2.00 5.00
23 Don Mattingly 3.00 8.00
24 Willie Mays 3.00 8.00
25 Andruw Jones 1.00 2.50
26 Andre Dawson .75 2.00
27 Carlton Fisk 1.00 2.50
28 Robin Yount 1.50 4.00
29 Joe Carter .75 2.00
30 Dale Murphy 1.00 2.50
31 Greg Maddux 2.00 5.00
32 Ichiro Suzuki 2.50 6.00
33 Jose Canseco 1.50 4.00
34 Nolan Ryan 4.00 10.00
35 Frank Thomas 1.25 3.00
36 Fred Lynn .75 2.00
37 Curt Schilling Phils .75 2.00
38 Curt Schilling Sox 1.00 2.50
39 Dave Parker .75 2.00
40 Randy Johnson M's 1.25 3.00
41 Randy Johnson Expos 1.25 3.00
42 Vladimir Guerrero 1.25 3.00
43 Bernie Williams 1.00 2.50
44 Wade Boggs 1.00 2.50
45 Pedro Martinez 1.00 2.50
46 Andy Pettitte 1.00 2.50
47 Fergie Jenkins .75 2.00
48 Darryl Strawberry .75 2.00
49 Rafael Palmeiro 1.00 2.50
50 Albert Pujols 2.50 6.00
51 Adrian Beltre .75 2.00
52 Albert Pujols 2.50 6.00
53 Andre Dawson .75 2.00
54 Carlos Beltran .75 2.00
55 Don Mattingly 3.00 8.00
56 Greg Maddux 2.00 5.00
57 Ivan Rodriguez 1.00 2.50
58 John Smoltz 1.00 2.50
59 Manny Ramirez 1.00 2.50
60 Mark Grace .75 2.00
61 Mark Teixeira 1.00 2.50
62 Mike Mussina 1.00 2.50
63 Paul Lo Duca .75 2.00
64 Pedro Martinez 1.00 2.50
65 Scott Rolen 1.00 2.50
66 Shawn Green .75 2.00
67 Tony Gwynn 2.00 5.00
68 Tony Oliva .75 2.00
69 Torii Hunter .75 2.00
70 Wade Boggs 1.00 2.50

2005 Absolute Memorabilia Heroes Button

PRINT RUNS B/WN 1-6 COPIES PER
SPECTRUM PRINT RUN 1 #'d SET
OVERALL AU-GU ODDS ONE PER PACK
NO PRICING DUE TO SCARCITY
54 Carlos Beltran/3
55 Don Mattingly/1
67 Tony Gwynn/6
70 Wade Boggs/3

2005 Absolute Memorabilia Heroes MLB Logo

PRINT RUNS B/WN 1-5 COPIES PER
SPECTRUM PRINT RUN 1 #'d SET
OVERALL AU-GU ODDS ONE PER PACK
NO PRICING DUE TO SCARCITY
56 Greg Maddux/5
57 Ivan Rodriguez/2
59 Manny Ramirez/1
64 Pedro Martinez/3

2005 Absolute Memorabilia Heroes Swatch Double

OVERALL AU-GU ODDS ONE PER PACK
PRINT RUNS B/WN 1-150 COPIES PER
NO PRICING ON QTY OF 1
1 Billy Martin Jsy-Pants/50 10.00 25.00
2 Rickey Henderson Bat-Jsy/50 5.00 12.00
3 Alan Trammell Bat-Jsy/50 4.00 10.00
4 Lenny Dykstra Bat-Jsy/50 4.00 10.00
5 Jeff Bagwell Bat-Jsy/50 4.00 10.00
6 Steve Garvey Bat-Jsy/50 4.00 10.00
7 Catfish Hunter Jsy-Jsy/25 6.00 15.00
8 Cal Ripken Jsy-Pants/50 15.00 40.00
9 Reggie Jackson Jkt-Jsy/50 5.00 12.00
10 Gary Sheffield Fld Glv-Jsy/50 3.00 8.00
11 Edgar Martinez Bat-Jsy/50 4.00 10.00
12 Roberto Alomar Jsy-Jsy/50 4.00 10.00
13 Luis Tiant Hat-Jsy/25 5.00 12.00
14 Jim Rice Jsy-Pants/50 4.00 10.00
15 Carlos Beltran Bat-Jsy/50 3.00 8.00
16 Hideo Nomo Bat-Jsy/50 6.00 15.00
17 Mark Grace Fld Glv-Jsy/50 4.00 10.00
18 Joe Cronin Jsy-Pants/50 10.00 25.00
19 Tony Gwynn Bat-Jsy/50 8.00 20.00
20 Bo Jackson Bat-Jsy/50 6.00 15.00
21 Roger Clemens Sox Jsy-Jsy/50 8.00 20.00
22 R.Clemens Yanks Jsy-Jsy/50 8.00 20.00
23 Don Mattingly Bat-Jsy/50 10.00 25.00
24 Willie Mays Bat-Jsy/50 20.00 50.00
25 Andruw Jones Bat-Jsy/50 4.00 10.00

26 Andre Dawson Jsy-Pants/50 4.00 10.00
28 Robin Yount Hat-Jsy/50 6.00 15.00
29 Joe Carter Bat-Jsy/50 4.00 10.00
30 Dale Murphy Bat-Jsy/50 5.00 12.00
31 Greg Maddux Jsy-Jsy/50 8.00 20.00
33 Jose Canseco Hat-Jsy/50 6.00 15.00
34 Nolan Ryan Bat-Jsy/50 12.50 30.00
35 Frank Thomas Jsy-Pants/50 5.00 12.00
36 Fred Lynn Bat-Jsy/50 4.00 10.00
37 Curt Schilling Phils Jsy-Jsy/50 3.00 8.00
38 Curt Schilling Sox Jsy-Jsy/50 4.00 10.00
39 Dave Parker Bat-Jsy/50 4.00 10.00
40 Randy Johnson M's Jsy-Jsy/50 5.00 12.00
41 R.Johnson Expos Bat-Jsy/25 6.00 15.00
42 Vladimir Guerrero Jsy-Jsy/50 5.00 12.00
43 Bernie Williams Jsy-Jsy/50 4.00 10.00
44 Wade Boggs Bat-Jsy/50 5.00 12.00
45 Pedro Martinez Jsy-Jsy/50 4.00 10.00
46 Andy Pettitte Jsy-Jsy/50 4.00 10.00
47 Fergie Jenkins Hat-Jsy/50 4.00 10.00
48 Darryl Strawberry Jsy-Pants/50 4.00 10.00
49 Rafael Palmeiro Bat-Jsy/50 4.00 10.00
50 Albert Pujols Jsy-Jsy/50 12.50 30.00
51 Adrian Beltre H-S/120 2.50 6.00
52 Albert Pujols B-J/150 10.00 25.00
53 Andre Dawson J-P/35 5.00 12.00
54 Carlos Beltran J-J/45 3.00 8.00
55 Don Mattingly B-H/1
56 Greg Maddux J-J/150 6.00 15.00
57 Ivan Rodriguez B-J/150 3.00 8.00
58 John Smoltz J-J/150 3.00 8.00
59 Manny Ramirez B-J/1
60 Mark Grace FG-J/25 5.00 12.00
61 Mark Teixeira B-J/1
62 Mike Mussina J-S/50 4.00 10.00
63 P.Lo Duca Bat-Chest Prot/150 2.50 6.00
64 Pedro Martinez J-J/50 4.00 10.00
65 Scott Rolen J-J/50 4.00 10.00
66 Shawn Green B-J/150 2.50 6.00
67 Tony Gwynn J-P/150 6.00 15.00
68 Tony Oliva B-J/150 3.00 8.00
69 Torii Hunter B-J/71 2.50 6.00

2005 Absolute Memorabilia Heroes Swatch Double Spectrum Prime

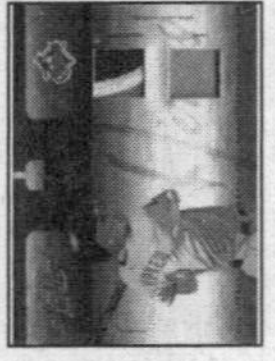

*PRIME p/r 100: .5X TO 1.2X DBL p/r 71-150
*PRIME p/r 45: .6X TO 1.5X DBL p/r 71-150
*PRIME p/r 25: .6X TO 1.5X DBL p/r 45-50
*PRIME p/r 25: .5X TO 1.2X DBL p/r 25-35
*PRIME p/r 15: 1X TO 2.5X DBL p/r 71-150
OVERALL AU-GU ODDS ONE PER PACK
PRINT RUNS B/WN 1-100 COPIES PER
NO PRICING ON QTY OF 10 OR LESS
27 Carlton Fisk Bat-Jsy/25 8.00 20.00
59 Manny Ramirez B-J/25 8.00 20.00

2005 Absolute Memorabilia Heroes Swatch Triple

*TRIP p/r 70-150: .5X TO 1.2X DBL p/r 71-150
*TRIP p/r 70-150: .3X TO .8X DBL p/r 25-35
*TRIP p/r 36-50: .6X TO 1.5X DBL p/r 71-150
*TRIP p/r 36-50: .5X TO 1.2X DBL p/r 45-50
*TRIP p/r 20-30: .75X TO 2X DBL p/r 71-150
*TRIP p/r 20-30: .6X TO 1.5X DBL p/r 45-50
*TRIP p/r 15: .75X TO 2X DBL p/r 45-50
*TRIP p/r 15: .6X TO 1.5X DBL p/r 25-35
OVERALL AU-GU ODDS ONE PER PACK
PRINT RUNS B/WN 1-150 COPIES PER
NO PRICING ON QTY OF 1
24 Willie Mays Bat-Jsy-Pants/25 40.00 80.00
55 D.Mattingly B-BG-H/70 15.00 40.00
59 Manny Ramirez B-J-S/20 6.00 15.00
61 Mark Teixeira B-FG-S/40 5.00 12.00

2005 Absolute Memorabilia Heroes Swatch Triple Spectrum Prime

*PRIME p/r 15: 1.25X TO 3X DBL p/r 45-50
*PRIME p/r 15: 1X TO 2.5X DBL p/r 25-35
OVERALL AU-GU ODDS ONE PER PACK
PRINT RUNS B/WN 1-100 COPIES PER
NO PRICING ON QTY OF 10 OR LESS
27 Carlton Fisk Bat-Jsy-Jsy/15 15.00 40.00
53 Andre Dawson B-J-P/95 6.00 15.00
54 Carlos Beltran J-J-J/70 6.00 15.00
56 Greg Maddux J-J-J/30 20.00 50.00
58 John Smoltz J-J-J/100 8.00 20.00
59 Manny Ramirez B-J-J/25 12.50 30.00
64 Pedro Martinez H-J-J/25 12.50 30.00
66 Shawn Green B-J-J/100 6.00 15.00
68 Tony Oliva B-J-J/75 6.00 15.00
69 Torii Hunter B-H-J/50 8.00 20.00

2005 Absolute Memorabilia Heroes Autograph

OVERALL AU-GU ODDS ONE PER PACK
PRINT RUNS B/WN 1-79 COPIES PER
NO PRICING ON QTY OF 8 OR LESS
51 Adrian Beltre/8
55 Don Mattingly/50 30.00 60.00
56 Greg Maddux/5
60 Mark Grace/1
61 Mark Teixeira/79 10.00 25.00
65 Scott Rolen/27 15.00 40.00
67 Tony Gwynn/19 30.00 60.00
69 Torii Hunter/50 8.00 20.00
70 Wade Boggs/26 15.00 40.00

2005 Absolute Memorabilia Heroes Autograph Spectrum

*SPEC p/r 50: .5X TO 1.2X AUTO p/r 79
OVERALL AU-GU ODDS ONE PER PACK
PRINT RUNS B/WN 1-50 COPIES PER
NO PRICING ON QTY OF 5 OR LESS

2005 Absolute Memorabilia Heroes Autograph Swatch Double Spectrum Prime

PRINT RUNS B/WN 1-20 COPIES PER
NO PRICING ON QTY OF 8 OR LESS
TRIPLE PRINT RUN B/WN 1-5 COPIES PER
NO TRIPLE PRICING DUE TO SCARCITY
OVERALL AU-GU ODDS ONE PER PACK
2 Rickey Henderson Bat-Jsy/5
3 Alan Trammell Bat-Jsy/15 20.00 50.00
4 Lenny Dykstra Bat-Jsy/15 20.00 50.00
5 Jeff Bagwell Bat-Jsy/5
6 Steve Garvey Bat-Jsy/15 20.00 50.00
8 Cal Ripken Jsy-Pants/8
9 Reggie Jackson Jkt-Jsy/15 40.00 80.00
10 Gary Sheffield Fld Glv-Jsy/15 40.00 80.00
11 Edgar Martinez Jsy-Jsy/15 40.00 80.00
12 Roberto Alomar Jsy-Jsy/15 40.00 80.00
13 Luis Tiant Hat-Jsy/15 12.50 30.00
14 Jim Rice Jsy-Pants/15 20.00 50.00
15 Carlos Beltran Jsy-Jsy/15 20.00 50.00
16 Hideo Nomo Bat-Jsy/5
17 Mark Grace Fld Glv-Jsy/15 20.00 50.00
19 Tony Gwynn Bat-Jsy/15 40.00 80.00
20 Bo Jackson Bat-Jsy/15 50.00 100.00
21 Roger Clemens Sox Jsy-Jsy/5
22 Roger Clemens Yanks Jsy-Jsy/5
23 Don Mattingly Bat-Jsy/15 50.00 100.00
24 Willie Mays Bat-Jsy/1
26 Andre Dawson Jsy-Pants/15 20.00 50.00
27 Carlton Fisk Bat-Jsy/15 40.00 80.00
28 Robin Yount Hat-Jsy/15 50.00 100.00
29 Joe Carter Bat-Jsy/5
30 Dale Murphy Bat-Jsy/15 40.00 80.00
31 Greg Maddux Jsy-Jsy/5
33 Jose Canseco Hat-Jsy/15 50.00 100.00
34 Nolan Ryan Bat-Jsy/15 125.00 200.00
35 Frank Thomas Jsy-Pants/15 50.00 100.00
36 Fred Lynn Bat-Jsy/15 20.00 50.00
37 Curt Schilling Phils Jsy-Jsy/5
38 Curt Schilling Sox Jsy-Jsy/5
39 Dave Parker Bat-Jsy/15 20.00 50.00
40 Randy Johnson M's Jsy-Jsy/5
41 Randy Johnson Expos Bat-Jsy/5
42 Vladimir Guerrero Jsy-Jsy/5
44 Wade Boggs Bat-Jsy/15 40.00 80.00
45 Pedro Martinez Jsy-Jsy/5
47 Fergie Jenkins Hat-Jsy/15 12.50 30.00
48 Darryl Strawberry Jsy-Pants/15 20.00 50.00
49 Rafael Palmeiro Bat-Jsy/5
50 Albert Pujols Jsy-Jsy/5
55 Don Mattingly B-J/1
56 Greg Maddux J-J/20 75.00 150.00
61 Mark Teixeira B-H/20 30.00 60.00
65 Scott Rolen J-J/1
67 Tony Gwynn J-P/1
69 Torii Hunter B-J/1
70 Wade Boggs B-J/1

2005 Absolute Memorabilia Marks of Fame

STATED PRINT RUN 150 SERIAL #'d SETS
*SPEC: 1.25X TO 3X BASIC
SPECTRUM PRINT RUN 25 #'d SETS
RANDOM INSERTS IN PACKS
1 Bobby Doerr 1.00 2.50
2 Reggie Jackson Yanks 1.25 3.00
3 Harmon Killebrew 2.00 5.00
4 Duke Snider 1.25 3.00
5 Brooks Robinson 1.25 3.00
6 Al Kaline 2.00 5.00
7 Carlton Fisk 1.25 3.00
8 Willie Stargell 1.25 3.00
9 Enos Slaughter 1.00 2.50
10 Nolan Ryan Rgr 5.00 12.00
11 Luis Aparicio R.Sox 1.00 2.50
12 Hoyt Wilhelm 1.00 2.50
13 Orlando Cepeda 1.00 2.50
14 Mike Schmidt 4.00 10.00
15 Frank Robinson 1.00 2.50
16 Whitey Ford 1.25 3.00
17 Don Sutton 1.00 2.50
18 Joe Morgan 1.00 2.50
19 Bob Feller 1.25 3.00
20 Lou Brock 1.25 3.00
21 Warren Spahn 1.25 3.00
22 Jim Palmer 1.00 2.50
23 Reggie Jackson Angels 1.25 3.00
24 Willie Mays 4.00 10.00
25 George Brett 4.00 10.00
26 Billy Williams 1.00 2.50
27 Juan Marichal 1.00 2.50
28 Early Wynn 1.00 2.50
29 Rod Carew 1.25 3.00
30 Maury Wills 1.00 2.50
31 Fergie Jenkins 1.00 2.50
32 Steve Carlton 1.00 2.50
33 Eddie Murray 2.00 5.00
34 Kirby Puckett 2.00 5.00
35 Johnny Bench 2.00 5.00
36 Gaylord Perry 1.00 2.50
37 Gary Carter 1.00 2.50
38 Tony Perez 1.00 2.50
39 Tony Oliva 1.00 2.50
40 Luis Aparicio W.Sox 1.00 2.50
41 Tom Seaver 1.25 3.00
42 Paul Molitor 1.00 2.50
43 Dennis Eckersley 1.00 2.50
44 Willie McCovey 1.25 3.00
45 Bob Gibson 1.25 3.00
46 Robin Roberts 1.00 2.50
47 Carl Yastrzemski 3.00 8.00
48 Ozzie Smith 3.00 8.00
49 Nolan Ryan Angels 5.00 12.00
50 Stan Musial 3.00 8.00
51 Bob Feller 1.00 2.50
52 Bob Gibson 1.25 3.00
53 Cal Ripken 6.00 15.00
54 Carl Yastrzemski 3.00 8.00
55 Carlton Fisk 1.25 3.00
56 Duke Snider Dgr 1.25 3.00
57 Duke Snider Mets 1.25 3.00
58 Gary Carter 1.00 2.50
59 George Brett 4.00 10.00
60 Johnny Bench 2.00 5.00
61 Juan Marichal 1.00 2.50
62 Kirby Puckett 2.00 5.00
63 Mike Schmidt 4.00 10.00
64 Nolan Ryan 5.00 12.00
65 Ozzie Smith 3.00 8.00
66 Paul Molitor 1.00 2.50
67 Phil Niekro 1.00 2.50
68 Ryne Sandberg 4.00 10.00
69 Wade Boggs 1.25 3.00
70 Willie McCovey 1.25 3.00

2005 Absolute Memorabilia Marks of Fame Button

PRINT RUNS B/WN 1-9 COPIES PER
SPECTRUM PRINT RUN 1 SERIAL #'d SET
OVERALL AU-GU ODDS ONE PER PACK
NO PRICING DUE TO SCARCITY
52 Bob Gibson/1
53 Cal Ripken/1
54 Carl Yastrzemski/8
55 Carlton Fisk/9
56 Duke Snider Dgr/3
57 Duke Snider Mets/4
58 Gary Carter/5
60 Johnny Bench/3
61 Juan Marichal/3
62 Kirby Puckett/5
64 Nolan Ryan/5
66 Paul Molitor/1
69 Wade Boggs/3

2005 Absolute Memorabilia Marks of Fame Swatch Double

OVERALL AU-GU ODDS ONE PER PACK
PRINT RUNS B/WN 1-50 COPIES PER
NO PRICING ON QTY OF 10 OR LESS
1 Bobby Doerr Bat-Pants/50 4.00 10.00
2 Reggie Jackson Yanks Bat-Pants/50 5.00 12.00
3 Harmon Killebrew Bat-Jsy/50 6.00 15.00
4 Duke Snider Jsy-Pants/25 6.00 15.00
5 Brooks Robinson Bat-Jsy/50 6.00 15.00
7 Carlton Fisk Bat-Jkt/50 5.00 12.00
8 Willie Stargell Bat-Jsy/50 5.00 12.00
9 Enos Slaughter Jsy-Jsy/50 4.00 10.00
10 Nolan Ryan Rgr Jsy-Pants/50 12.50 30.00
11 Luis Aparicio Bat-Jsy/50 4.00 10.00
12 Hoyt Wilhelm Jsy-Jsy/50 4.00 10.00
13 Orlando Cepeda Bat-Pants/50 4.00 10.00
14 Mike Schmidt Bat-Jsy/50 10.00 25.00
15 Frank Robinson Bat-Shoes/50 4.00 10.00
16 Whitey Ford Jsy/25 6.00 15.00
17 Don Sutton Jsy-Jsy/50 4.00 10.00
18 Joe Morgan Bat-Jsy/50 4.00 10.00
20 Lou Brock Bat-Jkt/50 5.00 12.00
21 Warren Spahn Jsy-Pants/50 6.00 15.00
22 Jim Palmer Hat-Pants/50 4.00 10.00
23 Reggie Jackson Angels Bat-Jsy/50 5.00 12.00
24 Willie Mays Bat-Jsy/25 30.00 60.00
25 George Brett Hat-Jsy/10
26 Billy Williams Jsy-Jsy/50 4.00 10.00
27 Juan Marichal Jsy-Pants/50 4.00 10.00
28 Early Wynn Jsy-Jsy/25 6.00 15.00
29 Rod Carew Bat-Jsy/50 5.00 12.00
30 Maury Wills Jsy-Jsy/1
31 Fergie Jenkins Fld Glv-Pants/50 4.00 10.00
32 Steve Carlton Bat-Pants/50 4.00 10.00
33 Eddie Murray Bat-Jsy/50 8.00 20.00
34 Kirby Puckett Bat-Jsy/50 6.00 15.00
35 Johnny Bench Bat-Jsy/50 6.00 15.00
36 Gaylord Perry Jsy-Jsy/50 4.00 10.00
37 Gary Carter Bat-Jsy/50 4.00 10.00
38 Tony Perez Fld Glv-Jsy/10
39 Tony Oliva Bat-Jsy/50 4.00 10.00
40 Luis Aparicio Bat-Pants/5
41 Tom Seaver Jsy-Pants/50 5.00 12.00
42 Paul Molitor Bat-Jsy/50 4.00 10.00
43 Dennis Eckersley Jsy-Jsy/50 4.00 10.00
44 Willie McCovey Jsy-Pants/50 5.00 12.00
47 Carl Yastrzemski Bat-Jsy/50 10.00 25.00
48 Ozzie Smith Hat-Pants/50 8.00 20.00
49 Nolan Ryan Angels Jkt-Jsy/50 12.50 30.00
50 Stan Musial Bat-Pants/50 12.50 30.00
53 Cal Ripken JK-P/100 10.00 25.00
54 Carl Yastrzemski B-H/70 10.00 25.00
55 Carlton Fisk B-J/1
57 Duke Snider J-P/100 4.00 10.00
58 Gary Carter FG-J/100 3.00 8.00
60 Johnny Bench J-P/1
61 Juan Marichal J-P/1
62 Kirby Puckett FG-S/20 8.00 20.00
64 Nolan Ryan J-P/1
66 Paul Molitor B-J/100 3.00 8.00
67 Phil Niekro B-J/10
68 Ryne Sandberg FG-J/1

2005 Absolute Memorabilia Marks of Fame Swatch Double Spectrum Prime

*PRIME p/r 44-50: .6X TO 1.5X DBL p/r 70-100
*PRIME p/r 25: .6X TO 1.5X DBL p/r 50
*PRIME p/r 25: .5X TO 1.2X DBL p/r 20-25
*PRIME p/r 15: 1X TO 2.5X DBL p/r 70-100
OVERALL AU-GU ODDS ONE PER PACK
PRINT RUNS B/WN 1-55 COPIES PER
NO PRICING ON QTY OF 10 OR LESS
21 Warren Spahn Jsy-Pants/25 40.00 80.00
24 Willie Mays Bat-Jsy/25 50.00 100.00
30 Maury Wills Jsy-Jsy/25 6.00 15.00
52 Bob Gibson J-J/75 5.00 12.00
67 Phil Niekro B-J/50 5.00 12.00
70 Willie McCovey J-J/44 6.00 15.00

2005 Absolute Memorabilia Marks of Fame Swatch Triple

*TRIP p/r 50-55: .6X TO 1.5X DBL p/r 70-100
*TRIP p/r 50-55: .4X TO 1X DBL p/r 20-25
*TRIP p/r 25: .6X TO 1.5X DBL p/r 50
OVERALL AU-GU ODDS ONE PER PACK
PRINT RUNS B/WN 1-55 COPIES PER
NO PRICING ON QTY OF 10 OR LESS
21 Warren Spahn Jsy-Jsy-Pants/25 40.00 80.00
24 Willie Mays Bat-Jsy-Pants/25 40.00 80.00

2005 Absolute Memorabilia Marks of Fame Swatch Triple Spectrum Prime

*PRIME p/r 15: 1.25X TO 3X DBL p/r 50
OVERALL AU-GU ODDS ONE PER PACK
PRINT RUNS B/WN 1-50 COPIES PER
NO PRICING ON QTY OF 10 OR LESS
21 Warren Spahn Jsy-Jsy-Pants/15 60.00 120.00
67 Phil Niekro B-J-J/50 6.00 15.00
70 Willie McCovey J-J-J/15 12.50 30.00

2005 Absolute Memorabilia Marks of Fame Autograph

OVERALL AU-GU ODDS ONE PER PACK
PRINT RUNS B/WN 2-200 COPIES PER
NO PRICING ON QTY OF 11 OR LESS
51 Bob Feller/150 6.00 15.00
52 Bob Gibson/150 10.00 25.00
53 Cal Ripken/8
55 Carlton Fisk/77 10.00 25.00
56 Duke Snider Dgr/150 10.00 25.00
57 Duke Snider Mets/150 10.00 25.00
58 Gary Carter/25 10.00 25.00
59 George Brett/54 40.00 80.00
60 Johnny Bench/200 15.00 40.00
61 Juan Marichal/19 12.50 30.00
62 Kirby Puckett/5
63 Mike Schmidt/35 20.00 50.00
64 Nolan Ryan/100 40.00 80.00
65 Ozzie Smith/150 15.00 40.00
66 Paul Molitor/11
67 Phil Niekro/4
68 Ryne Sandberg/100 20.00 50.00
69 Wade Boggs/26 15.00 40.00
70 Willie McCovey/2

2005 Absolute Memorabilia Marks of Fame Autograph Spectrum

*SPEC p/r 133: .4X TO 1X AUTO p/r 77-200
*SPEC p/r 50: .5X TO 1.2X AUTO p/r 77-200
*SPEC p/r 20-23: .6X TO 1.5X AUTOp/r77-200
OVERALL AU-GU ODDS ONE PER PACK
PRINT RUNS B/WN 1-133 COPIES PER
NO PRICING ON QTY OF 10 OR LESS

2005 Absolute Memorabilia Marks of Fame Autograph Swatch Single

OVERALL AU-GU ODDS ONE PER PACK
PRINT RUNS B/WN 1-125 COPIES PER
NO PRICING ON QTY OF 10 OR LESS
1 Bobby Doerr Pants/125 5.00 12.00
2 Reggie Jackson Yanks Pants/10
3 Harmon Killebrew Jsy/50 20.00 50.00
4 Duke Snider Jsy/25 20.00 50.00
5 Brooks Robinson Jsy/125 12.50 30.00
6 Al Kaline Bat/125 15.00 40.00
7 Carlton Fisk Jkt/50 15.00 40.00
10 Nolan Ryan Rgr Pants/50 50.00 100.00
11 Luis Aparicio Bos Jsy/125 8.00 20.00
12 Hoyt Wilhelm Jsy/10
13 Orlando Cepeda Pants/50 10.00 25.00
14 Mike Schmidt Jsy/50 30.00 60.00
15 Frank Robinson Bat/125 12.50 30.00
16 Whitey Ford Jsy/50 20.00 50.00
17 Don Sutton Jsy/125 5.00 12.00
19 Bob Feller Pants/125 12.50 30.00
20 Lou Brock Jkt/125 12.50 30.00
22 Jim Palmer Pants/50 10.00 25.00
23 Reggie Jackson Angels Jsy/10
24 Willie Mays Pants/25
25 George Brett Jsy/10
26 Billy Williams Pants/50 10.00 25.00
27 Juan Marichal Pants/125 8.00 20.00
29 Rod Carew Jsy/50 15.00 40.00
30 Maury Wills Jsy/10
31 Fergie Jenkins Pants/125 8.00 20.00
32 Steve Carlton Pants/125 8.00 20.00
34 Kirby Puckett Jsy/10
35 Johnny Bench Pants/50 20.00 50.00
36 Gaylord Perry Jsy/125 8.00 20.00
37 Gary Carter Pants/50 10.00 25.00
38 Tony Perez Jsy/50 10.00 25.00
39 Tony Oliva Jsy/125 8.00 20.00
40 Luis Aparicio Chi Bat/125 8.00 20.00
41 Tom Seaver Pants/50 20.00 50.00
42 Paul Molitor Pants/50 10.00 25.00
43 Dennis Eckersley Jsy/125 8.00 20.00
44 Willie McCovey Pants/50 15.00 40.00
45 Bob Gibson Hat/5
46 Robin Roberts Hat/50 10.00 25.00
47 Carl Yastrzemski Pants/10
48 Ozzie Smith Pants/50 20.00 50.00
49 Nolan Ryan Angels Jkt/50 50.00 100.00
50 Stan Musial Pants/50 40.00 80.00
51 Bob Feller Pants/15 30.00 60.00
52 Bob Gibson Jsy/113 12.50 30.00
53 Cal Ripken Jsy/25 75.00 150.00
55 Carlton Fisk Jsy/5
57 Duke Snider Mets Jsy/5
58 Gary Carter Jsy/100 8.00 20.00
59 George Brett Jsy/1
60 Johnny Bench Pants/9
61 Juan Marichal Pants/50 10.00 25.00
63 Mike Schmidt Sock/25 30.00 60.00
64 Nolan Ryan Jsy/50 50.00 100.00
66 Paul Molitor Jsy/48 10.00 25.00
70 Willie McCovey Jsy/44 15.00 40.00

2005 Absolute Memorabilia Marks of Fame Autograph Swatch Double

*DBL p/r 75-100: .4X TO 1X SNG p/r 100-125
*DBL p/r 75-100: .3X TO .8X SNG p/r 44-50
*DBL p/r 50: .5X TO 1.2X SNG p/r 100-125
*DBL p/r 50: .4X TO 1X SNG p/r 44-50
*DBL p/r 25-30: .6X TO 1.5X SNG p/r 100-125
*DBL p/r 25-30: .5X TO 1.2X SNG p/r 44-50
*DBL p/r 25-30: .4X TO 1X SNG p/r 25
OVERALL AU-GU ODDS ONE PER PACK
PRINT RUNS B/WN 1-100 COPIES PER
NO PRICING ON QTY OF 10 OR LESS
12 Hoyt Wilhelm Jsy-Jsy/25 20.00 50.00
53 Cal Ripken JK-P/25 75.00 150.00
55 Carlton Fisk B-J/30 20.00 50.00

2005 Absolute Memorabilia Marks of Fame Autograph Swatch Double Spectrum Prime

*PRIME p/r 20-25: .6X TO 1.5X SNG p/r 44-50
OVERALL AU-GU ODDS ONE PER PACK
PRINT RUNS B/WN 1-25 COPIES PER
NO PRICING ON QTY OF 10 OR LESS

2005 Absolute Memorabilia Marks of Fame Autograph Swatch Triple

PRINT RUNS B/WN 1-25 COPIES PER
NO PRICING ON QTY OF 10 OR LESS
PRIME PRINT RUNS B/WN 1-10 PER
NO PRIME PRICING DUE TO SCARCITY
OVERALL AU-GU ODDS ONE PER PACK
53 Cal Ripken JK-J-P/25 90.00 180.00
55 Carlton Fisk B-J-J/25 30.00 60.00

2005 Absolute Memorabilia Recollection Autographs

OVERALL AU-GU ODDS ONE PER PACK
NO PRICING ON QTY OF 18 OR LESS
PRINT RUNS B/WN 1-73 COPIES PER
DMU3 D.Murphy 87 Don DK/72 10.00 25.00
DMU6 D.Murphy 88 Don DK/73 10.00 25.00
DS1 Duke Snider 04 DK/20 15.00 40.00
DY1 Delmon Young 03 DK/46 20.00 50.00
HB1 Hank Blalock 02 DR/20 10.00 25.00
HB2 Hank Blalock 03 Don/20 10.00 25.00
KG2 Kirk Gibson 86 Don DK/20 10.00 25.00
MC2 Miguel Cabrera 04 DK/33 15.00 40.00
OS1 O.Smith 87 Don DK/30 20.00 50.00
OS8 O.Smith 03 DK/33 20.00 50.00

2005 Absolute Memorabilia Team Tandems

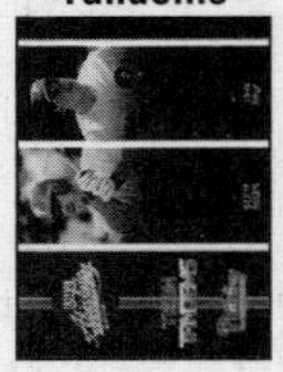

STATED PRINT RUN 250 SERIAL #'d SETS
*SPEC: .5X TO 1.2X BASIC
SPECTRUM PRINT RUN 150 #'d SETS
RANDOM INSERTS IN PACKS
1 Mark Prior / Kerry Wood 1.00 2.50
2 Barry Zito / Tim Hudson .75 2.00
3 Curt Schilling / Pedro Martinez 1.00 2.50
4 Will Clark / Matt Williams 1.00 2.50
5 Bernie Williams / Jason Giambi 1.00 2.50
6 Vernon Wells / Roy Halladay .75 2.00
7 Josh Beckett / A.J. Burnett .75 2.00
8 Dale Murphy / Phil Niekro 1.00 2.50
9 Mike Schmidt / Steve Carlton 3.00 8.00
10 Tony Oliva / Harmon Killebrew 1.25 3.00
11 Robin Yount / Paul Molitor 1.25 3.00
12 Francisco Rodriguez / Troy Percival .75 2.00
13 Ben Sheets / Danny Kolb .75 2.00
14 Andruw Jones / Rafael Furcal 1.00 2.50
15 Todd Helton / Preston Wilson .75 2.00
16 Wade Boggs / Fred McGriff 1.00 2.50
17 Manny Ramirez / David Ortiz 1.25 3.00
18 Miguel Cabrera / Dontrelle Willis 1.00 2.50
19 Edgar Renteria / Scott Rolen 1.00 2.50

20 Carlos Beltran .75 2.00
Jeff Kent
21 Eric Davis 1.00 2.50
Deion Sanders
22 Frank Thomas 1.25 3.00
Paul Konerko
23 Mike Piazza 1.25 3.00
Al Leiter
24 Sean Burroughs .75 2.00
Ryan Klesko
25 Ken Harvey .75 2.00
Mike Sweeney
26 Deion Sanders 2.50 6.00
Hideki Matsui
27 Steve Carlton .75 2.00
Mark Buehrle
28 Gaylord Perry 1.25 3.00
Randy Johnson
29 Joe Morgan .75 2.00
Steve Carlton
30 Vladimir Guerrero 1.25 3.00
Orlando Cabrera
31 Scott Rolen 1.00 2.50
John Kruk
32 Aaron Boone .75 2.00
Dmitri Young
33 Rickey Henderson 1.25 3.00
Vladimir Guerrero
34 Charles Johnson .75 2.00
Cliff Floyd
35 Cal Ripken 5.00 12.00
Rafael Palmeiro
36 Nolan Ryan 4.00 10.00
Francisco Rodriguez
37 Darin Erstad .75 2.00
Jim Edmonds
38 Troy Glaus 1.25 3.00
Rickey Henderson
39 Byung-Hyun Kim .75 2.00
Reggie Sanders
40 Andres Galarraga 1.00 2.50
David Justice
41 Brian Jordan .75 2.00
Ryan Klesko
42 Erik Bedard .75 2.00
Geronimo Gil
43 Brooks Robinson 1.00 2.50
Will Clark
44 Josh Towers .75 2.00
Erik Bedard
45 Nomar Garciaparra 1.25 3.00
Wade Boggs
46 Jason Varitek 1.25 3.00
Wade Boggs
47 Juan Cruz .75 2.00
Hee Seop Choi
48 Derrek Lee 1.00 2.50
Corey Patterson
49 Joe Borchard .75 2.00
Ray Durham
50 Eric Davis .75 2.00
Sean Casey
51 Dmitri Young .75 2.00
Wily Mo Pena
52 Early Wynn .75 2.00
Hal Newhouser
53 Sean Casey .75 2.00
Russell Branyan
54 Bert Blyleven 1.00 2.50
Jim Thome
55 Juan Uribe .75 2.00
Juan Pierre
56 Juan Encarnacion .75 2.00
Robert Fick
57 Dmitri Young .75 2.00
Juan Encarnacion
58 Magglio Ordonez .75 2.00
Bobby Higginson
59 Charles Johnson .75 2.00
Ryan Dempster
60 Cliff Floyd .75 2.00
Ryan Dempster
61 Mike Lowell .75 2.00
Cliff Floyd
62 Dontrelle Willis .75 2.00
Charles Johnson
63 Jose Cruz .75 2.00
Kirk Saarloos
64 Jeff Bagwell 1.00 2.50
Richard Hidalgo
65 Lance Berkman .75 2.00
Richard Hidalgo
66 Runelvys Hernandez .75 2.00
Mike Sweeney
67 Runelvys Hernandez .75 2.00
Willie Wilson
68 John Buck .75 2.00
Runelvys Hernandez
69 Angel Berroa .75 2.00
Jeremy Affeldt
70 Chan Ho Park .75 2.00
Kazuhisa Ishii
71 Shawn Green .75 2.00
Kazuhisa Ishii
72 Shawn Green 1.25 3.00
Rickey Henderson
73 Richie Sexson .75 2.00
Lyle Overbay
74 David Ortiz 1.25 3.00
J.C. Romero
75 David Ortiz 1.25 3.00
Kirby Puckett
76 Michael Barrett .75 2.00
Rondell White
77 Zach Day .75 2.00
Michael Barrett
78 Tony Armas Jr. .75 2.00
Zach Day
79 Rickey Henderson 1.25 3.00
Edgardo Alfonzo
80 Hideki Matsui 2.00 5.00
Bernie Williams
81 Don Mattingly 3.00 8.00
Hideki Matsui
82 Mark Ellis .75 2.00
Terrence Long
83 Ramon Hernandez .75 2.00
Erubiel Durazo
84 Brandon Duckworth .75 2.00
Anderson Machado
85 Craig Wilson .75 2.00
Freddy Sanchez
86 Brian Lawrence .75 2.00
Dennis Tankersley
87 Tony Gwynn 2.00 5.00
Trevor Hoffman
88 Andres Galarraga 1.00 2.50
Pedro Feliz
89 Jeff Kent .75 2.00
J.T. Snow
90 Freddy Garcia .75 2.00
John Olerud
91 Freddy Garcia 1.00 2.50
Edgar Martinez
92 So Taguchi .75 2.00
J.D. Drew
93 Ben Grieve .75 2.00
Brandon Backe
94 Dewon Brazelton .75 2.00
Joe Kennedy
95 Toby Hall .75 2.00
Pete LaForest
96 Frankie Francisco .75 2.00
Gabe Kapler
97 Travis Hafner .75 2.00
Doug Davis
98 Jeff Kent .75 2.00
Raul Mondesi
99 Shawn Green .75 2.00
Orlando Hudson
100 Marlon Byrd .75 2.00
Preston Wilson

2005 Absolute Memorabilia Team Tandems Swatch Single

OVERALL AU-GU ODDS ONE PER PACK
PRINT RUNS B/WN 5-150 COPIES PER
NO PRICING ON QTY OF 10 OR LESS
ALL ARE DUAL JERSEY UNLESS NOTED
1 Mark Prior Jsy 3.00 8.00
Kerry Wood Jsy/125
2 Barry Zito Jsy 2.50 6.00
Tim Hudson Jsy/125
3 Curt Schilling Jsy 3.00 8.00
Pedro Martinez Jsy/125
4 Will Clark Jsy 3.00 8.00
Matt Williams Jsy/125
5 Bernie Williams Jsy 3.00 8.00
Jason Giambi Jsy/125
6 Vernon Wells Jsy 2.50 6.00
Roy Halladay Jsy/125
7 Josh Beckett Jsy 2.50 6.00
A.J. Burnett Jsy/125
8 Dale Murphy Jsy 6.00 15.00
Phil Niekro Jsy/125
9 Mike Schmidt Jsy 6.00 15.00
Steve Carlton Jsy/125
10 Tony Oliva Jsy 10.00 25.00
Harmon Killebrew Jsy/50
11 Robin Yount Jsy 6.00 15.00
Paul Molitor Jsy/125
12 Francisco Rodriguez Jsy 4.00 10.00
Troy Percival Jsy/25
13 Ben Sheets Jsy 2.50 6.00
Danny Kolb Jsy/125
14 Andruw Jones Jsy 3.00 8.00
Rafael Furcal Jsy/125
15 Todd Helton Jsy 3.00 8.00
Preston Wilson Jsy/125
16 Wade Boggs Jsy 4.00 10.00
Fred McGriff Jsy/50
17 Manny Ramirez Jsy 5.00 12.00
David Ortiz Jsy/125
18 Miguel Cabrera Jsy 3.00 8.00
Dontrelle Willis Jsy/125
19 Edgar Renteria Jsy 3.00 8.00
Scott Rolen Jsy/125
20 Carlos Beltran Jsy 2.50 6.00
Jeff Kent Bat/125
21 Eric Davis Bat 3.00 8.00
Deion Sanders Jsy/125
22 Frank Thomas Jsy 5.00 12.00
Paul Konerko Jsy/50
23 Mike Piazza Jsy 4.00 10.00
Al Leiter Jsy/125
24 Sean Burroughs Jsy 2.50 6.00
Ryan Klesko Jsy/125
25 Ken Harvey Jsy 2.50 6.00
Mike Sweeney Jsy/125
26 Hideki Matsui Jsy 10.00 25.00
Deion Sanders Jsy/125
27 Steve Carlton Jsy 3.00 8.00
Mark Buehrle Jsy/50
28 Randy Johnson Jsy 4.00 10.00
Gaylord Perry Jsy/125
29 Joe Morgan Jsy 4.00 10.00
Steve Carlton Jsy/25
30 Vladimir Guerrero Jsy
Orlando Cabrera Jsy/10
31 Scott Rolen Jsy 3.00 8.00
John Kruk Jsy/125
32 Aaron Boone Jsy 2.50 6.00
Dmitri Young Jsy/125
33 Rickey Henderson Hat 6.00 15.00
Vladimir Guerrero Jsy/25
34 Cliff Floyd Jsy 2.50 6.00
Charles Johnson Jsy/125
35 Rafael Palmeiro Jsy 10.00 25.00
Cal Ripken Jsy/125
36 Nolan Ryan Jsy 10.00 25.00
Francisco Rodriguez Jsy/75
37 Darin Erstad Jsy 4.00 10.00
Jim Edmonds Bat/25
38 Troy Glaus Jsy 4.00 10.00
Rickey Henderson Bat/150
39 Byung-Hyun Kim Jsy 2.50 6.00
Reggie Sanders Jsy/150
40 Andres Galarraga Jsy 3.00 8.00
David Justice Jsy/150
41 Brian Jordan Jsy 2.50 6.00
Ryan Klesko Jsy/150
42 Erik Bedard Jsy
Geronimo Gil Jsy/5
43 Brooks Robinson Bat 3.00 8.00
Will Clark Bat/150
44 Josh Towers Pants 2.50 6.00
Erik Bedard Jsy/150
45 Nomar Garciaparra Bat 4.00 10.00
Wade Boggs Bat/150
46 Jason Varitek Bat 4.00 10.00
Wade Boggs Bat/150
47 Juan Cruz Hat 2.50 6.00
Hee Seop Choi Jsy/75
48 Derrek Lee Jsy 4.00 10.00
Corey Patterson Shoe/50
49 Joe Borchard Jsy 2.50 6.00
Ray Durham Jsy/75
50 Eric Davis Bat 2.50 6.00
Sean Casey Jsy/150
51 Dmitri Young Jsy 2.50 6.00
Wily Mo Pena Bat/150
52 Early Wynn Jsy 3.00 8.00
Hal Newhouser Jsy/150
53 Sean Casey Jsy 2.50 6.00
Russell Branyan Jsy/150
55 Juan Uribe Jsy 2.50 6.00
Juan Pierre Bat/150
56 Juan Encarnacion Jsy 2.50 6.00
Robert Fick Bat/150
57 Dmitri Young Jsy 2.50 6.00
Juan Encarnacion Jsy/150
58 Magglio Ordonez Bat 2.50 6.00
Bobby Higginson Bat/150
59 Charles Johnson Jsy 2.50 6.00
Ryan Dempster Jsy/150
60 Cliff Floyd Bat 2.50 6.00
Ryan Dempster Jsy/150
61 Mike Lowell Jsy 2.50 6.00
Cliff Floyd Bat/150
62 Dontrelle Willis Bat 2.50 6.00
Charles Johnson Jsy/150
63 Jose Cruz Jsy 2.50 6.00
Kirk Saarloos Jsy/150
64 Jeff Bagwell Pants 3.00 8.00
Richard Hidalgo Bat/150
65 Lance Berkman Bat 2.50 6.00
Richard Hidalgo Pants/150
66 Runelvys Hernandez Jsy 3.00 8.00
Mike Sweeney Bat/50
67 Runelvys Hernandez Jsy 3.00 8.00
Willie Wilson Bat/50
68 John Buck Bat 3.00 8.00
Runelvys Hernandez Jsy/50
69 Angel Berroa Bat 2.50 6.00
Jeremy Affeldt Shoe/100
70 Chan Ho Park Jsy 2.50 6.00
Kazuhisa Ishii Jsy/150
71 Shawn Green Bat 2.50 6.00
Kazuhisa Ishii Jsy/150
72 Shawn Green Bat 4.00 10.00
Rickey Henderson Bat/150
73 Richie Sexson Jsy 2.50 6.00
Lyle Overbay Jsy/100
74 David Ortiz Jsy 4.00 10.00
J.C. Romero Jsy/150
75 David Ortiz Jsy 4.00 10.00
Kirby Puckett Bat/150
76 Michael Barrett Jsy 3.00 8.00
Rondell White Jsy/150
77 Zach Day Jsy 3.00 8.00
Michael Barrett Jsy/50
78 Tony Armas Jr. Jsy 2.50 6.00
Zach Day Jsy/150
79 Rickey Henderson Jkt 4.00 10.00
Edgardo Alfonzo Bat/150
80 Hideki Matsui Bat 10.00 25.00
Bernie Williams Bat/150
81 Don Mattingly Bat 10.00 25.00
Hideki Matsui Bat/150
82 Mark Ellis Jsy 2.50 6.00
Terrence Long Jsy/150
83 Ramon Hernandez Jsy 2.50 6.00
Erubiel Durazo Bat/150
84 Brandon Duckworth Jsy 2.50 6.00
Anderson Machado Jsy/150
85 Craig Wilson Bat 2.50 6.00
Freddy Sanchez Bat/150
86 Brian Lawrence Bat 2.50 6.00
Dennis Tankersley Bat/150
87 Tony Gwynn Pants 6.00 15.00
Trevor Hoffman Jsy/150
88 Andres Galarraga Bat 4.00 10.00
Pedro Feliz Shoe/50
89 Jeff Kent Jsy 2.50 6.00
J.T. Snow Jsy/150
90 Freddy Garcia Jsy 3.00 8.00
John Olerud Jsy/50
91 Freddy Garcia Jsy 3.00 8.00
Edgar Martinez Jsy/100
92 So Taguchi Jsy 2.50 6.00
J.D. Drew Bat/150
93 Ben Grieve Jsy 2.50 6.00
Brandon Backe Jsy/100
94 Dewon Brazelton Jsy 2.50 6.00
Joe Kennedy Bat/75
95 Toby Hall Jsy 2.50 6.00
Pete LaForest Bat/150
96 Frankie Francisco Jsy 2.50 6.00
Gabe Kapler Jsy/100
97 Travis Hafner Jsy 2.50 6.00
Doug Davis Jsy/100
98 Jeff Kent Jsy 2.50 6.00
Raul Mondesi Jsy/100
100 Marlon Byrd Bat 2.50 6.00
Preston Wilson Bat/150

2005 Absolute Memorabilia Team Tandems Swatch Single Spectrum

*SPEC: p/r 75: .4X TO 1X SNG p/r 75-150
*SPEC: p/r 25: .6X TO 1.5X SNG p/r 75-150
*SPEC: p/r 25: .5X TO 1.2X SNG p/r 50
*SPEC: p/r 15: .6X TO 1.5X SNG p/r 50

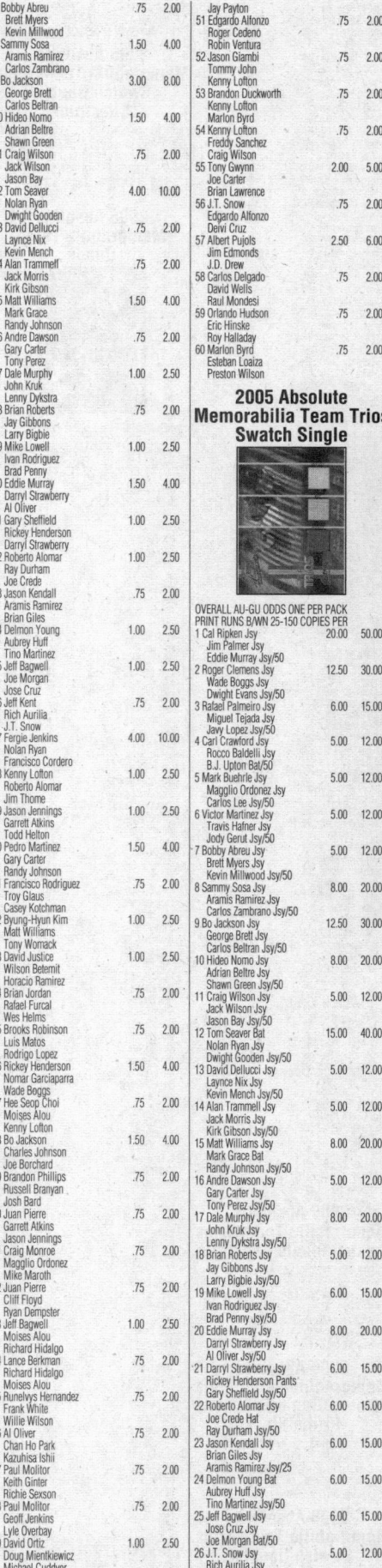

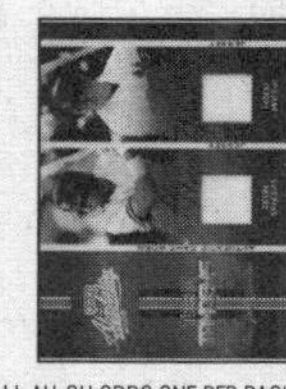

OVERALL AU-GU ODDS ONE PER PACK
PRINT RUNS B/WN 1-75 COPIES PER
NO PRICING ON QTY OF 10 OR LESS

2005 Absolute Memorabilia Team Tandems Swatch Single Spectrum Prime Black

*PRIMEp/r70-150: .5X TO 1.2X SNGp/r75-150
*PRIME p/r 70-150: .4X TO 1X SNG p/r 50
*PRIMEp/r40-65: .6X TO 1.5X SNGp/r75-150
*PRIME p/r 25: .75X TO 2X SNG p/r 75-150
*PRIME p/r 15: 1X TO 2.5X SNG p/r 75-150
*PRIME p/r 15: .75X TO 2X SNG p/r 50
*PRIME p/r 15: .6X TO 1.5X SNG p/r 25
OVERALL AU-GU ODDS ONE PER PACK
PRINT RUNS B/WN 1-150 COPIES PER
NO PRICING ON QTY OF 1
30 Vladimir Guerrero Jsy 10.00 25.00
Orlando Cabrera Jsy/15
42 Erik Bedard Jsy 4.00 10.00
Geronimo Gil Jsy/65
54 Bert Blyleven Jsy 4.00 10.00
Jim Thome Jsy/125

2005 Absolute Memorabilia Team Tandems Swatch Double

*DBL p/r 70-150: .6X TO 1.5X SNG p/r 75-150
*DBL p/r 70-150: .5X TO 1.2X SNG p/r 50
*DBL p/r 70-150: .4X TO 1X SNG p/r 25
*DBL p/r 50: .75X TO 2X SNG p/r 75-150
*DBL p/r 50: .6X TO 1.5X SNG p/r 50
*DBL p/r 50: .5X TO 1.2X SNG p/r 25
*DBL p/r 25: 1X TO 2.5X SNG p/r 75-150
*DBL p/r 25: .75X TO 2X SNG p/r 50
*DBL p/r 25: .6X TO 1.5X SNG p/r 25
OVERALL AU-GU ODDS ONE PER PACK
PRINT RUNS B/WN 1-150 COPIES PER
NO PRICING ON QTY OF 10 OR LESS
42 Geronimo Gil Bat-Jsy 4.00 10.00
Erik Bedard Bat-Jsy/150

2005 Absolute Memorabilia Team Tandems Swatch Double Spectrum

*SPECp/r70-100: .6X TO 1.5X SNGp/r75-150
*SPEC p/r 70-100: .5X TO 1.2X SNG p/r 50
*SPEC p/r 50-65: .75X TO 2X SNG p/r 75-150
*SPEC p/r 25: 1X TO 2.5X SNG p/r 75-150
*SPEC p/r 25: .6X TO 1.5X SNG p/r 25
OVERALL AU-GU ODDS ONE PER PACK
PRINT RUNS B/WN 1-100 COPIES PER
NO PRICING ON QTY OF 10 OR LESS
42 Erik Bedard Bat-Jsy 5.00 12.00
Geronimo Gil Bat-Jsy/65

2005 Absolute Memorabilia Team Tandems Swatch Double Spectrum Prime Black

*PRIME p/r 15: 1.5X TO 4X SNG p/r 125
*PRIME p/r 15: 1.25X TO 3X SNG p/r 50
*PRIME p/r 15: 1X TO 2.5X SNG p/r 25
OVERALL AU-GU ODDS ONE PER PACK
PRINT RUNS B/WN 1-15 COPIES PER
NO PRICING ON QTY OF 1
30 Vladimir Guerrero Jsy-Jsy 15.00 40.00
Orlando Cabrera Bat-Jsy/15

2005 Absolute Memorabilia Team Trios

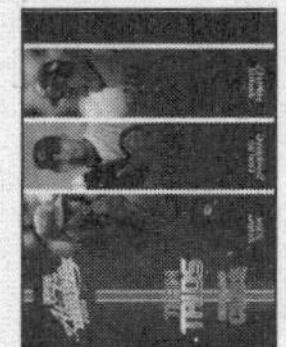

STATED PRINT RUN 200 SERIAL #'d SETS
*SPEC: .5X TO 1.2X BASIC
SPECTRUM PRINT RUN 125 #'d SETS
RANDOM INSERTS IN PACKS
1 Cal Ripken 5.00 12.00
Jim Palmer
Eddie Murray
2 Roger Clemens 2.00 5.00
Wade Boggs
Dwight Evans
3 Rafael Palmeiro 1.00 2.50
Miguel Tejada
Javy Lopez
4 Carl Crawford .75 2.00
Rocco Baldelli
B.J. Upton
5 Mark Buehrle .75 2.00
Magglio Ordonez
Carlos Lee
6 Victor Martinez .75 2.00
Travis Hafner
Jody Gerut
7 Bobby Abreu .75 2.00
Brett Myers
Kevin Millwood
8 Sammy Sosa 1.50 4.00
Aramis Ramirez
Carlos Zambrano
9 Bo Jackson 3.00 8.00
George Brett
Carlos Beltran
10 Hideo Nomo 1.50 4.00
Adrian Beltre
Shawn Green
11 Craig Wilson .75 2.00
Jack Wilson
Jason Bay
12 Tom Seaver 4.00 10.00
Nolan Ryan
Dwight Gooden
13 David Dellucci .75 2.00
Laynce Nix
Kevin Mench
14 Alan Trammell .75 2.00
Jack Morris
Kirk Gibson
15 Matt Williams 1.50 4.00
Mark Grace
Randy Johnson
16 Andre Dawson .75 2.00
Gary Carter
Tony Perez
17 Dale Murphy 1.00 2.50
John Kruk
Lenny Dykstra
18 Brian Roberts .75 2.00
Jay Gibbons
Larry Bigbie
19 Mike Lowell 1.00 2.50
Ivan Rodriguez
Brad Penny
20 Eddie Murray 1.50 4.00
Darryl Strawberry
Al Oliver
21 Gary Sheffield 1.00 2.50
Rickey Henderson
Darryl Strawberry
22 Roberto Alomar 1.00 2.50
Ray Durham
Joe Crede
23 Jason Kendall .75 2.00
Aramis Ramirez
Brian Giles
24 Delmon Young 1.00 2.50
Aubrey Huff
Tino Martinez
25 Jeff Bagwell 1.00 2.50
Joe Morgan
Jose Cruz
26 Jeff Kent .75 2.00
Rich Aurilia
J.T. Snow
27 Fergie Jenkins 4.00 10.00
Nolan Ryan
Francisco Cordero
28 Kenny Lofton 1.00 2.50
Roberto Alomar
Jim Thome
29 Jason Jennings 1.00 2.50
Garrett Atkins
Todd Helton
30 Pedro Martinez 1.50 4.00
Gary Carter
Randy Johnson
31 Francisco Rodriguez .75 2.00
Troy Glaus
Casey Kotchman
32 Byung-Hyun Kim 1.00 2.50
Matt Williams
Tony Womack
33 David Justice 1.00 2.50
Wilson Betemit
Horacio Ramirez
34 Brian Jordan .75 2.00
Rafael Furcal
Wes Helms
35 Brooks Robinson .75 2.00
Luis Matos
Rodrigo Lopez
36 Rickey Henderson 1.50 4.00
Nomar Garciaparra
Wade Boggs
37 Hee Seop Choi .75 2.00
Moises Alou
Kenny Lofton
38 Bo Jackson 1.50 4.00
Charles Johnson
Joe Borchard
39 Brandon Phillips .75 2.00
Russell Branyan
Josh Bard
40 Juan Pierre .75 2.00
Garrett Atkins
Jason Jennings
41 Craig Monroe .75 2.00
Magglio Ordonez
Mike Maroth
42 Juan Pierre .75 2.00
Cliff Floyd
Ryan Dempster
43 Jeff Bagwell 1.00 2.50
Moises Alou
Richard Hidalgo
44 Lance Berkman .75 2.00
Richard Hidalgo
Moises Alou
45 Runelvys Hernandez .75 2.00
Frank White
Willie Wilson
46 Al Oliver .75 2.00
Chan Ho Park
Kazuhisa Ishii
47 Paul Molitor .75 2.00
Keith Ginter
Richie Sexson
48 Paul Molitor .75 2.00
Geoff Jenkins
Lyle Overbay
49 David Ortiz 1.00 2.50
Doug Mientkiewicz
Michael Cuddyer
50 Cliff Floyd .75 2.00
Edgardo Alfonzo
Jay Payton
51 Edgardo Alfonzo .75 2.00
Roger Cedeno
Robin Ventura
52 Jason Giambi .75 2.00
Tommy John
Kenny Lofton
53 Brandon Duckworth .75 2.00
Kenny Lofton
Marlon Byrd
54 Kenny Lofton .75 2.00
Freddy Sanchez
Craig Wilson
55 Tony Gwynn 2.00 5.00
Joe Carter
Brian Lawrence
56 J.T. Snow .75 2.00
Edgardo Alfonzo
Deivi Cruz
57 Albert Pujols 2.50 6.00
Jim Edmonds
J.D. Drew
58 Carlos Delgado .75 2.00
David Wells
Raul Mondesi
59 Orlando Hudson .75 2.00
Eric Hinske
Roy Halladay
60 Marlon Byrd .75 2.00
Esteban Loaiza
Preston Wilson

2005 Absolute Memorabilia Team Trios Swatch Single

OVERALL AU-GU ODDS ONE PER PACK
PRINT RUNS B/WN 25-150 COPIES PER
1 Cal Ripken Jsy 20.00 50.00
Jim Palmer Jsy
Eddie Murray Jsy/50
2 Roger Clemens Jsy 12.50 30.00
Wade Boggs Jsy
Dwight Evans Jsy/50
3 Rafael Palmeiro Jsy 6.00 15.00
Miguel Tejada Jsy
Javy Lopez Jsy/50
4 Carl Crawford Jsy 5.00 12.00
Rocco Baldelli Jsy
B.J. Upton Bat/50
5 Mark Buehrle Jsy 5.00 12.00
Magglio Ordonez Jsy
Carlos Lee Jsy/50
6 Victor Martinez Jsy 5.00 12.00
Travis Hafner Jsy
Jody Gerut Jsy/50
7 Bobby Abreu Jsy 5.00 12.00
Brett Myers Jsy
Kevin Millwood Jsy/50
8 Sammy Sosa Jsy 8.00 20.00
Aramis Ramirez Jsy
Carlos Zambrano Jsy/50
9 Bo Jackson Jsy 12.50 30.00
George Brett Jsy
Carlos Beltran Jsy/50
10 Hideo Nomo Jsy 8.00 20.00
Adrian Beltre Jsy
Shawn Green Jsy/50
11 Craig Wilson Jsy 5.00 12.00
Jack Wilson Jsy
Jason Bay Jsy/50
12 Tom Seaver Bat 15.00 40.00
Nolan Ryan Jsy
Dwight Gooden Jsy/50
13 David Dellucci Jsy 5.00 12.00
Laynce Nix Jsy
Kevin Mench Jsy/50
14 Alan Trammell Jsy 5.00 12.00
Jack Morris Jsy
Kirk Gibson Jsy/50
15 Matt Williams Jsy 8.00 20.00
Mark Grace Bat
Randy Johnson Jsy/50
16 Andre Dawson Jsy 5.00 12.00
Gary Carter Jsy
Tony Perez Jsy/50
17 Dale Murphy Jsy 8.00 20.00
John Kruk Jsy
Lenny Dykstra Jsy/50
18 Brian Roberts Jsy 5.00 12.00
Jay Gibbons Jsy
Larry Bigbie Jsy/50
19 Mike Lowell Jsy 6.00 15.00
Ivan Rodriguez Jsy
Brad Penny Jsy/50
20 Eddie Murray Jsy 8.00 20.00
Darryl Strawberry Jsy
Al Oliver Jsy/50
21 Darryl Strawberry Jsy 6.00 15.00
Rickey Henderson Pants
Gary Sheffield Jsy/50
22 Roberto Alomar Jsy 6.00 15.00
Joe Crede Hat
Ray Durham Jsy/50
23 Jason Kendall Jsy 6.00 15.00
Brian Giles Jsy
Aramis Ramirez Jsy/25
24 Delmon Young Bat 6.00 15.00
Aubrey Huff Jsy
Tino Martinez Jsy/50
25 Jeff Bagwell Jsy 6.00 15.00
Jose Cruz Jsy
Joe Morgan Bat/50
26 J.T. Snow Jsy 5.00 12.00
Rich Aurilia Jsy
Jeff Kent Jsy/50
27 Fergie Jenkins Jsy 10.00 25.00

Nolan Ryan Jsy
Francisco Cordero Jsy/50
28 Kenny Lofton Fld Glv 6.00 15.00
Jim Thome Bat
Roberto Alomar Jsy/50
29 Garrett Atkins Jsy 6.00 15.00
Todd Helton Jsy
Jason Jennings Jsy/50
30 Gary Carter Jsy 8.00 20.00
Pedro Martinez Jsy
Randy Johnson Jsy/50
31 Francisco Rodriguez Jsy 4.00 10.00
Troy Glaus Bat
Casey Kotchman Bat/150
32 Byung-Hyun Kim Jsy 5.00 12.00
Matt Williams Bat
Tony Womack Jsy/150
33 David Justice Bat 5.00 12.00
Horacio Ramirez Fld Glv
Wilson Betemit Hat/50
34 Brian Jordan Jsy 4.00 10.00
Rafael Furcal Bat
Wes Helms Jsy/150
35 Brooks Robinson Bat 5.00 12.00
Luis Matos Jsy
Rodrigo Lopez Jsy/150
36 Rickey Henderson Bat 6.00 15.00
Nomar Garciaparra Bat
Wade Boggs Bat/150
37 Hee Seop Choi Jsy 4.00 10.00
Moises Alou Bat
Kenny Lofton Bat/150
38 Bo Jackson Bat 6.00 15.00
Charles Johnson Bat
Joe Borchard Bat/150
39 Brandon Phillips Bat 4.00 10.00
Russell Branyan Jsy
Josh Bard Jsy/150
40 Juan Pierre Bat 4.00 10.00
Jason Jennings Bat
Garrett Atkins Jsy/150
41 Craig Monroe Bat 4.00 10.00
Magglio Ordonez Bat
Mike Maroth Jsy/150
42 Juan Pierre Bat 4.00 10.00
Cliff Floyd Bat
Ryan Dempster Jsy/150
43 Jeff Bagwell Pants 5.00 12.00
Moises Alou Bat
Richard Hidalgo Pants/150
44 Lance Berkman Bat 4.00 10.00
Moises Alou Jsy
Richard Hidalgo Pants/150
45 Runelvys Hernandez Jsy 4.00 10.00
Frank White Bat
Willie Wilson Bat/150
46 Al Oliver Jsy 4.00 10.00
Chan Ho Park Jsy
Kazuhisa Ishii Jsy/150
47 Paul Molitor Bat 6.00 15.00
Richie Sexson Jsy
Keith Ginter Shoe/25
48 Paul Molitor Bat 4.00 10.00
Lyle Overbay Jsy
Geoff Jenkins Jsy/150
49 David Ortiz Jsy 5.00 12.00
Doug Mientkiewicz Bat
Michael Cuddyer Bat/150
50 Cliff Floyd Bat 4.00 10.00
Edgardo Alfonzo Bat
Jay Payton Jsy/150
51 Edgardo Alfonzo Bat 4.00 10.00
Robin Ventura Bat
Roger Cedeno Bat/150
52 Jason Giambi Jsy 4.00 10.00
Tommy John Bat
Kenny Lofton Bat/150
53 Brandon Duckworth Jsy 4.00 10.00
Kenny Lofton Bat
Marlon Byrd Bat/150
54 Kenny Lofton Bat 4.00 10.00
Craig Wilson Bat
Freddy Sanchez Bat/150
55 Tony Gwynn Pants 6.00 15.00
Joe Carter Bat
Brian Lawrence Jsy/150
56 J.T. Snow Jsy 4.00 10.00
Edgardo Alfonzo Bat
Deivi Cruz Bat/150
57 Albert Pujols Bat 10.00 25.00
Jim Edmonds Bat
J.D. Drew Bat/100
59 Orlando Hudson Bat 4.00 10.00
Eric Hinske Jsy
Roy Halladay Jsy/150
60 Marlon Byrd Bat 4.00 10.00
Preston Wilson Bat
Esteban Loaiza Bat/150

2005 Absolute Memorabilia Team Trios Swatch Single Spectrum

*SPEC p/r 50: .4X TO 1X SNG p/r 50
*SPEC p/r 25: .6X TO 1.5X SNG p/r 100-150
*SPEC p/r 25: .5X TO 1.2X SNG p/r 50
*SPEC p/r 25: .4X TO 1X SNG p/r 25
OVERALL AU-GU ODDS ONE PER PACK
PRINT RUNS B/WN 10-50 COPIES PER
NO PRICING ON QTY OF 10

2005 Absolute Memorabilia Team Trios Swatch Single Spectrum Prime Black

*PRIMEp/r40-50: .6X TO 1.5X SNGp/r100-150
*PRIMEp/r100-150:.5XTO1.2XSNGp/r100-150
OVERALL AU-GU ODDS ONE PER PACK
PRINT RUNS B/WN 10-150 COPIES PER
NO PRICING ON QTY OF 10

2005 Absolute Memorabilia Team Trios Swatch Double

*DBL p/r 100: .6X TO 1.5X SNG p/r 50
*DBL p/r 50: .75X TO 2X SNG p/r 50
*DBL p/r 25: 1X TO 2.5X SNG p/r 50
OVERALL AU-GU ODDS ONE PER PACK
PRINT RUNS B/WN 25-100 COPIES PER

2005 Absolute Memorabilia Team Trios Swatch Double Spectrum

*SPEC p/r 35: .5X TO 1.2X SNG p/r 50
PRINT RUNS B/WN 5-35 COPIES PER
NO PRICING ON QTY OF 10 OR LESS
PRIME BLACK PRINT RUNS B/WN 5-10 PER
NO PRIME BLK PRICING DUE TO SCARCITY
OVERALL AU-GU ODDS ONE PER PACK

2005 Absolute Memorabilia Team Quads

STATED PRINT RUN 150 SERIAL #'d SETS
*SPEC: .5X TO 1.2X BASIC
SPECTRUM PRINT RUN 100 #'d SETS
RANDOM INSERTS IN PACKS
1 Albert Pujols 3.00 8.00
Larry Walker
Scott Rolen
Jim Edmonds
2 Lou Boudreau 1.25 3.00
Bob Feller
Early Wynn
Hal Newhouser
3 Don Sutton 1.25 3.00
Rod Carew
Reggie Jackson
Tommy John
4 Jim Rice 1.25 3.00
Fred Lynn
Luis Tiant
Carlton Fisk
5 Hideki Matsui 3.00 8.00
Gary Sheffield
Mike Mussina
Jorge Posada
6 Greg Maddux 2.50 6.00
Tom Glavine
Chipper Jones
David Justice
7 Johnny Damon 1.25 3.00
Jermaine Dye
Eric Chavez
Mark Ellis
8 Vladimir Guerrero 1.50 4.00
Garret Anderson
Troy Glaus
Darin Erstad
9 Michael Young 1.25 3.00
Alfonso Soriano
Hank Blalock
Mark Teixeira
10 Torii Hunter 1.50 4.00
Shannon Stewart
Johan Santana
Jacque Jones
11 Mike Piazza 1.50 4.00
Kazuo Matsui
Jose Reyes
Tom Glavine
12 Roger Clemens 5.00 12.00
Nolan Ryan
Don Sutton
Randy Johnson
13 Tony Gwynn 2.50 6.00
Rickey Henderson
Steve Garvey
Willie McCovey
14 Sean Casey 1.00 2.50
Adam Dunn
Austin Kearns
Ryan Wagner
15 Nolan Ryan 5.00 12.00
Ivan Rodriguez
Juan Gonzalez
Rafael Palmeiro
16 Roger Clemens 4.00 10.00
Phil Rizzuto
Whitey Ford
Don Mattingly
17 Dennis Eckersley 3.00 8.00
Ozzie Smith
Edgar Renteria
Keith Hernandez
18 Willie Stargell 1.25 3.00
Bill Madlock
Dave Parker
Jason Bay
19 Mark Prior 1.25 3.00
Mark Grace
Andre Dawson
Ron Santo
20 Paul Molitor 1.50 4.00
Rod Carew
Kirby Puckett
Torii Hunter
21 Troy Glaus 1.50 4.00
Casey Kotchman
Darin Erstad
Rickey Henderson
22 Curt Schilling 1.00 2.50
Tony Womack
Matt Kata
Tony Clark
23 Dale Murphy 1.50 4.00
Chipper Jones
Kenny Lofton
Ryan Klesko
24 Greg Maddux 2.50 6.00
Tom Glavine
John Smoltz
Phil Niekro
25 Andres Galarraga 1.25 3.00
Deion Sanders
Kenny Lofton
Ryan Klesko
26 Luis Matos 1.25 3.00
Rodrigo Lopez
Brooks Robinson
Erik Bedard
27 Manny Ramirez 1.50 4.00
Jason Varitek
Wade Boggs
Nomar Garciaparra
28 Roger Clemens 2.50 6.00
Wade Boggs
Carlton Fisk
Nomar Garciaparra
29 David Ortiz 1.50 4.00
Trot Nixon
Jason Varitek
Manny Ramirez
30 Andre Dawson 1.50 4.00
Sammy Sosa
Hee Seop Choi
Kenny Lofton
31 Roberto Alomar 1.50 4.00
Frank Thomas
Ray Durham
Carl Everett
32 Bo Jackson 1.50 4.00
Joe Borchard
Carlos Lee
Charles Johnson
33 Bo Jackson 1.50 4.00
Magglio Ordonez
Carlton Fisk
Robin Ventura
34 Dave Concepcion 1.00 2.50
Joe Morgan
George Foster
Eric Davis
35 Adam Dunn 1.00 2.50
Sean Casey
Wily Mo Pena
Dmitri Young
36 Joe Morgan 1.00 2.50
George Foster
Paul O'Neill
Adam Dunn
37 C.C. Sabathia 1.00 2.50
Joe Carter
Russell Branyan
Sean Casey
38 Larry Walker 1.00 2.50
Clint Barmes
Charles Johnson
Garrett Atkins
39 Garrett Atkins 1.00 2.50
Jeff Baker
Jason Jennings
Juan Pierre
40 Bobby Higginson 1.00 2.50
Craig Monroe
Mike Maroth
Franklyn German
41 A.J. Burnett 1.00 2.50
Dontrelle Willis
Juan Pierre
Paul Lo Duca
42 Paul Lo Duca 1.00 2.50
Mike Lowell
Juan Pierre
Cliff Floyd
43 Craig Biggio 1.25 3.00
Jeff Bagwell
Moises Alou
Jason Lane
44 Jose Cruz 1.25 3.00
Kirk Saarloos
Jeff Bagwell
Richard Hidalgo
45 Joe Morgan 1.00 2.50
Wade Miller
Lance Berkman
Richard Hidalgo
46 Frank White 1.00 2.50
Willie Wilson
Angel Berroa
John Buck
47 Rickey Henderson 1.50 4.00
Kazuhisa Ishii
Shawn Green
Al Oliver
48 Chan Ho Park 1.00 2.50
Kazuhisa Ishii
Shawn Green
Kevin Brown
49 Paul Molitor 1.00 2.50
Richie Sexson
Lyle Overbay
Geoff Jenkins
50 Kirby Puckett 1.50 4.00
Harmon Killebrew
Paul Molitor
Tony Oliva
51 Kirby Puckett 1.50 4.00
David Ortiz
Michael Cuddyer
Matt Lawton
52 Kirby Puckett 1.50 4.00
Paul Molitor
David Ortiz
Michael Cuddyer
53 Tony Armas Jr. 1.00 2.50
Zach Day
Cliff Floyd
Jose Vidro
54 Javier Vazquez 1.00 2.50
Cliff Floyd
Tony Armas Jr.
Zach Day
55 Willie Mays 3.00 8.00
Mike Piazza
Edgardo Alfonzo
Robin Ventura
56 Rickey Henderson 2.00 5.00
Robin Ventura
David Wright
Edgardo Alfonzo
57 Don Mattingly 3.00 8.00
Jason Giambi
Bernie Williams
Jorge Posada
58 Mariano Rivera 1.50 4.00
Tommy John
Phil Niekro
Paul O'Neill
59 Wade Boggs 1.25 3.00
Robin Ventura
Paul O'Neill
Kenny Lofton
60 Erubiel Durazo 1.00 2.50
Mark Ellis
Ramon Hernandez
Terrence Long
61 Bobby Abreu 1.00 2.50
Joe Morgan
Kenny Lofton
Marlon Byrd
62 Kenny Lofton 1.00 2.50
Kevin Millwood
Marlon Byrd
Matt Kata
63 Kenny Lofton 1.00 2.50
Craig Wilson
Freddy Sanchez
Jason Bay
64 Tony Gwynn 2.00 5.00
Joe Carter
Trevor Hoffman
Brian Lawrence
65 Willie McCovey 1.25 3.00
Andres Galarraga
Kenny Lofton
Jose Cruz Jr.
66 Andres Galarraga 1.25 3.00
J.T. Snow
Jose Cruz Jr.
Deivi Cruz
67 John Olerud 1.00 2.50
Freddy Garcia
Chris Snelling
Bret Boone
68 Albert Pujols 3.00 8.00
Scott Rolen
J.D. Drew
So Taguchi
69 Brandon Backe 1.00 2.50
Chad Gaudin
Dewon Brazelton
Toby Hall
70 Wade Boggs 1.25 3.00
Delmon Young
Toby Hall
Joey Gathright
71 Alfonso Soriano 1.25 3.00
Hank Blalock
Mark Teixeira
Michael Young
72 Ivan Rodriguez 1.25 3.00
Kevin Mench
Gabe Kapler
Richard Hidalgo
73 Mark Teixeira 1.25 3.00
Travis Hafner
Gabe Kapler
Frankie Francisco
74 Shawn Green 1.00 2.50
Orlando Hudson
Josh Phelps
Shannon Stewart
75 Carlos Delgado 1.00 2.50
Josh Phelps
Raul Mondesi
Orlando Hudson

2005 Absolute Memorabilia Team Quads Swatch Single

OVERALL AU-GU ODDS ONE PER PACK
PRINT RUNS B/WN 25-150 COPIES PER
1 Albert Pujols Jsy 10.00 25.00
Larry Walker Bat
Scott Rolen Jsy
Jim Edmonds Jsy/100
2 Lou Boudreau Jsy 15.00 40.00
Bob Feller Pants
Early Wynn Jsy
Hal Newhouser Jsy/100
3 Don Sutton Jsy 6.00 15.00
Rod Carew Jkt
Reggie Jackson Jsy
Tommy John Jsy/100
4 Jim Rice Jsy 6.00 15.00
Fred Lynn Jsy
Luis Tiant Hat
Carlton Fisk Bat/100
5 Hideki Matsui Jsy 10.00 25.00
Gary Sheffield Jsy
Mike Mussina Jsy
Jorge Posada Jsy/100
6 Greg Maddux Jsy 10.00 25.00
Tom Glavine Jsy
Chipper Jones Jsy
David Justice Jsy/100
7 Johnny Damon Hat 6.00 15.00
Jermaine Dye Jsy
Eric Chavez Jsy
Mark Ellis Jsy/100
8 Vladimir Guerrero Jsy 8.00 20.00
Garret Anderson Jsy
Troy Glaus Jsy
Darin Erstad Jsy/100
9 Michael Young Jsy 6.00 15.00
Alfonso Soriano Jsy
Hank Blalock Jsy
Mark Teixeira Jsy/100
10 Torii Hunter Jsy 10.00 25.00
Shannon Stewart Jsy
Johan Santana Jsy
Jacque Jones Jsy/25
11 Mike Piazza Jsy 8.00 20.00
Kazuo Matsui Jsy
Jose Reyes Jsy
Tom Glavine Jsy/100
12 Roger Clemens Jsy 15.00 40.00
Nolan Ryan Jsy
Don Sutton Jsy
Randy Johnson Jsy/100
13 Tony Gwynn Jsy 10.00 25.00
Rickey Henderson Jsy
Steve Garvey Jsy
Willie McCovey Jsy/100
14 Sean Casey Jsy 5.00 12.00
Adam Dunn Jsy
Austin Kearns Jsy
Ryan Wagner Jsy/100
15 Nolan Ryan Jsy 12.50 30.00
Ivan Rodriguez Jsy
Juan Gonzalez Jsy
Rafael Palmeiro Jsy/100
16 Whitey Ford Jsy 20.00 50.00
Don Mattingly Jsy
Phil Rizzuto Pants
Roger Clemens Jsy/100
17 Ozzie Smith Pants 15.00 40.00
Dennis Eckersley Jsy
Keith Hernandez Jsy
Edgar Renteria Jsy/25
18 Willie Stargell Jsy 6.00 15.00
Dave Parker Jsy
Jason Bay Jsy
Bill Madlock Bat/100
19 Ron Santo Bat 6.00 15.00
Andre Dawson Jsy
Mark Grace Jsy
Mark Prior Jsy/100
20 Paul Molitor Jsy 8.00 20.00
Rod Carew Jsy
Kirby Puckett Jsy
Torii Hunter Jsy/100
21 Troy Glaus Jsy 8.00 20.00
Rickey Henderson Bat
Casey Kotchman Bat
Darin Erstad Jsy/150
22 Curt Schilling Jsy 5.00 12.00
Tony Womack Jsy
Matt Kata Bat
Tony Clark Bat/150
23 Dale Murphy Bat 8.00 20.00
Chipper Jones Bat
Kenny Lofton Bat
Ryan Klesko Jsy/150
24 Greg Maddux Jsy 10.00 25.00
Phil Niekro Bat
Tom Glavine Jsy
John Smoltz Jsy/150
25 Andres Galarraga Bat 6.00 15.00
Deion Sanders Bat
Kenny Lofton Bat
Ryan Klesko Jsy/150
26 Luis Matos Jsy 6.00 15.00
Rodrigo Lopez Jsy
Brooks Robinson Bat
Erik Bedard Jsy/150
27 Manny Ramirez Bat 8.00 20.00
Jason Varitek Bat
Wade Boggs Bat
Nomar Garciaparra Bat/150
28 Roger Clemens Jsy 10.00 25.00
Wade Boggs Bat
Carlton Fisk Bat
Nomar Garciaparra Bat/150
29 David Ortiz Jsy 8.00 20.00
Trot Nixon Jsy
Jason Varitek Bat
Manny Ramirez Bat/150
30 Andre Dawson Bat 8.00 20.00
Sammy Sosa Bat
Hee Seop Choi Jsy
Kenny Lofton Bat/150
31 Roberto Alomar Jsy 8.00 20.00
Frank Thomas Bat
Ray Durham Jsy
Carl Everett Bat/150
32 Bo Jackson Bat 8.00 20.00
Joe Borchard Bat
Carlos Lee Bat
Charles Johnson Bat/150
33 Bo Jackson Bat 8.00 20.00
Carlton Fisk Bat
Robin Ventura Bat
Magglio Ordonez Bat/150
34 Dave Concepcion Bat 5.00 12.00
Joe Morgan Bat
George Foster Bat
Eric Davis Bat/100
35 Adam Dunn Bat 5.00 12.00
Sean Casey Jsy
Wily Mo Pena Bat
Dmitri Young Jsy/150
36 Joe Morgan Bat 5.00 12.00
George Foster Bat
Paul O'Neill Bat
Adam Dunn Bat/150
37 C.C. Sabathia Jsy 5.00 12.00
Joe Carter Bat
Russell Branyan Jsy
Sean Casey Jsy/150
38 Larry Walker Jsy 5.00 12.00
Clint Barmes Bat
Charles Johnson Bat
Garrett Atkins Jsy/150
39 Garrett Atkins Jsy 5.00 12.00
Jeff Baker Bat
Jason Jennings Bat
Juan Pierre Bat/150
40 Bobby Higginson Bat 5.00 12.00
Craig Monroe Bat
Mike Maroth Jsy
Franklyn German Bat/150
41 A.J. Burnett Bat 5.00 12.00
Dontrelle Willis Bat
Juan Pierre Bat
Paul Lo Duca Bat/150
42 Paul Lo Duca Bat 5.00 12.00
Mike Lowell Jsy
Juan Pierre Bat
Cliff Floyd Jsy/150
43 Craig Biggio Bat 6.00 15.00
Jeff Bagwell Pants
Moises Alou Bat
Jason Lane Bat/150
44 Jose Cruz Jsy 6.00 15.00
Kirk Saarloos Jsy
Jeff Bagwell Pants
Richard Hidalgo Pants/150
45 Joe Morgan Bat 5.00 12.00
Wade Miller Fld Glv
Lance Berkman Bat
Richard Hidalgo Bat/150
46 Frank White Bat 5.00 12.00
Willie Wilson Bat
Angel Berroa Bat
John Buck Bat/150
47 Rickey Henderson Bat 8.00 20.00
Kazuhisa Ishii Jsy
Shawn Green Bat
Al Oliver Bat/150
48 Chan Ho Park Jsy 5.00 12.00
Kazuhisa Ishii Jsy
Shawn Green Bat
Kevin Brown Jsy/150
49 Paul Molitor Bat 5.00 12.00
Richie Sexson Pants
Lyle Overbay Jsy
Geoff Jenkins Jsy/100
50 Kirby Puckett Bat 8.00 20.00
Harmon Killebrew Jsy
Paul Molitor Jsy
Tony Oliva Jsy/150
51 Kirby Puckett Bat 8.00 20.00
David Ortiz Jsy
Michael Cuddyer Bat
Matt Lawton Bat/150
52 Kirby Puckett Bat 8.00 20.00
Paul Molitor Jsy
David Ortiz Jsy
Michael Cuddyer Bat/150
53 Tony Armas Jr. Jsy 5.00 12.00
Zach Day Jsy
Cliff Floyd Bat
Jose Vidro Bat/150
54 Javier Vazquez Jsy 5.00 12.00
Cliff Floyd Bat
Tony Armas Jr. Jsy
Zach Day Pants/150
55 Willie Mays Jsy 15.00 40.00
Mike Piazza Pants
Edgardo Alfonzo Bat
Robin Ventura Bat/150
56 Rickey Henderson Jkt 8.00 20.00
Robin Ventura Bat
David Wright Bat
Edgardo Alfonzo Bat/150
57 Don Mattingly Bat 20.00 50.00
Jason Giambi Jsy
Bernie Williams Bat
Jorge Posada Jsy/150
58 Mariano Rivera Jsy 8.00 20.00
Tommy John Bat
Phil Niekro Bat
Paul O'Neill Bat/100
59 Wade Boggs Bat 6.00 15.00
Robin Ventura Bat
Paul O'Neill Bat
Kenny Lofton Bat/150
60 Erubiel Durazo Bat 5.00 12.00
Ramon Hernandez Jsy
Terrence Long Jsy
Mark Ellis Jsy/150
61 Bobby Abreu Jsy 5.00 12.00
Joe Morgan Bat
Kenny Lofton Bat
Marlon Byrd Bat/75
62 Kenny Lofton Bat 5.00 12.00
Kevin Millwood Jsy
Marlon Byrd Bat
Matt Kata Bat/150
63 Kenny Lofton Bat 5.00 12.00
Craig Wilson Jsy
Freddy Sanchez Bat
Jason Bay Bat/150
64 Tony Gwynn Pants 8.00 20.00
Joe Carter Bat
Trevor Hoffman Jsy
Brian Lawrence Bat/150
65 Willie McCovey Jsy 6.00 15.00
Andres Galarraga Jsy
Kenny Lofton Bat
Jose Cruz Jr. Bat/150
66 Andres Galarraga Bat 6.00 15.00
J.T. Snow Jsy
Jose Cruz Jr. Bat
Deivi Cruz Bat/150
67 John Olerud Bat 5.00 12.00
Freddy Garcia Jsy
Chris Snelling Bat
Bret Boone Jsy/150
68 Albert Pujols Bat 10.00 25.00
Scott Rolen Jsy
J.D. Drew Bat
So Taguchi Bat/135
69 Brandon Backe Jsy 5.00 12.00
Chad Gaudin Jsy
Dewon Brazelton Jsy
Toby Hall Jsy/150
71 Alfonso Soriano Bat 6.00 15.00
Hank Blalock Jsy
Mark Teixeira Bat
Michael Young Bat/150
72 Ivan Rodriguez Jsy 6.00 15.00
Kevin Mench Jsy
Gabe Kapler Jsy
Richard Hidalgo Bat/150
73 Mark Teixeira Bat 6.00 15.00
Gabe Kapler Jsy
Frankie Francisco Jsy
Travis Hafner Jsy/150
74 Shawn Green Bat 5.00 12.00
Orlando Hudson Bat
Josh Phelps Bat
Shannon Stewart Bat/150
75 Carlos Delgado Bat 5.00 12.00
Orlando Hudson Bat

Josh Phelps Bat
Raul Mondesi Bat/150

2005 Absolute Memorabilia Team Quads Swatch Single Spectrum

*SPEC p/r 75-100: .4X TO 1X SNG p/r 75-150
*SPEC p/r 45-50: .5X TO 1.2X SNG p/r 75-150
*SPEC p/r 25-35: .6X TO 1.5X SNG p/r 75-150
OVERALL AU-GU ODDS ONE PER PACK
PRINT RUNS B/WN 10-100 COPIES PER
NO PRICING ON QTY OF 10

2005 Absolute Memorabilia Team Quads Swatch Single Spectrum Prime Black

*PRIMEp/r100-150:.6XT01.5XSNGp/r75-150
*PRIMEp/r50-60: .75X TO 2X SNGp/r75-150
OVERALL AU-GU ODDS ONE PER PACK
PRINT RUNS B/WN 10-150 COPIES PER
NO PRICING ON QTY OF 10

2005 Absolute Memorabilia Team Quads Swatch Double

*DBL p/r 75: .6X TO 1.5X SNG p/r 100
*DBL p/r 25: 1X TO 2.5X SNG p/r 100
*DBL p/r 25: .6X TO 1.5X SNG p/r 25
OVERALL AU-GU ODDS ONE PER PACK
PRINT RUNS B/WN 25-75 COPIES PER

2005 Absolute Memorabilia Team Quads Swatch Double Spectrum

*SPEC p/r 25: 1X TO 2.5X SNG p/r 100
PRINT RUNS B/WN 1-25 COPIES PER
NO PRICING ON QTY OF 10 OR LESS
PRIME BLK PRINT RUNS B/WN 1-5 PER
NO PRIME BLK PRICING DUE TO SCARCITY
OVERALL AU-GU ODDS ONE PER PACK

2005 Absolute Memorabilia Team Six

STATED PRINT RUN 100 SERIAL #'d SETS
*SPEC: .6X TO 1.5X BASIC
SPECTRUM PRINT RUN 50 #'d SETS
RANDOM INSERTS IN PACKS
1 Willie Mays 4.00 10.00
Willie McCovey
Juan Marichal
Gaylord Perry
Orlando Cepeda
Will Clark
2 Roger Clemens 3.00 8.00
Jeff Bagwell
Lance Berkman
Craig Biggio
Andy Pettitte
Roy Oswalt
3 Tom Seaver 2.50 6.00
Johnny Bench
Joe Morgan
Dave Concepcion
George Foster
Tony Perez
4 Marty Marion 4.00 10.00
Stan Musial
Bob Gibson
Lou Brock
Frankie Frisch
Red Schoendienst
5 Don Mattingly 5.00 12.00
Catfish Hunter
Dave Righetti
Tommy John
Phil Niekro
Reggie Jackson
6 Ernie Banks 3.00 8.00
Greg Maddux
Sammy Sosa
Fergie Jenkins
Nomar Garciaparra
Kerry Wood
7 Curt Schilling 1.25 3.00
Luis Gonzalez
Steve Finley
Junior Spivey
Brandon Webb
Lyle Overbay
8 Duke Snider 2.00 5.00
Rickey Henderson
Mike Piazza
Pedro Martinez
Don Sutton
Hideo Nomo
9 Vladimir Guerrero 2.00 5.00
Tim Salmon
Casey Kotchman
Francisco Rodriguez
Ramon Ortiz
Chone Figgins
10 Roger Clemens 4.00 10.00
Curt Schilling
Carl Yastrzemski
Bobby Doerr
Nomar Garciaparra
Wade Boggs
11 Edgar Martinez 3.00 8.00
Adrian Beltre
Rickey Henderson
Ichiro Suzuki
Bret Boone
Richie Sexson
12 Bo Jackson 2.00 5.00
Frank Thomas
Carlton Fisk
Sammy Sosa
Hoyt Wilhelm
Harold Baines
13 Mike Schmidt 4.00 10.00
Dale Murphy
Jim Thome
Curt Schilling
Bobby Abreu
Steve Carlton
14 Nolan Ryan 5.00 12.00
Gary Carter
Duke Snider
Mike Piazza
Rickey Henderson
Roberto Alomar
15 Dale Murphy 2.00 5.00
Deion Sanders
Gary Sheffield
J.D. Drew
David Justice
Chipper Jones
16 Rickey Henderson 2.00 5.00
Jim Edmonds
Troy Glaus
Casey Kotchman
Francisco Rodriguez
Darin Erstad
17 Curt Schilling 1.50 4.00
Matt Williams
Reggie Sanders
Byung-Hyun Kim
Travis Lee
Tony Womack
18 John Smoltz 3.00 8.00
Tom Glavine
Greg Maddux
Wes Helms
Kenny Lofton
Andruw Jones
19 Chipper Jones 2.00 5.00
Dale Murphy
Andruw Jones
Wes Helms
Rafael Furcal
Andres Galarraga
20 Brooks Robinson 1.50 4.00
Luis Matos
Rodrigo Lopez
Geronimo Gil
Josh Towers
Erik Bedard
21 Roger Clemens 4.00 10.00
Wade Boggs
Carlton Fisk
Rickey Henderson
Nomar Garciaparra
Bobby Doerr
22 David Ortiz 4.00 10.00
Roger Clemens
Nomar Garciaparra
Wade Boggs
Rickey Henderson
Jason Varitek
23 Andre Dawson 1.50 4.00
Aramis Ramirez
Derrek Lee
Kenny Lofton
Moises Alou
Hee Seop Choi
24 Sammy Sosa 2.00 5.00
Nomar Garciaparra
Derrek Lee
Hee Seop Choi
Kenny Lofton
Matt Lawton
25 Carlton Fisk 2.00 5.00
Frank Thomas
Magglio Ordonez
Carl Everett
Esteban Loaiza
Robin Ventura
26 Bo Jackson 2.00 5.00
Magglio Ordonez
Roberto Alomar
Robin Ventura
Kenny Lofton
Joe Borchard
27 Adam Dunn 1.25 3.00
Eric Davis
Joe Morgan
Paul O'Neill
Wily Mo Pena
Juan Encarnacion
28 Tony Perez 1.25 3.00
Dave Concepcion
George Foster
Dmitri Young
Adam Dunn
Eric Davis
29 Bert Blyleven 1.25 3.00
Early Wynn
Hal Newhouser
C.C. Sabathia
Joe Carter
Russell Branyan
30 Jim Thome 1.50 4.00
Victor Martinez
Sean Casey
Russell Branyan
Josh Bard
Kenny Lofton
31 Larry Walker 1.25 3.00
Clint Barmes
Garrett Atkins
Juan Pierre
Mike Hampton
Juan Uribe
32 Larry Walker 1.25 3.00
Jeff Baker
Juan Pierre
Garrett Atkins
Juan Uribe
Jason Jennings
33 Kirk Gibson 1.25 3.00
Magglio Ordonez
Brandon Inge
Bobby Higginson
Craig Monroe
Mike Maroth
34 Dontrelle Willis 1.25 3.00
Ryan Dempster
Juan Pierre
Mike Lowell
Cliff Floyd
Charles Johnson
35 Jeff Bagwell 1.50 4.00
Carlos Beltran
Lance Berkman
Richard Hidalgo
Jose Cruz
Jason Lane
36 Jeff Bagwell 1.50 4.00
Lance Berkman
Joe Morgan
Craig Biggio
Jason Lane
Jose Cruz
37 Roy Oswalt 1.50 4.00
Morgan Ensberg
Lance Berkman
Jeff Bagwell
Jason Lane
Craig Biggio
38 Frank White 1.25 3.00
Willie Wilson
Mike Sweeney
Angel Berroa
John Buck
Runelvys Hernandez
39 Hideo Nomo 2.00 5.00
Kazuhisa Ishii
Chan Ho Park
Rickey Henderson
Shawn Green
Al Oliver
40 Steve Garvey 2.00 5.00
Darryl Strawberry
Rickey Henderson
Kazuhisa Ishii
Paul Lo Duca
Kevin Brown
41 Johan Santana 2.00 5.00
Joe Mays
Justin Morneau
Torii Hunter
Shannon Stewart
Michael Cuddyer
42 Kirby Puckett 1.50 4.00
David Ortiz
Harmon Killebrew
Doug Mientkiewicz
Torii Hunter
Matt Lawton
43 Kirby Puckett 1.50 4.00
Shannon Stewart
David Ortiz
Doug Mientkiewicz
Torii Hunter
Michael Cuddyer
44 Tony Perez 1.25 3.00
Javier Vazquez
Rondell White
Cliff Floyd
Jose Vidro
Zach Day
45 Willie Mays 4.00 10.00
Roger Cedeno
Mike Piazza
Edgardo Alfonzo
Jay Payton
Robin Ventura
46 Mike Piazza 2.00 5.00
Robin Ventura
John Olerud
Roger Cedeno
Edgardo Alfonzo
Timo Perez
47 Roger Clemens 5.00 12.00
Don Mattingly
Wade Boggs
Jason Giambi
Jorge Posada
Hideki Matsui
48 Wade Boggs 1.50 4.00
Tommy John
Phil Niekro
Robin Ventura
Paul O'Neill
Kenny Lofton
49 Joe Morgan 1.25 3.00
Kenny Lofton
Kevin Millwood
Marlon Byrd
Matt Kata
Eric Valent
50 Bill Madlock 1.25 3.00
Kenny Lofton
Craig Wilson
Freddy Sanchez
Jason Bay
Jose Castillo
51 Tony Gwynn 2.50 6.00
Rickey Henderson
Joe Carter
Brian Lawrence
Robert Fick
Dennis Tankersley
52 Willie Mays 4.00 10.00
Willie McCovey
Joe Morgan
Matt Williams
J.T. Snow
Deivi Cruz
53 Stan Musial 4.00 10.00
Albert Pujols
Lou Brock
Enos Slaughter
Red Schoendienst
Will Clark
54 Bob Gibson 4.00 10.00
Albert Pujols
Jim Edmonds
J.D. Drew
Matt Morris
So Taguchi
55 Wade Boggs 1.50 4.00
Delmon Young
Rocco Baldelli
Joe Kennedy
Toby Hall
Pete LaForest
56 Alfonso Soriano 1.50 4.00
Mark Teixeira
Hank Blalock
Richard Hidalgo
Kevin Mench
Frankie Francisco
57 Nolan Ryan 4.00 10.00
Rafael Palmeiro
Ivan Rodriguez
Andres Galarraga
Doug Davis
Ricardo Rodriguez
58 Carlos Delgado 1.25 3.00
David Wells
Shawn Green
Roy Halladay
Josh Phelps
Orlando Hudson
59 Carlos Delgado 1.25 3.00
Joe Carter
Jeff Kent
John Olerud
Jose Cruz Jr.
Orlando Hudson
60 Shawn Green 1.25 3.00
Shannon Stewart
Joe Carter
Carlos Delgado
Orlando Hudson
Raul Mondesi

2005 Absolute Memorabilia Team Six Swatch Single

OVERALL AU-GU ODDS ONE PER PACK
PRINT RUNS B/WN 14-150 COPIES PER
NO PRICING ON QTY OF 14
1 Willie Mays Pants 50.00 100.00
Willie McCovey Jsy
Juan Marichal Jsy
Gaylord Perry Jsy
Orlando Cepeda Pants
Will Clark Jsy/50
2 Roger Clemens Jsy 15.00 40.00
Jeff Bagwell Jsy
Lance Berkman Jsy
Craig Biggio Jsy
Andy Pettitte Jsy
Roy Oswalt Jsy/50
3 Tom Seaver Jsy 20.00 50.00
Johnny Bench Jsy
Joe Morgan Bat
Dave Concepcion Jsy
George Foster Jsy
Tony Perez Fld Glv/15
4 Marty Marion Jsy 50.00 100.00
Stan Musial Pants
Bob Gibson Jsy
Lou Brock Jsy
Frankie Frisch Jkt
Red Schoendienst Jsy/15
5 Don Mattingly Jsy 30.00 60.00
Catfish Hunter Jsy
Dave Righetti Jsy
Tommy John Jsy
Phil Niekro Jsy
Reggie Jackson Jsy/50
6 Ernie Banks Jsy 15.00 40.00
Greg Maddux Jsy
Sammy Sosa Jsy
Fergie Jenkins Pants
Nomar Garciaparra Bat
Kerry Wood Jsy/50
7 Curt Schilling Jsy 8.00 20.00
Luis Gonzalez Jsy
Steve Finley Jsy
Junior Spivey Jsy
Brandon Webb Pants
Lyle Overbay Jsy/50
8 Duke Snider Pants 12.50 30.00
Rickey Henderson Jsy
Mike Piazza Jsy
Pedro Martinez Jsy
Don Sutton Jsy
Hideo Nomo Jsy/50
9 Vladimir Guerrero Jsy 12.50 30.00
Tim Salmon Jsy
Casey Kotchman Jsy
Francisco Rodriguez Jsy
Ramon Ortiz Jsy
Chone Figgins Jsy/50
10 Roger Clemens Jsy 20.00 50.00
Curt Schilling Jsy
Carl Yastrzemski Pants
Bobby Doerr Pants
Nomar Garciaparra Bat
Wade Boggs Jsy/50
12 Bo Jackson Jsy 12.50 30.00
Frank Thomas Jsy
Carlton Fisk Jkt
Sammy Sosa Jsy
Hoyt Wilhelm Jsy
Harold Baines Jsy/50
13 Mike Schmidt Jsy 15.00 40.00
Dale Murphy Jsy
Jim Thome Jsy
Curt Schilling Jsy
Bobby Abreu Jsy
Steve Carlton Jsy/50
14 Nolan Ryan Jsy 20.00 50.00
Gary Carter Pants
Duke Snider Pants
Mike Piazza Jsy
Rickey Henderson Jsy
Roberto Alomar Jsy/50
15 Dale Murphy Jsy 12.50 30.00
Deion Sanders Jsy
Gary Sheffield Jsy
J.D. Drew Bat
Chipper Jones Jsy
David Justice Jsy/50
16 Rickey Henderson Bat 10.00 25.00
Jim Edmonds Bat
Troy Glaus Jsy
Casey Kotchman Bat
Francisco Rodriguez Jsy
Darin Erstad Bat/150
17 Curt Schilling Jsy 8.00 20.00
Matt Williams Bat
Reggie Sanders Jsy
Byung-Hyun Kim Jsy
Travis Lee Jsy
Tony Womack Jsy/150
18 John Smoltz Jsy 15.00 40.00
Tom Glavine Jsy
Greg Maddux Jsy
Wes Helms Jsy
Kenny Lofton Bat
Andruw Jones Bat/150
19 Chipper Jones Bat 10.00 25.00
Dale Murphy Bat
Andruw Jones Bat
Wes Helms Jsy
Rafael Furcal Bat
Andres Galarraga Bat/150
20 Brooks Robinson Bat 8.00 20.00
Luis Matos Jsy
Rodrigo Lopez Jsy
Geronimo Gil Bat
Josh Towers Pants
Erik Bedard Bat/150
21 Roger Clemens Jsy 15.00 40.00
Wade Boggs Bat
Carlton Fisk Bat
Rickey Henderson Bat
Nomar Garciaparra Bat
Bobby Doerr Pants/150
22 David Ortiz Jsy 15.00 40.00
Roger Clemens Jsy
Nomar Garciaparra Bat
Wade Boggs Bat
Rickey Henderson Bat
Jason Varitek Bat/150
23 Andre Dawson Bat 8.00 20.00
Aramis Ramirez Jsy
Derrek Lee Jsy
Kenny Lofton Bat
Moises Alou Bat
Hee Seop Choi Jsy/150
24 Sammy Sosa Bat 10.00 25.00
Nomar Garciaparra Bat
Derrek Lee Bat
Hee Seop Choi Jsy
Kenny Lofton Bat
Matt Lawton Bat/150
25 Carlton Fisk Bat 10.00 25.00
Frank Thomas Bat
Magglio Ordonez Bat
Carl Everett Bat
Esteban Loaiza Bat
Robin Ventura Bat/150
26 Bo Jackson Jsy 10.00 25.00
Magglio Ordonez Bat
Roberto Alomar Jsy
Robin Ventura Bat
Kenny Lofton Bat
Joe Borchard Bat/150
27 Adam Dunn Bat 6.00 15.00
Eric Davis Bat
Joe Morgan Bat
Paul O'Neill Bat
Wily Mo Pena Bat
Juan Encarnacion Bat/150
28 Tony Perez Fld Glv 6.00 15.00
Dave Concepcion Jsy
George Foster Bat
Dmitri Young Jsy
Adam Dunn Bat
Eric Davis Bat/150
29 Bert Blyleven Jsy
Early Wynn Jsy
Hal Newhouser Jsy
C.C. Sabathia Jsy
Joe Carter Bat
Russell Branyan Jsy/14
30 Jim Thome Bat 8.00 20.00
Victor Martinez Jsy
Sean Casey Jsy
Russell Branyan Jsy
Josh Bard Jsy
Kenny Lofton Bat/150
31 Larry Walker Jsy 6.00 15.00
Clint Barmes Bat
Garrett Atkins Jsy
Juan Pierre Bat
Mike Hampton Jsy
Juan Uribe Jsy/150
32 Larry Walker Jsy 6.00 15.00
Jeff Baker Bat
Juan Pierre Bat
Garrett Atkins Jsy
Juan Uribe Jsy
Jason Jennings Bat/150
33 Kirk Gibson Bat 6.00 15.00
Magglio Ordonez Bat
Brandon Inge Jsy
Bobby Higginson Bat
Craig Monroe Bat
Mike Maroth Jsy/150
34 Dontrelle Willis Bat 6.00 15.00
Ryan Dempster Jsy
Juan Pierre Bat
Mike Lowell Bat
Cliff Floyd Bat
Charles Johnson Jsy/150
35 Jeff Bagwell Pants 8.00 20.00
Carlos Beltran Jsy
Lance Berkman Bat
Richard Hidalgo Bat
Jose Cruz Jsy
Jason Lane Bat/150
36 Jeff Bagwell Pants 8.00 20.00
Lance Berkman Bat
Joe Morgan Bat
Craig Biggio Bat
Jason Lane Bat
Jose Cruz Jsy/150
37 Roy Oswalt Bat 8.00 20.00
Morgan Ensberg Fld Glv
Lance Berkman Bat
Jeff Bagwell Pants
Jason Lane Bat
Craig Biggio Bat/150
38 Frank White Bat 6.00 15.00
Willie Wilson Bat
Mike Sweeney Bat
Angel Berroa Bat
John Buck Bat
Runelvys Hernandez Jsy/150
39 Hideo Nomo Pants 10.00 25.00
Kazuhisa Ishii Jsy
Chan Ho Park Jsy
Rickey Henderson Bat
Shawn Green Bat
Al Oliver Bat/75
40 Steve Garvey Bat 10.00 25.00
Darryl Strawberry Bat
Rickey Henderson Jsy
Kazuhisa Ishii Jsy
Paul Lo Duca Chest Prot
Kevin Brown Jsy/150
41 Johan Santana Jsy 8.00 20.00
Joe Mays Jsy
Justin Morneau Bat
Torii Hunter Bat
Shannon Stewart Bat
Michael Cuddyer Bat/150
42 Kirby Puckett Bat 10.00 25.00
David Ortiz Jsy
Harmon Killebrew Jsy
Doug Mientkiewicz Bat
Torii Hunter Bat
Matt Lawton Bat/150
43 Kirby Puckett Bat 10.00 25.00
Shannon Stewart Bat
David Ortiz Jsy
Doug Mientkiewicz Bat
Torii Hunter Bat
Michael Cuddyer Bat/150
44 Tony Perez Jsy 6.00 15.00
Javier Vazquez Jsy
Rondell White Jsy
Cliff Floyd Bat
Jose Vidro Bat
Zach Day Pants/150
45 Willie Mays Jsy 20.00 50.00
Roger Cedeno Bat
Mike Piazza Pants
Edgardo Alfonzo Bat
Jay Payton Jsy
Robin Ventura Bat/150
46 Mike Piazza Pants 10.00 25.00
Robin Ventura Bat
John Olerud Bat
Roger Cedeno Bat
Edgardo Alfonzo Bat
Timo Perez Bat/150
47 Roger Clemens Jsy 20.00 50.00
Don Mattingly Bat
Wade Boggs Bat
Jason Giambi Jsy
Jorge Posada Jsy
Hideki Matsui Bat/150
48 Wade Boggs Bat 8.00 20.00
Tommy John Pants
Phil Niekro Bat
Robin Ventura Bat
Paul O'Neill Bat
Kenny Lofton Bat/150
49 Joe Morgan Bat 6.00 15.00
Kenny Lofton Bat
Kevin Millwood Jsy
Marlon Byrd Bat
Matt Kata Bat
Eric Valent Shoe/150
50 Bill Madlock Bat 6.00 15.00
Kenny Lofton Bat
Craig Wilson Bat
Freddy Sanchez Bat
Jason Bay Bat
Jose Castillo Bat/150
51 Tony Gwynn Pants 10.00 25.00
Rickey Henderson Pants
Joe Carter Bat
Brian Lawrence Bat
Robert Fick Bat
Dennis Tankersley Bat/150
52 Willie Mays Bat 20.00 50.00
Willie McCovey Jsy
Joe Morgan Bat
Matt Williams Bat
J.T. Snow Jsy
Deivi Cruz Bat/150
54 Bob Gibson Jsy 15.00 40.00
Albert Pujols Bat
Jim Edmonds Bat
J.D. Drew Bat
Matt Morris Jsy
So Taguchi Bat/150
56 Alfonso Soriano Bat 8.00 20.00
Mark Teixeira Bat
Hank Blalock Bat
Richard Hidalgo Bat
Kevin Mench Jsy
Frankie Francisco Jsy/150
57 Nolan Ryan Jsy 15.00 40.00

Rafael Palmeiro Pants
Ivan Rodriguez Jsy
Andres Galarraga Bat
Doug Davis Jsy
Ricardo Rodriguez Bat/100
58 Carlos Delgado Jsy 6.00 15.00
David Wells Jsy
Shawn Green Bat
Roy Halladay Jsy
Josh Phelps Bat
Orlando Hudson Bat/150
59 Carlos Delgado Bat 6.00 15.00
Joe Carter Bat
Jeff Kent Jsy
John Olerud Bat
Jose Cruz Jr. Bat
Orlando Hudson Bat/150

2005 Absolute Memorabilia Team Six Swatch Single Spectrum

*SPEC p/r 75-100: .4X TO 1X SNG p/r 75-150
*SPEC p/r 50: .5X TO 1.2X SNG p/r 75-150
*SPEC p/r 25: .6X TO 1.5X SNG p/r 75-150
*SPEC p/r 25: .5X TO 1.2X SNG p/r 50
PRINT RUNS B/WN 1-100 COPIES PER
NO PRICING ON QTY OF 10 OR LESS
PRIME BLACK PRINT RUN 5 #'d SETS
NO PRIME BLK PRICING DUE TO SC ARCITY
OVERALL AU-GU ODDS ONE PER PACK

2005 Absolute Memorabilia Tools of the Trade Red

STATED PRINT RUN 250 SERIAL #'d SETS
*BLACK: .6X TO 1.5X BASIC
BLACK PRINT RUN 100 SERIAL #'d SETS
*BLUE: .5X TO 1.2X BASIC
BLUE PRINT RUN 150 SERIAL #'d SETS
REV.SPEC.BLACK PRINT RUN 5 #'d SETS
NO REV.SPEC.BLACK PRICING AVAILABLE
REV.SPEC.BLUE PRINT RUN 10 #'d SETS
NO REV.SPEC.BLUE PRICING AVAILABLE
*REV.SPEC.RED: 1X TO 2.5X BASIC
REV.SPEC.RED PRINT RUN 50 #'d SETS
RANDOM INSERTS IN PACKS
1 Ozzie Smith 2.50 6.00
2 Carlos Beltran Astros .75 2.00
3 Dale Murphy 1.00 2.50
4 Paul Molitor .75 2.00
5 George Brett 3.00 8.00
6 Stan Musial 2.50 6.00
7 Ivan Rodriguez M's 1.00 2.50
8 Carl Yastrzemski 2.50 6.00
9 Reggie Jackson A's 1.00 2.50
10 Hideo Nomo 1.25 3.00
11 Gary Sheffield .75 2.00
12 Roberto Alomar 1.00 2.50
13 Pedro Martinez 1.00 2.50
14 Ernie Banks 1.50 4.00
15 Tim Hudson .75 2.00
16 Dwight Gooden .75 2.00
17 Lance Berkman .75 2.00
18 Darryl Strawberry Mets .75 2.00
19 Larry Walker 1.00 2.50
20 Lou Brock 1.00 2.50
21 Roger Clemens 2.00 5.00
22 Paul Lo Duca .75 2.00
23 Don Mattingly 3.00 8.00
24 Willie Mays 3.00 8.00
25 Rafael Palmeiro 1.00 2.50
26 Roy Oswalt .75 2.00
27 Vladimir Guerrero 1.25 3.00
28 Austin Kearns .75 2.00
29 Rod Carew 1.00 2.50
30 Nolan Ryan Angels 4.00 10.00
31 Richie Sexson .75 2.00
32 Steve Carlton .75 2.00
33 Eddie Murray 1.50 4.00
34 Nolan Ryan Rgr 4.00 10.00
35 Mike Mussina O's 1.00 2.50
36 Sean Casey .75 2.00
37 Juan Gonzalez Rgr .75 2.00
38 Curt Schilling Sox 1.00 2.50
39 Darryl Strawberry Yanks .75 2.00
40 Alfonso Soriano .75 2.00
41 Tom Seaver 1.00 2.50
42 Mike Schmidt 3.00 8.00
43 Todd Helton 1.00 2.50
44 Reggie Jackson Yanks 1.00 2.50
45 Shawn Green .75 2.00
46 Mike Mussina Yanks 1.00 2.50
47 Tom Glavine 1.00 2.50
48 Torii Hunter .75 2.00
49 Kerry Wood .75 2.00
50 Carlos Delgado .75 2.00
51 Randy Johnson Astros 1.25 3.00
52 David Ortiz 1.25 3.00
53 Troy Glaus .75 2.00
54 Rickey Henderson Mets 1.00 2.50
55 Craig Biggio 1.00 2.50
56 Brad Penny .75 2.00
57 Gary Carter Mets 1.00 2.50
58 Andy Pettitte 1.00 2.50
59 Mark Prior 1.00 2.50
60 Kirby Puckett 1.50 4.00
61 Willie McCovey 1.00 2.50
62 Andre Dawson Expos .75 2.00
63 Greg Maddux 2.00 5.00
64 Adrian Beltre .75 2.00
65 Andruw Jones 1.00 2.50
66 Juan Gonzalez Indians .75 2.00
67 Frank Thomas 1.25 3.00
68 Victor Martinez .75 2.00
69 Randy Johnson D'backs 1.25 3.00
70 Andre Dawson Cubs .75 2.00
71 Adam Dunn .75 2.00
72 Carlton Fisk 1.00 2.50
73 Cal Ripken 5.00 12.00
74 Kenny Lofton .75 2.00
75 Barry Zito .75 2.00
76 Sammy Sosa 1.25 3.00
77 Deion Sanders 1.00 2.50
78 Tony Gwynn 2.00 5.00
79 Mike Piazza 1.25 3.00
80 Jeff Bagwell 1.00 2.50
81 Manny Ramirez 1.00 2.50
82 Carlos Beltran Royals .75 2.00
83 Mark Grace .75 2.00
84 Robin Yount 1.50 4.00
85 Albert Pujols 2.50 6.00
86 Dontrelle Willis .75 2.00
87 Jim Thome 1.00 2.50
88 Magglio Ordonez .75 2.00
89 Miguel Tejada .75 2.00
90 Mark Teixeira 1.00 2.50
91 Gary Carter Expos .75 2.00
92 Ivan Rodriguez Rgr 1.00 2.50
93 Jason Giambi .75 2.00
94 Rickey Henderson A's 1.00 2.50
95 Curt Schilling D'backs .75 2.00
96 Bobby Doerr .75 2.00
97 Chipper Jones 1.25 3.00
98 Eric Chavez .75 2.00
99 Johnny Bench 1.50 4.00
100 Harmon Killebrew 1.50 4.00
101 Andre Dawson .75 2.00
102 Babe Ruth 4.00 10.00
103 Bernie Williams 1.00 2.50
104 Billy Wagner .75 2.00
105 Billy Williams .75 2.00
106 Bo Jackson 1.50 4.00
107 Bob Gibson 1.00 2.50
108 Brad Penny .75 2.00
109 Burleigh Grimes 1.00 2.50
110 Cal Ripken 5.00 12.00
111 Casey Fossum .75 2.00
112 Curt Schilling .75 2.00
113 Dale Murphy 1.00 2.50
114 Darryl Strawberry .75 2.00
115 Dave Concepcion .75 2.00
116 Dave Winfield .75 2.00
117 David Cone .75 2.00
118 Fergie Jenkins .75 2.00
119 Gary Carter .75 2.00
120 Gary Sheffield .75 2.00
121 Gaylord Perry .75 2.00
122 Hank Aaron 3.00 8.00
123 Harmon Killebrew 1.50 4.00
124 Harold Baines .75 2.00
125 Hideki Matsui 2.00 5.00
126 Hideo Nomo 1.25 3.00
127 Hoyt Wilhelm .75 2.00
128 Jason Giambi Yanks .75 2.00
129 Jason Giambi A's .75 2.00
130 Jeff Bagwell 1.00 2.50
131 Jim Palmer .75 2.00
132 Jim Thorpe 2.50 6.00
133 Joe Mays .75 2.00
134 John Buck .75 2.00
135 John Kruk 1.00 2.50
136 Jorge Posada 1.00 2.50
137 Josh Beckett .75 2.00
138 Josh Phelps .75 2.00
139 Juan Pierre .75 2.00
140 Kazuhisa Ishii .75 2.00
141 Kenny Lofton .75 2.00
142 Kevin Brown .75 2.00
143 Kevin Millwood Braves .75 2.00
144 Kevin Millwood Phils .75 2.00
145 Lance Berkman .75 2.00
146 Lenny Dykstra .75 2.00
147 Lou Boudreau .75 2.00
148 Magglio Ordonez .75 2.00
149 Marcus Giles .75 2.00
150 Mark Grace .75 2.00
151 Mark Prior 1.00 2.50
152 Marlon Byrd .75 2.00
153 Miguel Tejada .75 2.00
154 Mike Lowell .75 2.00
155 Mike Piazza 1.25 3.00
156 Mike Sweeney .75 2.00
157 Morgan Ensberg .75 2.00
158 Nolan Ryan 4.00 10.00
159 Orel Hershiser .75 2.00
160 Ozzie Smith 2.50 6.00
161 Pedro Martinez 1.00 2.50
162 Phil Rizzuto 1.00 2.50
163 Rafael Furcal .75 2.00
164 Rafael Palmeiro 1.00 2.50
165 Randy Johnson D'backs 1.25 3.00
166 Randy Johnson Astros 1.25 3.00
167 Richie Sexson .75 2.00
168 Rickey Henderson Mets 1.50 4.00
169 Rickey Henderson A's 1.50 4.00
170 Rickey Henderson M's 1.50 4.00
171 Roberto Alomar 1.00 2.50
172 Roberto Clemente 4.00 10.00
173 Robin Yount 1.50 4.00
174 Rod Carew 1.00 2.50
175 Roger Clemens 2.00 5.00
176 Roger Maris A's 1.50 4.00
177 Roger Maris Yanks 1.50 4.00
178 Ron Cey .75 2.00
179 Ryan Klesko .75 2.00
180 Ryne Sandberg 3.00 8.00
181 Sammy Sosa 1.25 3.00
182 Shawn Green .75 2.00
183 Stan Musial 2.50 6.00
184 Steve Carlton .75 2.00
185 Ted Williams 3.00 8.00
186 Ted Williams 3.00 8.00
187 Tim Hudson .75 2.00
188 Todd Helton 1.00 2.50
189 Tom Glavine 1.00 2.50
190 Tom Seaver 1.00 2.50
191 Tommy John .75 2.00
192 Tony Gwynn 2.00 5.00
193 Vladimir Guerrero 1.25 3.00
194 Wade Boggs Sox 1.00 2.50
195 Wade Boggs Rays 1.00 2.50
196 Warren Spahn 1.00 2.50
197 Willie Mays 3.00 8.00
198 Willie McCovey 1.00 2.50
199 Willie Stargell 1.00 2.50
200 Yogi Berra 1.50 4.00

2005 Absolute Memorabilia Tools of the Trade Bat

OVERALL AU-GU ODDS ONE PER PACK
PRINT RUNS B/WN 1-250 COPIES PER
NO PRICING ON QTY OF 1
102 Babe Ruth/250 90.00 150.00
122 Hank Aaron/250 10.00 25.00
172 Roberto Clemente/250 15.00 40.00
176 Roger Maris A's/100 12.50 30.00
177 Roger Maris Yanks/61 15.00 40.00
185 Ted Williams/250 20.00 50.00
197 Willie Mays/50 15.00 40.00

2005 Absolute Memorabilia Tools of the Trade Bat Reverse

*REV p/r 100-150: .4X TO 1X BAT p/r 100-250
*REV p/r 50: .4X TO 1X BAT p/r 50-61
*REV p/r 24-35: .6X TO 1.5X BAT p/r 100-250
*REV p/r 24-35: .5X TO 1.2X BAT p/r 50-61
OVERALL AU-GU ODDS ONE PER BOX
PRINT RUNS B/WN 1-150 COPIES PER
NO PRICING ON QTY OF 1
102 Babe Ruth/150 90.00 150.00

2005 Absolute Memorabilia Tools of the Trade Bat Red

*RED p/r 50: .5X TO 1.2X BAT p/r 100-250
*RED p/r 21-25: .6X TO 1.5X BAT p/r 100-250
PRINT RUNS B/WN 1-50 COPIES PER
NO PRICING ON QTY OF 10 OR LESS
BLACK PRINT RUN 1 SERIAL #'d SET
NO BLACK PRICING DUE TO SCARCITY
OVERALL AU-GU ODDS ONE PER PACK
102 Babe Ruth/25 100.00 175.00

2005 Absolute Memorabilia Tools of the Trade Button Red

PRINT RUNS B/WN 1-21 COPIES PER
BLACK PRINT RUN 1 SERIAL #'d SET
OVERALL AU-GU ODDS ONE PER PACK
NO PRICING DUE TO SCARCITY
101 Andre Dawson/7
102 Babe Ruth/5
104 Billy Wagner/3
106 Bo Jackson/7
107 Bob Gibson/3
108 Brad Penny/3
110 Cal Ripken/1
111 Casey Fossum/7
112 Curt Schilling/3
113 Dale Murphy/15
114 Darryl Strawberry/12
116 Dave Winfield/5
119 Gary Carter/2
122 Hank Aaron/8
123 Harmon Killebrew/8
124 Harold Baines/7
125 Hideki Matsui/3
127 Hoyt Wilhelm/3
128 Jason Giambi Yanks/12
131 Jim Palmer/2
132 Jim Thorpe/3
135 John Kruk/2
138 Josh Phelps/7
144 Kevin Millwood Phils/7
146 Lenny Dykstra/3
154 Mike Lowell/10
158 Nolan Ryan/4
159 Orel Hershiser/5
161 Pedro Martinez/5
162 Phil Rizzuto/5
163 Rafael Furcal/3
165 Randy Johnson D'backs/10
168 Rickey Henderson Mets/2
169 Rickey Henderson A's/6
170 Rickey Henderson M's/11
171 Roberto Alomar/3
173 Robin Yount/3
174 Rod Carew/7
175 Roger Clemens/10
176 Roger Maris A's/3
177 Roger Maris Yanks/3
178 Ron Cey/3
179 Ryan Klesko/3
181 Sammy Sosa/21
183 Stan Musial/3
184 Steve Carlton/4
185 Ted Williams/4
189 Tom Glavine/11
192 Tony Gwynn/4
194 Wade Boggs Sox/3
195 Wade Boggs Rays/3
196 Warren Spahn/1
197 Willie Mays/5
198 Willie McCovey/8
199 Willie Stargell/4

2005 Absolute Memorabilia Tools of the Trade Jersey

OVERALL AU-GU ODDS ONE PER PACK
PRINT RUNS B/WN 1-250 COPIES PER
NO PRICING ON QTY OF 14 OR LESS
102 Babe Ruth/100 175.00 300.00
122 Hank Aaron/250 10.00 25.00
132 Jim Thorpe/250 50.00 100.00
177 R.Maris Yanks Pants/100 15.00 40.00
186 Ted Williams/75 30.00 60.00
197 Willie Mays/24 15.00 40.00

2005 Absolute Memorabilia Tools of the Trade Jersey Reverse

*REV p/r 150: .4X TO 1X JSY p/r 75-250
*REV p/r 41-50: .5X TO 1.2X JSY p/r 75-250
OVERALL AU-GU ODDS ONE PER PACK
PRINT RUNS B/WN 1-150 COPIES PER
NO PRICING ON QTY OF 10 OR LESS
102 Babe Ruth/50 175.00 300.00
132 Jim Thorpe/150 50.00 100.00
199 Willie Stargell/25 5.00 12.00

2005 Absolute Memorabilia Tools of the Trade Jersey Red

*RED p/r 25: .6X TO 1.5X JSY p/r 75-250
PRINT RUNS B/WN 1-25 COPIES PER
NO PRICING ON QTY OF 10 OR LESS
BLACK PRINT RUN 1 SERIAL #'d SET
NO BLACK PRICING DUE TO SCARCITY
OVERALL AU-GU ODDS ONE PER PACK
102 Babe Ruth/25 250.00 400.00
132 Jim Thorpe/25 75.00 150.00

2005 Absolute Memorabilia Tools of the Trade Laundry Tag Prime Red

OVERALL AU-GU ODDS ONE PER PACK
STATED PRINT RUN 1 SERIAL #'d SET
NO PRICING DUE TO SCARCITY

2005 Absolute Memorabilia Tools of the Trade MLB Logo Red

PRINT RUNS B/WN 1-5 COPIES PER
BLACK PRINT RUN 1 SERIAL #'d SET
OVERALL AU-GU ODDS ONE PER PACK
NO PRICING DUE TO SCARCITY
111 Casey Fossum/1
112 Curt Schilling/5
124 Harold Baines/1
128 Jason Giambi Yanks/1
133 Joe Mays/1
136 Jorge Posada/2
140 Kazuhisa Ishii/3
145 Lance Berkman/1
151 Mark Prior/1
155 Mike Piazza/1
167 Richie Sexson/3
168 R.Henderson Mets Jkt/1
170 R.Henderson M's/3
171 Roberto Alomar/1
179 Ryan Klesko/1
181 Sammy Sosa/5
182 Shawn Green/3
187 Tim Hudson/4
188 Todd Helton/2
189 Tom Glavine/3
193 Vladimir Guerrero/3

2005 Absolute Memorabilia Tools of the Trade Swatch Single Jumbo

*SNG p/r 75-250: .6X TO 1.5X DBL p/r 70-200
*SNG p/r 75-250: .5X TO 1.2X DBL p/r 50-60
*SNG p/r 75-250: .4X TO 1X DBL p/r 20-29
*SNG p/r 45-62: .75X TO 2X DBL p/r 70-200
*SNG p/r 45-62: .6X TO 1.5X DBL p/r 50-60
*SNG p/r 45-62: .5X TO 1.2X DBL p/r 20-29
*SNG p/r 25: 1X TO 2.5X DBL p/r 70-200
*SNG p/r 25: .75X TO 2X DBL p/r 50-60
*SNG p/r 25: .6X TO 1.5X DBL p/r 20-29
OVERALL AU-GU ODDS ONE PER PACK
PRINT RUNS B/WN 1-250 COPIES PER
NO PRICING ON QTY OF 10 OR LESS
37 J.Gonzalez Rgr Jsy/25 6.00 15.00
70 A.Dawson Cubs Jsy/250 6.00 15.00
98 Eric Chavez Jsy/100 4.00 10.00
102 Babe Ruth Jsy/95 1500.00 2500.00
104 Billy Wagner Jsy/250 4.00 10.00
105 Billy Williams Jsy/85 5.00 12.00
106 Bo Jackson Jsy/250 8.00 20.00
107 Bob Gibson Jsy/50 10.00 25.00
109 B.Grimes Pants/83 75.00 150.00
111 Casey Fossum Jsy/250 3.00 8.00
114 D.Strawberry Jsy/100 5.00 12.00
118 Fergie Jenkins Jsy/95 5.00 12.00
127 Hoyt Wilhelm Jsy/225 8.00 20.00
132 Jim Thorpe Jsy/200 200.00 300.00
136 Jorge Posada Jsy/250 6.00 15.00
138 Josh Phelps Jsy/200 3.00 8.00
139 Juan Pierre Jsy/250 4.00 10.00
142 Kevin Brown Jsy/250 4.00 10.00
143 K.Millwood Braves Jsy/250 4.00 10.00
144 K.Millwood Phils Jsy/250 4.00 10.00
146 Lenny Dykstra Jsy/100 5.00 12.00
147 Lou Boudreau Jsy/75 15.00 40.00
152 Marlon Byrd Jsy/250 5.00 12.00
154 Mike Lowell Jsy/200 4.00 10.00
159 Orel Hershiser Jsy/250 5.00 12.00
161 Pedro Martinez Jsy/175 5.00 12.00
162 Phil Rizzuto Jsy/100 15.00 40.00
176 R.Maris A's Jsy/199 40.00 80.00
177 R.Maris Yanks Jsy/250 40.00 80.00
178 Ron Cey Jsy/250 5.00 12.00
179 Ryan Klesko Jsy/250 4.00 10.00
185 Ted Williams Jsy/50 90.00 150.00
186 Ted Williams Jkt/100 60.00 120.00
198 W.McCovey Pants/100 8.00 20.00

2005 Absolute Memorabilia Tools of the Trade Swatch Single Jumbo Reverse

*REV p/r 75-150: .6X TO 1.5X DBL p/r 70-200
*REV p/r 75-150: .5X TO 1.2X DBL p/r 50-60
*REV p/r 75-150: .4X TO 1X DBL p/r 20-29
*REV p/r 44-59: .75X TO 2X DBL p/r 70-200
*REV p/r 20-25: 1X TO 2.5X DBL p/r 70-200
*REV p/r 20-25: .75X TO 2X DBL p/r 50-60
*REV p/r 20-25: .6X TO 1.5X DBL p/r 20-29
*REV p/r 15-17: 1.25X TO 3X DBL p/r 70-200
OVERALL AU-GU ODDS ONE PER PACK
PRINT RUNS B/WN 1-50 COPIES PER
NO PRICING ON QTY OF 10 OR LESS
70 A.Dawson Cubs Jsy/25 8.00 20.00
98 Eric Chavez Jsy/50 5.00 12.00
102 Babe Ruth Jsy/24 1200.00 2000.00
104 Billy Wagner Jsy/100 4.00 10.00
105 Billy Williams Jsy/25 8.00 20.00
106 Bo Jackson Jsy/150 8.00 20.00
107 Bob Gibson Jsy/25 12.50 30.00
109 B.Grimes Pants/23 100.00 175.00
111 Casey Fossum Jsy/150 3.00 8.00
114 Darryl Strawberry Jsy/25 8.00 20.00
118 Fergie Jenkins Jsy/25 8.00 20.00
127 Hoyt Wilhelm Jsy/50 10.00 25.00
132 Jim Thorpe Jsy/50 250.00 350.00
135 John Kruk Jsy/20 8.00 20.00
136 Jorge Posada Jsy/150 6.00 15.00
138 Josh Phelps Jsy/50 4.00 10.00
139 Juan Pierre Jsy/150 4.00 10.00
142 Kevin Brown Jsy/150 4.00 10.00
143 K.Millwood Braves Jsy/100 4.00 10.00
144 K.Millwood Phils Jsy/150 4.00 10.00
146 Lenny Dykstra Jsy/50 6.00 15.00
147 Lou Boudreau Jsy/25 20.00 50.00
154 Mike Lowell Jsy/100 4.00 10.00
159 Orel Hershiser Jsy/25 8.00 20.00
161 Pedro Martinez Jsy/100 5.00 12.00
176 R.Maris A's Jsy/50 50.00 100.00
177 R.Maris Yanks Jsy/59 50.00 100.00
179 Ryan Klesko Jsy/100 4.00 10.00
186 Ted Williams Jkt/25 100.00 175.00
198 W.McCovey Pants/44 10.00 25.00
200 Yogi Berra Pants/100 20.00 50.00

2005 Absolute Memorabilia Tools of the Trade Swatch Single Jumbo Prime Black

*BLACK p/r 25: .6X TO 1.5X RED p/r 75
*BLACK p/r 25: .5X TO 1.2X RED p/r 40-50
OVERALL AU-GU ODDS ONE PER PACK
PRINT RUNS B/WN 1-25 COPIES PER
NO PRICING ON QTY OF 10 OR LESS

2005 Absolute Memorabilia Tools of the Trade Swatch Single Jumbo Prime Red

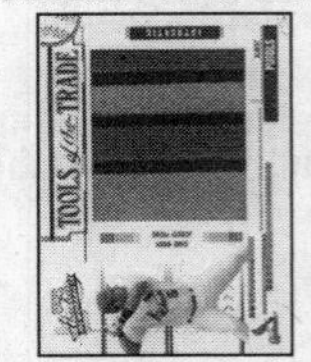

OVERALL AU-GU ODDS ONE PER PACK
PRINT RUNS B/WN 1-50 COPIES PER
NO PRICING ON QTY OF 10 OR LESS
*LISTED PRICES ARE FOR 3-COLOR PATCH
*ADD 20% FOR 4-COLOR+ PATCH
*REDUCE 20% FOR 2-COLOR PATCH
NO PRICING AVAIL.FOR LOGO PATCHES
LOGO PATCHES COMMAND BIG PREMIUMS
7 I.Rodriguez M's Jsy/25 40.00 80.00
10 Hideo Nomo Jsy/25 75.00 150.00
12 Roberto Alomar Jsy/25 40.00 80.00
15 Tim Hudson Jsy/50 20.00 50.00
17 Lance Berkman Jsy/25 20.00 50.00
19 Larry Walker Jsy/50 20.00 50.00
22 Paul Lo Duca Jsy/50 15.00 40.00
25 Rafael Palmeiro Jsy/25 40.00 80.00
27 Vladimir Guerrero Jsy/25 60.00 120.00
31 Richie Sexson Jsy/50 15.00 40.00
36 Sean Casey Jsy/50 15.00 40.00
43 Todd Helton Jsy/15 40.00 80.00
45 Shawn Green Jsy/50 15.00 40.00
47 Tom Glavine Jsy/50 40.00 80.00
50 Carlos Delgado Jsy/25 20.00 50.00
53 Troy Glaus Jsy/50 15.00 40.00
59 Mark Prior Jsy/25 40.00 80.00
63 Greg Maddux Jsy/25 125.00 200.00
64 Adrian Beltre Jsy/50 15.00 40.00
65 Andruw Jones Jsy/50 40.00 80.00
67 Frank Thomas Jsy/50 75.00 150.00
68 Victor Martinez Jsy/15 20.00 50.00
71 Adam Dunn Jsy/25 20.00 50.00
73 Cal Ripken Jsy/25 150.00 250.00
76 Sammy Sosa Jsy/50 50.00 100.00
78 Tony Gwynn Jsy/50 60.00 120.00
79 Mike Piazza Jsy/50 75.00 150.00
80 Jeff Bagwell Jsy/25 50.00 100.00
82 Carlos Beltran Royals Jsy/50 15.00 40.00
85 Albert Pujols Jsy/25 175.00 300.00
88 M.Ordonez Jsy/50 15.00 40.00
89 Miguel Tejada Jsy/50 20.00 50.00
90 Mark Teixeira Jsy/25 40.00 80.00
92 I.Rodriguez Rgr Jsy/25 40.00 80.00
98 Eric Chavez Jsy/15 20.00 50.00
112 Curt Schilling Jsy/35 40.00 80.00
115 D.Concepcion Jsy/50 40.00 80.00
117 David Cone Jsy/35 20.00 50.00
128 J.Giambi Yanks Jsy/15 40.00 80.00
138 Josh Phelps Jsy/45 10.00 25.00
142 Kevin Brown Jsy/30 20.00 50.00
143 K.Millwood Braves Jsy/40 15.00 40.00
144 K.Millwood Phils Jsy/75 10.00 25.00
152 Marlon Byrd Jsy/75 6.00 15.00
159 Orel Hershiser Jsy/25 50.00 100.00
161 P.Martinez Expos Jsy/25 50.00 100.00
168 R.Hend Mets Jkt/15 75.00 150.00
169 R.Hend A's Jsy/15 75.00 150.00
170 R.Hend M's Jsy/44 60.00 120.00
173 Robin Yount Jsy/50 60.00 120.00
181 Sammy Sosa Jsy/50 50.00 100.00
187 Tim Hudson Jsy/25 20.00 50.00
189 Tom Glavine Jsy/25 50.00 100.00
191 Tommy John Jsy/15 40.00 80.00
199 Willie Stargell Jsy/50 75.00 150.00

2005 Absolute Memorabilia Tools of the Trade Swatch Double

OVERALL AU-GU ODDS ONE PER PACK
PRINT RUNS B/WN 1-200 COPIES PER
NO PRICING ON QTY OF 10 OR LESS
B='s Bat, BL ='s Belt, BG ='s Batting Glove
CP ='s Chest Protector, FG ='s Fielding Glove
H ='s Hat, HM ='s Helmet, JK ='s Jacket
J ='s Jersey, P ='s Pants, SG ='s Shin Guard
S ='s Shoes, SO ='s Socks, ST ='s Stirrups
SW ='s Sweatband

1 Ozzie Smith Bat-Pants/50 8.00 20.00
2 Carlos Beltran Astros Jsy-Shoes/50 3.00 8.00
3 Dale Murphy Jsy-Jsy/50 5.00 12.00
4 Paul Molitor Jsy-Pants/150 3.00 8.00
5 George Brett Bat-Hat/25 12.50 30.00
6 Stan Musial Bat-Pants/25 15.00 40.00
7 Ivan Rodriguez M's Jsy-Jsy/150 3.00 8.00
8 Carl Yastrzemski Bat-Jsy/25 12.50 30.00
9 Reggie Jackson A's Jsy-Jsy/50 5.00 12.00
10 Hideo Nomo Jsy-Pants/150 5.00 12.00
11 Gary Sheffield Hat-Jsy/25 4.00 10.00
12 Roberto Alomar Bat-Jsy/150 3.00 8.00
13 Pedro Martinez Jsy-Pants/150 3.00 8.00
15 Tim Hudson Hat-Jsy/100 2.50 6.00
17 Lance Berkman Bat-Jsy/150 2.50 6.00
19 Larry Walker Jsy-Jsy/150 3.00 8.00
20 Lou Brock Bat-Jkt/150 4.00 10.00
21 Roger Clemens Bat-Jsy/150 6.00 15.00
22 Paul Lo Duca Bat-Jsy/50 3.00 8.00
23 Don Mattingly Btg Glv-Pants/50 10.00 25.00
24 Willie Mays Bat-Pants/25 30.00 60.00
25 Rafael Palmeiro Bat-Jsy/150 3.00 8.00
27 Vladimir Guerrero Bat-Jsy/150 4.00 10.00
29 Rod Carew Jkt-Jkt/150 4.00 10.00
30 N.Ryan Angels Bat-Jkt/150 10.00 25.00
31 Richie Sexson Hat-Jsy/150 2.50 6.00
32 Steve Carlton Bat-Hat/150 4.00 10.00
33 Eddie Murray Bat-Jsy/150 6.00 15.00
34 Nolan Ryan Rgr Bat-Jsy/150 10.00 25.00
35 Mike Mussina O's Jsy-Pants/125 3.00 8.00
36 Sean Casey Jsy-Pants/150 2.50 6.00
37 Juan Gonzalez Rgr Jsy-Pants/10
38 Curt Schilling Sox Jsy-Jsy/150 3.00 8.00
39 Darryl Strawberry Yanks Bat-Jsy/150 3.00 8.00
40 Alfonso Soriano Jsy-Jsy/5
41 Tom Seaver Jsy-Pants/150 4.00 10.00
42 Mike Schmidt Bat-Jsy/150 8.00 20.00
43 Todd Helton Bat-Jsy/150 3.00 8.00
45 Shawn Green Bat-Jsy/150 2.50 6.00
46 Mike Mussina Yanks Jsy-Shoes/1
47 Tom Glavine Bat-Jsy/150 3.00 8.00
49 Kerry Wood Fld Glv-Jsy/150 2.50 6.00
50 Carlos Delgado Bat-Jsy/100 2.50 6.00
51 Randy Johnson Astros Jsy-Pants/150 4.0010.00
52 David Ortiz Bat-Jsy/150 4.00 10.00
53 Troy Glaus Jsy-Jsy/150 2.50 6.00
54 Rickey Henderson Mets Bat-Jsy/150 4.0010.00
55 Craig Biggio Bat-Jsy/150 3.00 8.00
56 Brad Penny Fld Glv-Jsy/150 2.00 5.00
57 Gary Carter Mets Jsy-Pants/150 3.00 8.00
58 Andy Pettitte Jsy-Jsy/150 3.00 8.00
59 Mark Prior Fld Glv-Jsy/150 3.00 8.00
60 Kirby Puckett Bat-Fld Glv/100 5.00 12.00
61 Willie McCovey Jsy-Pants/150 4.00 10.00
62 A.Dawson Expos Bat-Jsy/20 5.00 12.00
63 Greg Maddux Bat-Jsy/50 8.00 20.00
64 Adrian Beltre Bat-Jsy/150 2.50 6.00
65 Andruw Jones Bat-Jsy/150 3.00 8.00
66 Juan Gonzalez Indians Bat-Jsy/5
67 Frank Thomas Jsy-Jsy/150 4.00 10.00
68 Victor Martinez Chest Prot-Jsy/150 2.50 6.00
69 Randy Johnson 4.00 10.00
D'backs Jsy-Pants/150
70 A.Dawson Cubs Jsy-Pants/5
71 Adam Dunn Bat-Jsy/95 2.50 6.00
72 Carlton Fisk Bat-Jsy/150 4.00 10.00
73 Cal Ripken Jsy-Pants/150 10.00 25.00
74 Kenny Lofton Bat-Hat/150 3.00 8.00
75 Barry Zito Jsy-Jsy/150 2.50 6.00
76 Sammy Sosa Bat-Jsy/150 4.00 10.00
77 Deion Sanders Jsy-Pants/150 6.00 15.00
78 Tony Gwynn Jsy-Pants/150 6.00 15.00
79 Mike Piazza Jsy-Pants/150 4.00 10.00
80 Jeff Bagwell Jsy-Pants/150 3.00 8.00
81 Manny Ramirez Bat-Jsy/150 3.00 8.00
82 Carlos Beltran Royals Hat-Jsy/10
83 Mark Grace Bat-Jsy/50 4.00 10.00
84 Robin Yount Bat-Jsy/150 5.00 12.00
85 Albert Pujols Bat-Jsy/150 10.00 25.00
86 Dontrelle Willis Bat-Jsy/150 2.50 6.00
88 Magglio Ordonez Bat-Shoes/150 2.50 6.00
89 Miguel Tejada Hat-Jsy/150 2.50 6.00
90 Mark Teixeira Fld Glv-Jsy/150 3.00 8.00
91 Gary Carter Expos Bat-Jsy/25 5.00 12.00
92 Ivan Rodriguez Rgr Chest Prot-Jsy/150 3.00 8.00
93 Jason Giambi Hat-Jsy/50 3.00 8.00
94 Rickey Henderson A's Bat-Pants/150 4.0010.00
95 Curt Schilling D'backs Jsy-Jsy/150 2.50 6.00
96 Bobby Doerr Bat-Pants/150 3.00 8.00
97 Chipper Jones Bat-Jsy/150 4.00 10.00
98 Eric Chavez Bat-Jsy/1
99 Johnny Bench Bat-Pants/150 5.00 12.00
100 Harmon Killebrew Hat-Jsy/50 10.00 25.00
101 Andre Dawson B-J/50 4.00 10.00
102 Babe Ruth B-P/150 150.00 250.00
103 Bernie Williams B-J/85 3.00 8.00
106 Bo Jackson B-J/1
108 Brad Penny FG-S/70 2.00 5.00
110 Cal Ripken JK-P/100 10.00 25.00
111 Casey Fossum J-S/1
112 Curt Schilling FG-J/100 2.50 6.00
113 Dale Murphy B-J/1
114 Darryl Strawberry B-J/1
115 Dave Concepcion B-J/60 5.00 12.00
116 Dave Winfield FG-H/75 3.00 8.00
120 Gary Sheffield FG-H/1
122 Hank Aaron B-J/200 12.50 30.00
123 Harmon Killebrew B-J/1
124 Harold Baines J-Jsy/75 3.00 8.00
125 Hideki Matsui B-P/150 8.00 20.00
126 Hideo Nomo J-P/125 4.00 10.00
128 Jason Giambi Yanks J-Jsy/100 2.50 6.00
129 Jason Giambi A's J-Jsy/1
130 Jeff Bagwell P-Pants/150 3.00 8.00
133 Joe Mays FG-J/150 2.00 5.00
134 John Buck B-CP/150 2.00 5.00
138 Josh Phelps B-J/1
139 Juan Pierre B-J/1
140 Kazuhisa Ishii J-Jsy/150 2.50 6.00
141 Kenny Lofton B-FG/125 3.00 8.00
142 Kevin Brown J-Jsy/1
144 Kevin Millwood Phils J-Jsy/1
145 Lance Berkman B-J/10
146 Lenny Dykstra B-J/1
148 M.Ordonez Bat-Btg Glv/1
149 Marcus Giles J-S/135 2.50 6.00
151 Mark Prior H-S/1
152 Marlon Byrd B-J/1
153 Miguel Tejada J-Jsy/75 2.50 6.00
154 Mike Lowell B-J/1
155 Mike Piazza B-P/150 4.00 10.00
156 M.Sweeney B-FG/55 3.00 8.00
157 M.Ensberg FG-H/55 3.00 8.00
161 Pedro Martinez J-Jsy/1
163 Rafael Furcal B-J/150 2.50 6.00
164 R.Palmeiro B-P/150 3.00 8.00
165 Randy Johnson D'backs J-Jsy/75 4.00 10.00
166 R.John Astros J-P/150 4.00 10.00
167 Richie Sexson J-P/150 2.50 6.00
168 R.Hend Mets B-JK/150 5.00 12.00
169 R.Hend A's J-P/100 5.00 12.00
170 R.Hend M's B-J/150 5.00 12.00
171 Roberto Alomar B-J/25 6.00 15.00
174 Rod Carew J-Jsy/29 6.00 15.00
175 Roger Clemens B-J/100 6.00 15.00
176 Roger Maris A's J-P/50 30.00 60.00
177 R.Maris Yanks J-P/150 20.00 50.00
181 Sammy Sosa B-J/150 4.00 10.00
182 Shawn Green B-J/150 2.50 6.00
184 Steve Carlton FG-P/150 3.00 8.00
185 Ted Williams JK-J/100 30.00 60.00
186 Ted Williams B-J/100 30.00 60.00
187 Tim Hudson H-J/150 2.50 6.00
188 Todd Helton B-J/150 3.00 8.00
189 Tom Glavine B-J/25 5.00 12.00
190 Tom Seaver J-P/150 4.00 10.00
191 Tommy John B-J/150 3.00 8.00
192 Tony Gwynn J-P/150 6.00 15.00
193 V.Guerrero B-J/100 4.00 10.00
196 Warren Spahn J-P/150 10.00 25.00
197 Willie Mays B-J/150 15.00 40.00
198 Willie McCovey J-P/10
199 Willie Stargell B-J/25 6.00 15.00
200 Yogi Berra J-P/25 12.50 30.00

2005 Absolute Memorabilia Tools of the Trade Swatch Double Prime Black

*PRIME p/r 100: .75X TO 2X DBL p/r 20-29
*PRIME p/r 45-50: .6X TO 1.5X DBL p/r 70-200
*PRIME p/r 45-50: .5X TO 1.2X DBL p/r 50-60
*PRIME p/r 45-50: .4X TO 1X DBL p/r 20-29
*PRIME p/r 20-35: .75X TO 2X DBL p/r 70-200
*PRIME p/r 20-35: .6X TO 1.5X DBL p/r 50-60
*PRIME p/r 20-35: .5X TO 1.2X DBL p/r 20-25
*PRIME p/r 15: 1X TO 2.5X DBL p/r 70-200
*PRIME p/r 15: .6X TO 1.5X DBL p/r 20-29
OVERALL AU-GU ODDS ONE PER PACK
PRINT RUNS B/WN 1-100 COPIES PER
NO PRICING ON QTY OF 10 OR LESS

16 Dwight Gooden Jsy-Shoes/20 6.00 15.00
18 Darryl Strawberry Mets Bat-Jsy/50 5.00 12.00
26 Roy Oswalt Jsy-Shoes/25 5.00 12.00
28 Austin Kearns Bat-Jsy/25 4.00 10.00
37 Juan Gonzalez Rgr Jsy-Pants/50 4.00 10.00
48 Torii Hunter Bat-Jsy/50 4.00 10.00
66 Juan Gonzalez Indians Bat-Jsy/50 4.00 10.00
82 Carlos Beltran Royals Hat-Jsy/25 5.00 12.00
104 Billy Wagner J-Jsy/25 5.00 12.00
105 Billy Williams J-Jsy/50 5.00 12.00
107 Bob Gibson J-Jsy/25 10.00 25.00
111 Casey Fossum J-Jsy/50 3.00 8.00
114 D.Strawberry B-J/35 6.00 15.00
119 Gary Carter B-JK/30 45.00 15.00
136 Jorge Posada J-Jsy/45 6.00 15.00
143 K.Millw Braves J-Jsy/35 5.00 12.00
144 K.Millw Phils J-Jsy/50 4.00 10.00
159 Orel Hershiser J-Jsy/15 8.00 20.00
161 Pedro Martinez J-Jsy/15 8.00 20.00

2005 Absolute Memorabilia Tools of the Trade Swatch Double Prime Red

*PRIMEp/r75-150: .5X TO 1.2X DBLp/r70-200
*PRIME p/r 75-150: .4X TO 1X DBL p/r 50-60
*PRIME p/r 75-150: .3X TO .8X DBL p/r 20-29
*PRIME p/r 40-55: .6X TO 1.5X DBL p/r 70-200
*PRIME p/r 40-55: .5X TO 1.2X DBL p/r 50-60
*PRIME p/r 40-55: .4X TO 1X DBL p/r 20-29
*PRIME p/r 20-35: .75X TO 2X DBL p/r 70-200
*PRIME p/r 20-35: .6X TO 1.5X DBL p/r 50-60
*PRIME p/r 20-35: .5X TO 1.2X DBL p/r 20-29
*PRIME p/r 15: 1X TO 2.5X DBL p/r 70-200
*PRIME p/r 15: .6X TO 1.5X DBL p/r 20-29
OVERALL AU-GU ODDS ONE PER PACK
PRINT RUNS B/WN 1-150 COPIES PER
NO PRICING ON QTY OF 12 OR LESS

14 Ernie Banks Bat-Jsy/25 30.00 60.00
16 Dwight Gooden Jsy-Shoes/50 5.00 12.00
18 Darryl Strawberry Mets Bat-Jsy/50 5.00 12.00
26 Roy Oswalt Jsy-Shoes/50 4.00 10.00
28 Austin Kearns Bat-Jsy/50 3.00 8.00
37 Juan Gonzalez Rgr Jsy-Pants/100 3.00 8.00
48 Torii Hunter Bat-Jsy/100 3.00 8.00
66 Juan Gonzalez Indians Bat-Jsy/100 3.00 8.00
70 Andre Dawson Cubs Jsy-Pants/15 8.00 20.00
82 Carlos Beltran Royals Hat-Jsy/50 4.00 10.00
87 Jim Thome Jsy-Jsy/25 6.00 15.00
98 Eric Chavez Bat-Jsy/25 5.00 12.00
104 Billy Wagner J-Jsy/90 3.00 8.00
105 Billy Williams J-Jsy/150 4.00 10.00
107 Bob Gibson J-Jsy/50 8.00 20.00
111 Casey Fossum J-Jsy/110 2.50 6.00
113 Dale Murphy B-J/15 10.00 25.00
114 Darryl Strawberry B-J/150 4.00 10.00
118 Fergie Jenkins J-Jsy/15 8.00 20.00
119 Gary Carter B-JK/50 5.00 12.00
121 Gaylord Perry J-Jsy/20 6.00 15.00
127 Hoyt Wilhelm J-Jsy/30 10.00 25.00
129 J.Giambi A's B-H/20 5.00 12.00
142 Kevin Brown J-Jsy/25 5.00 12.00
143 Kevin Millwood Braves J-Jsy/150 3.00 8.00
144 Kevin Millwood Phils J-Jsy/150 3.00 8.00
159 Orel Hershiser J-Jsy/55 5.00 12.00
161 Pedro Martinez J-Jsy/50 5.00 12.00

2005 Absolute Memorabilia Tools of the Trade Swatch Triple

*TRIP p/r 70-175: .5X TO 1.2X DBL p/r 70-200
*TRIP p/r 70-175: .4X TO 1X DBL p/r 50-60
*TRIP p/r 50-55: .4X TO 1X DBL p/r 20-29
*TRIP p/r 20-25: .75X TO 2X DBL p/r 70-200
*TRIP p/r 20-25: .6X TO 1.5X DBL p/r 50-60
*TRIP p/r 20-25: .5X TO 1.2X DBL p/r 20-29
*TRIP p/r 15: 1X TO 2.5X DBL p/r 70-200
*TRIP p/r 15: .75X TO 2X DBL p/r 50-60
OVERALL AU-GU ODDS ONE PER PACK
PRINT RUNS B/WN 1-175 COPIES PER
NO PRICING ON QTY OF 10 OR LESS

14 Ernie Banks Bat-Hat-Jsy/15 20.00 50.00
18 Darryl Strawberry Mets 8.00 20.00
{Bat-Fld Glv-Shoes/15
37 Juan Gonzalez Rgr Bat-Jsy-Pants/25 5.0012.00
70 A.Dawson Cubs Bat-Jsy-Pants/25 6.00 15.00
82 Carlos Beltran 6.00 15.00
Royals Bat-Jsy-Shoes/15
98 Eric Chavez Bat-Jsy-Jsy/25 5.00 12.00
102 Babe Ruth B-J-P/50 450.00 750.00
111 Casey Fossum FG-J-S/55 3.00 8.00
122 Hank Aaron B-H-J/175 15.00 40.00
138 Josh Phelps B-FG-J/115 2.50 6.00
139 Juan Pierre B-BG-J/100 3.00 8.00
142 Kevin Brown B-J-J/25 6.00 15.00
146 L.Dykstra B-FG-J/125 4.00 10.00
154 Mike Lowell B-J-J/175 3.00 8.00
176 R.Maris A's B-J-P/50 40.00 80.00
177 R.Maris Yanks B-J-P/100 30.00 60.00
179 Ryan Klesko FG-J-J/50 4.00 10.00
185 Ted Williams B-JK-J/50 90.00 150.00
186 Ted Williams B-JK-J/50 90.00 150.00
197 Willie Mays B-J-P/100 30.00 60.00
200 Yogi Berra J-J-P/25 20.00 50.00

2005 Absolute Memorabilia Tools of the Trade Swatch Triple Prime Black

*PRIME p/r 40-50: 1X TO 2.5X DBL p/r 70-200
*PRIME p/r 40-50: .75X TO 2X DBL p/r 50-60
*PRIMEp/r25-30: 1.25X TO 3X DBLp/r70-200
*PRIME p/r 25-30: .75X TO 2X DBL p/r 20-29
*PRIME p/r 15: 1.5X TO 4X DBL p/r 70-200
OVERALL AU-GU ODDS ONE PER PACK
PRINT RUNS B/WN 1-50 COPIES PER
NO PRICING ON QTY OF 10 OR LESS

26 Roy Oswalt Btg Glv-Fld Glv-Jsy/15 10.0025.00
37 J.Gonzalez Rgr Bat-Jsy-Pants/15 10.00 25.00
48 Torii Hunter Bat-Jsy-Jsy/15 10.00 25.00
66 Juan Gonzalez Indians Bat-Jsy-Jsy/15 10.00 25.00
111 Casey Fossum J-J-S/50 5.00 12.00
114 D.Strawberry B-J-J/50 8.00 20.00
119 Gary Carter BG-JK-S/30 10.00 25.00
127 Hoyt Wilhelm J-J-J/25 15.00 40.00
129 J.Giambi A's H-J-J/15 10.00 25.00
138 Josh Phelps FG-J-J/40 5.00 12.00
142 Kevin Brown B-J-J/50 6.00 15.00
144 K.Millw Phils J-J-J/50 6.00 15.00
151 Mark Prior B-H-H/25 10.00 25.00
152 Marlon Byrd B-J-J/50 5.00 12.00
161 Pedro Martinez B-J-J/25 10.00 25.00

2005 Absolute Memorabilia Tools of the Trade Swatch Triple Prime Red

*PRIME p/r 75-100: .75X TO 2X DBLp/r70-200
*PRIME p/r 75-100: .6X TO 1.5X DBLp/r 50-60
*PRIME p/r 40-65: 1X TO 2.5X DBL p/r 70-200
*PRIME p/r 40-65: .75X TO 2X DBL p/r 50-60
*PRIME p/r 40-65: .6X TO 1.5X DBL p/r 20-29
*PRIMEp/r24-35: 1.25X TO 3X DBLp/r70-200
*PRIMEp/r24-35: .75X TO 2X DBLp/r20-29
*PRIME p/r 15: 1.5X TO 4X DBL p/r 70-200
*PRIME p/r 15: 1.25X TO 3X DBL p/r 50-60
*PRIME p/r 15: 1X TO 2.5X DBL p/r 20-29
OVERALL AU-GU ODDS ONE PER PACK
PRINT RUNS B/WN 1-100 COPIES PER
NO PRICING ON QTY OF 10 OR LESS

26 Roy Oswalt Btg Glv-Fld Glv-Jsy/25 8.00 20.00
28 Austin Kearns Bat-Fld Glv-Jsy/15 8.00 20.00
37 Juan Gonzalez Rgr Bat-Jsy-Pants/25 8.00 20.00
40 Alfonso Soriano Bat-Jsy-Jsy/25 8.00 20.00
48 Torii Hunter Bat-Jsy-Jsy/25 8.00 20.00
66 Juan Gonzalez Indians Bat-Jsy-Jsy/25 8.00 20.00
70 Andre Dawson Cubs Bat-Jsy-Pants/15 12.50 30.00
87 Jim Thome Jsy-Jsy-Jsy/15 12.50 30.00
98 Eric Chavez Bat-Jsy-Jsy/15 10.00 25.00
111 Casey Fossum J-J-S/100 4.00 10.00
114 D.Strawberry B-J-J/100 6.00 15.00
119 Gary Carter BG-JK-S/50 8.00 20.00
122 Hank Aaron B-H-J/100 30.00 80.00
127 Hoyt Wilhelm J-J-J/75 10.00 25.00
129 J.Giambi A's H-J-J/35 8.00 20.00
138 Josh Phelps FG-J-J/75 4.00 10.00
142 Kevin-Brown B-J-J/100 5.00 12.00
144 K.Millw Phils J-J-J/100 5.00 12.00
151 Mark Prior B-H-H/40 8.00 20.00
152 Marlon Byrd B-J-J/100 4.00 10.00
161 Pedro Martinez B-J-J/75 6.00 15.00
197 Willie Mays B-J-P/24 75.00 150.00

2005 Absolute Memorabilia Tools of the Trade Swatch Quad

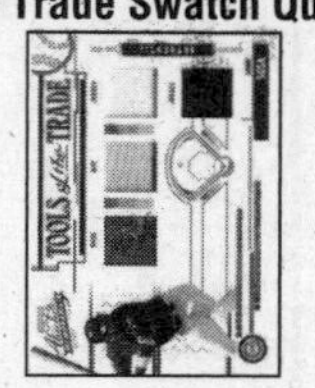

*QUAD p/r 75-150: .75X TO 2X DBL p/r 70-200
*QUAD p/r 75-150: .6X TO 1.5X DBL p/r 50-60
*QUAD p/r 75-150: .5X TO 1.2X DBL p/r 20-29
*QUAD p/r 50-65: 1X TO 2.5X DBL p/r 70-200
*QUAD p/r 50-65: .75X TO 2X DBL p/r 50-60
*QUAD p/r 20-35: 1.25X TO 3X DBL p/r 70-200
*QUAD p/r 20-35: 1X TO 2.5X DBL p/r 50-60
*QUAD p/r 20-35: .75X TO 2X DBL p/r 20-29
*QUAD p/r 15: 1.5X TO 4X DBL p/r 70-200
*QUAD p/r 15: 1.25X TO 3X DBL p/r 50-60
OVERALL AU-GU ODDS ONE PER PACK
PRINT RUNS B/WN 1-150 COPIES PER
NO PRICING ON QTY OF 10 OR LESS

14 Ernie Banks Bat-Hat-Jsy-Jsy/25 30.00 60.00
24 Willie Mays Bat-Jsy-Jsy-Pants/25 75.00150.00
26 Roy Oswalt 8.00 20.00
Btg Glv-Fld Glv-Jsy-Shoes/30
37 Juan Gonzalez 10.00 25.00
Rangers Bat-Hat-Jsy-Pants/15
46 Mike Mussina 10.00 25.00
Yanks Hat-Jsy-Jsy-Shoes/25
66 Juan Gonzalez Indians 8.00 20.00
Bat-Jsy-Jsy-Jsy/30
70 Andre Dawson 10.00 25.00
Cubs Bat-Jsy-Jsy-Pants/25
82 Carlos Beltran 8.00 20.00
Royals Bat-Hat-Jsy-Shoes/20
98 Eric Chavez Bat-Jsy-Jsy-Jsy/15 10.00 25.00
102 Babe Ruth B-J-J-P/20 700.00 1200.00
111 C.Fossum FG-H-J-S/150 4.00 10.00
113 Dale Murphy B-J-J-J/30 12.50 30.00
114 D.Straw B-FG-J-J/75 6.00 15.00
120 G.Sheffield B-FG-H-S/25 8.00 20.00
122 Hank Aaron B-H-J-J/150 30.00 60.00
129 J.Giam A's B-H-J-J/150 5.00 12.00
138 Josh Phelps B-FG-J-S/75 4.00 10.00
139 Juan Pierre B-H-J-S/112 5.00 12.00
151 Mark Prior B-H-J-S/50 8.00 20.00
152 Marlon Byrd B-J-J-S/35 6.00 15.00
161 P.Martinez B-J-J-P/150 6.00 15.00
173 Robin Yount H-HM-J-J/15 20.00 50.00
179 Ryan Klesko FG-H-J-J/25 8.00 20.00
186 T.Williams B-JK-J-J/50 125.00 200.00

2005 Absolute Memorabilia Tools of the Trade Swatch Quad Reverse

*REV p/r 100: .75X TO 2X DBL p/r 70-200
*REV p/r 40-65: 1X TO 2.5X DBL p/r 70-200
*REV p/r 20-35: 1.25X TO 3X DBL p/r 70-200
*REV p/r 20-35: .75X TO 2X DBL p/r 20-29
*REV p/r 15: 1.5X TO 4X DBL p/r 70-200
*REV p/r 15: 1.25X TO 3X DBL p/r 50-60
OVERALL AU-GU ODDS ONE PER PACK
PRINT RUNS B/WN 1-100 COPIES PER
NO PRICING ON QTY OF 10 OR LESS

111 C.Fossum FG-H-J-S/65 5.00 12.00
114 D.Straw B-FG-J-J/25 10.00 25.00
122 Hank Aaron B-H-J-J/100 30.00 60.00
129 J.Giambi A's B-H-J-J/50 6.00 15.00
138 Josh Phelps B-FG-J-S/25 6.00 15.00
139 Juan Pierre B-H-J-S/65 6.00 15.00
151 Mark Prior B-H-J-S/25 10.00 25.00
152 Marlon Byrd B-J-J-S/15 8.00 20.00
161 P.Martinez B-J-J-P/50 8.00 20.00

2005 Absolute Memorabilia Tools of the Trade Swatch Quad Prime Black

*PRIME p/r 25: 1.5X TO 4X DBL p/r 70-200
*PRIME p/r 25: 1.25X TO 3X DBL p/r 50-60
OVERALL AU-GU ODDS ONE PER PACK
PRINT RUNS B/WN 1-25 COPIES PER
NO PRICING ON QTY OF 5 OR LESS

119 G.Cart BG-CP-FG-JK/25 12.50 30.00
142 Kevin Brown B-J-J-J/25 10.00 25.00
148 M.Ordonez B-BG-J-S/25 10.00 25.00
154 Mike Lowell B-J-J-J/25 10.00 25.00

2005 Absolute Memorabilia Tools of the Trade Swatch Quad Prime Red

*PRIME p/r 50: 1.25X TO 3X DBL p/r 70-200
*PRIME p/r 50: 1X TO 2.5X DBL p/r 50-60
OVERALL AU-GU ODDS ONE PER PACK
PRINT RUNS B/WN 1-75 COPIES PER
NO PRICING ON QTY OF 12 OR LESS

119 G.Cart BG-CP-FG-JK/75 8.00 20.00
142 Kevin Brown B-J-J-J/50 8.00 20.00
148 M.Ordonez B-BG-J-S/50 8.00 20.00
154 Mike Lowell B-J-J-J/50 8.00 20.00
164 R.Palmeiro B-H-P-S/15 15.00 40.00
193 V.Guerrero B-FG-J-J/25 15.00 40.00

2005 Absolute Memorabilia Tools of the Trade Swatch Five

*FIVE p/r 75-150: 1X TO 2.5X DBL p/r 70-200
*FIVE p/r 75-150: .6X TO 1.5X DBL p/r 20-29
*FIVE p/r 40-50: 1.25X TO 3X DBL p/r 70-200
*FIVE p/r 40-50: 1X TO 2.5X DBL p/r 50-60
*FIVE p/r 20-35: 1.5X TO 4X DBL p/r 70-200
*FIVE p/r 20-35: 1.25X TO 3X DBL p/r 50-60
*FIVE p/r 20-35: 1X TO 2.5X DBL p/r 20-29
*FIVE p/r 15-17: 2X TO 5X DBL p/r 70-200
*FIVE p/r 15-17: 1.5X TO 4X DBL p/r 50-60
OVERALL AU-GU ODDS ONE PER PACK
PRINT RUNS B/WN 1-150 COPIES PER
NO PRICING ON QTY OF 10 OR LESS

26 Roy Oswalt 10.00 25.00
Bat-Btg Glv-Fld Glv-Jsy-Shoes/25
28 Austin Kearns 8.00 20.00
Bat-Hat-Jsy-Jsy-Shoes/25
82 Carlos Beltran Royals Bat-Hat-
Jsy-Jsy-Shoes/20 10.00 25.00
123 H.Kill B-H-J-J-S/25 20.00 50.00
129 J.Giam A's B-H-J-J-J/20 10.00 25.00
138 J.Phelps B-FG-H-J-S/15 10.00 25.00
145 L.Berk B-BG-FG-J-S/20 10.00 25.00
152 M.Byrd B-FG-H-J-S/25 8.00 20.00
179 R.Klesko BG-FG-H-J-J/25 10.00 25.00

2005 Absolute Memorabilia Tools of the Trade Swatch Five Reverse

*REV p/r 75-100: 1X TO 2.5X DBL p/r 70-200
*REV p/r 20-35: 1.5X TO 4X DBL p/r 70-200
*REV p/r 20-35: 1X TO 2.5X DBL p/r 20-29
*REV p/r 15: 2X TO 5X DBL p/r 70-200
*REV p/r 15: 1.5X TO 4X DBL p/r 50-60
*REV p/r 15: 1.25X TO 3X DBL p/r 20-29
OVERALL AU-GU ODDS ONE PER PACK
PRINT RUNS B/WN 1-15 COPIES PER
NO PRICING ON QTY OF 10 OR LESS

26 Roy Oswalt Bat-Btg Glv-Fld
Glv-Jsy-Shoes/15 12.50 30.00
28 Austin Kearns Bat-Hat-Jsy-
Jsy-Shoes/15 10.00 25.00
123 H.Kill B-H-J-J-S/15 30.00 60.00
152 M.Byrd B-FG-H-J-S/15 10.00 25.00

2005 Absolute Memorabilia Tools of the Trade Swatch Five Prime Red

*PRIME p/r 25: 2X TO 5X DBL p/r 70-200
*PRIME p/r 15: 1.5X TO 4X DBL p/r 20-29

PRINT RUNS B/WN 1-25 COPIES PER
NO PRICING ON QTY OF 10 OR LESS
PRIME BLACK PRINT B/WN 1-10 PER
NO PRIME BLACK PRICING DUE TO SCARCITY
OVERALL AU-GU ODDS ONE PER PACK

2005 Absolute Memorabilia Tools of the Trade Swatch Six

*SIX p/r 75-150: 1.5X TO 4X DBL p/r 70-200
*SIX p/r 50: 2X TO 5X DBL p/r 70-200
*SIX p/r 50: 1.5X TO 4X DBL p/r 50-60
*SIX p/r 25-30: 2.5X TO 6X DBL p/r 70-200
*SIX p/r 15: 3X TO 8X DBL p/r 70-200
*SIX p/r 15: 2.5X TO 6X DBL p/r 50-60
*SIX p/r 15: 2X TO 5X DBL p/r 20-29
OVERALL AU-GU ODDS ONE PER PACK
PRINT RUNS B/WN 1-150 COPIES PER
NO PRICING ON QTY OF 10 OR LESS

26 Roy Oswalt 20.00 50.00
Btg Glv-Fld Glv-Hat-Jsy-Jsy-Shoes/15
123 H.Kill B-H-J-J-P-S/30 30.00 80.00
138 J.Phelps B-FG-H-J-J-S/150 8.00 20.00
145 L.Berk B-BG-FG-H-J-S/25 15.00 40.00
152 M.Byrd B-BG-FG-H-J-S/150 8.00 20.00
179 R.Klesko BG-FG-H-J-J-S/100 10.00 25.00

2005 Absolute Memorabilia Tools of the Trade Swatch Six Reverse

*REV p/r 20-25: 2.5X TO 6X DBL p/r 70-200
OVERALL AU-GU ODDS ONE PER PACK
PRINT RUNS B/WN 1-50 COPIES PER
NO PRICING ON QTY OF 10 OR LESS

123 H.Kill B-H-J-J-P-S/15 50.00 100.00
138 J.Phelps B-FG-H-J-J-S/50 10.00 25.00
152 M.Byrd B-BG-FG-H-J-S/45 10.00 25.00
179 R.Klesko BG-FG-H-J-J-S/25 15.00 40.00

2005 Absolute Memorabilia Tools of the Trade Swatch Six Prime Black

*PRIME p/r 25: 3X TO 8X DBL p/r 70-200
OVERALL AU-GU ODDS ONE PER PACK
PRINT RUNS B/WN 1-25 COPIES PER
NO PRICING ON QTY OF 10 OR LESS

2005 Absolute Memorabilia Tools of the Trade Swatch Six Prime Red

*PRIME p/r 50: 2.5X TO 6X DBL p/r 70-200
*PRIME p/r 25: 3X TO 8X DBL p/r 70-200
OVERALL AU-GU ODDS ONE PER PACK
PRINT RUNS B/WN 1-50 COPIES PER
NO PRICING ON QTY OF 9 OR LESS

2005 Absolute Memorabilia Tools of the Trade Autograph

OVERALL AU-GU ODDS ONE PER PACK
PRINT RUNS B/WN 1-150 COPIES PER
NO PRICING ON QTY OF 11 OR LESS

105 Billy Williams/150 6.00 15.00
107 Bob Gibson/88 10.00 25.00
117 David Cone/75 6.00 15.00
118 Fergie Jenkins/100 6.00 15.00
119 Gary Carter/43 8.00 20.00
120 Gary Sheffield/36 12.50 30.00
121 Gaylord Perry/16 12.50 30.00
122 Hank Aaron/100 100.00 175.00
131 Jim Palmer/106 6.00 15.00
137 Josh Beckett/56 12.50 30.00
150 Mark Grace/50 8.00 20.00
158 Nolan Ryan/75 40.00 80.00
159 Orel Hershiser/21 10.00 25.00
160 Ozzie Smith/150 15.00 40.00
162 Phil Rizzuto/99 10.00 25.00
174 Rod Carew/150 10.00 25.00
178 Ron Cey/100 6.00 15.00

180 Ryne Sandberg/150 15.00 40.00
183 Stan Musial/150 30.00 60.00
184 Steve Carlton/150 6.00 15.00
188 Todd Helton/100 10.00 25.00
190 Tom Seaver/18 30.00 60.00
194 Wade Boggs Sox/70 10.00 25.00
195 Wade Boggs Rays/35 15.00 40.00

2005 Absolute Memorabilia Tools of the Trade Autograph Reverse

*REV p/r 75-100: .4X TO 1X AU p/r 70-150
*REV p/r 37-50: .5X TO 1.2X AU p/r 70-150
*REV p/r 37-50: .4X TO 1X AU p/r 36-56
*REV p/r 20-32: .6X TO 1.5X AU p/r 70-150
*REV p/r 20-32: .4X TO 1X AU p/r 21-35
*REV p/r 20-32: .3X TO .8X AU p/r 16-18
*REV p/r 15: .6X TO 1.5X AU p/r 36-56
OVERALL AU-GU ODDS ONE PER PACK
PRINT RUNS B/WN 1-100 COPIES PER
NO PRICING ON QTY OF 7 OR LESS
122 Hank Aaron/32 125.00 200.00
183 Stan Musial/100 30.00 60.00
192 Tony Gwynn/25 20.00 50.00

2005 Absolute Memorabilia Tools of the Trade Autograph Red

*RED p/r 25-30: .6X TO 1.5X AU p/r 70-150
*RED p/r 16-19: .75X TO 2X AU p/r 70-150
PRINT RUNS B/WN 1-30 COPIES PER
NO PRICING ON QTY OF 12 OR LESS
BLACK PRINT RUN 1 SERIAL #'d SET
BLACK CARD 175 PRINT RUN 4 #'d COPIES
NO BLACK PRICING DUE TO SCARCITY
OVERALL AU-GU ODDS ONE PER PACK
192 Tony Gwynn/19 20.00 50.00

2005 Absolute Memorabilia Tools of the Trade Autograph Bat

*BAT p/r 100: .3X TO .8X AU p/r 36-56
*BAT p/r 50: .5X TO 1.2X AU p/r 70-150
*BAT p/r 50: .3X TO .8X AU p/r 21-35
OVERALL AU-GU ODDS ONE PER PACK
PRINT RUNS B/WN 1-100 COPIES PER
NO PRICING ON QTY OF 7 OR LESS
113 Dale Murphy/100 10.00 25.00

2005 Absolute Memorabilia Tools of the Trade Autograph Bat Reverse

*BAT p/r 25: .6X TO 1.5X AU p/r 70-150
*BAT p/r 25: .5X TO 1.2X AU p/r 36-56
*BAT p/r 25: .4X TO 1X AU p/r 21-35
OVERALL AU-GU ODDS ONE PER PACK
PRINT RUNS B/WN 1-50 COPIES PER
NO PRICING ON QTY OF 3 OR LESS
113 Dale Murphy/50 12.50 30.00

2005 Absolute Memorabilia Tools of the Trade Autograph Bat Red

PRINT RUNS B/WN 1-10 COPIES PER
BLACK PRINT RUN 1 SERIAL #'d SET
OVERALL AU-GU ODDS ONE PER PACK
NO PRICING DUE TO SCARCITY

2005 Absolute Memorabilia Tools of the Trade Autograph Jersey

*JSY p/r 75-150: .4X TO 1X AU p/r 70-150
*JSY p/r 50: .5X TO 1.2X AU p/r 70-150
*JSY p/r 25-35: .6X TO 1.5X AU p/r 70-150
*JSY p/r 25-35: .5X TO 1.2X AU p/r 36-56
*JSY p/r 25-35: .3X TO .8X AU p/r 16-18
OVERALL AU-GU ODDS ONE PER PACK
PRINT RUNS B/WN 1-150 COPIES PER
NO PRICING ON QTY OF 10 OR LESS
113 Dale Murphy/50 12.50 30.00
122 Hank Aaron/50 125.00 200.00
135 John Kruk/150 6.00 15.00
192 Tony Gwynn/100 15.00 40.00

2005 Absolute Memorabilia Tools of the Trade Autograph Jersey Reverse

*JSY p/r 97-100: .4X TO 1X AU p/r 70-150
*JSY p/r 50: .5X TO 1.2X AU p/r 70-150
*JSY p/r 25: .6X TO 1.5X AU p/r 70-150
*JSY p/r 15: .6X TO 1.5X AU p/r 36-56
OVERALL AU-GU ODDS ONE PER PACK
PRINT RUNS B/WN 1-100 COPIES PER
NO PRICING ON QTY OF 10 OR LESS
113 Dale Murphy/25 15.00 40.00
122 Hank Aaron/25 125.00 200.00
123 Harmon Killebrew/15 30.00 60.00
135 John Kruk/100 6.00 15.00
192 Tony Gwynn/50 15.00 40.00

2005 Absolute Memorabilia Tools of the Trade Autograph Jersey Red

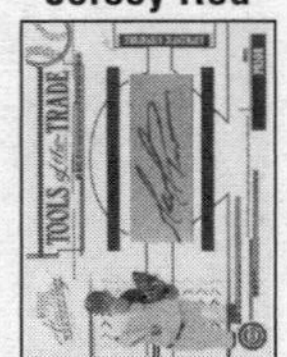

*RED p/r 25: .6X TO 1.5X AU p/r 70-150
OVERALL AU-GU ODDS ONE PER PACK
PRINT RUNS B/WN 1-25 COPIES PER
NO PRICING ON QTY OF 10 OR LESS
135 John Kruk/25 10.00 25.00
192 Tony Gwynn/25 20.00 50.00

2005 Absolute Memorabilia Tools of the Trade Autograph Swatch Single Jumbo

*SNG p/r 100: .5X TO 1.2X DBL p/r 75-100
*SNG p/r 44-50: .6X TO 1.5X DBL p/r 75-100
*SNG p/r 44-50: .5X TO 1.2X DBL p/r 40-65
OVERALL AU-GU ODDS ONE PER PACK
PRINT RUNS B/WN 1-100 COPIES PER
NO PRICING ON QTY OF 10 OR LESS
105 Billy Williams Jsy/25 12.50 30.00
118 Fergie Jenkins Jsy/25 12.50 30.00
135 John Kruk Jsy/25 12.50 30.00
159 Orel Hershiser Jsy/25 12.50 30.00
162 Phil Rizzuto Jsy/100 20.00 50.00
198 Willie McCovey Pants/44 15.00 40.00

2005 Absolute Memorabilia Tools of the Trade Autograph Swatch Single Jumbo Prime Red

PRINT RUNS B/WN 1-30 COPIES PER
NO PRICING ON QTY OF 10 OR LESS
PRIME BLACK PRINT RUNS B/WN 1-10 PER
NO PRIME BLK PRICING DUE TO SCARCITY
OVERALL AU-GU ODDS ONE PER PACK
121 Gaylord Perry Jsy/30 12.50 30.00

2005 Absolute Memorabilia Tools of the Trade Autograph Swatch Double

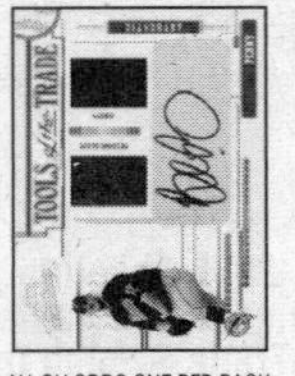

OVERALL AU-GU ODDS ONE PER PACK
PRINT RUNS B/WN 1-100 COPIES PER
NO PRICING ON QTY OF 10 OR LESS
1 Ozzie Smith Bat-Pants/25 30.00 60.00
2 Carlos Beltran Astros Jsy-Shoes/10
3 Dale Murphy Jsy-Jsy/50 15.00 40.00
4 Paul Molitor Jsy-Pants/25 12.50 30.00
5 George Brett Bat-Hat/5
6 Stan Musial Bat-Pants/10
10 Hideo Nomo Jsy-Pants/1
12 Roberto Alomar Bat-Jsy/10
13 Pedro Martinez Jsy-Pants/1
14 Ernie Banks Bat-Jsy/1
15 Tim Hudson Hat-Jsy/15 30.00 60.00
16 Dwight Gooden Jsy-Shoes/5
18 Darryl Strawberry Mets Bat-Jsy/1
20 Lou Brock Bat-Jkt/50 15.00 40.00
21 Roger Clemens Bat-Jsy/5
22 Paul Lo Duca Bat-Jsy/25 12.50 30.00
24 Willie Mays Bat-Pants/5
25 Rafael Palmeiro Bat-Jsy/1
26 Roy Oswalt Jsy-Shoes/1
30 Nolan Ryan Angels Bat-Jkt/15 75.00 150.00
34 Nolan Ryan Rgr Bat-Jsy/15 75.00 150.00
36 Sean Casey Jsy-Pants/50 10.00 25.00
37 Juan Gonzalez Rgr Jsy-Pants/25 12.50 30.00
38 Curt Schilling Sox Jsy-Jsy/5
39 Darryl Strawberry Yanks Bat-Jsy/50 10.0025.00
40 Alfonso Soriano Jsy-Jsy/1
41 Tom Seaver Jsy-Pants/25 30.00 60.00
42 Mike Schmidt Bat-Jsy/15 50.00 100.00
45 Shawn Green Bat-Jsy/1
48 Torii Hunter Bat-Jsy/40 10.00 25.00
49 Kerry Wood Fld Glv-Jsy/5
54 Rickey Henderson Mets Bat-Jsy/5
56 Brad Penny Fld Glv-Jsy/75 5.00 12.00
57 Gary Carter Mets Jsy-Pants/25 12.50 30.00
59 Mark Prior Fld Glv-Jsy/10
60 Kirby Puckett Bat-Fld Glv/1
61 Willie McCovey Jsy-Pants/15 30.00 60.00
62 Andre Dawson Expos Bat-Jsy/50 10.00 25.00
64 Adrian Beltre Bat-Jsy/50 10.00 25.00
66 Juan Gonzalez Indians Bat-Jsy/25 12.50 30.00
67 Frank Thomas Jsy-Jsy/10
68 Victor Martinez Chest Prot-Jsy/10
70 Andre Dawson Cubs Jsy-Pants/50 10.00 25.00
71 Adam Dunn Bat-Jsy/5
72 Carlton Fisk Bat-Jsy/15 30.00 60.00
73 Cal Ripken Jsy-Pants/25 75.00 150.00
75 Barry Zito Jsy-Jsy/5
78 Tony Gwynn Jsy-Pants/15 30.00 60.00
80 Jeff Bagwell Jsy-Pants/5
81 Manny Ramirez Bat-Jsy/5
82 Carlos Beltran Royals Hat-Jsy/10
83 Mark Grace Bat-Jsy/10
84 Robin Yount Bat-Jsy/10
85 Albert Pujols Bat-Jsy/1
86 Dontrelle Willis Bat-Jsy/1
88 Magglio Ordonez Bat-Shoes/25 12.50 30.00
90 Mark Teixeira Fld Glv-Jsy/1
91 Gary Carter Expos Bat-Jsy/25 12.50 30.00
94 Rickey Henderson A's Bat-Jsy/5
95 Curt Schilling D'backs Jsy-Jsy/5
96 Bobby Doerr Bat-Pants/50 6.00 15.00
97 Chipper Jones Bat-Jsy/10
98 Eric Chavez Bat-Jsy/25 12.50 30.00
99 Johnny Bench Bat-Pants/15 40.00 80.00
100 Harmon Killebrew Hat-Jsy/25 30.00 60.00
107 Bob Gibson J-Jsy/10
110 Cal Ripken J-Jsy/25 75.00 150.00
112 Curt Schilling J-Jsy/1
113 Dale Murphy B-J/1
114 Darryl Strawberry B-J/1
118 Fergie Jenkins FG-J/1
120 Gary Sheffield FG-H/50 15.00 40.00
122 Hank Aaron B-J/25 150.00 250.00
123 Harmon Killebrew B-J/65 20.00 50.00
126 Hideo Nomo J-P/30 150.00 250.00
130 Jeff Bagwell P-Pants/25 30.00 60.00
131 Jim Palmer H-P/40 10.00 25.00
137 Josh Beckett B-FG/10
146 Lenny Dykstra B-J/75 8.00 20.00
148 Magglio Ordonez B-BG/1
151 Mark Prior H-S/25 12.50 30.00
152 Marlon Byrd B-J/100 5.00 12.00
163 Rafael Furcal B-J/10
165 Randy Johnson D'backs J-Jsy/1
166 R.Johnson Astros J-P/1
174 Rod Carew J-Jsy/100 12.50 30.00
184 Steve Carlton FG-P/32 12.50 30.00
187 Tim Hudson H-J/15 30.00 60.00
188 Todd Helton B-J/17 30.00 60.00
190 Tom Seaver J-P/100 15.00 40.00
191 Tommy John B-J/5
192 Tony Gwynn J-P/50 15.00 40.00
198 Willie McCovey J-P/10

2005 Absolute Memorabilia Tools of the Trade Autograph Swatch Double Reverse

*REV p/r 75: .3X TO .8X DBL p/r 40-65
*REV p/r 41-50: .5X TO 1.2X DBL p/r 75-100
*REV p/r 41-50: .4X TO 1X DBL p/r 40-65
*REV p/r 25-29: .6X TO 1.5X DBL p/r 75-100
*REV p/r 25-29: .5X TO 1.2X DBL p/r 40-65
*REV p/r 25-29: .4X TO 1X DBL p/r 20-32
*REV p/r 15: .5X TO 1.2X DBL p/r 20-32
OVERALL AU-GU ODDS ONE PER PACK
PRINT RUNS B/WN 1-75 COPIES PER
NO PRICING ON QTY OF 10 OR LESS
113 Dale Murphy B-J/25 20.00 50.00
122 Hank Aaron B-J/15 150.00 250.00

2005 Absolute Memorabilia Tools of the Trade Autograph Swatch Double Prime Black

OVERALL AU-GU ODDS ONE PER PACK
PRINT RUNS B/WN 1-15 COPIES PER
NO PRICING ON QTY OF 10 OR LESS
159 Orel Hershiser J-Jsy/15 15.00 40.00

2005 Absolute Memorabilia Tools of the Trade Autograph Swatch Double Prime Red

*PRIME p/r 40-50: .6X TO 1.5X DBL p/r 75-100
*PRIME p/r 40-50: .5X TO 1.2X DBL p/r 40-65
*PRIME p/r 40-50: .4X TO 1X DBL p/r 20-32
*PRIME p/r 25: .75X TO 2X DBL p/r 75-100
*PRIME p/r 25: .5X TO 1.2X DBL p/r 20-32
*PRIME p/r 15: .75X TO 2X DBL p/r 40-65
*PRIME p/r 15: .6X TO 1.5X DBL p/r 20-32
OVERALL AU-GU ODDS ONE PER PACK
PRINT RUNS B/WN 1-50 COPIES PER
NO PRICING ON QTY OF 10 OR LESS
2 Carlos Beltran Astros Bat-Jsy/25 15.00 40.00
16 Dwight Gooden Jsy-Shoes/45 12.50 30.00
18 Darryl Strawberry Mets Bat-Jsy/50 12.50 30.00
82 Carlos Beltran Royals Hat-Jsy/25 15.00 40.00
148 Magglio Ordonez B-J/15 20.00 50.00
159 Orel Hershiser J-Jsy/25 15.00 40.00
163 Rafael Furcal B-J/15 20.00 50.00
198 Willie McCovey J-P/25 30.00 60.00

2005 Absolute Memorabilia Tools of the Trade Autograph Swatch Triple

*TRIP p/r 75-100: .5X TO 1.2X DBL p/r 75-100
*TRIP p/r 75-100: .4X TO 1X DBL p/r 40-65
*TRIP p/r 75-100: .3X TO .8X DBL p/r 20-32
*TRIP p/r 45-50: .6X TO 1.5X DBL p/r 75-100
*TRIP p/r 45-50: .5X TO 1.2X DBL p/r 40-65
*TRIP p/r 45-50: .4X TO 1X DBL p/r 20-32
*TRIP p/r 25-32: .75X TO 2X DBL p/r 75-100
*TRIP p/r 25-32: .6X TO 1.5X DBL p/r 40-65
*TRIP p/r 25-32: .5X TO 1.2X DBL p/r 25
*TRIP p/r 15: .6X TO 1.5X DBL p/r 20-32
OVERALL AU-GU ODDS ONE PER PACK
PRINT RUNS B/WN 1-100 COPIES PER
NO PRICING ON QTY OF 10 OR LESS
2 Carlos Beltran Astros Bat-Jsy-Jsy/25 15.0040.00
18 Darryl Strawberry Mets 10.00 25.00
Bat-Fld Glv-Shoes/75
73 Cal Ripken Bat-Jsy-Pants/25 90.00 180.00
82 Carlos Beltran 15.00 40.00
Royals Bat-Jsy-Shoes/25
108 Brad Penny FG-J-S/30 10.00 25.00
110 Cal Ripken JK-J-P/25 90.00 180.00
113 Dale Murphy B-J-J/45 20.00 50.00
122 Hank Aaron B-H-J/25 175.00 300.00
126 Hideo Nomo J-J-P/25 175.00 300.00
163 Rafael Furcal B-J-J/25 15.00 40.00
165 R.John D'backs J-J-P/15 60.00 120.00
166 R.John Astros H-J-P/50 40.00 80.00

2005 Absolute Memorabilia Tools of the Trade Autograph Swatch Triple Reverse

*REV p/r 50: .6X TO 1.5X DBL p/r 75-100
*REV p/r 50: .5X TO 1.2X DBL p/r 40-65
*REV p/r 25: .75X TO 2X DBL p/r 75-100
*REV p/r 25: .6X TO 1.5X DBL p/r 40-65
*REV p/r 25: .5X TO 1.2X DBL p/r 20-32
*REV p/r 15: 1X TO 2.5X DBL p/r 75-100
*REV p/r 15: .75X TO 2X DBL p/r 40-65
*REV p/r 15: .6X TO 1.5X DBL p/r 20-32
OVERALL AU-GU ODDS ONE PER PACK
PRINT RUNS B/WN 1-50 COPIES PER
NO PRICING ON QTY OF 10 OR LESS
18 Darryl Strawberry Mets 12.50 30.00
Bat-Fld Glv-Shoes/50
110 Cal Ripken JK-J-P/25 90.00 180.00
113 Dale Murphy B-J-J/15 30.00 60.00
122 Hank Aaron B-H-J/15 175.00 300.00
126 Hideo Nomo J-J-P/15 175.00 300.00
166 R.John Astros H-J-P/25 50.00 100.00

2005 Absolute Memorabilia Tools of the Trade Autograph Swatch Triple Prime Red

*PRIME p/r 25: 1X TO 2.5X DBL p/r 75-100
*PRIME p/r 25: .75X TO 2X DBL p/r 40-65
PRINT RUNS B/WN 1-25 COPIES PER
NO PRICING ON QTY OF 13 OR LESS
PRIME BLACK PRINT RUNS B/WN 1-10 PER
NO PRIME BLK PRICING DUE TO SCARCITY
OVERALL AU-GU ODDS ONE PER PACK
16 Dwight Gooden Bat-Jsy-Jsy/15 30.00 60.00
28 Austin Kearns Bat-Fld Glv-Jsy/25 12.50 30.00

2005 Absolute Memorabilia Tools of the Trade Autograph Swatch Quad

*QUAD p/r 25: 1X TO 2.5X DBL p/r 75-100
*QUAD p/r 25: .75X TO 2X DBL p/r 40-65
*QUAD p/r 25: .6X TO 1.5X DBL p/r 20-32
*QUAD p/r 25: .5X TO 1.2X DBL p/r 15
*QUAD p/r 15: 1X TO 2.5X DBL p/r 40-65
*QUAD p/r 15: .6X TO 1.5X DBL p/r 15-17
OVERALL AU-GU ODDS ONE PER PACK
PRINT RUNS B/WN 1-25 COPIES PER
NO PRICING ON QTY OF 10 OR LESS
23 Don Mattingly Bat-Jkt-Jsy-Shoes/25 60.00 120.00
73 Cal Ripken Bat-Hat-Jkt-Jsy/25 125.00 200.00
83 Mark Grace Bat-Fld Glv-Jsy-Jsy/15 30.0060.00
192 Tony Gwynn FG-J-P-S/25 60.00 120.00

2005 Absolute Memorabilia Tools of the Trade Autograph Swatch Quad Reverse

*REV p/r 15: 1.25X TO 3X DBL p/r 75-100
*REV p/r 15: 1X TO 2.5X DBL p/r 40-65
*REV p/r 15: .75X TO 2X DBL p/r 20-32
*REV p/r 15: .6X TO 1.5X DBL p/r 15-17
OVERALL AU-GU ODDS ONE PER PACK
PRINT RUNS B/WN 1-15 COPIES PER
NO PRICING ON QTY OF 10 OR LESS
23 Don Mattingly 75.00 150.00
Bat-Jkt-Jsy-Shoes/15
73 Cal Ripken Bat-Hat-Jkt-Jsy/15 150.00 250.00
77 Deion Sanders Bat-Jsy-Jsy-Pants/15 50.00
100.00

2005 Absolute Memorabilia Tools of the Trade Autograph Swatch Quad Prime Red

PRINT RUNS B/WN 1-10 COPIES PER
PRIME BLACK PRINT RUN 1 #'d SET
OVERALL AU-GU ODDS ONE PER PACK
NO PRICING DUE TO SCARCITY

2005 Artifacts

This product was released in April, 2005 but cards 201-285 were released within packs of '05 Upper Deck Update in February, 2006. The product was issued in four-card packs which came 10 packs to a box and 20 boxes to a case. The first 100 cards of the set feature active veterans while cards 101-150 feature leading prospects and cards 151-200 feature retired greats. Cards 101-150 were issued at a stated rate of one in five and were issued to a state print run of 1350 serial numbered sets while cards 151-200 were inserted at a stated rate of one in three and were issued to a stated print run of 1999 serial numbered sets. Cards 201-285 are serial #'d of 799.

COMP.SET w/o SP's (100) 15.00 40.00
COMMON CARD (1-100) .20 .50
COMMON CARD (101-150) 1.25 3.00
COMMON CARD (151-200) 1.25 3.00
COMMON CARD (201-285) 1.25 3.00
201-285 ISSUED IN 05 UD UPDATE PACKS
201-285: ONE #'d CARD OR AU PER PACK
201-285 PRINT RUN 799 SERIAL #'d SETS
1 Adam Dunn .20 .50
2 Adrian Beltre .20 .50
3 Albert Pujols 1.00 2.50
4 Alex Rodriguez .75 2.00
5 Alfonso Soriano .20 .50
6 Andruw Jones .30 .75
7 Andy Pettitte .30 .75
8 Aramis Ramirez .20 .50
9 Aubrey Huff .20 .50
10 Barry Larkin .30 .75
11 Ben Sheets .20 .50
12 Bernie Williams .30 .75
13 Bobby Abreu .20 .50
14 Brad Penny .20 .50
15 Bret Boone .20 .50
16 Brian Giles .20 .50
17 Carl Crawford .20 .50
18 Carl Pavano .20 .50
19 Carlos Beltran .20 .50
20 Carlos Delgado .20 .50
21 Carlos Guillen .20 .50
22 Carlos Lee .20 .50
23 Carlos Zambrano .20 .50
24 Chipper Jones .50 1.25
25 Craig Biggio .30 .75
26 Craig Wilson .20 .50
27 Curt Schilling .30 .75
28 David Ortiz .50 1.25
29 Derek Jeter 1.00 2.50
30 Eric Chavez .20 .50
31 Eric Gagne .20 .50
32 Frank Thomas .50 1.25
33 Garret Anderson .20 .50
34 Gary Sheffield .20 .50
35 Greg Maddux .75 2.00
36 Hank Blalock .20 .50
37 Hideki Matsui .75 2.00
38 Ichiro Suzuki 1.00 2.50
39 Ivan Rodriguez .30 .75
40 J.D. Drew .20 .50
41 Jake Peavy .20 .50
42 Jason Kendall .20 .50
43 Jason Schmidt .20 .50
44 Jeff Bagwell .30 .75
45 Jeff Kent .20 .50
46 Jim Edmonds .20 .50
47 Jim Thome .30 .75
48 Joe Mauer .50 1.25
49 Johan Santana .50 1.25
50 John Smoltz .30 .75
51 Jose Reyes .20 .50
52 Jose Vidro .20 .50
53 Josh Beckett .20 .50
54 Ken Griffey Jr. .75 2.00
55 Kerry Wood .20 .50
56 Kevin Brown .20 .50
57 Lance Berkman .20 .50
58 Larry Walker .30 .75
59 Livan Hernandez .20 .50
60 Luis Gonzalez .20 .50
61 Lyle Overbay .20 .50
62 Magglio Ordonez .20 .50
63 Manny Ramirez .30 .75
64 Mark Mulder .20 .50
65 Mark Prior .30 .75
66 Mark Teixeira .30 .75
67 Melvin Mora .20 .50
68 Michael Young .20 .50
69 Miguel Cabrera .30 .75
70 Miguel Tejada .20 .50
71 Mike Lowell .20 .50
72 Mike Mussina .30 .75
73 Mike Piazza .50 1.25
74 Mike Sweeney .20 .50
75 Nomar Garciaparra .50 1.25
76 Oliver Perez .20 .50
77 Paul Konerko .20 .50
78 Pedro Martinez .30 .75
79 Preston Wilson .20 .50
80 Rafael Furcal .20 .50
81 Rafael Palmeiro .30 .75
82 Randy Johnson .50 1.25
83 Richie Sexson .20 .50
84 Roger Clemens .75 2.00
85 Roy Halladay .20 .50
86 Roy Oswalt .20 .50
87 Sammy Sosa .50 1.25
88 Scott Podsednik .20 .50
89 Scott Rolen .30 .75
90 Shawn Green .20 .50
91 Steve Finley .20 .50
92 Tim Hudson .20 .50
93 Todd Helton .30 .75
94 Tom Glavine .30 .75
95 Torii Hunter .20 .50

96 Travis Hafner .20 .50
97 Troy Glaus .20 .50
98 Vernon Wells .20 .50
99 Victor Martinez .20 .50
100 Vladimir Guerrero .50 1.25
101 Aaron Rowand FS 1.25 3.00
102 Adam LaRoche FS 1.25 3.00
103 Adrian Gonzalez FS 1.25 3.00
104 Alexis Rios FS 1.25 3.00
105 Angel Guzman FS 1.25 3.00
106 B.J. Upton FS 1.25 3.00
107 Bobby Crosby FS 1.25 3.00
108 Bobby Madritsch FS 1.25 3.00
109 Brandon Claussen FS 1.25 3.00
110 Bucky Jacobsen FS 1.25 3.00
111 Casey Kotchman FS 1.25 3.00
112 Chad Cordero FS 1.25 3.00
113 Chase Utley FS 1.50 4.00
114 Chris Burke FS 1.25 3.00
115 Dallas McPherson FS 1.25 3.00
116 Daniel Cabrera FS 1.25 3.00
117 David DeJesus FS 1.25 3.00
118 David Wright FS 3.00 8.00
119 Eddy Rodriguez FS 1.25 3.00
120 Edwin Jackson FS 1.25 3.00
121 Gabe Gross FS 1.25 3.00
122 Garrett Atkins FS 1.25 3.00
123 Gavin Floyd FS 1.25 3.00
124 Gerald Laird FS 1.25 3.00
125 Guillermo Quiroz FS 1.25 3.00
126 J.D. Closser FS 1.25 3.00
127 Jason Bay FS 1.25 3.00
128 Jason DuBois FS 1.25 3.00
129 Jason Lane FS 1.25 3.00
130 Jayson Werth FS 1.25 3.00
131 Jeff Francis FS 1.25 3.00
132 Jesse Crain FS 1.25 3.00
133 Joe Blanton FS 1.25 3.00
134 Joe Mauer FS 2.00 5.00
135 Jose Capellan FS 1.25 3.00
136 Kevin Youkilis FS 1.25 3.00
137 Khalil Greene FS 1.50 4.00
138 Laynce Nix FS 1.25 3.00
139 Nick Swisher FS 1.25 3.00
140 Oliver Perez FS 1.25 3.00
141 Rickie Weeks FS 1.25 3.00
142 Robb Quinlan FS 1.25 3.00
143 Roman Colon FS 1.25 3.00
144 Ryan Howard FS 2.00 5.00
145 Ryan Wagner FS 1.25 3.00
146 Scott Kazmir FS 1.25 3.00
147 Scott Proctor FS 1.25 3.00
148 Wily Mo Pena FS 1.25 3.00
149 Yhency Brazoban FS 1.25 3.00
150 Zack Greinke FS 1.25 3.00
151 Al Kaline LGD 1.50 4.00
152 Babe Ruth LGD 4.00 10.00
153 Billy Williams LGD 1.25 3.00
154 Bob Feller LGD 1.25 3.00
155 Bob Gibson LGD 1.25 3.00
156 Bob Lemon LGD 1.25 3.00
157 Bobby Doerr LGD 1.25 3.00
158 Brooks Robinson LGD 1.25 3.00
159 Cal Ripken LGD 4.00 10.00
160 Christy Mathewson LGD 1.50 4.00
161 Cy Young LGD 1.50 4.00
162 Dizzy Dean LGD 1.25 3.00
163 Don Drysdale LGD 1.25 3.00
164 Eddie Mathews LGD 1.50 4.00
165 Enos Slaughter LGD 1.25 3.00
166 Ernie Banks LGD 1.50 4.00
167 Fergie Jenkins LGD 1.25 3.00
168 George Sisler LGD 1.25 3.00
169 Harmon Killebrew LGD 1.50 4.00
170 Honus Wagner LGD 1.50 4.00
171 Jackie Robinson LGD 1.50 4.00
172 Jimmie Foxx LGD 1.50 4.00
173 Joe DiMaggio LGD 2.00 5.00
174 Joe Morgan LGD 1.25 3.00
175 Juan Marichal LGD 1.25 3.00
176 Lou Brock LGD 1.25 3.00
177 Lou Gehrig LGD 2.00 5.00
178 Luis Aparicio LGD 1.25 3.00
179 Mel Ott LGD 1.25 3.00
180 Mickey Cochrane LGD 1.25 3.00
181 Mickey Mantle LGD 6.00 15.00
182 Mike Schmidt LGD 2.00 5.00
183 Nolan Ryan LGD 3.00 8.00
184 Pee Wee Reese LGD 1.25 3.00
185 Phil Rizzuto LGD 1.25 3.00
186 Ralph Kiner LGD 1.25 3.00
187 Rogers Hornsby LGD 1.25 3.00
188 Roy Campanella LGD 1.50 4.00
189 Satchel Paige LGD 1.50 4.00
190 Stan Musial LGD 1.50 4.00
191 Rick Ferrell LGD 1.25 3.00
192 Thurman Munson LGD 1.50 4.00
193 Tom Seaver LGD 1.25 3.00
194 Ty Cobb LGD 1.50 4.00
195 Walter Johnson LGD 1.50 4.00
196 Warren Spahn LGD 1.25 3.00
197 Whitey Ford LGD 1.25 3.00
198 Willie McCovey LGD 1.25 3.00
199 Willie Stargell LGD 1.25 3.00
200 Yogi Berra LGD 1.50 4.00
201 Adam Shabala FS RC 1.25 3.00
202 Ambiorix Burgos FS RC 1.25 3.00
203 Ambiorix Concepcion FS RC 1.25 3.00
204 Anibal Sanchez FS RC 3.00 8.00
205 Bill McCarthy FS RC 1.25 3.00
206 Brandon McCarthy FS RC 1.50 4.00
207 Brian Burres FS RC 1.25 3.00
208 Carlos Ruiz FS RC 1.25 3.00
209 Casey Rogowski FS RC 1.50 4.00
210 Chad Orvella FS RC 1.25 3.00
211 Chris Resop FS RC 1.25 3.00
212 Chris Roberson FS RC 1.25 3.00
213 Chris Seddon FS RC 1.25 3.00
214 Colter Bean FS RC 1.25 3.00
215 Dae-Sung Koo FS RC 1.25 3.00
216 Dave Gassner FS RC 1.25 3.00
217 Brian Anderson FS RC 1.50 4.00
218 D.J. Houlton FS RC 1.25 3.00
219 Derek Wathan FS RC 1.25 3.00
220 Devon Lowery FS RC 1.25 3.00
221 Enrique Gonzalez FS RC 1.25 3.00
222 Eude Brito FS RC 1.25 3.00
223 Francisco Butto FS RC 1.25 3.00
224 Franquelis Osoria FS RC 1.25 3.00
225 Garrett Jones FS RC 1.25 3.00
226 Geovany Soto FS RC 6.00 15.00
227 Hayden Penn FS RC 1.50 4.00
228 Ismael Ramirez FS RC 1.25 3.00
229 Jared Gothreaux FS RC 1.25 3.00
230 Jason Hammel FS RC 1.25 3.00
231 Jeff Miller FS RC 1.25 3.00
232 Jeff Niemann FS RC 1.50 4.00
233 Joel Peralta FS RC 1.25 3.00
234 John Hattig FS RC 1.25 3.00
235 Jorge Campillo FS RC 1.25 3.00
236 Juan Morillo FS RC 1.25 3.00
237 Justin Verlander FS RC 4.00 10.00
238 Ryan Garko FS RC 2.00 5.00
239 Keiichi Yabu FS RC 1.25 3.00
240 Kendry Morales FS RC 2.00 5.00
241 Luis Hernandez FS RC 1.25 3.00
242 Luis Pena FS RC 1.25 3.00
243 Luis O.Rodriguez FS RC 1.25 3.00
244 Luke Scott FS RC 2.00 5.00
245 Marcos Carvajal FS RC 1.25 3.00
246 Mark Woodyard FS RC 1.25 3.00
247 Matt A.Smith FS RC 1.25 3.00
248 Matthew Lindstrom FS RC 1.25 3.00
249 Miguel Negron FS RC 1.50 4.00
250 Mike Morse FS RC 1.25 3.00
251 Nate McLouth FS RC 1.50 4.00
252 Nelson Cruz FS RC 2.00 5.00
253 Nick Masset FS RC 1.25 3.00
254 Oscar Robles FS RC 1.25 3.00
255 Paulino Reynoso FS RC 1.25 3.00
256 Pedro Lopez FS RC 1.25 3.00
257 Pete Orr FS RC 1.25 3.00
258 Philip Humber FS RC 1.50 4.00
259 Prince Fielder FS RC 4.00 10.00
260 Randy Messenger FS RC 1.25 3.00
261 Randy Williams FS RC 1.25 3.00
262 Raul Tablado FS RC 1.25 3.00
263 Ronny Paulino FS RC 1.50 4.00
264 Russ Rohlicek FS RC 1.25 3.00
265 Russell Martin FS RC 2.50 6.00
266 Scott Baker FS RC 1.50 4.00
267 Scott Munter FS RC 1.25 3.00
268 Sean Thompson FS RC 1.25 3.00
269 Sean Tracey FS RC 1.25 3.00
270 Shane Costa FS RC 1.25 3.00
271 Stephen Drew FS RC 4.00 10.00
272 Steve Schmoll FS RC 1.25 3.00
273 Tadahito Iguchi FS RC 2.00 5.00
274 Tony Giarratano FS RC 1.25 3.00
275 Tony Pena FS RC 1.25 3.00
276 Travis Bowyer FS RC 1.25 3.00
277 Ubaldo Jimenez FS RC 2.50 6.00
278 Wladimir Balentien FS RC 1.50 4.00
279 Yorman Bazardo FS RC 1.25 3.00
280 Yuniesky Betancourt FS RC 2.00 5.00
281 Ryan Zimmerman FS RC 6.00 15.00
282 Chris Denorfia FS RC 1.50 4.00
283 Dana Eveland FS RC 1.25 3.00
284 Jermaine Van Buren FS 1.25 3.00
285 Mark McLemore FS RC 1.25 3.00

2005 Artifacts Rainbow Blue

*BLUE 1-100: 2.5X TO 6X BASIC
*BLUE 101-150: .6X TO 1.5X BASIC
*BLUE POST-WAR 151-200: .75X TO 2X
*BLUE PRE-WAR 151-200: .6X TO 1.5X
1-200 OVERALL PARALLEL ODDS 1:10
*BLUE 201-285: .6X TO 1.5X BASIC
201-285 ISSUED IN '05 UD UPDATE PACKS
201-285 ONE #'d CARD OR AU PER PACK
STATED PRINT RUN 100 SERIAL #'d SETS
1 Adam Dunn 1.25 3.00
181 Mickey Mantle LGD 20.00 50.00

2005 Artifacts Rainbow Gold

*GOLD 1-100: 6X TO 15X BASIC
*GOLD 101-150: 1.5X TO 4X BASIC
*GOLD POST-WAR 151-200: 2X TO 5X
*GOLD PRE-WAR 151-200: 1.5X TO 4X
1-200 OVERALL PARALLEL ODDS 1:10
201-285 ISSUED IN '05 UD UPDATE PACKS
201-285 ONE #'d CARD OR AU PER PACK
STATED PRINT RUN 25 SERIAL #'d SETS
201-285 NO PRICING DUE TO SCARCITY
1 Adam Dunn 3.00 8.00
181 Mickey Mantle LGD 60.00 120.00

2005 Artifacts Rainbow Platinum

1-200 OVERALL PARALLEL ODDS 1:10
201-285 ISSUED IN '05 UD UPDATE PACKS
201-285 ONE #'d CARD OR AU PER PACK
STATED PRINT RUN 1 SERIAL #'d SET
NO PRICING DUE TO SCARCITY
1 Adam Dunn

2005 Artifacts Rainbow Red

*RED 1-100: 4X TO 10X BASIC
*RED 101-150: 1X TO 2.5X BASIC
*RED POST-WAR 151-200: 1.25X TO 3X
*RED PRE-WAR 151-200: 1X TO 2.5X
1-200 OVERALL PARALLEL ODDS 1:10
*RED 201-285: 1X TO 2.5X BASIC
201-285 ISSUED IN '05 UD UPDATE PACKS
201-285 ONE #'d CARD OR AU PER PACK
STATED PRINT RUN 50 SERIAL #'d SETS
1 Adam Dunn 2.00 5.00
181 Mickey Mantle LGD 40.00 80.00

2005 Artifacts AL/NL Artifacts

OVERALL GAME-USED ODDS 1:3
PRINT RUNS B/WN 100-325 COPIES PER
AB Adrian Beltre Jsy/325 3.00 8.00
AD Andre Dawson Jsy/325 3.00 8.00
AH Aubrey Huff Jsy/325 3.00 8.00
AK Al Kaline Jsy/325 5.00 12.00
AO Akinori Otsuka Jsy/325 3.00 8.00
AP Albert Pujols Jsy/325 6.00 15.00
BA Bobby Abreu Jsy/325 3.00 8.00
BB Bert Blyleven Jsy/325 3.00 8.00
BC Bobby Crosby Jsy/325 3.00 8.00
BD Bobby Doerr Bat/325 3.00 8.00
BE Johnny Bench Jsy/325 5.00 12.00
BF Bob Feller Pants/325 4.00 10.00
BG Bob Gibson Pants/325 4.00 10.00
BPA Boog Powell Jsy/325 3.00 8.00
BPN Brad Penny Jsy/325 3.00 8.00
BR Brooks Robinson Jsy/325 4.00 10.00
BS Ben Sheets Jsy/325 3.00 8.00
BU B.J. Upton Jsy/325 3.00 8.00
CA Steve Carlton Jsy/325 3.00 8.00
CB Carlos Beltran Jsy/325 3.00 8.00
CK Casey Kotchman Jsy/325 3.00 8.00
CP Corey Patterson Jsy/325 3.00 8.00
CR Cal Ripken Jsy/325 10.00 25.00
CY Carl Yastrzemski Jsy/325 6.00 15.00
CZ Carlos Zambrano Jsy/325 3.00 8.00
DG Dwight Gooden Pants/325 3.00 8.00
DJ Derek Jeter Jsy/325 8.00 20.00
DK Dave Kingman Bat/325 3.00 8.00
DL Derrek Lee Jsy/325 3.00 8.00
DMA Dallas McPherson Jsy/325 3.00 8.00
DMN Dale Murphy Jsy/150 4.00 10.00
DO David Ortiz Jsy/325 3.00 8.00
DW David Wright Jsy/325 6.00 15.00
EC Eric Chavez Jsy/325 3.00 8.00
EG Eric Gagne Jsy/325 3.00 8.00
FL Fred Lynn Bat/325 3.00 8.00
FR Frank Robinson Jsy/325 3.00 8.00
GB George Brett Jsy/325 6.00 15.00
GI Brian Giles Jsy/325 3.00 8.00
GK George Kell Bat/325 3.00 8.00
GM Greg Maddux Jsy/275 6.00 15.00
GN Graig Nettles Jsy/325 3.00 8.00
GR Ken Griffey Sr. Jsy/325 3.00 8.00
HB Hank Blalock Jsy/325 3.00 8.00
HK Harmon Killebrew Jsy/325 5.00 12.00
JB Jason Bay Jsy/325 3.00 8.00
JK Jim Kaat Jsy/325 3.00 8.00
JM Joe Mauer Jsy/325 3.00 8.00
JPA Jim Palmer Jsy/325 3.00 8.00
JPN Jake Peavy Jsy/325 3.00 8.00
JRA Jim Rice Jsy/325 3.00 8.00
JRN Jose Reyes Jsy/250 3.00 8.00
JSA Johan Santana Jsy/325 4.00 10.00
JSN Jason Schmidt Jsy/325 3.00 8.00
KG Ken Griffey Jr. Jsy/325 6.00 15.00
KHA Kent Hrbek Jsy/325 3.00 8.00
KHN Keith Hernandez Bat/325 3.00 8.00
KL Khalil Greene Jsy/325 3.00 8.00
KW Kerry Wood Jsy/325 3.00 8.00
LN Laynce Nix Jsy/325 3.00 8.00
MA Don Mattingly Jsy/325 6.00 15.00
MC Miguel Cabrera Jsy/325 3.00 8.00
MG Marcus Giles Jsy/325 3.00 8.00
MK Mark Grace Jsy/175 4.00 10.00
ML Mike Lowell Jsy/325 3.00 8.00
MM Mark Mulder Jsy/325 3.00 8.00
MP Mark Prior Jsy/325 3.00 8.00
MS Mike Schmidt Jsy/325 6.00 15.00
MT Mark Teixeira Jsy/325 3.00 8.00
MW Maury Wills Jsy/325 3.00 8.00
MY Michael Young Jsy/325 3.00 8.00
NR Nolan Ryan Jsy/325 8.00 20.00
OC Orlando Cepeda Jsy/185 3.00 8.00
PM Paul Molitor Jsy/325 3.00 8.00
PN Phil Niekro Jsy/325 3.00 8.00
RCA Rod Carew Jsy/325 4.00 10.00
RCN Roger Clemens Jsy/325 4.00 10.00
RH Rich Harden Jsy/325 3.00 8.00
RJ Randy Johnson Jsy/325 4.00 10.00
RK Ralph Kiner Bat/325 4.00 10.00
RO Roy Oswalt Jsy/325 3.00 8.00
RP Rico Petrocelli Pants/325 3.00 8.00
RW Rickie Weeks Jsy/325 3.00 8.00
RY Robin Yount Jsy/325 5.00 12.00
SC Sean Casey Jsy/325 3.00 8.00
SL Sparky Lyle Pants/325 3.00 8.00
SM John Smoltz Jsy/325 3.00 8.00
SP Scott Podsednik Jsy/325 3.00 8.00
SR Scott Rolen Jsy/325 3.00 8.00
ST Shingo Takatsu Jsy/325 3.00 8.00
SU Bruce Sutter Jsy/325 3.00 8.00
TG Tony Gwynn Jsy/325 5.00 12.00
TH Travis Hafner Jsy/325 3.00 8.00
TS Tom Seaver Jsy/325 4.00 10.00
VM Victor Martinez Jsy/325 3.00 8.00
WB Wade Boggs Jsy/325 4.00 10.00
WC Will Clark Jsy/100 5.00 12.00
WM Willie McCovey Jsy/325 4.00 10.00
YB Yogi Berra Pants/325 6.00 15.00

2005 Artifacts AL/NL Artifacts Rainbow

*RAINBOW p/r 99: .5X TO 1.2X p/r 150-325
*RAINBOW p/r 50: .5X TO 1.2X p/r 100
OVERALL GAME-USED ODDS 1:3
PRINT RUNS B/WN 50-99 COPIES PER

2005 Artifacts AL/NL Artifacts Signatures

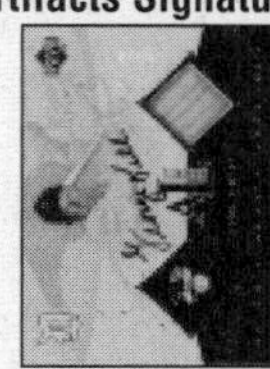

STATED PRINT RUN 30 SERIAL #'d SETS
RARE PRINT RUN 1 SERIAL #'d SET
NO RARE PRICING DUE TO SCARCITY
OVERALL AUTO ODDS 1:10
EXCHANGE DEADLINE 04/11/08
AB Adrian Beltre Jsy 10.00 25.00
AD Andre Dawson Jsy 10.00 25.00
AH Aubrey Huff Jsy 10.00 25.00
AK Al Kaline Jsy 30.00 60.00
AO Akinori Otsuka Jsy 15.00 40.00
AP Albert Pujols Jsy EXCH 150.00 250.00
BA Bobby Abreu Jsy EXCH 10.00 25.00
BB Bert Blyleven Jsy 10.00 25.00
BC Bobby Crosby Jsy EXCH 10.00 25.00
BD Bobby Doerr Bat 10.00 25.00
BE Johnny Bench Jsy 30.00 60.00
BF Bob Feller Pants 15.00 40.00
BG Bob Gibson Pants 15.00 40.00
BM Bill Mazeroski Jsy EXCH 15.00 40.00
BPA Boog Powell Jsy 15.00 40.00
BPN Brad Penny Jsy 10.00 25.00
BR Brooks Robinson Jsy 30.00 60.00
BS Ben Sheets Jsy EXCH 15.00 40.00
BU B.J. Upton Jsy 10.00 25.00
CA Steve Carlton Jsy 10.00 25.00
CB Carlos Beltran Jsy EXCH 10.00 25.00
CK Casey Kotchman Jsy 10.00 25.00
CP Corey Patterson Jsy EXCH 6.00 15.00
CR Cal Ripken Jsy 125.00 200.00
CY Carl Yastrzemski Jsy 40.00 80.00
CZ Carlos Zambrano Jsy 15.00 40.00
DG Dwight Gooden Pants 10.00 25.00
DJ Derek Jeter Jsy 125.00 200.00
DK Dave Kingman Bat 10.00 25.00
DL Derrek Lee Jsy 15.00 40.00
DMA Dallas McPherson Jsy EXCH 6.00 15.00
DMN Dale Murphy Jsy 15.00 40.00
DO David Ortiz Jsy 30.00 60.00
DW David Wright Jsy 40.00 80.00
EC Eric Chavez Jsy 10.00 25.00
EG Eric Gagne Jsy EXCH 15.00 40.00
FL Fred Lynn Bat 10.00 25.00
FR Frank Robinson Jsy 15.00 40.00
GB George Brett Jsy 50.00 100.00
GI Brian Giles Jsy 10.00 25.00
GK George Kell Bat 10.00 25.00
GM Greg Maddux Jsy EXCH
GN Graig Nettles Jsy 15.00 40.00
GR Ken Griffey Sr. Jsy 10.00 25.00
HB Hank Blalock Jsy 10.00 25.00
HK Harmon Killebrew Jsy 30.00 60.00
JB Jason Bay Jsy 10.00 25.00
JK Jim Kaat Jsy 10.00 25.00
JM Joe Mauer Jsy EXCH 15.00 40.00
JPA Jim Palmer Jsy 15.00 40.00
JPN Jake Peavy Jsy 15.00 40.00
JRA Jim Rice Jsy 10.00 25.00
JRN Jose Reyes Jsy EXCH 15.00 40.00
JSA Johan Santana Jsy EXCH 15.00 40.00
JSN Jason Schmidt Jsy 10.00 25.00
KG Ken Griffey Jr. Jsy 75.00 150.00
KHA Kent Hrbek Jsy 30.00 60.00
KHN Keith Hernandez Bat 10.00 25.00
KL Khalil Greene Jsy 15.00 40.00
KW Kerry Wood Jsy 15.00 40.00
LN Laynce Nix Jsy 6.00 15.00
MA Don Mattingly Jsy 50.00 100.00
MC Miguel Cabrera Jsy 15.00 40.00
MG Marcus Giles Jsy 10.00 25.00
MK Mark Grace Jsy 15.00 40.00
ML Mike Lowell Jsy 10.00 25.00
MM Mark Mulder Jsy 10.00 25.00
MP Mark Prior Jsy 15.00 40.00
MS Mike Schmidt Jsy 40.00 80.00
MT Mark Teixeira Jsy 15.00 40.00
MW Maury Wills Jsy 10.00 25.00
MY Michael Young Jsy EXCH 10.00 25.00
NR Nolan Ryan Jsy 75.00 150.00
OC Orlando Cepeda Jsy 15.00 40.00
PM Paul Molitor Jsy 10.00 25.00
PN Phil Niekro Jsy 10.00 25.00
RCA Rod Carew Jsy 15.00 40.00
RCN Roger Clemens Jsy EXCH 75.00 150.00
RH Rich Harden Jsy 10.00 25.00
RJ Randy Johnson Jsy EXCH
RK Ralph Kiner Bat 15.00 40.00
RO Roy Oswalt Jsy 10.00 25.00
RP Rico Petrocelli Pants 10.00 25.00
RW Rickie Weeks Jsy 10.00 25.00
RY Robin Yount Jsy 30.00 60.00
SC Sean Casey Jsy 10.00 25.00
SL Sparky Lyle Pants 10.00 25.00
SM John Smoltz Jsy EXCH 40.00 80.00
SP Scott Podsednik Jsy 15.00 40.00
SR Scott Rolen Jsy EXCH
ST Shingo Takatsu Jsy 10.00 25.00
SU Bruce Sutter Jsy 15.00 40.00
TG Tony Gwynn Jsy 40.00 80.00
TH Travis Hafner Jsy 10.00 25.00
TS Tom Seaver Jsy 30.00 60.00
VM Victor Martinez Jsy 10.00 25.00
WB Wade Boggs Jsy 15.00 40.00
WC Will Clark Jsy 30.00 60.00
WM Willie McCovey Jsy 30.00 60.00
YB Yogi Berra Pants 30.00 60.00

2005 Artifacts Autofacts

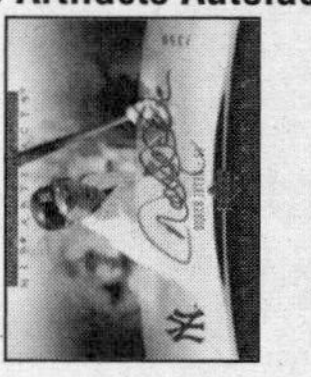

PRINT RUNS B/WN 15-699 COPIES PER
NO PRICING ON QTY OF 15
RAINBOW PRINT RUN 1 SERIAL #'d SET
NO RAINBOW PRICING DUE TO SCARCITY
OVERALL AUTO ODDS 1:10
EXCHANGE DEADLINE 04/11/08
AB Adrian Beltre/75 EXCH 6.00 15.00
AD Andre Dawson/25 10.00 25.00
AH Aubrey Huff/350 6.00 15.00
AK Al Kaline/15
AO Akinori Otsuka/599 10.00 25.00
BC Bobby Crosby/350 EXCH 6.00 15.00
BE Johnny Bench/15
BF Bob Feller/25 15.00 40.00
BH Burt Hooton/599 4.00 10.00
BM Bill Mazeroski/15
BP Brad Penny/599 4.00 10.00
BR Brooks Robinson/25 20.00 50.00
BS Ben Sheets/75 EXCH 10.00 25.00
BU B.J. Upton/599 6.00 15.00
CA Rod Carew/15
CB Carlos Beltran/15 EXCH
CK Casey Kotchman/599 6.00 15.00
CP Corey Patterson/75 EXCH 4.00 10.00
CR Cal Ripken/15
CY Carl Yastrzemski/15
DG1 Dwight Gooden Mets/350 6.00 15.00
DG2 Dwight Gooden Yanks/350 6.00 15.00
DJ Derek Jeter/350 75.00 150.00
DK Dave Kingman/75 6.00 15.00
DM Dale Murphy/75 10.00 25.00
DO David Ortiz/15
DW David Wright/599 30.00 60.00
EB Ernie Banks/15
EC Eric Chavez/25 10.00 25.00
EK Ed Kranepool/599 6.00 15.00
FL Fred Lynn/25 10.00 25.00
FR Bill Freehan/599 EXCH 4.00 10.00
GB George Brett/15
GI Marcus Giles/350 6.00 15.00
GK George Kell/15
GN Graig Nettles/75 6.00 15.00
GR Khalil Greene/599 10.00 25.00
HB Hank Blalock/25 10.00 25.00
HK Harmon Killebrew/15
HO Ken Holtzman/599 4.00 10.00
HR Kent Hrbek/599 6.00 15.00
JA Jake Peavy/75 10.00 25.00
JB Jason Bay/599 6.00 15.00
JK1 Jim Kaat Cards/458 6.00 15.00
JK2 Jim Kaat Twins/458 6.00 15.00
JL Jim Lonborg/599 4.00 10.00
JM Joe Mauer/25 EXCH 15.00 40.00
JP Jim Palmer/25 15.00 40.00
JR Ken Griffey Jr./699 30.00 60.00
JS Johan Santana/350 EXCH 15.00 40.00
KG1 Ken Griffey Sr. Reds/699 6.00 15.00
KG2 Ken Griffey Sr. Yanks/699 6.00 15.00
KH1 Keith Hernandez Mets/350 6.00 15.00
KH2 Keith Hernandez Cards/350 6.00 15.00
KW Kerry Wood/15
LD1 Lenny Dykstra Mets/599 6.00 15.00
LD2 Lenny Dykstra Phils/599 6.00 15.00
LN Laynce Nix/599 4.00 10.00
LT Luis Tiant/75 6.00 15.00
MA Don Mattingly/15
MC D.McPherson/599 EXCH 4.00 10.00
MG Mark Grace/25 15.00 40.00
MI Miguel Cabrera/25 15.00 40.00
ML Mike Lowell/75 6.00 15.00
MP Mark Prior/15
MS Mike Schmidt/15
MT Mark Teixeira/25 15.00 40.00
MW Maury Wills/15
MY Michael Young/599 EXCH 6.00 15.00
NG Nomar Garciaparra/15
NR Nolan Ryan/15
OC Orlando Cepeda/25 15.00 40.00
OP Oliver Perez/350 4.00 10.00
PE Jim Perry/599 4.00 10.00
PM Paul Molitor/15
PN1 Phil Niekro Braves/75 6.00 15.00
PN2 Phil Niekro Yanks/75 6.00 15.00
PO Boog Powell/350 6.00 15.00
RC Rocky Colavito/75 40.00 80.00
RH Rich Harden/599 6.00 15.00
RI Jim Rice/25 10.00 25.00
RK Ralph Kiner/25 15.00 40.00
RO Roy Oswalt/350 6.00 15.00
RP Rico Petrocelli/599 6.00 15.00
RW Rickie Weeks/75 6.00 15.00
RY Robin Yount/15
SC Steve Carlton/15
SF Sid Fernandez/599 6.00 15.00
SL1 Sparky Lyle Sox/599 6.00 15.00
SL2 Sparky Lyle Yanks/599 6.00 15.00
SP Scott Podsednik/75 10.00 25.00
ST Shingo Takatsu/599 6.00 15.00
SU Bruce Sutter/350 10.00 25.00
TG Tony Gwynn/15
TH Travis Hafner/599 6.00 15.00
VM Victor Martinez/599 6.00 15.00
WB Wade Boggs/15
WC Will Clark/15
WM Willie McCovey/15
YB Yogi Berra/15

2005 Artifacts Dual Artifacts

COMPLETE SET (100)
OVERALL GAME-USED ODDS 1:3
STATED PRINT RUN 99 SERIAL #'d SETS
CLARK/MCCOVEY PRINT RUN 56 #'d CARDS
KILLEB/MCCOVEY PRINT RUN 44 #'d CARDS
AB Bobby Abreu Jsy 4.00 10.00
Carlos Beltran Jsy
AD Adrian Beltre Jsy 4.00 10.00
Dallas McPherson Jsy
AG Bobby Abreu Jsy 8.00 20.00
Ken Griffey Jr. Jsy
BB George Brett Jsy 10.00 25.00
Wade Boggs Jsy
BC Adrian Beltre Jsy 4.00 10.00
Eric Chavez Jsy
BD Bob Gibson Pants 8.00 20.00
Dwight Gooden Pants
BE Bobby Crosby Jsy 4.00 10.00
Eric Chavez Jsy
BJ Brooks Robinson Jsy 8.00 20.00
Jim Palmer Jsy
BK Jason Bay Jsy 8.00 20.00
Ralph Kiner Bat
BM Brian Giles Jsy 4.00 10.00
Marcus Giles Jsy
BN Hank Blalock Jsy 4.00 10.00
Laynce Nix Jsy
BP Carlos Beltran Jsy 4.00 10.00
Corey Patterson Jsy
BR Ernie Banks Pants 8.00 20.00
Frank Robinson Jsy
BS Ben Sheets Jsy 4.00 10.00
Scott Podsednik Jsy
BY Hank Blalock Jsy 4.00 10.00
Michael Young Jsy
CB Jason Bay Jsy 4.00 10.00
Bobby Crosby Jsy
CC Miguel Cabrera Jsy 6.00 15.00
Orlando Cepeda Jsy
CG Dwight Gooden Pants 6.00 15.00
Gary Carter Jsy
CH Sean Casey Jsy 4.00 10.00
Travis Hafner Jsy
CK Harmon Killebrew Jsy 8.00 20.00
Rod Carew Jsy
CL Miguel Cabrera Jsy 6.00 15.00
Mike Lowell Jsy
CM Will Clark Jsy 12.50 30.00
Willie McCovey Jsy/56
CN Eric Chavez Jsy 6.00 15.00
Graig Nettles Jsy
CO Roger Clemens Jsy 6.00 15.00
Roy Oswalt Jsy
CR Bobby Crosby Jsy 15.00 40.00
Cal Ripken Jsy
DC Andre Dawson Jsy 6.00 15.00
Orlando Cepeda Jsy
DK Bobby Doerr Bat 6.00 15.00
George Kell Bat
FB Carlton Fisk Jsy 8.00 20.00
Johnny Bench Jsy
FW Bob Feller Pants 8.00 20.00
Kerry Wood Jsy
GB Brian Giles Jsy 4.00 10.00
Jason Bay Jsy
GC Ken Griffey Jr. Jsy 8.00 20.00
Sean Casey Jsy
GG Ken Griffey Sr. Jsy 10.00 25.00
Ken Griffey Jr. Jsy
GK Ken Griffey Jr. Jsy 8.00 20.00
Ralph Kiner Bat
GL Eric Gagne Jsy 6.00 15.00
Sparky Lyle Pants
GS Dwight Gooden Pants 8.00 20.00
Tom Seaver Jsy
HC Bobby Crosby Jsy 4.00 10.00
Rich Harden Jsy
HG Keith Hernandez Bat 8.00 20.00
Mark Grace Jsy
HH Aubrey Huff Jsy 4.00 10.00
Travis Hafner Jsy
HM Travis Hafner Jsy 4.00 10.00
Victor Martinez Jsy
HU Aubrey Huff Jsy 4.00 10.00
B.J. Upton Jsy
HW Harmon Killebrew Jsy 12.50 30.00
Willie McCovey Jsy/44
JG Derek Jeter Jsy 12.50 30.00
Khalil Greene Jsy
JJ Joe Mauer Jsy 6.00 15.00
Johan Santana Jsy

Card	Low	High
JR Jim Rice Jsy / Rico Petrocelli Pants	6.00	15.00
JW Derek Jeter Jsy / Maury Wills Jsy	12.50	30.00
JY Johnny Bench Jsy / Yogi Berra Pants	12.50	30.00
KB Jim Kaat Jsy / Bert Blyleven Jsy	6.00	15.00
KC Jim Kaat Jsy / Steve Carlton Jsy	6.00	15.00
KD Keith Hernandez Bat / Don Mattingly Jsy	10.00	25.00
KK Al Kaline Jsy / Ralph Kiner Bat	8.00	20.00
KM Al Kaline Jsy / Dale Murphy Jsy	8.00	20.00
KN Jim Kaat Jsy / Phil Niekro Jsy	6.00	15.00
LC Derrek Lee Jsy / Sean Casey Jsy	6.00	15.00
LG Derrek Lee Jsy / Mark Grace Jsy	8.00	20.00
LP Fred Lynn Bat / Rico Petrocelli Pants	6.00	15.00
LR Fred Lynn Bat / Jim Rice Jsy	6.00	15.00
MC Don Mattingly Jsy / Will Clark Jsy	10.00	25.00
MD Bill Mazeroski Jsy / Bobby Doerr Bat	8.00	20.00
MH Mark Mulder Jsy / Rich Harden Jsy	4.00	10.00
MK Bill Mazeroski Jsy / Ralph Kiner Bat	8.00	20.00
MM Joe Mauer Jsy / Victor Martinez Jsy	4.00	10.00
MS Dale Murphy Jsy / Mike Schmidt Jsy	12.50	30.00
MW Paul Molitor Jsy / Rickie Weeks Jsy	6.00	15.00
NL Graig Nettles Jsy / Sparky Lyle Pants	6.00	15.00
NT Laynce Nix Jsy / Mark Teixeira Jsy	8.00	20.00
NY Laynce Nix Jsy / Michael Young Jsy	6.00	15.00
OF David Ortiz Jsy / Carlton Fisk Jsy	8.00	20.00
OG Akinori Otsuka Jsy / Khalil Greene Jsy	6.00	15.00
OP Akinori Otsuka Jsy / Jake Peavy Jsy	6.00	15.00
OT Akinori Otsuka Jsy / Shingo Takatsu Jsy	6.00	15.00
PD Andre Dawson Jsy / Corey Patterson Jsy	6.00	15.00
PG Brad Penny Jsy / Eric Gagne Jsy	4.00	10.00
PH Jake Peavy Jsy / Rich Harden Jsy	4.00	10.00
PP Boog Powell Jsy / Jim Palmer Jsy	6.00	15.00
PR Boog Powell Jsy / Brooks Robinson Jsy	10.00	25.00
PS Brad Penny Jsy / Jason Schmidt Jsy	4.00	10.00
RB Ernie Banks Pants / Cal Ripken Jsy	20.00	50.00
RC Nolan Ryan Jsy / Steve Carlton Jsy	12.50	30.00
RJ Jose Reyes Jsy / Rickie Weeks Jsy	4.00	10.00
RP Frank Robinson Jsy / Boog Powell Jsy	6.00	15.00
RR Frank Robinson Jsy / Brooks Robinson Jsy	10.00	25.00
RW David Wright Jsy / Scott Rolen Jsy	6.00	15.00
SB Bert Blyleven Jsy / Johan Santana Jsy	8.00	20.00
SC Johan Santana Jsy / Roger Clemens Jsy	8.00	20.00
SF Ben Sheets Jsy / Bob Feller Pants	8.00	20.00
SG Bruce Sutter Jsy / Eric Gagne Jsy	6.00	15.00
SM Jason Schmidt Jsy / Mark Mulder Jsy	4.00	10.00
SO Ben Sheets Jsy / Roy Oswalt Jsy	4.00	10.00
SP Ben Sheets Jsy / Brad Penny Jsy	4.00	10.00
TH Mark Teixeira Jsy / Travis Hafner Jsy	6.00	15.00
TL Shingo Takatsu Jsy / Sparky Lyle Pants	6.00	15.00
TY Mark Teixeira Jsy / Michael Young Jsy	6.00	15.00
UJ B.J. Upton Jsy / Derek Jeter Jsy	12.50	30.00
WL David Wright Jsy / Mike Lowell Jsy	6.00	15.00
WR David Wright Jsy / Jose Reyes Jsy	8.00	20.00
YM Robin Yount Jsy / Paul Molitor Jsy	12.50	30.00
YP Carl Yastrzemski Jsy / Rico Petrocelli Pants	10.00	25.00
ZM Carlos Zambrano Jsy / Greg Maddux Jsy	8.00	20.00
ZP Carlos Zambrano Jsy / Mark Prior Jsy	6.00	15.00
ZW Carlos Zambrano Jsy / Kerry Wood Jsy	4.00	10.00

2005 Artifacts Dual Artifacts Rainbow

*RAINBOW: .6X TO 1.5X p/r 99
*RAINBOW: .5X TO 1.2X p/r 44-56
OVERALL GAME-USED ODDS 1:3
STATED PRINT RUN 25 SERIAL #'d SETS

2005 Artifacts Dual Artifacts Signatures

OVERALL AUTO ODDS 1:10
STATED PRINT RUN 10 SERIAL #'d SETS
NO PRICING DUE TO SCARCITY
EXCHANGE DEADLINE 04/11/08

AB Bobby Abreu Jsy / Carlos Beltran Jsy EXCH
AD Adrian Beltre Jsy / Dallas McPherson Jsy
AG Bobby Abreu Jsy / Ken Griffey Jr. Jsy EXCH
BB George Brett Jsy / Wade Boggs Jsy
BC Adrian Beltre Jsy / Eric Chavez Jsy EXCH
BD Bob Gibson Pants / Dwight Gooden Pants
BE Bobby Crosby Jsy / Eric Chavez Jsy
BJ Brooks Robinson Jsy / Jim Palmer Jsy
BK Jason Bay Jsy / Ralph Kiner Bat
BM Brian Giles Jsy / Marcus Giles Jsy
BN Hank Blalock Jsy / Laynce Nix Jsy
BP Carlos Beltran Jsy / Corey Patterson Jsy
BR Ernie Banks Pants / Frank Robinson Jsy
BS Ben Sheets Jsy / Scott Podsednik Jsy EXCH
BY Hank Blalock Jsy / Michael Young Jsy EXCH
CB Jason Bay Jsy / Bobby Crosby Jsy EXCH
CC Miguel Cabrera Jsy / Orlando Cepeda Jsy
CG Dwight Gooden Pants / Gary Carter Jsy
CH Sean Casey Jsy / Travis Hafner Jsy
CK Harmon Killebrew Jsy / Rod Carew Jsy
CL Miguel Cabrera Jsy / Mike Lowell Jsy
CM Will Clark Jsy / Willie McCovey Jsy
CN Eric Chavez Jsy / Graig Nettles Jsy
CO Roger Clemens Jsy / Roy Oswalt Jsy EXCH
CR Bobby Crosby Jsy / Cal Ripken Jsy EXCH
DC Andre Dawson Jsy / Orlando Cepeda Jsy
DK Bobby Doerr Bat / George Kell Bat
FB Carlton Fisk Jsy / Johnny Bench Jsy
FW Bob Feller Pants / Kerry Wood Jsy
GB Brian Giles Jsy / Jason Bay Jsy
GC Ken Griffey Jr. Jsy / Sean Casey Jsy
GG Ken Griffey Sr. Jsy / Ken Griffey Jr. Jsy
GK Ken Griffey Jr. Jsy / Ralph Kiner Bat
GL Eric Gagne Jsy / Sparky Lyle Pants EXCH
GS Dwight Gooden Pants / Tom Seaver Jsy
HC Bobby Crosby Jsy / Rich Harden Jsy EXCH
HG Keith Hernandez Bat / Mark Grace Jsy
HH Aubrey Huff Jsy / Travis Hafner Jsy EXCH
HM Travis Hafner Jsy / Victor Martinez Jsy
HU Aubrey Huff Jsy / B.J. Upton Jsy EXCH
HW Harmon Killebrew Jsy / Willie McCovey Jsy
JG Derek Jeter Jsy / Khalil Greene Jsy
JJ Joe Mauer Jsy / Johan Santana Jsy EXCH
JR Jim Rice Jsy / Rico Petrocelli Pants
JW Derek Jeter Jsy / Maury Wills Jsy EXCH
JY Johnny Bench Jsy / Yogi Berra Pants
KB Jim Kaat Jsy / Bert Blyleven Jsy
KC Jim Kaat Jsy / Steve Carlton Jsy
KD Keith Hernandez Bat / Don Mattingly Jsy
KK Al Kaline Jsy / Ralph Kiner Bat
KM Al Kaline Jsy / Dale Murphy Jsy EXCH
KN Jim Kaat Jsy / Phil Niekro Jsy
LC Derrek Lee Jsy / Sean Casey Jsy
LG Derrek Lee Jsy / Mark Grace Jsy
LP Fred Lynn Bat / Rico Petrocelli Pants
LR Fred Lynn Bat / Jim Rice Jsy
MC Don Mattingly Jsy / Will Clark Jsy
MD Bill Mazeroski Jsy / Bobby Doerr Bat
MH Mark Mulder Jsy / Rich Harden Jsy
MK Bill Mazeroski Jsy / Ralph Kiner Bat
MM Joe Mauer Jsy / Victor Martinez Jsy EXCH
MS Dale Murphy Jsy / Mike Schmidt Jsy
MW Paul Molitor Jsy / Rickie Weeks Jsy
NL Graig Nettles Jsy / Sparky Lyle Pants EXCH
NT Laynce Nix Jsy / Mark Teixeira Jsy
NY Laynce Nix Jsy / Michael Young Jsy EXCH
OF David Ortiz Jsy / Carlton Fisk Jsy
OG Akinori Otsuka Jsy / Khalil Greene Jsy
OP Akinori Otsuka Jsy / Jake Peavy Jsy
OT Akinori Otsuka Jsy / Shingo Takatsu Jsy
PD Andre Dawson Jsy / Corey Patterson Jsy EXCH
PG Brad Penny Jsy / Eric Gagne Jsy EXCH
PH Jake Peavy Jsy / Rich Harden Jsy
PP Boog Powell Jsy / Jim Palmer Jsy
PR Boog Powell Jsy / Brooks Robinson Jsy
PS Brad Penny Jsy / Jason Schmidt Jsy
RB Ernie Banks Pants / Cal Ripken Jsy
RC Nolan Ryan Jsy / Steve Carlton Jsy EXCH
RJ Jose Reyes Jsy / Rickie Weeks Jsy EXCH
RP Frank Robinson Jsy / Boog Powell Jsy
RR Frank Robinson Jsy / Brooks Robinson Jsy
RW David Wright Jsy / Scott Rolen Jsy EXCH
SB Bert Blyleven Jsy / Johan Santana Jsy EXCH
SC Johan Santana Jsy / Roger Clemens Jsy EXCH
SF Ben Sheets Jsy / Bob Feller Pants
SG Bruce Sutter Jsy / Eric Gagne Jsy EXCH
SM Jason Schmidt Jsy / Mark Mulder Jsy
SO Ben Sheets Jsy / Roy Oswalt Jsy EXCH
SP Ben Sheets Jsy / Brad Penny Jsy EXCH
TH Mark Teixeira Jsy / Travis Hafner Jsy
TL Shingo Takatsu Jsy / Sparky Lyle Pants
TY Mark Teixeira Jsy / Michael Young Jsy EXCH
UJ B.J. Upton Jsy / Derek Jeter Jsy
WL David Wright Jsy / Mike Lowell Jsy
WR David Wright Jsy / Jose Reyes Jsy EXCH
YM Robin Yount Jsy / Paul Molitor Jsy EXCH
YP Carl Yastrzemski Jsy / Rico Petrocelli Pants
ZM Carlos Zambrano Jsy / Greg Maddux Jsy
ZP Carlos Zambrano Jsy / Mark Prior Jsy
ZW Carlos Zambrano Jsy / Kerry Wood Jsy

2005 Artifacts Dual Artifacts Bat

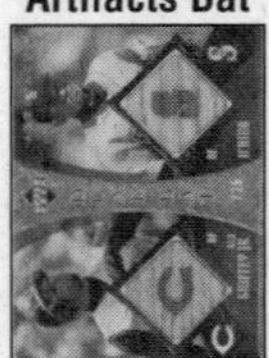

OVERALL GAME-USED ODDS 1:3
STATED PRINT RUN 25 SERIAL #'d SETS

Card	Low	High
BC Josh Beckett / Miguel Cabrera	10.00	25.00
BW Josh Beckett / Kerry Wood	6.00	15.00
DR Carlos Delgado / Manny Ramirez	10.00	25.00
GC Ken Griffey Jr. / Miguel Cabrera	15.00	40.00
GS Ken Griffey Jr. / Ichiro Suzuki	60.00	120.00
JP Derek Jeter / Mike Piazza	20.00	50.00
JR Derek Jeter / Manny Ramirez	20.00	50.00
RG Manny Ramirez / Vladimir Guerrero	10.00	25.00
RJ Cal Ripken / Derek Jeter	50.00	100.00
RT Cal Ripken / Miguel Tejada	40.00	80.00
SG Ichiro Suzuki / Vladimir Guerrero		
WP Kerry Wood / Mark Prior	10.00	25.00

2005 Artifacts MLB Apparel

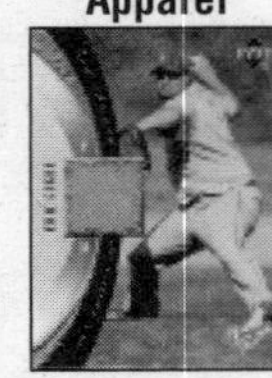

OVERALL GAME-USED ODDS 1:3
PRINT RUNS B/WN 100-325 COPIES PER

Card	Low	High
AB Adrian Beltre Jsy/325	3.00	8.00
AD Andre Dawson Jsy/325	3.00	8.00
AH Aubrey Huff Jsy/325	3.00	8.00
AK Al Kaline Jsy/325	5.00	12.00
AO Akinori Otsuka Jsy/325	3.00	8.00
BA Bobby Abreu Jsy/325	3.00	8.00
BB Bert Blyleven Jsy/150	3.00	8.00
BC Bobby Crosby Jsy/325	3.00	8.00
BE Johnny Bench Jsy/325	5.00	12.00
BF Bob Feller Pants/325	4.00	10.00
BG Bob Gibson Pants/325	4.00	10.00
BM Bill Mazeroski Jsy/100	5.00	12.00
BO Bret Boone Jsy/325	3.00	8.00
BP Boog Powell Jsy/325	3.00	8.00
BR Brooks Robinson Jsy/325	4.00	10.00
BS Ben Sheets Jsy/325	3.00	8.00
BU B.J. Upton Jsy/325	3.00	8.00
CA Steve Carlton Jsy/325	3.00	8.00
CB Carlos Beltran Jsy/325	3.00	8.00
CF Carlton Fisk R.Sox Jsy/175	4.00	10.00
CF1 Carlton Fisk W.Sox Jsy/175	4.00	10.00
CK Casey Kotchman Jsy/325	3.00	8.00
CL Roger Clemens Jsy/325	4.00	10.00
CP Corey Patterson Jsy/325	3.00	8.00
CR Cal Ripken Jsy/325	10.00	25.00
CY Carl Yastrzemski Jsy/325	6.00	15.00
CZ Carlos Zambrano Jsy/325	3.00	8.00
DG Dwight Gooden Pants/325	3.00	8.00
DJ Derek Jeter Jsy/325	8.00	20.00
DL Derrek Lee Jsy/325	3.00	8.00
DM Dale Murphy Jsy/150	4.00	10.00
DO David Ortiz Jsy/325	3.00	8.00
DW David Wright Jsy/325	6.00	15.00
EC Eric Chavez Jsy/325	3.00	8.00
EG Eric Gagne Jsy/325	3.00	8.00
FR Frank Robinson Jsy/325	3.00	8.00
GA Garret Anderson Jsy/325	3.00	8.00
GB George Brett Jsy/325	6.00	15.00
GC Gary Carter Jsy/325	3.00	8.00
GI Brian Giles Jsy/325	3.00	8.00
GN Graig Nettles Jsy/325	3.00	8.00
GR Ken Griffey Sr. Jsy/325	3.00	8.00
GS Marcus Giles Jsy/325	3.00	8.00
HB Hank Blalock Jsy/325	3.00	8.00
HK Harmon Killebrew Jsy/325	4.00	10.00
HU Tim Hudson Jsy/325	3.00	8.00
JB Jason Bay Jsy/325	3.00	8.00
JJ Jacque Jones Jsy/325	3.00	8.00
JK Jim Kaat Jsy/325	3.00	8.00
JM Joe Mauer Jsy/325	3.00	8.00
JP Jake Peavy Jsy/325	3.00	8.00
JR Jim Rice Jsy/325	3.00	8.00
JS Jason Schmidt Jsy/325	3.00	8.00
JV Jose Vidro Jsy/325	3.00	8.00
KG Ken Griffey Jr. Jsy/325	6.00	15.00
KH Kent Hrbek Jsy/325	3.00	8.00
KL Khalil Greene Jsy/325	3.00	8.00
KW Kerry Wood Jsy/325	3.00	8.00
LN Laynce Nix Jsy/325	3.00	8.00
MA Don Mattingly Jsy/325	6.00	15.00
MC Dallas McPherson Jsy/325	3.00	8.00
MI Miguel Cabrera Jsy/325	3.00	8.00
MK Mark Grace Jsy/175	4.00	10.00
ML Mike Lowell Jsy/325	3.00	8.00
MM Mark Mulder Jsy/325	3.00	8.00
MP Mark Prior Jsy/325	3.00	8.00
MS Mike Schmidt Jsy/325	6.00	15.00
MT Mark Teixeira Jsy/325	3.00	8.00
MW Maury Wills Jsy/325	3.00	8.00
MY Michael Young Jsy/325	3.00	8.00
NR Nolan Ryan Jsy/325	8.00	20.00
OC Orlando Cepeda Jsy/325	3.00	8.00
PA Jim Palmer Jsy/325	3.00	8.00
PE Brad Penny Jsy/325	3.00	8.00
PM Paul Molitor Jsy/325	3.00	8.00
PN Phil Niekro Jsy/325	3.00	8.00
RC Rod Carew Jsy/325	4.00	10.00
RE Jose Reyes Jsy/325	3.00	8.00
RH Rich Harden Jsy/325	3.00	8.00
RO Roy Oswalt Jsy/325	3.00	8.00
RP Rico Petrocelli Pants/325	3.00	8.00
RW Rickie Weeks Jsy/325	3.00	8.00
RY Robin Yount Jsy/325	5.00	12.00
SA Johan Santana Jsy/325	3.00	8.00
SC Sean Casey Jsy/325	3.00	8.00
SL Sparky Lyle Pants/325	3.00	8.00
SM John Smoltz Jsy/325	3.00	8.00
SP Scott Podsednik Jsy/325	3.00	8.00
SR Scott Rolen Jsy/325	3.00	8.00
ST Shingo Takatsu Jsy/325	3.00	8.00
SU Bruce Sutter Jsy/325	3.00	8.00
TG Tony Gwynn Jsy/325	5.00	12.00
TH Travis Hafner Jsy/325	3.00	8.00
TO Torii Hunter Jsy/325	3.00	8.00
TS Tom Seaver Jsy/300	4.00	10.00
VM Victor Martinez Jsy/325	3.00	8.00
WB Wade Boggs Jsy/325	4.00	10.00
WC Will Clark Jsy/100	4.00	10.00
WM Willie McCovey Jsy/325	4.00	10.00
YB Yogi Berra Pants/325	5.00	12.00

2005 Artifacts MLB Apparel Rainbow

*RAINBOW p/r 75-99: .5X TO 1.2X p/r 150-325
*RAINBOW p/r 75: .4X TO 1X p/r 100

*RAINBOW p/r 50: .5X TO 1.2X p/r 100
OVERALL GAME-USED ODDS 1:3
PRINT RUNS B/WN 50-99 COPIES PER

2005 Artifacts MLB Apparel Autographs

STATED PRINT RUN 30 SERIAL #'d SETS
RARE PRINT RUN 1 SERIAL #'d SET
NO RARE PRICING DUE TO SCARCITY
OVERALL AUTO ODDS 1:10
EXCHANGE DEADLINE 04/11/08

Card	Low	High
AB Adrian Beltre Jsy	10.00	25.00
AD Andre Dawson Jsy	10.00	25.00
AH Aubrey Huff Jsy	10.00	25.00
AK Al Kaline Jsy	30.00	60.00
AO Akinori Otsuka Jsy	15.00	40.00
BA Bobby Abreu Jsy EXCH	10.00	25.00
BB Bert Blyleven Jsy	10.00	25.00
BC Bobby Crosby Jsy EXCH	10.00	25.00
BE Johnny Bench Jsy	30.00	60.00
BF Bob Feller Pants	15.00	40.00
BG Bob Gibson Pants	15.00	40.00
BM Bill Mazeroski Jsy	15.00	40.00
BO Bret Boone Jsy	10.00	25.00
BP Boog Powell Jsy	15.00	40.00
BR Brooks Robinson Jsy	30.00	60.00
BS Ben Sheets Jsy EXCH	15.00	40.00
BU B.J. Upton Jsy	10.00	25.00
CA Steve Carlton Jsy	10.00	25.00
CB Carlos Beltran Jsy EXCH	10.00	25.00
CF Carlton Fisk R.Sox Jsy	15.00	40.00
CF1 Carlton Fisk W.Sox Jsy	15.00	40.00
CK Casey Kotchman Jsy	10.00	25.00
CL Roger Clemens Jsy EXCH	75.00	150.00
CP Corey Patterson Jsy EXCH	6.00	15.00
CR Cal Ripken Jsy	125.00	200.00
CY Carl Yastrzemski Jsy	40.00	80.00
CZ Carlos Zambrano Jsy	15.00	40.00
DG Dwight Gooden Pants	10.00	25.00
DJ Derek Jeter Jsy	125.00	200.00
DL Derrek Lee Jsy	15.00	40.00
DM Dale Murphy Jsy	15.00	40.00
DO David Ortiz Jsy	30.00	60.00
DW David Wright Jsy	50.00	100.00
EC Eric Chavez Jsy EXCH	10.00	25.00
EG Eric Gagne Jsy	15.00	40.00
FR Frank Robinson Jsy	15.00	40.00
GA Garret Anderson Jsy	10.00	25.00
GB George Brett Jsy	50.00	100.00
GC Gary Carter Jsy	10.00	25.00
GI Brian Giles Jsy	10.00	25.00
GN Graig Nettles Jsy	15.00	40.00
GR Ken Griffey Sr. Jsy	10.00	25.00
GS Marcus Giles Jsy	10.00	25.00
HB Hank Blalock Jsy	10.00	25.00
HK Harmon Killebrew Jsy	30.00	60.00
HU Tim Hudson Jsy	15.00	40.00
JB Jason Bay Jsy	10.00	25.00
JJ Jacque Jones Jsy	10.00	25.00
JK Jim Kaat Jsy	10.00	25.00
JM Joe Mauer Jsy EXCH	15.00	40.00
JP Jake Peavy Jsy	15.00	40.00
JR Jim Rice Jsy	10.00	25.00
JS Jason Schmidt Jsy	10.00	25.00
JV Jose Vidro Jsy	10.00	25.00
KG Ken Griffey Jr. Jsy	75.00	150.00
KH Kent Hrbek Jsy	30.00	60.00
KL Khalil Greene Jsy	15.00	40.00
KW Kerry Wood Jsy	15.00	40.00
LN Laynce Nix Jsy	6.00	15.00
MA Don Mattingly Jsy	50.00	100.00
MC Dallas McPherson Jsy EXCH	6.00	15.00
MI Miguel Cabrera Jsy	15.00	40.00
MK Mark Grace Jsy	15.00	40.00
ML Mike Lowell Jsy	10.00	25.00
MM Mark Mulder Jsy	10.00	25.00
MP Mark Prior Jsy	15.00	40.00
MS Mike Schmidt Jsy	40.00	80.00
MT Mark Teixeira Jsy	15.00	40.00
MW Maury Wills Jsy	10.00	25.00
MY Michael Young Jsy EXCH	10.00	25.00
NR Nolan Ryan Jsy	75.00	150.00
OC Orlando Cepeda Jsy	15.00	40.00
PA Jim Palmer Jsy	15.00	40.00
PE Brad Penny Jsy	10.00	25.00
PM Paul Molitor Jsy	10.00	25.00
PN Phil Niekro Jsy	10.00	25.00
RC Rod Carew Jsy	15.00	40.00
RE Jose Reyes Jsy EXCH	15.00	40.00
RH Rich Harden Jsy	10.00	25.00
RO Roy Oswalt Jsy	10.00	25.00
RP Rico Petrocelli Pants	10.00	25.00
RW Rickie Weeks Jsy	10.00	25.00
RY Robin Yount Jsy	30.00	60.00
SA Johan Santana Jsy EXCH	15.00	40.00
SC Sean Casey Jsy	10.00	25.00
SL Sparky Lyle Pants	10.00	25.00
SM John Smoltz Jsy EXCH	40.00	80.00
SP Scott Podsednik Jsy	15.00	40.00
SR Scott Rolen Jsy EXCH		
ST Shingo Takatsu Jsy	10.00	25.00
SU Bruce Sutter Jsy	15.00	40.00
TG Tony Gwynn Jsy	40.00	80.00
TH Travis Hafner Jsy	10.00	25.00
TO Torii Hunter Jsy	10.00	25.00
TS Tom Seaver Jsy	30.00	60.00
VM Victor Martinez Jsy	10.00	25.00
WB Wade Boggs Jsy	15.00	40.00
WC Will Clark Jsy	30.00	60.00
WM Willie McCovey Jsy	30.00	60.00
YB Yogi Berra Pants	30.00	60.00

2005 Artifacts Patches

PRINT RUNS B/WN 3-50 COPIES PER
NO PRICING ON QTY OF 11 OR LESS
ACTIVE PRICES ARE 1 OR 2 COLOR PATCH
ADD 20% FOR ACTIVE 3-COLOR
ADD 50% OR MORE FOR ACTIVE 4-COLOR+
RETIRED PRICES ARE 1 COLOR PATCH
ADD 20% FOR RETIRED 2-COLOR+
ADD 50% OR MORE FOR RETIRED 3-COLOR+
SIG PATCH PRINT RUN B/WN 4-10 PER
NO SIG PATCH PRICING DUE TO SCARCITY
OVERALL GAME-USED ODDS 1:3

Card	Low	High
AB Adrian Beltre/50	6.00	15.00
AD Andre Dawson/50	6.00	15.00
AH Aubrey Huff/50	6.00	15.00
AO Akinori Otsuka/50	10.00	25.00
BA Bobby Abreu/50	6.00	15.00
BB Bert Blyleven/50	6.00	15.00
BC Bobby Crosby/50	6.00	15.00
BE Johnny Bench/50	10.00	25.00
BG Bob Gibson/10		
BO Bret Boone/50	6.00	15.00
BP Boog Powell/50	10.00	25.00
BR Brooks Robinson/35	15.00	40.00
BS Ben Sheets/50	6.00	15.00
BU B.J. Upton/50	6.00	15.00
CA Steve Carlton/30	10.00	25.00
CB Carlos Beltran/50	6.00	15.00
CK Casey Kotchman/50	6.00	15.00
CL Roger Clemens/50	15.00	40.00
CP Corey Patterson/50	4.00	10.00
CR Cal Ripken/50	20.00	50.00
CY Carl Yastrzemski/50	15.00	40.00
CZ Carlos Zambrano/50	6.00	15.00
DG Dwight Gooden/50	6.00	15.00
DJ Derek Jeter/50	20.00	50.00
DL Derrek Lee/50	10.00	25.00
DM Dale Murphy/50	15.00	40.00
DO David Ortiz/50	10.00	25.00
DW David Wright/50	15.00	40.00
EC Eric Chavez/50	6.00	15.00
EG Eric Gagne/50	6.00	15.00
FR Frank Robinson/50	10.00	25.00
GA Garret Anderson/50	6.00	15.00
GB George Brett/50	15.00	40.00
GC Gary Carter/50	6.00	15.00
GI Brian Giles/50	6.00	15.00
GM Greg Maddux/50	15.00	40.00
GN Graig Nettles/50	10.00	25.00
GR Ken Griffey Sr./50	6.00	15.00
GS Marcus Giles/50	6.00	15.00
HB Hank Blalock/50	6.00	15.00
HK Harmon Killebrew/50	10.00	25.00
HU Tim Hudson/50	6.00	15.00
JB Jason Bay/50		
JJ Jacque Jones/50	6.00	15.00
JK Jim Kaat/50	6.00	15.00
JM Joe Mauer/50	10.00	25.00
JP Jake Peavy/50	10.00	25.00
JR Jim Rice/3		
JS Jason Schmidt/50	10.00	25.00
JV Jose Vidro/50	6.00	15.00
KG Ken Griffey Jr./50	10.00	25.00
KH Kent Hrbek/50	10.00	25.00
KL Khalil Greene/50	10.00	25.00
KW Kerry Wood/50	6.00	15.00
LN Laynce Nix/50	4.00	10.00
MA Don Mattingly/50	15.00	40.00
MC Dallas McPherson/50	4.00	10.00
MI Miguel Cabrera/50	10.00	25.00
MK Mark Grace/50	10.00	25.00
ML Mike Lowell/50	6.00	15.00
MM Mark Mulder/50	6.00	15.00
MP Mark Prior/50	10.00	25.00
MS Mike Schmidt/50	15.00	40.00
MT Mark Teixeira/50	10.00	25.00
MW Maury Wills/20	10.00	25.00
MY Michael Young/50	6.00	15.00
NR Nolan Ryan/50	20.00	50.00
OC Orlando Cepeda/3		
PA Jim Palmer/50	6.00	15.00
PE Brad Penny/50	6.00	15.00
PM Paul Molitor/9		
PN Phil Niekro/50	6.00	15.00
RC Rod Carew/50	10.00	25.00
RE Jose Reyes/50	6.00	15.00
RH Rich Harden/50	6.00	15.00
RJ Randy Johnson/50	10.00	25.00
RO Roy Oswalt/50	6.00	15.00
RW Rickie Weeks/50	6.00	15.00
RY Robin Yount/50	10.00	25.00
SA Johan Santana/50	10.00	25.00
SC Sean Casey/50	6.00	15.00
SM John Smoltz/50	10.00	25.00
SP Scott Podsednik/50	6.00	15.00
SR Scott Rolen/50	10.00	25.00
ST Shingo Takatsu/50	6.00	15.00
SU Bruce Sutter/50	6.00	15.00
TG Tony Gwynn/50	10.00	25.00
TH Travis Hafner/50	6.00	15.00
TO Torii Hunter/50	6.00	15.00
TS Tom Seaver/11		
VM Victor Martinez/50	6.00	15.00
WB Wade Boggs/50	10.00	25.00
WC Will Clark/20	15.00	40.00
WM Willie McCovey/50	10.00	25.00

2006 Artifacts

This 100-card set was released in July, 2006. The set was issued in four card packs with an $9.99 SRP. The product was issued in 10 pack boxes which came 20 boxes to a case.

COMPLETE SET (100) 15.00 40.00
COMMON CARD (1-100) .20 .50
COMMON ROOKIE .30 .75
1 Luis Gonzalez .20 .50
2 Conor Jackson (RC) .50 1.25
3 Joey Devine RC .30 .75
4 Andruw Jones .30 .75
5 Chipper Jones .50 1.25
6 John Smoltz .30 .75
7 Jeff Francoeur .50 1.25
8 Brian Roberts .20 .50
9 Miguel Tejada .20 .50
10 Nick Markakis (RC) .50 1.25
11 Curt Schilling .30 .75
12 David Ortiz .50 1.25
13 Johnny Damon .30 .75
14 Manny Ramirez .30 .75
15 Jonathan Papelbon (RC) 1.50 4.00
16 Aramis Ramirez .20 .50
17 Carlos Zambrano .20 .50
18 Derrek Lee .20 .50
19 Greg Maddux .75 2.00
20 Mark Prior .30 .75
21 Mark Buehrle .20 .50
22 Paul Konerko .20 .50
23 Adam Dunn .20 .50
24 Ken Griffey Jr. .75 2.00
25 Travis Hafner .20 .50
26 Victor Martinez .20 .50
27 Todd Helton .30 .75
28 Ivan Rodriguez .30 .75
29 Jeremy Bonderman .20 .50
30 Jeremy Hermida (RC) .30 .75
31 Carlos Delgado .20 .50
32 Dontrelle Willis .20 .50
33 Josh Beckett .20 .50
34 Miguel Cabrera .30 .75
35 Craig Biggio .30 .75
36 Lance Berkman .20 .50
37 Roger Clemens 1.00 2.50
38 Roy Oswalt .20 .50
39 Josh Willingham (RC) .30 .75
40 Hanley Ramirez (RC) .75 2.00
41 Prince Fielder (RC) 1.25 3.00
42 Zack Greinke .20 .50
43 Francisco Rodriguez .20 .50
44 Vladimir Guerrero .50 1.25
45 Tim Hamulack (RC) .30 .75
46 Jeff Kent .20 .50
47 Ben Sheets .20 .50
48 Rickie Weeks .20 .50
49 Francisco Liriano (RC) 1.50 4.00
50 Joe Mauer .30 .75
51 Johan Santana .30 .75
52 Justin Morneau .30 .75
53 Torii Hunter .20 .50
54 Carlos Beltran .20 .50
55 David Wright .75 2.00
56 Jose Reyes .50 1.25
57 Mike Piazza .50 1.25
58 Pedro Martinez .30 .75
59 Alex Rodriguez .75 2.00
60 Derek Jeter 1.25 3.00
61 Hideki Matsui .50 1.25
62 Randy Johnson .50 1.25
63 Justin Verlander (RC) 1.25 3.00
64 Bobby Crosby .20 .50
65 Eric Chavez .20 .50
66 Brian Anderson (RC) .30 .75
67 Bobby Abreu .20 .50
68 Pat Burrell .20 .50
69 Jason Bay .20 .50
70 Oliver Perez .20 .50
71 Chuck James (RC) .50 1.25
72 Brian Giles .20 .50
73 Jake Peavy .20 .50
74 Khalil Greene .30 .75
75 Jason Schmidt .20 .50
76 Kenji Johjima RC 1.50 4.00
77 Jeremy Accardo RC .30 .75
78 Adrian Beltre .20 .50
79 Ichiro Suzuki .75 2.00
80 Jeff Harris RC .30 .75
81 Felix Hernandez .30 .75
82 Albert Pujols 1.00 2.50
83 Chris Carpenter .20 .50
84 Jim Edmonds .30 .75
85 Scott Rolen .30 .75
86 Mike Jacobs (RC) .30 .75
87 Carl Crawford .20 .50
88 Anderson Hernandez (RC) .30 .75
89 Scott Kazmir .30 .75
90 Josh Rupe (RC) .30 .75
91 Scott Feldman RC .30 .75
92 Alfonso Soriano .20 .50
93 Hank Blalock .20 .50
94 Mark Teixeira .30 .75
95 Michael Young .20 .50
96 Roy Halladay .20 .50
97 Vernon Wells .20 .50
98 Jason Bergmann RC .30 .75
99 Ryan Zimmerman (RC) 2.00 5.00
100 Jose Vidro .20 .50

2006 Artifacts AL/NL Artifacts Blue

OVERALL GU ODDS 3:10
PRINT RUNS B/WN 200-325 COPIES PER
ADN Adam Dunn Jsy/250 3.00 8.00
AHN Aaron Harang Jsy/325 3.00 8.00

APN Albert Pujols Jsy/250 8.00 20.00
ASN Alfonso Soriano Jsy/325 3.00 8.00
BBA Ben Broussard Jsy/325 3.00 8.00
BHN Bill Hall Jsy/235 3.00 8.00
BLA Joe Blanton Jsy/325 3.00 8.00
BLN Brad Lidge Jsy/325 3.00 8.00
BMA Brandon McCarthy Jsy/325 3.00 8.00
BMN Brian McCann Jsy/325 4.00 10.00
CAN Chris Capuano Jsy/325 3.00 8.00
CBN Chris Burke Jsy/325 3.00 8.00
CCA Carl Crawford Jsy/325 3.00 8.00
CCN Chris Carpenter Jsy/325 4.00 10.00
CHN Chad Cordero Jsy/325 3.00 8.00
CJN Chipper Jones Jsy/325 4.00 10.00
CLA Cliff Lee Jsy/325 3.00 8.00
CLN Clint Barmes Jsy/325 3.00 8.00
COA Coco Crisp Jsy/325 3.00 8.00
CON Conor Jackson Jsy/325 3.00 8.00
CRA Joe Crede Jsy/325 3.00 8.00
CSA Chris Shelton Jsy/325 3.00 8.00
CUN Chase Utley Jsy/325 6.00 15.00
DAA Dan Johnson Jsy/325 3.00 8.00
DHA Dan Haren Jsy/325 3.00 8.00
DJA Derek Jeter Jsy/325 10.00 25.00
DLN Derrek Lee Jsy/325 3.00 8.00
DOA David Ortiz Jsy/325 4.00 10.00
DWN Dontrelle Willis Jsy/325 3.00 8.00
DYA Dmitri Young Jsy/325 3.00 8.00
ECA Eric Chavez Jsy/325 3.00 8.00
EGN Eric Gagne Jsy/325 3.00 8.00
ESA Ervin Santana Jsy/325 3.00 8.00
FHA Felix Hernandez Jsy/325 4.00 10.00
FLN Felipe Lopez Jsy/325 3.00 8.00
GAA Jon Garland Jsy/325 3.00 8.00
GAN Garrett Atkins Jsy/325 3.00 8.00
GCA Gustavo Chacin Jsy/325 3.00 8.00
GSA Grady Sizemore Jsy/325 4.00 10.00
HBA Hank Blalock Jsy/325 3.00 8.00
HSA Huston Street Jsy/325 3.00 8.00
IRA Ivan Rodriguez Jsy/325 3.00 8.00
JAN Jason Bay Jsy/325 3.00 8.00
JBA Jeremy Bonderman Jsy/325 3.00 8.00
JBN Jeff Bagwell Jsy/325 3.00 8.00
JCA Jorge Cantu Jsy/325 3.00 8.00
JEN Jim Edmonds Jsy/325 3.00 8.00
JFN Jeff Francoeur Jsy/325 6.00 15.00
JGA Jonny Gomes Jsy/325 3.00 8.00
JMA Joe Mauer Jsy/325 4.00 10.00
JNA Joe Nathan Jsy/325 3.00 8.00
JPA Joel Pineiro Jsy/325 3.00 8.00
JPN Jake Peavy Jsy/325 3.00 8.00
JRN Jose Reyes Jsy/325 3.00 8.00
JSN John Smoltz Jsy/250 3.00 8.00
JUA Justin Morneau Jsy/325 3.00 8.00
JVA Jason Varitek Jsy/325 4.00 10.00
JWA Jake Westbrook Jsy/325 3.00 8.00
JWN Jack Wilson Jsy/200 3.00 8.00
KGN Ken Griffey Jr. Jsy/325 6.00 15.00
LEN Carlos Lee Jsy/325 3.00 8.00
MAN Matt Cain Jsy/325 3.00 8.00
MBA Mark Buehrle Jsy/325 3.00 8.00
MCN Miguel Cabrera Jsy/325 4.00 10.00
MEN Morgan Ensberg Jsy/325 3.00 8.00
MGN Marcus Giles Jsy/325 3.00 8.00
MHN Matt Holliday Jsy/325 4.00 10.00
MLA Mark Loretta Jsy/325 3.00 8.00
MPN Mark Prior Jsy/325 3.00 8.00
MRA Manny Ramirez Jsy/325 3.00 8.00
MTA Miguel Tejada Jsy/325 3.00 8.00
MYA Michael Young Jsy/325 3.00 8.00
NJN Nick Johnson Jsy/325 3.00 8.00
NLN Noah Lowry Jsy/325 3.00 8.00
NSA Nick Swisher Jsy/325 3.00 8.00
PEA Jhonny Peralta Jsy/325 3.00 8.00
PFN Prince Fielder Jsy/325 4.00 10.00
PMN Pedro Martinez Jsy/325 4.00 10.00
RBA Rocco Baldelli Jsy/325 3.00 8.00
RCN Ryan Church Jsy/325 3.00 8.00
RHN Ramon Hernandez Jsy/325 3.00 8.00
RJA Randy Johnson Pants/235 4.00 10.00
RON Roy Oswalt Jsy/325 3.00 8.00
RWN Rickie Weeks Jsy/325 3.00 8.00
RYN Ryan Howard Jsy/325 10.00 25.00
RZN Ryan Zimmerman Jsy/325 6.00 15.00
SBA Scott Baker Jsy/325 3.00 8.00
SKA Scott Kazmir Jsy/325 3.00 8.00
SPA Scott Podsednik Jsy/325 3.00 8.00
THA Travis Hafner Jsy/325 3.00 8.00
THN Todd Helton Jsy/325 3.00 8.00
TIA Tadahito Iguchi Jsy/325 3.00 8.00
TRN Trevor Hoffman Jsy/325 3.00 8.00
VGA Vladimir Guerrero Jsy/325 4.00 10.00
VMA Victor Martinez Jsy/325 4.00 10.00
WRN David Wright Jsy/325 6.00 15.00
YMN Yadier Molina Jsy/325 3.00 8.00
ZDN Zach Duke Jsy/325 3.00 8.00

2006 Artifacts AL/NL Artifacts Green

*GREEN p/r 150: .5X TO 1.2X BLUE p/r 325
*GRN p/r 75-85: .5X TO 1.2X BLUEp/r200-250
*GRNp/r50-55: .6X TO 1.5X BLUEp/r200-250
OVERALL GU ODDS 3:10
PRINT RUNS B/WN 50-150 COPIES PER
FGA Freddy Garcia Jsy/75 5.00 12.00
JDA Jermaine Dye Jsy/150 4.00 10.00

2006 Artifacts AL/NL Artifacts Red

*RED p/r 150-250: .5X TO 1.2X BLUE p/r 325
*REDp/r150-250: .4X TO 1X BLUEp/r200-250
*REDp/r100-125: .5X TO 1.2XBLUEp/r200-250
OVERALL GU ODDS 3:10
PRINT RUNS B/WN 100-250 COPIES PER
FGA Freddy Garcia Jsy/175 4.00 10.00

2006 Artifacts Auto-Facts Signatures

OVERALL AU ODDS 1:10
PRINT RUNS B/WN 5-800 COPIES PER
NO DUFFY PRICING DUE TO SCARCITY
AD Andre Dawson/300 6.00 15.00
AH Aaron Harang/800 4.00 10.00
AJ Andruw Jones/150 30.00 60.00
AM Aaron Miles/494 4.00 10.00
AR Aaron Rowand/520 6.00 15.00
AV Andy Van Slyke/800 6.00 15.00
BE Jason Bergmann/800 4.00 10.00
BI Bill Madlock/300 4.00 10.00
BL Barry Larkin/300 15.00 40.00
BO Bo Jackson/250 20.00 50.00
BR Brian Roberts/200 6.00 15.00
BY Clete Boyer/484 4.00 10.00
CA Chris Capuano/800 6.00 15.00
CB Clint Barmes/800 4.00 10.00
CC Chris Chambliss/400 4.00 10.00
CD Chris Demaria/800 4.00 10.00
CH Chris Carpenter/51 15.00 40.00
CJ Conor Jackson/800 6.00 15.00
CK Jack Clark/800 4.00 10.00
CL Cliff Lee/800 4.00 10.00
CO Coco Crisp/800 6.00 15.00
CP Jose Capellan/800 4.00 10.00
CR Cal Ripken/100 60.00 120.00
CS Chris Shelton/750 6.00 15.00
CU Chase Utley/200 30.00 60.00
CY Chris Young/700 10.00 25.00
CZ Carlos Zambrano/300 10.00 25.00
DA Chris Denorfia/659 4.00 10.00
DE Joey Devine/350 4.00 10.00
DH Dan Haren/800 4.00 10.00
DJ Derek Jeter/100 75.00 150.00
DL Derrek Lee/300 10.00 25.00
DU Chris Duffy/5
DW David Wright/300 30.00 60.00
DY Dmitri Young/300 4.00 10.00
ED Eric Davis/487 6.00 15.00
FH Felix Hernandez/300 10.00 25.00
GA Garrett Atkins/800 4.00 10.00
GB George Bell/715 6.00 15.00
GC Gustavo Chacin/800 4.00 10.00
GF George Foster/300 4.00 10.00
GG Goose Gossage/300 6.00 15.00
GN Graig Nettles/300 6.00 15.00
GO Jonny Gomes/700 4.00 10.00
HR Hanley Ramirez/800 8.00 20.00
HS Huston Street/500 6.00 15.00
IK Ian Kinsler/800 6.00 15.00
JA Jeremy Accardo/800 4.00 10.00
JB Jason Bay/200 6.00 15.00
JC Joe Carter/400 6.00 15.00
JD Jermaine Dye/652 6.00 15.00
JE Jeff Harris/800 4.00 10.00
JK Jason Kubel/400 4.00 10.00
JL Jason Lane/800 4.00 10.00
JM Joe Mauer/400 15.00 40.00
JN Joe Nathan/800 6.00 15.00
JP Jhonny Peralta/700 4.00 10.00
JR Jim Rice/200 6.00 15.00
JS Johan Santana/150 30.00 60.00
JV Justin Verlander/700 15.00 40.00
JW Jake Westbrook/650 4.00 10.00
KG Ken Griffey Jr./800 30.00 60.00
KH Kent Hrbek/239 6.00 15.00
LA Luis Aparicio/250 6.00 15.00
LD Lenny Dykstra/412 4.00 10.00
MA Matt Cain/700 6.00 15.00
MC Miguel Cabrera/250 10.00 25.00
MG Marcus Giles/350 6.00 15.00
MO Magglio Ordonez/437 10.00 25.00
MW Maury Wills/150 6.00 15.00
MY Michael Young/600 6.00 15.00
NS Nick Swisher/700 6.00 15.00
PF Prince Fielder/200 15.00 40.00
PM Pedro Martinez/100 30.00 60.00
RC Ryan Church/800 4.00 10.00
RE Chris Resop/800 4.00 10.00
RJ Reggie Jackson/200 20.00 50.00
RW Rickie Weeks/91 8.00 20.00
RZ Ryan Zimmerman/800 15.00 40.00
SF Scott Feldman/800 4.00 10.00
SG Steve Garvey/300 6.00 15.00
TH Travis Hafner/400 6.00 15.00
TI Tadahito Iguchi/700 15.00 40.00
TM Tim Hamulack/742 4.00 10.00
TO Tony Oliva/300 6.00 15.00
TP Tony Perez/251 10.00 25.00
WI Dontrelle Willis/50 10.00 25.00
WT Willy Taveras/500 4.00 10.00
YM Yadier Molina/800 6.00 15.00

2006 Artifacts Awesome Artifacts Jumbos

OVERALL GU ODDS 3:10
PRINT RUNS B/WN 21-45 COPIES PER
NO PRICING ON QTY OF 25 OR LESS
AD Adam Dunn Jsy/45 6.00 15.00
AH Aaron Harang Jsy/45 6.00 15.00
AP Albert Pujols Jsy/45 20.00 50.00
AR Aaron Rowand Jsy/45 6.00 15.00
AS Alfonso Soriano Jsy/45 6.00 15.00
AV Andy Van Slyke Jsy/45 10.00 25.00
BA Jeff Bagwell Jsy/45 10.00 25.00
BH Bill Hall Jsy/45 6.00 15.00
BL Joe Blanton Jsy/45 6.00 15.00
BM Brandon McCarthy Jsy/45 6.00 15.00
BO Bo Jackson Jsy/45 15.00 40.00
BR Brian McCann Jsy/45 10.00 25.00
BU Chris Burke Jsy/45 6.00 15.00
CA Matt Cain Jsy/45 6.00 15.00
CB Clint Barmes Jsy/45 6.00 15.00
CC Carl Crawford Jsy/45 6.00 15.00
CF Carlton Fisk Jsy/45 10.00 25.00
CH Chris Carpenter Jsy/45 6.00 15.00
CJ Chipper Jones Jsy/45 15.00 40.00
CL Cliff Lee Jsy/45 6.00 15.00
CO Conor Jackson Jsy/45 8.00 20.00
CR Cal Ripken Jsy/45 30.00 60.00
CS Chris Shelton Jsy/45 6.00 15.00
CU Chase Utley Jsy/45 15.00 40.00
CY Carl Yastrzemski Pants/25
DA Dan Johnson Jsy/45 6.00 15.00
DD Don Drysdale Pants/25
DE Derrek Lee Jsy/45 6.00 15.00
DH Dan Haren Jsy/45 6.00 15.00
DJ Derek Jeter Jsy/45 30.00 60.00
DL Don Larsen Pants/25
DO David Ortiz Jsy/45 10.00 25.00
DP Dave Parker Jsy/45 6.00 15.00
DW David Wells Jsy/45 6.00 15.00
EC Eric Chavez Jsy/45 6.00 15.00
EG Eric Gagne Jsy/45 6.00 15.00
EM Eddie Mathews Pants/45 30.00 60.00
ES Ervin Santana Jsy/45 6.00 15.00
FG Freddy Garcia Jsy/21
FH Felix Hernandez Jsy/45 10.00 25.00
FT Frank Thomas Jsy/45 10.00 25.00
GA Jon Garland Jsy/45 6.00 15.00
GC Gustavo Chacin Jsy/45 6.00 15.00
GF Gavin Floyd Jsy/45 6.00 15.00
GP Gaylord Perry Jsy/45 6.00 15.00
GS Grady Sizemore Jsy/45 10.00 25.00
HA Hank Blalock Jsy/45 6.00 15.00
HB Harold Baines Jsy/45 6.00 15.00
HS Huston Street Jsy/45 6.00 15.00
IR Ivan Rodriguez Jsy/45 10.00 25.00
JA Jason Schmidt Jsy/45 6.00 15.00
JB Jason Bay Jsy/45 6.00 15.00
JE Jim Edmonds Jsy/45 6.00 15.00
JF Jeff Francoeur Jsy/45 15.00 40.00
JG Jonny Gomes Jsy/45 6.00 15.00
JL Jason Lane Jsy/45 6.00 15.00
JM Johnny Mize Bat/25
JO Joel Pineiro Jsy/45 6.00 15.00
JP Jake Peavy Jsy/45 6.00 15.00
JS John Smoltz Jsy/45 15.00 40.00
JU Justin Morneau Jsy/45 6.00 15.00
JV Jason Varitek Jsy/45 10.00 25.00
JW Jack Wilson Jsy/45 6.00 15.00
KG Ken Griffey Jr. Jsy/45 15.00 40.00
LG Lou Gehrig Bat/25
MB Mark Buehrle Jsy/45 6.00 15.00
MC Miguel Cabrera Jsy/45 10.00 25.00
ME Morgan Ensberg Jsy/45 6.00 15.00
MI Miguel Tejada Jsy/45 6.00 15.00
MP Mark Prior Jsy/45 6.00 15.00
MR Manny Ramirez Jsy/45 10.00 25.00
NJ Nick Johnson Jsy/45 6.00 15.00
NL Noah Lowry Jsy/45 10.00 25.00
NS Nick Swisher Jsy/45 6.00 15.00
PE Jhonny Peralta Jsy/45 6.00 15.00
PF Prince Fielder Jsy/45 10.00 25.00
PM Pedro Martinez Jsy/45 10.00 25.00
RA Randy Johnson Pants/45 10.00 25.00
RB Rocco Baldelli Jsy/45 6.00 15.00
RH Rogers Hornsby Pants/25
RJ Reggie Jackson Jsy/25
RO Roy Oswalt Jsy/45 6.00 15.00
RS Ron Santo Jsy/45 10.00 25.00
RW Rickie Weeks Jsy/45 10.00 25.00
RY Ryan Howard Jsy/45 20.00 50.00
RZ Ryan Zimmerman Jsy/45 15.00 40.00
SB Scott Baker Jsy/45 6.00 15.00
SG Steve Garvey Pants/45 6.00 15.00
SP Satchel Paige Pants/45 75.00 150.00
TH Todd Helton Jsy/45 10.00 25.00
TM Thurman Munson Pants/25
TR Trevor Hoffman Jsy/45 6.00 15.00
VG Vladimir Guerrero Jsy/45 10.00 25.00
WC Will Clark Pants/45 10.00 25.00
WE Jake Westbrook Jsy/45 6.00 15.00
WI Dontrelle Willis Jsy/45 6.00 15.00
WR David Wright Jsy/45 15.00 40.00
YM Yadier Molina Jsy/45 10.00 25.00
ZD Zach Duke Jsy/45 6.00 15.00

2006 Artifacts MLB Game-Used Apparel

OVERALL GU ODDS 3:10
STATED PRINT RUN 325 SERIAL #'d SETS
M.SCHMIDT PRINT RUN 85 #'d CARDS
AH Aaron Harang Jsy/325 3.00 8.00
AR Aaron Rowand Jsy/325 3.00 8.00

AT Garrett Atkins Jsy/325 3.00 8.00
AV Andy Van Slyke Jsy/325 3.00 8.00
BA Clint Barmes Jsy/325 3.00 8.00
BB Ben Broussard Jsy/325 3.00 8.00
BC Brian McCann Jsy/325 4.00 10.00
BI Bill Madlock Jsy/325 3.00 8.00
BL Brad Lidge Jsy/325 3.00 8.00
BM Brandon McCarthy Jsy/325 3.00 8.00
BO Bo Jackson Jsy/325 4.00 10.00
BP Boog Powell Jsy/325 3.00 8.00
BR Brian Roberts Jsy/325 3.00 8.00
BY Jason Bay Jsy/325 3.00 8.00
CA Carl Crawford Jsy/325 3.00 8.00
CB Chris Burke Jsy/325 3.00 8.00
CD Chad Cordero Jsy/325 3.00 8.00
CF Carlton Fisk Jsy/325 4.00 10.00
CH Chris Carpenter Jsy/325 4.00 10.00
CJ Conor Jackson Jsy/325 4.00 10.00
CK Casey Kotchman Jsy/325 3.00 8.00
CL Cliff Lee Jsy/325 3.00 8.00
CO Coco Crisp Jsy/325 3.00 8.00
CR Cal Ripken Jsy/325 10.00 25.00
CS Chris Capuano Jsy/325 3.00 8.00
CU Chase Utley Jsy/325 6.00 15.00
CY Carl Yastrzemski Pants/325 6.00 15.00
DA Dan Johnson Jsy/325 3.00 8.00
DH Dan Haren Jsy/325 3.00 8.00
DJ Derek Jeter Jsy/325 10.00 25.00
DL Derrek Lee Jsy/325 3.00 8.00
DO Don Larsen Pants/325 4.00 10.00
DW Dontrelle Willis Jsy/325 3.00 8.00
DY Dmitri Young Jsy/325 3.00 8.00
ES Ervin Santana Jsy/325 3.00 8.00
FH Felix Hernandez Jsy/325 4.00 10.00
FL Felipe Lopez Jsy/325 3.00 8.00
FM Fred McGriff Jsy/325 4.00 10.00
GA Jon Garland Jsy/325 3.00 8.00
GC Gustavo Chacin Jsy/325 3.00 8.00
GF Gavin Floyd Jsy/325 3.00 8.00
GG Goose Gossage Jsy/325 3.00 8.00
GN Graig Nettles Jsy/325 3.00 8.00
GO Adrian Gonzalez Jsy/325 3.00 8.00
GP Gaylord Perry Jsy/325 3.00 8.00
GS Grady Sizemore Jsy/325 4.00 10.00
HB Harold Baines Jsy/325 3.00 8.00
HO Ryan Howard Jsy/325 10.00 25.00
HS Huston Street Jsy/325 3.00 8.00
JE Jeremy Bonderman Jsy/325 3.00 8.00
JG Jonny Gomes Jsy/325 3.00 8.00
JH Jeremy Hermida Jsy/325 4.00 10.00
JK John Kruk Jsy/325 3.00 8.00
JL Jason Lane Jsy/325 3.00 8.00
JM Joe Mauer Jsy/325 4.00 10.00
JN Joe Nathan Jsy/325 3.00 8.00
JO Joe Blanton Jsy/325 3.00 8.00
JP Jhonny Peralta Jsy/325 3.00 8.00
JR Jose Reyes Jsy/325 3.00 8.00
JU Jorge Cantu Jsy/325 3.00 8.00
JW Jake Westbrook Jsy/325 3.00 8.00
JY Jeremy Reed Jsy/325 3.00 8.00
KE Jason Kendall Jsy/325 3.00 8.00
KG Ken Griffey Jr. Jsy/325 6.00 15.00
LE Carlos Lee Jsy/325 3.00 8.00
MA Matt Cain Jsy/325 3.00 8.00
MC Miguel Cabrera Jsy/325 4.00 10.00
MG Marcus Giles Jsy/325 3.00 8.00
MH Matt Holliday Jsy/325 4.00 10.00
ML Mark Loretta Jsy/325 3.00 8.00
MO Justin Morneau Jsy/325 3.00 8.00
MS Mike Schmidt Jsy/85 10.00 25.00
MY Michael Young Jsy/325 3.00 8.00
NL Noah Lowry Jsy/325 3.00 8.00
NS Nick Swisher Jsy/325 3.00 8.00
OR Magglio Ordonez Jsy/325 3.00 8.00
PE Jake Peavy Jsy/325 3.00 8.00
PF Prince Fielder Jsy/325
PI Joel Pineiro Jsy/325 3.00 8.00
RB Rocco Baldelli Jsy/325 3.00 8.00
RC Ryan Church Jsy/325 3.00 8.00
RH Ramon Hernandez Jsy/325 3.00 8.00
RO Roy Oswalt Jsy/325 3.00 8.00
RS Ron Santo Jsy/325 6.00 15.00
RW Rickie Weeks Jsy/325 3.00 8.00
RZ Ryan Zimmerman Jsy/325 6.00 15.00
SB Scott Baker Jsy/325 3.00 8.00
SG Steve Garvey Pants/325 3.00 8.00
SH Chris Shelton Jsy/325 3.00 8.00
SK Scott Kazmir Jsy/325 3.00 8.00
SP Scott Podsednik Jsy/325 3.00 8.00
ST So Taguchi Jsy/325 3.00 8.00
TI Tadahito Iguchi Jsy/325 3.00 8.00
WC Will Clark Pants/325 4.00 10.00
WR David Wright Jsy/325 6.00 15.00
YB Yuniesky Betancourt Jsy/325 3.00 8.00
YM Yadier Molina Jsy/325 4.00 10.00

2006 Artifacts MLB Game-Used Apparel Gold Limited

*GOLD p/r 150: .5X TO 1.2X BASIC p/r 325
*GOLD p/r 30: .6X TO 1.5X BASIC p/r 85
OVERALL GU ODDS 3:10
STATED PRINT RUN 150 SERIAL #'d SETS
M.SCHMIDT PRINT RUN 30 #'d SETS
JD Jermaine Dye Jsy/150 4.00 10.00

2006 Artifacts MLB Game-Used Apparel Silver Limited

*SILVER p/r 250: .5X TO 1.2X BASIC p/r 325
*SILVER p/r 50: .5X TO 1.2X BASIC p/r 85
OVERALL GU ODDS 3:10
STATED PRINT RUN 250 SERIAL #'d SETS
M.SCHMIDT PRINT RUN 50 #'d SETS

2006 Artifacts MLB Game-Used Apparel Autographs

OVERALL AU ODDS 1:10
STATED PRINT RUN 30 SERIAL #'d SETS
R.SANTO PRINT RUN 28 SERIAL #'d CARDS
HOWARD PRINT RUN 23 SERIAL #'d CARDS
NO HOWARD PRICING DUE TO SCARCITY
AH Aaron Harang Jsy/30 6.00 15.00
AR Aaron Rowand Jsy/30 10.00 25.00
AT Garrett Atkins Jsy/30 6.00 15.00
AV Andy Van Slyke Jsy/30 10.00 25.00
BA Clint Barmes Jsy/30 6.00 15.00
BB Ben Broussard Jsy/30 6.00 15.00
BI Bill Madlock Jsy/30 6.00 15.00
BL Brad Lidge Jsy/30 10.00 25.00
BM Brandon McCarthy Jsy/30 6.00 15.00
BO Bo Jackson Jsy/30 60.00 120.00
BP Boog Powell Jsy/30 10.00 25.00
BY Jason Bay Jsy/30 10.00 25.00
CA Carl Crawford Jsy/30 10.00 25.00
CB Chris Burke Jsy/30 6.00 15.00
CD Chad Cordero Jsy/30 6.00 15.00
CF Carlton Fisk Jsy/30 15.00 40.00
CH Chris Carpenter Jsy/30 30.00 60.00
CJ Conor Jackson Jsy/30 15.00 40.00
CK Casey Kotchman Jsy/30 10.00 25.00
CL Cliff Lee Jsy/30 6.00 15.00
CO Coco Crisp Jsy/30 15.00 40.00
CR Cal Ripken Jsy/30 125.00 200.00
CS Chris Capuano Jsy/30 10.00 25.00
CU Chase Utley Jsy/30 40.00 80.00
CY Carl Yastrzemski Pants/30 40.00 80.00
DA Dan Johnson Jsy/30 6.00 15.00
DH Dan Haren Jsy/30 6.00 15.00
DJ Derek Jeter Jsy/30 125.00 200.00
DL Derrek Lee Jsy/30 15.00 40.00
DO Don Larsen Pants/30 10.00 25.00
DW Dontrelle Willis Jsy/30 15.00 40.00
DY Dmitri Young Jsy/30 6.00 15.00
FH Felix Hernandez Jsy/30 20.00 50.00
FL Felipe Lopez Jsy/30 6.00 15.00
GC Gustavo Chacin Jsy/30 6.00 15.00
GG Goose Gossage Jsy/30 10.00 25.00
GN Graig Nettles Jsy/30 15.00 40.00
GO Adrian Gonzalez Jsy/30 6.00 15.00
GP Gaylord Perry Jsy/30 10.00 25.00
HB Harold Baines Jsy/30 10.00 25.00
HO Ryan Howard Jsy/23
HS Huston Street Jsy/30 10.00 25.00
JD Jermaine Dye Jsy/30 10.00 25.00
JE Jeremy Bonderman Jsy/30 10.00 25.00
JG Jonny Gomes Jsy/30 6.00 15.00
JH Jeremy Hermida Jsy/30 15.00 40.00
JK John Kruk Jsy/30 10.00 25.00
JM Joe Mauer Jsy/30 30.00 60.00
JN Joe Nathan Jsy/30 10.00 25.00
JO Joe Blanton Jsy/30 6.00 15.00
JP Jhonny Peralta Jsy/30 6.00 15.00
JR Jose Reyes Jsy/30 15.00 40.00
JW Jake Westbrook Jsy/30 6.00 15.00
KG Ken Griffey Jr. Jsy/30 75.00 150.00
LE Carlos Lee Jsy/30 10.00 25.00
MA Matt Cain Jsy/30 15.00 40.00
MC Miguel Cabrera Jsy/30 15.00 40.00
MG Marcus Giles Jsy/30 10.00 25.00
MO Justin Morneau Jsy/30 15.00 40.00
MS Mike Schmidt Jsy/30 40.00 80.00
MY Michael Young Jsy/30 10.00 25.00
NL Noah Lowry Jsy/30 15.00 40.00
NS Nick Swisher Jsy/30 10.00 25.00
OR Magglio Ordonez Jsy/30 15.00 40.00
PE Jake Peavy Jsy/30 15.00 40.00
PF Prince Fielder Jsy/30 30.00 60.00
PI Joel Pineiro Jsy/30 6.00 15.00
RC Ryan Church Jsy/30 6.00 15.00
RH Ramon Hernandez Jsy/30 6.00 15.00
RO Roy Oswalt Jsy/30 10.00 25.00
RS Ron Santo Jsy/28 40.00 80.00
RW Rickie Weeks Jsy/30 10.00 25.00
RZ Ryan Zimmerman Jsy/30 40.00 80.00
SB Scott Baker Jsy/30 6.00 15.00
SG Steve Garvey Pants/30 15.00 40.00
SH Chris Shelton Jsy/30 4.00 10.00
SK Scott Kazmir Jsy/30 15.00 40.00
SP Scott Podsednik Jsy/30 15.00 40.00
TI Tadahito Iguchi Jsy/30 30.00 60.00
WC Will Clark Pants/30 20.00 50.00
WR David Wright Jsy/30 50.00 100.00

YB Yuniesky Betancourt Jsy/30 10.00 25.00
YM Yadier Molina Jsy/30 15.00 40.00

2006 Artifacts MLB Game-Used Patch Apparel Autographs

OVERALL AU ODDS 1:10
STATED PRINT RUN 10 SERIAL #'d SETS
NO PRICING DUE TO SCARCITY

2006 Artifacts MLB Rare Apparel Autographs

OVERALL AU ODDS 1:10
STATED PRINT RUN 1 SERIAL #'d SET
NO PRICING DUE TO SCARCITY

2007 Artifacts

This 100-card set was released in July, 2007. The set was issued through both hobby and retail channels. The hobby version was issued in four-card packs which came 10 packs to a box. Cards numbered 1-70 feature veterans which were sequenced in team alphabetical order while cards numbered 71-100 featured 2007 rookies.

COMPLETE SET (100) 15.00 40.00
COMMON CARD (1-70) .15 .40
COMMON ROOKIE (71-100) .30 .75
1 Miguel Tejada .15 .40
2 David Ortiz .40 1.00
3 Manny Ramirez .25 .60
4 Curt Schilling .25 .60
5 Jim Thome .25 .60
6 Paul Konerko .15 .40
7 Jermaine Dye .15 .40
8 Travis Hafner .15 .40
9 Victor Martinez .15 .40
10 Grady Sizemore .25 .60
11 Ivan Rodriguez .25 .60
12 Magglio Ordonez .15 .40
13 Justin Verlander .40 1.00
14 Mark Teahen .15 .40
15 Vladimir Guerrero .40 1.00
16 Jered Weaver .25 .60
17 Justin Morneau .15 .40
18 Joe Mauer .25 .60
19 Torii Hunter .15 .40
20 Johan Santana .25 .60
21 Derek Jeter 1.00 2.50
22 Alex Rodriguez .60 1.50
23 Johnny Damon .25 .60
24 Huston Street .15 .40
25 Nick Swisher .15 .40
26 Ichiro Suzuki .60 1.50
27 Richie Sexson .15 .40
28 Carl Crawford .15 .40
29 Scott Kazmir .25 .60
30 Michael Young .15 .40
31 Mark Teixeira .25 .60
32 Vernon Wells .15 .40
33 Roy Halladay .15 .40
34 Brandon Webb .15 .40
35 Stephen Drew .25 .60
36 Chipper Jones .40 1.00
37 Andruw Jones .25 .60
38 Derrek Lee .15 .40
39 Aramis Ramirez .15 .40
40 Ken Griffey Jr. .60 1.50
41 Adam Dunn .15 .40
42 Todd Helton .25 .60
43 Matt Holliday .20 .50
44 Miguel Cabrera .25 .60
45 Hanley Ramirez .25 .60
46 Dontrelle Willis .15 .40
47 Lance Berkman .15 .40
48 Roy Oswalt .15 .40
49 Craig Biggio .25 .60
50 Nomar Garciaparra .40 1.00
51 Derek Lowe .15 .40
52 Prince Fielder .40 1.00
53 Rickie Weeks .15 .40
54 Jose Reyes .40 1.00
55 David Wright .60 1.50
56 Carlos Beltran .15 .40
57 Ryan Howard .60 1.50
58 Chase Utley .40 1.00
59 Jimmy Rollins .15 .40
60 Jason Bay .15 .40
61 Freddy Sanchez .15 .40
62 Trevor Hoffman .15 .40
63 Adrian Gonzalez .15 .40
64 Omar Vizquel .25 .60
65 Matt Cain .25 .60
66 Albert Pujols .75 2.00
67 Jim Edmonds .25 .60
68 Chris Carpenter .15 .40
69 David Eckstein .15 .40
70 Ryan Zimmerman .40 1.00
71 Alexi Casilla RC .50 1.25
72 Andrew Miller RC 2.00 5.00
73 Andy Cannizaro RC .30 .75
74 Brian Stokes (RC) .30 .75
75 Carlos Maldonado (RC) .30 .75
76 Cesar Jimenez RC .30 .75
77 Daisuke Matsuzaka RC 3.00 8.00
78 Delmon Young (RC) .50 1.25
79 Delwyn Young (RC) .30 .75
80 Fred Lewis (RC) .50 1.25
81 Glen Perkins (RC) .30 .75
82 Jeff Baker (RC) .30 .75
83 Jeff Fiorentino (RC) .30 .75
84 Jeff Salazar (RC) .30 .75
85 Jerry Owens (RC) .30 .75
86 Josh Fields (RC) .30 .75
87 Juan Perez RC .30 .75
88 Juan Salas (RC) .30 .75
89 Justin Hampson (RC) .30 .75
90 Kevin Kouzmanoff (RC) .30 .75
91 Michael Bourn (RC) .30 .75
92 Miguel Montero (RC) .30 .75
93 Mike Rabelo RC .30 .75
94 Oswaldo Navarro RC .30 .75
95 Philip Humber (RC) .30 .75
96 Ryan Braun RC .30 .75
97 Ryan Sweeney (RC) .30 .75
98 Sean Henn (RC) .30 .75
99 Jose Reyes RC .30 .75
100 Troy Tulowitzki (RC) .75 2.00

2007 Artifacts Antiquity Artifacts

RANDOM INSERTS IN PACKS
STATED PRINT RUN 199 SER.#'d SETS
AB Adrian Beltre 3.00 8.00
AJ Andruw Jones 3.00 8.00
AL Adam LaRoche 3.00 8.00
AP Albert Pujols 6.00 15.00
AR Aramis Ramirez 3.00 8.00
AT Garrett Atkins 3.00 8.00
BA Bobby Abreu 3.00 8.00
BC Bartolo Colon 3.00 8.00
BE Carlos Beltran 3.00 8.00
BG Brian Giles 3.00 8.00
BO Jeremy Bonderman 3.00 8.00
BR Brian Roberts 3.00 8.00
BU B.J. Upton 3.00 8.00
BW Billy Wagner 3.00 8.00
BZ Barry Zito 3.00 8.00
CA Miguel Cabrera 3.00 8.00
CB Craig Biggio 3.00 8.00
CC Carl Crawford 3.00 8.00
CF Chone Figgins 3.00 8.00
CH Chris Carpenter 3.00 8.00
CJ Chipper Jones 4.00 10.00
CL Carlos Lee 3.00 8.00
CR Cal Ripken Jr. 10.00 25.00
CS Curt Schilling 3.00 8.00
CU Chase Utley 4.00 10.00
DJ Derek Jeter 8.00 20.00
DO David Ortiz 4.00 10.00
DR J.D. Drew 3.00 8.00
DU Dan Uggla 3.00 8.00
DW Dontrelle Willis 3.00 8.00
EC Eric Chavez 3.00 8.00
ED Jim Edmonds 3.00 8.00
FG Freddy Garcia 3.00 8.00
FH Felix Hernandez 3.00 8.00
FL Francisco Liriano 3.00 8.00
FT Frank Thomas 4.00 10.00
GA Garret Anderson 3.00 8.00
GJ Geoff Jenkins 3.00 8.00
GM Greg Maddux 5.00 12.00
GR Ken Griffey Jr. 6.00 15.00
GS Grady Sizemore 3.00 8.00
HA Rich Harden 3.00 8.00
HB Hank Blalock 3.00 8.00
HO Trevor Hoffman 3.00 8.00
HR Hanley Ramirez 3.00 8.00
HS Huston Street 3.00 8.00
HU Torii Hunter 3.00 8.00
IR Ivan Rodriguez 3.00 8.00
JA Jason Bay 3.00 8.00
JC Jorge Cantu 3.00 8.00
JD Jermaine Dye 3.00 8.00
JE Johnny Estrada 3.00 8.00
JF Jeff Francoeur 4.00 10.00
JG Jason Giambi 3.00 8.00
JJ Josh Johnson 3.00 8.00
JK Jeff Kent 3.00 8.00
JM Joe Mauer 3.00 8.00
JP Jake Peavy 3.00 8.00
JR Jimmy Rollins 3.00 8.00
JS Jason Schmidt 3.00 8.00
JT Jim Thome 3.00 8.00
JV Justin Verlander 4.00 10.00
JZ Joel Zumaya 3.00 8.00
KG Khalil Greene 3.00 8.00
LB Lance Berkman 3.00 8.00
LG Luis Gonzalez 3.00 8.00
MO Justin Morneau 3.00 8.00
MR Manny Ramirez 3.00 8.00
MT Mark Teixeira 3.00 8.00
MY Michael Young 3.00 8.00
NS Nick Swisher 3.00 8.00
OR Magglio Ordonez 3.00 8.00
PA Jonathan Papelbon 4.00 10.00
PB Pat Burrell 3.00 8.00
PE Jhonny Peralta 3.00 8.00
PF Prince Fielder 4.00 10.00
PK Paul Konerko 3.00 8.00
PM Pedro Martinez 3.00 8.00
PO Jorge Posada 3.00 8.00
RC Roger Clemens 6.00 15.00
RE Jose Reyes 4.00 10.00
RH Roy Halladay 3.00 8.00
RJ Randy Johnson 4.00 10.00
RO Roy Oswalt 3.00 8.00
RW Rickie Weeks 3.00 8.00
RZ Ryan Zimmerman 4.00 10.00
SA Johan Santana 3.00 8.00
SK Scott Kazmir 3.00 8.00
SM John Smoltz 3.00 8.00
SR Scott Rolen 3.00 8.00
TE Miguel Tejada 3.00 8.00
TG Tom Glavine 3.00 8.00
TH Todd Helton 3.00 8.00
TI Tim Hudson 3.00 8.00
VA Jason Varitek 4.00 10.00
VG Vladimir Guerrero 4.00 10.00
VM Victor Martinez 3.00 8.00
VW Vernon Wells 3.00 8.00

2007 Artifacts Antiquity Artifacts Gold

*GOLD: .3X TO .75X BASIC
GOLD NOT SERIAL NUMBERED
RANDOM INSERTS IN RETAIL PACKS
TR Travis Hafner 2.50 6.00

2007 Artifacts Antiquity Artifacts Patch

*PATCH: .75X TO 2X BASIC
RANDOM INSERTS IN PACKS
STATED PRINT RUN 50 SER.#'d SETS
JB Josh Beckett 6.00 15.00
TR Travis Hafner 6.00 15.00
VA Jason Varitek 12.50 30.00

2007 Artifacts Autofacts

RANDOM INSERTS IN PACKS
EXCHANGE DEADLINE 6/14/2010
AD Adam Dunn 6.00 15.00
AK Austin Kearns 4.00 10.00
AL Adam LaRoche 4.00 10.00
AM Andrew Miller 15.00 40.00
AS Angel Sanchez 3.00 8.00
BB Boof Bonser 3.00 8.00
BC Bobby Crosby 3.00 8.00
BE Josh Beckett 15.00 40.00
BO Jeremy Bonderman 12.50 30.00
BR Brian Roberts
BT Jason Bartlett 3.00 8.00
BU Ambiorix Burgos 3.00 8.00
CH Cole Hamels 15.00 40.00
CJ Cesar Jimenez 3.00 8.00
CL Carlos Lee 6.00 15.00
CR Cal Ripken Jr.
CY Chris Young 6.00 15.00
CZ Carlos Zambrano 15.00 40.00
DJ Derek Jeter EXCH 75.00 125.00
DO David Ortiz 20.00 50.00
DW Dontrelle Willis 4.00 10.00
DY Delmon Young 6.00 15.00
EC Eric Chavez 4.00 10.00
FL Francisco Liriano
FT Frank Thomas
GA Garrett Atkins 4.00 10.00
HA Rich Harden 4.00 10.00
HG Hector Gimenez 3.00 8.00
HK Hong-Chih Kuo 10.00 25.00
HR Hanley Ramirez 10.00 25.00
IK Ian Kinsler 4.00 10.00
JA Joaquin Arias 3.00 8.00
JB Jason Bay 3.00 8.00
JC Jesse Crain 3.00 8.00
JE Johnny Estrada 4.00 10.00
JG Jonny Gomes 3.00 8.00
JJ Josh Johnson 3.00 8.00
JP Jake Peavy
JS John Smoltz 20.00 50.00
JT Jim Thome
JW Jered Weaver 4.00 10.00
JZ Joel Zumaya
KE Howie Kendrick 4.00 10.00
KG Ken Griffey Jr. EXCH 30.00 60.00
KM Kendry Morales 3.00 8.00
KN Jon Knott 3.00 8.00
KW Kerry Wood 10.00 25.00
MJ Mike Jacobs 6.00 15.00
MM Miguel Montero 3.00 8.00
MO Justin Morneau 10.00 25.00
PA Jonathan Papelbon 12.50 30.00
PE Jhonny Peralta 3.00 8.00
PH Philip Humber 3.00 8.00
PM Pedro Martinez 15.00 40.00
RA Chris Ray 3.00 8.00
RC Roger Clemens 75.00 125.00
RH Rich Hill 6.00 15.00
RW Rickie Weeks 4.00 10.00
SB Scott Baker 3.00 8.00
SD Stephen Drew 6.00 15.00
SK Scott Kazmir 5.00 12.00
SO Jeremy Sowers 3.00 8.00
SR Scott Rolen 10.00 25.00
TI Tadahito Iguchi 6.00 15.00
TT Troy Tulowitzki 10.00 25.00
UP B.J. Upton 6.00 15.00
VE Justin Verlander 10.00 25.00
VG Vladimir Guerrero 15.00 40.00
VM Victor Martinez 4.00 10.00
WI Josh Willingham 3.00 8.00
YB Yuniesky Betancourt 6.00 15.00
ZG Zack Greinke 3.00 8.00
ZS Zack Segovia 4.00 10.00

2007 Artifacts Awesome Artifacts

RANDOM INSERTS IN PACKS
PRINT RUNS B/WN 29-50 SER.#'d SETS
AD Adam Dunn 5.00 12.00
AG Adrian Gonzalez 5.00 12.00
AP Albert Pujols 15.00 40.00
AR Aramis Ramirez 5.00 12.00
AS Alfonso Soriano 5.00 12.00
BA Bobby Abreu 5.00 12.00
BC Bartolo Colon 5.00 12.00
BG Brian Giles 5.00 12.00
BI Craig Biggio 6.00 15.00
BR Brian Roberts 5.00 12.00
BW Billy Wagner 5.00 12.00
BZ Barry Zito 5.00 12.00
CA Carl Crawford 5.00 12.00
CB Carlos Beltran 5.00 12.00
CC Carl Crawford 5.00 12.00
CC Chris Carpenter 5.00 12.00
CD Carlos Delgado 5.00 12.00
CF Chone Figgins 5.00 12.00
CJ Chipper Jones 8.00 20.00
CL Carlos Lee 5.00 12.00
CR Cal Ripken Jr. 40.00 80.00
CS Curt Schilling 6.00 15.00
CU Chase Utley 8.00 20.00
DJ Derek Jeter 40.00 80.00
DO David Ortiz 8.00 20.00
DU Dan Uggla 6.00 15.00
DW Dontrelle Willis 5.00 12.00
EC Eric Chavez 5.00 12.00
FG Freddy Garcia 5.00 12.00
FH Felix Hernandez 6.00 15.00
FL Francisco Liriano 8.00 20.00
FT Frank Thomas 12.50 30.00
GA Garret Anderson 5.00 12.00
GM Greg Maddux 12.50 30.00
GR Khalil Greene 6.00 15.00
GS Grady Sizemore 6.00 15.00
HA Roy Halladay 5.00 12.00
HB Hank Blalock 5.00 12.00
HE Todd Helton 6.00 15.00
HR Hanley Ramirez 6.00 15.00
HS Huston Street 5.00 12.00
HU Torii Hunter 5.00 12.00
IK Ian Kinsler 5.00 12.00
IR Ivan Rodriguez 6.00 15.00
JA Jason Bay 5.00 12.00
JB Jeremy Bonderman 5.00 12.00
JC Jorge Cantu 5.00 12.00
JD Jermaine Dye 5.00 12.00
JE Jim Edmonds 6.00 15.00
JF Jeff Francoeur 12.50 30.00
JG Jason Giambi 5.00 12.00
JH Johnny Damon 6.00 15.00
JJ Josh Johnson 5.00 12.00
JK Jeff Kent 5.00 12.00
JM Joe Mauer 6.00 15.00
JO Josh Barfield 5.00 12.00
JP Jake Peavy 5.00 12.00
JR Jimmy Rollins 5.00 12.00
JS Jason Schmidt 5.00 12.00
JT Jim Thome 6.00 15.00
JV Justin Verlander 8.00 20.00
JW Jered Weaver 6.00 15.00
JZ Joel Zumaya 6.00 15.00
KG Ken Griffey Jr. 12.50 30.00
KM Kendry Morales 6.00 15.00
MC Miguel Cabrera 6.00 15.00
MO Justin Morneau 5.00 12.00
MR Manny Ramirez 6.00 15.00
MT Mark Teixeira 6.00 15.00
MY Michael Young 5.00 12.00
OR Magglio Ordonez 5.00 12.00
OS Roy Oswalt 5.00 12.00
PA Jonathan Papelbon 8.00 20.00
PB Pat Burrell 5.00 12.00
PE Jhonny Peralta 5.00 12.00
PF Prince Fielder 8.00 20.00
PO Jorge Posada 6.00 15.00
RC Robinson Cano 6.00 15.00
RE Jose Reyes 10.00 25.00
RF Rafael Furcal 5.00 12.00
RH Rich Harden 5.00 12.00
RJ Randy Johnson 8.00 20.00
RO Roger Clemens 15.00 40.00
RW Rickie Weeks 5.00 12.00
RZ Ryan Zimmerman 8.00 20.00
SK Scott Kazmir 6.00 15.00
SM John Smoltz 6.00 15.00
SR Scott Rolen 6.00 15.00
TG Tom Glavine 6.00 15.00
TH Trevor Hoffman 5.00 12.00
TI Tim Hudson 5.00 12.00
TR Travis Hafner 5.00 12.00
VA Jason Varitek 8.00 20.00
VG Vladimir Guerrero 8.00 20.00
VM Victor Martinez 5.00 12.00
VW Vernon Wells 5.00 12.00

2007 Artifacts Bat Knobs

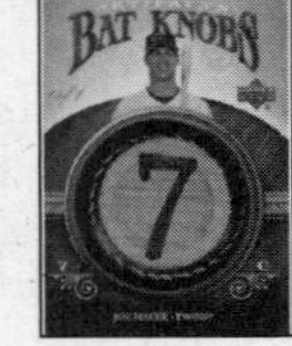

RANDOM INSERTS IN PACKS
STATED PRINT RUN 1 SER.#'d SET
NO PRICING DUE TO SCARCITY

2007 Artifacts Divisional Artifacts

RANDOM INSERTS IN PACKS
PRINT RUNS B/WN 117-199 COPIES PER
AA Aaron Rowand 3.00 8.00
AD Adam Dunn 3.00 8.00
AJ Andruw Jones 4.00 10.00
AL Adam LaRoche 3.00 8.00
AR Aramis Ramirez 3.00 8.00
BA Bobby Abreu 3.00 8.00
BC Bartolo Colon 3.00 8.00
BE Carlos Beltran 3.00 8.00
BG Brian Giles 3.00 8.00
BO Jeremy Bonderman 3.00 8.00
BR Brian Roberts 3.00 8.00
BW Billy Wagner 3.00 8.00
BZ Barry Zito 3.00 8.00
CA Robinson Cano 4.00 10.00
CB Craig Biggio 3.00 8.00
CC Carl Crawford 3.00 8.00
CD Carlos Delgado 3.00 8.00
CH Chris Carpenter 3.00 8.00
CJ Chipper Jones 4.00 10.00
CL Carlos Lee 3.00 8.00
CR Cal Ripken Jr. 10.00 25.00
CS Curt Schilling 3.00 8.00
CU Chase Utley 4.00 10.00
DJ Derek Jeter 8.00 20.00
DL Derrek Lee 3.00 8.00
DO David Ortiz 4.00 10.00
DU Dan Uggla 3.00 8.00
DW Dontrelle Willis 3.00 8.00
EC Eric Chavez 3.00 8.00
FG Freddy Garcia 3.00 8.00
FH Felix Hernandez 3.00 8.00
FL Francisco Liriano 3.00 8.00
FT Frank Thomas 4.00 10.00
GA Garret Anderson 3.00 8.00
GM Greg Maddux 5.00 12.00
GR Ken Griffey Jr. 6.00 15.00
GS Grady Sizemore 3.00 8.00
HA Rich Harden 3.00 8.00
HB Hank Blalock 3.00 8.00
HO Trevor Hoffman 3.00 8.00
HR Hanley Ramirez 3.00 8.00
HU Torii Hunter 3.00 8.00
IK Ian Kinsler 3.00 8.00
IR Ivan Rodriguez 3.00 8.00
JA Jason Bay 3.00 8.00
JC Jorge Cantu 3.00 8.00
JD Jermaine Dye 3.00 8.00
JE Jim Edmonds 3.00 8.00
JF Jeff Francoeur 4.00 10.00
JG Jason Giambi 3.00 8.00
JJ Josh Johnson 3.00 8.00
JK Jeff Kent 3.00 8.00
JM Joe Mauer 3.00 8.00
JN Joe Nathan 3.00 8.00
JO Josh Barfield 3.00 8.00
JP Jake Peavy 3.00 8.00
JR Jimmy Rollins 3.00 8.00
JS Jason Schmidt 3.00 8.00
JT Jim Thome 3.00 8.00
JV Justin Verlander 4.00 10.00
JW Jered Weaver 3.00 8.00
JZ Joel Zumaya 3.00 8.00
KG Khalil Greene 3.00 8.00
KM Kendry Morales 3.00 8.00
LB Lance Berkman 3.00 8.00
MC Miguel Cabrera 4.00 10.00
ME Melky Cabrera 3.00 8.00
MO Justin Morneau 3.00 8.00
MR Manny Ramirez 3.00 8.00
MT Mark Teixeira 3.00 8.00
MY Michael Young 3.00 8.00
NS Nick Swisher 3.00 8.00
OR Magglio Ordonez 3.00 8.00
PA Jonathan Papelbon 4.00 10.00
PB Pat Burrell 3.00 8.00
PE Jhonny Peralta 3.00 8.00
PF Prince Fielder 4.00 10.00
PK Paul Konerko 3.00 8.00
PO Jorge Posada 3.00 8.00
RC Roger Clemens 6.00 15.00
RE Jose Reyes 4.00 10.00
RH Roy Halladay 3.00 8.00
RJ Randy Johnson 3.00 8.00
RO Roy Oswalt 3.00 8.00
RW Rickie Weeks 3.00 8.00
RZ Ryan Zimmerman 4.00 10.00
SK Scott Kazmir 3.00 8.00
SM John Smoltz 3.00 8.00
SR Scott Rolen 3.00 8.00
TG Tom Glavine 3.00 8.00
TH Todd Helton 3.00 8.00
TI Tim Hudson 3.00 8.00
TR Travis Hafner 3.00 8.00
VA Jason Varitek 4.00 10.00
VG Vladimir Guerrero 4.00 10.00
VM Victor Martinez 3.00 8.00
VW Vernon Wells 3.00 8.00

2007 Artifacts Divisional Artifacts Gold

*GOLD: .3X TO .75X BASIC
RANDOMLY INSERTED IN RETAIL PACKS
GOLD NOT SERIAL NUMBERED
AP Albert Pujols 5.00 12.00
PM Pedro Martinez 2.50 6.00
TE Miguel Tejada 2.50 6.00

2007 Artifacts Divisional Artifacts Limited

*LIMITED: .4X TO 1X BASIC
RANDOM INSERTS IN PACKS
STATED PRINT RUN 130 SER.#'d SETS
AP Albert Pujols 6.00 15.00
PM Pedro Martinez 3.00 8.00
TE Miguel Tejada 3.00 8.00

2007 Artifacts Divisional Artifacts Autographs

RANDOM INSERTS IN PACKS
STATED PRINT RUN 25 SER.#'d SETS
NO PRICING DUE TO SCARCITY
AD Adam Dunn
BO Jeremy Bonderman
BR Brian Roberts
CB Craig Biggio
CC Carl Crawford
CF Aaron Rowand
CH Chris Carpenter
CL Carlos Lee
CR Cal Ripken Jr.
CS Curt Schilling
DJ Derek Jeter
DO David Ortiz
DU Dan Uggla
DW Dontrelle Willis
EC Eric Chavez
FH Felix Hernandez
FL Francisco Liriano
FT Frank Thomas
GA Garret Anderson
GM Greg Maddux
GR Ken Griffey Jr.
HA Rich Harden
HR Hanley Ramirez
HU Torii Hunter
IK Ian Kinsler
IR Ivan Rodriguez
JA Jason Bay
JB Josh Beckett
JD Jermaine Dye
JJ Josh Johnson
JM Joe Mauer
JN Joe Nathan
JO Josh Barfield
JP Jake Peavy
JT Jim Thome
JV Justin Verlander
JW Jered Weaver
JZ Joel Zumaya
KG Khalil Greene
KM Kendry Morales
MC Miguel Cabrera
MO Justin Morneau
MY Michael Young
PA Jonathan Papelbon
PB Pat Burrell
PE Jhonny Peralta
PM Pedro Martinez
RC Roger Clemens
RH Roy Halladay
RJ Randy Johnson
RW Rickie Weeks
RZ Ryan Zimmerman
SK Scott Kazmir
SM John Smoltz
SR Scott Rolen
TE Miguel Tejada
TG Tom Glavine
TI Tim Hudson
TR Travis Hafner
VG Vladimir Guerrero
VM Victor Martinez

2007 Artifacts MLB Apparel

RANDOM INSERTS IN PACKS
PRINT RUNS B/WN 25-199 COPIES PER
AD Adam Dunn 3.00 8.00
AJ Andruw Jones 4.00 10.00
AL Adam LaRoche 3.00 8.00
AP Albert Pujols 6.00 15.00
AR Aramis Ramirez 3.00 8.00
AT Garrett Atkins 3.00 8.00
BA Bobby Abreu 3.00 8.00
BC Bartolo Colon 3.00 8.00
BG Brian Giles 3.00 8.00
BI Craig Biggio 3.00 8.00
BO Jeremy Bonderman 3.00 8.00
BR Brian Roberts 3.00 8.00
BU B.J. Upton 3.00 8.00
BW Billy Wagner 3.00 8.00
BZ Barry Zito 3.00 8.00
CB Carlos Beltran 3.00 8.00
CC Carl Crawford 3.00 8.00
CH Cole Hamels 3.00 8.00
CJ Chipper Jones 4.00 10.00
CL Carlos Lee 3.00 8.00

CR Cal Ripken Jr.	10.00	25.00
CS Curt Schilling	3.00	8.00
CU Chase Utley	4.00	10.00
DJ Derek Jeter	8.00	20.00
DO David Ortiz	4.00	10.00
DU Dan Uggla	3.00	8.00
DW Dontrelle Willis	3.00	8.00
DY Jermaine Dye	3.00	8.00
EC Eric Chavez	3.00	8.00
ES Johnny Estrada	3.00	8.00
FG Freddy Garcia	3.00	8.00
FH Felix Hernandez	3.00	8.00
FL Francisco Liriano	3.00	8.00
FT Frank Thomas	4.00	10.00
GA Garret Anderson	3.00	8.00
GJ Geoff Jenkins	3.00	8.00
GM Greg Maddux	5.00	12.00
GR Khalil Greene	3.00	8.00
GS Grady Sizemore	3.00	8.00
HA Roy Halladay	3.00	8.00
HB Hank Blalock	3.00	8.00
HE Todd Helton	3.00	8.00
HO Trevor Hoffman	3.00	8.00
HR Hanley Ramirez	3.00	8.00
HU Torii Hunter	3.00	8.00
IR Ivan Rodriguez	3.00	8.00
JB Jason Bay	3.00	8.00
JC Jorge Cantu	3.00	8.00
JD J.D. Drew	3.00	8.00
JE Jim Edmonds	3.00	8.00
JF Jeff Francoeur	4.00	10.00
JG Jason Giambi	3.00	8.00
JJ Josh Johnson	3.00	8.00
JK Jeff Kent	3.00	8.00
JM Joe Mauer	3.00	8.00
JN Joe Nathan	3.00	8.00
JO Johnny Damon	3.00	8.00
JP Jake Peavy	3.00	8.00
JR Jimmy Rollins	3.00	8.00
JS Jason Schmidt	3.00	8.00
JT Jim Thome	3.00	8.00
JV Justin Verlander	4.00	10.00
JZ Joel Zumaya	3.00	8.00
KG Ken Griffey Jr.	6.00	15.00
LB Lance Berkman	3.00	8.00
LG Luis Gonzalez	3.00	8.00
MC Miguel Cabrera	4.00	10.00
MO Justin Morneau	3.00	8.00
MR Manny Ramirez	3.00	8.00
MT Mark Teixeira	3.00	8.00
MY Michael Young	3.00	8.00
OR Magglio Ordonez	3.00	8.00
PA Jonathan Papelbon	4.00	10.00
PB Pat Burrell	3.00	8.00
PE Jhonny Peralta	3.00	8.00
PF Prince Fielder	4.00	10.00
PM Pedro Martinez	3.00	8.00
PO Jorge Posada	3.00	8.00
RC Roger Clemens	6.00	15.00
RE Jose Reyes	4.00	10.00
RH Rich Harden	3.00	8.00
RI Mariano Rivera	4.00	10.00
RJ Randy Johnson	3.00	8.00
RO Roy Oswalt	3.00	8.00
RW Rickie Weeks	3.00	8.00
RZ Ryan Zimmerman	4.00	10.00
SA Johan Santana	3.00	8.00
SK Scott Kazmir	4.00	10.00
SM John Smoltz	3.00	8.00
SR Scott Rolen	3.00	8.00
TG Tom Glavine	3.00	8.00
TH Tim Hudson	3.00	8.00
TR Travis Hafner	3.00	8.00
VA Jason Varitek	4.00	10.00
VG Vladimir Guerrero	4.00	10.00
VM Victor Martinez	3.00	8.00
VW Vernon Wells	3.00	8.00

2007 Artifacts MLB Apparel Gold

*GOLD: .3X TO .75X BASIC
RANDOM INSERTS IN RETAIL PACKS
GOLD NOT SERIAL NUMBERED

AB Adrian Beltre	2.50	6.00
BE Josh Beckett SP		

2007 Artifacts MLB Apparel Limited

*LIMITED: .4X TO 1X BASIC
RANDOM INSERTS IN PACKS
PRINT RUNS B/WN 75-130 COPIES PER

AB Adrian Beltre	3.00	8.00
MT Miguel Tejada	3.00	8.00

2007 Artifacts MLB Apparel Rare Autographs

RANDOM INSERTS IN PACKS
STATED PRINT RUN 1 SER.#'d SET
NO PRICING DUE TO SCARCITY

2007 Artifacts MLB Apparel Autographs

RANDOM INSERTS IN PACKS
STATED PRINT RUN 25 SER.#'d SETS
NO PRICING DUE TO SCARCITY

1934-36 Batter-Up

The 1934-36 Batter-Up set, issued by National Chicle, contains 192 blank-backed die-cut cards. Numbers 1 to 80 are approximately 2 3/8" by 3 1/4" in size while 81 to 192 are 2 3/8" by 3". The latter are more difficult to find than the former. The pictures come in basic black and white or in tints of blue, brown, green, purple, red, or sepia. There are three combination cards (each featuring two players per card) in the high series (98, 111, and 115). Cards with the die-cut backing removed are graded fair at best.

COMPLETE SET (192)	10000.00	20000.00
COMMON CARD (1-80)	25.00	50.00
COMMON CARD (81-192)	50.00	100.00
WRAP.(1-CENT, CATCHER)	150.00	200.00
WRAP.(1-CENT, BAT)	500.00	600.00
1 Wally Berger	60.00	120.00
2 Ed Brandt	25.00	50.00
3 Al Lopez XRC	60.00	120.00
4 Dick Bartell	30.00	60.00
5 Carl Hubbell	75.00	150.00
6 Bill Terry	100.00	175.00
7 Pepper Martin	40.00	80.00
8 Jim Bottomley	60.00	120.00
9 Tommy Bridges	30.00	60.00
10 Rick Ferrell	60.00	120.00
11 Ray Benge	25.00	50.00
12 Wes Ferrell	30.00	60.00
13 Chalmer Cissell	25.00	50.00
14 Pie Traynor	75.00	150.00
15 Leroy Mahaffey	25.00	50.00
16 Chick Hafey XRC	60.00	120.00
17 Lloyd Waner	60.00	120.00
18 Jack Burns	25.00	50.00
19 Buddy Myer	30.00	60.00
20 Bob Johnson XRC	30.00	60.00
21 Arky Vaughan	60.00	120.00
22 Red Rolfe XRC	30.00	60.00
23 Lefty Gomez	100.00	175.00
24 Earl Averill	75.00	150.00
25 Mickey Cochrane	100.00	175.00
26 Van Lingle Mungo XRC	40.00	80.00
27 Mel Ott	150.00	250.00
28 Jimmie Foxx	200.00	300.00
29 Jimmy Dykes	30.00	60.00
30 Bill Dickey	150.00	250.00
31 Lefty Grove	150.00	250.00
32 Joe Cronin	100.00	175.00
33 Frankie Frisch	75.00	150.00
34 Al Simmons	75.00	150.00
35 Rogers Hornsby	200.00	300.00
36 Ted Lyons	60.00	120.00
37 Rabbit Maranville	60.00	120.00
38 Jimmy Wilson	30.00	60.00
39 Willie Kamm	25.00	50.00
40 Bill Hallahan	25.00	50.00
41 Gus Suhr	25.00	50.00
42 Charley Gehringer	75.00	150.00
43 Joe Heving XRC	25.00	50.00
44 Adam Comorosky	25.00	50.00
45 Tony Lazzeri	125.00	200.00
46 Sam Leslie XRC	25.00	50.00
47 Bob Smith	25.00	50.00
48 Willis Hudlin	25.00	50.00
49 Carl Reynolds	25.00	50.00
50 Fred Schulte	25.00	50.00
51 Cookie Lavagetto XRC	40.00	80.00
52 Hal Schumacher	30.00	60.00
53 Roger Cramer XRC	30.00	60.00
54 Sylvester Johnson XRC	25.00	50.00
55 Ollie Bejma XRC	25.00	50.00
56 Sam Byrd	25.00	50.00
57 Hank Greenberg XRC	200.00	300.00
58 Bill Knickerbocker XRC	25.00	50.00
59 Bill Urbanski	25.00	50.00
60 Eddie Morgan	25.00	50.00
61 Rabbit McNair XRC	25.00	50.00
62 Ben Chapman	30.00	60.00
63 Roy Johnson	25.00	50.00
64 Dizzy Dean	300.00	450.00
65 Zeke Bonura XRC	25.00	50.00
66 Fred Marberry	25.00	50.00
67 Gus Mancuso	25.00	50.00
68 Joe Vosmik XRC	25.00	50.00
69 Earl Grace RC	25.00	50.00
70 Tony Piet	25.00	50.00
71 Rollie Hemsley XRC	25.00	50.00
72 Fred Fitzsimmons	30.00	60.00
73 Hack Wilson	100.00	175.00
74 Chick Fullis XRC	25.00	50.00
75 Fred Frankhouse	25.00	50.00
76 Ethan Allen	25.00	50.00
77 Heinie Manush	60.00	120.00
78 Rip Collins XRC	25.00	50.00
79 Tony Cuccinello	25.00	50.00
80 Joe Kuhel	25.00	50.00
81 Tommy Bridges	60.00	120.00
82 Clint Brown XRC	50.00	100.00
83 Albert Blanche XRC	50.00	100.00
84 Boze Berger XRC	50.00	100.00
85 Goose Goslin	125.00	200.00
86 Lefty Gomez	150.00	250.00
87 Joe Glenn XRC	50.00	100.00
88 Cy Blanton XRC	50.00	100.00
89 Tom Carey XRC	50.00	100.00
90 Ralph Birkofer XRC	50.00	100.00
91 Fred Gabler XRC	50.00	100.00
92 Dick Coffman	50.00	100.00
93 Ollie Bejma XRC	50.00	100.00
94 Leroy Parmelee	50.00	100.00
95 Carl Reynolds	50.00	100.00
96 Ben Cantwell	50.00	100.00
97 Curtis Davis XRC	50.00	100.00
98 Earl Webb XRC	75.00	150.00
Wally Moses XRC		
99 Ray Benge	50.00	100.00
100 Pie Traynor	150.00	250.00
101 Phil Cavarretta XRC	60.00	120.00
102 Pep Young XRC	50.00	100.00
103 Willis Hudlin	50.00	100.00
104 Mickey Haslin XRC	50.00	100.00
105 Ossie Bluege	60.00	120.00
106 Paul Andrews XRC	50.00	100.00
107 Ed Brandt	50.00	100.00
108 Don Taylor XRC	50.00	100.00
109 Thornton Lee XRC	60.00	120.00
110 Hal Schumacher	60.00	120.00
111 Frank Hayes XRC	75.00	150.00
Ted Lyons		
112 Odell Hale XRC	50.00	100.00
113 Earl Averill	125.00	200.00
114 Italo Chelini XRC	50.00	100.00
115 Ivy Andrews	75.00	150.00
Jim Bottomley		
116 Bill Walker	50.00	100.00
117 Bill Dickey	250.00	350.00
118 Gerald Walker XRC	50.00	100.00
119 Ted Lyons	125.00	200.00
120 Eldon Auker XRC	50.00	100.00
121 Bill Hallahan	60.00	120.00
122 Fred Lindstrom	125.00	200.00
123 Oral Hildebrand XRC	50.00	100.00
124 Luke Appling XRC	150.00	250.00
125 Pepper Martin	60.00	120.00
126 Rick Ferrell	125.00	200.00
127 Ival Goodman XRC	50.00	100.00
128 Joe Kuhel	50.00	100.00
129 Ernie Lombardi XRC	125.00	200.00
130 Charley Gehringer	150.00	250.00
131 Van Lingle Mungo XRC	60.00	120.00
132 Larry French XRC	50.00	100.00
133 Buddy Myer	60.00	120.00
134 Mel Harder XRC	60.00	120.00
135 Augie Galan XRC	50.00	100.00
136 Gabby Hartnett	125.00	200.00
137 Stan Hack XRC	60.00	120.00
138 Billy Herman	125.00	200.00
139 Bill Jurges	50.00	100.00
140 Bill Lee XRC	60.00	120.00
141 Zeke Bonura XRC	50.00	100.00
142 Tony Piet	50.00	100.00
143 Paul Dean XRC	60.00	120.00
144 Jimmie Foxx	300.00	450.00
145 Joe Medwick XRC	150.00	250.00
146 Rip Collins XRC	50.00	100.00
147 Mel Almada XRC	50.00	100.00
148 Allan Cooke XRC	50.00	100.00
149 Moe Berg	300.00	450.00
150 Dolph Camilli XRC	60.00	120.00
151 Oscar Melillo XRC	50.00	100.00
152 Bruce Campbell XRC	50.00	100.00
153 Lefty Grove	250.00	350.00
154 Johnny Murphy XRC	60.00	120.00
155 Luke Sewell	60.00	120.00
156 Leo Durocher	200.00	300.00
157 Lloyd Waner	125.00	200.00
158 Guy Bush	50.00	100.00
159 Jimmy Dykes	60.00	120.00
160 Steve O'Neill XRC	60.00	120.00
161 General Crowder	60.00	120.00
162 Joe Cascarella XRC	60.00	120.00
163 Daniel Hafey XRC	60.00	120.00
164 Gilly Campbell XRC	50.00	100.00
165 Ray Hayworth XRC	50.00	100.00
166 Frank Demaree	50.00	100.00
167 John Babich XRC	50.00	100.00
168 Marvin Owen XRC	50.00	100.00
169 Ralph Kress	50.00	100.00
170 Mule Haas	50.00	100.00
171 Frank Higgins XRC	60.00	120.00
172 Wally Berger	60.00	120.00
173 Frankie Frisch	200.00	300.00
174 Wes Ferrell	60.00	120.00
175 Pete Fox XRC	50.00	100.00
176 John Vergez	50.00	100.00
177 Billy Rogell	50.00	100.00
178 Don Brennan XRC	50.00	100.00
179 Jim Bottomley	125.00	200.00
180 Travis Jackson	125.00	200.00
181 Red Rolfe XRC	60.00	120.00
182 Frank Crosetti	75.00	150.00
183 Joe Cronin	125.00	200.00
184 Schoolboy Rowe XRC	60.00	120.00
185 Chuck Klein	150.00	250.00
186 Lon Warneke	60.00	120.00
187 Gus Suhr	50.00	100.00
188 Ben Chapman	60.00	120.00
189 Clint Brown XRC	50.00	100.00
190 Paul Derringer XRC	60.00	120.00
191 John Burns XRC	50.00	100.00
192 John Broaca XRC	75.00	150.00

1959 Bazooka

The 23 full-color, unnumbered cards comprising the 1959 Bazooka set were cut from the bottom of the boxes of gum marketed nationally that year by Topps. Bazooka was the brand name which Topps had been using to sell its one cent bubblegum; this year Topps decided to distribute 25 dual pieces of Bazooka gum in a box. The cards themselves measure 2 13/16" by 4 15/16". Only nine cards were originally issued; 14 more were added to the set at a later date (these are marked with SP in the checklist). The latter are less plentiful and hence more valuable than the original nine. All the cards are blank backed and the catalog designation is R414-15. The prices below are for the cards cut from the box; complete boxes intact would be worth about 50 percent more. Hank Aaron's card can be found with his name in either white or yellow print. The Aaron variations are equally valued.

COMPLETE SET (23)	4000.00	8000.00
COMMON CARD (1-23)	25.00	50.00
COMMON CARD SP	100.00	200.00
1 Hank Aaron White Name	250.00	500.00
2 Richie Ashburn SP	200.00	400.00
3 Ernie Banks SP	300.00	600.00
4 Ken Boyer SP	150.00	300.00
5 Orlando Cepeda	100.00	200.00
6 Bob Cerv SP	100.00	200.00
7 Rocky Colavito SP	200.00	400.00
8 Del Crandall	25.00	50.00
9 Jim Davenport	25.00	50.00
10 Don Drysdale SP	250.00	500.00
11 Nellie Fox SP	200.00	400.00
12 Jackie Jensen SP	150.00	300.00
13 Harvey Kuenn SP	125.00	250.00
14 Mickey Mantle	750.00	1500.00
15 Willie Mays	300.00	600.00
16 Bill Mazeroski	100.00	200.00
17 Roy McMillan	25.00	50.00
18 Billy Pierce SP	125.00	250.00
19 Roy Sievers SP	100.00	200.00
20 Duke Snider SP	400.00	800.00
21 Gus Triandos SP	100.00	200.00
22 Bob Turley	50.00	100.00
23 Vic Wertz SP	100.00	200.00

1960 Bazooka

In 1960, Topps introduced a 36-card baseball player set in three card panels on the bottom of Bazooka gum boxes. The cards measure 1 13/16" by 2 3/4" and the panels measure 2 3/4" by 5 1/2". The cards carried full color pictures and were numbered at the bottom underneath the team position. The checklist below contains prices for individual cards. Complete panels of three would have a 50 percent more than the sum of the indiviudal cards (prices) on the panel and complete boxes would command a premium of another 50 percent above those prices.

COMPLETE INDIV.SET	600.00	1200.00
1 Ernie Banks	20.00	50.00
2 Bud Daley	8.00	20.00
3 Wally Moon	8.00	20.00
4 Hank Aaron	50.00	100.00
5 Milt Pappas	8.00	20.00
6 Dick Stuart	8.00	20.00
7 Roberto Clemente	100.00	200.00
8 Yogi Berra	40.00	80.00
9 Ken Boyer	8.00	20.00
10 Orlando Cepeda	12.50	30.00
11 Gus Triandos	8.00	20.00
12 Frank Malzone	8.00	20.00
13 Willie Mays	60.00	120.00
14 Camilo Pascual	8.00	20.00
15 Bob Cerv	8.00	20.00
16 Vic Power	8.00	20.00
17 Larry Sherry	8.00	20.00
18 Al Kaline	20.00	50.00
19 Warren Spahn	20.00	50.00
20 Harmon Killebrew	20.00	50.00
21 Jackie Jensen	8.00	20.00
22 Luis Aparicio	12.50	30.00
23 Gil Hodges	12.50	30.00
24 Richie Ashburn	15.00	40.00
25 Nellie Fox	15.00	40.00
26 Robin Roberts	15.00	40.00
27 Joe Cunningham	8.00	20.00
28 Early Wynn	12.50	30.00
29 Frank Robinson	20.00	50.00
30 Rocky Colavito	12.50	30.00
31 Mickey Mantle	150.00	300.00
32 Glen Hobbie	8.00	20.00
33 Roy McMillan	8.00	20.00
34 Harvey Kuenn	8.00	20.00
35 Johnny Antonelli	8.00	20.00
36 Del Crandall	8.00	20.00

1961 Bazooka

The 36 card set issued by Bazooka in 1961 follows the format established in 1960; three full color, numbered cards to each panel found on a Bazooka gum box. The individual cards measure 1 13/16" by 2 3/4" whereas the panels measure 2 3/4" by 5 1/2". The cards of 1960 and 1961 are similar in design but are easily distinguished from one another by their numbers. Complete panels of three would have a value of 40 percent more than the sum of the individual cards (prices) on the panel and complete boxes would command a premium of another 40 percent above those prices.

COMPLETE INDIV. SET	750.00	1500.00
1 Art Mahaffey	8.00	20.00
2 Mickey Mantle	250.00	500.00
3 Ron Santo	10.00	25.00
4 Bud Daley	8.00	20.00
5 Roger Maris	50.00	100.00
6 Eddie Yost	8.00	20.00
7 Minnie Minoso	10.00	25.00
8 Dick Groat	8.00	20.00
9 Frank Malzone	8.00	20.00
10 Dick Donovan	8.00	20.00
11 Eddie Mathews	40.00	80.00
12 Jim Lemon	8.00	20.00
13 Chuck Estrada	8.00	20.00
14 Ken Boyer	10.00	25.00
15 Harvey Kuenn	8.00	20.00
16 Ernie Broglio	8.00	20.00
17 Rocky Colavito	20.00	50.00
18 Ted Kluszewski	20.00	50.00
19 Ernie Banks	40.00	80.00
20 Al Kaline	40.00	80.00
21 Ed Bailey	8.00	20.00
22 Jim Perry	8.00	20.00
23 Willie Mays	75.00	150.00
24 Bill Mazeroski	20.00	50.00
25 Gus Triandos	8.00	20.00
26 Don Drysdale	30.00	60.00
27 Frank Herrera	8.00	20.00
28 Earl Battey	8.00	20.00
29 Warren Spahn	40.00	80.00
30 Gene Woodling	8.00	20.00
31 Frank Robinson	40.00	80.00
32 Pete Runnels	8.00	20.00
33 Woodie Held	8.00	20.00
34 Norm Larker	8.00	20.00
35 Luis Aparicio	20.00	50.00
36 Bill Tuttle	8.00	20.00

1962 Bazooka

The 1962 Bazooka set of 45 full color, blank backed, unnumbered cards was issued in panels of three on Bazooka bubble gum. The individual cards measure 1 13/16" by 2 3/4" whereas the panels measure 2 3/4" by 5 1/2". The cards below are numbered by panel alphabetically based on the last name of the player pictured on the far left card of the panel. The cards with SP in the checklist below are more difficult to obtain. Complete panels would have a value of 40 percent more than the sum of the individual cards (prices) on the panel and complete boxes would command a premium of another 40 percent above those prices.

COMPLETE INDIV. SET	1700.00	3400.00
COMMON CARD (1-45)	6.00	15.00
COMMON SP	100.00	200.00
1 Bob Allison SP	100.00	200.00
2 Eddie Mathews SP	250.00	500.00
3 Vada Pinson SP	125.00	250.00
4 Earl Battey	6.00	15.00
5 Warren Spahn	20.00	50.00
6 Lee Thomas	6.00	15.00
7 Orlando Cepeda	12.50	30.00
8 Woodie Held	6.00	15.00
9 Bob Aspromonte	6.00	15.00
10 Dick Howser	6.00	15.00
11 Roberto Clemente	100.00	200.00
12 Al Kaline	20.00	50.00
13 Joe Jay	6.00	15.00
14 Roger Maris	40.00	80.00
15 Frank Howard	8.00	20.00
16 Sandy Koufax	40.00	80.00
17 Jim Gentile	6.00	15.00
18 Johnny Callison	6.00	15.00
19 Jim Landis	6.00	15.00
20 Ken Boyer	8.00	20.00
21 Chuck Schilling	6.00	15.00
22 Art Mahaffey	6.00	15.00
23 Mickey Mantle	150.00	300.00
24 Dick Stuart	6.00	15.00
25 Ken McBride	6.00	15.00
26 Frank Robinson	20.00	50.00
27 Gil Hodges	15.00	40.00
28 Milt Pappas	6.00	15.00
29 Hank Aaron	50.00	100.00
30 Luis Aparicio	12.50	30.00
31 Johnny Romano SP	100.00	200.00
32 Ernie Banks SP	350.00	700.00
33 Norm Siebern SP	100.00	200.00
34 Ron Santo	10.00	25.00
35 Norm Cash	8.00	20.00
36 Jim Piersall	8.00	20.00
37 Don Schwall	6.00	15.00
38 Willie Mays	60.00	120.00
39 Norm Larker	6.00	15.00
40 Bill White	8.00	20.00
41 Whitey Ford	20.00	50.00
42 Rocky Colavito	12.50	30.00
43 Don Zimmer SP	50.00	100.00
44 Harmon Killebrew SP	350.00	700.00
45 Gene Woodling SP	100.00	200.00

1963 Bazooka

The 1963 Bazooka set of 36 full color, blank backed numbered cards was issued on Bazooka bubble gum boxes. This year marked a change in format from previous Bazooka issues with a smaller sized card being issued. The individual cards measure 1 9/16" by 2 1/2" whereas the panels measure 2 1/2" by 4 11/16". The card features a white strip with the player's name printed in black on the card. The number appears in the white border on the bottom of

the card. Three cards were issued per panel. Complete panels of three would have a value of 15 percent more than the sum of the individual cards (prices) on the panel and complete boxes would command a premium of another 30 percent above those prices.

COMPLETE INDIV.SET	400.00	800.00
1 Mickey Mantle	100.00	200.00
2 Bob Rodgers	3.00	8.00
3 Ernie Banks	20.00	50.00
4 Norm Siebern	3.00	8.00
5 Warren Spahn	15.00	40.00
6 Bill Mazeroski	8.00	20.00
7 Harmon Killebrew	15.00	40.00
8 Dick Farrell	3.00	8.00
9 Hank Aaron	40.00	80.00
10 Dick Donovan	3.00	8.00
11 Jim Gentile	3.00	8.00
12 Willie Mays	40.00	80.00
13 Camilo Pascual	3.00	8.00
14 Roberto Clemente	50.00	100.00
15 Johnny Callison	3.00	8.00
16 Carl Yastrzemski	15.00	40.00
17 Don Drysdale	12.50	30.00
18 Johnny Romano	3.00	8.00
19 Al Jackson	3.00	8.00
20 Ralph Terry	3.00	8.00
21 Bill Monbouquette	3.00	8.00
22 Orlando Cepeda	8.00	20.00
23 Stan Musial	20.00	50.00
24 Floyd Robinson	3.00	8.00
25 Chuck Hinton	3.00	8.00
26 Bob Purkey	3.00	8.00
27 Ken Hubbs	4.00	10.00
28 Bill White	4.00	10.00
29 Ray Herbert	3.00	8.00
30 Brooks Robinson	20.00	50.00
31 Frank Robinson	20.00	50.00
32 Lee Thomas	3.00	8.00
33 Rocky Colavito	8.00	20.00
34 Al Kaline	20.00	50.00
35 Art Mahaffey	3.00	8.00
36 Tommy Davis	3.00	8.00

1964 Bazooka

The 1964 Bazooka set of 36 full color, blank backed, numbered cards were issued in panels of three on the backs of Bazooka bubble gum boxes. The individual cards measure 1 9/16" by 2 1/2" whereas the panels measure 2 1/2" by 4 11/16". Many players who were in the 1963 set have the same number in this set; however, the pictures are different. Complete panels of three would have a value of 15 percent more than the sum of the individual cards (prices) on the panel and complete boxes would command a premium of another 40 percent above those prices.

COMPLETE INDIV. SET	500.00	1000.00
1 Mickey Mantle	100.00	200.00
2 Dick Groat	3.00	8.00
3 Steve Barber	3.00	8.00
4 Ken McBride	3.00	8.00
5 Warren Spahn	15.00	40.00
6 Bob Friend	3.00	8.00
7 Harmon Killebrew	15.00	40.00
8 Dick Farrell	3.00	8.00
9 Hank Aaron	40.00	80.00
10 Rich Rollins	3.00	8.00
11 Jim Gentile	3.00	8.00
12 Willie Mays	40.00	80.00
13 Camilo Pascual	3.00	8.00
14 Roberto Clemente	50.00	100.00
15 Johnny Callison	3.00	8.00
16 Carl Yastrzemski	20.00	50.00
17 Billy Williams	8.00	20.00
18 Johnny Romano	3.00	8.00
19 Jim Maloney	3.00	8.00
20 Norm Cash	4.00	10.00
21 Willie McCovey	8.00	20.00
22 Jim Fregosi	3.00	8.00
23 George Altman	3.00	8.00
24 Floyd Robinson	3.00	8.00
25 Chuck Hinton	3.00	8.00
26 Ron Hunt	3.00	8.00
27 Gary Peters	3.00	8.00
28 Dick Ellsworth	3.00	8.00
29 Elston Howard	4.00	10.00
30 Brooks Robinson	20.00	50.00
31 Frank Robinson	20.00	50.00
32 Sandy Koufax	40.00	80.00
33 Rocky Colavito	8.00	20.00
34 Al Kaline	20.00	50.00
35 Ken Boyer	4.00	10.00
36 Tommy Davis	3.00	8.00

1965 Bazooka

The 1965 Bazooka set of 36 full color, blank backed, numbered cards was issued in panels of three on the backs of Bazooka bubble gum boxes. The individual cards measure 1 9/16" by 2 1/2" whereas the panels measure 2 1/2" by 4 11/16". As in the previous two years some players have the same numbers on their cards; however all pictures

are different from the previous two years. Complete panels of three would have a value of 15 percent more than the sum of the individual cards (prices) on the panel and complete boxes would command a premium of another 40 percent above those prices.

COMPLETE INDIV. SET	400.00	800.00
1 Mickey Mantle	100.00	200.00
2 Larry Jackson	3.00	8.00
3 Chuck Hinton	3.00	8.00
4 Tony Oliva	6.00	15.00
5 Dean Chance	3.00	8.00
6 Jim O'Toole	3.00	8.00
7 Harmon Killebrew	12.50	30.00
8 Pete Ward	3.00	8.00
9 Hank Aaron	40.00	80.00
10 Dick Radatz	3.00	8.00
11 Boog Powell	4.00	10.00
12 Willie Mays	40.00	80.00
13 Bob Veale	3.00	8.00
14 Roberto Clemente	50.00	100.00
15 Johnny Callison	3.00	8.00
16 Joe Torre	6.00	15.00
17 Billy Williams	10.00	25.00
18 Bob Chance	3.00	8.00
19 Bob Aspromonte	3.00	8.00
20 Joe Christopher	3.00	8.00
21 Jim Bunning	8.00	20.00
22 Jim Fregosi	3.00	8.00
23 Bob Gibson	12.50	30.00
24 Juan Marichal	12.50	30.00
25 Dave Wickersham	3.00	8.00
26 Ron Hunt	3.00	8.00
27 Gary Peters	3.00	8.00
28 Ron Santo	6.00	15.00
29 Elston Howard	4.00	10.00
30 Brooks Robinson	15.00	40.00
31 Frank Robinson	15.00	40.00
32 Sandy Koufax	20.00	50.00
33 Rocky Colavito	8.00	20.00
34 Al Kaline	15.00	40.00
35 Ken Boyer	4.00	10.00
36 Tommy Davis	3.00	8.00

1966 Bazooka

The 1966 Bazooka set of 48 full color, blank backed, numbered cards was issued in panels of three on the backs of Bazooka bubble gum boxes. The individual cardsd measure 1 9/16" by 2 1/2" whereas the complete panels measure 2 1/2" by 4 11/16". The set is distinguishable from the previous years by mention of "48 card set" at the bottom of the card. Complete panels of three would have a value of 15 percent more than the sum of the individual cards (prices) on the panel and complete boxes would command a premium of another 40 percent above those prices.

COMPLETE INDIV. SET	500.00	1000.00
1 Sandy Koufax	20.00	50.00
2 Willie Horton	3.00	8.00
3 Frank Howard	4.00	10.00
4 Richie Allen	4.00	10.00
5 Mel Stottlemyre	4.00	10.00
6 Tony Conigliaro	5.00	12.00
7 Mickey Mantle	100.00	200.00
8 Leon Wagner	3.00	8.00
9 Ed Kranepool	3.00	8.00
10 Juan Marichal	10.00	25.00
11 Harmon Killebrew	10.00	25.00
12 Johnny Callison	3.00	8.00
13 Roy McMillan	3.00	8.00
14 Willie McCovey	10.00	25.00
15 Rocky Colavito	6.00	15.00
16 Willie Mays	40.00	80.00
17 Sam McDowell	3.00	8.00
18 Vern Law	3.00	8.00
19 Jim Fregosi	3.00	8.00
20 Ron Fairly	3.00	8.00
21 Bob Gibson	10.00	25.00
22 Carl Yastrzemski	12.50	30.00
23 Bill White	4.00	10.00
24 Bob Aspromonte	3.00	8.00
25 Dean Chance	3.00	8.00
26 Roberto Clemente	50.00	100.00
27 Tony Cloninger	3.00	8.00
28 Curt Blefary	3.00	8.00
29 Milt Pappas	3.00	8.00
30 Hank Aaron	40.00	80.00
31 Jim Bunning	6.00	15.00
32 Frank Robinson	12.50	30.00
33 Bill Skowron	4.00	10.00
34 Brooks Robinson	12.50	30.00
35 Jim Wynn	3.00	8.00
36 Joe Torre	5.00	12.00
37 Jim Grant	3.00	8.00
38 Pete Rose	30.00	60.00
39 Ron Santo	5.00	12.00
40 Tom Tresh	4.00	10.00
41 Tony Oliva	5.00	12.00
42 Don Drysdale	10.00	25.00
43 Pete Richert	3.00	8.00
44 Bert Campaneris	3.00	8.00
45 Jim Maloney	3.00	8.00
46 Al Kaline	12.50	30.00
47 Eddie Fisher	3.00	8.00
48 Billy Williams	8.00	20.00

1967 Bazooka

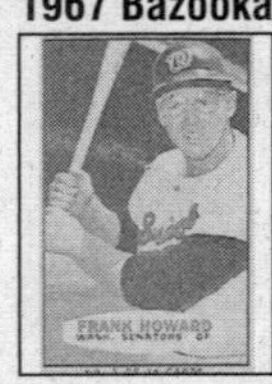

The 1967 Bazooka set of 48 full color, blank backed, numbered cards was issued in panels of three on the backs of Bazooka bubble gum boxes. The individual cards measure 1 9/16" by 2 1/2" whereas the complete panels measure 2 1/2" by 4 11/16". This set is virtually identical to the 1966 set with the exception of ten new cards as replacements for ten 1966 cards. The remaining 38 cards are identical in pose and number. The replacement cards are listed in the checklist below with an asterisk. Complete panels of three would have a value of 15 percent more than the sum of the individual cards (prices) on the panel and complete boxes would command a premium of another 40 percent above those prices.

COMPLETE INDIV. SET	500.00	1000.00
1 Rick Reichardt	3.00	8.00
2 Tommie Agee	3.00	8.00
3 Frank Howard	4.00	10.00
4 Richie Allen	4.00	10.00
5 Mel Stottlemyre	4.00	10.00
6 Tony Conigliaro	5.00	12.00
7 Mickey Mantle	100.00	200.00
8 Leon Wagner	3.00	8.00
9 Gary Peters	3.00	8.00
10 Juan Marichal	10.00	25.00
11 Harmon Killebrew	10.00	25.00
12 Johnny Callison	3.00	8.00
13 Denny McLain	5.00	12.00
14 Willie McCovey	10.00	25.00
15 Rocky Colavito	6.00	15.00
16 Willie Mays	40.00	80.00
17 Sam McDowell	3.00	8.00
18 Jim Kaat	5.00	12.00
19 Jim Fregosi	3.00	8.00
20 Ron Fairly	3.00	8.00
21 Bob Gibson	10.00	25.00
22 Carl Yastrzemski	12.50	30.00
23 Bill White	4.00	10.00
24 Bob Aspromonte	3.00	8.00
25 Dean Chance	3.00	8.00
26 Roberto Clemente	50.00	100.00
27 Tony Cloninger	3.00	8.00
28 Curt Blefary	3.00	8.00
29 Phil Regan	3.00	8.00
30 Hank Aaron	40.00	80.00
31 Jim Bunning	6.00	15.00
32 Frank Robinson	12.50	30.00
33 Ken Boyer	4.00	10.00
34 Brooks Robinson	12.50	30.00
35 Jim Wynn	3.00	8.00
36 Joe Torre	5.00	12.00
37 Tommy Davis	3.00	8.00
38 Pete Rose	30.00	60.00
39 Ron Santo	5.00	12.00
40 Tom Tresh	4.00	10.00
41 Tony Oliva	5.00	12.00
42 Don Drysdale	10.00	25.00
43 Pete Richert	3.00	8.00
44 Bert Campaneris	3.00	8.00
45 Jim Maloney	3.00	8.00
46 Al Kaline	12.50	30.00
47 Matty Alou	3.00	8.00
48 Billy Williams	8.00	20.00

2003 Bazooka

This 280 card set was released in March, 2003. The set was isssued in eight card packs that had an $2 SRP. These packs came 24 packs to a box and 10 boxes to a case. The Bazooka Joe card (number 7) was issued in a basic version as well as featuring a logo of all the major league teams. In addition, 20 cards from the set featured a fascimile signature of the featured player as well as a colorized Bazooka logo. These regular and special logo cards of those player were printed to the same quantity.

COMP.SET w/LOGO's (330)	40.00	80.00
COMPLETE SET (310)	30.00	60.00
COMP.SET w/o JOE's (280)	25.00	50.00
COMMON CARD (1-280)	.15	.40
COMMON ROOKIE	.15	.40
COMMON LOGO	.15	.40
1 Luis Castillo	.15	.40
2 Randy Winn	.15	.40
3 Orlando Hudson	.15	.40
3A Orlando Hudson Logo	.15	.40
4 Fernando Vina	.15	.40
5 Pat Burrell	.15	.40
6 Brad Wilkerson	.15	.40
7 Bazooka Joe	.15	.40
7AN Bazooka Joe Angels	.15	.40
7AS Bazooka Joe A's	.15	.40
7AT Bazooka Joe Astros	.15	.40
7BL Bazooka Joe Blue Jays	.15	.40
7BR Bazooka Joe Braves	.15	.40
7BW Bazooka Joe Brewers	.15	.40
7CA Bazooka Joe Cardinals	.15	.40
7CU Bazooka Joe Cubs	.15	.40
7DE Bazooka Joe Devil Rays	.15	.40
7DI Bazooka Joe Diamondbacks	.15	.40
7DO Bazooka Joe Dodgers	.15	.40
7EX Bazooka Joe Expos	.15	.40
7GI Bazooka Joe Giants	.15	.40
7IN Bazooka Joe Indians	.15	.40
7MA Bazooka Joe Mariners	.15	.40
7ME Bazooka Joe Mets	.15	.40
7MR Bazooka Joe Marlins	.15	.40
7OR Bazooka Joe Orioles	.15	.40
7PA Bazooka Joe Padres	.15	.40
7PH Bazooka Joe Phillies	.15	.40
7PI Bazooka Joe Pirates	.15	.40
7RA Bazooka Joe Rangers	.15	.40
7RC Bazooka Joe Rockies	.15	.40
7RD Bazooka Joe Reds	.15	.40
7RS Bazooka Joe Red Sox	.15	.40
7RY Bazooka Joe Royals	.15	.40
7TI Bazooka Joe Tigers	.15	.40
7TW Bazooka Joe Twins	.15	.40
7WS Bazooka Joe White Sox	.15	.40
7YA Bazooka Joe Yankees	.15	.40
8 Javy Lopez	.15	.40
9 Juan Pierre	.15	.40
10 Hideo Nomo	.40	1.00
11 Barry Larkin	.25	.60
12 Alfonso Soriano	.15	.40
12A Alfonso Soriano Logo	.15	.40
13 Rodrigo Lopez	.15	.40
14 Mark Ellis	.15	.40
15 Tim Salmon	.25	.60
16 Garret Anderson	.15	.40
16A Garret Anderson Logo	.15	.40
17 Aaron Boone	.15	.40
18 Jason Kendall	.15	.40
19 Hee Seop Choi	.15	.40
20 Jorge Posada	.25	.60
21 Sammy Sosa	.40	1.00
22 Mark Prior	.25	.60
22A Mark Prior Logo	.25	.60
23 Mark Teixeira	.25	.60
24 Manny Ramirez	.25	.60
25 Jim Thome	.25	.60
26 A.J. Pierzynski	.15	.40
27 Scott Rolen	.25	.60
28 Austin Kearns	.15	.40
29 Bret Boone	.15	.40
30 Ken Griffey Jr.	.60	1.50
31 Greg Maddux	.60	1.50
32 Derek Lowe	.15	.40
33 David Wells	.15	.40
34 A.J. Burnett	.15	.40
35 Randall Simon	.15	.40
36 Nick Johnson	.15	.40
37 Junior Spivey	.15	.40
38 Eric Gagne	.15	.40
39 Darin Erstad	.15	.40
40 Marty Cordova	.15	.40
41 Brett Myers	.15	.40
42 Mo Vaughn	.15	.40
43 Randy Wolf	.15	.40
44 Vicente Padilla	.15	.40
45 Elmer Dessens	.15	.40
46 Jason Simontacchi	.15	.40
47 John Mabry	.15	.40
48 Torii Hunter	.15	.40
48A Torii Hunter Logo	.15	.40
49 Lyle Overbay	.15	.40
50 Kirk Saarloos	.15	.40
51 Bernie Williams	.25	.60
52 Wade Miller	.15	.40
53 Bobby Abreu	.15	.40
54 Wilson Betemit	.15	.40
55 Edwin Almonte	.15	.40
56 Jarrod Washburn	.15	.40
57 Drew Henson	.15	.40
58 Tony Batista	.15	.40
59 Juan Rivera	.15	.40
60 Larry Walker	.15	.40
61 Brandon Phillips	.15	.40
62 Franklyn German	.15	.40
63 Victor Martinez	.25	.60
63A Victor Martinez Logo	.25	.60
64 Moises Alou	.15	.40
65 Nomar Garciaparra	.60	1.50
66 Willie Harris	.15	.40
67 Sean Casey	.15	.40
68 Omar Vizquel	.25	.60
69 Robert Fick	.15	.40
70 Curt Schilling	.15	.40
70A Curt Schilling Logo	.15	.40
71 Adam Kennedy	.15	.40
72 Scott Hairston	.15	.40
73 Jimmy Journell	.15	.40
74 Rafael Furcal	.15	.40
75 Barry Zito	.15	.40
76 Ed Rogers	.15	.40
77 Cliff Floyd	.15	.40
78 Matt Clement	.15	.40
79 Mike Lowell	.15	.40
80 Randy Johnson	.40	1.00
81 Craig Biggio	.25	.60
82 Carlos Beltran	.15	.40
83 Paul Lo Duca	.15	.40
84 Jose Vidro	.15	.40
85 Gary Sheffield	.15	.40
86 Jacque Jones	.15	.40
87 Corey Hart	.15	.40
88 Roberto Alomar	.25	.60
89 Robin Ventura	.15	.40
90 Pedro Martinez	.25	.60
91 Scott Hatteberg	.15	.40
92 Marlon Byrd	.15	.40
93 Pokey Reese	.15	.40
94 Sean Burroughs	.15	.40
95 Magglio Ordonez	.15	.40
96 Mariano Rivera	.40	1.00
97 John Olerud	.15	.40
98 Edgar Renteria	.15	.40
99 Ben Grieve	.15	.40
100 Barry Bonds	1.00	2.50
100A Barry Bonds Logo	1.00	2.50
101 Ivan Rodriguez	.25	.60
102 Josh Phelps	.15	.40
103 Nobuaki Yoshida RC	.20	.50
103A Nobuaki Yoshida Logo	.20	.50
104 Roy Halladay	.15	.40
105 Mark Buehrle	.15	.40
106 Chan Ho Park	.15	.40
107 Joe Kennedy	.15	.40
108 Shin-Soo Choo	.15	.40
108A Shin-Soo Choo Logo	.15	.40
109 Ryan Jensen	.15	.40
110 Todd Helton	.25	.60
111 Chris Duncan RC	1.25	3.00
112 Taggert Bozied	.15	.40
113 Sean Burnett	.15	.40
114 Mike Lieberthal	.15	.40
115 Josh Beckett	.15	.40
116 Andy Pettitte	.25	.60
117 Jose Reyes	.15	.40
117A Jose Reyes Logo	.15	.40
118 Bartolo Colon	.15	.40
119 Justin Morneau	.15	.40
120 Lance Berkman	.15	.40
121 Mike Wodnicki RC	.20	.50
122 Craig Brazell RC	.20	.50
122A Craig Brazell Logo	.20	.50
123 Troy Glaus	.15	.40
124 John Smoltz	.25	.60
125 Mike Sweeney	.15	.40
126 Jay Gibbons	.15	.40
127 Kerry Wood	.15	.40
128 Ellis Burks	.15	.40
129 Carlos Pena	.15	.40
130 Shawn Green	.15	.40
131 Jason Stokes	.15	.40
131A Jason Stokes Logo	.15	.40
132 Raul Ibanez	.15	.40
133 Francisco Rodriguez	.15	.40
133A Francisco Rodriguez Logo	.15	.40
134 Adrian Beltre	.15	.40
135 Richie Sexson	.15	.40
136 Paul Byrd	.15	.40
137 Bobby Kielty	.15	.40
138 Dewon Brazelton	.15	.40
139 Jeremy Griffiths RC	.20	.50
140 Vladimir Guerrero	.40	1.00
140A Vladimir Guerrero Logo	.40	1.00
141 Jake Peavy	.15	.40
142 Bryan Bullington RC	.20	.50
143 Orlando Cabrera	.15	.40
144 Scott Erickson	.15	.40
145 Doug Mientkiewicz	.15	.40
146 Derrek Lee	.25	.60
147 Daryl Clark RC	.20	.50
148 Trevor Hoffman	.15	.40
149 Gabe Gross	.15	.40
150 Roger Clemens	.75	2.00
151 Khalil Greene	.40	1.00
151A Khalil Greene Logo	.40	1.00
152 Cory Doyne RC	.20	.50
153 Brandon Roberson RC	.20	.50
154 Josh Fogg	.15	.40
155 Eric Chavez	.15	.40
156 Kris Benson	.15	.40
157 Billy Koch	.15	.40
158 Jermaine Dye	.15	.40
159 Kip Bouknight RC	.30	.75
160 Brian Giles	.15	.40
161 Justin Huber	.15	.40
162 Mike Restovich	.15	.40
163 Brandon Webb RC	1.00	2.50
164 Odalis Perez	.15	.40
165 Phil Nevin	.15	.40
166 Dontrelle Willis	.40	1.00
167 Aaron Heilman	.15	.40
168 Dustin Moseley RC	.20	.50
169 Rylan Reed RC	.20	.50
170 Miguel Tejada	.15	.40
171 Nic Jackson	.15	.40
172 Anthony Webster RC	.30	.75
173 Jorge Julio	.15	.40
174 Kevin Millwood	.15	.40
175 Brian Jordan	.15	.40
176 Terry Tiffee RC	.20	.50
177 Dallas McPherson	.15	.40
178 Freddy Garcia	.15	.40
179 Jaime Moyer	.15	.40
180 Rafael Palmeiro	.25	.60
181 Mike O'Keefe RC	.20	.50
182 Kevin Youkilis RC	.60	1.50
183 Kip Wells	.15	.40
184 Joe Mauer	.40	1.00
185 Edgar Martinez	.25	.60
186 Jamie Bubela RC	.20	.50
187 Jose Hernandez	.15	.40
188 Josh Hamilton	.30	.75
189 Matt Diaz RC	.30	.75
190 Chipper Jones	.40	1.00
191 Kevin Mench	.15	.40
192 Joey Gomes RC	.20	.50
193 Shannon Stewart	.15	.40
194 David Eckstein	.15	.40
195 Mike Piazza	.60	1.50
196 Damian Moss	.15	.40
197 Mike Fontenot	.15	.40
198 Shea Hillenbrand	.15	.40
199 Evel Bastida-Martinez RC	.20	.50
200 Jason Giambi	.15	.40
201 Aron Weston RC	.20	.50
202 Frank Thomas	.40	1.00
203 Carlos Lee	.15	.40
204 C.C. Sabathia	.15	.40
205 Jim Edmonds	.15	.40
206 Jemel Spearman RC	.20	.50
207 Jason Jennings	.15	.40
208 Jeremy Bonderman RC	1.00	2.50
209 Preston Wilson	.15	.40
210 Eric Hinske	.15	.40
210A Eric Hinske Logo	.15	.40
211 Will Smith	.15	.40
212 Matthew Hagen RC	.20	.50
213 Joe Randa	.15	.40
214 James Loney	.20	.50
215 Carlos Delgado	.15	.40
216 Chris Kroski RC	.20	.50
217 Cristian Guzman	.15	.40
218 Tomo Ohka	.15	.40
219 Al Leiter	.15	.40
220 Adam Dunn	.15	.40
221 Raul Mondesi	.15	.40
222 Donald Hood RC	.30	.75
223 Mark Mulder	.15	.40
224 Mike Williams	.15	.40
225 Ryan Klesko	.15	.40
226 Rich Aurilia	.15	.40
227 Chris Snelling	.15	.40
228 Gary Schneidmiller RC	.20	.50
229 Ichiro Suzuki	.75	2.00
229A Ichiro Suzuki Logo	.75	2.00
230 Luis Gonzalez	.15	.40
231 Rocco Baldelli	.15	.40
232 Callix Crabbe RC	.30	.75
233 Adrian Gonzalez	.15	.40
234 Corey Koskie	.15	.40
235 Tom Glavine	.25	.60
236 Kevin Beavers RC	.20	.50
237 Frank Catalanotto	.15	.40
238 Kevin Cash	.15	.40
239 Nick Trzesniak RC	.20	.50
240 Paul Konerko	.15	.40
241 Jose Cruz Jr.	.15	.40
242 Hank Blalock	.15	.40
243 J.D. Drew	.15	.40
244 Kazuhiro Sasaki	.15	.40
245 Jeff Bagwell	.25	.60
246 Jason Schmidt	.15	.40
247 Xavier Nady	.15	.40
248 Aramis Ramirez	.15	.40
249 Jimmy Rollins	.15	.40
250 Alex Rodriguez	.60	1.50
250A Alex Rodriguez Logo	.60	1.50
251 Terrence Long	.15	.40
252 Derek Jeter	1.00	2.50
253 Edgardo Alfonzo	.15	.40
254 Toby Hall	.15	.40
255 Kazuhisa Ishii	.15	.40
256 Brad Nelson	.15	.40
257 Kevin Brown	.15	.40
258 Roy Oswalt	.15	.40
259 Mike Cameron	.15	.40
260 Juan Gonzalez	.15	.40
261 Dmitri Young	.15	.40
262 Jose Jimenez	.15	.40
263 Wily Mo Pena	.15	.40
264 Joe Borchard	.15	.40
265 Mike Mussina	.25	.60
266 Fred McGriff	.25	.60
267 Johnny Damon	.25	.60
268 Joel Pineiro	.15	.40
269 Andruw Jones	.25	.60
270 Tim Hudson	.15	.40
271 Chad Tracy	.15	.40
272 Brad Fullmer	.15	.40
273 Boof Bonser	.15	.40
274 Clint Nageotte	.15	.40
275 Jeff Kent	.15	.40
276 Tino Martinez	.25	.60
277 Matt Morris	.15	.40
278 Jonny Gomes	.25	.60
279 Benito Santiago	.15	.40
280 Albert Pujols	.75	2.00
280A Albert Pujols Logo	.75	2.00

2003 Bazooka Minis

Issued at a stated rate of one per pack, this is a complete parallel of the Bazooka set. All the cards were issued in this parallel set including all 31 Bazooka Joe cards as well as the 20 logo variation cards. These cards measure approximately 2 1/4" by 3 1/8"/

*MINIS: .75X TO 2X BASIC
*MINIS JOE'S: .75X TO 2X BASIC JOE'S
*MINIS LOGO'S: .75X TO 2X BASIC LOGO'S
*MINI'S RC'S: .75X TO 2X BASIC RC'S

2003 Bazooka Silver

Issued at a stated rate of almost one per pack, this is a complete parallel to the Bazooka set. These cards can be identified by their silver borders. Again, all the Bazooka Joe varieties as well as the logo cards were issued in a silver version.

*SILVER: .75X TO 2X BASIC
*SILVER JOE'S: .75X TO 2X BASIC JOE'S
*SILVER LOGO'S: .75X TO 2X BASIC LOGO'S
*SILVER RC'S: .75X TO 2X BASIC

2003 Bazooka 4 on 1 Sticker

Inserted at a stated rate of one in four hobby and one in 6 retail packs, these 55 sticker cards feature four players on the front

1 Mark Prior	.50	1.25
Roy Oswalt		
Jarrod Washburn		
Barry Zito		
2 Troy Glaus	.40	1.00
Shea Hillenbrand		
Eric Chavez		
Eric Hinske		
3 Orlando Hudson	.50	1.25
Alfonso Soriano		
Roberto Alomar		
Jose Vidro		
4 Nomar Garciaparra	2.00	5.00
Derek Jeter		
Miguel Tejada		
Alex Rodriguez		
5 Jason Giambi	.50	1.25
Jim Thome		
Todd Helton		
Rafael Palmeiro		
6 Mike Williams	.50	1.25
Trevor Hoffman		
Billy Koch		
John Smoltz		
7 Jorge Posada	1.25	3.00
Mike Piazza		
A.J. Pierzynski		
Ivan Rodriguez		
8 Vladimir Guerrero	.75	2.00
Jim Edmonds		
Manny Ramirez		
Brad Wilkerson		
9 Shawn Green	.75	2.00
Sammy Sosa		
Torii Hunter		
Larry Walker		
10 Bernie Williams	1.50	4.00
Ken Griffey Jr.		
Ichiro Suzuki		
Adam Dunn		
11 John Olerud	.40	1.00
Mike Lieberthal		
Terrence Long		
Drew Henson		
12 Edgar Martinez	.50	1.25
Bret Boone		
Mo Vaughn		
Robert Fick		
13 Randy Johnson	1.50	4.00
Roger Clemens		
Pedro Martinez		
Greg Maddux		
14 Curt Schilling	.75	2.00
Tim Hudson		
Tom Glavine		
Kerry Wood		
15 Paul Konerko	.50	1.25
Mike Sweeney		
Cristian Guzman		
Scott Rolen		
16 Josh Phelps	.40	1.00
Brandon Phillips		
Hee Seop Choi		
Hank Blalock		
17 Benito Santiago	.50	1.25
Barry Larkin		
Gary Sheffield		
Carlos Delgado		
18 Juan Rivera	.40	1.00
Jose Reyes		
Sean Burroughs		
Carlos Pena		
19 Tony Batista	.50	1.25
Tim Salmon		
Jeff Bagwell		
Raul Ibanez		
20 Edgardo Alfonzo	.40	1.00
Nic Jackson		
Luis Castillo		
David Eckstein		
21 David Wells	.40	1.00
Ryan Klesko		
Phil Nevin		
Jeff Kent		
22 Derek Lowe	.40	1.00
Vicente Padilla		
Kevin Millwood		
Joel Pineiro		
23 Fernando Vina	.40	1.00
Darin Erstad		
Jimmy Rollins		
Doug Mientkiewicz		
24 Joe Mauer	.75	2.00
Justin Huber		
Jason Stokes		
Chad Tracy		
25 Austin Kearns	.40	1.00
Junior Spivey		
Brett Myers		
Victor Martinez		
26 Khalil Greene	1.00	2.50
Gabe Gross		
Kevin Cash		
James Loney		
27 Albert Pujols	1.50	4.00
Mark Buehrle		
Chipper Jones		
Lance Berkman		
28 Adam Kennedy	.50	1.25
Craig Biggio		
Johnny Damon		
Randy Winn		
29 Brian Giles	.40	1.00
J.D. Drew		
Marlon Byrd		
Joe Borchard		
30 Al Leiter	.50	1.25
Mike Mussina		
Bartolo Colon		
Freddy Garcia		
31 Jason Kendall	.40	1.00
Richie Sexson		
Mike Lowell		
Paul LoDuca		
32 Pat Burrell	.50	1.25
Garret Anderson		
Cliff Floyd		
Andrew Jones		
33 Xavier Nady	.40	1.00
Bobby Abreu		
Taggert Bozied		
Adrian Beltre		
34 Rocco Baldelli	.75	2.00
Dontrelle Willis		
Chris Snelling		
Mark Teixeira		
35 Willie Harris	.40	1.00
Nick Johnson		
Jason Jennings		
Kazuhisa Ishii		
36 Mark Mulder	.40	1.00

Sean Burnett
Paul Byrd
Josh Beckett
37 Corey Koskie .50 1.25
Aramis Ramirez
Tino Martinez
Moises Alou
38 Jose Cruz Jr. .40 1.00
Roy Halladay
Dewon Brazelton
Jonny Gomes
39 Odalis Perez .40 1.00
Kevin Brown
Matt Clement
Randy Wolf
40 Eric Gagne .40 1.00
Jose Jimenez
Franklyn German
Edwin Almonte
41 Luis Gonzalez .40 1.00
Shannon Stewart
Brian Jordan
Juan Gonzalez
42 Toby Hall .40 1.00
Joe Kennedy
Javier Lopez
Damian Moss
43 Magglio Ordonez .40 1.00
Carlos Lee
Randall Simon
Dmitri Young
44 Sean Casey .40 1.00
Aaron Boone
Jacque Jones
Michael Restovich
45 Adrian Gonzalez .75 2.00
Corey Hart
Fred McGriff
Frank Thomas
46 C.C. Sabathia .50 1.25
Omar Vizquel
Andy Pettitte
Robin Ventura
47 Jason Schmidt .40 1.00
Ellis Burks
Joe Randa
Kris Benson
48 Mike Cameron .40 1.00
Pokey Reese
Jermaine Dye
Preston Wilson
49 Chan Ho Park .75 2.00
Kazuhiro Sasaki
Tomo Ohka
Hideo Nomo
50 Jason Simontacchi .40 1.00
Kip Wells
Matt Morris
Rodrigo Lopez
51 Dallas McPherson 3.00 8.00
Josh Hamilton
Jeremy Bonderman
Aaron Heilman
52 Nobuaki Yoshida 2.00 5.00
Chris Duncan
Craig Brazell
Bryan Bullington
53 Daryl Clark 1.25 3.00
Brandon Webb
Dustin Moseley
Mike O'Keefe
54 Kevin Youkilis 1.25 3.00
Jaime Bubela
Matt Diaz
Joey Gomes
55 Chris Kroski .40 1.00
Donald Hood
Gary Schneidmiller
Callix Crabbe

2003 Bazooka Blasts Relics

Issued at different odds depending on what group the player belonged to, these 35 cards feature a game-used bat chip of the featured player.

GROUP A STATED ODDS 1:1666
GROUP B STATED ODDS 1:306
GROUP C STATED ODDS 1:197
GROUP D STATED ODDS 1:95
GROUP E STATED ODDS 1:52
GROUP F STATED ODDS 1:76
GROUP G STATED ODDS 1:326
GROUP H STATED ODDS 1:48
PARALLEL 25 ODDS 1:524
PARALLEL 25 PRINT RUN 25 #'d SETS
NO PARALLEL 25 PRICING DUE TO SCARCITY
AG Andres Galarraga C 3.00 8.00
ANR Aramis Ramirez E 3.00 8.00
AR Alex Rodriguez F 6.00 15.00
AS Alfonso Soriano D 3.00 8.00
BB Barry Bonds F 8.00 20.00
BW Bernie Williams D 4.00 10.00
CD Carlos Delgado D 3.00 8.00
CI Cesar Izturis B 4.00 10.00
CJ Chipper Jones E 4.00 10.00
DE Darin Erstad F 3.00 8.00
DH Drew Henson H 3.00 8.00
EM Edgar Martinez D 4.00 10.00
GS Gary Sheffield H 3.00 8.00
IR Ivan Rodriguez G 4.00 10.00
JD Johnny Damon H 4.00 10.00
JDD J.D. Drew B 4.00 10.00
JP Jorge Posada D 4.00 10.00
LB Lance Berkman E 3.00 8.00
LG Luis Gonzalez B 4.00 10.00
MP Mike Piazza H 6.00 15.00
MR Manny Ramirez F 4.00 10.00
MS Mike Sweeney C 3.00 8.00
NJ Nick Johnson B 4.00 10.00
PL Paul Lo Duca A 4.00 10.00
RA Roberto Alomar E 4.00 10.00
RH Rickey Henderson H 4.00 10.00
RK Ryan Klesko E 3.00 8.00
RM Raul Mondesi C 3.00 8.00
RP Rafael Palmeiro E 4.00 10.00
RV Robin Ventura F 3.00 8.00
SG Shawn Green D 3.00 8.00
TG Tony Gwynn H 6.00 15.00
TM Tino Martinez E 4.00 10.00
TS Tsuyoshi Shinjo E 3.00 8.00
WB Wilson Betemit E 3.00 8.00

2003 Bazooka Comics

Issued at a stated rate of one in four, these 24 comics, drawn in the style of the old Bazooka Joe comics, feature some of the leading players in the game.

COMPLETE SET (24) 10.00 25.00
1 Albert Pujols 1.00 2.50
2 Alex Rodriguez .75 2.00
3 Alfonso Soriano .40 1.00
4 Barry Zito .40 1.00
5 Chipper Jones .50 1.25
6 Derek Jeter 1.25 3.00
7 Greg Maddux .75 2.00
8 Ichiro Suzuki 1.00 2.50
9 Jason Giambi .40 1.00
10 Jim Thome .40 1.00
11 John Smoltz .40 1.00
12 Mike Piazza .75 2.00
13 Randy Johnson .50 1.25
14 Roger Clemens 1.00 2.50
15 Sammy Sosa .50 1.25
16 Shawn Green .40 1.00
17 Pedro Martinez .40 1.00
18 Manny Ramirez .40 1.00
19 Torii Hunter .40 1.00
20 Ivan Rodriguez .40 1.00
21 Miguel Tejada .40 1.00
22 Troy Glaus .40 1.00
23 Ken Griffey Jr. .75 2.00
24 Nomar Garciaparra .75 2.00

2003 Bazooka Piece of Americana Relics

These 30 cards, which feature game-work uniform swatches were issued at different odds depending on which group the card belonged to.

GROUP A STATED ODDS 1:1666
GROUP B STATED ODDS 1:611
GROUP C STATED ODDS 1:226
GROUP D STATED ODDS 1:118
GROUP E STATED ODDS 1:36
GROUP F STATED ODDS 1:73
GROUP G STATED ODDS 1:190
PARALLEL 25 ODDS 1:611
PARALLEL 25 PRINT RUN 25 #'d SETS
NO PARALLEL 25 PRICING DUE TO SCARCITY
ALL CARDS FEATURE JERSEY SWATCHES
AD Adam Dunn G 3.00 8.00
AH Aubrey Huff F 3.00 8.00
AJ Andruw Jones E 4.00 10.00
AL Al Leiter D 3.00 8.00
BB Bret Boone E 3.00 8.00
CB Craig Biggio E 4.00 10.00
CD Carlos Delgado E 3.00 8.00
CG Cristian Guzman E 3.00 8.00
CJ Chipper Jones E 4.00 10.00
CS Curt Schilling D 3.00 8.00
DB Dewon Brazelton F 3.00 8.00
FT Frank Thomas F 4.00 10.00
IR Ivan Rodriguez D 4.00 10.00
JB Jeff Bagwell A 6.00 15.00
JE Jim Edmonds E 3.00 8.00
JK Jeff Kent D 3.00 8.00
LW Larry Walker D 3.00 8.00
MM Mike Mussina C 4.00 10.00
MO Magglio Ordonez E 3.00 8.00
MP Mike Piazza E 6.00 15.00
NG Nomar Garciaparra B 8.00 20.00
PA Albert Pujols E 6.00 15.00
PL Paul Lo Duca B 4.00 10.00
PW Preston Wilson C 3.00 8.00
RF Rafael Furcal C 3.00 8.00
RP Rafael Palmeiro E 4.00 10.00
SG Shawn Green E 3.00 8.00
TG Tony Gwynn G 6.00 15.00
TH Todd Helton E 4.00 10.00
THA Toby Hall F 3.00 8.00

2003 Bazooka Stand-Ups

Issued at a stated rate of one in eight hobby and one in 24 retail, this 25 card set features a design similar to the 1964 Topps Stand-Up set.

1 Albert Pujols 2.50 6.00
2 Alfonso Soriano .75 2.00

3 Ichiro Suzuki 2.50 6.00
4 Sammy Sosa 1.25 3.00
5 Randy Johnson 1.25 3.00
6 Barry Bonds 3.00 8.00
7 Vladimir Guerrero 1.25 3.00
8 Nomar Garciaparra 2.00 5.00
9 Alex Rodriguez 2.00 5.00
10 Troy Glaus .75 2.00
11 Barry Zito .75 2.00
12 Derek Jeter 3.00 8.00
13 Lance Berkman .75 2.00
14 Larry Walker .75 2.00
15 Adam Dunn .75 2.00
16 Shawn Green .75 2.00
17 Curt Schilling .75 2.00
18 Todd Helton .75 2.00
19 Pedro Martinez .75 2.00
20 Pat Burrell .75 2.00
21 Miguel Tejada .75 2.00
22 Manny Ramirez .75 2.00
23 Mike Piazza 2.00 5.00
24 Jim Thome .75 2.00
25 Jason Giambi .75 2.00

2003 Bazooka Stand-Ups Red

Issued as an unperforated card on top of each Bazooka box, these four cards feature some of the leading players. These cards can be differentiated from the regular stand-ups as they have a red border.

COMPLETE SET (4) 3.00 8.00
1 Barry Bonds 1.50 4.00
2 Albert Pujols 1.25 3.00
3 Jim Thome .60 1.50
4 Barry Zito .60 1.50

2004 Bazooka

This 300 card set was released in March, 2004. This was issued in eight-card hobby and retail packs with an $2 SRP which came 24 packs to a box and 10 boxes to a case. Cards numbered 1-270 feature veterans while cards 271-300 are all Rookie Cards. It is also important to note that there were 30 variation cards issued as part of this set; each of these variations were produced in the same quantity as their counterpart and thus there is no scarcity and a set is considered complete at 330 cards.

COMPLETE SET (330) 35.00 60.00
COMMON CARD (1-270) .15 .40
COMMON CARD (271-300) .15 .40
1 Bobby Abreu .15 .40
2 Jesse Foppert .15 .40
3 Shea Hillenbrand .15 .40
4 Jose Lima .15 .40
5 Manny Ramirez .25 .60
6 Denny Neagle .15 .40
7 Frank Thomas .40 1.00
8 A.J. Burnett .15 .40
9 Carl Everett .15 .40
10A Scott Podsednik Blue Jsy .15 .40
10B Scott Podsednik White Jsy .15 .40
11 Travis Lee .15 .40
12 Mike Mussina .25 .60
13 Runelvys Hernandez .15 .40
14 Shannon Stewart .15 .40
15 Miguel Cabrera .25 .60
16 Edgardo Alfonzo .15 .40
17 Victor Zambrano .15 .40
18 Rafael Furcal .15 .40
19 Eric Hinske .15 .40
20 Paul Lo Duca .15 .40
21 Phil Nevin .15 .40
22 Aramis Ramirez .15 .40
23 Jim Thome .25 .60
24 Jeromy Burnitz .15 .40
25A Mark Prior Glove Chest .25 .60
25B Mark Prior Glove Face .25 .60
26 Ramon Hernandez .15 .40
27 Cliff Lee .15 .40
28 Greg Myers .15 .40
29 Robert Fick .15 .40
30 Mike Sweeney .15 .40
31 Carlos Zambrano .15 .40
32 Roberto Alomar .25 .60
33 Orlando Cabrera .15 .40
34 Orlando Hudson .15 .40
35A Nomar Garciaparra Batting .60 1.50
35B Nomar Garciaparra Fielding .60 1.50
36 Esteban Loaiza .15 .40
37 Laynce Nix .15 .40
38 Joe Randa .15 .40
39 Juan Uribe .15 .40
40 Pat Burrell .15 .40
41 Steve Finley .15 .40
42 Livan Hernandez .15 .40
43 Al Leiter .15 .40
44 Brett Myers .15 .40
45 Jody Gerut .15 .40
46 Mark Teixeira .25 .60
47 Barry Zito .15 .40
48 Moises Alou .15 .40
49 Mike Cameron .15 .40
50A Albert Pujols One Hand .75 2.00
50B Albert Pujols Two Hands .75 2.00
51 Tim Hudson .15 .40
52 Kenny Lofton .15 .40
53 Trot Nixon .15 .40
54 Tim Redding .15 .40
55 Marlon Byrd .15 .40
56 Javier Vazquez .15 .40
57 Sean Burroughs .15 .40
58 Cliff Floyd .15 .40
59 Juan Rivera .15 .40
60 Mike Lieberthal .15 .40
61 Xavier Nady .15 .40
62 Brad Radke .15 .40
63 Miguel Tejada .15 .40
64A Ichiro Suzuki Running .75 2.00
64B Ichiro Suzuki Throwing .75 2.00
65 Garret Anderson .15 .40
66 Sean Casey .15 .40
67A Jason Giambi Fielding .15 .40
67B Jason Giambi Hitting .15 .40
68 Aubrey Huff .15 .40
69 Javy Lopez .15 .40
70 Hideo Nomo .40 1.00
71 Mark Redman .15 .40
72 Jose Vidro .15 .40
73 Rich Aurilia .15 .40
74 Luis Castillo .15 .40
75 Jay Gibbons .15 .40
76 Torii Hunter .15 .40
77 Derek Lowe .15 .40
78 Wes Obermueller .15 .40
79 Edgar Renteria .15 .40
80 Jeff Bagwell .25 .60
81 Fernando Vina .15 .40
82 Frank Catalanotto .15 .40
83 Marcus Giles .15 .40
84 Raul Ibanez .15 .40
85 Mike Lowell .15 .40
86 Tomo Ohka .15 .40
87A Jose Reyes w/Bat .15 .40
87B Jose Reyes w/o Bat .15 .40
88 Omar Vizquel .25 .60
89 Shawn Chacon .15 .40
90 Rocco Baldelli .15 .40
91A Brian Giles w/Bat .15 .40
91B Brian Giles w/o Bat .15 .40
92 Kazuhisa Ishii .15 .40
93 Greg Maddux .60 1.50
94 John Olerud .15 .40
95 Eric Chavez .15 .40
96 Doug Waechter .15 .40
97 Tony Batista .15 .40
98 Jeriome Robertson .15 .40
99 Troy Glaus .15 .40
100A Eric Gagne Hand Out .15 .40
100B Eric Gagne Hand Up .15 .40
101A Pedro Martinez Leg Down .25 .60
101B Pedro Martinez Leg Up .25 .60
102 Magglio Ordonez .15 .40
103A Alex Rodriguez w/Bat .60 1.50
103B Alex Rodriguez w/o Bat .60 1.50
104 Jason Bay .15 .40
105 Larry Walker .15 .40
106 Matt Clement .15 .40
107 Tom Glavine .25 .60
108 Geoff Jenkins .15 .40
109 Victor Martinez .15 .40
110 David Ortiz .40 1.00
111 Ivan Rodriguez .25 .60
112 Jarrod Washburn .15 .40
113 Josh Beckett .15 .40
114 Bartolo Colon .15 .40
115 Juan Gonzalez .15 .40
116A Derek Jeter Fielding .75 2.00
116B Derek Jeter Hitting .75 2.00
117 Edgar Martinez .25 .60
118 Ramon Ortiz .15 .40
119 Scott Rolen .25 .60
120A Brandon Webb w/Ball .15 .40
120B Brandon Webb w/o Ball .15 .40
121 Carlos Beltran .15 .40
122 Jose Contreras .15 .40
123 Luis Gonzalez .15 .40
124 Jason Johnson .15 .40
125 Luis Matos .15 .40
126 Russ Ortiz .15 .40
127 Damian Rolls .15 .40
128 David Wells .15 .40
129 Adrian Beltre .15 .40
130 Shawn Green .15 .40
131 Nate Cornejo .15 .40
132 Nick Johnson .15 .40
133 Joe Mays .15 .40
134 Roy Oswalt .15 .40
135 C.C. Sabathia .15 .40
136A Vernon Wells Fielding .15 .40
136B Vernon Wells Hitting .15 .40
137 Kris Benson .15 .40
138 Carl Crawford .15 .40
139A Ken Griffey Jr. Fielding .60 1.50
139B Ken Griffey Jr. Hitting .60 1.50
140A Randy Johnson Black Jsy .40 1.00
140B Randy Johnson White Jsy .40 1.00
141 Fred McGriff .25 .60
142 Vicente Padilla .15 .40
143 Tim Salmon .25 .60
144 Kip Wells .15 .40
145 Lance Berkman .15 .40
146 Jose Cruz Jr. .15 .40
147 Marquis Grissom .15 .40
148 Jacque Jones .15 .40
149 Gil Meche .15 .40
150A Vladimir Guerrero Fielding .40 1.00
150B Vladimir Guerrero Hitting .40 1.00
151 Reggie Sanders .15 .40
152 Ty Wigginton .15 .40
153 Angel Berroa .15 .40
154 Johnny Damon .25 .60
155 Rafael Palmeiro .25 .60
156A Chipper Jones w/Bat .40 1.00
156B Chipper Jones w/o Bat .40 1.00
157 Kevin Millar .15 .40
158 Corey Patterson .15 .40
159A Johan Santana Both Feet .40 1.00
159B Johan Santana One Foot .40 1.00
160 Bernie Williams .25 .60
161 Craig Biggio .25 .60
162A Carlos Delgado Blue Jsy .15 .40
162B Carlos Delgado White Jsy .15 .40
163 Aaron Guiel .15 .40
164 Wade Miller .15 .40
165 Andruw Jones .25 .60
166 Jay Payton .15 .40
167 Benito Santiago .15 .40
168 Woody Williams .15 .40
169 Casey Blake .15 .40
170 Adam Dunn .15 .40
171 Jose Guillen .15 .40
172 Brian Jordan .15 .40
173 Kevin Millwood .15 .40
174 Carlos Pena .15 .40
175 Curt Schilling .25 .60
176 Jerome Williams .15 .40
177A Hank Blalock Grey Jsy .15 .40
177B Hank Blalock White Jsy .15 .40
178 Erubiel Durazo .15 .40
179 Cristian Guzman .15 .40
180 Austin Kearns .15 .40
181 Raul Mondesi .15 .40
182 Andy Pettitte .25 .60
183 Jason Schmidt .15 .40
184 Jeremy Bonderman .15 .40
185A Dontrelle Willis w/Ball .25 .60
185B Dontrelle Willis w/o Ball .25 .60
186 Ray Durham .15 .40
187 Jerry Hairston Jr. .15 .40
188 Jason Kendall .15 .40
189 Melvin Mora .15 .40
190 Jeff Kent .15 .40
191 Jae Weong Seo .15 .40
192 Jack Wilson .15 .40
193 Cesar Izturis .15 .40
194 Jermaine Dye .15 .40
195A Roy Halladay w/Ball .15 .40
195B Roy Halladay w/o Ball .15 .40
196 Jason Phillips .15 .40
197 Matt Morris .15 .40
198A Mike Piazza Fielding .60 1.50
198B Mike Piazza Running .60 1.50
199 Richie Sexson .15 .40
200 Alfonso Soriano .15 .40
201 Mark Mulder .15 .40
202 David Eckstein .15 .40
203 Mike Hampton .15 .40
204 Ryan Klesko .15 .40
205 Damian Moss .15 .40
206 Juan Pierre .15 .40
207 Ben Sheets .15 .40
208 Randy Winn .15 .40
209 Bret Boone .15 .40
210 Jim Edmonds .15 .40
211 Rich Harden .15 .40
212 Paul Konerko .15 .40
213 Jamie Moyer .15 .40
214 A.J. Pierzynski .15 .40
215 Gary Sheffield .15 .40
216 Randy Wolf .15 .40
217 Kevin Brown .15 .40
218 Morgan Ensberg .15 .40
219 Bo Hart .15 .40
220 Bill Mueller .15 .40
221 Corey Koskie .15 .40
222 Joel Pineiro .15 .40
223 Preston Wilson .15 .40
224 Aaron Boone .15 .40
225 Kerry Wood .15 .40
226 Darin Erstad .15 .40
227 Wes Helms .15 .40
228 Brian Lawrence .15 .40
229 Mark Buehrle .15 .40
230A Sammy Sosa w/Ball .40 1.00
230B Sammy Sosa w/Bat .40 1.00
231 Sidney Ponson .15 .40
232 Dmitri Young .15 .40
233 Ellis Burks .15 .40
234 Kelvim Escobar .15 .40
235 Todd Helton .25 .60
236 Matt Lawton .15 .40
237 Eric Munson .15 .40
238 Jorge Posada .25 .60
239 Mariano Rivera .40 1.00
240 Michael Young .15 .40
241 Ramon Nivar .15 .40
242 Edwin Jackson .15 .40
243 Felix Pie .25 .60
244 Joe Mauer .40 1.00
245 Grady Sizemore .40 1.00
246 Bobby Jenks .15 .40
247 Chad Billingsley .15 .40
248 Casey Kotchman .15 .40
249 Bobby Crosby .15 .40
250 Khalil Greene .25 .60
251 Danny Garcia .15 .40
252 Nick Markakis .15 .40
253 Bernie Castro .15 .40
254 Aaron Hill .15 .40
255 Josh Barfield .15 .40
256 Ryan Wagner .15 .40
257 Ryan Harvey .15 .40
258 Jimmy Gobble .15 .40
259 Ryan Madson .15 .40
260 Zack Greinke .15 .40
261 Rene Reyes .15 .40
262 Eric Duncan .15 .40
263 Chris Lubanski .15 .40
264 Jeff Mathis .15 .40
265 Rickie Weeks .15 .40
266 Justin Morneau .15 .40
267 Brian Snyder .15 .40
268 Neal Cotts .15 .40
269 Joe Borchard .15 .40
270 Larry Bigbie .15 .40
271 Marcus McBeth FY RC .15 .40
272 Tydus Meadows FY RC .15 .40
273 Zach Miner FY RC .50 1.25
274A A.Lerew w/Ball FY RC .30 .75
274B A.Lerew w/o Ball FY RC .30 .75
275A Y.Molina w/Bat FY RC .60 1.50
275B Y.Molina w/o Bat FY RC .60 1.50
276A Jon Knott Bat Up FY RC .15 .40
276B Jon Knott Bat Down FY RC .15 .40
277 Matthew Moses FY RC .50 1.25
278 Sung Jung FY RC .15 .40
279 Mike Gosling FY RC .15 .40
280 David Murphy FY RC .30 .75
281 Tim Frend FY RC .15 .40
282 Casey Myers FY RC .15 .40
283 Brayan Pena FY RC .15 .40
284 Omar Falcon FY RC .15 .40
285 Blake Hawksworth FY RC .20 .50
286 Jesse Roman FY RC .15 .40
287 Kyle Davies FY RC .75 2.00
288 Matt Creighton FY RC .15 .40
289 Rodney Choy Foo FY RC .15 .40
290 Kyle Sleeth FY RC .20 .50
291 Carlos Quentin FY RC 1.00 2.50
292 Khalid Ballouli FY RC .15 .40
293A Tim Stauffer w/Ball FY RC .30 .75
293B Tim Stauffer w/o Ball FY RC .30 .75
294 Craig Ansman FY RC .15 .40
295 Dioner Navarro FY RC .30 .75
296A Josh Labandeira w/Ball FY RC .15 .40
296B Josh Labandeira w/o Ball FY RC .15 .40
297 Jeffrey Allison FY RC .15 .40
298 Anthony Acevedo FY RC .15 .40
299 Brad Sullivan FY RC .20 .50
300 Conor Jackson FY RC 1.25 3.00

2004 Bazooka Red Chunks

*CHUNKS 1-270: .75X TO 2X BASIC
*CHUNKS 271-300: .75X TO 2X BASIC
ONE PER PACK

2004 Bazooka Minis

*MINIS 1-270: .75X TO 2X BASIC
*MINIS 271-300: .75X TO 2X BASIC
ONE PER PACK

2004 Bazooka 4 on 1 Sticker

STATED ODDS 1:4 H, 1:6 R
1 Rich Harden .40 1.00
Dontrelle Willis
Jerome Williams
Brandon Webb
2 Eric Duncan 1.50 4.00
Derek Jeter
Alfonso Soriano
Jason Giambi
3 Grady Sizemore 1.50 4.00
Rocco Baldelli
Ichiro Suzuki
Vladimir Guerrero
4 Roy Halladay .40 1.00
Pedro Martinez
Curt Schilling
Brett Myers
5 Alex Rodriguez 1.25 3.00
Angel Berroa
Jose Reyes
Khalil Greene
6 Kerry Wood .40 1.00
Adam Dunn
Jeff Kent
Scott Rolen
7 Miguel Cabrera .50 1.25
Scott Podsednik
Bo Hart
Mark Teixeira
8 Rickie Weeks 1.50 4.00
Josh Barfield
Albert Pujols
Vernon Wells
9 Torii Hunter 1.25 3.00
Garret Anderson
Bobby Abreu
Ken Griffey Jr.
10 Jay Gibbons 1.25 3.00
Chipper Jones
Mike Piazza
Mike Sweeney
11 David Ortiz .75 2.00
Nick Johnson
Carlos Delgado
Frank Thomas
12 Todd Helton .50 1.25
Jose Vidro

Mike Lowell
Miguel Tejada
13 Randy Wolf .75 2.00
Mark Mulder
Johan Santana
Randy Johnson
14 Bret Boone .40 1.00
Aubrey Huff
Eric Chavez
Javy Lopez
15 Jason Schmidt .50 1.25
Roy Oswalt
Joel Pineiro
Mark Prior
16 Kevin Millwood .50 1.25
Andy Pettitte
Matt Morris
Tim Hudson
17 Javier Vazquez .50 1.25
Esteban Loaiza
Orlando Cabrera
Roberto Alomar
18 Al Leiter .40 1.00
David Wells
Mike Hampton
Jarrod Washburn
19 Paul Lo Duca .50 1.25
Mike Lieberthal
Brian Giles
Andruw Jones
20 Magglio Ordonez .50 1.25
Corey Patterson
Aaron Boone
Jeff Bagwell
21 Troy Glaus .50 1.25
Edgar Martinez
Manny Ramirez
Raul Ibanez
22 Sammy Sosa .75 2.00
Barry Zito
Bartolo Colon
Austin Kearns
23 Jim Edmonds .40 1.00
Gary Sheffield
Preston Wilson
Shawn Green
24 Bernie Williams .40 1.00
Juan Pierre
Josh Beckett
Mike Mussina
25 Ramon Hernandez .40 1.00
Jason Kendall
Jason Phillips
A.J. Pierzynski
26 Pat Burrell .40 1.00
Laynce Nix
Mike Cameron
Cliff Floyd
27 Eric Gagne .40 1.00
Carl Crawford
Jose Guillen
Steve Finley
28 Ellis Burks .40 1.00
Livan Hernandez
Derek Lowe
Kazuhisa Ishii
29 Jorge Posada .50 1.25
Jeff Mathis
Victor Martinez
Ivan Rodriguez
30 Jim Thome .75 2.00
Marcus Giles
Nomar Garciaparra
Hank Blalock
31 Edgar Renteria .40 1.00
Bobby Crosby
Neal Cotts
Russ Ortiz
32 Zack Greinke .40 1.00
Cristian Guzman
Cesar Izturis
Kevin Brown
33 Bobby Jenks .40 1.00
Ramon Nivar
Richie Sexson
Ryan Klesko
34 Omar Vizquel .50 1.25
Carlos Pena
Rafael Furcal
Gil Meche
35 Kenny Lofton .50 1.25
Tim Salmon
Marquis Grissom
Craig Biggio
36 Kyle Davies 1.25 3.00
Anthony Lerew
Brayan Pena
Sung Jung
37 Rodney Choy Foo .75 2.00
Craig Ansman
David Murphy
Matthew Moses
38 Carlos Quentin 1.50 4.00
Dioner Navarro
Marcus McBeth
Josh Labandeira
39 Kyle Sleeth 2.00 5.00
Conor Jackson
Brad Sullivan
Jeffrey Allison
40 Yadier Molina 1.50 4.00
Jon Knott
Blake Hawksworth
Tim Stauffer

2004 Bazooka Adventures Relics

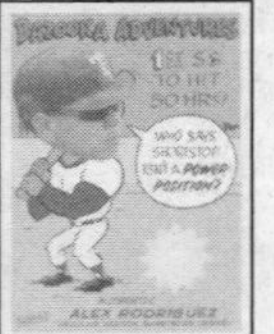

GROUP A ODDS 1:134 H, 1:187 R
GROUP B ODDS 1:207 H, 1:289 R
GROUP C ODDS 1:74 H, 1:104 R
GROUP D ODDS 1:57 H, 1:80 R
GROUP E ODDS 1:86 H, 1:119 R
OVERALL PARALLEL 25 ODDS 1:94
PARALLEL 25 PRINT RUN 25 #'d SETS
NO PARALLEL 25 PRICING DUE TO SCARCITY
AD1 Adam Dunn Stripe Jsy A 3.00 8.00
AD2 Adam Dunn Grey Jsy A 3.00 8.00
AJ Andruw Jones Jsy D 4.00 10.00
AP Albert Pujols Uni D 8.00 20.00
AR1 Alex Rodriguez Blue Jsy E 4.00 10.00
AR2 Alex Rodriguez White Jsy D 4.00 10.00
AS Alfonso Soriano Uni C 3.00 8.00
BG Ben Grieve Jsy A 3.00 8.00
BP Brad Penny Jsy A 3.00 8.00
BW Bernie Williams Jsy B 4.00 10.00
BZ Barry Zito Jsy B 3.00 8.00
CB Craig Biggio Uni A 4.00 10.00
CE Carl Everett Uni D 3.00 8.00
CF Cliff Floyd Jsy B 3.00 8.00
CG Cristian Guzman Jsy C 3.00 8.00
CJ Chipper Jones Jsy D 4.00 10.00
CS Curt Schilling Jsy A 4.00 10.00
DW Dontrelle Willis Uni D 4.00 10.00
EA Edgardo Alfonzo Uni D 3.00 8.00
EC Eric Chavez Uni A 3.00 8.00
GJ Geoff Jenkins Jsy E 3.00 8.00
GM Greg Maddux Jsy D 6.00 15.00
HN Hideo Nomo Jsy C 4.00 10.00
JB Jeff Bagwell Uni A 4.00 10.00
JDG Jeremy Giambi Jsy E 3.00 8.00
JG Jason Giambi Jsy D 3.00 8.00
JK Jason Kendall Jsy B 3.00 8.00
JO John Olerud Jsy E 3.00 8.00
JT Jim Thome Jsy C 4.00 10.00
JW Jarrod Washburn Uni C 3.00 8.00
KB Kevin Brown Jsy A 3.00 8.00
KM Kevin Millwood Jsy E 3.00 8.00
KW Kerry Wood Jsy A 3.00 8.00
LB Lance Berkman Jsy D 3.00 8.00
LC Luis Castillo Jsy D 3.00 8.00
LG Luis Gonzalez Uni A 3.00 8.00
LW Larry Walker Jsy A 3.00 8.00
MB Marlon Byrd Jsy C 3.00 8.00
MCM Mike Mussina Uni C 4.00 10.00
ML Mike Lowell Jsy D 3.00 8.00
MM Mark Mulder Uni A 3.00 8.00
MP1 M.Piazza 2nd Most Jsy C 6.00 15.00
MP2 M.Piazza 10 Straight Jsy D 6.00 15.00
MR Manny Ramirez Uni C 4.00 10.00
MT Miguel Tejada Uni E 3.00 8.00
MV Mo Vaughn Jsy A 3.00 8.00
NG Nomar Garciaparra Uni C 6.00 15.00
PB Pat Burrell Jsy E 3.00 8.00
PK Paul Konerko Jsy B 3.00 8.00
PL Paul Lo Duca Jsy C 3.00 8.00
PW Preston Wilson Jsy E 3.00 8.00
RJ Randy Johnson Jsy C 4.00 10.00
RP1 R.Palmeiro 500th HR Jsy D 4.00 10.00
RP2 R.Palmeiro 9 Straight Jsy D 4.00 10.00
SC Sean Casey Jsy D 3.00 8.00
SG Shawn Green Jsy C 3.00 8.00
TAH1 T.Hudson Most Wins Jsy B 3.00 8.00
TAH2 T.Hudson 3rd Best Uni D 3.00 8.00
TEG Troy Glaus Uni A 3.00 8.00
TG Tom Glavine Jsy A 4.00 10.00
TH Toby Hall Jsy A 3.00 8.00
TJS Tim Salmon Uni B 4.00 10.00
VG Vladimir Guerrero Jsy C 4.00 10.00

2004 Bazooka Blasts Bat Relics

GROUP A ODDS 1:62 H, 1:86 R
GROUP B ODDS 1:29 H, 1:40 R
OVERALL PARALLEL 25 ODDS 1:94
PARALLEL 25 PRINT RUN 25 #'d SETS
NO PARALLEL 25 PRICING DUE TO SCARCITY
AD Adam Dunn A 3.00 8.00
AG Adrian Gonzalez B 3.00 8.00
AH Aubrey Huff A 3.00 8.00
AJG Andres Galarraga A 3.00 8.00
ANR Aramis Ramirez B 3.00 8.00
AP Albert Pujols B 8.00 20.00
AR Alex Rodriguez B 4.00 10.00
AS Alfonso Soriano A 3.00 8.00
BB Bret Boone B 3.00 8.00
BF Brad Fullmer A 3.00 8.00
BW Bernie Williams A 4.00 10.00
CB Craig Biggio A 4.00 10.00
CC Carl Crawford A 3.00 8.00
CE Carl Everett B 3.00 8.00
CG Cristian Guzman A 3.00 8.00
CIB Carlos Beltran A 3.00 8.00
CJ Chipper Jones B 4.00 10.00
CL Carlos Lee A 3.00 8.00
CP Corey Patterson A 3.00 8.00
DM Doug Mientkiewicz A 3.00 8.00
EM Edgar Martinez B 4.00 10.00
FM Fred McGriff A 4.00 10.00
FT Frank Thomas B 4.00 10.00
GS Gary Sheffield B 3.00 8.00
HB Hank Blalock A 3.00 8.00
IR Ivan Rodriguez B 4.00 10.00
JAG Juan Gonzalez B 3.00 8.00
JB Jeff Bagwell A 4.00 10.00
JG Jason Giambi A 3.00 8.00
JNB Jeromy Burnitz A 3.00 8.00
JO John Olerud A 3.00 8.00
JP Jorge Posada A 4.00 10.00
JR Juan Rivera B 3.00 8.00
LB Lance Berkman B 3.00 8.00
LG Luis Gonzalez A 3.00 8.00
LW Larry Walker B 3.00 8.00
MA Moises Alou A 3.00 8.00
MAT Michael Tucker A 3.00 8.00
MCT Mark Teixeira A 4.00 10.00
MG Marquis Grissom B 3.00 8.00
ML Matt Lawton B 3.00 8.00
MO Magglio Ordonez B 3.00 8.00
MP Mike Piazza A 6.00 15.00
MR Manny Ramirez B 4.00 10.00
MT Miguel Tejada A 3.00 8.00
MV Mo Vaughn B 3.00 8.00
NG Nomar Garciaparra A 6.00 15.00
NH Nathan Haynes B 3.00 8.00
OV Omar Vizquel B 4.00 10.00
PK Paul Konerko A 3.00 8.00
PL Paul Lo Duca A 3.00 8.00
RA Roberto Alomar B 4.00 10.00
RB Rocco Baldelli A 3.00 8.00
RF Rafael Furcal B 3.00 8.00
RP Rafael Palmeiro B 4.00 10.00
RS Ruben Sierra B 3.00 8.00
RSA Rich Aurilia B 3.00 8.00
RW Rondell White B 3.00 8.00
SB Sean Burroughs B 3.00 8.00
SG Shawn Green B 3.00 8.00
SR Scott Rolen A 4.00 10.00
SS Shannon Stewart A 3.00 8.00
ST So Taguchi B 3.00 8.00
TB Tony Batista B 3.00 8.00
TG Troy Glaus A 3.00 8.00
TH Torii Hunter A 3.00 8.00
TJS Tim Salmon A 4.00 10.00
TKH Todd Helton B 4.00 10.00
TM Tino Martinez A 4.00 10.00
VG Vladimir Guerrero B 4.00 10.00
VW Vernon Wells A 3.00 8.00

2004 Bazooka Comics

COMPLETE SET (24) 10.00 25.00
STATED ODDS 1:4
BC1 Garret Anderson .40 1.00
BC2 Jeff Bagwell .40 1.00
BC3 Hank Blalock .40 1.00
BC4 Roy Halladay .40 1.00
BC5 Dontrelle Willis .40 1.00
BC6 Roger Clemens 1.00 2.50
BC7 Carlos Delgado .40 1.00
BC8 Rafael Furcal .40 1.00
BC9 Eric Gagne .40 1.00
BC10 Nomar Garciaparra .75 2.00
BC11 Derek Jeter 1.00 2.50
BC12 Esteban Loaiza .40 1.00
BC13 Kevin Millwood UER .40 1.00
Wrong date noted for his no-hitter
BC14 Bill Mueller .40 1.00
BC15 Rafael Palmeiro .40 1.00
BC16 Albert Pujols 1.00 2.50
BC17 Jose Reyes .40 1.00
BC18 Alex Rodriguez .75 2.00
BC19 Alfonso Soriano .40 1.00
BC20 Sammy Sosa .50 1.25
BC21 Ichiro Suzuki 1.00 2.50
BC22 Frank Thomas .50 1.25
BC23 Brad Wilkerson .40 1.00
BC24 Roy Oswalt .40 1.00
Pete Munro
Kirk Saarloos
Brad Lidge
Octavio Dotel
Billy Wagner

2004 Bazooka One-Liners Relics

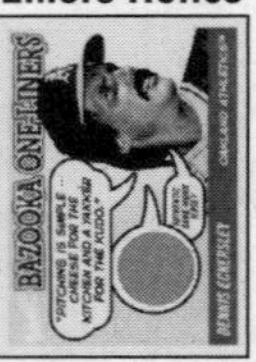

GROUP A ODDS 1:62 H, 1:86 R
GROUP B ODDS 1:98 H, 1:136 R
OVERALL PARALLEL 25 ODDS 1:94
PARALLEL 25 PRINT RUN 25 #'d SETS
NO PARALLEL 25 PRICING DUE TO SCARCITY
AD Andre Dawson Bat A 4.00 10.00
BB Bert Blyleven Jsy A 4.00 10.00
BC Bert Campaneris Jsy A 4.00 10.00
BM Bill Madlock Bat A 4.00 10.00
BS Bret Saberhagen Jsy A 4.00 10.00
CS Chris Sabo Bat A 4.00 10.00
CY Carl Yastrzemski Uni A 12.50 30.00
DA Dick Allen Bat A 4.00 10.00
DE Dennis Eckersley Jsy A 4.00 10.00
DJ1 David Justice Bat A 4.00 10.00
DJ2 David Justice Uni A 4.00 10.00
DM Dale Murphy Bat A 6.00 15.00
DP Dave Parker Jsy A 4.00 10.00
DW Dwight Gooden Jsy A 4.00 10.00
EM Eddie Murray Uni A 10.00 25.00
FR Frank Robinson Uni A 4.00 10.00
GB George Brett Jsy B 8.00 20.00
GC Gary Carter Bat A 4.00 10.00
GP Gaylord Perry Uni A 4.00 10.00
HK Harmon Killebrew Jsy A 12.50 30.00
JB Johnny Bench Bat B 6.00 15.00
JC Jose Canseco Bat B 6.00 15.00
JCA Joe Carter Jsy A 4.00 10.00
JK Jerry Koosman Jsy A 4.00 10.00
JM Joe Morgan Jsy A 4.00 10.00
KG1 Kirk Gibson Bat A 4.00 10.00
KG2 Kirk Gibson Jsy A 4.00 10.00
KH Keith Hernandez Bat B 4.00 10.00
KP1 Kirby Puckett Bat B 6.00 15.00
KP2 Kirby Puckett Jsy B 6.00 15.00
MS Mike Schmidt Jsy B 8.00 20.00
NR Nolan Ryan Jsy A 30.00 60.00
OC Orlando Cepeda Bat A 4.00 10.00
PN Phil Niekro Uni A 4.00 10.00
RC Rod Carew Bat B 6.00 15.00
RD Ron Darling Jsy A 4.00 10.00
RJ Reggie Jackson Jsy A 6.00 15.00
RS Red Schoendienst Bat B 4.00 10.00
RSA Ron Santo Bat A 6.00 15.00
RY Robin Yount Bat A 6.00 15.00
TM Tug McGraw Jsy A 6.00 15.00
TS Tom Seaver Uni A 6.00 15.00
WB1 Wade Boggs Bat B 6.00 15.00
WB2 Wade Boggs Jsy B 6.00 15.00
WM Willie Mays Uni A 30.00 60.00
WMC Willie McGee Bat A 6.00 15.00
WS Willie Stargell Bat A 6.00 15.00

2004 Bazooka Stand-Ups

STATED ODDS 1:8 H, 1:24 R
1 Jose Reyes .75 2.00
2 Jim Thome .75 2.00
3 Roy Halladay .75 2.00
4 Jason Giambi .75 2.00
5 Dontrelle Willis .75 2.00
6 Mike Piazza 2.00 5.00
7 Chipper Jones 1.25 3.00
8 Mark Prior .75 2.00
9 Todd Helton .75 2.00
10 Miguel Cabrera .75 2.00
11 Derek Jeter 2.50 6.00
12 Nomar Garciaparra 2.00 5.00
13 Alex Rodriguez 2.00 5.00
14 Miguel Tejada .75 2.00
15 Carlos Delgado .75 2.00
16 Pedro Martinez .75 2.00
17 Sammy Sosa 1.25 3.00
18 Ichiro Suzuki 2.50 6.00
19 Vladimir Guerrero 1.25 3.00
20 Alfonso Soriano .75 2.00
21 Eric Chavez .75 2.00
22 Albert Pujols 2.50 6.00
23 Ivan Rodriguez .75 2.00
24 Vernon Wells .75 2.00
25 Eric Gagne .75 2.00

2004 Bazooka Tattoos

STATED ODDS 1:4 H, 1:6 R
AD Adam Dunn .40 1.00
AJ Andruw Jones .60 1.50
AP Albert Pujols 2.00 5.00
AR Alex Rodriguez 1.50 4.00
AS Alfonso Soriano .40 1.00
BAZ Bazooka Logo .40 1.00
BP Brad Penny .40 1.00
BW Bernie Williams .60 1.50
BZ Barry Zito .40 1.00
CB Craig Biggio .60 1.50
CF Cliff Floyd .40 1.00
CG Cristian Guzman .40 1.00
CJ Chipper Jones 1.00 2.50
CS Curt Schilling .60 1.50
DW Dontrelle Willis .60 1.50
EC Eric Chavez .40 1.00
GJ Geoff Jenkins .40 1.00
GM Greg Maddux 1.50 4.00
HN Hideo Nomo 1.00 2.50
JB Jeff Bagwell .60 1.50
JG Jason Giambi .40 1.00
JK Jason Kendall .40 1.00
JO John Olerud .40 1.00
JT Jim Thome .60 1.50
JW Jarrod Washburn .40 1.00
KB Kevin Brown .40 1.00
KM Kevin Millwood .40 1.00
KW Kerry Wood .40 1.00
LB Lance Berkman .40 1.00
LC Luis Castillo .40 1.00
LG Luis Gonzalez .40 1.00
LW Larry Walker .40 1.00
MB Marlon Byrd .40 1.00
MCM Mike Mussina .60 1.50
ML Mike Lowell .40 1.00
MM Mark Mulder .40 1.00
MP Mike Piazza 1.50 4.00
MR Manny Ramirez .60 1.50
MT Miguel Tejada .40 1.00
NG Nomar Garciaparra 1.50 4.00
PB Pat Burrell .40 1.00
PK Paul Konerko .40 1.00
PL Paul Lo Duca .40 1.00
PW Preston Wilson .40 1.00
RJ Randy Johnson 1.00 2.50
RP Rafael Palmeiro .60 1.50
SC Sean Casey .40 1.00
SG Shawn Green .40 1.00
TAH Tim Hudson .40 1.00
TEG Troy Glaus .40 1.00
TG Tom Glavine .60 1.50
TH Toby Hall .40 1.00
TJS Tim Salmon .60 1.50
TOP Topps Logo .40 1.00
VG Vladimir Guerrero 1.00 2.50

2005 Bazooka

This 220-card set was released in late January-early February, 2005. The set was issued in eight card hobby packs which came 24 packs to a box and 12 boxes to a case. Cards numbered 1-170 feature leading veterans while cards numbered 171-190 feature leading prospects and cards numbered 191-220 feature players in their 1st year on Topps company cards.

COMPLETE SET (220) 30.00 60.00
COMMON CARD (1-170) .15 .40
COMMON CARD (171-190) .20 .50
COMMON CARD (191-220) .20 .50
1 Eric Gagne .15 .40
2 Aramis Ramirez .15 .40
3 Hank Blalock .15 .40
4 Jason Kendall .15 .40
5 Jeromy Burnitz .15 .40
6 Jose Guillen .15 .40
7 Tom Glavine .25 .60
8 Adrian Beltre .15 .40
9 Jason Bay .15 .40
10 Mark Teixeira .25 .60
11 Moises Alou .15 .40
12 Ronnie Belliard .15 .40
13 Aaron Guiel .15 .40
14 Vladimir Guerrero .40 1.00
15 Scott Podsednik .15 .40
16 Alfonso Soriano .15 .40
17 Craig Wilson .15 .40
18 Jose Reyes .15 .40
19 Mark Prior .25 .60
20 Preston Wilson .15 .40
21 Shawn Green .15 .40
22 Troy Glaus .15 .40
23 Dmitri Young .15 .40
24 Garret Anderson .15 .40
25 Kazuo Matsui .15 .40
26 Kerry Wood .15 .40
27 Michael Young .15 .40
28 Oliver Perez .15 .40
29 Bartolo Colon .15 .40
30 Richie Sexson .15 .40
31 Brad Penny .15 .40
32 Carlos Guillen .15 .40
33 Carlos Zambrano .15 .40
34 David Wright .60 1.50
35 Al Leiter .15 .40
36 Jack Wilson .15 .40
37 Ryan Drese .15 .40
38 Darin Erstad .15 .40
39 Derrek Lee .25 .60
40 Ivan Rodriguez .25 .60
41 Kenny Rogers .15 .40
42 Mike Piazza .40 1.00
43 Phil Nevin .15 .40
44 Geoff Jenkins .15 .40
45 Jorge Posada .25 .60
46 Khalil Greene .25 .60
47 Randy Johnson .40 1.00
48 Rondell White .15 .40
49 Sammy Sosa .40 1.00
50 Vernon Wells .15 .40
51 Ben Sheets .15 .40
52 Brian Giles .15 .40
53 Carlos Delgado .15 .40
54 Derek Jeter .75 2.00
55 Jeremy Bonderman .15 .40
56 Magglio Ordonez .15 .40
57 Chad Tracy .15 .40
58 Kevin Brown .15 .40
59 Luis Castillo .15 .40
60 Lyle Overbay .15 .40
61 Mark Buehrle .15 .40
62 Mark Loretta .15 .40
63 Orlando Hudson .15 .40
64 Adam Dunn .15 .40
65 Frank Thomas .40 1.00
66 Jake Peavy .15 .40
67 Jason Giambi .15 .40
68 Joe Mauer .40 1.00
69 Marcus Giles .15 .40
70 Mike Lowell .15 .40
71 Roy Halladay .15 .40
72 Aaron Rowand .15 .40
73 Alex Rodriguez .60 1.50
74 Brian Lawrence .15 .40
75 Gabe Gross .15 .40
76 Johnny Estrada .15 .40
77 Justin Morneau .15 .40
78 Miguel Cabrera .25 .60
79 Alex Rios .15 .40
80 Gary Sheffield .15 .40
81 Jason Schmidt .15 .40
82 Juan Pierre .15 .40
83 Paul Konerko .15 .40
84 Jermaine Dye .15 .40
85 Rafael Furcal .15 .40
86 Torii Hunter .15 .40
87 A.J. Pierzynski .15 .40
88 Carl Pavano .15 .40
89 Carlos Lee .15 .40
90 J.D. Drew .15 .40
91 Javier Vazquez .15 .40
92 Lew Ford .15 .40
93 Ted Lilly .15 .40
94 Austin Kearns .15 .40
95 Chipper Jones .40 1.00
96 Erubiel Durazo .15 .40
97 Johan Santana .40 1.00
98 Josh Beckett .15 .40
99 Mariano Rivera .40 1.00
100 Mark Mulder .15 .40
101 Andruw Jones .25 .60
102 Barry Zito .15 .40
103 Bret Boone .15 .40
104 Paul LoDuca .15 .40
105 Shannon Stewart .15 .40
106 Wily Mo Pena .15 .40
107 Dontrelle Willis .15 .40
108 Eric Chavez .15 .40
109 Jamie Moyer .15 .40
110 Joe Nathan .15 .40
111 Sidney Ponson .15 .40
112 John Smoltz .25 .60
113 Ichiro Suzuki .75 2.00
114 Javy Lopez .15 .40
115 Victor Martinez .15 .40
116 Ken Griffey Jr. .60 1.50
117 Lance Berkman .15 .40
118 Scott Hatteberg .15 .40
119 Jim Edmonds .15 .40
120 Kazuhisa Ishii .15 .40
121 Miguel Tejada .15 .40
122 Roger Clemens .60 1.50
123 Ryan Freel .15 .40
124 Albert Pujols .75 2.00
125 Hideo Nomo .40 1.00
126 Mark Kotsay .15 .40
127 Melvin Mora .15 .40
128 Roy Oswalt .15 .40
129 Sean Casey .15 .40
130 Casey Blake .15 .40
131 Edgar Renteria .15 .40
132 Jeff Kent .15 .40
133 Rafael Palmeiro .25 .60
134 Tim Hudson .15 .40
135 Barry Bonds 1.00 2.50
136 Andy Pettitte .25 .60
137 Brian Roberts .15 .40
138 Jose Vidro .15 .40
139 Omar Vizquel .25 .60
140 Rich Harden .15 .40
141 Scott Rolen .25 .60
142 Carlos Beltran .15 .40
143 Chris Carpenter .15 .40
144 Manny Ramirez .25 .60
145 Nick Johnson .15 .40
146 Pat Burrell .15 .40
147 C.C. Sabathia .15 .40
148 Johnny Damon .25 .60
149 Juan Rivera .15 .40
150 Ken Harvey .15 .40
151 Kevin Millwood .15 .40
152 Larry Walker .25 .60
153 Aubrey Huff .15 .40
154 Curt Schilling .25 .60
155 Jake Westbrook .15 .40
156 Randy Wolf .15 .40
157 Zach Day .15 .40
158 Zack Greinke .15 .40
159 Brad Wilkerson .15 .40
160 Carl Crawford .15 .40
161 Jim Thome .25 .60
162 Mike Sweeney .15 .40
163 Pedro Martinez .25 .60
164 Travis Hafner .15 .40
165 Bobby Abreu .15 .40
166 Cliff Floyd .15 .40
167 David DeJesus .15 .40
168 David Ortiz .40 1.00
169 Rocco Baldelli .15 .40
170 Todd Helton .25 .60
171 Dallas McPherson PROS .20 .50
172 Kevin Youkilis PROS .20 .50
173 Val Majewski PROS .20 .50
174 Grady Sizemore PROS .30 .75
175 Joey Gathright PROS .20 .50
176 Rickie Weeks PROS .20 .50
177 Jason Kubel PROS .20 .50
178 Robinson Cano PROS .30 .75
179 Nick Swisher PROS .30 .75
180 Ryan Howard PROS 1.00 2.50
181 Tim Stauffer PROS .20 .50
182 Merkin Valdez PROS .20 .50
183 B.J. Upton PROS .30 .75
184 Scott Kazmir PROS .40 1.00
185 Chris Burke PROS .20 .50
186 Felix Hernandez PROS .75 2.00
187 Freddy Guzman PROS .20 .50
188 Josh Labandeira PROS .20 .50
189 Willy Taveras PROS .20 .50
190 Casey Kotchman PROS .20 .50
191 Steve Doetsch FY RC .30 .75
192 Melky Cabrera FY RC .75 2.00
193 Luis Ramirez FY RC .20 .50
194 Chris Seddon FY RC .20 .50
195 Chad Orvella FY RC .20 .50
196 Ian Kinsler FY RC 1.00 2.50
197 Brandon Moss FY RC .75 2.00
198 Chadd Blasko FY RC .30 .75
199 Jeremy West FY RC .30 .75
200 Sean Marshall FY RC .75 2.00
201 Matt DeSalvo FY RC .30 .75
202 Ryan Sweeney FY RC .40 1.00
203 Matthew Lindstrom FY RC .20 .50
204 Ryan Goleski FY RC .30 .75
205 Brett Harper FY RC .30 .75
206 Chris Roberson FY RC .20 .50
207 Andre Ethier FY RC 2.00 5.00
208 Chris Denorfia FY RC .40 1.00
209 Darren Fenster FY RC .20 .50
210 Elvys Quezada FY RC .20 .50
211 Kevin West FY RC .20 .50
212 Chaz Lytle FY RC .30 .75
213 James Jurries FY RC .30 .75
214 Matt Rogelstad FY RC .30 .75
215 Wade Robinson FY RC .20 .50
216 Ian Bladergroen FY RC .30 .75
217 Jake Dittler FY .20 .50
218 Nate McLouth FY RC .20 .50
219 Kole Strayhorn FY RC .30 .75
220 Jose Vaquedano FY RC .20 .50

2005 Bazooka Gold Chunks

*GOLD 1-170: .75X TO 2X BASIC
*GOLD 171-190: .75X TO 2X BASIC
*GOLD 191-220: .75X TO 2X BASIC
ONE PER PACK

2005 Bazooka Minis

*MINIS 1-170: .75X TO 2X BASIC
*MINIS 171-190: .75X TO 2X BASIC
*MINIS 191-220: .75X TO 2X BASIC
ONE PER PACK

2005 Bazooka 4 on 1 Stickers

STATED ODDS 1:3 HOBBY, 1:6 RETAIL
ONE STICKER ALBUM PER HOBBY BOX
1 Alex Rodriguez 1.25 3.00
Hank Blalock
Scott Rolen
Mike Lowell
2 Jorge Posada .75 2.00
Ivan Rodriguez
Joe Mauer
Johnny Estrada
3 Ichiro Suzuki 1.50 4.00
Carlos Beltran
Jim Edmonds
Brian Giles
4 Jim Thome .50 1.25
Mark Teixeira
Paul Konerko
Lyle Overbay
5 Jose Reyes .40 1.00
Mark Loretta
Jose Vidro
Luis Castillo
6 Miguel Tejada 1.50 4.00
Derek Jeter
Michael Young
Edgar Renteria
7 Roy Oswalt .75 2.00
Rich Harden
Johan Santana
Mark Prior
8 Mariano Rivera .75 2.00
Eric Gagne
Joe Nathan
John Smoltz
9 Larry Walker .50 1.25
Carl Crawford
Preston Wilson
Garret Anderson
10 Wily Mo Pena .40 1.00
Mark Kotsay
Alex Rios
Geoff Jenkins
11 Victor Martinez 1.25 3.00
David Wright
Justin Morneau
Jason Bay
12 Carlos Lee .50 1.25
Andruw Jones
Ronnie Belliard
Eric Chavez
13 Vladimir Guerrero .75 2.00
Vernon Wells
Miguel Cabrera
Adrian Beltre
14 David Ortiz .50 1.25
Marcus Giles
Jeff Kent
Bobby Abreu
15 Juan Pierre .40 1.00
Torii Hunter
J.D. Drew
Austin Kearns
16 Bartolo Colon 1.25 3.00
Manny Ramirez
Ken Griffey Jr.
Dontrelle Willis
17 Andy Pettitte .75 2.00
Tim Hudson
Curt Schilling
Randy Johnson
18 Jamie Moyer .40 1.00
Zach Day
Al Leiter
Oliver Perez
19 Kazuo Matsui 1.25 3.00
Roger Clemens
Khalil Greene
Javier Vazquez
20 Pedro Martinez .75 2.00
Rocco Baldelli
Mike Piazza
Melvin Mora
21 Hideo Nomo .75 2.00
Kazuhisa Ishii
Ken Harvey
Mike Sweeney
22 Casey Blake .40 1.00
Ryan Freel
Bret Boone
Javy Lopez
23 Craig Wilson .40 1.00
Shawn Green
Aramis Ramirez
Darin Erstad
24 Troy Glaus .40 1.00
Lance Berkman
Scott Podsednik
Adam Dunn
25 Albert Pujols 1.50 4.00
Gary Sheffield
Chipper Jones
Magglio Ordonez
26 Johnny Damon .50 1.25
Carlos Zambrano
Jason Schmidt
Ted Lilly
27 Sidney Ponson .40 1.00
Chris Carpenter
C.C. Sabathia
Kevin Millwood
28 Carl Pavano .40 1.00
Mark Mulder
Rafael Furcal
Jack Wilson
29 Jeremy Bonderman .50 1.25
Jake Westbrook
Zack Greinke
Tom Glavine
30 Omar Vizquel .50 1.25
Carlos Guillen
Roy Halladay
Ben Sheets
31 Kerry Wood .40 1.00
Kevin Brown
Moises Alou
Travis Hafner
32 Nick Johnson .40 1.00
Erubiel Durazo
Alfonso Soriano
Jason Giambi
33 Chad Tracy .40 1.00
Richie Sexson
Aubrey Huff
Brian Roberts
34 Todd Helton .50 1.25
Dmitri Young
Jeromy Burnitz
Jose Guillen
35 Juan Rivera .75 2.00
Shannon Stewart
Sammy Sosa
Cliff Floyd
36 Pat Burrell .40 1.00
Gabe Gross
Aaron Guiel
Paul LoDuca
37 A.J. Pierzynski .40 1.00
Orlando Hudson
David DeJesus
Brian Lawrence
38 Josh Beckett .40 1.00
Barry Zito
Mark Buehrle
Randy Wolf
39 Brad Penny .40 1.00
Jake Peavy
Rondell White
Brad Wilkerson
40 Ryan Drese .40 1.00
Kenny Rogers
Jermaine Dye
Lew Ford
41 Aaron Rowand 2.00 5.00
Jason Kendall
Barry Bonds
Derrek Lee
42 Phil Nevin .75 2.00
Sean Casey
Rafael Palmeiro
Frank Thomas
43 Scott Hatteberg .50 1.25
Josh Labandeira
Jason Kubel
Nick Swisher
44 Freddy Guzman 1.50 4.00
Tim Stauffer
Merkin Valdez
Felix Hernandez
45 Willy Taveras .50 1.25
Grady Sizemore
Joey Gathright
Carlos Delgado
46 Scott Kazmir .40 1.00
Rickie Weeks
Dallas McPherson
Kevin Youkilis
47 Val Majewski .40 1.00
Casey Kotchman
Ryan Howard
Chris Burke
48 Robinson Cano .50 1.25
B.J. Upton
Jake Dittler
Ian Bladergroen
49 Brett Harper .50 1.25
James Jurries
Jeremy West
Matt Rogelstad
50 Darren Fenster 1.00 2.50
Chad Orvella
Brandon Moss
Ryan Sweeney
51 Chris Roberson 3.00 8.00
Steve Doetsch
Andre Ethier
Kevin West
52 Melky Cabrera 1.50 4.00
Ryan Goleski
Chris Denorfia
Chaz Lytle
53 Luis Ramirez 1.00 2.50
Matt DeSalvo
Sean Marshall
Jose Vaquedano
54 Chris Seddon .40 1.00
Chadd Blasko
Elvys Quezada
Wade Robinson
55 Nate McLouth 2.00 5.00
Matthew Lindstrom
Kole Strayhorn
Ian Kinsler
NNO Sticker Album .75 2.00

2005 Bazooka Blasts Bat Relics

GROUP A ODDS 1:649 H, 1:1205 R
GROUP B ODDS 1:47 H, 1:65 R
GROUP C ODDS 1:29 H, 1:45 R
GROUP D ODDS 1:93 H, 1:140 R
GROUP E ODDS 1:104 H, 1:158 R
GROUP A PRINT RUN 100 SETS
GROUP A ARE NOT SERIAL-NUMBERED
GROUP A PRINT RUN PROVIDED BY TOPPS
AB Angel Berroa C 3.00 8.00
AD Adam Dunn B 3.00 8.00
AG Adrian Gonzalez B 3.00 8.00
AG1 Alex Gonzalez C 3.00 8.00
AR Aramis Ramirez B 3.00 8.00
AR1 Alex Rodriguez A/100 * 10.00 25.00
BU B.J. Upton A/100 * 6.00 15.00
CB Craig Biggio A/100 * 6.00 15.00
CE Carl Everett C 3.00 8.00
CF Chone Figgins B 3.00 8.00
CG Cristian Guzman B 3.00 8.00
CGU Carlos Guillen B 3.00 8.00
CS Curt Schilling B 4.00 10.00
DL Derrek Lee B 4.00 10.00
DO David Ortiz A/100 * 6.00 15.00
DW David Wright A/100 * 6.00 15.00
GS Gary Sheffield E 3.00 8.00
HB Hank Blalock A/100 * 4.00 10.00
JB Jeromy Burnitz B 3.00 8.00
JC Jeff Conine D 3.00 8.00
JF Julio Franco C 3.00 8.00
JK Jeff Kent B 3.00 8.00
JV Jose Valentin C 3.00 8.00
JV1 Jose Vidro C 3.00 8.00
JW Jayson Werth B 3.00 8.00
KM Kaz Matsui A/100 * 6.00 15.00
LG Luis Gonzalez B 3.00 8.00
LH Livan Hernandez C 3.00 8.00
LW Larry Walker E 4.00 10.00
MC Miguel Cabrera A/100 * 6.00 15.00
ML Mike Lowell A/100 * 4.00 10.00
MO Magglio Ordonez C 3.00 8.00
MR Manny Ramirez C 4.00 10.00
MT Miguel Tejada B 3.00 8.00
MY Michael Young B 3.00 8.00
NG Nomar Garciaparra B 4.00 10.00
PK Paul Konerko D 3.00 8.00
PM Pedro Martinez B 4.00 10.00
PW Preston Wilson B 3.00 8.00
RA Roberto Alomar C 4.00 10.00
RB Ron Belliard C 3.00 8.00
RH Richard Hidalgo C 3.00 8.00
RS Ruben Sierra C 3.00 8.00
TC Tony Clark B 3.00 8.00
TH Todd Helton C 4.00 10.00
TM Tino Martinez B 4.00 10.00
VC Vinny Castilla D 3.00 8.00
VG Vladimir Guerrero A/100 * 4.00 10.00
VM Victor Martinez A/100 * 3.00 8.00

2005 Bazooka Comics

COMPLETE SET (24) 10.00 25.00
STATED ODDS 1:4 H
1 Randy Johnson .50 1.25
2 Gary Sheffield .40 1.00
3 Ken Griffey Jr. .75 2.00
4 Alex Rodriguez .75 2.00
5 Vladimir Guerrero .50 1.25
6 David Bell .40 1.00
7 Carlos Pena .40 1.00
8 Eric Gagne .40 1.00
9 Jim Thome .40 1.00
10 Cleveland Indians .40 1.00
11 Greg Maddux .75 2.00
12 Miguel Tejada .40 1.00
13 Ichiro Suzuki 1.00 2.50
14 Mariano Rivera .50 1.25
15 Juan Pierre .40 1.00
16 Carl Crawford .40 1.00
17 Mike Mussina .40 1.00
18 Vladimir Guerrero .50 1.25
19 Oliver Perez .40 1.00
20 Ichiro Suzuki 1.00 2.50
21 Johan Santana .50 1.25
22 Kevin Brown .40 1.00
23 Mike Piazza .50 1.25
24 Randy Johnson .50 1.25

2005 Bazooka Fun Facts Relics

GROUP A ODDS 1:3949 H, 1:6012 R
GROUP B ODDS 1:71 H, 1:108 R

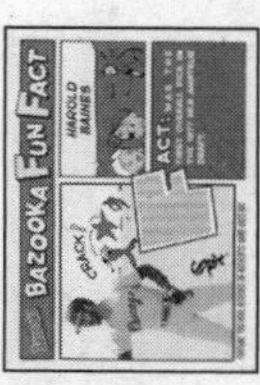

GROUP C ODDS 1:330 H, 1:500 R
GROUP D ODDS 1:83 H, 1:126 R
GROUP E ODDS 1:278 H, 1:423 R
GROUP F ODDS 1:209 H, 1:316 R
GROUP A PRINT RUN 100 SETS
GROUP A ARE NOT SERIAL-NUMBERED
GROUP A PRINT RUN PROVIDED BY TOPPS
CF Cecil Fielder Bat D 6.00 15.00
CS Cory Snyder Bat B 3.00 8.00
DD Darren Daulton Bat D 3.00 8.00
DE Darrell Evans Bat E 3.00 8.00
DJ1 Dave Justice Jsy C 3.00 8.00
DJ2 Dave Justice Bat D 3.00 8.00
DP Dave Parker Bat B 3.00 8.00
DS Darryl Strawberry Bat B 3.00 8.00
GB George Brett Bat B 6.00 15.00
GC Gary Carter Bat B 3.00 8.00
HB Harold Baines Bat D 3.00 8.00
HR Harold Reynolds Bat D 3.00 8.00
JC Jose Canseco Jsy C 6.00 15.00
JL Jim Leyritz Bat B 3.00 8.00
MR Mickey Rivers Bat B 3.00 8.00
MS Mike Schmidt Bat B 6.00 15.00
OS Ozzie Smith Bat A/100 * 15.00 40.00
RC Rod Carew Bat A/100 * 10.00 25.00
RK Ron Kittle Bat B 3.00 8.00
WB Wade Boggs Bat B 4.00 10.00
WH Willie Horton Bat B 3.00 8.00
WJ Wally Joyner Bat F 3.00 8.00
WW Walt Weiss Bat B 3.00 8.00

2005 Bazooka Moments Relics

GROUP A ODDS 1:1132 H, 1:1718 R
GROUP B ODDS 1:110 H, 1:167 R
GROUP A PRINT RUN 100 SETS
GROUP A ARE NOT SERIAL-NUMBERED
GROUP A PRINT RUN PROVIDED BY TOPPS
AP Albert Pujols Cap A/100 * 15.00 40.00
AR Alex Rodriguez Uni A/100 * 10.00 25.00
AS Alfonso Soriano Uni A/100 * 4.00 10.00
FT Frank Thomas Uni B 4.00 10.00
IR Ivan Rodriguez Uni A/100 * 6.00 15.00
JP Jorge Posada Uni A/100 * 6.00 15.00
KR Kenny Rogers Uni B 3.00 8.00
MB Matt Bush Jsy B 3.00 8.00
MM Mark Mulder Uni A/100 * 4.00 10.00
MP Mike Piazza Uni A/100 * 6.00 15.00
MT Mark Teixeira Uni B 4.00 10.00
RH Ramon Hernandez Uni B 3.00 8.00
TL Terrence Long Uni B 3.00 8.00

2005 Bazooka Tattoos

COMPLETE SET (25) 6.00 15.00
COMMON CARD (1-25) .40 1.00
STATED ODDS 1:4 HOBBY/RETAIL
1 Alex Rodriguez .40 1.00
2 Randy Johnson .40 1.00
3 Jim Thome .40 1.00
4 Pedro Martinez .40 1.00
5 Roger Clemens .40 1.00
6 Troy Glaus .40 1.00
7 Todd Helton .40 1.00
8 Albert Pujols .40 1.00
9 Sammy Sosa .40 1.00
10 David Wright .40 1.00
11 Mike Piazza .40 1.00
12 Gary Sheffield .40 1.00
13 David Ortiz .40 1.00
14 Hank Blalock .40 1.00
15 Miguel Tejada .40 1.00
16 Dontrelle Willis .40 1.00
17 Ivan Rodriguez .40 1.00
18 Nomar Garciaparra .40 1.00
19 Alfonso Soriano .40 1.00
20 Adrian Beltre .40 1.00
21 Torii Hunter .40 1.00
22 Brian Giles .40 1.00
23 Chipper Jones .40 1.00
24 Carlos Beltran .40 1.00
25 Manny Ramirez .40 1.00

2006 Bazooka

This 220-card set was released in March, 2006. The set was issued in eight-card hobby and retail packs with an $1.99 SRP. The first 200 card of the set are veterans while the final 20-cards in the set consist of players who qualified for the then-new RC designation which began in 2006.

COMPLETE SET (220) 15.00 40.00

COMMON CARD (1-200) .15 .40
COMMON CARD (201-220) .15 .40
1 Josh Gibson .60 1.50
2 Scott Podsednik .15 .40
3 Sammy Sosa .40 1.00
4 Ivan Rodriguez .25 .60
5 Derek Jeter 1.00 2.50
6 Manny Ramirez .25 .60
7 Nook Logan .15 .40
8 Adam Dunn .15 .40
9 Travis Hafner .15 .40
10 Felix Hernandez .25 .60
11 Larry Bigbie .15 .40
12 Magglio Ordonez .15 .40
13 Josh Beckett .15 .40
14 Mike Sweeney .15 .40
15 Mickey Mantle 2.00 5.00
16 Grady Sizemore .25 .60
17 Brian Fuentes .15 .40
18 Wily Mo Pena .15 .40
19 Morgan Ensberg .15 .40
20 Tim Hudson .15 .40
21 Justin Verlander .60 1.50
22 Jermaine Dye .15 .40
23 Miguel Cabrera .15 .40
24 Greg Maddux .60 1.50
25 Jason Giambi .15 .40
26 Ben Sheets .15 .40
27 Brad Radke .15 .40
28 Torii Hunter .15 .40
29 Mike Piazza .40 1.00
30 Jason Kendall .15 .40
31 Pat Burrell .15 .40
32 Khalil Greene .25 .60
33 Brian Roberts .15 .40
34 C.C. Sabathia .15 .40
35 Mike Mussina .25 .60
36 Bob Wickman .15 .40
37 Dmitri Young .15 .40
38 Dontrelle Willis .15 .40
39 David DeJesus .15 .40
40 J.D. Drew .15 .40
41 Chad Tracy .15 .40
42 Joe Mauer .40 1.00
43 Melvin Mora .15 .40
44 Carlos Zambrano .15 .40
45 Mariano Rivera .40 1.00
46 Coco Crisp .15 .40
47 Derrek Lee .25 .60
48 Cliff Floyd .15 .40
49 Willy Taveras .15 .40
50 Albert Pujols .75 2.00
51 Aaron Boone .15 .40
52 Mark Mulder .15 .40
53 Brad Wilkerson .15 .40
54 Hank Blalock .15 .40
55 Hideki Matsui .40 1.00
56 Victor Martinez .15 .40
57 Jeremy Bonderman .15 .40
58 Felipe Lopez .15 .40
59 Paul Lo Duca .15 .40
60 Derek Lowe .15 .40
61 Luis Gonzalez .15 .40
62 Paul Konerko .15 .40
63 Miguel Tejada .15 .40
64 Jeromy Burnitz .15 .40
65 Orlando Hernandez .15 .40
66 Curt Schilling .25 .60
67 Joe Nathan .15 .40
68 Jose Reyes .15 .40
69 David Wright .40 1.00
70 Eric Chavez .15 .40
71 Rich Harden .15 .40
72 A.J. Pierzynski .15 .40
73 Trevor Hoffman .15 .40
74 Adrian Beltre .15 .40
75 Alex Rodriguez .60 1.50
76 Jonathan Papelbon .75 2.00
77 Jorge Cantu .15 .40
78 Mark Teixeira .25 .60
79 Chien-Ming Wang .60 1.50
80 Jeff Francoeur .40 1.00
81 Ichiro Suzuki .60 1.50
82 Jhonny Peralta .15 .40
83 Todd Helton .25 .60
84 Brad Penny .15 .40
85 Shawn Chacon .15 .40
86 Billy Wagner .15 .40
87 Jason Schmidt .15 .40
88 Austin Kearns .15 .40
89 Chris Carpenter .15 .40
90 Chipper Jones .40 1.00
91 Shawn Green .15 .40
92 A.J. Burnett .15 .40
93 Joe Crede UER .15 .40
Comic on back talks about Rafael Palmeiro
94 Mark Prior .25 .60
95 Andy Pettitte .25 .60
96 Edgar Renteria .15 .40
97 Roy Halladay .15 .40
98 Eric Milton .15 .40
99 Craig Biggio .25 .60
100 Barry Bonds 1.00 2.50
101 Troy Glaus .15 .40
102 Aaron Rowand .15 .40
103 Aramis Ramirez .15 .40
104 Nomar Garciaparra .40 1.00
105 Randy Johnson .40 1.00
106 David Ortiz .40 1.00
107 Vinny Castilla .15 .40
108 Carl Crawford .15 .40
109 Zach Duke .15 .40
110 Barry Zito .15 .40
111 Darin Erstad .15 .40
112 Chris Capuano .15 .40
113 Javy Lopez .15 .40
114 Lew Ford .15 .40
115 Robinson Cano .25 .60
116 Ronnie Belliard .15 .40
117 Placido Polanco .15 .40
118 Rickie Weeks .15 .40
119 Brad Lidge .15 .40
120 Andruw Jones .25 .60
121 Nick Swisher .15 .40
122 Bartolo Colon .15 .40
123 Juan Pierre .15 .40
124 Johan Santana .40 1.00
125 Jorge Posada .25 .60
126 Jeff Francis .15 .40
127 Matt Holliday .20 .50
128 Carlos Delgado .15 .40
129 Zack Greinke .15 .40
130 Lyle Overbay .15 .40
131 Conor Jackson .15 .40
132 Mark Buehrle .15 .40
133 Chone Figgins .15 .40
134 Pedro Martinez .25 .60
135 Roger Clemens .75 2.00
136 Raul Ibanez .15 .40
137 Jim Edmonds .15 .40
138 Michael Young .15 .40
139 Preston Wilson .15 .40
140 Rafael Furcal .15 .40
141 Bobby Abreu .15 .40
142 Tadahito Iguchi .15 .40
143 B.J. Ryan .15 .40
144 Francisco Rodriguez UER .15 .40
Photo is Ervin Santana
145 J.T. Snow .15 .40
146 Aubrey Huff .15 .40
147 Mike Morse .15 .40
148 Jason Bay .15 .40
149 Roy Oswalt .15 .40
150 Carlos Beltran .15 .40
151 Carlos Lee .15 .40
152 Emil Brown .15 .40
153 Craig Monroe .15 .40
154 Kris Benson .15 .40
155 Gary Sheffield .15 .40
156 Jake Peavy .15 .40
157 David Eckstein .15 .40
158 Tom Glavine .25 .60
159 Jeff Kent .15 .40
160 Livan Hernandez .15 .40
161 Orlando Hudson .15 .40
162 Randy Winn .15 .40
163 Jimmy Rollins .15 .40
164 Luis Castillo .15 .40
165 Nick Johnson .15 .40
166 Johnny Damon .25 .60
167 Eric Gagne .15 .40
168 Geoff Jenkins .15 .40
169 Mike Cameron .15 .40
170 Marcus Giles .15 .40
171 Huston Street .15 .40
172 Moises Alou .15 .40
173 Scott Rolen .25 .60
174 Jose Vidro .15 .40
175 Alfonso Soriano .15 .40
176 Toby Hall .15 .40
177 Orlando Cabrera .15 .40
178 Brian Giles .15 .40
179 Erubiel Durazo .15 .40
180 Matt Morris .15 .40
181 Jack Wilson .15 .40
182 Brady Clark .15 .40
183 Shannon Stewart .15 .40
184 Kerry Wood .15 .40
185 Carl Pavano .15 .40
186 Chase Utley .25 .60
187 Omar Vizquel .25 .60
188 Vladimir Guerrero .40 1.00
189 Richie Sexson .15 .40
190 John Smoltz .25 .60
191 Garret Anderson UER .15 .40
Name spelled Garrett on front and back
192 Jon Garland .15 .40
193 Julio Lugo .15 .40
194 Rocco Baldelli .15 .40
195 Jaret Wright .15 .40
196 Matt Clement .15 .40
197 Vernon Wells .15 .40
198 Sean Casey .15 .40
199 Lance Berkman .15 .40
200 Justin Morneau .15 .40
201 Shaun Marcum (RC) .15 .40
202 Chuck James (RC) .15 .40
203 Hong-Chih Kuo (RC) .40 1.00
204 Darrell Rasner (RC) .15 .40
205 Anthony Reyes (RC) .25 .60
206 Francisco Liriano (RC) .75 2.00
207 Joe Saunders (RC) .15 .40
208 Fausto Carmona (RC) .15 .40
209 Charlton Jimerson (RC) .15 .40
210 Bryan Bullington (RC) .15 .40
211 Tom Gorzelanny (RC) .15 .40
212 Anderson Hernandez (RC) .15 .40
213 Ryan Garko (RC) .15 .40
214 John Koronka (RC) .15 .40
215 Chris Denorfia (RC) .15 .40
216 Jeff Mathis (RC) .15 .40
217 Jose Bautista (RC) .15 .40
218 Danny Sandoval RC .15 .40
219 Robert Andino RC .15 .40
220 Justin Huber (RC) .15 .40

2006 Bazooka Blue Fortune

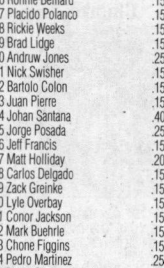

*BLUE 1-200: .75X TO 2X BASIC
*BLUE 201-220: .75X TO 2X BASIC
ONE PER PACK

2006 Bazooka Gold Chunks

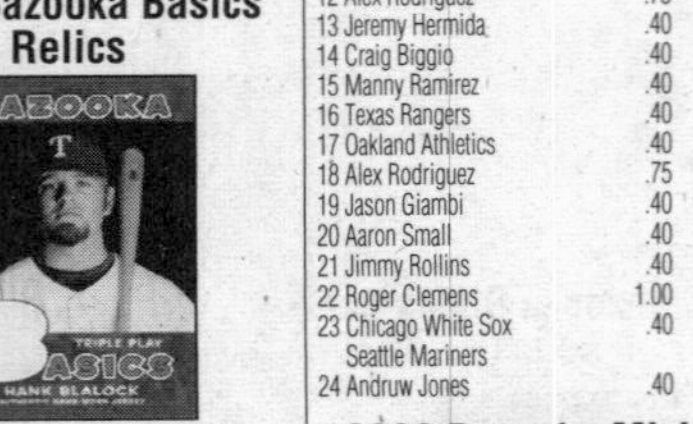

*GOLD 1-200: .75X TO 2X BASIC
*GOLD 201-220: .75X TO 2X BASIC
ONE CHUNK OR GU PER PACK

2006 Bazooka 4 on 1 Stickers

COMPLETE SET (55) 15.00 40.00
STATED ODDS 1:3 HOBBY, 1:6 RETAIL
1 Alex Rodriguez 4.00 10.00
Barry Bonds
Josh Gibson
Mickey Mantle
2 Carlos Delgado 1.25 3.00
David Ortiz
Jason Giambi
Chien-Ming Wang
3 Carl Crawford .40 1.00
Shannon Stewart
Torii Hunter
Vernon Wells
4 Jason Kendall .75 2.00
Javy Lopez
Joe Mauer
Jorge Posada
5 Andy Pettitte 1.50 4.00
Mike Mussina
Orlando Hernandez
Roger Clemens
6 Alfonso Soriano .50 1.25
Hank Blalock
Ivan Rodriguez
Rafael Palmeiro
7 Curt Schilling .50 1.25
Derek Lowe
Matt Clement
Pedro Martinez
8 Andruw Jones .75 2.00
Gary Sheffield
J.D. Drew
Vladimir Guerrero
9 Greg Maddux 1.25 3.00
John Smoltz
Tim Hudson
Tom Glavine
10 Albert Pujols 1.50 4.00
Derrek Lee
Justin Morneau
Mark Teixeira
11 B.J. Ryan .75 2.00
Bob Wickman
Mariano Rivera
Trevor Hoffman
12 Mike Cameron .75 2.00
Mike Morse
Mike Piazza
Mike Sweeney
13 David Eckstein .40 1.00
Jimmy Rollins
Michael Young
Orlando Cabrera
14 A.J. Burnett .40 1.00
A.J. Pierzynski
C.C. Sabathia
J.T. Snow
15 Chase Utley 1.25 3.00
Hideki Matsui
Ichiro Suzuki
Tadahito Iguchi
16 Barry Zito .50 1.25
Jeff Francis
Zach Duke
Zack Greinke
17 Marcus Giles .50 1.25
Mark Buehrle
Mark Mulder
Mark Prior
18 Bobby Abreu .75 2.00
Manny Ramirez
Sammy Sosa
Wily Mo Pena
19 Carlos Beltran .40 1.00
Juan Pierre
Preston Wilson
Scott Podsednik
20 Billy Wagner .40 1.00
Francisco Rodriguez
Huston Street
Joe Nathan
21 Eric Chavez .50 1.25
Melvin Mora
Morgan Ensberg
Scott Rolen
22 Garret Anderson .50 1.25
Jim Edmonds
Johnny Damon
Moises Alou
23 Derek Jeter 2.00 5.00
Edgar Renteria
Julio Lugo
Miguel Tejada
24 Brian Fuentes .50 1.25
Dontrelle Willis
Felix Hernandez
Rich Harden
25 Bartolo Colon .40 1.00
Carlos Zambrano
Jason Schmidt
Jeremy Bonderman
26 Chris Carpenter .75 2.00
Johan Santana
Randy Johnson
Roy Halladay
27 Josh Beckett .40 1.00
Kris Benson
Roy Oswalt
Shawn Chacon
28 Felipe Lopez .40 1.00
Jhonny Peralta
Jose Reyes
Rafael Furcal
29 Justin Verlander .40 1.00
Kerry Wood
Livan Hernandez
Matt Morris
30 Jack Wilson .75 2.00
Khalil Greene
Nomar Garciaparra
Omar Vizquel
31 Jason Bay .40 1.00
Pat Burrell
Rocco Baldelli
Shawn Green
32 Brad Lidge .40 1.00
Brad Penny
Brad Radke
Brian Roberts
33 Jeff Francoeur .75 2.00
Rickie Weeks
Robinson Cano
Willy Taveras
34 Geoff Jenkins .50 1.25
Lance Berkman
Larry Bigbie
Matt Holliday
35 Carlos Lee .40 1.00
Paul Lo
Toby Hall
Victor Martinez
36 Aramis Ramirez .75 2.00
Chipper Jones
David Wright
Troy Glaus
37 Aaron Rowand .40 1.00
Brad Wilkerson
Craig Monroe
Randy Winn
38 Aaron Boone .40 1.00
Adrian Beltre
Chone Figgins
Vinny Castilla
39 Adam Dunn .50 1.25
Cliff Floyd
Larry Walker
Luis Gonzalez
40 Jeff Kent .40 1.00
Jorge Cantu
Placido Polanco
Ronnie Belliard
41 Craig Biggio .50 1.25
Jose Vidro
Luis Castillo
Orlando Hudson
42 Brian Giles .50 1.25
Grady Sizemore
Lew Ford
Nick Swisher
43 Coco Crisp .40 1.00
David DeJesus
Emil Brown
Jeromy Burnitz
44 Eric Gagne .40 1.00
Eric Milton
Jake Peavy
Jaret Wright
45 Aubrey Huff .40 1.00
Austin Kearns
Brady Clark
Nook Logan
46 Ben Sheets .40 1.00
Carl Pavano
Chris Capuano
Jon Garland
47 Darin Erstad .40 1.00
Dmitri Young
Erubiel Durazo
Travis Hafner
48 Conor Jackson .50 1.25
Jermaine Dye
Magglio Ordonez
Miguel Cabrera
49 Chad Tracy .40 1.00
Lyle Overbay
Richie Sexson
Sean Casey
50 Nick Johnson .50 1.25
Paul Konerko
Raul Ibanez
Todd Helton
51 Chuck James .40 1.00
Darrell Rasner
Hong-Chih Kuo
Shaun Marcum
52 Anthony Reyes 1.25 3.00
Fausto Carmona
Francisco Liriano
Joe Saunders
53 Anderson Hernandez .40 1.00
Bryan Bullington
Charlton Jimerson
Tom Gorzelanny
54 Chris Denorfia .40 1.00
Jeff Mathis
John Koronka
Ryan Garko
55 Jose Bautista .40 1.00
Danny Sandoval
Robert Andino
Justin Huber

2006 Bazooka Basics Relics

GROUP A ODDS 1:285 H, 1:465 R
GROUP B ODDS 1:124 H, 1:204 R
GROUP C ODDS 1:95 H, 1:155 R
GROUP D ODDS 1:124 H, 1:204 R
AJ Andruw Jones Jsy B 4.00 10.00
AP Albert Pujols Jsy A 6.00 15.00
BA Bobby Abreu Jsy C 3.00 8.00
BR Brian Roberts Jsy C 3.00 8.00
BW Bernie Williams Uni C 4.00 10.00
CB Craig Biggio Jsy B 4.00 10.00
CD Carlos Delgado Jsy B 3.00 8.00
CJ Chipper Jones Jsy A 4.00 10.00
CS Curt Schilling Jsy B 4.00 10.00
DW Dontrelle Willis Jsy D 3.00 8.00
EG Eric Gagne Jsy A 3.00 8.00
HB Hank Blalock Jsy D 3.00 8.00
JD Johnny Damon Jsy B 4.00 10.00
JR Jose Reyes Jsy A 3.00 8.00
LB Lance Berkman Jsy C 3.00 8.00
MC Miguel Cabrera Uni C 4.00 10.00
MG Marcus Giles Jsy D 3.00 8.00
MH Matt Holliday Jsy A 4.00 10.00
ML Mike Lowell Uni C 3.00 8.00
MM Mark Mulder Uni B 3.00 8.00
MMU Mike Mussina Uni D 4.00 10.00
MR Manny Ramirez Jsy B 4.00 10.00
MT Mark Teixeira Jsy A 4.00 10.00
PM Pedro Martinez Uni B 4.00 10.00
SB Sean Burroughs Uni C 3.00 8.00
TH Tim Hudson Uni A 3.00 8.00

2006 Bazooka Blasts Bat Relics

GROUP A ODDS 1:4020 H, 1:6370 R
GROUP B ODDS 1:67 H, 1:108 R
GROUP C ODDS 1:29 H, 1:48 R
GROUP A PRINT RUN 100 SETS
GROUP A ARE NOT SERIAL-NUMBERED
GROUP A PRINT RUN PROVIDED BY TOPPS
AD Adam Dunn B 3.00 8.00
AJ Andruw Jones C 4.00 10.00
AR Alex Rodriguez B 4.00 10.00
ARA Aramis Ramirez C 3.00 8.00
BA Bobby Abreu C 3.00 8.00
BB Barry Bonds A/100 * 15.00 40.00
CB Carlos Beltran C 3.00 8.00
CC Coco Crisp B 3.00 8.00
CF Cliff Floyd C 3.00 8.00
CJ Chipper Jones C 4.00 10.00
CP Corey Patterson B 3.00 8.00
DL Derrek Lee C 4.00 10.00
DO David Ortiz B 4.00 10.00
DW David Wright C 4.00 10.00
GJ Geoff Jenkins B 3.00 8.00
GS Gary Sheffield C 3.00 8.00
HB Hank Blalock B 3.00 8.00
JB Jason Bay B 3.00 8.00
JD Johnny Damon C 4.00 10.00
JDD J.D. Drew B 3.00 8.00
JT Jim Thome B 4.00 10.00
MA Moises Alou C 3.00 8.00
ML Mark Loretta B 3.00 8.00
MM Mickey Mantle A/100 * 125.00 200.00
MP Mike Piazza B 4.00 10.00
MT Miguel Tejada B 3.00 8.00
PK Paul Konerko C 3.00 8.00
PL Paul LoDuca C 3.00 8.00
PW Preston Wilson C 3.00 8.00
SS Sammy Sosa B 4.00 10.00
TG Troy Glaus C 3.00 8.00
TN Trot Nixon B 3.00 8.00
VG Vladimir Guerrero C 4.00 10.00
VM Victor Martinez C 3.00 8.00

2006 Bazooka Comics

COMPLETE SET (24) 6.00 15.00
STATED ODDS 1:4 HOBBY
1 Greg Maddux .75 2.00
2 Alex Rodriguez .75 2.00
3 Trevor Hoffman .40 1.00
4 Rafael Palmeiro .40 1.00
5 Roy Oswalt .40 1.00
6 Bobby Abreu .40 1.00
7 Miguel Tejada .40 1.00
8 Vladimir Guerrero .50 1.25
9 Mark Teixeira .40 1.00
10 Zach Duke .40 1.00
11 Xavier Nady .40 1.00
12 Alex Rodriguez .75 2.00
13 Jeremy Hermida .40 1.00
14 Craig Biggio .40 1.00
15 Manny Ramirez .40 1.00
16 Texas Rangers .40 1.00
17 Oakland Athletics .40 1.00
18 Alex Rodriguez .75 2.00
19 Jason Giambi .40 1.00
20 Aaron Small .40 1.00
21 Jimmy Rollins .40 1.00
22 Roger Clemens 1.00 2.50
23 Chicago White Sox .40 1.00
Seattle Mariners
24 Andruw Jones .40 1.00

2006 Bazooka Mickey Mantle Jumbo Reprints

COMPLETE SET (16) 200.00 300.00
COMMON CARD (53-69) 10.00 25.00
ONE PER SEALED HOBBY BOX
1952 Mickey Mantle 1952 30.00 60.00
1953 Mickey Mantle 1953 10.00 25.00
1956 Mickey Mantle 1956 10.00 25.00
1957 Mickey Mantle 1957 10.00 25.00
1958 Mickey Mantle 1958 10.00 25.00
1959 Mickey Mantle 1959 10.00 25.00
1960 Mickey Mantle 1960 10.00 25.00
1961 Mickey Mantle 1961 10.00 25.00
1962 Mickey Mantle 1962 10.00 25.00
1963 Mickey Mantle 1963 10.00 25.00
1964 Mickey Mantle 1964 10.00 25.00
1965 Mickey Mantle 1965 10.00 25.00
1966 Mickey Mantle 1966 10.00 25.00
1967 Mickey Mantle 1967 10.00 25.00
1968 Mickey Mantle 1968 10.00 25.00
1969 Mickey Mantle 1969 10.00 25.00

2006 Bazooka Rewind Relics

GROUP A ODDS 1:2680 H, 1:4250 R
GROUP B ODDS 1:1066 H, 1:1700 R
GROUP C ODDS 1:400 H, 1:653 R
GROUP D ODDS 1:45 H, 1:74 R
GROUP E ODDS 1:56 H, 1:89 R
GROUP F ODDS 1:200 H, 1:324 R
GROUP G ODDS 1:251 H, 1:147 R
GROUP A PRINT RUN 100 SETS
GROUP A ARE NOT SERIAL-NUMBERED
GROUP A PRINT RUN PROVIDED BY TOPPS
NO GROUP A PRICING DUE TO SCARCITY
AJ Andruw Jones Uni C 4.00 10.00
AK Adam Kennedy Bat D 3.00 8.00
AML Adam LaRoche Jsy G 3.00 8.00
AP A.J. Pierzynski Bat D 3.00 8.00
AR Alex Rodriguez Bat D 6.00 15.00
ARO Aaron Rowand Bat E 3.00 8.00
BR Brian Roberts Bat C 3.00 8.00
BU B.J. Upton Jsy A/100 *
CB Clint Barmes Bat D 3.00 8.00
CBI Craig Biggio Jsy D 4.00 10.00
CC Carl Crawford Bat C 3.00 8.00
CE Carl Everett Uni C 3.00 8.00
CG Cristian Guzman Bat E 3.00 8.00
CJ Conor Jackson Jsy A/100 *
CL Carlos Lee Bat E 3.00 8.00
CU Chase Utley Bat D 4.00 10.00
DW Dontrelle Willis Jsy D 3.00 8.00
ER Edgar Renteria Bat E 3.00 8.00
FL Francisco Liriano Jsy B 6.00 15.00
FT Frank Thomas Bat D 4.00 10.00
HR Hanley Ramirez Jsy G 4.00 10.00
JB Jason Botts Bat D 3.00 8.00
JD Jermaine Dye Bat E 3.00 8.00
JDA Johnny Damon Bat E 4.00 10.00
JG Jon Garland Uni C 3.00 8.00
JGU Jose Guillen Bat D 3.00 8.00
JH Justin Huber Jsy F 3.00 8.00
JR Jimmy Rollins Bat D 3.00 8.00
JV Justin Verlander Jsy B 4.00 10.00
KT Kevin Thompson Jsy G 3.00 8.00
LB Lance Berkman Jsy D 3.00 8.00
MG Mark Grudzielanek Bat D 3.00 8.00
MJ Mike Jacobs Bat D 3.00 8.00
MR Manny Ramirez Uni E 4.00 10.00
NC Nelson Cruz Jsy G 3.00 8.00
NJ Nick Johnson Bat D 3.00 8.00
PB Pat Burrell Bat D 3.00 8.00
PK Paul Konerko Bat E 3.00 8.00
RC Robinson Cano Bat E 4.00 10.00
RG Ryan Garko Jsy B 3.00 8.00
RW Rickie Weeks Bat D 3.00 8.00
RWA Ryan Wagner Jsy D 3.00 8.00
SC Shin-Soo Choo Jsy F 3.00 8.00
SP Scott Podsednik Bat D 3.00 8.00
TS Termel Sledge Bat D 3.00 8.00
WB William Bergolla Jsy A/100 *
WB2 William Bergolla Jsy D 3.00 8.00
WT Willy Taveras Jsy D 3.00 8.00

2006 Bazooka Signature Line

GROUP A ODDS 1:21,250 H
GROUP B ODDS 1:3165 H
GROUP C ODDS 1:1261 H
GROUP D ODDS 1:314 H
GROUP A PRINT RUN 15 CARDS
GROUP B PRINT RUN 100 SETS
GROUP A-B ARE NOT SERIAL-NUMBERED
GROUP A-B PRINTS PROVIDED BY TOPPS
NO GROUP A PRICING DUE TO SCARCITY
AR Alex Rodriguez A/15 *
BM Brandon McCarthy D 6.00 15.00
KM Kevin Millar C 10.00 25.00
ML Victor Zambrano D 6.00 15.00
MM Mike Morse B/100 * 6.00 15.00

2006 Bazooka Stamps

COMPLETE SET (30) 12.50 30.00
STATED ODDS 1:3 HOBBY, 1:6 RETAIL
1 Bobby Abreu .40 1.00
2 Lance Berkman .40 1.00
3 Hank Blalock .40 1.00
4 Barry Bonds 1.50 4.00
5 Mark Buehrle .40 1.00
6 Miguel Cabrera .40 1.00
7 Jim Edmonds .40 1.00
8 Morgan Ensberg .40 1.00
9 Jeff Francoeur .60 1.50
10 Roy Halladay .40 1.00
11 Tim Hudson .40 1.00
12 Derek Jeter 1.50 4.00
13 Andruw Jones .40 1.00
14 Chipper Jones .60 1.50
15 Derrek Lee .40 1.00
16 Mickey Mantle 3.00 8.00
17 Victor Martinez .40 1.00
18 Justin Morneau .40 1.00
19 Manny Ramirez .40 1.00
20 Brian Roberts .40 1.00
21 Alex Rodriguez 1.00 2.50
22 Ivan Rodriguez .40 1.00
23 Johan Santana .40 1.00
24 Alfonso Soriano .40 1.00
25 Huston Street .40 1.00
26 Ichiro Suzuki 1.00 2.50
27 Mark Teixeira .40 1.00
28 Miguel Tejada .40 1.00
29 Rickie Weeks .40 1.00
30 Dontrelle Willis .40 1.00

1948 Bowman

The 48-card Bowman set of 1948 was the first major set of the post-war period. Each 2 1/16" by 2 1/2" card had a black and white photo of a current player, with his biographical information printed in black ink on a gray back. Due to the printing process and the 36-card sheet size upon which Bowman was then printing, the 12 cards marked with an SP in the checklist are scarcer numerically, as they were removed from the printing sheet in order to make room for the 12 high numbers (37-48). Cards were issued in one-card penny packs. Many cards are found with over-printed, transposed, or blank backs. The set features the Rookie Cards of Hall of Famers Yogi Berra, Ralph Kiner, Stan Musial, Red Schoendienst, and Warren Spahn. Half of the cards in the set feature New York players (Yankees or Giants).

COMPLETE SET (48) 3000.00 5000.00
COMMON CARD (1-36) 10.00 20.00
COMMON CARD (37-48) 15.00 30.00
WRAPPER (5-CENT) 600.00 700.00
WRAPPER (1-CENT)
1 Bob Elliott RC 75.00 125.00
2 Ewell Blackwell RC 35.00 60.00
3 Ralph Kiner RC 150.00 250.00
4 Johnny Mize RC 75.00 125.00
5 Bob Feller RC 150.00 250.00
6 Yogi Berra RC 500.00 800.00
7 Pete Reiser SP RC 75.00 125.00
8 Phil Rizzuto SP RC 200.00 350.00
9 Walker Cooper RC 10.00 20.00
10 Buddy Rosar RC 10.00 20.00
11 Johnny Lindell RC 12.50 25.00
12 Johnny Sain RC 50.00 80.00
13 Willard Marshall SP RC 20.00 40.00
14 Allie Reynolds RC 35.00 60.00
15 Eddie Joost 10.00 20.00
16 Jack Lohrke SP RC 20.00 40.00
17 Enos Slaughter RC 60.00 100.00
18 Warren Spahn RC 175.00 300.00
19 Tommy Henrich 35.00 60.00
20 Buddy Kerr SP RC 20.00 40.00
21 Ferris Fain RC 20.00 40.00
22 Floyd Bevens SP RC 30.00 50.00
23 Larry Jansen RC 12.50 25.00
24 Dutch Leonard SP 20.00 40.00
25 Barney McCosky 10.00 20.00
26 Frank Shea SP RC 30.00 50.00
27 Sid Gordon RC 12.50 25.00
28 Emil Verban SP RC 20.00 40.00
29 Joe Page SP RC 50.00 80.00
30 Whitey Lockman SP RC 30.00 50.00
31 Bill McCahan RC 10.00 20.00
32 Bill Rigney RC 10.00 20.00
33 Bill Johnson RC 12.50 25.00
34 Sheldon Jones SP RC 20.00 40.00
35 Snuffy Stirnweiss RC 20.00 40.00
36 Stan Musial RC 500.00 800.00
37 Clint Hartung RC 15.00 30.00
38 Red Schoendienst RC 125.00 200.00
39 Augie Galan RC 15.00 30.00
40 Marty Marion RC 50.00 80.00
41 Rex Barney RC 35.00 60.00
42 Ray Poat RC 15.00 30.00
43 Bruce Edwards RC 20.00 40.00
44 Johnny Wyrostek RC 15.00 30.00
45 Hank Sauer RC 35.00 60.00
46 Herman Wehmeier RC 15.00 30.00
47 Bobby Thomson RC 60.00 100.00
48 Dave Koslo RC 50.00 80.00

1949 Bowman

The cards in this 240-card set measure approximately 2 1/16" by 2 1/2". In 1949 Bowman took an intermediate step between black and white and full color with this set of tinted photos on colored backgrounds. Collectors should note the series price variations, which reflect some inconsistencies in the printing process. There are four major varieties in name printing, which are noted in the checklist below: NOF: name on front; NNOF: no name on front; PR: printed name on back; and SCR: script name on back. Cards were issued in five card nickel packs which came 24 packs to a box. These variations resulted when Bowman used twelve of the lower numbers to fill out the last press sheet of 36 cards, adding to numbers 217-240. Cards 1-3 and 5-73 can be found with either gray or white backs. Certain cards have been seen with a "gray" or "slate" background on the front. These cards are a result of a color printing error and are rarely seen on the secondary market so no value is established for them. Not all numbers are known to exist in this fashion. However, within the numbers between 75 and 107, slightly more of these cards have appeared on the market. Within the high numbers series (145-240), these cards have been seen but the appearance of these cards are very rare. Other cards are known to be extant with double printed backs. The set features the Rookie Cards of Hall of Famers Roy Campanella, Bob Lemon, Robin Roberts, Duke Snider, and Early Wynn as well as Rookie Cards of Richie Ashburn and Gil Hodges.

COMP. MASTER SET (252) 10000.0016000.00
COMPLETE SET (240) 10000.0015000.00
COMMON CARD (1-144) 7.50 15.00
COMMON (145-240) 30.00 50.00
WRAPPER (1-CENT,Rd,Wh,Bl)
WRAP.(5-CENT,GREEN) 200.00 250.00
WRAP.(5-CENT,BLUE) 150.00 200.00
1 Vern Bickford RC 75.00 125.00
2 Whitey Lockman 20.00 40.00
3 Bob Porterfield RC 7.50 15.00
4A Jerry Priddy NNOF RC 7.50 15.00
4B Jerry Priddy NOF 30.00 50.00
5 Hank Sauer 20.00 40.00
6 Phil Cavarretta RC 20.00 40.00
7 Joe Dobson RC 7.50 15.00
8 Murry Dickson RC 7.50 15.00
9 Ferris Fain 20.00 40.00
10 Ted Gray RC 7.50 15.00
11 Lou Boudreau MG RC 50.00 80.00
12 Cass Michaels RC 7.50 15.00
13 Bob Chesnes RC 7.50 15.00
14 Curt Simmons RC 20.00 40.00
15 Ned Garver RC 7.50 15.00
16 Al Kozar RC 7.50 15.00
17 Earl Torgeson RC 7.50 15.00
18 Bobby Thomson 20.00 40.00
19 Bobby Brown RC 35.00 60.00
20 Gene Hermanski RC 7.50 15.00
21 Frank Baumholtz RC 12.50 25.00
22 Peanuts Lowrey RC 7.50 15.00
23 Bobby Doerr 50.00 80.00
24 Stan Musial 350.00 600.00
25 Carl Scheib RC 7.50 15.00
26 George Kell RC 50.00 80.00
27 Bob Feller 200.00 300.00
28 Don Kolloway RC 7.50 15.00
29 Ralph Kiner 75.00 125.00
30 Andy Seminick 20.00 40.00
31 Dick Kokos RC 7.50 15.00
32 Eddie Yost RC 35.00 60.00
33 Warren Spahn 125.00 200.00
34 Dave Koslo 7.50 15.00
35 Vic Raschi RC 35.00 60.00
36 Pee Wee Reese 125.00 200.00
37 Johnny Wyrostek 7.50 15.00
38 Emil Verban 7.50 15.00
39 Billy Goodman RC 12.50 25.00
40 George Munger RC 7.50 15.00
41 Lou Brissie RC 7.50 15.00
42 Hoot Evers RC 7.50 15.00
43 Dale Mitchell RC 20.00 40.00
44 Dave Philley RC 7.50 15.00

45 Wally Westlake RC 7.50 15.00
46 Robin Roberts RC 150.00 250.00
47 Johnny Sain 35.00 60.00
48 Willard Marshall 7.50 15.00
49 Frank Shea 12.50 25.00
50 Jackie Robinson RC 900.00 1500.00
51 Herman Wehmeier 7.50 15.00
52 Johnny Schmitz RC 7.50 15.00
53 Jack Kramer RC 7.50 15.00
54 Marty Marion 35.00 60.00
55 Eddie Joost 7.50 15.00
56 Pat Mullin RC 7.50 15.00
57 Gene Bearden RC 20.00 40.00
58 Bob Elliott 20.00 40.00
59 Jack Lohrke 7.50 15.00
60 Yogi Berra 175.00 300.00
61 Rex Barney 20.00 40.00
62 Grady Hatton RC 7.50 15.00
63 Andy Pafko RC 20.00 40.00
64 Dom DiMaggio 35.00 60.00
65 Enos Slaughter 50.00 80.00
66 Elmer Valo RC 7.50 15.00
67 Alvin Dark RC 20.00 40.00
68 Sheldon Jones 7.50 15.00
69 Tommy Henrich 20.00 40.00
70 Carl Furillo RC 90.00 150.00
71 Vern Stephens RC 7.50 15.00
72 Tommy Holmes RC 20.00 40.00
73 Billy Cox RC 20.00 40.00
74 Tom McBride RC 7.50 15.00
75 Eddie Mayo RC 7.50 15.00
76 Bill Nicholson RC 12.50 25.00
77 Ernie Bonham RC 7.50 15.00
78A Sam Zoldak RC NNOF 7.50 15.00
78B Sam Zoldak NOF 30.00 50.00
79 Ron Northey RC 7.50 15.00
80 Bill McCahan 7.50 15.00
81 Virgil Stallcup RC 7.50 15.00
82 Joe Page 35.00 60.00
83A Bob Scheffing NNOF RC 7.50 15.00
83B Bob Scheffing NOF 30.00 50.00
84 Roy Campanella RC 500.00 800.00
85A Johnny Mize NNOF 60.00 100.00
85B Johnny Mize NOF 90.00 150.00
86 Johnny Pesky RC 35.00 60.00
87 Randy Gumpert RC 7.50 15.00
88A Bill Salkeld NNOF RC 7.50 15.00
88B Bill Salkeld NOF 30.00 50.00
89 Mizell Platt RC 7.50 15.00
90 Gil Coan RC 7.50 15.00
91 Dick Wakefield RC 7.50 15.00
92 Willie Jones RC 20.00 40.00
93 Ed Stevens RC 7.50 15.00
94 Mickey Vernon RC 20.00 40.00
95 Howie Pollet RC 7.50 15.00
96 Taft Wright 7.50 15.00
97 Danny Litwhiler RC 7.50 15.00
98A Phil Rizzuto NNOF 125.00 200.00
98B Phil Rizzuto NOF 150.00 250.00
99 Frank Gustine RC 7.50 15.00
100 Gil Hodges RC 150.00 250.00
101 Sid Gordon 7.50 15.00
102 Stan Spence RC 7.50 15.00
103 Joe Tipton RC 7.50 15.00
104 Eddie Stanky RC 20.00 40.00
105 Bill Kennedy RC 7.50 15.00
106 Jake Early RC 7.50 15.00
107 Eddie Lake RC 7.50 15.00
108 Ken Heintzelman RC 7.50 15.00
109A Ed Fitzgerald SCR RC 7.50 15.00
109B Ed Fitzgerald PR 35.00 60.00
110 Early Wynn RC 90.00 150.00
111 Red Schoendienst 60.00 100.00
112 Sam Chapman 20.00 40.00
113 Ray LaManno RC 7.50 15.00
114 Allie Reynolds 35.00 60.00
115 Dutch Leonard 7.50 15.00
116 Joe Hatten RC 7.50 15.00
117 Walker Cooper 7.50 15.00
118 Sam Mele RC 7.50 15.00
119 Floyd Baker RC 7.50 15.00
120 Cliff Fannin RC 7.50 15.00
121 Mark Christman RC 7.50 15.00
122 George Vico RC 7.50 15.00
123 Johnny Blatnik UER 7.50 15.00
Card spelled as Blatnick
124A D.Murtaugh SCR RC 20.00 40.00
124B D.Murtaugh PR 35.00 60.00
125 Ken Keltner RC 12.50 25.00
126A Al Brazle SCR RC 7.50 15.00
126B Al Brazle PR 35.00 60.00
127A Hank Majeski SCR RC 7.50 15.00
127B Hank Majeski PR 35.00 60.00
128 Johnny VanderMeer 35.00 60.00
129 Bill Johnson 20.00 40.00
130 Harry Walker RC 7.50 15.00
131 Paul Lehner RC 7.50 15.00
132A Al Evans SCR RC 7.50 15.00
132B Al Evans PR 35.00 60.00
133 Aaron Robinson RC 7.50 15.00
134 Hank Borowy RC 7.50 15.00
135 Stan Rojek RC 7.50 15.00
136 Hank Edwards RC 7.50 15.00
137 Ted Wilks RC 7.50 15.00
138 Buddy Rosar 7.50 15.00
139 Hank Arft RC 7.50 15.00
140 Ray Scarborough RC 7.50 15.00
141 Tony Lupien RC 7.50 15.00
142 Eddie Waitkus RC 20.00 40.00
143A Bob Dillinger SCR RC 12.50 25.00
143B Bob Dillinger PR 35.00 60.00
144 Mickey Haefner RC 7.50 15.00
145 Sylvester Donnelly RC 30.00 50.00
146 Mike McCormick RC 30.00 50.00
147 Bert Singleton RC 30.00 50.00
148 Bob Swift RC 30.00 50.00
149 Roy Partee RC 30.00 50.00
150 Allie Clark RC 30.00 50.00
151 Mickey Harris RC 30.00 50.00
152 Clarence Maddern RC 30.00 50.00
153 Phil Masi RC 30.00 50.00
154 Clint Hartung 35.00 60.00
155 Mickey Guerra RC 30.00 50.00
156 Al Zarilla RC 30.00 50.00
157 Walt Masterson RC 30.00 50.00
158 Harry Brecheen RC 35.00 60.00
159 Glen Moulder RC 30.00 50.00
160 Jim Blackburn RC 30.00 50.00
161 Jocko Thompson RC 30.00 50.00
162 Preacher Roe RC 75.00 125.00
163 Clyde McCullough RC 30.00 50.00
164 Vic Wertz RC 50.00 80.00
165 Snuffy Stirnweiss 50.00 80.00
166 Mike Tresh RC 30.00 50.00
167 Babe Martin RC 30.00 50.00
168 Doyle Lade RC 30.00 50.00
169 Jeff Heath RC 35.00 60.00
170 Bill Rigney 35.00 60.00
171 Dick Fowler RC 30.00 50.00
172 Eddie Pellagrini RC 30.00 50.00
173 Eddie Stewart RC 30.00 50.00
174 Terry Moore RC 50.00 80.00
175 Luke Appling 90.00 150.00
176 Ken Raffensberger RC 30.00 50.00
177 Stan Lopata RC 35.00 60.00
178 Tom Brown RC 35.00 60.00
179 Hugh Casey 50.00 80.00
180 Connie Berry 30.00 50.00
181 Gus Niarhos RC 30.00 50.00
182 Hal Peck RC 30.00 50.00
183 Lou Stringer RC 30.00 50.00
184 Bob Chipman RC 30.00 50.00
185 Pete Reiser 50.00 80.00
186 Buddy Kerr 30.00 50.00
187 Phil Marchildon RC 30.00 50.00
188 Karl Drews RC 30.00 50.00
189 Earl Wooten RC 30.00 50.00
190 Jim Hearn RC 30.00 50.00
191 Joe Haynes RC 30.00 50.00
192 Harry Gumbert 30.00 50.00
193 Ken Trinkle RC 30.00 50.00
194 Ralph Branca RC 60.00 100.00
195 Eddie Bockman RC 30.00 50.00
196 Fred Hutchinson RC 35.00 60.00
197 Johnny Lindell 35.00 60.00
198 Steve Gromek RC 30.00 50.00
199 Tex Hughson RC 30.00 50.00
200 Jess Dobernic RC 30.00 50.00
201 Sibby Sisti RC 30.00 50.00
202 Larry Jansen 35.00 60.00
203 Barney McCosky 30.00 50.00
204 Bob Savage RC 30.00 50.00
205 Dick Sisler RC 35.00 60.00
206 Bruce Edwards 30.00 50.00
207 Johnny Hopp RC 30.00 50.00
208 Dizzy Trout 35.00 60.00
209 Charlie Keller 50.00 80.00
210 Joe Gordon RC 50.00 80.00
211 Boo Ferriss RC 30.00 50.00
212 Ralph Hamner RC 30.00 50.00
213 Red Barrett RC 30.00 50.00
214 Richie Ashburn RC 350.00 600.00
215 Kirby Higbe 30.00 50.00
216 Schoolboy Rowe 35.00 60.00
217 Marino Pieretti RC 30.00 50.00
218 Dick Kryhoski RC 30.00 50.00
219 Virgil Trucks RC 35.00 60.00
220 Johnny McCarthy 30.00 50.00
NY Giants Cap but listed as Sioux City MG
221 Bob Muncrief RC 30.00 50.00
222 Alex Kellner RC 30.00 50.00
223 Bobby Hofman RC 30.00 50.00
224 Satchel Paige RC 1000.00 1500.00
225 Jerry Coleman RC 50.00 80.00
226 Duke Snider RC 600.00 1000.00
227 Fritz Ostermueller 30.00 50.00
228 Jackie Mayo RC 30.00 50.00
229 Ed Lopat RC 90.00 150.00
230 Augie Galan 35.00 60.00
231 Earl Johnson RC 30.00 50.00
232 George McQuinn 35.00 60.00
233 Larry Doby RC 175.00 300.00
234 Rip Sewell RC 30.00 50.00
235 Jim Russell RC 30.00 50.00
236 Fred Sanford RC 30.00 50.00
237 Monte Kennedy RC 30.00 50.00
238 Bob Lemon RC 125.00 200.00
239 Frank McCormick 30.00 50.00
240 Babe Young UER 60.00 100.00
(Photo actually Bobby Young)

1950 Bowman

The cards in this 252-card set measure approximately 2 1/16" by 2 1/2". This set, marketed in 1950 by Bowman, represented a major improvement in terms of quality over their previous efforts. Each card was a beautifully colored line drawing developed from a simple photograph. The first 72 cards are the scarcest in the set, while the final 72 cards may be found with or without the copyright line. This was the only Bowman sports set to carry the famous "5-Star" logo. Cards were issued in five-card nickel packs. Key rookies in this set are Hank Bauer, Don Newcombe, and Al Rosen.

COMPLETE SET (252) 6000.00 8500.00
COMMON CARD (1-72) 30.00 50.00
COMMON CARD (73-252) 7.50 15.00
WRAPPER (1-cent) 200.00 250.00
WRAPPER (5-cent) 200.00 250.00
1 Mel Parnell RC 90.00 150.00
2 Vern Stephens 35.00 60.00
3 Dom DiMaggio 50.00 80.00
4 Gus Zernial RC 35.00 60.00
5 Bob Kuzava RC 30.00 50.00
6 Bob Feller 175.00 300.00
7 Jim Hegan 35.00 60.00
8 George Kell 35.00 60.00
9 Vic Wertz 35.00 60.00
10 Tommy Henrich 50.00 80.00
11 Phil Rizzuto 175.00 300.00
12 Joe Page 50.00 80.00
13 Ferris Fain 35.00 60.00
14 Alex Kellner 30.00 50.00
15 Al Kozar 30.00 50.00
16 Roy Sievers RC 50.00 80.00
17 Sid Hudson 30.00 50.00
18 Eddie Robinson RC 30.00 50.00
19 Warren Spahn 175.00 300.00
20 Bob Elliott 35.00 60.00
21 Pee Wee Reese 175.00 300.00
22 Jackie Robinson 700.00 1200.00
23 Don Newcombe RC 90.00 150.00
24 Johnny Schmitz 30.00 50.00
25 Hank Sauer 35.00 60.00
26 Grady Hatton 30.00 50.00
27 Herman Wehmeier 30.00 50.00
28 Bobby Thomson 50.00 80.00
29 Eddie Stanky 35.00 60.00
30 Eddie Waitkus 35.00 60.00
31 Del Ennis 50.00 80.00
32 Robin Roberts 90.00 150.00
33 Ralph Kiner 60.00 100.00
34 Murry Dickson 30.00 50.00
35 Enos Slaughter 60.00 100.00
36 Eddie Kazak RC 35.00 60.00
37 Luke Appling 50.00 80.00
38 Bill Wight RC 30.00 50.00
39 Larry Doby 60.00 100.00
40 Bob Lemon 50.00 80.00
41 Hoot Evers 30.00 50.00
42 Art Houtteman RC 30.00 50.00
43 Bobby Doerr 50.00 80.00
44 Joe Dobson 30.00 50.00
45 Al Zarilla 30.00 50.00
46 Yogi Berra 250.00 400.00
47 Jerry Coleman 50.00 80.00
48 Lou Brissie 30.00 50.00
49 Elmer Valo 30.00 50.00
50 Dick Kokos 30.00 50.00
51 Ned Garver 35.00 60.00
52 Sam Mele 30.00 50.00
53 Clyde Vollmer RC 30.00 50.00
54 Gil Coan 30.00 50.00
55 Buddy Kerr 30.00 50.00
56 Del Crandall RC 35.00 60.00
57 Vern Bickford 30.00 50.00
58 Carl Furillo 50.00 80.00
59 Ralph Branca 50.00 80.00
60 Andy Pafko 35.00 60.00
61 Bob Rush RC 30.00 50.00
62 Ted Kluszewski 75.00 125.00
63 Ewell Blackwell 35.00 60.00
64 Alvin Dark 35.00 60.00
65 Dave Koslo 30.00 50.00
66 Larry Jansen 35.00 60.00
67 Willie Jones 35.00 60.00
68 Curt Simmons 35.00 60.00
69 Wally Westlake 30.00 50.00
70 Bob Chesnes 30.00 50.00
71 Red Schoendienst 50.00 80.00
72 Howie Pollet 30.00 50.00
73 Willard Marshall 7.50 15.00
74 Johnny Antonelli RC 35.00 60.00
75 Roy Campanella 175.00 300.00
76 Rex Barney 20.00 40.00
77 Duke Snider 175.00 300.00
78 Mickey Owen 12.50 25.00
79 Johnny VanderMeer 20.00 40.00
80 Howard Fox RC 7.50 15.00
81 Ron Northey 7.50 15.00
82 Whitey Lockman 12.50 25.00
83 Sheldon Jones 7.50 15.00
84 Richie Ashburn 75.00 125.00
85 Ken Heintzelman 7.50 15.00
86 Stan Rojek 7.50 15.00
87 Bill Werle RC 7.50 15.00
88 Marty Marion 20.00 40.00
89 George Munger 7.50 15.00
90 Harry Brecheen 20.00 40.00
91 Cass Michaels 7.50 15.00
92 Hank Majeski 7.50 15.00
93 Gene Bearden 20.00 40.00
94 Lou Boudreau MG 35.00 60.00
95 Aaron Robinson 7.50 15.00
96 Virgil Trucks 12.50 25.00
97 Maurice McDermott RC 7.50 15.00
98 Ted Williams 600.00 1000.00
99 Billy Goodman 12.50 25.00
100 Vic Raschi 35.00 60.00
101 Bobby Brown 35.00 60.00
102 Billy Johnson 12.50 25.00
103 Eddie Joost 7.50 15.00
104 Sam Chapman 7.50 15.00
105 Bob Dillinger 7.50 15.00
106 Cliff Fannin 7.50 15.00
107 Sam Dente RC 7.50 15.00
108 Ray Scarborough 7.50 15.00
109 Sid Gordon 7.50 15.00
110 Tommy Holmes 12.50 25.00
111 Walker Cooper 7.50 15.00
112 Gil Hodges 75.00 125.00
113 Gene Hermanski 7.50 15.00
114 Wayne Terwilliger RC 7.50 15.00
115 Roy Smalley 7.50 15.00
116 Virgil Stallcup 7.50 15.00
117 Bill Rigney 7.50 15.00
118 Clint Hartung 7.50 15.00
119 Dick Sisler 12.50 25.00
120 John Thompson 7.50 15.00
121 Andy Seminick 12.50 25.00
122 Johnny Hopp 12.50 25.00
123 Dino Restelli RC 7.50 15.00
124 Clyde McCullough 7.50 15.00
125 Del Rice RC 7.50 15.00
126 Al Brazle 7.50 15.00
127 Dave Philley 7.50 15.00
128 Phil Masi 7.50 15.00
129 Joe Gordon 12.50 25.00
130 Dale Mitchell 12.50 25.00
131 Steve Gromek 7.50 15.00
132 Mickey Vernon 12.50 25.00
133 Don Kolloway 7.50 15.00
134 Paul Trout 7.50 15.00
135 Pat Mullin 7.50 15.00
136 Buddy Rosar 7.50 15.00
137 Johnny Pesky 12.50 25.00
138 Allie Reynolds 35.00 60.00
139 Johnny Mize 50.00 80.00
140 Pete Suder RC 7.50 15.00
141 Joe Coleman RC 12.50 25.00
142 Sherman Lollar RC 20.00 40.00
143 Eddie Stewart 7.50 15.00
144 Al Evans 7.50 15.00
145 Jack Graham RC 7.50 15.00
146 Floyd Baker 7.50 15.00
147 Mike Garcia RC 20.00 40.00
148 Early Wynn 50.00 80.00
149 Bob Swift 7.50 15.00
150 George Vico 7.50 15.00
151 Fred Hutchinson 12.50 25.00
152 Ellis Kinder RC 7.50 15.00
153 Walt Masterson 7.50 15.00
154 Gus Niarhos 7.50 15.00
155 Frank Shea 12.50 25.00
156 Fred Sanford 12.50 25.00
157 Mike Guerra 7.50 15.00
158 Paul Lehner 7.50 15.00
159 Joe Tipton 7.50 15.00
160 Mickey Harris 7.50 15.00
161 Sherry Robertson RC 7.50 15.00
162 Eddie Yost 12.50 25.00
163 Earl Torgeson 7.50 15.00
164 Sibby Sisti 7.50 15.00
165 Bruce Edwards 7.50 15.00
166 Joe Hatton 7.50 15.00
167 Preacher Roe 35.00 60.00
168 Bob Scheffing 7.50 15.00
169 Hank Edwards 7.50 15.00
170 Dutch Leonard 7.50 15.00
171 Harry Gumbert 7.50 15.00
172 Peanuts Lowrey 7.50 15.00
173 Lloyd Merriman RC 7.50 15.00
174 Hank Thompson RC 20.00 40.00
175 Monte Kennedy 7.50 15.00
176 Sylvester Donnelly 7.50 15.00
177 Hank Borowy 7.50 15.00
178 Ed Fitzgerald 7.50 15.00
179 Chuck Diering RC 7.50 15.00
180 Harry Walker 12.50 25.00
181 Marino Pieretti 7.50 15.00
182 Sam Zoldak 7.50 15.00
183 Mickey Haefner 7.50 15.00
184 Randy Gumpert 7.50 15.00
185 Howie Judson RC 7.50 15.00
186 Ken Keltner 12.50 25.00
187 Lou Stringer 7.50 15.00
188 Earl Johnson 7.50 15.00
189 Owen Friend RC 7.50 15.00
190 Ken Wood RC 7.50 15.00
191 Dick Starr RC 7.50 15.00
192 Bob Chipman 7.50 15.00
193 Pete Reiser 20.00 40.00
194 Billy Cox 35.00 60.00
195 Phil Cavarretta 20.00 40.00
196 Doyle Lade 7.50 15.00
197 Johnny Wyrostek 7.50 15.00
198 Danny Litwhiler 7.50 15.00
199 Jack Kramer 7.50 15.00
200 Kirby Higbe 12.50 25.00
201 Pete Castiglione RC 7.50 15.00
202 Cliff Chambers RC 7.50 15.00
203 Danny Murtaugh 12.50 25.00
204 Granny Hamner RC 20.00 40.00
205 Mike Goliat RC 7.50 15.00
206 Stan Lopata 12.50 25.00
207 Max Lanier RC 7.50 15.00
208 Jim Hearn 7.50 15.00
209 Johnny Lindell 7.50 15.00
210 Ted Gray 7.50 15.00
211 Charlie Keller 20.00 40.00
212 Jerry Priddy 7.50 15.00
213 Carl Scheib 7.50 15.00
214 Dick Fowler 7.50 15.00
215 Ed Lopat 35.00 60.00
216 Bob Porterfield 12.50 25.00
217 Casey Stengel MG 75.00 125.00
218 Cliff Mapes RC 12.50 25.00
219 Hank Bauer RC 60.00 100.00
220 Leo Durocher MG 35.00 60.00
221 Don Mueller RC 20.00 40.00
222 Bobby Morgan RC 7.50 15.00
223 Jim Russell 7.50 15.00
224 Jack Banta RC 7.50 15.00
225 Eddie Sawyer MG RC 12.50 25.00
226 Jim Konstanty RC 35.00 60.00
227 Bob Miller RC 12.50 25.00
228 Bill Nicholson 12.50 25.00
229 Frankie Frisch MG 35.00 60.00
230 Bill Serena RC 7.50 15.00
231 Preston Ward RC 7.50 15.00
232 Al Rosen RC 35.00 60.00
233 Allie Clark 7.50 15.00
234 Bobby Shantz RC 35.00 60.00
235 Harold Gilbert RC 7.50 15.00
236 Bob Cain RC 7.50 15.00
237 Bill Salkeld 7.50 15.00
238 Nippy Jones RC 7.50 15.00
239 Bill Howerton RC 7.50 15.00
240 Eddie Lake 7.50 15.00
241 Neil Berry RC 7.50 15.00
242 Dick Kryhoski 7.50 15.00
243 Johnny Groth RC 7.50 15.00
244 Dale Coogan RC 7.50 15.00
245 Al Papai RC 7.50 15.00
246 Walt Dropo RC 20.00 40.00
247 Irv Noren RC 12.50 25.00
248 Sam Jethroe RC 35.00 60.00
249 Snuffy Stirnweiss 12.50 25.00
250 Ray Coleman RC 7.50 15.00
251 Les Moss RC 7.50 15.00
252 Billy DeMars RC 35.00 60.00

1951 Bowman

The cards in this 324-card set measure approximately 2 1/16" by 3 1/8". Many of the obverses of the cards appearing in the 1951 Bowman set are enlargements of those appearing in the previous year. The high number series (253-324) is highly valued and contains the true "Rookie" cards of Mickey Mantle and Willie Mays. Card number 195 depicts Paul Richards in caricature. George Kell's card (number 46) incorrectly lists him as being in the "1941" Bowman series. Cards were issued either in one card penny packs which came 120 to a box or in six-card nickel packs which came 24 to a box. Player names are found printed in a panel on the front of the card. These cards were supposedly also sold in sheets in variety stores in the Philadelphia area.

COMPLETE SET (324) 15000.00 20000.00
COMMON CARD (1-252) 10.00 20.00
COMMON (253-324) 30.00 50.00
WRAPPER (1-cent) 150.00 200.00
WRAPPER (5-cent) 200.00 250.00
1 Whitey Ford RC 1500.00 2500.00
2 Yogi Berra 250.00 400.00
3 Robin Roberts 60.00 100.00
4 Del Ennis 12.50 25.00
5 Dale Mitchell 12.50 25.00
6 Don Newcombe 35.00 60.00
7 Gil Hodges 75.00 125.00
8 Paul Lehner 10.00 20.00
9 Sam Chapman 10.00 20.00
10 Red Schoendienst 35.00 60.00
11 George Munger 10.00 20.00
12 Hank Majeski 10.00 20.00
13 Eddie Stanky 12.50 25.00
14 Alvin Dark 20.00 40.00
15 Johnny Pesky 12.50 25.00
16 Maurice McDermott 10.00 20.00
17 Pete Castiglione 10.00 20.00
18 Gil Coan 10.00 20.00
19 Sid Gordon 10.00 20.00
20 Del Crandall UER 12.50 25.00
(Misspelled Crandell on card)
21 Snuffy Stirnweiss 12.50 25.00
wearing St.L.Browns hat
22 Hank Sauer 12.50 25.00
23 Hoot Evers 10.00 20.00
24 Ewell Blackwell 20.00 40.00
25 Vic Raschi 35.00 60.00
26 Phil Rizzuto 90.00 150.00
27 Jim Konstanty 12.50 25.00
28 Eddie Waitkus 10.00 20.00
29 Allie Clark 10.00 20.00
30 Bob Feller 75.00 125.00
31 Roy Campanella 175.00 300.00
32 Duke Snider 150.00 250.00
33 Bob Hooper RC 10.00 20.00
34 Marty Marion 20.00 40.00
35 Al Zarilla 10.00 20.00
36 Joe Dobson 10.00 20.00
37 Whitey Lockman 20.00 40.00
38 Al Evans 10.00 20.00
39 Ray Scarborough 10.00 20.00
40 Gus Bell RC 35.00 60.00
41 Eddie Yost 12.50 25.00
42 Vern Bickford 10.00 20.00
43 Billy DeMars 10.00 20.00
44 Roy Smalley 10.00 20.00
45 Art Houtteman 10.00 20.00
46 George Kell 1941 UER 35.00 60.00
47 Grady Hatton 10.00 20.00
48 Ken Raffensberger 10.00 20.00
49 Jerry Coleman 12.50 25.00
50 Johnny Mize 50.00 80.00
51 Andy Seminick 10.00 20.00
52 Dick Sisler 20.00 40.00
53 Bob Lemon 35.00 60.00
54 Ray Boone RC 20.00 40.00
55 Gene Hermanski 10.00 20.00
56 Ralph Branca 35.00 60.00
57 Alex Kellner 10.00 20.00
58 Enos Slaughter 35.00 60.00
59 Randy Gumpert 10.00 20.00
60 Chico Carrasquel RC 35.00 60.00
61 Jim Hearn 12.50 25.00
62 Lou Boudreau MG 35.00 60.00
63 Bob Dillinger 10.00 20.00
64 Bill Werle 10.00 20.00
65 Mickey Vernon 20.00 40.00
66 Bob Elliott 12.50 25.00
67 Roy Sievers 12.50 25.00
68 Dick Kokos 10.00 20.00
69 Johnny Schmitz 10.00 20.00
70 Ron Northey 10.00 20.00
71 Jerry Priddy 10.00 20.00
72 Lloyd Merriman 10.00 20.00
73 Tommy Byrne RC 10.00 20.00
74 Billy Johnson 12.50 25.00
75 Russ Meyer RC 12.50 25.00
76 Stan Lopata 12.50 25.00
77 Mike Goliat 10.00 20.00
78 Early Wynn 35.00 60.00
79 Jim Hegan 12.50 25.00
80 Pee Wee Reese 125.00 200.00
81 Carl Furillo 35.00 60.00
82 Joe Tipton 10.00 20.00
83 Carl Scheib 10.00 20.00
84 Barney McCosky 10.00 20.00
85 Eddie Kazak 10.00 20.00
86 Harry Brecheen 12.50 25.00
87 Floyd Baker 10.00 20.00
88 Eddie Robinson 10.00 20.00
89 Hank Thompson 12.50 25.00
90 Dave Koslo 10.00 20.00
91 Clyde Vollmer 10.00 20.00
92 Vern Stephens 12.50 25.00
93 Danny O'Connell RC 10.00 20.00
94 Clyde McCullough 10.00 20.00
95 Sherry Robertson 10.00 20.00
96 Sandy Consuegra RC 10.00 20.00
97 Bob Kuzava 10.00 20.00
98 Willard Marshall 10.00 20.00
99 Earl Torgeson 10.00 20.00
100 Sherm Lollar 12.50 25.00
101 Owen Friend 10.00 20.00
102 Dutch Leonard 10.00 20.00
103 Andy Pafko 20.00 40.00
104 Virgil Trucks 12.50 25.00
105 Don Kolloway 10.00 20.00
106 Pat Mullin 10.00 20.00
107 Johnny Wyrostek 10.00 20.00
108 Virgil Stallcup 10.00 20.00
109 Allie Reynolds 35.00 60.00
110 Bobby Brown 20.00 40.00
111 Curt Simmons 12.50 25.00
112 Willie Jones 10.00 20.00
113 Bill Nicholson 10.00 20.00
114 Sam Zoldak 10.00 20.00
Pictured in Indians uniform
115 Steve Gromek 10.00 20.00
116 Bruce Edwards 10.00 20.00
117 Eddie Miksis RC 10.00 20.00
118 Preacher Roe 35.00 60.00
119 Eddie Joost 10.00 20.00
120 Joe Coleman 12.50 25.00
121 Gerry Staley RC 10.00 20.00
122 Joe Garagiola RC 60.00 100.00
123 Howie Judson 10.00 20.00
124 Gus Niarhos 10.00 20.00
125 Bill Rigney 12.50 25.00
126 Bobby Thomson 35.00 60.00
127 Sal Maglie RC 35.00 60.00
128 Ellis Kinder 10.00 20.00
129 Matt Batts 10.00 20.00
130 Tom Saffell RC 10.00 20.00
131 Cliff Chambers 10.00 20.00
132 Cass Michaels 10.00 20.00
133 Sam Dente 10.00 20.00
134 Warren Spahn 90.00 150.00
135 Walker Cooper 10.00 20.00
136 Ray Coleman 10.00 20.00
137 Dick Starr 10.00 20.00
138 Phil Cavarretta 12.50 25.00
139 Doyle Lade 10.00 20.00
140 Eddie Lake 10.00 20.00
141 Fred Hutchinson 12.50 25.00
142 Aaron Robinson 10.00 20.00
143 Ted Kluszewski 50.00 80.00
144 Herman Wehmeier 10.00 20.00
145 Fred Sanford 12.50 25.00
146 Johnny Hopp 12.50 25.00
147 Ken Heintzelman 10.00 20.00
148 Granny Hamner 10.00 20.00
149 Bubba Church RC 10.00 20.00
150 Mike Garcia 12.50 25.00
151 Larry Doby 35.00 60.00
152 Cal Abrams RC 10.00 20.00
153 Rex Barney 12.50 25.00
154 Pete Suder 10.00 20.00
155 Lou Brissie 10.00 20.00
156 Del Rice 10.00 20.00
157 Al Brazle 10.00 20.00
158 Chuck Diering 10.00 20.00
159 Eddie Stewart 10.00 20.00
160 Phil Masi 10.00 20.00
161 Wes Westrum RC 10.00 20.00
162 Larry Jansen 12.50 25.00
163 Monte Kennedy 10.00 20.00
164 Bill Wight 10.00 20.00
165 Ted Williams UER 500.00 800.00
Wrong birthdate
166 Stan Rojek 10.00 20.00
Pictured in Pirates uniform
167 Murry Dickson 10.00 20.00
168 Sam Mele 10.00 20.00
169 Sid Hudson 10.00 20.00
170 Sibby Sisti 10.00 20.00
171 Buddy Kerr 10.00 20.00
172 Ned Garver 10.00 20.00
173 Hank Arft 10.00 20.00
174 Mickey Owen 12.50 25.00
175 Wayne Terwilliger 10.00 20.00
176 Vic Wertz 20.00 40.00
177 Charlie Keller 12.50 25.00
178 Ted Gray 10.00 20.00
179 Danny Litwhiler 10.00 20.00
180 Howie Fox 10.00 20.00
181 Casey Stengel MG 50.00 80.00
182 Tom Ferrick RC 10.00 20.00
183 Hank Bauer 35.00 60.00
184 Eddie Sawyer MG 20.00 40.00
185 Jimmy Bloodworth 10.00 20.00
186 Richie Ashburn 60.00 100.00
187 Al Rosen 20.00 40.00
188 Bobby Avila RC 12.50 25.00
189 Erv Palica RC 10.00 20.00
190 Joe Hatten 10.00 20.00
191 Billy Hitchcock RC 10.00 20.00
192 Hank Wyse RC 10.00 20.00
193 Ted Wilks 10.00 20.00
194 Peanuts Lowrey 10.00 20.00
195 Paul Richards MG 12.50 25.00
(Caricature)
196 Billy Pierce RC 35.00 60.00
197 Bob Cain 10.00 20.00
198 Monte Irvin RC 75.00 125.00
199 Sheldon Jones 10.00 20.00
200 Jack Kramer 10.00 20.00
Pictured in NY Giants uniform
201 Steve O'Neill MG RC 10.00 20.00
202 Mike Guerra 10.00 20.00
203 Vernon Law RC 35.00 60.00
204 Vic Lombardi RC 10.00 20.00
205 Mickey Grasso RC 10.00 20.00
206 Conrado Marrero RC 10.00 20.00
207 Billy Southworth MG RC 10.00 20.00
208 Blix Donnelly 10.00 20.00
209 Ken Wood 10.00 20.00
210 Les Moss 10.00 20.00
Pictured in St.L.Browns uniform
211 Hal Jeffcoat RC 10.00 20.00
212 Bob Rush 10.00 20.00
213 Neil Berry 10.00 20.00
214 Bob Swift 10.00 20.00
215 Ken Peterson 10.00 20.00
216 Connie Ryan RC 10.00 20.00
217 Joe Page 12.50 25.00
218 Ed Lopat 35.00 60.00
219 Gene Woodling RC 35.00 60.00
220 Bob Miller 10.00 20.00
221 Dick Whitman RC 10.00 20.00
222 Thurman Tucker RC 10.00 20.00
223 Johnny VanderMeer 20.00 40.00
224 Billy Cox 20.00 40.00
225 Dan Bankhead RC 20.00 40.00
226 Jimmy Dykes MG 10.00 20.00
227 Bobby Shantz UER 12.50 25.00
Sic, Schantz
228 Cloyd Boyer RC 12.50 25.00
229 Bill Howerton 10.00 20.00
Pictured in St.L.Cardinals uniform
230 Max Lanier 10.00 20.00
231 Luis Aloma RC 10.00 20.00
232 Nelson Fox RC 150.00 250.00
233 Leo Durocher MG 35.00 60.00
234 Clint Hartung 12.50 25.00
235 Jack Lohrke 10.00 20.00
236 Buddy Rosar 10.00 20.00
237 Billy Goodman 12.50 25.00
238 Pete Reiser 20.00 40.00
239 Bill MacDonald RC 10.00 20.00
240 Joe Haynes 10.00 20.00
241 Irv Noren 12.50 25.00

242 Sam Jethroe 12.50 25.00
243 Johnny Antonelli 12.50 25.00
244 Cliff Fannin 10.00 20.00
245 John Berardino RC 35.00 60.00
246 Bill Serena 10.00 20.00
247 Bob Ramazzotti RC 10.00 20.00
248 Johnny Klippstein RC 10.00 20.00
249 Johnny Groth 10.00 20.00
250 Hank Borowy 10.00 20.00
251 Willard Ramsdell RC 10.00 20.00
252 Dixie Howell RC 10.00 20.00
253 Mickey Mantle RC 5000.00 8000.00
254 Jackie Jensen RC 60.00 100.00
255 Milo Candini RC 30.00 50.00
256 Ken Silvestri RC 30.00 50.00
257 Birdie Tebbetts RC 35.00 60.00
258 Luke Easter RC 35.00 60.00
259 Chuck Dressen MG 35.00 60.00
260 Carl Erskine RC 60.00 100.00
261 Wally Moses 35.00 60.00
262 Gus Zernial 35.00 60.00
263 Howie Pollet 35.00 60.00
Pictured in Cardinals uniform
264 Don Richmond RC 30.00 50.00
265 Steve Bilko RC 30.00 50.00
266 Harry Dorish RC 30.00 50.00
267 Ken Holcombe RC 30.00 50.00
268 Don Mueller 35.00 60.00
269 Ray Noble RC 30.00 50.00
270 Willard Nixon RC 30.00 50.00
271 Tommy Wright RC 30.00 50.00
272 Billy Meyer MG RC 30.00 50.00
273 Danny Murtaugh 35.00 60.00
274 George Metkovich RC 30.00 50.00
275 Bucky Harris MG 50.00 80.00
276 Frank Quinn RC 30.00 50.00
277 Roy Hartsfield RC 30.00 50.00
278 Norman Roy RC 30.00 50.00
279 Jim Delsing RC 30.00 50.00
280 Howie Pollet 30.00 50.00
Pictured in Cardinals uniform
281 Al Widmar RC 30.00 50.00
282 Frank Frisch MG 60.00 100.00
283 Walt Dubiel RC 30.00 50.00
284 Gene Bearden 35.00 60.00
285 Johnny Lipon RC 30.00 50.00
286 Bob Usher RC 30.00 50.00
287 Jim Blackburn 30.00 50.00
288 Bobby Adams 30.00 50.00
289 Cliff Mapes 35.00 60.00
290 Bill Dickey CO 90.00 150.00
291 Tommy Henrich CO 50.00 80.00
292 Eddie Pellagrini 30.00 50.00
293 Ken Johnson RC 30.00 50.00
294 Jocko Thompson 30.00 50.00
295 Al Lopez MG RC 75.00 125.00
296 Bob Kennedy RC 35.00 60.00
297 Dave Philley 30.00 50.00
298 Joe Astroth RC 30.00 50.00
299 Clyde King RC 30.00 50.00
300 Hal Rice RC 30.00 50.00
301 Tommy Glaviano RC 30.00 50.00
302 Jim Busby RC 30.00 50.00
303 Marv Rotblatt RC 30.00 50.00
304 Al Gettell RC 30.00 50.00
305 Willie Mays RC 1800.00 2500.00
306 Jim Piersall RC 75.00 125.00
307 Walt Masterson 30.00 50.00
308 Ted Beard RC 30.00 50.00
309 Mel Queen RC 30.00 50.00
310 Erv Dusak RC 30.00 50.00
311 Mickey Harris 30.00 50.00
312 Gene Mauch RC 35.00 60.00
313 Ray Mueller RC 30.00 50.00
314 Johnny Sain 50.00 80.00
315 Zack Taylor MG 30.00 50.00
316 Duane Pillette RC 30.00 50.00
317 Smoky Burgess RC 50.00 80.00
318 Warren Hacker RC 30.00 50.00
319 Red Rolfe MG 35.00 60.00
320 Hal White RC 30.00 50.00
321 Earl Johnson 30.00 50.00
322 Luke Sewell MG 35.00 60.00
323 Joe Adcock RC 50.00 80.00
324 Johnny Pramesa RC 75.00 125.00

1952 Bowman

The cards in this 252-card set measure approximately 2 1/16" by 3 1/8". While the Bowman set of 1952 retained the card size introduced in 1951, it employed a modification of color tones from the two preceding years. The cards also appeared with a facsimile autograph on the front and, for the first time since 1949, premium advertising on the back. The 1952 set was apparently sold in sheets as well as in gum packs. Artwork for 15 cards that were never issued was discovered in the early 1980s. Cards were issued in one card penny packs or five card nickel packs. The five cent packs came 24 to a box. Notable Rookie Cards in this set are Lew Burdette, Gil McDougald, and Minnie Minoso.

COMPLETE SET (252) 5500.00 8500.00
COMMON CARD (1-216) 7.50 15.00
COMMON (217-252) 35.00 60.00
WRAPPER (1-cent) 150.00 200.00
WRAPPER (5-cent) 75.00 100.00
1 Yogi Berra 350.00 600.00
2 Bobby Thomson 20.00 40.00
3 Fred Hutchinson 12.50 25.00
4 Robin Roberts 50.00 80.00
5 Minnie Minoso RC 75.00 125.00
6 Virgil Stallcup 7.50 15.00
7 Mike Garcia 12.50 25.00
8 Pee Wee Reese 90.00 150.00
9 Vern Stephens 12.50 25.00
10 Bob Hooper 7.50 15.00
11 Ralph Kiner 35.00 60.00
12 Max Surkont RC 7.50 15.00
13 Cliff Mapes 7.50 15.00
14 Cliff Chambers 7.50 15.00
15 Sam Mele 7.50 15.00
16 Turk Lown RC 7.50 15.00
17 Ed Lopat 20.00 40.00
18 Don Mueller 12.50 25.00
19 Bob Cain 7.50 15.00
20 Willie Jones 7.50 15.00
21 Nellie Fox 60.00 100.00
22 Willard Ramsdell 7.50 15.00
23 Bob Lemon 35.00 60.00
24 Carl Furillo 20.00 40.00
25 Mickey McDermott 7.50 15.00
26 Eddie Joost 7.50 15.00
27 Joe Garagiola 20.00 40.00
28 Roy Hartsfield 7.50 15.00
29 Ned Garver 7.50 15.00
30 Red Schoendienst 35.00 60.00
31 Eddie Yost 12.50 25.00
32 Eddie Miksis 7.50 15.00
33 Gil McDougald RC 50.00 80.00
34 Alvin Dark 12.50 25.00
35 Granny Hamner 7.50 15.00
36 Cass Michaels 7.50 15.00
37 Vic Raschi 12.50 25.00
38 Whitey Lockman 12.50 25.00
39 Vic Wertz 12.50 25.00
40 Bubba Church 7.50 15.00
41 Chico Carrasquel 12.50 25.00
42 Johnny Wyrostek 7.50 15.00
43 Bob Feller 90.00 150.00
44 Roy Campanella 150.00 250.00
45 Johnny Pesky 12.50 25.00
46 Carl Scheib 7.50 15.00
47 Pete Castiglione 7.50 15.00
48 Vern Bickford 7.50 15.00
49 Jim Hearn 7.50 15.00
50 Gerry Staley 7.50 15.00
51 Gil Coan 7.50 15.00
52 Phil Rizzuto 90.00 150.00
53 Richie Ashburn 75.00 125.00
54 Billy Pierce 12.50 25.00
55 Ken Raffensberger 7.50 15.00
56 Clyde King 12.50 25.00
57 Clyde Vollmer 7.50 15.00
58 Hank Majeski 7.50 15.00
59 Murry Dickson 7.50 15.00
60 Sid Gordon 7.50 15.00
61 Tommy Byrne 7.50 15.00
62 Joe Presko RC 7.50 15.00
63 Irv Noren 7.50 15.00
64 Roy Smalley 7.50 15.00
65 Hank Bauer 20.00 40.00
66 Sal Maglie 12.50 25.00
67 Johnny Groth 7.50 15.00
68 Jim Busby 7.50 15.00
69 Joe Adcock 12.50 25.00
70 Carl Erskine 20.00 40.00
71 Vernon Law 12.50 25.00
72 Earl Torgeson 7.50 15.00
73 Jerry Coleman 12.50 25.00
74 Wes Westrum 12.50 25.00
75 George Kell 35.00 60.00
76 Del Ennis 12.50 25.00
77 Eddie Robinson 7.50 15.00
78 Lloyd Merriman 7.50 15.00
79 Lou Brissie 7.50 15.00
80 Gil Hodges 60.00 100.00
81 Billy Goodman 12.50 25.00
82 Gus Zernial 12.50 25.00
83 Howie Pollet 7.50 15.00
84 Sam Jethroe 12.50 25.00
85 Marty Marion CO 12.50 25.00
86 Cal Abrams 7.50 15.00
87 Mickey Vernon 12.50 25.00
88 Bruce Edwards 7.50 15.00
89 Billy Hitchcock 7.50 15.00
90 Larry Jansen 12.50 25.00
91 Don Kolloway 7.50 15.00
92 Eddie Waitkus 12.50 25.00
93 Paul Richards MG 12.50 25.00
94 Luke Sewell MG 12.50 25.00
95 Luke Easter 12.50 25.00
96 Ralph Branca 12.50 25.00
97 Willard Marshall 7.50 15.00
98 Jimmy Dykes MG 12.50 25.00
99 Clyde McCullough 7.50 15.00
100 Sibby Sisti 7.50 15.00
101 Mickey Mantle 1500.00 2500.00
102 Peanuts Lowrey 7.50 15.00
103 Joe Haynes 7.50 15.00
104 Hal Jeffcoat 7.50 15.00
105 Bobby Brown 12.50 25.00
106 Randy Gumpert 7.50 15.00
107 Del Rice 7.50 15.00
108 George Metkovich 7.50 15.00
109 Tom Morgan RC 7.50 15.00
110 Max Lanier 7.50 15.00
111 Hoot Evers 7.50 15.00
112 Smoky Burgess 12.50 25.00
113 Al Zarilla 7.50 15.00
114 Frank Hiller RC 7.50 15.00
115 Larry Doby 35.00 60.00
116 Duke Snider 125.00 200.00
117 Bill Wight 7.50 15.00
118 Ray Murray RC 7.50 15.00
119 Bill Howerton 7.50 15.00
120 Chet Nichols RC 7.50 15.00
121 Al Corwin RC 7.50 15.00
122 Billy Johnson 7.50 15.00
123 Sid Hudson 7.50 15.00
124 Birdie Tebbetts 7.50 15.00
125 Howie Fox 7.50 15.00
126 Phil Cavarretta 12.50 25.00
127 Dick Sisler 7.50 15.00
128 Don Newcombe 35.00 60.00
129 Gus Niarhos 7.50 15.00
130 Allie Clark 7.50 15.00
131 Bob Swift 7.50 15.00
132 Dave Cole RC 7.50 15.00
133 Dick Kryhoski 7.50 15.00
134 Al Brazle 7.50 15.00
135 Mickey Harris 7.50 15.00
136 Gene Hermanski 7.50 15.00
137 Stan Rojek 7.50 15.00
138 Ted Wilks 7.50 15.00
139 Jerry Priddy 7.50 15.00
140 Ray Scarborough 7.50 15.00
141 Hank Edwards 7.50 15.00
142 Early Wynn 35.00 60.00
143 Sandy Consuegra 7.50 15.00
144 Joe Hatton 7.50 15.00
145 Johnny Mize 35.00 60.00
146 Leo Durocher MG 35.00 60.00
147 Marlin Stuart RC 7.50 15.00
148 Ken Heintzelman 7.50 15.00
149 Howie Judson 7.50 15.00
150 Herman Wehmeier 7.50 15.00
151 Al Rosen 12.50 25.00
152 Billy Cox 7.50 15.00
153 Fred Hatfield RC 7.50 15.00
154 Ferris Fain 12.50 25.00
155 Billy Meyer MG 7.50 15.00
156 Warren Spahn 75.00 125.00
157 Jim Delsing 7.50 15.00
158 Bucky Harris MG 20.00 40.00
159 Dutch Leonard 7.50 15.00
160 Eddie Stanky 12.50 25.00
161 Jackie Jensen 20.00 40.00
162 Monte Irvin 35.00 60.00
163 Johnny Lipon 7.50 15.00
164 Connie Ryan 7.50 15.00
165 Saul Rogovin RC 7.50 15.00
166 Bobby Adams 7.50 15.00
167 Bobby Avila 12.50 25.00
168 Preacher Roe 12.50 25.00
169 Walt Dropo 12.50 25.00
170 Joe Astroth 7.50 15.00
171 Mel Queen 7.50 15.00
172 Ebba St.Claire RC 7.50 15.00
173 Gene Bearden 7.50 15.00
174 Mickey Grasso 7.50 15.00
175 Randy Jackson RC 7.50 15.00
176 Harry Brecheen 12.50 25.00
177 Gene Woodling 12.50 25.00
178 Dave Williams RC 12.50 25.00
179 Pete Suder 7.50 15.00
180 Ed Fitzgerald 7.50 15.00
181 Joe Collins RC 12.50 25.00
182 Dave Koslo 7.50 15.00
183 Pat Mullin 7.50 15.00
184 Curt Simmons 12.50 25.00
185 Eddie Stewart 7.50 15.00
186 Frank Smith RC 7.50 15.00
187 Jim Hegan 12.50 25.00
188 Chuck Dressen MG 12.50 25.00
189 Jimmy Piersall 12.50 25.00
190 Dick Fowler 7.50 15.00
191 Bob Friend RC 20.00 40.00
192 John Cusick RC 7.50 15.00
193 Bobby Young RC 7.50 15.00
194 Bob Porterfield 7.50 15.00
195 Frank Baumholtz 7.50 15.00
196 Stan Musial 300.00 500.00
197 Charlie Silvera RC 7.50 15.00
198 Chuck Diering 7.50 15.00
199 Ted Gray 7.50 15.00
200 Ken Silvestri 7.50 15.00
201 Ray Coleman 7.50 15.00
202 Harry Perkowski RC 7.50 15.00
203 Steve Gromek 7.50 15.00
204 Andy Pafko 12.50 25.00
205 Walt Masterson 7.50 15.00
206 Elmer Valo 7.50 15.00
207 George Strickland RC 7.50 15.00
208 Walker Cooper 7.50 15.00
209 Dick Littlefield RC 7.50 15.00
210 Archie Wilson RC 7.50 15.00
211 Paul Minner RC 7.50 15.00
212 Solly Hemus RC 7.50 15.00
213 Monte Kennedy 7.50 15.00
214 Ray Boone 7.50 15.00
215 Sheldon Jones 7.50 15.00
216 Matt Batts 7.50 15.00
217 Casey Stengel MG 90.00 150.00
218 Willie Mays 900.00 1500.00
219 Neil Berry 35.00 60.00
220 Russ Meyer 35.00 60.00
221 Lou Kretlow RC 35.00 60.00
222 Dixie Howell 35.00 60.00
223 Harry Simpson RC 35.00 60.00
224 Johnny Schmitz 35.00 60.00
225 Del Wilber RC 35.00 60.00
226 Alex Kellner 35.00 60.00
227 Clyde Sukeforth CO RC 35.00 60.00
228 Bob Chipman 35.00 60.00
229 Hank Arft 35.00 60.00
230 Frank Shea 35.00 60.00
231 Dee Fondy RC 35.00 60.00
232 Enos Slaughter 60.00 100.00
233 Bob Kuzava 35.00 60.00
234 Fred Fitzsimmons CO 35.00 60.00
235 Steve Souchock RC 35.00 60.00
236 Tommy Brown 35.00 60.00
237 Sherm Lollar 35.00 60.00
238 Roy McMillan RC 35.00 60.00
239 Dale Mitchell 35.00 60.00
240 Billy Loes RC 35.00 60.00
241 Mel Parnell 35.00 60.00
242 Everett Kell RC 35.00 60.00
243 George Munger 35.00 60.00
244 Lew Burdette RC 50.00 80.00
245 George Schmees RC 35.00 60.00
246 Jerry Snyder RC 35.00 60.00
247 Johnny Pramesa 35.00 60.00
248 Bill Werle 35.00 60.00
Full name in signature
248A Bill Werle 35.00 60.00
Signature on front has no W
249 Hank Thompson 35.00 60.00
250 Ike Delock RC 35.00 60.00
251 Jack Lohrke 35.00 60.00
252 Frank Crosetti CO 75.00 125.00

1953 Bowman Black and White

The cards in this 64-card set measure approximately 2 1/2" by 3 3/4". Some collectors believe that the high cost of producing the 1953 color series forced Bowman to issue this set in black and white, since the two sets are identical in design except for the element of color. This set was also produced in fewer numbers than its color counterpart, and is popular among collectors for the challenge involved in completing it and the lack of short prints. Cards were issued in one-card penny packs which came 120 to a box and five-card nickel packs. There are no key Rookie Cards in this set. Recently, a variation of the Hal Bevan card (number 43) was discovered, that card exists with him being born in either 1930 or 1950. The 1950 version is much more difficult.

COMPLETE SET (64) 2000.00 3000.00
WRAPPER (1-CENT) 300.00 350.00
1 Gus Bell 75.00 125.00
2 Willard Nixon 25.00 40.00
3 Bill Rigney 25.00 40.00
4 Pat Mullin 25.00 40.00
5 Dee Fondy 25.00 40.00
6 Ray Murray 25.00 40.00
7 Andy Seminick 25.00 40.00
8 Pete Suder 25.00 40.00
9 Walt Masterson 25.00 40.00
10 Dick Sisler 35.00 60.00
11 Dick Gernert 25.00 40.00
12 Randy Jackson 25.00 40.00
13 Joe Tipton 25.00 40.00
14 Bill Nicholson 35.00 60.00
15 Johnny Mize 75.00 125.00
16 Stu Miller RC 35.00 60.00
17 Virgil Trucks 35.00 60.00
18 Billy Hoeft 25.00 40.00
19 Paul LaPalme 25.00 40.00
20 Eddie Robinson 25.00 40.00
21 Clarence Podbielan 25.00 40.00
22 Matt Batts 25.00 40.00
23 Wilmer Mizell 35.00 60.00
24 Del Wilber 25.00 40.00
25 Johnny Sain 50.00 80.00
26 Preacher Roe 50.00 80.00
27 Bob Lemon 100.00 175.00
28 Hoyt Wilhelm 75.00 125.00
29 Sid Hudson 25.00 40.00
30 Walker Cooper 25.00 40.00
31 Gene Woodling 50.00 80.00
32 Rocky Bridges 25.00 40.00
33 Bob Kuzava 25.00 40.00
34 Ebba St.Claire 25.00 40.00
35 Johnny Wyrostek 25.00 40.00
36 Jimmy Piersall 50.00 80.00
37 Hal Jeffcoat 25.00 40.00
38 Dave Cole 25.00 40.00
39 Casey Stengel MG 200.00 350.00
40 Larry Jansen 35.00 60.00
41 Bob Ramazzotti 25.00 40.00
42 Howie Judson 25.00 40.00
43 Hal Bevan ERR RC 25.00 40.00
Born in 1950
43A Hal Bevan COR 25.00 40.00
Born in 1930
44 Jim Delsing 25.00 40.00
45 Irv Noren 35.00 60.00
46 Bucky Harris MG 50.00 80.00
47 Jack Lohrke 25.00 40.00
48 Steve Ridzik RC 25.00 40.00
49 Floyd Baker 25.00 40.00
50 Dutch Leonard 25.00 40.00
51 Lou Burdette 50.00 80.00
52 Ralph Branca 50.00 80.00
53 Morrie Martin 25.00 40.00
54 Bill Miller 25.00 40.00
55 Don Johnson 25.00 40.00
56 Roy Smalley 25.00 40.00
57 Andy Pafko 35.00 60.00
58 Jim Konstanty 35.00 60.00
59 Duane Pillette 25.00 40.00
60 Billy Cox 50.00 80.00
61 Tom Gorman RC 25.00 40.00
62 Keith Thomas RC 25.00 40.00
63 Steve Gromek 25.00 40.00
64 Andy Hansen 50.00 80.00

1953 Bowman Color

The cards in this 160-card set measure approximately 2 1/2" by 3 3/4". The 1953 Bowman Color set, considered by many to be the best looking set of the modern era, contains Kodachrome photographs with no names or facsimile autographs on the face. Cards were issued in five-card nickel packs in a 24 pack box with each pack having gum in it. The entire low number run were also printed in three card strips; it is believed that these three card strips in numerical order were box toppers to retailers. The box features an endorsement from Joe DiMaggio. Numbers 113 to 160 are somewhat more difficult to obtain, with numbers 113 to 128 being the most difficult. There are two cards of Al Corwin (126 and 149). There are no key Rookie Cards in this set.

COMPLETE SET (160) 9000.00 15000.00
COMMON CARD (1-112) 20.00 40.00
COMMON (113-128) 50.00 80.00
COMMON (129-160) 45.00 75.00
WRAPPER (1-cent) 300.00 400.00
WRAPPER (5-CENT) 250.00 300.00
1 Dave Williams 100.00 175.00
2 Vic Wertz 30.00 50.00
3 Sam Jethroe 30.00 50.00
4 Art Houtteman 20.00 40.00
5 Sid Gordon 20.00 40.00
6 Joe Ginsberg 20.00 40.00
7 Harry Chiti RC 20.00 40.00
8 Al Rosen 30.00 50.00
9 Phil Rizzuto 150.00 225.00
10 Richie Ashburn 90.00 150.00
11 Bobby Shantz 30.00 50.00
12 Carl Erskine 35.00 60.00
13 Gus Zernial 30.00 50.00
14 Billy Loes 30.00 50.00
15 Jim Busby 20.00 40.00
16 Bob Friend 30.00 50.00
17 Gerry Staley 20.00 40.00
18 Nellie Fox 90.00 150.00
19 Alvin Dark 30.00 50.00
20 Don Lenhardt 20.00 40.00
21 Joe Garagiola 35.00 60.00
22 Bob Porterfield 20.00 40.00
23 Herman Wehmeier 20.00 40.00
24 Jackie Jensen 35.00 60.00
25 Hoot Evers 20.00 40.00
26 Roy McMillan 30.00 50.00
27 Vic Raschi 35.00 60.00
28 Smoky Burgess 30.00 50.00
29 Bobby Avila 30.00 50.00
30 Phil Cavarretta 30.00 50.00
31 Jimmy Dykes MG 30.00 50.00
32 Stan Musial 350.00 600.00
33 Pee Wee Reese 500.00 1000.00
34 Gil Coan 20.00 40.00
35 Maurice McDermott 20.00 40.00
36 Minnie Minoso 50.00 80.00
37 Jim Wilson 20.00 40.00
38 Harry Byrd RC 20.00 40.00
39 Paul Richards MG 30.00 50.00
40 Larry Doby 60.00 100.00
41 Sammy White 20.00 40.00
42 Tommy Brown 20.00 40.00
43 Mike Garcia 30.00 50.00
44 Yogi Berra 500.00 800.00
Hank Bauer
Mickey Mantle
45 Walt Dropo 30.00 50.00
46 Roy Campanella 200.00 350.00
47 Ned Garver 20.00 40.00
48 Hank Sauer 30.00 50.00
49 Eddie Stanky MG 30.00 50.00
50 Lou Kretlow 20.00 40.00
51 Monte Irvin 50.00 80.00
52 Marty Marion MG 30.00 50.00
53 Del Rice 20.00 40.00
54 Chico Carrasquel 20.00 40.00
55 Leo Durocher MG 50.00 80.00
56 Bob Cain 20.00 40.00
57 Lou Boudreau MG 50.00 80.00
58 Willard Marshall 20.00 40.00
59 Mickey Mantle 1200.00 2000.00
60 Granny Hamner 20.00 40.00
61 George Kell 50.00 80.00
62 Ted Kluszewski 60.00 100.00
63 Gil McDougald 50.00 80.00
64 Curt Simmons 30.00 50.00
65 Robin Roberts 75.00 125.00
66 Mel Parnell 30.00 50.00
67 Mel Clark RC 20.00 40.00
68 Allie Reynolds 35.00 60.00
69 Charlie Grimm MG 30.00 50.00
70 Clint Courtney RC 20.00 40.00
71 Paul Minner 20.00 40.00
72 Ted Gray 20.00 40.00
73 Billy Pierce 30.00 50.00
74 Don Mueller 30.00 50.00
75 Saul Rogovin 20.00 40.00
76 Jim Hearn 20.00 40.00
77 Mickey Grasso 20.00 40.00
78 Carl Furillo 35.00 60.00
79 Ray Boone 30.00 50.00
80 Ralph Kiner 60.00 100.00
81 Enos Slaughter 60.00 100.00
82 Joe Astroth 20.00 40.00
83 Jack Daniels RC 20.00 40.00
84 Hank Bauer 35.00 60.00
85 Solly Hemus 20.00 40.00
86 Harry Simpson 20.00 40.00
87 Harry Perkowski 20.00 40.00
88 Joe Dobson 20.00 40.00
89 Sandy Consuegra 20.00 40.00
90 Joe Nuxhall 30.00 50.00
91 Steve Souchock 20.00 40.00
92 Gil Hodges 175.00 300.00
93 Phil Rizzuto 175.00 300.00
Billy Martin
94 Bob Addis 20.00 40.00
95 Wally Moses CO 30.00 50.00
96 Sal Maglie 30.00 50.00
97 Eddie Mathews 200.00 350.00
98 Hector Rodriguez RC 20.00 40.00
99 Warren Spahn 200.00 350.00
100 Bill Wight 20.00 40.00
101 Red Schoendienst 50.00 80.00
102 Jim Hegan 30.00 50.00
103 Del Ennis 30.00 50.00
104 Luke Easter 30.00 50.00
105 Eddie Joost 20.00 40.00
106 Ken Raffensberger 20.00 40.00
107 Alex Kellner 20.00 40.00
108 Bobby Adams 20.00 40.00
109 Ken Wood 20.00 40.00
110 Bob Rush 20.00 40.00
111 Jim Dyck RC 20.00 40.00
112 Toby Atwell 20.00 40.00
113 Karl Drews 50.00 80.00
114 Bob Feller 350.00 500.00
115 Cloyd Boyer 50.00 80.00
116 Eddie Yost 60.00 100.00
117 Duke Snider 350.00 600.00
118 Billy Martin 250.00 400.00
119 Dale Mitchell 60.00 100.00
120 Marlin Stuart 50.00 80.00
121 Yogi Berra 500.00 800.00
122 Bill Serena 50.00 80.00
123 Johnny Lipon 50.00 80.00
124 Charlie Dressen MG 60.00 100.00
125 Fred Hatfield 50.00 80.00
126 Al Corwin 50.00 80.00
127 Dick Kryhoski 50.00 80.00
128 Whitey Lockman 60.00 100.00
129 Russ Meyer 45.00 75.00
130 Cass Michaels 45.00 75.00
131 Connie Ryan 45.00 75.00
132 Fred Hutchinson 60.00 90.00
133 Willie Jones 45.00 75.00
134 Johnny Pesky 60.00 90.00
135 Bobby Morgan 45.00 75.00
136 Jim Brideweser RC 45.00 75.00
137 Sam Dente 45.00 75.00
138 Bubba Church 45.00 75.00
139 Pete Runnels 60.00 90.00
140 Al Brazle 45.00 75.00
141 Frank Shea 45.00 75.00
142 Larry Miggins RC 45.00 75.00
143 Al Lopez MG 70.00 110.00
144 Warren Hacker 45.00 75.00
145 George Shuba 60.00 90.00
146 Early Wynn 125.00 200.00
147 Clem Koshorek 45.00 75.00
148 Billy Goodman 60.00 90.00
149 Al Corwin 45.00 75.00
150 Carl Scheib 45.00 75.00
151 Joe Adcock 70.00 110.00
152 Clyde Vollmer 45.00 75.00
153 Whitey Ford 500.00 800.00
154 Turk Lown 45.00 75.00
155 Allie Clark 45.00 75.00
156 Max Surkont 45.00 75.00
157 Sherm Lollar 60.00 90.00
158 Howard Fox 45.00 75.00
159 Mickey Vernon UER 60.00 90.00
(Photo actually
Floyd Baker)
160 Cal Abrams 300.00 500.00

1954 Bowman

The cards in this 224-card set measure approximately 2 1/2" by 3 3/4". The set was distributed in two separate series: 1-128 in first series and 129-224 in second series. A contractual problem apparently resulted in the deletion of the number 66 Ted Williams card from this Bowman set, thereby creating a scarcity that is highly valued among collectors. The set price below does NOT include number 66 Williams but does include number 66 Jim Piersall, the apparent replacement for Williams in spite of the fact that Piersall was already number 210 to appear later in the set. Many errors in players' statistics exist (and some were corrected) while a few players' names were printed on the front, instead of appearing as a facsimile autograph. Most of these differences are so minor that there is no price differential for either card. The cards which changes were made on are numbers 12, 22,25,26,35,38,41,43,47,53,61,67,80,81,82,85,93,94,99,103,105,124,138,139, 140,145,153,156,174,179,185,212,216 and 217. The set was issued in seven-card nickel packs and one-card penny packs. The penny packs were issued 120 to a box while the nickel packs were issued 24 to a box. The notable Rookie Cards in this set are Harvey Kuenn and Don Larsen.

COMPLETE SET (224) 2500.00 4000.00
WRAP.(1-CENT, DATED) 100.00 150.00
WRAP.(1-CENT, UNDATED) 150.00 200.00
WRAP.(5-CENT, DATED) 100.00 150.00
WRAP.(5-CENT, UNDATED) 50.00 60.00
1 Phil Rizzuto 100.00 175.00
2 Jackie Jensen 15.00 30.00
3 Marion Fricano 6.00 12.00
4 Bob Hooper 6.00 12.00
5 Billy Hunter 6.00 12.00
6 Nellie Fox 50.00 80.00
7 Walt Dropo 10.00 20.00
8 Jim Busby 6.00 12.00
9 Dave Williams 6.00 12.00
10 Carl Erskine 10.00 20.00
11 Sid Gordon 6.00 12.00
12A Roy McMillan 10.00 20.00
551/1290 At Bat
12B Roy McMillan 10.00 20.00
557/1296 At Bat
13 Paul Minner 6.00 12.00
14 Gerry Staley 6.00 12.00
15 Richie Ashburn 50.00 80.00
16 Jim Wilson 6.00 12.00
17 Tom Gorman 6.00 12.00
18 Hoot Evers 6.00 12.00
19 Bobby Shantz 10.00 20.00
20 Art Houtteman 6.00 12.00
21 Vic Wertz 10.00 20.00
22A Sam Mele 6.00 12.00
213/1661 Putouts
22B Sam Mele 6.00 12.00
217/1665 Putouts
23 Harvey Kuenn RC 15.00 30.00
24 Bob Porterfield 6.00 12.00
25A Wes Westrum 10.00 20.00
1.000/.987 Fielding Avg.
25B Wes Westrum 10.00 20.00
.982/.986 Fielding Avg.
26A Billy Cox 10.00 20.00
1.000/.960 Fielding Avg.
26B Billy Cox 10.00 20.00
.972/.960 Fielding Avg.
27 Dick Cole RC 6.00 12.00
28A Jim Greengrass 6.00 12.00
Birthplace Addison, NJ
28B Jim Greengrass 6.00 12.00
Birthplace Addison, NY
29 Johnny Klippstein 6.00 12.00
30 Del Rice 6.00 12.00
31 Smoky Burgess 10.00 20.00
32 Del Crandall 10.00 20.00
33A Vic Raschi 10.00 20.00
No Trade
33B Vic Raschi 15.00 30.00
Traded to St.Louis
34 Sammy White 6.00 12.00
35A Eddie Joost 6.00 12.00
Quiz Answer is 8
35B Eddie Joost 6.00 12.00
Quiz Answer is 33
36 George Strickland 6.00 12.00
37 Dick Kokos 6.00 12.00

38A Minnie Minoso 15.00 30.00
.895/.961 Fielding Avg.
38B Minnie Minoso 15.00 30.00
.963/.963 Fielding Avg.
39 Ned Garver 6.00 12.00
40 Gil Coan 6.00 12.00
41A Alvin Dark 10.00 20.00
.986/.960 Fielding Avg.
41B Alvin Dark 10.00 20.00
.968/.960 Fielding Avg.
42 Billy Loes 10.00 20.00
43A Bob Friend 10.00 20.00
20 Shutouts in Quiz
43B Bob Friend 10.00 20.00
16 Shutouts in Quiz
44 Harry Perkowski 6.00 12.00
45 Ralph Kiner 25.00 50.00
46 Rip Repulski 6.00 12.00
47A Granny Hamner 6.00 12.00
.970/.953 Fielding Avg.
47B Granny Hamner 6.00 12.00
.953/.951 Fielding Avg.
48 Jack Dittmer 6.00 12.00
49 Harry Byrd 6.00 12.00
50 George Kell 25.00 50.00
51 Alex Kellner 6.00 12.00
52 Joe Ginsberg 6.00 12.00
53A Don Lenhardt 6.00 12.00
.969/.984 Fielding Avg.
53B Don Lenhardt 6.00 12.00
.966/.983 Fielding Avg.
54 Chico Carrasquel 6.00 12.00
55 Jim Delsing 6.00 12.00
56 Maurice McDermott 6.00 12.00
57 Hoyt Wilhelm 25.00 50.00
58 Pee Wee Reese 50.00 80.00
59 Bob Schultz 6.00 12.00
60 Fred Baczewski RC 6.00 12.00
61A Eddie Miksis 6.00 12.00
.954/.962 Fielding Avg.
61B Eddie Miksis 6.00 12.00
.954/.961 Fielding Avg.
62 Enos Slaughter 25.00 50.00
63 Earl Torgeson 6.00 12.00
64 Eddie Mathews 50.00 80.00
65 Mickey Mantle 900.00 1500.00
66A Ted Williams 1800.00 3000.00
66B Jimmy Piersall 50.00 80.00
67A Carl Scheib 6.00 12.00
.306 Pct. Two Lines under Bio
67B Carl Scheib 6.00 12.00
.306 Pct. One Line under Bio
67C Carl Scheib 6.00 12.00
.300 Pct.
68 Bobby Avila 10.00 20.00
69 Clint Courtney 6.00 12.00
70 Willard Marshall 6.00 12.00
71 Ted Gray 6.00 12.00
72 Eddie Yost 10.00 20.00
73 Don Mueller 10.00 20.00
74 Jim Gilliam 15.00 30.00
75 Max Surkont 6.00 12.00
76 Joe Nuxhall 10.00 20.00
77 Bob Rush 6.00 12.00
78 Sal Yvars 6.00 12.00
79 Curt Simmons 10.00 20.00
80A Johnny Logan 6.00 12.00
106 Runs
80B Johnny Logan 6.00 12.00
100 Runs
81A Jerry Coleman 10.00 20.00
1.000/.975 Fielding Avg.
81B Jerry Coleman 10.00 20.00
.952/.975 Fielding Avg.
82A Bill Goodman 10.00 20.00
.965/.986 Fielding Avg.
82B Bill Goodman 10.00 20.00
.972/.985 Fielding Avg.
83 Ray Murray 6.00 12.00
84 Larry Doby 25.00 50.00
85A Jim Dyck 6.00 12.00
.926/.956 Fielding Avg.
85B Jim Dyck 6.00 12.00
.947/.960 Fielding Avg.
86 Harry Dorish 6.00 12.00
87 Don Lund 6.00 12.00
88 Tom Umphlett RC 6.00 12.00
89 Willie Mays 300.00 500.00
90 Roy Campanella 90.00 150.00
91 Cal Abrams 6.00 12.00
92 Ken Raffensberger 6.00 12.00
93A Bill Serena 6.00 12.00
.983/.966 Fielding Avg.
93B Bill Serena 6.00 12.00
.977/.966 Fielding Avg.
94A Solly Hemus 6.00 12.00
476/1343 Assists
94B Solly Hemus 6.00 12.00
477/1343 Assists
95 Robin Roberts 25.00 50.00
96 Joe Adcock 10.00 20.00
97 Gil McDougald 10.00 20.00
98 Ellis Kinder 6.00 12.00
99A Peter Suder 6.00 12.00
.985/.974 Fielding Avg.
99B Peter Suder 6.00 12.00
.978/.974 Fielding Avg.
100 Mike Garcia 10.00 20.00
101 Don Larsen RC 50.00 80.00
102 Billy Pierce 10.00 20.00
103A Stephen Souchock 6.00 12.00
144/1192 Putouts
103B Stephen Souchock 6.00 12.00
147/1195 Putouts
104 Frank Shea 6.00 12.00
105A Sal Maglie 10.00 20.00
Quiz Answer is 8
105B Sal Maglie 10.00 20.00
Quiz Answer is 1904
106 Clem Labine 10.00 20.00
107 Paul LaPalme 6.00 12.00
108 Bobby Adams 6.00 12.00
109 Roy Smalley 6.00 12.00
110 Red Schoendienst 25.00 50.00
111 Murry Dickson 6.00 12.00
112 Andy Pafko 10.00 20.00
113 Allie Reynolds 10.00 20.00
114 Willard Nixon 6.00 12.00
115 Don Bollweg 6.00 12.00
116 Luke Easter 10.00 20.00
117 Dick Kryhoski 6.00 12.00
118 Bob Boyd 6.00 12.00
119 Fred Hatfield 6.00 12.00
120 Mel Hoderlein RC 6.00 12.00
121 Ray Katt RC 6.00 12.00
122 Carl Furillo 15.00 30.00
123 Toby Atwell 6.00 12.00
124A Gus Bell 10.00 20.00
15/27 Errors
124B Gus Bell 10.00 20.00
11/26 Errors
125 Warren Hacker 6.00 12.00
126 Cliff Chambers 6.00 12.00
127 Del Ennis 10.00 20.00
128 Ebba St.Claire 6.00 12.00
129 Hank Bauer 15.00 30.00
130 Milt Bolling 6.00 12.00
131 Joe Astroth 6.00 12.00
132 Bob Feller 50.00 80.00
133 Duane Pillette 6.00 12.00
134 Luis Aloma 6.00 12.00
135 Johnny Pesky 10.00 20.00
136 Clyde Vollmer 6.00 12.00
137 Al Corwin 6.00 12.00
138A Gil Hodges 50.00 80.00
.993/.991 Fielding Avg.
138B Gil Hodges 50.00 80.00
.992/.991 Fielding Avg.
139A Preston Ward 6.00 12.00
.961/.992 Fielding Avg.
139B Preston Ward 6.00 12.00
.990/.992 Fielding Avg.
140A Saul Rogovin 6.00 12.00
7-12 W-L 2 Strikeouts
140B Saul Rogovin 6.00 12.00
7-12 W-L 62 Strikeouts
140C Saul Rogovin 6.00 12.00
8-12 W-L
141 Joe Garagiola 15.00 30.00
142 Al Brazle 6.00 12.00
143 Willie Jones 6.00 12.00
144 Ernie Johnson RC 15.00 30.00
145A Billy Martin 50.00 80.00
.985/.983 Fielding Avg.
145B Billy Martin 50.00 80.00
.983/.982 Fielding Avg.
146 Dick Gernert 6.00 12.00
147 Joe DeMaestri 6.00 12.00
148 Dale Mitchell 10.00 20.00
149 Bob Young 6.00 12.00
150 Cass Michaels 6.00 12.00
151 Pat Mullin 6.00 12.00
152 Mickey Vernon 10.00 20.00
153A Whitey Lockman 10.00 20.00
100/331 Assists
153B Whitey Lockman 10.00 20.00
102/333 Assists
154 Don Newcombe 15.00 30.00
155 Frank Thomas RC 10.00 20.00
156A Rocky Bridges 6.00 12.00
320/467 Assists
156B Rocky Bridges 6.00 12.00
328/475 Assists
157 Turk Lown 6.00 12.00
158 Stu Miller 10.00 20.00
159 Johnny Lindell 6.00 12.00
160 Danny O'Connell 6.00 12.00
161 Yogi Berra 100.00 175.00
162 Ted Lepcio 6.00 12.00
163A Dave Philley 10.00 20.00
No Trade 152 Games
163B Dave Philley 15.00 30.00
Traded to Cleveland 152 Games
163C Dave Philley 15.00 30.00
Traded to Cleveland 157 Games
164 Early Wynn 25.00 50.00
165 Johnny Groth 6.00 12.00
166 Sandy Consuegra 6.00 12.00
167 Billy Hoeft 6.00 12.00
168 Ed Fitzgerald 6.00 12.00
169 Larry Jansen 10.00 20.00
170 Duke Snider 150.00 250.00
171 Carlos Bernier 6.00 12.00
172 Andy Seminick 6.00 12.00
173 Dee Fondy 6.00 12.00
174A Pete Castiglione 6.00 12.00
.966/.959 Fielding Avg.
174B Pete Castiglione 6.00 12.00
.970/.959 Fielding Avg.
175 Mel Clark 6.00 12.00
176 Vern Bickford 6.00 12.00
177 Whitey Ford 60.00 100.00
178 Del Wilber 6.00 12.00
179A Morris Martin 6.00 12.00
44 ERA
179B Morris Martin 6.00 12.00
4.44 ERA
180 Joe Tipton 6.00 12.00
181 Les Moss 6.00 12.00
182 Sherm Lollar 10.00 20.00
183 Matt Batts 6.00 12.00
184 Mickey Grasso 6.00 12.00
185A Daryl Spencer 6.00 12.00
.941/.944 Fielding Avg. RC
185B Daryl Spencer 6.00 12.00
.933/.936 Fielding Avg.
186 Russ Meyer 6.00 12.00
187 Vern Law 10.00 20.00
188 Frank Smith 6.00 12.00
189 Randy Jackson 6.00 12.00
190 Joe Presko 6.00 12.00
191 Karl Drews 6.00 12.00
192 Lou Burdette 10.00 20.00
193 Eddie Robinson 6.00 12.00
194 Sid Hudson 6.00 12.00
195 Bob Cain 6.00 12.00
196 Bob Lemon 25.00 50.00
197 Lou Kretlow 6.00 12.00
198 Virgil Trucks 6.00 12.00
199 Steve Gromek 6.00 12.00
200 Conrado Marrero 6.00 12.00
201 Bobby Thomson 15.00 30.00
202 George Shuba 10.00 20.00
203 Vic Janowicz 10.00 20.00
204 Jack Collum RC 6.00 12.00
205 Hal Jeffcoat 6.00 12.00
206 Steve Bilko 6.00 12.00
207 Stan Lopata 6.00 12.00
208 Johnny Antonelli 10.00 20.00
209 Gene Woodling 6.00 12.00
UER Reversed Photo
210 Jimmy Piersall 15.00 30.00
211 Al Robertson RC 6.00 12.00
212A Owen Friend 6.00 12.00
.964/.957 Fielding Avg.
212B Owen Friend 6.00 12.00
.967/.958 Fielding Avg.
213 Dick Littlefield 6.00 12.00
214 Ferris Fain 10.00 20.00
215 Johnny Bucha 6.00 12.00
216A Jerry Snyder 6.00 12.00
.988/.988 Fielding Avg.
216B Jerry Snyder 6.00 12.00
.968/.968 Fielding Avg.
217A Henry Thompson 10.00 20.00
.956/.951 Fielding Avg.
217B Henry Thompson 10.00 20.00
.958/.952 Fielding Avg.
218 Preacher Roe 10.00 20.00
219 Hal Rice 6.00 12.00
220 Hobie Landrith RC 6.00 12.00
221 Frank Baumholtz 6.00 12.00
222 Memo Luna RC 6.00 12.00
223 Steve Ridzik 6.00 12.00
224 Bill Bruton 25.00 50.00

1955 Bowman

The cards in this 320-card set measure approximately 2 1/2" by 3 3/4". The Bowman set of 1955 is known as the "TV set" because each player photograph is cleverly shown within a television set design. The set contains umpire cards, some transposed pictures (e.g., Johnsons and Bollings), an incorrect spelling for Harvey Kuenn, and a traded line for Palica (all of which are noted in the checklist below). Some three-card advertising strips exist, the backs of these panels contain advertising for Bowman products. Print advertisements for these cards featured Willie Mays along with publicizing the great value in nine cards for a nickel. Advertising panels seen include Nellie Fox/Carl Furillo/Carl Erskine; Hank Aaron/Johnny Logan/Eddie Miksis; Bob Rush/Ray Katt/Willie Mays; Steve Gromek/Milt Bolling/Vern Stephens, Russ Kemmerer/ Hal Jeffcoat/Dee Fondy and a Bob Darnell/Early Wynn/Pee Wee Reese. Cards were issued either in nine-card nickel packs or one card penny packs. Cello packs containing approximately 20 cards have also been seen, albeit on a very limited basis. The notable Rookie Cards in this set are Elston Howard and Don Zimmer. Hall of Fame umpires pictured in the set are Al Barlick, Jocko Conlon and Cal Hubbard. Undated five cent wrappers are also known to exist for this set.

COMPLETE SET (320) 3500.00 6000.00
COMMON CARD (1-96) 6.00 12.00
COMMON CARD (97-224) 5.00 10.00
COMMON (225-320) 7.50 15.00
COMMON UMP. 225-320 18.00 30.00
WRAPPER (1-CENT) 50.00 60.00
WRAPPER (5-CENT) 50.00 60.00
1 Hoyt Wilhelm 60.00 100.00
2 Alvin Dark 7.50 15.00
3 Joe Coleman 7.50 15.00
4 Eddie Waitkus 7.50 15.00
5 Jim Robertson 6.00 12.00
6 Pete Suder 6.00 12.00
7 Gene Baker RC 6.00 12.00
8 Warren Hacker 6.00 12.00
9 Gil McDougald 10.00 20.00
10 Phil Rizzuto 75.00 125.00
11 Bill Bruton 7.50 15.00
12 Andy Pafko 7.50 15.00
13 Clyde Vollmer 6.00 12.00
14 Gus Keriazakos RC 6.00 12.00
15 Frank Sullivan RC 6.00 12.00
16 Jimmy Piersall 10.00 20.00
17 Del Ennis 7.50 15.00
18 Stan Lopata 7.50 15.00
19 Bobby Avila 7.50 15.00
20 Al Smith 7.50 15.00
21 Don Hoak 6.00 12.00
22 Roy Campanella 75.00 125.00
23 Al Kaline 90.00 150.00
24 Al Aber 6.00 12.00
25 Minnie Minoso 15.00 30.00
26 Virgil Trucks 7.50 15.00
27 Preston Ward 6.00 12.00
28 Dick Cole 6.00 12.00
29 Red Schoendienst 15.00 30.00
30 Bill Sarni 6.00 12.00
31 Johnny Temple RC 7.50 15.00
32 Wally Post 7.50 15.00
33 Nellie Fox 30.00 50.00
34 Clint Courtney 6.00 12.00
35 Bill Tuttle RC 6.00 12.00
36 Wayne Belardi RC 6.00 12.00
37 Pee Wee Reese 60.00 100.00
38 Early Wynn 15.00 30.00
39 Bob Darnell RC 7.50 15.00
40 Vic Wertz 7.50 15.00
41 Mel Clark 6.00 12.00
42 Bob Greenwood RC 6.00 12.00
43 Bob Buhl 7.50 15.00
44 Danny O'Connell 6.00 12.00
45 Tom Umphlett 6.00 12.00
46 Mickey Vernon 7.50 15.00
47 Sammy White 6.00 12.00
48A Milt Bolling ERR 10.00 20.00
(Name on back is
Frank Bolling)
48B Milt Bolling COR 10.00 20.00
49 Jim Greengrass 6.00 12.00
50 Hobie Landrith 6.00 12.00
51 Elvin Tappe RC UER 6.00 12.00
Some information about Ted Tappe on the card
52 Hal Rice 6.00 12.00
53 Alex Kellner 6.00 12.00
54 Don Bollweg 6.00 12.00
55 Cal Abrams 6.00 12.00
56 Billy Cox 7.50 15.00
57 Bob Friend 7.50 15.00
58 Frank Thomas 7.50 15.00
59 Whitey Ford 60.00 100.00
60 Enos Slaughter 15.00 30.00
61 Paul LaPalme 6.00 12.00
62 Royce Lint RC 6.00 12.00
63 Irv Noren 7.50 15.00
64 Curt Simmons 7.50 15.00
65 Don Zimmer RC 10.00 20.00
66 George Shuba 10.00 20.00
67 Don Larsen 10.00 20.00
68 Elston Howard RC 50.00 80.00
69 Billy Hunter 6.00 12.00
70 Lou Burdette 10.00 20.00
71 Dave Jolly 6.00 12.00
72 Chet Nichols 6.00 12.00
73 Eddie Yost 7.50 15.00
74 Jerry Snyder 6.00 12.00
75 Brooks Lawrence RC 6.00 12.00
76 Tom Poholsky 6.00 12.00
77 Jim McDonald RC 6.00 12.00
78 Gil Coan 6.00 12.00
79 Willie Miranda 6.00 12.00
80 Lou Limmer 6.00 12.00
81 Bobby Morgan 6.00 12.00
82 Lee Walls RC 6.00 12.00
83 Max Surkont 6.00 12.00
84 George Freese RC 6.00 12.00
85 Cass Michaels 6.00 12.00
86 Ted Gray 6.00 12.00
87 Randy Jackson 6.00 12.00
88 Steve Bilko 6.00 12.00
89 Lou Boudreau MG 15.00 30.00
90 Art Ditmar RC 6.00 12.00
91 Dick Marlowe RC 6.00 12.00
92 George Zuverink 6.00 12.00
93 Andy Seminick 6.00 12.00
94 Hank Thompson 7.50 15.00
95 Sal Maglie 7.50 15.00
96 Ray Narleski RC 6.00 12.00
97 Johnny Podres 15.00 30.00
98 Jim Gilliam 10.00 20.00
99 Jerry Coleman 7.50 15.00
100 Tom Morgan 5.00 10.00
101A Don Johnson ERR 10.00 20.00
(Photo actually
Ernie Johnson)
101B Don Johnson COR 10.00 20.00
102 Bobby Thomson 7.50 15.00
103 Eddie Mathews 50.00 80.00
104 Bob Porterfield 5.00 10.00
105 Johnny Schmitz 5.00 10.00
106 Del Rice 5.00 10.00
107 Solly Hemus 5.00 10.00
108 Lou Kretlow 5.00 10.00
109 Vern Stephens 7.50 15.00
110 Bob Miller 5.00 10.00
111 Steve Ridzik 5.00 10.00
112 Granny Hamner 5.00 10.00
113 Bob Hall RC 5.00 10.00
114 Vic Janowicz 7.50 15.00
115 Roger Bowman RC 5.00 10.00
116 Sandy Consuegra 5.00 10.00
117 Johnny Groth 5.00 10.00
118 Bobby Adams 5.00 10.00
119 Joe Astroth 5.00 10.00
120 Ed Burtschy RC 5.00 10.00
121 Rufus Crawford RC 5.00 10.00
122 Al Corwin 5.00 10.00
123 Marv Grissom RC 5.00 10.00
124 Johnny Antonelli 7.50 15.00
125 Paul Giel RC 7.50 15.00
126 Billy Goodman 7.50 15.00
127 Hank Majeski 5.00 10.00
128 Mike Garcia 7.50 15.00
129 Hal Naragon RC 5.00 10.00
130 Richie Ashburn 30.00 50.00
131 Willard Marshall 5.00 10.00
132A Harvey Kueen ERR 30.00 50.00
(Sic& Kuenn)
132B Harvey Kuenn COR 15.00 30.00
133 Charles King RC 5.00 10.00
134 Bob Feller 50.00 80.00
135 Lloyd Merriman 5.00 10.00
136 Rocky Bridges 5.00 10.00
137 Bob Talbot 5.00 10.00
138 Davey Williams 7.50 15.00
139 Shantz Brothers 7.50 15.00
Wilmer Shantz
Bobby Shantz
140 Bobby Shantz 7.50 15.00
141 Wes Westrum 7.50 15.00
142 Rudy Regalado RC 5.00 10.00
143 Don Newcombe 15.00 30.00
144 Art Houtteman 5.00 10.00
145 Bob Nieman RC 5.00 10.00
146 Don Liddle 5.00 10.00
147 Sam Mele 5.00 10.00
148 Bob Chakales 5.00 10.00
149 Cloyd Boyer 5.00 10.00
150 Billy Klaus RC 5.00 10.00
151 Jim Brideweser 5.00 10.00
152 Johnny Klippstein 5.00 10.00
153 Eddie Robinson 5.00 10.00
154 Frank Lary RC 7.50 15.00
155 Gerry Staley 5.00 10.00
156 Jim Hughes 7.50 15.00
157A Ernie Johnson ERR 10.00 20.00
(Photo actually
Don Johnson)
157B Ernie Johnson COR 10.00 20.00
158 Gil Hodges 30.00 50.00
159 Harry Byrd 5.00 10.00
160 Bill Skowron 10.00 20.00
161 Matt Batts 5.00 10.00
162 Charlie Maxwell 5.00 10.00
163 Sid Gordon 7.50 15.00
164 Toby Atwell 5.00 10.00
165 Maurice McDermott 5.00 10.00
166 Jim Busby 5.00 10.00
167 Bob Grim RC 10.00 20.00
168 Yogi Berra 75.00 125.00
169 Carl Furillo 15.00 30.00
170 Carl Erskine 10.00 20.00
171 Robin Roberts 30.00 50.00
172 Willie Jones 5.00 10.00
173 Chico Carrasquel 5.00 10.00
174 Sherm Lollar 7.50 15.00
175 Wilmer Shantz RC 5.00 10.00
176 Joe DeMaestri 5.00 10.00
177 Willard Nixon 5.00 10.00
178 Tom Brewer RC 5.00 10.00
179 Hank Aaron 150.00 250.00
180 Johnny Logan 7.50 15.00
181 Eddie Miksis 5.00 10.00
182 Bob Rush 5.00 10.00
183 Ray Katt 5.00 10.00
184 Willie Mays 150.00 250.00
185 Vic Raschi 5.00 10.00
186 Alex Grammas 5.00 10.00
187 Fred Hatfield 5.00 10.00
188 Ned Garver 5.00 10.00
189 Jack Collum 5.00 10.00
190 Fred Baczewski 5.00 10.00
191 Bob Lemon 15.00 30.00
192 George Strickland 5.00 10.00
193 Howie Judson 5.00 10.00
194 Joe Nuxhall 7.50 15.00
195A Erv Palica 7.50 15.00
(Without trade)
195B Erv Palica 20.00 40.00
(With trade)
196 Russ Meyer 7.50 15.00
197 Ralph Kiner 15.00 30.00
198 Dave Pope RC 5.00 10.00
199 Vern Law 7.50 15.00
200 Dick Littlefield 5.00 10.00
201 Allie Reynolds 10.00 20.00
202 Mickey Mantle UER 500.00 800.00
Birthdate listed as 10/30/31
Should be 10/20/31
203 Steve Gromek 5.00 10.00
204A Frank Bolling ERR RC 10.00 20.00
(Name on back is
Milt Bolling)
204B Frank Bolling COR 10.00 20.00
205 Rip Repulski 5.00 10.00
206 Ralph Beard RC 5.00 10.00
207 Frank Shea 5.00 10.00
208 Ed Fitzgerald 5.00 10.00
209 Smoky Burgess 7.50 15.00
210 Earl Torgeson 5.00 10.00
211 Sonny Dixon RC 5.00 10.00
212 Jack Dittmer 5.00 10.00
213 George Kell 15.00 30.00
214 Billy Pierce 7.50 15.00
215 Bob Kuzava 5.00 10.00
216 Preacher Roe 10.00 20.00
217 Del Crandall 7.50 15.00
218 Joe Adcock 7.50 15.00
219 Whitey Lockman 7.50 15.00
220 Jim Hearn 5.00 10.00
221 Hector Brown 5.00 10.00
222 Russ Kemmerer RC 5.00 10.00
223 Hal Jeffcoat 5.00 10.00
224 Dee Fondy 5.00 10.00
225 Paul Richards MG 7.50 15.00
226 Bill McKinley UMP 18.00 30.00
227 Frank Baumholtz 7.50 15.00
228 John Phillips RC 7.50 15.00
229 Jim Brosnan RC 10.00 20.00
230 Al Brazle 7.50 15.00
231 Jim Konstanty 10.00 20.00
232 Birdie Tebbetts MG 10.00 20.00
233 Bill Serena 7.50 15.00
234 Dick Bartell CO 10.00 20.00
235 Joe Paparella UMP 18.00 30.00
236 Murry Dickson 7.50 15.00
237 Johnny Wyrostek 7.50 15.00
238 Eddie Stanky MG 10.00 20.00
239 Edwin Rommel UMP 20.00 40.00
240 Billy Loes 10.00 20.00
241 Johnny Pesky CO 10.00 20.00
242 Ernie Banks 200.00 350.00
243 Gus Bell 10.00 20.00
244 Duane Pillette 7.50 15.00
245 Bill Miller 7.50 15.00
246 Hank Bauer 15.00 30.00
247 Dutch Leonard CO 7.50 15.00
248 Harry Dorish 7.50 15.00
249 Billy Gardner RC 10.00 20.00
250 Larry Napp UMP 18.00 30.00
251 Stan Jok 7.50 15.00
252 Roy Smalley 7.50 15.00
253 Jim Wilson 7.50 15.00
254 Bennett Flowers RC 7.50 15.00
255 Pete Runnels 10.00 20.00
256 Owen Friend 7.50 15.00
257 Tom Alston RC 7.50 15.00
258 John Stevens UMP 18.00 30.00
259 Don Mossi RC 15.00 30.00
260 Edwin Hurley UMP 18.00 30.00
261 Walt Moryn RC 10.00 20.00
262 Jim Lemon 7.50 15.00
263 Eddie Joost 7.50 15.00
264 Bill Henry RC 7.50 15.00
265 Albert Barlick UMP 50.00 80.00
266 Mike Fornieles 7.50 15.00
267 Jim Honochick UMP 50.00 80.00
268 Roy Lee Hawes RC 7.50 15.00
269 Joe Amalfitano RC 10.00 20.00
270 Chico Fernandez RC 10.00 20.00
271 Bob Hooper 7.50 15.00
272 John Flaherty UMP 18.00 30.00
273 Bubba Church 7.50 15.00
274 Jim Delsing 7.50 15.00
275 William Grieve UMP 18.00 30.00
276 Ike Delock 7.50 15.00
277 Ed Runge UMP 18.00 30.00
278 Charlie Neal RC 20.00 40.00
279 Hank Soar UMP 20.00 40.00
280 Clyde McCullough 7.50 15.00
281 Charles Berry UMP 20.00 40.00
282 Phil Cavarretta 10.00 20.00
283 Nestor Chylak UMP 50.00 80.00
284 Bill Jackowski UMP 18.00 30.00
285 Walt Dropo 10.00 20.00
286 Frank Secory UMP 18.00 30.00
287 Ron Mrozinski RC 7.50 15.00
288 Dick Smith RC 7.50 15.00
289 Arthur Gore UMP 18.00 30.00
290 Hershell Freeman RC 7.50 15.00
291 Frank Dascoli UMP 18.00 30.00
292 Marv Blaylock RC 7.50 15.00
293 Thomas Gorman UMP 20.00 40.00
294 Wally Moses CO 7.50 15.00
295 Lee Ballanfant UMP 18.00 30.00
296 Bill Virdon RC 15.00 30.00
297 Dusty Boggess UMP 18.00 30.00
298 Charlie Grimm MG 10.00 20.00
299 Lon Warneke UMP 20.00 40.00
300 Tommy Byrne 10.00 20.00
301 William Engeln UMP 18.00 30.00
302 Frank Malzone RC 15.00 30.00
303 Jocko Conlan UMP 50.00 80.00
304 Harry Chiti 7.50 15.00
305 Frank Umont UMP 18.00 30.00
306 Bob Cerv 10.00 20.00
307 Babe Pinelli UMP 20.00 40.00
308 Al Lopez MG 30.00 50.00
309 Hal Dixon UMP 18.00 30.00
310 Ken Lehman RC 7.50 15.00
311 Lawrence Goetz UMP 18.00 30.00
312 Bill Wight 7.50 15.00
313 Augie Donatelli UMP 30.00 50.00
314 Dale Mitchell 10.00 20.00
315 Cal Hubbard UMP 50.00 80.00
316 Marion Fricano 7.50 15.00
317 W. Summers UMP 10.00 20.00
318 Sid Hudson 7.50 15.00
319 Al Schroll RC 7.50 15.00
320 George Susce RC 30.00 50.00

1954 Bowman Advertising Strips

These strips were issued in four card salesman's sample and feature the actual card along with a diamond advertising in the back middle which notates these cards as 1954 Bowman's Advertising Samples.

COMPLETE SET 500.00 1000.00
1 Martin Fricano 300.00 600.00
Bob Hooper
Sid Gordon
Roy McMillan
2 Harvey Kuenn 300.00 600.00
Bob Porterfield
Smoky Burgess
Del Crandall

1955 Bowman Advertising Strips

For Bowman's final set; these advertising panels have been seen. The fronts are standard 1955 Bowman cards while the backs have advertising information.

COMPLETE SET 4500.00 9000.00
1 Nellie Fox 500.00 1000.00
Carl Furillo
Carl Erskine
2 Hank Aaron 750.00 1500.00
Johnny Logan
Eddie Miksis
3 Bob Rush 750.00 1500.00
Ray Katt
Willie Mays
4 Steve Gromek 250.00 500.00
Milt Bolling
Vern Stephens
5 Bob Darnell 600.00 1200.00
Early Wynn
Pee Wee Reese
6 Russ Kemmerer 250.00 500.00
Hal Jeffcoat
Dee Fondy
7 Don Bollweg 250.00 500.00
Cal Abrams
Billy Cox
8 Mickey Mantle 2500.00 5000.00
Steve Gromek
Milt Bolling
9 Stan Lopata 250.00 500.00
Bobby Avila
Al Smith

1982 Bowman 1952 Extension

In 1980, 15 unissued pieces of artwork initially intended to be used by Bowman Gum in their 1952 baseball card set were discovered. This set consists of 15 cards made from this original artwork. The backs have been created to resemble the original 1952 series, and the set has been numbered 253-267 (the next 15 cards in the 1952 Bowman sequence). The facsimile autograph on the original 1952 Bowmans has been omitted from the cards in this set. This set was originally available from the producer for $3 per set.

COMPLETE SET (15) 2.00 5.00
253 Bob Kennedy .08 .25
254 Barney McCosky .08 .25
255 Chris Van Cuyk .08 .25
256 Morrie Martin .08 .25
257 Jim Wilson .08 .25
258 Bob Thorpe .08 .25
259 Bill Henry .08 .25
260 Bob Addis .08 .25
261 Terry Moore CO .30 .75
262 Joe Dobson .08 .25
263 John Merson .08 .25
264 Virgil Trucks .20 .50

Card	Low	High
265 Johnny Hopp	.08	.25
267 George Shuba	.20	.50

1989 Bowman

The 1989 Bowman set, produced by Topps, contains 484 slightly oversized cards (measuring 2 1/2" by 3 3/4"). The cards were released in midseason 1989 in wax, rack, cello and factory set formats. The fronts have white-bordered color photos with facsimile autographs and small Bowman logos. The backs feature charts detailing 1988 player performances vs. each team. The cards are ordered alphabetically according to teams in the AL and NL. Cards 258-261 form a father/son subset. Rookie Cards in this set include Sandy Alomar Jr., Steve Finley, Ken Griffey Jr., Tino Martinez, Gary Sheffield, John Smoltz and Robin Ventura.

Card	Low	High
COMPLETE SET (484)	10.00	25.00
COMP.FACT.SET (484)	10.00	25.00
1 Oswald Peraza	.01	.05
2 Brian Holton	.01	.05
3 Jose Bautista RC	.02	.10
4 Pete Harnisch RC	.08	.25
5 Dave Schmidt	.01	.05
6 Gregg Olson RC	.08	.25
7 Jeff Ballard	.01	.05
8 Bob Melvin	.01	.05
9 Cal Ripken	.30	.75
10 Randy Milligan	.01	.05
11 Juan Bell RC	.02	.10
12 Billy Ripken	.01	.05
13 Jim Traber	.01	.05
14 Pete Stanicek	.01	.05
15 Steve Finley RC	.30	.75
16 Larry Sheets	.01	.05
17 Phil Bradley	.01	.05
18 Brady Anderson RC	.15	.40
19 Lee Smith	.02	.10
20 Tom Fischer	.01	.05
21 Mike Boddicker	.01	.05
22 Rob Murphy	.01	.05
23 Wes Gardner	.01	.05
24 John Dopson	.01	.05
25 Bob Stanley	.01	.05
26 Roger Clemens	.40	1.00
27 Rich Gedman	.01	.05
28 Marty Barrett	.01	.05
29 Luis Rivera	.01	.05
30 Jody Reed	.01	.05
31 Nick Esasky	.01	.05
32 Wade Boggs	.05	.15
33 Jim Rice	.02	.10
34 Mike Greenwell	.01	.05
35 Dwight Evans	.05	.15
36 Ellis Burks	.02	.10
37 Chuck Finley	.02	.10
38 Kirk McCaskill	.01	.05
39 Jim Abbott RC*	.40	1.00
40 Bryan Harvey RC *	.08	.25
41 Bert Blyleven	.02	.10
42 Mike Witt	.01	.05
43 Bob McClure	.01	.05
44 Bill Schroeder	.01	.05
45 Lance Parrish	.02	.10
46 Dick Schofield	.01	.05
47 Wally Joyner	.02	.10
48 Jack Howell	.01	.05
49 Johnny Ray	.01	.05
50 Chili Davis	.02	.10
51 Tony Armas	.02	.10
52 Claudell Washington	.01	.05
53 Brian Downing	.02	.10
54 Devon White	.02	.10
55 Bobby Thigpen	.01	.05
56 Bill Long	.01	.05
57 Jerry Reuss	.01	.05
58 Shawn Hillegas	.01	.05
59 Melido Perez	.01	.05
60 Jeff Bittiger	.01	.05
61 Jack McDowell	.02	.10
62 Carlton Fisk	.05	.15
63 Steve Lyons	.01	.05
64 Ozzie Guillen	.02	.10
65 Robin Ventura RC	.30	.75
66 Fred Manrique	.01	.05
67 Dan Pasqua	.01	.05
68 Ivan Calderon	.01	.05
69 Ron Kittle	.01	.05
70 Daryl Boston	.01	.05
71 Dave Gallagher	.01	.05
72 Harold Baines	.02	.10
73 Charles Nagy RC	.08	.25
74 John Farrell	.01	.05
75 Kevin Wickander	.01	.05
76 Greg Swindell	.01	.05
77 Mike Walker	.01	.05
78 Doug Jones	.01	.05
79 Rich Yett	.01	.05
80 Tom Candiotti	.01	.05
81 Jesse Orosco	.01	.05
82 Bud Black	.01	.05
83 Andy Allanson	.01	.05
84 Pete O'Brien	.01	.05
85 Jerry Browne	.01	.05
86 Brook Jacoby	.01	.05
87 Mark Lewis RC	.08	.25
88 Luis Aguayo	.01	.05
89 Cory Snyder	.01	.05
90 Oddibe McDowell	.01	.05
91 Joe Carter	.02	.10
92 Frank Tanana	.02	.10
93 Jack Morris	.02	.10
94 Doyle Alexander	.01	.05
95 Steve Searcy	.01	.05
96 Randy Bockus	.01	.05
97 Jeff M. Robinson	.01	.05
98 Mike Henneman	.01	.05
99 Paul Gibson	.01	.05
100 Frank Williams	.01	.05
101 Matt Nokes	.01	.05
102 Rico Brogna RC UER (Misspelled Ricco on card back)	.15	.40
103 Lou Whitaker	.02	.10
104 Al Pedrique	.01	.05
105 Alan Trammell	.02	.10
106 Chris Brown	.01	.05
107 Pat Sheridan	.01	.05
108 Chet Lemon	.02	.10
109 Keith Moreland	.01	.05
110 Mel Stottlemyre Jr.	.01	.05
111 Bret Saberhagen	.02	.10
112 Floyd Bannister	.01	.05
113 Jeff Montgomery	.01	.05
114 Steve Farr	.01	.05
115 Tom Gordon UER RC (Front shows autograph of Don Gordon)	.15	.40
116 Charlie Leibrandt	.01	.05
117 Mark Gubicza	.01	.05
118 Mike Macfarlane RC	.08	.25
119 Bob Boone	.02	.10
120 Kurt Stillwell	.01	.05
121 George Brett	.25	.60
122 Frank White	.02	.10
123 Kevin Seitzer	.01	.05
124 Willie Wilson	.02	.10
125 Pat Tabler	.01	.05
126 Bo Jackson	.08	.25
127 Hugh Walker RC	.02	.10
128 Danny Tartabull	.01	.05
129 Teddy Higuera	.01	.05
130 Don August	.01	.05
131 Juan Nieves	.01	.05
132 Mike Birkbeck	.01	.05
133 Dan Plesac	.01	.05
134 Chris Bosio	.01	.05
135 Bill Wegman	.01	.05
136 Chuck Crim	.01	.05
137 B.J. Surhoff	.02	.10
138 Joey Meyer	.01	.05
139 Dale Sveum	.01	.05
140 Paul Molitor	.02	.10
141 Jim Gantner	.01	.05
142 Gary Sheffield RC	.60	1.50
143 Greg Brock	.01	.05
144 Robin Yount	.15	.40
145 Glenn Braggs	.01	.05
146 Rob Deer	.01	.05
147 Fred Toliver	.01	.05
148 Jeff Reardon	.02	.10
149 Allan Anderson	.01	.05
150 Frank Viola	.02	.10
151 Shane Rawley	.01	.05
152 Juan Berenguer	.01	.05
153 Johnny Ard	.01	.05
154 Tim Laudner	.01	.05
155 Brian Harper	.01	.05
156 Al Newman	.01	.05
157 Kent Hrbek	.02	.10
158 Gary Gaetti	.02	.10
159 Wally Backman	.01	.05
160 Gene Larkin	.01	.05
161 Greg Gagne	.01	.05
162 Kirby Puckett	.08	.25
163 Dan Gladden	.01	.05
164 Randy Bush	.01	.05
165 Dave LaPoint	.01	.05
166 Andy Hawkins	.01	.05
167 Dave Righetti	.02	.10
168 Lance McCullers	.01	.05
169 Jimmy Jones	.01	.05
170 Al Leiter	.08	.25
171 John Candelaria	.01	.05
172 Don Slaught	.01	.05
173 Jamie Quirk	.01	.05
174 Rafael Santana	.01	.05
175 Mike Pagliarulo	.01	.05
176 Don Mattingly	.25	.60
177 Ken Phelps	.01	.05
178 Steve Sax	.01	.05
179 Dave Winfield	.02	.10
180 Stan Jefferson	.01	.05
181 Rickey Henderson	.08	.25
182 Bob Brower	.01	.05
183 Roberto Kelly	.01	.05
184 Curt Young	.01	.05
185 Gene Nelson	.01	.05
186 Bob Welch	.02	.10
187 Rick Honeycutt	.01	.05
188 Dave Stewart	.02	.10
189 Mike Moore	.01	.05
190 Dennis Eckersley	.05	.15
191 Eric Plunk	.01	.05
192 Storm Davis	.01	.05
193 Terry Steinbach	.02	.10
194 Ron Hassey	.01	.05
195 Stan Royer RC	.02	.10
196 Walt Weiss	.01	.05
197 Mark McGwire	.40	1.00
198 Carney Lansford	.02	.10
199 Glenn Hubbard	.01	.05
200 Dave Henderson	.01	.05
201 Jose Canseco	.08	.25
202 Dave Parker	.02	.10
203 Scott Bankhead	.01	.05
204 Tom Niedenfuer	.01	.05
205 Mark Langston	.01	.05
206 Erik Hanson RC	.08	.25
207 Mike Jackson	.01	.05
208 Dave Valle	.01	.05
209 Scott Bradley	.01	.05
210 Harold Reynolds	.02	.10
211 Tino Martinez RC	.75	2.00
212 Rich Renteria	.01	.05
213 Rey Quinones	.01	.05
214 Jim Presley	.01	.05
215 Alvin Davis	.01	.05
216 Edgar Martinez	.08	.25
217 Darnell Coles	.01	.05
218 Jeffrey Leonard	.01	.05
219 Jay Buhner	.02	.10
220 Ken Griffey Jr. RC	2.50	6.00
221 Drew Hall	.01	.05
222 Bobby Witt	.01	.05
223 Jamie Moyer	.02	.10
224 Charlie Hough	.02	.10
225 Nolan Ryan	.40	1.00
226 Jeff Russell	.01	.05
227 Jim Sundberg	.02	.10
228 Julio Franco	.02	.10
229 Buddy Bell	.02	.10
230 Scott Fletcher	.01	.05
231 Jeff Kunkel	.01	.05
232 Steve Buechele	.01	.05
233 Monty Fariss	.01	.05
234 Rick Leach	.01	.05
235 Ruben Sierra	.02	.10
236 Cecil Espy	.01	.05
237 Rafael Palmeiro	.08	.25
238 Pete Incaviglia	.01	.05
239 Dave Stieb	.02	.10
240 Jeff Musselman	.01	.05
241 Mike Flanagan	.01	.05
242 Todd Stottlemyre	.01	.05
243 Jimmy Key	.02	.10
244 Tony Castillo RC	.02	.10
245 Alex Sanchez RC	.01	.05
246 Tom Henke	.01	.05
247 John Cerutti	.01	.05
248 Ernie Whitt	.01	.05
249 Bob Brenly	.01	.05
250 Rance Mulliniks	.01	.05
251 Kelly Gruber	.01	.05
252 Ed Sprague RC	.08	.25
253 Fred McGriff	.05	.15
254 Tony Fernandez	.01	.05
255 Tom Lawless	.01	.05
256 George Bell	.02	.10
257 Jesse Barfield	.02	.10
258 Roberto Alomar / Sandy Alomar	.05	.15
259 Ken Griffey Jr. / Ken Griffey Sr.	.40	1.00
260 Cal Ripken Jr. / Cal Ripken Sr.	.08	.25
261 Mel Stottlemyre Jr. / Mel Stottlemyre Sr.	.01	.05
262 Zane Smith	.01	.05
263 Charlie Puleo	.01	.05
264 Derek Lilliquist RC	.02	.10
265 Paul Assenmacher	.01	.05
266 John Smoltz RC	.60	1.50
267 Tom Glavine	.08	.25
268 Steve Avery RC	.08	.25
269 Pete Smith	.01	.05
270 Jody Davis	.01	.05
271 Bruce Benedict	.01	.05
272 Andres Thomas	.01	.05
273 Gerald Perry	.01	.05
274 Ron Gant	.02	.10
275 Darrell Evans	.02	.10
276 Dale Murphy	.05	.15
277 Dion James	.01	.05
278 Lonnie Smith	.01	.05
279 Geronimo Berroa	.01	.05
280 Steve Wilson RC	.02	.10
281 Rick Sutcliffe	.02	.10
282 Kevin Coffman	.01	.05
283 Mitch Williams	.01	.05
284 Greg Maddux	.20	.50
285 Paul Kilgus	.01	.05
286 Mike Harkey RC	.02	.10
287 Lloyd McClendon	.01	.05
288 Damon Berryhill	.01	.05
289 Ty Griffin	.01	.05
290 Ryne Sandberg	.15	.40
291 Mark Grace	.08	.25
292 Curt Wilkerson	.01	.05
293 Vance Law	.01	.05
294 Shawon Dunston	.01	.05
295 Jerome Walton RC	.08	.25
296 Mitch Webster	.01	.05
297 Dwight Smith RC	.08	.25
298 Andre Dawson	.02	.10
299 Jeff Sellers	.01	.05
300 Jose Rijo	.02	.10
301 John Franco	.02	.10
302 Rick Mahler	.01	.05
303 Ron Robinson	.01	.05
304 Danny Jackson	.01	.05
305 Rob Dibble RC	.15	.40
306 Tom Browning	.02	.10
307 Bo Diaz	.01	.05
308 Manny Trillo	.01	.05
309 Chris Sabo RC *	.15	.40
310 Ron Oester	.01	.05
311 Barry Larkin	.05	.15
312 Todd Benzinger	.01	.05
313 Paul O'Neill	.05	.15
314 Kal Daniels	.01	.05
315 Joel Youngblood	.01	.05
316 Eric Davis	.02	.10
317 Dave Smith	.01	.05
318 Mark Portugal	.01	.05
319 Brian Meyer	.01	.05
320 Jim Deshaies	.01	.05
321 Juan Agosto	.01	.05
322 Mike Scott	.02	.10
323 Rick Rhoden	.01	.05
324 Jim Clancy	.01	.05
325 Larry Andersen	.01	.05
326 Alex Trevino	.01	.05
327 Alan Ashby	.01	.05
328 Craig Reynolds	.01	.05
329 Bill Doran	.01	.05
330 Rafael Ramirez	.01	.05
331 Glenn Davis	.01	.05
332 Willie Ansley RC	.02	.10
333 Gerald Young	.01	.05
334 Cameron Drew	.01	.05
335 Jay Howell	.01	.05
336 Tim Belcher	.01	.05
337 Fernando Valenzuela	.02	.10
338 Ricky Horton	.01	.05
339 Tim Leary	.01	.05
340 Bill Bene	.01	.05
341 Orel Hershiser	.02	.10
342 Mike Scioscia	.02	.10
343 Rick Dempsey	.01	.05
344 Willie Randolph	.02	.10
345 Alfredo Griffin	.01	.05
346 Eddie Murray	.08	.25
347 Mickey Hatcher	.01	.05
348 Mike Sharperson	.01	.05
349 John Shelby	.01	.05
350 Mike Marshall	.01	.05
351 Kirk Gibson	.02	.10
352 Mike Davis	.01	.05
353 Bryn Smith	.01	.05
354 Pascual Perez	.01	.05
355 Kevin Gross	.01	.05
356 Andy McGaffigan	.01	.05
357 Brian Holman RC *	.02	.10
358 Dave Wainhouse RC	.02	.10
359 Dennis Martinez	.02	.10
360 Tim Burke	.01	.05
361 Nelson Santovenia	.01	.05
362 Tim Wallach	.01	.05
363 Spike Owen	.01	.05
364 Rex Hudler	.01	.05
365 Andres Galarraga	.02	.10
366 Otis Nixon	.01	.05
367 Hubie Brooks	.01	.05
368 Mike Aldrete	.01	.05
369 Tim Raines	.02	.10
370 Dave Martinez	.01	.05
371 Bob Ojeda	.01	.05
372 Ron Darling	.02	.10
373 Wally Whitehurst RC	.02	.10
374 Randy Myers	.02	.10
375 David Cone	.02	.10
376 Dwight Gooden	.02	.10
377 Sid Fernandez	.01	.05
378 Dave Proctor	.01	.05
379 Gary Carter	.02	.10
380 Keith Miller	.01	.05
381 Gregg Jefferies	.01	.05
382 Tim Teufel	.01	.05
383 Kevin Elster	.01	.05
384 Dave Magadan	.01	.05
385 Keith Hernandez	.02	.10
386 Mookie Wilson	.02	.10
387 Darryl Strawberry	.02	.10
388 Kevin McReynolds	.01	.05
389 Mark Carreon	.01	.05
390 Jeff Parrett	.01	.05
391 Mike Maddux	.01	.05
392 Don Carman	.01	.05
393 Bruce Ruffin	.01	.05
394 Ken Howell	.01	.05
395 Steve Bedrosian	.01	.05
396 Floyd Youmans	.01	.05
397 Larry McWilliams	.01	.05
398 Pat Combs RC *	.02	.10
399 Steve Lake	.01	.05
400 Dickie Thon	.01	.05
401 Ricky Jordan RC *	.08	.25
402 Mike Schmidt	.20	.50
403 Tom Herr	.01	.05
404 Chris James	.01	.05
405 Juan Samuel	.01	.05
406 Von Hayes	.01	.05
407 Ron Jones	.02	.10
408 Curt Ford	.01	.05
409 Bob Walk	.01	.05
410 Jeff D. Robinson	.01	.05
411 Jim Gott	.01	.05
412 Scott Medvin	.01	.05
413 John Smiley	.01	.05
414 Bob Kipper	.01	.05
415 Brian Fisher	.01	.05
416 Doug Drabek	.01	.05
417 Mike LaValliere	.01	.05
418 Ken Oberkfell	.01	.05
419 Sid Bream	.01	.05
420 Austin Manahan	.01	.05
421 Jose Lind	.01	.05
422 Bobby Bonilla	.02	.10
423 Glenn Wilson	.01	.05
424 Andy Van Slyke	.05	.15
425 Gary Redus	.01	.05
426 Barry Bonds	.60	1.50
427 Don Heinkel	.01	.05
428 Ken Dayley	.01	.05
429 Todd Worrell	.01	.05
430 Brad DuVall	.01	.05
431 Jose DeLeon	.01	.05
432 Joe Magrane	.01	.05
433 John Ericks	.01	.05
434 Frank DiPino	.01	.05
435 Tony Pena	.01	.05
436 Ozzie Smith	.15	.40
437 Terry Pendleton	.02	.10
438 Jose Oquendo	.01	.05
439 Tim Jones	.01	.05
440 Pedro Guerrero	.02	.10
441 Milt Thompson	.01	.05
442 Willie McGee	.02	.10
443 Vince Coleman	.01	.05
444 Tom Brunansky	.01	.05
445 Walt Terrell	.01	.05
446 Eric Show	.01	.05
447 Mark Davis	.01	.05
448 Andy Benes RC	.15	.40
449 Ed Whitson	.01	.05
450 Dennis Rasmussen	.01	.05
451 Bruce Hurst	.01	.05
452 Pat Clements	.01	.05
453 Benito Santiago	.02	.10
454 Sandy Alomar Jr. RC	.15	.40
455 Garry Templeton	.02	.10
456 Jack Clark	.02	.10
457 Tim Flannery	.01	.05
458 Roberto Alomar	.08	.25
459 Carmelo Martinez	.01	.05
460 John Kruk	.02	.10
461 Tony Gwynn	.10	.30
462 Jerald Clark RC	.02	.10
463 Don Robinson	.01	.05
464 Craig Lefferts	.01	.05
465 Kelly Downs	.01	.05
466 Rick Reuschel	.02	.10
467 Scott Garrelts	.01	.05
468 Wil Tejada	.01	.05
469 Kirt Manwaring	.01	.05
470 Terry Kennedy	.01	.05
471 Jose Uribe	.01	.05
472 Royce Clayton RC	.15	.40
473 Robby Thompson	.01	.05
474 Kevin Mitchell	.02	.10
475 Ernie Riles	.01	.05
476 Will Clark	.05	.15
477 Donell Nixon	.01	.05
478 Candy Maldonado	.01	.05
479 Tracy Jones	.01	.05
480 Brett Butler	.02	.10
481 Checklist 1-121	.01	.05
482 Checklist 122-242	.01	.05
483 Checklist 243-363	.01	.05
484 Checklist 364-484	.01	.05

1989 Bowman Tiffany

This is a parallel to the regular 1989 Bowman set. This set was issued with a glossy front and white-stock backs, thus joining other sets known in the Topps family as "Tiffany" sets. The set measure 2 1/2" by 3 3/4" and was issued in factory set form only. In addition to the 484 regular cards, the 11 Reprint inserts were also included in the factory set. Reportedly, only 6,000 factory sets were printed.

Card	Low	High
COMP.FACT.SET (495)	125.00	200.00
*STARS: 6X TO 15X BASIC CARDS		
*ROOKIES: 6X TO 15X BASIC CARDS		
211 Tino Martinez	6.00	15.00
220 Ken Griffey Jr.	40.00	80.00

1989 Bowman Reprint Inserts

The 1989 Bowman Reprint Inserts set contains 11 cards measuring approximately 2 1/2" by 3 3/4". The fronts depict reproduced actual size "classic" Bowman cards, which are noted as reprints. The backs are devoted to a sweepstakes entry form. One of these reprint cards was included in each 1989 Bowman wax pack thus making these "reprints" quite easy to find. Since the cards are unnumbered, they are ordered below in alphabetical order by player's name and year within player.

Card	Low	High
*TIFFANY: 10X TO 20X HI COLUMN		
ONE TIFF.REP.SET PER TIFF.FACT.SET		
1 Richie Ashburn 49	.15	.40
2 Yogi Berra 48	.08	.25
3 Whitey Ford 51	.15	.40
4 Gil Hodges 49	.20	.50
5 Mickey Mantle 51	.40	1.00
6 Mickey Mantle 53	.40	1.00
7 Willie Mays 51	.20	.50
8 Satchel Paige 49	.20	.50
9 Jackie Robinson 50	.20	.50
10 Duke Snider 49	.08	.25
11 Ted Williams 54	.20	.50

1990 Bowman

The 1990 Bowman set (produced by Topps) consists of 528 standard-size cards. The cards were issued in wax packs and factory sets. Each wax pack contained one of 11 different 1950's retro art cards. Unlike most sets, player selection focused primarily on rookies instead of proven major leaguers. The cards feature a white border with the player's photo inside and the Bowman logo on top. The card numbering is in team order with the teams themselves being ordered alphabetically within each league. Notable Rookie Cards include Moises Alou, Travis Fryman, Juan Gonzalez, Chuck Knoblauch, Ray Lankford, Sammy Sosa, Frank Thomas, Mo Vaughn, Larry Walker, and Bernie Williams.

Card	Low	High
COMPLETE SET (528)	10.00	25.00
COMP.FACT.SET (528)	10.00	25.00
1 Tommy Greene RC	.02	.10
2 Tom Glavine	.05	.15
3 Andy Nezelek	.01	.05
4 Mike Stanton RC	.08	.25
5 Rick Luecken RC	.01	.05
6 Kent Mercker RC	.08	.25
7 Derek Lilliquist	.01	.05
8 Charlie Leibrandt	.01	.05
9 Steve Avery	.01	.05
10 John Smoltz	.08	.25
11 Mark Lemke	.01	.05
12 Lonnie Smith	.01	.05
13 Oddibe McDowell	.01	.05
14 Tyler Houston RC	.08	.25
15 Jeff Blauser	.01	.05
16 Ernie Whitt	.01	.05
17 Alexis Infante	.01	.05
18 Jim Presley	.01	.05
19 Dale Murphy	.05	.15
20 Nick Esasky	.01	.05
21 Rick Sutcliffe	.02	.10
22 Mike Bielecki	.01	.05
23 Steve Wilson	.01	.05
24 Kevin Blankenship	.01	.05
25 Mitch Williams	.01	.05
26 Dean Wilkins RC	.01	.05
27 Greg Maddux	.15	.40
28 Mike Harkey	.01	.05
29 Mark Grace	.05	.15
30 Ryne Sandberg	.15	.40
31 Greg Smith RC	.01	.05
32 Dwight Smith	.01	.05
33 Damon Berryhill	.01	.05
34 E.Cunningham UER RC (Errant * by the word in)	.02	.10
35 Jerome Walton	.01	.05
36 Lloyd McClendon	.01	.05
37 Ty Griffin	.01	.05
38 Shawon Dunston	.01	.05
39 Andre Dawson	.02	.10
40 Luis Salazar	.01	.05
41 Tim Layana RC	.01	.05
42 Rob Dibble	.02	.10
43 Tom Browning	.01	.05
44 Danny Jackson	.01	.05
45 Jose Rijo	.01	.05
46 Scott Scudder	.01	.05
47 Randy Myers UER (Career ERA .274, should be 2.74)	.02	.10
48 Brian Lane RC	.02	.10
49 Paul O'Neill	.05	.15
50 Barry Larkin	.05	.15
51 Reggie Jefferson RC	.08	.25
52 Jeff Branson RC	.02	.10
53 Chris Sabo	.01	.05
54 Joe Oliver	.01	.05
55 Todd Benzinger	.01	.05
56 Rolando Roomes	.01	.05
57 Hal Morris	.01	.05
58 Eric Davis	.02	.10
59 Scott Bryant RC	.01	.05
60 Ken Griffey Sr.	.02	.10
61 Darryl Kile RC	.20	.50
62 Dave Smith	.01	.05
63 Mark Portugal	.01	.05
64 Jeff Juden RC	.02	.10
65 Bill Gullickson	.01	.05
66 Danny Darwin	.01	.05
67 Larry Andersen	.01	.05
68 Jose Cano RC	.01	.05
69 Dan Schatzeder	.01	.05
70 Jim Deshaies	.01	.05
71 Mike Scott	.01	.05
72 Gerald Young	.01	.05
73 Ken Caminiti	.02	.10
74 Ken Oberkfell	.01	.05
75 Dave Rohde RC	.01	.05
76 Bill Doran	.01	.05
77 Andujar Cedeno RC	.02	.10
78 Craig Biggio	.08	.25
79 Karl Rhodes RC	.08	.25
80 Glenn Davis	.01	.05
81 Eric Anthony RC	.02	.10
82 John Wetteland	.08	.25
83 Jay Howell	.01	.05
84 Orel Hershiser	.02	.10
85 Tim Belcher	.01	.05
86 Kiki Jones RC	.01	.05
87 Mike Hartley RC	.01	.05
88 Ramon Martinez	.01	.05
89 Mike Scioscia	.01	.05
90 Willie Randolph	.02	.10
91 Juan Samuel	.01	.05
92 Jose Offerman RC	.08	.25
93 Dave Hansen RC	.08	.25
94 Jeff Hamilton	.01	.05
95 Alfredo Griffin	.01	.05
96 Tom Goodwin RC	.08	.25
97 Kirk Gibson	.02	.10
98 Jose Vizcaino RC	.08	.25
99 Kal Daniels	.01	.05
100 Hubie Brooks	.01	.05
101 Eddie Murray	.08	.25
102 Dennis Boyd	.01	.05
103 Tim Burke	.01	.05
104 Bill Sampen RC	.01	.05
105 Brett Gideon	.01	.05
106 Mark Gardner RC	.02	.10
107 Howard Farmer RC	.01	.05
108 Mel Rojas RC	.02	.10
109 Kevin Gross	.01	.05
110 Dave Schmidt	.01	.05
111 Dennis Martinez	.02	.10
112 Jerry Goff RC	.01	.05
113 Andres Galarraga	.02	.10
114 Tim Wallach	.01	.05
115 Marquis Grissom RC	.20	.50
116 Spike Owen	.01	.05
117 Larry Walker RC	.40	1.00
118 Tim Raines	.02	.10
119 Delino DeShields RC	.08	.25
120 Tom Foley	.01	.05
121 Dave Martinez	.01	.05
122 Frank Viola UER (Career ERA .384 should be 3.84)	.01	.05
123 Julio Valera RC	.01	.05
124 Alejandro Pena	.01	.05
125 David Cone	.02	.10
126 Dwight Gooden	.02	.10
127 Kevin D. Brown RC	.01	.05
128 John Franco	.02	.10
129 Terry Bross RC	.01	.05
130 Blaine Beatty RC	.01	.05
131 Sid Fernandez	.01	.05
132 Mike Marshall	.01	.05
133 Howard Johnson	.01	.05
134 Jaime Roseboro RC	.01	.05
135 Alan Zinter RC	.02	.10
136 Keith Miller	.01	.05
137 Kevin Elster	.01	.05
138 Kevin McReynolds	.01	.05
139 Barry Lyons	.01	.05
140 Gregg Jefferies	.02	.10
141 Darryl Strawberry	.02	.10
142 Todd Hundley RC	.08	.25
143 Scott Service	.01	.05
144 Chuck Malone RC	.01	.05
145 Steve Ontiveros	.01	.05
146 Roger McDowell	.01	.05
147 Ken Howell	.01	.05
148 Pat Combs	.01	.05
149 Jeff Parrett	.01	.05
150 Chuck McElroy RC	.01	.05
151 Jason Grimsley RC	.02	.10
152 Len Dykstra	.02	.10
153 Mickey Morandini RC	.08	.25

154 John Kruk .02 .10
155 Dickie Thon .01 .05
156 Ricky Jordan .01 .05
157 Jeff Jackson RC .02 .10
158 Darren Daulton .02 .10
159 Tom Herr .01 .05
160 Von Hayes .01 .05
161 Dave Hollins RC .08 .25
162 Carmelo Martinez .01 .05
163 Bob Walk .01 .05
164 Doug Drabek .01 .05
165 Walt Terrell .01 .05
166 Bill Landrum .01 .05
167 Scott Ruskin RC .01 .05
168 Bob Patterson .01 .05
169 Bobby Bonilla .02 .10
170 Jose Lind .01 .05
171 Andy Van Slyke .05 .15
172 Mike LaValliere .01 .05
173 Willie Greene RC .02 .10
174 Jay Bell .02 .10
175 Sid Bream .01 .05
176 Tom Prince .01 .05
177 Wally Backman .01 .05
178 Moises Alou RC .30 .75
179 Steve Carter .01 .05
180 Gary Redus .01 .05
181 Barry Bonds .40 1.00
182 Don Slaught UER .01 .05
(Card back shows
headings for a pitcher)
183 Joe Magrane .01 .05
184 Bryn Smith .01 .05
185 Todd Worrell .01 .05
186 Jose DeLeon .01 .05
187 Frank DiPino .01 .05
188 John Tudor .01 .05
189 Howard Hilton RC .01 .05
190 John Ericks .01 .05
191 Ken Dayley .01 .05
192 Ray Lankford RC .20 .50
193 Todd Zeile .02 .10
194 Willie McGee .02 .10
195 Ozzie Smith .15 .40
196 Milt Thompson .01 .05
197 Terry Pendleton .02 .10
198 Vince Coleman .01 .05
199 Paul Coleman RC .02 .10
200 Jose Oquendo .01 .05
201 Pedro Guerrero .01 .05
202 Tom Brunansky .01 .05
203 Roger Smithberg RC .01 .05
204 Eddie Whitson .01 .05
205 Dennis Rasmussen .01 .05
206 Craig Lefferts .01 .05
207 Andy Benes .02 .10
208 Bruce Hurst .01 .05
209 Eric Show .01 .05
210 Rafael Valdez RC .01 .05
211 Joey Cora .02 .10
212 Thomas Howard .01 .05
213 Rob Nelson .01 .05
214 Jack Clark .02 .10
215 Garry Templeton .01 .05
216 Fred Lynn .01 .05
217 Tony Gwynn .10 .30
218 Benito Santiago .02 .10
219 Mike Pagliarulo .01 .05
220 Joe Carter .02 .10
221 Roberto Alomar .05 .15
222 Bip Roberts .01 .05
223 Rick Reuschel .01 .05
224 Russ Swan RC .01 .05
225 Eric Gunderson RC .01 .05
226 Steve Bedrosian .01 .05
227 Mike Remlinger RC .01 .05
228 Scott Garrelts .01 .05
229 Ernie Camacho .01 .05
230 Andres Santana RC .02 .10
231 Will Clark .05 .15
232 Kevin Mitchell .01 .05
233 Robby Thompson .01 .05
234 Bill Bathe .01 .05
235 Tony Perezchica .01 .05
236 Gary Carter .02 .10
237 Brett Butler .02 .10
238 Matt Williams .02 .10
239 Earnie Riles .01 .05
240 Kevin Bass .01 .05
241 Terry Kennedy .01 .05
242 Steve Hosey RC .02 .10
243 Ben McDonald RC .08 .25
244 Jeff Ballard .01 .05
245 Joe Price .01 .05
246 Curt Schilling .40 1.00
247 Pete Harnisch .01 .05
248 Mark Williamson .01 .05
249 Gregg Olson .02 .10
250 Chris Myers RC .01 .05
251A David Segui ERR .20 .50
(Missing vital stats
at top of card back
under name)
251B David Segui COR RC .20 .50
252 Joe Orsulak .01 .05
253 Craig Worthington .01 .05
254 Mickey Tettleton .01 .05
255 Cal Ripken .30 .75
256 Bill Ripken .01 .05
257 Randy Milligan .01 .05
258 Brady Anderson .02 .10
259 Chris Hoiles RC UER .08 .25
Baltimore is spelled Balitmore
260 Mike Devereaux .01 .05
261 Phil Bradley .01 .05
262 Leo Gomez RC .02 .10
263 Lee Smith .02 .10
264 Mike Rochford .01 .05
265 Jeff Reardon .02 .10
266 Wes Gardner .01 .05
267 Mike Boddicker .01 .05
268 Roger Clemens .40 1.00
269 Rob Murphy .01 .05
270 Mickey Pina RC .01 .05
271 Tony Pena .01 .05
272 Jody Reed .01 .05
273 Kevin Romine .01 .05
274 Mike Greenwell .01 .05
275 Mo Vaughn RC .40 1.00
276 Danny Heep .01 .05
277 Scott Cooper RC .02 .10
278 Greg Blosser RC .02 .10
279 Dwight Evans UER .05 .15
(* by 1990 Team
Breakdown)
280 Ellis Burks .05 .15
281 Wade Boggs .05 .15
282 Marty Barrett .01 .05
283 Kirk McCaskill .01 .05
284 Mark Langston .01 .05
285 Bert Blyleven .02 .10
286 Mike Fetters RC .08 .25
287 Kyle Abbott RC .01 .05
288 Jim Abbott .05 .15
289 Chuck Finley .02 .10
290 Gary DiSarcina RC .08 .25
291 Dick Schofield .01 .05
292 Devon White .02 .10
293 Bobby Rose .01 .05
294 Brian Downing .01 .05
295 Lance Parrish .01 .05
296 Jack Howell .01 .05
297 Claudell Washington .01 .05
298 John Orton RC .02 .10
299 Wally Joyner .02 .10
300 Lee Stevens .02 .10
301 Chili Davis .02 .10
302 Johnny Ray .01 .05
303 Greg Hibbard RC .02 .10
304 Eric King .01 .05
305 Jack McDowell .01 .05
306 Bobby Thigpen .01 .05
307 Adam Peterson .01 .05
308 Scott Radinsky RC .08 .25
309 Wayne Edwards RC .01 .05
310 Melido Perez .01 .05
311 Robin Ventura .08 .25
312 Sammy Sosa RC 1.25 3.00
313 Dan Pasqua .01 .05
314 Carlton Fisk .05 .15
315 Ozzie Guillen .02 .10
316 Ivan Calderon .01 .05
317 Daryl Boston .01 .05
318 Craig Grebeck RC .08 .25
319 Scott Fletcher .01 .05
320 Frank Thomas RC .75 2.00
321 Steve Lyons .01 .05
322 Carlos Martinez .01 .05
323 Joe Skalski .01 .05
324 Tom Candiotti .01 .05
325 Greg Swindell .01 .05
326 Steve Olin RC .08 .25
327 Kevin Wickander .01 .05
328 Doug Jones .01 .05
329 Jeff Shaw .01 .05
330 Kevin Bearse RC .01 .05
331 Dion James .01 .05
332 Jerry Browne .01 .05
333 Joey Belle .08 .25
334 Felix Fermin .01 .05
335 Candy Maldonado .01 .05
336 Cory Snyder .01 .05
337 Sandy Alomar Jr. .02 .10
338 Mark Lewis .01 .05
339 Carlos Baerga RC .08 .25
340 Chris James .01 .05
341 Brook Jacoby .01 .05
342 Keith Hernandez .02 .10
343 Frank Tanana .01 .05
344 Scott Aldred RC .01 .05
345 Mike Henneman .01 .05
346 Steve Wapnick RC .01 .05
347 Greg Gohr RC .02 .10
348 Eric Stone RC .01 .05
349 Brian DuBois RC .01 .05
350 Kevin Ritz RC .01 .05
351 Rico Brogna .08 .25
352 Mike Heath .01 .05
353 Alan Trammell .02 .10
354 Chet Lemon .01 .05
355 Dave Bergman .01 .05
356 Lou Whitaker .02 .10
357 Cecil Fielder UER .02 .10
* by 1990 Team Breakdown
358 Milt Cuyler RC .02 .10
359 Tony Phillips .02 .10
360 Travis Fryman RC .20 .50
361 Ed Romero .01 .05
362 Lloyd Moseby .01 .05
363 Mark Gubicza .01 .05
364 Bret Saberhagen .02 .10
365 Tom Gordon .02 .10
366 Steve Farr .01 .05
367 Kevin Appier .02 .10
368 Storm Davis .01 .05
369 Mark Davis .01 .05
370 Jeff Montgomery .02 .10
371 Frank White .02 .10
372 Brent Mayne RC .08 .25
373 Bob Boone .02 .10
374 Jim Eisenreich .01 .05
375 Danny Tartabull .01 .05
376 Kurt Stillwell .01 .05
377 Bill Pecota .01 .05
378 Bo Jackson .08 .25
379 Bob Hamelin RC .08 .25
380 Kevin Seitzer .01 .05
381 Rey Palacios .01 .05
382 George Brett .25 .60
383 Gerald Perry .01 .05
384 Teddy Higuera .01 .05
385 Tom Filer .01 .05
386 Dan Plesac .01 .05
387 Cal Eldred RC .08 .25
388 Jaime Navarro .01 .05
389 Chris Bosio .01 .05
390 Randy Veres .01 .05
391 Gary Sheffield .08 .25
392 George Canale RC .01 .05
393 B.J. Surhoff .02 .10
394 Tim McIntosh RC .01 .05
395 Greg Brock .01 .05
396 Greg Vaughn .01 .05
397 Darryl Hamilton .01 .05
398 Dave Parker .02 .10
399 Paul Molitor .02 .10
400 Jim Gantner .01 .05
401 Rob Deer .01 .05
402 Billy Spiers .01 .05
403 Glenn Braggs .01 .05
404 Robin Yount .15 .40
405 Rick Aguilera .02 .10
406 Johnny Ard .01 .05
407 Kevin Tapani RC .08 .25
408 Park Pittman RC .01 .05
409 Allan Anderson .01 .05
410 Juan Berenguer .01 .05
411 Willie Banks RC .02 .10
412 Rich Yett .01 .05
413 Dave West .01 .05
414 Greg Gagne .01 .05
415 Chuck Knoblauch RC .20 .50
416 Randy Bush .01 .05
417 Gary Gaetti .02 .10
418 Kent Hrbek .02 .10
419 Al Newman .01 .05
420 Danny Gladden .01 .05
421 Paul Sorrento RC .08 .25
422 Derek Parks RC .02 .10
423 Scott Leius RC .02 .10
424 Kirby Puckett .08 .25
425 Willie Smith .01 .05
426 Dave Righetti .01 .05
427 Jeff D. Robinson .01 .05
428 Alan Mills RC .02 .10
429 Tim Leary .01 .05
430 Pascual Perez .01 .05
431 Alvaro Espinoza .01 .05
432 Dave Winfield .02 .10
433 Jesse Barfield .01 .05
434 Randy Velarde .01 .05
435 Rick Cerone .01 .05
436 Steve Balboni .01 .05
437 Mel Hall .01 .05
438 Bob Geren .01 .05
439 Bernie Williams RC .60 1.50
440 Kevin Maas RC .08 .25
441 Mike Blowers RC .02 .10
442 Steve Sax .01 .05
443 Don Mattingly .25 .60
444 Roberto Kelly .01 .05
445 Mike Moore .01 .05
446 Reggie Harris RC .02 .10
447 Scott Sanderson .01 .05
448 Dave Otto .01 .05
449 Dave Stewart .02 .10
450 Rick Honeycutt .01 .05
451 Dennis Eckersley .02 .10
452 Carney Lansford .02 .10
453 Scott Hemond RC .02 .10
454 Mark McGwire .40 1.00
455 Felix Jose .01 .05
456 Terry Steinbach .01 .05
457 Rickey Henderson .08 .25
458 Dave Henderson .01 .05
459 Mike Gallego .01 .05
460 Jose Canseco .05 .15
461 Walt Weiss .01 .05
462 Ken Phelps .01 .05
463 Darren Lewis RC .02 .10
464 Ron Hassey .01 .05
465 Roger Salkeld RC .02 .10
466 Scott Bankhead .01 .05
467 Keith Comstock .01 .05
468 Randy Johnson .20 .50
469 Erik Hanson .01 .05
470 Mike Schooler .01 .05
471 Gary Eave RC .01 .05
472 Jeffrey Leonard .01 .05
473 Dave Valle .01 .05
474 Omar Vizquel .08 .25
475 Pete O'Brien .01 .05
476 Henry Cotto .01 .05
477 Jay Buhner .02 .10
478 Harold Reynolds .02 .10
479 Alvin Davis .01 .05
480 Darnell Coles .01 .05
481 Ken Griffey Jr. .30 .75
482 Greg Briley .01 .05
483 Scott Bradley .01 .05
484 Tino Martinez .20 .50
485 Jeff Russell .01 .05
486 Nolan Ryan .40 1.00
487 Robb Nen RC .20 .50
488 Kevin Brown .02 .10
489 Brian Bohanon RC .02 .10
490 Ruben Sierra .02 .10
491 Pete Incaviglia .01 .05
492 Juan Gonzalez RC .40 1.00
493 Steve Buechele .01 .05
494 Scott Coolbaugh .01 .05
495 Geno Petralli .01 .05
496 Rafael Palmeiro .05 .15
497 Julio Franco .02 .10
498 Gary Pettis .01 .05
499 Donald Harris RC .01 .05
500 Monty Fariss .01 .05
501 Harold Baines .02 .10
502 Cecil Espy .01 .05
503 Jack Daugherty RC .01 .05
504 Willie Blair RC .02 .10
505 Dave Stieb .02 .10
506 Tom Henke .01 .05
507 John Cerutti .01 .05
508 Paul Kilgus .01 .05
509 Jimmy Key .02 .10
510 John Olerud RC .40 1.00
511 Ed Sprague .02 .10
512 Manuel Lee .01 .05
513 Fred McGriff .08 .25
514 Glenallen Hill .01 .05
515 George Bell .01 .05
516 Mookie Wilson .02 .10
517 Luis Sojo RC .08 .25
518 Nelson Liriano .01 .05
519 Kelly Gruber .01 .05
520 Greg Myers .01 .05
521 Pat Borders .01 .05
522 Junior Felix .01 .05
523 Eddie Zosky RC .02 .10
524 Tony Fernandez .01 .05
525 Checklist 1-132 UER .01 .05
(No copyright mark
on the back)
526 Checklist 133-264 .01 .05
527 Checklist 265-396 .01 .05
528 Checklist 397-528 .01 .05

1990 Bowman Tiffany

These 528 standard-size cards were issued as a factory set by Topps. These cards parallel the regular Bowman issue except they have glossy fronts and a very easy to read white stock back. In addition to the 528 basic cards, the 11 insert art cards were also included in the factory set. According to published reports at the time, approximately 3,000 of these sets were produced.

COMP.FACT.SET (539) 100.00 200.00
*STARS: 6X TO 15X BASIC CARDS
*ROOKIES: 4X TO 10X BASIC CARDS

1990 Bowman Art Inserts

These standard-size cards were included as an insert in every 1990 Bowman pack. This set, which consists of 11 superstars, depicts drawings by Craig Pursley with the backs being descriptions of the 1990 Bowman sweepstakes. We have checklisted the set alphabetically by player. All the cards in this set can be found with either one asterisk or two on the back.

COMPLETE SET (11) .75 2.00
*TIFFANY: 8X TO 20X BASIC ART INSERT
ONE TIFF.REP.SET PER TIFF.FACT.SET
1 Will Clark .05 .15
2 Mark Davis .01 .05
3 Dwight Gooden .02 .10
4 Bo Jackson .08 .25
5 Don Mattingly .25 .60
6 Kevin Mitchell .01 .05
7 Gregg Olson .02 .10
8 Nolan Ryan .40 1.00
9 Bret Saberhagen .02 .10
10 Jerome Walton .01 .05
11 Robin Yount .15 .40

1990 Bowman Insert Lithographs

These 11" by 14" lithographs were issued through both Topps dealer network and through a pack/wrapper redemption. The fronts of the lithographs are larger versions of the 1990 Bowman insert sets. These lithos were drawn by Craig Pursley and are signed by the artist and are come either with or without serial numbering to 500. The backs are blank but we are sequencing them in the same order as the 1990 Bowman inserts. The lithos which the artist signed are worth approximately 2X to 3X the regular lithographs.

COMPLETE SET (11) 240.00 600.00
1 Will Clark 20.00 50.00
2 Mark Davis 10.00 25.00
3 Dwight Gooden 12.50 30.00
4 Bo Jackson 20.00 50.00
5 Don Mattingly 40.00 100.00
6 Kevin Mitchell 10.00 25.00
7 Gregg Olson 10.00 25.00
8 Nolan Ryan 100.00 250.00
9 Bret Saberhagen 12.50 30.00
10 Jerome Walton 10.00 25.00
11 Robin Yount 25.00 60.00

1991 Bowman

This single-series 704-card standard-size set marked the third straight year that Topps issued a set weighted towards prospects using the Bowman name. Cards were issued in wax packs and factory sets. The cards share a design very similar to the 1990 Bowman set with white borders enframing a color photo. The player name, however, is more prominent than in the previous year set. The cards are arranged in team order by division as follows: AL East, AL West, NL East, and NL West. Subsets include Rod Carew Tribute (1-5), Minor League MVP's (180-185/693-698), AL Silver Sluggers (367-375), NL Silver Sluggers (376-384) and checklists (699-704). Rookie Cards in this set include Jeff Bagwell, Jeromy Burnitz, Carl Everett, Chipper Jones, Eric Karros, Ryan Klesko, Kenny Lofton, Javier Lopez, Raul Mondesi, Mike Mussina, Ivan "Pudge" Rodriguez, Tim Salmon, Jim Thome, and Rondell White. There are two instances of misnumbering in the set; Ken Griffey (should be 255) and Ken Griffey Jr. are both numbered 246 and Donovan Osborne (should be 406) and Thomson/Branca share number 410.

COMPLETE SET (704) 15.00 40.00
COMP.FACT.SET (704) 15.00 40.00
1 Rod Carew I .05 .15
2 Rod Carew II .05 .15
3 Rod Carew III .05 .15
4 Rod Carew IV .05 .15
5 Rod Carew V .05 .15
6 Willie Fraser .01 .05
7 John Olerud .02 .10
8 William Suero RC .01 .05
9 Roberto Alomar .05 .15
10 Todd Stottlemyre .01 .05
11 Joe Carter .02 .10
12 Steve Karsay RC .20 .50
13 Mark Whiten .01 .05
14 Pat Borders .01 .05
15 Mike Timlin RC .20 .50
16 Tom Henke .01 .05
17 Eddie Zosky .01 .05
18 Kelly Gruber .01 .05
19 Jimmy Key .02 .10
20 Jerry Schunk RC .01 .05
21 Manuel Lee .01 .05
22 Dave Stieb .01 .05
23 Pat Hentgen RC .20 .50
24 Glenallen Hill .01 .05
25 Rene Gonzales .01 .05
26 Ed Sprague .01 .05
27 Ken Dayley .01 .05
28 Pat Tabler .01 .05
29 Denis Boucher RC .05 .15
30 Devon White .02 .10
31 Dante Bichette .02 .10
32 Paul Molitor .02 .10
33 Greg Vaughn .01 .05
34 Dan Plesac .01 .05
35 Chris George RC .05 .15
36 Tim McIntosh .01 .05
37 Franklin Stubbs .01 .05
38 Bo Dodson RC .05 .15
39 Ron Robinson .01 .05
40 Ed Nunez .01 .05
41 Greg Brock .01 .05
42 Jaime Navarro .01 .05
43 Chris Bosio .01 .05
44 B.J. Surhoff .02 .10
45 Chris Johnson RC .01 .05
46 Willie Randolph .02 .10
47 Narciso Elvira RC .01 .05
48 Jim Gantner .01 .05
49 Kevin Brown .01 .05
50 Julio Machado .01 .05
51 Chuck Crim .01 .05
52 Gary Sheffield .02 .10
53 Angel Miranda RC .05 .15
54 Ted Higuera .01 .05
55 Robin Yount .15 .40
56 Cal Eldred .01 .05
57 Sandy Alomar Jr. .01 .05
58 Greg Swindell .01 .05
59 Brook Jacoby .01 .05
60 Efrain Valdez RC .01 .05
61 Ever Magallanes RC .01 .05
62 Tom Candiotti .01 .05
63 Eric King .01 .05
64 Alex Cole .01 .05
65 Charles Nagy .01 .05
66 Mitch Webster .01 .05
67 Chris James .01 .05
68 Jim Thome RC 1.50 4.00
69 Carlos Baerga .01 .05
70 Mark Lewis .01 .05
71 Jerry Browne .01 .05
72 Jesse Orosco .01 .05
73 Mike Huff .01 .05
74 Jose Escobar RC .01 .05
75 Jeff Manto .01 .05
76 Turner Ward RC .05 .15
77 Doug Jones .01 .05
78 Bruce Egloff RC .01 .05
79 Tim Costo RC .05 .15
80 Beau Allred .01 .05
81 Albert Belle .02 .10
82 John Farrell .01 .05
83 Glenn Davis .01 .05
84 Joe Orsulak .01 .05
85 Mark Williamson .01 .05
86 Ben McDonald .01 .05
87 Billy Ripken .01 .05
88 Leo Gomez UER .01 .05
Baltimore is spelled Balitmore
89 Bob Melvin .01 .05
90 Jeff M. Robinson .01 .05
91 Jose Mesa .01 .05
92 Gregg Olson .01 .05
93 Mike Devereaux .01 .05
94 Luis Mercedes RC .05 .15
95 Arthur Rhodes RC .20 .50
96 Juan Bell .01 .05
97 Mike Mussina RC 1.50 4.00
98 Jeff Ballard .01 .05
99 Chris Hoiles .01 .05
100 Brady Anderson .02 .10
101 Bob Milacki .01 .05
102 David Segui .01 .05
103 Dwight Evans .05 .15
104 Cal Ripken .30 .75
105 Mike Linskey RC .01 .05
106 Jeff Tackett RC .05 .15
107 Jeff Reardon .02 .10
108 Dana Kiecker .01 .05
109 Ellis Burks .02 .10
110 Dave Owen .01 .05
111 Danny Darwin .01 .05
112 Mo Vaughn .02 .10
113 Jeff McNeely RC .05 .15
114 Tom Bolton .01 .05
115 Greg Blosser .01 .05
116 Mike Greenwell .01 .05
117 Phil Plantier RC .05 .15
118 Roger Clemens .30 .75
119 John Marzano .01 .05
120 Jody Reed .01 .05
121 Scott Taylor RC .05 .15
122 Jack Clark .02 .10
123 Derek Livernois RC .01 .05
124 Tony Pena .01 .05
125 Tom Brunansky .01 .05
126 Carlos Quintana .01 .05
127 Tim Naehring .01 .05
128 Matt Young .01 .05
129 Wade Boggs .05 .15
130 Kevin Morton RC .01 .05
131 Pete Incaviglia .01 .05
132 Rob Deer .01 .05
133 Bill Gullickson .01 .05
134 Rico Brogna .01 .05
135 Lloyd Moseby .01 .05
136 Cecil Fielder .02 .10
137 Tony Phillips .01 .05
138 Mark Leiter RC .05 .15
139 John Cerutti .01 .05
140 Mickey Tettleton .01 .05
141 Milt Cuyler .01 .05
142 Greg Gohr .01 .05
143 Tony Bernazard .01 .05
144 Dan Gakeler RC .01 .05
145 Travis Fryman .02 .10
146 Dan Petry .01 .05
147 Scott Aldred .01 .05
148 John DeSilva RC .01 .05
149 Rusty Meacham RC .05 .15
150 Lou Whitaker .02 .10
151 Dave Haas RC .01 .05
152 Luis de los Santos .01 .05
153 Ivan Cruz RC .01 .05
154 Alan Trammell .02 .10
155 Pat Kelly RC .01 .05
156 Carl Everett RC .60 1.50
157 Greg Cadaret .01 .05
158 Kevin Maas .01 .05
159 Jeff Johnson RC .01 .05
160 Willie Smith .01 .05
161 Gerald Williams RC .20 .50
162 Mike Humphreys RC .05 .15
163 Alvaro Espinoza .01 .05
164 Matt Nokes .01 .05
165 Wade Taylor RC .01 .05
166 Roberto Kelly .01 .05
167 John Habyan .01 .05
168 Steve Farr .01 .05
169 Jesse Barfield .01 .05
170 Steve Sax .01 .05
171 Jim Leyritz .01 .05
172 Robert Eenhoorn RC .05 .15
173 Bernie Williams .08 .25
174 Scott Lusader .01 .05
175 Torey Lovullo .01 .05
176 Chuck Cary .01 .05
177 Scott Sanderson .01 .05
178 Don Mattingly .25 .60
179 Mel Hall .01 .05
180 Juan Gonzalez .08 .25
181 Hensley Meulens .01 .05
182 Jose Offerman .01 .05
183 Jeff Bagwell RC 1.25 3.00
184 Jeff Conine RC .40 1.00
185 Henry Rodriguez RC .20 .50
186 Jimmie Reese CO .02 .10
187 Kyle Abbott .01 .05
188 Lance Parrish .02 .10
189 Rafael Montalvo RC .01 .05
190 Floyd Bannister .01 .05
191 Dick Schofield .01 .05
192 Scott Lewis RC .01 .05
193 Jeff D. Robinson .01 .05
194 Kent Anderson .01 .05
195 Wally Joyner .02 .10
196 Chuck Finley .02 .10
197 Luis Sojo .01 .05
198 Jeff Richardson RC .01 .05
199 Dave Parker .02 .10
200 Jim Abbott .05 .15
201 Junior Felix .01 .05
202 Mark Langston .01 .05
203 Tim Salmon RC .60 1.50
204 Cliff Young .01 .05
205 Scott Bailes .01 .05
206 Bobby Rose .01 .05
207 Gary Gaetti .02 .10
208 Ruben Amaro RC .05 .15
209 Luis Polonia .01 .05
210 Dave Winfield .02 .10
211 Bryan Harvey .01 .05
212 Mike Moore .01 .05
213 Rickey Henderson .08 .25
214 Steve Chitren RC .01 .05
215 Bob Welch .01 .05
216 Terry Steinbach .01 .05
217 Earnest Riles .01 .05
218 Todd Van Poppel RC .20 .50
219 Mike Gallego .01 .05
220 Curt Young .01 .05
221 Todd Burns .01 .05
222 Vance Law .01 .05
223 Eric Show .01 .05
224 Don Peters RC .01 .05
225 Dave Stewart .02 .10
226 Dave Henderson .01 .05
227 Jose Canseco .05 .15
228 Walt Weiss .01 .05
229 Dann Howitt .01 .05
230 Willie Wilson .01 .05
231 Harold Baines .02 .10
232 Scott Hemond .01 .05
233 Joe Slusarski RC .01 .05
234 Mark McGwire .30 .75
235 K.Dressendorfer RC .05 .15
236 Craig Paquette RC .20 .50
237 Dennis Eckersley .02 .10
238 Dana Allison RC .01 .05
239 Scott Bradley .01 .05
240 Brian Holman .01 .05
241 Mike Schooler .01 .05
242 Rich DeLucia RC .01 .05
243 Edgar Martinez .05 .15
244 Henry Cotto .01 .05
245 Omar Vizquel .05 .15
246 Ken Griffey Jr. .20 .50
(See also 255)
247 Jay Buhner .02 .10
248 Bill Krueger .01 .05
249 Dave Fleming RC .05 .15

250 Patrick Lennon RC .01 .05
251 Dave Valle .01 .05
252 Harold Reynolds .02 .10
253 Randy Johnson .10 .30
254 Scott Bankhead .01 .05
255 Ken Griffey Sr. UER .01 .05
(Card number is 246)
256 Greg Briley .01 .05
257 Tino Martinez .08 .25
258 Alvin Davis .01 .05
259 Pete O'Brien .01 .05
260 Erik Hanson .01 .05
261 Bret Boone RC .60 1.50
262 Roger Salkeld .01 .05
263 Dave Burba RC .20 .50
264 Kerry Woodson RC .05 .15
265 Julio Franco .02 .10
266 Dan Peltier RC .05 .15
267 Jeff Russell .01 .05
268 Steve Buechele .01 .05
269 Donald Harris .01 .05
270 Robb Nen .05 .15
271 Rich Gossage .02 .10
272 Ivan Rodriguez RC 1.50 4.00
273 Jeff Huson .01 .05
274 Kevin Brown .02 .10
275 Dan Smith RC .05 .15
276 Gary Pettis .01 .05
277 Jack Daugherty .01 .05
278 Mike Jeffcoat .01 .05
279 Brad Arnsberg .01 .05
280 Nolan Ryan .40 1.00
281 Eric McCray RC .01 .05
282 Scott Chiamparino .01 .05
283 Ruben Sierra .02 .10
284 Geno Petralli .01 .05
285 Monty Fariss .01 .05
286 Rafael Palmeiro .05 .15
287 Bobby Witt .01 .05
288 Dean Palmer UER .02 .10
Photo is Dan Peltier
289 Tony Scruggs RC .01 .05
290 Kenny Rogers .02 .10
291 Bret Saberhagen .02 .10
292 Brian McRae RC .20 .50
293 Storm Davis .01 .05
294 Danny Tartabull .01 .05
295 David Howard RC .01 .05
296 Mike Boddicker .01 .05
297 Joel Johnston RC .05 .15
298 Tim Spehr RC .01 .05
299 Hector Wagner RC .01 .05
300 George Brett .25 .60
301 Mike Macfarlane .01 .05
302 Kirk Gibson .02 .10
303 Harvey Pulliam RC .05 .15
304 Jim Eisenreich .01 .05
305 Kevin Seitzer .01 .05
306 Mark Davis .01 .05
307 Kurt Stillwell .01 .05
308 Jeff Montgomery .01 .05
309 Kevin Appier .02 .10
310 Bob Hamelin .01 .05
311 Tom Gordon .01 .05
312 Kerwin Moore RC .05 .15
313 Hugh Walker .01 .05
314 Terry Shumpert .01 .05
315 Warren Cromartie .01 .05
316 Gary Thurman .01 .05
317 Steve Bedrosian .01 .05
318 Danny Gladden .01 .05
319 Jack Morris .02 .10
320 Kirby Puckett .08 .25
321 Kent Hrbek .02 .10
322 Kevin Tapani .01 .05
323 Denny Neagle RC .20 .50
324 Rich Garces RC .05 .15
325 Larry Casian RC .01 .05
326 Shane Mack .01 .05
327 Allan Anderson .01 .05
328 Junior Ortiz .01 .05
329 Paul Abbott RC .05 .15
330 Chuck Knoblauch .05 .15
331 Chili Davis .02 .10
332 Todd Ritchie RC .20 .50
333 Brian Harper .01 .05
334 Rick Aguilera .02 .10
335 Scott Erickson .01 .05
336 Pedro Munoz RC .05 .15
337 Scott Leius .01 .05
338 Greg Gagne .01 .05
339 Mike Pagliarulo .01 .05
340 Terry Leach .01 .05
341 Willie Banks .01 .05
342 Bobby Thigpen .01 .05
343 Roberto Hernandez RC .20 .50
344 Melido Perez .01 .05
345 Carlton Fisk .05 .15
346 Norberto Martin RC .01 .05
347 Johnny Ruffin RC .05 .15
348 Jeff Carter .01 .05
349 Lance Johnson .01 .05
350 Sammy Sosa .08 .25
351 Alex Fernandez .01 .05
352 Jack McDowell .01 .05
353 Bob Wickman RC .60 1.50
354 Wilson Alvarez .01 .05
355 Charlie Hough .02 .10
356 Ozzie Guillen .02 .10
357 Cory Snyder .01 .05
358 Robin Ventura .02 .10
359 Scott Fletcher .01 .05
360 Cesar Bernhardt RC .01 .05
361 Dan Pasqua .01 .05
362 Tim Raines .02 .10
363 Brian Drahman RC .01 .05
364 Wayne Edwards .01 .05
365 Scott Radinsky .01 .05
366 Frank Thomas .08 .25
367 Cecil Fielder SLUG .01 .05
368 Julio Franco SLUG .01 .05
369 Kelly Gruber SLUG .01 .05
370 Alan Trammell SLUG .02 .10
371 R.Henderson SLUG .05 .15
372 Jose Canseco SLUG .02 .10
373 Ellis Burks SLUG .01 .05
374 Lance Parrish SLUG .01 .05
375 Dave Parker SLUG .01 .05
376 Eddie Murray SLUG .05 .15
377 Ryne Sandberg SLUG .08 .25
378 Matt Williams SLUG .01 .05
379 Barry Larkin SLUG .02 .10
380 Barry Bonds SLUG .20 .50
381 Bobby Bonilla SLUG .01 .05
382 D.Strawberry SLUG .01 .05
383 Benny Santiago SLUG .01 .05
384 Don Robinson SLUG .01 .05
385 Paul Coleman .01 .05
386 Milt Thompson .01 .05
387 Lee Smith .02 .10
388 Ray Lankford .02 .10
389 Tom Pagnozzi .01 .05
390 Ken Hill .01 .05
391 Jamie Moyer .02 .10
392 Greg Carmona RC .01 .05
393 John Ericks .01 .05
394 Bob Tewksbury .01 .05
395 Jose Oquendo .01 .05
396 Rheal Cormier RC .05 .15
397 Mike Milchin RC .01 .05
398 Ozzie Smith .15 .40
399 Aaron Holbert RC .05 .15
400 Jose DeLeon .01 .05
401 Felix Jose .01 .05
402 Juan Agosto .01 .05
403 Pedro Guerrero .02 .10
404 Todd Zeile .01 .05
405 Gerald Perry .01 .05
406 D.Osborne UER RC .05 .15
Card number is 410)
407 Bryn Smith .01 .05
408 Bernard Gilkey .01 .05
409 Rex Hudler .01 .05
410 Bobby Thomson .08 .25
Ralph Branca
Shot Heard Round the World
See also 406
411 Lance Dickson RC .05 .15
412 Danny Jackson .01 .05
413 Jerome Walton .01 .05
414 Sean Cheetham RC .01 .05
415 Joe Girardi .01 .05
416 Ryne Sandberg .15 .40
417 Mike Harkey .01 .05
418 George Bell .01 .05
419 Rick Wilkins RC .05 .15
420 Earl Cunningham .01 .05
421 Heathcliff Slocumb RC .05 .15
422 Mike Bielecki .01 .05
423 Jessie Hollins RC .05 .15
424 Shawon Dunston .01 .05
425 Dave Smith .01 .05
426 Greg Maddux .15 .40
427 Jose Vizcaino .01 .05
428 Luis Salazar .01 .05
429 Andre Dawson .02 .10
430 Rick Sutcliffe .02 .10
431 Paul Assenmacher .01 .05
432 Erik Pappas RC .01 .05
433 Mark Grace .05 .15
434 Dennis Martinez .02 .10
435 Marquis Grissom .02 .10
436 Wil Cordero RC .20 .50
437 Tim Wallach .01 .05
438 Brian Barnes RC .01 .05
439 Barry Jones .01 .05
440 Ivan Calderon .01 .05
441 Stan Spencer RC .01 .05
442 Larry Walker .08 .25
443 Chris Haney RC .05 .15
444 Hector Rivera RC .01 .05
445 Delino DeShields .02 .10
446 Andres Galarraga .02 .10
447 Gilberto Reyes .01 .05
448 Willie Greene .01 .05
449 Greg Colbrunn RC .20 .50
450 Rondell White RC .40 1.00
451 Steve Frey .01 .05
452 Shane Andrews RC .05 .15
453 Mike Fitzgerald .01 .05
454 Spike Owen .01 .05
455 Dave Martinez .01 .05
456 Dennis Boyd .01 .05
457 Eric Bullock .01 .05
458 Reid Cornelius RC .05 .15
459 Chris Nabholz .01 .05
460 David Cone .02 .10
461 Hubie Brooks .01 .05
462 Sid Fernandez .01 .05
463 Doug Simons RC .01 .05
464 Howard Johnson .01 .05
465 Chris Donnels RC .01 .05
466 Anthony Young RC .05 .15
467 Todd Hundley .01 .05
468 Rick Cerone .01 .05
469 Kevin Elster .01 .05
470 Wally Whitehurst .01 .05
471 Vince Coleman .01 .05
472 Dwight Gooden .02 .10
473 Charlie O'Brien .01 .05
474 Jeromy Burnitz RC .40 1.00
475 John Franco .02 .10
476 Daryl Boston .01 .05
477 Frank Viola .02 .10
478 D.J. Dozier .01 .05
479 Kevin McReynolds .01 .05
480 Tom Herr .01 .05
481 Gregg Jefferies .01 .05
482 Pete Schourek RC .05 .15
483 Ron Darling .01 .05
484 Dave Magadan .01 .05
485 Andy Ashby RC .20 .50
486 Dale Murphy .05 .15
487 Von Hayes .01 .05
488 Kim Batiste RC .05 .15
489 Tony Longmire RC .05 .15
490 Wally Backman .01 .05
491 Jeff Jackson .01 .05
492 Mickey Morandini .01 .05
493 Darrel Akerfelds .01 .05
494 Ricky Jordan .01 .05
495 Randy Ready .01 .05
496 Darrin Fletcher .01 .05
497 Chuck Malone .01 .05
498 Pat Combs .01 .05
499 Dickie Thon .01 .05
500 Roger McDowell .01 .05
501 Len Dykstra .02 .10
502 Joe Boever .01 .05
503 John Kruk .02 .10
504 Terry Mulholland .01 .05
505 Wes Chamberlain RC .05 .15
506 Mike Lieberthal RC .40 1.00
507 Darren Daulton .02 .10
508 Charlie Hayes .01 .05
509 John Smiley .01 .05
510 Gary Varsho .01 .05
511 Curt Wilkerson .01 .05
512 Orlando Merced RC .05 .15
513 Barry Bonds .40 1.00
514 Mike LaValliere .01 .05
515 Doug Drabek .01 .05
516 Gary Redus .01 .05
517 W.Pennyfeather RC .05 .15
518 Randy Tomlin RC .05 .15
519 Mike Zimmerman RC .05 .15
520 Jeff King .01 .05
521 Kurt Miller RC .05 .15
522 Jay Bell .02 .10
523 Bill Landrum .01 .05
524 Zane Smith .01 .05
525 Bobby Bonilla .02 .10
526 Bob Walk .01 .05
527 Austin Manahan .01 .05
528 Joe Ausanio RC .01 .05
529 Andy Van Slyke .05 .15
530 Jose Lind .01 .05
531 Carlos Garcia RC .05 .15
532 Don Slaught .01 .05
533 Gen.Colin Powell .20 .50
534 Frank Bolick RC .05 .15
535 Gary Scott RC .01 .05
536 Nikco Riesgo RC .01 .05
537 Reggie Sanders RC .60 1.50
538 Tim Howard RC .05 .15
539 Ryan Bowen RC .05 .15
540 Eric Anthony .01 .05
541 Jim Deshaies .01 .05
542 Tom Nevers RC .05 .15
543 Ken Caminiti .02 .10
544 Karl Rhodes .01 .05
545 Xavier Hernandez .01 .05
546 Mike Scott .01 .05
547 Jeff Juden .01 .05
548 Darryl Kile .01 .05
549 Willie Ansley .01 .05
550 Luis Gonzalez RC .60 1.50
551 Mike Simms RC .01 .05
552 Mark Portugal .01 .05
553 Jimmy Jones .01 .05
554 Jim Clancy .01 .05
555 Pete Harnisch .01 .05
556 Craig Biggio .05 .15
557 Eric Yelding .01 .05
558 Dave Rohde .01 .05
559 Casey Candaele .01 .05
560 Curt Schilling .08 .25
561 Steve Finley .02 .10
562 Javier Ortiz .01 .05
563 Andujar Cedeno .01 .05
564 Rafael Ramirez .01 .05
565 Kenny Lofton RC .60 1.50
566 Steve Avery .01 .05
567 Lonnie Smith .01 .05
568 Kent Mercker .01 .05
569 Chipper Jones RC 2.50 6.00
570 Terry Pendleton .02 .10
571 Otis Nixon .01 .05
572 Juan Berenguer .01 .05
573 Charlie Leibrandt .01 .05
574 David Justice .02 .10
575 Keith Mitchell RC .05 .15
576 Tom Glavine .05 .15
577 Greg Olson .01 .05
578 Rafael Belliard .01 .05
579 Ben Rivera RC .05 .15
580 John Smoltz .05 .15
581 Tyler Houston .01 .05
582 Mark Wohlers RC .20 .50
583 Ron Gant .02 .10
584 Ramon Caraballo RC .05 .15
585 Sid Bream .01 .05
586 Jeff Treadway .01 .05
587 Javy Lopez RC 1.25 3.00
588 Deion Sanders .05 .15
589 Mike Heath .01 .05
590 Ryan Klesko RC .40 1.00
591 Bob Ojeda .01 .05
592 Alfredo Griffin .01 .05
593 Raul Mondesi RC .40 1.00
594 Greg Smith .01 .05
595 Orel Hershiser .02 .10
596 Juan Samuel .01 .05
597 Brett Butler .02 .10
598 Gary Carter .02 .10
599 Stan Javier .01 .05
600 Kal Daniels .01 .05
601 Jamie McAndrew RC .05 .15
602 Mike Sharperson .01 .05
603 Jay Howell .01 .05
604 Eric Karros RC .60 1.50
605 Tim Belcher .01 .05
606 Dan Opperman RC .01 .05
607 Lenny Harris .01 .05
608 Tom Goodwin .01 .05
609 Darryl Strawberry .02 .10
610 Ramon Martinez .01 .05
611 Kevin Gross .01 .05
612 Zakary Shinall RC .01 .05
613 Mike Scioscia .01 .05
614 Eddie Murray .08 .25
615 Ronnie Walden RC .05 .15
616 Will Clark .05 .15
617 Adam Hyzdu RC .20 .50
618 Matt Williams .02 .10
619 Don Robinson .01 .05
620 Jeff Brantley .01 .05
621 Greg Litton .01 .05
622 Steve Decker RC .01 .05
623 Robby Thompson .01 .05
624 Mark Leonard RC .01 .05
625 Kevin Bass .01 .05
626 Scott Garrelts .01 .05
627 Jose Uribe .01 .05
628 Eric Gunderson .01 .05
629 Steve Hosey .01 .05
630 Trevor Wilson .01 .05
631 Terry Kennedy .01 .05
632 Dave Righetti .02 .10
633 Kelly Downs .01 .05
634 Johnny Ard .01 .05
635 E.Christopherson RC .05 .15
636 Kevin Mitchell .01 .05
637 John Burkett .01 .05
638 Kevin Rogers RC .05 .15
639 Bud Black .01 .05
640 Willie McGee .02 .10
641 Royce Clayton .01 .05
642 Tony Fernandez .01 .05
643 Ricky Bones RC .05 .15
644 Thomas Howard .01 .05
645 Dave Staton RC .05 .15
646 Jim Presley .01 .05
647 Tony Gwynn .10 .30
648 Marty Barrett .01 .05
649 Scott Coolbaugh .01 .05
650 Craig Lefferts .01 .05
651 Eddie Whitson .01 .05
652 Oscar Azocar .01 .05
653 Wes Gardner .01 .05
654 Bip Roberts .01 .05
655 Robbie Beckett RC .05 .15
656 Benito Santiago .02 .10
657 Greg W.Harris .01 .05
658 Jerald Clark .01 .05
659 Fred McGriff .05 .15
660 Larry Andersen .01 .05
661 Bruce Hurst .01 .05
662 Steve Martin UER RC .05 .15
Card said he pitched at Waterloo
he's an outfielder)
663 Rafael Valdez .01 .05
664 Paul Faries RC .01 .05
665 Andy Benes .01 .05
666 Randy Myers .01 .05
667 Rob Dibble .02 .10
668 Glenn Sutko RC .01 .05
669 Glenn Braggs .01 .05
670 Billy Hatcher .01 .05
671 Joe Oliver .01 .05
672 Freddie Benavides RC .05 .15
673 Barry Larkin .05 .15
674 Chris Sabo .01 .05
675 Mariano Duncan .01 .05
676 Chris Jones RC .01 .05
677 Gino Minutelli RC .01 .05
678 Reggie Jefferson .01 .05
679 Jack Armstrong .01 .05
680 Chris Hammond .01 .05
681 Jose Rijo .01 .05
682 Bill Doran .01 .05
683 Terry Lee RC .01 .05
684 Tom Browning .01 .05
685 Paul O'Neill .05 .15
686 Eric Davis .02 .10
687 Dan Wilson RC .20 .50
688 Ted Power .01 .05
689 Tim Layana .01 .05
690 Norm Charlton .01 .05
691 Hal Morris .01 .05
692 Rickey Henderson .05 .15
693 Sam Militello RC .05 .15
694 Matt Mieske RC .05 .15
695 Paul Russo RC .05 .15
696 Domingo Mota MVP .01 .05
697 Todd Guggiana RC .05 .15
698 Marc Newfield RC .05 .15
699 Checklist 1-122 .01 .05
700 Checklist 123-244 .01 .05
701 Checklist 245-366 .01 .05
702 Checklist 367-471 .01 .05
703 Checklist 472-593 .01 .05
704 Checklist 594-704 .01 .05

1992 Bowman

This 705-card standard-size set was issued in one comprehensive series. Unlike the previous Bowman issues, the 1992 set was radically upgraded to slick stock with gold foil subset cards in an attempt to reposition the brand as a premium level product. It initially stumbled out of the gate, but its superior selection of prospects enabled it to eventually gain acceptance in the hobby and now stands as one of the more important issues of the 1990's. Cards were distributed in plastic wrap packs, retail jumbo packs and special 80-card retail carton packs. Card fronts feature posed and action color player photos on a UV-coated white card face. Forty-five foil cards inserted at a stated rate of one per wax pack and two per jumbo (23 regular cards) pack. These foil cards feature past and present Team USA players and minor league POY Award winners. Each foil card has an extremely slight variation in that the photos are cropped differently. There is no additional value to either version. Some of the regular and special cards picture prospects in civilian clothing who were still in the farm system. Rookie Cards in this set include Garret Anderson, Carlos Delgado, Mike Hampton, Brian Jordan, Mike Piazza, Manny Ramirez and Mariano Rivera.

COMPLETE SET (705) 75.00 150.00
1 Ivan Rodriguez .50 1.25
2 Kirk McCaskill .20 .50
3 Scott Livingstone .20 .50
4 Salomon Torres RC .20 .50
5 Carlos Hernandez .20 .50
6 Dave Hollins .20 .50
7 Scott Fletcher .20 .50
8 Jorge Fabregas RC .20 .50
9 Andujar Cedeno .20 .50
10 Howard Johnson .20 .50
11 Trevor Hoffman RC 4.00 10.00
12 Roberto Kelly .20 .50
13 Gregg Jefferies .20 .50
14 Marquis Grissom .20 .50
15 Mike Ignasiak .20 .50
16 Jack Morris .20 .50
17 William Pennyfeather .20 .50
18 Todd Stottlemyre .20 .50
19 Chito Martinez .20 .50
20 Roberto Alomar .30 .75
21 Sam Militello .20 .50
22 Hector Fajardo RC .20 .50
23 Paul Quantrill RC .20 .50
24 Chuck Knoblauch .20 .50
25 Reggie Jefferson .20 .50
26 Jeremy McGarity RC .20 .50
27 Jerome Walton .20 .50
28 Chipper Jones 5.00 12.00
29 Brian Barber RC .20 .50
30 Ron Darling .20 .50
31 Roberto Petagine RC .20 .50
32 Chuck Finley .20 .50
33 Edgar Martinez .30 .75
34 Napoleon Robinson .20 .50
35 Andy Van Slyke .30 .75
36 Bobby Thigpen .20 .50
37 Travis Fryman .20 .50
38 Eric Christopherson .20 .50
39 Terry Mulholland .20 .50
40 Darryl Strawberry .20 .50
41 Manny Alexander RC .20 .50
42 Tracy Sanders RC .20 .50
43 Pete Incaviglia .20 .50
44 Kim Batiste .20 .50
45 Frank Rodriguez .20 .50
46 Greg Swindell .20 .50
47 Delino DeShields .20 .50
48 John Ericks .20 .50
49 Franklin Stubbs .20 .50
50 Tony Gwynn .60 1.50
51 Clifton Garrett RC .20 .50
52 Mike Gardella .20 .50
53 Scott Erickson .20 .50
54 Gary Caraballo RC .20 .50
55 Jose Oliva RC .20 .50
56 Brook Fordyce .20 .50
57 Mark Whiten .20 .50
58 Joe Slusarski .20 .50
59 J.R. Phillips RC .20 .50
60 Barry Bonds 1.50 4.00
61 Bob Milacki .20 .50
62 Keith Mitchell .20 .50
63 Angel Miranda .20 .50
64 Raul Mondesi .20 .50
65 Brian Koelling RC .20 .50
66 Brian McRae .20 .50
67 John Patterson RC .20 .50
68 John Wetteland .20 .50
69 Wilson Alvarez .20 .50
70 Wade Boggs .30 .75
71 Darryl Ratliff RC .20 .50
72 Jeff Jackson .20 .50
73 Jeremy Hernandez RC .20 .50
74 Darryl Hamilton .20 .50
75 Rafael Belliard .20 .50
76 Rick Trlicek RC .20 .50
77 Felipe Crespo RC .20 .50
78 Carney Lansford .20 .50
79 Ryan Long RC .20 .50
80 Kirby Puckett .50 1.25
81 Earl Cunningham .20 .50
82 Pedro Martinez 4.00 10.00
83 Scott Hatteberg RC .40 1.00
84 Juan Gonzalez UER .30 .75
(65 doubles vs. Tigers)
85 Robert Nutting RC .20 .50
86 Pokey Reese RC .40 1.00
87 Dave Silvestri .20 .50
88 Scott Ruffcorn RC .20 .50
89 Rick Aguilera .20 .50
90 Cecil Fielder .20 .50
91 Kirk Dressendorfer .20 .50
92 Jerry DiPoto RC .20 .50
93 Mike Felder .20 .50
94 Craig Paquette .20 .50
95 Elvin Paulino RC .20 .50
96 Donovan Osborne .20 .50
97 Hubie Brooks .20 .50
98 Derek Lowe RC 1.50 4.00
99 David Zancanaro .20 .50
100 Ken Griffey Jr. .75 2.00
101 Todd Hundley .20 .50
102 Mike Trombley RC .20 .50
103 Ricky Gutierrez RC .40 1.00
104 Braulio Castillo .20 .50
105 Craig Lefferts .20 .50
106 Rick Sutcliffe .20 .50
107 Dean Palmer .20 .50
108 Henry Rodriguez .20 .50
109 Mark Clark RC .40 1.00
110 Kenny Lofton .30 .75
111 Mark Carreon .20 .50
112 J.T. Bruett .20 .50
113 Gerald Williams .20 .50
114 Frank Thomas .50 1.25
115 Kevin Reimer .20 .50
116 Sammy Sosa .50 1.25
117 Mickey Tettleton .20 .50
118 Reggie Sanders .20 .50
119 Trevor Wilson .20 .50
120 Cliff Brantley .20 .50
121 Spike Owen .20 .50
122 Jeff Montgomery .20 .50
123 Alex Sutherland .20 .50
124 Brien Taylor RC .40 1.00
125 Brian Williams RC .20 .50
126 Kevin Seitzer .20 .50
127 Carlos Delgado RC 4.00 10.00
128 Gary Scott .20 .50
129 Scott Cooper .20 .50
130 Domingo Jean RC .20 .50
131 Pat Mahomes RC .40 1.00
132 Mike Boddicker .20 .50
133 Roberto Hernandez .20 .50
134 Dave Valle .20 .50
135 Kurt Stillwell .20 .50
136 Brad Pennington RC .20 .50
137 Jermaine Swinton RC .20 .50
138 Ryan Hawblitzel RC .20 .50
139 Tito Navarro RC .20 .50
140 Sandy Alomar Jr. .20 .50
141 Todd Benzinger .20 .50
142 Danny Jackson .20 .50
143 Melvin Nieves RC .20 .50
144 Jim Campanis .20 .50
145 Luis Gonzalez .20 .50
146 D.Doorneweerd RC .20 .50
147 Charlie Hayes .20 .50
148 Greg Maddux .75 2.00
149 Brian Harper .20 .50
150 Brent Miller RC .20 .50
151 Shawn Estes RC .40 1.00
152 Mike Williams RC .40 1.00
153 Charlie Hough .20 .50
154 Randy Myers .20 .50
155 Kevin Young RC .40 1.00
156 Rick Wilkins .20 .50
157 Terry Shumpert .20 .50
158 Steve Karsay .20 .50
159 Gary DiSarcina .20 .50
160 Deion Sanders .30 .75
161 Tom Browning .20 .50
162 Dickie Thon .20 .50
163 Luis Mercedes .20 .50
164 Riccardo Ingram .20 .50
165 Tavo Alvarez RC .20 .50
166 Rickey Henderson .50 1.25
167 Jaime Navarro .20 .50
168 Billy Ashley RC .20 .50
169 Phil Dauphin RC .20 .50
170 Ivan Cruz .20 .50
171 Harold Baines .20 .50
172 Bryan Harvey .20 .50
173 Alex Cole .20 .50
174 Curtis Shaw RC .20 .50
175 Matt Williams .20 .50
176 Felix Jose .20 .50
177 Sam Horn .20 .50
178 Randy Johnson .50 1.25
179 Ivan Calderon .20 .50
180 Steve Avery .20 .50
181 William Suero .20 .50
182 Bill Swift .20 .50
183 Howard Battle RC .20 .50
184 Ruben Amaro .20 .50
185 Jim Abbott .30 .75
186 Mike Fitzgerald .20 .50
187 Bruce Hurst .20 .50
188 Jeff Juden .20 .50
189 Jeromy Burnitz .20 .50
190 Dave Burba .20 .50
191 Kevin Brown .20 .50
192 Patrick Lennon .20 .50
193 Jeff McNeely .20 .50
194 Wil Cordero .20 .50
195 Chili Davis .20 .50
196 Milt Cuyler .20 .50
197 Von Hayes .20 .50
198 Todd Revenig RC .20 .50
199 Joel Johnston .20 .50
200 Jeff Bagwell .50 1.25
201 Alex Fernandez .20 .50
202 Todd Jones RC 1.00 2.50
203 Charles Nagy .20 .50
204 Tim Raines .20 .50
205 Kevin Maas .20 .50
206 Julio Franco .20 .50
207 Randy Velarde .20 .50
208 Lance Johnson .20 .50
209 Scott Leius .20 .50
210 Derek Lee .20 .50
211 Joe Sondrini RC .20 .50
212 Royce Clayton .20 .50
213 Chris George .20 .50
214 Gary Sheffield .20 .50
215 Mark Gubicza .20 .50
216 Mike Moore .20 .50
217 Rick Huisman RC .20 .50
218 Jeff Russell .20 .50
219 D.J. Dozier .20 .50
220 Dave Martinez .20 .50
221 Alan Newman RC .20 .50
222 Nolan Ryan 1.50 4.00
223 Teddy Higuera .20 .50
224 Damon Buford RC .20 .50
225 Ruben Sierra .20 .50
226 Tom Nevers .20 .50
227 Tommy Greene .20 .50
228 Nigel Wilson RC .20 .50
229 John DeSilva .20 .50
230 Bobby Witt .20 .50
231 Greg Cadaret .20 .50
232 John Vander Wal RC .40 1.00
233 Jack Clark .20 .50
234 Bill Doran .20 .50
235 Bobby Bonilla .20 .50
236 Steve Olin .20 .50
237 Derek Bell .20 .50
238 David Cone .20 .50
239 Victor Cole .20 .50
240 Rod Bolton RC .20 .50
241 Tom Pagnozzi .20 .50
242 Rob Dibble .20 .50
243 Michael Carter RC .20 .50
244 Don Peters .20 .50
245 Mike LaValliere .20 .50
246 Joe Perona RC .20 .50
247 Mitch Williams .20 .50
248 Jay Buhner .20 .50
249 Andy Benes .20 .50
250 Alex Ochoa RC .20 .50
251 Greg Blosser .20 .50
252 Jack Armstrong .20 .50
253 Juan Samuel .20 .50
254 Terry Pendleton .20 .50
255 Ramon Martinez .20 .50
256 Rico Brogna .20 .50
257 John Smiley .20 .50
258 Carl Everett .30 .75
259 Tim Salmon .30 .75
260 Will Clark .30 .75
261 Ugueth Urbina RC .40 1.00
262 Jason Wood RC .20 .50
263 Dave Magadan .20 .50
264 Dante Bichette .20 .50
265 Jose DeLeon .20 .50
266 Mike Neill RC .40 1.00
267 Paul O'Neill .30 .75
268 Anthony Young .20 .50
269 Greg W. Harris .20 .50
270 Todd Van Poppel .20 .50
271 Pedro Castellano RC .20 .50
272 Tony Phillips .20 .50
273 Mike Gallego .20 .50
274 Steve Cooke RC .20 .50
275 Robin Ventura .20 .50
276 Kevin Mitchell .20 .50
277 Doug Linton RC .20 .50
278 Robert Eenhoorn .20 .50
279 Gabe White RC .20 .50
280 Dave Stewart .20 .50

281 Mo Sanford .20 .50
282 Greg Perschke .20 .50
283 Kevin Flora RC .20 .50
284 Jeff Williams RC .40 1.00
285 Keith Miller .20 .50
286 Andy Ashby .20 .50
287 Doug Dascenzo .20 .50
288 Eric Karros .20 .50
289 Glenn Murray RC .20 .50
290 Troy Percival RC 1.25 3.00
291 Orlando Merced .20 .50
292 Peter Hoy .20 .50
293 Tony Fernandez .20 .50
294 Juan Guzman .20 .50
295 Jesse Barfield .20 .50
296 Sid Fernandez .20 .50
297 Scott Cepicky .20 .50
298 Garret Anderson RC 2.00 5.00
299 Cal Eldred .20 .50
300 Ryne Sandberg 1.00 2.50
301 Jim Gantner .20 .50
302 Mariano Rivera RC 10.00 25.00
303 Ron Lockett RC .20 .50
304 Jose Offerman .20 .50
305 Dennis Martinez .20 .50
306 Luis Ortiz RC .20 .50
307 David Howard .20 .50
308 Russ Springer RC .40 1.00
309 Chris Howard .20 .50
310 Kyle Abbott .20 .50
311 Aaron Sele RC .40 1.00
312 David Justice .20 .50
313 Pete O'Brien .20 .50
314 Greg Hansell RC .20 .50
315 Dave Winfield .20 .50
316 Lance Dickson .20 .50
317 Eric King .20 .50
318 Vaughn Eshelman RC .20 .50
319 Tim Belcher .20 .50
320 Andres Galarraga .20 .50
321 Scott Bullett RC .20 .50
322 Doug Strange .20 .50
323 Jerald Clark .20 .50
324 Dave Righetti .20 .50
325 Greg Hibbard .20 .50
326 Eric Hillman RC .20 .50
327 Shane Reynolds RC .40 1.00
328 Chris Hammond .20 .50
329 Albert Belle .20 .50
330 Rich Becker RC .20 .50
331 Eddie Williams .20 .50
332 Donald Harris .20 .50
333 Dave Smith .20 .50
334 Steve Fireovid .20 .50
335 Steve Buechele .20 .50
336 Mike Schooler .20 .50
337 Kevin McReynolds .20 .50
338 Hensley Meulens .20 .50
339 Benji Gil RC .40 1.00
340 Don Mattingly 1.25 3.00
341 Alvin Davis .20 .50
342 Alan Mills .20 .50
343 Kelly Downs .20 .50
344 Leo Gomez .20 .50
345 Tarrik Brock RC .20 .50
346 Ryan Turner RC .20 .50
347 John Smoltz .30 .75
348 Bill Sampen .20 .50
349 Paul Byrd RC 1.25 3.00
350 Mike Bordick .20 .50
351 Jose Lind .20 .50
352 David Wells .20 .50
353 Barry Larkin .30 .75
354 Bruce Ruffin .20 .50
355 Luis Rivera .20 .50
356 Sid Bream .20 .50
357 Julian Vasquez RC .20 .50
358 Jason Bere RC .40 1.00
359 Ben McDonald .20 .50
360 Scott Stahoviak RC .20 .50
361 Kirt Manwaring .20 .50
362 Jeff Johnson .20 .50
363 Rob Deer .20 .50
364 Tony Pena .20 .50
365 Melido Perez .20 .50
366 Clay Parker .20 .50
367 Dale Sveum .20 .50
368 Mike Scioscia .20 .50
369 Roger Salkeld .20 .50
370 Mike Stanley .20 .50
371 Jack McDowell .20 .50
372 Tim Wallach .20 .50
373 Billy Ripken .20 .50
374 Mike Christopher .20 .50
375 Paul Molitor .20 .50
376 Dave Stieb .20 .50
377 Pedro Guerrero .20 .50
378 Russ Swan .20 .50
379 Bob Ojeda .20 .50
380 Donn Pall .20 .50
381 Eddie Zosky .20 .50
382 Darnell Coles .20 .50
383 Tom Smith RC .20 .50
384 Mark McGwire 1.25 3.00
385 Gary Carter .20 .50
386 Rich Amaral RC .20 .50
387 Alan Embree RC .40 1.00
388 Jonathan Hurst RC .20 .50
389 Bobby Jones RC .40 1.00
390 Rico Rossy .20 .50
391 Dan Smith .20 .50
392 Terry Steinbach .20 .50
393 Jon Farrell RC .20 .50
394 Dave Anderson .20 .50
395 Benny Santiago .20 .50
396 Mark Wohlers .20 .50
397 Mo Vaughn .20 .50
398 Randy Kramer .20 .50
399 John Jaha RC .40 1.00
400 Cal Ripken 1.50 4.00
401 Ryan Bowen .20 .50
402 Tim McIntosh .20 .50
403 Bernard Gilkey .20 .50
404 Junior Felix .20 .50
405 Cris Colon RC .20 .50
406 Marc Newfield .20 .50
407 Bernie Williams .30 .75
408 Jay Howell .20 .50
409 Zane Smith .20 .50
410 Jeff Shaw .20 .50
411 Kerry Woodson .20 .50
412 Wes Chamberlain .20 .50
413 Dave Mlicki RC .40 1.00
414 Benny Distefano .20 .50
415 Kevin Rogers .20 .50
416 Tim Naehring .20 .50
417 Clemente Nunez RC .20 .50
418 Luis Sojo .20 .50
419 Kevin Ritz .20 .50
420 Omar Olivares .20 .50
421 Manuel Lee .20 .50
422 Julio Valera .20 .50
423 Omar Vizquel .30 .75
424 Darren Burton RC .20 .50
425 Mel Hall .20 .50
426 Dennis Powell .20 .50
427 Lee Stevens .20 .50
428 Glenn Davis .20 .50
429 Willie Greene .20 .50
430 Kevin Wickander .20 .50
431 Dennis Eckersley .20 .50
432 Joe Orsulak .20 .50
433 Eddie Murray .50 1.25
434 Matt Stairs RC .40 1.00
435 Wally Joyner .20 .50
436 Rondell White .20 .50
437 Rob Maurer .20 .50
438 Joe Redfield .20 .50
439 Mark Lewis .20 .50
440 Darren Daulton .20 .50
441 Mike Henneman .20 .50
442 John Cangelosi .20 .50
443 Vince Moore RC .20 .50
444 John Wehner .20 .50
445 Kent Hrbek .20 .50
446 Mark McLemore .20 .50
447 Bill Wegman .20 .50
448 Robby Thompson .20 .50
449 Mark Anthony RC .20 .50
450 Archi Cianfrocco RC .20 .50
451 Johnny Ruffin .20 .50
452 Javy Lopez .75 2.00
453 Greg Gohr .20 .50
454 Tim Scott .20 .50
455 Stan Belinda .20 .50
456 Darrin Jackson .20 .50
457 Chris Gardner .20 .50
458 Esteban Beltre .20 .50
459 Phil Plantier .20 .50
460 Jim Thome 3.00 8.00
461 Mike Piazza RC 8.00 20.00
462 Matt Sinatro .20 .50
463 Scott Servais .20 .50
464 Brian Jordan RC .75 2.00
465 Doug Drabek .20 .50
466 Carl Willis .20 .50
467 Bret Barberie .20 .50
468 Hal Morris .20 .50
469 Steve Sax .20 .50
470 Jerry Willard .20 .50
471 Dan Wilson .20 .50
472 Chris Hoiles .20 .50
473 Rheal Cormier .20 .50
474 John Morris .20 .50
475 Jeff Reardon .20 .50
476 Mark Leiter .20 .50
477 Tom Gordon .20 .50
478 Kent Bottenfield RC .40 1.00
479 Gene Larkin .20 .50
480 Dwight Gooden .20 .50
481 B.J. Surhoff .20 .50
482 Andy Stankiewicz .20 .50
483 Tino Martinez .30 .75
484 Craig Biggio .30 .75
485 Denny Neagle .20 .50
486 Rusty Meacham .20 .50
487 Kal Daniels .20 .50
488 Dave Henderson .20 .50
489 Tim Costo .20 .50
490 Doug Davis .20 .50
491 Frank Viola .20 .50
492 Cory Snyder .20 .50
493 Chris Martin .20 .50
494 Dion James .20 .50
495 Randy Tomlin .20 .50
496 Greg Vaughn .20 .50
497 Dennis Cook .20 .50
498 Rosario Rodriguez .20 .50
499 Dave Staton .20 .50
500 George Brett 1.25 3.00
501 Brian Barnes .20 .50
502 Butch Henry RC .20 .50
503 Harold Reynolds .20 .50
504 David Nied RC .20 .50
505 Lee Smith .20 .50
506 Steve Chitren .20 .50
507 Ken Hill .20 .50
508 Robbie Beckett .20 .50
509 Troy Afenir .20 .50
510 Kelly Gruber .20 .50
511 Bret Boone .30 .75
512 Jeff Branson .20 .50
513 Mike Jackson .20 .50
514 Pete Harnisch .20 .50
515 Chad Kreuter .20 .50
516 Joe Vitko RC .20 .50
517 Orel Hershiser .20 .50
518 John Doherty RC .20 .50
519 Jay Bell .20 .50
520 Mark Langston .20 .50
521 Dann Howitt .20 .50
522 Bobby Reed RC .20 .50
523 Bobby Munoz RC .20 .50
524 Todd Ritchie .20 .50
525 Bip Roberts .20 .50
526 Pat Listach RC .40 1.00
527 Scott Brosius RC .75 2.00
528 John Roper RC .20 .50
529 Phil Hiatt RC .20 .50
530 Denny Walling .20 .50
531 Carlos Baerga .20 .50
532 Manny Ramirez RC 8.00 20.00
533 Pat Clements UER .20 .50
(Mistakenly numbered 553)
534 Ron Gant .20 .50
535 Pat Kelly .20 .50
536 Bill Spiers .20 .50
537 Darren Reed .20 .50
538 Ken Caminiti .20 .50
539 Butch Huskey RC .20 .50
540 Matt Nokes .20 .50
541 John Kruk .20 .50
542 John Jaha FOIL .20 .50
543 Justin Thompson RC .20 .50
544 Steve Hosey .20 .50
545 Joe Kmak .20 .50
546 John Franco .20 .50
547 Devon White .20 .50
548 Elston Hansen FOIL SP RC .20 .50
549 Ryan Klesko .20 .50
550 Danny Tartabull .20 .50
551 Frank Thomas FOIL .50 1.25
552 Kevin Tapani .20 .50
553 Willie Banks .20 .50
(See also 533)
554 B.J. Wallace FOIL RC .20 .50
555 Orlando Miller RC .20 .50
556 Mark Smith RC .20 .50
557 Tim Wallach FOIL .20 .50
558 Bill Gullickson .20 .50
559 Derek Bell FOIL .20 .50
560 Joe Randa FOIL RC 1.25 3.00
561 Frank Seminara RC .20 .50
562 Mark Gardner .20 .50
563 Rick Greene FOIL RC .20 .50
564 Gary Gaetti .20 .50
565 Ozzie Guillen .20 .50
566 Charles Nagy FOIL .20 .50
567 Mike Milchin .20 .50
568 Ben Shelton RC .20 .50
569 Chris Roberts FOIL .20 .50
570 Ellis Burks .20 .50
571 Scott Scudder .20 .50
572 Jim Abbott FOIL .30 .75
573 Joe Carter .20 .50
574 Steve Finley .20 .50
575 Jim Olander FOIL .20 .50
576 Carlos Garcia .20 .50
577 Gregg Olson .20 .50
578 Greg Swindell FOIL .20 .50
579 Matt Williams FOIL .20 .50
580 Mark Grace .30 .75
581 Howard House FOIL RC .20 .50
582 Luis Polonia .20 .50
583 Erik Hanson .20 .50
584 Salomon Torres FOIL .20 .50
585 Carlton Fisk .30 .75
586 Bret Saberhagen .20 .50
587 Chad McConnell FOIL RC .20 .50
588 Jimmy Key .20 .50
589 Mike Macfarlane .20 .50
590 Barry Bonds FOIL 1.50 4.00
591 Jamie McAndrew .20 .50
592 Shane Mack .20 .50
593 Kerwin Moore .20 .50
594 Joe Oliver .20 .50
595 Chris Sabo .20 .50
596 Alex Gonzalez RC .40 1.00
597 Brett Butler .20 .50
598 Mark Hutton RC .20 .50
599 Andy Benes FOIL .20 .50
600 Jose Canseco .30 .75
601 Darryl Kile .20 .50
602 Matt Stairs FOIL .20 .50
603 Rob Butler FOIL RC .20 .50
604 Willie McGee .20 .50
605 Jack McDowell FOIL .20 .50
606 Tom Candiotti .20 .50
607 Ed Martel RC .20 .50
608 Matt Mieske FOIL .20 .50
609 Darrin Fletcher .20 .50
610 Rafael Palmeiro .30 .75
611 Bill Swift FOIL .20 .50
612 Mike Mussina .50 1.25
613 Vince Coleman .20 .50
614 Scott Cepicky COR .20 .50
614A S.Cepicky FOIL UER .20 .50
Bats: LEFLT
615 Mike Greenwell .20 .50
616 Kevin McGehee RC .20 .50
617 J.Hammonds FOIL .20 .50
618 Scott Taylor .20 .50
619 Dave Otto .20 .50
620 Mark McGwire FOIL 1.25 3.00
621 Kevin Tatar RC .20 .50
622 Steve Farr .20 .50
623 Ryan Klesko FOIL .20 .50
624 Dave Fleming .20 .50
625 Andre Dawson .20 .50
626 Tino Martinez FOIL .30 .75
627 Chad Curtis RC .40 1.00
628 Mickey Morandini .20 .50
629 Gregg Olson FOIL .20 .50
630 Lou Whitaker .20 .50
631 Arthur Rhodes .20 .50
632 Brandon Wilson RC .20 .50
633 Lance Jennings RC .20 .50
634 Allen Watson RC .20 .50
635 Len Dykstra .20 .50
636 Joe Girardi .20 .50
637 Kiki Hernandez FOIL RC .20 .50
638 Mike Hampton RC .75 2.00
639 Al Osuna .20 .50
640 Kevin Appier .20 .50
641 Rick Helling FOIL .20 .50
642 Jody Reed .20 .50
643 Ray Lankford .20 .50
644 John Olerud .20 .50
645 Paul Molitor FOIL .20 .50
646 Pat Borders .20 .50
647 Mike Morgan .20 .50
648 Larry Walker .30 .75
649 P.Castellano FOIL .20 .50
650 Fred McGriff .30 .75
651 Walt Weiss .20 .50
652 Calvin Murray FOIL RC .40 1.00
653 Dave Nilsson .20 .50
654 Greg Pirkl RC .20 .50
655 Robin Ventura FOIL .20 .50
656 Mark Portugal .20 .50
657 Roger McDowell .20 .50
658 Rick Hirtensteiner FOIL RC .20 .50
659 Glenallen Hill .20 .50
660 Greg Gagne .20 .50
661 Charles Johnson FOIL .20 .50
662 Brian Hunter .20 .50
663 Mark Lemke .20 .50
664 Tim Belcher FOIL .20 .50
665 Rich DeLucia .20 .50
666 Bob Walk .20 .50
667 Joe Carter FOIL .20 .50
668 Jose Guzman .20 .50
669 Otis Nixon .20 .50
670 Phil Nevin FOIL .20 .50
671 Eric Davis .20 .50
672 Damion Easley RC .40 1.00
673 Will Clark FOIL .30 .75
674 Mark Kiefer RC .20 .50
675 Ozzie Smith .75 2.00
676 Manny Ramirez FOIL 5.00 12.00
677 Gregg Olson .20 .50
678 Cliff Floyd RC 1.25 3.00
679 Duane Singleton RC .20 .50
680 Jose Rijo .20 .50
681 Willie Randolph .20 .50
682 Michael Tucker FOIL RC .40 1.00
683 Darren Lewis .20 .50
684 Dale Murphy .30 .75
685 Mike Pagliarulo .20 .50
686 Paul Miller RC .20 .50
687 Mike Robertson RC .20 .50
688 Mike Devereaux .20 .50
689 Pedro Astacio RC .40 1.00
690 Alan Trammell .20 .50
691 Roger Clemens 1.00 2.50
692 Bud Black .20 .50
693 Turk Wendell RC .40 1.00
694 Barry Larkin FOIL .30 .75
695 Todd Zeile .20 .50
696 Pat Hentgen .20 .50
697 Eddie Taubensee RC .40 1.00
698 Guillermo Velasquez RC .20 .50
699 Tom Glavine .30 .75
700 Robin Yount .75 2.00
701 Checklist 1-141 .20 .50
702 Checklist 142-282 .20 .50
703 Checklist 283-423 .20 .50
704 Checklist 424-564 .20 .50
705 Checklist 565-705 .20 .50

1993 Bowman

This 708-card standard-size set (produced by Topps) was issued in one series and features one of the more comprehensive selection of prospects and rookies available that year. Cards were distributed in 14-card plastic wrapped packs and jumbo packs. Each 14-card pack contained one silver foil bordered subset card. The basic issue card fronts feature white-bordered color action player photos. The 48 foil subset cards (339-374 and 693-704) feature sixteen 1992 MVPs of the Minor Leagues, top prospects and a few father/son combinations. Rookie Cards in this set include James Baldwin, Roger Cedeno, Derek Jeter, Jason Kendall, Andy Pettitte, Jose Vidro and Preston Wilson.

COMPLETE SET (708) 15.00 40.00
1 Glenn Davis .05 .15
2 Hector Roa RC .08 .25
3 Ken Ryan RC .08 .25
4 Derek Wallace RC .08 .25
5 Jorge Fabregas .05 .15
6 Joe Oliver .05 .15
7 Brandon Wilson .05 .15
8 Mark Thompson RC .08 .25
9 Tracy Sanders .05 .15
10 Rich Renteria .05 .15
11 Lou Whitaker .10 .30
12 Brian L. Hunter RC .20 .50
13 Joe Vitiello .05 .15
14 Eric Karros .10 .30
15 Joe Kmak .05 .15
16 Tavo Alvarez .05 .15
17 Steve Dunn RC .08 .25
18 Tony Fernandez .05 .15
19 Melido Perez .05 .15
20 Mike Lieberthal .10 .30
21 Terry Steinbach .05 .15
22 Stan Belinda .05 .15
23 Jay Buhner .10 .30
24 Allen Watson .05 .15
25 Daryl Henderson RC .08 .25
26 Ray McDavid RC .08 .25
27 Shawn Green .40 1.00
28 Bud Black .05 .15
29 Sherman Obando RC .08 .25
30 Mike Hostetler RC .08 .25
31 Nate Minchey RC .08 .25
32 Randy Myers .05 .15
33 Brian Grebeck .05 .15
34 John Roper .05 .15
35 Larry Thomas .05 .15
36 Alex Cole .05 .15
37 Tom Kramer RC .08 .25
38 Matt Whisenant RC .08 .25
39 Chris Gomez RC .20 .50
40 Luis Gonzalez .10 .30
41 Kevin Appier .10 .30
42 Omar Daal RC .08 .25
43 Duane Singleton .05 .15
44 Bill Risley .05 .15
45 Pat Meares RC .20 .50
46 Butch Huskey .05 .15
47 Bobby Munoz .05 .15
48 Juan Bell .05 .15
49 Scott Lydy RC .08 .25
50 Dennis Moeller .05 .15
51 Marc Newfield .05 .15
52 Tripp Cromer RC .08 .25
53 Kurt Miller .05 .15
54 Jim Pena .05 .15
55 Juan Guzman .05 .15
56 Matt Williams .10 .30
57 Harold Reynolds .10 .30
58 Donnie Elliott RC .08 .25
59 Jon Shave RC .08 .25
60 Kevin Roberson RC .08 .25
61 Hilly Hathaway RC .08 .25
62 Jose Rijo .05 .15
63 Kerry Taylor RC .05 .15
64 Ryan Hawblitzel .05 .15
65 Glenallen Hill .05 .15
66 Ramon Martinez RC .08 .25
67 Travis Fryman .10 .30
68 Tom Nevers .05 .15
69 Phil Hiatt .05 .15
70 Tim Wallach .05 .15
71 B.J. Surhoff .10 .30
72 Rondell White .10 .30
73 Denny Hocking RC .20 .50
74 Mike Oquist RC .08 .25
75 Paul O'Neill .20 .50
76 Willie Banks .05 .15
77 Bob Welch .05 .15
78 Jose Sandoval RC .08 .25
79 Bill Haselman .05 .15
80 Rheal Cormier .05 .15
81 Dean Palmer .10 .30
82 Pat Gomez RC .08 .25
83 Steve Karsay .05 .15
84 Carl Hanselman RC .08 .25
85 T.R. Lewis RC .08 .25
86 Chipper Jones .30 .75
87 Scott Hatteberg .05 .15
88 Greg Hibbard .05 .15
89 Lance Painter RC .08 .25
90 Chad Mottola RC .20 .50
91 Jason Bere .05 .15
92 Dante Bichette .10 .30
93 Sandy Alomar Jr. .05 .15
94 Carl Everett .10 .30
95 Danny Bautista RC .20 .50
96 Steve Finley .10 .30
97 David Cone .10 .30
98 Todd Hollandsworth .05 .15
99 Matt Mieske .05 .15
100 Larry Walker .10 .30
101 Shane Mack .05 .15
102 Aaron Ledesma RC .08 .25
103 Andy Pettitte RC 3.00 8.00
104 Kevin Stocker .05 .15
105 Mike Mohler RC .08 .25
106 Tony Menendez .05 .15
107 Derek Lowe .10 .30
108 Basil Shabazz .05 .15
109 Dan Smith .05 .15
110 Scott Sanders RC .20 .50
111 Todd Stottlemyre .05 .15
112 Benji Simonton RC .08 .25
113 Rick Sutcliffe .10 .30
114 Lee Heath RC .08 .25
115 Jeff Russell .05 .15
116 Dave Stevens RC .08 .25
117 Mark Holzemer RC .08 .25
118 Tim Belcher .05 .15
119 Bobby Thigpen .05 .15
120 Roger Bailey RC .08 .25
121 Tony Mitchell RC .08 .25
122 Junior Felix .05 .15
123 Rich Robertson RC .08 .25
124 Andy Cook RC .08 .25
125 Brian Bevil RC .08 .25
126 Darryl Strawberry .10 .30
127 Cal Eldred .05 .15
128 Cliff Floyd .10 .30
129 Alan Newman .05 .15
130 Howard Johnson .05 .15
131 Jim Abbott .20 .50
132 Chad McConnell .05 .15
133 Miguel Jimenez RC .08 .25
134 Brett Backlund RC .08 .25
135 John Cummings RC .08 .25
136 Brian Barber .05 .15
137 Rafael Palmeiro .20 .50
138 Tim Worrell RC .08 .25
139 Jose Pett RC .08 .25
140 Barry Bonds .75 2.00
141 Damon Buford .05 .15
142 Jeff Blauser .05 .15
143 Frankie Rodriguez .05 .15
144 Mike Morgan .05 .15
145 Gary DiSarcina .05 .15
146 Pokey Reese .05 .15
147 Johnny Ruffin .05 .15
148 David Nied .05 .15
149 Charles Nagy .05 .15
150 Mike Myers RC .08 .25
151 Kenny Carlyle RC .08 .25
152 Eric Anthony .05 .15
153 Jose Lind .05 .15
154 Pedro Martinez .60 1.50
155 Mark Kiefer .05 .15
156 Tim Laker RC .08 .25
157 Pat Mahomes .05 .15
158 Bobby Bonilla .10 .30
159 Domingo Jean .05 .15
160 Darren Daulton .10 .30
161 Mark McGwire .75 2.00
162 Jason Kendall RC .75 2.00
163 Desi Relaford .05 .15
164 Ozzie Canseco .05 .15
165 Rick Helling .05 .15
166 Steve Pegues RC .08 .25
167 Paul Molitor .10 .30
168 Larry Carter RC .05 .15
169 Arthur Rhodes .05 .15
170 Damon Hollins RC .20 .50
171 Frank Viola .10 .30
172 Steve Trachsel RC .40 1.00
173 J.T. Snow RC .40 1.00
174 Keith Gordon RC .08 .25
175 Carlton Fisk .20 .50
176 Jason Bates RC .08 .25
177 Mike Crosby RC .08 .25
178 Benny Santiago .10 .30
179 Mike Moore .05 .15
180 Jeff Juden .05 .15
181 Darren Burton .05 .15
182 Todd Williams RC .20 .50
183 John Jaha .05 .15
184 Mike Lansing RC .20 .50
185 Pedro Grifol RC .08 .25
186 Vince Coleman .05 .15
187 Pat Kelly .05 .15
188 Clemente Alvarez RC .08 .25
189 Ron Darling .05 .15
190 Orlando Merced .05 .15
191 Chris Bosio .05 .15
192 Steve Dixon RC .08 .25
193 Doug Dascenzo .05 .15
194 Ray Holbert RC .08 .25
195 Howard Battle .05 .15
196 Willie McGee .10 .30
197 John O'Donoghue RC .08 .25
198 Steve Avery .05 .15
199 Greg Blosser .05 .15
200 Ryne Sandberg .50 1.25
201 Joe Grahe .05 .15
202 Dan Wilson .10 .30
203 Domingo Martinez RC .08 .25
204 Andres Galarraga .10 .30
205 Jamie Taylor RC .08 .25
206 Darrell Whitmore RC .08 .25
207 Ben Blomdahl RC .08 .25
208 Doug Drabek .05 .15
209 Keith Miller .05 .15
210 Billy Ashley .05 .15
211 Mike Farrell RC .08 .25
212 John Wetteland .10 .30
213 Randy Tomlin .05 .15
214 Sid Fernandez .05 .15
215 Quilvio Veras RC .20 .50
216 Dave Hollins .05 .15
217 Mike Neill .05 .15
218 Andy Van Slyke .20 .50
219 Bret Boone .10 .30
220 Tom Pagnozzi .05 .15
221 Mike Welch RC .08 .25
222 Frank Seminara .05 .15
223 Ron Villone .05 .15
224 D.J. Thielen RC .08 .25
225 Cal Ripken 1.00 2.50
226 Pedro Borbon Jr. RC .08 .25
227 Carlos Quintana .05 .15
228 Tommy Shields .05 .15
229 Tim Salmon .20 .50
230 John Smiley .05 .15
231 Ellis Burks .10 .30
232 Pedro Castellano .05 .15
233 Paul Byrd .10 .30
234 Bryan Harvey .05 .15
235 Scott Livingstone .05 .15
236 James Mouton RC .08 .25
237 Joe Randa .10 .30
238 Pedro Astacio .05 .15
239 Darryl Hamilton .05 .15
240 Joey Eischen RC .08 .25
241 Edgar Herrera RC .08 .25
242 Dwight Gooden .10 .30
243 Sam Militello .05 .15
244 Ron Blazier RC .08 .25
245 Ruben Sierra .10 .30
246 Al Martin .05 .15
247 Mike Felder .05 .15
248 Bob Tewksbury .05 .15
249 Craig Lefferts .05 .15
250 Luis Lopez RC .08 .25
251 Devon White .10 .30
252 Will Clark .20 .50
253 Mark Smith .05 .15
254 Terry Pendleton .10 .30
255 Aaron Sele .05 .15
256 Jose Viera RC .08 .25
257 Damion Easley .05 .15
258 Rod Lofton RC .08 .25
259 Chris Snopek RC .08 .25
260 Q.McCracken RC .20 .50
261 Mike Matthews RC .08 .25
262 Hector Carrasco RC .08 .25
263 Rick Greene .05 .15
264 Chris Holt RC .20 .50
265 George Brett .75 2.00
266 Rick Gorecki RC .08 .25
267 Francisco Gamez RC .08 .25
268 Marquis Grissom .10 .30
269 Kevin Tapani UER .05 .15
(Misspelled Tapan
on card front)
270 Ryan Thompson .05 .15
271 Gerald Williams .05 .15
272 Paul Fletcher RC .08 .25
273 Lance Blankenship .05 .15
274 Marty Neff RC .08 .25
275 Shawn Estes .05 .15
276 Rene Arocha RC .20 .50
277 Scott Eyre RC .08 .25
278 Phil Plantier .05 .15
279 Paul Spoljaric RC .08 .25
280 Chris Gambs .05 .15
281 Harold Baines .10 .30
282 Jose Oliva .05 .15
283 Matt Whiteside RC .08 .25
284 Brant Brown RC .20 .50
285 Russ Springer .05 .15
286 Chris Sabo .05 .15
287 Ozzie Guillen .10 .30
288 Marcus Moore RC .08 .25
289 Chad Ogea .05 .15
290 Walt Weiss .05 .15
291 Brian Edmondson .05 .15
292 Jimmy Gonzalez .05 .15
293 Danny Miceli RC .20 .50
294 Jose Offerman .05 .15
295 Greg Vaughn .05 .15
296 Frank Bolick .05 .15
297 Mike Maksudian RC .08 .25
298 John Franco .10 .30
299 Danny Tartabull .05 .15
300 Len Dykstra .10 .30
301 Bobby Witt .05 .15
302 Trey Beamon RC .08 .25
303 Tino Martinez .20 .50
304 Aaron Holbert .05 .15
305 Juan Gonzalez .10 .30
306 Billy Hall RC .08 .25
307 Duane Ward .05 .15
308 Rod Beck .05 .15
309 Jose Mercedes RC .08 .25
310 Otis Nixon .05 .15
311 Gettys Glaze RC .08 .25
312 Candy Maldonado .05 .15
313 Chad Curtis .05 .15
314 Tim Costo .05 .15
315 Mike Robertson .05 .15
316 Nigel Wilson .05 .15
317 Greg McMichael RC .20 .50
318 Scott Pose RC .08 .25
319 Ivan Cruz .05 .15
320 Greg Swindell .05 .15
321 Kevin McReynolds .05 .15
322 Tom Candiotti .05 .15
323 Rob Wishnevski RC .08 .25
324 Ken Hill .05 .15

325 Kirby Puckett .30 .75
326 Tim Bogar RC .08 .25
327 Mariano Rivera 1.00 2.50
328 Mitch Williams .05 .15
329 Craig Paquette .05 .15
330 Jay Bell .10 .30
331 Jose Martinez RC .08 .25
332 Rob Deer .05 .15
333 Brook Fordyce .05 .15
334 Matt Nokes .05 .15
335 Derek Lee .05 .15
336 Paul Ellis RC .08 .25
337 Desi Wilson RC .08 .25
338 Roberto Alomar .20 .50
339 Jim Tatum FOIL RC .08 .25
340 J.T. Snow FOIL .40 1.00
341 Tim Salmon FOIL .20 .50
342 Russ Davis FOIL RC .20 .50
343 Javy Lopez FOIL .20 .50
344 Troy O'Leary FOIL RC .20 .50
345 M.Cordova FOIL RC .20 .50
346 Bubba Smith RC FOIL .08 .25
347 Chipper Jones FOIL .30 .75
348 Jessie Hollins FOIL .05 .15
349 Willie Greene FOIL .05 .15
350 Mark Thompson FOIL .05 .15
351 Nigel Wilson FOIL .05 .15
352 Todd Jones FOIL .10 .30
353 Raul Mondesi FOIL .10 .30
354 Cliff Floyd FOIL .10 .30
355 Bobby Jones FOIL .10 .30
356 Kevin Stocker FOIL .05 .15
357 M.Cummings FOIL .05 .15
358 Allen Watson FOIL .05 .15
359 Ray McDavid FOIL .05 .15
360 Steve Hosey FOIL .05 .15
361 B.Pennington FOIL .05 .15
362 F.Rodriguez FOIL .05 .15
363 Troy Percival FOIL .20 .50
364 Jason Bere FOIL .05 .15
365 Manny Ramirez FOIL .50 1.25
366 J.Thompson FOIL .05 .15
367 Joe Vitiello FOIL .05 .15
368 Tyrone Hill FOIL .05 .15
369 David McCarty FOIL .05 .15
370 Brien Taylor FOIL .05 .15
371 T.Van Poppel FOIL .05 .15
372 Marc Newfield FOIL .05 .15
373 T.Lowery RC FOIL .20 .50
374 Alex Gonzalez FOIL .05 .15
375 Ken Griffey Jr. .50 1.25
376 Donovan Osborne .05 .15
377 Ritchie Moody RC .08 .25
378 Shane Andrews .05 .15
379 Carlos Delgado .30 .75
380 Bill Swift .05 .15
381 Leo Gomez .05 .15
382 Ron Gant .10 .30
383 Scott Fletcher .05 .15
384 Matt Walbeck RC .20 .50
385 Chuck Finley .10 .30
386 Kevin Mitchell .05 .15
387 Wilson Alvarez UER .05 .15
(Misspelled Alverez on card front)
388 John Burke RC .08 .25
389 Alan Embree .05 .15
390 Trevor Hoffman .30 .75
391 Alan Trammell .10 .30
392 Todd Jones .10 .30
393 Felix Jose .05 .15
394 Orel Hershiser .10 .30
395 Pat Listach .05 .15
396 Gabe White .05 .15
397 Dan Serafini RC .08 .25
398 Todd Hundley .05 .15
399 Wade Boggs .20 .50
400 Tyler Green .05 .15
401 Mike Bordick .05 .15
402 Scott Bullett .05 .15
403 LaGrande Russell RC .08 .25
404 Ray Lankford .10 .30
405 Nolan Ryan 1.25 3.00
406 Robbie Beckett .05 .15
407 Brent Bowers RC .08 .25
408 Adell Davenport RC .08 .25
409 Brady Anderson .10 .30
410 Tom Glavine .20 .50
411 Doug Hecker RC .08 .25
412 Jose Guzman .05 .15
413 Luis Polonia .05 .15
414 Brian Williams .05 .15
415 Bo Jackson .30 .75
416 Eric Young .05 .15
417 Kenny Lofton .10 .30
418 Orestes Destrade .05 .15
419 Tony Phillips .05 .15
420 Jeff Bagwell .20 .50
421 Mark Gardner .05 .15
422 Brett Butler .10 .30
423 Graeme Lloyd RC .20 .50
424 Delino DeShields .05 .15
425 Scott Erickson .05 .15
426 Jeff Kent .30 .75
427 Jimmy Key .10 .30
428 Mickey Morandini .05 .15
429 Marcos Armas RC .08 .25
430 Don Slaught .05 .15
431 Randy Johnson .30 .75
432 Omar Olivares .05 .15
433 Charlie Leibrandt .05 .15
434 Kurt Stillwell .05 .15
435 Scott Brow RC .08 .25
436 Robby Thompson .05 .15
437 Ben McDonald .05 .15
438 Deion Sanders .20 .50
439 Tony Pena .05 .15
440 Mark Grace .20 .50
441 Eduardo Perez .05 .15
442 Tim Pugh RC .08 .25
443 Scott Ruffcorn .05 .15
444 Jay Gainer RC .08 .25
445 Albert Belle .10 .30
446 Bret Barberie .05 .15
447 Justin Mashore .05 .15
448 Pete Harnisch .05 .15
449 Greg Gagne .05 .15
450 Eric Davis .10 .30
451 Dave Mlicki .05 .15
452 Moises Alou .10 .30
453 Rick Aguilera .05 .15
454 Eddie Murray .30 .75
455 Bob Wickman .05 .15
456 Wes Chamberlain .05 .15
457 Brent Gates .05 .15
458 Paul Wagner .05 .15
459 Mike Hampton .10 .30
460 Ozzie Smith .50 1.25
461 Tom Henke .05 .15
462 Ricky Gutierrez .05 .15
463 Jack Morris .10 .30
464 Joel Chimelis .05 .15
465 Gregg Olson .05 .15
466 Javy Lopez .20 .50
467 Scott Cooper .05 .15
468 Willie Wilson .05 .15
469 Mark Langston .05 .15
470 Barry Larkin .20 .50
471 Rod Bolton .05 .15
472 Freddie Benavides .05 .15
473 Ken Ramos RC .08 .25
474 Chuck Carr .05 .15
475 Cecil Fielder .10 .30
476 Eddie Taubensee .05 .15
477 Chris Eddy RC .08 .25
478 Greg Hansell .05 .15
479 Kevin Reimer .05 .15
480 Dennis Martinez .10 .30
481 Chuck Knoblauch .10 .30
482 Mike Draper .05 .15
483 Spike Owen .05 .15
484 Terry Mulholland .05 .15
485 Dennis Eckersley .10 .30
486 Blas Minor .05 .15
487 Dave Fleming .05 .15
488 Dan Cholowsky .05 .15
489 Ivan Rodriguez .20 .50
490 Gary Sheffield .10 .30
491 Ed Sprague .05 .15
492 Steve Hosey .05 .15
493 Jimmy Haynes RC .20 .50
494 John Smoltz .20 .50
495 Andre Dawson .10 .30
496 Rey Sanchez .05 .15
497 Ty Van Burkleo .05 .15
498 Bobby Ayala RC .08 .25
499 Tim Raines .10 .30
500 Charlie Hayes .05 .15
501 Paul Sorrento .05 .15
502 Richie Lewis RC .08 .25
503 Jason Pfaff RC .08 .25
504 Ken Caminiti .10 .30
505 Mike Macfarlane .05 .15
506 Jody Reed .05 .15
507 Bobby Hughes RC .08 .25
508 Wil Cordero .05 .15
509 George Tsamis RC .08 .25
510 Bret Saberhagen .10 .30
511 Derek Jeter RC 10.00 25.00
512 Gene Schall .05 .15
513 Curtis Shaw .05 .15
514 Steve Cooke .05 .15
515 Edgar Martinez .20 .50
516 Mike Milchin .05 .15
517 Billy Ripken .05 .15
518 Andy Benes .05 .15
519 Juan de la Rosa RC .08 .25
520 John Burkett .05 .15
521 Alex Ochoa .05 .15
522 Tony Tarasco RC .20 .50
523 Luis Ortiz .05 .15
524 Rick Wilkins .05 .15
525 Chris Turner RC .08 .25
526 Rob Dibble .10 .30
527 Jack McDowell .05 .15
528 Daryl Boston .05 .15
529 Bill Wertz RC .08 .25
530 Charlie Hough .10 .30
531 Sean Bergman .05 .15
532 Doug Jones .05 .15
533 Jeff Montgomery .05 .15
534 Roger Cedeno RC .20 .50
535 Robin Yount .50 1.25
536 Mo Vaughn .10 .30
537 Brian Harper .05 .15
538 Juan Castillo RC .05 .15
539 Steve Farr .05 .15
540 John Kruk .10 .30
541 Troy Neel .05 .15
542 Danny Clyburn RC .08 .25
543 Jim Converse RC .08 .25
544 Gregg Jefferies .05 .15
545 Jose Canseco .20 .50
546 Julio Bruno RC .08 .25
547 Rob Butler .05 .15
548 Royce Clayton .05 .15
549 Chris Hoiles .05 .15
550 Greg Maddux .50 1.25
551 Joe Ciccarella RC .08 .25
552 Ozzie Timmons .05 .15
553 Chili Davis .10 .30
554 Brian Koelling .05 .15
555 Frank Thomas .30 .75
556 Vinny Castilla .30 .75
557 Reggie Jefferson .05 .15
558 Rob Natal .05 .15
559 Mike Henneman .05 .15
560 Craig Biggio .20 .50
561 Billy Brewer .05 .15
562 Dan Melendez .05 .15
563 Kenny Felder RC .08 .25
564 Miguel Batista RC .40 1.00
565 Dave Winfield .10 .30
566 Al Shirley .05 .15
567 Robert Eenhoorn .05 .15
568 Mike Williams .05 .15
569 Tanyon Sturtze RC .20 .50
570 Tim Wakefield .30 .75
571 Greg Pirkl .05 .15
572 Sean Lowe RC .08 .25
573 Terry Burrows RC .08 .25
574 Kevin Higgins .05 .15
575 Joe Carter .10 .30
576 Kevin Rogers .05 .15
577 Manny Alexander .05 .15
578 David Justice .10 .30
579 Brian Conroy RC .08 .25
580 Jessie Hollins .05 .15
581 Ron Watson RC .08 .25
582 Bip Roberts .05 .15
583 Tom Urbani RC .08 .25
584 Jason Hutchins RC .08 .25
585 Carlos Baerga .05 .15
586 Jeff Mutis .05 .15
587 Justin Thompson .05 .15
588 Orlando Miller .05 .15
589 Brian McRae .05 .15
590 Ramon Martinez .05 .15
591 Dave Nilsson .05 .15
592 Jose Vidro RC .75 2.00
593 Rich Becker .05 .15
594 Preston Wilson RC .60 1.50
595 Don Mattingly .75 2.00
596 Tony Longmire .05 .15
597 Kevin Seitzer .05 .15
598 Midre Cummings RC .08 .25
599 Omar Vizquel .20 .50
600 Lee Smith .10 .30
601 David Hulse RC .08 .25
602 Darrell Sherman RC .08 .25
603 Alex Gonzalez .05 .15
604 Geronimo Pena .05 .15
605 Mike Devereaux .05 .15
606 S.Hitchcock RC .20 .50
607 Mike Greenwell .05 .15
608 Steve Buechele .05 .15
609 Troy Percival .20 .50
610 Roberto Kelly .05 .15
611 James Baldwin RC .20 .50
612 Jerald Clark .05 .15
613 Albie Lopez RC .08 .25
614 Dave Magadan .05 .15
615 Mickey Tettleton .05 .15
616 Sean Runyan RC .08 .25
617 Bob Hamelin .05 .15
618 Raul Mondesi .10 .30
619 Tyrone Hill .05 .15
620 Darrin Fletcher .05 .15
621 Mike Trombley .05 .15
622 Jeromy Burnitz .10 .30
623 Bernie Williams .20 .50
624 Mike Farmer RC .08 .25
625 Rickey Henderson .30 .75
626 Carlos Garcia .05 .15
627 Jeff Darwin RC .08 .25
628 Todd Zeile .05 .15
629 Benji Gil .05 .15
630 Tony Gwynn .40 1.00
631 Aaron Small RC .40 1.00
632 Joe Rosselli RC .08 .25
633 Mike Mussina .20 .50
634 Ryan Klesko .10 .30
635 Roger Clemens .60 1.50
636 Sammy Sosa .30 .75
637 Orlando Palmeiro RC .08 .25
638 Willie Greene .05 .15
639 George Bell .05 .15
640 Garvin Alston RC .08 .25
641 Pete Janicki RC .08 .25
642 Chris Sheff RC .08 .25
643 Felipe Lira RC .08 .25
644 Roberto Petagine .05 .15
645 Wally Joyner .10 .30
646 Mike Piazza 1.25 3.00
647 Jaime Navarro .05 .15
648 Jeff Hartsock .05 .15
649 David McCarty .05 .15
650 Bobby Jones .10 .30
651 Mark Hutton .05 .15
652 Kyle Abbott .05 .15
653 Steve Cox RC .08 .25
654 Jeff King .05 .15
655 Norm Charlton .05 .15
656 Mike Gulan RC .08 .25
657 Julio Franco .10 .30
658 C.Cairncross RC .08 .25
659 John Olerud .10 .30
660 Salomon Torres .05 .15
661 Brad Pennington .05 .15
662 Melvin Nieves .05 .15
663 Ivan Calderon .05 .15
664 Turk Wendell .20 .50
665 Chris Pritchett .05 .15
666 Reggie Sanders .10 .30
667 Robin Ventura .10 .30
668 Joe Girardi .05 .15
669 Manny Ramirez .50 1.25
670 Jeff Conine .10 .30
671 Greg Gohr .05 .15
672 Andujar Cedeno .05 .15
673 Les Norman RC .08 .25
674 Mike James RC .08 .25
675 Marshall Boze RC .08 .25
676 B.J. Wallace .05 .15
677 Kent Hrbek .10 .30
678 Jack Voigt RC .08 .25
679 Brien Taylor .05 .15
680 Curt Schilling .10 .30
681 Todd Van Poppel .05 .15
682 Kevin Young .10 .30
683 Tommy Adams .05 .15
684 Bernard Gilkey .05 .15
685 Kevin Brown .10 .30
686 Fred McGriff .20 .50
687 Pat Borders .05 .15
688 Kirt Manwaring .05 .15
689 Sid Bream .05 .15
690 John Valentin .05 .15
691 Steve Olsen RC .08 .25
692 Roberto Mejia RC .08 .25
693 Carlos Delgado FOIL .30 .75
694 S.Gibraltar FOIL RC .08 .25
695 Gary Mota FOIL RC .08 .25
696 Jose Malave FOIL RC .08 .25
697 Larry Sutton FOIL RC .08 .25
698 Dan Frye FOIL RC .08 .25
699 Tim Clark FOIL RC .08 .25
700 Brian Rupp FOIL RC .08 .25
701 Felipe Alou FOIL .10 .30
Moises Alou
702 Barry Bonds FOIL .40 1.00
Bobby Bonds
703 Ken Griffey Sr. FOIL .30 .75
Ken Griffey Jr.
704 Brian McRae FOIL .05 .15
Hal McRae
705 Checklist 1 .05 .15
706 Checklist 2 .05 .15
707 Checklist 3 .05 .15
708 Checklist 4 .05 .15

1994 Bowman Previews

This 10-card standard-size set served as a preview to the 1994 Bowman set. The cards were randomly inserted one in every 24 1994 Stadium Club second series pack. The backs are identical to the basic issue with a horizontal layout containing a player photo, text and statistics.

COMPLETE SET (10) 10.00 25.00
1 Frank Thomas 2.00 5.00
2 Mike Piazza 4.00 10.00
3 Albert Belle .75 2.00
4 Javier Lopez .75 2.00
5 Cliff Floyd .75 2.00
6 Alex Gonzalez .50 1.25
7 Ricky Bottalico .30 .75
8 Tony Clark 1.25 3.00
9 Mac Suzuki .75 2.00
10 James Mouton Foil .50 1.25

1994 Bowman

The 1994 Bowman set consists of 682 standard-size, full-bleed cards primarily distributed in plastic wrap packs and jumbo packs. There are 52 Foil cards (337-388) that include a number of top young stars and prospects. These foil cards were issued one per foil pack and two per jumbo. Rookie Cards of note include Edgardo Alfonzo, Tony Clark, Jermaine Dye, Brad Fullmer, Richard Hidalgo, Derrek Lee, Chan Ho Park, Jorge Posada, Edgar Renteria and Billy Wagner.

COMPLETE SET (682) 30.00 60.00
1 Joe Carter .15 .40
2 Marcus Moore .08 .25
3 Doug Creek RC .15 .40
4 Pedro Martinez .40 1.00
5 Ken Griffey Jr. .60 1.50
6 Greg Swindell .08 .25
7 J.J. Johnson .08 .25
8 Homer Bush RC .15 .40
9 Arquimedez Pozo RC .15 .40
10 Bryan Harvey .08 .25
11 J.T. Snow .15 .40
12 Alan Benes RC .40 1.00
13 Chad Kreuter .08 .25
14 Eric Karros .15 .40
15 Frank Thomas .40 1.00
16 Bret Saberhagen .15 .40
17 Terrell Lowery .08 .25
18 Rod Bolton .08 .25
19 Harold Baines .15 .40
20 Matt Walbeck .08 .25
21 Tom Glavine .25 .60
22 Todd Jones .08 .25
23 Alberto Castillo RC .15 .40
24 Ruben Sierra .15 .40
25 Don Mattingly 1.00 2.50
26 Mike Morgan .08 .25
27 Jim Musselwhite RC .15 .40
28 Matt Brunson RC .15 .40
29 A.Meinershagen RC .15 .40
30 Joe Girardi .08 .25
31 Shane Halter .08 .25
32 Jose Paniagua RC .40 1.00
33 Paul Perkins RC .15 .40
34 John Hudek RC .15 .40
35 Frank Viola .15 .40
36 David Lamb RC .15 .40
37 Marshall Boze .08 .25
38 Jorge Posada RC 3.00 8.00
39 Brian Anderson RC .40 1.00
40 Mark Whiten .08 .25
41 Sean Bergman .08 .25
42 Jose Parra RC .15 .40
43 Mike Robertson .08 .25
44 Pete Walker RC .15 .40
45 Juan Gonzalez .15 .40
46 Cleveland Ladell RC .15 .40
47 Mark Smith .08 .25
48 Kevin Jarvis UER .15 .40
(team listed as Yankees on back)
49 Amaury Telemaco RC .15 .40
50 Andy Van Slyke .25 .60
51 Rikkert Faneyte RC .15 .40
52 Curtis Shaw .08 .25
53 Matt Drews RC .15 .40
54 Wilson Alvarez .08 .25
55 Manny Ramirez .40 1.00
56 Bobby Munoz .08 .25
57 Ed Sprague .08 .25
58 Jamey Wright RC .40 1.00
59 Jeff Montgomery .08 .25
60 Kirk Rueter .08 .25
61 Edgar Martinez .25 .60
62 Luis Gonzalez .15 .40
63 Tim Vanegmond RC .15 .40
64 Bip Roberts .08 .25
65 John Jaha .08 .25
66 Chuck Carr .08 .25
67 Chuck Finley .15 .40
68 Aaron Holbert .08 .25
69 Cecil Fielder .15 .40
70 Tom Engle RC .15 .40
71 Ron Karkovice .08 .25
72 Joe Orsulak .08 .25
73 Duff Brumley RC .15 .40
74 Craig Clayton RC .15 .40
75 Cal Ripken 1.25 3.00
76 Brad Fullmer RC .40 1.00
77 Tony Tarasco .08 .25
78 Terry Farrar RC .15 .40
79 Matt Williams .15 .40
80 Rickey Henderson .40 1.00
81 Terry Mulholland .08 .25
82 Sammy Sosa .40 1.00
83 Paul Sorrento .08 .25
84 Pete Incaviglia .08 .25
85 Darren Hall RC .15 .40
86 Scott Klingenbeck .08 .25
87 Dario Perez RC .15 .40
88 Ugueth Urbina .08 .25
89 Dave Vanhof RC .15 .40
90 Domingo Jean .08 .25
91 Otis Nixon .08 .25
92 Andres Berumen .08 .25
93 Jose Valentin .08 .25
94 Edgar Renteria RC 2.00 5.00
95 Chris Turner .08 .25
96 Ray Lankford .15 .40
97 Danny Bautista .08 .25
98 Chan Ho Park RC .60 1.50
99 Glenn DiSarcina RC .15 .40
100 Butch Huskey .08 .25
101 Ivan Rodriguez .25 .60
102 Johnny Ruffin .08 .25
103 Alex Ochoa .08 .25
104 Torii Hunter RC 2.00 5.00
105 Ryan Klesko .15 .40
106 Jay Bell .15 .40
107 Kurt Peltzer RC .15 .40
108 Miguel Jimenez .08 .25
109 Russ Davis .08 .25
110 Derek Wallace .08 .25
111 Keith Lockhart RC .40 1.00
112 Mike Lieberthal .15 .40
113 Dave Stewart .15 .40
114 Tom Schmidt .08 .25
115 Brian McRae .08 .25
116 Moises Alou .15 .40
117 Dave Fleming .08 .25
118 Jeff Bagwell .25 .60
119 Luis Ortiz .08 .25
120 Tony Gwynn .50 1.25
121 Jaime Navarro .08 .25
122 Benito Santiago .15 .40
123 Darrell Whitmore .08 .25
124 John Mabry RC .40 1.00
125 Mickey Tettleton .08 .25
126 Tom Candiotti .08 .25
127 Tim Raines .15 .40
128 Bobby Bonilla .15 .40
129 John Dettmer .08 .25
130 Hector Carrasco .08 .25
131 Chris Hoiles .08 .25
132 Rick Aguilera .08 .25
133 David Justice .15 .40
134 Esteban Loaiza RC .60 1.50
135 Barry Bonds 1.00 2.50
136 Bob Welch .08 .25
137 Mike Stanley .08 .25
138 Roberto Hernandez .08 .25
139 Sandy Alomar Jr. .08 .25
140 Darren Daulton .15 .40
141 Angel Martinez RC .15 .40
142 Howard Johnson .08 .25
143 Bob Hamelin UER .08 .25
(name and card number colors don't match)
144 J.J. Thobe RC .15 .40
145 Roger Salkeld .08 .25
146 Orlando Miller .08 .25
147 Dmitri Young .15 .40
148 Tim Hyers RC .15 .40
149 Mark Loretta RC 2.00 5.00
150 Chris Hammond .08 .25
151 Joel Moore RC .15 .40
152 Todd Zeile .08 .25
153 Wil Cordero .08 .25
154 Chris Smith .08 .25
155 James Baldwin .08 .25
156 Edgardo Alfonzo RC .40 1.00
157 Kym Ashworth RC .15 .40
158 Paul Bako RC .15 .40
159 Rick Krivda RC .15 .40
160 Pat Mahomes .08 .25
161 Damon Hollins .08 .25
162 Felix Martinez RC .15 .40
163 Jason Myers RC .15 .40
164 Izzy Molina RC .15 .40
165 Brien Taylor .08 .25
166 Kevin Orie RC .15 .40
167 Casey Whitten RC .15 .40
168 Tony Longmire .08 .25
169 John Olerud .15 .40
170 Mark Thompson .08 .25
171 Jorge Fabregas .08 .25
172 John Wetteland .15 .40
173 Dan Wilson .08 .25
174 Doug Drabek .08 .25
175 Jeff McNeely .08 .25
176 Melvin Nieves .08 .25
177 Doug Glanville RC .40 1.00
178 Javier De La Hoya RC .15 .40
179 Chad Curtis .08 .25
180 Brian Barber .08 .25
181 Mike Henneman .08 .25
182 Jose Offerman .08 .25
183 Robert Ellis RC .15 .40
184 John Franco .15 .40
185 Benji Gil .08 .25
186 Hal Morris .08 .25
187 Chris Sabo .08 .25
188 Blaise Ilsley RC .15 .40
189 Steve Avery .08 .25
190 Rick White RC .15 .40
191 Rod Beck .08 .25
192 Mark McGwire UER 1.00 2.50
(No card number on back)
193 Jim Abbott .25 .60
194 Randy Myers .08 .25
195 Kenny Lofton .15 .40
196 Mariano Duncan .08 .25
197 Lee Daniels RC .15 .40
198 Armando Reynoso .08 .25
199 Joe Randa .15 .40
200 Cliff Floyd .15 .40
201 Tim Harkrider RC .15 .40
202 Kevin Gallaher RC .15 .40
203 Scott Cooper .08 .25
204 Phil Stidham RC .15 .40
205 Jeff D'Amico RC .15 .40
206 Matt Whisenant .08 .25
207 De Shawn Warren .08 .25
208 Rene Arocha .08 .25
209 Tony Clark RC .60 1.50
210 Jason Jacome RC .15 .40
211 Scott Christman RC .15 .40
212 Bill Pulsipher .15 .40
213 Dean Palmer .15 .40
214 Chad Mottola .08 .25
215 Manny Alexander .08 .25
216 Rich Becker .08 .25
217 Andre King RC .15 .40
218 Carlos Garcia .08 .25
219 Ron Pezzoni RC .15 .40
220 Steve Karsay .08 .25
221 Jose Musset RC .15 .40
222 Karl Rhodes .08 .25
223 Frank Cimorelli RC .15 .40
224 Kevin Jordan RC .15 .40
225 Duane Ward .08 .25
226 John Burke .08 .25
227 Mike Macfarlane .08 .25
228 Mike Lansing .08 .25
229 Chuck Knoblauch .15 .40
230 Ken Caminiti .15 .40
231 Gar Finnvold RC .15 .40
232 Derrek Lee RC 3.00 8.00
233 Brady Anderson .15 .40
234 Vic Darensbourg RC .15 .40
235 Mark Langston .08 .25
236 T.J. Mathews RC .15 .40
237 Lou Whitaker .15 .40
238 Roger Cedeno .08 .25
239 Alex Fernandez .08 .25
240 Ryan Thompson .08 .25
241 Kerry Lacy RC .15 .40
242 Reggie Sanders .15 .40
243 Brad Pennington .08 .25
244 Bryan Eversgerd RC .15 .40
245 Greg Maddux .60 1.50
246 Jason Kendall .15 .40
247 J.R. Phillips .08 .25
248 Bobby Witt .08 .25
249 Paul O'Neill .25 .60
250 Ryne Sandberg .60 1.50
251 Charles Nagy .08 .25
252 Kevin Stocker .08 .25
253 Shawn Green .40 1.00
254 Charlie Hayes .08 .25
255 Donnie Elliott .08 .25
256 Rob Fitzpatrick RC .15 .40
257 Tim Davis .08 .25
258 James Mouton .08 .25
259 Mike Greenwell .08 .25
260 Ray McDavid .08 .25
261 Mike Kelly .08 .25
262 Andy Larkin RC .15 .40
263 Marquis Riley UER .08 .25
(No card number on back)
264 Bob Tewksbury .08 .25
265 Brian Edmondson .08 .25
266 Eduardo Lantigua RC .15 .40
267 Brandon Wilson .08 .25
268 Mike Welch .08 .25
269 Tom Henke .08 .25
270 Pokey Reese .08 .25
271 Greg Zaun RC .40 1.00
272 Todd Ritchie .08 .25
273 Javier Lopez .15 .40
274 Kevin Young .08 .25
275 Kirt Manwaring .08 .25
276 Bill Taylor RC .15 .40
277 Robert Eenhoorn .08 .25
278 Jessie Hollins .08 .25
279 Julian Tavarez RC .40 1.00
280 Gene Schall .08 .25
281 Paul Molitor .15 .40
282 Neifi Perez RC .40 1.00
283 Greg Gagne .08 .25
284 Marquis Grissom .15 .40
285 Randy Johnson .40 1.00
286 Pete Harnisch .08 .25
287 Joel Bennett RC .15 .40
288 Derek Bell .08 .25
289 Darryl Hamilton .08 .25
290 Gary Sheffield .15 .40
291 Eduardo Perez .08 .25
292 Basil Shabazz .08 .25
293 Eric Davis .15 .40
294 Pedro Astacio .08 .25
295 Robin Ventura .15 .40
296 Jeff Kent .25 .60
297 Rick Helling .08 .25
298 Joe Oliver .08 .25
299 Lee Smith .15 .40
300 Dave Winfield .15 .40
301 Deion Sanders .25 .60
302 R.Manzanillo RC .15 .40
303 Mark Portugal .08 .25
304 Brent Gates .08 .25
305 Wade Boggs .25 .60
306 Rick Wilkins .08 .25
307 Carlos Baerga .08 .25
308 Curt Schilling .15 .40
309 Shannon Stewart .40 1.00
310 Darren Holmes .08 .25
311 Robert Toth RC .15 .40
312 Gabe White .08 .25
313 Mac Suzuki RC .40 1.00
314 Alvin Morman RC .15 .40
315 Mo Vaughn .15 .40
316 Bryce Florie RC .15 .40
317 Gabby Martinez RC .15 .40
318 Carl Everett .15 .40
319 Kerwin Moore .08 .25
320 Tom Pagnozzi .08 .25
321 Chris Gomez .08 .25
322 Todd Williams .08 .25
323 Pat Hentgen .08 .25
324 Kirk Presley RC .15 .40
325 Kevin Brown .15 .40
326 J.Isringhausen RC 1.25 3.00
327 Rick Forney RC .15 .40
328 Carlos Pulido RC .15 .40
329 Terrell Wade RC .15 .40
330 Al Martin .08 .25

331 Dan Carlson RC .15 .40
332 Mark Acre RC .15 .40
333 Sterling Hitchcock .08 .25
334 Jon Ratliff RC .15 .40
335 Alex Ramirez RC .15 .40
336 Phil Geisler RC .08 .25
337 E.Zambrano FOIL RC .15 .40
338 Jim Thome FOIL .25 .60
339 James Mouton FOIL .08 .25
340 Cliff Floyd FOIL .15 .40
341 Carlos Delgado FOIL .25 .60
342 R.Petagine FOIL .08 .25
343 Tim Clark FOIL .08 .25
344 Bubba Smith FOIL .08 .25
345 Randy Curtis FOIL RC .15 .40
346 Joe Biasucci FOIL RC .15 .40
347 D.J. Boston FOIL RC .15 .40
348 R.Rivera FOIL RC .15 .40
349 Bryan Link FOIL RC .15 .40
350 Mike Bell FOIL RC .15 .40
351 M.Watson FOIL RC .15 .40
352 Jason Myers FOIL .08 .25
353 Chipper Jones FOIL .40 1.00
354 B.Kieschnick FOIL .15 .40
355 Pokey Reese FOIL .08 .25
356 John Burke FOIL .08 .25
357 Kurt Miller FOIL .08 .25
358 Orlando Miller FOIL .08 .25
359 T.Hollandsworth FOIL .08 .25
360 Rondell White FOIL .15 .40
361 Bill Pulsipher FOIL .15 .40
362 Tyler Green FOIL .08 .25
363 M.Cummings FOIL .08 .25
364 Brian Barber FOIL .08 .25
365 Melvin Nieves FOIL .08 .25
366 Salomon Torres FOIL .08 .25
367 Alex Ochoa FOIL .08 .25
368 F.Rodriguez FOIL .08 .25
369 Brian Anderson FOIL .15 .40
370 James Baldwin FOIL .08 .25
371 Manny Ramirez FOIL .40 1.00
372 J.Thompson FOIL .08 .25
373 Johnny Damon FOIL .25 .60
374 Jeff D'Amico FOIL .15 .40
375 Rich Becker FOIL .08 .25
376 Derek Jeter FOIL 1.25 3.00
377 Steve Karsay FOIL .08 .25
378 Mac Suzuki FOIL .15 .40
379 Benji Gil FOIL .08 .25
380 Alex Gonzalez FOIL .08 .25
381 Jason Bere FOIL .08 .25
382 Brett Butler FOIL .15 .40
383 Jeff Conine FOIL .15 .40
384 Darren Daulton FOIL .15 .40
385 Jeff Kent FOIL .25 .60
386 Don Mattingly FOIL 1.00 2.50
387 Mike Piazza FOIL .75 2.00
388 Ryne Sandberg FOIL .60 1.50
389 Rich Amaral .08 .25
390 Craig Biggio .25 .60
391 Jeff Suppan RC .75 2.00
392 Andy Benes .08 .25
393 Cal Eldred .08 .25
394 Jeff Conine .15 .40
395 Tim Salmon .25 .60
396 Ray Suplee RC .15 .40
397 Tony Phillips .08 .25
398 Ramon Martinez .08 .25
399 Julio Franco .15 .40
400 Dwight Gooden .15 .40
401 Kevin Lomon RC .15 .40
402 Jose Rijo .08 .25
403 Mike Devereaux .08 .25
404 Mike Zolecki RC .15 .40
405 Fred McGriff .25 .60
406 Danny Clyburn .08 .25
407 Robby Thompson .08 .25
408 Terry Steinbach .08 .25
409 Luis Polonia .08 .25
410 Mark Grace .25 .60
411 Albert Belle .15 .40
412 John Kruk .15 .40
413 Scott Spiezio RC .40 1.00
414 Ellis Burks UER .15 .40
(Name spelled Elkis on front)
415 Joe Vitiello .08 .25
416 Tim Costo .08 .25
417 Marc Newfield .08 .25
418 Oscar Henriquez RC .15 .40
419 Matt Perisho RC .15 .40
420 Julio Bruno .08 .25
421 Kenny Felder .08 .25
422 Tyler Green .08 .25
423 Jim Edmonds .40 1.00
424 Ozzie Smith .60 1.50
425 Rick Greene .08 .25
426 Todd Hollandsworth .08 .25
427 Eddie Pearson RC .15 .40
428 Quilvio Veras .08 .25
429 Kenny Rogers .15 .40
430 Willie Greene .08 .25
431 Vaughn Eshelman .08 .25
432 Pat Meares .08 .25
433 Jermaine Dye RC 2.50 6.00
434 Steve Cooke .08 .25
435 Bill Swift .08 .25
436 Fausto Cruz RC .15 .40
437 Mark Hutton .08 .25
438 B.Kieschnick RC .15 .40
439 Yorkis Perez .08 .25
440 Len Dykstra .15 .40
441 Pat Borders .08 .25
442 Doug Walls RC .15 .40
443 Wally Joyner .15 .40
444 Ken Hill .08 .25
445 Eric Anthony .08 .25
446 Mitch Williams .08 .25
447 Cory Bailey RC .15 .40
448 Dave Staton .08 .25
449 Greg Vaughn .08 .25
450 Dave Magadan .08 .25
451 Chili Davis .15 .40
452 Gerald Santos RC .15 .40
453 Joe Perona .08 .25
454 Delino DeShields .08 .25
455 Jack McDowell .08 .25
456 Todd Hundley .08 .25
457 Ritchie Moody .08 .25
458 Bret Boone .15 .40
459 Ben McDonald .08 .25
460 Kirby Puckett .40 1.00
461 Gregg Olson .08 .25
462 Rich Aude RC .15 .40
463 John Burkett .08 .25
464 Troy Neel .08 .25
465 Jimmy Key .15 .40
466 Ozzie Timmons .08 .25
467 Eddie Murray .40 1.00
468 Mark Tranberg RC .15 .40
469 Alex Gonzalez .08 .25
470 David Nied .08 .25
471 Barry Larkin .25 .60
472 Brian Looney RC .15 .40
473 Shawn Estes .08 .25
474 A.J. Sager RC .15 .40
475 Roger Clemens .75 2.00
476 Vince Moore .08 .25
477 Scott Karl RC .15 .40
478 Kurt Miller .08 .25
479 Garret Anderson .40 1.00
480 Allen Watson .08 .25
481 Jose Lima RC .40 1.00
482 Rick Gorecki .08 .25
483 Jimmy Hurst RC .15 .40
484 Preston Wilson .15 .40
485 Will Clark .25 .60
486 Mike Ferry RC .15 .40
487 Curtis Goodwin RC .15 .40
488 Mike Myers .08 .25
489 Chipper Jones .40 1.00
490 Jeff King .08 .25
491 W.VanLandingham RC .15 .40
492 Carlos Reyes RC .15 .40
493 Andy Pettitte .40 1.00
494 Brant Brown .08 .25
495 Daron Kirkreit .08 .25
496 Ricky Bottalico RC .15 .40
497 Devon White .15 .40
498 Jason Johnson RC .40 1.00
499 Vince Coleman .08 .25
500 Larry Walker .15 .40
501 Bobby Ayala .08 .25
502 Steve Finley .15 .40
503 Scott Fletcher .08 .25
504 Brad Ausmus .25 .60
505 Scott Talanoa RC .15 .40
506 Orestes Destrade .08 .25
507 Gary DiSarcina .08 .25
508 Willie Smith RC .15 .40
509 Alan Trammell .15 .40
510 Mike Piazza .75 2.00
511 Ozzie Guillen .15 .40
512 Jeromy Burnitz .15 .40
513 Darren Oliver RC .40 1.00
514 Kevin Mitchell .08 .25
515 Rafael Palmeiro .25 .60
516 David McCarty .08 .25
517 Jeff Blauser .08 .25
518 Trey Beamon .08 .25
519 Royce Clayton .08 .25
520 Dennis Eckersley .15 .40
521 Bernie Williams .25 .60
522 Steve Buechele .08 .25
523 Dennis Martinez .15 .40
524 Dave Hollins .08 .25
525 Joey Hamilton .08 .25
526 Andres Galarraga .15 .40
527 Jeff Granger .08 .25
528 Joey Eischen .08 .25
529 Desi Relaford .08 .25
530 Roberto Petagine .08 .25
531 Andre Dawson .15 .40
532 Ray Holbert .08 .25
533 Duane Singleton .08 .25
534 Kurt Abbott RC .15 .40
535 Bo Jackson .40 1.00
536 Gregg Jefferies .08 .25
537 David Mysel .08 .25
538 Raul Mondesi .15 .40
539 Chris Snopek .08 .25
540 Brook Fordyce .08 .25
541 Ron Frazier RC .15 .40
542 Brian Koelling .08 .25
543 Jimmy Haynes .08 .25
544 Marty Cordova .08 .25
545 Jason Green RC .15 .40
546 Orlando Merced .08 .25
547 Lou Pote RC .15 .40
548 Todd Van Poppel .08 .25
549 Pat Kelly .08 .25
550 Turk Wendell .08 .25
551 Herbert Perry RC .15 .40
552 Ryan Karp RC .15 .40
553 Juan Guzman .08 .25
554 Bryan Rekar RC .15 .40
555 Kevin Appier .15 .40
556 Chris Schwab RC .15 .40
557 Jay Buhner .15 .40
558 Andujar Cedeno .08 .25
559 Ryan McGuire RC .15 .40
560 Ricky Gutierrez .08 .25
561 Keith Kimsey RC .15 .40
562 Tim Clark .08 .25
563 Damion Easley .08 .25
564 Clint Davis RC .15 .40
565 Mike Moore .08 .25
566 Orel Hershiser .15 .40
567 Jason Bere .08 .25
568 Kevin McReynolds .08 .25
569 Leland Macon RC .15 .40
570 John Courtright RC .15 .40
571 Sid Fernandez .08 .25
572 Chad Roper .08 .25
573 Terry Pendleton .15 .40
574 Danny Miceli .08 .25
575 Joe Rosselli .08 .25
576 Mike Bordick .08 .25
577 Danny Tartabull .08 .25
578 Jose Guzman .08 .25
579 Omar Vizquel .25 .60
580 Tommy Greene .08 .25
581 Paul Spoljaric .08 .25
582 Walt Weiss .08 .25
583 Oscar Jimenez RC .15 .40
584 Rod Henderson .08 .25
585 Derek Lowe .15 .40
586 Richard Hidalgo RC .40 1.00
587 Shayne Bennett RC .15 .40
588 Tim Belk RC .15 .40
589 Matt Mieske .08 .25
590 Nigel Wilson .08 .25
591 Jeff Knox RC .15 .40
592 Bernard Gilkey .08 .25
593 David Cone .15 .40
594 Paul LoDuca RC 2.00 5.00
595 Scott Ruffcorn .08 .25
596 Chris Roberts .08 .25
597 Oscar Munoz RC .15 .40
598 Scott Sullivan RC .15 .40
599 Matt Jarvis RC .15 .40
600 Jose Canseco .25 .60
601 Tony Graffanino RC .60 1.50
602 Don Slaught .08 .25
603 Brett King RC .15 .40
604 Jose Herrera RC .15 .40
605 Melido Perez .08 .25
606 Mike Hubbard RC .15 .40
607 Chad Ogea .08 .25
608 Wayne Gomes RC .40 1.00
609 Roberto Alomar .25 .60
610 Angel Echevarria RC .15 .40
611 Jose Lind .08 .25
612 Darrin Fletcher .08 .25
613 Chris Bosio .08 .25
614 Darryl Kile .15 .40
615 Frankie Rodriguez .08 .25
616 Phil Plantier .08 .25
617 Pat Listach .08 .25
618 Charlie Hough .15 .40
619 Ryan Hancock RC .15 .40
620 Darrel Deak RC .15 .40
621 Travis Fryman .15 .40
622 Brett Butler .15 .40
623 Lance Johnson .08 .25
624 Pete Smith .08 .25
625 James Hurst RC .15 .40
626 Roberto Kelly .08 .25
627 Mike Mussina .25 .60
628 Kevin Tapani .08 .25
629 John Smoltz .25 .60
630 Midre Cummings .08 .25
631 Salomon Torres .08 .25
632 Willie Adams .08 .25
633 Derek Jeter 1.25 3.00
634 Steve Trachsel .08 .25
635 Albie Lopez .08 .25
636 Jason Moler .08 .25
637 Carlos Delgado .25 .60
638 Roberto Mejia .08 .25
639 Darren Burton .08 .25
640 B.J. Wallace .08 .25
641 Brad Clontz RC .15 .40
642 Billy Wagner RC 1.50 4.00
643 Aaron Sele .08 .25
644 Cameron Cairncross .08 .25
645 Brian Harper .08 .25
646 Marc Valdes UER .08 .25
(No card number on back)
647 Mark Ratekin .08 .25
648 Terry Bradshaw RC .15 .40
649 Justin Thompson .08 .25
650 Mike Busch RC .15 .40
651 Joe Hall RC .15 .40
652 Bobby Jones .08 .25
653 Kelly Stinnett RC .40 1.00
654 Rod Steph RC .15 .40
655 Jay Powell RC .40 1.00
656 K.Garagozzo RC UER .15 .40
No card number on back
657 Todd Dunn .08 .25
658 Charles Peterson RC .15 .40
659 Darren Lewis .08 .25
660 John Wasdin RC .15 .40
661 Tate Seefried RC .15 .40
662 Hector Trinidad RC .15 .40
663 John Carter RC .08 .25
664 Larry Mitchell .08 .25
665 David Catlett RC .15 .40
666 Dante Bichette .15 .40
667 Felix Jose .08 .25
668 Rondell White .15 .40
669 Tino Martinez .25 .60
670 Brian L. Hunter .08 .25
671 Jose Malave .08 .25
672 Archi Cianfrocco .08 .25
673 Mike Matheny RC .60 1.50
674 Bret Barberie .08 .25
675 Andrew Lorraine RC .15 .40
676 Brian Jordan .15 .40
677 Tim Belcher .08 .25
678 Antonio Osuna RC .15 .40
679 Checklist .08 .25
680 Checklist .08 .25
681 Checklist .08 .25
682 Checklist .08 .25

1995 Bowman

Cards from this 439-card standard-size prospect-oriented set were primarily issued in plastic wrapped packs and jumbo packs. Card fronts feature white borders enframing full color photos. The left border is a reversed negative of the photo. The set includes 54 silver foil subset cards (221-274). The foil subset, largely comprising of minor league stars, have embossed borders and are found one per pack and two per jumbo pack. Rookie Cards of note include Bob Abreu, Bartolo Colon, Vladmir Guerrero, Andruw Jones, Hideo Nomo and Scott Rolen.

COMPLETE SET (439) 90.00 150.00
1 Billy Wagner .30 .75
2 Chris Widger .08 .25
3 Brent Bowers .08 .25
4 Bob Abreu RC 3.00 8.00
5 Lou Collier RC .40 1.00
6 Juan Acevedo RC .20 .50
7 Jason Kelley RC .20 .50
8 Brian Sackinsky .08 .25
9 Scott Christman .08 .25
10 Damon Hollins .08 .25
11 Willis Otanez RC .20 .50
12 Jason Ryan RC .20 .50
13 Jason Giambi .30 .75
14 Andy Taulbee RC .20 .50
15 Mark Thompson .08 .25
16 Hugo Pivaral RC .20 .50
17 Brien Taylor .08 .25
18 Antonio Osuna .08 .25
19 Edgardo Alfonzo .08 .25
20 Carl Everett .08 .25
21 Matt Drews .08 .25
22 Bartolo Colon RC 1.50 4.00
23 Andruw Jones RC 10.00 25.00
24 Robert Person RC .40 1.00
25 Derrek Lee .50 1.25
26 John Ambrose RC .20 .50
27 Eric Knowles RC .20 .50
28 Chris Roberts .08 .25
29 Don Wengert .08 .25
30 Marcus Jensen RC .40 1.00
31 Brian Barber .08 .25
32 Kevin Brown C .20 .50
33 Benji Gil .08 .25
34 Mike Hubbard .08 .25
35 Bart Evans RC .20 .50
36 Enrique Wilson RC .20 .50
37 Brian Buchanan RC .20 .50
38 Ken Ray RC .20 .50
39 Micah Franklin RC .20 .50
40 Ricky Otero RC .20 .50
41 Jason Kendall .20 .50
42 Jimmy Hurst .08 .25
43 Jerry Wolak RC .20 .50
44 Jayson Peterson RC .20 .50
45 Allen Battle RC .20 .50
46 Scott Stahoviak .08 .25
47 Steve Schrenk RC .20 .50
48 Travis Miller RC .20 .50
49 Eddie Rios RC .20 .50
50 Mike Hampton .20 .50
51 Chad Frontera RC .20 .50
52 Tom Evans .08 .25
53 C.J. Nitkowski .08 .25
54 Clay Caruthers RC .20 .50
55 Shannon Stewart .20 .50
56 Jorge Posada .50 1.25
57 Aaron Holbert .08 .25
58 Harry Berrios RC .20 .50
59 Steve Rodriguez .08 .25
60 Shane Andrews .08 .25
61 Will Cunnane RC .20 .50
62 Richard Hidalgo .08 .25
63 Bill Selby RC .20 .50
64 Jay Cranford RC .20 .50
65 Jeff Suppan .20 .50
66 Curtis Goodwin .08 .25
67 John Thomson RC .40 1.00
68 Justin Thompson .08 .25
69 Troy Percival .20 .50
70 Matt Wagner RC .20 .50
71 Terry Bradshaw .08 .25
72 Greg Hansell .08 .25
73 John Burke .08 .25
74 Jeff D'Amico .08 .25
75 Ernie Young .08 .25
76 Jason Bates .08 .25
77 Chris Stynes .08 .25
78 Cade Gaspar RC .20 .50
79 Melvin Nieves .08 .25
80 Rick Gorecki .08 .25
81 Felix Rodriguez RC .20 .50
82 Ryan Hancock .08 .25
83 Chris Carpenter RC 3.00 8.00
84 Ray McDavid .08 .25
85 Chris Wimmer .08 .25
86 Doug Glanville .08 .25
87 DeShawn Warren .08 .25
88 Damian Moss RC .20 .50
89 Rafael Orellano RC .20 .50
90 Vladimir Guerrero RC 12.50 30.00
91 Raul Casanova RC .20 .50
92 Karim Garcia RC .20 .50
93 Bryce Florie .08 .25
94 Kevin Orie .08 .25
95 Ryan Nye RC .20 .50
96 Matt Sachse RC .20 .50
97 Ivan Arteaga RC .20 .50
98 Glenn Murray .08 .25
99 Stacy Hollins RC .20 .50
100 Jim Pittsley .08 .25
101 Craig Mattson RC .20 .50
102 Neifi Perez .08 .25
103 Keith Williams .08 .25
104 Roger Cedeno .08 .25
105 Tony Terry RC .20 .50
106 Jose Malave .08 .25
107 Joe Rosselli .08 .25
108 Kevin Jordan .08 .25
109 Sid Roberson RC .20 .50
110 Alan Embree .08 .25
111 Terrell Wade .08 .25
112 Bob Wolcott .08 .25
113 Carlos Perez RC .40 1.00
114 Mike Bovee RC .20 .50
115 Tommy Davis RC .20 .50
116 Jeremey Kendall RC .20 .50
117 Rich Aude .08 .25
118 Rick Huisman .08 .25
119 Tim Belk .08 .25
120 Edgar Renteria .20 .50
121 Calvin Maduro RC .20 .50
122 Jerry Martin RC .20 .50
123 Ramon Fermin RC .20 .50
124 Kimera Bartee RC .20 .50
125 Mark Farris .08 .25
126 Frank Rodriguez .08 .25
127 Bobby Higginson RC .75 2.00
128 Bret Wagner .08 .25
129 Edwin Diaz RC .20 .50
130 Jimmy Haynes .08 .25
131 Chris Weinke RC .40 1.00
132 Damian Jackson RC .20 .50
133 Felix Martinez .08 .25
134 Edwin Hurtado RC .20 .50
135 Matt Raleigh RC .20 .50
136 Paul Wilson .08 .25
137 Ron Villone .08 .25
138 E.Stuckenschneider RC .20 .50
139 Tate Seefried .08 .25
140 Rey Ordonez RC .75 2.00
141 Eddie Pearson .08 .25
142 Kevin Gallaher .08 .25
143 Torii Hunter .30 .75
144 Daron Kirkreit .08 .25
145 Craig Wilson .08 .25
146 Ugueth Urbina .08 .25
147 Chris Snopek .08 .25
148 Kym Ashworth .08 .25
149 Wayne Gomes .08 .25
150 Mark Loretta .20 .50
151 Ramon Morel RC .20 .50
152 Trot Nixon .20 .50
153 Desi Relaford .08 .25
154 Scott Sullivan .08 .25
155 Marc Barcelo .08 .25
156 Willie Adams .08 .25
157 Derrick Gibson RC .20 .50
158 Brian Meadows RC .20 .50
159 Julian Tavarez .08 .25
160 Bryan Rekar .08 .25
161 Steve Gibralter .08 .25
162 Esteban Loaiza .08 .25
163 John Wasdin .08 .25
164 Kirk Presley .08 .25
165 Mariano Rivera .60 1.50
166 Andy Larkin .08 .25
167 Sean Whiteside RC .20 .50
168 Matt Apana RC .20 .50
169 Shawn Senior RC .20 .50
170 Scott Gentile .08 .25
171 Quilvio Veras .08 .25
172 Eli Marrero RC .60 1.50
173 Mendy Lopez RC .20 .50
174 Homer Bush .08 .25
175 Brian Stephenson RC .20 .50
176 Jon Nunnally .08 .25
177 Jose Herrera .08 .25
178 Corey Avrard RC .20 .50
179 David Bell .08 .25
180 Jason Isringhausen .20 .50
181 Jamey Wright .08 .25
182 Lonell Roberts RC .20 .50
183 Marty Cordova .08 .25
184 Amaury Telemaco .08 .25
185 John Mabry .08 .25
186 Andrew Vessel RC .20 .50
187 Jim Cole RC .20 .50
188 Marquis Riley .08 .25
189 Todd Dunn .08 .25
190 John Carter .08 .25
191 Donnie Sadler RC .40 1.00
192 Mike Bell .08 .25
193 Chris Cumberland RC .20 .50
194 Jason Schmidt .50 1.25
195 Matt Brunson .08 .25
196 James Baldwin .08 .25
197 Bill Simas RC .20 .50
198 Gus Gandarillas .20 .50
199 Mac Suzuki .08 .25
200 Rick Holifield RC .20 .50
201 Fernando Lunar RC .20 .50
202 Kevin Jarvis .08 .25
203 Everett Stull .08 .25
204 Steve Wojciechowski .08 .25
205 Shawn Estes .08 .25
206 Jermaine Dye .20 .50
207 Marc Kroon .08 .25
208 Peter Munro RC .40 1.00
209 Pat Watkins .08 .25
210 Matt Smith .08 .25
211 Joe Vitiello .08 .25
212 Gerald Witasick Jr. .08 .25
213 Freddy A. Garcia RC .20 .50
214 Glenn Dishman RC .20 .50
215 Jay Canizaro RC .20 .50
216 Angel Martinez .08 .25
217 Yamil Benitez RC .20 .50
218 Fausto Macey RC .20 .50
219 Eric Owens .20 .50
220 Checklist .08 .25
221 D.Hosey FOIL RC .20 .50
222 B.Woodall FOIL RC .20 .50
223 Billy Ashley FOIL .08 .25
224 M.Grudzielanek FOIL RC .75 2.00
225 M.Johnson FOIL RC .40 1.00
226 Tim Unroe FOIL RC .20 .50
227 Todd Greene FOIL .08 .25
228 Larry Sutton FOIL .08 .25
229 Derek Jeter FOIL 1.50 4.00
230 Sal Fasano FOIL RC .20 .50
231 Ruben Rivera FOIL .08 .25
232 Chris Truby FOIL RC .20 .50
233 John Donati FOIL .08 .25
234 D.Conner FOIL RC .20 .50
235 Sergio Nunez FOIL RC .20 .50
236 Ray Brown FOIL RC .20 .50
237 Juan Melo FOIL RC .20 .50
238 Hideo Nomo FOIL RC 2.00 5.00
239 Jamie Bluma RC FOIL .20 .50
240 Jay Payton FOIL RC .75 2.00
241 Paul Konerko FOIL 1.50 4.00
242 Scott Elarton FOIL RC .40 1.00
243 Jeff Abbott FOIL RC .40 1.00
244 Jim Brower FOIL RC .40 1.00
245 Geoff Blum FOIL RC .20 .50
246 Aaron Boone FOIL RC .75 2.00
247 J.R. Phillips FOIL .75 2.00
248 Alex Ochoa FOIL .08 .25
249 N.Garciaparra FOIL 1.50 4.00
250 Garret Anderson FOIL .20 .50
251 Ray Durham FOIL .20 .50
252 Paul Shuey FOIL .08 .25
253 Tony Clark FOIL .08 .25
254 Johnny Damon FOIL .30 .75
255 Duane Singleton FOIL .08 .25
256 LaTroy Hawkins FOIL .08 .25
257 Andy Pettitte FOIL .30 .75
258 Ben Grieve FOIL .08 .25
259 Marc Newfield FOIL .08 .25
260 Terrell Lowery FOIL .08 .25
261 Shawn Green FOIL .20 .50
262 Chipper Jones FOIL .50 1.25
263 B.Kieschnick FOIL .08 .25
264 Pokey Reese FOIL .08 .25
265 Doug Million FOIL .08 .25
266 Marc Valdes FOIL .08 .25
267 Brian L.Hunter FOIL .08 .25
268 T.Hollandsworth FOIL .08 .25
269 Rod Henderson FOIL .08 .25
270 Bill Pulsipher FOIL .08 .25
271 Scott Rolen FOIL RC 5.00 12.00
272 Trey Beamon FOIL .08 .25
273 Alan Benes FOIL .08 .25
274 D.Hermanson FOIL .08 .25
275 Ricky Bottalico .08 .25
276 Albert Belle .20 .50
277 Deion Sanders .30 .75
278 Matt Williams .20 .50
279 Jeff Bagwell .30 .75
280 Kirby Puckett .50 1.25
281 Dave Hollins .08 .25
282 Don Mattingly 1.25 3.00
283 Joey Hamilton .08 .25
284 Bobby Bonilla .20 .50
285 Moises Alou .20 .50
286 Tom Glavine .30 .75
287 Brett Butler .20 .50
288 Chris Hoiles .08 .25
289 Kenny Rogers .20 .50
290 Larry Walker .20 .50
291 Tim Raines .20 .50
292 Kevin Appier .20 .50
293 Roger Clemens 1.00 2.50
294 Chuck Carr .08 .25
295 Randy Myers .08 .25
296 Dave Nilsson .08 .25
297 Joe Carter .20 .50
298 Chuck Finley .20 .50
299 Ray Lankford .20 .50
300 Roberto Kelly .08 .25
301 Jon Lieber .08 .25
302 Travis Fryman .20 .50
303 Mark McGwire 1.25 3.00
304 Tony Gwynn .60 1.50
305 Kenny Lofton .20 .50
306 Mark Whiten .08 .25
307 Doug Drabek .08 .25
308 Terry Steinbach .08 .25
309 Ryan Klesko .20 .50
310 Mike Piazza .75 2.00
311 Ben McDonald .08 .25
312 Reggie Sanders .20 .50
313 Alex Fernandez .08 .25
314 Aaron Sele .08 .25
315 Gregg Jefferies .08 .25
316 Rickey Henderson .50 1.25
317 Brian Anderson .08 .25
318 Jose Valentin .08 .25
319 Rod Beck .08 .25
320 Marquis Grissom .20 .50
321 Ken Griffey Jr. .75 2.00
322 Bret Saberhagen .20 .50
323 Juan Gonzalez .20 .50
324 Paul Molitor .20 .50
325 Gary Sheffield .20 .50
326 Darren Daulton .20 .50
327 Bill Swift .08 .25
328 Brian McRae .08 .25
329 Robin Ventura .20 .50
330 Lee Smith .20 .50
331 Fred McGriff .30 .75
332 Delino DeShields .08 .25
333 Edgar Martinez .30 .75
334 Mike Mussina .30 .75
335 Orlando Merced .08 .25
336 Carlos Baerga .08 .25
337 Wil Cordero .08 .25
338 Tom Pagnozzi .08 .25
339 Pat Hentgen .08 .25
340 Chad Curtis .08 .25
341 Darren Lewis .08 .25
342 Jeff Kent .20 .50
343 Bip Roberts .08 .25
344 Ivan Rodriguez .30 .75
345 Jeff Montgomery .20 .50
346 Hal Morris .08 .25
347 Danny Tartabull .08 .25
348 Raul Mondesi .20 .50
349 Ken Hill .08 .25
350 Pedro Martinez .30 .75
351 Frank Thomas .50 1.25
352 Manny Ramirez .30 .75
353 Tim Salmon .30 .75
354 W. VanLandingham .08 .25
355 Andres Galarraga .20 .50
356 Paul O'Neill .30 .75
357 Brady Anderson .20 .50
358 Ramon Martinez .20 .50
359 John Olerud .20 .50
360 Ruben Sierra .20 .50
361 Cal Eldred .08 .25
362 Jay Buhner .20 .50
363 Jay Bell .20 .50
364 Wally Joyner .20 .50
365 Chuck Knoblauch .20 .50
366 Len Dykstra .20 .50
367 John Wetteland .20 .50
368 Roberto Alomar .30 .75
369 Craig Biggio .30 .75
370 Ozzie Smith .75 2.00
371 Terry Pendleton .20 .50
372 Sammy Sosa .50 1.25
373 Carlos Garcia .08 .25
374 Jose Rijo .08 .25
375 Chris Gomez .08 .25
376 Barry Bonds 1.25 3.00
377 Steve Avery .08 .25
378 Rick Wilkins .08 .25
379 Pete Harnisch .08 .25
380 Dean Palmer .20 .50
381 Bob Hamelin .08 .25
382 Jason Bere .08 .25
383 Jimmy Key .20 .50
384 Dante Bichette .20 .50
385 Rafael Palmeiro .30 .75
386 David Justice .20 .50
387 Chili Davis .20 .50
388 Mike Greenwell .20 .50
389 Todd Zeile .08 .25
390 Jeff Conine .20 .50
391 Rick Aguilera .08 .25
392 Eddie Murray .50 1.25
393 Mike Stanley .08 .25
394 Cliff Floyd UER .20 .50
(numbered 294)
395 Randy Johnson .50 1.25
396 David Nied .08 .25
397 Devon White .20 .50
398 Royce Clayton .08 .25
399 Andy Benes .08 .25
400 John Hudek .08 .25
401 Bobby Jones .08 .25

402 Eric Karros .20 .50
403 Will Clark .30 .75
404 Mark Langston .08 .25
405 Kevin Brown .20 .50
406 Greg Maddux .75 2.00
407 David Cone .20 .50
408 Wade Boggs .30 .75
409 Steve Trachsel .08 .25
410 Greg Vaughn .08 .25
411 Mo Vaughn .20 .50
412 Wilson Alvarez .08 .25
413 Cal Ripken 1.50 4.00
414 Rico Brogna .08 .25
415 Barry Larkin .30 .75
416 Cecil Fielder .20 .50
417 Jose Canseco .30 .75
418 Jack McDowell .08 .25
419 Mike Lieberthal .20 .50
420 Andrew Lorraine .08 .25
421 Rich Becker .08 .25
422 Tony Phillips .08 .25
423 Scott Ruffcorn .08 .25
424 Jeff Granger .08 .25
425 Greg Pirkl .08 .25
426 Dennis Eckersley .20 .50
427 Jose Lima .08 .25
428 Russ Davis .08 .25
429 Armando Benitez .08 .25
430 Alex Gonzalez .08 .25
431 Carlos Delgado .20 .50
432 Chan Ho Park .20 .50
433 Mickey Tettleton .08 .25
434 Dave Winfield .20 .50
435 John Burkett .08 .25
436 Orlando Miller .08 .25
437 Rondell White .20 .50
438 Jose Oliva .08 .25
439 Checklist .08 .25

1995 Bowman Gold Foil

Numbered 221-274, this 54-card standard-size set is the gold insert parallel version of the silver foil subset found in the basic issue. The odds of finding a gold foil version are one in six packs.

COMPLETE SET (54) 75.00 150.00
*STARS: .6X TO 1.5X BASIC CARDS
*ROOKIES: .5X TO 1.2X BASIC

1996 Bowman

The 1996 Bowman set was issued in one series totalling 385 cards. The 11-card packs retailed for $2.50 each. The fronts feature color action player photos in a tan-checkered frame with the player's name printed in silver foil at the bottom. The backs carry another color player photo with player information, 1995 and career player statistics. Each pack contained 10 regular issue cards plus either one foil parallel or an insert card. In a special promotional program, Topps offered collector's a $100 guarantee on complete sets. To get the guarantee, collectors had to mail in a Guaranteed Value Certificate request form, found in packs, along with a $5 processing and registration fee before the December 31st, 1996 deadline. Collectors would then receive a $100 Guaranteed Value Certificate, of which they could mail back to Topps between August 31st, 1999 and December 31st, 1999, along with their complete set, to receive $100. A reprint version of the 1952 Bowman Mickey Mantle card was randomly inserted into packs. Rookie Cards in this set include Russell Branyan, Mike Cameron, Luis Castillo, Ryan Dempster, Livan Hernandez, Geoff Jenkins, Ben Petrick and Mike Sweeney.

COMPLETE SET (385) 20.00 50.00
1 Cal Ripken 1.00 2.50
2 Ray Durham .10 .30
3 Ivan Rodriguez .20 .50
4 Fred McGriff .20 .50
5 Hideo Nomo .30 .75
6 Troy Percival .10 .30
7 Moises Alou .10 .30
8 Mike Stanley .10 .30
9 Jay Buhner .10 .30
10 Shawn Green .10 .30
11 Ryan Klesko .10 .30
12 Andres Galarraga .10 .30
13 Dean Palmer .10 .30
14 Jeff Conine .10 .30
15 Brian L.Hunter .10 .30
16 J.T. Snow .10 .30
17 Larry Walker .10 .30
18 Barry Larkin .20 .50
19 Alex Gonzalez .10 .30
20 Edgar Martinez .20 .50
21 Mo Vaughn .10 .30
22 Mark McGwire .75 2.00
23 Jose Canseco .20 .50
24 Jack McDowell .10 .30
25 Dante Bichette .10 .30
26 Wade Boggs .20 .50
27 Mike Piazza .50 1.25
28 Ray Lankford .10 .30
29 Craig Biggio .20 .50
30 Rafael Palmeiro .20 .50
31 Ron Gant .10 .30
32 Javy Lopez .10 .30
33 Brian Jordan .10 .30
34 Paul O'Neill .20 .50
35 Mark Grace .20 .50
36 Matt Williams .10 .30
37 Pedro Martinez UER .20 .50
Wrong birthdate
38 Rickey Henderson .30 .75
39 Bobby Bonilla .10 .30
40 Todd Hollandsworth .10 .30
41 Jim Thome .20 .50
42 Gary Sheffield .30 .75
43 Tim Salmon .20 .50
44 Gregg Jefferies .10 .30
45 Roberto Alomar .20 .50
46 Carlos Baerga .10 .30
47 Mark Grudzielanek .10 .30
48 Randy Johnson .30 .75
49 Tino Martinez .20 .50
50 Robin Ventura .10 .30
51 Ryne Sandberg .50 1.25
52 Jay Bell .10 .30
53 Jason Schmidt .20 .50
54 Frank Thomas .30 .75
55 Kenny Lofton .10 .30
56 Ariel Prieto .10 .30
57 David Cone .10 .30
58 Reggie Sanders .10 .30
59 Michael Tucker .10 .30
60 Vinny Castilla .10 .30
61 Len Dykstra .10 .30
62 Todd Hundley .10 .30
63 Brian McRae .10 .30
64 Dennis Eckersley .10 .30
65 Rondell White .10 .30
66 Eric Karros .10 .30
67 Greg Maddux .50 1.25
68 Kevin Appier .10 .30
69 Eddie Murray .30 .75
70 John Olerud .10 .30
71 Tony Gwynn .40 1.00
72 David Justice .10 .30
73 Ken Caminiti .10 .30
74 Terry Steinbach .10 .30
75 Alan Benes .10 .30
76 Chipper Jones .30 .75
77 Jeff Bagwell .20 .50
78 Barry Bonds .75 2.00
79 Ken Griffey Jr. .60 1.50
80 Roger Cedeno .10 .30
81 Joe Carter .10 .30
82 Henry Rodriguez .10 .30
83 Jason Isringhausen .10 .30
84 Chuck Knoblauch .10 .30
85 Manny Ramirez .20 .50
86 Tom Glavine .20 .50
87 Jeffrey Hammonds .10 .30
88 Paul Molitor .10 .30
89 Roger Clemens .60 1.50
90 Greg Vaughn .10 .30
91 Marty Cordova .10 .30
92 Albert Belle .10 .30
93 Mike Mussina .20 .50
94 Garret Anderson .10 .30
95 Juan Gonzalez .10 .30
96 John Valentin .10 .30
97 Jason Giambi .10 .30
98 Kirby Puckett .30 .75
99 Jim Edmonds .10 .30
100 Cecil Fielder .10 .30
101 Mike Aldrete .10 .30
102 Marquis Grissom .10 .30
103 Derek Bell .10 .30
104 Raul Mondesi .10 .30
105 Sammy Sosa .30 .75
106 Travis Fryman .10 .30
107 Rico Brogna .10 .30
108 Will Clark .20 .50
109 Bernie Williams .20 .50
110 Brady Anderson .10 .30
111 Torii Hunter .10 .30
112 Derek Jeter .75 2.00
113 Mike Kusiewicz RC .20 .50
114 Scott Rolen .30 .75
115 Ramon Castro .10 .30
116 Jose Guillen RC 1.25 3.00
117 Wade Walker RC .20 .50
118 Shawn Senior .10 .30
119 Onan Masaoka RC .40 1.00
120 Marlon Anderson RC .40 1.00
121 Katsuhiro Maeda RC .40 1.00
122 G.Stephenson RC .20 .50
123 Butch Huskey .10 .30
124 D'Angelo Jimenez RC .40 1.00
125 Tony Mounce RC .20 .50
126 Jay Canizaro .10 .30
127 Juan Melo .10 .30
128 Steve Gibralter .10 .30
129 Freddy Garcia .10 .30
130 Julio Santana UER .10 .30
Card has him born in 1993
131 Richard Hidalgo .10 .30
132 Jermaine Dye .10 .30
133 Willie Adams .10 .30
134 Everett Stull .10 .30
135 Ramon Morel .10 .30
136 Chan Ho Park .10 .30
137 Jamey Wright .10 .30
138 Luis R.Garcia RC .20 .50
139 Dan Serafini .10 .30
140 Ryan Dempster RC .75 2.00
141 Tate Seefried .10 .30
142 Jimmy Hurst .10 .30
143 Travis Miller .10 .30
144 Curtis Goodwin .10 .30
145 Rocky Coppinger RC .20 .50
146 Enrique Wilson .10 .30
147 Jaime Bluma .10 .30
148 Andrew Vessel .10 .30
149 Damian Moss .10 .30
150 Shawn Gallagher RC .20 .50
151 Pat Watkins .10 .30
152 Jose Paniagua .10 .30
153 Danny Graves .10 .30
154 Bryon Gainey RC .20 .50
155 Steve Soderstrom .10 .30
156 Cliff Brumbaugh RC .20 .50
157 Eugene Kingsale RC .20 .50
158 Lou Collier .10 .30
159 Todd Walker .10 .30
160 Kris Detmers RC .20 .50
161 Josh Booty RC .20 .50
162 Greg Whiteman RC .20 .50
163 Damian Jackson .10 .30
164 Tony Clark .10 .30
165 Jeff D'Amico .10 .30
166 Johnny Damon .20 .50
167 Rafael Orellano .10 .30
168 Ruben Rivera .10 .30
169 Alex Ochoa .10 .30
170 Jay Powell .10 .30
171 Tom Evans .10 .30
172 Ron Villone .10 .30
173 Shawn Estes .10 .30
174 John Wasdin .10 .30
175 Bill Simas .10 .30
176 Kevin Brown .10 .30
177 Shannon Stewart .10 .30
178 Todd Greene .10 .30
179 Bob Wolcott .10 .30
180 Chris Snopek .10 .30
181 Nomar Garciaparra .60 1.50
182 Cameron Smith RC .20 .50
183 Matt Drews .10 .30
184 Jimmy Haynes .10 .30
185 Chris Carpenter .20 .50
186 Desi Relaford .10 .30
187 Ben Grieve .10 .30
188 Mike Bell .10 .30
189 Luis Castillo RC .60 1.50
190 Ugueth Urbina .10 .30
191 Paul Wilson .10 .30
192 Andruw Jones .50 1.25
193 Wayne Gomes .10 .30
194 Craig Counsell RC .60 1.50
195 Jim Cole .10 .30
196 Brooks Kieschnick .10 .30
197 Trey Beamon .10 .30
198 Marino Santana RC .20 .50
199 Bob Abreu .30 .75
200 Pokey Reese .10 .30
201 Dante Powell .10 .30
202 George Arias .10 .30
203 Jorge Velandia RC .20 .50
204 George Lombard RC .20 .50
205 Byron Browne RC .20 .50
206 John Frascatore .10 .30
207 Terry Adams .10 .30
208 Wilson Delgado RC .20 .50
209 Billy McMillon .10 .30
210 Jeff Abbott .10 .30
211 Trot Nixon .10 .30
212 Amaury Telemaco .10 .30
213 Scott Sullivan .10 .30
214 Justin Thompson .10 .30
215 Decomba Conner .10 .30
216 Ryan McGuire .10 .30
217 Matt Luke .10 .30
218 Doug Million .10 .30
219 Jason Dickson RC .20 .50
220 Ramon Hernandez RC .75 2.00
221 Mark Bellhorn RC .75 2.00
222 Eric Ludwick RC .20 .50
223 Luke Wilcox RC .20 .50
224 Marty Malloy RC .20 .50
225 Gary Coffee RC .20 .50
226 Wendell Magee RC .20 .50
227 Brett Tomko RC .40 1.00
228 Derek Lowe .10 .30
229 Jose Rosado RC .20 .50
230 Steve Bourgeois RC .20 .50
231 Neil Weber RC .20 .50
232 Jeff Ware .10 .30
233 Edwin Diaz .10 .30
234 Greg Norton .10 .30
235 Aaron Boone .10 .30
236 Jeff Suppan .10 .30
237 Bret Wagner .10 .30
238 Elieser Marrero .10 .30
239 Will Cunnane .10 .30
240 Brian Barkley RC .20 .50
241 Jay Payton .10 .30
242 Marcus Jensen .10 .30
243 Ryan Nye .10 .30
244 Chad Mottola .10 .30
245 Scott McClain RC .20 .50
246 Jessie Ibarra RC .20 .50
247 Mike Darr RC .20 .50
248 Bobby Estalella RC .20 .50
249 Michael Barrett .10 .30
250 Jamie Lopiccolo RC .20 .50
251 Shane Spencer RC .40 1.00
252 Ben Petrick RC .20 .50
253 Jason Bell RC .20 .50
254 Arnold Gooch RC .20 .50
255 T.J. Mathews .10 .30
256 Jason Ryan .10 .30
257 Pat Cline RC .20 .50
258 Rafael Carmona RC .20 .50
259 Carl Pavano RC .75 2.00
260 Ben Davis .10 .30
261 Matt Lawton RC .40 1.00
262 Kevin Sefcik RC .20 .50
263 Chris Fussell RC .20 .50
264 Mike Cameron RC .60 1.50
265 Marty Janzen RC .20 .50
266 Livan Hernandez RC .75 2.00
267 Raul Ibanez RC .75 2.00
268 Juan Encarnacion .10 .30
269 David Yocum RC .20 .50
270 Jonathan Johnson RC .20 .50
271 Reggie Taylor .10 .30
272 Danny Buxbaum RC .20 .50
273 Jacob Cruz .10 .30
274 Bobby Morris RC .20 .50
275 Andy Fox RC .20 .50
276 Greg Keagle .10 .30
277 Charles Peterson .10 .30
278 Derrek Lee .20 .50
279 Bryant Nelson RC .20 .50
280 Antone Williamson .10 .30
281 Scott Elarton .10 .30
282 Shad Williams RC .20 .50
283 Rich Hunter RC .20 .50
284 Chris Sheff .10 .30
285 Derrick Gibson .10 .30
286 Felix Rodriguez .10 .30
287 Brian Banks RC .20 .50
288 Jason McDonald .10 .30
289 Glendon Rusch RC .40 1.00
290 Gary Rath .10 .30
291 Peter Munro .10 .30
292 Tom Fordham .10 .30
293 Jason Kendall .10 .30
294 Russ Johnson .10 .30
295 Joe Long .10 .30
296 Robert Smith RC .20 .50
297 Jarrod Washburn RC .60 1.50
298 Dave Coggin RC .20 .50
299 Jeff Yoder RC .20 .50
300 Jed Hansen RC .20 .50
301 Matt Morris RC 1.00 2.50
302 Josh Bishop RC .20 .50
303 Dustin Hermanson .10 .30
304 Mike Gulan .10 .30
305 Felipe Crespo .10 .30
306 Quinton McCracken .10 .30
307 Jim Bonnici RC .20 .50
308 Sal Fasano .10 .30
309 Gabe Alvarez RC .20 .50
310 Heath Murray RC .20 .50
311 Javier Valentin RC .20 .50
312 Bartolo Colon .30 .75
313 Olmedo Saenz .10 .30
314 Norm Hutchins RC .20 .50
315 Chris Holt .10 .30
316 David Doster RC .20 .50
317 Robert Person .10 .30
318 Donne Wall RC .20 .50
319 Adam Riggs RC .20 .50
320 Homer Bush .10 .30
321 Brad Rigby RC .20 .50
322 Lou Merloni RC .20 .50
323 Neifi Perez .10 .30
324 Chris Cumberland .10 .30
325 Alvie Shepherd RC .20 .50
326 Jarrod Patterson RC .20 .50
327 Ray Ricken RC .20 .50
328 Danny Klassen RC .20 .50
329 David Miller RC .20 .50
330 Chad Alexander RC .20 .50
331 Matt Beaumont .10 .30
332 Damon Hollins .10 .30
333 Todd Dunn .10 .30
334 Mike Sweeney RC .75 2.00
335 Richie Sexson .20 .50
336 Billy Wagner .20 .50
337 Ron Wright RC .20 .50
338 Paul Konerko .30 .75
339 Tommy Phelps RC .20 .50
340 Karim Garcia .10 .30
341 Mike Grace RC .20 .50
342 Russell Branyan RC .40 1.00
343 Randy Winn RC .60 1.50
344 A.J. Pierzynski RC 1.50 4.00
345 Mike Busby RC .20 .50
346 Matt Beech RC .20 .50
347 Jose Cepeda RC .20 .50
348 Brian Stephenson .10 .30
349 Rey Ordonez .10 .30
350 Rich Aurilia RC .40 1.00
351 Edgard Velazquez RC .20 .50
352 Raul Casanova .10 .30
353 Carlos Guillen RC .75 2.00
354 Bruce Aven RC .20 .50
355 Ryan Jones RC .20 .50
356 Derek Aucoin RC .20 .50
357 Brian Rose RC .20 .50
358 Richard Almanzar RC .20 .50
359 Fletcher Bates RC .20 .50
360 Russ Ortiz RC .60 1.50
361 Wilton Guerrero RC .20 .50
362 Geoff Jenkins RC .60 1.50
363 Pete Janicki .10 .30
364 Yamil Benitez .10 .30
365 Aaron Holbert .10 .30
366 Tim Belk .10 .30
367 Terrell Wade .10 .30
368 Terrence Long .10 .30
369 Brad Fullmer .10 .30
370 Matt Wagner .10 .30
371 Craig Wilson RC .20 .50
372 Mark Loretta .10 .30
373 Eric Owens .10 .30
374 Vladimir Guerrero .60 1.50
375 Tommy Davis .10 .30
376 Donnie Sadler .10 .30
377 Edgar Renteria .10 .30
378 Todd Helton .60 1.50
379 Ralph Milliard RC .20 .50
380 Darin Blood RC .20 .50
381 Shayne Bennett .10 .30
382 Mark Redman .10 .30
383 Felix Martinez .10 .30
384 Sean Watkins RC .20 .50
385 Oscar Henriquez .10 .30
M20 Mickey Mantle 2.00 5.00
1952 Bowman Reprint
NNO Checklists .10 .30

1996 Bowman Foil

These parallel foil cards were seeded at an approximate rate of one per pack. Packs that did not contain a Foil card had a Bowman's Best Preview or Minor League Player of the Year insert card instead. The striking silver foil card fronts differ them from the base 1996 Bowman cards.

COMPLETE SET (385) 150.00 300.00
*STARS: 1X TO 2.5X BASIC CARDS
*ROOKIES: 1.25X TO 2.5X BASIC CARDS

1996 Bowman Minor League POY

Randomly inserted in packs at a rate of one in 12, this 15-card set features top minor league prospects for Player of the Year Candidates. The fronts carry a color player photo with red-and-silver foil printing. The backs display player information including his career bests.

COMPLETE SET (15) 10.00 25.00
1 Andruw Jones 1.25 3.00
2 Derrick Gibson .30 .75
3 Bob Abreu .75 2.00
4 Todd Walker .30 .75
5 Jamey Wright .30 .75
6 Wes Helms .60 1.50
7 Karim Garcia .30 .75
8 Bartolo Colon .75 2.00
9 Alex Ochoa .30 .75
10 Mike Sweeney .75 2.00
11 Ruben Rivera .30 .75
12 Gabe Alvarez .20 .50
13 Billy Wagner .30 .75
14 Vladimir Guerrero 1.50 4.00
15 Edgard Velazquez .20 .50

1997 Bowman

The 1997 Bowman set was issued in two series (series one numbers 1-221, series two numbers 222-441) and was distributed in 10 card packs with a suggested retail price of $2.50. The 441-card set features color photos of 300 top prospects with silver and blue foil stamping and 140 veteran stars designated by silver and red foil stamping. An unannounced Hideki Irabu red bordered card (number 441) was also included in series two packs. Players that were featured for the first time on a Bowman card also carried a blue foil "1st Bowman Card" logo on the card front. Topps offered collectors a $125 guarantee on complete sets. To get the guarantee, collectors had to mail in the Guaranteed Certificate Request Form which was found in every three packs of either series along with a $5 registration and processing fee. To redeem the guarantee, collectors had to send a complete set of Bowman regular cards (441 cards in both series) along with the certificate to Topps between August 31 and December 31 in the year 2000. Rookie Cards in this set include Adrian Beltre, Kris Benson, Eric Chavez, Jose Cruz Jr, Travis Lee, Aramis Ramirez, Miguel Tejada and Kerry Wood. Please note that cards 155 and 158 don't exist. Calvin "Pokey" Reese and George Arias are both numbered 156 (Reese is an uncorrected error - should be numbered 155). Chris Carpenter and Eric Milton are both numbered 159 (Carpenter is an uncorrected error - should be numbered 158).

COMPLETE SET (441) 25.00 60.00
COMP. SERIES 1 (221) 12.50 30.00
COMP. SERIES 2 (220) 12.50 30.00
1 Derek Jeter .75 2.00
2 Edgar Renteria .10 .30
3 Chipper Jones .30 .75
4 Hideo Nomo .30 .75
5 Tim Salmon .20 .50
6 Jason Giambi .10 .30
7 Robin Ventura .10 .30
8 Tony Clark .10 .30
9 Barry Larkin .20 .50
10 Paul Molitor .10 .30
11 Bernard Gilkey .10 .30
12 Jack McDowell .10 .30
13 Andy Benes .10 .30
14 Ryan Klesko .10 .30
15 Mark McGwire .75 2.00
16 Ken Griffey Jr. .50 1.25
17 Robb Nen .10 .30
18 Cal Ripken 1.00 2.50
19 John Valentin .10 .30
20 Ricky Bottalico .10 .30
21 Mike Lansing .10 .30
22 Ryne Sandberg .50 1.25
23 Carlos Delgado .10 .30
24 Craig Biggio .20 .50
25 Eric Karros .10 .30
26 Kevin Appier .10 .30
27 Mariano Rivera .30 .75
28 Vinny Castilla .10 .30
29 Juan Gonzalez .10 .30
30 Al Martin .10 .30
31 Jeff Cirillo .10 .30
32 Eddie Murray .30 .75
33 Ray Lankford .10 .30
34 Manny Ramirez .20 .50
35 Roberto Alomar .20 .50
36 Will Clark .20 .50
37 Chuck Knoblauch .10 .30
38 Harold Baines .10 .30
39 Trevor Hoffman .10 .30
40 Edgar Martinez .20 .50
41 Geronimo Berroa .10 .30
42 Rey Ordonez .10 .30
43 Mike Stanley .10 .30
44 Mike Mussina .20 .50
45 Kevin Brown .10 .30
46 Dennis Eckersley .10 .30
47 Henry Rodriguez .10 .30
48 Tino Martinez .20 .50
49 Eric Young .10 .30
50 Bret Boone .10 .30
51 Raul Mondesi .10 .30
52 Sammy Sosa .30 .75
53 John Smoltz .20 .50
54 Billy Wagner .10 .30
55 Jeff D'Amico .10 .30
56 Ken Caminiti .10 .30
57 Jason Kendall .10 .30
58 Wade Boggs .20 .50
59 Andres Galarraga .10 .30
60 Jeff Brantley .10 .30
61 Mel Rojas .10 .30
62 Brian L. Hunter .10 .30
63 Bobby Bonilla .10 .30
64 Roger Clemens .60 1.50
65 Jeff Kent .10 .30
66 Matt Williams .10 .30
67 Albert Belle .10 .30
68 Jeff King .10 .30
69 John Wetteland .10 .30
70 Deion Sanders .20 .50
71 Bubba Trammell RC .25 .60
72 Felix Heredia RC .15 .40
73 Billy Koch RC .40 1.00
74 Sidney Ponson RC .40 1.00
75 Ricky Ledee RC .25 .60
76 Brett Tomko .10 .30
77 Braden Looper RC .15 .40
78 Damian Jackson .10 .30
79 Jason Dickson .10 .30
80 Chad Green RC .15 .40
81 R.A. Dickey RC .15 .40
82 Jeff Liefer .10 .30
83 Matt Wagner .10 .30
84 Richard Hidalgo .10 .30
85 Adam Riggs .10 .30
86 Robert Smith .10 .30
87 Chad Hermansen RC .15 .40
88 Felix Martinez .10 .30
89 J.J. Johnson .10 .30
90 Todd Dunwoody .10 .30
91 Katsuhiro Maeda .10 .30
92 Darin Erstad .10 .30
93 Elieser Marrero .10 .30
94 Bartolo Colon .10 .30
95 Chris Fussell .10 .30
96 Ugueth Urbina .10 .30
97 Josh Paul RC .15 .40
98 Jaime Bluma .10 .30
99 Seth Greisinger RC .15 .40
100 Jose Cruz Jr. RC .25 .60
101 Todd Dunn .10 .30
102 Joe Young RC .15 .40
103 Jonathan Johnson .10 .30
104 Justin Towle RC .15 .40
105 Brian Rose .10 .30
106 Jose Guillen .10 .30
107 Andruw Jones .20 .50
108 Mark Kotsay RC .60 1.50
109 Wilton Guerrero .10 .30
110 Jacob Cruz .10 .30
111 Mike Sweeney .10 .30
112 Julio Mosquera .10 .30
113 Matt Morris .10 .30
114 Wendell Magee .10 .30
115 John Thomson .10 .30
116 Javier Valentin .10 .30
117 Tom Fordham .10 .30
118 Ruben Rivera .10 .30
119 Mike Drumright RC .15 .40
120 Chris Holt .10 .30
121 Sean Maloney .10 .30
122 Michael Barrett .10 .30
123 Tony Saunders RC .15 .40
124 Kevin Brown C .10 .30
125 Richard Almanzar .10 .30
126 Mark Redman .10 .30
127 Anthony Sanders RC .15 .40
128 Jeff Abbott .10 .30
129 Eugene Kingsale .10 .30
130 Paul Konerko .20 .50
131 Randall Simon RC .25 .60
132 Andy Larkin .10 .30
133 Rafael Medina .10 .30
134 Mendy Lopez .10 .30
135 Freddy Adrian Garcia .10 .30
136 Karim Garcia .10 .30
137 Larry Rodriguez RC .15 .40
138 Carlos Guillen .10 .30
139 Aaron Boone .10 .30
140 Donnie Sadler .10 .30
141 Brooks Kieschnick .10 .30
142 Scott Spiezio .10 .30
143 Everett Stull .10 .30
144 Enrique Wilson .10 .30
145 Milton Bradley RC .75 2.00
146 Kevin Orie .10 .30
147 Derek Wallace .10 .30
148 Russ Johnson .10 .30
149 Joe Lagarde RC .15 .40
150 Luis Castillo .10 .30
151 Jay Payton .10 .30
152 Joe Long .10 .30
153 Livan Hernandez .10 .30
154 Vladimir Nunez RC .25 .60
155 Pokey Reese UER .10 .30
Card actually numbered 156
156 George Arias .10 .30
157 Homer Bush .10 .30
158 Chris Carpenter UER .10 .30
Card numbered 159
159 Eric Milton RC .25 .60
160 Richie Sexson .10 .30
161 Carl Pavano .10 .30
162 Chris Gissell RC .15 .40
163 Mac Suzuki .10 .30
164 Pat Cline .10 .30
165 Ron Wright .10 .30
166 Dante Powell .10 .30
167 Mark Bellhorn .10 .30
168 George Lombard .10 .30
169 Pee Wee Lopez RC .15 .40
170 Paul Wilder RC .15 .40
171 Brad Fullmer .10 .30
172 Willie Martinez RC .15 .40
173 Dario Veras RC .15 .40
174 Dave Coggin .10 .30
175 Kris Benson RC .40 1.00
176 Torii Hunter .10 .30
177 D.T. Cromer .10 .30
178 Nelson Figueroa RC .15 .40
179 Hiram Bocachica RC .15 .40

180 Shane Monahan .10 .30
181 Jimmy Anderson RC .15 .40
182 Juan Melo .10 .30
183 Pablo Ortega RC .15 .40
184 Calvin Pickering RC .15 .40
185 Reggie Taylor .10 .30
186 Jeff Farnsworth RC .15 .40
187 Terrence Long .10 .30
188 Geoff Jenkins .10 .30
189 Steve Rain RC .15 .40
190 Nerio Rodriguez RC .15 .40
191 Derrick Gibson .10 .30
192 Darin Blood .10 .30
193 Ben Davis .10 .30
194 Adrian Beltre RC 1.25 3.00
195 Damian Sapp RC UER .15 .40
196 Kerry Wood RC 2.00 5.00
197 Nate Rolison RC .15 .40
198 Fernando Tatis RC .15 .40
199 Brad Penny RC 1.25 3.00
200 Jake Westbrook RC .40 1.00
201 Edwin Diaz .10 .30
202 Joe Fontenot RC .25 .60
203 Matt Halloran RC .15 .40
204 Blake Stein RC .15 .40
205 Onan Masaoka .10 .30
206 Ben Petrick .10 .30
207 Matt Clement RC .40 1.00
208 Todd Greene .10 .30
209 Ray Ricken .10 .30
210 Eric Chavez RC 1.50 4.00
211 Edgard Velazquez .10 .30
212 Bruce Chen RC .40 1.00
213 Danny Patterson .10 .30
214 Jeff Yoder .10 .30
215 Luis Ordaz RC .15 .40
216 Chris Widger .10 .30
217 Jason Brester .10 .30
218 Carlton Loewer .10 .30
219 Chris Reitsma RC .25 .60
220 Neifi Perez .10 .30
221 Hideki Irabu RC .25 .60
222 Ellis Burks .10 .30
223 Pedro Martinez UER .20 .50
Wrong birthdate
224 Kenny Lofton .10 .30
225 Randy Johnson .30 .75
226 Terry Steinbach .10 .30
227 Bernie Williams .20 .50
228 Dean Palmer .10 .30
229 Alan Benes .10 .30
230 Marquis Grissom .10 .30
231 Gary Sheffield .10 .30
232 Curt Schilling .10 .30
233 Reggie Sanders .10 .30
234 Bobby Higginson .10 .30
235 Moises Alou .10 .30
236 Tom Glavine .20 .50
237 Mark Grace .20 .50
238 Ramon Martinez .10 .30
239 Rafael Palmeiro .20 .50
240 John Olerud .10 .30
241 Dante Bichette .10 .30
242 Greg Vaughn .10 .30
243 Jeff Bagwell .20 .50
244 Barry Bonds .75 2.00
245 Pat Hentgen .10 .30
246 Jim Thome .20 .50
247 J.Allensworth .10 .30
248 Andy Pettitte .20 .50
249 Jay Bell .10 .30
250 John Jaha .10 .30
251 Jim Edmonds .10 .30
252 Ron Gant .10 .30
253 David Cone .10 .30
254 Jose Canseco .20 .50
255 Jay Buhner .10 .30
256 Greg Maddux .50 1.25
257 Brian McRae .10 .30
258 Lance Johnson .10 .30
259 Travis Fryman .10 .30
260 Paul O'Neill .20 .50
261 Ivan Rodriguez .20 .50
262 Gregg Jefferies .10 .30
263 Fred McGriff .20 .50
264 Derek Bell .10 .30
265 Jeff Conine .10 .30
266 Mike Piazza .50 1.25
267 Mark Grudzielanek .10 .30
268 Brady Anderson .10 .30
269 Marty Cordova .10 .30
270 Ray Durham .10 .30
271 Joe Carter .10 .30
272 Brian Jordan .10 .30
273 David Justice .10 .30
274 Tony Gwynn .40 1.00
275 Larry Walker .10 .30
276 Cecil Fielder .10 .30
277 Mo Vaughn .10 .30
278 Alex Fernandez .10 .30
279 Michael Tucker .10 .30
280 Jose Valentin .10 .30
281 Sandy Alomar Jr. .10 .30
282 Todd Hollandsworth .10 .30
283 Rico Brogna .10 .30
284 Rusty Greer .10 .30
285 Roberto Hernandez .10 .30
286 Hal Morris .10 .30
287 Johnny Damon .20 .50
288 Todd Hundley .10 .30
289 Rondell White .10 .30
290 Frank Thomas .30 .75
291 Don Denbow RC .15 .40
292 Derrek Lee .20 .50
293 Todd Walker .10 .30
294 Scott Rolen .20 .50
295 Wes Helms .10 .30
296 Bob Abreu .20 .50
297 John Patterson RC .60 1.50
298 Alex Gonzalez RC .40 1.00
299 Grant Roberts RC .15 .40
300 Jeff Suppan .10 .30
301 Luke Wilcox .10 .30
302 Marlon Anderson .10 .30
303 Ray Brown .10 .30
304 Mike Caruso RC .15 .40
305 Sam Marsonek RC .15 .40
306 Brady Raggio RC .15 .40
307 Kevin McGlinchy RC .25 .60
308 Roy Halladay RC 2.00 5.00
309 Jeremi Gonzalez RC .15 .40
310 Aramis Ramirez RC 1.50 4.00
311 Dee Brown RC .15 .40
312 Justin Thompson .10 .30
313 Jay Tessmer RC .15 .40
314 Mike Johnson RC .15 .40
315 Danny Clyburn .10 .30
316 Bruce Aven .10 .30
317 Keith Foulke RC .60 1.50
318 Jimmy Osting RC .25 .60
319 Val.De Los Santos RC .15 .40
320 Shannon Stewart .10 .30
321 Willie Adams .10 .30
322 Larry Barnes RC .15 .40
323 Mark Johnson RC .15 .40
324 Chris Stowers RC .15 .40
325 Brandon Reed .10 .30
326 Randy Winn .10 .30
327 Steve Chavez RC .15 .40
328 Nomar Garciaparra .50 1.25
329 Jacque Jones RC .60 1.50
330 Chris Clemons .10 .30
331 Todd Helton .30 .75
332 Ryan Brannan RC .15 .40
333 Alex Sanchez RC .25 .60
334 Arnold Gooch .10 .30
335 Russell Branyan .10 .30
336 Daryle Ward .15 .40
337 John LeRoy RC .15 .40
338 Steve Cox .10 .30
339 Kevin Witt .10 .30
340 Norm Hutchins .10 .30
341 Gabby Martinez .10 .30
342 Kris Detmers .10 .30
343 Mike Villano RC .15 .40
344 Preston Wilson .10 .30
345 James Manias RC .15 .40
346 Deivi Cruz RC .25 .60
347 Donzell McDonald RC .15 .40
348 Rod Myers RC .15 .40
349 Shawn Chacon RC .40 1.00
350 Elvin Hernandez RC .25 .60
351 Orlando Cabrera RC .60 1.50
352 Brian Banks .10 .30
353 Robbie Bell .15 .40
354 Brad Rigby .10 .30
355 Scott Elarton .10 .30
356 Kevin Sweeney RC .15 .40
357 Steve Soderstrom .10 .30
358 Ryan Nye .10 .30
359 Marlon Allen RC .10 .30
360 Donny Leon RC .15 .40
361 Garrett Neubart RC .25 .60
362 Abraham Nunez RC .25 .60
363 Adam Eaton RC .40 1.00
364 Octavio Dotel RC .25 .60
365 Dean Crow RC .15 .40
366 Jason Baker RC .15 .40
367 Sean Casey .40 1.00
368 Joe Lawrence RC .15 .40
369 Adam Johnson RC .15 .40
370 S.Schoeneweis RC .25 .60
371 Gerald Witasick Jr. .10 .30
372 Ronnie Belliard RC .50 1.25
373 Russ Ortiz .10 .30
374 Robert Stratton RC .25 .60
375 Bobby Estalella .10 .30
376 Corey Lee RC .15 .40
377 Carlos Beltran .75 2.00
378 Mike Cameron .10 .30
379 Scott Randall RC .15 .40
380 Corey Erickson RC .15 .40
381 Jay Canizaro .10 .30
382 Kerry Robinson RC .15 .40
383 Todd Noel RC .15 .40
384 A.J. Zapp RC .15 .40
385 Jarrod Washburn .10 .30
386 Ben Grieve .10 .30
387 Javier Vazquez RC .60 1.50
388 Tony Graffanino .10 .30
389 Travis Lee RC .25 .60
390 DaRond Stovall .10 .30
391 Dennis Reyes RC .25 .60
392 Danny Buxbaum .10 .30
393 Marc Lewis RC .15 .40
394 Kelvim Escobar RC .40 1.00
395 Danny Klassen .10 .30
396 Ken Cloude RC .15 .40
397 Gabe Alvarez .10 .30
398 Jaret Wright RC .25 .60
399 Raul Casanova .10 .30
400 Clayton Bruner RC .15 .40
401 Jason Marquis RC .40 1.00
402 Marc Kroon .10 .30
403 Jamey Wright .10 .30
404 Matt Snyder RC .15 .40
405 Josh Garrett RC .15 .40
406 Juan Encarnacion .10 .30
407 Heath Murray .10 .30
408 Brett Herbison RC .25 .60
409 Brent Butler RC .15 .40
410 Danny Peoples RC .15 .40
411 Miguel Tejada RC 2.00 5.00
412 Damian Moss .10 .30
413 Jim Pittsley .10 .30
414 Dmitri Young .10 .30
415 Glendon Rusch .10 .30
416 Vladimir Guerrero .30 .75
417 Cole Liniak RC .25 .60
418 R.Hernandez UER .10 .30
Card back says 1st Bowman card is 1997, he had a 1996 Bowman
419 Cliff Politte RC .15 .40
420 Mel Rosario RC .15 .40
421 Jorge Carrion RC .15 .40
422 John Barnes RC .15 .40
423 Chris Stowe RC .15 .40
424 Vernon Wells RC 2.00 5.00
425 Brett Caradonna RC .15 .40
426 Scott Hodges RC .15 .40
427 Jon Garland RC 1.00 2.50
428 Nathan Haynes RC .15 .40
429 Geoff Goetz RC .15 .40
430 Adam Kennedy RC .40 1.00
431 T.J. Tucker RC .15 .40
432 Aaron Akin RC .15 .40
433 Jayson Werth RC .40 1.00
434 Glenn Davis RC .15 .40
435 Mark Mangum RC .15 .40
436 Troy Cameron RC .15 .40
437 J.J. Davis RC .15 .40
438 Lance Berkman RC 4.00 10.00
439 Jason Standridge RC .15 .40
440 Jason Dellaero RC .25 .60
441 Hideki Irabu .25 .60

1997 Bowman International

Inserted one in every pack, this 441-card set is parallel to the regular Bowman set. The difference is found in the flag in the background of each card that tells in what country the pictured player was born.

COMPLETE SET (441) 60.00 160.00
COMP.SERIES 1 (221) 30.00 80.00
COMP.SERIES 2 (220) 30.00 80.00
*STARS: 1X TO 2.5X BASIC CARDS
*ROOKIES: .5X TO 1.2X BASIC CARDS

1997 Bowman 1998 ROY Favorites

Randomly inserted in 1997 Bowman Series two packs at the rate of one in 12, this 15-card set features color photos of prospective 1998 Rookie of the Year candidates.

COMPLETE SET (15) 6.00 15.00
ROY1 Jeff Abbott .40 1.00
ROY2 Karim Garcia .40 1.00
ROY3 Todd Helton 1.00 2.50
ROY4 Richard Hidalgo .40 1.00
ROY5 Geoff Jenkins .40 1.00
ROY6 Russ Johnson .40 1.00
ROY7 Paul Konerko .60 1.50
ROY8 Mark Kotsay .75 2.00
ROY9 Ricky Ledee .30 .75
ROY10 Travis Lee .30 .75
ROY11 Derrek Lee .60 1.50
ROY12 Elieser Marrero .40 1.00
ROY13 Juan Melo .40 1.00
ROY14 Brian Rose .40 1.00
ROY15 Fernando Tatis .20 .50

1997 Bowman Certified Blue Ink Autographs

Randomly inserted in first and second series packs at a rate of one in 96 and ANCO packs at one in 115, this 90-card set features color player photos of top prospects with blue ink autographs and printed on sturdy 16 pt. card stock with the Topps Certified Autograph Issue Stamp. The Derek Jeter blue ink and green ink versions are seeded in every 1,928 packs.

*BLACK INK: .5X TO 1.2X BLUE INK
BLACK STATED ODDS 1:503, ANCO 1:600
*GOLD INK: 1X TO 2.5X BLUE INK
GOLD: STATED ODDS 1:1509, ANCO 1:1795
*GREEN JETER: SAME VALUE AS BLUE INK
D.JETER BLUE SER.1 ODDS 1:1928
D.JETER GREEN SER.2 ODDS 1:1928
CA1 Jeff Abbott 3.00 8.00
CA2 Bob Abreu 15.00 40.00
CA3 Willie Adams 3.00 8.00
CA4 Brian Banks 3.00 8.00
CA5 Kris Benson 5.00 12.00
CA6 Darin Blood 3.00 8.00
CA7 Jaime Bluma 3.00 8.00
CA8 Kevin L. Brown 3.00 8.00
CA9 Ray Brown 3.00 8.00
CA10 Homer Bush 3.00 8.00
CA11 Mike Cameron 5.00 12.00
CA12 Jay Canizaro 3.00 8.00
CA13 Luis Castillo 5.00 12.00
CA14 Dave Coggin 3.00 8.00
CA15 Bartolo Colon 5.00 12.00
CA16 Rocky Coppinger 3.00 8.00
CA17 Jacob Cruz 3.00 8.00
CA18 Jose Cruz Jr. 3.00 8.00
CA19 Jeff D'Amico 3.00 8.00
CA20 Ben Davis 3.00 8.00
CA21 Mike Drumright 3.00 8.00
CA22 Scott Elarton 3.00 8.00
CA23 Darin Erstad 5.00 12.00
CA24 Bobby Estalella 3.00 8.00
CA25 Joe Fontenot 3.00 8.00
CA26 Tom Fordham 3.00 8.00
CA27 Brad Fullmer 3.00 8.00
CA28 Chris Fussell 3.00 8.00
CA29 Karim Garcia 3.00 8.00
CA30 Kris Detmers 3.00 8.00
CA31 Todd Greene 3.00 8.00
CA32 Ben Grieve 3.00 8.00
CA33 Vladimir Guerrero 15.00 40.00
CA34 Jose Guillen 5.00 12.00
CA35 Roy Halladay 60.00 100.00
CA36 Wes Helms 3.00 8.00
CA37 Chad Hermansen 3.00 8.00
CA38 Richard Hidalgo 3.00 8.00
CA39 Todd Hollandsworth 3.00 8.00
CA40 Damian Jackson 3.00 8.00
CA41 Derek Jeter 75.00 150.00
CA42 Andruw Jones 15.00 40.00
CA43 Brooks Kieschnick 3.00 8.00
CA44 Eugene Kingsale 3.00 8.00
CA45 Paul Konerko 15.00 40.00
CA46 Marc Kroon 3.00 8.00
CA47 Derrek Lee 15.00 40.00
CA48 Travis Lee 3.00 8.00
CA49 Terrence Long 3.00 8.00
CA50 Curt Lyons 3.00 8.00
CA51 Eli Marrero 3.00 8.00
CA52 Rafael Medina 3.00 8.00
CA53 Juan Melo 3.00 8.00
CA54 Shane Monahan 3.00 8.00
CA55 Julio Mosquera 3.00 8.00
CA56 Heath Murray 3.00 8.00
CA57 Ryan Nye 3.00 8.00
CA58 Kevin Orie 3.00 8.00
CA59 Russ Ortiz 5.00 12.00
CA60 Carl Pavano 5.00 12.00
CA61 Jay Payton 3.00 8.00
CA62 Neifi Perez 3.00 8.00
CA63 Sidney Ponson 5.00 12.00
CA64 Pokey Reese 5.00 12.00
CA65 Ray Ricken 3.00 8.00
CA66 Brad Rigby 3.00 8.00
CA67 Adam Riggs 3.00 8.00
CA68 Ruben Rivera 3.00 8.00
CA69 J.J. Johnson 3.00 8.00
CA70 Scott Rolen 15.00 40.00
CA71 Tony Saunders 3.00 8.00
CA72 Donnie Sadler 3.00 8.00
CA73 Richie Sexson 5.00 12.00
CA74 Scott Spiezio 3.00 8.00
CA75 Everett Stull 3.00 8.00
CA76 Mike Sweeney 5.00 12.00
CA77 Fernando Tatis 3.00 8.00
CA78 Miguel Tejada 50.00 100.00
CA79 Justin Thompson 3.00 8.00
CA80 Justin Towle 3.00 8.00
CA81 Billy Wagner 15.00 40.00
CA82 Todd Walker 5.00 12.00
CA83 Luke Wilcox 3.00 8.00
CA84 Paul Wilder 3.00 8.00
CA85 Enrique Wilson 3.00 8.00
CA86 Kerry Wood 50.00 100.00
CA87 Jamey Wright 3.00 8.00
CA88 Ron Wright 3.00 8.00
CA89 Dmitri Young 5.00 12.00
CA90 Nelson Figueroa 3.00 8.00

1997 Bowman International Best

Randomly inserted in series two packs at the rate of one in 12, this 20-card set features color photos of both prospects and veterans from far and wide who have made an impact on the game.

COMPLETE SET (20) 20.00 50.00
*ATOMIC: 1.5X TO 4X BASIC INT.BEST
ATOMIC SER.2 STATED ODDS 1:96
*REFRACTORS: .75X TO 2X BASIC INT.BEST
REFRACTOR SER.2 STATED ODDS 1:48
BBI1 Frank Thomas 1.25 3.00
BBI2 Ken Griffey Jr. 2.00 5.00
BBI3 Juan Gonzalez .50 1.25
BBI4 Bernie Williams .75 2.00
BBI5 Hideo Nomo 1.25 3.00
BBI6 Sammy Sosa 1.25 3.00
BBI7 Larry Walker .50 1.25
BBI8 Vinny Castilla .50 1.25
BBI9 Mariano Rivera 1.25 3.00
BBI10 Rafael Palmeiro .75 2.00
BBI11 Nomar Garciaparra 2.00 5.00
BBI12 Todd Walker .50 1.25
BBI13 Andruw Jones .75 2.00
BBI14 Vladimir Guerrero 1.25 3.00
BBI15 Ruben Rivera .50 1.25
BBI16 Bob Abreu .75 2.00
BBI17 Karim Garcia .50 1.25
BBI18 Katsuhiro Maeda .50 1.25
BBI19 Jose Cruz Jr. .50 1.25
BBI20 Damian Moss .50 1.25

1997 Bowman Scout's Honor Roll

Randomly inserted in first series packs at a rate of one in 12, this 15-card set features color photos of top prospects and rookies printed on double-etched foil cards.

COMPLETE SET (15) 12.50 25.00
1 Dmitri Young .30 .75
2 Bob Abreu .50 1.25
3 Vladimir Guerrero .75 2.00
4 Paul Konerko .50 1.25
5 Kevin Orie .30 .75
6 Todd Walker .30 .75
7 Ben Grieve .30 .75
8 Darin Erstad .30 .75
9 Derrek Lee .50 1.25
10 Jose Cruz Jr. .30 .75
11 Scott Rolen .50 1.25
12 Travis Lee .30 .75
13 Andruw Jones .50 1.25
14 Wilton Guerrero .30 .75
15 Nomar Garciaparra 1.25 3.00

1998 Bowman Previews

Randomly inserted in Stadium Club first series hobby and retail packs at the rate of one in 12 and first series Home Team Advantage packs at a rate of one in four, this 10-card set is a sneak preview of the Bowman series and features color photos of top players. The cards are numbered with a BP prefix on the backs.

COMPLETE SET (10) 10.00 25.00
BP1 Nomar Garciaparra 1.50 4.00
BP2 Scott Rolen .60 1.50
BP3 Ken Griffey Jr. 1.50 4.00
BP4 Frank Thomas 1.00 2.50
BP5 Larry Walker .40 1.00
BP6 Mike Piazza 1.50 4.00
BP7 Chipper Jones 1.00 2.50
BP8 Tino Martinez .60 1.50
BP9 Mark McGwire 2.50 6.00
BP10 Barry Bonds 2.50 6.00

1998 Bowman Prospect Previews

Randomly seeded in Stadium Club second series hobby and retail packs at a rate of one in twelve and second series Home Team Advantage packs at a rate of one in four, this ten card set previewed the upcoming 1998 Bowman brand, featuring a selection of top youngsters expected to make an impact in 1998.

COMPLETE SET (10) 4.00 10.00
BP1 Ben Grieve .40 1.00
BP2 Brad Fullmer .40 1.00
BP3 Ryan Anderson .40 1.00
BP4 Mark Kotsay .50 1.25
BP5 Bobby Estalella .40 1.00
BP6 Juan Encarnacion .40 1.00
BP7 Todd Helton .60 1.50
BP8 Mike Lowell 2.00 5.00
BP9 A.J. Hinch .40 1.00
BP10 Richard Hidalgo .40 1.00

1998 Bowman

The complete 1998 Bowman set was distributed amongst two series with a total of 441 cards. The 10-card packs retailed for $2.50 each. Series one contains 221 cards while series two contains 220 cards. Each player's facsimile signature taken from the contract they signed with Topps is also on the left border. Players new to Bowman are marked with the new Bowman Rookie Card stamp. Notable Rookie Cards include Ryan Anderson, Jack Cust, Troy Glaus, Orlando Hernandez, Gabe Kapler, Ruben Mateo, Kevin Millwood and Magglio Ordonez. The 1991 BBM (Major Japanese Card set) cards of Shigetoshi Hasegawa, Hideki Irabu and Hideo Nomo (All of which are considered Japanese Rookie Cards) were randomly inserted into these packs.

COMPLETE SET (441) 20.00 50.00
COMP. SERIES 1 (221) 10.00 25.00
COMP. SERIES 2 (220) 10.00 25.00
1 Nomar Garciaparra .50 1.25
2 Scott Rolen .20 .50
3 Andy Pettitte .20 .50
4 Ivan Rodriguez .20 .50
5 Mark McGwire .75 2.00
6 Jason Dickson .10 .30
7 Jose Cruz Jr. .10 .30
8 Jeff Kent .10 .30
9 Mike Mussina .20 .50
10 Jason Kendall .10 .30
11 Brett Tomko .10 .30
12 Jeff King .10 .30
13 Brad Radke .10 .30
14 Robin Ventura .10 .30
15 Jeff Bagwell .20 .50
16 Greg Maddux .50 1.25
17 John Jaha .10 .30
18 Mike Piazza .50 1.25
19 Edgar Martinez .20 .50
20 David Justice .10 .30
21 Todd Hundley .10 .30
22 Tony Gwynn .40 1.00
23 Larry Walker .10 .30
24 Bernie Williams .20 .50
25 Edgar Renteria .10 .30
26 Rafael Palmeiro .20 .50
27 Tim Salmon .20 .50
28 Matt Morris .10 .30
29 Shawn Estes .10 .30
30 Vladimir Guerrero .30 .75
31 Fernando Tatis .10 .30
32 Justin Thompson .10 .30
33 Ken Griffey Jr. .50 1.25
34 Edgardo Alfonzo .10 .30
35 Mo Vaughn .10 .30
36 Marty Cordova .10 .30
37 Craig Biggio .20 .50
38 Roger Clemens .60 1.50
39 Mark Grace .20 .50
40 Ken Caminiti .10 .30
41 Tony Womack .10 .30
42 Albert Belle .10 .30
43 Tino Martinez .20 .50
44 Sandy Alomar Jr. .10 .30
45 Jeff Cirillo .10 .30
46 Jason Giambi .10 .30
47 Darin Erstad .10 .30
48 Livan Hernandez .10 .30
49 Mark Grudzielanek .10 .30
50 Sammy Sosa .30 .75
51 Curt Schilling .10 .30
52 Brian Hunter .10 .30
53 Neifi Perez .10 .30
54 Todd Walker .10 .30
55 Jose Guillen .10 .30
56 Jim Thome .20 .50
57 Tom Glavine .20 .50
58 Todd Greene .10 .30
59 Rondell White .10 .30
60 Roberto Alomar .20 .50
61 Tony Clark .10 .30
62 Vinny Castilla .10 .30
63 Barry Larkin .20 .50
64 Hideki Irabu .10 .30
65 Johnny Damon .20 .50
66 Juan Gonzalez .10 .30
67 John Olerud .10 .30
68 Gary Sheffield .10 .30
69 Raul Mondesi .10 .30
70 Chipper Jones .30 .75
71 David Ortiz 1.00 2.50
72 Warren Morris RC .15 .40
73 Alex Gonzalez .10 .30
74 Nick Bierbrodt .10 .30
75 Roy Halladay .10 .30
76 Danny Buxbaum .10 .30
77 Adam Kennedy .10 .30
78 Jared Sandberg .10 .30
79 Michael Barrett .10 .30
80 Gil Meche .25 .60
81 Jayson Werth .10 .30
82 Abraham Nunez .10 .30
83 Ben Petrick .10 .30
84 Brett Caradonna .10 .30
85 Mike Lowell RC 1.25 3.00
86 Clayton Bruner .10 .30
87 John Curtice RC .25 .60
88 Bobby Estalella .10 .30
89 Juan Melo .10 .30
90 Arnold Gooch .10 .30
91 Kevin Millwood RC .60 1.50
92 Richie Sexson .10 .30
93 Orlando Cabrera .10 .30
94 Pat Cline .10 .30
95 Anthony Sanders .10 .30
96 Russ Johnson .10 .30
97 Ben Grieve .10 .30
98 Kevin McGlinchy .10 .30
99 Paul Wilder .10 .30
100 Russ Ortiz .10 .30
101 Ryan Jackson RC .15 .40
102 Heath Murray .10 .30
103 Brian Rose .10 .30
104 R.Radmanovich RC .15 .40
105 Ricky Ledee .10 .30
106 Jeff Wallace RC .15 .40
107 Ryan Minor RC .15 .40
108 Dennis Reyes .10 .30
109 James Manias .10 .30
110 Chris Carpenter .10 .30
111 Daryle Ward .10 .30
112 Vernon Wells .10 .30
113 Chad Green .10 .30
114 Mike Stoner RC .15 .40
115 Brad Fullmer .10 .30
116 Adam Eaton .10 .30
117 Jeff Liefer .10 .30
118 Corey Koskie RC .40 1.00
119 Todd Helton .20 .50
120 Jaime Jones RC .15 .40
121 Mel Rosario .10 .30
122 Geoff Goetz .10 .30
123 Adrian Beltre .10 .30
124 Jason Dellaero .10 .30
125 Gabe Kapler RC .40 1.00
126 Scott Schoeneweis .10 .30
127 Ryan Brannan .10 .30
128 Aaron Akin .10 .30
129 Ryan Anderson RC .15 .40
130 Brad Penny .10 .30
131 Bruce Chen .10 .30
132 Eli Marrero .10 .30
133 Eric Chavez .10 .30
134 Troy Glaus RC 1.50 4.00
135 Troy Cameron .10 .30
136 Brian Sikorski RC .15 .40
137 Mike Kinkade RC .15 .40
138 Braden Looper .10 .30
139 Mark Mangum .10 .30
140 Danny Peoples .10 .30
141 J.J. Davis .10 .30
142 Ben Davis .10 .30
143 Jacque Jones .10 .30
144 Derrick Gibson .10 .30
145 Bronson Arroyo .60 1.50
146 L.De Los Santos RC UER .15 .40
has hitting stat line instead of pitching
147 Jeff Abbott .10 .30

148 Mike Cuddyer RC .60 1.50
149 Jason Romano .10 .30
150 Shane Monahan .10 .30
151 Ntema Ndungidi RC .15 .40
152 Alex Sanchez .10 .30
153 Jack Cust RC .75 2.00
154 Brent Butler .10 .30
155 Ramon Hernandez .10 .30
156 Norm Hutchins .10 .30
157 Jason Marquis .10 .30
158 Jacob Cruz .10 .30
159 Rob Burger RC .15 .40
160 Dave Coggin .10 .30
161 Preston Wilson .10 .30
162 Jason Fitzgerald RC .15 .40
163 Dan Serafini .10 .30
164 Peter Munro .10 .30
165 Trot Nixon .10 .30
166 Homer Bush .10 .30
167 Dermal Brown .10 .30
168 Chad Hermansen .10 .30
169 Julio Moreno RC .15 .40
170 John Roskos RC .15 .40
171 Grant Roberts .10 .30
172 Ken Cloude .10 .30
173 Jason Brester .10 .30
174 Jason Conti .10 .30
175 Jon Garland .10 .30
176 Robbie Bell .10 .30
177 Nathan Haynes .10 .30
178 Ramon Ortiz RC .25 .60
179 Shannon Stewart .10 .30
180 Pablo Ortega .10 .30
181 Jimmy Rollins RC 2.50 6.00
182 Sean Casey .10 .30
183 Ted Lilly RC .40 1.00
184 Chris Enochs RC .15 .40
185 M.Ordonez UER RC 2.00 5.00
Front photo is Mario Valdez
186 Mike Drumright .10 .30
187 Aaron Boone .10 .30
188 Matt Clement .10 .30
189 Todd Dunwoody .10 .30
190 Larry Rodriguez .10 .30
191 Todd Noel .10 .30
192 Geoff Jenkins .10 .30
193 George Lombard .10 .30
194 Lance Berkman .10 .30
195 Marcus McCain .10 .30
196 Ryan McGuire .10 .30
197 Jhensy Sandoval .10 .30
198 Corey Lee .10 .30
199 Mario Valdez .10 .30
200 Robert Fick RC .25 .60
201 Donnie Sadler .10 .30
202 Marc Kroon .10 .30
203 David Miller .10 .30
204 Jarrod Washburn .10 .30
205 Miguel Tejada .30 .75
206 Raul Ibanez .10 .30
207 John Patterson .10 .30
208 Calvin Pickering .10 .30
209 Felix Martinez .10 .30
210 Mark Redman .10 .30
211 Scott Elarton .10 .30
212 Jose Amado RC .15 .40
213 Kerry Wood .10 .30
214 Dante Powell .10 .30
215 Aramis Ramirez .10 .30
216 A.J. Hinch .10 .30
217 Dustin Carr RC .15 .40
218 Mark Kotsay .10 .30
219 Jason Standridge .10 .30
220 Luis Ordaz .10 .30
221 O.Hernandez RC .75 2.00
222 Cal Ripken 1.00 2.50
223 Paul Molitor .10 .30
224 Derek Jeter .75 2.00
225 Barry Bonds .75 2.00
226 Jim Edmonds .10 .30
227 John Smoltz .20 .50
228 Eric Karros .10 .30
229 Ray Lankford .10 .30
230 Rey Ordonez .10 .30
231 Kenny Lofton .10 .30
232 Alex Rodriguez .50 1.25
233 Dante Bichette .10 .30
234 Pedro Martinez .20 .50
235 Carlos Delgado .10 .30
236 Rod Beck .10 .30
237 Matt Williams .10 .30
238 Charles Johnson .10 .30
239 Rico Brogna .10 .30
240 Frank Thomas .30 .75
241 Paul O'Neill .20 .50
242 Jaret Wright .10 .30
243 Brant Brown .10 .30
244 Ryan Klesko .10 .30
245 Chuck Finley .10 .30
246 Derek Bell .10 .30
247 Delino DeShields .10 .30
248 Chan Ho Park .10 .30
249 Wade Boggs .20 .50
250 Jay Buhner .10 .30
251 Butch Huskey .10 .30
252 Steve Finley .10 .30
253 Will Clark .20 .50
254 John Valentin .10 .30
255 Bobby Higginson .10 .30
256 Darryl Strawberry .10 .30
257 Randy Johnson .30 .75
258 Al Martin .10 .30
259 Travis Fryman .10 .30
260 Fred McGriff .20 .50
261 Jose Valentin .10 .30
262 Andruw Jones .20 .50
263 Kenny Rogers .10 .30
264 Moises Alou .10 .30
265 Denny Neagle .10 .30
266 Ugueth Urbina .10 .30
267 Derrek Lee .20 .50
268 Ellis Burks .10 .30
269 Mariano Rivera .30 .75
270 Dean Palmer .10 .30
271 Eddie Taubensee .10 .30
272 Brady Anderson .10 .30
273 Brian Giles .10 .30
274 Quinton McCracken .10 .30
275 Henry Rodriguez .10 .30
276 Andres Galarraga .10 .30
277 Jose Canseco .20 .50
278 David Segui .10 .30
279 Bret Saberhagen .10 .30
280 Kevin Brown .20 .50
281 Chuck Knoblauch .10 .30
282 Jeromy Burnitz .10 .30
283 Jay Bell .10 .30
284 Manny Ramirez .20 .50
285 Rick Helling .10 .30
286 Francisco Cordova .10 .30
287 Bob Abreu .10 .30
288 J.T. Snow .10 .30
289 Hideo Nomo .30 .75
290 Brian Jordan .10 .30
291 Javy Lopez .10 .30
292 Travis Lee .10 .30
293 Russell Branyan .10 .30
294 Paul Konerko .10 .30
295 Masato Yoshii RC .25 .60
296 Kris Benson .10 .30
297 Juan Encarnacion .10 .30
298 Eric Milton .10 .30
299 Mike Caruso .10 .30
300 R.Aramboles RC .15 .40
301 Bobby Smith .10 .30
302 Billy Koch .10 .30
303 Richard Hidalgo .10 .30
304 Justin Baughman RC .15 .40
305 Chris Gissell .10 .30
306 Donnie Bridges RC .15 .40
307 Nelson Lara RC .15 .40
308 Randy Wolf RC .25 .60
309 Jason LaRue RC .25 .60
310 Jason Gooding RC .15 .40
311 Edgard Clemente .10 .30
312 Andrew Vessel .10 .30
313 Chris Reitsma .10 .30
314 Jesus Sanchez RC .15 .40
315 Buddy Carlyle RC .15 .40
316 Randy Winn .10 .30
317 Luis Rivera RC .15 .40
318 Marcus Thames RC 1.00 2.50
319 A.J. Pierzynski .10 .30
320 Scott Randall .10 .30
321 Damian Sapp .10 .30
322 Ed Yarnall RC .15 .40
323 Luke Allen RC .15 .40
324 J.D. Smart .10 .30
325 Willie Martinez .10 .30
326 Alex Ramirez .10 .30
327 Eric DuBose RC .15 .40
328 Kevin Witt .10 .30
329 Dan McKinley RC .15 .40
330 Cliff Politte .10 .30
331 Vladimir Nunez .10 .30
332 John Halama RC .15 .40
333 Nerio Rodriguez .10 .30
334 Desi Relaford .10 .30
335 Robinson Checo .10 .30
336 John Nicholson .10 .30
337 Tom LaRosa RC .15 .40
338 Kevin Nicholson RC .15 .40
339 Javier Vazquez .10 .30
340 A.J. Zapp .10 .30
341 Tom Evans .10 .30
342 Kerry Robinson .10 .30
343 Gabe Gonzalez RC .15 .40
344 Ralph Milliard .10 .30
345 Enrique Wilson .10 .30
346 Elvin Hernandez .10 .30
347 Mike Lincoln RC .15 .40
348 Cesar King RC .15 .40
349 Cristian Guzman RC .25 .60
350 Donzell McDonald .10 .30
351 Jim Parque RC .15 .40
352 Mike Saipe RC .15 .40
353 Carlos Febles RC .25 .60
354 Dernell Stenson RC .15 .40
355 Mark Osborne RC .15 .40
356 Odalis Perez RC .60 1.50
357 Jason Dewey RC .15 .40
358 Joe Fontenot .10 .30
359 Jason Grilli RC .15 .40
360 Kevin Haverbusch RC .15 .40
361 Jay Yennaco RC .15 .40
362 Brian Buchanan .10 .30
363 John Barnes .10 .30
364 Chris Fussell .10 .30
365 Kevin Gibbs RC .15 .40
366 Joe Lawrence .10 .30
367 DaRond Stovall .10 .30
368 Brian Fuentes RC .15 .40
369 Jimmy Anderson .10 .30
370 Lariel Gonzalez RC .15 .40
371 Scott Williamson RC .15 .40
372 Milton Bradley .10 .30
373 Jason Halper RC .15 .40
374 Brent Billingsley RC .15 .40
375 Joe DePastino RC .15 .40
376 Jake Westbrook .10 .30
377 Octavio Dotel .10 .30
378 Jason Williams RC .15 .40
379 Julio Ramirez RC .15 .40
380 Seth Greisinger .10 .30
381 Mike Judd RC .15 .40
382 Ben Ford RC .15 .40
383 Tom Bennett RC .15 .40
384 Adam Butler RC .15 .40
385 Wade Miller RC .40 1.00
386 Kyle Peterson RC .15 .40
387 Tommy Peterman RC .15 .40
388 Onan Masaoka .10 .30
389 Jason Rakers RC .15 .40
390 Rafael Medina .10 .30
391 Luis Lopez RC .15 .40
392 Jeff Yoder .10 .30
393 Vance Wilson RC .15 .40
394 F.Seguignol RC .15 .40
395 Ron Wright .10 .30
396 Ruben Mateo RC .15 .40
397 Steve Lomasney RC .25 .60
398 Damian Jackson .10 .30
399 Mike Jerzembeck RC .15 .40
400 Luis Rivas RC .40 1.00
401 Kevin Burford RC .15 .40
402 Glenn Davis .10 .30
403 Robert Luce RC .15 .40
404 Cole Liniak .10 .30
405 Matt LeCroy RC .25 .60
406 Jeremy Giambi RC .25 .60
407 Shawn Chacon .10 .30
408 Dewayne Wise RC .15 .40
409 Steve Woodard .10 .30
410 F.Cordero RC .40 1.00
411 Damon Minor RC .15 .40
412 Lou Collier .10 .30
413 Justin Towle .10 .30
414 Juan LeBron .10 .30
415 Michael Coleman .10 .30
416 Felix Rodriguez .10 .30
417 Paul Ah Yat RC .15 .40
418 Kevin Barker RC .15 .40
419 Brian Meadows .10 .30
420 Darnell McDonald RC .15 .40
421 Matt Kinney RC .15 .40
422 Mike Vavrek RC .15 .40
423 Courtney Duncan RC .15 .40
424 Kevin Millar RC .60 1.50
425 Ruben Rivera .10 .30
426 Steve Shoemaker RC .15 .40
427 Dan Reichert RC .15 .40
428 Carlos Lee RC 1.25 3.00
429 Rod Barajas .40 1.00
430 Pablo Ozuna RC .25 .60
431 Todd Belitz RC .15 .40
432 Sidney Ponson .10 .30
433 Steve Carver RC .15 .40
434 Esteban Yan RC .25 .60
435 Cedrick Bowers .10 .30
436 Marlon Anderson .10 .30
437 Carl Pavano .10 .30
438 Jae Weong Seo RC .25 .60
439 Jose Taveras RC .15 .40
440 Matt Anderson RC .15 .40
441 Darron Ingram RC .15 .40
NNO S.Hasegawa '91 BBM 4.00 10.00
NNO H.Irabu '91 BBM 4.00 10.00
NNO H.Nomo '91 BBM 10.00 25.00

1998 Bowman Golden Anniversary

Randomly inserted in first series packs at a rate of one in 237 and second series packs at a rate of one in 194, this 441-card set is a parallel to the Bowman base set. The set celebrates Bowman's 50th birthday. Each card is highlighted by gold-stamped facsimile autographs (instead of silver foil on the basic cards) and are sequentially numbered to 50.

*STARS: 12.5X TO 30X BASIC CARDS
*ROOKIES: 10X TO 20X BASIC CARDS
424 Kevin Millar 15.00 30.00

1998 Bowman International

Inserted one per pack, this 441-card set is a parallel to the Bowman base set. The set allows collectors to see where their favorite players were born and learn the vitals on each of them as translated in the player's home language.

COMPLETE SET (441) 60.00 150.00
COMP. SERIES 1 (221) 30.00 75.00
COMP. SERIES 2 (220) 30.00 75.00
*STARS: 1.25X TO 3X BASIC CARDS
*ROOKIES: .6X TO 1.5X BASIC CARDS

1998 Bowman 1999 ROY Favorites

Randomly inserted in second series packs at a rate of one in 12, this 10-card insert features color action photography on borderless, double-etched foil cards. The players featured on these cards were among the leading early candidates for the 1999 ROY award.

COMPLETE SET (10) 8.00 20.00
ROY1 Adrian Beltre .50 1.25
ROY2 Troy Glaus 1.50 4.00
ROY3 Chad Hermansen .50 1.25
ROY4 Matt Clement .50 1.25
ROY5 Eric Chavez .50 1.25
ROY6 Kris Benson .50 1.25
ROY7 Richie Sexson .50 1.25
ROY8 Randy Wolf 1.00 2.50
ROY9 Ryan Minor .60 1.50
ROY10 Alex Gonzalez .50 1.25

1998 Bowman Certified Blue Autographs

Randomly inserted in first series packs at a rate of one in 149 and second series packs at a rate of one in 122.

*GOLD FOIL: 1.5X TO 4X BLUE AU'S
SER.1 GOLD FOIL STATED ODDS 1:2976
SER.2 GOLD FOIL STATED ODDS 1:2445
*SILVER FOIL: .75X TO 2X BLUE AU'S
SER.1 SILVER FOIL STATED ODDS 1:992
SER.2 SILVER FOIL STATED ODDS 1:815
1 Adrian Beltre 6.00 15.00
2 Brad Fullmer 4.00 10.00
3 Ricky Ledee 4.00 10.00
4 David Ortiz 25.00 50.00
5 Fernando Tatis 4.00 10.00
6 Kerry Wood 10.00 25.00
7 Mel Rosario 4.00 10.00
8 Cole Liniak 4.00 10.00
9 A.J. Hinch 4.00 10.00
10 Jhensy Sandoval 4.00 10.00
11 Jose Cruz Jr. 4.00 10.00
12 Richard Hidalgo 4.00 10.00
13 Geoff Jenkins 6.00 15.00
14 Carl Pavano 6.00 15.00
15 Richie Sexson 6.00 15.00
16 Tony Womack 4.00 10.00
17 Scott Rolen 10.00 25.00
18 Ryan Minor 4.00 10.00
19 Eli Marrero 4.00 10.00
20 Jason Marquis 6.00 15.00
21 Mike Lowell 15.00 40.00
22 Todd Helton 10.00 25.00
23 Chad Green 4.00 10.00
24 Scott Elarton 4.00 10.00
25 Russell Branyan 4.00 10.00
26 Mike Drumright 4.00 10.00
27 Ben Grieve 4.00 10.00
28 Jacque Jones 6.00 15.00
29 Jared Sandberg 4.00 10.00
30 Grant Roberts 4.00 10.00
31 Mike Stoner 4.00 10.00
32 Brian Rose 4.00 10.00
33 Randy Winn 4.00 10.00
34 Justin Towle 4.00 10.00
35 Anthony Sanders 4.00 10.00
36 Rafael Medina 4.00 10.00
37 Corey Lee 4.00 10.00
38 Mike Kinkade 4.00 10.00
39 Norm Hutchins 4.00 10.00
40 Jason Brester 4.00 10.00
41 Ben Davis 4.00 10.00
42 Nomar Garciaparra 20.00 50.00
43 Jeff Liefer 4.00 10.00
44 Eric Milton 4.00 10.00
45 Preston Wilson 6.00 15.00
46 Miguel Tejada 15.00 40.00
47 Luis Ordaz 4.00 10.00
48 Travis Lee 4.00 10.00
49 Kris Benson 6.00 15.00
50 Jacob Cruz 4.00 10.00
51 Dermal Brown 4.00 10.00
52 Marc Kroon 4.00 10.00
53 Chad Hermansen 4.00 10.00
54 Roy Halladay 10.00 25.00
55 Eric Chavez 10.00 25.00
56 Jason Conti 4.00 10.00
57 Juan Encarnacion 6.00 15.00
58 Paul Wilder 4.00 10.00
59 Aramis Ramirez 10.00 25.00
60 Cliff Politte 4.00 10.00
61 Todd Dunwoody 4.00 10.00
62 Paul Konerko 10.00 25.00
63 Shane Monahan 4.00 10.00
64 Alex Sanchez 4.00 10.00
65 Jeff Abbott 4.00 10.00
66 John Patterson 6.00 15.00
67 Peter Munro 4.00 10.00
68 Jarrod Washburn 4.00 10.00
69 Derrek Lee 10.00 25.00
70 Ramon Hernandez 4.00 10.00

1998 Bowman Minor League MVP's

Randomly inserted in second series packs at a rate of one in 12, this 11-card insert features former Minor League MVP award winners in color action photography.

COMPLETE SET (11) 10.00 25.00
MVP1 Jeff Bagwell .60 1.50
MVP2 Andres Galarraga .40 1.00
MVP3 Juan Gonzalez .40 1.00
MVP4 Tony Gwynn 1.25 3.00
MVP5 Vladimir Guerrero 1.00 2.50
MVP6 Derek Jeter 2.50 6.00
MVP7 Andruw Jones .60 1.50
MVP8 Tino Martinez .60 1.50
MVP9 Manny Ramirez .60 1.50
MVP10 Gary Sheffield .60 1.50
MVP11 Jim Thome .60 1.50

1998 Bowman Scout's Choice

Randomly inserted in first series packs at a rate of one in 12, this borderless 21-card set is an insert featuring leading minor league prospects.

COMPLETE SET (21) 10.00 25.00

SC1 Paul Konerko .75 2.00
SC2 Richard Hidalgo .75 2.00
SC3 Mark Kotsay .75 2.00
SC4 Ben Grieve .75 2.00
SC5 Chad Hermansen .75 2.00
SC6 Matt Clement .75 2.00
SC7 Brad Fullmer .75 2.00
SC8 Eli Marrero .75 2.00
SC9 Kerry Wood 1.00 2.50
SC10 Adrian Beltre .75 2.00
SC11 Ricky Ledee .75 2.00
SC12 Travis Lee .75 2.00
SC13 Abraham Nunez .75 2.00
SC14 Brian Rose .75 2.00
SC15 Dermal Brown .75 2.00
SC16 Juan Encarnacion .75 2.00
SC17 Aramis Ramirez .75 2.00
SC18 Todd Helton 1.25 3.00
SC19 Kris Benson .75 2.00
SC20 Russell Branyan .75 2.00
SC21 Mike Stoner 1.00 2.50

1999 Bowman Pre-Production

This six-card set was issued to preview the 1999 Bowman set. The cards are numbered with a "PP" prefix and feature a mixture of veterans and young players. The set was distributed to dealers and hobby media in complete set form within a clear cello wrap several months prior to the shipping of 1999 Bowman series one.

COMPLETE SET (6) 2.00 5.00
PP1 Andres Galarraga .60 1.50
PP2 Raul Mondesi .40 1.00
PP3 Vinny Castilla .40 1.00
PP4 Corey Koskie UER .40 1.00
Birthyear listed as 1967
PP5 Octavio Dotel .60 1.50
PP6 Dernell Stenson .20 .50

1999 Bowman

The 1999 Bowman set was issued in two series and was distributed in 10 card packs with a suggested retail price of $3.00. The 440-card set featured the newest faces and potential talent that would carry Major League Baseball into the next millennium. This set features 300 top prospects and and 140 veterans. Prospect cards are designated with a silver and blue design while the veteran cards are shown with a silver and red design. Prospects making their debut on a Bowman card each featured a "Bowman Rookie Card" stamp on front. Notable Rookie Cards include Pat Burrell, Sean Burroughs, Carl Crawford, Adam Dunn, Rafael Furcal, Tim Hudson, Nick Johnson, Austin Kearns, Corey Patterson, Wily Mo Pena, Adam Piatt and Alfonso Soriano.

COMPLETE SET (440) 30.00 80.00
COMP. SERIES 1 (220) 12.50 30.00
COMP. SERIES 2 (220) 20.00 50.00
1 Ben Grieve .10 .30
2 Kerry Wood .10 .30
3 Ruben Rivera .10 .30
4 Sandy Alomar Jr. .10 .30
5 Cal Ripken 1.00 2.50
6 Mark McGwire .75 2.00
7 Vladimir Guerrero .30 .75
8 Moises Alou .10 .30
9 Jim Edmonds .10 .30
10 Greg Maddux .50 1.25
11 Gary Sheffield .10 .30
12 John Valentin .10 .30
13 Chuck Knoblauch .10 .30
14 Tony Clark .10 .30
15 Rusty Greer .10 .30
16 Al Leiter .10 .30
17 Travis Lee .10 .30
18 Jose Cruz Jr. .10 .30
19 Pedro Martinez .20 .50
20 Paul O'Neill .20 .50
21 Todd Walker .10 .30
22 Vinny Castilla .10 .30
23 Barry Larkin .20 .50
24 Curt Schilling .10 .30
25 Jason Kendall .10 .30
26 Scott Erickson .10 .30
27 Andres Galarraga .10 .30
28 Jeff Shaw .10 .30
29 John Olerud .10 .30
30 Orlando Hernandez .10 .30
31 Larry Walker .10 .30
32 Andruw Jones .20 .50
33 Jeff Cirillo .10 .30
34 Barry Bonds .75 2.00
35 Manny Ramirez .20 .50
36 Mark Kotsay .10 .30
37 Ivan Rodriguez .20 .50
38 Jeff King .10 .30
39 Brian Hunter .10 .30
40 Ray Durham .10 .30
41 Bernie Williams .20 .50
42 Darin Erstad .10 .30
43 Chipper Jones .30 .75
44 Pat Hentgen .10 .30
45 Eric Young .10 .30
46 Jaret Wright .10 .30
47 Juan Guzman .10 .30
48 Jorge Posada .20 .50
49 Bobby Higginson .10 .30
50 Jose Guillen .10 .30
51 Trevor Hoffman .10 .30
52 Ken Griffey Jr. .50 1.25
53 David Justice .10 .30
54 Matt Williams .10 .30
55 Eric Karros .10 .30
56 Derek Bell .10 .30
57 Ray Lankford .10 .30
58 Mariano Rivera .30 .75
59 Brett Tomko .10 .30
60 Mike Mussina .20 .50
61 Kenny Lofton .10 .30
62 Chuck Finley .10 .30
63 Alex Gonzalez .10 .30
64 Mark Grace .20 .50
65 Raul Mondesi .10 .30
66 David Cone .10 .30
67 Brad Fullmer .10 .30
68 Andy Benes .10 .30
69 John Smoltz .20 .50
70 Shane Reynolds .10 .30
71 Bruce Chen .10 .30
72 Adam Kennedy .10 .30
73 Jack Cust .10 .30
74 Matt Clement .10 .30
75 Derrick Gibson .10 .30
76 Darnell McDonald .10 .30
77 Adam Everett RC .40 1.00
78 Ricardo Aramboles .10 .30
79 Mark Quinn RC .15 .40
80 Jason Rakers .10 .30
81 Seth Etherton RC .15 .40
82 Jeff Urban RC .25 .60
83 Manny Aybar .10 .30
84 Mike Nannini RC .15 .40
85 Onan Masaoka .10 .30
86 Rod Barajas .10 .30
87 Mike Frank .10 .30
88 Scott Randall .10 .30
89 Justin Bowles RC .15 .40
90 Chris Haas .10 .30
91 Arturo McDowell RC .15 .40
92 Matt Belisle RC .15 .40
93 Scott Elarton .10 .30
94 Vernon Wells .10 .30
95 Pat Cline .10 .30
96 Ryan Anderson .10 .30
97 Kevin Barker .10 .30
98 Ruben Mateo .10 .30
99 Robert Fick .10 .30
100 Corey Koskie .10 .30
101 Ricky Ledee .10 .30
102 Rick Elder RC .15 .40
103 Jack Cressend RC .15 .40
104 Joe Lawrence .10 .30
105 Mike Lincoln .10 .30
106 Kit Pellow RC .15 .40
107 Matt Burch RC .25 .60
108 Cole Liniak .10 .30
109 Jason Dewey .10 .30
110 Cesar King .10 .30
111 Julio Ramirez .10 .30
112 Jake Westbrook .10 .30
113 Eric Valent RC .25 .60
114 Roosevelt Brown RC .15 .40
115 Choo Freeman RC .25 .60
116 Juan Melo .10 .30
117 Jason Grilli .10 .30
118 Jared Sandberg .10 .30
119 Glenn Davis .10 .30
120 David Riske RC .15 .40
121 Jacque Jones .10 .30
122 Corey Lee .10 .30
123 Michael Barrett .10 .30
124 Lariel Gonzalez .10 .30
125 Mitch Meluskey .10 .30
126 Freddy Adrian Garcia .10 .30
127 Tony Torcato RC .15 .40
128 Jeff Liefer .10 .30
129 Ntema Ndungidi .10 .30
130 Andy Brown RC .15 .40
131 Ryan Mills RC .15 .40
132 Andy Abad RC .15 .40
133 Carlos Febles .10 .30
134 Jason Tyner RC .15 .40
135 Mark Osborne .10 .30
136 Phil Norton RC .15 .40
137 Nathan Haynes .10 .30
138 Roy Halladay .10 .30
139 Juan Encarnacion .10 .30
140 Brad Penny .10 .30
141 Grant Roberts .10 .30
142 Aramis Ramirez .10 .30
143 Cristian Guzman .10 .30
144 Mamon Tucker RC .15 .40
145 Ryan Bradley .10 .30
146 Brian Simmons .10 .30
147 Dan Reichert .10 .30
148 Russ Branyan .10 .30
149 Victor Valencia RC .20 .50
150 Scott Schoeneweis .10 .30
151 Sean Spencer RC .15 .40
152 Odalis Perez .10 .30
153 Joe Fontenot .10 .30
154 Milton Bradley .10 .30
155 Josh McKinley RC .15 .40
156 Terrence Long .10 .30
157 Danny Klassen .10 .30
158 Paul Hoover RC .25 .60
159 Ron Belliard .10 .30
160 Armando Rios .10 .30
161 Ramon Hernandez .10 .30
162 Jason Conti .10 .30

163 Chad Hermansen .10 .30
164 Jason Standridge .10 .30
165 Jason Dellaero .10 .30
166 John Curtice .10 .30
167 Clayton Andrews RC .15 .40
168 Jeremy Giambi .10 .30
169 Alex Ramirez .10 .30
170 Gabe Molina RC .15 .40
171 M.Encarnacion RC .15 .40
172 Mike Zywica RC .15 .40
173 Chip Ambres RC .15 .40
174 Trot Nixon .10 .30
175 Pat Burrell RC 1.25 3.00
176 Jeff Yoder .10 .30
177 Chris Jones RC .15 .40
178 Kevin Witt .10 .30
179 Keith Luuloa RC .15 .40
180 Billy Koch .10 .30
181 Damaso Marte RC .15 .40
182 Ryan Glynn RC .15 .40
183 Calvin Pickering .10 .30
184 Michael Cuddyer .10 .30
185 Nick Johnson RC .75 2.00
186 D.Mientkiewicz RC .40 1.00
187 Nate Cornejo RC .15 .40
188 Octavio Dotel .10 .30
189 Wes Helms .10 .30
190 Nelson Lara .10 .30
191 Chuck Abbott RC .15 .40
192 Tony Armas Jr. .10 .30
193 Gil Meche .10 .30
194 Ben Petrick .10 .30
195 Chris George RC .15 .40
196 Scott Hunter RC .15 .40
197 Ryan Brannan .10 .30
198 Amaury Garcia RC .25 .60
199 Chris Gissell .10 .30
200 Austin Kearns RC 1.25 3.00
201 Alex Gonzalez .10 .30
202 Wade Miller .10 .30
203 Scott Williamson .10 .30
204 Chris Enochs .10 .30
205 Fernando Seguignol .10 .30
206 Marlon Anderson .10 .30
207 Todd Sears RC .15 .40
208 Nate Bump RC .15 .40
209 J.M. Gold RC .15 .40
210 Matt LeCroy .10 .30
211 Alex Hernandez .10 .30
212 Luis Rivera .10 .30
213 Troy Cameron .10 .30
214 Alex Escobar RC .25 .60
215 Jason LaRue .10 .30
216 Kyle Peterson .10 .30
217 Brent Butler .10 .30
218 Dernell Stenson .10 .30
219 Adrian Beltre .10 .30
220 Daryle Ward .10 .30
221 Jim Thome .20 .50
222 Cliff Floyd .10 .30
223 Rickey Henderson .30 .75
224 Garret Anderson .10 .30
225 Ken Caminiti .10 .30
226 Bret Boone .10 .30
227 Jeromy Burnitz .10 .30
228 Steve Finley .10 .30
229 Miguel Tejada .10 .30
230 Greg Vaughn .10 .30
231 Jose Offerman .10 .30
232 Andy Ashby .10 .30
233 Albert Belle .10 .30
234 Fernando Tatis .10 .30
235 Todd Helton .20 .50
236 Sean Casey .10 .30
237 Brian Giles .10 .30
238 Andy Pettitte .20 .50
239 Fred McGriff .20 .50
240 Roberto Alomar .20 .50
241 Edgar Martinez .20 .50
242 Lee Stevens .10 .30
243 Shawn Green .10 .30
244 Ryan Klesko .10 .30
245 Sammy Sosa .30 .75
246 Todd Hundley .10 .30
247 Shannon Stewart .10 .30
248 Randy Johnson .30 .75
249 Rondell White .10 .30
250 Mike Piazza .50 1.25
251 Craig Biggio .20 .50
252 David Wells .10 .30
253 Brian Jordan .10 .30
254 Edgar Renteria .10 .30
255 Bartolo Colon .10 .30
256 Frank Thomas .30 .75
257 Will Clark .20 .50
258 Dean Palmer .10 .30
259 Dmitri Young .10 .30
260 Scott Rolen .20 .50
261 Jeff Kent .10 .30
262 Dante Bichette .10 .30
263 Nomar Garciaparra .50 1.25
264 Tony Gwynn .40 1.00
265 Alex Rodriguez .50 1.25
266 Jose Canseco .20 .50
267 Jason Giambi .10 .30
268 Jeff Bagwell .20 .50
269 Carlos Delgado .10 .30
270 Tom Glavine .20 .50
271 Eric Davis .10 .30
272 Edgardo Alfonzo .10 .30
273 Tim Salmon .20 .50
274 Johnny Damon .20 .50
275 Rafael Palmeiro .20 .50
276 Denny Neagle .10 .30
277 Neifi Perez .10 .30
278 Roger Clemens .60 1.50
279 Brant Brown .10 .30
280 Kevin Brown .20 .50
281 Jay Bell .10 .30
282 Jay Buhner .10 .30
283 Matt Lawton .10 .30
284 Robin Ventura .10 .30
285 Juan Gonzalez .10 .30
286 Mo Vaughn .10 .30
287 Kevin Millwood .10 .30
288 Tino Martinez .20 .50
289 Justin Thompson .10 .30
290 Derek Jeter .75 2.00
291 Ben Davis .10 .30
292 Mike Lowell .10 .30
293 Calvin Murray .10 .30
294 Micah Bowie RC .15 .40
295 Lance Berkman .10 .30
296 Jason Marquis .10 .30
297 Chad Green .10 .30
298 Dee Brown .10 .30
299 Jerry Hairston Jr. .10 .30
300 Gabe Kapler .10 .30
301 Brent Stentz RC .25 .60
302 Scott Mullen RC .15 .40
303 Brandon Reed .10 .30
304 Shea Hillenbrand RC .60 1.50
305 J.D. Closser RC .25 .60
306 Gary Matthews Jr. .10 .30
307 Toby Hall RC .25 .60
308 Jason Phillips RC .15 .40
309 Jose Macias RC .15 .40
310 Jung Bong RC .15 .40
311 Ramon Soler RC .15 .40
312 Kelly Dransfeldt RC .15 .40
313 Carl. E. Hernandez RC .25 .60
314 Kevin Haverbusch .10 .30
315 Aaron Myette RC .15 .40
316 Chad Harville RC .15 .40
317 Kyle Farnsworth RC .25 .60
318 Gookie Dawkins RC .25 .60
319 Willie Martinez .10 .30
320 Carlos Lee .10 .30
321 Carlos Pena RC .30 .75
322 Peter Bergeron RC .15 .40
323 A.J. Burnett RC .60 1.50
324 Bucky Jacobsen RC .25 .60
325 Mo Bruce RC .15 .40
326 Reggie Taylor .10 .30
327 Jackie Rexrode .10 .30
328 Alvin Morrow RC .15 .40
329 Carlos Beltran .20 .50
330 Eric Chavez .10 .30
331 John Patterson .10 .30
332 Jayson Werth .10 .30
333 Richie Sexson .10 .30
334 Randy Wolf .10 .30
335 Eli Marrero .10 .30
336 Paul LoDuca .10 .30
337 J.D Smart .10 .30
338 Ryan Minor .10 .30
339 Kris Benson .10 .30
340 George Lombard .10 .30
341 Troy Glaus .20 .50
342 Eddie Yarnall .10 .30
343 Kip Wells RC .25 .60
344 C.C. Sabathia RC 1.25 3.00
345 Sean Burroughs RC .40 1.00
346 Felipe Lopez RC 1.00 2.50
347 Ryan Rupe RC .15 .40
348 Orber Moreno RC .15 .40
349 Rafael Roque RC .15 .40
350 Alfonso Soriano RC 2.50 6.00
351 Pablo Ozuna .10 .30
352 Corey Patterson RC .60 1.50
353 Braden Looper .10 .30
354 Robbie Bell .10 .30
355 Mark Mulder RC 1.00 2.50
356 Angel Pena .10 .30
357 Kevin McGlinchy .10 .30
358 M.Restovich RC .25 .60
359 Eric DuBose .10 .30
360 Geoff Jenkins .10 .30
361 Mark Harriger RC .15 .40
362 Junior Herndon RC .15 .40
363 Tim Raines Jr. RC .15 .40
364 Rafael Furcal RC 1.00 2.50
365 Marcus Giles RC .60 1.50
366 Ted Lilly .10 .30
367 Jorge Toca RC .25 .60
368 David Kelton RC .15 .40
369 Adam Dunn RC 2.00 5.00
370 Guillermo Mota RC .15 .40
371 Brett Laxton RC .15 .40
372 Travis Harper RC .25 .60
373 Tom Davey RC .15 .40
374 Darren Blakely RC .15 .40
375 Tim Hudson RC 1.50 4.00
376 Jason Romano .10 .30
377 Dan Reichert .10 .30
378 Julio Lugo RC .40 1.00
379 Jose Garcia RC .15 .40
380 Erubiel Durazo RC .25 .60
381 Jose Jimenez .10 .30
382 Chris Fussell .10 .30
383 Steve Lomasney .10 .30
384 Juan Pena RC .25 .60
385 Allen Levrault RC .15 .40
386 Juan Rivera RC .60 1.50
387 Steve Colyer RC .15 .40
388 Joe Nathan RC .75 2.00
389 Ron Walker RC .15 .40
390 Nick Bierbrodt .10 .30
391 Luke Prokopec RC .15 .40
392 Dave Roberts RC .40 1.00
393 Mike Darr .10 .30
394 Abraham Nunez RC .25 .60
395 G.Chiaramonte RC .15 .40
396 J.Van Buren RC .15 .40
397 Mike Kusiewicz .10 .30
398 Matt Wise RC .15 .40
399 Joe McEwing RC .25 .60
400 Matt Holliday RC 2.50 6.00
401 Willi Mo Pena RC 2.00 5.00
402 Ruben Quevedo RC .15 .40
403 Rob Ryan RC .15 .40
404 Freddy Garcia RC .60 1.50
405 Kevin Eberwein RC .15 .40
406 Jesus Colome RC .15 .40
407 Chris Singleton .10 .30
408 Bubba Crosby RC .40 1.00
409 Jesus Cordero RC .15 .40
410 Donny Leon .10 .30
411 G.Tomlinson RC .25 .60
412 Jeff Winchester RC .15 .40
413 Adam Piatt RC .15 .40
414 Robert Stratton .10 .30
415 T.J. Tucker .10 .30
416 Ryan Langerhans RC .40 1.00
417 A.Shumaker RC .15 .40
418 Matt Miller RC .15 .40
419 Doug Clark RC .15 .40
420 Kory DeHaan RC .15 .40
421 David Eckstein RC 1.25 3.00
422 Brian Cooper RC .15 .40
423 Brady Clark RC .60 1.50
424 Chris Magruder RC .25 .60
425 Bobby Seay RC .15 .40
426 Aubrey Huff RC .75 2.00
427 Mike Jerzembeck .10 .30
428 Matt Blank RC .25 .60
429 Benny Agbayani RC .25 .60
430 Kevin Beirne RC .15 .40
431 Josh Hamilton RC 2.50 6.00
432 Josh Girdley RC .15 .40
433 Kyle Snyder RC .15 .40
434 Mike Paradis RC .15 .40
435 Jason Jennings RC .40 1.00
436 David Walling RC .15 .40
437 Omar Ortiz RC .25 .60
438 Jay Gehrke RC .25 .60
439 Casey Burns RC .25 .60
440 Carl Crawford RC 1.50 4.00

1999 Bowman Gold

Randomly inserted in first series packs at a rate of one in 111 and second series packs at a rate of one in 59, this 440-card set is a parallel to the Bowman base set. The set features facsimile autographs printed in gold foil with gold border designs. Each card is serial numbered to 99 on the back.

*STARS: 10X TO 25X BASIC CARDS
*ROOKIES: 4X TO 10X BASIC CARDS
431 Josh Hamilton 40.00 80.00

1999 Bowman International

Inserted one per pack, this 440-card set is a parallel to the Bowman base set. Card fronts contain each player's nationality with a background photograph of a landmark native to his homeland. Card backs contain vital information which are translated into the player's home language giving the collector insight into the player's background. Card fronts are printed on a distinctive foil board.

COMPLETE SET (440) 100.00 200.00
COMP.SERIES 1 (220) 40.00 80.00
COMP.SERIES 2 (220) 60.00 120.00
*STARS: 1X TO 2.5X BASIC CARDS
*ROOKIES: .6X TO 1.5X BASIC CARDS

1999 Bowman Autographs

This set contains a selection of top young prospects, all of whom participated by signing their cards in blue ink. Card rarity is differentiated by either a blue, silver or gold foil Topps Certified Autograph Issue Stamp. The insert rates for Blue are at a rate of one in 162; Silver one in 485 and Gold one in 1,194.

BA1 Ruben Mateo B 4.00 10.00
BA2 Troy Glaus G 12.50 30.00
BA3 Ben Davis G 6.00 15.00
BA4 Jayson Werth B 4.00 10.00
BA5 Jerry Hairston Jr. S 4.00 10.00
BA6 Darnell McDonald B 4.00 10.00
BA7 Calvin Pickering S 6.00 15.00
BA8 Ryan Minor S 6.00 15.00
BA9 Alex Escobar B 4.00 10.00
BA10 Grant Roberts B 4.00 10.00
BA11 Carlos Guillen B 10.00 25.00
BA12 Ryan Anderson S 6.00 15.00
BA13 Gil Meche S 6.00 15.00
BA14 Russell Branyan S 6.00 15.00
BA15 Alex Ramirez S 6.00 15.00
BA16 Jason Rakers S 6.00 15.00
BA17 Eddie Yarnall B 4.00 10.00
BA18 Freddy Garcia B 10.00 25.00
BA19 Jason Conti B 4.00 10.00
BA20 Corey Koskie B 6.00 15.00
BA21 Roosevelt Brown B 4.00 10.00
BA22 Willie Martinez B 4.00 10.00
BA23 Mike Jerzembeck B 4.00 10.00
BA24 Lariel Gonzalez B 4.00 10.00
BA25 F.Seguignol B 6.00 15.00
BA26 Robert Fick S 6.00 15.00
BA27 J.D. Smart B 4.00 10.00
BA28 Ryan Mills B 4.00 10.00
BA29 Chad Hermansen G 6.00 15.00
BA30 Jason Grilli B 4.00 10.00
BA31 Michael Cuddyer B 4.00 10.00
BA32 Jacque Jones S 10.00 25.00
BA33 Reggie Taylor B 4.00 10.00
BA34 Richie Sexson G 10.00 25.00
BA35 Michael Barrett B 4.00 10.00
BA36 Paul LoDuca B 6.00 15.00
BA37 Adrian Beltre G 10.00 25.00
BA38 Peter Bergeron B 4.00 10.00
BA39 Joe Fontenot B 4.00 10.00
BA40 Randy Wolf B 6.00 15.00
BA41 Nick Johnson B 12.50 30.00
BA42 Ryan Bradley B 4.00 10.00
BA43 Mike Lowell S 10.00 25.00
BA44 Ricky Ledee G 4.00 10.00
BA45 Mike Lincoln S 6.00 15.00
BA46 Jeremy Giambi B 4.00 10.00
BA47 Dermal Brown S 6.00 15.00
BA48 Derrick Gibson B 4.00 10.00
BA49 Scott Randall B 4.00 10.00
BA50 Ben Petrick S 6.00 15.00
BA51 Jason LaRue B 6.00 15.00
BA52 Cole Liniak B 4.00 10.00
BA53 John Curtice B 4.00 10.00
BA54 Jackie Rexrode B 4.00 10.00
BA55 John Patterson B 6.00 15.00
BA56 Brad Penny S 10.00 25.00
BA57 Jared Sandberg B 6.00 15.00
BA58 Kerry Wood G 15.00 40.00
BA59 Eli Marrero S 6.00 15.00
BA60 Jason Marquis B 6.00 15.00
BA61 George Lombard S 6.00 15.00
BA62 Bruce Chen S 6.00 15.00
BA63 Kevin Witt S 6.00 15.00
BA64 Vernon Wells B 12.50 30.00
BA65 Billy Koch B 6.00 15.00
BA66 Roy Halladay G 15.00 40.00
BA67 Nathan Haynes B 4.00 10.00
BA68 Ben Grieve G 10.00 25.00
BA69 Alex Chavez G 10.00 25.00
BA70 Lance Berkman S 15.00 40.00

1999 Bowman 2000 ROY Favorites

Randomly inserted in second series packs at a rate of one in twelve, this 10-card insert set features borderless, double-etched foil cards and feature players that had serious potential to win the 2000 Rookie of the Year award.

COMPLETE SET (10) 5.00 10.00
ROY1 Ryan Anderson .20 .50
ROY2 Pat Burrell .75 2.00
ROY3 A.J. Burnett .40 1.00
ROY4 Ruben Mateo .20 .50
ROY5 Alex Escobar .20 .50
ROY6 Pablo Ozuna .20 .50
ROY7 Mark Mulder .60 1.50
ROY8 Corey Patterson .40 1.00
ROY9 George Lombard .20 .50
ROY10 Nick Johnson .40 1.00

1999 Bowman Early Risers

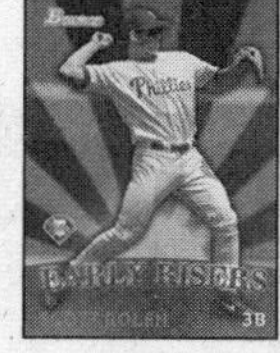

Randomly inserted in second series packs at a rate of one in twelve, this 11-card insert set features current superstars who have already won a ROY award and who continue to prove their worth on the diamond.

COMPLETE SET (11) 10.00 25.00
ER1 Mike Piazza 1.00 2.50
ER2 Cal Ripken 2.00 5.00
ER3 Jeff Bagwell .40 1.00
ER4 Ben Grieve .25 .60
ER5 Kerry Wood .25 .60
ER6 Mark McGwire 1.50 4.00
ER7 Nomar Garciaparra 1.00 2.50
ER8 Derek Jeter 1.50 4.00
ER9 Scott Rolen .40 1.00
ER10 Jose Canseco .40 1.00
ER11 Raul Mondesi .25 .60

1999 Bowman Late Bloomers

Randomly inserted in first series packs at a rate of one in twelve, this 10-card insert set features late round picks from previous drafts. Players featured include Mike Piazza and Jim Thome.

COMPLETE SET (10) 4.00 8.00
LB1 Mike Piazza 1.00 2.50
LB2 Jim Thome .40 1.00
LB3 Larry Walker .25 .60
LB4 Vinny Castilla .25 .60
LB5 Andy Pettitte .40 1.00
LB6 Jim Edmonds .25 .60
LB7 Kenny Lofton .25 .60
LB8 John Smoltz .40 1.00
LB9 Mark Grace .40 1.00
LB10 Trevor Hoffman .25 .60

1999 Bowman Scout's Choice

Randomly inserted in first series packs at a rate of one in twelve, this 21-card insert set features a selection of gifted prospects.

COMPLETE SET (21) 10.00 20.00
SC1 Ruben Mateo .40 1.00
SC2 Ryan Anderson .40 1.00
SC3 Pat Burrell 1.00 2.50
SC4 Troy Glaus .60 1.50
SC5 Eric Chavez .40 1.00
SC6 Adrian Beltre .40 1.00
SC7 Bruce Chen .40 1.00
SC8 Carlos Beltran .60 1.50
SC9 Alex Gonzalez .40 1.00
SC10 Carlos Lee .40 1.00
SC11 George Lombard .40 1.00
SC12 Matt Clement .40 1.00
SC13 Calvin Pickering .40 1.00
SC14 Marlon Anderson .40 1.00
SC15 Chad Hermansen .40 1.00
SC16 Russell Branyan .40 1.00
SC17 Jeremy Giambi .40 1.00
SC18 Ricky Ledee .40 1.00
SC19 John Patterson .40 1.00
SC20 Roy Halladay .40 1.00
SC21 Michael Barrett .40 1.00

2000 Bowman Pre-Production

This three card set of sample cards was distributed within a sealed, clear, cello poly-wrap to dealers and hobby media several weeks prior to the national release of 2000 Bowman.

COMPLETE SET (3) 2.00 4.00
PP1 Chipper Jones .80 2.00
PP2 Adam Piatt .40 1.00
PP3 Josh Hamilton 1.50 4.00

2000 Bowman

The 2000 Bowman product was released in May, 2000 as a 440-card set. The set features 140 veteran players and 300 rookies and prospects. Each pack contained 10 cards and carried a suggested retail price of $3.00. Rookie Cards include Rick Asadoorian, Bobby Bradley, Kevin Mench, Nick Neugebauer, Ben Sheets and Barry Zito.

COMPLETE SET (440) 25.00 60.00
1 Vladimir Guerrero .30 .75
2 Chipper Jones .30 .75
3 Todd Walker .10 .30
4 Barry Larkin .20 .50
5 Bernie Williams .20 .50
6 Todd Helton .20 .50
7 Jermaine Dye .10 .30
8 Brian Giles .10 .30
9 Freddy Garcia .10 .30
10 Greg Vaughn .10 .30
11 Alex Gonzalez .10 .30
12 Luis Gonzalez .10 .30
13 Ron Belliard .10 .30
14 Ben Grieve .10 .30
15 Carlos Delgado .10 .30
16 Brian Jordan .10 .30
17 Fernando Tatis .10 .30
18 Ryan Rupe .10 .30
19 Miguel Tejada .10 .30
20 Mark Grace .20 .50
21 Kenny Lofton .10 .30
22 Eric Karros .10 .30
23 Cliff Floyd .10 .30
24 John Halama .10 .30
25 Cristian Guzman .10 .30
26 Scott Williamson .10 .30
27 Mike Lieberthal .10 .30
28 Tim Hudson .10 .30
29 Warren Morris .10 .30
30 Pedro Martinez .20 .50
31 John Smoltz .20 .50
32 Ray Durham .10 .30
33 Chad Allen .10 .30
34 Tony Clark .10 .30
35 Tino Martinez .20 .50
36 J.T. Snow .10 .30
37 Kevin Brown .10 .30
38 Bartolo Colon .10 .30
39 Rey Ordonez .10 .30
40 Jeff Bagwell .20 .50
41 Ivan Rodriguez .20 .50
42 Eric Chavez .10 .30
43 Eric Milton .10 .30
44 Jose Canseco .20 .50
45 Shawn Green .10 .30
46 Rich Aurilia .10 .30
47 Roberto Alomar .20 .50
48 Brian Daubach .10 .30
49 Maggio Ordonez .10 .30
50 Derek Jeter .75 2.00
51 Kris Benson .10 .30
52 Albert Belle .10 .30
53 Rondell White .10 .30
54 Justin Thompson .10 .30
55 Nomar Garciaparra .50 1.25
56 Chuck Finley .10 .30
57 Omar Vizquel .20 .50
58 Luis Castillo .10 .30
59 Richard Hidalgo .10 .30
60 Barry Bonds .75 2.00
61 Craig Biggio .20 .50
62 Doug Glanville .10 .30
63 Gabe Kapler .10 .30
64 Johnny Damon .20 .50
65 Pokey Reese .10 .30
66 Andy Pettitte .20 .50
67 B.J. Surhoff .10 .30
68 Richie Sexson .10 .30
69 Javy Lopez .10 .30
70 Raul Mondesi .10 .30
71 Darin Erstad .10 .30
72 Kevin Millwood .10 .30
73 Ricky Ledee .10 .30
74 John Olerud .10 .30
75 Sean Casey .10 .30
76 Carlos Febles .10 .30
77 Paul O'Neill .20 .50
78 Bob Abreu .10 .30
79 Neifi Perez .10 .30
80 Tony Gwynn .40 1.00
81 Russ Ortiz .10 .30
82 Matt Williams .10 .30
83 Chris Carpenter .10 .30
84 Roger Cedeno .10 .30
85 Tim Salmon .20 .50
86 Billy Koch .10 .30
87 Jeromy Burnitz .10 .30
88 Edgardo Alfonzo .10 .30
89 Jay Bell .10 .30
90 Manny Ramirez .20 .50
91 Frank Thomas .30 .75
92 Mike Mussina .20 .50
93 J.D. Drew .10 .30
94 Adrian Beltre .10 .30
95 Alex Rodriguez .50 1.25
96 Larry Walker .10 .30
97 Juan Encarnacion .10 .30
98 Mike Sweeney .10 .30
99 Rusty Greer .10 .30
100 Randy Johnson .30 .75
101 Jose Vidro .10 .30
102 Preston Wilson .10 .30
103 Greg Maddux .50 1.25
104 Jason Giambi .10 .30
105 Cal Ripken 1.00 2.50
106 Carlos Beltran .10 .30
107 Vinny Castilla .10 .30
108 Mariano Rivera .30 .75
109 Mo Vaughn .10 .30
110 Rafael Palmeiro .20 .50
111 Shannon Stewart .10 .30
112 Mike Hampton .10 .30
113 Joe Nathan .10 .30
114 Ben Davis .10 .30
115 Andruw Jones .20 .50
116 Robin Ventura .10 .30
117 Damion Easley .10 .30
118 Jeff Cirillo .10 .30
119 Kerry Wood .10 .30
120 Scott Rolen .20 .50
121 Sammy Sosa .30 .75
122 Ken Griffey Jr. .50 1.25
123 Shane Reynolds .10 .30
124 Troy Glaus .10 .30
125 Tom Glavine .20 .50
126 Michael Barrett .10 .30
127 Al Leiter .10 .30
128 Jason Kendall .10 .30
129 Roger Clemens .60 1.50
130 Juan Gonzalez .10 .30
131 Corey Koskie .10 .30
132 Curt Schilling .10 .30
133 Mike Piazza .50 1.25
134 Gary Sheffield .10 .30
135 Jim Thome .20 .50
136 Orlando Hernandez .10 .30
137 Ray Lankford .10 .30
138 Geoff Jenkins .10 .30
139 Jose Lima .10 .30
140 Mark McGwire .75 2.00
141 Adam Platt .10 .30
142 Pat Manning RC .10 .30
143 Marcos Castillo RC .10 .30
144 Lesli Brea RC .10 .30
145 Humberto Cota RC .20 .50
146 Ben Petrick .10 .30
147 Kip Wells .10 .30
148 Wily Pena .10 .30
149 Chris Wakeland RC .10 .30
150 Brad Baker RC .10 .30
151 Robbie Morrison RC .10 .30
152 Reggie Taylor .10 .30
153 Matt Ginter RC .10 .30
154 Peter Bergeron .10 .30
155 Roosevelt Brown .10 .30
156 Matt Cepicky RC .10 .30
157 Ramon Castro .10 .30
158 Brad Baisley RC .10 .30
159 Jeff Goldbach RC .10 .30
160 Mitch Meluskey .10 .30
161 Chad Harville .10 .30
162 Brian Cooper .10 .30
163 Marcus Giles .10 .30
164 Jim Morris .30 .75
165 Geoff Goetz .10 .30
166 Bobby Bradley RC .10 .30
167 Rob Bell .10 .30
168 Joe Crede .60 1.50
169 Michael Restovich .10 .30

2000 Bowman

170 Quincy Foster RC .10 .30
171 Enrique Cruz RC .10 .30
172 Mark Quinn .10 .30
173 Nick Johnson .10 .30
174 Jeff Liefer .10 .30
175 Kevin Mench RC .75 2.00
176 Steve Lomasney .10 .30
177 Jayson Werth .10 .30
178 Tim Drew .10 .30
179 Chip Ambres .10 .30
180 Ryan Anderson .10 .30
181 Matt Blank .10 .30
182 G.Chiaramonte .10 .30
183 Corey Myers RC .10 .30
184 Jeff Yoder .10 .30
185 Craig Dingman RC .10 .30
186 Jon Hamilton RC .10 .30
187 Toby Hall .10 .30
188 Russell Branyan .10 .30
189 Brian Falkenborg RC .10 .30
190 Aaron Harang RC 1.00 2.50
191 Juan Pena .10 .30
192 Travis Thompson RC .10 .30
193 Alfonso Soriano .30 .75
194 Alejandro Diaz RC .10 .30
195 Carlos Pena .10 .30
196 Kevin Nicholson .10 .30
197 Mo Bruce .10 .30
198 C.C. Sabathia .10 .30
199 Carl Crawford .10 .30
200 Rafael Furcal .10 .30
201 Andrew Beinbrink RC .10 .30
202 Jimmy Osting .10 .30
203 Aaron McNeal RC .10 .30
204 Brett Laxton .10 .30
205 Chris George .10 .30
206 Felipe Lopez .10 .30
207 Ben Sheets RC 1.00 2.50
208 Mike Meyers RC .20 .50
209 Jason Conti .10 .30
210 Milton Bradley .10 .30
211 Chris Mears RC .10 .30
212 Carlos Hernandez RC .30 .75
213 Jason Romano .10 .30
214 Geofrey Tomlinson .10 .30
215 Jimmy Rollins .10 .30
216 Pablo Ozuna .10 .30
217 Steve Cox .10 .30
218 Terrence Long .10 .30
219 Jeff DaVanon RC .20 .50
220 Rick Ankiel .10 .30
221 Jason Standridge .10 .30
222 Tony Armas Jr. .10 .30
223 Jason Tyner .10 .30
224 Ramon Ortiz .10 .30
225 Daryle Ward .10 .30
226 Enger Veras RC .10 .30
227 Chris Jones .10 .30
228 Eric Cammack RC .10 .30
229 Ruben Mateo .10 .30
230 Ken Harvey RC .20 .50
231 Jake Westbrook .10 .30
232 Rob Purvis RC .10 .30
233 Choo Freeman .10 .30
234 Aramis Ramirez .10 .30
235 A.J. Burnett .10 .30
236 Kevin Barker .10 .30
237 Chance Caple RC .10 .30
238 Jarrod Washburn .10 .30
239 Lance Berkman .10 .30
240 Michael Wenner RC .10 .30
241 Alex Sanchez .10 .30
242 Pat Daneker .10 .30
243 Grant Roberts .10 .30
244 Mark Ellis RC .20 .50
245 Donny Leon .10 .30
246 David Eckstein .10 .30
247 Dicky Gonzalez RC .10 .30
248 John Patterson .10 .30
249 Chad Green .10 .30
250 Scot Shields RC .10 .30
251 Troy Cameron .10 .30
252 Jose Molina .10 .30
253 Rob Pugmire RC .10 .30
254 Rick Elder .10 .30
255 Sean Burroughs .10 .30
256 Josh Kalinowski RC .10 .30
257 Matt LeCroy .10 .30
258 Alex Graman RC .10 .30
259 Tomo Ohka RC .20 .50
260 Brady Clark .10 .30
261 Rico Washington RC .10 .30
262 Gary Matthews Jr. .10 .30
263 Matt Wise .10 .30
264 Keith Reed RC .10 .30
265 Santiago Ramirez RC .10 .30
266 Ben Broussard RC .50 1.25
267 Ryan Langerhans .10 .30
268 Juan Rivera .10 .30
269 Shawn Gallagher .10 .30
270 Jorge Toca .10 .30
271 Brad Lidge .20 .50
272 Leoncio Estrella RC .10 .30
273 Ruben Quevedo .10 .30
274 Jack Cust .10 .30
275 T.J. Tucker .10 .30
276 Mike Colangelo .10 .30
277 Brian Schneider .10 .30
278 Calvin Murray .10 .30
279 Josh Girdley .10 .30
280 Mike Paradis .10 .30
281 Chad Hermansen .10 .30
282 Ty Howington RC .10 .30
283 Aaron Myette .10 .30
284 D'Angelo Jimenez .10 .30
285 Dernell Stenson .10 .30
286 Jerry Hairston Jr. .10 .30
287 Gary Majewski RC .20 .50
288 Derrin Ebert .10 .30
289 Steve Fish RC .10 .30
290 Carlos E. Hernandez .10 .30
291 Allen Levrault .10 .30
292 Sean McNally RC .10 .30
293 Randey Dorame RC .10 .30
294 Wes Anderson RC .10 .30
295 B.J. Ryan .10 .30
296 Alan Webb RC .10 .30
297 Brandon Inge RC .75 2.00
298 David Walling .10 .30
299 Sun Woo Kim RC .10 .30
300 Pat Burrell .10 .30
301 Rick Guttormson RC .10 .30
302 Gil Meche .10 .30
303 Carlos Zambrano RC 2.00 5.00
304 Eric Byrnes UER RC .20 .50
Bo Porter pictured
305 Robb Quinlan RC .20 .50
306 Jackie Rexrode .10 .30
307 Nate Bump .10 .30
308 Sean DePaula RC .10 .30
309 Matt Riley .10 .30
310 Ryan Minor .10 .30
311 J.J. Davis .10 .30
312 Randy Wolf .10 .30
313 Jason Jennings .10 .30
314 Scott Seabol RC .10 .30
315 Doug Davis .10 .30
316 Todd Moser RC .10 .30
317 Rob Ryan .10 .30
318 Bubba Crosby .10 .30
319 Ryan Knox RC .50 1.25
320 Mario Encarnacion .10 .30
321 F.Rodriguez RC 1.25 3.00
322 Michael Cuddyer .10 .30
323 Ed Yarnall .10 .30
324 Cesar Saba RC .10 .30
325 Gookie Dawkins .10 .30
326 Alex Escobar .10 .30
327 Julio Zuleta RC .10 .30
328 Josh Hamilton .40 1.00
329 Nick Neugebauer RC .10 .30
330 Matt Belisle .10 .30
331 Kurt Ainsworth RC .10 .30
332 Tim Raines Jr. .10 .30
333 Eric Munson .10 .30
334 Donzell McDonald .10 .30
335 Larry Bigbie RC .30 .75
336 Matt Watson RC .10 .30
337 Aubrey Huff .10 .30
338 Julio Ramirez .10 .30
339 Jason Grabowski RC .10 .30
340 Jon Garland .10 .30
341 Austin Kearns .10 .30
342 Josh Pressley RC .10 .30
343 Miguel Olivo RC .30 .75
344 Julio Lugo .10 .30
345 Roberto Vaz .10 .30
346 Ramon Soler .10 .30
347 Brandon Phillips RC .60 1.50
348 Vince Faison RC .10 .30
349 Mike Venafro .10 .30
350 Rick Asadoorian RC .20 .50
351 B.J. Garbe RC .10 .30
352 Dan Reichert .10 .30
353 Jason Stumm RC .10 .30
354 Ruben Salazar RC .10 .30
355 Francisco Cordero .10 .30
356 Juan Guzman RC .10 .30
357 Mike Bacsik RC .10 .30
358 Jared Sandberg .10 .30
359 Rod Barajas .10 .30
360 Junior Brignac RC .10 .30
361 J.M. Gold .10 .30
362 Octavio Dotel .10 .30
363 David Kelton .10 .30
364 Scott Morgan .10 .30
365 Wascar Serrano RC .10 .30
366 Wilton Veras .10 .30
367 Eugene Kingsale .10 .30
368 Ted Lilly .10 .30
369 George Lombard .10 .30
370 Chris Haas .10 .30
371 Wilton Pena RC .10 .30
372 Vernon Wells .10 .30
373 Jason Royer RC .10 .30
374 Jeff Heaverlo RC .10 .30
375 Calvin Pickering .10 .30
376 Mike Lamb RC .30 .75
377 Kyle Snyder .10 .30
378 Javier Cardona RC .10 .30
379 Aaron Rowand RC .75 2.00
380 Dee Brown .10 .30
381 Brett Myers RC .60 1.50
382 Abraham Nunez .10 .30
383 Eric Valent .10 .30
384 Jody Gerut RC .20 .50
385 Adam Dunn .30 .75
386 Jay Gehrke .10 .30
387 Omar Ortiz .10 .30
388 Darnell McDonald .10 .30
389 Tony Schrager RC .10 .30
390 J.D. Closser .10 .30
391 Ben Christensen RC .10 .30
392 Adam Kennedy .10 .30
393 Nick Green RC .10 .30
394 Ramon Hernandez .10 .30
395 Roy Oswalt RC 4.00 10.00
396 Andy Tracy RC .10 .30
397 Eric Gagne .30 .75
398 Michael Tejera RC .10 .30
399 Adam Everett .10 .30
400 Corey Patterson .10 .30
401 Gary Knotts RC .10 .30
402 Ryan Christianson RC .10 .30
403 Eric Ireland RC .10 .30
404 Andrew Good RC .10 .30
405 Brad Penny .10 .30
406 Jason LaRue .10 .30
407 Kit Pellow .10 .30
408 Kevin Beirne .10 .30
409 Kelly Dransfeldt .10 .30
410 Jason Grilli .10 .30
411 Scott Downs RC .10 .30
412 Jesus Colome .10 .30
413 John Sneed RC .10 .30
414 Tony McKnight .10 .30
415 Luis Rivera .10 .30
416 Adam Eaton .10 .30
417 Mike MacDougal RC .20 .50
418 Mike Nannini .10 .30
419 Barry Zito RC 1.50 4.00
420 DeWayne Wise .10 .30
421 Jason Dellaero .10 .30
422 Chad Moeller .10 .30
423 Jason Marquis .10 .30
424 Tim Redding RC .20 .50
425 Mark Mulder .10 .30
426 Josh Paul .10 .30
427 Chris Enochs .10 .30
428 W.Rodriguez RC .10 .30
429 Kevin Witt .10 .30
430 Scott Sobkowiak RC .10 .30
431 McKay Christensen .10 .30
432 Jung Bong .10 .30
433 Keith Evans RC .10 .30
434 Garry Maddox Jr. RC .10 .30
435 Ramon Santiago RC .10 .30
436 Alex Cora .10 .30
437 Carlos Lee .10 .30
438 Jason Repko RC .30 .75
439 Matt Burch .10 .30
440 Shawn Sonnier RC .10 .30

2000 Bowman Gold

Randomly inserted into hobby/retail packs at one in 64, this 440-card insert is a complete parallel of the Bowman base set. Each card features a gold facsimile autograph that runs down the right side of the card. Each card in the set is also individually serial numbered to 99.

*STARS: 10X TO 25X BASIC CARDS
*ROOKIES: 5X TO 12X BASIC CARDS

2000 Bowman Retro/Future

Randomly inserted into hobby/retail packs at one per pack, this 440-card insert is a complete parallel of the Bowman base set. Each card features a television border similar to that of the classic 1955 Bowman set.

COMPLETE SET (440) 75.00 200.00
*STARS: 1X TO 2.5X BASIC CARDS
*ROOKIES: .6X TO 1.5X BASIC CARDS

2000 Bowman Autographs

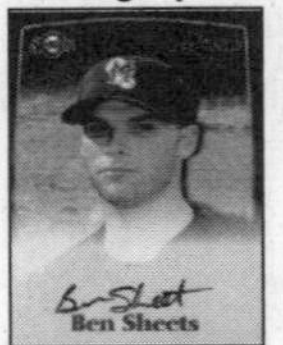

Randomly inserted into packs, this 40-card insert features autographed cards from young players like Corey Patterson, Ruben Mateo, and Alfonso Soriano. Please note that this is a three tiered autographed set. Cards that are marked with a "B" are part of the Blue Tier (1:144 HOB/RET, 1:69 HTC). Cards marked with an "S" are part of the Silver Tier (1:312 HOB/RET, 1:148 HTC), and cards marked with a "G" are part of the Gold Tier (1:1604 HOB/RET, 1:762 HTC).

AD Adam Dunn B 10.00 25.00
AH Aubrey Huff B 4.00 10.00
AK Austin Kearns B 4.00 10.00
AP Adam Piatt S 6.00 15.00
AS Alfonso Soriano S 12.50 30.00
BP Ben Petrick G 10.00 25.00
BS Ben Sheets B 12.50 30.00
BWP Brad Penny B 4.00 10.00
CA Chip Ambres B 4.00 10.00
CB Carlos Beltran G 10.00 25.00
CF Choo Freeman B 4.00 10.00
CP Corey Patterson S 6.00 15.00
DB Dee Brown S 6.00 15.00
DK David Kelton B 4.00 10.00
EV Eric Valent B 4.00 10.00
EY Ed Yarnall S 6.00 15.00
JC Jack Cust S 6.00 15.00
JDC J.D. Closser B 4.00 10.00
JDD J.D. Drew G 10.00 25.00
JJ Jason Jennings B 4.00 10.00
JR Jason Romano B 4.00 10.00
JV Jose Vidro S 6.00 15.00
JZ Julio Zuleta B 4.00 10.00
KJW Kevin Witt S 6.00 15.00
KLW Kerry Wood S 10.00 25.00
LB Lance Berkman S 10.00 25.00
MC Michael Cuddyer S 6.00 15.00
MJR Mike Restovich B 4.00 10.00
MM Mike Meyers B 4.00 10.00
MQ Mark Quinn S 6.00 15.00
MR Matt Riley S 6.00 15.00
NJ Nick Johnson S 8.00 20.00
RA Rick Ankiel G 20.00 50.00
RF Rafael Furcal S 8.00 20.00
RM Ruben Mateo G 10.00 25.00
SB Sean Burroughs S 6.00 15.00
SC Steve Cox B 4.00 10.00
SD Scott Downs S 6.00 15.00
SW Scott Williamson G 10.00 25.00
VW Vernon Wells G 10.00 25.00

2000 Bowman Early Indications

Randomly inserted into hobby/retail packs at one in 24, this 10-card insert features players that put up big numbers early on in their careers. Card backs carry an "E" prefix.

COMPLETE SET (10) 20.00 50.00
E1 Nomar Garciaparra 2.00 5.00
E2 Cal Ripken 4.00 10.00
E3 Derek Jeter 3.00 8.00
E4 Mark McGwire 3.00 8.00
E5 Alex Rodriguez 2.00 5.00
E6 Chipper Jones 1.25 3.00
E7 Todd Helton .75 2.00
E8 Vladimir Guerrero 1.25 3.00
E9 Mike Piazza 2.00 5.00
E10 Jose Canseco .75 2.00

2000 Bowman Major Power

Randomly inserted into hobby/retail packs at one in 24, this 10-card insert features the major league's top sluggers. Card backs carry a "MP" prefix.

COMPLETE SET (10) 20.00 50.00
MP1 Mark McGwire 3.00 8.00
MP2 Chipper Jones 1.25 3.00
MP3 Alex Rodriguez 2.00 5.00
MP4 Sammy Sosa 1.25 3.00
MP5 Rafael Palmeiro .75 2.00
MP6 Ken Griffey Jr. 2.00 5.00
MP7 Nomar Garciaparra 2.00 5.00
MP8 Barry Bonds 3.00 8.00
MP9 Derek Jeter 3.00 8.00
MP10 Jeff Bagwell .75 2.00

2000 Bowman Tool Time

Randomly inserted into hobby/retail packs at one in eight, this 20-card insert grades the major league's top prospects on their batting, power, speed, arm strength, and defensive skills. Card backs carry a "TT" prefix.

COMPLETE SET (20) 8.00 20.00
TT1 Pat Burrell .40 1.00
TT2 Aaron Rowand .75 2.00
TT3 Chris Wakeland .40 1.00
TT4 Ruben Mateo .40 1.00
TT5 Pat Burrell .40 1.00
TT6 Adam Piatt .40 1.00
TT7 Nick Johnson .40 1.00
TT8 Jack Cust .40 1.00
TT9 Rafael Furcal .40 1.00
TT10 Julio Ramirez .40 1.00
TT11 Gookie Dawkins .40 1.00
TT12 Corey Patterson .40 1.00
TT13 Ruben Mateo .40 1.00
TT14 Jason Dellaero .40 1.00
TT15 Sean Burroughs .40 1.00
TT16 Ryan Langerhans .40 1.00
TT17 D'Angelo Jimenez .40 1.00
TT18 Corey Patterson .40 1.00
TT19 Troy Cameron .40 1.00
TT20 Michael Cuddyer .40 1.00

2000 Bowman Draft Picks

The 2000 Bowman Draft Picks set was released in November, 2000 as a 110-card set. Each factory set was initially distributed in a tight, clear cello wrap and contained the 110-card set plus one of 60 different autographs. Topps announced that due to the unavailability of certain players previously scheduled to sign autographs, a small quantity (less than ten percent) of autographed cards from the 2000 Topps Baseball Rookies/Traded set were be included into its 2000 Bowman Baseball Draft Picks set. Rookie Cards include Chin-Feng Chen, Adrian Gonzalez, Kazuhiro Sasaki, Grady Sizemore and Chin-Hui Tsao.

COMP.FACT.SET (111) 20.00 40.00
COMPLETE SET (110) 10.00 25.00
1 Pat Burrell .10 .30
2 Rafael Furcal .10 .30
3 Grant Roberts .10 .30
4 Barry Zito .60 1.50
5 Julio Zuleta .10 .30
6 Mark Mulder .10 .30
7 Rob Bell .10 .30
8 Adam Piatt .10 .30
9 Mike Lamb .25 .60
10 Pablo Ozuna .10 .30
11 Jason Tyner .10 .30
12 Jason Marquis .10 .30
13 Eric Munson .10 .30
14 Seth Etherton .10 .30
15 Milton Bradley .10 .30
16 Nick Green .10 .30
17 Chin-Feng Chen RC .25 .60
18 Matt Boone RC .10 .30
19 Kevin Gregg RC .10 .30
20 Eddy Garabito RC .10 .30
21 Aaron Capista RC .10 .30
22 Esteban German RC .10 .30
23 Derek Thompson RC .10 .30
24 Phil Merrell RC .10 .30
25 Brian O'Connor RC .10 .30
26 Yamid Haad .10 .30
27 Hector Mercado RC .10 .30
28 Jason Woolf RC .10 .30
29 Eddy Furniss RC .10 .30
30 Cha Sueng Baek RC .10 .30
31 Colby Lewis RC .10 .30
32 Pasqual Coco RC .10 .30
33 Jorge Cantu RC 1.00 2.50
34 Erasmo Ramirez RC .10 .30
35 Bobby Kielty RC .15 .40
36 Joaquin Benoit RC .10 .30
37 Brian Esposito RC .10 .30
38 Michael Wenner .10 .30
39 Juan Rincon RC .10 .30
40 Yorvit Torrealba RC .25 6.00
41 Chad Durham RC .10 .30
42 Jim Mann RC .10 .30
43 Shane Loux RC .10 .30
44 Luis Rivas .10 .30
45 Ken Chenard RC .10 .30
46 Mike Lockwood RC .10 .30
47 Yovanny Lara RC .10 .30
48 Bubba Carpenter RC .10 .30
49 Ryan Dittfurth RC .10 .30
50 John Stephens RC .10 .30
51 Pedro Feliz RC .40 1.00
52 Kenny Kelly RC .10 .30
53 Neil Jenkins RC .10 .30
54 Mike Glendenning RC .10 .30
55 Bo Porter .10 .30
56 Eric Byrnes .10 .30
57 Tony Alvarez RC .10 .30
58 Kazuhiro Sasaki RC .25 .60
59 Chad Durbin RC .10 .30
60 Mike Bynum RC .10 .30
61 Travis Wilson RC .10 .30
62 Jose Leon RC .10 .30
63 Ryan Vogelsong RC .10 .30
64 Geraldo Guzman RC .10 .30
65 Craig Anderson RC .10 .30
66 Carlos Silva RC .15 .40
67 Brad Thomas RC .10 .30
68 Chin-Hui Tsao RC .75 2.00
69 Mark Buehrle RC 1.50 4.00
70 Juan Salas RC .10 .30
71 Denny Abreu RC .10 .30
72 Keith McDonald RC .10 .30
73 Chris Richard RC .10 .30
74 Tomas De la Rosa RC .10 .30
75 Vicente Padilla RC .15 .40
76 Justin Brunette RC .10 .30
77 Scott Linebrink RC .10 .30
78 Jeff Sparks RC .10 .30
79 Tike Redman RC .25 .60
80 John Lackey RC 1.00 2.50
81 Joe Strong RC .10 .30
82 Brian Tollberg RC .10 .30
83 Steve Sisco RC .10 .30
84 Chris Clapinski RC .10 .30
85 Augie Ojeda RC .10 .30
86 Adrian Gonzalez RC 1.25 3.00
87 Mike Stodolka RC .10 .30
88 Adam Johnson RC .10 .30
89 Matt Wheatland RC .10 .30
90 Corey Smith RC .10 .30
91 Rocco Baldelli RC .75 2.00
92 Keith Bucktrot RC .10 .30
93 Adam Wainwright RC .50 1.25
94 Blaine Boyer RC .10 .30
95 Aaron Herr RC .15 .40
96 Scott Thorman RC .40 1.00
97 Bryan Digby RC .10 .30
98 Josh Shortslef RC .20 .50
99 Sean Smith RC .10 .30
100 Alex Cruz RC .10 .30
101 Marc Love RC .10 .30
102 Kevin Lee RC .10 .30
103 Victor Ramos RC .10 .30
104 Jason Kaanoi RC .10 .30
105 Luis Escobar RC .10 .30
106 Tripper Johnson RC .10 .30
107 Phil Dumatrait RC .10 .30
108 Bryan Edwards RC .10 .30
109 Grady Sizemore RC 4.00 10.00
110 Thomas Mitchell RC .10 .30

2000 Bowman Draft Picks Autographs

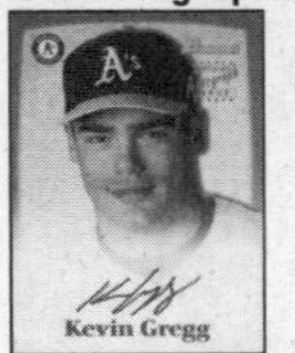

Inserted into 2000 Bowman Draft Pick sets at one per set, this 55-card insert features autographed cards of some of the hottest prospects in baseball. Card backs carry a "BDPA" prefix. Please note that cards BDPA16, BDPA32, BDPA34, BDPA45, BDPA56 do not exist.

BDPA1 Pat Burrell 6.00 15.00
BDPA2 Rafael Furcal 6.00 15.00
BDPA3 Grant Roberts 4.00 10.00
BDPA4 Barry Zito 15.00 40.00
BDPA5 Julio Zuleta 4.00 10.00
BDPA6 Mark Mulder 6.00 15.00
BDPA7 Rob Bell 4.00 10.00
BDPA8 Adam Piatt 4.00 10.00
BDPA9 Mike Lamb 6.00 15.00
BDPA10 Pablo Ozuna 4.00 10.00
BDPA11 Jason Tyner 4.00 10.00
BDPA12 Jason Marquis 6.00 15.00
BDPA13 Eric Munson 4.00 10.00
BDPA14 Seth Etherton 4.00 10.00
BDPA15 Milton Bradley 6.00 15.00
BDPA17 Michael Wenner 4.00 10.00
BDPA18 M.Glendenning 4.00 10.00
BDPA19 Tony Alvarez 4.00 10.00
BDPA20 Adrian Gonzalez 40.00 80.00
BDPA21 Corey Smith 4.00 10.00
BDPA22 Matt Wheatland 4.00 10.00
BDPA23 Adam Johnson 4.00 10.00
BDPA24 Mike Stodolka 4.00 10.00
BDPA25 Rocco Baldelli 60.00 100.00
BDPA26 Juan Rincon 4.00 10.00
BDPA27 Chad Durbin 4.00 10.00
BDPA28 Yorvit Torrealba 10.00 25.00
BDPA29 Nick Green 4.00 10.00
BDPA30 Derek Thompson 4.00 10.00
BDPA31 John Lackey 30.00 60.00
BDPA33 Kevin Gregg 4.00 10.00
BDPA35 Denny Abreu 4.00 10.00
BDPA36 Brian Tollberg 4.00 10.00
BDPA37 Yamid Haad 4.00 10.00
BDPA38 Grady Sizemore 200.00 300.00
BDPA39 Carlos Silva 4.00 10.00
BDPA40 Jorge Cantu 30.00 60.00
BDPA41 Bobby Kielty 4.00 10.00
BDPA42 Scott Thorman 30.00 80.00
BDPA43 Juan Salas 4.00 10.00
BDPA44 Phil Dumatrait 4.00 10.00
BDPA46 Mike Lockwood 4.00 10.00
BDPA47 Yovanny Lara 4.00 10.00
BDPA48 Tripper Johnson 4.00 10.00
BDPA49 Colby Lewis 4.00 10.00
BDPA50 Neil Jenkins 4.00 10.00
BDPA51 Keith Bucktrot 4.00 10.00
BDPA52 Eric Byrnes 4.00 10.00
BDPA53 Aaron Herr 4.00 10.00
BDPA54 Erasmo Ramirez 4.00 10.00
BDPA55 Chris Richard 4.00 10.00
BDPA57 Mike Bynum 4.00 10.00
BDPA58 Brian Esposito 4.00 10.00
BDPA59 Chris Clapinski 4.00 10.00
BDPA60 Augie Ojeda 4.00 10.00

2001 Bowman Promos

This three-card set was distributed in a sealed plastic cello wrap to dealers and hobby media a few months prior to the release of 2001 Bowman to allow a sneak preview of the upcoming brand. The promos can be readily identified from base issue cards by their PP prefixed numbering on back.

COMPLETE SET (3) 2.40 6.00
PP1 Barry Bonds .80 2.00
PP2 Roger Clemens 1.20 3.00
PP3 Adrian Gonzalez .60 1.50

2001 Bowman

Issued in one series, this 440 card set features a mix of 140 veteran cards along with 300 cards of young players. The cards were issued in either 10-card retail or hobby packs or 21-card hobby collector packs. The 10 card packs had an SRP of $3 while the jumbo packs had an SRP of $6. The 10 card packs were inserted 24 packs to a box and 12 boxes to a case. The 21 card packs were inserted 12 packs per box and eight boxes per case. An exchange card with a redemption deadline of May 31st, 2002, good for a signed Sean Burroughs baseball, was randomly seeded into packs at a miniscule rate of 1:30,432. Only eighty exchange cards were produced. In addition, a special card featuring game-used jersey swatches of A.L. and N.L. Rookie of the Year winners Kazuhiro Sasaki and Rafael Furcal was randomly seeded into packs at the following rates; hobby 1:2,202 and Home Team Advantage 1:1,045.

COMPLETE SET (440) 90.00 150.00
COMMON CARD (1-440) .10 .30
COMMON RC .15 .40
1 Jason Giambi .10 .30
2 Rafael Furcal .10 .30
3 Rick Ankiel .10 .30
4 Freddy Garcia .10 .30
5 Magglio Ordonez .10 .30
6 Bernie Williams .20 .50
7 Kenny Lofton .10 .30
8 Al Leiter .10 .30
9 Albert Belle .10 .30
10 Craig Biggio .20 .50
11 Mark Mulder .10 .30
12 Carlos Delgado .10 .30
13 Darin Erstad .10 .30
14 Richie Sexson .10 .30

15 Randy Johnson .30 .75
16 Greg Maddux .50 1.25
17 Cliff Floyd .10 .30
18 Mark Buehrle .20 .50
19 Chris Singleton .10 .30
20 Orlando Hernandez .10 .30
21 Javier Vazquez .10 .30
22 Jeff Kent .10 .30
23 Jim Thome .20 .50
24 John Olerud .10 .30
25 Jason Kendall .10 .30
26 Scott Rolen .20 .50
27 Tony Gwynn .40 1.00
28 Edgardo Alfonzo .10 .30
29 Pokey Reese .10 .30
30 Todd Helton .20 .50
31 Mark Quinn .10 .30
32 Dan Tosca RC .15 .40
33 Dean Palmer .10 .30
34 Jacque Jones .10 .30
35 Ray Durham .10 .30
36 Rafael Palmeiro .20 .50
37 Carl Everett .10 .30
38 Ryan Dempster .10 .30
39 Randy Wolf .10 .30
40 Vladimir Guerrero .30 .75
41 Livan Hernandez .10 .30
42 Mo Vaughn .10 .30
43 Shannon Stewart .10 .30
44 Preston Wilson .10 .30
45 Jose Vidro .10 .30
46 Fred McGriff .20 .50
47 Kevin Brown .10 .30
48 Peter Bergeron .10 .30
49 Miguel Tejada .10 .30
50 Chipper Jones .30 .75
51 Edgar Martinez .20 .50
52 Tony Batista .10 .30
53 Jorge Posada .20 .50
54 Ricky Ledee .10 .30
55 Sammy Sosa .30 .75
56 Steve Cox .10 .30
57 Tony Armas Jr. .10 .30
58 Gary Sheffield .10 .30
59 Bartolo Colon .10 .30
60 Pat Burrell .10 .30
61 Jay Payton .10 .30
62 Sean Casey .10 .30
63 Larry Walker .10 .30
64 Mike Mussina .20 .50
65 Nomar Garciaparra .50 1.25
66 Darren Dreifort .10 .30
67 Richard Hidalgo .10 .30
68 Troy Glaus .10 .30
69 Ben Grieve .10 .30
70 Jim Edmonds .10 .30
71 Raul Mondesi .10 .30
72 Andruw Jones .20 .50
73 Luis Castillo .10 .30
74 Mike Sweeney .10 .30
75 Derek Jeter .75 2.00
76 Ruben Mateo .10 .30
77 Carlos Lee .10 .30
78 Cristian Guzman .10 .30
79 Mike Hampton .10 .30
80 J.D. Drew .10 .30
81 Matt Lawton .10 .30
82 Moises Alou .10 .30
83 Terrence Long .10 .30
84 Geoff Jenkins .10 .30
85 Manny Ramirez Sox .20 .50
86 Johnny Damon .20 .50
87 Barry Larkin .20 .50
88 Pedro Martinez .20 .50
89 Juan Gonzalez .10 .30
90 Roger Clemens .60 1.50
91 Carlos Beltran .10 .30
92 Brad Radke .10 .30
93 Orlando Cabrera .10 .30
94 Roberto Alomar .20 .50
95 Barry Bonds .75 2.00
96 Tim Hudson .10 .30
97 Tom Glavine .20 .50
98 Jeromy Burnitz .10 .30
99 Adrian Beltre .10 .30
100 Mike Piazza .50 1.25
101 Kerry Wood .10 .30
102 Steve Finley .10 .30
103 Alex Cora .10 .30
104 Bob Abreu .10 .30
105 Neifi Perez .10 .30
106 Mark Redman .10 .30
107 Paul Konerko .10 .30
108 Jermaine Dye .10 .30
109 Brian Giles .10 .30
110 Ivan Rodriguez .20 .50
111 Vinny Castilla .10 .30
112 Adam Kennedy .10 .30
113 Eric Chavez .10 .30
114 Billy Koch .10 .30
115 Shawn Green .10 .30
116 Matt Williams .10 .30
117 Greg Vaughn .10 .30
118 Gabe Kapler .10 .30
119 Jeff Cirillo .10 .30
120 Frank Thomas .30 .75
121 David Justice .10 .30
122 Cal Ripken 1.00 2.50
123 Rich Aurilia .10 .30
124 Curt Schilling .10 .30
125 Barry Zito .20 .50
126 Brian Jordan .10 .30
127 Chan Ho Park .10 .30
128 J.T. Snow .10 .30
129 Kazuhiro Sasaki .10 .30
130 Alex Rodriguez .50 1.25
131 Mariano Rivera .30 .75
132 Eric Milton .10 .30
133 Andy Pettitte .20 .50
134 Scott Elarton .10 .30
135 Ken Griffey Jr. .50 1.25
136 Bengie Molina .10 .30
137 Jeff Bagwell .20 .50
138 Kevin Millwood .10 .30
139 Tino Martinez .20 .50
140 Mark McGwire .75 2.00
141 Larry Barnes .10 .30
142 John Buck RC .40 1.00
143 Freddie Bynum RC .15 .40
144 Abraham Nunez .10 .30
145 Felix Diaz RC .15 .40
146 Horacio Estrada .10 .30
147 Ben Diggins .10 .30
148 Tsuyoshi Shinjo RC .40 1.00
149 Rocco Baldelli .10 .30
150 Rod Barajas .10 .30
151 Luis Terrero .10 .30
152 Milton Bradley .10 .30
153 Kurt Ainsworth .10 .30
154 Russell Branyan .10 .30
155 Ryan Anderson .10 .30
156 Mitch Jones RC .25 .60
157 Chip Ambres .10 .30
158 Steve Bennett RC .15 .40
159 Ivanon Coffie .10 .30
160 Sean Burroughs .10 .30
161 Keith Bucktrot .10 .30
162 Tony Alvarez .10 .30
163 Joaquin Benoit .10 .30
164 Rick Asadoorian .10 .30
165 Ben Broussard .10 .30
166 Ryan Madson RC .50 1.25
167 Dee Brown .10 .30
168 Sergio Contreras RC .25 .60
169 John Barnes .10 .30
170 Ben Washburn RC .15 .40
171 Erick Almonte RC .15 .40
172 Shawn Fagan RC .15 .40
173 Gary Johnson RC .15 .40
174 Brady Clark .10 .30
175 Grant Roberts .10 .30
176 Tony Torcato .10 .30
177 Ramon Castro .10 .30
178 Esteban German .10 .30
179 Joe Hamer RC .25 .60
180 Nick Neugebauer .10 .30
181 Dernell Stenson .10 .30
182 Yhency Brazoban RC .40 1.00
183 Aaron Myette .10 .30
184 Juan Sosa .10 .30
185 Brandon Inge .10 .30
186 Domingo Guante RC .15 .40
187 Adrian Brown .10 .30
188 Deivi Mendez RC .15 .40
189 Luis Matos .10 .30
190 Pedro Liriano RC .25 .60
191 Donnie Bridges .10 .30
192 Alex Cintron .10 .30
193 Jace Brewer .10 .30
194 Ron Davenport RC .25 .60
195 Jason Belcher RC .15 .40
196 Adrian Hernandez RC .15 .40
197 Bobby Kielty .10 .30
198 Reggie Griggs RC .25 .60
199 R. Abercrombie RC .40 1.00
200 Troy Farnsworth RC .25 .60
201 Matt Belisle .10 .30
202 Miguel Villilo RC .25 .60
203 Adam Everett .10 .30
204 John Lackey .10 .30
205 Pasqual Coco .10 .30
206 Adam Wainwright .10 .30
207 Matt White RC .25 .60
208 Chin-Feng Chen .10 .30
209 Jeff Andra RC .15 .40
210 Willie Bloomquist .10 .30
211 Wes Anderson .10 .30
212 Enrique Cruz .10 .30
213 Jerry Hairston Jr. .10 .30
214 Mike Bynum .10 .30
215 Brian Hitchcox RC .15 .40
216 Ryan Christianson .10 .30
217 J.J. Davis .10 .30
218 Jovanny Cedeno .10 .30
219 Elvin Nina .10 .30
220 Alex Graman .10 .30
221 Arturo McDowell .10 .30
222 Deivis Santos RC .15 .40
223 Jody Gerut .10 .30
224 Sun Woo Kim .10 .30
225 Jimmy Rollins .10 .30
226 Ntema Ndungidi .10 .30
227 Ruben Salazar .10 .30
228 Josh Girdley .10 .30
229 Carl Crawford .10 .30
230 Luis Montanez RC .30 .75
231 Ramon Carvajal RC .25 .60
232 Matt Riley .10 .30
233 Ben Davis .10 .30
234 Jason Grabowski .10 .30
235 Chris George .10 .30
236 Hank Blalock RC 2.00 5.00
237 Roy Oswalt .30 .75
238 Eric Reynolds RC .15 .40
239 Brian Cole .10 .30
240 Denny Bautista RC .40 1.00
241 Hector Garcia RC .15 .40
242 Joe Thurston RC .25 .60
243 Brad Cresse .10 .30
244 Corey Patterson .10 .30
245 Brett Evert RC .15 .40
246 Elpidio Guzman RC .15 .40
247 Vernon Wells .10 .30
248 Roberto Miniel RC .25 .60
249 Brian Bass RC .15 .40
250 Mark Burnett RC .25 .60
251 Juan Silvestre .10 .30
252 Pablo Ozuna .10 .30
253 Jayson Werth .10 .30
254 Russ Jacobson .10 .30
255 Chad Hermansen .10 .30
256 Travis Hafner RC 4.00 10.00
257 Brad Baker .10 .30
258 Gookie Dawkins .10 .30
259 Michael Cuddyer .10 .30
260 Mark Buehrle .20 .50
261 Ricardo Aramboles .10 .30
262 Esix Snead RC .15 .40
263 Wilson Betemit RC 1.25 3.00
264 Albert Pujols RC 20.00 50.00
265 Joe Lawrence .10 .30
266 Ramon Ortiz .10 .30
267 Ben Sheets .20 .50
268 Luke Lockwood RC .25 .60
269 Toby Hall .10 .30
270 Jack Cust .10 .30
271 Pedro Feliz UER .10 .30
No facsimile signature on card
272 Noel Devarez RC .25 .60
273 Josh Beckett .20 .50
274 Alex Escobar .10 .30
275 Doug Gredvig RC .15 .40
276 Marcus Giles .10 .30
277 Jon Rauch .10 .30
278 Brian Schmitt RC .15 .40
279 Seung Song RC .25 .60
280 Kevin Mench .10 .30
281 Adam Eaton .10 .30
282 Shawn Sonnier .10 .30
283 Andy Van Hekken RC .15 .40
284 Aaron Rowand .10 .30
285 Tony Blanco RC .25 .60
286 Ryan Kohlmeier .10 .30
287 C.C. Sabathia .10 .30
288 Bubba Crosby .10 .30
289 Josh Hamilton .25 .60
290 Dee Haynes RC .15 .40
291 Jason Marquis .10 .30
292 Julio Zuleta .10 .30
293 Carlos Hernandez .10 .30
294 Matt Lecroy .10 .30
295 Andy Beal RC .15 .40
296 Carlos Pena .10 .30
297 Reggie Taylor .10 .30
298 Bob Keppel RC .15 .40
299 Miguel Cabrera UER .60 1.50
Photo is Manuel Esquivia
300 Ryan Franklin .10 .30
301 Brandon Phillips .10 .30
302 Victor Hall RC .25 .60
303 Tony Pena Jr. .10 .30
304 Jim Journell RC .25 .60
305 Cristian Guerrero .10 .30
306 Miguel Olivo .10 .30
307 Jin Ho Cho .10 .30
308 Choo Freeman .10 .30
309 Danny Borrell RC .15 .40
310 Doug Mientkiewicz .10 .30
311 Aaron Herr .10 .30
312 Keith Ginter .10 .30
313 Felipe Lopez .10 .30
314 Jeff Goldbach .10 .30
315 Travis Harper .10 .30
316 Paul LoDuca .10 .30
317 Joe Torres .10 .30
318 Eric Byrnes .10 .30
319 George Lombard .10 .30
320 Dave Krynzel .10 .30
321 Ben Christensen .10 .30
322 Aubrey Huff .10 .30
323 Lyle Overbay .10 .30
324 Sean McGowan .10 .30
325 Jeff Heaverlo .10 .30
326 Timo Perez .10 .30
327 Octavio Martinez RC .25 .60
328 Vince Faison .10 .30
329 David Parrish RC .15 .40
330 Bobby Bradley .15 .40
331 Jason Miller RC .15 .40
332 Corey Spencer RC .15 .40
333 Craig House .10 .30
334 Maxim St. Pierre RC .25 .60
335 Adam Johnson .10 .30
336 Joe Crede .30 .75
337 Greg Nash RC .15 .40
338 Chad Durbin .10 .30
339 Pat Magness RC .25 .60
340 Matt Wheatland .10 .30
341 Julio Lugo .10 .30
342 Grady Sizemore .60 1.50
343 Adrian Gonzalez .10 .30
344 Tim Raines Jr. .10 .30
345 Ranier Olmedo RC .25 .60
346 Phil Dumatrait .10 .30
347 Brandon Mims RC .15 .40
348 Jason Jennings .10 .30
349 Phil Wilson RC .25 .60
350 Jason Hart .10 .30
351 Cesar Izturis .10 .30
352 Matt Butler RC .25 .60
353 David Kelton .10 .30
354 Luke Prokopec .10 .30
355 Corey Smith .10 .30
356 Joel Pineiro .25 .60
357 Ken Chenard .10 .30
358 Keith Reed .10 .30
359 David Walling .10 .30
360 Alexis Gomez RC .15 .40
361 Justin Morneau RC 4.00 10.00
362 Josh Fogg RC .25 .60
363 J.R. House .10 .30
364 Andy Tracy .10 .30
365 Kenny Kelly .10 .30
366 Aaron McNeal .10 .30
367 Nick Johnson .10 .30
368 Brian Esposito .10 .30
369 Charles Frazier RC .15 .40
370 Scott Heard .10 .30
371 Pat Strange .10 .30
372 Mike Meyers .10 .30
373 Ryan Ludwick RC 2.50 6.00
374 Brad Wilkerson .10 .30
375 Allen Levrault .10 .30
376 Seth McClung RC .25 .60
377 Joe Nathan .10 .30
378 Rafael Soriano RC .25 .60
379 Chris Richard .10 .30
380 Jared Sandberg .10 .30
381 Tike Redman .10 .30
382 Adam Dunn UER .20 .50
Card lists him as a pitcher
383 Jared Abruzzo RC .15 .40
384 Jason Richardson RC .15 .40
385 Matt Holliday .15 .40
386 Darwin Cubillan RC .15 .40
387 Mike Nannini .10 .30
388 Blake Williams RC .15 .40
389 V. Pascucci RC .25 .60
390 Jon Garland .10 .30
391 Josh Pressley .10 .30
392 Jose Ortiz .10 .30
393 Ryan Hannaman RC .25 .60
394 Steve Smyth RC .25 .60
395 John Patterson .10 .30
396 Chad Petty RC .15 .40
397 Jake Peavy RC 2.50 6.00
UER last name misspelled Peavey
398 Onix Mercado RC .25 .60
399 Jason Romano .10 .30
400 Luis Torres RC .25 .60
401 Casey Fossum RC .25 .60
402 Eduardo Figueroa RC .15 .40
403 Bryan Barnowski RC .15 .40
404 Tim Redding .10 .30
405 Jason Standridge .10 .30
406 Marvin Seale RC .25 .60
407 Todd Moser .10 .30
408 Alex Gordon .10 .30
409 Steve Smitherman RC .25 .60
410 Ben Petrick .10 .30
411 Eric Munson .10 .30
412 Luis Rivas .10 .30
413 Matt Ginter .10 .30
414 Alfonso Soriano .20 .50
415 Rafael Boitel RC .15 .40
416 Dany Morban RC .15 .40
417 Justin Woodrow RC .25 .60
418 Wilfredo Rodriguez .10 .30
419 Derrick Van Dusen RC .15 .40
420 Josh Spoerl RC .25 .60
421 Juan Pierre .10 .30
422 J.C. Romero .10 .30
423 Ed Rogers RC .15 .40
424 Tomo Ohka .10 .30
425 Ben Hendrickson RC .15 .40
426 Carlos Zambrano .20 .50
427 Brett Myers .10 .30
428 Scott Seabol .10 .30
429 Thomas Mitchell .10 .30
430 Jose Reyes RC 6.00 15.00
431 Kip Wells .10 .30
432 Donzell McDonald .10 .30
433 Adam Pettyjohn RC .15 .40
434 Austin Kearns .10 .30
435 Rico Washington .10 .30
436 Doug Nickle RC .15 .40
437 Steve Lomasney .10 .30
438 Jason Jones RC .15 .40
439 Bobby Seay .10 .30
440 Justin Wayne RC .25 .60
ROYR Kazuhiro Sasaki 6.00 15.00
Rafael Furcal ROY Jsy
NNO Sean Burroughs Ball/80 6.00 15.00

2001 Bowman Gold

Inserted one per pack, these 440 cards are a parallel to the basic Bowman set.

*STARS: 1.25X TO 3X BASIC CARDS
*ROOKIES: .6X TO 1.5X BASIC
264 Albert Pujols 40.00 80.00
430 Jose Reyes 8.00 20.00

2001 Bowman Autographs

Inserted at a rate of one in 74 hobby packs and one in 35 HTA packs, these 40 cards feature autographs from some of the leading prospects in the Bowman set. Dustin McGowan did not return his cards in time for inclusion in the product and exchange cards with a redemption deadline of April 30th, 2003 were seeded into packs in their place.

BAAE Alex Escobar 4.00 10.00
BAAG Adrian Gonzalez 6.00 15.00
BAAJ Adam Johnson 4.00 10.00
BAAP Albert Pujols 225.00 450.00
BAADP Adam Piatt 4.00 10.00
BAAJG Alex Graman 4.00 10.00
BAAKG Alex Gordon 4.00 10.00
BABB Brian Barnowski 4.00 10.00
BABD Ben Diggins 4.00 10.00
BABS Ben Sheets 10.00 25.00
BABW Brad Wilkerson 6.00 15.00
BABZ Barry Zito 10.00 25.00
BACG Cristian Guerrero 4.00 10.00
BADK Dave Krynzel 4.00 10.00
BADM D. McGowan EXCH 6.00 15.00
BADWK David Kelton 4.00 10.00
BAFB Freddie Bynum 4.00 10.00
BAJB Jason Botts 6.00 15.00
BAJD Jose Diaz 6.00 15.00
BAJH Josh Hamilton 20.00 50.00
BAJM Justin Morneau 100.00 150.00
BAJP Josh Pressley 4.00 10.00
BAJRH J.R. House 4.00 10.00
BAJWH Jason Hart 4.00 10.00
BAKM Kevin Mench 6.00 15.00
BALM Luis Montanez 15.00 40.00
BALO Lyle Overbay 6.00 15.00
BAMV Miguel Villilo 4.00 10.00
BAND Noel Devarez 4.00 10.00
BAPL Pedro Liriano 4.00 10.00
BARF Rafael Furcal 6.00 15.00
BARJ Russ Jacobson 4.00 10.00
BASB Sean Burroughs 4.00 10.00
BASM S. McGowan EXCH 4.00 10.00
BASS Shawn Sonnier 4.00 10.00
BASU Sixto Urena 4.00 10.00
BASDS Steve Smyth 4.00 10.00
BATH Travis Hafner 30.00 60.00
BATJ Tripper Johnson 4.00 10.00
BAWB Wilson Betemit 10.00 25.00

2001 Bowman AutoProofs

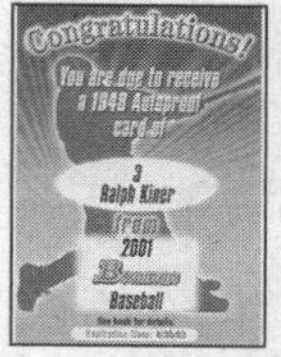

Congratulations!
You are due to receive a 1948 Autograph card of
3
Ralph Kiner
from
2001
Bowman
Baseball

Inserted at a rate of 1 in 18,239 hobby packs and 1 in 8,306 HTA packs; these 10 cards feature players signing their actual Bowman Rookie Cards. Each player signed 25 cards for this promotion. Hank Bauer, Pat Burrell, Carlos Delgado, Chipper Jones, Ralph Kiner, Gil McDougald, and Ivan Rodriguez did not return their cards in time for inclusion in this product and exchange cards with a redemption deadline of April 30th, 2003 were seeded in to packs in their place.

1 Hank Bauer 50
2 Pat Burrell 99
3 Carlos Delgado 92
4 Carl Erskine 51
5 Rafael Furcal 99
6 Chipper Jones 91
7 Ralph Kiner 48
8 Don Larsen 54
9 Gil McDougald 52
10 Ivan Rodriguez EXCH

2001 Bowman Futures Game Relics

Inserted at overall odds of one in 82 hobby packs and one in 39 HTA packs, these 34 cards feature relics used by the featured players in the futures game. These cards were inserted at different ratios and our checklist provides that information as to what group each insert belongs to.

FGRAE Alex Escobar A 4.00 10.00
FGRAM Aaron Myette B 4.00 10.00
FGRBB Bobby Bradley B 4.00 10.00
FGRBP Ben Petrick C 4.00 10.00
FGRBS Ben Sheets B 6.00 15.00
FGRBW Brad Wilkerson C 4.00 10.00
FGRBZ Barry Zito B 6.00 15.00
FGRCA Craig Anderson B 4.00 10.00
FGRCC Chin-Feng Chen A 15.00 40.00
FGRCG Chris George D 4.00 10.00
FGRCH C. Hernandez D 4.00 10.00
FGRCP Corey Patterson A 4.00 10.00
FGRCP Carlos Pena A 4.00 10.00
FGRCT Chin-Hui Tsao D 10.00 25.00
FGREM Eric Munson A 4.00 10.00
FGRFL Felipe Lopez A 4.00 10.00
FGRGR Grant Roberts D 4.00 10.00
FGRJC Jack Cust A 4.00 10.00
FGRJH Josh Hamilton A 8.00 20.00
FGRJR Jason Romano C 4.00 10.00
FGRJZ Julio Zuleta A 4.00 10.00
FGRKA Kurt Ainsworth B 4.00 10.00
FGRMB Mike Bynum D 4.00 10.00
FGRMG Marcus Giles A 4.00 10.00
FGRNN N. Ndungidi A 4.00 10.00
FGRRA Ryan Anderson B 4.00 10.00
FGRRC Ramon Castro C 4.00 10.00
FGRRD R. Dorame D 4.00 10.00
FGRRO Ramon Ortiz D 4.00 10.00
FGRSK Sun Woo Kim D 4.00 10.00
FGRTD Travis Dawkins C 4.00 10.00
FGRTO Tomokazu Ohka B 4.00 10.00
FGRTW Travis Wilson A 4.00 10.00
FGRVW Vernon Wells C 4.00 10.00

2001 Bowman Multiple Game Relics

Issued at overall odds of one in 1,476 hobby packs and one in 701 HTA packs, these cards have three different pieces of memorabilia on them. These cards feature a piece of a jersey, helmet and a base fragment.

MGRAE Alex Escobar B 10.00 25.00
MGRBP Ben Petrick A 10.00 25.00
MGRBW B. Wilkerson B 10.00 25.00
MGRCC C. Chen A 90.00 150.00
MGRCP Carlos Pena A 10.00 25.00
MGREM Eric Munson B 10.00 25.00
MGRFL Felipe Lopez A 12.50 30.00
MGRJC Jack Cust A 10.00 25.00
MGRJH Josh Hamilton B 20.00 50.00
MGRJR Jason Romano A 10.00 25.00
MGRJZ Julio Zuleta A 10.00 25.00
MGRMG Marcus Giles A 12.50 30.00
MGRNN N. Ndungidi A 10.00 25.00
MGRRC Ramon Castro A 10.00 25.00
MGRTD Travis Dawkins A 10.00 25.00
MGRTW Travis Wilson A 10.00 25.00
MGRVW Vernon Wells A 12.50 30.00
MGRDCP C. Patterson B 10.00 25.00

2001 Bowman Multiple Game Relics Autograph

Inserted in packs at a rate of one in 18,259 Hobby and one in 8,306 HTA packs, these five cards feature not only three pieces of memorabilia from the featured players but also included an authentic signature.

AMGRAE Alex Escobar
AMGRBW Brad Wilkerson
AMGRCP Corey Patterson
AMGREM Eric Munson
AMGRJH Josh Hamilton

2001 Bowman Rookie Reprints

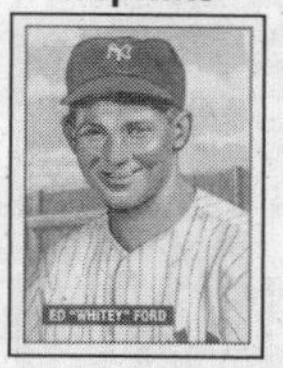

Inserted at a rate of one in 12, these 25 cards feature reprint cards of various stars who made their debut between 1948 and 1955.

COMPLETE SET (25) 25.00 60.00
1 Yogi Berra 2.00 5.00
2 Ralph Kiner 1.25 3.00
3 Stan Musial 4.00 10.00
4 Warren Spahn 1.25 3.00
5 Roy Campanella 2.00 5.00
6 Bob Lemon 1.25 3.00
7 Robin Roberts 1.25 3.00
8 Duke Snider 1.25 3.00
9 Early Wynn 1.25 3.00
10 Richie Ashburn 1.25 3.00
11 Gil Hodges 2.00 5.00
12 Hank Bauer 1.25 3.00
13 Don Newcombe 1.25 3.00
14 Al Rosen 1.25 3.00
15 Willie Mays 5.00 12.00
16 Joe Garagiola 1.25 3.00
17 Whitey Ford 1.25 3.00
18 Lew Burdette 1.25 3.00
19 Gil McDougald 1.25 3.00
20 Minnie Minoso 1.25 3.00
21 Eddie Mathews 2.00 5.00
22 Harvey Kuenn 1.25 3.00
23 Don Larsen 1.25 3.00
24 Elston Howard 1.25 3.00
25 Don Zimmer 1.25 3.00

2001 Bowman Rookie Reprints Autographs

Inserted at a rate of one in 2,467 hobby packs and one in 1,162 HTA packs, these 10 cards feature the players signing their rookie reprint cards. Duke Snider did not return his card in time for inclusion in packs. His card was redeemable until April 30, 2003. Please note that card number 7 does not exist. Though the cards lack serial-numbering, Topps did announce that only 100 sets were produced. Card number 7 does not exist.

1 Yogi Berra 40.00 80.00
2 Willie Mays 150.00 250.00
3 Stan Musial 75.00 150.00
4 Duke Snider 30.00 60.00
5 Warren Spahn 30.00 60.00
6 Ralph Kiner 10.00 25.00
8 Don Larsen 10.00 25.00
9 Don Zimmer 10.00 25.00
10 Minnie Minoso 10.00 25.00

2001 Bowman Rookie Reprints Relic Bat

Issued at a rate of one in 1,954 hobby packs and one in 928 HTA packs, these five cards feature not only the rookie reprint of these players but also a piece of a bat they used during their career.

1 Willie Mays 40.00 80.00
2 Duke Snider 10.00 25.00
3 Minnie Minoso 6.00 15.00
4 Hank Bauer 6.00 15.00
5 Gil McDougald 6.00 15.00

2001 Bowman Rookie Reprints Relic Bat Autographs

Issued at a rate of one in 18,259 hobby packs and one in 8,306 HTA packs, these five cards feature not only the rookie reprint of these players but also a piece of a bat they used during their career as well as an authentic autograph.

1 Willie Mays
2 Duke Snider
3 Minnie Minoso
4 Hank Bauer
5 Gil McDougald

2001 Bowman Draft Picks

Issued as a 112-card factory set with a SRP of $45.99, these sets feature 100 cards of young players along with an autograph and relic card in each box. Twelve sets were included in each case. Cards BDP51 and BDP71 featuring Alex Herrera and Brad Thomas are uncorrected errors in that the card backs were switched for each player.

COMP.FACT.SET (112) 30.00 60.00
COMPLETE SET (110) 20.00 50.00
BDP1 Alfredo Amezaga RC .10 .30
BDP2 Andrew Good .10 .30
BDP3 Kelly Johnson RC 1.25 3.00
BDP4 Larry Bigbie .10 .30
BDP5 Matt Thompson RC .15 .40
BDP6 Wilton Chavez RC .15 .40
BDP7 Joe Borchard RC .15 .40
BDP8 David Espinosa .10 .30
BDP9 Zach Day RC .15 .40
BDP10 Brad Hawpe RC 1.00 2.50
BDP11 Nate Cornejo .10 .30
BDP12 Matt Cooper RC .15 .40
BDP13 Brad Lidge .10 .30
BDP14 Angel Berroa RC .25 .60
BDP15 L. Matthews RC .15 .40
BDP16 Jose Garcia .10 .30
BDP17 Grant Balfour RC .10 .30
BDP18 Ron Chiavacci RC .10 .30
BDP19 Jae Seo .10 .30
BDP20 Juan Rivera .10 .30
BDP21 D'Angelo Jimenez .10 .30
BDP22 Juan A.Pena RC .15 .40
BDP23 Marlon Byrd RC .15 .40
BDP24 Sean Burnett .10 .30
BDP25 Josh Pearce RC .15 .40
BDP26 B. Duckworth RC .10 .30
BDP27 Jack Taschner RC .10 .30
BDP28 Marcus Thames .10 .30
BDP29 Brent Abernathy .10 .30
BDP30 David Elder RC .10 .30
BDP31 Scott Cassidy RC .15 .40
BDP32 D. Tankersley RC .10 .30
BDP33 Denny Stark .10 .30
BDP34 Dave Williams RC .10 .30
BDP35 Boof Bonser RC .10 .30
BDP36 Kris Foster RC .10 .30
BDP37 Luis Garcia RC .15 .40
BDP38 Shawn Chacon .10 .30
BDP39 Mike Rivera RC .15 .40
BDP40 Will Smith RC .15 .40
BDP41 M. Ensberg RC .75 2.00
BDP42 Ken Harvey .10 .30
BDP43 R. Rodriguez RC .15 .40
BDP44 Jose Mieses RC .15 .40
BDP45 Luis Maza RC .15 .40
BDP46 Julio Perez RC .15 .40
BDP47 Dustan Mohr RC .15 .40
BDP48 Randy Flores RC .10 .30
BDP49 Covelli Crisp RC 2.00 5.00
BDP50 Kevin Reese RC .15 .40
BDP51 Brad Thomas UER .10 .30
Card back is BDP71 Alex Herrera
BDP52 Xavier Nady .10 .30
BDP53 Ryan Vogelsong .10 .30
BDP54 Carlos Silva .10 .30
BDP55 Dan Wright .10 .30
BDP56 Brent Butler .10 .30
BDP57 Brandon Knight RC .10 .30
BDP58 Brian Reith RC .10 .30
BDP59 M. Valenzuela RC .15 .40
BDP60 Bobby Hill RC .15 .40
BDP61 Rich Rundles RC .15 .40
BDP62 Rick Elder .10 .30
BDP63 J.D. Closser .10 .30
BDP64 Scot Shields .10 .30
BDP65 Miguel Olivo .10 .30
BDP66 Stubby Clapp RC .10 .30
BDP67 J. Williams RC .25 .60
BDP68 Jason Lane RC .25 .60
BDP69 Chase Utley RC 10.00 25.00
BDP70 Erik Bedard RC 2.00 5.00
BDP71 A. Herrera UER RC .10 .30
Card back is BDP51 Brad Thomas
BDP72 Juan Cruz RC .15 .40
BDP73 Billy Martin RC .10 .30
BDP74 Ronnie Merrill RC .15 .40
BDP75 Jason Kinchen RC .10 .30
BDP76 Wilkin Ruan RC .15 .40
BDP77 Cody Ransom RC .10 .30
BDP78 Bud Smith RC .10 .30
BDP79 Wily Mo Pena .10 .30
BDP80 Jeff Nettles RC .15 .40
BDP81 Jamal Strong RC .10 .30
BDP82 Bill Ortega RC .10 .30
BDP83 Mike Bell .10 .30
BDP84 Ichiro Suzuki RC 3.00 8.00
BDP85 F. Rodney RC .10 .30
BDP86 Chris Smith RC .10 .30
BDP87 J.VanBenschoten RC .15 .40
BDP88 Bobby Crosby RC 1.50 4.00
BDP89 Kenny Baugh RC .10 .30
BDP90 Jake Gautreau RC .10 .30
BDP91 Gabe Gross RC .25 .60
BDP92 Kris Honel RC .15 .40
BDP93 Dan Denham RC .10 .30
BDP94 Aaron Heilman RC .15 .40
BDP95 Irvin Guzman RC 1.50 4.00
BDP96 Mike Jones RC .25 .60
BDP97 J. Griffin RC .15 .40
BDP98 Macay McBride RC .40 1.00
BDP99 J. Rheinecker RC .40 1.00
BDP100 B. Sardinha RC .10 .30
BDP101 J. Weintraub RC .10 .30
BDP102 J.D. Martin RC .10 .30
BDP103 Jayson Nix RC .15 .40
BDP104 Noah Lowry RC 1.00 2.50
BDP105 Richard Lewis RC .15 .40
BDP106 B. Hennessey RC .25 .60
BDP107 Jeff Mathis RC .25 .60
BDP108 Jon Skaggs RC .15 .40
BDP109 Justin Pope RC .15 .40
BDP110 Josh Burrus RC .15 .40

2001 Bowman Draft Picks Autographs

Inserted one per Bowman draft pick factory set, these 37 cards feature autographs of some of the leading players from the Bowman Draft Pick set.

BDPAAA A. Amezaga 4.00 10.00
BDPAAC Alex Cintron 4.00 10.00
BDPAAE Adam Everett 4.00 10.00
BDPAAF Alex Fernandez 4.00 10.00
BDPAAG Alexis Gomez 4.00 10.00
BDPAAH Aaron Herr 4.00 10.00
BDPAAK Austin Kearns 6.00 15.00
BDPABB Bobby Bradley 4.00 10.00
BDPABH Beau Hale 4.00 10.00
BDPABP Brandon Phillips 4.00 10.00
BDPABS Bud Smith 4.00 10.00
BDPACG C. Guerrero 4.00 10.00
BDPACI Cesar Izturis 4.00 10.00
BDPACP Christian Parra 4.00 10.00
BDPAER Ed Rogers 4.00 10.00
BDPAFL Felipe Lopez 6.00 15.00
BDPAGA Garrett Atkins 30.00 60.00
BDPAGJ Gary Johnson 4.00 10.00
BDPAJA Jared Abruzzo 4.00 10.00
BDPAJK Joe Kennedy 6.00 15.00
BDPAJL John Lackey 6.00 15.00
BDPAJP Joel Pineiro 6.00 15.00
BDPAJT Joe Torres 4.00 10.00
BDPANJ Nick Johnson 6.00 15.00
BDPANR Nick Regilio 4.00 10.00
BDPARC Ryan Church 6.00 15.00
BDPARD Ryan Dittfurth 4.00 10.00
BDPARL Ryan Ludwick 20.00 50.00
BDPARO Roy Oswalt 15.00 40.00
BDPASH Scott Heard 4.00 10.00
BDPASS Scott Seabol 4.00 10.00
BDPATO Tomo Ohka 6.00 15.00
BDPAANC A. Cameron 4.00 10.00
BDPABJS Brian Specht 4.00 10.00
BDPAJMW Justin Wayne 4.00 10.00
BDPARMM Ryan Madson 8.00 20.00
BDPAROC R. Carvajal 4.00 10.00

2001 Bowman Draft Picks Futures Game Relics

Inserted one per factory set, these 26 cards feature relics from the futures game.

FGRAA Alfredo Amezaga 2.00 5.00
FGRAD Adam Dunn 3.00 8.00
FGRAG Adrian Gonzalez 2.00 5.00
FGRAH Alex Herrera 2.00 5.00
FGRBM Brett Myers 2.00 5.00
FGRCD Cody Ransom 2.00 5.00
FGRCG Chris George 2.00 5.00
FGRCH Carlos Hernandez 2.00 5.00
FGRCU Chase Utley 30.00 60.00
FGREB Erik Bedard 4.00 10.00
FGRGB Grant Balfour 2.00 5.00
FGRHB Hank Blalock 4.00 10.00
FGRJB Joe Borchard 2.00 5.00
FGRJC Juan Cruz 2.00 5.00
FGRJP Josh Pearce 2.00 5.00
FGRJR Juan Rivera 2.00 5.00
FGRJAP Juan A.Pena 2.00 5.00
FGRLG Luis Garcia 2.00 5.00
FGRMC Miguel Cabrera 6.00 15.00
FGRMR Mike Rivera 2.00 5.00
FGRRR R. Rodriguez 2.00 5.00
FGRSC Scott Chiasson 2.00 5.00
FGRSS Seung Song 2.00 5.00
FGRTB Toby Hall 2.00 5.00
FGRWB Wilson Betemit 4.00 10.00
FGRWP Wily Mo Pena 2.00 5.00

2001 Bowman Draft Picks Relics

Inserted one per factory set, these six cards feature relics from some of the most popular prospects in the Bowman Draft Pick set.

BDPRCI Cesar Izturis 4.00 10.00
BDPRGJ Gary Johnson 4.00 10.00
BDPRNR Nick Regilio 4.00 10.00
BDPRRC Ryan Church 6.00 15.00
BDPRBJS Brian Specht 4.00 10.00
BDPRJRH J.R. House 4.00 10.00

2002 Bowman

This 440 card set was issued in May, 2002. It was issued in 10 card packs which were packed 24 packs to a box and 12 boxes per case. These packs had an SRP of $3 per pack. The first 110 cards of this set featured veterans while the rest of the set featured rookies and prospects.

COMPLETE SET (440) 40.00 80.00
COMMON CARD (1-110) .10 .30
COMMON CARD (111-440) .10 .30
1 Adam Dunn .10 .30
2 Derek Jeter .75 2.00
3 Alex Rodriguez .50 1.25
4 Miguel Tejada .10 .30
5 Nomar Garciaparra .50 1.25
6 Toby Hall .10 .30
7 Brandon Duckworth .10 .30
8 Paul LoDuca .10 .30
9 Brian Giles .10 .30
10 C.C. Sabathia .10 .30
11 Curt Schilling .10 .30
12 Tsuyoshi Shinjo .10 .30
13 Ramon Hernandez .10 .30
14 Jose Cruz Jr. .10 .30
15 Albert Pujols .60 1.50
16 Joe Mays .10 .30
17 Javy Lopez .10 .30
18 J.T. Snow .10 .30
19 David Segui .10 .30
20 Jorge Posada .20 .50
21 Doug Mientkiewicz .10 .30
22 Jerry Hairston Jr. .10 .30
23 Bernie Williams .20 .50
24 Mike Sweeney .10 .30
25 Jason Giambi .10 .30
26 Ryan Dempster .10 .30
27 Ryan Klesko .10 .30
28 Mark Quinn .10 .30
29 Jeff Kent .10 .30
30 Eric Chavez .10 .30
31 Adrian Beltre .10 .30
32 Andruw Jones .20 .50
33 Alfonso Soriano .10 .30
34 Aramis Ramirez .10 .30
35 Greg Maddux .50 1.25
36 Andy Pettitte .20 .50
37 Bartolo Colon .10 .30
38 Ben Sheets .10 .30
39 Bobby Higginson .10 .30
40 Ivan Rodriguez .20 .50
41 Brad Penny .10 .30
42 Carlos Lee .10 .30
43 Damion Easley .10 .30
44 Preston Wilson .10 .30
45 Jeff Bagwell .20 .50
46 Eric Milton .10 .30
47 Rafael Palmeiro .20 .50
48 Gary Sheffield .10 .30
49 J.D. Drew .10 .30
50 Jim Thome .20 .50
51 Ichiro Suzuki .60 1.50
52 Bud Smith .10 .30
53 Chan Ho Park .10 .30
54 D'Angelo Jimenez .10 .30
55 Ken Griffey Jr. .50 1.25
56 Wade Miller .10 .30
57 Vladimir Guerrero .30 .75
58 Troy Glaus .10 .30
59 Shawn Green .10 .30
60 Kerry Wood .10 .30
61 Jack Wilson .10 .30
62 Kevin Brown .10 .30
63 Marcus Giles .10 .30
64 Pat Burrell .10 .30
65 Larry Walker .10 .30
66 Sammy Sosa .30 .75
67 Raul Mondesi .10 .30
68 Tim Hudson .10 .30
69 Lance Berkman .10 .30
70 Mike Mussina .20 .50
71 Barry Zito .10 .30
72 Jimmy Rollins .10 .30
73 Barry Bonds .75 2.00
74 Craig Biggio .20 .50
75 Todd Helton .20 .50
76 Roger Clemens .60 1.50
77 Frank Catalanotto .10 .30
78 Josh Towers .10 .30
79 Roy Oswalt .10 .30
80 Chipper Jones .30 .75
81 Cristian Guzman .10 .30
82 Darin Erstad .10 .30
83 Freddy Garcia .10 .30
84 Jason Tyner .10 .30
85 Carlos Delgado .10 .30
86 Jon Lieber .10 .30
87 Juan Pierre .10 .30
88 Matt Morris .10 .30
89 Phil Nevin .10 .30
90 Jim Edmonds .10 .30
91 Magglio Ordonez .10 .30
92 Mike Hampton .10 .30
93 Rafael Furcal .10 .30
94 Richie Sexson .10 .30
95 Luis Gonzalez .10 .30
96 Scott Rolen .20 .50
97 Tim Redding .10 .30
98 Moises Alou .10 .30
99 Jose Vidro .10 .30
100 Mike Piazza .50 1.25
101 Pedro Martinez UER .20 .50
Career strikeout total incorrect
102 Geoff Jenkins .10 .30
103 Johnny Damon Sox .20 .50
104 Mike Cameron .10 .30
105 Randy Johnson .30 .75
106 David Eckstein .10 .30
107 Javier Vazquez .10 .30
108 Mark Mulder .10 .30
109 Robert Fick .10 .30
110 Roberto Alomar .20 .50
111 Wilson Betemit .10 .30
112 Chris Tritle RC .10 .30
113 Ed Rogers .10 .30
114 Juan Pena .10 .30
115 Josh Beckett .15 .40
116 Juan Cruz .10 .30
117 Noochie Varner RC .15 .40
118 Taylor Buchholz RC .25 .60
119 Mike Rivera .10 .30
120 Hank Blalock .25 .60
121 Hansel Izquierdo RC .15 .40
122 Orlando Hudson .10 .30
123 Bill Hall .15 .40
124 Jose Reyes .25 .60
125 Juan Rivera .10 .30
126 Eric Valent .10 .30
127 Scotty Layfield RC .15 .40
128 Austin Kearns .10 .30
129 Nic Jackson RC .15 .40
130 Chris Baker RC .15 .40
131 Chad Qualls RC .20 .50
132 Marcus Thames .10 .30
133 Nathan Haynes .10 .30
134 Brett Evert .10 .30
135 Joe Borchard .10 .30
136 Ryan Christianson .10 .30
137 Josh Hamilton .25 .60
138 Corey Patterson .10 .30
139 Travis Wilson .10 .30
140 Alex Escobar .10 .30
141 Alexis Gomez .10 .30
142 Nick Johnson .15 .40
143 Kenny Kelly .10 .30
144 Marlon Byrd .10 .30
145 Kory DeHaan .10 .30
146 Matt Belisle .10 .30
147 Carlos Hernandez .10 .30
148 Sean Burroughs .10 .30
149 Angel Berroa .10 .30
150 Aubrey Huff .15 .40
151 Travis Hafner .15 .40
152 Brandon Berger .10 .30
153 David Krynzel .10 .30
154 Ruben Salazar .10 .30
155 J.R. House .10 .30
156 Juan Silvestre .10 .30
157 Dewon Brazelton .10 .30
158 Jayson Werth .10 .30
159 Larry Barnes .10 .30
160 Elvis Pena .10 .30
161 Ruben Gotay RC .20 .50
162 Tommy Marx RC .15 .40
163 John Suomi RC .15 .40
164 Javier Colina .15 .40
165 Greg Sain RC .15 .40
166 Robert Cosby RC .15 .40
167 Angel Pagan RC .20 .50
168 Ralph Santana RC .15 .40
169 Joe Orloski RC .15 .40
170 Shayne Wright RC .15 .40
171 Jay Caligiuri RC .15 .40
172 Greg Montalbano RC .15 .40
173 Rich Harden RC 1.25 3.00
174 Rich Thompson RC .15 .40
175 Fred Bastardo RC .15 .40
176 Alejandro Giron RC .15 .40
177 Jesus Medrano RC .15 .40
178 Kevin Deaton RC .15 .40
179 Mike Rosamond RC .15 .40
180 Jon Guzman RC .15 .40
181 Gerard Oakes RC .15 .40
182 Francisco Liriano RC 3.00 8.00
183 Matt Allegra RC .15 .40
184 Mike Snyder RC .15 .40
185 James Shanks RC .15 .40
186 Anderson Hernandez RC .15 .40
187 Dan Trumble RC .15 .40
188 Luis DePaula RC .15 .40
189 Randall Shelley RC .15 .40
190 Richard Lane RC .15 .40
191 Antwon Rollins RC .15 .40
192 Ryan Bukvich RC .15 .40
193 Derrick Lewis .10 .30
194 Eric Miller RC .15 .40
195 Justin Schuda RC .15 .40
196 Brian West RC .15 .40
197 Adam Roller RC .15 .40
198 Neal Frendling RC .15 .40
199 Jeremy Hill RC .15 .40
200 James Barrett RC .15 .40
201 Brett Kay RC .15 .40
202 Ryan Mottl RC .15 .40
203 Brad Nelson RC .15 .40
204 Juan M. Gonzalez RC .15 .40
205 Curtis Legendre RC .15 .40
206 Ronald Acuna RC .15 .40
207 Chris Flinn RC .15 .40
208 Nick Alvarez RC .15 .40
209 Jason Ellison RC .30 .75
210 Blake McGinley RC .15 .40
211 Dan Phillips RC .15 .40
212 Demetrius Heath RC .15 .40
213 Eric Bruntlett RC .15 .40
214 Joe Jiannetti RC .15 .40
215 Mike Hill RC .15 .40
216 Ricardo Cordova RC .15 .40
217 Mark Hamilton RC .15 .40
218 David Mattox RC .15 .40
219 Jose Morban RC .15 .40
220 Scott Wiggins RC .10 .30
221 Steve Green .10 .30
222 Brian Rogers .10 .30
223 Chin-Hui Tsao .15 .40
224 Kenny Baugh .10 .30
225 Nate Teut .10 .30
226 Josh Wilson RC .15 .40
227 Christian Parker .10 .30
228 Tim Raines Jr. .10 .30
229 Anastacio Martinez RC .15 .40
230 Richard Lewis .10 .30
231 Tim Kalita RC .15 .40
232 Edwin Almonte RC .15 .40
233 Hee-Seop Choi .10 .30
234 Ty Howington .10 .30
235 Victor Alvarez RC .15 .40
236 Morgan Ensberg .15 .40
237 Jeff Austin RC .15 .40
238 Luis Terrero .10 .30
239 Adam Wainwright .10 .30
240 Clint Weibl RC .10 .30
241 Eric Cyr .10 .30
242 Marlyn Tisdale RC .15 .40
243 John VanBenschoten .10 .30
244 Ryan Raburn RC .15 .40
245 Miguel Cabrera .60 1.50
246 Jung Bong .10 .30
247 Raul Chavez RC .10 .30
248 Erik Bedard .15 .40
249 Chris Snelling RC .25 .60
250 Joe Rogers RC .15 .40
251 Nate Field RC .10 .30
252 Matt Herges RC .10 .30
253 Matt Childers RC .15 .40
254 Erick Almonte .10 .30
255 Nick Neugebauer .10 .30
256 Ron Calloway RC .15 .40
257 Seung Song .10 .30
258 Brandon Phillips .10 .30
259 Cole Barthel RC .10 .30
260 Jason Lane .15 .40
261 Jae Seo .10 .30
262 Randy Flores .10 .30
263 Scott Chiasson .10 .30
264 Chase Utley 1.00 2.50
265 Tony Alvarez .10 .30
266 Ben Howard RC .15 .40
267 Nelson Castro RC .15 .40
268 Mark Lukasiewicz RC .10 .30
269 Eric Glaser RC .15 .40
270 Rob Henkel RC .15 .40
271 Jose Valverde RC .15 .40
272 Ricardo Rodriguez .10 .30
273 Chris Smith .10 .30
274 Mark Prior .25 .60
275 Miguel Olivo .10 .30
276 Ben Broussard .10 .30
277 Zach Sorensen .10 .30
278 Brian Mallette RC .10 .30
279 Brad Wilkerson .10 .30
280 Carl Crawford .15 .40
281 Chone Figgins RC .60 1.50
282 Jimmy Alvarez RC .15 .40
283 Gavin Floyd RC .40 1.00
284 Josh Bonifay RC .15 .40
285 Garrett Guzman RC .15 .40
286 Blake Williams .10 .30
287 Matt Holliday .10 .30
288 Ryan Madson .10 .30
289 Luis Torres .10 .30
290 Jeff Verplancke RC .15 .40
291 Nate Espy RC .15 .40
292 Jeff Lincoln RC .15 .40
293 Ryan Snare RC .15 .40
294 Jose Ortiz .10 .30
295 Eric Munson .10 .30
296 Denny Bautista .10 .30
297 Willy Aybar .15 .40
298 Kelly Johnson .25 .60
299 Justin Morneau .15 .40
300 Derrick Van Dusen .10 .30
301 Chad Petty .10 .30
302 Mike Restovich .10 .30
303 Shawn Fagan .10 .30
304 Yurendell DeCaster RC .15 .40
305 Justin Wayne .10 .30
306 Mike Peeples RC .15 .40
307 Joel Guzman .40 1.00
308 Ryan Vogelsong .10 .30
309 Jorge Padilla RC .15 .40
310 Grady Sizemore .40 1.00
311 Joe Jester RC .15 .40
312 Jim Journell .10 .30
313 Bobby Seay .10 .30
314 Ryan Church RC .40 1.00
315 Grant Balfour .10 .30
316 Mitch Jones .10 .30
317 Travis Foley RC .15 .40
318 Bobby Crosby .40 1.00
319 Adrian Gonzalez .10 .30
320 Ronnie Merrill .10 .30
321 Joel Pineiro .10 .30
322 John-Ford Griffin .10 .30
323 Brian Forystek RC .15 .40
324 Sean Douglass .10 .30
325 Manny Delcarmen RC .20 .50
326 Donnie Bridges .10 .30
327 Jim Kavourias RC .15 .40
328 Gabe Gross .10 .30
329 Jon Rauch .10 .30
330 Bill Ortega .10 .30
331 Joey Hammond RC .15 .40
332 Ramon Moreta RC .15 .40
333 Ron Davenport .10 .30
334 Brett Myers .15 .40
335 Carlos Pena .10 .30
336 Ezequiel Astacio RC .15 .40
337 Edwin Yan RC .15 .40
338 Josh Girdley .10 .30
339 Shaun Boyd .10 .30
340 Juan Rincon .10 .30
341 Chris Duffy RC .20 .50
342 Jason Kinchen .10 .30
343 Brad Thomas .10 .30
344 David Kelton .10 .30
345 Rafael Soriano .10 .30
346 Colin Young RC .15 .40
347 Eric Byrnes .10 .30
348 Chris Narveson RC .20 .50
349 John Rheinecker .10 .30
350 Mike Wilson RC .15 .40
351 Justin Sherrod RC .15 .40
352 Deivi Mendez .15 .40
353 Wily Mo Pena .15 .40
354 Brett Roneberg RC .15 .40
355 Trey Lunsford RC .15 .40
356 Jimmy Gobble RC .15 .40
357 Brent Butler .10 .30
358 Aaron Heilman .10 .30
359 Wilkin Ruan .10 .30
360 Brian Wolfe RC .15 .40
361 Cody Ransom .10 .30
362 Koyie Hill .10 .30
363 Scott Cassidy .10 .30
364 Tony Fontana RC .15 .40
365 Mark Teixeira .60 1.50
366 Doug Sessions RC .15 .40
367 Victor Hall .10 .30
368 Josh Cisneros RC .15 .40
369 Kevin Mench .10 .30
370 Tike Redman .10 .30
371 Jeff Heaverlo .10 .30
372 Carlos Brackley RC .15 .40
373 Brad Hawpe .10 .30
374 Jesus Colome .10 .30
375 David Espinosa .10 .30
376 Jesse Foppert RC .20 .50
377 Ross Peeples RC .15 .40
378 Alex Requena RC .15 .40
379 Joe Mauer RC 5.00 12.00
380 Carlos Silva .10 .30
381 David Wright RC 8.00 20.00
382 Craig Kuzmic RC .15 .40
383 Pete Zamora RC .15 .40
384 Matt Parker RC .15 .40
385 Keith Ginter .10 .30
386 Gary Cates Jr. .15 .40
387 Justin Reid RC .15 .40
388 Jake Mauer RC .15 .40
389 Dennis Tankersley .10 .30
390 Josh Barfield RC 1.00 2.50
391 Luis Maza .10 .30
392 Henry Pichardo RC .15 .40
393 Michael Floyd RC .15 .40
394 Clint Nageotte RC .20 .50
395 Raymond Cabrera RC .15 .40
396 Mauricio Lara RC .15 .40
397 Alejandro Cadena RC .15 .40
398 Jonny Gomes RC 1.00 2.50
399 Jason Bulger RC .15 .40
400 Bobby Jenks RC .60 1.50
401 David Gil RC .15 .40
402 Joel Crump RC .15 .40
403 Kazuhisa Ishii RC .30 .75
404 So Taguchi RC .30 .75
405 Ryan Doumit RC .25 .60
406 Macay McBride .15 .40
407 Brandon Claussen .10 .30
408 Chin-Feng Chen .15 .40
409 Josh Phelps .10 .30
410 Freddie Money RC .20 .50
411 Cliff Bartosh RC .15 .40
412 Josh Pearce .10 .30
413 Lyle Overbay .10 .30
414 Ryan Anderson .10 .30
415 Terrance Hill RC .15 .40
416 John Rodriguez RC .20 .50
417 Richard Stahl .10 .30
418 Brian Specht .10 .30
419 Chris Latham RC .10 .30
420 Carlos Cabrera RC .15 .40
421 Jose Bautista RC .40 1.00
422 Kevin Frederick RC .15 .40
423 Jerome Williams .10 .30
424 Napoleon Calzado RC .15 .40
425 Benito Baez .10 .30
426 Xavier Nady .10 .30
427 Jason Botts RC .25 .60
428 Steve Bechler RC .15 .40
429 Reed Johnson RC .40 1.00
430 Mark Outlaw RC .15 .40
431 Billy Sylvester .10 .30
432 Luke Lockwood .10 .30
433 Jake Peavy .25 .60
434 Alfredo Amezaga .10 .30
435 Aaron Cook RC .15 .40
436 Josh Shaffer RC .15 .40
437 Dan Wright .10 .30
438 Ryan Gripp RC .15 .40
439 Alex Herrera .10 .30
440 Jason Bay RC 2.00 5.00

2002 Bowman Gold

Inserted one per pack, this is a parallel to the 2002 Bowman set. These cards can be differentiated by the Bowman logo and the facsimile signature in gold foil stamping.

*RED 1-110: 1.25X TO 3X BASIC
*BLUE 111-440: .75X TO 2X BASIC
*BLUE ROOKIES 111-440: .75X TO 2X BASIC

182 Francisco Liriano 5.00 12.00
381 David Wright 10.00 25.00

2002 Bowman Uncirculated

Inserted at a stated rate of one per box, these cards were issued as redemptions through the Pit.Com. These cards were printed to a stated print run of 672 sets and could be redeemed and were kept in special holders. The cards could be exchanged until December 31, 2002 with delivery beginning July 7, 2002.

112 Chris Tritle
117 Noochie Varner
118 Taylor Buchholz
121 Hansel Izquierdo
123 Bill Hall
127 Scotty Layfield
129 Nic Jackson
130 Chris Baker
131 Chad Qualls
161 Ruben Gotay
162 Tommy Marx
163 John Suomi
164 Javier Colina
165 Greg Sain
222 Brian Rogers
229 Anastacio Martinez
230 Richard Lewis
231 Tim Kalita
232 Edwin Almonte
235 Victor Alvarez
237 Jeff Austin
240 Clint Weibl
244 Ryan Raburn
249 Chris Snelling
250 Joe Rogers
251 Nate Field
253 Matt Childers
256 Ron Calloway
259 Cole Barthel
266 Ben Howard
267 Nelson Castro
269 Eric Glaser
270 Rob Henkel
271 Jose Valverde
278 Brian Mallette
281 Chone Figgins
282 Jimmy Alvarez
283 Gavin Floyd
284 Josh Bonifay
285 Garrett Guzman
290 Jeff Verplancke
291 Nate Espy
293 Ryan Snare
304 Yurendell De Caster
306 Mike Peeples
309 Jorge Padilla
311 Joe Jester
314 Ryan Church
317 Travis Foley
323 Brian Forystek
325 Manny Delcarmen
327 Jim Kavourias
331 Joey Hammond
336 Ezequiel Astacio
337 Edwin Yan
341 Chris Duffy
348 Chris Narveson
351 Justin Sherrod
354 Brett Roneberg
355 Trey Lunsford
356 Jimmy Gobble
360 Brian Wolfe
362 Koyie Hill
364 Tony Fontana
366 Doug Sessions
372 Carlos Brackley
376 Jesse Foppert
377 Ross Peeples
378 Alex Requena
379 Joe Mauer 12.50 30.00
381 David Wright 30.00 60.00
382 Craig Kuzmic
383 Pete Zamora
384 Matt Parker
386 Gary Cates Jr
387 Justin Reid
388 Jake Mauer
390 Josh Barfield
392 Henry Pichardo
393 Michael Floyd
394 Clint Nageotte
395 Raymond Cabrera
396 Mauricio Lara
397 Alejandro Cadena
398 Jonny Gomes
399 Jason Bulger
400 Bobby Jenks
401 David Gil
402 Joel Crump
403 Kazuhisa Ishii
404 So Taguchi
405 Ryan Doumit
410 Freddie Money
411 Cliff Bartosh
415 Terrance Hill
416 John Rodriguez
419 Chris Latham
420 Carlos Cabrera
421 Jose Bautista
422 Kevin Frederick
424 Napoleon Calzado
425 Benito Baez
427 Jason Botts
428 Steve Bechler
429 Reed Johnson
430 Mark Outlaw
436 Josh Shaffer
437 Dan Wright
438 Ryan Gripp
440 Jason Bay
NNO Exchange Card

2002 Bowman Autographs

Inserted in packs at overall odds of one in 40 hobby packs, one in 24 HTA packs and one in 53 retail packs, this 45 card set featued autographs of leading rookies and prospects.

GROUP A 1:67 H, 1:39 HTA, 1:89 R
GROUP B 1:129 H, 1:74 HTA, 1:170 R
GROUP C 1:881 H, 1:507 HTA, 1:1165 R
GROUP D 1:1558 H, 1:896 HTA, 1:2060 R
GROUP E 1:1685 H, 1:968 HTA, 1:2238 R
OVERALL ODDS 1:40 H, 1:24 HTA, 1:53 R
ONE ADD'L AUTO PER SEALED HTA BOX
BAAA Alfredo Amezaga A 4.00 10.00
BAAH Aubrey Huff A 4.00 10.00
BABA Brandon Claussen A 4.00 10.00
BABC Ben Christensen A 4.00 10.00
BABD Brian Cardwell A 4.00 10.00
BABBC Boof Bonser A 4.00 10.00
BABJC Brian Specht C 4.00 10.00
BABSS Bud Smith B 4.00 10.00
BACK Charles Kegley A 4.00 10.00
BACR Cody Ransom B 4.00 10.00
BACS Chris Smith B 4.00 10.00
BACT Chris Tritle B 4.00 10.00
BACU Chase Utley A 60.00 120.00
BADV Domingo Valdez A 4.00 10.00
BADW Dan Wright B 4.00 10.00
BAGA Garrett Atkins A 8.00 20.00
BAGJ Gary Johnson C 4.00 10.00
BAHB Hank Blalock B 6.00 15.00
BAJB Josh Beckett B 15.00 40.00
BAJD Jeff Davanon A 4.00 10.00
BAJL Jason Lane A 6.00 15.00
BAJP Juan Pena A 4.00 10.00
BAJS Juan Silvestre A 4.00 10.00
BAJAB Jason Botts B 6.00 15.00
BAJLW Jerome Williams A 4.00 10.00
BAKG Keith Ginter B 4.00 10.00
BALB Larry Bigbie A 6.00 15.00
BAMB Marlon Byrd B 4.00 10.00
BAMC Matt Cooper A 4.00 10.00
BAMD Manny Delcarmen A 4.00 10.00
BAME Morgan Ensberg A 6.00 15.00
BAMP Mark Prior B 6.00 15.00
BANJ Nick Johnson B 6.00 15.00
BANN Nick Neugebauer E 4.00 10.00
BANV Noochie Varner B 4.00 10.00
BARF Randy Flores D 4.00 10.00
BARF Ryan Franklin B 4.00 10.00
BARH Ryan Hannaman A 4.00 10.00
BARO Roy Oswalt B 6.00 15.00
BARV Ryan Vogelsong B 4.00 10.00
BATB Tony Blanco A 4.00 10.00
BATH Toby Hall B 4.00 10.00
BATS Termel Sledge B 4.00 10.00
BAWB Wilson Betemit B 4.00 10.00
BAWS Will Smith A 4.00 10.00

2002 Bowman Futures Game Autograph Relics

Inserted at overall odds of one in 196 hobby packs, one in 113 HTA packs and one in 259 retail packs for jersey cards and one in 126 HTA packs for base cards, these cards feature pieces of memorabilia and the player's autograph from the 2001 Futures Game.

GROUP A JSY 1:2193 H, 1:1262 HTA, 1:2898 R
GROUP B JSY 1:1599 H, 1:923 HTA, 1:2125 R
GROUP C JSY 1:522 H, 1:301 HTA, 1:688 R
GROUP D JSY 1:1533 H, 1:882 HTA, 1:2028 R
GROUP E JSY 1:1425 H, 1:822 HTA, 1:1882 R
GROUP F JSY 1:1316 H, 1:759 HTA, 1:1738 R
OVERALL JSY 1:196 H, 1:113 HTA, 1:259 R
BASE ODDS 1:126 HTA
CH Carlos Hernandez Jsy B 10.00 25.00
CP Carlos Pena Jsy D 10.00 25.00
DT Dennis Tankersley Jsy E 10.00 25.00
JRH J.R. House Jsy C 10.00 25.00
JW Jerome Williams Jsy F 10.00 25.00
NJ Nick Johnson Jsy C 10.00 25.00
RL Ryan Ludwick Jsy C 15.00 40.00
TH Toby Hall Base 10.00 25.00
WB Wilson Betemit Jsy A 10.00 25.00

2002 Bowman Game Used Relics

Inserted at an overall stated odd of one in 74 hobby packs, one in 43 HTA packs and one in 99 retail packs, these 26 cards features some of the leading prospects from the set along a piece of game-used memorabilia.

GROUP A BAT 1:3236 H, 1:1866 HTA, 1:4331 R
GROUP B BAT 1:1472 H, 1:849 HTA, 1:1949 R

GROUP C BAT 1:1647 H, 1:948 HTA, 1:2180 R
GROUP D BAT 1:894 H, 1:515 HTA, 1:1180 R
GROUP E BAT 1:375 H, 1:216 HTA, 1:496 R
GROUP F BAT 1:1042 H, 1:601 HTA, 1:1381 R
GROUP G BAT 1:939 H, 1:541 HTA, 1:1237 R
OVERALL BAT 1:135 H, 1:78 HTA, 1:179 R
GROUP A JSY 1:2085 H,1:1202 HTA,1:2762 R
GROUP B JSY 1:1916 H, 1:528 HTA, 1:1213 R
GROUP C JSY 1:223 H, 1:129 HTA, 1:295 R
OVERALL JSY 1:165 H, 1:95 HTA, 1:219 R
OVERALL RELIC 1:74 H, 1:43 HTA, 1: R
BRAB Angel Berroa Bat B 4.00 10.00
BRAC Antoine Cameron Bat C 4.00 10.00
BRAE Adam Everett Bat E 3.00 8.00
BRAF Alex Fernandez Bat B 4.00 10.00
BRAF Alex Fernandez Jsy C 3.00 8.00
BRAG Alexis Gomez Bat A 4.00 10.00
BRAK Austin Kearns Bat E 3.00 8.00
BRALC Alex Cintron Bat E 3.00 8.00
BRCG Cristian Guerrero Bat E 3.00 8.00
BRCI Cesar Izturis Bat D 3.00 8.00
BRCP Corey Patterson Bat B 4.00 10.00
BRCY Colin Young Jsy C 3.00 8.00
BRDJ D'Angelo Jimenez Bat C 4.00 10.00
BRFJ Forrest Johnson Bat G 3.00 8.00
BRGA Garrett Atkins Bat F 4.00 10.00
BRJA Jared Abruzzo Bat D 3.00 8.00
BRJA Jared Abruzzo Jsy C 3.00 8.00
BRJL Jason Lane Jsy B 3.00 8.00
BRJS Jamal Strong Jsy A 3.00 8.00
BRNC Nate Cornejo Jsy C 3.00 8.00
BRNN Nick Neugebauer Jsy C 3.00 8.00
BRRC Ryan Church Bat D 3.00 8.00
BRRD Ryan Dittfurth Jsy C 3.00 8.00
BRRM Ryan Madson Bat E 3.00 8.00
BRRS Ruben Salazar Bat A 4.00 10.00
BRRST Richard Stahl Jsy B 3.00 8.00

2002 Bowman Draft

This 165 card set was issued in December, 2002. These cards were issued in seven card packs which came 24 packs to a box and 10 boxes to a case. Each pack contained four regular Bowman Draft Pick Cards, two Bowman Chrome Draft cards and one Bowman gold card.

COMPLETE SET (165) 25.00 50.00
BDP1 Clint Everts RC .20 .50
BDP2 Fred Lewis RC .15 .40
BDP3 Jon Broxton RC .40 1.00
BDP4 Jason Anderson RC .15 .40
BDP5 Mike Eusebio RC .15 .40
BDP6 Zack Greinke RC 1.50 4.00
BDP7 Joe Blanton RC .75 2.00
BDP8 Sergio Santos RC .20 .50
BDP9 Jason Cooper RC .15 .40
BDP10 Delwyn Young RC .40 1.00
BDP11 Jeremy Hermida RC 2.00 5.00
BDP12 Dan Ortmeier RC .20 .50
BDP13 Kevin Jepsen RC .20 .50
BDP14 Russ Adams RC .20 .50
BDP15 Mike Nixon RC .15 .40
BDP16 Nick Swisher RC 2.00 5.00
BDP17 Cole Hamels RC 5.00 12.00
BDP18 Brian Dopirak RC .40 1.00
BDP19 James Loney RC 2.50 6.00
BDP20 Denard Span RC .75 2.00
BDP21 Billy Petrick RC .15 .40
BDP22 Jared Doyle RC .15 .40
BDP23 Jeff Francoeur RC 6.00 15.00
BDP24 Nick Bourgeois RC .15 .40
BDP25 Matt Cain RC 2.50 6.00
BDP26 John McCurdy RC .15 .40
BDP27 Mark Kiger RC .15 .40
BDP28 Bill Murphy RC .15 .40
BDP29 Matt Craig RC .20 .50
BDP30 Mike Megrew RC .15 .40
BDP31 Ben Crockett RC .15 .40
BDP32 Luke Hagerty RC .15 .40
BDP33 Matt Whitney RC .15 .40
BDP34 Dan Meyer RC .20 .50
BDP35 Jeremy Brown RC .15 .40
BDP36 Doug Johnson RC .15 .40
BDP37 Steve Obenchain RC .15 .40
BDP38 Matt Clanton RC .15 .40
BDP39 Mark Teahen RC .40 1.00
BDP40 Tom Carrow RC .15 .40
BDP41 Micah Sehilling RC .15 .40
BDP42 Blair Johnson RC .15 .40
BDP43 Jason Pridie RC .15 .40
BDP44 Joey Votto RC 1.25 3.00
BDP45 Taber Lee RC .15 .40
BDP46 Adam Peterson RC .15 .40
BDP47 Adam Donachie RC .15 .40
BDP48 Josh Murray RC .15 .40
BDP49 Brent Clevlen RC .75 2.00
BDP50 Chad Pleiness RC .15 .40
BDP51 Zach Hammes RC .15 .40
BDP52 Chris Snyder RC .20 .50
BDP53 Chris Smith RC .15 .40
BDP54 Justin Maureau RC .15 .40
BDP55 David Bush RC .40 1.00
BDP56 Tim Gilhooly RC .15 .40
BDP57 Blair Barbier RC .15 .40
BDP58 Zach Segovia RC .15 .40
BDP59 Jeremy Reed RC .40 1.00
BDP60 Matt Pender RC .15 .40
BDP61 Eric Thomas RC .15 .40
BDP62 Justin Jones RC .20 .50
BDP63 Brian Slocum RC .15 .40
BDP64 Larry Broadway RC .15 .40
BDP65 Bo Flowers RC .15 .40
BDP66 Scott White RC .15 .40
BDP67 Steve Stanley RC .15 .40
BDP68 Alex Merricks RC .15 .40
BDP69 Josh Womack RC .15 .40
BDP70 Dave Jensen RC .15 .40
BDP71 Curtis Granderson RC 2.00 5.00
BDP72 Pat Osborn RC .15 .40
BDP73 Nic Carter RC .15 .40
BDP74 Mitch Talbot RC .15 .40
BDP75 Don Murphy RC .15 .40
BDP76 Val Majewski RC .15 .40
BDP77 Javy Rodriguez RC .15 .40
BDP78 Fernando Pacheco RC .15 .40
BDP79 Steve Russell RC .15 .40
BDP80 Jon Slack RC .15 .40
BDP81 John Baker RC .15 .40
BDP82 Aaron Coonrod RC .15 .40
BDP83 Josh Johnson RC 2.00 5.00
BDP84 Jake Blalock RC 2.00 5.00
BDP85 Alex Hart RC .15 .40
BDP86 Wes Bankston RC .75 2.00
BDP87 Josh Rupe RC .15 .40
BDP88 Dan Cevette RC .15 .40
BDP89 Kiel Fisher RC .20 .50
BDP90 Alan Rick RC .15 .40
BDP91 Charlie Morton RC .15 .40
BDP92 Chad Spann RC .15 .40
BDP93 Kyle Boyer RC .15 .40
BDP94 Bob Malek RC .15 .40
BDP95 Ryan Rodriguez RC .15 .40
BDP96 Jordan Renz RC .15 .40
BDP97 Randy Frye RC .15 .40
BDP98 Rich Hill RC 2.00 5.00
BDP99 B.J. Upton RC 2.00 5.00
BDP100 Dan Christensen RC .15 .40
BDP101 Casey Kotchman RC .40 1.00
BDP102 Eric Good RC .10 .30
BDP103 Mike Fontenot RC .15 .40
BDP104 John Webb RC .15 .40
BDP105 Jason Dubois RC .20 .50
BDP106 Ryan Kibler RC .15 .40
BDP107 Jhonny Peralta RC 1.00 2.50
BDP108 Kirk Saarloos RC .15 .40
BDP109 Rhett Parrott RC .15 .40
BDP110 Jason Grove RC .15 .40
BDP111 Colt Griffin RC .15 .40
BDP112 Dallas McPherson RC .40 1.00
BDP113 Oliver Perez RC .40 1.00
BDP114 Mar. McDougall RC .15 .40
BDP115 Mike Wood RC .15 .40
BDP116 Scott Hairston RC .20 .50
BDP117 Jason Simontacchi RC .15 .40
BDP118 Taggert Bozied RC .20 .50
BDP119 Shelley Duncan RC 1.25 3.00
BDP120 Dontrelle Willis RC 2.00 5.00
BDP121 Sean Burnett .10 .30
BDP122 Aaron Cook .10 .30
BDP123 Brett Evert .10 .30
BDP124 Jimmy Journell .10 .30
BDP125 Brett Myers .10 .30
BDP126 Brad Baker .10 .30
BDP127 Billy Traber RC .15 .40
BDP128 Adam Wainwright .10 .30
BDP129 Jason Young RC .10 .30
BDP130 John Buck .10 .30
BDP131 Kevin Cash RC .15 .40
BDP132 Jason Stokes RC .20 .50
BDP133 Drew Henson .10 .30
BDP134 Chad Tracy RC .40 1.00
BDP135 Orlando Hudson .10 .30
BDP136 Brandon Phillips .10 .30
BDP137 Joe Borchard .10 .30
BDP138 Marlon Byrd .10 .30
BDP139 Carl Crawford .10 .30
BDP140 Michael Restovich .10 .30
BDP141 Corey Hart RC .60 1.50
BDP142 Edwin Almonte .10 .30
BDP143 Francis Beltran RC .15 .40
BDP144 Jorge De La Rosa RC .15 .40
BDP145 Gerardo Garcia RC .15 .40
BDP146 Franklyn German RC .15 .40
BDP147 Francisco Liriano 1.25 3.00
BDP148 Francisco Rodriguez .10 .30
BDP149 Ricardo Rodriguez .10 .30
BDP150 Seung Song .10 .30
BDP151 John Stephens .10 .30
BDP152 Justin Huber RC .30 .75
BDP153 Victor Martinez .30 .75
BDP154 Hee Seop Choi .10 .30
BDP155 Justin Morneau .10 .30
BDP156 Miguel Cabrera .50 1.25
BDP157 Victor Diaz RC .30 .75
BDP158 Jose Reyes .20 .50
BDP159 Omar Infante .10 .30
BDP160 Angel Berroa .10 .30
BDP161 Tony Alvarez .10 .30
BDP162 Shin Soo Choo RC .30 .75
BDP163 Wily Mo Pena .10 .30
BDP164 Andres Torres .10 .30
BDP165 Jose Lopez RC .75 2.00

2002 Bowman Draft Gold

Issued one per pack, this is a parallel to the Bowman Draft Set. These cards have the player's fascimile autograph set off in gold foil.

*GOLD: 1.25X TO 3X BASIC
*GOLD RC'S: .6X TO 1.5X BASIC
BDP17 Cole Hamels 6.00 15.00
BDP23 Jeff Francoeur 6.00 15.00
BDP147 Francisco Liriano 2.50 6.00

2002 Bowman Draft Fabric of the Future Relics

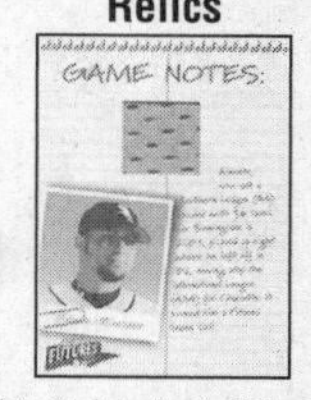

Inserted at a stated rate of one in 55, these 28 cards feature prospects from the 2002 All-Star Futures Game who are very close to be major leaguers. All of these cards have a game-worn jersey relic piece on them.

STATED ODDS 1:55
ALL CARDS FEATURE JERSEY SWATCHES
AB Angel Berroa 3.00 8.00
AT Andres Torres 3.00 8.00
AW Adam Wainwright 3.00 8.00
BM Brett Myers 3.00 8.00
BT Billy Traber 2.00 5.00
CC Carl Crawford 4.00 10.00
CH Corey Hart 4.00 10.00
CT Chad Tracy 3.00 8.00
DH Drew Henson 3.00 8.00
EA Edwin Almonte 2.00 5.00
FB Francis Beltran 2.00 5.00
FG Franklyn German 2.00 5.00
FL Francisco Liriano 4.00 10.00
GG Gerardo Garcia 2.00 5.00
HC Hee Seop Choi 4.00 10.00
JH Justin Huber 3.00 8.00
JK Josh Karp 2.00 5.00
JL Jose Lopez 3.00 8.00
JR Jorge De La Rosa 2.00 5.00
JS1 Jason Stokes 2.00 5.00
JS2 John Stephens 3.00 8.00
KC Kevin Cash 2.00 5.00
MR Michael Restovich 3.00 8.00
SB Sean Burnett 3.00 8.00
SC Shin Soo Choo 3.00 8.00
TA Tony Alvarez 3.00 8.00
VD Victor Diaz 3.00 8.00
WP Wily Mo Pena 4.00 10.00

2002 Bowman Draft Freshman Fiber

Issued at a stated rate of one in 605 for the bat cards and one in 45 for the jersey cards, these 13 cards feature some of the leading young players in the game along with a game-worn piece.

AH Aubrey Huff Jsy 2.00 5.00
AK Austin Kearns Bat 3.00 8.00
BA Brent Abernathy Jsy 2.00 5.00
DB Dewon Brazelton Jsy 2.00 5.00
JH Josh Hamilton Jsy 6.00 15.00
JK Joe Kennedy Jsy 2.00 5.00
JS Jared Sandberg Jsy 2.00 5.00
JV John VanBenschoten Jsy 2.00 5.00
JWS Jason Standridge Jsy 2.00 5.00
MB Marlon Byrd Bat 3.00 8.00
MT Mark Teixeira Bat 6.00 15.00
NB Nick Bierbrodt Jsy 2.00 5.00
TH Toby Hall Jsy 2.00 5.00

2002 Bowman Draft Signs of the Future

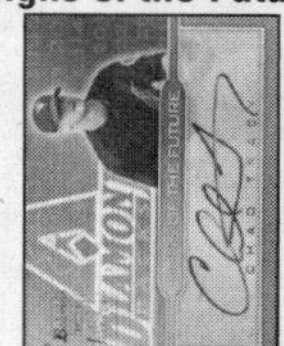

Inserted at different odds depending on what group the player belonged to, these 21 cards feature authentic autographs of the featured player.

GROUP A ODDS 1:100
GROUP B ODDS 1:110
GROUP C ODDS 1:1028
GROUP D ODDS 1:1103
GROUP E ODDS 1:386
GROUP F ODDS 1:2807
BI Brandon Inge E 4.00 10.00
BK Bob Keppel C 4.00 10.00
BP Brandon Phillips B 4.00 10.00
BS Bud Smith E 4.00 10.00
CP Christian Parra D 4.00 10.00
CT Chad Tracy A 6.00 15.00
DD Dan Denham A 4.00 10.00
EB Erik Bedard A 4.00 10.00
JEM Justin Morneau B 10.00 25.00
JM Jake Mauer B 4.00 10.00
JR Juan Rivera B 4.00 10.00
JW Jerome Williams F 4.00 10.00
KH Kris Honel A 4.00 10.00
LB Larry Bigbie E 4.00 10.00
LN Lance Niekro A 6.00 15.00
ME Morgan Ensberg E 4.00 10.00
MF Mike Fontenot A 4.00 10.00
MJ Mitch Jones A 4.00 10.00
NJ Nic Jackson B 4.00 10.00
TB Taylor Buchholz B 4.00 10.00
TL Todd Linden B 6.00 15.00

2003 Bowman

This 330 card set was released in May, 2003. These cards were mixed between veteran cards with red borders on the bottom (1-155) and rookie/prospect cards with blue on the bottom (156-330). This set was issued in 10 card packs which came 24 packs to a box and 12 boxes to a case with an $3 SRP per pack. A special card was inserted featured game-used relics of the two 2002 Major League Rookie of the Years.

COMPLETE SET (330) 25.00 60.00
COMMON CARD (1-155) .10 .30
COMMON CARD (156-330) .10 .30
1 Garret Anderson .10 .30
2 Derek Jeter .75 2.00
3 Gary Sheffield .10 .30
4 Matt Morris .10 .30
5 Derek Lowe .10 .30
6 Andy Van Hekken .10 .30
7 Sammy Sosa .30 .75
8 Ken Griffey Jr. .50 1.25
9 Omar Vizquel .20 .50
10 Jorge Posada .20 .50
11 Lance Berkman .10 .30
12 Mike Sweeney .10 .30
13 Adrian Beltre .10 .30
14 Richie Sexson .10 .30
15 A.J. Pierzynski .10 .30
16 Bartolo Colon .10 .30
17 Mike Mussina .20 .50
18 Paul Byrd .10 .30
19 Bobby Abreu .10 .30
20 Miguel Tejada .10 .30
21 Aramis Ramirez .10 .30
22 Edgardo Alfonzo .10 .30
23 Edgar Martinez .20 .50
24 Albert Pujols .60 1.50
25 Carl Crawford .10 .30
26 Eric Hinske .10 .30
27 Tim Salmon .20 .50
28 Luis Gonzalez .10 .30
29 Jay Gibbons .10 .30
30 John Smoltz .20 .50
31 Tim Wakefield .10 .30
32 Mark Prior .20 .50
33 Magglio Ordonez .10 .30
34 Adam Dunn .10 .30
35 Larry Walker .10 .30
36 Luis Castillo .10 .30
37 Wade Miller .10 .30
38 Carlos Beltran .10 .30
39 Odalis Perez .10 .30
40 Alex Sanchez .10 .30
41 Torii Hunter .10 .30
42 Cliff Floyd .10 .30
43 Andy Pettitte .20 .50
44 Francisco Rodriguez .10 .30
45 Eric Chavez .10 .30
46 Kevin Millwood .10 .30
47 Dennis Tankersley .10 .30
48 Hideo Nomo .30 .75
49 Freddy Garcia .10 .30
50 Randy Johnson .30 .75
51 Aubrey Huff .10 .30
52 Carlos Delgado .10 .30
53 Troy Glaus .10 .30
54 Junior Spivey .10 .30
55 Mike Hampton .10 .30
56 Sidney Ponson .10 .30
57 Aaron Boone .10 .30
58 Kerry Wood .10 .30
59 Runelvys Hernandez .10 .30
60 Nomar Garciaparra .50 1.25
61 Todd Helton .20 .50
62 Mike Lowell .10 .30
63 Roy Oswalt .10 .30
64 Raul Ibanez .10 .30
65 Brian Jordan .10 .30
66 Geoff Jenkins .10 .30
67 Jermaine Dye .10 .30
68 Tom Glavine .20 .50
69 Bernie Williams .20 .50
70 Vladimir Guerrero .30 .75
71 Mark Mulder .10 .30
72 Jimmy Rollins .10 .30
73 Oliver Perez .10 .30
74 Rich Aurilia .10 .30
75 Joel Pineiro .10 .30
76 J.D. Drew .10 .30
77 Ivan Rodriguez .20 .50
78 Josh Phelps .10 .30
79 Darin Erstad .10 .30
80 Curt Schilling .10 .30
81 Paul Lo Duca .10 .30
82 Marty Cordova .10 .30
83 Manny Ramirez .20 .50
84 Bobby Hill .10 .30
85 Paul Konerko .10 .30
86 Austin Kearns .10 .30
87 Jason Jennings .10 .30
88 Brad Penny .10 .30
89 Jeff Bagwell .20 .50
90 Shawn Green .10 .30
91 Jason Schmidt .10 .30
92 Doug Mientkiewicz .10 .30
93 Jose Vidro .10 .30
94 Bret Boone .10 .30
95 Jason Giambi .10 .30
96 Barry Zito .10 .30
97 Roy Halladay .10 .30

98 Pat Burrell .10 .30
99 Sean Burroughs .10 .30
100 Barry Bonds .75 2.00
101 Kazuhiro Sasaki .10 .30
102 Fernando Vina .10 .30
103 Chan Ho Park .10 .30
104 Andruw Jones .20 .50
105 Adam Kennedy .10 .30
106 Shea Hillenbrand .10 .30
107 Greg Maddux .50 1.25
108 Jim Edmonds .10 .30
109 Pedro Martinez .20 .50
110 Moises Alou .10 .30
111 Jeff Weaver .10 .30
112 C.C. Sabathia .10 .30
113 Robert Fick .10 .30
114 A.J. Burnett .10 .30
115 Jeff Kent .10 .30
116 Kevin Brown .10 .30
117 Rafael Furcal .10 .30
118 Cristian Guzman .10 .30
119 Brad Wilkerson .10 .30
120 Mike Piazza .50 1.25
121 Alfonso Soriano .10 .30
122 Mark Ellis .10 .30
123 Vicente Padilla .10 .30
124 Eric Gagne .10 .30
125 Ryan Klesko .10 .30
126 Ichiro Suzuki .60 1.50
127 Tony Batista .10 .30
128 Roberto Alomar .20 .50
129 Alex Rodriguez .50 1.25
130 Jim Thome .20 .50
131 Jarrod Washburn .10 .30
132 Orlando Hudson .10 .30
133 Chipper Jones .30 .75
134 Rodrigo Lopez .10 .30
135 Johnny Damon .20 .50
136 Matt Clement .10 .30
137 Frank Thomas .30 .75
138 Ellis Burks .10 .30
139 Carlos Pena .10 .30
140 Josh Beckett .10 .30
141 Joe Randa .10 .30
142 Brian Giles .10 .30
143 Kazuhisa Ishii .10 .30
144 Corey Koskie .10 .30
145 Orlando Cabrera .10 .30
146 Mark Buehrle .10 .30
147 Roger Clemens .60 1.50
148 Tim Hudson .10 .30
149 Randy Wolf UER .10 .30
resume says AL leaders; he pitches in NL
150 Josh Fogg .10 .30
151 Phil Nevin .10 .30
152 John Olerud .10 .30
153 Scott Rolen .20 .50
154 Joe Kennedy .10 .30
155 Rafael Palmeiro .20 .50
156 Chad Hutchinson .10 .30
157 Quincy Carter XRC .15 .40
158 Hee Seop Choi .10 .30
159 Joe Borchard .10 .30
160 Brandon Phillips .10 .30
161 Wily Mo Pena .10 .30
162 Victor Martinez .20 .50
163 Jason Stokes .20 .50
164 Ken Harvey .10 .30
165 Juan Rivera .10 .30
166 Jose Contreras RC .60 1.50
167 Dan Haren RC .40 1.00
168 Michel Hernandez RC .15 .40
169 Eider Torres RC .15 .40
170 Chris De La Cruz RC .15 .40
171 Ramon Nivar-Martinez RC .15 .40
172 Mike Adams RC .15 .40
173 Justin Arneson RC .15 .40
174 Jamie Athas RC .15 .40
175 Dwaine Bacon RC .15 .40
176 Clint Barmes RC .40 1.00
177 B.J. Barns RC .15 .40
178 Tyler Johnson RC .15 .40
179 Bobby Basham RC .15 .40
180 T.J. Bohn RC .15 .40
181 J.D. Durbin RC .15 .40
182 Brandon Bowe RC .15 .40
183 Craig Brazell RC .15 .40
184 Dusty Brown RC .15 .40
185 Brian Bruney RC .20 .50
186 Greg Bruso RC .15 .40
187 Jaime Bubela RC .15 .40
188 Bryan Bullington RC .15 .40
189 Brian Burgamy RC .15 .40
190 Eny Cabreja RC .50 1.25
191 Daniel Cabrera RC .30 .75
192 Ryan Cameron RC .15 .40
193 Lance Caraccioli RC .15 .40
194 David Cash RC .15 .40
195 Bernie Castro RC .15 .40
196 Ismael Castro RC .20 .50
197 Daryl Clark RC .15 .40
198 Jeff Clark RC .15 .40
199 Chris Colton RC .15 .40
200 Dexter Cooper RC .15 .40
201 Callix Crabbe RC .20 .50
202 Chien-Ming Wang RC 2.50 6.00
203 Eric Crozier RC .20 .50
204 Nook Logan RC .20 .50
205 David DeJesus RC .30 .75
206 Matt DeMarco RC .15 .40
207 Chris Duncan RC 1.50 4.00
208 Eric Eckenstahler .10 .30
209 Willie Eyre RC .15 .40
210 Evel Bastida-Martinez RC .15 .40
211 Chris Fallon RC .15 .40
212 Mike Flannery RC .15 .40
213 Mike Oâ™Keefe RC .15 .40
214 Ben Francisco RC .15 .40
215 Kason Gabbard RC .15 .40
216 Mike Gallo RC .15 .40
217 Jairo Garcia RC .20 .50
218 Angel Garcia RC .20 .50
219 Michael Garciaparra RC .10 .30
220 Joey Gomes RC .15 .40
221 Dusty Gomon RC .20 .50
222 Bryan Grace RC .15 .40
223 Tyson Graham RC .15 .40
224 Henry Guerrero RC .15 .40
225 Franklin Gutierrez RC .40 1.00
226 Carlos Guzman RC .20 .50
227 Matthew Hagen RC .15 .40
228 Josh Hall RC .15 .40
229 Rob Hammock RC .15 .40
230 Brendan Harris RC .20 .50
231 Gary Harris RC .15 .40
232 Clay Hensley RC .15 .40
233 Michael Hinckley RC .20 .50
234 Luis Hodge RC .15 .40
235 Donnie Hood RC .20 .50
236 Travis Ishikawa RC .40 1.00
237 Edwin Jackson RC .20 .50
238 Ardley Jansen RC .20 .50
239 Ferenc Jongejan RC .15 .40
240 Matt Kata RC .15 .40
241 Kazuhiro Takeoka RC .15 .40
242 Beau Kemp RC .15 .40
243 Il Kim RC .15 .40
244 Brennan King RC .15 .40
245 Chris Kroski RC .15 .40
246 Jason Kubel RC .75 2.00
247 Pete LaForest RC .15 .40
248 Wil Ledezma RC .15 .40
249 Jeremy Bonderman RC 1.25 3.00
250 Gonzalo Lopez RC .15 .40
251 Brian Luderer RC .15 .40
252 Ruddy Lugo RC .15 .40
253 Wayne Lydon RC .15 .40
254 Mark Malaska RC .15 .40
255 Andy Marte RC 1.25 3.00
256 Tyler Martin RC .15 .40
257 Branden Florence RC .15 .40
258 Aneudis Mateo RC .15 .40
259 Derell McCall RC .15 .40
260 Brian McCann RC 3.00 8.00
261 Mike McNutt RC .15 .40
262 Jacabo Meque RC .15 .40
263 Derek Michaelis RC .15 .40
264 Aaron Miles RC .20 .50
265 Jose Morales RC .15 .40
266 Dustin Moseley RC .15 .40
267 Adrian Myers RC .15 .40
268 Dan Neil RC .15 .40
269 Jon Nelson RC .20 .50
270 Mike Neu RC .15 .40
271 Leigh Neuage RC .15 .40
272 Wes O'Brien RC .15 .40
273 Trent Oeltjen RC .20 .50
274 Tim Olson RC .15 .40
275 David Pahucki RC .15 .40
276 Nathan Panther RC .15 .40
277 Arnie Munoz RC .15 .40
278 Dave Pember RC .15 .40
279 Jason Perry RC .20 .50
280 Matthew Peterson RC .15 .40
281 Ryan Shealy RC 1.00 2.50
282 Jorge Piedra RC .20 .50
283 Simon Pond RC .15 .40
284 Aaron Rakers RC .15 .40
285 Hanley Ramirez RC 2.00 5.00
286 Manuel Ramirez RC .20 .50
287 Kevin Randel RC .15 .40
288 Darrell Rasner RC .15 .40
289 Prentice Redman RC .15 .40
290 Eric Reed RC .15 .40
291 Wilton Reynolds RC .20 .50
292 Eric Riggs RC .20 .50
293 Carlos Rijo RC .15 .40
294 Rajai Davis RC .15 .40
295 Aron Weston RC .15 .40
296 Arturo Rivas RC .15 .40
297 Kyle Roat RC .15 .40
298 Bubba Nelson RC .20 .50
299 Levi Robinson RC .15 .40
300 Ray Sadler RC .15 .40
301 Gary Schneidmiller RC .15 .40
302 Jon Schuerholz RC .15 .40
303 Corey Shafer RC .15 .40
304 Brian Shackelford RC .15 .40
305 Bill Simon RC .15 .40
306 Haj Turay RC .10 .30
307 Sean Smith RC .20 .50
308 Ryan Spataro RC .15 .40
309 Jemel Spearman RC .15 .40
310 Keith Stamler RC .15 .40
311 Luke Steidlmayer RC .15 .40
312 Adam Stern RC .10 .30
313 Jay Sitzman RC .15 .40
314 Thomari Story-Harden RC .20 .50
315 Terry Tiffee RC .15 .40
316 Nick Trzesniak RC .15 .40
317 Denny Tussen RC .15 .40
318 Scott Tyler RC .20 .50
319 Shane Victorino RC .40 1.00
320 Doug Waechter RC .20 .50
321 Brandon Watson RC .15 .40
322 Todd Wellemeyer RC .15 .40
323 Eli Whiteside RC .15 .40
324 Josh Willingham RC .40 1.00
325 Travis Wong RC .20 .50
326 Brian Wright RC .15 .40
327 Kevin Youkilis RC 1.25 3.00
328 Andy Sisco RC .10 .30
329 Dustin Yount RC .20 .50
330 Andrew Dominique RC .15 .40
NNO Eric Hinske Bat 6.00 15.00
Jason Jennings Jsy
ROY Relic

2003 Bowman Gold

COMPLETE SET (330) 75.00 150.00
*RED 1-155: 1.25X TO 3X BASIC
*BLUE 156-330: 1.25X TO 3X BASIC
*BLUE ROOKIES: .75X TO 2X BASIC
ONE PER PACK

2003 Bowman Uncirculated Metallic Gold

These cards were originally issued as exchange cards in the silver packs which were inserted one per hobby box. In addition, these exchange cards were seeded into retail packs at a stated rate of one in 49. These cards could be mailed into the Pit.Com for redemption for a hermetically sealed card. Please note that the original stated print run for these cards are 230 sets. These cards could be redeemed until April 30th, 2004.

NNO Exchange Card

2003 Bowman Uncirculated Silver

These cards were issued at a stated rate of one per silver pack, which were inserted one per sealed hobby box. This is a parallel set to the basic Bowman set and each card was issued in already sealed holder. Please note that each card was issued to a stated print run of 250 serial numbered sets. In addition, a few cards were issued as redemption cards for the entire Uncirculated Silver set. These cards could be redeemed until April 30th, 2004.

*UNC.SILVER 1-155: 5X TO 12X BASIC
*UNC.SILVER 156-330: 5X TO 12X BASIC
*UNC.SILVER ROOKIES: 2.5X TO 6X BASIC
202 Chien-Ming Wang 15.00 40.00
NNO Set Exchange Card

2003 Bowman Future Fiber Bats

GROUP A ODDS 1:96 H, 1:34 HTA, 1:196 R
GROUP B ODDS 1:393 H, 1:140 HTA, 1:803 R
AG Adrian Gonzalez A 3.00 8.00
AH Aubrey Huff A 3.00 8.00
AK Austin Kearns A 3.00 8.00
BS Bud Smith B 3.00 8.00
CD Chris Duffy B 3.00 8.00
CK Casey Kotchman A 3.00 8.00
DH Drew Henson A 3.00 8.00
DW David Wright A 15.00 40.00
ES Esix Snead A 3.00 8.00
EY Edwin Yan B 3.00 8.00
FS Freddy Sanchez A 3.00 8.00
HB Hank Blalock A 3.00 8.00
JB Jason Botts A 2.00 5.00
JDM Jake Mauer A 3.00 8.00
JG Jason Grove A 3.00 8.00
JH Josh Hamilton A 6.00 15.00
JM Joe Mauer A 6.00 15.00
JW Justin Wayne B 3.00 8.00
KC Kevin Cash B 3.00 8.00
KD Kory DeHaan A 3.00 8.00
MR Michael Restovich A 3.00 8.00
NH Nathan Haynes A 3.00 8.00
PF Pedro Feliz A 3.00 8.00
RB Rocco Baldelli B 3.00 8.00
RJ Reed Johnson A 3.00 8.00
RK Ryan Langerhans A 3.00 8.00
RS Randall Shelley A 3.00 8.00
SB Sean Burroughs A 3.00 8.00
ST So Taguchi A 3.00 8.00
TW Travis Wilson A 3.00 8.00
WB Wilson Betemit A 3.00 8.00
WR Wilkin Ruan B 3.00 8.00
XN Xavier Nady A 3.00 8.00

2003 Bowman Futures Game Base Autograph

STATED ODDS 1:141 HTA
JR Jose Reyes 12.50 30.00

2003 Bowman Futures Game Gear Jersey Relics

STATED ODDS 1:26 H, 1:9 HTA, 1:52 R
AC Aaron Cook 3.00 8.00
AW Adam Wainwright 3.00 8.00
BB Brad Baker 3.00 8.00
BE Brett Evert 3.00 8.00
BH Bill Hall 3.00 8.00
BM Brett Myers 3.00 8.00
BP Brandon Phillips 3.00 8.00

BT Billy Traber 3.00 8.00
CC Carl Crawford 3.00 8.00
CH Corey Hart 3.00 8.00
CT Chad Tracy 3.00 8.00
DH Drew Henson 3.00 8.00
EA Edwin Almonte 3.00 8.00
FB Francis Beltran 3.00 8.00
FL Francisco Liriano 6.00 15.00
FR Francisco Rodriguez 3.00 8.00
GG Gerardo Garcia 3.00 8.00
HC Hee Seop Choi 3.00 8.00
JB John Buck 3.00 8.00
JDR Jorge De La Rosa 3.00 8.00
JEB Joe Borchard 3.00 8.00
JH Justin Huber 3.00 8.00
JJ Jimmy Journell 3.00 8.00
JK Josh Karp 3.00 8.00
JL Jose Lopez 4.00 10.00
JM Justin Morneau 3.00 8.00
JMS John Stephens 3.00 8.00
JR Jose Reyes 3.00 8.00
JS Jason Stokes 3.00 8.00
JY Jason Young 3.00 8.00
KC Kevin Cash 3.00 8.00
LO Lyle Overbay 3.00 8.00
MB Marlon Byrd 3.00 8.00
MC Miguel Cabrera 4.00 10.00
MR Michael Restovich 3.00 8.00
OH Orlando Hudson 3.00 8.00
OI Omar Infante 3.00 8.00
RD Ryan Dittfurth 3.00 8.00
RR Ricardo Rodriguez 3.00 8.00
SB Sean Burnett 3.00 8.00
SC Shin Soo Choo 3.00 8.00
SS Seung Song 3.00 8.00
TA Tony Alvarez 3.00 8.00
VD Victor Diaz 3.00 8.00
VM Victor Martinez 4.00 10.00
WP Wily Mo Pena 3.00 8.00

2003 Bowman Signs of the Future

GROUP A ODDS 1:39 H, 1:13 HTA, 1:79 R
GROUP B ODDS 1:183 H, 1:65 HTA, 1:374 R
GROUP C ODDS 1:2288 H, 1:816 HTA, 1:4720 R
*RED INK: 1.25X TO 3X GROUP A
*RED INK: 1.25X TO 3X GROUP B
*RED INK: .75X TO 2X GROUP C
RED INK ODDS 1:687 H, 1:245 HTA, 1:1402 R
AV Andy Van Hekken A 4.00 10.00
BB Bryan Bullington A 3.00 8.00
BJ Bobby Jenks B 6.00 15.00
BK Ben Kozlowski A 4.00 10.00
BL Brandon League B 4.00 10.00
BS Brian Slocum A 4.00 10.00
CH Cole Hamels A 40.00 80.00
CJH Corey Hart A 4.00 10.00
CMH Chad Hutchinson C 4.00 10.00
CP Chris Piersoll B 4.00 10.00
DG Doug Gredvig A 4.00 10.00
DHM Dustin McGowan A 4.00 10.00
DL Donald Levinski A 3.00 8.00
DS Doug Sessions B 4.00 10.00
FL Fred Lewis A 4.00 10.00
FS Freddy Sanchez B 6.00 15.00
HR Hanley Ramirez A 30.00 60.00
JA Jason Arnold B 4.00 10.00
JB John Buck A 4.00 10.00
JC Jesus Cota B 4.00 10.00
JG Jason Grove B 4.00 10.00
JGU Jeremy Guthrie A 4.00 10.00
JL James Loney A 10.00 25.00
JOG Jonny Gomes B 6.00 15.00
JR Jose Reyes A 12.50 30.00
JRH Joel Hanrahan A 4.00 10.00
JSC Jason St. Clair B 4.00 10.00
KG Khalil Greene A 12.50 30.00
KH Koyie Hill B 4.00 10.00
MT Mitch Talbot A 4.00 10.00
NC Nelson Castro B 4.00 10.00
OV Oscar Villareal A 3.00 8.00
PR Prentice Redman A 3.00 8.00
QC Quincy Carter C 6.00 15.00
RC Ryan Church B 6.00 15.00
RS Ryan Snare B 4.00 10.00
TL Todd Linden B 4.00 10.00
VM Val Majewski A 4.00 10.00
ZG Zack Greinke A 6.00 15.00
ZS Zach Segovia A 4.00 10.00

2003 Bowman Signs of the Future Dual

STAT.ODDS 1:9220 H,1:3264 HTA,1:20,390 R
CH Quincy Carter 20.00 50.00
Chad Hutchinson

2003 Bowman Draft

This 165-card standard-size set was released in December, 2003. The set was issued in 10 card packs with a $2.99 SRP which came 24 packs to a box and 10 boxes to a case. Please note that each Draft pack included 2 Chrome cards.

COMPLETE SET (165) 20.00 50.00
1 Dontrelle Willis .30 .75
2 Freddy Sanchez .10 .30
3 Miguel Cabrera .30 .75
4 Ryan Ludwick .10 .30
5 Ty Wigginton .10 .30
6 Mark Teixeira .20 .50
7 Trey Hodges .10 .30
8 Laynce Nix .10 .30
9 Antonio Perez .10 .30
10 Jody Gerut .10 .30
11 Jae Weong Seo .10 .30
12 Erick Almonte .10 .30
13 Lyle Overbay .10 .30
14 Billy Traber .10 .30
15 Andres Torres .10 .30
16 Jose Valverde .10 .30
17 Aaron Heilman .10 .30
18 Brandon Larson .10 .30
19 Jung Bong .10 .30
20 Jesse Foppert .10 .30
21 Angel Berroa .10 .30
22 Jeff DaVanon .10 .30
23 Kurt Ainsworth .10 .30
24 Brandon Claussen .10 .30
25 Xavier Nady .10 .30
26 Travis Hafner .10 .30
27 Jerome Williams .10 .30
28 Jose Reyes .10 .30
29 Sergio Mitre RC .20 .50
30 Bo Hart RC .15 .40
31 Adam Miller RC 1.00 2.50
32 Brian Finch RC .15 .40
33 Taylor Mattingly RC .20 .50
34 Daric Barton RC 1.00 2.50
35 Chris Ray RC .40 1.00
36 Jarrod Saltalamacchia RC 3.00 8.00
37 Dennis Dove RC .20 .50
38 James Houser RC .20 .50
39 Clint King RC .20 .50
40 Lou Palmisano RC .20 .50
41 Dan Moore RC .15 .40
42 Craig Stansberry RC .20 .50
43 Jo Jo Reyes RC .50 1.25
44 Jake Stevens RC .20 .50
45 Tom Gorzelanny RC .50 1.25
46 Brian Marshall RC .15 .40
47 Scott Beerer RC .15 .40
48 Javi Herrera RC .20 .50
49 Steve LeRud RC .20 .50
50 Josh Banks RC .30 .75
51 Jon Papelbon RC 5.00 12.00
52 Juan Valdes RC .20 .50
53 Beau Vaughan RC .20 .50
54 Matt Chico RC .20 .50
55 Todd Jennings RC .20 .50
56 Anthony Gwynn RC .50 1.25
57 Matt Harrison RC .30 .75
58 Aaron Marsden RC .20 .50
59 Casey Abrams RC .15 .40
60 Cory Stuart RC .15 .40
61 Mike Wagner RC .15 .40
62 Jordan Pratt RC .20 .50
63 Andre Randolph RC .20 .50
64 Blake Balkcom RC .20 .50
65 Josh Muecke RC .15 .40
66 Jamie D'Antona RC .30 .75
67 Cole Seifrig RC .15 .40
68 Josh Anderson RC .20 .50
69 Matt Lorenzo RC .20 .50
70 Nate Spears RC .20 .50
71 Chris Goodman RC .15 .40
72 Brian McFall RC .15 .40
73 Billy Hogan RC .20 .50
74 Jamie Romak RC .20 .50
75 Jeff Cook RC .20 .50
76 Brooks McNiven RC .15 .40
77 Xavier Paul RC .20 .50
78 Bob Zimmerman RC UER .15 .40
Name is spelled Zimmermann
79 Mickey Hall RC .20 .50
80 Shaun Marcum RC .20 .50
81 Matt Nachreiner RC .20 .50
82 Chris Kinsey RC .15 .40
83 Jonathan Fulton RC .20 .50
84 Edgardo Baez RC .20 .50
85 Robert Valido RC .20 .50
86 Kenny Lewis RC .20 .50
87 Trent Peterson RC .15 .40
88 Johnny Woodard RC .20 .50
89 Wes Littleton RC .20 .50
90 Sean Rodriguez RC .60 1.50
91 Kyle Pearson RC .15 .40
92 Josh Rainwater RC .20 .50
93 Travis Schlichting RC .20 .50
94 Tim Battle RC .20 .50
95 Aaron Hill RC .60 1.50
96 Bob McCrory RC .15 .40
97 Rick Guarno RC .20 .50
98 Brandon Yarbrough RC .15 .40
99 Peter Stonard RC .15 .40
100 Darin Downs RC .20 .50
101 Matt Bruback RC .10 .30
102 Danny Garcia RC .15 .40
103 Cory Stewart RC .15 .40
104 Ferdin Tejeda RC .15 .40
105 Kade Johnson RC .15 .40
106 Andrew Brown RC .20 .50
107 Aquilino Lopez RC .15 .40
108 Stephen Randolph RC .15 .40
109 Dave Matranga RC .15 .40
110 Dustin McGowan RC .20 .50
111 Juan Camacho RC .15 .40
112 Cliff Lee .10 .30
113 Jeff Duncan RC .15 .40
114 C.J. Wilson .10 .30
115 Brandon Roberson RC .15 .40
116 David Corrente RC .15 .40
117 Kevin Beavers RC .15 .40
118 Anthony Webster RC .20 .50
119 Oscar Villarreal RC .15 .40
120 Hong-Chih Kuo RC 1.00 2.50
121 Josh Barfield .10 .30
122 Denny Bautista .10 .30
123 Chris Burke RC .50 1.25
124 Robinson Cano RC 3.00 8.00
125 Jose Castillo .10 .30
126 Neal Cotts .10 .30
127 Jorge De La Rosa .10 .30
128 J.D. Durbin .15 .40
129 Edwin Encarnacion .40 1.00
130 Gavin Floyd .10 .30
131 Alexis Gomez .10 .30
132 Edgar Gonzalez RC .15 .40
133 Khalil Greene .30 .75
134 Zack Greinke .10 .30
135 Franklin Gutierrez .20 .50
136 Rich Harden .20 .50
137 J.J. Hardy RC 2.00 5.00
138 Ryan Howard RC 6.00 15.00
139 Justin Huber .10 .30
140 David Kelton .10 .30
141 Dave Krynzel .10 .30
142 Pete LaForest .15 .40
143 Adam LaRoche .10 .30
144 Preston Larrison RC .20 .50
145 John Maine RC 2.00 5.00
146 Andy Marte .50 1.25
147 Jeff Mathis .10 .30
148 Joe Mauer UER .30 .75
Card has playing for New Haven
149 Clint Nageotte .10 .30
150 Chris Narveson .10 .30
151 Ramon Nivar .15 .40
152 Felix Pie RC 2.00 5.00
153 Guillermo Quiroz RC .15 .40
154 Rene Reyes .10 .30
155 Royce Ring .10 .30
156 Alexis Rios .40 1.00
157 Grady Sizemore .30 .75
158 Stephen Smitherman .10 .30
159 Seung Song .10 .30
160 Scott Thorman .10 .30
161 Chad Tracy .10 .30
162 Chin-Hui Tsao .10 .30
163 John VanBenschoten .10 .30
164 Kevin Youkilis 1.50 4.00
165 Chien-Ming Wang 2.00 5.00

2003 Bowman Draft Gold

COMPLETE SET (165) 50.00 100.00
*GOLD: 1.25X TO 3X BASIC
*GOLD RC'S: .6X TO 1.5X BASIC
*GOLD RC YR: .6X TO 1.5X BASIC
ONE PER PACK
51 Jon Papelbon 6.00 15.00
138 Ryan Howard 8.00 20.00
165 Chien-Ming Wang 2.50 6.00

2003 Bowman Draft Fabric of the Future Jersey Relics

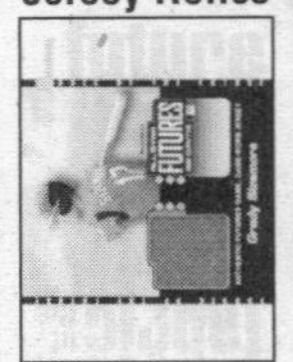

GROUP A ODDS 1:721 H, 1:720 R
GROUP B ODDS 1:315 H/R
GROUP C ODDS 1:98 H/R
GROUP D ODDS 1:81 H, 1:82 R
GROUP E ODDS 1:263 H/R
GROUP F ODDS 1:241 H, 1:240 R
AL Adam LaRoche D 2.00 5.00
AM Andy Marte D 4.00 10.00
CN Chris Narveson C 2.00 5.00
EG Edgar Gonzalez D 2.00 5.00
FG Franklin Gutierrez C 3.00 8.00
FP Felix Pie A 4.00 10.00
GF Gavin Floyd E 2.00 5.00
GS Grady Sizemore D 4.00 10.00
JB Josh Barfield B 3.00 8.00
JD J.D. Durbin D 2.00 5.00
JH Justin Huber D 2.00 5.00
JM Joe Mauer C 5.00 12.00
JSM Jeff Mathis B 2.00 5.00
KG Khalil Greene D 4.00 10.00
RC Robinson Cano C 8.00 20.00
RH Rich Harden C 4.00 10.00
RJH Ryan Howard F 12.50 30.00
RR Rene Reyes E 2.00 5.00
RRR Royce Ring F 2.00 5.00
ZG Zack Greinke C 3.00 8.00

2003 Bowman Draft Prospect Premiums Relics

GROUP A ODDS 1:216 H/R
GROUP B ODDS 1:470 H, 1:469 R
AK Austin Kearns Jsy B 2.00 5.00
BH Brendan Harris Bat A 3.00 8.00
BM Brett Myers Jsy B 2.00 5.00
CC Carl Crawford Bat A 3.00 8.00

CS Chris Snelling Bat A 3.00 8.00
CU Chase Utley Bat A 8.00 20.00
HB Hank Blalock Bat A 3.00 8.00
JM Justin Morneau Bat A 3.00 8.00
JT Joe Thurston Bat A 3.00 8.00
NH Nathan Haynes Bat A 3.00 8.00
RB Rocco Baldelli Bat A 3.00 8.00
TH Travis Hafner Bat A 3.00 8.00

2003 Bowman Draft Signs of the Future

GROUP A ODDS 1:720 H, 1:720 R
GROUP B ODDS 1:491 H, 1:491 R
GROUP C ODDS 1:2160 H, 1:12,185 R
AT Andres Torres A 4.00 10.00
CS Cory Stewart B 4.00 10.00
DT Dennis Tankersley A 4.00 10.00
JA Jason Arnold B 4.00 10.00
ZG Zack Greinke C 6.00 15.00

2004 Bowman

This 330-card set was released in May, 2004. The set was issued in hobby, retail and HTA versions. The hobby version was 10 card packs with an $3 SRP which came 24 packs to a box and 12 boxes to a case. The HTA version had 21 card packs with an $6 SRP which came 12 packs to a box and eight boxes to a case. Meanwhile the Retail version consisted of seven card packs with an $3 SRP which came 24 packs to a box and 12 boxes to a case. Cards numbered 1 through 144 feature veterans while cards cards 145 through 165 feature prospects and cards numbered 166 through 330 feature Rookie Cards. Please note that there is a special card featuring memorabilia pieces from 2003 ROY's Dontrelle Willis and Angel Berroa which we have notated at the end of our checklist.

COMPLETE SET (330) 40.00 80.00
ROY ODDS 1:829 H, 1:284 HTA, 1:1632 R
1 Garret Anderson .10 .30
2 Larry Walker .10 .30
3 Derek Jeter .60 1.50
4 Curt Schilling .20 .50
5 Carlos Zambrano .10 .30
6 Shawn Green .10 .30
7 Manny Ramirez .20 .50
8 Randy Johnson .30 .75
9 Jeremy Bonderman .10 .30
10 Alfonso Soriano .10 .30
11 Scott Rolen .20 .50
12 Kerry Wood .10 .30
13 Eric Gagne .10 .30
14 Ryan Klesko .10 .30
15 Kevin Millar .10 .30
16 Ty Wigginton .10 .30
17 David Ortiz .30 .75
18 Luis Castillo .10 .30
19 Bernie Williams .20 .50
20 Edgar Renteria .10 .30
21 Matt Kata .10 .30
22 Bartolo Colon .10 .30
23 Derrek Lee .20 .50
24 Gary Sheffield .10 .30
25 Nomar Garciaparra .50 1.25
26 Kevin Millwood .10 .30
27 Corey Patterson .10 .30
28 Carlos Beltran .10 .30
29 Mike Lieberthal .10 .30
30 Troy Glaus .10 .30
31 Preston Wilson .10 .30
32 Jorge Posada .20 .50
33 Bo Hart .10 .30
34 Mark Prior .20 .50
35 Hideo Nomo .30 .75
36 Jason Kendall .10 .30
37 Roger Clemens .60 1.50
38 Dmitri Young .10 .30
39 Jason Giambi .10 .30
40 Jim Edmonds .10 .30
41 Ryan Ludwick .10 .30
42 Brandon Webb .10 .30
43 Todd Helton .20 .50
44 Jacque Jones .10 .30
45 Jamie Moyer .10 .30
46 Tim Salmon .20 .50
47 Kelvim Escobar .10 .30
48 Tony Batista .10 .30
49 Nick Johnson .10 .30
50 Jim Thome .20 .50
51 Casey Blake .10 .30
52 Trot Nixon .10 .30
53 Luis Gonzalez .10 .30
54 Dontrelle Willis .20 .50
55 Mike Mussina .20 .50
56 Carl Crawford .10 .30
57 Mark Buehrle .10 .30
58 Scott Podsednik .10 .30
59 Brian Giles .10 .30
60 Rafael Furcal .10 .30
61 Miguel Cabrera .20 .50
62 Rich Harden .10 .30
63 Mark Teixeira .20 .50
64 Frank Thomas .30 .75
65 Johan Santana .30 .75
66 Jason Schmidt .10 .30
67 Aramis Ramirez .10 .30
68 Jose Reyes .10 .30
69 Magglio Ordonez .10 .30
70 Mike Sweeney .10 .30
71 Eric Chavez .10 .30
72 Rocco Baldelli .10 .30
73 Sammy Sosa .30 .75
74 Javy Lopez .10 .30
75 Roy Oswalt .10 .30
76 Raul Ibanez .10 .30
77 Ivan Rodriguez .20 .50
78 Jerome Williams .10 .30
79 Carlos Lee .10 .30
80 Geoff Jenkins .10 .30
81 Sean Burroughs .10 .30
82 Marcus Giles .10 .30
83 Mike Lowell .10 .30
84 Barry Zito .10 .30
85 Aubrey Huff .10 .30
86 Esteban Loaiza .10 .30
87 Torii Hunter .10 .30
88 Phil Nevin .10 .30
89 Andruw Jones .20 .50
90 Josh Beckett .10 .30
91 Mark Mulder .10 .30
92 Hank Blalock .10 .30
93 Jason Phillips .10 .30
94 Russ Ortiz .10 .30
95 Juan Pierre .10 .30
96 Tom Glavine .20 .50
97 Gil Meche .10 .30
98 Ramon Ortiz .10 .30
99 Richie Sexson .10 .30
100 Albert Pujols .60 1.50
101 Javier Vazquez .10 .30
102 Johnny Damon .20 .50
103 Alex Rodriguez Yanks .50 1.25
104 Omar Vizquel .20 .50
105 Chipper Jones .30 .75
106 Lance Berkman .20 .50
107 Tim Hudson .10 .30
108 Carlos Delgado .10 .30
109 Austin Kearns .10 .30
110 Orlando Cabrera .10 .30
111 Edgar Martinez .20 .50
112 Melvin Mora .10 .30
113 Jeff Bagwell .20 .50
114 Marlon Byrd .10 .30
115 Vernon Wells .10 .30
116 C.C. Sabathia .10 .30
117 Cliff Floyd .10 .30
118 Ichiro Suzuki .60 1.50
119 Miguel Olivo .10 .30
120 Mike Piazza .50 1.25
121 Adam Dunn .10 .30
122 Paul Lo Duca .10 .30
123 Brett Myers .10 .30
124 Michael Young .10 .30
125 Sidney Ponson .10 .30
126 Greg Maddux .50 1.25
127 Vladimir Guerrero .30 .75
128 Miguel Tejada .20 .50
129 Andy Pettitte .20 .50
130 Rafael Palmeiro .20 .50
131 Ken Griffey Jr. .50 1.25
132 Shannon Stewart .10 .30
133 Joel Pineiro .10 .30
134 Luis Matos .10 .30
135 Jeff Kent .10 .30
136 Randy Wolf .10 .30
137 Chris Woodward .10 .30
138 Jody Gerut .10 .30
139 Jose Vidro .10 .30
140 Bret Boone .10 .30
141 Bill Mueller .10 .30
142 Angel Berroa .10 .30
143 Bobby Abreu .10 .30
144 Roy Halladay .10 .30
145 Delmon Young .20 .50
146 Jonny Gomes .10 .30
147 Rickie Weeks .20 .50
148 Edwin Jackson .10 .30
149 Neal Cotts .10 .30
150 Jason Bay .10 .30
151 Khalil Greene .20 .50
152 Joe Mauer .30 .75
153 Bobby Jenks .10 .30
154 Chin-Feng Chen .10 .30
155 Chien-Ming Wang .40 1.00
156 Mickey Hall .10 .30
157 James Houser .10 .30
158 Jay Sborz .10 .30
159 Jonathan Fulton .10 .30
160 Steven Lerud .10 .30
161 Grady Sizemore .30 .75
162 Felix Pie .20 .50
163 Dustin McGowan .10 .30
164 Chris Lubanski .10 .30
165 Tom Gorzelanny .10 .30
166 Rudy Guillen FY RC .30 .75
167 Bobby Brownlie FY RC .40 1.00
168 Conor Jackson FY RC 1.25 3.00
169 Matt Moses FY RC .40 1.00
170 Ervin Santana FY RC .60 1.50
171 Merkin Valdez FY RC .20 .50
172 Erick Aybar FY RC .40 1.00
173 Brad Sullivan FY RC .20 .50
174 David Aardsma FY RC .20 .50
175 Brad Snyder FY RC .40 1.00
176 Alberto Callaspo FY RC .30 .75
177 Brandon Medders FY RC .15 .40
178 Zach Miner FY RC .50 1.25
179 Charlie Zink FY RC .15 .40
180 Adam Greenberg FY RC .30 .75
181 Kevin Howard FY RC .20 .50
182 Wanell Severino FY RC .15 .40
183 Kevin Kouzmanoff FY RC .75 2.00
184 Joel Zumaya FY RC 2.00 5.00
185 Skip Schumaker FY RC .15 .40
186 Nic Ungs FY RC .15 .40
187 Todd Self FY RC .20 .50
188 Brian Steffek FY RC .10 .30
189 Brock Peterson FY RC .15 .40
190 Greg Thissen FY RC .10 .30
191 Frank Brooks FY RC .10 .30
192 Estee Harris FY RC .20 .50
193 Chris Mabeus FY RC .15 .40
194 Dan Giese FY RC .15 .40
195 Jared Wells FY RC .10 .30
196 Carlos Sosa FY RC .15 .40
197 Bobby Madritsch FY .10 .30
198 Calvin Hayes FY RC .20 .50
199 Omar Quintanilla FY RC .20 .50
200 Chris O'Riordan FY RC .15 .40
201 Tim Hutting FY RC .10 .30
202 Carlos Quentin FY RC 1.00 2.50
203 Brayan Pena FY RC .15 .40
204 Jeff Salazar FY RC .40 1.00
205 David Murphy FY RC .30 .75
206 Alberto Garcia FY RC .20 .50
207 Ramon Ramirez FY RC .15 .40
208 Luis Bolivar FY RC .20 .50
209 Rodney Choy Foo FY RC .10 .30
210 Kyle Sleeth FY RC .20 .50
211 Anthony Acevedo FY RC .15 .40
212 Chad Santos FY RC .15 .40
213 Jason Frasor FY RC .10 .30
214 Jesse Roman FY RC .10 .30
215 James Tomlin FY RC .15 .40
216 Josh Labandeira FY RC .15 .40
217 Joaquin Arias FY RC .30 .75
218 Don Sutton FY UER RC .40 1.00
Nick Swisher pictured
219 Danny Gonzalez FY RC .10 .30
220 Javier Guzman FY RC .20 .50
221 Anthony Lerew FY RC .30 .75
222 Jon Knott FY RC .15 .40
223 Jesse English FY RC .15 .40
224 Felix Hernandez FY RC 3.00 8.00
225 Travis Hanson FY RC .20 .50
226 Jesse Floyd FY RC .15 .40
227 Nick Gorneault FY RC .20 .50
228 Craig Ansman FY RC .15 .40
229 Wardell Starling FY RC .15 .40
230 Carl Loadenthal FY RC .20 .50
231 Dave Crouthers FY RC .10 .30
232 Harvey Garcia FY RC .10 .30
233 Casey Kopitzke FY RC .10 .30
234 Ricky Nolasco FY RC .50 1.25
235 Miguel Perez FY RC .15 .40
236 Ryan Mulhern FY RC .15 .40
237 Chris Aguila FY RC .15 .40
238 Brooks Conrad FY RC .20 .50
239 Damaso Espino FY RC .10 .30
240 Jereme Milons FY RC .20 .50
241 Luke Hughes FY RC .20 .50
242 Kory Casto FY RC .20 .50
243 Jose Valdez FY RC .15 .40
244 J.T. Stotts FY RC .10 .30
245 Lee Gwaltney FY RC .10 .30
246 Yoann Torrealba FY RC .10 .30
247 Omar Falcon FY RC .15 .40
248 Jon Coutlangus FY RC .10 .30
249 George Sherrill FY RC .15 .40
250 John Santor FY RC .15 .40
251 Tony Richie FY RC .15 .40
252 Kevin Richardson FY RC .10 .30
253 Tim Bittner FY RC .15 .40
254 Dustin Nippert FY RC .50 1.25
255 Jose Capellan FY RC .20 .50
256 Donald Levinski FY RC .10 .30
257 Jerome Gamble FY RC .10 .30
258 Jeff Keppinger FY RC .75 2.00
259 Jason Szuminski FY RC .10 .30
260 Akinori Otsuka FY RC .20 .50
261 Ryan Budde FY RC .15 .40
262 Shingo Takatsu FY RC .30 .75
263 Jeff Allison FY RC .15 .40
264 Hector Gimenez FY RC .10 .30
265 Tim Frend FY RC .10 .30
266 Tom Farmer FY RC .15 .40
267 Shawn Hill FY RC .15 .40
268 Lastings Milledge FY RC 2.00 5.00
269 Scott Proctor FY RC .20 .50
270 Jorge Mejia FY RC .15 .40
271 Terry Jones FY RC .20 .50
272 Zach Duke FY RC .75 2.00
273 Tim Stauffer FY RC .30 .75
274 Luke Anderson FY RC .10 .30
275 Hunter Brown FY RC .10 .30
276 Matt Lemanczyk FY RC .15 .40
277 Fernando Cortez FY RC .10 .30
278 Vince Perkins FY RC .20 .50
279 Tommy Murphy FY RC .15 .40
280 Mike Gosling FY RC .10 .30
281 Paul Bacot FY RC .20 .50
282 Matt Capps FY RC .15 .40
283 Juan Gutierrez FY RC .15 .40
284 Teodoro Encarnacion FY RC .20 .50
285 Juan Cedeno FY RC .15 .40
286 Matt Creighton FY RC .15 .40
287 Ryan Hankins FY RC .10 .30
288 Leo Nunez FY RC .15 .40
289 Dave Wallace FY RC .15 .40
290 Rob Tejeda FY RC .30 .75
291 Lincoln Holdzkom FY RC .15 .40
292 Jason Hirsh FY RC .60 1.50
293 Tydus Meadows FY RC .15 .40
294 Khalid Ballouli FY RC .10 .30
295 Benji DeQuin FY RC .10 .30
296 Tyler Davidson FY RC .60 1.50
297 Brant Colamarino FY RC .30 .75
298 Marcus McBeth FY RC .10 .30
299 Brad Eldred FY RC .25 .60
300 David Pauley FY RC .50 1.25
301 Yadier Molina FY RC .60 1.50
302 Chris Shelton FY RC .50 1.25
303 Travis Blackley FY RC .15 .40
304 Jon DeVries FY RC .15 .40
305 Sheldon Fulse FY RC .10 .30
306 Vito Chiaravalloti FY RC .15 .40
307 Warner Madrigal FY RC .30 .75
308 Reid Gorecki FY RC .15 .40
309 Sung Jung FY RC .15 .40
310 Pete Shier FY RC .10 .30
311 Michael Mooney FY RC .10 .30
312 Kenny Perez FY RC .15 .40
313 Michael Mallory FY RC .15 .40
314 Ben Himes FY RC .10 .30
315 Ivan Ochoa FY RC .15 .40
316 Donald Kelly FY RC .15 .40
317 Logan Kensing FY RC .15 .40
318 Kevin Davidson FY RC .10 .30
319 Brian Pilkington FY RC .10 .30
320 Alex Romero FY RC .15 .40
321 Chad Chop FY RC .15 .40
322 Dioner Navarro FY RC .30 .75
323 Casey Myers FY RC .10 .30
324 Mike Rouse FY RC .15 .40
325 Sergio Silva FY RC .10 .30
326 J.J. Furmaniak FY RC .30 .75
327 Brad Vericker FY RC .15 .40
328 Blake Hawksworth FY RC .20 .50
329 Brock Jacobsen FY RC .10 .30
330 Alec Zumwalt FY RC .10 .30
BW Angel Berroa Bat 6.00 15.00
Dontrelle Willis Jsy ROY

2004 Bowman 1st Edition

*1ST EDITION 1-165: .75X TO 2X BASIC
*1ST EDITION 166-330: .75X TO 2X BASIC
ISSUED IN FIRST EDITION PACKS

2004 Bowman Gold

COMPLETE SET (330) 60.00 150.00
*GOLD 1-165: 1.25X TO 3X BASIC
*GOLD 166-330: 1X TO 2.5X BASIC
ONE PER HOBBY PACK
ONE PER HTA PACK
ONE PER RETAIL PACK

2004 Bowman Uncirculated Gold

ONE EXCH.CARD PER SILVER PACK
ONE SILVER PACK PER SEALED HOBBY BOX
ONE SILVER PACK PER SEALED HTA BOX
STATED ODDS 1:44 RETAIL
STATED PRINT RUN 210 SETS
SEE WWW.THEPIT.COM FOR PRICING
NNO Exchange Card 2.00 5.00

2004 Bowman Uncirculated Silver

*UNC.SILVER 1-165: 5X TO 12X BASIC
*UNC.SILVER 166-330: 3X TO 8X BASIC
ONE PER SILVER PACK
ONE SILVER PACK PER SEALED HOBBY BOX
ONE SILVER PACK PER SEALED HTA BOX
SET EXCH.CARD ODDS 1:9159 H, 1:3718 HTA
STATED PRINT RUN 245 SERIAL #'d SETS
1ST 100 SETS PRINTED HELD FOR EXCH.
LAST 145 SETS PRINTED DIST.IN BOXES
EXCHANGE DEADLINE 05/31/06
NNO Set Exchange Card/100 300.00 500.00

2004 Bowman Autographs

STATED ODDS 1:72 H, 1:24 HTA, 1:139 R
RED INK ODDS 1:1466 H,1:501 HTA,1:2901 R
RED INK PRINT RUN 25 SETS
RED INK ARE NOT SERIAL-NUMBERED
RED INK PRINT RUN PROVIDED BY TOPPS
NO RED INK PRICING DUE TO SCARCITY
161 Grady Sizemore 12.50 30.00
162 Felix Pie 6.00 15.00
163 Dustin McGowan 3.00 8.00
164 Chris Lubanski 4.00 10.00
165 Tom Gorzelanny 3.00 8.00
166 Rudy Guillen 4.00 10.00
167 Bobby Brownlie 4.00 10.00
168 Conor Jackson 10.00 25.00
169 Matt Moses 6.00 15.00
170 Ervin Santana 5.00 12.00
171 Merkin Valdez 4.00 10.00
172 Erick Aybar 8.00 20.00
173 Brad Sullivan 4.00 10.00
174 David Aardsma 4.00 10.00
175 Brad Snyder 4.00 10.00

2004 Bowman Relics

GROUP A 1:346 H, 1:118 HTA, 1:1685 R
GROUP B 1:133 H, 1:44 HTA, 1:269 R
HS JSY MEANS HIGH SCHOOL JERSEY
154 Chin-Feng Chen Jsy B 6.00 15.00
155 Chien-Ming Wang Uni B 6.00 15.00
156 Mickey Hall HS Jsy B 3.00 8.00
157 James Houser HS Jsy A 3.00 8.00
158 Jay Sborz HS Jsy B 3.00 8.00
159 Jonathan Fulton HS Jsy B 3.00 8.00
160 Steve Lerud HS Jsy B 3.00 8.00
164 Chris Lubanski HS Jsy B 3.00 8.00
192 Estee Harris HS Jsy A 3.00 8.00
221 Anthony Lerew Jsy B 3.00 8.00

2004 Bowman Base of the Future Autograph

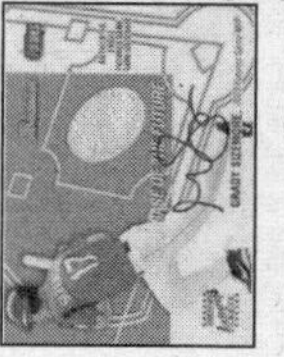

STATED ODDS 1:110 HTA
RED INK ODDS 1:5112 HTA
RED INK PRINT RUN 25 SERIAL #'d CARDS
NO RED INK PRICING DUE TO SCARCITY
GS Grady Sizemore 15.00 40.00

2004 Bowman Futures Game Gear Jersey Relics

GROUP A 1:167 H, 1:58 HTA, 1:333 R
GROUP B 1:71 H, 1:23 HTA, 1:148 R
GROUP C 1:181 H, 1:63 HTA, 1:362 R
GROUP D 1:173 H, 1:59 HTA, 1:341 R
GROUP E 1:145 H, 1:70 HTA, 1:318 R
AR Alexis Rios A 3.00 8.00
CB Chris Burke B 3.00 8.00
CN Clint Nageotte B 3.00 8.00
CT Chad Tracy B 3.00 8.00
CW Chien-Ming Wang C 15.00 40.00
DB Denny Bautista D 3.00 8.00
DBK Dave Krynzel B 3.00 8.00
DK David Kelton E 3.00 8.00
EE Edwin Encarnacion A 3.00 8.00
EJ Edwin Jackson C 3.00 8.00
ES Ervin Santana D 4.00 10.00
GQ Guillermo Quiroz A 3.00 8.00
JC Jose Castillo E 3.00 8.00
JD Jorge De La Rosa C 3.00 8.00
JH J.J. Hardy A 3.00 8.00
JM John Maine B 4.00 10.00
JV John VanBenschoten B 3.00 8.00
KY Kevin Youkilis E 3.00 8.00
MV Merkin Valdez E 3.00 8.00
NC Neal Cotts D 3.00 8.00
PL Pete LaForest B 3.00 8.00
PWL Preston Larrison B 3.00 8.00
RN Ramon Nivar A 3.00 8.00
SH Shawn Hill D 3.00 8.00
SJS Seung Song B 3.00 8.00
SS Stephen Smitherman B 3.00 8.00
ST Scott Thorman C 3.00 8.00
TB Travis Blackley B 3.00 8.00

2004 Bowman Signs of the Future

GROUP A 1:75 H, 1:25 HTA, 1:147 R
GROUP B 1:847 H, 1:289 HTA, 1:1675 R
GROUP C 1:582 H, 1:198 HTA, 1:1148 R
GROUP D 1:315 H, 1:105 HTA, 1:605 R
RED INK ODDS 1:1466 H,1:501 HTA,1:2901 R
RED INK PRINT RUN 25 SETS
RED INK CARDS ARE NOT SERIAL #'d
RED INK PRINT RUN PROVIDED BY TOPPS
NO RED INK PRICING DUE TO SCARCITY
AH Aaron Hill A 6.00 15.00
BC Brent Clevlen A 8.00 20.00
BF Brian Finch D 4.00 10.00
BM Brandon Medders A 3.00 8.00
BS Brian Snyder D 4.00 10.00
BW Brandon Wood B 8.00 20.00
CS Corey Shafer A 3.00 8.00
DS Denard Span A 3.00 8.00
ED Eric Duncan D 6.00 15.00
GS Grady Sizemore D 15.00 40.00
IC Ismael Castro A 3.00 8.00
JB Justin Backsmeyer D 4.00 10.00
JH James Houser A 3.00 8.00
JV Joey Votto A 10.00 25.00
MM Matt Murton D 6.00 15.00
NM Nick Markakis C 6.00 15.00
RH Ryan Harvey C 4.00 10.00
TJ Tyler Johnson A 3.00 8.00
TL Todd Linden A 3.00 8.00

2004 Bowman Draft

This 165-card set was released in November-December, 2004. The set was issued in seven-card hobby and retail packs, both with an $3 SRP which were issued 24 packs to a box and 10 boxes to a case. The hobby and retial packs can be differentiated by the insert odds.

COMPLETE SET (165) 15.00 40.00
COMMON CARD (1-165) .10 .30
COMMON RC (1-165) .10 .30
COMMON RC YR .10 .30
PLATES ODDS 1:559 HOBBY
PLATES PRINT RUN 1 SERIAL #'d SET
BLACK-CYAN-MAGENTA-YELLOW EXIST
NO PLATES PRICING DUE TO SCARCITY
1 Lyle Overbay .10 .30
2 David Newhan .10 .30
3 J.R. House .10 .30
4 Chad Tracy .10 .30
5 Humberto Quintero .10 .30
6 Dave Bush .10 .30
7 Scott Hairston .10 .30
8 Mike Wood .10 .30
9 Alexis Rios .10 .30
10 Sean Burnett .10 .30
11 Wilson Valdez .10 .30
12 Lew Ford .10 .30
13 Freddy Thon RC .15 .40
14 Zack Greinke .10 .30
15 Bucky Jacobsen .10 .30
16 Kevin Youkilis .10 .30
17 Grady Sizemore .30 .75
18 Denny Bautista .10 .30
19 David DeJesus .10 .30
20 Casey Kotchman .10 .30
21 David Kelton .10 .30
22 Charles Thomas RC .15 .40
23 Kazuhito Tadano RC .20 .50
24 Justin Leone RC .20 .50
25 Eduardo Villacis RC .15 .40
26 Brian Dallimore RC .15 .40
27 Nick Green .10 .30
28 Sam McConnell RC .15 .40
29 Brad Halsey RC .20 .50
30 Roman Colon RC UER .10 .30
Letter T missing in how acquired -- Free Agen
31 Josh Fields RC .75 2.00
32 Cody Bunkelman RC .20 .50
33 Jay Rainville RC .50 1.25
34 Richie Robnett RC .40 1.00
35 Jon Peterson RC .30 .75
36 Huston Street RC .75 2.00
37 Erick San Pedro RC .15 .40
38 Cory Dunlap RC .50 1.25
39 Kurt Suzuki RC .40 1.00
40 Anthony Swarzak RC .30 .75
41 Ian Desmond RC .50 1.25
42 Chris Covington RC .20 .50
43 Christian Garcia RC .30 .75
44 Gaby Hernandez RC .50 1.25
45 Steven Register RC .15 .40
46 Eduardo Morlan RC .30 .75
47 Collin Balester RC .20 .50
48 Nathan Phillips RC .20 .50
49 Dan Schwartzbauer RC .20 .50
50 Rafael Gonzalez RC .15 .40
51 K.C. Herren RC .30 .75
52 William Susdorf RC .15 .40
53 Rob Johnson RC .20 .50
54 Louis Marson RC .30 .75
55 Joe Koshansky RC .75 2.00
56 Jamar Walton RC .30 .75
57 Mark Lowe RC .60 1.50
58 Matt Macri RC .40 1.00
59 Donny Lucy RC .15 .40
60 Mike Ferris RC .20 .50
61 Mike Nickeas RC .20 .50
62 Eric Hurley RC .40 1.00
63 Scott Elbert RC .40 1.00
64 Blake DeWitt RC .60 1.50
65 Danny Putnam RC .30 .75
66 J.P. Howell RC .40 1.00
67 John Wiggins RC .15 .40
68 Justin Orenduff RC .30 .75
69 Ray Liotta RC .50 1.25
70 Billy Buckner RC .20 .50
71 Eric Campbell RC .75 2.00
72 Olin Wick RC .30 .75
73 Sean Gamble RC .20 .50
74 Seth Smith RC .40 1.00
75 Wade Davis RC .60 1.50
76 Joe Jacobitz RC .15 .40
77 J.A. Happ RC .30 .75
78 Eric Ridener RC .15 .40

79 Matt Tuiasosopo RC .75 2.00
80 Brad Bergesen RC .15 .40
81 Javy Guerra RC .20 .50
82 Buck Shaw RC .20 .50
83 Paul Janish RC .30 .75
84 Sean Kazmar RC .15 .40
85 Josh Johnson RC .20 .50
86 Angel Salome RC .50 1.25
87 Jordan Parraz RC .30 .75
88 Kelvin Vazquez RC .15 .40
89 Grant Hansen RC .15 .40
90 Matt Fox RC .15 .40
91 Trevor Plouffe RC .50 1.25
92 Wes Whisler RC .15 .40
93 Curtis Thigpen RC .30 .75
94 Donnie Smith RC .20 .50
95 Luis Rivera RC .20 .50
96 Jesse Hoover RC .20 .50
97 Jason Vargas RC .60 1.50
98 Clary Carlsen RC .15 .40
99 Mark Robinson RC .15 .40
100 J.C. Holt RC .20 .50
101 Chad Blackwell RC .15 .40
102 Daryl Jones RC .40 1.00
103 Jonathan Tierce RC .15 .40
104 Patrick Bryant RC .15 .40
105 Eddie Prasch RC .20 .50
106 Mitch Einertson RC .20 .50
107 Kyle Waldrop RC .40 1.00
108 Jeff Marquez RC .20 .50
109 Zach Jackson RC .30 .75
110 Josh Wahpepah RC .15 .40
111 Adam Lind RC .75 2.00
112 Kyle Bloom RC .20 .50
113 Ben Harrison RC .15 .40
114 Taylor Tankersley RC .20 .50
115 Steven Jackson RC .15 .40
116 David Purcey RC .30 .75
117 Jacob McGee RC .40 1.00
118 Lucas Harrell RC .15 .40
119 Brandon Allen RC .40 1.00
120 Van Pope RC .20 .50
121 Jeff Francis .10 .30
122 Joe Blanton .10 .30
123 Wil Ledezma .10 .30
124 Bryan Bullington .10 .30
125 Jairo Garcia .10 .30
126 Matt Cain .40 1.00
127 Arnie Munoz .10 .30
128 Clint Everts .10 .30
129 Jesus Cota .10 .30
130 Gavin Floyd .10 .30
131 Edwin Encarnacion .10 .30
132 Koyie Hill .10 .30
133 Ruben Gotay .10 .30
134 Jeff Mathis .10 .30
135 Andy Marte .20 .50
136 Dallas McPherson .10 .30
137 Justin Morneau .10 .30
138 Rickie Weeks .10 .30
139 Joel Guzman .20 .50
140 Shin Soo Choo .10 .30
141 Yusmeiro Petit RC .75 2.00
142 Jorge Cortes RC .15 .40
143 Val Majewski .10 .30
144 Felix Pie .20 .50
145 Aaron Hill .10 .30
146 Jose Capellan .10 .30
147 Dioner Navarro .20 .50
148 Fausto Carmona RC .60 1.50
149 Robinzon Diaz RC .15 .40
150 Felix Hernandez 1.50 4.00
151 Andres Blanco RC .15 .40
152 Jason Kubel .10 .30
153 Willy Taveras RC .40 1.00
154 Merkin Valdez .20 .50
155 Robinson Cano .30 .75
156 Bill Murphy .10 .30
157 Chris Burke .10 .30
158 Kyle Sleeth .10 .30
159 B.J. Upton .20 .50
160 Tim Stauffer .20 .50
161 David Wright .75 2.00
162 Conor Jackson .50 1.25
163 Brad Thompson RC .30 .75
164 Delmon Young .20 .50
165 Jeremy Reed .10 .30

2004 Bowman Draft Gold

COMPLETE SET (165) 25.00 60.00
*GOLD RC's: .6X TO 1.5X BASIC
*GOLD RC YR: .6X TO 1.5X BASIC
ONE PER PACK

2004 Bowman Draft Red

STATED ODDS 1:4471 HOBBY
STATED PRINT RUN 1 SERIAL #'d SET
NO PRICING DUE TO SCARCITY

2004 Bowman Draft AFLAC Promos

Little is known about how many of these six cards have appeared on the secondary market. A few of these cards surfaced in the AFLAC redemption packs issued to dealers. These cards were issued instead of some of the standard 12 cards in those packs. If you know of other cards issued this way or can provide extra information, that would be very appreciated.

DISTRIBUTED TO DEALERS
11 Cameron Maybin
15 Ryan DeLaughter
17 Jeremy Hellickson
18 Austin Jackson
19 Ryan Mitchell
30 Ralphie Henriquez
38 Kent Matthes

2004 Bowman Draft AFLAC

COMP.FACT.SET (12) 5.00 12.00
ONE SET VIA MAIL PER AFLAC EXCH.CARD
ONE EXCH.PER '04 BOW.DRAFT HOBBY BOX
EXCH.CARD DEADLINE WAS 11/30/05
SETS ACTUALLY SENT OUT JANUARY, 2006
1 C.J. Henry .50 1.25
2 John Drennen .40 1.00
3 Beau Jones .30 .75
4 Jeff Lyman .20 .50
5 Andrew McCutchen 1.25 3.00
6 Chris Volstad 1.00 2.50
7 Jonathan Egan .20 .50
8 P.J. Phillips .30 .75
9 Steve Johnson .20 .50
10 Ryan Tucker .20 .50
11 Cameron Maybin 4.00 10.00
12 Shane Funk .20 .50

2004 Bowman Draft Futures Game Jersey Relics

STATED ODDS 1:31 HOBBY, 1:30 RETAIL
146 Jose Capellan 3.00 8.00
147 Dioner Navarro 3.00 8.00
148 Fausto Carmona 4.00 10.00
149 Robinzon Diaz 2.00 5.00
150 Felix Hernandez 10.00 25.00
151 Andres Blanco 2.00 5.00
152 Jason Kubel 2.00 5.00
153 Willy Taveras 3.00 8.00
154 Merkin Valdez 3.00 8.00
155 Robinson Cano 6.00 15.00
156 Bill Murphy 2.00 5.00
157 Chris Burke 2.00 5.00
158 Kyle Sleeth 3.00 8.00
159 B.J. Upton 3.00 8.00
160 Tim Stauffer 3.00 8.00
161 David Wright 12.50 30.00
162 Conor Jackson 3.00 8.00
163 Brad Thompson 3.00 8.00
164 Delmon Young 3.00 8.00
165 Jeremy Reed 2.00 5.00

2004 Bowman Draft Prospect Premiums Relics

GROUP A ODDS 1:145 H, 1:153 R
GROUP B ODDS 1:387 H, 1:411 R
AB Angel Berroa Bat A 2.00 5.00
BU B.J. Upton Bat B 3.00 8.00
CJ Conor Jackson Bat B 3.00 8.00
CQ Carlos Quentin Bat B 3.00 8.00
DN Dioner Navarro Bat A 2.00 5.00
DY Delmon Young Bat A 3.00 8.00
EJ Edwin Jackson Jsy A 2.00 5.00
JR Jeremy Reed Bat A 2.00 5.00
KC Kevin Cash Bat B 2.00 5.00
LM Lastings Milledge Bat A 4.00 10.00
NS Nick Swisher Bat B 2.00 5.00
RH Ryan Harvey Bat A 2.00 5.00

2004 Bowman Draft Signs of the Future

GROUP A ODDS 1:127 H, 1:127 R
GROUP B ODDS 1:509 H, 1:511 R

EXCHANGE DEADLINE 11/30/05
AL Adam Loewen A 6.00 15.00
CC Chad Cordero B 6.00 15.00
JH James Houser B 4.00 10.00
PM Paul Maholm A 4.00 10.00
TP Tyler Pelland A 4.00 10.00
TT Terry Tiffee A 4.00 10.00

2005 Bowman

This 330-card set was released in May, 2005. The set was issued in 10-card hobby and retail packs which had an $3 SRP and which came 24 packs to a box and 12 boxes to a case. These cards were also issued in "HTA" or jumbo packs with an $6 SRP which had 21 cards per pack and came 12 packs to a box and eight boxes to a case. The first 140 cards in this set feature active veterans while cards number 141 through 165 feature leading prospects and cards 166 through 330 feature Rookie Cards. There was also a card randomly inserted into packs featuring game-used relics of the 2004 Rookies of the Year.

COMPLETE SET (330) 40.00 80.00
COMMON CARD (1-140) .10 .30
COMMON CARD (141-165) .15 .40
COMMON CARD (166-330) .15 .40
PLATE ODDS 1:695 HOBBY, 1:177 HTA
PLATE PRINT RUN 1 SET PER COLOR
BLACK-CYAN-MAGENTA-YELLOW ISSUED
NO PLATE PRICING DUE TO SCARCITY
ROY ODDS 1:668 H, 1:248 HTA, 1:1535 R
1 Gavin Floyd .10 .30
2 Eric Chavez .10 .30
3 Miguel Tejada .10 .30
4 Dmitri Young .10 .30
5 Hank Blalock .10 .30
6 Kerry Wood .10 .30
7 Andy Pettitte .20 .50
8 Pat Burrell .10 .30
9 Johnny Estrada .10 .30
10 Frank Thomas .30 .75
11 Juan Pierre .10 .30
12 Tom Glavine .20 .50
13 Lyle Overbay .10 .30
14 Jim Edmonds .10 .30
15 Steve Finley .10 .30
16 Jermaine Dye .10 .30
17 Omar Vizquel .20 .50
18 Nick Johnson .10 .30
19 Brian Giles .10 .30
20 Justin Morneau .10 .30
21 Preston Wilson .10 .30
22 Wily Mo Pena .10 .30
23 Rafael Palmeiro .20 .50
24 Scott Kazmir .10 .30
25 Derek Jeter .60 1.50
26 Barry Zito .10 .30
27 Mike Lowell .10 .30
28 Jason Bay .10 .30
29 Ken Harvey .10 .30
30 Nomar Garciaparra .30 .75
31 Roy Halladay .10 .30
32 Todd Helton .20 .50
33 Mark Kotsay .10 .30
34 Jake Peavy .10 .30
35 David Wright .50 1.25
36 Dontrelle Willis .10 .30
37 Marcus Giles .10 .30
38 Chone Figgins .10 .30
39 Sidney Ponson .10 .30
40 Randy Johnson .30 .75
41 John Smoltz .20 .50
42 Kevin Millar .10 .30
43 Mark Teixeira .20 .50
44 Alex Rios .10 .30
45 Mike Piazza .30 .75
46 Victor Martinez .10 .30
47 Jeff Bagwell .20 .50
48 Shawn Green .10 .30
49 Ivan Rodriguez .20 .50
50 Alex Rodriguez .50 1.25
51 Kazuo Matsui .10 .30
52 Mark Mulder .10 .30
53 Michael Young .10 .30
54 Javy Lopez .10 .30
55 Johnny Damon .20 .50
56 Jeff Francis .10 .30
57 Rich Harden .10 .30
58 Bobby Abreu .10 .30
59 Mark Loretta .10 .30
60 Gary Sheffield .10 .30
61 Jamie Moyer .10 .30
62 Garret Anderson .10 .30
63 Vernon Wells .10 .30
64 Orlando Cabrera .10 .30
65 Magglio Ordonez .10 .30
66 Ronnie Belliard .10 .30
67 Carlos Lee .10 .30
68 Carl Pavano .10 .30
69 Jon Lieber .10 .30
70 Aubrey Huff .10 .30
71 Rocco Baldelli .10 .30
72 Jason Schmidt .10 .30
73 Bernie Williams .20 .50
74 Hideki Matsui .50 1.25
75 Ken Griffey Jr. .50 1.25
76 Josh Beckett .10 .30
77 Mark Buehrle .10 .30
78 David Ortiz .30 .75
79 Luis Gonzalez .10 .30
80 Scott Rolen .20 .50
81 Joe Mauer .30 .75
82 Jose Reyes .10 .30
83 Adam Dunn .10 .30
84 Greg Maddux .50 1.25
85 Bartolo Colon .10 .30
86 Bret Boone .10 .30
87 Mike Mussina .20 .50
88 Ben Sheets .10 .30
89 Lance Berkman .10 .30
90 Miguel Cabrera .20 .50
91 C.C. Sabathia .10 .30
92 Mike Maroth .10 .30
93 Andruw Jones .20 .50
94 Jack Wilson .10 .30
95 Ichiro Suzuki .60 1.50
96 Geoff Jenkins .10 .30
97 Zack Greinke .10 .30
98 Jorge Posada .20 .50
99 Travis Hafner .10 .30
100 Barry Bonds .75 2.00
101 Aaron Rowand .10 .30
102 Aramis Ramirez .10 .30
103 Curt Schilling .20 .50
104 Melvin Mora .10 .30
105 Albert Pujols .60 1.50
106 Austin Kearns .10 .30
107 Shannon Stewart .10 .30
108 Carl Crawford .10 .30
109 Carlos Zambrano .10 .30
110 Roger Clemens .50 1.25
111 Javier Vazquez .10 .30
112 Randy Wolf .10 .30
113 Chipper Jones .30 .75
114 Larry Walker .20 .50
115 Alfonso Soriano .10 .30
116 Brad Wilkerson .10 .30
117 Bobby Crosby .10 .30
118 Jim Thome .20 .50
119 Oliver Perez .10 .30
120 Vladimir Guerrero .30 .75
121 Roy Oswalt .10 .30
122 Torii Hunter .10 .30
123 Rafael Furcal .10 .30
124 Luis Castillo .10 .30
125 Carlos Beltran .10 .30
126 Mike Sweeney .10 .30
127 Johan Santana .30 .75
128 Tim Hudson .10 .30
129 Troy Glaus .10 .30
130 Manny Ramirez .20 .50
131 Jeff Kent .10 .30
132 Jose Vidro .10 .30
133 Edgar Renteria .10 .30
134 Russ Ortiz .10 .30
135 Sammy Sosa .30 .75
136 Carlos Delgado .10 .30
137 Richie Sexson .10 .30
138 Pedro Martinez .20 .50
139 Adrian Beltre .10 .30
140 Mark Prior .20 .50
141 Omar Quintanilla .15 .40
142 Carlos Quentin .20 .50
143 Dan Johnson .20 .50
144 Jake Stevens .15 .40
145 Nate Schierholtz .20 .50
146 Neil Walker .15 .40
147 Bill Bray .15 .40
148 Taylor Tankersley .15 .40
149 Trevor Plouffe .20 .50
150 Felix Hernandez .75 2.00
151 Philip Hughes .20 .50
152 James Houser UER .15 .40
Facsimile Signature is J.R. House
153 David Murphy .15 .40
154 Ervin Santana UER .15 .40
Card has Johan Santana's facsimile autograph
155 Anthony Whittington .15 .40
156 Chris Lambert .15 .40
157 Jeremy Sowers .20 .50
158 Giovanny Gonzalez .15 .40
159 Blake DeWitt .20 .50
160 Thomas Diamond .20 .50
161 Greg Golson .15 .40
162 David Aardsma .15 .40
163 Paul Maholm .15 .40
164 Mark Rogers .20 .50
165 Homer Bailey .20 .50
166 Chip Cannon FY RC .40 1.00
167 Tony Giarratano FY RC .20 .50
168 Darren Fenster FY RC .20 .50
169 Elvys Quezada FY RC .20 .50
170 Glen Perkins FY RC .40 1.00
171 Ian Kinsler FY RC 1.25 3.00
172 Mike Bourn FY RC .40 1.00
173 Jeremy West FY RC .30 .75
174 Justin Verlander FY RC 2.00 5.00
175 Kevin West FY RC .20 .50
176 Luis Hernandez FY RC .20 .50
177 Matt Campbell FY RC .20 .50
178 Nate McLouth FY RC .40 1.00
179 Ryan Goleski FY RC .20 .50
180 Matthew Lindstrom FY RC .20 .50
181 Matt DeSalvo FY RC .30 .75
182 Kole Strayhorn FY RC .20 .50
183 Jose Vaquedano FY RC .20 .50
184 James Jurries FY RC .30 .75
185 Ian Bladergroen FY RC .30 .75
186 Eric Nielsen FY RC .20 .50
187 Chris Vines FY RC .20 .50
188 Chris Denorfia FY RC .40 1.00
189 Kevin Melillo FY RC .40 1.00
190 Melky Cabrera FY RC 1.00 2.50
191 Ryan Sweeney FY RC .50 1.25
192 Sean Marshall FY RC .75 2.00
193 Andy LaRoche FY RC 1.50 4.00
194 Tyler Pelland FY RC .20 .50
195 Mike Morse FY RC .25 .60
196 Wes Swackhamer FY RC .20 .50
197 Wade Robinson FY RC .20 .50
198 Dan Santin FY RC .20 .50
199 Steve Doetsch FY RC .30 .75
200 Shane Costa FY RC .20 .50
201 Scott Mathieson FY RC .40 1.00
202 Ben Jones FY RC .40 1.00
203 Michael Rogers FY RC .20 .50
204 Matt Rogelstad FY RC .20 .50
205 Luis Ramirez FY RC .20 .50
206 Landon Powell FY RC .30 .75
207 Erik Cordier FY RC .20 .50
208 Chris Seddon FY RC .20 .50
209 Chris Roberson FY RC .20 .50
210 Thomas Oldham FY RC .20 .50
211 Dana Eveland FY RC .20 .50
212 Cody Haerther FY RC .20 .50
213 Danny Core FY RC .20 .50
214 Craig Tatum FY RC .20 .50
215 Elliot Johnson FY RC .20 .50
216 Ender Chavez FY RC .20 .50
217 Errol Simonitsch FY RC .30 .75
218 Matt Van Der Bosch FY RC .20 .50
219 Eulogio de la Cruz FY RC .20 .50
220 C.J. Smith FY RC .20 .50
221 Adam Boeve FY RC .20 .50
222 Adam Harben FY RC .30 .75
223 Baltazar Lopez FY RC .20 .50
224 Russ Martin FY RC .75 2.00
225 Brian Bannister FY RC .40 1.00
226 Brian Miller FY RC .20 .50
227 Casey McGehee FY RC .20 .50
228 Humberto Sanchez FY RC .75 2.00
229 Javon Moran FY RC .20 .50
230 Brandon McCarthy FY RC .60 1.50
231 Danny Zell FY RC .20 .50
232 Jake Postlewait FY RC .20 .50
233 Juan Tejeda FY RC .20 .50
234 Keith Ramsey FY RC .20 .50
235 Lorenzo Scott FY RC .20 .50
236 Wladimir Balentien FY RC .40 1.00
237 Martin Prado FY RC .20 .50
238 Matt Albers FY RC .50 1.25
239 Brian Schweiger FY RC .20 .50
240 Brian Stavisky FY RC .20 .50
241 Pat Misch FY RC .20 .50
242 Pat Osborn FY .15 .40
243 Ryan Feierabend FY RC .20 .50
244 Shaun Marcum FY .15 .40
245 Kevin Collins FY RC .20 .50
246 Stuart Pomeranz FY RC .20 .50
247 Tetsu Yofu FY RC .20 .50
248 Hernan Iribarren FY RC .30 .75
249 Mike Spidale FY RC .20 .50
250 Tony Arnerich FY RC .20 .50
251 Manny Parra FY RC .50 1.25
252 Drew Anderson FY RC .20 .50
253 T.J. Beam FY RC .40 1.00
254 Pedro Lopez FY RC .20 .50
255 Andy Sides FY RC .20 .50
256 Bear Bay FY RC .30 .75
257 Bill McCarthy FY RC .20 .50
258 Daniel Haigwood FY RC .40 1.00
259 Brian Sprout FY RC .40 1.00
260 Bryan Triplett FY RC .20 .50
261 Steven Bondurant FY RC .20 .50
262 Darwinson Salazar FY RC .20 .50
263 David Shepard FY RC .20 .50
264 Johan Silva FY RC .20 .50
265 J.B. Thurmond FY RC .20 .50
266 Brandon Moorhead FY RC .20 .50
267 Kyle Nichols FY RC .30 .75
268 Jonathan Sanchez FY RC .50 1.25
269 Mike Esposito FY RC .20 .50
270 Erik Schindewolf FY RC .20 .50
271 Peeter Ramos FY RC .20 .50
272 Juan Senreiso FY RC .20 .50
273 Matthew Kemp FY RC 1.50 4.00
274 Vinny Rottino FY RC .20 .50
275 Micah Furtado FY RC .20 .50
276 George Kottaras FY RC .40 1.00
277 Billy Butler FY RC 1.50 4.00
278 Buck Coats FY RC .20 .50
279 Kenny Durost FY RC .20 .50
280 Nick Touchstone FY RC .20 .50
281 Jerry Owens FY RC .30 .75
282 Stefan Bailie FY RC .20 .50
283 Jesse Gutierrez FY RC .20 .50
284 Chuck Tiffany FY RC .50 1.25
285 Brendan Ryan FY RC .20 .50
286 Hayden Penn FY RC .40 1.00
287 Shawn Bowman FY RC .30 .75
288 Alexander Smit FY RC .20 .50
289 Micah Schnurstein FY RC .20 .50
290 Jared Gothreaux FY RC .20 .50
291 Jair Jurrjens FY RC .60 1.50
292 Bobby Livingston FY RC .20 .50
293 Ryan Speier FY RC .20 .50
294 Zach Parker FY RC .20 .50
295 Christian Colonel FY RC .20 .50
296 Scott Mitchinson FY RC .20 .50
297 Neil Wilson FY RC .20 .50
298 Chuck James FY RC .75 2.00
299 Heath Totten FY RC .20 .50
300 Sean Tracey FY RC .20 .50
301 Ismael Ramirez FY RC .20 .50
302 Matt Brown FY RC .20 .50
303 Franklin Morales FY RC .30 .75
304 Brandon Sing FY RC .30 .75
305 D.J. Houlton FY RC .20 .50
306 Jayce Tingler FY RC .20 .50
307 Mitchell Arnold FY RC .20 .50
308 Jim Burt FY RC .20 .50
309 Jason Motte FY RC .20 .50
310 David Gassner FY RC .20 .50
311 Andy Santana FY RC UER .20 .50
Spelled Santan
312 Kelvin Pichardo FY RC .20 .50
313 Carlos Carrasco FY RC .50 1.25
314 Willy Mota FY RC .20 .50
315 Frank Mata FY RC .20 .50
316 Carlos Gonzalez FY RC 1.25 3.00
317 Jeff Niemann FY RC .40 1.00
318 Chris B.Young FY RC 1.00 2.50
319 Billy Sadler FY RC .20 .50
320 Ricky Barrett FY RC .20 .50
321 Ben Harrison FY .15 .40
322 Steve Nelson FY RC .20 .50
323 Daryl Thompson FY RC .20 .50
324 Philip Humber FY RC .40 1.00
325 Jeremy Harts FY RC .20 .50
326 Nick Masset FY RC .20 .50
327 Mike Rodriguez FY RC .20 .50
328 Mike Garber FY RC .20 .50
329 Kennard Bibbs FY RC .20 .50
330 Ryan Garko FY RC .60 1.50
BC Jason Bay Bat 6.00 15.00
Bobby Crosby Bat ROY

2005 Bowman 1st Edition

This parallel set was issued in 1st Edition boxes - of which were produced exclusively for hobby shops. Each sealed case contained two boxes. Each box contained 20 packs and each pack contained 10 cards. Each pack carried suggested retail price of $2.99. No insert cards were made available in these packs.

*1ST EDITION 1-165: .75X TO 2X BASIC
*1ST EDITION 166-330: .75X TO 2X BASIC
ISSUED IN 1ST EDITION PACKS

2005 Bowman Gold

COMPLETE SET (330) 75.00 150.00
*GOLD 1-165: 1.25X TO 3X BASIC
*GOLD 166-330: .75X TO 2X BASIC
ONE PER HOBBY PACK
ONE PER HTA PACK
ONE PER RETAIL PACK

2005 Bowman Red

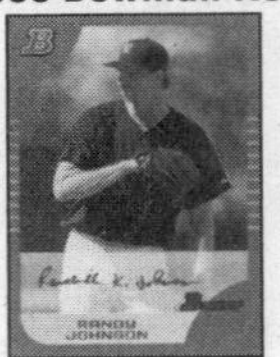

STATED ODDS 1:2768 H, 1:708 HTA
STATED PRINT RUN 1 SERIAL #'d SET
NO PRICING DUE TO SCARCITY

2005 Bowman White

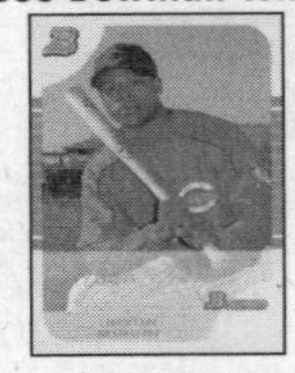

*WHITE 1-165: 4X TO 10X BASIC
*WHITE 166-330: 3X TO 8X BASIC
STATED ODDS 1:23 HOBBY, 1:6 HTA
STATED PRINT RUN 240 SERIAL #'d SETS
UNCIRCULATED EXCH.ODDS 1:94 H, 1:23 R
FOUR PIT.COM CARDS PER UNCIRC.EXCH
UNCIRCULATED EXCH DEADLINE 12/31/05
50% OF PRINT SEEDED INTO PACKS
50% OF PRINT AVAIL VIA PIT.COM EXCH
313 Carlos Carrasco FY 15.00 40.00
NNO Uncirculated EXCH Card 6.00 15.00

2005 Bowman Autographs

GROUP A ODDS 1:74 H, 1:26 HTA, 1:118 R
GROUP B ODDS 1:95 H, 1:33 HTA, 1:212 R
RED INK ODDS 1:1599 H, 1:599 HTA, 1:3672 R
RED INK PRINT RUN 25 SETS
RED INK ARE NOT SERIAL-NUMBERED
RED INK PRINT RUN PROVIDED BY TOPPS
NO RED INK PRICING DUE TO SCARCITY
GROUP A IS CARDS 141-151
GROUP B IS CARDS 152-165
EXCHANGE DEADLINE 05/31/07
141 Omar Quintanilla A 4.00 10.00
142 Carlos Quentin A 6.00 15.00
143 Dan Johnson A 4.00 10.00
144 Jake Stevens A 4.00 10.00
145 Nate Schierholtz A 4.00 10.00
146 Neil Walker A 4.00 10.00
147 Bill Bray A 4.00 10.00
148 Taylor Tankersley A 4.00 10.00
149 Trevor Plouffe A 4.00 10.00
150 Felix Hernandez A 15.00 40.00
151 Philip Hughes A 15.00 40.00
152 James Houser B 4.00 10.00
153 David Murphy B 4.00 10.00
154 Ervin Santana B 4.00 10.00
155 Anthony Whittington B 4.00 10.00
156 Chris Lambert B 4.00 10.00
157 Jeremy Sowers B 6.00 15.00
158 Giovanny Gonzalez B 4.00 10.00
159 Blake DeWitt B 10.00 25.00
160 Thomas Diamond B 6.00 15.00
161 Greg Golson B 4.00 10.00
162 David Aardsma B EXCH 4.00 10.00
163 Paul Maholm B 4.00 10.00

Card	Low	High
164 Mark Rogers B	6.00	15.00
165 Homer Bailey B	10.00	25.00

2005 Bowman Relics

STATED ODDS 1:50 H, 1:19 HTA, 1:114 R

Card	Low	High
2 Eric Chavez Jsy	3.00	8.00
5 Hank Blalock Bat	3.00	8.00
23 Rafael Palmeiro Bat	4.00	10.00
43 Mark Teixeira Bat	4.00	10.00
49 Ivan Rodriguez Bat	4.00	10.00
50 Alex Rodriguez Bat	6.00	15.00
60 Gary Sheffield Bat	3.00	8.00
65 Magglio Ordonez Bat	3.00	8.00
78 David Ortiz Bat	4.00	10.00
83 Adam Dunn Jsy	3.00	8.00
90 Miguel Cabrera Bat	4.00	10.00
93 Andruw Jones Bat	4.00	10.00
100 Barry Bonds Jsy	10.00	25.00
104 Melvin Mora Jsy	3.00	8.00
105 Albert Pujols Bat	6.00	15.00
115 Alfonso Soriano Bat	3.00	8.00
120 Vladimir Guerrero Bat	4.00	10.00
125 Carlos Beltran Bat	3.00	8.00
130 Manny Ramirez Bat	4.00	10.00
135 Sammy Sosa Bat	4.00	10.00

2005 Bowman A-Rod Throwback

Card	Low	High
COMPLETE SET (4)	3.00	8.00
STATED ODDS 1:12 HOBBY		
94 Alex Rodriguez 1994	.75	2.00
95 Alex Rodriguez 1995	.75	2.00
96 Alex Rodriguez 1996	.75	2.00
97 Alex Rodriguez 1997	.75	2.00

2005 Bowman A-Rod Throwback Autographs

1994 BOW ODDS 1:108,288 HTA
1995 BOW ODDS 1:27,684 H, 1:13,536 HTA
1996 BOW ODDS 1:9039 H, 1:4922 HTA
1996 BOW.DRAFT ODDS 1:44,837 H
1997 BOW ODDS 1:6815 H, 1:3734 HTA
1997 BOW.DRAFT ODDS 1:8664 H
1994 PRINT RUN 1 SERIAL #'d CARD
1995 PRINT RUN 25 SERIAL #'d CARDS
1996 PRINT RUN 75 SERIAL #'d CARDS
1997 PRINT RUN 225 SERIAL #'d CARDS
NO PRICING ON QTY OF 25 OR LESS
75 OF 99 1996 CARDS ARE IN BOWMAN
25 OF 99 1996 CARDS ARE IN BOW.DRAFT
100 OF 225 1997 CARDS ARE IN BOWMAN
125 OF 225 1997 CARDS ARE IN BOW.DRAFT

Card	Low	High
94A Alex Rodriguez 1994/1		
95A Alex Rodriguez 1995/25		
96A Alex Rodriguez 1996/99	125.00	200.00
97A Alex Rodriguez 1997/225	60.00	120.00

2005 Bowman A-Rod Throwback Jersey Relics

1994 ODDS 1:108,288 HTA
1995 ODDS 1:27,684 H, 1:13,536 HTA
1996 ODDS 1:6815 H, 1:3734 HTA
1997 ODDS 1:849 H, 1:461 HTA
1994 PRINT RUN 1 SERIAL #'d CARD
1995 PRINT RUN 25 SERIAL #'d CARDS
1996 PRINT RUN 99 SERIAL #'d CARDS
1997 PRINT RUN 800 SERIAL #'d CARDS
NO PRICING ON QTY OF 25 OR LESS

Card	Low	High
94R Alex Rodriguez 1994/1		
95R Alex Rodriguez 1995/25		
96R Alex Rodriguez 1996/99	15.00	40.00
97R Alex Rodriguez 1997/800	6.00	15.00

2005 Bowman A-Rod Throwback Posters

ONE PER SEALED HOBBY BOX
05 POSTER ISSUED IN BECKETT MONTHLY

Card	Low	High
1994 Alex Rodriguez 1994	.40	1.00
1995 Alex Rodriguez 1995	.40	1.00
1996 Alex Rodriguez 1996	.40	1.00
1997 Alex Rodriguez 1997	.40	1.00
2005 Alex Rodriguez 2005	.40	1.00

2005 Bowman Base of the Future Autograph Relic

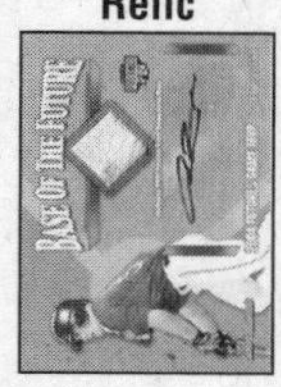

STATED ODDS 1:106 HTA
RED INK ODDS 1:4708 HTA
RED INK PRINT RUN 25 CARDS
RED INK IS NOT SERIAL-NUMBERED
RED INK PRINT RUN PROVIDED BY TOPPS
NO RED INK PRICING DUE TO SCARCITY

Card	Low	High
AH Aaron Hill	6.00	15.00

2005 Bowman Futures Game Gear Jersey Relics

STATED ODDS 1:36 H, 1:14 HTA, 1:83 R

Card	Low	High
AH Aaron Hill	2.00	5.00
AM Arnie Munoz	2.00	5.00
AMA Andy Marte	3.00	8.00
BB Bryan Bullington	2.00	5.00
CE Clint Everts	2.00	5.00
DM Dallas McPherson	2.00	5.00
EE Edwin Encarnacion	3.00	8.00
FP Felix Pie	3.00	8.00
GF Gavin Floyd	2.00	5.00
JB Joe Blanton	2.00	5.00
JC Jesus Cota	2.00	5.00
JCO Jorge Cortes	2.00	5.00
JF Jeff Francis	2.00	5.00
JG Jairo Garcia	2.00	5.00
JGU Joel Guzman	3.00	8.00
JM Jeff Mathis	2.00	5.00
JMO Justin Morneau	3.00	8.00
KH Koyie Hill	2.00	5.00
MC Matt Cain	4.00	10.00
RG Ruben Gotay	2.00	5.00
RW Rickie Weeks	3.00	8.00
SC Shin Soo Choo	2.00	5.00
VM Val Majewski	2.00	5.00
WL Wilfredo Ledezma	2.00	5.00
YP Yusmeiro Petit	3.00	8.00

2005 Bowman Signs of the Future

GROUP A ODDS 1:252 H, 1:93 HTA, 1:571 R
GROUP B ODDS 1:219 H, 1:82 HTA, 1:502 R
GROUP C ODDS 1:167 H, 1:63 HTA,1:382 R
GROUP D ODDS 1:636 H, 1:239 HTA, 1:1448 R
D.WRIGHT PRINT RUN 100 CARDS
D.WRIGHT IS NOT SERIAL-NUMBERED
D.WRIGHT PRINT RUN GIVEN BY TOPPS
EXCHANGE DEADLINE 05/31/07

Card	Low	High
AL Adam Loewen C	4.00	10.00
AW Anthony Whittington B	4.00	10.00
BB Brian Bixler B	4.00	10.00
BC Bobby Crosby B	6.00	15.00
BD Blake DeWitt C	6.00	15.00
BMS Brad Snyder C EXCH	4.00	10.00
BS Brad Sullivan C	4.00	10.00
CC Chad Cordero D	4.00	10.00
CG Christian Garcia C	4.00	10.00
DM Dallas McPherson B	4.00	10.00
DP Dan Putnam B	4.00	10.00
DW David Wright D/100 *	20.00	50.00
ES Ervin Santana D	4.00	10.00
HS Huston Street C	8.00	20.00
JR Jay Rainville C	4.00	10.00
JS Jay Sborz C	4.00	10.00
KW Kyle Waldrop B	4.00	10.00
MC Melky Cabrera C	15.00	40.00
PH Philip Hughes C	20.00	50.00
PM Paul Maholm C	4.00	10.00
RC Robinson Cano D	15.00	40.00
RR Richie Robnett A	4.00	10.00
RW Ryan Wagner C	4.00	10.00
SK Scott Kazmir D	8.00	20.00
SO Scott Olson D	4.00	10.00
TG Tom Gorzelanny C	4.00	10.00
TH Tim Hutting A	3.00	8.00
TP Trevor Plouffe D	6.00	15.00
TT Taylor Tankersley D	4.00	10.00

2005 Bowman Two of a Kind Autographs

STATED ODDS 1:55,368 H, 1:21,658 HTA
STATED PRINT RUN 13 SERIAL #'d CARDS
NO PRICING DUE TO SCARCITY
ARHA Alex Rodriguez
Hank Aaron

2005 Bowman Draft

This 165-card set was released in November, 2005. The set was issued in seven-card packs (which included two Bowman Chrome Draft Cards) with an $2 SRP which came 24 packs to a box and 10 boxes to a case.

Card	Low	High
COMPLETE SET (165)	15.00	40.00
COMMON CARD (1-165)	.10	.30
COMMON RC	.10	.30
COMMON RC YR	.10	.30
OVERALL PLATE ODDS 1:826 HOBBY		
PLATE PRINT RUN 1 SET PER COLOR		
BLACK-CYAN-MAGENTA-YELLOW ISSUED		
NO PLATE PRICING DUE TO SCARCITY		
1 Rickie Weeks	.10	.30
2 Kyle Davies	.10	.30
3 Garrett Atkins	.10	.30
4 Chien-Ming Wang	.40	1.00
5 Dallas McPherson	.10	.30
6 Dan Johnson	.10	.30
7 Andy Sisco	.10	.30
8 Ryan Doumit	.10	.30
9 J.P. Howell	.10	.30
10 Tim Stauffer	.10	.30
11 Willy Taveras	.10	.30
12 Aaron Hill	.10	.30
13 Victor Diaz	.10	.30
14 Wilson Betemit	.10	.30
15 Ervin Santana UER	.10	.30
Facsimile Signature is Johan Santana		
16 Mike Morse	.10	.30
17 Yadier Molina	.10	.30
18 Kelly Johnson	.10	.30
19 Clint Barmes	.10	.30
20 Robinson Cano	.20	.50
21 Brad Thompson	.10	.30
22 Jorge Cantu	.10	.30
23 Brad Halsey	.10	.30
24 Lance Niekro	.10	.30
25 D.J. Houlton	.10	.30
26 Ryan Church	.10	.30
27 Hayden Penn	.30	.75
28 Chris Young	.10	.30
29 Chad Orvella RC	.10	.30
30 Mark Teahen	.10	.30
31 Mark McCormick FY RC	.20	.50
32 Jay Bruce FY RC UER	3.00	8.00
Card has drafted by the wrong team		
33 Beau Jones FY RC	.20	.50
34 Tyler Greene FY RC	.30	.75
35 Zach Ward FY RC	.10	.30
36 Josh Bell FY RC	.30	.75
37 Josh Wall FY RC	.20	.50
38 Nick Webber FY RC	.10	.30
39 Travis Buck FY RC	.40	1.00
40 Kyle Winters FY RC	.20	.50
41 Mitch Boggs FY RC	.10	.30
42 Tommy Mendoza FY RC	.30	.75
43 Brad Corley FY RC	.20	.50
44 Drew Butera FY RC	.10	.30
45 Ryan Mount FY RC	.30	.75
46 Tyler Herron FY RC	.20	.50
47 Nick Weglarz FY RC	.20	.50
48 Brandon Erbe FY RC	.40	1.00
49 Cody Allen FY RC	.10	.30
50 Eric Fowler FY RC	.10	.30
51 James Boone FY RC	.20	.50
52 Josh Flores FY RC	.50	1.25
53 Brandon Monk FY RC	.20	.50
54 Kieron Pope FY RC	.30	.75
55 Kyle Cofield FY RC	.10	.30
56 Brent Lillibridge FY RC	.20	.50
57 Daryl Jones FY	.10	.30
58 Eli Iorg FY RC	.20	.50
59 Brett Hayes FY RC	.10	.30
60 Mike Durant FY RC	.30	.75
61 Michael Bowden FY RC	.75	2.00
62 Paul Kelly FY RC	.20	.50
63 Andrew McCutchen FY RC	.75	2.00
64 Travis Wood FY RC	.40	1.00
65 Cesar Ramos FY RC	.20	.50
66 Chaz Roe FY RC	.20	.50
67 Matt Torra FY RC	.20	.50
68 Kevin Slowey FY RC	.60	1.50
69 Trayvon Robinson FY RC	.20	.50
70 Reid Engel FY RC	.10	.30
71 Kris Harvey FY RC	.20	.50
72 Craig Italiano FY RC	.30	.75
73 Matt Maloney FY RC	.40	1.00
74 Sean West FY RC	.30	.75
75 Henry Sanchez FY RC	.20	.50
76 Scott Blue FY RC	.10	.30
77 Jordan Schafer FY RC	.60	1.50
78 Chris Robinson FY RC	.20	.50
79 Chris Hobdy FY RC	.10	.30
80 Brandon Durden FY RC	.10	.30
81 Clay Buchholz FY RC	2.50	6.00
82 Josh Geer FY RC	.10	.30
83 Sam LeCure FY RC	.10	.30
84 Justin Thomas FY RC	.10	.30
85 Brett Gardner FY RC	.20	.50
86 Tommy Manzella FY RC	.10	.30
87 Matt Green FY RC	.10	.30
88 Yunel Escobar FY RC	.75	2.00
89 Mike Costanzo FY RC	.30	.75
90 Nick Hundley FY RC	.10	.30
91 Zach Simons FY RC	.10	.30
92 Jacob Marceaux FY RC	.10	.30
93 Jed Lowrie FY RC	.20	.50
94 Brandon Snyder FY RC	.40	1.00
95 Matt Goyen FY RC	.10	.30
96 Jon Egan FY RC	.20	.50
97 Drew Thompson FY RC	.20	.50
98 Bryan Anderson FY RC	.40	1.00
99 Clayton Richard FY RC	.10	.30
100 Jimmy Shull FY RC	.20	.50
101 Mark Pawelek FY RC	.60	1.50
102 P.J. Phillips FY RC	.30	.75
103 John Drennen FY RC	.50	1.25
104 Nolan Reimold FY RC	.40	1.00
105 Troy Tulowitzki FY RC	1.50	4.00
106 Kevin Whelan FY RC	.15	.40
107 Wade Townsend FY RC	.20	.50
108 Micah Owings FY RC	.50	1.25
109 Ryan Tucker FY RC	.20	.50
110 Jeff Clement FY RC	.60	1.50
111 Josh Sullivan FY RC	.10	.30
112 Jeff Lyman FY RC	.20	.50
113 Brian Bogusevic FY RC	.10	.30
114 Trevor Bell FY RC	.20	.50
115 Brent Cox FY RC	.20	.50
116 Michael Billek FY RC	.10	.30
117 Garrett Olson FY RC	.20	.50
118 Steven Johnson FY RC	.10	.30
119 Chase Headley FY RC	.30	.75
120 Daniel Carte FY RC	.20	.50
121 Francisco Liriano PROS	.60	1.50
122 Fausto Carmona PROS	.10	.30
123 Zach Jackson PROS	.10	.30
124 Adam Loewen PROS	.10	.30
125 Chris Lambert PROS	.10	.30
126 Scott Mathieson FY	.10	.30
127 Paul Maholm PROS	.10	.30
128 Fernando Nieve PROS	.10	.30
129 Justin Verlander FY	.60	1.50
130 Yusmeiro Petit PROS	.20	.50
131 Joel Zumaya PROS	.10	.30
132 Merkin Valdez PROS	.10	.30
133 Ryan Garko FY	.20	.50
134 Edison Volquez FY RC	1.50	4.00
135 Russ Martin FY	.30	.75
136 Conor Jackson PROS	.10	.30
137 Miguel Montero FY RC	.40	1.00
138 Josh Barfield PROS	.10	.30
139 Delmon Young PROS	.20	.50
140 Andy LaRoche FY	.30	.75
141 William Bergolla PROS	.10	.30
142 B.J. Upton PROS	.10	.30
143 Hernan Iribarren FY	.10	.30
144 Brandon Wood PROS	.30	.75
145 Jose Bautista PROS	.10	.30
146 Edwin Encarnacion PROS	.10	.30
147 Javier Herrera FY RC	.30	.75
148 Jeremy Hermida PROS	.30	.75
149 Frank Diaz PROS RC	.10	.30
150 Chris B.Young FY	.40	1.00
151 Shin-Soo Choo PROS	.10	.30
152 Kevin Thompson PROS RC	.10	.30
153 Hanley Ramirez PROS	.20	.50
154 Lastings Milledge PROS	.10	.30
155 Luis Montanez PROS	.10	.30
156 Justin Huber PROS	.10	.30
157 Zach Duke PROS	.20	.50
158 Jeff Francoeur PROS	.30	.75
159 Melky Cabrera FY	.40	1.00
160 Bobby Jenks PROS	.10	.30
161 Ian Snell PROS	.10	.30
162 Fernando Cabrera PROS	.10	.30
163 Troy Patton PROS	.20	.50
164 Anthony Lerew PROS	.10	.30
165 Nelson Cruz FY RC	.30	.75

2005 Bowman Draft Gold

Card	Low	High
COMPLETE SET (165)	25.00	60.00

*GOLD: 1.25X TO 3X BASIC
*GOLD: .6X TO 1.5X BASIC RC
*GOLD: .6X TO 1.5X BASIC RC YR
ONE PER PACK

2005 Bowman Draft Red

STATED ODDS 1:6609 HOBBY
STATED PRINT RUN 1 SERIAL #'d SET
NO PRICING DUE TO SCARCITY

2005 Bowman Draft White

*WHITE: 4X TO 10X BASIC
*WHITE: 3X TO 8X BASIC RC
*WHITE: 2.5X TO 6X BASIC RC YR
STATED ODDS 1:35 HOBBY, 1:72 RETAIL
STATED PRINT RUN 225 SERIAL #'d SETS

Card	Low	High
32 Jay Bruce FY	20.00	50.00
81 Clay Buchholz FY	20.00	50.00
105 Troy Tulowitzki FY	15.00	40.00
134 Edison Volquez FY	10.00	25.00

2005 Bowman Draft Futures Game Jersey Relics

STATED ODDS 1:24 HOBBY

Card	Low	High
121 Francisco Liriano	6.00	15.00
122 Fausto Carmona	4.00	10.00
123 Zach Jackson	3.00	8.00
124 Adam Loewen	3.00	8.00
125 Chris Lambert	3.00	8.00
126 Scott Mathieson	3.00	8.00
127 Paul Maholm	3.00	8.00
128 Fernando Nieve	3.00	8.00
129 Justin Verlander	6.00	15.00
130 Yusmeiro Petit	3.00	8.00
131 Joel Zumaya	3.00	8.00
132 Merkin Valdez	3.00	8.00
133 Ryan Garko	3.00	8.00
134 Edison Volquez	6.00	15.00
135 Russ Martin	4.00	10.00
136 Conor Jackson	3.00	8.00
137 Miguel Montero	4.00	10.00
138 Josh Barfield	3.00	8.00
139 Delmon Young	3.00	8.00
140 Andy LaRoche	4.00	10.00
141 William Bergolla	3.00	8.00
142 B.J. Upton	3.00	8.00
143 Hernan Iribarren	3.00	8.00
144 Brandon Wood	6.00	15.00
145 Jose Bautista	3.00	8.00
146 Edwin Encarnacion	3.00	8.00
147 Javier Herrera	3.00	8.00
148 Jeremy Hermida	3.00	8.00
149 Frank Diaz	3.00	8.00
150 Chris B.Young	6.00	15.00

2005 Bowman Draft A-Rod Throwback Autograph

SEE 2005 BOWMAN A-ROD AU'S FOR INFO

2005 Bowman Draft Signs of the Future

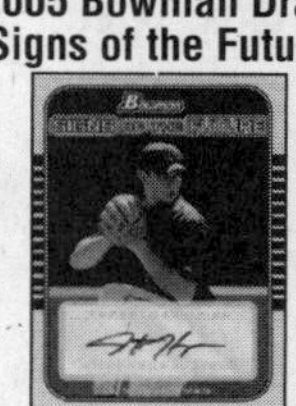

GROUP A ODDS 1:232 H, 1:232 R
GROUP B ODDS 1:823 H, 1:819 R
GROUP C ODDS 1:232 H, 1:232 R
GROUP D ODDS 1:1157 H, 1:1166 R
GROUP E ODDS 1:348 H, 1:349 R
GROUP F ODDS 1:1746 H, 1:1749 R

Card	Low	High
AG Angel Guzman E	3.00	8.00
BB Bill Bray E	3.00	8.00
DL Donald Lucey F	3.00	8.00
DM David Murphy E	3.00	8.00
DP David Purcey C	3.00	8.00
GG Greg Golson C	3.00	8.00
HB Homer Bailey D	6.00	15.00
JF Jeff Frazier C	3.00	8.00
JH Justin Hoyman A	3.00	8.00
JJ Justin Jones B	3.00	8.00
JP Jonathan Poterson C	3.00	8.00
JS Jeremy Sowers E	4.00	10.00
RR Richie Robnett A	3.00	8.00
TL Tyler Lumsden A	3.00	8.00

2005 Bowman Draft AFLAC Exchange Cards

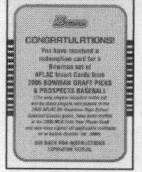

STATED ODDS 1:32 HOBBY
PLATES PRINT RUN 1 SET PER COLOR
NO PLATES PRICING DUE TO SCARCITY
EXCHANGE DEADLINE 12/25/06

Card	Low	High
1 Basic Set	3.00	8.00
2 Printing Plates Set/4		

2005 Bowman Draft AFLAC

Card	Low	High
COMP.FACT.SET (14)	4.00	10.00
STATED ODDS 1:32 '05 BOW.DRAFT HOB.		
EXCHANGE DEADLINE 12/26/06		
ONE SET VIA MAIL PER AFLAC EXCH.CARD		
SETS ACTUALLY SENT OUT JANUARY, 2007		
PLATE PRINT RUN 1 SET PER COLOR		
BLACK-CYAN-MAGENTA-YELLOW ISSUED		
NO PLATE PRICING DUE TO SCARCITY		
1 Billy Rowell	1.00	2.50
2 Kasey Kiker	.30	.75
3 Chris Marrero	.60	1.50
4 Jeremy Jeffress	.30	.75
5 Kyle Drabek	.60	1.50
6 Chris Parmelee	.60	1.50
7 Colton Willems	.30	.75
8 Cody Johnson	.30	.75
9 Hank Conger	.60	1.50
10 Cory Rasmus	.30	.75
11 David Christensen	.30	.75
12 Chris Tillman	.30	.75
13 Torre Langley	.30	.75
14 Robby Alcombrack	.30	.75

2006 Bowman

This 231-card set was released in May, 2006. The first 200 cards in the set consist of veterans while the last 31 cards in the set are players who were Rookie Cards under the then-new rules used in 2006. Cards number 219 and 220 come either signed or unsigned. The cards were issued in 10-card hobby packs with an $3 SRP which came 24 packs to a box and 12 boxes to a case. In addition, these cards were issued in 21-card HTA packs with an $6 SRP which were produced in 12-pack boxes which came eight boxes to a case and also in 10-card retail packs with an $3 SRP which came 24 packs to a box and 12 boxes to a case.

Card	Low	High
COMP.SET w/o AU's (220)	15.00	40.00
COMP.SET w/PROS (330)	40.00	80.00
COMMON CARD (1-200)	.10	.30
COMMON ROOKIE (201-220)	.15	.40
219-220 AU ODDS 1:1150 HOBBY, 1:699 HTA		
COMMON AUTO (221-231)	4.00	10.00
221-231 AU ODDS 1:82 HOBBY, 1:40 HTA		
1-220 PLATE ODDS 1:588 HOBBY, 1:575 HTA		
221-231 AU PLATES 1:15,700 H, 1:4100 HTA		
PLATE PRINT RUN 1 SET PER COLOR		
BLACK-CYAN-MAGENTA-YELLOW ISSUED		
NO PLATE PRICING DUE TO SCARCITY		
1 Nick Swisher	.12	.30
2 Ted Lilly	.12	.30
3 John Smoltz	.20	.50
4 Lyle Overbay	.12	.30
5 Alfonso Soriano	.12	.30
6 Javier Vazquez	.12	.30
7 Ronnie Belliard	.12	.30
8 Jose Reyes	.30	.75
9 Brian Roberts	.12	.30
10 Curt Schilling	.20	.50
11 Adam Dunn	.12	.30
12 Zack Greinke	.12	.30
13 Carlos Guillen	.12	.30
14 Jon Garland	.12	.30
15 Robinson Cano	.20	.50
16 Chris Burke	.10	.30
17 Barry Zito	.10	.30
18 Russ Adams	.10	.30
19 Chris Capuano	.10	.30
20 Scott Rolen	.20	.50
21 Kerry Wood	.10	.30
22 Scott Kazmir	.20	.50
23 Brandon Webb	.10	.30
24 Jeff Kent	.10	.30
25 Albert Pujols	.60	1.50
26 C.C. Sabathia	.10	.30
27 Adrian Beltre	.10	.30
28 Brad Wilkerson	.10	.30
29 Randy Wolf	.10	.30
30 Jason Bay	.10	.30
31 Austin Kearns	.10	.30
32 Clint Barmes	.10	.30
33 Mike Sweeney	.10	.30
34 Justin Verlander	.50	1.25
35 Justin Morneau	.10	.30
36 Scott Podsednik	.10	.30
37 Jason Giambi	.10	.30
38 Steve Finley	.10	.30
39 Morgan Ensberg	.10	.30
40 Eric Chavez	.10	.30
41 Roy Halladay	.10	.30
42 Horacio Ramirez	.10	.30

43 Ben Sheets	.10	.30
44 Chris Carpenter	.10	.30
45 Andruw Jones	.20	.50
46 Carlos Zambrano	.10	.30
47 Jonny Gomes	.10	.30
48 Shawn Green	.10	.30
49 Moises Alou	.10	.30
50 Ichiro Suzuki	.50	1.25
51 Juan Pierre	.10	.30
52 Grady Sizemore	.20	.50
53 Kazuo Matsui	.10	.30
54 Jose Vidro	.10	.30
55 Jake Peavy	.10	.30
56 Dallas Mcpherson	.10	.30
57 Ryan Howard	.50	1.25
58 Zach Duke	.10	.30
59 Michael Young	.10	.30
60 Todd Helton	.20	.50
61 David Dejesus	.10	.30
62 Ivan Rodriguez	.20	.50
63 Johan Santana	.20	.50
64 Danny Haren	.10	.30
65 Derek Jeter	.75	2.00
66 Greg Maddux	.50	1.25
67 Jorge Cantu	.10	.30
68 Conor Jackson	.10	.30
69 Victor Martinez	.10	.30
70 David Wright	.50	1.25
71 Ryan Church	.10	.30
72 Khalil Greene	.20	.50
73 Jimmy Rollins	.10	.30
74 Hank Blalock	.10	.30
75 Pedro Martinez	.20	.50
76 Jon Papelbon	.75	2.00
77 Felipe Lopez	.10	.30
78 Jeff Francis	.10	.30
79 Andy Sisco	.10	.30
80 Hideki Matsui	.50	1.25
81 Ken Griffey Jr.	.50	1.25
82 Nomar Garciaparra	.30	.75
83 Kevin Millwood	.10	.30
84 Paul Konerko	.10	.30
85 A.J. Burnett	.10	.30
86 Mike Piazza	.30	.75
87 Brian Giles	.10	.30
88 Johnny Damon	.20	.50
89 Jim Thome	.20	.50
90 Roger Clemens	.60	1.50
91 Aaron Rowand	.10	.30
92 Rafael Furcal	.10	.30
93 Gary Sheffield	.10	.30
94 Mike Cameron	.10	.30
95 Carlos Delgado	.10	.30
96 Jorge Posada	.20	.50
97 Denny Bautista	.10	.30
98 Mike Maroth	.10	.30
99 Brad Radke	.10	.30
100 Alex Rodriguez	.50	1.25
101 Freddy Garcia	.10	.30
102 Oliver Perez	.10	.30
103 Jon Lieber	.10	.30
104 Melvin Mora	.10	.30
105 Travis Hafner	.10	.30
106 Matt Cain	.20	.50
107 Derek Lowe	.10	.30
108 Luis Castillo	.10	.30
109 Livan Hernandez	.10	.30
110 Tadahito Iguchi	.10	.30
111 Shawn Chacon	.10	.30
112 Frank Thomas	.30	.75
113 Josh Beckett	.12	.30
114 Aubrey Huff	.10	.30
115 Derrek Lee	.10	.30
116 Chien-Ming Wang	.50	1.25
117 Joe Crede	.10	.30
118 Torii Hunter	.10	.30
119 J.D. Drew	.10	.30
120 Troy Glaus	.10	.30
121 Sean Casey	.10	.30
122 Edgar Renteria	.10	.30
123 Craig Wilson	.10	.30
124 Adam Eaton	.10	.30
125 Jeff Francoeur	.30	.75
126 Bruce Chen	.10	.30
127 Cliff Floyd	.10	.30
128 Jeremy Reed	.10	.30
129 Jake Westbrook	.10	.30
130 Wily Mo Pena	.10	.30
131 Toby Hall	.10	.30
132 David Ortiz	.30	.75
133 David Eckstein	.10	.30
134 Brady Clark	.10	.30
135 Marcus Giles	.10	.30
136 Aaron Hill	.10	.30
137 Mark Kotsay	.10	.30
138 Carlos Lee	.10	.30
139 Roy Oswalt	.10	.30
140 Chone Figgins	.10	.30
141 Mike Mussina	.20	.50
142 Orlando Hernandez	.10	.30
143 Magglio Ordonez	.10	.30
144 Jim Edmonds	.20	.50
145 Bobby Abreu	.10	.30
146 Nick Johnson	.10	.30
147 Carlos Beltran	.10	.30
148 Jhonny Peralta	.10	.30
149 Pedro Feliz	.10	.30
150 Miguel Tejada	.10	.30
151 Luis Gonzalez	.10	.30
152 Carl Crawford	.10	.30
153 Yadier Molina	.10	.30
154 Rich Harden	.10	.30
155 Tim Wakefield	.10	.30
156 Rickie Weeks	.10	.30
157 Johnny Estrada	.10	.30
158 Gustavo Chacin	.10	.30
159 Dan Johnson	.10	.30
160 Willy Taveras	.10	.30
161 Garret Anderson	.10	.30
162 Randy Johnson	.30	.75
163 Jermaine Dye	.10	.30
164 Joe Mauer	.20	.50
165 Ervin Santana	.10	.30
166 Jeremy Bonderman	.10	.30
167 Garrett Atkins	.10	.30
168 Manny Ramirez	.20	.50
169 Brad Eldred	.10	.30
170 Chase Utley	.30	.75
171 Mark Loretta	.10	.30
172 John Patterson	.10	.30
173 Tom Glavine	.20	.50
174 Dontrelle Willis	.10	.30
175 Mark Teixeira	.20	.50
176 Felix Hernandez	.20	.50
177 Cliff Lee	.10	.30
178 Jason Schmidt	.10	.30
179 Chad Tracy	.10	.30
180 Rocco Baldelli	.10	.30
181 Aramis Ramirez	.10	.30
182 Andy Pettitte	.20	.50
183 Mark Mulder	.10	.30
184 Geoff Jenkins	.10	.30
185 Chipper Jones	.30	.75
186 Vernon Wells	.10	.30
187 Bobby Crosby	.10	.30
188 Lance Berkman	.10	.30
189 Vladimir Guerrero	.30	.75
190 Jose Capellan	.10	.30
191 Brad Penny	.10	.30
192 Jose Guillen	.10	.30
193 Brett Myers	.10	.30
194 Miguel Cabrera	.20	.50
195 Bartolo Colon	.10	.30
196 Craig Biggio	.20	.50
197 Tim Hudson	.10	.30
198 Mark Prior	.20	.50
199 Mark Buehrle	.10	.30
200 Barry Bonds	.75	2.00
201 Anderson Hernandez (RC)	.15	.40
202 Charlton Jimerson (RC)	.15	.40
203 Jeremy Accardo RC	.15	.40
204 Hanley Ramirez (RC)	.40	1.00
205 Matt Capps (RC)	.15	.40
206 John-Ford Griffin (RC)	.15	.40
207 Chuck James (RC)	.25	.60
208 Jaime Bubela (RC)	.15	.40
209 Mark Woodyard (RC)	.15	.40
210 Jason Botts (RC)	.15	.40
211 Chris Demaria RC	.15	.40
212 Miguel Perez (RC)	.15	.40
213 Tom Gorzelanny (RC)	.15	.40
214 Adam Wainwright (RC)	.15	.40
215 Ryan Garko (RC)	.15	.40
216 Jason Bergmann RC	.15	.40
217 J.J. Furmaniak (RC)	.15	.40
218 Francisco Liriano (RC)	.75	2.00
219 Kenji Johjima RC	.75	2.00
219a Kenji Johjima AU	30.00	60.00
220 Craig Hansen RC	.60	1.50
220a Craig Hansen AU	20.00	50.00
221 Ryan Zimmerman AU (RC)	20.00	50.00
222 Joey Devine AU RC	4.00	10.00
223 Scott Olsen AU (RC)	4.00	10.00
224 Darrel Rasner AU (RC)	4.00	10.00
225 Craig Breslow AU RC	4.00	10.00
226 Reggie Abercrombie AU (RC)	4.00	10.00
227 Dan Uggla AU (RC)	6.00	15.00
228 Willie Eyre AU (RC)	4.00	10.00
229 Joel Zumaya AU (RC)	12.50	30.00
230 Ricky Nolasco AU (RC)	4.00	10.00
231 Ian Kinsler AU (RC)	10.00	25.00

2006 Bowman Blue

*BLUE 1-200: 2X TO 5X BASIC
*BLUE 76/201-220: 2X TO 5X BASIC
*BLUE 221-231: 4.X TO 1X BASIC AU
1-220 ODDS 1:8 HOBBY, 1:4 HTA
221-231 AU ODDS 1:225 HOBBY, 1:115 HTA
STATED PRINT RUN 500 SERIAL #'d SETS

227 Dan Uggla AU	10.00	25.00

2006 Bowman Gold

*GOLD 1-200: 1.25X TO 3X BASIC
*GOLD 201-220: 1X TO 2.5X BASIC
ONE PER HOBBY PACK
ONE PER HTA PACK

2006 Bowman Red

STATED ODDS 1:3750 HOBBY, 1:1754 HTA
221-231 AU ODDS 1:114,583 H, 1:58,464 HTA
STATED PRINT RUN 1 SERIAL #'d SET
NO PRICING DUE TO SCARCITY

2006 Bowman White

*WHITE 1-200: 3X TO 8X BASIC
*WHITE 76/201-220: 3X TO 8X BASIC
*WHITE 221-231: .6X TO 1.5X BASIC AU
1-220 ODDS 1:32 HOBBY, 1:15 HTA
221-231 AU ODDS 1:1020 HOBBY, 1:500 HTA
STATED PRINT RUN 120 SERIAL #'d SETS

227 Dan Uggla AU	20.00	50.00

2006 Bowman Prospects

For the first time, the non-major league prospects in Bowman had their own seperate set. These cards were inserted at a stated rate of two cards for every Bowman hobby pack and four cards for every HTA pack. The final 14 cards in this insert set were signed and were inserted at a stated rate of one in 62 hobby and one in 35 HTA.

COMP.SET w/o AU's (110)	25.00	50.00
COMMON CARD (B1-B110)	.15	.40

B1-B110 STATED ODDS 2:1 HOBBY, 4:1 HTA
B111-B124 AU ODDS 1:62 HOBBY, 1:35 HTA
B1-B110 PLATE ODDS 1:588 H, 1:575 HTA
B111-B124 AU PLATE 1:15,700 H, 1:4100 HTA
PLATE PRINT RUN 1 PER COLOR
BLACK-CYAN-MAGENTA-YELLOW ISSUED
NO PLATE PRICING DUE TO SCARCITY

B1 Alex Gordon	.75	2.00
B2 Jonathan George	.15	.40
B3 Scott Walter	.15	.40
B4 Brian Holliday	.15	.40
B5 Ben Copeland	.25	.60
B6 Bobby Wilson	.25	.60
B7 Mayker Sandoval	.15	.40
B8 Alejandro de Aza	.40	1.00
B9 David Munoz	.15	.40
B10 Josh LeBlanc	.15	.40
B11 Philippe Valiquette	.15	.40
B12 Edwin Bellorin	.25	.60
B13 Jason Quarles	.15	.40
B14 Mark Trumbo	.40	1.00
B15 Steve Kelly	.15	.40
B16 Jamie Hoffman	.15	.40
B17 Joe Bauserman	.15	.40
B18 Nick Adenhart	.75	2.00
B19 Mike Butia	.15	.40
B20 Jon Weber	.15	.40
B21 Luis Valdez	.15	.40
B22 Rafael Rodriguez	.25	.60
B23 Wyatt Toregas	.25	.60
B24 John Vanden Berg	.15	.40
B25 Mike Connolly	.15	.40
B26 Mike O'Connor	.15	.40
B27 Garrett Mock	.15	.40
B28 Bill Layman	.15	.40
B29 Luis Pena	.15	.40
B30 Billy Killian	.15	.40
B31 Ross Ohlendorf	.15	.40
B32 Marc Keiser	.15	.40
B33 Ryan Costello	.15	.40
B34 Dale Thayer	.15	.40
B35 Steve Garrabrants	.15	.40
B36 Samuel Deduno	.15	.40
B37 Juan Portes	.40	1.00
B38 Javier Martinez	.15	.40
B39 Clint Sammons	.15	.40
B40 Andrew Kown	.25	.60
B41 Matt Tolbert	.15	.40
B42 Michael Ekstrom	.15	.40
B43 Shawn Norris	.15	.40
B44 Diory Hernandez	.15	.40
B45 Chris Maples	.15	.40
B46 Aaron Hathaway	.15	.40
B47 Steven Baker	.15	.40
B48 Greg Creek	.15	.40
B49 Collin Mahoney	.15	.40
B50 Corey Ragsdale	.15	.40
B51 Ariel Nunez	.15	.40
B52 Max Ramirez	.50	1.25
B53 Eric Rodland	.15	.40
B54 Dante Brinkley	.15	.40
B55 Casey Craig	.15	.40
B56 Ryan Spilborghs	.25	.60
B57 Fredy Deza	.15	.40
B58 Jeff Frazier	.15	.40
B59 Vince Cordova	.15	.40
B60 Oswaldo Navarro	.15	.40
B61 Jarod Rine	.15	.40
B62 Jordan Tata	.15	.40
B63 Ben Julianel	.15	.40
B64 Yung-Chi Chen	1.00	2.50
B65 Carlos Torres	.25	.60
B66 Juan Francia	.15	.40
B67 Brett Smith	.15	.40
B68 Francisco Leandro	.15	.40
B69 Chris Turner	.40	1.00
B70 Matt Joyce	.25	.60
B71 Jason Jones	.15	.40
B72 Jose Diaz	.15	.40
B73 Kevin Ool	.15	.40
B74 Nate Bumstead	.15	.40
B75 Omir Santos	.15	.40
B76 Shawn Riggans	.15	.40
B77 Ofilio Castro	.15	.40
B78 Mike Rozier	.15	.40
B79 Wilkin Ramirez	.40	1.00
B80 Yobal Duenas	.15	.40
B81 Adam Bourassa	.15	.40
B82 Tony Granadillo	.25	.60
B83 Brad McCann	.50	1.25
B84 Dustin Majewski	.15	.40
B85 Kelvin Jimenez	.15	.40
B86 Mark Reed	.50	1.25
B87 Asdrubal Cabrera	.50	1.25
B88 James Barthmaier	.25	.60
B89 Brandon Boggs	.15	.40
B90 Raul Valdez	.15	.40
B91 Jose Campusano	.15	.40
B92 Henry Owens	.25	.60
B93 Tug Hulett	.15	.40
B94 Nate Gold	.25	.60
B95 Lee Mitchell	.15	.40
B96 John Hardy	.15	.40
B97 Aaron Wideman	.15	.40
B98 Brandon Roberts	.15	.40
B99 Lou Santangelo	.15	.40
B100 Kyle Kendrick	.50	1.25
B101 Michael Collins	.40	1.00
B102 Camilo Vazquez	.15	.40
B103 Mark McLemore	.15	.40
B104 Alexander Peralta	.15	.40
B105 Josh Whitesell	.15	.40
B106 Carlos Guevara	.15	.40
B107 Michael Aubrey	.25	.60
B108 Brandon Chaves	.15	.40
B109 Leonard Davis	.15	.40
B110 Kendry Morales	.40	1.00
B111 Koby Clemens AU	10.00	25.00
B112 Lance Broadway AU	6.00	15.00
B113 Cameron Maybin AU	30.00	60.00
B114 Mike Aviles AU	4.00	10.00
B115 Kyle Blanks AU	10.00	25.00
B116 Chris Dickerson AU	6.00	15.00
B117 Sean Gallagher AU	10.00	25.00
B118 Jamar Hill AU	4.00	10.00
B119 Garrett Mock AU	4.00	10.00
B120 Kendry Morales AU	8.00	20.00
B121 Russ Rohlicek AU	4.00	10.00
B122 Clete Thomas AU	4.00	10.00
B123 Josh Kinney AU	4.00	10.00
B124 Justin Huber AU	4.00	10.00

2006 Bowman Prospects Blue

*BLUE B1-B110: 1.5X TO 4X BASIC
*BLUE B111-B124: .4X TO 1X BASIC
B1-B110 ODDS 1:8 HOBBY, 1:4 HTA
B111-B124 AU ODDS 1:170 H, 1:100 HTA
STATED PRINT RUN 500 SERIAL #'d SETS

B113 Cameron Maybin AU	40.00	80.00

2006 Bowman Prospects Gold

*GOLD B1-B110: .75X TO 2X BASIC
ONE PER HOBBY PACK
ONE PER HTA PACK

2006 Bowman Prospects Red

B1-B110 ODDS 1:3750 HOBBY, 1:1754 HTA
B111-B124 AU ODDS 1:80,208 H, 1:56,464 HTA
STATED PRINT RUN 1 SERIAL #'d SET
NO PRICING DUE TO SCARCITY

2006 Bowman Prospects White

*WHITE B1-B110: 2.5X TO 6X BASIC
*WHITE B111-B124: .6X TO 1.5X BASIC
B1-B110 ODDS 1:32 HOBBY, 1:15 HTA
B111-B124 AU ODDS 1:750 H, 1:450 HTA
STATED PRINT RUN 120 SERIAL #'d SETS

B113 Cameron Maybin AU	125.00	250.00

2006 Bowman Base of the Future

STATED ODDS 1:173 HTA
RED INK ODDS 1:7800 HTA
NO RED INK PRICING DUE TO SCARCITY

JH Justin Huber	4.00	10.00

2006 Bowman Signs of the Future

ONE PER SEALED HTA BOX
GROUP A ODDS 1:5 HTA BOXES, 1:150 RETAIL
GROUP B ODDS 1:4 HTA BOXES, 1:105 RETAIL
GROUP C-D ODDS 1:6 HTA BOXES, 1:200 R
GROUP E ODDS 1:19 HTA BOXES, 1:1050 R

AT Aaron Thompson D	4.00	10.00
BB Brian Bogusevic A	4.00	10.00
BC Ben Copeland C	4.00	10.00
CR Cesar Ramos E	4.00	10.00
DS Denard Span B	6.00	15.00
GO Garrett Olson C	4.00	10.00
HS Henry Sanchez D	4.00	10.00
JC Jeff Clement B	10.00	25.00
JD John Drennen C	4.00	10.00
JE Jacoby Ellsbury D UER	30.00	60.00
The words the signing run together instead of being seperated		
JM John Mayberry Jr. E	4.00	10.00
MB Michael Bowden B	8.00	20.00
MC Mike Costanzo D	4.00	10.00
RB Ryan Braun E	15.00	40.00
RR Ricky Romero B	4.00	10.00
RT Ryan Tucker C	4.00	10.00
SW Sean West D	4.00	10.00
TB Travis Buck D	6.00	15.00
TC Trevor Crowe B	4.00	10.00
TT Troy Tulowitzki A	12.50	30.00
YE Yunel Escobar A	10.00	25.00

2006 Bowman Draft

COMPLETE SET (55)	6.00	15.00
COMMON RC (1-55)	.15	.40

APPX. TWO PER HOBBY/RETAL PACK
ODDS INFO PROVIDED BY BECKETT
OVERALL PLATE ODDS 1:990 HOBBY
PLATE PRINT RUN 1 SET PER COLOR
BLACK-CYAN-MAGENTA-YELLOW ISSUED
NO PLATE PRICING DUE TO SCARCITY

1 Matt Kemp (RC)	.25	.60
2 Taylor Tankersley (RC)	.15	.40
3 Mike Napoli RC	.40	1.00
4 Brian Bannister (RC)	.15	.40
5 Melky Cabrera (RC)	.25	.60
6 Bill Bray (RC)	.15	.40
7 Brian Anderson (RC)	.15	.40
8 Jered Weaver (RC)	.50	1.25
9 Chris Duncan (RC)	.25	.60
10 Boof Bonser (RC)	.25	.60
11 Mike Rouse (RC)	.15	.40
12 David Pauley (RC)	.15	.40
13 Russ Martin (RC)	.25	.60
14 Jeremy Sowers (RC)	.15	.40
15 Kevin Reese (RC)	.15	.40
16 John Rheinecker (RC)	.15	.40
17 Tommy Murphy (RC)	.15	.40
18 Sean Marshall (RC)	.15	.40
19 Jason Kubel (RC)	.15	.40
20 Chad Billingsley (RC)	.25	.60
21 Kendry Morales (RC)	.25	.60
22 Jon Lester RC	1.00	2.50
23 Brandon Fahey RC	.15	.40
24 Josh Johnson (RC)	.25	.60
25 Kevin Frandsen (RC)	.15	.40
26 Casey Janssen RC	.25	.60
27 Scott Thorman (RC)	.15	.40
28 Scott Mathieson (RC)	.15	.40
29 Jeremy Hermida (RC)	.15	.40
30 Dustin Nippert (RC)	.15	.40
31 Kevin Thompson (RC)	.15	.40
32 Bobby Livingston (RC)	.15	.40
33 Travis Ishikawa (RC)	.15	.40
34 Jeff Mathis (RC)	.15	.40
35 Charlie Haeger RC	.25	.60
36 Josh Willingham (RC)	.15	.40
37 Taylor Buchholz (RC)	.15	.40
38 Joel Guzman (RC)	.15	.40
39 Zach Jackson (RC)	.15	.40
40 Howie Kendrick (RC)	.40	1.00
41 T.J. Beam (RC)	.15	.40
42 Ty Taubenheim RC	.25	.60
43 Erick Aybar (RC)	.15	.40
44 Anibal Sanchez (RC)	.25	.60
45 Michael Pelfrey RC	.60	1.50
46 Shawn Hill (RC)	.15	.40
47 Chris Roberson (RC)	.15	.40
48 Carlos Villanueva RC	.15	.40
49 Andre Ethier (RC)	.40	1.00
50 Anthony Reyes (RC)	.25	.60
51 Franklin Gutierrez (RC)	.15	.40
52 Angel Guzman (RC)	.15	.40
53 Michael O'Connor RC	.15	.40
54 James Shields RC	.15	.40
55 Nate McLouth (RC)	.15	.40

2006 Bowman Draft Gold

COMPLETE SET (55)	8.00	20.00

*GOLD: .75X TO 2X BASIC
APPX. ODDS 1:3 HOBBY, 1:3 RETAIL
ODDS INFO PROVIDED BY BECKETT

2006 Bowman Draft Red

STATED ODDS 1:7934 HOBBY
STATED PRINT RUN 1 SERIAL #'d SET
NO PRICING DUE TO SCARCITY

2006 Bowman Draft White

*WHITE: 2.5X TO 6X BASIC
STATED ODDS 1:43 H,1:93 R
STATED PRINT RUN 225 SER.#'d SETS

2006 Bowman Draft Draft Picks

COMPLETE SET (65)	8.00	20.00

APPX. ODDS 1:1 HOBBY, 1:1 RETAIL
ODDS INFO PROVIDED BY BECKETT
OVERALL PLATE ODDS 1:990 HOBBY
PLATE PRINT RUN 1 SET PER COLOR
BLACK-CYAN-MAGENTA-YELLOW ISSUED
NO PLATE PRICING DUE TO SCARCITY

1 Tyler Colvin	.50	1.25
2 Chris Marrero	.60	1.50
3 Hank Conger	.75	2.00
4 Chris Parmelee	1.00	2.50
5 Jason Place	.75	2.00
6 Billy Rowell	1.25	3.00
7 Travis Snider	1.25	3.00
8 Colton Willems	.40	1.00
9 Chase Fontaine	.15	.40
10 Jon Jay	.40	1.00
11 Wade Leblanc	.15	.40
12 Justin Masterson	1.00	2.50
13 Gary Daley	.15	.40
14 Justin Edwards	.15	.40
15 Charlie Yarbrough	.15	.40
16 Cyle Hankerd	.40	1.00
17 Zach McAllister	.15	.40
18 Tyler Robertson	.15	.40
19 Joe Smith	.15	.40
20 Nate Culp	.15	.40
21 John Holdzkom	.15	.40
22 Patrick Bresnehan	.15	.40
23 Chad Lee	.15	.40
24 Ryan Morris	.15	.40
25 D'Arby Myers	.25	.60
26 Garrett Olson	.15	.40
27 Jon Still	.15	.40
28 Brandon Rice	.15	.40
29 Chris Davis	1.00	2.50
30 Zack Daeges	.15	.40
31 Bobby Henson	.15	.40
32 George Kontos	.15	.40
33 Jermaine Mitchell	.25	.60
34 Adam Coe	.15	.40
35 Dustin Richardson	.15	.40
36 Allen Craig	.15	.40
37 Austin McClune	.15	.40
38 Doug Fister	.15	.40
39 Corey Madden	.15	.40
40 Justin Jacobs	.15	.40
41 Jim Negrych	.15	.40
42 Tyler Norrick	.15	.40
43 Adam Davis	.15	.40
44 Brett Logan	.15	.40
45 Brian Omogrosso	.15	.40
46 Kyle Drabek	.50	1.25
47 Jamie Ortiz	.40	1.00
48 Alex Presley	.15	.40
49 Terrance Warren	.15	.40
50 David Christensen	.25	.60
51 Helder Velazquez	.15	.40
52 Matt McBride	.15	.40
53 Quintin Berry	.15	.40
54 Michael Eisenberg	.15	.40
55 Dan Garcia	.15	.40
56 Scott Cousins	.15	.40

57 Sean Land .15 .40
58 Kristopher Medlen .15 .40
59 Tyler Reves .15 .40
60 John Shelby .15 .40
61 Jordan Newton .15 .40
62 Ricky Orta .15 .40
63 Jason Donald .15 .40
64 David Huff .15 .40
65 Brett Sinkbeil .15 .40

2006 Bowman Draft Draft Picks Gold

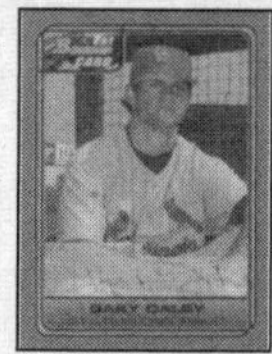

*GOLD: .75X TO 2X BASIC
APPX. ODDS 1:2 HOBBY, 1:2 RETAIL
ODDS INFO PROVIDED BY BECKETT

2006 Bowman Draft Draft Picks Red

STATED ODDS 1:7934 HOBBY
STATED PRINT RUN 1 SERIAL #'d SET
NO PRICING DUE TO SCARCITY

2006 Bowman Draft Draft Picks White

*WHITE: 2.5X TO 6X BASIC
STATED ODDS 1:43 H,1:93 R
STATED PRINT RUN 225 SER.#'d SETS
29 Chris Davis 12.50 30.00

2006 Bowman Draft Future's Game Prospects

COMPLETE SET (45) 6.00 15.00
APPX. ODDS 1:1 HOBBY, 1:1 RETAIL
ODDS INFO PROVIDED BY BECKETT
OVERALL PLATE ODDS 1:990 HOBBY
PLATE PRINT RUN 1 SET PER COLOR
BLACK-CYAN-MAGENTA-YELLOW ISSUED
NO PLATE PRICING DUE TO SCARCITY
1 Nick Adenhart .40 1.00
2 Joel Guzman .15 .40
3 Ryan Braun 1.25 3.00
4 Carlos Carrasco .25 .60
5 Neil Walker .15 .40
6 Pablo Sandoval .15 .40
7 Gio Gonzalez .15 .40
8 Joey Votto .15 .40
9 Luis Cruz .15 .40
10 Nolan Reimold .15 .40
11 Juan Salas .15 .40
12 Josh Fields .15 .40
13 Yovani Gallardo .40 1.00
14 Radhames Liz .40 1.00
15 Eric Patterson .15 .40
16 Cameron Maybin .60 1.50
17 Edgar Martinez .15 .40
18 Hunter Pence 1.50 4.00
19 Philip Hughes .40 1.00
20 Trent Oeltjen .15 .40
21 Nick Pereira .15 .40
22 Wladimir Balentien .15 .40
23 Stephen Drew .40 1.00
24 Davis Romero .15 .40
25 Joe Koshansky .15 .40
26 Chin Lung Hu .50 1.25
27 Jason Hirsh .15 .40
28 Jose Tabata .60 1.50
29 Eric Hurley .15 .40
30 Yung Chi Chen .50 1.25
31 Howie Kendrick .40 1.00
32 Humberto Sanchez .15 .40
33 Alex Gordon 1.00 2.50
34 Yunel Escobar .15 .40
35 Travis Buck .15 .40
36 Billy Butler .40 1.00
37 Homer Bailey .40 1.00
38 George Kottaras .15 .40
39 Kurt Suzuki .15 .40
40 Joaquin Arias .15 .40
41 Matt Lindstrom .15 .40
42 Sean Smith .15 .40
43 Carlos Gonzalez .15 .40
44 Jaime Garcia .25 .60
45 Jose Garcia .15 .40

2006 Bowman Draft Future's Game Prospects Gold

*GOLD: 1X TO 2.5X BASIC
APPX. ODDS 1:6 HOBBY, 1:6 RETAIL
ODDS INFO PROVIDED BY BECKETT
16 Cameron Maybin 1.25 3.00
18 Hunter Pence 6.00 15.00
26 Chin Lung Hu 1.00 2.50
28 Jose Tabata 1.25 3.00
30 Yung Chi Chen 1.00 2.50
33 Alex Gordon 2.00 5.00

2006 Bowman Draft Future's Game Prospects Red

STATED ODDS 1:7934 HOBBY
STATED PRINT RUN 1 SERIAL #'d SET
NO PRICING DUE TO SCARCITY

2006 Bowman Draft Future's Game Prospects White

*WHITE: 2.5X TO 6X BASIC
STATED ODDS 1:43 H,1:93 R
STATED PRINT RUN 225 SER.#'d SETS
18 Hunter Pence 10.00 25.00
26 Chin Lung Hu 5.00 12.00
30 Yung Chi Chen 5.00 12.00
33 Alex Gordon 10.00 25.00

2006 Bowman Draft Future's Game Prospects Relics

GROUP A ODDS 1:285 H,1:285 R
GROUP B ODDS 1:26 H,1:25 R
PRICES LISTED FOR JSY SWATCHES
NO PATCH PRICING DUE TO SCARCITY
1 Nick Adenhart Jsy B 4.00 10.00
2 Joel Guzman Jsy B 2.50 6.00
3 Ryan Braun Jsy B 8.00 20.00
4 Carlos Carrasco Jsy B 2.50 6.00
6 Pablo Sandoval Jsy B 2.50 6.00
7 Gio Gonzalez Jsy B 2.50 6.00
8 Joey Votto Jsy B 2.50 6.00
9 Luis Cruz Jsy B 2.50 6.00
10 Nolan Reimold Jsy B 2.50 6.00
11 Juan Salas Jsy B 2.50 6.00
12 Josh Fields Jsy B 2.50 6.00
13 Yovani Gallardo Jsy B 6.00 15.00
14 Radhames Liz Jsy B 2.50 6.00
15 Eric Patterson Jsy A 2.50 6.00
16 Cameron Maybin Jsy B 6.00 15.00
17 Edgar Martinez Jsy B 2.50 6.00
18 Hunter Pence Jsy B 6.00 15.00
19 Philip Hughes Jsy B 6.00 15.00
20 Trent Oeltjen Jsy B 2.50 6.00
21 Nick Pereira Jsy B 2.50 6.00
22 Wladimir Balentien Jsy B 2.50 6.00
23 Stephen Drew Jsy B 3.00 8.00
24 Davis Romero Jsy A 2.50 6.00
25 Joe Koshansky Jsy B 2.50 6.00
26 Chin-Lung Hu Jsy Black B 10.00 25.00
26b Chin-Lung Hu Jsy Red 60.00 120.00
26c Chin-Lung Hu Jsy Yellow 50.00 100.00
27 Jason Hirsh Jsy B 2.50 6.00
28 Jose Tabata Jsy B 4.00 10.00
29 Eric Hurley Jsy B 2.50 6.00
30 Yung-Chi Chen Jsy Black B 10.00 25.00
30b Yung-Chi Chen Jsy Red 60.00 120.00
30c Yung-Chi Chen Jsy Yellow 50.00 100.00
31 Howie Kendrick Jsy A 3.00 8.00
32 Humberto Sanchez Jsy B 2.50 6.00
33 Alex Gordon Jsy B 6.00 15.00
34 Yunel Escobar Jsy A 6.00 15.00
35 Travis Buck Jsy B 6.00 15.00
36 Billy Butler Jsy B 4.00 10.00
37 Homer Bailey Jsy B 4.00 10.00
38 George Kottaras Jsy B 2.50 6.00
39 Kurt Suzuki Jsy B 2.50 6.00
40 Joaquin Arias Jsy B 2.50 6.00
43 Carlos Gonzalez Jsy B 2.50 6.00
44 Jaime Garcia Jsy B 2.50 6.00
45 Jose Garcia Jsy B 2.50 6.00

2006 Bowman Draft Head of the Class Dual Autograph

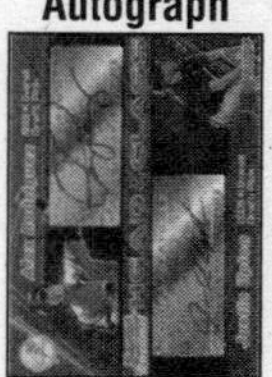

STATED ODDS 1:7640 HOBBY
STATED PRINT RUN 174 SER.#'d SETS
GOLD REF. ODDS 1:56,000 HOBBY
GOLD REF. PRINT RUN 25 SER.#'d SETS
NO GOLD PRICING DUE TO SCARCITY
SUPERFRAC. ODDS 1:261,680 HOBBY
SUPERFRAC. PRINT RUN 1 SER.#'d SET
NO SUPERFRAC.PRICING DUE TO SCARCITY
RU Alex Rodriguez 150.00 250.00
Justin Upton

2006 Bowman Draft Head of the Class Dual Autograph Refractor

STATED ODDS 1:27,000 HOBBY
STATED PRINT RUN 50 SERIAL #'d SETS
RU Alex Rodriguez 175.00 300.00
Justin Upton

2006 Bowman Draft Signs of the Future

GROUP A ODDS 1:973 H, 1:973 R
GROUP B ODDS 1:324 H, 1:323 R
GROUP C ODDS 1:430 H, 1:431 R
GROUP D ODDS 1:1140 H, 1:1140 R
GROUP E ODDS 1:322 H, 1:323 R
GROUP F ODDS 1:387 H, 1:388 R
AG Alex Gordon A 20.00 50.00
BJ Beau Jones B 3.00 8.00
BS Brandon Snyder A 4.00 10.00
CDR Chaz Roe C 3.00 8.00
CI Chris Iannetta A 4.00 10.00
CR Clayton Richard B 3.00 8.00
CRA Cesar Ramos F 3.00 8.00
CTI Craig Italiano C 3.00 8.00
DJ Daryl Jones B 3.00 8.00
HS Henry Sanchez E 3.00 8.00
JB Jay Bruce D 12.50 30.00
JC Jeff Clement B 6.00 15.00
JM Jacob Marceaux C 3.00 8.00
KC Koby Clemens A 8.00 20.00
MC Mike Costanzo F 3.00 8.00
MM Mark McCormick E 3.00 8.00
MO Micah Owings B 6.00 15.00
TB Travis Buck B 4.00 10.00
WT Wade Townsend E 3.00 8.00

2007 Bowman

This 237-card set was released in June, 2007. This set was issued through both hobby and retail channels. The hobby version came in 10-card packs with an $3 SRP which came 24 packs to a box and 12 boxes to a case. In addition, hobby HTA packs were also produced and those packs contained 32 cards with an $10 SRP. Those packs were issued 12 to a box and eight boxes to a case. Card #219, Hideki Okajima comes in three versions; a standard version, an signed version in English and a signed Japanese version. In addition, card number 234 was never issued. Cards number 1-200 feature veterans, cards numbered 201-219 feature 2007 rookies and the aforementioned Okajima signed versions and cards numbered 221-236 are signed. Those cards were inserted into packs at a stated rate of one in 98 hobby and one in 25 HTA packs.

COMP.SET w/o AU's (221) 20.00 50.00
COMMON CARD (1-200) .12 .30
COMMON ROOKIE (201-220) .15 .40
COMMON AUTO (221-236) 4.00 10.00
219/221-236 AU ODDS 1:98 HOBBY, 1:25 HTA
BONDS ODDS 1:51 HTA, 1:610 RETAIL
1-220 PLATE ODDS 1:1468 H, 1:212 HTA
221-231 AU PLATES 1:8200 H, 1:1150 HTA
BONDS PLATE ODDS 1:106,000 HTA
PLATE PRINT RUN 1 SET PER COLOR
BLACK-CYAN-MAGENTA-YELLOW ISSUED
NO PLATE PRICING DUE TO SCARCITY
1 Hanley Ramirez .20 .50
2 Justin Verlander .30 .75
3 Ryan Zimmerman .30 .75
4 Jered Weaver .20 .50
5 Stephen Drew .20 .50
6 Jonathan Papelbon .30 .75
7 Melky Cabrera .12 .30
8 Francisco Liriano .30 .75
9 Prince Fielder .30 .75
10 Dan Uggla .20 .50
11 Jeremy Sowers .12 .30
12 Carlos Quentin .12 .30
13 Chuck James .12 .30
14 Andre Ethier .20 .50
15 Cole Hamels UER .30 .75
(Utley pictured on back)
16 Kenji Johjima .30 .75
17 Chad Billingsley .12 .30
18 Ian Kinsler .12 .30
19 Jason Hirsh .12 .30
20 Nick Markakis .20 .50
21 Jeremy Hermida .12 .30
22 Ryan Shealy .12 .30
23 Scott Olsen .12 .30
24 Russell Martin .12 .30
25 Conor Jackson .12 .30
26 Erik Bedard .12 .30
27 Brian McCann .12 .30
28 Michael Barrett .12 .30
29 Brandon Phillips .12 .30
30 Garrett Atkins .12 .30
31 Freddy Garcia .12 .30
32 Mark Loretta .12 .30
33 Craig Biggio .20 .50
34 Jeremy Bonderman .12 .30
35 Johan Santana .20 .50
36 Jorge Posada .20 .50
37 Brian Bannister .12 .30
38 Carlos Delgado .12 .30
39 Gary Matthews Jr. .12 .30
40 Mike Cameron .12 .30
41 Adrian Beltre .12 .30
42 Freddy Sanchez .12 .30
43 Austin Kearns .12 .30
44 Mark Buehrle .12 .30
45 Miguel Cabrera .20 .50
46 Josh Beckett .20 .50
47 Chone Figgins .12 .30
48 Edgar Renteria .12 .30
49 Derek Lowe .12 .30
50 Ryan Howard .50 1.25
51 Shawn Green .12 .30
52 Jason Giambi .12 .30
53 Ervin Santana .12 .30
54 Jack Wilson .12 .30
55 Roy Oswalt .12 .30
56 Dan Haren .12 .30
57 Jose Vidro .12 .30
58 Kevin Millwood .12 .30
59 Jim Edmonds .20 .50
60 Carl Crawford .12 .30
61 Randy Wolf .12 .30
62 Paul LoDuca .12 .30
63 Johnny Estrada .12 .30
64 Brian Roberts .12 .30
65 Manny Ramirez .20 .50
66 Jose Contreras .12 .30
67 Josh Barfield .12 .30
68 Juan Pierre .12 .30
69 David DeJesus .12 .30
70 Gary Sheffield .12 .30
71 Jon Lieber .12 .30
72 Randy Johnson .30 .75
73 Rickie Weeks .12 .30
74 Brian Giles .12 .30
75 Ichiro Suzuki .50 1.25
76 Nick Swisher .12 .30
77 Justin Morneau .12 .30
78 Scott Kazmir .20 .50
79 Lyle Overbay .12 .30
80 Alfonso Soriano .12 .30
81 Brandon Webb .12 .30
82 Joe Crede .12 .30
83 Corey Patterson .12 .30
84 Kenny Rogers .12 .30
85 Ken Griffey Jr .50 1.25
86 Cliff Lee .12 .30
87 Mike Lowell .12 .30
88 Marcus Giles .12 .30
89 Orlando Cabrera .12 .30
90 Derek Jeter .75 2.00
91 Josh Johnson .12 .30
92 Carlos Guillen .12 .30
93 Bill Hall .12 .30
94 Michael Cuddyer .12 .30
95 Miguel Tejada .12 .30
96 Todd Helton .20 .50
97 C.C. Sabathia .12 .30
98 Tadahito Iguchi .12 .30
99 Jose Reyes .30 .75
100 David Wright .50 1.25
101 Barry Zito .12 .30
102 Jake Peavy .12 .30
103 Richie Sexson .12 .30
104 A.J. Burnett .12 .30
105 Eric Chavez .12 .30
106 Jorge Cantu .12 .30
107 Grady Sizemore .20 .50
108 Bronson Arroyo .12 .30
109 Mike Mussina .20 .50
110 Magglio Ordonez .12 .30
111 Anibal Sanchez .12 .30
112 Jeff Francoeur .30 .75
113 Kevin Youkilis .12 .30
114 Aubrey Huff .12 .30
115 Carlos Zambrano .12 .30
116 Mark Teahen .12 .30
117 Carlos Silva .12 .30
118 Pedro Martinez .20 .50
119 Hideki Matsui .30 .75
120 Mike Piazza .30 .75
121 Jason Schmidt .12 .30
122 Greg Maddux .50 1.25
123 Joe Blanton .12 .30
124 Chris Carpenter .12 .30
125 David Ortiz .30 .75
126 Alex Rios .12 .30
127 Nick Johnson .12 .30
128 Carlos Lee .12 .30
129 Pat Burrell .12 .30
130 Ben Sheets .12 .30
131 Kazuo Matsui .12 .30
132 Adam Dunn .12 .30
133 Jermaine Dye .12 .30
134 Curt Schilling .20 .50
135 Chad Tracy .12 .30
136 Vladimir Guerrero .30 .75
137 Melvin Mora .12 .30
138 John Smoltz .20 .50
139 Craig Monroe .12 .30
140 Dontrelle Willis .12 .30
141 Jeff Francis .12 .30
142 Chipper Jones .30 .75
143 Frank Thomas .30 .75
144 Brett Myers .12 .30
145 Xavier Nady .12 .30
146 Robinson Cano .20 .50
147 Jeff Kent .12 .30
148 Scott Rolen .20 .50
149 Roy Halladay .20 .50
150 Joe Mauer .20 .50
151 Bobby Abreu .12 .30
152 Matt Cain .20 .50
153 Hank Blalock .12 .30
154 Chris Capuano .12 .30
155 Jake Westbrook .12 .30
156 Javier Vazquez .12 .30
157 Garret Anderson .12 .30
158 Aramis Ramirez .12 .30
159 Mark Kotsay .12 .30
160 Matt Kemp .12 .30
161 Adrian Gonzalez .12 .30
162 Felix Hernandez .20 .50
163 David Eckstein .12 .30
164 Curtis Granderson .12 .30
165 Paul Konerko .12 .30
166 Orlando Hudson .12 .30
167 Tim Hudson .12 .30
168 J.D. Drew .12 .30
169 Chien-Ming Wang .50 1.25
170 Jimmy Rollins .12 .30
171 Matt Morris .12 .30
172 Raul Ibanez .12 .30
173 Mark Teixeira .20 .50
174 Ted Lilly .12 .30
175 Albert Pujols .60 1.50
176 Carlos Beltran .12 .30
177 Lance Berkman .12 .30
178 Ivan Rodriguez .20 .50
179 Torii Hunter .12 .30
180 Johnny Damon .20 .50
181 Chase Utley .30 .75
182 Jason Bay .12 .30
183 Jeff Weaver .12 .30
184 Troy Glaus .12 .30
185 Rocco Baldelli .12 .30
186 Rafael Furcal .12 .30
187 Jim Thome .20 .50
188 Travis Hafner .12 .30
189 Matt Holliday .30 .75
190 Andruw Jones .20 .50
191 Ramon Hernandez .12 .30
192 Victor Martinez .12 .30
193 Aaron Hill .12 .30
194 Michael Young .12 .30
195 Vernon Wells .12 .30
196 Mark Mulder .12 .30
197 Derrek Lee .12 .30
198 Tom Glavine .20 .50
199 Chris Young .12 .30
200 Alex Rodriguez .50 1.25
201 Delmon Young (RC) .25 .60
202 Alexi Casilla RC .25 .60
203 Shawn Riggans (RC) .15 .40
204 Jeff Baker (RC) .15 .40
205 Hector Gimenez (RC) .15 .40
206 Ubaldo Jimenez (RC) .15 .40
207 Adam Lind (RC) .15 .40
208 Joaquin Arias (RC) .15 .40
209 David Murphy (RC) .15 .40
210 Daisuke Matsuzaka RC 2.00 5.00
211 Jerry Owens (RC) .15 .40
212 Ryan Sweeney (RC) .15 .40
213 Kei Igawa RC .60 1.50
214 Fred Lewis (RC) .25 .60
215 Philip Humber (RC) .15 .40
216 Kevin Hooper (RC) .15 .40
217 Jeff Fiorentino (RC) .15 .40
218 Michael Bourn (RC) .15 .40
219 Hideki Okajima RC .75 2.00
219b Hideki Okajima English AU 8.00 20.00
219c Hideki Okajima Japanese AU 30.00 60.00
220 Josh Fields (RC) .15 .40
221 Andrew Miller AU RC 10.00 25.00
222 Troy Tulowitzki AU (RC) 12.50 30.00
223 Ryan Braun AU RC 10.00 25.00
224 Oswaldo Navarro AU RC 4.00 10.00
225 Philip Humber AU (RC) 4.00 10.00
226 Mitch Maier AU RC 4.00 10.00
227 Jerry Owens AU (RC) 4.00 10.00
228 Mike Rabelo AU RC 4.00 10.00
229 Delwyn Young AU (RC) 4.00 10.00
230 Miguel Montero AU (RC) 4.00 10.00
231 Akinori Iwamura AU RC 8.00 20.00
232 Matt Lindstrom AU (RC) 4.00 10.00
233 Josh Hamilton AU (RC) 15.00 40.00
235 Elijah Dukes AU RC 6.00 15.00
236 Sean Henn AU (RC) 4.00 10.00
237 Barry Bonds .60 1.50

2007 Bowman Blue

*BLUE 1-200: 2X TO 5X BASIC
*BLUE 201-220: 2X TO 5X BASIC
*BLUE 219 AU/221-236: .4X TO 1X BASIC AU
1-220 ODDS 1:17 HOB, 1:3 HTA, 1:30 RET
221-236 AU ODDS 1:241 HOBBY, 1:60 HTA
BONDS ODDS 1:1261 HTA, 1:15,500 RETAIL
STATED PRINT RUN 500 SERIAL #'d SETS
219b Hideki Okajima English AU 10.00 25.00
237 Barry Bonds 6.00 15.00

2007 Bowman Gold

*GOLD 1-200: 1.2X TO 3X BASIC
*GOLD 201-220: 1.2X TO 3X BASIC
OVERALL GOLD ODDS 1 PER PACK
210 Daisuke Matsuzaka 4.00 10.00

2007 Bowman Orange

*ORANGE 1-200: 3X TO 8X BASIC
*ORANGE 201-220: 3X TO 8X BASIC
*ORANGE 219 AU/221-236: .5X TO 1.2X BASIC AU
1-220 ODDS 1:33 HOB, 1:6 HTA, 1:65 RET
221-236 AU ODDS 1:486 HOBBY, 1:119 HTA
BONDS ODDS 1:2521 HTA, 1:30,000 RETAIL
STATED PRINT RUN 250 SERIAL #'d SETS
219b Hideki Okajima English AU 30.00 60.00
219c Hideki Okajima Japanese AU 40.00 80.00
221 Andrew Miller AU 15.00 40.00
222 Troy Tulowitzki AU 20.00 50.00
233 Josh Hamilton AU 20.00 50.00
237 Barry Bonds 10.00 25.00

2007 Bowman Red

1-220 ODDS 1:6036 HOBBY, 1:1400 HTA
221-236 AU ODDS 1:222,220 H, 1:27,000 HTA
BONDS ODDS 1:211,776 HTA
STATED PRINT RUN 1 SER.#'d SET
NO PRICING DUE TO SCARCITY

2007 Bowman Prospects

COMP.SET w/o AU's (110) 20.00 50.00
111-135 AU ODDS 1:64 HOBBY, 1:16 HTA
1-110 PLATE ODDS 1:1468 H, 1:212 HTA
111-135 AU PLATES 1:8200 H, 1:1150 HTA
PLATE PRINT RUN 1 SET PER COLOR
BLACK-CYAN-MAGENTA-YELLOW ISSUED
NO PLATE PRICING DUE TO SCARCITY
BP1 Cooper Brannon .20 .50
BP2 Jason Taylor .50 1.25
BP3 Shawn O'Malley .20 .50
BP4 Robert Alcombrack .20 .50
BP5 Dellin Betances .60 1.50
BP6 Jeremy Papelbon .20 .50
BP7 Adam Carr .20 .50
BP8 Matthew Clarkson .20 .50
BP9 Darin McDonald .20 .50
BP10 Brandon Rice .20 .50
BP11 Matthew Sweeney .50 1.25

BP12 Scott Deal .20 .50
BP13 Brennan Boesch .20 .50
BP14 Scott Taylor .20 .50
BP15 Michael Brantley .50 1.25
BP16 Yahmed Yema .20 .50
BP17 Brandon Morrow .30 .75
BP18 Cole Garner .20 .50
BP19 Erik Lis .30 .75
BP20 Lucas French .20 .50
BP21 Aaron Cunningham .60 1.50
BP22 Ryan Schreppel .20 .50
BP23 Kevin Russo .20 .50
BP24 Yohan Pino .30 .75
BP25 Michael Sullivan .20 .50
BP26 Trey Shields .20 .50
BP27 Daniel Matienzo .20 .50
BP28 Chuck Lofgren .50 1.25
BP29 Gerrit Simpson .20 .50
BP30 David Haehnel .20 .50
BP31 Marvin Lowrance .20 .50
BP32 Kevin Ardoin .20 .50
BP33 Edwin Maysonet .20 .50
BP34 Derek Griffith .20 .50
BP35 Sam Fuld .50 1.25
BP36 Chase Wright .50 1.25
BP37 Brandon Roberts .20 .50
BP38 Kyle Aselton .20 .50
BP39 Steven Sollmann .20 .50
BP40 Mike Devaney .20 .50
BP41 Charlie Fermaint .20 .50
BP42 Jesse Litsch .30 .75
BP43 Bryan Hansen .20 .50
BP44 Ramon Garcia .20 .50
BP45 John Otness .20 .50
BP46 Trey Hearne .20 .50
BP47 Habelito Hernandez .20 .50
BP48 Edgar Garcia .20 .50
BP49 Seth Fortenberry .20 .50
BP50 Reid Brignac .50 1.25
BP51 Derek Rodriguez .20 .50
BP52 Ervin Alcantara .20 .50
BP53 Thomas Hottovy .20 .50
BP54 Jesus Flores .20 .50
BP55 Matt Palmer .20 .50
BP56 Brian Henderson .20 .50
BP57 John Gragg .20 .50
BP58 Jay Garthwaite .20 .50
BP59 Esmerling Vasquez .20 .50
BP60 Gilberto Mejia .20 .50
BP61 Aaron Jensen .20 .50
BP62 Cedric Brooks .20 .50
BP63 Brandon Mann .20 .50
BP64 Myron Leslie .20 .50
BP65 Ray Aguilar .20 .50
BP66 Jesus Guzman .30 .75
BP67 Sean Thompson .20 .50
BP68 Jarrett Hoffpauir .20 .50
BP69 Matt Goodson .20 .50
BP70 Neal Musser .20 .50
BP71 Tony Abreu .50 1.25
BP72 Tony Peguero .20 .50
BP73 Michael Bertram .20 .50
BP74 Randy Wells .20 .50
BP75 Bradley Davis .20 .50
BP76 Jay Sawatski .20 .50
BP77 Vic Buttler .20 .50
BP78 Jose Oyervidez .20 .50
BP79 Doug Deeds .20 .50
BP80 Dan Dement .20 .50
BP81 Spike Lundberg .20 .50
BP82 Ricardo Nanita .20 .50
BP83 Brad Knox .20 .50
BP84 Will Venable .30 .75
BP85 Greg Smith .20 .50
BP86 Pedro Powell .20 .50
BP87 Gabriel Medina .20 .50
BP88 Duke Sardinha .20 .50
BP89 Mike Madsen .20 .50
BP90 Rayner Bautista .20 .50
BP91 T.J. Nall .20 .50
BP92 Neil Sellers .20 .50
BP93 Andrew Dobies .20 .50
BP94 Leo Daigle .20 .50
BP95 Brian Duensing .20 .50
BP96 Vincent Blue .20 .50
BP97 Fernando Rodriguez .20 .50
BP98 Derin McMains .20 .50
BP99 Adam Bass .20 .50
BP100 Justin Ruggiano .20 .50
BP101 Jared Burton .20 .50
BP102 Mike Parisi .20 .50
BP103 Aaron Peel .20 .50
BP104 Evan Englebrook .20 .50
BP105 Sendy Vasquez .20 .50
BP106 Desmond Jennings .75 2.00
BP107 Clay Harris .20 .50
BP108 Cody Strait .20 .50
BP109 Ryan Mullins .20 .50
BP110 Ryan Webb .20 .50
BP111 Kyle Drabek AU 4.00 10.00
BP112 Evan Longoria AU 40.00 80.00
BP113 Tyler Colvin AU 6.00 15.00
BP114 Matt Long AU 4.00 10.00
BP115 Jeremy Jeffress AU 4.00 10.00
BP116 Kasey Kiker AU 4.00 10.00
BP117 Hank Conger AU 4.00 10.00
BP118 Cody Johnson AU 4.00 10.00
BP119 David Huff AU 4.00 10.00
BP120 Tommy Hickman AU 4.00 10.00
BP121 Chris Parmelee AU 6.00 15.00
BP122 Dustin Evans AU 4.00 10.00
BP123 Brett Sinkbeil AU 4.00 10.00
BP124 Andrew Carpenter AU 4.00 10.00
BP125 Colten Willems AU 4.00 10.00
BP126 Matt Antonelli AU 4.00 10.00
BP127 Marcus Sanders AU 4.00 10.00
BP128 Joshua Rodriguez AU 4.00 10.00
BP129 Keith Weiser AU 4.00 10.00
BP130 Chad Tracy AU 4.00 10.00
BP131 Matthew Sulentic AU 6.00 15.00
BP132 Adam Ottavino AU 4.00 10.00
BP133 Jarrod Saltalamacchia AU 8.00 20.00
BP134 Kyle Blanks AU 4.00 10.00
BP135 Brad Eldred AU 4.00 10.00

2007 Bowman Prospects Blue

*BLUE 1-110: 2X TO 5X BASIC
*BLUE 111-135: .4X TO 1X BASIC AU
1-110 ODDS 1:17 HOB, 1:3 HTA, 1:30 RET

111-135 AU ODDS 1:156 HOBBY, 1:38 HTA
STATED PRINT RUN 500 SERIAL #'d SETS
BP111 Kyle Drabek AU 6.00 15.00
BP112 Evan Longoria AU 50.00 100.00

2007 Bowman Prospects Gold

*GOLD 1-110: .75X TO 2X BASIC
OVERALL GOLD ODDS 1 PER PACK

2007 Bowman Prospects Orange

*ORANGE 1-110: 2.5X TO 6X BASIC
*ORANGE 111-135: .5X TO 1.2X BASIC AU
1-110 ODDS 1:33 HOB, 1:6 HTA, 1:65 RET
111-135 AU ODDS 1:311 HOBBY, 1:77 HTA
STATED PRINT RUN 250 SERIAL #'d SETS
BP111 Kyle Drabek AU 10.00 25.00
BP112 Evan Longoria AU 50.00 100.00
BP113 Tyler Colvin AU 12.50 30.00
BP115 Jeremy Jeffress AU 6.00 15.00
BP117 Hank Conger AU 8.00 20.00
BP121 Chris Parmelee AU 10.00 25.00
BP131 Matthew Sulentic AU 10.00 25.00

2007 Bowman Prospects Red

1-110 ODDS 1:6036 HOBBY, 1:1400 HTA
111-135 AU ODDS 80,000 H, 1:19,252 HTA
STATED PRINT RUN 1 SER.#'d SET
NO PRICING DUE TO SCARCITY

2007 Bowman Signs of the Future

GROUP A ODDS 1:2725 RETAIL
GROUP B ODDS 1:385 RETAIL
GROUP C ODDS 1:268 RETAIL
GROUP D ODDS 1:82 RETAIL
GROUP E ODDS 1:83 RETAIL
GROUP F ODDS 1:89 RETAIL
PRINTING PLATE ODDS 1:8200 H, 1:1150 HTA
PLATE PRINT RUN 1 SET PER COLOR
BLACK-CYAN-MAGENTA-YELLOW ISSUED
NO PLATE PRICING DUE TO SCARCITY
AM Andrew McCutchen 6.00 15.00
AR Adam Russell 3.00 8.00
BB Brian Bixler 3.00 8.00
BM Brandon Moss 4.00 10.00
CG Chris Getz 3.00 8.00
CJS Chris Seddon 3.00 8.00
CL Chris Lubanski 4.00 10.00
CM Chris McConnell 3.00 8.00
JW Jared Wells 3.00 8.00
CS Chad Santos 3.00 8.00
DB Dellin Betances 30.00 60.00
DS Denard Span 4.00 10.00
EH Estee Harris 6.00 15.00
ER Eric Reed 6.00 15.00
FP Felix Pie 8.00 20.00
JB John Baker 3.00 8.00
CR Chris Robinson 3.00 8.00
JBC J. Brent Cox 6.00 15.00
JC Jesus Cota 3.00 8.00
JCB Jordan Brown 3.00 8.00
JD John Drennen 6.00 15.00
JBB John Bowker 3.00 8.00
JJ Jair Jurrjens 12.50 30.00
MM Matt Merricks 3.00 8.00
BF Ben Fritz 3.00 8.00
KC Koby Clemens 6.00 15.00
KD Kyle Drabek 12.50 30.00
KS Kurt Suzuki 4.00 10.00
MA Mike Aviles 3.00 8.00
ME Mike Edwards 3.00 8.00
JDA Jaime D'Antona 3.00 8.00
MN Mike Neu 3.00 8.00
MR Michael Rogers 3.00 8.00
RB Reid Brignac 6.00 15.00
RG Richie Gardner 4.00 10.00
RO Ross Ohlendorf 6.00 15.00
SG Sean Gallagher 4.00 10.00
SK Shane Komine 4.00 10.00
TT Taylor Teagarden 10.00 25.00

2007 Bowman Draft

This 54-card set, featuring 2007 rookies, was released in December, 2007. The set was issued in seven-card packs, which included two Bowman Chrome Draft cards, which came 24 packs to a box and 10 boxes per case.

COMMON RC (1-54) .15 .40
SEE 07 BOWMAN FOR BONDS PRICING
OVERALL PLATE ODDS 1:1294 HOBBY
PLATE PRINT RUN 1 SET PER COLOR
BLACK-CYAN-MAGENTA-YELLOW ISSUED
NO PLATE PRICING DUE TO SCARCITY
BDP1 Travis Buck (RC) .15 .40
BDP2 Matt Chico (RC) .15 .40
BDP3 Justin Upton RC 1.00 2.50
BDP4 Chase Wright RC .40 1.00
BDP5 Kevin Kouzmanoff (RC) .15 .40
BDP6 John Danks RC .15 .40
BDP7 Alejandro De Aza RC .25 .60
BDP8 Jamie Vermilyea RC .15 .40
BDP9 Jesus Flores RC .15 .40
BDP10 Glen Perkins (RC) .15 .40
BDP11 Tim Lincecum RC 1.25 3.00
BDP12 Cameron Maybin RC .75 2.00
BDP13 Brandon Morrow RC .40 1.00
BDP14 Mike Rabelo RC .15 .40
BDP15 Alex Gordon RC .75 2.00
BDP16 Zack Segovia (RC) .15 .40
BDP17 Jon Knott (RC) .15 .40
BDP18 Joba Chamberlain RC 1.50 4.00
BDP19 Danny Putnam (RC) .15 .40
BDP20 Matt DeSalvo (RC) .15 .40
BDP21 Fred Lewis (RC) .25 .60
BDP22 Sean Gallagher (RC) .15 .40
BDP23 Brandon Wood (RC) .15 .40
BDP24 Dennis Dove (RC) .15 .40
BDP25 Hunter Pence (RC) .75 2.00
BDP26 Jarrod Saltalamacchia (RC) .25 .60
BDP27 Ben Francisco (RC) .15 .40
BDP28 Doug Slaten RC .15 .40
BDP29 Tony Abreu RC .40 1.00
BDP30 Billy Butler (RC) .25 .60
BDP31 Jesse Litsch RC .25 .60
BDP32 Nate Schierholtz (RC) .15 .40
BDP33 Jared Burton RC .15 .40
BDP34 Matt Brown RC .15 .40
BDP35 Dallas Braden RC .25 .60
BDP36 Carlos Gomez RC .25 .60
BDP37 Brian Stokes (RC) .15 .40
BDP38 Kory Casto (RC) .15 .40
BDP39 Mark McLemore (RC) .15 .40
BDP40 Andy LaRoche (RC) .15 .40
BDP41 Tyler Clippard (RC) .25 .60
BDP42 Curtis Thigpen (RC) .15 .40
BDP43 Yunel Escobar (RC) .15 .40
BDP44 Andy Sonnanstine RC .15 .40
BDP45 Felix Pie (RC) .15 .40
BDP46 Homer Bailey (RC) .25 .60
BDP47 Kyle Kendrick RC .40 1.00
BDP48 Angel Sanchez RC .15 .40
BDP49 Phil Hughes (RC) .75 2.00
BDP50 Ryan Braun (RC) 1.00 2.50
BDP51 Kevin Slowey (RC) .40 1.00
BDP52 Brendan Ryan (RC) .15 .40
BDP53 Yovani Gallardo (RC) .50 1.25
BDP54 Mark Reynolds RC .60 1.50

2007 Bowman Draft Blue

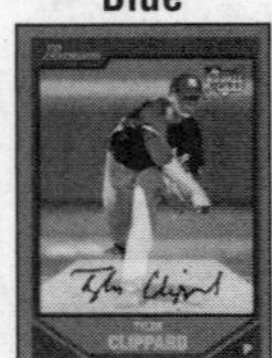

*BLUE: 1.2X TO 3X BASIC
STATED ODDS 1:29 HOBBY,1:84 RETAIL
STATED PRINT RUN 399 SER.#'d SETS
237 Barry Bonds 1.50 4.00

2007 Bowman Draft Gold

*GOLD: .6X TO 1.5X BASIC
APPX.GOLD ODDS ONE PER PACK
237 Barry Bonds .75 2.00

2007 Bowman Draft Red

STATED ODDS 1:10,377 HOBBY
STATED PRINT RUN ONE SER.#'d SET
NO PRICING DUE TO SCARCITY

2007 Bowman Draft Draft Picks

OVERALL PLATE ODDS 1:1294 HOBBY
PLATE PRINT RUN 1 SET PER COLOR
BLACK-CYAN-MAGENTA-YELLOW ISSUED
NO PLATE PRICING DUE TO SCARCITY
BDPP1 Cody Crowell .15 .40
BDPP2 Karl Bolt .25 .60
BDPP3 Corey Brown .25 .60
BDPP4 Tyler Mach .25 .60
BDPP5 Trevor Pippin .25 .60
BDPP6 Ed Easley .15 .40
BDPP7 Cory Luebke .15 .40
BDPP8 Darin Mastroianni .15 .40
BDPP9 Ryan Zink .25 .60
BDPP10 Brandon Hamilton .15 .40
BDPP11 Kyle Lotzkar .25 .60
BDPP12 Freddie Freeman .40 1.00
BDPP13 Nicholas Barnese .25 .60
BDPP14 Travis d'Arnaud .15 .40
BDPP15 Eric Eiland .15 .40
BDPP16 John Ely .15 .40
BDPP17 Oliver Marmol .15 .40
BDPP18 Eric Sogard .15 .40
BDPP19 Lars Davis .15 .40
BDPP20 Sam Runion .15 .40
BDPP21 Austin Gallagher .50 1.25
BDPP22 Matt West .25 .60
BDPP23 Derek Norris .15 .40
BDPP24 Taylor Holiday .25 .60
BDPP25 Dustin Biell .15 .40
BDPP26 Julio Borbon .50 1.25
BDPP27 Brant Rustich .25 .60
BDPP28 Andrew Lambo .60 1.50
BDPP29 Cory Kluber .15 .40
BDPP30 Justin Jackson .25 .60
BDPP31 Scott Carroll .15 .40
BDPP32 Danny Rams .15 .40
BDPP33 Thomas Eager .15 .40
BDPP34 Matt Dominguez .60 1.50
BDPP35 Steven Souza .15 .40
BDPP36 Craig Heyer .15 .40
BDPP37 Michael Taylor .15 .40
BDPP38 Drew Bowman .15 .40
BDPP39 Frank Gailey .15 .40
BDPP40 Jeremy Hefner .15 .40
BDPP41 Reynaldo Navarro .25 .60
BDPP42 Daniel Descalso .15 .40
BDPP43 Leroy Hunt .15 .40
BDPP44 Jason Kiley .15 .40
BDPP45 Ryan Pope .40 1.00
BDPP46 Josh Horton .15 .40
BDPP47 Jason Monti .15 .40
BDPP48 Richard Lucas .15 .40
BDPP49 Jonathan Lucroy .40 1.00
BDPP50 Sean Doolittle .40 1.00
BDPP51 Mike McDade .25 .60
BDPP52 Charlie Culberson .25 .60
BDPP53 Michael Moustakas 1.25 3.00
BDPP54 Jason Heyward 1.50 4.00
BDPP55 David Price 1.50 4.00
BDPP56 Brad Mills .15 .40
BDPP57 John Tolisano .50 1.25
BDPP58 Jarrod Parker .75 2.00
BDPP59 Wendell Fairley .50 1.25
BDPP60 Gary Gattis .15 .40
BDPP61 Madison Bumgarner .75 2.00
BDPP62 Danny Payne .15 .40
BDPP63 Jake Smolinski .50 1.25
BDPP64 Matt LaPorta 1.25 3.00
BDPP65 Jackson Williams .15 .40

2007 Bowman Draft Draft Picks Blue

*BLUE: 2X TO 5X BASIC
STATED ODDS 1:29 HOBBY,1:84 RETAIL
STATED PRINT RUN 399 SER.#'d SETS
BDPP55 David Price 12.50 30.00

2007 Bowman Draft Draft Picks Gold

*GOLD: .75X TO 2X BASIC
APPX.GOLD ODDS ONE PER PACK
BDPP55 David Price 2.50 6.00

2007 Bowman Draft Draft Picks Red

STATED ODDS 1:10,377 HOBBY
STATED PRINT RUN ONE SER.#'d SET
NO PRICING DUE TO SCARCITY

2007 Bowman Draft Future's Game Prospects

OVERALL PLATE ODDS 1:1294 HOBBY
PLATE PRINT RUN 1 SET PER COLOR
BLACK-CYAN-MAGENTA-YELLOW ISSUED
NO PLATE PRICING DUE TO SCARCITY
BDPP66 Pedro Beato .12 .30
BDPP67 Collin Balester .12 .30
BDPP68 Carlos Carrasco .12 .30
BDPP69 Clay Buchholz .75 2.00
BDPP70 Emiliano Fruto .12 .30
BDPP71 Joba Chamberlain 1.25 3.00
BDPP72 Deolis Guerra 1.00 2.50
BDPP73 Kevin Mulvey .30 .75
BDPP74 Franklin Morales .12 .30
BDPP75 Luke Hochevar .40 1.00
BDPP76 Henry Sosa .20 .50
BDPP77 Clayton Kershaw .60 1.50
BDPP78 Rich Thompson .12 .30
BDPP79 Chuck Lofgren .30 .75
BDPP80 Rick VandenHurk .20 .50
BDPP81 Michael Madsen .12 .30
BDPP82 Robinzon Diaz .12 .30
BDPP83 Jeff Niemann .12 .30
BDPP84 Max Ramirez .12 .30
BDPP85 Geovany Soto .50 1.25
BDPP86 Elvis Andrus .20 .50
BDPP87 Bryan Anderson .12 .30
BDPP88 German Duran .50 1.25
BDPP89 J.R. Towles .40 1.00
BDPP90 Alcides Escobar .12 .30
BDPP91 Brian Bocock .12 .30
BDPP92 Chin-Lung Hu .50 1.25
BDPP93 Adrian Cardenas .30 .75
BDPP94 Freddy Sandoval .12 .30
BDPP95 Chris Coghlan .12 .30
BDPP96 Craig Stansberry .12 .30
BDPP97 Brent Lillibridge .12 .30
BDPP98 Joey Votto .20 .50
BDPP99 Evan Longoria 1.50 4.00
BDPP100 Wladimir Balentien .12 .30
BDPP101 Johnny Whittleman .12 .30
BDPP102 Gorkys Hernandez .30 .75
BDPP103 Jay Bruce .75 2.00
BDPP104 Matt Tolbert .12 .30
BDPP105 Jacoby Ellsbury 1.25 3.00
BDPP106 Michael Saunders .40 1.00
BDPP107 Cameron Maybin .60 1.50
BDPP108 Carlos Gonzalez .12 .30
BDPP109 Colby Rasmus .60 1.50
BDPP110 Justin Upton .75 2.00

2007 Bowman Draft Future's Game Prospects Blue

*BLUE: 1.2X TO 3X BASIC
STATED ODDS 1:29 HOBBY,1:84 RETAIL
STATED PRINT RUN 399 SER.#'d SETS

2007 Bowman Draft Future's Game Prospects Gold

*GOLD: .6X TO 1.5X BASIC
APPX.GOLD ODDS ONE PER PACK

2007 Bowman Draft Future's Game Prospects Red

STATED ODDS 1:10,377 HOBBY
STATED PRINT RUN ONE SER.#'d SET
NO PRICING DUE TO SCARCITY

2007 Bowman Draft Future's Game Prospects Jerseys

STATED ODDS 1:24 RETAIL
BDPP68 Carlos Carrasco 3.00 8.00
BDPP69 Clay Buchholz 5.00 12.00
BDPP71 Joba Chamberlain 10.00 25.00
BDPP73 Kevin Mulvey 3.00 8.00
BDPP74 Franklin Morales 3.00 8.00
BDPP75 Luke Hochevar 3.00 8.00
BDPP78 Rich Thompson 3.00 8.00
BDPP83 Jeff Niemann 3.00 8.00
BDPP84 Max Ramirez 3.00 8.00
BDPP89 J.R. Towles 3.00 8.00
BDPP95 Chris Coghlan 3.00 8.00
BDPP96 Craig Stansberry 3.00 8.00
BDPP97 Brent Lillibridge 3.00 8.00
BDPP98 Joey Votto 3.00 8.00
BDPP102 Gorkys Hernandez 3.00 8.00
BDPP105 Jacoby Ellsbury 8.00 20.00
BDPP106 Michael Saunders 3.00 8.00
BDPP107 Cameron Maybin 5.00 12.00
BDPP108 Carlos Gonzalez 3.00 8.00
BDPP110 Justin Upton 6.00 15.00

2007 Bowman Draft Future's Game Prospects Patches

STATED ODDS 1:384 HOBBY
STATED PRINT RUN 99 SER.#'d SETS
BDPP66 Pedro Beato 10.00 25.00
BDPP67 Collin Balester 10.00 25.00
BDPP68 Carlos Carrasco 12.50 30.00
BDPP69 Clay Buchholz 15.00 40.00
BDPP70 Emiliano Fruto 4.00 10.00
BDPP71 Joba Chamberlain 20.00 50.00
BDPP72 Deolis Guerra 12.50 30.00
BDPP73 Kevin Mulvey 6.00 15.00
BDPP74 Franklin Morales 6.00 15.00
BDPP75 Luke Hochevar 10.00 25.00
BDPP76 Henry Sosa 6.00 15.00
BDPP77 Clayton Kershaw 10.00 25.00
BDPP78 Rich Thompson 6.00 15.00
BDPP79 Chuck Lofgren 6.00 15.00
BDPP80 Rick VandenHurk 6.00 15.00
BDPP81 Michael Madsen 4.00 10.00
BDPP82 Robinzon Diaz 4.00 10.00
BDPP83 Jeff Niemann 6.00 15.00
BDPP84 Max Ramirez 10.00 25.00
BDPP85 Geovany Soto 15.00 40.00
BDPP86 Elvis Andrus 10.00 25.00
BDPP87 Bryan Anderson 10.00 25.00
BDPP88 German Duran 6.00 15.00
BDPP89 J.R. Towles 6.00 15.00
BDPP90 Alcides Escobar 6.00 15.00
BDPP91 Brian Bocock 6.00 15.00
BDPP92 Chin-Lung Hu 20.00 50.00
BDPP93 Adrian Cardenas 15.00 40.00
BDPP94 Freddy Sandoval 6.00 15.00
BDPP95 Chris Coghlan 6.00 15.00
BDPP96 Craig Stansberry 4.00 10.00
BDPP97 Brent Lillibridge 6.00 15.00
BDPP98 Joey Votto 10.00 25.00
BDPP99 Evan Longoria 15.00 40.00
BDPP100 Wladimir Balentien 6.00 15.00
BDPP101 Johnny Whittleman 6.00 15.00
BDPP102 Gorkys Hernandez 10.00 25.00
BDPP103 Jay Bruce 15.00 40.00
BDPP104 Matt Tolbert 15.00 40.00
BDPP105 Jacoby Ellsbury 15.00 40.00
BDPP106 Michael Saunders 10.00 25.00
BDPP107 Cameron Maybin 12.50 30.00
BDPP108 Carlos Gonzalez 10.00 25.00
BDPP109 Colby Rasmus 12.50 30.00
BDPP110 Justin Upton 15.00 40.00

2007 Bowman Draft Head of the Class Dual Autograph

STATED ODDS 1:4965 HOBBY
STATED PRINT RUN 174 SER.#'d SETS
EXCHANGE DEADLINE 12/31/2009
GH Jonathan Gilmore 30.00 60.00
Jason Heyward
HP Luke Hochevar 50.00 100.00
David Price EXCH

2007 Bowman Draft Head of the Class Dual Autograph Refractors

*REF: .6X TO 1.5X BASIC
STATED ODDS 1:18,000 HOBBY
STATED PRINT RUN 50 SER.#'d SETS
EXCHANGE DEADLINE 12/31/2009

2007 Bowman Draft Head of the Class Dual Autograph Gold Refractors

STATED ODDS 1:34,500 HOBBY
STATED PRINT RUN 25 SER.#'d SETS
NO PRICING DUE TO SCARCITY
EXCHANGE DEADLINE 12/31/2009

2007 Bowman Draft Head of the Class Dual Autograph SuperFractors

STATED ODDS 1:809,400 HOBBY
STATED PRINT RUN ONE SER.#'d SET
NO PRICING DUE TO SCARCITY

2007 Bowman Draft Signs of the Future

GROUP A ODDS 1:233 RETAIL
GROUP B ODDS 1:30 RETAIL
GROUP C ODDS 1:194 RETAIL
GROUP D ODDS 1:146 RETAIL
GROUP E ODDS 1:2945 RETAIL
AL Anthony Lerew 6.00 15.00
AM Adam Miller 5.00 12.00
BA Brandon Allen 3.00 8.00
CD Chris Dickerson 3.00 8.00
CM Casey McGehee 3.00 8.00
CMC Chris McConnell 4.00 10.00
CMM Carlos Marmol 6.00 15.00
CV Carlos Villanueva 3.00 8.00
FM Fernando Martinez 12.50 30.00
JGA Jamie Garcia 3.00 8.00
JK John Koronka 3.00 8.00
JR John Rheinecker 3.00 8.00
JV Jonathan Van Every 3.00 8.00
PH Philip Humber 4.00 10.00
RD Ryan Delaughter 3.00 8.00
SM Sergio Mitre 3.00 8.00
TC Trevor Crowe 3.00 8.00

2008 Bowman

COMP.SET w/o AU's (220) 10.00 25.00
COMMON CARD (1-200) .12 .30
COMMON ROOKIE (201-220) .15 .40
COMMON AUTO (221-230) 4.00 10.00
AU RC ODDS 1:233 HOBBY
1-220 PLATE ODDS 1:732 HOBBY
221-231 AU PLATES 1:4700 HOBBY
PLATE PRINT RUN 1 SET PER COLOR
BLACK-CYAN-MAGENTA-YELLOW ISSUED
NO PLATE PRICING DUE TO SCARCITY
1 Ryan Braun .40 1.00
2 David DeJesus .12 .30
3 Brandon Phillips .12 .30
4 Mark Teixeira .20 .50
5 Daisuke Matsuzaka .50 1.25
6 Justin Upton .30 .75
7 Jered Weaver .12 .30
8 Todd Helton .20 .50
9 Cameron Maybin .30 .75
10 Erik Bedard .12 .30
11 Jason Bay .12 .30
12 Cole Hamels .30 .75
13 Bobby Abreu .12 .30
14 Carlos Zambrano .12 .30
15 Vladimir Guerrero .30 .75
16 Joe Blanton .12 .30
17 Bengie Molina .12 .30
18 Paul Maholm .12 .30
19 Adrian Gonzalez .20 .50
20 Brandon Webb .20 .50
21 Carl Crawford .12 .30
22 A.J. Burnett .12 .30
23 Dmitri Young .12 .30
24 Jeremy Hermida .12 .30
25 C.C. Sabathia .12 .30
26 Adam Dunn .12 .30
27 Matt Garza .12 .30
28 Adrian Beltre .12 .30
29 Kevin Millwood .12 .30
30 Manny Ramirez .30 .75
31 Javier Vazquez .12 .30
32 Carlos Delgado .12 .30
33 Jason Schmidt .12 .30
34 Torii Hunter .12 .30
35 Ivan Rodriguez .20 .50
36 Nick Markakis .20 .50
37 Gil Meche .12 .30
38 Garrett Atkins .12 .30
39 Fausto Carmona .12 .30
40 Joe Mauer .20 .50
41 Tom Glavine .20 .50
42 Hideki Matsui .30 .75
43 Scott Rolen .20 .50
44 Tim Lincecum .30 .75
45 Prince Fielder .30 .75
46 Ted Lilly .12 .30
47 Frank Thomas .30 .75
48 Tom Gorzelanny .12 .30
49 Lance Berkman .20 .50
50 David Ortiz .30 .75
51 Dontrelle Willis .12 .30
52 Travis Hafner .12 .30
53 Aaron Harang .12 .30
54 Chris Young .12 .30
55 Vernon Wells .12 .30
56 Francisco Liriano .20 .50
57 Eric Chavez .12 .30
58 Phil Hughes .40 1.00
59 Melvin Mora .12 .30
60 Johan Santana .20 .50
61 Brian McCann .20 .50
62 Pat Burrell .12 .30
63 Chris Carpenter .12 .30
64 Brian Giles .12 .30
65 Jose Reyes .20 .50
66 Hanley Ramirez .30 .75
67 Ubaldo Jimenez .12 .30
68 Felix Pie .12 .30
69 Jeremy Bonderman .12 .30
70 Jimmy Rollins .20 .50
71 Miguel Tejada .12 .30
72 Derek Lowe .12 .30
73 Alex Gordon .30 .75
74 John Maine .12 .30
75 Alfonso Soriano .20 .50
76 Richie Sexson .12 .30
77 Ben Sheets .20 .50
78 Hunter Pence .30 .75
79 Magglio Ordonez .20 .50
80 Josh Beckett .20 .50
81 Victor Martinez .12 .30
82 Mark Buehrle .12 .30
83 Jason Varitek .30 .75
84 Chien-Ming Wang .50 1.25
85 Ken Griffey Jr. .50 1.25
86 Billy Butler .12 .30
87 Brad Penny .12 .30
88 Carlos Beltran .12 .30
89 Curt Schilling .20 .50
90 Jorge Posada .20 .50
91 Andruw Jones .12 .30
92 Bobby Crosby .12 .30
93 Freddy Sanchez .12 .30
94 Barry Zito .12 .30
95 Miguel Cabrera .20 .50
96 B.J. Upton .20 .50
97 Matt Cain .12 .30
98 Lyle Overbay .12 .30
99 Austin Kearns .12 .30
100 Alex Rodriguez .50 1.25
101 Rich Harden .12 .30
102 Justin Morneau .12 .30
103 Oliver Perez .12 .30
104 Gary Matthews .12 .30
105 Matt Holliday .20 .50
106 Justin Verlander .20 .50
107 Orlando Cabrera .12 .30
108 Rich Hill .12 .30
109 Tim Hudson .12 .30
110 Ryan Zimmerman .20 .50
111 Roy Oswalt .12 .30
112 Nick Swisher .12 .30
113 Raul Ibanez .12 .30
114 Kelly Johnson .12 .30
115 Alex Rios .12 .30
116 John Lackey .12 .30
117 Robinson Cano .20 .50
118 Michael Young .12 .30
119 Jeff Francis .12 .30
120 Grady Sizemore .20 .50
121 Mike Lowell .12 .30
122 Aramis Ramirez .12 .30
123 Stephen Drew .12 .30
124 Yovani Gallardo .12 .30
125 Chase Utley .30 .75
126 Dan Haren .12 .30
127 Jose Vidro .12 .30
128 Ronnie Belliard .12 .30
129 Yunel Escobar .12 .30
130 Greg Maddux .40 1.00
131 Garret Anderson .12 .30
132 Aubrey Huff .12 .30
133 Paul Konerko .12 .30
134 Dan Uggla .20 .50
135 Roy Halladay .12 .30
136 Andre Ethier .20 .50
137 Orlando Hernandez .12 .30
138 Troy Tulowitzki .20 .50
139 Carlos Guillen .12 .30
140 Scott Kazmir .20 .50
141 Aaron Rowand .12 .30
142 Jim Edmonds .20 .50
143 Jermaine Dye .12 .30
144 Orlando Hudson .12 .30
145 Derrek Lee .20 .50
146 Travis Buck .12 .30
147 Zack Greinke .12 .30
148 Jeff Kent .12 .30
149 John Smoltz .30 .75
150 David Wright .40 1.00
151 Joba Chamberlain .40 1.00
152 Adam LaRoche .12 .30
153 Kevin Youkilis .20 .50
154 Troy Glaus .20 .50
155 Nick Johnson .12 .30
156 J.J. Hardy .12 .30
157 Felix Hernandez .20 .50
158 Khalil Greene .20 .50
159 Gary Sheffield .12 .30
160 Albert Pujols .60 1.50
161 Chuck James .12 .30
162 Rocco Baldelli .12 .30
163 Eric Byrnes .12 .30
164 Brad Hawpe .12 .30
165 Delmon Young .20 .50
166 Chris Young .12 .30
167 Brian Roberts .20 .50
168 Russell Martin .12 .30
169 Hank Blalock .12 .30
170 Yadier Molina .20 .50
171 Jeremy Guthrie .12 .30
172 Chipper Jones .40 1.00
173 Johnny Damon .20 .50
174 Ryan Garko .12 .30
175 Jake Peavy .20 .50
176 Chone Figgins .12 .30
177 Edgar Renteria .12 .30
178 Jim Thome .20 .50
179 Carlos Pena .30 .75
180 Corey Patterson .12 .30
181 Dustin Pedroia .50 1.25
182 Brett Myers .12 .30
183 Josh Hamilton .40 1.00
184 Randy Johnson .30 .75
185 Ichiro Suzuki .50 1.25
186 Aaron Hill .12 .30
187 Jarrod Saltalamacchia .12 .30
188 Michael Cuddyer .12 .30
189 Jeff Francoeur .20 .50
190 Derek Jeter .75 2.00
191 Curtis Granderson .12 .30
192 James Loney .20 .50
193 Brian Bannister .12 .30
194 Carlos Lee .12 .30
195 Pedro Martinez .20 .50
196 Asdrubal Cabrera .12 .30
197 Kenji johjima .12 .30
198 Bartolo Colon .12 .30
199 Jacoby Ellsbury .50 1.25
200 Ryan Howard .40 1.00
201 Radhames Liz RC .25 .60
202 Justin Ruggiano RC .25 .60
203 Lance Broadway (RC) .15 .40
204 Joey Votto (RC) .40 1.00
205 Billy Buckner (RC) .15 .40
206 Joe Koshansky (RC) .15 .40
207 Ross Detwiler RC .40 1.00
208 Chin-Lung Hu (RC) .25 .60
209 Luke Hochevar RC .40 1.00
210 Jeff Clement (RC) .15 .40
211 Troy Patton (RC) .15 .40
212 Hiroki Kuroda RC .25 .60
213 Emilio Bonifacio RC .25 .60
214 Armando Galarraga RC .25 .60
215 Josh Anderson (RC) .15 .40
216 Nick Blackburn RC .25 .60
217 Seth Smith (RC) .15 .40
218 Jonathan Meloan RC .25 .60
219 Alberto Gonzalez RC .25 .60
220 Josh Banks (RC) .15 .40
221 Clay Buchholz AU (RC) 6.00 15.00
222 Nyjer Morgan AU (RC) 4.00 10.00
223 Brandon Jones AU RC 4.00 10.00
224 Sam Fuld AU RC 4.00 10.00
225 Daric Barton AU (RC) 4.00 10.00
226 Chris Seddon AU (RC) 4.00 10.00
227 J.R. Towles AU RC 4.00 10.00
228 Steve Pearce AU RC 4.00 10.00
229 Ross Ohlendorf AU RC 4.00 10.00
230 Clint Sammons AU (RC) 4.00 10.00

2008 Bowman Blue

*BLUE 1-200: 2X TO 5X BASIC
*BLUE 201-220: 2X TO 5X BASIC
*BLUE AU 221-230: .4X TO 1X BASIC AU
1-220 ODDS 1:14 HOBBY,1:32 RETAIL
221-230 AU ODDS 1:620 HOBBY
STATED PRINT RUN 500 SERIAL #'d SETS
221 Clay Buchholz AU 10.00 25.00

2008 Bowman Gold

*GOLD 1-200: 1.2X TO 3X BASIC
*GOLD 201-220: 1.2X TO 3X BASIC
OVERALL GOLD ODDS 1 PER PACK

2008 Bowman Orange

*ORANGE 1-200: 2.5X TO 6X BASIC
*ORANGE 201-220: 2.5X TO 6X BASIC
*ORANGE AU 221-230: .5X TO 1.2X BASIC AU
1-220 ODDS 1:26 HOBBY,1:65 RETAIL
221-230 AU ODDS 1:1160 HOBBY
STATED PRINT RUN 250 SERIAL #'d SETS
221 Clay Buchholz AU 12.50 30.00

2008 Bowman Red

1-220 ODDS 1:4512 HOBBY
221-230 AU ODDS 1:243,648 HOBBY
STATED PRINT RUN 1 SER.#'d SET
NO PRICING DUE TO SCARCITY

2008 Bowman Prospects

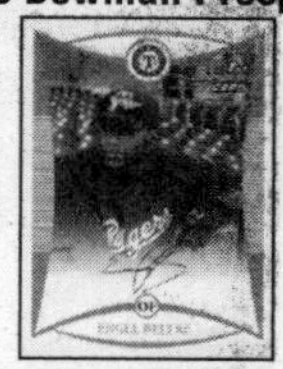

PRINTING PLATE ODDS 1:732 HOBBY
PLATE PRINT RUN 1 SET PER COLOR
BLACK-CYAN-MAGENTA-YELLOW ISSUED
NO PLATE PRICING DUE TO SCARCITY
BP1 Max Sapp .25 .60
BP2 Jamie Richmond .15 .40
BP3 Darren Ford .15 .40
BP4 Sergio Romo .15 .40
BP5 Jacob Butler .15 .40
BP6 Glenn Gibson .15 .40
BP7 Tom Hagan .15 .40
BP8 Michael McCormick .15 .40
BP9 Gregorio Petit .25 .60
BP10 Bobby Parnell .15 .40
BP11 Jeff Kindel .25 .60
BP12 Anthony Claggett .25 .60
BP13 Christopher Frey .15 .40
BP14 Jonah Nickerson .25 .60
BP15 Anthony Martinez .15 .40
BP16 Rusty Ryal .25 .60
BP17 Justin Berg .25 .60
BP18 Gerardo Parra .15 .40
BP19 Wesley Wright .15 .40
BP20 Stephen Chapman .15 .40
BP21 Chance Chapman .15 .40
BP22 Brett Pill .15 .40
BP23 Zachary Phillips .25 .60
BP24 John Raynor .40 1.00
BP25 Danny Duffy .15 .40
BP26 Brian Finegan .15 .40
BP27 Jonathan Venters .15 .40
BP28 Steve Tolleson .15 .40
BP29 Ben Jukich .25 .60
BP30 Matthew Weston .15 .40
BP31 Kyle Mura .15 .40
BP32 Luke Hetherington .15 .40
BP33 Michael Daniel .25 .60
BP34 Jake Renshaw .15 .40
BP35 Greg Halman .50 1.25
BP36 Ryan Khoury .15 .40
BP37 Ryan Ouellette .15 .40
BP38 Mike Brantley .15 .40
BP39 Eric Brown .15 .40
BP40 Jose Duarte .15 .40
BP41 Eli Tintor .15 .40
BP42 Kent Sakamoto .15 .40
BP43 Luke Montz .25 .60
BP44 Alex Cobb .15 .40
BP45 Michael McKenry .15 .40
BP46 Javier Castillo .15 .40
BP47 Jeffrey Stevens .15 .40
BP48 Greg Burns .15 .40
BP49 Blake Johnson .15 .40
BP50 Austin Jackson 1.00 2.50
BP51 Anthony Recker .15 .40
BP52 Luis Durango .75 2.00
BP53 Engel Beltre .50 1.25
BP54 Seth Bynum .15 .40
BP55 Ryan Strieby .25 .60
BP56 Iggy Suarez .15 .40
BP57 Ryan Morris .25 .60
BP58 Scott Van Slyke .15 .40
BP59 Tyler Kolodny .50 1.25
BP60 Joseph Martinez .15 .40
BP61 Aaron Mathews .15 .40
BP62 Phillip Cuadrado .15 .40
BP63 Alex Liddi .25 .60
BP64 Alex Burnett .25 .60
BP65 Brian Barton .25 .60
BP66 David Welch .15 .40
BP67 Kyle Reynolds .15 .40
BP68 Francisco Hernandez .15 .40
BP69 Logan Morrison .75 2.00
BP70 Ronald Ramirez .15 .40
BP71 Brad Miller .15 .40
BP72 Braedyn Pruitt .25 .60
BP73 Jason Fernandez .25 .60
BP74 Joseph Mahoney .15 .40
BP75 Quentin Davis .25 .60
BP76 P.J. Walters .40 1.00
BP77 Jordan Czarniecki .15 .40
BP78 Jonathan Mota .15 .40
BP79 Michael Hernandez .15 .40
BP80 James Guerrero .15 .40
BP81 Chris Johnson .25 .60
BP82 Daniel Cortes .40 1.00
BP83 Sal Sanchez .25 .60
BP84 Sean Henry .15 .40
BP85 Caleb Gindl .15 .40
BP86 Tommy Everidge .15 .40
BP87 Matt Rizzotti .15 .40
BP88 Luis Munoz .15 .40
BP89 Matthew Klimas .15 .40
BP90 Angel Reyes .15 .40
BP91 Sean Danielson .15 .40
BP92 Omar Poveda .25 .60
BP93 Mario Lisson .15 .40
BP94 Brian Mathews .15 .40
BP95 Matthew Buschmann .15 .40
BP96 Greg Thomson .15 .40
BP97 Matt Inouye .15 .40
BP98 Aneury Rodriguez .60 1.50
BP99 Brad Harman .25 .60
BP100 Aaron Bates .40 1.00
BP101 Graham Taylor .15 .40
BP102 Ken Holmberg .15 .40
BP103 Greg Dowling .15 .40
BP104 Ronnie Ray .15 .40
BP105 Michael Wlodarczyk .15 .40
BP106 Jose Martinez .50 1.25
BP107 Jason Stephens .25 .60
BP108 Will Rhymes .15 .40
BP109 Joey Side .15 .40
BP110 Brandon Waring .50 1.25

2008 Bowman Prospects Blue

*BLUE 1-110: 1.2X TO 3X BASIC
1-110 ODDS 1:14 HOBBY,1:32 RETAIL
STATED PRINT RUN 500 SER.#'d SETS

2008 Bowman Prospects Gold

*GOLD 1-110: .75X TO 2X BASIC
OVERALL GOLD ODDS 1 PER PACK

2008 Bowman Prospects Orange

*ORANGE 1-110: 2X TO 5X BASIC
1-110 ODDS 1:26 HOBBY,1:65 RETAIL
STATED PRINT RUN 250 SER.#'d SETS

2008 Bowman Prospects Red

STATED ODDS 1:4512 HOBBY
STATED PRINT RUN 1 SER.#'d SET
NO PRICING DUE TO SCARCITY

2008 Bowman Scouts Autographs

GROUP A ODDS 1:176 HOB,1:410 RET
GROUP B ODDS 1:390 HOB,1:910 RET
EXCHANGE DEADLINE 5/31/2010
AS Alex Smith B 3.00 8.00
BB Bill Buck B 3.00 8.00
BE Bob Engle B 3.00 8.00
BF Bob Fontaine Jr. A 3.00 8.00
BS Bowman Scout A 3.00 8.00
CB Chris Bourjos A 3.00 8.00
DJ Dave Jennings B 3.00 8.00
DL Don Lyle B 3.00 8.00
DO Dan Ontiveros B 3.00 8.00
JC Jerome Cochran B EXCH 3.00 8.00
JD Jon Deeble A EXCH 3.00 8.00
JH Josue Herrera B 3.00 8.00
JL Jerry Lafferty A 3.00 8.00
JM Joe Mason B EXCH 3.00 8.00
LW Leon Wurth A 3.00 8.00
MR Mike Rizzo A 3.00 8.00
RA Ralph Avila A 3.00 8.00
TC Ty Coslow A 3.00 8.00
TCU Tom Couston A 3.00 8.00
TD Tony DeMacio A 3.00 8.00
TK Tim Kelly B 3.00 8.00

2008 Bowman Signs of the Future

GROUP A ODDS 1:26 RETAIL
GROUP B ODDS 1:305 RETAIL
EXCHANGE DEADLINE 5/31/2010
PLATE PRINT RUN 1 SET PER COLOR
BLACK-CYAN-MAGENTA-YELLOW ISSUED
NO PLATE PRICING DUE TO SCARCITY
AC Adam Carr 3.00 8.00
BK Brad Knox 3.00 8.00
BO Brian Omogrosso 3.00 8.00
BW Brian Wilson 3.00 8.00
CN Chris Nowak 4.00 10.00
CR Colby Rasmus 10.00 25.00
CT Clayton Tanner 3.00 8.00
CTI Chris Tillman 6.00 15.00
DS David Shafer 3.00 8.00
EJ Elliot Johnson 3.00 8.00
GM Garrett Mock 3.00 8.00
GP Gerardo Parra 4.00 10.00
GS Greg Smith 4.00 10.00
JE Jack Egbert 3.00 8.00
JG Jaime Garcia 3.00 8.00
JH Joel Hanrahan 3.00 8.00
JHI Jamar Hill 3.00 8.00
JHU Jon Huber 3.00 8.00
JJ Jason Jaramillo 3.00 8.00
JK Josh Kroeger 3.00 8.00
JL Jeff Locke 4.00 10.00
JM Jose Mijares EXCH 3.00 8.00
JV Jonathan Van Every 3.00 8.00
KB Kyle Bloom 3.00 8.00
LM Lou Marson 3.00 8.00
MC Mike Costanzo 3.00 8.00
ME Mitch Einertson 4.00 10.00
MP Matt Peterson 3.00 8.00
RK Ryan Kalish 8.00 20.00
RS Ryan Speier 3.00 8.00
SR Steven Register 3.00 8.00
TC Tyler Colvin 3.00 8.00
TM Tommy Manzella 3.00 8.00
TO Tim Olson 3.00 8.00
WI Will Inman 4.00 10.00

2008 Bowman Draft

This set was released on November 28, 2008. The base set consists of 55 cards.

COMPLETE SET (55) 10.00 25.00
COMMON CARD (1-55) .20 .50
OVERALL PLATE ODDS 1:750 HOBBY
PLATE PRINT RUN 1 SET PER COLOR
BLACK-CYAN-MAGENTA-YELLOW ISSUED
NO PLATE PRICING DUE TO SCARCITY
BDP1 Nick Adenhart (RC) .20 .50
BDP2 Michael Aubrey RC .30 .75
BDP3 Mike Aviles RC .30 .75
BDP4 Burke Badenhop RC .30 .75
BDP5 Wladimir Balentien (RC) .20 .50
BDP6 Collin Balester (RC) .20 .50
BDP7 Josh Banks (RC) .20 .50
BDP8 Wes Bankston (RC) .20 .50
BDP9 Joey Votto (RC) .50 1.25
BDP10 Mitch Boggs (RC) .20 .50
BDP11 Jay Bruce (RC) .75 2.00
BDP12 Chris Carter (RC) .30 .75
BDP13 Justin Christian RC .50 1.25
BDP14 Chris Davis RC .50 1.25
BDP15 Blake DeWitt (RC) .50 1.25
BDP16 Nick Evans RC .20 .50
BDP17 Jaime Garcia RC .20 .50
BDP18 Brett Gardner (RC) .50 1.25
BDP19 Carlos Gonzalez (RC) .20 .50
BDP20 Matt Harrison (RC) .20 .50
BDP21 Micah Hoffpauir RC .30 .75
BDP22 Nick Hundley (RC) .20 .50
BDP23 Eric Hurley (RC) .20 .50
BDP24 Elliot Johnson (RC) .20 .50
BDP25 Matt Joyce RC .50 1.25
BDP26 Clayton Kershaw RC .60 1.50
BDP27 Evan Longoria RC 1.50 4.00
BDP28 Matt Macri (RC) .20 .50
BDP29 Chris Perez RC .30 .75
BDP30 Max Ramirez RC .20 .50
BDP31 Greg Reynolds RC .30 .75
BDP32 Brooks Conrad (RC) .20 .50
BDP33 Max Scherzer RC .50 1.25
BDP34 Daryl Thompson (RC) .20 .50
BDP35 Taylor Teagarden RC .30 .75
BDP36 Rich Thompson RC .30 .75
BDP37 Ryan Tucker (RC) .20 .50
BDP38 Jonathan Van Every RC .20 .50
BDP39 Chris Volstad (RC) .20 .50
BDP40 Michael Hollimon RC .20 .50
BDP41 Brad Ziegler RC .50 1.25
BDP42 Jamie D'Antona (RC) .20 .50
BDP43 Clayton Richard (RC) .20 .50
BDP44 Edgar Gonzalez (RC) .20 .50
BDP45 Bryan LaHair RC .20 .50
BDP46 Warner Madrigal (RC) .20 .50
BDP47 Reid Brignac (RC) .30 .75
BDP48 David Robertson RC .30 .75
BDP49 Nick Stavinoha RC .30 .75
BDP50 Jai Miller (RC) .20 .50
BDP51 Charlie Morton (RC) .20 .50
BDP52 Brandon Boggs (RC) .30 .75
BDP53 Joe Mather RC .30 .75
BDP54 Gregorio Petit RC .30 .75
BDP55 Jeff Samardzija RC .60 1.50

2008 Bowman Draft Blue

*BLUE: 1X TO 2.5X BASIC
STATED ODDS 1:19 HOBBY
STATED PRINT RUN 399 SER.#'d SETS

2008 Bowman Draft Gold

*GOLD: .6X TO 1.5X BASIC
APPX.GOLD ODDS ONE PER PACK

2008 Bowman Draft Red

STATED ODDS 1:6025 HOBBY
STATED PRINT RUN 1 SER.#'d SET
NO PRICING DUE TO SCARCITY

2008 Bowman Draft AFLAC Autographs

STATED ODDS 1:215 HOBBY
AF AnthonyÂ Ferrara 8.00 20.00
AN Adrian Nieto 8.00 20.00
BB Blake Beavan 15.00 40.00
DB Drake Britton 8.00 20.00
DR Danny Rams 10.00 25.00
FF Freddie Freeman 60.00 120.00
IG IsaacÂ Galloway 20.00 50.00
JG Jon Gilmore 20.00 50.00
JH Jason Heyward 200.00 350.00
JS Josh Smoker 15.00 40.00
JT John Tolisano 10.00 25.00
JV Josh Vitters 40.00 80.00
MB Madison Bumgarner 60.00 120.00
MM Michael Main 20.00 50.00
NN Nick Noonan 20.00 50.00
PD Paul Demny 10.00 25.00
QM QuintonÂ Miller 8.00 20.00
RP Rick Porcello 100.00 175.00
TA Tim Alderson 50.00 100.00
XA Xavier Avery 15.00 40.00

2008 Bowman Draft Prospects

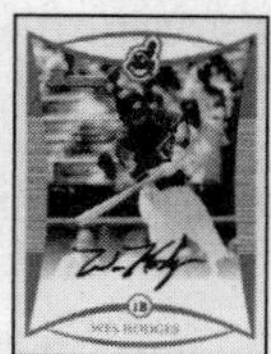

COMPLETE SET (110) 12.50 30.00
COMMON CARD (1-65) .20 .50
OVERALL PLATE ODDS 1:750 HOBBY
PLATE PRINT RUN 1 SET PER COLOR
BLACK-CYAN-MAGENTA-YELLOW ISSUED
NO PLATE PRICING DUE TO SCARCITY
BDPP1 Rick Porcello DP 1.00 2.50
BDPP2 Braeden Schlehuber DP .20 .50
BDPP3 Kenny Wilson DP .20 .50
BDPP4 Jeff Lanning DP .20 .50
BDPP5 Kevin Dubler DP .20 .50
BDPP6 Eric Campbell DP .30 .75
BDPP7 Tyler Chatwood DP .20 .50
BDPP8 Tyreace House DP .20 .50
BDPP9 Adrian Nieto DP .30 .75
BDPP10 Robbie Grossman DP .30 .75
BDPP11 Jordan Danks DP .50 1.25
BDPP12 Jay Austin DP .30 .75
BDPP13 Ryan Perry DP .30 .75
BDPP14 Ryan Chaffee DP .30 .75
BDPP15 Niko Vasquez DP .50 1.25
BDPP16 Shane Dyer DP .20 .50
BDPP17 Benji Gonzalez DP .20 .50
BDPP18 Miles Reagan DP .20 .50
BDPP19 Anthony Ferrara DP .20 .50
BDPP20 Markus Brisker DP .20 .50
BDPP21 Justin Bristow DP .20 .50
BDPP22 Richard Bleier DP .30 .75
BDPP23 Jeremy Beckham DP .30 .75
BDPP24 Xavier Avery DP .50 1.25
BDPP25 Christian Vazquez DP .30 .75
BDPP26 Nick Romero DP .20 .50
BDPP27 Trey Watten DP .20 .50
BDPP28 Brett Jacobson DP .20 .50
BDPP29 Tyler Sample DP .20 .50
BDPP30 T.J. Steele DP .30 .75
BDPP31 Christian Friedrich DP .50 1.25
BDPP32 Graham Hicks DP .30 .75
BDPP33 Shane Peterson DP .30 .75
BDPP34 Brett Hunter DP .30 .75
BDPP35 Tim Federowicz DP .30 .75
BDPP36 Isaac Galloway DP .30 .75
BDPP37 Logan Schafer DP .20 .50
BDPP38 Paul Demny DP .20 .50
BDPP39 Clayton Shunick DP .20 .50
BDPP40 Andrew Liebel DP .20 .50
BDPP41 Brandon Crawford DP .30 .75
BDPP42 Blake Tekotte DP .30 .75
BDPP43 Jason Corder DP .20 .50
BDPP44 Bryan Shaw DP .20 .50
BDPP45 Edgar Olmos DP .20 .50
BDPP46 Dusty Coleman DP .20 .50
BDPP47 Johnny Giavotella DP .20 .50
BDPP48 Tyson Ross DP .30 .75
BDPP49 Brent Morel DP .20 .50
BDPP50 Dennis Raben DP .30 .75
BDPP51 Jake Odorizzi DP .50 1.25
BDPP52 Ryne White DP .30 .75
BDPP53 Devaris Strange-Gordon DP .20 .50
BDPP54 Tim Murphy DP .20 .50
BDPP55 Jake Jefferies DP .20 .50
BDPP56 Anthony Capra DP .20 .50
BDPP57 Kyle Weiland DP .50 1.25
BDPP58 Anthony Bass DP .30 .75
BDPP59 Scott Green DP .20 .50
BDPP60 Zeke Spruill DP .50 1.25
BDPP61 L.J. Hoes DP .50 1.25
BDPP62 Tyler Cline DP .20 .50
BDPP63 Matt Cerda DP .20 .50
BDPP64 Bobby Lanigan DP .20 .50
BDPP65 Mike Sheridan DP .20 .50
BDPP66 Carlos Carrasco FG .20 .50
BDPP67 Nate Schierholtz FG .20 .50
BDPP68 Jesus Delgado FG .20 .50
BDPP69 Andrew McCutchen FG .30 .75
BDPP70 Shairon Martis FG .20 .50
BDPP71 Matt LaPorta FG .50 1.25
BDPP72 Eddie Morlan FG .20 .50
BDPP73 Greg Golson FG .20 .50
BDPP74 Julio Pimentel FG .20 .50
BDPP75 Dexter Fowler FG .20 .50
BDPP76 Henry Rodriguez FG .20 .50
BDPP77 Cliff Pennington FG .20 .50
BDPP78 Hector Rondon FG .20 .50
BDPP79 Wes Hodges FG .20 .50
BDPP80 Polin Trinidad FG .20 .50
BDPP81 Chris Getz FG .20 .50
BDPP82 Welington Castillo FG .20 .50
BDPP83 Mat Gamel FG .30 .75
BDPP84 Pablo Sandoval FG .20 .50
BDPP85 Jason Donald FG .20 .50
BDPP86 Jesus Montero FG .30 .75
BDPP87 Jamie D'Antona FG .20 .50
BDPP88 Will Inman FG .20 .50
BDPP89 Elvis Andrus FG .20 .50
BDPP90 Taylor Teagarden FG .30 .75
BDPP91 Scott Campbell FG .20 .50
BDPP92 Jake Arrieta FG .20 .50
BDPP93 Juan Francisco FG .20 .50
BDPP94 Lou Marson FG .20 .50
BDPP95 Luke Hughes FG .20 .50
BDPP96 Bryan Anderson FG .20 .50
BDPP97 Ramiro Pena FG .20 .50
BDPP98 Jesse Todd FG .20 .50
BDPP99 Gorkys Hernandez FG .20 .50
BDPP100 Casey Weathers FG .20 .50
BDPP101 Fernando Martinez FG .30 .75
BDPP102 Clayton Richard FG .20 .50
BDPP103 Gerardo Parra FG .20 .50
BDPP104 Kevin Pucetas FG .30 .75
BDPP105 Wilkin Ramirez FG .20 .50
BDPP106 Ryan Mattheus FG .20 .50
BDPP107 Angel Villalona FG .50 1.25
BDPP108 Brett Anderson FG .20 .50
BDPP109 Chris Valaika FG .20 .50
BDPP110 Trevor Cahill FG .20 .50

2008 Bowman Draft Prospects Blue

*BLUE: 1.5X TO 4X BASIC
STATED ODDS 1:19 HOBBY
STATED PRINT RUN 399 SER.#'d SETS

2008 Bowman Draft Prospects Gold

*GOLD: .75X TO 2X BASIC
APPX.GOLD ODDS ONE PER PACK

2008 Bowman Draft Prospects Red

STATED ODDS 1:6025 HOBBY
STATED PRINT RUN 1 SER.#'d SET
NO PRICING DUE TO SCARCITY

2008 Bowman Draft Prospects Jerseys

RANDOM INSERTS IN RETAIL PACKS
NO PRICING DUE TO LACK OF MARKET INFO
BDPP68 Jesus Delgado FG
BDPP69 Andrew McCutchen FG
BDPP70 Shairon Martis FG
BDPP71 Matt LaPorta FG
BDPP72 Eddie Morlan FG
BDPP74 Julio Pimentel FG
BDPP75 Dexter Fowler FG
BDPP77 Cliff Pennington FG
BDPP80 Polin Trinidad FG
BDPP82 Welington Castillo FG
BDPP87 Jamie D'Antona FG
BDPP88 Will Inman FG
BDPP93 Juan Francisco FG
BDPP94 Lou Marson FG
BDPP96 Bryan Anderson FG
BDPP97 Ramiro Pena FG
BDPP98 Jesse Todd FG
BDPP102 Clayton Richard FG
BDPP103 Gerardo Parra FG
BDPP105 Wilkin Ramirez FG

2008 Bowman Draft Signs of the Future

RANDOM INSERTS IN RETAIL PACKS
NO PRICING DUE TO LACK OF MARKET INFO
AC Adrain Cardenas
BP Billy Petrick
BS Brad Salmon
CW Corey Wimberly
DM Daniel Murphy
DS David Shafer
EM Evan MacLane
FG Freddy Galvis
GK George Kontos
JW Johnny Whittleman
KD Kyle Drabek
OP Omar Poveda
OS Oswaldo Sosa
TD Travis D'Arnaud
TS Travis Snider

1997 Bowman Chrome

The 1997 Bowman Chrome set was issued in one series totalling 300 cards and was distributed in four-card packs with a suggested retail price of $3.00. The cards parallel the 1997 Bowman brand and the 300 card set represents a selection of top cards taken from the 441-card 1997 Bowman set. The product was released in the Winter, after the end of the 1997 season. The fronts feature color action player photos printed on dazzling chromium stock. The backs carry player information. Rookie Cards in this set include Adrian Beltre, Kris Benson, Lance Berkman, Kris Benson, Eric Chavez, Jose Cruz Jr., Travis Lee, Aramis Ramirez, Miguel Tejada, Vernon Wells and Kerry Wood.

COMPLETE SET (300) 75.00 150.00
1 Derek Jeter 1.25 3.00
2 Chipper Jones .50 1.25
3 Hideo Nomo .50 1.25
4 Tim Salmon .30 .75
5 Robin Ventura .20 .50
6 Tony Clark .20 .50
7 Barry Larkin .30 .75
8 Paul Molitor .30 .75
9 Andy Benes .20 .50
10 Ryan Klesko .20 .50
11 Mark McGwire 1.25 3.00
12 Ken Griffey Jr. .75 2.00
13 Robb Nen .20 .50
14 Cal Ripken 1.50 4.00
15 John Valentin .20 .50
16 Ricky Bottalico .20 .50
17 Mike Lansing .20 .50
18 Ryne Sandberg .75 2.00
19 Carlos Delgado .20 .50
20 Craig Biggio .30 .75
21 Eric Karros .20 .50
22 Kevin Appier .20 .50
23 Mariano Rivera .50 1.25
24 Vinny Castilla .20 .50
25 Juan Gonzalez .20 .50
26 Al Martin .20 .50
27 Jeff Cirillo .20 .50
28 Ray Lankford .20 .50
29 Manny Ramirez .30 .75
30 Roberto Alomar .30 .75
31 Will Clark .30 .75
32 Chuck Knoblauch .20 .50
33 Harold Baines .20 .50
34 Edgar Martinez .30 .75
35 Mike Mussina .30 .75
36 Kevin Brown .20 .50
37 Dennis Eckersley .20 .50
38 Tino Martinez .30 .75
39 Raul Mondesi .20 .50
40 Sammy Sosa .50 1.25
41 John Smoltz .30 .75
42 Billy Wagner .20 .50
43 Ken Caminiti .20 .50
44 Wade Boggs .30 .75
45 Andres Galarraga .20 .50
46 Roger Clemens 1.00 2.50
47 Matt Williams .20 .50
48 Albert Belle .20 .50
49 Jeff King .20 .50
50 John Wetteland .20 .50
51 Deion Sanders .30 .75
52 Ellis Burks .20 .50
53 Pedro Martinez .30 .75
54 Kenny Lofton .20 .50
55 Randy Johnson .50 1.25
56 Bernie Williams .30 .75
57 Marquis Grissom .20 .50
58 Gary Sheffield .20 .50
59 Curt Schilling .20 .50
60 Reggie Sanders .20 .50
61 Bobby Higginson .20 .50
62 Moises Alou .20 .50
63 Tom Glavine .30 .75
64 Mark Grace .30 .75
65 Rafael Palmeiro .30 .75
66 John Olerud .20 .50
67 Dante Bichette .20 .50
68 Jeff Bagwell .30 .75
69 Barry Bonds 1.25 3.00
70 Pat Hentgen .20 .50
71 Jim Thome .30 .75
72 Andy Pettitte .30 .75
73 Jay Bell .20 .50
74 Jim Edmonds .20 .50
75 Ron Gant .20 .50
76 David Cone .20 .50
77 Jose Canseco .30 .75
78 Jay Buhner .20 .50
79 Greg Maddux .75 2.00
80 Lance Johnson .20 .50
81 Travis Fryman .20 .50
82 Paul O'Neill .30 .75
83 Ivan Rodriguez .30 .75
84 Fred McGriff .30 .75
85 Mike Piazza .75 2.00
86 Brady Anderson .20 .50
87 Marty Cordova .20 .50
88 Joe Carter .20 .50
89 Brian Jordan .20 .50
90 David Justice .20 .50
91 Tony Gwynn .60 1.50
92 Larry Walker .20 .50
93 Mo Vaughn .20 .50
94 Sandy Alomar Jr. .20 .50
95 Rusty Greer .20 .50
96 Roberto Hernandez .20 .50
97 Hal Morris .20 .50
98 Todd Hundley .20 .50
99 Rondell White .20 .50
100 Frank Thomas .50 1.25
101 Bubba Trammell RC .60 1.50
102 Sidney Ponson RC 1.00 2.50
103 Ricky Ledee RC .60 1.50
104 Brett Tomko .20 .50
105 Braden Looper RC .40 1.00
106 Jason Dickson .20 .50
107 Chad Green RC .40 1.00
108 R.A. Dickey RC .40 1.00
109 Jeff Liefer .20 .50
110 Richard Hidalgo .20 .50
111 Chad Hermansen RC .40 1.00
112 Felix Martinez .20 .50
113 J.J. Johnson .20 .50
114 Todd Dunwoody .20 .50
115 Katsuhiro Maeda .20 .50
116 Darin Erstad .20 .50
117 Elieser Marrero .20 .50
118 Bartolo Colon .20 .50
119 Ugueth Urbina .20 .50
120 Jaime Bluma .20 .50
121 Seth Greisinger RC .40 1.00
122 Jose Cruz Jr. RC .60 1.50
123 Todd Dunn .20 .50
124 Justin Towle RC .40 1.00
125 Brian Rose .20 .50
126 Jose Guillen .20 .50
127 Andruw Jones .30 .75
128 Mark Kotsay RC 1.50 4.00
129 Wilton Guerrero .20 .50
130 Jacob Cruz .20 .50
131 Mike Sweeney .20 .50
132 Matt Morris .20 .50
133 John Thomson .20 .50
134 Javier Valentin .20 .50
135 Mike Drumright RC .40 1.00
136 Michael Barrett .20 .50
137 Tony Saunders RC .40 1.00
138 Kevin Brown .20 .50
139 Anthony Sanders RC .40 1.00
140 Jeff Abbott .20 .50
141 Eugene Kingsale .20 .50
142 Paul Konerko .30 .75
143 Randall Simon RC .60 1.50
144 Freddy Adrian Garcia .20 .50
145 Karim Garcia .20 .50
146 Carlos Guillen .20 .50
147 Aaron Boone .20 .50
148 Donnie Sadler .20 .50
149 Brooks Kieschnick .20 .50
150 Scott Spiezio .20 .50
151 Kevin Orie .20 .50
152 Russ Johnson .20 .50
153 Livan Hernandez .20 .50
154 Vladimir Nunez RC .40 1.00
155 Pokey Reese .20 .50
156 Chris Carpenter .20 .50
157 Eric Milton RC .60 1.50
158 Richie Sexson .20 .50
159 Carl Pavano .20 .50
160 Pat Cline .20 .50
161 Ron Wright .20 .50
162 Dante Powell .20 .50
163 Mark Bellhorn .20 .50
164 George Lombard .20 .50
165 Paul Wilder RC .40 1.00
166 Brad Fullmer .20 .50
167 Kris Benson RC 1.00 2.50
168 Torii Hunter .20 .50
169 D.T. Cromer RC .40 1.00
170 Nelson Figueroa RC .40 1.00
171 Hiram Bocachica RC .40 1.00
172 Shane Monahan .20 .50
173 Juan Melo .20 .50
174 Calvin Pickering RC .40 1.00
175 Reggie Taylor .20 .50
176 Geoff Jenkins .20 .50
177 Steve Rain RC .40 1.00
178 Nerio Rodriguez RC .40 1.00
179 Derrick Gibson .20 .50
180 Darin Blood .20 .50
181 Ben Davis .20 .50
182 Adrian Beltre RC 3.00 8.00
183 Kerry Wood RC 5.00 12.00
184 Nate Rolison RC .40 1.00
185 Fernando Tatis RC .40 1.00
186 Jake Westbrook RC 1.00 2.50
187 Edwin Diaz .20 .50
188 Joe Fontenot RC .40 1.00
189 Matt Halloran RC .40 1.00
190 Matt Clement RC 1.00 2.50
191 Todd Greene .20 .50
192 Eric Chavez RC 4.00 10.00
193 Edgard Velazquez .20 .50
194 Bruce Chen RC 1.00 2.50
195 Jason Brester .20 .50
196 Chris Reitsma RC .60 1.50
197 Neifi Perez .20 .50
198 Hideki Irabu RC .60 1.50
199 Don Denbow RC .40 1.00
200 Derrek Lee .30 .75
201 Todd Walker .20 .50
202 Scott Rolen .30 .75
203 Wes Helms .20 .50
204 Bob Abreu .30 .75
205 John Patterson RC 1.50 4.00
206 Alex Gonzalez RC 1.00 2.50
207 Grant Roberts RC .40 1.00
208 Jeff Suppan .20 .50
209 Luke Wilcox .20 .50
210 Marlon Anderson .20 .50
211 Mike Caruso RC .40 1.00
212 Roy Halladay RC 4.00 10.00
213 Jeremi Gonzalez RC .40 1.00
214 Aramis Ramirez RC 4.00 10.00
215 Dee Brown RC .40 1.00
216 Justin Thompson .20 .50
217 Danny Clyburn .20 .50
218 Bruce Aven .20 .50
219 Keith Foulke RC 1.50 4.00
220 Shannon Stewart .20 .50
221 Larry Barnes RC .40 1.00
222 Mark Johnson RC .40 1.00
223 Randy Winn .20 .50
224 Nomar Garciaparra .75 2.00
225 Jacque Jones RC 1.50 4.00
226 Chris Clemons .20 .50
227 Todd Helton .50 1.25
228 Ryan Brannan RC .40 1.00
229 Alex Sanchez RC .60 1.50
230 Russell Branyan .20 .50
231 Daryle Ward .40 1.00
232 Kevin Witt .20 .50
233 Gabby Martinez .20 .50
234 Preston Wilson .20 .50
235 Donzell McDonald RC .40 1.00
236 Orlando Cabrera RC 1.50 4.00
237 Brian Banks .20 .50
238 Robbie Bell .40 1.00
239 Brad Rigby .20 .50
240 Scott Elarton .20 .50
241 Donny Leon RC .40 1.00
242 Abraham Nunez RC .40 1.00
243 Adam Eaton RC 1.00 2.50
244 Octavio Dotel RC .60 1.50
245 Sean Casey 1.00 2.50
246 Joe Lawrence RC .40 1.00
247 Adam Johnson RC .40 1.00
248 Ronnie Belliard RC 1.25 3.00
249 Bobby Estalella .20 .50
250 Corey Lee RC .40 1.00
251 Mike Cameron .20 .50
252 Kerry Robinson RC .40 1.00
253 A.J. Zapp RC .40 1.00
254 Jarrod Washburn .20 .50
255 Ben Grieve .20 .50
256 Javier Vazquez RC 1.50 4.00
257 Travis Lee RC .60 1.50
258 Dennis Reyes RC .40 1.00
259 Danny Buxbaum .20 .50
260 Kelvim Escobar RC 1.00 2.50
261 Danny Klassen .20 .50
262 Ken Cloude RC .40 1.00
263 Gabe Alvarez .20 .50
264 Clayton Bruner RC .40 1.00
265 Jason Marquis RC 1.00 2.50
266 Jamey Wright .20 .50
267 Matt Snyder RC .40 1.00
268 Josh Garrett RC .40 1.00
269 Juan Encarnacion .20 .50
270 Heath Murray .20 .50
271 Brent Butler RC .40 1.00
272 Danny Peoples RC .40 1.00
273 Miguel Tejada RC 5.00 12.00
274 Jim Pittsley .20 .50
275 Dmitri Young .20 .50
276 Vladimir Guerrero .50 1.25
277 Cole Liniak RC .40 1.00
278 Ramon Hernandez .20 .50
279 Cliff Politte RC .40 1.00
280 Mel Rosario RC .40 1.00
281 Jorge Carrion RC .40 1.00
282 John Barnes RC .40 1.00
283 Chris Stowe RC .40 1.00
284 Vernon Wells RC 5.00 12.00
285 Brett Caradonna RC .40 1.00
286 Scott Hodges RC .40 1.00
287 Jon Garland RC 2.50 6.00
288 Nathan Haynes RC .40 1.00
289 Geoff Goetz RC .40 1.00
290 Adam Kennedy RC 1.00 2.50
291 T.J. Tucker RC .40 1.00
292 Aaron Akin RC .40 1.00
293 Jayson Werth RC 1.25 3.00
294 Glenn Davis RC .40 1.00
295 Mark Mangum RC .40 1.00
296 Troy Cameron RC .40 1.00
297 J.J. Davis RC .40 1.00
298 Lance Berkman RC 6.00 15.00
299 Jason Standridge RC .40 1.00
300 Jason Dellaero RC .40 1.00

1997 Bowman Chrome International

Randomly inserted in packs at the rate of one in four, this 300-card set is parallel to the base set and is distinguished by the flag on the background of each card front identifying the country where that player was born.

*STARS: 1.25X TO 3X BASIC CARDS
*ROOKIES: .4X TO 1X BASIC CARDS
298 Lance Berkman 20.00 50.00

1997 Bowman Chrome International Refractors

Randomly inserted in packs at the rate of one in 24, this 300-card set is a parallel version of the Bowman Chrome International set and is similar in design. The difference is found in the refractive quality of the card front.

*STARS: 6X TO 15X BASIC CARDS
*ROOKIES: 2X TO 5X BASIC CARDS
183 Kerry Wood 30.00 60.00
273 Miguel Tejada 30.00 60.00
284 Vernon Wells 30.00 60.00
298 Lance Berkman 75.00 150.00

1997 Bowman Chrome Refractors

Randomly inserted in packs at the rate of one in 12, this 300-card set is parallel to the base set and is similar in design. The difference can be found in the refractive quality of the cards fronts.

*STARS: 3X TO 8X BASIC CARDS
*ROOKIES: 1.5X TO 4X BASIC CARDS
183 Kerry Wood 20.00 50.00
273 Miguel Tejada 20.00 50.00
284 Vernon Wells 20.00 50.00
298 Lance Berkman 30.00 60.00

1997 Bowman Chrome 1998 ROY Favorites

Randomly inserted in packs at the rate of one in 24, cards from this 15-card set features color action photos of 1998 Rookie of the Year prospective candidates printed on chromium cards.

COMPLETE SET (15) 12.50 25.00
*REFRACTORS: .75X TO 2X BASIC ROY
REFRACTOR STATED ODDS 1:72
ROY1 Jeff Abbott .60 1.50
ROY2 Karim Garcia .60 1.50
ROY3 Todd Helton 1.50 4.00
ROY4 Richard Hidalgo .60 1.50
ROY5 Geoff Jenkins .60 1.50
ROY6 Russ Johnson .60 1.50
ROY7 Paul Konerko 1.00 2.50
ROY8 Mark Kotsay 1.00 2.50
ROY9 Ricky Ledee .40 1.00
ROY10 Travis Lee .40 1.00
ROY11 Derrek Lee 1.00 2.50
ROY12 Elieser Marrero .60 1.50
ROY13 Juan Melo .60 1.50
ROY14 Brian Rose .60 1.50
ROY15 Fernando Tatis .25 .60

1997 Bowman Chrome Scout's Honor Roll

Randomly inserted in packs at a rate of one in 12, this 15-card set features color photos of top prospects and rookies printed on chromium cards. The backs carry player information.

COMPLETE SET (15) 15.00 30.00
*REF: .75X TO 2X BASIC CHR.HONOR
REFRACTOR STATED ODDS 1:36
SHR1 Dmitri Young .50 1.25
SHR2 Bob Abreu .75 2.00
SHR3 Vladimir Guerrero 1.25 3.00
SHR4 Paul Konerko .75 2.00
SHR5 Kevin Orie .50 1.25
SHR6 Todd Walker .50 1.25
SHR7 Ben Grieve .50 1.25
SHR8 Darin Erstad .50 1.25
SHR9 Derrek Lee .75 2.00
SHR10 Jose Cruz Jr. .50 1.25
SHR11 Scott Rolen .75 2.00
SHR12 Travis Lee .50 1.25
SHR13 Andruw Jones .75 2.00
SHR14 Wilton Guerrero .50 1.25
SHR15 Nomar Garciaparra 2.00 5.00

1998 Bowman Chrome

The 1998 Bowman Chrome set was issued in two separate series with a total of 441 cards. The four-card packs retailed for $3.00 each. These cards are parallel to the regular Bowman set but with a premium Chrome finish. Unlike the 1997 brand, the 1998 issue parallels the entire Bowman brand. Rookie Cards include Ryan Anderson, Jack Cust, Troy Glaus, Orlando Hernandez, Gabe Kapler, Carlos Lee, Ted Lilly, Ruben Mateo, Kevin Millwood, Magglio Ordonez and Jimmy Rollins.

COMPLETE SET (441) 60.00 160.00
COMP. SERIES 1 (221) 30.00 80.00
COMP. SERIES 2 (220) 30.00 80.00
1 Nomar Garciaparra .75 2.00
2 Scott Rolen .30 .75
3 Andy Pettitte .30 .75
4 Ivan Rodriguez .30 .75
5 Mark McGwire 1.25 3.00
6 Jason Dickson .20 .50
7 Jose Cruz Jr. .20 .50
8 Jeff Kent .20 .50
9 Mike Mussina .30 .75
10 Jason Kendall .20 .50
11 Brett Tomko .20 .50
12 Jeff King .20 .50
13 Brad Radke .20 .50
14 Robin Ventura .20 .50
15 Jeff Bagwell .30 .75
16 Greg Maddux .75 2.00
17 John Jaha .20 .50
18 Mike Piazza .75 2.00
19 Edgar Martinez .30 .75
20 David Justice .20 .50
21 Todd Hundley .20 .50
22 Tony Gwynn .60 1.50
23 Larry Walker .20 .50
24 Bernie Williams .30 .75
25 Edgar Renteria .20 .50
26 Rafael Palmeiro .30 .75
27 Tim Salmon .30 .75
28 Matt Morris .20 .50
29 Shawn Estes .20 .50
30 Vladimir Guerrero .50 1.25
31 Fernando Tatis .20 .50
32 Justin Thompson .20 .50
33 Ken Griffey Jr. .75 2.00
34 Edgardo Alfonzo .20 .50
35 Mo Vaughn .20 .50
36 Marty Cordova .20 .50
37 Craig Biggio .30 .75
38 Roger Clemens 1.00 2.50
39 Mark Grace .30 .75
40 Ken Caminiti .20 .50
41 Tony Womack .20 .50
42 Albert Belle .20 .50
43 Tino Martinez .30 .75
44 Sandy Alomar Jr. .20 .50
45 Jeff Cirillo .20 .50
46 Jason Giambi .20 .50
47 Darin Erstad .20 .50
48 Livan Hernandez .20 .50
49 Mark Grudzielanek .20 .50
50 Sammy Sosa .50 1.25
51 Curt Schilling .20 .50
52 Brian Hunter .20 .50
53 Neifi Perez .20 .50
54 Todd Walker .20 .50
55 Jose Guillen .20 .50
56 Jim Thome .30 .75
57 Tom Glavine .30 .75
58 Todd Greene .20 .50
59 Rondell White .20 .50
60 Roberto Alomar .30 .75
61 Tony Clark .20 .50
62 Vinny Castilla .20 .50
63 Barry Larkin .30 .75
64 Hideki Irabu .20 .50
65 Johnny Damon .30 .75
66 Juan Gonzalez .20 .50
67 John Olerud .20 .50
68 Gary Sheffield .20 .50
69 Raul Mondesi .20 .50
70 Chipper Jones .50 1.25
71 David Ortiz 2.50 6.00
72 Warren Morris RC .40 1.00
73 Alex Gonzalez .20 .50
74 Nick Bierbrodt .20 .50
75 Roy Halladay .20 .50
76 Danny Buxbaum .20 .50
77 Adam Kennedy .20 .50
78 Jared Sandberg .20 .50
79 Michael Barrett .20 .50
80 Gil Meche .60 1.50
81 Jayson Werth .20 .50
82 Abraham Nunez .20 .50
83 Ben Petrick .20 .50
84 Brett Caradonna .20 .50
85 Mike Lowell RC 2.50 6.00
86 Clay Bruner .20 .50
87 John Curtice RC .60 1.50
88 Bobby Estalella .20 .50
89 Juan Melo .20 .50
90 Arnold Gooch .20 .50
91 Kevin Millwood RC 1.50 4.00
92 Richie Sexson .20 .50
93 Orlando Cabrera .20 .50
94 Pat Cline .20 .50
95 Anthony Sanders .20 .50
96 Russ Johnson .20 .50
97 Ben Grieve .20 .50
98 Kevin McGlinchy .20 .50
99 Paul Wilder .20 .50
100 Russ Ortiz .20 .50
101 Ryan Jackson RC .40 1.00
102 Heath Murray .20 .50
103 Brian Rose .20 .50
104 R.Radmanovich RC .40 1.00
105 Ricky Ledee .20 .50
106 Jeff Wallace RC .40 1.00
107 Ryan Minor RC .40 1.00
108 Dennis Reyes .20 .50
109 James Manias .20 .50
110 Chris Carpenter .20 .50
111 Daryle Ward .20 .50
112 Vernon Wells .20 .50
113 Chad Green .20 .50
114 Mike Stoner RC .40 1.00
115 Brad Fullmer .20 .50
116 Adam Eaton .20 .50
117 Jeff Liefer .20 .50
118 Corey Koskie RC 1.00 2.50
119 Todd Helton .30 .75
120 Jaime Jones RC .40 1.00
121 Mel Rosario .20 .50
122 Geoff Goetz .20 .50
123 Adrian Beltre .20 .50
124 Jason Dellaero .20 .50
125 Gabe Kapler RC 1.00 2.50
126 Scott Schoeneweis .20 .50
127 Ryan Brannan .20 .50
128 Aaron Akin .20 .50
129 Ryan Anderson RC .40 1.00
130 Brad Penny .20 .50
131 Bruce Chen .20 .50
132 Eli Marrero .20 .50
133 Eric Chavez .20 .50
134 Troy Glaus RC 3.00 8.00
135 Troy Cameron .20 .50
136 Brian Sikorski RC .40 1.00
137 Mike Kinkade RC .40 1.00
138 Braden Looper .20 .50
139 Mark Mangum .20 .50
140 Danny Peoples .20 .50
141 J.J. Davis .20 .50
142 Ben Davis .20 .50
143 Jacque Jones .20 .50
144 Derrick Gibson .20 .50
145 Bronson Arroyo 1.50 4.00
146 L.De Los Santos RC .40 1.00
147 Jeff Abbott .20 .50
148 Mike Cuddyer RC 1.50 4.00
149 Jason Romano .20 .50
150 Shane Monahan .20 .50
151 Ntema Ndungidi RC .40 1.00
152 Alex Sanchez .20 .50
153 Jack Cust RC 3.00 8.00
154 Brent Butler .20 .50
155 Ramon Hernandez .20 .50
156 Norm Hutchins .20 .50
157 Jason Marquis .20 .50
158 Jacob Cruz .20 .50
159 Rob Burger RC .40 1.00
160 Dave Coggin .20 .50
161 Preston Wilson .20 .50
162 Jason Fitzgerald RC .40 1.00
163 Dan Serafini .20 .50
164 Pete Munro .20 .50
165 Trot Nixon .20 .50
166 Homer Bush .20 .50
167 Dermal Brown .20 .50
168 Chad Hermansen .20 .50
169 Julio Moreno RC .40 1.00
170 John Roskos RC .40 1.00
171 Grant Roberts .20 .50
172 Ken Cloude .20 .50
173 Jason Brester .20 .50
174 Jason Conti .20 .50
175 Jon Garland .20 .50
176 Robbie Bell .20 .50
177 Nathan Haynes .20 .50
178 Ramon Ortiz RC .60 1.50
179 Shannon Stewart .20 .50
180 Pablo Ortega .20 .50
181 Jimmy Rollins RC 4.00 10.00
182 Sean Casey .20 .50
183 Ted Lilly RC 1.00 2.50
184 Chris Enochs RC .40 1.00
185 Magglio Ordonez UER RC 4.00 10.00
Front picture is Mario Valdez
186 Mike Drumright .20 .50
187 Aaron Boone .20 .50
188 Matt Clement .20 .50
189 Todd Dunwoody .20 .50
190 Larry Rodriguez .20 .50
191 Todd Noel .20 .50
192 Geoff Jenkins .20 .50
193 George Lombard .20 .50
194 Lance Berkman .20 .50
195 Marcus McCain .20 .50
196 Ryan McGuire .20 .50
197 Jhensy Sandoval .20 .50
198 Corey Lee .20 .50
199 Mario Valdez .20 .50
200 Robert Fick RC .60 1.50
201 Donnie Sadler .20 .50
202 Marc Kroon .20 .50
203 David Miller .20 .50
204 Jarrod Washburn .20 .50
205 Miguel Tejada .50 1.25
206 Raul Ibanez .20 .50
207 John Patterson .20 .50
208 Calvin Pickering .20 .50
209 Felix Martinez .20 .50
210 Mark Redman .20 .50
211 Scott Elarton .20 .50
212 Jose Amado RC .40 1.00
213 Kerry Wood .20 .50
214 Dante Powell .20 .50
215 Aramis Ramirez .20 .50
216 A.J. Hinch .20 .50
217 Dustin Carr RC .40 1.00

218 Mark Kotsay .20 .50
219 Jason Standridge .20 .50
220 Luis Ordaz .20 .50
221 O.Hernandez RC 2.00 5.00
222 Cal Ripken 1.50 4.00
223 Paul Molitor .20 .50
224 Derek Jeter 1.25 3.00
225 Barry Bonds 1.25 3.00
226 Jim Edmonds .20 .50
227 John Smoltz .30 .75
228 Eric Karros .20 .50
229 Ray Lankford .20 .50
230 Rey Ordonez .20 .50
231 Kenny Lofton .20 .50
232 Alex Rodriguez .75 2.00
233 Dante Bichette .20 .50
234 Pedro Martinez .30 .75
235 Carlos Delgado .20 .50
236 Rod Beck .20 .50
237 Matt Williams .20 .50
238 Charles Johnson .20 .50
239 Rico Brogna .20 .50
240 Frank Thomas .50 1.25
241 Paul O'Neill .30 .75
242 Jaret Wright .20 .50
243 Brant Brown .20 .50
244 Ryan Klesko .20 .50
245 Chuck Finley .20 .50
246 Derek Bell .20 .50
247 Delino DeShields .20 .50
248 Chan Ho Park .20 .50
249 Wade Boggs .30 .75
250 Jay Buhner .20 .50
251 Butch Huskey .20 .50
252 Steve Finley .20 .50
253 Will Clark .30 .75
254 John Valentin .20 .50
255 Bobby Higginson .20 .50
256 Darryl Strawberry .20 .50
257 Randy Johnson .50 1.25
258 Al Martin .20 .50
259 Travis Fryman .20 .50
260 Fred McGriff .30 .75
261 Jose Valentin .20 .50
262 Andruw Jones .30 .75
263 Kenny Rogers .20 .50
264 Moises Alou .20 .50
265 Denny Neagle .20 .50
266 Ugueth Urbina .20 .50
267 Derrek Lee .30 .75
268 Ellis Burks .20 .50
269 Mariano Rivera .50 1.25
270 Dean Palmer .20 .50
271 Eddie Taubensee .20 .50
272 Brady Anderson .20 .50
273 Brian Giles .20 .50
274 Quinton McCracken .20 .50
275 Henry Rodriguez .20 .50
276 Andres Galarraga .20 .50
277 Jose Canseco .30 .75
278 David Segui .20 .50
279 Bret Saberhagen .20 .50
280 Kevin Brown .30 .75
281 Chuck Knoblauch .20 .50
282 Jeromy Burnitz .20 .50
283 Jay Bell .20 .50
284 Manny Ramirez .30 .75
285 Rick Helling .20 .50
286 Francisco Cordova .20 .50
287 Bob Abreu .20 .50
288 J.T. Snow .20 .50
289 Hideo Nomo .50 1.25
290 Brian Jordan .20 .50
291 Javy Lopez .20 .50
292 Travis Lee .20 .50
293 Russell Branyan .20 .50
294 Paul Konerko .20 .50
295 Masato Yoshii RC .60 1.50
296 Kris Benson .20 .50
297 Juan Encarnacion .20 .50
298 Eric Milton .20 .50
299 Mike Caruso .20 .50
300 R. Aramboles RC .40 1.00
301 Bobby Smith .20 .50
302 Billy Koch .20 .50
303 Richard Hidalgo .20 .50
304 Justin Baughman RC .40 1.00
305 Chris Gissell .20 .50
306 Donnie Bridges RC .40 1.00
307 Nelson Lara RC .40 1.00
308 Randy Wolf RC .60 1.50
309 Jason LaRue RC .60 1.50
310 Jason Gooding RC .40 1.00
311 Edgard Clemente .20 .50
312 Andrew Vessel .20 .50
313 Chris Reitsma .20 .50
314 Jesus Sanchez RC .40 1.00
315 Buddy Carlyle RC .40 1.00
316 Randy Winn .20 .50
317 Luis Rivera RC .40 1.00
318 Marcus Thames RC 2.50 6.00
319 A.J. Pierzynski .20 .50
320 Scott Randall .20 .50
321 Damian Sapp .20 .50
322 Ed Yarnall RC .40 1.00
323 Luke Allen RC .40 1.00
324 J.D. Smart .20 .50
325 Willie Martinez .20 .50
326 Alex Ramirez .20 .50
327 Eric DuBose RC .40 1.00
328 Kevin Witt .20 .50
329 Dan McKinley RC .40 1.00
330 Cliff Politte .20 .50
331 Vladimir Nunez .20 .50
332 John Halama RC .40 1.00
333 Nerio Rodriguez .20 .50
334 Desi Relaford .20 .50
335 Robinson Checo .20 .50
336 John Nicholson .30 .75
337 Tom LaRosa RC .40 1.00
338 Kevin Nicholson RC .40 1.00
339 Javier Vazquez .20 .50
340 A.J. Zapp .20 .50
341 Tom Evans .20 .50
342 Kerry Robinson .20 .50
343 Gabe Gonzalez RC .40 1.00
344 Ralph Milliard .20 .50
345 Enrique Wilson .20 .50
346 Elvin Hernandez .20 .50
347 Mike Lincoln RC .40 1.00
348 Cesar King RC .40 1.00
349 Cristian Guzman RC .60 1.50
350 Donzell McDonald .20 .50
351 Jim Parque RC .40 1.00
352 Mike Saipe RC .40 1.00
353 Carlos Febles RC .60 1.50
354 Dernell Stenson RC .40 1.00
355 Mark Osborne RC .40 1.00
356 Odalis Perez RC 1.50 4.00
357 Jason Dewey RC .40 1.00
358 Joe Fontenot .20 .50
359 Jason Grilli RC .40 1.00
360 Kevin Haverbusch RC .40 1.00
361 Jay Yennaco RC .40 1.00
362 Brian Buchanan .20 .50
363 John Barnes .20 .50
364 Chris Fussell .20 .50
365 Kevin Gibbs RC .40 1.00
366 Joe Lawrence .20 .50
367 DaRond Stovall .20 .50
368 Brian Fuentes RC .40 1.00
369 Jimmy Anderson .20 .50
370 Lariel Gonzalez RC .40 1.00
371 Scott Williamson RC .40 1.00
372 Milton Bradley .20 .50
373 Jason Halper RC .40 1.00
374 Brent Billingsley RC .40 1.00
375 Joe DePastino RC .40 1.00
376 Jake Westbrook .20 .50
377 Octavio Dotel .20 .50
378 Jason Williams RC .40 1.00
379 Julio Ramirez RC .40 1.00
380 Seth Greisinger .20 .50
381 Mike Judd RC .40 1.00
382 Ben Ford RC .40 1.00
383 Tom Bennett RC .40 1.00
384 Adam Butler RC .40 1.00
385 Wade Miller RC 1.00 2.50
386 Kyle Peterson RC .40 1.00
387 Tommy Peterman RC .40 1.00
388 Onan Masaoka .20 .50
389 Jason Rakers RC .40 1.00
390 Rafael Medina .20 .50
391 Luis Lopez RC .40 1.00
392 Jeff Yoder .20 .50
393 Vance Wilson RC .40 1.00
394 F. Seguignol RC .40 1.00
395 Ron Wright .20 .50
396 Ruben Mateo RC .40 1.00
397 Steve Lomasney RC .60 1.50
398 Damian Jackson .20 .50
399 Mike Jerzembeck RC .40 1.00
400 Luis Rivas RC 1.00 2.50
401 Kevin Burford RC .40 1.00
402 Glenn Davis .20 .50
403 Robert Luce RC .40 1.00
404 Cole Liniak .20 .50
405 Matt LeCroy RC .60 1.50
406 Jeremy Giambi RC .60 1.50
407 Shawn Chacon .20 .50
408 Dewayne Wise RC .40 1.00
409 Steve Woodard .20 .50
410 F.Cordero RC 1.00 2.50
411 Damon Minor RC .40 1.00
412 Lou Collier .20 .50
413 Justin Towle .20 .50
414 Juan LeBron .20 .50
415 Michael Coleman .20 .50
416 Felix Rodriguez .20 .50
417 Paul Ah Yat RC .40 1.00
418 Kevin Barker RC .40 1.00
419 Brian Meadows .20 .50
420 Darnell McDonald RC .40 1.00
421 Matt Kinney RC .40 1.00
422 Mike Vavrek RC .40 1.00
423 Courtney Duncan RC .40 1.00
424 Kevin Millar RC 1.50 4.00
425 Ruben Rivera .20 .50
426 Steve Shoemaker RC .40 1.00
427 Dan Reichert RC .40 1.00
428 Carlos Lee RC 2.50 6.00
429 Rod Barajas 1.00 2.50
430 Pablo Ozuna RC .60 1.50
431 Todd Belitz RC .40 1.00
432 Sidney Ponson .20 .50
433 Steve Carver RC .40 1.00
434 Esteban Yan RC .60 1.50
435 Cedrick Bowers .20 .50
436 Marlon Anderson .20 .50
437 Carl Pavano .20 .50
438 Jae Weong Seo RC .60 1.50
439 Jose Taveras RC .40 1.00
440 Matt Anderson RC .40 1.00
441 Darron Ingram RC .40 1.00

1998 Bowman Chrome Golden Anniversary

Randomly inserted in first series packs at a rate of one in 164 and second series packs at a rate of one in 133, this 441-card set is a parallel to the Bowman Chrome base set. The set is sequentially numbered to 50 and is highlighted by gold facsimile signatures.

*STARS: 6X TO 15X BASIC CARDS
*ROOKIES: 3X TO 8X BASIC CARDS

1998 Bowman Chrome International

Randomly inserted in packs at a rate of one in four, this 441-card set is a parallel to the Bowman Chrome base set. These cards are differentiated by maps of the player's hometown area in the background of each-card front.

COMPLETE SET (441) 350.00 700.00
COMP. SERIES 1 (221) 200.00 400.00
COMP. SERIES 2 (220) 150.00 300.00

*STARS: 1.5X TO 4X BASIC CARDS
*ROOKIES: .4X TO 1X BASIC CARDS

1998 Bowman Chrome International Refractors

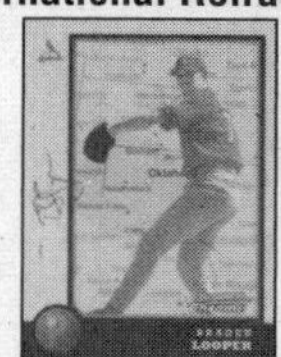

Randomly inserted in packs at a rate of one in 24, this 441-card set is a parallel to the Bowman Chrome base set. These cards are differentiated by maps of the player's hometown area in the background of each card front.

*STARS: 5X TO 12X BASIC CARDS
*ROOKIES: 2X TO 5X BASIC CARDS

1998 Bowman Chrome Refractors

Randomly inserted in packs at a rate of one in 12, this 441-card set is a parallel of the Bowman Chrome base set. The refractive quality of the card fronts differentiate themselves from basic issue cards.

*STARS: 3X TO 8X BASIC CARDS
*ROOKIES: 1.5X TO 4X BASIC CARDS

1998 Bowman Chrome Reprints

Randomly inserted in first and second packs at a rate of one in 12, these cards are replicas of classic Bowman Rookie Cards from 1948-1955 and 1989-present. Odd numbered cards (1, 3, 5 etc) were distributed in first series packs and even numbered cards in second series packs. The upgraded Chrome silver-colored stock gives them a striking appearance and makes them easy to differentiate from the originals.

COMPLETE SET (50) 60.00 160.00
COMPLETE SERIES 1 (25) 30.00 80.00
COMPLETE SERIES 2 (25) 30.00 80.00
*REFRACTORS: 1X TO 2.5X BASIC REPRINTS
REFRACTOR STATED ODDS 1:36
1 Yogi Berra 1.50 4.00
2 Jackie Robinson 1.50 4.00
3 Don Newcombe .60 1.50
4 Satchell Paige 1.50 4.00
5 Willie Mays 4.00 10.00
6 Gil McDougald .60 1.50
7 Don Larsen .60 1.50
8 Elston Howard 1.00 2.50
9 Robin Ventura .60 1.50
10 Brady Anderson .60 1.50
11 Gary Sheffield .60 1.50
12 Tino Martinez 1.00 2.50
13 Ken Griffey Jr. 2.50 6.00
14 John Smoltz 1.00 2.50
15 Sandy Alomar Jr. .40 1.00
16 Larry Walker .60 1.50
17 Todd Hundley .40 1.00
18 Mo Vaughn .60 1.50
19 Sammy Sosa 1.50 4.00
20 Frank Thomas 1.50 4.00
21 Chuck Knoblauch .60 1.50
22 Bernie Williams 1.00 2.50
23 Juan Gonzalez .60 1.50
24 Mike Mussina 1.00 2.50
25 Jeff Bagwell 1.00 2.50
26 Tim Salmon 1.00 2.50
27 Ivan Rodriguez 1.00 2.50
28 Kenny Lofton .60 1.50
29 Chipper Jones 1.50 4.00
30 Javy Lopez .60 1.50
31 Ryan Klesko .60 1.50
32 Raul Mondesi .60 1.50
33 Jim Thome 1.00 2.50
34 Carlos Delgado .60 1.50
35 Mike Piazza 2.50 6.00
36 Manny Ramirez 1.00 2.50
37 Andy Pettitte 1.00 2.50
38 Derek Jeter 4.00 10.00
39 Brad Fullmer .40 1.00
40 Richard Hidalgo .40 1.00
41 Tony Clark .40 1.00
42 Andruw Jones 1.00 2.50
43 Vladimir Guerrero 1.50 4.00
44 Nomar Garciaparra 2.50 6.00
45 Paul Konerko .60 1.50
46 Ben Grieve .40 1.00
47 Hideo Nomo 1.50 4.00
48 Scott Rolen 1.00 2.50
49 Jose Guillen .60 1.50
50 Livan Hernandez .60 1.50

1999 Bowman Chrome

The 1999 Bowman Chrome set was issued in two distinct series and were distributed in four card packs with a suggested retail price of $3.00. The set contains 440 regular cards printed on brilliant chromium 18-pt. Stock. Within the set are 300 top prospects that are designated with silver and blue foil. Each player's facsimile rookie signature are featured on these cards. There are also 140 vereran stars designated with a red and silver foil stamp. The backs contain information on each player's rookie and most recent season, career statistics and a scouting report from early league days Rookie Cards include Pat Burrell, Carl Crawford, Adam Dunn, Rafael Furcal, Freddy Garcia, Tim Hudson, Nick Johnson, Austin Kearns, Willy Mo Pena, Adam Piatt, Corey Patterson and Alfonso Soriano.

COMPLETE SET (440) 100.00 200.00
COMP. SERIES 1 (220) 40.00 80.00
COMP. SERIES 2 (220) 60.00 120.00
1 Ben Grieve .20 .50
2 Kerry Wood .20 .50
3 Ruben Rivera .20 .50
4 Sandy Alomar Jr. .20 .50
5 Cal Ripken 1.50 4.00
6 Mark McGwire 1.25 3.00
7 Vladimir Guerrero .50 1.25
8 Moises Alou .20 .50
9 Jim Edmonds .20 .50
10 Greg Maddux .75 2.00
11 Gary Sheffield .20 .50
12 John Valentin .20 .50
13 Chuck Knoblauch .20 .50
14 Tony Clark .20 .50
15 Rusty Greer .20 .50
16 Al Leiter .20 .50
17 Travis Lee .20 .50
18 Jose Cruz Jr. .20 .50
19 Pedro Martinez .30 .75
20 Paul O'Neill .30 .75
21 Todd Walker .20 .50
22 Vinny Castilla .20 .50
23 Barry Larkin .30 .75
24 Curt Schilling .20 .50
25 Jason Kendall .20 .50
26 Scott Erickson .20 .50
27 Andres Galarraga .20 .50
28 Jeff Shaw .20 .50
29 John Olerud .20 .50
30 Orlando Hernandez .20 .50
31 Larry Walker .20 .50
32 Andruw Jones .30 .75
33 Jeff Cirillo .20 .50
34 Barry Bonds 1.25 3.00
35 Manny Ramirez .30 .75
36 Mark Kotsay .20 .50
37 Ivan Rodriguez .30 .75
38 Jeff King .20 .50
39 Brian Hunter .20 .50
40 Ray Durham .20 .50
41 Bernie Williams .30 .75
42 Darin Erstad .20 .50
43 Chipper Jones .50 1.25
44 Pat Hentgen .20 .50
45 Eric Young .20 .50
46 Jaret Wright .20 .50
47 Juan Guzman .20 .50
48 Jorge Posada .30 .75
49 Bobby Higginson .20 .50
50 Jose Guillen .20 .50
51 Trevor Hoffman .20 .50
52 Ken Griffey Jr. .75 2.00
53 David Justice .20 .50
54 Matt Williams .20 .50
55 Eric Karros .20 .50
56 Derek Bell .20 .50
57 Ray Lankford .20 .50
58 Mariano Rivera .50 1.25
59 Brett Tomko .20 .50
60 Mike Mussina .30 .75
61 Kenny Lofton .20 .50
62 Chuck Finley .20 .50
63 Alex Gonzalez .20 .50
64 Mark Grace .30 .75
65 Raul Mondesi .20 .50
66 David Cone .20 .50
67 Brad Fullmer .20 .50
68 Andy Benes .20 .50
69 John Smoltz .30 .75
70 Shane Reynolds .20 .50
71 Bruce Chen .20 .50
72 Adam Kennedy .20 .50
73 Jack Cust .20 .50
74 Matt Clement .20 .50
75 Derrick Gibson .20 .50
76 Darnell McDonald .20 .50
77 Adam Everett RC 1.00 2.50
78 Ricardo Aramboles .20 .50
79 Mark Quinn RC .40 1.00
80 Jason Rakers .20 .50
81 Seth Etherton RC .40 1.00
82 Jeff Urban RC .40 1.00
83 Manny Aybar .20 .50
84 Mike Nannini RC .40 1.00
85 Onan Masaoka .20 .50
86 Rod Barajas .20 .50
87 Mike Frank .20 .50
88 Scott Randall .20 .50
89 Justin Bowles RC .40 1.00
90 Chris Haas .20 .50
91 Arturo McDowell RC .40 1.00
92 Matt Belisle RC .40 1.00
93 Scott Elarton .20 .50
94 Vernon Wells .20 .50
95 Pat Cline .20 .50
96 Ryan Anderson .20 .50
97 Kevin Barker .20 .50
98 Ruben Mateo .20 .50
99 Robert Fick .20 .50
100 Corey Koskie .20 .50
101 Ricky Ledee .20 .50
102 Rick Elder RC .40 1.00
103 Jack Cressend RC .40 1.00
104 Joe Lawrence .20 .50
105 Mike Lincoln .20 .50
106 Kit Pellow RC .40 1.00
107 Matt Burch RC .40 1.00
108 Cole Liniak .20 .50
109 Jason Dewey .20 .50
110 Cesar King .20 .50
111 Julio Ramirez .20 .50
112 Jake Westbrook .20 .50
113 Eric Valent RC .60 1.50
114 Roosevelt Brown RC .40 1.00
115 Choo Freeman RC .60 1.50
116 Juan Melo .20 .50
117 Jason Grilli .20 .50
118 Jared Sandberg .20 .50
119 Glenn Davis .20 .50
120 David Riske RC .40 1.00
121 Jacque Jones .20 .50
122 Corey Lee .20 .50
123 Michael Barrett .20 .50
124 Lariel Gonzalez .20 .50
125 Mitch Meluskey .20 .50
126 Freddy Adrian Garcia .20 .50
127 Tony Torcato RC .40 1.00
128 Jeff Liefer .20 .50
129 Ntema Ndungidi .20 .50
130 Andy Brown RC .40 1.00
131 Ryan Mills RC .40 1.00
132 Andy Abad RC .40 1.00
133 Carlos Febles .20 .50
134 Jason Tyner RC .40 1.00
135 Mark Osborne .20 .50
136 Phil Norton RC .40 1.00
137 Nathan Haynes .20 .50
138 Roy Halladay .20 .50
139 Juan Encarnacion .20 .50
140 Brad Penny .20 .50
141 Grant Roberts .20 .50
142 Aramis Ramirez .20 .50
143 Cristian Guzman .20 .50
144 Mamon Tucker RC .40 1.00
145 Ryan Bradley .20 .50
146 Brian Simmons .20 .50
147 Dan Reichert .20 .50
148 Russell Branyan .20 .50
149 Victor Valencia RC .40 1.00
150 Scott Schoeneweis .20 .50
151 Sean Spencer RC .40 1.00
152 Odalis Perez .20 .50
153 Joe Fontenot .20 .50
154 Milton Bradley .20 .50
155 Josh McKinley RC .40 1.00
156 Terrence Long .20 .50
157 Danny Klassen .20 .50
158 Paul Hoover RC .40 1.00
159 Ron Belliard .20 .50
160 Armando Rios .20 .50
161 Ramon Hernandez .20 .50
162 Jason Conti .20 .50
163 Chad Hermansen .20 .50
164 Jason Standridge .20 .50
165 Jason Dellaero .20 .50
166 John Curtice .20 .50
167 Clayton Andrews RC .40 1.00
168 Jeremy Giambi .20 .50
169 Alex Ramirez .20 .50
170 Gabe Molina RC .40 1.00
171 M.Encarnacion RC .40 1.00
172 Mike Zywica RC .40 1.00
173 Chip Ambres RC .40 1.00
174 Trot Nixon .20 .50
175 Pat Burrell RC 3.00 8.00
176 Jeff Yoder .20 .50
177 Chris Jones RC .40 1.00
178 Kevin Witt .20 .50
179 Keith Luuloa RC .40 1.00
180 Billy Koch .20 .50
181 Damaso Marte RC .40 1.00
182 Ryan Glynn RC .40 1.00
183 Calvin Pickering .20 .50
184 Michael Cuddyer .20 .50
185 Nick Johnson RC 2.00 5.00
186 D.Mientkiewicz RC 1.00 2.50
187 Nate Cornejo RC .40 1.00
188 Octavio Dotel .20 .50
189 Wes Helms .20 .50
190 Nelson Lara .20 .50
191 Chuck Abbott RC .40 1.00
192 Tony Armas Jr. .20 .50
193 Gil Meche .20 .50
194 Ben Petrick .20 .50
195 Chris George RC .40 1.00
196 Scott Hunter RC .40 1.00
197 Ryan Brannan .20 .50
198 Amaury Garcia RC .40 1.00
199 Chris Gissell .20 .50
200 Austin Kearns RC 3.00 8.00
201 Alex Gonzalez .20 .50
202 Wade Miller .20 .50
203 Scott Williamson .20 .50
204 Chris Enochs .20 .50
205 Fernando Seguignol .20 .50
206 Marlon Anderson .20 .50
207 Todd Sears RC .40 1.00
208 Nate Bump RC .40 1.00
209 J.M. Gold RC .40 1.00
210 Matt LeCroy .20 .50
211 Alex Hernandez .20 .50
212 Luis Rivera .20 .50
213 Troy Cameron .20 .50
214 Alex Escobar RC .60 1.50
215 Jason LaRue .20 .50
216 Kyle Peterson .20 .50
217 Brent Butler .20 .50
218 Dernell Stenson .20 .50
219 Adrian Beltre .20 .50
220 Daryle Ward .20 .50
221 Jim Thome .30 .75
222 Cliff Floyd .20 .50
223 Rickey Henderson .50 1.25
224 Garret Anderson .20 .50
225 Ken Caminiti .20 .50
226 Bret Boone .20 .50
227 Jeromy Burnitz .20 .50
228 Steve Finley .20 .50
229 Miguel Tejada .20 .50
230 Greg Vaughn .20 .50
231 Jose Offerman .20 .50
232 Andy Ashby .20 .50
233 Albert Belle .20 .50
234 Fernando Tatis .20 .50
235 Todd Helton .30 .75
236 Sean Casey .20 .50
237 Brian Giles .20 .50
238 Andy Pettitte .30 .75
239 Fred McGriff .30 .75
240 Roberto Alomar .30 .75
241 Edgar Martinez .30 .75
242 Lee Stevens .20 .50
243 Shawn Green .20 .50
244 Ryan Klesko .20 .50
245 Sammy Sosa .50 1.25
246 Todd Hundley .20 .50
247 Shannon Stewart .20 .50
248 Randy Johnson .50 1.25
249 Rondell White .20 .50
250 Mike Piazza .75 2.00
251 Craig Biggio .30 .75
252 David Wells .20 .50
253 Brian Jordan .20 .50
254 Edgar Renteria .20 .50
255 Bartolo Colon .20 .50
256 Frank Thomas .50 1.25
257 Will Clark .30 .75
258 Dean Palmer .20 .50
259 Dmitri Young .20 .50
260 Scott Rolen .30 .75
261 Jeff Kent .20 .50
262 Dante Bichette .20 .50
263 Nomar Garciaparra .75 2.00
264 Tony Gwynn .60 1.50
265 Alex Rodriguez .75 2.00
266 Jose Canseco .30 .75
267 Jason Giambi .20 .50
268 Jeff Bagwell .30 .75
269 Carlos Delgado .20 .50
270 Tom Glavine .30 .75
271 Eric Davis .20 .50
272 Edgardo Alfonzo .20 .50
273 Tim Salmon .30 .75
274 Johnny Damon .30 .75
275 Rafael Palmeiro .30 .75
276 Denny Neagle .20 .50
277 Neifi Perez .20 .50
278 Roger Clemens 1.00 2.50
279 Brant Brown .20 .50
280 Kevin Brown .30 .75
281 Jay Bell .20 .50
282 Jay Buhner .20 .50
283 Matt Lawton .20 .50
284 Robin Ventura .20 .50
285 Juan Gonzalez .20 .50
286 Mo Vaughn .20 .50
287 Kevin Millwood .20 .50
288 Tino Martinez .30 .75
289 Justin Thompson .20 .50
290 Derek Jeter 1.25 3.00
291 Ben Davis .20 .50
292 Mike Lowell .20 .50
293 Calvin Murray .20 .50
294 Micah Bowie RC .40 1.00
295 Lance Berkman .20 .50
296 Jason Marquis .20 .50
297 Chad Green .20 .50
298 Dee Brown .20 .50
299 Jerry Hairston Jr. .20 .50
300 Gabe Kapler .20 .50
301 Brent Stentz RC .40 1.00
302 Scott Mullen RC .40 1.00
303 Brandon Reed .20 .50
304 Shea Hillenbrand RC 1.50 4.00
305 J.D. Closser RC .60 1.50
306 Gary Matthews Jr. .20 .50
307 Toby Hall RC .60 1.50
308 Jason Phillips RC .40 1.00
309 Jose Macias RC .40 1.00
310 Jung Bong RC .40 1.00
311 Ramon Soler RC .40 1.00
312 Kelly Dransfeldt RC .40 1.00
313 Carlos E. Hernandez RC .60 1.50
314 Kevin Haverbusch .20 .50
315 Aaron Myette RC .40 1.00
316 Chad Harville RC .40 1.00
317 Kyle Farnsworth RC .60 1.50
318 Gookie Dawkins RC .60 1.50
319 Willie Martinez .20 .50
320 Carlos Lee .20 .50
321 Carlos Pena RC 1.25 3.00
322 Peter Bergeron RC .40 1.00
323 A.J. Burnett RC 1.50 4.00
324 Bucky Jacobsen RC .60 1.50
325 Mo Bruce RC .40 1.00
326 Reggie Taylor .20 .50
327 Jackie Rexrode .20 .50
328 Alvin Morrow RC .40 1.00
329 Carlos Beltran .30 .75
330 Eric Chavez .20 .50
331 John Patterson .20 .50
332 Jayson Werth .20 .50
333 Richie Sexson .20 .50
334 Randy Wolf .20 .50
335 Eli Marrero .20 .50
336 Paul LoDuca .20 .50
337 J.D Smart .20 .50
338 Ryan Minor .20 .50
339 Kris Benson .20 .50
340 George Lombard .20 .50
341 Troy Glaus .30 .75
342 Eddie Yarnall .20 .50
343 Kip Wells RC .60 1.50
344 C.C. Sabathia RC 4.00 10.00

345 Sean Burroughs RC	1.00	2.50
346 Felipe Lopez RC	2.50	6.00
347 Ryan Rupe RC	.40	1.00
348 Orber Moreno RC	.40	1.00
349 Rafael Roque RC	.40	1.00
350 Alfonso Soriano RC	5.00	12.00
351 Pablo Ozuna	.20	.50
352 Corey Patterson RC	1.50	4.00
353 Braden Looper	.20	.50
354 Robbie Bell	.20	.50
355 Mark Mulder RC	2.50	6.00
356 Angel Pena	.20	.50
357 Kevin McGlinchy	.20	.50
358 M.Restovich RC	.60	1.50
359 Eric DuBose	.20	.50
360 Geoff Jenkins	.20	.50
361 Mark Harriger RC	.40	1.00
362 Junior Herndon RC	.40	1.00
363 Tim Raines Jr. RC	.40	1.00
364 Rafael Furcal RC	2.50	6.00
365 Marcus Giles RC	1.50	4.00
366 Ted Lilly	.20	.50
367 Jorge Toca RC	.60	1.50
368 David Kelton RC	.40	1.00
369 Adam Dunn RC	5.00	12.00
370 Guillermo Mota RC	.40	1.00
371 Brett Laxton RC	.40	1.00
372 Travis Harper RC	.40	1.00
373 Tom Davey RC	.40	1.00
374 Darren Blakely RC	.40	1.00
375 Tim Hudson RC	3.00	8.00
376 Jason Romano	.20	.50
377 Dan Reichert	.20	.50
378 Julio Lugo RC	1.00	2.50
379 Jose Garcia RC	.40	1.00
380 Erubiel Durazo RC	.60	1.50
381 Jose Jimenez	.20	.50
382 Chris Fussell	.20	.50
383 Steve Lomasney	.20	.50
384 Juan Pena RC	.40	1.00
385 Allen Levrault RC	.40	1.00
386 Juan Rivera RC	1.50	4.00
387 Steve Colyer RC	.40	1.00
388 Joe Nathan RC	2.00	5.00
389 Ron Walker RC	.40	1.00
390 Nick Bierbrodt	.20	.50
391 Luke Prokopec RC	.40	1.00
392 Dave Roberts RC	1.00	2.50
393 Mike Darr	.20	.50
394 Abraham Nunez RC	.60	1.50
395 G.Chiaramonte RC	.40	1.00
396 J.Van Buren RC	.40	1.00
397 Mike Kusiewicz	.20	.50
398 Matt Wise RC	.40	1.00
399 Joe McEwing RC	.60	1.50
400 Matt Holliday RC	5.00	12.00
401 Willi Mo Pena RC	5.00	12.00
402 Ruben Quevedo RC	.40	1.00
403 Rob Ryan RC	.40	1.00
404 Freddy Garcia RC	1.50	4.00
405 Kevin Eberwein RC	.40	1.00
406 Jesus Colome RC	.40	1.00
407 Chris Singleton	.20	.50
408 Bubba Crosby RC	1.00	2.50
409 Jesus Cordero RC	.40	1.00
410 Donny Leon	.20	.50
411 G.Tomlinson RC	.40	1.00
412 Jeff Winchester RC	.40	1.00
413 Adam Piatt RC	.40	1.00
414 Robert Stratton	.20	.50
415 T.J. Tucker	.20	.50
416 Ryan Langerhans RC	1.00	2.50
417 A.Shumaker RC	.40	1.00
418 Matt Miller RC	.40	1.00
419 Doug Clark RC	.40	1.00
420 Kory DeHaan RC	.40	1.00
421 David Eckstein RC	3.00	8.00
422 Brian Cooper RC	.40	1.00
423 Brady Clark RC	1.50	4.00
424 Chris Magruder RC	.40	1.00
425 Bobby Seay RC	.40	1.00
426 Aubrey Huff RC	2.00	5.00
427 Mike Jerzembeck	.20	.50
428 Matt Blank RC	.40	1.00
429 Benny Agbayani RC	.60	1.50
430 Kevin Beirne RC	.40	1.00
431 Josh Hamilton RC	8.00	20.00
432 Josh Girdley RC	.40	1.00
433 Kyle Snyder RC	.40	1.00
434 Mike Paradis RC	.40	1.00
435 Jason Jennings RC	1.00	2.50
436 David Walling RC	.40	1.00
437 Omar Ortiz RC	.40	1.00
438 Jay Gehrke RC	.60	1.50
439 Casey Burns RC	.40	1.00
440 Carl Crawford RC	4.00	10.00

1999 Bowman Chrome Gold

Randomly inserted in first series packs a rate of one in twelve , and second series packs at one in 24, this 440-card set is highlighted by gold facsimile signatures and borders and is a parallel to the 1999 Bowman Chrome base set.

*SER.1 STARS: 2.5X TO 6X BASIC CARDS		
*SER.1 ROOKIES: .75X TO 2X BASIC		
*SER.2 STARS: 3X TO 8X BASIC CARDS		
*SER.2 ROOKIES: 1X TO 2.5X BASIC		
369 Adam Dunn	12.50	30.00
400 Matt Holliday	20.00	50.00

1999 Bowman Chrome Gold Refractors

Randomly inserted in first series packs at a rate of one in 305 and second series packs at a rate of one in 200, this 440-card set is a parallel insert to the Bowman Chrome base set. Gold foil fascimile signatures and refractive chrome fronts highlight the design. In addition, only 25 serial numbered sets were printed.

*STARS: 20X TO 50X BASIC CARDS

1999 Bowman Chrome International

Randomly inserted in first series packs at a rate of one in four, and second series packs at a rate of one in 12, this 440-card set is a parallel insert to the Bowman Chrome Base set. Metallic foil fronts and backgrounds taken from notable scenes of the featured players hometown highlight the design.

COMPLETE SET (440)	450.00	900.00
COMP. SERIES 1 (220)	150.00	300.00
COMP. SERIES 2 (220)	300.00	600.00
*SER.1 STARS: 1.25X TO 3X BASIC CARDS		
*SER.1 ROOKIES: .4X TO 1X BASIC		
*SER.2 STARS: 2X TO 5X BASIC CARDS		
*SER.2 ROOKIES: .5X TO 1.2X BASIC		
369 Adam Dunn	6.00	15.00
431 Josh Hamilton	12.50	30.00

1999 Bowman Chrome International Refractors

Randomly inserted in first series packs at a rate of one in 76 and second series packs at a rate of one in 50, this 440-card set is a refractive parallel insert to the Bowman Chrome International set. Only 100 serial numbered sets were printed.

*STARS: 6X TO 15X BASIC CARDS		
*ROOKIES: 4X TO 8X BASIC		
369 Adam Dunn	50.00	100.00
400 Matt Holliday	60.00	120.00
431 Josh Hamilton	100.00	200.00
440 Carl Crawford	40.00	100.00

1999 Bowman Chrome Refractors

Randomly inserted at a rate of one in twelve, this 440-card set is a parallel insert to the Bowman Chrome base set. The refractive sheen of each card highlights the design.

*STARS: 4X TO 10X BASIC CARDS		
*ROOKIES: 1.5X TO 4X BASIC		
431 Josh Hamilton	50.00	100.00

1999 Bowman Chrome 2000 ROY Favorites

Randomly inserted in second series packs at a rate of one in 20, this 10-card insert set features borderless, double-etched foil cards and feature players that had potential to win Rookie of the Year honors for the 2000 seasons.

COMPLETE SET (10)	8.00	20.00
*REF: .75X TO 2X BASIC CHR.2000 ROY		
REFRACTOR SER.2 STATED ODDS 1:100		
ROY1 Ryan Anderson	.40	1.00
ROY2 Pat Burrell	1.25	3.00
ROY3 A.J. Burnett	.60	1.50
ROY4 Ruben Mateo	.40	1.00
ROY5 Alex Escobar	.40	1.00
ROY6 Pablo Ozuna	.40	1.00
ROY7 Mark Mulder	1.00	2.50
ROY8 Corey Patterson	.60	1.50
ROY9 George Lombard	.40	1.00
ROY10 Nick Johnson	.60	1.50

1999 Bowman Chrome Diamond Aces

Randomly inserted in first series packs at the rate of one in 21, this 18-card set features nine emerging stars such as Pat Burrell and Troy Glaus as well as nine proven veterans including Derek Jeter and Ken Griffey Jr.

COMPLETE SET (18)	30.00	80.00
*REF: .75X TO 2X BASIC CHR.ACES		
REFRACTOR SER.1 ODDS 1:84		
DA1 Troy Glaus	1.00	2.50
DA2 Eric Chavez	.60	1.50
DA3 Fernando Seguignol	.60	1.50
DA4 Ryan Anderson	.60	1.50
DA5 Ruben Mateo	.60	1.50
DA6 Carlos Beltran	1.00	2.50
DA7 Adrian Beltre	.60	1.50
DA8 Bruce Chen	.60	1.50
DA9 Pat Burrell	2.00	5.00
DA10 Mike Piazza	2.50	6.00
DA11 Ken Griffey Jr.	2.50	6.00
DA12 Chipper Jones	1.50	4.00
DA13 Derek Jeter	4.00	10.00
DA14 Mark McGwire	4.00	10.00
DA15 Nomar Garciaparra	2.50	6.00
DA16 Sammy Sosa	1.50	4.00
DA17 Juan Gonzalez	.60	1.50
DA18 Alex Rodriguez	2.50	6.00

1999 Bowman Chrome Impact

Randomly inserted in second series packs at the rate of one in 15, this 15-card insert set features 20 players separated into three distinct categories; Early Impact, Initial Impact and Lasting Impact.

COMPLETE SET (20)	30.00	80.00
*REF 1-10: .75X TO 2X BASIC IMPACT		
*REF 11-20: .75X TO 2X BASIC IMPACT		
REFRACTOR SER.2 STATED ODDS 1:75		
I1 Alfonso Soriano	2.00	5.00
I2 Pat Burrell	1.25	3.00
I3 Ruben Mateo	.50	1.25
I4 A.J. Burnett	.50	1.25
I5 Corey Patterson	.75	2.00
I6 Daryle Ward	.50	1.25
I7 Eric Chavez	.50	1.25
I8 Troy Glaus	.75	2.00
I9 Sean Casey	.50	1.25
I10 Joe McEwing	.20	.50
I11 Gabe Kapler	.50	1.25
I12 Michael Barrett	.50	1.25
I13 Sammy Sosa	1.25	3.00
I14 Alex Rodriguez	2.00	5.00
I15 Mark McGwire	3.00	8.00
I16 Derek Jeter	3.00	8.00
I17 Nomar Garciaparra	2.00	5.00
I18 Mike Piazza	2.00	5.00
I19 Chipper Jones	1.25	3.00
I20 Ken Griffey Jr.	2.00	5.00

1999 Bowman Chrome Scout's Choice

Randomly inserted in first series packs at the rate of one in twelve, this 21-card insert set features borderless, double-etched foil cards showcase a selection of the game's top young prospects.

COMPLETE SET (21)	10.00	25.00
*REFRACTORS: .75X TO 2X BASIC SCOUT'S		
REFRACTOR SER.1 ODDS 1:48		
SC1 Ruben Mateo	.60	1.50
SC2 Ryan Anderson	.60	1.50
SC3 Pat Burrell	1.25	3.00
SC4 Troy Glaus	1.00	2.50
SC5 Eric Chavez	.60	1.50
SC6 Adrian Beltre	.60	1.50
SC7 Bruce Chen	.60	1.50
SC8 Carlos Beltran	1.00	2.50
SC9 Alex Gonzalez	.60	1.50
SC10 Carlos Lee	.60	1.50
SC11 George Lombard	.60	1.50
SC12 Matt Clement	.60	1.50
SC13 Calvin Pickering	.60	1.50
SC14 Marlon Anderson	.60	1.50
SC15 Chad Hermansen	.60	1.50
SC16 Russell Branyan	.60	1.50
SC17 Jeremy Giambi	.60	1.50
SC18 Ricky Ledee	.60	1.50
SC19 John Patterson	.60	1.50
SC20 Roy Halladay	.60	1.50
SC21 Michael Barrett	.60	1.50

2000 Bowman Chrome

The 2000 Bowman Chrome product was released in late July, 2000 as a 440-card set that featured 140 veteran players (1-140), and 300 rookies and prospects (141-440). Each pack contained four cards, and carried a suggested retail price of $3.00. Rookie Cards include Rick Asadoorian, Bobby Bradley, Kevin Mench, Ben Sheets and Barry Zito. In addition, Topps designated five prospects as Bowman Chrome "exclusives" whereby their only appearance in a Topps brand for the year 2000 would be in this set. Jason Hart and Chin-Hui Tsao highlight this selection of Bowman Chrome exclusive Rookie Cards.

COMPLETE SET (440)	60.00	120.00
1 Vladimir Guerrero	.50	1.25
2 Chipper Jones	.50	1.25
3 Todd Walker	.20	.50
4 Barry Larkin	.30	.75
5 Bernie Williams	.30	.75
6 Todd Helton	.30	.75
7 Jermaine Dye	.20	.50
8 Brian Giles	.20	.50
9 Freddy Garcia	.20	.50
10 Greg Vaughn	.20	.50
11 Alex Gonzalez	.20	.50
12 Luis Gonzalez	.20	.50
13 Ron Belliard	.20	.50
14 Ben Grieve	.20	.50
15 Carlos Delgado	.20	.50
16 Brian Jordan	.20	.50
17 Fernando Tatis	.20	.50
18 Ryan Rupe	.20	.50
19 Miguel Tejada	.20	.50
20 Mark Grace	.30	.75
21 Kenny Lofton	.20	.50
22 Eric Karros	.20	.50
23 Cliff Floyd	.20	.50
24 John Halama	.20	.50
25 Cristian Guzman	.20	.50
26 Scott Williamson	.20	.50
27 Mike Lieberthal	.20	.50
28 Tim Hudson	.20	.50
29 Warren Morris	.20	.50
30 Pedro Martinez	.30	.75
31 John Smoltz	.30	.75
32 Ray Durham	.20	.50
33 Chad Allen	.20	.50
34 Tony Clark	.20	.50
35 Tino Martinez	.30	.75
36 J.T. Snow	.20	.50
37 Kevin Brown	.30	.75
38 Bartolo Colon	.20	.50
39 Rey Ordonez	.20	.50
40 Jeff Bagwell	.30	.75
41 Ivan Rodriguez	.30	.75
42 Eric Chavez	.20	.50
43 Eric Milton	.20	.50
44 Jose Canseco	.30	.75
45 Shawn Green	.20	.50
46 Rich Aurilia	.20	.50
47 Roberto Alomar	.30	.75
48 Brian Daubach	.20	.50
49 Magglio Ordonez	.20	.50
50 Derek Jeter	1.25	3.00
51 Kris Benson	.20	.50
52 Albert Belle	.20	.50
53 Rondell White	.20	.50
54 Justin Thompson	.20	.50
55 Nomar Garciaparra	.75	2.00
56 Chuck Finley	.20	.50
57 Omar Vizquel	.30	.75
58 Luis Castillo	.20	.50
59 Richard Hidalgo	.20	.50
60 Barry Bonds	1.25	3.00
61 Craig Biggio	.30	.75
62 Doug Glanville	.20	.50
63 Gabe Kapler	.20	.50
64 Johnny Damon	.30	.75
65 Pokey Reese	.20	.50
66 Andy Pettitte	.30	.75
67 B.J. Surhoff	.20	.50
68 Richie Sexson	.20	.50
69 Javy Lopez	.20	.50
70 Raul Mondesi	.20	.50
71 Darin Erstad	.20	.50
72 Kevin Millwood	.20	.50
73 Ricky Ledee	.20	.50
74 John Olerud	.20	.50
75 Sean Casey	.20	.50
76 Carlos Febles	.20	.50
77 Paul O'Neill	.30	.75
78 Bob Abreu	.20	.50
79 Neifi Perez	.20	.50
80 Tony Gwynn	.60	1.50
81 Russ Ortiz	.20	.50
82 Matt Williams	.20	.50
83 Chris Carpenter	.20	.50
84 Roger Cedeno	.20	.50
85 Tim Salmon	.30	.75
86 Billy Koch	.20	.50
87 Jeromy Burnitz	.20	.50
88 Edgardo Alfonzo	.20	.50
89 Jay Bell	.20	.50
90 Manny Ramirez	.30	.75
91 Frank Thomas	.50	1.25
92 Mike Mussina	.30	.75
93 J.D. Drew	.20	.50
94 Adrian Beltre	.20	.50
95 Alex Rodriguez	.75	2.00
96 Larry Walker	.20	.50
97 Juan Encarnacion	.20	.50
98 Mike Sweeney	.20	.50
99 Rusty Greer	.20	.50
100 Randy Johnson	.50	1.25
101 Jose Vidro	.20	.50
102 Preston Wilson	.20	.50
103 Greg Maddux	.75	2.00
104 Jason Giambi	.20	.50
105 Cal Ripken	1.50	4.00
106 Carlos Beltran	.20	.50
107 Vinny Castilla	.20	.50
108 Mariano Rivera	.50	1.25
109 Mo Vaughn	.20	.50
110 Rafael Palmeiro	.30	.75
111 Shannon Stewart	.20	.50
112 Mike Hampton	.20	.50
113 Joe Nathan	.20	.50
114 Ben Davis	.20	.50
115 Andruw Jones	.30	.75
116 Robin Ventura	.20	.50
117 Damion Easley	.20	.50
118 Jeff Cirillo	.20	.50
119 Kerry Wood	.20	.50
120 Scott Rolen	.30	.75
121 Sammy Sosa	.50	1.25
122 Ken Griffey Jr.	.75	2.00
123 Shane Reynolds	.20	.50
124 Troy Glaus	.20	.50
125 Tom Glavine	.30	.75
126 Michael Barrett	.20	.50
127 Al Leiter	.20	.50
128 Jason Kendall	.20	.50
129 Roger Clemens	1.00	2.50
130 Juan Gonzalez	.20	.50
131 Corey Koskie	.20	.50
132 Curt Schilling	.20	.50
133 Mike Piazza	.75	2.00
134 Gary Sheffield	.20	.50
135 Jim Thome	.30	.75
136 Orlando Hernandez	.20	.50
137 Ray Lankford	.20	.50
138 Geoff Jenkins	.20	.50
139 Jose Lima	.20	.50
140 Mark McGwire	1.25	3.00
141 Adam Piatt	.20	.50
142 Pat Manning RC	.30	.75
143 Marcos Castillo RC	.30	.75
144 Lesli Brea RC	.30	.75
145 Humberto Cota RC	.50	1.25
146 Ben Petrick	.20	.50
147 Kip Wells	.20	.50
148 Wily Pena	.20	.50
149 Chris Wakeland RC	.30	.75
150 Brad Baker RC	.30	.75
151 Robbie Morrison RC	.30	.75
152 Reggie Taylor	.20	.50
153 Matt Ginter RC	.30	.75
154 Peter Bergeron	.20	.50
155 Roosevelt Brown	.20	.50
156 Matt Cepicky RC	.30	.75
157 Ramon Castro	.20	.50
158 Brad Baisley RC	.30	.75
159 Jason Hart RC	.30	.75
160 Mitch Meluskey	.20	.50
161 Chad Harville	.20	.50
162 Brian Cooper	.20	.50
163 Marcus Giles	.20	.50
164 Jim Morris	.50	1.25
165 Geoff Goetz	.20	.50
166 Bobby Bradley RC	.30	.75
167 Rob Bell	.20	.50
168 Joe Crede	1.00	2.50
169 Michael Restovich	.20	.50
170 Quincy Foster RC	.30	.75
171 Enrique Cruz RC	.30	.75
172 Mark Quinn	.20	.50
173 Nick Johnson	.20	.50
174 Jeff Liefer	.20	.50
175 Kevin Mench RC	2.00	5.00
176 Steve Lomasney	.20	.50
177 Jayson Werth	.20	.50
178 Tim Drew	.20	.50
179 Chip Ambres	.20	.50
180 Ryan Anderson	.20	.50
181 Matt Blank	.20	.50
182 G. Chiaramonte	.20	.50
183 Corey Myers RC	.30	.75
184 Jeff Yoder	.20	.50
185 Craig Dingman RC	.30	.75
186 Jon Hamilton RC	.30	.75
187 Toby Hall	.20	.50
188 Russell Branyan	.20	.50
189 Brian Falkenborg RC	.30	.75
190 Aaron Harang RC	2.00	5.00
191 Juan Pena	.20	.50
192 Chin-Hui Tsao RC	2.00	5.00
193 Alfonso Soriano	.50	1.25
194 Alejandro Diaz RC	.30	.75
195 Carlos Pena	.20	.50
196 Kevin Nicholson	.20	.50
197 Mo Bruce	.20	.50
198 C.C. Sabathia	.20	.50
199 Carl Crawford	.20	.50
200 Rafael Furcal	.20	.50
201 Andrew Beinbrink RC	.30	.75
202 Jimmy Osting	.20	.50
203 Aaron McNeal RC	.30	.75
204 Brett Laxton	.20	.50
205 Chris George	.20	.50
206 Felipe Lopez	.20	.50
207 Ben Sheets RC	2.50	6.00
208 Mike Meyers RC	.50	1.25
209 Jason Conti	.20	.50
210 Milton Bradley	.20	.50
211 Chris Mears RC	.30	.75
212 Carlos Hernandez RC	.50	1.25
213 Jason Romano	.20	.50
214 Geofrey Tomlinson	.20	.50
215 Jimmy Rollins	.20	.50
216 Pablo Ozuna	.20	.50
217 Steve Cox	.20	.50
218 Terrence Long	.20	.50
219 Jeff DaVanon RC	.50	1.25
220 Rick Ankiel	.20	.50
221 Jason Standridge	.20	.50
222 Tony Armas Jr.	.20	.50
223 Jason Tyner	.20	.50
224 Ramon Ortiz	.20	.50
225 Daryle Ward	.20	.50
226 Enger Veras RC	.30	.75
227 Chris Jones	.20	.50
228 Eric Cammack RC	.30	.75
229 Ruben Mateo	.20	.50
230 Ken Harvey RC	.50	1.25
231 Jake Westbrook	.20	.50
232 Rob Purvis RC	.30	.75
233 Choo Freeman	.20	.50
234 Aramis Ramirez	.20	.50
235 A.J. Burnett	.20	.50
236 Kevin Barker	.20	.50
237 Chance Caple RC	.30	.75
238 Jarrod Washburn	.20	.50
239 Lance Berkman	.20	.50
240 Michael Wenner RC	.30	.75
241 Alex Sanchez	.20	.50
242 Pat Daneker	.20	.50
243 Grant Roberts	.20	.50
244 Mark Ellis RC	.50	1.25
245 Donny Leon	.20	.50
246 David Eckstein	.20	.50
247 Dicky Gonzalez RC	.30	.75
248 John Patterson	.20	.50
249 Chad Green	.20	.50
250 Scot Shields RC	.30	.75
251 Troy Cameron	.20	.50
252 Jose Molina	.20	.50
253 Rob Pugmire RC	.30	.75
254 Rick Elder	.20	.50
255 Sean Burroughs	.20	.50
256 Josh Kalinowski RC	.30	.75
257 Matt LeCroy	.20	.50
258 Alex Graman RC	.30	.75
259 Juan Silvestre RC	.30	.75
260 Brady Clark	.20	.50
261 Rico Washington RC	.30	.75
262 Gary Matthews Jr.	.20	.50
263 Matt Wise	.20	.50
264 Keith Reed RC	.30	.75
265 Santiago Ramirez RC	.30	.75
266 Ben Broussard RC	1.25	3.00
267 Ryan Langerhans	.20	.50
268 Juan Rivera	.20	.50
269 Shawn Gallagher	.20	.50
270 Jorge Toca	.20	.50
271 Brad Lidge	.30	.75
272 Leoncio Estrella RC	.30	.75
273 Ruben Quevedo	.20	.50
274 Jack Cust	.20	.50
275 T.J. Tucker	.20	.50
276 Mike Colangelo	.20	.50
277 Brian Schneider	.20	.50
278 Calvin Murray	.20	.50
279 Josh Girdley	.20	.50
280 Mike Paradis	.20	.50
281 Chad Hermansen	.20	.50
282 Ty Howington RC	.30	.75
283 Aaron Myette	.20	.50
284 D'Angelo Jimenez	.20	.50
285 Dernell Stenson	.20	.50
286 Jerry Hairston Jr.	.20	.50
287 Gary Majewski RC	.50	1.25
288 Derrin Ebert	.20	.50
289 Steve Fish RC	.30	.75
290 Carlos E. Hernandez	.20	.50
291 Allen Levrault	.20	.50
292 Sean McNally RC	.30	.75
293 Randey Dorame RC	.30	.75
294 Wes Anderson RC	.30	.75
295 B.J. Ryan	.20	.50
296 Alan Webb RC	.30	.75
297 Brandon Inge RC	2.00	5.00
298 David Walling	.20	.50
299 Sun Woo Kim RC	.30	.75
300 Pat Burrell	.20	.50
301 Rick Guttormson RC	.30	.75
302 Gil Meche	.20	.50
303 Carlos Zambrano RC	4.00	10.00
304 Eric Byrnes UER RC	.40	1.00
Bo Porter pictured		
305 Robb Quinlan RC	.50	1.25
306 Jackie Rexrode	.20	.50
307 Nate Bump	.20	.50
308 Sean DePaula RC	.30	.75
309 Matt Riley	.20	.50
310 Ryan Minor	.20	.50
311 J.J. Davis	.20	.50
312 Randy Wolf	.20	.50
313 Jason Jennings	.20	.50
314 Scott Seabol RC	.30	.75
315 Doug Davis	.20	.50
316 Todd Moser RC	.30	.75
317 Rob Ryan	.20	.50
318 Bubba Crosby	.20	.50
319 Lyle Overbay RC	1.25	3.00
320 Mario Encarnacion	.20	.50
321 F.Rodriguez RC	2.50	6.00
322 Michael Cuddyer	.20	.50
323 Ed Yarnall	.20	.50
324 Cesar Saba RC	.30	.75
325 Gookie Dawkins	.20	.50
326 Alex Escobar	.20	.50
327 Julio Zuleta RC	.30	.75
328 Josh Hamilton	.60	1.50
329 Carlos Urquiola RC	.30	.75
330 Matt Belisle	.20	.50
331 Kurt Ainsworth RC	.30	.75
332 Tim Raines Jr.	.20	.50
333 Eric Munson	.20	.50
334 Donzell McDonald	.20	.50
335 Larry Bigbie RC	.75	2.00
336 Matt Watson RC	.30	.75
337 Aubrey Huff	.20	.50
338 Julio Ramirez	.20	.50
339 Jason Grabowski RC	.30	.75
340 Jon Garland	.20	.50
341 Austin Kearns	.20	.50
342 Josh Pressley RC	.30	.75
343 Miguel Olivo RC	.75	2.00
344 Julio Lugo	.20	.50
345 Roberto Vaz	.20	.50
346 Ramon Soler	.20	.50
347 Brandon Phillips RC	1.50	4.00
348 Vince Faison RC	.30	.75
349 Mike Venafro	.20	.50
350 Rick Asadoorian RC	.50	1.25
351 B.J. Garbe RC	.30	.75

352 Dan Reichert .20 .50
353 Jason Stumm RC .30 .75
354 Ruben Salazar RC .30 .75
355 Francisco Cordero .20 .50
356 Juan Guzman RC .30 .75
357 Mike Bacsik RC .30 .75
358 Jared Sandberg .20 .50
359 Rod Barajas .20 .50
360 Junior Brignac RC .30 .75
361 J.M. Gold .20 .50
362 Octavio Dotel .20 .50
363 David Kelton .20 .50
364 Scott Morgan .20 .50
365 Wascar Serrano RC .30 .75
366 Wilton Veras .20 .50
367 Eugene Kingsale .20 .50
368 Ted Lilly .20 .50
369 George Lombard .20 .50
370 Chris Haas .20 .50
371 Wilton Pena RC .30 .75
372 Vernon Wells .20 .50
373 Keith Ginter RC .30 .75
374 Jeff Heaverlo RC .30 .75
375 Calvin Pickering .20 .50
376 Mike Lamb RC .75 2.00
377 Kyle Snyder .20 .50
378 Javier Cardona RC .30 .75
379 Aaron Rowand RC 2.00 5.00
380 Dee Brown .20 .50
381 Brett Myers RC 1.50 4.00
382 Abraham Nunez .20 .50
383 Eric Valent .20 .50
384 Jody Gerut RC .50 1.25
385 Adam Dunn .50 1.25
386 Jay Gehrke .20 .50
387 Omar Ortiz .20 .50
388 Darnell McDonald .20 .50
389 Tony Schrager RC .30 .75
390 J.D. Closser .20 .50
391 Ben Christensen RC .30 .75
392 Adam Kennedy .20 .50
393 Nick Green RC .30 .75
394 Ramon Hernandez .20 .50
395 Roy Oswalt RC 6.00 15.00
396 Andy Tracy RC .30 .75
397 Eric Gagne .50 1.25
398 Michael Tejera RC .30 .75
399 Adam Everett .20 .50
400 Corey Patterson .20 .50
401 Gary Knotts RC .30 .75
402 Ryan Christianson RC .30 .75
403 Eric Ireland RC .30 .75
404 Andrew Good RC .30 .75
405 Brad Penny .20 .50
406 Jason LaRue .20 .50
407 Kit Pellow .20 .50
408 Kevin Beirne .20 .50
409 Kelly Dransfeldt .20 .50
410 Jason Grilli .20 .50
411 Scott Downs RC .30 .75
412 Jesus Colome .20 .50
413 John Sneed RC .30 .75
414 Tony McKnight .20 .50
415 Luis Rivera .20 .50
416 Adam Eaton .20 .50
417 Mike MacDougal RC .50 1.25
418 Mike Nannini .20 .50
419 Barry Zito RC 4.00 10.00
420 DeWayne Wise .20 .50
421 Jason Dellaero .20 .50
422 Chad Moeller .20 .50
423 Jason Marquis .20 .50
424 Tim Redding RC .50 1.25
425 Mark Mulder .20 .50
426 Josh Paul .20 .50
427 Chris Enochs .20 .50
428 W.Rodriguez RC .30 .75
429 Kevin Witt .20 .50
430 Scott Sobkowiak RC .30 .75
431 McKay Christensen .20 .50
432 Jung Bong .20 .50
433 Keith Evans RC .30 .75
434 Garry Maddox Jr. RC .30 .75
435 Ramon Santiago RC .30 .75
436 Alex Cora .20 .50
437 Carlos Lee .20 .50
438 Jason Repko RC .75 2.00
439 Matt Burch .20 .50
440 Shawn Sonnier RC .30 .75

2000 Bowman Chrome Oversize

Inserted into hobby boxes as a chip-topper at one per box, this eight-card oversized set features some of the Major Leagues most promising young players.

COMPLETE SET (8) 6.00 15.00
1 Pat Burrell .50 1.25
2 Josh Hamilton 1.25 3.00
3 Rafael Furcal .20 .50
4 Corey Patterson .30 .75
5 A.J. Burnett .30 .75
6 Eric Munson .30 .75
7 Nick Johnson .20 .50
8 Alfonso Soriano .20 .50

2000 Bowman Chrome Refractors

Randomly inserted into packs at one in 12, this 440-card insert is a complete parallel of the Bowman Chrome base set. This parallel was produced using Topps' refractor technology.

*STARS: 3X TO 8X BASIC CARDS
*ROOKIES: 2X TO 5X BASIC CARDS

2000 Bowman Chrome Retro/Future

Randomly inserted into hobby/retail packs at one in six, this 440-card insert is a complete parallel of the Bowman Chrome base set. Each card features a television border similar to that of the 1955 Bowman set.

*STARS: 1.5X TO 4X BASIC CARDS
*ROOKIES: .5X TO 1.2X BASIC CARDS

2000 Bowman Chrome Retro/Future Refractors

Randomly inserted into hobby/retail packs at one in 60, this 440-card insert is a complete parallel of the Bowman Chrome base set. Each card features a television border similar to that of the 1955 Bowman set. These cards were produced using Topps' refractor technology.

*STARS: 6X TO 15X BASIC CARDS
*ROOKIES: 4X TO 10X BASIC CARDS

2000 Bowman Chrome Bidding for the Call

Randomly inserted into packs at one in 16, this 15-card insert features players that are looking to break into the Major Leagues during the 2000 season. Card backs carry a "BC" prefix. It's worth noting that top prospect Chin-Feng Chen's very first MLB-licensed card was included in this set.

COMPLETE SET (15) 12.50 30.00
*REFRACTORS: 1.25X TO 3X BASIC BID
REFRACTOR STATED ODDS 1:160
BC1 Adam Piatt .40 1.00
BC2 Pat Burrell .40 1.00
BC3 Mark Mulder .40 1.00
BC4 Nick Johnson .40 1.00
BC5 Alfonso Soriano .75 2.00
BC6 Chin-Feng Chen .40 1.00
BC7 Scott Sobkowiak .40 1.00
BC8 Corey Patterson .40 1.00
BC9 Jack Cust .40 1.00
BC10 Sean Burroughs .40 1.00
BC11 Josh Hamilton 1.50 4.00
BC12 Corey Myers .40 1.00
BC13 Eric Munson .40 1.00
BC14 Wes Anderson .40 1.00
BC15 Lyle Overbay .75 2.00

2000 Bowman Chrome Meteoric Rise

Randomly inserted into packs at one in 24, this 10-card insert features players that have risen to the occasion during their careers. Card backs carry a "MR" prefix.

COMPLETE SET (10) 20.00 50.00
*REF: 1.25X TO 3X BASIC METEORIC 1.25 3.00
REFRACTOR STATED ODDS 1:240
MR1 Nomar Garciaparra 2.00 5.00
MR2 Mark McGwire 3.00 8.00
MR3 Ken Griffey Jr. 2.00 5.00
MR4 Chipper Jones 1.25 3.00
MR5 Manny Ramirez .75 2.00
MR6 Mike Piazza 2.00 5.00
MR7 Cal Ripken 4.00 10.00
MR8 Ivan Rodriguez .75 2.00
MR9 Greg Maddux 2.00 5.00
MR10 Randy Johnson 1.25 3.00

2000 Bowman Chrome Rookie Class 2000

Randomly inserted into packs at one in 24, this 10-card insert features players that made their Major League debuts in 2000. Card backs carry a "RC" prefix.

COMPLETE SET (10) 8.00 20.00
*REF: 1.25X TO 3X BASIC ROOKIE CLASS 1.00 2.50
REFRACTOR STATED ODDS 1:240
RC1 Pat Burrell .60 1.50
RC2 Rick Ankiel .60 1.50
RC3 Ruben Mateo .60 1.50
RC4 Vernon Wells .60 1.50
RC5 Mark Mulder .60 1.50
RC6 A.J. Burnett .60 1.50
RC7 Chad Hermansen .60 1.50
RC8 Corey Patterson .60 1.50
RC9 Rafael Furcal .60 1.50
RC10 Mike Lamb 1.00 2.50

2000 Bowman Chrome Teen Idols

Randomly inserted into packs at one in 16, this 15-card insert set features Major League players that either made it to the majors as teenagers or are top current prospects who are still in their teens in 2000. Card backs carry a "TI" prefix.

COMPLETE SET (15) 20.00 50.00
*SINGLES: 1X TO 2.5X BASIC CARDS 1.00 2.50
*REFRACTORS: 1.25X TO 3X BASIC TEEN
REFRACTOR STATED ODDS 1:160
TI1 Alex Rodriguez 2.50 6.00
TI2 Andruw Jones 1.00 2.50
TI3 Juan Gonzalez .60 1.50
TI4 Ivan Rodriguez 1.00 2.50
TI5 Ken Griffey Jr. 2.50 6.00
TI6 Bobby Bradley .60 1.50
TI7 Brett Myers 1.00 2.50
TI8 C.C. Sabathia .60 1.50
TI9 Ty Howington .60 1.50
TI10 Brandon Phillips 1.50 4.00
TI11 Rick Asadoorian .60 1.50
TI12 Wily Mo Pena .60 1.50
TI13 Sean Burroughs .60 1.50
TI14 Josh Hamilton 1.50 4.00
TI15 Rafael Furcal .60 1.50

2000 Bowman Chrome Draft Picks

The 2000 Bowman Chrome Draft Picks and Prospects set was released in December, 2000 as a 110-card parallel of the 2000 Bowman Draft Picks set. This product was distributed only in factory set form. Each set features Topps' Chrome technology. A limited selection of prospects were switched out from the Bowman checklist and are available exclusively in this Bowman Chrome set. The most notable of these players include Timo Perez and Jon Rauch. Other notable Rookie Cards include Chin-Feng Chen and Adrian Gonzalez.

COMP.FACT.SET (110) 20.00 50.00
1 Pat Burrell .20 .50
2 Rafael Furcal .20 .50
3 Grant Roberts .20 .50
4 Barry Zito 1.50 4.00
5 Julio Zuleta .20 .50
6 Mark Mulder .20 .50
7 Rob Bell .20 .50
8 Adam Piatt .20 .50
9 Mike Lamb .30 .75
10 Pablo Ozuna .20 .50
11 Jason Tyner .20 .50
12 Jason Marquis .20 .50
13 Eric Munson .20 .50
14 Seth Etherton .20 .50
15 Milton Bradley .20 .50
16 Nick Green .20 .50
17 Chin-Feng Chen RC .60 1.50
18 Matt Boone RC .20 .50
19 Kevin Gregg RC .20 .50
20 Eddy Garabito RC .20 .50
21 Aaron Capista RC .20 .50
22 Esteban German RC .20 .50
23 Derek Thompson RC .20 .50
24 Phil Merrell RC .20 .50
25 Brian O'Connor RC .20 .50
26 Yamid Haad .20 .50
27 Hector Mercado RC .20 .50
28 Jason Woolf RC .20 .50
29 Eddy Furniss RC .20 .50
30 Cha Sueng Baek RC .20 .50
31 Colby Lewis RC .20 .50
32 Pasqual Coco RC .20 .50
33 Jorge Cantu RC 2.00 5.00
34 Erasmo Ramirez RC .20 .50
35 Bobby Kielty RC .40 1.00
36 Joaquin Benoit RC .20 .50
37 Brian Esposito RC .20 .50
38 Michael Wenner .20 .50
39 Juan Rincon RC .20 .50
40 Yorvit Torrealba RC .40 1.00
41 Chad Durham RC .20 .50
42 Jim Mann RC .20 .50
43 Shane Loux RC .20 .50
44 Luis Rivas .20 .50
45 Ken Chenard RC .20 .50
46 Mike Lockwood RC .20 .50
47 Yovanny Lara RC .20 .50
48 Bubba Carpenter RC .20 .50
49 Ryan Dittfurth RC .20 .50
50 John Stephens RC .20 .50
51 Pedro Feliz RC 1.00 2.50
52 Kenny Kelly RC .20 .50
53 Neil Jenkins RC .20 .50
54 Mike Glendenning RC .20 .50
55 Bo Porter .20 .50
56 Eric Byrnes .20 .50
57 Tony Alvarez RC .20 .50
58 Kazuhiro Sasaki RC .60 1.50
59 Chad Durbin RC .20 .50
60 Mike Bynum RC .20 .50
61 Travis Wilson RC .20 .50
62 Jose Leon RC .20 .50
63 Ryan Vogelsong RC .20 .50
64 Geraldo Guzman RC .20 .50
65 Craig Anderson RC .20 .50
66 Carlos Silva RC .40 1.00
67 Brad Thomas RC .20 .50
68 Chin-Hui Tsao .60 1.50
69 Mark Buehrle RC 3.00 8.00
70 Juan Salas RC .20 .50
71 Denny Abreu RC .20 .50
72 Keith McDonald RC .20 .50
73 Chris Richard RC .20 .50
74 Tomas De la Rosa RC .20 .50
75 Vicente Padilla RC .40 1.00
76 Justin Brunette RC .20 .50
77 Scott Linebrink RC .20 .50
78 Jeff Sparks RC .20 .50
79 Tike Redman RC .60 1.50
80 John Lackey RC 2.00 5.00
81 Joe Strong RC .20 .50
82 Brian Tollberg RC .20 .50
83 Steve Sisco RC .20 .50
84 Chris Clapinski RC .20 .50
85 Augie Ojeda RC .20 .50
86 Adrian Gonzalez RC 2.50 6.00
87 Mike Stodolka RC .20 .50
88 Adam Johnson RC .20 .50
89 Matt Wheatland RC .20 .50
90 Corey Smith RC .20 .50
91 Rocco Baldelli RC 2.00 5.00
92 Keith Bucktrot RC .20 .50
93 Adam Wainwright RC 1.00 2.50
94 Blaine Boyer RC .20 .50
95 Aaron Herr RC .40 1.00
96 Scott Thorman RC 1.00 2.50
97 Bryan Digby RC .20 .50
98 Josh Shortslef RC .20 .50
99 Sean Smith RC .20 .50
100 Alex Cruz RC .20 .50
101 Marc Love RC .20 .50
102 Kevin Lee RC .20 .50
103 Timo Perez RC .40 1.00
104 Alex Cabrera RC .40 1.00
105 Shane Heams RC .20 .50
106 Tripper Johnson RC .20 .50
107 Brent Abernathy RC .20 .50
108 John Cotton RC .20 .50
109 Brad Wilkerson RC 1.00 2.50
110 Jon Rauch RC .20 .50

2001 Bowman Chrome

The 2001 Bowman Chrome set was distributed in four-card packs with a suggested retail price of $3.99. This 352-card set consists of 110 leading hitters and pitchers (1-110), 110 rising young stars (201-310), 110 top rookies including 20 not found in the regular Bowman set (111-200, 311-330), 20 autographed rookie refractor cards (331-350) each serial numbered to 500 copies and two Ichiro Suzuki Rookie Cards (351) in available in English and Japanese text variations. Both Ichiro cards were only available via mail redemption whereby exchange cards were seeded into packs. In addition, an exchange card was seeded into packs for the Albert Pujols signed Rookie Card. The deadline to send these cards in was June 30th, 2003.

COMP.SET w/o SP's (220) 20.00 50.00
COMMON (1-110/201-310) .20 .50
COMMON (111-200/311-330) 2.00 5.00
COMMON (331-350) 20.00 50.00
1 Jason Giambi .20 .50
2 Rafael Furcal .20 .50
3 Bernie Williams .30 .75
4 Kenny Lofton .20 .50
5 Al Leiter .20 .50
6 Albert Belle .20 .50
7 Craig Biggio .30 .75
8 Mark Mulder .20 .50
9 Carlos Delgado .20 .50
10 Darin Erstad .20 .50
11 Richie Sexson .20 .50
12 Randy Johnson .50 1.25
13 Greg Maddux .75 2.00
14 Orlando Hernandez .20 .50
15 Javier Vazquez .20 .50
16 Jeff Kent .20 .50
17 Jim Thome .30 .75
18 John Olerud .20 .50
19 Jason Kendall .20 .50
20 Scott Rolen .30 .75
21 Tony Gwynn .60 1.50
22 Edgardo Alfonzo .20 .50
23 Pokey Reese .20 .50
24 Todd Helton .30 .75
25 Mark Quinn .20 .50
26 Dean Palmer .20 .50
27 Ray Durham .20 .50
28 Rafael Palmeiro .30 .75
29 Carl Everett .20 .50
30 Vladimir Guerrero .50 1.25
31 Livan Hernandez .20 .50
32 Preston Wilson .20 .50
33 Jose Vidro .20 .50
34 Fred McGriff .30 .75
35 Kevin Brown .20 .50
36 Miguel Tejada .20 .50
37 Chipper Jones .50 1.25
38 Edgar Martinez .30 .75
39 Tony Batista .20 .50
40 Jorge Posada .30 .75
41 Sammy Sosa .50 1.25
42 Gary Sheffield .20 .50
43 Bartolo Colon .20 .50
44 Pat Burrell .20 .50
45 Jay Payton .20 .50
46 Mike Mussina .30 .75
47 Nomar Garciaparra .75 2.00
48 Darren Dreifort .20 .50
49 Richard Hidalgo .20 .50
50 Troy Glaus .20 .50
51 Ben Grieve .20 .50
52 Jim Edmonds .20 .50
53 Raul Mondesi .20 .50
54 Andruw Jones .30 .75
55 Mike Sweeney .20 .50
56 Derek Jeter 1.25 3.00
57 Ruben Mateo .20 .50
58 Cristian Guzman .20 .50
59 Mike Hampton .20 .50
60 J.D. Drew .20 .50
61 Matt Lawton .20 .50
62 Moises Alou .20 .50
63 Terrence Long .20 .50
64 Geoff Jenkins .20 .50
65 Manny Ramirez Sox .30 .75
66 Johnny Damon .30 .75
67 Pedro Martinez .30 .75
68 Juan Gonzalez .20 .50
69 Roger Clemens 1.00 2.50
70 Carlos Beltran .20 .50
71 Roberto Alomar .30 .75
72 Barry Bonds 1.25 3.00
73 Tim Hudson .20 .50
74 Tom Glavine .30 .75
75 Jeromy Burnitz .20 .50
76 Adrian Beltre .20 .50
77 Mike Piazza .75 2.00
78 Kerry Wood .20 .50
79 Steve Finley .20 .50
80 Bob Abreu .20 .50
81 Neifi Perez .20 .50
82 Mark Redman .20 .50
83 Paul Konerko .20 .50
84 Jermaine Dye .20 .50
85 Brian Giles .20 .50
86 Ivan Rodriguez .30 .75
87 Adam Kennedy .20 .50
88 Eric Chavez .20 .50
89 Billy Koch .20 .50
90 Shawn Green .20 .50
91 Matt Williams .20 .50
92 Greg Vaughn .20 .50
93 Jeff Cirillo .20 .50
94 Frank Thomas .50 1.25
95 David Justice .20 .50
96 Cal Ripken 1.50 4.00
97 Curt Schilling .20 .50
98 Barry Zito .30 .75
99 Brian Jordan .20 .50
100 Chan Ho Park .20 .50
101 J.T. Snow .20 .50
102 Kazuhiro Sasaki .20 .50
103 Alex Rodriguez .75 2.00
104 Mariano Rivera .50 1.25
105 Eric Milton .20 .50
106 Andy Pettitte .30 .75
107 Ken Griffey Jr. .75 2.00
108 Bengie Molina .20 .50
109 Jeff Bagwell .30 .75
110 Mark McGwire 1.25 3.00
111 Dan Tosca RC 2.00 5.00
112 Sergio Contreras RC 3.00 8.00
113 Mitch Jones RC 3.00 8.00
114 Ramon Carvajal RC 3.00 8.00
115 Ryan Madson RC 4.00 10.00
116 Hank Blalock RC 12.50 30.00
117 Ben Washburn RC 2.00 5.00
118 Erick Almonte RC 2.00 5.00
119 Shawn Fagan RC 3.00 8.00
120 Gary Johnson RC 2.00 5.00
121 Brett Evert RC 2.00 5.00
122 Joe Hamer RC 3.00 8.00
123 Yhency Brazoban RC 4.00 10.00
124 Domingo Guante RC 2.00 5.00
125 Deivi Mendez RC 2.00 5.00
126 Adrian Hernandez RC 2.00 5.00
127 R. Abercrombie RC 4.00 10.00
128 Steve Bennett RC 2.00 5.00
129 Matt White RC 3.00 8.00
130 Brian Hitchcox RC 2.00 5.00
131 Deivis Santos RC 2.00 5.00
132 Luis Montanez RC 4.00 10.00
133 Eric Reynolds RC 2.00 5.00
134 Denny Bautista RC 4.00 10.00
135 Hector Garcia RC 2.00 5.00
136 Joe Thurston RC 3.00 8.00
137 Tsuyoshi Shinjo RC 4.00 10.00
138 Elpidio Guzman RC 2.00 5.00
139 Brian Bass RC 2.00 5.00
140 Mark Burnett RC 3.00 8.00
141 Russ Jacobson UER 2.00 5.00
Last name misspelled Jacobsen on front
142 Travis Hafner RC 12.50 30.00
143 Wilson Betemit RC 6.00 15.00
144 Luke Lockwood RC 3.00 8.00
145 Noel Devarez RC 3.00 8.00
146 Doug Gredvig RC 2.00 5.00
147 Seung Song RC 3.00 8.00
148 Andy Van Hekken RC 2.00 5.00
149 Ryan Kohlmeier 2.00 5.00
150 Dee Haynes RC 2.00 5.00
151 Jim Journell RC 3.00 8.00
152 Chad Petty RC 2.00 5.00
153 Danny Borrell RC 2.00 5.00
154 Dave Krynzel 2.00 5.00
155 Octavio Martinez RC 3.00 8.00
156 David Parrish RC 2.00 5.00
157 Jason Miller RC 2.00 5.00
158 Corey Spencer RC 2.00 5.00
159 Maxim St. Pierre RC 3.00 8.00
160 Pat Magness RC 3.00 8.00
161 Ranier Olmedo RC 3.00 8.00
162 Brandon Mims RC 2.00 5.00
163 Phil Wilson RC 3.00 8.00
164 Jose Reyes RC 50.00 100.00
165 Matt Butler RC 3.00 8.00
166 Joel Pineiro 3.00 8.00
167 Ken Chenard 2.00 5.00
168 Alexis Gomez RC 2.00 5.00
169 Justin Morneau RC 40.00 80.00
170 Josh Fogg RC 3.00 8.00
171 Charles Frazier RC 2.00 5.00
172 Ryan Ludwick RC 10.00 25.00
173 Seth McClung RC 3.00 8.00
174 Justin Wayne RC 3.00 8.00
175 Rafael Soriano RC 3.00 8.00
176 Jared Abruzzo RC 2.00 5.00
177 Jason Richardson RC 2.00 5.00
178 Darwin Cubillan RC 2.00 5.00
179 Blake Williams RC 2.00 5.00
180 V. Pascucci RC 3.00 8.00
181 Ryan Hannaman RC 3.00 8.00
182 Steve Smyth RC 3.00 8.00
183 Jake Peavy RC 30.00 60.00
184 Onix Mercado RC 3.00 8.00
185 Luis Torres RC 3.00 8.00
186 Casey Fossum RC 2.00 5.00
187 Eduardo Figueroa RC 2.00 5.00
188 Bryan Barnowski RC 2.00 5.00
189 Jason Standridge 2.00 5.00
190 Marvin Seale RC 3.00 8.00
191 Steve Smitherman RC 3.00 8.00
192 Rafael Boitel RC 2.00 5.00
193 Dany Morban RC 2.00 5.00
194 Justin Woodrow RC 3.00 8.00
195 Ed Rogers RC 2.00 5.00
196 Ben Hendrickson RC 2.00 5.00
197 Thomas Mitchell 2.00 5.00
198 Adam Pettyjohn RC 2.00 5.00
199 Doug Nickle RC 2.00 5.00
200 Jason Jones RC 2.00 5.00
201 Larry Barnes .20 .50
202 Ben Diggins .20 .50
203 Dee Brown .20 .50
204 Rocco Baldelli .20 .50
205 Luis Terrero .20 .50
206 Milton Bradley .20 .50
207 Kurt Ainsworth .20 .50
208 Sean Burroughs .20 .50
209 Rick Asadoorian .20 .50
210 Ramon Castro .20 .50
211 Nick Neugebauer .20 .50
212 Aaron Myette .20 .50
213 Luis Matos .20 .50
214 Donnie Bridges .20 .50
215 Alex Cintron .20 .50
216 Bobby Kielty .20 .50
217 Matt Belisle .20 .50
218 Adam Everett .20 .50
219 John Lackey .20 .50
220 Adam Wainwright .20 .50
221 Jerry Hairston Jr. .20 .50
222 Mike Bynum .20 .50
223 Ryan Christianson .20 .50
224 J.J. Davis .20 .50
225 Alex Graman .20 .50
226 Abraham Nunez .20 .50
227 Sun Woo Kim .20 .50
228 Jimmy Rollins .20 .50
229 Ruben Salazar .20 .50
230 Josh Girdley .20 .50
231 Carl Crawford .20 .50
232 Ben Davis .20 .50
233 Jason Grabowski .20 .50
234 Chris George .20 .50
235 Roy Oswalt .50 1.25
236 Brian Cole .20 .50
237 Corey Patterson .20 .50
238 Vernon Wells .20 .50
239 Brad Baker .20 .50
240 Gookie Dawkins .20 .50
241 Michael Cuddyer .20 .50
242 Ricardo Aramboles .20 .50
243 Ben Sheets .30 .75
244 Toby Hall .20 .50
245 Jack Cust .20 .50
246 Pedro Feliz .20 .50
247 Josh Beckett .30 .75
248 Alex Escobar .20 .50
249 Marcus Giles .20 .50
250 Jon Rauch .20 .50
251 Kevin Mench .20 .50
252 Shawn Sonnier .20 .50
253 Aaron Rowand .20 .50
254 C.C. Sabathia .20 .50
255 Bubba Crosby .20 .50
256 Josh Hamilton .40 1.00
257 Carlos Hernandez .20 .50
258 Carlos Pena .20 .50
259 Miguel Cabrera 1.50 4.00
260 Brandon Phillips .20 .50
261 Tony Pena Jr. .20 .50
262 Cristian Guerrero .20 .50
263 Jin Ho Cho .20 .50
264 Aaron Herr .20 .50
265 Keith Ginter .20 .50

266 Felipe Lopez .20 .50
267 Travis Harper .20 .50
268 Joe Torres .20 .50
269 Eric Byrnes .20 .50
270 Ben Christensen .20 .50
271 Aubrey Huff .20 .50
272 Lyle Overbay .20 .50
273 Vince Faison .20 .50
274 Bobby Bradley .20 .50
275 Joe Crede .50 1.25
276 Matt Wheatland .20 .50
277 Grady Sizemore .75 2.00
278 Adrian Gonzalez .20 .50
279 Tim Raines Jr. .20 .50
280 Phil Dumatrait .20 .50
281 Jason Hart .20 .50
282 David Kelton .20 .50
283 David Walling .20 .50
284 J.R. House .20 .50
285 Kenny Kelly .20 .50
286 Aaron McNeal .20 .50
287 Nick Johnson .20 .50
288 Scott Heard .20 .50
289 Brad Wilkerson .20 .50
290 Allen Levrault .20 .50
291 Chris Richard .20 .50
292 Jared Sandberg .20 .50
293 Tike Redman .20 .50
294 Adam Dunn .30 .75
295 Josh Pressley .20 .50
296 Jose Ortiz .20 .50
297 Jason Romano .20 .50
298 Tim Redding .20 .50
299 Alex Gordon .20 .50
300 Ben Petrick .20 .50
301 Eric Munson .20 .50
302 Luis Rivas .20 .50
303 Matt Ginter .20 .50
304 Alfonso Soriano .30 .75
305 Wilfredo Rodriguez .20 .50
306 Brett Myers .20 .50
307 Scott Seabol .20 .50
308 Tony Alvarez .20 .50
309 Donzell McDonald .20 .50
310 Austin Kearns .20 .50
311 Will Ohman RC 3.00 8.00
312 Ryan Soules RC 2.00 5.00
313 Cody Ross RC 2.00 5.00
314 Bill Whitecotton RC 2.00 5.00
315 Mike Burns RC 3.00 8.00
316 Manuel Acosta RC 2.00 5.00
317 Lance Niekro RC 4.00 10.00
318 Travis Thompson RC 3.00 8.00
319 Zach Sorensen RC 3.00 8.00
320 Austin Evans RC 2.00 5.00
321 Brad Stiles RC 2.00 5.00
322 Joe Kennedy RC 4.00 10.00
323 Luke Martin RC 3.00 8.00
324 Juan Diaz RC 3.00 8.00
325 Pat Hallmark RC 2.00 5.00
326 Christian Parker RC 2.00 5.00
327 Ronny Corona RC 3.00 8.00
328 Jermaine Clark RC 2.00 5.00
329 Scott Dunn RC 3.00 8.00
330 Scott Chiasson RC 3.00 8.00
331 Greg Nash AU RC 20.00 50.00
332 Brad Cresse AU 20.00 50.00
333 John Buck AU RC 40.00 80.00
334 Freddie Bynum AU RC 20.00 50.00
335 Felix Diaz AU RC 20.00 50.00
336 Jason Belcher AU RC 20.00 50.00
337 T.Farnsworth AU RC 20.00 50.00
338 Roberto Miniel AU RC 20.00 50.00
339 Esix Snead AU RC 20.00 50.00
340 Albert Pujols AU RC 1500.00 2500.00
341 Jeff Andra AU RC 20.00 50.00
342 Victor Hall AU RC 20.00 50.00
343 Pedro Liriano AU RC 20.00 50.00
344 Andy Beal AU RC 20.00 50.00
345 Bob Keppel AU RC 20.00 50.00
346 Brian Schmitt AU RC 20.00 50.00
347 Ron Davenport AU RC 90.00 150.00
348 Tony Blanco AU RC 20.00 50.00
349 Reggie Griggs AU RC 20.00 50.00
350 D. Van Dusen AU RC 20.00 50.00
351A I. Suzuki English RC 60.00 100.00
351B I. Suzuki Japan RC 60.00 100.00

2001 Bowman Chrome Gold Refractors

Randomly inserted in packs at the rate of one in 47, this 330-card set is a parallel version of the base set with a distinctive gold refractive quality. Only 99 serially numbered sets were produced. Exchange cards with a redemption deadline of June 30th, 2003 for two separate Ichiro Suzuki issues were seeded into packs. One of the features English text on the card back with 50 copies produced and the other features Japanese text on the card back with 49 copies produced. Both cards were serial-numbered together resulting in an intermingled print run of 99 copies with English cards featuring odd serial-numbering (i.e. 1/99, 3/99, 5/99 etc.) and Japanese cards featuring even serial-numbering (i.e. 2/99, 4/99, 6/99 etc.).

*STARS: 8X TO 20X BASIC CARDS
*ROOKIES: 1.5X TO 4X BASIC CARDS
ICHIRO JAPAN PRINT RUN 49 #'d CARDS
ICHIRO ENGLISH ARE EVEN SERIAL #'d
ICHIRO ENGLISH ARE ODD SERIAL #'d
172 Ryan Ludwick 100.00 200.00
183 Jake Peavy 200.00 300.00
NNOA Ichiro Suzuki English/50 EXCH 250.00 400.00
NNOB Ichiro Suzuki Japan/49 EXCH 250.00 400.00

2001 Bowman Chrome X-Fractors

Randomly inserted in packs at the rate of one in 23, this 330-card set is a parallel version of the base set highlighted by a distinct background pattern. Exchange cards with a redemption deadline of June 30th, 2003 for two separate Ichiro Suzuki issues (English text and Japanese text) were randomly seeded into packs.

*STARS: 4X TO 10X BASIC CARDS
*ROOKIES: .75X TO 2X BASIC CARDS
172 Ryan Ludwick 50.00 100.00
183 Jake Peavy 75.00 150.00

2001 Bowman Chrome Futures Game Relics

Randomly inserted in packs at the rate of one in 460, this 30-card set features color photos of players who participated in the 2000 Futures Game in Atlanta with pieces of game-worn uniform numbers and letters embedded in the cards.

FGRAE Alex Escobar 3.00 8.00
FGRAM Aaron Myette 3.00 8.00
FGRBB Bobby Bradley 3.00 8.00
FGRBP Ben Petrick 3.00 8.00
FGRBS Ben Sheets 6.00 15.00
FGRBW Brad Wilkerson 3.00 8.00
FGRBZ Barry Zito 6.00 15.00
FGRCA Craig Anderson 3.00 8.00
FGRCC Chin-Feng Chen 30.00 60.00
FGRCG Chris George 3.00 8.00
FGRCH Carlos Hernandez 4.00 10.00
FGRCP Carlos Pena 3.00 8.00
FGRCT Chin-Hui Tsao 40.00 80.00
FGREM Eric Munson 3.00 8.00
FGRFL Felipe Lopez 4.00 10.00
FGRJC Jack Cust 3.00 8.00
FGRJH Josh Hamilton 6.00 15.00
FGRJR Jason Romano 3.00 8.00
FGRJZ Julio Zuleta 3.00 8.00
FGRKA Kurt Ainsworth 3.00 8.00
FGRMB Mike Bynum 3.00 8.00
FGRMG Marcus Giles 4.00 10.00
FGRNN Ntema Ndungidi 3.00 8.00
FGRRA Ryan Anderson 3.00 8.00
FGRRC Ramon Castro 3.00 8.00
FGRRD Randey Dorame 3.00 8.00
FGRSK Sun Woo Kim 3.00 8.00
FGRTO Tomo Ohka 3.00 8.00
FGRTW Travis Wilson 3.00 8.00
FGRDCP Corey Patterson 3.00 8.00

2001 Bowman Chrome Rookie Reprints

Randomly inserted in packs at the rate of one in 12, this 25-card set feature reprints of classic 1948-1955 Bowman rookies printed on polished Chrome finishes.

COMPLETE SET (25) 20.00 50.00
*REFRACTORS: .75X TO 2X BASIC REPRINT
REFRACTOR STATED ODDS 1:203
REF.PRINT RUN 299 SERIAL #'d SETS
1 Yogi Berra 3.00 8.00
2 Ralph Kiner 1.50 4.00
3 Stan Musial 5.00 12.00
4 Warren Spahn 1.50 4.00
5 Roy Campanella 3.00 8.00
6 Bob Lemon 1.50 4.00
7 Robin Roberts 1.50 4.00
8 Duke Snider 1.50 4.00
9 Early Wynn 1.50 4.00
10 Richie Ashburn 1.50 4.00
11 Gil Hodges 2.50 6.00
12 Hank Bauer 1.50 4.00
13 Don Newcombe 1.50 4.00
14 Al Rosen 1.50 4.00
15 Willie Mays 6.00 15.00
16 Joe Garagiola 1.50 4.00
17 Whitey Ford 1.50 4.00
18 Lew Burdette 1.50 4.00
19 Gil McDougald 1.50 4.00
20 Minnie Minoso 1.50 4.00
21 Eddie Mathews 2.50 6.00
22 Harvey Kuenn 1.50 4.00
23 Don Larsen 1.50 4.00
24 Elston Howard 1.50 4.00
25 Don Zimmer 1.50 4.00

2001 Bowman Chrome Rookie Reprints Relics

This six-card insert set features color player photos with pieces of their Rookie Season game-worn jerseys or game-used bats embedded in the cards. The insertion rate for the Mike Piazza Bat card is one in 3674 and one in 244 for the jersey cards. Three cards are Bowman Rookie card reprints and three cards are re-created "cards that never were."

1 David Justice Jsy 4.00 10.00
2 Richie Sexson Jsy 4.00 10.00
3 Sean Casey Jsy 4.00 10.00
4 Mike Piazza Bat 15.00 40.00
5 Carlos Delgado Jsy 4.00 10.00
6 Chipper Jones Jsy 6.00 15.00

2002 Bowman Chrome

This 405 card set was issued in July, 2002. It was issued in four card packs with an SRP of $4 which were packed 18 packs to a box and 12 boxes to a case. The first 110 card of the set featured veteran players. The next grouping of cards (111-383) featured a mix of rookies and prospect cards. The then final grouping (384-405) featured signed rookie cards. Both So Taguchi and Kazuhisa Ishii were also printed without autographs on their cards. An exchange was inserted into packs for Jake Mauer's autographed RC. The exchange card was intended to be card number 388 in the checklist but the actual Mauer autograph mailed out to collectors was card number 324. Thus, this set actually has two cards numbered 324 (the Jake Mauer autograph and a basic-issue Ben Broussard card) and no number 388.

COMP.RED SET (110) 15.00 40.00
COMP.BLUE w/o SP's (110) 15.00 40.00
COMMON RED (1-110) .20 .50
COMMON BLUE (111-383) .30 .75
COMMON AU (324B/384-405) 4.00 10.00
324B/384-405 GROUP A AUTO ODDS 1:28
403-404 GROUP B AUTO ODDS 1:1290
324B/384-405 OVERALL AUTO ODDS 1:27
1 Adam Dunn .20 .50
2 Derek Jeter 1.25 3.00
3 Alex Rodriguez .75 2.00
4 Miguel Tejada .20 .50
5 Nomar Garciaparra .75 2.00
6 Toby Hall .20 .50
7 Brandon Duckworth .20 .50
8 Paul LoDuca .20 .50
9 Brian Giles .20 .50
10 C.C. Sabathia .20 .50
11 Curt Schilling .20 .50
12 Tsuyoshi Shinjo .20 .50
13 Ramon Hernandez .20 .50
14 Jose Cruz Jr. .20 .50
15 Albert Pujols 1.00 2.50
16 Joe Mays .20 .50
17 Javy Lopez .20 .50
18 J.T. Snow .20 .50
19 David Segui .20 .50
20 Jorge Posada .30 .75
21 Doug Mientkiewicz .20 .50
22 Jerry Hairston Jr. .20 .50
23 Bernie Williams .30 .75
24 Mike Sweeney .20 .50
25 Jason Giambi .20 .50
26 Ryan Dempster .20 .50
27 Ryan Klesko .20 .50
28 Mark Quinn .20 .50
29 Jeff Kent .20 .50
30 Eric Chavez .20 .50
31 Adrian Beltre .20 .50
32 Andruw Jones .30 .75
33 Alfonso Soriano .20 .50
34 Aramis Ramirez .20 .50
35 Greg Maddux .75 2.00
36 Andy Pettitte .30 .75
37 Bartolo Colon .20 .50
38 Ben Sheets .20 .50
39 Bobby Higginson .20 .50
40 Ivan Rodriguez .30 .75
41 Brad Penny .20 .50
42 Carlos Lee .20 .50
43 Damion Easley .20 .50
44 Preston Wilson .20 .50
45 Jeff Bagwell .30 .75
46 Eric Milton .20 .50
47 Rafael Palmeiro .30 .75
48 Gary Sheffield .20 .50
49 J.D. Drew .20 .50
50 Jim Thome .30 .75
51 Ichiro Suzuki 1.00 2.50
52 Bud Smith .20 .50
53 Chan Ho Park .20 .50
54 D'Angelo Jimenez .20 .50
55 Ken Griffey Jr. .75 2.00
56 Wade Miller .20 .50
57 Vladimir Guerrero .50 1.25
58 Troy Glaus .20 .50
59 Shawn Green .20 .50
60 Kerry Wood .20 .50
61 Jack Wilson .20 .50
62 Kevin Brown .20 .50
63 Marcus Giles .20 .50
64 Pat Burrell .20 .50
65 Larry Walker .20 .50
66 Sammy Sosa .50 1.25
67 Raul Mondesi .20 .50
68 Tim Hudson .20 .50
69 Lance Berkman .20 .50
70 Mike Mussina .30 .75
71 Barry Zito .20 .50
72 Jimmy Rollins .20 .50
73 Barry Bonds 1.25 3.00
74 Craig Biggio .30 .75
75 Todd Helton .30 .75
76 Roger Clemens 1.00 2.50
77 Frank Catalanotto .20 .50
78 Josh Towers .20 .50
79 Roy Oswalt .20 .50
80 Chipper Jones .50 1.25
81 Cristian Guzman .20 .50
82 Darin Erstad .20 .50
83 Freddy Garcia .20 .50
84 Jason Tyner .20 .50
85 Carlos Delgado .20 .50
86 Jon Lieber .20 .50
87 Juan Pierre .20 .50
88 Matt Morris .20 .50
89 Phil Nevin .20 .50
90 Jim Edmonds .20 .50
91 Maggio Ordonez .20 .50
92 Mike Hampton .20 .50
93 Rafael Furcal .20 .50
94 Richie Sexson .20 .50
95 Luis Gonzalez .20 .50
96 Scott Rolen .30 .75
97 Tim Redding .20 .50
98 Moises Alou .20 .50
99 Jose Vidro .20 .50
100 Mike Piazza .75 2.00
101 Pedro Martinez .30 .75
102 Geoff Jenkins .20 .50
103 Johnny Damon Sox .30 .75
104 Mike Cameron UER .30 .75
Card has fascimile autograph of Troy Cameron
105 Randy Johnson .50 1.25
106 David Eckstein .20 .50
107 Javier Vazquez .20 .50
108 Mark Mulder .20 .50
109 Robert Fick .20 .50
110 Roberto Alomar .30 .75
111 Wilson Betemit .30 .75
112 Chris Tritle SP RC 2.00 5.00
113 Ed Rogers .30 .75
114 Juan Pena .30 .75
115 Josh Beckett .50 1.25
116 Juan Cruz .30 .75
117 Noochie Varner SP RC 2.00 5.00
118 Blake Williams .30 .75
119 Mike Rivera .30 .75
120 Hank Blalock .75 2.00
121 Hansel Izquierdo SP RC 2.00 5.00
122 Orlando Hudson .30 .75
123 Bill Hall SP 2.00 5.00
124 Jose Reyes .75 2.00
125 Juan Rivera .30 .75
126 Eric Valent .30 .75
127 Scotty Layfield SP RC 2.00 5.00
128 Austin Kearns .30 .75
129 Nic Jackson SP RC 2.00 5.00
130 Scott Chiasson .30 .75
131 Chad Qualls SP RC 3.00 8.00
132 Marcus Thames .30 .75
133 Nathan Haynes .30 .75
134 Joe Borchard .30 .75
135 Josh Hamilton .60 1.50
136 Corey Patterson .30 .75
137 Travis Wilson .30 .75
138 Alex Escobar .30 .75
139 Alexis Gomez .30 .75
140 Nick Johnson .50 1.25
141 Marlon Byrd .30 .75
142 Kory DeHaan .30 .75
143 Carlos Hernandez .30 .75
144 Sean Burroughs .30 .75
145 Angel Berroa .30 .75
146 Aubrey Huff .50 1.25
147 Travis Hafner .50 1.25
148 Brandon Berger .30 .75
149 J.R. House .30 .75
150 Dewon Brazelton .30 .75
151 Jayson Werth .30 .75
152 Larry Barnes .30 .75
153 Ruben Gotay SP RC 3.00 8.00
154 Tommy Marx SP RC 2.00 5.00
155 John Suomi SP RC 2.00 5.00
156 Javier Colina SP 2.00 5.00
157 Greg Sain SP RC 2.00 5.00
158 Robert Cosby SP RC 2.00 5.00
159 Angel Pagan SP RC 3.00 8.00
160 Ralph Santana RC .50 1.25
161 Joe Orloski RC .50 1.25
162 Shayne Wright SP RC 2.00 5.00
163 Jay Caligiuri SP RC 2.00 5.00
164 Greg Montalbano SP RC 2.00 5.00
165 Rich Harden SP RC 10.00 25.00
166 Rich Thompson SP RC 2.00 5.00
167 Fred Bastardo SP RC 2.00 5.00
168 Alejandro Giron SP RC 2.00 5.00
169 Jesus Medrano SP RC 2.00 5.00
170 Kevin Deaton SP RC 2.00 5.00
171 Mike Rosamond RC .50 1.25
172 Jon Guzman SP RC 2.00 5.00
173 Gerard Oakes SP RC 2.00 5.00
174 Francisco Liriano SP RC 15.00 40.00
175 Matt Allegra SP RC 2.00 5.00
176 Mike Snyder SP RC 2.00 5.00
177 James Shanks SP RC 2.00 5.00
178 And. Hernandez SP RC 2.00 5.00
179 Dan Trumble SP RC 2.00 5.00
180 Luis DePaula SP RC 2.00 5.00
181 Randall Shelley SP RC 2.00 5.00
182 Richard Lane SP RC 2.00 5.00
183 Antwon Rollins SP RC 2.00 5.00
184 Ryan Bukvich SP RC 2.00 5.00
185 Derrick Lewis SP 2.00 5.00
186 Eric Miller SP RC 2.00 5.00
187 Justin Schuda SP RC 2.00 5.00
188 Brian West SP RC 2.00 5.00
189 Brad Wilkerson .30 .75
190 Neal Frendling SP RC 2.00 5.00
191 Jeremy Hill SP RC 2.00 5.00
192 James Barrett SP RC 2.00 5.00
193 Brett Kay SP RC 2.00 5.00
194 Ryan Mottl SP RC 2.00 5.00
195 Brad Nelson SP RC 2.00 5.00
196 Juan M. Gonzalez SP RC 2.00 5.00
197 Curtis Legendre SP RC 2.00 5.00
198 Ronald Acuna SP RC 2.00 5.00
199 Chris Flinn SP RC 2.00 5.00
200 Nick Alvarez SP RC 2.00 5.00
201 Jason Ellison SP RC 4.00 10.00
202 Blake McGinley SP RC 2.00 5.00
203 Dan Phillips SP RC 2.00 5.00
204 Demetrius Heath SP RC 2.00 5.00
205 Eric Bruntlett SP RC 2.00 5.00
206 Joe Jiannetti SP RC 2.00 5.00
207 Mike Hill SP RC 2.00 5.00
208 Ricardo Cordova SP RC 2.00 5.00
209 Mark Hamilton SP RC 2.00 5.00
210 David Mattox SP RC 2.00 5.00
211 Jose Morban SP RC 2.00 5.00
212 Scott Wiggins SP RC 2.00 5.00
213 Steve Green .30 .75
214 Brian Rogers SP 2.00 5.00
215 Kenny Baugh .30 .75
216 Anastacio Martinez SP RC 2.00 5.00
217 Richard Lewis .30 .75
218 Tim Kalita SP RC 2.00 5.00
219 Edwin Almonte SP RC 2.00 5.00
220 Hee Seop Choi .30 .75
221 Ty Howington .30 .75
222 Victor Alvarez SP RC 2.00 5.00
223 Morgan Ensberg .50 1.25
224 Jeff Austin SP RC 2.00 5.00
225 Clint Weibl SP RC 2.00 5.00
226 Eric Cyr .30 .75
227 Marlyn Tisdale SP RC 2.00 5.00
228 John VanBenschoten .30 .75
229 David Krynzel .30 .75
230 Raul Chavez SP RC 2.00 5.00
231 Brett Evert .30 .75
232 Joe Rogers SP RC 2.00 5.00
233 Adam Wainwright .30 .75
234 Matt Herges RC .30 .75
235 Matt Childers SP RC 2.00 5.00
236 Nick Neugebauer .30 .75
237 Carl Crawford .50 1.25
238 Seung Song .30 .75
239 Randy Flores .30 .75
240 Jason Lane .50 1.25
241 Chase Utley 4.00 10.00
242 Ben Howard SP RC 2.00 5.00
243 Eric Glaser SP RC 2.00 5.00
244 Josh Wilson RC .50 1.25
245 Jose Valverde SP RC 2.00 5.00
246 Chris Smith .30 .75
247 Mark Prior .75 2.00
248 Brian Mallette SP RC 2.00 5.00
249 Chone Figgins SP RC 3.00 8.00
250 Jimmy Alvarez SP RC 2.00 5.00
251 Luis Terrero .30 .75
252 Josh Bonifay SP RC 2.00 5.00
253 Garrett Guzman SP RC 2.00 5.00
254 Jeff Verplancke SP RC 2.00 5.00
255 Nate Espy SP RC 2.00 5.00
256 Jeff Lincoln SP RC 2.00 5.00
257 Ryan Snare SP RC 2.00 5.00
258 Jose Ortiz .30 .75
259 Denny Bautista .30 .75
260 Willy Aybar .30 .75
261 Kelly Johnson 1.25 3.00
262 Shawn Fagan .30 .75
263 Yurendell DeCaster SP RC 2.00 5.00
264 Mike Peeples SP RC 2.00 5.00
265 Joel Guzman 1.25 3.00
266 Ryan Vogelsong .30 .75
267 Jorge Padilla SP RC 2.00 5.00
268 Joe Jester SP RC 2.00 5.00
269 Ryan Church SP RC 4.00 10.00
270 Mitch Jones .30 .75
271 Travis Foley SP RC 2.00 5.00
272 Bobby Crosby 1.25 3.00
273 Adrian Gonzalez .30 .75
274 Ronnie Merrill .30 .75
275 Joel Pineiro .30 .75
276 John-Ford Griffin .30 .75
277 Brian Forystek SP RC 2.00 5.00
278 Sean Douglass .30 .75
279 Manny Delcarmen SP RC 3.00 8.00
280 Jim Kavourias SP RC 2.00 5.00
281 Gabe Gross .30 .75
282 Bill Ortega .30 .75
283 Joey Hammond SP RC 2.00 5.00
284 Brett Myers .50 1.25
285 Carlos Pena .30 .75
286 Ezequiel Astacio SP RC 2.00 5.00
287 Edwin Yan SP RC 2.00 5.00
288 Chris Duffy SP RC 3.00 8.00
289 Jason Kinchen .30 .75
290 Rafael Soriano .30 .75
291 Colin Young RC 2.00 5.00
292 Eric Byrnes .30 .75
293 Chris Narveson SP RC 3.00 8.00
294 John Rheinecker .30 .75
295 Mike Wilson SP RC 2.00 5.00
296 Justin Sherrod SP RC 2.00 5.00
297 Deivi Mendez .30 .75
298 Wily Mo Pena .50 1.25
299 Brett Roneberg SP RC 2.00 5.00
300 Trey Lunsford SP RC 2.00 5.00
301 Christian Parker .30 .75
302 Brent Butler .30 .75
303 Aaron Heilman .30 .75
304 Wilkin Ruan .30 .75
305 Kenny Kelly .30 .75
306 Cody Ransom .30 .75
307 Koyie Hill SP 2.00 5.00
308 Tony Fontana SP RC 2.00 5.00
309 Mark Teixeira 2.00 5.00
310 Doug Sessions SP RC 2.00 5.00
311 Josh Cisneros SP RC 2.00 5.00
312 Carlos Brackley SP RC 2.00 5.00
313 Tim Raines Jr. .30 .75
314 Ross Peeples SP RC 2.00 5.00
315 Alex Requena SP RC 2.00 5.00
316 Chin-Hui Tsao .50 1.25
317 Tony Alvarez .30 .75
318 Craig Kuzmic SP RC 2.00 5.00
319 Pete Zamora SP RC 2.00 5.00
320 Matt Parker SP RC 2.00 5.00
321 Keith Ginter .30 .75
322 Gary Cates Jr. SP RC 2.00 5.00
323 Matt Belisle .30 .75
324A Ben Broussard .30 .75
324B Ja.Mauer AU A RC EXCH UER 4.00 10.00
Card was mistakenly numbered as 324
325 Dennis Tankersley .30 .75
326 Juan Silvestre .30 .75
327 Henry Pichardo SP RC 2.00 5.00
328 Michael Floyd SP RC 2.00 5.00
329 Clint Nageotte SP RC 3.00 8.00
330 Raymond Cabrera SP RC 2.00 5.00
331 Mauricio Lara SP RC 2.00 5.00
332 Alejandro Cadena SP RC 2.00 5.00
333 Jonny Gomes SP RC 6.00 15.00
334 Jason Bulger SP RC 2.00 5.00
335 Nate Teut .30 .75
336 David Gil SP RC 2.00 5.00
337 Joel Crump SP RC 2.00 5.00
338 Brandon Phillips .30 .75
339 Macay McBride .50 1.25
340 Brandon Claussen .30 .75
341 Josh Phelps .30 .75
342 Freddie Money SP RC 2.00 5.00
343 Cliff Bartosh SP RC 2.00 5.00
344 Terrance Hill SP RC 2.00 5.00
345 John Rodriguez SP RC 3.00 8.00
346 Chris Latham SP RC 2.00 5.00
347 Carlos Cabrera SP RC 2.00 5.00
348 Jose Bautista SP RC 4.00 10.00
349 Kevin Frederick SP RC 2.00 5.00
350 Jerome Williams .30 .75
351 Napoleon Calzado SP RC 2.00 5.00
352 Benito Baez SP 2.00 5.00
353 Xavier Nady .30 .75
354 Jason Botts SP RC 3.00 8.00
355 Steve Bechler SP RC 2.00 5.00
356 Reed Johnson SP RC 4.00 10.00
357 Mark Outlaw SP RC 2.00 5.00
358 Jake Peavy .75 2.00
359 Josh Shaffer SP RC 2.00 5.00
360 Dan Wright SP 2.00 5.00
361 Ryan Gripp SP RC 2.00 5.00
362 Nelson Castro SP RC 2.00 5.00
363 Jason Bay SP RC 5.00 12.00
364 Franklyn German SP RC 2.00 5.00
365 Corwin Malone SP RC 2.00 5.00
366 Kelly Ramos SP RC 2.00 5.00
367 John Ennis SP RC 2.00 5.00
368 George Perez SP 2.00 5.00
369 Rene Reyes SP RC 2.00 5.00
370 Rolando Viera SP RC 2.00 5.00
371 Earl Snyder SP RC 2.00 5.00
372 Kyle Kane SP RC 2.00 5.00
373 Mario Ramos SP RC 2.00 5.00
374 Tyler Yates SP RC 2.00 5.00
375 Jason Young SP RC 2.00 5.00
376 Chris Bootcheck SP RC 2.00 5.00
377 Jesus Cota SP RC 2.00 5.00
378 Corky Miller SP 2.00 5.00
379 Matt Erickson SP RC 2.00 5.00
380 Justin Huber SP RC 4.00 10.00
381 Felix Escalona SP RC 2.00 5.00
382 Kevin Cash SP RC 2.00 5.00
383 J.J. Putz SP RC 3.00 8.00
384 Chris Snelling AU A RC 8.00 20.00
385 David Wright AU A RC 150.00 250.00
386 Brian Wolfe AU A RC 4.00 10.00
387 Justin Reid AU A RC 4.00 10.00
389 Ryan Raburn AU A RC 4.00 10.00
390 Josh Barfield AU A RC 25.00 50.00
391 Joe Mauer AU A RC 60.00 120.00
392 Bobby Jenks AU A RC 4.00 10.00
393 Rob Henkel AU A RC 4.00 10.00
394 Jimmy Gobble AU A RC 4.00 10.00
395 Jesse Foppert AU A RC 4.00 10.00
396 Gavin Floyd AU A RC 6.00 15.00
397 Nate Field AU A RC 4.00 10.00
398 Ryan Doumit AU A RC 6.00 15.00
399 Ron Calloway AU A RC 4.00 10.00
400 Taylor Buchholz AU A RC 4.00 10.00
401 Adam Roller AU A RC 4.00 10.00
402 Cole Barthel AU A RC 4.00 10.00
403 Kazuhisa Ishii SP RC 3.00 8.00
403A Kazuhisa Ishii AU B 30.00 50.00
404 So Taguchi SP RC 3.00 8.00
404A So Taguchi AU B 30.00 50.00
405 Chris Baker AU A RC 4.00 10.00

2002 Bowman Chrome Facsimile Autograph Variations

This 20 card partial parallel to the Bowman Chrome set were issued in this special version with a facsimile autograph as part of the card. These cards were not originally expected to be issued and caused some confusion in the secondary market upon the product's release. It's estimated that as few as 50 copies of each card were produced.

118 Taylor Buchholz
130 Chris Baker
189 Adam Roller
229 Ryan Raburn
231 Chris Snelling
233 Nate Field
237 Ron Calloway
239 Cole Barthel
244 Rob Henkel
251 Gavin Floyd
301 Jimmy Gobble
305 Brian Wolfe
313 Jesse Foppert
316 Joe Mauer
317 David Wright
323 Justin Reid
324 Jake Mauer
326 Josh Barfield
335 Bobby Jenks
338 Ryan Doumit

2002 Bowman Chrome Uncirculated

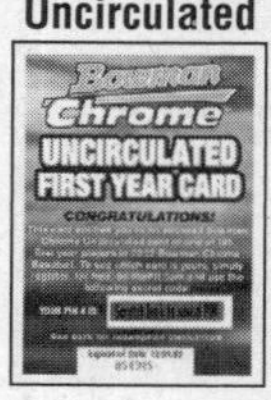

Issued as one per box chip topper exchange cards, these cards parallel the Bowman Chrome Rookie Cards. Each card, which needed to be redeemed from ThePit.Com comes in a special "case" which guarantees the card has never been handled. Most of these cards are traded there so we will only price copies which are actually "in-hand" or actually physically owned by the user. 350 of each basic card was produced and a mere 10 of each autograph card was made in Uncirculated format. The deadline to redeem the scratch off exchange cards was December 31st, 2002.

112 Chris Tritle
117 Noochie Varner
121 Hansel Izquierdo
123 Bill Hall
127 Scotty Layfield
129 Nic Jackson
131 Chad Qualls
153 Ruben Gotay
154 Tommy Marx
155 John Suomi
156 Javier Colina
157 Greg Sain
158 Robert Crosby
159 Angel Pagan
162 Shayne Wright
163 Jay Caliguiri
164 Greg Montalbano
165 Rich Harden
166 Rich Thompson
167 Fred Bastardo
168 Alejandro Giron
169 Jesus Medrano
170 Kevin Deaton
172 Jon Guzman
173 Gerard Oakes
174 Francisco Liriano
175 Matt Allegra
176 Mike Snyder
178 Anderson Hernandez
179 Dan Trumble
180 Luis DePaula
181 Randall Shelley
182 Richard Lane
183 Antwon Rollins
184 Ryan Bukvich
185 Derrick Lewis
186 Eric Miller
187 Justin Schuda
188 Brian West
190 Neal Frendling
191 Jeremy Hill
192 James Barrett
193 Brett Kay
194 Ryan Mottl
195 Brad Nelson
196 Juan M. Gonzalez
197 Curtis Legendre
198 Ronald Acuna
199 Chris Flinn
200 Nick Alvarez
201 Jason Ellison
202 Blake McGinley
203 Dan Phillips
204 Demetrius Heath
205 Eric Bruntlett
206 Joe Jiannetti
207 Mike Hill
208 Ricardo Cordova
209 Mark Hamilton
210 David Mattox
211 Jose Morban
212 Scott Wiggins
214 Brian Rogers
216 Anastacio Martinez
218 Tim Kalita
219 Edwin Almonte
222 Victor Alvarez
224 Jeff Austin
225 Clint Weibl
227 Marlyn Tisdale
230 Raul Chavez
232 Joe Rogers
235 Matt Childers
242 Ben Howard
243 Eric Glaser
245 Jose Valverde
248 Brian Mallette
249 Chone Figgins
250 Jimmy Alvarez
252 Josh Bonifay
253 Garrett Guzman
254 Jeff Verplancke
255 Nate Espy
256 Jeff Lincoln
257 Ryan Snare
263 Yurendell DeCaster
264 Mike Peeples
267 Jorge Padilla
268 Joe Jester
269 Ryan Church
271 Travis Foley
277 Brian Forystek
279 Manny Delcarmen
280 Jim Kavourias
283 Joey Hammond
286 Ezequiel Astacio
287 Edwin Yan
288 Chris Duffy
293 Chris Narveson
295 Mike Wilson
296 Justin Sherrod
299 Brett Roneberg
300 Trey Lunsford
307 Koyie Hill
308 Tony Fontana
310 Doug Sessions
311 Josh Cisneros
312 Carlos Brackley
314 Ross Peeples
315 Alex Requena
318 Craig Kuzmic
319 Pete Zamora
320 Matt Parker
322 Gary Cates Jr.
324 Jake Mauer AU
327 Henry Pichardo
328 Michael Floyd
329 Clint Nageotte
330 Raymond Cabrera
331 Mauricio Lara
332 Alejandro Cadena
333 Jonny Gomes
334 Jason Bulger
336 David Gil
337 Joel Crump
342 Freddie Money
343 Cliff Bartosh
344 Terrance Hill
345 John Rodriguez
346 Chris Latham
347 Carlos Cabrera
348 Jose Bautista
349 Kevin Frederick
351 Napolean Calzado
352 Benito Baez
354 Jason Botts
355 Steve Bechler
356 Reed Johnson
357 Mark Outlaw
359 Josh Shaffer
360 Dan Wright
361 Ryan Gripp
362 Nelson Castro
363 Jason Bay
364 Franklyn German
365 Corwin Malone
366 Kelly Ramos
367 John Ennis
368 George Perez
369 Rene Reyes
370 Rolando Viera
371 Earl Snyder
372 Kyle Kane
373 Mario Ramos
374 Tyler Yates
375 Jason Young
376 Chris Bootcheck
377 Jesus Cota
378 Corky Miller
379 Matt Erickson
380 Justin Huber
381 Felix Escalona
382 Kevin Cash
383 J.J. Putz
384 Chris Snelling AU
385 David Wright AU
386 Brian Wolfe AU
387 Justin Reid AU
389 Ryan Raburn AU
390 Josh Barfield AU
391 Joe Mauer AU
392 Bobby Jenks AU
393 Rob Henkel AU
394 Jimmy Gobble AU
395 Jesse Foppert AU
396 Gavin Floyd AU
397 Nate Field AU
398 Ryan Doumit AU
399 Ron Calloway AU
400 Taylor Buchholz AU
401 Adam Roller AU
402 Cole Barthel AU
403 Kazuhisa Ishii
403A Kazuhisa Ishii AU
404 So Taguchi
404A So Taguchi AU
405 Chris Baker AU
NNO Exchange Card

2002 Bowman Chrome Refractors

This is a complete parallel set to the Bowman Chrome set. These cards were issued in several different tiers but it is important to note that most of these cards have a stated print run of 500 sets. The Ishii and Taguchi autograph cards have a stated print run of 100 sets.

*REF RED: 1.5X TO 4X BASIC
*REF BLUE: 1X TO 2.5X BASIC
*REF BLUE SP: .6X TO 1.5X BASIC
*REF AU: .5X TO 1.2X BASIC AU'S
324B/384-405 GROUP A AUTO ODDS 1:88
403-404 GROUP B AUTO ODDS 1:4392
324B/384-405 OVERALL AUTO ODDS 1:86
1-383/403-404 PRINT 500 SERIAL #'d SETS
324B/384-405 GROUP A PRINT RUN 500 SETS
403-404 GROUP B PRINT RUN 100 SETS

159 Angel Pagan	8.00	20.00
165 Rich Harden	30.00	60.00
174 Francisco Liriano	50.00	100.00
363 Jason Bay	20.00	50.00
385 David Wright AU A	200.00	300.00
391 Joe Mauer AU A	150.00	300.00
392 Bobby Jenks AU A	5.00	12.00
403 Kazuhisa Ishii AU B	40.00	80.00
404 So Taguchi AU B	30.00	60.00

2002 Bowman Chrome Gold Refractors

This is a complete parallel set to the Bowman Chrome set. These cards were issued in several different tiers but it is important to note that most of these cards have a stated print run of 50 sets. The Ishii and Taguchi autograph cards have a stated print run of 10 sets.

*GOLD REF RED: 5X TO 12X BASIC
*GOLD REF BLUE: 4X TO 10X BASIC
*GOLD REF BLUE SP: 2X TO 5X BASIC
*GOLD REF AU: 1.5X TO 4X BASIC
384-405 GROUP A AUTO ODDS 1:879
403-404 GROUP B AUTO ODDS 1:59,616
324B/384-405 OVERALL AUTO ODDS 1:866
1-383/403-404 PRINT 50 SERIAL #'d SETS
324B/384-405 GROUP A AU PRINT 50 SETS
403-404 GROUP B AU PRINT RUN 10 SETS

159 Angel Pagan	20.00	50.00
165 Rich Harden	100.00	200.00
174 Francisco Liriano	300.00	600.00
241 Chase Utley	75.00	150.00
363 Jason Bay	125.00	250.00
385 David Wright AU A	1000.00	1500.00
391 Joe Mauer AU A	600.00	1000.00
392 Bobby Jenks AU A	15.00	40.00

2002 Bowman Chrome X-Fractors

This is a complete parallel set to the Bowman Chrome set. These cards were issued in several different tiers but it is important to note that most of these cards have a stated print run of 250 sets. The Ishii and Taguchi autograph cards have a stated print run of 50 sets.

*XFRACT RED: 3X TO 8X BASIC
*XFRACT BLUE: 1.5X TO 4X BASIC
*XFRACT BLUE SP: .75X TO 2X BASIC
*XFRACT AU: .75X TO 2X BASIC
324B/384-405 GROUP A AUTO ODDS 1:176
403-404 GROUP B AUTO ODDS 1:9072
324B/384-405 OVERALL AUTO ODDS 1:173
1-383/403-404 PRINT 250 SERIAL #'d SETS
324B/384-405 GROUP A PRINT RUN 250 SETS
403-404 GROUP B PRINT RUN 50 SETS

159 Angel Pagan	10.00	25.00
165 Rich Harden	50.00	100.00
174 Francisco Liriano	60.00	120.00
363 Jason Bay	30.00	60.00
385 David Wright AU A	375.00	500.00
391 Joe Mauer AU A	250.00	400.00
392 Bobby Jenks AU A	8.00	20.00
403 Kazuhisa Ishii AU B	60.00	100.00
404 So Taguchi AU B	60.00	100.00

2002 Bowman Chrome Reprints

Isssued at stated odds of one in six, these 20 cards feature reprint cards of players who have made their debut since Bowman was reintroduced as a major brand in 1989.

COMPLETE SET (20)	10.00	25.00
*BLACK REF: .6X TO 1.5X BASIC REPRINTS		
BLACK REFRACTOR ODDS 1:18		
BCRAJ Andruw Jones 95	.75	2.00
BCRBC Bartolo Colon 95	.75	2.00
BCRBW Bernie Williams 90	.75	2.00
BCRCD Carlos Delgado 92	.75	2.00
BCRCJ Chipper Jones 91	1.00	2.50
BCRDJ Derek Jeter 93	3.00	8.00
BCRFT Frank Thomas 90	1.00	2.50
BCRGS Gary Sheffield 89	.75	2.00
BCRIR Ivan Rodriguez 91	.75	2.00
BCRJB Jeff Bagwell 91	.75	2.00
BCRJG Juan Gonzalez 90	.75	2.00
BCRJK Jason Kendall 93	.75	2.00
BCRJP Jorge Posada 94	.75	2.00
BCRKG Ken Griffey Jr. 89	2.00	5.00
BCRLG Luis Gonzalez 91	.75	2.00
BCRLW Larry Walker 90	.75	2.00
BCRMP Mike Piazza 92	2.00	5.00
BCRMS Mike Sweeney 96	.75	2.00
BCRSR Scott Rolen 95	.75	2.00
BCRVG Vladimir Guerrero 95	1.00	2.50

2002 Bowman Chrome Draft

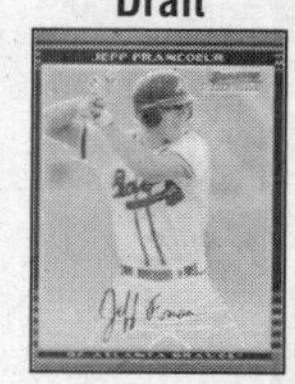

Inserted two per Bowman Draft pack, this is a parallel to the Bowman Draft Pick set. Each of these cards uses the Topps "Chrome" technology and these cards were inserted two per bowman draft pack. Cards numbered 166 through 175 are not parallels to the regular Bowman cards and they feature autographs of the players. Those ten cards were issued at a stated rate of one in 45 Bowman Draft packs.

COMPLETE SET (175)	200.00	350.00
COMP.SET w/o AU'S (165)	135.00	200.00
COMMON CARD (1-165)	.15	.40
COMMON CARD (166-175)	4.00	10.00
1 Clint Everts RC	.60	1.50
2 Fred Lewis RC	.40	1.00
3 Jon Broxton RC	1.25	3.00
4 Jason Anderson RC	.40	1.00
5 Mike Eusebio RC	.40	1.00
6 Zack Greinke RC	2.50	6.00
7 Joe Blanton RC	2.00	5.00
8 Sergio Santos RC	.60	1.50
9 Jason Cooper RC	.40	1.00
10 Delwyn Young RC	1.25	3.00
11 Jeremy Hermida RC	5.00	12.00
12 Dan Ortmeier RC	.60	1.50
13 Kevin Jepsen RC	.60	1.50
14 Russ Adams RC	.60	1.50
15 Mike Nixon RC	.40	1.00
16 Nick Swisher RC	6.00	15.00
17 Cole Hamels RC	15.00	40.00
18 Brian Dopirak RC	1.25	3.00
19 James Loney RC	5.00	12.00
20 Denard Span RC	1.50	4.00
21 Billy Petrick RC	.40	1.00
22 Jared Doyle RC	.40	1.00
23 Jeff Francoeur RC	20.00	40.00
24 Nick Bourgeois RC	.40	1.00
25 Matt Cain RC	6.00	15.00
26 John McCurdy RC	.40	1.00
27 Mark Kiger RC	.40	1.00
28 Bill Murphy RC	.40	1.00
29 Matt Craig RC	.60	1.50
30 Mike Megrew RC	.40	1.00
31 Ben Crockett RC	.40	1.00
32 Luke Hagerty RC	.40	1.00
33 Matt Whitney RC	.40	1.00
34 Dan Meyer RC	.60	1.50
35 Jeremy Brown RC	.40	1.00
36 Doug Johnson RC	.40	1.00
37 Steve Obenchain RC	.40	1.00
38 Matt Clanton RC	.40	1.00
39 Mark Teahen RC	1.25	3.00
40 Tom Carrow RC	.40	1.00
41 Micah Schilling RC	.40	1.00
42 Blair Johnson RC	.40	1.00
43 Jason Pridie RC	.40	1.00
44 Joey Votto RC	5.00	12.00
45 Taber Lee RC	.40	1.00
46 Adam Peterson RC	.40	1.00
47 Adam Donachie RC	.40	1.00
48 Josh Murray RC	.40	1.00
49 Brent Clevlen RC	2.50	6.00
50 Chad Pleiness RC	.40	1.00
51 Zach Hammes RC	.40	1.00
52 Chris Snyder RC	.60	1.50
53 Chris Smith RC	.40	1.00
54 Justin Maureau RC	.40	1.00
55 David Bush RC	1.25	3.00
56 Tim Gilhooly RC	.40	1.00
57 Blair Barbier RC	.40	1.00
58 Zach Segovia RC	.40	1.00
59 Jeremy Reed RC	1.25	3.00
60 Matt Pender RC	.40	1.00
61 Eric Thomas RC	.40	1.00
62 Justin Jones RC	.60	1.50
63 Brian Slocum RC	.40	1.00
64 Larry Broadway RC	.40	1.00
65 Bo Flowers RC	.40	1.00
66 Scott White RC	.40	1.00
67 Steve Stanley RC	.40	1.00
68 Alex Merricks RC	.40	1.00
69 Josh Womack RC	.40	1.00
70 Dave Jensen RC	.40	1.00
71 Curtis Granderson RC	5.00	12.00
72 Pat Osborn RC	.40	1.00
73 Nic Carter RC	.40	1.00
74 Mitch Talbot RC	.40	1.00
75 Don Murphy RC	.40	1.00
76 Val Majewski RC	.40	1.00
77 Javy Rodriguez RC	.40	1.00
78 Fernando Pacheco RC	.40	1.00
79 Steve Russell RC	.40	1.00
80 Jon Slack RC	.40	1.00
81 John Baker RC	.40	1.00
82 Aaron Coonrod RC	.40	1.00
83 Josh Johnson RC	4.00	10.00
84 Jake Blalock RC	.60	1.50
85 Alex Hart RC	.40	1.00
86 Wes Bankston RC	2.50	6.00
87 Josh Rupe RC	.40	1.00
88 Dan Cevette RC	.40	1.00
89 Kiel Fisher RC	.60	1.50
90 Alan Rick RC	.40	1.00
91 Charlie Morton RC	.40	1.00
92 Chad Spann RC	.40	1.00
93 Kyle Boyer RC	.40	1.00
94 Bob Malek RC	.40	1.00
95 Ryan Rodriguez RC	.40	1.00
96 Jordan Renz RC	.40	1.00
97 Randy Frye RC	.40	1.00
98 Rich Hill RC	5.00	12.00
99 B.J. Upton RC	5.00	12.00
100 Dan Christensen RC	.40	1.00
101 Casey Kotchman RC	2.50	6.00
102 Eric Good RC	.40	1.00
103 Mike Fontenot RC	.40	1.00
104 John Webb RC	.40	1.00
105 Jason Dubois RC	.60	1.50
106 Ryan Kibler RC	.40	1.00
107 Jhonny Peralta RC	3.00	8.00
108 Kirk Saarloos RC	.40	1.00
109 Rhett Parrott RC	.40	1.00
110 Jason Grove RC	.40	1.00
111 Colt Griffin RC	.40	1.00
112 Dallas McPherson RC UER Reversed Negative	1.25	3.00
113 Oliver Perez RC	1.25	3.00
114 Marshall McDougall RC	.40	1.00
115 Mike Wood RC	.40	1.00
116 Scott Hairston RC	.60	1.50
117 Jason Simontacchi RC	.40	1.00
118 Taggert Bozied RC	.60	1.50
119 Shelley Duncan RC	4.00	10.00
120 Dontrelle Willis RC	6.00	15.00
121 Sean Burnett	.15	.40
122 Aaron Cook	.25	.60
123 Brett Evert	.15	.40
124 Jimmy Journell	.15	.40
125 Brett Myers	.25	.60
126 Brad Baker	.15	.40
127 Billy Traber RC	.40	1.00
128 Adam Wainwright	.15	.40
129 Jason Young	.40	1.00
130 John Buck	.15	.40
131 Kevin Cash	.40	1.00
132 Jason Stokes RC	.60	1.50
133 Drew Henson	.15	.40
134 Chad Tracy RC	2.00	5.00
135 Orlando Hudson	.15	.40
136 Brandon Phillips	.15	.40
137 Joe Borchard	.15	.40
138 Marlon Byrd	.15	.40
139 Carl Crawford	.25	.60
140 Michael Restovich	.15	.40
141 Corey Hart RC	2.00	5.00
142 Edwin Almonte	.25	.60
143 Francis Beltran RC	.40	1.00
144 Jorge De La Rosa RC	.40	1.00
145 Gerardo Garcia RC	.40	1.00
146 Franklyn German RC	.40	1.00
147 Francisco Liriano	4.00	10.00
148 Francisco Rodriguez	.25	.60
149 Ricardo Rodriguez	.15	.40
150 Seung Song	.15	.40
151 John Stephens	.15	.40
152 Justin Huber RC	1.00	2.50
153 Victor Martinez	.60	1.50
154 Hee Seop Choi	.15	.40
155 Justin Morneau	.25	.60
156 Miguel Cabrera	1.00	2.50
157 Victor Diaz RC	1.00	2.50
158 Jose Reyes	.40	1.00
159 Omar Infante	.15	.40
160 Angel Berroa	.15	.40
161 Tony Alvarez	.15	.40
162 Shin Soo Choo RC	1.00	2.50
163 Wily Mo Pena	.25	.60
164 Andres Torres	.15	.40
165 Jose Lopez RC	2.50	6.00
166 Scott Moore AU RC	4.00	10.00
167 Chris Gruler AU RC	4.00	10.00
168 Joe Saunders AU RC	5.00	12.00
169 Jeff Francis AU RC	6.00	15.00
170 Royce Ring AU RC	4.00	10.00
171 Greg Miller AU RC	6.00	15.00
172 Brandon Weeden AU RC	4.00	10.00
173 Drew Meyer AU RC	4.00	10.00
174 Khalil Greene AU RC	30.00	60.00
175 Mark Schramek AU RC	4.00	10.00

2002 Bowman Chrome Draft Refractors

Issued at a stated rate of one in 11 Bowman Draft packs, these cards are refractor parallels of the Bowman Chrome Draft set. Cards 1-165 have a stated print run of 300 serial numbered sets. Cards numbered 166 through 175, which are autographed, but lack serial-numbering, were issued at a stated rate of one in 154 Bowman Draft packs.

*REFRACTOR 1-165: 2.5X TO 6X BASIC
*REFRACTOR RC 1-165: 2X TO 5X BASIC
*REFRACTOR 166-175: .5X TO 1.2X BASIC

11 Jeremy Hermida	40.00	80.00
16 Nick Swisher	40.00	80.00
17 Cole Hamels	50.00	100.00
19 James Loney	20.00	50.00
23 Jeff Francoeur	90.00	150.00
25 Matt Cain	50.00	100.00
83 Josh Johnson	20.00	50.00
99 B.J. Upton	20.00	50.00
113 Oliver Perez	8.00	20.00
119 Shelley Duncan	15.00	40.00
120 Dontrelle Willis	30.00	60.00
147 Francisco Liriano	60.00	120.00
168 Joe Saunders AU	10.00	25.00
169 Jeff Francis AU	8.00	20.00
174 Khalil Greene AU	40.00	80.00

2002 Bowman Chrome Draft Gold Refractors

Issued at a stated rate of one in 67 Bowman Draft packs, these cards are gold refractors of the Bowman Chrome Draft set. Cards 1-165 have a stated print run of 50 serial numbered sets. Cards numbered 166 through 175, which are autographed but lack serial-numbering, were issued at a stated rate of one in 1546 Bowman Draft cards and there is no pricing provided on these cards due to market scarcity. Though never confirmed by the manufacturer, based upon research conducted by the Price Guide staff at Beckett Baseball, it's estimated that as few as 35 copies of AU subset card were produced.

*GOLD REF 1-165: 8X TO 20X BASIC
*GOLD REF RC 1-165: 10X TO 20X BASIC
1-165 ODDS 1:67 BOWMAN DRAFT
166-175 AU ODDS 1:1546 BOWMAN DRAFT
1-165 PRINT RUN 50 SERIAL #'d SETS
166-175 ARE NOT SERIAL-NUMBERED
166-175 NO PRICING DUE TO SCARCITY

3 Jon Broxton	40.00	80.00
6 Zack Greinke	125.00	200.00
11 Jeremy Hermida	175.00	300.00
16 Nick Swisher	150.00	250.00
17 Cole Hamels	250.00	350.00
19 James Loney	250.00	350.00
23 Jeff Francoeur	350.00	500.00
25 Matt Cain	150.00	300.00
39 Mark Teahen	40.00	80.00
44 Joey Votto	100.00	200.00
71 Curtis Granderson	200.00	300.00
83 Josh Johnson	150.00	250.00
86 Wes Bankston	40.00	80.00
98 Rich Hill	125.00	300.00
99 B.J. Upton	100.00	200.00
113 Oliver Perez	40.00	80.00
119 Shelley Duncan	100.00	200.00
120 Dontrelle Willis	125.00	200.00
147 Francisco Liriano	125.00	250.00

2002 Bowman Chrome Draft X-Fractors

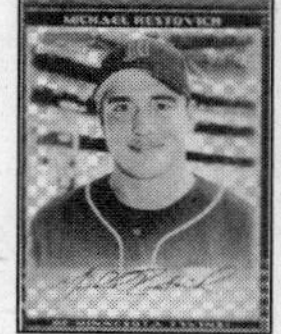

Issued at a stated rate of one in 22 Bowman Draft packs, these cards are x-fractor parallels of the Bowman Chrome Draft set. Cards 1-165 have a stated print run of 150 serial numbered sets. Cards numbered 166 through 175, which are autographed but lack serial-numbering, were issued at a stated rate of one in 309 Bowman Draft packs.

*X-FRACTOR 1-165: 3X TO 8X BASIC
*X-FRACTOR RC 1-165: 3X TO 6X BASIC
*X-FRACTOR 166-175: .75X TO 1.5X BASIC

11 Jeremy Hermida	50.00	100.00
16 Nick Swisher	50.00	100.00
17 Cole Hamels	60.00	120.00
19 James Loney	60.00	120.00
23 Jeff Francoeur	125.00	200.00
25 Matt Cain	60.00	120.00
39 Mark Teahen	12.50	30.00
83 Josh Johnson	40.00	80.00
99 B.J. Upton	30.00	60.00
113 Oliver Perez	12.50	30.00
119 Shelley Duncan	30.00	60.00
120 Dontrelle Willis	40.00	80.00
147 Francisco Liriano	75.00	150.00
168 Joe Saunders AU	12.50	30.00
169 Jeff Francis AU	10.00	25.00
174 Khalil Greene AU	50.00	100.00

2003 Bowman Chrome

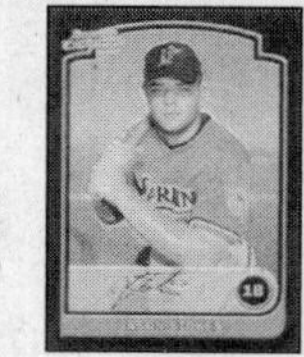

This 351 card set was released in July, 2003. The set was issued in four-card packs with an $4 SRP which came 18 to a box and 12 boxes to a case. Cards numbered 1 through 165 feature veteran players while cards 166 through 330 feature rookie players. Cards numbered 331 through 350 feature autograph cards of Rookie Cards. Each of those cards, with the exception of Jose Contreras (number 332) was issued to a stated print run of 1700 sets and were seeded at a stated rate of one in 26. The Contreras card was issued to a stated print run of 340 cards and was issued at a stated rate of one in 3,3351 packs. The final card of the set features baseball legend Willie Mays. That card was issued as a box-loader and an authentic autograph on that card was also randomly inserted into packs. The autograph card was inserted at a stated rate of one in 384 box loader packs and was issued to a stated print run of 150 sets. Bryan Bullington did not return his cards in time for pack out and those cards could be redeemed until July 31st, 2005.

COMPLETE SET (351)	300.00	500.00
COMP.SET w/o AU'S (331)	75.00	150.00
COMMON CARD (1-165)	.20	.50
COMMON CARD (166-330)	.20	.50
COMMON RC (156-330)	.40	1.00
COMP.SET w/o AU'S INCLUDES 351 MAYS		
MAYS AU IS NOT PART OF 351-CARD SET		
1 Garret Anderson	.20	.50

2 Derek Jeter 1.25 3.00
3 Gary Sheffield .20 .50
4 Matt Morris .20 .50
5 Derek Lowe .20 .50
6 Andy Van Hekken .20 .50
7 Sammy Sosa .50 1.25
8 Ken Griffey Jr. .75 2.00
9 Omar Vizquel .30 .75
10 Jorge Posada .30 .75
11 Lance Berkman .20 .50
12 Mike Sweeney .20 .50
13 Adrian Beltre .20 .50
14 Richie Sexson .20 .50
15 A.J. Pierzynski .20 .50
16 Bartolo Colon .20 .50
17 Mike Mussina .30 .75
18 Paul Byrd .20 .50
19 Bobby Abreu .20 .50
20 Miguel Tejada .20 .50
21 Aramis Ramirez .20 .50
22 Edgardo Alfonzo .20 .50
23 Edgar Martinez .30 .75
24 Albert Pujols 1.00 2.50
25 Carl Crawford .20 .50
26 Eric Hinske .20 .50
27 Tim Salmon .30 .75
28 Luis Gonzalez .20 .50
29 Jay Gibbons .20 .50
30 John Smoltz .20 .50
31 Tim Wakefield .20 .50
32 Mark Prior .30 .75
33 Magglio Ordonez .20 .50
34 Adam Dunn .20 .50
35 Larry Walker .20 .50
36 Luis Castillo .20 .50
37 Wade Miller .20 .50
38 Carlos Beltran .20 .50
39 Odalis Perez .20 .50
40 Alex Sanchez .20 .50
41 Torii Hunter .20 .50
42 Cliff Floyd .20 .50
43 Andy Pettitte .30 .75
44 Francisco Rodriguez .20 .50
45 Eric Chavez .20 .50
46 Kevin Millwood .20 .50
47 Dennis Tankersley .20 .50
48 Hideo Nomo .50 1.25
49 Freddy Garcia .20 .50
50 Randy Johnson .50 1.25
51 Aubrey Huff .20 .50
52 Carlos Delgado .20 .50
53 Troy Glaus .20 .50
54 Junior Spivey .20 .50
55 Mike Hampton .20 .50
56 Sidney Ponson .20 .50
57 Aaron Boone .20 .50
58 Kerry Wood .20 .50
59 Willie Harris .20 .50
60 Nomar Garciaparra .75 2.00
61 Todd Helton .30 .75
62 Mike Lowell .20 .50
63 Roy Oswalt .20 .50
64 Raul Ibanez .20 .50
65 Brian Jordan .20 .50
66 Geoff Jenkins .20 .50
67 Jermaine Dye .20 .50
68 Tom Glavine .30 .75
69 Bernie Williams .30 .75
70 Vladimir Guerrero .50 1.25
71 Mark Mulder .20 .50
72 Jimmy Rollins .20 .50
73 Oliver Perez .20 .50
74 Rich Aurilia .20 .50
75 Joel Pineiro .20 .50
76 J.D. Drew .20 .50
77 Ivan Rodriguez .30 .75
78 Josh Phelps .20 .50
79 Darin Erstad .20 .50
80 Curt Schilling .30 .75
81 Paul Lo Duca .20 .50
82 Marty Cordova .20 .50
83 Manny Ramirez .30 .75
84 Bobby Hill .20 .50
85 Paul Konerko .20 .50
86 Austin Kearns .20 .50
87 Jason Jennings .20 .50
88 Brad Penny .20 .50
89 Jeff Bagwell .30 .75
90 Shawn Green .20 .50
91 Jason Schmidt .20 .50
92 Doug Mientkiewicz .20 .50
93 Jose Vidro .20 .50
94 Bret Boone .20 .50
95 Jason Giambi .20 .50
96 Barry Zito .20 .50
97 Roy Halladay .20 .50
98 Pat Burrell .20 .50
99 Sean Burroughs .20 .50
100 Barry Bonds 1.25 3.00
101 Kazuhiro Sasaki .20 .50
102 Fernando Vina .20 .50
103 Chan Ho Park .20 .50
104 Andruw Jones .30 .75
105 Adam Kennedy .20 .50
106 Shea Hillenbrand .20 .50
107 Greg Maddux .75 2.00
108 Jim Edmonds .20 .50
109 Pedro Martinez .30 .75
110 Moises Alou .20 .50
111 Jeff Weaver .20 .50
112 C.C. Sabathia .20 .50
113 Robert Fick .20 .50
114 A.J. Burnett .20 .50
115 Jeff Kent .20 .50
116 Kevin Brown .20 .50
117 Rafael Furcal .20 .50
118 Cristian Guzman .20 .50
119 Brad Wilkerson .20 .50
120 Mike Piazza .75 2.00
121 Alfonso Soriano .20 .50
122 Mark Ellis .20 .50
123 Vicente Padilla .20 .50
124 Eric Gagne .20 .50
125 Ryan Klesko .20 .50
126 Ichiro Suzuki 1.00 2.50
127 Tony Batista .20 .50
128 Roberto Alomar .30 .75
129 Alex Rodriguez .75 2.00
130 Jim Thome .30 .75
131 Jarrod Washburn .20 .50
132 Orlando Hudson .20 .50
133 Chipper Jones .50 1.25
134 Rodrigo Lopez .20 .50
135 Johnny Damon .30 .75
136 Matt Clement .20 .50
137 Frank Thomas .50 1.25
138 Ellis Burks .20 .50
139 Carlos Pena .20 .50
140 Josh Beckett .20 .50
141 Joe Randa .20 .50
142 Brian Giles .20 .50
143 Kazuhisa Ishii .20 .50
144 Corey Koskie .20 .50
145 Orlando Cabrera .20 .50
146 Mark Buehrle .20 .50
147 Roger Clemens 1.00 2.50
148 Tim Hudson .20 .50
149 Randy Wolf .20 .50
150 Josh Fogg .20 .50
151 Phil Nevin .20 .50
152 John Olerud .20 .50
153 Scott Rolen .30 .75
154 Joe Kennedy .20 .50
155 Rafael Palmeiro .30 .75
156 Chad Hutchinson .20 .50
157 Quincy Carter XRC .60 1.50
158 Hee Seop Choi .20 .50
159 Joe Borchard .20 .50
160 Brandon Phillips .20 .50
161 Wily Mo Pena .20 .50
162 Victor Martinez .30 .75
163 Jason Stokes .20 .50
164 Ken Harvey .20 .50
165 Juan Rivera .20 .50
166 Joe Valentine RC .60 1.50
167 Dan Haren RC 1.50 4.00
168 Michel Hernandez RC .60 1.50
169 Eider Torres RC .60 1.50
170 Chris De La Cruz RC .60 1.50
171 Ramon Nivar-Martinez RC .60 1.50
172 Mike Adams RC .60 1.50
173 Justin Arneson RC .60 1.50
174 Jamie Athas RC .60 1.50
175 Dwaine Bacon RC .60 1.50
176 Clint Barmes RC 1.50 4.00
177 B.J. Barns RC .60 1.50
178 Tyler Johnson RC .60 1.50
179 Brandon Webb RC 6.00 15.00
180 T.J. Bohn RC .60 1.50
181 Ozzie Chavez RC .60 1.50
182 Brandon Bowe RC .60 1.50
183 Craig Brazell RC .60 1.50
184 Dusty Brown RC .60 1.50
185 Brian Bruney RC .75 2.00
186 Greg Bruso RC .60 1.50
187 Jaime Bubela RC .60 1.50
188 Matt Diaz RC 1.25 3.00
189 Brian Burgamy RC .60 1.50
190 Eny Cabreja RC 2.00 5.00
191 Daniel Cabrera RC 1.25 3.00
192 Ryan Cameron RC .60 1.50
193 Lance Caracciolli RC .60 1.50
194 David Cash RC .60 1.50
195 Bernie Castro RC .60 1.50
196 Ismael Castro RC .75 2.00
197 Cory Doyne RC .60 1.50
198 Jeff Clark RC .60 1.50
199 Chris Colton RC .60 1.50
200 Dexter Cooper RC .60 1.50
201 Callix Crabbe RC .75 2.00
202 Chien-Ming Wang RC 6.00 15.00
203 Eric Crozier RC .75 2.00
204 Nook Logan RC .75 2.00
205 David DeJesus RC 1.25 3.00
206 Matt DeMarco RC .60 1.50
207 Chris Duncan RC 5.00 12.00
208 Eric Eckenstahler .20 .50
209 Willie Eyre RC .60 1.50
210 Evel Bastida-Martinez RC .60 1.50
211 Chris Fallon RC .60 1.50
212 Mike Flannery RC .60 1.50
213 Mike Oâ ™Keefe RC .60 1.50
214 Lew Ford RC .75 2.00
215 Kason Gabbard RC .60 1.50
216 Mike Gallo RC .60 1.50
217 Jairo Garcia RC .75 2.00
218 Angel Garcia RC .75 2.00
219 Michael Garciaparra RC .60 1.50
220 Jeremy Griffiths RC .60 1.50
221 Dusty Gomon RC .75 2.00
222 Bryan Grace RC .60 1.50
223 Tyson Graham RC .60 1.50
224 Henry Guerrero RC .60 1.50
225 Franklin Gutierrez RC 1.50 4.00
226 Carlos Guzman RC .75 2.00
227 Matthew Hagen RC .60 1.50
228 Josh Hall RC .60 1.50
229 Rob Hammock RC .60 1.50
230 Brendan Harris RC .75 2.00
231 Gary Harris RC .60 1.50
232 Clay Hensley RC .60 1.50
233 Michael Hinckley RC .75 2.00
234 Luis Hodge RC .60 1.50
235 Donnie Hood RC .75 2.00
236 Matt Hensley RC .60 1.50
237 Edwin Jackson RC .75 2.00
238 Ardley Jansen RC .75 2.00
239 Ferenc Jongejan RC .60 1.50
240 Matt Kata RC .60 1.50
241 Kazuhiro Takeoka RC .60 1.50
242 Charlie Manning RC .60 1.50
243 Il Kim RC .60 1.50
244 Brennan King RC .60 1.50
245 Chris Kroski RC .60 1.50
246 David Martinez RC .60 1.50
247 Pete LaForest RC .60 1.50
248 Wil Ledezma RC .60 1.50
249 Jeremy Bonderman RC 4.00 10.00
250 Gonzalo Lopez RC .60 1.50
251 Brian Luderer RC .60 1.50
252 Ruddy Lugo RC .60 1.50
253 Wayne Lydon RC .60 1.50
254 Mark Malaska RC .60 1.50
255 Andy Marte RC 4.00 10.00
256 Tyler Martin RC .60 1.50
257 Branden Florence RC .60 1.50
258 Aneudis Mateo RC .60 1.50
259 Derell McCall RC .60 1.50
260 Elizardo Ramirez RC .75 2.00
261 Mike McNutt RC .60 1.50
262 Jacobo Meque RC .60 1.50
263 Derek Michaelis RC .60 1.50
264 Aaron Miles RC .75 2.00
265 Jose Morales RC .60 1.50
266 Dustin Moseley RC .60 1.50
267 Adrian Myers RC .60 1.50
268 Dan Neil RC .60 1.50
269 Jon Nelson RC .75 2.00
270 Mike Neu RC .60 1.50
271 Leigh Neuage RC .60 1.50
272 Wes O'Brien RC .60 1.50
273 Trent Oeltjen RC .75 2.00
274 Tim Olson RC .60 1.50
275 David Pahucki RC .60 1.50
276 Nathan Panther RC .60 1.50
277 Arnie Munoz RC .60 1.50
278 Dave Pember RC .60 1.50
279 Jason Perry RC .75 2.00
280 Matthew Peterson RC .60 1.50
281 Greg Aquino RC .60 1.50
282 Jorge Piedra RC .75 2.00
283 Simon Pond RC .60 1.50
284 Aaron Rakers RC .60 1.50
285 Felix Sanchez RC .60 1.50
286 Manuel Ramirez RC .75 2.00
287 Kevin Randel RC .60 1.50
288 Kelly Shoppach RC 1.25 3.00
289 Prentice Redman RC .60 1.50
290 Eric Reed RC .60 1.50
291 Wilton Reynolds RC .75 2.00
292 Eric Riggs RC .75 2.00
293 Carlos Rijo RC .60 1.50
294 Tyler Adamczyk RC .60 1.50
295 Jon-Mark Sprowl RC .60 1.50
296 Arturo Rivas RC .60 1.50
297 Kyle Roat RC .60 1.50
298 Bubba Nelson RC .30 .75
299 Levi Robinson RC .60 1.50
300 Ray Sadler RC .60 1.50
301 Rylan Reed RC .60 1.50
302 Jon Schuerholz RC .60 1.50
303 Nobuaki Yoshida RC .60 1.50
304 Brian Shackelford RC .60 1.50
305 Bill Simon RC .60 1.50
306 Haj Turay RC .40 1.00
307 Sean Smith RC .75 2.00
308 Ryan Spataro RC .60 1.50
309 Jemel Spearman RC .60 1.50
310 Keith Stamler RC .60 1.50
311 Luke Steidlmayer RC .60 1.50
312 Adam Stern RC .40 1.00
313 Jay Sitzman RC .60 1.50
314 Mike Wodnicki RC .60 1.50
315 Terry Tiffee RC .60 1.50
316 Nick Trzesniak RC .60 1.50
317 Denny Tussen RC .60 1.50
318 Scott Tyler RC .75 2.00
319 Shane Victorino RC 1.50 4.00
320 Doug Waechter RC .75 2.00
321 Brandon Watson RC .60 1.50
322 Todd Wellemeyer RC .60 1.50
323 Eli Whiteside RC .60 1.50
324 Josh Willingham RC 1.50 4.00
325 Travis Wong RC .75 2.00
326 Brian Wright RC .60 1.50
327 Felix Pie RC 5.00 12.00
328 Andy Sisco RC .20 .50
329 Dustin Yount RC .75 2.00
330 Andrew Dominique RC .60 1.50
331 Brian McCann AU A RC 20.00 50.00
332 Jose Contreras AU B RC 30.00 60.00
333 Corey Shafer AU A RC 4.00 10.00
334 Hanley Ramirez AU A RC 100.00 200.00
335 Ryan Shealy AU A RC 4.00 10.00
336 Kevin Youkilis AU A RC 20.00 50.00
337 Jason Kubel AU A RC 5.00 12.00
338 Aron Weston AU A RC 4.00 10.00
338B Rajai Davis AU A ERR
339 J.D. Durbin AU A RC 4.00 10.00
340 G. Schneidmiller AU A RC 4.00 10.00
341 Travis Ishikawa AU A RC 4.00 10.00
342 Ben Francisco AU A RC 4.00 10.00
343 Bobby Basham AU A RC 4.00 10.00
344 Joey Gomes AU A RC 4.00 10.00
345 Beau Kemp AU A RC 4.00 10.00
346 T.Story-Harden AU A RC 4.00 10.00
347 Daryl Clark AU A RC 4.00 10.00
348 Bryan Bullington AU A RC 4.00 10.00
349 Rajai Davis AU A RC 4.00 10.00
350 Darrell Rasner AU A RC 4.00 10.00
351 Willie Mays .75 2.00
351AU Willie Mays AU 150.00 250.00

2003 Bowman Chrome Refractors

This is a complete parallel to the regular Bowman Chrome set. Cards numbered 1-330 were issued at a stated rate of one in four hobby packs. Cards numbers 331-350 (with the exception of number 332) were issued at a stated rate of one in 92 packs. Those cards were issued to a stated print run of 500 sets. Card number 332 was issued at a stated rate of one in 11,479 packs and was issued to a stated print run of 100 sets. Card number 351 featuring Willie Mays was issued at a stated rate of one in 12 box loader packs.

*REF 1-155: 1.5X TO 4X BASIC
*REF 156-330: 2X TO 5X BASIC
*REF 156-330 RC'S: 1X TO 2.5X BASIC
*REF AU A 331/333-350: .5X TO 1.2X BASIC
*REF MAYS: 2X TO 5X BASIC
167 Dan Haren 5.00 12.00
179 Brandon Webb 20.00 50.00
202 Chien-Ming Wang 20.00 50.00
207 Chris Duncan 12.50 30.00
237 Edwin Jackson 4.00 10.00
319 Shane Victorino 6.00 15.00
327 Felix Pie 12.50 30.00
332 Jose Contreras AU B 30.00 60.00
334 Hanley Ramirez AU A 150.00 250.00
336 Kevin Youkilis AU A 50.00 100.00

2003 Bowman Chrome Blue Refractors

These cards were issued at a stated rate of one per box loader pack. Each of those packs contained an exchange card for an uncirculated card of which had to be redeemed from ThePit.Com by November 30th, 2005.

*BLUE: 1.5X TO 4X BASIC
167 Dan Haren 12.50 30.00
179 Brandon Webb 30.00 60.00
202 Chien-Ming Wang 60.00 120.00
207 Chris Duncan 20.00 50.00
319 Shane Victorino 10.00 25.00
327 Felix Pie 15.00 40.00
NNO Exchange Card

2003 Bowman Chrome Gold Refractors

This is a full parallel to the 2003 Bowman Chrome set. Cards 1-330 were issued at a stated rate of one per box loader pack. The cards 331-350 were inserted at much tougher odds. Cards 331-350 (except for number 332) were issued at a stated rate of one in 1202 hobby packs and were issued to a stated print run of 50 sets. Card number 332 was issued at a stated rate of one in 177,606 hobby packs and was issued to a stated run of 10 sets. The Willie Mays card (number 351) was issued at a stated rate of one in 116 box loader packs. There were also cards inserted for a complete set of these randomly inserted in packs at a stated rate of one in 78,936 packs. That exchange card was issued to a stated print run on 10 sets and those cards could be redeemed until November 30th, 2005.

*GOLD REF 1-155: 3X TO 8X BASIC
*GOLD REF 156-330: 3X TO 8X BASIC
*GOLD REF RC'S 156-330: 3X TO 8X BASIC
1-330 ODDS ONE PER BOX LOADER PACK
1-330 PRINT RUN 170 SERIAL #'d SETS
179 Brandon Webb 125.00 250.00
202 Chien-Ming Wang 300.00 400.00
207 Chris Duncan 60.00 120.00
237 Edwin Jackson 20.00 50.00
255 Andy Marte 90.00 150.00
319 Shane Victorino 20.00 50.00
327 Felix Pie 75.00 150.00
331 Brian McCann AU A 125.00 250.00
333 Corey Shafer AU A 30.00 60.00
334 Hanley Ramirez AU A 600.00 900.00
335 Ryan Shealy AU A 30.00 60.00
336 Kevin Youkilis AU A 125.00 250.00
337 Jason Kubel AU A 40.00 80.00
338 Aron Weston AU A 30.00 60.00
339 J.D. Durbin AU A 30.00 60.00
340 Gary Schneidmiller AU A 30.00 60.00
341 Travis Ishikawa AU A 30.00 60.00
342 Ben Francisco AU A 30.00 60.00
343 Bobby Basham AU A 30.00 60.00
344 Joey Gomes AU A 30.00 60.00
345 Beau Kemp AU A 30.00 60.00
346 Thomari Story-Harden AU A 30.00 60.00
347 Daryl Clark AU A 30.00 60.00
348 Bryan Bullington AU A 30.00 60.00
349 Rajai Davis AU A 30.00 60.00
350 Darrell Rasner AU A 30.00 60.00
NNO Set Exchange Card

2003 Bowman Chrome X-Fractors

This is a complete parallel to the basic Bowman Chrome set. Cards numbered 1-330 were issued at a stated rate of one in nine hobby packs. Cards numbered 331-350 (with the exception of number 332) were issued at a stated rate of one in 199 hobby packs and were issued to a stated print run of 250 sets. The Jose Contreras Card (number 332) was issued at a stated rate of one in 22,959 sets and was issued to a stated print run of 50 sets. The Willie Mays card (number 351) was issued at a stated rate of one in 58 box loader packs.

*X-FR 1-155: 2.5X TO 6X BASIC
*X-FR 156-330: 2.5X TO 6X BASIC
*X-FR RC'S 156-330: 1.25X TO 3X BASIC
*X-FR AU A 331/333-350: .6X TO 1.5X BASIC
*X-FR MAYS: 4X TO 10X BASIC
167 Dan Haren 10.00 25.00
179 Brandon Webb 30.00 60.00
202 Chien-Ming Wang 40.00 80.00
207 Chris Duncan 30.00 60.00
237 Edwin Jackson 5.00 12.00
249 Jeremy Bonderman 20.00 50.00
319 Shane Victorino 8.00 20.00
327 Felix Pie 30.00 60.00
332 Jose Contreras AU B 40.00 80.00
334 Hanley Ramirez AU A 200.00 300.00
336 Kevin Youkilis AU A 60.00 120.00

2003 Bowman Chrome Draft

This 176-card set was inserted as part of the 2003 Bowman Draft Packs. Each pack contained 2 Bowman Chrome Cards numbered between 1-165. In addition, cards numbered 166 through 176 were inserted at a stated rate of one in 41 packs. Each of those cards can be easily idenitifed as they were autographed. Please note that these cards were issued as a mix of live and exchange cards with a deadline for redeeming the exchange cards of November 30, 2005.

COMPLETE SET (176) 400.00 550.00
COMP.SET w/o AU'S (165) 50.00 100.00
COMMON CARD (1-165) .15 .40
1-165 TWO PER BOWMAN DRAFT PACK
COMMON CARD (166-176) 4.00 10.00
166-176 STATED ODDS 1:41 H/R
LUBANSKI IS AN SP BY 1000 COPIES
1 Dontrelle Willis .60 1.50
2 Freddy Sanchez .15 .40
3 Miguel Cabrera .60 1.50
4 Ryan Ludwick .15 .40
5 Ty Wigginton .15 .40
6 Mark Teixeira .40 1.00
7 Trey Hodges .15 .40
8 Laynce Nix .25 .60
9 Antonio Perez .15 .40
10 Jody Gerut .15 .40
11 Jae Weong Seo .15 .40
12 Erick Almonte .15 .40
13 Lyle Overbay .15 .40
14 Billy Traber .15 .40
15 Andres Torres .15 .40
16 Jose Valverde .15 .40
17 Aaron Heilman .15 .40
18 Brandon Larson .15 .40
19 Jung Bong .15 .40
20 Jesse Foppert .15 .40
21 Angel Berroa .15 .40
22 Jeff DaVanon .15 .40
23 Kurt Ainsworth .15 .40
24 Brandon Claussen .15 .40
25 Xavier Nady .15 .40
26 Travis Hafner .25 .60
27 Jerome Williams .15 .40
28 Jose Reyes .25 .60
29 Sergio Mitre RC .60 1.50
30 Bo Hart RC .40 1.00
31 Adam Miller RC 4.00 10.00
32 Brian Finch RC .40 1.00
33 Taylor Mattingly RC .60 1.50
34 Daric Barton RC 2.50 6.00
35 Chris Ray RC 1.25 3.00
36 Jarrod Saltalamacchia RC 6.00 15.00
37 Dennis Dove RC .60 1.50
38 James Houser RC .60 1.50
39 Clint King RC .60 1.50
40 Lou Palmisano RC .60 1.50
41 Dan Moore RC .40 1.00
42 Craig Stansberry RC .60 1.50
43 Jo Jo Reyes RC 1.25 3.00
44 Jake Stevens RC .60 1.50
45 Tom Gorzelanny RC 2.00 5.00
46 Brian Marshall RC .40 1.00
47 Scott Beerer RC .40 1.00
48 Javi Herrera RC .60 1.50
49 Steve LeRud RC .60 1.50
50 Josh Banks RC 1.00 2.50
51 Jon Papelbon RC 6.00 15.00
52 Juan Valdes RC .60 1.50
53 Beau Vaughan RC .60 1.50
54 Matt Chico RC .60 1.50
55 Todd Jennings RC .60 1.50
56 Anthony Gwynn RC 1.50 4.00
57 Matt Harrison RC 1.00 2.50
58 Aaron Marsden RC .60 1.50
59 Casey Abrams RC .40 1.00
60 Cory Stuart RC .40 1.00
61 Mike Wagner RC .40 1.00
62 Jordan Pratt RC .60 1.50
63 Andre Randolph RC .60 1.50
64 Blake Balkcom RC .60 1.50
65 Josh Muecke RC .40 1.00
66 Jamie D'Antona RC 1.00 2.50
67 Cole Seifrig RC .40 1.00
68 Josh Anderson RC .60 1.50
69 Matt Lorenzo RC .60 1.50
70 Nate Spears RC .60 1.50
71 Chris Goodman RC .40 1.00
72 Brian McFall RC .40 1.00
73 Billy Hogan RC .60 1.50
74 Jamie Romak RC .60 1.50
75 Jeff Cook RC .60 1.50
76 Brooks McNiven RC .40 1.00
77 Xavier Paul RC .60 1.50
78 Bob Zimmerman RC UER .40 1.00
Name is really Zimmermann
79 Mickey Hall RC .60 1.50
80 Shaun Marcum RC .60 1.50
81 Matt Nachreiner RC .60 1.50
82 Chris Kinsey RC .40 1.00
83 Jonathan Fulton RC .60 1.50
84 Edgardo Baez RC .60 1.50
85 Robert Valido RC .60 1.50
86 Kenny Lewis RC .60 1.50
87 Trent Peterson RC .40 1.00
88 Johnny Woodard RC .60 1.50
89 Wes Littleton RC .60 1.50
90 Sean Rodriguez RC 2.00 5.00
91 Kyle Pearson RC .40 1.00
92 Josh Rainwater RC .60 1.50
93 Travis Schlichting RC .60 1.50
94 Tim Battle RC 1.00 2.50
95 Aaron Hill RC 2.00 5.00
96 Bob McCrory RC .40 1.00
97 Rick Guarno RC .60 1.50
98 Brandon Yarbrough RC .40 1.00
99 Peter Stonard RC .40 1.00
100 Darin Downs RC .60 1.50
101 Matt Bruback RC .40 1.00
102 Danny Garcia RC .40 1.00
103 Cory Stewart RC .40 1.00
104 Ferdin Tejeda RC .40 1.00
105 Kade Johnson RC .40 1.00
106 Andrew Brown RC .60 1.50
107 Aquilino Lopez RC .40 1.00
108 Stephen Randolph RC .40 1.00
109 Dave Matranga RC .40 1.00
110 Dustin McGowan RC .60 1.50
111 Juan Camacho RC .40 1.00
112 Cliff Lee 1.50 4.00
113 Jeff Duncan RC .40 1.00
114 C.J. Wilson .15 .40
115 Brandon Roberson RC .40 1.00
116 David Corrente RC .40 1.00
117 Kevin Beavers RC .40 1.00
118 Anthony Webster RC .60 1.50
119 Oscar Villarreal RC .40 1.00
120 Hong-Chih Kuo RC 3.00 8.00
121 Josh Barfield .25 .60
122 Denny Bautista .15 .40
123 Chris Burke RC 1.50 4.00
124 Robinson Cano RC 8.00 20.00
125 Jose Castillo .15 .40
126 Neal Cotts .15 .40
127 Jorge De La Rosa .15 .40
128 J.D. Durbin .20 .50
129 Edwin Encarnacion .75 2.00
130 Gavin Floyd .15 .40
131 Alexis Gomez .15 .40
132 Edgar Gonzalez RC .40 1.00
133 Khalil Greene .60 1.50
134 Zack Greinke .25 .60
135 Franklin Gutierrez .60 1.50
136 Rich Harden .40 1.00
137 J.J. Hardy RC 4.00 10.00
138 Ryan Howard RC 12.50 30.00
139 Justin Huber .15 .40
140 David Kelton .15 .40
141 Dave Krynzel .15 .40
142 Pete LaForest .20 .50
143 Adam LaRoche .15 .40
144 Preston Larrison RC .40 1.00
145 John Maine RC 5.00 12.00
146 Andy Marte 1.50 4.00
147 Jeff Mathis .15 .40
148 Joe Mauer .60 1.50
149 Clint Nageotte .15 .40
150 Chris Narveson .15 .40
151 Ramon Nivar .20 .50
152 Felix Pie 2.00 5.00
153 Guillermo Quiroz RC .40 1.00
154 Rene Reyes .15 .40
155 Royce Ring .15 .40
156 Alexis Rios 1.25 3.00
157 Grady Sizemore .60 1.50
158 Stephen Smitherman .15 .40
159 Seung Song .15 .40
160 Scott Thorman .15 .40
161 Chad Tracy .15 .40
162 Chin-Hui Tsao .25 .60
163 John VanBenschoten .15 .40
164 Kevin Youkilis 2.00 5.00
165 Chien-Ming Wang 2.50 6.00
166 Chris Lubanski AU SP RC 10.00 25.00
167 Ryan Harvey AU RC 4.00 10.00
168 Matt Murton AU RC 4.00 10.00
169 Jay Sborz AU RC 4.00 10.00
170 Brandon Wood AU RC 20.00 50.00
171 Nick Markakis AU RC 30.00 60.00
172 Rickie Weeks AU RC 10.00 25.00
173 Eric Duncan AU RC 6.00 15.00
174 Chad Billingsley AU RC 15.00 40.00
175 Ryan Wagner AU RC 4.00 10.00
176 Delmon Young AU RC 30.00 60.00

2003 Bowman Chrome Draft Refractors

*REFRACTOR 1-165: 1.5X TO 4X BASIC
*REFRACTOR RC 1-165: 1.25X TO 3X BASIC
*REFRACTOR RC YR 1-165: 1.5X TO 4X BASIC
*REFRACTOR AU 166-176: .6X TO 1.5X BASIC
1-165 ODDS 1:11 BOWMAN DRAFT H/R
166-176 AU ODDS 1:196 BOW.DRAFT HOBBY
166-176 AU ODDS 1:198 BOW.DRAFT RETAIL
166-176 AU PRINT RUN 500 SETS
166-176 AU PRINT RUN PROVIDED BY TOPPS
166-176 AU'S ARE NOT SERIAL-NUMBERED
31 Adam Miller 15.00 40.00
36 Jarrod Saltalamacchia 15.00 40.00
51 Jon Papelbon 30.00 60.00
56 Anthony Gwynn 6.00 15.00
112 Cliff Lee 6.00 15.00
120 Hong-Chih Kuo 12.50 30.00
124 Robinson Cano 50.00 100.00
137 J.J. Hardy 15.00 40.00
138 Ryan Howard 50.00 100.00
145 John Maine 20.00 50.00
152 Felix Pie 8.00 20.00
165 Chien-Ming Wang 12.50 30.00
171 Nick Markakis AU 60.00 120.00
176 Delmon Young AU 150.00 250.00

2003 Bowman Chrome Draft Gold Refractors

*GOLD REF 1-165: 8X TO 20X BASIC
*GOLD REF RC 1-165: 10X TO 20X BASIC
*GOLD REF RC YR 1-165: 7.5X TO 15X BASIC
1-165 ODDS 1:98 BOWMAN DRAFT HOBBY
166-176 AU ODDS 1:1479 BOW.DRAFT HOBBY
1-165 PRINT RUN 50 SERIAL #'d SETS

166-176 AU PRINT RUN 50 SETS
166-176 AU PRINT RUN PROVIDED BY TOPPS
166-176 AU'S ARE NOT SERIAL-NUMBERED
GOLD REF ARE HOBBY-ONLY DISTRIBUTION

Card	Low	High
31 Adam Miller	150.00	250.00
36 Jarrod Saltalamacchia	150.00	250.00
51 Jon Papelbon	125.00	250.00
112 Cliff Lee	40.00	80.00
120 Hong-Chih Kuo	100.00	200.00
123 Chris Burke	100.00	200.00
124 Robinson Cano	175.00	300.00
137 J.J. Hardy	200.00	300.00
138 Ryan Howard	400.00	600.00
145 John Maine	200.00	275.00
152 Felix Pie	50.00	100.00
165 Chien-Ming Wang	60.00	120.00
166 Chris Lubanski AU	30.00	60.00
167 Ryan Harvey AU	30.00	60.00
168 Matt Murton AU	30.00	60.00
169 Jay Sborz AU	30.00	60.00
170 Brandon Wood AU	300.00	600.00
171 Nick Markakis AU	350.00	550.00
172 Rickie Weeks AU	125.00	250.00
173 Eric Duncan AU	40.00	80.00
174 Chad Billingsley AU	250.00	350.00
175 Ryan Wagner AU	30.00	60.00
176 Delmon Young AU	500.00	700.00

2003 Bowman Chrome Draft X-Fractors

*X-FRACTOR 1-165: 3X TO 8X BASIC
*X-FRACTOR RC 1-165: 2.5X TO 6X BASIC
*X-FRACTOR RC YR 1-165: 2.5X TO 6X BASIC
*X-FRACTOR AU 166-176: .75X TO 2X BASIC
1-165 ODDS 1:50 BOWMAN DRAFT HOBBY
1-165 ODDS 1:52 BOWMAN DRAFT RETAIL
166-176 AU ODDS 1:393 BOW.DRAFT HOBBY
166-176 AU ODDS 1:394 BOW.DRAFT RETAIL
1-165 PRINT RUN 130 SERIAL #'d SETS
166-176 AU PRINT RUN 250 SETS
166-176 AU PRINT RUN PROVIDED BY TOPPS
166-176 AU'S ARE NOT SERIAL-NUMBERED

Card	Low	High
31 Adam Miller	30.00	60.00
45 Tom Gorzelanny	15.00	40.00
51 Jon Papelbon	40.00	80.00
90 Sean Rodriguez	20.00	50.00
95 Aaron Hill	20.00	50.00
112 Cliff Lee	12.50	30.00
120 Hong-Chih Kuo	20.00	50.00
124 Robinson Cano	100.00	150.00
137 J.J. Hardy	30.00	60.00
138 Ryan Howard	125.00	250.00
145 John Maine	40.00	80.00
165 Chien-Ming Wang	20.00	50.00
171 Nick Markakis AU	75.00	150.00
176 Delmon Young AU	250.00	350.00

2004 Bowman Chrome

This 350-card set was released in August, 2004. The set was issued in four card packs with an $4 SRP which came 18 packs and 12 boxes to a case. The first 144 cards feature veterans while cards numbered 145 through 165 feature leading prospects. Cards numbered 166 through 350 are all Rookie Cards with the last 20 cards of the set being autographed. The Autographed cards (331-350) were inserted at a stated rate of one in 25 with a stated print run of 2000 sets. The Bobby Brownlie cards were issued as exchange cards with a stated expiry date of August 31, 2006.

Card	Low	High
COMPLETE SET (350)	250.00	400.00
COMP.SET w/o AU's (330)	60.00	120.00
COMMON CARD (1-150)	.20	.50
COMMON CARD (151-165)	.20	.50
COMMON AUTO (331-350)	4.00	10.00
331-350 AU'S ARE NOT SERIAL-NUMBERED		
331-350 PRINT RUN PROVIDED BY TOPPS		
1 Garret Anderson	.20	.50
2 Larry Walker	.20	.50
3 Derek Jeter	1.00	2.50
4 Curt Schilling	.30	.75
5 Carlos Zambrano	.20	.50
6 Shawn Green	.20	.50
7 Manny Ramirez	.30	.75
8 Randy Johnson	.50	1.25
9 Jeremy Bonderman	.20	.50
10 Alfonso Soriano	.20	.50
11 Scott Rolen	.30	.75
12 Kerry Wood	.20	.50
13 Eric Gagne	.20	.50
14 Ryan Klesko	.20	.50
15 Kevin Millar	.20	.50
16 Ty Wigginton	.20	.50
17 David Ortiz	.50	1.25
18 Luis Castillo	.20	.50
19 Bernie Williams	.30	.75
20 Edgar Renteria	.20	.50
21 Matt Kata	.20	.50
22 Bartolo Colon	.20	.50
23 Derrek Lee	.30	.75
24 Gary Sheffield	.20	.50
25 Nomar Garciaparra	.75	2.00
26 Kevin Millwood	.20	.50
27 Corey Patterson	.20	.50
28 Carlos Beltran	.20	.50
29 Mike Lieberthal	.20	.50
30 Troy Glaus	.20	.50
31 Preston Wilson	.20	.50
32 Jorge Posada	.30	.75
33 Bo Hart	.20	.50
34 Mark Prior	.30	.75
35 Hideo Nomo	.50	1.25
36 Jason Kendall	.20	.50
37 Roger Clemens	1.00	2.50
38 Dmitri Young	.20	.50
39 Jason Giambi	.20	.50
40 Jim Edmonds	.20	.50
41 Ryan Ludwick	.20	.50
42 Brandon Webb	.20	.50
43 Todd Helton	.30	.75
44 Jacque Jones	.20	.50
45 Jamie Moyer	.20	.50
46 Tim Salmon	.30	.75
47 Kelvim Escobar	.20	.50
48 Tony Batista	.20	.50
49 Nick Johnson	.20	.50
50 Jim Thome	.30	.75
51 Casey Blake	.20	.50
52 Trot Nixon	.20	.50
53 Luis Gonzalez	.20	.50
54 Dontrelle Willis	.30	.75
55 Mike Mussina	.30	.75
56 Carl Crawford	.20	.50
57 Mark Buehrle	.20	.50
58 Scott Podsednik	.20	.50
59 Brian Giles	.20	.50
60 Rafael Furcal	.20	.50
61 Miguel Cabrera	.30	.75
62 Rich Harden	.20	.50
63 Mark Teixeira	.30	.75
64 Frank Thomas	.50	1.25
65 Johan Santana	.50	1.25
66 Jason Schmidt	.20	.50
67 Aramis Ramirez	.20	.50
68 Jose Reyes	.20	.50
69 Magglio Ordonez	.20	.50
70 Mike Sweeney	.20	.50
71 Eric Chavez	.20	.50
72 Rocco Baldelli	.20	.50
73 Sammy Sosa	.50	1.25
74 Javy Lopez	.20	.50
75 Roy Oswalt	.20	.50
76 Raul Ibanez	.20	.50
77 Ivan Rodriguez	.30	.75
78 Jerome Williams	.20	.50
79 Carlos Lee	.20	.50
80 Geoff Jenkins	.20	.50
81 Sean Burroughs	.20	.50
82 Marcus Giles	.20	.50
83 Mike Lowell	.20	.50
84 Barry Zito	.20	.50
85 Aubrey Huff	.20	.50
86 Esteban Loaiza	.20	.50
87 Torii Hunter	.20	.50
88 Phil Nevin	.20	.50
89 Andruw Jones	.30	.75
90 Josh Beckett	.20	.50
91 Mark Mulder	.20	.50
92 Hank Blalock	.20	.50
93 Jason Phillips	.20	.50
94 Russ Ortiz	.20	.50
95 Juan Pierre	.20	.50
96 Tom Glavine	.30	.75
97 Gil Meche	.20	.50
98 Ramon Ortiz	.20	.50
99 Richie Sexson	.20	.50
100 Albert Pujols	1.00	2.50
101 Javier Vazquez	.20	.50
102 Johnny Damon	.30	.75
103 Alex Rodriguez	.75	2.00
104 Omar Vizquel	.30	.75
105 Chipper Jones	.50	1.25
106 Lance Berkman	.20	.50
107 Tim Hudson	.20	.50
108 Carlos Delgado	.20	.50
109 Austin Kearns	.20	.50
110 Orlando Cabrera	.20	.50
111 Edgar Martinez	.30	.75
112 Melvin Mora	.20	.50
113 Jeff Bagwell	.30	.75
114 Marlon Byrd	.20	.50
115 Vernon Wells	.20	.50
116 C.C. Sabathia	.20	.50
117 Cliff Floyd	.20	.50
118 Ichiro Suzuki	1.00	2.50
119 Miguel Olivo	.20	.50
120 Mike Piazza	.75	2.00
121 Adam Dunn	.20	.50
122 Paul Lo Duca	.20	.50
123 Brett Myers	.20	.50
124 Michael Young	.20	.50
125 Sidney Ponson	.20	.50
126 Greg Maddux	.75	2.00
127 Vladimir Guerrero	.50	1.25
128 Miguel Tejada	.20	.50
129 Andy Pettitte	.30	.75
130 Rafael Palmeiro	.30	.75
131 Ken Griffey Jr.	.75	2.00
132 Shannon Stewart	.20	.50
133 Joel Pineiro	.20	.50
134 Luis Matos	.20	.50
135 Jeff Kent	.20	.50
136 Randy Wolf	.20	.50
137 Chris Woodward	.20	.50
138 Jody Gerut	.20	.50
139 Jose Vidro	.20	.50
140 Bret Boone	.20	.50
141 Bill Mueller	.20	.50
142 Angel Berroa	.20	.50
143 Bobby Abreu	.20	.50
144 Roy Halladay	.20	.50
145 Delmon Young	.30	.75
146 Jonny Gomes	.20	.50
147 Rickie Weeks	.20	.50
148 Edwin Jackson	.20	.50
149 Neal Cotts	.20	.50
150 Jason Bay	.20	.50
151 Khalil Greene	.40	1.00
152 Joe Mauer	.50	1.25
153 Bobby Jenks	.30	.75
154 Chin-Feng Chen	.30	.75
155 Chien-Ming Wang	.75	2.00
156 Mickey Hall	.20	.50
157 James Houser	.20	.50
158 Jay Sborz	.20	.50
159 Jonathan Fulton	.20	.50
160 Steven Lerud	.20	.50
161 Grady Sizemore	.60	1.50
162 Felix Pie	.75	2.00
163 Dustin McGowan	.20	.50
164 Chris Lubanski	.30	.75
165 Tom Gorzelanny	.20	.50
166 Rudy Guillen RC	1.25	3.00
167 Aarom Baldiris RC	.75	2.00
168 Conor Jackson RC	4.00	10.00
169 Matt Moses RC	1.50	4.00
170 Ervin Santana RC	2.50	6.00
171 Merkin Valdez RC	.75	2.00
172 Erick Aybar RC	1.25	3.00
173 Brad Sullivan RC	.75	2.00
174 Joey Gathright RC	1.50	4.00
175 Brad Snyder RC	1.50	4.00
176 Alberto Callaspo RC	1.25	3.00
177 Brandon Medders RC	.60	1.50
178 Zach Miner RC	2.00	5.00
179 Charlie Zink RC	.40	1.00
180 Adam Greenberg RC	1.25	3.00
181 Kevin Howard RC	.75	2.00
182 Wanell Severino RC	.40	1.00
183 Chin-Lung Hu RC	2.00	5.00
184 Joel Zumaya RC	5.00	12.00
185 Skip Schumaker RC	.60	1.50
186 Nic Ungs RC	.60	1.50
187 Todd Self RC	.75	2.00
188 Brian Steffek RC	.40	1.00
189 Brock Peterson RC	.60	1.50
190 Greg Thissen RC	.60	1.50
191 Frank Brooks RC	.40	1.00
192 Scott Olsen RC	2.50	6.00
193 Chris Mabeus RC	.60	1.50
194 Dan Giese RC	.60	1.50
195 Jared Wells RC	.40	1.00
196 Carlos Sosa RC	.60	1.50
197 Bobby Madritsch	.40	1.00
198 Calvin Hayes RC	.75	2.00
199 Omar Quintanilla RC	.75	2.00
200 Chris O'Riordan RC	.60	1.50
201 Tim Hutting RC	.40	1.00
202 Carlos Quentin RC	4.00	10.00
203 Brayan Pena RC	.60	1.50
204 Jeff Salazar RC	1.50	4.00
205 David Murphy RC	1.25	3.00
206 Alberto Garcia RC	.75	2.00
207 Ramon Ramirez RC	.60	1.50
208 Luis Bolivar RC	.60	1.50
209 Rodney Choy Foo RC	.40	1.00
210 Fausto Carmona RC	3.00	8.00
211 Anthony Acevedo RC	.60	1.50
212 Chad Santos RC	.60	1.50
213 Jason Frasor RC	.60	1.50
214 Jesse Roman RC	.40	1.00
215 James Tomlin RC	.40	1.00
216 Josh Labandeira RC	.60	1.50
217 Ryan Meaux RC	.60	1.50
218 Don Sutton RC	1.50	4.00
219 Danny Gonzalez RC	.60	1.50
220 Javier Guzman RC	.75	2.00
221 Anthony Lerew RC	1.25	3.00
222 Jon Connolly RC	1.50	4.00
223 Jesse English RC	.60	1.50
224 Hector Made RC	1.25	3.00
225 Travis Hanson RC	.75	2.00
226 Jesse Floyd RC	.60	1.50
227 Nick Gorneault RC	.75	2.00
228 Craig Ansman RC	.60	1.50
229 Paul McAnulty RC	1.25	3.00
230 Carl Loadenthal RC	.75	2.00
231 Dave Crouthers RC	.40	1.00
232 Harvey Garcia RC	.40	1.00
233 Casey Kopitzke RC	.40	1.00
234 Ricky Nolasco RC	2.00	5.00
235 Miguel Perez RC	.40	1.00
236 Ryan Mulhern RC	.60	1.50
237 Chris Aguila RC	.60	1.50
238 Brooks Conrad RC	.75	2.00
239 Damaso Espino RC	.40	1.00
240 Jereme Milons RC	.75	2.00
241 Luke Hughes RC	.40	1.00
242 Kory Casto RC	.75	2.00
243 Jose Valdez RC	.60	1.50
244 J.T. Stotts RC	.40	1.00
245 Lee Gwaltney RC	.40	1.00
246 Yoann Torrealba RC	.40	1.00
247 Omar Falcon RC	.60	1.50
248 Jon Coutlangus RC	.40	1.00
249 George Sherrill RC	.40	1.00
250 John Santor RC	.40	1.00
251 Tony Richie RC	.60	1.50
252 Kevin Richardson RC	.60	1.50
253 Tim Bittner RC	.60	1.50
254 Chris Saenz RC	.60	1.50
255 Jose Capellan RC	.75	2.00
256 Donald Levinski RC	.40	1.00
257 Jerome Gamble RC	.40	1.00
258 Jeff Keppinger RC	2.50	6.00
259 Jason Szuminski RC	.40	1.00
260 Akinori Otsuka RC	.60	1.50
261 Ryan Budde RC	.60	1.50
262 Marland Williams RC	.75	2.00
263 Jeff Allison RC	.60	1.50
264 Hector Gimenez RC	.40	1.00
265 Tim Frend RC	.60	1.50
266 Tom Farmer RC	.60	1.50
267 Shawn Hill RC	.60	1.50
268 Mike Huggins RC	.60	1.50
269 Scott Proctor RC	.75	2.00
270 Jorge Mejia RC	.60	1.50
271 Terry Jones RC	.75	2.00
272 Zach Duke RC	3.00	8.00
273 Jesse Crain RC	1.25	3.00
274 Luke Anderson RC	.40	1.00
275 Hunter Brown RC	.40	1.00
276 Matt Lemanczyk RC	.60	1.50
277 Fernando Cortez RC	.40	1.00
278 Vince Perkins RC	.75	2.00
279 Tommy Murphy RC	.60	1.50
280 Mike Gosling RC	.40	1.00
281 Paul Bacot RC	.75	2.00
282 Matt Capps RC	.60	1.50
283 Juan Gutierrez RC	.60	1.50
284 Teodoro Encarnacion RC	.75	2.00
285 Chad Bentz RC	.60	1.50
286 Kazuo Matsui RC	.75	2.00
287 Ryan Hankins RC	.40	1.00
288 Leo Nunez RC	.60	1.50
289 Dave Wallace RC	.60	1.50
290 Rob Tejeda RC	1.25	3.00
291 Paul Maholm RC	1.50	4.00
292 Casey Daigle RC	.60	1.50
293 Tydus Meadows RC	.40	1.00
294 Khalid Ballouli RC	.40	1.00
295 Benji DeQuin RC	.40	1.00
296 Tyler Davidson RC	.75	2.00
297 Brant Colamarino RC	1.25	3.00
298 Marcus McBeth RC	.40	1.00
299 Brad Eldred RC	.75	2.00
300 David Pauley RC	2.00	5.00
301 Yadier Molina RC	2.50	6.00
302 Chris Shelton RC	2.00	5.00
303 Nyjer Morgan RC	.40	1.00
304 Jon DeVries RC	.60	1.50
305 Sheldon Fulse RC	.40	1.00
306 Vito Chiaravalloti RC	.60	1.50
307 Warner Madrigal RC	1.25	3.00
308 Reid Gorecki RC	.60	1.50
309 Sung Jung RC	.40	1.00
310 Pete Shier RC	.40	1.00
311 Michael Mooney RC	.60	1.50
312 Kenny Perez RC	.60	1.50
313 Michael Mallory RC	.60	1.50
314 Ben Himes RC	.40	1.00
315 Ivan Ochoa RC	.60	1.50
316 Donald Kelly RC	.60	1.50
317 Tom Mastny RC	.60	1.50
318 Kevin Davidson RC	.40	1.00
319 Brian Pilkington RC	.40	1.00
320 Alex Romero RC	.60	1.50
321 Chad Chop RC	.60	1.50
322 Kody Kirkland RC	.75	2.00
323 Casey Myers RC	.40	1.00
324 Mike Rouse RC	.60	1.50
325 Sergio Silva RC	.40	1.00
326 J.J. Furmaniak RC	1.25	3.00
327 Brad Vericker RC	.60	1.50
328 Blake Hawksworth RC	.75	2.00
329 Brock Jacobsen RC	.40	1.00
330 Alec Zumwalt RC	.40	1.00
331 Wardell Starling AU RC	4.00	10.00
332 Estee Harris AU RC	4.00	10.00
333 Kyle Sleeth AU RC	4.00	10.00
334 Dioner Navarro AU RC	6.00	15.00
335 Logan Kensing AU RC	4.00	10.00
336 Travis Blackley AU RC	4.00	10.00
337 Lincoln Holdzkom AU RC	4.00	10.00
338 Jason Hirsh AU RC	10.00	25.00
339 Juan Cedeno AU RC	4.00	10.00
340 Matt Creighton AU RC	4.00	10.00
341 Tim Stauffer AU RC	6.00	15.00
342 Shingo Takatsu AU RC	6.00	15.00
343 Lastings Milledge AU RC	20.00	50.00
344 Dustin Nippert AU RC	4.00	10.00
345 Felix Hernandez AU RC	60.00	120.00
346 Joaquin Arias AU RC	6.00	15.00
347 Kevin Kouzmanoff AU RC	10.00	25.00
348 B.Brownlie AU RC	4.00	10.00
349 David Aardsma AU RC	4.00	10.00
350 Jon Knott AU RC	6.00	15.00

2004 Bowman Chrome Refractors

*REF 1-150: 1.5X TO 4X BASIC
*REF 151-165: 2X TO 5X BASIC
*REF 166-330: 1X TO 2.5X BASIC
1-330 STATED ODDS 1:4 HOBBY
*REF AU 331-350: .5X TO 1.2X BASIC
331-350 AU ODDS 1:100 HOBBY
331-350 AU PRINT RUN 500 SETS
331-350 AU'S ARE NOT SERIAL-NUMBERED
331-350 PRINT RUN PROVIDED BY TOPPS
EXCHANGE DEADLINE 08/31/06

Card	Low	High
183 Chin-Lung Hu	20.00	50.00
202 Carlos Quentin	12.50	30.00
258 Jeff Keppinger	10.00	25.00
334 Dioner Navarro AU	8.00	20.00
342 Shingo Takatsu AU	8.00	20.00
343 Lastings Milledge AU	30.00	60.00
345 Felix Hernandez AU	100.00	200.00
347 Kevin Kouzmanoff AU	15.00	40.00

2004 Bowman Chrome Blue Refractors

*BLUE REF 166-330: 1.25X TO 3X BASIC
EXCH.CARDS AVAIL VIA PIT.COM WEBSITE
ONE EXCH.CARD PER BOX-LOADER PACK
ONE BOX-LOADER PACK PER HOBBY BOX
STATED PRINT RUN 290 SETS

Card	Low	High
168 Conor Jackson	15.00	40.00
176 Alberto Callaspo	12.50	30.00
183 Chin-Lung Hu	20.00	50.00
184 Joel Zumaya	25.00	60.00
202 Carlos Quentin	15.00	40.00
205 David Murphy	10.00	25.00
258 Jeff Keppinger	15.00	40.00
299 Brad Eldred	2.50	6.00
NNO Exchange Card		

2004 Bowman Chrome Gold Refractors

*GOLD REF 1-150: 5X TO 12X BASIC
*GOLD REF 151-165: 8X TO 20X BASIC
*GOLD REF 166-330: 6X TO 15X BASIC
1-330 STATED ODDS 1:60 HOBBY
1-330 PRINT RUN 50 SERIAL #'d SETS
*GOLD REF 331-350: 2X TO 4X BASIC
331-350 AU ODDS 1:1003 HOBBY
331-350 AU STATED PRINT RUN 50 SETS
331-350 AU'S ARE NOT SERIAL-NUMBERED
331-350 PRINT RUN PROVIDED BY TOPPS
EXCHANGE DEADLINE 08/31/06

Card	Low	High
154 Chin-Feng Chen	30.00	60.00
168 Conor Jackson	175.00	300.00
170 Ervin Santana	75.00	150.00
174 Joey Gathright	12.50	30.00
176 Alberto Callaspo	60.00	120.00
183 Chin-Lung Hu	60.00	120.00
184 Joel Zumaya	125.00	250.00
192 Scott Olsen	60.00	120.00
202 Carlos Quentin	125.00	250.00
210 Fausto Carmona	100.00	200.00
242 Kory Casto	30.00	60.00
258 Jeff Keppinger	100.00	200.00
272 Zach Duke	75.00	150.00
286 Kazuo Matsui	12.50	30.00
299 Brad Eldred	30.00	60.00
328 Blake Hawksworth	15.00	40.00
333 Kyle Sleeth AU	30.00	60.00
334 Dioner Navarro AU	30.00	60.00
336 Travis Blackley AU	20.00	50.00
341 Tim Stauffer AU	30.00	60.00
342 Shingo Takatsu AU	30.00	60.00
343 Lastings Milledge AU	200.00	400.00
344 Dustin Nippert AU	50.00	100.00
345 Felix Hernandez AU	600.00	800.00
346 Joaquin Arias AU	30.00	60.00
347 Kevin Kouzmanoff AU	100.00	200.00
349 David Aardsma AU	20.00	50.00

2004 Bowman Chrome X-Fractors

*X-FR 1-150: 3X TO 8X BASIC
*X-FR 151-165: 4X TO 10X BASIC
*X-FR 166-330: 2X TO 5X BASIC
1-330 ODDS ONE PER BOX LOADER PACK
ONE BOX LOADER PACK PER HOBY BOX
INSTANT WIN 1-330 ODDS 1:103,968 H
1-330 PRINT RUN 172 SERIAL #'d SETS
SETS 1-10 AVAIL.VIA INSTANT WIN CARD
SETS 11-172 ISSUED IN BOX-LOADER PACKS
*X-FR AU 331-350: .6X TO 1.5X BASIC
331-350 AU ODDS 1:200 HOBBY
331-350 AU STATED PRINT RUN 250 SETS
331-350 AU'S ARE NOT SERIAL-NUMBERED
331-350 PRINT RUNS PROVIDED BY TOPPS
EXCHANGE DEADLINE 08/31/06

Card	Low	High
168 Conor Jackson	30.00	60.00
176 Alberto Callaspo	20.00	50.00
183 Chin-Lung Hu	30.00	60.00
184 Joel Zumaya	30.00	60.00
202 Carlos Quentin	30.00	60.00
258 Jeff Keppinger	20.00	50.00
299 Brad Eldred	4.00	10.00
334 Dioner Navarro AU	10.00	25.00
342 Shingo Takatsu AU	10.00	25.00
343 Lastings Milledge AU	60.00	120.00
345 Felix Hernandez AU	200.00	300.00
347 Kevin Kouzmanoff AU	30.00	60.00
NNO Complete 1-330 Instant Win/10		

2004 Bowman Chrome Stars of the Future

STATED ODDS 1:600 HOBBY
STATED PRINT RUN 500 SETS
CARDS ARE NOT SERIAL-NUMBERED
PRINT RUN INFO PROVIDED BY TOPPS
REFRACTORS RANDOM INSERTS IN PACKS
NO REFRACTOR PRICING DUE TO SCARCITY
EXCHANGE DEADLINE 08/31/06

Card	Low	High
LHC Chris Lubanski Ryan Harvey Chad Cordero	15.00	40.00
MHD Nick Markakis Aaron Hill Eric Duncan	20.00	50.00
YSS Delmon Young Kyle Sleeth Tim Stauffer	20.00	50.00

2004 Bowman Chrome Draft

This 175-card set was issued as part of the Bowman Draft release. The first 165 cards were issued at a stated rate of two per Bowman Draft pack while the final 10 cards, all of which were autographed, were issued at a stated rate of one in 60 hobby and retail packs and were issued to a stated print run of 1695 sets.

Card	Low	High
COMPLETE SET (175)	175.00	300.00
COMP.SET w/o SP's (165)	50.00	100.00
COMMON CARD (1-165)	.15	.40
COMMON RC YR	.15	.40
1-165 TWO PER BOWMAN DRAFT PACK		
166-175 ODDS 1:60 BOWMAN DRAFT HOBBY		
166-175 ODDS 1:60 BOWMAN DRAFT RETAIL		
166-175 STATED PRINT RUN 1695 SETS		
166-175 ARE NOT SERIAL-NUMBERED		
166-175 PRINT RUN PROVIDED BY TOPPS		
PLATES 1-165 ODDS 1:559 HOBBY		
PLATES 166-175 ODDS 1:18,354 HOBBY		
PLATES PRINT RUN 1 SERIAL #'d SET		
BLACK-CYAN-MAGENTA-YELLOW EXIST		
NO PLATES PRICING DUE TO SCARCITY		
1 Lyle Overbay	.15	.40
2 David Newhan	.15	.40
3 J.R. House	.15	.40
4 Chad Tracy	.15	.40
5 Humberto Quintero	.15	.40
6 Dave Bush	.15	.40
7 Scott Hairston	.15	.40
8 Mike Wood	.15	.40
9 Alexis Rios	.25	.60
10 Sean Burnett	.15	.40
11 Wilson Valdez	.15	.40
12 Lew Ford	.15	.40
13 Freddy Thon RC	.40	1.00
14 Zack Greinke	.25	.60
15 Bucky Jacobsen	.15	.40
16 Kevin Youkilis	.15	.40
17 Grady Sizemore	.60	1.50
18 Denny Bautista	.15	.40
19 David DeJesus	.15	.40
20 Casey Kotchman	.25	.60
21 David Kelton	.15	.40
22 Charles Thomas RC	.40	1.00
23 Kazuhito Tadano RC	.60	1.50
24 Justin Leone RC	.60	1.50
25 Eduardo Villacis RC	.40	1.00
26 Brian Dallimore RC	.40	1.00
27 Nick Green	.15	.40
28 Sam McConnell RC	.40	1.00
29 Brad Halsey RC	.60	1.50
30 Roman Colon RC	.40	1.00
31 Josh Fields RC	2.50	6.00
32 Cody Bunkelman RC	.60	1.50
33 Jay Rainville RC	1.50	4.00
34 Richie Robnett RC	1.25	3.00
35 Jon Poterson RC	1.00	2.50
36 Huston Street RC	2.00	5.00
37 Erick San Pedro RC	.40	1.00
38 Cory Dunlap RC	1.25	3.00
39 Kurt Suzuki RC	1.25	3.00
40 Anthony Swarzak RC	1.00	2.50
41 Ian Desmond RC	1.50	4.00
42 Chris Covington RC	.60	1.50
43 Christian Garcia RC	1.00	2.50
44 Gaby Hernandez RC	1.50	4.00
45 Steven Register RC	.40	1.00
46 Eduardo Morlan RC	1.25	3.00
47 Collin Balester RC	.60	1.50
48 Nathan Phillips RC	.60	1.50
49 Dan Schwartzbauer RC	.60	1.50
50 Rafael Gonzalez RC	.40	1.00
51 K.C. Herren RC	1.00	2.50
52 William Susdorf RC	.40	1.00
53 Rob Johnson RC	.60	1.50
54 Louis Marson RC	1.00	2.50
55 Joe Koshansky RC	2.50	6.00
56 Jamar Walton RC	1.00	2.50
57 Mark Lowe RC	2.00	5.00
58 Matt Macri RC	1.25	3.00
59 Donny Lucy RC	.40	1.00
60 Mike Ferris RC	.60	1.50
61 Mike Nickeas RC	.60	1.50
62 Eric Hurley RC	1.25	3.00
63 Scott Elbert RC	1.25	3.00
64 Blake DeWitt RC	2.00	5.00
65 Danny Putnam RC	1.00	2.50
66 J.P. Howell RC	1.25	3.00
67 John Wiggins RC	.40	1.00
68 Justin Orenduff RC	1.00	2.50
69 Ray Liotta RC	1.25	3.00
70 Billy Buckner RC	.60	1.50
71 Eric Campbell RC	2.50	6.00
72 Olin Wick RC	1.00	2.50
73 Sean Gamble RC	.60	1.50
74 Seth Smith RC	1.25	3.00
75 Wade Davis RC	2.00	5.00
76 Joe Jacobitz RC	.40	1.00
77 J.A. Happ RC	1.00	2.50
78 Eric Ridener RC	.40	1.00
79 Matt Tuiasosopo RC	1.50	4.00

80 Brad Bergesen RC .40 1.00
81 Javy Guerra RC .60 1.50
82 Buck Shaw RC .60 1.50
83 Paul Janish RC .75 2.00
84 Sean Kazmar RC .40 1.00
85 Josh Johnson RC .60 1.50
86 Angel Salome RC 1.50 4.00
87 Jordan Parraz RC 1.00 2.50
88 Kelvin Vazquez RC .40 1.00
89 Grant Hansen RC .40 1.00
90 Matt Fox RC .40 1.00
91 Trevor Plouffe RC 1.50 4.00
92 Wes Whisler RC .40 1.00
93 Curtis Thigpen RC 1.00 2.50
94 Donnie Smith RC .60 1.50
95 Luis Rivera RC .60 1.50
96 Jesse Hoover RC .60 1.50
97 Jason Vargas RC 1.50 4.00
98 Clary Carlsen RC .40 1.00
99 Mark Robinson RC .40 1.00
100 J.C. Holt RC .60 1.50
101 Chad Blackwell RC .40 1.00
102 Daryl Jones RC 1.25 3.00
103 Jonathan Tierce RC .40 1.00
104 Patrick Bryant RC .40 1.00
105 Eddie Prasch RC .60 1.50
106 Mitch Einertson RC .75 2.00
107 Kyle Waldrop RC 1.25 3.00
108 Jeff Marquez RC .60 1.50
109 Zach Jackson RC 1.00 2.50
110 Josh Wahpepah RC .40 1.00
111 Adam Lind RC 3.00 8.00
112 Kyle Bloom RC .60 1.50
113 Ben Harrison RC .40 1.00
114 Taylor Tankersley RC .60 1.50
115 Steven Jackson RC .40 1.00
116 David Purcey RC 1.00 2.50
117 Jacob McGee RC 2.00 5.00
118 Lucas Harrell RC .40 1.00
119 Brandon Allen RC 1.25 3.00
120 Van Pope RC .60 1.50
121 Jeff Francis .25 .60
122 Joe Blanton .25 .60
123 Wil Ledezma .15 .40
124 Bryan Bullington .15 .40
125 Jairo Garcia .15 .40
126 Matt Cain .75 2.00
127 Arnie Munoz .15 .40
128 Clint Everts .15 .40
129 Jesus Cota .15 .40
130 Gavin Floyd .15 .40
131 Edwin Encarnacion .25 .60
132 Koyie Hill .15 .40
133 Ruben Gotay .15 .40
134 Jeff Mathis .15 .40
135 Andy Marte .40 1.00
136 Dallas McPherson .25 .60
137 Justin Morneau .25 .60
138 Rickie Weeks .25 .60
139 Joel Guzman .40 1.00
140 Shin Soo Choo .15 .40
141 Yusmeiro Petit RC 2.00 5.00
142 Jorge Cortes RC .40 1.00
143 Val Majewski .15 .40
144 Felix Pie .40 1.00
145 Aaron Hill .15 .40
146 Jose Capellan .25 .60
147 Dioner Navarro .40 1.00
148 Fausto Carmona 1.00 2.50
149 Robinzon Diaz RC .40 1.00
150 Felix Hernandez 6.00 15.00
151 Andres Blanco RC .40 1.00
152 Jason Kubel .15 .40
153 Willy Taveras RC 1.00 2.50
154 Merkin Valdez .40 1.00
155 Robinson Cano .60 1.50
156 Bill Murphy .15 .40
157 Chris Burke .25 .60
158 Kyle Sleeth .15 .40
159 B.J. Upton .40 1.00
160 Tim Stauffer .40 1.00
161 David Wright 1.50 4.00
162 Conor Jackson 1.50 4.00
163 Brad Thompson RC 1.00 2.50
164 Delmon Young .40 1.00
165 Jeremy Reed .25 .60
166 Matt Bush AU RC 10.00 25.00
167 Mark Rogers AU RC 8.00 20.00
168 Thomas Diamond AU RC UER 6.00 15.00
Many errors in informational blurb
169 Greg Golson AU RC 8.00 20.00
170 Homer Bailey AU RC 30.00 60.00
171 Chris Lambert AU RC 4.00 10.00
172 Neil Walker AU RC 12.50 30.00
173 Bill Bray AU RC 4.00 10.00
174 Philip Hughes AU RC 40.00 80.00
175 Gio Gonzalez AU RC 12.50 30.00

2004 Bowman Chrome Draft Refractors

*REF 1-165: 8X TO 20X BASIC
*REF RC 1-165: 1.25X TO 3X BASIC
*REF RC YR 1-165: 1.5X TO 4X BASIC
1-165 ODDS 1:11 BOWMAN DRAFT HOBBY
1-165 ODDS 1:11 BOWMAN DRAFT RETAIL
*REF AU 166-175: .6X TO 1.5X BASIC
166-175 AU ODDS BOW.DRAFT 1:204 HOB
166-175 AU ODDS BOW.DRAFT 1:204 RET
166-175 STATED PRINT RUN 500 SETS
166-175 ARE NOT SERIAL-NUMBERED
166-175 PRINT RUN PROVIDED BY TOPPS
150 Felix Hernandez 30.00 60.00
166 Matt Bush AU 15.00 40.00
170 Homer Bailey AU 40.00 80.00
172 Neil Walker AU 20.00 50.00
174 Philip Hughes AU 50.00 100.00

2004 Bowman Chrome Draft Gold Refractors

*GOLD REF 1-165: 8X TO 20X BASIC
*GOLD REF RC 1-165: 8X TO 20X BASIC
*GOLD REF RC YR 1-165: 6X TO 15X BASIC
1-165 ODDS 1:119 BOWMAN DRAFT HOBBY
1-165 ODDS 1:205 BOWMAN DRAFT RETAIL
1-165 PRINT RUN 50 SERIAL #'d SETS
*GOLD REF 166-175: 4X TO 10X BASIC
166-175 AU ODDS 1:2045 BOW.DRAFT HOB
166-175 AU ODDS 1:2055 BOW.DRAFT RET
166-175 STATED PRINT RUN 50 SETS
166-175 ARE NOT SERIAL-NUMBERED
166-175 PRINT RUN PROVIDED BY TOPPS
31 Josh Fields 75.00 150.00
55 Joe Koshansky 75.00 150.00
79 Matt Tuiasosopo 60.00 120.00
106 Mitch Einertson 40.00 80.00
111 Adam Lind 125.00 200.00
150 Felix Hernandez 100.00 200.00
166 Matt Bush AU 125.00 200.00
167 Mark Rogers AU 90.00 150.00
168 Thomas Diamond AU 60.00 120.00
169 Greg Golson AU 75.00 150.00
170 Homer Bailey AU 300.00 500.00
172 Neil Walker AU 125.00 200.00
174 Philip Hughes AU 300.00 600.00

2004 Bowman Chrome Draft Red Refractors

STATED ODDS 1:4471 BOW.DRAFT HOBBY
STATED PRINT RUN 1 SERIAL #'d SET
NO PRICING DUE TO SCARCITY

2004 Bowman Chrome Draft X-Fractors

*XF 1-165: 3X TO 8X BASIC
*XF RC 1-165: 2.5X TO 6X BASIC
*XF RC YR 1-165: 2.5X TO 6X BASIC
1-165 ODDS 1:48 BOWMAN DRAFT HOBBY
1-165 ODDS 1:80 BOWMAN DRAFT RETAIL
1-165 PRINT RUN 125 SERIAL #'d SETS
*XF AU 166-175: .75X TO 2X BASIC
166-175 AU ODDS 1:407 BOW.DRAFT HOB
166-175 AU ODDS 1:407 BOW.DRAFT RET
166-175 STATED PRINT RUN 250 SETS
166-175 ARE NOT SERIAL-NUMBERED
166-175 PRINT RUN PROVIDED BY TOPPS
63 Scott Elbert 10.00 25.00
79 Matt Tuiasosopo 15.00 40.00
150 Felix Hernandez 50.00 100.00
166 Matt Bush AU 20.00 50.00
170 Homer Bailey AU 60.00 120.00
172 Neil Walker AU 30.00 60.00
174 Philip Hughes AU 75.00 150.00
175 Gio Gonzalez AU 30.00 60.00

2004 Bowman Chrome Draft AFLAC

COMP.FACT.SET (12) 20.00 50.00
ONE SET VIA MAIL PER AFLAC EXCH.CARD
ONE EXCH.PER '04 BOW.DRAFT HOBBY BOX
EXCH.CARD DEADLINE WAS 11/30/05
SETS ACTUALLY SENT OUT JANUARY, 2006
1 C.J. Henry 1.50 4.00
2 John Drennen 1.25 3.00
3 Beau Jones 1.00 2.50
4 Jeff Lyman .60 1.50
5 Andrew McCutchen 4.00 10.00
6 Chris Volstad 1.00 2.50
7 Jonathan Egan .60 1.50
8 P.J. Phillips .60 1.50
9 Steve Johnson .60 1.50
10 Ryan Tucker 1.00 2.50
11 Cameron Maybin 10.00 25.00
12 Shane Funk .60 1.50

2004 Bowman Chrome Draft AFLAC Refractors

COMP.FACT.SET (12) 60.00 120.00
*REF: 1.5X TO 4X BASIC
ONE SET VIA MAIL PER AFLAC EXCH.CARD
ONE EXCH.PER '04 BOW.DRAFT HOBBY BOX
STATED PRINT RUN 550 SERIAL #'d SETS
EXCH.CARD DEADLINE WAS 11/30/05
SETS ACTUALLY SENT OUT JANUARY, 2006
5 Andrew McCutchen 20.00 50.00
11 Cameron Maybin 60.00 120.00

2004 Bowman Chrome Draft AFLAC X-Fractors

COMP.FACT.SET (12) 175.00 300.00
*X-FRAC: 4X TO 10X BASIC
ONE SET VIA MAIL PER AFLAC EXCH.CARD
ONE EXCH.PER '04 BOW.DRAFT HOBBY BOX
STATED PRINT RUN 125 SERIAL #'d SETS
EXCH.CARD DEADLINE WAS 11/30/05
SETS ACTUALLY SENT OUT JANUARY, 2006
11 Cameron Maybin 150.00 250.00

2004 Bowman Chrome Draft AFLAC Autograph Refractors

ONE SET VIA MAIL PER GOLD EXCH.CARD
STATED PRINT RUN 125 SERIAL #'d SETS
SETS ACTUALLY SENT OUT JUNE, 2006
AM Andrew McCutchen 300.00 400.00
CH C.J. Henry 75.00 125.00
CM Cameron Maybin 300.00 600.00
JU Justin Upton 800.00 1000.00

2005 Bowman Chrome

This 353-card set was released in August, 2005. The set was issued in four card packs with an $4 SRP which came 18 packs to a box and 12 boxes to a case. Cards 1-140 feature active veterans while cards 141-165 feature leading prospects and cards 166-330 feature Rookies. Cards 331-353 are signed Rookie Cards which were inserted into boxes at a stated rate of one in 28 packs.

COMP.SET w/o AU's (330) 60.00 120.00
COMMON CARD (1-140) .20 .50
COMMON CARD (141-165) .20 .50
COMMON CARD (166-330) .40 1.00
COMMON AUTO (331-353) 4.00 10.00
1-330 PLATE ODDS 1:779 HOBBY
331-353 AU PLATE ODDS 1:10,996 HOBBY
PLATE PRINT RUN 1 SET PER COLOR
BLACK-CYAN-MAGENTA-YELLOW ISSUED
NO PLATE PRICING DUE TO SCARCITY
1 Gavin Floyd .20 .50
2 Eric Chavez .20 .50
3 Miguel Tejada .20 .50
4 Dmitri Young .20 .50
5 Hank Blalock .20 .50
6 Kerry Wood .20 .50
7 Andy Pettitte .30 .75
8 Pat Burrell .20 .50
9 Johnny Estrada .20 .50
10 Frank Thomas .50 1.25
11 Juan Pierre .20 .50
12 Tom Glavine .30 .75
13 Lyle Overbay .20 .50
14 Jim Edmonds .20 .50
15 Steve Finley .20 .50
16 Jermaine Dye .20 .50
17 Omar Vizquel .30 .75
18 Nick Johnson .20 .50
19 Brian Giles .20 .50
20 Justin Morneau .20 .50
21 Preston Wilson .20 .50
22 Wily Mo Pena .20 .50
23 Rafael Palmeiro .30 .75
24 Scott Kazmir .20 .50
25 Derek Jeter 1.00 2.50
26 Barry Zito .20 .50
27 Mike Lowell .20 .50
28 Jason Bay .20 .50
29 Ken Harvey .20 .50
30 Nomar Garciaparra .50 1.25
31 Roy Halladay .20 .50
32 Todd Helton .30 .75
33 Mark Kotsay .20 .50
34 Jake Peavy .20 .50
35 David Wright .75 2.00
36 Dontrelle Willis .20 .50
37 Marcus Giles .20 .50
38 Chone Figgins .20 .50
39 Sidney Ponson .20 .50
40 Randy Johnson .50 1.25
41 John Smoltz .50 1.25
42 Kevin Millar .20 .50
43 Mark Teixeira .30 .75
44 Alex Rios .20 .50
45 Mike Piazza .50 1.25
46 Victor Martinez .20 .50
47 Jeff Bagwell .30 .75
48 Shawn Green .20 .50
49 Ivan Rodriguez .30 .75
50 Alex Rodriguez .75 2.00
51 Kazuo Matsui .20 .50
52 Mark Mulder .20 .50
53 Michael Young .20 .50
54 Javy Lopez .20 .50
55 Johnny Damon .30 .75
56 Jeff Francis .20 .50
57 Rich Harden .20 .50
58 Bobby Abreu .20 .50
59 Mark Loretta .20 .50
60 Gary Sheffield .20 .50
61 Jamie Moyer .20 .50
62 Garret Anderson .20 .50
63 Vernon Wells .20 .50
64 Orlando Cabrera .20 .50
65 Magglio Ordonez .20 .50
66 Ronnie Belliard .20 .50
67 Carlos Lee .20 .50
68 Carl Pavano .20 .50
69 Jon Lieber .20 .50
70 Aubrey Huff .20 .50
71 Rocco Baldelli .20 .50
72 Jason Schmidt .20 .50
73 Bernie Williams .30 .75
74 Hideki Matsui .75 2.00
75 Ken Griffey Jr. .75 2.00
76 Josh Beckett .20 .50
77 Mark Buehrle .20 .50
78 David Ortiz .50 1.25
79 Luis Gonzalez .20 .50
80 Scott Rolen .30 .75
81 Joe Mauer .50 1.25
82 Jose Reyes .20 .50
83 Adam Dunn .20 .50
84 Greg Maddux .75 2.00
85 Bartolo Colon .20 .50
86 Bret Boone .20 .50
87 Mike Mussina .30 .75
88 Ben Sheets .20 .50
89 Lance Berkman .20 .50
90 Miguel Cabrera .30 .75
91 C.C. Sabathia .20 .50
92 Mike Maroth .20 .50
93 Andruw Jones .30 .75
94 Jack Wilson .20 .50
95 Ichiro Suzuki 1.00 2.50
96 Geoff Jenkins .20 .50
97 Zack Greinke .20 .50
98 Jorge Posada .30 .75
99 Travis Hafner .20 .50
100 Barry Bonds 1.25 3.00
101 Aaron Rowand .20 .50
102 Aramis Ramirez .20 .50
103 Curt Schilling .30 .75
104 Melvin Mora .20 .50
105 Albert Pujols 1.00 2.50
106 Austin Kearns .20 .50
107 Shannon Stewart .20 .50
108 Carl Crawford .20 .50
109 Carlos Zambrano .20 .50
110 Roger Clemens .75 2.00
111 Javier Vazquez .20 .50
112 Randy Wolf .20 .50
113 Chipper Jones .50 1.25
114 Larry Walker .30 .75
115 Alfonso Soriano .30 .75
116 Brad Wilkerson .20 .50
117 Bobby Crosby .20 .50
118 Jim Thome .30 .75
119 Oliver Perez .20 .50
120 Vladimir Guerrero .50 1.25
121 Roy Oswalt .20 .50
122 Torii Hunter .20 .50
123 Rafael Furcal .20 .50
124 Luis Castillo .20 .50
125 Carlos Beltran .20 .50
126 Mike Sweeney .20 .50
127 Johan Santana .50 1.25
128 Tim Hudson .20 .50
129 Troy Glaus .20 .50
130 Manny Ramirez .30 .75
131 Jeff Kent .20 .50
132 Jose Vidro .20 .50
133 Edgar Renteria .20 .50
134 Russ Ortiz .20 .50
135 Sammy Sosa .50 1.25
136 Carlos Delgado .20 .50
137 Richie Sexson .20 .50
138 Pedro Martinez .30 .75
139 Adrian Beltre .20 .50
140 Mark Prior .30 .75
141 Omar Quintanilla .20 .50
142 Carlos Quentin .30 .75
143 Dan Johnson .20 .50
144 Jake Stevens .20 .50
145 Nate Schierholtz .30 .75
146 Neil Walker .20 .50
147 Bill Bray .20 .50
148 Taylor Tankersley .20 .50
149 Trevor Plouffe .30 .75
150 Felix Hernandez 2.50 6.00
151 Philip Hughes .75 2.00
152 James Houser .20 .50
153 David Murphy .20 .50
154 Ervin Santana UER .30 .75
Facsimile signature is Johan Santana
155 Anthony Whittington .20 .50
156 Chris Lambert .20 .50
157 Jeremy Sowers .30 .75
158 Giovanny Gonzalez .30 .75
159 Blake DeWitt .30 .75
160 Thomas Diamond .30 .75
161 Greg Golson .30 .75
162 David Aardsma .20 .50
163 Paul Maholm .20 .50
164 Mark Rogers .30 .75
165 Homer Bailey .30 .75
166 Elvin Puello RC .60 1.50
167 Tony Giarratano RC .60 1.50
168 Darren Fenster RC .60 1.50
169 Elvys Quezada RC .60 1.50
170 Glen Perkins RC 1.25 3.00
171 Ian Kinsler RC 2.50 6.00
172 Adam Bostick RC .60 1.50
173 Jeremy West RC .75 2.00
174 Brett Harper RC .75 2.00
175 Kevin West RC .60 1.50
176 Luis Hernandez RC .60 1.50
177 Matt Campbell RC .60 1.50
178 Nate McLouth RC 1.50 4.00
179 Ryan Goleski RC .75 2.00
180 Matthew Lindstrom RC .60 1.50
181 Matt DeSalvo RC .75 2.00
182 Kole Strayhorn RC .60 1.50
183 Jose Vaquedano RC .60 1.50
184 James Jurries RC .75 2.00
185 Ian Bladergroen RC .75 2.00
186 Kila Kaaihue RC 1.50 4.00
187 Luke Scott RC 2.50 6.00
188 Chris Denorfia RC 1.50 4.00
189 Jai Miller RC .75 2.00
190 Melky Cabrera RC 3.00 8.00
191 Ryan Sweeney RC 1.50 4.00
192 Sean Marshall RC 2.50 6.00
193 Erick Abreu RC 1.25 3.00
194 Tyler Pelland RC .75 2.00
195 Cole Armstrong RC .60 1.50
196 John Hudgins RC .60 1.50
197 Wade Robinson RC .60 1.50
198 Dan Santin RC .60 1.50
199 Steve Doetsch RC .60 1.50
200 Shane Costa RC .60 1.50
201 Scott Mathieson RC 1.25 3.00
202 Ben Jones RC .75 2.00
203 Michael Rogers RC .60 1.50
204 Matt Rogelstad RC .60 1.50
205 Luis Ramirez RC .60 1.50
206 Landon Powell RC .75 2.00
207 Erik Cordier RC .60 1.50
208 Chris Seddon RC .60 1.50
209 Chris Roberson RC .60 1.50
210 Thomas Oldham RC .60 1.50
211 Dana Eveland RC .60 1.50
212 Cody Haerther RC .60 1.50
213 Danny Core RC .60 1.50
214 Craig Tatum RC .60 1.50
215 Elliot Johnson RC .60 1.50
216 Ender Chavez RC .60 1.50
217 Errol Simonitsch RC .75 2.00
218 Matt Van Der Bosch RC .60 1.50
219 Eulogio de la Cruz RC .60 1.50
220 Drew Toussaint RC .60 1.50
221 Adam Boeve RC .60 1.50
222 Adam Harben RC .75 2.00
223 Baltazar Lopez RC .60 1.50
224 Russ Martin RC 2.00 5.00
225 Brian Bannister RC 1.50 4.00
226 Chris Walker RC .60 1.50
227 Casey McGehee RC .60 1.50
228 Humberto Sanchez RC 2.50 6.00
229 Javon Moran RC .60 1.50
230 Brandon McCarthy RC 2.00 5.00
231 Danny Zell RC .60 1.50
232 Kevin Barry RC .60 1.50
233 Juan Tejeda RC .60 1.50
234 Keith Ramsey RC .60 1.50
235 Lorenzo Scott RC .60 1.50
236 Jon Barratt RC .60 1.50
237 Martin Prado RC .60 1.50
238 Matt Albers RC 1.50 4.00
239 Brian Schweiger RC .60 1.50
240 Raul Tablado RC .60 1.50
241 Pat Misch RC .60 1.50
242 Pat Osborn .60 1.50
243 Ryan Feierabend RC .60 1.50
244 Shaun Marcum .40 1.00
245 Kevin Collins RC .60 1.50
246 Stuart Pomeranz RC .60 1.50
247 Tetsu Yofu RC .60 1.50
248 Hernan Iribarren RC .75 2.00
249 Mike Spidale RC .60 1.50
250 Tony Arnerich RC .60 1.50
251 Manny Parra RC 2.00 5.00
252 Drew Anderson RC .60 1.50
253 T.J. Beam RC 1.25 3.00
254 Claudio Arias RC .75 2.00
255 Andy Sides RC .60 1.50
256 Bear Bay RC .75 2.00
257 Bill McCarthy RC .60 1.50
258 Daniel Haigwood RC 1.25 3.00
259 Brian Sprout RC .75 2.00
260 Bryan Triplett RC .60 1.50
261 Steven Bondurant RC .60 1.50
262 Darwinson Salazar RC .60 1.50
263 David Shepard RC .60 1.50
264 Johan Silva RC .60 1.50
265 J.B. Thurmond RC .60 1.50
266 Brandon Moorhead RC .60 1.50
267 Kyle Nichols RC .75 2.00
268 Jonathan Sanchez RC 2.00 5.00
269 Mike Esposito RC .60 1.50
270 Erik Schindewolf RC .60 1.50
271 Peeter Ramos RC .60 1.50
272 Juan Senreiso RC .60 1.50
273 Travis Chick RC .75 2.00
274 Vinny Rottino RC .60 1.50
275 Micah Furtado RC .60 1.50
276 George Kottaras RC 1.25 3.00
277 Abel Gomez RC .75 2.00
278 Buck Coats RC .60 1.50
279 Kenny Durost RC .60 1.50
280 Nick Touchstone RC .60 1.50
281 Jerry Owens RC .75 2.00
282 Stefan Bailie RC .60 1.50
283 Jesse Gutierrez RC .60 1.50
284 Chuck Tiffany RC 1.50 4.00
285 Brendan Ryan RC .60 1.50
286 Julio Pimentel RC .75 2.00
287 Shawn Bowman RC .75 2.00
288 Alexander Smit RC .60 1.50
289 Micah Schnurstein RC .60 1.50
290 Jared Gothreaux RC .60 1.50
291 Jair Jurrjens RC 1.50 4.00
292 Bobby Livingston RC .60 1.50
293 Ryan Speier RC .60 1.50
294 Zach Parker RC .60 1.50
295 Christian Colonel RC .60 1.50
296 Scott Mitchinson RC .60 1.50
297 Neil Wilson RC .60 1.50
298 Chuck James RC 2.50 6.00
299 Heath Totten RC .60 1.50
300 Sean Tracey RC .60 1.50
301 Tadahito Iguchi RC 2.00 5.00
302 Matt Brown RC .60 1.50
303 Franklin Morales RC 1.25 3.00
304 Brandon Sing RC .75 2.00
305 D.J. Houlton RC .60 1.50
306 Jayce Tingler RC .60 1.50
307 Mitchell Arnold RC .60 1.50
308 Jim Burt RC .60 1.50
309 Jason Motte RC .60 1.50
310 David Gassner RC .60 1.50
311 Andy Santana RC .60 1.50
312 Kelvin Pichardo RC .60 1.50
313 Carlos Carrasco RC 2.00 5.00
314 Willy Mota RC .60 1.50
315 Frank Mata RC .60 1.50
316 Carlos Gonzalez RC 3.00 8.00
317 Jesse Floyd .40 1.00
318 Chris B.Young RC 3.00 8.00
319 Billy Sadler RC .60 1.50
320 Ricky Barrett RC .60 1.50
321 Ben Harrison .60 1.50
322 Steve Nelson RC .60 1.50
323 Daryl Thompson RC .60 1.50
324 Davis Romero RC .60 1.50
325 Jeremy Harts RC .60 1.50
326 Nick Masset RC .60 1.50
327 Thomas Pauly RC .60 1.50
328 Mike Garber RC .60 1.50
329 Kennard Bibbs RC .60 1.50
330 Colter Bean RC .60 1.50
331 Justin Verlander AU RC 50.00 100.00
332 Chip Cannon AU RC 10.00 25.00
333 Kevin Melillo AU RC 6.00 15.00
334 Jake Postlewait AU RC 4.00 10.00
335 Wes Swackhamer AU RC 4.00 10.00
336 Mike Rodriguez AU RC 4.00 10.00
337 Philip Humber AU RC 10.00 25.00
338 Jeff Niemann AU RC 12.50 30.00
339 Brian Miller AU RC 4.00 10.00
340 Chris Vines AU RC 4.00 10.00
341 Andy LaRoche AU RC 10.00 25.00
342 Mike Bourn AU RC 10.00 25.00
343 Eric Nielsen AU RC 4.00 10.00
344 Wladimir Balentien AU RC 20.00 50.00
345 Ismael Ramirez AU RC 4.00 10.00
346 Pedro Lopez AU RC 4.00 10.00
347 Shawn Bowman AU 6.00 15.00
348 Hayden Penn AU RC 10.00 25.00
349 Matthew Kemp AU RC 20.00 50.00
350 Brian Stavisky AU RC 4.00 10.00
351 C.J. Smith AU RC 4.00 10.00
352 Mike Morse AU RC 5.00 12.00
353 Billy Butler AU RC 50.00 100.00

2005 Bowman Chrome Refractors

*REF 1-140: 1.5X TO 4X BASIC
*REF 141-165: 1.25X TO 3X BASIC
*REF 166-330: 1X TO 2.5X BASIC
1-330 ODDS 1:4 HOBBY, 1:6 RETAIL
*REF AU 331-353: .5X TO 1.2X BASIC AU
331-353 AU ODDS 1:88 HOB, 1:259 RET
331-353 PRINT RUN 500 SERIAL #'d SETS
150 Felix Hernandez 5.00 12.00
171 Ian Kinsler 10.00 25.00
178 Nate McLouth 8.00 20.00
187 Luke Scott 8.00 20.00
225 Brian Bannister 6.00 15.00
251 Manny Parra 6.00 15.00
303 Franklin Morales 10.00 25.00
313 Carlos Carrasco 12.50 30.00
331 Justin Verlander AU 75.00 150.00
341 Andy LaRoche AU 30.00 60.00
349 Matthew Kemp AU 40.00 80.00
352 Mike Morse AU 12.50 30.00
353 Billy Butler AU 75.00 150.00

2005 Bowman Chrome Blue Refractors

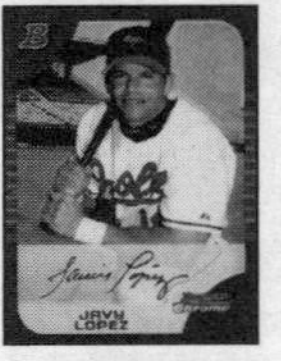

*BLUE REF 1-140: 3X TO 8X BASIC
*BLUE REF 141-165: 2.5X TO 6X BASIC
*BLUE REF 166-330: 2X TO 5X BASIC
1-330 ODDS 1:20 HOBBY, 1:69 RETAIL
*BLUE REF AU 331-353: 1.25X TO 2.5X BASIC
331-353 AU ODDS 1:294 HOB, 1:866 RET
STATED PRINT RUN 150 SERIAL #'d SETS
150 Felix Hernandez 10.00 25.00
171 Ian Kinsler 30.00 60.00
178 Nate McLouth 20.00 50.00
192 Sean Marshall 20.00 40.00
224 Russ Martin 12.50 30.00
225 Brian Bannister 40.00 80.00
251 Manny Parra 15.00 40.00
303 Franklin Morales 30.00 60.00
313 Carlos Carrasco 30.00 60.00
316 Carlos Gonzalez 40.00 80.00
318 Chris B.Young 40.00 80.00
331 Justin Verlander AU 150.00 250.00
332 Chip Cannon AU 15.00 40.00
341 Andy LaRoche AU 125.00 200.00
342 Mike Bourn AU 50.00 100.00
344 Wladimir Balentien AU 90.00 150.00
349 Matthew Kemp AU 60.00 120.00
353 Billy Butler AU 200.00 300.00

2005 Bowman Chrome Gold Refractors

*GOLD REF 1-140: 8X TO 20X BASIC
*GOLD REF 141-165: 6X TO 15X BASIC
*GOLD REF 166-330: 10X TO 25X BASIC

1-330 ODDS 1:61 HOBBY, 1:206 RETAIL
*GOLD REF AU 331-353: 3X TO 6X BASIC
331-353 AU ODDS 1:880 HOB, 1:2612 RET
STATED PRINT RUN 50 SERIAL #'d SETS
100 Barry Bonds 50.00 100.00
150 Felix Hernandez 25.00 60.00
171 Ian Kinsler 100.00 200.00
178 Nate McLouth 75.00 150.00
190 Melky Cabrera 175.00 300.00
224 Russ Martin 150.00 250.00
225 Brian Bannister 75.00 150.00
228 Humberto Sanchez 50.00 100.00
251 Manny Parra 75.00 150.00
303 Franklin Morales 75.00 150.00
313 Carlos Carrasco 75.00 150.00
316 Carlos Gonzalez 150.00 250.00
318 Chris B.Young 100.00 200.00
331 Justin Verlander AU 500.00 800.00
332 Chip Cannon AU 60.00 120.00
333 Kevin Melillo AU 30.00 60.00
334 Jake Postlewait AU 30.00 60.00
335 Wes Swackhamer AU 30.00 60.00
336 Mike Rodriguez AU 30.00 60.00
337 Philip Humber AU 150.00 250.00
338 Jeff Niemann AU 100.00 200.00
339 Brian Miller AU 30.00 60.00
340 Chris Vines AU 30.00 60.00
341 Andy LaRoche AU 300.00 500.00
342 Mike Bourn AU 100.00 200.00
343 Eric Nielsen AU 30.00 60.00
344 Wladimir Balentien AU 200.00 300.00
345 Ismael Ramirez AU 30.00 60.00
346 Pedro Lopez AU 30.00 60.00
347 Shawn Bowman AU 50.00 100.00
348 Hayden Penn AU 75.00 150.00
349 Matthew Kemp AU 100.00 200.00
350 Brian Stavisky AU 30.00 60.00
351 C.J. Smith AU 30.00 60.00
352 Mike Morse AU 60.00 120.00
353 Billy Butler AU 500.00 650.00

2005 Bowman Chrome Green Refractors

*GREEN: 1.5X TO 4X BASIC
ISSUED VIA THE PIT.COM
STATED PRINT RUN 225 SERIAL #'d SETS
171 Ian Kinsler 30.00 60.00
178 Nate McLouth 15.00 40.00
190 Melky Cabrera 12.50 30.00
192 Sean Marshall 15.00 30.00
224 Russ Martin 15.00 40.00
225 Brian Bannister 12.50 30.00
251 Manny Parra 15.00 40.00
303 Franklin Morales 15.00 40.00
313 Carlos Carrasco 15.00 40.00
316 Carlos Gonzalez 20.00 50.00

2005 Bowman Chrome Red Refractors

1-330 ODDS 1:606 H, 1:2112 R
331-353 AU ODDS 1:8773 H, 1:32,160 R
STATED PRINT RUN 5 SERIAL #'d SETS
NO PRICING DUE TO SCARCITY

2005 Bowman Chrome Super-Fractors

1-330 STATED ODDS 1:3117 H
331-353 AU STATED ODDS 1:47,238 H
STATED PRINT RUN 1 SERIAL #'d SET
NO PRICING DUE TO SCARCITY

2005 Bowman Chrome X-Fractors

*X-FRACTOR 1-140: 2X TO 5X BASIC
*X-FRACTOR 141-165: 1.5X TO 4X BASIC
*X-FRACTOR 166-330: 2X TO 5X BASIC
1-330 ODDS 1:13 HOBBY, 1:61 RETAIL
*X-FRACT AU 331-353: 1X TO 2X BASIC AU
331-353 AU ODDS 1:196 HOB, 1:573 RET
STATED PRINT RUN 225 SERIAL #'d SETS
150 Felix Hernandez 6.00 15.00
171 Ian Kinsler 12.50 30.00
178 Nate McLouth 10.00 25.00
225 Brian Bannister 12.50 30.00
251 Manny Parra 15.00 40.00
303 Franklin Morales 20.00 50.00
316 Carlos Gonzalez 20.00 50.00
331 Justin Verlander AU 100.00 175.00
338 Jeff Niemann AU 20.00 50.00
341 Andy LaRoche AU 50.00 100.00
344 Wladimir Balentien AU 60.00 120.00
349 Matthew Kemp AU 50.00 100.00
352 Mike Morse AU 20.00 50.00
353 Billy Butler AU 100.00 175.00

2005 Bowman Chrome A-Rod Throwback

COMPLETE SET (4) 4.00 10.00
COMMON CARD (94-97) 1.25 3.00
STATED ODDS 1:9 HOBBY, 1:12 RETAIL
*REF: 1X TO 2.5X BASIC
REFRACTOR ODDS 1:445 HOBBY
REFRACTOR PRINT RUN 499 #'d SETS
SUPER-FRACTOR ODDS 1:226,044 HOBBY
SUPER-FRACTOR PRINT RUN 1 #'d SET
NO SUPER-FRACTOR PRICING AVAILABLE
*X-FRACTOR: 1.5X TO 4X BASIC
X-FRACTOR ODDS 1:2241 HOBBY
X-FRACTOR PRINT RUN 99 #'d SETS
94AR Alex Rodriguez 1994 1.25 3.00
95AR Alex Rodriguez 1995 1.25 3.00
96AR Alex Rodriguez 1996 1.25 3.00
97AR Alex Rodriguez 1997 1.25 3.00

2005 Bowman Chrome A-Rod Throwback Autographs

1994 CARD STATED ODDS 1:614,088 H
1995 CARD STATED ODDS 1:36,122 H
1996 CARD STATED ODDS 1:18,061 H
1997 CARD STATED ODDS 1:9042 H
1994 CARD PRINT RUN 1 #'d CARD
1995 CARD PRINT RUN 25 #'d CARDS
1996 CARD PRINT RUN 50 #'d CARDS
1997 CARD PRINT RUN 99 #'d CARDS
NO PRICING ON 1994 CARD AVAILABLE
94AR A.Rodriguez 1994 SF/1
95AR A.Rodriguez 1995 XF/25
96AR A.Rodriguez 1996 RF/50 125.00 200.00
97AR A.Rodriguez 1997 CH/99 75.00 150.00

2005 Bowman Chrome Two of a Kind Autographs

STATED ODDS 1:76,761 HOBBY
STATED PRINT RUN 13 SERIAL #'d CARDS
NO PRICING DUE TO SCARCITY
ARCR Alex Rodriguez
Cal Ripken/13

2005 Bowman Chrome Draft

These cards were issued two per Bowman Draft Pack. Cards numbered 166 through 180, which were not issued as regular Bowman cards feature signed cards of some leading prospects. Those cards were issued at different odds depending on the player who signed the cards.

COMP.SET w/o SP's (165) 50.00 100.00
COMMON CARD (1-165) .15 .40
COMMON RC .40 1.00
COMMON RC YR .15 .40
1-165 TWO PER BOWMAN DRAFT PACK
166-180 GROUP A ODDS 1:671 H, 1:643 R
166-180 GROUP B ODDS 1:69 H, 1:69 R
1-165 PLATE ODDS 1:826 HOBBY
166-180 AU PLATE ODDS 1:18,411 HOBBY
PLATE PRINT RUN 1 SET PER COLOR
BLACK-CYAN-MAGENTA-YELLOW ISSUED
NO PLATE PRICING DUE TO SCARCITY
1 Rickie Weeks .25 .60
2 Kyle Davies .15 .40
3 Garrett Atkins .15 .40
4 Chien-Ming Wang .75 2.00
5 Dallas McPherson .15 .40
6 Dan Johnson .25 .60
7 Andy Sisco .15 .40
8 Ryan Doumit .15 .40
9 J.P. Howell .15 .40
10 Tim Stauffer .15 .40
11 Willy Taveras .25 .60
12 Aaron Hill .15 .40
13 Victor Diaz .15 .40
14 Wilson Betemit .15 .40
15 Ervin Santana .25 .60
16 Mike Morse .25 .60
17 Yadier Molina .25 .60
18 Kelly Johnson .15 .40
19 Clint Barmes .25 .60
20 Robinson Cano .40 1.00
21 Brad Thompson .15 .40
22 Jorge Cantu .25 .60
23 Brad Halsey .15 .40
24 Lance Niekro .25 .60
25 D.J. Houlton .15 .40
26 Ryan Church .15 .40
27 Hayden Penn .60 1.50
28 Chris Young .15 .40
29 Chad Orvella RC .40 1.00
30 Mark Teahen .15 .40
31 Mark McCormick FY RC .60 1.50
32 Jay Bruce FY RC 5.00 12.00
33 Beau Jones FY RC 1.00 2.50
34 Tyler Greene FY RC 1.00 2.50
35 Zach Ward FY RC .40 1.00
36 Josh Bell FY RC 1.50 4.00
37 Josh Wall FY RC .60 1.50
38 Nick Webber FY RC .40 1.00
39 Travis Buck FY RC 1.25 4.00
40 Kyle Winters FY RC .60 1.50
41 Mitch Boggs FY RC .40 1.00
42 Tommy Mendoza FY RC 1.00 2.50
43 Brad Corley FY RC .60 1.50
44 Drew Butera FY RC .40 1.00
45 Ryan Mount FY RC 1.00 2.50
46 Tyler Herron FY RC .60 1.50
47 Nick Weglarz FY RC 1.00 2.50
48 Brandon Erbe FY RC 1.50 4.00
49 Cody Allen FY RC .40 1.00
50 Eric Fowler FY RC .40 1.00
51 James Boone FY RC .60 1.50
52 Josh Flores FY RC 1.50 4.00
53 Brandon Monk FY RC .60 1.50
54 Kieron Pope FY RC 1.00 2.50
55 Kyle Cofield FY RC .40 1.00
56 Brent Lillibridge FY RC .60 1.50
57 Daryl Jones FY RC .40 1.00
58 Eli Iorg FY RC .60 1.50
59 Brett Hayes FY RC .40 1.00
60 Mike Durant FY RC 1.25 3.00
61 Michael Bowden FY RC 2.00 5.00
62 Paul Kelly FY RC .60 1.50
63 Andrew McCutchen FY RC 3.00 8.00
64 Travis Wood FY RC 1.25 3.00
65 Cesar Ramos FY RC .60 1.50
66 Chaz Roe FY RC .60 1.50
67 Matt Torra FY RC .60 1.50
68 Kevin Slowey FY RC 2.50 6.00
69 Trayvon Robinson FY RC .60 1.50
70 Reid Engel FY RC .40 1.00
71 Kris Harvey FY RC .60 1.50
72 Craig Italiano FY RC 1.00 2.50
73 Matt Maloney FY RC 1.25 3.00
74 Sean West FY RC 1.25 3.00
75 Henry Sanchez FY RC 1.00 2.50
76 Scott Blue FY RC .40 1.00
77 Jordan Schafer FY RC 3.00 8.00
78 Chris Robinson FY RC .60 1.50
79 Chris Hobdy FY RC .40 1.00
80 Brandon Durden FY RC .40 1.00
81 Clay Buchholz FY RC 6.00 15.00
82 Josh Geer FY RC .40 1.00
83 Sam LeCure FY RC .40 1.00
84 Justin Thomas FY RC .40 1.00
85 Brett Gardner FY RC 1.00 2.50
86 Tommy Manzella FY RC .40 1.00
87 Matt Green FY RC .40 1.00
88 Yunel Escobar FY RC 2.00 5.00
89 Mike Costanzo FY RC 1.25 3.00
90 Nick Hundley FY RC .40 1.00
91 Zach Simons FY RC .40 1.00
92 Jacob Marceaux FY RC .40 1.00
93 Jed Lowrie FY RC 2.50 6.00
94 Brandon Snyder FY RC 1.25 3.00
95 Matt Goyen FY RC .40 1.00
96 Jon Egan FY RC .60 1.50
97 Drew Thompson FY RC .60 1.50
98 Bryan Anderson FY RC 1.50 4.00
99 Clayton Richard FY RC .40 1.00
100 Jimmy Shull FY RC .60 1.50
101 Mark Pawelek FY RC 2.00 5.00
102 P.J. Phillips FY RC 1.00 2.50
103 John Drennen FY RC 1.50 4.00
104 Nolan Reimold FY RC 2.00 5.00
105 Troy Tulowitzki FY RC 4.00 10.00
106 Kevin Whelan FY RC .50 1.25
107 Wade Townsend FY RC .60 1.50
108 Micah Owings FY RC 1.00 2.50
109 Ryan Tucker FY RC .60 1.50
110 Jeff Clement FY RC 3.00 8.00
111 Josh Sullivan FY RC .40 1.00
112 Jeff Lyman FY RC .60 1.50
113 Brian Bogusevic FY RC .60 1.50
114 Trevor Bell FY RC .60 1.50
115 Brent Cox FY RC .60 1.50
116 Michael Billek FY RC .40 1.00
117 Garrett Olson FY RC .60 1.50
118 Steven Johnson FY RC .60 1.50
119 Chase Headley FY RC 2.00 5.00
120 Daniel Carte FY RC .60 1.50
121 Francisco Liriano PROS 1.00 2.50
122 Fausto Carmona PROS .15 .40
123 Zach Jackson PROS .15 .40
124 Adam Loewen PROS .15 .40
125 Chris Lambert PROS .15 .40
126 Scott Mathieson FY .25 .60
127 Paul Maholm PROS .25 .60
128 Fernando Nieve PROS .15 .40
129 Justin Verlander FY 1.50 4.00
130 Yusmeiro Petit PROS .40 1.00
131 Joel Zumaya PROS .60 1.50
132 Merkin Valdez PROS .15 .40
133 Ryan Garko FY RC 1.50 4.00
134 Edison Volquez FY RC 5.00 12.00
135 Russ Martin FY .60 1.50
136 Conor Jackson PROS .25 .60
137 Miguel Montero FY RC 1.50 4.00
138 Josh Barfield PROS .25 .60
139 Delmon Young PROS .40 1.00
140 Andy LaRoche FY .60 1.50
141 William Bergolla PROS .15 .40
142 B.J. Upton PROS .25 .60
143 Hernan Iribarren FY .25 .60
144 Brandon Wood PROS .50 1.25
145 Jose Bautista PROS .15 .40
146 Edwin Encarnacion PROS .25 .60
147 Javier Herrera FY RC 1.00 2.50
148 Jeremy Hermida PROS .60 1.50
149 Frank Diaz PROS RC .40 1.00
150 Chris B.Young FY 1.25 3.00
151 Shin-Soo Choo PROS .15 .40
152 Kevin Thompson PROS RC .40 1.00
153 Hanley Ramirez PROS .40 1.00
154 Lastings Milledge PROS .25 .60
155 Luis Montanez PROS .15 .40
156 Justin Huber PROS .15 .40
157 Zach Duke PROS .30 .75
158 Jeff Francoeur PROS .50 1.25
159 Melky Cabrera FY 1.25 3.00
160 Bobby Jenks PROS .25 .60
161 Ian Snell PROS .15 .40
162 Fernando Cabrera PROS .15 .40
163 Troy Patton PROS .40 1.00
164 Anthony Lerew PROS .25 .60
165 Nelson Cruz FY RC 1.25 3.00
166 Stephen Drew AU A RC 20.00 50.00
167 Jered Weaver AU A RC 20.00 50.00
168 Ryan Braun AU B RC 100.00 200.00
169 John Mayberry Jr. AU B RC 12.50 30.00
170 Aaron Thompson AU B RC 6.00 15.00
171 Cesar Carrillo AU B RC 10.00 25.00
172 Jacoby Ellsbury AU B RC 60.00 120.00
173 Matt Garza AU B RC 15.00 40.00
174 Cliff Pennington AU B RC 4.00 10.00
175 Colby Rasmus AU B RC 50.00 100.00
176 Chris Volstad AU B RC 12.50 30.00
177 Ricky Romero AU B RC 6.00 15.00
178 Ryan Zimmerman AU B RC 50.00 100.00
179 C.J. Henry AU B RC 10.00 25.00
180 Eddy Martinez AU B RC 6.00 15.00

2005 Bowman Chrome Draft Refractors

*REF 1-165: 8X TO 20X BASIC
*REF 1-165: 1.25X TO 3X BASIC RC
*REF 1-165: 1.25X TO 3X BASIC RC YR
1-165 ODDS 1:11 BOWMAN DRAFT HOBBY
1-165 ODDS 1:11 BOWMAN DRAFT RETAIL
*REF AU 166-180: .6X TO 1.5X BASIC
166-180 AU ODDS BOW.DRAFT 1:204 HOB
166-180 AU ODDS 1:186 BOW.DRAFT RET
166-180 PRINT RUN 500 SERIAL #'d SETS
32 Jay Bruce FY 20.00 50.00
36 Josh Bell FY 6.00 15.00
61 Michael Bowden FY 10.00 25.00
68 Kevin Slowey FY 10.00 25.00
77 Jordan Schafer FY 15.00 40.00
81 Clay Buchholz FY 30.00 60.00
85 Brett Gardner FY 6.00 15.00
88 Yunel Escobar FY 12.50 30.00
105 Troy Tulowitzki FY 12.50 30.00
119 Chase Headley FY 10.00 25.00
134 Edison Volquez FY 12.50 30.00
135 Russ Martin FY 6.00 15.00
166 Stephen Drew AU 60.00 120.00
167 Jered Weaver AU 40.00 80.00
168 Ryan Braun AU 150.00 300.00
172 Jacoby Ellsbury AU 60.00 120.00
173 Matt Garza AU 20.00 50.00
175 Colby Rasmus AU 100.00 150.00
178 Ryan Zimmerman AU 75.00 150.00

2005 Bowman Chrome Draft Blue Refractors

*BLUE 1-165: 4X TO 10X BASIC
*BLUE 1-165: 4X TO 10X BASIC RC
*BLUE 1-165: 3X TO 8X BASIC RC YR
1-165 ODDS 1:52 BOWMAN DRAFT HOBBY
1-165 ODDS 1:107 BOWMAN DRAFT RETAIL
*BLUE AU 166-180: 1.25X TO 2.5X BASIC
166-180 AU ODDS 1:619 BOW.DRAFT HOB
166-180 AU ODDS 1:619 BOW.DRAFT RET
STATED PRINT RUN 150 SERIAL #'d SETS
32 Jay Bruce FY 125.00 250.00
39 Travis Buck FY 30.00 60.00
61 Michael Bowden FY 40.00 80.00
68 Kevin Slowey FY 30.00 60.00
77 Jordan Schafer FY 75.00 125.00
81 Clay Buchholz FY 150.00 225.00
85 Brett Gardner FY 15.00 40.00
88 Yunel Escobar FY 40.00 80.00
93 Jed Lowrie FY 20.00 50.00
101 Mark Pawelek FY 20.00 50.00
105 Troy Tulowitzki FY 100.00 150.00
108 Micah Owings FY 15.00 40.00
119 Chase Headley FY 30.00 60.00
134 Edison Volquez FY 75.00 150.00
135 Russ Martin FY 10.00 25.00
150 Chris B.Young FY 50.00 80.00
166 Stephen Drew AU 150.00 250.00
167 Jered Weaver AU 75.00 150.00
168 Ryan Braun AU 300.00 500.00
172 Jacoby Ellsbury AU 175.00 300.00
173 Matt Garza AU 75.00 150.00
175 Colby Rasmus AU 275.00 350.00
178 Ryan Zimmerman AU 125.00 250.00

2005 Bowman Chrome Draft Gold Refractors

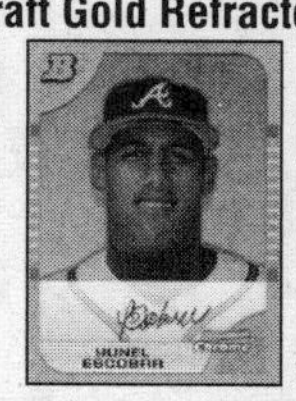

*GOLD REF 1-165: 10X TO 25X BASIC
*GOLD REF 1-165: 12.5X TO 25X BASIC RC
*GOLD REF 1-165: 12.5X TO 30X BASIC RC YR
1-165 ODDS 1:155 BOWMAN DRAFT HOBBY
1-165 ODDS 1:323 BOWMAN DRAFT HOBBY
*GOLD REF AU 166-180: 4X TO 8X BASIC
166-180 AU ODDS 1:1857 BOW.DRAFT HOB
166-180 AU ODDS 1:1856 BOW.DRAFT RET
STATED PRINT RUN 50 SERIAL #'d SETS
32 Jay Bruce FY 300.00 500.00
61 Michael Bowden FY 100.00 200.00
63 Andrew McCutchen FY 250.00 350.00
68 Kevin Slowey FY 150.00 250.00
77 Jordan Schafer FY 150.00 250.00
81 Clay Buchholz FY 350.00 450.00
85 Brett Gardner FY 100.00 200.00
88 Yunel Escobar FY 60.00 120.00
105 Troy Tulowitzki FY 250.00 350.00
108 Micah Owings FY 60.00 120.00
110 Jeff Clement FY 300.00 500.00
119 Chase Headley FY 150.00 200.00
134 Edison Volquez FY 250.00 350.00
135 Russ Martin FY 60.00 120.00
159 Melky Cabrera FY 90.00 150.00
166 Stephen Drew AU 375.00 500.00
167 Jered Weaver AU 300.00 600.00
168 Ryan Braun AU 1000.00 1400.00
172 Jacoby Ellsbury AU 500.00 700.00
173 Matt Garza AU 125.00 250.00
175 Colby Rasmus AU 400.00 550.00
178 Ryan Zimmerman AU 600.00 800.00

2005 Bowman Chrome Draft Red Refractors

1-165 ODDS 1:6609 HOBBY
166-180 AU ODDS 1:73,645 HOBBY
STATED PRINT RUN 1 SERIAL #'d SET
NO PRICING DUE TO SCARCITY

2005 Bowman Chrome Draft SuperFractors

1-165 ODDS 1:6609 HOBBY
166-180 AU ODDS 1:73,645 HOBBY
STATED PRINT RUN 1 SERIAL #'d SET
NO PRICING DUE TO SCARCITY

2005 Bowman Chrome Draft X-Fractors

*XF 1-165: 2X TO 5X BASIC
*XF 1-165: 2.5X TO 6X BASIC RC
*XF 1-165: 2X TO 5X BASIC RC YR
1-165 ODDS 1:31 BOWMAN DRAFT HOBBY
1-165 ODDS 1:64 BOWMAN DRAFT RETAIL
*XF AU 166-180: 1X TO 2X BASIC
166-180 AU ODDS 1:372 BOW.DRAFT HOB
166-180 AU ODDS 1:371 BOW.DRAFT RET
STATED PRINT RUN 250 SERIAL #'d SETS
32 Jay Bruce FY 40.00 80.00
61 Michael Bowden FY 20.00 50.00
68 Kevin Slowey FY 15.00 40.00
77 Jordan Schafer FY 40.00 80.00
81 Clay Buchholz FY 60.00 120.00
85 Brett Gardner FY 6.00 15.00
88 Yunel Escobar FY 40.00 80.00
101 Mark Pawelek FY 12.50 30.00
105 Troy Tulowitzki FY 50.00 100.00
108 Micah Owings FY 10.00 25.00
110 Jeff Clement FY 20.00 50.00
119 Chase Headley FY 15.00 40.00
134 Edison Volquez FY 20.00 50.00
135 Russ Martin FY 12.50 30.00
150 Chris B.Young FY 15.00 40.00
166 Stephen Drew AU 75.00 150.00
167 Jered Weaver AU 75.00 150.00
168 Ryan Braun AU 300.00 400.00
172 Jacoby Ellsbury AU 100.00 200.00
173 Matt Garza AU 30.00 60.00
175 Colby Rasmus AU 150.00 250.00
178 Ryan Zimmerman AU 100.00 200.00

2005 Bowman Chrome Draft AFLAC Exchange Cards

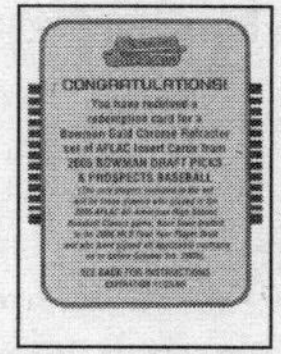

BASIC ODDS 1:109 BOW.DRAFT H
REFRACTOR ODDS 1:2184 BOW.DRAFT H
X-FRACTOR ODDS 1:4369 BOW.DRAFT H
BLUE REF ODDS 1:7261 BOW.DRAFT H
GOLD REF ODDS 1:21,937 BOW.DRAFT H
RED REF ODDS 1:1,031,040 BOW.DRAFT H
SUP-FRAC ODDS 1:1,031,040 BOW.DRAFT H
REFRACTOR PRINT RUN 500 CARDS
X-FRACTOR PRINT RUN 250 CARDS
BLUE REF PRINT RUN 150 CARDS
GOLD REF PRINT RUN 50 CARDS
RED REF PRINT RUN 1 CARD
SUPER-FRACTOR PRINT RUN 1 CARD
PLATES PRINT RUN 1 SET PER COLOR
NO RED/SUPER PRICING DUE TO SCARCITY
NO PLATES PRICING DUE TO SCARCITY
EXCHANGE DEADLINE 12/26/06
1 Basic Set 15.00 30.00
2 Printing Plates Set/4
3 Refractor Set/500 90.00 150.00
4 Blue Refractor Set/150 250.00 400.00
5 Gold Refractor Set/50 700.00 1000.00
6 Red Refractor Set/1
7 Super-Fractor Set/1
8 X-Fractor Set/250 175.00 300.00

2005 Bowman Chrome Draft AFLAC

COMP.FACT.SET (14) 12.50 30.00
ONE SET VIA MAIL PER AFLAC EXCH.CARD
BASIC ODDS 1:109 '05 BOW.DRAFT HOB.
SETS ACTUALLY SENT OUT JANUARY, 2007
EXCHANGE DEADLINE 12/26/06
PLATE PRINT RUN 1 SET PER COLOR
BLACK-CYAN-MAGENTA-YELLOW ISSUED
NO PLATE PRICING DUE TO SCARCITY
1 Billy Rowell 3.00 8.00
2 Kasey Kiker 1.00 2.50
3 Chris Marrero 2.50 6.00
4 Jeremy Jeffress .60 1.50
5 Kyle Drabek .60 1.50
6 Chris Parmelee 1.25 3.00
7 Colton Willems .60 1.50
8 Cody Johnson .75 2.00
9 Hank Conger 1.00 2.50
10 Cory Rasmus .60 1.50
11 David Christensen .60 1.50
12 Chris Tillman .60 1.50
13 Torre Langley .60 1.50
14 Robby Alcombrack .60 1.50

2005 Bowman Chrome Draft AFLAC Refractors

COMP.FACT.SET (14) 60.00 120.00
*REF: 2X TO 5X BASIC
ONE SET VIA MAIL PER EXCH.CARD
STATED ODDS 1:2184 BOW.DRAFT H
STATED PRINT RUN 500 SER.#'d SETS
EXCHANGE DEADLINE 12/26/06
SETS ACTUALLY SENT OUT JANUARY, 2007

2005 Bowman Chrome Draft AFLAC Blue Refractors

COMP.FACT.SET (14) 250.00 350.00
*BLUE REF: 8X TO 20X BASIC
ONE SET VIA MAIL PER EXCH.CARD
STATED ODDS 1:7261 BOW.DRAFT H
STATED PRINT RUN 150 SER.#'d SETS
EXCHANGE DEADLINE 12/26/06
SETS ACTUALLY SENT OUT JANUARY, 2007
1 Billy Rowell 50.00 100.00
3 Chris Marrero 60.00 120.00
5 Kyle Drabek 15.00 40.00
6 Chris Parmelee 15.00 40.00
9 Hank Conger 12.50 30.00

2005 Bowman Chrome Draft AFLAC Gold Refractors

ONE SET VIA MAIL PER EXCH.CARD
STATED ODDS 1:21,937 BOW.DRAFT H
STATED PRINT RUN 50 SER.#'d SETS
EXCHANGE DEADLINE 12/26/06
SETS ACTUALLY SENT OUT JANUARY, 2007
1 Billy Rowell 200.00 300.00
2 Kasey Kiker 50.00 100.00
3 Chris Marrero 100.00 200.00
4 Jeremy Jeffress 50.00 100.00
5 Kyle Drabek 75.00 150.00

6 Chris Parmelee 60.00 120.00
7 Colton Willems 50.00 100.00
8 Cody Johnson 60.00 120.00
9 Hank Conger 60.00 120.00
10 Cory Rasmus 50.00 100.00
11 David Christensen 40.00 80.00
12 Chris Tillman 40.00 80.00
13 Torre Langley 50.00 100.00
14 Robby Alcombrack 40.00 80.00

2005 Bowman Chrome Draft AFLAC Red Refractors

STATED ODDS 1:1,031,040 BOW.DRAFT H
STATED PRINT RUN 1 SER.#'d SET
NO PRICING DUE TO SCARCITY
ONE SET VIA MAIL PER EXCH.CARD
EXCHANGE DEADLINE 12/26/06
SETS ACTUALLY SENT OUT JANUARY, 2007

2005 Bowman Chrome Draft AFLAC SuperFractors

STATED ODDS 1:1,031,040 BOW.DRAFT H
STATED PRINT RUN 1 SER.#'d SET
NO PRICING DUE TO SCARCITY
ONE SET VIA MAIL PER EXCH.CARD
EXCHANGE DEADLINE 12/26/06
SETS ACTUALLY SENT OUT JANUARY, 2007

2005 Bowman Chrome Draft AFLAC X-Fractors

COMP.FACT.SET (14) 150.00 250.00
*X-FRAC: 4X TO 10X BASIC
STATED ODDS 1:4369 BOW.DRAFT H
ONE SET VIA MAIL PER EXCH.CARD
STATED PRINT RUN 250 SER.#'d SETS
EXCHANGE DEADLINE 12/26/06
SETS ACTUALLY SENT OUT JANUARY, 2007
1 Billy Rowell 30.00 60.00

2006 Bowman Chrome

This 224-card set was released in August, 2006. The set was issued in four card hobby packs with an $3 SRP which came 18 packs to a box and 12 boxes to a case. Card number 219, Kenji Johjima was available in both a regular and an autographed version. Cards numbered 221 through 224 were only available in a signed form. The first 200-cards of this set feature veterans while the rest of this set features players who qualified for the Rookie Card designation under the new Rookie Card rules which began in 2006.

COMP.SET w/o AU's (220) 30.00 60.00
COMMON CARD (1-200) .20 .50
COMMON ROOKIE (201-220) .25 .60
219 AU ODDS 1:2734 HOBBY, 1:6617 RETAIL
221-224 AU ODDS 1:27 HOBBY, 1:65 RETAIL
1-220 PLATE ODDS 1:836 HOBBY
219 AU PLATE ODDS 1:292,536 HOBBY
221-224 AU PLATES ODDS 1:9,000 HOBBY
PLATE PRINT RUN 1 SET PER COLOR
BLACK-CYAN-MAGENTA-YELLOW ISSUED
NO PLATE PRICING DUE TO SCARCITY
1 Nick Swisher .20 .50
2 Ted Lilly .20 .50
3 John Smoltz .30 .75
4 Lyle Overbay .20 .50
5 Alfonso Soriano .20 .50
6 Javier Vazquez .20 .50
7 Ronnie Belliard .20 .50
8 Jose Reyes .50 1.25
9 Brian Roberts .20 .50
10 Curt Schilling .30 .75
11 Adam Dunn .20 .50
12 Zack Greinke .20 .50
13 Carlos Guillen .20 .50
14 Jon Garland .20 .50
15 Robinson Cano .30 .75
16 Chris Burke .20 .50
17 Barry Zito .20 .50
18 Russ Adams .20 .50
19 Chris Capuano .20 .50
20 Scott Rolen .30 .75
21 Kerry Wood .20 .50
22 Scott Kazmir .30 .75
23 Brandon Webb .20 .50
24 Jeff Kent .20 .50
25 Albert Pujols 1.00 2.50
26 C.C. Sabathia .20 .50
27 Adrian Beltre .20 .50
28 Brad Wilkerson .20 .50
29 Randy Wolf .20 .50
30 Jason Bay .20 .50
31 Austin Kearns .20 .50
32 Clint Barmes .20 .50
33 Mike Sweeney .20 .50
34 Kevin Youkilis .20 .50
35 Justin Morneau .20 .50
36 Scott Podsednik .20 .50
37 Jason Giambi .20 .50
38 Steve Finley .20 .50
39 Morgan Ensberg .20 .50
40 Eric Chavez .20 .50
41 Roy Halladay .20 .50
42 Horacio Ramirez .20 .50
43 Ben Sheets .20 .50
44 Chris Carpenter .20 .50
45 Andruw Jones .30 .75
46 Carlos Zambrano .20 .50
47 Jonny Gomes .20 .50
48 Shawn Green .20 .50
49 Moises Alou .20 .50
50 Ichiro Suzuki .75 2.00
51 Juan Pierre .20 .50
52 Grady Sizemore .30 .75
53 Kazuo Matsui .20 .50
54 Jose Vidro .20 .50
55 Jake Peavy .20 .50
56 Dallas McPherson .20 .50
57 Ryan Howard .75 2.00
58 Zach Duke .20 .50
59 Michael Young .20 .50
60 Todd Helton .30 .75
61 David DeJesus .20 .50
62 Ivan Rodriguez .30 .75
63 Johan Santana .30 .75
64 Danny Haren .20 .50
65 Derek Jeter 1.25 3.00
66 Greg Maddux .75 2.00
67 Jorge Cantu .20 .50
68 J.J. Hardy .20 .50
69 Victor Martinez .20 .50
70 David Wright .75 2.00
71 Ryan Church .20 .50
72 Khalil Greene .30 .75
73 Jimmy Rollins .20 .50
74 Hank Blalock .20 .50
75 Pedro Martinez .30 .75
76 Chris Shelton .20 .50
77 Felipe Lopez .20 .50
78 Jeff Francis .20 .50
79 Andy Sisco .20 .50
80 Hideki Matsui .50 1.25
81 Ken Griffey Jr. .75 2.00
82 Nomar Garciaparra .50 1.25
83 Kevin Millwood .20 .50
84 Paul Konerko .20 .50
85 A.J. Burnett .20 .50
86 Mike Piazza .50 1.25
87 Brian Giles .20 .50
88 Johnny Damon .30 .75
89 Jim Thome .30 .75
90 Roger Clemens 1.00 2.50
91 Aaron Rowand .20 .50
92 Rafael Furcal .20 .50
93 Gary Sheffield .20 .50
94 Mike Cameron .20 .50
95 Carlos Delgado .20 .50
96 Jorge Posada .30 .75
97 Denny Bautista .20 .50
98 Mike Maroth .20 .50
99 Brad Radke .20 .50
100 Alex Rodriguez .75 2.00
101 Freddy Garcia .20 .50
102 Oliver Perez .20 .50
103 Jon Lieber .20 .50
104 Melvin Mora .20 .50
105 Travis Hafner .20 .50
106 Alex Rios .20 .50
107 Derek Lowe .20 .50
108 Luis Castillo .20 .50
109 Livan Hernandez .20 .50
110 Tadahito Iguchi .20 .50
111 Shawn Chacon .20 .50
112 Frank Thomas .50 1.25
113 Josh Beckett .20 .50
114 Aubrey Huff .20 .50
115 Derrek Lee .20 .50
116 Chien-Ming Wang .75 2.00
117 Joe Crede .20 .50
118 Torii Hunter .20 .50
119 J.D. Drew .20 .50
120 Troy Glaus .20 .50
121 Sean Casey .20 .50
122 Edgar Renteria .20 .50
123 Craig Wilson .20 .50
124 Adam Eaton .20 .50
125 Jeff Francoeur .50 1.25
126 Bruce Chen .20 .50
127 Cliff Floyd .20 .50
128 Jeremy Reed .20 .50
129 Jake Westbrook .20 .50
130 Wily Mo Pena .20 .50
131 Toby Hall .20 .50
132 David Ortiz .50 1.25
133 David Eckstein .20 .50
134 Brady Clark .20 .50
135 Marcus Giles .20 .50
136 Aaron Hill .20 .50
137 Mark Kotsay .20 .50
138 Carlos Lee .20 .50
139 Roy Oswalt .20 .50
140 Chone Figgins .20 .50
141 Mike Mussina .30 .75
142 Orlando Hernandez .20 .50
143 Magglio Ordonez .20 .50
144 Jim Edmonds .30 .75
145 Bobby Abreu .20 .50
146 Nick Johnson .20 .50
147 Carlos Beltran .20 .50
148 Jhonny Peralta .20 .50
149 Pedro Feliz .20 .50
150 Miguel Tejada .20 .50
151 Luis Gonzalez .20 .50
152 Carl Crawford .20 .50
153 Yadier Molina .20 .50
154 Rich Harden .20 .50
155 Tim Wakefield .20 .50
156 Rickie Weeks .20 .50
157 Johnny Estrada .20 .50
158 Gustavo Chacin .20 .50
159 Dan Johnson .20 .50
160 Willy Taveras .20 .50
161 Garret Anderson .20 .50
162 Randy Johnson .50 1.25
163 Jermaine Dye .20 .50
164 Joe Mauer .30 .75
165 Ervin Santana .20 .50
166 Jeremy Bonderman .20 .50
167 Garrett Atkins .20 .50
168 Manny Ramirez .30 .75
169 Brad Eldred .20 .50
170 Chase Utley .50 1.25
171 Mark Loretta .20 .50
172 John Patterson .20 .50
173 Tom Glavine .30 .75
174 Dontrelle Willis .20 .50
175 Mark Teixeira .30 .75
176 Felix Hernandez .30 .75
177 Cliff Lee .20 .50
178 Jason Schmidt .20 .50
179 Chad Tracy .20 .50
180 Rocco Baldelli .20 .50
181 Aramis Ramirez .20 .50
182 Andy Pettitte .30 .75
183 Mark Mulder .20 .50
184 Geoff Jenkins .20 .50
185 Chipper Jones .50 1.25
186 Vernon Wells .20 .50
187 Bobby Crosby .20 .50
188 Lance Berkman .20 .50
189 Vladimir Guerrero .50 1.25
190 Coco Crisp .20 .50
191 Brad Penny .20 .50
192 Jose Guillen .20 .50
193 Brett Myers .20 .50
194 Miguel Cabrera .30 .75
195 Bartolo Colon .20 .50
196 Craig Biggio .30 .75
197 Tim Hudson .20 .50
198 Mark Prior .30 .75
199 Mark Buehrle .20 .50
200 Barry Bonds 1.00 2.50
201 Anderson Hernandez (RC) .25 .60
202 Jose Capellan (RC) .25 .60
203 Jeremy Accardo RC .25 .60
204 Hanley Ramirez (RC) .60 1.50
205 Matt Capps (RC) .25 .60
206 Jonathan Papelbon (RC) 1.25 3.00
207 Chuck James (RC) .40 1.00
208 Matt Cain (RC) .40 1.00
209 Cole Hamels (RC) 1.00 2.50
210 Jason Botts (RC) .25 .60
211 Lastings Milledge (RC) .40 1.00
212 Conor Jackson (RC) .40 1.00
213 Yusmeiro Petit (RC) .25 .60
214 Alay Soler RC .25 .60
215 Willy Aybar (RC) .25 .60
216 Adam Loewen (RC) .25 .60
217 Justin Verlander (RC) 1.00 2.50
218 Francisco Liriano (RC) .60 1.50
219 Kenji Johjima RC 1.25 3.00
219a Kenji Johjima AU 60.00 120.00
220 Craig Hansen RC 1.00 2.50
221 Prince Fielder AU (RC) 20.00 50.00
222 Josh Barfield AU (RC) 6.00 15.00
223 Fausto Carmona AU (RC) 12.50 30.00
224 James Loney AU (RC) 15.00 40.00

2006 Bowman Chrome Refractors

*REF 1-200: 1.5X TO 4X BASIC
*REF 201-220: 1X TO 2.5X BASIC
1-220 ODDS 1:4 HOB, 1:6 RET
219 AU ODDS 1:5100 HOB, 1:12,432 RET
219 AU PRINT RUN 250 SERIAL #'d CARDS
*REF AU 221-224: .5X TO 1.2X BASIC
221-224 AU ODDS 1:82 HOB, 1:200 RET
221-224 AU PRINT RUN 500 SER.#'d SETS
116 Chien-Ming Wang 6.00 15.00
220 Craig Hansen 3.00 8.00
221 Prince Fielder AU 40.00 80.00
223 Fausto Carmona AU 20.00 50.00
224 James Loney AU 40.00 80.00
219a Kenji Johjima AU/250 30.00 60.00

2006 Bowman Chrome Blue Refractors

*BLUE REF 1-200: 4X TO 10X BASIC
*BLUE REF 201-220: 4X TO 10X BASIC
1-220 ODDS 1:25 HOB, 1:73 RET
219 AU ODDS 1:16,877 HOB, 1:61,760 RET
219 AU PRINT RUN 75 SERIAL #'d CARDS
*BLUE REF AU 221-224: .75X TO 2X BASIC
221-224 AU ODDS 1:266 HOB, 1:890 RET
STATED PRINT RUN 150 SERIAL #'d SETS
116 Chien-Ming Wang 20.00 50.00
224 James Loney AU 50.00 100.00
219a Kenji Johjima AU/75 50.00 100.00

2006 Bowman Chrome Gold Refractors

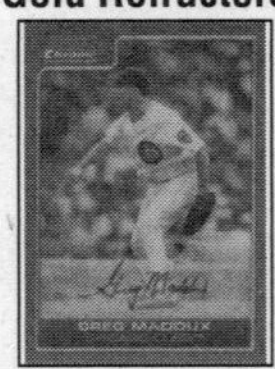

*GOLD REF 1-200: 8X TO 20X BASIC
*GOLD REF 201-220: 6X TO 15X BASIC
1-220 ODDS 1:74 HOB, 1:247 RET
219 AU ODDS 1:26,000 HOB, 1:52,937 RET
*GOLD REF AU 221-224: 2X TO 5X BASIC
221-224 AU ODDS 1:820 HOB, 1:1910 RET
STATED PRINT RUN 50 SERIAL #'d SETS
116 Chien-Ming Wang 150.00 300.00
221 Prince Fielder AU 250.00 400.00
223 Fausto Carmona AU 90.00 150.00
224 James Loney AU 125.00 250.00
219a Kenji Johjima AU 60.00 120.00

2006 Bowman Chrome Orange Refractors

*ORANGE REF 1-200: 15X TO 40X BASIC
1-220 ODDS 1:181 HOB, 1:182 RET
219 AU ODDS 1:62,686 HOB, 1:62,607 RET
221-224 AU ODDS 1:1640 HOB, 1:3820 RET
STATED PRINT RUN 25 SERIAL #'d SETS
NO RC/AU PRICING DUE TO SCARCITY
116 Chien-Ming Wang 150.00 300.00

2006 Bowman Chrome Red Refractors

1-220 ODDS 1:906 HOB, 1:908 RET
219 AU ODDS 1:438,929 HOBBY
221-224 AU ODDS 1:8250 H,1:19,500 R
STATED PRINT RUN 5 SERIAL #'d SETS
NO PRICING DUE TO SCARCITY

2006 Bowman Chrome SuperFractors

1-220 ODDS 1:3350 HOBBY
219 AU ODDS 1:877,608 HOBBY
221-224 AU ODDS 1:35,592 HOBBY
STATED PRINT RUN 1 SERIAL #'d SET
NO PRICING DUE TO SCARCITY

2006 Bowman Chrome X-Fractors

*X-FRACTOR 1-200: 3X TO 8X BASIC
*X-FRACTOR 201-220: 2.5X TO 6X BASIC
1-220 ODDS 1:15 HOB, 1:44 RET
1-220 PRINT RUN 250 SERIAL #'d SETS
219 AU ODDS 1:10,205 HOB 1:28,500 RET
219 AU PRINT RUN 125 SERIAL #'d CARDS
*X-FRAC AU 221-224: .6X TO 1.5X BASIC
221-224 AU ODDS 1:182 HOB, 1:478 RET
221-224 AU PRINT RUN 225 SERIAL #'d SETS
116 Chien-Ming Wang 15.00 40.00
217 Justin Verlander 8.00 20.00
221 Prince Fielder AU 50.00 100.00
223 Fausto Carmona AU 20.00 50.00
224 James Loney AU 40.00 80.00
219a Kenji Johjima AU/125 40.00 80.00

2006 Bowman Chrome Prospects

COMP.SET w/o AU's (220) 75.00 150.00
COMP.SERIES 1 SET (110) 30.00 60.00
COMP.SERIES 2 SET (110) 40.00 80.00
1-110 TWO PER HOBBY PACK
1-110 FOUR PER HTA PACK
111-220 TWO PER HOB/RET PACKS
221-247 AU ODDS 1:27 HOB, 1:65 RET
1-110 PLATE ODDS 1:588 HOB,1:575 HTA
111-220 PLATE ODDS 1:836 HOBBY
221-247 AU PLATES 1: 9000 HOBBY
PLATE PRINT RUN 1 PER COLOR
BLACK-CYAN-MAGENTA-YELLOW ISSUED
NO PLATE PRICING DUE TO SCARCITY
1-110 ISSUED IN BOWMAN PACKS
111-247 ISSUED IN BOW.CHROME PACKS
EXCHANGE DEADLINE 8/31/08
BC1 Alex Gordon 6.00 15.00
BC2 Jonathan George .40 1.00
BC3 Scott Walter .40 1.00
BC4 Brian Holliday .40 1.00
BC5 Ben Copeland .60 1.50
BC6 Bobby Wilson .60 1.50
BC7 Mayker Sandoval .40 1.00
BC8 Alejandro de Aza 1.00 2.50
BC9 David Munoz .40 1.00
BC10 Josh LeBlanc .40 1.00
BC11 Philippe Valiquette .40 1.00
BC12 Edwin Bellorin .60 1.50
BC13 Jason Quarles .40 1.00
BC14 Mark Trumbo 1.00 2.50
BC15 Steve Kelly .40 1.00
BC16 Jamie Hoffman .40 1.00
BC17 Joe Bauserman .40 1.00
BC18 Nick Adenhart 2.00 5.00
BC19 Mike Butia .40 1.00
BC20 Jon Weber .40 1.00
BC21 Luis Valdez .40 1.00
BC22 Rafael Rodriguez .60 1.50
BC23 Wyatt Toregas .60 1.50
BC24 John Vanden Berg .40 1.00
BC25 Mike Connolly .40 1.00
BC26 Mike O'Connor .40 1.00
BC27 Garrett Mock .40 1.00
BC28 Bill Layman .40 1.00
BC29 Luis Pena .40 1.00
BC30 Billy Killian .40 1.00
BC31 Ross Ohlendorf .40 1.00
BC32 Marc Kaiser .40 1.00
BC33 Ryan Costello .40 1.00
BC34 Dale Thayer .40 1.00
BC35 Steve Garrabrants .40 1.00
BC36 Samuel Deduno .40 1.00
BC37 Juan Portes 1.00 2.50
BC38 Javier Martinez .40 1.00
BC39 Clint Sammons .40 1.00
BC40 Andrew Kown .60 1.50
BC41 Matt Tolbert .40 1.00
BC42 Michael Ekstrom .40 1.00
BC43 Shawn Norris .40 1.00
BC44 Diory Hernandez .40 1.00
BC45 Chris Maples .40 1.00
BC46 Aaron Hathaway .40 1.00
BC47 Steven Baker .40 1.00
BC48 Greg Creek .40 1.00
BC49 Collin Mahoney .40 1.00
BC50 Corey Ragsdale .40 1.00
BC51 Ariel Nunez .40 1.00
BC52 Max Ramirez 1.25 3.00
BC53 Eric Rodland .40 1.00
BC54 Dante Brinkley .40 1.00
BC55 Casey Craig .40 1.00
BC56 Ryan Spilborghs .60 1.50
BC57 Fredy Deza .40 1.00
BC58 Jeff Frazier .40 1.00
BC59 Vince Cordova .40 1.00
BC60 Oswaldo Navarro .40 1.00
BC61 Jarod Rine .40 1.00
BC62 Jordan Tata .40 1.00
BC63 Ben Julianel .40 1.00
BC64 Yung-Chi Chen 3.00 8.00
BC65 Carlos Torres .60 1.50
BC66 Juan Francia .40 1.00
BC67 Brett Smith .40 1.00
BC68 Francisco Leandro .40 1.00
BC69 Chris Turner 1.00 2.50
BC70 Matt Joyce .60 1.50
BC71 Sean Jones .40 1.00
BC72 Jose Diaz .40 1.00
BC73 Kevin Ool .40 1.00
BC74 Nate Bumstead .40 1.00
BC75 Omir Santos .40 1.00
BC76 Shawn Riggans .40 1.00
BC77 Ofilio Castro .40 1.00
BC78 Mike Rozier .40 1.00
BC79 Wilkin Ramirez 1.00 2.50
BC80 Yobal Duenas .40 1.00
BC81 Adam Bourassa .40 1.00
BC82 Tony Granadillo .60 1.50
BC83 Brad McCann 1.25 3.00
BC84 Dustin Majewski .40 1.00
BC85 Kelvin Jimenez .40 1.00
BC86 Mark Reed 1.25 3.00
BC87 Asdrubal Cabrera 1.50 4.00
BC88 James Barthmaier .60 1.50
BC89 Brandon Boggs .40 1.00
BC90 Raul Valdez .40 1.00
BC91 Jose Campusano .40 1.00
BC92 Henry Owens .60 1.50
BC93 Tug Hulett .40 1.00
BC94 Nate Gold .60 1.50
BC95 Lee Mitchell .40 1.00
BC96 John Hardy .40 1.00
BC97 Aaron Wideman .40 1.00
BC98 Brandon Roberts .40 1.00
BC99 Lou Santangelo .40 1.00
BC100 Kyle Kendrick 1.25 3.00
BC101 Michael Collins 1.00 2.50
BC102 Camilo Vazquez .40 1.00
BC103 Mark McLemore .40 1.00
BC104 Alexander Peralta .40 1.00
BC105 Josh Whitesell .40 1.00
BC106 Carlos Guevara .40 1.00
BC107 Michael Aubrey .60 1.50
BC108 Brandon Chaves .40 1.00
BC109 Leonard Davis .40 1.00
BC110 Kendry Morales 1.00 2.50
BC111 Koby Clemens 1.25 3.00
BC112 Lance Broadway 1.00 2.50
BC113 Cameron Maybin 5.00 12.00
BC114 Mike Aviles .40 1.00
BC115 Kyle Blanks 1.00 2.50
BC116 Chris Dickerson 1.25 3.00
BC117 Sean Gallagher 1.50 4.00
BC118 Jamar Hill .40 1.00
BC119 Garrett Mock .40 1.00
BC120 Russ Rohlicek .40 1.00
BC121 Clete Thomas .60 1.50
BC122 Elvis Andrus 3.00 8.00
BC123 Brandon Moss .40 1.00
BC124 Mark Holliman .40 1.00
BC125 Jose Tabata 4.00 10.00
BC126 Corey Wimberly 1.00 2.50
BC127 Bobby Wilson .60 1.50
BC128 Edward Mujica .40 1.00
BC129 Hunter Pence 6.00 15.00
BC130 Adam Heether .40 1.00
BC131 Andy Wilson .40 1.00
BC132 Radhames Liz 1.50 4.00
BC133 Garrett Patterson .40 1.00
BC134 Carlos Gomez 4.00 10.00
BC135 Jared Lansford .40 1.00
BC136 Jose Arredondo 1.00 2.50
BC137 Renee Cortez .40 1.00
BC138 Francisco Rosario .40 1.00
BC139 Brian Stokes .40 1.00
BC140 Will Thompson .40 1.00
BC141 Ernesto Frieri .40 1.00
BC142 Jose Mijares .40 1.00
BC143 Jeremy Slayden 1.00 2.50
BC144 Brandon Fahey .40 1.00
BC145 Jason Windsor .40 1.00
BC146 Shawn Nottingham .40 1.00
BC147 Dallas Trahern .40 1.00
BC148 Jon Niese 2.00 5.00
BC149 A.J. Shappi .40 1.00
BC150 Jordan Pals .60 1.50
BC151 Tim Moss .60 1.50
BC152 Stephen Marek .60 1.50
BC153 Mat Gamel 2.50 6.00
BC154 Sean Henn .40 1.00
BC155 Matt Guillory .40 1.00
BC156 Brandon Jones 1.50 4.00
BC157 Gary Galvez .40 1.00
BC158 Shane Lindsay 1.00 2.50
BC159 Jesus Reina .40 1.00
BC160 Lorenzo Cain 2.00 5.00
BC161 Chris Britton .40 1.00
BC162 Yovani Gallardo 3.00 8.00
BC163 Matt Walker .40 1.00
BC164 Shaun Cumberland .40 1.00
BC165 Ryan Patterson 1.00 2.50
BC166 Michael Hollimon .40 1.00
BC167 Eude Brito .40 1.00
BC168 John Bowker .40 1.00
BC169 James Avery .40 1.00
BC170 John Bannister .40 1.00
BC171 Juan Ciriaco .40 1.00
BC172 Manuel Corpas .40 1.00
BC173 Leo Rosales .40 1.00
BC174 Tim Kennelly .40 1.00
BC175 Adam Russell .40 1.00
BC176 Jeremy Hellickson 2.00 5.00
BC177 Ryan Klosterman .40 1.00
BC178 Evan Meek .40 1.00
BC179 Steve Murphy 1.00 2.50
BC180 Scott Feldman .40 1.00
BC181 Pablo Sandoval 1.25 3.00
BC182 Dexter Fowler 1.00 2.50
BC183 Jairo Cuevas .40 1.00
BC184 Andrew Pinckney .60 1.50
BC185 Marino Salas .40 1.00
BC186 Justin Christian .40 1.00
BC187 Ching-Lung Lo 2.00 5.00
BC188 Randy Roth 1.00 2.50
BC189 Andy Sonnanstine 1.00 2.50
BC190 Josh Outman 2.00 5.00
BC191 Yuber Rodriguez .40 1.00
BC192 Hainley Statia 1.00 2.50
BC193 Kevin Estrada .40 1.00
BC194 Jeff Karstens 1.00 2.50
BC195 Corey Coles .40 1.00
BC196 Gustavo Espinoza .40 1.00
BC197 Brian Horwitz .40 1.00
BC198 Landon Jacobsen .40 1.00
BC199 Ben Krosschell .40 1.00
BC200 Jason Jaramillo .40 1.00
BC201 Josh Wilson .40 1.00
BC202 Jason Ray .40 1.00
BC203 Brent Dlugach .40 1.00
BC204 Cesar Jimenez .40 1.00
BC205 Eric Haberer .40 1.00
BC206 Felipe Paulino .40 1.00
BC207 Alcides Escobar .60 1.50
BC208 Jose Ascanio .40 1.00
BC209 Yoel Hernandez .40 1.00
BC210 Geoff Vandel .40 1.00
BC211 Travis Denker 1.00 2.50
BC212 Ramon Alvarado .40 1.00
BC213 Welinson Baez .60 1.50
BC214 Chris Kolkhorst .40 1.00
BC215 Emiliano Fruto .40 1.00
BC216 Luis Cota .40 1.00
BC217 Mark Worrell .40 1.00
BC218 Cla Meredith .60 1.50
BC219 Emmanuel Garcia .60 1.50
BC220 B.J. Szymanski .60 1.50
BC221 Alex Gordon AU 40.00 80.00
BC222 Mark Pawelek AU EXCH 8.00 20.00
BC223 Justin Upton AU 50.00 100.00
BC224 Sean West AU 6.00 15.00
BC225 Tyler Greene AU 6.00 15.00
BC226 Josh Kinney AU 6.00 15.00
BC227 Pedro Lopez AU 6.00 15.00
BC228 Troy Patton AU 8.00 20.00
BC229 Chris Iannetta AU 12.50 30.00
BC230 Jared Wells AU 6.00 15.00
BC231 Brandon Wood AU 8.00 20.00
BC232 Josh Geer AU 6.00 15.00
BC233 Cesar Carrillo AU 6.00 15.00
BC234 Franklin Gutierrez AU 6.00 15.00
BC235 Matt Garza AU 10.00 25.00
BC236 Eli Iorg AU 6.00 15.00
BC237 Trevor Bell AU 6.00 15.00
BC238 Jeff Lyman AU 6.00 15.00
BC239 Jon Lester AU 20.00 50.00
BC240 Kendry Morales AU 10.00 25.00
BC241 J. Brent Cox AU 6.00 15.00
BC242 Jose Bautista AU 6.00 15.00
BC243 Josh Sullivan AU 6.00 15.00
BC244 Brandon Snyder AU 6.00 15.00
BC245 Elvin Puello AU 6.00 15.00
BC246 Henry Sanchez AU EXCH 6.00 15.00
BC247 Jacob Marceaux AU 6.00 15.00

2006 Bowman Chrome Prospects Refractors

*REF 1-110: 1.25X TO 3X BASIC
*REF 111-220: 1.25X TO 3X BASIC
1-110 ODDS 1:36 HOBBY, 1:12 HTA
111-220 ODDS 1:22 HOBBY, 1:81 RETAIL
*REF AU 221-247: .5X TO 1.2X BASIC
221-247 AU ODDS 1:82 HOB, 1:200 RET

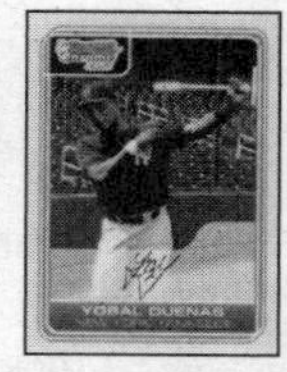

STATED PRINT RUN 500 SERIAL #'d SETS
1-110 ISSUED IN BOWMAN PACKS
111-247 ISSUED IN BOW.CHROME PACKS
EXCHANGE DEADLINE 8/31/08
BC1 Alex Gordon 20.00 50.00
BC8 Alejandro de Aza 8.00 20.00
BC52 Max Ramirez 10.00 25.00
BC64 Yung-Chi Chen 15.00 40.00
BC113 Cameron Maybin 20.00 50.00
BC116 Chris Dickerson 6.00 15.00
BC125 Jose Tabata 3.00 8.00
BC129 Hunter Pence 20.00 50.00
BC134 Carlos Gomez 12.50 30.00
BC153 Mat Gamel 20.00 50.00
BC162 Yovani Gallardo 15.00 40.00
BC181 Pablo Sandoval 6.00 15.00
BC187 Ching-Lung Lo 12.50 30.00
BC221 Alex Gordon AU 100.00 175.00
BC223 Justin Upton AU 100.00 200.00
BC239 Jon Lester AU 30.00 60.00

2006 Bowman Chrome Prospects Blue Refractors

*BLUE REF 1-220: 2.5X TO 6X BASIC
1-110 ODDS 1:118 HOBBY, 1:39 HTA
111-220 ODDS 1:25 HOBBY
*BLUE AU 221-247: .75X TO 2X BASIC
221-247 AU ODDS 1:266 HOB, 1:890 RET
STATED PRINT RUN 150 SERIAL #'d SETS
1-110 ISSUED IN BOWMAN PACKS
111-247 ISSUED IN BOW.CHROME PACKS
EXCHANGE DEADLINE 8/31/08
BC1 Alex Gordon 75.00 150.00
BC8 Alejandro de Aza 15.00 40.00
BC52 Max Ramirez 20.00 50.00
BC64 Yung-Chi Chen 40.00 80.00
BC113 Cameron Maybin 75.00 150.00
BC116 Chris Dickerson 15.00 40.00
BC122 Elvis Andrus 30.00 60.00
BC125 Jose Tabata 75.00 150.00
BC129 Hunter Pence 100.00 150.00
BC134 Carlos Gomez 40.00 80.00
BC153 Mat Gamel 75.00 150.00
BC162 Yovani Gallardo 40.00 80.00
BC181 Pablo Sandoval 15.00 40.00
BC187 Ching-Lung Lo 40.00 80.00
BC221 Alex Gordon AU 250.00 350.00
BC223 Justin Upton AU 250.00 500.00
BC228 Troy Patton AU 20.00 50.00
BC229 Chris Iannetta AU 40.00 80.00
BC239 Jon Lester AU 60.00 120.00

2006 Bowman Chrome Prospects Gold Refractors

*GOLD REF 1-110: 10X TO 25X BASIC
*GOLD REF 111-220: 8X TO 20X BASIC
1-110 ODDS 1:355 HOBBY, 1:116 HTA
111-220 ODDS: 1:74 HOBBY
COMMON AUTO (221-247) 30.00 60.00
221-247 AU ODDS 1:820 HOB, 1:1910 RET
STATED PRINT RUN 50 SERIAL #'d SETS
1-110 ISSUED IN BOWMAN PACKS
111-247 ISSUED IN BOW.CHROME PACKS
EXCHANGE DEADLINE 8/31/08
BC1 Alex Gordon 150.00 300.00
BC8 Alejandro de Aza 40.00 80.00
BC52 Max Ramirez 40.00 80.00
BC64 Yung-Chi Chen 125.00 250.00
BC87 Asdrubal Cabrera 60.00 120.00
BC113 Cameron Maybin 250.00 400.00
BC116 Chris Dickerson 40.00 80.00
BC122 Elvis Andrus 100.00 175.00
BC125 Jose Tabata 250.00 350.00
BC129 Hunter Pence 250.00 400.00
BC134 Carlos Gomez 125.00 200.00
BC153 Mat Gamel 200.00 300.00
BC160 Lorenzo Cain 60.00 120.00
BC162 Yovani Gallardo 60.00 120.00
BC176 Jeremy Hellickson 75.00 150.00
BC181 Pablo Sandoval 40.00 80.00
BC187 Ching-Lung Lo 125.00 200.00
BC221 Alex Gordon AU 600.00 700.00
BC222 Mark Pawelek AU EXCH 50.00 100.00
BC223 Justin Upton AU 500.00 700.00
BC226 Josh Kinney AU 20.00 50.00
BC228 Troy Patton AU 40.00 80.00
BC229 Chris Iannetta AU 75.00 150.00
BC231 Brandon Wood AU 50.00 100.00
BC235 Matt Garza AU 60.00 120.00
BC239 Jon Lester AU 100.00 200.00
BC240 Kendry Morales AU 75.00 150.00

2006 Bowman Chrome Prospects Orange Refractors

1-110 ODDS 1:710 HOBBY, 1:233 HTA
111-220 ODDS 1:181 HOBBY
221-247 AU ODDS 1:1640 HOB, 1:3820 RET
STATED PRINT RUN 25 SERIAL #'d SETS
1-110 ISSUED IN BOWMAN PACKS
111-247 ISSUED IN BOW.CHROME PACKS
NO PRICING DUE TO SCARCITY
EXCHANGE DEADLINE 8/31/08

2006 Bowman Chrome Prospects Red Refractors

1-110 ODDS 1:3000 HOBBY, 1:690 HTA
111-220 ODDS 1:906 HOBBY
221-247 AU ODDS 1:8250 H, 1:19,500 R
STATED PRINT RUN 5 SERIAL #'d SETS
NO PRICING DUE TO SCARCITY
1-110 ISSUED IN BOWMAN PACKS
111-247 ISSUED IN BOW.CHROME PACKS
EXCHANGE DEADLINE 8/31/08

2006 Bowman Chrome Prospects SuperFractors

1-110 ODDS 1:15,425 HOBBY, 1:3373 HTA
111-220 ODDS 1:3350 HOBBY
221-247 AU ODDS 1:35,592 HOBBY
STATED PRINT RUN 1 SERIAL #'d SET
NO PRICING DUE TO SCARCITY
1-110 ISSUED IN BOWMAN PACKS
111-247 ISSUED IN BOW.CHROME PACKS
EXCHANGE DEADLINE 8/31/08

2006 Bowman Chrome Prospects X-Fractors

*X-F 1-220: 1.5X TO 4X BASIC
1-110 ODDS 1:72 HOBBY, 1:23 HTA
111-220 ODDS 1:15 HOBBY
1-220 PRINT RUN 250 SERIAL #'d SETS
*X-F AU 221-247: .6X TO 1.5X BASIC
221-247 AU ODDS 1:182 HOB, 1:478 RET
221-247 AU PRINT RUN 225 SERIAL #'d SETS
1-110 ISSUED IN BOWMAN PACKS
111-247 ISSUED IN BOW.CHROME PACKS
EXCHANGE DEADLINE 8/31/08
BC1 Alex Gordon 40.00 80.00
BC52 Max Ramirez 15.00 40.00
BC64 Yung-Chi Chen 40.00 80.00
BC113 Cameron Maybin 30.00 60.00
BC116 Chris Dickerson 10.00 25.00
BC122 Elvis Andrus 15.00 40.00
BC125 Jose Tabata 30.00 60.00
BC129 Hunter Pence 30.00 60.00
BC153 Mat Gamel 30.00 60.00
BC162 Yovani Gallardo 10.00 25.00
BC181 Pablo Sandoval 10.00 25.00
BC187 Ching-Lung Lo 20.00 50.00
BC221 Alex Gordon AU 150.00 200.00
BC223 Justin Upton AU 125.00 250.00
BC239 Jon Lester AU 40.00 80.00

2006 Bowman Chrome Draft

This 55-card set was issued at a stated rate of one card in every other pack of Bowman Draft Picks. All fifty-five cards in this set feature players who made their major league debut in 2006.

COMPLETE SET (55) 15.00 40.00
COMMON RC (1-55) .40 1.00
APPX. ODDS 1:2 HOBBY, 1:2 RETAIL
ODDS INFO PROVIDED BY BECKETT
OVERALL PLATE ODDS 1:990 HOBBY
PLATE PRINT RUN 1 SET PER COLOR
BLACK-CYAN-MAGENTA-YELLOW ISSUED
NO PLATE PRICING DUE TO SCARCITY
1 Matt Kemp (RC) .60 1.50
2 Taylor Tankersley (RC) .40 1.00
3 Mike Napoli RC 1.00 2.50
4 Brian Bannister (RC) .40 1.00
5 Melky Cabrera (RC) .60 1.50
6 Bill Bray (RC) .40 1.00
7 Brian Anderson (RC) .40 1.00
8 Jered Weaver (RC) 1.25 3.00
9 Chris Duncan (RC) .60 1.50
10 Boof Bonser (RC) .60 1.50
11 Mike Rouse (RC) .40 1.00
12 David Pauley (RC) .40 1.00
13 Russ Martin (RC) .60 1.50
14 Jeremy Sowers (RC) .40 1.00
15 Kevin Reese (RC) .40 1.00
16 John Rheinecker (RC) .40 1.00
17 Tommy Murphy (RC) .40 1.00
18 Sean Marshall (RC) .40 1.00
19 Jason Kubel (RC) .40 1.00
20 Chad Billingsley (RC) .60 1.50
21 Kendry Morales (RC) .60 1.50
22 Jon Lester RC 2.00 5.00
23 Brandon Fahey RC .40 1.00
24 Josh Johnson (RC) .60 1.50
25 Kevin Frandsen (RC) .40 1.00
26 Casey Janssen RC .60 1.50
27 Scott Thorman (RC) .40 1.00
28 Scott Mathieson (RC) .40 1.00
29 Jeremy Hermida (RC) .40 1.00
30 Dustin Nippert (RC) .40 1.00
31 Kevin Thompson (RC) .40 1.00
32 Bobby Livingston (RC) .40 1.00
33 Travis Ishikawa (RC) .40 1.00
34 Jeff Mathis (RC) .40 1.00
35 Charlie Haeger RC .60 1.50
36 Josh Willingham (RC) .40 1.00
37 Taylor Buchholz (RC) .40 1.00
38 Joel Guzman (RC) .40 1.00
39 Zach Jackson (RC) .40 1.00
40 Howie Kendrick (RC) 1.00 2.50
41 T.J. Beam (RC) .40 1.00
42 Ty Taubenheim RC .60 1.50
43 Erick Aybar (RC) .40 1.00
44 Anibal Sanchez (RC) .60 1.50
45 Michael Pelfrey RC 3.00 8.00
46 Shawn Hill (RC) .40 1.00
47 Chris Roberson (RC) .40 1.00
48 Carlos Villanueva RC .40 1.00
49 Andre Ethier (RC) 1.00 2.50
50 Anthony Reyes (RC) .60 1.50
51 Franklin Gutierrez (RC) .40 1.00
52 Angel Guzman (RC) .40 1.00
53 Michael O'Connor RC .40 1.00
54 James Shields RC .40 1.00
55 Nate McLouth (RC) .40 1.00

2006 Bowman Chrome Draft Refractors

*REF: 1.25X TO 3X BASIC
STATED ODDS 1:11 HOBBY, 1:11 RETAIL
3 Mike Napoli 2.00 5.00
8 Jered Weaver 2.50 6.00
22 Jon Lester 4.00 10.00
40 Howie Kendrick 2.00 5.00
45 Michael Pelfrey 8.00 20.00
49 Andre Ethier 2.00 5.00

2006 Bowman Chrome Draft Blue Refractors

*BLUE REF: 3X TO 8X BASIC
STATED ODDS 1:50 HOBBY, 1:94 RETAIL
STATED PRINT RUN 199 SER.#'d SETS
3 Mike Napoli 5.00 12.00
8 Jered Weaver 6.00 15.00
22 Jon Lester 15.00 40.00
40 Howie Kendrick 5.00 12.00
45 Michael Pelfrey 40.00 80.00
49 Andre Ethier 5.00 12.00

2006 Bowman Chrome Draft Gold Refractors

*GOLD REF: 5X TO 12X BASIC
STATED ODDS 1:197 H, 1:388 R
STATED PRINT RUN 50 SER.#'d SETS
3 Mike Napoli 12.50 30.00
5 Melky Cabrera 10.00 25.00
8 Jered Weaver 10.00 25.00
22 Jon Lester 40.00 80.00
30 Dustin Nippert 8.00 20.00
35 Charlie Haeger 10.00 25.00
40 Howie Kendrick 10.00 25.00
41 T.J. Beam 8.00 20.00
42 Ty Taubenheim 8.00 20.00
45 Michael Pelfrey 150.00 250.00
49 Andre Ethier 10.00 25.00
53 Michael O'Connor 6.00 15.00

2006 Bowman Chrome Draft Orange Refractors

STATED ODDS 1:395 HOBBY, 1:770 RETAIL
STATED PRINT RUN 25 SERIAL #'d SETS
NO PRICING DUE TO SCARCITY

2006 Bowman Chrome Draft Red Refractors

STATED ODDS 1:1585 HOBBY
STATED PRINT RUN 5 SERIAL #'d SETS
NO PRICING DUE TO SCARCITY

2006 Bowman Chrome Draft SuperFractors

STATED ODDS 1:7934 HOBBY
STATED PRINT RUN 1 SERIAL #'d SET
NO PRICING DUE TO SCARCITY

2006 Bowman Chrome Draft X-Fractors

*X-F: 2X TO 5X BASIC
STATED ODDS 1:32 H, 1:74 R
STATED PRINT RUN 299 SER.#'d SETS
3 Mike Napoli 3.00 8.00
8 Jered Weaver 4.00 10.00
22 Jon Lester 10.00 25.00
40 Howie Kendrick 3.00 8.00
45 Michael Pelfrey 12.50 30.00
49 Andre Ethier 3.00 8.00

2006 Bowman Chrome Draft Draft Picks

APPX. ODDS 1:1 HOBBY, 1:1 RETAIL
ODDS INFO PROVIDED BY BECKETT
66-90 AU ODDS 1:50 HOB.,1:51 RET.
1-65 PLATE ODDS 1:990 HOBBY
66-90 AU PLATE ODDS 1:13,200 HOBBY
PLATE PRINT RUN 1 SET PER COLOR
BLACK-CYAN-MAGENTA-YELLOW ISSUED
NO PLATE PRICING DUE TO SCARCITY
1 Tyler Colvin 1.25 3.00
2 Chris Marrero 2.50 6.00
3 Hank Conger 1.25 3.00

4 Chris Parmelee 2.50 6.00
5 Jason Place 1.50 4.00
6 Billy Rowell 2.00 5.00
7 Travis Snider 3.00 8.00
8 Colton Willems 1.00 2.50
9 Chase Fontaine .40 1.00
10 Jon Jay .60 1.50
11 Wade Leblanc .40 1.00
12 Justin Masterson 3.00 8.00
13 Gary Daley .40 1.00
14 Justin Edwards .40 1.00
15 Charlie Yarbrough .40 1.00
16 Cyle Hankerd 1.00 2.50
17 Zach McAllister .40 1.00
18 Tyler Robertson .40 1.00
19 Joe Smith .40 1.00
20 Nate Culp .40 1.00
21 John Holdzkom .40 1.00
22 Patrick Bresnehan
23 Chad Lee .40 1.00
24 Ryan Morris .40 1.00
25 D'Arby Myers .60 1.50
26 Garrett Olson
27 Jon Still .40 1.00
28 Brandon Rice .40 1.00
29 Chris Davis 3.00 8.00
30 Zack Daeges .40 1.00
31 Bobby Henson .40 1.00
32 George Kontos .40 1.00
33 Jermaine Mitchell .60 1.50
34 Adam Coe .60 1.50
35 Dustin Richardson .40 1.00
36 Allen Craig .40 1.00
37 Austin McClune .40 1.00
38 Doug Fister .40 1.00
39 Corey Madden .40 1.00
40 Justin Jacobs .40 1.00
41 Jim Negrych .40 1.00
42 Tyler Norrick .40 1.00
43 Adam Davis .40 1.00
44 Brett Logan .40 1.00
45 Brian Omogrosso .40 1.00
46 Kyle Drabek 1.25 3.00
47 Jamie Ortiz 1.00 2.50
48 Alex Presley .40 1.00
49 Terrance Warren .40 1.00
50 David Christensen .60 1.50
51 Helder Velazquez .40 1.00
52 Matt McBride .40 1.00
53 Quintin Berry .40 1.00
54 Michael Eisenberg .40 1.00
55 Dan Garcia .40 1.00
56 Scott Cousins .40 1.00
57 Sean Land .40 1.00
58 Kristopher Medlen .40 1.00
59 Tyler Reves .40 1.00
60 John Shelby .40 1.00
61 Jordan Newton .40 1.00
62 Ricky Orta .40 1.00
63 Jason Donald .40 1.00
64 David Huff .40 1.00
65 Brett Sinkbeil .60 1.50
66 Evan Longoria AU 125.00 225.00
67 Cody Johnson AU 15.00 40.00
68 Kris Johnson AU 6.00 15.00
69 Kasey Kiker AU 10.00 25.00
70 Ronnie Bourquin AU 6.00 15.00
71 Adrian Cardenas AU 15.00 40.00
72 Matt Antonelli AU 20.00 50.00
73 Brooks Brown AU 4.00 10.00
74 Steven Evarts AU 6.00 15.00
75 Joshua Butler AU 4.00 10.00
76 Chad Huffman AU 4.00 10.00
77 Steven Wright AU 4.00 10.00
78 Cory Rasmus AU 6.00 15.00
79 Brad Furnish AU 4.00 10.00
80 Andrew Carpenter AU 8.00 20.00
81 Dustin Evans AU 4.00 10.00
82 Tommy Hickman AU 8.00 20.00
83 Matt Long AU 4.00 10.00
84 Clayton Kershaw AU 40.00 80.00
85 Kyle McCulloch AU 6.00 15.00
86 Pedro Beato AU 10.00 25.00
87 Kyler Burke AU 8.00 20.00
88 Stephen Englund AU 8.00 20.00
89 Michael Felix AU 4.00 10.00
90 Sean Watson AU 4.00 10.00

2006 Bowman Chrome Draft Draft Picks Refractors

*REF 1-65: 1.25X TO 3X BASIC
1-65 ODDS 1:11 HOBBY, 1:11 RETAIL
*REF AU 66-90: .5X TO 1.2X BASIC AU
AU 66-90 ODDS 1:156 HOB, 1:157 RET
66-90 AU PRINT RUN 500 SER.#'d SETS
7 Travis Snider 20.00 50.00
12 Justin Masterson 12.50 30.00
29 Chris Davis 15.00 40.00
66 Evan Longoria AU 150.00 300.00
68 Kris Johnson AU 10.00 25.00
84 Clayton Kershaw AU 60.00 120.00
86 Pedro Beato AU 15.00 40.00

2006 Bowman Chrome Draft Draft Picks Blue Refractors

*BLUE REF 1-65: 5X TO 12X BASIC
1-65 STATED ODDS 1:50 H, 1:94 R
1-65 PRINT RUN 199 SER.#'d SETS
*BLUE AU 66-90: 1.25X TO 3X BASIC AU
66-90 STATED ODDS 1:535 H, 1:535 R
66-90 PRINT RUN 150 SER.#'d SETS
1 Tyler Colvin 20.00 50.00
2 Chris Marrero 60.00 120.00
4 Chris Parmelee 30.00 60.00
5 Jason Place 20.00 50.00
7 Travis Snider 75.00 150.00
10 Jon Jay 15.00 40.00
11 Wade Leblanc 10.00 25.00
12 Justin Masterson 40.00 80.00
16 Cyle Hankerd 20.00 50.00
18 Tyler Robertson 10.00 25.00
25 D'Arby Myers 10.00 25.00
29 Chris Davis 60.00 120.00
32 George Kontos 10.00 25.00
33 Jermaine Mitchell 12.50 30.00
34 Adam Coe 8.00 20.00
46 Kyle Drabek 20.00 50.00
49 Terrance Warren 6.00 15.00
51 Helder Velazquez 8.00 20.00
52 Matt McBride 10.00 25.00
60 John Shelby 10.00 25.00
65 Brett Sinkbeil 8.00 20.00
66 Evan Longoria AU 300.00 400.00
71 Adrian Cardenas AU 75.00 150.00
82 Tommy Hickman AU 40.00 80.00
84 Clayton Kershaw AU 150.00 300.00

2006 Bowman Chrome Draft Draft Picks Gold Refractors

*GOLD REF 1-65: 10X TO 25X BASIC
1-65 STATED ODDS 1:197 H, 1:388 R
66-90 AU ODDS 1:1575 H, 1:1600 R
STATED PRINT RUN 50 SER.#'d SETS
1 Tyler Colvin 60.00 120.00
2 Chris Marrero 150.00 250.00
3 Hank Conger 60.00 120.00
4 Chris Parmelee 90.00 150.00
5 Jason Place 60.00 120.00
6 Billy Rowell 200.00 400.00
7 Travis Snider 250.00 400.00
8 Colton Willems 60.00 120.00
10 Jon Jay 60.00 120.00
12 Justin Masterson 125.00 250.00
16 Cyle Hankerd 60.00 120.00
17 Zach McAllister 12.50 30.00
24 Ryan Morris 12.50 30.00
25 D'Arby Myers 30.00 60.00
27 Jon Still 10.00 25.00
28 Brandon Rice 12.50 30.00
29 Chris Davis 250.00 350.00
32 George Kontos 12.50 30.00
33 Jermaine Mitchell 50.00 100.00
34 Adam Coe 30.00 60.00
37 Austin McClune 15.00 40.00
46 Kyle Drabek 60.00 150.00
50 David Christensen 30.00 60.00
51 Helder Velazquez 12.50 30.00
55 Dan Garcia 15.00 40.00
56 Scott Cousins 12.50 30.00
60 John Shelby 12.50 30.00
65 Brett Sinkbeil 30.00 60.00
66 Evan Longoria AU 600.00 800.00
67 Cody Johnson AU 100.00 200.00
68 Kris Johnson AU 60.00 120.00
69 Kasey Kiker AU 100.00 200.00
70 Ronnie Bourquin AU 60.00 120.00
71 Adrian Cardenas AU 200.00 300.00
72 Matt Antonelli AU 250.00 300.00
73 Brooks Brown AU 40.00 80.00
74 Steven Evarts AU 60.00 120.00
75 Joshua Butler AU 40.00 80.00
77 Steven Wright AU 40.00 80.00
78 Cory Rasmus AU 75.00 150.00
79 Brad Furnish AU 30.00 60.00
80 Andrew Carpenter AU 40.00 80.00
81 Dustin Evans AU 30.00 60.00
82 Tommy Hickman AU 100.00 200.00
83 Matt Long AU 30.00 60.00
84 Clayton Kershaw AU 400.00 700.00
85 Kyle McCulloch AU 60.00 120.00
86 Pedro Beato AU 75.00 150.00
87 Kyler Burke AU 60.00 120.00
88 Stephen Englund AU 75.00 150.00
89 Michael Felix AU 50.00 100.00
90 Sean Watson AU 30.00 60.00

2006 Bowman Chrome Draft Draft Picks Orange Refractors

1-65 STATD ODDS 1:395 HOB.,1:770 RET.
66-90 AU ODDS 1:3232 HOB.,1:3232 RET.

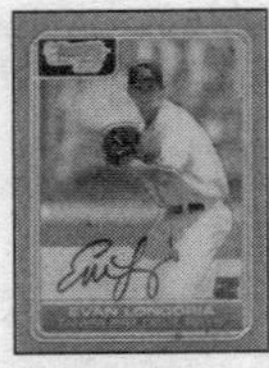

STATED PRINT RUN 25 SERIAL #'d SETS
NO PRICING DUE TO SCARCITY

2006 Bowman Chrome Draft Draft Picks Red Refractors

1-65 ODDS 1:1585 HOBBY
66-90 AU ODDS 1:13,166 HOBBY
STATED PRINT RUN 5 SERIAL #'d SETS
NO PRICING DUE TO SCARCITY

2006 Bowman Chrome Draft Draft Picks SuperFractors

1-65 STATED ODDS 1:7934 HOBBY
66-90 AU STATED ODDS 53,812 HOBBY
STATED PRINT RUN 1 SERIAL #'d SET
NO PRICING DUE TO SCARCITY

2006 Bowman Chrome Draft Draft Picks X-Fractors

*X-F 1-65: 2X TO 5X BASIC
1-65 STATED ODDS 1:32 H, 1:74 R
1-65 PRINT RUN 299 SER.#'d SETS
*X-F AU 66-90: .75X TO 2X BASIC
66-90 AU STATED ODDS 1:351 H, 1:353 R
66-90 AU PRINT RUN 225 SER.#'d SETS

1 Tyler Colvin	10.00	25.00
2 Chris Marrero	40.00	80.00
6 Billy Rowell	20.00	50.00
7 Travis Snider	30.00	60.00
12 Justin Masterson	15.00	40.00
16 Cyle Hankerd	8.00	20.00
29 Chris Davis	20.00	50.00
46 Kyle Drabek	8.00	20.00
50 David Christensen	6.00	15.00
66 Evan Longoria AU	250.00	350.00
67 Cody Johnson AU	30.00	60.00
68 Kris Johnson AU	15.00	40.00
71 Adrian Cardenas AU	30.00	60.00
82 Tommy Hickman AU	20.00	50.00
84 Clayton Kershaw AU	90.00	150.00

2006 Bowman Chrome Draft Future's Game Prospects

COMPLETE SET (45) 10.00 25.00
APPX. ODDS 1:2 HOBBY, 1:2 RETAIL
ODDS INFO PROVIDED BY BECKETT
OVERALL PLATE ODDS 1:990 HOBBY
PLATE PRINT RUN 1 SET PER COLOR
BLACK-CYAN-MAGENTA-YELLOW ISSUED
NO PLATE PRICING DUE TO SCARCITY

1 Nick Adenhart	1.00	2.50
2 Joel Guzman	.40	1.00
3 Ryan Braun	1.50	4.00
4 Carlos Carrasco	.60	1.50
5 Neil Walker	.40	1.00
6 Pablo Sandoval	.40	1.00
7 Gio Gonzalez	.60	1.50
8 Joey Votto	.40	1.00
9 Luis Cruz	.40	1.00
10 Nolan Reimold	.40	1.00
11 Juan Salas	.40	1.00
12 Josh Fields	.40	1.00
13 Yovani Gallardo	1.00	2.50
14 Radhames Liz	1.00	2.50
15 Eric Patterson	.40	1.00
16 Cameron Maybin	1.25	3.00
17 Edgar Martinez	.40	1.00
18 Hunter Pence	1.50	4.00
19 Philip Hughes	1.00	2.50
20 Trent Oeltjen	.40	1.00
21 Nick Pereira	.40	1.00
22 Wladimir Balentien	.40	1.00
23 Stephen Drew	1.00	2.50
24 Davis Romero	.40	1.00
25 Joe Koshansky	.40	1.00
26 Chin Lung Hu	1.25	3.00
27 Jason Hirsh	.40	1.00
28 Jose Tabata	1.25	3.00
29 Eric Hurley	.40	1.00
30 Yung Chi Chen	1.25	3.00
31 Howie Kendrick	1.00	2.50
32 Humberto Sanchez	.40	1.00
33 Alex Gordon	2.50	6.00
34 Yunel Escobar	.40	1.00
35 Travis Buck	.40	1.00
36 Billy Butler	1.00	2.50
37 Homer Bailey	1.00	2.50
38 George Kottaras	.40	1.00
39 Kurt Suzuki	.40	1.00
40 Joaquin Arias	.40	1.00
41 Matt Lindstrom	.40	1.00
42 Sean Smith	.40	1.00
43 Carlos Gonzalez	.40	1.00
44 Jaime Garcia	.60	1.50
45 Jose Garcia	.40	1.00

2006 Bowman Chrome Draft Future's Game Prospects Refractors

*REF: .75X TO 2X BASIC
STATED ODDS 1:11 HOBBY, 1:11 RETAIL

3 Ryan Braun	10.00	25.00
13 Yovani Gallardo	6.00	15.00
16 Cameron Maybin	5.00	12.00
18 Hunter Pence	6.00	15.00
26 Chin Lung Hu	5.00	12.00
28 Jose Tabata	3.00	8.00
30 Yung Chi Chen	6.00	15.00
33 Alex Gordon	10.00	25.00

2006 Bowman Chrome Draft Future's Game Prospects Blue Refractors

*BLUE REF: 1.5X TO 4X BASIC
STATED ODDS 1:50 HOBBY, 1:94 RETAIL
STATED PRINT RUN 199 SER.#'d SETS

3 Ryan Braun	20.00	50.00
13 Yovani Gallardo	15.00	40.00
16 Cameron Maybin	10.00	25.00
18 Hunter Pence	20.00	50.00
26 Chin Lung Hu	20.00	50.00
28 Jose Tabata	10.00	25.00
30 Yung Chi Chen	30.00	60.00
33 Alex Gordon	20.00	50.00
44 Jaime Garcia	6.00	15.00

2006 Bowman Chrome Draft Future's Game Prospects Gold Refractors

*GOLD REF: 4X TO 10X BASIC
STATED ODDS 1:197 H, 1:388 R
STATED PRINT RUN 50 SER.#'d SETS

1 Nick Adenhart	12.50	30.00
3 Ryan Braun	40.00	80.00
4 Carlos Carrasco	8.00	20.00
9 Luis Cruz	10.00	25.00
12 Josh Fields	6.00	15.00
13 Yovani Gallardo	30.00	60.00
16 Cameron Maybin	40.00	80.00
18 Hunter Pence	100.00	150.00
19 Philip Hughes	20.00	50.00
26 Chin Lung Hu	75.00	150.00
28 Jose Tabata	40.00	80.00
30 Yung Chi Chen	100.00	175.00
33 Alex Gordon	60.00	120.00
35 Travis Buck	6.00	15.00
44 Jaime Garcia	30.00	60.00

2006 Bowman Chrome Draft Future's Game Prospects Orange Refractors

STATED ODDS 1:395 HOBBY, 1:770 RETAIL
STATED PRINT RUN 25 SERIAL #'d SETS
NO PRICING DUE TO SCARCITY

2006 Bowman Chrome Draft Future's Game Prospects Red Refractors

STATED ODDS 1:1585 HOBBY
STATED PRINT RUN 5 SERIAL #'d SETS
NO PRICING DUE TO SCARCITY

2006 Bowman Chrome Draft Future's Game Prospects SuperFractors

STATED ODDS 1:7934 HOBBY
STATED PRINT RUN 1 SERIAL #'d SET
NO PRICING DUE TO SCARCITY

2006 Bowman Chrome Draft Future's Game Prospects X-Fractors

*X-F: 1.25X TO 3X BASIC
STATED ODDS 1:32 H, 1:74 R
STATED PRINT RUN 299 SER.#'d SETS

3 Ryan Braun	12.50	30.00
13 Yovani Gallardo	10.00	25.00
16 Cameron Maybin	6.00	15.00
18 Hunter Pence	10.00	25.00
19 Philip Hughes	3.00	8.00
26 Chin Lung Hu	12.50	30.00
28 Jose Tabata	6.00	15.00
30 Yung Chi Chen	15.00	40.00
33 Alex Gordon	12.50	30.00

2007 Bowman Chrome

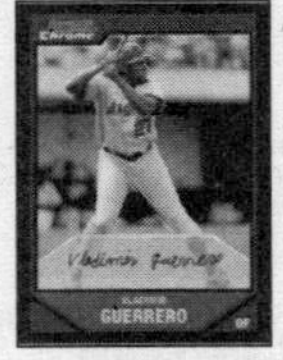

This 220-card set was released in August, 2007. The set was issued through both hobby and retail channels. The hobby version was issued on in standard (no HTA) packs and those four-card packs with an $4 SRP were issued 18 packs per box and 12 boxes per case. Cards numbered 1-190 feature veterans while cards 191-220 honored 2007 rookies.

COMPLETE SET (220) 30.00 60.00
COMMON CARD (1-190) .20 .50
COMMON ROOKIE (191-220) .30 .75
1-220 PLATE ODDS 1:1054 HOBBY
PLATE PRINT RUN 1 SET PER COLOR
BLACK-CYAN-MAGENTA-YELLOW ISSUED
NO PLATE PRICING DUE TO SCARCITY

1 Hanley Ramirez	.30	.75
2 Justin Verlander	.50	1.25
3 Ryan Zimmerman	.50	1.25
4 Jered Weaver	.30	.75
5 Stephen Drew	.30	.75
6 Jonathan Papelbon	.50	1.25
7 Melky Cabrera	.20	.50
8 Francisco Liriano	.50	1.25
9 Prince Fielder	.50	1.25
10 Dan Uggla	.30	.75
11 Jeremy Sowers	.20	.50
12 Carlos Quentin	.20	.50
13 Chuck James	.20	.50
14 Andre Ethier	.30	.75
15 Cole Hamels	.50	1.25
16 Kenji Johjima	.50	1.25
17 Chad Billingsley	.20	.50
18 Ian Kinsler	.20	.50
19 Jason Hirsh	.20	.50
20 Nick Markakis	.30	.75
21 Jeremy Hermida	.20	.50
22 Ryan Shealy	.20	.50
23 Scott Olsen	.20	.50
24 Russell Martin	.20	.50
25 Conor Jackson	.20	.50
26 Erik Bedard	.20	.50
27 Brian McCann	.20	.50
28 Michael Barrett	.20	.50
29 Brandon Phillips	.20	.50
30 Garrett Atkins	.20	.50
31 Freddy Garcia	.20	.50
32 Mark Loretta	.20	.50
33 Craig Biggio	.30	.75
34 Jeremy Bonderman	.20	.50
35 Johan Santana	.30	.75
36 Jorge Posada	.30	.75
37 Victor Martinez	.20	.50
38 Carlos Delgado	.20	.50
39 Gary Matthews Jr.	.20	.50
40 Mike Cameron	.20	.50
41 Adrian Beltre	.20	.50
42 Freddy Sanchez	.20	.50
43 Austin Kearns	.20	.50
44 Mark Buehrle	.20	.50
45 Miguel Cabrera	.30	.75
46 Josh Beckett	.30	.75
47 Chone Figgins	.20	.50
48 Edgar Renteria	.20	.50
49 Derek Lowe	.20	.50
50 Ryan Howard	.75	2.00
51 Shawn Green	.20	.50
52 Jason Giambi	.20	.50
53 Ervin Santana	.20	.50
54 Aaron Hill	.20	.50
55 Roy Oswalt	.20	.50
56 Dan Haren	.20	.50
57 Jose Vidro	.20	.50
58 Kevin Millwood	.20	.50
59 Jim Edmonds	.30	.75
60 Carl Crawford	.20	.50
61 Randy Wolf	.20	.50
62 Paul LoDuca	.20	.50
63 Johnny Estrada	.20	.50
64 Brian Roberts	.20	.50
65 Manny Ramirez	.30	.75
66 Jose Contreras	.20	.50
67 Josh Barfield	.20	.50
68 Juan Pierre	.20	.50
69 David DeJesus	.20	.50
70 Gary Sheffield	.20	.50
71 Michael Young	.20	.50
72 Randy Johnson	.50	1.25
73 Rickie Weeks	.20	.50
74 Brian Giles	.20	.50
75 Ichiro Suzuki	.75	2.00
76 Nick Swisher	.20	.50
77 Justin Morneau	.20	.50
78 Scott Kazmir	.30	.75
79 Lyle Overbay	.20	.50
80 Alfonso Soriano	.20	.50
81 Brandon Webb	.20	.50
82 Joe Crede	.20	.50
83 Corey Patterson	.20	.50
84 Kenny Rogers	.20	.50
85 Ken Griffey Jr.	.75	2.00
86 Cliff Lee	.20	.50
87 Mike Lowell	.20	.50
88 Marcus Giles	.20	.50
89 Orlando Cabrera	.20	.50
90 Derek Jeter	1.25	3.00
91 Ramon Hernandez	.20	.50
92 Carlos Guillen	.20	.50
93 Bill Hall	.20	.50
94 Michael Cuddyer	.20	.50
95 Miguel Tejada	.20	.50
96 Todd Helton	.30	.75
97 C.C. Sabathia	.20	.50
98 Tadahito Iguchi	.20	.50
99 Jose Reyes	.50	1.25
100 David Wright	.75	2.00
101 Barry Zito	.20	.50
102 Jake Peavy	.20	.50
103 Richie Sexson	.20	.50
104 A.J. Burnett	.20	.50
105 Eric Chavez	.20	.50
106 Vernon Wells	.20	.50
107 Grady Sizemore	.30	.75
108 Bronson Arroyo	.20	.50
109 Mike Mussina	.30	.75
110 Magglio Ordonez	.20	.50
111 Anibal Sanchez	.20	.50
112 Jeff Francoeur	.50	1.25
113 Kevin Youkilis	.20	.50
114 Aubrey Huff	.20	.50
115 Carlos Zambrano	.20	.50
116 Mark Teahen	.20	.50
117 Mark Mulder	.20	.50
118 Pedro Martinez	.30	.75
119 Hideki Matsui	.50	1.25
120 Mike Piazza	.50	1.25
121 Jason Schmidt	.20	.50
122 Greg Maddux	.75	2.00
123 Joe Blanton	.20	.50
124 Chris Carpenter	.20	.50
125 David Ortiz	.50	1.25
126 Alex Rios	.20	.50
127 Nick Johnson	.20	.50
128 Carlos Lee	.20	.50
129 Pat Burrell	.20	.50
130 Ben Sheets	.20	.50
131 Derrek Lee	.20	.50
132 Adam Dunn	.20	.50
133 Jermaine Dye	.20	.50
134 Curt Schilling	.30	.75
135 Chad Tracy	.20	.50
136 Vladimir Guerrero	.50	1.25
137 Melvin Mora	.20	.50
138 John Smoltz	.30	.75
139 Craig Monroe	.20	.50
140 Dontrelle Willis	.20	.50
141 Jeff Francis	.20	.50
142 Chipper Jones	.50	1.25
143 Frank Thomas	.50	1.25
144 Brett Myers	.20	.50
145 Tom Glavine	.30	.75
146 Robinson Cano	.30	.75
147 Jeff Kent	.20	.50
148 Scott Rolen	.30	.75
149 Roy Halladay	.20	.50
150 Joe Mauer	.30	.75
151 Bobby Abreu	.20	.50
152 Matt Cain	.30	.75
153 Hank Blalock	.20	.50
154 Chris Young	.20	.50
155 Jake Westbrook	.20	.50
156 Javier Vazquez	.20	.50
157 Garret Anderson	.20	.50
158 Aramis Ramirez	.20	.50
159 Mark Kotsay	.20	.50
160 Matt Kemp	.20	.50
161 Adrian Gonzalez	.20	.50
162 Felix Hernandez	.30	.75
163 David Eckstein	.20	.50
164 Curtis Granderson	.20	.50
165 Paul Konerko	.20	.50
166 Alex Rodriguez	.75	2.00
167 Tim Hudson	.20	.50
168 J.D. Drew	.20	.50
169 Chien-Ming Wang	.75	2.00
170 Jimmy Rollins	.20	.50
171 Matt Morris	.20	.50
172 Raul Ibanez	.20	.50
173 Mark Teixeira	.30	.75
174 Ted Lilly	.20	.50
175 Albert Pujols	1.00	2.50
176 Carlos Beltran	.20	.50
177 Lance Berkman	.20	.50
178 Ivan Rodriguez	.30	.75
179 Torii Hunter	.20	.50
180 Johnny Damon	.30	.75
181 Chase Utley	.50	1.25
182 Jason Bay	.20	.50
183 Jeff Weaver	.20	.50
184 Troy Glaus	.20	.50
185 Rocco Baldelli	.20	.50
186 Rafael Furcal	.20	.50
187 Jim Thome	.30	.75
188 Travis Hafner	.20	.50
189 Matt Holliday	.50	1.25
190 Andruw Jones	.30	.75
191 Andrew Miller RC	2.00	5.00
192 Ryan Braun RC	.30	.75
193 Oswaldo Navarro RC	.30	.75
194 Mike Rabelo RC	.30	.75
195 Delwyn Young (RC)	.30	.75
196 Miguel Montero (RC)	.30	.75
197 Matt Lindstrom (RC)	.30	.75
198 Josh Hamilton (RC)	.75	2.00
199 Elijah Dukes RC	.50	1.25
200 Sean Henn (RC)	.30	.75
201 Delmon Young (RC)	.50	1.25
202 Alexi Casilla RC	.50	1.25
203 Hunter Pence (RC)	1.50	4.00
204 Jeff Baker (RC)	.30	.75
205 Hector Gimenez (RC)	.30	.75
206 Ubaldo Jimenez (RC)	.30	.75
207 Adam Lind (RC)	.30	.75
208 Joaquin Arias (RC)	.30	.75
209 David Murphy (RC)	.30	.75
210 Daisuke Matsuzaka RC	3.00	8.00
211 Jerry Owens (RC)	.30	.75
212 Ryan Sweeney (RC)	.30	.75
213 Kei Igawa RC	.75	2.00
214 Mitch Maier RC	.30	.75
215 Philip Humber (RC)	.30	.75
216 Troy Tulowitzki (RC)	.75	2.00
217 Tim Lincecum RC	4.00	10.00
218 Michael Bourn (RC)	.30	.75
219 Hideki Okajima RC	1.50	4.00
220 Josh Fields (RC)	.30	.75

2007 Bowman Chrome Refractors

*REF 1-190: 1.25X TO 3X BASIC
*REF 191-220: .75X TO 2X BASIC
1-220 ODDS 1:4 HOBBY, 1:6 RETAIL

217 Tim Lincecum	6.00	15.00

2007 Bowman Chrome Blue Refractors

*BLUE REF 1-190: 3X TO 8X BASIC
*BLUE REF 191-220: 2X TO 5X BASIC
1-220 ODDS 1:30 HOBBY, 1:205 RETAIL
STATED PRINT RUN 150 SERIAL #'d SETS

169 Chien-Ming Wang	10.00	25.00
210 Daisuke Matsuzaka	20.00	50.00
217 Tim Lincecum	30.00	60.00

2007 Bowman Chrome Gold Refractors

*GOLD REF 1-190: 8X TO 20X BASIC
*GOLD REF 191-220: 5X TO 12X BASIC
1-220 ODDS 1:88 HOBBY, 1:615 RETAIL
STATED PRINT RUN 50 SERIAL #'d SETS

90 Derek Jeter	15.00	40.00
169 Chien-Ming Wang	50.00	80.00
191 Andrew Miller	50.00	100.00
202 Alexi Casilla	10.00	25.00
203 Hunter Pence	20.00	50.00
210 Daisuke Matsuzaka	75.00	150.00
213 Kei Igawa	12.50	30.00
217 Tim Lincecum	100.00	200.00
219 Hideki Okajima	15.00	40.00

2007 Bowman Chrome Orange Refractors

*ORANGE REF 1-190: 10X TO 25X BASIC
1-220 ODDS 1:176 HOBBY, 1:1220 RETAIL
STATED PRINT RUN 25 SERIAL #'d SETS
NO RC 191-220 PRICING DUE TO SCARCITY

75 Ichiro Suzuki	40.00	80.00
85 Ken Griffey Jr.	40.00	80.00
169 Chien-Ming Wang	60.00	120.00

2007 Bowman Chrome Red Refractors

1-220 ODDS 1:882 HOBBY, 1:6000 RETAIL
STATED PRINT RUN 5 SERIAL #'d SETS
NO PRICING DUE TO SCARCITY

2007 Bowman Chrome SuperFractors

1-220 ODDS 1:4218 HOBBY
STATED PRINT RUN 1 SERIAL #'d SET
NO PRICING DUE TO SCARCITY

2007 Bowman Chrome X-Fractors

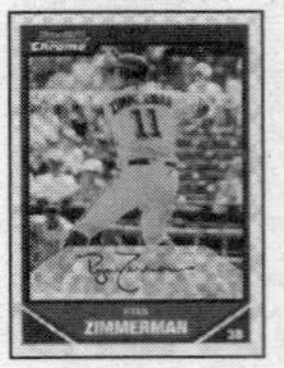

*X-FRACTOR 1-190: 2.5X TO 6X BASIC
*X-FRACTOR 191-220: 1.5X TO 4X BASIC
1-220 ODDS 1:18 HOBBY, 1:123 RETAIL
STATED PRINT RUN 250 SER.#'d SETS

169 Chien-Ming Wang	6.00	15.00
210 Daisuke Matsuzaka	12.50	30.00
217 Tim Lincecum	15.00	40.00

2007 Bowman Chrome Prospects

COMP.SET w/o AU's (220)	40.00	100.00
COMP.SERIES 1 SET (110)	20.00	50.00
COMP.SERIES 2 SET (110)	20.00	50.00

COMMON AUTO (221-256) 3.00 8.00
AU MINORS 4.00 10.00
221-256 AU ODDS 1:29 HOB, 1:59 RET
1-110 PLATE ODDS 1:1468 H, 1:212 HTA
111-220 PLATE ODDS 1:1054 HOBBY
221-256 AU PLATE ODDS 1:9668 HOBBY
PLATE PRINT RUN 1 SET PER COLOR
BLACK-CYAN-MAGENTA-YELLOW ISSUED
NO PLATE PRICING DUE TO SCARCITY
1-110 ISSUED IN BOWMAN PACKS
111-256 ISSUED IN BOW.CHROME PACKS
EXCHANGE DEADLINE 8/31/2009
BC1 Cooper Brannon .30 .75
BC2 Jason Taylor .50 1.25
BC3 Shawn O'Malley .30 .75
BC4 Robert Alcombrack .30 .75
BC5 Dellin Betances 1.00 2.50
BC6 Jeremy Papelbon .30 .75
BC7 Adam Carr .30 .75
BC8 Matthew Clarkson .30 .75
BC9 Darin McDonald .30 .75
BC10 Brandon Rice .30 .75
BC11 Matthew Sweeney 1.00 2.50
BC12 Scott Deal .30 .75
BC13 Brennan Boesch .30 .75
BC14 Scott Taylor .30 .75
BC15 Michael Brantley .75 2.00
BC16 Yahmed Yema .30 .75
BC17 Brandon Morrow .75 2.00
BC18 Cole Garner .30 .75
BC19 Erik Lis .50 1.25
BC20 Lucas French .30 .75
BC21 Aaron Cunningham 1.00 2.50
BC22 Ryan Schreppel .30 .75
BC23 Kevin Russo .30 .75
BC24 Yohan Pino .50 1.25
BC25 Michael Sullivan .30 .75
BC26 Trey Shields .30 .75
BC27 Daniel Matienzo .30 .75
BC28 Chuck Lofgren .75 2.00
BC29 Gerrit Simpson .30 .75
BC30 David Haehnel .30 .75
BC31 Marvin Lowrance .30 .75
BC32 Kevin Ardoin .30 .75
BC33 Edwin Maysonet .30 .75
BC34 Derek Griffith .30 .75
BC35 Sam Fuld .75 2.00
BC36 Chase Wright .75 2.00
BC37 Brandon Roberts .30 .75
BC38 Kyle Aselton .30 .75
BC39 Steven Sollmann .30 .75
BC40 Mike Devaney .30 .75
BC41 Charlie Fermaint .30 .75
BC42 Jesse Litsch .50 1.25
BC43 Bryan Hansen .30 .75
BC44 Ramon Garcia .30 .75
BC45 John Otness .30 .75
BC46 Trey Hearne .30 .75
BC47 Habelito Hernandez .30 .75
BC48 Edgar Garcia .30 .75
BC49 Seth Fortenberry .30 .75
BC50 Reid Brignac .75 2.00
BC51 Derek Rodriguez .30 .75
BC52 Ervin Alcantara .30 .75
BC53 Thomas Hottovy .30 .75
BC54 Jesus Flores .30 .75
BC55 Matt Palmer .30 .75
BC56 Brian Henderson .30 .75
BC57 John Gragg .30 .75
BC58 Jay Garthwaite .30 .75
BC59 Esmerling Vasquez .30 .75
BC60 Gilberto Mejia .30 .75
BC61 Aaron Jensen .30 .75
BC62 Cedric Brooks .30 .75
BC63 Brandon Mann .30 .75
BC64 Myron Leslie .30 .75
BC65 Ray Aguilar .30 .75
BC66 Jesus Guzman .50 1.25
BC67 Sean Thompson .30 .75
BC68 Jarrett Hoffpauir .30 .75
BC69 Matt Goodson .30 .75
BC70 Neal Musser .30 .75
BC71 Tony Abreu .75 2.00
BC72 Tony Peguero .30 .75
BC73 Michael Bertram .30 .75
BC74 Randy Wells .30 .75
BC75 Bradley Davis .30 .75
BC76 Jay Sawatski .30 .75
BC77 Vic Butler .30 .75
BC78 Jose Oyervidez .30 .75
BC79 Doug Deeds .30 .75
BC80 Dan Dement .30 .75
BC81 Spike Lundberg .30 .75
BC82 Ricardo Nanita .30 .75
BC83 Brad Knox .30 .75
BC84 Will Venable .50 1.25
BC85 Greg Smith .30 .75
BC86 Pedro Powell .30 .75
BC87 Gabriel Medina .30 .75
BC88 Duke Sardinha .30 .75
BC89 Mike Madsen .30 .75
BC90 Rayner Bautista .30 .75
BC91 T.J. Nall .30 .75
BC92 Neil Sellers .30 .75
BC93 Andrew Dobies .30 .75
BC94 Leo Daigle .30 .75
BC95 Brian Duensing .30 .75
BC96 Vincent Blue .30 .75
BC97 Fernando Rodriguez .30 .75
BC98 Derin McMains .30 .75
BC99 Adam Bass .30 .75
BC100 Justin Ruggiano .30 .75
BC101 Jared Burton .30 .75
BC102 Mike Parisi .30 .75
BC103 Aaron Peel .30 .75
BC104 Evan Englebrook .30 .75
BC105 Sendy Vasquez .30 .75
BC106 Desmond Jennings 1.25 3.00
BC107 Clay Harris .30 .75
BC108 Cody Strait .30 .75
BC109 Ryan Mullins .30 .75
BC110 Ryan Webb .30 .75
BC111 Mike Carp .50 1.25
BC112 Gregory Porter .30 .75
BC113 Joe Ness .30 .75
BC114 Matt Camp .30 .75
BC115 Carlos Fisher .30 .75
BC116 Bryan Bass .30 .75
BC117 Jeff Baisley .50 1.25
BC118 Burke Badenhop .50 1.25
BC119 Grant Psomas .30 .75
BC120 Eric Young Jr. .50 1.25
BC121 Henry Rodriguez .75 2.00
BC122 Carlos Fernandez-Oliva .50 1.25
BC123 Chris Errecart .50 1.25
BC124 Brandon Hynick 1.25 3.00
BC125 Jose Constanza .30 .75
BC126 Steve Delabar .30 .75
BC127 Raul Barron .30 .75
BC128 Nick DeBarr .30 .75
BC129 Reegie Corona .50 1.25
BC130 Thomas Fairchild .30 .75
BC131 Bryan Byrne .30 .75
BC132 Kurt Mertins .30 .75
BC133 Erik Averill .30 .75
BC134 Matt Young .30 .75
BC135 Ryan Rogowski .30 .75
BC136 Andrew Bailey .75 2.00
BC137 Jonathan Van Every .30 .75
BC138 Scott Shoemaker .30 .75
BC139 Steve Singleton .30 .75
BC140 Mitch Atkins .30 .75
BC141 Robert Rohrbaugh .50 1.25
BC142 Ole Sheldon .30 .75
BC143 Adam Ricks .30 .75
BC144 Daniel Mayora .75 2.00
BC145 Johnny Cueto 3.00 8.00
BC146 Jim Fasano .30 .75
BC147 Jared Goedert .75 2.00
BC148 Jonathan Ash .30 .75
BC149 Derek Miller .50 1.25
BC150 Juan Miranda .50 1.25
BC151 J.R. Mathes .30 .75
BC152 Craig Cooper .50 1.25
BC153 Drew Locke .30 .75
BC154 Michael MacDonald .30 .75
BC155 Ryan Norwood .30 .75
BC156 Tony Butler 1.25 3.00
BC157 Pat Dobson .30 .75
BC158 Cody Ehlers .30 .75
BC159 Dan Fournier .30 .75
BC160 Joe Gaetti .30 .75
BC161 Mark Wagner .50 1.25
BC162 Tommy Hanson 1.50 4.00
BC163 Sharlon Schoop .30 .75
BC164 Woods Fines .30 .75
BC165 Chad Boyd .30 .75
BC166 Kala Kaaihue .75 2.00
BC167 Chris Salamida .30 .75
BC168 Brendan Katin .30 .75
BC169 Terrance Blunt .30 .75
BC170 Tobi Stoner .30 .75
BC171 Phil Coke .75 2.00
BC172 O.D. Gonzalez .30 .75
BC173 Christopher Cody .30 .75
BC174 Cedric Hunter .75 2.00
BC175 Whit Robbins .30 .75
BC176 Chris Begg .30 .75
BC177 Nathan Southard .30 .75
BC178 Dan Brauer .30 .75
BC179 Jared Keel .30 .75
BC180 Chance Douglass .30 .75
BC181 Daniel Murphy 2.50 6.00
BC182 Anthony Hatch .30 .75
BC183 Justin Byler .30 .75
BC184 Scott Lewis .75 2.00
BC185 Andrew Fie .30 .75
BC186 Chorye Spoone .50 1.25
BC187 Cole Bruce .30 .75
BC188 Adam Cowart .75 2.00
BC189 Chris Nowak .30 .75
BC190 Gorkys Hernandez .75 2.00
BC191 Devin Ivany .30 .75
BC192 Jordan Smith .30 .75
BC193 Philip Britton .30 .75
BC194 Cole Gillespie .50 1.25
BC195 Brett Anderson 1.00 2.50
BC196 Joe Mather .30 .75
BC197 Eddie Degerman .30 .75
BC198 Ronald Prettyman .30 .75
BC199 Patrick Reilly .30 .75
BC200 Tyler Clippard .50 1.25
BC201 Nick Van Stratten .30 .75
BC202 Todd Redmond .30 .75
BC203 Michael Martinez .30 .75
BC204 Alberto Bastardo .30 .75
BC205 Vasili Spanos .30 .75
BC206 Shane Benson .30 .75
BC207 Brent Johnson .30 .75
BC208 Brett Campbell .30 .75
BC209 Dustin Martin .30 .75
BC210 Chris Carter 1.25 3.00
BC211 Alfred Joseph .30 .75
BC212 Carlos Leon .30 .75
BC213 Gabriel Sanchez .50 1.25
BC214 Carlos Corporan .30 .75
BC215 Kevin Frostad .30 .75
BC216 Karl Gelinas .30 .75
BC217 Ryan Finan .30 .75
BC218 Noe Rodriguez .30 .75
BC219 Archie Gilbert .30 .75
BC220 Jeff Locke 1.25 3.00
BC221 Fernando Martinez AU 40.00 80.00
BC222 Jeremy Papelbon AU 3.00 8.00
BC223 Ryan Adams AU 3.00 8.00
BC224 Chris Perez AU 5.00 12.00
BC225 J.R. Towles AU 5.00 12.00
BC226 Tommy Mendoza AU 3.00 8.00
BC227 Jeff Samardzija AU 20.00 50.00
BC228 Sergio Perez AU 3.00 8.00
BC229 Justin Reed AU 3.00 8.00
BC230 Luke Hochevar AU 5.00 12.00
BC231 Ivan De Jesus Jr. AU 6.00 15.00
BC232 Kevin Mulvey AU 5.00 12.00
BC233 Chris Coghlan AU 5.00 12.00
BC234 Trevor Cahill AU 15.00 40.00
BC235 Peter Bourjos AU 6.00 15.00
BC236 Joba Chamberlain AU 60.00 120.00
BC237 Josh Rodriguez AU 3.00 8.00
BC238 Tim Lincecum AU 60.00 120.00
BC239 Josh Papelbon AU 4.00 10.00
BC240 Greg Reynolds AU 3.00 8.00
BC241 Wes Hodges AU 8.00 20.00
BC242 Chad Reineke AU 4.00 10.00
BC243 Emmanuel Burriss AU 5.00 12.00
BC244 Henry Sosa AU 5.00 12.00
BC245 Cesar Nicolas AU 3.00 8.00
BC246 Young Il Jung AU 3.00 8.00
BC247 Eric Patterson AU 3.00 8.00
BC248 Hunter Pence AU 10.00 25.00
BC249 Dellin Betances AU 12.50 30.00
BC250 Will Venable AU 4.00 10.00
BC251 Zach McAllister AU 6.00 15.00
BC252 Mark Hamilton AU 3.00 8.00
BC253 Paul Estrada AU 3.00 8.00
BC254 Brad Lincoln AU 4.00 10.00
BC255 Cedric Hunter AU 8.00 20.00
BC256 Chad Rodgers AU 3.00 8.00

2007 Bowman Chrome Prospects Refractors

*REF 1-110: 2X TO 5X BASIC CHROME
*REF 111-220: 2X TO 5X BASIC CHROME
1-110 ODDS 1:48 H, 1:8 HTA, 1:142 R
111-220 ODDS 1:27 HOB, 1:186 RET
*REF AU 221-256: .5X TO 1.2X BASIC
221-256 AU ODDS 1:89 HOB, 1:197 RET
STATED PRINT RUN 500 SERIAL #'d SETS
1-110 ISSUED IN BOWMAN PACKS
111-256 ISSUED IN BOW.CHROME PACKS
EXCHANGE DEADLINE 8/31/2009
BC5 Dellin Betances 20.00 50.00
BC17 Brandon Morrow 5.00 12.00
BC145 Johnny Cueto 15.00 40.00
BC162 Tommy Hanson 12.50 30.00
BC181 Daniel Murphy 15.00 40.00
BC221 Fernando Martinez AU 75.00 150.00
BC227 Jeff Samardzija AU 30.00 60.00
BC234 Trevor Cahill AU 30.00 60.00
BC235 Peter Bourjos AU 10.00 25.00
BC236 Joba Chamberlain AU 100.00 200.00
BC238 Tim Lincecum AU 100.00 200.00
BC249 Dellin Betances AU 30.00 60.00
BC255 Cedric Hunter AU 15.00 40.00

2007 Bowman Chrome Prospects Blue Refractors

*BLUE 1-110: 4X TO 10X BASIC CHROME
*BLUE 111-220: 4X TO 10X BASIC CHROME
1-110 ODDS 1:481 H, 1:80 HTA, 1:1375 R
111-220 ODDS 1:30 H, 1:205 R
*BLUE AU 221-256: 1X TO 2.5X BASIC
221-256 AU ODDS 1:296 HOB, 1:825 RET
STATED PRINT RUN 150 SER.#'d SETS
1-110 ISSUED IN BOWMAN PACKS
111-256 ISSUED IN BOW.CHROME PACKS
EXCHANGE DEADLINE 8/31/2009
BC5 Dellin Betances 50.00 100.00
BC11 Matthew Sweeney 20.00 50.00
BC13 Brennan Boesch 8.00 20.00
BC15 Michael Brantley 15.00 40.00
BC17 Brandon Morrow 20.00 50.00
BC19 Erik Lis 10.00 25.00
BC21 Aaron Cunningham 15.00 40.00
BC28 Chuck Lofgren 10.00 25.00
BC36 Chase Wright 6.00 15.00
BC42 Jesse Litsch 6.00 15.00
BC48 Edgar Garcia 6.00 15.00
BC49 Seth Fortenberry 6.00 15.00
BC50 Reid Brignac 10.00 25.00
BC71 Tony Abreu 20.00 50.00
BC84 Will Venable 5.00 12.00
BC95 Brian Duensing 8.00 20.00
BC106 Desmond Jennings 30.00 60.00
BC124 Brandon Hynick 20.00 50.00
BC129 Reegie Corona 10.00 25.00
BC145 Johnny Cueto 40.00 80.00
BC161 Mark Wagner 10.00 25.00
BC162 Tommy Hanson 30.00 60.00
BC166 Kala Kaaihue 20.00 50.00
BC181 Daniel Murphy 50.00 100.00
BC186 Chorye Spoone 6.00 15.00
BC200 Tyler Clippard 6.00 15.00
BC210 Chris Carter 30.00 60.00
BC220 Jeff Locke 15.00 40.00
BC221 Fernando Martinez AU 200.00 300.00
BC227 Jeff Samardzija AU 50.00 100.00
BC234 Trevor Cahill AU 60.00 120.00
BC236 Joba Chamberlain AU 200.00 300.00
BC238 Tim Lincecum AU 300.00 400.00
BC244 Henry Sosa AU 12.50 30.00
BC249 Dellin Betances AU 50.00 100.00
BC255 Cedric Hunter AU 50.00 100.00

2007 Bowman Chrome Prospects Gold Refractors

*GOLD 1-110: 12X TO 30X BASIC CHROME
*GOLD 111-220: 12X TO 30X BASIC CHROME

1-110 ODDS 1:481 H, 1:80 HTA, 1:1375 R
111-220 ODDS 1:88 HOB, 1:615 RET
221-256 AU ODDS 1:889 HOB, 1:8500 RET
STATED PRINT RUN 50 SER.#'d SETS
1-110 ISSUED IN BOWMAN PACKS
111-256 ISSUED IN BOW.CHROME PACKS
EXCHANGE DEADLINE 8/31/2009
BC5 Dellin Betances 150.00 250.00
BC11 Matthew Sweeney 60.00 100.00
BC17 Brandon Morrow 100.00 200.00
BC19 Erik Lis 30.00 60.00
BC21 Aaron Cunningham 60.00 120.00
BC54 Jesus Flores 20.00 50.00
BC71 Tony Abreu 60.00 120.00
BC84 Will Venable 50.00 80.00
BC85 Greg Smith 30.00 60.00
BC95 Brian Duensing 30.00 60.00
BC106 Desmond Jennings 100.00 150.00
BC109 Ryan Mullins 20.00 50.00
BC120 Eric Young Jr. 40.00 80.00
BC122 Carlos Fernandez-Oliva 20.00 50.00
BC123 Chris Errecart 30.00 60.00
BC140 Mitch Atkins 15.00 40.00
BC145 Johnny Cueto 150.00 250.00
BC147 Jared Goedert 40.00 80.00
BC161 Mark Wagner 20.00 50.00
BC162 Tommy Hanson 75.00 150.00
BC168 Brendan Katin 15.00 40.00
BC181 Daniel Murphy 125.00 250.00
BC190 Gorkys Hernandez 125.00 250.00
BC194 Cole Gillespie 20.00 50.00
BC210 Chris Carter 125.00 200.00
BC221 Fernando Martinez AU 300.00 500.00
BC222 Jeremy Papelbon AU 30.00 60.00
BC223 Ryan Adams AU 30.00 60.00
BC224 Chris Perez AU 40.00 80.00
BC225 J.R. Towles AU 50.00 100.00
BC226 Tommy Mendoza AU 30.00 60.00
BC227 Jeff Samardzija AU 250.00 400.00
BC228 Sergio Perez AU 30.00 60.00
BC229 Justin Reed AU 30.00 60.00
BC230 Luke Hochevar AU 40.00 80.00
BC231 Ivan De Jesus Jr. AU 40.00 80.00
BC232 Kevin Mulvey AU 30.00 60.00
BC233 Chris Coghlan AU 30.00 60.00
BC234 Trevor Cahill AU 200.00 300.00
BC235 Peter Bourjos AU 50.00 100.00
BC236 Joba Chamberlain AU 800.00 1200.00
BC237 Josh Rodriguez AU 30.00 60.00
BC238 Tim Lincecum AU 600.00 800.00
BC239 Josh Papelbon AU 30.00 60.00
BC240 Greg Reynolds AU 30.00 60.00
BC242 Chad Reineke AU 30.00 60.00
BC243 Emmanuel Burriss AU 30.00 60.00
BC244 Henry Sosa AU 50.00 100.00
BC245 Cesar Nicolas AU 30.00 60.00
BC246 Young Il Jung AU 30.00 60.00
BC247 Eric Patterson AU 30.00 60.00
BC248 Hunter Pence AU 60.00 120.00
BC249 Dellin Betances AU 100.00 200.00
BC250 Will Venable AU 40.00 80.00
BC251 Zach McAllister AU 40.00 80.00
BC252 Mark Hamilton AU 40.00 80.00
BC253 Paul Estrada AU 30.00 60.00
BC254 Brad Lincoln AU 30.00 60.00
BC255 Cedric Hunter AU 75.00 150.00
BC256 Chad Rodgers AU 30.00 60.00

2007 Bowman Chrome Prospects Orange Refractors

1-110 ODDS 1:961 H, 1:160 HTA, 1:2800 R
111-220 ODDS 1:176 HOB, 1:1220 RET
221-256 AU ODDS 1:1780 HOB, 1:3650 RET
STATED PRINT RUN 25 SER.#'d SETS
1-110 ISSUED IN BOWMAN PACKS
111-220 ISSUED IN BOW.CHROME PACKS
NO PRICING DUE TO SCARCITY
EXCHANGE DEADLINE 8/31/2009

2007 Bowman Chrome Prospects Red Refractors

1-110 ODDS 1:4817 H, 1:799 HTA, 1:14,000 R
111-220 ODDS 1:882 H, 1:6000 R
221-256 AU ODDS 1:8914 H,1:18,000 R
STATED PRINT RUN 5 SER.#'d SETS
1-110 ISSUED IN BOWMAN PACKS
111-220 ISSUED IN BOW.CHROME PACKS
NO PRICING DUE TO SCARCITY
EXCHANGE DEADLINE 8/31/2009

2007 Bowman Chrome Prospects SuperFractors

1-110 ODDS 1:18,803 H, 1:4073 HTA
111-220 ODDS 1:4218 HOBBY
221-256 AU ODDS 1:39,392 HOB
STATED PRINT RUN 1 SER.#'d SET
1-110 ISSUED IN BOWMAN PACKS
111-220 ISSUED IN BOW.CHROME PACKS
NO PRICING DUE TO SCARCITY
EXCHANGE DEADLINE 8/31/2009

2007 Bowman Chrome Prospects X-Fractors

*X-F 1-110: 2.5X TO 6X BASIC CHROME
*X-F 111-220: 2.5X TO 6X BASIC CHROME
1-110 ODDS 1:87 H, 1:15 HTA, 1:260 R
111-220 ODDS 1:18 H, 1:123 R
1-110 PRINT RUN 275 SER.#'d SETS
111-220 PRINT RUN 250 SER.#'d SETS
*X-F AU 221-256: .6X TO 1.5X BASIC
221-256 AU ODDS 1:198 HOB, 1:480 RET
211-256 PRINT RUN 225 SERIAL #'d SETS
1-110 ISSUED IN BOWMAN PACKS
111-256 ISSUED IN BOW.CHROME PACKS
EXCHANGE DEADLINE 8/31/2009
BC2 Jason Taylor 6.00 15.00
BC5 Dellin Betances 20.00 50.00
BC6 Jeremy Papelbon 4.00 10.00
BC11 Matthew Sweeney 12.50 30.00
BC17 Brandon Morrow 12.50 30.00
BC19 Erik Lis 10.00 25.00
BC42 Jesse Litsch 5.00 12.00
BC71 Tony Abreu 12.50 30.00
BC84 Will Venable 4.00 10.00
BC106 Desmond Jennings 10.00 25.00
BC145 Johnny Cueto 20.00 50.00
BC162 Tommy Hanson 20.00 50.00
BC181 Daniel Murphy 20.00 50.00
BC190 Gorkys Hernandez 15.00 40.00
BC210 Chris Carter 10.00 25.00
BC221 Fernando Martinez AU 75.00 150.00
BC227 Jeff Samardzija AU 40.00 80.00
BC234 Trevor Cahill AU 40.00 80.00
BC235 Peter Bourjos AU 12.50 30.00
BC236 Joba Chamberlain AU 150.00 250.00
BC238 Tim Lincecum AU 150.00 250.00
BC241 Wes Hodges AU 15.00 40.00
BC249 Dellin Betances AU 40.00 80.00
BC255 Cedric Hunter AU 20.00 50.00

2007 Bowman Chrome Draft

This 55-card set, was inserted at a stated rate of two per Bowman Draft pack. This set was also released in December, 2007. In addition to the same 54 players from the basic Bowman Draft set, card #237 featuring Barry Bonds was also included in this set.

COMPLETE SET (55) 15.00 40.00
COMMON RC (1-55) .25 .60
OVERALL PLATE ODDS 1:1294 HOBBY
PLATE PRINT RUN 1 SET PER COLOR
BLACK-CYAN-MAGENTA-YELLOW ISSUED
NO PLATE PRICING DUE TO SCARCITY
BDP1 Travis Buck (RC) .25 .60
BDP2 Matt Chico (RC) .25 .60
BDP3 Justin Upton RC 1.50 4.00
BDP4 Chase Wright RC .60 1.50
BDP5 Kevin Kouzmanoff (RC) .25 .60
BDP6 John Danks RC .25 .60
BDP7 Alejandro De Aza RC .40 1.00
BDP8 Jamie Vermilyea RC .25 .60
BDP9 Jesus Flores RC .25 .60
BDP10 Glen Perkins (RC) .25 .60
BDP11 Tim Lincecum RC 2.00 5.00
BDP12 Cameron Maybin RC 1.25 3.00
BDP13 Brandon Morrow RC .60 1.50
BDP14 Mike Rabelo RC .25 .60
BDP15 Alex Gordon RC 1.25 3.00
BDP16 Zack Segovia (RC) .25 .60
BDP17 Jon Knott (RC) .25 .60
BDP18 Joba Chamberlain RC 2.50 6.00
BDP19 Danny Putnam (RC) .25 .60
BDP20 Matt DeSalvo (RC) .25 .60
BDP21 Fred Lewis (RC) .40 1.00
BDP22 Sean Gallagher (RC) .25 .60
BDP23 Brandon Wood (RC) .25 .60
BDP24 Dennis Dove (RC) .25 .60
BDP25 Hunter Pence (RC) 1.25 3.00
BDP26 Jarrod Saltalamacchia (RC) .40 1.00
BDP27 Ben Francisco (RC) .25 .60
BDP28 Doug Slaten RC .25 .60
BDP29 Tony Abreu RC .60 1.50
BDP30 Billy Butler (RC) .40 1.00
BDP31 Jesse Litsch RC .40 1.00
BDP32 Nate Schierholtz (RC) .25 .60
BDP33 Jared Burton RC .25 .60
BDP34 Matt Brown RC .25 .60
BDP35 Dallas Braden RC .40 1.00
BDP36 Carlos Gomez RC .40 1.00
BDP37 Brian Stokes (RC) .25 .60
BDP38 Kory Casto (RC) .25 .60
BDP39 Mark McLemore (RC) .25 .60
BDP40 Andy LaRoche (RC) .25 .60
BDP41 Tyler Clippard (RC) .40 1.00
BDP42 Curtis Thigpen (RC) .25 .60
BDP43 Yunel Escobar (RC) .25 .60
BDP44 Andy Sonnanstine RC .25 .60
BDP45 Felix Pie (RC) .25 .60
BDP46 Homer Bailey (RC) .40 1.00
BDP47 Kyle Kendrick RC .60 1.50
BDP48 Angel Sanchez RC .25 .60
BDP49 Phil Hughes (RC) 1.25 3.00
BDP50 Ryan Braun (RC) 1.50 4.00
BDP51 Kevin Slowey (RC) .60 1.50
BDP52 Brendan Ryan (RC) .25 .60
BDP53 Yovani Gallardo (RC) .75 2.00
BDP54 Mark Reynolds RC 1.00 2.50
237 Barry Bonds 1.25 3.00

2007 Bowman Chrome Draft Refractors

*REF: 1X TO 2.5X BASIC
STATED ODDS 1:11 HOBBY,1:11 RETAIL
BDP54 Mark Reynolds 8.00 20.00

2007 Bowman Chrome Draft Blue Refractors

*BLUE REF: 2X TO 5X BASIC
STATED ODDS 1:58 HOBBY,1:171 RETAIL
STATED PRINT RUN 199 SER.#'d SETS
BDP54 Mark Reynolds 20.00 50.00

2007 Bowman Chrome Draft Gold Refractors

*GOLD REF: 5X TO 12X BASIC
STATED ODDS 1:232 H, 1:659 R
STATED PRINT RUN 50 SER.#'d SETS
BDP18 Joba Chamberlain 60.00 120.00
BDP54 Mark Reynolds 50.00 100.00

2007 Bowman Chrome Draft Orange Refractors

STATED ODDS 1:463 H, 1:1349 R
STATED PRINT RUN 25 SER.#'d SETS
NO PRICING DUE TO SCARCITY

2007 Bowman Chrome Draft Red Refractors

STATED ODDS 1:2300 H, 1:7080 R
STATED PRINT RUN 5 SER.#'d SETS
NO PRICING DUE TO SCARCITY

2007 Bowman Chrome Draft SuperFractors

STATED ODDS 1:10,377 HOBBY
STATED PRINT RUN 1 SER.#'d SETS
NO PRICING DUE TO SCARCITY

2007 Bowman Chrome Draft X-Fractors

*X-F: 1.5X TO 4X BASIC
STATED ODDS 1:39 HOBBY,1:106 RETAIL
STATED PRINT RUN 299 SER.#'d SETS

2007 Bowman Chrome Draft Draft Picks

66-95 AU ODDS 1:38 HOBBY,1:575 RETAIL
1-65 PLATE ODDS 1:1294 HOBBY
66-95 AU PLATE ODDS 1:14,255 HOBBY

PLATE PRINT RUN 1 SET PER COLOR
BLACK-CYAN-MAGENTA-YELLOW ISSUED
NO PLATE PRICING DUE TO SCARCITY
BDPP1 Cody Crowell .30 .75
BDPP2 Karl Bolt .50 1.25
BDPP3 Corey Brown .50 1.25
BDPP4 Tyler Mach .50 1.25
BDPP5 Trevor Pippin .50 1.25
BDPP6 Ed Easley .30 .75
BDPP7 Cory Luebke .30 .75
BDPP8 Darin Mastroianni .30 .75
BDPP9 Ryan Zink .50 1.25
BDPP10 Brandon Hamilton .30 .75
BDPP11 Kyle Lotzkar .50 1.25
BDPP12 Freddie Freeman .75 2.00
BDPP13 Nicholas Barnese .50 1.25
BDPP14 Travis d'Arnaud .30 .75
BDPP15 Eric Eiland .30 .75
BDPP16 John Ely .30 .75
BDPP17 Oliver Marmol .30 .75
BDPP18 Eric Sogard .30 .75
BDPP19 Lars Davis .30 .75
BDPP20 Sam Runion .30 .75
BDPP21 Austin Gallagher 1.00 2.50
BDPP22 Matt West .50 1.25
BDPP23 Derek Norris .30 .75
BDPP24 Taylor Holiday .50 1.25
BDPP25 Dustin Biell .30 .75
BDPP26 Julio Borbon 1.00 2.50
BDPP27 Brant Rustich .50 1.25
BDPP28 Andrew Lambo 1.25 3.00
BDPP29 Cory Kluber .30 .75
BDPP30 Justin Jackson .50 1.25
BDPP31 Scott Carroll .30 .75
BDPP32 Danny Rams .30 .75
BDPP33 Thomas Eager .30 .75
BDPP34 Matt Dominguez 1.25 3.00
BDPP35 Steven Souza .30 .75
BDPP36 Craig Heyer .30 .75
BDPP37 Michael Taylor .30 .75
BDPP38 Drew Bowman .30 .75
BDPP39 Frank Gailey .30 .75
BDPP40 Jeremy Hefner .30 .75
BDPP41 Reynaldo Navarro .50 1.25
BDPP42 Daniel Descalso .30 .75
BDPP43 Leroy Hunt .30 .75
BDPP44 Jason Kiley .30 .75
BDPP45 Ryan Pope .75 2.00
BDPP46 Josh Horton .30 .75
BDPP47 Jason Monti .30 .75
BDPP48 Richard Lucas .30 .75
BDPP49 Jonathan Lucroy .75 2.00
BDPP50 Sean Doolittle .75 2.00
BDPP51 Mike McDade .50 1.25
BDPP52 Charlie Culberson .50 1.25
BDPP53 Michael Moustakas 2.50 6.00
BDPP54 Jason Heyward 3.00 8.00
BDPP55 David Price 3.00 8.00
BDPP56 Brad Mills .30 .75
BDPP57 John Tolisano 1.00 2.50
BDPP58 Jarrod Parker 1.50 4.00
BDPP59 Wendell Fairley 1.00 2.50
BDPP60 Gary Gattis .30 .75
BDPP61 Madison Bumgarner 1.50 4.00
BDPP62 Danny Payne .30 .75
BDPP63 Jake Smolinski 1.00 2.50
BDPP64 Matt LaPorta 2.50 6.00
BDPP65 Jackson Williams .30 .75
BDPP111 Daniel Moskos AU 4.00 10.00
BDPP112 Ross Detwiler AU 5.00 12.00
BDPP113 Tim Alderson AU 12.50 30.00
BDPP114 Beau Mills AU 12.50 30.00
BDPP115 Devin Mesoraco AU 6.00 15.00
BDPP116 Kyle Lotzkar AU 4.00 10.00
BDPP117 Blake Beavan AU 6.00 15.00
BDPP118 Peter Kozma AU 5.00 12.00
BDPP119 Chris Withrow AU 6.00 15.00
BDPP120 Cory Luebke AU 3.00 8.00
BDPP121 Nick Schmidt AU 3.00 8.00
BDPP122 Michael Main AU 6.00 15.00
BDPP123 Aaron Poreda AU 5.00 12.00
BDPP124 James Simmons AU 5.00 12.00
BDPP125 Ben Revere AU 10.00 25.00
BDPP126 Joe Savery AU 5.00 12.00
BDPP127 Jonathan Gilmore AU 6.00 15.00
BDPP128 Todd Frazier AU 5.00 12.00
BDPP129 Matt Mangini AU 3.00 8.00
BDPP130 Casey Weathers AU 3.00 8.00
BDPP131 Nick Noonan AU 8.00 20.00
BDPP132 Kellen Kulbacki AU 6.00 15.00
BDPP133 Michael Burgess AU 12.50 30.00
BDPP134 Nick Hagadone AU 6.00 15.00
BDPP135 Clayton Mortensen AU 4.00 10.00
BDPP136 Justin Jackson AU 4.00 10.00
BDPP137 Ed Easley AU 3.00 8.00
BDPP138 Corey Brown AU 3.00 8.00
BDPP139 Danny Payne AU 3.00 8.00
BDPP140 Travis d'Arnaud AU 6.00 15.00

2007 Bowman Chrome Draft Draft Picks Refractors

*REF 1-65: 1.5X TO 4X BASIC
1-65 ODDS 1:11 HOBBY,1:11 RETAIL
*REF AU 66-95: .5X TO 1.2X BASIC AU
AU 66-95 ODDS 1:118 H, 1:1700 R
66-95 AU PRINT RUN 500 SER.#'d SETS
BDPP55 David Price 10.00 25.00
BDPP117 Blake Beavan AU 10.00 25.00
BDPP125 Ben Revere AU 12.50 30.00

2007 Bowman Chrome Draft Draft Picks Blue Refractors

*BLUE REF 1-65: 4X TO 10X BASIC
1-65 ODDS 1:58 HOBBY, 1:171 HOBBY
1-65 PRINT RUN 199 SER.#'d SETS
*BLUE REF AU 66-95: 1X TO 2.5X BASIC AU
AU 66-95 ODDS 1:400 H, 1:12,000 R
66-95 AU PRINT RUN 150 SER.#'d SETS
BDPP15 Eric Eiland 6.00 15.00
BDPP22 Matt West 10.00 25.00
BDPP28 Andrew Lambo 15.00 40.00
BDPP34 Matt Dominguez 30.00 60.00
BDPP37 Michael Taylor 10.00 25.00
BDPP52 Charlie Culberson 10.00 25.00
BDPP53 Michael Moustakas 60.00 120.00
BDPP54 Jason Heyward 75.00 150.00
BDPP55 David Price 60.00 120.00
BDPP58 Jarrod Parker 30.00 60.00
BDPP59 Wendell Fairley 30.00 60.00
BDPP61 Madison Bumgarner 20.00 50.00
BDPP64 Matt LaPorta 60.00 120.00
BDPP122 Michael Main AU 30.00 60.00
BDPP125 Ben Revere AU 40.00 80.00
BDPP133 Michael Burgess AU 60.00 120.00
BDPP140 Travis d'Arnaud AU 40.00 80.00

2007 Bowman Chrome Draft Draft Picks Gold Refractors

*GOLD REF 1-65: 10X TO 25X BASIC
1-65 ODDS 1:232 H, 1:659 R
1-65 PRINT RUN 50 SER.#'d SETS
COMMON AUTO (66-95) 40.00 80.00
AU 66-95 ODDS 1:1270 H, 1:9440 R
66-95 AU PRINT RUN 50 SER.#'d SETS
BDPP3 Corey Brown 15.00 40.00
BDPP10 Brandon Hamilton 20.00 50.00
BDPP12 Freddie Freeman 60.00 120.00
BDPP13 Nicholas Barnese 40.00 80.00
BDPP15 Eric Eiland 20.00 50.00
BDPP20 Sam Runion 15.00 40.00
BDPP21 Austin Gallagher 40.00 80.00
BDPP22 Matt West 40.00 80.00
BDPP28 Andrew Lambo 100.00 150.00
BDPP32 Danny Rams 15.00 40.00
BDPP34 Matt Dominguez 100.00 175.00
BDPP35 Steven Souza 20.00 50.00
BDPP37 Michael Taylor 30.00 60.00
BDPP40 Jeremy Hefner 12.50 30.00
BDPP41 Reynaldo Navarro 30.00 60.00
BDPP46 Josh Horton 12.50 30.00
BDPP50 Sean Doolittle 60.00 120.00
BDPP52 Charlie Culberson 20.00 50.00
BDPP53 Michael Moustakas 300.00 350.00
BDPP54 Jason Heyward 200.00 300.00
BDPP55 David Price 200.00 300.00
BDPP57 John Tolisano 40.00 80.00
BDPP58 Jarrod Parker 100.00 175.00
BDPP59 Wendell Fairley 40.00 80.00
BDPP61 Madison Bumgarner 90.00 150.00
BDPP64 Matt LaPorta 250.00 350.00
BDPP111 Daniel Moskos AU 30.00 60.00
BDPP112 Ross Detwiler AU 50.00 100.00
BDPP113 Tim Alderson AU 150.00 250.00
BDPP114 Beau Mills AU 150.00 250.00
BDPP115 Devin Mesoraco AU 60.00 120.00
BDPP116 Kyle Lotzkar AU 40.00 80.00
BDPP117 Blake Beavan AU 60.00 120.00
BDPP118 Peter Kozma AU 30.00 60.00
BDPP119 Chris Withrow AU 40.00 80.00
BDPP120 Cory Luebke AU 30.00 60.00
BDPP121 Nick Schmidt AU 30.00 60.00
BDPP122 Michael Main AU 60.00 120.00
BDPP123 Aaron Poreda AU 50.00 100.00
BDPP124 James Simmons AU 30.00 60.00
BDPP125 Ben Revere AU 90.00 150.00
BDPP126 Joe Savery AU 30.00 60.00
BDPP127 Jonathan Gilmore AU 40.00 80.00
BDPP128 Todd Frazier AU 30.00 60.00
BDPP129 Matt Mangini AU 30.00 60.00
BDPP130 Casey Weathers AU 30.00 60.00
BDPP131 Nick Noonan AU 75.00 150.00
BDPP132 Kellen Kulbacki AU 40.00 80.00
BDPP133 Michael Burgess AU 250.00 350.00
BDPP134 Nick Hagadone AU 60.00 120.00
BDPP135 Clayton Mortensen AU 30.00 60.00
BDPP136 Justin Jackson AU 50.00 100.00
BDPP137 Ed Easley AU 30.00 60.00
BDPP138 Corey Brown AU 30.00 60.00
BDPP139 Danny Payne AU 30.00 60.00
BDPP140 Travis d'Arnaud AU 75.00 150.00

2007 Bowman Chrome Draft Draft Picks Orange Refractors

1-65 STATED ODDS 1:463 H,1:1349 R
66-95 AU ODDS 1:2345 H, 1:28,320 R
STATED PRINT RUN 25 SERIAL #'d SETS
NO PRICING DUE TO SCARCITY

2007 Bowman Chrome Draft Draft Picks Red Refractors

1-65 STATED ODDS 1:2300 H, 1:7080 R
66-95 AU ODDS 1:11,400 HOBBY
STATED PRINT RUN 5 SERIAL #'d SETS
NO PRICING DUE TO SCARCITY

2007 Bowman Chrome Draft Draft Picks SuperFractors

1-65 STATED ODDS 1:10,377 HOBBY
66-95 AU ODDS 1:57,814 HOBBY
STATED PRINT RUN 1 SERIAL #'d SET
NO PRICING DUE TO SCARCITY

2007 Bowman Chrome Draft Draft Picks X-Fractors

*X-F 1-65: 2.5X TO 6X BASIC
1-65 STATED ODDS 1:39 H, 1:106 R
1-65 PRINT RUN 299 SER.#'d SETS
*X-F AU 66-95: .6X TO 1.5X BASIC
66-95 AU STATED ODDS 1:262 H,1:14,000 R
66-95 AU PRINT RUN 225 SER.#'d SETS
BDPP53 Michael Moustakas 30.00 60.00
BDPP54 Jason Heyward 30.00 60.00
BDPP55 David Price 20.00 50.00
BDPP61 Madison Bumgarner 12.50 30.00
BDPP64 Matt LaPorta 30.00 60.00
BDPP117 Blake Beavan AU 12.50 30.00
BDPP125 Ben Revere AU 15.00 40.00

2007 Bowman Chrome Draft Future's Game Prospects

OVERALL PLATE ODDS 1:1294 HOBBY
PLATE PRINT RUN 1 SET PER COLOR
BLACK-CYAN-MAGENTA-YELLOW ISSUED
NO PLATE PRICING DUE TO SCARCITY
BDPP66 Pedro Beato .20 .50
BDPP67 Collin Balester .20 .50
BDPP68 Carlos Carrasco .20 .50
BDPP69 Clay Buchholz 1.25 3.00
BDPP70 Emiliano Fruto .20 .50
BDPP71 Joba Chamberlain 2.00 5.00
BDPP72 Deolis Guerra 1.50 4.00
BDPP73 Kevin Mulvey .50 1.25
BDPP74 Franklin Morales .20 .50
BDPP75 Luke Hochevar .60 1.50
BDPP76 Henry Sosa .30 .75
BDPP77 Clayton Kershaw 1.00 2.50
BDPP78 Rich Thompson .20 .50
BDPP79 Chuck Lofgren .50 1.25
BDPP80 Rick VandenHurk .30 .75
BDPP81 Michael Madsen .20 .50
BDPP82 Robinzon Diaz .20 .50
BDPP83 Jeff Niemann .20 .50
BDPP84 Max Ramirez .20 .50
BDPP85 Geovany Soto .75 2.00
BDPP86 Elvis Andrus .30 .75
BDPP87 Bryan Anderson .20 .50
BDPP88 German Duran .75 2.00
BDPP89 J.R. Towles .60 1.50
BDPP90 Alcides Escobar .20 .50
BDPP91 Brian Bocock .20 .50
BDPP92 Chin-Lung Hu .75 2.00
BDPP93 Adrian Cardenas .50 1.25
BDPP94 Freddy Sandoval .20 .50
BDPP95 Chris Coghlan .20 .50
BDPP96 Craig Stansberry .20 .50
BDPP97 Brent Lillibridge .20 .50
BDPP98 Joey Votto .30 .75
BDPP99 Evan Longoria 2.50 6.00
BDPP100 Wladimir Balentien .20 .50
BDPP101 Johnny Whittleman .20 .50
BDPP102 Gorkys Hernandez .50 1.25
BDPP103 Jay Bruce 1.25 3.00
BDPP104 Matt Tolbert .20 .50
BDPP105 Jacoby Ellsbury 2.00 5.00
BDPP106 Michael Saunders .60 1.50
BDPP107 Cameron Maybin 1.00 2.50
BDPP108 Carlos Gonzalez .20 .50
BDPP109 Colby Rasmus 1.00 2.50
BDPP110 Justin Upton 1.25 3.00

2007 Bowman Chrome Draft Future's Game Prospects Refractors

*REF: 1X TO 2.5X BASIC
STATED ODDS 1:11 HOBBY,1:11 RETAIL
BDPP77 Clayton Kershaw 3.00 8.00
BDPP99 Evan Longoria 8.00 20.00
BDPP103 Jay Bruce 5.00 12.00

2007 Bowman Chrome Draft Future's Game Prospects Blue Refractors

*BLUE REF: 2X TO 5X BASIC
STATED ODDS 1:58 HOBBY,1:171 RETAIL
STATED PRINT RUN 199 SER.#'d SETS
BDPP72 Deolis Guerra 20.00 50.00
BDPP77 Clayton Kershaw 10.00 25.00
BDPP88 German Duran 6.00 15.00
BDPP103 Jay Bruce 10.00 25.00

2007 Bowman Chrome Draft Future's Game Prospects Gold Refractors

*GOLD REF: 5X TO 12X BASIC
STATED ODDS 1:232 H, 1:659 R
STATED PRINT RUN 50 SER.#'d SETS
BDPP71 Joba Chamberlain 50.00 100.00
BDPP72 Deolis Guerra 100.00 175.00
BDPP77 Clayton Kershaw 12.50 30.00
BDPP85 Geovany Soto 30.00 60.00
BDPP88 German Duran 20.00 50.00
BDPP92 Chin-Lung Hu 50.00 100.00
BDPP93 Adrian Cardenas 15.00 40.00
BDPP99 Evan Longoria 40.00 80.00
BDPP103 Jay Bruce 15.00 40.00

2007 Bowman Chrome Draft Future's Game Prospects Orange Refractors

STATED ODDS 1:463 H, 1:1349 R
STATED PRINT RUN 25 SER.#'d SETS
NO PRICING DUE TO SCARCITY

2007 Bowman Chrome Draft Future's Game Prospects Red Refractors

STATED ODDS 1:2300 H, 1:7080 R
STATED PRINT RUN 5 SER.#'d SETS
NO PRICING DUE TO SCARCITY

2007 Bowman Chrome Draft Future's Game Prospects SuperFractors

STATED ODDS 1:10,377 HOBBY
STATED PRINT RUN 1 SER.#'d SETS
NO PRICING DUE TO SCARCITY

2007 Bowman Chrome Draft Future's Game Prospects X-Fractors

*X-F: 1.5X TO 4X BASIC
STATED ODDS 1:39 HOBBY,1:106 RETAIL
STATED PRINT RUN 299 SER.#'d SETS
BDPP72 Deolis Guerra 10.00 25.00
BDPP77 Clayton Kershaw 6.00 15.00
BDPP99 Evan Longoria 12.50 30.00
BDPP103 Jay Bruce 10.00 25.00

2007 Bowman Chrome Draft Future's Game Prospects Bases

STATED ODDS 1:633 HOBBY
STATED PRINT RUN 135 SER.#'d SETS
BDPP86 Elvis Andrus 4.00 10.00
BDPP87 Bryan Anderson 3.00 8.00
BDPP88 German Duran 3.00 8.00
BDPP89 J.R. Towles 3.00 8.00
BDPP91 Brian Bocock 3.00 8.00
BDPP92 Chin-Lung Hu 10.00 25.00
BDPP93 Adrian Cardenas 3.00 8.00
BDPP94 Freddy Sandoval 3.00 8.00
BDPP95 Chris Coghlan 3.00 8.00
BDPP97 Brent Lillibridge 4.00 10.00
BDPP98 Joey Votto 3.00 8.00
BDPP99 Evan Longoria 12.50 30.00
BDPP101 Johnny Whittleman 3.00 8.00
BDPP102 Gorkys Hernandez 4.00 10.00
BDPP103 Jay Bruce 6.00 15.00
BDPP105 Jacoby Ellsbury 6.00 15.00
BDPP106 Michael Saunders 4.00 10.00
BDPP108 Carlos Gonzalez 3.00 8.00
BDPP109 Colby Rasmus 6.00 15.00
BDPP110 Justin Upton 10.00 25.00

2008 Bowman Chrome

COMPLETE SET (220) 15.00 40.00
COMMON CARD (1-190) .20 .50
COMMON ROOKIE (1-220) .60 1.50
1-220 PLATE ODDS 1:1382 HOBBY
PLATE PRINT RUN 1 SET PER COLOR
BLACK-CYAN-MAGENTA-YELLOW ISSUED
NO PLATE PRICING DUE TO SCARCITY
1 Ryan Braun .60 1.50
2 David DeJesus .20 .50
3 Brandon Phillips .20 .50
4 Mark Teixeira .30 .75
5 Daisuke Matsuzaka .75 2.00
6 Justin Upton .50 1.25
7 Jered Weaver .20 .50
8 Todd Helton .30 .75
9 Adam Jones .20 .50
10 Erik Bedard .20 .50
11 Jason Bay .20 .50
12 Cole Hamels .50 1.25
13 Bobby Abreu .20 .50
14 Carlos Zambrano .20 .50
15 Vladimir Guerrero .50 1.25
16 Joe Blanton .20 .50
17 Paul Maholm .20 .50
18 Adrian Gonzalez .30 .75
19 Brandon Webb .30 .75
20 Carl Crawford .20 .50
21 A.J. Burnett .20 .50
22 Dmitri Young .20 .50
23 Jeremy Hermida .20 .50
24 C.C. Sabathia .20 .50
25 Adam Dunn .20 .50
26 Matt Garza .20 .50
27 Adrian Beltre .20 .50
28 Kevin Milwood .20 .50
29 Manny Ramirez .50 1.25
30 Javier Vazquez .20 .50
31 Carlos Delgado .20 .50
32 Torii Hunter .20 .50
33 Ivan Rodriguez .30 .75
34 Nick Markakis .30 .75
35 Gil Meche .20 .50
36 Garrett Atkins .20 .50
37 Fausto Carmona .20 .50
38 Joe Mauer .30 .75
39 Tom Glavine .30 .75
40 Hideki Matsui .50 1.25
41 Scott Rolen .30 .75
42 Tim Lincecum .50 1.25
43 Prince Fielder .50 1.25
44 Kazuo Matsui .20 .50
45 Tom Gorzelanny .20 .50
46 Lance Berkman .30 .75
47 David Ortiz .50 1.25
48 Dontrelle Willis .20 .50
49 Travis Hafner .20 .50
50 Aaron Harang .20 .50
51 Chris Young .20 .50
52 Vernon Wells .20 .50
53 Francisco Liriano .30 .75
54 Eric Chavez .20 .50
55 Phil Hughes .50 1.25
56 Melvin Mora .20 .50
57 Johan Santana .30 .75
58 Brian McCann .30 .75
59 Pat Burrell .20 .50
60 Chris Carpenter .20 .50
61 Brian Giles .20 .50
62 Jose Reyes .30 .75
63 Hanley Ramirez .50 1.25
64 Ubaldo Jimenez .20 .50
65 Felix Pie .20 .50
66 Jeremy Bonderman .20 .50
67 Jimmy Rollins .30 .75
68 Miguel Tejada .20 .50
69 Derek Lowe .20 .50
70 Alex Gordon .50 1.25
71 John Maine .20 .50
72 Alfonso Soriano .30 .75
73 Ben Sheets .30 .75
74 Hunter Pence .50 1.25
75 Magglio Ordonez .30 .75
76 Josh Beckett .30 .75
77 Victor Martinez .20 .50
78 Mark Buehrle .20 .50
79 Jason Varitek .50 1.25
80 Chien-Ming Wang .60 1.50
81 Ken Griffey Jr. .75 2.00
82 Billy Butler .20 .50
83 Brad Penny .20 .50
84 Carlos Beltran .20 .50
85 Curt Schilling .30 .75
86 Jorge Posada .30 .75
87 Andruw Jones .20 .50
88 Bobby Crosby .20 .50
89 Freddy Sanchez .20 .50
90 Barry Zito .20 .50
91 Miguel Cabrera .30 .75
92 B.J. Upton .30 .75
93 Matt Cain .20 .50
94 Lyle Overbay .20 .50
95 Austin Kearns .20 .50
96 Alex Rodriguez .75 2.00
97 Rich Harden .20 .50
98 Justin Morneau .30 .75
99 Oliver Perez .20 .50
100 Gary Matthews .20 .50
101 Matt Holliday .30 .75
102 Justin Verlander .30 .75
103 Orlando Cabrera .20 .50
104 Rich Hill .20 .50
105 Tim Hudson .20 .50
106 Ryan Zimmerman .30 .75
107 Roy Oswalt .20 .50
108 Nick Swisher .20 .50
109 Raul Ibanez .20 .50
110 Kelly Johnson .20 .50
111 Alex Rios .20 .50
112 John Lackey .20 .50
113 Robinson Cano .30 .75
114 Michael Young .20 .50
115 Jeff Francis .20 .50
116 Grady Sizemore .30 .75
117 Mike Lowell .20 .50
118 Aramis Ramirez .20 .50
119 Stephen Drew .20 .50
120 Yovani Gallardo .20 .50
121 Chase Utley .50 1.25
122 Dan Haren .20 .50
123 Yunel Escobar .20 .50
124 Greg Maddux .60 1.50
125 Garret Anderson .20 .50
126 Aubrey Huff .20 .50
127 Paul Konerko .20 .50
128 Dan Uggla .30 .75
129 Roy Halladay .20 .50
130 Andre Ethier .30 .75
131 Orlando Hernandez .20 .50
132 Troy Tulowitzki .30 .75
133 Carlos Guillen .20 .50
134 Scott Kazmir .30 .75
135 Aaron Rowand .20 .50
136 Jim Edmonds .30 .75
137 Jermaine Dye .20 .50
138 Orlando Hudson .20 .50
139 Derrek Lee .30 .75
140 Travis Buck .20 .50
141 Zack Greinke .20 .50
142 Jeff Kent .20 .50
143 John Smoltz .50 1.25
144 David Wright .60 1.50
145 Joba Chamberlain .60 1.50
146 Adam LaRoche .20 .50
147 Kevin Youkilis .30 .75
148 Troy Glaus .30 .75
149 Nick Johnson .20 .50
150 J.J. Hardy .20 .50
151 Felix Hernandez .30 .75
152 Gary Sheffield .20 .50
153 Albert Pujols 1.00 2.50
154 Chuck James .20 .50
155 Kosuke Fukudome RC 4.00 10.00
155b Kosuke Fukudome Japan 4.00 10.00
155c Kosuke Fukudome 10.00 25.00
No Signature/1600 *
156 Eric Byrnes .20 .50
157 Brad Hawpe .20 .50
158 Delmon Young .30 .75
159 Brian Roberts .30 .75
160 Russ Martin .30 .75
161 Hank Blalock .20 .50
162 Yadier Molina .30 .75
163 Jeremy Guthrie .20 .50
164 Chipper Jones .60 1.50
165 Johnny Damon .30 .75
166 Ryan Garko .20 .50
167 Jake Peavy .30 .75
168 Chone Figgins .20 .50
169 Edgar Renteria .20 .50
170 Jim Thome .30 .75
171 Carlos Pena .50 1.25
172 Dustin Pedroia .75 2.00
173 Brett Myers .20 .50
174 Josh Hamilton .60 1.50
175 Randy Johnson .50 1.25
176 Ichiro Suzuki .75 2.00
177 Aaron Hill .20 .50
178 Corey Hart .20 .50
179 Jarrod Saltalamacchia .20 .50
180 Jeff Francoeur .30 .75
181 Derek Jeter 1.25 3.00
182 Curtis Granderson .20 .50
183 James Loney .30 .75
184 Brian Bannister .20 .50
185 Carlos Lee .20 .50
186 Pedro Martinez .30 .75
187 Asdrubal Cabrera .20 .50
188 Kenji Johjima .20 .50
189 Jacoby Ellsbury .75 2.00
190 Ryan Howard .60 1.50
191 Sean Rodriguez (RC) .60 1.50
192 Justin Ruggiano RC 1.00 2.50
193 Jed Lowrie (RC) 1.50 4.00
194 Joey Votto (RC) 1.50 4.00
195 Denard Span (RC) 1.00 2.50
196 Brad Harman RC 1.00 2.50
197 Jeff Niemann (RC) .60 1.50
198 Chin-Lung Hu (RC) 1.00 2.50
199 Luke Hochevar RC 1.50 4.00
200 German Duran RC 1.00 2.50
201 Troy Patton (RC) .60 1.50
202 Hiroki Kuroda RC 1.00 2.50
203 David Purcey (RC) .60 1.50
204 Armando Galarraga RC 1.00 2.50
205 John Bowker (RC) .60 1.50
206 Nick Blackburn RC 1.00 2.50
207 Hernan Iribarren (RC) 1.00 2.50
208 Greg Smith RC .60 1.50
209 Alberto Gonzalez RC 1.00 2.50
210 Justin Masterson RC 3.00 8.00
211 Brian Barton RC 1.00 2.50
212 Robinzon Diaz (RC) .60 1.50
213 Clete Thomas RC 1.00 2.50
214 Kazuo Fukumori RC 1.00 2.50
215 Jayson Nix (RC) .60 1.50
216 Evan Longoria RC 5.00 12.00
217 Johnny Cueto RC 1.00 2.50
218 Matt Tolbert RC 1.00 2.50
219 Masahide Kobayashi RC 1.00 2.50
220 Callix Crabbe (RC) .60 1.50

2008 Bowman Chrome Refractors

*REF 1-190: 1X TO 2.5X BASIC
*REF 1-221: .6X TO 1.5X BASIC
1-221 ODDS

2008 Bowman Chrome Blue Refractors

*BLUE REF 1-190: 2.5X TO 6X BASIC
*BLUE REF 1-221: 1.2X TO 3X BASIC
1-221 ODDS 1:66 HOBBY
STATED PRINT RUN 150 SERIAL #'d SETS
193 Jed Lowrie 10.00 25.00
198 Chin-Lung Hu 10.00 25.00
204 Armando Galarraga 10.00 25.00
216 Evan Longoria 40.00 80.00

2008 Bowman Chrome Gold Refractors

*GOLD REF 1-190: 4X TO 10X BASIC
*GOLD REF 1-221: 2X TO 5X BASIC
1-221 ODDS 1:197 HOBBY
STATED PRINT RUN 50 SERIAL #'d SETS
5 Daisuke Matsuzaka 12.50 30.00
40 Hideki Matsui 8.00 20.00
42 Tim Lincecum 15.00 40.00
80 Chien-Ming Wang 60.00 120.00
96 Alex Rodriguez 20.00 50.00
153 Albert Pujols 30.00 60.00
155 Kosuke Fukudome 40.00 80.00
155b Kosuke Fukudome Japan 40.00 80.00
176 Ichiro Suzuki 20.00 50.00
181 Derek Jeter 30.00 60.00
189 Jacoby Ellsbury 15.00 40.00
193 Jed Lowrie 15.00 40.00
198 Chin-Lung Hu 30.00 60.00
204 Armando Galarraga 30.00 60.00
210 Justin Masterson 20.00 50.00
216 Evan Longoria 60.00 120.00

2008 Bowman Chrome Orange Refractors

STATED ODDS 1:393 HOBBY
STATED PRINT RUN 25 SER.#'d SETS
NO PRICING DUE TO SCARCITY

2008 Bowman Chrome Red Refractors

STATED ODDS 1:1972 HOBBY
STATED PRINT RUN 5 SER.#'d SETS
NO PRICING DUE TO SCARCITY

2008 Bowman Chrome SuperFractors

STATED ODDS 1:8308 HOBBY
STATED PRINT RUN 1 SER.#'d SET
NO PRICING DUE TO SCARCITY

2008 Bowman Chrome X-Fractors

*X-FRACTOR 1-190: 2X TO 5X BASIC
*X-FRACTOR 1-221: 1X TO 2.5X BASIC
1-221 ODDS 1:40 HOBBY
STATED PRINT RUN 250 SER.#'d SETS
155 Kosuke Fukudome 10.00 25.00
155b Kosuke Fukudome Japan 10.00 25.00
193 Jed Lowrie 8.00 20.00
198 Chin-Lung Hu 5.00 12.00
204 Armando Galarraga 8.00 20.00
216 Evan Longoria 20.00 50.00

2008 Bowman Chrome Head of the Class Dual Autograph

STATED ODDS 1:1773 HOBBY
STATED PRINT RUN 350 SER.#'d SETS
CH Joba Chamberlain 40.00 80.00
Phil Hughes
FL Prince Fielder 20.00 50.00
Matt LaPorta
LP Evan Logoria 75.00 150.00
David Price

2008 Bowman Chrome Head of the Class Dual Autograph X-Fractors

*X-F: .6X TO 1.5X BASIC
STATED ODDS 1:12,823 HOBBY
STATED PRINT RUN 50 SER.#'d SETS

2008 Bowman Chrome Head of the Class Dual Autograph Refractors

*REF: .5X TO 1.2X BASIC
STATED ODDS 1:6298 HOBBY
STATED PRINT RUN 99 SER.#'d SETS
LP Evan Logoria 125.00 250.00
David Price

2008 Bowman Chrome Head of the Class Dual Autograph SuperFractors

STATED ODDS 1:589,824 HOBBY
STATED PRINT RUN 1 SER.#'d SET
NO PRICING DUE TO SCARCITY

2008 Bowman Chrome Prospects

COMP.SET w/o AU's (220) 40.00 100.00
COMP.SET w/o AU's (1-110) 20.00 50.00
COMP.SET w/o AU's (131-240) 20.00 50.00
111-130 AU ODDS 1:37 HOBBY
241-285 AU ODDS 1:31 HOBBY
1-110 PLATE ODDS 1:732 HOBBY
111-130 AU PLATE ODDS 1:4700 HOBBY
131-240 PLATE ODDS 1:1132 HOBBY
241-285 AU PLATES 1:10,471 HOBBY
PLATE PRINT RUN 1 SET PER COLOR
BLACK-CYAN-MAGENTA-YELLOW ISSUED
NO PLATE PRICING DUE TO SCARCITY
BCP1 Max Sapp .30 .75
BCP2 Jamie Richmond .20 .50
BCP3 Darren Ford .20 .50
BCP4 Sergio Romo .20 .50
BCP5 Jacob Butler .20 .50
BCP6 Glenn Gibson .20 .50
BCP7 Tom Hagan .20 .50
BCP8 Michael McCormick .20 .50
BCP9 Gregorio Petit .30 .75
BCP10 Bobby Parnell .30 .75
BCP11 Jeff Kindel .30 .75
BCP12 Anthony Claggett .30 .75
BCP13 Christopher Frey .20 .50
BCP14 Jonah Nickerson .20 .50
BCP15 Anthony Martinez .20 .50
BCP16 Rusty Ryal .30 .75
BCP17 Justin Berg .30 .75
BCP18 Gerardo Parra .20 .50
BCP19 Wesley Wright .20 .50
BCP20 Stephen Chapman .20 .50
BCP21 Chance Chapman .20 .50
BCP22 Brett Pill .20 .50
BCP23 Zachary Phillips .30 .75
BCP24 John Raynor .50 1.25
BCP25 Danny Duffy .20 .50
BCP26 Brian Finegan .20 .50
BCP27 Jonathan Venters .20 .50
BCP28 Steve Tolleson .20 .50
BCP29 Ben Jukich .30 .75
BCP30 Matthew Weston .20 .50
BCP31 Kyle Mura .20 .50
BCP32 Luke Hetherington .20 .50
BCP33 Michael Daniel .30 .75
BCP34 Jake Renshaw .20 .50
BCP35 Greg Halman .60 1.50
BCP36 Ryan Khoury .20 .50
BCP37 Ryan Ouellette .20 .50
BCP38 Mike Brantley .20 .50
BCP39 Eric Brown .20 .50
BCP40 Jose Duarte .20 .50
BCP41 Eli Tintor .20 .50
BCP42 Kent Sakamoto .20 .50
BCP43 Luke Montz .30 .75
BCP44 Alex Cobb .20 .50
BCP45 Michael McKenry .20 .50
BCP46 Javier Castillo .20 .50
BCP47 Jeffrey Stevens .20 .50
BCP48 Greg Burns .20 .50
BCP49 Blake Johnson .20 .50
BCP50 Austin Jackson 1.25 3.00
BCP51 Anthony Recker .20 .50
BCP52 Luis Durango 1.00 2.50
BCP53 Engel Beltre .60 1.50
BCP54 Seth Bynum .20 .50
BCP55 Ryan Strieby .30 .75
BCP56 Iggy Suarez .20 .50
BCP57 Ryan Morris .30 .75
BCP58 Scott Van Slyke .20 .50
BCP59 Tyler Kolodny .60 1.50
BCP60 Joseph Martinez .20 .50
BCP61 Aaron Mathews .20 .50
BCP62 Phillip Cuadrado .20 .50
BCP63 Alex Liddi .30 .75
BCP64 Alex Burnett .30 .75
BCP65 Brian Barton .30 .75
BCP66 David Welch .20 .50
BCP67 Kyle Reynolds .20 .50
BCP68 Francisco Hernandez .20 .50
BCP69 Logan Morrison 1.00 2.50
BCP70 Ronald Ramirez .20 .50
BCP71 Brad Miller .20 .50
BCP72 Braedyn Pruitt .30 .75
BCP73 Jason Fernandez .30 .75
BCP74 Joseph Mahoney .20 .50
BCP75 Quentin Davis .30 .75
BCP76 P.J. Walters .50 1.25
BCP77 Jordan Czarniecki .20 .50
BCP78 Jonathan Mota .20 .50
BCP79 Michael Hernandez .20 .50
BCP80 James Guerrero .20 .50
BCP81 Chris Johnson .30 .75
BCP82 Daniel Cortes .50 1.25
BCP83 Sal Sanchez .30 .75
BCP84 Sean Henry .20 .50
BCP85 Caleb Gindl .20 .50
BCP86 Tommy Everidge .20 .50
BCP87 Matt Rizzotti .20 .50
BCP88 Luis Munoz .20 .50
BCP89 Matthew Klimas .20 .50
BCP90 Angel Reyes .20 .50
BCP91 Sean Danielson .20 .50
BCP92 Omar Poveda .30 .75
BCP93 Mario Lisson .20 .50
BCP94 Brian Mathews .20 .50
BCP95 Matthew Buschmann .20 .50
BCP96 Greg Thomson .20 .50
BCP97 Matt Inouye .20 .50
BCP98 Aneury Rodriguez .75 2.00
BCP99 Brad Harman .30 .75
BCP100 Aaron Bates .50 1.25
BCP101 Graham Taylor .20 .50
BCP102 Ken Holmberg .20 .50
BCP103 Greg Dowling .20 .50
BCP104 Ronnie Ray .20 .50
BCP105 Michael Wlodarczyk .20 .50
BCP106 Jose Martinez .60 1.50
BCP107 Jason Stephens .30 .75
BCP108 Will Rhymes .20 .50
BCP109 Joey Side .20 .50
BCP110 Brandon Waring .60 1.50
BCP111 David Price AU 40.00 80.00
BCP112 Michael Moustakas AU 15.00 40.00
BCP113 Matt LaPorta AU 30.00 60.00
BCP114 Wendell Fairley AU 4.00 10.00
BCP115 Josh Vitters AU 12.50 30.00
BCP116 Jonathan Bachanov AU 4.00 10.00
BCP117 Edward Kunz AU 4.00 10.00
BCP118 Matt Dominguez AU 6.00 15.00
BCP119 Kyle Lotzkar AU 4.00 10.00
BCP120 Madison Bumgarner AU 15.00 40.00
BCP121 Jason Heyward AU 20.00 50.00
BCP122 Julio Borbon AU 4.00 10.00
BCP123 Josh Smoker AU 4.00 10.00
BCP124 Jarrod Parker AU 8.00 20.00
BCP125 Kevin Ahrens AU 4.00 10.00
BCP126 J.P. Arencibia AU 6.00 15.00
BCP127 Josh Bell AU 4.00 10.00
BCP128 Scott Cousins AU 4.00 10.00
BCP129 Brandon Hynick AU 4.00 10.00
BCP130 Alan Johnson AU 4.00 10.00
BCP131 Zhenwang Zhang .30 .75
BCP132 Chris Nash .20 .50
BCP133 Sergio Morales .20 .50
BCP134 Carlos Santana 1.25 3.00
BCP135 Carlos Monasterios .20 .50
BCP136 Quincy Latimore .20 .50
BCP137 Yamaico Navarro .60 1.50
BCP138 Ryan Mullins .20 .50
BCP139 Collin DeLome .30 .75
BCP140 Hector Correa .20 .50
BCP141 Mitch Canham .20 .50
BCP142 Robert Fish .20 .50
BCP143 Ryan Royster .20 .50
BCP144 Eric Barrett .20 .50
BCP145 Deibinson Romero .30 .75
BCP146 Jeff Gerbe .20 .50
BCP147 Lucas Duda .30 .75
BCP148 Bryan Morris .30 .75
BCP149 Andrew Romine .20 .50
BCP150 Glenn Gibson .20 .50
BCP151 Danny Brezeale .20 .50
BCP152 Shairon Martis .20 .50
BCP153 Helder Velazquez .20 .50
BCP154 Alan Farina .20 .50
BCP155 Brandon Barnes .20 .50
BCP156 Waldis Joaquin .20 .50
BCP157 Luis De La Cruz .20 .50
BCP158 Yunesky Sanchez .20 .50
BCP159 Mitch Hilligross .20 .50
BCP160 Vin Mazzaro .60 1.50
BCP161 Marcus Davis .20 .50
BCP162 Tony Barnette .20 .50
BCP163 Joe Benson .50 1.25
BCP164 Jake Arrieta .20 .50
BCP165 Alfredo Silverio .50 1.25
BCP166 Duane Below .20 .50
BCP167 Kai Liu .30 .75
BCP168 Zach Britton .30 .75
BCP169 Jamie Pedroza .30 .75
BCP170 Frank Herrmann .20 .50
BCP171 Justin Turner .30 .75
BCP172 Jeff Manship .20 .50
BCP173 Paul Winterling .20 .50
BCP174 Nathan Vineyard .30 .75
BCP175 Jason Delaney .20 .50
BCP176 Ivan Nova .30 .75
BCP177 Esmailyn Gonzalez .60 1.50
BCP178 Brett Cecil .50 1.25
BCP179 Jose Martinez .20 .50
BCP180 Brad Peacock .30 .75
BCP181 Justin Snyder .30 .75
BCP182 Steve Garrison .20 .50
BCP183 Joe Mahoney .20 .50
BCP184 Graham Godfrey .20 .50
BCP185 Larry Williams .20 .50
BCP186 Jeremy Haynes .20 .50
BCP187 Brent Brewer .50 1.25
BCP188 Jhoulys Chacin 1.50 4.00
BCP189 Nevin Ashley .30 .75
BCP190 Justin Cassel .20 .50
BCP191 Jon Jay .20 .50
BCP192 Chris Huseby .20 .50
BCP193 D.J. Jones .30 .75
BCP194 David Bromberg .30 .75
BCP195 Juan Francisco .20 .50
BCP196 Zach Jevne .20 .50
BCP197 Darwin Barney .30 .75
BCP198 Jose Ortegano .30 .75
BCP199 Dominic Brown 1.00 2.50
BCP200 Kyle Ginley .20 .50
BCP201 David Wood .20 .50
BCP202 Jhonny Nunez .20 .50
BCP203 Carlos Rivero .50 1.25
BCP204 Anthony Varvaro .20 .50
BCP205 Christian Lopez .20 .50
BCP206 Travis Banwart .20 .50
BCP207 Rhyne Hughes .20 .50
BCP208 Heath Rollins .30 .75
BCP209 Zack Cozart .30 .75
BCP210 Mike Dunn .20 .50
BCP211 Chris Pettit .20 .50
BCP212 Dan Berlind .20 .50
BCP213 Ernesto Mejia .30 .75
BCP214 Hector Rondon .30 .75
BCP215 Jose Vallejo .30 .75
BCP216 Kyle Schmidt .20 .50
BCP217 Bubba Bell .50 1.25
BCP218 Charlie Furbush .20 .50
BCP219 Pedro Baez .50 1.25
BCP220 Brandon MaGee .20 .50
BCP221 Clint Robinson .20 .50
BCP222 Fabio Castillo .30 .75
BCP223 Brad Emaus .30 .75
BCP224 Mike DeJesus .20 .50
BCP225 Brandon Laird .50 1.25
BCP226 R.J. Seidel .20 .50
BCP227 Agustin Murillo .20 .50
BCP228 Trevor Reckling .60 1.50
BCP229 Hector Gomez .50 1.25
BCP230 Jordan Norberto .20 .50
BCP231 Steve Hill .20 .50
BCP232 Hassan Pena .20 .50
BCP233 Justin Henry .30 .75
BCP234 Chase Lirette .20 .50
BCP235 Christian Marrero .30 .75
BCP236 Will Kline .20 .50
BCP237 Johan Limonta .20 .50
BCP238 Duke Welker .20 .50
BCP239 Jeudy Valdez .30 .75
BCP240 Elvin Ramirez .20 .50
BCP241 Josh Kreuzer AU 4.00 10.00
BCP242 Ryan Zink AU 5.00 12.00
BCP243 Matt Harrison AU 4.00 10.00
BCP244 Dustin Richardson AU 6.00 15.00
BCP245 Fautino De Los Santos AU 6.00 15.00
BCP246 Austin Jackson AU 20.00 50.00
BCP247 Jordan Schafer AU 10.00 25.00
BCP248 Daryl Thompson AU 5.00 12.00
BCP249 Lars Anderson AU 40.00 80.00
BCP250 Tim Bascom AU 6.00 15.00
BCP251 Brandon Hicks AU 6.00 15.00
BCP252 David Kopp AU 5.00 12.00
BCP253 Danny Lehmann AU 4.00 10.00
BCP254 Jordan Zimmerman AU UER 6.00 15.00
Last name misspelled
BCP255 Cale Iorg AU 4.00 10.00
BCP256 Austin Romine AU 10.00 25.00
BCP257 Chaz Roe AU 6.00 15.00
BCP258 Danny Rams AU 6.00 15.00
BCP259 Daniel Bard AU 8.00 20.00
BCP260 Engel Beltre AU 20.00 50.00
BCP261 Michael Watt AU 6.00 15.00
BCP262 Brennan Boesch AU 5.00 12.00
BCP263 Matt Latos AU 8.00 20.00
BCP264 John Jaso AU 6.00 15.00
BCP265 Adrian Alaniz AU 4.00 10.00
BCP266 Matt Green AU 4.00 10.00
BCP267 Andrew Lambo AU 10.00 25.00
BCP268 Michael McCardell AU 6.00 15.00
BCP269 Chris Valaika AU 8.00 20.00
BCP270 Cole Rohrbough AU 8.00 20.00
BCP271 Andrew Brackman AU 10.00 25.00
BCP272 Bud Norris AU 5.00 12.00
BCP273 Ryan Kalish AU 10.00 25.00
BCP274 Jake McGee AU 5.00 12.00
BCP275 Aaron Cunningham AU 6.00 15.00
BCP276 Mitch Boggs AU 4.00 10.00
BCP277 Bradley Suttle AU 6.00 15.00
BCP278 Henry Rodriguez AU 6.00 15.00
BCP279 Mario Lisson AU 4.00 10.00
BCP280 Ludovicus Van Mil AU 5.00 12.00
BCP281 Angel Villalona AU 30.00 60.00
BCP282 Mark Melancon AU 8.00 20.00
BCP283 Brian Dinkelman AU 4.00 10.00
BCP284 Daniel McCutchen AU 4.00 10.00
BCP285 Rene Tosoni AU 5.00 12.00

2008 Bowman Chrome Prospects Refractors

*REF 1-110: 2.5X TO 6X BASIC
*REF 131-240: 2.5X TO 6X BASIC
1-110 ODDS 1:34 HOBBY,1:88 RETAIL
131-240 ODDS 1:40 HOBBY
1-110 PRINT RUN 599 SER.#'d SETS
131-240 PRINT RUN 500 SER.#'d SETS
*REF AU 111-130: .5X TO 1.2X BASIC
*REF AU 241-285: .5X TO 1.2X BASIC
111-130 AU ODDS 1:113 HOBBY
241-285 AU ODDS 1:88 HOBBY
111-130 AU PRINT RUN 500 SER.#'d SETS
241-285 AU PRINT RUN 500 SER.#'d SETS
BCP111 David Price AU 50.00 100.00
BCP113 Matt LaPorta AU 40.00 80.00
BCP273 Ryan Kalish AU 15.00 40.00
BCP275 Aaron Cunningham AU 10.00 25.00
BCP282 Mark Melancon AU 12.50 30.00

2008 Bowman Chrome Prospects Blue Refractors

*BLUE 1-110: 5X TO 12X BASIC
*BLUE 131-240: 5X TO 12X BASIC
1-110 ODDS 1:126 HOBBY,1:350 RETAIL
131-240 ODDS 1:131 HOBBY
1-110 PRINT RUN 150 SER.#'d SETS
131-240 PRINT RUN 150 SER.#'d SETS
*BLUE AU 111-130: 1.2X TO 3X BASIC
*BLUE AU 241-285: 1.2X TO 3X BASIC
111-130 AU ODDS 1:372 HOBBY
241-285 AU ODDS 1:295 HOBBY
111-130 AU PRINT RUN 150 SER.#'d SETS
241-285 AU PRINT RUN 150 SER.#'d SETS
BCP18 Gerardo Parra 20.00 50.00
BCP25 Danny Duffy 20.00 50.00
BCP35 Greg Halman 40.00 80.00
BCP50 Austin Jackson 40.00 80.00
BCP53 Engel Beltre 20.00 50.00
BCP55 Ryan Strieby 15.00 40.00
BCP69 Logan Morrison 30.00 60.00
BCP110 Brandon Waring 40.00 80.00
BCP111 David Price AU 100.00 200.00
BCP113 Matt LaPorta AU 100.00 200.00
BCP126 J.P. Arencibia AU 20.00 50.00
BCP134 Carlos Santana 30.00 60.00
BCP137 Yamaico Navarro 30.00 60.00
BCP141 Mitch Canham 6.00 15.00
BCP143 Ryan Royster 10.00 25.00
BCP169 Jamie Pedroza 6.00 15.00
BCP177 Esmailyn Gonzalez 15.00 40.00
BCP178 Brett Cecil 10.00 25.00
BCP179 Jose Martinez 20.00 50.00
BCP194 David Bromberg 10.00 25.00
BCP225 Brandon Laird 10.00 25.00
BCP228 Trevor Reckling 20.00 50.00
BCP229 Hector Gomez 12.50 30.00
BCP249 Lars Anderson AU 150.00 250.00
BCP260 Engel Beltre AU 60.00 120.00

2008 Bowman Chrome Prospects Gold Refractors

*GOLD 1-110: 12X TO 30X BASIC
*GOLD 131-240: 12X TO 30X BASIC
1-110 ODDS 1:380 HOB, 1:1040 RET
131-240 ODDS 1:393 HOBBY
1-110 PRINT RUN 50 SER.#'d SETS
131-240 PRINT RUN 50 SER.#'d SETS
111-130 AU ODDS 1:1155 HOBBY
241-285 AU ODDS 1:953 HOBBY
111-130 AU PRINT RUN 50 SER.#'d SETS
241-285 AU PRINT RUN 50 SER.#'d SETS
BCP2 Jamie Richmond 15.00 40.00
BCP11 Jeff Kindel 30.00 60.00
BCP18 Gerardo Parra 40.00 80.00
BCP25 Danny Duffy 40.00 80.00
BCP35 Greg Halman 90.00 150.00
BCP43 Luke Montz 20.00 50.00
BCP50 Austin Jackson 60.00 120.00
BCP53 Engel Beltre 40.00 80.00
BCP55 Ryan Strieby 20.00 50.00
BCP58 Scott Van Slyke 20.00 50.00
BCP69 Logan Morrison 90.00 150.00
BCP92 Omar Poveda 30.00 60.00
BCP110 Brandon Waring 90.00 150.00
BCP111 David Price AU 250.00 400.00
BCP112 Michael Moustakas AU 150.00 250.00
BCP113 Matt LaPorta AU 350.00 500.00
BCP114 Wendell Fairley AU 30.00 60.00
BCP115 Josh Vitters AU 150.00 250.00
BCP116 Jonathan Bachanov AU 30.00 60.00
BCP118 Matt Dominguez AU 60.00 120.00
BCP120 Madison Bumgarner AU 150.00 250.00
BCP121 Jason Heyward AU 250.00 350.00
BCP123 Josh Smoker AU 30.00 60.00
BCP124 Jarrod Parker AU 90.00 150.00
BCP125 Kevin Ahrens AU 30.00 60.00
BCP126 J.P. Arencibia AU 100.00 175.00
BCP143 Ryan Royster 12.50 30.00
BCP164 Jake Arrieta 60.00 120.00
BCP193 D.J. Jones 20.00 50.00
BCP194 David Bromberg 20.00 50.00
BCP195 Juan Francisco 60.00 120.00
BCP199 Dominic Brown 60.00 120.00
BCP203 Carlos Rivero 30.00 60.00
BCP229 Hector Gomez 30.00 60.00
BCP245 Fautino De Los Santos AU 60.00 120.00
BCP246 Austin Jackson AU 200.00 300.00
BCP247 Jordan Schafer AU 60.00 120.00
BCP249 Lars Anderson AU 300.00 400.00
BCP256 Austin Romine AU 60.00 120.00
BCP259 Daniel Bard AU 60.00 120.00
BCP260 Engel Beltre AU 150.00 250.00
BCP263 Matt Latos AU 75.00 150.00
BCP267 Andrew Lambo AU 150.00 250.00
BCP270 Cole Rohrbough AU 60.00 120.00
BCP271 Andrew Brackman AU 100.00 150.00
BCP273 Ryan Kalish AU 75.00 150.00
BCP274 Jake McGee AU 30.00 60.00
BCP275 Aaron Cunningham AU 50.00 100.00
BCP277 Bradley Suttle AU 60.00 120.00
BCP281 Angel Villalona AU 350.00 450.00
BCP282 Mark Melancon AU 40.00 80.00

2008 Bowman Chrome Prospects Orange Refractors

1-110 ODDS 1:750 HOB, 1:2075 RET
111-130 AU ODDS 1:2495 HOBBY
131-240 ODDS 1:785 HOBBY
241-285 AU ODDS 1:1784 HOBBY
STATED PRINT RUN 25 SER.#'d SETS
NO PRICING DUE TO SCARCITY

2008 Bowman Chrome Prospects Red Refractors

1-110 ODDS 1:3600 HOBBY
111-130 AU ODDS 1:11,075 HOBBY
131-240 ODDS 1:3924 HOBBY
241-285 AU ODDS 1:8549 HOBBY
STATED PRINT RUN 5 SER.#'d SETS
NO PRICING DUE TO SCARCITY

2008 Bowman Chrome Prospects SuperFractors

1-110 ODDS 1:18,274 HOBBY
111-130 AU ODDS 1:55,000 HOBBY
131-240 ODDS 1:16,694 HOBBY
241-285 AU ODDS 1:40,216 HOBBY
STATED PRINT RUN 1 SER.#'d SET
NO PRICING DUE TO SCARCITY

2008 Bowman Chrome Prospects X-Fractors

*X-F 1-110: 3X TO 8X BASIC
*X-F 131-240: 3X TO 8X BASIC
1-110 ODDS 1:65 HOBBY,1:188 RETAIL
131-240 ODDS 1:79 HOBBY
1-110 PRINT RUN 275 SER.#'d SETS
131-240 PRINT RUN 250 SER.#'d SETS
*X-F AU 111-130: .6X TO 1.5X BASIC
*X-F AU 241-285: .6X TO 1.5X BASIC
111-130 X-F AU ODDS 1:226 HOBBY
241-285 X-F AU ODDS 1:175 HOBBY
111-130 AU PRINT RUN 275 SER.#'d SETS
241-285 AU PRINT RUN 250 SER.#'d SETS
BCP35 Greg Halman 15.00 40.00
BCP69 Logan Morrison 15.00 40.00
BCP111 David Price AU 75.00 150.00
BCP113 Matt LaPorta AU 50.00 100.00
BCP120 Madison Bumgarner AU 40.00 80.00
BCP263 Matt Latos AU 15.00 40.00
BCP267 Andrew Lambo AU 40.00 80.00
BCP273 Ryan Kalish AU 20.00 50.00
BCP275 Aaron Cunningham AU 12.50 30.00
BCP282 Mark Melancon AU 15.00 40.00

2008 Bowman Chrome Draft

This set was released on Nobember 28, 2008. The base set consists of 60 cards.

COMP.SET w/o AU's (55) 12.50 30.00
COMMON CARD (1-60) .25 .60
COMMON AUTO 4.00 10.00
AU ODDS 1:627 HOBBY
OVERALL PLATE ODDS 1:750 HOBBY
AUTO PLATE ODDS 1:49,870 HOBBY
PLATE PRINT RUN 1 SET PER COLOR
BLACK-CYAN-MAGENTA-YELLOW ISSUED
NO PLATE PRICING DUE TO SCARCITY
BDP1 Nick Adenhart (RC) .25 .60
BDP2 Michael Aubrey RC .40 1.00
BDP3 Mike Aviles RC .40 1.00
BDP4 Burke Badenhop RC .40 1.00
BDP5 Wladimir Balentien (RC) .25 .60
BDP6a Collin Balester (RC) .25 .60
BDP6b Collin Balester AU 4.00 10.00
BDP7 Josh Banks (RC) .25 .60
BDP8 Wes Bankston (RC) .25 .60
BDP9 Joey Votto (RC) .60 1.50
BDP10 Mitch Boggs (RC) .25 .60
BDP11 Jay Bruce (RC) 1.00 2.50
BDP12 Chris Carter (RC) .40 1.00
BDP13 Justin Christian RC .60 1.50
BDP14 Chris Davis RC .60 1.50
BDP15a Blake DeWitt (RC) .60 1.50
BDP15b Blake DeWitt AU 8.00 20.00
BDP16 Nick Evans RC .25 .60
BDP17 Jaime Garcia RC .25 .60
BDP18 Brett Gardner (RC) .60 1.50
BDP19 Carlos Gonzalez (RC) .25 .60
BDP20 Matt Harrison (RC) .25 .60
BDP21 Micah Hoffpauir RC .40 1.00
BDP22 Nick Hundley (RC) .25 .60
BDP23 Eric Hurley (RC) .25 .60
BDP24 Elliot Johnson (RC) .25 .60
BDP25 Matt Joyce RC .60 1.50
BDP26a Clayton Kershaw RC .75 2.00
BDP26b Clayton Kershaw AU 10.00 25.00
BDP27a Evan Longoria RC 2.00 5.00
BDP27b Evan Longoria AU 40.00 80.00
BDP28 Matt Macri (RC) .25 .60
BDP29 Chris Perez RC .40 1.00
BDP30 Max Ramirez RC .25 .60
BDP31 Greg Reynolds RC .40 1.00
BDP32 Brooks Conrad (RC) .25 .60
BDP33 Max Scherzer RC .60 1.50
BDP34 Daryl Thompson (RC) .40 1.00
BDP35 Taylor Teagarden RC .40 1.00
BDP36 Rich Thompson RC .40 1.00
BDP37 Ryan Tucker (RC) .25 .60
BDP38 Jonathan Van Every RC .25 .60
BDP39a Chris Volstad (RC) .25 .60
BDP39b Chris Volstad AU 4.00 10.00
BDP40 Michael Hollimon RC .25 .60
BDP41 Brad Ziegler RC .60 1.50
BDP42 Jamie D'Antona (RC) .25 .60
BDP43 Clayton Richard (RC) .25 .60
BDP44 Edgar Gonzalez (RC) .25 .60
BDP45 Bryan LaHair RC .25 .60
BDP46 Warner Madrigal (RC) .25 .60
BDP47 Reid Brignac (RC) .40 1.00
BDP48 David Robertson RC .40 1.00
BDP49 Nick Stavinoha RC .40 1.00
BDP50 Jai Miller (RC) .25 .60
BDP51 Charlie Morton (RC) .25 .60
BDP52 Brandon Boggs (RC) .40 1.00
BDP53 Joe Mather RC .40 1.00
BDP54 Gregorio Petit RC .40 1.00
BDP55 Jeff Samardzija RC .75 2.00

2008 Bowman Chrome Draft Refractors

*REF: 1X TO 2.5X BASIC
RANDOM INSERTS IN PACKS
*REF AU: .5X TO 1.2X BASIC AU
REF AUTO ODDS 1:2,000 PACKS
REF AUTO PRINT RUN 99 SER.#'d SETS

2008 Bowman Chrome Draft Blue Refractors

*BLUE REF: 2.5X TO 6X BASIC
STATED ODDS 1:76 HOBBY
STATED PRINT RUN 99 SER.#'d SETS

2008 Bowman Chrome Draft Gold Refractors

*GOLD REF: 5X TO 12X BASIC
STATED ODDS 1:150 HOBBY
STATED PRINT RUN 50 SER.#'d SETS
*GODL REF AU: 1.2X TO 3X BASIC AU
GLD.REF AUTO ODDS 1:3965 PACKS
GLD.REF AU PRINT RUN 50 SER.#'d SETS

2008 Bowman Chrome Draft Orange Refractors

STATED ODDS 1:301 HOBBY
AUTO ODDS 1:7962 HOBBY
STATED PRINT RUN 25 SER.#'d SETS
NO PRICING DUE TO SCARCITY

2008 Bowman Chrome Draft Red Refractors

STATED ODDS 1:1518 HOBBY
AUTO ODDS 1:39,500 HOBBY
STATED PRINT RUN 5 SER.#'d SETS
NO PRICING DUE TO SCARCITY

2008 Bowman Chrome Draft SuperFractors

STATED ODDS 1:6025 HOBBY
AUTO ODDS 1:189,500 HOBBY
STATED PRINT RUN 1 SER.#'d SET
NO PRICING DUE TO SCARCITY

2008 Bowman Chrome Draft X-Fractors

*X-F: 1.2X TO 3X BASIC
STATED ODDS 1:38 HOBBY
STATED PRINT RUN 199 SER.#'d SETS

2008 Bowman Chrome Draft Prospects

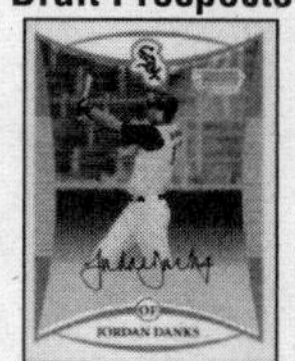

COMP.SET w/o AU's (110) 20.00 50.00
STATED AUTO ODDS 1:38 HOBBY
OVERALL PLATE ODDS 1:750 HOBBY
AUTO PLATE ODDS 1:13,742 HOBBY
PLATE PRINT RUN 1 SET PER COLOR
BLACK-CYAN-MAGENTA-YELLOW ISSUED
NO PLATE PRICING DUE TO SCARCITY
EXCHANGE DEADLINE 11/30/2010
BDPP1 Rick Porcello DP 1.50 4.00
BDPP2 Braeden Schlehuber DP .30 .75
BDPP3 Kenny Wilson DP .30 .75
BDPP4 Jeff Lanning DP .30 .75
BDPP5 Kevin Dubler DP .30 .75
BDPP6 Eric Campbell DP .50 1.25
BDPP7 Tyler Chatwood DP .30 .75
BDPP8 Tyreace House DP .30 .75
BDPP9 Adrian Nieto DP .50 1.25
BDPP10 Robbie Grossman DP .50 1.25
BDPP11 Jordan Danks DP .75 2.00
BDPP12 Jay Austin DP .50 1.25
BDPP13 Ryan Perry DP .50 1.25
BDPP14 Ryan Chaffee DP .50 1.25
BDPP15 Niko Vasquez DP .75 2.00
BDPP16 Shane Dyer DP .30 .75
BDPP17 Benji Gonzalez DP .30 .75
BDPP18 Miles Reagan DP .30 .75
BDPP19 Anthony Ferrara DP .30 .75
BDPP20 Markus Brisker DP .30 .75
BDPP21 Justin Bristow DP .30 .75
BDPP22 Richard Bleier DP .50 1.25
BDPP23 Jeremy Beckham DP .50 1.25
BDPP24 Xavier Avery DP .75 2.00
BDPP25 Christian Vazquez DP .50 1.25
BDPP26 Nick Romero DP .30 .75
BDPP27 Trey Watten DP .30 .75
BDPP28 Brett Jacobson DP .30 .75
BDPP29 Tyler Sample DP .30 .75

BDPP30 T.J. Steele DP .50 1.25
BDPP31 Christian Friedrich DP .75 2.00
BDPP32 Graham Hicks DP .50 1.25
BDPP33 Shane Peterson DP .50 1.25
BDPP34 Brett Hunter DP .30 .75
BDPP35 Tim Federowicz DP .50 1.25
BDPP36 Isaac Galloway DP .50 1.25
BDPP37 Logan Schafer DP .30 .75
BDPP38 Paul Demny DP .30 .75
BDPP39 Clayton Shunick DP .30 .75
BDPP40 Andrew Liebel DP .30 .75
BDPP41 Brandon Crawford DP .50 1.25
BDPP42 Blake Tekotte DP .50 1.25
BDPP43 Jason Corder DP .30 .75
BDPP44 Bryan Shaw DP .30 .75
BDPP45 Edgar Olmos DP .30 .75
BDPP46 Dusty Coleman DP .30 .75
BDPP47 Johnny Giavotella DP .30 .75
BDPP48 Tyson Ross DP .50 1.25
BDPP49 Brent Morel DP .30 .75
BDPP50 Dennis Raben DP .50 1.25
BDPP51 Jake Odorizzi DP .75 2.00
BDPP52 Ryne White DP .50 1.25
BDPP53 Devaris Strange-Gordon DP .30 .75
BDPP54 Tim Murphy DP .30 .75
BDPP55 Jake Jefferies DP .30 .75
BDPP56 Anthony Capra DP .30 .75
BDPP57 Kyle Weiland DP .75 2.00
BDPP58 Anthony Bass DP .50 1.25
BDPP59 Scott Green DP .30 .75
BDPP60 Zeke Spruill DP .75 2.00
BDPP61 L.J. Hoes DP .75 2.00
BDPP62 Tyler Cline DP .30 .75
BDPP63 Matt Cerda DP .30 .75
BDPP64 Bobby Lanigan DP .30 .75
BDPP65 Mike Sheridan DP .30 .75
BDPP66 Carlos Carrasco FG .30 .75
BDPP67 Nate Schierholtz FG .30 .75
BDPP68 Jesus Delgado FG .30 .75
BDPP69 Andrew McCutchen FG .50 1.25
BDPP70 Shairon Martis FG .30 .75
BDPP71 Matt LaPorta FG .75 2.00
BDPP72 Eddie Morlan FG .30 .75
BDPP73 Greg Golson FG .30 .75
BDPP74 Julio Pimentel FG .30 .75
BDPP75 Dexter Fowler FG .30 .75
BDPP76 Henry Rodriguez FG .30 .75
BDPP77 Cliff Pennington FG .30 .75
BDPP78 Hector Rondon FG .30 .75
BDPP79 Wes Hodges FG .30 .75
BDPP80 Polin Trinidad FG .30 .75
BDPP81 Chris Getz FG .30 .75
BDPP82 Welington Castillo FG .30 .75
BDPP83 Mat Gamel FG .50 1.25
BDPP84 Pablo Sandoval FG .30 .75
BDPP85 Jason Donald FG .30 .75
BDPP86 Jesus Montero FG .50 1.25
BDPP87 Jamie D'Antona FG .30 .75
BDPP88 Will Inman FG .30 .75
BDPP89 Elvis Andrus FG .30 .75
BDPP90 Taylor Teagarden FG .50 1.25
BDPP91 Scott Campbell FG .30 .75
BDPP92 Jake Arrieta FG .30 .75
BDPP93 Juan Francisco FG .30 .75
BDPP94 Lou Marson FG .30 .75
BDPP95 Luke Hughes FG .30 .75
BDPP96 Bryan Anderson FG .30 .75
BDPP97 Ramiro Pena FG .30 .75
BDPP98 Jesse Todd FG .30 .75
BDPP99 Gorkys Hernandez FG .30 .75
BDPP100 Casey Weathers FG .30 .75
BDPP101 Fernando Martinez FG .50 1.25
BDPP102 Clayton Richard FG .30 .75
BDPP103 Gerardo Parra FG .30 .75
BDPP104 Kevin Pucetas FG .50 1.25
BDPP105 Wilkin Ramirez FG .30 .75
BDPP106 Ryan Mattheus FG .30 .75
BDPP107 Angel Villalona FG .75 2.00
BDPP108 Brett Anderson FG .30 .75
BDPP109 Chris Valaika FG .30 .75
BDPP110 Trevor Cahill FG .30 .75
BDPP111 Wilmer Flores AU EXCH 20.00 50.00
BDPP112 Lonnie Chisenhall AU 6.00 15.00
BDPP113 Carlos Gutierrez AU 4.00 10.00
BDPP114 Derek Holland AU 10.00 25.00
BDPP115 Michael Stanton AU 30.00 60.00
BDPP116 Ike Davis AU 8.00 20.00
BDPP117 Anthony Hewitt AU 6.00 15.00
BDPP118 Gordon Beckham AU 30.00 60.00
BDPP119 Daniel Schlereth AU 4.00 10.00
BDPP120 Zach Collier AU 8.00 20.00
BDPP121 Evan Frederickson AU 4.00 10.00
BDPP122 Mike Montgomery AU 6.00 15.00
BDPP123 Cody Adams AU 4.00 10.00
BDPP124 Brad Hand AU 4.00 10.00
BDPP125 Josh Reddick AU 12.50 30.00
BDPP126 Michel Inoa AU EXCH 12.50 30.00
BDPP127 Jesus Montero AU EXCH 20.00 50.00
BDPP128 Buster Posey AU 40.00 80.00

2008 Bowman Chrome Draft Prospects Refractors

*REF: 1.5X TO 4X BASIC
RANDOM INSERTS IN PACKS
*REF AU: .5X TO 1.2X BASIC
REF.AU ODDS 1:118 HOBBY
REF.AU PRINT RUN 500 SER.#'d SETS
EXCHANGE DEADLINE 11/30/2010

2008 Bowman Chrome Draft Prospects Blue Refractors

*BLUE REF: 4X TO 10X BASIC
STATED ODDS 1:76 HOBBY
STATED PRINT RUN 99 SER.#'d SETS
*BLUE REF AU: 1X TO 2.5X BASIC
BLUE REF.AU ODDS 1:396 HOBBY
BLUE REF.AU PRINT RUN 150 SER.#'d SETS
EXCHANGE DEADLINE 11/30/2010
BDPP1 Rick Porcello DP 40.00 80.00
BDPP36 Isaac Galloway DP 15.00 40.00
BDPP111 Wilmer Flores AU EXCH 100.00 200.00
BDPP115 Michael Stanton AU 100.00 150.00
BDPP122 Mike Montgomery AU 20.00 50.00
BDPP126 Michel Inoa AU EXCH 40.00 100.00
BDPP127 Jesus Montero AU EXCH 90.00 150.00

2008 Bowman Chrome Draft Prospects Gold Refractors

*GOLD REF: 12.5X TO 30X BASIC
STATED ODDS 1:150 HOBBY
STATED PRINT RUN 50 SER.#'d SETS
*GOLD REF AU: 2.5X TO 6X BASIC
GOLD REF.AU ODDS 1:1258 HOBBY
GOLD AU PRINT RUN 50 SER.#'d SETS
EXCHANGE DEADLINE 11/30/2010
BDPP1 Rick Porcello DP 150.00 200.00
BDPP9 Adrian Nieto DP 20.00 50.00
BDPP36 Isaac Galloway DP 30.00 60.00
BDPP50 Dennis Raben DP 30.00 60.00
BDPP51 Jake Odorizzi DP 30.00 60.00
BDPP57 Kyle Weiland DP 30.00 60.00
BDPP111 Wilmer Flores AU EXCH 350.00 500.00
BDPP112 Lonnie Chisenhall AU 60.00 120.00
BDPP115 Michael Stanton AU 250.00 350.00
BDPP118 Gordon Beckham AU 250.00 350.00
BDPP126 Michel Inoa AU EXCH 150.00 350.00
BDPP127 Jesus Montero AU EXCH 300.00 400.00
BDPP128 Buster Posey AU 450.00 600.00

2008 Bowman Chrome Draft Prospects Orange Refractors

STATED ODDS 1:301 HOBBY
AUTO ODDS 1:2700 HOBBY
STATED PRINT RUN 25 SER.#'d SETS
NO PRICING DUE TO SCARCITY

2008 Bowman Chrome Draft Prospects Red Refractors

STATED ODDS 1:518 HOBBY
AUTO ODDS 1:11,017 HOBBY
STATED PRINT RUN 5 SER.#'d SETS
NO PRICING DUE TO SCARCITY

2008 Bowman Chrome Draft Prospects SuperFractors

STATED ODDS 1:6025 HOBBY
AUTO ODDS 1:55,736 HOBBY
STATED PRINT RUN 1 SER.#'d SET
NO PRICING DUE TO SCARCITY

2008 Bowman Chrome Draft Prospects X-Fractors

*X-F: 2.5X TO 6X BASIC
STATED ODDS 1:38 HOBBY
STATED PRINT RUN 199 SER.#'d SETS
*X-F AU: .6X TO 1.5X BASIC
X-F.AU ODDS 1:270 HOBBY
X-F.AU PRINT RUN 225 SER.#'d SETS
EXCHANGE DEADLINE 11/30/2010
BDPP1 Rick Porcello DP 20.00 50.00

2001 Bowman Heritage Promos

This five-card set was distributed to collectors and dealers who attended the 2001 National Convention in Cleveland, a few months prior to the release of 2001 Bowman Heritage to allow a sneak preview of the upcoming brand. Please note that a sealed piece of gum was issued in the cello packs. Five hundred of each of these cards were produced and those cards were available at various corporate booths at the National. The Albert Pujols card was available only at the Beckett booth.

COMPLETE SET (5) 90.00 150.00
ONE SET PER ATTENDEE AT 01 CLEVELAND NAT'L
STATED PRINT RUN 500 SETS
PRINT RUN INFO PROVIDED BY TOPPS
1 Roberto Alomar 4.00 10.00
2 Albert Pujols 75.00 125.00
3 C.C. Sabathia 4.00 10.00
4 Mark McGwire 10.00 25.00
5 Juan Gonzalez 3.20 8.00

2001 Bowman Heritage

This 440-card product was issued in 10 card packs, along with a slab of gum, with an SRP of $3 per pack. The packs were issued 16 to a box with 24 boxes to a case. Cards numbered 331-440 were inserted at a rate of one every two packs.

COMPLETE SET (440) 125.00 200.00
COMP.SET w/o SP's (330) 20.00 50.00
COMMON CARD (1-330) .15 .40
COMMON RC (1-330) .15 .40
COMMON (331-440) .75 2.00
1 Chipper Jones .40 1.00
2 Pete Harnisch .15 .40
3 Brian Giles .15 .40
4 J.T. Snow .15 .40
5 Bartolo Colon .15 .40
6 Jorge Posada .25 .60
7 Shawn Green .15 .40
8 Derek Jeter 1.00 2.50
9 Benito Santiago .15 .40
10 Ramon Hernandez .15 .40
11 Bernie Williams .25 .60
12 Greg Maddux .60 1.50
13 Barry Bonds 1.00 2.50
14 Roger Clemens .75 2.00
15 Miguel Tejada .15 .40
16 Pedro Feliz .15 .40
17 Jim Edmonds .15 .40
18 Tom Glavine .25 .60
19 David Justice .15 .40
20 Rich Aurilia .15 .40
21 Jason Giambi .15 .40
22 Orlando Hernandez .15 .40
23 Shawn Estes .15 .40
24 Nelson Figueroa .15 .40
25 Terrence Long .15 .40
26 Mike Mussina .25 .60
27 Eric Davis .15 .40
28 Jimmy Rollins .15 .40
29 Andy Pettitte .25 .60
30 Shawon Dunston .15 .40
31 Tim Hudson .15 .40
32 Jeff Kent .15 .40
33 Scott Brosius .15 .40
34 Livan Hernandez .15 .40
35 Alfonso Soriano .25 .60
36 Mark McGwire 1.00 2.50
37 Russ Ortiz .15 .40
38 Fernando Vina .15 .40
39 Ken Griffey Jr. .60 1.50
40 Edgar Renteria .15 .40
41 Kevin Brown .15 .40
42 Robb Nen .15 .40
43 Paul LoDuca .15 .40
44 Bobby Abreu .15 .40
45 Adam Dunn .25 .60
46 Osvaldo Fernandez .15 .40
47 Marvin Benard .15 .40
48 Mark Gardner .15 .40
49 Alex Rodriguez .60 1.50
50 Preston Wilson .15 .40
51 Roberto Alomar .25 .60
52 Ben Davis .15 .40
53 Derek Bell .15 .40
54 Ken Caminiti .15 .40
55 Barry Zito .25 .60
56 Scott Rolen .25 .60
57 Geoff Jenkins .15 .40
58 Mike Cameron .15 .40
59 Ben Grieve .15 .40
60 Chuck Knoblauch .15 .40
61 Matt Lawton .15 .40
62 Chan Ho Park .15 .40
63 Lance Berkman .15 .40
64 Carlos Beltran .15 .40
65 Dean Palmer .15 .40
66 Alex Gonzalez .15 .40
67 Larry Walker .15 .40
68 Magglio Ordonez .15 .40
69 Ellis Burks .15 .40
70 Mark Mulder .15 .40
71 Randy Johnson .40 1.00
72 John Smoltz .25 .60
73 Jerry Hairston Jr. .15 .40
74 Pedro Martinez .25 .60
75 Fred McGriff .25 .60
76 Sean Casey .15 .40
77 C.C. Sabathia .15 .40
78 Todd Helton .25 .60
79 Brad Penny .15 .40
80 Mike Sweeney .15 .40
81 Billy Wagner .15 .40
82 Mark Buehrle .25 .60
83 Cristian Guzman .15 .40
84 Jose Vidro .15 .40
85 Pat Burrell .15 .40
86 Jermaine Dye .15 .40
87 Brandon Inge .15 .40
88 David Wells .15 .40
89 Mike Piazza .60 1.50
90 Jose Cabrera .15 .40
91 Cliff Floyd .15 .40
92 Matt Morris .15 .40
93 Raul Mondesi .15 .40
94 Joe Kennedy RC .25 .60
95 Jack Wilson RC .25 .60
96 Andruw Jones .25 .60
97 Mariano Rivera .40 1.00
98 Mike Hampton .15 .40
99 Roger Cedeno .15 .40
100 Jose Cruz .15 .40
101 Mike Lowell .15 .40
102 Pedro Astacio .15 .40
103 Joe Mays .15 .40
104 John Franco .15 .40
105 Tim Redding .15 .40
106 Sandy Alomar Jr. .15 .40
107 Bret Boone .15 .40
108 Josh Towers RC .25 .60
109 Matt Stairs .15 .40
110 Chris Truby .15 .40
111 Jeff Suppan .15 .40
112 J.C. Romero .15 .40
113 Felipe Lopez .15 .40
114 Ben Sheets .25 .60
115 Frank Thomas .40 1.00
116 A.J. Burnett .15 .40
117 Tony Clark .15 .40
118 Mac Suzuki .15 .40
119 Brad Radke .15 .40
120 Jeff Shaw .15 .40
121 Nick Neugebauer .15 .40
122 Kenny Lofton .15 .40
123 Jacque Jones .15 .40
124 Brent Mayne .15 .40
125 Carlos Hernandez .15 .40
126 Shane Spencer .15 .40
127 John Lackey .15 .40
128 Sterling Hitchcock .15 .40
129 Darren Dreifort .15 .40
130 Rusty Greer .15 .40
131 Michael Cuddyer .15 .40
132 Tyler Houston .15 .40
133 Chin-Feng Chen .15 .40
134 Ken Harvey .15 .40
135 Marquis Grissom .15 .40
136 Russell Branyan .15 .40
137 Eric Karros .15 .40
138 Josh Beckett .25 .60
139 Todd Zeile .15 .40
140 Corey Koskie .15 .40
141 Steve Sparks .15 .40
142 Bobby Seay .15 .40
143 Tim Raines Jr. .15 .40
144 Julio Zuleta .15 .40
145 Jose Lima .15 .40
146 Dante Bichette .15 .40
147 Randy Keisler .15 .40
148 Brent Butler .15 .40
149 Antonio Alfonseca .15 .40
150 Bryan Rekar .15 .40
151 Jeffrey Hammonds .15 .40
152 Larry Bigbie .15 .40
153 Blake Stein .15 .40
154 Robin Ventura .15 .40
155 Rondell White .15 .40
156 Juan Silvestre .15 .40
157 Marcus Thames .15 .40
158 Sidney Ponson .15 .40
159 Juan A. Pena RC .15 .40
160 C.J. Nitkowski .15 .40
161 Adam Everett .15 .40
162 Eric Munson .15 .40
163 Jason Isringhausen .15 .40
164 Brad Fullmer .15 .40
165 Miguel Olivo .15 .40
166 Fernando Tatis .15 .40
167 Freddy Garcia .15 .40
168 Tom Goodwin .15 .40
169 Armando Benitez .15 .40
170 Paul Konerko .15 .40
171 Jeff Cirillo .15 .40
172 Shane Reynolds .15 .40
173 Kevin Tapani .15 .40
174 Joe Crede .40 1.00
175 Omar Infante RC .15 .40
176 Jake Peavy RC 2.00 5.00
177 Corey Patterson .15 .40
178 Mike Penney RC .15 .40
179 Jeromy Burnitz .15 .40
180 David Segui .15 .40
181 Marcus Giles .15 .40
182 Paul O'Neill .25 .60
183 John Olerud .15 .40
184 Andy Benes .15 .40
185 Brad Cresse .15 .40
186 Ricky Ledee .15 .40
187 Allen Levrault UER .15 .40
Last name misspelled Leverault
188 Royce Clayton .15 .40
189 Kelly Johnson RC 1.25 3.00
190 Quilvio Veras .15 .40
191 Mike Williams .15 .40
192 Jason Lane RC .25 .60
193 Rick Helling .15 .40
194 Tim Wakefield .15 .40
195 James Baldwin .15 .40
196 Cody Ransom RC .15 .40
197 Bobby Kielty .15 .40
198 Bobby Jones .15 .40
199 Steve Cox .15 .40
200 Jamal Strong RC .15 .40
201 Steve Lomasney .15 .40
202 Brian Cardwell RC .15 .40
203 Mike Matheny .15 .40
204 Jeff Randazzo RC .15 .40
205 Aubrey Huff .15 .40
206 Chuck Finley .15 .40
207 Denny Bautista RC .25 .60
208 Terry Mulholland .15 .40
209 Rey Ordonez .15 .40
210 Keith Surkont RC .15 .40
211 Orlando Cabrera .15 .40
212 Juan Encarnacion .15 .40
213 Dustin Hermanson .15 .40
214 Luis Rivas .15 .40
215 Mark Quinn .15 .40
216 Randy Velarde .15 .40
217 Billy Koch .15 .40
218 Ryan Rupe .15 .40
219 Keith Ginter .15 .40
220 Woody Williams .15 .40
221 Ryan Franklin .15 .40
222 Aaron Myette .15 .40
223 Joe Borchard RC .15 .40
224 Nate Cornejo .15 .40
225 Julian Tavarez .15 .40
226 Kevin Millwood .15 .40
227 Travis Hafner RC 2.00 5.00
228 Charles Nagy .15 .40
229 Mike Lieberthal .15 .40
230 Jeff Nelson .15 .40
231 Ryan Dempster .15 .40
232 Andres Galarraga .15 .40
233 Chad Durbin .15 .40
234 Timo Perez .15 .40
235 Troy O'Leary .15 .40
236 Kevin Young .15 .40
237 Gabe Kapler .15 .40
238 Juan Cruz RC .15 .40
239 Masato Yoshii .15 .40
240 Aramis Ramirez .15 .40
241 Matt Cooper RC .15 .40
242 Randy Flores RC .15 .40
243 Rafael Furcal .15 .40
244 David Eckstein .15 .40
245 Matt Clement .15 .40
246 Craig Biggio .25 .60
247 Rick Reed .15 .40
248 Jose Macias .15 .40
249 Alex Escobar .15 .40
250 Roberto Hernandez .15 .40
251 Andy Ashby .15 .40
252 Tony Armas Jr. .15 .40
253 Jamie Moyer .15 .40
254 Jason Tyner .15 .40
255 Charles Kegley RC .15 .40
256 Jeff Conine .15 .40
257 Francisco Cordova .15 .40
258 Ted Lilly .15 .40
259 Joe Randa .15 .40
260 Jeff D'Amico .15 .40
261 Albie Lopez .15 .40
262 Kevin Appier .15 .40
263 Richard Hidalgo .15 .40
264 Omar Daal .15 .40
265 Ricky Gutierrez .15 .40
266 John Rocker .15 .40
267 Ray Lankford .15 .40
268 Beau Hale RC .15 .40
269 Tony Blanco RC .15 .40
270 Derrek Lee UER .25 .60
First name misspelled Derrick
271 Jamey Wright .15 .40
272 Alex Gordon .15 .40
273 Jeff Weaver .15 .40
274 Jaret Wright .15 .40
275 Jose Hernandez .15 .40
276 Bruce Chen .15 .40
277 Todd Hollandsworth .15 .40
278 Wade Miller .15 .40
279 Luke Prokopec .15 .40
280 Rafael Soriano RC .15 .40
281 Damion Easley .15 .40
282 Darren Oliver .15 .40
283 B. Duckworth RC .15 .40
284 Aaron Herr .15 .40
285 Ray Durham .15 .40
286 Wilmy Caceras RC .15 .40
287 Ugueth Urbina .15 .40
288 Scott Seabol .15 .40
289 Lance Niekro RC .25 .60
290 Trot Nixon .15 .40
291 Adam Kennedy .15 .40
292 Brian Schmitt RC .15 .40
293 Grant Roberts .15 .40
294 Benny Agbayani .15 .40
295 Travis Lee .15 .40
296 Erick Almonte RC .15 .40
297 Jim Thome .25 .60
298 Eric Young .15 .40
299 Dan Denham RC .15 .40
300 Boof Bonser RC .15 .40
301 Denny Neagle .15 .40
302 Kenny Rogers .15 .40
303 J.D. Closser .15 .40
304 Chase Utley RC 5.00 12.00
305 Rey Sanchez .15 .40
306 Sean McGowan .15 .40
307 Justin Pope RC .15 .40
308 Torii Hunter .15 .40
309 B.J. Surhoff .15 .40
310 Aaron Heilman RC .20 .50
311 Gabe Gross RC .25 .60
312 Lee Stevens .15 .40
313 Todd Hundley .15 .40
314 Macay McBride RC .40 1.00
315 Edgar Martinez .25 .60
316 Omar Vizquel .25 .60
317 Reggie Sanders .15 .40
318 John-Ford Griffin RC .15 .40
319 Tim Salmon UER .15 .40
Photo is Troy Glaus
320 Pokey Reese .15 .40
321 Jay Payton .15 .40
322 Doug Glanville .15 .40
323 Greg Vaughn .15 .40
324 Ruben Sierra .15 .40
325 Kip Wells .15 .40
326 Carl Everett .15 .40
327 Garret Anderson .15 .40
328 Jay Bell .15 .40
329 Barry Larkin .25 .60
330 Jeff Mathis RC .25 .60
331 Adrian Gonzalez SP .75 2.00
332 Juan Rivera SP .75 2.00
333 Tony Alvarez SP .75 2.00
334 Xavier Nady SP .75 2.00
335 Josh Hamilton SP 1.50 4.00
336 Will Smith SP RC .75 2.00
337 Israel Alcantara SP .75 2.00
338 Chris George SP .75 2.00
339 Sean Burroughs SP .75 2.00
340 Jack Cust SP .75 2.00
341 Henry Mateo SP RC .75 2.00
342 Carlos Pena SP .75 2.00
343 J.R. House SP .75 2.00
344 Carlos Silva SP .75 2.00
345 Mike Rivera SP RC .75 2.00
346 Adam Johnson SP .75 2.00
347 Scott Heard SP .75 2.00
348 Alex Cintron SP .75 2.00
349 Miguel Cabrera SP 3.00 8.00
350 Nick Johnson SP .75 2.00
351 Albert Pujols SP RC 20.00 50.00
352 Ichiro Suzuki SP RC 12.50 30.00
353 Carlos Delgado SP .75 2.00
354 Troy Glaus SP .75 2.00
355 Sammy Sosa SP 1.25 3.00
356 Ivan Rodriguez SP 1.25 3.00
357 Vladimir Guerrero SP 1.25 3.00
358 Manny Ramirez Sox SP 1.25 3.00
359 Luis Gonzalez SP .75 2.00
360 Roy Oswalt SP 1.25 3.00
361 Moises Alou SP .75 2.00
362 Juan Gonzalez SP .75 2.00
363 Tony Gwynn SP 1.50 4.00
364 Hideo Nomo SP 1.25 3.00
365 T. Shinjo SP RC 1.25 3.00
366 Kazuhiro Sasaki SP .75 2.00
367 Cal Ripken SP 4.00 10.00
368 Rafael Palmeiro SP 1.25 3.00
369 J.D. Drew SP .75 2.00
370 Doug Mientkiewicz SP .75 2.00
371 Jeff Bagwell SP 1.25 3.00
372 Darin Erstad SP .75 2.00
373 Tom Gordon SP .75 2.00
374 Ben Petrick SP .75 2.00
375 Eric Milton SP .75 2.00
376 N. Garciaparra SP 2.00 5.00
377 Julio Lugo SP .75 2.00
378 Tino Martinez SP 1.25 3.00
379 Javier Vazquez SP .75 2.00
380 Jeremy Giambi SP .75 2.00
381 Marty Cordova SP .75 2.00
382 Adrian Beltre SP .75 2.00
383 John Burkett SP .75 2.00
384 Aaron Boone SP .75 2.00
385 Eric Chavez SP .75 2.00
386 Curt Schilling SP .75 2.00
387 Cory Lidle UER .75 2.00
First name misspelled Corey
388 Jason Schmidt SP .75 2.00
389 Johnny Damon SP 1.25 3.00
390 Steve Finley SP .75 2.00
391 Edgardo Alfonzo SP .75 2.00
392 Jose Valentin SP .75 2.00
393 Jose Canseco SP 1.25 3.00
394 Ryan Klesko SP .75 2.00
395 David Cone SP .75 2.00
396 Jason Kendall UER .75 2.00
Last name misspelled Kendell
397 Placido Polanco SP .75 2.00
398 Glendon Rusch SP .75 2.00
399 Aaron Sele SP .75 2.00
400 D'Angelo Jimenez SP .75 2.00
401 Mark Grace SP 1.25 3.00
402 Al Leiter SP .75 2.00
403 Brian Jordan SP .75 2.00
404 Phil Nevin SP .75 2.00
405 Brent Abernathy SP .75 2.00
406 Kerry Wood SP .75 2.00
407 Alex Gonzalez SP .75 2.00
408 Robert Fick SP .75 2.00
409 Dmitri Young UER .75 2.00
First name misspelled Dimitri
410 Wes Helms SP .75 2.00
411 Trevor Hoffman SP .75 2.00
412 Rickey Henderson SP 1.25 3.00
413 Bobby Higginson SP .75 2.00
414 Gary Sheffield SP .75 2.00
415 Darryl Kile SP .75 2.00
416 Richie Sexson SP .75 2.00
417 F. Menechino SP RC .75 2.00
418 Javy Lopez SP .75 2.00
419 Carlos Lee SP .75 2.00
420 Jon Lieber SP .75 2.00
421 Hank Blalock SP RC 2.50 6.00
422 Marlon Byrd SP RC .15 .40
423 Jason Kinchen SP RC .75 2.00
424 M. Ensberg SP RC UER 2.00 5.00
Front photo is Adam Everett
425 Greg Nash SP RC .75 2.00
426 D. Tankersley SP RC .75 2.00
427 Nate Murphy SP RC .75 2.00
428 Chris Smith SP RC .75 2.00
429 Jake Gautreau SP RC .75 2.00
430 J. VanBenschoten SP RC .75 2.00
431 T.Thompson SP RC .75 2.00
432 O.Hudson SP RC 1.25 3.00
433 J.Williams SP RC 1.25 3.00
434 Kevin Reese SP RC .75 2.00
435 Ed Rogers SP RC .75 2.00
436 Ryan Jamison SP RC .75 2.00
437 A. Pettyjohn SP RC .75 2.00
438 Hee Seop Choi SP RC 1.25 3.00
439 J. Morneau SP RC 4.00 10.00
440 Mitch Jones SP RC .75 2.00

2001 Bowman Heritage Chrome

Inserted at a rate of one in 12 packs, the first 110 cards of this set are featured in this partial parallel set. Please see the multipliers to assess the values for the individual cards.

*CHROME STARS: 4X TO 10X BASIC CARDS
*CHROME RC'S: 2.5X TO 6X BASIC CARDS

2001 Bowman Heritage 1948 Reprints

Issued one per two packs, these 13 cards feature reprints of the featured players 1948 Bowman card.

COMPLETE SET (13) 4.00 10.00
1 Ralph Kiner .40 1.00
2 Johnny Mize .40 1.00
3 Bobby Thomson .40 1.00
4 Yogi Berra .60 1.50
5 Phil Rizzuto .50 1.25
6 Bob Feller .40 1.00
7 Enos Slaughter .40 1.00
8 Stan Musial .75 2.00
9 Hank Sauer .40 1.00
10 Ferris Fain .40 1.00
11 Red Schoendienst .40 1.00
12 Allie Reynolds UER .40 1.00
Original Card number is incorrect
13 Johnny Sain .40 1.00

2001 Bowman Heritage 1948 Reprints Autographs

Inserted at an overall rate of one in 1,523 these two cards have autographs from the feature players on their 1948 reprint cards.

1 Warren Spahn 1 30.00 60.00
2 Bob Feller 2 20.00 50.00

2001 Bowman Heritage 1948 Reprints Relics

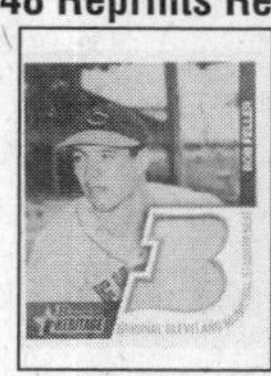

Issued at an overall odds of one in 53, these 12 cards feature relic cards from the featured players. The cards featuring pieces of actual seats were inserted at a rate of one in 291 while the odds for bats were one in 2,113 and the odds for jerseys were one in 2,905.

BHMBF Bob Feller Seat A 6.00 15.00
BHMBT Bobby Thomson Seat C 6.00 15.00
BHMES Enos Slaughter Seat C 6.00 15.00
BHMFF Ferris Fain Seat A 6.00 15.00
BHMHS Hank Sauer Seat A 6.00 15.00
BHMJM Johnny Mize Seat C 8.00 20.00
BHMPR Phil Rizzuto Seat B 8.00 20.00
BHMRK Ralph Kiner Seat B 6.00 15.00
BHMRS R.Schoendienst Bat 6.00 15.00
BHMSM1 Stan Musial Seat C 12.50 30.00
BHMYB1 Yogi Berra Seat B 10.00 25.00
BHMYB2 Yogi Berra Jsy 15.00 40.00

2001 Bowman Heritage Autographs

Inserted at overall odds of one in 358, these three cards feature active players who signed cards for the Bowman Heritage set.

HAAR Alex Rodriguez B 60.00 120.00
HABB Barry Bonds A 100.00 175.00
HARC Roger Clemens A 60.00 120.00

2002 Bowman Heritage

This 440 card standard-size, designed in the style of the 1954 Bowman set, was released in August, 2002. The 10-card packs had an SRP of $3 per pack and were issued 24 packs to a box and 16 boxes to a case. 110 cards were issued in shorter supply than the rest of the set and we have notated that information next to the player's name in our checklist. There were two versions of card number 66 which paid tribute to the Ted Williams/Jim Piersall numbering issue in the original 1954 Bowman set.

COMP.SET w/o SP's (324) 25.00 50.00
COMMON CARD (1-439) .15 .40
COMMON SP .75 2.00
1 Brent Abernathy .15 .40
2 Jermaine Dye .15 .40
3 James Shanks RC .15 .40
4 Chris Flinn RC .15 .40
5 Mike Peeples SP RC .75 2.00
6 Gary Sheffield .15 .40
7 Livan Hernandez SP .75 2.00
8 Jeff Austin RC .15 .40
9 Jeremy Giambi .15 .40
10 Adam Roller RC .15 .40
11 Sandy Alomar Jr. SP .75 2.00
12 Matt Williams SP .75 2.00
13 Hee Seop Choi .15 .40
14 Jose Offerman .15 .40
15 Robin Ventura .15 .40
16 Craig Biggio .25 .60
17 David Wells .15 .40
18 Rob Henkel RC .15 .40
19 Edgar Martinez .25 .60
20 Matt Morris SP .75 2.00
21 Jose Valentin .15 .40
22 Barry Bonds 1.00 2.50
23 Justin Schuda RC .15 .40
24 Josh Phelps .15 .40
25 John Rodriguez RC .20 .50
26 Angel Pagan RC 1.25 3.00
27 Aramis Ramirez .15 .40
28 Jack Wilson .15 .40
29 Roger Clemens .75 2.00
30 Kazuhisa Ishii RC .20 .50
31 Carlos Beltran .15 .40
32 Drew Henson SP .75 2.00
33 Kevin Young SP .75 2.00
34 Juan Cruz SP .75 2.00
35 Curtis Legendre RC .15 .40
36 Jose Morban RC .15 .40
37 Ricardo Cordova SP RC .75 2.00
38 Adam Everett .15 .40
39 Mark Prior .25 .60
40 Jose Bautista RC .40 1.00
41 Travis Foley RC .15 .40
42 Kerry Wood .15 .40
43 B.J. Surhoff .15 .40
44 Moises Alou .15 .40
45 Joey Hammond .15 .40
46 Eric Bruntlett RC .15 .40
47 Carlos Guillen .15 .40
48 Joe Crede .15 .40
49 Dan Phillips RC .15 .40
50 Jason LaRue .15 .40
51 Javy Lopez .15 .40
52 Larry Bigbie SP .75 2.00
53 Chris Baker RC .15 .40
54 Marty Cordova .15 .40
55 C.C. Sabathia .15 .40
56 Mike Piazza .60 1.50
57 Brian Giles .15 .40
58 Mike Bordick SP .75 2.00
59 Tyler Houston SP .75 2.00
60 Gabe Kapler .15 .40
61 Ben Broussard .15 .40
62 Steve Finley SP .75 2.00
63 Koyie Hill .15 .40
64 Jeff D'Amico .15 .40
65 Edwin Almonte RC .15 .40
66 Pedro Martinez .25 .60
66B Nomar Garciaparra 66 .60 1.50
67 Travis Fryman SP .75 2.00
68 Brady Clark SP .75 2.00
69 Reed Johnson SP RC 1.50 4.00
70 Mark Grace SP 1.25 3.00
71 Tony Batista SP .75 2.00
72 Roy Oswalt .15 .40
73 Pat Burrell SP .75 2.00
74 Dennis Tankersley .15 .40
75 Ramon Ortiz .15 .40
76 Neal Frendling SP RC .75 2.00
77 Omar Vizquel SP 1.25 3.00
78 Hideo Nomo .40 1.00
79 Orlando Hernandez SP .75 2.00
80 Andy Pettitte .25 .60
81 Cole Barthel RC .15 .40
82 Bret Boone .15 .40
83 Alfonso Soriano .15 .40
84 Brandon Duckworth .15 .40
85 Ben Grieve .15 .40
86 Mike Rosamond SP RC .75 2.00
87 Luke Prokopec .15 .40
88 Chone Figgins RC .60 1.50
89 Rick Ankiel SP .75 2.00
90 David Eckstein .15 .40
91 Corey Koskie .15 .40
92 David Justice .15 .40
93 Jimmy Alvarez RC .15 .40
94 Jason Schmidt .15 .40
95 Reggie Sanders .15 .40
96 Victor Alvarez RC .15 .40
97 Brett Roneberg RC .15 .40
98 D'Angelo Jimenez .15 .40
99 Hank Blalock .25 .60
100 Juan Rivera .15 .40
101 Mark Buehrle SP .75 2.00
102 Juan Uribe .15 .40
103 Royce Clayton SP .75 2.00
104 Brett Kay RC .15 .40
105 John Olerud .15 .40
106 Richie Sexson .15 .40
107 Chipper Jones .40 1.00
108 Adam Dunn .15 .40
109 Tim Salmon SP 1.25 3.00
110 Eric Karros .15 .40
111 Jose Vidro .15 .40
112 Jerry Hairston Jr. .15 .40
113 Anastacio Martinez RC .15 .40
114 Robert Fick SP .75 2.00
115 Randy Johnson .40 1.00
116 Trot Nixon SP .75 2.00
117 Nick Bierbrodt SP .75 2.00
118 Jim Edmonds .15 .40
119 Rafael Palmeiro .25 .60
120 Jose Macias .15 .40
121 Josh Beckett .15 .40
122 Sean Douglass .15 .40
123 Jeff Kent .15 .40
124 Tim Redding .15 .40
125 Xavier Nady .15 .40
126 Carl Everett .15 .40
127 Joe Randa .15 .40
128 Luke Hudson SP .75 2.00
129 Eric Miller RC .15 .40
130 Melvin Mora .15 .40
131 Adrian Gonzalez .15 .40
132 Larry Walker SP .75 2.00
133 Nic Jackson SP RC .75 2.00
134 Mike Lowell SP .75 2.00
135 Jim Thome .25 .60
136 Eric Milton .15 .40
137 Rich Thompson SP RC .75 2.00
138 Placido Polanco SP .75 2.00
139 Juan Pierre .15 .40
140 David Segui .15 .40
141 Chuck Finley .15 .40
142 Felipe Lopez .15 .40
143 Toby Hall .15 .40
144 Fred Bastardo RC .15 .40
145 Troy Glaus .15 .40
146 Todd Helton .25 .60
147 Ruben Gotay SP RC 1.25 3.00
148 Darin Erstad .15 .40
149 Ryan Gripp SP RC .75 2.00
150 Orlando Cabrera .15 .40
151 Jason Young RC .15 .40
152 Sterling Hitchcock SP .75 2.00
153 Miguel Tejada .15 .40
154 Al Leiter .15 .40
155 Taylor Buchholz RC .20 .50
156 Juan M. Gonzalez RC .15 .40
157 Damion Easley .15 .40
158 Jimmy Gobble RC .15 .40
159 Dennis Ulacia SP RC .75 2.00
160 Shane Reynolds SP .75 2.00
161 Javier Colina .15 .40
162 Frank Thomas .40 1.00
163 Chuck Knoblauch .15 .40
164 Sean Burroughs .15 .40
165 Greg Maddux .60 1.50
166 Jason Ellison RC .30 .75
167 Tony Womack .15 .40
168 Randall Shelley SP RC .75 2.00
169 Jason Marquis .15 .40
170 Brian Jordan .15 .40
171 Vicente Padilla .15 .40
172 Barry Zito .15 .40
173 Matt Allegra SP RC .75 2.00
174 Ralph Santana SP RC .75 2.00
175 Carlos Lee .15 .40
176 Richard Hidalgo SP .75 2.00
177 Kevin Deaton RC .15 .40
178 Juan Encarnacion .15 .40
179 Mark Quinn .15 .40
180 Rafael Furcal .15 .40
181 Garret Anderson UER .15 .40
Photo is Chone Figgins
182 David Wright RC 6.00 15.00
183 Jose Reyes .25 .60
184 Mario Ramos SP RC .75 2.00
185 J.D. Drew .15 .40
186 Juan Gonzalez .15 .40
187 Nick Neugebauer .15 .40
188 Alejandro Giron RC .15 .40
189 John Burkett .15 .40
190 Ben Sheets .15 .40
191 Vinny Castilla SP .75 2.00
192 Cory Lidle .15 .40
193 Fernando Vina .15 .40
194 Russell Branyan SP .75 2.00
195 Ben Davis .15 .40
196 Angel Berroa .15 .40
197 Alex Gonzalez .15 .40
198 Jared Sandberg .15 .40
199 Travis Lee SP .75 2.00
200 Luis DePaula SP .75 2.00
201 Ramon Hernandez SP .75 2.00
202 Brandon Inge .15 .40
203 Aubrey Huff .15 .40
204 Mike Rivera .15 .40
205 Brad Nelson RC .15 .40
206 Colt Griffin SP RC .75 2.00
207 Joel Pineiro .15 .40
208 Adam Pettyjohn .15 .40
209 Mark Redman .15 .40
210 Roberto Alomar SP 1.25 3.00
211 Denny Neagle .15 .40
212 Adam Kennedy .15 .40
213 Jason Arnold SP RC .75 2.00
214 Jamie Moyer .15 .40
215 Aaron Boone .15 .40
216 Doug Glanville .15 .40
217 Nick Johnson SP .75 2.00
218 Mike Cameron SP .75 2.00
219 Tim Wakefield SP .75 2.00
220 Todd Stottlemyre SP .75 2.00
221 Mo Vaughn SP .75 2.00
222 Vladimir Guerrero .40 1.00
223 Bill Ortega .15 .40
224 Kevin Brown .15 .40
225 Peter Bergeron SP .75 2.00
226 Shannon Stewart SP .75 2.00
227 Eric Chavez .15 .40
228 Clint Weibl RC .15 .40
229 Todd Hollandsworth SP .75 2.00
230 Jeff Bagwell .25 .60
231 Chad Qualls RC .20 .50
232 Ben Howard RC .15 .40
233 Rondell White SP .75 2.00
234 Fred McGriff .25 .60
235 Steve Cox SP .75 2.00
236 Chris Tritle RC .15 .40
237 Eric Valent .15 .40
238 Joe Mauer RC 3.00 8.00
239 Shawn Green .15 .40
240 Jimmy Rollins .15 .40
241 Edgar Renteria .15 .40
242 Edwin Yan RC .15 .40
243 Noochie Varner RC .15 .40
244 Kris Benson SP .75 2.00
245 Mike Hampton .15 .40
246 So Taguchi RC .20 .50
247 Sammy Sosa .40 1.00
248 Terrence Long .15 .40
249 Jason Bay RC 2.00 5.00
250 Kevin Millar SP .75 2.00
251 Albert Pujols .75 2.00
252 Chris Latham RC .15 .40
253 Eric Byrnes .15 .40
254 Napoleon Calzado SP RC .75 2.00
255 Bobby Higginson .15 .40
256 Ben Molina .15 .40
257 Torii Hunter SP .75 2.00
258 Jason Giambi .15 .40
259 Bartolo Colon .15 .40
260 Benito Baez .15 .40
261 Ichiro Suzuki .75 2.00
262 Mike Sweeney .15 .40
263 Brian West RC .15 .40
264 Brad Penny .15 .40
265 Kevin Millwood SP .75 2.00
266 Orlando Hudson .15 .40
267 Doug Mientkiewicz .15 .40
268 Luis Gonzalez SP .75 2.00
269 Jay Caligiuri RC .15 .40
270 Nate Cornejo SP .75 2.00
271 Lee Stevens .15 .40
272 Eric Hinske .15 .40
273 Antwon Rollins RC .15 .40
274 Bobby Jenks RC .60 1.50
275 Joe Mays .15 .40
276 Josh Shaffer RC .15 .40
277 Jonny Gomes RC 1.00 2.50
278 Bernie Williams .25 .60
279 Ed Rogers .15 .40
280 Carlos Delgado .15 .40
281 Raul Mondesi SP .75 2.00
282 Jose Ortiz .15 .40
283 Cesar Izturis .15 .40
284 Ryan Dempster SP .75 2.00
285 Brian Daubach .15 .40
286 Hansel Izquierdo RC .15 .40
287 Mike Lieberthal SP .75 2.00
288 Marcus Thames .15 .40
289 Nomar Garciaparra .60 1.50
290 Brad Fullmer .15 .40
291 Tino Martinez .25 .60
292 James Barrett RC .15 .40
293 Jacque Jones .15 .40
294 Nick Alvarez SP RC .75 2.00
295 Jason Grove SP RC .75 2.00
296 Mike Wilson SP RC .75 2.00
297 J.T. Snow .15 .40
298 Cliff Floyd .15 .40
299 Todd Hundley SP .75 2.00
300 Tony Clark SP .75 2.00
301 Demetrius Heath RC .15 .40
302 Morgan Ensberg .15 .40
303 Cristian Guzman .15 .40
304 Frank Catalanotto .15 .40
305 Jeff Weaver .15 .40
306 Tim Hudson .15 .40
307 Scott Wiggins SP RC .75 2.00
308 Shea Hillenbrand SP .75 2.00
309 Todd Walker SP .75 2.00
310 Tsuyoshi Shinjo .15 .40
311 Adrian Beltre .15 .40
312 Craig Kuzmic RC .15 .40
313 Paul Konerko .15 .40
314 Scott Hairston RC .20 .50
315 Chan Ho Park .15 .40
316 Jorge Posada .25 .60
317 Chris Snelling RC .30 .75
318 Keith Foulke .15 .40
319 John Smoltz .25 .60
320 Ryan Church SP RC 1.50 4.00
321 Mike Mussina .25 .60
322 Tony Armas Jr. SP .75 2.00
323 Craig Counsell .15 .40
324 Marcus Giles .15 .40
325 Greg Vaughn .15 .40
326 Curt Schilling .15 .40
327 Jeromy Burnitz .15 .40
328 Eric Byrnes .15 .40
329 Johnny Damon Sox .25 .60
330 Michael Floyd SP RC .75 2.00
331 Edgardo Alfonzo .15 .40
332 Jeremy Hill RC .15 .40
333 Josh Bonifay RC .15 .40
334 Byung-Hyun Kim .15 .40
335 Keith Ginter .15 .40
336 Ronald Acuna SP RC .75 2.00
337 Mike Hill SP RC .75 2.00
338 Sean Casey .15 .40
339 Matt Anderson SP .75 2.00
340 Dan Wright .15 .40
341 Ben Petrick .15 .40
342 Mike Sirotka SP .75 2.00
343 Alex Rodriguez .60 1.50
344 Einar Diaz .15 .40
345 Derek Jeter 1.00 2.50
346 Jeff Conine .15 .40
347 Ray Durham SP .75 2.00
348 Wilson Betemit SP .75 2.00
349 Jeffrey Hammonds .15 .40
350 Dan Trumble RC .15 .40
351 Phil Nevin SP .75 2.00
352 A.J. Burnett .15 .40
353 Bill Mueller .15 .40
354 Charles Nagy .15 .40
355 Rusty Greer SP .75 2.00
356 Jason Botts RC .20 .50
357 Magglio Ordonez .15 .40
358 Kevin Appier .15 .40
359 Brad Radke .15 .40
360 Chris George .15 .40
361 Chris Piersoll RC .15 .40
362 Ivan Rodriguez .25 .60
363 Jim Kavourias RC .15 .40
364 Rick Helling SP .75 2.00
365 Dean Palmer .15 .40
366 Rich Aurilia SP .75 2.00
367 Ryan Vogelsong .15 .40
368 Matt Lawton .15 .40
369 Wade Miller .15 .40
370 Dustin Hermanson .15 .40
371 Craig Wilson .15 .40
372 Todd Zeile SP .75 2.00
373 Jon Guzman RC .15 .40
374 Ellis Burks .15 .40
375 Robert Cosby SP RC .75 2.00
376 Jason Kendall .15 .40
377 Scott Rolen SP 1.25 3.00
378 Andruw Jones .25 .60
379 Greg Sain RC .15 .40
380 Paul LoDuca .15 .40
381 Scotty Layfield RC .15 .40
382 Tomo Ohka .15 .40
383 Garrett Guzman RC .15 .40
384 Jack Cust SP .75 2.00
385 Shayne Wright RC .15 .40
386 Derrek Lee .25 .60
387 Jesus Medrano RC .15 .40
388 Javier Vazquez .15 .40
389 Preston Wilson SP .75 2.00
390 Gavin Floyd RC .40 1.00
391 Sidney Ponson SP .75 2.00
392 Jose Hernandez .15 .40
393 Scott Erickson SP .75 2.00
394 Jose Valverde RC .15 .40
395 Mark Hamilton SP RC .75 2.00
396 Brad Cresse .15 .40
397 Danny Bautista .15 .40
398 Ray Lankford SP .75 2.00
399 Miguel Batista SP .75 2.00
400 Brent Butler .15 .40
401 Manny Delcarmen SP RC 1.25 3.00
402 Kyle Farnsworth SP .75 2.00
403 Freddy Garcia .15 .40
404 Joe Jiannetti RC .15 .40
405 Josh Barfield RC 1.00 2.50
406 Corey Patterson .15 .40
407 Josh Towers .15 .40
408 Carlos Pena .15 .40
409 Jeff Cirillo .15 .40
410 Jon Lieber .15 .40
411 Woody Williams SP .75 2.00
412 Richard Lane SP RC .75 2.00
413 Alex Gonzalez .15 .40
414 Wilkin Ruan .15 .40
415 Geoff Jenkins .15 .40
416 Carlos Hernandez .15 .40
417 Matt Clement SP .75 2.00
418 Jose Cruz Jr. .15 .40
419 Jake Mauer RC .15 .40
420 Matt Childers RC .15 .40
421 Tom Glavine SP 1.25 3.00
422 Ken Griffey Jr. .60 1.50
423 Anderson Hernandez RC .15 .40
424 John Suomi RC .15 .40
425 Doug Sessions RC .15 .40
426 Jaret Wright .15 .40
427 Rolando Viera SP RC .75 2.00
428 Aaron Sele .15 .40
429 Dmitri Young .15 .40
430 Ryan Klesko .15 .40
431 Kevin Tapani SP .75 2.00
432 Joe Kennedy .15 .40
433 Austin Kearns .15 .40
434 Roger Cedeno SP .75 2.00
435 Lance Berkman .15 .40
436 Frank Menechino .15 .40
437 Brett Myers .15 .40
438 Bob Abreu .15 .40
439 Shawn Estes SP .75 2.00

2002 Bowman Heritage Black Box

Issued at stated odds of one in two packs, these 55 cards form a partial parallel of the Bowman Heritage set. These cards can be notated by the players "signature" being placed in a black box.

13 Hee Seop Choi .30 .75
22 Barry Bonds 2.00 5.00
23 Justin Schuda .25 .60
27 Aramis Ramirez .30 .75
30 Kazuhisa Ishii .30 .75
39 Mark Prior .50 1.25
41 Travis Foley .25 .60
56 Mike Piazza 1.25 3.00
66 Nomar Garciaparra .50 1.25
72 Roy Oswalt .30 .75
96 Victor Alvarez .25 .60
99 Hank Blalock .50 1.25
107 Chipper Jones .75 2.00
108 Adam Dunn .30 .75
120 Jose Macias .30 .75
121 Josh Beckett .30 .75
139 Juan Pierre .30 .75
143 Toby Hall .30 .75
145 Troy Glaus .30 .75
146 Todd Helton .50 1.25
153 Miguel Tejada .30 .75
167 Tony Womack .30 .75
180 Rafael Furcal .30 .75
182 David Wright 6.00 15.00
185 J.D. Drew .30 .75
222 Vladimir Guerrero .75 2.00
227 Eric Chavez .30 .75
238 Joe Mauer 5.00 12.00
240 Jimmy Rollins .30 .75
246 So Taguchi .30 .75
247 Sammy Sosa .75 2.00
251 Albert Pujols 1.50 4.00
258 Jason Giambi .30 .75
261 Ichiro Suzuki 1.50 4.00
266 Orlando Hudson .30 .75
269 Jay Caligiuri .25 .60
274 Bobby Jenks 1.00 2.50
275 Joe Mays .30 .75
277 Jonny Gomes 1.50 4.00
310 Tsuyoshi Shinjo .30 .75
314 Scott Hairston .30 .75
316 Jorge Posada .50 1.25
317 Chris Snelling .50 1.25
335 Keith Ginter .30 .75
343 Alex Rodriguez 1.25 3.00
345 Derek Jeter 2.00 5.00
362 Ivan Rodriguez .50 1.25
390 Gavin Floyd .60 1.50
396 Brad Cresse .30 .75
405 Josh Barfield 1.50 4.00
414 Wilkin Ruan .30 .75
416 Carlos Hernandez .30 .75
418 Jose Cruz Jr. .30 .75
422 Ken Griffey Jr. 1.25 3.00
433 Austin Kearns .30 .75

2002 Bowman Heritage Chrome Refractors

Issued at stated odds of one in 16, these 110 cards partially parallel the regular Bowman Heritage set. Please note that although the numbering is different, the cards are the same as the regular cards except for the Chrome technology used. These cards were issued to a stated print run of 350 serial numbered sets.

*CHROME: 4X TO 10X BASIC CARDS
*CHROME SP's: .75X TO 2X BASIC SP'S
*CHROME RC's: 3X TO 8X BASIC RC'S

2002 Bowman Heritage Gold Chrome Refractors

Issued at stated odds of one in 32, these 110 cards partially parallel the regular Bowman Heritage set. Please note that although the numbering is different, the cards are the same as the regular cards except for the Chrome technology used. Each card was issued to a stated print run of 175 serial numbered sets.

*GOLD: 6X TO 15X BASIC CARDS
*GOLD SP'S: 1.25X TO 3X BASIC SP'S
*GOLD RC'S: 5X TO 12X BASIC RC'S

2002 Bowman Heritage 1954 Reprints

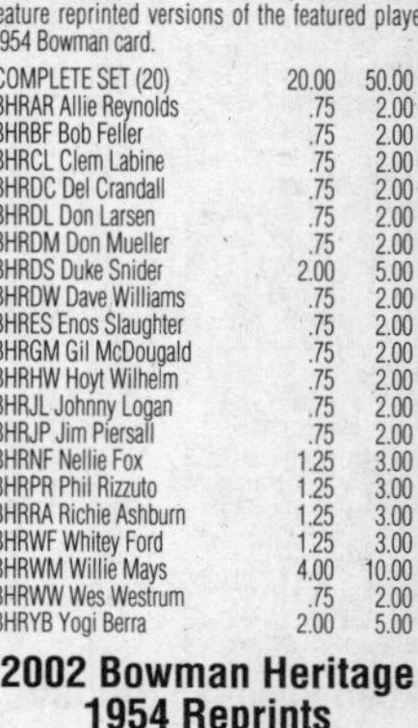

Issued at stated odds of one in 12, these 20 cards feature reprinted versions of the featured player 1954 Bowman card.

COMPLETE SET (20) 20.00 50.00
BHRAR Allie Reynolds .75 2.00
BHRBF Bob Feller .75 2.00
BHRCL Clem Labine .75 2.00
BHRDC Del Crandall .75 2.00
BHRDL Don Larsen .75 2.00
BHRDM Don Mueller .75 2.00
BHRDS Duke Snider 2.00 5.00
BHRDW Dave Williams .75 2.00
BHRES Enos Slaughter .75 2.00
BHRGM Gil McDougald .75 2.00
BHRHW Hoyt Wilhelm .75 2.00
BHRJL Johnny Logan .75 2.00
BHRJP Jim Piersall .75 2.00
BHRNF Nellie Fox 1.25 3.00
BHRPR Phil Rizzuto 1.25 3.00
BHRRA Richie Ashburn 1.25 3.00
BHRWF Whitey Ford 1.25 3.00
BHRWM Willie Mays 4.00 10.00
BHRWW Wes Westrum .75 2.00
BHRYB Yogi Berra 2.00 5.00

2002 Bowman Heritage 1954 Reprints Autographs

Inserted at stated odds of one in 126, these six cards have autographs of the featured player on their 1954 Reprint card.

*SPEC.ED: .75X TO 2X BASIC AUTOS
SPEC.ED STATED ODDS 1:1910
SPEC.ED. PRINT RUN 54 SERIAL #'d SETS
BHRACL Clem Labine 10.00 25.00
BHRADC Del Crandall 15.00 40.00
BHRADM Don Mueller 10.00 25.00
BHRADW Dave Williams 10.00 25.00
BHRAJL Johnny Logan 15.00 40.00
BHRAYB Yogi Berra 40.00 80.00

2002 Bowman Heritage Autographs

Issued at overall stated odds of one in 45, these 13 cards feature players signing copies of their Bowman Heritage card. Please note that these cards were issued in three different groups with differing odds and we have noted which players belong to which group in our checklist.

GROUP A STATED ODDS 1:620
GROUP B STATED ODDS 1:89
GROUP C STATED ODDS 1:103
OVERALL STATED ODDS 1:45
BHAAP Albert Pujols A 200.00 350.00
BHACI Cesar Izturis B 4.00 10.00
BHADH Drew Henson B 4.00 10.00
BHAHB Hank Blalock C 6.00 15.00
BHAJM Joe Mauer C 40.00 80.00
BHAJR Juan Rivera C 6.00 15.00
BHAKG Keith Ginter B 4.00 10.00
BHAKI Kazuhisa Ishii A 12.50 30.00
BHALB Lance Berkman B 10.00 25.00
BHAMP Mark Prior B 6.00 15.00
BHAPL Paul LoDuca C 6.00 15.00

BHARO Roy Oswalt B 6.00 15.00
BHATH Toby Hall B 4.00 10.00

2002 Bowman Heritage Relics

Inserted in packs at overall stated odds of one in 47 for Jersey cards and one in 75 for Uniform cards, these 26 cards feature game-worn swatches on them. Many cards belong to different groups and we have noted that information next to their name in our checklist.

GROUP A JSY ODDS 1:1910
GROUP B JSY ODDS 1:1551
GROUP C JSY ODDS 1:138
GROUP D JSY ODDS 1:207
GROUP E JSY ODDS 1:165
GROUP F JSY ODDS 1:2072
GROUP G JSY ODDS 1:653
GROUP A UNI ODDS 1:1551
GROUP B UNI ODDS 1:855
GROUP C UNI ODDS 1:124
GROUP D UNI ODDS 1:284
BHAP Albert Pujols Uni C 8.00 20.00
BHBB Barry Bonds Uni D 10.00 25.00
BHCD Carlos Delgado Jsy G 4.00 10.00
BHCJ Chipper Jones Jsy C 6.00 15.00
BHDE Darin Erstad Uni C 4.00 10.00
BHEA Edgardo Alfonzo Jsy C 4.00 10.00
BHEC Eric Chavez Jsy C 4.00 10.00
BHEM Edgar Martinez Jsy C 6.00 15.00
BHFT Frank Thomas Jsy F 6.00 15.00
BHGM Greg Maddux Jsy C 6.00 15.00
BHIR Ivan Rodriguez Uni B 6.00 15.00
BHJB Josh Beckett Jsy E 4.00 10.00
BHJE Jim Edmonds Jsy D 4.00 10.00
BHJS John Smoltz Jsy C 6.00 15.00
BHJT Jim Thome Jsy E 6.00 15.00
BHKS Kazuhiro Sasaki Jsy C 4.00 10.00
BHLW Larry Walker Jsy C 4.00 10.00
BHMP Mike Piazza Uni A 6.00 15.00
BHMR Mariano Rivera Uni C 6.00 15.00
BHNG Nomar Garciaparra Jsy A 8.00 20.00
BHPK Paul Konerko Jsy E 4.00 10.00
BHPW Preston Wilson Jsy B 4.00 10.00
BHSR Scott Rolen Jsy C 6.00 15.00
BHTG Tony Gwynn Jsy D 6.00 15.00
BHTH Todd Helton Jsy D 6.00 15.00
BHTS Tim Salmon Uni C 6.00 15.00

2003 Bowman Heritage

This 300-card standard-size set was released in December, 2003. The set was issued in four-card packs with an $3 SRP which came 24 packs to a box and 10 boxes to a case. This set was designed in the style of what the 1956 Bowman set would have been if that set had been issued. Cards numbered 161 through 170 feature players who debuted in the 2003 season and each of those players have a double image. Cards numbered 171-180 featured retired greats and those cards were issued in three styles: Regular design, Double Image and Knothole Design. Cards number 180 through 300 are all Rookie Cards and all those cards are issued in the knothole design.

COMPLETE SET (300) 60.00 120.00
1 Jorge Posada .25 .60
2 Todd Helton .25 .60
3 Marcus Giles .15 .40
4 Eric Chavez .15 .40
5 Edgar Martinez .25 .60
6 Luis Gonzalez .15 .40
7 Corey Patterson .15 .40
8 Preston Wilson .15 .40
9 Ryan Klesko .15 .40
10 Randy Johnson .40 1.00
11 Jose Guillen .15 .40
12 Carlos Lee .15 .40
13 Steve Finley .15 .40
14 A.J. Pierzynski .15 .40
15 Troy Glaus .15 .40
16 Darin Erstad .15 .40
17 Moises Alou .15 .40
18 Torii Hunter .15 .40
19 Marlon Byrd .15 .40
20 Mark Prior .25 .60
21 Shannon Stewart .15 .40
22 Craig Biggio .25 .60
23 Johnny Damon .25 .60
24 Robert Fick .15 .40
25 Jason Giambi .15 .40
26 Fernando Vina .15 .40
27 Aubrey Huff .15 .40
28 Benito Santiago .15 .40
29 Jay Gibbons .15 .40
30 Ken Griffey Jr. .60 1.50
31 Rocco Baldelli .15 .40
32 Pat Burrell .15 .40
33 A.J. Burnett .15 .40
34 Omar Vizquel .25 .60
35 Greg Maddux .60 1.50
36 Cliff Floyd .15 .40
37 C.C. Sabathia .15 .40
38 Geoff Jenkins .15 .40
39 Ty Wigginton .15 .40
40 Jeff Kent .15 .40
41 Orlando Hudson .15 .40
42 Edgardo Alfonzo .15 .40
43 Greg Myers .15 .40
44 Melvin Mora .15 .40
45 Sammy Sosa .40 1.00
46 Russ Ortiz .15 .40
47 Josh Beckett .15 .40
48 David Wells .15 .40
49 Woody Williams .15 .40
50 Alex Rodriguez .60 1.50
51 Randy Wolf .15 .40
52 Carlos Beltran .15 .40
53 Austin Kearns .15 .40
54 Trot Nixon .15 .40
55 Ivan Rodriguez .25 .60
56 Shea Hillenbrand .15 .40
57 Roberto Alomar .25 .60
58 John Olerud .15 .40
59 Michael Young .25 .60
60 Garret Anderson .15 .40
61 Mike Lieberthal .15 .40
62 Adam Dunn .15 .40
63 Raul Ibanez .15 .40
64 Kenny Lofton .15 .40
65 Ichiro Suzuki .75 2.00
66 Jarrod Washburn .15 .40
67 Shawn Chacon .15 .40
68 Alex Gonzalez .15 .40
69 Roy Halladay .15 .40
70 Vladimir Guerrero .40 1.00
71 Hee Seop Choi .15 .40
72 Jody Gerut .15 .40
73 Ray Durham .15 .40
74 Mark Teixeira .25 .60
75 Hank Blalock .15 .40
76 Jerry Hairston Jr. .15 .40
77 Erubiel Durazo .15 .40
78 Frank Catalanotto .15 .40
79 Jacque Jones .15 .40
80 Bobby Abreu .15 .40
81 Mike Hampton .15 .40
82 Zach Day .15 .40
83 Jimmy Rollins .15 .40
84 Joel Pineiro .15 .40
85 Brett Myers .15 .40
86 Frank Thomas .40 1.00
87 Aramis Ramirez .15 .40
88 Paul Lo Duca .15 .40
89 Dmitri Young .15 .40
90 Brian Giles .15 .40
91 Jose Cruz Jr. .15 .40
92 Derek Lowe .15 .40
93 Mark Buehrle .15 .40
94 Wade Miller .15 .40
95 Derek Jeter 1.00 2.50
96 Bret Boone .15 .40
97 Tony Batista .15 .40
98 Sean Casey .15 .40
99 Eric Hinske .15 .40
100 Albert Pujols .75 2.00
101 Runelvys Hernandez .15 .40
102 Vernon Wells .15 .40
103 Kerry Wood .15 .40
104 Lance Berkman .15 .40
105 Alfonso Soriano .15 .40
106 Bill Mueller .15 .40
107 Bartolo Colon .15 .40
108 Andy Pettitte .25 .60
109 Rafael Furcal .15 .40
110 Dontrelle Willis .40 1.00
111 Carl Crawford .15 .40
112 Scott Rolen .25 .60
113 Chipper Jones .40 1.00
114 Magglio Ordonez .15 .40
115 Bernie Williams .25 .60
116 Roy Oswalt .15 .40
117 Kevin Brown .15 .40
118 Cristian Guzman .15 .40
119 Kazuhisa Ishii .15 .40
120 Larry Walker .15 .40
121 Miguel Tejada .15 .40
122 Manny Ramirez .25 .60
123 Mike Mussina .25 .60
124 Mike Lowell .15 .40
125 Scott Podsednik .15 .40
126 Aaron Boone .15 .40
127 Carlos Delgado .15 .40
128 Jose Vidro .15 .40
129 Brad Radke .15 .40
130 Rafael Palmeiro .25 .60
131 Mark Mulder .15 .40
132 Jason Schmidt .15 .40
133 Gary Sheffield .15 .40
134 Richie Sexson .15 .40
135 Barry Zito .15 .40
136 Tom Glavine .25 .60
137 Jim Edmonds .15 .40
138 Andruw Jones .25 .60
139 Pedro Martinez .25 .60
140 Curt Schilling .15 .40
141 Phil Nevin .15 .40
142 Nomar Garciaparra .60 1.50
143 Vicente Padilla .15 .40
144 Kevin Millwood .15 .40
145 Shawn Green .15 .40
146 Jeff Bagwell .25 .60
147 Hideo Nomo .40 1.00
148 Fred McGriff .25 .60
149 Matt Morris .15 .40
150 Roger Clemens .75 2.00
151 Jerome Williams .15 .40
152 Orlando Cabrera .15 .40
153 Tim Hudson .15 .40
154 Mike Sweeney .15 .40
155 Jim Thome .25 .60
156 Rich Aurilia .15 .40
157 Mike Piazza .60 1.50
158 Edgar Renteria .15 .40
159 Javy Lopez .15 .40
160 Jamie Moyer .15 .40
161 Miguel Cabrera DI .40 1.00
162 Adam Loewen DI RC .40 1.00
163 Jose Reyes DI .15 .40
164 Zack Greinke DI .15 .40
165 Gavin Floyd DI .15 .40
166 Jeremy Guthrie DI .15 .40
167 Victor Martinez DI .25 .60
168 Rich Harden DI .25 .60
169 Joe Mauer DI .40 1.00
170 Khalil Greene DI .40 1.00
171A Willie Mays .75 2.00
171B Willie Mays DI .75 2.00
171C Willie Mays KN .75 2.00
172A Phil Rizzuto .25 .60
172B Phil Rizzuto DI .25 .60
172C Phil Rizzuto KN .25 .60
173A Al Kaline .40 1.00
173B Al Kaline DI .40 1.00
173C Al Kaline KN .40 1.00
174A Warren Spahn .25 .60
174B Warren Spahn DI .25 .60
174C Warren Spahn KN .25 .60
175A Jimmy Piersall .15 .40
175B Jimmy Piersall DI .15 .40
175C Jimmy Piersall KN .15 .40
176A Luis Aparicio .15 .40
176B Luis Aparicio DI .15 .40
176C Luis Aparicio KN .15 .40
177A Whitey Ford .25 .60
177B Whitey Ford DI .25 .60
177C Whitey Ford KN .25 .60
178A Harmon Killebrew .40 1.00
178B Harmon Killebrew DI .40 1.00
178C Harmon Killebrew KN .40 1.00
179A Duke Snider .25 .60
179B Duke Snider DI .25 .60
179C Duke Snider KN .25 .60
180A Roberto Clemente 1.00 2.50
180B Roberto Clemente DI 1.00 2.50
180C Roberto Clemente KN 1.00 2.50
181 David Martinez KN RC .15 .40
182 Felix Pie KN RC 1.50 4.00
183 Kevin Correia KN RC .15 .40
184 Brandon Webb KN RC 1.00 2.50
185 Matt Diaz KN RC .30 .75
186 Lew Ford KN RC .20 .50
187 Jeremy Griffiths KN RC .15 .40
188 Matt Hensley KN RC .15 .40
189 Danny Garcia KN RC .15 .40
190 Elizardo Ramirez KN RC .20 .50
191 Greg Aquino KN RC .15 .40
192 Felix Sanchez KN RC .15 .40
193 Kelly Shoppach KN RC .30 .75
194 Bubba Nelson KN RC .20 .50
195 Mike Oâ™Keefe KN RC .15 .40
196 Hanley Ramirez KN RC 1.50 4.00
197 Todd Wellemeyer KN RC .15 .40
198 Dustin Moseley KN RC .15 .40
199 Eric Crozier KN RC .20 .50
200 Ryan Shealy KN RC 1.00 2.50
201 Jeremy Bonderman KN RC 1.00 2.50
202 Bo Hart KN RC .15 .40
203 Dusty Brown KN RC .15 .40
204 Rob Hammock KN RC .15 .40
205 Jorge Piedra KN RC .20 .50
206 Jason Kubel KN RC .60 1.50
207 Stephen Randolph KN RC .15 .40
208 Andy Sisco KN RC .15 .40
209 Matt Kata KN RC .15 .40
210 Robinson Cano KN RC 3.00 8.00
211 Ben Francisco KN RC .15 .40
212 Arnie Munoz KN RC .15 .40
213 Ozzie Chavez KN RC .15 .40
214 Beau Kemp KN RC .15 .40
215 Travis Wong KN RC .20 .50
216 Brian McCann KN RC 2.50 6.00
217 Aquilino Lopez KN RC .15 .40
218 Bobby Basham KN RC .15 .40
219 Tim Olson KN RC .15 .40
220 Nathan Panther KN RC .15 .40
221 Wil Ledezma KN RC .15 .40
222 Josh Willingham KN RC .40 1.00
223 David Cash KN RC .15 .40
224 Oscar Villarreal KN RC .15 .40
225 Jeff Duncan KN RC .15 .40
226 Dan Haren KN RC .40 1.00
227 Michel Hernandez KN RC .15 .40
228 Matt Murton KN RC .75 2.00
229 Clay Hensley KN RC .15 .40
230 Tyler Johnson KN RC .15 .40
231 Tyler Martin KN RC .15 .40
232 J.D. Durbin KN RC .15 .40
233 Shane Victorino KN RC .40 1.00
234 Rajai Davis KN RC .15 .40
235 Chien-Ming Wang KN RC 2.00 5.00
236 Travis Ishikawa KN RC .30 .75
237 Eric Eckenstahler KN RC .15 .40
238 Dustin McGowan KN RC .20 .50
239 Prentice Redman KN RC .15 .40
240 Haj Turay KN RC .15 .40
241 Matt DeMarco KN RC .15 .40
242 Lou Palmisano KN RC .20 .50
243 Eric Reed KN RC .15 .40
244 Willie Eyre KN RC .15 .40
245 Ferdin Tejeda KN RC .15 .40
246 Michael Garciaparra KN RC .15 .40
247 Michael Hinckley KN RC .20 .50
248 Branden Florence KN RC .15 .40
249 Trent Oeltjen KN RC .20 .50
250 Mike Neu KN RC .15 .40
251 Chris Lubanski KN RC .40 1.00
252 Brandon Wood KN RC 4.00 10.00
253 Delmon Young KN RC 2.00 5.00
254 Matt Harrison KN RC .30 .75
255 Chad Billingsley KN RC 1.25 3.00
256 Josh Anderson KN RC .20 .50
257 Brian McFall KN RC .15 .40
258 Ryan Wagner KN RC .15 .40
259 Billy Hogan KN RC .20 .50
260 Nate Spears KN RC .20 .50
261 Ryan Harvey KN RC .75 2.00
262 Wes Littleton KN RC .20 .50
263 Xavier Paul KN RC .15 .40
264 Sean Rodriguez KN RC .75 2.00
265 Brian Finch KN RC .15 .40
266 Josh Rainwater KN RC .20 .50
267 Brian Snyder KN RC .20 .50
268 Eric Duncan KN RC .75 2.00
269 Rickie Weeks KN RC 1.25 3.00
270 Tim Battle KN RC .30 .75
271 Scott Beerer KN RC .15 .40
272 Aaron Hill KN RC .40 1.00
273 Casey Abrams KN RC .30 .75
274 Jonathan Fulton KN RC .20 .50
275 Todd Jennings KN RC .20 .50
276 Jordan Pratt KN RC .20 .50
277 Tom Gorzelanny KN RC .50 1.25
278 Matt Lorenzo KN RC .20 .50
279 Jarrod Saltalamacchia KN RC 2.00 5.00
280 Mike Wagner KN RC .15 .40

2003 Bowman Heritage Autographs

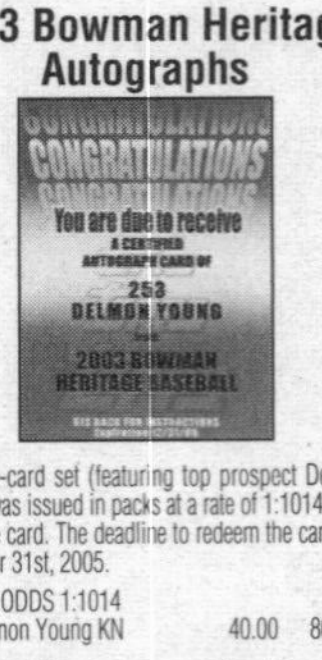

This one-card set (featuring top prospect Delmon Young) was issued in packs at a rate of 1:1014 as an exchange card. The deadline to redeem the card was December 31st, 2005.

STATED ODDS 1:1014
253 Delmon Young KN 40.00 80.00

2003 Bowman Heritage Box Toppers

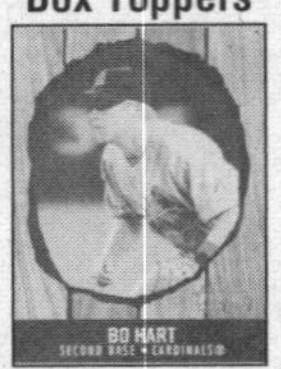

COMPLETE SET (8) 10.00 25.00
*BOX TOPPER: .4X TO 1X BASIC
ONE PER SEALED BOX

2003 Bowman Heritage Facsimile Signature

*FACSIMILE 161-170: 1X TO 2.5X BASIC
*FACSIMILE 171A-180C: 1X TO 2.5X BASIC
*FACSIMILE 181-280: .6X TO 1.5X BASIC
ONE PER PACK

2003 Bowman Heritage Gold Rainbow

STATED ODDS 1:4178
STATED PRINT RUN 1 SERIAL #'d SET
NO PRICING DUE TO SCARCITY

2003 Bowman Heritage Rainbow

COMPLETE SET (100) 30.00 80.00
*RAINBOW: .5X TO 1.2X BASIC
ONE PER PACK

2003 Bowman Heritage Diamond Cuts Relics

BAT ODDS 1:133
JSY GROUP A ODDS 1:28
JSY GROUP B ODDS 1:936
JSY GROUP C ODDS 1:626
UNI ODDS 1:35
GOLD STATED ODDS 1:8193
GOLD PRINT RUN 1 SERIAL #'d SET
NO GOLD PRICING DUE TO SCARCITY
*RED BAT: .6X TO 1.5X BASIC BAT
*RED JSY: 1X TO 2.5X BASIC JSY
*RED UNI: 1X TO 2.5X BASIC UNI
RED STATED ODDS 1:143
RED PRINT RUN 56 SERIAL #'d SETS
AJ Andruw Jones Jsy A 4.00 10.00
AK Austin Kearns Jsy A 3.00 8.00
AP Albert Pujols Bat 10.00 25.00
AR1 Alex Rodriguez Bat 6.00 15.00
AR2 Alex Rodriguez Jsy A 4.00 10.00
AS Alfonso Soriano Bat 4.00 10.00
BB Bret Boone Jsy A 3.00 8.00
BM Brett Myers Jsy A 3.00 8.00
BW Bernie Williams Uni 4.00 10.00
BZ Barry Zito Uni 3.00 8.00
CB Craig Biggio Uni 4.00 10.00
CF Cliff Floyd Uni 3.00 8.00
CG Cristian Guzman Jsy A 3.00 8.00
CJ1 Chipper Jones Bat 6.00 15.00
CJ2 Chipper Jones Jsy A 4.00 10.00
EC Eric Chavez Uni 3.00 8.00
GS Gary Sheffield Uni 3.00 8.00
HB Hank Blalock Bat 4.00 10.00
HN Hideo Nomo Jsy A 4.00 10.00
JA Jeremy Affeldt Uni 3.00 8.00
JB Jeff Bagwell Jsy A 4.00 10.00
JE Jim Edmonds Uni 3.00 8.00
JG Jason Giambi Uni 3.00 8.00
JJ Jason Jennings Jsy A 3.00 8.00
JL Javy Lopez Jsy A 3.00 8.00
JLP Josh Phelps Jsy C 3.00 8.00
JR Jose Reyes Jsy A 3.00 8.00
JV Javier Vazquez Jsy A 3.00 8.00
JW Jarrod Washburn Uni 3.00 8.00
KI Kazuhiro Sasaki Jsy A 3.00 8.00
KM Kevin Millwood Jsy A 3.00 8.00
KW Kerry Wood Uni 3.00 8.00
MA Moises Alou Jsy C 3.00 8.00
MG Mark Grace Jsy B 4.00 10.00
ML Mike Lowell Jsy A 3.00 8.00
MM Mark Mulder Uni 3.00 8.00
MS Mike Sweeney Jsy A 3.00 8.00
MT Miguel Tejada Uni 3.00 8.00
PL Paul Lo Duca Jsy A 3.00 8.00
PM Pedro Martinez Jsy A 4.00 10.00
RC Roberto Clemente Bat 40.00 80.00
RH Rickey Henderson Bat 6.00 15.00
RP1 Rafael Palmeiro Bat 6.00 15.00
RP2 Rafael Palmeiro Uni 4.00 10.00
SR1 Scott Rolen Bat 6.00 15.00
SR2 Scott Rolen Uni 4.00 10.00
SS1 Sammy Sosa Bat 6.00 15.00
SS2 Sammy Sosa Jsy A 4.00 10.00
TA Tony Armas Jr. Jsy A 3.00 8.00
TG Troy Glaus Uni 3.00 8.00
TH Todd Helton Jsy A 4.00 10.00
THA Tim Hudson Uni 3.00 8.00
TW Ty Wigginton Uni 3.00 8.00
VG Vladimir Guerrero Bat 6.00 15.00
VW Vernon Wells Jsy A 3.00 8.00

2003 Bowman Heritage Olbermann Autograph

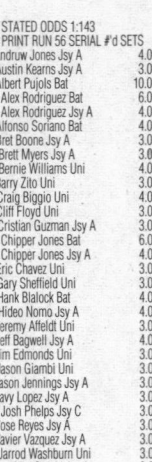

STATED ODDS 1:1421
KOA Keith Olbermann 40.00 80.00

2003 Bowman Heritage Signs of Greatness

STATED ODDS 1:30
RED INK STATED ODDS 1:32,141
RED INK PRINT RUN 1 SERIAL #'d SET
NO RED INK PRICING DUE TO SCARCITY
BF Brian Finch 3.00 8.00
BS Brian Snyder 3.00 8.00
CB Chad Billingsley 10.00 25.00
DW Dontrelle Willis 10.00 25.00
FP Felix Pie 15.00 40.00
JD Jeff Duncan 3.00 8.00
KY Kevin Youkilis 10.00 25.00
MM Matt Murton 6.00 15.00
RC Robinson Cano 75.00 150.00
RH Rich Harden 4.00 10.00
RW Rickie Weeks 10.00 25.00
TG Tom Gorzelanny 10.00 25.00

2004 Bowman Heritage

This 352-card set was released in December, 2004. The set was issued in eight-card packs with an $3 SRP which came 24 packs to a box and 10 boxes to a case. This set was issued in the style of 1955 Bowman and featured several twists similar to the original set including some cards in which the biographies did not match the player pictured and a card number #140 featuring a pair of brothers. (as the original 55 set had pictures of the Shantz brothers at #140). There were also short prints scattered throughout the set as well as the first major manufacturer cards of many current umpires.

COMPLETE SET (351) 175.00 300.00
COMP.SET w/o SP's (300) 25.00 50.00
SP STATED ODDS 1:3 HOBBY, 1:3 RETAIL
SP's: 2/9/13/21/25/40B/46/48B/50/55/61
SP's: 77/80/87/89/95/100/104/109/127/130
SP's: 132/141/183A/189/204/206/208/210
SP's: 213/216/220/224/228/234/240/243
SP's: 246/249/259/268/270-271/282/291
SP's: 304/318/327/334/342/348
PLATES STATED ODDS 1:240 HOBBY
PLATES PRINT RUN 1 #'d SET PER COLOR
PLATES: BLACK, CYAN, MAGENTA & YELLOW
NO PLATES PRICING DUE TO SCARCITY
ROOP BINDER ODDS 1:240 HOBBY
ROOP BINDER EXCH.DEADLINE 12/31/05
1 Tom Glavine .25 .60
2 Mike Piazza SP 3.00 8.00
3 Sidney Ponson .15 .40
4 Jerry Hairston Jr. .15 .40
5 Jermaine Dye .15 .40
6 Bobby Crosby .15 .40
7 Carlos Zambrano .15 .40
8 Moises Alou .15 .40
9 Alex Rodriguez SP 3.00 8.00
10 Derek Jeter .75 2.00
11 Rafael Furcal .15 .40
12 J.D. Drew .15 .40
13 Joe Mauer SP 2.50 6.00
14 Brad Radke .15 .40
15 Johnny Damon .25 .60
16 Derek Lowe .15 .40
17 Pat Burrell .15 .40
18 Mike Lieberthal .15 .40
19 Cliff Lee .15 .40
20 Ronnie Belliard .15 .40
21 Eric Gagne SP 2.00 5.00
22 Brad Penny .15 .40
23 Al Kaline RET .60 1.50
24 Mike Maroth .15 .40
25 Magglio Ordonez SP 2.00 5.00
26 Mark Buehrle .15 .40
27 Jack Wilson .15 .40
28 Oliver Perez .15 .40
29 Red Schoendienst RET .25 .60
30 Yadier Molina FY RC .75 2.00
31 Ryan Freel .15 .40
32 Adam Dunn .15 .40
33 Paul Konerko .15 .40
34 Esteban Loaiza .15 .40
35 Ivan Rodriguez .25 .60
36 Carlos Guillen .15 .40
37 Adrian Beltre .15 .40
38 C.C. Sabathia .15 .40
39 Hideo Nomo .40 1.00
40A Victor Martinez .15 .40
40B V.Martinez Pedro Stats SP 2.00 5.00
41 Bobby Abreu .15 .40
42 Randy Wolf .15 .40
43 Johnny Estrada .15 .40
44 Russ Ortiz .15 .40
45 Kenny Rogers .15 .40
46 Hank Blalock SP 2.00 5.00
47 David Ortiz .40 1.00
48A Pedro Martinez .25 .60
48B P.Martinez Victor Stats SP 3.00 8.00
49 Austin Kearns .15 .40
50 Ken Griffey Jr. SP 3.00 8.00
51 Mark Prior .25 .60
52 Kerry Wood .15 .40
53 Eric Chavez .15 .40
54 Tim Hudson .15 .40
55 Rafael Palmeiro SP 3.00 8.00
56 Javy Lopez .15 .40
57 Jason Bay .15 .40
58 Craig Wilson .15 .40
59 Whitey Ford RET .40 1.00
60 Jason Giambi .15 .40
61 Scott Rolen SP 3.00 8.00
62 Matt Morris .15 .40
63 Javier Vazquez .15 .40
64 Jim Thome .25 .60
65 Don Zimmer RET .25 .60
66 Shawn Green .15 .40
67 Don Larsen RET .40 1.00
68 Gary Sheffield .15 .40
69 Jorge Posada .25 .60
70 Bernie Williams .25 .60
71 Chipper Jones .40 1.00
72 Andruw Jones .25 .60
73 John Thomson .15 .40
74 Jim Edmonds .15 .40
75 Albert Pujols .75 2.00
76 Chris Carpenter .15 .40
77 Aubrey Huff SP 2.00 5.00
78 Carl Crawford .15 .40
79 Victor Zambrano .15 .40
80 Alfonso Soriano SP 2.00 5.00
81 Lance Berkman .15 .40
82 Mike Sweeney .15 .40
83 Ken Harvey .15 .40
84 Angel Berroa .15 .40
85 A.J. Burnett .15 .40
86 Mike Lowell .15 .40
87 Miguel Cabrera SP 3.00 8.00
88 Preston Wilson .15 .40
89 Todd Helton SP 3.00 8.00
90 Larry Walker Cards .25 .60
91 Vladimir Guerrero .40 1.00
92 Garret Anderson .15 .40
93 Bartolo Colon .15 .40
94 Scott Hairston .15 .40
95 Richie Sexson SP 2.00 5.00
96 Sean Casey .15 .40
97 John Podres RET .25 .60
98 Andy Pettitte .25 .60
99 Roy Oswalt .15 .40
100 Roger Clemens SP 3.00 8.00
101 Scott Podsednik .15 .40
102 Ben Sheets .15 .40
103 Lyle Overbay .15 .40
104 Nick Johnson SP 2.00 5.00
105 Zach Day .15 .40
106 Jose Reyes .15 .40
107 Khalil Greene .25 .60
108 Sean Burroughs .15 .40

109 David Wells SP 2.00 5.00
110 Jason Schmidt .15 .40
111 Neifi Perez .15 .40
112 Edgar Renteria .15 .40
113 Rich Aurilia .15 .40
114 Edgar Martinez .25 .60
115 Joel Pineiro .15 .40
116 Mark Teixeira .25 .60
117 Michael Young .15 .40
118 Ricardo Rodriguez .15 .40
119 Carlos Delgado .15 .40
120 Roy Halladay .15 .40
121 Jose Guillen .15 .40
122 Troy Glaus .15 .40
123 Shea Hillenbrand .15 .40
124 Luis Gonzalez .15 .40
125 Horacio Ramirez .15 .40
126 Melvin Mora .15 .40
127 Miguel Tejada SP 2.00 5.00
128 Manny Ramirez .25 .60
129 Tim Wakefield .15 .40
130 Curt Schilling SP 3.00 8.00
131 Aramis Ramirez .15 .40
132 Sammy Sosa SP 3.00 8.00
133 Matt Clement .15 .40
134 Juan Uribe .15 .40
135 Dontrelle Willis .25 .60
136 Paul Lo Duca .15 .40
137 Juan Pierre .15 .40
138 Kevin Brown .15 .40
139 Brian Giles .15 .40
Marcus Giles
140 Brian Giles .15 .40
141 Nomar Garciaparra SP 3.00 8.00
142 Cesar Izturis .15 .40
143 Don Newcombe RET .25 .60
144 Craig Biggio .25 .60
145 Carlos Beltran .15 .40
146 Torii Hunter .15 .40
147 Livan Hernandez .15 .40
148 Cliff Floyd .15 .40
149 Barry Zito .15 .40
150 Mark Mulder .15 .40
151 Rocco Baldelli .15 .40
152 Bret Boone .15 .40
153 Jamie Moyer .15 .40
154 Ichiro Suzuki .75 2.00
155 Brett Myers .15 .40
156 Carl Pavano .15 .40
157 Josh Beckett .15 .40
158 Randy Johnson .40 1.00
159 Trot Nixon .15 .40
160 Dmitri Young .15 .40
161 Jacque Jones .15 .40
162 Lew Ford .15 .40
163 Jose Vidro .15 .40
164 Mark Kotsay .15 .40
165 A.J. Pierzynski .15 .40
166 Dewon Brazelton .15 .40
167 Jeromy Burnitz .15 .40
168 Johan Santana .40 1.00
169 Greg Maddux .60 1.50
170 Carl Erskine RET .25 .60
171 Robin Roberts RET .25 .60
172 Freddy Garcia .15 .40
173 Carlos Lee .15 .40
174 Jeff Bagwell .25 .60
175 Jeff Kent .15 .40
176 Kazuhisa Ishii .15 .40
177 Orlando Cabrera .15 .40
178 Shannon Stewart .15 .40
179 Mike Cameron .15 .40
180 Mike Mussina .25 .60
181 Frank Thomas .40 1.00
182 Jaret Wright .15 .40
183A Alex Gonzalez Marlins SP 2.00 5.00
183B Alex Gonzalez Padres .15 .40
184 Matt Lawton .15 .40
185 Derrek Lee .25 .60
186 Omar Vizquel .25 .60
187 Jeremy Bonderman .15 .40
188 Jake Westbrook .15 .40
189 Zack Greinke SP 2.00 5.00
190 Chad Tracy .15 .40
191 Rondell White .15 .40
192 Alex Gonzalez .15 .40
193 Geoff Jenkins .15 .40
194 Ralph Kiner RET .40 1.00
195 Al Leiter .15 .40
196 Kevin Millwood .15 .40
197 Jason Kendall .15 .40
198 Kris Benson .15 .40
199 Ryan Klesko .15 .40
200 Mark Loretta .15 .40
201 Richard Hidalgo .15 .40
202 Reed Johnson .15 .40
203 Luis Castillo .15 .40
204 Jon Zeringue DP SP RC 2.00 5.00
205 Matt Bush DP RC 1.00 2.50
206 Kurt Suzuki DP SP RC 2.50 6.00
207 Mark Rogers DP RC .75 2.00
208 Jason Vargas DP SP RC 2.00 5.00
209 Homer Bailey DP RC 1.50 4.00
210 Ray Liotta DP SP RC 2.00 5.00
211 Eric Campbell DP RC 1.25 3.00
212 Thomas Diamond DP RC 1.00 2.50
213 Gaby Hernandez DP SP RC 3.00 8.00
214 Neil Walker DP RC .75 2.00
215 Bill Bray DP RC .30 .75
216 Wade Davis DP SP RC 3.00 8.00
217 David Purcey DP RC .60 1.50
218 Scott Elbert DP RC .75 2.00
219 Josh Fields DP RC 1.50 4.00
220 Josh Johnson DP SP RC 2.00 5.00
221 Chris Lambert DP RC .40 1.00
222 Trevor Plouffe DP RC 1.00 2.50
223 Bruce Froemming UMP .20 .50
224 Matt Macri DP SP RC 1.50 4.00
225 Greg Golson DP RC 1.00 2.50
226 Philip Hughes DP RC 4.00 10.00
227 Kyle Waldrop DP RC .75 2.00
228 Matt Tuiasosopo DP SP RC 3.00 8.00
229 Richie Robnett DP RC .75 2.00
230 Taylor Tankersley DP RC .40 1.00
231 Blake DeWitt DP RC 1.25 3.00
232 Charlie Reliford UMP .20 .50
233 Eric Hurley DP RC .75 2.00
234 Jordan Parraz DP SP RC 2.00 5.00
235 J.P. Howell DP RC .75 2.00
236 Dana DeMuth UMP .20 .50
237 Zach Jackson DP RC .60 1.50
238 Justin Orenduff DP RC .60 1.50
239 Brad Thompson FY RC .30 .75
240 J.C. Holt DP SP RC 2.00 5.00
241 Matt Fox DP RC .30 .75
242 Danny Putnam DP RC .60 1.50
243 Daryl Jones DP SP RC 2.00 5.00
244 Jon Poterson DP RC .30 .75
245 Gio Gonzalez DP RC 1.00 2.50
246 Lucas Harrell DP SP RC 2.00 5.00
247 Jerry Crawford UMP .20 .50
248 Jay Rainville DP RC 1.00 2.50
249 Donnie Smith DP SP RC 2.00 5.00
250 Huston Street DP RC 1.25 3.00
251 Jeff Marquez DP RC .40 1.00
252 Reid Brignac DP RC 1.25 3.00
253 Yusmeiro Petit FY RC .75 2.00
254 K.C. Herren DP RC .60 1.50
255 Dale Scott UMP .20 .50
256 Erick San Pedro DP RC .30 .75
257 Ed Montague UMP .20 .50
258 Billy Buckner DP RC .40 1.00
259 Mitch Einertson DP SP RC 2.00 5.00
260 Aarom Baldiris FY RC .20 .50
261 Conor Jackson FY RC 1.25 3.00
262 Rick Reed UMP .20 .50
263 Ervin Santana FY RC UER .75 2.00
Facsimile Signature is Johan Santana
264 Gerry Davis UMP .20 .50
265 Merkin Valdez FY RC .20 .50
266 Joey Gathright FY RC .40 1.00
267 Alberto Callaspo FY RC .30 .75
268 Carlos Quentin FY SP RC 4.00 10.00
269 Gary Darling UMP .20 .50
270 Jeff Salazar FY SP RC 2.00 5.00
271 Akinori Otsuka FY SP RC 2.00 5.00
272 Joe Brinkman UMP .20 .50
273 Omar Quintanilla FY RC .20 .50
274 Brian Runge UMP .20 .50
275 Tom Mastny FY RC .15 .40
276 John Hirschbeck UMP .20 .50
277 Warner Madrigal FY RC .30 .75
278 Joe West UMP .20 .50
279 Paul Maholm FY RC .40 1.00
280 Larry Young UMP .20 .50
281 Mike Reilly UMP .20 .50
282 Kazuo Matsui FY SP RC 2.00 5.00
283 Randy Marsh UMP .20 .50
284 Frank Francisco FY RC .15 .40
285 Zach Duke FY RC .75 2.00
286 Tim McClelland UMP .20 .50
287 Jesse Crain FY RC .30 .75
288 Hector Gimenez FY RC .15 .40
289 Marland Williams FY RC .20 .50
290 Brian Gorman UMP .20 .50
291 Jose Capellan FY SP RC 2.00 5.00
292 Tim Welke UMP .20 .50
293 Javier Guzman FY RC .20 .50
294 Paul McAnulty FY RC .30 .75
295 Hector Made FY RC .30 .75
296 Jon Connolly FY RC .40 1.00
297 Don Sutton FY RC .40 1.00
298 Fausto Carmona FY RC .75 2.00
299 Ramon Ramirez FY RC .15 .40
300 Brad Snyder FY RC .40 1.00
301 Chin-Lung Hu FY RC .50 1.25
302 Rudy Guillen FY RC .30 .75
303 Matt Moses FY RC .40 1.00
304 Brad Halsey FY SP RC 2.00 5.00
305 Erick Aybar FY RC .40 1.00
306 Brad Sullivan FY RC .20 .50
307 Nick Gorneault FY RC .20 .50
308 Craig Ansman FY RC .15 .40
309 Ricky Nolasco FY RC .50 1.25
310 Luke Hughes FY RC .15 .40
311 Danny Gonzalez FY RC .15 .40
312 Josh Labandeira FY RC .15 .40
313 Donald Levinski FY RC .15 .40
314 Vince Perkins FY RC .20 .50
315 Tommy Murphy FY RC .15 .40
316 Chad Bentz FY RC .15 .40
317 Chris Shelton FY RC .75 2.00
318 Nyjer Morgan FY SP RC 2.00 5.00
319 Koby Kirkland FY RC .20 .50
320 Blake Hawksworth FY RC .20 .50
321 Alex Romero FY RC .15 .40
322 Mike Gosling FY RC .15 .40
323 Ryan Budde FY RC .15 .40
324 Kevin Howard FY RC .20 .50
325 Wanell Macia FY RC .15 .40
326 Travis Blackley FY RC .15 .40
327 Kazuhito Tadano FY SP RC 2.00 5.00
328 Shingo Takatsu FY RC .30 .75
329 Joaquin Arias FY RC .30 .75
330 Juan Cedeno FY RC .15 .40
331 Bobby Brownlie FY RC .40 1.00
332 Lastings Milledge FY RC 2.00 5.00
333 Estee Harris FY RC .20 .50
334 Tim Stauffer FY SP RC 2.00 5.00
335 Jon Knott FY RC .15 .40
336 David Aardsma FY RC .20 .50
337 Wardell Starling FY RC .15 .40
338 Dioner Navarro FY RC .30 .75
339 Logan Kensing FY RC .15 .40
340 Jason Hirsh FY RC .75 2.00
341 Matt Creighton FY RC .15 .40
342 Felix Hernandez FY SP RC 8.00 20.00
343 Kyle Sleeth FY RC .20 .50
344 Dustin Nippert FY RC .20 .50
345 Anthony Lerew FY RC .30 .75
346 Chris Saenz FY RC .15 .40
347 Steve Palermo SUP .40 1.00
348 Barry Bonds SP 6.00 15.00
MJ Roop Binder EXCH

2004 Bowman Heritage Black and White

COMPLETE SET (351) 225.00 325.00
*B/W: 1X TO 2.5X BASIC
*B/W: .6X TO 1.5X BASIC RC
*B/W: .5X TO 1.2X BASIC DP RC
*B/W: .12X TO .3X BASIC SP
*B/W: .06X TO .15X BASIC SP RC
*B/W: .1X TO .25X BASIC DP SP RC
ONE PER PACK
342 Felix Hernandez FY 6.00 15.00

2004 Bowman Heritage Mahogany

STATED ODDS 1:39 HOBBY
STATED PRINT RUN 25 SERIAL #'d SETS
NO RC YR PRICING DUE TO SCARCITY
9 Alex Rodriguez 40.00 80.00
10 Derek Jeter 50.00 100.00
23 Al Kaline RET 40.00 80.00
50 Ken Griffey Jr. 40.00 80.00
75 Albert Pujols 125.00 200.00
100 Roger Clemens 40.00 80.00
154 Ichiro Suzuki 50.00 100.00
169 Greg Maddux 40.00 80.00
348 Barry Bonds 125.00 200.00

2004 Bowman Heritage Commissioner's Cut

STATED ODDS 1:320,720 HOBBY
STATED PRINT RUN 1 SERIAL #'d SET
NO PRICING DUE TO SCARCITY
FF Ford Frick

2004 Bowman Heritage Signs of Authority

STATED ODDS 1:49 HOBBY, 1:107 RETAIL
*RED: 1X TO 2.5X BASIC
RED STATED ODDS 1:499 HOB, 1:1019 RET
RED PRINT RUN 55 SERIAL #'d SETS
BF Bruce Froemming 6.00 15.00
BG Brian Gorman 6.00 15.00
BR Brian Runge 6.00 15.00
CM Charlie Reliford 6.00 15.00
DD Dana DeMuth 6.00 15.00
DS Dale Scott 6.00 15.00
EM Ed Montague 6.00 15.00
ER Rick Reed 6.00 15.00
GD Gerry Davis 6.00 15.00
GDA Gary Darling 6.00 15.00
JB Joe Brinkman 6.00 15.00
JC Jerry Crawford 6.00 15.00
JH John Hirschbeck 6.00 15.00
JW Joe West 6.00 15.00
LY Larry Young 6.00 15.00
MR Mike Reilly 6.00 15.00
RM Randy Marsh 6.00 15.00
SP Steve Palermo 6.00 15.00
TM Tim McClelland 6.00 15.00
TW Tim Welke 6.00 15.00

2004 Bowman Heritage Signs of Glory

STATED ODDS 1:246 HOBBY, 1:503 RETAIL
*RED: 1.25X TO 3X BASIC
RED ODDS 1:2019 HOBBY, 1:3961 RETAIL
RED PRINT RUN 55 SERIAL #'d SETS
BK Bob Kuzava 10.00 25.00
BS Bobby Shantz 10.00 25.00
GK George Kell 10.00 25.00
MS Bill Skowron 10.00 25.00
PR Preacher Roe 10.00 25.00

2004 Bowman Heritage Signs of Greatness

STATED ODDS 1:57 HOBBY, 1:122 RETAIL
*RED: 1.5X TO 4X BASIC
RED ODDS 1:999 HOBBY, 1:2038 RETAIL
RED PRINT RUN 55 SERIAL #'d SETS
CL Chris Lambert 3.00 8.00
GG Greg Golson 5.00 12.00
JM Jeff Marquez 3.00 8.00
JR Jay Rainville 5.00 12.00
MB Matt Bush 6.00 15.00
MR Mark Rogers 5.00 12.00
NW Neil Walker 8.00 20.00
PH Philip Hughes 20.00 50.00
TD Thomas Diamond 6.00 15.00
TP Trevor Plouffe 5.00 12.00

2004 Bowman Heritage Threads of Greatness

GROUP A ODDS 1:339 H, 1:799 R
GROUP B ODDS 1:229 H, 1:534 R
GROUP C ODDS 1:128 H, 1:279 R
GROUP D ODDS 1:48 H, 1:109 R
GROUP E ODDS 1:261 H, 1:621 R
GROUP F ODDS 1:26 H, 1:49 R
*RED: 1X TO 2.5X BASIC C-F
*RED: .75X TO 2X BASIC B
*RED: .6X TO 1.5X BASIC A
RED ODDS 1:115 HOBBY, 1:264 RETAIL
RED PRINT RUN 55 SERIAL #'d SETS
AB Adrian Beltre Bat C 2.00 5.00
AEP Andy Pettitte Uni F 3.00 8.00
AGB Armando Benitez Jsy F 2.00 5.00
AJ Andruw Jones Bat A 6.00 15.00
AMB Angel Berroa Bat B 3.00 8.00
AP Albert Pujols Jsy B 8.00 20.00
AP2 Albert Pujols Bat F 6.00 15.00
AR Alex Rodriguez Bat A 10.00 25.00
AS Alfonso Soriano Bat D 2.00 5.00
BB Bret Boone Bat C 2.00 5.00
BB2 Bret Boone Jsy F 2.00 5.00
BC Bobby Cox Uni F 3.00 8.00
BW Bernie Williams Bat C 3.00 8.00
BZ Barry Zito Uni F 2.00 5.00
CE Carl Everett Uni F 2.00 5.00
CS C.C. Sabathia Jsy F 2.00 5.00
DJ Dave Justice Uni F 3.00 8.00
DW Dontrelle Willis Jsy D 3.00 8.00
EC Eric Chavez Bat D 2.00 5.00
EC2 Eric Chavez Uni D 2.00 5.00
FT Frank Thomas Jsy F 3.00 8.00
GS Gary Sheffield Bat D 2.00 5.00
HB Hank Blalock Bat A 4.00 10.00
HB2 Hank Blalock Jsy F 2.00 5.00
HN Hideo Nomo Jsy E 3.00 8.00
JAG Juan Gonzalez Jsy B 3.00 8.00
JB Jeff Bagwell Bat C 3.00 8.00
JB2 Jeff Bagwell Jsy F 3.00 8.00
JD Johnny Damon Uni D 3.00 8.00
JDS Jason Schmidt Jsy C 2.00 5.00
JG Jason Giambi Uni F 2.00 5.00
JG2 Jason Giambi Jsy D 2.00 5.00
JL Javy Lopez Jsy B 3.00 8.00
JM Joe Mauer Bat B 4.00 10.00
JO John Olerud Bat E 3.00 8.00
JO2 John Olerud Jsy F 3.00 8.00
JPB Josh Beckett Jsy A 4.00 10.00
JPB2 Josh Beckett Bat D 2.00 5.00
JR Jose Reyes Jsy A 4.00 10.00
JS John Smoltz Jsy B 4.00 10.00
JS2 John Smoltz Jsy F 3.00 8.00
JT Jim Thome Jsy D 3.00 8.00
JT2 Jim Thome Bat E 3.00 8.00
JW Jarrod Washburn Uni F 2.00 5.00
KM Kevin Millwood Jsy F 2.00 5.00
KW Kerry Wood Jsy B 3.00 8.00
KW2 Kerry Wood Bat D 2.00 5.00
LB Lance Berkman Bat D 2.00 5.00
LB2 Lance Berkman Jsy D 2.00 5.00
MA Moises Alou Jsy A 4.00 10.00
MC Miguel Cabrera Bat D 3.00 8.00
MCD Mike McDougal Jsy F 2.00 5.00
MCT Mark Teixeira Jsy D 3.00 8.00
ML Mike Lowell Jsy F 2.00 5.00
MM Mark Mulder White Uni F 2.00 5.00
MM2 Mark Mulder White Uni F 2.00 5.00
MP Mike Piazza Bat D 4.00 10.00
MP2 Mike Piazza Jsy A 6.00 15.00
MR Manny Ramirez Uni B 4.00 10.00
MR2 Manny Ramirez Bat D 3.00 8.00
MS Mike Sweeney Bat F 2.00 5.00
MT Miguel Tejada Bat A 4.00 10.00
MT2 Miguel Tejada White Uni F 2.00 5.00
MT3 Miguel Tejada Gray Uni F 2.00 5.00
MY Michael Young Jsy A 4.00 10.00
NG Nomar Garciaparra Bat F 4.00 10.00
OV Omar Vizquel Bat C 3.00 8.00
PB Pat Burrell Bat D 2.00 5.00
PL Paul LoDuca Bat C 2.00 5.00
RB Rocco Baldelli Bat B 3.00 8.00
RC Roger Clemens Uni F 4.00 10.00
RH Roy Halladay Jsy F 2.00 5.00
RS Ruben Sierra Bat C 2.00 5.00
SS Sammy Sosa Blue Jsy A 6.00 15.00
SS2 Sammy Sosa Bat C 3.00 8.00
SS3 Sammy Sosa White Jsy F 3.00 8.00
TB Tony Batista Jsy D 2.00 5.00
TH Todd Helton Jsy D 3.00 8.00
VW Vernon Wells Jsy D 2.00 5.00
WB Wade Boggs Jsy A 6.00 15.00

2005 Bowman Heritage

This 350-card set was released in December, 2005. The set was issued in eight-card hobby and retail packs with an $3 SRP which came 24 packs to a box and 10 boxes to a case. Cards numbered 2 through 201 feature leading current major league players. Cards numbered 1 and 202 through 300 feature leading prospects. Cards numbered 301 through 350 were printed in shorter quantities than other cards in this set. Those cards which feature veteran players from 301 through 324 and leading prospects from 325-350 were issued at stated rates of one in three hobby or retail packs. Please note that card #350, originally issued as a "Mystery Redemption", turned out to be Mickey Mantle.

COMPLETE SET (350) 175.00 300.00
COMP.SET w/o SP's (300) 25.00 50.00
COMMON CARD (1-300) .15 .40
COMMON RC (1-300) .15 .40
COMMON SP (301-350) 2.00 5.00
COM.SP RC (301-350) 2.00 5.00
301-350 SP ODDS 1:3 H, 1:3 R
PLATES STATED ODDS 1:343 HOBBY
PLATES PRINT RUN 1 #'d SET PER COLOR
PLATES: BLACK, CYAN, MAGENTA & YELLOW
NO PLATES PRICING DUE TO SCARCITY
ROOP BINDER EXCH ODDS 1:240 H
ROOP BINDER EXCH.DEADLINE 12/31/07
1 Steven White FY RC .15 .40
2 Jorge Posada .25 .60
3 Brett Myers .15 .40
4 Pat Burrell .15 .40
5 Grady Sizemore .25 .60
6 Jeff Weaver .15 .40
7 Jeff Kent .15 .40
8 Mark Kotsay .15 .40
9 Nick Swisher .25 .60
10 Scott Rolen .25 .60
11 Matt Morris .15 .40
12 Luis Castillo .15 .40
13 Pedro Feliz .15 .40
14 Omar Vizquel .25 .60
15 Edgar Renteria .15 .40
16 David Wells .15 .40
17 Chad Cordero .15 .40
18 Brad Wilkerson .15 .40
19 Kelly Johnson .15 .40
20 Johnny Estrada .15 .40
21 Brian Roberts .15 .40
22 Jeromy Burnitz .15 .40
23 Magglio Ordonez .15 .40
24 Adam Dunn .15 .40
25 Randy Johnson .40 1.00
26 Derek Jeter .75 2.00
27 Jon Lieber .15 .40
28 Jim Thome .25 .60
29 Ronnie Belliard .15 .40
30 Jake Westbrook .15 .40
31 Bengie Molina .15 .40
32 J.D. Drew .15 .40
33 Rich Harden .15 .40
34 David Eckstein .15 .40
35 Scott Podsednik .15 .40
36 Mark Buehrle .15 .40
37 Barry Bonds 1.00 2.50
38 Brian Schneider .15 .40
39 Tim Wakefield .15 .40
40 Craig Wilson .15 .40
41 Jose Vidro .15 .40
42 Jacque Jones .15 .40
43 Felix Hernandez .40 1.00
44 Nomar Garciaparra .40 1.00
45 Neifi Perez .15 .40
46 Brandon Inge .15 .40
47 Felipe Lopez .15 .40
48 Ken Griffey Jr. .60 1.50
49 Robinson Cano .25 .60
50 Jason Giambi .15 .40
51 Mike Lieberthal .15 .40
52 Bobby Abreu .15 .40
53 C.C. Sabathia .15 .40
54 Aaron Boone .15 .40
55 Milton Bradley .15 .40
56 Derek Lowe .15 .40
57 Barry Zito .15 .40
58 Jim Edmonds .15 .40
59 Jon Garland .15 .40
60 Tadahito Iguchi RC .60 1.50
61 Jason Schmidt .15 .40
62 David Ortiz .40 1.00
63 Matt Lawton .15 .40
64 Zach Duke .25 .60
65 Gary Sheffield .15 .40
66 Chipper Jones .40 1.00
67 Sammy Sosa .40 1.00
68 Rafael Palmeiro .25 .60
69 Carlos Zambrano .15 .40
70 Aramis Ramirez .15 .40
71 Chris Shelton .25 .60
72 Wily Mo Pena .15 .40
73 Mike Mussina .25 .60
74 Chien-Ming Wang .60 1.50
75 Randy Wolf .15 .40
76 Jimmy Rollins .15 .40
77 Chase Utley .25 .60
78 Kevin Millwood .15 .40
79 Victor Martinez .15 .40
80 Morgan Ensberg .15 .40
81 Bartolo Colon .15 .40
82 Bobby Crosby .15 .40
83 Dan Johnson .15 .40
84 Dan Haren .15 .40
85 Yadier Molina .15 .40
86 Mark Mulder .15 .40
87 Russell Branyan .15 .40
88 Lyle Overbay .15 .40
89 Edgardo Alfonzo .15 .40
90 Mike Matheny .15 .40
91 J.T. Snow .15 .40
92 Curt Schilling .25 .60
93 Oliver Perez .15 .40
94 Mark Redman .15 .40
95 Esteban Loaiza .15 .40
96 Livan Hernandez .15 .40
97 Ryan Church .15 .40
98 Kyle Davies .15 .40
99 Mike Hampton .15 .40
100 Jeff Francoeur .40 1.00
101 Javy Lopez .15 .40
102 Mark Prior .25 .60
103 Kerry Wood .15 .40
104 Carlos Guillen .15 .40
105 Dmitri Young .15 .40
106 David Wright .60 1.50
107 Cliff Floyd .15 .40
108 Carlos Beltran .15 .40
109 Melky Cabrera RC .75 2.00
110 Carl Pavano .15 .40
111 Jamie Moyer .15 .40
112 Joel Pineiro .15 .40
113 Adrian Beltre .15 .40
114 Jhonny Peralta .15 .40
115 Travis Hafner .15 .40
116 Cesar Izturis .15 .40
117 Brad Penny .15 .40
118 Garret Anderson .15 .40
119 Scott Kazmir .15 .40
120 Aubrey Huff .15 .40
121 Larry Walker .25 .60
122 Albert Pujols .75 2.00
123 Paul Konerko .15 .40
124 Frank Thomas .40 1.00
125 Phil Nevin .15 .40
126 Brian Giles .15 .40
127 Ramon Hernandez .15 .40
128 Johnny Damon .25 .60
129 Trot Nixon .15 .40
130 Rocco Baldelli .15 .40
131 Carl Crawford .15 .40
132 Alfonso Soriano .15 .40
133 Mark Teixeira .25 .60
134 Gustavo Chacin .15 .40
135 Vernon Wells .15 .40
136 Erik Bedard .15 .40
137 Daniel Cabrera .15 .40
138 Michael Barrett .15 .40
139 Greg Maddux .60 1.50
140 Javier Vazquez .15 .40
141 Chad Tracy .15 .40
142 Michael Young .15 .40
143 Kenny Rogers .15 .40
144 Mike Piazza .40 1.00
145 Jose Reyes .15 .40
146 Geoff Jenkins .15 .40
147 Carlos Lee .15 .40
148 Brady Clark .15 .40
149 Torii Hunter .15 .40
150 Johan Santana .40 1.00
151 Steve Finley .15 .40
152 Darin Erstad .15 .40
153 Jake Peavy .15 .40
154 Xavier Nady .15 .40
155 Ryan Klesko .15 .40
156 Ichiro Suzuki .75 2.00
157 Richie Sexson .15 .40
158 Raul Ibanez .15 .40
159 Freddy Garcia .15 .40
160 Brad Hawpe .15 .40
161 Jeff Francis .15 .40
162 Todd Helton .25 .60
163 Clint Barmes .15 .40
164 Rodrigo Lopez .15 .40
165 Melvin Mora .15 .40
166 Brandon Webb .15 .40
167 Shawn Green .15 .40
168 Moises Alou .15 .40
169 Matt Clement .15 .40
170 John Smoltz .25 .60
171 Rafael Furcal .15 .40
172 Jeff Bagwell .25 .60
173 Roger Clemens .60 1.50
174 Dontrelle Willis .15 .40
175 Paul Lo Duca .15 .40
176 Zack Greinke .15 .40
177 David DeJesus .15 .40
178 Mike Sweeney .15 .40
179 Ben Sheets .15 .40
180 Doug Davis .15 .40
181 Mike Cameron .15 .40
182 Lance Berkman .15 .40
183 Craig Biggio .25 .60
184 Shannon Stewart .15 .40
185 Joe Mauer .40 1.00
186 Justin Morneau .15 .40
187 Mike Maroth .15 .40
188 Ivan Rodriguez .25 .60
189 Luis Gonzalez .15 .40
190 Troy Glaus .15 .40
191 Adam Eaton .15 .40
192 Khalil Greene .25 .60
193 Mike Lowell .15 .40
194 Miguel Cabrera .25 .60
195 Roy Halladay .15 .40
196 Ted Lilly .15 .40
197 Alex Rios .15 .40
198 Josh Beckett .15 .40
199 A.J. Burnett .15 .40
200 Juan Pierre .15 .40
201 Marcus Giles .15 .40
202 Craig Tatum FY RC .15 .40
203 Hayden Penn FY RC .30 .75
204 C.J. Smith FY RC .15 .40
205 Matt Albers FY RC .40 1.00
206 Jared Gothreaux FY RC .15 .40
207 Mike Rodriguez FY RC .15 .40
208 Hernan Iribarren FY RC .20 .50
209 Manny Parra FY RC .12 .30
210 Kevin Collins FY RC .15 .40
211 Buck Coats FY RC .15 .40
212 Jeremy West FY RC .30 .75
213 Ian Bladergroen FY RC .20 .50
214 Chuck Tiffany FY RC .40 1.00
215 Andy LaRoche FY RC 1.25 3.00
216 Frank Diaz FY RC .15 .40
217 Jai Miller FY RC .20 .50
218 Tony Giarratano FY RC .15 .40
219 Danny Zell FY RC .15 .40
220 Justin Verlander FY RC 1.50 4.00
221 Ryan Sweeney FY RC .40 1.00
222 Brandon McCarthy FY RC .50 1.25
223 Jerry Owens FY RC .20 .50
224 Glen Perkins FY RC .30 .75
225 Kevin West FY RC .15 .40
226 Billy Butler FY RC 1.50 4.00
227 Shane Costa FY RC .15 .40
228 Erik Schindewolf FY RC .15 .40
229 Miguel Montero FY RC .50 1.25

230 Stephen Drew FY RC 2.00 5.00
231 Matt DeSalvo FY RC .20 .50
232 Ben Jones FY RC .20 .50
233 Bill McCarthy FY RC .15 .40
234 Chuck James FY RC .60 1.50
235 Brandon Sing FY RC .20 .50
236 Andy Santana FY RC .15 .40
237 Brendan Ryan FY RC .15 .40
238 Wes Swackhamer FY RC .15 .40
239 Jeff Niemann FY RC .30 .75
240 Ian Kinsler FY RC 1.00 2.50
241 Micah Furtado FY RC .15 .40
242 Ryan Mount FY RC .30 .75
243 P.J. Phillips FY RC .30 .75
244 Trevor Bell FY RC .30 .75
245 Jered Weaver FY RC 2.00 5.00
246 Eddy Martinez FY RC .40 1.00
247 Brian Bannister FY RC .30 .75
248 Philip Humber FY RC .30 .75
249 Michael Rogers FY RC .15 .40
250 Landon Powell FY RC .20 .50
251 Kennard Bibbs FY RC .15 .40
252 Nelson Cruz FY RC .50 1.25
253 Paul Kelly FY RC .20 .50
254 Kevin Slowey FY RC .50 1.25
255 Brandon Snyder FY RC .60 1.50
256 Nolan Reimold FY RC .50 1.25
257 Brian Stavisky FY RC .15 .40
258 Javier Herrera FY RC .75 2.00
259 Russ Martin FY RC .50 1.25
260 Matthew Kemp FY RC 2.00 5.00
261 Wade Townsend FY RC .20 .50
262 Nick Touchstone FY RC .15 .40
263 Ryan Feierabend FY RC .15 .40
264 Bobby Livingston FY RC .15 .40
265 Wladimir Balentien FY RC .30 .75
266 Keiichi Yabu FY RC .15 .40
267 Craig Italiano FY RC .30 .75
268 Ryan Goleski FY RC .15 .40
269 Ryan Garko FY RC .50 1.25
270 Mike Bourn FY RC .30 .75
271 Scott Mathieson FY RC .30 .75
272 Scott Mitchinson FY RC .15 .40
273 Tyler Greene FY RC .30 .75
274 Mark McCormick FY RC .20 .50
275 Daryl Jones FY .20 .50
276 Travis Chick FY RC .20 .50
277 Luis Hernandez FY RC .15 .40
278 Steve Doetsch FY RC .15 .40
279 Chris Vines FY RC .15 .40
280 Mike Costanzo FY RC .50 1.25
281 Matt Maloney FY RC .40 1.00
282 Matt Goyen FY RC .15 .40
283 Jacob Marceaux FY RC .15 .40
284 David Gassner FY RC .15 .40
285 Ricky Barrett FY RC .15 .40
286 Jon Egan FY RC .20 .50
287 Scott Blue FY RC .15 .40
288 Steven Bondurant FY RC .15 .40
289 Kevin Melillo FY RC .30 .75
290 Brad Corley FY RC .20 .50
291 Brent Lillibridge FY RC .15 .40
292 Mike Morse FY RC .30 .75
293 Justin Thomas FY RC .15 .40
294 Nick Webber FY RC .15 .40
295 Mitch Boggs FY RC .15 .40
296 Jeff Lyman FY RC .20 .50
297 Jordan Schafer FY RC .40 1.00
298 Ismael Ramirez FY RC .15 .40
299 Chris B.Young FY RC .75 2.00
300 Brian Miller FY RC .15 .40
301 Jason Bay SP 2.00 5.00
302 Tim Hudson SP 2.00 5.00
303 Miguel Tejada SP 2.00 5.00
304 Jeremy Bonderman SP 2.00 5.00
305 Alex Rodriguez SP 3.00 8.00
306 Rickie Weeks SP 2.00 5.00
307 Manny Ramirez SP 3.00 8.00
308 Nick Johnson SP 2.00 5.00
309 Andruw Jones SP 2.00 5.00
310 Hideki Matsui SP 2.50 6.00
311 Jeremy Reed SP 2.00 5.00
312 Dallas McPherson SP 2.00 5.00
313 Vladimir Guerrero SP 3.00 8.00
314 Eric Chavez SP 2.00 5.00
315 Chris Carpenter SP 2.00 5.00
316 Aaron Hill SP 2.00 5.00
317 Derrek Lee SP 3.00 8.00
318 Mark Loretta SP 2.00 5.00
319 Garrett Atkins SP 2.00 5.00
320 Hank Blalock SP 2.00 5.00
321 Chris Young SP 2.00 5.00
322 Roy Oswalt SP 2.00 5.00
323 Carlos Delgado SP 2.00 5.00
324 Pedro Martinez SP 3.00 8.00
325 Jeff Clement FY SP RC 4.00 10.00
326 Jimmy Shull FY SP RC 2.00 5.00
327 Daniel Carte FY SP RC 2.00 5.00
328 Travis Buck FY SP RC 2.50 6.00
329 Chris Volstad FY SP RC 2.00 5.00
330 A.McCutchen FY SP RC 4.00 10.00
331 Cliff Pennington FY SP RC 2.00 5.00
332 John Mayberry Jr. FY SP RC 2.00 5.00
333 C.J. Henry FY SP RC 3.00 8.00
334 Ricky Romero FY SP RC 2.00 5.00
335 Aaron Thompson FY SP RC 2.00 5.00
336 Cesar Carrillo FY SP RC 2.00 5.00
337 Jacoby Ellsbury FY SP RC 8.00 20.00
338 Matt Garza FY SP RC 3.00 8.00
339 Colby Rasmus FY SP RC 5.00 12.00
340 Ryan Zimmerman FY SP RC 6.00 15.00
341 Ryan Braun FY SP RC 6.00 15.00
342 Brent Lillibridge FY SP 2.00 5.00
343 Jay Bruce FY SP RC 6.00 15.00
344 Matt Green FY SP RC 2.00 5.00
345 Brent Cox FY SP RC 2.00 5.00
346 Jed Lowrie FY SP RC 2.00 5.00
347 Beau Jones FY SP RC 2.00 5.00
348 Eli Iorg FY SP RC 2.00 5.00
349 Chaz Roe FY SP RC 2.00 5.00
350 Mickey Mantle 10.00 25.00
NNO Roop Binder Redemption 6.00 15.00

2005 Bowman Heritage Draft Pick Variation

COMPLETE SET (25) 30.00 60.00
*DP VAR: .4X TO 1X BASIC
ONE 5-CARD DPV PACK PER HOBBY BOX
337 Jacoby Ellsbury 8.00 20.00

2005 Bowman Heritage Mahogany

COMPLETE SET (350) 225.00 325.00
*MAH 1-300: 1X TO 2.5X BASIC
*MAH 1-300: .6X TO 1.5X BASIC RC
COMMON (301-324) .40 1.00
ONE MAHOGANY OR RELIC PER PACK
ON AVG. 22 MAHOG'S PER 24 CT. BOX
150 Johan Santana 1.00 2.50
185 Joe Mauer 1.00 2.50
301 Jason Bay .60 1.50
302 Tim Hudson .60 1.50
303 Miguel Tejada .60 1.50
304 Jeremy Bonderman .60 1.50
305 Alex Rodriguez 1.50 4.00
306 Rickie Weeks .60 1.50
307 Manny Ramirez 1.00 2.50
308 Nick Johnson .60 1.50
309 Andruw Jones 1.00 2.50
310 Hideki Matsui 1.50 4.00
311 Jeremy Reed .60 1.50
312 Dallas McPherson .60 1.50
313 Vladimir Guerrero 1.00 2.50
314 Eric Chavez .60 1.50
315 Chris Carpenter .60 1.50
316 Aaron Hill .60 1.50
317 Derrek Lee 1.00 2.50
318 Mark Loretta .60 1.50
319 Garrett Atkins .60 1.50
320 Hank Blalock .60 1.50
321 Chris Young .60 1.50
322 Roy Oswalt .60 1.50
323 Carlos Delgado .60 1.50
324 Pedro Martinez 1.00 2.50
325 Jeff Clement 2.00 5.00
326 Jimmy Shull .30 .75
327 Daniel Carte .50 1.25
329 Chris Volstad .60 1.50
330 Andrew McCutchen 1.50 4.00
331 Cliff Pennington .50 1.25
332 John Mayberry Jr. .60 1.50
333 C.J. Henry 1.00 2.50
334 Ricky Romero .50 1.25
335 Aaron Thompson .50 1.25
336 Cesar Carrillo .60 1.50
337 Jacoby Ellsbury 6.00 15.00
338 Matt Garza 1.25 3.00
339 Colby Rasmus 4.00 10.00
340 Ryan Zimmerman 4.00 10.00
341 Ryan Braun 10.00 25.00
342 Brent Lillibridge .25 .60
343 Jay Bruce 6.00 15.00
344 Matt Green .25 .60
345 Brent Cox .30 .75
346 Jed Lowrie .50 1.25
347 Beau Jones .60 1.50
348 Eli Iorg .50 1.25
349 Chaz Roe .30 .75
350 Mystery Redemption 10.00 25.00

2005 Bowman Heritage Mini

COMPLETE SET (350) 225.00 325.00
*MINI 1-300: 1X TO 2.5X BASIC
*MINI 1-300: .6X TO 1.5X BASIC RC
ONE MINI OR BLUE/RED BACK PER PACK
ON AVG. 20 MINI'S PER 24 CT. BOX
150 Johan Santana 1.00 2.50
185 Joe Mauer 1.00 2.50
301 Jason Bay .40 1.00
302 Tim Hudson .40 1.00
303 Miguel Tejada .40 1.00
304 Jeremy Bonderman .40 1.00
305 Alex Rodriguez 1.50 4.00
306 Rickie Weeks .40 1.00
307 Manny Ramirez .60 1.50
308 Nick Johnson .40 1.00
309 Andruw Jones .60 1.50
310 Hideki Matsui 1.50 4.00
311 Jeremy Reed .40 1.00
312 Dallas McPherson .40 1.00
313 Vladimir Guerrero 1.00 2.50
314 Eric Chavez .40 1.00
315 Chris Carpenter .40 1.00
316 Aaron Hill .40 1.00
317 Derrek Lee .60 1.50
318 Mark Loretta .40 1.00
319 Garrett Atkins .40 1.00
320 Hank Blalock .40 1.00
321 Chris Young .40 1.00
322 Roy Oswalt .40 1.00
323 Carlos Delgado .40 1.00
324 Pedro Martinez .60 1.50
325 Jeff Clement 2.00 5.00
326 Jimmy Shull .30 .75
327 Daniel Carte .50 1.25
329 Chris Volstad .60 1.50
330 Andrew McCutchen 1.50 4.00
331 Cliff Pennington .50 1.25
332 John Mayberry Jr. .60 1.50
333 C.J. Henry 1.00 2.50
334 Ricky Romero .50 1.25
335 Aaron Thompson .50 1.25
336 Cesar Carrillo .60 1.50
337 Jacoby Ellsbury 6.00 15.00
338 Matt Garza 1.25 3.00
339 Colby Rasmus 4.00 10.00
340 Ryan Zimmerman 4.00 10.00
341 Ryan Braun 10.00 25.00
342 Brent Lillibridge .25 .60
343 Jay Bruce 6.00 15.00
344 Matt Green .25 .60
345 Brent Cox .30 .75
346 Jed Lowrie .50 1.25
347 Beau Jones .60 1.50
348 Eli Iorg .50 1.25
349 Chaz Roe .30 .75
350 Mystery Redemption 10.00 25.00

2005 Bowman Heritage Red

STATED ODDS 1:1374 HOBBY
STATED PRINT RUN 1 SERIAL #'d SET
NO PRICING DUE TO SCARCITY

2005 Bowman Heritage 51 Topps Heritage Blue Backs

OVERALL 51 HERITAGE ODDS 1:6 H/R
1 Adam Dunn 1.50 4.00
2 Zach Duke 1.50 4.00
3 Alex Rodriguez 3.00 8.00
4 Vladimir Guerrero 2.00 5.00
5 Andruw Jones 1.50 4.00
6 Travis Chick 1.25 3.00
7 Alfonso Soriano 1.50 4.00
8 Scott Rolen 1.50 4.00
9 Brian Bannister 1.50 4.00
10 Randy Johnson 2.00 5.00
11 Barry Bonds 5.00 12.00
12 Pat Burrell 1.50 4.00
13 Barry Zito 1.50 4.00
14 Nomar Garciaparra 2.00 5.00
15 C.C. Sabathia 1.50 4.00
16 Miguel Tejada 1.50 4.00
17 Hideki Matsui 3.00 8.00
18 John Smoltz 1.50 4.00
19 Ken Griffey Jr. 3.00 8.00
20 Chris Carpenter 1.50 4.00
21 Ian Kinsler 2.50 6.00
22 Chuck Tiffany 1.50 4.00
23 Gary Sheffield 1.50 4.00
24 Mark Mulder 1.50 4.00
25 Ichiro Suzuki 4.00 10.00
26 Kerry Wood 1.50 4.00
27 Jose Reyes 1.50 4.00
28 Derrek Lee 1.50 4.00
29 Justin Verlander 4.00 10.00
30 Johnny Damon 1.50 4.00
31 Chris Volstad 1.50 4.00
32 Jeremy Bonderman 1.50 4.00
33 David Ortiz 2.00 5.00
34 Morgan Ensberg 1.50 4.00
35 Mark Buehrle 1.50 4.00
36 Chuck James 2.50 6.00
37 Miguel Cabrera 1.50 4.00
38 Magglio Ordonez 1.50 4.00
39 Michael Young 1.50 4.00
40 Carlos Beltran 1.50 4.00
41 Nick Johnson 1.50 4.00
42 Billy Butler 4.00 10.00
43 Brian Giles 1.50 4.00
44 Paul Konerko 1.50 4.00
45 Roy Oswalt 1.50 4.00
46 Bobby Abreu 1.50 4.00
47 Sammy Sosa 2.00 5.00
48 Aramis Ramirez UER 1.50 4.00
Bio refers to Anthony Reyes
49 Torii Hunter 1.50 4.00
50 Aubrey Huff 1.50 4.00
51 Vernon Wells 1.50 4.00
52 Joe Mauer 3.00 8.00

2005 Bowman Heritage 51 Topps Heritage Red Backs

OVERALL 51 HERITAGE ODDS 1:6 H/R
1 Andy LaRoche 3.00 8.00
2 Mike Piazza 2.00 5.00
3 Pedro Martinez 1.50 4.00

4 Wladimir Balentien 1.50 4.00
5 Tim Hudson 1.50 4.00
6 Richie Sexson 1.50 4.00
7 Carlos Delgado 1.50 4.00
8 Derek Jeter 4.00 10.00
9 Ryan Zimmerman 6.00 15.00
10 Mark Teixeira 1.50 4.00
11 David Wright 3.00 8.00
12 Jake Peavy 1.50 4.00
13 Jose Vidro 1.50 4.00
14 Jim Thome 1.50 4.00
15 Carlos Zambrano 1.50 4.00
16 Hank Blalock 1.50 4.00
17 Johan Santana 2.00 5.00
18 Cliff Pennington 1.50 4.00
19 Rafael Palmeiro 1.50 4.00
20 Curt Schilling 1.50 4.00
21 Brandon McCarthy 2.00 5.00
22 Stephen Drew 6.00 15.00
23 Jeff Niemann 1.50 4.00
24 Eric Chavez 1.50 4.00
25 Hernan Iribarren 1.25 3.00
26 Jered Weaver 5.00 12.00
27 Edgar Renteria 1.50 4.00
28 Travis Hafner 1.50 4.00
29 Frank Thomas 2.00 5.00
30 Brian Roberts 1.50 4.00
31 Anthony Reyes 2.50 6.00
32 Scott Kazmir 1.50 4.00
33 Carlos Lee 1.50 4.00
34 Jimmy Rollins 1.50 4.00
35 Garrett Anderson 1.50 4.00
36 Jason Schmidt 1.50 4.00
37 Jon Garland 1.50 4.00
38 Dontrelle Willis 1.50 4.00
39 C.J. Henry 2.00 5.00
40 Greg Maddux 3.00 8.00
41 Todd Helton 1.50 4.00
42 Ivan Rodriguez 1.50 4.00
43 Chipper Jones 2.00 5.00
44 Rich Harden 1.50 4.00
45 Mark Prior 1.50 4.00
46 Roy Halladay 1.50 4.00
47 Albert Pujols 4.00 10.00
48 Roger Clemens 3.00 8.00
49 Andrew McCutchen 3.00 8.00
50 Scott Podsednik 1.50 4.00
51 Manny Ramirez 1.50 4.00
52 Carl Crawford 1.50 4.00
53 Jim Edmonds 1.50 4.00
54 Wily Mo Pena 1.50 4.00

2005 Bowman Heritage Future Greatness Jersey Relics

GROUP A ODDS 1:1004 H, 1:3350 R
GROUP B ODDS 1:270 H, 1:1237 R
GROUP C ODDS 1:205 H, 1:875 R
GROUP D ODDS 1:61 H, 1:210 R
GROUP E ODDS 1:141 H, 1:500 R
*RAINBOW: .75X TO 2X GRP C-E
*RAINBOW: .75X TO 2X GRP B
*RAINBOW: .5X TO 1.2X GRP A
OVERALL RAINBOW ODDS 1:183 H, 1:735 R
RAINBOW PRINT RUN 51 SERIAL #'d SETS
OVERALL RAINBOW RED ODDS 1:7841 H
RAINBOW RED PRINT RUN 1 #'d SET
NO R'BOW RED PRICING DUE TO SCARCITY
AH Aaron Hill D 2.00 5.00
AM Arnie Munoz D 2.00 5.00
AMA Andy Marte D 3.00 8.00
BB Bryan Bullington D 2.00 5.00
BT Brad Thompson A 3.00 8.00
CE Clint Everts B 3.00 8.00
DM Dallas McPherson C 2.00 5.00
DY Delmon Young A 6.00 15.00
EE Edwin Encarnacion C 3.00 8.00
FC Fausto Carmona A 3.00 8.00
FP Felix Pie C 3.00 8.00
GF Gavin Floyd D 2.00 5.00
JB Joe Blanton D 3.00 8.00
JC Jorge Cortes B 2.00 5.00
JCO Jesus Cota D 2.00 5.00
JF Jeff Francis D 3.00 8.00
JG Joel Guzman E 3.00 8.00
JGA Jairo Garcia B 2.00 5.00
JK Jason Kubel A 3.00 8.00
JM Justin Morneau D 3.00 8.00
JMA Jeff Mathis B 3.00 8.00
JP Juan Perez E 2.00 5.00
KH Koyie Hill B 2.00 5.00
MC Matt Cain D 4.00 10.00
RG Ruben Gotay B 2.00 5.00
RW Rickie Weeks D 3.00 8.00
SC Shin Soo Choo C 3.00 8.00
TB Tony Blanco E 2.00 5.00
VM Val Majewski D 2.00 5.00
WL Wil Ledezma E 2.00 5.00
YP Yusmeiro Petit D 3.00 8.00

2005 Bowman Heritage Pieces of Greatness Relics

GROUP A ODDS 1:167 H, 1:555 R
GROUP B ODDS 1:47 H, 1:155 R
GROUP C ODDS 1:55 H, 1:188 R
AD Adam Dunn Bat A 3.00 8.00
AP Albert Pujols Jsy B 6.00 15.00
AR Alex Rodriguez Bat A 6.00 15.00
BB Barry Bonds Uni A 8.00 20.00
BC Bobby Crosby Uni C 3.00 8.00
BM Brett Myers Jsy A 3.00 8.00
BR Brian Roberts Bat B 3.00 8.00
BZ Barry Zito Uni C 3.00 8.00
CB Carlos Beltran Bat B 3.00 8.00
CD Carlos Delgado Bat B 3.00 8.00
DW Dontrelle Willis Jsy C 3.00 8.00
DWR David Wright Bat B 4.00 10.00
EC Eric Chavez Uni C 3.00 8.00
IS Ichiro Suzuki Jsy C 6.00 15.00
JB Josh Beckett Uni B 3.00 8.00
JD Johnny Damon Bat B 3.00 8.00
JG Josh Gibson Seat C 6.00 15.00
JK Jeff Kent Bat A 3.00 8.00
JS John Smoltz Jsy B 3.00 8.00
JT Jim Thome Bat B 3.00 8.00
MC Miguel Cabrera Bat A 3.00 8.00
MM Mark Mulder Uni B 3.00 8.00
MMO Melvin Mora Bat B 3.00 8.00
MR Manny Ramirez Bat B 3.00 8.00
MT Miguel Tejada Bat C 3.00 8.00
PK Paul Konerko Bat B 3.00 8.00
PM Pedro Martinez Bat B 3.00 8.00
RC Roger Clemens Jsy A 6.00 15.00
RH Rich Harden Jsy A 3.00 8.00
TG Troy Glaus Bat B 3.00 8.00
TH Todd Helton Jsy B 3.00 8.00

2005 Bowman Heritage Pieces of Greatness Rainbow Relics

*RAINBOW: .75X TO 2X GRP B-C
*RAINBOW: .75X TO 2X GRP A
OVERALL RAINBOW ODDS 1:183 H, 1:735 R
STATED PRINT RUN 51 SERIAL #'d SETS
RED STATED ODDS 1:7841 HOBBY
RED PRINT RUN 1 SERIAL #'d SET
NO RED PRICING DUE TO SCARCITY
BB Barry Bonds Uni 30.00 60.00
IS Ichiro Suzuki Jsy 30.00 60.00
JG Josh Gibson Seat 30.00 60.00

2005 Bowman Heritage Signs of Greatness

GROUP A ODDS 1:153 H, 1:154 R
GROUP B ODDS 1:40 H, 1:40 R
GROUP C ODDS 1:74 H, 1:75 R
*RED INK: 1.25X TO 3X BASIC
RED INK ODDS 1:634 H, 1:635 R
RED INK PRINT RUN 51 SERIAL #'d SETS
NO RC YR RED INK PRICING AVAILABLE
AG Angel Guzman C 3.00 8.00
AM Andrew McCutchen B 10.00 25.00
BL Brent Lillibridge B 3.00 8.00
CT Curtis Thigpen A 3.00 8.00
DJ Dan Johnson A 4.00 10.00
DL Donny Lucey A 3.00 8.00
DP David Purcey C 5.00 12.00
EM Eddy Martinez B 5.00 12.00
HS Huston Street C 6.00 15.00
JB Jay Bruce B 40.00 80.00
JH J.P. Howell C 3.00 8.00
JJ Jason Jaramillo B 3.00 8.00
JM John Mayberry Jr. B 5.00 12.00
JP Jon Papelbon C 30.00 60.00
JZ Jon Zeringue B 3.00 8.00
MB Matt Bush A 4.00 10.00
MG Matt Green B 3.00 8.00
PB Patrick Bryant A 3.00 8.00
PH Philip Humber B 6.00 15.00
RB Ryan Braun B 40.00 80.00
RR Ricky Romero B 5.00 12.00
RZ Ryan Zimmerman B 25.00 50.00
SE Scott Elbert C 3.00 8.00
TC Travis Chick B 3.00 8.00
TD Thomas Diamond B 3.00 8.00
WW Wesley Whisler B 3.00 8.00
ZJ Zach Jackson A 3.00 8.00

2006 Bowman Heritage

This 300-card set was released in December, 2006. The set was issued in eight-card hobby packs with an $3 SRP which came packaged 24 packs to a box and 12 boxes to a case. The first 200 cards in the set are veterans while their are two rookie subsets (201-250, 276-300). Interestingly, the even numbered cards between 200 and 300 were all short printed.

COMPLETE SET (300) 75.00 150.00
COMP.SET w/o SP's (250) 15.00 40.00
COMMON CARD (1-300) .15 .40
COMMON RC (1-300) .15 .40
COMMON SP (202-300) 2.00 5.00
COM.SP RC (202-300) 2.00 5.00
202-300 SP ODDS 1:3 H, 1:3 R
SP CL: EVEN #s B/WN 202-300
OVERALL PLATE ODDS 1:497 HOBBY
PLATE PRINT RUN 1 SET PER COLOR
BLACK-CYAN-MAGENTA-YELLOW ISSUED
NO PLATE PRICING DUE TO SCARCITY
1 David Wright .60 1.50
2 Andruw Jones .25 .60
3 Ryan Howard .60 1.50
4 Jason Bay .15 .40
5 Paul Konerko .15 .40
6 Jake Peavy .15 .40
7 Todd Jones .15 .40
8 Troy Glaus .15 .40
9 Rocco Baldelli .15 .40
10 Rafael Furcal .15 .40
11 Freddy Sanchez .15 .40
12 Jermaine Dye .15 .40
13 A.J. Burnett .15 .40
14 Michael Cuddyer .15 .40
15 Barry Zito .15 .40
16 Chipper Jones .40 1.00
17 Paul LoDuca .15 .40
18 Mark Mulder .15 .40
19 Raul Ibanez .15 .40
20 Carlos Delgado .15 .40
21 Marcus Giles .15 .40
22 Dan Haren .15 .40
23 Justin Morneau .15 .40
24 Livan Hernandez .15 .40
25 Ken Griffey Jr. .60 1.50
26 Aaron Hill .15 .40
27 Tadahito Iguchi .15 .40
28 Nate Robertson .15 .40
29 Kevin Millwood .15 .40
30 Jim Thome .25 .60
31 Aubrey Huff .15 .40
32 Dontrelle Willis .15 .40
33 Khalil Greene .25 .60
34 Doug Davis .15 .40
35 Ivan Rodriguez .25 .60
36 Rickie Weeks .15 .40
37 Jhonny Peralta .15 .40
38 Yadier Molina .15 .40
39 Eric Chavez .15 .40
40 Alfonso Soriano .15 .40
41 Pat Burrell .15 .40
42 B.J. Ryan .15 .40
43 Carl Crawford .15 .40
44 Preston Wilson .15 .40
45 Jorge Posada .25 .60
46 Carlos Zambrano .15 .40
47 Mark Teahen .15 .40
48 Nick Johnson .15 .40
49 Mark Kotsay .15 .40
50 Derek Jeter 1.00 2.50
51 Moises Alou .15 .40
52 Ryan Freel .15 .40
53 Shannon Stewart .15 .40
54 Casey Blake .15 .40
55 Edgar Renteria .15 .40
56 Frank Thomas .40 1.00
57 Ty Wigginton .15 .40
58 Jeff Kent .15 .40
59 Chien-Ming Wang .60 1.50
60 Josh Beckett .15 .40
61 Chase Utley .40 1.00
62 Gary Matthews .15 .40
63 Torii Hunter .15 .40
64 Bobby Jenks .15 .40
65 Wilson Betemit .15 .40
66 Jeremy Bonderman .15 .40
67 Scott Rolen .25 .60
68 Brad Penny .15 .40
69 Jacque Jones .15 .40
70 Jose Reyes .15 .40
71 Brian Roberts .15 .40
72 John Smoltz .25 .60
73 Johnny Estrada .15 .40
74 Ronnie Belliard .15 .40
75 Vladimir Guerrero .40 1.00
76 A.J. Pierzynski .15 .40
77 Garrett Atkins .15 .40
78 Adam LaRoche .15 .40
79 Mark Loretta .15 .40
80 Todd Helton .25 .60
81 Jose Vidro .15 .40
82 Carlos Guillen .15 .40
83 Michael Barrett .15 .40
84 Lyle Overbay .15 .40
85 Travis Hafner .15 .40
86 Shea Hillenbrand .15 .40
87 Julio Lugo .15 .40
88 Tim Hudson .15 .40
89 Scott Podsednik .15 .40
90 Roy Halladay .15 .40
91 Bartolo Colon .15 .40
92 Ryan Langerhans .15 .40
93 Tom Glavine .25 .60
94 Kenny Rogers .15 .40
95 Robinson Cano .25 .60
96 Mark Prior .25 .60
97 Jason Schmidt .15 .40

98 Bengie Molina .15 .40
99 Jon Lieber .15 .40
100 Alex Rodriguez .60 1.50
101 Scott Kazmir .25 .60
102 Jeff Francoeur .40 1.00
103 Chris Carpenter .15 .40
104 Juan Uribe .15 .40
105 Mariano Rivera .40 1.00
106 Rich Harden .15 .40
107 Jack Wilson .15 .40
108 Austin Kearns .15 .40
109 Marcus Thames .15 .40
110 Miguel Tejada .15 .40
111 Chone Figgins .15 .40
112 Bronson Arroyo .15 .40
113 Chad Cordero .15 .40
114 Bill Hall .15 .40
115 Curt Schilling .25 .60
116 David Eckstein .15 .40
117 Ramon Hernandez .15 .40
118 Eric Byrnes .15 .40
119 Clint Barmes .15 .40
120 Bobby Abreu .15 .40
121 Joe Crede .15 .40
122 Derek Lowe .15 .40
123 Jason Marquis .15 .40
124 Erik Bedard .15 .40
125 Derrek Lee .15 .40
126 Brian McCann .15 .40
127 Magglio Ordonez .15 .40
128 Ben Sheets .15 .40
129 Brandon Inge .15 .40
130 Miguel Cabrera .25 .60
131 Jim Edmonds .25 .60
132 John Lackey .15 .40
133 Kevin Mench .15 .40
134 Adrian Beltre .15 .40
135 Curtis Granderson .15 .40
136 Shawn Green .15 .40
137 Jose Contreras .15 .40
138 Joe Nathan .15 .40
139 Bobby Crosby .15 .40
140 Johnny Damon .25 .60
141 Brad Hawpe .15 .40
142 Brandon Phillips .15 .40
143 Victor Martinez .15 .40
144 Jimmy Rollins .15 .40
145 Corey Patterson .15 .40
146 Grady Sizemore .25 .60
147 Placido Polanco .15 .40
148 Mike Lowell .15 .40
149 Francisco Rodriguez .15 .40
150 Ichiro Suzuki .60 1.50
151 Kris Benson .15 .40
152 Scott Hatteberg .15 .40
153 Akinori Otsuka .15 .40
154 Cesar Izturis .15 .40
155 Roger Clemens .75 2.00
156 Kerry Wood .15 .40
157 Tom Gordon .15 .40
158 Sean Casey .15 .40
159 Jose Lopez .15 .40
160 Orlando Hernandez .15 .40
161 Aramis Ramirez .15 .40
162 J.D. Drew .15 .40
163 David DeJesus .15 .40
164 Craig Biggio .25 .60
165 Brett Myers .15 .40
166 C.C. Sabathia .15 .40
167 Zach Duke .15 .40
168 Luis Castillo .15 .40
169 Hideki Matsui .40 1.00
170 Brian Giles .15 .40
171 Coco Crisp .15 .40
172 Richie Sexson .15 .40
173 Nomar Garciaparra .40 1.00
174 Roy Oswalt .15 .40
175 David Ortiz .40 1.00
176 Matt Morris .15 .40
177 Felipe Lopez .15 .40
178 Garret Anderson .15 .40
179 Kevin Youkilis .15 .40
180 Alex Rios .15 .40
181 Jon Garland .15 .40
182 Luis Gonzalez .15 .40
183 Cliff Floyd .15 .40
184 Juan Encarnacion .15 .40
185 Nick Swisher .15 .40
186 Mike Cameron .15 .40
187 Jose Castillo .15 .40
188 Ray Durham .15 .40
189 Jorge Cantu .15 .40
190 Andy Pettitte .15 .40
191 Chad Tracy .15 .40
192 Adrian Gonzalez .15 .40
193 Jose Valentin .15 .40
194 Mark Buehrle .15 .40
195 Huston Street .15 .40
196 Chris Capuano .15 .40
197 Aaron Rowand .15 .40
198 Billy Wagner .15 .40
199 Orlando Cabrera .15 .40
200 Albert Pujols .75 2.00
201 Dan Uggla (RC) .40 1.00
202 Alay Soler SP RC 2.00 5.00
203 Matt Kemp (RC) .25 .60
204 Mike Napoli SP RC 2.00 5.00
205 Joel Zumaya (RC) .40 1.00
206 Mike Pelfrey SP RC 3.00 8.00
207 Ian Kinsler (RC) .25 .60
208 Josh Willingham SP (RC) 2.00 5.00
209 Erick Aybar (RC) .15 .40
210 Willie Eyre SP (RC) 2.00 5.00
211 Kendry Morales (RC) .25 .60
212 Scott Thorman SP (RC) 2.00 5.00
213 Hanley Ramirez (RC) .40 1.00
214 Boof Bonser SP (RC) 2.00 5.00
215 Anthony Reyes (RC) .25 .60
216 Justin Huber SP (RC) 2.00 5.00
217 Yusmeiro Petit (RC) .15 .40
218 Jason Bartlett SP (RC) 2.00 5.00
219 Shin-Soo Choo (RC) .25 .60
220 Francisco Liriano SP (RC) 2.00 5.00
221 Craig Hansen RC .60 1.50
222 Ricky Nolasco SP (RC) 2.00 5.00
223 Adam Loewen (RC) .15 .40
224 Scott Olsen SP (RC) 2.00 5.00
225 Cole Hamels (RC) .40 1.00
226 Martin Prado SP (RC) 2.00 5.00
227 James Loney (RC) .25 .60
228 Kevin Thompson SP (RC) 2.00 5.00
229 Adam Jones RC .50 1.25
230 Josh Johnson SP (RC) 2.00 5.00
231 Anderson Hernandez (RC) .15 .40
232 Tony Gwynn Jr. SP (RC) 2.00 5.00
233 Casey Janssen RC .25 .60
234 Taylor Tankersley SP (RC) 2.00 5.00
235 Mike Thompson RC .15 .40
236 Jeremy Sowers SP (RC) 2.00 5.00
237 Anibal Sanchez (RC) .25 .60
238 Adam Wainwright SP (RC) 2.00 5.00
239 Rich Hill (RC) .15 .40
240 Russ Martin SP (RC) 2.00 5.00
241 Joe Inglett RC .15 .40
242 Tony Pena SP (RC) 2.00 5.00
243 Josh Sharpless RC .15 .40
244 Darrell Rasner SP (RC) 2.00 5.00
245 Joe Saunders (RC) .15 .40
246 Jon Lester SP RC 2.00 5.00
247 Jeremy Hermida (RC) .15 .40
248 Chad Billingsley SP (RC) 2.00 5.00
249 Bobby Livingston (RC) .15 .40
250 Justin Verlander SP (RC) 2.00 5.00
251 Mickey Mantle 3.00 8.00
252 Hank Blalock SP 2.00 5.00
253 Manny Ramirez .25 .60
254 Mike Mussina SP 3.00 8.00
255 Greg Maddux .60 1.50
Wearing a Cubs Cap; Back Notates Trade to Dodgers
256 Jason Giambi SP 2.00 5.00
257 Mark Teixeira .25 .60
258 Carlos Beltran SP 2.00 5.00
259 Matt Holliday .20 .50
260 Pedro Martinez SP 3.00 8.00
261 Joe Mauer .25 .60
262 Melvin Mora SP 2.00 5.00
263 Mike Piazza .40 1.00
264 B.J. Upton SP 2.00 5.00
265 Vernon Wells .15 .40
266 Gary Sheffield SP 2.00 5.00
267 Randy Johnson .40 1.00
268 Ryan Zimmerman SP 2.00 5.00
269 Lance Berkman .15 .40
270 Johan Santana SP 3.00 8.00
271 Carlos Lee .15 .40
272 Brandon Webb SP 2.00 5.00
273 Adam Dunn .15 .40
274 Michael Young SP 2.00 5.00
275 Barry Bonds .75 2.00
276 Jonathan Papelbon SP (RC) 2.00 5.00
277 Howie Kendrick (RC) .40 1.00
278 Melky Cabrera SP (RC) 2.00 5.00
279 Jered Weaver (RC) .50 1.25
280 Josh Barfield SP (RC) 2.00 5.00
281 Chuck James (RC) .25 .60
282 Lastings Milledge SP (RC) 2.00 5.00
283 Nick Markakis (RC) .25 .60
284 Jose Capellan SP (RC) 2.00 5.00
285 Prince Fielder (RC) .60 1.50
286 Jason Botts SP (RC) 2.00 5.00
287 Eliezer Alfonzo RC .15 .40
288 Sean Marshall SP (RC) 2.00 5.00
289 Ryan Garko (RC) .15 .40
290 Stephen Drew SP (RC) 2.00 5.00
291 Joel Guzman (RC) .15 .40
292 Hong-Chih Kuo SP (RC) 2.00 5.00
293 Zach Miner (RC) .15 .40
294 Angel Guzman SP (RC) 2.00 5.00
295 Andre Ethier (RC) .40 1.00
296 Fausto Carmona SP (RC) 2.00 5.00
297 Ronny Paulino (RC) .15 .40
298 Matt Cain SP (RC) 2.00 5.00
299 Carlos Quentin (RC) .25 .60
300 Kenji Johjima SP RC 2.00 5.00

2006 Bowman Heritage Black

STATED ODDS 1:1990 HOBBY
STATED PRINT RUN 1 SERIAL #'d SET
NO PRICING DUE TO SCARCITY

2006 Bowman Heritage Mini

COMPLETE SET (300) 100.00 200.00
*MINI 1-300: 1X TO 2.5X BASIC
*MINI 1-300: 1X TO 2.5X BASIC RC
COMMON BASIC SP (202-300) .40 1.00
BASIC SP SEMIS 202-300 .60 1.50
BASIC SP UNLISTED 202-300 1.00 2.50
OVERALL ODDS ONE PER PACK
NO SHORT PRINTS IN MINI SET
206 Mike Pelfrey 1.50 4.00
220 Francisco Liriano 2.00 5.00
232 Tony Gwynn Jr. 1.25 3.00
246 Jon Lester 1.25 3.00
250 Justin Verlander 1.50 4.00
251 Mickey Mantle 4.00 10.00
268 Ryan Zimmerman 2.50 6.00
276 Jonathan Papelbon 2.00 5.00
300 Kenji Johjima 2.00 5.00

2006 Bowman Heritage Chrome

*CHROME 1-300: 1X TO 2.5X BASIC
*CHROME 1-300: 1X TO 2.5X BASIC RC
COMMON BASIC SP (202-300) .40 1.00
BASIC SP SEMIS 202-300 .60 1.50
BASIC SP UNLISTED 202-300 1.00 2.50
APPX. ODDS ONE PER PACK
ON AVG. 22 CHROME PER 24 CT.BOX
NO SHORT PRINTS IN CHROME SET
206 Mike Pelfrey 1.50 4.00
220 Francisco Liriano 2.00 5.00
232 Tony Gwynn Jr. 1.25 3.00
246 Jon Lester 1.25 3.00
250 Justin Verlander 1.50 4.00
251 Mickey Mantle 4.00 10.00
268 Ryan Zimmerman 2.50 6.00
276 Jonathan Papelbon 2.00 5.00
300 Kenji Johjima 2.00 5.00

2006 Bowman Heritage White

*WHITE 1-300: .4X TO 1X BASIC
*WHITE 1-300: .4X TO 1X BASIC RC
COMMON BASIC SP (202-300) .40 1.00
BASIC SP SEMIS 202-300 .60 1.50
BASIC SP UNLISTED 202-300 1.00 2.50
STATED ODDS 1:6 HOBBY, 1:6 RETAIL
NO SHORT PRINTS IN WHITE SET
206 Mike Pelfrey 1.50 4.00
220 Francisco Liriano .75 2.00
232 Tony Gwynn Jr. 1.25 3.00
246 Jon Lester 1.25 3.00
250 Justin Verlander .60 1.50
268 Ryan Zimmerman 2.50 6.00
276 Jonathan Papelbon 2.00 5.00
300 Kenji Johjima 2.00 5.00

2006 Bowman Heritage Mini Draft Pick Variations

*DP VAR: 1X TO 2.5X BASIC
ONE 5-CARD DPV PACK PER HOBBY BOX
76 Evan Longoria 5.00 12.00
77 Adrian Cardenas 1.25 3.00
82 Matthew Sulentic .75 2.00
85 Clayton Kershaw 1.25 3.00
87 Chris Parmelee 1.25 3.00
88 Billy Rowell 1.50 4.00
90 Chris Marrero .75 2.00
95 Chad Huffman .75 2.00

2006 Bowman Heritage Pieces of Greatness

GROUP A ODDS 1:98 H, 1:99 R
GROUP B ODDS 1:82 H, 1:82 R
GROUP C ODDS 1:28 H, 1:28 R
GROUP D ODDS 1:43 H, 1:43 R
AD Adam Dunn Bat A 3.00 8.00
AJ Andruw Jones Jsy D 3.00 8.00
AJ2 Andruw Jones Bat C 3.00 8.00
AJP A.J. Pierzynski Bat A 3.00 8.00
AL Adam LaRoche Jsy B 3.00 8.00
AP Albert Pujols Bat C 8.00 20.00
AP2 Albert Pujols Jsy D 6.00 15.00
AR Alex Rodriguez Bat A 6.00 15.00
ARA Aramis Ramirez Bat A 3.00 8.00
BB Barry Bonds Jsy A 6.00 15.00
BR Brian Roberts Bat B 3.00 8.00
BW Brad Wilkerson Bat A 3.00 8.00
BZ Barry Zito Jsy C 3.00 8.00
CB Craig Biggio Jsy C 3.00 8.00
CF Cliff Floyd Bat B 3.00 8.00
CJ Chipper Jones Bat C 4.00 10.00
CJ2 Chipper Jones Jsy D 4.00 10.00
CS Curt Schilling Jsy C 3.00 8.00
CU Chase Utley Bat A 4.00 10.00
DE David Eckstein Bat A 3.00 8.00
DL Derrek Lee Bat B 3.00 8.00
DO David Ortiz Bat C 4.00 10.00
DW Dontrelle Willis Jsy D 3.00 8.00
EE Edwin Encarnacion Jsy C 3.00 8.00
GM Greg Maddux Bat B 4.00 10.00
GS Gary Sheffield Bat D 3.00 8.00
HB Hank Blalock Bat A 3.00 8.00
JD Jermaine Dye Bat C 3.00 8.00
JF Jeff Francoeur Bat A 4.00 10.00
JK Jeff Kent Jsy C 3.00 8.00
JL Javy Lopez Jsy C 3.00 8.00
JT Jim Thome Bat C 3.00 8.00
LB Lance Berkman Jsy C 3.00 8.00
MB Milton Bradley Bat A 3.00 8.00
ME Morgan Ensberg Jsy C 3.00 8.00
ML Mike Lowell Bat A 3.00 8.00
MO Magglio Ordonez Bat C 3.00 8.00
MR Manny Ramirez Bat D 3.00 8.00
MY Michael Young Jsy C 3.00 8.00
NJ Nick Johnson Bat B 3.00 8.00
NS Nick Swisher Bat C 3.00 8.00
RC Robinson Cano Bat C 4.00 10.00
RF Rafael Furcal Bat C 3.00 8.00
RH Ryan Howard Jsy C 6.00 15.00
SP Scott Podsednik Bat B 3.00 8.00
TH Torii Hunter Bat B 3.00 8.00
THE Todd Helton Jsy D 3.00 8.00
VG Vladimir Guerrero Bat B 4.00 10.00
VM Victor Martinez Bat B 3.00 8.00
XN Xavier Nady Bat C 3.00 8.00

2006 Bowman Heritage Pieces of Greatness White

*WHITE: .5X TO 1.2X GRP C-D
*WHITE: .5X TO 1.2X GRP A-B
OVERALL WHITE ODDS 1:387 H,1:387 R
STATED PRINT RUN 49 SERIAL #'d SETS
BLACK STATED ODDS 1:12,016 HOBBY
BLACK PRINT RUN 1 SERIAL #'d SET
NO BLACK PRICING DUE TO SCARCITY
AP Albert Pujols Bat 20.00 50.00
AP2 Albert Pujols Jsy 20.00 50.00
AR Alex Rodriguez Bat 12.50 30.00
BB Barry Bonds Jsy 20.00 50.00
GM Greg Maddux Bat 10.00 25.00
RC Robinson Cano Bat 8.00 20.00
RH Ryan Howard Jsy 12.50 30.00

2006 Bowman Heritage Prospects

COMMON CARD (1-100) .15 .40
OVERALL PLATE ODDS 1:1494 HOBBY
PLATE PRINT RUN 1 SET PER COLOR
BLACK-CYAN-MAGENTA-YELLOW ISSUED
NO PLATE PRICING DUE TO SCARCITY
1 Justin Upton 3.00 8.00
2 Koby Clemens .40 1.00
3 Lance Broadway .40 1.00
4 Cameron Maybin .75 2.00
5 Garrett Mock .15 .40
6 Alex Gordon 3.00 8.00
7 Ben Copeland .25 .60
8 Nick Adenhart .75 2.00
9 Yung-Chi Chen 1.25 3.00
10 Tim Moss .25 .60
11 Francisco Leandro .15 .40
12 Brad McCann .50 1.25
13 Dallas Trahern .15 .40
14 Dustin Majewski .15 .40
15 James Barthmaier .25 .60
16 Nate Gold .25 .60
17 John Hardy .15 .40
18 Mark McLemore .15 .40
19 Michael Aubrey .25 .60
20 Mark Holliman UER .15 .40
Mike Holliman pictured on card
21 Bobby Wilson .25 .60
22 Radhames Liz .60 1.50
23 Jose Tabata .40 1.00
24 Jared Lansford .15 .40
25 Brent Dlugach .15 .40
26 Steve Garrabrants .15 .40
27 Eric Haberer .15 .40
28 Chris Dickerson .50 1.25
29 Welinson Baez .25 .60
30 Chris Kolkhorst .15 .40
31 Brandon Moss .15 .40
32 Corey Wimberly .40 1.00
33 Ryan Patterson .40 1.00
34 Michael Hollimon .15 .40
35 John Bannister .15 .40
36 Pablo Sandoval .50 1.25
37 Dexter Fowler .40 1.00
38 Elvis Andrus 1.25 3.00
39 Jason Windsor .15 .40
40 B.J. Szymanski .25 .60
41 Yovani Gallardo .60 1.50
42 John Bowker .15 .40
43 Justin Christian .15 .40
44 Andy Sonnanstine .40 1.00
45 Jeremy Slayden .40 1.00
46 Brandon Hicks .40 1.00
47 Travis Denker .40 1.00
48 Emmanuel Garcia .25 .60
49 Landon Jacobsen .15 .40
50 Kevin Estrada .15 .40
51 Ross Ohlendorf .15 .40
52 Wyatt Toregas .25 .60
53 Andrew Kown .25 .60
54 Steve Kelly .15 .40
55 Mike Butia .15 .40
56 Mike Connolly .15 .40
57 Brian Horwitz .15 .40
58 Dale Thayer .15 .40
59 Diory Hernandez .15 .40
60 Samuel Deduno .15 .40
61 Jamie Hoffman .15 .40
62 Matt Tolbert .15 .40
63 Michael Ekstrom .15 .40
64 Chris Maples .15 .40
65 Adam Coe .15 .40
66 Max Ramirez .50 1.25
67 Evan MacLane .15 .40
68 Jose Campusano .15 .40
69 Lou Santangelo .15 .40
70 Shawn Riggans .15 .40
71 Kyle Kendrick .50 1.25
72 Oswaldo Navarro .15 .40
73 Eric Rodland .15 .40
74 Omir Santos .15 .40
75 Kyle McCulloch .50 1.25
76 Evan Longoria 3.00 8.00
77 Adrian Cardenas 1.00 2.50
78 Steven Wright .15 .40
79 Andrew Carpenter .15 .40
80 Dustin Evans .15 .40
81 Chad Tracy .15 .40
82 Matthew Sulentic .75 2.00
83 Adam Ottavino .15 .40
84 Matt Long .15 .40
85 Clayton Kershaw 1.00 2.50
86 Matt Antonelli .15 .40
87 Chris Parmelee 1.00 2.50
88 Billy Rowell 1.25 3.00
89 Chase Fontaine .15 .40
90 Chris Marrero .60 1.50
91 Jamie Ortiz .40 1.00
92 Sean Watson .15 .40
93 Brooks Brown .15 .40
94 Brad Furnish .15 .40
95 Chad Huffman .50 1.25
96 Pedro Beato .15 .40
97 Kyler Burke .15 .40
98 Stephen Englund .15 .40
99 Tyler Norrick .15 .40
100 Brett Sinkbeil .15 .40

2006 Bowman Heritage Prospects Black

STATED ODDS 1:6008 HOBBY
STATED PRINT RUN 1 SERIAL #'d SET
NO PRICING DUE TO SCARCITY

2006 Bowman Heritage Prospects White

*WHITE: .4X TO 1X BASIC
STATED ODDS 1:6 HOBBY, 1:6 RETAIL

2006 Bowman Heritage Signs of Greatness

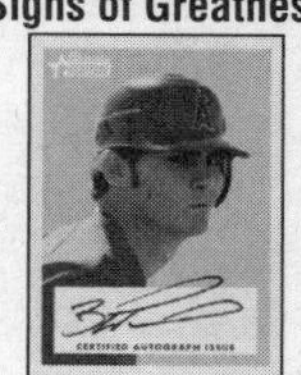

The John Drennan card was never produced.
GROUP A ODDS 1:719 H, 1:719 R
GROUP B ODDS 1:42 H, 1:42 R
GROUP C ODDS 1:61 H, 1:63 R
GROUP D ODDS 1:2172 H, 1:2175 R
RED INK ODDS 1:9737 HOBBY
RED INK PRINT RUN 5 SERIAL #'d SETS
NO RED INK PRICING DUE TO SCARCITY
SILVER INK ODDS 28,238 H,1:9500 R
SILVER INK PRINT RUN 1 SER.#'d SET
NO SILVER PRICING DUE TO SCARCITY
EXCHANGE DEADLINE 12/31/08
AG Alex Gordon B 30.00 60.00
BB Brian Bogusevic B 3.00 8.00
BS Brandon Snyder B 3.00 8.00
BW Brandon Wood A 6.00 15.00
CI Craig Italiano B 3.00 8.00
CM Cameron Maybin B 20.00 50.00
JC Jesus Cota B 3.00 8.00
JCL Jeff Clement B EXCH 5.00 12.00
JD John Drennen B EXCH 3.00 8.00
JH Justin Huber C EXCH 3.00 8.00
JS Jarrod Saltalamacchia C 6.00 15.00
JU Justin Upton D 40.00 80.00
KC Koby Clemens C EXCH 8.00 20.00
KW Kevin Whelan B 3.00 8.00
LB Lance Broadway B 4.00 10.00
MM Matt Maloney B 6.00 15.00
RT Ryan Tucker C 3.00 8.00
SG Sean Gallagher B 5.00 12.00
SL Sam LeCure C 3.00 8.00
ST Steve Tolleson B 3.00 8.00
TC Trevor Crowe B EXCH 6.00 15.00
WT Wade Townsend C 3.00 8.00

2007 Bowman Heritage

This 296-card set was released in November, 2007. The set was issued through hobby and retail channels. The hobby packs consisted of eight cards which came 24 packs to a box and 12 boxes to a case. Cards numbered 1-200 were veterans while cards numbered 201-251 were 2007 rookies. In addition, cards numbered 181-200 and 226-250 were issued both with facsimile signatures and without signatures. The cards without signatures were printed in shorter quantity and were inserted at a stated rate of one in three hobby packs. Our complete set price also includes the five Mickey Mantle cards listed as a seperate set.

COMP.SET w/o SPs (251) 15.00 40.00
COMMON CARD (1-200) .15 .40
COMMON ROOKIE (201-251) .20 .50
COMMON SP (181-200) 1.25 3.00
COMMON SP RC (226-250) 1.50 4.00
SP ODDS 1:3 HOBBY
NO SIG CARDS ARE SHORT PRINTS
COMP.SET INCLUDES ALL MANTLE VAR.
OVERALL PLATE ODDS 1:463 HOBBY
PLATE PRINT RUN 1 SET PER COLOR
BLACK-CYAN-MAGENTA-YELLOW ISSUED
NO PLATE PRICING DUE TO SCARCITY
1 Jeff Francoeur .40 1.00
2 Jered Weaver .25 .60
3 Derrek Lee .15 .40
4 Todd Helton .25 .60
5 Shawn Hill .15 .40
6 Ivan Rodriguez .25 .60
7 Mickey Mantle 2.00 5.00
8 Ramon Hernandez .15 .40
9 Randy Johnson .40 1.00
10 Jermaine Dye .15 .40
11 Brian Roberts .15 .40
12 Hank Blalock .15 .40
13 Chien-Ming Wang .60 1.50
14 Mike Lowell .15 .40
15 Brandon Webb .15 .40
16 Kelly Johnson .15 .40
17 Nick Johnson .15 .40
18 Zach Duke .15 .40
19 Aaron Hill .15 .40
20 Miguel Tejada .15 .40
21 Mark Buehrle .15 .40
22 Michael Young .15 .40
23 Carlos Delgado .15 .40
24 Anibal Sanchez .15 .40
25 Vladimir Guerrero .40 1.00
26 Russell Martin .15 .40
27 Lance Berkman .15 .40
28 Bobby Crosby .15 .40
29 Javier Vazquez .15 .40
30 Manny Ramirez .25 .60
31 Rich Hill .15 .40
32 Mike Sweeney .15 .40
33 Jeff Kent .15 .40
34 Noah Lowry .15 .40
35 Alfonso Soriano .15 .40
36 Paul Lo Duca .15 .40
37 J.D. Drew .15 .40
38 C.C Sabathia .15 .40
39 Craig Biggio .25 .60
40 Adam Dunn .15 .40
41 Josh Beckett .25 .60
42 Carlos Guillen .15 .40
43 Jeff Francis .15 .40
44 Orlando Hudson .15 .40
45 Grady Sizmore .25 .60
46 Jason Jennings .15 .40
47 Mark Teixeira .25 .60
48 Freddy Garcia .15 .40
49 Adrian Gonzalez .15 .40
50 Albert Pujols .75 2.00
51 Tom Glavine .25 .60
52 J.J. Hardy .15 .40
53 Bobby Abreu .15 .40
54 Bartolo Colon .15 .40
55 Garrett Atkins .15 .40
56 Moises Alou .15 .40
57 Cliff Lee .15 .40
58 Michael Cuddyer .15 .40
59 Brandon Phillips .15 .40
60 Jeremy Bonderman .15 .40
61 Rickie Weeks .15 .40
62 Chris Carpenter .15 .40
63 Frank Thomas .40 1.00
64 Victor Martinez .15 .40
65 Dontrelle Willis .15 .40
66 Jim Thome .25 .60
67 Aaron Rowand .15 .40
68 Andy Pettitte .25 .60
69 Brian McCann .15 .40
70 Roger Clemens .60 1.50
71 Gary Matthews .15 .40
72 Bronson Arroyo .15 .40
73 Jeremy Hermida .15 .40
74 Eric Chavez .15 .40

75 David Ortiz .40 1.00
76 Stephen Drew .25 .60
77 Ronnie Belliard .15 .40
78 James Shields .15 .40
79 Richie Sexson .15 .40
80 Johan Santana .25 .60
81 Orlando Cabrera .15 .40
82 Aramis Ramirez .15 .40
83 Greg Maddux .60 1.50
84 Reggie Sanders .15 .40
85 Carlos Zambrano .15 .40
86 Bengie Molina .15 .40
87 David DeJesus .15 .40
88 Adam Wainwright .15 .40
89 Conor Jackson .15 .40
90 David Wright .60 1.50
91 Ryan Garko .15 .40
92 Bill Hall .15 .40
93 Marcus Giles .15 .40
94 Kenny Rogers .15 .40
95 Joe Mauer .25 .60
96 Hanley Ramirez .25 .60
97 Brian Giles .15 .40
98 Dan Haren .15 .40
99 Robinson Cano .25 .60
100 Ryan Howard .60 1.50
101 Andruw Jones .25 .60
102 Aaron Harang .15 .40
103 Hideki Matsui .40 1.00
104 Nick Swisher .15 .40
105 Pedro Martinez .25 .60
106 Felipe Lopez .15 .40
107 Erik Bedard .15 .40
108 Rafael Furcal .15 .40
109 Curt Schilling .25 .60
110 Jose Reyes .40 1.00
111 Adam LaRoche .15 .40
112 Mike Mussina .25 .60
113 Melvin Mora .15 .40
114 Zack Greinke .15 .40
115 Justin Morneau .15 .40
116 Ervin Santana .15 .40
117 Ken Griffey Jr. .60 1.50
118 David Eckstein .15 .40
119 Jamie Moyer .15 .40
120 Jorge Posada .25 .60
121 Justin Verlander .40 1.00
122 Sammy Sosa .40 1.00
123 Jason Schmidt .15 .40
124 Josh Willingham .15 .40
125 Roy Oswalt .15 .40
126 Travis Hafner .15 .40
127 John Maine .15 .40
128 Willy Taveras .15 .40
129 Magglio Ordonez .15 .40
130 Barry Zito .15 .40
131 Prince Fielder .40 1.00
132 Michael Barrett .15 .40
133 Livan Hernandez .15 .40
134 Troy Glaus .15 .40
135 Rocco Baldelli .15 .40
136 Jason Giambi .15 .40
137 Austin Kearns .15 .40
138 Dan Uggla .25 .60
139 Pat Burrell .15 .40
140 Carlos Beltran .15 .40
141 Carlos Quentin .15 .40
142 Johnny Estrada .15 .40
143 Torii Hunter .15 .40
144 Carlos Lee .15 .40
145 Mike Piazza .40 1.00
146 Mark Teahen .15 .40
147 Juan Pierre .15 .40
148 Paul Konerko .15 .40
149 Freddy Sanchez .15 .40
150 Derek Jeter 1.00 2.50
151 Orlando Hernandez .15 .40
152 Raul Ibanez .15 .40
153 John Smoltz .25 .60
154 Scott Rolen .25 .60
155 Jimmy Rollins .15 .40
156 A.J. Burnett .15 .40
157 Jason Varitek .40 1.00
158 Ben Sheets .15 .40
159 Matt Cain .25 .60
160 Carl Crawford .15 .40
161 Jeff Suppan .15 .40
162 Tadahito Iguchi .15 .40
163 Kevin Millwood .15 .40
164 Chris Duncan .15 .40
165 Rich Harden .15 .40
166 Joe Crede .15 .40
167 Chipper Jones .40 1.00
168 Gary Sheffield .15 .40
169 Cole Hamels .40 1.00
170 Jason Bay .15 .40
171 Jhonny Peralta .15 .40
172 Aubrey Huff .15 .40
173 Xavier Nady .15 .40
174 Kazuo Matsui .15 .40
175 Vernon Wells .15 .40
176 Johnny Damon .25 .60
177 Jim Edmonds .25 .60
178 Jose Vidro .15 .40
179 Garret Anderson .15 .40
180 Alex Rios .15 .40
181a Ichiro Suzuki .60 1.50
181b Ichiro Suzuki SP 3.00 8.00
182a Jake Peavy .15 .40
182b Jake Peavy SP 1.25 4.00
183a Ian Kinsler .15 .40
183b Ian Kinsler SP 1.25 4.00
184a Tom Gorzelanny .15 .40
184b Tom Gorzelanny SP 1.25 4.00
185a Miguel Cabrera .25 .60
185b Miguel Cabrera SP 2.00 5.00
186a Scott Kazmir .25 .60
186b Scott Kazmir SP 2.00 5.00
187a Matt Holliday .40 1.00
187b Matt Holliday SP 2.00 5.00
188a Roy Halladay .15 .40
188b Roy Halladay SP 1.25 4.00
189a Ryan Zimmerman .40 1.00
189b Ryan Zimmerman SP 2.00 5.00
190a Alex Rodriguez .60 1.50
190b Alex Rodriguez SP 3.00 8.00
191a Kenji Johjima .40 1.00
191b Kenji Johjima SP 2.00 5.00
192a Gil Meche .15 .40
192b Gil Meche SP 1.25 4.00
193a Chase Utley .40 1.00
193b Chase Utley SP 2.00 5.00
194a Jeremy Sowers .15 .40
194b Jeremy Sowers SP 1.25 3.00
195a John Lackey .15 .40
195b John Lackey SP 1.25 3.00
196a Nick Markakis .25 .60
196b Nick Markakis SP 2.00 5.00
197a Tim Hudson .15 .40
197b Tim Hudson SP 1.25 3.00
198a B.J. Upton .15 .40
198b B.J. Upton SP 1.25 3.00
199a Felix Hernandez .25 .60
199b Felix Hernandez SP 2.00 5.00
200a Barry Bonds .75 2.00
200b Barry Bonds SP 4.00 10.00
201 Jarrod Saltalamacchia (RC) .30 .75
202 Tim Lincecum RC 1.50 4.00
203 Kory Casto (RC) .20 .50
204 Sean Henn (RC) .20 .50
205 Hector Gimenez (RC) .20 .50
206 Homer Bailey (RC) .30 .75
207 Yunel Escobar (RC) .20 .50
208 Matt Lindstrom (RC) .20 .50
209 Tyler Clippard (RC) .30 .75
210 Joe Smith RC .20 .50
211 Tony Abreu RC .50 1.25
212 Billy Butler (RC) .30 .75
213 Gustavo Molina RC .20 .50
214 Brian Stokes (RC) .20 .50
215 Kevin Slowey (RC) .50 1.25
216 Curtis Thigpen (RC) .20 .50
217 Carlos Gomez RC .30 .75
218 Rick Vanden Hurk RC .30 .75
219 Michael Bourn (RC) .20 .50
220 Jeff Baker (RC) .20 .50
221 Andy LaRoche (RC) .20 .50
222 Andy Sonnanstine RC .20 .50
223 Chase Wright RC .50 1.25
224 Mark Reynolds RC .75 2.00
225 Matt Chico (RC) .20 .50
226a Hunter Pence (RC) 1.00 2.50
226b Hunter Pence SP 3.00 8.00
227a John Danks RC .20 .50
227b John Danks SP 1.50 4.00
228a Elijah Dukes RC .30 .75
228b Elijah Dukes SP 2.50 6.00
229a Kei Igawa RC .50 1.25
229b Kei Igawa SP 2.50 6.00
230a Felix Pie (RC) .20 .50
230b Felix Pie SP 1.50 4.00
231a Jesus Flores RC .20 .50
231b Jesus Flores SP 1.50 4.00
232a Dallas Braden RC .30 .75
232b Dallas Braden SP 2.50 6.00
233a Akinori Iwamura RC .50 1.25
233b Akinori Iwamura SP 2.50 6.00
234a Ryan Braun (RC) 1.25 3.00
234b Ryan Braun SP 3.00 8.00
235a Alex Gordon RC 1.00 2.50
235b Alex Gordon SP 3.00 8.00
236a Micah Owings (RC) .20 .50
236b Micah Owings SP 1.50 4.00
237a Kevin Kouzmanoff (RC) .20 .50
237b Kevin Kouzmanoff SP 1.50 4.00
238a Glen Perkins (RC) .20 .50
238b Glen Perkins SP 1.50 4.00
239a Danny Putnam (RC) .20 .50
239b Danny Putnam SP 1.50 4.00
240a Philip Hughes (RC) 1.00 2.50
240b Philip Hughes SP 3.00 8.00
241a Ryan Sweeney (RC) .20 .50
241b Ryan Sweeney SP 1.50 4.00
242a Josh Hamilton (RC) .50 1.25
242b Josh Hamilton SP 5.00 12.00
243a Hideki Okajima RC 1.00 2.50
243b Hideki Okajima SP 3.00 8.00
244a Adam Lind (RC) .20 .50
244b Adam Lind SP 1.50 4.00
245a Travis Buck (RC) .20 .50
245b Travis Buck SP 1.50 4.00
246a Miguel Montero (RC) .20 .50
246b Miguel Montero SP 1.50 4.00
247a Brandon Morrow RC .40 1.00
247b Brandon Morrow SP 2.50 6.00
248a Troy Tulowitzki (RC) .50 1.25
248b Troy Tulowitzki SP 2.50 6.00
249a Delmon Young (RC) .30 .75
249b Delmon Young SP 2.50 6.00
250a Daisuke Matsuzaka RC 2.00 5.00
250b Daisuke Matsuzaka SP 4.00 10.00
251 Joba Chamberlain RC 3.00 8.00

2007 Bowman Heritage Black

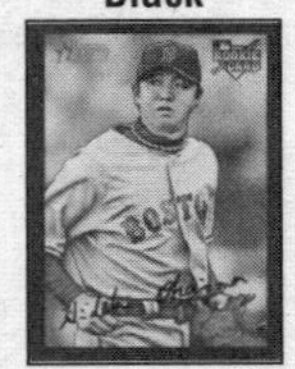

*BLACK 1-200: 8X TO 20X BASIC
*BLACK 201-251: 6X TO 15X BASIC RC
COMMON BASIC SP (180-250) 3.00 8.00
BASIC SP SEMIS 5.00 12.00
BASIC SP UNLISTED 8.00 20.00
STATED ODDS 1:52 HOBBY, 1:97 RETAIL
NO SHORT PRINTS IN BLACK SET
7 Mickey Mantle 40.00 80.00
50 Albert Pujols 15.00 40.00
181a Ichiro Suzuki 40.00 80.00
181b Ichiro Suzuki No Sig 40.00 80.00
190b Alex Rodriguez No Sig 12.00 30.00
200b Barry Bonds No Sig 15.00 40.00
226b Hunter Pence No Sig 15.00 40.00
234b Ryan Braun No Sig 20.00 50.00
235b Alex Gordon No Sig 15.00 40.00
240b Philip Hughes No Sig 15.00 40.00
243b Hideki Okajima No Sig 15.00 40.00
250b Daisuke Matsuzaka No Sig 30.00 80.00
251 Joba Chamberlain 50.00 100.00

2007 Bowman Heritage Rainbow Foil

COMPLETE SET (299) 75.00 150.00
*CHROME 1-200: 1X TO 2.5X BASIC
*CHROME 201-250: .75X TO 2X BASIC RC
COMMON BASIC SP (180-250) .40 1.00
BASIC SP SEMIS .60 1.50
BASIC SP UNLISTED 1.00 2.50
APPX.ODDS 1:1 HOBBY
NO SHORT PRINTS IN CHROME SET
COMP.SET INCLUDES ALL MANTLE VAR.
181b Ichiro Suzuki No Sig 1.50 4.00
190b Alex Rodriguez No Sig 1.50 4.00
200b Barry Bonds No Sig 2.00 5.00
226b Hunter Pence No Sig 2.00 5.00
234b Ryan Braun No Sig 2.50 6.00
235b Alex Gordon No Sig 2.00 5.00
240b Philip Hughes No Sig 2.00 5.00
243b Hideki Okajima No Sig 2.00 5.00
250b Daisuke Matsuzaka No Sig 4.00 10.00

2007 Bowman Heritage Red

STATED ODDS 1:1569 HOBBY
STATED PRINT RUN 1 SER.#'d SET
NO PRICING DUE TO SCARCITY

2007 Bowman Heritage Mantle Short Prints

COMPLETE SET (5) 12.50 30.00
COMMON CARD 2.50 6.00
OVERALL SP ODDS 1:3 HOBBY
OVERALL PLATE ODDS 1:463 HOBBY
PLATE PRINT RUN 1 SET PER COLOR
BLACK-CYAN-MAGENTA-YELLOW ISSUED
NO PLATE PRICING DUE TO SCARCITY

2007 Bowman Heritage Mantle Short Prints Black

COMMON CARD 40.00 80.00
OVERALL BLACK ODDS 1:52 HOB,1:97 RET
STATED PRINT RUN 52 SER.#'d SETS

2007 Bowman Heritage Mantle Short Prints Rainbow Foil

COMPLETE SET (5) 15.00 40.00
COMMON CARD 3.00 8.00
OVERALL FOIL ODDS ONE PER PACK

2007 Bowman Heritage Mantle Short Prints Red

OVERALL RED ODDS 1:1569 HOBBY
STATED PRINT RUN 1 SER.#'d SET
NO PRICING DUE TO SCARCITY

2007 Bowman Heritage Pieces of Greatness

GROUP A ODDS 1:83 HOBBY,1:166 RETAIL
GROUP B ODDS 1:22 HOBBY,1:46 RETAIL
GROUP C ODDS 1:119 HOBBY,1:238 RETAIL
GROUP D ODDS 1:325 HOBBY,1:660 RETAIL
GROUP E ODDS 1:104 HOBBY,1:211 RETAIL
GROUP F ODDS 1:67 HOBBY,1:687 RETAIL
GROUP G ODDS 1:452 HOBBY,1:953 RETAIL
AD Adam Dunn Jsy C 3.00 8.00
AE Andre Ethier Jsy B 3.00 8.00
AG Alex Gonzalez Bat B 3.00 8.00
AJ Andruw Jones Bat C 3.00 8.00
AL Adam LaRoche Jsy B 3.00 8.00
AR Aramis Ramirez Bat A 3.00 8.00
ARO Alex Rodriguez Bat C 6.00 15.00
BB Barry Bonds Jsy A 6.00 15.00
BC Bobby Crosby Bat B 3.00 8.00
BG Brian Giles Bat A 3.00 8.00
BL Brad Lidge Jsy E 3.00 8.00
BZ Barry Zito Pants C 3.00 8.00
CB Craig Biggio Jsy B 3.00 8.00
CBE Carlos Beltran Bat B 3.00 8.00
CH Cole Hamels Jsy A 4.00 10.00
CK Cory Koskie Bat B 3.00 8.00
CP Corey Patterson Bat B 3.00 8.00
CS Curt Schilling Jsy C 3.00 8.00
CT Chad Tracy Bat B 3.00 8.00
CU Chase Utley Bat A 4.00 10.00
DE Darin Erstad Bat B 3.00 8.00
DO David Ortiz Bat B 3.00 8.00
DO2 David Ortiz Jsy A 3.00 8.00
DW Dontrelle Willis Jsy E 3.00 8.00
DWR David Wright Pants A 5.00 12.00
EC Eric Chavez Pants B 3.00 8.00
FT Frank Thomas Bat A 4.00 10.00
GM Greg Maddux Bat A 4.00 10.00
GS Gary Sheffield Bat B 3.00 8.00
GSI Grady Sizmore Jsy B 3.00 8.00
HM Hideki Matsui Bat A 4.00 10.00
IR Ivan Rodriguez Jsy E 3.00 8.00
JB Jeremy Bonderman Jsy B 3.00 8.00
JD Johnny Damon Bat A 3.00 8.00
JDD J.D. Drew Jsy B 3.00 8.00
JE Juan Encarnacion Bat B 3.00 8.00
JF Jeff Franceour Bat B 3.00 8.00
JFR Jeff Francis Jsy B 3.00 8.00
JK Jeff Kent Jsy A 3.00 8.00
JM Joe Mauer Bat B 3.00 8.00
JR Jose Reyes Jsy B 4.00 10.00
LB Lance Berkman Jsy A 3.00 8.00
LG Luis Gonzalez Bat B 3.00 8.00
MC Miguel Cabrera Jsy B 3.00 8.00
ML Mike Lowell Pants A 3.00 8.00
MM Mark Mulder Pants E 3.00 8.00
MO Magglio Ordonez Bat D 3.00 8.00
MP Mike Piazza Bat E 4.00 10.00
MR Manny Ramirez Jsy C 3.00 8.00
MR2 Manny Ramirez Bat G 3.00 8.00
MT Mark Teixeira Bat A 3.00 8.00
MTE Miguel Tejada Pants B 3.00 8.00
NS Nick Swisher Bat A 3.00 8.00
PK Paul Konerko Pants B 3.00 8.00
PK2 Paul Konerko Jsy B 3.00 8.00
RB Rocco Baldelli Jsy F 3.00 8.00
RC Robinson Cano Bat B 4.00 10.00
RC2 Robinson Cano Jsy B 4.00 10.00
RF Rafael Furcal Bat B 3.00 8.00
RH Rich Harden Jsy B 3.00 8.00
SG Shawn Green Bat B 3.00 8.00
TH Todd Helton Jsy B 3.00 8.00
TH2 Todd Helton Bat B 3.00 8.00
THU Tim Hudson Pants A 3.00 8.00
TI Tadahito Iguchi Bat A 3.00 8.00
TN Trot Nixon Bat A 3.00 8.00
TW Tim Wakefield Pants B 3.00 8.00
VG Vladimir Guerrero Bat B 3.00 8.00
YM Yadier Molina Jsy D 3.00 8.00

2007 Bowman Heritage Pieces of Greatness Black

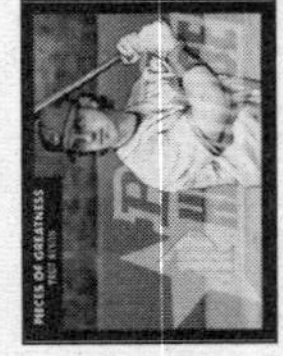

*BLACK: .75X TO 2X BASIC
STATED ODDS 1:221 HOBBY,1:429 RETAIL
STATED PRINT RUN 52 SER.#'d SETS

2007 Bowman Heritage Pieces of Greatness Red

STATED ODDS 1:6854 HOBBY
STATED PRINT RUN 1 SER.#'d SET
NO PRICING DUE TO SCARCITY

2007 Bowman Heritage Prospects

COMPLETE SET (100) 15.00 40.00
STATED ODDS TWO PER PACK
OVERALL PLATE ODDS 1:1175 HOBBY
PLATE PRINT RUN 1 SET PER COLOR
BLACK-CYAN-MAGENTA-YELLOW ISSUED
NO PLATE PRICING DUE TO SCARCITY
BHP1 Thomas Fairchild .20 .50
BHP2 Peter Bourjos .20 .50
BHP3 Brett Campbell .20 .50
BHP4 Cesar Nicolas .20 .50
BHP5 Kala Kaaihue .50 1.25
BHP6 Zach McAllister .30 .75
BHP7 Chad Reineke .20 .50
BHP8 Anthony Hatch .20 .50
BHP9 Cedric Hunter .50 1.25
BHP10 Chris Carter .75 2.00
BHP11 Tommy Hanson 1.00 2.50
BHP12 Dellin Betances .60 1.50
BHP13 John Otness .20 .50
BHP14 Derin McMains .20 .50
BHP15 Greg Reynolds .60 1.50
BHP16 Jonathan Van Every .20 .50
BHP17 Eddie Degerman .20 .50
BHP18 Cody Strait .20 .50
BHP19 Noe Rodriguez .20 .50
BHP20 Young-Il Jung .50 1.25
BHP21 Reegie Corona .30 .75
BHP22 Carlos Corporan .20 .50
BHP23 Chance Douglass .20 .50
BHP24 Leo Daigle .20 .50
BHP25 Jeff Samardzija 2.00 5.00
BHP26 Mark Wagner .30 .75
BHP27 Chuck Lofgren .50 1.25
BHP28 Bryan Byrne .20 .50
BHP29 Daniel Mayora .50 1.25
BHP30 Gorkys Hernandez .50 1.25
BHP31 Joshua Rodriguez .20 .50
BHP32 Brad Knox .20 .50
BHP33 Scott Lewis .50 1.25
BHP34 Joe Gaetti .20 .50
BHP35 Michael Saunders .60 1.50
BHP36 Brendan Katin .20 .50
BHP37 Brennan Boesch .20 .50
BHP38 Jay Garthwaite .20 .50
BHP39 Mike Devaney .20 .50
BHP40 J.R. Towles .60 1.50
BHP41 Joe Ness .20 .50
BHP42 Michael Martinez .20 .50
BHP43 Justin Byler .20 .50
BHP44 Chris Coghlan .20 .50
BHP45 Eric Young Jr. .30 .75
BHP46 J.R. Mathes .20 .50
BHP47 Ivan De Jesus Jr. .30 .75
BHP48 Woods Fines .20 .50
BHP49 Andrew Fie .20 .50
BHP50 Luke Hochevar .60 1.50
BHP51 Will Venable .30 .75
BHP52 Todd Redmond .20 .50
BHP53 Matthew Sweeney .60 1.50
BHP54 Trevor Cahill .50 1.25
BHP55 Mike Carp .30 .75
BHP56 Henry Sosa .30 .75
BHP57 Emerson Frostad .20 .50
BHP58 Jeremy Jeffress .20 .50
BHP59 Whit Robbins .20 .50
BHP60 Joba Chamberlain 3.00 8.00
BHP61 Raul Barron .20 .50
BHP62 Aaron Cunningham .60 1.50
BHP63 Greg Smith .20 .50
BHP64 Jeff Baisley .30 .75
BHP65 Vic Buttler .20 .50
BHP66 Steve Singleton .20 .50
BHP67 Josh Papelbon .20 .50
BHP68 Ryan Finan .20 .50
BHP69 Deolis Guerra 1.50 4.00
BHP70 Vasili Spanos .20 .50
BHP71 Patrick Reilly .20 .50
BHP72 Thomas Hottovy .20 .50
BHP73 Daniel Murphy 1.50 4.00
BHP74 Matt Young .20 .50
BHP75 Brian Bocock .20 .50
BHP76 Chris Salamida .20 .50
BHP77 Nathan Southard .20 .50
BHP78 Brandon Hynick .75 2.00
BHP79 Chris Nowak .20 .50
BHP80 Reid Brignac .50 1.25
BHP81 Cole Garner .20 .50
BHP82 Nick Van Stratten .20 .50
BHP83 Jeremy Papelbon .20 .50
BHP84 Jarrett Hoffpauir .20 .50
BHP85 Kevin Mulvey .50 1.25
BHP86 Matt Miller .20 .50
BHP87 Devin Ivany .20 .50
BHP88 Marcus Sanders .20 .50
BHP89 Michael MacDonald .20 .50
BHP90 Gabriel Sanchez .30 .75
BHP91 Ryan Norwood .20 .50
BHP92 Jim Fasano .20 .50
BHP93 Ryan Adams .30 .75
BHP94 Evan Englebrook .20 .50
BHP95 Juan Miranda .30 .75
BHP96 Gregory Porter .20 .50
BHP97 Shane Benson .20 .50
BHP98 Sam Fuld .50 1.25
BHP99 Cooper Brannan .20 .50
BHP100 Fernando Martinez 1.50 4.00

2007 Bowman Heritage Prospects Black

*BLACK: 4X TO 10X BASIC
STATED ODDS 1:153 HOBBY,1:295 RETAIL
STATED PRINT RUN 52 SER.#'d SETS
BHP25 Jeff Samardzija 20.00 50.00
BHP60 Joba Chamberlain 50.00 100.00
BHP73 Daniel Murphy 15.00 40.00

2007 Bowman Heritage Prospects Red

STATED ODDS 1:4740 HOBBY
STATED PRINT RUN 1 SER.#'d SET
NO PRICING DUE TO SCARCITY

2007 Bowman Heritage Red Man Box Topper

ONE PER HOBBY BOX TOPPER
AG Alex Gordon 3.00 8.00
AK Akinori Iwamura 2.50 6.00
AP Albert Pujols 5.00 12.00
AR Alex Rodriguez 4.00 10.00
AS Alfonso Soriano 2.00 5.00
BB Barry Bonds 3.00 8.00
DM Daisuke Matsuzaka 4.00 10.00
DO David Ortiz 2.50 6.00
DW David Wright 3.00 8.00
DY Delmon Young 2.00 5.00
FH Matt Holliday 2.50 6.00
FP Felix Pie 2.00 5.00
HM Hideki Matsui 2.50 6.00
HP Hunter Pence 3.00 8.00
IS Ichiro Suzuki 3.00 8.00
JH Josh Hamilton 6.00 15.00
JR Jose Reyes 2.50 6.00
KI Kei Igawa 2.50 6.00
MC Miguel Cabrera 2.00 5.00
MM Mickey Mantle 6.00 15.00
MR Manny Ramirez 2.00 5.00
PH Phil Hughes 3.00 8.00
RH Ryank Howard 3.00 8.00
TT Troy Tulowitzki 3.00 8.00
VG Vladimir Guerrero 2.50 6.00

2007 Bowman Heritage Signs of Greatness

GROUP A ODDS 1:339 HOBBY,1:405 RETAIL
GROUP B ODDS 1:47 HOBBY,1:53 RETAIL
GROUP C ODDS 1:58 HOBBY, 1:68 RETAIL
GROUP D ODDS 1:350 HOBBY,1:410 RETAIL
GROUP E ODDS 1:238 HOBBY,1:232 RETAIL
GROUP F ODDS 1:389 HOBBY,1:445 RETAIL
GROUP G ODDS 1:4450 HOBBY,1:4800 RETAIL
GROUP H ODDS 1:8100 HOBBY,1:7850 RETAIL
EXCH DEADLINE 10/31/2009
AF Andrew Fie G 3.00 8.00
AO Adam Ottavino D 3.00 8.00
BJ Blake Johnson C 3.00 8.00
BL Brad Lincoln E 3.00 8.00
CA Carlos Arroyo D 3.00 8.00
CC Carl Crawford C 4.00 10.00
CH Cole Hamels C 12.50 30.00
CJ Chipper Jones B 30.00 60.00
CS Chorye Spoone G 3.00 8.00
DW David Wright A 40.00 80.00
EJ Elliot Johnson F 3.00 8.00
GG Glenn Gibson F 3.00 8.00
GM Garrett Mock D 3.00 8.00
JB John Buck D 3.00 8.00
JC Jorge Cantu D 3.00 8.00
JCB Jordan Brown F 6.00 15.00
JH J.P. Howell C 3.00 8.00
JL Jeff Locke G 8.00 20.00
JM Jeff Manship F 6.00 15.00
JP Jorge Posada C 30.00 60.00

JT J.R. Towles G 6.00 15.00
JW Johnny Whittleman H 3.00 8.00
MM Matt Maloney E 3.00 8.00
MT Mike Thompson F 3.00 8.00
NR Nolan Reimold C 4.00 10.00
RD Rajai Davis E 3.00 8.00
SE Stephen Englund G 3.00 8.00
SJ Seth Johnston G 3.00 8.00
SK Sean Kazmar G 3.00 8.00
SP Steve Pearce G 10.00 25.00
SS Scott Sizemore F 4.00 10.00
TG Tony Giarratano F 3.00 8.00
WCS Cody Strait G 3.00 8.00
WJB Joe Benson F 5.00 12.00

2007 Bowman Heritage Signs of Greatness Black

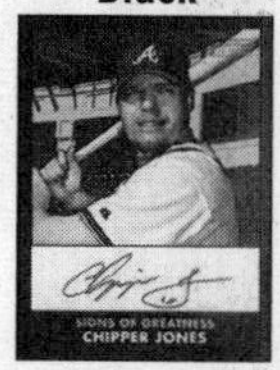

*BLACK: .75X TO 2X BASIC
STATED ODDS 1:590 HOBBY,1:695 RETAIL
STATED PRINT RUN 52 SER.#'d SETS
EXCH DEADLINE 10/31/2009
CJ Chipper Jones 75.00 150.00
DW David Wright 60.00 120.00
JL Jeff Locke 40.00 80.00
NR Nolan Reimold 15.00 40.00
SP Steve Pearce 60.00 120.00

2007 Bowman Heritage Signs of Greatness Red

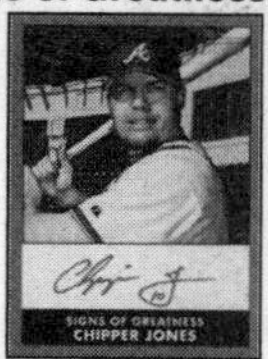

STATED ODDS 1:14,500 HOBBY
STATED PRINT RUN 1 SER.#'d SET
NO PRICING DUE TO SCARCITY

2006 Bowman Originals

This fifty-five card set was released in December, 2006. The set was issued in seven-card packs (five base cards plus 2 encased buy-back cards) which had an $75 SRP. The packs came six per box and there were also eight boxes per case.

COMMON CARD (1-35) .40 1.00
COMMON ROOKIE (36-55) .50 1.25
OVERALL PRINTING PLATE ODDS 1:86
PLATE PRINT RUN 1 SET PER COLOR
BLACK-CYAN-MAGENTA-YELLOW ISSUED
NO PLATE PRICING DUE TO SCARCITY
1 David Wright 1.50 4.00
2 Derek Jeter 2.50 6.00
3 Eric Chavez .40 1.00
4 Ken Griffey Jr. 1.50 4.00
5 Albert Pujols 2.00 5.00
6 Ryan Howard 1.50 4.00
7 Joe Mauer .60 1.50
8 Andruw Jones .60 1.50
9 Nomar Garciaparra 1.00 2.50
10 Michael Young .40 1.00
11 Miguel Tejada .40 1.00
12 Alfonso Soriano .40 1.00
13 Alex Rodriguez 1.50 4.00
14 Paul Konerko .40 1.00
15 Carl Crawford .40 1.00
16 Nick Johnson .40 1.00
17 Jim Thome .60 1.50
18 Ivan Rodriguez .60 1.50
19 Chipper Jones 1.00 2.50
20 Pedro Martinez .60 1.50
21 Carlos Delgado .40 1.00
22 Roger Clemens 2.00 5.00
23 Mark Teixeira .60 1.50
24 Manny Ramirez .60 1.50
25 Barry Bonds 2.00 5.00
26 Vernon Wells .40 1.00
27 Vladimir Guerrero 1.00 2.50
28 Miguel Cabrera .60 1.50
29 Victor Martinez .40 1.00
30 Derrek Lee .40 1.00
31 Carlos Lee .40 1.00
32 Ichiro Suzuki 1.50 4.00
33 Johan Santana .60 1.50
34 David Ortiz 1.00 2.50
35 Jason Bay .40 1.00
36 Kendry Morales (RC) 1.00 2.50
37 Nick Markakis (RC) .75 2.00
38 Conor Jackson (RC) .75 2.00
39 Justin Verlander (RC) 2.00 5.00
40 Ryan Zimmerman (RC) 2.50 6.00
41 Jeremy Hermida (RC) .75 2.00
42 Dan Uggla (RC) 1.25 3.00
43 Matt Kemp (RC) .75 2.00
44 Lastings Milledge (RC) .75 2.00
45 Kenji Johjima RC 2.00 5.00
46 Ian Kinsler (RC) .75 2.00
47 Hanley Ramirez (RC) 1.25 3.00
48 Melky Cabrera (RC) 2.00 5.00
49 Willy Aybar (RC) .50 1.25
50 Jonathan Papelbon (RC) 2.00 5.00
51 Prince Fielder (RC) 1.50 4.00
52 Cole Hamels (RC) 1.25 3.00
53 Josh Barfield (RC) .50 1.25
54 Alay Soler RC .50 1.50
55 Russ Martin (RC) .60 1.50

2006 Bowman Originals Black

*BLACK: 1X TO 2.5X BASIC
*BLACK RC: .75X TO 2X BASIC RC
STATED ODDS 1:4
STATED PRINT RUN 99 SERIAL #'d SETS
32 Ichiro Suzuki 6.00 15.00

2006 Bowman Originals Blue

*BLUE: .6X TO 1.5X BASIC
*BLUE RC: .5X TO 1.2X BASIC RC
STATED ODDS 1:2
STATED PRINT RUN 249 SERIAL #'d SETS
32 Ichiro Suzuki 4.00 10.00

2006 Bowman Originals Red

STATED ODDS 1:347
STATED PRINT RUN 1 SERIAL #'d SET
NO PRICING DUE TO SCARCITY

2006 Bowman Originals Buyback Autographs

GROUP A ODDS 1:3600
GROUP B ODDS 1:768
GROUP C ODDS 1:38
GROUP D ODDS 1:3
GROUP E ODDS 1:26
GROUP F ODDS 1:1
GROUP G ODDS 1:31
GROUP A PRINT RUN B/WN 10-20 PER
GROUP B PRINT RUN 50 CARDS
GROUP C PRINT RUN B/WN 1-61 PER
GROUP D PRINT RUN B/WN 1-466 PER
GROUP E PRINT RUN B/WN 1-472 PER
GROUP F PRINT RUN B/WN 1-1000 PER
GROUP G PRINT RUN B/WN 1-544 PER
NO PRICING ON QTY OF 25 OR LESS
1 Adam Loewen 03 BH/2 F
2 Adam Loewen 05 BDP/198 F 5.00 12.00
3 Adam Loewen 05 BCDPREF/3 F
4 Adam Loewen 05 BCDPREL/1 F
5 Adam Loewen 05 BCDPREL/2 F
6 Adam Loewen 05 BCDPWHITE/1 F
7 Adam Loewen 05 BCDPXF/1 F
8 Adam Loewen 05 BDP/1 F
9 Adam Loewen 05 BDP/1 F
10 Adam Loewen 05 BDP/1 F
11 Adam Loewen 05 BDP/719 F 4.00 10.00
12 Adam Loewen 05 BDPGLD/68 F 5.00 12.00
13 Adam Loewen 06 BC/4 F
14 Adam Loewen 06 BCREF/1 F
15 Adrian Gonzalez 00 B/976 F 8.00 20.00
16 Adrian Gonzalez 02 B/24 F
17 Albert Pujols 01 B/1 C
18 Albert Pujols 02 B/50 C 175.00 300.00
19 Albert Pujols 02 BB/1 C
20 Albert Pujols 02 BC/1 C
21 Albert Pujols 02 BH/1 C
22 Albert Pujols 03 BCXF/1 C
23 Albert Pujols 04 BC/1 C
24 Albert Pujols 05 B/44 C 175.00 300.00
25 Alex Gordon 06 BCPROS/32 C 250.00 400.00
26 Alex Gordon 06 BPROS/49 C 200.00 400.00
27 Alex Gordon 06 BPROSGLD/19 C
28 Alex Rodriguez 00 B/9 C
29 Alex Rodriguez 01 BC/2 C
30 Alex Rodriguez 01 BH/22 C
31 Alex Rodriguez 02 B/1 C
32 Alex Rodriguez 02 BC/1 C
33 Alex Rodriguez 02 BH/21 C
34 Alex Rodriguez 03 B/7 C
35 Alex Rodriguez 04 B/9 C
36 Alex Rodriguez 04 BFE/1 C
37 Alex Rodriguez 05 B/2 C
38 Alex Rodriguez 94 B/2 C
39 Alex Rodriguez 95 BC/1 C
40 Alex Rodriguez 96 B/1 C
41 Alex Rodriguez 96 BC/1 C
42 Alex Rodriguez 97 B/2 C
43 Alex Rodriguez 97 BC/1 C
44 Alex Rodriguez 98 B/5 C
45 Alex Rodriguez 98 BC/4 C
46 Alex Rodriguez 99 B/8 C
47 Andrew McCutchen 04 BAFLAC/391 F 15.00 40.00
48 Andrew McCutchen 04 BCAFLAC/15 F
49 Andrew McCutchen 05 BDP/1 F
50 Andrew McCutchen 05 BDP/561 F 6.00 15.00
51 Andrew McCutchen 06 BDPGLD/33 F 30.00 60.00
52 Andruw Jones 02 BC/22 C
53 Andruw Jones 03 BC/24 C
54 Andruw Jones 04 B/15 C
55 Andruw Jones 04 B/48 C 30.00 60.00
56 Andruw Jones 04 BH/28 C 30.00 60.00
57 Andruw Jones 04 BH/34 C 30.00 60.00
58 Andy LaRoche 05 B/66 F 12.50 30.00
59 Andy LaRoche 05 BCDP/14 F
60 Andy LaRoche 05 BCDPREF/2 F
61 Andy LaRoche 05 BCDPXF/1 F
62 Andy LaRoche 05 BDP/12 F
63 Andy LaRoche 05 BDP/734 F 6.00 15.00
64 Andy LaRoche 05 BDPGLD/60 F 12.50 30.00
65 Andy LaRoche 05 BDPREL/7 F
66 Andy LaRoche 05 BDPWHT/1 F
67 Andy LaRoche 05 BS/5 F
68 Andy LaRoche 05 BWHT/1 F
69 B.J. Upton 02 BCDP/1 F
70 B.J. Upton 02 BDP/5 F
71 B.J. Upton 03 BDPGLD/1 F
72 B.J. Upton 04 BCDP/10 F
73 B.J. Upton 04 BCDP/3 F
74 B.J. Upton 04 BCDPGLD/6 F
75 B.J. Upton 04 BDP/120 F 12.50 30.00
76 B.J. Upton 04 BDPREL/4 F
77 B.J. Upton 05 BCDP/136 F 12.50 30.00
78 B.J. Upton 05 BCDPBLUE/1 F
79 B.J. Upton 05 BCDPGLD/2 F
80 B.J. Upton 05 BCDPREF/5 F
81 B.J. Upton 05 BCDPREF/5 F
82 B.J. Upton 05 BDGLD/24 F
83 B.J. Upton 05 BDP/1 F
84 B.J. Upton 05 BDP/2 F
85 B.J. Upton 05 BDP/667 F 8.00 20.00
86 B.J. Upton 05 BDPREL/7 F
87 B.J. Upton Jsy 05 BDPREL/4 F
88a Barry Bonds 05 B/20 A
88b Barry Bonds 05 BC/10 A
89 Beau Jones 05 BAFLAC/329 F 4.00 10.00
90 Beau Jones 05 BAFLAC/33 F 8.00 20.00
91 Beau Jones 05 BCDP/2 F
92 Beau Jones 05 BCDP/63 F 6.00 15.00
93 Beau Jones 05 BCDPREF/6 F
94 Beau Jones 05 BCDPXF/3 F
95 Beau Jones 05 BDP/576 F 4.00 10.00
96 Beau Jones 05 BH/1 F
97 Beau Jones 06 BDPGLD/20 F
98 Billy Buckner 04 BC/182 E 6.00 15.00
99 Billy Buckner 04 BCDPXF/1 E
100 Billy Buckner 04 BDP/432 E 4.00 10.00
101 Billy Buckner 04 BDPGLD/33 E 8.00 20.00
102 Billy Buckner 04 BH/99 E 6.00 15.00
103 Billy Buckner 04 BS/3 E
104 Billy Wagner 01 BH/99 D 8.00 20.00
105 Billy Wagner 01 BHCHR/5 D
106 Billy Wagner 94 B/7 D
107 Billy Wagner 94 BB/19 D
108 Billy Wagner 94 BB/37 D 10.00 25.00
109 Billy Wagner 95 B/56 D 8.00 20.00
110 Billy Wagner 96 B/47 D 10.00 25.00
111 Billy Wagner 96 BB/64 D 8.00 20.00
112 Billy Wagner 96 BBREF/10 D
113 Billy Wagner 96 BBXF/4 D
114 Billy Wagner 96 BPOY/13 D
115 Billy Wagner 96 BVAR/4 D
116 Billy Wagner 97 B/90 D 8.00 20.00
117 Billy Wagner 97 BC/38 D 10.00 25.00
118 Billy Wagner 97 BCFLG/3 D
119 Billy Wagner 97 BCFLGREF/1 D
120 Billy Wagner 97 BFLG/4 D
121 Brandon Phillips 00 BC/1 F
122 Brandon Phillips 00 BCTI/4 F
123 Brandon Phillips 01 B/26 F 6.00 15.00
124 Brandon Phillips 01 BC/46 F 6.00 15.00
125 Brandon Phillips 01 BCXF/2 F
126 Brandon Phillips 02 B/335 F 4.00 10.00
127 Brandon Phillips 02 BC/67 F 5.00 12.00
128 Brandon Phillips 02 BCDP/28 F 6.00 15.00
129 Brandon Phillips 02 BCREF/3 F
130 Brandon Phillips 02 BCXF/1 F
131 Brandon Phillips 02 BDP/140 F 5.00 12.00
132 Brandon Phillips 02 BDPGLD/1 F
133 Brandon Phillips 02 BDPGLD/32 F 6.00 15.00
134 Brandon Phillips 02 BGLD/12 F
135 Brandon Phillips 03 B/257 F 4.00 10.00
136 Brandon Phillips 03 BC/35 F 6.00 15.00
137 Brandon Phillips 03 BCREF/1 F
138 Brandon Phillips 03 BGLD/10 F
139 Brandon Snyder 05 BCDP/1 D
140 Brandon Snyder 05 BCDP/14 D
141 Brandon Snyder 05 BDP/461 D 4.00 10.00
142 Brandon Snyder 05 BDPGLD/1 D
143 Brandon Snyder 05 BH/24 D
144 Brandon Wood 04 BH/2 F
145 Brandon Wood 05 BCDP/239 F 6.00 15.00
146 Brandon Wood 05 BCDPGLD/1 F
147 Brandon Wood 05 BCREF/11 F
148 Brandon Wood 05 BCXF/6 F
149 Brandon Wood 05 BDGLD/2 F
150 Brandon Wood 05 BDP/627 F 6.00 15.00
151 Brandon Wood 05 BDP/9 F
152 Brandon Wood 05 BDPGLD/1 F
153 Brandon Wood 05 BDPGLD/100 F 6.00 15.00
154 Brandon Wood 05 BDPREL/12 F
155 Brent Cox 05 BCDP/240 F 5.00 12.00
156 Brent Cox 05 BCREF/1 F
157 Brent Cox 05 BCXF/1 F
158 Brent Cox 05 BDP/2 F
159 Brent Cox 05 BDP/688 F 4.00 10.00
160 Brent Cox 05 BDPGLD/1 F
161 Brent Cox 05 BDPGLD/66 F 5.00 12.00
162 Brent Cox 05 BH/1 F
163 Brent Cox 05 BH/3 F
164 Carl Crawford 00 B/1 F
165 Carl Crawford 00 B/40 F 20.00 50.00
166 Carl Crawford 00 BC/18 F
167 Carl Crawford 00 BC/37 F 20.00 50.00
168 Carl Crawford 00 BC/4 F
169 Carl Crawford 01 B/20 F
170 Carl Crawford 01 BC/10 F
171 Carl Crawford 02 B/279 F 4.00 10.00
172 Carl Crawford 02 BC/14 F
173 Carl Crawford 02 BDP/13 F
174 Carl Crawford 02 BDPGLD/2 F
175 Carl Crawford 03 B/12 F
176 Carl Crawford 03 BC/5 F
177 Carl Crawford 03 BH/5 F
178 Carl Crawford 04 B/30 F 20.00 50.00
179 Carl Crawford 04 BC/13 F
180 Carl Crawford 04 BH/13 F
181 Carl Crawford 05 B/71 F 5.00 12.00
182 Carl Crawford 05 BC/6 F
183 Carl Crawford 05 BGLD/1 F
184 Carl Crawford 05 BH/71 F 5.00 12.00
185 Carl Crawford 06 B/1 F
186 Carl Crawford 06 B/334 F 4.00 10.00
187 Carlos Silva 00 B/2 F
188 Carlos Silva 00 B/996 F 4.00 10.00
189 Cesar Ramos 05 BCDP/16 F
190 Cesar Ramos 05 BCDP/161 F 5.00 12.00
191 Cesar Ramos 05 BCDPREF/2 F
192 Cesar Ramos 05 BCDPXF/1 F
193 Cesar Ramos 05 BCDPXF/3 F
194 Cesar Ramos 05 BDP/3 F
195 Cesar Ramos 05 BDP/5 F
196 Cesar Ramos 05 BDP/732 F 4.00 10.00
197 Cesar Ramos 05 BDPGLD/76 F 5.00 12.00
198 Cesar Ramos 05 BS/25 F
199 Chase Utley 01 BH/1 D
200 Chase Utley 02 B/303 D 30.00 60.00
201 Chase Utley 02 BC/23 D
202 Chase Utley 05 BH/23 D
203 Chase Utley 06 B/150 D 20.00 50.00
204 Chaz Roe 05 BCDP/132 F 5.00 12.00
205 Chaz Roe 05 BCDP/5 F
206 Chaz Roe 05 BCDPREF/2 F
207 Chaz Roe 05 BCDPXF/1 F
208 Chaz Roe 05 BDP/4 F
209 Chaz Roe 05 BDP/7 F
210 Chaz Roe 05 BDP/774 F 4.00 10.00
211 Chaz Roe 05 BDPBLUE/1 F
212 Chaz Roe 05 BDPGLD/73 F 5.00 12.00
213 Chaz Roe 05 BDPWHT/4 F
214 Chaz Roe 05 BH/4 F
215 Chien-Ming Wang 03 B/25 C
216 Chien-Ming Wang 03 BDP/25 C
217 Chien-Ming Wang 04 B/25 C
218 Chien-Ming Wang 05 B/25 C
219 Chipper Jones 02 B/20 C
220 Chipper Jones 02 BC/20 C
221 Chipper Jones 03 BC/20 C
222 Chipper Jones 04 BH/20 C
223 Chipper Jones 05 B/20 C
224 Chris B. Young 05 B/81 F 15.00 40.00
225 Chris B. Young 05 BC/6 F
226 Chris B. Young 05 BCDPREF/2 F
227 Chris B. Young 05 BDP/17 F
228 Chris B. Young 05 BDP/558 F 8.00 20.00
229 Chris B. Young 05 BDPGLD/88 F 20.00 50.00
230 Chris B. Young 05 BDPREL/3 F
231 Chris B. Young 05 BDPXF/2 F
232 Chris B. Young 05 BH/44 F 20.00 50.00
233 Chris B. Young 05 BHVAR/2 F
234 Chris R. Young 05 BCDP/1 F
235 Chris R. Young 05 BCDP/146 F 12.50 30.00
236 Chris R. Young 05 BCDP/19 F
237 Chris R. Young 05 BCDPREF/1 F
238 Chris R. Young 05 BCDPREF/5 F
239 Chris R. Young 05 BCXF/4 F
240 Chris R. Young 05 BDP/1 F
241 Chris R. Young 05 BDP/3 F
242 Chris R. Young 05 BDP/772 F 10.00 25.00
243 Chris R. Young 05 BDPGLD/70 F 12.50 30.00
244 Chris R. Young 05 BDPWHT/3 F
245 Clint Barmes 03 B/61 F 5.00 12.00
246 Clint Barmes 05 BCDP/113 F 5.00 12.00
247 Clint Barmes 05 BCDPREF/7 F
248 Clint Barmes 05 BDP/1 F
249 Clint Barmes 05 BDP/430 F 4.00 10.00
250 Clint Barmes 05 BH/14 F
251 Clint Barmes 06 B/375 F 4.00 10.00
252 Conor Jackson 04 B/78 F 8.00 20.00
253 Conor Jackson 04 BDP/10 F
254 Conor Jackson 04 BDPREL/3 F
255 Conor Jackson 04 BPPREL/1 F
256 Conor Jackson 05 BCDPREF/2 F
257 Conor Jackson 05 BDP/2 F
258 Conor Jackson 05 BDP/457 F 5.00 12.00
259 Conor Jackson 05 BDPREL/2 F
260 Conor Jackson 05 BDPREL/5 F
261 Conor Jackson 06 B/360 F 5.00 12.00
262 Conor Jackson 06 BC/1 F
263 Conor Jackson 06 BCORG/1 F
264 Conor Jackson 06 BCREF/10 F
265 Craig Italiano 05 BCDP/163 F 5.00 12.00
266 Craig Italiano 05 BCDPBLUE/1 F
267 Craig Italiano 05 BCDPREF/5 F
268 Craig Italiano 05 BDP/658 F 4.00 10.00
269 Craig Italiano 05 BDPGLD/160 F 5.00 12.00
270 Craig Italiano 05 BDPWHT/1 F
271 Craig Italiano 05 BH/1 F
272 Craig Italiano 05 BH/7 F
273 Craig Italiano 05 BS/3 F
274 Craig Italiano 05 BSREF/1 F
275 Dan Johnson 05 B/4 F
276 Dan Johnson 05 BCDP/101 F 5.00 12.00
277 Dan Johnson 05 BCDP/18 F
278 Dan Johnson 05 BCDPREF/1 F
279 Dan Johnson 05 BCDPREF/3 F
280 Dan Johnson 05 BDP/1 F
281 Dan Johnson 05 BDP/575 F 4.00 10.00
282 Dan Johnson 05 BDPGLD/9 F
283 Dan Johnson 05 BH/29 F 6.00 15.00
284 Dan Johnson 06 B/276 F 4.00 10.00
285 Dan Johnson 06 BC/1 F
286 Dan Johnson 06 BCREF/1 F
287 David Wright 02 B/264 F 50.00 100.00
288 David Wright 02 BH/1 F
289 David Wright 04 BCDP/7 F
290 David Wright 04 BDP/45 F 40.00 80.00
291 David Wright 04 BDPGLD/2 F
292 David Wright 05 B/64 F 40.00 80.00
293 David Wright 05 BC/1 F
294 David Wright 05 BH/62 F 40.00 80.00
295 David Wright 06 B/543 F 30.00 60.00
296 David Wright 06 BGLD/5 F
297 Derrek Lee 04 B/61 C 5.00 12.00
298 Derrek Lee 05 BSREL/4 C
299 Derrek Lee 05 BSRELREF/1 C
300 Derrek Lee 06 B/20 C
301 Derrek Lee 06 BCORG/1 C
302 Derrek Lee 06 BCREF/13 C
303 Dontrelle Willis 02 BCDP/1 F
304 Dontrelle Willis 02 BDP/10 F
305 Dontrelle Willis 03 BCDP/10 F
306 Dontrelle Willis 03 BDP/24 F
307 Dontrelle Willis 04 B/78 F 8.00 20.00
308 Dontrelle Willis 04 BC/8 F
309 Dontrelle Willis 04 BCREF/1 F
310 Dontrelle Willis 04 BH/79 F 8.00 20.00
311 Dontrelle Willis 05 B/147 F 8.00 20.00
312 Dontrelle Willis 05 BB/1 F
313 Dontrelle Willis 05 BC/36 F 10.00 25.00
314 Dontrelle Willis 05 BCREF/1 F
315 Dontrelle Willis 05 BH/55 F 8.00 20.00
316 Dontrelle Willis 05 BHVAR/1 F
317 Dontrelle Willis 05 BSREL/14 F
318 Dontrelle Willis 05 BSVARREF/1 F
319 Dontrelle Willis 06 B/525 F 5.00 12.00
320 Dontrelle Willis 06 BCORG/1 F
321 Dontrelle Willis 06 BGLD/7 F
322 Eli Iorg 05 BCDP/1 F
323 Eli Iorg 05 BCDP/4 F
324 Eli Iorg 05 BCDPREF/2 F
325 Eli Iorg 05 BDP/1 F
326 Eli Iorg 05 BDP/11 F
327 Eli Iorg 05 BDP/672 F 4.00 10.00
328 Eli Iorg 05 BDPGLD/151 F 5.00 12.00
329 Eli Iorg 05 BDPWHT/1 F
330 Eli Iorg 05 BH/1 F
331 Eli Iorg 05 BH/2 F
332 Eric Chavez 02 B/301 D 4.00 10.00
333 Eric Chavez 02 BC/7 D
334 Eric Chavez 03 BC/25 D
335 Eric Chavez 05 B/70 D 5.00 12.00
336 Eric Chavez 05 BH/62 D 5.00 12.00
337 Eric Chavez 05 BS/1 D
338 Eric Chavez 06 B/34 D 6.00 15.00
339 Ervin Santana 04 B/76 F 6.00 15.00
340 Ervin Santana 04 BH/62 F 15.00 40.00
341 Ervin Santana 05 B/67 F 5.00 12.00
342 Ervin Santana 05 BC/4 F
343 Ervin Santana 05 BCDP/109 F 5.00 12.00
344 Ervin Santana 05 BCDP/22 F
345 Ervin Santana 05 BCDPREF/5 F
346 Ervin Santana 05 BCGLD/1 F
347 Ervin Santana 05 BDP/1 F
348 Ervin Santana 05 BDP/51 F 5.00 12.00
349 Ervin Santana 05 BDP/544 F 4.00 10.00
350 Ervin Santana 05 BDPGLD/13 F
351 Ervin Santana 06 B/369 F 4.00 10.00
352 Fausto Carmona 04 BC/2 D
353 Fausto Carmona 04 BC/23 D
354 Fausto Carmona 04 BDP/56 D 15.00 40.00
355 Fausto Carmona 04 BDPGLD/1 D
356 Fausto Carmona 05 BCDP/14 D
357 Fausto Carmona 05 BDP/263 D 15.00 40.00
358 Fausto Carmona 05 BDPGLD/10 D
359 Francisco Cordero 00 B/140 D 5.00 12.00
360 Francisco Cordero 00 BC/64 D 5.00 12.00
361 Francisco Cordero 00 BCREF/2 D
362 Francisco Cordero 00 BCTV/1 D
363 Francisco Cordero 00 BTV/8 D
364 Francisco Cordero 98 B/138 D 5.00 12.00
365 Francisco Cordero 98 BB/87 D 5.00 12.00
366 Francisco Cordero 98 BBREF/1 D
367 Francisco Cordero 98 BC/49 D 6.00 15.00
368 Francisco Cordero 98 BCMAP/1 D
369 Francisco Cordero 98 BMAP/9 D
370 Francisco Liriano 02 B/212 F 30.00 60.00
371 Francisco Liriano 02 BDP/63 F 15.00 40.00
372 Francisco Liriano 05 B/4 F
373 Francisco Liriano 05 BCDP/142 F 15.00 40.00
374 Francisco Liriano 05 BDP/1 F
375 Francisco Liriano 05 BDP/350 F 10.00 25.00
376 Francisco Liriano 05 BDPREL/2 F
377 Francisco Liriano 05 BDPREL/9 F
378 Francisco Liriano 06 B/222 F 8.00 20.00
379 Garrett Atkins 05 BCDP/10 F
380 Garrett Atkins 05 BCDPREF/2 F
381 Garrett Atkins 05 BDP/1 F
382 Garrett Atkins 05 BDP/4 F
383 Garrett Atkins 05 BDP/581 F 4.00 10.00
384 Garrett Atkins 05 BDPGLD/1 F
385 Garrett Atkins 05 BDPGLD/27 F 6.00 15.00
386 Garrett Atkins 06 B/209 F 5.00 12.00
387 Garrett Atkins 06 B/4 F
388 Garrett Atkins 06 BBLUE/1 F
389 Garrett Atkins 06 BCREF/6 F
390 Garrett Atkins 06 BGLD/38 F 6.00 15.00
391 Gustavo Chacin 05 BH/30 D 6.00 15.00
392 Gustavo Chacin 05 BHVAR/1 D
393 Gustavo Chacin 06 B/468 D 4.00 10.00
394 Gustavo Chacin 06 BGLD/1 D
395 Hanley Ramirez 05 BCDP/1 F
396 Hanley Ramirez 05 BCDP/98 F 12.50 30.00
397 Hanley Ramirez 05 BCDPGLD/1 F
398 Hanley Ramirez 05 BDP/2 F
399 Hanley Ramirez 05 BDP/435 F 8.00 20.00
400 Hanley Ramirez 06 B/466 F 8.00 20.00
401 Huston Street 05 BCDP/24
402 Huston Street 05 BDP/54 5.00 12.00
403 Huston Street 05 BDPGLD/17
404 Jason Bay 02 B/298 D 12.50 30.00
405 Jason Bay 02 BC/24 D
406 Jason Bay 04 BH/58 D 6.00 15.00
407 Jason Bay 05 B/70 D 6.00 15.00
408 Jason Bay 06 B/50 D 6.00 15.00
409 Jason Botts 02 B/269 F 4.00 10.00
410 Jason Botts 02 BBREL/2 F
411 Jason Botts 02 BC/2 F
412 Jason Botts 02 BH/46 F 6.00 15.00
413 Jason Botts 06 B/29 F 6.00 15.00
414 Jason Botts 06 B/577 F 4.00 10.00
415 Jason Botts 06 BCGLD/1 F
416 Jason Botts 06 BCREF/1 F
417 Jason Botts 06 BCREF/12 F
418 Jason Botts 06 BGLD/31 F 6.00 15.00
419 Jason Kubel 03 B/77 D 5.00 12.00
420 Jason Kubel 03 BH/5 D
421 Jason Kubel 03 BHREF/1 D
422 Jason Kubel 03 BHREF/15 D
423 Jason Kubel 03 BHVAR/2 D
424 Jason Kubel 04 BCDP/127 D 5.00 12.00
425 Jason Kubel 04 BCDPGLD/1 D
426 Jason Kubel 04 BCDPREF/5 D
427 Jason Kubel 04 BCDPXF/4 D
428 Jason Kubel 04 BDP/232 D 5.00 12.00
429 Jason Kubel 04 BDPGLD/25 D
430 Jason Kubel 04 BDPREL/5 D
431 Jason Kubel 05 BGREL/1 D
432 Jason Marquis 00 B/9 F
433 Jason Marquis 00 B/944 F 4.00 10.00
434 Jason Marquis 00 BC/16 F
435 Jason Marquis 97 BC/1 F
436 Jason Marquis 98 B/26 F 6.00 15.00
437 Jason Marquis 98 BVAR/4 F
438 Jay Bruce 05 BDP/434 D 30.00 60.00
439 Jay Bruce 05 BDPGLD/66 D 50.00 100.00
440 Jed Lowrie 05 BCDP/4 F
441 Jed Lowrie 05 BCREF/6 F
442 Jed Lowrie 05 BDP/716 F 10.00 25.00
443 Jed Lowrie 05 BDPGLD/141 F 10.00 25.00
444 Jed Lowrie 05 BDPWHT/4 F
445 Jed Lowrie 05 BH/2 F
446 Jed Lowrie 05 BH/4 F
447 Jeff Mathis 01 BDP/71 D 5.00 12.00
448 Jeff Mathis 01 BH/1 D
449 Jeff Mathis 03 BCDP/8 D
450 Jeff Mathis 03 BCREF/1 D
451 Jeff Mathis 03 BDP/127 D 5.00 12.00
452 Jeff Mathis 03 BDPGLD/6 D
453 Jeff Mathis 04 BCDP/97 D 5.00 12.00
454 Jeff Mathis 04 BDP/185 D 5.00 12.00
455 Jeff Mathis 04 BDPGLD/4 D
456 Jerome Williams 01 BDP/8 D
457 Jerome Williams 02 B/292 D 4.00 10.00
458 Jerome Williams 02 BC/10 D
459 Jerome Williams 03 BCDP/45 D 6.00 15.00
460 Jerome Williams 03 BDP/48 D 6.00 15.00
461 Jerome Williams 04 B/97 D 5.00 12.00
462 Joel Guzman 02 B/274 D 4.00 10.00
463 Joel Guzman 02 BC/21 D
464 Joel Guzman 02 BCREF/1 D
465 Joel Guzman 02 BDP/90 D 10.00 25.00
466 Joel Guzman 04 BC/54 D 5.00 12.00
467 Joel Guzman 05 BDP/53 D 5.00 12.00
468 Joel Guzman 05 BREL/1 D
469 Joel Zumaya 04 B/96 F 20.00 50.00
470 Joel Zumaya 04 BC/18 F
471 Joel Zumaya 04 BFE/2 F
472 Joel Zumaya 05 BCDP/233 F 12.50 30.00
473 Joel Zumaya 05 BCDP/7 F
474 Joel Zumaya 05 BCDPREF/2 F
475 Joel Zumaya 05 BCDPREF/4 F
476 Joel Zumaya 05 BCDPXF/1 F
477 Joel Zumaya 05 BDP/1 F
478 Joel Zumaya 05 BDP/582 F 10.00 25.00
479 Joel Zumaya 05 BDPGLD/57 F 20.00 50.00
480 Joel Zumaya 05 BDPREL/2 F
481 Joel Zumaya 05 BDPREL/3 F
482 John Drennen 05 BAFLAC/2 D
483 John Drennen 05 BAFLAC/78 D 8.00 20.00
484 John Drennen 06 BCDP/23 D
485 John Drennen 06 BDP/2 D
486 John Drennen 06 BDP/387 D 4.00 10.00
487 John Drennen 06 BDPGLD/9 D
488 John Drennen 06 BS/3 D
489 John Van Benschoten 01 BDP/51 D 5.00 12.00
490 John Van Benschoten 02 B/272 D 4.00 10.00
491 John Van Benschoten 02 BGLD/1 D
492 John Van Benschoten 03 BCDP/26 D 6.00 15.00
493 John Van Benschoten 03 BDP/130 D 5.00 12.00
494 John Van Benschoten 03 BDPGLD/20 D
495 Jonny Gomes 02 B/341 F 4.00 10.00
496 Jonny Gomes 02 BC/27 F 6.00 15.00
497 Jonny Gomes 02 BGLD/1 F
498 Jonny Gomes 02 BH/9 F
499 Jonny Gomes 04 B/175 F 5.00 12.00
500 Jonny Gomes 04 BC/25 F
501 Jonny Gomes 04 BCREF/2 F
502 Jonny Gomes 04 BFE/9 F
503 Jonny Gomes 04 BGLD/8 F
504 Jonny Gomes 06 B/1 F
505 Jonny Gomes 06 B/14 F
506 Jonny Gomes 06 B/363 F 4.00 10.00
507 Jonny Gomes 06 BC/17 F
508 Jonny Gomes 06 BCREF/12 F
509 Jonny Gomes 06 BCXF/1 F
510 Jonny Gomes 06 BGLD/8 F
511 Josh Barfield 02 B/178 F 8.00 20.00
512 Josh Barfield 02 BBREL/1 F
513 Josh Barfield 02 BH/1 F
514 Josh Barfield 03 BCDP/1 F
515 Josh Barfield 03 BCDPREF/2 F
516 Josh Barfield 03 BCDPXF/1 F
517 Josh Barfield 03 BDP/18 F
518 Josh Barfield 03 BDPGLD/4 F
519 Josh Barfield 03 BFOTF/1 F
520 Josh Barfield 05 BCDPBLUE/1 F
521 Josh Barfield 05 BCDPREF/6 F
522 Josh Barfield 05 BDP/12 F
523 Josh Barfield 05 BDP/2 F
524 Josh Barfield 05 BDP/557 F 4.00 10.00
525 Josh Barfield 05 BDPGLD/1 F
526 Josh Barfield 05 BDPGLD/31 F 6.00 15.00
527 Josh Barfield 05 BDPREL/5 F
528 Josh Barfield 05 BDPWHT/1 F
529 Josh Geer 05 BCDP/138 D 5.00 12.00
530 Josh Geer 05 BCDPREF/1 D
531 Josh Geer 05 BDP/343 D 4.00 10.00
532 Josh Geer 05 BDPGLD/18 D
533 Justin Huber 02 BC/2 F
534 Justin Huber 02 BDP/26 F 12.50 30.00
535 Justin Huber 02 BDPGLD/2 F
536 Justin Huber 03 BCDP/37 F 12.50 30.00
537 Justin Huber 03 BCDPREF/3 F
538 Justin Huber 03 BCDPXF/2 F
539 Justin Huber 03 BDP/99 F 5.00 12.00
540 Justin Huber 03 BDPGLD/7 F
541 Justin Huber 04 BFOTF/1 F
542 Justin Huber 05 BCDPREF/1 F
543 Justin Huber 05 BCDPREF/2 F
544 Justin Huber 05 BDP/1 F
545 Justin Huber 05 BDP/572 F 4.00 10.00
546 Justin Huber 05 BDP/6 F
547 Justin Huber 05 BDPGLD/32 F 6.00 15.00

548 Justin Huber 05 BDPWHT/1 F
549 Justin Huber 05 BDPXF/1 F
550 Justin Upton 04 BAFLAC/1000 F 40.00 80.00
551 Kevin Gregg 00 B/988 F 4.00 10.00
552 Kevin Gregg 00 BC/1 F
553 Lastings Milledge 04 B/1 F
554 Lastings Milledge 04 B/158 F 12.50 30.00
555 Lastings Milledge 04 B/7 F
556 Lastings Milledge 04 BGLD/3 F
557 Lastings Milledge 04 BPPREL/3 F
558 Lastings Milledge 05 BCDP/166 F 12.50 30.00
559 Lastings Milledge 05 BCDPGLD/1 F
560 Lastings Milledge 05 BDP/632 F 10.00 25.00
561 Lastings Milledge 05 BDPGLD/27 F 15.00 40.00
562 Lastings Milledge 05 BDPWHT/1 F
563 Mark Loretta 05 B/110 D 5.00 12.00
564 Mark Loretta 05 BC/23 D
565 Mark Loretta 05 BH/73 D 5.00 12.00
566 Mark Loretta 06 B/289 D 4.00 10.00
567 Mark Loretta 06 BC/3 D
568 Mark Loretta 06 BGLD/1 D
569 Mark Loretta 96 B/1 D
570 Mark Mulder 02 B/20 C
571 Mark Mulder 02 BC/20 C
572 Mark Mulder 04 B/20 C
573 Mark Mulder 04 BH/20 C
574 Mark Mulder 05 B/20 C
575 Matt Cain 02 BCDP/1 D
576 Matt Cain 02 BCDPREF/9 D
577 Matt Cain 02 BDP/1 D
578 Matt Cain 02 BDPGLD/1 D
579 Matt Cain 03 BDPGLD/2 D
580 Matt Cain 04 BCDP/11 D
581 Matt Cain 04 BCDP/4 D
582 Matt Cain 04 BDP/36 D 10.00 25.00
583 Matt Cain 04 BDPGLD/7 D
584 Matt Cain 05 BHREL/1 D
585 Matt Cain 06 B/1 D
586 Matt Cain 06 B/389 D 6.00 15.00
587 Matt Cain 06 BC/16 D
588 Matt Cain 06 BCXF/2 D
589 Matt Cain 06 BGLD/20 D
590 Matt Maloney 05 B/350 D 6.00 15.00
591 Matt Maloney 05 B/4 D
592 Matt Maloney 05 BCDP/1 D
593 Matt Maloney 05 BCDPREF/3 D
594 Matt Maloney 05 BDPGLD/20 D
595 Matt Maloney 05 BH/50 D 30.00 60.00
596 Matt Maloney 05 BS/13 D
597 Matt Maloney 05 BS/4 D
598 Matt Torra 05 BCDP/1 D
599 Matt Torra 05 BS/1 D
600 Matt Torra 05 BS/13 D
601 Matt Torra 06 BDP/456 D 4.00 10.00
602 Matt Torra 06 BDPGLD/4 D
603 Melky Cabrera 05 B/95 F 20.00 50.00
604 Melky Cabrera 05 BC/1 F
605 Melky Cabrera 05 BC/10 F
606 Melky Cabrera 05 BCDP/191 F 20.00 50.00
607 Melky Cabrera 05 BCDP/25 F
608 Melky Cabrera 05 BCDPREF/1 F
609 Melky Cabrera 05 BCDPXF/1 F
610 Melky Cabrera 05 BDP/1 F
611 Melky Cabrera 05 BDP/22 F
612 Melky Cabrera 05 BDP/606 F 10.00 25.00
613 Melky Cabrera 05 BDPGLD/60 F 20.00 50.00
614 Melky Cabrera 05 BFE/12 F
615 Melky Cabrera 05 BH/24 F
616 Merkin Valdez 04 B/70 D 5.00 12.00
617 Merkin Valdez 04 BCDP/2 D
618 Merkin Valdez 04 BDPGLD/1 D
619 Merkin Valdez 04 BH/66 D 5.00 12.00
620 Merkin Valdez 05 BCDP/25 D
621 Merkin Valdez 05 BDP/325 D 4.00 10.00
622 Merkin Valdez 05 BDP/41 D 6.00 15.00
623 Merkin Valdez 05 BDPGLD/8 D
624 Merkin Valdez 05 BDPREL/3 D
625 Micah Owings 05 BDPGLD/3 E
626 Micah Owings 05 BDPWHT/1 E
627 Micah Owings 06 BDP/648 F 6.00 15.00
628 Micah Owings 06 BDPGLD/138 F 12.50 30.00
629 Michael Bowden 05 BCDP/24 D
630 Michael Bowden 05 BDP/11 D
631 Michael Bowden 05 BDP/449 D 15.00 40.00
632 Michael Bowden 05 BDPGLD/27 D 40.00 80.00
633 Miguel Cabrera 02 B/130 D 10.00 25.00
634 Miguel Cabrera 03 B/70 D 10.00 25.00
635 Miguel Cabrera 04 B/70 D 10.00 25.00
636 Miguel Cabrera 05 B/1 D
637 Miguel Cabrera 05 B/69 D 10.00 25.00
638 Miguel Cabrera 05 BH/1 D
639 Miguel Cabrera 05 BH/63 D 12.50 30.00
640 Miguel Cabrera 06 B/3 D
641 Miguel Cabrera 06 B/98 D 10.00 25.00
642 Mike Costanzo 05 BS/9 D
643 Mike Costanzo 05 BSREF/1 D
644 Mike Costanzo 06 BCDP/13 D
645 Mike Costanzo 06 BDP/466 D 5.00 12.00
646 Mike Costanzo 06 BDPGLD/10 D
647 Mike Costanzo 06 BDPWHT/1 D
648 Mike Lamb 00 B/993 F 4.00 10.00
649 Morgan Ensberg 01 BDP/74 D 5.00 12.00
650 Morgan Ensberg 02 B/334 D 4.00 10.00
651 Morgan Ensberg 02 BC/23 D
652 Morgan Ensberg 02 BH/1 D
653 Morgan Ensberg 05 BH/1 D
654 Morgan Ensberg 06 B/15 D
655 Morgan Ensberg 06 B/64 D 5.00 12.00
656 Morgan Ensberg 06 BCGLD/3 D
657 Morgan Ensberg 06 BCREF/1 D
658 Nick Swisher 03 BCDP/9 D
659 Nick Swisher 03 BDP/5 D
660 Nick Swisher 05 BH/15 D
661 Nick Swisher 05 BH/73 D 5.00 12.00
662 Nick Swisher 06 B/1 D
663 Nick Swisher 06 B/342 D 4.00 10.00
664 Nick Swisher 06 BC/16 D
665 Nick Swisher 06 BCGLD/1 D
666 Nick Swisher 06 BCORG/1 D
667 Nick Swisher 06 BCREF/7 D
668 Nick Swisher 06 BGLD/31 D 6.00 15.00
669 Nolan Reimold 05 BCDP/2 D
670 Nolan Reimold 05 BCDP/30 D 20.00 50.00
671 Nolan Reimold 05 BDP/419 D 6.00 15.00
672 Nolan Reimold 05 BDPGLD/7 D
673 Nolan Reimold 05 BH/1 D
674 Nolan Reimold 05 BH/41 D 20.00 50.00
675 Nolan Reimold 05 BHVAR/1 D
676 Nolan Reimold 05 BPREL/1 D
677 Rich Harden 02 B/263 D 10.00 25.00
678 Rich Harden 03 B/70 D 5.00 12.00
679 Rich Harden 03 BDP/68 D 6.00 15.00
680 Rich Harden 03 BH/1 D
681 Rich Harden 04 B/87 D 5.00 12.00
682 Rich Harden 05 B/82 D 5.00 12.00
683 Rich Harden 05 BH/2 D
684 Rich Harden 06 BC/2 D
685 Rich Harden 06 BCREF/10 D
686 Ricky Nolasco 04 B/256 D 4.00 10.00
687 Ricky Nolasco 04 BC/148 D 5.00 12.00
688 Ricky Nolasco 04 BCBLUE/10 D
689 Ricky Nolasco 04 BCREF/5 D
690 Ricky Nolasco 04 BCXF/1 D
691 Ricky Nolasco 04 BFE/6 D
692 Ricky Nolasco 04 BGLD/12 D
693 Ricky Nolasco 04 BH/52 D 5.00 12.00
694 Ricky Nolasco 04 BHVAR/5 D
695 Robinson Cano 03 BDP/2 D
696 Robinson Cano 03 BDPGLD/1 D
697 Robinson Cano 04 BCDP/1 D
698 Robinson Cano 04 BDP/72 D 15.00 40.00
699 Robinson Cano 04 BDPGLD/1 D
700 Robinson Cano 05 BCDP/1 D
701 Robinson Cano 05 BCDP/90 D 15.00 40.00
702 Robinson Cano 05 BDP/222 D 15.00 40.00
703 Robinson Cano 05 BDPGLD/10 D
704 Robinson Cano 05 BH/1 D
705 Robinson Cano 06 B/101 D 15.00 40.00
706 Roy Oswalt 02 B/199 D 6.00 15.00
707 Roy Oswalt 02 BC/14 D
708 Roy Oswalt 03 BC/25 D
709 Roy Oswalt 04 B/61 D 8.00 20.00
710 Roy Oswalt 04 BH/63 D 15.00 40.00
711 Roy Oswalt 05 B/96 D 8.00 20.00
712 Roy Oswalt 06 B/42 D 10.00 25.00
713 Russ Martin 05 B/96 F 20.00 50.00
714 Russ Martin 05 BC/6 F
715 Russ Martin 05 BCDP/252 F 15.00 40.00
716 Russ Martin 05 BCDPREF/4 F
717 Russ Martin 05 BDP/2 F
718 Russ Martin 05 BDP/577 F 10.00 25.00
719 Russ Martin 05 BDPGLD/33 F 20.00 50.00
720 Russ Martin 05 BDPREL/3 F
721 Russ Martin 05 BDPREL/8 F
722 Russ Martin 05 BH/21 F
723 Ryan Garko 05 BC/3 F
724 Ryan Garko 05 BDP/394 F 4.00 10.00
725 Ryan Garko 05 BDPGLD/14 F
726 Ryan Garko 06 B/580 F 4.00 10.00
727 Ryan Garko 06 BGLD/2 F
728 Ryan Howard 03 BDP/50 B 150.00 250.00
729 Scott Elbert 04 BCDP/60 D 10.00 25.00
730 Scott Elbert 04 BCDPREF/1 D
731 Scott Elbert 04 BDP/330 D 8.00 20.00
732 Scott Elbert 04 BDPGLD/9 D
733 Scott Elbert 04 BH/79 D 15.00 40.00
734 Scott Kazmir 05 B/155 F 8.00 20.00
735 Scott Kazmir 05 BFE/7 F
736 Scott Kazmir 05 BH/99 F 10.00 25.00
737 Scott Kazmir 06 B/1 F
738 Scott Kazmir 06 B/661 F 8.00 20.00
739 Scott Kazmir 06 BC/10 F
740 Scott Kazmir 06 BCGLD/1 F
741 Scott Kazmir 06 BCREF/7 F
742 Scott Kazmir 06 BGLD/26 F 10.00 25.00
743 Scott Mathieson 05 B/3 E
744 Scott Mathieson 05 B/72 E 5.00 12.00
745 Scott Mathieson 05 BCBREF/4 E
746 Scott Mathieson 05 BCDP/20 E
747 Scott Mathieson 05 BCGRN/5 E
748 Scott Mathieson 05 BCREF/2 E
749 Scott Mathieson 05 BCREF/3 E
750 Scott Mathieson 05 BCREF/4 E
751 Scott Mathieson 05 BCXF/1 E
752 Scott Mathieson 05 BCXF/1 E
753 Scott Mathieson 05 BDP/1 E
754 Scott Mathieson 05 BDP/472 E 4.00 10.00
755 Scott Mathieson 05 BDPGLD/16 E
756 Scott Mathieson 05 BDPREL/16 E
757 Scott Mathieson 05 BDPWHT/1 E
758 Scott Mathieson 05 BH/19 E
759 Scott Thorman 00 B/980 F 4.00 10.00
760 Scott Thorman 03 BDP/20 F
761 Sean West 05 BCDP/70 D 12.50 30.00
762 Sean West 05 BCXF/1 D
763 Sean West 05 BDP/1 D
764 Sean West 05 BDP/394 D 4.00 10.00
765 Sean West 05 BDPGLD/35 D 10.00 25.00
766 Shaun Marcum 03 BCDP/153 D 5.00 12.00
767 Shaun Marcum 03 BDP/138 D 5.00 12.00
768 Shaun Marcum 03 BDPGLD/33 D 6.00 15.00
769 Shaun Marcum 05 B/133 D 5.00 12.00
770 Shaun Marcum 05 BC/26 D 6.00 15.00
771 Shaun Marcum 05 BCREF/1 D
772 Shaun Marcum 05 BFE/13 D
773 Shaun Marcum 05 BGLD/2 D
774 Shaun Marcum 05 BWHT/1 D
775 Travis Buck 05 BCDP/134 F 8.00 20.00
776 Travis Buck 05 BCREF/1 F
777 Travis Buck 05 BDP/747 F 5.00 12.00
778 Travis Buck 05 BDPGLD/60 F 20.00 50.00
779 Travis Buck 05 BH/1 F
780 Travis Buck 05 BH/2 F
781 Travis Buck 05 BHVAR/10 F
782 Travis Buck 05 BS/44 F 20.00 50.00
783 Travis Buck 05 BSREF/1 F
784 Travis Hafner 02 B/280 F 6.00 15.00
785 Travis Hafner 02 BC/16 F
786 Travis Hafner 02 BCREF/1 F
787 Travis Hafner 03 BCDP/45 F 10.00 25.00
788 Travis Hafner 03 BCDPREF/1 F
789 Travis Hafner 03 BCDPXF/1 F
790 Travis Hafner 03 BDP/114 F 6.00 15.00
791 Travis Hafner 03 BDPGLD/2 F
792 Travis Hafner 05 B/96 F 6.00 15.00
793 Travis Hafner 05 BCGLD/1 F
794 Travis Hafner 06 B/386 F 6.00 15.00
795 Travis Hafner 06 B/9 F
796 Travis Hafner 06 BC/18 F
797 Travis Hafner 06 BCBLUE/1 F
798 Travis Hafner 06 BCORG/1 F
799 Travis Hafner 06 BCREF/7 F
800 Travis Hafner 06 BGLD/1 F
801 Trevor Bell 05 BCREF/2 F
802 Trevor Bell 05 BDP/1 F
803 Trevor Bell 05 BDP/2 F
804 Trevor Bell 05 BDP/689 F 4.00 10.00
805 Trevor Bell 05 BDPGLD/1 F
806 Trevor Bell 05 BDPGLD/134 F 5.00 12.00
807 Trevor Bell 05 BH/28 F 6.00 15.00
808 Trevor Bell 05 BHVAR/1 F
809 Troy Patton 05 BCDP/211 F 8.00 20.00
810 Troy Patton 05 BCDPREF/2 F
811 Troy Patton 05 BDP/1 F
812 Troy Patton 05 BDP/3 F
813 Troy Patton 05 BDP/736 F 4.00 10.00
814 Troy Patton 05 BDPGLD/50 F 5.00 12.00
815 Troy Patton 05 BDPWHT/1 F
816 Vernon Wells 00 B/1 F
817 Vernon Wells 00 B/56 F 15.00 40.00
818 Vernon Wells 00 BB/1 F
819 Vernon Wells 00 BC/11 F
820 Vernon Wells 01 B/29 F 15.00 40.00
821 Vernon Wells 01 BC/10 F
822 Vernon Wells 03 BH/16 F
823 Vernon Wells 04 B/96 F 10.00 25.00
824 Vernon Wells 04 BC/7 F
825 Vernon Wells 05 B/1 F
826 Vernon Wells 05 B/100 F 10.00 25.00
827 Vernon Wells 05 BC/25 F
828 Vernon Wells 05 BH/52 F 10.00 25.00
829 Vernon Wells 05 BHVAR/3 F
830 Vernon Wells 06 B/4 F
831 Vernon Wells 06 B/426 F 6.00 15.00
832 Vernon Wells 06 BC/11 F
833 Vernon Wells 06 BCGLD/1 F
834 Vernon Wells 06 BCORG/1 F
835 Vernon Wells 06 BCREF/1 F
836 Vernon Wells 97 B/5 F
837 Vernon Wells 98 B/2 F
838 Vernon Wells 98 B/40 F 20.00 50.00
839 Vernon Wells 98 BC/1 F
840 Vernon Wells 98 BC/13 F
841 Vernon Wells 98 BVAR/6 F
842 Vernon Wells 99 B/68 F 10.00 25.00
843 Vernon Wells 99 BB/4 F
844 Vernon Wells 99 BC/15 F
845 Vladimir Guerrero 02 B/12 C
846 Vladimir Guerrero 02 BC/1 C
847 Vladimir Guerrero 02 BC/21 C
848 Vladimir Guerrero 04 BH/20 C
849 Vladimir Guerrero 05 B/45 C 20.00 50.00
850 Vladimir Guerrero 95 BB/1 C
851 Wade Townsend 05 BCDP/53 D 5.00 12.00
852 Wade Townsend 05 BDP/1 D
853 Wade Townsend 05 BDP/423 D 4.00 10.00
854 Wade Townsend 05 BDPGLD/10 D
855 Wade Townsend 05 BH/14 D
856 Wily Mo Pena 00 B/79 D 5.00 12.00
857 Wily Mo Pena 00 BB/27 D 6.00 15.00
858 Wily Mo Pena 00 BC/21 D
859 Wily Mo Pena 00 BTV/10 D
860 Wily Mo Pena 02 B/134 D 5.00 12.00
861 Wily Mo Pena 02 BC/19 D
862 Wily Mo Pena 02 BC/2 D
863 Wily Mo Pena 02 BDP/70 D 5.00 12.00
864 Wily Mo Pena 02 BDPGLD/2 D
865 Wily Mo Pena 03 B/62 D 5.00 12.00
866 Wily Mo Pena 05 B/69 D 5.00 12.00
867 Xavier Nady 01 BB/3 F
868 Xavier Nady 01 BDP/192 F 5.00 12.00
869 Xavier Nady 02 B/294 F 4.00 10.00
870 Xavier Nady 02 BC/41 F 6.00 15.00
871 Xavier Nady 02 BCGLD/1 F
872 Xavier Nady 02 BCREF/2 F
873 Xavier Nady 02 BGLD/8 F
874 Xavier Nady 02 BH/21 F
875 Xavier Nady 03 BCDP/72 F 5.00 12.00
876 Xavier Nady 03 BCDPGLD/1 F
877 Xavier Nady 03 BDP/213 F 5.00 12.00
878 Xavier Nady 03 BDPGLD/33 F 6.00 15.00
879 Xavier Nady 05 BH/105 F 5.00 12.00
880 Xavier Nady 05 BHVAR/14 F
881 Yunel Escobar 05 BCDPREF/1 D
882 Yunel Escobar 05 BS/7 D
883 Yunel Escobar 06 BCDP/1 D
884 Yunel Escobar 06 BCDP/28 D 15.00 40.00
885 Yunel Escobar 06 BDP/395 D 15.00 40.00
886 Yunel Escobar 06 BDPGLD/69 D 30.00 60.00
887 Yusmeiro Petit 04 BCDP/15 F
888 Yusmeiro Petit 04 BDP/102 F 5.00 12.00
889 Yusmeiro Petit 04 BDPGLD/6 F
890 Yusmeiro Petit 04 BH/1 F
891 Yusmeiro Petit 04 BH/68 F 5.00 12.00
892 Yusmeiro Petit 04 BS/4 F
893 Yusmeiro Petit 05 BCDP/160 F 5.00 12.00
894 Yusmeiro Petit 05 BCDP/19 F
895 Yusmeiro Petit 05 BCDP/2 F
896 Yusmeiro Petit 05 BDP/13 F
897 Yusmeiro Petit 05 BDP/630 F 4.00 10.00
898 Yusmeiro Petit 05 BDPGLD/11 F
899 Chris Tillman 05 BAFLAC/100

2006 Bowman Originals Prospects

COMMON CARD (1-55) .40 1.00
OVERALL PRINTING PLATE ODDS 1:86
PLATE PRINT RUN 1 SET PER COLOR
BLACK-CYAN-MAGENTA-YELLOW ISSUED
NO PLATE PRICING DUE TO SCARCITY
1 Cameron Maybin 4.00 10.00
2 Koby Clemens 1.00 2.50
3 Lance Broadway 1.00 2.50
4 Chris Dickerson .60 1.50
5 Garrett Mock .40 1.00
6 Ben Copeland .60 1.50
7 Nick Adenhart 2.50 6.00
8 Brad McCann 1.25 3.00
9 Dustin Majewski .40 1.00
10 Jimmy Barthmaier .60 1.50
11 Michael Aubrey .60 1.50
12 Evan Longoria 6.00 15.00
13 Clayton Kershaw 2.50 6.00
14 Juan Francia .40 1.00
15 Elvis Andrus 2.50 6.00
16 Mark Trumbo 1.00 2.50
17 Shawn Riggans .40 1.00
18 Asdrubal Cabrera 1.25 3.00
19 Mark McLemore .40 1.00
20 Radhames Liz 1.50 4.00
21 Mat Gamel 1.00 2.50
22 Wilkin Ramirez 1.00 2.50
23 Jared Lansford .40 1.00
24 Hunter Pence 3.00 8.00
25 Justin Upton 3.00 8.00
26 Brent Dlugach .40 1.00
27 B.J. Szymanski .60 1.50
28 Stephen Marek .60 1.50
29 Shaun Cumberland .40 1.00
30 Yovani Gallardo 1.50 4.00
31 Will Venable .40 1.00
32 A.J. Shappi .40 1.00
33 Dallas Trahern .40 1.00
34 Jason Jaramillo .40 1.00
35 Jose Tabata 4.00 10.00
36 Jose Campusano .40 1.00
37 Ryan Patterson 1.00 2.50
38 Andrew Pinckney .60 1.50
39 Dexter Fowler 1.00 2.50
40 Cody Johnson .40 1.00
41 Steve Murphy 1.00 2.50
42 Mark Reed 1.25 3.00
43 Chris Iannetta .40 1.00
44 Michael Hollimon UER .40 1.00
Mark Holliman is pictured on this card
45 Omir Santos .40 1.00
46 Diory Hernandez .40 1.00
47 Matt Tolbert .40 1.00
48 Jeff Frazier .40 1.00
49 Max Ramirez 1.50 4.00
50 Alex Gordon 4.00 10.00
51 Steve Garrabrants .40 1.00
52 Steven Baker .40 1.00
53 Ryan Klosterman .40 1.00
54 Michael Collins 1.00 2.50
55 Corey Wimberly 1.00 2.50

2006 Bowman Originals Prospects Black

*BLACK: .75X TO 2X BASIC
STATED ODDS 1:4
STATED PRINT RUN 99 SERIAL #'d SETS
1 Cameron Maybin 15.00 40.00
12 Evan Longoria 30.00 60.00
15 Elvis Andrus 10.00 25.00
24 Hunter Pence 20.00 50.00
25 Justin Upton 12.50 30.00
35 Jose Tabata 15.00 40.00
50 Alex Gordon 12.50 30.00

2006 Bowman Originals Prospects Blue

*BLUE: .6X TO 1.5X BASIC
STATED ODDS 1:2
STATED PRINT RUN 249 SERIAL #'d SETS
12 Evan Longoria 20.00 50.00
25 Justin Upton 6.00 15.00

2006 Bowman Originals Prospects Red

STATED ODDS 1:347
STATED PRINT RUN 1 SERIAL #'d SET
NO PRICING DUE TO SCARCITY

2004 Bowman Sterling

This 138-card set was released in December, 2004. The set was issued in five-card packs with a $50 SRP and they came six packs to a box and four boxes to a case. Just about every basic card is a "hit" as the cards are either memorabilia cards of veterans, or rookie cards with the possibility of them being either autographed or with a jersey swatch on it. Despite the high price point for the packs, this product did extremely well in the secondary market.

FY ODDS APPX.TWO PER HOBBY PACK
FY AU ODDS APPX.ONE PER HOBBY PACK
AU-GU ODDS APPX.ONE PER HOBBY PACK
AU-GU 1:2 WRAPPER ODDS IS AN ERROR
GU ODDS APPX. 1.5 PER HOBBY PACK
GU 1:2 WRAPPER ODDS IS AN ERROR
AB Angel Berroa Bat 2.00 5.00
ABA Aarom Baldiris FY RC 2.00 5.00
AC Alberto Callaspo FY AU RC 8.00 20.00
AD Adam Dunn Bat 2.00 5.00
AER Alex Rodriguez Bat 6.00 15.00
AJ Andruw Jones Jsy 3.00 8.00
AK Austin Kearns Jsy 2.00 5.00
ANR Aramis Ramirez Bat 2.00 5.00
AP Albert Pujols Jsy 8.00 20.00
AR Alex Romero FY AU RC 3.00 8.00
AW Adam Wainwright AU Jsy 10.00 25.00
AWH A.Whittington FY RC 2.00 5.00
AZ Alec Zumwalt FY AU RC 3.00 8.00
BB Brian Bixler AU Jsy RC 4.00 10.00
BBR Bill Bray FY RC 1.50 4.00
BBU Billy Buckner FY RC 2.00 5.00
BC2 Bobby Crosby Jsy 2.00 5.00
BD Blake DeWitt AU Jsy RC 6.00 15.00
BE Brad Eldred FY RC 2.00 5.00
BH B.Hawksworth FY AU RC 4.00 10.00
BT Brad Thompson FY RC 2.00 5.00
BU B.J. Upton AU Bat 12.50 30.00
BW Bernie Williams Jsy 3.00 8.00
CA Chris Aguila FY AU RC 3.00 8.00
CB Craig Biggio Jsy 3.00 8.00
CC Chad Cordero AU Jsy 6.00 15.00
CG Christian Garcia AU Jsy RC 6.00 15.00
CH Chin-Lung Hu FY RC 6.00 15.00
CIB Carlos Beltran Bat 2.00 5.00
CJ Conor Jackson FY RC 8.00 20.00
CL Chris Lubanski AU Bat 4.00 10.00
CLA Chris Lambert FY RC 2.00 5.00
CN Chris Nelson FY RC 3.00 8.00
CQ Carlos Quentin FY AU RC 12.50 30.00
CT Curtis Thigpen FY RC 2.00 5.00
DD David DeJesus AU Jsy 6.00 15.00
DP Danny Putnam AU Jsy RC 4.00 10.00
DPU David Purcey FY RC 2.00 5.00
DW David Wright AU Jsy 30.00 50.00
DWW Dontrelle Willis Jsy 3.00 8.00
DY Delmon Young AU Bat 12.50 30.00
EG Eric Gagne Jsy 2.00 5.00
EH Eric Hurley FY RC 2.00 5.00
ESP Erick San Pedro FY RC 1.50 4.00
FC Fausto Carmona FY RC 4.00 10.00
FG Freddy Guzman FY RC 1.50 4.00
FH Felix Hernandez FY RC 12.50 30.00
FP Felix Pie AU Jsy 10.00 25.00
FT Frank Thomas Bat 3.00 8.00
GG Greg Golson FY RC 3.00 8.00
GH Gaby Hernandez FY RC 3.00 8.00
GIG Gio Gonzalez FY RC 3.00 8.00
GS Gary Sheffield Bat 2.00 5.00
HB Homer Bailey AU Jsy RC 15.00 40.00
HC Hee Seop Choi Bat 2.00 5.00
HG Hector Gimenez FY AU RC 3.00 8.00
HJB Hank Blalock Bat 2.00 5.00
HM Hector Made FY RC 2.00 5.00
HS Huston Street AU Jsy RC 10.00 25.00
IR Ivan Rodriguez Bat 3.00 8.00
JB Jeff Bagwell Jsy 3.00 8.00
JC Jose Capellan FY RC 2.00 5.00
JCR Jesse Crain FY RC 2.00 5.00
JD Johnny Damon Bat 3.00 8.00
JE Johnny Estrada Bat 2.00 5.00
JFI Josh Fields FY RC 5.00 12.00
JG Joey Gathright FY RC 2.00 5.00
JH Jesse Hoover FY RC 2.00 5.00
JK Jason Kendall Bat 2.00 5.00
JM Jeff Marquez AU Jsy RC 6.00 15.00
JO Justin Orenduff FY RC 2.00 5.00
JP Juan Pierre Bat 2.00 5.00
JPH J.P. Howell FY RC 2.00 5.00
JR Jay Rainville FY AU RC 5.00 12.00
JS Jeremy Sowers FY AU RC 15.00 30.00
JZ Jon Zeringue FY RC 2.00 5.00
KCH K.C. Herren FY RC 2.00 5.00
KS Kurt Suzuki FY RC 2.50 6.00
KT Kazuhito Tadano FY RC 2.00 5.00
KW Kerry Wood Jsy 2.00 5.00
KWA Kyle Waldrop AU Jsy RC 6.00 15.00
LB Lance Berkman Jsy 2.00 5.00
LC Luis Castillo Jsy 2.00 5.00
LH Linc Holdzkom FY AU RC 3.00 8.00
LN Laynce Nix Bat 2.00 5.00
MA Moises Alou Bat 2.00 5.00
MAM Mark Mulder Jsy 2.00 5.00
MAR Manny Ramirez Bat 3.00 8.00
MB Matt Bush AU Jsy RC 10.00 25.00
MC Miguel Cabrera Bat 3.00 8.00
MCT Mark Teixeira Bat 3.00 8.00
ME Mitch Einertson FY RC 2.00 5.00
MF Mike Ferris FY RC 2.00 5.00
MFO Matt Fox FY RC 1.50 4.00
MJP Mike Piazza Bat 3.00 8.00
MM Matt Moses FY AU RC 6.00 15.00
MMC Matt Macri FY RC 2.50 6.00
MP Mark Prior Jsy 3.00 8.00
MR Mike Rouse FY AU RC 3.00 8.00
MRO Mark Rogers FY RC 3.00 8.00
MT M.Tuiasosopo AU Bat RC 12.50 30.00
MT1 Miguel Tejada Bat 2.00 5.00
MT2 Miguel Tejada Jsy 2.00 5.00
MW Marland Williams FY RC 2.00 5.00
MY Michael Young Bat 2.00 5.00
NJ Nick Johnson Bat 2.00 5.00
NM Nyjer Morgan FY RC 1.50 4.00
NS Nate Schierholtz FY RC 3.00 8.00
NW Neil Walker FY RC 3.00 8.00
OQ Omar Quintanilla FY RC 2.00 5.00
PGM Paul Maholm FY RC 3.00 8.00
PH Philip Hughes FY RC 10.00 25.00
PL Paul LoDuca Bat 2.00 5.00
PR Pokey Reese Bat 2.00 5.00
RB Rocco Baldelli Bat 2.00 5.00
RBR Reid Brignac FY RC 4.00 10.00
RC Robinson Cano AU Jsy 20.00 50.00
RH Ryan Harvey AU Bat 6.00 15.00
RJH Richard Hidalgo Bat 2.00 5.00
RM Ryan Meaux FY AU RC 3.00 8.00
RO Russ Ortiz Jsy 2.00 5.00
RP Rafael Palmeiro Bat 3.00 8.00
SK Scott Kazmir AU Jsy RC 10.00 25.00
SO Scott Olsen AU Jsy RC 15.00 30.00
SS Sammy Sosa Jsy 3.00 8.00
SSM Seth Smith FY RC 3.00 8.00
TD Thomas Diamond FY RC 3.00 8.00
TG Troy Glaus Bat 2.00 5.00
TLH Todd Helton Bat 3.00 8.00
TM Tino Martinez Bat 3.00 8.00
TMG Tom Glavine Jsy 3.00 8.00
TP Trevor Plouffe AU Jsy RC 6.00 15.00
TT T.Tankersley AU Jsy RC 4.00 10.00
VG Vladimir Guerrero Bat 3.00 8.00
VP Vince Perkins FY AU RC 4.00 10.00
YP Yusmeiro Petit FY RC 4.00 10.00
ZD Zach Duke FY RC 4.00 10.00
ZJ Zach Jackson FY RC 2.00 5.00

2004 Bowman Sterling Refractors

*REF.FY: 1.25X TO 3X BASIC
FY ODDS 1:4 HOBBY
*REF.FY AU: 1X TO 2.5X BASIC FY AU
FY AU ODDS 1:8 HOBBY
*REF.AU-GU: .6X TO 1.5X BASIC AU-GU
AU-GU ODDS 1:9 HOBBY
*REF.GU: .6X TO 1.5X BASIC GU
GU ODDS 1:5 HOBBY
STATED PRINT RUN 199 SERIAL #'d SETS
AW Adam Wainwright AU Jsy 15.00 40.00
BD Blake DeWitt AU Jsy 8.00 20.00
BE Brad Eldred FY 8.00 20.00
CH Chin-Lung Hu FY 40.00 80.00
CJ Conor Jackson FY 25.00 60.00
CN Chris Nelson FY 10.00 25.00
CQ Carlos Quentin FY AU 30.00 60.00
DW David Wright AU Jsy 30.00 60.00
DY Delmon Young AU Bat 15.00 40.00
FH Felix Hernandez FY 50.00 100.00
FP Felix Pie AU Jsy 12.50 30.00
HB Homer Bailey AU Jsy 60.00 120.00
JS Jeremy Sowers FY AU 30.00 60.00
MB Matt Bush AU Jsy 20.00 50.00
RC Robinson Cano AU Jsy 40.00 80.00
SK Scott Kazmir AU Jsy 20.00 50.00

2004 Bowman Sterling Black Refractors

FY ODDS 1:28 HOBBY
FY PRINT RUN 16 SERIAL #'d SETS
FY AU ODDS 1:64 HOBBY
FY AU PRINT RUN 25 SERIAL #'d SETS
AU-GU ODDS 1:37 HOBBY
AU-GU PRINT RUN 25 SERIAL #'d SETS
GU ODDS 1:28 HOBBY
GU PRINT RUN 16 SERIAL #'d SETS
ISSUED IN HOBBY BOX LOADER PACKS
NO PRICING DUE TO SCARCITY

2004 Bowman Sterling Red Refractors

FY ODDS 1:449 HOBBY
FY AU ODDS 1:1507 HOBBY
AU-GU ODDS 1:917 HOBBY
GU ODDS 1:449 HOBBY
STATED PRINT RUN 1 SERIAL #'d SET
NO PRICING DUE TO SCARCITY
ISSUED IN HOBBY BOX LOADER PACKS

2004 Bowman Sterling Original Autographs

GROUP A ODDS 1:221 HOBBY
GROUP B ODDS 1:25 HOBBY
GROUP A = A.ROD/BONDS
GROUP B = CHAVEZ/REYES/SORIANO
PRINT RUNS B/WN 1-106 COPIES PER
NO PRICING ON QTY OF 25 OR LESS
ISSUED IN HOBBY BOX LOADER PACKS
AR1 Alex Rodriguez 98B
AR2 Alex Rodriguez 99B/8

AR3 Alex Rodriguez 99BC
AR4 Alex Rodriguez 00B/16
AR5 Alex Rodriguez 00BC/6
AR6 Alex Rodriguez 01B
AR7 Alex Rodriguez 01BC/7
AR8 Alex Rodriguez 02B/3
AR9 Alex Rodriguez 02BC
AR10 Alex Rodriguez 03B/19
AR11 Alex Rodriguez 03BC/28 75.00 150.00
AS1 Alfonso Soriano 99B
AS2 Alfonso Soriano 99BC/1
AS3 Alfonso Soriano 00B
AS4 Alfonso Soriano 00BC/8
AS5 Alfonso Soriano 01B/7
AS6 Alfonso Soriano 01BC/13
AS7 Alfonso Soriano 02B/54 15.00 40.00
AS8 Alfonso Soriano 02BC/33 20.00 50.00
AS9 Alfonso Soriano 03B/102 15.00 40.00
AS10 Alfonso Soriano 03BC/49 15.00 40.00
AS11 Alfonso Soriano 04B/26 20.00 50.00
AS12 Alfonso Soriano 04BC
BB1 Barry Bonds 98BC/6
BB2 Barry Bonds 01BC/3
BB3 Barry Bonds 03BC/1
EC1 Eric Chavez 97B/8
EC2 Eric Chavez 98B/14
EC3 Eric Chavez 98BC/10
EC4 Eric Chavez 99B
EC5 Eric Chavez 99BC
EC6 Eric Chavez 00B/10
EC7 Eric Chavez 00BC/9
EC8 Eric Chavez 01B
EC9 Eric Chavez 01BC/16
EC10 Eric Chavez 02B/68 10.00 25.00
EC11 Eric Chavez 02BC/21 12.50 30.00
EC12 Eric Chavez 03B/106 10.00 25.00
EC13 Eric Chavez 03BC/22 12.50 30.00
JR1 Jose Reyes 02B/52 15.00 40.00
JR2 Jose Reyes 02BD/22 20.00 50.00
JR3 Jose Reyes 02BD/34 20.00 50.00
JR4 Jose Reyes 02BC/31 20.00 50.00
JR5 Jose Reyes 02BCD/41 15.00 40.00
JR6 Jose Reyes 03BD/92 15.00 40.00
JR7 Jose Reyes 03BCD

2005 Bowman Sterling

COMMON CARD 1.50 4.00
BASIC CARDS APPX.TWO PER HOBBY PACK
BASIC CARDS APPX.TWO PER RETAIL PACK
AU GROUP A ODDS 1:2 HOBBY
AU GROUP B ODDS 1:3 HOBBY
AU-GU GROUP A ODDS 1:2 H, 1:2 R
AU-GU GROUP B ODDS 1:37 H, 1:37 R
AU-GU GROUP C ODDS 1:11 H, 1:11 R
AU-GU GROUP D ODDS 1:10 H, 1:10 R
AU-GU GROUP E ODDS 1:27 H, 1:27 R
AU-GU GROUP F ODDS 1:13 H, 1:13 R
GU GROUP A ODDS 1:3 H, 1:3 R
GU GROUP B ODDS 1:5 H, 1:5 R
GU GROUP C ODDS 1:6 H, 1:6 R
ACL Andy LaRoche RC 3.00 8.00
AL Adam Lind AU Bat B 10.00 25.00
AM A.McCutchen AU Jsy D RC 20.00 50.00
AP Albert Pujols Jsy B 6.00 15.00
AR Alex Rodriguez Jsy UER 6.00 15.00
Card states Game-Used Bat
ARA Aramis Ramirez Bat A 2.00 5.00
AS Alfonso Soriano Bat E 2.00 5.00
AT Aaron Thompson AU A RC 4.00 10.00
BA Brian Anderson RC 2.50 6.00
BB Billy Buckner AU Jsy A 4.00 10.00
BBU Billy Butler RC 5.00 12.00
BC Brent Cox AU Jsy D RC 6.00 15.00
BCR Brad Corley RC 2.00 5.00
BE Brad Eldred AU Jsy C 4.00 10.00
BH Brett Hayes RC 1.50 4.00
BJ Beau Jones AU Jsy A RC 8.00 20.00
BL B.Livingston AU Jsy A RC 4.00 10.00
BLB Barry Bonds Jsy C 6.00 15.00
BM B.McCarthy AU Jsy A RC 10.00 25.00
BMU Bill Mueller Jsy C 2.00 5.00
BRB Brian Bogusevic RC 1.50 4.00
BS Brandon Sing AU A RC 4.00 10.00
BSN Brandon Snyder RC 3.00 8.00
BZ Barry Zito Uni A 2.00 5.00
CB Carlos Beltran Bat A 2.00 5.00
CBU Clay Buchholz RC 12.50 30.00
CC Cesar Carrillo RC 2.50 6.00
CD Carlos Delgado Jsy A 2.00 5.00
CH C.J. Henry AU B RC 5.00 12.00
CHE Chase Headley RC 3.00 8.00
CI Craig Italiano RC 2.00 5.00
CJ Chuck James RC 4.00 10.00
CLT Chuck Tiffany RC 2.00 5.00
CN Chris Nelson AU Jsy A 4.00 10.00
CP Cliff Pennington AU B RC 4.00 10.00
CPP C.Pignatiello AU Jsy A RC 4.00 10.00
CR Colby Rasmus AU Jsy A RC 20.00 50.00
CRA Cesar Ramos RC 2.00 5.00
CRO Chaz Roe AU Jsy A RC 6.00 15.00
CS C.J. Smith AU Jsy A RC 4.00 10.00
CSU Curt Schilling Jsy C 3.00 8.00
CT Curtis Thigpen AU Jsy A 4.00 10.00
CV Chris Volstad AU B RC 4.00 10.00
DC Dan Carte RC 2.00 5.00
DL Derrek Lee Bat A 3.00 8.00
DO David Ortiz Bat A 3.00 8.00
DP Dustin Pedroia AU Jsy A 60.00 120.00
DT Drew Thompson RC 2.00 5.00
DW Dontrelle Willis Jsy C 2.00 5.00
EC Eric Chavez Uni B 2.00 5.00
EI Eli Iorg AU Jsy C RC 6.00 15.00
EM Eddy Martinez AU A RC 4.00 10.00
GK George Kottaras AU A RC 4.00 10.00
GM Greg Maddux Jsy C 4.00 10.00
GO Garrett Olson AU A RC 6.00 15.00
GS Gary Sheffield Bat A 2.00 5.00
HAS Henry Sanchez RC 2.50 6.00
HB Hank Blalock Bat A 2.00 5.00
HI Hernan Iribarren RC 2.00 5.00
HM Hideki Matsui AS Jsy C 6.00 15.00
HS Hum Sanchez AU A RC 8.00 20.00
IR Ivan Rodriguez Bat A 3.00 8.00
JB Jay Bruce AU Jsy D RC 30.00 60.00
JBE Josh Beckett Uni A 2.00 5.00
JC Jeff Clement RC 6.00 15.00
JCN John Nelson AU Uni A RC 4.00 10.00
JD Johnny Damon Bat A 3.00 8.00
JDR John Drennen RC 3.00 8.00
JE J.Ellsbury AU Jsy E RC 50.00 100.00
JEG Jon Egan RC 2.00 5.00
JF Josh Fields AU Jsy A 5.00 12.00
JG Josh Geer AU Jsy A RC 4.00 10.00
JGI Josh Gibson Seat C 6.00 15.00
JL Jed Lowrie AU Jsy F RC 15.00 40.00
JLY Jeff Lyman RC 2.00 5.00
JM John Mayberry Jr. AU A RC 6.00 15.00
JMA Jacob Marceaux RC 1.50 4.00
JN Jeff Niemann AU Jsy A RC 6.00 15.00
JO Justin Olson AU Jsy A RC 4.00 10.00
JP Jorge Posada Bat A 3.00 8.00
JPE Jim Edmonds Jsy B 2.00 5.00
JS John Smoltz Jsy A 3.00 8.00
JV J.Verlander AU Jsy A RC 30.00 60.00
JW Josh Wall RC 2.00 5.00
JWE Jered Weaver RC 6.00 15.00
KG Khalil Greene Jsy B 3.00 8.00
KM Kevin Millar Bat A 2.00 5.00
KS Kevin Slowey RC 6.00 15.00
KW Kevin Whelan RC 2.00 5.00
LWJ Chipper Jones Bat A 3.00 8.00
MA Matt Albers AU A RC 4.00 10.00
MAM Matt Maloney RC 2.50 6.00
MB M.Bowden AU Jsy A RC 20.00 50.00
MC Mike Conroy AU Jsy A RC 4.00 10.00
MCA Miguel Cabrera Jsy A 3.00 8.00
MCO Mike Costanzo RC 3.00 8.00
MG Matt Green AU A RC 3.00 8.00
MGA Matt Garza RC 4.00 10.00
MGI Marcus Giles AS Jsy B 2.00 5.00
MM Mark Mulder Uni B 2.00 5.00
MMC Mark McCormick RC 2.00 5.00
MP Mike Piazza Bat B 3.00 8.00
MPR Mark Prior Jsy B 3.00 8.00
MR Manny Ramirez Bat A 3.00 8.00
MT Miguel Tejada Uni A 2.00 5.00
MTE Mark Teixeira Bat A 3.00 8.00
MTO Matt Torra RC 2.00 5.00
MY Michael Young Bat A 2.00 5.00
NH Nick Hundley RC 1.50 4.00
NR Nolan Reimold RC 3.00 8.00
NW Nick Webber RC 1.50 4.00
PH Philip Humber AU Jsy A RC 10.00 25.00
PK Paul Kelly RC 2.00 5.00
PL Paul Lo Duca Bat A 2.00 5.00
PM Pedro Martinez Jsy A 3.00 8.00
PP P.J. Phillips RC 2.00 5.00
RB Ryan Braun AU A RC 60.00 120.00
RBE Ronnie Belliard Bat A 2.00 5.00
RF Rafael Furcal Jsy A 2.00 5.00
RM Russ Martin AU Jsy F RC 10.00 25.00
RMO Ryan Mount RC 2.00 5.00
RR Ricky Romero RC 2.00 5.00
RT Raul Tablado AU Jsy A RC 4.00 10.00
RZ Ryan Zimmerman RC 10.00 25.00
SD Stephen Drew RC 8.00 20.00
SE Scott Elbert AU Jsy A 4.00 10.00
SM Steve Marek AU Jsy A RC 4.00 10.00
SR Scott Rolen Jsy B 3.00 8.00
SS Sammy Sosa Bat A 3.00 8.00
SW Steven White AU B RC 3.00 8.00
TB Trevor Bell AU Jsy C RC 6.00 15.00
TBU Travis Buck RC 3.00 8.00
TC Travis Chick AU A RC 3.00 8.00
TG Tyler Greene RC 2.00 5.00
TH Torii Hunter Bat A 2.00 5.00
THE Tyler Herron RC 2.00 5.00
THU Tim Hudson Uni A 2.00 5.00
TI Tadahito Iguchi RC 2.00 5.00
TLH Todd Helton Jsy B 3.00 8.00
TM Tyler Minges AU Jsy A RC 4.00 10.00
TMI Tino Martinez Bat A 3.00 8.00
TN Trot Nixon Bat A 2.00 5.00
TT Troy Tulowitzki RC 5.00 12.00
TW Travis Wood RC 2.50 6.00
VG Vladimir Guerrero Bat A 3.00 8.00
VM Victor Martinez Bat A 2.00 5.00
WT Wade Townsend RC 2.00 5.00
YE Yunel Escobar RC 6.00 15.00
ZS Zach Simons RC 1.50 4.00

2005 Bowman Sterling Refractors

*REF: 1.25X TO 3X BASIC
BASIC ODDS 1:6 H, 1:6 R
*REF AU: 1X TO 2.5X BASIC AU
AU ODDS 1:13 HOBBY
*REF AU-GU: .6X TO 1.5X BASIC AU-GU
AU-GU ODDS 1:9 H, 1:9 R
*REF GU: .6X TO 1.5X BASIC GU
GU ODDS 1:6 H, 1: R
STATED PRINT RUN 199 SERIAL #'d SETS
AL Adam Lind AU Bat 20.00 50.00
AM A.McCutchen AU Jsy 50.00 100.00
BE Brad Eldred AU Jsy 12.50 30.00
CBU Clay Buchholz 60.00 120.00
CH C.J. Henry AU 15.00 40.00
CHE Chase Headley 20.00 50.00
CR Colby Rasmus AU Jsy 75.00 150.00
CV Chris Volstad AU 10.00 25.00
DP Dustin Pedroia AU Jsy 75.00 150.00
JB Jay Bruce AU Jsy 100.00 200.00
JC Jeff Clement 30.00 60.00
JE Jacoby Ellsbury AU Jsy 100.00 200.00
JL Jed Lowrie AU Jsy 40.00 80.00
JN Jeff Niemann AU Jsy 15.00 40.00
JV Justin Verlander AU Jsy 40.00 80.00
KS Kevin Slowey 12.50 30.00
MB Michael Bowden AU Jsy 30.00 60.00
RB Ryan Braun AU 150.00 250.00
RM Russ Martin AU Jsy 12.50 30.00
RZ Ryan Zimmerman 20.00 50.00
SD Stephen Drew 30.00 60.00
TBU Travis Buck 12.50 30.00

2005 Bowman Sterling Black Refractors

BASIC ODDS 1:5 BOX-LOADER
NO BASIC PRICING DUE TO SCARCITY
AU ODDS 1:17 BOX-LOADER
NO AU PRICING DUE TO SCARCITY
AU-GU ODDS 1:8 BOX-LOADER
NO AU-GU PRICING DUE TO SCARCITY
*BLACK GU: 2X TO 5X BASIC GU
GU ODDS 1:5 BOX-LOADER
ONE BOX-LOADER PACK PER HOBBY BOX
STATED PRINT RUN 25 SERIAL #'d SETS
BLB Barry Bonds Jsy 60.00 120.00

2005 Bowman Sterling Red Refractors

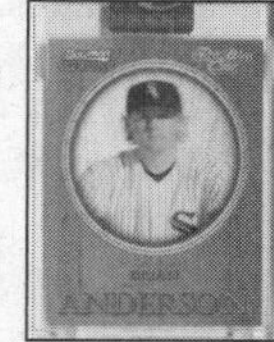

BASIC ODDS 1:128 BOX-LOADER
AU ODDS 1:428 BOX-LOADER
AU-GU ODDS 1:182 BOX-LOADER
GU ODDS 1:128 BOX-LOADER
ONE BOX-LOADER PACK PER HOBBY BOX
STATED PRINT RUN 1 SERIAL #'d SET
NO PRICING DUE TO SCARCITY

2005 Bowman Sterling MLB Logo Patch Autograph

STATED ODDS 1:665 BOX-LOADER
ONE BOX-LOADER PACK PER HOBBY BOX
STATED PRINT RUN 1 SERIAL #'d SET
NO PRICING DUE TO SCARCITY
BB Billy Buckner
CS C.J. Smith
CT Curtis Thigpen
DP Dustin Pedroia
JF Josh Fields
JN Jeff Niemann
JV Justin Verlander
PH Philip Humber
SE Scott Elbert

2005 Bowman Sterling Original Autographs

GROUP A ODDS 1:665 BOX-LOADER
GROUP B ODDS 1:250 BOX-LOADER
GROUP C ODDS 1:63 BOX-LOADER
GROUP D ODDS 1:50 BOX-LOADER
GROUP E ODDS 1:42 BOX-LOADER
GROUP F ODDS 1:28 BOX-LOADER
GROUP G ODDS 1:25 BOX-LOADER
GROUP H ODDS 1:20 BOX-LOADER
GROUP I ODDS 1:6 BOX-LOADER
ONE BOX-LOADER PACK PER HOBBY BOX
PRINT RUNS B/WN 1-160 COPIES PER
NO PRICING ON QTY OF 13 OR LESS
AJ1 Andruw Jones 98 B/18 20.00 50.00
AJ2 Andruw Jones 99 B/18 20.00 50.00
AJ3 Andruw Jones 99 BC/4
AJ4 Andruw Jones 00 BC/8
AJ5 Andruw Jones 01 BC/5
AJ6 Andruw Jones 02 B/122 10.00 25.00
AJ7 Andruw Jones 02 BC/13
AJ8 Andruw Jones 03 B/112 10.00 25.00
AJ9 Andruw Jones 03 BC/18 20.00 50.00
AJ10 Andruw Jones 04 B/71 10.00 25.00
AP1 Albert Pujols 03 B/7
AP2 Albert Pujols 03 BC/11
AP3 Albert Pujols 04 B/7
AP4 Albert Pujols 04 BC/1
BB1 Barry Bonds 97 BC Int'l/1
BB2 Barry Bonds 99 BC/2
DL1 Derrek Lee 95 B/27 10.00 25.00
DL2 Derrek Lee 96 B/29 10.00 25.00
DL3 Derrek Lee 96 BB/15 12.50 30.00
DL4 Derrek Lee 97 BC/16 12.50 30.00
DL5 Derrek Lee 98 B/22 10.00 25.00
DL6 Derrek Lee 04 B/92 6.00 15.00
DL7 Derrek Lee 04 BC/26
DW1 David Wright 04 BD/98 30.00 60.00
DW2 David Wright 04 BCD/15
DW3 David Wright 05 B/139 30.00 60.00
GA1 Garret Anderson 96 B/3
GA2 Garret Anderson 99 B/8
GA3 Garret Anderson 03 B/33 6.00 15.00
GA4 Garret Anderson 04 B/33 6.00 15.00
GA5 Garret Anderson 04 BC/36 6.00 15.00
GA6 Garret Anderson 05 B/48 5.00 12.00
GS1 Gary Sheffield 90 B/1
GS2 Gary Sheffield 91 B/2
GS3 Gary Sheffield 92 B/3
GS4 Gary Sheffield 94 B/5
GS5 Gary Sheffield 95 B/1
GS6 Gary Sheffield 96 B/2
GS7 Gary Sheffield 97 B/3
GS8 Gary Sheffield 98 B/10
GS9 Gary Sheffield 98 BC/1
GS10 Gary Sheffield 99 B/9
GS11 Gary Sheffield 99 BC/4
GS12 Gary Sheffield 00 B/9
GS13 Gary Sheffield 00 BC/1
GS14 Gary Sheffield 01 B/5
GS15 Gary Sheffield 01 BC/4
GS16 Gary Sheffield 02 B/7
GS17 Gary Sheffield 03 B/12
GS18 Gary Sheffield 03 BC/6
GS19 Gary Sheffield 04 BC/1
JR1 Jeremy Reed 04 BD/82 4.00 10.00
JR2 Jeremy Reed 04 BCD/48 5.00 12.00
MC1 M.Cabrera 02 B/7
MC2 M.Cabrera 02 BD/26 20.00 50.00
MC3 M.Cabrera 02 BCD/2
MC4 M.Cabrera 03 BD/27 20.00 50.00
MC5 M.Cabrera 03 BCD/25 20.00 50.00
MC6 M.Cabrera 04 B/127 12.50 30.00
MC7 M.Cabrera 04 BC/25 20.00 50.00
MC8 M.Cabrera 05 B/154 12.50 30.00
MC9 M.Cabrera 05 BC/25 20.00 50.00
MK1 Mark Kotsay 97 B/18 20.00 50.00
MK2 Mark Kotsay 97 BC/5
MK3 Mark Kotsay 98 B/56 8.00 20.00
MK4 Mark Kotsay 98 BC/23 10.00 25.00
MK5 Mark Kotsay 99 B/75 6.00 15.00
MK6 Mark Kotsay 99 BC/23 10.00 25.00
MK7 Mark Kotsay 05 B/160 6.00 15.00
MK8 Mark Kotsay 05 BC/46 8.00 20.00
MY1 Michael Young 04 B/148 6.00 15.00
MY2 Michael Young 04 BC/64 8.00 20.00
MY3 Michael Young 05 B/92 6.00 15.00

2006 Bowman Sterling

This 117-card set was released in January, 2007. This set was issued in five-card packs with an $50 SRP which came six packs per box and eight boxes per case. The set is a mix of game-used relics from veteran playerfs and players who were rookies in 2006. Some of the rookies either signed some of the cards or signed some of the cards and had a game-used relic included as well as their signature.

COMMON ROOKIE 1.25 3.00
COMMON AUTO RC 3.00 8.00
AU RC AUTO ODDS 1:4 HOBBY
COMMON AU-GU RC 4.00 10.00
AU-GU RC ODDS 1:4 HOBBY
COMMON GU VET 2.50 6.00
GU VET ODDS 1:4 HOBBY
OVERALL PLATE ODDS 1:23 BOXES
PLATE PRINT RUN 1 SET PER COLOR
BLACK-CYAN-MAGENTA-YELLOW ISSUED
NO PLATE PRICING DUE TO SCARCITY
EXCHANGE DEADLINE 12/31/08
AD Adam Dunn Jsy 2.50 6.00
AE Andre Ethier AU (RC) 10.00 25.00
AER Alex Rodriguez Bat 10.00 25.00
AJ Andruw Jones Jsy 3.00 8.00
ALR Anthony Reyes Jsy AU (RC) EXCH 6.00 15.00
ALS Alay Soler RC 1.25 3.00
AP Albert Pujols Jsy 8.00 20.00
AP2 Albert Pujols Bat 8.00 20.00
APS Alfonso Soriano Bat 4.00 10.00
AR Aramis Ramirez Bat UER 3.00 8.00
Front of card denotes game used jersey
AS Anibal Sanchez (RC) 1.50 4.00
BA Brian Anderson (RC) 1.25 3.00
BB Brian Bannister (RC) 1.25 3.00
BL Bobby Livingston Jsy AU (RC) 4.00 10.00
BLB Barry Bonds Bat 6.00 15.00
BON Boof Bonser (RC) 1.50 4.00
BR Brian Roberts Jsy 2.50 6.00
BZ Ben Zobrist (RC) 1.50 4.00
CB Carlos Beltran Jsy 2.50 6.00
CB2 Carlos Beltran Bat 2.50 6.00
CC Chris Carpenter Jsy 4.00 10.00
CH Cole Hamels Jsy AU (RC) 20.00 50.00
CHJ Chuck James (RC) 1.50 4.00
CI Chris Iannetta Jsy AU RC 8.00 20.00
CJ Conor Jackson (RC) 1.50 4.00
CJJ Casey Janssen RC 1.50 4.00
CQ Carlos Quentin (RC) 1.50 4.00
CRB Chad Billingsley (RC) 1.50 4.00
CRH Craig Hansen RC 2.00 5.00
CS Curt Schilling Jsy 3.00 8.00
DG David Gassner (RC) 1.25 3.00
DO David Ortiz Bat 4.00 10.00
DP David Pauley (RC) 1.25 3.00
DU Dan Uggla (RC) 2.00 5.00
DW David Wright Jsy 6.00 15.00
DWW Dontrelle Willis Jsy 2.50 6.00
EC Eric Chavez Pants 2.50 6.00
EG Enrique Gonzalez (RC) 1.25 3.00
FG Franklin Gutierrez (RC) 1.25 3.00
FL Francisco Liriano (RC) 2.50 6.00
GS Grady Sizemore Jsy 4.00 10.00
HB Hank Blalock Jsy 2.50 6.00
HK1 Howie Kendrick (RC) 2.00 5.00
HK2 Howie Kendrick Jsy AU (RC) EXCH 8.00 20.00
HM Hideki Matsui Bat 6.00 15.00
HP Hayden Penn (RC) 1.25 3.00
HR Hanley Ramirez (RC) 2.00 5.00
IK Ian Kinsler AU (RC) 10.00 25.00
IR Ivan Rodriguez Jsy 3.00 8.00
IS Ichiro Suzuki Jsy 10.00 25.00
JAS Johan Santana Jsy 4.00 10.00
JB Jason Bulger Jsy AU (RC) EXCH 4.00 10.00
JBS Jeremy Sowers (RC) 1.25 3.00
JCB Jason Botts AU (RC) 3.00 8.00
JD Joey Devine RC 1.25 3.00
JDD Johnny Damon Bat 4.00 10.00
JHT Jim Thome Bat 4.00 10.00
JI Joe Inglett AU RC 5.00 12.00
JJ Josh Johnson (RC) 1.50 4.00
JK Jeff Karstens RC 2.00 5.00
JL James Loney (RC) 1.50 4.00
JLB Josh Barfield AU (RC) 3.00 8.00
JM Jeff Mathis (RC) 1.25 3.00
JP Jonathan Papelbon (RC) 3.00 8.00
JRH Rich Harden Jsy 2.50 6.00
JS James Shields RC 1.25 3.00
JT Jack Taschner Jsy AU (RC) 4.00 10.00
JTA Jordan Tata RC 1.25 3.00
JTL Jon Lester Jsy AU RC 20.00 50.00
JV Justin Verlander (RC) 3.00 8.00
JW Jered Weaver (RC) 2.50 6.00
JZ Joel Zumaya (RC) 2.00 5.00
KF Kevin Frandsen (RC) 1.25 3.00
KJ Kenji Johjima RC 3.00 8.00
KM Kendry Morales (RC) 1.50 4.00
LB Lance Berkman Jsy 3.00 8.00
LM Lastings Milledge AU (RC) 8.00 20.00
LWJ Chipper Jones Jsy 4.00 10.00
MC Miguel Cabrera Jsy 3.00 8.00
MC2 Miguel Cabrera Bat 3.00 8.00
MCC Melky Cabrera (RC) 1.50 4.00
MCM Mickey Mantle Bat 30.00 60.00
MCT Mark Teixeira Bat 3.00 8.00
ME Morgan Ensberg Jsy 2.50 6.00
MJP Mike Piazza Bat 4.00 10.00
MK Matt Kemp (RC) 1.50 4.00
MM Mark Mulder Pants 2.50 6.00
MN Mike Napoli Jsy AU RC EXCH 6.00 15.00
MP Martin Prado Jsy AU (RC) 8.00 20.00
MPP Mike Pelfrey RC 6.00 15.00
MR Manny Ramirez Jsy 4.00 10.00
MR2 Manny Ramirez Bat 4.00 10.00
MS Matt Smith (RC) 1.50 4.00
MT Miguel Tejada Pants 2.50 6.00
NM Nick Markakis (RC) 1.50 4.00
PF Prince Fielder Jsy AU (RC) 20.00 50.00
PK Paul Konerko Bat 3.00 8.00
PM Pedro Martinez Pants 3.00 8.00
RC Robinson Cano Bat 5.00 12.00
RH Ryan Howard Jsy 8.00 20.00
RK Ryan Garko (RC) 1.25 3.00
RM Russ Martin (RC) 1.50 4.00
RN Ricky Nolasco AU (RC) 3.00 8.00
RP Ronny Paulino Jsy AU (RC) 6.00 15.00
RZ Ryan Zimmerman (RC) 3.00 8.00
SD Stephen Drew (RC) 2.00 5.00
SM Scott Mathieson (RC) 1.25 3.00
SO Scott Olsen (RC) 1.25 3.00
SR Scott Rolen Pants 3.00 8.00
ST Scott Thorman Jsy AU (RC) EXCH 5.00 12.00
TGJ Tony Gwynn Jr (RC) 2.50 6.00
TH Todd Helton Jsy 3.00 8.00
TT Taylor Tankersley (RC) 1.25 3.00
VG Vladimir Guerrero Jsy 3.00 8.00
WA Willy Aybar (RC) 1.25 3.00
YP Yusmeiro Petit Jsy AU (RC) 4.00 10.00
ZM Zach Miner AU (RC) 3.00 8.00

2006 Bowman Sterling Refractors

*REF RC: .6X TO 1.5X BASIC
RC ODDS 1:6 HOBBY
*REF AU RC: .6X TO 1.5X BASIC AU
AU RC ODDS 1:5 HOBBY
*REF AU-GU RC: .5X TO 1.2X BASIC AU-GU
AU-GU RC ODDS 1:20 HOBBY
*REF GU VET: .5X TO 1.2X BASIC GU
GU VET ODDS 1:7 HOBBY
STATED PRINT RUN 199 SERIAL #'d SETS
EXCHANGE DEADLINE 12/31/08
ALR Anthony Reyes Jsy AU EXCH 10.00 25.00
BLB Barry Bonds Bat 12.50 30.00
CH Cole Hamels Jsy AU 40.00 80.00
CI Chris Iannetta Jsy AU 12.50 30.00
HK2 Howie Kendrick Jsy AU EXCH 12.50 30.00
HM Hideki Matsui Bat 12.50 30.00
IK Ian Kinsler AU 12.50 30.00
JP Jonathan Papelbon 6.00 15.00
JTL Jon Lester Jsy AU 40.00 80.00
MCM Mickey Mantle Bat 40.00 80.00
MPP Mike Pelfrey 12.50 30.00
PF Prince Fielder Jsy AU 30.00 60.00
RZ Ryan Zimmerman 8.00 20.00

2006 Bowman Sterling Black Refractors

STATED BLK RC ODDS 1:8 BOXES
STATED BLK AU-GU RC 1:26 BOXES
STATED BLK VET GU ODDS 1:8 BOXES
STATED PRINT RUN 25 SERIAL #'d SETS
NO PRICING DUE TO SCARCITY
EXCHANGE DEADLINE 12/31/08

2006 Bowman Sterling Gold Refractors

STATED GOLD RC ODDS 1:18 BOXES
STATED PRINT RUN 10 SERIAL #'d SETS
NO PRICING DUE TO SCARCITY

2006 Bowman Sterling Red Refractors

STATED RED RC ODDS 1:182 BOXES
STATED RED AU-GU RC 1:610 BOXES
STATED RED VET GU ODDS 1:199 BOXES
STATED PRINT RUN 1 SERIAL #'d SET
NO PRICING DUE TO SCARCITY
EXCHANGE DEADLINE 12/31/08

2006 Bowman Sterling Original Autographs

GROUP A ODDS 1:356 BOXES
GROUP B ODDS 1:90 BOXES
GROUP C ODDS 1:45 BOXES
GROUP D ODDS 1:8 BOXES
PRINT RUNS B/WN 1-233 COPIES PER
NO PRICING ON QTY OF 25 OR LESS
EXCHANGE DEADLINE 12/31/08
BB1 Barry Bonds 05 B/20 B
BB2 Barry Bonds 05 BCBREF/1 B
BB3 Barry Bonds 06 B/32 B
CJ1 Chipper Jones 98 B/5 C
CJ2 Chipper Jones 01 B/10 C
CJ3 Chipper Jones 02 B/20 C
CJ4 Chipper Jones 02 BC/20 C
CJ5 Chipper Jones 03 BC/20 C
CJ6 Chipper Jones 04 BH/20 C
CJ7 Chipper Jones 05 B/20 C
CJ9 Chipper Jones 99 B/7 C
JD1 Johnny Damon 96 B/2 C
JD10 Johnny Damon 04 BH/25 C
JD11 Johnny Damon 06 B/1 C
JD2 Johnny Damon 97 B/1 C
JD3 Johnny Damon 98 B/1 C
JD4 Johnny Damon 01 BB/1 C
JD5 Johnny Damon 02 B/47 C 10.00 25.00
JD6 Johnny Damon 02 BC/22 C
JD7 Johnny Damon 02 BH/1 C
JD8 Johnny Damon 03 B/1 C
JD9 Johnny Damon 03 BH/1 C
JM1 Justin Morneau 02 B/199 D 12.50 30.00
JM2 Justin Morneau 06 B/48 D 15.00 40.00
JN Joe Nathan EXCH 6.00 15.00
JN1 Joe Nathan 99 B/96 D
JN10 Joe Nathan 01 BG/8 D
JN2 Joe Nathan 99 BVAR/6 D
JN3 Joe Nathan 99 BC/22 D
JN4 Joe Nathan 99 BCVAR/1 D
JN5 Joe Nathan 00 B/54 D
JN6 Joe Nathan 00 BTV/15 D
JN7 Joe Nathan 00 BC/36 D
JN8 Joe Nathan 00 BCREF/1 D
JN9 Joe Nathan 01 B/61 D
JP1 Jonathan Papelbon 03 BD/71 D 30.00 60.00
JP2 Jonathan Papelbon 06 B/225 D 15.00 40.00
JP3 Jonathan Papelbon 06 BG/2 D
JV1 Justin Verlander 05 BD/233 D 15.00 40.00
JV2 Justin Verlander 05 BDG/8 D
JV3 Justin Verlander 06 B/59 D 20.00 50.00
MG1 Marcus Giles 00 B/9 B

MG2 Marcus Giles 01 B/10 B
MG3 Marcus Giles 01 BC/20 B
MR1 Manny Ramirez 97 B/9 A

2006 Bowman Sterling Prospects

COMMON CARD 1.50 4.00
GROUP A AUTO ODDS 1:2 HOBBY
GROUP B AUTO ODDS 1:2 HOBBY
OVERALL PLATE ODDS 1:23 BOXES
PLATE PRINT RUN 1 SET PER COLOR
BLACK-CYAN-MAGENTA-YELLOW ISSUED
NO PLATE PRICING DUE TO SCARCITY
EXCHANGE DEADLINE 12/31/08
AC Adrian Cardenas AU A 10.00 25.00
ADC Adam Coe 1.50 4.00
AG Alex Gordon AU B 30.00 60.00
AJC Asdrubal Cabrera 1.50 4.00
AO Adam Ottovino AU A 5.00 12.00
AP Andrew Pinckney 1.50 4.00
AS A.J. Shappi 1.50 4.00
BA Brandon Allen AU B 3.00 8.00
BB Brooks Brown AU A 3.00 8.00
BC Ben Copeland 1.50 4.00
BD Brent Dlugach 1.50 4.00
BF Brad Furnish AU A 3.00 8.00
BH Brett Hayes AU B 3.00 8.00
BJ Brandon Jones 2.50 6.00
BJS B.J. Szymanski 1.50 4.00
BM Brandon Moss AU A 3.00 8.00
BR Billy Rowell AU A EXCH 20.00 50.00
BS Brandon Snyder AU B 3.00 8.00
BSI Brett Sinkbeil AU B 6.00 15.00
BW Brandon Wood AU B 6.00 15.00
BWM Brad McCann 2.00 5.00
CD Chris Dickerson AU A 10.00 25.00
CD Chris Dickerson 1.50 4.00
CH Chase Headley AU B 10.00 25.00
CHH Chad Huffman AU B 10.00 25.00
CJ Cody Johnson AU B 8.00 20.00
CK Clayton Kershaw AU A 12.50 30.00
CM Cameron Maybin AU A 15.00 40.00
CMT Matt Tolbert 1.50 4.00
CP Chris Parmelee AU B 12.50 30.00
CR Cory Rasmus AU A 5.00 12.00
CT Chad Tracy AU A 3.00 8.00
CW Colton Willems AU B 10.00 25.00
CWW Corey Wimberly 2.50 6.00
DE Dustin Evans AU A 3.00 8.00
DF Dexter Fowler 2.00 5.00
DH Daniel Haigwood AU B 3.00 8.00
DHU David Huff AU B 3.00 8.00
DIH Diory Hernandez 1.50 4.00
DM Dustin Majewski 1.50 4.00
DT Dallas Trahern 1.50 4.00
EA Elvis Andrus 4.00 10.00
EL Evan Longoria AU B 60.00 120.00
EM Evan MacLane 1.50 4.00
EP Elvin Puello AU A 3.00 8.00
GLM Garrett Mock 1.50 4.00
GM Garrett Mock AU B 3.00 8.00
HC Hank Conger AU B 10.00 25.00
HP Hunter Pence 12.50 30.00
JAC Jose Campusano 1.50 4.00
JBU Joshua Butler AU A 3.00 8.00
JC Jeff Clement AU B 6.00 15.00
JF Juan Francia 1.50 4.00
JJ Jeremy Jeffress AU B 8.00 20.00
JJ Jason Jaramillo 1.50 4.00
JKF Jeff Frazier 1.50 4.00
JN Jason Neighborgall AU B 3.00 8.00
JR Joshua Rodriguez AU A 3.00 8.00
JRB Jimmy Barthmaier 1.50 4.00
JS Jarrod Saltalamacchia AU A 8.00 20.00
JT Jose Tabata 5.00 12.00
JTL Jared Lansford 1.50 4.00
JU Justin Upton AU B 30.00 60.00
JW Johnny Whittleman AU B 8.00 20.00
KB Kyler Burke AU A 3.00 8.00
KC Koby Clemens AU A 10.00 25.00
KD Kyle Drabek AU B 10.00 25.00
KJ Kris Johnson AU A 5.00 12.00
KK Kasey Kiker AU B 5.00 12.00
KM Kyle McCulloch AU B 3.00 8.00
LH Luke Hochevar AU A 5.00 12.00
MA Mike Aviles AU B 3.00 8.00
MAA Matt Antonelli AU B 4.00 10.00
MC Michael Collins 2.50 6.00
MF Michael Felix AU A 3.00 8.00
MG Mat Gamel 4.00 10.00
MH Michael Hollimon 1.50 4.00
MM Mark McCormick AU B 3.00 8.00
MO Micah Owings AU B 6.00 15.00
MR Mark Reed 2.50 6.00
MRA Michael Aubrey 1.50 4.00
MRR Max Ramirez 2.50 6.00
MSM Mark McLemore 1.50 4.00
MT Mark Trumbo 2.50 6.00
NA Nick Adenhart 2.50 6.00
ON Oswaldo Navarro 1.50 4.00
OS Omir Santos 1.50 4.00
PB Pedro Beato AU A 5.00 12.00
PL Pedro Lopez AU A 3.00 8.00
RB Ronny Bourquin AU B 3.00 8.00
RK Ryan Klosterman 1.50 4.00
RL Radhames Liz 2.50 6.00
RP Ryan Patterson 2.50 6.00
SC Shaun Cumberland 1.50 4.00
SE Steven Evarts AU A 3.00 8.00
SGG Steve Garrabrants 1.50 4.00
SM Stephen Marek 1.50 4.00
SMM Steve Murphy 2.50 6.00
SR Shawn Riggans 1.50 4.00
SW Steven Wright AU A 3.00 8.00
SWA Sean Watson AU B 3.00 8.00
TB Travis Buck AU B 6.00 15.00
TC Trevor Crowe AU A 15.00 40.00
TC Tyler Colvin AU B 10.00 25.00
TP Troy Patton AU A 10.00 25.00
WR Wilkin Ramirez 2.00 5.00
WT Wade Townsend AU B 3.00 8.00
WV Will Venable 1.50 4.00
YC Yung-Chi Chen 6.00 15.00
YG Yovani Gallardo 3.00 8.00

2006 Bowman Sterling Prospects Refractors

*REF: .75X TO 2X BASIC
REF ODDS 1:6 HOBBY
*REF AU: .75X TO 2X BASIC AU
AU ODDS 1:5 HOBBY
STATED PRINT RUN 199 SERIAL #'d SETS
EXCHANGE DEADLINE 12/31/08
AG Alex Gordon AU 75.00 150.00
BJ Brandon Jones 8.00 20.00
BR Billy Rowell AU EXCH 40.00 80.00
CK Clayton Kershaw AU 60.00 120.00
CM Cameron Maybin AU 60.00 120.00
CP Chris Parmelee AU EXCH 40.00 80.00
EA Elvis Andrus 10.00 25.00
EL Evan Longoria AU 100.00 200.00
HC Hank Conger AU 20.00 50.00
HP Hunter Pence 50.00 100.00
JT Jose Tabata 30.00 60.00
JU Justin Upton AU 90.00 150.00
JW Johnny Whittleman AU 15.00 40.00
KB Kyler Burke AU 10.00 25.00
KD Kyle Drabek AU 20.00 50.00
KK Kasey Kiker AU 12.50 30.00
LH Luke Hochevar AU 20.00 50.00
MG Mat Gamel 20.00 50.00
MO Micah Owings AU 12.50 30.00
MRR Max Ramirez 8.00 20.00
PB Pedro Beato AU 12.50 30.00
TB Travis Buck AU 10.00 25.00
TC Trevor Crowe AU 30.00 60.00
WV Will Venable 8.00 20.00
YC Yung-Chi Chen 30.00 60.00
YG Yovani Gallardo 20.00 50.00

2006 Bowman Sterling Prospects Black Refractors

STATED BLACK ODDS 1:8 BOXES
STATED BLACK AU ODDS 1:6 BOXES
STATED PRINT RUN 25 SERIAL #'d SETS
NO PRICING DUE TO SCARCITY

2006 Bowman Sterling Prospects Gold Refractors

STATED GOLD ODDS 1:18 BOXES
STATED PRINT RUN 10 SERIAL #'d SETS
NO PRICING DUE TO SCARCITY

2006 Bowman Sterling Prospects Red Refractors

STATED RED ODDS 1:182 BOXES
STATED RED AU ODDS 1:133 BOXES
STATED PRINT RUN 1 SERIAL #'d SET
NO PRICING DUE TO SCARCITY
EXCHANGE DEADLINE 12/31/08

2007 Bowman Sterling

This 117-card set was released in January, 2008. The set was issued in five-card mini-boxes, with an $50 SRP, which came six mini-boxes per display box, four display boxes per carton and two cartons per case.

COMMON ROOKIE 1.00 2.50
COMMON AUTO RC 3.00 8.00
AU RC AUTO ODDS 1:2 PACKS
COMMON GU VET 2.50 6.00
GU VET GROUP A ODDS 1:5 PACKS
GU VET GROUP B ODDS 1:3 PACKS
GU VET GROUP C ODDS 1:253 PACKS
PRINTING PLATE ODDS 1:29 BOXES
PRINTING PLATE AU ODDS 1:41 BOXES
PLATE PRINT RUN 1 SET PER COLOR
BLACK-CYAN-MAGENTA-YELLOW ISSUED
NO PLATE PRICING DUE TO SCARCITY
AAL Adam Lind (RC) 1.00 2.50
AER Alex Rodriguez Bat A 6.00 15.00
AG Alex Gordon RC 2.50 6.00
AI Akinori Iwamura RC 1.50 4.00
AJ Andruw Jones Bat B 2.50 6.00
AL Andy LaRoche (RC) 1.00 2.50
AM Andrew Miller RC 2.50 6.00
AP Albert Pujols Jsy A 5.00 12.00
AR Alex Rios Jsy B 2.50 6.00
AS Alfonso Soriano Bat B 2.50 6.00
AS Andy Sonnanstine RC 1.00 2.50
BB Billy Butler (RC) 1.25 3.00
BF Ben Francisco (RC) 1.00 2.50
BLB Barry Bonds Pants A 4.00 10.00
BP Brad Penny Jsy B 2.50 6.00
BR Brian Roberts Jsy A 2.50 6.00
BS Brian Stokes (RC) 1.00 2.50
BU B.J. Upton Bat B 2.50 6.00
BW Brandon Webb Jsy B 2.50 6.00
BW Brandon Wood (RC) 1.00 2.50
CAB Craig Biggio Jsy B 3.00 8.00
CAG Carlos Guillen Jsy B 2.50 6.00
CG Carlos Gomez RC 1.25 3.00
CH Cole Hamels Jsy A 5.00 12.00
CH Chase Headley AU (RC) 4.00 10.00
CL Carlos Lee Jsy B 2.50 6.00
CM Cameron Maybin AU RC 6.00 15.00
CMS Curt Schilling Jsy B 2.50 6.00
CT Curtis Thigpen (RC) 1.00 2.50
DDY Dmitri Young Jsy B 2.50 6.00
DM Daisuke Matsuzaka RC 3.00 8.00
DMM David Murphy (RC) 1.00 2.50
DO David Ortiz Bat B 3.00 8.00
DP Danny Putnam (RC) 1.00 2.50
DW David Wright Bat B 4.00 10.00
DWW Dontrelle Willis Jsy B 2.50 6.00
DY Delmon Young (RC) 1.25 3.00
EC Eric Chavez Pants B 2.50 6.00
FL Fred Lewis (RC) 1.25 3.00
FP Felix Pie AU (RC) 3.00 8.00
GO Garrett Olson (RC) 1.00 2.50
GP Glen Perkins AU (RC) 4.00 10.00
HB Homer Bailey AU (RC) 4.00 10.00
HG Hector Gimenez (RC) 1.00 2.50
HO Hideki Okajima RC 2.50 6.00
HP Hunter Pence (RC) 2.50 6.00
IS Ichiro Suzuki Bat B 5.00 12.00
JAV Jason Varitek Jsy B 3.00 8.00
JB Jeff Baker (RC) 1.00 2.50
JBR Jose Reyes Jsy A 3.00 8.00
JC1 Joba Chamberlain RC 5.00 12.00
JC2 Joba Chamberlain AU 40.00 80.00
JD John Danks AU RC 4.00 10.00
JDF Josh Fields (RC) 1.00 2.50
JE Jim Edmonds Jsy B 3.00 8.00
JE Jacoby Ellsbury (RC) 5.00 12.00
JF Jesus Flores RC 1.00 2.50
JH Josh Hamilton AU (RC) 15.00 40.00
JL Jesse Litsch AU RC 3.00 8.00
JQF Jake Fox RC 1.00 2.50
JR Jo-Jo Reyes (RC) 1.00 2.50
JS Johan Santana Jsy A 3.00 8.00
JS Jarrod Saltalamacchia AU (RC) 4.00 10.00
JU Justin Upton RC 2.50 6.00
JV Justin Verlander Jsy B 3.00 8.00
KI Kei Igawa RC 1.50 4.00
KK Kevin Kouzmanoff (RC) 1.00 2.50
KKS Kurt Suzuki AU (RC) 3.00 8.00
KRK Kyle Kendrick AU RC 3.00 8.00
KS Kevin Slowey AU (RC) 6.00 15.00
LB Lance Berkman Jsy B 2.50 6.00
MAR Manny Ramirez Bat B 2.50 6.00
MB Michael Bourn (RC) 1.00 2.50
MC Melky Cabrera Bat B 2.50 6.00
MC Matt Chico AU (RC) 3.00 8.00
MCT Mark Teixeira Bat A 2.50 6.00
MF Mike Fontenot (RC) 1.00 2.50
MH Matt Holliday Jsy B 3.00 8.00
MJO Magglio Ordonez Bat B 2.50 6.00
MK Masumi Kuwata RC 1.25 3.00
MM Mickey Mantle Jsy C 40.00 80.00
MM Miguel Montero (RC) 1.00 2.50
MO Micah Owings (RC) 1.00 2.50
MP Manny Parra (RC) 1.00 2.50
MR Mark Reynolds RC 2.50 6.00
MSM Mark McLemore (RC) 1.00 2.50
MT Miguel Tejada Pants B 2.50 6.00
MY Michael Young Jsy B 2.50 6.00
NG Nick Gorneault AU (RC) 3.00 8.00
NS Nate Schierholtz AU (RC) 5.00 12.00
OC Orlando Cabrera Jsy 2.50 6.00
PF Prince Fielder Jsy A 3.00 8.00
PH Phil Hughes (RC) 2.50 6.00
PH Phil Hughes AU (RC) 6.00 15.00
RB Rocco Baldelli Jsy B 2.50 6.00
RB Ryan Braun AU (RC) 15.00 40.00
RC Roger Clemens Jsy B 4.00 10.00
RJC Robinson Cano Bat B 3.00 8.00
RJH Ryan Howard Bat A 4.00 10.00
RS Ryan Sweeney (RC) 1.00 2.50
RV Rick Vanden Hurk RC 1.25 3.00
RZ Ryan Zimmerman Bat B 3.00 8.00
SD Shelley Duncan (RC) 1.00 2.50
SG Sean Gallagher (RC) 1.00 2.50
SK Scott Kazmir Jsy B 2.50 6.00
TA Tony Abreu RC 1.50 4.00
TB Travis Buck (RC) 1.00 2.50
TC Tyler Clippard (RC) 1.25 3.00
TH Tim Hudson Jsy B 2.50 6.00
TL Tim Lincecum AU RC 40.00 80.00
TLH Todd Helton Bat A 2.50 6.00
TM Travis Metcalf RC 1.25 3.00
TW Tim Wakefield Jsy B 2.50 6.00
UJ Ubaldo Jimenez (RC) 1.00 2.50
VG Vladimir Guerrero Jsy A 2.50 6.00
YE Yunel Escobar (RC) 1.00 2.50
YG Yovani Gallardo AU (RC) 6.00 15.00

2007 Bowman Sterling Refractors

*REF RC: .6X TO 1.5X BASIC
RC ODDS 1:7 PACKS
*REF AU RC: .5X TO 1.2X BASIC AU
AU RC ODDS 1:5 PACKS
*REF GU VET: .5X TO 1.2X BASIC GU
GU VET ODDS 1:8 PACKS
STATED PRINT RUN 199 SERIAL #'d SETS
DM Daisuke Matsuzaka 8.00 20.00
JC1 Joba Chamberlain 12.50 30.00
JC2 Joba Chamberlain AU 60.00 120.00
JE Jacoby Ellsbury 10.00 25.00
JH Josh Hamilton AU 30.00 60.00
KS Kevin Slowey AU 10.00 25.00
MK Masumi Kuwata 5.00 12.00
PH Phil Hughes 5.00 12.00
PH Phil Hughes AU 10.00 25.00
TL Tim Lincecum AU 60.00 120.00

2007 Bowman Sterling Black Refractors

STATED BLK RC ODDS 1:11 BOXES
STATED BLK RELIC ODDS 1:10 BOXES
STATED BLK AU RC ODDS 1:7 BOXES
STATED PRINT RUN 25 SER.#'d SETS
NO PRICING DUE TO SCARCITY

2007 Bowman Sterling Red Refractors

STATED RED RC ODDS 1:230 BOXES
STATED RED RELIC ODDS 1:246 BOXES
STATED RED AU RC ODDS 1:164 BOXES
STATED PRINT RUN 1 SER.#'d SET
NO PRICING DUE TO SCARCITY

2007 Bowman Sterling Dual Autographs

STATED ODDS 1:5 BOXES
STATED PRINT RUN 275 SER.#'d SETS
BV Jay Bruce 30.00 60.00
Joey Votto
CH Shin Soo Choo 8.00 20.00
Chin-Lung Hu
GM Deolis Guerra 8.00 20.00
Fernando Martinez
HC Phil Hughes 40.00 80.00
Joba Chamberlain
HP Luke Hochevar 20.00 50.00
David Price
LC Evan Longoria 30.00 60.00
Carl Crawford
MM John Maine 4.00 10.00
Lastings Milledge
PB Hunter Pence 30.00 60.00
Ryan Braun
PP Jeremy Papelbon 4.00 10.00
Josh Papelbon
PS Felix Pie 30.00 60.00
Jeff Samardzija

2007 Bowman Sterling Dual Autographs Refractors

*REF: .4X TO 1X BASIC
STATED ODDS 1:6 BOXES
STATED PRINT RUN 199 SER.#'d SETS

2007 Bowman Sterling Dual Autographs Black Refractors

STATED ODDS 1:46 BOXES
STATED PRINT RUN 25 SER.#'d SETS
NO PRICING DUE TO SCARCITY

2007 Bowman Sterling Dual Autographs Red Refractors

STATED ODDS 1:1080 BOXES
STATED PRINT RUN 1 SER.#'d SET
NO PRICING DUE TO SCARCITY

2007 Bowman Sterling Prospects

COMMON CARD .75 2.00
COMMON AUTO 3.00 8.00
STATED AU ODDS 1:1 PACKS
COMMON AU-GU 3.00 8.00
AU-GU ODDS 1:5 PACKS
PRINTING PLATE ODDS 1:29 BOXES
PRINTING PLATE AU ODDS 1:41 BOXES
PLATE PRINT RUN 1 SET PER COLOR
BLACK-CYAN-MAGENTA-YELLOW ISSUED
NO PLATE PRICING DUE TO SCARCITY
AC Adrian Cardenas Jsy AU 4.00 10.00
AF Andrew Fie .75 2.00
ALC Aaron Cunningham 2.00 5.00
AP Aaron Poreda AU 4.00 10.00
BB Brian Bocock Jsy AU 3.00 8.00
BB Blake Beavan AU 5.00 12.00
BEL Brad Lincoln .75 2.00
BH Brandon Hamilton .75 2.00
BHB Burke Badenhop 1.25 3.00
BL Bryan LaHair AU 3.00 8.00
BM Brandon MaGee AU 3.00 8.00
BMI Beau Mills AU 6.00 15.00
BR Ben Revere AU 5.00 12.00
BWH Brandon Hynick 2.50 6.00
CB Collin Balester Jsy AU 3.00 8.00
CC Chris Carter 2.50 6.00
CD Chance Douglass .75 2.00
CG Cole Gillespie AU 3.00 8.00
CH Chin-Lung Hu Jsy AU 10.00 25.00
CH Cedric Hunter 2.00 5.00
CK Clayton Kershaw Jsy AU 12.50 30.00
CL Chuck Lofgren Jsy AU 4.00 10.00
CM Clayton Mortensen AU 3.00 8.00
CN Chris Nowak .75 2.00
CR Colby Rasmus Jsy AU 10.00 25.00
CS Cody Strait .75 2.00
CW Chris Withrow AU 4.00 10.00
CWW Casey Weathers AU 3.00 8.00
DB Daniel Bard AU 6.00 15.00
DBE Dellin Betances 2.00 5.00
DG Deolis Guerra Jsy AU 5.00 12.00
DI Devin Ivany .75 2.00
DJ Desmond Jennings 2.50 6.00
DL Drew Locke .75 2.00
DM Daniel Moskos AU 3.00 8.00
DME Devin Mesoraco AU 3.00 8.00
DMM Derek Miller 1.25 3.00
DPP David Price AU 40.00 80.00
DS James Simmons AU 3.00 8.00
EE Ed Easley .75 2.00
EL Evan Longoria Jsy AU 60.00 120.00
EL Erik Lis AU 3.00 8.00
EM Emerson Frostad .75 2.00
EY Eric Young Jr. 1.25 3.00
FF Freddie Freeman 2.00 5.00
GD German Duran Jsy AU 3.00 8.00
GH Gorkys Hernandez 2.00 5.00
GP Gregory Porter .75 2.00
GR Greg Reynolds 2.00 5.00
GS Greg Smith 1.25 3.00
HS Henry Sosa Jsy AU 4.00 10.00
ID Ivan De Jesus Jr. 1.25 3.00
IS Ian Stewart Jsy AU 5.00 12.00
JA J.P. Arencibia AU 4.00 10.00
JAA James Avery AU 3.00 8.00
JB Jay Bruce Jsy AU 20.00 50.00
JB Joe Benson AU 3.00 8.00
JBO Julio Borbon AU 3.00 8.00
JG Jonathan Gilmore AU 3.00 8.00
JGA Joe Gaetti .75 2.00
JGO Jared Goedert 2.00 5.00
JH Jason Heyward AU 20.00 50.00
JJ Justin Jackson 1.25 3.00
JL Jeff Locke 2.50 6.00
JM Joe Mather .75 2.00
JO Josh Outman AU 3.00 8.00
JP Jason Place 1.25 3.00
JPA Jeremy Papelbon .75 2.00
JPP Josh Papelbon .75 2.00
JS Joe Savery AU 3.00 8.00
JS Jeff Samardzija 3.00 8.00
JSM Jake Smolinski 2.00 5.00
JT J.R. Towles 2.00 5.00
JV Joey Votto Jsy AU 12.50 30.00
JV Josh Vitters AU 12.50 30.00
JVE Jonathan Van Every .75 2.00
JW Johnny Whittleman Jsy AU 3.00 8.00
KA Kevin Ahrens AU 3.00 8.00
KK Kellen Kulbacki AU 3.00 8.00
KK Kala Kaaihue 2.00 5.00
MB Michael Burgess AU 6.00 15.00
MBB Madison Bumgarner AU 15.00 40.00
MC Mike Carp 1.25 3.00
MCA Mitch Canham AU 3.00 8.00
MD Mike Daniel AU 3.00 8.00
MDE Mike Devaney .75 2.00
MDO Matt Dominguez AU 6.00 15.00
MH Mark Hamilton .75 2.00
MIM Michael Main AU 3.00 8.00
MLP Matt LaPorta AU 30.00 60.00
MM Michael Madsen Jsy AU 3.00 8.00
MM Matt McBride AU 3.00 8.00
MMG Matt Mangini AU 3.00 8.00
MP Mike Parisi AU 3.00 8.00
MS Michael Saunders 2.00 5.00
MY Matt Young .75 2.00
NH Nick Hagadone AU 4.00 10.00
NN Nick Noonan AU 5.00 12.00
NS Nick Schmidt AU 3.00 8.00
OS Ole Sheldon .75 2.00
PB Pedro Beato Jsy AU 3.00 8.00
PK Peter Kozma AU 3.00 8.00
RD Ross Detwiler AU 3.00 8.00
RM Ryan Mount AU 3.00 8.00
RT Rich Thompson .75 2.00
SF Sam Fuld 2.00 5.00
SP Steve Pearce Jsy AU 6.00 15.00
TA Tim Alderson AU 8.00 20.00
TF Todd Frazier AU 5.00 12.00
TF Thomas Fairchild .75 2.00
TM Thomas Manzella AU 3.00 8.00
TS Travis Snider AU 15.00 40.00
TW Ty Weeden AU 3.00 8.00
VB Vic Buttler .75 2.00
VS Vasili Spanos .75 2.00
WF Wendell Fairley AU 4.00 10.00
WT Wade Townsend AU 3.00 8.00
ZM Zach McAllister 1.25 3.00

2007 Bowman Sterling Prospects Refractors

*REF: .75X TO 2X BASIC
REF ODDS 1:7 PACKS
*REF AU: .75X TO 2X BASIC AU
REF AU ODDS 1:5 PACKS
*REF AU-GU RC: .5X TO 1.2X BASIC AU-GU
REF AU-GU ODDS 1:20 PACKS
STATED PRINT RUN 199 SERIAL #'d SETS
DG Deolis Guerra Jsy AU 10.00 25.00
DJ Desmond Jennings 10.00 25.00
DPP David Price AU 75.00 150.00
EL Evan Longoria Jsy AU 75.00 150.00
IS Ian Stewart Jsy AU 10.00 25.00
JA J.P. Arencibia AU 15.00 40.00
JB Jay Bruce Jsy AU 20.00 50.00
JBO Julio Borbon AU 15.00 40.00
JH Jason Heyward AU 75.00 150.00
JL Jeff Locke 6.00 15.00
JS Jeff Samardzija 10.00 25.00
JV Joey Votto Jsy AU 15.00 40.00
JV Josh Vitters AU 50.00 100.00
MB Michael Burgess AU 20.00 50.00
MBB Madison Bumgarner AU 50.00 100.00
MDO Matt Dominguez AU 30.00 60.00
MLP Matt LaPorta AU 75.00 150.00
SP Steve Pearce Jsy AU 12.50 30.00
TF Todd Frazier AU 15.00 40.00
TS Travis Snider AU 60.00 120.00

2007 Bowman Sterling Prospects Black Refractors

STATED BLK PROS ODDS 1:11 BOXES
STATED BLK RELIC ODDS 1:10 BOXES
STATED BLK AU PROS ODDS 1:7 BOXES
STATED BLK AU RELIC ODDS 1:26 BOXES
STATED PRINT RUN 25 SER.#'d SETS
NO PRICING DUE TO SCARCITY

2007 Bowman Sterling Prospects Red Refractors

STATED RED PROS ODDS 1:230 BOXES
STATED RED RELIC ODDS 1:246 BOXES
STATED RED AU PROS ODDS 1:164 BOXES
STATED RED AU RELIC ODDS 1:675 BOXES
STATED PRINT RUN 1 SER.#'d SET
NO PRICING DUE TO SCARCITY

1994 Bowman's Best

This 200-card standard-size set (produced by Topps) consists of 90 veteran stars, 90 rookies and prospects and 20 Mirror Image cards. The veteran cards have red fronts and are designated 1R-90R. The rookies and prospects cards have blue fronts and are designated 1B-90B. The Mirror Image cards feature a veteran star and a prospect matched by position in a horizontal design. These cards are numbered 91-110. Subsets featured are Super Vet (1R-6R), Super Rookie (82R-90R), and Blue Chip (1B-11B). Rookie Cards include Edgardo Alfonzo, Tony Clark, Brad Fullmer, Chan Ho Park, Jorge Posada and Edgar Renteria.

COMPLETE SET (200) 15.00 40.00
B1 Chipper Jones .50 1.25
B2 Derek Jeter 1.50 4.00
B3 Bill Pulsipher .20 .50
B4 James Baldwin .08 .25
B5 Brooks Kieschnick RC .08 .25
B6 Justin Thompson .08 .25
B7 Midre Cummings .08 .25
B8 Joey Hamilton .08 .25
B9 Pokey Reese .08 .25
B10 Brian Barber .08 .25
B11 John Burke .08 .25
B12 DeShawn Warren .08 .25
B13 Edgardo Alfonzo RC .40 1.00
B14 Eddie Pearson RC .20 .50
B15 Jimmy Haynes .08 .25
B16 Danny Bautista .08 .25
B17 Roger Cedeno .08 .25
B18 Jon Lieber .20 .50
B19 Billy Wagner RC 2.00 5.00
B20 Tate Seefried RC .20 .50
B21 Chad Mottola .08 .25
B22 Jose Malave .08 .25
B23 Terrell Wade RC .20 .50
B24 Shane Andrews .08 .25
B25 Chan Ho Park RC .60 1.50
B26 Kirk Presley RC .20 .50
B27 Robbie Beckett .08 .25
B28 Orlando Miller .08 .25
B29 Jorge Posada RC 4.00 10.00
B30 Frankie Rodriguez .08 .25
B31 Brian L. Hunter .08 .25
B32 Billy Ashley .08 .25
B33 Rondell White .20 .50
B34 John Roper .08 .25
B35 Marc Valdes .08 .25
B36 Scott Ruffcorn .08 .25
B37 Rod Henderson .08 .25
B38 Curtis Goodwin RC .20 .50
B39 Russ Davis .08 .25
B40 Rick Gorecki .08 .25
B41 Johnny Damon .50 1.25
B42 Roberto Petagine .08 .25
B43 Chris Snopek .08 .25
B44 Mark Acre RC .20 .50
B45 Todd Hollandsworth .08 .25
B46 Shawn Green .50 1.25
B47 John Carter RC .20 .50
B48 Jim Pittsley RC .20 .50
B49 John Wasdin RC .20 .50
B50 D.J. Boston RC .20 .50
B51 Tim Clark .08 .25
B52 Alex Ochoa .08 .25
B53 Chad Roper .08 .25
B54 Mike Kelly .08 .25
B55 Brad Fullmer RC .40 1.00
B56 Carl Everett .20 .50
B57 Tim Belk RC .20 .50
B58 Jimmy Hurst RC .20 .50
B59 Mac Suzuki RC .40 1.00
B60 Mike Moore .08 .25
B61 Alan Benes RC .20 .50
B62 Tony Clark RC .60 1.50
B63 Edgar Renteria RC 2.00 5.00
B64 Trey Beamon .08 .25
B65 LaTroy Hawkins RC .40 1.00
B66 Wayne Gomes RC .40 1.00
B67 Ray McDavid .08 .25
B68 John Dettmer .08 .25
B69 Willie Greene .08 .25
B70 Dave Stevens .08 .25
B71 Kevin Orie RC .08 .25
B72 Chad Ogea .08 .25
B73 Ben Van Ryn RC .20 .50
B74 Kym Ashworth RC .20 .50
B75 Dmitri Young .20 .50
B76 Herbert Perry RC .20 .50
B77 Joey Eischen .08 .25
B78 Arquimedez Pozo RC .20 .50
B79 Ugueth Urbina .08 .25
B80 Keith Williams RC .20 .50
B81 John Frascatore RC .20 .50
B82 Garey Ingram RC .20 .50
B83 Aaron Small .20 .50
B84 Olmedo Saenz RC .20 .50
B85 Jesus Tavarez RC .20 .50

B86 Jose Silva RC .40 1.00
B87 Jay Witasick RC .20 .50
B88 Jay Maldonado RC .20 .50
B89 Keith Heberling RC .20 .50
B90 Rusty Greer RC .60 1.50
R1 Paul Molitor .20 .50
R2 Eddie Murray .50 1.25
R3 Ozzie Smith .75 2.00
R4 Rickey Henderson .50 1.25
R5 Lee Smith .20 .50
R6 Dave Winfield .20 .50
R7 Roberto Alomar .30 .75
R8 Matt Williams .20 .50
R9 Mark Grace .30 .75
R10 Lance Johnson .08 .25
R11 Darren Daulton .20 .50
R12 Tom Glavine .30 .75
R13 Gary Sheffield .20 .50
R14 Rod Beck .08 .25
R15 Fred McGriff .30 .75
R16 Joe Carter .20 .50
R17 Dante Bichette .20 .50
R18 Danny Tartabull .08 .25
R19 Juan Gonzalez .20 .50
R20 Steve Avery .08 .25
R21 John Wetteland .08 .25
R22 Ben McDonald .08 .25
R23 Jack McDowell .08 .25
R24 Jose Canseco .30 .75
R25 Tim Salmon .30 .75
R26 Wilson Alvarez .08 .25
R27 Gregg Jefferies .08 .25
R28 John Burkett .08 .25
R29 Greg Vaughn .08 .25
R30 Robin Ventura .20 .50
R31 Paul O'Neill .30 .75
R32 Cecil Fielder .20 .50
R33 Kevin Mitchell .08 .25
R34 Jeff Conine .20 .50
R35 Carlos Baerga .08 .25
R36 Greg Maddux .75 2.00
R37 Roger Clemens 1.00 2.50
R38 Deion Sanders .30 .75
R39 Delino DeShields .08 .25
R40 Ken Griffey Jr. .75 2.00
R41 Albert Belle .20 .50
R42 Wade Boggs .30 .75
R43 Andres Galarraga .20 .50
R44 Aaron Sele .08 .25
R45 Don Mattingly 1.25 3.00
R46 David Cone .20 .50
R47 Len Dykstra .20 .50
R48 Brett Butler .20 .50
R49 Bill Swift .08 .25
R50 Bobby Bonilla .20 .50
R51 Rafael Palmeiro .30 .75
R52 Moises Alou .20 .50
R53 Jeff Bagwell .30 .75
R54 Mike Mussina .30 .75
R55 Frank Thomas .50 1.25
R56 Jose Rijo .08 .25
R57 Ruben Sierra .20 .50
R58 Randy Myers .08 .25
R59 Barry Bonds 1.25 3.00
R60 Jimmy Key .20 .50
R61 Travis Fryman .20 .50
R62 John Olerud .20 .50
R63 David Justice .20 .50
R64 Ray Lankford .20 .50
R65 Bob Tewksbury .08 .25
R66 Chuck Carr .08 .25
R67 Jay Buhner .20 .50
R68 Kenny Lofton .20 .50
R69 Marquis Grissom .20 .50
R70 Sammy Sosa .50 1.25
R71 Cal Ripken 1.50 4.00
R72 Ellis Burks .20 .50
R73 Jeff Montgomery .08 .25
R74 Julio Franco .20 .50
R75 Kirby Puckett .50 1.25
R76 Larry Walker .20 .50
R77 Andy Van Slyke .30 .75
R78 Tony Gwynn .60 1.50
R79 Will Clark .30 .75
R80 Mo Vaughn .20 .50
R81 Mike Piazza 1.00 2.50
R82 James Mouton .08 .25
R83 Carlos Delgado .30 .75
R84 Ryan Klesko .20 .50
R85 Javier Lopez .20 .50
R86 Raul Mondesi .20 .50
R87 Cliff Floyd .20 .50
R88 Manny Ramirez .50 1.25
R89 Hector Carrasco .08 .25
R90 Jeff Granger .08 .25
X91 Frank Thomas .30 .75
Dmitri Young
X92 Fred McGriff .20 .50
Brooks Kieschnick
X93 Matt Williams .08 .25
Shane Andrews
X94 Cal Ripken .75 2.00
Kevin Orie
X95 Barry Larkin .75 2.00
Derek Jeter
X96 Ken Griffey Jr. .40 1.00
Johnny Damon
X97 Barry Bonds .60 1.50
Rondell White
X98 Albert Belle .20 .50
Jimmy Hurst
X99 Raul Mondesi .20 .50
Ruben Rivera RC
X100 Roger Clemens .50 1.25
Scott Ruffcorn
X101 Greg Maddux .50 1.25
John Wasdin
X102 Tim Salmon .30 .75
Chad Mottola
X103 Carlos Baerga .08 .25
Arquimedez Pozo
X104 Mike Piazza .50 1.25
Bobby Hughes
X105 Carlos Delgado .30 .75
Melvin Nieves
X106 Javier Lopez 1.00 2.50
Jorge Posada
X107 Manny Ramirez .50 1.25
Jose Malave
X108 Travis Fryman .30 .75
Chipper Jones
X109 Steve Avery .08 .25
Bill Pulsipher
X110 John Olerud .50 1.25
Shawn Green

1994 Bowman's Best Refractors

This 200-card standard-size set is a parallel to the basic Bowman's Best issue. The cards were randomly inserted in packs at a rate of one in nine packs. The only difference is the refractive coating on front that allows for a brighter, shinier appearance.

*RED STARS: 4X TO 10X BASIC CARDS
*BLUE STARS: 4X TO 10X BASIC CARDS
*BLUE ROOKIES: 1.5X TO 4X BASIC
*MIRROR IMAGE STARS: 2X TO 5X BASIC
B63 Edgar Renteria 8.00 20.00

1995 Bowman's Best

This 195 card standard-size set (produced by Topps) consists of 90 veteran stars, 90 rookies and prospects and 15 dual player Mirror Image cards. The packs contain seven cards and the suggested retail price was $5. The veteran cards have red fronts and are designated R1-R90. Cards of rookies and prospects have blue fronts and are designated B1-B90. The Mirror Image cards feature a veteran star and a prospect matched by position in a horizontal design. These cards are numbered X1-X15. Rookie Cards include Bob Abreu, Bartolo Colon, Scott Elarton, Juan Encarnacion, Vladimir Guerrero, Andruw Jones, Hideo Nomo, Rey Ordonez, Scott Rolen and Richie Sexson.

COMPLETE SET (195) 125.00 250.00
COMMON CARD (B1-R90) .20 .50
COMMON CARD (X1-X15) .20 .50
B1 Derek Jeter 1.25 3.00
B2 Vladimir Guerrero RC 15.00 40.00
B3 Bob Abreu RC 5.00 12.00
B4 Chan Ho Park .20 .50
B5 Paul Wilson .20 .50
B6 Chad Ogea .20 .50
B7 Andruw Jones RC 10.00 25.00
B8 Brian Barber .20 .50
B9 Andy Larkin .20 .50
B10 Richie Sexson RC 4.00 10.00
B11 Everett Stull .20 .50
B12 Brooks Kieschnick .20 .50
B13 Matt Murray .20 .50
B14 John Wasdin .20 .50
B15 Shannon Stewart .20 .50
B16 Luis Ortiz .20 .50
B17 Marc Kroon .20 .50
B18 Todd Greene .20 .50
B19 Juan Acevedo RC .40 1.00
B20 Tony Clark .20 .50
B21 Jermaine Dye .20 .50
B22 Derrek Lee .50 1.25
B23 Pat Watkins .20 .50
B24 Pokey Reese .20 .50
B25 Ben Grieve .20 .50
B26 Julio Santana RC .20 .50
B27 Felix Rodriguez RC .40 1.00
B28 Paul Konerko 3.00 8.00
B29 Nomar Garciaparra 2.00 5.00
B30 Pat Ahearne RC .20 .50
B31 Jason Schmidt .50 1.25
B32 Billy Wagner .30 .75
B33 Rey Ordonez RC 1.25 3.00
B34 Curtis Goodwin .20 .50
B35 Sergio Nunez RC .40 1.00
B36 Tim Belk .20 .50
B37 Scott Elarton RC .75 2.00
B38 Jason Isringhausen .20 .50
B39 Trot Nixon .20 .50
B40 Sid Roberson RC .40 1.00
B41 Ron Villone .20 .50
B42 Ruben Rivera .20 .50
B43 Rick Huisman .20 .50
B44 Todd Hollandsworth .20 .50
B45 Johnny Damon .30 .75
B46 Garret Anderson .20 .50
B47 Jeff D'Amico .20 .50
B48 Dustin Hermanson .20 .50
B49 Juan Encarnacion RC 1.25 3.00
B50 Andy Pettitte .30 .75
B51 Chris Stynes .20 .50
B52 Troy Percival .20 .50
B53 LaTroy Hawkins .20 .50
B54 Roger Cedeno .20 .50
B55 Alan Benes .20 .50
B56 Karim Garcia RC .40 1.00
B57 Andrew Lorraine .20 .50
B58 Gary Rath RC .40 1.00
B59 Bret Wagner .20 .50
B60 Jeff Suppan .20 .50
B61 Bill Pulsipher .20 .50
B62 Jay Payton RC 1.25 3.00
B63 Alex Ochoa .20 .50
B64 Ugueth Urbina .20 .50
B65 Armando Benitez .20 .50
B66 George Arias .20 .50
B67 Raul Casanova RC .40 1.00
B68 Matt Drews .20 .50
B69 Jimmy Haynes .20 .50
B70 Jimmy Hurst .20 .50
B71 C.J. Nitkowski .20 .50
B72 Tommy Davis RC .40 1.00
B73 Bartolo Colon RC 3.00 8.00
B74 Chris Carpenter RC 5.00 12.00
B75 Trey Beamon .20 .50
B76 Bryan Rekar .20 .50
B77 James Baldwin .20 .50
B78 Marc Valdes .20 .50
B79 Tom Fordham RC .40 1.00
B80 Marc Newfield .20 .50
B81 Angel Martinez .20 .50
B82 Brian L. Hunter .20 .50
B83 Jose Herrera .20 .50
B84 Glenn Dishman RC .40 1.00
B85 Jacob Cruz RC .75 2.00
B86 Paul Shuey .20 .50
B87 Scott Rolen RC 8.00 20.00
B88 Doug Million .20 .50
B89 Desi Relaford .20 .50
B90 Michael Tucker .20 .50
R1 Randy Johnson .50 1.25
R2 Joe Carter .20 .50
R3 Chili Davis .20 .50
R4 Moises Alou .20 .50
R5 Gary Sheffield .20 .50
R6 Kevin Appier .20 .50
R7 Denny Neagle .20 .50
R8 Ruben Sierra .20 .50
R9 Darren Daulton .20 .50
R10 Cal Ripken 1.50 4.00
R11 Bobby Bonilla .20 .50
R12 Manny Ramirez .30 .75
R13 Barry Bonds 1.25 3.00
R14 Eric Karros .20 .50
R15 Greg Maddux .75 2.00
R16 Jeff Bagwell .30 .75
R17 Paul Molitor .20 .50
R18 Ray Lankford .20 .50
R19 Mark Grace .30 .75
R20 Kenny Lofton .20 .50
R21 Tony Gwynn .60 1.50
R22 Will Clark .30 .75
R23 Roger Clemens 1.00 2.50
R24 Dante Bichette .20 .50
R25 Barry Larkin .30 .75
R26 Wade Boggs .30 .75
R27 Kirby Puckett .50 1.25
R28 Cecil Fielder .20 .50
R29 Jose Canseco .30 .75
R30 Juan Gonzalez .20 .50
R31 David Cone .20 .50
R32 Craig Biggio .30 .75
R33 Tim Salmon .30 .75
R34 David Justice .20 .50
R35 Sammy Sosa .50 1.25
R36 Mike Piazza .75 2.00
R37 Carlos Baerga .20 .50
R38 Jeff Conine .20 .50
R39 Rafael Palmeiro .30 .75
R40 Bret Saberhagen .20 .50
R41 Len Dykstra .20 .50
R42 Mo Vaughn .20 .50
R43 Wally Joyner .20 .50
R44 Chuck Knoblauch .20 .50
R45 Robin Ventura .20 .50
R46 Don Mattingly 1.25 3.00
R47 Dave Hollins .20 .50
R48 Andy Benes .20 .50
R49 Ken Griffey Jr. .75 2.00
R50 Albert Belle .20 .50
R51 Matt Williams .20 .50
R52 Rondell White .20 .50
R53 Raul Mondesi .20 .50
R54 Brian Jordan .20 .50
R55 Greg Vaughn .20 .50
R56 Fred McGriff .30 .75
R57 Roberto Alomar .30 .75
R58 Dennis Eckersley .20 .50
R59 Lee Smith .20 .50
R60 Eddie Murray .50 1.25
R61 Kenny Rogers .20 .50
R62 Ron Gant .20 .50
R63 Larry Walker .20 .50
R64 Chad Curtis .20 .50
R65 Frank Thomas .50 1.25
R66 Paul O'Neill .30 .75
R67 Kevin Seitzer .20 .50
R68 Marquis Grissom .20 .50
R69 Mark McGwire 1.50 4.00
R70 Travis Fryman .20 .50
R71 Andres Galarraga .20 .50
R72 Carlos Perez RC .75 2.00
R73 Tyler Green .20 .50
R74 Marty Cordova .20 .50
R75 Shawn Green .20 .50
R76 Vaughn Eshelman .20 .50
R77 John Mabry .20 .50
R78 Jason Bates .20 .50
R79 Jon Nunnally .20 .50
R80 Ray Durham .20 .50
R81 Edgardo Alfonzo .20 .50
R82 Esteban Loaiza .20 .50
R83 Hideo Nomo RC 3.00 8.00
R84 Orlando Miller .20 .50
R85 Alex Gonzalez .20 .50
R86 M.Grudzielanek RC 1.25 3.00
R87 Julian Tavarez .20 .50
R88 Benji Gil .20 .50
R89 Quilvio Veras .20 .50
R90 Ricky Bottalico .20 .50
X1 Ben Davis RC .60 1.50
Ivan Rodriguez
X2 Mark Redman RC .60 1.50
Manny Ramirez
X3 Reggie Taylor RC .60 1.50
Deion Sanders
X4 Ryan Jaroncyk RC .20 .50
Shawn Green
X5 Juan LeBron RC 3.00 8.00
Juan Gonzalez UER
Card pictures Carlos Beltran instead of Juan LeBron.
X6 Tony McKnight RC .20 .50
Craig Biggio
X7 Michael Barrett RC .60 1.50
Travis Fryman
X8 Corey Jenkins RC .20 .50
Mo Vaughn
X9 Ruben Rivera .50 1.25
Frank Thomas
X10 Curtis Goodwin .20 .50
Kenny Lofton
X11 Brian L. Hunter .30 .75
Tony Gwynn
X12 Todd Greene .50 1.25
Ken Griffey Jr.
X13 Karim Garcia .20 .50
Matt Williams
X14 Billy Wagner .30 .75
Randy Johnson
X15 Pat Watkins .30 .75
Jeff Bagwell

1995 Bowman's Best Refractors

Randomly inserted at a rate of one in six packs, this set is a parallel to the basic Bowman's Best issue. As far as the refractive qualities, the final 15 Mirror Image cards (X1-X15) are considered diffractors which reflects light in a different manner than the typical refractor. Unlike the 180 red and blue Refractors, the Mirror Image Diffractors are seeded into packs at a rate of 1:12. The veteran red refractor cards have been seen with or without the word refractor on the back. These cards without the refractor markings are valued at the same price as the regular refractors.

*STARS: 4X TO 10X BASIC CARDS
*RCs: 1.5X TO 4X BASIC CARDS
*MIRROR IMAGE: 1.25X TO 3X BASIC CARDS
B2 Vladimir Guerrero 150.00 250.00
B3 Bob Abreu 40.00 80.00
B7 Andruw Jones 75.00 150.00
B10 Richie Sexson 20.00 50.00
B73 Bartolo Colon 15.00 40.00
B74 Chris Carpenter 30.00 60.00
B87 Scott Rolen 60.00 120.00
X5 Juan LeBron 10.00 25.00
Juan Gonzalez UER
Card pictures Carlos Beltran instead of Juan LeBron.

1995 Bowman's Best Jumbo Refractors

This ten-card set was produced for various retail outlets. One card was inserted into each specially marked retail Topps box. According to Treat, Inc. there are no more than 9,000 of each card issued. Each over-sized card measures approximately 4" by 6". The most available of these cards are Albert Belle and Greg Maddux since they were distributed nationally. The other eight players were issued on a more regional basis. The cards are an exact parallel of the standard-size Refractor inserts except for their larger size.

COMPLETE SET (10) 50.00 125.00
COMMON CARD (1-10) 2.00 5.00
COMMON DP 1.50 4.00
1 Albert Belle DP 1.50 4.00
2 Ken Griffey Jr 6.00 15.00
3 Tony Gwynn 6.00 15.00
4 Greg Maddux DP 3.00 8.00
5 Hideo Nomo 6.00 15.00
6 Mike Piazza 6.00 15.00
7 Cal Ripken 12.50 30.00
8 Sammy Sosa 5.00 12.00
9 Frank Thomas 4.00 10.00
10 Mo Vaughn 2.00 5.00

1996 Bowman's Best Previews

Printed with Finest technology, this 30-card set features the hottest 15 top prospects and 15 veterans and was randomly inserted in 1996 Bowman packs at the rate of one in 12. The fronts display a color action player photo. The backs carry player information.

COMPLETE SET (30) 25.00 60.00
*REFRACTORS: .5X TO 1.2X BASIC PREVIEWS
REFRACTOR STATED ODDS 1:24
*ATOMIC: 1X TO 2.5X BASIC PREVIEWS
ATOMIC STATED ODDS 1:48
BBP1 Chipper Jones 1.00 2.50
BBP2 Alan Benes .40 1.00
BBP3 Brooks Kieschnick .40 1.00
BBP4 Barry Bonds 2.50 6.00
BBP5 Rey Ordonez .40 1.00
BBP6 Tim Salmon .60 1.50
BBP7 Mike Piazza 1.50 4.00
BBP8 Billy Wagner .40 1.00
BBP9 Andruw Jones 1.50 4.00
BBP10 Tony Gwynn 1.25 3.00
BBP11 Paul Wilson .40 1.00
BBP12 Pokey Reese .40 1.00
BBP13 Frank Thomas 1.00 2.50
BBP14 Greg Maddux 1.50 4.00
BBP15 Derek Jeter 2.50 6.00
BBP16 Jeff Bagwell .60 1.50
BBP17 Barry Larkin .60 1.50
BBP18 Todd Greene .40 1.00
BBP19 Ruben Rivera .40 1.00
BBP20 Richard Hidalgo .40 1.00
BBP21 Larry Walker .40 1.00
BBP22 Carlos Baerga .40 1.00
BBP23 Derrick Gibson .40 1.00
BBP24 Richie Sexson .60 1.50
BBP25 Mo Vaughn .40 1.00
BBP26 Hideo Nomo 1.00 2.50
BBP27 N.Garciaparra 2.00 5.00
BBP28 Cal Ripken 3.00 8.00
BBP29 Karim Garcia .40 1.00
BBP30 Ken Griffey Jr. 1.50 4.00

1996 Bowman's Best

This 180-card set was (produced by Topps) issued in packs of six cards at the cost of $4.99 per pack. The fronts feature a color action player cutout of 90 outstanding veteran players on a chromium gold background design and 90 up and coming prospects and rookies on a silver design. The backs carry a color player portrait, player information and statistics. Card number 33 was never actually issued. Instead, both Roger Clemens and Rafael Palmeiro are erroneously numbered 32. A chrome reprint of the 1952 Bowman Mickey Mantle was inserted at the rate of one in 24 packs. A Refractor version of the Mantle was seeded at 1:96 packs and an Atomic Refractor version was seeded at 1:192. Notable Rookie Cards include Geoff Jenkins and Mike Sweeney.

COMPLETE SET (180) 15.00 40.00
1 Hideo Nomo .40 1.00
2 Edgar Martinez .25 .60
3 Cal Ripken 1.25 3.00
4 Wade Boggs .25 .60
5 Cecil Fielder .15 .40
6 Albert Belle .15 .40
7 Chipper Jones .40 1.00
8 Ryne Sandberg .60 1.50
9 Tim Salmon .25 .60
10 Barry Bonds 1.00 2.50
11 Ken Caminiti .15 .40
12 Ron Gant .15 .40
13 Frank Thomas .40 1.00
14 Dante Bichette .15 .40
15 Jason Kendall .15 .40
16 Mo Vaughn .15 .40
17 Rey Ordonez .15 .40
18 Henry Rodriguez .15 .40
19 Ryan Klesko .15 .40
20 Jeff Bagwell .25 .60
21 Randy Johnson .40 1.00
22 Jim Edmonds .15 .40
23 Kenny Lofton .15 .40
24 Andy Pettitte .25 .60
25 Brady Anderson .15 .40
26 Mike Piazza .60 1.50
27 Greg Vaughn .15 .40
28 Joe Carter .15 .40
29 Jason Giambi .15 .40
30 Ivan Rodriguez .25 .60
31 Jeff Conine .15 .40
32 Rafael Palmeiro .25 .60
33 Roger Clemens UER .75 2.00
Actually card #32
34 Chuck Knoblauch .15 .40
35 Reggie Sanders .15 .40
36 Andres Galarraga .15 .40
37 Paul O'Neill .25 .60
38 Tony Gwynn .50 1.25
39 Paul Wilson .15 .40
40 Garret Anderson .15 .40
41 David Justice .15 .40
42 Eddie Murray .40 1.00
43 Mike Grace RC .20 .50
44 Marty Cordova .15 .40
45 Kevin Appier .15 .40
46 Raul Mondesi .15 .40
47 Jim Thome .25 .60
48 Sammy Sosa .40 1.00
49 Craig Biggio .25 .60
50 Marquis Grissom .15 .40
51 Alan Benes .15 .40
52 Manny Ramirez .25 .60
53 Gary Sheffield .15 .40
54 Mike Mussina .25 .60
55 Robin Ventura .15 .40
56 Johnny Damon .25 .60
57 Jose Canseco .25 .60
58 Juan Gonzalez .15 .40
59 Tino Martinez .25 .60
60 Brian Hunter .15 .40
61 Fred McGriff .25 .60
62 Jay Buhner .15 .40
63 Carlos Delgado .15 .40
64 Moises Alou .15 .40
65 Roberto Alomar .25 .60
66 Barry Larkin .25 .60
67 Vinny Castilla .15 .40
68 Ray Durham .15 .40
69 Travis Fryman .15 .40
70 Jason Isringhausen .15 .40
71 Ken Griffey Jr. .60 1.50
72 John Smoltz .25 .60
73 Matt Williams .15 .40
74 Chan Ho Park .15 .40
75 Mark McGwire 1.25 3.00
76 Jeffrey Hammonds .15 .40
77 Will Clark .25 .60
78 Kirby Puckett .40 1.00
79 Derek Jeter 1.00 2.50
80 Derek Bell .15 .40
81 Eric Karros .15 .40
82 Len Dykstra .15 .40
83 Larry Walker .15 .40
84 Mark Grudzielanek .15 .40
85 Greg Maddux .60 1.50
86 Carlos Baerga .15 .40
87 Paul Molitor .15 .40
88 John Valentin .15 .40
89 Mark Grace .25 .60
90 Ray Lankford .15 .40
91 Andruw Jones .60 1.50
92 Nomar Garciaparra .75 2.00
93 Alex Ochoa .15 .40
94 Derrick Gibson .15 .40
95 Jeff D'Amico .15 .40
96 Ruben Rivera .15 .40
97 Vladimir Guerrero .75 2.00
98 Pokey Reese .15 .40
99 Richard Hidalgo .15 .40
100 Bartolo Colon .40 1.00
101 Karim Garcia .15 .40
102 Ben Davis .15 .40
103 Jay Powell .15 .40
104 Chris Snopek .15 .40
105 Glendon Rusch RC .40 1.00
106 Enrique Wilson .15 .40
107 A.Alfonseca RC .40 1.00
108 Wilton Guerrero RC .20 .50
109 Jose Guillen RC 1.50 4.00
110 Miguel Mejia RC .20 .50
111 Jay Payton .15 .40
112 Scott Elarton .15 .40
113 Brooks Kieschnick .15 .40
114 Dustin Hermanson .15 .40
115 Roger Cedeno .15 .40
116 Matt Wagner .15 .40
117 Lee Daniels .15 .40
118 Ben Grieve .15 .40
119 Ugueth Urbina .15 .40
120 Danny Graves .15 .40
121 Dan Donato RC .20 .50
122 Matt Ruebel RC .20 .50
123 Mark Sievert RC .20 .50
124 Chris Stynes .15 .40
125 Jeff Abbott .15 .40
126 Rocky Coppinger RC .20 .50
127 Jermaine Dye .15 .40
128 Todd Greene .15 .40
129 Chris Carpenter .25 .60
130 Edgar Renteria .15 .40
131 Matt Drews .15 .40
132 Edgard Velazquez RC .20 .50
133 Casey Whitten .15 .40
134 Ryan Jones RC .20 .50
135 Todd Walker .15 .40
136 Geoff Jenkins RC .75 2.00
137 Matt Morris RC 1.50 4.00
138 Richie Sexson .25 .60
139 Todd Dunwoody RC .20 .50
140 Gabe Alvarez RC .20 .50
141 J.J. Johnson .15 .40
142 Shannon Stewart .15 .40
143 Brad Fullmer .15 .40
144 Julio Santana .15 .40
145 Scott Rolen .40 1.00
146 Amaury Telemaco .15 .40
147 Trey Beamon .15 .40
148 Billy Wagner .15 .40
149 Todd Hollandsworth .15 .40
150 Doug Million .15 .40
151 Javier Valentin RC .20 .50
152 Wes Helms RC .40 1.00
153 Jeff Suppan .15 .40
154 Luis Castillo RC .60 1.50
155 Bob Abreu .40 1.00
156 Paul Konerko .40 1.00
157 Jamey Wright .15 .40
158 Eddie Pearson .15 .40
159 Jimmy Haynes .15 .40
160 Derrek Lee .25 .60
161 Damian Moss .15 .40
162 Carlos Guillen RC 1.00 2.50
163 Chris Fussell RC .20 .50
164 Mike Sweeney RC 1.00 2.50
165 Donnie Sadler .15 .40
166 Desi Relaford .15 .40
167 Steve Gibralter .15 .40
168 Neifi Perez .15 .40
169 Antone Williamson .15 .40
170 Marty Janzen RC .20 .50
171 Todd Helton .75 2.00
172 Raul Ibanez RC .75 2.00
173 Bill Selby .15 .40
174 Shane Monahan RC .20 .50
175 Robin Jennings .15 .40
176 Bobby Chouinard .15 .40
177 Einar Diaz .15 .40
178 Jason Thompson RC .15 .40
179 Rafael Medina RC .20 .50
180 Kevin Orie .15 .40
NNO Mickey Mantle 4.00 10.00
1952 Bowman Atomic Ref.
NNO Mickey Mantle 2.00 5.00
1952 Bowman Refractor
NNO Mickey Mantle 1.00 2.50
1952 Bowman Chrome

1996 Bowman's Best Atomic Refractors

Inserted one in every 48 hobby packs and one in every 80 retail packs, this 180-card set is parallel to the 1996 Bowman's Best set. It is similar in design to the regular set but was printed with sparkling refractor technology.

*GOLD STARS: 6X TO 15X BASIC CARDS
*SILVER STARS: 6X TO 15X BASIC CARDS
*ROOKIES: 4X TO 10X BASIC CARDS

1996 Bowman's Best Refractors

This 180-card set is parallel to the regular 1996 Bowman Best set and is similar in design. The difference is in the refractive quality of the cards. The cards were inserted at the rate of one in every 12 hobby packs and one in every 20 retail packs.

*GOLD STARS: 3X TO 8X BASIC CARDS
*SILVER STARS: 3X TO 8X BASIC CARDS
*ROOKIES: 2X TO 5X BASIC CARDS

1996 Bowman's Best Cuts

Randomly inserted in hobby packs at a rate of one in 24 and retail packs at a rate on one in 40, this chromium card die-cut set features 15 top hobby stars.

COMPLETE SET (15) 30.00 80.00
*REFRACTORS: .6X TO 1.5X BASIC CUTS
REF.STATED ODDS 1:48 HOB, 1:80 RET
*ATOMIC: 1X TO 2.5X BASIC CUTS
ATOMIC STATED ODDS 1:96 HOB, 1:160 RET
1 Ken Griffey Jr. 2.50 6.00
2 Jason Isringhausen .60 1.50
3 Derek Jeter 4.00 10.00
4 Andruw Jones 2.50 6.00
5 Chipper Jones 1.50 4.00
6 Ryan Klesko .60 1.50
7 Raul Mondesi .60 1.50
8 Hideo Nomo 1.50 4.00
9 Mike Piazza 2.50 6.00
10 Manny Ramirez 1.00 2.50
11 Cal Ripken 5.00 12.00
12 Ruben Rivera .60 1.50
13 Tim Salmon 1.00 2.50
14 Frank Thomas 1.50 4.00
15 Jim Thome 1.00 2.50

1996 Bowman's Best Mirror Image

Randomly inserted in hobby packs at a rate of one in 48 and retail packs at a rate of one in 80, this 10-card set features four top players on a single card at one of ten different positions. The fronts display a color photo of an AL veteran with a semicircle containing a color portrait of a prospect who plays the same position. The backs carry a color photo of an NL veteran with a semicircle color portrait of a prospect.

COMPLETE SET (10) 30.00 80.00
*REFRACTORS: .6X TO 1.5X BASIC CARDS
REFRACTOR ODDS 1:96 HOB, 1:160 RET
*ATOMIC REFRACTORS: 1.25X TO 3X BASIC CARDS
ATOMIC ODDS 1:192 HOB, 1:320 RET
1 Jeff Bagwell 1.50 4.00
Todd Helton
Frank Thomas
Richie Sexson
2 Craig Biggio 1.50 4.00
Luis Castillo
Roberto Alomar
Desi Relaford
3 Chipper Jones 1.50 4.00
Scott Rolen
Wade Boggs
George Arias
4 Barry Larkin 6.00 15.00
Neifi Perez
Cal Ripken
Mark Bellhorn
5 Larry Walker 1.50 4.00
Karim Garcia
Albert Belle
Ruben Rivera
6 Barry Bonds 6.00 15.00
Andruw Jones
Kenny Lofton
Donnie Sadler
7 Tony Gwynn 4.00 10.00
Vladimir Guerrero
Ken Griffey
Ben Grieve
8 Mike Piazza 4.00 10.00
Ben Davis
Ivan Rodriguez
Javier Valentin
9 Greg Maddux 5.00 12.00
Jamey Wright
Mike Mussina
Bartolo Colon
10 Tom Glavine 1.50 4.00
Billy Wagner
Randy Johnson
Jarrod Washburn

1997 Bowman's Best Preview

Randomly inserted in 1997 Bowman Series 1 packs at a rate of one in 12, this 20-card set features color photos of 10 rookies and 10 veterans that would be appearing in the 1997 Bowman's Best set. The background of each card features a flag of the featured player's homeland.

COMPLETE SET (20) 40.00 80.00
*REF: .75X TO 2X BASIC PREVIEWS
REFRACTOR STATED ODDS 1:48
*ATOMIC REF: 1.5X TO 4X BASIC PREVIEWS
ATOMIC STATED ODDS 1:96
1 Frank Thomas 1.50 4.00
2 Ken Griffey Jr. 2.50 6.00
3 Barry Bonds 4.00 10.00
4 Derek Jeter 4.00 10.00
5 Chipper Jones 1.50 4.00
6 Mark McGwire 5.00 12.00
7 Cal Ripken 5.00 12.00
8 Kenny Lofton .60 1.50
9 Gary Sheffield .60 1.50
10 Jeff Bagwell .60 1.50
11 Wilton Guerrero .60 1.50
12 Scott Rolen 1.00 2.50
13 Todd Walker .60 1.50
14 Ruben Rivera .60 1.50
15 Andruw Jones 1.00 2.50
16 Nomar Garciaparra 2.50 6.00
17 Vladimir Guerrero 1.50 4.00
18 Miguel Tejada 1.50 4.00
19 Bartolo Colon .60 1.50
20 Katsuhiro Maeda .60 1.50

1997 Bowman's Best

The 1997 Bowman's Best set (produced by Topps) was issued in one series totalling 200 cards and was distributed in six-card packs (SRP $4.99). The fronts feature borderless color player photos printed on chromium card stock. The cards of the 100 current veteran stars display a classic gold design while the cards of the 100 top prospects carry a sleek silver design. Rookie Cards include Adrian Beltre, Kris Benson, Jose Cruz Jr., Travis Lee, Fernando Tatis, Miguel Tejada and Kerry Wood.

COMPLETE SET (200) 15.00 40.00
1 Ken Griffey Jr. .60 1.50
2 Cecil Fielder .15 .40
3 Albert Belle .15 .40
4 Todd Hundley .15 .40
5 Mike Piazza .60 1.50
6 Matt Williams .15 .40
7 Mo Vaughn .15 .40
8 Ryne Sandberg .60 1.50
9 Chipper Jones .40 1.00
10 Edgar Martinez .25 .60
11 Kenny Lofton .15 .40
12 Ron Gant .15 .40
13 Moises Alou .15 .40
14 Pat Hentgen .15 .40
15 Steve Finley .15 .40
16 Mark Grace .25 .60
17 Jay Buhner .15 .40
18 Jeff Conine .15 .40
19 Jim Edmonds .15 .40
20 Todd Hollandsworth .15 .40
21 Andy Pettitte .25 .60
22 Jim Thome .25 .60
23 Eric Young .15 .40
24 Ray Lankford .15 .40
25 Marquis Grissom .15 .40
26 Tony Clark .15 .40
27 Jermaine Allensworth .15 .40
28 Ellis Burks .15 .40
29 Tony Gwynn .50 1.25
30 Barry Larkin .25 .60
31 John Olerud .15 .40
32 Mariano Rivera .40 1.00
33 Paul Molitor .15 .40
34 Ken Caminiti .15 .40
35 Gary Sheffield .15 .40
36 Al Martin .15 .40
37 John Valentin .15 .40
38 Frank Thomas .40 1.00
39 John Jaha .15 .40
40 Greg Maddux .60 1.50
41 Alex Fernandez .15 .40
42 Dean Palmer .15 .40
43 Bernie Williams .25 .60
44 Deion Sanders .25 .60
45 Mark McGwire 1.25 3.00
46 Brian Jordan .15 .40
47 Bernard Gilkey .15 .40
48 Will Clark .25 .60
49 Kevin Appier .15 .40
50 Tom Glavine .25 .60
51 Chuck Knoblauch .15 .40
52 Rondell White .15 .40
53 Greg Vaughn .15 .40
54 Mike Mussina .25 .60
55 Brian McRae .15 .40
56 Chili Davis .15 .40
57 Wade Boggs .25 .60
58 Jeff Bagwell .25 .60
59 Roberto Alomar .25 .60
60 Dennis Eckersley .15 .40
61 Ryan Klesko .15 .40
62 Manny Ramirez .25 .60
63 John Wetteland .15 .40
64 Cal Ripken 1.25 3.00
65 Edgar Renteria .15 .40
66 Tino Martinez .25 .60
67 Larry Walker .15 .40
68 Gregg Jefferies .15 .40
69 Lance Johnson .15 .40
70 Carlos Delgado .15 .40
71 Craig Biggio .25 .60
72 Jose Canseco .25 .60
73 Barry Bonds 1.00 2.50
74 Juan Gonzalez .15 .40
75 Eric Karros .15 .40
76 Reggie Sanders .15 .40
77 Robin Ventura .15 .40
78 Hideo Nomo .40 1.00
79 David Justice .15 .40
80 Vinny Castilla .15 .40
81 Travis Fryman .15 .40
82 Derek Jeter 1.00 2.50
83 Sammy Sosa .40 1.00
84 Ivan Rodriguez .25 .60
85 Rafael Palmeiro .25 .60
86 Roger Clemens .75 2.00
87 Jason Giambi .15 .40
88 Andres Galarraga .15 .40
89 Jermaine Dye .15 .40
90 Joe Carter .15 .40
91 Brady Anderson .15 .40
92 Derek Bell .15 .40
93 Randy Johnson .40 1.00
94 Fred McGriff .25 .60
95 John Smoltz .25 .60
96 Harold Baines .15 .40
97 Raul Mondesi .15 .40
98 Tim Salmon .25 .60
99 Carlos Baerga .15 .40
100 Dante Bichette .15 .40
101 Vladimir Guerrero .40 1.00
102 Richard Hidalgo .15 .40
103 Paul Konerko .25 .60
104 Alex Gonzalez RC .40 1.00
105 Jason Dickson .15 .40
106 Jose Rosado .15 .40
107 Todd Walker .15 .40
108 Seth Greisinger RC .15 .40
109 Todd Helton .40 1.00
110 Ben Davis .15 .40
111 Bartolo Colon .15 .40
112 Elieser Marrero .15 .40
113 Jeff D'Amico .15 .40
114 Miguel Tejada RC 1.50 4.00
115 Darin Erstad .15 .40
116 Kris Benson RC .40 1.00
117 Adrian Beltre RC 1.25 3.00
118 Neifi Perez .15 .40
119 Pokey Reese .15 .40
120 Carl Pavano .15 .40
121 Juan Melo .15 .40
122 Kevin McGlinchy RC .15 .40
123 Pat Cline .15 .40
124 Felix Heredia RC .15 .40
125 Aaron Boone .15 .40
126 Glendon Rusch .15 .40
127 Mike Cameron .15 .40
128 Justin Thompson .15 .40
129 Chad Hermansen RC .15 .40
130 Sidney Ponson RC .40 1.00
131 Willie Martinez RC .15 .40
132 Paul Wilder RC .15 .40
133 Geoff Jenkins .15 .40
134 Roy Halladay RC 1.50 4.00
135 Carlos Guillen .15 .40
136 Tony Batista .15 .40
137 Todd Greene .15 .40
138 Luis Castillo .15 .40
139 Jimmy Anderson RC .15 .40
140 Edgard Velazquez .15 .40
141 Chris Snopek .15 .40
142 Ruben Rivera .15 .40
143 Javier Valentin .15 .40
144 Brian Rose .15 .40
145 Fernando Tatis RC .15 .40
146 Dean Crow RC .15 .40
147 Karim Garcia .15 .40
148 Dante Powell .15 .40
149 Hideki Irabu RC .25 .60
150 Matt Morris .15 .40
151 Wes Helms .15 .40
152 Russ Johnson .15 .40
153 Jarrod Washburn .15 .40
154 Kerry Wood RC 1.50 4.00
155 Joe Fontenot RC .15 .40
156 Eugene Kingsale .15 .40
157 Terrence Long .15 .40
158 Calvin Maduro .15 .40
159 Jeff Suppan .15 .40
160 DaRond Stovall .15 .40
161 Mark Redman .15 .40
162 Ken Cloude RC .15 .40
163 Bobby Estalella .15 .40
164 Abraham Nunez RC .15 .40
165 Derrick Gibson .15 .40
166 Mike Drumright RC .15 .40
167 Katsuhiro Maeda .15 .40
168 Jeff Liefer .15 .40
169 Ben Grieve .15 .40
170 Bob Abreu .25 .60
171 Shannon Stewart .15 .40
172 Braden Looper RC .30 .75
173 Brant Brown .15 .40
174 Marlon Anderson .15 .40
175 Brad Fullmer .15 .40
176 Carlos Beltran .75 2.00
177 Nomar Garciaparra .60 1.50
178 Derrek Lee .25 .60
179 Val.De Los Santos RC .15 .40
180 Dmitri Young .15 .40
181 Jamey Wright .15 .40
182 Hiram Bocachica RC .15 .40
183 Wilton Guerrero .15 .40
184 Chris Carpenter .15 .40
185 Scott Spiezio .15 .40
186 Andruw Jones .25 .60
187 Travis Lee RC .25 .60
188 Jose Cruz Jr. RC .25 .60
189 Jose Guillen .15 .40
190 Jeff Abbott .15 .40
191 Ricky Ledee RC .25 .60
192 Mike Sweeney .15 .40
193 Donnie Sadler .15 .40
194 Scott Rolen .25 .60
195 Kevin Orie .15 .40
196 Jason Conti RC .15 .40
197 Mark Kotsay RC .60 1.50
198 Eric Milton RC .25 .60
199 Russell Branyan .15 .40
200 Alex Sanchez RC .25 .60

1997 Bowman's Best Atomic Refractors

Randomly inserted in packs at a rate of one in 24, cards from this 200 card set parallel the regular Bowman's Best set and were printed with sparkling cross-weave refractor technology.

*STARS: 5X TO 12X BASIC CARDS
*ROOKIES: 3X TO 8X BASIC CARDS

1997 Bowman's Best Refractors

Randomly inserted in packs at a rate of one in 12, this 200 card set is parallel to the regular set and is similar in design. The difference is found in the refractive quality of the cards.

*STARS: 2.5X TO 6X BASIC CARDS
*ROOKIES: 1.5X TO 4X BASIC CARDS

1997 Bowman's Best Autographs

Randomly inserted in packs at a rate of 1:170, this 10-card set features five silver rookie cards and five gold veteran cards with authentic autographs and a "Certified Autograph Issue" stamp.

*REF.STARS: .75X TO 2X BASIC CARDS
REFRACTOR STATED ODDS 1:2036
*ATOMIC STARS: 1.5X TO 4X BASIC CARDS
ATOMIC STATED ODDS 1:6107
SKIP-NUMBERED 10-CARD SET
29 Tony Gwynn 15.00 40.00
33 Paul Molitor 6.00 15.00
82 Derek Jeter 60.00 120.00
91 Brady Anderson 6.00 15.00
98 Tim Salmon 10.00 25.00
107 Todd Walker 6.00 15.00
183 Wilton Guerrero 2.00 5.00
185 Scott Spiezio 2.00 5.00
188 Jose Cruz Jr. 6.00 15.00
194 Scott Rolen 10.00 25.00

1997 Bowman's Best Best Cuts

Randomly inserted in packs at a rate of one in 24, this 20-card set features color player photos printed on intricate, Laser Cut Chromium card stock.

COMPLETE SET (20) 75.00 150.00
*REFRACTOR: .6X TO 1.5X BASIC CUTS
REFRACTOR STATED ODDS 1:48
*ATOMIC: 1X TO 2.5X BASIC CUTS
ATOMIC STATED ODDS 1:96
BC1 Derek Jeter 6.00 15.00
BC2 Chipper Jones 2.50 6.00
BC3 Frank Thomas 2.50 6.00

BC4 Cal Ripken 8.00 20.00
BC5 Mark McGwire 8.00 20.00
BC6 Ken Griffey Jr. 4.00 10.00
BC7 Jeff Bagwell 1.50 4.00
BC8 Mike Piazza 4.00 10.00
BC9 Ken Caminiti 1.00 2.50
BC10 Albert Belle 1.00 2.50
BC11 Jose Cruz Jr. 1.00 2.50
BC12 Wilton Guerrero 1.00 2.50
BC13 Darin Erstad 1.00 2.50
BC14 Andruw Jones 1.50 4.00
BC15 Scott Rolen 1.50 4.00
BC16 Jose Guillen 1.00 2.50
BC17 Bob Abreu 1.50 4.00
BC18 Vladimir Guerrero 2.50 6.00
BC19 Todd Walker 1.00 2.50
BC20 Nomar Garciaparra 4.00 10.00

1997 Bowman's Best Mirror Image

Randomly inserted in packs at a rate of one in 48, this 10-card set features color photos of four of the best players in the same position printed on double-sided chromium card stock. Two veterans and two rookies appear on each card. The veteran players are displayed in the larger photos with the rookies appearing in smaller corner photos.

COMPLETE SET (10) 40.00 80.00
*REFRACTORS: .6X TO 1.5X BASIC CARDS
REFRACTOR STATED ODDS 1:96
*ATOMIC REF: 1.25X TO 3X BASIC MI
ATOMIC STATED ODDS 1:192
*INVERTED: 2X VALUE OF NON-INVERTED
INVERTED: RANDOM INSERTS IN PACKS
INVERTED HAVE LARGER ROOKIE PHOTOS
MI1 Nomar Garciaparra 5.00 12.00
Derek Jeter
Hiram Bocachica
Barry Larkin
MI2 Travis Lee 2.00 5.00
Frank Thomas
Derrick Lee
Jeff Bagwell
MI3 Kerry Wood 2.00 5.00
Greg Maddux
Kris Benson
John Smoltz
MI4 Kevin Brown 3.00 8.00
Ivan Rodriguez
Eli Marrero
Mike Piazza
MI5 Jose Cruz Jr. 5.00 12.00
Ken Griffey Jr.
Andruw Jones
Barry Bonds
MI6 Jose Guillen 1.25 3.00
Juan Gonzalez
Richard Hidalgo
Gary Sheffield
MI7 Paul Konerko 5.00 12.00
Mark McGwire
Todd Helton
Rafael Palmeiro
MI8 Wilton Guerrero 1.25 3.00
Craig Biggio
Donnie Sadler
Chuck Knoblauch
MI9 Russell Branyan 1.50 4.00
Matt Williams
Adrian Beltre
Chipper Jones
MI10 Bob Abreu 2.00 5.00
Kenny Lofton
Vladimir Guerrero
Albert Belle

1997 Bowman's Best Jumbo

This 16-card set features selected cards from the 1997 regular Bowman's Best set in a 4" by 6" jumbo version available to Stadium Club members only by mail. Only 675 of each of the 16 cards were produced for this jumbo version. The cards are checklisted according to their number in the regular size set.

*REFRACTORS: 4X BASIC JUMBOS
*ATOMIC REFRACTORS: 8X BASIC JUMBOS
1 Ken Griffey Jr. 3.00 8.00
5 Mike Piazza 3.00 8.00
9 Chipper Jones 3.00 8.00
11 Kenny Lofton .75 2.00
29 Tony Gwynn 3.00 8.00
33 Paul Molitor 1.50 4.00
38 Frank Thomas 1.25 3.00
45 Mark McGwire 3.00 8.00
64 Cal Ripken Jr. 6.00 15.00
73 Barry Bonds 3.00 8.00
74 Juan Gonzalez .75 2.00
82 Derek Jeter 6.00 15.00
101 Vladimir Guerrero 1.50 4.00
177 Nomar Garciaparra 2.50 6.00
186 Andruw Jones 2.00 5.00
188 Jose Cruz Jr. .75 2.00

1998 Bowman's Best

The 1998 Bowman's Best set (produced by Topps) consists of 200 standard size cards and was released in August, 1998. The six-card packs retailed for a suggested price of $5 each. The card fronts feature 100 action photos with a gold background showcasing today's veteran players and 100 photos (combining posed shots with action shots) with a silver background showcasing rookies. The Bowman's Best logo sits in the upper right corner and the featured player's name sits in the lower left corner. Rookie Cards include Ryan Anderson, Troy Glaus, Orlando Hernandez, Carlos Lee, Ruben Mateo and Magglio Ordonez.

COMPLETE SET (200) 15.00 40.00
1 Mark McGwire 1.00 2.50
2 Jeromy Burnitz .15 .40
3 Barry Bonds 1.00 2.50
4 Dante Bichette .15 .40
5 Chipper Jones .40 1.00
6 Frank Thomas .40 1.00
7 Kevin Brown .25 .60
8 Juan Gonzalez .15 .40
9 Jay Buhner .15 .40
10 Chuck Knoblauch .15 .40
11 Cal Ripken 1.25 3.00
12 Matt Williams .15 .40
13 Jim Edmonds .15 .40
14 Manny Ramirez .25 .60
15 Tony Clark .15 .40
16 Mo Vaughn .15 .40
17 Bernie Williams .25 .60
18 Scott Rolen .25 .60
19 Gary Sheffield .15 .40
20 Albert Belle .15 .40
21 Mike Piazza .60 1.50
22 John Olerud .15 .40
23 Tony Gwynn .50 1.25
24 Jay Bell .15 .40
25 Jose Cruz Jr. .15 .40
26 Justin Thompson .15 .40
27 Ken Griffey Jr. .60 1.50
28 Sandy Alomar Jr. .15 .40
29 Mark Grudzielanek .15 .40
30 Mark Grace .25 .60
31 Ron Gant .15 .40
32 Javy Lopez .15 .40
33 Jeff Bagwell .25 .60
34 Fred McGriff .25 .60
35 Rafael Palmeiro .25 .60
36 Vinny Castilla .15 .40
37 Andy Benes .15 .40
38 Pedro Martinez .25 .60
39 Andy Pettitte .25 .60
40 Marty Cordova .15 .40
41 Rusty Greer .15 .40
42 Kevin Orie .15 .40
43 Chan Ho Park .15 .40
44 Ryan Klesko .15 .40
45 Alex Rodriguez .60 1.50
46 Travis Fryman .15 .40
47 Jeff King .15 .40
48 Roger Clemens .75 2.00
49 Darin Erstad .15 .40
50 Brady Anderson .15 .40
51 Jason Kendall .15 .40
52 John Valentin .15 .40
53 Ellis Burks .15 .40
54 Brian Hunter .15 .40
55 Paul O'Neill .25 .60
56 Ken Caminiti .15 .40
57 David Justice .15 .40
58 Eric Karros .15 .40
59 Pat Hentgen .15 .40
60 Greg Maddux .60 1.50
61 Craig Biggio .25 .60
62 Edgar Martinez .25 .60
63 Mike Mussina .25 .60
64 Larry Walker .15 .40
65 Tino Martinez .25 .60
66 Jim Thome .25 .60
67 Tom Glavine .25 .60
68 Raul Mondesi .15 .40
69 Marquis Grissom .15 .40
70 Randy Johnson .40 1.00
71 Steve Finley .15 .40
72 Jose Guillen .15 .40
73 Nomar Garciaparra .60 1.50
74 Wade Boggs .25 .60
75 Bobby Higginson .15 .40
76 Robin Ventura .15 .40
77 Derek Jeter 1.00 2.50
78 Andruw Jones .25 .60
79 Ray Lankford .15 .40
80 Vladimir Guerrero .40 1.00
81 Kenny Lofton .15 .40
82 Ivan Rodriguez .25 .60
83 Neifi Perez .15 .40
84 John Smoltz .25 .60
85 Tim Salmon .25 .60
86 Carlos Delgado .15 .40
87 Sammy Sosa .40 1.00

88 Jaret Wright .15 .40
89 Roberto Alomar .25 .60
90 Paul Molitor .15 .40
91 Dean Palmer .15 .40
92 Barry Larkin .25 .60
93 Jason Giambi .15 .40
94 Curt Schilling .15 .40
95 Eric Young .15 .40
96 Denny Neagle .15 .40
97 Moises Alou .15 .40
98 Livan Hernandez .15 .40
99 Todd Hundley .15 .40
100 Andres Galarraga .15 .40
101 Travis Lee .15 .40
102 Lance Berkman .15 .40
103 Orlando Cabrera .15 .40
104 Mike Lowell RC 1.25 3.00
105 Ben Grieve .15 .40
106 Jae Weong Seo RC .25 .60
107 Richie Sexson .15 .40
108 Eli Marrero .15 .40
109 Aramis Ramirez .15 .40
110 Paul Konerko .15 .40
111 Carl Pavano .15 .40
112 Brad Fullmer .15 .40
113 Matt Clement .15 .40
114 Donzell McDonald .15 .40
115 Todd Helton .25 .60
116 Mike Caruso .15 .40
117 Donnie Sadler .15 .40
118 Bruce Chen .15 .40
119 Jarrod Washburn .15 .40
120 Adrian Beltre .15 .40
121 Ryan Jackson RC .15 .40
122 Kevin Millar RC .60 1.50
123 Corey Koskie RC .40 1.00
124 Dermal Brown .15 .40
125 Kerry Wood .15 .40
126 Juan Melo .15 .40
127 Ramon Hernandez .15 .40
128 Roy Halladay .15 .40
129 Ron Wright .15 .40
130 Darnell McDonald RC .25 .60
131 Odalis Perez RC .60 1.50
132 Alex Cora RC .25 .60
133 Justin Towle .15 .40
134 Juan Encarnacion .15 .40
135 Brian Rose .15 .40
136 Russell Branyan .15 .40
137 Cesar King RC .15 .40
138 Ruben Rivera .15 .40
139 Ricky Ledee .15 .40
140 Vernon Wells .15 .40
141 Luis Rivas RC .40 1.00
142 Brent Butler .15 .40
143 Karim Garcia .15 .40
144 George Lombard .15 .40
145 Masato Yoshii RC .25 .60
146 Braden Looper .15 .40
147 Alex Sanchez .15 .40
148 Kris Benson .15 .40
149 Mark Kotsay .15 .40
150 Richard Hidalgo .15 .40
151 Scott Elarton .15 .40
152 Ryan Minor RC .15 .40
153 Troy Glaus RC 1.50 4.00
154 Carlos Lee RC 1.25 3.00
155 Michael Coleman .15 .40
156 Jason Grilli RC .15 .40
157 Julio Ramirez RC .15 .40
158 Randy Wolf RC .25 .60
159 Ryan Brannan .15 .40
160 Edgard Clemente .15 .40
161 Miguel Tejada .40 1.00
162 Chad Hermansen .15 .40
163 Ryan Anderson RC .15 .40
164 Ben Petrick .15 .40
165 Alex Gonzalez .15 .40
166 Ben Davis .15 .40
167 John Patterson .15 .40
168 Cliff Politte .15 .40
169 Randall Simon .15 .40
170 Javier Vazquez .15 .40
171 Kevin Witt .15 .40
172 Geoff Jenkins .15 .40
173 David Ortiz 1.50 4.00
174 Derrick Gibson .15 .40
175 Abraham Nunez .15 .40
176 A.J. Hinch .15 .40
177 Ruben Mateo RC .15 .40
178 Magglio Ordonez RC 2.00 5.00
179 Todd Dunwoody .15 .40
180 Daryle Ward .15 .40
181 Mike Kinkade RC .15 .40
182 Willie Martinez .15 .40
183 O.Hernandez RC .75 2.00
184 Eric Milton .15 .40
185 Eric Chavez .15 .40
186 Damian Jackson .15 .40
187 Jim Parque RC .25 .60
188 Dan Reichert RC .25 .60
189 Mike Drumright .15 .40
190 Todd Walker .15 .40
191 Shane Monahan .15 .40
192 Derrek Lee .25 .60
193 Jeremy Giambi RC .25 .60
194 Dan McKinley RC .15 .40
195 Tony Armas Jr. RC .25 .60
196 Matt Anderson RC .15 .40
197 Jim Chamblee RC .15 .40
198 F.Cordero RC .40 1.00
199 Calvin Pickering .15 .40
200 Reggie Taylor .15 .40

1998 Bowman's Best Atomic Refractors

The 1998 Bowman's Best Atomic Refractor set consists of 200 cards and is a parallel to the 1998 Bowman's Best base set. The cards are randomly inserted in packs at a rate of one in 82. The entire set is sequentially numbered to 100. Each card front featured a kaleidescopic refractive background.

*STARS: 8X TO 20X BASIC CARDS
*ROOKIES: 5X TO 12X BASIC CARDS
122 Kevin Millar 8.00 20.00

1998 Bowman's Best Refractors

The 1998 Bowman's Best Refractor set consists of 200 cards and is a parallel to the 1998 Bowman's Best base set. The cards are randomly inserted in packs at a rate of one in 20. The entire set is sequentially numbered to 400.

*STARS: 5X TO 12X BASIC CARDS
*ROOKIES: 2.5X TO 6X BASIC CARDS
122 Kevin Millar 4.00 10.00

1998 Bowman's Best Autographs

Randomly inserted in packs at a rate of one in 180, this 10-card set is an insert to the 1998 Bowman's Best brand. The fronts feature five gold veteran and five silver prospect cards sporting a Topps "Certified Autograph Issue" logo for authentication. The cards are designed in an identical manner to the basic issue 1998 Bowman's Best set except, of course, for the autograph and the certification logo.

*REFRACTORS: .75X TO 1.5X BASIC AU'S
REFRACTOR STATED ODDS 1:2158
*ATOMICS: 2X TO 4X BASIC AU'S
ATOMIC STATED ODDS 1:6437
SKIP-NUMBERED 10-CARD SET
5 Chipper Jones 20.00 50.00
10 Chuck Knoblauch 6.00 15.00
15 Tony Clark 4.00 10.00
20 Albert Belle 6.00 15.00
25 Jose Cruz Jr. 4.00 10.00
105 Ben Grieve 4.00 10.00
110 Paul Konerko 10.00 25.00
115 Todd Helton 10.00 25.00
120 Adrian Beltre 6.00 15.00
125 Kerry Wood 10.00 25.00

1998 Bowman's Best Mirror Image Fusion

Randomly inserted in packs at a rate of one in 12, this 20-card set is an insert to the 1998 Bowman's Best brand. The fronts feature a Major League veteran player with his positional protÃ©gÃ© on the flip side. The player's name runs along the bottom of the card.

COMPLETE SET (20) 60.00 150.00
*REFRACTORS: 1.25X TO 3X BASIC MIRROR
REFRACTOR STATED ODDS 1:809
REF.PRINT RUN 100 SERIAL #'d SETS
ATOMIC STATED ODDS 1:3237
ATOMIC PRINT RUN 25 SERIAL #'d SETS
NO ATOMIC PRICING DUE TO SCARCITY
MI1 Frank Thomas / David Ortiz 2.50 6.00
MI2 Chuck Knoblauch / Enrique Wilson 1.00 2.50
MI3 Nomar Garciaparra / Miguel Tejada 4.00 10.00
MI4 Alex Rodriguez / Mike Caruso 4.00 10.00
MI5 Cal Ripken / Ryan Minor 8.00 20.00
MI6 Ken Griffey Jr. / Ben Grieve 4.00 10.00
MI7 Juan Gonzalez / Juan Encarnacion 1.00 2.50
MI8 Jose Cruz Jr. / Ruben Mateo 1.00 2.50
MI9 Randy Johnson / Ryan Anderson 2.00 5.00
MI10 Ivan Rodriguez / A.J. Hinch 1.50 4.00
MI11 Jeff Bagwell / Paul Konerko 1.50 4.00
MI12 Mark McGwire / Travis Lee 6.00 15.00
MI13 Craig Biggio / Chad Hermansen 1.50 4.00
MI14 Mark Grudzielanek / Alex Gonzalez 1.00 2.50
MI15 Chipper Jones / Adrian Beltre 2.00 5.00
MI16 Larry Walker / Mark Kotsay 1.00 2.50
MI17 Tony Gwynn / George Lombard 3.00 8.00
MI18 Barry Bonds / Richard Hidalgo 6.00 15.00
MI19 Greg Maddux / Kerry Wood 3.00 8.00
MI20 Mike Piazza / Ben Petrick 4.00 10.00

1998 Bowman's Best Performers

Randomly inserted in packs at a rate of one in six, this 10-card set is an insert to the 1998 Bowman's Best brand. The card fronts feature full color game-action photos of ten players with the best Minor League stats of 1997. The featured player's name is found below the photo with both Bowman's Best logo and the team logo above the photo.

COMPLETE SET (10) 6.00 15.00
*REFRACTORS: 5X TO 12X BASIC PERF.
REFRACTOR STATED ODDS 1:809
REF.PRINT RUN 200 SERIAL #'d SETS
*ATOMIC: 12.5X TO 30X BASIC PERF.
ATOMIC STATED ODDS 1:3237
ATOMIC PRINT RUN 50 SERIAL #'d SETS
BP1 Ben Grieve .60 1.50
BP2 Travis Lee .60 1.50
BP3 Ryan Minor .60 1.50
BP4 Todd Helton 1.00 2.50
BP5 Brad Fullmer .60 1.50
BP6 Paul Konerko .60 1.50
BP7 Adrian Beltre .60 1.50
BP8 Richie Sexson .60 1.50
BP9 Aramis Ramirez .60 1.50
BP10 Russell Branyan .60 1.50

1999 Bowman's Best Pre-Production

These three cards were distributed as a complete set in a sealed poly-bag and sent to dealers and hobby media several weeks prior to the national release of 1999 Bowman's Best. The cards were created to preview the upcoming product and are almost identical in design to their basic issue counterparts. The key difference is the card numbering. These pre-production cards are numbered PP1-PP3, whereas the basic issue cards of Anderson, Lopez and Gold are all numbered within the context of the 180-card standard set.

COMPLETE SET (3) 1.00 2.50
PP1 Javy Lopez .60 1.50
PP2 Marlon Anderson .20 .50
PP3 J.M. Gold .20 .50

1999 Bowman's Best

The 1999 Bowman's Best set (produced by Topps) consists of 200 standard size cards. The six-card packs, released in August, 1999, retailed for a suggested price of $5 each. The cards are printed on 27-pt. Serillusion stock and feature 85 veteran stars in a striking gold series, 15 Best Performers bonus subset captured in a bronze series, 50 rookies highlighted in a brilliant blue series and 50 prospects shown in a captivating silver series. The fifty rookies and prospects (cards 151-200) were seeded at a rate of one per pack. Notable Rookie Cards included Pat Burrell, Sean Burroughs, Nick Johnson, Austin Kearns, Corey Patterson and Alfonso Soriano.

COMPLETE SET (200) 15.00 40.00
COMP.SET w/o SP's (150) 10.00 25.00
COMMON CARD (1-150) .15 .40
COMMON (151-200) .20 .50
1 Chipper Jones .40 1.00
2 Brian Jordan .15 .40
3 David Justice .15 .40
4 Jason Kendall .15 .40
5 Mo Vaughn .15 .40
6 Jim Edmonds .15 .40
7 Wade Boggs .25 .60
8 Jeromy Burnitz .15 .40
9 Todd Hundley .15 .40
10 Rondell White .15 .40
11 Cliff Floyd .15 .40
12 Sean Casey .15 .40
13 Bernie Williams .25 .60
14 Dante Bichette .15 .40
15 Greg Vaughn .15 .40
16 Andres Galarraga .15 .40
17 Ray Durham .15 .40
18 Jim Thome .25 .60
19 Gary Sheffield .15 .40
20 Frank Thomas .40 1.00
21 Orlando Hernandez .15 .40
22 Ivan Rodriguez .25 .60
23 Jose Cruz Jr. .15 .40
24 Jason Giambi .15 .40
25 Craig Biggio .25 .60
26 Kerry Wood .15 .40
27 Manny Ramirez .25 .60
28 Curt Schilling .15 .40
29 Mike Mussina .25 .60
30 Tim Salmon .25 .60
31 Mike Piazza .60 1.50
32 Roberto Alomar .25 .60
33 Larry Walker .15 .40
34 Barry Larkin .25 .60
35 Nomar Garciaparra .60 1.50
36 Paul O'Neill .25 .60
37 Todd Walker .15 .40
38 Eric Karros .15 .40
39 Brad Fullmer .15 .40
40 John Olerud .15 .40
41 Todd Helton .25 .60
42 Raul Mondesi .15 .40
43 Jose Canseco .25 .60
44 Matt Williams .15 .40
45 Ray Lankford .15 .40
46 Carlos Delgado .15 .40
47 Darin Erstad .15 .40
48 Vladimir Guerrero .40 1.00
49 Robin Ventura .15 .40
50 Alex Rodriguez .60 1.50
51 Vinny Castilla .15 .40
52 Tony Clark .15 .40
53 Pedro Martinez .25 .60
54 Rafael Palmeiro .25 .60
55 Scott Rolen .25 .60
56 Tino Martinez .25 .60
57 Tony Gwynn .50 1.25
58 Barry Bonds 1.00 2.50
59 Kenny Lofton .15 .40
60 Javy Lopez .15 .40
61 Mark Grace .25 .60
62 Travis Lee .15 .40
63 Kevin Brown .25 .60
64 Al Leiter .15 .40
65 Albert Belle .15 .40
66 Sammy Sosa .40 1.00
67 Greg Maddux .60 1.50
68 Mark Kotsay .15 .40
69 Dmitri Young .15 .40
70 Mark McGwire 1.00 2.50
71 Juan Gonzalez .15 .40
72 Andruw Jones .25 .60
73 Derek Jeter 1.00 2.50
74 Randy Johnson .40 1.00
75 Cal Ripken 1.25 3.00
76 Shawn Green .15 .40
77 Moises Alou .15 .40
78 Tom Glavine .25 .60
79 Sandy Alomar Jr. .15 .40
80 Ken Griffey Jr. .60 1.50
81 Ryan Klesko .15 .40
82 Jeff Bagwell .25 .60
83 Ben Grieve .15 .40
84 John Smoltz .25 .60
85 Roger Clemens .75 2.00
86 Ken Griffey Jr. BP .40 1.00
87 Roger Clemens BP .40 1.00
88 Derek Jeter BP .50 1.25
89 Nomar Garciaparra BP .30 .75
90 Mark McGwire BP .50 1.25
91 Sammy Sosa BP .25 .60
92 Alex Rodriguez BP .30 .75
93 Greg Maddux BP .30 .75
94 Vladimir Guerrero BP .25 .60
95 Chipper Jones BP .25 .60
96 Kerry Wood BP .15 .40
97 Ben Grieve BP .15 .40
98 Tony Gwynn BP .25 .60
99 Juan Gonzalez BP .15 .40
100 Mike Piazza BP .30 .75
101 Eric Chavez .15 .40
102 Billy Koch .15 .40
103 Dernell Stenson .15 .40
104 Marlon Anderson .15 .40
105 Ron Belliard .15 .40
106 Bruce Chen .15 .40
107 Carlos Beltran .25 .60
108 Chad Hermansen .15 .40
109 Ryan Anderson .15 .40
110 Michael Barrett .15 .40
111 Matt Clement .15 .40
112 Ben Davis .15 .40
113 Calvin Pickering .15 .40
114 Brad Penny .15 .40
115 Paul Konerko .15 .40
116 Alex Gonzalez .15 .40
117 George Lombard .15 .40
118 John Patterson .15 .40
119 Rob Bell .15 .40
120 Ruben Mateo .15 .40
121 Troy Glaus .25 .60
122 Ryan Bradley .15 .40
123 Carlos Lee .15 .40
124 Gabe Kapler .15 .40
125 Ramon Hernandez .15 .40
126 Carlos Febles .15 .40
127 Mitch Meluskey .15 .40
128 Michael Cuddyer .15 .40
129 Pablo Ozuna .15 .40
130 Jayson Werth .15 .40
131 Ricky Ledee .15 .40
132 Jeremy Giambi .15 .40
133 Danny Klassen .15 .40
134 Mark DeRosa .15 .40
135 Randy Wolf .15 .40
136 Roy Halladay .15 .40
137 Derrick Gibson .15 .40
138 Ben Petrick .15 .40
139 Warren Morris .15 .40
140 Lance Berkman .15 .40
141 Russell Branyan .15 .40
142 Adrian Beltre .15 .40
143 Juan Encarnacion .15 .40
144 Fernando Seguignol .15 .40
145 Corey Koskie .15 .40
146 Preston Wilson .15 .40
147 Homer Bush .15 .40
148 Daryle Ward .15 .40
149 Joe McEwing RC .25 .60
150 Peter Bergeron RC .20 .50
151 Pat Burrell RC 1.25 3.00
152 Choo Freeman RC .25 .60
153 Matt Belisle RC .20 .50
154 Carlos Pena RC .30 .75
155 A.J. Burnett RC .60 1.50
156 D.Mientkiewicz RC .40 1.00
157 Sean Burroughs RC .40 1.00
158 Mike Zywica RC .20 .50
159 Corey Patterson RC .60 1.50
160 Austin Kearns RC 1.25 3.00
161 Chip Ambres RC .20 .50
162 Kelly Dransfeldt RC .20 .50
163 Mike Nannini RC .20 .50
164 Mark Mulder RC 1.00 2.50
165 Jason Tyner RC .20 .50
166 Bobby Seay RC .20 .50
167 Alex Escobar RC .25 .60
168 Nick Johnson RC .60 1.50
169 Alfonso Soriano RC 3.00 8.00
170 Clayton Andrews RC .20 .50
171 C.C. Sabathia RC 1.50 4.00
172 Matt Holliday RC 3.00 8.00
173 Brad Lidge RC 1.50 4.00
174 Kit Pellow RC .20 .50
175 J.M. Gold RC .20 .50
176 Roosevelt Brown RC .20 .50
177 Eric Valent RC .25 .60
178 Adam Everett RC .40 1.00
179 Jorge Toca RC .25 .60
180 Matt Roney RC .20 .50
181 Andy Brown RC .20 .50
182 Phil Norton RC .20 .50
183 Mickey Lopez RC .20 .50
184 Chris George RC .20 .50
185 Arturo McDowell RC .20 .50
186 Jose Fernandez RC .20 .50
187 Seth Etherton RC .20 .50
188 Josh McKinley RC .20 .50
189 Nate Cornejo RC .20 .50
190 G.Chiaramonte RC .20 .50
191 Mamon Tucker RC .20 .50
192 Ryan Mills RC .20 .50
193 Chad Moeller RC .20 .50
194 Tony Torcato RC .20 .50
195 Jeff Winchester RC .20 .50
196 Rick Elder RC .20 .50
197 Matt Burch RC .25 .60
198 Jeff Urban RC .25 .60
199 Chris Jones RC .20 .50
200 Masao Kida RC .25 .60

1999 Bowman's Best Atomic Refractors

Randomly inserted at a rate of one in 62, this 200-card set is a parallel of the Bowman's Best Base set. Each card in this set is sequentially numbered to 100 and feature a refractive kaleidescope treatment on front.

*STARS: 10X TO 25X BASIC CARDS
*ROOKIES: 7.5X TO 15X BASIC CARDS

1999 Bowman's Best Refractors

Randomly inserted at a rate of one in 15, this 200-card set is a parallel of the Bowman's Best Base set and features iridescent select metallization technology. Each card in this set is sequentially numbered to 400.

*STARS: 5X TO 12X BASIC CARDS
*ROOKIES: 4X TO 8X BASIC CARDS

1999 Bowman's Best Franchise Best Mach I

Randomly inserted in packs at the rate of one in 41, this 10-card set features color photos of some of the Major's top stars printed on die-cut Serillusion stock and sequentially numbered to 3,000.

COMPLETE SET (10) 30.00 60.00
*MACH II: .75X TO 2X MACH I
MACH II STATED ODDS 1:124
MACH II PRINT RUN 1000 SERIAL #'d SETS
*MACH III: 1.25X TO 3X MACH I
MACH III STATED ODDS 1:248
MACH III PRINT RUN 500 SERIAL #'d SETS
FB1 Mark McGwire 4.00 10.00
FB2 Ken Griffey Jr. 2.50 6.00
FB3 Sammy Sosa 1.50 4.00
FB4 Nomar Garciaparra 2.50 6.00
FB5 Alex Rodriguez 2.50 6.00
FB6 Derek Jeter 4.00 10.00
FB7 Mike Piazza 2.50 6.00
FB8 Frank Thomas 1.50 4.00
FB9 Chipper Jones 1.50 4.00
FB10 Juan Gonzalez .60 1.50

1999 Bowman's Best Franchise Favorites

Randomly inserted in packs at the rate of one in 40, this six-card set features color photos of retired legends and current stars in three versions. Version A pictures the current star; Version B, a retired great; and Version C pairs the current star with the retired legend.

COMPLETE SET (6) 40.00 80.00
FR1A Derek Jeter 8.00 20.00
FR1B Don Mattingly 8.00 20.00
FR1C Derek Jeter / Don Mattingly 10.00 25.00
FR2A Scott Rolen 3.00 8.00
FR2B Mike Schmidt 5.00 12.00
FR2C Scott Rolen / Mike Schmidt 8.00 20.00

1999 Bowman's Best Franchise Favorites Autographs

This six-card set is an autographed parallel version of the regular insert set with the "Topps Certified Autograph Issue" stamp. The insertion rate for these cards are: Versions A and B, 1:1550 packs; and Version C, 1:6174. Version C cards feature autographs from both players.

FR1A Derek Jeter 60.00 120.00
FR1B Don Mattingly 30.00 60.00
FR1C Derek Jeter / Don Mattingly 175.00 300.00
FR2A Scott Rolen 10.00 25.00
FR2B Mike Schmidt 20.00 50.00
FR2C Scott Rolen / Mike Schmidt 60.00 120.00

1999 Bowman's Best Future Foundations Mach I

Randomly inserted into packs at the rate of one in 41, this 10-card set features color photos of some of the top young stars printed on die-cut Serillusion stock and sequentially numbered to 3,000.

COMPLETE SET (10) 15.00 30.00
*MACH II: .75X TO 2X MACH I
MACH II STATED ODDS 1:124
MACH II PRINT RUN 1000 SERIAL #'d SETS
*MACH III: 1.25X TO 3X MACH I
MACH III STATED ODDS 1:248
MACH III PRINT RUN 500 SERIAL #'d SETS
FF1 Ruben Mateo .40 1.00
FF2 Troy Glaus 1.00 2.50
FF3 Eric Chavez .60 1.50
FF4 Pat Burrell 1.50 4.00
FF5 Adrian Beltre .60 1.50
FF6 Ryan Anderson .40 1.00
FF7 Alfonso Soriano 2.00 5.00
FF8 Brad Penny .40 1.00
FF9 Derrick Gibson .40 1.00
FF10 Bruce Chen .40 1.00

1999 Bowman's Best Mirror Image

Randomly inserted into packs at the rate of one in 24, this 10-card double-sided set features color photos of a veteran ballplayer on one side and a hot prospect on the other.

COMPLETE SET (10) 30.00 60.00
*REFRACTORS: .75X TO 2X BASIC MIR.IMAGE

REFRACTOR STATED ODDS 1:96
*ATOMIC: 1.25X TO 3X BASIC MIR.IMAGE
ATOMIC STATED ODDS 1:192

Card	Low	High
M1 Alex Rodriguez Alex Gonzalez	2.00	5.00
M2 Ken Griffey Jr. Ruben Mateo	2.00	5.00
M3 Derek Jeter Alfonso Soriano	4.00	10.00
M4 Sammy Sosa Corey Patterson	1.25	3.00
M5 Greg Maddux Bruce Chen	2.00	5.00
M6 Chipper Jones Eric Chavez	1.00	2.50
M7 Vladimir Guerrero Carlos Beltran	1.00	2.50
M8 Frank Thomas Nick Johnson	1.00	2.50
M9 Nomar Garciaparra Pablo Ozuna	2.00	5.00
M10 Mark McGwire Pat Burrell	3.00	8.00

1999 Bowman's Best Rookie Locker Room Autographs

Randomly inserted into packs at the rate of one in 248, this five-card set features autographed color photos of top prospects with the "Topps Certified Autograph Issue" logo stamp.

Card	Low	High
RA1 Pat Burrell	8.00	20.00
RA2 Michael Barrett	4.00	10.00
RA3 Troy Glaus	6.00	15.00
RA4 Gabe Kapler	4.00	10.00
RA5 Eric Chavez	4.00	10.00

1999 Bowman's Best Rookie Locker Room Game Used Bats

Randomly inserted into packs at the rate of one in 517, this six-card set features color photos of top players with pieces of game-used bats embedded into the cards.

Card	Low	High
RB1 Pat Burrell	6.00	15.00
RB2 Michael Barrett	3.00	8.00
RB3 Troy Glaus	4.00	10.00
RB4 Gabe Kapler	3.00	8.00
RB5 Eric Chavez	3.00	8.00
RB6 Richie Sexson	3.00	8.00

1999 Bowman's Best Rookie Locker Room Game Worn Jerseys

Randomly inserted into packs at the rate of one in 538, this four-card set features color photos of some of the hottest young stars with pieces of their game-used jerseys embedded in the cards.

Card	Low	High
RJ1 Richie Sexson	4.00	10.00
RJ2 Michael Barrett	4.00	10.00
RJ3 Troy Glaus	6.00	15.00
RJ4 Eric Chavez	4.00	10.00

1999 Bowman's Best Rookie of the Year

Randomly inserted into packs at the rate of one in 95, this two-card set features color photos of the 1998 American and National League Rookies of the Year printed on Serillusion card stock. An autographed version of Ben Grieve's card with the "Topps Certified Autograph Issue" stamp was inserted at the rate of 1:1239 packs.

Card	Low	High
ROY1 Ben Grieve	1.00	2.50
ROY2 Kerry Wood	1.00	2.50
ROY1A Ben Grieve AU	6.00	15.00

2000 Bowman's Best Pre-Production

This three card set of sample cards was distributed within a sealed, clear, cello poly-wrap to dealers and hobby media several weeks prior to the national release of 2000 Bowman's Best.

Card	Low	High
COMPLETE SET (3)	1.50	6.00
PP1 Larry Walker	.40	1.00
PP2 Adam Dunn	1.50	4.00
PP3 Brett Myers	.60	1.50

2000 Bowman's Best Previews

Randomly inserted into Bowman hobby/retail packs at one in 18, this 10-card insert set features preview cards from the 2000 Bowman's Best product. Card backs carry a "BB" prefix.

Card	Low	High
COMPLETE SET (10)	15.00	40.00
BB1 Derek Jeter	2.50	6.00
BB2 Ken Griffey Jr.	1.50	4.00
BB3 Nomar Garciaparra	1.50	4.00
BB4 Mike Piazza	1.50	4.00
BB5 Alex Rodriguez	1.50	4.00
BB6 Sammy Sosa	1.00	2.50
BB7 Mark McGwire	2.50	6.00
BB8 Pat Burrell	.40	1.00
BB9 Josh Hamilton	1.50	4.00
BB10 Adam Piatt	.40	1.00

2000 Bowman's Best

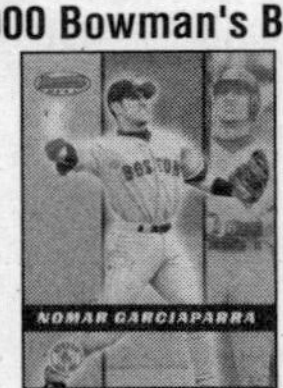

The 2000 Bowman's Best set (produced by Topps) was released in early August, 2000 and features a 200-card base set broken into tiers as follows: Base Veterans/Prospects (1-150) and Rookies (151-200) which were serial numbered to 2999. Each pack contained four cards, and carried a suggested retail of $5.00. Rookie Cards include Rick Asadoorian, Willie Bloomquist, Bobby Bradley, Ben Broussard, Chin-Feng Chen and Barry Zito. The added element of serial-numbered Rookie Cards was extremely popular with collectors and a much-need jolt of life for the Bowman's Best brand (which had been badly overshadowed for two years by the Bowman Chrome Brand).

Card	Low	High
COMP.SET w/o RC's (150)	15.00	40.00
COMMON CARD (1-150)	.15	.40
COMMON (151-200)	2.00	5.00
1 Nomar Garciaparra	.60	1.50
2 Chipper Jones	.40	1.00
3 Tony Clark	.15	.40
4 Bernie Williams	.25	.60
5 Barry Bonds	1.00	2.50
6 Jermaine Dye	.15	.40
7 John Olerud	.15	.40
8 Mike Hampton	.15	.40
9 Cal Ripken	1.25	3.00
10 Jeff Bagwell	.25	.60
11 Troy Glaus	.15	.40
12 J.D. Drew	.15	.40
13 Jeromy Burnitz	.15	.40
14 Carlos Delgado	.15	.40
15 Shawn Green	.15	.40
16 Kevin Millwood	.15	.40
17 Rondell White	.15	.40
18 Scott Rolen	.25	.60
19 Jeff Cirillo	.15	.40
20 Barry Larkin	.25	.60
21 Brian Giles	.15	.40
22 Roger Clemens	.75	2.00
23 Manny Ramirez	.25	.60
24 Alex Gonzalez	.15	.40
25 Mark Grace	.25	.60
26 Fernando Tatis	.15	.40
27 Randy Johnson	.40	1.00
28 Roger Cedeno	.15	.40
29 Brian Jordan	.15	.40
30 Kevin Brown	.15	.40
31 Greg Vaughn	.15	.40
32 Roberto Alomar	.25	.60
33 Larry Walker	.15	.40
34 Rafael Palmeiro	.25	.60
35 Curt Schilling	.15	.40
36 Orlando Hernandez	.15	.40
37 Todd Walker	.15	.40
38 Juan Gonzalez	.15	.40
39 Sean Casey	.15	.40
40 Tony Gwynn	.50	1.25
41 Albert Belle	.15	.40
42 Gary Sheffield	.15	.40
43 Michael Barrett	.15	.40
44 Preston Wilson	.15	.40
45 Jim Thome	.25	.60
46 Shannon Stewart	.15	.40
47 Mo Vaughn	.15	.40
48 Ben Grieve	.15	.40
49 Adrian Beltre	.15	.40
50 Sammy Sosa	.40	1.00
51 Bob Abreu	.15	.40
52 Edgardo Alfonzo	.15	.40
53 Carlos Febles	.15	.40
54 Frank Thomas	.40	1.00
55 Alex Rodriguez	.60	1.50
56 Cliff Floyd	.15	.40
57 Jose Canseco	.25	.60
58 Erubiel Durazo	.15	.40
59 Tim Hudson	.15	.40
60 Craig Biggio	.25	.60
61 Eric Karros	.15	.40
62 Mike Mussina	.25	.60
63 Robin Ventura	.15	.40
64 Carlos Beltran	.15	.40
65 Pedro Martinez	.25	.60
66 Gabe Kapler	.15	.40
67 Jason Kendall	.15	.40
68 Derek Jeter	1.00	2.50
69 Magglio Ordonez	.15	.40
70 Mike Piazza	.60	1.50
71 Mike Lieberthal	.15	.40
72 Andres Galarraga	.15	.40
73 Raul Mondesi	.15	.40
74 Eric Chavez	.15	.40
75 Greg Maddux	.60	1.50
76 Matt Williams	.15	.40
77 Kris Benson	.15	.40
78 Ivan Rodriguez	.25	.60
79 Pokey Reese	.15	.40
80 Vladimir Guerrero	.40	1.00
81 Mark McGwire	1.00	2.50
82 Vinny Castilla	.15	.40
83 Todd Helton	.25	.60
84 Andruw Jones	.25	.60
85 Ken Griffey Jr.	.60	1.50
86 Mark McGwire BP	.50	1.25
87 Derek Jeter BP	.50	1.25
88 Chipper Jones BP	.25	.60
89 Nomar Garciaparra BP	.40	1.00
90 Sammy Sosa BP	.25	.60
91 Cal Ripken BP	.60	1.50
92 Juan Gonzalez BP	.15	.40
93 Alex Rodriguez BP	.40	1.00
94 Barry Bonds BP	.50	1.25
95 Sean Casey BP	.15	.40
96 Vladimir Guerrero BP	.25	.60
97 Mike Piazza BP	.40	1.00
98 Shawn Green BP	.15	.40
99 Jeff Bagwell BP	.15	.40
100 Ken Griffey Jr. BP	.40	1.00
101 Rick Ankiel	.15	.40
102 John Patterson	.15	.40
103 David Walling	.15	.40
104 Michael Restovich	.15	.40
105 A.J. Burnett	.15	.40
106 Pablo Ozuna	.15	.40
107 Chad Hermansen	.15	.40
108 Choo Freeman	.15	.40
109 Mark Quinn	.15	.40
110 Corey Patterson	.15	.40
111 Ramon Ortiz	.15	.40
112 Vernon Wells	.15	.40
113 Milton Bradley	.15	.40
114 Gookie Dawkins	.15	.40
115 Sean Burroughs	.15	.40
116 Wily Mo Pena	.15	.40
117 Dee Brown	.15	.40
118 C.C. Sabathia	.15	.40
119 Adam Kennedy	.15	.40
120 Octavio Dotel	.15	.40
121 Kip Wells	.15	.40
122 Ben Petrick	.15	.40
123 Mark Mulder	.15	.40
124 Jason Standridge	.15	.40
125 Adam Piatt	.15	.40
126 Steve Lomasney	.15	.40
127 Jayson Werth	.15	.40
128 Alex Escobar	.15	.40
129 Ryan Anderson	.15	.40
130 Adam Dunn	.40	1.00
131 Ted Lilly	.15	.40
132 Brad Penny	.15	.40
133 Daryle Ward	.15	.40
134 Eric Munson	.15	.40
135 Nick Johnson	.15	.40
136 Jason Jennings	.15	.40
137 Tim Raines Jr.	.15	.40
138 Ruben Mateo	.15	.40
139 Jack Cust	.15	.40
140 Rafael Furcal	.15	.40
141 Eric Gagne	.40	1.00
142 Tony Armas Jr.	.15	.40
143 Mike Paradis	.15	.40
144 Peter Bergeron	.15	.40
145 Alfonso Soriano	.40	1.00
146 Josh Hamilton	.60	1.50
147 Michael Cuddyer	.15	.40
148 Jay Gehrke	.15	.40
149 Josh Girdley	.15	.40
150 Pat Burrell	.15	.40
151 Brett Myers RC	5.00	12.00
152 Scott Seabol RC	2.00	5.00
153 Keith Reed RC	2.00	5.00
154 F.Rodriguez RC	5.00	12.00
155 Barry Zito RC	12.50	30.00
156 Pat Manning RC	2.00	5.00
157 Ben Christensen RC	2.00	5.00
158 Corey Myers RC	2.00	5.00
159 Wascar Serrano RC	2.00	5.00
160 Wes Anderson RC	2.00	5.00
161 Andy Tracy RC	2.00	5.00
162 Cesar Saba RC	2.00	5.00
163 Mike Lamb RC	3.00	8.00
164 Bobby Bradley RC	2.00	5.00
165 Vince Faison RC	2.00	5.00
166 Ty Howington RC	2.00	5.00
167 Ken Harvey RC UER Card has pitching stats on the back	2.00	5.00
168 Josh Kalinowski RC	2.00	5.00
169 Ruben Salazar RC	2.00	5.00
170 Aaron Rowand RC	4.00	10.00
171 Ramon Santiago RC	2.00	5.00
172 Scott Sobkowiak RC	2.00	5.00
173 Lyle Overbay RC	3.00	8.00
174 Rico Washington RC	2.00	5.00
175 Rick Asadoorian RC	2.00	5.00
176 Matt Ginter RC	2.00	5.00
177 Jason Stumm RC	2.00	5.00
178 B.J. Garbe RC	2.00	5.00
179 Mike MacDougal RC	2.00	5.00
180 Ryan Christianson RC	2.00	5.00
181 Kurt Ainsworth RC	2.00	5.00
182 Brad Baisley RC	2.00	5.00
183 Ben Broussard RC	5.00	12.00
184 Aaron McNeal RC	2.00	5.00
185 John Sneed RC	2.00	5.00
186 Junior Brignac RC	2.00	5.00
187 Chance Caple RC	2.00	5.00
188 Scott Downs RC	2.00	5.00
189 Matt Cepicky RC	2.00	5.00
190 Chin-Feng Chen RC	15.00	30.00
191 Johan Santana RC	40.00	80.00
192 Brad Baker RC	2.00	5.00
193 Jason Repko RC	3.00	8.00
194 Craig Dingman RC	2.00	5.00
195 Chris Wakeland RC	2.00	5.00
196 Rogelio Arias RC	2.00	5.00
197 Luis Matos RC	2.00	5.00
198 Rob Ramsay	2.00	5.00
199 Willie Bloomquist RC	15.00	30.00
200 Tony Pena Jr. RC	2.00	5.00

2000 Bowman's Best Autographed Baseball Redemptions

Randomly inserted into packs at one in 688, this five-card insert features exchange cards for actual autographed baseballs from some of the Major League's hottest prospects. Please note the deadline to return these cards to Topps was June 30th, 2001.

Card	Low	High
1 Josh Hamilton	15.00	40.00
2 Rick Ankiel	15.00	40.00
3 Alfonso Soriano	30.00	60.00
4 Nick Johnson	15.00	40.00
5 Corey Patterson	15.00	40.00

2000 Bowman's Best Bets

Randomly inserted into packs at one in 15, this 10-card insert features prospects that are sure bets to excel at the Major League level. Card backs carry a "BBB" prefix.

Card	Low	High
COMPLETE SET (10)	10.00	25.00
BBB1 Pat Burrell	.60	1.50
BBB2 Alfonso Soriano	1.50	4.00
BBB3 Corey Patterson	.60	1.50
BBB4 Eric Munson	.60	1.50
BBB5 Sean Burroughs	.60	1.50
BBB6 Rafael Furcal	.60	1.50
BBB7 Rick Ankiel	.60	1.50
BBB8 Nick Johnson	.60	1.50
BBB9 Ruben Mateo	.60	1.50
BBB10 Josh Hamilton	1.50	4.00

2000 Bowman's Best Franchise 2000

Randomly inserted into packs at one in 18, this 25-card set features players that teams build around. Card backs carry an "F" prefix.

Card	Low	High
COMPLETE SET (25)	60.00	150.00
F1 Cal Ripken	8.00	20.00
F2 Nomar Garciaparra	4.00	10.00
F3 Frank Thomas	2.50	6.00
F4 Manny Ramirez	1.50	4.00
F5 Juan Gonzalez	1.00	2.50
F6 Carlos Beltran	1.00	2.50
F7 Derek Jeter	6.00	15.00
F8 Alex Rodriguez	4.00	10.00
F9 Ben Grieve	1.00	2.50
F10 Jose Canseco	1.50	4.00
F11 Ivan Rodriguez	1.50	4.00
F12 Mo Vaughn	1.00	2.50
F13 Randy Johnson	2.50	6.00
F14 Chipper Jones	2.50	6.00
F15 Sammy Sosa	2.50	6.00
F16 Ken Griffey Jr.	4.00	10.00
F17 Larry Walker	1.00	2.50
F18 Preston Wilson	1.00	2.50
F19 Jeff Bagwell	1.50	4.00
F20 Shawn Green	1.00	2.50
F21 Vladimir Guerrero	2.50	6.00
F22 Mike Piazza	4.00	10.00
F23 Scott Rolen	1.50	4.00
F24 Tony Gwynn	3.00	8.00
F25 Barry Bonds	6.00	15.00

2000 Bowman's Best Franchise Favorites

Randomly inserted into packs at one in 17, this six-card insert features players (past and present) that are franchise favorites. Card backs carry a "FR" prefix.

Card	Low	High
COMPLETE SET (6)	12.50	30.00
FR1A Sean Casey	1.00	2.50
FR1B Johnny Bench	1.50	4.00
FR1C Sean Casey Johnny Bench	1.50	4.00
FR2A Cal Ripken	4.00	10.00
FR2B Brooks Robinson	1.00	2.50
FR2C Cal Ripken Brooks Robinson	4.00	10.00

2000 Bowman's Best Franchise Favorites Autographs

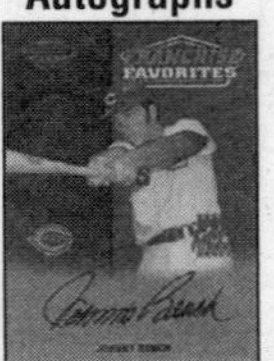

Randomly inserted into packs, this six-card insert is a complete parallel of the Franchise Favorites insert. Each of these cards were autographed by the players, and the set was broken into tiers as folllows: Group A (Sean Casey and Cal Ripken) were inserted at one in 1291, Group B (Johnny Bench and Brooks Robinson) were inserted at one in 1291, and Group C (Casey/Bench, and Ripken/Robinson) were inserted into packs at one in 1,513. The overall odds of getting an autograph cards were one in 574. Card backs carry a "FR" prefix.

Card	Low	High
FR1A Sean Casey A	10.00	25.00
FR1B Johnny Bench B	30.00	60.00
FR1C Sean Casey Johnny Bench	60.00	120.00
FR2A Cal Ripken A	60.00	120.00
FR2B Brooks Robinson B	15.00	40.00
FR2C Cal Ripken Brooks Robinson	150.00	250.00

2000 Bowman's Best Locker Room Collection Autographs

Randomly inserted into packs, this 19-card insert features autographed cards of top Major League prospects. Card backs carry an "LRCA" prefix. Please note that these cards were broken into two groups. Group A cards were inserted at one in 1033 packs, and Group B cards were inserted at one in 61.

Card	Low	High
LRCA1 Carlos Beltran B	6.00	15.00
LRCA2 Rick Ankiel A	10.00	25.00
LRCA3 Vernon Wells A	6.00	15.00
LRCA4 Ruben Mateo A	4.00	10.00
LRCA5 Ben Petrick A	4.00	10.00
LRCA6 Adam Piatt A	4.00	10.00
LRCA7 Eric Munson A	4.00	10.00
LRCA8 Alfonso Soriano A	15.00	40.00
LRCA9 Kerry Wood B	10.00	25.00
LRCA10 Jack Cust A	4.00	10.00
LRCA11 Rafael Furcal A	8.00	20.00
LRCA12 Josh Hamilton A	15.00	40.00
LRCA13 Brad Penny A	6.00	15.00
LRCA14 Dee Brown A	4.00	10.00
LRCA15 Milton Bradley A	6.00	15.00
LRCA16 Ryan Anderson A	4.00	10.00
LRCA17 John Patterson A	6.00	15.00
LRCA18 Nick Johnson A	6.00	15.00
LRCA19 Peter Bergeron A	4.00	10.00

2000 Bowman's Best Locker Room Collection Bats

Randomly inserted into packs at one in 376, this 11-card insert features game-used bat cards of some of the hottest prospects in baseball. Card backs carry a "LRCL" prefix.

Card	Low	High
LRCLAP Adam Piatt	3.00	8.00
LRCLBP Ben Petrick	3.00	8.00
LRCLBP Brad Penny	4.00	10.00
LRCLCB Carlos Beltran	4.00	10.00
LRCLDB Dee Brown	3.00	8.00
LRCLEM Eric Munson	3.00	8.00
LRCLJD J.D. Drew	4.00	10.00
LRCLPB Pat Burrell	4.00	10.00
LRCLRA Rick Ankiel	6.00	15.00
LRCLRF Rafael Furcal	4.00	10.00
LRCLVW Vernon Wells	4.00	10.00

2000 Bowman's Best Locker Room Collection Jerseys

Randomly inserted into packs at one in 206, this five-card insert features swatches from actual game-used jerseys. Card backs carry a "LRCJ" prefix.

Card	Low	High
LRCJ1 Carlos Beltran	4.00	10.00
LRCJ2 Rick Ankiel	6.00	15.00
LRCJ3 Mark Quinn	3.00	8.00
LRCJ4 Ben Petrick	3.00	8.00
LRCJ5 Adam Piatt	3.00	8.00

2000 Bowman's Best Selections

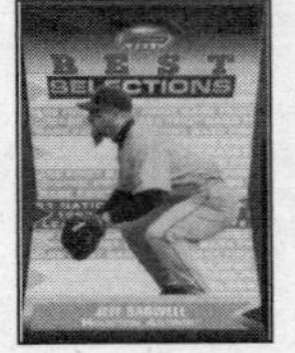

Randomly inserted into packs at one in 30, this 15-card insert features players that turned out to be outstanding draft selections. Card backs carry a "BBS" prefix.

Card	Low	High
COMPLETE SET (15)	50.00	120.00
BBS1 Alex Rodriguez	4.00	10.00
BBS2 Ken Griffey Jr.	4.00	10.00
BBS3 Pat Burrell	1.00	2.50
BBS4 Mark McGwire	6.00	15.00
BBS5 Derek Jeter	6.00	15.00
BBS6 Nomar Garciaparra	4.00	10.00
BBS7 Mike Piazza	4.00	10.00
BBS8 Josh Hamilton	2.50	6.00
BBS9 Cal Ripken	8.00	20.00
BBS10 Jeff Bagwell	1.50	4.00
BBS11 Chipper Jones	2.50	6.00
BBS12 Jose Canseco	1.50	4.00
BBS13 Carlos Beltran	1.00	2.50
BBS14 Kerry Wood	1.00	2.50
BBS15 Ben Grieve	1.00	2.50

2000 Bowman's Best Year by Year

Randomly inserted into packs at one in 23, this 10-card insert features duos that made their Major League debuts in the same year. Card backs carry a "YY" prefix.

Card	Low	High
COMPLETE SET (10)	30.00	80.00
YY1 Sammy Sosa Ken Griffey Jr.	3.00	8.00
YY2 Nomar Garciaparra Vladimir Guerrero	3.00	8.00
YY3 Alex Rodriguez Jeff Cirillo	3.00	8.00
YY4 Mike Piazza Pedro Martinez	3.00	8.00
YY5 Derek Jeter Edgardo Alfonzo	5.00	12.00
YY6 Alfonso Soriano Rick Ankiel	.75	2.00
YY7 Mark McGwire Barry Bonds	5.00	12.00
YY8 Juan Gonzalez Larry Walker	.75	2.00
YY9 Ivan Rodriguez Jeff Bagwell	1.25	3.00
YY10 Shawn Green Manny Ramirez	1.25	3.00

2001 Bowman's Best Promos

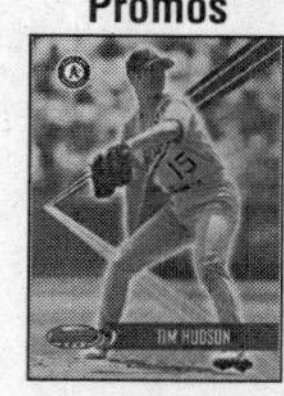

This three-card set was distributed in a sealed plastic cello wrap to dealers and hobby media a few months prior to the release of 2001 Bowman's Best to allow a sneak preview of the upcoming brand. The promos can be readily identified from base issue cards by their PP prefixed numbering on back.

COMPLETE SET (3) 2.00 5.00
PP1 Todd Helton .80 2.00
PP2 Tim Hudson .80 2.00
PP3 Vernon Wells .40 1.00

2001 Bowman's Best

This 200-card set features color action player photos printed in an all new design and leading technology. The set was distributed in five-card packs with a suggested retail price of $5 and includes 35 Rookie and 15 Exclusive Rookie cards sequentially numbered to 2,999.

COMP.SET w/o SP's (150) 20.00 50.00
COMMON CARD (1-150) .15 .40
COMMON (151-200) 2.00 5.00
1 Vladimir Guerrero .40 1.00
2 Miguel Tejada .15 .40
3 Geoff Jenkins .15 .40
4 Jeff Bagwell .25 .60
5 Todd Helton .25 .60
6 Ken Griffey Jr. .60 1.50
7 Nomar Garciaparra .60 1.50
8 Chipper Jones .40 1.00
9 Darin Erstad .15 .40
10 Frank Thomas .40 1.00
11 Jim Thome .25 .60
12 Preston Wilson .15 .40
13 Kevin Brown .15 .40
14 Derek Jeter 1.00 2.50
15 Scott Rolen .25 .60
16 Ryan Klesko .15 .40
17 Jeff Kent .15 .40
18 Raul Mondesi .15 .40
19 Greg Vaughn .15 .40
20 Bernie Williams .25 .60
21 Mike Piazza .60 1.50
22 Richard Hidalgo .15 .40
23 Dean Palmer .15 .40
24 Roberto Alomar .25 .60
25 Sammy Sosa .40 1.00
26 Randy Johnson .40 1.00
27 Manny Ramirez Sox .25 .60
28 Roger Clemens .75 2.00
29 Terrence Long .15 .40
30 Jason Kendall .15 .40
31 Richie Sexson .15 .40
32 David Wells .15 .40
33 Andruw Jones .25 .60
34 Pokey Reese .15 .40
35 Juan Gonzalez .15 .40
36 Carlos Beltran .15 .40
37 Shawn Green .15 .40
38 Mariano Rivera .40 1.00
39 John Olerud .15 .40
40 Jim Edmonds .15 .40
41 Andres Galarraga .15 .40
42 Carlos Delgado .15 .40
43 Kris Benson .15 .40
44 Andy Pettitte .25 .60
45 Jeff Cirillo .15 .40
46 Magglio Ordonez .15 .40
47 Tom Glavine .25 .60
48 Garret Anderson .15 .40
49 Cal Ripken 1.25 3.00
50 Pedro Martinez .25 .60
51 Barry Bonds 1.00 2.50
52 Alex Rodriguez .60 1.50
53 Ben Grieve .15 .40
54 Edgar Martinez .25 .60
55 Jason Giambi .15 .40
56 Jeromy Burnitz .15 .40
57 Mike Mussina .25 .60
58 Moises Alou .15 .40
59 Sean Casey .15 .40
60 Greg Maddux .60 1.50
61 Tim Hudson .15 .40
62 Mark McGwire 1.00 2.50
63 Rafael Palmeiro .25 .60
64 Tony Batista .15 .40
65 Kazuhiro Sasaki .15 .40
66 Jorge Posada .25 .60
67 Johnny Damon .25 .60
68 Brian Giles .15 .40
69 Jose Vidro .15 .40
70 Jermaine Dye .15 .40
71 Craig Biggio .25 .60
72 Larry Walker .15 .40
73 Eric Chavez .15 .40
74 David Segui .15 .40
75 Tim Salmon .25 .60
76 Javy Lopez .15 .40
77 Paul Konerko .15 .40
78 Barry Larkin .25 .60
79 Mike Hampton .15 .40
80 Bobby Higginson .15 .40
81 Mark Mulder .15 .40
82 Pat Burrell .15 .40
83 Kerry Wood .15 .40
84 J.T. Snow .15 .40
85 Ivan Rodriguez .25 .60
86 Edgardo Alfonzo .15 .40
87 Orlando Hernandez .15 .40
88 Gary Sheffield .15 .40
89 Mike Sweeney .15 .40
90 Carlos Lee .15 .40
91 Rafael Furcal .15 .40
92 Troy Glaus .15 .40
93 Bartolo Colon .15 .40
94 Cliff Floyd .15 .40
95 Barry Zito .25 .60
96 J.D. Drew .15 .40
97 Eric Karros .15 .40
98 Jose Valentin .15 .40
99 Ellis Burks .15 .40
100 David Justice .15 .40
101 Larry Barnes .15 .40
102 Rod Barajas .15 .40
103 Tony Pena Jr. .15 .40
104 Jerry Hairston Jr. .15 .40
105 Keith Ginter .15 .40
106 Corey Patterson .15 .40
107 Aaron Rowand .15 .40
108 Miguel Olivo .15 .40
109 Gookie Dawkins .15 .40
110 C.C. Sabathia .15 .40
111 Ben Petrick .15 .40
112 Eric Munson .15 .40
113 Ramon Castro .15 .40
114 Alex Escobar .15 .40
115 Josh Hamilton .30 .75
116 Jason Marquis .15 .40
117 Ben Davis .15 .40
118 Alex Cintron .15 .40
119 Julio Zuleta .15 .40
120 Ben Broussard .15 .40
121 Adam Everett .15 .40
122 Ramon Carvajal RC .15 .40
123 Felipe Lopez .15 .40
124 Alfonso Soriano .25 .60
125 Jayson Werth .15 .40
126 Donzell McDonald .15 .40
127 Jason Hart .15 .40
128 Joe Crede .40 1.00
129 Sean Burroughs .15 .40
130 Jack Cust .15 .40
131 Corey Smith .15 .40
132 Adrian Gonzalez .15 .40
133 J.R. House .15 .40
134 Steve Lomasney .15 .40
135 Tim Raines Jr. .15 .40
136 Tony Alvarez .15 .40
137 Doug Mientkiewicz .15 .40
138 Rocco Baldelli .15 .40
139 Jason Romano .15 .40
140 Vernon Wells .15 .40
141 Mike Bynum .15 .40
142 Xavier Nady .15 .40
143 Brad Wilkerson .15 .40
144 Ben Diggins .15 .40
145 Aubrey Huff .15 .40
146 Eric Byrnes .15 .40
147 Alex Gordon .15 .40
148 Roy Oswalt .40 1.00
149 Brian Esposito .15 .40
150 Scott Seabol .15 .40
151 Erick Almonte RC 2.00 5.00
152 Gary Johnson RC 2.00 5.00
153 Pedro Liriano RC 2.00 5.00
154 Matt White RC 2.00 5.00
155 Luis Montanez RC 2.50 6.00
156 Brad Cresse 2.00 5.00
157 Wilson Betemit RC 3.00 8.00
158 Octavio Martinez RC 2.00 5.00
159 Adam Pettyjohn RC 2.00 5.00
160 Corey Spencer RC 2.00 5.00
161 Mark Burnett RC 2.00 5.00
162 Ichiro Suzuki RC 25.00 50.00
163 Alexis Gomez RC 2.00 5.00
164 Greg Nash RC 2.00 5.00
165 Roberto Miniel RC 2.00 5.00
166 Justin Morneau RC 20.00 40.00
167 Ben Washburn RC 2.00 5.00
168 Bob Keppel RC 2.00 5.00
169 Deivi Mendez RC 2.00 5.00
170 Tsuyoshi Shinjo RC 3.00 8.00
171 Jared Abruzzo RC 2.00 5.00
172 Derrick Van Dusen RC 2.00 5.00
173 Hee Seop Choi RC 3.00 8.00
174 Albert Pujols RC 125.00 250.00
175 Travis Hafner RC 15.00 30.00
176 Ron Davenport RC 2.00 5.00
177 Luis Torres RC 2.00 5.00
178 Jake Peavy RC 10.00 25.00
179 Elvis Corporan RC 2.00 5.00
180 Dave Krynzel 2.00 5.00
181 Tony Blanco RC 2.00 5.00
182 Elpidio Guzman RC 2.00 5.00
183 Matt Butler RC 2.00 5.00
184 Joe Thurston RC 2.00 5.00
185 Andy Beal RC 2.00 5.00
186 Kevin Nulton RC 2.00 5.00
187 Sneideer Santos RC 2.00 5.00
188 Joe Dillon RC 2.00 5.00
189 Jeremy Blevins RC 2.00 5.00
190 Chris Amador RC 2.00 5.00
191 Mark Hendrickson RC 2.00 5.00
192 Willy Aybar RC 2.00 5.00
193 Antoine Cameron RC 2.00 5.00
194 J.J. Johnson RC 2.00 5.00
195 Ryan Ketchner RC 2.00 5.00
196 Bjorn Ivy RC 2.00 5.00
197 Josh Kroeger RC 2.00 5.00
198 Ty Wigginton RC 3.00 8.00
199 Stubby Clapp RC 2.00 5.00
200 Jerrod Riggan RC 2.00 5.00

2001 Bowman's Best Autographs

Randomly inserted in packs at the rate of one in 95, this seven-card set features autographed photos of top players.

BBAAG Adrian Gonzalez 6.00 15.00
BBABC Brad Cresse 4.00 10.00
BBAJH Josh Hamilton 20.00 50.00
BBAJR Jon Rauch 4.00 10.00
BBAJRH J.R. House 4.00 10.00
BBASB Sean Burroughs 4.00 10.00
BBATL Terrence Long 4.00 10.00

2001 Bowman's Best Exclusive Autographs

Randomly inserted in packs at the rate of one in 50, this nine-card set features autographed player photos. Stubby Clapp was an exchange card.

BBEABI Bjorn Ivy 3.00 8.00
BBEAJB Jeremy Blevins 3.00 8.00
BBEAJJ J.J. Johnson 3.00 8.00
BBEAJR Jerrod Riggan 3.00 8.00
BBEAMH M. Hendrickson 3.00 8.00
BBEASC Stubby Clapp 3.00 8.00
BBEASS Sneideer Santos 3.00 8.00
BBEATW Ty Wigginton 4.00 10.00
BBEAWA Willy Aybar 3.00 8.00

2001 Bowman's Best Franchise Favorites

Randomly inserted in packs at the rate of one in 16, this nine-card set features color photos of past and present players that are franchise favorites.

COMPLETE SET (9) 20.00 50.00
FFAR Alex Rodriguez 3.00 8.00
FFDE Darin Erstad 1.50 4.00
FFDM Don Mattingly 5.00 12.00
FFDW Dave Winfield 1.50 4.00
FFEJ Darin Erstad 1.50 4.00
Reggie Jackson
FFMW Don Mattingly 5.00 12.00
Dave Winfield
FFNR Nolan Ryan 5.00 12.00
FFRJ Reggie Jackson 1.50 4.00
FFRR Nolan Ryan 5.00 12.00
Alex Rodriguez

2001 Bowman's Best Franchise Favorites Autographs

Randomly inserted in packs, this nine-card set is an autographed parallel version of the regular insert set.

FFAAR Alex Rodriguez 60.00 120.00
FFADE Darin Erstad 6.00 15.00
FFADM Don Mattingly 30.00 60.00
FFADW Dave Winfield 10.00 25.00
FFAEJ Darin Erstad 40.00 80.00
Reggie Jackson
FFAMW Don Mattingly 125.00 200.00
Dave Winfield
FFANR Nolan Ryan 50.00 100.00
FFARJ Reggie Jackson 15.00 40.00
FFARR Nolan Ryan 250.00 400.00
Alex Rodriguez

2001 Bowman's Best Franchise Favorites Relics

Randomly inserted in packs at the rate of one in 58, this 12-card set features color player photos of franchise favorites along with memorabilia pieces.

FFRAR Alex Rodriguez 10.00 25.00
Jsy
FFRBB Craig Biggio Uni 15.00 40.00
Jeff Bagwell Uni
FFRCB Craig Biggio 6.00 15.00
Uni
FFRDE Darin Erstad Jsy 4.00 10.00
FFRDM Don Mattingly 15.00 40.00
Jsy
FFRDW Dave Winfield Jsy 4.00 10.00
FFREJ Darin Erstad Jsy 15.00 40.00
Reggie Jackson Jsy
FFRJB Jeff Bagwell 6.00 15.00
Uni
FFRMW Don Mattingly Jsy 50.00 100.00
Dave Winfield Jsy
FFRNR Nolan Ryan Jsy 20.00 50.00
FFRRJ Reggie Jackson 6.00 15.00
Jsy
FFRRR Nolan Ryan Jsy 40.00 80.00
Alex Rodriguez Jsy

2001 Bowman's Best Franchise Futures

Randomly inserted into packs at the rate of one in 24, this 12-card set displays color photos of top young players.

COMPLETE SET (12) 12.50 30.00
FF1 Josh Hamilton 1.50 4.00
FF2 Wes Helms .75 2.00
FF3 Alfonso Soriano .75 2.00
FF4 Nick Johnson .75 2.00
FF5 Jose Ortiz .75 2.00
FF6 Ben Sheets .75 2.00
FF7 Sean Burroughs .75 2.00
FF8 Ben Petrick .75 2.00
FF9 Corey Patterson .75 2.00
FF10 J.R. House .75 2.00
FF11 Alex Escobar .75 2.00
FF12 Travis Hafner 2.50 6.00

2001 Bowman's Best Impact Players

Randomly inserted in packs at the rate of one in seven, this 20-card set features color action photos of top players who have made their mark on the game.

COMPLETE SET (20) 12.50 30.00
IP1 Mark McGwire 2.00 5.00
IP2 Sammy Sosa .75 2.00
IP3 Manny Ramirez .50 1.25
IP4 Troy Glaus .40 1.00
IP5 Ken Griffey Jr. 1.25 3.00
IP6 Gary Sheffield .40 1.00
IP7 Vladimir Guerrero .75 2.00
IP8 Carlos Delgado .40 1.00
IP9 Jason Giambi .40 1.00
IP10 Frank Thomas .75 2.00
IP11 Vernon Wells .40 1.00
IP12 Carlos Pena .40 1.00
IP13 Joe Crede .75 2.00
IP14 Keith Ginter .40 1.00
IP15 Aubrey Huff .40 1.00
IP16 Brad Cresse .40 1.00
IP17 Austin Kearns .40 1.00
IP18 Nick Johnson .40 1.00
IP19 Josh Hamilton .75 2.00
IP20 Corey Patterson .40 1.00

2001 Bowman's Best Locker Room Collection Jerseys

Randomly inserted in packs at the rate of one in 133, this five-card set features color player photos with swatches of jerseys embedded in the cards and carry the "LRCL" prefix.

LRCJEC Eric Chavez 4.00 10.00
LRCJJP Jay Payton 3.00 8.00
LRCJMM Mark Mulder 4.00 10.00
LRCJPR Pokey Reese 3.00 8.00
LRCJPW Preston Wilson 4.00 10.00

2001 Bowman's Best Locker Room Collection Lumber

Randomly inserted in packs at the rate of one in 267, this five-card set features color player photos with pieces of actual bats embedded in the cards and carry the "LRCL" prefix.

LRCLAG Adrian Gonzalez 3.00 8.00
LRCLCP Corey Patterson 3.00 8.00
LRCLEM Eric Munson 3.00 8.00
LRCLPB Pat Burrell 4.00 10.00
LRCLSB Sean Burroughs 3.00 8.00

2001 Bowman's Best Rookie Fever

Randomly inserted in packs at the rate of one in 10, this 10-card set features color photos of top players during their rookie year. Card backs display the "RF" prefix.

COMPLETE SET (10) 6.00 15.00
RF1 Chipper Jones .60 1.50
RF2 Preston Wilson .40 1.00
RF3 Todd Helton .40 1.00
RF4 Jay Payton .40 1.00
RF5 Ivan Rodriguez .40 1.00
RF6 Manny Ramirez .40 1.00
RF7 Derek Jeter 1.50 4.00
RF8 Orlando Hernandez .40 1.00
RF9 Mark Quinn .40 1.00
RF10 Terrence Long .40 1.00

2002 Bowman's Best

This 181 card set was released in August, 2002. The set was issued in five card packs which were issued 10 packs to a box and 10 boxes to a case with an SRP of $15. The first 90 cards of the set featured veteran players while cards 91 through 181 featured prospects or rookies along with either an autograph or a game-used bat piece of the featured player. The higher numbered cards were issued in different seeding ratios and we have notated the group the player belongs to next to their name in our checklist. Card number 181 features Kaz Ishii and was issued as an exchange card which could be redeemed until December 31, 2002.

COMP.SET w/o SP's (90) 40.00 100.00
COMMON CARD (1-90) .30 .75
COMMON AUTO A (91-180) 3.00 8.00
AUTO GROUP A ODDS 1:3
COMMON AUTO B (91-180) 4.00 10.00
AUTO GROUP B ODDS 1:19
COMMON BAT (91-180) 2.00 5.00
91-180 BAT STATED ODDS 1:5
181 ISHII BAT EXCHANGE ODDS 1:131
1 Josh Beckett .30 .75
2 Derek Jeter 2.00 5.00
3 Alex Rodriguez 1.25 3.00
4 Miguel Tejada .30 .75
5 Nomar Garciaparra 1.25 3.00
6 Aramis Ramirez .30 .75
7 Jeremy Giambi .30 .75
8 Bernie Williams .50 1.25
9 Juan Pierre .30 .75
10 Chipper Jones .75 2.00
11 Jimmy Rollins .30 .75
12 Alfonso Soriano .30 .75
13 Mark Prior .50 1.25
14 Paul Konerko .30 .75
15 Tim Hudson .30 .75
16 Doug Mientkiewicz .30 .75
17 Todd Helton .50 1.25
18 Moises Alou .30 .75
19 Juan Gonzalez .30 .75
20 Jorge Posada .50 1.25
21 Jeff Kent .30 .75
22 Roger Clemens 1.50 4.00
23 Phil Nevin .30 .75
24 Brian Giles .30 .75
25 Carlos Delgado .30 .75
26 Jason Giambi .30 .75
27 Vladimir Guerrero .75 2.00
28 Cliff Floyd .30 .75
29 Shea Hillenbrand .30 .75
30 Ken Griffey Jr. 1.25 3.00
31 Mike Piazza 1.25 3.00
32 Carlos Pena .30 .75
33 Larry Walker .30 .75
34 Magglio Ordonez .30 .75
35 Mike Mussina .50 1.25
36 Andruw Jones .50 1.25
37 Nick Johnson .30 .75
38 Curt Schilling .30 .75
39 Eric Chavez .30 .75
40 Bartolo Colon .30 .75
41 Eric Hinske .30 .75
42 Sean Burroughs .30 .75
43 Randy Johnson .75 2.00
44 Adam Dunn .30 .75
45 Pedro Martinez .50 1.25
46 Garret Anderson .30 .75
47 Jim Thome .50 1.25
48 Gary Sheffield .30 .75
49 Tsuyoshi Shinjo .30 .75
50 Albert Pujols 1.50 4.00
51 Ichiro Suzuki 1.50 4.00
52 C.C. Sabathia .30 .75
53 Bobby Abreu .30 .75
54 Ivan Rodriguez .50 1.25
55 J.D. Drew .30 .75
56 Jacque Jones .30 .75
57 Jason Kendall .30 .75
58 Javier Vazquez .30 .75
59 Jeff Bagwell .50 1.25
60 Greg Maddux 1.25 3.00
61 Jim Edmonds .30 .75
62 Hank Blalock .50 1.25
63 Jose Vidro .30 .75
64 Kevin Brown .30 .75
65 Mark Teixeira .75 2.00
66 Sammy Sosa .75 2.00
67 Lance Berkman .30 .75
68 Mark Mulder .30 .75
69 Marty Cordova .30 .75
70 Frank Thomas .75 2.00
71 Mike Cameron .30 .75
72 Mike Sweeney .30 .75
73 Barry Bonds 2.00 5.00
74 Troy Glaus .30 .75
75 Barry Zito .30 .75
76 Pat Burrell .30 .75
77 Paul LoDuca .30 .75
78 Rafael Palmeiro .50 1.25
79 Austin Kearns .30 .75
80 Darin Erstad .30 .75
81 Richie Sexson .30 .75
82 Roberto Alomar .50 1.25
83 Roy Oswalt .30 .75
84 Ryan Klesko .30 .75
85 Luis Gonzalez .30 .75
86 Scott Rolen .50 1.25
87 Shannon Stewart .30 .75
88 Shawn Green .30 .75
89 Toby Hall .30 .75
90 Bret Boone .30 .75
91 Casey Kotchman Bat RC 3.00 8.00
92 Jose Valverde AU A RC 3.00 8.00
93 Cole Barthel Bat RC 2.00 5.00
94 Brad Nelson AU A RC 3.00 8.00
95 Mauricio Lara AU A RC 3.00 8.00
96 Ryan Gripp Bat RC 2.00 5.00
97 Brian West AU A RC 3.00 8.00
98 Chris Piersoll AU B RC 4.00 10.00
99 Ryan Church AU B RC 6.00 15.00
100 Javier Colina AU A 3.00 8.00
101 Juan M. Gonzalez AU A RC 3.00 8.00
102 Benito Baez AU A 3.00 8.00
103 Mike Hill Bat RC 2.00 5.00
104 Jason Grove AU B RC 4.00 10.00
105 Koyie Hill AU B 4.00 10.00
106 Mark Outlaw AU A RC 3.00 8.00
107 Jason Bay Bat RC 6.00 15.00
108 Jorge Padilla AU A RC 3.00 8.00
109 Pete Zamora AU A RC 3.00 8.00
110 Joe Mauer AU A RC 40.00 80.00
111 Franklyn German AU A RC 3.00 8.00
112 Chris Flinn AU A RC 3.00 8.00
113 David Wright Bat RC 50.00 80.00
114 An. Martinez AU A RC 3.00 8.00
115 Nic Jackson Bat RC 2.00 5.00
116 Rene Reyes AU A RC 3.00 8.00
117 Colin Young AU A RC 3.00 8.00
118 Joe Orloski AU A RC 3.00 8.00
119 Mike Wilson AU A RC 3.00 8.00
120 Rich Thompson AU A RC 3.00 8.00
121 Jake Mauer AU B RC 4.00 10.00
122 Mario Ramos AU A RC 3.00 8.00
123 Doug Sessions AU B RC 4.00 10.00
124 Doug Devore Bat RC 2.00 5.00
125 Travis Foley AU A RC 3.00 8.00
126 Chris Baker AU A RC 3.00 8.00
127 Michael Floyd AU A RC 3.00 8.00
128 Josh Barfield Bat RC 4.00 10.00
129 Jose Bautista Bat RC 3.00 8.00
130 Gavin Floyd AU A RC 6.00 15.00
131 Jason Botts Bat RC 2.00 5.00
132 Clint Nageotte AU A RC 4.00 10.00
133 Jesus Cota AU B RC 4.00 10.00
134 Ron Calloway Bat RC 2.00 5.00
135 Kevin Cash Bat RC 2.00 5.00
136 Jonny Gomes AU B RC 10.00 25.00
137 Dennis Ulacia AU A RC 3.00 8.00
138 Ryan Snare AU A RC 3.00 8.00
139 Kevin Deaton AU A RC 3.00 8.00
140 Bobby Jenks AU B RC 6.00 15.00
141 Casey Kotchman AU A RC 6.00 15.00
142 Adam Walker AU A RC 3.00 8.00
143 Mike Gonzalez AU A RC 3.00 8.00
144 Ruben Gotay Bat RC 3.00 8.00
145 Jason Grove Bat RC 2.00 5.00
146 Freddy Sanchez AU B RC 12.50 30.00
147 Jason Arnold AU B RC 4.00 10.00
148 Scott Hairston AU A RC 4.00 10.00
149 Jason St. Clair AU B RC 4.00 10.00
150 Chris Tritle Bat RC 2.00 5.00
151 Edwin Yan Bat RC 2.00 5.00
152 Freddy Sanchez Bat RC 5.00 12.00
153 Greg Sain Bat RC 2.00 5.00
154 Yurendell De Caster Bat RC 2.00 5.00
155 Noochie Varner Bat RC 2.00 5.00
156 Nelson Castro AU B RC 4.00 10.00
157 Randall Shelley Bat RC 2.00 5.00
158 Reed Johnson Bat RC 3.00 8.00
159 Ryan Raburn AU A RC 3.00 8.00
160 Jose Morban Bat RC 2.00 5.00
161 Justin Schuda AU A RC 3.00 8.00

162 Henry Pichardo AU A RC 3.00 8.00
163 Josh Bard AU A RC 3.00 8.00
164 Josh Bonifay AU A RC 3.00 8.00
165 Brandon League AU B RC 4.00 10.00
166 Jorge-Julio DePaula AU A RC 3.00 8.00
167 Todd Linden AU B RC 6.00 15.00
168 Francisco Liriano AU A RC 60.00 120.00
169 Chris Snelling AU A RC 5.00 12.00
170 Blake McGinley AU A RC 3.00 8.00
171 Cody McKay AU A RC 3.00 8.00
172 Jason Stanford AU A RC 3.00 8.00
173 Lenny Dinardo AU A RC 3.00 8.00
174 Greg Montalbano AU A RC 3.00 8.00
175 Earl Snyder AU A RC 3.00 8.00
176 Justin Huber AU A RC 6.00 15.00
177 Chris Narveson AU A RC 3.00 8.00
178 Jon Switzer AU A RC 3.00 8.00
179 Ronald Acuna AU A RC 3.00 8.00
180 Chris Duffy Bat RC 3.00 8.00
181 Kazuhisa Ishii Bat RC 3.00 8.00

2002 Bowman's Best Blue

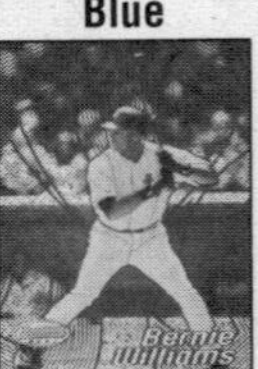

This 181 card set is a parallel of the regular Bowman's Best set. These cards were seeded into packs at different rates which we have notated. These card can be differentiated by their "blue" coloring. Cards numbered from 1 through 90 were issued to a stated print run of 300 serial numbered sets. Card number 181 features Kaz Ishii and was issued as an exchange card which could be redeemed until December 31, 2002.

*BLUE 1-90: 1X TO 2.5X BASIC
1-90 STATED ODDS 1:6
1-90 PRINT RUN 300 SERIAL #'d SETS
*BLUE AUTO: .4X TO 1X BASIC AU A
*BLUE AUTO: .3X TO .8X BASIC AU B
AUTO STATED ODDS 1:6
*BLUE BAT: .4X TO 1X BASIC BAT
BAT STATED ODDS 1:14
ISHII BAT EXCHANGE ODDS 1:335
ISHII BAT EXCHANGE DEADLINE 12/31/02
BLUE BATS FEATURE TEAM LOGOS!
110 Joe Mauer AU 50.00 100.00
113 David Wright Bat 50.00 80.00
140 Bobby Jenks AU 6.00 15.00
168 Francisco Liriano AU 75.00 150.00
181 Kazuhisa Ishii Bat 3.00 8.00

2002 Bowman's Best Gold

This 181 card set is a parallel of the regular Bowman's Best set. These cards were seeded into packs at different rates which we have notated. These card can be differentiated by their "gold" coloring. Cards numbered from 1 through 90 were limited to a stated print run of 50 serial numbered sets. Card number 181 features Kaz Ishii and was issued as an exchange card which could be redeemed until December 31, 2002.

*GOLD 1-90: 3X TO 8X BASIC
1-90 STATED ODDS 1:31
1-90 PRINT RUN 50 SERIAL #'d SETS
*GOLD AUTO: 1X TO 2.5X BASIC AU A
*GOLD AUTO: .75X TO 2X BASIC AU B
GOLD AUTO STATED ODDS 1:51
*GOLD BAT: 1X TO 2.5X BASIC BAT
GOLD BAT STATED ODDS 1:115
ISHII BAT EXCHANGE ODDS 1:3444
ISHII BAT EXCHANGE DEADLINE 12/31/02
GOLD BATS FEATURE FACSIMILE AUTOS!
113 David Wright Bat 150.00 250.00
168 Francisco Liriano AU 300.00 600.00
181 Kazuhisa Ishii Bat 8.00 20.00

2002 Bowman's Best Red

This 181 card set is a parallel of the regular Bowman's Best set. These cards were seeded into packs at different rates which we have notated. These card can be differentiated by their "red" coloring. Cards numbered from 1 through 90 were limited to a stated print run of 200 serial numbered sets. Card number 181 features Kaz Ishii and was issued as an exchange card which could be redeemed until December 31, 2002.

*RED 1-90: 1.25X TO 3X BASIC
1-90 PRINT RUN 200 SERIAL #'d SETS
*RED AUTO: .6X TO 1.5X BASIC AU A
*RED AUTO: .5X TO 1.2X BASIC AU B
AUTO STATED ODDS 1:17
*RED BATS: .6X TO 1.5X BASIC BATS
BAT STATED ODDS 1:39
ISHII BAT EXCHANGE ODDS 1:1117
ISHII BAT EXCHANGE DEADLINE 12/31/02
RED BATS FEATURE STATISTICS!
113 David Wright Bat 60.00 120.00
168 Francisco Liriano AU 100.00 200.00
181 Kazuhisa Ishii Bat 5.00 12.00

2002 Bowman's Best Uncirculated

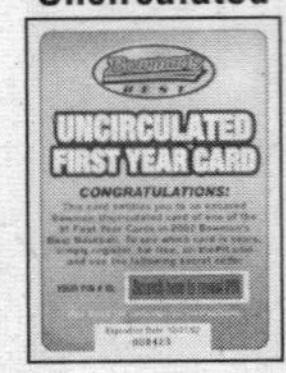

Ninety-one different scratch-off redemption cards were inserted into packs at overall odds of one in 92. Once the cards were scratched, a code number was revealed whereby collectors could enter the code at the Topps website to reveal which specific player they had won the rights to. The actual "Uncirculated" cards were straight parallels of the basic Bowman's Best autographed rookie cards - except these were sealed inside a hard plastic case of which was affixed with a tamper-proof Topps holographic logo. These cards were printed to a stated print run of 20 sets and there is no pricing provided due to scarcity. The deadline to redeem the cards was December 31st, 2002.

COMMON EXCH
AU STATED ODDS 1:129
BAT STATED ODDS 1:322
OVERALL STATED ODDS 1:92

2003 Bowman's Best

This 130 card set was released in September, 2003. This set was issued in five card packs which contained an autograph card. Each of these packs had an SRP of $15 and these packs were issued 10 to a box and 10 boxes to a case. This set was designed to be checklisted alphabetically as no numbering was used for this set. The first year cards which are autographed have the lettering FY AU RC after their name in the checklist. A few first year players had some cards issued with an bat piece included. Those bat cards were issued one per box-loader pack. In addition, high draft pick Bryan Bullington signed some of the actual boxes and those boxes were issued at a stated rate of one in 106.

COMP.SET w/o SP's (50) 15.00 40.00
COMMON CARD .40 1.00
COMMON AUTO 3.00 8.00
COMMON BAT 1.50 4.00
AB Andrew Brown FY AU RC 4.00 10.00
AK Austin Kearns .40 1.00
AM Aneudis Mateo FY AU RC 3.00 8.00
AP Albert Pujols 1.25 3.00
AR Alex Rodriguez 1.00 2.50
AS Alfonso Soriano .40 1.00
AW Aron Weston FY AU RC 3.00 8.00
BB Bryan Bullington FY AU RC 3.00 8.00
BC Bernie Castro FY RC .40 1.00
BFL Br. Florence FY AU RC 3.00 8.00
BFR Ben Francisco FY AU RC 3.00 8.00
BH Brendan Harris FY AU RC 4.00 10.00
BJH Bo Hart FY RC .40 1.00
BK Beau Kemp FY AU RC 3.00 8.00
BLB Barry Bonds 1.50 4.00
BM Brian McCann FY AU RC 20.00 50.00
BSG Brian Giles .40 1.00
BWB Bobby Basham FY AU RC 3.00 8.00
BZ Barry Zito .40 1.00
CAD Carlos Duran FY AU RC 3.00 8.00
CDC C. De La Cruz FY AU RC 3.00 8.00
CJ Chipper Jones .60 1.50
CJW C.J. Wilson FY AU 3.00 8.00
CM Charlie Manning FY AU RC 3.00 8.00
CMS Curt Schilling .40 1.00
CS Cory Stewart FY AU RC 3.00 8.00
CSS Corey Shafer FY AU RC 3.00 8.00
CW Chien-Ming Wang FY RC 5.00 12.00
CWA Chien-Ming Wang FY AU 150.00 250.00
DAM D. Moseley FY AU RC 3.00 8.00
DC David Cash FY AU RC 3.00 8.00
DH Dan Haren FY AU RC 10.00 25.00
DJ Derek Jeter 1.50 4.00
DM David Martinez FY AU RC 3.00 8.00
DMM D. McGowan FY AU RC 4.00 10.00
DR Darrell Rasner FY AU RC 3.00 8.00
DW Doug Waechter FY AU RC 4.00 10.00
DY Dustin Yount FY RC .60 1.50
ERA El. Ramirez FY AU RC 4.00 10.00
ERI Eric Riggs FY AU RC 4.00 10.00
ET Eider Torres FY AU RC 3.00 8.00
FP Felix Pie FY AU RC 12.50 30.00
FS Felix Sanchez FY AU RC 3.00 8.00
FT Ferdin Tejeda FY AU RC 3.00 8.00
GA Greg Aquino FY AU RC 3.00 8.00
GB Gregor Blanco FY AU RC 3.00 8.00
GJA Garret Anderson .40 1.00
GM Greg Maddux 1.00 2.50
GS G. Schneidmiller FY AU RC 3.00 8.00
HR Hanley Ramirez FY AU RC 60.00 120.00
HRB Hanley Ramirez FY Bat 10.00 25.00
HT Haj Turay FY RC .40 1.00
IS Ichiro Suzuki 1.25 3.00
JB Jeremy Bonderman FY RC 1.50 4.00
JC Jose Contreras FY RC .60 1.50
JDD J.D. Durbin FY AU RC 3.00 8.00
JFK Jeff Kent .40 1.00
JG Joey Gomes FY AU RC 3.00 8.00
JGB Joey Gomes FY Bat 1.50 4.00
JGG Jason Giambi .40 1.00
JK Jason Kubel FY AU RC 10.00 25.00
JKB Jason Kubel FY Bat 2.50 6.00
JLB Jaime Bubela FY AU RC 3.00 8.00
JM Jose Morales FY AU RC 3.00 8.00
JMS Jon-Mark Sprowl FY RC .40 1.00
JRG Jeremy Griffiths FY AU RC 3.00 8.00
JT Jim Thome .40 1.00
JV Joe Valentine FY AU RC 3.00 8.00
JW Josh Willingham FY AU RC 10.00 25.00
KBS Kelly Shoppach FY Bat 2.00 5.00
KG Ken Griffey Jr. 1.00 2.50
KJ Kade Johnson FY AU RC 3.00 8.00
KS Kelly Shoppach FY AU RC 4.00 10.00
KY Kevin Youkilis FY AU RC 12.50 30.00
KYE Kevin Youkilis FY Bat 6.00 15.00
LB Lance Berkman .40 1.00
LF Lew Ford FY AU RC 4.00 10.00
LFJ Lew Ford FY Bat 2.00 5.00
LW Larry Walker .40 1.00
MB Matt Bruback FY RC .40 1.00
MD Matt Diaz FY RC .75 2.00
MDA Matt Diaz FY AU 4.00 10.00
MDH Matt Hensley FY AU RC 3.00 8.00
MDM Mark Malaska FY AU RC 3.00 8.00
MH Mi. Hernandez FY AU RC 3.00 8.00
MHI Mi. Hinckley FY AU RC 4.00 10.00
MJP Mike Piazza 1.00 2.50
MK Matt Kata FY AU RC 3.00 8.00
MNH Matt Hagen FY AU RC 3.00 8.00
MO Mike O'Keefe FY RC .40 1.00
MOR Magglio Ordonez .40 1.00
MP Mark Prior .40 1.00
MR Manny Ramirez .40 1.00
MS Mike Sweeney .40 1.00
MT Miguel Tejada .40 1.00
NG Nomar Garciaparra 1.00 2.50
NL Nook Logan FY AU RC 4.00 10.00
OC Ozzie Chavez FY AU RC 3.00 8.00
PB Pat Burrell .40 1.00
PL Pete LaForest FY AU RC 3.00 8.00
PM Pedro Martinez .40 1.00
PR Prentice Redman FY AU RC 3.00 8.00
RC Ryan Cameron FY AU RC 3.00 8.00
RD Rajai Davis FY AU RC 3.00 8.00
RH Ryan Howard FY AU RC 125.00 250.00
RHJ Ryan Howard FY Bat 30.00 60.00
RJ Randy Johnson .60 1.50
RLD Rajai Davis FY Bat 1.50 4.00
RM R. Nivar-Martinez FY RC .40 1.00
RS Ryan Shealy FY AU RC 12.50 30.00
RSB Ryan Shealy FY Bat 5.00 12.00
RWH Rob. Hammock FY AU RC 3.00 8.00
SG Shawn Green .40 1.00
SS Sammy Sosa .60 1.50
ST Scott Tyler FY AU RC 4.00 10.00
SV Shane Victorino FY RC 1.50 4.00
TA Tyler Adamczyk FY AU RC 3.00 8.00
TH Todd Helton .40 1.00
TI Travis Ishikawa FY AU RC 4.00 10.00
TJ Tyler Johnson FY AU RC 3.00 8.00
TJB T.J. Bohn FY RC .40 1.00
TKH Torii Hunter .40 1.00
TO Tim Olson FY AU RC 3.00 8.00
TS T.Story-Harden FY AU RC 3.00 8.00
TSB T.Story-Harden FY Bat 1.50 4.00
TT Terry Tiffee FY RC .40 1.00
VG Vladimir Guerrero .60 1.50
WE Willie Eyre FY AU RC 3.00 8.00
WL Wil Ledezma FY AU RC 3.00 8.00
WRC Roger Clemens 1.25 3.00
NNO Bryan Bullington Opened Box AU 10.00 25.00
NNO Bryan Bullington Sealed Box AU

2003 Bowman's Best Blue

*BLUE: 1.5X TO 4X BASIC
*BLUE FY: 3X TO 8X BASIC FY
BLUE STATED ODDS 1:28
BLUE PRINT RUN 100 SERIAL #'d SETS
*BLUE AUTO: 1X TO 2.5X BASIC AUTO
BLUE AUTO ODDS 1:32
BLUE AUTO PRINT RUN 50 SETS
BLUE AUTO'S NOT SERIAL-NUMBERED
BLUE AU PRINT RUNS PROVIDED BY TOPPS
*BLUE BAT: 1X TO 2.5X BASIC FY BAT
BLUE BAT ODDS 1:22 BOXLOADER PACKS
BLUE BAT PRINT RUN 50 SETS
BLUE BATS NOT SERIAL-NUMBERED
BLUE BAT PRINTS PROVIDED BY TOPPS
BM Brian McCann FY AU 50.00 100.00
CW Chien-Ming Wang FY 40.00 80.00
CWA Chien-Ming Wang FY AU 300.00 500.00
DH Dan Haren FY AU 50.00 100.00
FP Felix Pie FY AU 100.00 200.00
HR Hanley Ramirez FY AU 400.00 475.00
KY Kevin Youkilis FY AU 30.00 60.00
RH Ryan Howard FY AU 600.00 900.00
RHJ Ryan Howard FY Bat 150.00 300.00

2003 Bowman's Best Red

*RED: 3X TO 8X BASIC RED
*RED FY: 4X TO 10X BASIC FY
RED STATED ODDS 1:55

RED STATED PRINT RUN 50 SERIAL #'d SETS
RED AUTO ODDS 1:63
RED AUTO PRINT RUN 25 SETS
RED AU PRINT RUNS PROVIDED BY TOPPS
RED AUTOS NOT SERIAL-NUMBERED
NO RED AUTO PRICING DUE TO SCARCITY
RED BAT ODDS 1:44 BOXLOADER PACKS
RED BAT PRINT RUN 25 SETS
RED BAT PRINT RUNS PROVIDED BY TOPPS
RED BATS NOT SERIAL-NUMBERED
NO RED BAT PRICING DUE TO SCARCITY
BWB Bobby Basham FY AU
CW Chien-Ming Wang FY 75.00 150.00

2003 Bowman's Best Double Play Autographs

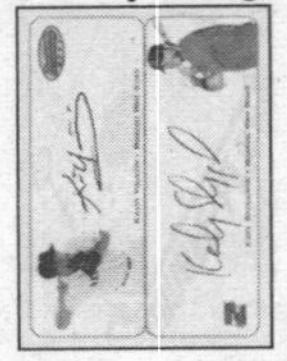

STATED ODDS 1:55
EB Elizardo Ramirez / Bryan Bullington 10.00 25.00
GK Joey Gomes / Jason Kubel 15.00 40.00
HV Dan Haren / Joe Valentine 10.00 25.00
LL Nook Logan / Wil Ledezma 6.00 15.00
RS Prentice Redman / Gary Schneidmiller 6.00 15.00
SB Corey Shafer / Gregor Blanco 6.00 15.00
SR Felix Sanchez / Darrell Rasner 6.00 15.00
YS Kevin Youkilis / Kelly Shoppach 15.00 40.00

2003 Bowman's Best Triple Play Autographs

STATED ODDS 1:219
BCS Andrew Brown / David Cash / Cory Stewart 12.50 30.00
DRS Rajai Davis / Hanley Ramirez / Ryan Shealy 30.00 60.00

2004 Bowman's Best

This 108-card set was released in September, 2004. The set was issued in five-card packs with an $15 SRP which came 10 packs to a box and 10 boxes to a case. In an interesting twist, the cards are numbered using the initials of the players instead of using a numbering system. Fifty cards in this set feature veteran players and the rest of the set features either rookie cards some of whom signed cardd for this product.

COMP.SET w/o SP'S (50) 10.00 25.00
COMMON CARD .40 1.00
COMMON RC .40 1.00
ONE AUTO PER HOBBY PACK
ONE RELIC PER BOX-LOADER PACK
ONE BOX-LOADER PACK PER HOBBY BOX
STAUFFER BOX RANDOM IN HOBBY CASES
OVERALL AU PLATE ODDS 1:391 HOBBY
AU PLATE PRINT RUN 1 SET PER COLOR
BLACK-CYAN-MAGENTA-YELLOW ISSUED
NO AU PLATE PRICING DUE TO SCARCITY
AER Alex Rodriguez 1.00 2.50
AG Adam Greenberg FY AU RC 4.00 10.00
AL Anthony Lerew FY RC .60 1.50
AO Akinori Otsuka FY RC .40 1.00
AP Albert Pujols 1.25 3.00
AS Alfonso Soriano .40 1.00
BB Bobby Brownlie FY AU RC 4.00 10.00
BEM Brandon Medders FY AU RC 3.00 8.00
BG Brian Giles .40 1.00
BMS Brad Snyder FY AU RC 4.00 10.00
BP Brayan Pena FY AU RC 3.00 8.00
BS Brad Sullivan FY AU RC 4.00 10.00
CB Carlos Beltran .40 1.00
CD Carlos Delgado .40 1.00
CJ Conor Jackson FY AU RC 10.00 25.00
CLH Chin-Lung Hu FY RC 1.00 2.50
CMA Craig Ansman FY AU RC 3.00 8.00
CMS Curt Schilling .40 1.00
CZ Charlie Zink FY AU RC 3.00 8.00
DA David Aardsma FY AU RC 4.00 10.00
DC Dave Crouthers FY AU RC 3.00 8.00
DDN Dustin Nippert FY AU RC 4.00 10.00
DG Danny Gonzalez FY RC .40 1.00
DK Donald Kelly FY AU RC 3.00 8.00
DL Donald Levinski FY AU RC 3.00 8.00
DM David Murphy FY AU RC 6.00 15.00
DN Dioner Navarro FY AU RC 4.00 10.00
DS Don Sutton FY RC 1.00 2.50
EA Erick Aybar FY AU RC 6.00 15.00
EC Eric Chavez .40 1.00
EH Estee Harris FY AU RC 4.00 10.00
ES Ervin Santana FY AU RC 10.00 25.00
FH Felix Hernandez FY AU RC 30.00 60.00
GA Garret Anderson .40 1.00
HB Hank Blalock .40 1.00
HM Hector Made FY RC .60 1.50
IR Ivan Rodriguez .40 1.00
IS Ichiro Suzuki 1.25 3.00
JA Joaquin Arias FY AU RC 6.00 10.00
JAV Jose Vidro .40 1.00
JC Juan Cedeno FY AU RC 3.00 8.00
JDS Jason Schmidt .40 1.00
JE Jesse English FY AU RC 3.00 8.00
JGG Jason Giambi .40 1.00
JH Jason Hirsh FY AU RC 10.00 25.00
JJC Jon Connolly FY RC .75 2.00
JK Jon Knott FY AU RC 3.00 8.00
JL Josh Labandeira FY AU RC 3.00 8.00
JLO Javy Lopez .40 1.00
JP Jorge Posada .40 1.00
JRG Joey Gathright FY RC .75 2.00
JS Jeff Salazar FY AU RC 4.00 10.00
JSZ Jason Szuminski FY AU RC 3.00 8.00
JT Jim Thome .40 1.00
KC Kory Casto FY AU RC 6.00 15.00
KK Kevin Kouzmanoff FY AU RC 15.00 40.00
KM Kazuo Matsui FY Uni RC 2.00 5.00
KRK Kody Kirkland FY Bat RC 2.00 5.00
KS Kyle Sleeth FY RC .60 1.50
KT Kazuhito Tadano FY Jsy RC 3.00 8.00
LK Logan Kensing FY AU RC 3.00 8.00
LM Lastings Milledge FY AU RC 12.50 30.00
LO Lyle Overbay .40 1.00
LTH Luke Hughes FY AU RC 3.00 8.00
LWJ Chipper Jones .60 1.50
MAR Manny Ramirez .40 1.00
MDC Matt Creighton FY AU RC 3.00 8.00
MG Mike Gosling FY RC .40 1.00
MJP Mike Piazza 1.00 2.50
MO Magglio Ordonez .40 1.00
MT Miguel Tejada .40 1.00
MTC Miguel Cabrera .40 1.00
MV Merkin Valdez FY AU RC 3.00 8.00
MWP Mark Prior .40 1.00
MY Michael Young .40 1.00
NAG Nomar Garciaparra 1.00 2.50
NG Nick Gorneault FY RC .60 1.50
NU Nic Ungs FY AU RC 3.00 8.00
OQ Omar Quintanilla FY AU RC 4.00 10.00
PM Paul Maholm FY AU RC 10.00 25.00
PMM Paul McAnulty FY RC .60 1.50
RB Ryan Budde FY AU RC 3.00 8.00
RC Roger Clemens 1.25 3.00
RG Rudy Guillen FY AU RC 4.00 10.00
RJ Randy Johnson .60 1.50
RN Ricky Nolasco FY AU RC 8.00 20.00
RR Ramon Ramirez FY AU RC 3.00 8.00
RS Richie Sexson .40 1.00
RT Rob Tejeda FY AU RC 6.00 15.00
SH Shawn Hill FY AU RC 3.00 8.00
SR Scott Rolen .40 1.00
SS Sammy Sosa .60 1.50
ST Shingo Takatsu FY Jsy RC 3.00 8.00
TB Travis Blackley FY Jsy RC 2.00 5.00
TD Tyler Davidson FY AU RC 4.00 10.00
TJ Terry Jones FY RC .60 1.50
TJS Tim Stauffer FY AU RC 4.00 10.00
TLH Todd Helton .40 1.00
TOH Travis Hanson FY AU RC 4.00 10.00
TRM Tom Mastny FY AU RC 3.00 8.00
TS Todd Self FY RC .60 1.50
VC Vito Chiaravalloti FY AU RC 3.00 8.00
VG Vladimir Guerrero .60 1.50
WM Warner Madrigal FY RC .60 1.50
WS Wardell Starling FY AU RC 3.00 8.00
YM Yadier Molina FY AU RC 8.00 20.00
ZD Zach Duke FY AU RC 20.00 40.00
NNO Tim Stauffer AU Box/100 10.00 25.00

2004 Bowman's Best Green

*GREEN: 1.5X TO 4X BASIC
*GREEN RC'S: 3X TO 8X BASIC RC'S
GREEN ODDS 1:18
GREEN PRINT RUN 100 SERIAL #'d SETS
*GREEN AU'S: 1X TO 2.5X BASIC AU'S
GREEN AU ODDS 1:32 HOBBY
GREEN AU PRINT RUN 50 SETS
GREEN AUTOS NOT SERIAL-NUMBERED
AUTO PRINT RUNS PROVIDED BY TOPPS
*GREEN RELICS: .75X TO 2X BASIC RELICS
GREEN RELIC ODDS 1:31 HOBBY BOXES
GREEN RELIC PRINT RUN 50 SETS
GREEN RELICS NOT SERIAL-NUMBERED
RELIC PRINT RUNS PROVIDED BY TOPPS
CJ Conor Jackson FY AU 50.00 100.00
ES Ervin Santana FY AU 30.00 60.00
FH Felix Hernandez FY AU 400.00 600.00
KK Kevin Kouzmanoff FY AU 50.00 100.00
LM Lastings Milledge FY AU 90.00 150.00
ZD Zach Duke FY AU 50.00 100.00

2004 Bowman's Best Red

*RED: 5X TO 12X BASIC
RED ODDS 1:90 HOBBY
RED PRINT RUN 20 SERIAL #'d SETS
NO RED RC PRICING DUE TO SCARCITY
RED AUTO ODDS 1:156 HOBBY
RED AU PRINT RUN 10 SETS
RED AU'S ARE NOT SERIAL-NUMBERED
PRINT RUN INFO PROVIDED BY TOPPS
NO RED AU PRICING DUE TO SCARCITY
RED RELIC ODDS 1:154 HOBBY BOXES
RED RELIC PRINT RUN 10 SETS
RED RELICS ARE NOT SERIAL-NUMBERED
PRINT RUN INFO PROVIDED BY TOPPS
NO RED RELIC PRICING DUE TO SCARCITY

2004 Bowman's Best Double Play Autographs

STATED ODDS 1:33 HOBBY
STATED PRINT RUN 236 SETS
CARDS ARE NOT SERIAL NUMBERED
PRINT RUN INFO PROVIDED BY TOPPS
CC Matt Creighton / Dave Crouthers 8.00 20.00
EN Jesse English / Ricky Nolasco 10.00 25.00
HJ Travis Hanson / Conor Jackson 10.00 25.00
MH Lastings Milledge / Estee Harris 20.00 50.00
MN Brandon Medders / Dustin Nippert 6.00 15.00
QS Omar Quintanilla / Brad Snyder 6.00 15.00
SC Tim Stauffer / Vito Chiaravalloti 6.00 15.00
SK Jeff Salazar / Jon Knott 6.00 15.00
SV Ervin Santana / Merkin Valdez 6.00 15.00
UK Nic Ungs / Kevin Kouzmanoff 12.50 30.00

2004 Bowman's Best Triple Play Autographs

STATED ODDS 1:109 HOBBY
STATED PRINT RUN 236 SETS
CARDS ARE NOT SERIAL NUMBERED
PRINT RUN INFO PROVIDED BY TOPPS
ALS David Aardsma / Donald Levinski / Brad Sullivan 10.00 25.00
CBA Juan Cedeno / Bobby Brownlie / Joaquin Arias 10.00 25.00
SSV Tim Stauffer / Ervin Santana / Merkin Valdez 15.00 40.00

2005 Bowman's Best

This 143-card set was released in September, 2005. The set was issued in five-card packs with an $10 SRP which came 10 packs to a box and 10 boxes to a case. The first 30 cards in the set feature active veterans while cards 31 through 143 feature Rookie Cards. Cards 101 through 143 are all autographed, and while most of them are Rookie Cards, a few of the cards are not Rookie Cards as the players had cards in the 31-100 grouping. Cards number 101 through 143 were issued at a stated rate of one in five hobby packs and those cards were issued to a stated print run of 974 serial numbered sets.

COMP.SET w/o SP's (100) 25.00 50.00
COMMON CARD (1-30) .20 .50
COMMON CARD (31-100) .40 1.00
COMMON AU (101-143) 3.00 8.00
OVERALL 1-100 PLATE ODDS 1:345 H
OVERALL 101-143 AU PLATE ODDS 1:805 H
PLATE PRINT RUN 1 SET PER COLOR
BLACK-CYAN-MAGENTA-YELLOW ISSUED
NO PLATE PRICING DUE TO SCARCITY
1 Jose Vidro .20 .50
2 Adam Dunn .20 .50
3 Manny Ramirez .30 .75
4 Miguel Tejada .20 .50
5 Ken Griffey Jr. .75 2.00
6 Pedro Martinez .30 .75
7 Alex Rodriguez .75 2.00
8 Ichiro Suzuki 1.00 2.50
9 Alfonso Soriano .20 .50
10 Brian Giles .20 .50
11 Roger Clemens .75 2.00
12 Todd Helton .30 .75
13 Ivan Rodriguez .30 .75
14 David Ortiz .30 .75
15 Sammy Sosa .50 1.25
16 Chipper Jones .50 1.25
17 Mark Buehrle .20 .50
18 Miguel Cabrera .30 .75
19 Johan Santana .50 1.25
20 Randy Johnson .50 1.25
21 Jim Thome .30 .75
22 Vladimir Guerrero .50 1.25
23 Dontrelle Willis .20 .50
24 Nomar Garciaparra .50 1.25
25 Barry Bonds 1.25 3.00
26 Curt Schilling .30 .75
27 Carlos Beltran .20 .50
28 Albert Pujols 1.00 2.50
29 Mark Prior .30 .75
30 Derek Jeter 1.00 2.50
31 Ryan Garko FY RC 1.25 3.00
32 Eulogio De La Cruz FY RC .40 1.00
33 Luke Scott FY RC 1.25 3.00
34 Shane Costa FY RC .40 1.00
35 Casey McGehee FY RC .40 1.00
36 Jered Weaver FY RC 5.00 12.00
37 Kevin Melillo FY RC .75 2.00
38 D.J. Houlton FY RC .40 1.00
39 Brandon Moorhead FY RC .40 1.00
40 Jerry Owens FY RC .60 1.50
41 Elliot Johnson FY RC .40 1.00
42 Kevin West FY RC .40 1.00
43 Hernan Iribarren FY RC .60 1.50
44 Miguel Montero FY RC 2.00 5.00
45 Craig Tatum FY RC .40 1.00
46 Ryan Sweeney FY RC 1.00 2.50
47 Micah Furtado FY RC .40 1.00
48 Cody Haerther FY RC .40 1.00
49 Erick Abreu FY RC .75 2.00
50 Chuck Tiffany FY RC 1.00 2.50
51 Tadahito Iguchi FY RC 1.50 4.00
52 Frank Diaz FY RC .40 1.00
53 Errol Simonitsch FY RC .60 1.50
54 Wade Robinson FY RC .40 1.00
55 Adam Boeve FY RC .40 1.00
56 Steven Bondurant FY RC .40 1.00
57 Jason Motte FY RC .40 1.00
58 Juan Senreiso FY RC .40 1.00
59 Vinny Rottino FY RC .40 1.00
60 Jai Miller FY RC .60 1.50
61 Thomas Pauly FY RC .40 1.00
62 Tony Giarratano FY RC .40 1.00
63 Alexander Smit FY RC .40 1.00
64 Keiichi Yabu FY RC .40 1.00
65 Brian Bannister FY RC 1.00 2.50
66 Kennard Bibbs FY RC .40 1.00
67 Anthony Reyes FY RC 2.00 5.00
68 Thomas Oldham FY RC .40 1.00
69 Ben Harrison FY .40 1.00
70 Daryl Thompson FY RC .40 1.00
71 Kevin Collins FY RC .40 1.00
72 Wes Swackhamer FY RC .40 1.00
73 Landon Powell FY RC .60 1.50
74 Matt Brown FY RC .40 1.00
75 Russ Martin FY RC 1.25 3.00
76 Nick Touchstone FY RC .40 1.00
77 Steven White FY RC .40 1.00
78 Ian Bladergroen FY RC .60 1.50
79 Sean Marshall FY RC 1.50 4.00
80 Nick Masset FY RC .40 1.00
81 Ryan Goleski FY RC .40 1.00
82 Matt Campbell FY RC .40 1.00
83 Manny Parra FY RC 1.00 2.50
84 Melky Cabrera FY RC 2.00 5.00
85 Ryan Feierabend FY RC .40 1.00
86 Nate McLouth FY RC .60 1.50
87 Glen Perkins FY RC .75 2.00
88 Kila Kaaihue FY RC 1.00 2.50
89 Dana Eveland FY RC .40 1.00
90 Tyler Pelland FY RC .60 1.50
91 Matt Van Der Bosch FY RC .40 1.00
92 Andy Santana FY RC .40 1.00
93 Eric Nielsen FY RC .40 1.00
94 Brendan Ryan FY RC .40 1.00
95 Ian Kinsler FY RC 3.00 8.00
96 Matthew Kemp FY RC 3.00 8.00
97 Stephen Drew FY RC 4.00 10.00
98 Peeter Ramos FY RC .40 1.00
99 Chris Seddon FY RC .40 1.00
100 Chuck James FY RC 1.50 4.00
101 Travis Chick FY AU RC 4.00 10.00
102 Justin Verlander FY AU RC 20.00 50.00
103 Billy Butler FY AU RC 20.00 50.00
104 Chris B.Young FY AU RC 35.00 60.00
105 Jake Postlewait FY AU RC 3.00 8.00
106 C.J. Smith FY AU RC 3.00 8.00
107 Mike Rodriguez FY AU RC 3.00 8.00
108 Philip Humber FY AU RC 10.00 25.00
109 Jeff Niemann FY AU RC 4.00 10.00
110 Brian Miller FY AU RC 3.00 8.00
111 Chris Vines FY AU RC 3.00 8.00
112 Andy LaRoche FY AU RC 12.50 30.00
113 Mike Bourn FY AU RC 4.00 10.00
114 Wlad Balentein FY AU RC 12.50 30.00
115 Ismael Ramirez FY AU RC 3.00 8.00
116 Hayden Penn FY AU RC 4.00 10.00
117 Pedro Lopez FY AU RC 3.00 8.00
118 Shawn Bowman FY AU RC 4.00 10.00
119 Chad Orvella FY AU RC 3.00 8.00
120 Sean Tracey FY AU RC 3.00 8.00
121 Bobby Livingston FY AU RC 3.00 8.00
122 Michael Rogers FY AU RC 3.00 8.00
123 Willy Mota FY AU RC 3.00 8.00
124 Bran McCarthy FY AU RC 10.00 25.00
125 Mike Morse FY AU RC 3.00 8.00
126 Matt Lindstrom FY AU RC 3.00 8.00
127 Brian Stavisky FY AU RC 3.00 8.00
128 Richie Gardner FY AU RC 3.00 8.00
129 Scott Mitchinson FY AU RC 3.00 8.00
130 Billy McCarthy FY AU RC 3.00 8.00
131 Brandon Sing FY AU RC 4.00 10.00
132 Matt Albers FY AU RC 4.00 10.00
133 George Kottaras FY AU RC 4.00 10.00
134 Luis Hernandez FY AU RC 3.00 8.00
135 Juan Sanchez FY AU RC 12.50 30.00
136 Buck Coats FY AU RC 3.00 8.00
137 Jon Barratt FY AU RC 3.00 8.00
138 Raul Tablado FY AU RC 3.00 8.00
139 Jake Mullinax FY AU RC 3.00 8.00
140 Edgar Varela FY AU RC 3.00 8.00
141 Ryan Garko FY AU 6.00 15.00
142 Nate McLouth FY AU 10.00 25.00
143 Shane Costa FY AU 3.00 8.00

2005 Bowman's Best Black

STATED ODDS 1:1386 HOBBY
STATED PRINT RUN 1 SERIAL #'d SET
NO PRICING DUE TO SCARCITY

2005 Bowman's Best Blue

*BLUE 1-30: 1.25X TO 3X BASIC
*BLUE 31-100: .6X TO 1.5X BASIC
1-100 ODDS 1:4 HOBBY
1-100 PRINT RUN 499 #'d SETS
*BLUE AU 101-143: .5X TO 1.2X BASIC
AU 101-143 PRINT RUN 299 #'d SETS
AU 101-143 ODDS 1:14 HOBBY
97 Stephen Drew FY 8.00 20.00

2005 Bowman's Best Gold

*GOLD 1-30: 6X TO 15X BASIC
1-100 ODDS 1:69 HOBBY
1-100 PRINT RUN 25 #'d SETS
31-100 NO PRICING DUE TO SCARCITY
AU 101-143 ODDS 1:159 HOBBY
AU 101-143 PRINT RUN 25 #'d SETS
AU 101-143 NO PRICING DUE TO SCARCITY

2005 Bowman's Best Green

*GREEN 1-30: 1X TO 2.5X BASIC
*GREEN 31-100: .5X TO 1.2X BASIC
1-100 ODDS 1:2 HOBBY
1-100 PRINT RUN 899 #'d SETS
*GREEN AU 101-143: .5X TO 1.2X BASIC
AU 101-143 ODDS 1:10 HOBBY
AU 101-143 PRINT RUN 399 #'d SETS
95 Ian Kinsler FY 6.00 15.00
97 Stephen Drew FY 6.00 15.00

2005 Bowman's Best Red

*RED 1-30: 1.5X TO 4X BASIC
*RED 31-100: 1X TO 2.5X BASIC
1-100 ODDS 1:9 HOBBY
1-100 PRINT RUN 199 #'d SETS
*RED AU 101-143: .6X TO 1.5X BASIC
AU 101-143 ODDS 1:20 HOBBY
AU 101-143 PRINT RUN 199 #'d SETS
97 Stephen Drew FY 12.50 30.00

2005 Bowman's Best Silver

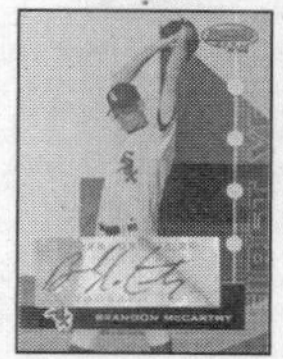

*SILVER 1-30: 2.5X TO 6X BASIC
*SILVER 31-100: 1.25X TO 3X BASIC
1-100 ODDS 1:18 HOBBY
1-100 PRINT RUN 99 #'d SETS
*SILVER AU 101-143: .75X TO 2X BASIC
AU 101-143 ODDS 1:41 HOBBY
AU 101-143 PRINT RUN 99 #'d SETS
97 Stephen Drew FY 25.00 60.00

2005 Bowman's Best A-Rod Throwback Autograph

STATED ODDS 1:1402 HOBBY
STATED PRINT RUN 100 SERIAL #'d CARDS
AR Alex Rodriguez 1994 90.00 150.00

2005 Bowman's Best Mirror Image Spokesmen Dual Autograph

STATED ODDS 1:16,300 HOBBY
STATED PRINT RUN 10 SERIAL #'d CARDS
NO PRICING DUE TO SCARCITY
BR Barry Bonds
Alex Rodriguez

2005 Bowman's Best Mirror Image Throwback Dual Autograph

STATED ODDS 1:2835 HOBBY
STATED PRINT RUN 50 SERIAL #'d CARDS
RR Alex Rodriguez 250.00 400.00
Cal Ripken

2005 Bowman's Best Shortstops Triple Autograph

STATED ODDS 1:5927 HOBBY
STATED PRINT RUN 25 SERIAL #'d CARDS
NO PRICING DUE TO SCARCITY
RRB Alex Rodriguez
Cal Ripken
Matt Bush

2007 Bowman's Best

This 117-card set was released in January, 2008. The set consists of 33 base veteran cards, the last 11 of those cards also come in an autographed form. In addition, cards numbered 34-51 feature signed veterans. Cards numbered 52-81 are 2007 rookies which were inserted at a stated rate of one in two packs and those cards were issued to a stated print run of 799 serial numbered sets. The last 10 numbers in those rookies also come in a signed version which were inserted at a stated rate of one in 11. The set concludes with 18 signed 2007 rookie cards and those cards were also inserted at a stated rate of one in two. This set was issued in five-card packs with an $20 SRP which came five packs to a mini-box, three mini-boxes per full box and eight full boxes per case.

COMP.SET w/o AU (33) 6.00 15.00
COMMON CARD (1-33) .20 .50
COMMON AU VET VAR (23-33) 6.00 15.00
AU VET VAR GROUP A 1:15 PACKS
AU VET VAR GROUP B 1:122 PACKS
AU VET VAR GROUP C 1:381 PACKS
AU VET VAR GROUP D 1:113 PACKS
COMMON AU VET (34-51) 3.00 8.00
AU VET ODDS 1:2 PACKS
COMMON RC (52-81) .40 1.00
RC ODDS 1:2 PACKS
RC PRINT RUN 799 SER.#'d SETS
GU-RC ODDS 1:35 PACKS
COMMON AU VAR RC (71-81) 3.00 8.00
AU VAR RC ODDS 1:11 PACKS
COMMON AU RC (82-99) 3.00 8.00
AU RC ODDS 1:2 PACKS
PRINTING PLATE ODDS 1:88 PACKS
PRINTING PLATE AU ODDS 1:173 PACKS
PRINTING PLATE GU ODDS 1:8945 PACKS
PLATE PRINT RUN 1 SET PER COLOR
BLACK-CYAN-MAGENTA-YELLOW ISSUED
NO PLATE PRICING DUE TO SCARCITY
1 Jose Reyes .50 1.25
2 Derek Jeter 1.25 3.00
3 Vladimir Guerrero .50 1.25
4 Ichiro Suzuki .75 2.00
5 Jason Bay .20 .50
6 Joe Mauer .30 .75
7 Alfonso Soriano .20 .50
8 David Ortiz .50 1.25
9 Andruw Jones .30 .75
10 Roger Clemens .75 2.00
11 Grady Sizemore .30 .75
12 Magglio Ordonez .20 .50
13 Carl Crawford .20 .50
14 Chase Utley .50 1.25
15 Mark Teixeira .30 .75
16 Ryan Zimmerman .50 1.25
17 Ken Griffey Jr. .75 2.00
18 Derrek Lee .20 .50
19 Barry Bonds 1.00 2.50
20 Chipper Jones .50 1.25
21 Vernon Wells .20 .50
22 Manny Ramirez .30 .75
23a Alex Rodriguez .75 2.00
23b Alex Rodriguez AU A 90.00 150.00
24a Ryan Howard .75 2.00
24b Ryan Howard AU B 20.00 50.00
25a Tom Glavine .30 .75
25b Tom Glavine AU D 15.00 40.00
26a Gary Sheffield .20 .50
26b Gary Sheffield AU A 8.00 20.00
27a Miguel Cabrera .30 .75
27b Miguel Cabrera AU A 8.00 20.00
28a Robinson Cano .30 .75
28b Robinson Cano AU A 10.00 25.00
29a David Wright .75 2.00
29b David Wright AU A 20.00 50.00
30a Jim Thome .30 .75
30b Jim Thome AU A 10.00 25.00
31a Albert Pujols 1.00 2.50
31b Albert Pujols AU C 150.00 200.00
32 Jorge Posada .30 .75
33a Brian McCann .20 .50
33b Brian McCann AU A 6.00 15.00
34 Josh Barfield AU 3.00 8.00
35 Melky Cabrera AU 8.00 20.00
36 Bill Hall AU 3.00 8.00
37 Cole Hamels AU 12.50 30.00
38 Adam LaRoche AU 3.00 8.00
39 Matt Holliday AU 8.00 20.00
40 Jeremy Hermida AU 3.00 8.00
41 Jonathan Papelbon AU 8.00 20.00
42 Hanley Ramirez AU 10.00 25.00
43 Justin Verlander AU 8.00 20.00
44 Andre Ethier AU 5.00 12.00
46 Erik Bedard AU 5.00 12.00
47 Freddy Sanchez AU 3.00 8.00
48 Adrian Gonzalez AU 5.00 12.00
49 Russell Martin AU 5.00 12.00
50 B.J. Upton AU 10.00 25.00
51 Prince Fielder AU 15.00 40.00
52 Tony Abreu RC 1.00 2.50
53 Ben Francisco (RC) .40 1.00
54 Billy Butler (RC) .60 1.50
55 Philip Hughes (RC) 2.00 5.00
56 Josh Fields (RC) .40 1.00
57 Carlos Gomez RC .60 1.50
58 Akinori Iwamura RC 1.00 2.50
59 Matt Brown RC .40 1.00
60 Jesus Flores RC .40 1.00
61 Mike Fontenot (RC) .40 1.00
62 Ryan Feierabend (RC) .40 1.00
63 Miguel Montero (RC) .40 1.00
64a Daisuke Matsuzaka RC 4.00 10.00
64b Daisuke Matsuzaka Jsy 10.00 25.00
65 Kei Igawa RC 1.00 2.50
66 Shawn Riggans (RC) .40 1.00
67 Masumi Kuwata RC 3.00 8.00
68 Kevin Slowey (RC) 1.00 2.50
69 Josh Hamilton (RC) 1.00 2.50
70 Curtis Thigpen (RC) .40 1.00
71a Justin Upton RC 2.50 6.00
71b Justin Upton AU 40.00 80.00
72a Delmon Young (RC) .60 1.50
72b Delmon Young AU 8.00 20.00
73a Brandon Wood (RC) .40 1.00
73b Brandon Wood AU 6.00 15.00
74a Felix Pie (RC) .50 1.25
74b Felix Pie AU 4.00 10.00
75a Alex Gordon RC 2.00 5.00
75b Alex Gordon AU 15.00 40.00
76a Mark Reynolds RC 1.50 4.00
76b Mark Reynolds AU 20.00 50.00
77a Tyler Clippard (RC) .60 1.50
77b Tyler Clippard AU 4.00 10.00
78a Adam Lind (RC) .40 1.00
78b Adam Lind AU 3.00 8.00
79a Hunter Pence (RC) 2.00 5.00
79b Hunter Pence AU 20.00 50.00
80 Micah Owings (RC) .40 1.00
81a Jarrod Saltalamacchia (RC) .60 1.50
81b Jarrod Saltalamacchia AU 6.00 15.00
82 Kevin Kouzmanoff AU (RC) 3.00 8.00
83 Glen Perkins AU (RC) 3.00 8.00
84 Michael Bourn AU (RC) 3.00 8.00
85 Andrew Miller AU RC 6.00 15.00
86 Fred Lewis AU (RC) 3.00 8.00
88 Joba Chamberlain AU RC 30.00 60.00
89 Hideki Okajima AU RC 10.00 25.00
90 Troy Tulowitzki AU (RC) 10.00 25.00
91 Ryan Sweeney AU (RC) 3.00 8.00
92 Matt Lindstrom AU (RC) 3.00 8.00
93 Tim Lincecum AU RC 30.00 60.00
94 Homer Bailey AU (RC) 4.00 10.00
95 Matt DeSalvo AU (RC) 3.00 8.00
96 Alejandro De Aza AU RC 3.00 8.00
97 Ryan Braun AU (RC) 30.00 60.00
99 Andy LaRoche AU (RC) 6.00 15.00

2007 Bowman's Best Blue

*VET BLUE: 3X TO 8X BASIC VET
VET ODDS 1:11 PACKS
*AU VET BLUE: .5X TO 1.2X BASIC AU VET
AU VET ODDS 1:14 PACKS
*RC BLUE: 1X TO 2.5X BASIC RC
RC ODDS 1:12 PACKS
*AU RC BLUE: .5X TO 1.2X BASIC AU RC
AU RC ODDS 1:15 PACKS
*GU-RC BLUE: .75X TO 2X BASIC GU-RC
GU-RC ODDS 1:361 PACKS
STATED PRINT RUN 99 SER.#'d SETS
93 Tim Lincecum AU 60.00 120.00

2007 Bowman's Best Gold

*VET GOLD: 4X TO 10X BASIC VET
VET ODDS 1:22 PACKS
*AU VET GOLD: .6X TO 1.5X BASIC AU VET
AU VET ODDS 1:28 PACKS
*RC GOLD: 1.5X TO 4X BASIC RC
RC ODDS 1:24 PACKS
*AU RC GOLD: .6X TO 1.5X BASIC AU RC
AU RC ODDS 1:29 PACKS
*GU-RC GOLD: 1X TO 2.5X BASIC GU-RC
GU-RC ODDS 1:715 PACKS
STATED PRINT RUN 50 SER.#'d SETS
31b Albert Pujols AU 200.00 300.00
88 Joba Chamberlain AU 75.00 150.00
93 Tim Lincecum AU 100.00 200.00

2007 Bowman's Best Green

*VET GREEN: 1.5X TO 4X BASIC VET
VET ODDS 1:5 PACKS
*RC GREEN: .75X TO 2X BASIC RC
RC ODDS 1:5 PACKS
STATED PRINT RUN 249 SER.#'d SETS
64a Daisuke Matsuzaka 6.00 15.00

2007 Bowman's Best Red

VET ODDS 1:1073 PACKS
AU VET ODDS 1:1325 PACKS
RC ODDS 1:1221 PACKS
AU RC ODDS 1:1376 PACKS
GU-RC ODDS 1:27,456 PACKS
STATED PRINT RUN 1 SER.#'d SETS
NO PRICING DUE TO SCARCITY

2007 Bowman's Best Alex Rodriguez 500

COMMON CARD 1.50 4.00
STATED ODDS 1:
COMMON BLUE 8.00 20.00
BLUE ODDS 1:1107 PACKS
BLUE PRINT RUN 33 SER.#'d SETS
GOLD ODDS 1:2532 PACKS
GOLD PRINT RUN 15 SER.#'d SETS
NO GOLD PRICING DUE TO SCARCITY
COMMON GREEN 5.00 12.00
GREEN ODDS 1:361 PACKS
GREEN PRINT RUN 99 SER.#'d SETS
AR Alex Rodriguez 1.50 4.00

2007 Bowman's Best Barry Bonds 756

STATED ODDS 1:20 PACKS
PRINTING PLATE ODDS 1:8945 PACKS
PLATE PRINT RUN 1 SET PER COLOR
BLACK-CYAN-MAGENTA-YELLOW ISSUED
NO PLATE PRICING DUE TO SCARCITY
BB Barry Bonds 1.25 3.00

2007 Bowman's Best Prospects

COMMON PROSPECT (1-40) 2.00 5.00
PROSPECT STATED ODDS 1:2 PACKS
PROSPECT PRINT RUN 499 SER.#'d SETS
COMMON PROS.AU VAR (37-40) 3.00 8.00
PROS AU VAR ODDS 1:26 PACKS
COMMON PROS.AUTO (41-60) 3.00 8.00
PROS.AUTO ODDS 1:26 PACKS
PRINTING PLATE ODDS 1:88 PACKS
PRINTING PLATE AU ODDS 1:173 PACKS
PLATE PRINT RUN 1 SET PER COLOR
BLACK-CYAN-MAGENTA-YELLOW ISSUED
NO PLATE PRICING DUE TO SCARCITY
BBP1 Greg Smith 4.00 10.00
BBP2 J.R. Towles 2.50 6.00
BBP3 Jeff Locke 8.00 20.00
BBP4 Henry Sosa 2.50 6.00
BBP5 Ivan De Jesus Jr. 2.50 6.00
BBP6 Brad Lincoln 2.00 5.00
BBP7 Josh Papelbon 2.50 6.00
BBP8 Mark Hamilton 2.00 5.00
BBP9 Sam Fuld 3.00 8.00
BBP10 Thomas Fairchild 2.00 5.00
BBP11 Chris Carter 3.00 8.00
BBP12 Chuck Lofgren 2.00 5.00
BBP13 Joe Gaetti 2.00 5.00
BBP14 Zach McAllister 2.00 5.00
BBP15 Cole Gillespie 2.00 5.00
BBP16 Jeremy Papelbon 2.00 5.00
BBP17 Mike Carp 2.50 6.00
BBP18 Cody Strait 2.00 5.00
BBP19 Gorkys Hernandez 3.00 8.00
BBP20 Andrew Fie 2.50 6.00
BBP21 Erik Lis 2.50 6.00
BBP22 Chance Douglass 2.00 5.00
BBP23 Vasili Spanos 2.00 5.00
BBP24 Desmond Jennings 3.00 8.00
BBP25 Vic Buttler 2.50 6.00
BBP26 Cedric Hunter 2.50 6.00
BBP27 Emerson Frostad 2.00 5.00
BBP28 Mike Devaney 2.00 5.00
BBP29 Eric Young Jr. 2.00 5.00
BBP30 Evan Englebrook 2.00 5.00
BBP31 Aaron Cunningham 2.50 6.00
BBP32 Dellin Betances 3.00 8.00
BBP33 Michael Saunders 3.00 8.00
BBP34 Deolis Guerra 2.50 6.00
BBP35 Brian Bocock 3.00 8.00
BBP36 Rich Thompson 2.00 5.00
BBP37a Greg Reynolds 2.50 6.00
BBP37b Greg Reynolds AU 5.00 12.00
BBP38a Jeff Samardzija 4.00 10.00
BBP38b Jeff Samardzija AU 12.50 30.00
BBP39a Evan Longoria 2.50 6.00
BBP39b Evan Longoria AU 40.00 80.00
BBP40a Luke Hochevar 3.00 8.00
BBP40b Luke Hochevar AU 15.00 40.00
BBP41 James Avery AU 3.00 8.00
BBP42 Joe Mather AU 4.00 10.00
BBP43 Hank Conger AU 4.00 10.00
BBP44 Adam Miller AU 4.00 10.00
BBP45 Clayton Kershaw AU 10.00 25.00
BBP46 Adam Ottavino AU 3.00 8.00
BBP47 Jason Place AU 5.00 12.00
BBP48 Billy Rowell AU 5.00 12.00
BBP49 Brett Sinkbeil AU 3.00 8.00
BBP50 Colton Willems AU 3.00 8.00
BBP51 Cameron Maybin AU 6.00 15.00
BBP52 Jeremy Jeffress AU 4.00 10.00
BBP53 Fernando Martinez AU 20.00 50.00
BBP54 Chris Marrero AU 20.00 50.00
BBP55 Kyle McCulloch AU 3.00 8.00
BBP56 Chris Parmelee AU 4.00 10.00
BBP57 Emmanuel Burris AU 4.00 10.00
BBP58 Chris Coghlan AU 5.00 12.00
BBP59 Chris Perez AU 4.00 10.00
BBP60 David Huff AU 4.00 10.00

2007 Bowman's Best Prospects Blue

*PROS BLUE: .6X TO 1.5X BASIC PROS
PROS ODDS 1:9 PACKS
*PROS AU BLUE: .6X TO 1.5X BASIC PROS AU
PROS AU ODDS 1:16 PACKS
STATED PRINT RUN 99 SER.#'d SETS
BBP45 Clayton Kershaw AU 20.00 50.00
BBP53 Fernando Martinez AU 100.00 150.00

2007 Bowman's Best Prospects Gold

*PROS GOLD: .75X TO 2X BASIC PROS
PROS ODDS 1:18 PACKS
*PROS AU GOLD: .75X TO 2X BASIC PROS AU
PROS AU ODDS 1:31 PACKS
STATED PRINT RUN 50 SER.#'d SETS
BBP38b Jeff Samardzija AU 40.00 80.00
BBP45 Clayton Kershaw AU 30.00 60.00
BBP48 Billy Rowell AU 20.00 50.00
BBP53 Fernando Martinez AU 150.00 200.00
BBP54 Chris Marrero AU 60.00 120.00

2007 Bowman's Best Prospects Green

PROS GREEN: .5X TO 1.2X BASIC PROS
STATED ODDS 1:4 PACKS
STATED PRINT RUN 249 SER.#'d SETS

2007 Bowman's Best Prospects Red

PROS. ODDS 1:908 PACKS
PROS. AU ODDS 1:1453 PACKS
STATED PRINT RUN 1 SER.#'d SET
NO PRICING DUE TO SCARCITY

1914 Cracker Jack

The cards in this 144-card set measure approximately 2 1/4" by 3". This "Series of colored pictures of Famous Ball Players and Managers" was issued in packages of Cracker Jack in 1914. The cards have tinted photos set against red backgrounds and many are found with caramel stains. The set also contains Federal League players. The company claims to have printed 15 million cards. The 1914 series can be distinguished from the 1915 issue by the advertising found on the back of the cards. Team names are included for some players to show differences between the 1914 and 1915 issue.

COMPLETE SET (144) 70000.00 140000.00
1 Otto Knabe 300.00 600.00
2 Frank Baker 750.00 1500.00
3 Joe Tinker 1000.00 2000.00
4 Larry Doyle 200.00 400.00

5 Ward Miller	200.00	400.00
6 Eddie Plank	750.00	1500.00
Phila. AL		
7 Eddie Collins	750.00	1500.00
Phila. AL		
8 Rube Oldring	200.00	400.00
9 Artie Hoffman	200.00	400.00
10 John McInnis	200.00	400.00
11 George Stovall	200.00	400.00
12 Connie Mack MG	750.00	1500.00
13 Art Wilson	200.00	400.00
14 Sam Crawford	750.00	1500.00
15 Reb Russell	200.00	400.00
16 Howie Camnitz	200.00	400.00
17 Roger Bresnahan	750.00	1500.00
18 Johnny Evers	750.00	1500.00
19 Chief Bender	750.00	1500.00
Phila. AL		
20 Cy Falkenberg	200.00	400.00
21 Heinie Zimmerman	200.00	400.00
22 Joe Wood	1250.00	2500.00
23 Chas.Comiskey OWN	750.00	1500.00
24 George Mullen	200.00	400.00
25 Michael Simon	200.00	400.00
26 James Scott	200.00	400.00
27 Bill Carrigan	200.00	400.00
28 Jack Barry	200.00	400.00
29 Vean Gregg	200.00	400.00
Cleveland		
30 Ty Cobb	5000.00	10000.00
31 Heinie Wagner	200.00	400.00
32 Mordecai Brown	750.00	1500.00
33 Amos Strunk	200.00	400.00
34 Ira Thomas	300.00	600.00
35 Harry Hooper	750.00	1500.00
36 Ed Walsh	750.00	1500.00
37 Grover C. Alexander	2000.00	4000.00
38 Red Dooin	200.00	400.00
Phila. NL		
39 Chick Gandil	750.00	1500.00
40 Jimmy Austin	200.00	400.00
St.L. AL		
41 Tommy Leach	200.00	400.00
42 Al Bridwell	200.00	400.00
43 Rube Marquard	750.00	1500.00
NY NL		
44 Charles Tesreau	200.00	400.00
45 Fred Luderus	200.00	400.00
46 Bob Groom	200.00	400.00
47 Josh Devore	200.00	400.00
Phila. NL		
48 Harry Lord	300.00	600.00
49 John Miller	200.00	400.00
50 John Hummell	200.00	400.00
51 Nap Rucker	200.00	400.00
52 Zach Wheat	750.00	1500.00
53 Otto Miller	200.00	400.00
54 Marty O'Toole	200.00	400.00
55 Dick Hoblitzel	200.00	400.00
Cinc.		
56 Clyde Milan	200.00	400.00
57 Walter Johnson	2000.00	4000.00
58 Wally Schang	200.00	400.00
59 Harry Gessler	200.00	400.00
60 Rollie Zeider	300.00	600.00
61 Ray Schalk	1000.00	2000.00
62 Jay Cashion	300.00	600.00
63 Babe Adams	200.00	400.00
64 Jimmy Archer	200.00	400.00
65 Tris Speaker	750.00	1500.00
66 Napoleon Lajoie	1250.00	2500.00
Cleve.		
67 Otis Crandall	200.00	400.00
68 Honus Wagner	4000.00	8000.00
69 John McGraw MG	750.00	1500.00
70 Fred Clarke	600.00	1200.00
71 Chief Meyers	200.00	400.00
72 John Boehling	200.00	400.00
73 Max Carey	750.00	1500.00
74 Frank Owens	200.00	400.00
75 Miller Huggins	600.00	1200.00
76 Claude Hendrix	200.00	400.00
77 Hughie Jennings MG	750.00	1500.00
78 Fred Merkle	200.00	400.00
79 Ping Bodie	200.00	400.00
80 Ed Ruelbach	200.00	400.00
81 Jim C. Delehanty	200.00	400.00
82 Gavvy Cravath	200.00	400.00
83 Russ Ford	200.00	400.00
84 Elmer E. Knetzer	200.00	400.00
85 Buck Herzog	200.00	400.00
86 Burt Shotton	200.00	400.00
87 Forrest Cady	200.00	400.00
88 Christy Mathewson	20000.00	50000.00
Pitching		
89 Lawrence Cheney	200.00	400.00
90 Frank Smith	200.00	400.00
91 Roger Peckinpaugh	200.00	400.00
92 Al Demaree N.Y. NL	200.00	400.00
93 Del Pratt	200.00	400.00
Throwing		
94 Eddie Cicotte	750.00	1500.00
95 Ray Keating	200.00	400.00
96 Beals Becker	200.00	400.00
97 John(Rube) Benton	200.00	400.00
98 Frank LaPorte	200.00	400.00
99 Frank Chance	2000.00	4000.00
100 Thomas Seaton	200.00	400.00
101 Frank Schulte	200.00	400.00
102 Ray Fisher	200.00	400.00
103 Joe Jackson	10000.00	20000.00
104 Vic Saier	200.00	400.00
105 James Lavender	200.00	400.00
106 Joe Birmingham	200.00	400.00
107 Tom Downey	200.00	400.00
108 Sherry Magee	200.00	400.00
Phila. NL		
109 Fred Blanding	200.00	400.00
110 Bob Bescher	200.00	400.00
111 Jim Callahan	200.00	400.00
112 Ed Sweeney	200.00	400.00
113 George Suggs	200.00	400.00
114 Geo.J. Moriarty	200.00	400.00
115 Addison Brennan	200.00	400.00
116 Rollie Zeider	200.00	400.00
117 Ted Easterly	200.00	400.00
118 Ed Konetchy	200.00	400.00
Pittsburgh		
119 George Perring	200.00	400.00
120 Mike Doolan	200.00	400.00
121 Hub Perdue	200.00	400.00
Boston NL		
122 Owen Bush	200.00	400.00
123 Slim Sallee	200.00	400.00
124 Earl Moore	200.00	400.00
125 Bert Niehoff	200.00	400.00
126 Walter Blair	200.00	400.00
127 Butch Schmidt	200.00	400.00
128 Steve Evans	200.00	400.00
129 Ray Caldwell	200.00	400.00
130 Ivy Wingo	200.00	400.00
131 George Baumgardner	200.00	400.00
132 Les Nunamaker	200.00	400.00
133 Branch Rickey MG	1000.00	2000.00
134 Armando Marsans	200.00	400.00
Cincinnati		
135 Bill Killefer	200.00	400.00
136 Rabbit Maranville	750.00	1500.00
137 William Rariden	200.00	400.00
138 Hank Gowdy	200.00	400.00
139 Rebel Oakes	200.00	400.00
140 Danny Murphy	200.00	400.00
141 Cy Barger	200.00	400.00
142 Eugene Packard	200.00	400.00
143 Jake Daubert	200.00	400.00
144 James C. Walsh	200.00	400.00

1915 Cracker Jack

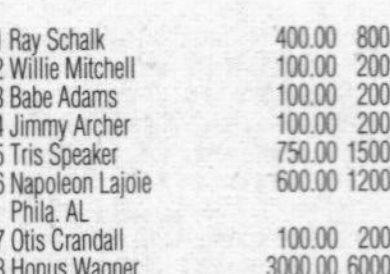

The cards in this 176-card set measure approximately 2 1/4" by 3". When flipped over, a 1915 "series of 176" Cracker Jack card shows the back printing upside-down. Cards were available in boxes of Cracker Jack or from the company for "100 Cracker Jack coupons, or one coupon and 25 cents." An album was available for "50 coupons or one coupon and 10 cents." Because of this send-in offer, the 1915 Cracker Jack cards are noticeably easier to find than the 1914 Cracker Jack cards, although obviously neither set is plentiful. The set essentially duplicates E145-1 (1914 Cracker Jack) except for some additional cards and new poses. Players in the Federal League are indicated by FED in the checklist below.

COMPLETE SET (176)	35000.00	70000.00
COMMON CARD (1-144)	100.00	200.00
COMM. CARD (145-176)	125.00	250.00
1 Otto Knabe	300.00	600.00
2 Frank Baker	500.00	1000.00
3 Joe Tinker	400.00	800.00
4 Larry Doyle	125.00	250.00
5 Ward Miller	100.00	200.00
6 Eddie Plank	750.00	1500.00
St.L. FED		
7 Eddie Collins	400.00	800.00
Chicago AL		
8 Rube Oldring	100.00	200.00
9 Artie Hoffman	100.00	200.00
10 John McInnis	100.00	200.00
11 George Stovall	100.00	200.00
12 Connie Mack MG	400.00	800.00
13 Art Wilson	100.00	200.00
14 Sam Crawford	400.00	800.00
15 Reb Russell	100.00	200.00
16 Howie Camnitz	100.00	200.00
17 Roger Bresnahan	300.00	600.00
18 Johnny Evers	400.00	800.00
19 Chief Bender	400.00	800.00
Baltimore FED		
20 Cy Falkenberg	100.00	200.00
21 Heinie Zimmerman	100.00	200.00
22 Joe Wood	500.00	1000.00
23 C. Comiskey OWN	500.00	1000.00
24 George Mullen	100.00	200.00
25 Michael Simon	100.00	200.00
26 James Scott	100.00	200.00
27 Bill Carrigan	100.00	200.00
28 Jack Barry	125.00	250.00
29 Vean Gregg	100.00	200.00
Boston AL		
30 Ty Cobb	3000.00	6000.00
31 Heinie Wagner	100.00	200.00
32 Mordecai Brown	500.00	1000.00
33 Amos Strunk	100.00	200.00
34 Ira Thomas	100.00	200.00
35 Harry Hooper	300.00	600.00
36 Ed Walsh	400.00	800.00
37 Grover C. Alexander	1000.00	2000.00
38 Red Dooin	100.00	200.00
Cincinnati		
39 Chick Gandil	400.00	800.00
40 Jimmy Austin	125.00	250.00
Pitts. FED UER		
Biographical Information is wrong		
41 Tommy Leach	100.00	200.00
42 Al Bridwell	100.00	200.00
43 Rube Marquard	300.00	600.00
Brooklyn FED		
Although card says Federals, Marquard was in fact a Dodger in 1915		
44 Charles(Jeff) Tesreau	100.00	200.00
45 Fred Luderus	100.00	200.00
46 Bob Groom	100.00	200.00
47 Josh Devore	100.00	200.00
Boston NL		
48 Steve O'Neill	100.00	200.00
49 John Miller	100.00	200.00
50 John Hummell	100.00	200.00
51 Nap Rucker	100.00	200.00
52 Zach Wheat	300.00	600.00
53 Otto Miller	100.00	200.00
54 Marty O'Toole	100.00	200.00
55 Dick Hoblitzel	100.00	200.00
Boston AL		
56 Clyde Milan	100.00	200.00
57 Walter Johnson	1500.00	3000.00
58 Wally Schang	100.00	200.00
59 Harry Gessler	100.00	200.00
60 Oscar Dugey	100.00	200.00
61 Ray Schalk	400.00	800.00
62 Willie Mitchell	100.00	200.00
63 Babe Adams	100.00	200.00
64 Jimmy Archer	100.00	200.00
65 Tris Speaker	750.00	1500.00
66 Napoleon Lajoie	600.00	1200.00
Phila. AL		
67 Otis Crandall	100.00	200.00
68 Honus Wagner	3000.00	6000.00
69 John McGraw MG	400.00	800.00
70 Fred Clarke	300.00	600.00
71 Chief Meyers	125.00	250.00
72 John Boehling	100.00	200.00
73 Max Carey	400.00	800.00
74 Frank Owens	100.00	200.00
75 Miller Huggins	300.00	600.00
76 Claude Hendrix	100.00	200.00
77 Hughie Jennings MG	300.00	600.00
78 Fred Merkle	100.00	200.00
79 Ping Bodie	100.00	200.00
80 Ed Ruelbach	100.00	200.00
81 Jim C. Delehanty	100.00	200.00
82 Gavvy Cravath	100.00	200.00
83 Russ Ford	100.00	200.00
84 Elmer E. Knetzer	100.00	200.00
85 Buck Herzog	100.00	200.00
86 Burt Shotton	100.00	200.00
87 Forrest Cady	100.00	200.00
88 Christy Mathewson	1750.00	3500.00
Portrait		
89 Lawrence Cheney	100.00	200.00
90 Frank Smith	100.00	200.00
91 Roger Peckinpaugh	100.00	200.00
92 Al Demaree	100.00	200.00
Phila. NL		
93 Del Pratt	125.00	250.00
Portrait		
94 Eddie Cicotte	450.00	900.00
95 Ray Keating	100.00	200.00
96 Beals Becker	125.00	250.00
97 John(Rube) Benton	100.00	200.00
98 Frank LaPorte	100.00	200.00
99 Hal Chase	250.00	500.00
100 Thomas Seaton	100.00	200.00
101 Frank Schulte	100.00	200.00
102 Ray Fisher	100.00	200.00
103 Joe Jackson	7500.00	15000.00
104 Vic Saier	100.00	200.00
105 James Lavender	100.00	200.00
106 Joe Birmingham MG	100.00	200.00
107 Thomas Downey	100.00	200.00
108 Sherry Magee	100.00	200.00
Boston NL		
109 Fred Blanding	100.00	200.00
110 Bob Bescher	100.00	200.00
111 Herbie Moran	100.00	200.00
112 Ed Sweeney	100.00	200.00
113 George Suggs	100.00	200.00
114 Geo.J. Moriarty	100.00	200.00
115 Addison Brennan	100.00	200.00
116 Rollie Zeider	100.00	200.00
117 Ted Easterly	100.00	200.00
118 Ed Konetchy	100.00	200.00
Pitts. FED		
119 George Perring	100.00	200.00
120 Mike Doolan	100.00	200.00
121 Hub Perdue	100.00	200.00
St. Louis NL		
122 Owen Bush	100.00	200.00
123 Slim Sallee	100.00	200.00
124 Earl Moore	100.00	200.00
125 Bert Niehoff	100.00	200.00
Phila. NL		
126 Walter Blair	100.00	200.00
127 Butch Schmidt	100.00	200.00
128 Steve Evans	100.00	200.00
129 Ray Caldwell	100.00	200.00
130 Ivy Wingo	100.00	200.00
131 Geo. Baumgardner	100.00	200.00
132 Les Nunamaker	100.00	200.00
133 Branch Rickey MG	600.00	1200.00
134 Armando Marsans	125.00	250.00
St.L. FED		
135 William Killefer	100.00	200.00
136 Rabbit Maranville	300.00	600.00
137 William Rariden	100.00	200.00
138 Hank Gowdy	100.00	200.00
139 Rebel Oakes	100.00	200.00
140 Danny Murphy	100.00	200.00
141 Cy Barger	100.00	200.00
142 Eugene Packard	100.00	200.00
143 Jake Daubert	100.00	200.00
144 James C. Walsh	100.00	200.00
145 Ted Cather	125.00	250.00
146 George Tyler	125.00	250.00
147 Lee Magee	125.00	250.00
148 Owen Wilson	125.00	250.00
149 Hal Janvrin	125.00	250.00
150 Doc Johnston	125.00	250.00
151 George Whitted	125.00	250.00
152 George McQuillen	125.00	250.00
153 Bill James	125.00	250.00
154 Dick Rudolph	125.00	250.00
155 Joe Connolly	125.00	250.00
156 Jean Dubuc	125.00	250.00
157 George Kaiserling	125.00	250.00
158 Fritz Maisel	125.00	250.00
159 Heinie Groh	125.00	250.00
160 Benny Kauff	125.00	250.00
161 Edd Roush	500.00	1000.00
162 George Stallings MG	125.00	250.00
163 Bert Whaling	125.00	250.00
164 Bob Shawkey	125.00	250.00
165 Eddie Murphy	125.00	250.00
166 Joe Bush	125.00	250.00
167 Clark Griffith	300.00	600.00
168 Vin Campbell	125.00	250.00
169 Raymond Collins	125.00	250.00
170 Hans Lobert	125.00	250.00
171 Earl Hamilton	125.00	250.00
172 Erskine Mayer	125.00	250.00
173 Tilly Walker	125.00	250.00
174 Robert Veach	125.00	250.00
175 Joseph Benz	125.00	250.00
176 Hippo Vaughn	300.00	600.00

2002 Diamond Kings

This 160 card set was issued in two separate series. The first 150 cards were issued within the Diamond Kings brand of which was distributed in May, 2002.

These cards were issued in four card packs with an SRP of $3.99 which came 24 packs to a box and 20 boxes to a case. Cards numbered 101 through 150 were printed in shorter supply than the other cards. Cards numbered 101 through 121 feature prospect while cards numbered 122 through 150 featured retired veterans. These cards were all issued at a stated rate of one in three packs. Cards 151-160 were issued within packs of 2002 Donruss the Rookies in mid-December, 2002 at the following ratios: hobby 1:10, retail 1:12. This set was noteworthy as Donruss/Playoff created a full set based on the tradition began in 1982 when the first Diamond King cards were created.

COMP.LOW SET (150)	100.00	200.00
COMP.LOW w/o SP's (100)	20.00	50.00
COMP.UPDATE SET (10)	15.00	40.00
COMMON CARD (1-100)	.20	.50
COMMON PROSPECT (101-150)	1.50	4.00
COMMON RETIRED (101-150)	1.50	4.00
COMMON CARD (151-160)	1.50	4.00
1 Vladimir Guerrero	.50	1.25
2 Adam Dunn	.20	.50
3 Tsuyoshi Shinjo	.20	.50
4 Adrian Beltre	.20	.50
5 Troy Glaus	.20	.50
6 Albert Pujols	1.00	2.50
7 Trot Nixon	.20	.50
8 Alex Rodriguez	.75	2.00
9 Tom Glavine	.30	.75
10 Alfonso Soriano	.30	.75
11 Todd Helton	.30	.75
12 Joe Torre	.30	.75
13 Tim Hudson	.20	.50
14 Andruw Jones	.30	.75
15 Shawn Green	.20	.50
16 Aramis Ramirez	.20	.50
17 Shannon Stewart	.20	.50
18 Barry Bonds	1.25	3.00
19 Sean Casey	.20	.50
20 Barry Larkin	.30	.75
21 Scott Rolen	.30	.75
22 Barry Zito	.20	.50
23 Sammy Sosa	.50	1.25
24 Bartolo Colon	.20	.50
25 Ryan Klesko	.20	.50
26 Ben Grieve	.20	.50
27 Roy Oswalt	.20	.50
28 Kazuhiro Sasaki	.20	.50
29 Roger Clemens	1.00	2.50
30 Bernie Williams	.30	.75
31 Roberto Alomar	.30	.75
32 Bobby Abreu	.20	.50
33 Robert Fick	.20	.50
34 Bret Boone	.20	.50
35 Rickey Henderson	.50	1.25
36 Brian Giles	.20	.50
37 Richie Sexson	.20	.50
38 Bud Smith	.20	.50
39 Richard Hidalgo	.20	.50
40 C. C. Sabathia	.20	.50
41 Rich Aurilia	.20	.50
42 Carlos Beltran	.20	.50
43 Raul Mondesi	.20	.50
44 Carlos Delgado	.20	.50
45 Randy Johnson	.50	1.25
46 Chan Ho Park	.20	.50
47 Rafael Palmeiro	.30	.75
48 Chipper Jones	.50	1.25
49 Phil Nevin	.20	.50
50 Cliff Floyd	.20	.50
51 Pedro Martinez	.30	.75
52 Craig Biggio	.30	.75
53 Paul LoDuca	.20	.50
54 Cristian Guzman	.20	.50
55 Pat Burrell	.20	.50
56 Curt Schilling	.20	.50
57 Orlando Cabrera	.20	.50
58 Darin Erstad	.20	.50
59 Omar Vizquel	.30	.75
60 Derek Jeter	1.25	3.00
61 Nomar Garciaparra	.75	2.00
62 Edgar Martinez	.30	.75
63 Moises Alou	.20	.50
64 Eric Chavez	.20	.50
65 Mike Sweeney	.20	.50
66 Frank Thomas	.50	1.25
67 Mike Piazza	.75	2.00
68 Gary Sheffield	.20	.50
69 Mike Mussina	.30	.75
70 Greg Maddux	.75	2.00
71 Juan Gonzalez	.20	.50
72 Hideo Nomo	.50	1.25
73 Miguel Tejada	.20	.50
74 Ichiro Suzuki	1.00	2.50
75 Matt Morris	.20	.50
76 Ivan Rodriguez	.30	.75
77 Mark Mulder	.20	.50
78 J.D. Drew	.20	.50
79 Mark Grace	.30	.75
80 Jason Giambi	.20	.50
81 Mark Buehrle	.20	.50
82 Jose Vidro	.20	.50
83 Manny Ramirez	.30	.75
84 Jeff Bagwell	.30	.75
85 Magglio Ordonez	.20	.50
86 Ken Griffey Jr.	.75	2.00
87 Luis Gonzalez	.20	.50
88 Jim Edmonds	.20	.50
89 Larry Walker	.20	.50
90 Jim Thome	.30	.75
91 Lance Berkman	.20	.50
92 Jorge Posada	.30	.75
93 Kevin Brown	.20	.50
94 Joe Mays	.20	.50
95 Kerry Wood	.20	.50
96 Mark Ellis	.20	.50
97 Austin Kearns	.20	.50
98 Jorge De La Rosa RC	.20	.50
99 Brandon Berger	.20	.50
100 Ryan Ludwick	.20	.50
101 Marlon Byrd SP	1.50	4.00
102 Brandon Backe SP RC	1.50	4.00
103 Juan Cruz SP	1.50	4.00
104 Anderson Machado SP RC	1.50	4.00
105 So Taguchi SP RC	1.50	4.00
106 Dewon Brazelton SP	1.50	4.00
107 Josh Beckett SP	1.50	4.00
108 John Buck SP	1.50	4.00
109 Jorge Padilla SP RC	1.50	4.00
110 Hee Seop Choi SP	1.50	4.00
111 Angel Berroa SP	1.50	4.00
112 Mark Teixeira SP	2.00	5.00
113 Victor Martinez SP	2.00	5.00
114 Kazuhisa Ishii SP RC	1.50	4.00
115 Dennis Tankersley SP	1.50	4.00
116 Wilson Valdez SP RC	1.50	4.00
117 Antonio Perez SP	1.50	4.00
118 Ed Rogers SP	1.50	4.00
119 Wilson Betemit SP	1.50	4.00
120 Mike Rivera SP	1.50	4.00
121 Mark Prior SP	1.25	3.00
122 Roberto Clemente SP	3.00	8.00
123 Roberto Clemente SP	3.00	8.00
124 Roberto Clemente SP	3.00	8.00
125 Roberto Clemente SP	3.00	8.00
126 Roberto Clemente SP	3.00	8.00
127 Babe Ruth SP	4.00	10.00
128 Ted Williams SP	3.00	8.00
129 Andre Dawson SP	1.50	4.00
130 Eddie Murray SP	2.00	5.00
131 Juan Marichal SP	1.50	4.00
132 Kirby Puckett SP	2.00	5.00
133 Alan Trammell SP	1.50	4.00
134 Bobby Doerr SP	1.50	4.00
135 Carlton Fisk SP	1.50	4.00
136 Eddie Mathews SP	2.00	5.00
137 Mike Schmidt SP	4.00	10.00
138 Catfish Hunter SP	1.50	4.00
139 Nolan Ryan SP UER	5.00	12.00
Wrong year notated for no-hitter		
140 George Brett SP	4.00	10.00
141 Gary Carter SP	1.50	4.00
142 Paul Molitor SP	1.50	4.00
143 Lou Gehrig SP	2.50	6.00
144 Ryne Sandberg SP	4.00	10.00
145 Tony Gwynn SP	2.50	6.00
146 Ron Santo SP	1.50	4.00
147 Cal Ripken SP	6.00	15.00
148 Al Kaline SP	2.00	5.00
149 Bo Jackson SP	2.00	5.00
150 Don Mattingly SP	4.00	10.00
151 Chris Snelling RC	1.50	4.00
152 Satoru Komiyama RC	1.50	4.00
153 Oliver Perez RC	1.50	4.00
154 Kirk Saarloos RC	1.50	4.00
155 Rene Reyes RC	1.50	4.00
156 Runelvys Hernandez RC	1.50	4.00
157 Rodrigo Rosario RC	1.50	4.00
158 Jason Simontacchi RC	1.50	4.00
159 Miguel Asencio RC	1.50	4.00
160 Aaron Cook RC	1.50	4.00

2002 Diamond Kings Bronze Foil

Inserted at a stated rate of one in six packs, this is a parallel to the Diamond Kings sets. These cards have white frames with bronze highlights.

*BRONZE 1-100: 1.5X TO 4X BASIC
*BRONZE 101-121: .4X TO 1X BASIC
*BRONZE 122-150: .4X TO 1X BASIC
*BRONZE 151-160: 1X TO 2.5X BASIC

2002 Diamond Kings Gold Foil

Randomly inserted in packs, this is a parallel to the Diamond Kings set. These cards can be differentiated by their having black frames with gold accents. 100 serial-numbered sets were printed.

*GOLD 1-100: 6X TO 15X BASIC
*GOLD 101-121: 1.5X TO 4X BASIC
*GOLD 122-150: 2.5X TO 6X BASIC
*GOLD 151-160: 1.5X TO 4X BASIC
1-150 RANDOM INSERTS IN PACKS
151-160 RANDOM IN DONRUSS ROOK.PACKS

2002 Diamond Kings Silver Foil

Randomly inserted in packs, this is a parallel to the Diamond Kings set. These cards can be differentiated by the grey frames and with silver accents. Cards 1-150 are serial-numbered to 400 and 151-160 to 250.

*SILVER 1-100: 3X TO 8X BASIC
*SILVER 101-121: .75X TO 2X BASIC
*SILVER 122-150: 1.25X TO 3X BASIC
*SILVER 151-160: 1.25X TO 3X BASIC
151-160 PRINT RUN 250 SERIAL #'d SETS

2002 Diamond Kings Diamond Cut Collection

These 100 cards were inserted at an approximate rate of one per hobby box and as random inserts in retail packs. These cards feature a mix of autograph and memorabilia cards. The bat cards of Tony Gwynn and Kazuhisa Ishii were not ready by the time this product packed out. Thus, exchange cards with a deadline of November 1st, 2003 were seeded into packs. Serial-numbered print runs range between 100-500 copies per card.

DC1 Vladimir Guerrero AU/400	15.00	40.00
DC2 Mark Prior AU/400	10.00	25.00
DC3 Victor Martinez AU/500	15.00	40.00
DC4 Marlon Byrd AU/500	4.00	10.00
DC5 Bud Smith AU/400	4.00	10.00
DC6 Joe Mays AU/500	4.00	10.00
DC7 Troy Glaus AU/500	6.00	15.00
DC8 Ron Santo AU/500	10.00	25.00
DC9 Roy Oswalt AU/500	6.00	15.00
DC10 Angel Berroa AU/500	4.00	10.00
DC11 Mark Buehrle AU/500	10.00	25.00
DC12 John Buck AU/500	4.00	10.00
DC13 Barry Larkin AU/250	20.00	50.00
DC14 Gary Carter AU/250	10.00	25.00
DC15 Mark Teixeira AU/300	15.00	40.00
DC16 Alan Trammell AU/500	6.00	15.00
DC17 Kazuhisa Ishii AU/100	15.00	40.00
DC18 Rafael Palmeiro AU/125	30.00	60.00
DC19 Austin Kearns AU/500	4.00	10.00
DC20 Joe Torre AU/125	30.00	60.00
DC21 J.D. Drew AU/400	6.00	15.00
DC22 So Taguchi AU/400	12.50	30.00
DC23 Juan Marichal AU/500	6.00	15.00
DC24 Bobby Doerr AU/500	10.00	25.00
DC25 Carlos Beltran AU/500	6.00	15.00
DC26 Robert Fick AU/500	4.00	10.00
DC27 Albert Pujols AU/200	150.00	250.00
DC28 Shannon Stewart AU/500	6.00	15.00
DC29 Antonio Perez AU/500	4.00	10.00
DC30 Wilson Betemit AU/500	4.00	10.00
DC31 Alex Rodriguez Jsy/500	6.00	15.00
DC32 Curt Schilling Jsy/500	3.00	8.00
DC33 George Brett Jsy/300	10.00	25.00
DC34 Hideo Nomo Jsy/100	6.00	15.00
DC35 Ivan Rodriguez Jsy/500	4.00	10.00
DC36 Don Mattingly Jsy/200	10.00	25.00
DC37 Joe Mays Jsy/500	3.00	8.00
DC38 Lance Berkman Jsy/400	3.00	8.00
DC39 Tony Gwynn Jsy/500	6.00	15.00
DC40 Darin Erstad Jsy/500	3.00	8.00
DC41 Adrian Beltre Jsy/400	3.00	8.00
DC42 Frank Thomas Jsy/500	4.00	10.00
DC43 Cal Ripken Jsy/300	15.00	40.00
DC44 Jose Vidro Jsy/500	3.00	8.00
DC45 Randy Johnson Jsy/300	4.00	10.00
DC46 Carlos Delgado Jsy/500	3.00	8.00
DC47 Roger Clemens Jsy/400	6.00	15.00
DC48 Luis Gonzalez Jsy/500	3.00	8.00
DC49 Marlon Byrd Jsy/500	3.00	8.00
DC50 Carlton Fisk Jsy/500	4.00	10.00
DC51 Manny Ramirez Jsy/500	4.00	10.00
DC52 Vladimir Guerrero Jsy/500	4.00	10.00
DC53 Barry Larkin Jsy/500	3.00	8.00
DC54 Aramis Ramirez Jsy/500	3.00	8.00
DC55 Todd Helton Jsy/300	4.00	10.00
DC56 Carlos Beltran Jsy/250	3.00	8.00
DC57 Jeff Bagwell Jsy/250	4.00	10.00
DC58 Larry Walker Jsy/500	3.00	8.00
DC59 Al Kaline Jsy/200	4.00	10.00
DC60 Chipper Jones Jsy/500	4.00	10.00
DC61 Bernie Williams Jsy/500	4.00	10.00
DC62 Bud Smith Jsy/500	3.00	8.00
DC63 Edgar Martinez Jsy/500	4.00	10.00
DC64 Pedro Martinez Jsy/500	4.00	10.00
DC65 Andre Dawson Jsy/200	3.00	8.00
DC66 Mike Piazza Jsy/100	10.00	25.00
DC67 Barry Zito Jsy/500	3.00	8.00
DC68 Bo Jackson Jsy/300	4.00	10.00
DC69 Nolan Ryan Jsy/400	15.00	40.00
DC70 Troy Glaus Jsy/500	3.00	8.00
DC71 Jorge Posada Jsy/500	4.00	10.00
DC72 Ted Williams Jsy/100	50.00	100.00
DC73 N.Garciaparra Jsy/500	6.00	15.00
DC74 Catfish Hunter Jsy/100	6.00	15.00
DC75 Gary Carter Jsy/500	3.00	8.00
DC76 Craig Biggio Jsy/500	4.00	10.00
DC77 Andruw Jones Jsy/500	4.00	10.00
DC78 R.Henderson Jsy/300	4.00	10.00
DC79 Greg Maddux Jsy/400	6.00	15.00
DC80 Kerry Wood Jsy/500	3.00	8.00
DC81 Alex Rodriguez Bat/500	6.00	15.00
DC82 Don Mattingly Bat/425	10.00	25.00
DC83 Craig Biggio Bat/500	6.00	15.00
DC84 Kazuhisa Ishii Bat/375	4.00	10.00
DC85 Eddie Murray Bat/500	6.00	15.00
DC86 Carlton Fisk Bat/500	6.00	15.00
DC87 Tsuyoshi Shinjo Bat/500	4.00	10.00
DC88 Bo Jackson Bat/500	6.00	15.00
DC89 Eddie Mathews Bat/100	10.00	25.00
DC90 Chipper Jones Bat/500	6.00	15.00
DC91 Adam Dunn Bat/375	4.00	10.00
DC92 Tony Gwynn Bat/200	6.00	15.00
DC93 Kirby Puckett Bat/500	6.00	15.00
DC94 Andre Dawson Bat/500	4.00	10.00

DC95 Bernie Williams Bat/500	6.00	15.00
DC96 Rob. Clemente Bat/300	40.00	80.00
DC97 Babe Ruth Bat/100	150.00	250.00
DC98 Roberto Alomar Bat/500	6.00	15.00
DC99 Frank Thomas Bat/500	6.00	15.00
DC100 So Taguchi Bat/500	4.00	10.00

2002 Diamond Kings DK Originals

Randomly inserted in packs, these 15 cards are printed to a stated print run of 1000 serial numbered sets. These cards are printed on canvas board with a vintage Diamond King look to them.

COMPLETE SET (15)	75.00	150.00
DK1 Alex Rodriguez	5.00	12.00
DK2 Kazuhisa Ishii	3.00	8.00
DK3 Pedro Martinez	3.00	8.00
DK4 Nomar Garciaparra	5.00	12.00
DK5 Albert Pujols	6.00	15.00
DK6 Chipper Jones	3.00	8.00
DK7 So Taguchi	3.00	8.00
DK8 Jeff Bagwell	3.00	8.00
DK9 Vladimir Guerrero	3.00	8.00
DK10 Derek Jeter	8.00	20.00
DK11 Sammy Sosa	3.00	8.00
DK12 Ichiro Suzuki	6.00	15.00
DK13 Barry Bonds	8.00	20.00
DK14 Jason Giambi	3.00	8.00
DK15 Mike Piazza	5.00	12.00

2002 Diamond Kings Heritage Collection

Inserted in packs to a stated rate of one in 23 hobby and one in 46 retail packs, these 25 cards feature many of baseball's all-time greats highlighted on canvas board stock.

COMPLETE SET (25)	100.00	200.00
HC1 Lou Gehrig	4.00	10.00
HC2 Nolan Ryan	6.00	15.00
HC3 Ryne Sandberg	4.00	10.00
HC4 Ted Williams	5.00	12.00
HC5 Roberto Clemente	6.00	15.00
HC6 Mike Schmidt	5.00	12.00
HC7 Roger Clemens	5.00	12.00
HC8 Kirby Puckett	2.00	5.00
HC9 Andre Dawson	1.50	4.00
HC10 Carlton Fisk	1.50	4.00
HC11 Don Mattingly	5.00	12.00
HC12 Juan Marichal	1.50	4.00
HC13 George Brett	5.00	12.00
HC14 Bo Jackson	2.00	5.00
HC15 Eddie Mathews	2.00	5.00
HC16 Randy Johnson	2.00	5.00
HC17 Alan Trammell	1.50	4.00
HC18 Tony Gwynn	3.00	8.00
HC19 Paul Molitor	1.50	4.00
HC20 Barry Bonds	6.00	15.00
HC21 Eddie Murray	2.00	5.00
HC22 Catfish Hunter	1.50	4.00
HC23 Rickey Henderson	2.00	5.00
HC24 Cal Ripken	8.00	20.00
HC25 Babe Ruth	6.00	15.00

2002 Diamond Kings Recollection Autographs

Randomly inserted in packs, these cards are original Diamond Kings which Donruss/Playoff bought back and had the feature player sign. These cards are all numbered to differing amounts and we have notated that information in our checklist. No pricing is provided on quantities of 25 or less.

47 Alan Trammell 88 DK/110	15.00	40.00

2002 Diamond Kings T204

Randomly inserted in packs, these 25 cards are printed to a stated print run of 1000 serial numbered sets. These cards are designed just like the Ramly T204 set which was issued early in the 20th century.

COMPLETE SET (25)	125.00	250.00
RC1 Vladimir Guerrero	3.00	8.00
RC2 Jeff Bagwell	2.00	5.00
RC3 Barry Bonds	8.00	20.00
RC4 Rickey Henderson	3.00	8.00
RC5 Mike Piazza	5.00	12.00
RC6 Derek Jeter	8.00	20.00
RC7 Kazuhisa Ishii	2.00	5.00
RC8 Ichiro Suzuki	6.00	15.00
RC9 Chipper Jones	3.00	8.00
RC10 Sammy Sosa	3.00	8.00
RC11 Don Mattingly	6.00	15.00
RC12 Shawn Green	2.00	5.00
RC13 Nomar Garciaparra	5.00	12.00
RC14 Luis Gonzalez	2.00	5.00
RC15 Albert Pujols	6.00	15.00
RC16 Cal Ripken	10.00	25.00
RC17 Todd Helton	2.00	5.00
RC18 Hideo Nomo	3.00	8.00
RC19 Alex Rodriguez	5.00	12.00
RC20 So Taguchi	2.00	5.00
RC21 Lance Berkman	2.00	5.00
RC22 Tony Gwynn	4.00	10.00
RC23 Roger Clemens	6.00	15.00
RC24 Jason Giambi	2.00	5.00
RC25 Ken Griffey Jr.	5.00	12.00

2002 Diamond Kings Timeline

Issued at a stated rate of one in 60 hobby and one in 120 retail packs, these 10 cards feature two players who have something in common.

COMPLETE SET (10)	60.00	120.00
TL1 Lou Gehrig Don Mattingly	6.00	15.00
TL2 Hideo Nomo Ichiro Suzuki	4.00	10.00
TL3 Cal Ripken Alex Rodriguez	8.00	20.00
TL4 Mike Schmidt Scott Rolen	5.00	12.00
TL5 Ichiro Suzuki Albert Pujols	5.00	12.00
TL6 Curt Schilling Randy Johnson	4.00	10.00
TL7 Chipper Jones Eddie Mathews	4.00	10.00
TL8 Lou Gehrig Cal Ripken	8.00	20.00
TL9 Derek Jeter Roger Clemens	6.00	15.00
TL10 Kazuhisa Ishii SoTaguchi	4.00	10.00

2002 Diamond Kings Hawaii

These cards were distributed in six-card cello-wrapped packets at the eBay booth of the Hawaii Trade Conference "Meet the Industry" event in late February, 2002. Each attendee received one packet at the presentation. The cards parallel the basic issue 2002 Donruss Diamond Kings distributed later that year, but can be readily distinguished by the "2002 Hawaii Trade Conference" gold foil logo stamped on the front.

*PARALLEL 20'S RANDOMLY INSERTED INTO PACKS
*PARALLEL: NO PRICING DUE TO SCARCITY
*BLUE PORT: RANDOMLY INSERTED INTO PACKS

*BLUE PORT: SERIAL #'D TO 1 OR 5
*BLUE PORT: NO PRICING DUE TO SCARCITY

2003 Diamond Kings Samples

Issued one per Beckett Baseball Card Magazine, these cards were issued to preview the 2003 Donruss Diamond Kings set. These cards parallel the regular set except the word "sample" is stamped in silver on the back.

*SAMPLES: 1.5X TO 4X BASIC CARDS

2003 Diamond Kings Samples Gold

Randomly inserted in Beckett Baseball Card Magazine, these cards feature the word "sample" on the back printed in gold. Usually the gold samples comprise 10 percent of all the samples produced.

*GOLD SAMPLES: 4X TO 10X BASIC CARDS

2003 Diamond Kings

This 200-card set was released in two separate series. The primary Diamond Kings product - containing cards 1-176 from the basic set - was issued in March, 2003. These cards were issued in five card packs with an $4 SRP. These packs came 24 packs to a box and 20 boxes to a case. Cards numbered 151 through 158 feature some of the leading rookie prospects and those cards were issued at a stated rate of one in six. Cards numbered 159 through 175 feature retired greats and those cards were also issued at a stated rate of one in six. Card number 176 features Cuban refugee Jose Contreras who was signed to a free agent contract before the 2003 season began. The Contreras card was not on the original checklist and is believed to be considerably scarcer than other RC's from the first series set. Cards 177-189/191-201 were distributed at a rate of 1:24 packs of DLP Rookies and Traded in December, 2003. Please note, card 190 does not exist.

COMP.LO SET (176)	60.00	150.00
COMP.LO SET w/o SP's (150)	20.00	50.00
COMMON CARD (1-150)	.20	.50
COMMON CARD (151-158)	.75	2.00
COMMON CARD (159-175)	1.50	4.00
COMMON CARD (177-201)	1.50	4.00
1 Darin Erstad	.20	.50
2 Garret Anderson	.20	.50
3 Troy Glaus	.20	.50
4 David Eckstein	.20	.50
5 Jarrod Washburn	.20	.50
6 Adam Kennedy	.20	.50
7 Jay Gibbons	.20	.50
8 Tony Batista	.20	.50
9 Melvin Mora	.20	.50
10 Rodrigo Lopez	.20	.50
11 Manny Ramirez	.30	.75
12 Pedro Martinez	.30	.75
13 Nomar Garciaparra	.75	2.00
14 Rickey Henderson	.50	1.25
15 Johnny Damon	.30	.75
16 Derek Lowe	.20	.50
17 Cliff Floyd	.20	.50
18 Frank Thomas	.50	1.25
19 Magglio Ordonez	.20	.50
20 Paul Konerko	.20	.50
21 Mark Buehrle	.20	.50
22 C.C. Sabathia	.20	.50
23 Omar Vizquel	.30	.75
24 Jim Thome	.30	.75
25 Ellis Burks	.20	.50
26 Robert Fick	.20	.50
27 Bobby Higginson	.20	.50
28 Randall Simon	.20	.50
29 Carlos Pena	.20	.50
30 Carlos Beltran	.20	.50
31 Paul Byrd	.20	.50
32 Raul Ibanez	.20	.50
33 Mike Sweeney	.20	.50
34 Torii Hunter	.20	.50
35 Corey Koskie	.20	.50
36 A.J. Pierzynski	.20	.50
37 Cristian Guzman	.20	.50
38 Jacque Jones	.20	.50
39 Derek Jeter	1.25	3.00
40 Bernie Williams	.30	.75
41 Roger Clemens	1.00	2.50
42 Mike Mussina	.30	.75
43 Jorge Posada	.30	.75
44 Alfonso Soriano	.20	.50
45 Jason Giambi	.20	.50
46 Robin Ventura	.20	.50
47 David Wells	.20	.50
48 Tim Hudson	.20	.50
49 Barry Zito	.20	.50
50 Mark Mulder	.20	.50
51 Miguel Tejada	.20	.50
52 Eric Chavez	.20	.50
53 Jermaine Dye	.20	.50
54 Ichiro Suzuki	1.00	2.50
55 Edgar Martinez	.30	.75
56 John Olerud	.20	.50
57 Dan Wilson	.20	.50
58 Joel Pineiro	.20	.50
59 Kazuhiro Sasaki	.20	.50
60 Freddy Garcia	.20	.50
61 Aubrey Huff	.20	.50
62 Steve Cox	.20	.50
63 Randy Winn	.20	.50
64 Alex Rodriguez	.75	2.00
65 Juan Gonzalez	.20	.50
66 Rafael Palmeiro	.30	.75
67 Ivan Rodriguez	.30	.75
68 Kenny Rogers	.20	.50
69 Carlos Delgado	.20	.50
70 Eric Hinske	.20	.50
71 Roy Halladay	.20	.50
72 Vernon Wells	.20	.50
73 Shannon Stewart	.20	.50
74 Curt Schilling	.20	.50
75 Randy Johnson	.50	1.25
76 Luis Gonzalez	.20	.50
77 Mark Grace	.30	.75
78 Junior Spivey	.20	.50
79 Greg Maddux	.75	2.00
80 Tom Glavine	.30	.75
81 John Smoltz	.30	.75
82 Chipper Jones	.50	1.25
83 Gary Sheffield	.20	.50
84 Andruw Jones	.30	.75
85 Kerry Wood	.20	.50
86 Fred McGriff	.30	.75
87 Sammy Sosa	.50	1.25
88 Mark Prior	.30	.75
89 Ken Griffey Jr.	.75	2.00
90 Barry Larkin	.30	.75
91 Adam Dunn	.20	.50
92 Sean Casey	.20	.50
93 Austin Kearns	.20	.50
94 Aaron Boone	.20	.50
95 Larry Walker	.20	.50
96 Todd Helton	.30	.75
97 Jason Jennings	.20	.50
98 Jay Payton	.20	.50
99 Josh Beckett	.20	.50
100 Mike Lowell	.20	.50
101 A.J. Burnett	.20	.50
102 Jeff Bagwell	.30	.75
103 Craig Biggio	.30	.75
104 Lance Berkman	.20	.50
105 Roy Oswalt	.20	.50
106 Wade Miller	.20	.50
107 Shawn Green	.20	.50
108 Adrian Beltre	.20	.50
109 Hideo Nomo	.50	1.25
110 Kazuhisa Ishii	.20	.50
111 Odalis Perez	.20	.50
112 Paul Lo Duca	.20	.50
113 Ben Sheets	.20	.50
114 Richie Sexson	.20	.50
115 Jose Hernandez	.20	.50
116 Vladimir Guerrero	.50	1.25
117 Jose Vidro	.20	.50
118 Tomo Ohka	.20	.50
119 Andres Galarraga	.20	.50
120 Bartolo Colon	.20	.50
121 Mike Piazza	.75	2.00
122 Roberto Alomar	.30	.75
123 Mo Vaughn	.20	.50
124 Al Leiter	.20	.50
125 Edgardo Alfonzo	.20	.50
126 Pat Burrell	.20	.50
127 Bobby Abreu	.20	.50
128 Mike Lieberthal	.20	.50
129 Vicente Padilla	.20	.50
130 Marlon Byrd	.20	.50
131 Jason Kendall	.20	.50
132 Brian Giles	.20	.50
133 Aramis Ramirez	.20	.50
134 Kip Wells	.20	.50
135 Ryan Klesko	.20	.50
136 Phil Nevin	.20	.50
137 Brian Lawrence	.20	.50
138 Sean Burroughs	.20	.50
139 Mark Kotsay	.20	.50
140 Barry Bonds	1.25	3.00
141 Jeff Kent	.20	.50
142 Benito Santiago	.20	.50
143 Kirk Rueter	.20	.50
144 Jason Schmidt	.20	.50
145 Jim Edmonds	.20	.50
146 J.D. Drew	.20	.50
147 Albert Pujols	1.00	2.50
148 Tino Martinez	.30	.75
149 Matt Morris	.20	.50
150 Scott Rolen	.30	.75
151 Joe Borchard ROO	.75	2.00
152 Cliff Lee ROO	.75	2.00
153 Brian Tallet ROO	.75	2.00
154 Freddy Sanchez ROO	.75	2.00
155 Chone Figgins ROO	.75	2.00
156 Kevin Cash ROO	.75	2.00
157 Justin Wayne ROO	.75	2.00
158 Ben Kozlowski ROO	.75	2.00
159 Babe Ruth RET	4.00	10.00
160 Jackie Robinson RET	2.00	5.00
161 Ozzie Smith RET	3.00	8.00
162 Lou Gehrig RET	2.50	6.00
163 Stan Musial RET	2.50	6.00
164 Mike Schmidt RET	4.00	10.00
165 Carlton Fisk RET	2.00	5.00
166 George Brett RET	4.00	10.00
167 Dale Murphy RET	3.00	8.00
168 Cal Ripken RET	5.00	12.00
169 Tony Gwynn RET	2.00	5.00
170 Don Mattingly RET	4.00	10.00
171 Jack Morris RET	1.50	4.00
172 Ty Cobb RET	2.00	5.00
173 Nolan Ryan RET	4.00	10.00
174 Ryne Sandberg RET	3.00	8.00
175 Thurman Munson RET	2.00	5.00
176 Jose Contreras ROO RC	2.00	5.00
177 Hideki Matsui ROO RC	4.00	10.00
178 Jeremy Bonderman ROO RC	4.00	10.00
179 Brandon Webb ROO RC	3.00	8.00
180 Adam Loewen ROO RC	2.00	5.00
181 Chien-Ming Wang ROO RC	5.00	12.00
182 Hong-Chih Kuo ROO RC	3.00	8.00
183 Clint Barmes ROO RC	1.25	3.00
184 Guillermo Quiroz ROO RC	1.50	4.00
185 Edgar Gonzalez ROO RC	1.50	4.00
186 Todd Wellemeyer ROO RC	1.50	4.00
187 Dan Haren ROO RC	2.00	5.00
188 Dustin McGowan ROO RC	2.00	5.00
189 Preston Larrison ROO RC	2.00	5.00
191 Kevin Youkilis ROO RC	2.50	6.00
192 Bubba Nelson ROO RC	2.00	5.00
193 Chris Burke ROO RC	2.00	5.00
194 J.D. Durbin ROO RC	1.50	4.00
195 Ryan Howard ROO RC	8.00	20.00
196 Jason Kubel ROO RC	2.00	5.00
197 Brendan Harris ROO RC	2.00	5.00
198 Brian Bruney ROO RC	2.00	5.00
199 Ramon Nivar ROO RC	1.50	4.00
200 Rickie Weeks ROO RC	3.00	8.00
201 Delmon Young ROO RC	4.00	10.00

2003 Diamond Kings Bronze Foil

Randomly inserted in packs, this is a parallel to the Diamond Kings set. Cards 177-201 were randomly seeded into packs of DLP Rookies and Traded and unlike the first 176 cards are serial numbered to 200 copies per. The bronze cards can be identified by the white frames and the bronze foil used for the cards.

*BRONZE 1-150: 1.5X TO 4X BASIC
*BRONZE 151-158: .6X TO 1.5X BASIC
*BRONZE 159-175: .6X TO 1.5X BASIC
*BRONZE 176: .4X TO 1X BASIC
*BRZ 177-189/191-201: .5X TO 1.2X BASIC

181 Chien-Ming Wang ROO	20.00	50.00
182 Hong-Chih Kuo ROO	12.50	30.00
195 Ryan Howard ROO	12.50	30.00

2003 Diamond Kings Gold Foil

Randomly inserted into packs, this is a parallel to the Diamond Kings insert set. Cards 177-201 were randomly seeded into packs of DLP Rookies and Traded. These cards feature black frames which surround the gold foil usage. Cards 1-176 were issued to a stated print run of 100 serial numbered sets and 177-201 to a stated print run of 50 serial numbered copies per.

*GOLD 1-150: 6X TO 15X BASIC
*GOLD 151-158: 2X TO 5X BASIC
*GOLD 176: 1X TO 2.5X BASIC
*GOLD 177-201: 1.25X TO 3X BASIC

159 Babe Ruth RET	20.00	50.00
160 Jackie Robinson RET	10.00	25.00
161 Ozzie Smith RET	15.00	40.00
162 Lou Gehrig RET	12.50	30.00
163 Stan Musial RET	15.00	40.00
164 Mike Schmidt RET	20.00	50.00
165 Carlton Fisk RET	10.00	25.00
166 George Brett RET	20.00	50.00
167 Dale Murphy RET	25.00	60.00
168 Cal Ripken RET	30.00	80.00
169 Tony Gwynn RET	12.50	30.00
170 Don Mattingly RET	20.00	50.00
171 Jack Morris RET	8.00	20.00
172 Ty Cobb RET	15.00	40.00
173 Nolan Ryan RET	25.00	60.00
174 Ryne Sandberg RET	25.00	60.00
175 Thurman Munson RET	15.00	40.00
181 Chien-Ming Wang ROO	50.00	100.00
182 Hong-Chih Kuo ROO	30.00	60.00
195 Ryan Howard ROO	50.00	100.00
200 Rickie Weeks ROO	12.30	30.00
201 Delmon Young ROO	15.00	40.00

2003 Diamond Kings Silver Foil

Randomly inserted into packs, this is a parallel to the Diamond Kings set. Cards 177-201 were randomly seeded into packs of DLP Rookies and Traded. These cards can be identified by the grey frames surrounding the silver foil. Cards 1-176 were serial numbered to 400 and 177-201 were serial numbered to 100.

*SILVER 1-150: 3X TO 8X BASIC
*SILVER 151-158: 1X TO 2.5X BASIC
*SILVER 159-175: 1X TO 2.5X BASIC
*SILVER 176: .5X TO 1.2X BASIC
*SILVER 177-201: .6X TO 1.5X BASIC

181 Chien-Ming Wang ROO	30.00	60.00
182 Hong-Chih Kuo ROO	15.00	40.00
195 Ryan Howard ROO	20.00	50.00

2003 Diamond Kings Diamond Cut Collection

Randomly inserted into packs, this 110 card set features either an autograph or a game-used memorabilia piece. Since these cards are issued to a varying amount of cards, we have notated that information next to the player's name in our checklist.

1 Barry Zito AU/75	30.00	60.00
2 Edgar Martinez AU/125	30.00	60.00
3 Jay Gibbons AU/150	10.00	25.00
4 Joe Borchard AU/150	10.00	25.00
5 Marlon Byrd AU/150	10.00	25.00
6 Adam Dunn AU/150	20.00	50.00
7 Torii Hunter AU/150	12.50	30.00
8 Vladimir Guerrero AU/25		
9 Wade Miller AU/150	10.00	25.00
10 Alfonso Soriano AU/100	20.00	50.00
11 Brian Lawrence AU/150	10.00	25.00
12 Cliff Floyd AU/150	12.50	30.00
13 Dale Murphy AU/75	30.00	60.00
14 Jack Morris AU/150	12.50	30.00
15 Eric Hinske AU/150	10.00	25.00
16 Jason Jennings AU/150	10.00	25.00
17 Mark Buehrle AU/150	20.00	50.00
18 Mark Prior AU/150	10.00	25.00
19 Mark Mulder AU/150	12.50	30.00
20 Mike Sweeney AU/150	12.50	30.00
21 Nolan Ryan AU/50	150.00	250.00
22 Don Mattingly AU/75	75.00	150.00
23 Andruw Jones AU/75	30.00	60.00
24 Aubrey Huff AU/150	12.50	30.00
25 Rickey Henderson AU/25		
26 Nolan Ryan Jsy/250	20.00	50.00
27 Ozzie Smith Jsy/400	6.00	15.00
28 Rickey Henderson Jsy/300	4.00	10.00
29 Jack Morris Jsy/500	3.00	8.00
30 George Brett Jsy/350	8.00	20.00
31 Cal Ripken Jsy/300	15.00	40.00
32 Ryne Sandberg Jsy/450	8.00	20.00
33 Don Mattingly Jsy/400	8.00	20.00
34 Tony Gwynn Jsy/400	6.00	15.00
35 Dale Murphy Jsy/350	4.00	10.00
36 Carlton Fisk Jsy/400	4.00	10.00
37 Stan Musial Jsy/50		
38 Lou Gehrig Jsy/50	150.00	250.00
39 Garret Anderson Jsy/450	3.00	8.00
40 Pedro Martinez Jsy/400	4.00	10.00
41 Nomar Garciaparra Jsy/350	6.00	15.00
42 Magglio Ordonez Jsy/450	3.00	8.00
43 C.C. Sabathia Jsy/500	3.00	8.00
44 Omar Vizquel Jsy/250	6.00	15.00
45 Jim Thome Jsy/500	4.00	10.00
46 Torii Hunter Jsy/500	3.00	8.00
47 Roger Clemens Jsy/500	6.00	15.00
48 Alfonso Soriano Jsy/400	3.00	8.00
49 Tim Hudson Jsy/500	3.00	8.00
50 Barry Zito Jsy/350	3.00	8.00
51 Mark Mulder Jsy/500	3.00	8.00
52 Miguel Tejada Jsy/400	3.00	8.00
53 John Olerud Jsy/350	3.00	8.00
54 Alex Rodriguez Jsy/500	6.00	15.00
55 Rafael Palmeiro Jsy/500	4.00	10.00
56 Curt Schilling Jsy/500	3.00	8.00
57 Randy Johnson Jsy/400	4.00	10.00
58 Greg Maddux Jsy/350	6.00	15.00
59 John Smoltz Jsy/400	4.00	10.00
60 Chipper Jones Jsy/450	4.00	10.00
61 Andruw Jones Jsy/500	4.00	10.00
62 Kerry Wood Jsy/500	3.00	8.00
63 Mark Prior Jsy/500	4.00	10.00
64 Adam Dunn Jsy/350	3.00	8.00
65 Larry Walker Jsy/500	3.00	8.00
66 Todd Helton Jsy/500	4.00	10.00
67 Jeff Bagwell Jsy/500	4.00	10.00
68 Roy Oswalt Jsy/500	3.00	8.00
69 Hideo Nomo Jsy/150	6.00	15.00
70 Kazuhisa Ishii Jsy/250	4.00	10.00
71 Vladimir Guerrero Jsy/500	4.00	10.00
72 Mike Piazza Jsy/500	6.00	15.00
73 Joe Borchard Jsy/500	3.00	8.00
74 Ryan Klesko Jsy/500	3.00	8.00
75 Shawn Green Jsy/500	3.00	8.00
76 George Brett Bat/350	8.00	20.00
77 Ozzie Smith Bat/450	6.00	15.00
78 Cal Ripken Bat/150	20.00	50.00
79 Don Mattingly Bat/400	8.00	20.00
80 Babe Ruth Bat/50	150.00	250.00
81 Dale Murphy Bat/350	4.00	10.00
82 Rickey Henderson Bat/500	4.00	10.00
83 Ivan Rodriguez Bat/500	4.00	10.00
84 Marlon Byrd Bat/500	3.00	8.00
85 Eric Chavez Bat/500	3.00	8.00
86 Nomar Garciaparra Bat/500	6.00	15.00
87 Alex Rodriguez Bat/500	6.00	15.00
88 Vladimir Guerrero Bat/500	4.00	10.00
89 Paul Lo Duca Bat/500	3.00	8.00
90 Richie Sexson Bat/500	3.00	8.00
91 Mike Piazza Bat/350	6.00	15.00
92 J.D. Drew Bat/500	3.00	8.00
93 Juan Gonzalez Bat/500	3.00	8.00
94 Pat Burrell Bat/500	3.00	8.00
95 Adam Dunn Bat/250	4.00	10.00
96 Mike Schmidt Bat/500	8.00	20.00
97 Ryne Sandberg Bat/500	8.00	20.00
98 Edgardo Alfonzo Bat/500	3.00	8.00
99 Andruw Jones Bat/500	4.00	10.00
100 Carlos Beltran Bat/500	3.00	8.00
101 Jeff Bagwell Bat/500	4.00	10.00
102 Lance Berkman Bat/500	3.00	8.00
103 Luis Gonzalez Bat/500	3.00	8.00
104 Carlos Delgado Bat/500	3.00	8.00
105 Jim Edmonds Bat/250	4.00	10.00
106 Alf Soriano Hat-Jsy/75	10.00	25.00
107 Greg Maddux Jsy-AU/50	100.00	200.00
108 Ty Cobb Pants-Bat/25		
109 Adam Dunn Bat-AU/50	40.00	80.00
110 R.Henderson Jsy-Bat/50	10.00	25.00

2003 Diamond Kings DK Evolution

Issued at a stated rate of one in 18 hobby and one in 36 retail, this 25 card set features both the original photo as well as the artwork.

1 Cal Ripken	8.00	20.00
2 Ichiro Suzuki	5.00	12.00
3 Randy Johnson	2.50	6.00

4 Pedro Martinez	2.00	5.00
5 Nolan Ryan	6.00	15.00
6 Derek Jeter	6.00	15.00
7 Kerry Wood	2.00	5.00
8 Alex Rodriguez	4.00	10.00
9 Magglio Ordonez	2.00	5.00
10 Greg Maddux	4.00	10.00
11 Todd Helton	2.00	5.00
12 Sammy Sosa	2.50	6.00
13 Lou Gehrig	5.00	12.00
14 Lance Berkman	2.00	5.00
15 Barry Zito	2.00	5.00
16 Barry Bonds	6.00	15.00
17 Tom Glavine	2.00	5.00
18 Shawn Green	2.00	5.00
19 Roger Clemens	5.00	12.00
20 Nomar Garciaparra	4.00	10.00
21 Tony Gwynn	3.00	8.00
22 Vladimir Guerrero	2.50	6.00
23 Albert Pujols	5.00	12.00
24 Chipper Jones	2.50	6.00
25 Alfonso Soriano	2.00	5.00

2003 Diamond Kings Heritage Collection

Issued at a stated rate of one in 23, this 25 card set features a mix of past and present superstars spotlighted with silver holo-foil on canvas board.

1 Ozzie Smith	4.00	10.00
2 Lou Gehrig	5.00	12.00
3 Stan Musial	4.00	10.00
4 Mike Schmidt	5.00	12.00
5 Carlton Fisk	2.00	5.00
6 George Brett	5.00	12.00
7 Dale Murphy	2.00	5.00
8 Cal Ripken	8.00	20.00
9 Tony Gwynn	3.00	8.00
10 Don Mattingly	5.00	12.00
11 Jack Morris	2.00	5.00
12 Ty Cobb	4.00	10.00
13 Nolan Ryan	6.00	15.00
14 Ryne Sandberg	5.00	12.00
15 Thurman Munson	2.50	6.00
16 Ichiro Suzuki	5.00	12.00
17 Derek Jeter	6.00	15.00
18 Greg Maddux	4.00	10.00
19 Sammy Sosa	2.50	6.00
20 Pedro Martinez	2.00	5.00
21 Alex Rodriguez	4.00	10.00
22 Roger Clemens	5.00	12.00
23 Barry Bonds	6.00	15.00
24 Lance Berkman	2.00	5.00
25 Vladimir Guerrero	2.50	6.00

2003 Diamond Kings HOF Heroes Reprints

Issued in the style of the 1983 Donruss Hall of Fame Heroes set, this set was issued at a stated rate of one in 43 hobby and one in 67 retail.

1 Bob Feller	3.00	8.00
2 Al Kaline	3.00	8.00
3 Lou Boudreau	3.00	8.00
4 Duke Snider	3.00	8.00
5 Jackie Robinson	3.00	8.00
6 Early Wynn	3.00	8.00
7 Yogi Berra	3.00	8.00
8 Stan Musial	4.00	10.00
9 Ty Cobb	4.00	10.00
10 Ted Williams	5.00	12.00

2003 Diamond Kings HOF Heroes Reprints Materials

Randomly inserted into packs, these cards parallel the HOF Heroes Reprint set. Each card has a game-used memorabilia piece used by that player during his career. Each of these cards were issued to a stated print run of 50 serial numbered sets.

1 Bob Feller Jsy
2 Al Kaline Bat
3 Lou Boudreau Jsy
4 Duke Snider Bat
5 Jackie Robinson Jsy
6 Early Wynn Jsy
7 Yogi Berra Bat
8 Stan Musial Bat
9 Ty Cobb Bat
10 Ted Williams Jsy

2003 Diamond Kings Recollection

Randomly inserted into packs, these 14 cards feature older repurchased Diamond King subset cards or 1983 Hall of Fame Heroes cards. As each of these cards were issued to a stated print run of 15 or fewer copies, no pricing is available due to market scarcity.

5 Lou Boudreau 83 HOF/3
15 Roberto Clemente 83 HOF/5
16 Roberto Clemente 87 DK/9
17 Ty Cobb 83 DK/10
18 Ty Cobb 83 HOF/5
34 Lou Gehrig 85 DK/10
44 Monte Irvin 83 HOF/5
48 Bob Lemon 83 HOF/5
66 Dan Quisenberry 85 DK/2
69 Jackie Robinson 83 HOF/5
82 Willie Stargell 83 DK/15
83 Willie Stargell 91 DK/6
90 Ted Williams 83 HOF/4
92 Early Wynn 83 HOF/5

2003 Diamond Kings Recollection Autographs

Randomly inserted in packs, these cards feature not only repurchased Donruss Diamond King cards but also an authentic autograph of the featured player. These cards were issued to a varying print run amount and we have notated that information next to the player's name in our checklist. Please note that for cards with a print run of 40 of fewer, no pricing is provided due to market scarcity.

SEE BECKETT.COM FOR PRINT RUNS
NO PRICING ON QTY OF 40 OR LESS

2 Brandon Berger 02 DK/99	6.00	15.00

2003 Diamond Kings Team Timeline

Randomly inserted into packs, these 10 cards feature both an active and retired player from the same team, Each of these cards are printed on canvas board and were issued to a stated print run of 1000 sets.

1 Nolan Ryan Roy Oswalt	6.00	15.00
2 Dale Murphy Chipper Jones	3.00	8.00
3 Stan Musial Jim Edmonds	4.00	10.00
4 George Brett Mike Sweeney	6.00	15.00
5 Tony Gwynn Ryan Klesko	3.00	8.00
6 Carlton Fisk Magglio Ordonez	3.00	8.00
7 Mike Schmidt Pat Burrell	6.00	15.00
8 Don Mattingly Bernie Williams	6.00	15.00
9 Ryne Sandberg Kerry Wood	6.00	15.00
10 Lou Gehrig Alfonso Soriano	5.00	12.00

2003 Diamond Kings Team Timeline Jerseys

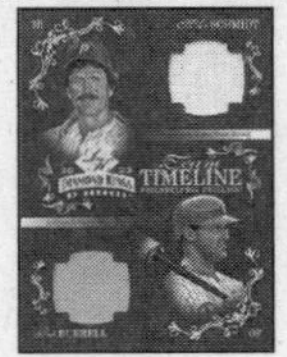

Randomly inserted into packs, this is a parallel to the Team Timeline insert set. Each of these cards feature two game-worn jersey swatches and were issued to a stated print run of 100 serial numbered sets.

1 Nolan Ryan Roy Oswalt	60.00	120.00
2 Dale Murphy Chipper Jones	15.00	40.00
3 Stan Musial Jim Edmonds	20.00	50.00
4 George Brett Mike Sweeney	40.00	80.00
5 Tony Gwynn Ryan Klesko	20.00	50.00
6 Carlton Fisk Magglio Ordonez	15.00	40.00
7 Mike Schmidt Pat Burrell	40.00	80.00
8 Don Mattingly Bernie Williams	40.00	80.00
9 Ryne Sandberg Kerry Wood	40.00	80.00
10 Lou Gehrig Alfonso Soriano/50	150.00	250.00

2003 Diamond Kings Atlantic City National

Collectors who opened enough packs of Donruss product at the Donruss corporate booth at the 2003 National held in Atlantic City received copies of these Diamond King cards. The fronts of the card had special Atlantic City embossing while the backs were serial numbered to a stated print of five serial numbered copies. Due to market scarcity, no pricing is provided for these cards.

PRINT RUN 5 SERIAL #'d SETS

2003 Diamond Kings Chicago Collection

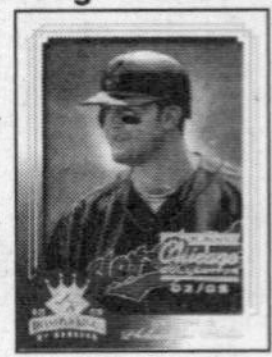

These cards were issued at the March, 2003 Chicago Sun-Times show. These cards parallel the Donruss Diamond King set and were available to collectors who opened three packs at the Donruss booth. For each three packs collectors opened, they received a specially stamped Diamond Kings cards stamped as "March Chicago Collection" and also with a stamped serial number. Each of these cards were issued to a stated print run of five serial numbered sets and no pricing is available due to market scarcity.

DIST.AT MARCH 03 SUN TIMES SHOW
STATED PRINT RUN 5 SERIAL #'d SETS
NO PRICING DUE TO SCARCITY

2003 Diamond Kings Heritage Collection Hawaii

These cards, which parallel the Diamond Kings Heritage Collection set were distributed at the Hawaii Trade Show conference. These cards were issued to a stated print run of 20 serial numbered sets and no pricing is available due to market scarcity.

DISTRIBUTED AT 2003 HAWAII CONFERENCE
STATED PRINT RUN 20 SERIAL #'d SETS
NO PRICING DUE TO SCARCITY

2003 Diamond Kings Team Timeline Hawaii

This set parallels the Team Timeline insert set. Each of these cards were specially distributed at the Hawaii Conference and were issued to a stated print run of 50 serial numbered sets.

*HAWAII: 2X TO 5X BASIC TIMELINE
DISTRIBUTED AT 2003 HAWAII CONFERENCE
STATED PRINT RUN 50 SERIAL #'d SETS

2003 Diamond Kings HOF Heroes Reprints Hawaii

These cards, which parallel the HOF Heroes Reprint set was distributed at the 2003 Hawaii Conference. These cards were issued to a stated print run of 50 serial numbered sets.

*HAWAII: 1X TO 2.5X BASIC HOF REPRINTS
DISTRIBUTED AT 2003 HAWAII CONFERENCE
STATED PRINT RUN 50 SERIAL #'d SETS

2004 Diamond Kings

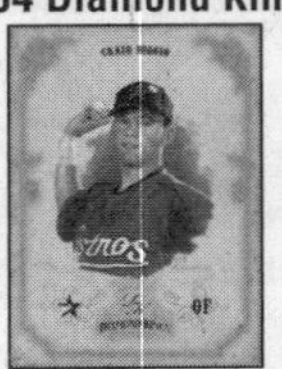

This 175-card set was released in February, 2004. This set was issued in five-card packs with an $6 SRP which came 12 packs to a box and 16 boxes to a case. This product has a dizzying amount of parallels and insert cards which included DK Materials which had two memorabilia pieces on each card and DK Combos which had not only those two memorabilia pieces but also had an authentic autograph from the player. In addition, many other insert sets were issued including a 134-card recollection autograph insert set as well as many other insert sets. This product; despite the seeming never-ending array of parallel and insert sets which made identifying cards difficult actually became one of the hobby hits of the first part of 2004. Cards numbered 1 through 150 feature current major leaguers while cards 151 through 158 are a flashback featuring some of today's players in an then and now format and cards numbered 159 through 175 are a legends subset. Cards numbered 151 through 175 were randomly inserted into packs.

COMPLETE SET w/Sepia (200)	75.00	200.00
COMPLETE SET (175)	40.00	100.00
COMP.SET w/o SP's (150)	15.00	40.00
COMMON CARD (1-150)	.20	.50
COMMON CARD (151-175)	1.25	3.00
151-175 RANDOM INSERTS IN PACKS		
1 Alex Rodriguez	.75	2.00
2 Andruw Jones	.30	.75
3 Nomar Garciaparra	.75	2.00
4 Kerry Wood	.20	.50
5 Magglio Ordonez	.20	.50
6 Victor Martinez	.20	.50
7 Jeremy Bonderman	.20	.50
8 Josh Beckett	.20	.50
9 Jeff Kent	.20	.50
10 Carlos Beltran	.20	.50
11 Hideo Nomo	.50	1.25
12 Richie Sexson	.20	.50
13 Jose Vidro	.20	.50
14 Jae Weong Seo	.20	.50
15 Alfonso Soriano	.20	.50
16 Barry Zito	.20	.50
17 Brett Myers	.20	.50
18 Brian Giles	.20	.50
19 Edgar Martinez	.30	.75
20 Jim Edmonds	.20	.50
21 Rocco Baldelli	.20	.50
22 Mark Teixeira	.30	.75
23 Carlos Delgado	.20	.50
24 Julius Matos	.20	.50
25 Jose Reyes	.20	.50
26 Marlon Byrd	.20	.50
27 Albert Pujols	1.00	2.50
28 Vernon Wells	.20	.50
29 Garret Anderson	.20	.50
30 Jerome Williams	.20	.50
31 Chipper Jones	.50	1.25
32 Rich Harden	.20	.50
33 Manny Ramirez	.30	.75
34 Derek Jeter	1.00	2.50
35 Brandon Webb	.20	.50
36 Mark Prior	.30	.75
37 Roy Halladay	.20	.50
38 Frank Thomas	.50	1.25
39 Rafael Palmeiro	.30	.75
40 Adam Dunn	.20	.50
41 Aubrey Huff	.20	.50
42 Todd Helton	.30	.75
43 Matt Morris	.20	.50
44 Dontrelle Willis	.30	.75
45 Lance Berkman	.20	.50
46 Mike Sweeney	.20	.50
47 Kazuhisa Ishii	.20	.50
48 Torii Hunter	.20	.50
49 Vladimir Guerrero	.50	1.25
50 Mike Piazza	.75	2.00
51 Alexis Rios	.20	.50
52 Shannon Stewart	.20	.50
53 Eric Hinske	.20	.50
54 Jason Jennings	.20	.50
55 Jason Giambi	.20	.50
56 Brandon Claussen	.20	.50
57 Joe Thurston	.20	.50
58 Ramon Nivar	.20	.50
59 Jay Gibbons	.20	.50
60 Eric Chavez	.20	.50
61 Jimmy Gobble	.20	.50
62 Walter Young	.20	.50
63 Mark Grace	.30	.75
64 Austin Kearns	.20	.50
65 Bob Abreu	.20	.50
66 Hee Seop Choi	.20	.50
67 Brandon Phillips	.20	.50
68 Rickie Weeks	.20	.50
69 Luis Gonzalez	.20	.50
70 Mariano Rivera	.50	1.25
71 Jason Lane	.20	.50
72 Xavier Nady	.20	.50
73 Runelvys Hernandez	.20	.50
74 Aramis Ramirez	.20	.50
75 Ichiro Suzuki	1.00	2.50
76 Cliff Lee	.20	.50
77 Chris Snelling	.20	.50
78 Ryan Wagner	.20	.50
79 Miguel Tejada	.20	.50
80 Juan Gonzalez	.20	.50
81 Joe Borchard	.20	.50
82 Gary Sheffield	.20	.50
83 Wade Miller	.20	.50
84 Jeff Bagwell	.30	.75
85 Ryan Church	.20	.50
86 Adrian Beltre	.20	.50
87 Jeff Baker	.20	.50
88 Adam Loewen	.20	.50
89 Bernie Williams	.30	.75
90 Pedro Martinez	.30	.75
91 Carlos Rivera	.20	.50
92 Junior Spivey	.20	.50
93 Tim Hudson	.20	.50
94 Troy Glaus	.20	.50
95 Ken Griffey Jr.	.75	2.00
96 Alexis Gomez	.20	.50
97 Antonio Perez	.20	.50
98 Dan Haren	.20	.50
99 Ivan Rodriguez	.30	.75
100 Randy Johnson	.50	1.25
101 Lyle Overbay	.20	.50
102 Oliver Perez	.20	.50
103 Miguel Cabrera	.30	.75
104 Scott Rolen	.30	.75
105 Roger Clemens	1.00	2.50
106 Brian Tallet	.20	.50
107 Nic Jackson	.20	.50
108 Angel Berroa	.20	.50
109 Hank Blalock	.20	.50
110 Ryan Klesko	.20	.50
111 Jose Castillo	.20	.50
112 Paul Konerko	.20	.50
113 Greg Maddux	.75	2.00
114 Mark Mulder	.20	.50
115 Pat Burrell	.20	.50
116 Garrett Atkins	.20	.50
117 Jeremy Guthrie	.20	.50
118 Orlando Cabrera	.20	.50
119 Nick Johnson	.20	.50
120 Tom Glavine	.30	.75
121 Morgan Ensberg	.20	.50
122 Sean Casey	.20	.50
123 Orlando Hudson	.20	.50
124 Hideki Matsui	.75	2.00
125 Craig Biggio	.30	.75
126 Adam LaRoche	.20	.50
127 Hong-Chih Kuo	.20	.50
128 Paul Lo Duca	.20	.50
129 Shawn Green	.20	.50
130 Luis Castillo	.20	.50
131 Joe Crede	.20	.50
132 Ken Harvey	.20	.50
133 Freddy Sanchez	.20	.50
134 Roy Oswalt	.20	.50
135 Curt Schilling	.30	.75
136 Alfredo Amezaga	.20	.50
137 Chien-Ming Wang	.75	2.00
138 Barry Larkin	.30	.75
139 Trot Nixon	.20	.50
140 Jim Thome	.30	.75
141 Bret Boone	.20	.50
142 Jacque Jones	.20	.50
143 Travis Hafner	.20	.50
144 Sammy Sosa	.50	1.25
145 Mike Mussina	.30	.75
146 Vinny Chulk	.20	.50
147 Chad Gaudin	.20	.50
148 Delmon Young	.30	.75
149 Mike Lowell	.20	.50
150 Rickey Henderson	.50	1.25
151 Roger Clemens FB	2.50	6.00
152 Mark Grace FB	1.50	4.00
153 Rickey Henderson FB	1.50	4.00
154 Alex Rodriguez FB	2.00	5.00
155 Rafael Palmeiro FB	1.50	4.00
156 Greg Maddux FB	2.00	5.00
157 Mike Piazza FB	2.00	5.00
158 Mike Mussina FB	1.50	4.00
159 Dale Murphy LGD	1.50	4.00
160 Cal Ripken LGD	4.00	10.00
161 Carl Yastrzemski LGD	2.00	5.00
162 Marty Marion LGD	1.25	3.00
163 Don Mattingly LGD	2.50	6.00
164 Robin Yount LGD	1.50	4.00
165 Andre Dawson LGD	1.25	3.00
166 Jim Palmer LGD	1.25	3.00
167 George Brett LGD	2.50	6.00
168 Whitey Ford LGD	1.50	4.00
169 Roy Campanella LGD	1.50	4.00
170 Roger Maris LGD	1.50	4.00
171 Duke Snider LGD	1.50	4.00
172 Steve Carlton LGD	1.25	3.00
173 Stan Musial LGD	2.00	5.00
174 Nolan Ryan LGD	3.00	8.00
175 Deion Sanders LGD	1.50	4.00

2004 Diamond Kings Sepia

*SEPIA: .75X TO 2X BASIC
RANDOM INSERTS IN PACKS

2004 Diamond Kings Bronze

*BRONZE 1-150: 3X TO 8X BASIC
*BRONZE 151-175: 1.25X TO 3X BASIC
RANDOM INSERTS IN PACKS
STATED PRINT RUN 100 SERIAL #'d SETS

2004 Diamond Kings Bronze Sepia

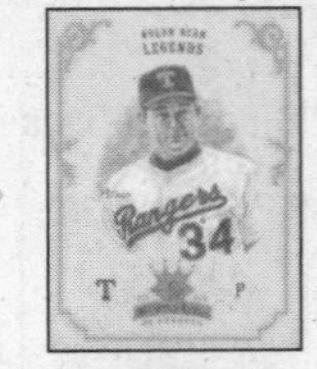

*BRONZE SEPIA: 1.25X TO 3X BASIC
RANDOM INSERTS IN PACKS
STATED PRINT RUN 100 SERIAL #'d SETS

2004 Diamond Kings Platinum

RANDOM INSERTS IN PACKS
STATED PRINT RUN 1 SERIAL #'d SET
NO PRICING DUE TO SCARCITY

2004 Diamond Kings Platinum Sepia

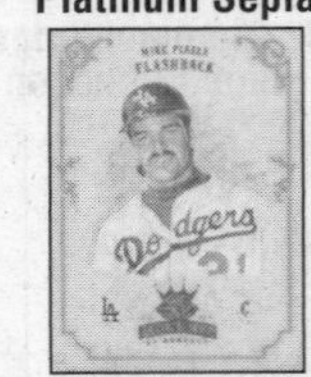

RANDOM INSERTS IN PACKS
STATED PRINT RUN 1 SERIAL #'d SET
NO PRICING DUE TO SCARCITY

2004 Diamond Kings Silver

*SILVER 1-150: 5X TO 12X BASIC
*SILVER 151-175: 2X TO 5X BASIC
RANDOM INSERTS IN PACKS
STATED PRINT RUN 50 SERIAL #'d SETS

2004 Diamond Kings Silver Sepia

*SILVER SEPIA: 2X TO 5X BASIC
RANDOM INSERTS IN PACKS
STATED PRINT RUN 50 SERIAL #'d SETS

2004 Diamond Kings Framed Platinum Grey

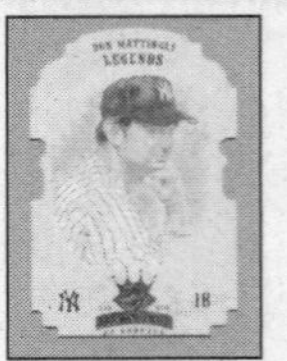

RANDOM INSERTS IN PACKS
STATED PRINT RUN 1 SERIAL #'d SET
NO PRICING DUE TO SCARCITY

2004 Diamond Kings Framed Bronze

*FRAMED BRZ 1-150: 1.5X TO 4X BASIC
*FRAMED BRZ 151-175: .75X TO 2X BASIC
STATED ODDS 1:6

2004 Diamond Kings Framed Bronze Sepia

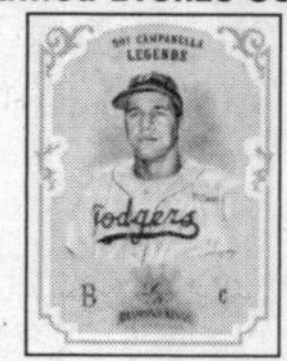

*FRAMED BRZ.SEPIA: .75X TO 2X BASIC
STATED ODDS 1:6

2004 Diamond Kings Framed Gold

*FRAMED GOLD 1-150: 10X TO 25X BASIC
*FRAMED GOLD 150-175: 4X TO 10X BASIC
RANDOM INSERTS IN PACKS
STATED PRINT RUN 25 SERIAL #'d SETS

2004 Diamond Kings Framed Gold Sepia

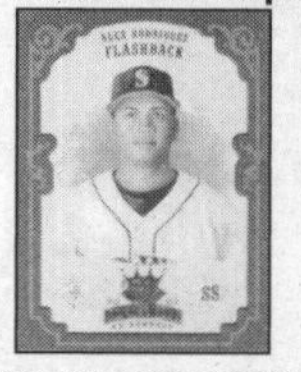

*FRAMED GOLD SEPIA: 4X TO 10X BASIC
RANDOM INSERTS IN PACKS
STATED PRINT RUN 25 SERIAL #'d SETS

2004 Diamond Kings Framed Platinum Black

RANDOM INSERTS IN PACKS
STATED PRINT RUN 1 SERIAL #'d SET
NO PRICING DUE TO SCARCITY

2004 Diamond Kings Framed Platinum Black Sepia

RANDOM INSERTS IN PACKS
STATED PRINT RUN 1 SERIAL #'d SET
NO PRICING DUE TO SCARCITY

2004 Diamond Kings Framed Platinum Grey Sepia

RANDOM INSERTS IN PACKS
STATED PRINT RUN 1 SERIAL #'d SET
NO PRICING DUE TO SCARCITY

2004 Diamond Kings Framed Platinum White

RANDOM INSERTS IN PACKS
STATED PRINT RUN 1 SERIAL #'d SET
NO PRICING DUE TO SCARCITY

2004 Diamond Kings Framed Platinum White Sepia

RANDOM INSERTS IN PACKS
STATED PRINT RUN 1 SERIAL #'d SET
NO PRICING DUE TO SCARCITY

2004 Diamond Kings Framed Silver

*FRAMED SLV 1-150: 4X TO 10X BASIC
*FRAMED SLV 151-175: 1.5X TO 4X BASIC
RANDOM INSERTS IN PACKS
STATED PRINT RUN 100 SERIAL #'d SETS

2004 Diamond Kings Framed Silver Sepia

*FRAMED SLV SEPIA: 1.5X TO 4X BASIC
RANDOM INSERTS IN PACKS
STATED PRINT RUN 100 SERIAL #'d SETS

2004 Diamond Kings DK Combos Bronze

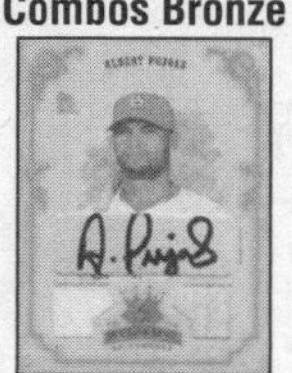

RANDOM INSERTS IN PACKS
PRINT RUNS B/WN 1-30 COPIES PER
NO PRICING ON QTY OF 10 OR LESS

26 Marlon Byrd Bat-Jsy/30	12.50	30.00
32 Rich Harden Jsy-Jsy/15	20.00	50.00
35 Brandon Webb Bat-Jsy/15	15.00	40.00
41 Aubrey Huff Bat-Jsy/15	20.00	50.00
53 Eric Hinske Bat-Jsy/30	12.50	30.00
57 Joe Thurston Bat-Jsy/25	12.50	30.00
59 Jay Gibbons Jsy-Jsy/15	15.00	40.00
62 Walter Young Bat-Bat/15	15.00	40.00
65 Bob Abreu Bat-Jsy/15	20.00	50.00
71 Jason Lane Bat-Hat/15	20.00	50.00
73 Run Hernandez Jsy-Jsy/15	15.00	40.00
74 Aramis Ramirez Bat-Bat/15	40.00	80.00
77 Chris Snelling Bat-Bat/15	15.00	40.00
81 Joe Borchard Bat-Jsy/15	15.00	40.00
92 Junior Spivey Bat-Jsy/15	15.00	40.00
98 Dan Haren Bat-Jsy/15	15.00	40.00
101 Lyle Overbay Bat-Jsy/30	12.50	30.00
103 Miguel Cabrera Bat-Jsy/30	30.00	60.00
108 Angel Berroa Bat-Pants/30	12.50	30.00
109 Hank Blalock Bat-Jsy/30	15.00	40.00
111 Jose Castillo Bat-Bat/15	15.00	40.00
121 Morgan Ensberg Bat-Jsy/30	15.00	40.00
123 Orlando Hudson Bat-Jsy/30	12.50	30.00
126 Adam LaRoche Bat-Bat/30	12.50	30.00
127 Hong-Chih Kuo Bat-Bat/15	75.00	150.00
130 Luis Castillo Bat-Jsy/30	12.50	30.00
133 Freddy Sanchez Bat-Bat/15	15.00	40.00
136 Alfredo Amezaga Bat-Jsy/15	15.00	40.00
143 Travis Hafner Bat-Jsy/30	15.00	40.00
147 Chad Gaudin Jsy-Jsy/25	12.50	30.00

2004 Diamond Kings DK Combos Bronze Sepia

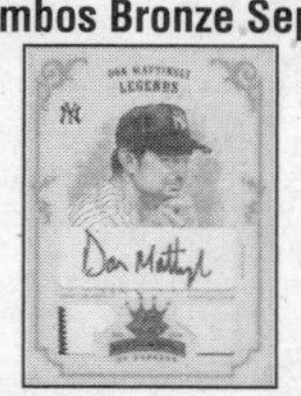

RANDOM INSERTS IN PACKS
PRINT RUNS B/WN 1-5 COPIES PER
NO PRICING DUE TO SCARCITY

2004 Diamond Kings DK Combos Gold

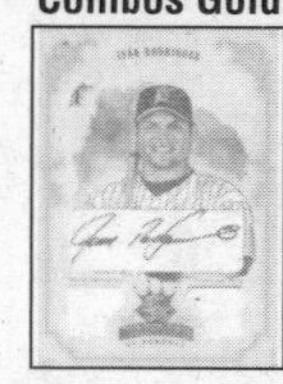

RANDOM INSERTS IN PACKS
PRINT RUNS B/WN 1-5 COPIES PER
NO PRICING DUE TO SCARCITY

2004 Diamond Kings DK Combos Gold Sepia

RANDOM INSERTS IN PACKS
STATED PRINT RUN 1 SERIAL #'d SET
NO PRICING DUE TO SCARCITY

2004 Diamond Kings DK Combos Platinum

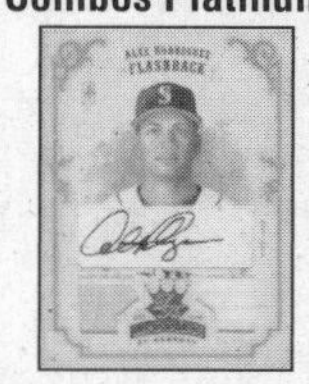

RANDOM INSERTS IN PACKS
STATED PRINT RUN 1 SERIAL #'d SET
NO PRICING DUE TO SCARCITY

2004 Diamond Kings DK Combos Platinum Sepia

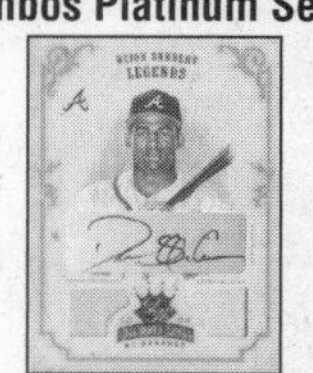

RANDOM INSERTS IN PACKS
STATED PRINT RUN RUN 1 SERIAL #'d SET
NO PRICING DUE TO SCARCITY

2004 Diamond Kings DK Combos Silver

RANDOM INSERTS IN PACKS
PRINT RUNS B/WN 1-15 COPIES PER
NO PRICING ON QTY OF 10 OR LESS

26 Marlon Byrd Bat-Jsy/15	15.00	40.00
101 Lyle Overbay Bat-Jsy/15	15.00	40.00
103 Miguel Cabrera Bat-Jsy/15	40.00	80.00
108 Angel Berroa Bat-Pants/15	15.00	40.00
109 Hank Blalock Bat-Jsy/15	20.00	50.00
121 Morgan Ensberg Bat-Jsy/15	20.00	50.00
123 Orlando Hudson Bat-Jsy/15	15.00	40.00
126 Adam LaRoche Bat-Bat/15	15.00	40.00
130 Luis Castillo Bat-Jsy/15	15.00	40.00
143 Travis Hafner Bat-Jsy/15	20.00	50.00

2004 Diamond Kings DK Combos Silver Sepia

RANDOM INSERTS IN PACKS
PRINT RUNS B/WN 1-3 COPIES PER
NO PRICING DUE TO SCARCITY

2004 Diamond Kings DK Combos Framed Bronze

RANDOM INSERTS IN PACKS
PRINT RUNS B/WN 1-25 COPIES PER
NO PRICING ON QTY OF 10 OR LESS

26 Marlon Byrd Bat-Jsy/25	10.00	25.00
35 Brandon Webb Bat-Jsy/25	10.00	25.00
53 Eric Hinske Bat-Jsy/25	10.00	25.00
57 Joe Thurston Bat-Jsy/25	10.00	25.00
59 Jay Gibbons Jsy-Jsy/25	10.00	25.00
62 Walter Young Bat-Bat/25	10.00	25.00
65 Bob Abreu Bat-Jsy/25	15.00	40.00
71 Jason Lane Bat-Hat/25	15.00	40.00
74 Aramis Ramirez Bat-Bat/25	20.00	50.00
77 Chris Snelling Bat-Bat/25	10.00	25.00
81 Joe Borchard Bat-Jsy/25	10.00	25.00
92 Junior Spivey Bat-Jsy/25	10.00	25.00
97 Antonio Perez Bat-Pants/25	10.00	25.00
98 Dan Haren Bat-Jsy/25	10.00	25.00
101 Lyle Overbay Bat-Jsy/25	10.00	25.00
103 Miguel Cabrera Bat-Jsy/25	20.00	50.00
107 Nic Jackson Bat-Bat/25	10.00	25.00
108 Angel Berroa Bat-Pants/25	10.00	25.00
109 Hank Blalock Bat-Jsy/25	15.00	40.00
110 Ryan Klesko Bat-Jsy/15	20.00	50.00
111 Jose Castillo Bat-Bat/25	10.00	25.00
112 Paul Konerko Bat-Jsy/15	30.00	60.00
121 Morgan Ensberg Bat-Jsy/25	15.00	40.00
123 Orlando Hudson Bat-Jsy/25	10.00	25.00
126 Adam LaRoche Bat-Bat/25	10.00	25.00
127 Hong-Chih Kuo Bat-Bat/25	20.00	50.00
130 Luis Castillo Bat-Jsy/25	10.00	25.00
133 Freddy Sanchez Bat-Bat/15	12.50	30.00
136 Alfredo Amezaga Bat-Jsy/15	12.50	30.00
143 Travis Hafner Bat-Jsy/15	20.00	50.00
147 Chad Gaudin Jsy-Jsy/25	10.00	25.00

2004 Diamond Kings DK Combos Framed Bronze Sepia

RANDOM INSERTS IN PACKS
PRINT RUNS B/WN 1-5 COPIES PER
NO PRICING DUE TO SCARCITY

2004 Diamond Kings DK Combos Framed Gold

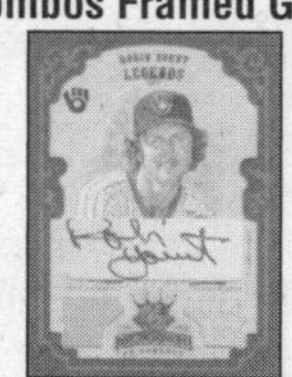

RANDOM INSERTS IN PACKS
PRINT RUNS B/WN 1-5 COPIES PER
NO PRICING DUE TO SCARCITY

2004 Diamond Kings DK Combos Framed Gold Sepia

RANDOM INSERTS IN PACKS
PRINT RUNS B/WN 1-5 COPIES PER
NO PRICING DUE TO SCARCITY

2004 Diamond Kings DK Combos Framed Platinum Black

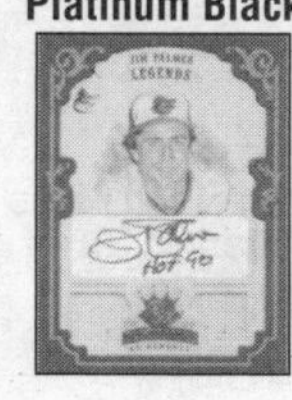

RANDOM INSERTS IN PACKS
STATED PRINT RUN 1 SERIAL #'d SET
NO PRICING DUE TO SCARCITY

2004 Diamond Kings DK Combos Framed Platinum Black Sepia

RANDOM INSERTS IN PACKS
STATED PRINT RUN 1 SERIAL #'d SET
NO PRICING DUE TO SCARCITY

2004 Diamond Kings DK Combos Framed Platinum Grey

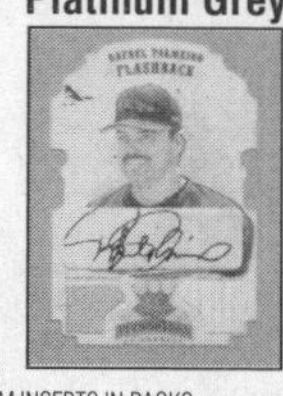

RANDOM INSERTS IN PACKS
STATED PRINT RUN 1 SERIAL #'d SET
NO PRICING DUE TO SCARCITY

2004 Diamond Kings DK Combos Framed Platinum Grey Sepia

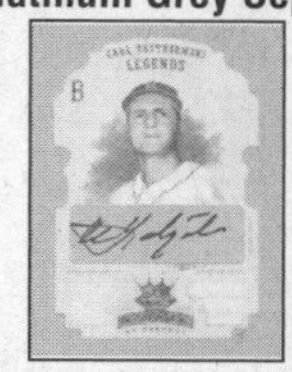

RANDOM INSERTS IN PACKS
STATED PRINT RUN 1 SERIAL #'d SET
NO PRICING DUE TO SCARCITY

2004 Diamond Kings DK Combos Framed Platinum White

RANDOM INSERTS IN PACKS
STATED PRINT RUN 1 SERIAL #'d SET
NO PRICING DUE TO SCARCITY

2004 Diamond Kings DK Combos Framed Platinum White Sepia

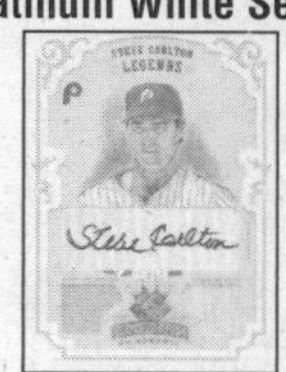

RANDOM INSERTS IN PACKS
STATED PRINT RUN 1 SERIAL #'d SET
NO PRICING DUE TO SCARCITY

2004 Diamond Kings DK Combos Framed Silver

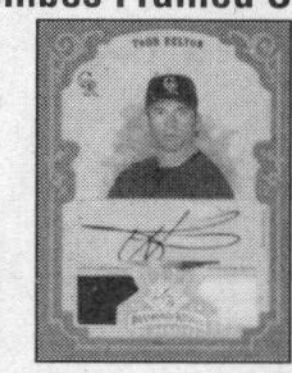

RANDOM INSERTS IN PACKS
PRINT RUNS B/WN 1-15 COPIES PER
NO PRICING ON QTY OF 10 OR LESS

110 Ryan Klesko Bat-Jsy/15	20.00	50.00

2004 Diamond Kings DK Combos Framed Silver Sepia

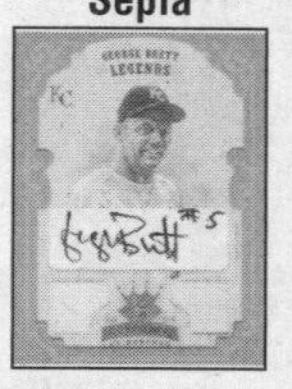

RANDOM INSERTS IN PACKS
PRINT RUNS B/WN 1-5 COPIES PER
NO PRICING DUE TO SCARCITY

2004 Diamond Kings DK Materials Bronze

RANDOM INSERTS IN PACKS
PRINT RUNS B/WN 1-150 COPIES PER
NO PRICING ON QTY OF 5 OR LESS

1 Alex Rodriguez Bat-Jsy/150	10.00	25.00
2 Andruw Jones Bat-Jsy/150	6.00	15.00
3 Nomar Garciaparra Bat-Jsy/150	10.00	25.00
4 Kerry Wood Bat-Jsy/150	4.00	10.00
5 Magglio Ordonez Bat-Jsy/150	4.00	10.00
6 Victor Martinez Bat-Bat/100	4.00	10.00
7 Jeremy Bonderman Jsy-Jsy/30	6.00	15.00
8 Josh Beckett Bat-Jsy/150	4.00	10.00
9 Jeff Kent Bat-Jsy/150	4.00	10.00
10 Carlos Beltran Bat-Jsy/150	4.00	10.00
11 Hideo Nomo Bat-Jsy/150	8.00	20.00
12 Richie Sexson Bat-Jsy/150	4.00	10.00
13 Jose Vidro Bat-Jsy/50	4.00	10.00
14 Jae Seo Jsy-Jsy/100	4.00	10.00
15 Alfonso Soriano Bat-Jsy/150	4.00	10.00
16 Barry Zito Bat-Jsy/100	4.00	10.00
17 Brett Myers Jsy-Jsy/30	6.00	15.00
18 Brian Giles Bat-Bat/100	4.00	10.00
19 Edgar Martinez Bat-Jsy/150	6.00	15.00
20 Jim Edmonds Bat-Jsy/150	4.00	10.00
21 Rocco Baldelli Bat-Jsy/100	4.00	10.00
22 Mark Teixeira Bat-Jsy/100	6.00	15.00
23 Carlos Delgado Bat-Jsy/150	4.00	10.00
25 Jose Reyes Bat-Jsy/100	4.00	10.00
26 Marlon Byrd Bat-Jsy/100	4.00	10.00
27 Albert Pujols Bat-Jsy/150	15.00	40.00
28 Vernon Wells Bat-Jsy/150	4.00	10.00
29 Garret Anderson Bat-Jsy/15	10.00	25.00
30 Jerome Williams Jsy-Jsy/100	4.00	10.00
31 Chipper Jones Bat-Jsy/150	8.00	20.00
32 Rich Harden Jsy-Jsy/100	4.00	10.00
33 Manny Ramirez Bat-Jsy/150	6.00	15.00
34 Derek Jeter Base-Base/100	12.50	30.00
35 Brandon Webb Bat-Jsy/100	4.00	10.00
36 Mark Prior Bat-Jsy/100	6.00	15.00
37 Roy Halladay Jsy-Jsy/100	4.00	10.00
38 Frank Thomas Bat-Jsy/150	8.00	20.00
39 Rafael Palmeiro Bat-Jsy/150	6.00	15.00
40 Adam Dunn Bat-Jsy/150	4.00	10.00
41 Aubrey Huff Bat-Jsy/30	6.00	15.00
42 Todd Helton Bat-Jsy/150	6.00	15.00
43 Matt Morris Jsy-Jsy/100	4.00	10.00
44 Dontrelle Willis Bat-Jsy/100	6.00	15.00
45 Lance Berkman Bat-Jsy/150	4.00	10.00
46 Mike Sweeney Bat-Jsy/100	4.00	10.00
47 Kazuhisa Ishii Bat-Jsy/100	4.00	10.00
48 Torii Hunter Bat-Jsy/100	4.00	10.00
49 Vladimir Guerrero Bat-Jsy/100	8.00	20.00
50 Mike Piazza Bat-Jsy/150	10.00	25.00
51 Alexis Rios Bat-Bat/150	4.00	10.00
52 Shannon Stewart Bat-Bat/100	4.00	10.00
53 Eric Hinske Bat-Jsy/100	4.00	10.00
54 Jason Jennings Bat-Jsy/150	4.00	10.00
55 Jason Giambi Bat-Jsy/150	4.00	10.00
56 Brandon Claussen Fld Glv-Shoe/5		
57 Joe Thurston Bat-Jsy/150	4.00	10.00
58 Ramon Nivar Bat-Jsy/100	4.00	10.00
59 Jay Gibbons Jsy-Jsy/100	4.00	10.00
60 Eric Chavez Bat-Jsy/150	4.00	10.00
62 Walter Young Bat-Bat/100	4.00	10.00
63 Mark Grace Bat-Jsy/150	6.00	15.00
64 Austin Kearns Bat-Jsy/150	4.00	10.00
65 Bob Abreu Bat-Jsy/150	4.00	10.00
66 Hee Seop Choi Bat-Jsy/100	4.00	10.00
67 Brandon Phillips Bat-Bat/100	4.00	10.00
68 Rickie Weeks Bat-Bat/100	4.00	10.00
69 Luis Gonzalez Bat-Jsy/150	4.00	10.00
70 Mariano Rivera Jsy-Jsy/100	8.00	20.00
71 Jason Lane Bat-Hat/15	10.00	25.00
72 Xavier Nady Bat-Hat/5		
73 Run Hernandez Jsy-Jsy/30	6.00	15.00
74 Aramis Ramirez Bat-Bat/1		
75 Ichiro Suzuki Ball-Base/15	50.00	100.00
77 Chris Snelling Bat-Bat/30	6.00	15.00
79 Miguel Tejada Bat-Jsy/150	4.00	10.00
80 Juan Gonzalez Bat-Jsy/150	4.00	10.00
81 Joe Borchard Bat-Jsy/15	10.00	25.00
82 Gary Sheffield Bat-Jsy/150	4.00	10.00
83 Wade Miller Bat-Jsy/50	4.00	10.00
84 Jeff Bagwell Bat-Jsy/150	6.00	15.00
86 Adrian Beltre Bat-Jsy/100	4.00	10.00
87 Jeff Baker Bat-Bat/100	4.00	10.00
89 Bernie Williams Bat-Jsy/150	6.00	15.00
90 Pedro Martinez Bat-Jsy/100	6.00	15.00
92 Junior Spivey Bat-Jsy/100	4.00	10.00
93 Tim Hudson Bat-Jsy/150	4.00	10.00
94 Troy Glaus Bat-Jsy/100	4.00	10.00
95 Ken Griffey Jr. Base-Base/100	8.00	20.00
96 Alexis Gomez Bat-Bat/30	6.00	15.00
97 Antonio Perez Bat-Pants/100	4.00	10.00

98 Dan Haren Bat-Jsy/100 4.00 10.00
99 Ivan Rodriguez Bat-Jsy/150 6.00 15.00
100 Randy Johnson Bat-Jsy/100 8.00 20.00
101 Lyle Overbay Bat-Jsy/100 4.00 10.00
103 Miguel Cabrera Bat-Jsy/100 6.00 15.00
104 Scott Rolen Bat-Jsy/100 6.00 15.00
105 Roger Clemens Bat-Jsy/100 12.50 30.00
107 Nic Jackson Bat-Bat/100 4.00 10.00
108 Angel Berroa Bat-Pants/30 6.00 15.00
109 Hank Blalock Bat-Jsy/100 4.00 10.00
110 Ryan Klesko Bat-Jsy/100 4.00 10.00
111 Jose Castillo Bat-Bat/100 4.00 10.00
112 Paul Konerko Bat-Jsy/100 4.00 10.00
113 Greg Maddux Bat-Jsy/100 10.00 25.00
114 Mark Mulder Bat-Jsy/100 4.00 10.00
115 Pat Burrell Bat-Jsy/100 4.00 10.00
116 Garrett Atkins Jsy-Jsy/100 4.00 10.00
118 Orlando Cabrera Bat-Jsy/100 4.00 10.00
119 Nick Johnson Bat-Jsy/100 4.00 10.00
120 Tom Glavine Bat-Jsy/100 6.00 15.00
121 Morgan Ensberg Bat-Jsy/100 4.00 10.00
122 Sean Casey Bat-Hat/15 10.00 25.00
123 Orlando Hudson Bat-Jsy/100 4.00 10.00
124 Hideki Matsui Ball-Base/15 40.00 80.00
125 Craig Biggio Bat-Jsy/100 6.00 15.00
126 Adam LaRoche Bat-Bat/100 4.00 10.00
127 Hong-Chih Kuo Bat-Bat/100 4.00 10.00
128 Paul LoDuca Bat-Jsy/100 4.00 10.00
129 Shawn Green Bat-Jsy/100 4.00 10.00
130 Luis Castillo Bat-Jsy/100 4.00 10.00
131 Joe Crede Bat-Btg Glv/5
132 Ken Harvey Bat-Bat/100 4.00 10.00
133 Freddy Sanchez Bat-Bat/100 4.00 10.00
134 Roy Oswalt Bat-Jsy/100 4.00 10.00
135 Curt Schilling Bat-Jsy/100 6.00 15.00
136 Alfredo Amezaga Bat-Jsy/15 10.00 25.00
138 Barry Larkin Bat-Jsy/15 15.00 40.00
139 Trot Nixon Bat-Bat/100 4.00 10.00
140 Jim Thome Bat-Jsy/100 6.00 15.00
141 Bret Boone Bat-Jsy/100 4.00 10.00
142 Jacque Jones Bat-Jsy/100 4.00 10.00
143 Travis Hafner Bat-Jsy/100 4.00 10.00
144 Sammy Sosa Bat-Jsy/100 8.00 20.00
145 Mike Mussina Bat-Jsy/100 6.00 15.00
147 Chad Gaudin Jsy-Jsy/100 4.00 10.00
149 Mike Lowell Bat-Jsy/100 4.00 10.00
150 R.Henderson Bat-Jsy/100 8.00 20.00
151 R.Clemens FB Bat-Jsy/100 12.50 30.00
152 Mark Grace FB Bat-Jsy/15 15.00 40.00
153 R.Henderson FB Bat-Jsy/30 12.50 30.00
154 A.Rodriguez FB Bat-Jsy/100 10.00 25.00
155 R.Palmeiro FB Bat-Jsy/100 6.00 15.00
156 G.Maddux FB Bat-Bat/100 10.00 25.00
157 Mike Piazza FB Bat-Jsy/100 10.00 25.00
158 M.Mussina FB Bat-Jsy/100 6.00 15.00
159 Dale Murphy LGD Bat-Jsy/30 10.00 25.00
160 Cal Ripken LGD Bat-Jsy/100 20.00 50.00
161 C.Yaz LGD Bat-Jsy/100 10.00 25.00
162 M.Marion LGD Jsy-Jsy/30 6.00 15.00
163 D.Mattingly LGD Bat-Jsy/100 15.00 40.00
164 R.Yount LGD Bat-Jsy/100 8.00 20.00
165 A.Dawson LGD Bat-Jsy/30 6.00 15.00
166 Jim Palmer LGD Jsy-Jsy/5
167 George Brett LGD Bat-Jsy/30 30.00 60.00
168 W.Ford LGD Jsy-Pants/30 10.00 25.00
169 R.Campy LGD Bat-Pants/15 20.00 50.00
170 R.Maris LGD Bat-Jsy/15 60.00 120.00
171 Duke Snider LGD Bat-Jsy/4
172 S.Carlton LGD Bat-Jsy/100 4.00 10.00
173 Stan Musial LGD Bat-Jsy/30 20.00 50.00
174 Nolan Ryan LGD Bat-Jsy/30 30.00 60.00
175 D.Sanders LGD Bat-Jsy/100 6.00 15.00

2004 Diamond Kings DK Materials Bronze Sepia

RANDOM INSERTS IN PACKS
PRINT RUNS B/WN 4-50 COPIES PER
NO PRICING ON QTY OF 5 OR LESS
151 R.Clemens FB Bat-Jsy/30 20.00 50.00
152 Mark Grace FB Bat-Jsy/15 15.00 40.00
153 R.Henderson FB Bat-Jsy/15 20.00 50.00
154 A.Rodriguez FB Bat-Jsy/30 20.00 50.00
155 R.Palmeiro FB Bat-Jsy/50 6.00 15.00
156 G.Maddux FB Bat-Bat/50 15.00 40.00
157 Mike Piazza FB Bat-Jsy/50 15.00 40.00
158 M.Mussina FB Bat-Jsy/50 6.00 15.00
159 Dale Murphy LGD Bat-Jsy/15 15.00 40.00
160 Cal Ripken LGD Bat-Jsy/50 40.00 80.00
161 C.Yaz LGD Bat-Jsy/50 15.00 40.00
162 M.Marion LGD Jsy-Jsy/15 10.00 25.00
163 D.Mattingly LGD Bat-Jsy/50 20.00 50.00
164 R.Yount LGD Bat-Jsy/50 10.00 25.00
165 A.Dawson LGD Bat-Jsy/15 10.00 25.00
166 Jim Palmer LGD Jsy-Jsy/5
167 G.Brett LGD Bat-Jsy/15 50.00 100.00
168 W.Ford LGD Jsy-Pants/15 15.00 40.00
169 R.Campy LGD Bat-Pants/15 20.00 50.00
170 R.Maris LGD Bat-Jsy/15 60.00 120.00
171 Duke Snider LGD Bat-Jsy/4
172 S.Carlton LGD Bat-Jsy/50 4.00 10.00
173 Stan Musial LGD Bat-Jsy/15 40.00 80.00
174 Nolan Ryan LGD Bat-Jsy/15 50.00 100.00
175 D.Sanders LGD Bat-Jsy/50 6.00 15.00

2004 Diamond Kings DK Materials Gold

RANDOM INSERTS IN PACKS
PRINT RUNS B/WN 1-50 COPIES PER
NO PRICING ON QTY OF 5 OR LESS
1 Alex Rodriguez Bat-Jsy/25 20.00 50.00
2 Andruw Jones Bat-Jsy/25 10.00 25.00
3 Nomar Garciaparra Bat-Jsy/25 20.00 50.00
4 Kerry Wood Bat-Jsy/25 6.00 15.00
5 Magglio Ordonez Bat-Jsy/25 6.00 15.00
6 Victor Martinez Bat-Bat/50 4.00 10.00
7 Jeremy Bonderman Jsy-Jsy/5

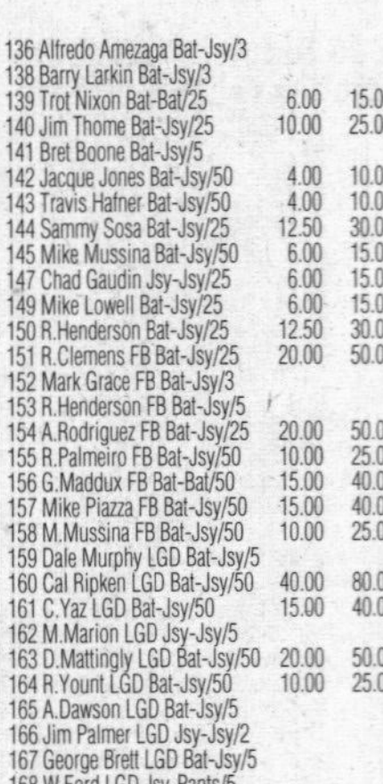

8 Josh Beckett Bat-Jsy/25 6.00 15.00
9 Jeff Kent Bat-Jsy/25 6.00 15.00
10 Carlos Beltran Bat-Jsy/25 6.00 15.00
11 Hideo Nomo Bat-Jsy/25 12.50 30.00
12 Richie Sexson Bat-Jsy/25 6.00 15.00
13 Jose Vidro Bat-Jsy/25 6.00 15.00
14 Jae Seo Jsy-Jsy/25 6.00 15.00
15 Alfonso Soriano Bat-Jsy/25 6.00 15.00
16 Barry Zito Bat-Jsy/25 6.00 15.00
17 Brett Myers Jsy-Jsy/5
18 Brian Giles Bat-Bat/25 6.00 15.00
19 Edgar Martinez Bat-Jsy/25 10.00 25.00
20 Jim Edmonds Bat-Jsy/25 6.00 15.00
21 Rocco Baldelli Bat-Jsy/25 6.00 15.00
22 Mark Teixeira Bat-Jsy/25 10.00 25.00
23 Carlos Delgado Bat-Jsy/25
25 Jose Reyes Bat-Jsy/25 6.00 15.00
26 Marlon Byrd Bat-Jsy/25 6.00 15.00
27 Albert Pujols Bat-Jsy/25 30.00 60.00
28 Vernon Wells Bat-Jsy/25 6.00 15.00
29 Garret Anderson Bat-Jsy/3
30 Jerome Williams Jsy-Jsy/50 4.00 10.00
31 Chipper Jones Bat-Jsy/25 12.50 30.00
32 Rich Harden Jsy-Jsy/50 4.00 10.00
33 Manny Ramirez Bat-Jsy/25 10.00 25.00
34 Derek Jeter Base-Base/50 15.00 40.00
35 Brandon Webb Bat-Jsy/50 4.00 10.00
36 Mark Prior Bat-Jsy/25 10.00 25.00
37 Roy Halladay Jsy-Jsy/25 6.00 15.00
38 Frank Thomas Bat-Jsy/25 12.50 30.00
39 Rafael Palmeiro Bat-Jsy/50 6.00 15.00
40 Adam Dunn Bat-Jsy/25 6.00 15.00
41 Aubrey Huff Bat-Jsy/5
42 Todd Helton Bat-Jsy/25 10.00 25.00
43 Matt Morris Jsy-Jsy/25 6.00 15.00
44 Dontrelle Willis Bat-Jsy/25 10.00 25.00
45 Lance Berkman Bat-Jsy/25 6.00 15.00
46 Mike Sweeney Bat-Jsy/25 6.00 15.00
47 Kazuhisa Ishii Bat-Jsy/25 6.00 15.00
48 Torii Hunter Bat-Jsy/25 6.00 15.00
49 Vladimir Guerrero Bat-Jsy/25 12.50 30.00
50 Mike Piazza Bat-Jsy/25 20.00 50.00
51 Alexis Rios Bat-Bat/25 6.00 15.00
52 Shannon Stewart Bat-Bat/50 4.00 10.00
53 Eric Hinske Bat-Jsy/50 4.00 10.00
54 Jason Jennings Bat-Jsy/25 6.00 15.00
55 Jason Giambi Bat-Jsy/25 6.00 15.00
56 Brandon Claussen Fld Glv-Shoe/1
57 Joe Thurston Bat-Jsy/50 4.00 10.00
58 Ramon Nivar Bat-Jsy/50 4.00 10.00
59 Jay Gibbons Jsy-Jsy/25 6.00 15.00
60 Eric Chavez Bat-Jsy/25 6.00 15.00
62 Walter Young Bat-Bat/50 4.00 10.00
63 Mark Grace Bat-Jsy/25 10.00 25.00
64 Austin Kearns Bat-Jsy/25 6.00 15.00
65 Bob Abreu Bat-Jsy/25 6.00 15.00
66 Hee Seop Choi Bat-Jsy/25 6.00 15.00
67 Brandon Phillips Bat-Bat/50 4.00 10.00
68 Rickie Weeks Bat-Bat/50 4.00 10.00
69 Luis Gonzalez Bat-Jsy/25 6.00 15.00
70 Mariano Rivera Jsy-Jsy/50 10.00 25.00
71 Jason Lane Bat-Hat/3
72 Xavier Nady Bat-Hat/2
73 Run Hernandez Jsy-Jsy/5
74 Aramis Ramirez Bat-Bat/1
75 Ichiro Suzuki Ball-Base/3
77 Chris Snelling Bat-Bat/5
79 Miguel Tejada Bat-Jsy/50 4.00 10.00
80 Juan Gonzalez Bat-Jsy/25 6.00 15.00
81 Joe Borchard Bat-Jsy/3
82 Gary Sheffield Bat-Jsy/25 6.00 15.00
83 Wade Miller Bat-Jsy/3
84 Jeff Bagwell Bat-Jsy/25 10.00 25.00
86 Adrian Beltre Bat-Jsy/25 6.00 15.00
87 Jeff Baker Bat-Bat/50 4.00 10.00
89 Bernie Williams Bat-Jsy/25 10.00 25.00
90 Pedro Martinez Bat-Jsy/25 10.00 25.00
92 Junior Spivey Bat-Jsy/25 6.00 15.00
93 Tim Hudson Bat-Jsy/25 6.00 15.00
94 Troy Glaus Bat-Jsy/25 6.00 15.00
95 Ken Griffey Jr. Base-Base/50 12.50 30.00
96 Alexis Gomez Bat-Bat/5
97 Antonio Perez Bat-Pants/50 4.00 10.00
98 Dan Haren Bat-Jsy/25 6.00 15.00
99 Ivan Rodriguez Bat-Jsy/25 10.00 25.00
100 Randy Johnson Bat-Jsy/25 12.50 30.00
101 Lyle Overbay Bat-Jsy/50 4.00 10.00
103 Miguel Cabrera Bat-Jsy/25 10.00 25.00
104 Scott Rolen Bat-Jsy/25 10.00 25.00
105 Roger Clemens Bat-Jsy/25 20.00 50.00
107 Nic Jackson Bat-Bat/30 6.00 15.00
108 Angel Berroa Bat-Pants/3
109 Hank Blalock Bat-Jsy/25 6.00 15.00
110 Ryan Klesko Bat-Jsy/25 6.00 15.00
111 Jose Castillo Bat-Bat/50 4.00 10.00
112 Paul Konerko Bat-Jsy/25 6.00 15.00
113 Greg Maddux Bat-Jsy/25 20.00 50.00
114 Mark Mulder Bat-Jsy/25 6.00 15.00
115 Pat Burrell Bat-Jsy/25 6.00 15.00
116 Garrett Atkins Jsy-Jsy/50 4.00 10.00
118 Orlando Cabrera Bat-Jsy/25 6.00 15.00
119 Nick Johnson Bat-Jsy/25 6.00 15.00
120 Tom Glavine Bat-Jsy/25 10.00 25.00
121 Morgan Ensberg Bat-Jsy/25 6.00 15.00
122 Sean Casey Bat-Hat/3
123 Orlando Hudson Bat-Jsy/25 6.00 15.00
124 Hideki Matsui Ball-Base/3
125 Craig Biggio Bat-Jsy/25 10.00 25.00
126 Adam LaRoche Bat-Bat/50 4.00 10.00
127 Hong-Chih Kuo Bat-Bat/50 4.00 10.00
128 Paul LoDuca Bat-Jsy/25 6.00 15.00
129 Shawn Green Bat-Jsy/25 6.00 15.00
130 Luis Castillo Bat-Jsy/25 6.00 15.00
131 Joe Crede Bat-Btg Glv/1
132 Ken Harvey Bat-Bat/50 4.00 10.00
133 Freddy Sanchez Bat-Bat/50 4.00 10.00
134 Roy Oswalt Bat-Jsy/50 4.00 10.00
135 Curt Schilling Bat-Jsy/25 10.00 25.00
136 Alfredo Amezaga Bat-Jsy/3
138 Barry Larkin Bat-Jsy/3
139 Trot Nixon Bat-Bat/25 6.00 15.00
140 Jim Thome Bat-Jsy/25 10.00 25.00
141 Bret Boone Bat-Jsy/5
142 Jacque Jones Bat-Jsy/50 4.00 10.00
143 Travis Hafner Bat-Jsy/50 4.00 10.00
144 Sammy Sosa Bat-Jsy/25 12.50 30.00
145 Mike Mussina Bat-Jsy/50 6.00 15.00
147 Chad Gaudin Jsy-Jsy/25 6.00 15.00
149 Mike Lowell Bat-Jsy/25 6.00 15.00
150 R.Henderson Bat-Jsy/25 12.50 30.00
151 R.Clemens FB Bat-Jsy/25 20.00 50.00
152 Mark Grace FB Bat-Jsy/3
153 R.Henderson FB Bat-Jsy/5
154 A.Rodriguez FB Bat-Jsy/25 20.00 50.00
155 R.Palmeiro FB Bat-Jsy/50 10.00 25.00
156 G.Maddux FB Bat-Bat/50 15.00 40.00
157 Mike Piazza FB Bat-Jsy/50 15.00 40.00
158 M.Mussina FB Bat-Jsy/50 10.00 25.00
159 Dale Murphy LGD Bat-Jsy/5
160 Cal Ripken LGD Bat-Jsy/50 40.00 80.00
161 C.Yaz LGD Bat-Jsy/50 15.00 40.00
162 M.Marion LGD Jsy-Jsy/5
163 D.Mattingly LGD Bat-Jsy/50 20.00 50.00
164 R.Yount LGD Bat-Jsy/50 10.00 25.00
165 A.Dawson LGD Bat-Jsy/5
166 Jim Palmer LGD Jsy-Jsy/2
167 George Brett LGD Bat-Jsy/5
168 W.Ford LGD Jsy-Pants/5
169 R.Campy LGD Bat-Pants/3
170 Roger Maris LGD Bat-Jsy/3
171 Duke Snider LGD Bat-Jsy/1
172 S.Carlton LGD Bat-Jsy/50 4.00 10.00
173 Stan Musial LGD Bat-Jsy/5
174 Nolan Ryan LGD Bat-Jsy/5
175 D.Sanders LGD Bat-Jsy/50 6.00 15.00

2004 Diamond Kings DK Materials Gold Sepia

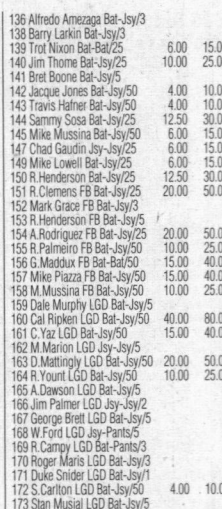

RANDOM INSERTS IN PACKS
PRINT RUNS B/WN 1-15 COPIES PER
NO PRICING ON QTY OF 5 OR LESS
151 R.Clemens FB Bat-Jsy/5
152 Mark Grace FB Bat-Jsy/3
153 R.Henderson FB Bat-Jsy/3
154 A.Rodriguez FB Bat-Jsy/5
155 R.Palmeiro FB Bat-Jsy/15 15.00 40.00
156 G.Maddux FB Bat-Bat/15 30.00 60.00
157 Mike Piazza FB Bat-Jsy/15 30.00 60.00
158 M.Mussina FB Bat-Jsy/15 15.00 40.00
159 Dale Murphy LGD Bat-Jsy/3
160 Cal Ripken LGD Bat-Jsy/15 75.00 150.00
161 C.Yaz LGD Bat-Jsy/15 40.00 80.00
162 M.Marion LGD Jsy-Jsy/3
163 D.Mattingly LGD Bat-Jsy/15 50.00 100.00
164 R.Yount LGD Bat-Jsy/15 20.00 50.00
165 A.Dawson LGD Bat-Jsy/3
166 Jim Palmer LGD Jsy-Jsy/2
167 George Brett LGD Bat-Jsy/3
168 W.Ford LGD Jsy-Pants/3
169 R.Campy LGD Bat-Pants/3
170 Roger Maris LGD Bat-Jsy/3
171 Duke Snider LGD Bat-Jsy/1
172 S.Carlton LGD Bat-Jsy/15 10.00 25.00
173 Stan Musial LGD Bat-Jsy/3
174 Nolan Ryan LGD Bat-Jsy/3
175 D.Sanders LGD Bat-Jsy/15 15.00 40.00

2004 Diamond Kings DK Materials Platinum

RANDOM INSERTS IN PACKS
STATED PRINT RUN 1 SERIAL #'d SET
NO PRICING DUE TO SCARCITY

2004 Diamond Kings DK Materials Platinum Sepia

RANDOM INSERTS IN PACKS
STATED PRINT RUN 1 SERIAL #'d SET
NO PRICING DUE TO SCARCITY

2004 Diamond Kings DK Materials Silver

RANDOM INSERTS IN PACKS
PRINT RUNS B/WN 1-50 COPIES PER
NO PRICING ON QTY OF 6 OR LESS
1 Alex Rodriguez Bat-Jsy/50 15.00 40.00

2 Andruw Jones Bat-Jsy/50 6.00 15.00
3 Nomar Garciaparra Bat-Jsy/50 15.00 40.00
4 Kerry Wood Bat-Jsy/50 4.00 10.00
5 Magglio Ordonez Bat-Jsy/50 4.00 10.00
6 Victor Martinez Bat-Bat/50 4.00 10.00
7 Jeremy Bonderman Jsy-Jsy/15 10.00 25.00
8 Josh Beckett Bat-Jsy/50 4.00 10.00
9 Jeff Kent Bat-Jsy/50 4.00 10.00
10 Carlos Beltran Bat-Jsy/50 4.00 10.00
11 Hideo Nomo Bat-Jsy/50 10.00 25.00
12 Richie Sexson Bat-Jsy/50 4.00 10.00
13 Jose Vidro Bat-Jsy/30 6.00 15.00
14 Jae Seo Jsy-Jsy/50 4.00 10.00
15 Alfonso Soriano Bat-Jsy/50 4.00 10.00
16 Barry Zito Bat-Jsy/50 4.00 10.00
17 Brett Myers Jsy-Jsy/15 10.00 25.00
18 Brian Giles Bat-Bat/50 4.00 10.00
19 Edgar Martinez Bat-Jsy/50 6.00 15.00
20 Jim Edmonds Bat-Jsy/50 4.00 10.00
21 Rocco Baldelli Bat-Jsy/50 4.00 10.00
22 Mark Teixeira Bat-Jsy/50 6.00 15.00
23 Carlos Delgado Bat-Jsy/50 4.00 10.00
25 Jose Reyes Bat-Jsy/50 4.00 10.00
26 Marlon Byrd Bat-Jsy/50 4.00 10.00
27 Albert Pujols Bat-Jsy/50 20.00 50.00
28 Vernon Wells Bat-Jsy/50 4.00 10.00
29 Garret Anderson Bat-Jsy/6
30 Jerome Williams Jsy-Jsy/50 4.00 10.00
31 Chipper Jones Bat-Jsy/50 10.00 25.00
32 Rich Harden Jsy-Jsy/50 4.00 10.00
33 Manny Ramirez Bat-Jsy/50 6.00 15.00
34 Derek Jeter Base-Base/50 15.00 40.00
35 Brandon Webb Bat-Jsy/50 4.00 10.00
36 Mark Prior Bat-Jsy/50 6.00 15.00
37 Roy Halladay Jsy-Jsy/50 4.00 10.00
38 Frank Thomas Bat-Jsy/50 10.00 25.00
39 Rafael Palmeiro Bat-Jsy/50 6.00 15.00
40 Adam Dunn Bat-Jsy/50 4.00 10.00
41 Aubrey Huff Bat-Jsy/15 10.00 25.00
42 Todd Helton Bat-Jsy/50 6.00 15.00
43 Matt Morris Jsy-Jsy/50 4.00 10.00
44 Dontrelle Willis Bat-Jsy/50 6.00 15.00
45 Lance Berkman Bat-Jsy/50 4.00 10.00
46 Mike Sweeney Bat-Jsy/50 4.00 10.00
47 Kazuhisa Ishii Bat-Jsy/50 4.00 10.00
48 Torii Hunter Bat-Jsy/50 4.00 10.00
49 Vladimir Guerrero Bat-Jsy/50 10.00 25.00
50 Mike Piazza Bat-Jsy/50 15.00 40.00
51 Alexis Rios Bat-Bat/50 4.00 10.00
52 Shannon Stewart Bat-Bat/50 4.00 10.00
53 Eric Hinske Bat-Jsy/50 4.00 10.00
54 Jason Jennings Bat-Jsy/50 4.00 10.00
55 Jason Giambi Bat-Jsy/50 4.00 10.00
56 Brandon Claussen Fld Glv-Shoe/1
57 Joe Thurston Bat-Jsy/50 4.00 10.00
58 Ramon Nivar Bat-Jsy/50 4.00 10.00
59 Jay Gibbons Jsy-Jsy/50 4.00 10.00
60 Eric Chavez Bat-Jsy/50 4.00 10.00
62 Walter Young Bat-Bat/50 4.00 10.00
63 Mark Grace Bat-Jsy/50 6.00 15.00
64 Austin Kearns Bat-Jsy/50 4.00 10.00
65 Bob Abreu Bat-Jsy/50 4.00 10.00
66 Hee Seop Choi Bat-Jsy/50 4.00 10.00
67 Brandon Phillips Bat-Bat/50 4.00 10.00
68 Rickie Weeks Bat-Bat/50 4.00 10.00
69 Luis Gonzalez Bat-Jsy/50 4.00 10.00
70 Mariano Rivera Jsy-Jsy/50 10.00 25.00
71 Jason Lane Bat-Hat/6
72 Xavier Nady Bat-Hat/3
73 Run Hernandez Jsy-Jsy/15 10.00 25.00
74 Aramis Ramirez Bat-Bat/1
75 Ichiro Suzuki Ball-Base/6
77 Chris Snelling Bat-Bat/15 10.00 25.00
79 Miguel Tejada Bat-Jsy/50 4.00 10.00
80 Juan Gonzalez Bat-Jsy/50 4.00 10.00
81 Joe Borchard Bat-Jsy/6
82 Gary Sheffield Bat-Jsy/50 4.00 10.00
83 Wade Miller Bat-Jsy/6
84 Jeff Bagwell Bat-Jsy/50 6.00 15.00
86 Adrian Beltre Bat-Jsy/50 4.00 10.00
87 Jeff Baker Bat-Bat/50 4.00 10.00
89 Bernie Williams Bat-Jsy/50 6.00 15.00
90 Pedro Martinez Bat-Jsy/50 6.00 15.00
92 Junior Spivey Bat-Jsy/50 4.00 10.00
93 Tim Hudson Bat-Jsy/50 4.00 10.00
94 Troy Glaus Bat-Jsy/50 4.00 10.00
95 Ken Griffey Jr. Base-Base/50 12.50 30.00
96 Alexis Gomez Bat-Bat/15 10.00 25.00
97 Antonio Perez Bat-Pants/50 4.00 10.00
98 Dan Haren Bat-Jsy/50 4.00 10.00
99 Ivan Rodriguez Bat-Jsy/50 6.00 15.00
100 Randy Johnson Bat-Jsy/50 10.00 25.00
101 Lyle Overbay Bat-Jsy/50 4.00 10.00
103 Miguel Cabrera Bat-Jsy/50 6.00 15.00
104 Scott Rolen Bat-Jsy/50 6.00 15.00
105 Roger Clemens Bat-Jsy/50 15.00 40.00
107 Nic Jackson Bat-Bat/50 4.00 10.00
108 Angel Berroa Bat-Pants/6
109 Hank Blalock Bat-Jsy/50 4.00 10.00
110 Ryan Klesko Bat-Jsy/50 4.00 10.00
111 Jose Castillo Bat-Bat/50 4.00 10.00
112 Paul Konerko Bat-Jsy/50 4.00 10.00
113 Greg Maddux Bat-Jsy/50 15.00 40.00
114 Mark Mulder Bat-Jsy/50 4.00 10.00
115 Pat Burrell Bat-Jsy/50 4.00 10.00
116 Garrett Atkins Jsy-Jsy/50 4.00 10.00
118 Orlando Cabrera Bat-Jsy/50 4.00 10.00
119 Nick Johnson Bat-Jsy/50 4.00 10.00
120 Tom Glavine Bat-Jsy/50 6.00 15.00
121 Morgan Ensberg Bat-Jsy/50 4.00 10.00
122 Sean Casey Bat-Hat/6
123 Orlando Hudson Bat-Jsy/50 4.00 10.00
124 Hideki Matsui Ball-Base/6
125 Craig Biggio Bat-Jsy/50 6.00 15.00
126 Adam LaRoche Bat-Bat/50 4.00 10.00
127 Hong-Chih Kuo Bat-Bat/50 4.00 10.00
128 Paul LoDuca Bat-Jsy/50 4.00 10.00
129 Shawn Green Bat-Jsy/50 4.00 10.00
130 Luis Castillo Bat-Jsy/50 4.00 10.00
131 Joe Crede Bat-Btg Glv/1
132 Ken Harvey Bat-Bat/50 4.00 10.00
133 Freddy Sanchez Bat-Bat/50 4.00 10.00
134 Roy Oswalt Bat-Jsy/50 4.00 10.00
135 Curt Schilling Bat-Jsy/50 6.00 15.00
136 Alfredo Amezaga Bat-Jsy/6
138 Barry Larkin Bat-Jsy/6
139 Trot Nixon Bat-Bat/50 4.00 10.00
140 Jim Thome Bat-Jsy/50 6.00 15.00
141 Bret Boone Bat-Jsy/50 4.00 10.00
142 Jacque Jones Bat-Jsy/50 4.00 10.00
143 Travis Hafner Bat-Jsy/50 4.00 10.00
144 Sammy Sosa Bat-Jsy/50 10.00 25.00
145 Mike Mussina Bat-Jsy/50 6.00 15.00
147 Chad Gaudin Jsy-Jsy/50 4.00 10.00
149 Mike Lowell Bat-Jsy/50 4.00 10.00
150 R.Henderson Bat-Jsy/50 10.00 25.00
151 R.Clemens FB Bat-Jsy/50 15.00 40.00
152 Mark Grace FB Bat-Jsy/6
153 R.Henderson FB Bat-Jsy/15 20.00 50.00
154 A.Rodriguez FB Bat-Jsy/30 20.00 50.00
155 R.Palmeiro FB Bat-Jsy/50 6.00 15.00
156 G.Maddux FB Bat-Bat/50 15.00 40.00
157 Mike Piazza FB Bat-Jsy/50 15.00 40.00
158 M.Mussina FB Bat-Jsy/50 6.00 15.00
159 Dale Murphy LGD Bat-Jsy/15
160 Cal Ripken LGD Bat-Jsy/50 40.00 80.00
161 C.Yaz LGD Bat-Jsy/50 15.00 40.00
162 M.Marion LGD Jsy-Jsy/15 10.00 25.00
163 D.Mattingly LGD Bat-Jsy/50 20.00 50.00
164 R.Yount LGD Bat-Jsy/50 10.00 25.00
165 A.Dawson LGD Bat-Jsy/15 10.00 25.00
166 Jim Palmer LGD Jsy-Jsy/3
167 G.Brett LGD Bat-Jsy/15 50.00 100.00
168 W.Ford LGD Jsy-Pants/15 15.00 40.00
169 R.Campy LGD Bat-Pants/6
170 Roger Maris LGD Bat-Jsy/6
171 Duke Snider LGD Bat-Jsy/1
172 S.Carlton LGD Bat-Jsy/50 4.00 10.00
173 Stan Musial LGD Bat-Jsy/15 40.00 80.00
174 Nolan Ryan LGD Bat-Jsy/15 50.00 100.00
175 D.Sanders LGD Bat-Jsy/50 6.00 15.00

2004 Diamond Kings DK Materials Silver Sepia

RANDOM INSERTS IN PACKS
PRINT RUNS B/WN 1-30 COPIES PER
NO PRICING ON QTY OF 6 OR LESS
151 R.Clemens FB Bat-Jsy/15 30.00 60.00
152 Mark Grace FB Bat-Jsy/6
153 R.Henderson FB Bat-Jsy/6
154 A.Rodriguez FB Bat-Jsy/15 30.00 60.00
155 R.Palmeiro FB Bat-Jsy/30 10.00 25.00
156 G.Maddux FB Bat-Bat/30 20.00 50.00
157 Mike Piazza FB Bat-Jsy/30 20.00 50.00
158 M.Mussina FB Bat-Jsy/30 10.00 25.00
159 Dale Murphy LGD Bat-Jsy/6
160 Cal Ripken LGD Bat-Jsy/30 50.00 100.00
161 C.Yaz LGD Bat-Jsy/30 20.00 50.00
162 M.Marion LGD Jsy-Jsy/6
163 D.Mattingly LGD Bat-Jsy/30 30.00 60.00
164 R.Yount LGD Bat-Jsy/30 12.50 30.00
165 A.Dawson LGD Bat-Jsy/6
166 Jim Palmer LGD Jsy-Jsy/3
167 George Brett LGD Bat-Jsy/6
168 W.Ford LGD Jsy-Pants/6
169 R.Campy LGD Bat-Pants/6
170 Roger Maris LGD Bat-Jsy/6
171 Duke Snider LGD Bat-Jsy/1
172 S.Carlton LGD Bat-Jsy/30 6.00 15.00
173 Stan Musial LGD Bat-Jsy/6
174 Nolan Ryan LGD Bat-Jsy/6
175 D.Sanders LGD Bat-Jsy/30 10.00 25.00

2004 Diamond Kings DK Materials Framed Bronze

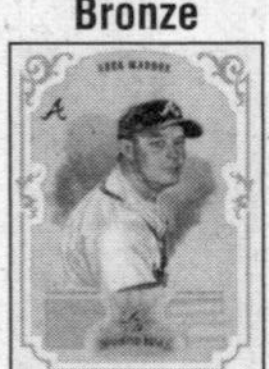

RANDOM INSERTS IN PACKS
PRINT RUNS B/WN 1-100 COPIES PER
NO PRICING ON QTY OF 10 OR LESS
1 Alex Rodriguez Bat-Jsy/100 10.00 25.00
2 Andruw Jones Bat-Jsy/100 6.00 15.00
3 Nomar Garciaparra Bat-Jsy/100 10.00 25.00
4 Kerry Wood Bat-Jsy/100 4.00 10.00
5 Magglio Ordonez Bat-Jsy/100 4.00 10.00
6 Victor Martinez Bat-Bat/100 4.00 10.00
7 Jeremy Bonderman Jsy-Jsy/25 6.00 15.00
8 Josh Beckett Bat-Jsy/100 4.00 10.00
9 Jeff Kent Bat-Jsy/100 4.00 10.00
10 Carlos Beltran Bat-Jsy/100 4.00 10.00
11 Hideo Nomo Bat-Jsy/100 8.00 20.00
12 Richie Sexson Bat-Jsy/100 4.00 10.00
13 Jose Vidro Bat-Jsy/50 4.00 10.00
14 Jae Seo Jsy-Jsy/100 4.00 10.00
15 Alfonso Soriano Bat-Jsy/100 4.00 10.00
16 Barry Zito Bat-Jsy/100 4.00 10.00
17 Brett Myers Jsy-Jsy/25 6.00 15.00
18 Brian Giles Bat-Bat/100 4.00 10.00
19 Edgar Martinez Bat-Jsy/100 6.00 15.00
20 Jim Edmonds Bat-Jsy/100 4.00 10.00
21 Rocco Baldelli Bat-Jsy/100 4.00 10.00
22 Mark Teixeira Bat-Jsy/100 6.00 15.00
23 Carlos Delgado Bat-Jsy/100 4.00 10.00
25 Jose Reyes Bat-Jsy/100 4.00 10.00
26 Marlon Byrd Bat-Jsy/100 4.00 10.00
27 Albert Pujols Bat-Jsy/100 15.00 40.00
28 Vernon Wells Bat-Jsy/100 4.00 10.00
29 Garret Anderson Bat-Jsy/25 6.00 15.00
30 Jerome Williams Jsy-Jsy/100 4.00 10.00
31 Chipper Jones Bat-Jsy/100 8.00 20.00
32 Rich Harden Jsy-Jsy/100 4.00 10.00
33 Manny Ramirez Bat-Jsy/100 6.00 15.00
34 Derek Jeter Base-Base/100 12.50 30.00
35 Brandon Webb Bat-Jsy/100 4.00 10.00
36 Mark Prior Bat-Jsy/100 6.00 15.00
37 Roy Halladay Jsy-Jsy/75 4.00 10.00
38 Frank Thomas Bat-Jsy/100 8.00 20.00
39 Rafael Palmeiro Bat-Jsy/100 6.00 15.00
40 Adam Dunn Bat-Jsy/100 4.00 10.00
41 Aubrey Huff Bat-Jsy/25 6.00 15.00
42 Todd Helton Bat-Jsy/100 6.00 15.00
43 Matt Morris Jsy-Jsy/100 4.00 10.00
44 Dontrelle Willis Bat-Jsy/100 6.00 15.00
45 Lance Berkman Bat-Jsy/100 4.00 10.00
46 Mike Sweeney Bat-Jsy/100 4.00 10.00
47 Kazuhisa Ishii Bat-Jsy/100 4.00 10.00
48 Torii Hunter Bat-Jsy/100 4.00 10.00
49 Vladimir Guerrero Bat-Jsy/100 8.00 20.00
50 Mike Piazza Bat-Jsy/100 10.00 25.00
51 Alexis Rios Bat-Bat/100 4.00 10.00
52 Shannon Stewart Bat-Bat/100. 4.00 10.00
53 Eric Hinske Bat-Jsy/100 4.00 10.00
54 Jason Jennings Bat-Jsy/100 4.00 10.00
55 Jason Giambi Bat-Jsy/100 4.00 10.00
56 Brandon Claussen Fld Glv-Shoe/5
57 Joe Thurston Bat-Jsy/100 4.00 10.00
58 Ramon Nivar Bat-Jsy/100 4.00 10.00
59 Jay Gibbons Jsy-Jsy/100 4.00 10.00
60 Eric Chavez Bat-Jsy/100 4.00 10.00
62 Walter Young Bat-Bat/100 4.00 10.00
63 Mark Grace Bat-Jsy/100 6.00 15.00
64 Austin Kearns Bat-Jsy/50 4.00 10.00
65 Bob Abreu Bat-Jsy/100 4.00 10.00
66 Hee Seop Choi Bat-Jsy/100 4.00 10.00
67 Brandon Phillips Bat-Bat/100 4.00 10.00
68 Rickie Weeks Bat-Bat/100 4.00 10.00
69 Luis Gonzalez Bat-Jsy/100 4.00 10.00
70 Mariano Rivera Jsy-Jsy/100 8.00 20.00
71 Jason Lane Bat-Hat/25 6.00 15.00
72 Xavier Nady Bat-Hat/10
73 Run Hernandez Jsy-Jsy/50 4.00 10.00
74 Aramis Ramirez Bat-Bat/1
75 Ichiro Suzuki Ball-Base/25 40.00 80.00
77 Chris Snelling Bat-Bat/25 6.00 15.00
79 Miguel Tejada Bat-Jsy/100 4.00 10.00
80 Juan Gonzalez Bat-Jsy/100 4.00 10.00
81 Joe Borchard Bat-Jsy/25 6.00 15.00
82 Gary Sheffield Bat-Jsy/100 4.00 10.00
83 Wade Miller Bat-Jsy/25 6.00 15.00
84 Jeff Bagwell Bat-Jsy/100 6.00 15.00
86 Adrian Beltre Bat-Jsy/100 4.00 10.00
87 Jeff Baker Bat-Bat/100 4.00 10.00
89 Bernie Williams Bat-Jsy/100 6.00 15.00
90 Pedro Martinez Bat-Jsy/100 6.00 15.00
92 Junior Spivey Bat-Jsy/100 4.00 10.00
93 Tim Hudson Bat-Jsy/100 4.00 10.00
94 Troy Glaus Bat-Jsy/100 4.00 10.00
95 Ken Griffey Jr. Base-Base/100 8.00 20.00
96 Alexis Gomez Bat-Bat/30 6.00 15.00
97 Antonio Perez Bat-Pants/100 4.00 10.00
98 Dan Haren Bat-Jsy/100 4.00 10.00
99 Ivan Rodriguez Bat-Jsy/100 6.00 15.00
100 Randy Johnson Bat-Jsy/100 8.00 20.00
101 Lyle Overbay Bat-Jsy/100 4.00 10.00
103 Miguel Cabrera Bat-Jsy/100 6.00 15.00
104 Scott Rolen Bat-Jsy/100 6.00 15.00
105 Roger Clemens Bat-Jsy/100 12.50 30.00
107 Nic Jackson Bat-Bat/100 4.00 10.00
108 Angel Berroa Bat-Pants/25 6.00 15.00
109 Hank Blalock Bat-Jsy/100 4.00 10.00
110 Ryan Klesko Bat-Jsy/100 4.00 10.00
111 Jose Castillo Bat-Bat/100 4.00 10.00
112 Paul Konerko Bat-Jsy/50 4.00 10.00
113 Greg Maddux Bat-Jsy/100 10.00 25.00
114 Mark Mulder Bat-Jsy/100 4.00 10.00
115 Pat Burrell Bat-Jsy/100 4.00 10.00
116 Garrett Atkins Jsy-Jsy/100 4.00 10.00
118 Orlando Cabrera Bat-Jsy/100 4.00 10.00
119 Nick Johnson Bat-Jsy/100
120 Tom Glavine Bat-Jsy/100 6.00 15.00
121 Morgan Ensberg Bat-Jsy/100 4.00 10.00
122 Sean Casey Bat-Hat/25 6.00 15.00
123 Orlando Hudson Bat-Jsy/100 4.00 10.00
124 Hideki Matsui Ball-Base/25 30.00 60.00
125 Craig Biggio Bat-Jsy/25 10.00 25.00
126 Adam LaRoche Bat-Bat/100 4.00 10.00
127 Hong-Chih Kuo Bat-Bat/100 4.00 10.00
128 Paul LoDuca Bat-Jsy/100 4.00 10.00
129 Shawn Green Bat-Jsy/100 4.00 10.00
130 Luis Castillo Bat-Jsy/100 4.00 10.00
131 Joe Crede Bat-Btg Glv/5
132 Ken Harvey Bat-Bat/100 4.00 10.00
133 Freddy Sanchez Bat-Bat/100 4.00 10.00
134 Roy Oswalt Bat-Jsy/100 4.00 10.00
135 Curt Schilling Bat-Jsy/100 6.00 15.00
136 Alfredo Amezaga Bat-Jsy/25 6.00 15.00
138 Barry Larkin Bat-Jsy/25 10.00 25.00
139 Trot Nixon Bat-Bat/100 4.00 10.00
140 Jim Thome Bat-Jsy/100 6.00 15.00
141 Bret Boone Bat-Jsy/100 4.00 10.00
142 Jacque Jones Bat-Jsy/100 4.00 10.00
143 Travis Hafner Bat-Jsy/100 4.00 -10.00
144 Sammy Sosa Bat-Jsy/100 8.00 20.00
145 Mike Mussina Bat-Jsy/100 6.00 15.00
147 Chad Gaudin Jsy-Jsy/50 4.00 10.00
149 Mike Lowell Bat-Jsy/100 4.00 10.00
150 R.Henderson Bat-Jsy/100 8.00 20.00
151 R.Clemens FB Bat-Jsy/25 20.00 50.00
152 Mark Grace FB Bat-Jsy/25 10.00 25.00
153 R.Henderson FB Bat-Jsy/25 12.50 30.00
154 A.Rodriguez FB Bat-Jsy/25 20.00 50.00
155 R.Palmeiro FB Bat-Jsy/100 6.00 15.00
156 G.Maddux FB Bat-Bat/100 10.00 25.00
157 Mike Piazza FB Bat-Jsy/100 10.00 25.00
158 M.Mussina FB Bat-Jsy/100 6.00 15.00
159 Dale Murphy LGD Bat-Jsy/25 10.00 25.00
160 Cal Ripken LGD Bat-Jsy/100 20.00 50.00
161 C.Yaz LGD Bat-Jsy/100 10.00 25.00
162 M.Marion LGD Jsy-Jsy/25 6.00 15.00
163 D.Mattingly LGD Bat-Jsy/100 15.00 40.00
164 R.Yount LGD Bat-Jsy/100 8.00 20.00
165 A.Dawson LGD Bat-Jsy/25 6.00 15.00

166 Jim Palmer LGD Jsy-Jsy/5
167 George Brett LGD Bat-Jsy/25 30.00 60.00
168 W.Ford LGD Jsy-Pants/25 10.00 25.00
169 R.Campy LGD Bat-Pants/25 12.50 30.00
170 R. Maris LGD Bat-Jsy/25 50.00 100.00
171 Duke Snider LGD Bat-Jsy/4
172 S.Carlton LGD Bat-Jsy/100 4.00 10.00
173 Stan Musial LGD Bat-Jsy/25 20.00 50.00
174 Nolan Ryan LGD Bat-Jsy/25 30.00 60.00
175 D.Sanders LGD Bat-Jsy/100 6.00 15.00

2004 Diamond Kings DK Materials Framed Bronze Sepia

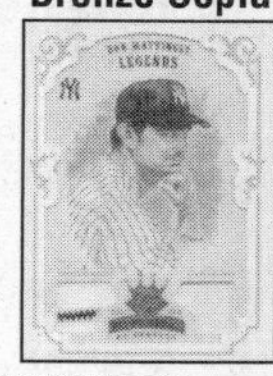

RANDOM INSERTS IN PACKS
PRINT RUNS B/WN 4-50 COPIES PER
NO PRICING ON QTY OF 5 OR LESS
151 R.Clemens FB Bat-Jsy/25 20.00 50.00
152 Mark Grace FB Bat-Jsy/25 10.00 25.00
153 R.Henderson FB Bat-Jsy/25 12.50 30.00
154 A.Rodriguez FB Bat-Jsy/25 20.00 50.00
155 R.Palmeiro FB Bat-Bat/50 6.00 15.00
156 G.Maddux FB Bat-Bat/50 15.00 40.00
157 Mike Piazza FB Bat-Jsy/50 15.00 40.00
158 M.Mussina FB Bat-Jsy/50 6.00 15.00
159 Dale Murphy LGD Bat-Jsy/15 15.00 40.00
160 Cal Ripken LGD Bat-Jsy/50 40.00 80.00
161 C.Yaz LGD Bat-Jsy/50 15.00 40.00
162 M.Marion LGD Jsy-Jsy/15 10.00 25.00
163 D.Mattingly LGD Bat-Jsy/50 20.00 50.00
164 R.Yount LGD Bat-Jsy/50 10.00 25.00
165 A.Dawson LGD Bat-Jsy/15 10.00 25.00
166 Jim Palmer LGD Jsy-Jsy/5
167 G.Brett LGD Bat-Jsy/15 50.00 100.00
168 W.Ford LGD Jsy-Pants/15 15.00 40.00
169 R.Campy LGD Bat-Pants/15 20.00 50.00
170 R.Maris LGD Bat-Jsy/15 60.00 120.00
171 Duke Snider LGD Bat-Jsy/5
172 S.Carlton LGD Bat-Jsy/15 10.00 25.00
173 Stan Musial LGD Bat-Jsy/15 40.00 80.00
174 Nolan Ryan LGD Bat-Jsy/15 50.00 100.00
175 D.Sanders LGD Bat-Jsy/50 6.00 15.00

2004 Diamond Kings DK Materials Framed Gold

RANDOM INSERTS IN PACKS
PRINT RUNS B/WN 1-50 COPIES PER
NO PRICING ON QTY OF 10 OR LESS
1 Alex Rodriguez Bat-Jsy/10
2 Andruw Jones Bat-Jsy/10
3 Nomar Garciaparra Bat-Jsy/10
4 Kerry Wood Bat-Jsy/10
5 Magglio Ordonez Bat-Jsy/10
6 Victor Martinez Bat-Bat/50 4.00 10.00
7 Jeremy Bonderman Jsy-Jsy/5
8 Josh Beckett Bat-Jsy/10
9 Jeff Kent Bat-Jsy/10
10 Carlos Beltran Bat-Jsy/10
11 Hideo Nomo Bat-Jsy/10
12 Richie Sexson Bat-Jsy/5
13 Jose Vidro Bat-Jsy/5
14 Jae Seo Jsy-Jsy/10
15 Alfonso Soriano Bat-Jsy/10
16 Barry Zito Bat-Jsy/10
17 Brett Myers Jsy-Jsy/5
18 Brian Giles Bat-Bat/10
19 Edgar Martinez Bat-Jsy/5
20 Jim Edmonds Bat-Jsy/5
21 Rocco Baldelli Bat-Jsy/5
22 Mark Teixeira Bat-Jsy/5
23 Carlos Delgado Bat-Jsy/10
25 Jose Reyes Bat-Jsy/10
26 Marlon Byrd Bat-Jsy/25 6.00 15.00
27 Albert Pujols Bat-Jsy/5
28 Vernon Wells Bat-Jsy/10
29 Garret Anderson Bat-Jsy/10
31 Chipper Jones Bat-Jsy/10
32 Rich Harden Jsy-Jsy/50 4.00 10.00
33 Manny Ramirez Bat-Jsy/10
34 Derek Jeter Base-Base/50 15.00 40.00
35 Brandon Webb Bat-Jsy/50 4.00 10.00
36 Mark Prior Bat-Jsy/10
37 Roy Halladay Jsy-Jsy/5
38 Frank Thomas Bat-Jsy/10
39 Rafael Palmeiro Bat-Jsy/50 6.00 15.00
40 Adam Dunn Bat-Jsy/10
41 Aubrey Huff Bat-Jsy/5
42 Todd Helton Bat-Jsy/10
43 Matt Morris Jsy-Jsy/10
44 Dontrelle Willis Bat-Jsy/10
45 Lance Berkman Bat-Jsy/10
46 Mike Sweeney Bat-Jsy/10
47 Kazuhisa Ishii Bat-Jsy/10
48 Torii Hunter Bat-Jsy/10
49 Vladimir Guerrero Bat-Jsy/10
50 Mike Piazza Bat-Jsy/50 15.00 40.00
51 Alexis Rios Bat-Bat/50 4.00 10.00
52 Shannon Stewart Bat-Bat/50 4.00 10.00
53 Eric Hinske Bat-Jsy/50 4.00 10.00
54 Jason Jennings Bat-Jsy/10
55 Jason Giambi Bat-Jsy/10
56 Brandon Claussen Fld Glv-Shoe/5
57 Joe Thurston Bat-Jsy/50 4.00 10.00
58 Ramon Nivar Bat-Jsy/50 4.00 10.00
59 Jay Gibbons Jsy-Jsy/10
60 Eric Chavez Bat-Jsy/10
62 Walter Young Bat-Bat/50 4.00 10.00
63 Mark Grace Bat-Jsy/5
64 Austin Kearns Bat-Jsy/5
65 Bob Abreu Bat-Jsy/10
66 Hee Seop Choi Bat-Jsy/10
67 Brandon Phillips Bat-Bat/50 4.00 10.00
68 Rickie Weeks Bat-Bat/50 4.00 10.00
69 Luis Gonzalez Bat-Jsy/10
70 Mariano Rivera Jsy-Jsy/50 10.00 25.00
71 Jason Lane Bat-Hat/5
72 Xavier Nady Bat-Hat/5
73 Run Hernandez Jsy-Jsy/5
74 Aramis Ramirez Bat-Bat/1
75 Ichiro Suzuki Ball-Base/5
77 Chris Snelling Bat-Bat/5
79 Miguel Tejada Bat-Jsy/50 4.00 10.00
80 Juan Gonzalez Bat-Jsy/10
81 Joe Borchard Bat-Jsy/5
82 Gary Sheffield Bat-Jsy/10
83 Wade Miller Bat-Jsy/5
84 Jeff Bagwell Bat-Jsy/10
86 Adrian Beltre Bat-Jsy/5
87 Jeff Baker Bat-Bat/50 4.00 10.00
89 Bernie Williams Bat-Jsy/10
90 Pedro Martinez Bat-Jsy/10
92 Junior Spivey Bat-Jsy/5
93 Tim Hudson Bat-Jsy/5
94 Troy Glaus Bat-Jsy/10
95 Ken Griffey Jr. Base-Base/50 12.50 30.00
96 Alexis Gomez Bat-Bat/5
97 Antonio Perez Bat-Pants/50 4.00 10.00
98 Dan Haren Bat-Jsy/50 4.00 10.00
99 Ivan Rodriguez Bat-Jsy/10
100 Randy Johnson Bat-Jsy/10
101 Lyle Overbay Bat-Jsy/50 4.00 10.00
103 Miguel Cabrera Bat-Jsy/10
104 Scott Rolen Bat-Jsy/10
105 Roger Clemens Bat-Jsy/10
107 Nic Jackson Bat-Bat/30 6.00 15.00
108 Angel Berroa Bat-Pants/5
109 Hank Blalock Bat-Jsy/5
110 Ryan Klesko Bat-Jsy/10
111 Jose Castillo Bat-Bat/50 4.00 10.00
112 Paul Konerko Bat-Jsy/10
113 Greg Maddux Bat-Jsy/10
114 Mark Mulder Bat-Jsy/10
115 Pat Burrell Bat-Jsy/10
116 Garrett Atkins Jsy-Jsy/50 4.00 10.00
118 Orlando Cabrera Bat-Jsy/5
119 Nick Johnson Bat-Jsy/10
120 Tom Glavine Bat-Jsy/10
121 Morgan Ensberg Bat-Jsy/10
122 Sean Casey Bat-Hat/5
123 Orlando Hudson Bat-Jsy/10
124 Hideki Matsui Ball-Base/5
125 Craig Biggio Bat-Jsy/10
126 Adam LaRoche Bat-Bat/25
127 Hong-Chih Kuo Bat-Bat/50 4.00 10.00
128 Paul LoDuca Bat-Jsy/10
129 Shawn Green Bat-Jsy/10
130 Luis Castillo Bat-Jsy/10
131 Joe Crede Bat-Btg Glv/5
132 Ken Harvey Bat-Bat/50 4.00 10.00
133 Freddy Sanchez Bat-Bat/50 4.00 10.00
134 Roy Oswalt Bat-Jsy/50 4.00 10.00
135 Curt Schilling Bat-Jsy/10
136 Alfredo Amezaga Bat-Jsy/5
138 Barry Larkin Bat-Jsy/5
139 Trot Nixon Bat-Bat/10
140 Jim Thome Bat-Jsy/10
141 Bret Boone Bat-Jsy/5
142 Jacque Jones Bat-Jsy/50 4.00 10.00
143 Travis Hafner Bat-Jsy/50 4.00 10.00
144 Sammy Sosa Bat-Jsy/10
145 Mike Mussina Bat-Jsy/50 6.00 15.00
147 Chad Gaudin Jsy-Jsy/10
149 Mike Lowell Bat-Jsy/10
150 R.Henderson Bat-Jsy/10
151 R.Clemens FB Bat-Jsy/5
152 Mark Grace FB Bat-Jsy/5
153 R.Henderson FB Bat-Jsy/5
154 A.Rodriguez FB Bat-Jsy/5
155 R.Palmeiro FB Bat-Bat/50 6.00 15.00
156 G.Maddux FB Bat-Bat/50 15.00 40.00
157 Mike Piazza FB Bat-Jsy/50 15.00 40.00
158 M.Mussina FB Bat-Jsy/50 6.00 15.00
159 Dale Murphy LGD Bat-Jsy/5
160 Cal Ripken LGD Bat-Jsy/50 40.00 80.00
161 C.Yaz LGD Bat-Jsy/50 15.00 40.00
162 M.Marion LGD Jsy-Jsy/5
163 D.Mattingly LGD Bat-Jsy/50 20.00 50.00
164 R.Yount LGD Bat-Jsy/50 10.00 25.00
165 A.Dawson LGD Bat-Jsy/5
166 Jim Palmer LGD Jsy-Jsy/5
167 George Brett LGD Bat-Jsy/5
168 W.Ford LGD Jsy-Pants/5
169 R.Campy LGD Bat-Pants/5
170 Roger Maris LGD Bat-Jsy/5
171 Duke Snider LGD Bat-Jsy/1
172 S.Carlton LGD Bat-Jsy/15 10.00 25.00
173 Stan Musial LGD Bat-Jsy/5
174 Nolan Ryan LGD Bat-Jsy/5
175 D.Sanders LGD Bat-Jsy/50 6.00 15.00

2004 Diamond Kings DK Materials Framed Gold Sepia

RANDOM INSERTS IN PACKS
PRINT RUNS B/WN 1-15 COPIES PER
NO PRICING ON QTY OF 5 OR LESS
151 R.Clemens FB Bat-Jsy/5
152 Mark Grace FB Bat-Jsy/5
153 R.Henderson FB Bat-Jsy/5
154 A.Rodriguez FB Bat-Jsy/5
155 R.Palmeiro FB Bat-Bat/15 15.00 40.00
156 G.Maddux FB Bat-Bat/15 30.00 60.00
157 Mike Piazza FB Bat-Jsy/15 30.00 60.00
158 M.Mussina FB Bat-Jsy/15 15.00 40.00
159 Dale Murphy LGD Bat-Jsy/5
160 Cal Ripken LGD Bat-Jsy/15 75.00 150.00
161 C.Yaz LGD Bat-Jsy/15 40.00 80.00
162 M.Marion LGD Jsy-Jsy/5
163 D.Mattingly LGD Bat-Jsy/15 50.00 100.00
164 R.Yount LGD Bat-Jsy/15
165 A.Dawson LGD Bat-Jsy/5
166 Jim Palmer LGD Jsy-Jsy/5
167 George Brett LGD Bat-Jsy/5
168 W.Ford LGD Jsy-Pants/5
169 R.Campy LGD Bat-Pants/5
170 Roger Maris LGD Bat-Jsy/5
171 Duke Snider LGD Bat-Jsy/1
172 S.Carlton LGD Bat-Jsy/5
173 Stan Musial LGD Bat-Jsy/5
174 Nolan Ryan LGD Bat-Jsy/5
175 D.Sanders LGD Bat-Jsy/15 15.00 40.00

2004 Diamond Kings DK Materials Framed Platinum Black

RANDOM INSERTS IN PACKS
STATED PRINT RUN 1 SERIAL #'d SET
NO PRICING DUE TO SCARCITY

2004 Diamond Kings DK Materials Framed Platinum Black Sepia

RANDOM INSERTS IN PACKS
STATED PRINT RUN 1 SERIAL #'d SET
NO PRICING DUE TO SCARCITY

2004 Diamond Kings DK Materials Framed Platinum Grey

RANDOM INSERTS IN PACKS
STATED PRINT RUN 1 SERIAL #'d SET
NO PRICING DUE TO SCARCITY

2004 Diamond Kings DK Materials Framed Platinum Grey Sepia

RANDOM INSERTS IN PACKS
STATED PRINT RUN 1 SERIAL #'d SET
NO PRICING DUE TO SCARCITY

2004 Diamond Kings DK Materials Framed Platinum White

RANDOM INSERTS IN PACKS
STATED PRINT RUN 1 SERIAL #'d SET
NO PRICING DUE TO SCARCITY

2004 Diamond Kings DK Materials Framed Platinum White Sepia

RANDOM INSERTS IN PACKS
STATED PRINT RUN 1 SERIAL #'d SET
NO PRICING DUE TO SCARCITY

2004 Diamond Kings DK Materials Framed Silver

RANDOM INSERTS IN PACKS
PRINT RUNS B/WN 1-75 COPIES PER

NO PRICING ON QTY OF 10 OR LESS
1 Alex Rodriguez Bat-Jsy/25 20.00 50.00
2 Andruw Jones Bat-Jsy/50 10.00 25.00
3 Nomar Garciaparra Bat-Jsy/25 20.00 50.00
4 Kerry Wood Bat-Jsy/25 6.00 15.00
5 Magglio Ordonez Bat-Jsy/25 6.00 15.00
6 Victor Martinez Bat-Bat/50 4.00 10.00
7 Jeremy Bonderman Jsy-Jsy/10
8 Josh Beckett Bat-Jsy/25 6.00 15.00
9 Jeff Kent Bat-Jsy/25 6.00 15.00
10 Carlos Beltran Bat-Jsy/25 6.00 15.00
11 Hideo Nomo Bat-Jsy/25 12.50 30.00
12 Richie Sexson Bat-Jsy/25 6.00 15.00
13 Jose Vidro Bat-Jsy/25 6.00 15.00
14 Jae Seo Jsy-Jsy/25 6.00 15.00
15 Alfonso Soriano Bat-Jsy/25 6.00 15.00
16 Barry Zito Bat-Jsy/25 6.00 15.00
17 Brett Myers Jsy-Jsy/10
18 Brian Giles Bat-Bat/25 6.00 15.00
19 Edgar Martinez Bat-Jsy/25 10.00 25.00
20 Jim Edmonds Bat-Jsy/25 6.00 15.00
21 Rocco Baldelli Bat-Jsy/25 6.00 15.00
22 Mark Teixeira Bat-Jsy/25 10.00 25.00
23 Carlos Delgado Bat-Jsy/25 6.00 15.00
25 Jose Reyes Bat-Jsy/25 6.00 15.00
26 Marlon Byrd Bat-Jsy/50 4.00 10.00
27 Albert Pujols Bat-Jsy/25 30.00 60.00
28 Vernon Wells Bat-Jsy/25 6.00 15.00
29 Garret Anderson Bat-Jsy/25 6.00 15.00
31 Chipper Jones Bat-Jsy/25 12.50 30.00
32 Rich Harden Jsy-Jsy/50 4.00 10.00
33 Manny Ramirez Bat-Jsy/25 10.00 25.00
34 Derek Jeter Base-Base/50 15.00 40.00
35 Brandon Webb Bat-Jsy/50 4.00 10.00
36 Mark Prior Bat-Jsy/25 10.00 25.00
37 Roy Halladay Jsy-Jsy/10
38 Frank Thomas Bat-Jsy/25 12.50 30.00
39 Rafael Palmeiro Bat-Bat/50 6.00 15.00
40 Adam Dunn Bat-Jsy/25 6.00 15.00
41 Aubrey Huff Bat-Jsy/10
42 Todd Helton Bat-Jsy/25 10.00 25.00
43 Matt Morris Jsy-Jsy/25 6.00 15.00
44 Dontrelle Willis Bat-Jsy/25 10.00 25.00
45 Lance Berkman Bat-Jsy/25 6.00 15.00
46 Mike Sweeney Bat-Jsy/25
47 Kazuhisa Ishii Bat-Jsy/25 6.00 15.00
48 Torii Hunter Bat-Jsy/25 6.00 15.00
49 Vladimir Guerrero Bat-Jsy/25 12.50 30.00
50 Mike Piazza Bat-Jsy/50 15.00 40.00
51 Alexis Rios Bat-Bat/50 4.00 10.00
52 Shannon Stewart Bat-Bat/50 4.00 10.00
53 Eric Hinske Bat-Jsy/50 4.00 10.00
54 Jason Jennings Bat-Jsy/25 6.00 15.00
55 Jason Giambi Bat-Jsy/25 6.00 15.00
56 Brandon Claussen Fld Glv-Shoe/5
57 Joe Thurston Bat-Jsy/50 4.00 10.00
58 Ramon Nivar Bat-Jsy/50 4.00 10.00
59 Jay Gibbons Jsy-Jsy/25 6.00 15.00
60 Eric Chavez Bat-Jsy/25 6.00 15.00
62 Walter Young Bat-Bat/50 4.00 10.00
63 Mark Grace Bat-Jsy/25 10.00 25.00
64 Austin Kearns Bat-Jsy/25 6.00 15.00
65 Bob Abreu Bat-Jsy/25 6.00 15.00
66 Hee Seop Choi Bat-Jsy/25 6.00 15.00
67 Brandon Phillips Bat-Bat/50 4.00 10.00
68 Rickie Weeks Bat-Bat/50 4.00 10.00
69 Luis Gonzalez Bat-Jsy/25 6.00 15.00
70 Mariano Rivera Jsy-Jsy/75 10.00 25.00
71 Jason Lane Bat-Hat/25 6.00 15.00
72 Xavier Nady Bat-Hat/10
73 Run Hernandez Jsy-Jsy/10
74 Aramis Ramirez Bat-Bat/1
75 Ichiro Suzuki Ball-Base/10
77 Chris Snelling Bat-Bat/10
79 Miguel Tejada Bat-Jsy/50 4.00 10.00
80 Juan Gonzalez Bat-Jsy/25 6.00 15.00
81 Joe Borchard Bat-Jsy/25 6.00 15.00
82 Gary Sheffield Bat-Jsy/25 6.00 15.00
83 Wade Miller Bat-Jsy/25 6.00 15.00
84 Jeff Bagwell Bat-Jsy/25 10.00 25.00
86 Adrian Beltre Bat-Jsy/25 6.00 15.00
87 Jeff Baker Bat-Bat/50 4.00 10.00
89 Bernie Williams Bat-Jsy/25 10.00 25.00
90 Pedro Martinez Bat-Jsy/25 10.00 25.00
92 Junior Spivey Bat-Jsy/25 6.00 15.00
93 Tim Hudson Bat-Jsy/25 6.00 15.00
94 Troy Glaus Bat-Jsy/25 6.00 15.00
95 Ken Griffey Jr. Base-Base/50 12.50 30.00
96 Alexis Gomez Bat-Bat/15
97 Antonio Perez Bat-Pants/50 4.00 10.00
98 Dan Haren Bat-Jsy/50 4.00 10.00
99 Ivan Rodriguez Bat-Jsy/25 10.00 25.00
100 Randy Johnson Bat-Jsy/25 12.50 30.00
101 Lyle Overbay Bat-Jsy/50 4.00 10.00
103 Miguel Cabrera Bat-Jsy/25 10.00 25.00
104 Scott Rolen Bat-Jsy/25 10.00 25.00
105 Roger Clemens Bat-Jsy/25 20.00 50.00
107 Nic Jackson Bat-Bat/50 4.00 10.00
108 Angel Berroa Bat-Pants/25 6.00 15.00
109 Hank Blalock Bat-Jsy/25 6.00 15.00
110 Ryan Klesko Bat-Jsy/25 6.00 15.00
111 Jose Castillo Bat-Bat/50 4.00 10.00
112 Paul Konerko Bat-Jsy/25 6.00 15.00
113 Greg Maddux Bat-Jsy/25 20.00 50.00
114 Mark Mulder Bat-Jsy/25 6.00 15.00
115 Pat Burrell Bat-Jsy/25 6.00 15.00
116 Garrett Atkins Jsy-Jsy/50 4.00 10.00
118 Orlando Cabrera Bat-Jsy/25 6.00 15.00
119 Nick Johnson Bat-Jsy/25 6.00 15.00
120 Tom Glavine Bat-Jsy/25 10.00 25.00
121 Morgan Ensberg Bat-Jsy/25 6.00 15.00
122 Sean Casey Bat-Hat/25 6.00 15.00
123 Orlando Hudson Bat-Jsy/25 6.00 15.00
124 Hideki Matsui Ball-Base/10
125 Craig Biggio Bat-Jsy/25 10.00 25.00
126 Adam LaRoche Bat-Bat/50 4.00 10.00
127 Hong-Chih Kuo Bat-Bat/50 4.00 10.00
128 Paul LoDuca Bat-Jsy/25 6.00 15.00
129 Shawn Green Bat-Jsy/25 6.00 15.00
130 Luis Castillo Bat-Jsy/25 6.00 15.00
131 Joe Crede Bat-Btg Glv/5
132 Ken Harvey Bat-Bat/50 4.00 10.00
133 Freddy Sanchez Bat-Bat/50 4.00 10.00
134 Roy Oswalt Bat-Jsy/50 4.00 10.00
135 Curt Schilling Bat-Jsy/25 10.00 25.00
136 Alfredo Amezaga Bat-Jsy/25 6.00 15.00
138 Barry Larkin Bat-Jsy/25 10.00 25.00
139 Trot Nixon Bat-Bat/25 6.00 15.00
140 Jim Thome Bat-Jsy/25 10.00 25.00
141 Bret Boone Bat-Jsy/50 4.00 10.00
142 Jacque Jones Bat-Jsy/50 4.00 10.00
143 Travis Hafner Bat-Jsy/50 4.00 10.00
144 Sammy Sosa Bat-Jsy/25 12.50 30.00
145 Mike Mussina Bat-Jsy/50 6.00 15.00
147 Chad Gaudin Jsy-Jsy/25 6.00 15.00
149 Mike Lowell Bat-Jsy/25 6.00 15.00
150 R.Henderson Bat-Jsy/25 12.50 30.00
151 R.Clemens FB Bat-Jsy/15 30.00 60.00
152 Mark Grace FB Bat-Jsy/15 15.00 40.00
153 R.Henderson FB Bat-Jsy/15 10.00 25.00
154 A.Rodriguez FB Bat-Jsy/15 30.00 60.00
155 R.Palmeiro FB Bat-Jsy/50 6.00 15.00
156 G.Maddux FB Bat-Bat/50 15.00 40.00
157 Mike Piazza FB Bat-Jsy/50 15.00 40.00
158 M.Mussina FB Bat-Jsy/50 6.00 15.00
159 Dale Murphy LGD Bat-Jsy/15 15.00 40.00
160 Cal Ripken LGD Bat-Jsy/50 40.00 80.00
161 C.Yaz LGD Bat-Jsy/50 15.00 40.00
162 M.Marion LGD Jsy-Jsy/15 10.00 25.00
163 D.Mattingly LGD Bat-Jsy/50 20.00 50.00
164 R.Yount LGD Bat-Jsy/50 10.00 25.00
165 A.Dawson LGD Bat-Jsy/15 10.00 25.00
166 Jim Palmer LGD Jsy-Jsy/5
167 G.Brett LGD Bat-Jsy/15 50.00 100.00
168 W.Ford LGD Jsy-Pants/15 15.00 40.00
169 R.Campy LGD Bat-Pants/15 20.00 50.00
170 R.Maris LGD Bat-Jsy/15 60.00 120.00
171 Duke Snider LGD Bat-Jsy/1
172 S.Carlton LGD Bat-Jsy/50 4.00 10.00
173 Stan Musial LGD Bat-Jsy/15 40.00 80.00
174 Nolan Ryan LGD Bat-Jsy/15 50.00 100.00
175 D.Sanders LGD Bat-Jsy/50 6.00 15.00

2004 Diamond Kings DK Materials Framed Silver Sepia

RANDOM INSERTS IN PACKS
PRINT RUNS B/WN 1-30 COPIES PER
NO PRICING ON QTY OF 10 OR LESS
151 R.Clemens FB Bat-Jsy/15 30.00 60.00
152 Mark Grace FB Bat-Jsy/15 15.00 40.00
153 R.Henderson FB Bat-Jsy/15 20.00 50.00
154 A.Rodriguez FB Bat-Jsy/15 30.00 60.00
155 R.Palmeiro FB Bat-Jsy/30 10.00 25.00
156 G.Maddux FB Bat-Bat/30 20.00 50.00
157 Mike Piazza FB Bat-Jsy/30 20.00 50.00
158 M.Mussina FB Bat-Jsy/30 10.00 25.00
159 Dale Murphy LGD Bat-Jsy/10
160 Cal Ripken LGD Bat-Jsy/30 50.00 100.00
161 C.Yaz LGD Bat-Jsy/30 20.00 50.00
162 M.Marion LGD Jsy-Jsy/10
163 D.Mattingly LGD Bat-Jsy/30 30.00 60.00
164 R.Yount LGD Bat-Jsy/30 12.50 30.00
165 A.Dawson LGD Bat-Jsy/10
166 Jim Palmer LGD Jsy-Jsy/5
167 George Brett LGD Bat-Jsy/10
168 W.Ford LGD Jsy-Pants/10
169 R.Campy LGD Bat-Pants/10
170 Roger Maris LGD Bat-Jsy/10
171 Duke Snider LGD Bat-Jsy/1
172 S.Carlton LGD Bat-Jsy/10
173 Stan Musial LGD Bat-Jsy/10
174 Nolan Ryan LGD Bat-Jsy/10
175 D.Sanders LGD Bat-Jsy/30 10.00 25.00

2004 Diamond Kings DK Signatures Bronze

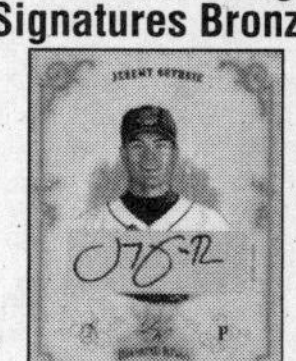

RANDOM INSERTS IN PACKS
PRINT RUNS B/WN 1-200 COPIES PER
NO PRICING ON QTY OF 10 OR LESS
1 Alex Rodriguez/1
2 Andruw Jones/2
4 Kerry Wood/1
5 Magglio Ordonez/2
6 Victor Martinez/200 6.00 15.00
7 Jeremy Bonderman/1
8 Josh Beckett/2
9 Jeff Kent/2
10 Carlos Beltran/8
11 Hideo Nomo/1
12 Richie Sexson/5
13 Jose Vidro/200 4.00 10.00
14 Jae Seo/200 6.00 15.00
17 Brett Myers/200 6.00 15.00
19 Edgar Martinez/25 30.00 60.00
20 Jim Edmonds/1
21 Rocco Baldelli/10
22 Mark Teixeira/5
26 Marlon Byrd/200 4.00 10.00
27 Albert Pujols/1
28 Vernon Wells/10
29 Garret Anderson/5
31 Chipper Jones/1
32 Rich Harden/200 6.00 15.00
35 Brandon Webb/25 6.00 15.00
36 Mark Prior/1
38 Frank Thomas/2
39 Rafael Palmeiro/1
40 Adam Dunn/5
41 Aubrey Huff/100 6.00 15.00
42 Todd Helton/1
44 Dontrelle Willis/15 20.00 50.00
45 Lance Berkman/1
46 Mike Sweeney/8
48 Torii Hunter/100 6.00 15.00
49 Vladimir Guerrero/1
50 Mike Piazza/1
51 Alexis Rios/200 6.00 15.00
52 Shannon Stewart/200 6.00 15.00
53 Eric Hinske/25 6.00 15.00
54 Jason Jennings/15 10.00 25.00
56 Brandon Claussen/200 4.00 10.00
57 Joe Thurston/200 4.00 10.00
58 Ramon Nivar/100 4.00 10.00
59 Jay Gibbons/25 6.00 15.00
60 Eric Chavez/2
61 Jimmy Gobble/100 4.00 10.00
62 Walter Young/200 4.00 10.00
63 Mark Grace/1
64 Austin Kearns/2
65 Bob Abreu/15 12.50 30.00
67 Brandon Phillips/100 4.00 10.00
68 Rickie Weeks/30 10.00 25.00
70 Mariano Rivera/10
71 Jason Lane/200 6.00 15.00
72 Xavier Nady/1
73 Runelvys Hernandez/50 5.00 12.00
74 Aramis Ramirez/100 6.00 15.00
76 Cliff Lee/200 4.00 10.00
77 Chris Snelling/200 4.00 10.00
78 Ryan Wagner/100 4.00 10.00
80 Juan Gonzalez/2
81 Joe Borchard/200 4.00 10.00
82 Gary Sheffield/10
83 Wade Miller/5
84 Jeff Bagwell/1
85 Ryan Church/200 6.00 15.00
86 Adrian Beltre/5
87 Jeff Baker/100 4.00 10.00
88 Adam Loewen/100 4.00 10.00
90 Pedro Martinez/1
91 Carlos Rivera/100 4.00 10.00
92 Junior Spivey/25 6.00 15.00
93 Tim Hudson/2
94 Troy Glaus/5
96 Alexis Gomez/200 4.00 10.00
97 Antonio Perez/46 5.00 12.00
98 Dan Haren/100 4.00 10.00
99 Ivan Rodriguez/5
100 Randy Johnson/1
101 Lyle Overbay/200 4.00 10.00
102 Oliver Perez/200 6.00 15.00
103 Miguel Cabrera/100 10.00 25.00
104 Scott Rolen/2
106 Brian Tallet/200 4.00 10.00
107 Nic Jackson/100 4.00 10.00
108 Angel Berroa/25 6.00 15.00
109 Hank Blalock/25 10.00 25.00
110 Ryan Klesko/3
111 Jose Castillo/200 4.00 10.00
112 Paul Konerko/8
113 Greg Maddux/1
114 Mark Mulder/25 10.00 25.00
116 Garrett Atkins/100 4.00 10.00
117 Jeremy Guthrie/200 4.00 10.00
118 Orlando Cabrera/75 8.00 20.00
120 Tom Glavine/2
121 Morgan Ensberg/200 6.00 15.00
122 Sean Casey/10
123 Orlando Hudson/100 4.00 10.00
125 Craig Biggio/2
126 Adam LaRoche/100 4.00 10.00
127 Hong-Chih Kuo/25 40.00 80.00
128 Paul LoDuca/1
130 Luis Castillo/25 6.00 15.00
131 Joe Crede/100 6.00 15.00
132 Ken Harvey/200 4.00 10.00
133 Freddy Sanchez/50 6.00 15.00
134 Roy Oswalt/8
135 Curt Schilling/1
136 Alfredo Amezaga/90 4.00 10.00
137 Chien-Ming Wang/25 125.00 200.00
139 Trot Nixon/15 12.50 30.00
142 Jacque Jones/25 10.00 25.00
143 Travis Hafner/200 6.00 15.00
144 Sammy Sosa/1
145 Mike Mussina/1
146 Vinny Chulk/200 4.00 10.00
147 Chad Gaudin/100 4.00 10.00
148 Delmon Young/25 15.00 40.00
149 Mike Lowell/25 10.00 25.00
151 Roger Clemens FB/1
152 Mark Grace FB/1
154 Alex Rodriguez FB/1
155 Rafael Palmeiro FB/1
156 Greg Maddux FB/1
157 Mike Piazza FB/1
158 Mike Mussina FB/1
159 Dale Murphy LGD/1
160 Cal Ripken LGD/1
161 Carl Yastrzemski LGD/1
162 Marty Marion LGD/15 12.50 30.00
163 Don Mattingly LGD/1
164 Robin Yount LGD/1
166 Jim Palmer LGD/1
168 Whitey Ford LGD/1
171 Duke Snider LGD/1
172 Steve Carlton LGD/1
173 Stan Musial LGD/1
174 Nolan Ryan LGD/1
175 Deion Sanders LGD/1

2004 Diamond Kings DK Signatures Bronze Sepia

RANDOM INSERTS IN PACKS
PRINT RUNS B/WN 1-15 COPIES PER
NO PRICING ON QTY OF 1 OR LESS
162 Marty Marion LGD/15 12.50 30.00

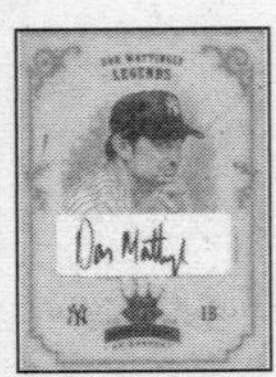

2004 Diamond Kings DK Signatures Gold

RANDOM INSERTS IN PACKS
PRINT RUNS B/WN 1-50 COPIES PER
NO PRICING ON QTY OF 12 OR LESS

26 Marlon Byrd/15 10.00 25.00
32 Rich Harden/50 8.00 20.00
51 Alexis Rios/50 8.00 20.00
56 Brandon Claussen/50 5.00 12.00
57 Joe Thurston/50 5.00 12.00
62 Walter Young/50 5.00 12.00
71 Jason Lane/40 8.00 20.00
77 Chris Snelling/50 5.00 12.00
81 Joe Borchard/50 5.00 12.00
85 Ryan Church/50 8.00 20.00
96 Alexis Gomez/50 5.00 12.00
101 Lyle Overbay/50 5.00 12.00
102 Oliver Perez/50 8.00 20.00
106 Brian Tallet/50 5.00 12.00
107 Nic Jackson/50 5.00 12.00
121 Morgan Ensberg/48 8.00 20.00
146 Vinny Chulk/50 5.00 12.00

2004 Diamond Kings DK Signatures Gold Sepia

RANDOM INSERTS IN PACKS
PRINT RUNS B/WN 1-3 COPIES PER
NO PRICING DUE TO SCARCITY

2004 Diamond Kings DK Signatures Platinum

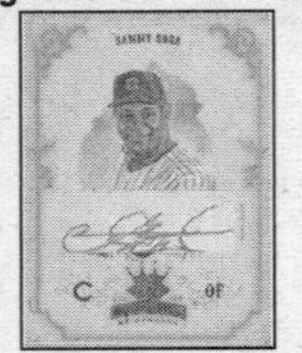

RANDOM INSERTS IN PACKS
STATED PRINT RUN 1 SERIAL #'d SET
NO PRICING DUE TO SCARCITY

2004 Diamond Kings DK Signatures Platinum Sepia

RANDOM INSERTS IN PACKS
STATED PRINT RUN 1 SERIAL #'d SET
NO PRICING DUE TO SCARCITY

2004 Diamond Kings DK Signatures Silver

RANDOM INSERTS IN PACKS
PRINT RUNS B/WN 1-100 COPIES PER
NO PRICING ON QTY OF 10 OR LESS

1 Alex Rodriguez/1
2 Andruw Jones/1
4 Kerry Wood/1
5 Magglio Ordonez/1
6 Victor Martinez/49 8.00 20.00
7 Jeremy Bonderman/1
8 Josh Beckett/1
9 Jeff Kent/1
10 Carlos Beltran/5
11 Hideo Nomo/1
12 Richie Sexson/3
13 Jose Vidro/20 8.00 20.00
14 Jae Seo/80 6.00 15.00
17 Brett Myers/90 6.00 15.00
19 Edgar Martinez/15 40.00 80.00
20 Jim Edmonds/1
21 Rocco Baldelli/5
22 Mark Teixeira/3
26 Marlon Byrd/100 4.00 10.00
27 Albert Pujols/1
28 Vernon Wells/5
29 Garret Anderson/3
31 Chipper Jones/1
32 Rich Harden/100 6.00 15.00
35 Brandon Webb/15 10.00 25.00
36 Mark Prior/1
38 Frank Thomas/1
39 Rafael Palmeiro/1
40 Adam Dunn/3
41 Aubrey Huff/40 10.00 25.00
42 Todd Helton/1
44 Dontrelle Willis/5
45 Lance Berkman/1
46 Mike Sweeney/5
48 Torii Hunter/30 10.00 25.00
49 Vladimir Guerrero/1
50 Mike Piazza/1
51 Alexis Rios/100 6.00 15.00
52 Shannon Stewart/30 10.00 25.00
53 Eric Hinske/15 10.00 25.00
54 Jason Jennings/5
56 Brandon Claussen/100 4.00 10.00
57 Joe Thurston/100 4.00 10.00
58 Ramon Nivar/30 6.00 15.00
59 Jay Gibbons/15 10.00 25.00
60 Eric Chavez/1
61 Jimmy Gobble/30 6.00 15.00
62 Walter Young/100 4.00 10.00
63 Mark Grace/1
64 Austin Kearns/1
65 Bob Abreu/6
67 Brandon Phillips/30 6.00 15.00
68 Rickie Weeks/20 10.00 25.00
70 Mariano Rivera/5
71 Jason Lane/100 6.00 15.00
72 Xavier Nady/1
73 Runelvys Hernandez/30 6.00 15.00
74 Aramis Ramirez/30 10.00 25.00
76 Cliff Lee/100 4.00 10.00
77 Chris Snelling/100 4.00 10.00
78 Ryan Wagner/30 6.00 15.00
80 Juan Gonzalez/3
81 Joe Borchard/100 4.00 10.00
82 Gary Sheffield/5
83 Wade Miller/3
84 Jeff Bagwell/1
85 Ryan Church/100 6.00 15.00
86 Adrian Beltre/3
87 Jeff Baker/30 6.00 15.00
88 Adam Loewen/30 6.00 15.00
90 Pedro Martinez/1
91 Carlos Rivera/15
92 Junior Spivey/15 10.00 25.00
93 Tim Hudson/1
94 Troy Glaus/3
96 Alexis Gomez/100 4.00 10.00
97 Antonio Perez/15 10.00 25.00
98 Dan Haren/30 6.00 15.00
99 Ivan Rodriguez/3
100 Randy Johnson/1
101 Lyle Overbay/100 4.00 10.00
102 Oliver Perez/100 6.00 15.00
103 Miguel Cabrera/30 15.00 40.00
104 Scott Rolen/1
105 Roger Clemens/1
106 Brian Tallet/100 4.00 10.00
107 Nic Jackson/100 4.00 10.00
108 Angel Berroa/5
109 Hank Blalock/30 10.00 25.00
110 Ryan Klesko/5
111 Jose Castillo/100 4.00 10.00
112 Paul Konerko/5
113 Greg Maddux/1
114 Mark Mulder/15 12.50 30.00
116 Garrett Atkins/30 6.00 15.00
117 Jeremy Guthrie/30 6.00 15.00
118 Orlando Cabrera/15 12.50 30.00
120 Tom Glavine/1
121 Morgan Ensberg/50 8.00 20.00
122 Sean Casey/5
123 Orlando Hudson/30 6.00 15.00
125 Craig Biggio/1
126 Adam LaRoche/30 6.00 15.00
127 Hong-Chih Kuo/15 60.00 120.00
128 Paul LoDuca/1
130 Luis Castillo/15 10.00 25.00
131 Joe Crede/35 6.00 15.00
132 Ken Harvey/30 6.00 15.00
133 Freddy Sanchez/15 10.00 25.00
134 Roy Oswalt/5
135 Curt Schilling/1
136 Alfredo Amezaga/30 6.00 15.00
137 Chien-Ming Wang/15 150.00 250.00
139 Trot Nixon/6
142 Jacque Jones/10
143 Travis Hafner/30 10.00 25.00
144 Sammy Sosa/1
145 Mike Mussina/1
146 Vinny Chulk/100 4.00 10.00
147 Chad Gaudin/30 6.00 15.00
148 Delmon Young/10
149 Mike Lowell/15 12.50 30.00
151 Roger Clemens FB/1
152 Mark Grace FB/1
154 Alex Rodriguez FB/1
155 Rafael Palmeiro FB/1
156 Greg Maddux FB/1
157 Mike Piazza FB/1
158 Mike Mussina FB/1
159 Dale Murphy LGD/1
160 Cal Ripken LGD/1
161 Carl Yastrzemski LGD/1
162 Marty Marion LGD/10
163 Don Mattingly LGD/1
164 Robin Yount LGD/1
166 Jim Palmer LGD/1
167 George Brett LGD/1
168 Whitey Ford LGD/1
171 Duke Snider LGD/1
172 Steve Carlton LGD/1
173 Stan Musial LGD/1
174 Nolan Ryan LGD/1
175 Deion Sanders LGD/1

2004 Diamond Kings DK Signatures Silver Sepia

RANDOM INSERTS IN PACKS
PRINT RUNS B/WN 1-10 COPIES PER
NO PRICING DUE TO SCARCITY

2004 Diamond Kings DK Signatures Framed Bronze

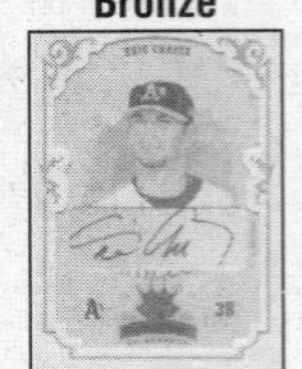

RANDOM INSERTS IN PACKS
PRINT RUNS B/WN 1-50 COPIES PER
NO PRICING ON QTY OF 10 OR LESS

1 Alex Rodriguez/1
2 Andruw Jones/5
4 Kerry Wood/1
5 Magglio Ordonez/10
6 Victor Martinez/50 8.00 20.00
7 Jeremy Bonderman/1
8 Josh Beckett/5
9 Jeff Kent/5
10 Carlos Beltran/10
11 Hideo Nomo/1
12 Richie Sexson/10
13 Jose Vidro/25 8.00 20.00
14 Jae Seo/50 8.00 20.00
17 Brett Myers/25 10.00 25.00
19 Edgar Martinez/25 30.00 60.00
20 Jim Edmonds/1
21 Rocco Baldelli/25 10.00 25.00
22 Mark Teixeira/1
26 Marlon Byrd/50 5.00 12.00
27 Albert Pujols/1
28 Vernon Wells/25 10.00 25.00
29 Garret Anderson/10
31 Chipper Jones/1
32 Rich Harden/50 8.00 20.00
35 Brandon Webb/25 8.00 20.00
36 Mark Prior/1
38 Frank Thomas/5
39 Rafael Palmeiro/1
40 Adam Dunn/25 15.00 40.00
41 Aubrey Huff/25 10.00 25.00
42 Todd Helton/1
44 Dontrelle Willis/25 15.00 40.00
45 Lance Berkman/1
46 Mike Sweeney/10
48 Torii Hunter/25 10.00 25.00
49 Vladimir Guerrero/1
50 Mike Piazza/1
51 Alexis Rios/50 8.00 20.00
52 Shannon Stewart/25 10.00 25.00
53 Eric Hinske/25 8.00 20.00
54 Jason Jennings/25 8.00 20.00
56 Brandon Claussen/50 5.00 12.00
57 Joe Thurston/50 5.00 12.00
58 Ramon Nivar/25 8.00 20.00
59 Jay Gibbons/25 8.00 20.00
60 Eric Chavez/10
61 Jimmy Gobble/50 5.00 12.00
62 Walter Young/50 5.00 12.00
63 Mark Grace/1
64 Austin Kearns/5
65 Bob Abreu/25 10.00 25.00
67 Brandon Phillips/50 5.00 12.00
68 Rickie Weeks/25 10.00 25.00
70 Mariano Rivera /10
71 Jason Lane/25 10.00 25.00
72 Xavier Nady/1
73 Runelvys Hernandez/25 8.00 20.00
74 Aramis Ramirez/25 10.00 25.00
76 Cliff Lee/50 5.00 12.00
77 Chris Snelling/50 5.00 12.00
78 Ryan Wagner/25 8.00 20.00
80 Juan Gonzalez/5
81 Joe Borchard/50 5.00 12.00
82 Gary Sheffield/10
83 Wade Miller/5
84 Jeff Bagwell/1
85 Ryan Church/50 8.00 20.00
86 Adrian Beltre/10
87 Jeff Baker/25 8.00 20.00
88 Adam Loewen/25 8.00 20.00
90 Pedro Martinez/1
91 Carlos Rivera/50 5.00 12.00
92 Junior Spivey/25
93 Tim Hudson/10
94 Troy Glaus/25 15.00 40.00
96 Alexis Gomez/50 5.00 12.00
97 Antonio Perez/25 8.00 20.00
98 Dan Haren/25 8.00 20.00
99 Ivan Rodriguez/5
100 Randy Johnson/1
101 Lyle Overbay/50 5.00 12.00
102 Oliver Perez/50 8.00 20.00
103 Miguel Cabrera/50 12.50 30.00
104 Scott Rolen/5
106 Brian Tallet/50 5.00 12.00
107 Nic Jackson/50 5.00 12.00
108 Angel Berroa/25 8.00 20.00
109 Hank Blalock/25 10.00 25.00
110 Ryan Klesko/5
111 Jose Castillo/50 5.00 12.00
112 Paul Konerko/15 20.00 50.00
113 Greg Maddux/1
114 Mark Mulder/25 10.00 25.00
116 Garrett Atkins/50 5.00 12.00
117 Jeremy Guthrie/25 8.00 20.00
118 Orlando Cabrera/25 10.00 25.00
120 Tom Glavine/5
121 Morgan Ensberg/50 8.00 20.00
122 Sean Casey/5
123 Orlando Hudson/50 5.00 12.00
125 Craig Biggio/5
126 Adam LaRoche/50 5.00 12.00
127 Hong-Chih Kuo/25 40.00 80.00
128 Paul LoDuca/1
130 Luis Castillo/25 8.00 20.00
131 Joe Crede/50 8.00 20.00
132 Ken Harvey/25 8.00 20.00
133 Freddy Sanchez/25 8.00 20.00
134 Roy Oswalt/20 10.00 25.00
135 Curt Schilling/1
136 Alfredo Amezaga/25 8.00 20.00
137 Chien-Ming Wang/25 125.00 200.00
139 Trot Nixon/25 10.00 25.00
142 Jacque Jones/25 10.00 25.00
143 Travis Hafner/25 10.00 25.00
144 Sammy Sosa/1
145 Mike Mussina/1
146 Vinny Chulk/50 5.00 12.00
147 Chad Gaudin/25 8.00 20.00
148 Delmon Young/25 15.00 40.00
149 Mike Lowell/25 10.00 25.00
151 Roger Clemens FB/1
152 Mark Grace FB/1
154 Alex Rodriguez FB/1
155 Rafael Palmeiro FB/1
156 Greg Maddux FB/1
157 Mike Piazza FB/1
158 Mike Mussina FB/1
159 Dale Murphy LGD/1
160 Cal Ripken LGD/1
161 Carl Yastrzemski LGD/1
162 Marty Marion LGD/25 10.00 25.00
163 Don Mattingly LGD/1
164 Robin Yount LGD/1
166 Jim Palmer LGD/1
167 George Brett LGD/1
168 Whitey Ford LGD/1
171 Duke Snider LGD/1
172 Steve Carlton LGD/1
173 Stan Musial LGD/1
174 Nolan Ryan LGD/1
175 Deion Sanders LGD/1

2004 Diamond Kings DK Signatures Framed Bronze Sepia

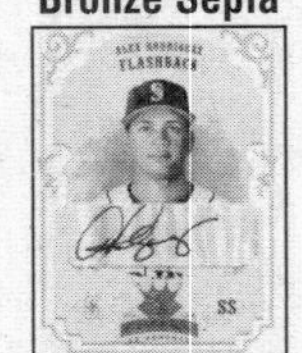

RANDOM INSERTS IN PACKS
PRINT RUNS B/WN 1-25 COPIES PER
NO PRICING ON QTY OF 1 OR LESS

162 Marty Marion LGD/25 10.00 25.00

2004 Diamond Kings DK Signatures Framed Gold

RANDOM INSERTS IN PACKS
PRINT RUNS B/WN 1-5 COPIES PER
NO PRICING DUE TO SCARCITY

2004 Diamond Kings DK Signatures Framed Gold Sepia

RANDOM INSERTS IN PACKS
PRINT RUNS B/WN 1-5 COPIES PER
NO PRICING DUE TO SCARCITY

2004 Diamond Kings DK Signatures Framed Platinum Black

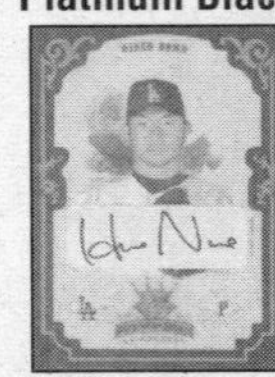

RANDOM INSERTS IN PACKS
STATED PRINT RUN 1 SERIAL #'d SET
NO PRICING DUE TO SCARCITY

2004 Diamond Kings DK Signatures Framed Platinum Black Sepia

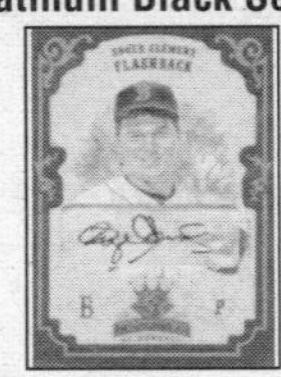

RANDOM INSERTS IN PACKS
STATED PRINT RUN 1 SERIAL #'d SET
NO PRICING DUE TO SCARCITY

2004 Diamond Kings DK Signatures Framed Platinum Grey

RANDOM INSERTS IN PACKS
STATED PRINT RUN 1 SERIAL #'d SET
NO PRICING DUE TO SCARCITY

2004 Diamond Kings DK Signatures Framed Platinum Grey Sepia

RANDOM INSERTS IN PACKS
STATED PRINT RUN 1 SERIAL #'d SET
NO PRICING DUE TO SCARCITY

2004 Diamond Kings DK Signatures Framed Platinum White

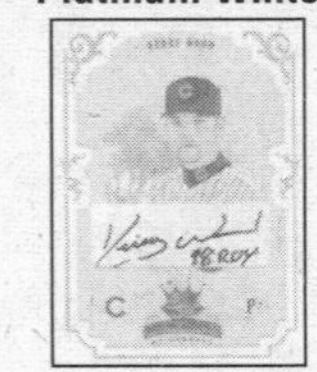

RANDOM INSERTS IN PACKS
STATED PRINT RUN 1 SERIAL #'d SET
NO PRICING DUE TO SCARCITY

2004 Diamond Kings DK Signatures Framed Platinum White Sepia

RANDOM INSERTS IN PACKS
STATED PRINT RUN 1 SERIAL #'d SET
NO PRICING DUE TO SCARCITY

2004 Diamond Kings DK Signatures Framed Silver

RANDOM INSERTS IN PACKS
PRINT RUNS B/WN 1-25 COPIES PER
NO PRICING ON QTY OF 10 OR LESS

1 Alex Rodriguez/1
2 Andruw Jones/5
4 Kerry Wood/1
5 Magglio Ordonez/10
6 Victor Martinez/15 12.50 30.00
7 Jeremy Bonderman/1
8 Josh Beckett/5
9 Jeff Kent/5
10 Carlos Beltran/10
11 Hideo Nomo/1
12 Richie Sexson/10
13 Jose Vidro/10
14 Jae Seo/15 12.50 30.00
17 Brett Myers/10
19 Edgar Martinez/10
20 Jim Edmonds/1
21 Rocco Baldelli/15 12.50 30.00
22 Mark Teixeira/1
26 Marlon Byrd/15 10.00 25.00
27 Albert Pujols/1
28 Vernon Wells/10
29 Garret Anderson/10
31 Chipper Jones/1
32 Rich Harden/25 10.00 25.00
35 Brandon Webb/15 10.00 25.00
36 Mark Prior/1
38 Frank Thomas/5
39 Rafael Palmeiro/1
40 Adam Dunn/5
41 Aubrey Huff/10
42 Todd Helton/1
44 Dontrelle Willis/10
45 Lance Berkman/1
46 Mike Sweeney/10
47 Kazuhisa Ishii/1
48 Torii Hunter/10
49 Vladimir Guerrero/1
50 Mike Piazza/1
51 Alexis Rios/25 10.00 25.00
52 Shannon Stewart/5
53 Eric Hinske/15
54 Jason Jennings/10
56 Brandon Claussen/25 8.00 20.00
57 Joe Thurston/25 8.00 20.00
58 Ramon Nivar/15 10.00 25.00
59 Jay Gibbons/15 10.00 25.00
60 Eric Chavez/10
61 Jimmy Gobble/15 10.00 25.00
62 Walter Young/25 8.00 20.00
63 Mark Grace/1
64 Austin Kearns/5
65 Bob Abreu/10
67 Brandon Phillips/15 10.00 25.00
68 Rickie Weeks/10
70 Mariano Rivera/5
71 Jason Lane/10
72 Xavier Nady/1
73 Runelvys Hernandez/15 10.00 25.00
74 Aramis Ramirez/10
76 Cliff Lee/15 10.00 25.00
77 Chris Snelling/25 8.00 20.00
78 Ryan Wagner/10
80 Juan Gonzalez/5
81 Joe Borchard/25 8.00 20.00
82 Gary Sheffield/5
83 Wade Miller/3
84 Jeff Bagwell/1
85 Ryan Church/25 10.00 25.00
86 Adrian Beltre/10
87 Jeff Baker/10
88 Adam Loewen/10
90 Pedro Martinez/1
91 Carlos Rivera/15 10.00 25.00
92 Junior Spivey/10
93 Tim Hudson/10
94 Troy Glaus/5
96 Alexis Gomez/25 8.00 20.00
97 Antonio Perez/10
98 Dan Haren/15
99 Ivan Rodriguez/5
100 Randy Johnson/1
101 Lyle Overbay/25 8.00 20.00
102 Oliver Perez/25 10.00 25.00
103 Miguel Cabrera/10
104 Scott Rolen/5
105 Roger Clemens/1
106 Brian Tallet/25 8.00 20.00
107 Nic Jackson/25 8.00 20.00
108 Angel Berroa/5
109 Hank Blalock/10
110 Ryan Klesko/5
111 Jose Castillo/15 10.00 25.00
112 Paul Konerko/10
113 Greg Maddux/1
114 Mark Mulder/10
116 Garrett Atkins/15
117 Jeremy Guthrie/10
118 Orlando Cabrera/10
120 Tom Glavine/5
121 Morgan Ensberg/15 12.50 30.00
122 Sean Casey/5
123 Orlando Hudson/15 10.00 25.00
125 Craig Biggio/5
126 Adam LaRoche/15 10.00 25.00
127 Hong-Chih Kuo/10
128 Paul LoDuca/1
130 Luis Castillo/15 10.00 25.00
131 Joe Crede/10
132 Ken Harvey/15
133 Freddy Sanchez/15 10.00 25.00

134 Roy Oswalt/10
135 Curt Schilling/1
136 Alfredo Amezaga/15 10.00 25.00
137 Chien-Ming Wang/15 150.00 250.00
139 Trot Nixon/10
142 Jacque Jones/10
143 Travis Hafner/10
144 Sammy Sosa/1
145 Mike Mussina/1
146 Vinny Chulk/25 8.00 20.00
147 Chad Gaudin/15 10.00 25.00
148 Delmon Young/10
149 Mike Lowell/15 12.50 30.00
151 Roger Clemens FB/1
152 Mark Grace FB/1
154 Alex Rodriguez FB/1
155 Rafael Palmeiro FB/1
156 Greg Maddux FB/1
157 Mike Piazza FB/1
158 Mike Mussina FB/1
159 Dale Murphy LGD/1
160 Cal Ripken LGD/1
161 Carl Yastrzemski LGD/1
162 Marty Marion LGD/10
163 Don Mattingly LGD/1
164 Robin Yount LGD/1
166 Jim Palmer LGD/1
167 George Brett LGD/1
168 Whitey Ford LGD/1
171 Duke Snider LGD/1
172 Steve Carlton LGD/1
173 Stan Musial LGD/1
174 Nolan Ryan LGD/1
175 Deion Sanders LGD/1

2004 Diamond Kings DK Signatures Framed Silver Sepia

RANDOM INSERTS IN PACKS
PRINT RUNS B/WN 1-10 COPIES PER
NO PRICING DUE TO SCARCITY

2004 Diamond Kings Diamond Cut Bats

RANDOM INSERTS IN PACKS
PRINT RUNS B/WN 1-100 COPIES PER
NO PRICING ON QTY OF 1 OR LESS
1 Alex Rodriguez/100 10.00 25.00
2 Nomar Garciaparra/100 10.00 25.00
3 Hideo Nomo/100 6.00 15.00
4 Alfonso Soriano/100 4.00 10.00
6 Edgar Martinez/100 6.00 15.00
7 Rocco Baldelli/100 4.00 10.00
8 Mark Teixeira/100 6.00 15.00
9 Albert Pujols/100 12.50 30.00
10 Vernon Wells/100 4.00 10.00
11 Garret Anderson/100 4.00 10.00
14 Brandon Webb/100 4.00 10.00
15 Mark Prior/100 6.00 15.00
16 Rafael Palmeiro/100 6.00 15.00
17 Adam Dunn/100 4.00 10.00
18 Dontrelle Willis/100 6.00 15.00
19 Kazuhisa Ishii/100 4.00 10.00
20 Torii Hunter/100 4.00 10.00
21 Vladimir Guerrero/100 6.00 15.00
22 Mike Piazza/100 10.00 25.00
23 Jason Giambi/100 4.00 10.00
26 Bob Abreu/100 4.00 10.00
27 Hee Seop Choi/100 4.00 10.00
28 Rickie Weeks/100 4.00 10.00
30 Troy Glaus/100 4.00 10.00
31 Ivan Rodriguez/100 6.00 15.00
32 Hank Blalock/100 4.00 10.00
33 Greg Maddux/100 10.00 25.00
34 Nick Johnson/100 4.00 10.00
35 Shawn Green/100 4.00 10.00
36 Sammy Sosa/100 6.00 15.00
37 Dale Murphy/50 10.00 25.00
38 Cal Ripken/50 30.00 60.00
39 Carl Yastrzemski/100 10.00 25.00
41 Don Mattingly/100 12.50 30.00
43 George Brett/50 15.00 40.00
45 Duke Snider/1
46 Steve Carlton/50 6.00 15.00
47 Stan Musial/25 20.00 50.00
48 Nolan Ryan/50 20.00 50.00
49 Deion Sanders/50 10.00 25.00
50 Roberto Clemente/25 75.00 150.00

2004 Diamond Kings Diamond Cut Combos Material

RANDOM INSERTS IN PACKS
PRINT RUNS B/WN 1-50 COPIES PER
NO PRICING ON QTY OF 8 OR LESS
1 Alex Rodriguez Bat-Jsy/50 15.00 40.00
2 Nomar Garciaparra Bat-Jsy/50 15.00 40.00
3 Hideo Nomo Bat-Jsy/25 15.00 40.00
4 Alfonso Soriano Bat-Jsy/50 6.00 15.00
6 Edgar Martinez Bat-Jsy/25 15.00 40.00
7 Rocco Baldelli Bat-Jsy/25 10.00 25.00

8 Mark Teixeira Bat-Jsy/25 15.00 40.00
9 Albert Pujols Bat-Jsy/50 20.00 50.00
10 Vernon Wells Bat-Jsy/25 10.00 25.00
11 Garret Anderson Bat-Jsy/25 10.00 25.00
14 Brandon Webb Bat-Jsy/25 10.00 25.00
15 Mark Prior Bat-Jsy/50 10.00 25.00
16 Rafael Palmeiro Bat-Jsy/25 15.00 40.00
17 Adam Dunn Bat-Jsy/25 10.00 25.00
18 Dontrelle Willis Bat-Jsy/25 15.00 40.00
19 Kazuhisa Ishii Bat-Jsy/25 10.00 25.00
20 Torii Hunter Bat-Jsy/25 10.00 25.00
21 Vladimir Guerrero Bat-Jsy/25 15.00 40.00
22 Mike Piazza Bat-Jsy/50 15.00 40.00
23 Jason Giambi Bat-Jsy/25 10.00 25.00
26 Bob Abreu Bat-Jsy/50 6.00 15.00
27 Hee Seop Choi Bat-Jsy/50 6.00 15.00
30 Troy Glaus Bat-Jsy/25 10.00 25.00
31 Ivan Rodriguez Bat-Jsy/25 15.00 40.00
32 Hank Blalock Bat-Jsy/25 10.00 25.00
33 Greg Maddux Bat-Jsy/50 15.00 40.00
34 Nick Johnson Bat-Jsy/25 10.00 25.00
35 Shawn Green Bat-Jsy/25 10.00 25.00
36 Sammy Sosa Bat-Jsy/50 10.00 25.00
37 Dale Murphy Bat-Jsy/3
38 Cal Ripken Bat-Jsy/8
39 Carl Yastrzemski Bat-Jsy/8
41 Don Mattingly Bat-Jsy/23 40.00 80.00
42 Jim Palmer Jsy-Jsy/22 12.50 30.00
43 George Brett Bat-Jsy/5
44 Whitey Ford Jsy-Pants/16 20.00 50.00
45 Duke Snider Bat-Jsy/1
46 Steve Carlton Bat-Jsy/32 10.00 25.00
47 Stan Musial Bat-Jsy/6
48 Nolan Ryan Bat-Jsy/34 30.00 60.00
49 Deion Sanders Bat-Jsy/24 20.00 50.00
50 Roberto Clemente Bat-Jsy/21

2004 Diamond Kings Diamond Cut Combos Signature

RANDOM INSERTS IN PACKS
PRINT RUNS B/WN 1-32 COPIES PER
NO PRICING ON QTY OF 10 OR LESS
1 Alex Rodriguez Jsy/3
3 Hideo Nomo Jsy/1
5 Brett Myers Jsy/5
6 Edgar Martinez Jsy/5
7 Rocco Baldelli Jsy/10
8 Mark Teixeira Jsy/10
9 Albert Pujols Jsy/5
10 Vernon Wells Jsy/5
11 Garret Anderson Jsy/5
13 Rich Harden Jsy/1
14 Brandon Webb Jsy/10
15 Mark Prior Jsy/5
16 Rafael Palmeiro Jsy/5
17 Adam Dunn Jsy/5
18 Dontrelle Willis Jsy/10
19 Kazuhisa Ishii Jsy/1
20 Torii Hunter Jsy/5
21 Vladimir Guerrero Jsy/5
22 Mike Piazza Jsy/1
26 Bob Abreu Jsy/10
30 Troy Glaus Jsy/10
31 Ivan Rodriguez Jsy/10
32 Hank Blalock Jsy/10
33 Greg Maddux Jsy/1
37 Dale Murphy Jsy/3
38 Cal Ripken Jsy/8
39 Carl Yastrzemski Jsy/8
40 Marty Marion Jsy/25 15.00 40.00
41 Don Mattingly Jsy/23 75.00 150.00
42 Jim Palmer Jsy/22 20.00 50.00
43 George Brett Jsy/1
44 Whitey Ford Jsy/16 40.00 80.00
45 Duke Snider Jsy/4
46 Steve Carlton Jsy/32 15.00 40.00
47 Stan Musial Jsy/6
48 Nolan Ryan Jsy/1
49 Deion Sanders Jsy/1

2004 Diamond Kings Diamond Cut Jerseys

RANDOM INSERTS IN PACKS
PRINT RUNS B/WN 10-100 COPIES PER
NO PRICING ON QTY OF 10 OR LESS
1 Alex Rodriguez/100 10.00 25.00
2 Nomar Garciaparra/100 10.00 25.00
3 Hideo Nomo/50 10.00 25.00
4 Alfonso Soriano/100 4.00 10.00
5 Brett Myers/50 6.00 15.00
6 Edgar Martinez/100 6.00 15.00
7 Rocco Baldelli/100 4.00 10.00
8 Mark Teixeira/100 6.00 15.00
9 Albert Pujols/100 12.50 30.00
10 Vernon Wells/100 4.00 10.00
11 Garret Anderson/50 6.00 15.00
12 Jerome Williams/100 4.00 10.00
13 Rich Harden/100 4.00 10.00
14 Brandon Webb/100 4.00 10.00
15 Mark Prior/100 6.00 15.00
16 Rafael Palmeiro/100 6.00 15.00
17 Adam Dunn/100 4.00 10.00
18 Dontrelle Willis/100 6.00 15.00
19 Kazuhisa Ishii/100 4.00 10.00
20 Torii Hunter/100 4.00 10.00
21 Vladimir Guerrero/50 10.00 25.00
22 Mike Piazza/100 10.00 25.00
23 Jason Giambi/100 4.00 10.00
25 Ramon Nivar/100 4.00 10.00
26 Bob Abreu/100 4.00 10.00
27 Hee Seop Choi/100 4.00 10.00
30 Troy Glaus/100 4.00 10.00
31 Ivan Rodriguez/100 6.00 15.00
32 Hank Blalock/100 4.00 10.00
33 Greg Maddux/100 10.00 25.00
34 Nick Johnson/100 4.00 10.00
35 Shawn Green/100 4.00 10.00
36 Sammy Sosa/100 6.00 15.00
37 Dale Murphy/50 10.00 25.00
38 Cal Ripken/50 30.00 60.00
39 Carl Yastrzemski/100 10.00 25.00
40 Marty Marion/50 6.00 15.00
41 Don Mattingly/100 12.50 30.00
42 Jim Palmer/25 10.00 25.00
43 George Brett/50 15.00 40.00
44 Whitey Ford/25 15.00 40.00
45 Duke Snider/10
46 Steve Carlton/50 6.00 15.00
47 Stan Musial/10
48 Nolan Ryan/50 20.00 50.00
49 Deion Sanders/50 10.00 25.00
50 Roberto Clemente/10

2004 Diamond Kings Diamond Cut Signatures

RANDOM INSERTS IN PACKS
PRINT RUNS B/WN 1-50 COPIES PER
NO PRICING ON QTY OF 10 OR LESS
1 Alex Rodriguez/1
3 Hideo Nomo/1
5 Brett Myers/10
6 Edgar Martinez/5
7 Rocco Baldelli/25 10.00 25.00
8 Mark Teixeira/25 15.00 40.00
9 Albert Pujols/1
10 Vernon Wells/5
11 Garret Anderson/5
13 Rich Harden/50 8.00 20.00
14 Brandon Webb/50 6.00 15.00
15 Mark Prior/5
16 Rafael Palmeiro/5
17 Adam Dunn/5
18 Dontrelle Willis/10
19 Kazuhisa Ishii/1
20 Torii Hunter/25 15.00 40.00
21 Vladimir Guerrero/5
22 Mike Piazza/1
24 Ryan Wagner/50 6.00 15.00
25 Ramon Nivar/50 6.00 15.00
26 Bob Abreu/10
28 Rickie Weeks/50 8.00 20.00
29 Adam Loewen/50 6.00 15.00
30 Troy Glaus/10
31 Ivan Rodriguez/10
32 Hank Blalock/25 10.00 25.00
33 Greg Maddux/1
36 Sammy Sosa/1
37 Dale Murphy/3
38 Cal Ripken/8
39 Carl Yastrzemski/8
40 Marty Marion/25 10.00 25.00
41 Don Mattingly/23 60.00 120.00
42 Jim Palmer/22 12.50 30.00
43 George Brett/1
44 Whitey Ford/16 20.00 50.00
45 Duke Snider/4
46 Steve Carlton/32 15.00 40.00
47 Stan Musial/6
48 Nolan Ryan/34 75.00 150.00
49 Deion Sanders/1

2004 Diamond Kings Gallery of Stars

STATED ODDS 1:37
1 Nolan Ryan 4.00 10.00
2 Cal Ripken 5.00 12.00
3 George Brett 3.00 8.00
4 Don Mattingly 3.00 8.00
5 Deion Sanders 2.50 6.00
6 Mike Piazza 2.50 6.00
7 Hideo Nomo 1.50 4.00
8 Rickey Henderson 1.50 4.00
9 Roger Clemens 3.00 8.00
10 Greg Maddux 2.50 6.00
11 Albert Pujols 3.00 8.00
12 Alex Rodriguez 2.50 6.00
13 Dale Murphy 1.50 4.00
14 Mark Prior 1.50 4.00
15 Dontrelle Willis 1.50 4.00

2004 Diamond Kings Gallery of Stars Signatures

RANDOM INSERTS IN PACKS
PRINT RUNS B/WN 1-10 COPIES PER
NO PRICING DUE TO SCARCITY

2004 Diamond Kings Heritage Collection

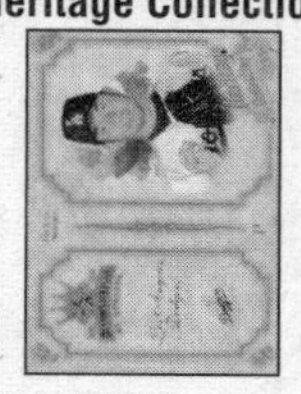

RANDOM INSERTS IN PACKS
1 Dale Murphy 1.50 4.00
2 Cal Ripken 5.00 12.00
3 Carl Yastrzemski 2.50 6.00
4 Don Mattingly 3.00 8.00
5 Jim Palmer 1.25 3.00
6 Andre Dawson 1.25 3.00
7 Roy Campanella 1.50 4.00
8 George Brett 3.00 8.00
9 Duke Snider 1.50 4.00
10 Marty Marion 1.25 3.00
11 Deion Sanders 1.50 4.00
12 Whitey Ford 1.50 4.00
13 Stan Musial 2.50 6.00
14 Nolan Ryan 4.00 10.00
15 Steve Carlton 1.25 3.00
16 Robin Yount 1.50 4.00
17 Albert Pujols 3.00 8.00
18 Alex Rodriguez 2.50 6.00
19 Mike Piazza 2.50 6.00
20 Roger Clemens 3.00 8.00
21 Hideo Nomo 1.50 4.00
22 Mark Prior 1.50 4.00
23 Roger Maris 1.50 4.00
24 Greg Maddux 2.50 6.00
25 Mark Grace 1.50 4.00

2004 Diamond Kings Heritage Collection Bats

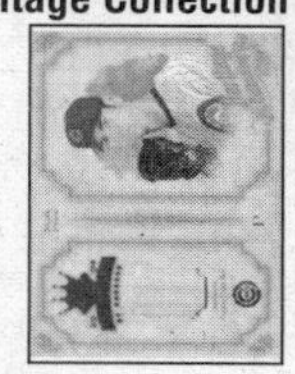

RANDOM INSERTS IN PACKS
PRINT RUNS B/WN 1-50 COPIES PER
NO PRICING ON QTY OF 1 OR LESS
1 Dale Murphy/50 10.00 25.00
2 Cal Ripken/50 30.00 60.00
3 Carl Yastrzemski/50 12.50 30.00
4 Don Mattingly/50 15.00 40.00
6 Andre Dawson/25 10.00 25.00
7 Roy Campanella/25 15.00 40.00
8 George Brett/25 30.00 60.00
9 Duke Snider/1
11 Deion Sanders/50 10.00 25.00
13 Stan Musial/25 20.00 50.00
14 Nolan Ryan/25 30.00 60.00
15 Steve Carlton/25 10.00 25.00
16 Robin Yount/50 10.00 25.00
17 Albert Pujols/50 15.00 40.00
18 Alex Rodriguez/50 12.50 30.00
19 Mike Piazza/50 12.50 30.00
20 Roger Clemens/50 12.50 30.00
21 Hideo Nomo/50 10.00 25.00
22 Mark Prior/50 10.00 25.00
23 Roger Maris/25 40.00 80.00
24 Greg Maddux/50 12.50 30.00
25 Mark Grace/50 10.00 25.00

2004 Diamond Kings Heritage Collection Jerseys

RANDOM INSERTS IN PACKS
PRINT RUNS B/WN 10-50 COPIES PER
NO PRICING ON QTY OF 10 OR LESS
1 Dale Murphy/50 10.00 25.00
2 Cal Ripken/50 30.00 60.00
3 Carl Yastrzemski/50 12.50 30.00
4 Don Mattingly/50 15.00 40.00
5 Jim Palmer/10
6 Andre Dawson/25 10.00 25.00
7 Roy Campanella Pants/25 15.00 40.00
8 George Brett/25 30.00 60.00
9 Duke Snider/10
10 Marty Marion/50 6.00 15.00
11 Deion Sanders/50 10.00 25.00
12 Whitey Ford/25 15.00 40.00
13 Stan Musial/10
14 Nolan Ryan/25 30.00 60.00
15 Steve Carlton/25 10.00 25.00
16 Robin Yount/50 10.00 25.00
17 Albert Pujols/50 15.00 40.00
18 Alex Rodriguez/50 15.00 40.00
19 Mike Piazza/50 12.50 30.00
20 Roger Clemens/50 12.50 30.00
21 Hideo Nomo/50 10.00 25.00
22 Mark Prior/50 10.00 25.00
23 Roger Maris/25 40.00 80.00
24 Greg Maddux/50 12.50 30.00
25 Mark Grace/50 10.00 25.00

2004 Diamond Kings Heritage Collection Signatures

RANDOM INSERTS IN PACKS
PRINT RUNS B/WN 1-16 COPIES PER
NO PRICING ON QTY OF 10 OR LESS
12 Whitey Ford/16 20.00 50.00

2004 Diamond Kings HOF Heroes

RANDOM INSERTS IN PACKS
PRINT RUNS B/WN 100-1000 COPIES PER
1 George Brett #45/1000 3.00 8.00
2 George Brett #45/500 5.00 12.00
3 George Brett #45/250 8.00 20.00
4 Mike Schmidt #46/1000 3.00 8.00
5 Mike Schmidt #46/250 8.00 20.00
6 Nolan Ryan #47/1000 4.00 10.00
7 Nolan Ryan #47/500 6.00 15.00
8 Nolan Ryan #47/250 10.00 25.00
9 Roberto Clemente #48/1000 4.00 10.00
10 Roberto Clemente #48/500 6.00 15.00
11 Roberto Clemente #48/250 10.00 25.00
12 Roberto Clemente #48/100 12.50 30.00
13 Carl Yastrzemski #49/1000 2.50 6.00
14 Robin Yount #50/1000 2.00 5.00
15 Whitey Ford #51/1000 2.00 5.00
16 Duke Snider #52/1000 2.00 5.00
17 Duke Snider #52/250 6.00 15.00
18 Carlton Fisk #53/1000 2.00 5.00
19 Ozzie Smith #54/1000 2.50 6.00
20 Kirby Puckett #55/1000 2.00 5.00
21 Bobby Doerr #56/1000 1.50 4.00
22 Frank Robinson #57/1000 1.50 4.00
23 Ralph Kiner #58/1000 1.50 4.00
24 Al Kaline #59/1000 2.00 5.00
25 Bob Feller #60/1000 1.50 4.00
26 Yogi Berra #61/1000 2.00 5.00
27 Stan Musial #62/1000 2.50 6.00
28 Stan Musial #62/500 4.00 10.00
29 Stan Musial #62/250 6.00 15.00
30 Jim Palmer #63/1000 1.50 4.00
31 Johnny Bench #64/1000 2.00 5.00
32 Steve Carlton #65/1000 1.50 4.00
33 Gary Carter #66/1000 1.50 4.00
34 Roy Campanella #67/1000 2.00 5.00
35 Roy Campanella #67/250 6.00 15.00

2004 Diamond Kings HOF Heroes Bats

RANDOM INSERTS IN PACKS
PRINT RUNS B/WN 1-25 COPIES PER
NO PRICING ON QTY OF 5 OR LESS
1 George Brett #45/25 20.00 50.00
2 George Brett #45/25 20.00 50.00
3 George Brett #45/25 20.00 50.00
4 Mike Schmidt #46/25 20.00 50.00
5 Mike Schmidt #46/25 20.00 50.00
6 Nolan Ryan #47/25 30.00 60.00
7 Nolan Ryan #47/25 30.00 60.00
8 Nolan Ryan #47/25 30.00 60.00
9 Roberto Clemente #48/5
10 Roberto Clemente #48/5
11 Roberto Clemente #48/5
12 Roberto Clemente #48/5
13 Carl Yastrzemski #49/25 20.00 50.00
14 Robin Yount #50/25 15.00 40.00
16 Duke Snider #52/1
17 Duke Snider #52/1
18 Carlton Fisk #53/25 15.00 40.00
19 Ozzie Smith #54/25 20.00 50.00
20 Kirby Puckett #55/25 15.00 40.00
21 Bobby Doerr #56/25 10.00 25.00
22 Frank Robinson #57/25 10.00 25.00
23 Ralph Kiner #58/25 10.00 25.00
24 Al Kaline #59/25 15.00 40.00
26 Yogi Berra #61/5
27 Stan Musial #62/5
28 Stan Musial #62/5
29 Stan Musial #62/5
31 Johnny Bench #64/25 15.00 40.00
32 Steve Carlton #65/25 10.00 25.00
33 Gary Carter #66/25 10.00 25.00
34 Roy Campanella #67/25 15.00 40.00
35 Roy Campanella #67/25 15.00 40.00

2004 Diamond Kings HOF Heroes Combos

RANDOM INSERTS IN PACKS
PRINT RUNS B/WN 1-25 COPIES PER
NO PRICING ON QTY OF 10 OR LESS
1 George Brett #45 Bat-Jsy/25 30.00 60.00
2 George Brett #45 Bat-Jsy/25 30.00 60.00
3 George Brett #45 Bat-Jsy/25 30.00 60.00
4 Mike Schmidt #46 Bat-Jsy/25 30.00 60.00
5 Mike Schmidt #46 Bat-Jsy/25 30.00 60.00
6 Nolan Ryan #47 Bat-Jsy/25 40.00 80.00
7 Nolan Ryan #47 Bat-Jsy/25 40.00 80.00
8 Nolan Ryan #47 Bat-Jsy/25 40.00 80.00
9 Roberto Clemente #48 Bat-Jsy/5
10 Roberto Clemente #48 Bat-Jsy/5
11 Roberto Clemente #48 Bat-Jsy/5
12 Roberto Clemente #48 Bat-Jsy/5
13 C.Yastrzemski #49 Bat-Jsy/25 30.00 60.00
14 Robin Yount #50 Bat-Jsy/25 20.00 50.00
15 Whitey Ford #51 Jsy-Pants/25 20.00 50.00
16 Duke Snider #52 Bat-Jsy/1
17 Duke Snider #52 Bat-Jsy/1
18 Carlton Fisk #53 Bat-Jsy/25 20.00 50.00
19 Ozzie Smith #54 Bat-Jsy/25 30.00 60.00
20 Kirby Puckett #55 Bat-Jsy/25 20.00 50.00
21 Bobby Doerr #56 Bat-Jsy/25 12.50 30.00
22 Frank Robinson #57 Bat-Jsy/10
23 Ralph Kiner #58 Bat-Bat/25 12.50 30.00
24 Al Kaline #59 Bat-Jsy/25 20.00 50.00
25 Bob Feller #60 Jsy-Jsy/10
26 Yogi Berra #61 Bat-Jsy/5
27 Stan Musial #62 Bat-Jsy/5
28 Stan Musial #62 Bat-Jsy/5
29 Stan Musial #62 Bat-Jsy/5
30 Jim Palmer #63 Jsy-Jsy/5
31 Johnny Bench #64 Bat-Jsy/1
32 Steve Carlton #65 Bat-Jsy/25 12.50 30.00
33 Gary Carter #66 Bat-Jsy/25 12.50 30.00
34 R.Campy #67 Bat-Pants/25 20.00 50.00
35 R.Campy #67 Bat-Pants/25 20.00 50.00

2004 Diamond Kings HOF Heroes Jerseys

RANDOM INSERTS IN PACKS
PRINT RUNS B/WN 1-25 COPIES PER
NO PRICING ON QTY OF 10 OR LESS
1 George Brett #45/25 20.00 50.00
2 George Brett #45/25 20.00 50.00
3 George Brett #45/25 20.00 50.00
4 Mike Schmidt #46/25 20.00 50.00
5 Mike Schmidt #46/25 20.00 50.00
6 Nolan Ryan #47/25 30.00 60.00
7 Nolan Ryan #47/25 30.00 60.00
8 Nolan Ryan #47/25 30.00 60.00
9 Roberto Clemente #48/5
10 Roberto Clemente #48/5
11 Roberto Clemente #48/5
12 Roberto Clemente #48/5
13 Carl Yastrzemski #49/25 20.00 50.00
14 Robin Yount #50/25 15.00 40.00
15 Whitey Ford #51/25 15.00 40.00
16 Duke Snider #52/10
17 Duke Snider #52/10
18 Carlton Fisk #53/25 15.00 40.00
19 Ozzie Smith #54/25 20.00 50.00
20 Kirby Puckett #55/25 15.00 40.00
21 Bobby Doerr #56/25 10.00 25.00
22 Frank Robinson #57/10
24 Al Kaline #59/25 15.00 40.00
25 Bob Feller #60/10
26 Yogi Berra #61/5
27 Stan Musial #62/5
28 Stan Musial #62/5
29 Stan Musial #62/5
30 Jim Palmer #63/5
31 Johnny Bench #64/1
32 Steve Carlton #65/25 10.00 25.00

33 Gary Carter #66/25 10.00 25.00
34 Roy Campanella #67 Pants/25 15.00 40.00
35 Roy Campanella #67 Pants/25 15.00 40.00

2004 Diamond Kings HOF Heroes Signatures

RANDOM INSERTS IN PACKS
PRINT RUNS B/WN 4-32 COPIES PER
NO PRICING ON QTY OF 10 OR LESS
1 George Brett #45/5
2 George Brett #45/5
3 George Brett #45/5
6 Nolan Ryan #47/5
7 Nolan Ryan #47/5
8 Nolan Ryan #47/5
13 Carl Yastrzemski #49/8
14 Robin Yount #50/19 50.00 100.00
15 Whitey Ford #51/16 20.00 50.00
16 Duke Snider #52/4
17 Duke Snider #52/4
18 Carlton Fisk #53/5
19 Ozzie Smith #54/5
20 Kirby Puckett #55/5
21 Bobby Doerr #56/10
22 Frank Robinson #57/20 20.00 50.00
23 Ralph Kiner #58/4
24 Al Kaline #59/6
25 Bob Feller #60/19 12.50 30.00
26 Yogi Berra #61/8
27 Stan Musial #62/6
28 Stan Musial #62/6
29 Stan Musial #62/6
30 Jim Palmer #63/22 12.50 30.00
31 Johnny Bench #64/5
32 Steve Carlton #65/32 10.00 25.00
33 Gary Carter #66/5

2004 Diamond Kings Recollection Autographs

RANDOM INSERTS IN PACKS
PRINT RUNS B/WN 1-159 COPIES PER
NO PRICING ON QTY OF 14 OR LESS
1 Sandy Alomar Jr. 91 DK/8
2 Rich Aurilia 02 DK/2
3 Jeff Bagwell 93 TP Gall/1
4 Jeff Bagwell 02 DK/2
5 Jeff Bagwell 03 DK/1
6 Clint Barmes 03 DK Black/82 5.00 12.00
7 Clint Barmes 03 DK Blue/72 6.00 15.00
8 Carlos Beltran 02 DK/23 10.00 25.00
9 Carlos Beltran 03 DK/99 6.00 15.00
10 Adrian Beltre 02 DK/40 8.00 20.00
11 Johnny Bench 83 DK/3
12 Johnny Bench 01 DK Rep/1
13 Yogi Berra 83 HOF/4
14 Craig Biggio 91 DK/10
15 Craig Biggio 03 DK/1
16 Wade Boggs 84 DK/13
17 George Brett 03 DK/1
18 John Buck 02 DK/13
19 Chris Burke 03 DK/150 6.00 15.00
20 Marlon Byrd 02 DK/23 6.00 15.00
21 Marlon Byrd 03 DK/100 4.00 10.00
22 Rod Carew 01 DK Rep/1
23 Steve Carlton 01 DK Rep/6
24 Kevin Cash 03 DK/103 4.00 10.00
25 Jose Cruz 85 DK/59 5.00 12.00
26 J.D. Durbin 03 DK/151 4.00 10.00
27 Jim Edmonds 03 DK/24 15.00 40.00
28 Bob Feller 84 HOF/5
29 Bob Feller 03 DK HOF/18 15.00 40.00
30 Carlton Fisk 02 DK/13
31 Carlton Fisk 02 DK Her/5
32 Julio Franco 87 DK/25 10.00 25.00
33 Freddy Garcia 03 DK/50 8.00 20.00
34 Jay Gibbons 03 DK/100 4.00 10.00
35 Juan Gonzalez 03 DK/10
36 Mark Grace 02 DK/5
37 Mark Grace 03 DK/7
38 Shawn Green 02 DK/2
39 Brendan Harris 03 DK/150 4.00 10.00
40 Rickey Henderson 02 DK/1
41 Rickey Henderson 03 DK/2
42 Ru.Hernandez 02 DK/100 4.00 10.00
43 Eric Hinske 03 DK/20 6.00 15.00
44 Tim Hudson 02 DK/25 15.00 40.00
45 Tim Hudson 03 DK/25 15.00 40.00
46 Aubrey Huff 03 DK/99 6.00 15.00
47 Monte Irvin 84 HOF/7
48 Bo Jackson 02 DK/5
49 Jason Jennings 03 DK/50 5.00 12.00
50 Tommy John 88 DK Black/62 8.00 20.00
51 Tommy John 88 DK Blue/7
52 Howard Johnson 90 DK/52 5.00 12.00
53 Andruw Jones 03 DK/14
54 Austin Kearns 02 DK/25 6.00 15.00
55 Austin Kearns 03 DK/25 6.00 15.00
56 Ralph Kiner 83 HOF/5
57 Carney Lansford 85 DK Black/12
58 Carney Lansford 85 DK Blue/4
59 P.Larrison 03 DK Black/74 8.00 20.00
60 Pr.Larrison 03 DK Blue/77 8.00 20.00
61 Greg Maddux 02 DK/1
62 Greg Maddux 03 DK/2
63 Don Mattingly 85 DK/4
64 Don Mattingly 89 DK/5
65 Don Mattingly 02 DK Time/1
66 Don Mattingly 03 DK/5
67 Dustin McGowan 03 DK/159 4.00 10.00
68 Paul Molitor 02 DK Her/5
69 Melvin Mora 03 DK/101 6.00 15.00
70 Joe Morgan 01 DK Rep/2
71 Jack Morris 03 DK/60 8.00 20.00
72 Jack Morris 03 DK Her/19 15.00 40.00
73 Dale Murphy 03 DK Black/3
74 Dale Murphy 03 DK Blue/47 12.50 30.00
75 Dale Murphy 03 DK Her Black/8
76 Dale Murphy 03 DK Her Blue/10
77 Dale Murphy 03 DK Time/18 30.00 60.00
78 Stan Musial 83 HOF/3
79 Stan Musial 03 DK/2
80 Mike Mussina 03 DK/1
81 Phil Niekro 82 DK/10
82 Magglio Ordonez 03 DK/25 15.00 40.00
83 Magglio Ordonez 03 DK Ins/10
84 Roy Oswalt 03 DK/10
85 Dave Parker 82 DK/20 10.00 25.00
86 Dave Parker 90 DK/18 15.00 40.00
87 Tony Pena 85 DK/7
88 Jorge Posada 02 DK/25 15.00 40.00
89 Mark Prior 03 DK/25 10.00 25.00
90 Cal Ripken 02 DK/2
91 Cal Ripken 03 DK/3
92 Mike Rivera 02 DK/24 6.00 15.00
93 Robin Roberts 84 HOF Black/6
94 Robin Roberts 84 HOF Blue/1
95 Frank Robinson 83 HOF/8
96 Alex Rodriguez 03 DK/1
97 Ivan Rodriguez 03 DK/22 30.00 60.00
98 Scott Rolen 02 DK/5
99 Scott Rolen 03 DK/2
100 Rodrigo Rosario 02 DK/50 5.00 12.00
101 Nolan Ryan 02 DK/3
102 Nolan Ryan 03 DK/5
103 Nolan Ryan 03 DK Bronze/1
104 Nolan Ryan 03 DK Evol/1
105 Ron Santo 02 DK/29 15.00 40.00
106 Richie Sexson 02 DK/25 10.00 25.00
107 Richie Sexson 03 DK/25 10.00 25.00
108 Gary Sheffield 03 DK/11
109 Chris Snelling 02 DK/46 5.00 12.00
110 Duke Snider 83 HOF/4
111 J.T. Snow 93 TP Gall Black/1
112 J.T. Snow 93 TP Gall Blue/1
113 Sammy Sosa 99 Retro DK/2
114 Sammy Sosa 01 DK/2
115 Sammy Sosa 03 DK/3
116 Sammy Sosa 03 DK Ins/1
117 Junior Spivey 03 DK Black/12
118 Junior Spivey 03 DK Blue/13
119 Shannon Stewart 02 DK/50 8.00 20.00
120 S.Stewart 03 DK Black/92 6.00 15.00
121 Shannon Stewart 03 DK Blue/9
122 Frank Thomas 01 DK Black/1
123 Frank Thomas 01 DK Blue/1
124 Frank Thomas 00 Retro DK Black/2
125 Frank Thomas 00 Retro DK Blue/1
126 G.Thomas 82 DK Black/22 6.00 15.00
127 G.Thomas 82 DK Blue/20 6.00 15.00
128 Alan Trammell 02 DK/29 10.00 25.00
129 Alan Trammell 02 DK Her/25 10.00 25.00
130 Robin Ventura 03 DK/25 10.00 25.00
131 Jose Vidro 03 DK/25 6.00 15.00
132 Rickie Weeks 03 DK/52 12.50 30.00
133 Kevin Youkilis 03 DK/153 6.00 15.00
134 Barry Zito 03 DK/5

2004 Diamond Kings Team Timeline

STATED ODDS 1:29
1 Deion Sanders 1.50 4.00
Andruw Jones
2 Rickie Weeks 1.50 4.00
Robin Yount
3 Don Mattingly 3.00 8.00
Whitey Ford
4 Chipper Jones 1.50 4.00
Dale Murphy
5 Nomar Garciaparra 2.50 6.00
Bobby Doerr
6 Mark Prior 1.50 4.00
Sammy Sosa
7 Hideo Nomo 1.50 4.00
Kazuhisa Ishii
8 Andre Dawson 1.50 4.00
Mark Grace
9 Roger Clemens 3.00 8.00
Carl Yastrzemski
10 Mike Mussina 5.00 12.00
Cal Ripken
11 Stan Musial 3.00 8.00
Albert Pujols
12 Jim Palmer 1.50 4.00
Mike Mussina
13 Marty Marion 2.50 6.00
Stan Musial
14 George Brett 3.00 8.00
Mike Sweeney
15 Roger Clemens 3.00 8.00
Roger Maris
16 Duke Snider 1.50 4.00
Shawn Green
17 Jim Thome 3.00 8.00
Mike Schmidt
18 Nolan Ryan 4.00 10.00
Alex Rodriguez
19 Roy Campanella 2.50 6.00
Mike Piazza

2004 Diamond Kings Team Timeline Bats

RANDOM INSERTS IN PACKS
STATED PRINT RUN 25 SERIAL #'d SETS
SNIDER/GREEN PRINT 1 SERIAL #'d CARD
SNIDER/GREEN TOO SCARCE TO PRICE
1 Deion Sanders 12.50 30.00
Andruw Jones
2 Rickie Weeks 20.00 50.00
Robin Yount
3 Don Mattingly 50.00 100.00
Whitey Ford
4 Chipper Jones 30.00 60.00
Dale Murphy
5 Nomar Garciaparra 20.00 50.00
Bobby Doerr
6 Mark Prior 20.00 50.00
Sammy Sosa
7 Hideo Nomo 30.00 60.00
Kazuhisa Ishii
8 Andre Dawson 12.50 30.00
Mark Grace
9 Roger Clemens 30.00 60.00
Carl Yastrzemski
10 Mike Mussina 60.00 120.00
Cal Ripken
11 Stan Musial 50.00 100.00
Albert Pujols
12 Jim Palmer 12.50 30.00
Mike Mussina
13 Marty Marion
Stan Musial
14 George Brett 20.00 50.00
Mike Sweeney
15 Roger Clemens 50.00 100.00
Roger Maris
16 Duke Snider/1
Shawn Green
17 Jim Thome 30.00 60.00
Mike Schmidt
18 Nolan Ryan 40.00 80.00
Alex Rodriguez
19 Roy Campanella 30.00 60.00
Mike Piazza

2004 Diamond Kings Team Timeline Jerseys

PRINT RUNS B/WN 10-25 COPIES PER
NO PRICING ON QTY OF 10 OR LESS
PRIME PRINT RUN 1 SERIAL #'d SET
NO PRIME PRICING DUE TO SCARCITY
RANDOM INSERTS IN PACKS
R.WEEKS IS A BAT SWATCH
R.CAMPANELLA IS A PANTS SWATCH
1 Deion Sanders/25 12.50 30.00
Andruw Jones
2 Rickie Weeks/25 20.00 50.00
Robin Yount
3 Don Mattingly/25 50.00 100.00
Whitey Ford
4 Chipper Jones/25 30.00 60.00
Dale Murphy
5 Nomar Garciaparra/25 20.00 50.00
Bobby Doerr
6 Mark Prior/25 20.00 50.00
Sammy Sosa
7 Hideo Nomo/25 30.00 60.00
Kazuhisa Ishii
8 Andre Dawson/25 12.50 30.00
Mark Grace
9 Roger Clemens/25 30.00 60.00
Carl Yastrzemski
10 Mike Mussina/25 60.00 120.00
Cal Ripken
11 Stan Musial/10
Albert Pujols
12 Jim Palmer/10
Mike Mussina
13 Marty Marion/10
Stan Musial
14 George Brett/25 20.00 50.00
Mike Sweeney
15 Roger Clemens/25 50.00 100.00
Roger Maris
16 Duke Snider/10
Shawn Green
17 Jim Thome/25 30.00 60.00
Mike Schmidt
18 Nolan Ryan/25 40.00 80.00
Alex Rodriguez
19 Roy Campanella Pants/25 30.00 60.00
Mike Piazza

2004 Diamond Kings Timeline

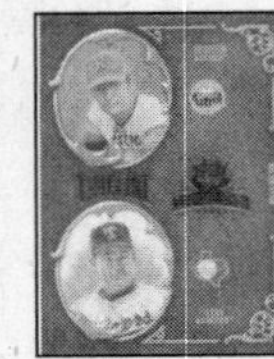

STATED ODDS 1:92
1 Roger Clemens 3.00 8.00
2 Mark Grace 1.50 4.00
3 Mike Mussina 1.50 4.00
4 Mike Piazza 2.50 6.00
5 Nolan Ryan 4.00 10.00
6 Rickey Henderson 1.50 4.00

2004 Diamond Kings Timeline Bats

RANDOM INSERTS IN PACKS
STATED PRINT RUN 25 SERIAL #'d SETS
1 Roger Clemens Sox-Yanks 20.00 50.00
2 Mark Grace Cubs-D'backs 15.00 40.00
3 Mike Mussina O's-Yanks 15.00 40.00
4 Mike Piazza Dodgers-Mets 20.00 50.00
5 Nolan Ryan Astros-Rangers 40.00 80.00
6 Rickey Henderson A's-Dodgers 15.00 40.00

2004 Diamond Kings Timeline Jerseys

STATED PRINT RUN 25 SERIAL #'d SETS
PRIME PRINT RUN 1 SERIAL #'d SET
NO PRIME PRICING DUE TO SCARCITY
RANDOM INSERTS IN PACKS
1 Roger Clemens Sox-Yanks 30.00 60.00
2 Mark Grace Cubs-D'backs 20.00 50.00
3 Mike Mussina O's-Yanks 20.00 50.00
4 Mike Piazza Dodgers-Mets 30.00 60.00
5 Nolan Ryan Astros-Rangers 50.00 100.00
6 Rickey Henderson A's-Dodgers 20.00 50.00

2005 Diamond Kings

This 300-card first series was released in February, 2005. The series was issued in five card packs with an $6 SRP which came 12 packs to a box and 16 boxes to a case. Although there are no short prints in this set, cards numbered 281-300 feature retired greats. An 150-card update set was released in July, 2005. The second series was also issued in five-card packs with $6 SRP which came 12 packs to a box and 16 boxes to a case.

COMPLETE SET (450) 90.00 180.00
COMP.SERIES 1 SET (300) 60.00 120.00
COMP.SERIES 2 SET (150) 30.00 60.00
COMMON CARD .20 .50
COMMON RC .20 .50
COMMON RETIRED .20 .50
COMP.SET DOES NOT CONTAIN ANY SP's
1 Garret Anderson .20 .50
2 Vladimir Guerrero .50 1.25
3 Jose Guillen .20 .50
4 Troy Glaus UER .20 .50
Previous Diamond King appearences in wrong years
5 Tim Salmon .30 .75
6 Casey Kotchman .20 .50
7 Chone Figgins .20 .50
8 Robb Quinlan .20 .50
9 Francisco Rodriguez .20 .50
10 Troy Glavine .20 .50
11 Randy Johnson .50 1.25
12 Brandon Webb .20 .50
13 Richie Sexson .20 .50
14 Shea Hillenbrand .20 .50
15 Chad Tracy .20 .50
16 Alex Cintron .20 .50
17 Luis Gonzalez .20 .50
18 Rafael Furcal .20 .50
19 Andruw Jones .30 .75
20 Marcus Giles .20 .50
21 John Smoltz .30 .75
22 Adam LaRoche .20 .50
23 Russ Ortiz .20 .50
24 J.D. Drew .20 .50
25 Chipper Jones .50 1.25
26 Nick Green .20 .50
27 Rafael Palmeiro O's .30 .75
28 Miguel Tejada .20 .50
29 Javy Lopez .20 .50
30 Luis Matos .20 .50
31 Larry Bigbie .20 .50
32 Rodrigo Lopez .20 .50
33 Brian Roberts .20 .50
34 Melvin Mora .20 .50
35 Adam Loewen .20 .50
36 Manny Ramirez .30 .75
37 Jason Varitek .50 1.25
38 Trot Nixon .20 .50
39 Curt Schilling .30 .75
40 Keith Foulke .20 .50
41 Pedro Martinez .30 .75
42 Johnny Damon .30 .75
43 Kevin Youkilis .20 .50
44 Orlando Cabrera Sox .20 .50
45 Abe Alvarez .20 .50
46 David Ortiz .50 1.25
47 Kerry Wood .20 .50
48 Mark Prior .30 .75
49 Aramis Ramirez .20 .50
50 Greg Maddux Cubs .75 2.00
51 Carlos Zambrano .20 .50
52 Derrek Lee .30 .75
53 Corey Patterson .20 .50
54 Moises Alou .20 .50
55 Matt Clement .20 .50
56 Sammy Sosa .50 1.25
57 Nomar Garciaparra Cubs .50 1.25
58 Todd Walker .20 .50
59 Angel Guzman .20 .50
60 Magglio Ordonez .20 .50
61 Carlos Lee .20 .50
62 Joe Crede .20 .50
63 Paul Konerko .20 .50
64 Shingo Takatsu .20 .50
65 Frank Thomas .50 1.25
66 Freddy Garcia .20 .50
67 Aaron Rowand .20 .50
68 Jose Contreras .20 .50
69 Adam Dunn .20 .50
70 Austin Kearns .20 .50
71 Barry Larkin .30 .75
72 Ken Griffey Jr. .75 2.00
73 Ryan Wagner .20 .50
74 Sean Casey .20 .50
75 Danny Graves .20 .50
76 C.C. Sabathia .20 .50
77 Jody Gerut .20 .50
78 Omar Vizquel .30 .75
79 Victor Martinez .20 .50
80 Matt Lawton .20 .50
81 Jake Westbrook .20 .50
82 Kazuhito Tadano .20 .50
83 Travis Hafner .20 .50
84 Todd Helton .30 .75
85 Preston Wilson .20 .50
86 Matt Holliday .25 .60
87 Jeromy Burnitz .20 .50
88 Vinny Castilla .20 .50
89 Jeremy Bonderman .20 .50
90 Ivan Rodriguez Tigers .30 .75
91 Carlos Guillen .20 .50
92 Brandon Inge .20 .50
93 Rondell White .20 .50
94 Dontrelle Willis .20 .50
95 Miguel Cabrera .30 .75
96 Josh Beckett .20 .50
97 Mike Lowell .20 .50
98 Luis Castillo .20 .50
99 Juan Pierre .20 .50
100 Paul LoDuca Marlins .20 .50
101 Guillermo Mota .20 .50
102 Craig Biggio .30 .75
103 Lance Berkman .20 .50
104 Roy Oswalt .20 .50
105 Roger Clemens Astros .75 2.00
106 Jeff Kent .20 .50
107 Morgan Ensberg .20 .50
108 Jeff Bagwell .30 .75
109 Carlos Beltran Astros .20 .50
110 Angel Berroa .20 .50
111 Mike Sweeney .20 .50
112 Jeremy Affeldt .20 .50
113 Zack Greinke .20 .50
114 Juan Gonzalez .20 .50
115 Andres Blanco .20 .50
116 Shawn Green .20 .50
117 Milton Bradley .20 .50
118 Adrian Beltre .20 .50
119 Hideo Nomo .50 1.25
120 Steve Finley .20 .50
121 Eric Gagne .20 .50
122 Brad Penny Dgr .20 .50
123 Scott Podsednik .20 .50
124 Ben Sheets .20 .50
125 Lyle Overbay .20 .50
126 Junior Spivey .20 .50
127 Bill Hall .20 .50
128 Rickie Weeks .20 .50
129 Jacque Jones .20 .50
130 Torii Hunter .20 .50
131 Johan Santana .50 1.25
132 Lew Ford .20 .50
133 Joe Mauer .50 1.25
134 Justin Morneau .20 .50
135 Jason Kubel .20 .50
136 Jose Vidro .20 .50
137 Chad Cordero .20 .50
138 Brad Wilkerson .20 .50
139 Nick Johnson .20 .50
140 Livan Hernandez .20 .50
141 Tom Glavine .30 .75
142 Jae Weong Seo .20 .50
143 Jose Reyes .20 .50
144 Al Leiter .20 .50
145 Mike Piazza .50 1.25
146 Kazuo Matsui .20 .50
147 Richard Hidalgo Mets .20 .50
148 David Wright .75 2.00
149 Mariano Rivera .50 1.25
150 Mike Mussina .30 .75
151 Alex Rodriguez .75 2.00
152 Derek Jeter 1.00 2.50
153 Jorge Posada .30 .75
154 Jason Giambi .20 .50
155 Gary Sheffield .20 .50
156 Bubba Crosby .20 .50
157 Javier Vazquez .20 .50
158 Kevin Brown .20 .50
159 Tom Gordon .20 .50
160 Esteban Loaiza Yanks .20 .50
161 Hideki Matsui .75 2.00
162 Eric Chavez .20 .50
163 Mark Mulder .20 .50
164 Barry Zito .20 .50
165 Tim Hudson .20 .50
166 Jermaine Dye .20 .50
167 Octavio Dotel .20 .50
168 Bobby Crosby .20 .50
169 Mark Kotsay .20 .50
170 Scott Hatteberg .20 .50
171 Jim Thome Phils .30 .75
172 Bobby Abreu .20 .50
173 Kevin Millwood .20 .50
174 Mike Lieberthal .20 .50
175 Jimmy Rollins .20 .50
176 Chase Utley .30 .75
177 Randy Wolf .20 .50
178 Craig Wilson .20 .50
179 Jason Kendall .20 .50
180 Jack Wilson .20 .50
181 Jose Castillo .20 .50
182 Rob Mackowiak .20 .50
183 Oliver Perez .20 .50
184 Jason Bay .20 .50
185 Sean Burroughs .20 .50
186 Jay Payton .20 .50
187 Brian Giles .20 .50
188 Akinori Otsuka .20 .50
189 Jake Peavy .20 .50
190 Phil Nevin .20 .50
191 Mark Loretta .20 .50
192 Khalil Greene .30 .75
193 Trevor Hoffman .20 .50
194 Freddy Guzman .20 .50
195 Jerome Williams .20 .50
196 Jason Schmidt .20 .50
197 Todd Linden .20 .50
198 Merkin Valdez .20 .50
199 J.T. Snow .20 .50
200 A.J. Pierzynski .20 .50
201 Edgar Martinez .30 .75
202 Ichiro Suzuki 1.00 2.50
203 Raul Ibanez .20 .50
204 Bret Boone .20 .50
205 Shigetoshi Hasegawa .20 .50
206 Miguel Olivo .20 .50
207 Bucky Jacobsen .20 .50
208 Jamie Moyer .20 .50
209 Jim Edmonds .20 .50
210 Scott Rolen .30 .75
211 Edgar Renteria .20 .50
212 Dan Haren .20 .50
213 Matt Morris .20 .50
214 Albert Pujols 1.00 2.50
215 Larry Walker Cards .30 .75
216 Jason Isringhausen .20 .50
217 Chris Carpenter .20 .50
218 Jason Marquis .20 .50
219 Jeff Suppan .20 .50
220 Aubrey Huff .20 .50
221 Carl Crawford .20 .50
222 Rocco Baldelli .20 .50
223 Fred McGriff .30 .75
224 Dewon Brazelton .20 .50
225 B.J. Upton .30 .75
226 Joey Gathright .20 .50
227 Scott Kazmir .20 .50
228 Hank Blalock .20 .50
229 Mark Teixeira .30 .75
230 Michael Young .20 .50
231 Adrian Gonzalez .20 .50
232 Laynce Nix .20 .50
233 Alfonso Soriano Rgr .20 .50
234 Rafael Palmeiro Rgr .30 .75
235 Kevin Mench .20 .50
236 David Dellucci .20 .50
237 Francisco Cordero .20 .50
238 Kenny Rogers .20 .50
239 Roy Halladay .20 .50
240 Carlos Delgado .20 .50
241 Alexis Rios .20 .50
242 Vernon Wells .20 .50
243 Yadier Molina .20 .50
244 Rene Rivera .20 .50
245 Logan Kensing .20 .50
246 Gavin Floyd .20 .50
247 Russ Adams .20 .50
248 Dioner Navarro .20 .50
249 Ryan Howard 1.25 3.00
250 Ryan Church .20 .50
251 Jeff Francis .20 .50
252 John VanBenschoten .20 .50
253 Yhency Brazoban .20 .50
254 Dave Krynzel .20 .50
255 Victor Diaz .20 .50
256 Jairo Garcia .20 .50
257 Scott Proctor .20 .50
258 Shawn Hill .20 .50
259 Jeff Baker .20 .50
260 Matt Peterson .20 .50
261 Josh Kroeger .20 .50
262 Grady Sizemore .30 .75
263 Clint Nageotte .20 .50
264 Andy Green .20 .50
265 Justin Verlander RC 1.50 4.00
266 Jim Thome Indians .30 .75
267 Larry Walker Rockies .30 .75
268 Ivan Rodriguez Rgr .30 .75
269 Brad Penny Marlins .20 .50
270 Carlos Beltran Royals .20 .50
271 Paul LoDuca Dgr .20 .50
272 Orlando Cabrera Expos .20 .50
273 Nomar Garciaparra Sox .50 1.25
274 Esteban Loaiza Sox .20 .50
275 Richard Hidalgo Astros .20 .50
276 John Olerud .20 .50
277 Greg Maddux Braves .75 2.00
278 Roger Clemens Yanks .75 2.00
279 Alfonso Soriano Yanks .20 .50
280 Dale Murphy .30 .75
281 Cal Ripken 2.00 5.00
282 Dwight Evans .30 .75
283 Ron Santo .30 .75
284 Andre Dawson .20 .50
285 Harold Baines .20 .50
286 Jack Morris .20 .50
287 Kirk Gibson .20 .50
288 Bo Jackson .50 1.25
289 Orel Hershiser .20 .50
290 Maury Wills .20 .50
291 Tony Oliva .20 .50
292 Darryl Strawberry .20 .50
293 Roger Maris .50 1.25
294 Don Mattingly 1.00 2.50
295 Rickey Henderson .50 1.25

296 Dave Stewart .20 .50
297 Dave Parker .20 .50
298 Steve Garvey .20 .50
299 Matt Williams .20 .50
300 Keith Hernandez .20 .50
301 John Lackey .20 .50
302 Vladimir Guerrero Angels .50 1.25
303 Garret Anderson .20 .50
304 Dallas McPherson .20 .50
305 Orlando Cabrera .20 .50
306 Steve Finley Angels .20 .50
307 Luis Gonzalez .20 .50
308 Randy Johnson D'backs .50 1.25
309 Scott Hairston .20 .50
310 Shawn Green .20 .50
311 Troy Glaus .20 .50
312 Javier Vazquez .20 .50
313 Russ Ortiz .20 .50
314 Chipper Jones .50 1.25
315 Johnny Estrada .20 .50
316 Andruw Jones .30 .75
317 Tim Hudson .20 .50
318 Danny Kolb .20 .50
319 Jay Gibbons .20 .50
320 Melvin Mora .20 .50
321 Rafael Palmeiro O's .30 .75
322 Val Majewski .20 .50
323 David Ortiz .50 1.25
324 Manny Ramirez .30 .75
325 Edgar Renteria .20 .50
326 Matt Clement .20 .50
327 Curt Schilling Sox .30 .75
328 Sammy Sosa Cubs .50 1.25
329 Mark Prior .30 .75
330 Greg Maddux .75 2.00
331 Nomar Garciaparra .50 1.25
332 Frank Thomas .50 1.25
333 Mark Buehrle .20 .50
334 Jermaine Dye .20 .50
335 Scott Podsednik .20 .50
336 Sean Casey .20 .50
337 Adam Dunn .20 .50
338 Ken Griffey Jr. .75 2.00
339 Travis Hafner .20 .50
340 Victor Martinez .20 .50
341 Cliff Lee .20 .50
342 Todd Helton .30 .75
343 Preston Wilson .20 .50
344 Ivan Rodriguez Tigers .30 .75
345 Dmitri Young .20 .50
346 Nate Robertson .20 .50
347 Miguel Cabrera .30 .75
348 Jeff Bagwell .30 .75
349 Andy Pettitte .30 .75
350 Roger Clemens Astros .75 2.00
351 Ken Harvey .20 .50
352 Denny Bautista .20 .50
353 Hideo Nomo .50 1.25
354 Kazuhisa Ishii .20 .50
355 Edwin Jackson .20 .50
356 J.D. Drew .20 .50
357 Jeff Kent .20 .50
358 Geoff Jenkins .20 .50
359 Carlos Lee .20 .50
360 Shannon Stewart .20 .50
361 Joe Nathan .20 .50
362 Johan Santana .50 1.25
363 Mike Piazza Mets .50 1.25
364 Kazuo Matsui .20 .50
365 Carlos Beltran .20 .50
366 Pedro Martinez .30 .75
367 Ambiorix Concepcion RC .20 .50
368 Hideki Matsui .75 2.00
369 Bernie Williams .30 .75
370 Gary Sheffield Yanks .20 .50
371 Randy Johnson Yanks .50 1.25
372 Jaret Wright .20 .50
373 Carl Pavano .20 .50
374 Derek Jeter 1.00 2.50
375 Alex Rodriguez .75 2.00
376 Eric Byrnes .20 .50
377 Rich Harden .20 .50
378 Mark Mulder A's .20 .50
379 Nick Swisher .30 .75
380 Eric Chavez .20 .50
381 Jason Kendall .20 .50
382 Marlon Byrd .20 .50
383 Pat Burrell .20 .50
384 Brett Myers .20 .50
385 Jim Thome .30 .75
386 Jason Bay .20 .50
387 Jake Peavy .20 .50
388 Moises Alou .20 .50
389 Omar Vizquel .30 .75
390 Travis Blackley .20 .50
391 Jose Lopez .20 .50
392 Jeremy Reed .20 .50
393 Adrian Beltre .20 .50
394 Richie Sexson .20 .50
395 Wladimir Balentien RC .50 1.25
396 Ichiro Suzuki 1.00 2.50
397 Albert Pujols 1.00 2.50
398 Scott Rolen Cards .30 .75
399 Mark Mulder Cards .20 .50
400 David Eckstein .20 .50
401 Delmon Young .30 .75
402 Aubrey Huff .20 .50
403 Alfonso Soriano .20 .50
404 Hank Blalock .20 .50
405 Richard Hidalgo .20 .50
406 Vernon Wells .20 .50
407 Orlando Hudson .20 .50
408 Alexis Rios .20 .50
409 Shea Hillenbrand .20 .50
410 Jose Guillen .20 .50
411 Vinny Castilla .20 .50
412 Jose Vidro .20 .50
413 Nick Johnson .20 .50
414 Livan Hernandez .20 .50
415 Miguel Tejada .20 .50
416 Gary Sheffield Braves .20 .50
417 Curt Schilling D'backs .20 .50
418 Rafael Palmeiro Rgr .30 .75
419 Scott Rolen Phils .30 .75
420 Aramis Ramirez .20 .50
421 Vladimir Guerrero Expos .50 1.25
422 Steve Finley D'backs .20 .50
423 Roger Clemens Sox .75 2.00
424 Mike Piazza Dgr .50 1.25
425 Ivan Rodriguez M's .30 .75
426 David Justice .60 1.50
427 Mark Grace .30 .75
428 Alan Trammell .20 .50
429 Bert Blyleven .20 .50
430 Dwight Gooden .20 .50
431 Deion Sanders .30 .75
432 Joe Torre MG .30 .75
433 Jose Canseco .50 1.25
434 Tony Gwynn .60 1.50
435 Will Clark .30 .75
436 Marty Marion .20 .50
437 Nolan Ryan 1.25 3.00
438 Billy Martin .30 .75
439 Carlos Delgado .20 .50
440 Magglio Ordonez .20 .50
441 Sammy Sosa O's .50 1.25
442 Keiichi Yabu RC .20 .50
443 Yuniesky Betancourt RC .75 2.00
444 Jeff Niemann RC .50 1.25
445 Brandon McCarthy RC .60 1.50
446 Phil Humber RC .50 1.25
447 Tadahito Iguchi RC .75 2.00
448 Cal Ripken 2.00 5.00
449 Ryne Sandberg 1.00 2.50
450 Willie Mays 1.00 2.50

2005 Diamond Kings B/W

*B/W: .6X TO 1.5X BASIC
SER.2 STATED ODDS 1:2

2005 Diamond Kings Non-Canvas

RANDOM INSERTS IN PACKS
STATED PRINT RUN 20 SETS
PRINT RUN INFO PROVIDED BY DONRUSS
NO PRICING DUE TO SCARCITY

2005 Diamond Kings Non-Canvas B/W

RANDOM INSERTS IN SER.2 PACKS
STATED PRINT RUN 20 SETS
PRINT RUN INFO PROVIDED BY DONRUSS
NO PRICING DUE TO SCARCITY

2005 Diamond Kings Bronze

*BRONZE 1-300: 2X TO 5X BASIC
*BRONZE 1-300: 1.25X TO 3X BASIC RC's
1-300 INSERT ODDS 10 PER SER.1 BOX
1-300 PRINT RUN 100 SERIAL #'d SETS
*BRONZE 301-450: 2.5X TO 6X BASIC
*BRONZE 301-450: 1.5X TO 4X BASIC RC's
301-450 INSERT ODDS 12 PER SER.2 BOX
301-450 PRINT RUN 50 SERIAL #'d SETS

2005 Diamond Kings Bronze B/W

*BRONZE B/W: 2X TO 5X BASIC
OVERALL INSERT ODDS 12 PER SER.2 BOX
STATED PRINT RUN 100 SERIAL #'d SETS

2005 Diamond Kings Gold

*GOLD 1-300: 4X TO 10X BASIC
1-300 INSERT ODDS 10 PER SER.1 BOX
1-300 PRINT RUN 25 SERIAL #'d SETS
NO PRICING ON CARD 265 VERLANDER
301-450 INSERT ODDS 12 PER SER.2 BOX
301-450 PRINT RUN 10 SERIAL #'d SETS
301-450 NO PRICING DUE TO SCARCITY

2005 Diamond Kings Gold B/W

*GOLD B/W: 4X TO 10X BASIC
OVERALL INSERT ODDS 12 PER SER.2 BOX
STATED PRINT RUN 25 SERIAL #'d SETS

2005 Diamond Kings Platinum

1-300 INSERT ODDS 10 PER SER.1 BOX
301-450 INSERT ODDS 12 PER SER.2 BOX
STATED PRINT RUN 1 SERIAL #'d SET
NO PRICING DUE TO SCARCITY

2005 Diamond Kings Platinum B/W

OVERALL INSERT ODDS 12 PER SER.2 BOX
STATED PRINT RUN 1 SERIAL #'d SET
NO PRICING DUE TO SCARCITY

2005 Diamond Kings Silver

*SILVER 1-300: 2.5X TO 6X BASIC
*SILVER 1-300: 1.5X TO 4X BASIC RC's
1-300 INSERT ODDS 10 PER SER.1 BOX
1-300 PRINT RUN 50 SERIAL #'d SETS
*SILVER: 4X TO 10X BASIC
301-450 INSERT ODDS 12 PER SER.2 BOX
301-450 PRINT RUN 25 SERIAL #'d SETS
301-450 NO RC PRICING DUE TO SCARCITY

2005 Diamond Kings Silver B/W

*SILVER B/W: 2.5X TO 6X BASIC
OVERALL INSERT ODDS 12 PER SER.2 BOX
STATED PRINT RUN 50 SERIAL #'d SETS

2005 Diamond Kings Framed Black

*BLACK: 5X TO 12X BASIC
STATED PRINT RUN 25 SERIAL #'d SETS
NO RC PRICING DUE TO SCARCITY
PLATINUM PRINT RUN 1 SERIAL #'d SET
NO PLAT.PRICING DUE TO SCARCITY
OVERALL INSERT ODDS 10 PER SER.1 BOX
OVERALL INSERT ODDS 12 PER SER.2 BOX

2005 Diamond Kings Framed Black B/W

*BLACK: 5X TO 12X BASIC
STATED PRINT RUN 25 SERIAL #'d SETS
PLATINUM PRINT RUN 1 SERIAL #'d SET
NO PLAT.PRICING DUE TO SCARCITY
OVERALL INSERT ODDS 12 PER SER.2 BOX

2005 Diamond Kings Framed Blue

*BLUE: 2.5X TO 6X BASIC
*BLUE: 1.5X TO 4X BASIC RC's
STATED PRINT RUN 100 SERIAL #'d SETS
PLATINUM PRINT RUN 1 SERIAL #'d SET
NO PLAT.PRICING DUE TO SCARCITY
1-300 INSERT ODDS 10 PER SER.1 BOX
301-450 INSERT ODDS 12 PER SER.2 BOX

2005 Diamond Kings Framed Blue B/W

*BLUE B/W: 2.5X TO 6X BASIC
STATED PRINT RUN 100 SERIAL #'d SETS
PLATINUM PRINT RUN 1 SERIAL #'d SET
NO PLAT.PRICING DUE TO SCARCITY
OVERALL INSERT ODDS 12 PER SER.2 BOX

2005 Diamond Kings Framed Green

*GREEN: 3X TO 8X BASIC
*GREEN: 2X TO 5X BASIC RC's
STATED PRINT RUN 50 SERIAL #'d SETS
PLATINUM PRINT RUN 1 SERIAL #'d SET
NO PLAT.PRICING DUE TO SCARCITY
1-300 INSERT ODDS 10 PER SER.1 BOX
301-450 INSERT ODDS 12 PER SER.2 BOX

2005 Diamond Kings Framed Green B/W

*GREEN B/W: 3X TO 8X BASIC
STATED PRINT RUN 50 SERIAL #'d SETS
PLATINUM PRINT RUN 1 SERIAL #'d SET
NO PLAT.PRICING DUE TO SCARCITY
OVERALL INSERT ODDS 12 PER SER.2 BOX

2005 Diamond Kings Framed Red

*RED: 1X TO 2.5X BASIC
*RED: .6X TO 1.5X BASIC RC's
1-300 SER.1 STATED ODDS 1:3
301-450 SER.2 STATED ODDS 1:3
PLAT.1-300: INSERTS 10 PER SER.1 BOX
PLAT.301-450: INSERTS 12 PER SER.2 BOX
PLATINUM PRINT RUN 1 SERIAL #'d SET
NO PLAT.PRICING DUE TO SCARCITY

2005 Diamond Kings Framed Red B/W

*RED: 1X TO 2.5X BASIC
OVERALL FRAMED RED ODDS 1:3
PLAT: INSERT ODDS 12 PER SER.2 BOX
PLATINUM PRINT RUN 1 SERIAL #'d SET
NO PLAT.PRICING DUE TO SCARCITY

2005 Diamond Kings Materials Bronze

OVERALL AU-GU ODDS 1:6
PRINT RUNS B/WN 10-200 COPIES PER
NO PRICING ON QTY OF 10 OR LESS
1 G.Anderson Bat-Jsy/200 2.50 6.00
2 Vlad Guerrero Bat-Jsy/200 4.00 10.00
4 Troy Glaus Bat-Jsy/200 2.50 6.00
5 Tim Salmon Bat-Jsy/200 3.00 8.00
7 Chone Figgins Bat-Jsy/200 2.50 6.00
10 Troy Percival Jsy-Jsy/200 2.50 6.00
11 Randy Johnson Bat-Bat/10
12 B.Webb Bat-Pants/200 2.50 6.00
13 Richie Sexson Bat-Bat/200 2.50 6.00
17 Luis Gonzalez Jsy-Jsy/200 2.50 6.00
18 Rafael Furcal Bat-Jsy/200 2.50 6.00
19 Andruw Jones Bat-Jsy/200 3.00 8.00
21 John Smoltz Jsy-Jsy/200 3.00 8.00
24 J.D. Drew Bat-Bat/200 2.50 6.00
25 Chipper Jones Bat-Jsy/200 4.00 10.00
27 R.Palmeiro O's Bat-Jsy/200 3.00 8.00
28 Miguel Tejada Bat-Jsy/200 2.50 6.00
29 Javy Lopez Bat-Jsy/25 5.00 12.00
30 Luis Matos Jsy-Jsy/100 3.00 8.00
31 Larry Bigbie Jsy-Jsy/200 2.50 6.00
32 Rodrigo Lopez Jsy-Jsy/200 2.50 6.00
34 Melvin Mora Bat-Jsy/200 2.50 6.00
36 Manny Ramirez Bat-Jsy/200 3.00 8.00
38 Trot Nixon Bat-Bat/200 3.00 8.00
39 Curt Schilling Bat-Jsy/200 3.00 8.00
41 Pedro Martinez Bat-Jsy/200 3.00 8.00
42 Johnny Damon Bat-Bat/200 3.00 8.00
43 Kevin Youkilis Bat-Bat/200 2.50 6.00
46 David Ortiz Bat-Jsy/200 4.00 10.00
47 Kerry Wood Jsy-Pants/200 2.50 6.00
48 Mark Prior Bat-Jsy/200 3.00 8.00
49 Aramis Ramirez Bat-Jsy/200 2.50 6.00
50 G.Madd Cubs Bat-Jsy/100 6.00 15.00
51 C.Zambrano Jsy-Jsy/200 2.50 6.00
52 Derrek Lee Bat-Bat/200 3.00 8.00
54 Moises Alou Bat-Bat/200 2.50 6.00
56 Sammy Sosa Bat-Jsy/200 4.00 10.00
57 N.G'parra Cubs Bat-Bat/200 4.00 10.00
60 M.Ordonez Bat-Jsy/200 2.50 6.00
61 Carlos Lee Bat-Jsy/200 2.50 6.00
62 Joe Crede Bat-Bat/200 2.50 6.00
65 Frank Thomas Bat-Jsy/200 4.00 10.00
69 Adam Dunn Bat-Jsy/200 2.50 6.00
70 Austin Kearns Bat-Bat/200 2.50 6.00
74 Sean Casey Jsy-Pants/200 2.50 6.00
76 C.C. Sabathia Jsy-Jsy/200 2.50 6.00
77 Jody Gerut Bat-Jsy/200 2.50 6.00
78 Omar Vizquel Bat-Jsy/200 3.00 8.00
79 Victor Martinez Bat-Jsy/200 2.50 6.00
80 Matt Lawton Bat-Bat/200 2.50 6.00
84 Todd Helton Bat-Jsy/200 3.00 8.00
85 Preston Wilson Bat-Jsy/200 2.50 6.00
90 I.Rod Tigers Bat-Jsy/200 3.00 8.00
92 Brandon Inge Bat-Jsy/200 2.50 6.00
94 Dontrelle Willis Jsy-Jsy/200 2.50 6.00
95 Miguel Cabrera Bat-Jsy/200 3.00 8.00
96 Josh Beckett Bat-Bat/100 3.00 8.00
97 Mike Lowell Bat-Jsy/100 3.00 8.00
98 Luis Castillo Bat-Bat/200 2.50 6.00
99 Juan Pierre Bat-Bat/200 2.50 6.00
100 P.LoDuca M's Bat-Bat/200 2.50 6.00
102 Craig Biggio Bat-Pants/200 3.00 8.00
103 L.Berkman Bat-Jsy/200 2.50 6.00
104 Roy Oswalt Jsy-Jsy/200 2.50 6.00
105 R.Clem Astros Bat-Jsy/200 5.00 12.00
106 Jeff Kent Bat-Jsy/100 3.00 8.00
108 Jeff Bagwell Bat-Jsy/200 3.00 8.00
109 C.Belt Astros Bat-Jsy/200 2.50 6.00
110 Angel Berroa Bat-Bat/200 2.50 6.00
111 Mike Sweeney Bat-Jsy/200 2.50 6.00
112 J.Affeldt Pants-Pants/200 2.50 6.00
114 Juan Gonzalez Bat-Jsy/200 2.50 6.00
116 Shawn Green Bat-Jsy/200 2.50 6.00
118 Adrian Beltre Bat-Jsy/200 2.50 6.00
119 Hideo Nomo Bat-Jsy/200 4.00 10.00
123 S.Podsednik Jsy-Jsy/200 2.50 6.00
124 Ben Sheets Bat-Pants/200 2.50 6.00
125 Lyle Overbay Jsy-Jsy/200 2.50 6.00
126 Junior Spivey Jsy-Jsy/200 2.50 6.00
127 Bill Hall Bat-Jsy/200 2.50 6.00
129 Jacque Jones Bat-Jsy/200 2.50 6.00
130 Torii Hunter Bat-Jsy/200 2.50 6.00
131 Johan Santana Jsy-Jsy/200 4.00 10.00
132 Lew Ford Bat-Jsy/200 2.50 6.00
136 Jose Vidro Bat-Jsy/200 2.50 6.00
138 Brad Wilkerson Bat-Bat/100 3.00 8.00
139 Nick Johnson Bat-Bat/100 3.00 8.00
140 L.Hernandez Jsy-Jsy/25 5.00 12.00
141 Tom Glavine Bat-Bat/200 3.00 8.00
143 Jose Reyes Bat-Jsy/200 2.50 6.00
144 Al Leiter Jsy-Jsy/200 2.50 6.00
145 Mike Piazza Jsy-Jsy/100 5.00 12.00
146 Kazuo Matsui Bat-Jsy/200 2.50 6.00
147 R.Hidalgo Mets Bat-Bat/200 2.50 6.00
149 Mariano Rivera Jsy-Jsy/100 5.00 12.00
150 Mike Mussina Bat-Jsy/200 3.00 8.00
153 Jorge Posada Bat-Jsy/200 3.00 8.00
154 Jason Giambi Bat-Jsy/200 2.50 6.00
155 Gary Sheffield Bat-Jsy/200 2.50 6.00
158 Kevin Brown Bat-Bat/100 3.00 8.00
160 E.Loaiza Yanks Bat-Bat/100 3.00 8.00
161 H.Matsui Jsy-Pants/200 6.00 15.00
162 Eric Chavez Bat-Jsy/200 2.50 6.00
163 Mark Mulder Bat-Bat/25 5.00 12.00
164 Barry Zito Bat-Jsy/200 2.50 6.00
165 Tim Hudson Bat-Jsy/200 2.50 6.00
166 Jermaine Dye Bat-Jsy/200 2.50 6.00
168 Bobby Crosby Jsy-Jsy/200 2.50 6.00
171 J.Thome Phils Bat-Jsy/200 3.00 8.00
172 Bobby Abreu Jsy-Jsy/200 2.50 6.00
173 Kevin Millwood Jsy-Jsy/200 2.50 6.00
178 Craig Wilson Bat-Jsy/200 2.50 6.00
180 Jack Wilson Bat-Bat/200 2.50 6.00
181 Jose Castillo Bat-Bat/200 2.50 6.00
184 Jason Bay Bat-Jsy/200 2.50 6.00
185 S.Burroughs Bat-Jsy/200 2.50 6.00
187 Brian Giles Bat-Bat/100 3.00 8.00
193 Trevor Hoffman Jsy-Jsy/200 2.50 6.00
199 J.T. Snow Jsy-Jsy/25 5.00 12.00
200 A.J. Pierzynski Jsy-Jsy/100 3.00 8.00
201 Edgar Martinez Bat-Bat/200 3.00 8.00
204 Bret Boone Jsy-Jsy/200 2.50 6.00
208 Jamie Moyer Jsy-Jsy/50 4.00 10.00
209 Jim Edmonds Bat-Jsy/200 2.50 6.00
210 Scott Rolen Bat-Jsy/200 3.00 8.00
211 Edgar Renteria Bat-Jsy/200 2.50 6.00
212 Dan Haren Bat-Jsy/100 3.00 8.00
213 Matt Morris Jsy-Jsy/100 3.00 8.00
214 Albert Pujols Jsy-Jsy/200 8.00 20.00
215 L.Walker Cards Bat-Bat/200 3.00 8.00
220 Aubrey Huff Bat-Bat/100 3.00 8.00
221 Carl Crawford Jsy-Jsy/200 2.50 6.00
222 Rocco Baldelli Bat-Jsy/200 2.50 6.00
223 Fred McGriff Bat-Jsy/200 3.00 8.00
224 D.Brazelton Jsy-Jsy/200 2.50 6.00
225 B.J. Upton Bat-Bat/200 3.00 8.00
226 Joey Gathright Bat-Jsy/200 2.50 6.00
228 Hank Blalock Bat-Jsy/100 3.00 8.00
229 Mark Teixeira Bat-Jsy/200 3.00 8.00
230 Michael Young Bat-Jsy/200 2.50 6.00
232 Laynce Nix Bat-Jsy/200 2.50 6.00
233 A.Soriano Rgr Bat-Jsy/200 2.50 6.00
234 R.Palmeiro Rgr Bat-Jsy/200 3.00 8.00
235 Kevin Mench Bat-Jsy/200 2.50 6.00
236 David Dellucci Jsy-Jsy/200 4.00 10.00
237 F.Cordero Jsy-Jsy/200 2.50 6.00
239 Roy Halladay Jsy-Jsy/200 2.50 6.00
240 Carlos Delgado Bat-Jsy/200 2.50 6.00
242 Vernon Wells Bat-Jsy/200 2.50 6.00
267 L.Walk Rockies Jsy-Jsy/200 2.50 6.00
268 I.Rodriguez Rgr Jsy-Jsy/200 3.00 8.00
269 B.Penny M's Bat-Jsy/200 2.50 6.00
270 C.Belt Royals Bat-Jsy/200 2.50 6.00
271 P.LoDuca Dgr Bat-Jsy/200 2.50 6.00
273 N.G'parra Sox Bat-Bat/100 5.00 12.00
274 E.Loaiza Sox Bat-Bat/100 3.00 8.00
275 R.Hidal Astros Jkt-Pants/200 2.50 6.00
276 John Olerud Bat-Jsy/200 2.50 6.00
277 G.Madd Braves Jsy-Jsy/200 5.00 12.00
278 R.Clem Yanks Bat-Jsy/200 5.00 12.00
279 A.Sor Yanks Bat-Jsy/200 2.50 6.00
280 Dale Murphy Jsy-Jsy/200 4.00 10.00
281 Cal Ripken Bat-Jsy/200 12.50 30.00
282 Dwight Evans Bat-Jsy/200 4.00 10.00
283 Ron Santo Bat-Bat/200 4.00 10.00
284 Andre Dawson Bat-Jsy/100 4.00 10.00
285 Harold Baines Bat-Jsy/200 3.00 8.00
286 Jack Morris Jsy-Jsy/100 4.00 10.00
287 Kirk Gibson Bat-Jsy/200 3.00 8.00
288 Bo Jackson Bat-Jsy/200 5.00 12.00
289 Orel Hershiser Jsy-Jsy/50 5.00 12.00
290 Maury Wills Jsy-Jsy/10
291 Tony Oliva Bat-Jsy/200 3.00 8.00
292 D.Strawberry Bat-Jsy/100 4.00 10.00
293 Roger Maris Bat-Jsy/100 20.00 50.00
294 Don Mattingly Bat-Jsy/100 10.00 25.00
295 R.Henderson Bat-Jsy/100 6.00 15.00
297 Dave Parker Bat-Jsy/200 3.00 8.00
298 Steve Garvey Bat-Jsy/200 3.00 8.00
299 Matt Williams Jsy-Jsy/200 3.00 8.00
300 K.Hernandez Bat-Jsy/200 3.00 8.00
302 V.Guer Angels Jsy-Jsy/200 4.00 10.00
303 G.Anderson Bat-Jsy/200 2.50 6.00
307 Luis Gonzalez Jsy-Jsy/200 2.50 6.00
308 Randy Johnson D'backs Bat-Jsy/1
310 Shawn Green Bat-Bat/200 2.50 6.00
311 Troy Glaus Bat-Bat/200 2.50 6.00
314 Chipper Jones Jsy-Jsy/100 5.00 12.00
315 Johnny Estrada Jsy-Jsy/200 2.50 6.00
316 Andruw Jones Bat-Jsy/200 3.00 8.00
319 Jay Gibbons Bat-Bat/200 2.50 6.00
320 Melvin Mora Jsy-Jsy/200 2.50 6.00
321 R.Palmeiro O's Bat-Jsy/200 3.00 8.00
323 David Ortiz Bat-Jsy/200 4.00 10.00
324 M.Ramirez Bat-Jsy/200 3.00 8.00
327 C.Schill Sox Jsy-Jsy/200 3.00 8.00
328 S.Sosa Cubs Bat-Jsy/100 5.00 12.00
329 Mark Prior Bat-Jsy/200 3.00 8.00
330 Greg Maddux Jsy-Jsy/25 10.00 25.00
332 F.Thomas Bat-Pants/200 4.00 10.00
333 Mark Buehrle Bat-Jsy/200 2.50 6.00
336 Sean Casey Bat-Jsy/200 2.50 6.00
337 Adam Dunn Bat-Jsy/200 2.50 6.00
339 Travis Hafner Jsy-Jsy/100 3.00 8.00
340 Victor Martinez Bat-Jsy/100 3.00 8.00
341 Cliff Lee Jsy-Jsy/200 2.50 6.00
342 Todd Helton Bat-Jsy/25 6.00 15.00
343 P.Wilson Jsy-Jsy/200 2.50 6.00
344 I.Rod Tigers Bat-Jsy/200 3.00 8.00
347 M.Cabrera Bat-Jsy/200 3.00 8.00
348 Jeff Bagwell Bat-Jsy/200 3.00 8.00
349 Andy Pettitte Bat-Jsy/200 3.00 8.00
350 R.Clem Astros Bat-Jsy/100 6.00 15.00
351 Ken Harvey Jsy-Jsy/200 2.50 6.00
353 Hideo Nomo Bat-Jsy/200 4.00 10.00
354 Kazuhisa Ishii Jsy-Jsy/200 2.50 6.00
355 E.Jackson Jsy-Jsy/200 2.50 6.00
356 J.D. Drew Bat-Bat/200 2.50 6.00
357 Jeff Kent Bat-Bat/25 5.00 12.00
358 G.Jenkins Jsy-Pants/200 2.50 6.00
359 Carlos Lee Bat-Bat/200 2.50 6.00
360 S.Stewart Jsy-Jsy/200 2.50 6.00
362 J.Santana Jsy-Jsy/100 4.00 10.00
363 M.Piaz Mets Jsy-Jsy/100 5.00 12.00
364 Kazuo Matsui Jsy-Jsy/100 3.00 8.00
365 Carlos Beltran Bat-Bat/10
366 P.Martinez Bat-Bat/100 4.00 10.00
368 Hideki Matsui Bat-Jsy/100 6.00 15.00
369 B.Williams Bat-Jsy/200 3.00 8.00
370 G.Shef Yanks Bat-Jsy/100 3.00 8.00
371 R.John Yanks Bat-Bat/25 8.00 20.00
378 M.Mulder A's Bat-Bat/50 4.00 10.00
380 Eric Chavez Jsy-Jsy/100 3.00 8.00
382 Marlon Byrd Bat-Jsy/200 2.50 6.00
383 Pat Burrell Jsy-Jsy/200 2.50 6.00
385 Jim Thome Bat-Bat/200 3.00 8.00
386 Jason Bay Bat-Jsy/1
388 Moises Alou Bat-Bat/200 2.50 6.00
393 Adrian Beltre Bat-Bat/50 4.00 10.00
394 R.Sexson Bat-Bat/200 2.50 6.00
397 Albert Pujols Bat-Jsy/200 8.00 20.00
398 S.Rolen Cards Bat-Jsy/200 3.00 8.00
401 D.Young Bat-Bat/200 3.00 8.00
402 Aubrey Huff Bat-Bat/50 4.00 10.00
403 A.Soriano Bat-Jsy/200 2.50 6.00
404 Hank Blalock Bat-Jsy/200 2.50 6.00
405 R.Hidalgo Bat-Bat/200 2.50 6.00
406 Vernon Wells Jsy-Jsy/200 2.50 6.00
407 O.Hudson Bat-Bat/200 2.50 6.00
412 Jose Vidro Bat-Jsy/5
415 M.Tejada Jsy-Jsy/200 2.50 6.00
416 G.Shef Braves Bat-Bat/200 2.50 6.00
417 C.Schil D'back J-J/200 2.50 6.00
418 R.Palm Rgr Bat-Pants/50 5.00 12.00
419 S.Rolen Phils Bat-Jsy/200 3.00 8.00
420 A.Ramirez Jsy-Jsy/200 2.50 6.00
421 V.Guer Guerrero Expos Bat-Bat/200 4.0010.00
422 S.Finley D'backs J-J/200 2.50 6.00
423 R.Clem Sox Bat-Jsy/200 5.00 12.00

424 M.Piaz Dgr Jsy-Jsy/200 4.00 10.00
425 I.Rod M's Bat-Jsy/200 3.00 8.00
426 David Justice Jsy-Jsy/200 5.00 12.00
427 Mark Grace Bat-Jsy/25 8.00 20.00
428 Alan Trammell Bat-Jsy/100 4.00 10.00
429 Bert Blyleven Jsy-Jsy/1
430 D.Gooden Bat-Jsy/200 3.00 8.00
431 D.Sanders Bat-Jsy/200 4.00 10.00
432 Joe Torre MG Bat-Bat/100 5.00 12.00
433 Jose Canseco Jsy-Jsy/100 6.00 15.00
434 T.Gwynn Bat-Pants/200 5.00 12.00
435 Will Clark Bat-Jsy/100 5.00 12.00
436 Marty Marion Jsy-Jsy/1
437 Nolan Ryan Bat-Jsy/50 12.50 30.00
438 Billy Martin Jsy-Pants/200 4.00 10.00
439 C.Delgado Bat-Bat/100 3.00 8.00
440 M.Ordonez Bat-Jsy/200 2.50 6.00
441 S.Sosa O's Bat-Bat/25 8.00 20.00
449 R.Sandberg Bat-Jsy/100 8.00 20.00
450 Willie Mays Bat-Pants/5

2005 Diamond Kings Materials Bronze B/W

*BRZ B/W p/r 100: .5X TO 1.2X BRZ p/r 200
*BRZ B/W p/r 100: .4X TO 1X BRZ p/r 100
*BRZ B/W p/r 50: .6X TO 1.5X BRZ p/r 200
*BRZ B/W p/r 50: .5X TO 1.2X BRZ p/r 100
OVERALL AU-GU ODDS 1:6
PRINT RUNS B/WN 10-100 COPIES PER
NO PRICING ON QTY OF 10
73 Ryan Wagner Jsy-Jsy/100 3.00 8.00

2005 Diamond Kings Materials Gold

*GOLD p/r 50: .6X TO 1.5X BRZ p/r 200
*GOLD p/r 50: .5X TO 1.2X BRZ p/r 100
*GOLD p/r 50: .4X TO 1X BRZ p/r 50
*GOLD p/r 50: .3X TO .8X BRZ p/r 25
*GOLD p/r 25: .75X TO 2X BRZ p/r 200
*GOLD p/r 25: .6X TO 1.5X BRZ p/r 100
*GOLD p/r 25: .5X TO 1.2X BRZ p/r 50
*GOLD p/r 25: .4X TO 1X BRZ p/r 25
OVERALL AU-GU ODDS 1:6
PRINT RUNS B/WN 25-50 COPIES PER
6 C.Kotchman Jsy-Jsy/50 4.00 10.00
9 Francisco Rodriguez Jsy-Jsy/50 4.00 10.00
11 Randy Johnson Bat-Bat/25 8.00 20.00
20 Marcus Giles Jsy-Jsy/50 4.00 10.00
26 Nick Green Bat-Jsy/50 4.00 10.00
33 Brian Roberts Jsy-Jsy/50 4.00 10.00
55 Matt Clement Jsy-Jsy/50 4.00 10.00
73 Ryan Wagner Jsy-Jsy/50 4.00 10.00
89 J.Bonderman Jsy-Jsy/50 4.00 10.00
107 Morgan Ensberg Jsy-Jsy/50 4.00 10.00

2005 Diamond Kings Materials Gold B/W

*GOLD B/W p/r 50: .6X TO 1.5X BRZ p/r 200
*GOLD B/W p/r 50: .5X TO 1.2X BRZ p/r 100
*GOLD B/W p/r 25: .75X TO 2X BRZ p/r 200
OVERALL AU-GU ODDS 1:6
PRINT RUNS B/WN 25-50 COPIES PER
11 Randy Johnson Bat-Bat/25 8.00 20.00
73 Ryan Wagner Jsy-Jsy/50 4.00 10.00

2005 Diamond Kings Materials Platinum

OVERALL AU-GU ODDS 1:6
STATED PRINT RUN 1 SERIAL #'d SET
NO PRICING DUE TO SCARCITY

2005 Diamond Kings Materials Platinum B/W

OVERALL AU-GU ODDS 1:6
STATED PRINT RUN 1 SERIAL #'d SET
NO PRICING DUE TO SCARCITY

2005 Diamond Kings Materials Silver

*SILV p/r 100: .5X TO 1.2X BRZ p/r 200
*SILV p/r 100: .4X TO 1X BRZ p/r 100
*SILV p/r 100: .25X TO .6X BRZ p/r 25
*SILV p/r 50: .6X TO 1.5X BRZ p/r 200
*SILV p/r 50: .5X TO 1.2X BRZ p/r 100
*SILV p/r 50: .4X TO 1X BRZ p/r 50
*SILV p/r 25: .6X TO 1.5X BRZ p/r 100
*SILV p/r 25: .5X TO 1.2X BRZ p/r 50
*SILV p/r 25: .4X TO 1X BRZ p/r 25
OVERALL AU-GU ODDS 1:6
PRINT RUNS B/WN 1-100 COPIES PER
NO PRICING ON QTY OF 10 OR LESS
6 C.Kotchman Jsy-Jsy/100 3.00 8.00
9 F.Rodriguez Jsy-Jsy/100 3.00 8.00
11 Randy Johnson Bat-Bat/25 8.00 20.00
20 Marcus Giles Jsy-Jsy/100 3.00 8.00
26 Nick Green Bat-Jsy/100 3.00 8.00
33 Brian Roberts Jsy-Jsy/100 3.00 8.00
37 Jason Varitek Bat-Bat/50 6.00 15.00
55 Matt Clement Jsy-Jsy/100 3.00 8.00
71 Barry Larkin Bat-Bat/50 5.00 12.00
73 Ryan Wagner Jsy-Jsy/100 3.00 8.00
83 Travis Hafner Jsy-Jsy/50 4.00 10.00
89 J.Bonderman Jsy-Jsy/100 3.00 8.00
107 Morgan Ensberg Jsy-Jsy/100 3.00 8.00

2005 Diamond Kings Materials Silver B/W

*SILV B/W p/r 100: .5X TO 1.2X BRZ p/r 200
*SILV B/W p/r 100: .4X TO 1X BRZ p/r 100
*SILV B/W p/r 50: .6X TO 1.5X BRZ p/r 200
*SILV B/W p/r 50: .5X TO 1.2X BRZ p/r 100
*SILV B/W p/r 25: .75X TO 2X BRZ p/r 200
*SILV B/W p/r 25: .6X TO 1.5X BRZ p/r 100
OVERALL AU-GU ODDS 1:6
PRINT RUNS B/WN 25-100 COPIES PER
11 Randy Johnson Bat-Bat/25 8.00 20.00
73 Ryan Wagner Jsy-Jsy/100 3.00 8.00

2005 Diamond Kings Materials Framed Black

1-300 PRINT RUN 10 SERIAL #'d SETS
301-450 PRINT RUN 1 SERIAL #'d SET
PLATINUM PRINT RUN 1 SERIAL #'d SET
OVERALL AU-GU ODDS 1:6
NO PRICING DUE TO SCARCITY

2005 Diamond Kings Materials Framed Black B/W

STATED PRINT RUN 1 SERIAL #'d SET
PLATINUM PRINT RUN 1 SERIAL #'d SET
OVERALL AU-GU ODDS 1:6
NO PRICING DUE TO SCARCITY

2005 Diamond Kings Materials Framed Blue

*BLUE p/r 100: .5X TO 1.2X BRZ p/r 200
*BLUE p/r 100: .4X TO 1X BRZ p/r 100
*BLUE p/r 100: .3X TO .8X BRZ p/r 50
*BLUE p/r 100: .25X TO .6X BRZ p/r 25
*BLUE p/r 50: .6X TO 1.5X BRZ p/r 200
*BLUE p/r 50: .5X TO 1.2X BRZ p/r 100
*BLUE p/r 50: .4X TO 1X BRZ p/r 50
*BLUE p/r 50: .3X TO .8X BRZ p/r 25
*BLUE p/r 25: .75X TO 2X BRZ p/r 200
*BLUE p/r 25: .4X TO 1X BRZ p/r 25
1-300 PRINT RUN 50 SERIAL #'d SETS
301-450 PRINT RUNS B/WN 1-100 PER
301-450 NO PRICE ON QTY OF 10 OR LESS
PLATINUM PRINT RUN 1 SERIAL #'d SET
NO PLAT.PRICING DUE TO SCARCITY
OVERALL AU-GU ODDS 1:6 PACKS

2005 Diamond Kings Materials Framed Blue B/W

*BLUE B/W p/r 25: .75X TO 2X BRZ p/r 200
*BLUE B/W p/r 25: .6X TO 1.5X BRZ p/r 100
STATED PRINT RUN 25 SERIAL #'d SETS
PLATINUM PRINT RUN 1 SERIAL #'d SET
NO PLAT.PRICING DUE TO SCARCITY
OVERALL AU-GU ODDS 1:6
73 Ryan Wagner Jsy-Jsy/25 5.00 12.00

2005 Diamond Kings Materials Framed Green

*GREEN p/r 25: .75X TO 2X BRZ p/r 200
*GREEN p/r 25: .6X TO 1.5X BRZ p/r 100
*GREEN p/r 25: .5X TO 1.2X BRZ p/r 50
*GREEN p/r 25: .4X TO 1X BRZ p/r 25

1-300 PRINT RUN 25 SERIAL #'d SETS
301-450 PRINT RUNS B/WN 1-25 PER
301-450 NO PRICES ON QTY OF 10 OR LESS
PLATINUM PRINT RUN 1 SERIAL #'d SET
NO PLAT.PRICING DUE TO SCARCITY
OVERALL AU-GU ODDS 1:6
11 Randy Johnson Bat-Jsy 8.00 20.00

2005 Diamond Kings Materials Framed Green B/W

*GRN B/W p/r 25: .75X TO 2X BRZ p/r 200
*GRN B/W p/r 25: .6X TO 1.5X BRZ p/r 100
STATED PRINT RUN 25 SERIAL #'d SETS
PLATINUM PRINT RUN 1 SERIAL #'d SET
NO PLAT.PRICING DUE TO SCARCITY
OVERALL AU-GU ODDS 1:6
73 Ryan Wagner Jsy-Jsy/25 5.00 12.00

2005 Diamond Kings Materials Framed Red

*RED p/r 200: .4X TO 1X BRZ p/r 200
*RED p/r 200: .3X TO .8X BRZ p/r 100
*RED p/r 100: .5X TO 1.2X BRZ p/r 200
*RED p/r 100: .4X TO 1X BRZ p/r 100
*RED p/r 100: .3X TO .8X BRZ p/r 50
*RED p/r 100: .25X TO .6X BRZ p/r 25
*RED p/r 50: .6X TO 1.5X BRZ p/r 200
*RED p/r 50: .5X TO 1.2X BRZ p/r 100
*RED p/r 50: .4X TO 1X BRZ p/r 50
*RED p/r 50: .3X TO .8X BRZ p/r 25
*RED p/r 25: .75X TO 2X BRZ p/r 200
*RED p/r 25: .6X TO 1.5X BRZ p/r 100
*RED p/r 25: .4X TO 1X BRZ p/r 25
PRINT RUNS B/WN 25-100 COPIES PER
PLATINUM PRINT RUN 1 SERIAL #'d SET
NO PLAT.PRICING DUE TO SCARCITY
OVERALL AU-GU ODDS 1:6
6 C.Kotchman Jsy-Jsy/100 3.00 8.00
9 F.Rodriguez Jsy-Jsy/100 3.00 8.00
11 Randy Johnson Bat-Bat/50 6.00 15.00
20 Marcus Giles Jsy-Jsy/100 3.00 8.00
26 Nick Green Bat-Jsy/100 3.00 8.00
33 Brian Roberts Jsy-Jsy/100 3.00 8.00
37 Jason Varitek Bat-Bat/25 8.00 20.00
55 Matt Clement Jsy-Jsy/100 3.00 8.00
71 Barry Larkin Bat-Bat/100 4.00 10.00
73 Ryan Wagner Jsy-Jsy/100 3.00 8.00
83 Travis Hafner Jsy-Jsy/50 4.00 10.00
89 J.Bonderman Jsy-Jsy/100 3.00 8.00
107 Morg Ensberg Jsy-Jsy/100 3.00 8.00
190 Phil Nevin Jsy-Jsy/50 4.00 10.00
195 Jerome Williams Jsy-Jsy/50 4.00 10.00
266 J.Thome Indians Bat-Bat/25 6.00 15.00
272 O.Cabrera Expos Bat-Jsy/50 4.00 10.00
290 Maury Wills Jsy-Jsy/25 5.00 12.00
365 Carlos Beltran Bat-Bat/25 5.00 12.00
412 Jose Vidro Bat-Jsy/25 5.00 12.00

2005 Diamond Kings Materials Framed Red B/W

*RED B/W p/r 100: .5X TO 1.2X BRZ p/r 200
*RED B/W p/r 100: .4X TO 1X BRZ p/r 100
*RED B/W p/r 50: .6X TO 1.5X BRZ p/r 200
*RED B/W p/r 50: .5X TO 1.2X BRZ p/r 100
*RED B/W p/r 50: .4X TO 1X BRZ p/r 100
PRINT RUNS B/WN 25-100 COPIES PER
PLATINUM PRINT RUN 1 SERIAL #'d SET
NO PLAT.PRICING DUE TO SCARCITY
OVERALL AU-GU ODDS 1:6
73 Ryan Wagner Jsy-Jsy/100 3.00 8.00

2005 Diamond Kings Signature Black

OVERALL AU-GU ODDS 1:6
STATED PRINT RUN 1 SERIAL #'d SET
NO PRICING DUE TO SCARCITY

2005 Diamond Kings Signature Bronze

OVERALL AU-GU ODDS 1:6
PRINT RUNS B/WN 1-100 COPIES PER
NO PRICING ON QTY OF 10 OR LESS
NO RC YR PRICING ON QTY OF 25 OR LESS
1 Garret Anderson/10
3 Jose Guillen/100 6.00 15.00
5 Tim Salmon/100 10.00 25.00
6 Casey Kotchman/100 6.00 15.00
7 Chone Figgins/100 6.00 15.00
8 Robb Quinlan/100 4.00 10.00
9 Francisco Rodriguez/50 12.50 30.00
10 Troy Percival/50 8.00 20.00
11 Randy Johnson/1
12 Brandon Webb/10
14 Shea Hillenbrand/100 6.00 15.00
15 Chad Tracy/100 4.00 10.00
16 Alex Cintron/100 4.00 10.00
18 Rafael Furcal/10
19 Andruw Jones/1
22 Adam LaRoche/50 5.00 12.00
23 Russ Ortiz/50 5.00 12.00
24 J.D. Drew/1
25 Chipper Jones/1
26 Nick Green/100 4.00 10.00
27 Rafael Palmeiro O's/1
30 Luis Matos/100 4.00 10.00
31 Larry Bigbie/100 6.00 15.00
32 Rodrigo Lopez/100 4.00 10.00
33 Brian Roberts/100 6.00 15.00
34 Melvin Mora/100 6.00 15.00
36 Manny Ramirez/1
38 Trot Nixon/10
39 Curt Schilling/1
40 Keith Foulke/50 12.50 30.00
41 Pedro Martinez/1
43 Kevin Youkilis/100 4.00 10.00
44 Orlando Cabrera Sox/50 8.00 20.00
45 Abe Alvarez/100 6.00 15.00
46 David Ortiz/10
47 Kerry Wood/1
48 Mark Prior/1
49 Aramis Ramirez/10
50 Greg Maddux Cubs/1
51 Carlos Zambrano/50 12.50 30.00
52 Derrek Lee/10
55 Matt Clement/5
56 Sammy Sosa/1
58 Todd Walker/50 5.00 12.00
59 Angel Guzman/100 4.00 10.00
60 Magglio Ordonez/5
61 Carlos Lee/100 6.00 15.00
63 Paul Konerko/10
64 Shingo Takatsu/10
65 Frank Thomas/1
68 Jose Contreras/1
69 Adam Dunn/1
70 Austin Kearns/5
71 Barry Larkin/1
73 Ryan Wagner/100 4.00 10.00
74 Sean Casey/5
75 Danny Graves/100 4.00 10.00
76 C.C. Sabathia/50 8.00 20.00
77 Jody Gerut/100 4.00 10.00
78 Omar Vizquel/5
79 Victor Martinez/50 8.00 20.00
82 Kazuhito Tadano/100 6.00 15.00
83 Travis Hafner/100 6.00 15.00
84 Todd Helton/1
89 Jeremy Bonderman/100 6.00 15.00
92 Brandon Inge/100 4.00 10.00
94 Dontrelle Willis/1
95 Miguel Cabrera/10
96 Josh Beckett/1
97 Mike Lowell/5
100 Paul LoDuca Marlins/5
101 Guillermo Mota/50 5.00 12.00
102 Craig Biggio/1
103 Lance Berkman/1
104 Roy Oswalt/5
105 Roger Clemens Astros/1
107 Morgan Ensberg/100 6.00 15.00
108 Jeff Bagwell/1
109 Carlos Beltran Astros/1
110 Angel Berroa/10
112 Jeremy Affeldt/100 4.00 10.00
114 Juan Gonzalez/5
116 Shawn Green/1
117 Milton Bradley/100 6.00 15.00
118 Adrian Beltre/5
119 Hideo Nomo/1
120 Steve Finley/10
122 Brad Penny Dgr/100 4.00 10.00
123 Scott Podsednik/50 12.50 30.00
124 Ben Sheets/5
125 Lyle Overbay/100 4.00 10.00
127 Bill Hall/100 4.00 10.00
128 Rickie Weeks/5
129 Jacque Jones/10
130 Torii Hunter/5
131 Johan Santana/10
132 Lew Ford/100 4.00 10.00
135 Jason Kubel/100 4.00 10.00
136 Jose Vidro/10
137 Chad Cordero/100 6.00 15.00
139 Nick Johnson/10
140 Livan Hernandez/25 10.00 25.00
141 Tom Glavine/1
142 Jae Weong Seo/10
145 Mike Piazza/1
148 David Wright/10
150 Mike Mussina/1
155 Gary Sheffield/1
156 Bubba Crosby/100 4.00 10.00
159 Tom Gordon/25 10.00 25.00
160 Esteban Loaiza Yanks/100 6.00 15.00
162 Eric Chavez/1
163 Mark Mulder/1
164 Barry Zito/1
165 Tim Hudson/1
166 Jermaine Dye/50 8.00 20.00
167 Octavio Dotel/50 8.00 20.00
168 Bobby Crosby/100 6.00 15.00
174 Mike Lieberthal/100 6.00 15.00
177 Randy Wolf/100 6.00 15.00
178 Craig Wilson/100 4.00 10.00
180 Jack Wilson/100 6.00 15.00
181 Jose Castillo/100 4.00 10.00
184 Jason Bay/100 6.00 15.00
185 Sean Burroughs/10
186 Jay Payton/50 5.00 12.00
188 Akinori Otsuka/10
189 Jake Peavy/50 12.50 30.00
194 Freddy Guzman/100 4.00 10.00
195 Jerome Williams/10
197 Todd Linden/50 5.00 12.00
198 Merkin Valdez/100 6.00 15.00
199 J.T. Snow/10
201 Edgar Martinez/5
203 Raul Ibanez/100 6.00 15.00
205 Shigetoshi Hasegawa/5
206 Miguel Olivo/100 4.00 10.00
207 Bucky Jacobsen/100 4.00 10.00
208 Jamie Moyer/50 8.00 20.00
209 Jim Edmonds/1
210 Scott Rolen/1
211 Edgar Renteria/5
212 Dan Haren/100 4.00 10.00
214 Albert Pujols/1
219 Jeff Suppan/100 6.00 15.00
220 Aubrey Huff/50 8.00 20.00
221 Carl Crawford/25 10.00 25.00
223 Fred McGriff/5
224 Dewon Brazelton/100 4.00 10.00
225 B.J. Upton/5
226 Joey Gathright/100 4.00 10.00
227 Scott Kazmir/25 10.00 25.00
228 Hank Blalock/5
229 Mark Teixeira/5
230 Michael Young/50 8.00 20.00
231 Adrian Gonzalez/100 6.00 15.00
232 Laynce Nix/100 4.00 10.00
233 Alfonso Soriano Rgr/1
234 Rafael Palmeiro Rgr/1
236 David Dellucci/100 12.50 30.00
237 Francisco Cordero/100 6.00 15.00
239 Roy Halladay/1
241 Alexis Rios/100 6.00 15.00
242 Vernon Wells/5
243 Yadier Molina/5
248 Dioner Navarro/100 6.00 15.00
253 Yhency Brazoban/100 4.00 10.00
257 Scott Proctor/100 4.00 10.00
260 Matt Peterson/100 4.00 10.00
269 Brad Penny Marlins/50 5.00 12.00
270 Carlos Beltran Royals/1
271 Paul LoDuca Dgr/5
272 Orlando Cabrera Expos/50 8.00 20.00
274 Esteban Loaiza Sox/100 6.00 15.00
277 Greg Maddux Braves/1
278 Roger Clemens Yanks/1
279 Alfonso Soriano Yanks/1
280 Dale Murphy/10
281 Cal Ripken/1
282 Dwight Evans/10
283 Ron Santo/10
284 Andre Dawson/50 8.00 20.00
285 Harold Baines/100 6.00 15.00
286 Jack Morris/100 6.00 15.00
287 Kirk Gibson/5
288 Bo Jackson/1
289 Orel Hershiser/1
290 Maury Wills/100 6.00 15.00
291 Tony Oliva/10
292 Darryl Strawberry/100 6.00 15.00
294 Don Mattingly/1
295 Rickey Henderson/1
296 Dave Stewart/10
297 Dave Parker/100 6.00 15.00
298 Steve Garvey/10
299 Matt Williams/25 15.00 40.00
300 Keith Hernandez/10
303 Garret Anderson/50 8.00 20.00
304 Dallas McPherson/100 4.00 10.00
305 Orlando Cabrera/25 10.00 25.00
306 Steve Finley Angels/50 8.00 20.00
310 Shawn Green/1
313 Russ Ortiz/50 5.00 12.00
314 Chipper Jones/1
315 Johnny Estrada/100 4.00 10.00
317 Tim Hudson/25 15.00 40.00
318 Danny Kolb/100 4.00 10.00
319 Jay Gibbons/50 5.00 12.00
320 Melvin Mora/50 8.00 20.00
323 David Ortiz/10
324 Manny Ramirez/1
325 Edgar Renteria/50 8.00 20.00
326 Matt Clement/10
327 Curt Schilling Sox/1
329 Mark Prior/10
330 Greg Maddux/1
332 Frank Thomas/10
333 Mark Buehrle/50 8.00 20.00
336 Sean Casey/25 10.00 25.00
339 Travis Hafner/50 8.00 20.00
340 Victor Martinez/50 8.00 20.00
341 Cliff Lee/100 4.00 10.00
342 Todd Helton/1
343 Preston Wilson/50 8.00 20.00
347 Miguel Cabrera/10
348 Jeff Bagwell/1
350 Roger Clemens Astros/1
351 Ken Harvey/100 4.00 10.00
353 Hideo Nomo/1
354 Kazuhisa Ishii/5
355 Edwin Jackson/100 4.00 10.00
359 Carlos Lee/100 6.00 15.00
360 Shannon Stewart/25 10.00 25.00
361 Joe Nathan/100 6.00 15.00
362 Johan Santana/10
365 Carlos Beltran/1
366 Pedro Martinez/1
370 Gary Sheffield Yanks/1
371 Randy Johnson Yanks/1
376 Eric Byrnes/100 4.00 10.00
377 Rich Harden/100 6.00 15.00
378 Mark Mulder A's/25 10.00 25.00
380 Eric Chavez/25 10.00 25.00
382 Marlon Byrd/100 4.00 10.00
384 Brett Myers/100 6.00 15.00
386 Jason Bay/50 8.00 20.00
387 Jake Peavy/50 12.50 30.00
389 Omar Vizquel/10
393 Adrian Beltre/1
397 Albert Pujols/1
398 Scott Rolen Cards/10
399 Mark Mulder Cards/10
401 Delmon Young/10
402 Aubrey Huff/50 8.00 20.00
403 Alfonso Soriano/10
406 Vernon Wells/5
407 Orlando Hudson/25 6.00 15.00
408 Alexis Rios/5
410 Jose Guillen/25 10.00 25.00
412 Jose Vidro/1
413 Nick Johnson/5
414 Livan Hernandez/5
416 Gary Sheffield Braves/1
417 Curt Schilling D'backs/1
419 Scott Rolen Phils/5
422 Steve Finley D'backs/5
423 Roger Clemens Sox/1
427 Mark Grace/1
428 Alan Trammell/5
429 Bert Blyleven/25 8.00 20.00
430 Dwight Gooden/50 8.00 20.00
431 Deion Sanders/1
432 Joe Torre MG/5
433 Jose Canseco/1
434 Tony Gwynn/1
435 Will Clark/1
436 Marty Marion/50 8.00 20.00
437 Nolan Ryan/1
440 Magglio Ordonez/5
444 Jeff Niemann/25
445 Brandon McCarthy/25
446 Phil Humber/25
449 Ryne Sandberg/5
450 Willie Mays/1

2005 Diamond Kings Signature Bronze B/W

*BRZ B/W p/r 100: .4X TO 1X BRZ p/r 100
*BRZ B/W p/r 50: .4X TO 1X BRZ p/r 50
*BRZ B/W p/r 25: .4X TO 1X BRZ p/r 25
OVERALL AU-GU ODDS 1:6
PRINT RUNS B/WN 1-100 COPIES PER
NO PRICING ON QTY OF 10 OR LESS
185 Sean Burroughs/25 6.00 15.00

2005 Diamond Kings Signature Gold

*GOLD p/r 50: .5X TO 1.2X BRZ p/r 100
*GOLD p/r 25: .6X TO 1.5X BRZ p/r 100
*GOLD p/r 25: .5X TO 1.2X BRZ p/r 50
*GOLD p/r 25: .4X TO 1X BRZ p/r 25
OVERALL AU-GU ODDS 1:6
PRINT RUNS B/WN 1-50 COPIES PER
NO PRICING ON QTY OF 10 OR LESS
115 Andres Blanco/25 6.00 15.00
325 Edgar Renteria/25 10.00 25.00

2005 Diamond Kings Signature Gold B/W

*GOLD B/W p/r 25: .6X TO 1.5X BRZ p/r 100
OVERALL AU-GU ODDS 1:6
PRINT RUNS B/WN 1-25 COPIES PER
NO PRICING ON QTY OF 10 OR LESS
185 Sean Burroughs/25 6.00 15.00

2005 Diamond Kings Signature Platinum

OVERALL AU-GU ODDS 1:6
STATED PRINT RUN 1 SERIAL #'d SET
NO PRICING DUE TO SCARCITY

2005 Diamond Kings Signature Platinum B/W

OVERALL AU-GU ODDS 1:6
STATED PRINT RUN 1 SERIAL #'d SET
NO PRICING DUE TO SCARCITY

2005 Diamond Kings Signature Silver

*SILV p/r 100: .4X TO 1X BRZ p/r 100
*SILV p/r 50: .5X TO 1.2X BRZ p/r 100
*SILV p/r 50: .4X TO 1X BRZ p/r 50
*SILV p/r 25: .6X TO 1.5X BRZ p/r 100
*SILV p/r 25: .5X TO 1.2X BRZ p/r 50
*SILV p/r 25: .4X TO 1X BRZ p/r 25
OVERALL AU-GU ODDS 1:6

PRINT RUNS B/WN 1-100 COPIES PER
NO PRICING ON QTY OF 10 OR LESS
115 Andres Blanco/50 5.00 12.00

2005 Diamond Kings Signature Silver B/W

*SILV B/W p/r 50: .5X TO 1.2X BRZ p/r 100
*SILV B/W p/r 25: .6X TO 1.5X BRZ p/r 100
OVERALL AU-GU ODDS 1:6
PRINT RUNS B/WN 1-50 COPIES PER
NO PRICING ON QTY OF 10 OR LESS

2005 Diamond Kings Signature Framed Black

STATED PRINT RUN 1 SERIAL #'d SET
NO PRICING DUE TO SCARCITY
PLATINUM PRINT RUN 1 #'d SET
NO PLAT.PRICING DUE TO SCARCITY
OVERALL AU-GU ODDS 1:6

2005 Diamond Kings Signature Framed Black B/W

STATED PRINT RUN 1 SERIAL #'d SET
PLATINUM PRINT RUN 1 SERIAL #'d SET
OVERALL AU-GU ODDS 1:6
NO PRICING DUE TO SCARCITY

2005 Diamond Kings Signature Framed Blue

*BLUE p/r 50: .5X TO 1.2X BRZ p/r 100
*BLUE p/r 25: .6X TO 1.5X BRZ p/r 100
PRINT RUNS B/WN 1-50 COPIES PER
NO PRICING ON QTY OF 10 OR LESS
PLATINUM PRINT RUN 1 SERIAL #'d SET
NO PLAT.PRICING DUE TO SCARCITY
OVERALL AU-GU ODDS 1:6
115 Andres Blanco/25 6.00 15.00

2005 Diamond Kings Signature Framed Blue B/W

*BLUE B/W p/r 50: .5X TO 1.2X BRZ p/r 100
*BLUE B/W p/r 25: .6X TO 1.5X BRZ p/r 100
PRINT RUNS B/WN 1-50 COPIES PER
NO PRICING ON QTY OF 10 OR LESS
PLATINUM PRINT RUN 1 SERIAL #'d SET
NO PLAT.PRICING DUE TO SCARCITY
OVERALL AU-GU ODDS 1:6

2005 Diamond Kings Signature Framed Green

*GRN p/r 25: .6X TO 1.5X BRZ p/r 100
PRINT RUNS B/WN 1-25 COPIES PER
NO PRICING ON QTY OF 10 OR LESS
PLATINUM PRINT RUN 1 SERIAL #'d SET
NO PLATINUM PRICING DUE TO SCARCITY
OVERALL AU-GU ODDS 1:6

2005 Diamond Kings Signature Framed Green B/W

*GREEN B/W p/r 25: .6X TO 1.5X BRZ p/r 100
PRINT RUNS B/WN 1-25 COPIES PER
NO PRICING ON QTY OF 10 OR LESS
PLATINUM PRINT RUN 1 SERIAL #'d SET
NO PLAT.PRICING DUE TO SCARCITY
OVERALL AU-GU ODDS 1:6

2005 Diamond Kings Signature Framed Red

*RED p/r 100: .4X TO 1X BRZ p/r 100
*RED p/r 50: .5X TO 1.2X BRZ p/r 100
*RED p/r 50: .4X TO 1X BRZ p/r 50
*RED p/r 25: .6X TO 1.5X BRZ p/r 100
*RED p/r 25: .5X TO 1.2X BRZ p/r 50
*RED p/r 25: .4X TO 1X BRZ p/r 25
PRINT RUNS B/WN 1-100 COPIES PER
NO PRICING ON QTY OF 14 OR LESS
PLATINUM PRINT RUN 1 SERIAL #'d SET
NO PLAT.PRICING DUE TO SCARCITY
OVERALL AU-GU ODDS 1:6

2005 Diamond Kings Signature Framed Red B/W

*RED B/W p/r 100: .4X TO 1X BRZ p/r 100
*RED B/W p/r 50: .5X TO 1.2X BRZ p/r 100
*RED B/W p/r 50: .4X TO 1X BRZ p/r 50
*RED B/W p/r 25: .6X TO 1.5X BRZ p/r 100
*RED B/W p/r 25: .5X TO 1.2X BRZ p/r 50
*RED B/W p/r 25: .4X TO 1X BRZ p/r 25
PRINT RUNS B/WN 1-100 COPIES PER
NO PRICING ON QTY OF 10 OR LESS
PLATINUM PRINT RUN 1 SERIAL #'d SET
NO PLAT.PRICING DUE TO SCARCITY
OVERALL AU-GU ODDS 1:6

2005 Diamond Kings Signature Materials Black

OVERALL AU-GU ODDS 1:6
STATED PRINT RUN 1 SERIAL #'d SET
NO PRICING DUE TO SCARCITY

2005 Diamond Kings Signature Materials Bronze

OVERALL AU-GU ODDS 1:6
PRINT RUNS B/WN 1-200 COPIES PER
NO PRICING ON QTY OF 10 OR LESS
1 Garret Anderson Bat-Jsy/50 10.00 25.00
7 Chone Figgins Bat-Jsy/200 6.00 15.00
18 Rafael Furcal Bat-Jsy/50 10.00 25.00
19 Andruw Jones Bat-Jsy/25 20.00 50.00
25 Chipper Jones Bat-Jsy/10
27 R.Palmeiro O's Bat-Jsy/10
31 Larry Bigbie Jsy-Jsy/200 6.00 15.00
32 Rodrigo Lopez Jsy-Jsy/200 4.00 10.00
38 Trot Nixon Jsy-Jsy/100 12.50 30.00
39 Curt Schilling Bat-Jsy/5
41 Pedro Martinez Bat-Jsy/5
46 David Ortiz Bat-Jsy/100 15.00 40.00
47 Kerry Wood Jsy-Pants/10
48 Mark Prior Bat-Jsy/25 15.00 40.00
49 A.Ramirez Bat-Jsy/100 8.00 20.00
50 Greg Maddux Cubs Jsy-Jsy/5
51 C.Zambrano Jsy-Jsy/200 10.00 25.00
52 Derrek Lee Bat-Bat/100 12.50 30.00
56 Sammy Sosa Bat-Jsy/5
60 Magglio Ordonez Bat-Jsy/10
61 Carlos Lee Bat-Jsy/100 5.00 12.00
69 Adam Dunn Bat-Jsy/10
74 Sean Casey Jsy-Pants/10
76 C.C. Sabathia Jsy-Jsy/100 8.00 20.00
78 Omar Vizquel Jsy-Jsy/25 20.00 50.00
84 Todd Helton Bat-Jsy/1
94 Dontrelle Willis Jsy-Jsy/10
95 Miguel Cabrera Bat-Jsy/25 20.00 50.00
97 Mike Lowell Bat-Jsy/10
100 P.LoDuca Marlins Bat-Bat/10
102 Craig Biggio Bat-Pants/10
103 Lance Berkman Bat-Jsy/5
105 R.Clemens Astros Bat-Jsy/1
108 Jeff Bagwell Bat-Jsy/5
109 C.Belt Astros Bat-Jsy/50 10.00 25.00
110 Angel Berroa Bat-Bat/10
112 J.Affeldt Pants-Pants/100 5.00 12.00
114 Juan Gonzalez Bat-Jsy/10
116 Shawn Green Bat-Jsy/1
127 Bill Hall Bat-Bat/100 5.00 12.00
129 Jacque Jones Bat-Jsy/50 10.00 25.00
130 Torii Hunter Bat-Jsy/10
131 Johan Santana Jsy-Jsy/50 15.00 40.00
132 Lew Ford Bat-Jsy/200 4.00 10.00
139 Nick Johnson Bat-Bat/50 10.00 25.00
141 Tom Glavine Bat-Bat/5
145 Mike Piazza Bat-Jsy/1
150 Mike Mussina Bat-Jsy/5
153 Jorge Posada Bat-Jsy/25 20.00 50.00
155 Gary Sheffield Bat-Bat/10
162 Eric Chavez Bat-Jsy/25 12.50 30.00
164 Barry Zito Bat-Jsy/10
165 Tim Hudson Bat-Jsy/10
178 Craig Wilson Bat-Jsy/200 4.00 10.00
185 S.Burroughs Bat-Jsy/100 5.00 12.00
201 Edgar Martinez Bat-Bat/25 20.00 50.00
209 Jim Edmonds Bat-Jsy/10
211 Edgar Renteria Bat-Jsy/50 10.00 25.00
214 Albert Pujols Jsy-Jsy/5
221 Carl Crawford Jsy-Jsy/200 6.00 15.00
223 Fred McGriff Bat-Jsy/10
229 Mark Teixeira Bat-Jsy/25 20.00 50.00
230 Michael Young Bat-Jsy/100 8.00 20.00
232 Laynce Nix Bat-Jsy/200 4.00 10.00
233 A.Soriano Rgr Bat-Jsy/25 12.50 30.00
234 R.Palmeiro Rgr Bat-Jsy/10
239 Roy Halladay Jsy-Jsy/25 12.50 30.00
269 B.Penny M's Bat-Jsy/100 5.00 12.00
277 G. Maddux Braves Jsy-Jsy/5
278 R.Clemens Yanks Bat-Jsy/5
280 Dale Murphy Jsy-Jsy/50 15.00 40.00
281 Cal Ripken Bat-Jsy/5
282 Dwight Evans Bat-Jsy/50 15.00 40.00
283 Ron Santo Bat-Bat/100 15.00 40.00
284 Andre Dawson Bat-Jsy/100 8.00 20.00
286 Jack Morris Jsy-Jsy/100 8.00 20.00
287 Kirk Gibson Bat-Jsy/25 12.50 30.00
289 Orel Hershiser Jsy-Jsy/25 12.50 30.00
291 Tony Oliva Bat-Jsy/100 8.00 20.00
294 Don Mattingly Bat-Jsy/25 40.00 80.00
295 R.Henderson Bat-Jsy/10
297 Dave Parker Bat-Jsy/100 8.00 20.00
298 Steve Garvey Bat-Jsy/50 10.00 25.00
300 K.Hernandez Bat-Jsy/100 8.00 20.00
303 G.Anderson Bat-Jsy/50 10.00 25.00
310 Shawn Green Bat-Bat/1
314 Chipper Jones Bat-Jsy/1
315 Johnny Estrada Jsy-Jsy/50 6.00 15.00
317 Tim Hudson Bat-Bat/10
319 Jay Gibbons Bat-Bat/50 6.00 15.00
320 Melvin Mora Jsy-Jsy/50 10.00 25.00
321 Rafael Palmeiro O's Bat-Jsy/1
323 David Ortiz Jsy-Jsy/25 30.00 60.00
324 Manny Ramirez Bat-Jsy/1
327 Curt Schilling Sox Jsy-Jsy/5
329 Mark Prior Bat-Jsy/10
330 Greg Maddux Bat-Jsy/1
332 Frank Thomas Bat-Jsy/10
333 Mark Buehrle Jsy-Jsy/25 12.50 30.00
336 Sean Casey Bat-Jsy/10
339 Travis Hafner Jsy-Jsy/25 12.50 30.00
340 Victor Martinez Jsy-Jsy/25 12.50 30.00
341 Cliff Lee Jsy-Jsy/25 8.00 20.00
342 Todd Helton Bat-Bat/5
343 P.Wilson Bat-Jsy/25 12.50 30.00
347 Miguel Cabrera Bat-Jsy/10
348 Jeff Bagwell Bat-Jsy/5
350 Roger Clemens Astros Bat-Jsy/1
351 Ken Harvey Jsy-Jsy/25 8.00 20.00
353 Hideo Nomo Bat-Jsy/1
360 Shannon Stewart Jsy-Jsy/10
362 Johan Santana Jsy-Jsy/10
365 Carlos Beltran Bat-Bat/1
366 Pedro Martinez Bat-Bat/1
370 Gary Sheffield Yanks Bat-Jsy/1
371 Randy Johnson Yanks Bat-Bat/1
378 Mark Mulder A's Jsy-Jsy/10
380 Eric Chavez Bat-Jsy/10
382 Marlon Byrd Bat-Jsy/50 6.00 15.00
386 Jason Bay Bat-Jsy/1
393 Adrian Beltre Bat-Bat/1
397 Albert Pujols Bat-Jsy/1
398 Scott Rolen Cards Bat-Jsy/10
401 Delmon Young Bat-Bat/25 20.00 50.00
402 Aubrey Huff Bat-Bat/10
403 Alfonso Soriano Jsy-Jsy/10
406 Vernon Wells Jsy-Jsy/10
407 O.Hudson Bat-Bat/25 8.00 20.00
416 Gary Sheffield Braves Bat-Jsy/5
417 Curt Schilling D'backs Jsy-Jsy/5
419 S.Rolen Phils Bat-Jsy/25 20.00 50.00
422 Steve Finley D'backs Jsy-Jsy/10
423 Roger Clemens Sox Bat-Jsy/1
426 David Justice Bat-Jsy/1
427 Mark Grace Bat-Jsy/10
428 Alan Trammell Bat-Jsy/25 12.50 30.00
429 Bert Blyleven Jsy-Jsy/1
430 D.Gooden Bat-Jsy/25 12.50 30.00
431 Deion Sanders Bat-Jsy/1
432 Joe Torre MG Bat-Bat/10
434 Tony Gwynn Bat-Jsy/25 30.00 60.00
435 Will Clark Bat-Jsy/10
436 Marty Marion Jsy-Jsy/1
437 Nolan Ryan Bat-Jsy/10
440 Magglio Ordonez Bat-Bat/10
441 Sammy Sosa O's Bat-Bat/1
449 Ryne Sandberg Jsy-Jsy/5
450 Willie Mays Bat-Jsy/1

2005 Diamond Kings Signature Materials Bronze B/W

*BRZ B/W p/r 100: .5X TO 1.2X BRZ p/r 200
*BRZ B/W p/r 50: .5X TO 1.2X BRZ p/r 100
*BRZ B/W p/r 25: .75X TO 2X BRZ p/r 200
*BRZ B/W p/r 25: .6X TO 1.5X BRZ p/r 100
OVERALL AU-GU ODDS 1:6
PRINT RUNS B/WN 1-100 COPIES PER
NO PRICING ON QTY OF 10 OR LESS
73 Ryan Wagner Jsy-Jsy/50 6.00 15.00
97 Mike Lowell Jsy-Jsy/25 8.00 20.00
136 Jose Vidro Bat-Bat/50 6.00 15.00
180 Jack Wilson Bat-Bat/100 5.00 12.00
271 P.Lo Duca Dgr Bat-Bat/25 12.50 30.00
285 Harold Baines Bat-Jsy/50 10.00 25.00

2005 Diamond Kings Signature Materials Gold

*GOLD p/r 50: .6X TO 1.5X BRZ p/r 200
*GOLD p/r 50: .5X TO 1.2X BRZ p/r 100
*GOLD p/r 50: .4X TO 1X BRZ p/r 50

*GOLD p/r 25: .5X TO 1.2X BRZ p/r 50
*GOLD p/r 25: .4X TO 1X BRZ p/r 25
OVERALL AU-GU ODDS 1:6
PRINT RUNS B/WN 1-50 COPIES PER
NO PRICING ON QTY OF 10 OR LESS
104 Roy Oswalt Jsy-Jsy/50 10.00 25.00
285 Harold Baines Bat-Jsy/50 10.00 25.00
299 Matt Williams Jsy-Jsy/25 20.00 50.00

2005 Diamond Kings Signature Materials Gold B/W

*GOLD B/W p/r 25: .75X TO 2X BRZ p/r 200
*GOLD B/W p/r 25: .6X TO 1.5X BRZ p/r 100
OVERALL AU-GU ODDS 1:6
PRINT RUNS B/WN 1-25 COPIES PER
NO PRICING ON QTY OF 10 OR LESS
73 Ryan Wagner Jsy-Jsy/25 8.00 20.00
97 Mike Lowell Jsy-Jsy/25 8.00 20.00
136 Jose Vidro Bat-Bat/25 8.00 20.00
180 Jack Wilson Bat-Bat/25 8.00 20.00
271 P.Lo Duca Dgr Bat-Bat/25 12.50 30.00
285 Harold Baines Bat-Jsy/25 12.50 30.00

2005 Diamond Kings Signature Materials Platinum

OVERALL AU-GU ODDS 1:6
STATED PRINT RUN 1 SERIAL #'d SET
NO PRICING DUE TO SCARCITY

2005 Diamond Kings Signature Materials Platinum B/W

OVERALL AU-GU ODDS 1:6
STATED PRINT RUN 1 SERIAL #'d SET
NO PRICING DUE TO SCARCITY

2005 Diamond Kings Signature Materials Silver

*SILV p/r 100: .5X TO 1.2X BRZ p/r 200
*SILV p/r 100: .4X TO 1X BRZ p/r 100
*SILV p/r 50: .5X TO 1.2X BRZ p/r 100
*SILV p/r 50: .4X TO 1X BRZ p/r 50
*SILV p/r 25: .5X TO 1.2X BRZ p/r 50
*SILV p/r 25: .4X TO 1X BRZ p/r 25
OVERALL AU-GU ODDS 1:6
PRINT RUNS B/WN 1-100 COPIES PER
NO PRICING ON QTY OF 10 OR LESS
104 Roy Oswalt Jsy-Jsy/50 10.00 25.00
285 Harold Baines Bat-Jsy/50 10.00 25.00
299 Matt Williams Jsy-Jsy/25 20.00 50.00
354 Kazuhisa Ishii Jsy-Jsy/25 12.50 30.00

2005 Diamond Kings Signature Materials Silver B/W

*SILV B/W p/r 50: .6X TO 1.5X BRZ p/r 200
*SILV B/W p/r 50: .5X TO 1.2X BRZ p/r 100
*SILV B/W p/r 25: .75X TO 2X BRZ p/r 200
*SILV B/W p/r 25: .6X TO 1.5X BRZ p/r 100
OVERALL AU-GU ODDS 1:6
PRINT RUNS B/WN 1-50 COPIES PER
NO PRICING ON QTY OF 10 OR LESS
73 Ryan Wagner Jsy-Jsy/50 6.00 15.00
97 Mike Lowell Jsy-Jsy/25 8.00 20.00
136 Jose Vidro Bat-Bat/50 6.00 15.00
180 Jack Wilson Bat-Bat/50 6.00 15.00
271 P.Lo Duca Dgr Bat-Bat/25 12.50 30.00
285 Harold Baines Bat-Jsy/25 12.50 30.00

2005 Diamond Kings Signature Materials Framed Black

PRINT RUNS B/WN 1-10 COPIES PER
PLATINUM PRINT RUN 1 SERIAL #'d SET
OVERALL AU-GU ODDS 1:6
NO PRICING DUE TO SCARCITY

2005 Diamond Kings Signature Materials Framed Black B/W

STATED PRINT RUN 1 SERIAL #'d SET
PLATINUM PRINT RUN 1 SERIAL #'d SET
OVERALL AU-GU ODDS 1:6
NO PRICING DUE TO SCARCITY

2005 Diamond Kings Signature Materials Framed Blue

*BLUE p/r 50: .6X TO 1.5X BRZ p/r 200
*BLUE p/r 50: .5X TO 1.2X BRZ p/r 100
*BLUE p/r 50: .4X TO 1X BRZ p/r 50
*BLUE p/r 25: .5X TO 1.2X BRZ p/r 50
PRINT RUNS B/WN 1-50 COPIES PER
NO PRICING ON QTY OF 10 OR LESS
PLATINUM PRINT RUN 1 SERIAL #'d SET
NO PLAT.PRICING DUE TO SCARCITY
OVERALL AU-GU ODDS 1:6

2005 Diamond Kings Signature Materials Framed Blue B/W

*BLUE B/W p/r 25: .75X TO 2X BRZ p/r 200
*BLUE B/W p/r 25: .6X TO 1.5X BRZ p/r 100
PRINT RUNS B/WN 1-25 COPIES PER
NO PRICING ON QTY OF 10 OR LESS
PLATINUM PRINT RUN 1 SERIAL #'d SET
NO PLAT.PRICING DUE TO SCARCITY
OVERALL AU-GU ODDS 1:6
73 Ryan Wagner Jsy-Jsy/25 8.00 20.00
97 Mike Lowell Jsy-Jsy/25 8.00 20.00
180 Jack Wilson Bat-Bat/25 8.00 20.00
271 P.Lo Duca Dgr Bat-Bat/25 12.50 30.00

2005 Diamond Kings Signature Materials Framed Green

*GRN p/r 25: .75X TO 2X BRZ p/r 200
*GRN p/r 25: .6X TO 1.5X BRZ p/r 100
*GRN p/r 25: .5X TO 1.2X BRZ p/r 50
PRINT RUNS B/WN 1-25 COPIES PER
NO PRICING ON QTY OF 10 OR LESS
PLATINUM PRINT RUN 1 SERIAL #'d SET
NO PLAT.PRICING DUE TO SCARCITY
OVERALL AU-GU ODDS 1:6
299 Matt Williams Jsy-Jsy/25 20.00 50.00

2005 Diamond Kings Signature Materials Framed Green B/W

*GREEN B/W p/r 25: .75X TO 2X BRZ p/r 200
*GREEN B/W p/r 25: .6X TO 1.5X BRZ p/r 100
PRINT RUNS B/WN 1-25 COPIES PER
NO PRICING ON QTY OF 10 OR LESS
PLATINUM PRINT RUN 1 SERIAL #'d SET
NO PLAT.PRICING DUE TO SCARCITY
OVERALL AU-GU ODDS 1:6
73 Ryan Wagner Jsy-Jsy/25 8.00 20.00
97 Mike Lowell Jsy-Jsy/25 8.00 20.00
180 Jack Wilson Bat-Bat/25 8.00 20.00
271 P.Lo Duca Dgr Bat-Bat/25 12.50 30.00
285 Harold Baines Bat-Jsy/25 12.50 30.00

2005 Diamond Kings Signature Materials Framed Red

*RED p/r 100: .5X TO 1.2X BRZ p/r 200
*RED p/r 100: .4X TO 1X BRZ p/r 100
*RED p/r 50: .5X TO 1.2X BRZ p/r 100
*RED p/r 50: .4X TO 1X BRZ p/r 50
*RED p/r 25: .5X TO 1.2X BRZ p/r 50
PRINT RUNS B/WN 1-100 COPIES PER
NO PRICING ON QTY OF 10 OR LESS
PLATINUM PRINT RUN 1 SERIAL #'d SET
NO PLAT.PRICING DUE TO SCARCITY
OVERALL AU-GU ODDS 1:6

2005 Diamond Kings Signature Materials Framed Red B/W

*RED B/W p/r 25: .75X TO 2X BRZ p/r 200
*RED B/W p/r 25: .6X TO 1.5X BRZ p/r 100
PRINT RUNS B/WN 1-50 COPIES PER
NO PRICING ON QTY OF 10 OR LESS
PLATINUM PRINT RUN 1 SERIAL #'d SET
NO PLAT.PRICING DUE TO SCARCITY
OVERALL AU-GU ODDS 1:6

2005 Diamond Kings Diamond Cuts Bat

*BAT p/r 200: .4X TO 1X JSY p/r 200
*BAT p/r 200: .4X TO 1X JSY p/r 100
*BAT p/r 200: .3X TO .8X JSY p/r 50
*BAT p/r 100: .5X TO 1.2X JSY p/r 200
*BAT p/r 100: .3X TO .8X JSY p/r 50
*BAT p/r 50: .6X TO 1.5X JSY p/r 200
*BAT p/r 50: .5X TO 1.2X JSY p/r 100
*BAT p/r 50: .4X TO 1X JSY p/r 50
OVERALL AU-GU ODD 1:6
PRINT RUNS B/WN 50-200 COPIES PER
16 Derrek Lee/200 2.50 6.00
47 Tim Salmon/200 2.50 6.00
49 Torii Hunter/200 2.00 5.00

2005 Diamond Kings Diamond Cuts Combos

*COMBO p/r 200: .5X TO 1.2X JSY p/r 200
*COMBO p/r 100: .6X TO 1.5X JSY p/r 200
*COMBO p/r 100: .5X TO 1.2X JSY p/r 100
*COMBO p/r 100: .4X TO 1X JSY p/r 50
*COMBO p/r 50: .75X TO 2X JSY p/r 200
*COMBO p/r 50: .6X TO 1.5X JSY p/r 100
*COMBO p/r 50: .5X TO 1.2X JSY p/r 50
PRINT RUNS B/WN 25-200 COPIES PER
PRIME PRINT RUN 1 SERIAL #'d SET
NO PRIME PRICING DUE TO SCARCITY
OVERALL AU-GU ODDS 1:6
49 Torii Hunter Bat-Jsy/25 5.00 12.00

2005 Diamond Kings Diamond Cuts Jersey

PRINT RUNS B/WN 50-200 COPIES PER
PRIME PRINT RUN 1 SERIAL #'d SET
NO PRIME PRICING DUE TO SCARCITY
OVERALL AU-GU ODDS 1:6
1 Adam Dunn/50 3.00 8.00
2 Adrian Beltre/200 2.00 5.00
3 Alfonso Soriano/50 3.00 8.00
4 Andruw Jones/200 2.50 6.00
5 Andy Pettitte/100 3.00 8.00
6 Aramis Ramirez/200 2.00 5.00
7 Brian Giles/200 2.00 5.00
8 C.C. Sabathia/200 2.00 5.00
9 Carl Crawford/200 2.00 5.00
10 Carlos Beltran/200 2.00 5.00
11 Carlos Lee/200 2.00 5.00
12 Craig Wilson/200 2.00 5.00
13 Curt Schilling/50 4.00 10.00
14 Darin Erstad/200 2.00 5.00
17 Fred McGriff/200 2.50 6.00
18 Greg Maddux/50 6.00 15.00
19 Ivan Rodriguez/200 2.50 6.00
20 Jason Bay/200 2.00 5.00
21 Jason Giambi/200 2.00 5.00
22 Jay Gibbons/100 2.50 6.00
23 Jeff Kent/200 2.00 5.00
24 John Olerud/200 2.00 5.00
25 Juan Gonzalez Pants/200 2.00 5.00
26 Junior Spivey/200 2.00 5.00
27 Kazuhisa Ishii/200 2.00 5.00
28 Kevin Brown/200 2.00 5.00
29 Larry Walker Rockies/200 2.00 5.00
30 Lyle Overbay/200 2.00 5.00

31 Mark Teixeira/100 3.00 8.00
32 Melvin Mora/200 2.00 5.00
33 Michael Young/200 2.00 5.00
34 Miguel Tejada/200 2.00 5.00
35 Mike Mussina/100 3.00 8.00
36 Paul LoDuca/50 3.00 8.00
37 Preston Wilson/200 2.00 5.00
38 Randy Johnson/200 3.00 8.00
39 Richie Sexson/200 2.00 5.00
40 Roger Clemens/50 6.00 15.00
41 Scott Rolen/50 4.00 10.00
42 Sean Burroughs/200 2.00 5.00
43 Sean Casey/200 2.00 5.00
44 Shannon Stewart/100 2.50 6.00
45 Shawn Green/200 2.00 5.00
46 Steve Finley/200 2.00 5.00
48 Tom Glavine/200 2.50 6.00
50 Travis Hafner/50 2.50 6.00

2005 Diamond Kings Diamond Cuts Signature

*SIG p/r 100: .3X TO .8X SIG.JSY p/r 100
*SIG p/r 100: .25X TO .6X SIG.JSY p/r 50
*SIG p/r 50: .3X TO .8X SIG.JSY p/r 50
*SIG p/r 25: .5X TO 1.2X SIG.JSY p/r 100
*SIG p/r 25: .3X TO .8X SIG.JSY p/r 25
OVERALL AU-GU ODDS 1:6
PRINT RUNS B/WN 1-100 COPIES PER
NO PRICING ON QTY OF 10 OR LESS
20 Jason Bay/100 6.00 15.00
22 Jay Gibbons/100 4.00 10.00
47 Tim Salmon/100 10.00 25.00

2005 Diamond Kings Diamond Cuts Signature Bat

*SIG.BAT p/r 100: .4X TO 1X SIG.JSY p/r 100
*SIG.BAT p/r 50: .5X TO 1.2X SIG.JSY p/r 100
*SIG.BAT p/r 25: .4X TO 1X SIG.JSY p/r 25
OVERALL AU-GU ODDS 1:6
PRINT RUNS B/WN 1-100 COPIES PER
NO PRICING ON QTY OF 10 OR LESS
1 Adam Dunn/25 20.00 50.00
10 Carlos Beltran/50 10.00 25.00
16 Derrek Lee/100 12.50 30.00
17 Fred McGriff/25 30.00 60.00
22 Jay Gibbons/100 5.00 12.00
49 Torii Hunter/25 12.50 30.00
53 Carlos Beltran/25 12.50 30.00

2005 Diamond Kings Diamond Cuts Signature Combos

*SIG.COM p/r 100: .4X TO 1X SIG.JSY p/r 100
*SIG.COM p/r 50: .5X TO 1.2X SIG.JSY p/r 100
*SIG.COM p/r 25: .6X TO 1.5X SIG.JSY p/r 100
*SIG.COM p/r 25: .5X TO 1.2X SIG.JSY p/r 50
*SIG.COM p/r 25: .4X TO 1X SIG.JSY p/r 25
PRINT RUNS B/WN 1-100 COPIES PER
NO PRICING ON QTY OF 10 OR LESS
PRIME PRINT RUN 1 SERIAL #'d SET
NO PRIME PRICING DUE TO SCARCITY
OVERALL AU-GU ODDS 1:6
1 Adam Dunn Bat-Jsy/25 20.00 50.00
17 Fred McGriff Bat-Jsy/25 30.00 60.00
22 Jay Gibbons Bat-Bat/50 6.00 15.00
25 Juan Gonzalez Bat-Jsy/100 8.00 20.00
49 Torii Hunter Bat-Jsy/25 12.50 30.00
51 Aramis Ramirez Jsy-Jsy/24 12.50 30.00
54 Craig Biggio Bat-Pants/25 20.00 50.00

2005 Diamond Kings Diamond Cuts Signature Jersey

PRINT RUNS B/WN 5-100 COPIES PER
NO PRICING ON QTY OF 10 OR LESS
PRIME PRINT RUN 1 SERIAL #'d SET
NO PRIME PRICING DUE TO SCARCITY
OVERALL AU-GU ODDS 1:6
1 Adam Dunn/10
2 Adrian Beltre/100 8.00 20.00
3 Alfonso Soriano/10
4 Andruw Jones/10
5 Andy Pettitte/10
6 Aramis Ramirez/100 8.00 20.00
8 C.C. Sabathia/100 8.00 20.00
9 Carl Crawford/50 10.00 25.00
11 Carlos Lee/100 8.00 20.00
12 Craig Wilson/100 5.00 12.00
13 Curt Schilling/5
17 Fred McGriff/10
18 Greg Maddux/5
25 Juan Gonzalez Pants/10
27 Kazuhisa Ishii/10
30 Lyle Overbay/100 5.00 12.00
31 Mark Teixeira/25 20.00 50.00
32 Melvin Mora/50 10.00 25.00
33 Michael Young/100 8.00 20.00
35 Mike Mussina/5
36 Paul LoDuca/25 12.50 30.00
38 Randy Johnson/5
40 Roger Clemens/5
41 Scott Rolen/10
42 Sean Burroughs/50 6.00 15.00
43 Sean Casey/25 12.50 30.00
44 Shannon Stewart/25 12.50 30.00
45 Shawn Green/5
46 Steve Finley/25 12.50 30.00
50 Travis Hafner/50 10.00 25.00
51 Aramis Ramirez/10
54 Craig Biggio Pants/10
55 Jim Edmonds/5
56 Johan Santana/25 20.00 50.00
57 Mark Mulder/25 12.50 30.00
59 Tim Hudson/10
60 Victor Martinez/25 12.50 30.00

2005 Diamond Kings Gallery of Stars

SER.2 STATED ODDS 1:8
1 Andre Dawson .75 2.00
2 Bob Feller .75 2.00
3 Bobby Doerr .75 2.00
4 C.C. Sabathia .75 2.00
5 Carl Crawford .75 2.00
6 Dale Murphy 1.25 3.00
7 Danny Kolb .75 2.00
8 Darryl Strawberry .75 2.00
9 Dave Parker .75 2.00
10 David Ortiz 1.25 3.00
11 Dwight Gooden .75 2.00
12 Garret Anderson .75 2.00
13 Jack Morris .75 2.00
14 Jacque Jones .75 2.00
15 Jim Palmer .75 2.00
16 Johan Santana 1.25 3.00
17 Ken Harvey .75 2.00
18 Lyle Overbay .75 2.00
19 Marty Marion .75 2.00
20 Melvin Mora .75 2.00
21 Michael Young .75 2.00
22 Miguel Cabrera 1.25 3.00
23 Preston Wilson .75 2.00
24 Sean Casey .75 2.00
25 Victor Martinez .75 2.00

2005 Diamond Kings Gallery of Stars Bat

*BAT p/r 200: .3X TO .8X JSY p/r 100
*BAT p/r 100: .4X TO 1X JSY p/r 100
*BAT p/r 100: .3X TO .8X JSY p/r 50
*BAT p/r 100: .25X TO .6X JSY p/r 25
*BAT p/r 50: .5X TO 1.2X JSY p/r 100
OVERALL AU-GU ODDS 1:6
PRINT RUNS B/WN 50-200 COPIES PER

2005 Diamond Kings Gallery of Stars Combos

*COMBO p/r 200: .3X TO .8X JSY p/r 100
*COMBO p/r 100: .5X TO 1.2X JSY p/r 100
*COMBO p/r 100: .4X TO 1X JSY p/r 50
*COMBO p/r 100: .3X TO .8X JSY p/r 25
*COMBO p/r 50: .6X TO 1.5X JSY p/r 100
*COMBO p/r 50: .5X TO 1.2X JSY p/r 50
PRINT RUNS B/WN 50-200 COPIES PER
PRIME PRINT RUN 1 SERIAL #'d SET
NO PRIME PRICING DUE TO SCARCITY
OVERALL AU-GU ODDS 1:6

2005 Diamond Kings Gallery of Stars Jersey

PRINT RUNS B/WN 25-100 COPIES PER
PRIME PRINT RUN 1 SERIAL #'d SET
NO PRIME PRICING DUE TO SCARCITY
OVERALL AU-GU ODDS 1:6
1 Andre Dawson/100 3.00 8.00
2 Bob Feller Pants/50 5.00 12.00
3 Bobby Doerr Pants/100 3.00 8.00
4 C.C. Sabathia/100 2.50 6.00
5 Carl Crawford/100 2.50 6.00
6 Dale Murphy/100 4.00 10.00
8 Darryl Strawberry/25 5.00 12.00
9 Dave Parker/100 3.00 8.00
10 David Ortiz/100 3.00 8.00
11 Dwight Gooden/25 5.00 12.00
12 Garret Anderson/50 3.00 8.00
13 Jack Morris/100 3.00 8.00
14 Jacque Jones/100 2.50 6.00
15 Jim Palmer Pants/50 4.00 10.00
17 Ken Harvey/100 2.50 6.00
18 Lyle Overbay/100 2.50 6.00
20 Melvin Mora/100 2.50 6.00
21 Michael Young/100 2.50 6.00
22 Miguel Cabrera/100 3.00 8.00
23 Preston Wilson/100 2.50 6.00
24 Sean Casey/100 2.50 6.00
25 Victor Martinez/25 4.00 10.00

2005 Diamond Kings Gallery of Stars Signature

*SIG p/r 100: .3X TO .8X SIG.JSY p/r 100
*SIG p/r 100: .25X TO .6X SIG.JSY p/r 50
*SIG p/r 100: .2X TO .5X SIG.JSY p/r 25
*SIG p/r 50: .4X TO 1X SIG.JSY p/r 100
*SIG p/r 50: .25X TO .6X SIG.JSY p/r 25
*SIG p/r 25: .5X TO 1.2X SIG.JSY p/r 100
*SIG p/r 25: .3X TO .8X SIG.JSY p/r 25
OVERALL AU-GU ODDS 1:6
PRINT RUNS B/WN 5-100 COPIES PER
NO PRICING ON QTY OF 10 OR LESS
7 Danny Kolb/100 4.00 10.00
8 Darryl Strawberry/100 6.00 15.00

2005 Diamond Kings Gallery of Stars Signature Bat

*BAT p/r 200: .3X TO .8X SIG.JSY p/r 100
*BAT p/r 100: .3X TO .8X SIG.JSY p/r 50
*BAT p/r 100: .25X TO .6X SIG.JSY p/r 25
*BAT p/r 50: .3X TO .8X SIG.JSY p/r 25
*BAT p/r 25: .6X TO 1.5X SIG.JSY p/r 100
*BAT p/r 25: .4X TO 1X SIG.JSY p/r 25
OVERALL AU-GU ODDS 1:6
PRINT RUNS B/WN 25-200 COPIES PER
21 Michael Young/100 8.00 20.00
22 Miguel Cabrera/50 15.00 40.00

2005 Diamond Kings Gallery of Stars Signature Combos

*SIG.COM p/r 200: .5X TO 1.2X SIG.JSYp/r100
*SIG.COM p/r 100: .4X TO 1X SIG.JSY p/r 100
*SIG.COM p/r 100: .3X TO .8X SIG.JSY p/r 50
*SIG.COM p/r 50: .4X TO 1X SIG.JSY p/r 50
*SIG.COM p/r 50: .3X TO .8X SIG.JSY p/r 25
*SIG.COM p/r 25: .6X TO 1.5X SIG.JSY p/r 100
*SIG.COM p/r 25: .4X TO 1X SIG.JSY p/r 25
PRINT RUNS B/WN 25-200 COPIES PER
PRIME PRINT RUN 1 SERIAL #'d SET
NO PRIME PRICING DUE TO SCARCITY
OVERALL AU-GU ODDS 1:6
21 Michael Young Bat-Jsy/50 10.00 25.00
22 Miguel Cabrera Bat-Jsy/50 15.00 40.00

2005 Diamond Kings Gallery of Stars Signature Jersey

PRINT RUNS B/WN 25-100 COPIES PER
PRIME PRINT RUN 1 SERIAL #'d SET
NO PRIME PRICING DUE TO SCARCITY
OVERALL AU-GU ODDS 1:6
1 Andre Dawson/25 12.50 30.00
2 Bob Feller Pants/50 15.00 40.00
3 Bobby Doerr Pants/100 8.00 20.00
4 C.C. Sabathia/100 8.00 20.00
5 Carl Crawford/50 10.00 25.00
6 Dale Murphy/50 15.00 40.00
9 Dave Parker/100 8.00 20.00
10 David Ortiz/50 20.00 50.00
11 Dwight Gooden/50 10.00 25.00
12 Garret Anderson/50 10.00 25.00
13 Jack Morris/50 10.00 25.00
14 Jacque Jones/25 12.50 30.00
15 Jim Palmer Pants/25 12.50 30.00
17 Ken Harvey/100 5.00 12.00
18 Lyle Overbay/100 5.00 12.00
19 Marty Marion/25 12.50 30.00
20 Melvin Mora/100 8.00 20.00
24 Sean Casey/25 12.50 30.00
25 Victor Martinez/100 8.00 20.00

2005 Diamond Kings Heritage Collection

1-25 STATED ODDS 1:21 SER.1 PACKS
26-35 STATED ODDS 1:76 SER.2 PACKS
1 Andre Dawson 1.00 2.50
2 Bob Gibson 1.00 2.50
3 Cal Ripken 5.00 12.00
4 Dale Murphy 1.00 2.50
5 Darryl Strawberry 1.00 2.50
6 Dennis Eckersley 1.00 2.50
7 Don Mattingly 3.00 8.00
8 Duke Snider 1.00 2.50
9 Dwight Gooden 1.00 2.50
10 Eddie Murray 1.50 4.00
11 Frank Robinson 1.00 2.50
12 Gary Carter 1.00 2.50
13 George Brett 3.00 8.00
14 Harmon Killebrew 1.50 4.00
15 Jack Morris 1.00 2.50
16 Jim Palmer 1.00 2.50
17 Lou Brock 1.00 2.50
18 Mike Schmidt 3.00 8.00
19 Nolan Ryan 4.00 10.00
20 Ozzie Smith 2.50 6.00
21 Phil Niekro 1.00 2.50
22 Rod Carew 1.00 2.50
23 Rollie Fingers 1.00 2.50
24 Steve Carlton 1.00 2.50
25 Tony Gwynn 2.00 5.00
26 Curt Schilling 1.00 2.50
27 Bobby Doerr 1.00 2.50
28 Edgar Martinez 1.00 2.50
29 Jim Thorpe 2.00 5.00
30 Mark Grace 1.00 2.50
31 Matt Williams 1.00 2.50
32 Paul Molitor 1.00 2.50
33 Robin Yount 1.50 4.00
34 Ryne Sandberg 3.00 8.00
35 Will Clark 1.00 2.50

2005 Diamond Kings Heritage Collection Bat

*BAT p/r 100: .4X TO 1X JSY p/r 100
*BAT p/r 100: .3X TO .8X JSY p/r 50
*BAT p/r 50: .5X TO 1.2X JSY p/r 100
*BAT p/r 50: .4X TO 1X JSY p/r 50
*BAT p/r 50: .3X TO .8X JSY p/r 25
OVERALL AU-GU ODDS 1:6
PRINT RUNS B/WN 50-100 COPIES PER
11 Frank Robinson/50 4.00 10.00

2005 Diamond Kings Heritage Collection Combos

*COMBO p/r 100: .5X TO 1.2X JSY p/r 100
*COMBO p/r 100: .4X TO 1X JSY p/r 50
*COMBO p/r 50: .6X TO 1.5X JSY p/r 100
*COMBO p/r 50: .5X TO 1.2X JSY p/r 50
*COMBO p/r 25: .75X TO 2X JSY p/r 100
*COMBO p/r 25: .6X TO 1.5X JSY p/r 50
PRINT RUNS B/WN 25-100 COPIES PER
PRIME PRINT RUN 1 SERIAL #'d SET
NO PRIME PRICING DUE TO SCARCITY
OVERALL AU-GU ODDS 1:6

2005 Diamond Kings Heritage Collection Jersey

PRINT RUNS B/WN 25-100 COPIES PER
PRIME PRINT RUN 1 SERIAL #'d SET
NO PRIME PRICING DUE TO SCARCITY
OVERALL AU-GU ODDS 1:6
1 Andre Dawson/100 3.00 8.00
2 Bob Gibson/50 5.00 12.00
3 Cal Ripken/100 12.50 30.00
4 Dale Murphy/100 4.00 10.00
5 Darryl Strawberry/25 5.00 12.00
6 Dennis Eckersley/100 3.00 8.00
7 Don Mattingly/100 8.00 20.00
8 Duke Snider/50 5.00 12.00
9 Dwight Gooden/100 3.00 8.00
10 Eddie Murray/100 5.00 12.00
12 Gary Carter/100 3.00 8.00
13 George Brett/50 10.00 25.00
14 Harmon Killebrew/100 5.00 12.00
15 Jack Morris/100 3.00 8.00
16 Jim Palmer/100 3.00 8.00
17 Lou Brock/100 4.00 10.00
18 Mike Schmidt Jkt/100 8.00 20.00
19 Nolan Ryan/100 8.00 20.00
20 Ozzie Smith Pants/100 6.00 15.00
21 Phil Niekro/100 4.00 10.00
22 Rod Carew/100 4.00 10.00
23 Rollie Fingers/50 4.00 10.00
24 Steve Carlton/50 4.00 10.00
25 Tony Gwynn/100 5.00 12.00

2005 Diamond Kings Heritage Collection Signature

*SIG p/r 50: .4X TO 1X SIG.JSY p/r 100
*SIG p/r 25: .5X TO 1.2X SIG.JSY p/r 100
*SIG p/r 25: .4X TO 1X SIG.JSY p/r 50
OVERALL AU-GU ODDS 1:6
PRINT RUNS B/WN 1-50 COPIES PER
NO PRICING ON QTY OF 10 OR LESS

2005 Diamond Kings Heritage Collection Signature Bat

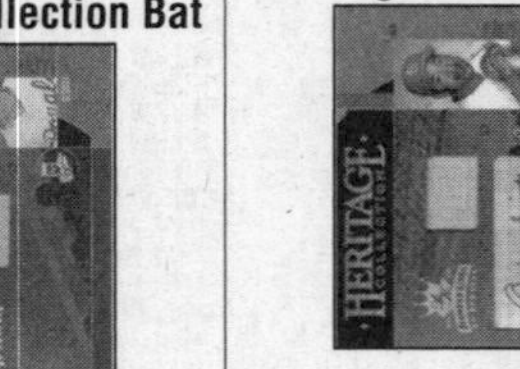

*SIG.BAT p/r 100: .4X TO 1X SIG.JSY p/r 100
*SIG.BAT p/r 50: .5X TO 1.2X SIG.JSY p/r 100
*SIG.BAT p/r 50: .4X TO 1X SIG.JSY p/r 50
*SIG.BATp/r20-25: .5X TO 1.2X SIG.JSYp/r50
*SIG.BAT p/r 20-25: .4X TO 1X SIG.JSY p/r 25
OVERALL AU-GU ODDS 1:6
PRINT RUNS B/WN 5-100 COPIES PER
NO PRICING ON QTY OF 10 OR LESS
11 Frank Robinson/25 20.00 50.00
25 Tony Gwynn/25 30.00 60.00

2005 Diamond Kings Heritage Collection Signature Combos

*SIG.COM p/r 100: .4X TO 1X SIG.JSY p/r 100
*SIG.COM p/r 50: .5X TO 1.2X SIG.JSY p/r 100
*SIG.COM p/r 50: .4X TO 1X SIG.JSY p/r 50
*SIG.COM p/r 50: .3X TO .8X SIG.JSY p/r 25
*SIG.COM p/r 25: .6X TO 1.5X SIG.JSY p/r 100
*SIG.COM p/r 25: .5X TO 1.2X SIG.JSY p/r 50
*SIG.COM p/r 25: .4X TO 1X SIG.JSY p/r 25
PRINT RUNS B/WN 5-100 COPIES PER
NO PRICING ON QTY OF 10 OR LESS
PRIME PRINT RUN 1 SERIAL #'d SET
NO PRIME PRICING DUE TO SCARCITY
OVERALL AU-GU ODDS 1:6
25 Tony Gwynn Bat-Jsy/25 30.00 60.00

2005 Diamond Kings Heritage Collection Signature Jersey

PRINT RUNS B/WN 5-100 COPIES PER
NO PRICING ON QTY OF 10 OR LESS
PRIME PRINT RUN 1 SERIAL #'d SET
NO PRIME PRICING DUE TO SCARCITY
OVERALL AU-GU ODDS 1:6
1 Andre Dawson/100 8.00 20.00
2 Bob Gibson/25 20.00 50.00
3 Cal Ripken/5
4 Dale Murphy/50 15.00 40.00
5 Darryl Strawberry Pants/100 8.00 20.00
6 Dennis Eckersley/50 10.00 25.00
7 Don Mattingly/25 40.00 80.00
8 Duke Snider/50 15.00 40.00
9 Dwight Gooden/100 8.00 20.00
10 Eddie Murray/5
11 Frank Robinson/25 20.00 50.00
12 Gary Carter/50 10.00 25.00
13 George Brett/5
14 Harmon Killebrew/50 20.00 50.00
15 Jack Morris/100 8.00 20.00
16 Jim Palmer/25 12.50 30.00
17 Lou Brock/50 15.00 40.00
18 Mike Schmidt Jkt/5
19 Nolan Ryan/10
20 Ozzie Smith/25 30.00 60.00
21 Phil Niekro/25 12.50 30.00
22 Rod Carew/25 20.00 50.00
23 Rollie Fingers/25 12.50 30.00
24 Steve Carlton/25 12.50 30.00
25 Tony Gwynn/10
26 Curt Schilling/10
27 Bobby Doerr Pants/25 12.50 30.00
28 Edgar Martinez/25 20.00 50.00
30 Mark Grace/10
31 Matt Williams/25 20.00 50.00
32 Paul Molitor/10
33 Robin Yount/10
34 Ryne Sandberg/5
35 Will Clark/25 20.00 50.00

2005 Diamond Kings HOF Heroes

1-50 STATED ODDS 1:5 SER.1 PACKS
51-100 STATED ODDS 1:7 SER.2 PACKS
NON CANVAS RANDOM IN PACKS
NON-CANVAS PRINT RUN 20 SETS
NON-CANVAS PRINT RUN INFO BY DONRUSS
NO NON-CANVAS PRICING AVAILABLE
*BRONZE 1-50: .75X TO 2X BASIC
*BRONZE 51-100: 1X TO 2.5X BASIC
BRONZE 1-50 PRINT RUN 100 #'d SETS
BRONZE 51-100 PRINT RUN 50 #'d SETS
*GOLD 1-50: 1.5X TO 4X BASIC
GOLD 1-50 PRINT RUN 25 #'d SETS
GOLD 51-100 PRINT RUN 10 #'d SETS
GOLD 51-100 NO PRICING AVAILABLE
PLATINUM PRINT RUN 1 SERIAL #'d SET
NO PLATINUM PRICING DUE TO SCARCITY
*SILVER 1-50: 1.25X TO 3X BASIC
*SILVER 51-100: 2X TO 5X BASIC
SILVER 1-50 PRINT RUN 50 #'d SETS
SILVER 51-100 PRINT RUN 25 #'d SETS
*FRAME BLK: 2X TO 5X BASIC
FRAME BLK PRINT RUN 25 #'d SETS
FRAME BLK PLAT. PRINT RUN 1 #'d SET
NO FRAME BLK PLAT.PRICING AVAIL.
*FRAME BLUE: 1X TO 2.5X BASIC
FRAME BLUE PRINT RUN 100 #'d SETS

FRAME BLUE PLAT.PRINT RUN 1 #'d SET
NO FRAME BLUE PLAT.PRICING AVAIL.
*FRAME GRN: 1.25X TO 3X BASIC
FRAME GRN PRINT RUN 50 #'d SETS
FRAME GRN PLAT.PRINT RUN 1 #'d SET
NO FRAME GRN PLAT.PRICING AVAIL.
*FRAME RED: .6X TO 1.5X BASIC
FRAME RED STATED ODDS 1:18
FRAME RED PLAT.PRINT RUN 1 #'d SET
NO FRAME RED PLAT.PRICING AVAIL.
OVERALL INSERT ODDS 10 PER SER.1 BOX
OVERALL INSERT ODDS 12 PER SER.2 BOX
1 Phil Niekro .75 2.00
2 Brooks Robinson .75 2.00
3 Jim Palmer .75 2.00
4 Carl Yastrzemski 2.00 5.00
5 Ted Williams 2.00 5.00
6 Duke Snider .75 2.00
7 Burleigh Grimes .75 2.00
8 Don Sutton .75 2.00
9 Nolan Ryan 3.00 8.00
10 Fergie Jenkins .75 2.00
11 Carlton Fisk .75 2.00
12 Tom Seaver .75 2.00
13 Bob Feller .75 2.00
14 Nolan Ryan 3.00 8.00
15 George Brett 2.50 6.00
16 Warren Spahn .75 2.00
17 Paul Molitor .75 2.00
18 Rod Carew .75 2.00
19 Harmon Killebrew 1.25 3.00
20 Monte Irvin .75 2.00
21 Gary Carter .75 2.00
22 Phil Rizzuto .75 2.00
23 Babe Ruth 3.00 8.00
24 Reggie Jackson .75 2.00
25 Mike Schmidt 2.50 6.00
26 Roberto Clemente 2.50 6.00
27 Juan Marichal .75 2.00
28 Willie McCovey .75 2.00
29 Stan Musial 1.50 4.00
30 Ozzie Smith 2.00 5.00
31 Dennis Eckersley .75 2.00
32 Phil Niekro .75 2.00
33 Jim Palmer .75 2.00
34 Carl Yastrzemski 2.00 5.00
35 Duke Snider .75 2.00
36 Don Sutton .75 2.00
37 Nolan Ryan 3.00 8.00
38 Carlton Fisk .75 2.00
39 Tom Seaver .75 2.00
40 Bob Feller .75 2.00
41 Nolan Ryan 3.00 8.00
42 George Brett 2.50 6.00
43 Harmon Killebrew 1.25 3.00
44 Gary Carter .75 2.00
45 Mike Schmidt 2.50 6.00
46 Stan Musial 1.50 4.00
47 Ozzie Smith 2.00 5.00
48 Dennis Eckersley .75 2.00
49 Fergie Jenkins .75 2.00
50 Brooks Robinson .75 2.00
51 Eddie Murray 1.25 3.00
52 Frank Robinson .75 2.00
53 Carlton Fisk .75 2.00
54 Ted Williams 2.00 5.00
55 Rod Carew .75 2.00
56 Ernie Banks 1.25 3.00
57 Luis Aparicio .75 2.00
58 Johnny Bench 1.25 3.00
59 Al Kaline 1.25 3.00
60 George Kell .75 2.00
61 Robin Yount 1.25 3.00
62 Nolan Ryan 3.00 8.00
63 Whitey Ford .75 2.00
64 Reggie Jackson .75 2.00
65 Babe Ruth 3.00 8.00
66 Rollie Fingers .75 2.00
67 Steve Carlton .75 2.00
68 Robin Roberts .75 2.00
69 Ralph Kiner .75 2.00
70 Willie Stargell .75 2.00
71 Roberto Clemente 2.50 6.00
72 Gaylord Perry .75 2.00
73 Bob Gibson .75 2.00
74 Lou Brock .75 2.00
75 Frankie Frisch .75 2.00
76 Eddie Murray 1.25 3.00
77 Frank Robinson .75 2.00
78 Carlton Fisk .75 2.00
79 Ted Williams 2.00 5.00
80 Rod Carew .75 2.00
81 Ernie Banks 1.25 3.00
82 Luis Aparicio .75 2.00
83 Johnny Bench 1.25 3.00
84 Al Kaline 1.25 3.00
85 Willie Mays 2.50 6.00
86 Robin Yount 1.25 3.00
87 Nolan Ryan 3.00 8.00
88 Whitey Ford .75 2.00
89 Reggie Jackson .75 2.00
90 Babe Ruth 3.00 8.00
91 Rollie Fingers .75 2.00
92 Steve Carlton .75 2.00
93 Wade Boggs Yanks .75 2.00
94 Wade Boggs Sox .75 2.00
95 Willie Stargell .75 2.00
96 Roberto Clemente 2.50 6.00
97 Gaylord Perry .75 2.00
98 Bob Gibson .75 2.00
99 Lou Brock .75 2.00
100 Frankie Frisch .75 2.00

2005 Diamond Kings HOF Heroes Materials Bronze

OVERALL AU-GU ODDS 1:6 PACKS
PRINT RUNS B/WN 1-100 COPIES PER
NO PRICING ON QTY OF 10 OR LESS
1 Phil Niekro Bat-Jsy/100 4.00 10.00
2 B.Robinson Bat-Jsy/100 5.00 12.00
3 Jim Palmer Jsy-Pants/100 4.00 10.00
4 C.Yastrzemski Bat-Pants/50 10.00 25.00
5 Ted Williams Bat-Jsy/1
6 Duke Snider Jsy-Pants/50 6.00 15.00
7 B.Grimes Pants-Pants/25 25.00 60.00
8 Don Sutton Jsy-Jsy/100 4.00 10.00
9 Nolan Ryan Bat-Jkt/50 12.50 30.00
10 F.Jenkins Pants-Pants/100 4.00 10.00
11 Carlton Fisk Bat-Jkt/100 5.00 12.00
12 Tom Seaver Jsy-Pants/50 6.00 15.00
13 Bob Feller Pants-Pants/25 8.00 20.00
14 Nolan Ryan Bat-Jsy/50 12.50 30.00
15 George Brett Bat-Bat/25 15.00 40.00
16 W.Spahn Jsy-Pants/25 10.00 25.00
17 Paul Molitor Bat-Jsy/100 4.00 10.00
18 Rod Carew Bat-Jsy/50 6.00 15.00
19 H.Killebrew Bat-Jsy/50 8.00 20.00
21 Gary Carter Bat-Jsy/100 4.00 10.00
23 Babe Ruth Bat-Pants/25 200.00 350.00
24 R.Jackson Bat-Jkt/100 6.00 15.00
25 Mike Schmidt Bat-Jkt/50 12.50 30.00
26 R.Clemente Bat-Bat/50 25.00 60.00
27 J.Marichal Pants-Pants/25 6.00 15.00
28 W.McCovey Jsy-Pants/100 5.00 12.00
29 Stan Musial Bat-Bat/25 12.50 30.00
30 Ozzie Smith Bat-Pants/100 8.00 20.00
31 D.Eckersley Jsy-Jsy/100 4.00 10.00
32 Phil Niekro Bat-Jsy/100 4.00 10.00
33 Jim Palmer Jsy-Pants/25 6.00 15.00
34 C.Yaz Bat-Pants/25 12.50 30.00
35 Duke Snider Jsy-Pants/25 8.00 20.00
36 Don Sutton Jsy-Jsy/100 4.00 10.00
37 Nolan Ryan Bat-Jkt/25 15.00 40.00
38 Carlton Fisk Bat-Jkt/100 5.00 12.00
39 Tom Seaver Bat-Jsy/25 8.00 20.00
40 Bob Feller Pants-Pants/25 8.00 20.00
41 Nolan Ryan Bat-Jkt/25 15.00 40.00
42 George Brett Bat-Bat/25 15.00 40.00
43 H.Killebrew Bat-Jsy/25 10.00 25.00
44 Gary Carter Bat-Jsy/100 4.00 10.00
45 Mike Schmidt Bat-Jsy/25 15.00 40.00
46 Stan Musial Bat-Bat/25 12.50 30.00
47 Ozzie Smith Bat-Pants/100 8.00 20.00
48 D.Eckersley Jsy-Jsy/100 4.00 10.00
49 F.Jenkins Pants-Pants/25 6.00 15.00
50 B.Robinson Bat-Jsy/25 8.00 20.00
51 Eddie Murray Bat-Pants/50 8.00 20.00
52 Frank Robinson Bat-Bat/50 5.00 12.00
53 Carlton Fisk Bat-Bat/50 5.00 12.00
54 Ted Williams Bat-Bat/25 25.00 60.00
55 Rod Carew Bat-Jkt/Jsy/50 6.00 15.00
56 Ernie Banks Bat-Pants/50 8.00 20.00
57 Luis Aparicio Bat-Bat/50 5.00 12.00
58 Johnny Bench Bat-Jsy/25 8.00 20.00
59 Al Kaline Bat-Bat/25 10.00 25.00
61 Robin Yount Bat-Jsy/25 8.00 20.00
62 Nolan Ryan Bat-Jsy/25 15.00 40.00
63 Whitey Ford Jsy-Jsy/25 10.00 25.00
64 R.Jackson Bat-Pants/50 6.00 15.00
65 Babe Ruth Bat-Pants/25 200.00 350.00
66 Rollie Fingers Jsy-Jsy/50 5.00 12.00
67 Steve Carlton Bat-Jsy/50 5.00 12.00
70 Willie Stargell Bat-Jsy/50 6.00 15.00
71 R.Clemente Bat-Bat/25 30.00 80.00
72 Gaylord Perry Jsy-Jsy/50 5.00 12.00
73 Bob Gibson Jsy-Jsy/25 8.00 20.00
74 Lou Brock Bat-Jsy/50 6.00 15.00
75 Frankie Frisch Jkt-Jkt/50 8.00 20.00
76 Eddie Murray Bat-Bat/50 8.00 20.00
77 Frank Robinson Bat-Bat/50 5.00 12.00
78 Carlton Fisk Bat-Bat/50 5.00 12.00
79 Ted Williams Bat-Bat/25 30.00 80.00
80 Rod Carew Bat-Jkt/50 6.00 15.00
81 Ernie Banks Bat-Jsy/25 10.00 25.00
82 Luis Aparicio Bat-Bat/50 5.00 12.00
83 Johnny Bench Bat-Jsy/50 8.00 20.00
84 Al Kaline Bat-Bat/10
86 Robin Yount Bat-Jsy/50 8.00 20.00
87 Nolan Ryan Bat-Jsy/25 15.00 40.00
88 Whitey Ford Jsy-Jsy/25 10.00 25.00
89 R.Jackson Pants-Pants/50 6.00 15.00
90 Babe Ruth Bat-Pants/10
91 Rollie Fingers Jsy-Jsy/50 5.00 12.00
92 Steve Carlton Bat-Jsy/50 5.00 12.00
95 Willie Stargell Jsy-Jsy/50 6.00 15.00
96 Roberto Clemente Bat-Bat/10
97 Gaylord Perry Jsy-Jsy/50 5.00 12.00
98 Bob Gibson Jsy-Jsy/10
99 Lou Brock Bat-Jsy/50 6.00 15.00
100 Frankie Frisch Jkt-Jkt/50 8.00 20.00

2005 Diamond Kings HOF Heroes Materials Gold

*GOLD p/r 25: .6X TO 1.5X BRZ p/r 100
*GOLD p/r 25: .5X TO 1.2X BRZ p/r 50
*GOLD p/r 25: .4X TO 1X BRZ p/r 25
OVERALL AU-GU ODDS 1:6
PRINT RUNS B/WN 1-25 COPIES PER
NO PRICING ON QTY OF 10 OR LESS
96 R.Clemente Bat-Bat/25 30.00 80.00
98 Bob Gibson Jsy-Jsy/25 8.00 20.00

2005 Diamond Kings HOF Heroes Materials Platinum

OVERALL AU-GU ODDS 1:6
STATED PRINT RUN 1 SERIAL #'d SET
NO PRICING DUE TO SCARCITY

2005 Diamond Kings HOF Heroes Materials Silver

*SILV p/r 50: .5X TO 1.2X BRZ p/r 100
*SILV p/r 50: .4X TO 1X BRZ p/r 50
*SILV p/r 50: .3X TO .8X BRZ p/r 25
*SILV p/r 25: .6X TO 1.5X BRZ p/r 100
*SILV p/r 25: .5X TO 1.2X BRZ p/r 50
*SILV p/r 25: .4X TO 1X BRZ p/r 25
OVERALL AU-GU ODDS 1:6
PRINT RUNS B/WN 10-50 COPIES PER
NO PRICING ON QTY OF 10
65 Babe Ruth Pants-Pants/25 200.00 350.00

2005 Diamond Kings HOF Heroes Materials Framed Black

PRINT RUNS B/WN 1-10 COPIES PER
PLATINUM PRINT RUN 1 SERIAL #'d SET
OVERALL AU-GU ODDS 1:6
NO PRICING DUE TO SCARCITY

2005 Diamond Kings HOF Heroes Materials Framed Blue

*BLUE p/r 25: .6X TO 1.5X BRZ p/r 100
*BLUE p/r 25: .5X TO 1.2X BRZ p/r 50
*BLUE p/r 25: .4X TO 1X BRZ p/r 25
PRINT RUNS B/WN 1-25 COPIES PER
NO PRICING ON QTY OF 10 OR LESS
PLATINUM PRINT RUN 1 SERIAL #'d SET
NO PLAT.PRICING DUE TO SCARCITY
OVERALL AU-GU ODDS 1:6
65 Babe Ruth Pants-Pants/25 200.00 350.00

2005 Diamond Kings HOF Heroes Materials Framed Green

PRINT RUNS B/WN 1-10 COPIES PER
PLATINUM PRINT RUN 1 SERIAL #'d SET
OVERALL AU-GU ODDS 1:6
NO PRICING DUE TO SCARCITY

2005 Diamond Kings HOF Heroes Materials Framed Red

*RED p/r 50: .5X TO 1.2X BRZ p/r 100
*RED p/r 50: .4X TO 1X BRZ p/r 50
*RED p/r 50: .3X TO .8X BRZ p/r 25
*RED p/r 25: .6X TO 1.5X BRZ p/r 100
*RED p/r 25: .5X TO 1.2X BRZ p/r 50
*RED p/r 25: .4X TO 1X BRZ p/r 25
PRINT RUNS B/WN 5-50 COPIES PER
NO PRICING ON QTY OF 10 OR LESS
PLATINUM PRINT RUN 1 SERIAL #'d SET
NO PLATINUM PRICING DUE TO SCARCITY
OVERALL AU-GU ODDS 1:6
5 Ted Williams Bat-Jsy/50 25.00 60.00
65 Babe Ruth Pants-Pants/50 175.00 300.00
90 Babe Ruth Bat-Pants/50 175.00 300.00
96 R.Clemente Bat-Bat/50 25.00 60.00

2005 Diamond Kings HOF Heroes Signature Bronze

OVERALL AU-GU ODDS 1:6
PRINT RUNS B/WN 1-25 COPIES PER
NO PRICING ON QTY OF 10 OR LESS
1 Phil Niekro/5
2 Brooks Robinson/5
3 Jim Palmer/5
4 Carl Yastrzemski/1
6 Duke Snider/1
8 Don Sutton/5
9 Nolan Ryan/1
10 Fergie Jenkins/10
11 Carlton Fisk/1
12 Tom Seaver/1
13 Bob Feller/25 15.00 40.00
14 Nolan Ryan/1
15 George Brett/1
17 Paul Molitor/1
18 Rod Carew/1
19 Harmon Killebrew/5
20 Monte Irvin/5
21 Gary Carter/5
22 Phil Rizzuto/5
24 Reggie Jackson/1
25 Mike Schmidt/1
27 Juan Marichal/5
28 Willie McCovey/1
29 Stan Musial/1
30 Ozzie Smith/1
31 Dennis Eckersley/5
32 Phil Niekro/5
33 Jim Palmer/5
34 Carl Yastrzemski/1
35 Duke Snider/1
36 Don Sutton/5
37 Nolan Ryan/1
38 Carlton Fisk/1
39 Tom Seaver/1
40 Bob Feller/25 15.00 40.00
41 Nolan Ryan/1
42 George Brett/1
43 Harmon Killebrew/5
44 Gary Carter/5
45 Mike Schmidt/1
46 Stan Musial/1
47 Ozzie Smith/1
48 Dennis Eckersley/5
49 Fergie Jenkins/10
50 Brooks Robinson/5
52 Frank Robinson/25 15.00 40.00
53 Carlton Fisk/10
55 Rod Carew/10
56 Ernie Banks/5
57 Luis Aparicio/25 10.00 25.00
58 Johnny Bench/10
59 Al Kaline/25 20.00 50.00
60 George Kell/25 10.00 25.00
61 Robin Yount/5
62 Nolan Ryan/5
63 Whitey Ford/5
64 Reggie Jackson/5
66 Rollie Fingers/25 10.00 25.00
67 Steve Carlton/25 10.00 25.00
68 Robin Roberts/25 10.00 25.00
69 Ralph Kiner/25 20.00 50.00
72 Gaylord Perry/25 10.00 25.00
73 Bob Gibson/5
74 Lou Brock/25 15.00 40.00
77 Frank Robinson/10
78 Carlton Fisk/5
80 Rod Carew/10
81 Ernie Banks/5
82 Luis Aparicio/25 10.00 25.00
83 Johnny Bench/5
84 Al Kaline/25 20.00 50.00
85 Willie Mays/25
86 Robin Yount/5
87 Nolan Ryan/5
88 Whitey Ford/5
89 Reggie Jackson/5
91 Rollie Fingers/25 10.00 25.00
92 Steve Carlton/25 10.00 25.00
93 Wade Boggs Yanks/25 15.00 40.00
94 Wade Boggs Sox/25 15.00 40.00
97 Gaylord Perry/25 10.00 25.00
98 Bob Gibson/5
99 Lou Brock/25 15.00 40.00

2005 Diamond Kings HOF Heroes Signature Gold

OVERALL AU-GU ODDS 1:6
PRINT RUNS B/WN 1-10 COPIES PER
NO PRICING DUE TO SCARCITY

2005 Diamond Kings HOF Heroes Signature Platinum

OVERALL AU-GU ODDS 1:6
STATED PRINT RUN 1 SERIAL #'d SET
NO PRICING DUE TO SCARCITY

2005 Diamond Kings HOF Heroes Signature Silver

*SILV p/r 25: .4X TO 1X BRZ p/r 25
OVERALL AU-GU ODDS 1:6
PRINT RUNS B/WN 1-25 COPIES PER
NO PRICING ON QTY OF 10 OR LESS
85 Willie Mays/25

2005 Diamond Kings HOF Heroes Signature Framed Black

STATED PRINT RUN 1 SERIAL #'d SET
PLATINUM PRINT RUN 1 SERIAL #'d SET
OVERALL AU-GU ODDS 1:6
NO PRICING DUE TO SCARCITY

2005 Diamond Kings HOF Heroes Signature Framed Blue

PRINT RUNS B/WN 1-10 COPIES PER
PLATINUM PRINT RUN 1 SERIAL #'d SET
OVERALL AU-GU ODDS 1:6
NO PRICING DUE TO SCARCITY

2005 Diamond Kings HOF Heroes Signature Framed Green

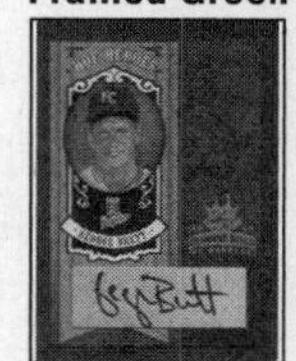

PRINT RUNS B/WN 1-10 COPIES PER
PLATINUM PRINT RUN 1 SERIAL #'d SET
OVERALL AU-GU ODDS 1:6
NO PRICING DUE TO SCARCITY

2005 Diamond Kings HOF Heroes Signature Framed Red

*SILV p/r 25: .4X TO 1X BRZ p/r 25
PRINT RUNS B/WN 1-25 COPIES PER
NO PRICING ON QTY OF 10 OR LESS
PLATINUM PRINT RUN 1 SERIAL #'d SET
NO PLAT.PRICING DUE TO SCARCITY
OVERALL AU-GU ODDS 1:6
85 Willie Mays/25

2005 Diamond Kings HOF Heroes Signature Materials Bronze

OVERALL AU-GU ODDS 1:6
PRINT RUNS B/WN 5-50 COPIES PER
NO PRICING ON QTY OF 10 OR LESS
2 B.Robinson Bat-Jsy/25 20.00 50.00
3 Jim Palmer Jsy-Jsy/25 12.50 30.00
4 C.Yastrzemski Bat-Pants/5
6 Duke Snider Jsy-Pants/25 20.00 50.00
8 Don Sutton Jsy-Jsy/25 12.50 30.00
9 Nolan Ryan Jkt-Jsy/10
10 F.Jenkins Pants-Pants/25 12.50 30.00
11 Carlton Fisk Bat-Jkt/10
12 Tom Seaver Bat-Jsy/10
13 Bob Feller Pants-Pants/50 15.00 40.00
14 Nolan Ryan Jkt-Jsy/10
15 George Brett Bat-Bat/5
17 Paul Molitor Bat-Jsy/10
18 Rod Carew Bat-Jsy/50 15.00 40.00
19 H.Killebrew Bat-Jsy/25 30.00 60.00
21 Gary Carter Bat-Jsy/50 10.00 25.00
24 Reggie Jackson Bat-Jkt/10
25 Mike Schmidt Bat-Jsy/10
27 J.Marichal Pants-Pants/25 12.50 30.00
28 W.McCovey Jsy-Pants/25 20.00 50.00
29 Stan Musial Bat-Bat/25 50.00 100.00
30 Ozzie Smith Bat-Pants/25 30.00 60.00
31 D.Eckersley Jsy-Jsy/25 12.50 30.00
32 Phil Niekro Bat-Jsy/25 12.50 30.00
33 Jim Palmer Jsy-Pants/25 12.50 30.00
34 C.Yastrzemski Bat-Pants/5
35 Duke Snider Jsy-Pants/25 20.00 50.00
36 Don Sutton Jsy-Jsy/25 12.50 30.00
37 Nolan Ryan Bat-Jkt/10
38 Carlton Fisk Bat-Jkt/10
39 Tom Seaver Jsy-Pants/10
40 Bob Feller Pants-Pants/50 15.00 40.00
41 Nolan Ryan Jsy-Jsy/10
42 George Brett Bat-Bat/5
43 H.Killebrew Bat-Jsy/50 20.00 50.00
44 Gary Carter Bat-Jsy/50 10.00 25.00
45 Mike Schmidt Bat-Jkt/5
46 Stan Musial Bat-Bat/10
47 Ozzie Smith Bat-Pants/25 30.00 60.00
48 D.Eckersley Jsy-Jsy/50 10.00 25.00
49 F.Jenkins Pants-Pants/25 12.50 30.00
50 B.Robinson Bat-Jsy/25 20.00 50.00
53 Carlton Fisk Bat-Jkt/5
55 Rod Carew Bat-Jkt/10
58 Johnny Bench Bat-Jsy/10
61 Robin Yount Bat-Jsy/25 30.00 60.00
62 Nolan Ryan Bat-Jsy/5
63 Whitey Ford Jsy-Jsy/5
64 Reggie Jackson Bat-Pants/5
66 Rollie Fingers Jsy-Jsy/50 10.00 25.00
67 Steve Carlton Bat-Jsy/10
72 Gaylord Perry Jsy-Jsy/50 10.00 25.00
74 Lou Brock Jsy-Jsy/50 15.00 40.00
77 Frank Robinson Bat-Bat/10
78 Carlton Fisk Bat-Jsy/5
80 Rod Carew Bat-Jsy/50 15.00 40.00
83 Johnny Bench Bat-Jsy/5
86 Robin Yount Bat-Jsy/10
87 Nolan Ryan Bat-Jsy/10
88 Whitey Ford Jsy-Jsy/5
89 Reggie Jackson Bat-Pants/5
91 Rollie Fingers Jsy-Jsy/10
92 Steve Carlton Bat-Jsy/10
99 Lou Brock Bat-Jsy/25 20.00 50.00

2005 Diamond Kings HOF Heroes Signature Materials Gold

*GOLD: p/r 25: .5X TO 1.2X BRZ p/r 50
*GOLD: p/r 25: .4X TO 1X BRZ p/r 25
OVERALL AU-GU ODDS 1:6
PRINT RUNS B/WN 5-25 COPIES PER
NO PRICING ON QTY OF 10 OR LESS
91 Rollie Fingers Jsy-Jsy/25 12.50 30.00

2005 Diamond Kings HOF Heroes Signature Materials Platinum

OVERALL AU-GU ODDS 1:6
STATED PRINT RUN 1 SERIAL #'d SET
NO PRICING DUE TO SCARCITY

2005 Diamond Kings HOF Heroes Signature Materials Silver

*SILV p/r 50: .4X TO 1X BRZ p/r 50
*SILV p/r 25: .5X TO 1.2X BRZ p/r 50
*SILV p/r 25: .4X TO 1X BRZ p/r 25
OVERALL AU-GU ODDS 1:6
PRINT RUNS B/WN 5-50 COPIES PER
NO PRICING ON QTY OF 10 OR LESS
91 Rollie Fingers Jsy-Jsy/50 10.00 25.00

2005 Diamond Kings HOF Heroes Signature Materials Framed Black

PRINT RUNS B/WN 5-10 COPIES PER
PLATINUM PRINT RUN 1 SERIAL #'d SET
OVERALL AU-GU ODDS 1:6
NO PRICING DUE TO SCARCITY

2005 Diamond Kings HOF Heroes Signature Materials Framed Blue

*BLUE p/r 25: .5X TO 1.2X BRZ p/r 50
*BLUE p/r 25: .4X TO 1X BRZ p/r 25
PRINT RUNS B/WN 5-25 COPIES PER
NO PRICING ON QTY OF 10 OR LESS
PLATINUM PRINT RUN 1 SERIAL #'d SET
NO PLAT.PRICING DUE TO SCARCITY
OVERALL AU-GU ODDS 1:6
53 Carlton Fisk Bat-Jsy/25 12.50 30.00
55 Rod Carew Bat-Jkt/25 20.00 50.00
58 Johnny Bench Bat-Jsy/25 30.00 60.00
62 Nolan Ryan Bat-Jsy/25 60.00 120.00
63 Whitey Ford Jsy-Jsy/25 20.00 50.00
64 R.Jackson Bat-Pants/25 30.00 60.00
67 Steve Carlton Bat-Jsy/25 12.50 30.00
77 Frank Robinson Bat-Bat/25 20.00 50.00
78 Carlton Fisk Bat-Bat/25 12.50 30.00
83 Johnny Bench Bat-Jsy/25 30.00 60.00
86 Robin Yount Bat-Jsy/25 30.00 60.00
87 Nolan Ryan Bat-Jsy/25 60.00 120.00
88 Whitey Ford Jsy-Jsy/25 20.00 50.00
89 R.Jackson Bat-Pants/25 30.00 60.00
91 Rollie Fingers Jsy-Jsy/25 12.50 30.00
92 Steve Carlton Jsy-Pants/25 12.50 30.00

2005 Diamond Kings HOF Heroes Signature Materials Framed Green

PRINT RUNS B/WN 5-10 COPIES PER
PLATINUM PRINT RUN 1 SERIAL #'d SET
OVERALL AU-GU ODDS 1:6
NO PRICING DUE TO SCARCITY

2005 Diamond Kings HOF Heroes Signature Materials Framed Red

*RED p/r 50: .4X TO 1X BRZ p/r 50
*RED p/r 25: .5X TO 1.2X BRZ p/r 50
*RED p/r 25: .4X TO 1X BRZ p/r 25
PRINT RUNS B/WN 5-50 COPIES PER
NO PRICING ON QTY OF 10 OR LESS
PLATINUM PRINT RUN 1 SERIAL #'d SET
NO PLAT.PRICING DUE TO SCARCITY
OVERALL AU-GU ODDS 1:6
91 Rollie Fingers Jsy-Jsy/50 10.00 25.00

2005 Diamond Kings HOF Sluggers

RANDOM INSERTS IN SER.2 PACKS
1 Duke Snider 1.25 3.00
2 Eddie Murray 1.25 3.00
3 Frank Robinson .75 2.00
4 George Brett 2.50 6.00
5 Harmon Killebrew 1.25 3.00
6 Mike Schmidt 2.50 6.00
7 Reggie Jackson 1.25 3.00
8 Roberto Clemente 3.00 8.00
9 Stan Musial 2.00 5.00
10 Willie Mays 2.50 6.00

2005 Diamond Kings HOF Sluggers Bat

*BAT p/r 50: .4X TO 1X JSY p/r 25
*BAT p/r 50: .3X TO .8X JSY p/r 25
OVERALL AU-GU ODDS 1:6
PRINT RUNS B/WN 10-50 COPIES PER
NO PRICING ON QTY OF 10
3 Frank Robinson/50 4.00 10.00
4 George Brett/50 10.00 25.00
8 Roberto Clemente/50 20.00 50.00

2005 Diamond Kings HOF Sluggers Combos

*COMBO p/r 50: .5X TO 1.2X JSY p/r 50
*COMBO p/r 25: .6X TO 1.5X JSY p/r 50
OVERALL AU-GU ODDS 1:6
PRINT RUNS B/WN 5-50 COPIES PER
NO PRICING ON QTY OF 10 OR LESS
4 George Brett Bat-Hat/50 12.50 30.00

2005 Diamond Kings HOF Sluggers Jersey

OVERALL AU-GU ODDS 1:6
PRINT RUNS B/WN 5-50 COPIES PER
NO PRICING ON QTY OF 5
1 Duke Snider Pants/25 6.00 15.00
2 Eddie Murray/50 6.00 15.00
5 Harmon Killebrew/25 8.00 20.00
6 Mike Schmidt/50 10.00 25.00
7 Reggie Jackson Pants/50 5.00 12.00
8 Roberto Clemente/5
9 Stan Musial Pants/25 12.50 30.00
10 Willie Mays Pants/50 12.50 30.00

2005 Diamond Kings Masters of the Game

RANDOM INSERTS IN SER.2 PACKS
1 Albert Pujols 2.50 6.00
2 Cal Ripken 4.00 10.00
3 Don Mattingly 2.50 6.00
4 Greg Maddux 2.00 5.00
5 Jim Thorpe 2.00 5.00
6 Nolan Ryan 3.00 8.00
7 Randy Johnson 1.25 3.00
8 Roberto Clemente 3.00 8.00
9 Roger Clemens 2.00 5.00
10 Willie Mays 2.50 6.00

2005 Diamond Kings Masters of the Game Bat

*BAT p/r 100: .3X TO .8X JSY p/r 50
*BAT p/r 50: .3X TO .8X JSY p/r 25
*BAT p/r 25: .4X TO 1X JSY p/r 25
OVERALL AU-GU ODDS 1:6
PRINT RUNS B/WN 25-100 COPIES PER
8 Roberto Clemente/50 20.00 50.00

2005 Diamond Kings Masters of the Game Combos

*COMBO p/r 50: .5X TO 1.2X JSY p/r 50
*COMBO p/r 25: .6X TO 1.5X JSY p/r 25
OVERALL AU-GU ODDS 1:6
PRINT RUNS B/WN 25-50 COPIES PER

2005 Diamond Kings Masters of the Game Jersey

OVERALL AU-GU ODDS 1:6
PRINT RUNS B/WN 25-50 COPIES PER
1 Albert Pujols/50 10.00 25.00
2 Cal Ripken/50 15.00 40.00
3 Don Mattingly/25 12.50 30.00
4 Greg Maddux/50 6.00 15.00
5 Jim Thorpe/25 125.00 200.00
6 Nolan Ryan/50 10.00 25.00
7 Randy Johnson/25 6.00 15.00
9 Roger Clemens/50 6.00 15.00
10 Willie Mays Pants/25 15.00 40.00

2005 Diamond Kings Recollection Autographs Gold

RANDOM INSERTS IN PACKS
STATED PRINT RUN 1 SERIAL #'d SET
NO PRICING DUE TO SCARCITY

2005 Diamond Kings Recollection Autographs Platinum

RANDOM INSERTS IN PACKS
STATED PRINT RUN 1 SERIAL #'d SET
NO PRICING DUE TO SCARCITY

2005 Diamond Kings Recollection Autographs Silver

RANDOM INSERTS IN PACKS
STATED PRINT RUN 1 SERIAL #'d SET
NO PRICING DUE TO SCARCITY

2005 Diamond Kings Team Timeline

1-25 STATED ODDS 1:21 SER.1 PACKS
26-30 RANDOM INSERTS IN SER.2 PACKS
1 Albert Pujols 3.00 8.00
Scott Rolen
2 Roger Clemens 2.50 6.00
Andy Pettitte
3 Tim Hudson 1.25 3.00
Mark Mulder
4 Hank Blalock 1.50 4.00
Mark Teixeira
5 Miguel Cabrera 1.50 4.00
Mike Lowell
6 Greg Maddux 2.50 6.00
Sammy Sosa
7 Miguel Tejada 5.00 12.00
Cal Ripken
8 Vladimir Guerrero 1.50 4.00
Reggie Jackson
9 Mike Schmidt 3.00 8.00
Jim Thome
10 Chipper Jones 2.50 6.00
Greg Maddux
11 George Brett 3.00 8.00
Ken Harvey
12 Don Mattingly 3.00 8.00
Hideki Matsui
13 Torii Hunter 1.50 4.00
Johan Santana
14 Carlos Delgado 1.25 3.00
Vernon Wells
15 Todd Helton 1.50 4.00
Larry Walker
16 Duke Snider 1.50 4.00
Adrian Beltre
17 Al Kaline 1.50 4.00
Ivan Rodriguez
18 Rafael Palmeiro 1.50 4.00
Eddie Murray
19 Manny Ramirez 2.50 6.00
Carl Yastrzemski
20 Ralph Kiner 1.25 3.00
Jason Bay
21 Johnny Bench 1.50 4.00
Adam Dunn
22 Robin Yount 1.50 4.00
Lyle Overbay
23 Nolan Ryan 4.00 10.00
Randy Johnson
24 Gary Carter 1.50 4.00
Mike Piazza
25 Carlton Fisk 1.50 4.00
Frank Thomas
26 Nolan Ryan 4.00 10.00
Mike Piazza
27 Roger Clemens 2.50 6.00
Jeff Bagwell
28 Cal Ripken 5.00 12.00
Sammy Sosa
29 Willie Mays 3.00 8.00
Jim Thorpe
30 Albert Pujols 3.00 8.00
Stan Musial

2005 Diamond Kings Team Timeline Materials Bat

*BAT p/r 75-100: .4X TO 1X JSY p/r 100
*BAT p/r 50: .5X TO 1.2X JSY p/r 100
*BAT p/r 50: .3X TO .8X JSY p/r 25
*BAT p/r 25: .6X TO 1.5X JSY p/r 100
*BAT p/r 25: .5X TO 1.2X JSY p/r 50
*BAT p/r 25: .4X TO 1X JSY p/r 25
OVERALL AU-GU ODDS 1:6
PRINT RUNS B/WN 25-100 COPIES PER
5 Miguel Cabrera 6.00 15.00
Mike Lowell/100
17 Al Kaline 12.50 30.00
Ivan Rodriguez/25
28 Cal Ripken 25.00 60.00
Sammy Sosa/50

2005 Diamond Kings Team Timeline Materials Jersey

PRINT RUNS B/WN 25-100 COPIES PER
PRIME PRINT RUN 1 SERIAL #'d SET

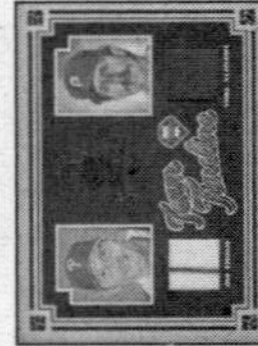

NO PRIME PRICING DUE TO SCARCITY
OVERALL AU-GU ODDS 1:6
1 Albert Pujols 12.50 30.00
Scott Rolen/100
2 Roger Clemens 10.00 25.00
Andy Pettitte/100
3 Tim Hudson 5.00 12.00
Mark Mulder/100
4 Hank Blalock 6.00 15.00
Mark Teixeira/100
7 Miguel Tejada 20.00 50.00
Cal Ripken/100
8 Vladimir Guerrero 8.00 20.00
Reggie Jackson/100
9 Mike Schmidt Jkt 15.00 40.00
Jim Thome/100
10 Chipper Jones 15.00 40.00
Greg Maddux/100
12 Don Mattingly Jkt 20.00 50.00
Hideki Matsui/100
14 Carlos Delgado 5.00 12.00
Vernon Wells/100
15 Todd Helton 6.00 15.00
Larry Walker/100
16 Duke Snider 5.00 12.00
Adrian Beltre/100
18 Rafael Palmeiro 8.00 20.00
Eddie Murray/100
19 Manny Ramirez 15.00 40.00
Carl Yastrzemski/100
21 Johnny Bench 8.00 20.00
Adam Dunn/100
22 Robin Yount 8.00 20.00
Lyle Overbay/100
23 Nolan Ryan 15.00 40.00
Randy Johnson/100
24 Gary Carter 8.00 20.00
Mike Piazza/100
25 Carlton Fisk 8.00 20.00
Frank Thomas/100
26 Nolan Ryan 15.00 40.00
Mike Piazza/50
27 Roger Clemens 10.00 25.00
Jeff Bagwell/25
29 Willie Mays 125.00 200.00
Jim Thorpe/25
30 Albert Pujols 25.00 60.00
Stan Musial/25

2005 Diamond Kings Timeline

1-25 STATED ODDS 1:21 SER.1 PACKS
26-30 RANDOM INSERTS IN SER.2 PACKS
1 Roger Clemens Sox-Yanks 2.50 6.00
2 Nolan Ryan Angels-Astros 4.00 10.00
3 Carlos Beltran Royals-Astros 1.25 3.00
4 Ivan Rodriguez Rgr-M's 1.50 4.00
5 Jim Thome Indians-Phils 1.50 4.00
6 Mike Piazza Dgr-Mets 1.50 4.00
7 Miguel Tejada A's-O's 1.25 3.00
8 Rafael Palmeiro O's-Rgr 1.50 4.00
9 Greg Maddux Braves-Cubs 2.50 6.00
10 Tom Glavine Braves-Mets 1.50 4.00
11 Vlad Guerrero Expos-Angels 1.50 4.00
12 Curt Schilling D'backs-Sox 1.50 4.00
13 Mike Mussina O's-Yanks 1.50 4.00
14 Rickey Henderson A's-Dgr 1.50 4.00
15 Scott Rolen Phils-Cards 1.50 4.00
16 Alfonso Soriano Yanks-Rgr 1.50 4.00
17 Gary Sheffield Braves-Yanks 1.25 3.00
18 Carlton Fisk R.Sox-W.Sox 1.50 4.00
19 Aramis Ramirez Pirates-Cubs 1.25 3.00
20 Mark Grace Cubs-D'backs 1.50 4.00
21 Jason Giambi A's-Yanks 1.25 3.00
22 Juan Gonzalez Rgr-Royals 1.25 3.00
23 Brad Penny M's-Dgr 1.25 3.00
24 N.Garciaparra Sox-Cubs 1.50 4.00
25 Larry Walker Rockies-Cards 1.25 3.00
26 Curt Schilling Phils-D'backs 1.25 3.00
27 R.Jackson Angels-Yanks 1.50 4.00
28 Gary Carter Expos-Mets 1.25 3.00
29 Roger Clemens Sox-Astros 2.50 6.00
30 Nolan Ryan Mets-Astros 4.00 10.00

2005 Diamond Kings Timeline Materials Bat

*BAT p/r 100: .5X TO 1.2X JSY p/r 200
*BAT p/r 100: .4X TO 1X JSY p/r 100
*BAT p/r 50: .4X TO 1X JSY p/r 50
*BAT p/r 50: .3X TO .8X JSY p/r 25
*BAT p/r 25: .6X TO 1.5X JSY p/r 100
*BAT p/r 25: .5X TO 1.2X JSY p/r 50
OVERALL AU-GU ODDS 1:6
PRINT RUNS B/WN 25-100 COPIES PER
5 J.Thome Indians-Phils/25 10.00 25.00
10 T.Glavine Braves-Mets/100 6.00 15.00
17 G.Sheff Braves-Yanks/100 5.00 12.00
20 M.Grace Cubs-D'backs/100 6.00 15.00
25 L.Walk Rockies-Cards/100 5.00 12.00

2005 Diamond Kings Timeline Materials Jersey

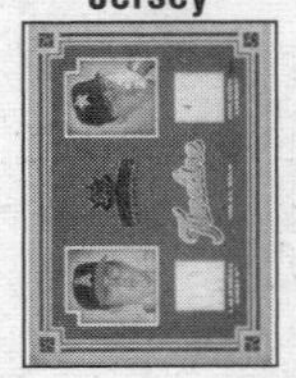

PRINT RUNS B/WN 25-200 COPIES PER
PRIME PRINT RUN 1 SERIAL #'d SET
NO PRIME PRICING DUE TO SCARCITY
OVERALL AU-GU ODDS 1:6
1 R.Clemens Sox-Yanks/50 12.50 30.00
2 N.Ryan Angels-Astros/50 25.00 60.00
3 C.Belt Royals-Astros/100 5.00 12.00
4 I.Rodriguez Rgr-M's/200 5.00 12.00
6 M.Piazza Dgr-Mets/100 8.00 20.00
7 M.Tejada A's-O's/100 5.00 12.00
8 R.Palmeiro O's-Rgr/100 6.00 15.00
9 G.Madd Braves-Cubs/50 12.50 30.00
11 V.Guer Expos-Angels/100 8.00 20.00
12 C.Schilling D'backs-Sox/100 6.00 15.00
13 M.Mussina O's-Yanks/100 6.00 15.00
14 R.Henderson A's-Dgr/100 10.00 25.00
15 S.Rolen Phils-Cards/100 6.00 15.00
16 A.Soriano Yanks-Rgr/50 6.00 15.00
18 C.Fisk R.Sox-W.Sox/100 6.00 15.00
19 A.Ramirez Pirates-Cubs/100 5.00 12.00
21 J.Giambi A's-Yanks/100 5.00 12.00
22 J.Gonzalez Rgr-Royals/100 5.00 12.00
26 C.Schill Phils-D'backs/50 6.00 15.00
27 R.Jack Ang-Yank Pants/50 10.00 25.00
28 G.Carter Expos-Mets/25 10.00 25.00
29 R.Clemens Sox-Astros/50 12.50 30.00
30 N.Ryan Mets-Astros/25 30.00 80.00

2005 Diamond Kings Hawaii

ISSUED AT 05 HAWAII TRADE CONFERENCE
STATED PRINT RUN 10 SERIAL #'d SETS
NO PRICING DUE TO SCARCITY

1934-36 Diamond Stars

The cards in this 108-card set measure approximately 2 3/8" by 2 7/8". The Diamond Stars set, produced by National Chicle from 1934-36, is also commonly known by its catalog designation, R327. The year of production can be determined by the statistics contained on the back of the card. There are 170 possible front/back combinations counting blue (B) and green (G) backs over all three years. The last twelve cards are repeat players and are quite scarce. The checklist below lists the year(s) and back color(s) for the cards. Cards 32 through 72 were issued only in 1935 with green ink on back. Cards 73 through 84 were issued three ways: 35B, 35G, and 36B. Card numbers 85 through 108 were issued only in 1936 with blue ink on back. The complete set price below refers to the set of all variations listed explicitly below. A blank-backed proof sheet of 12 additional (never-issued) cards was discovered in 1980.

COMPLETE SET (119) 9000.00 15000.00
COMMON CARD (1-31) 30.00 50.00
COMMON CARD (32-84) 35.00 60.00
COMMON CARD (85-96) 60.00 100.00
COMMON CARD (97-108) 125.00 200.00
WRAP.(1-CENT, BLUE) 200.00 250.00
WRAP.(1-CENT, YELLOW) 150.00 200.00
WRAP.(1-CENT, CLEAR) 150.00 200.00
1 Lefty Grove 450.00 750.00
34G, 35G
2A Al Simmons 90.00 150.00
34G, 35G
Sox on uniform
2B Al Simmons 125.00 200.00
36B
No name on uniform
3 Rabbit Maranville 90.00 150.00
34G, 35G
4 Buddy Myer 35.00 60.00
34G, 35G, 36B
5 Tommy Bridges 35.00 60.00
34G, 35G, 36B
6 Max Bishop 35.00 60.00
34G, 35G
7 Lew Fonseca 35.00 60.00
34G, 35G
8 Joe Vosmik XRC (34G,35G,36B) 30.00 50.00
9 Mickey Cochrane 100.00 175.00
34G, 35G, 36B
10A Leroy Mahaffey 30.00 50.00
34G, 35G
A's on uniform
10B Leroy Mahaffey 50.00 80.00
36B
No name on uniform
11 Bill Dickey 125.00 200.00

34G, 35G
12A Fred Walker XRC (34G) 50.00 80.00
12B Fred Walker 35G 50.00 80.00
(Ruth to Boston
mentioned on back
12C Fred Walker 36B 60.00 100.00
13 George Blaeholder 30.00 50.00
34G, 35G
14 Bill Terry 100.00 175.00
34G, 35G
15A Dick Bartell 34G 60.00 100.00
Philadelphia Nationals
on card back
15B Dick Bartell 35G 50.00 80.00
New York Giants
on card back
16 Lloyd Waner 75.00 125.00
34G, 35G, 36B
17 Frankie Frisch 75.00 125.00
34G, 35G
18 Chick Hafey XRC (34G,35G) 75.00 125.00
19 Van Mungo XRC (34G,35G) 50.00 80.00
20 Frank Hogan 35.00 60.00
34G, 35G
21A Johnny Vergez 34G 50.00 80.00
New York Giants
on card back
21B Johnny Vergez 35G 35.00 60.00
Philadelphia Phillies
on card back
22 Jimmy Wilson 35.00 60.00
34G, 35G, 36B
23 Bill Hallahan 30.00 50.00
34G, 35G
24 Earl Adams 30.00 50.00
34G, 35G
25 Wally Berger 35G 35.00 60.00
26 Pepper Martin 50.00 80.00
35G, 36B
27 Pie Traynor 35G 90.00 150.00
28 Al Lopez 35G 90.00 150.00
29 Red Rolfe 35G 50.00 80.00
30A Heinie Manush 35G 90.00 150.00
W on sleeve
30B Heinie Manush 36B 125.00 200.00
No W on sleeve
31A Kiki Cuyler 35G 75.00 125.00
Chicago Cubs
31B Kiki Cuyler 36B 100.00 175.00
Cincinnati Reds
32 Sam Rice (35G) 75.00 125.00
33 Schoolboy Rowe (35G) 50.00 80.00
34 Stan Hack (35G) 50.00 80.00
35 Earl Averill (35G) 75.00 125.00
36A Earnie Lombardi 175.00 300.00
(Sic, Ernie)
36B Ernie Lombardi (35G) 125.00 200.00
37 Billy Urbanski (35G) 35.00 60.00
38 Ben Chapman (35G) 50.00 80.00
39 Carl Hubbell (35G) 125.00 200.00
40 Blondy Ryan (35G) 35.00 60.00
41 Harvey Hendrick XRC (35G) 35.00 60.00
42 Jimmy Dykes (35G) 50.00 80.00
43 Ted Lyons (35G) 75.00 125.00
44 Rogers Hornsby (35G) 250.00 400.00
45 Jo Jo White XRC (35G) 35.00 60.00
46 Red Lucas (35G) 35.00 60.00
47 Bob Bolton XRC (35G) 35.00 60.00
48 Rick Ferrell (35G) 75.00 125.00
49 Buck Jordan (35G) 35.00 60.00
50 Mel Ott (35G) 175.00 300.00
51 John Whitehead XRC (35G) 35.00 60.00
52 Tuck Stainback XRC (35G) 35.00 60.00
53 Oscar Melillo (35G) 35.00 60.00
54A Hank Greenburg 350.00 600.00
(Sic, Greenberg)
54B Hank Greenberg (35G) 250.00 400.00
55 Tony Cuccinello (35G) 50.00 80.00
56 Gus Suhr (35G) 35.00 60.00
57 Cy Blanton (35G) 35.00 60.00
58 Glenn Myatt (35G) 35.00 60.00
59 Jim Bottomley (35G) 75.00 125.00
60 Red Ruffing (35G) 90.00 150.00
61 Bill Werber (35G) 50.00 80.00
62 Fred Frankhouse (35G) 35.00 60.00
63 Travis Jackson (35G) 75.00 125.00
64 Jimmie Foxx (35G) 250.00 400.00
65 Zeke Bonura (35G) 35.00 60.00
66 Ducky Medwick (35G) 125.00 200.00
67 Marvin Owen (35G) 50.00 80.00
68 Sam Leslie (35G) 35.00 60.00
69 Earl Grace (35G) 35.00 60.00
70 Hal Trosky (35G) 50.00 80.00
71 Ossie Bluege (35G) 50.00 80.00
72 Tony Piet (35G) 35.00 60.00
73 Fritz Ostermueller 50.00 80.00
35G, 35B, 36B
74 Tony Lazzeri 125.00 200.00
35G, 35B, 36B
75 Jack Burns 50.00 80.00
35G, 35B, 36B
76 Billy Rogell 50.00 80.00
35G, 35B, 36B
77 Charley Gehringer 100.00 175.00
35G, 35B, 36B
78 Joe Kuhel 50.00 80.00
35G, 35B, 36B
79 Willis Hudlin 50.00 80.00
35G, 35B, 36B
80 Lou Chiozza 50.00 80.00
35G, 35B, 36B
81 Bill Delancey XRC (35G,35B,36B) 35.00 60.00
82A Johnny Babich 50.00 80.00
(Dodgers on uniorm
35G, 35B)
82B Johnny Babich 75.00 125.00
(No name on
uniform; 36B)
83 Paul Waner 90.00 150.00
35G, 35B, 36B
84 Sam Byrd 50.00 80.00
35G, 35B, 36B
85 Moose Solters (36B) 60.00 100.00
86 Frank Crosetti (36B) 90.00 150.00
87 Steve O'Neill MG (36B) 75.00 125.00
88 George Selkirk XRC (36B) 75.00 125.00
89 Joe Stripp (36B) 75.00 125.00
90 Ray Hayworth (36B) 75.00 125.00
91 Bucky Harris MG XRC (36B) 125.00 200.00
92 Ethan Allen (36B) 60.00 100.00
93 General Crowder (36B) 60.00 100.00
94 Wes Ferrell (36B) 90.00 150.00
95 Luke Appling (36B) 150.00 250.00
96 Lew Riggs XRC (36B) 60.00 100.00
97 Al Lopez (36B) 250.00 400.00
98 Schoolboy Rowe (36B) 125.00 200.00
99 Pie Traynor (36B) 300.00 500.00
100 Earl Averill (36B) 250.00 400.00
101 Dick Bartell (36B) 125.00 200.00
102 Van Lingle Mungo (36B) 150.00 250.00
103 Bill Dickey (36B) 400.00 700.00
104 Red Rolfe (36B) 125.00 200.00
105 Ernie Lombardi (36B) 250.00 400.00
106 Red Lucas (36B) 125.00 200.00
107 Stan Hack (36B) 125.00 200.00
108 Wally Berger (36B) 175.00 300.00

1981 Donruss

In 1981 Donruss launched itself into the baseball card market with a 600-card set. Wax packs contained 15 cards as well as a piece of gum. This would be the only year that Donruss was allowed to have any confectionary product in their packs. The standard-size cards are printed on thin stock and more than one pose exists for several popular players. Numerous errors of the first print run were later corrected by the company. These are marked P1 and P2 in our checklist below. According to published reports at the time, approximately 500 sets were made available in uncut sheet form. The key Rookie Cards in this set are Danny Ainge, Tim Raines, and Jeff Reardon.

COMPLETE SET (605) 20.00 50.00
1 Ozzie Smith 1.25 3.00
2 Rollie Fingers .08 .25
3 Rick Wise .02 .10
4 Gene Richards .02 .10
5 Alan Trammell .20 .50
6 Tom Brookens .02 .10
7A Duffy Dyer P1 .08 .25
(1980 batting average
has decimal
7B Duffy Dyer P2 .02 .10
(1980 batting average
has no decim
8 Mark Fidrych .08 .25
9 Dave Rozema .02 .10
10 Ricky Peters RC .02 .10
11 Mike Schmidt 1.00 2.50
12 Willie Stargell .20 .50
13 Tim Foli .02 .10
14 Manny Sanguillen .08 .25
15 Grant Jackson .02 .10
16 Eddie Solomon .02 .10
17 Omar Moreno .02 .10
18 Joe Morgan .20 .50
19 Rafael Landestoy .02 .10
20 Bruce Bochy .02 .10
21 Joe Sambito .02 .10
22 Manny Trillo .02 .10
23A Dave Smith P1 .20 .50
Line box around stats
is not complete
23B Dave Smith RC .20 .50
P2 Box totally encloses
stats at top
24 Terry Puhl .02 .10
25 Bump Wills .02 .10
26A John Ellis P1 ERR .20 .50
(Photo on front
shows Danny Wa
26B John Ellis P2 COR .08 .25
27 Jim Kern .02 .10
28 Richie Zisk .02 .10
29 John Mayberry .02 .10
30 Bob Davis .02 .10
31 Jackson Todd .02 .10
32 Alvis Woods .02 .10
33 Steve Carlton .20 .50
34 Lee Mazzilli .08 .25
35 John Stearns .02 .10
36 Roy Lee Jackson RC .02 .10
37 Mike Scott .08 .25
38 Lamar Johnson .02 .10
39 Kevin Bell .02 .10
40 Ed Farmer .02 .10
41 Ross Baumgarten .02 .10
42 Leo Sutherland RC .02 .10
43 Dan Meyer .02 .10
44 Ron Reed .02 .10
45 Mario Mendoza .02 .10
46 Rick Honeycutt .02 .10
47 Glenn Abbott .02 .10
48 Leon Roberts .02 .10
49 Rod Carew .20 .50
50 Bert Campaneris .08 .25
51A Tom Donahue P1 ERR .08 .25
(Name on front
misspelled Don
51B Tom Donohue RC .02 .10
P2 COR
52 Dave Frost .02 .10
53 Ed Halicki .02 .10
54 Dan Ford .02 .10
55 Garry Maddox .02 .10
56A Steve Garvey P1 .08 .25
Surpassed 25 HR
56B Steve Garvey P2 21HR .08 .25
57 Bill Russell .08 .25
58 Don Sutton .08 .25
59 Reggie Smith .08 .25
60 Rick Monday .08 .25
61 Ray Knight .08 .25
62 Johnny Bench .40 1.00
63 Mario Soto .08 .25
64 Doug Bair .02 .10
65 George Foster .08 .25
66 Jeff Burroughs .08 .25
67 Keith Hernandez .08 .25
68 Tom Herr .02 .10
69 Bob Forsch .02 .10
70 John Fulgham .02 .10
71A Bobby Bonds P1 ERR .40 1.00
986 lifetime HR
71B Bobby Bonds P2 COR .20 .50
326 lifetime HR
72A Rennie Stennett P1 .08 .25
Breaking broke leg
72B Rennie Stennett P2 .02 .10
Word broke deleted
73 Joe Strain .02 .10
74 Ed Whitson .02 .10
75 Tom Griffin .02 .10
76 Billy North .02 .10
77 Gene Garber .02 .10
78 Mike Hargrove .02 .10
79 Dave Rosello .02 .10
80 Ron Hassey .02 .10
81 Sid Monge .02 .10
82A Joe Charboneau P1 .40 1.00
'78 highlights
For some reason
82B Joe Charboneau RC .40 1.00
P2 Phrase For some reason deleted
83 Cecil Cooper .08 .25
84 Sal Bando .08 .25
85 Moose Haas .02 .10
86 Mike Caldwell .02 .10
87A Larry Hisle P1 .08 .25
('77 highlights& line
ends with %
87B Larry Hisle P2 .02 .10
Correct line 28 HR
88 Luis Gomez .02 .10
89 Larry Parrish .02 .10
90 Gary Carter .20 .50
91 Bill Gullickson RC .20 .50
92 Fred Norman .02 .10
93 Tommy Hutton .02 .10
94 Carl Yastrzemski .60 1.50
95 Glenn Hoffman RC .02 .10
96 Dennis Eckersley .20 .50
97A Tom Burgmeier P1 .08 .25
ERR Throws: Right
97B Tom Burgmeier P2 .02 .10
COR Throws: Left
98 Win Remmerswaal RC .02 .10
99 Bob Horner .08 .25
100 George Brett 1.00 2.50
101 Dave Chalk .02 .10
102 Dennis Leonard .02 .10
103 Renie Martin .02 .10
104 Amos Otis .08 .25
105 Graig Nettles .08 .25
106 Eric Soderholm .02 .10
107 Tommy John .08 .25
108 Tom Underwood .02 .10
109 Lou Piniella .08 .25
110 Mickey Klutts .02 .10
111 Bobby Murcer .08 .25
112 Eddie Murray .60 1.50
113 Rick Dempsey .02 .10
114 Scott McGregor .02 .10
115 Ken Singleton .08 .25
116 Gary Roenicke .02 .10
117 Dave Revering .02 .10
118 Mike Norris .02 .10
119 Rickey Henderson 2.50 6.00
120 Mike Heath .02 .10
121 Dave Cash .02 .10
122 Randy Jones .08 .25
123 Eric Rasmussen .02 .10
124 Jerry Mumphrey .02 .10
125 Richie Hebner .02 .10
126 Mark Wagner .02 .10
127 Jack Morris .20 .50
128 Dan Petry .02 .10
129 Bruce Robbins .02 .10
130 Champ Summers .02 .10
131 Pete Rose P1 1.25 3.00
Last line ends with
see card 251
131B Pete Rose P2 .75 2.00
132 Willie Stargell .20 .50
133 Ed Ott .02 .10
134 Jim Bibby .02 .10
135 Bert Blyleven .08 .25
136 Dave Parker .08 .25
137 Bill Robinson .02 .10
138 Enos Cabell .02 .10
139 Dave Bergman .02 .10
140 J.R. Richard .08 .25
141 Ken Forsch .02 .10
142 Larry Bowa UER .08 .25
143 Frank LaCorte UER .02 .10
Photo actually Randy Niemann
144 Denny Walling .02 .10
145 Buddy Bell .08 .25
146 Fergie Jenkins .08 .25
147 Dannny Darwin .08 .25
148 John Grubb .02 .10
149 Alfredo Griffin .02 .10
150 Jerry Garvin .02 .10
151 Paul Mirabella RC .02 .10
152 Rick Bosetti .02 .10
153 Dick Ruthven .02 .10
154 Frank Taveras .02 .10
155 Craig Swan .02 .10
156 Jeff Reardon RC .40 1.00
157 Steve Henderson .02 .10
158 Jim Morrison .02 .10
159 Glenn Borgmann .02 .10
160 LaMarr Hoyt RC .20 .50
161 Rich Wortham .02 .10
162 Thad Bosley .02 .10
163 Julio Cruz .02 .10
164A Del Unser P1 .08 .25
No 3B heading
164B Del Unser P2 .02 .10
(Batting record on back
corrected (
165 Jim Anderson .02 .10
166 Jim Beattie .02 .10
167 Shane Rawley .02 .10
168 Joe Simpson .02 .10
169 Rod Carew .20 .50
170 Fred Patek .02 .10
171 Frank Tanana .08 .25
172 Alfredo Martinez RC .02 .10
173 Chris Knapp .02 .10
174 Joe Rudi .08 .25
175 Greg Luzinski .08 .25
176 Steve Garvey .20 .50
177 Joe Ferguson .02 .10
178 Bob Welch .08 .25
179 Dusty Baker .08 .25
180 Rudy Law .02 .10
181 Dave Concepcion .08 .25
182 Johnny Bench .40 1.00
183 Mike LaCoss .02 .10
184 Ken Griffey .08 .25
185 Dave Collins .02 .10
186 Brian Asselstine .02 .10
187 Garry Templeton .08 .25
188 Mike Phillips .02 .10
189 Pete Vuckovich .02 .10
190 John Urrea .02 .10
191 Tony Scott .02 .10
192 Darrell Evans .08 .25
193 Milt May .02 .10
194 Bob Knepper .02 .10
195 Randy Moffitt .02 .10
196 Larry Herndon .02 .10
197 Rick Camp .02 .10
198 Andre Thornton .08 .25
199 Tom Veryzer .02 .10
200 Gary Alexander .02 .10
201 Rick Waits .02 .10
202 Rick Manning .02 .10
203 Paul Molitor .40 1.00
204 Jim Gantner .02 .10
205 Paul Mitchell .02 .10
206 Reggie Cleveland .02 .10
207 Sixto Lezcano .02 .10
208 Bruce Benedict .02 .10
209 Rodney Scott .02 .10
210 John Tamargo .02 .10
211 Bill Lee .08 .25
212 Andre Dawson .20 .50
213 Rowland Office .02 .10
214 Carl Yastrzemski .60 1.50
215 Jerry Remy .02 .10
216 Mike Torrez .02 .10
217 Skip Lockwood .02 .10
218 Fred Lynn .08 .25
219 Chris Chambliss .08 .25
220 Willie Aikens .02 .10
221 John Wathan .02 .10
222 Dan Quisenberry .02 .10
223 Willie Wilson .08 .25
224 Clint Hurdle .02 .10
225 Bob Watson .02 .10
226 Jim Spencer .02 .10
227 Ron Guidry .08 .25
228 Reggie Jackson .40 1.00
229 Oscar Gamble .02 .10
230 Jeff Cox RC .02 .10
231 Luis Tiant .08 .25
232 Rich Dauer .02 .10
233 Dan Graham .02 .10
234 Mike Flanagan .02 .10
235 John Lowenstein .02 .10
236 Benny Ayala .02 .10
237 Wayne Gross .02 .10
238 Rick Langford .02 .10
239 Tony Armas .08 .25
240A Bob Lacy P1 ERR .20 .50
(Name misspelled
Bob Lacy)
240B Bob Lacey P2 COR .02 .10
241 Gene Tenace .08 .25
242 Bob Shirley .02 .10
243 Gary Lucas RC .02 .10
244 Jerry Turner .02 .10
245 John Wockenfuss .02 .10
246 Stan Papi .02 .10
247 Milt Wilcox .02 .10
248 Dan Schatzeder .02 .10
249 Steve Kemp .02 .10
250 Jim Lentine RC .02 .10
251 Pete Rose 1.25 3.00
252 Bill Madlock .08 .25
253 Dale Berra .02 .10
254 Kent Tekulve .02 .10
255 Enrique Romo .02 .10
256 Mike Easler .02 .10
257 Chuck Tanner MG .02 .10
258 Art Howe .02 .10
259 Alan Ashby .02 .10
260 Nolan Ryan 2.00 5.00
261A Vern Ruhle P1 ERR .20 .50
(Photo on front
actually Ken F
261B Vern Ruhle P2 COR .08 .25
262 Bob Boone .08 .25
263 Cesar Cedeno .08 .25
264 Jeff Leonard .08 .25
265 Pat Putnam .02 .10
266 Jon Matlack .02 .10
267 Dave Rajsich .02 .10
268 Billy Sample .02 .10
269 Damaso Garcia RC .02 .10
270 Tom Buskey .02 .10
271 Joey McLaughlin .02 .10
272 Barry Bonnell .02 .10
273 Tug McGraw .08 .25
274 Mike Jorgensen .02 .10
275 Pat Zachry .02 .10
276 Neil Allen .02 .10
277 Joel Youngblood .02 .10
278 Greg Pryor .02 .10
279 Britt Burns RC .02 .10
280 Rich Dotson RC .02 .10
281 Chet Lemon .08 .25
282 Rusty Kuntz RC .02 .10
283 Ted Cox .02 .10
284 Sparky Lyle .08 .25
285 Larry Cox .02 .10
286 Floyd Bannister .02 .10
287 Byron McLaughlin .02 .10
288 Rodney Craig .02 .10
289 Bobby Grich .08 .25
290 Dickie Thon .02 .10
291 Mark Clear .02 .10
292 Dave Lemanczyk .02 .10
293 Jason Thompson .02 .10
294 Rick Miller .02 .10
295 Lonnie Smith .08 .25
296 Ron Cey .08 .25
297 Steve Yeager .08 .25
298 Bobby Castillo .02 .10
299 Manny Mota .08 .25
300 Jay Johnstone .02 .10
301 Dan Driessen .02 .10
302 Joe Nolan RC .02 .10
303 Paul Householder RC .02 .10
304 Harry Spilman .02 .10
305 Cesar Geronimo .02 .10
306A Gary Mathews P1 ERR .20 .50
Name misspelled
306B Gary Matthews P2 .08 .25
COR
307 Ken Reitz .02 .10
308 Ted Simmons .08 .25
309 John Littlefield RC .02 .10
310 George Frazier .02 .10
311 Dane Iorg .02 .10
312 Mike Ivie .02 .10
313 Dennis Littlejohn .02 .10
314 Gary Lavelle .02 .10
315 Jack Clark .08 .25
316 Jim Wohlford .02 .10
317 Rick Matula .02 .10
318 Toby Harrah .08 .25
319A Dwane Kuiper P1 ERR .08 .25
Name misspelled
319B Duane Kuiper P2 COR .02 .10
320 Len Barker .08 .25
321 Victor Cruz .02 .10
322 Dell Alston .02 .10
323 Robin Yount .60 1.50
324 Charlie Moore .02 .10
325 Lary Sorensen .02 .10
326A Gorman Thomas P1 .20 .50
(2nd line on back:
30 HR mark
326B Gorman Thomas P2 .08 .25
(%%30 HR mark 3rd–)
327 Bob Rodgers MG .02 .10
328 Phil Niekro .08 .25
329 Chris Speier .02 .10
330A Steve Rodgers P1 .08 .25
ERR Name misspelled
330B Steve Rogers P2 COR .08 .25
331 Woodie Fryman .02 .10
332 Warren Cromartie .02 .10
333 Jerry White .02 .10
334 Tony Perez .20 .50
335 Carlton Fisk .20 .50
336 Dick Drago .02 .10
337 Steve Renko .02 .10
338 Jim Rice .08 .25
339 Jerry Royster .02 .10
340 Frank White .08 .25
341 Jamie Quirk .02 .10
342A Paul Spittorff P1 ERR .08 .25
Name misspelled
342B Paul Splittorff .02 .10
P2 COR
343 Marty Pattin .02 .10
344 Pete LaCock .02 .10
345 Willie Randolph .08 .25
346 Rick Cerone .02 .10
347 Rich Gossage .08 .25
348 Reggie Jackson .40 1.00
349 Ruppert Jones .02 .10
350 Dave McKay RC .02 .10
351 Yogi Berra CO .40 1.00
352 Doug DeCinces .08 .25
353 Jim Palmer .20 .50
354 Tippy Martinez .02 .10
355 Al Bumbry .08 .25
356 Earl Weaver MG .08 .25
357A Bob Picciolo P1 ERR .08 .25
Name misspelled
357B Bob Picciolo P2 COR .02 .10
358 Matt Keough .02 .10
359 Dwayne Murphy .02 .10
360 Brian Kingman .02 .10
361 Bill Fahey .02 .10
362 Steve Mura .02 .10
363 Dennis Kinney RC .02 .10
364 Dave Winfield .20 .50
365 Lou Whitaker .20 .50
366 Lance Parrish .08 .25
367 Tim Corcoran .02 .10
368 Pat Underwood .02 .10
369 Al Cowens .02 .10
370 Sparky Anderson MG .08 .25
371 Pete Rose 1.25 3.00
372 Phil Garner .08 .25
373 Steve Nicosia .02 .10
374 John Candelaria .08 .25
375 Don Robinson .08 .25
376 Lee Lacy .02 .10
377 John Milner .02 .10
378 Craig Reynolds .02 .10
379A Luis Pujois P1 ERR .08 .25
(Name misspelled)
379B Luis Pujols P2 COR .02 .10
380 Joe Niekro .02 .10
381 Joaquin Andujar .08 .25
382 Keith Moreland RC .08 .25
383 Jose Cruz .08 .25
384 Bill Virdon MG .02 .10
385 Jim Sundberg .08 .25
386 Doc Medich .02 .10
387 Al Oliver .08 .25
388 Jim Norris .02 .10
389 Bob Bailor .02 .10
390 Ernie Whitt .02 .10
391 Otto Velez .02 .10
392 Roy Howell .02 .10
393 Bob Walk RC .20 .50
394 Doug Flynn .02 .10
395 Pete Falcone .02 .10
396 Tom Hausman .02 .10
397 Elliott Maddox .02 .10
398 Mike Squires .02 .10
399 Marvis Foley RC .02 .10
400 Steve Trout .02 .10
401 Wayne Nordhagen .02 .10
402 Tony LaRussa MG .08 .25
403 Bruce Bochte .02 .10
404 Bake McBride .08 .25
405 Jerry Narron .02 .10
406 Rob Dressler .02 .10
407 Dave Heaverlo .02 .10
408 Tom Paciorek .08 .25
409 Carney Lansford .08 .25
410 Brian Downing .08 .25
411 Don Aase .02 .10
412 Jim Barr .02 .10
413 Don Baylor .08 .25
414 Jim Fregosi MG .02 .10
415 Dallas Green MG .02 .10
416 Dave Lopes .08 .25
417 Jerry Reuss .08 .25
418 Rick Sutcliffe .08 .25
419 Derrel Thomas .02 .10
420 Tom Lasorda MG .20 .50
421 Charlie Leibrandt RC .20 .50
422 Tom Seaver .40 1.00
423 Ron Oester .02 .10
424 Junior Kennedy .02 .10
425 Tom Seaver .40 1.00
426 Bobby Cox MG .08 .25
427 Leon Durham RC .20 .50
428 Terry Kennedy .02 .10
429 Silvio Martinez .02 .10
430 George Hendrick .08 .25
431 Red Schoendienst MG .20 .50
432 Johnnie LeMaster .02 .10
433 Vida Blue .08 .25
434 John Montefusco .02 .10
435 Terry Whitfield .02 .10
436 Dave Bristol MG .02 .10
437 Dale Murphy .20 .50
438 Jerry Dybzinski RC .02 .10
439 Jorge Orta .02 .10
440 Wayne Garland .02 .10
441 Miguel Dilone .02 .10
442 Dave Garcia MG .02 .10
443 Don Money .02 .10
444A Buck Martinez P1 ERR .08 .25
Reverse negative
444B Buck Martinez .02 .10
P2 COR
445 Jerry Augustine .02 .10
446 Ben Oglivie .08 .25
447 Jim Slaton .02 .10
448 Doyle Alexander .02 .10
449 Tony Bernazard .02 .10
450 Scott Sanderson .02 .10
451 David Palmer .02 .10
452 Stan Bahnsen .02 .10
453 Dick Williams MG .02 .10
454 Rick Burleson .02 .10
455 Gary Allenson .02 .10
456 Bob Stanley .02 .10
457A John Tudor P1 ERR .40 1.00
Lifetime W-L 9.7
457B John Tudor RC .40 1.00
P2 COR Lifetime W-L 9-7
458 Dwight Evans .20 .50
459 Glenn Hubbard .02 .10
460 U.L. Washington .02 .10
461 Larry Gura .02 .10
462 Rich Gale .02 .10
463 Hal McRae .08 .25
464 Jim Frey MG RC .02 .10
465 Bucky Dent .08 .25
466 Dennis Werth RC .02 .10
467 Ron Davis .02 .10
468 Reggie Jackson .40 1.00
469 Bobby Brown .02 .10
470 Mike Davis RC .20 .50
471 Gaylord Perry .08 .25
472 Mark Belanger .02 .10
473 Jim Palmer .20 .50
474 Sammy Stewart .02 .10
475 Tim Stoddard .02 .10
476 Steve Stone .02 .10
477 Jeff Newman .02 .10
478 Steve McCatty .02 .10
479 Billy Martin MG .20 .50
480 Mitchell Page .02 .10
481 Steve Carlton CY .08 .25
482 Bill Buckner .08 .25
483A Ivan DeJesus P1 ERR .08 .25
Lifetime hits 702
483B Ivan DeJesus P2 COR .02 .10
Lifetime hits 642
484 Cliff Johnson .02 .10
485 Lenny Randle .02 .10
486 Larry Milbourne .02 .10
487 Roy Smalley .02 .10
488 John Castino .02 .10
489 Ron Jackson .02 .10
490A Dave Roberts P1 .08 .25
(Career Highlights:
Showed pop
490B Dave Roberts P2 .02 .10
(%%Declared himself–)
491 George Brett MVP .60 1.50
492 Mike Cubbage .02 .10
493 Rob Wilfong .02 .10
494 Danny Goodwin .02 .10
495 Jose Morales .02 .10
496 Mickey Rivers .02 .10
497 Mike Edwards .02 .10
498 Mike Sadek .02 .10
499 Lenn Sakata .02 .10
500 Gene Michael MG .02 .10
501 Dave Roberts .02 .10
502 Steve Dillard .02 .10
503 Jim Essian .02 .10
504 Rance Mulliniks .02 .10
505 Darrell Porter .02 .10
506 Joe Torre MG .08 .25
507 Terry Crowley .02 .10
508 Bill Travers .02 .10
509 Nelson Norman .02 .10
510 Bob McClure .02 .10
511 Steve Howe RC .20 .50
512 Dave Rader .02 .10
513 Mick Kelleher .02 .10
514 Kiko Garcia .02 .10
515 Larry Biittner .02 .10
516A Willie Norwood P1 .08 .25
(Career Highlights
%%Spent mos
516B Willie Norwood P2 .02 .10
(%%Traded to Seattle–)
517 Bo Diaz .02 .10
518 Juan Beniquez .02 .10
519 Scott Thompson .02 .10
520 Jim Tracy RC .40 1.00
521 Carlos Lezcano RC .02 .10
522 Joe Amalfitano MG .02 .10
523 Preston Hanna .02 .10
524A Ray Burris P1 .02 .10

(Career Highlights:
%%Went on ...-
524B Ray Burris P2 .02 .10
(%%Drafted by ...-)
525 Broderick Perkins .02 .10
526 Mickey Hatcher .02 .10
527 John Goryl MG .02 .10
528 Dick Davis .02 .10
529 Butch Wynegar .02 .10
530 Sal Butera RC .02 .10
531 Jerry Koosman .08 .25
532A Geoff Zahn P1 .08 .25
(Career Highlights:
%%Was 2nd in-)
532B Geoff Zahn P2 .02 .10
(%%Signed a 3 year-)
533 Dennis Martinez .08 .25
534 Gary Thomasson .02 .10
535 Steve Macko .02 .10
536 Jim Kaat .08 .25
537 George Brett .60 1.50
Rod Carew
538 Tim Raines RC 1.00 2.50
539 Keith Smith .02 .10
540 Ken Macha .02 .10
541 Burt Hooton .02 .10
542 Butch Hobson .02 .10
543 Bill Stein .02 .10
544 Dave Stapleton RC .02 .10
545 Bob Pate RC .02 .10
546 Doug Corbett RC .02 .10
547 Darrell Jackson .02 .10
548 Pete Redfern .02 .10
549 Roger Erickson .02 .10
550 Al Hrabosky .08 .25
551 Dick Tidrow .02 .10
552 Dave Ford RC .02 .10
553 Dave Kingman .08 .25
554A Mike Vail P1 .08 .25
(Career Highlights:
%%After two ...
554B Mike Vail P2 .02 .10
(%%Traded to ...-)
555A Jerry Martin P1 .08 .25
(Career Highlights:
%%Overcame a
555B Jerry Martin P2 .02 .10
(%%Traded to ...-)
556A Jesus Figueroa P1 .08 .25
(Career Highlights:
%%Had an
556B Jesus Figueroa RC .02 .10
(P2 Traded to ...-)
557 Don Stanhouse .02 .10
558 Barry Foote .02 .10
559 Tim Blackwell .02 .10
560 Bruce Sutter .20 .50
561 Rick Reuschel .08 .25
562 Lynn McGlothen .02 .10
563A Bob Owchinko P1 .08 .25
(Career Highlights:
%%Traded to
563B Bob Owchinko P2 .02 .10
(%%Involved in a ...-)
564 John Verhoeven .02 .10
565 Ken Landreaux .02 .10
566A Glen Adams P1 ERR .08 .25
Name misspelled
566B Glenn Adams P2 COR .02 .10
567 Hosken Powell .02 .10
568 Dick Noles .02 .10
569 Danny Ainge RC 1.25 3.00
570 Bobby Mattick MG RC .02 .10
571 Joe Lefebvre RC .02 .10
572 Bobby Clark .02 .10
573 Dennis Lamp .02 .10
574 Randy Lerch .02 .10
575 Mookie Wilson RC 1.25 3.00
576 Ron LeFlore .08 .25
577 Jim Dwyer .02 .10
578 Bill Castro .02 .10
579 Greg Minton .02 .10
580 Mark Littell .02 .10
581 Andy Hassler .02 .10
582 Dave Stieb .08 .25
583 Ken Oberkfell .02 .10
584 Larry Bradford .02 .10
585 Fred Stanley .02 .10
586 Bill Caudill .02 .10
587 Doug Capilla .02 .10
588 George Riley RC .02 .10
589 Willie Hernandez .02 .10
590 Mike Schmidt MVP 1.00 2.50
591 Steve Stone CY .02 .10
592 Rick Sofield .02 .10
593 Bombo Rivera .02 .10
594 Gary Ward .02 .10
595A Dave Edwards P1 .08 .25
(Career Highlights:
%%Sidelined
595B Dave Edwards P2 .02 .10
(%%Traded to ...-)
596 Mike Proly .02 .10
597 Tommy Boggs .02 .10
598 Greg Gross .02 .10
599 Elias Sosa .02 .10
600 Pat Kelly .02 .10
601A Checklist 1-120 P1 .08 .25
ERR Unnumbered
51 Donahue
601B Checklist 1-120 P2 .20 .50
COR Unnumbered
51 Donohue
602 Checklist 121-240 .08 .25
Unnumbered
603A Checklist 241-360 P1 .08 .25
ERR Unnumbered
(306 Mathews
603B Checklist 241-360 P2 .08 .25
COR Unnumbered
(306 Matthew
604A Checklist 361-480 P1 .08 .25
ERR Unnumbered
379 Pujois
604B Checklist 361-480 P2 .08 .25
COR Unnumbered
379 Pujols
605A Checklist 481-600 P1 .08 .25
ERR Unnumbered
(566 Glen Ad
605B Checklist 481-600 P2 .08 .25
COR Unnumbered
(566 Glenn A

1982 Donruss

The 1982 Donruss set contains 653 numbered standard-size cards and seven unnumbered checklists. The first 26 cards of this set are entitled Diamond Kings (DK) and feature the artwork of Dick Perez of Perez-Steele Galleries. The set was marketed with puzzle pieces in 15-card packs rather than with bubble gum. Those 15-card packs with an 30 cent SRP were issued 36 packs to a box and 20 boxes to a case. There are 63 pieces to the puzzle, which, when put together, make a collage of Babe Ruth entitled "Hall of Fame Diamond King." The card stock in this year's Donruss cards is considerably thicker than the 1981 cards. The seven unnumbered checklist cards are arbitrarily assigned numbers 654 through 660 and are listed at the end of the list below. Notable Rookie Cards in this set include Brett Butler, Cal Ripken Jr., Lee Smith and Dave Stewart.

COMPLETE SET (660) 30.00 60.00
COMP.FACT.SET (660) 30.00 60.00
COMP.RUTH PUZZLE 5.00 10.00
1 Pete Rose DK 1.00 2.50
2 Gary Carter DK .07 .20
3 Steve Garvey DK .07 .20
4 Vida Blue DK .07 .20
5 Alan Trammell DK .07 .20
COR
5A Alan Trammell DK ERR .07 .20
(Name misspelled)
6 Len Barker DK .02 .10
7 Dwight Evans DK .15 .40
8 Rod Carew DK .15 .40
9 George Hendrick DK .07 .20
10 Phil Niekro DK .07 .20
11 Richie Zisk DK .02 .10
12 Dave Parker DK .07 .20
13 Nolan Ryan DK 1.50 4.00
14 Ivan DeJesus DK .02 .10
15 George Brett DK .75 2.00
16 Tom Seaver DK .15 .40
17 Dave Kingman DK .07 .20
18 Dave Winfield DK .07 .20
19 Mike Norris DK .02 .10
20 Carlton Fisk DK .15 .40
21 Ozzie Smith DK .60 1.50
22 Roy Smalley DK .02 .10
23 Buddy Bell DK .07 .20
24 Ken Singleton DK .07 .20
25 John Mayberry DK .02 .10
26 Gorman Thomas DK .07 .20
27 Earl Weaver MG .07 .20
28 Rollie Fingers .07 .20
29 Sparky Anderson MG .07 .20
30 Dennis Eckersley .15 .40
31 Dave Winfield .07 .20
32 Burt Hooton .02 .10
33 Rick Waits .02 .10
34 George Brett .75 2.00
35 Steve McCatty .02 .10
36 Steve Rogers .07 .20
37 Bill Stein .02 .10
38 Steve Renko .02 .10
39 Mike Squires .02 .10
40 George Hendrick .07 .20
41 Bob Knepper .02 .10
42 Steve Carlton .15 .40
43 Larry Biittner .02 .10
44 Chris Welsh .02 .10
45 Steve Nicosia .02 .10
46 Jack Clark .07 .20
47 Chris Chambliss .07 .20
48 Ivan DeJesus .02 .10
49 Lee Mazzilli .07 .20
50 Julio Cruz .02 .10
51 Pete Redfern .02 .10
52 Dave Stieb .07 .20
53 Doug Corbett .02 .10
54 Jorge Bell RC .40 1.00
55 Joe Simpson .02 .10
56 Rusty Staub .07 .20
57 Hector Cruz .02 .10
58 Claudell Washington .02 .10
59 Enrique Romo .02 .10
60 Gary Lavelle .02 .10
61 Tim Flannery .02 .10
62 Joe Nolan .02 .10
63 Larry Bowa .07 .20
64 Sixto Lezcano .02 .10
65 Joe Sambito .02 .10
66 Bruce Kison .02 .10
67 Wayne Nordhagen .02 .10
68 Woodie Fryman .02 .10
69 Billy Sample .02 .10
70 Amos Otis .07 .20
71 Matt Keough .02 .10
72 Toby Harrah .07 .20
73 Dave Righetti RC .60 1.50
74 Carl Yastrzemski .50 1.25
75 Bob Welch .07 .20
76 Alan Trammell COR .07 .20
76A Alan Trammell ERR .07 .20
(Name misspelled)
77 Rick Dempsey .02 .10
78 Paul Molitor .07 .20
79 Dennis Martinez .07 .20
80 Jim Slaton .02 .10
81 Champ Summers .02 .10
82 Carney Lansford .07 .20
83 Barry Foote .02 .10
84 Steve Garvey .07 .20
85 Rick Manning .02 .10
86 John Wathan .02 .10
87 Brian Kingman .02 .10
88 Andre Dawson UER .07 .20
(Middle name Fernando
should be Nolan)
89 Jim Kern .02 .10
90 Bobby Grich .07 .20
91 Bob Forsch .02 .10
92 Art Howe .02 .10
93 Marty Bystrom .02 .10
94 Ozzie Smith .60 1.50
95 Dave Parker .07 .20
96 Doyle Alexander .02 .10
97 Al Hrabosky .02 .10
98 Frank Taveras .02 .10
99 Tim Blackwell .02 .10
100 Floyd Bannister .02 .10
101 Alfredo Griffin .02 .10
102 Dave Engle .02 .10
103 Mario Soto .07 .20
104 Ross Baumgarten .02 .10
105 Ken Singleton .07 .20
106 Ted Simmons .07 .20
107 Jack Morris .07 .20
108 Bob Watson .02 .10
109 Dwight Evans .15 .40
110 Tom Lasorda MG .15 .40
111 Bert Blyleven .07 .20
112 Dan Quisenberry .02 .10
113 Rickey Henderson 1.00 2.50
114 Gary Carter .07 .20
115 Brian Downing .07 .20
116 Al Oliver .07 .20
117 LaMarr Hoyt .02 .10
118 Cesar Cedeno .07 .20
119 Keith Moreland .02 .10
120 Bob Shirley .02 .10
121 Terry Kennedy .02 .10
122 Frank Pastore .02 .10
123 Gene Garber .02 .10
124 Tony Pena .07 .20
125 Allen Ripley .02 .10
126 Randy Martz .02 .10
127 Richie Zisk .02 .10
128 Mike Scott .07 .20
129 Lloyd Moseby .02 .10
130 Rob Wilfong .02 .10
131 Tim Stoddard .02 .10
132 Gorman Thomas .07 .20
133 Dan Petry .02 .10
134 Bob Stanley .02 .10
135 Lou Piniella .07 .20
136 Pedro Guerrero .07 .20
137 Len Barker .02 .10
138 Rich Gale .02 .10
139 Wayne Gross .02 .10
140 Tim Wallach RC .40 1.00
141 Gene Mauch MG .02 .10
142 Doc Medich .02 .10
143 Tony Bernazard .02 .10
144 Bill Virdon MG .02 .10
145 John Littlefield .02 .10
146 Dave Bergman .02 .10
147 Dick Davis .02 .10
148 Tom Seaver .30 .75
149 Matt Sinatro .02 .10
150 Chuck Tanner MG .02 .10
151 Leon Durham .02 .10
152 Gene Tenace .07 .20
153 Al Bumbry .02 .10
154 Mark Brouhard .02 .10
155 Rick Peters .02 .10
156 Jerry Remy .02 .10
157 Rick Reuschel .07 .20
158 Steve Howe .02 .10
159 Alan Bannister .02 .10
160 U.L. Washington .02 .10
161 Rick Langford .02 .10
162 Bill Gullickson .02 .10
163 Mark Wagner .02 .10
164 Geoff Zahn .02 .10
165 Ron LeFlore .07 .20
166 Dane Iorg .02 .10
167 Joe Niekro .02 .10
168 Pete Rose 1.00 2.50
169 Dave Collins .02 .10
170 Rick Wise .02 .10
171 Jim Bibby .02 .10
172 Larry Herndon .02 .10
173 Bob Horner .07 .20
174 Steve Dillard .02 .10
175 Mookie Wilson .07 .20
176 Dan Meyer .02 .10
177 Fernando Arroyo .02 .10
178 Jackson Todd .02 .10
179 Darrell Jackson .02 .10
180 Alvis Woods .02 .10
181 Jim Anderson .02 .10
182 Dave Kingman .07 .20
183 Steve Henderson .02 .10
184 Brian Asselstine .02 .10
185 Rod Scurry .02 .10
186 Fred Breining .02 .10
187 Danny Boone .02 .10
188 Junior Kennedy .02 .10
189 Sparky Lyle .07 .20
190 Whitey Herzog MG .07 .20
191 Dave Smith .02 .10
192 Ed Ott .02 .10
193 Greg Luzinski .07 .20
194 Bill Lee .07 .20
195 Don Zimmer MG .07 .20
196 Hal McRae .07 .20
197 Mike Norris .02 .10
198 Duane Kuiper .02 .10
199 Rick Cerone .02 .10
200 Jim Rice .07 .20
201 Steve Yeager .07 .20
202 Tom Brookens .02 .10
203 Jose Morales .02 .10
204 Roy Howell .02 .10
205 Tippy Martinez .02 .10
206 Moose Haas .02 .10
207 Al Cowens .02 .10
208 Dave Stapleton .02 .10
209 Bucky Dent .07 .20
210 Ron Cey .07 .20
211 Jorge Orta .02 .10
212 Jamie Quirk .02 .10
213 Jeff Jones .02 .10
214 Tim Raines .15 .40
215 Jon Matlack .02 .10
216 Rod Carew .15 .40
217 Jim Kaat .07 .20
218 Joe Pittman .02 .10
219 Larry Christenson .02 .10
220 Juan Bonilla RC .05 .15
221 Mike Easler .02 .10
222 Vida Blue .07 .20
223 Rick Camp .02 .10
224 Mike Jorgensen .02 .10
225 Jody Davis .02 .10
226 Mike Parrott .02 .10
227 Jim Clancy .02 .10
228 Hosken Powell .02 .10
229 Tom Hume .02 .10
230 Britt Burns .02 .10
231 Jim Palmer .07 .20
232 Bob Rodgers MG .02 .10
233 Milt Wilcox .02 .10
234 Dave Revering .02 .10
235 Mike Torrez .02 .10
236 Robert Castillo .02 .10
237 Von Hayes RC .20 .50
238 Renie Martin .02 .10
239 Dwayne Murphy .02 .10
240 Rodney Scott .02 .10
241 Fred Patek .02 .10
242 Mickey Rivers .02 .10
243 Steve Trout .02 .10
244 Jose Cruz .07 .20
245 Manny Trillo .02 .10
246 Lary Sorensen .02 .10
247 Dave Edwards .02 .10
248 Dan Driessen .02 .10
249 Tommy Boggs .02 .10
250 Dale Berra .02 .10
251 Ed Whitson .02 .10
252 Lee Smith RC .75 2.00
253 Tom Paciorek .02 .10
254 Pat Zachry .02 .10
255 Luis Leal .02 .10
256 John Castino .02 .10
257 Rich Dauer .02 .10
258 Cecil Cooper .07 .20
259 Dave Rozema .02 .10
260 John Tudor .07 .20
261 Jerry Mumphrey .02 .10
262 Jay Johnstone .02 .10
263 Bo Diaz .02 .10
264 Dennis Leonard .02 .10
265 Jim Spencer .02 .10
266 John Milner .02 .10
267 Don Aase .02 .10
268 Jim Sundberg .07 .20
269 Lamar Johnson .02 .10
270 Frank LaCorte .02 .10
271 Barry Evans .02 .10
272 Enos Cabell .02 .10
273 Del Unser .02 .10
274 George Foster .07 .20
275 Brett Butler RC .40 1.00
276 Lee Lacy .02 .10
277 Ken Reitz .02 .10
278 Keith Hernandez .07 .20
279 Doug DeCinces .07 .20
280 Charlie Moore .02 .10
281 Lance Parrish .07 .20
282 Ralph Houk MG .02 .10
283 Rich Gossage .07 .20
284 Jerry Reuss .02 .10
285 Mike Stanton .02 .10
286 Frank White .07 .20
287 Bob Owchinko .02 .10
288 Scott Sanderson .02 .10
289 Bump Wills .02 .10
290 Dave Frost .02 .10
291 Chet Lemon .07 .20
292 Tito Landrum .02 .10
293 Vern Ruhle .02 .10
294 Mike Schmidt .75 2.00
295 Sam Mejias .02 .10
296 Gary Lucas .02 .10
297 John Candelaria .02 .10
298 Jerry Martin .02 .10
299 Dale Murphy .15 .40
300 Mike Lum .02 .10
301 Tom Hausman .02 .10
302 Glenn Abbott .02 .10
303 Roger Erickson .02 .10
304 Otto Velez .02 .10
305 Danny Goodwin .02 .10
306 John Mayberry .02 .10
307 Lenny Randle .02 .10
308 Bob Bailor .02 .10
309 Jerry Morales .02 .10
310 Rufino Linares .02 .10
311 Kent Tekulve .02 .10
312 Joe Morgan .07 .20
313 John Urrea .02 .10
314 Paul Householder .02 .10
315 Garry Maddox .02 .10
316 Mike Ramsey .02 .10
317 Alan Ashby .02 .10
318 Bob Clark .02 .10
319 Tony LaRussa MG .07 .20
320 Charlie Lea .02 .10
321 Danny Darwin .02 .10
322 Cesar Geronimo .02 .10
323 Tom Underwood .02 .10
324 Andre Thornton .02 .10
325 Rudy May .02 .10
326 Frank Tanana .07 .20
327 Dave Lopes .07 .20
328 Richie Hebner .02 .10
329 Mike Flanagan .02 .10
330 Mike Caldwell .02 .10
331 Scott McGregor .02 .10
332 Jerry Augustine .02 .10
333 Stan Papi .02 .10
334 Rick Miller .02 .10
335 Graig Nettles .07 .20
336 Dusty Baker .07 .20
337 Dave Garcia MG .02 .10
338 Larry Gura .02 .10
339 Cliff Johnson .02 .10
340 Warren Cromartie .02 .10
341 Steve Comer .02 .10
342 Rick Burleson .02 .10
343 John Martin RC .05 .15
344 Craig Reynolds .02 .10
345 Mike Proly .02 .10
346 Ruppert Jones .02 .10
347 Omar Moreno .02 .10
348 Greg Minton .02 .10
349 Rick Mahler .02 .10
350 Alex Trevino .02 .10
351 Mike Krukow .02 .10
352A Shane Rawley ERR .15 .40
(Photo actually
Jim Anderson)
352B Shane Rawley COR .02 .10
353 Garth Iorg .02 .10
354 Pete Mackanin .02 .10
355 Paul Moskau .02 .10
356 Richard Dotson .02 .10
357 Steve Stone .02 .10
358 Larry Hisle .02 .10
359 Aurelio Lopez .02 .10
360 Oscar Gamble .02 .10
361 Tom Burgmeier .02 .10
362 Terry Forster .07 .20
363 Joe Charboneau .07 .20
364 Ken Brett .02 .10
365 Tony Armas .07 .20
366 Chris Speier .02 .10
367 Fred Lynn .07 .20
368 Buddy Bell .07 .20
369 Jim Essian .02 .10
370 Terry Puhl .02 .10
371 Greg Gross .02 .10
372 Bruce Sutter .15 .40
373 Joe Lefebvre .02 .10
374 Ray Knight .07 .20
375 Bruce Benedict .02 .10
376 Tim Foli .02 .10
377 Al Holland .02 .10
378 Ken Kravec .02 .10
379 Jeff Burroughs .02 .10
380 Pete Falcone .02 .10
381 Ernie Whitt .02 .10
382 Brad Havens .02 .10
383 Terry Crowley .02 .10
384 Don Money .02 .10
385 Dan Schatzeder .02 .10
386 Gary Allenson .02 .10
387 Yogi Berra CO .30 .75
388 Ken Landreaux .02 .10
389 Mike Hargrove .02 .10
390 Darryl Motley .02 .10
391 Dave McKay .02 .10
392 Stan Bahnsen .02 .10
393 Ken Forsch .02 .10
394 Mario Mendoza .02 .10
395 Jim Morrison .02 .10
396 Mike Ivie .02 .10
397 Broderick Perkins .02 .10
398 Darrell Evans .07 .20
399 Ron Reed .02 .10
400 Johnny Bench .30 .75
401 Steve Bedrosian RC .20 .50
402 Bill Robinson .02 .10
403 Bill Buckner .07 .20
404 Ken Oberkfell .02 .10
405 Cal Ripken RC 10.00 25.00
406 Jim Gantner .02 .10
407 Kirk Gibson .30 .75
408 Tony Perez .15 .40
409 Tommy John UER .07 .20
(Text says 52-56 as
Yankee, should be
52-26)
410 Dave Stewart RC .60 1.50
411 Dan Spillner .02 .10
412 Willie Aikens .02 .10
413 Mike Heath .02 .10
414 Ray Burris .02 .10
415 Leon Roberts .02 .10
416 Mike Witt .20 .50
417 Bob Molinaro .02 .10
418 Steve Braun .02 .10
419 Nolan Ryan UER 1.50 4.00
(Nisnumbering of
Nolan's no-hitters
on card back)
420 Tug McGraw .07 .20
421 Dave Concepcion .07 .20
422A Juan Eichelberger .15 .40
ERR (Photo actually
Gary Lucas)
422B Juan Eichelberger .02 .10
COR
423 Rick Rhoden .02 .10
424 Frank Robinson MG .15 .40
425 Eddie Miller .02 .10
426 Bill Caudill .02 .10
427 Doug Flynn .02 .10
428 Larry Andersen UER .02 .10
(Misspelled Anderson
on card front)
429 Al Williams .02 .10
430 Jerry Garvin .02 .10
431 Glenn Adams .02 .10
432 Barry Bonnell .02 .10
433 Jerry Narron .02 .10
434 John Stearns .02 .10
435 Mike Tyson .02 .10
436 Glenn Hubbard .02 .10
437 Eddie Solomon .02 .10
438 Jeff Leonard .02 .10
439 Randy Bass .20 .50
440 Mike LaCoss .02 .10
441 Gary Matthews .07 .20
442 Mark Littell .02 .10
443 Don Sutton .07 .20
444 John Harris .02 .10
445 Vada Pinson CO .07 .20
446 Elias Sosa .02 .10
447 Charlie Hough .07 .20
448 Willie Wilson .07 .20
449 Fred Stanley .02 .10
450 Tom Veryzer .02 .10
451 Ron Davis .02 .10
452 Mark Clear .02 .10
453 Bill Russell .07 .20
454 Lou Whitaker .07 .20
455 Dan Graham .02 .10
456 Reggie Cleveland .02 .10
457 Sammy Stewart .02 .10
458 Pete Vuckovich .02 .10
459 John Wockenfuss .02 .10
460 Glenn Hoffman .02 .10
461 Willie Randolph .07 .20
462 Fernando Valenzuela .30 .75
463 Ron Hassey .02 .10
464 Paul Splittorff .02 .10
465 Rob Picciolo .02 .10
466 Larry Parrish .02 .10
467 Johnny Grubb .02 .10
468 Dan Ford .02 .10
469 Silvio Martinez .02 .10
470 Kiko Garcia .02 .10
471 Bob Boone .07 .20
472 Luis Salazar .02 .10
473 Randy Niemann UER .02 .10
Card says Pirate, but in an Astro uniform
474 Tom Griffin .02 .10
475 Phil Niekro .07 .20
476 Hubie Brooks .02 .10
477 Dick Tidrow .02 .10
478 Jim Beattie .02 .10
479 Damaso Garcia .02 .10
480 Mickey Hatcher .02 .10
481 Joe Price .02 .10
482 Ed Farmer .02 .10
483 Eddie Murray .30 .75
484 Ben Oglivie .07 .20
485 Kevin Saucier .02 .10
486 Bobby Murcer .07 .20
487 Bill Campbell .02 .10
488 Reggie Smith .07 .20
489 Wayne Garland .02 .10
490 Jim Wright .02 .10
491 Billy Martin MG .15 .40
492 Jim Fanning MG .02 .10
493 Don Baylor .07 .20
494 Rick Honeycutt .02 .10
495 Carlton Fisk .15 .40
496 Denny Walling .02 .10
497 Bake McBride .07 .20
498 Darrell Porter .02 .10
499 Gene Richards .02 .10
500 Ron Oester .02 .10
501 Ken Dayley .02 .10
502 Jason Thompson .02 .10
503 Milt May .02 .10
504 Doug Bird .02 .10
505 Bruce Bochte .02 .10
506 Neil Allen .02 .10
507 Joey McLaughlin .02 .10
508 Butch Wynegar .02 .10
509 Gary Roenicke .02 .10
510 Robin Yount .50 1.25
511 Dave Tobik .02 .10
512 Rich Gedman .20 .50
513 Gene Nelson .02 .10
514 Rick Monday .07 .20
515 Miguel Dilone .02 .10
516 Clint Hurdle .02 .10
517 Jeff Newman .02 .10
518 Grant Jackson .02 .10
519 Andy Hassler .02 .10
520 Pat Putnam .02 .10
521 Greg Pryor .02 .10
522 Tony Scott .02 .10
523 Steve Mura .02 .10
524 Johnnie LeMaster .02 .10
525 Dick Ruthven .02 .10
526 John McNamara MG .02 .10
527 Larry McWilliams .02 .10
528 Johnny Ray RC .20 .50
529 Pat Tabler .02 .10
530 Tom Herr .02 .10
531A SD Chicken .40 1.00
ERR (Without TM)
531B San Diego Chicken .40 1.00
COR (With TM)
532 Sal Butera .02 .10
533 Mike Griffin .02 .10
534 Kelvin Moore .02 .10
535 Reggie Jackson .15 .40
536 Ed Romero .02 .10
537 Derrel Thomas .02 .10
538 Mike O'Berry .02 .10
539 Jack O'Connor .02 .10
540 Bob Ojeda RC .20 .50
541 Roy Lee Jackson .02 .10
542 Lynn Jones .02 .10
543 Gaylord Perry .07 .20
544A Phil Garner ERR .07 .20
(Reverse negative)
544B Phil Garner COR .07 .20
545 Garry Templeton .07 .20
546 Rafael Ramirez .02 .10
547 Jeff Reardon .07 .20
548 Ron Guidry .07 .20
549 Tim Laudner .02 .10
550 John Henry Johnson .02 .10
551 Chris Bando .02 .10
552 Bobby Brown .02 .10
553 Larry Bradford .02 .10
554 Scott Fletcher RC .20 .50
555 Jerry Royster .02 .10
556 Shooty Babitt UER .02 .10
(Spelled Babbitt
on front)
557 Kent Hrbek RC .40 1.00
558 Ron Guidry .07 .20
Tommy John
559 Mark Bomback .02 .10
560 Julio Valdez .02 .10
561 Buck Martinez .02 .10
562 Mike A. Marshall RC .20 .50
563 Rennie Stennett .02 .10
564 Steve Crawford .02 .10
565 Bob Babcock .02 .10
566 Johnny Podres CO .07 .20
567 Paul Serna .02 .10
568 Harold Baines .07 .20
569 Dave LaRoche .02 .10
570 Lee May .02 .10
571 Gary Ward .02 .10
572 John Denny .02 .10
573 Roy Smalley .02 .10
574 Bob Brenly RC .40 1.00
575 Reggie Jackson .07 .20
Dave Winfield
576 Luis Pujols .02 .10
577 Butch Hobson .02 .10
578 Harvey Kuenn MG .02 .10
579 Cal Ripken Sr. CO .07 .20
580 Juan Berenguer .02 .10
581 Benny Ayala .02 .10
582 Vance Law .02 .10
583 Rick Leach .02 .10
584 George Frazier .02 .10
585 Phillies Finest .60 1.50

Pete Rose
Mike Schmidt
586 Joe Rudi .07 .20
587 Juan Beniquez .02 .10
588 Luis DeLeon .02 .10
589 Craig Swan .02 .10
590 Dave Chalk .02 .10
591 Billy Gardner MG .02 .10
592 Sal Bando .07 .20
593 Bert Campaneris .07 .20
594 Steve Kemp .02 .10
595A Randy Lerch ERR .15 .40
(Braves)
595B Randy Lerch COR .02 .10
(Brewers)
596 Bryan Clark RC .05 .15
597 Dave Ford .02 .10
598 Mike Scioscia .07 .20
599 John Lowenstein .02 .10
600 Rene Lachemann MG .02 .10
601 Mick Kelleher .02 .10
602 Ron Jackson .02 .10
603 Jerry Koosman .07 .20
604 Dave Goltz .02 .10
605 Ellis Valentine .02 .10
606 Lonnie Smith .02 .10
607 Joaquin Andujar .07 .20
608 Garry Hancock .02 .10
609 Jerry Turner .02 .10
610 Bob Bonner .02 .10
611 Jim Dwyer .02 .10
612 Terry Bulling .02 .10
613 Joel Youngblood .02 .10
614 Larry Milbourne .02 .10
615 Gene Roof UER .02 .10
(Name on front
is Phil Roof)
616 Keith Drumwright .02 .10
617 Dave Rosello .02 .10
618 Rickey Keeton .02 .10
619 Dennis Lamp .02 .10
620 Sid Monge .02 .10
621 Jerry White .02 .10
622 Luis Aguayo .02 .10
623 Jamie Easterly .02 .10
624 Steve Sax RC .40 1.00
625 Dave Roberts .02 .10
626 Rick Bosetti .02 .10
627 Terry Francona RC 1.25 3.00
628 Tom Seaver .30 .75
Johnny Bench
629 Paul Mirabella .02 .10
630 Rance Mulliniks .02 .10
631 Kevin Hickey RC .05 .15
632 Reid Nichols .02 .10
633 Dave Geisel .02 .10
634 Ken Griffey .07 .20
635 Bob Lemon MG .15 .40
636 Orlando Sanchez .02 .10
637 Bill Almon .02 .10
638 Danny Ainge .07 .20
639 Willie Stargell .15 .40
640 Bob Sykes .02 .10
641 Ed Lynch .02 .10
642 John Ellis .02 .10
643 Ferguson Jenkins .07 .20
644 Lenn Sakata .02 .10
645 Julio Gonzalez .02 .10
646 Jesse Orosco .02 .10
647 Jerry Dybzinski .02 .10
648 Tommy Davis CO .07 .20
649 Ron Gardenhire RC .20 .50
650 Felipe Alou CO .07 .20
651 Harvey Haddix CO .07 .20
652 Willie Upshaw .20 .50
653 Bill Madlock .07 .20
654A DK Checklist 1-26 .15 .40
ERR (Unnumbered)
(With Trammel)
654B DK Checklist 1-26 .07 .20
COR (Unnumbered)
(With Trammell)
655 Checklist 27-130 .07 .20
(Unnumbered)
656 Checklist 131-234 .07 .20
(Unnumbered)
657 Checklist 235-338 .07 .20
(Unnumbered)
658 Checklist 339-442 .07 .20
(Unnumbered)
659 Checklist 443-544 .07 .20
(Unnumbered)
660 Checklist 545-653 .07 .20
(Unnumbered)

1983 Donruss

The 1983 Donruss baseball set leads off with a 26-card Diamond Kings (DK) series. Of the remaining 634 standard-size cards, two are combination cards, one portrays the San Diego Chicken, one shows the completed Ty Cobb puzzle, and seven are unnumbered checklist cards. The seven unnumbered checklist cards are arbitrarily assigned numbers 654 through 660 and are listed at the end of the list below. All cards measure the standard size. Card fronts feature full color photos around a framed white broder. Several printing variations are available but the complete set price below includes only the more common of each variation pair. Cards were issued in 15-card packs which included a three-piece Ty Cobb puzzle panel (21 different panels were needed to complete the puzzle). Notable Rookie Cards include Wade Boggs, Tony Gwynn and Ryne Sandberg.

COMPLETE SET (660) 30.00 60.00
COMP.FACT.SET (660) 40.00 80.00
COMP.COBB PUZZLE 2.00 5.00

1 Fernando Valenzuela DK .07 .20
2 Rollie Fingers DK .07 .20
3 Reggie Jackson DK .15 .40
4 Jim Palmer DK .07 .20
5 Jack Morris DK .07 .20
6 George Foster DK .07 .20
7 Jim Sundberg DK .07 .20
8 Willie Stargell DK .15 .40
9 Dave Stieb DK .07 .20
10 Joe Niekro DK .02 .10
11 Rickey Henderson DK .60 1.50
12 Dale Murphy DK .15 .40
13 Toby Harrah DK .07 .20
14 Bill Buckner DK .07 .20
15 Willie Wilson DK .07 .20
16 Steve Carlton DK .15 .40
17 Ron Guidry DK .07 .20
18 Steve Rogers DK .07 .20
19 Kent Hrbek DK .07 .20
20 Keith Hernandez DK .07 .20
21 Floyd Bannister DK .02 .10
22 Johnny Bench DK .30 .75
23 Britt Burns DK .02 .10
24 Joe Morgan DK .07 .20
25 Carl Yastrzemski DK .30 .75
26 Terry Kennedy DK .02 .10
27 Gary Roenicke .02 .10
28 Dwight Bernard .02 .10
29 Pat Underwood .02 .10
30 Gary Allenson .02 .10
31 Ron Guidry .07 .20
32 Burt Hooton .02 .10
33 Chris Bando .02 .10
34 Vida Blue .07 .20
35 Rickey Henderson .60 1.50
36 Ray Burris .02 .10
37 John Butcher .02 .10
38 Don Aase .02 .10
39 Jerry Koosman .07 .20
40 Bruce Sutter .15 .40
41 Jose Cruz .07 .20
42 Pete Rose 1.00 2.50
43 Cesar Cedeno .07 .20
44 Floyd Chiffer .02 .10
45 Larry McWilliams .02 .10
46 Alan Fowlkes .02 .10
47 Dale Murphy .15 .40
48 Doug Bird .02 .10
49 Hubie Brooks .07 .20
50 Floyd Bannister .02 .10
51 Jack O'Connor .02 .10
52 Steve Senteney .02 .10
53 Gary Gaetti RC .40 1.00
54 Damaso Garcia .02 .10
55 Gene Nelson .02 .10
56 Mookie Wilson .07 .20
57 Allen Ripley .02 .10
58 Bob Horner .07 .20
59 Tony Pena .02 .10
60 Gary Lavelle .02 .10
61 Tim Lollar .02 .10
62 Frank Pastore .02 .10
63 Garry Maddox .02 .10
64 Bob Forsch .02 .10
65 Harry Spilman .02 .10
66 Geoff Zahn .02 .10
67 Salome Barojas .02 .10
68 David Palmer .02 .10
69 Charlie Hough .07 .20
70 Dan Quisenberry .07 .20
71 Tony Armas .07 .20
72 Rick Sutcliffe .07 .20
73 Steve Balboni .02 .10
74 Jerry Remy .02 .10
75 Mike Scioscia .07 .20
76 John Wockenfuss .02 .10
77 Jim Palmer .07 .20
78 Rollie Fingers .07 .20
79 Joe Nolan .02 .10
80 Pete Vuckovich .02 .10
81 Rick Leach .02 .10
82 Rick Miller .02 .10
83 Graig Nettles .07 .20
84 Ron Cey .07 .20
85 Miguel Dilone .02 .10
86 John Wathan .02 .10
87 Kelvin Moore .02 .10
88A Byrn Smith ERR .07 .20
(Sic, Bryn)
88B Bryn Smith COR .15 .40
89 Dave Hostetler .02 .10
90 Rod Carew .15 .40
91 Lonnie Smith .02 .10
92 Bob Knepper .02 .10
93 Marty Bystrom .02 .10
94 Chris Welsh .02 .10
95 Jason Thompson .02 .10
96 Tom O'Malley .02 .10
97 Phil Niekro .07 .20
98 Neil Allen .02 .10
99 Bill Buckner .07 .20
100 Ed VandeBerg .02 .10
101 Jim Clancy .02 .10
102 Robert Castillo .02 .10
103 Bruce Berenyi .02 .10
104 Carlton Fisk .15 .40
105 Mike Flanagan .02 .10
106 Cecil Cooper .07 .20
107 Jack Morris .07 .20
108 Mike Morgan .02 .10
109 Luis Aponte .02 .10
110 Pedro Guerrero .07 .20
111 Len Barker .02 .10
112 Willie Wilson .07 .20
113 Dave Beard .02 .10
114 Mike Gates .02 .10
115 Reggie Jackson .15 .40
116 George Wright RC .20 .50
117 Vance Law .02 .10
118 Nolan Ryan 1.50 4.00
119 Mike Krukow .02 .10
120 Ozzie Smith .50 1.25
121 Broderick Perkins .02 .10
122 Tom Seaver .30 .75
123 Chris Chambliss .07 .20
124 Chuck Tanner MG .02 .10
125 Johnnie LeMaster .02 .10
126 Mel Hall RC .20 .50
127 Bruce Bochte .02 .10
128 Charlie Puleo .02 .10
129 Luis Leal .02 .10
130 John Pacella .02 .10
131 Glenn Gulliver .02 .10
132 Don Money .02 .10
133 Dave Rozema .02 .10
134 Bruce Hurst .02 .10
135 Rudy May .02 .10
136 Tom Lasorda MG .15 .40
137 Dan Spillner UER .02 .10
(Photo actually
Ed Whitson)
138 Jerry Martin .02 .10
139 Mike Norris .02 .10
140 Al Oliver .07 .20
141 Daryl Sconiers .02 .10
142 Lamar Johnson .02 .10
143 Harold Baines .07 .20
144 Alan Ashby .02 .10
145 Garry Templeton .07 .20
146 Al Holland .02 .10
147 Bo Diaz .02 .10
148 Dave Concepcion .07 .20
149 Rick Camp .02 .10
150 Jim Morrison .02 .10
151 Randy Martz .02 .10
152 Keith Hernandez .07 .20
153 John Lowenstein .02 .10
154 Mike Caldwell .02 .10
155 Milt Wilcox .02 .10
156 Rich Gedman .02 .10
157 Rich Gossage .07 .20
158 Jerry Reuss .02 .10
159 Ron Hassey .02 .10
160 Larry Gura .02 .10
161 Dwayne Murphy .02 .10
162 Woodie Fryman .02 .10
163 Steve Comer .02 .10
164 Ken Forsch .02 .10
165 Dennis Lamp .02 .10
166 David Green RC .20 .50
167 Terry Puhl .02 .10
168 Mike Schmidt .75 2.00
(Wearing 37
rather than 20)
169 Eddie Milner .02 .10
170 John Curtis .02 .10
171 Don Robinson .02 .10
172 Rich Gale .02 .10
173 Steve Bedrosian .02 .10
174 Willie Hernandez .02 .10
175 Ron Gardenhire .02 .10
176 Jim Beattie .02 .10
177 Tim Laudner .02 .10
178 Buck Martinez .02 .10
179 Kent Hrbek .07 .20
180 Alfredo Griffin .02 .10
181 Larry Andersen .02 .10
182 Pete Falcone .02 .10
183 Jody Davis .02 .10
184 Glenn Hubbard .02 .10
185 Dale Berra .02 .10
186 Greg Minton .02 .10
187 Gary Lucas .02 .10
188 Dave Van Gorder .02 .10
189 Bob Dernier .02 .10
190 Willie McGee RC .60 1.50
191 Dickie Thon .02 .10
192 Bob Boone .07 .20
193 Britt Burns .02 .10
194 Jeff Reardon .07 .20
195 Jon Matlack .02 .10
196 Don Slaught RC .20 .50
197 Fred Stanley .02 .10
198 Rick Manning .02 .10
199 Dave Righetti .07 .20
200 Dave Stapleton .02 .10
201 Steve Yeager .07 .20
202 Enos Cabell .02 .10
203 Sammy Stewart .02 .10
204 Moose Haas .02 .10
205 Lenn Sakata .02 .10
206 Charlie Moore .02 .10
207 Alan Trammell .07 .20
208 Jim Rice .07 .20
209 Roy Smalley .02 .10
210 Bill Russell .07 .20
211 Andre Thornton .02 .10
212 Willie Aikens .02 .10
213 Dave McKay .02 .10
214 Tim Blackwell .02 .10
215 Buddy Bell .07 .20
216 Doug DeCinces .02 .10
217 Tom Herr .02 .10
218 Frank LaCorte .02 .10
219 Steve Carlton .15 .40
220 Terry Kennedy .02 .10
221 Mike Easler .02 .10
222 Jack Clark .07 .20
223 Gene Garber .02 .10
224 Scott Holman .02 .10
225 Mike Proly .02 .10
226 Terry Bulling .02 .10
227 Jerry Garvin .02 .10
228 Ron Davis .02 .10
229 Tom Hume .02 .10
230 Marc Hill .02 .10
231 Dennis Martinez .07 .20
232 Jim Gantner .02 .10
233 Larry Pashnick .02 .10
234 Dave Collins .02 .10
235 Tom Burgmeier .02 .10
236 Ken Landreaux .02 .10
237 John Denny .02 .10
238 Hal McRae .07 .20
239 Matt Keough .02 .10
240 Doug Flynn .02 .10
241 Fred Lynn .07 .20
242 Billy Sample .02 .10
243 Tom Paciorek .02 .10
244 Joe Sambito .02 .10
245 Sid Monge .02 .10
246 Ken Oberkfell .02 .10
247 Joe Pittman UER .02 .10
(Photo actually
Juan Eichelberger)
248 Mario Soto .07 .20
249 Claudell Washington .02 .10
250 Rick Rhoden .02 .10
251 Darrell Evans .07 .20
252 Steve Henderson .02 .10
253 Manny Castillo .02 .10
254 Craig Swan .02 .10
255 Joey McLaughlin .02 .10
256 Pete Redfern .02 .10
257 Ken Singleton .07 .20
258 Robin Yount .50 1.25
259 Elias Sosa .02 .10
260 Bob Ojeda .02 .10
261 Bobby Murcer .07 .20
262 Candy Maldonado RC .20 .50
263 Rick Waits .02 .10
264 Greg Pryor .02 .10
265 Bob Owchinko .02 .10
266 Chris Speier .02 .10
267 Bruce Kison .02 .10
268 Mark Wagner .02 .10
269 Steve Kemp .02 .10
270 Phil Garner .07 .20
271 Gene Richards .02 .10
272 Renie Martin .02 .10
273 Dave Roberts .02 .10
274 Dan Driessen .02 .10
275 Rufino Linares .02 .10
276 Lee Lacy .02 .10
277 Ryne Sandberg RC 4.00 10.00
278 Darrell Porter .02 .10
279 Cal Ripken 2.50 6.00
280 Jamie Easterly .02 .10
281 Bill Fahey .02 .10
282 Glenn Hoffman .02 .10
283 Willie Randolph .07 .20
284 Fernando Valenzuela .07 .20
285 Alan Bannister .02 .10
286 Paul Splittorff .02 .10
287 Joe Rudi .07 .20
288 Bill Gullickson .02 .10
289 Danny Darwin .02 .10
290 Andy Hassler .02 .10
291 Ernesto Escarrega .02 .10
292 Steve Mura .02 .10
293 Tony Scott .02 .10
294 Manny Trillo .02 .10
295 Greg Harris .02 .10
296 Luis DeLeon .02 .10
297 Kent Tekulve .02 .10
298 Atlee Hammaker .02 .10
299 Bruce Benedict .02 .10
300 Fergie Jenkins .07 .20
301 Dave Kingman .07 .20
302 Bill Caudill .02 .10
303 John Castino .02 .10
304 Ernie Whitt .02 .10
305 Randy Johnson .02 .10
306 Garth Iorg .02 .10
307 Gaylord Perry .07 .20
308 Ed Lynch .02 .10
309 Keith Moreland .02 .10
310 Rafael Ramirez .02 .10
311 Bill Madlock .07 .20
312 Milt May .02 .10
313 John Montefusco .02 .10
314 Wayne Krenchicki .02 .10
315 George Vukovich .02 .10
316 Joaquin Andujar .07 .20
317 Craig Reynolds .02 .10
318 Rick Burleson .02 .10
319 Richard Dotson .02 .10
320 Steve Rogers .07 .20
321 Dave Schmidt .02 .10
322 Bud Black RC .20 .50
323 Jeff Burroughs .02 .10
324 Von Hayes .02 .10
325 Butch Wynegar .02 .10
326 Carl Yastrzemski .50 1.25
327 Ron Roenicke .02 .10
328 Howard Johnson RC .40 1.00
329 Rick Dempsey UER .02 .10
(Posing as a left-
handed batter)
330A Jim Slaton .02 .10
(Bio printed
black on white)
330B Jim Slaton .07 .20
(Bio printed
black on yellow)
331 Benny Ayala .02 .10
332 Ted Simmons .07 .20
333 Lou Whitaker .07 .20
334 Chuck Rainey .02 .10
335 Lou Piniella .07 .20
336 Steve Sax .07 .20
337 Toby Harrah .07 .20
338 George Brett .75 2.00
339 Dave Lopes .07 .20
340 Gary Carter .07 .20
341 John Grubb .02 .10
342 Tim Foli .02 .10
343 Jim Kaat .07 .20
344 Mike LaCoss .02 .10
345 Larry Christenson .02 .10
346 Juan Bonilla .02 .10
347 Omar Moreno .02 .10
348 Chili Davis .07 .20
349 Tommy Boggs .02 .10
350 Rusty Staub .07 .20
351 Bump Wills .02 .10
352 Rick Sweet .02 .10
353 Jim Gott RC .20 .50
354 Terry Felton .02 .10
355 Jim Kern .02 .10
356 Bill Almon UER .02 .10
(Expos/Mets in 1983,
not Padres/Mets)
357 Tippy Martinez .02 .10
358 Roy Howell .02 .10
359 Dan Petry .02 .10
360 Jerry Mumphrey .02 .10
361 Mark Clear .02 .10
362 Mike Marshall .02 .10
363 Lary Sorensen .02 .10
364 Amos Otis .07 .20
365 Rick Langford .02 .10
366 Brad Mills .02 .10
367 Brian Downing .07 .20
368 Mike Richardt .02 .10
369 Aurelio Rodriguez .02 .10
370 Dave Smith .02 .10
371 Tug McGraw .07 .20
372 Doug Bair .02 .10
373 Ruppert Jones .02 .10
374 Alex Trevino .02 .10
375 Ken Dayley .02 .10
376 Rod Scurry .02 .10
377 Bob Brenly .02 .10
378 Scot Thompson .02 .10
379 Julio Cruz .02 .10
380 John Stearns .02 .10
381 Dale Murray .02 .10
382 Frank Viola RC .60 1.50
383 Al Bumbry .02 .10
384 Ben Oglivie .07 .20
385 Dave Tobik .02 .10
386 Bob Stanley .02 .10
387 Andre Robertson .02 .10
388 Jorge Orta .02 .10
389 Ed Whitson .02 .10
390 Don Hood .02 .10
391 Tom Underwood .02 .10
392 Tim Wallach .07 .20
393 Steve Renko .02 .10
394 Mickey Rivers .02 .10
395 Greg Luzinski .07 .20
396 Art Howe .02 .10
397 Alan Wiggins .02 .10
398 Jim Barr .02 .10
399 Ivan DeJesus .02 .10
400 Tom Lawless .02 .10
401 Bob Walk .02 .10
402 Jimmy Smith .02 .10
403 Lee Smith .15 .40
404 George Hendrick .07 .20
405 Eddie Murray .30 .75
406 Marshall Edwards .02 .10
407 Lance Parrish .07 .20
408 Carney Lansford .07 .20
409 Dave Winfield .07 .20
410 Bob Welch .07 .20
411 Larry Milbourne .02 .10
412 Dennis Leonard .02 .10
413 Dan Meyer .02 .10
414 Charlie Lea .02 .10
415 Rick Honeycutt .02 .10
416 Mike Witt .02 .10
417 Steve Trout .02 .10
418 Glenn Brummer .02 .10
419 Denny Walling .02 .10
420 Gary Matthews .07 .20
421 Charlie Leibrandt UER .02 .10
(Liebrandt on
front of card)
422 J.Eichelberger UER .02 .10
Photo actually
Joe Pittman
423 Cecilio Guante UER .02 .10
(Listed as Matt
on card)
424 Bill Laskey .02 .10
425 Jerry Royster .02 .10
426 Dickie Noles .02 .10
427 George Foster .07 .20
428 Mike Moore RC .20 .50
429 Gary Ward .02 .10
430 Barry Bonnell .02 .10
431 Ron Washington .02 .10
432 Rance Mulliniks .02 .10
433 Mike Stanton .02 .10
434 Jesse Orosco .02 .10
435 Larry Bowa .07 .20
436 Biff Pocoroba .02 .10
437 Johnny Ray .02 .10
438 Joe Morgan .07 .20
439 Eric Show RC .20 .50
440 Larry Biittner .02 .10
441 Greg Gross .02 .10
442 Gene Tenace .07 .20
443 Danny Heep .02 .10
444 Bobby Clark .02 .10
445 Kevin Hickey .02 .10
446 Scott Sanderson .02 .10
447 Frank Tanana .07 .20
448 Cesar Geronimo .02 .10
449 Jimmy Sexton .02 .10
450 Mike Hargrove .02 .10
451 Doyle Alexander .02 .10
452 Dwight Evans .15 .40
453 Terry Forster .07 .20
454 Tom Brookens .02 .10
455 Rich Dauer .02 .10
456 Rob Picciolo .02 .10
457 Terry Crowley .02 .10
458 Ned Yost .02 .10
459 Kirk Gibson .07 .20
460 Reid Nichols .02 .10
461 Oscar Gamble .02 .10
462 Dusty Baker .07 .20
463 Jack Perconte .02 .10
464 Frank White .07 .20
465 Mickey Klutts .02 .10
466 Warren Cromartie .02 .10
467 Larry Parrish .02 .10
468 Bobby Grich .07 .20
469 Dane Iorg .02 .10
470 Joe Niekro .02 .10
471 Ed Farmer .02 .10
472 Tim Flannery .02 .10
473 Dave Parker .07 .20
474 Jeff Leonard .02 .10
475 Al Hrabosky .02 .10
476 Ron Hodges .02 .10
477 Leon Durham .02 .10
478 Jim Essian .02 .10
479 Roy Lee Jackson .02 .10
480 Brad Havens .02 .10
481 Joe Price .02 .10
482 Tony Bernazard .02 .10
483 Scott McGregor .02 .10
484 Paul Molitor .07 .20
485 Mike Ivie .02 .10
486 Ken Griffey .07 .20
487 Dennis Eckersley .15 .40
488 Steve Garvey .07 .20
489 Mike Fischlin .02 .10
490 U.L. Washington .02 .10
491 Steve McCatty .02 .10
492 Roy Johnson .02 .10
493 Don Baylor .07 .20
494 Bobby Johnson .02 .10
495 Mike Squires .02 .10
496 Bert Roberge .02 .10
497 Dick Ruthven .02 .10
498 Tito Landrum .02 .10
499 Sixto Lezcano .02 .10
500 Johnny Bench .30 .75
501 Larry Whisenton .02 .10
502 Manny Sarmiento .02 .10
503 Fred Breining .02 .10
504 Bill Campbell .02 .10
505 Todd Cruz .02 .10
506 Bob Bailor .02 .10
507 Dave Stieb .07 .20
508 Al Williams .02 .10
509 Dan Ford .02 .10
510 Gorman Thomas .07 .20
511 Chet Lemon .07 .20
512 Mike Torrez .02 .10
513 Shane Rawley .02 .10
514 Mark Belanger .02 .10
515 Rodney Craig .02 .10
516 Onix Concepcion .02 .10
517 Mike Heath .02 .10
518 Andre Dawson UER .07 .20
(Middle name Fernando,
should be Nolan)
519 Luis Sanchez .02 .10
520 Terry Bogener .02 .10
521 Rudy Law .02 .10
522 Ray Knight .07 .20
523 Joe Lefebvre .02 .10
524 Jim Wohlford .02 .10
525 Julio Franco RC 2.50 6.00
526 Ron Oester .02 .10
527 Rick Mahler .02 .10
528 Steve Nicosia .02 .10
529 Junior Kennedy .02 .10
530A Whitey Herzog MG .07 .20
(Bio printed
black on white)
530B Whitey Herzog MG .07 .20
(Bio printed
black on yellow)
531A Don Sutton .07 .20
(Blue border
on photo)
531B Don Sutton .07 .20
(Green border
on photo)
532 Mark Brouhard .02 .10
533A S.Anderson MG .07 .20
Bio printed
black on white
533B S.Anderson MG .07 .20
Bio printed
black on yellow
534 Roger LaFrancois .02 .10
535 George Frazier .02 .10
536 Tom Niedenfuer .02 .10
537 Ed Glynn .02 .10
538 Lee May .02 .10
539 Bob Kearney .02 .10
540 Tim Raines .07 .20
541 Paul Mirabella .02 .10
542 Luis Tiant .07 .20
543 Ron LeFlore .07 .20
544 Dave LaPoint .02 .10
545 Randy Moffitt .02 .10
546 Luis Aguayo .02 .10
547 Brad Lesley .05 .15
548 Luis Salazar .02 .10
549 John Candelaria .02 .10
550 Dave Bergman .02 .10
551 Bob Watson .02 .10
552 Pat Tabler .02 .10
553 Brent Gaff .02 .10
554 Al Cowens .02 .10
555 Tom Brunansky .07 .20
556 Lloyd Moseby .02 .10
557A Pascual Perez ERR .75 2.00
(Twins in glove)
557B Pascual Perez COR .07 .20
(Braves in glove)
558 Willie Upshaw .02 .10
559 Richie Zisk .02 .10
560 Pat Zachry .02 .10
561 Jay Johnstone .02 .10
562 Carlos Diaz RC .05 .15
563 John Tudor .07 .20
564 Frank Robinson MG .15 .40
565 Dave Edwards .02 .10
566 Paul Householder .02 .10
567 Ron Reed .02 .10
568 Mike Ramsey .02 .10
569 Kiko Garcia .02 .10
570 Tommy John .07 .20
571 Tony LaRussa MG .07 .20
572 Joel Youngblood .02 .10
573 Wayne Tolleson .02 .10
574 Keith Creel .02 .10
575 Billy Martin MG .15 .40
576 Jerry Dybzinski .02 .10
577 Rick Cerone .02 .10
578 Tony Perez .15 .40
579 Greg Brock .02 .10
580 Glenn Wilson .20 .50
581 Tim Stoddard .02 .10
582 Bob McClure .02 .10
583 Jim Dwyer .02 .10
584 Ed Romero .02 .10
585 Larry Herndon .02 .10
586 Wade Boggs RC 4.00 10.00
587 Jay Howell .02 .10
588 Dave Stewart .07 .20
589 Bert Blyleven .07 .20
590 Dick Howser MG .02 .10
591 Wayne Gross .02 .10
592 Terry Francona .07 .20
593 Don Werner .02 .10
594 Bill Stein .02 .10
595 Jesse Barfield .07 .20
596 Bob Molinaro .02 .10
597 Mike Vail .02 .10
598 Tony Gwynn RC 6.00 15.00
599 Gary Rajsich .02 .10
600 Jerry Ujdur .02 .10
601 Cliff Johnson .02 .10
602 Jerry White .02 .10
603 Bryan Clark .02 .10
604 Joe Ferguson .02 .10
605 Guy Sularz .02 .10
606A Ozzie Virgil .07 .20
(Green border
on photo)
606B Ozzie Virgil .07 .20
(Orange border
on photo)
607 Terry Harper .02 .10

608 Harvey Kuenn MG .02 .10
609 Jim Sundberg .07 .20
610 Willie Stargell .15 .40
611 Reggie Smith .07 .20
612 Rob Wilfong .02 .10
613 Joe Niekro .07 .20
Phil Niekro
614 Lee Elia MG .02 .10
615 Mickey Hatcher .02 .10
616 Jerry Hairston .02 .10
617 John Martin .02 .10
618 Wally Backman .02 .10
619 Storm Davis RC .20 .50
620 Alan Knicely .02 .10
621 John Stuper .02 .10
622 Matt Sinatro .02 .10
623 Geno Petralli .20 .50
624 Duane Walker .02 .10
625 Dick Williams MG .02 .10
626 Pat Corrales MG .02 .10
627 Vern Ruhle .02 .10
628 Joe Torre MG .07 .20
629 Anthony Johnson .02 .10
630 Steve Howe .02 .10
631 Gary Woods .02 .10
632 LaMarr Hoyt .02 .10
633 Steve Swisher .02 .10
634 Terry Leach .02 .10
635 Jeff Newman .02 .10
636 Brett Butler .07 .20
637 Gary Gray .02 .10
638 Lee Mazzilli .07 .20
639A Ron Jackson ERR 8.00 20.00
(A's in glove)
639B Ron Jackson COR .02 .10
(Angels in glove,
red border
on photo)
639C Ron Jackson COR .15 .40
(Angels in glove,
green border
on photo)
640 Juan Beniquez .02 .10
641 Dave Rucker .02 .10
642 Luis Pujols .02 .10
643 Rick Monday .07 .20
644 Hosken Powell .02 .10
645 The Chicken .15 .40
646 Dave Engle .02 .10
647 Dick Davis .02 .10
648 Frank Robinson .15 .40
Vida Blue
Joe Morgan
649 Al Chambers .02 .10
650 Jesus Vega .02 .10
651 Jeff Jones .02 .10
652 Marvis Foley .02 .10
653 Ty Cobb Puzzle Card .30 .75
654A Dick Perez/Diamond .15 .40
King Checklist 1-26
(Unnumbered) ERR
(Word 'checklist'
omitted from back)
654B Dick Perez/Diamond .15 .40
King Checklist 1-26
(Unnumbered) COR
(Word 'checklist'
is on back)
655 Checklist 27-130 .02 .10
(Unnumbered)
656 Checklist 131-234 .02 .10
(Unnumbered)
657 Checklist 235-338 .02 .10
(Unnumbered)
658 Checklist 339-442 .02 .10
(Unnumbered)
659 Checklist 443-544 .02 .10
(Unnumbered)
660 Checklist 545-653 .02 .10
(Unnumbered)

1984 Donruss

The 1984 Donruss set contains a total of 660 standard-size cards; however, only 658 are numbered. The first 26 cards in the set are again Diamond Kings (DK). A new feature, Rated Rookies (RR), was introduced with this set with Bill Madden's 20 selections comprising numbers 27 through 46. Two "Living Legend" cards designated A (featuring Gaylord Perry and Rollie Fingers) and B (featuring Johnny Bench and Carl Yastrzemski) were issued as bonus cards in wax packs, but were not issued in the factory sets sold to hobby dealers. The seven unnumbered checklist cards are arbitrarily assigned numbers 652 through 658 and are listed at the end of the list below. The attractive card front designs changed considerably from the previous two years. This set has since grown in stature to be recognized as one of the finest produced in the 1980's. The backs contain statistics and are printed in green and black ink. The cards, issued amongst other ways in 15 card packs which had a 30 cent SRP, were distributed with a three-piece puzzle panel of Duke Snider. There are no extra variation cards included in the complete set price below. The variation cards apparently resulted from a different printing for the factory sets as the Darling and Stenhouse no number variations as well as the Perez-Steele errors were corrected in the factory sets which were released later in the year. The factory sets were shipped 15 to a case. The Diamond King cards found in packs spelled Perez-Steele as Perez-Steel. Rookie Cards in this set include Joe Carter, Don Mattingly, Darryl Strawberry, and Andy Van Slyke. The Joe Carter card is almost never found well centered.

COMPLETE SET (660) 70.00 120.00
COMP.FACT.SET (658) 70.00 120.00
COMP.SNIDER PUZZLE 2.00 5.00
1 Robin Yount DK COR 1.00 2.50
1A Robin Yount DK ERR 2.00 5.00
2 Dave Concepcion DK .30 .75
COR
2A Dave Concepcion DK .30 .75
ERR (Perez Steel)
3 Dwayne Murphy DK .08 .25
COR
3A Dwayne Murphy DK .08 .25
ERR (Perez Steel)
4 John Castino DK COR .08 .25
4A John Castino DK ERR .08 .25
(Perez Steel)
5 Leon Durham DK COR .30 .75
5A Leon Durham DK ERR .08 .25
(Perez Steel)
6 Rusty Staub DK COR .30 .75
6A Rusty Staub DK ERR .30 .75
(Perez Steel)
7 Jack Clark DK COR .30 .75
7A Jack Clark DK ERR .30 .75
(Perez Steel)
8 Dave Dravecky DK .08 .25
COR
8A Dave Dravecky DK .08 .25
ERR (Perez Steel)
9 Al Oliver DK COR .30 .75
9A Al Oliver DK ERR .30 .75
(Perez Steel)
10 Dave Righetti DK .30 .75
COR
10A Dave Righetti DK .30 .75
ERR (Perez Steel)
11 Hal McRae DK COR .30 .75
11A Hal McRae DK ERR .30 .75
(Perez Steel)
12 Ray Knight DK COR .30 .75
12A Ray Knight DK ERR .30 .75
(Perez Steel)
13 Bruce Sutter DK COR .60 1.50
13A Bruce Sutter DK ERR .60 1.50
(Perez Steel)
14 Bob Horner DK COR .30 .75
14A Bob Horner DK ERR .30 .75
(Perez Steel)
15 Lance Parrish DK .30 .75
COR
15A Lance Parrish DK .30 .75
ERR (Perez Steel)
16 Matt Young DK COR .30 .75
16A Matt Young DK ERR .30 .75
(Perez Steel)
17 Fred Lynn DK COR .30 .75
17A Fred Lynn DK ERR .30 .75
(Perez Steel)
(A's logo on back)
18 Ron Kittle DK COR .08 .25
18A Ron Kittle DK ERR .08 .25
(Perez Steel)
19 Jim Clancy DK COR .08 .25
19A Jim Clancy DK ERR .08 .25
(Perez Steel)
20 Bill Madlock DK COR .30 .75
20A Bill Madlock DK ERR .30 .75
(Perez Steel)
21 Larry Parrish DK .08 .25
COR
21A Larry Parrish DK .08 .25
ERR (Perez Steel)
22 Eddie Murray DK COR 1.25 3.00
22A Eddie Murray DK ERR 1.25 3.00
23 Mike Schmidt DK COR 2.00 5.00
23A M.Schmidt DK ERR 2.00 5.00
24 Pedro Guerrero DK .30 .75
COR
24A Pedro Guerrero DK .30 .75
ERR (Perez Steel)
25 Andre Thornton DK .08 .25
COR
25A Andre Thornton DK .08 .25
ERR (Perez Steel)
26 Wade Boggs DK COR 1.25 3.00
26A Wade Boggs DK ERR 1.25 3.00
27 Joel Skinner RC .08 .25
28 Tommy Dunbar RC .08 .25
29A Mike Stenhouse RC .08 .25
ERR No number on back
29B Mike Stenhouse RR 1.25 3.00
COR Numbered on back
30A Ron Darling RC .75 2.00
ERR No number on back
30B Ron Darling RR COR 1.25 3.00
(Numbered on back)
31 Dion James RC .08 .25
32 Tony Fernandez RC .75 2.00
33 Angel Salazar RC .08 .25
34 Kevin McReynolds RC .75 2.00
35 Dick Schofield RC .40 1.00
36 Brad Komminsk RC .08 .25
37 Tim Teufel RR RC .40 1.00
38 Doug Frobel RC .08 .25
39 Greg Gagne RC .40 1.00
40 Mike Fuentes RC .08 .25
41 Joe Carter RR RC 3.00 8.00
42 Mike C. Brown RC .08 .25
(Angels OF)
43 Mike Jeffcoat RC .08 .25
44 Sid Fernandez RC .75 2.00
45 Brian Dayett RC .08 .25
46 Chris Smith RC .08 .25
47 Eddie Murray 1.25 3.00
48 Robin Yount 2.00 5.00
49 Lance Parrish .60 1.50
50 Jim Rice .30 .75
51 Dave Winfield .30 .75
52 Fernando Valenzuela .30 .75
53 George Brett 3.00 8.00
54 Rickey Henderson 2.00 5.00
55 Gary Carter .30 .75
56 Buddy Bell .30 .75
57 Reggie Jackson .60 1.50
58 Harold Baines .30 .75
59 Ozzie Smith 2.00 5.00
60 Nolan Ryan UER 6.00 15.00
(Text on back refers to 1972 as
the year he struck out 383;
the year was 1973)
61 Pete Rose 4.00 10.00
62 Ron Oester .08 .25
63 Steve Garvey .30 .75
64 Jason Thompson .08 .25
65 Jack Clark .30 .75
66 Dale Murphy .60 1.50
67 Leon Durham .08 .25
68 Darryl Strawberry RC 3.00 8.00
69 Richie Zisk .08 .25
70 Kent Hrbek .30 .75
71 Dave Stieb .30 .75
72 Ken Schrom .08 .25
73 George Bell .30 .75
74 John Moses .08 .25
75 Ed Lynch .08 .25
76 Chuck Rainey .08 .25
77 Biff Pocoroba .08 .25
78 Cecilio Guante .08 .25
79 Jim Barr .08 .25
80 Kurt Bevacqua .08 .25
81 Tom Foley .08 .25
82 Joe Lefebvre .08 .25
83 Andy Van Slyke RC 1.50 4.00
84 Bob Lillis MG .08 .25
85 Ricky Adams .08 .25
86 Jerry Hairston .08 .25
87 Bob James .08 .25
88 Joe Altobelli MG .08 .25
89 Ed Romero .08 .25
90 John Grubb .08 .25
91 John Henry Johnson .08 .25
92 Juan Espino .08 .25
93 Candy Maldonado .08 .25
94 Andre Thornton .08 .25
95 Onix Concepcion .08 .25
96 Donnie Hill UER .08 .25
(Listed as P,
should be 2B)
97 Andre Dawson UER .30 .75
(Wrong middle name,
should be Nolan)
98 Frank Tanana .30 .75
99 Curtis Wilkerson .08 .25
100 Larry Gura .08 .25
101 Dwayne Murphy .08 .25
102 Tom Brennan .08 .25
103 Dave Righetti .30 .75
104 Steve Sax .08 .25
105 Dan Petry .30 .75
106 Cal Ripken 5.00 12.00
107 Paul Molitor UER .30 .75
('83 stats should
say .270 BA, 608 AB,
and 164 hits)
108 Fred Lynn .30 .75
109 Neil Allen .08 .25
110 Joe Niekro .08 .25
111 Steve Carlton .60 1.50
112 Terry Kennedy .08 .25
113 Bill Madlock .30 .75
114 Chili Davis .30 .75
115 Jim Gantner .08 .25
116 Tom Seaver 1.25 3.00
117 Bill Buckner .30 .75
118 Bill Caudill .08 .25
119 Jim Clancy .08 .25
120 John Castino .08 .25
121 Dave Concepcion .30 .75
122 Greg Luzinski .30 .75
123 Mike Boddicker .08 .25
124 Pete Ladd .08 .25
125 Juan Berenguer .08 .25
126 John Montefusco .08 .25
127 Ed Jurak .08 .25
128 Tom Niedenfuer .08 .25
129 Bert Blyleven .30 .75
130 Bud Black .08 .25
131 Gorman Heimueller .08 .25
132 Dan Schatzeder .08 .25
133 Ron Jackson .08 .25
134 Tom Henke RC .75 2.00
135 Kevin Hickey .08 .25
136 Mike Scott .30 .75
137 Bo Diaz .08 .25
138 Glenn Brummer .08 .25
139 Sid Monge .08 .25
140 Rich Gale .08 .25
141 Brett Butler .30 .75
142 Brian Harper RC .40 1.00
143 John Rabb .08 .25
144 Gary Woods .08 .25
145 Pat Putnam .08 .25
146 Jim Acker .08 .25
147 Mickey Hatcher .08 .25
148 Todd Cruz .08 .25
149 Tom Tellmann .08 .25
150 John Wockenfuss .08 .25
151 Wade Boggs UER 3.00 8.00
1983 runs 10; should be 100
152 Don Baylor .30 .75
153 Bob Welch .30 .75
154 Alan Bannister .08 .25
155 Willie Aikens .08 .25
156 Jeff Burroughs .08 .25
157 Bryan Little .08 .25
158 Bob Boone .30 .75
159 Dave Hostetler .08 .25
160 Jerry Dybzinski .08 .25
161 Mike Madden .08 .25
162 Luis DeLeon .08 .25
163 Willie Hernandez .08 .25
164 Frank Pastore .08 .25
165 Rick Camp .08 .25
166 Lee Mazzilli .30 .75
167 Scot Thompson .08 .25
168 Bob Forsch .08 .25
169 Mike Flanagan .08 .25
170 Rick Manning .08 .25
171 Chet Lemon .30 .75
172 Jerry Remy .08 .25
173 Ron Guidry .30 .75
174 Pedro Guerrero .30 .75
175 Willie Wilson .30 .75
176 Carney Lansford .30 .75
177 Al Oliver .30 .75
178 Jim Sundberg .30 .75
179 Bobby Grich .30 .75
180 Rich Dotson .08 .25
181 Joaquin Andujar .30 .75
182 Jose Cruz .30 .75
183 Mike Schmidt 3.00 8.00
184 Gary Redus RC .40 1.00
185 Garry Templeton .30 .75
186 Tony Pena .08 .25
187 Greg Minton .08 .25
188 Phil Niekro .30 .75
189 Ferguson Jenkins .30 .75
190 Mookie Wilson .30 .75
191 Jim Beattie .08 .25
192 Gary Ward .08 .25
193 Jesse Barfield .30 .75
194 Pete Filson .08 .25
195 Roy Lee Jackson .08 .25
196 Rick Sweet .08 .25
197 Jesse Orosco .08 .25
198 Steve Lake .08 .25
199 Ken Dayley .08 .25
200 Manny Sarmiento .08 .25
201 Mark Davis .08 .25
202 Tim Flannery .08 .25
203 Bill Scherrer .08 .25
204 Al Holland .08 .25
205 Dave Von Ohlen .08 .25
206 Mike LaCoss .08 .25
207 Juan Beniquez .08 .25
208 Juan Agosto .08 .25
209 Bobby Ramos .08 .25
210 Al Bumbry .08 .25
211 Mark Brouhard .08 .25
212 Howard Bailey .08 .25
213 Bruce Hurst .08 .25
214 Bob Shirley .08 .25
215 Pat Zachry .08 .25
216 Julio Franco 1.25 3.00
217 Mike Armstrong .08 .25
218 Dave Beard .08 .25
219 Steve Rogers .30 .75
220 John Butcher .08 .25
221 Mike Smithson .08 .25
222 Frank White .30 .75
223 Mike Heath .08 .25
224 Chris Bando .08 .25
225 Roy Smalley .08 .25
226 Dusty Baker .30 .75
227 Lou Whitaker .30 .75
228 John Lowenstein .08 .25
229 Ben Oglivie .30 .75
230 Doug DeCinces .08 .25
231 Lonnie Smith .08 .25
232 Ray Knight .30 .75
233 Gary Matthews .30 .75
234 Juan Bonilla .08 .25
235 Rod Scurry .08 .25
236 Atlee Hammaker .08 .25
237 Mike Caldwell .08 .25
238 Keith Hernandez .30 .75
239 Larry Bowa .30 .75
240 Tony Bernazard .08 .25
241 Damaso Garcia .08 .25
242 Tom Brunansky .08 .25
243 Dan Driessen .08 .25
244 Ron Kittle .08 .25
245 Tim Stoddard .08 .25
246 Bob L. Gibson RC .08 .25
(Brewers Pitcher)
247 Marty Castillo .08 .25
248 Don Mattingly RC 10.00 25.00
UER trailing on back
249 Jeff Newman .08 .25
250 Alejandro Pena RC .75 2.00
251 Toby Harrah .30 .75
252 Cesar Geronimo .08 .25
253 Tom Underwood .08 .25
254 Doug Flynn .08 .25
255 Andy Hassler .08 .25
256 Odell Jones .08 .25
257 Rudy Law .08 .25
258 Harry Spilman .08 .25
259 Marty Bystrom .08 .25
260 Dave Rucker .08 .25
261 Ruppert Jones .08 .25
262 Jeff R. Jones .08 .25
(Reds OF)
263 Gerald Perry .40 1.00
264 Gene Tenace .30 .75
265 Brad Wellman .08 .25
266 Dickie Noles .08 .25
267 Jamie Allen .08 .25
268 Jim Gott .08 .25
269 Ron Davis .08 .25
270 Benny Ayala .08 .25
271 Ned Yost .08 .25
272 Dave Rozema .08 .25
273 Dave Stapleton .08 .25
274 Lou Piniella .30 .75
275 Jose Morales .08 .25
276 Broderick Perkins .08 .25
277 Butch Davis RC .08 .25
278 Tony Phillips RC .75 2.00
279 Jeff Reardon .30 .75
280 Ken Forsch .08 .25
281 Pete O'Brien RC .40 1.00
282 Tom Paciorek .08 .25
283 Frank LaCorte .08 .25
284 Tim Lollar .08 .25
285 Greg Gross .08 .25
286 Alex Trevino .08 .25
287 Gene Garber .08 .25
288 Dave Parker .30 .75
289 Lee Smith .30 .75
290 Dave LaPoint .08 .25
291 John Shelby .08 .25
292 Charlie Moore .08 .25
293 Alan Trammell .30 .75
294 Tony Armas .30 .75
295 Shane Rawley .08 .25
296 Greg Brock .08 .25
297 Hal McRae .30 .75
298 Mike Davis .08 .25
299 Tim Raines .30 .75
300 Bucky Dent .30 .75
301 Tommy John .30 .75
302 Carlton Fisk .60 1.50
303 Darrell Porter .08 .25
304 Dickie Thon .08 .25
305 Garry Maddox .08 .25
306 Cesar Cedeno .30 .75
307 Gary Lucas .08 .25
308 Johnny Ray .08 .25
309 Andy McGaffigan .08 .25
310 Claudell Washington .08 .25
311 Ryne Sandberg 5.00 12.00
312 George Foster .30 .75
313 Spike Owen RC .40 1.00
314 Gary Gaetti .60 1.50
315 Willie Upshaw .08 .25
316 Al Williams .08 .25
317 Jorge Orta .08 .25
318 Orlando Mercado .08 .25
319 Junior Ortiz .08 .25
320 Mike Proly .08 .25
321 Randy Johnson UER .08 .25
('72-'82 stats are
from Twins' Randy John-
son, '83 stats are from
Braves' Randy Johnson)
322 Jim Morrison .08 .25
323 Max Venable .08 .25
324 Tony Gwynn 5.00 12.00
325 Duane Walker .08 .25
326 Ozzie Virgil .08 .25
327 Jeff Lahti .08 .25
328 Bill Dawley .08 .25
329 Rob Wilfong .08 .25
330 Marc Hill .08 .25
331 Ray Burris .08 .25
332 Allan Ramirez .08 .25
333 Chuck Porter .08 .25
334 Wayne Krenchicki .08 .25
335 Gary Allenson .08 .25
336 Bobby Meacham .08 .25
337 Joe Beckwith .08 .25
338 Rick Sutcliffe .30 .75
339 Mark Huismann .08 .25
340 Tim Conroy .08 .25
341 Scott Sanderson .08 .25
342 Larry Biittner .08 .25
343 Dave Stewart .30 .75
344 Darryl Motley .08 .25
345 Chris Codiroli .08 .25
346 Rich Behenna .08 .25
347 Andre Robertson .08 .25
348 Mike Marshall .08 .25
349 Larry Herndon .30 .75
350 Rich Dauer .08 .25
351 Cecil Cooper .30 .75
352 Rod Carew .60 1.50
353 Willie McGee .30 .75
354 Phil Garner .30 .75
355 Joe Morgan .30 .75
356 Luis Salazar .08 .25
357 John Candelaria .08 .25
358 Bill Laskey .08 .25
359 Bob McClure .08 .25
360 Dave Kingman .30 .75
361 Ron Cey .30 .75
362 Matt Young RC .40 1.00
363 Lloyd Moseby .08 .25
364 Frank Viola .60 1.50
365 Eddie Milner .08 .25
366 Floyd Bannister .08 .25
367 Dan Ford .08 .25
368 Moose Haas .08 .25
369 Doug Bair .08 .25
370 Ray Fontenot .08 .25
371 Luis Aponte .08 .25
372 Jack Fimple .08 .25
373 Neal Heaton .08 .25
374 Greg Pryor .08 .25
375 Wayne Gross .08 .25
376 Charlie Lea .08 .25
377 Steve Lubratich .08 .25
378 Jon Matlack .08 .25
379 Julio Cruz .08 .25
380 John Mizerock .08 .25
381 Kevin Gross RC .40 1.00
382 Mike Ramsey .08 .25
383 Doug Gwosdz .08 .25
384 Kelly Paris .08 .25
385 Pete Falcone .08 .25
386 Milt May .08 .25
387 Fred Breining .08 .25
388 Craig Lefferts RC .08 .25
389 Steve Henderson .08 .25
390 Randy Moffitt .08 .25
391 Ron Washington .08 .25
392 Gary Roenicke .08 .25
393 Tom Candiotti RC .75 2.00
394 Larry Pashnick .08 .25
395 Dwight Evans .60 1.50
396 Rich Gossage .30 .75
397 Derrel Thomas .08 .25
398 Juan Eichelberger .08 .25
399 Leon Roberts .08 .25
400 Dave Lopes .30 .75
401 Bill Gullickson .08 .25
402 Geoff Zahn .08 .25
403 Billy Sample .08 .25
404 Mike Squires .08 .25
405 Craig Reynolds .08 .25
406 Eric Show .08 .25
407 John Denny .08 .25
408 Dann Bilardello .08 .25
409 Bruce Benedict .08 .25
410 Kent Tekulve .08 .25
411 Mel Hall .30 .75
412 John Stuper .08 .25
413 Rick Dempsey .08 .25
414 Don Sutton .30 .75
415 Jack Morris .30 .75
416 John Tudor .30 .75
417 Willie Randolph .30 .75
418 Jerry Reuss .08 .25
419 Don Slaught .30 .75
420 Steve McCatty .08 .25
421 Tim Wallach .30 .75
422 Larry Parrish .08 .25
423 Brian Downing .30 .75
424 Britt Burns .08 .25
425 David Green .08 .25
426 Jerry Mumphrey .08 .25
427 Ivan DeJesus .08 .25
428 Mario Soto .30 .75
429 Gene Richards .08 .25
430 Dale Berra .08 .25
431 Darrell Evans .30 .75
432 Glenn Hubbard .08 .25
433 Jody Davis .08 .25
434 Danny Heep .08 .25
435 Ed Nunez RC .08 .25
436 Bobby Castillo .08 .25
437 Ernie Whitt .08 .25
438 Scott Ullger .08 .25
439 Doyle Alexander .08 .25
440 Domingo Ramos .08 .25
441 Craig Swan .08 .25
442 Warren Brusstar .08 .25
443 Len Barker .08 .25
444 Mike Easler .08 .25
445 Renie Martin .08 .25
446 D.Rasmussen RC .40 1.00
447 Ted Power .08 .25
448 Charles Hudson .08 .25
449 Danny Cox RC .08 .25
450 Kevin Bass .08 .25
451 Daryl Sconiers .08 .25
452 Scott Fletcher .08 .25
453 Bryn Smith .08 .25
454 Jim Dwyer .08 .25
455 Rob Picciolo .08 .25
456 Enos Cabell .08 .25
457 Dennis Boyd .30 .75
458 Butch Wynegar .08 .25
459 Burt Hooton .08 .25
460 Ron Hassey .08 .25
461 Danny Jackson RC .40 1.00
462 Bob Kearney .08 .25
463 Terry Francona .30 .75
464 Wayne Tolleson .08 .25
465 Mickey Rivers .08 .25
466 John Wathan .08 .25
467 Bill Almon .08 .25
468 George Vukovich .08 .25
469 Steve Kemp .08 .25
470 Ken Landreaux .08 .25
471 Milt Wilcox .08 .25
472 Tippy Martinez .08 .25
473 Ted Simmons .30 .75
474 Tim Foli .08 .25
475 George Hendrick .30 .75
476 Terry Puhl .08 .25
477 Von Hayes .08 .25
478 Bobby Brown .08 .25
479 Lee Lacy .08 .25
480 Joel Youngblood .08 .25
481 Jim Slaton .08 .25
482 Mike Fitzgerald .08 .25
483 Keith Moreland .08 .25
484 Ron Roenicke .08 .25
485 Luis Leal .08 .25
486 Bryan Oelkers .08 .25
487 Bruce Berenyi .08 .25
488 LaMarr Hoyt .08 .25
489 Joe Nolan .08 .25
490 Marshall Edwards .08 .25
491 Mike Laga .30 .75
492 Rick Cerone .08 .25
493 Rick Miller UER .08 .25
(Listed as Mike
on card front)
494 Rick Honeycutt .08 .25
495 Mike Hargrove .08 .25
496 Joe Simpson .08 .25
497 Keith Atherton .08 .25
498 Chris Welsh .08 .25
499 Bruce Kison .08 .25
500 Bobby Johnson .08 .25
501 Jerry Koosman .30 .75
502 Frank DiPino .08 .25
503 Tony Perez .60 1.50
504 Ken Oberkfell .08 .25
505 Mark Thurmond .08 .25
506 Joe Price .08 .25
507 Pascual Perez .08 .25
508 Marvell Wynne .40 1.00
509 Mike Krukow .08 .25
510 Dick Ruthven .08 .25
511 Al Cowens .08 .25
512 Cliff Johnson .08 .25
513 Randy Bush .08 .25
514 Sammy Stewart .08 .25
515 Bill Schroeder .08 .25
516 Aurelio Lopez .30 .75
517 Mike C. Brown .08 .25
518 Graig Nettles .30 .75
519 Dave Sax .08 .25
520 Jerry Willard .08 .25
521 Paul Splittorff .08 .25
522 Tom Burgmeier .08 .25
523 Chris Speier .08 .25
524 Bobby Clark .08 .25
525 George Wright .08 .25
526 Dennis Lamp .08 .25
527 Tony Scott .08 .25
528 Ed Whitson .08 .25
529 Ron Reed .08 .25
530 Charlie Puleo .08 .25
531 Jerry Royster .08 .25
532 Don Robinson .08 .25
533 Steve Trout .08 .25
534 Bruce Sutter .60 1.50
535 Bob Horner .30 .75
536 Pat Tabler .08 .25
537 Chris Chambliss .30 .75
538 Bob Ojeda .08 .25
539 Alan Ashby .08 .25
540 Jay Johnstone .08 .25
541 Bob Dernier .08 .25
542 Brook Jacoby .40 1.00
543 U.L. Washington .08 .25
544 Danny Darwin .08 .25
545 Kiko Garcia .08 .25
546 Vance Law UER .08 .25
(Listed as P
on card front)
547 Tug McGraw .30 .75
548 Dave Smith .08 .25
549 Len Matuszek .08 .25
550 Tom Hume .08 .25
551 Dave Dravecky .08 .25
552 Rick Rhoden .08 .25
553 Duane Kuiper .08 .25
554 Rusty Staub .30 .75
555 Bill Campbell .08 .25
556 Mike Torrez .08 .25
557 Dave Henderson .30 .75
558 Len Whitehouse .08 .25
559 Barry Bonnell .08 .25
560 Rick Lysander .08 .25
561 Garth Iorg .08 .25
562 Bryan Clark .08 .25
563 Brian Giles .08 .25
564 Vern Ruhle .08 .25
565 Steve Bedrosian .08 .25
566 Larry McWilliams .08 .25
567 Jeff Leonard UER .08 .25

(Listed as P
on card front)
568 Alan Wiggins .08 .25
569 Jeff Russell RC .40 1.00
570 Salome Barojas .08 .25
571 Dane Iorg .08 .25
572 Bob Knepper .08 .25
573 Gary Lavelle .08 .25
574 Gorman Thomas .30 .75
575 Manny Trillo .08 .25
576 Jim Palmer .30 .75
577 Dale Murray .08 .25
578 Tom Brookens .30 .75
579 Rich Gedman .08 .25
580 Bill Doran RC .40 1.00
581 Steve Yeager .30 .75
582 Dan Spillner .08 .25
583 Dan Quisenberry .08 .25
584 Rance Mulliniks .08 .25
585 Storm Davis .08 .25
586 Dave Schmidt .08 .25
587 Bill Russell .30 .75
588 Pat Sheridan .08 .25
589 Rafael Ramirez .08 .25
UER (A's on front)
590 Bud Anderson .08 .25
591 George Frazier .08 .25
592 Lee Tunnell .08 .25
593 Kirk Gibson 1.25 3.00
594 Scott McGregor .08 .25
595 Bob Bailor .08 .25
596 Tom Herr .08 .25
597 Luis Sanchez .08 .25
598 Dave Engle .08 .25
599 Craig McMurtry .08 .25
600 Carlos Diaz .08 .25
601 Tom O'Malley .08 .25
602 Nick Esasky .08 .25
603 Ron Hodges .08 .25
604 Ed VandeBerg .08 .25
605 Alfredo Griffin .08 .25
606 Glenn Hoffman .08 .25
607 Hubie Brooks .08 .25
608 Richard Barnes UER .08 .25
(Photo actually
Neal Heaton)
609 Greg Walker .40 1.00
610 Ken Singleton .30 .75
611 Mark Clear .08 .25
612 Buck Martinez .08 .25
613 Ken Griffey .30 .75
614 Reid Nichols .08 .25
615 Doug Sisk .08 .25
616 Bob Brenly .08 .25
617 Joey McLaughlin .08 .25
618 Glenn Wilson .30 .75
619 Bob Stoddard .08 .25
620 Lenn Sakata UER .08 .25
(Listed as Len
on card front)
621 Mike Young RC .08 .25
622 John Stefero .08 .25
623 Carmelo Martinez .08 .25
624 Dave Bergman .08 .25
625 Runnin' Reds UER 1.25 3.00
(Sic, Redbirds)
David Green
Willie McGee
Lonnie Smith
Ozzie Smith
626 Rudy May .08 .25
627 Matt Keough .08 .25
628 Jose DeLeon RC .40 1.00
629 Jim Essian .08 .25
630 Darnell Coles RC .40 1.00
631 Mike Warren .08 .25
632 Del Crandall MG .08 .25
633 Dennis Martinez .30 .75
634 Mike Moore .08 .25
635 Lary Sorensen .08 .25
636 Ricky Nelson .08 .25
637 Omar Moreno .08 .25
638 Charlie Hough .30 .75
639 Dennis Eckersley .60 1.50
640 Walt Terrell .08 .25
641 Denny Walling .08 .25
642 Dave Anderson RC .08 .25
643 Jose Oquendo RC .40 1.00
644 Bob Stanley .08 .25
645 Dave Geisel .08 .25
646 Scott Garrelts .08 .25
647 Gary Pettis .08 .25
648 Duke Snider .60 1.50
Puzzle Card
649 Johnnie LeMaster .08 .25
650 Dave Collins .08 .25
651 The Chicken .60 1.50
652 DK Checklist 1-26 .30 .75
(Unnumbered)
653 Checklist 27-130 .08 .25
(Unnumbered)
654 Checklist 131-234 .08 .25
(Unnumbered)
655 Checklist 235-338 .08 .25
(Unnumbered)
656 Checklist 339-442 .08 .25
(Unnumbered)
657 Checklist 443-546 .08 .25
(Unnumbered)
658 Checklist 547-651 .08 .25
(Unnumbered)
A Living Legends A 1.00 2.50
Gaylord Perry
Rollie Fingers
B Living Legends B 2.00 5.00
Carl Yastrzemski
Johnny Bench

1985 Donruss

The 1985 Donruss set consists of 660 standard-size cards. The wax packs, packed 36 packs to a box and 20 boxes to a case, contained 15 cards and a Lou Gehrig puzzle panel. The fronts feature full color photos framed by jet black borders (making the cards condition sensitive). The first 26 cards of the set feature Diamond Kings (DK), for the fourth year in a row; the artwork on the Diamond Kings was again produced by the Perez-Steele Galleries. Cards 27-46 feature Rated Rookies (RR). The unnumbered checklist cards are arbitrarily numbered below as numbers 654 through 660. Rookie Cards in this set include Roger Clemens, Eric Davis, Shawon Dunston, Dwight Gooden, Orel Hershiser, Jimmy Key, Terry Pendleton, Kirby Puckett and Bret Saberhagen.

COMPLETE SET (660) 30.00 60.00
COMP.FACT.SET (660) 50.00 100.00
COMP.GEHRIG PUZZLE 1.50 4.00
1 Ryne Sandberg DK .50 1.25
2 Doug DeCinces DK .05 .15
3 Richard Dotson DK .05 .15
4 Bert Blyleven DK .15 .40
5 Lou Whitaker DK .15 .40
6 Dan Quisenberry DK .05 .15
7 Don Mattingly DK 1.00 2.50
8 Carney Lansford DK .15 .40
9 Frank Tanana DK .15 .40
10 Willie Upshaw DK .05 .15
11 C.Washington DK .05 .15
12 Mike Marshall DK .05 .15
13 Joaquin Andujar DK .15 .40
14 Cal Ripken DK 1.00 2.50
15 Jim Rice DK .15 .40
16 Don Sutton DK .15 .40
17 Frank Viola DK .15 .40
18 Alvin Davis DK .15 .40
19 Mario Soto DK .15 .40
20 Jose Cruz DK .15 .40
21 Charlie Lea DK .05 .15
22 Jesse Orosco DK .05 .15
23 Juan Samuel DK .05 .15
24 Tony Pena DK .05 .15
25 Tony Gwynn DK .50 1.25
26 Bob Brenly DK .05 .15
27 Danny Tartabull RC .40 1.00
28 Mike Bielecki RC .08 .25
29 Steve Lyons RC .20 .50
30 Jeff Reed RC .08 .25
31 Tony Brewer RC .08 .25
32 John Morris RC .08 .25
33 Daryl Boston RC .08 .25
34 Al Pulido RC .08 .25
35 Steve Kiefer RC .08 .25
36 Larry Sheets RC .08 .25
37 Scott Bradley RC .08 .25
38 Calvin Schiraldi RC .20 .50
39 Shawon Dunston RC .40 1.00
40 Charlie Mitchell RC .08 .25
41 Billy Hatcher RC .20 .50
42 Russ Stephans RC .08 .25
43 Alejandro Sanchez RC .08 .25
44 Steve Jeltz RC .08 .25
45 Jim Traber RC .08 .25
46 Doug Loman RC .08 .25
47 Eddie Murray .50 1.25
48 Robin Yount .75 2.00
49 Lance Parrish .15 .40
50 Jim Rice .15 .40
51 Dave Winfield .15 .40
52 Fernando Valenzuela .15 .40
53 George Brett 1.25 3.00
54 Dave Kingman .15 .40
55 Gary Carter .15 .40
56 Buddy Bell .15 .40
57 Reggie Jackson .30 .75
58 Harold Baines .15 .40
59 Ozzie Smith .75 2.00
60 Nolan Ryan UER 2.50 6.00
(Set strikeout record
in 1973, not 1972)
61 Mike Schmidt 1.25 3.00
62 Dave Parker .15 .40
63 Tony Gwynn 1.00 2.50
64 Tony Pena .05 .15
65 Jack Clark .15 .40
66 Dale Murphy .30 .75
67 Ryne Sandberg 1.00 2.50
68 Keith Hernandez .15 .40
69 Alvin Davis RC .20 .50
70 Kent Hrbek .15 .40
71 Willie Upshaw .05 .15
72 Dave Engle .05 .15
73 Alfredo Griffin .05 .15
74A Jack Perconte .05 .15
(Career Highlights
takes four lines)
74B Jack Perconte .05 .15
(Career Highlights
takes three lines)
75 Jesse Orosco .05 .15
76 Jody Davis .05 .15
77 Bob Horner .15 .40
78 Larry McWilliams .05 .15
79 Joel Youngblood .05 .15
80 Alan Wiggins .05 .15
81 Ron Oester .05 .15
82 Ozzie Virgil .05 .15
83 Ricky Horton .05 .15
84 Bill Doran .05 .15
85 Rod Carew .30 .75
86 LaMarr Hoyt .05 .15
87 Tim Wallach .05 .15
88 Mike Flanagan .05 .15
89 Jim Sundberg .15 .40
90 Chet Lemon .15 .40
91 Bob Stanley .05 .15
92 Willie Randolph .15 .40
93 Bill Russell .15 .40
94 Julio Franco .15 .40
95 Dan Quisenberry .05 .15
96 Bill Caudill .05 .15
97 Bill Gullickson .05 .15
98 Danny Darwin .05 .15
99 Curtis Wilkerson .05 .15
100 Bud Black .05 .15
101 Tony Phillips .05 .15
102 Tony Bernazard .05 .15
103 Jay Howell .05 .15
104 Burt Hooton .05 .15
105 Milt Wilcox .05 .15
106 Rich Dauer .05 .15
107 Don Sutton .15 .40
108 Mike Witt .05 .15
109 Bruce Sutter .15 .40
110 Enos Cabell .05 .15
111 John Denny .05 .15
112 Dave Dravecky .05 .15
113 Marvell Wynne .05 .15
114 Johnnie LeMaster .05 .15
115 Chuck Porter .05 .15
116 John Gibbons RC .05 .15
117 Keith Moreland .05 .15
118 Darnell Coles .05 .15
119 Dennis Lamp .05 .15
120 Ron Davis .05 .15
121 Nick Esasky .05 .15
122 Vance Law .05 .15
123 Gary Roenicke .05 .15
124 Bill Schroeder .05 .15
125 Dave Rozema .05 .15
126 Bobby Meacham .05 .15
127 Marty Barrett .05 .15
128 R.J. Reynolds .05 .15
129 Ernie Camacho UER .05 .15
(Photo actually
Rich Thompson)
130 Jorge Orta .05 .15
131 Lary Sorensen .05 .15
132 Terry Francona .15 .40
133 Fred Lynn .15 .40
134 Bob Jones .05 .15
135 Jerry Hairston .05 .15
136 Kevin Bass .05 .15
137 Garry Maddox .05 .15
138 Dave LaPoint .05 .15
139 Kevin McReynolds .15 .40
140 Wayne Krenchicki .05 .15
141 Rafael Ramirez .05 .15
142 Rod Scurry .05 .15
143 Greg Minton .05 .15
144 Tim Stoddard .05 .15
145 Steve Henderson .05 .15
146 George Bell .15 .40
147 Dave Meier .05 .15
148 Sammy Stewart .05 .15
149 Mark Brouhard .05 .15
150 Larry Herndon .05 .15
151 Oil Can Boyd .05 .15
152 Brian Dayett .05 .15
153 Tom Niedenfuer .05 .15
154 Brook Jacoby .05 .15
155 Onix Concepcion .05 .15
156 Tim Conroy .05 .15
157 Joe Hesketh .05 .15
158 Brian Downing .15 .40
159 Tommy Dunbar .05 .15
160 Marc Hill .05 .15
161 Phil Garner .15 .40
162 Jerry Davis .05 .15
163 Bill Campbell .05 .15
164 John Franco RC .40 1.00
165 Len Barker .05 .15
166 Benny Distefano .05 .15
167 George Frazier .05 .15
168 Tito Landrum .05 .15
169 Cal Ripken 2.00 5.00
170 Cecil Cooper .15 .40
171 Alan Trammell .15 .40
172 Wade Boggs .50 1.25
173 Don Baylor .15 .40
174 Pedro Guerrero .15 .40
175 Frank White .15 .40
176 Rickey Henderson .60 1.50
177 Charlie Lea .05 .15
178 Pete O'Brien .05 .15
179 Doug DeCinces .05 .15
180 Ron Kittle .05 .15
181 George Hendrick .15 .40
182 Joe Niekro .05 .15
183 Juan Samuel .05 .15
184 Mario Soto .15 .40
185 Rich Gossage .15 .40
186 Johnny Ray .05 .15
187 Bob Brenly .05 .15
188 Craig McMurtry .05 .15
189 Leon Durham .05 .15
190 Dwight Gooden RC 1.25 3.00
191 Barry Bonnell .05 .15
192 Tim Teufel .05 .15
193 Dave Stieb .15 .40
194 Mickey Hatcher .05 .15
195 Jesse Barfield .15 .40
196 Al Cowens .05 .15
197 Hubie Brooks .05 .15
198 Steve Trout .05 .15
199 Glenn Hubbard .05 .15
200 Bill Madlock .15 .40
201 Jeff D. Robinson .05 .15
202 Eric Show .05 .15
203 Dave Concepcion .15 .40
204 Ivan DeJesus .05 .15
205 Neil Allen .05 .15
206 Jerry Mumphrey .05 .15
207 Mike C. Brown .05 .15
208 Carlton Fisk .30 .75
209 Bryn Smith .05 .15
210 Tippy Martinez .05 .15
211 Dion James .05 .15
212 Willie Hernandez .05 .15
213 Mike Easler .05 .15
214 Ron Guidry .15 .40
215 Rick Honeycutt .05 .15
216 Brett Butler .15 .40
217 Larry Gura .05 .15
218 Ray Burris .05 .15
219 Steve Rogers .15 .40
220 Frank Tanana UER .15 .40
(Bats Left listed
twice on card back)
221 Ned Yost .05 .15
222 Bret Saberhagen RC .60 1.50
UER 18 career IP on back
223 Mike Davis .05 .15
224 Bert Blyleven .15 .40
225 Steve Kemp .05 .15
226 Jerry Reuss .05 .15
227 Darrell Evans UER .15 .40
(80 homers in 1980)
228 Wayne Gross .05 .15
229 Jim Gantner .05 .15
230 Bob Boone .15 .40
231 Lonnie Smith .05 .15
232 Frank DiPino .05 .15
233 Jerry Koosman .15 .40
234 Graig Nettles .15 .40
235 John Tudor .15 .40
236 John Rabb .05 .15
237 Rick Manning .05 .15
238 Mike Fitzgerald .05 .15
239 Gary Matthews .15 .40
240 Jim Presley .20 .50
241 Dave Collins .05 .15
242 Gary Gaetti .15 .40
243 Dann Bilardello .05 .15
244 Rudy Law .05 .15
245 John Lowenstein .05 .15
246 Tom Tellmann .05 .15
247 Howard Johnson .15 .40
248 Ray Fontenot .05 .15
249 Tony Armas .15 .40
250 Candy Maldonado .05 .15
251 Mike Jeffcoat .05 .15
252 Dane Iorg .05 .15
253 Bruce Bochte .05 .15
254 Pete Rose Expos 1.50 4.00
255 Don Aase .05 .15
256 George Wright .05 .15
257 Britt Burns .05 .15
258 Mike Scott .15 .40
259 Len Matuszek .05 .15
260 Dave Rucker .05 .15
261 Craig Lefferts .05 .15
262 Jay Tibbs .05 .15
263 Bruce Benedict .05 .15
264 Don Robinson .05 .15
265 Gary Lavelle .05 .15
266 Scott Sanderson .05 .15
267 Matt Young .05 .15
268 Ernie Whitt .05 .15
269 Houston Jimenez .05 .15
270 Ken Dixon .05 .15
271 Pete Ladd .05 .15
272 Juan Berenguer .05 .15
273 Roger Clemens RC 8.00 20.00
274 Rick Cerone .05 .15
275 Dave Anderson .05 .15
276 George Vukovich .05 .15
277 Greg Pryor .05 .15
278 Mike Warren .05 .15
279 Bob James .05 .15
280 Bobby Grich .15 .40
281 Mike Mason RC .08 .25
282 Ron Reed .05 .15
283 Alan Ashby .05 .15
284 Mark Thurmond .05 .15
285 Joe Lefebvre .05 .15
286 Ted Power .05 .15
287 Chris Chambliss .15 .40
288 Lee Tunnell .05 .15
289 Rich Bordi .05 .15
290 Glenn Brummer .05 .15
291 Mike Boddicker .05 .15
292 Rollie Fingers .15 .40
293 Lou Whitaker .15 .40
294 Dwight Evans .30 .75
295 Don Mattingly 2.00 5.00
296 Mike Marshall .05 .15
297 Willie Wilson .15 .40
298 Mike Heath .05 .15
299 Tim Raines .15 .40
300 Larry Parrish .15 .40
301 Geoff Zahn .05 .15
302 Rich Dotson .05 .15
303 David Green .05 .15
304 Jose Cruz .15 .40
305 Steve Carlton .15 .40
306 Gary Redus .05 .15
307 Steve Garvey .15 .40
308 Jose DeLeon .05 .15
309 Randy Lerch .05 .15
310 Claudell Washington .05 .15
311 Lee Smith .15 .40
312 Darryl Strawberry .50 1.25
313 Jim Beattie .05 .15
314 John Butcher .05 .15
315 Damaso Garcia .05 .15
316 Mike Smithson .05 .15
317 Luis Leal .05 .15
318 Ken Phelps .05 .15
319 Wally Backman .05 .15
320 Ron Cey .15 .40
321 Brad Komminsk .05 .15
322 Jason Thompson .05 .15
323 Frank Williams .05 .15
324 Tim Lollar .05 .15
325 Eric Davis RC 1.25 3.00
326 Von Hayes .05 .15
327 Andy Van Slyke .30 .75
328 Craig Reynolds .05 .15
329 Dick Schofield .05 .15
330 Scott Fletcher .05 .15
331 Jeff Reardon .15 .40
332 Rick Dempsey .05 .15
333 Ben Oglivie .15 .40
334 Dan Petry .05 .15
335 Jackie Gutierrez .05 .15
336 Dave Righetti .15 .40
337 Alejandro Pena .05 .15
338 Mel Hall .05 .15
339 Pat Sheridan .05 .15
340 Keith Atherton .05 .15
341 David Palmer .05 .15
342 Gary Ward .05 .15
343 Dave Stewart .15 .40
344 Mark Gubicza RC .20 .50
345 Carney Lansford .15 .40
346 Jerry Willard .05 .15
347 Ken Griffey .15 .40
348 Franklin Stubbs .05 .15
349 Aurelio Lopez .05 .15
350 Al Bumbry .05 .15
351 Charlie Moore .05 .15
352 Luis Sanchez .05 .15
353 Darrell Porter .05 .15
354 Bill Dawley .05 .15
355 Charles Hudson .05 .15
356 Garry Templeton .15 .40
357 Cecilio Guante .05 .15
358 Jeff Leonard .05 .15
359 Paul Molitor .15 .40
360 Ron Gardenhire .05 .15
361 Larry Bowa .15 .40
362 Bob Kearney .05 .15
363 Garth Iorg .05 .15
364 Tom Brunansky .05 .15
365 Brad Gulden .05 .15
366 Greg Walker .05 .15
367 Mike Young .05 .15
368 Rick Waits .05 .15
369 Doug Bair .05 .15
370 Bob Shirley .05 .15
371 Bob Ojeda .05 .15
372 Bob Welch .15 .40
373 Neal Heaton .05 .15
374 Danny Jackson UER .05 .15
(Photo actually
Frank Wills)
375 Donnie Hill .05 .15
376 Mike Stenhouse .05 .15
377 Bruce Kison .05 .15
378 Wayne Tolleson .05 .15
379 Floyd Bannister .05 .15
380 Vern Ruhle .05 .15
381 Tim Corcoran .05 .15
382 Kurt Kepshire .05 .15
383 Bobby Brown .05 .15
384 Dave Van Gorder .05 .15
385 Rick Mahler .05 .15
386 Lee Mazzilli .15 .40
387 Bill Laskey .05 .15
388 Thad Bosley .05 .15
389 Al Chambers .05 .15
390 Tony Fernandez .15 .40
391 Ron Washington .05 .15
392 Bill Swaggerty .05 .15
393 Bob L. Gibson .05 .15
394 Marty Castillo .05 .15
395 Steve Crawford .05 .15
396 Clay Christiansen .05 .15
397 Bob Bailor .05 .15
398 Mike Hargrove .05 .15
399 Charlie Leibrandt .05 .15
400 Tom Burgmeier .05 .15
401 Razor Shines .05 .15
402 Rob Wilfong .05 .15
403 Tom Henke .15 .40
404 Al Jones .05 .15
405 Mike LaCoss .05 .15
406 Luis DeLeon .05 .15
407 Greg Gross .05 .15
408 Tom Hume .05 .15
409 Rick Camp .05 .15
410 Milt May .05 .15
411 Henry Cotto RC .08 .25
412 David Von Ohlen .05 .15
413 Scott McGregor .05 .15
414 Ted Simmons .15 .40
415 Jack Morris .15 .40
416 Bill Buckner .15 .40
417 Butch Wynegar .05 .15
418 Steve Sax .05 .15
419 Steve Balboni .05 .15
420 Dwayne Murphy .05 .15
421 Andre Dawson .15 .40
422 Charlie Hough .15 .40
423 Tommy John .15 .40
424A Tom Seaver ERR .30 .75
(Photo actually
Floyd Bannister)
424B Tom Seaver COR 4.00 10.00
425 Tom Herr .05 .15
426 Terry Puhl .05 .15
427 Al Holland .05 .15
428 Eddie Milner .05 .15
429 Terry Kennedy .05 .15
430 John Candelaria .05 .15
431 Manny Trillo .05 .15
432 Ken Oberkfell .05 .15
433 Rick Sutcliffe .15 .40
434 Ron Darling .15 .40
435 Spike Owen .05 .15
436 Frank Viola .15 .40
437 Lloyd Moseby .05 .15
438 Kirby Puckett RC 4.00 10.00
439 Jim Clancy .05 .15
440 Mike Moore .05 .15
441 Doug Sisk .05 .15
442 Dennis Eckersley .30 .75
443 Gerald Perry .05 .15
444 Dale Berra .05 .15
445 Dusty Baker .15 .40
446 Ed Whitson .05 .15
447 Cesar Cedeno .15 .40
448 Rick Schu .05 .15
449 Joaquin Andujar .15 .40
450 Mark Bailey .05 .15
451 Ron Romanick .05 .15
452 Julio Cruz .05 .15
453 Miguel Dilone .05 .15
454 Storm Davis .05 .15
455 Jaime Cocanower .05 .15
456 Barbaro Garbey .05 .15
457 Rich Gedman .05 .15
458 Phil Niekro .15 .40
459 Mike Scioscia .15 .40
460 Pat Tabler .05 .15
461 Darryl Motley .05 .15
462 Chris Codiroli .05 .15
463 Doug Flynn .05 .15
464 Billy Sample .05 .15
465 Mickey Rivers .05 .15
466 John Wathan .05 .15
467 Bill Krueger .05 .15
468 Andre Thornton .05 .15
469 Rex Hudler .05 .15
470 Sid Bream RC .20 .50
471 Kirk Gibson .15 .40
472 John Shelby .05 .15
473 Moose Haas .05 .15
474 Doug Corbett .05 .15
475 Willie McGee .15 .40
476 Bob Knepper .05 .15
477 Kevin Gross .05 .15
478 Carmelo Martinez .05 .15
479 Kent Tekulve .05 .15
480 Chili Davis .15 .40
481 Bobby Clark .05 .15
482 Mookie Wilson .15 .40
483 Dave Owen .05 .15
484 Ed Nunez .05 .15
485 Rance Mulliniks .05 .15
486 Ken Schrom .05 .15
487 Jeff Russell .05 .15
488 Tom Paciorek .05 .15
489 Dan Ford .05 .15
490 Mike Caldwell .05 .15
491 Scottie Earl .05 .15
492 Jose Rijo RC .40 1.00
493 Bruce Hurst .05 .15
494 Ken Landreaux .05 .15
495 Mike Fischlin .05 .15
496 Don Slaught .05 .15
497 Steve McCatty .05 .15
498 Gary Lucas .05 .15
499 Gary Pettis .05 .15
500 Marvis Foley .05 .15
501 Mike Squires .05 .15
502 Jim Pankovits .05 .15
503 Luis Aguayo .05 .15
504 Ralph Citarella .05 .15
505 Bruce Bochy .05 .15
506 Bob Owchinko .05 .15
507 Pascual Perez .05 .15
508 Lee Lacy .05 .15
509 Atlee Hammaker .05 .15
510 Bob Dernier .05 .15
511 Ed VandeBerg .05 .15
512 Cliff Johnson .05 .15
513 Len Whitehouse .05 .15
514 Dennis Martinez .15 .40
515 Ed Romero .05 .15
516 Rusty Kuntz .05 .15
517 Rick Miller .05 .15
518 Dennis Rasmussen .05 .15
519 Steve Yeager .15 .40
520 Chris Bando .05 .15
521 U.L. Washington .05 .15
522 Curt Young .05 .15
523 Angel Salazar .05 .15
524 Curt Kaufman .05 .15
525 Odell Jones .05 .15
526 Juan Agosto .05 .15
527 Denny Walling .05 .15
528 Andy Hawkins .05 .15
529 Sixto Lezcano .05 .15
530 Skeeter Barnes RC .08 .25
531 Randy Johnson .05 .15
532 Jim Morrison .05 .15
533 Warren Brusstar .05 .15
534A Terry Pendleton RC .40 1.00
ERR Wrong first name as Jeff
534B Terry Pendleton COR .40 1.00
535 Vic Rodriguez .05 .15
536 Bob McClure .05 .15
537 Dave Bergman .05 .15
538 Mark Clear .05 .15
539 Mike Pagliarulo .05 .15
540 Terry Whitfield .05 .15
541 Joe Beckwith .05 .15
542 Jeff Burroughs .05 .15
543 Dan Schatzeder .05 .15
544 Donnie Scott .05 .15
545 Jim Slaton .05 .15
546 Greg Luzinski .15 .40
547 Mark Salas .05 .15
548 Dave Smith .05 .15
549 John Wockenfuss .05 .15
550 Frank Pastore .05 .15
551 Tim Flannery .05 .15
552 Rick Rhoden .05 .15
553 Mark Davis .05 .15
554 Jeff Dedmon .05 .15
555 Gary Woods .05 .15
556 Danny Heep .05 .15
557 Mark Langston RC .40 1.00
558 Darrell Brown .05 .15
559 Jimmy Key RC .40 1.00
560 Rick Lysander .05 .15
561 Doyle Alexander .05 .15
562 Mike Stanton .05 .15
563 Sid Fernandez .15 .40
564 Richie Hebner .05 .15
565 Alex Trevino .05 .15
566 Brian Harper .05 .15
567 Dan Gladden RC .20 .50
568 Luis Salazar .05 .15
569 Tom Foley .05 .15
570 Larry Andersen .05 .15
571 Danny Cox .05 .15
572 Joe Sambito .05 .15
573 Juan Beniquez .05 .15
574 Joel Skinner .05 .15
575 Randy St.Claire .05 .15
576 Floyd Rayford .05 .15
577 Roy Howell .05 .15
578 John Grubb .05 .15
579 Ed Jurak .05 .15
580 John Montefusco .05 .15
581 Orel Hershiser RC 1.25 3.00
582 Tom Waddell .05 .15
583 Mark Huismann .05 .15
584 Joe Morgan .15 .40
585 Jim Wohlford .05 .15
586 Dave Schmidt .05 .15
587 Jeff Kunkel .05 .15
588 Hal McRae .15 .40
589 Bill Almon .05 .15
590 Carmelo Castillo .05 .15
591 Omar Moreno .05 .15
592 Ken Howell .05 .15
593 Tom Brookens .05 .15
594 Joe Nolan .05 .15
595 Willie Lozado .05 .15
596 Tom Nieto .05 .15
597 Walt Terrell .05 .15
598 Al Oliver .15 .40
599 Shane Rawley .05 .15
600 Denny Gonzalez .05 .15
601 Mark Grant .05 .15
602 Mike Armstrong .05 .15
603 George Foster .15 .40
604 Dave Lopes .15 .40
605 Salome Barojas .05 .15
606 Roy Lee Jackson .05 .15
607 Pete Filson .05 .15
608 Duane Walker .05 .15
609 Glenn Wilson .05 .15
610 Rafael Santana .05 .15
611 Roy Smith .05 .15
612 Ruppert Jones .05 .15
613 Joe Cowley .05 .15

614 Al Nipper UER .05 .15
(Photo actually
Mike Brown)
615 Gene Nelson .05 .15
616 Joe Carter .50 1.25
617 Ray Knight .15 .40
618 Chuck Rainey .05 .15
619 Dan Driessen .05 .15
620 Daryl Sconiers .05 .15
621 Bill Stein .05 .15
622 Roy Smalley .05 .15
623 Ed Lynch .05 .15
624 Jeff Stone RC .05 .15
625 Bruce Berenyi .05 .15
626 Kelvin Chapman .05 .15
627 Joe Price .05 .15
628 Steve Bedrosian .05 .15
629 Vic Mata .05 .15
630 Mike Krukow .05 .15
631 Phil Bradley .20 .50
632 Jim Gott .05 .15
633 Randy Bush .05 .15
634 Tom Browning RC .20 .50
635 Lou Gehrig .50 1.25
Puzzle Card
636 Reid Nichols .05 .15
637 Dan Pasqua RC .20 .50
638 German Rivera .05 .15
639 Don Schulze .05 .15
640A Mike Jones .05 .15
(Career Highlights,
takes five lines)
640B Mike Jones .05 .15
(Career Highlights,
takes four lines)
641 Pete Rose 1.50 4.00
642 Wade Rowdon .05 .15
643 Jerry Narron .05 .15
644 Darrell Miller .05 .15
645 Tim Hulett RC .08 .25
646 Andy McGaffigan .05 .15
647 Kurt Bevacqua .05 .15
648 John Russell .05 .15
649 Ron Robinson .05 .15
650 Donnie Moore .05 .15
651A Two for the Title .75 2.00
Dave Winfield
Don Mattingly
(Yellow letters)
651B Two for the Title 2.00 5.00
Dave Winfield
Don Mattingly
(White letters)
652 Tim Laudner .05 .15
653 Steve Farr RC .20 .50
654 DK Checklist 1-26 .05 .15
(Unnumbered)
655 Checklist 27-130 .05 .15
(Unnumbered)
656 Checklist 131-234 .05 .15
(Unnumbered)
657 Checklist 235-338 .05 .15
(Unnumbered)
658 Checklist 339-442 .05 .15
(Unnumbered)
659 Checklist 443-546 .05 .15
(Unnumbered)
660 Checklist 547-653 .05 .15
(Unnumbered)

1986 Donruss

The 1986 Donruss set consists of 660 standard-size cards. Wax packs, packed 36 packs to a box and 20 boxes to a case, contained 15 cards plus a Hank Aaron puzzle panel. The card fronts feature blue borders, the standard team logo, player's name, position, and Donruss logo. The first 26 cards of the set are Diamond Kings (DK), for the fifth year in a row; the artwork on the Diamond Kings was again produced by the Perez-Steele Galleries. Cards 27-46 again feature Rated Rookies (RR). The unnumbered checklist cards are arbitrarily numbered below as numbers 654 through 660. Rookie Cards in this set include Jose Canseco, Darren Daulton, Len Dykstra, Cecil Fielder, Andres Galarraga, Fred McGriff and Paul O'Neill.

COMPLETE SET (660) 15.00 40.00
COMP.FACT.SET (660) 15.00 40.00
COMP.AARON PUZZLE .75 2.00
1 Kirk Gibson DK .08 .25
2 Rich Gossage DK .08 .25
3 Willie McGee DK .08 .25
4 George Bell DK .08 .25
5 Tony Armas DK .08 .25
6 Chili Davis DK .08 .25
7 Cecil Cooper DK .08 .25
8 Mike Boddicker DK .05 .15
9 Dave Lopes DK .08 .25
10 Bill Doran DK .05 .15
11 Bret Saberhagen DK .08 .25
12 Brett Butler DK .08 .25
13 Harold Baines DK .08 .25
14 Mike Davis DK .05 .15
15 Tony Perez DK .20 .50
16 Willie Randolph DK .08 .25
17 Bob Boone DK .08 .25
18 Orel Hershiser DK .20 .50
19 Johnny Ray DK .05 .15
20 Gary Ward DK .05 .15
21 Rick Mahler DK .05 .15
22 Phil Bradley DK .05 .15
23 Jerry Koosman DK .08 .25
24 Tom Brunansky DK .05 .15
25 Andre Dawson DK .05 .15
26 Dwight Gooden DK .30 .75
27 Kal Daniels RR .20 .50
28 Fred McGriff RR RC 3.00 8.00
29 Cory Snyder RR .05 .15
30 Jose Guzman RR RC .05 .15
31 Ty Gainey RC .05 .15
32 Johnny Abrego RC .05 .15
33A A.Galarraga RR RC .60 1.50
No accent
33B A.Galarraga RR RC .60 1.50
Accent over e
34 Dave Shipanoff RC .05 .15
35 M.McLemore RR RC .40 1.00
36 Marty Clary RC .05 .15
37 Paul O'Neill RR RC 1.50 4.00
38 Danny Tartabull RR .08 .25
39 Jose Canseco RR RC 4.00 10.00
40 Juan Nieves RC .05 .15
41 Lance McCullers RC .05 .15
42 Rick Surhoff RC .05 .15
43 Todd Worrell RR RC .20 .50
44 Bob Kipper RC .05 .15
45 John Habyan RR RC .05 .15
46 Mike Woodard RC .05 .15
47 Mike Boddicker .05 .15
48 Robin Yount .50 1.25
49 Lou Whitaker .08 .25
50 Oil Can Boyd .05 .15
51 Rickey Henderson .30 .75
52 Mike Marshall .05 .15
53 George Brett .75 2.00
54 Dave Kingman .08 .25
55 Hubie Brooks .05 .15
56 Oddibe McDowell .05 .15
57 Doug DeCinces .05 .15
58 Britt Burns .05 .15
59 Ozzie Smith .50 1.25
60 Jose Cruz .08 .25
61 Mike Schmidt .75 2.00
62 Pete Rose 1.00 2.50
63 Steve Garvey .08 .25
64 Tony Pena .05 .15
65 Chili Davis .08 .25
66 Dale Murphy .20 .50
67 Ryne Sandberg .60 1.50
68 Gary Carter .08 .25
69 Alvin Davis .05 .15
70 Kent Hrbek .08 .25
71 George Bell .08 .25
72 Kirby Puckett .75 2.00
73 Lloyd Moseby .05 .15
74 Bob Kearney .05 .15
75 Dwight Gooden .30 .75
76 Gary Matthews .05 .15
77 Rick Mahler .05 .15
78 Benny Distefano .05 .15
79 Jeff Leonard .05 .15
80 Kevin McReynolds .08 .25
81 Ron Oester .05 .15
82 John Russell .05 .15
83 Tommy Herr .05 .15
84 Jerry Mumphrey .05 .15
85 Ron Romanick .05 .15
86 Daryl Boston .05 .15
87 Andre Dawson .08 .25
88 Eddie Murray .30 .75
89 Dion James .05 .15
90 Chet Lemon .08 .25
91 Bob Stanley .05 .15
92 Willie Randolph .08 .25
93 Mike Scioscia .08 .25
94 Tom Waddell .05 .15
95 Danny Jackson .05 .15
96 Mike Davis .05 .15
97 Mike Fitzgerald .05 .15
98 Gary Ward .05 .15
99 Pete O'Brien .05 .15
100 Bret Saberhagen .08 .25
101 Alfredo Griffin .05 .15
102 Brett Butler .08 .25
103 Ron Guidry .08 .25
104 Jerry Reuss .05 .15
105 Jack Morris .08 .25
106 Rick Dempsey .05 .15
107 Ray Burris .05 .15
108 Brian Downing .08 .25
109 Willie McGee .08 .25
110 Bill Doran .05 .15
111 Kent Tekulve .05 .15
112 Tony Gwynn .50 1.25
113 Marvell Wynne .05 .15
114 David Green .05 .15
115 Jim Gantner .05 .15
116 George Foster .08 .25
117 Steve Trout .05 .15
118 Mark Langston .08 .25
119 Tony Fernandez .08 .25
120 John Butcher .05 .15
121 Ron Robinson .05 .15
122 Dan Spillner .05 .15
123 Mike Young .05 .15
124 Paul Molitor .08 .25
125 Kirk Gibson .08 .25
126 Ken Griffey .08 .25
127 Tony Armas .08 .25
128 Mariano Duncan RC .20 .50
129 Pat Tabler .05 .15
130 Frank White .08 .25
131 Carney Lansford .08 .25
132 Vance Law .05 .15
133 Dick Schofield .05 .15
134 Wayne Tolleson .05 .15
135 Greg Walker .05 .15
136 Denny Walling .05 .15
137 Ozzie Virgil .05 .15
138 Ricky Horton .05 .15
139 LaMarr Hoyt .05 .15
140 Wayne Krenchicki .05 .15
141 Glenn Hubbard .05 .15
142 Cecilio Guante .05 .15
143 Mike Krukow .05 .15
144 Lee Smith .08 .25
145 Edwin Nunez .05 .15
146 Dave Stieb .08 .25
147 Mike Smithson .05 .15
148 Ken Dixon .05 .15
149 Danny Darwin .05 .15
150 Chris Pittaro .05 .15
151 Bill Buckner .08 .25
152 Mike Pagliarulo .05 .15
153 Bill Russell .08 .25
154 Brook Jacoby .05 .15
155 Pat Sheridan .05 .15
156 Mike Gallego RC .05 .15
157 Jim Wohlford .05 .15
158 Gary Pettis .05 .15
159 Toby Harrah .08 .25
160 Richard Dotson .05 .15
161 Bob Knepper .05 .15
162 Dave Dravecky .05 .15
163 Greg Gross .05 .15
164 Eric Davis .30 .75
165 Gerald Perry .05 .15
166 Rick Rhoden .05 .15
167 Keith Moreland .05 .15
168 Jack Clark .08 .25
169 Storm Davis .05 .15
170 Cecil Cooper .08 .25
171 Alan Trammell .08 .25
172 Roger Clemens 2.00 5.00
173 Don Mattingly 1.00 2.50
174 Pedro Guerrero .08 .25
175 Willie Wilson .08 .25
176 Dwayne Murphy .05 .15
177 Tim Raines .08 .25
178 Larry Parrish .05 .15
179 Mike Witt .05 .15
180 Harold Baines .08 .25
181 Vince Coleman RC .40 1.00
UER BA 2.67 on back
182 Jeff Heathcock .05 .15
183 Steve Carlton .08 .25
184 Mario Soto .08 .25
185 Rich Gossage .08 .25
186 Johnny Ray .05 .15
187 Dan Gladden .05 .15
188 Bob Horner .08 .25
189 Rick Sutcliffe .08 .25
190 Keith Hernandez .08 .25
191 Phil Bradley .05 .15
192 Tom Brunansky .05 .15
193 Jesse Barfield .08 .25
194 Frank Viola .08 .25
195 Willie Upshaw .05 .15
196 Jim Beattie .05 .15
197 Darryl Strawberry .20 .50
198 Ron Cey .08 .25
199 Steve Bedrosian .05 .15
200 Steve Kemp .05 .15
201 Manny Trillo .05 .15
202 Garry Templeton .08 .25
203 Dave Parker .08 .25
204 John Denny .05 .15
205 Terry Pendleton .08 .25
206 Terry Puhl .05 .15
207 Bobby Grich .08 .25
208 Ozzie Guillen RC .75 2.00
209 Jeff Reardon .08 .25
210 Cal Ripken 1.25 3.00
211 Bill Schroeder .05 .15
212 Dan Petry .05 .15
213 Jim Rice .08 .25
214 Dave Righetti .08 .25
215 Fernando Valenzuela .08 .25
216 Julio Franco .08 .25
217 Darryl Motley .05 .15
218 Dave Collins .05 .15
219 Tim Wallach .05 .15
220 George Wright .05 .15
221 Tommy Dunbar .05 .15
222 Steve Balboni .05 .15
223 Jay Howell .05 .15
224 Joe Carter .08 .25
225 Ed Whitson .05 .15
226 Orel Hershiser .30 .75
227 Willie Hernandez .05 .15
228 Lee Lacy .05 .15
229 Rollie Fingers .08 .25
230 Bob Boone .08 .25
231 Joaquin Andujar .08 .25
232 Craig Reynolds .05 .15
233 Shane Rawley .05 .15
234 Eric Show .05 .15
235 Jose DeLeon .05 .15
236 Jose Uribe .05 .15
237 Moose Haas .05 .15
238 Wally Backman .05 .15
239 Dennis Eckersley .20 .50
240 Mike Moore .05 .15
241 Damaso Garcia .05 .15
242 Tim Teufel .05 .15
243 Dave Concepcion .08 .25
244 Floyd Bannister .05 .15
245 Fred Lynn .08 .25
246 Charlie Moore .05 .15
247 Walt Terrell .05 .15
248 Dave Winfield .08 .25
249 Dwight Evans .20 .50
250 Dennis Powell .05 .15
251 Andre Thornton .05 .15
252 Onix Concepcion .05 .15
253 Mike Heath .05 .15
254A David Palmer ERR .05 .15
(Position 2B)
254B David Palmer COR .20 .50
(Position P)
255 Donnie Moore .05 .15
256 Curtis Wilkerson .05 .15
257 Julio Cruz .05 .15
258 Nolan Ryan 1.50 4.00
259 Jeff Stone .05 .15
260 John Tudor .08 .25
261 Mark Thurmond .05 .15
262 Jay Tibbs .05 .15
263 Rafael Ramirez .05 .15
264 Larry McWilliams .05 .15
265 Mark Davis .05 .15
266 Bob Dernier .05 .15
267 Matt Young .05 .15
268 Jim Clancy .05 .15
269 Mickey Hatcher .05 .15
270 Sammy Stewart .05 .15
271 Bob L. Gibson .05 .15
272 Nelson Simmons .05 .15
273 Rich Gedman .05 .15
274 Butch Wynegar .05 .15
275 Ken Howell .05 .15
276 Mel Hall .05 .15
277 Jim Sundberg .08 .25
278 Chris Codiroli .05 .15
279 Herm Winningham .05 .15
280 Rod Carew .20 .50
281 Don Slaught .05 .15
282 Scott Fletcher .05 .15
283 Bill Dawley .05 .15
284 Andy Hawkins .05 .15
285 Glenn Wilson .05 .15
286 Nick Esasky .05 .15
287 Claudell Washington .05 .15
288 Lee Mazzilli .08 .25
289 Jody Davis .05 .15
290 Darrell Porter .05 .15
291 Scott McGregor .05 .15
292 Ted Simmons .08 .25
293 Aurelio Lopez .05 .15
294 Marty Barrett .05 .15
295 Dale Berra .05 .15
296 Greg Brock .05 .15
297 Charlie Leibrandt .05 .15
298 Bill Krueger .05 .15
299 Bryn Smith .05 .15
300 Burt Hooton .05 .15
301 Stu Cliburn .05 .15
302 Luis Salazar .05 .15
303 Ken Dayley .05 .15
304 Frank DiPino .05 .15
305 Von Hayes .05 .15
306 Gary Redus .05 .15
307 Craig Lefferts .05 .15
308 Sammy Khalifa .05 .15
309 Scott Garrelts .05 .15
310 Rick Cerone .05 .15
311 Shawon Dunston .08 .25
312 Howard Johnson .08 .25
313 Jim Presley .05 .15
314 Gary Gaetti .08 .25
315 Luis Leal .05 .15
316 Mark Salas .05 .15
317 Bill Caudill .05 .15
318 Dave Henderson .05 .15
319 Rafael Santana .05 .15
320 Leon Durham .05 .15
321 Bruce Sutter .08 .25
322 Jason Thompson .05 .15
323 Bob Brenly .05 .15
324 Carmelo Martinez .05 .15
325 Eddie Milner .05 .15
326 Juan Samuel .05 .15
327 Tom Nieto .05 .15
328 Dave Smith .05 .15
329 Urbano Lugo .05 .15
330 Joel Skinner .05 .15
331 Bill Gullickson .05 .15
332 Floyd Rayford .05 .15
333 Ben Oglivie .08 .25
334 Lance Parrish .08 .25
335 Jackie Gutierrez .05 .15
336 Dennis Rasmussen .05 .15
337 Terry Whitfield .05 .15
338 Neal Heaton .05 .15
339 Jorge Orta .05 .15
340 Donnie Hill .05 .15
341 Joe Hesketh .05 .15
342 Charlie Hough .08 .25
343 Dave Rozema .05 .15
344 Greg Pryor .05 .15
345 Mickey Tettleton RC .20 .50
346 George Vukovich .05 .15
347 Don Baylor .08 .25
348 Carlos Diaz .05 .15
349 Barbaro Garbey .05 .15
350 Larry Sheets .05 .15
351 Ted Higuera RC .20 .50
352 Juan Beniquez .05 .15
353 Bob Forsch .05 .15
354 Mark Bailey .05 .15
355 Larry Andersen .05 .15
356 Terry Kennedy .05 .15
357 Don Robinson .05 .15
358 Jim Gott .05 .15
359 Earnie Riles .05 .15
360 John Christensen .05 .15
361 Ray Fontenot .05 .15
362 Spike Owen .05 .15
363 Jim Acker .05 .15
364 Ron Davis .05 .15
365 Tom Hume .05 .15
366 Carlton Fisk .20 .50
367 Nate Snell .05 .15
368 Rick Manning .05 .15
369 Darrell Evans .08 .25
370 Ron Hassey .05 .15
371 Wade Boggs .20 .50
372 Rick Honeycutt .05 .15
373 Chris Bando .05 .15
374 Bud Black .05 .15
375 Steve Henderson .05 .15
376 Charlie Lea .05 .15
377 Reggie Jackson .20 .50
378 Dave Schmidt .05 .15
379 Bob James .05 .15
380 Glenn Davis .05 .15
381 Tim Corcoran .05 .15
382 Danny Cox .05 .15
383 Tim Flannery .05 .15
384 Tom Browning .05 .15
385 Rick Camp .05 .15
386 Jim Morrison .05 .15
387 Dave LaPoint .05 .15
388 Dave Lopes .08 .25
389 Al Cowens .05 .15
390 Doyle Alexander .05 .15
391 Tim Laudner .05 .15
392 Don Aase .05 .15
393 Jaime Cocanower .05 .15
394 Randy O'Neal .05 .15
395 Mike Easler .05 .15
396 Scott Bradley .05 .15
397 Tom Niedenfuer .05 .15
398 Jerry Willard .05 .15
399 Lonnie Smith .05 .15
400 Bruce Bochte .05 .15
401 Terry Francona .08 .25
402 Jim Slaton .05 .15
403 Bill Stein .05 .15
404 Tim Hulett .05 .15
405 Alan Ashby .05 .15
406 Tim Stoddard .05 .15
407 Garry Maddox .05 .15
408 Ted Power .05 .15
409 Len Barker .05 .15
410 Denny Gonzalez .05 .15
411 George Frazier .05 .15
412 Andy Van Slyke .20 .50
413 Jim Dwyer .05 .15
414 Paul Householder .05 .15
415 Alejandro Sanchez .05 .15
416 Steve Crawford .05 .15
417 Dan Pasqua .05 .15
418 Enos Cabell .05 .15
419 Mike Jones .05 .15
420 Steve Kiefer .05 .15
421 Tim Burke .05 .15
422 Mike Mason .05 .15
423 Ruppert Jones .05 .15
424 Jerry Hairston .05 .15
425 Tito Landrum .05 .15
426 Jeff Calhoun .05 .15
427 Don Carman .05 .15
428 Tony Perez .20 .50
429 Jerry Davis .05 .15
430 Bob Walk .05 .15
431 Brad Wellman .05 .15
432 Terry Forster .08 .25
433 Billy Hatcher .05 .15
434 Clint Hurdle .05 .15
435 Ivan Calderon RC .20 .50
436 Pete Filson .05 .15
437 Tom Henke .08 .25
438 Dave Engle .05 .15
439 Tom Filer .05 .15
440 Gorman Thomas .08 .25
441 Rick Aguilera RC .20 .50
442 Scott Sanderson .05 .15
443 Jeff Dedmon .05 .15
444 Joe Orsulak RC .20 .50
445 Atlee Hammaker .05 .15
446 Jerry Royster .05 .15
447 Buddy Bell .08 .25
448 Dave Rucker .05 .15
449 Ivan DeJesus .05 .15
450 Jim Pankovits .05 .15
451 Jerry Narron .05 .15
452 Bryan Little .05 .15
453 Gary Lucas .05 .15
454 Dennis Martinez .08 .25
455 Ed Romero .05 .15
456 Bob Melvin .05 .15
457 Glenn Hoffman .05 .15
458 Bob Shirley .05 .15
459 Bob Welch .08 .25
460 Carmen Castillo .05 .15
461 Dave Leeper .05 .15
462 Tim Birtsas .05 .15
463 Randy St.Claire .05 .15
464 Chris Welsh .05 .15
465 Greg Harris .05 .15
466 Lynn Jones .05 .15
467 Dusty Baker .08 .25
468 Roy Smith .05 .15
469 Andre Robertson .05 .15
470 Ken Landreaux .05 .15
471 Dave Bergman .05 .15
472 Gary Roenicke .05 .15
473 Pete Vuckovich .05 .15
474 Kirk McCaskill RC .20 .50
475 Jeff Lahti .05 .15
476 Mike Scott .08 .25
477 Darren Daulton RC .40 1.00
478 Graig Nettles .08 .25
479 Bill Almon .05 .15
480 Greg Minton .05 .15
481 Randy Ready .05 .15
482 Len Dykstra RC .60 1.50
483 Thad Bosley .05 .15
484 Harold Reynolds RC .60 1.50
485 Al Oliver .08 .25
486 Roy Smalley .05 .15
487 John Franco .08 .25
488 Juan Agosto .05 .15
489 Al Pardo .05 .15
490 Bill Wegman RC .05 .15
491 Frank Tanana .08 .25
492 Brian Fisher RC .05 .15
493 Mark Clear .05 .15
494 Len Matuszek .05 .15
495 Ramon Romero .05 .15
496 John Wathan .05 .15
497 Rob Picciolo .05 .15
498 U.L. Washington .05 .15
499 John Candelaria .05 .15
500 Duane Walker .05 .15
501 Gene Nelson .05 .15
502 John Mizerock .05 .15
503 Luis Aguayo .05 .15
504 Kurt Kepshire .05 .15
505 Ed Wojna .05 .15
506 Joe Price .05 .15
507 Milt Thompson RC .20 .50
508 Junior Ortiz .05 .15
509 Vida Blue .08 .25
510 Steve Engel .05 .15
511 Karl Best .05 .15
512 Cecil Fielder RC .75 2.00
513 Frank Eufemia .05 .15
514 Tippy Martinez .05 .15
515 Billy Joe Robidoux .05 .15
516 Bill Scherrer .05 .15
517 Bruce Hurst .05 .15
518 Rich Bordi .05 .15
519 Steve Yeager .08 .25
520 Tony Bernazard .05 .15
521 Hal McRae .08 .25
522 Jose Rijo .08 .25
523 Mitch Webster .05 .15
524 Jack Howell .05 .15
525 Alan Bannister .05 .15
526 Ron Kittle .05 .15
527 Phil Garner .08 .25
528 Kurt Bevacqua .05 .15
529 Kevin Gross .05 .15
530 Bo Diaz .05 .15
531 Ken Oberkfell .05 .15
532 Rick Reuschel .08 .25
533 Ron Meridith .05 .15
534 Steve Braun .05 .15
535 Wayne Gross .05 .15
536 Ray Searage .05 .15
537 Tom Brookens .05 .15
538 Al Nipper .05 .15
539 Billy Sample .05 .15
540 Steve Sax .05 .15
541 Dan Quisenberry .05 .15
542 Tony Phillips .05 .15
543 Floyd Youmans .05 .15
544 Steve Buechele RC .20 .50
545 Craig Gerber .05 .15
546 Joe DeSa .05 .15
547 Brian Harper .05 .15
548 Kevin Bass .05 .15
549 Tom Foley .05 .15
550 Dave Van Gorder .05 .15
551 Bruce Bochy .05 .15
552 R.J. Reynolds .05 .15
553 Chris Brown RC .05 .15
554 Bruce Benedict .05 .15
555 Warren Brusstar .05 .15
556 Danny Heep .05 .15
557 Darnell Coles .05 .15
558 Greg Gagne .05 .15
559 Ernie Whitt .05 .15
560 Ron Washington .05 .15
561 Jimmy Key .08 .25
562 Billy Swift .05 .15
563 Ron Darling .08 .25
564 Dick Ruthven .05 .15
565 Zane Smith .05 .15
566 Sid Bream .05 .15
567A J.Youngblood ERR .05 .15
Position P
567B J.Youngblood COR .20 .50
Position IF
568 Mario Ramirez .05 .15
569 Tom Runnells .05 .15
570 Rick Schu .05 .15
571 Bill Campbell .05 .15
572 Dickie Thon .05 .15
573 Al Holland .05 .15
574 Reid Nichols .05 .15
575 Bert Roberge .05 .15
576 Mike Flanagan .05 .15
577 Tim Leary .05 .15
578 Mike Laga .05 .15
579 Steve Lyons .05 .15
580 Phil Niekro .08 .25
581 Gilberto Reyes .05 .15
582 Jamie Easterly .05 .15
583 Mark Gubicza .05 .15
584 Stan Javier RC .20 .50
585 Bill Laskey .05 .15
586 Jeff Russell .05 .15
587 Dickie Noles .05 .15
588 Steve Farr .05 .15
589 Steve Ontiveros RC .05 .15
590 Mike Hargrove .05 .15
591 Marty Bystrom .05 .15
592 Franklin Stubbs .05 .15
593 Larry Herndon .05 .15
594 Bill Swaggerty .05 .15
595 Carlos Ponce .05 .15
596 Pat Perry .05 .15
597 Ray Knight .08 .25
598 Steve Lombardozzi .05 .15
599 Brad Havens .05 .15
600 Pat Clements .05 .15
601 Joe Niekro .05 .15
602 Hank Aaron .30 .75
Puzzle Card
603 Dwayne Henry .05 .15
604 Mookie Wilson .08 .25
605 Buddy Biancalana .05 .15
606 Rance Mulliniks .05 .15
607 Alan Wiggins .05 .15
608 Joe Cowley .05 .15
609 Tom Seaver .20 .50
(Green borders
on name)
609B Tom Seaver .75 2.00
(Yellow borders
on name)
610 Neil Allen .05 .15
611 Don Sutton .08 .25
612 Fred Toliver .05 .15
613 Jay Baller .05 .15
614 Marc Sullivan .05 .15
615 John Grubb .05 .15
616 Bruce Kison .05 .15
617 Bill Madlock .08 .25
618 Chris Chambliss .08 .25
619 Dave Stewart .08 .25
620 Tim Lollar .05 .15
621 Gary Lavelle .05 .15
622 Charles Hudson .05 .15
623 Joel Davis .05 .15
624 Joe Johnson .05 .15
625 Sid Fernandez .05 .15
626 Dennis Lamp .05 .15
627 Terry Harper .05 .15
628 Jack Lazorko .05 .15
629 Roger McDowell RC .20 .50
630 Mark Funderburk .05 .15
631 Ed Lynch .05 .15
632 Rudy Law .05 .15
633 Roger Mason RC .05 .15
634 Mike Felder RC .05 .15
635 Ken Schrom .05 .15
636 Bob Ojeda .05 .15
637 Ed VandeBerg .05 .15
638 Bobby Meacham .05 .15
639 Cliff Johnson .05 .15
640 Garth Iorg .05 .15
641 Dan Driessen .05 .15
642 Mike Brown OF .05 .15
643 John Shelby .05 .15
644 Pete Rose RB .30 .75
645 Phil Niekro .08 .25
Joe Niekro
646 Jesse Orosco .05 .15
647 Billy Beane RC .40 1.00
648 Cesar Cedeno .08 .25
649 Bert Blyleven .08 .25
650 Max Venable .05 .15
651 Vince Coleman .05 .15
Willie McGee
652 Calvin Schiraldi .05 .15
653 Pete Rose KING .30 .75
654 Dia. Kings CL 1-26 .05 .15
Unnumbered
655A CL 1: 27-130 .05 .15
(Unnumbered)
(45 Beane ERR)
655B CL 1: 27-130 .05 .15
(Unnumbered)
(45 Habyan COR)
656 CL 2: 131-234 .05 .15
(Unnumbered)
657 CL 3: 235-338 .05 .15
(Unnumbered)

658 CL 4: 339-442 .05 .15
(Unnumbered)
659 CL 5: 443-546 .05 .15
(Unnumbered)
660 CL 6: 547-653 .05 .15
(Unnumbered)

1986 Donruss Rookies

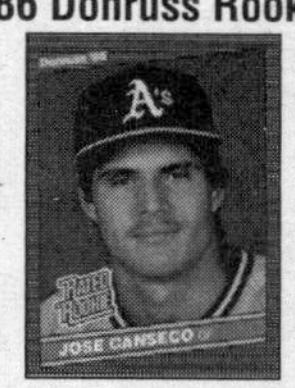

The 1986 Donruss "The Rookies" set features 56 full-color standard-size cards plus a 15-piece puzzle of Hank Aaron. The set was distributed through hobby dealers, packed in 60-set cases, in a small green, cellophane wrapped factory box. Although the set was wrapped in cellophane, the top card was number one Joyner, resulting in a percentage of the Joyner cards arriving in less than perfect condition. Donruss fixed the problem after it was called to their attention and even went so far as to include a customer service phone number in their second printing. Card fronts are similar in design to the 1986 Donruss regular issue except for the presence of "The Rookies" logo in the lower left corner and a bluish green border instead of a blue border. The key extended Rookie Cards in this set are Barry Bonds, Bobby Bonilla, Will Clark, Bo Jackson, Wally Joyner and John Kruk.

COMP.FACT.SET (56) 10.00 25.00
1 Wally Joyner XRC .40 1.00
2 Tracy Jones .05 .15
3 Allan Anderson XRC .05 .15
4 Ed Correa .05 .15
5 Reggie Williams .05 .15
6 Charlie Kerfeld .05 .15
7 Andres Galarraga .60 1.50
8 Bob Tewksbury XRC .20 .50
9 Al Newman XRC .08 .25
10 Andres Thomas .05 .15
11 Barry Bonds XRC 5.00 12.00
12 Juan Nieves .05 .15
13 Mark Eichhorn .05 .15
14 Dan Plesac XRC .20 .50
15 Cory Snyder .05 .15
16 Kelly Gruber .05 .15
17 Kevin Mitchell XRC .40 1.00
18 Steve Lombardozzi .05 .15
19 Mitch Williams XRC .20 .50
20 John Cerutti .05 .15
21 Todd Worrell .20 .50
22 Jose Canseco 1.50 4.00
23 Pete Incaviglia XRC .20 .50
24 Jose Guzman .05 .15
25 Scott Bailes .05 .15
26 Greg Mathews .05 .15
27 Eric King .05 .15
28 Paul Assenmacher .20 .50
29 Jeff Sellers .05 .15
30 Bobby Bonilla XRC .40 1.00
31 Doug Drabek XRC .40 1.00
32 Will Clark UER .75 2.00
(Listed as throwing right, should be left) XRC
33 Bip Roberts XRC .20 .50
34 Jim Deshaies XRC .05 .15
35 Mike LaValliere XRC .20 .50
36 Scott Bankhead .05 .15
37 Dale Sveum .05 .15
38 Bo Jackson XRC 2.00 5.00
39 Robby Thompson XRC .20 .50
40 Eric Plunk .05 .15
41 Bill Bathe .05 .15
42 John Kruk XRC .60 1.50
43 Andy Allanson XRC .05 .15
44 Mark Portugal XRC .20 .50
45 Danny Tartabull .08 .25
46 Bob Kipper .05 .15
47 Gene Walter .05 .15
48 Rey Quinones UER .05 .15
(Misspelled Quinonez)
49 Bobby Witt XRC .20 .50
50 Bill Mooneyham .05 .15
51 John Cangelosi .05 .15
52 Ruben Sierra XRC .60 1.50
53 Rob Woodward .05 .15
54 Ed Hearn XRC .05 .15
55 Joel McKeon .05 .15
56 Checklist 1-56 .05 .15

1987 Donruss

This set consists of 660 standard-size cards. Cards were primarily distributed in 15-card wax packs, rack packs and a factory set. All packs included a Roberto Clemente puzzle panel and the factory sets contained a complete puzzle. The regular-issue cards feature a black and gold border on the front. The backs of the cards in the factory sets are oriented differently than cards taken from wax packs, giving the appearance that one version or the other is upside down when sorting from the card backs. There are no premiums or discounts for either version. The popular Diamond King subset returns for the sixth consecutive year. Some of the Diamond King (1-26) selections are repeats from prior years; Perez-Steele Galleries had indicated in 1987 that a five-year rotation would be maintained in order to avoid depleting the pool of available worthy "kings" on some of the teams. The rich selection of Rookie Cards in this set include Barry Bonds, Bobby Bonilla, Kevin Brown, Will Clark, David Cone, Chuck Finley, Bo Jackson, Wally Joyner, Barry Larkin, Greg Maddux and Rafael Palmeiro.

COMPLETE SET (660) 15.00 40.00
COMP.FACT.SET (660) 20.00 50.00
COMP.CLEMENTE PUZZLE .60 1.50
1 Wally Joyner DK .15 .40
2 Roger Clemens DK .75 2.00
3 Dale Murphy DK .08 .25
4 Darryl Strawberry DK .05 .15
5 Ozzie Smith DK .25 .60
6 Jose Canseco DK .40 1.00
7 Charlie Hough DK .05 .15
8 Brook Jacoby DK .02 .10
9 Fred Lynn DK .05 .15
10 Rick Rhoden DK .02 .10
11 Chris Brown DK .02 .10
12 Von Hayes DK .02 .10
13 Jack Morris DK .05 .15
14A Kevin McReynolds DK .15 .40
ERR (Yellow strip missing on back)
14B Kevin McReynolds DK .02 .10
COR
15 George Brett DK .40 1.00
16 Ted Higuera DK .02 .10
17 Hubie Brooks DK .02 .10
18 Mike Scott DK .05 .15
19 Kirby Puckett DK .30 .75
20 Dave Winfield DK .05 .15
21 Lloyd Moseby DK .02 .10
22A Eric Davis DK ERR .15 .40
(Yellow strip missing on back)
22B Eric Davis DK COR .08 .25
23 Jim Presley DK .02 .10
24 Keith Moreland DK .02 .10
25A Greg Walker DK ERR .15 .40
(Yellow strip missing on back)
25B Greg Walker DK COR .02 .10
26 Steve Sax DK .02 .10
27 DK Checklist 1-26 .02 .10
28 B.J. Surhoff RR RC .25 .60
29 Randy Myers RR RC .25 .60
30 Ken Gerhart RC .05 .15
31 Benito Santiago .05 .15
32 Greg Swindell RR RC .15 .40
33 Mike Birkbeck RC .05 .15
34 Terry Steinbach RR RC .25 .60
35 Bo Jackson RR RC 2.00 5.00
36 Greg Maddux UER RC 4.00 10.00
middle name misspelled Allen
37 Jim Lindeman RC .05 .15
38 Devon White RR RC .25 .60
39 Eric Bell RC .05 .15
40 Willie Fraser RC .05 .15
41 Jerry Browne RR RC .05 .15
42 Chris James RR RC .05 .15
43 Rafael Palmeiro RR RC 2.00 5.00
44 Pat Dodson RC .05 .15
45 Duane Ward RR RC .15 .40
46 Mark McGwire RR 3.00 8.00
47 Bruce Fields UER RC .05 .15
(Photo actually Darnell Coles)
48 Eddie Murray .15 .40
49 Ted Higuera .02 .10
50 Kirk Gibson .05 .15
51 Oil Can Boyd .02 .10
52 Don Mattingly .50 1.25
53 Pedro Guerrero .05 .15
54 George Brett .40 1.00
55 Jose Rijo .05 .15
56 Tim Raines .05 .15
57 Ed Correa .02 .10
58 Mike Witt .02 .10
59 Greg Walker .02 .10
60 Ozzie Smith .25 .60
61 Glenn Davis .02 .10
62 Glenn Wilson .02 .10
63 Tom Browning .02 .10
64 Tony Gwynn .25 .60
65 R.J. Reynolds .02 .10
66 Will Clark RC .60 1.50
67 Ozzie Virgil .02 .10
68 Rick Sutcliffe .05 .15
69 Gary Carter .05 .15
70 Mike Moore .02 .10
71 Bert Blyleven .05 .15
72 Tony Fernandez .02 .10
73 Kent Hrbek .05 .15
74 Lloyd Moseby .02 .10
75 Alvin Davis .02 .10
76 Keith Hernandez .05 .15
77 Ryne Sandberg .30 .75
78 Dale Murphy .08 .25
79 Sid Bream .02 .10
80 Chris Brown .02 .10
81 Steve Garvey .05 .15
82 Mario Soto .05 .15
83 Shane Rawley .02 .10
84 Willie McGee .05 .15
85 Jose Cruz .05 .15
86 Brian Downing .05 .15
87 Ozzie Guillen .08 .25
88 Hubie Brooks .02 .10
89 Cal Ripken .60 1.50
90 Juan Nieves .02 .10
91 Lance Parrish .05 .15
92 Jim Rice .05 .15
93 Ron Guidry .05 .15
94 Fernando Valenzuela .05 .15
95 Andy Allanson RC .02 .10
96 Willie Wilson .05 .15
97 Jose Canseco .40 1.00
98 Jeff Reardon .05 .15
99 Bobby Witt RC .15 .40
100 Checklist 28-133 .02 .10
101 Jose Guzman .02 .10
102 Steve Balboni .02 .10
103 Tony Phillips .02 .10
104 Brook Jacoby .02 .10
105 Dave Winfield .05 .15
106 Orel Hershiser .08 .25
107 Lou Whitaker .05 .15
108 Fred Lynn .05 .15
109 Bill Wegman .02 .10
110 Donnie Moore .02 .10
111 Jack Clark .05 .15
112 Bob Knepper .02 .10
113 Von Hayes .02 .10
114 Bip Roberts RC .15 .40
115 Tony Pena .02 .10
116 Scott Garrelts .02 .10
117 Paul Molitor .05 .15
118 Darryl Strawberry .05 .15
119 Shawon Dunston .02 .10
120 Jim Presley .02 .10
121 Jesse Barfield .05 .15
122 Gary Gaetti .05 .15
123 Kurt Stillwell .02 .10
124 Joel Davis .02 .10
125 Mike Boddicker .02 .10
126 Robin Yount .25 .60
127 Alan Trammell .05 .15
128 Dave Righetti .05 .15
129 Dwight Evans .08 .25
130 Mike Scioscia .05 .15
131 Julio Franco .05 .15
132 Bret Saberhagen .05 .15
133 Mike Davis .02 .10
134 Joe Hesketh .02 .10
135 Wally Joyner RC .25 .60
136 Don Slaught .02 .10
137 Daryl Boston .02 .10
138 Nolan Ryan .75 2.00
139 Mike Schmidt .40 1.00
140 Tommy Herr .02 .10
141 Garry Templeton .05 .15
142 Kal Daniels .02 .10
143 Billy Sample .02 .10
144 Johnny Ray .02 .10
145 Rob Thompson RC .15 .40
146 Bob Dernier .02 .10
147 Danny Tartabull .02 .10
148 Ernie Whitt .02 .10
149 Kirby Puckett .30 .75
150 Mike Young .02 .10
151 Ernest Riles .02 .10
152 Frank Tanana .05 .15
153 Rich Gedman .02 .10
154 Willie Randolph .05 .15
155 Bill Madlock .05 .15
156 Joe Carter .05 .15
157 Danny Jackson .02 .10
158 Carney Lansford .05 .15
159 Bryn Smith .02 .10
160 Gary Pettis .02 .10
161 Oddibe McDowell .02 .10
162 John Cangelosi .02 .10
163 Mike Scott .05 .15
164 Eric Show .02 .10
165 Juan Samuel .02 .10
166 Nick Esasky .02 .10
167 Zane Smith .02 .10
168 Mike C. Brown .02 .10
169 Keith Moreland .02 .10
170 John Tudor .05 .15
171 Ken Dixon .02 .10
172 Jim Gantner .02 .10
173 Jack Morris .05 .15
174 Bruce Hurst .02 .10
175 Dennis Rasmussen .02 .10
176 Mike Marshall .02 .10
177 Dan Quisenberry .02 .10
178 Eric Plunk .02 .10
179 Tim Wallach .02 .10
180 Steve Buechele .02 .10
181 Don Sutton .05 .15
182 Dave Schmidt .02 .10
183 Terry Pendleton .05 .15
184 Jim Deshaies RC .05 .15
185 Steve Bedrosian .02 .10
186 Pete Rose .50 1.25
187 Dave Dravecky .02 .10
188 Rick Reuschel .05 .15
189 Dan Gladden .02 .10
190 Rick Mahler .02 .10
191 Thad Bosley .02 .10
192 Ron Darling .05 .15
193 Matt Young .02 .10
194 Tom Brunansky .02 .10
195 Dave Stieb .05 .15
196 Frank Viola .05 .15
197 Tom Henke .02 .10
198 Karl Best .02 .10
199 Dwight Gooden .08 .25
200 Checklist 134-239 .02 .10
201 Steve Trout .02 .10
202 Rafael Ramirez .02 .10
203 Bob Walk .02 .10
204 Roger Mason .02 .10
205 Terry Kennedy .02 .10
206 Ron Oester .02 .10
207 John Russell .02 .10
208 Greg Mathews .02 .10
209 Charlie Kerfeld .02 .10
210 Reggie Jackson .08 .25
211 Floyd Bannister .02 .10
212 Vance Law .02 .10
213 Rich Bordi .02 .10
214 Dan Plesac .02 .10
215 Dave Collins .02 .10
216 Bob Stanley .02 .10
217 Joe Niekro .02 .10
218 Tom Niedenfuer .02 .10
219 Brett Butler .05 .15
220 Charlie Leibrandt .02 .10
221 Steve Ontiveros .02 .10
222 Tim Burke .02 .10
223 Curtis Wilkerson .02 .10
224 Pete Incaviglia RC .15 .40
225 Lonnie Smith .02 .10
226 Chris Codiroli .02 .10
227 Scott Bailes .02 .10
228 Rickey Henderson .15 .40
229 Ken Howell .02 .10
230 Darnell Coles .02 .10
231 Don Aase .02 .10
232 Tim Leary .02 .10
233 Bob Boone .05 .15
234 Ricky Horton .02 .10
235 Mark Bailey .02 .10
236 Kevin Gross .02 .10
237 Lance McCullers .02 .10
238 Cecilio Guante .02 .10
239 Bob Melvin .02 .10
240 Billy Joe Robidoux .02 .10
241 Roger McDowell .02 .10
242 Leon Durham .02 .10
243 Ed Nunez .02 .10
244 Jimmy Key .05 .15
245 Mike Smithson .02 .10
246 Bo Diaz .02 .10
247 Carlton Fisk .08 .25
248 Larry Sheets .02 .10
249 Juan Castillo RC .05 .15
250 Eric King .02 .10
251 Doug Drabek RC .25 .60
252 Wade Boggs .08 .25
253 Mariano Duncan .02 .10
254 Pat Tabler .02 .10
255 Frank White .05 .15
256 Alfredo Griffin .02 .10
257 Floyd Youmans .02 .10
258 Rob Wilfong .02 .10
259 Pete O'Brien .02 .10
260 Tim Hulett .02 .10
261 Dickie Thon .02 .10
262 Darren Daulton .05 .15
263 Vince Coleman .02 .10
264 Andy Hawkins .02 .10
265 Eric Davis .08 .25
266 Andres Thomas .02 .10
267 Mike Diaz .02 .10
268 Chili Davis .05 .15
269 Jody Davis .02 .10
270 Phil Bradley .02 .10
271 George Bell .05 .15
272 Keith Atherton .02 .10
273 Storm Davis .02 .10
274 Rob Deer .02 .10
275 Walt Terrell .02 .10
276 Roger Clemens .75 2.00
277 Mike Easler .02 .10
278 Steve Sax .02 .10
279 Andre Thornton .02 .10
280 Jim Sundberg .05 .15
281 Bill Bathe .02 .10
282 Jay Tibbs .02 .10
283 Dick Schofield .02 .10
284 Mike Mason .02 .10
285 Jerry Hairston .02 .10
286 Bill Doran .02 .10
287 Tim Flannery .02 .10
288 Gary Redus .02 .10
289 John Franco .05 .15
290 Paul Assenmacher .15 .40
291 Joe Orsulak .02 .10
292 Lee Smith .05 .15
293 Mike Laga .02 .10
294 Rick Dempsey .02 .10
295 Mike Felder .02 .10
296 Tom Brookens .02 .10
297 Al Nipper .02 .10
298 Mike Pagliarulo .02 .10
299 Franklin Stubbs .02 .10
300 Checklist 240-345 .02 .10
301 Steve Farr .02 .10
302 Bill Mooneyham .02 .10
303 Andres Galarraga .05 .15
304 Scott Fletcher .02 .10
305 Jack Howell .02 .10
306 Russ Morman .02 .10
307 Todd Worrell .02 .10
308 Dave Smith .02 .10
309 Jeff Stone .02 .10
310 Ron Robinson .02 .10
311 Bruce Bochy .02 .10
312 Jim Winn .02 .10
313 Mark Davis .02 .10
314 Jeff Dedmon .02 .10
315 Jamie Moyer RC .40 1.00
316 Wally Backman .02 .10
317 Ken Phelps .02 .10
318 Steve Lombardozzi .02 .10
319 Rance Mulliniks .02 .10
320 Tim Laudner .02 .10
321 Mark Eichhorn .02 .10
322 Lee Guetterman .02 .10
323 Sid Fernandez .02 .10
324 Jerry Mumphrey .02 .10
325 David Palmer .02 .10
326 Bill Almon .02 .10
327 Candy Maldonado .02 .10
328 John Kruk RC .40 1.00
329 John Denny .02 .10
330 Milt Thompson .02 .10
331 Mike LaValliere RC .15 .40
332 Alan Ashby .02 .10
333 Doug Corbett .02 .10
334 Ron Karkovice RC .15 .40
335 Mitch Webster .02 .10
336 Lee Lacy .02 .10
337 Glenn Braggs RC .05 .15
338 Dwight Lowry .02 .10
339 Don Baylor .05 .15
340 Brian Fisher .02 .10
341 Reggie Williams .02 .10
342 Tom Candiotti .02 .10
343 Rudy Law .02 .10
344 Curt Young .02 .10
345 Mike Fitzgerald .02 .10
346 Ruben Sierra RC .40 1.00
347 Mitch Williams RC .15 .40
348 Jorge Orta .02 .10
349 Mickey Tettleton .02 .10
350 Ernie Camacho .02 .10
351 Ron Kittle .02 .10
352 Ken Landreaux .02 .10
353 Chet Lemon .05 .15
354 John Shelby .02 .10
355 Mark Clear .02 .10
356 Doug DeCinces .02 .10
357 Ken Dayley .02 .10
358 Phil Garner .05 .15
359 Steve Jeltz .02 .10
360 Ed Whitson .02 .10
361 Barry Bonds RC 5.00 12.00
362 Vida Blue .05 .15
363 Cecil Cooper .05 .15
364 Bob Ojeda .02 .10
365 Dennis Eckersley .08 .25
366 Mike Morgan .02 .10
367 Willie Upshaw .02 .10
368 Allan Anderson RC .02 .10
369 Bill Gullickson .02 .10
370 Bobby Thigpen RC .15 .40
371 Juan Beniquez .02 .10
372 Charlie Moore .02 .10
373 Dan Petry .02 .10
374 Rod Scurry .02 .10
375 Tom Seaver .08 .25
376 Ed VandeBerg .02 .10
377 Tony Bernazard .02 .10
378 Greg Pryor .02 .10
379 Dwayne Murphy .02 .10
380 Andy McGaffigan .02 .10
381 Kirk McCaskill .02 .10
382 Greg Harris .02 .10
383 Rich Dotson .02 .10
384 Craig Reynolds .02 .10
385 Greg Gross .02 .10
386 Tito Landrum .02 .10
387 Craig Lefferts .02 .10
388 Dave Parker .05 .15
389 Bob Horner .05 .15
390 Pat Clements .02 .10
391 Jeff Leonard .02 .10
392 Chris Speier .02 .10
393 John Moses .02 .10
394 Garth Iorg .02 .10
395 Greg Gagne .02 .10
396 Nate Snell .02 .10
397 Bryan Clutterbuck .02 .10
398 Darrell Evans .05 .15
399 Steve Crawford .02 .10
400 Checklist 346-451 .02 .10
401 Phil Lombardi .02 .10
402 Rick Honeycutt .02 .10
403 Ken Schrom .02 .10
404 Bud Black .02 .10
405 Donnie Hill .02 .10
406 Wayne Krenchicki .02 .10
407 Chuck Finley RC .25 .60
408 Toby Harrah .05 .15
409 Steve Lyons .02 .10
410 Kevin Bass .02 .10
411 Marvell Wynne .02 .10
412 Ron Roenicke .02 .10
413 Tracy Jones .02 .10
414 Gene Garber .02 .10
415 Mike Bielecki .02 .10
416 Frank DiPino .02 .10
417 Andy Van Slyke .08 .25
418 Jim Dwyer .02 .10
419 Ben Oglivie .05 .15
420 Dave Bergman .02 .10
421 Joe Sambito .02 .10
422 Bob Tewksbury RC .15 .40
423 Len Matuszek .02 .10
424 Mike Kingery RC .05 .15
425 Dave Kingman .05 .15
426 Al Newman RC .02 .10
427 Gary Ward .02 .10
428 Ruppert Jones .02 .10
429 Harold Baines .05 .15
430 Pat Perry .02 .10
431 Terry Puhl .02 .10
432 Don Carman .02 .10
433 Eddie Milner .02 .10
434 LaMarr Hoyt .02 .10
435 Rick Rhoden .02 .10
436 Jose Uribe .02 .10
437 Ken Oberkfell .02 .10
438 Ron Davis .02 .10
439 Jesse Orosco .02 .10
440 Scott Bradley .02 .10
441 Randy Bush .02 .10
442 John Cerutti .02 .10
443 Roy Smalley .02 .10
444 Kelly Gruber .02 .10
445 Bob Kearney .02 .10
446 Ed Hearn RC .02 .10
447 Scott Sanderson .02 .10
448 Bruce Benedict .02 .10
449 Junior Ortiz .02 .10
450 Mike Aldrete .02 .10
451 Kevin McReynolds .02 .10
452 Rob Murphy .02 .10
453 Kent Tekulve .02 .10
454 Curt Ford .02 .10
455 Dave Lopes .05 .15
456 Bob Grich .05 .15
457 Jose DeLeon .02 .10
458 Andre Dawson .05 .15
459 Mike Flanagan .02 .10
460 Joey Meyer .05 .15
461 Chuck Cary .02 .10
462 Bill Buckner .05 .15
463 Bob Shirley .02 .10
464 Jeff Hamilton .02 .10
465 Phil Niekro .05 .15
466 Mark Gubicza .02 .10
467 Jerry Willard .02 .10
468 Bob Sebra .02 .10
469 Larry Parrish .02 .10
470 Charlie Hough .05 .15
471 Hal McRae .05 .15
472 Dave Leiper .02 .10
473 Mel Hall .02 .10
474 Dan Pasqua .02 .10
475 Bob Welch .05 .15
476 Johnny Grubb .02 .10
477 Jim Traber .02 .10
478 Chris Bosio RC .15 .40
479 Mark McLemore .05 .15
480 John Morris .02 .10
481 Billy Hatcher .02 .10
482 Dan Schatzeder .02 .10
483 Rich Gossage .05 .15
484 Jim Morrison .02 .10
485 Bob Brenly .02 .10
486 Bill Schroeder .02 .10
487 Mookie Wilson .05 .15
488 Dave Martinez RC .15 .40
489 Harold Reynolds .05 .15
490 Jeff Hearron .02 .10
491 Mickey Hatcher .02 .10
492 Barry Larkin RC .60 1.50
493 Bob James .02 .10
494 John Habyan .02 .10
495 Jim Adduci .02 .10
496 Mike Heath .02 .10
497 Tim Stoddard .02 .10
498 Tony Armas .05 .15
499 Dennis Powell .02 .10
500 Checklist 452-557 .02 .10
501 Chris Bando .02 .10
502 David Cone RC .40 1.00
503 Jay Howell .02 .10
504 Tom Foley .02 .10
505 Ray Chadwick .02 .10
506 Mike Loynd RC .05 .15
507 Neil Allen .02 .10
508 Danny Darwin .02 .10
509 Rick Schu .02 .10
510 Jose Oquendo .02 .10
511 Gene Walter .02 .10
512 Terry McGriff .02 .10
513 Ken Griffey .05 .15
514 Benny Distefano .02 .10
515 Terry Mulholland RC .15 .40
516 Ed Lynch .02 .10
517 Bill Swift .02 .10
518 Manny Lee .02 .10
519 Andre David .02 .10
520 Scott McGregor .02 .10
521 Rick Manning .02 .10
522 Willie Hernandez .02 .10
523 Marty Barrett .02 .10
524 Wayne Tolleson .02 .10
525 Jose Gonzalez RC .05 .15
526 Cory Snyder .02 .10
527 Buddy Biancalana .02 .10
528 Moose Haas .02 .10
529 Wilfredo Tejada .02 .10
530 Stu Cliburn .02 .10
531 Dale Mohorcic .02 .10
532 Ron Hassey .02 .10
533 Ty Gainey .02 .10
534 Jerry Royster .02 .10
535 Mike Maddux RC .02 .10
536 Ted Power .02 .10
537 Ted Simmons .05 .15
538 Rafael Belliard RC .15 .40
539 Chico Walker .02 .10
540 Bob Forsch .02 .10
541 John Stefero .02 .10
542 Dale Sveum .02 .10
543 Mark Thurmond .02 .10
544 Jeff Sellers .02 .10
545 Joel Skinner .02 .10
546 Alex Trevino .02 .10
547 Randy Kutcher .02 .10
548 Joaquin Andujar .05 .15
549 Casey Candaele .02 .10
550 Jeff Russell .02 .10
551 John Candelaria .02 .10
552 Joe Cowley .02 .10
553 Danny Cox .02 .10
554 Denny Walling .02 .10
555 Bruce Ruffin RC .05 .15
556 Buddy Bell .05 .15
557 Jimmy Jones RC .05 .15
558 Bobby Bonilla RC .25 .60
559 Jeff D. Robinson .02 .10
560 Ed Olwine .02 .10
561 Glenallen Hill RC .15 .40
562 Lee Mazzilli .05 .15
563 Mike G. Brown P .02 .10
564 George Frazier .02 .10
565 Mike Sharperson RC .05 .15
566 Mark Portugal RC .15 .40
567 Rick Leach .02 .10
568 Mark Langston .02 .10
569 Rafael Santana .02 .10
570 Manny Trillo .02 .10
571 Cliff Speck .02 .10
572 Bob Kipper .02 .10
573 Kelly Downs RC .05 .15
574 Randy Asadoor .02 .10
575 Dave Magadan RC .15 .40
576 Marvin Freeman RC .05 .15
577 Jeff Lahti .02 .10
578 Jeff Calhoun .02 .10
579 Gus Polidor .02 .10
580 Gene Nelson .02 .10
581 Tim Teufel .02 .10
582 Odell Jones .02 .10
583 Mark Ryal .02 .10
584 Randy O'Neal .02 .10
585 Mike Greenwell RC .15 .40
586 Ray Knight .05 .15
587 Ralph Bryant .02 .10
588 Carmen Castillo .02 .10
589 Ed Wojna .02 .10
590 Stan Javier .02 .10
591 Jeff Musselman .02 .10
592 Mike Stanley RC .15 .40
593 Darrell Porter .02 .10
594 Drew Hall .02 .10
595 Rob Nelson .02 .10
596 Bryan Oelkers .02 .10
597 Scott Nielsen .02 .10
598 Brian Holton .02 .10
599 Kevin Mitchell RC .25 .60
600 Checklist 558-660 .02 .10
601 Jackie Gutierrez .02 .10
602 Barry Jones .02 .10
603 Jerry Narron .02 .10
604 Steve Lake .02 .10
605 Jim Pankovits .02 .10
606 Ed Romero .02 .10
607 Dave LaPoint .02 .10
608 Don Robinson .02 .10
609 Mike Krukow .02 .10
610 Dave Valle RC .05 .15
611 Len Dykstra .05 .15
612 R.Clemente PUZ .20 .50
613 Mike Trujillo .02 .10
614 Damaso Garcia .02 .10
615 Neal Heaton .02 .10
616 Juan Berenguer .02 .10
617 Steve Carlton .05 .15
618 Gary Lucas .02 .10
619 Geno Petralli .02 .10
620 Rick Aguilera .05 .15
621 Fred McGriff .30 .75
622 Dave Henderson .02 .10
623 Dave Clark RC .05 .15
624 Angel Salazar .02 .10
625 Randy Hunt .02 .10
626 John Gibbons .02 .10
627 Kevin Brown RC .60 1.50
628 Bill Dawley .02 .10
629 Aurelio Lopez .02 .10
630 Charles Hudson .02 .10
631 Ray Soff .02 .10
632 Ray Hayward .02 .10

633 Spike Owen .02 .10
634 Glenn Hubbard .02 .10
635 Kevin Elster RC .15 .40
636 Mike LaCoss .02 .10
637 Dwayne Henry .02 .10
638 Rey Quinones .02 .10
639 Jim Clancy .02 .10
640 Larry Andersen .02 .10
641 Calvin Schiraldi .02 .10
642 Stan Jefferson .02 .10
643 Marc Sullivan .02 .10
644 Mark Grant .02 .10
645 Cliff Johnson .02 .10
646 Howard Johnson .05 .15
647 Dave Sax .02 .10
648 Dave Stewart .05 .15
649 Danny Heep .02 .10
650 Joe Johnson .02 .10
651 Bob Brower .02 .10
652 Rob Woodward .02 .10
653 John Mizerock .02 .10
654 Tim Pyznarski .02 .10
655 Luis Aquino .02 .10
656 Mickey Brantley .02 .10
657 Doyle Alexander .02 .10
658 Sammy Stewart .02 .10
659 Jim Acker .02 .10
660 Pete Ladd .02 .10

1987 Donruss Rookies

The 1987 Donruss "The Rookies" set features 56 full-color standard-size cards plus a 15-piece puzzle of Roberto Clemente. The set was distributed in factory set form packaged in a small green and black box through hobby dealers. Card fronts are similar in design to the 1987 Donruss regular issue except for the presence of "The Rookies" logo in the lower left corner and a green border instead of a black border. The key extended Rookie Cards in this set are Ellis Burks and Matt Williams. The second Donruss-issued cards of Greg Maddux and Rafael Palmeiro are also in this set. Because itâ ™s the first card in the set (of which came in a tightly-sealed cello wrap, the Mark McGwire card is quite condition sensitive.

COMP.FACT.SET (56) 10.00 25.00
1 Mark McGwire 4.00 10.00
2 Eric Bell .05 .15
3 Mark Williamson .02 .10
4 Mike Greenwell .15 .40
5 Ellis Burks XRC .25 .60
6 DeWayne Buice .02 .10
7 Mark McLemore .08 .25
8 Devon White .25 .60
9 Willie Fraser .05 .15
10 Les Lancaster .02 .10
11 Ken Williams XRC .02 .10
12 Matt Nokes XRC .15 .40
13 Jeff M. Robinson .02 .10
14 Bo Jackson 2.00 5.00
15 Kevin Seitzer XRC .15 .40
16 Billy Ripken XRC .15 .40
17 B.J. Surhoff .25 .60
18 Chuck Crim .02 .10
19 Mike Birkbeck .05 .15
20 Chris Bosio .15 .40
21 Les Straker .02 .10
22 Mark Davidson .02 .10
23 Gene Larkin XRC .15 .40
24 Ken Gerhart .02 .10
25 Luis Polonia XRC .15 .40
26 Terry Steinbach .25 .60
27 Mickey Brantley .02 .10
28 Mike Stanley .15 .40
29 Jerry Browne .05 .15
30 Todd Benzinger XRC .15 .40
31 Fred McGriff .60 1.50
32 Mike Henneman XRC .15 .40
33 Casey Candaele .02 .10
34 Dave Magadan .15 .40
35 David Cone .40 1.00
36 Mike Jackson XRC .15 .40
37 John Mitchell XRC .05 .15
38 Mike Dunne .02 .10
39 John Smiley XRC .15 .40
40 Joe Magrane XRC .05 .15
41 Jim Lindeman .05 .15
42 Shane Mack .02 .10
43 Stan Jefferson .02 .10
44 Benito Santiago .08 .25
45 Matt Williams XRC 1.00 2.50
46 Dave Meads .02 .10
47 Rafael Palmeiro 2.00 5.00
48 Bill Long .02 .10
49 Bob Brower .02 .10
50 James Steels .02 .10
51 Paul Noce .02 .10
52 Greg Maddux 3.00 8.00
53 Jeff Musselman .02 .10
54 Brian Holton .02 .10
55 Chuck Jackson .02 .10
56 Checklist 1-56 .02 .10

1987 Donruss Opening Day

This innovative set of 272 standard-size cards features a card for each of the players in the starting line-ups of all the teams on Opening Day 1987. The set was packaged in a specially designed box. Cards are very similar in design to the 1987 regular Donruss issue except that these "OD" cards have a maroon border instead of a black border. Teams in the same city share a checklist card. A 15-piece puzzle of Roberto Clemente is also included with every complete set. The error on Barry Bonds (picturing Johnny Ray by mistake) was corrected very early in the press run; supposedly less than one percent of the sets have the error. Players in this set in their Rookie Card year include Will Clark, Bo Jackson, Wally Joyner and Barry Larkin.

COMP.FACT. SET (272) 15.00 40.00
163A LISTED IN NEAR MINT CONDITION
1 Doug DeCinces .02 .10
2 Mike Witt .02 .10
3 George Hendrick .05 .15
4 Dick Schofield .02 .10
5 Devon White .25 .60
6 Butch Wynegar .02 .10
7 Wally Joyner .08 .25
8 Mark McLemore .05 .15
9 Brian Downing .05 .15
10 Gary Pettis .02 .10
11 Bill Doran .02 .10
12 Phil Garner .05 .15
13 Jose Cruz .05 .15
14 Kevin Bass .02 .10
15 Mike Scott .05 .15
16 Glenn Davis .02 .10
17 Alan Ashby .02 .10
18 Billy Hatcher .02 .10
19 Craig Reynolds .02 .10
20 Carney Lansford .05 .15
21 Mike Davis .02 .10
22 Reggie Jackson .08 .25
23 Mickey Tettleton .02 .10
24 Jose Canseco .60 1.50
25 Rob Nelson .02 .10
26 Tony Phillips .02 .10
27 Dwayne Murphy .02 .10
28 Alfredo Griffin .02 .10
29 Curt Young .02 .10
30 Willie Upshaw .02 .10
31 Mike Sharperson .02 .10
32 Rance Mulliniks .02 .10
33 Ernie Whitt .02 .10
34 Jesse Barfield .05 .15
35 Tony Fernandez .02 .10
36 Lloyd Moseby .02 .10
37 Jimmy Key .05 .15
38 Fred McGriff .30 .75
39 George Bell .05 .15
40 Dale Murphy .08 .25
41 Rick Mahler .02 .10
42 Ken Griffey .05 .15
43 Andres Thomas .02 .10
44 Dion James .02 .10
45 Ozzie Virgil .02 .10
46 Ken Oberkfell .02 .10
47 Gary Roenicke .02 .10
48 Glenn Hubbard .02 .10
49 Bill Schroeder .02 .10
50 Greg Brock .02 .10
51 Billy Joe Robidoux .02 .10
52 Glenn Braggs .05 .15
53 Jim Gantner .02 .10
54 Paul Molitor .05 .15
55 Dale Sveum .02 .10
56 Ted Higuera .02 .10
57 Rob Deer .02 .10
58 Robin Yount .25 .60
59 Jim Lindeman .05 .15
60 Vince Coleman .02 .10
61 Tommy Herr .02 .10
62 Terry Pendleton .05 .15
63 John Tudor .05 .15
64 Tony Pena .02 .10
65 Ozzie Smith .25 .60
66 Tito Landrum .02 .10
67 Jack Clark .05 .15
68 Bob Dernier .02 .10
69 Rick Sutcliffe .05 .15
70 Andre Dawson .05 .15
71 Keith Moreland .02 .10
72 Jody Davis .02 .10
73 Brian Dayett .02 .10
74 Leon Durham .02 .10
75 Ryne Sandberg .30 .75
76 Shawon Dunston .02 .10
77 Mike Marshall .02 .10
78 Bill Madlock .05 .15
79 Orel Hershiser .08 .25
80 Mike Ramsey .02 .10
81 Ken Landreaux .02 .10
82 Mike Scioscia .05 .15
83 Franklin Stubbs .02 .10
84 Mariano Duncan .02 .10
85 Steve Sax .02 .10
86 Mitch Webster .02 .10
87 Reid Nichols .02 .10
88 Tim Wallach .02 .10
89 Floyd Youmans .02 .10
90 Andres Galarraga .05 .15
91 Hubie Brooks .02 .10
92 Jeff Reed .02 .10
93 Alonzo Powell .02 .10
94 Vance Law .02 .10
95 Bob Brenly .02 .10
96 Will Clark .75 2.00
97 Chili Davis .05 .15
98 Mike Krukow .02 .10
99 Jose Uribe .02 .10
100 Chris Brown .02 .10
101 Robby Thompson .15 .40
102 Candy Maldonado .02 .10
103 Jeff Leonard .02 .10
104 Tom Candiotti .02 .10
105 Chris Bando .02 .10
106 Cory Snyder .02 .10
107 Pat Tabler .02 .10
108 Andre Thornton .02 .10
109 Joe Carter .05 .15
110 Tony Bernazard .02 .10
111 Julio Franco .05 .15
112 Brook Jacoby .02 .10
113 Brett Butler .05 .15
114 Donell Nixon .02 .10
115 Alvin Davis .02 .10
116 Mark Langston .02 .10
117 Harold Reynolds .05 .15
118 Ken Phelps .02 .10
119 Mike Kingery .05 .15
120 Dave Valle .05 .15
121 Rey Quinones .02 .10
122 Phil Bradley .02 .10
123 Jim Presley .02 .10
124 Keith Hernandez .05 .15
125 Kevin McReynolds .02 .10
126 Rafael Santana .02 .10
127 Bob Ojeda .02 .10
128 Darryl Strawberry .05 .15
129 Mookie Wilson .05 .15
130 Gary Carter .05 .15
131 Tim Teufel .02 .10
132 Howard Johnson .05 .15
133 Cal Ripken .60 1.50
134 Rick Burleson .02 .10
135 Fred Lynn .05 .15
136 Eddie Murray .15 .40
137 Ray Knight .05 .15
138 Alan Wiggins .02 .10
139 John Shelby .02 .10
140 Mike Boddicker .02 .10
141 Ken Gerhart .02 .10
142 Terry Kennedy .02 .10
143 Steve Garvey .05 .15
144 Marvell Wynne .02 .10
145 Kevin Mitchell .08 .25
146 Tony Gwynn .25 .60
147 Joey Cora .15 .40
148 Benito Santiago .05 .15
149 Eric Show .02 .10
150 Garry Templeton .05 .15
151 Carmelo Martinez .02 .10
152 Von Hayes .02 .10
153 Lance Parrish .05 .15
154 Milt Thompson .02 .10
155 Mike Easler .02 .10
156 Juan Samuel .02 .10
157 Steve Jeltz .02 .10
158 Glenn Wilson .02 .10
159 Shane Rawley .02 .10
160 Mike Schmidt .40 1.00
161 Andy Van Slyke .08 .25
162 Johnny Ray .02 .10
163A Barry Bonds ERR (Photo actually Johnny Ray wearing a black shirt) 175.00 300.00
163B Barry Bonds COR 5.00 12.00
164 Junior Ortiz .02 .10
165 Rafael Belliard .15 .40
166 Bob Patterson .02 .10
167 Bobby Bonilla .25 .60
168 Sid Bream .02 .10
169 Jim Morrison .02 .10
170 Jerry Browne .05 .15
171 Scott Fletcher .02 .10
172 Ruben Sierra .40 1.00
173 Larry Parrish .02 .10
174 Pete O'Brien .02 .10
175 Pete Incaviglia .15 .40
176 Don Slaught .02 .10
177 Oddibe McDowell .02 .10
178 Charlie Hough .05 .15
179 Steve Buechele .02 .10
180 Bob Stanley .02 .10
181 Wade Boggs .08 .25
182 Jim Rice .05 .15
183 Bill Buckner .05 .15
184 Dwight Evans .08 .25
185 Spike Owen .02 .10
186 Don Baylor .05 .15
187 Marc Sullivan .02 .10
188 Marty Barrett .02 .10
189 Dave Henderson .02 .10
190 Bo Diaz .02 .10
191 Barry Larkin .75 2.00
192 Kal Daniels .02 .10
193 Terry Francona .05 .15
194 Tom Browning .02 .10
195 Ron Oester .02 .10
196 Buddy Bell .05 .15
197 Eric Davis .08 .25
198 Dave Parker .05 .15
199 Steve Balboni .02 .10
200 Danny Tartabull .02 .10
201 Ed Hearn .02 .10
202 Buddy Biancalana .02 .10
203 Danny Jackson .02 .10
204 Frank White .05 .15
205 Bo Jackson 2.00 5.00
206 George Brett .40 1.00
207 Kevin Seitzer .05 .15
208 Willie Wilson .05 .15
209 Orlando Mercado .02 .10
210 Darrell Evans .05 .15
211 Larry Herndon .02 .10
212 Jack Morris .05 .15
213 Chet Lemon .05 .15
214 Mike Heath .02 .10
215 Darnell Coles .02 .10
216 Alan Trammell .05 .15
217 Terry Harper .02 .10
218 Lou Whitaker .05 .15
219 Gary Gaetti .05 .15
220 Tom Nieto .02 .10
221 Kirby Puckett .30 .75
222 Tom Brunansky .02 .10
223 Greg Gagne .02 .10
224 Dan Gladden .02 .10
225 Mark Davidson .02 .10
226 Bert Blyleven .05 .15
227 Steve Lombardozzi .02 .10
228 Kent Hrbek .05 .15
229 Gary Redus .02 .10
230 Ivan Calderon .02 .10
231 Tim Hulett .02 .10
232 Carlton Fisk .08 .25
233 Greg Walker .02 .10
234 Ron Karkovice .15 .40
235 Ozzie Guillen .08 .25
236 Harold Baines .05 .15
237 Donnie Hill .02 .10
238 Rich Dotson .02 .10
239 Mike Pagliarulo .02 .10
240 Joel Skinner .02 .10
241 Don Mattingly .50 1.25
242 Gary Ward .02 .10
243 Dave Winfield .05 .15
244 Dan Pasqua .02 .10
245 Wayne Tolleson .02 .10
246 Willie Randolph .05 .15
247 Dennis Rasmussen .02 .10
248 Rickey Henderson .15 .40
249 Angels Logo .01 .05
250 Astros Logo .01 .05
251 A's Logo .01 .05
252 Blue Jays Logo .01 .05
253 Braves Logo .01 .05
254 Brewers Logo .01 .05
255 Cardinals Logo .01 .05
256 Dodgers Logo .01 .05
257 Expos Logo .01 .05
258 Giants Logo .01 .05
259 Indians Logo .01 .05
260 Mariners Logo .01 .05
261 Orioles Logo .01 .05
262 Padres Logo .01 .05
263 Phillies Logo .01 .05
264 Pirates Logo .01 .05
265 Rangers Logo .01 .05
266 Red Sox Logo .01 .05
267 Reds Logo .01 .05
268 Royals Logo .01 .05
269 Tigers Logo .01 .05
270 Twins Logo .01 .05
271 Chicago Logos .01 .05
272 New York Logos .01 .05

1988 Donruss

This set consists of 660 standard-size cards. For the seventh straight year, wax packs consisted of 15 cards plus a puzzle panel (featuring Stan Musial this time around). Cards were also distributed in rack packs and retail and hobby factory sets. Card fronts feature a distinctive black and blue border on the front. The card front border design pattern of the factory set card fronts is oriented differently from that of the regular wax pack cards. No premium or discount exists for either version. Subsets include Diamond Kings (1-27) and Rated Rookies (28-47). Cards marked as SP (short printed) from 648-660 are more difficult to find than the other 13 SP's in the lower 600s. These 26 cards listed as SP were apparently pulled from the printing sheet to make room for the 26 Bonus MVP cards. Six of the checklist cards were done two different ways to reflect the inclusion or exclusion of the Bonus MVP cards in the wax packs. In the checklist below, the A variations (for the checklist cards) are from the wax packs and the B variations are from the factory-collated sets. The key Rookie Cards in this set are Roberto Alomar, Jay Bell, Jay Buhner, Ellis Burks, Ken Caminiti, Tom Glavine, Mark Grace and Matt Williams. There was also a Kirby Puckett card issued as the package back of Donruss blister packs; it uses a different photo from both of Kirby's regular and Bonus MVP cards and is unnumbered on the back.

COMPLETE SET (660) 4.00 10.00
COMP.FACT.SET (660) 6.00 15.00
COMMON CARD (1-660) .01 .05
COMMON SP (648-660) .02 .10
1 Mark McGwire DK .30 .75
2 Tim Raines DK .02 .10
3 Benito Santiago DK .02 .10
4 Alan Trammell DK .02 .10
5 Danny Tartabull DK .01 .05
6 Ron Darling DK .02 .10
7 Paul Molitor DK .02 .10
8 Devon White DK .02 .10
9 Andre Dawson DK .01 .05
10 Julio Franco DK .02 .10
11 Scott Fletcher DK .01 .05
12 Tony Fernandez DK .01 .05
13 Shane Rawley DK .01 .05
14 Kal Daniels DK .01 .05
15 Jack Clark DK .02 .10
16 Dwight Evans DK .05 .15
17 Tommy John DK .02 .10
18 Andy Van Slyke DK .05 .15
19 Gary Gaetti DK .02 .10
20 Mark Langston DK .01 .05
21 Will Clark DK .07 .20
22 Glenn Hubbard DK .01 .05
23 Billy Hatcher DK .01 .05
24 Bob Welch DK .02 .10
25 Ivan Calderon DK .01 .05
26 Cal Ripken DK .15 .40
27 DK Checklist 1-26 .01 .05
28 Mackey Sasser RR RC .08 .25
29 Jeff Treadway RR RC .08 .25
30 Mike Campbell RR .01 .05
31 Lance Johnson RR RC .08 .25
32 Nelson Liriano RR .01 .05
33 Shawn Abner RR .01 .05
34 Roberto Alomar RR RC .75 2.00
35 Shawn Hillegas RR .01 .05
36 Joey Meyer RR .01 .05
37 Kevin Elster RR .01 .05
38 Jose Lind RR RC .08 .25
39 Kirt Manwaring RR RC .08 .25
40 Mark Grace RR RC .75 2.00
41 Jody Reed RR RC .08 .25
42 John Farrell RR RC .02 .10
43 Al Leiter RR RC .30 .75
44 Gary Thurman RR .01 .05
45 Vicente Palacios RR .01 .05
46 Eddie Williams RR RC .02 .10
47 Jack McDowell RR RC .15 .40
48 Ken Dixon .01 .05
49 Mike Birkbeck .01 .05
50 Eric King .01 .05
51 Roger Clemens .40 1.00
52 Pat Clements .01 .05
53 Fernando Valenzuela .02 .10
54 Mark Gubicza .01 .05
55 Jay Howell .01 .05
56 Floyd Youmans .01 .05
57 Ed Correa .01 .05
58 DeWayne Buice .01 .05
59 Jose DeLeon .01 .05
60 Danny Cox .01 .05
61 Nolan Ryan .40 1.00
62 Steve Bedrosian .01 .05
63 Tom Browning .01 .05
64 Mark Davis .01 .05
65 R.J. Reynolds .01 .05
66 Kevin Mitchell .02 .10
67 Ken Oberkfell .01 .05
68 Rick Sutcliffe .02 .10
69 Dwight Gooden .02 .10
70 Scott Bankhead .01 .05
71 Bert Blyleven .02 .10
72 Jimmy Key .02 .10
73 Les Straker .01 .05
74 Jim Clancy .01 .05
75 Mike Moore .01 .05
76 Ron Darling .02 .10
77 Ed Lynch .01 .05
78 Dale Murphy .05 .15
79 Doug Drabek .01 .05
80 Scott Garrelts .01 .05
81 Ed Whitson .01 .05
82 Rob Murphy .01 .05
83 Shane Rawley .01 .05
84 Greg Mathews .01 .05
85 Jim Deshaies .01 .05
86 Mike Witt .01 .05
87 Donnie Hill .01 .05
88 Jeff Reed .01 .05
89 Mike Boddicker .01 .05
90 Ted Higuera .01 .05
91 Walt Terrell .01 .05
92 Bob Stanley .01 .05
93 Dave Righetti .02 .10
94 Orel Hershiser .02 .10
95 Chris Bando .01 .05
96 Bret Saberhagen .02 .10
97 Curt Young .01 .05
98 Tim Burke .01 .05
99 Charlie Hough .02 .10
100A Checklist 28-137 .01 .05
100B Checklist 28-133 .01 .05
101 Bobby Witt .01 .05
102 George Brett .20 .50
103 Mickey Tettleton .01 .05
104 Scott Bailes .01 .05
105 Mike Pagliarulo .01 .05
106 Mike Scioscia .02 .10
107 Tom Brookens .01 .05
108 Ray Knight .02 .10
109 Dan Plesac .01 .05
110 Wally Joyner .02 .10
111 Bob Forsch .01 .05
112 Mike Scott .02 .10
113 Kevin Gross .01 .05
114 Benito Santiago .02 .10
115 Bob Kipper .01 .05
116 Mike Krukow .01 .05
117 Chris Bosio .01 .05
118 Sid Fernandez .01 .05
119 Jody Davis .01 .05
120 Mike Morgan .01 .05
121 Mark Eichhorn .01 .05
122 Jeff Reardon .02 .10
123 John Franco .02 .10
124 Richard Dotson .01 .05
125 Eric Bell .01 .05
126 Juan Nieves .01 .05
127 Jack Morris .02 .10
128 Rick Rhoden .01 .05
129 Rich Gedman .01 .05
130 Ken Howell .01 .05
131 Brook Jacoby .01 .05
132 Danny Jackson .01 .05
133 Gene Nelson .01 .05
134 Neal Heaton .01 .05
135 Willie Fraser .01 .05
136 Jose Guzman .01 .05
137 Ozzie Guillen .02 .10
138 Bob Knepper .01 .05
139 Mike Jackson RC .08 .25
140 Joe Magrane RC .08 .25
141 Jimmy Jones .01 .05
142 Ted Power .01 .05
143 Ozzie Virgil .01 .05
144 Felix Fermin .01 .05
145 Kelly Downs .01 .05
146 Shawon Dunston .01 .05
147 Scott Bradley .01 .05
148 Dave Stieb .02 .10
149 Frank Viola .02 .10
150 Terry Kennedy .01 .05
151 Bill Wegman .01 .05
152 Matt Nokes RC .08 .25
153 Wade Boggs .05 .15
154 Wayne Tolleson .01 .05
155 Mariano Duncan .01 .05
156 Julio Franco .02 .10
157 Charlie Leibrandt .01 .05
158 Terry Steinbach .02 .10
159 Mike Fitzgerald .01 .05
160 Jack Lazorko .01 .05
161 Mitch Williams .01 .05
162 Greg Walker .01 .05
163 Alan Ashby .01 .05
164 Tony Gwynn .10 .30
165 Bruce Ruffin .01 .05
166 Ron Robinson .01 .05
167 Zane Smith .01 .05
168 Junior Ortiz .01 .05
169 Jamie Moyer .02 .10
170 Tony Pena .01 .05
171 Cal Ripken .30 .75
172 B.J. Surhoff .02 .10
173 Lou Whitaker .02 .10
174 Ellis Burks RC .15 .40
175 Ron Guidry .02 .10
176 Steve Sax .01 .05
177 Danny Tartabull .01 .05
178 Carney Lansford .02 .10
179 Casey Candaele .01 .05
180 Scott Fletcher .01 .05
181 Mark McLemore .01 .05
182 Ivan Calderon .01 .05
183 Jack Clark .02 .10
184 Glenn Davis .01 .05
185 Luis Aguayo .01 .05
186 Bo Diaz .01 .05
187 Stan Jefferson .01 .05
188 Sid Bream .01 .05
189 Bob Brenly .01 .05
190 Dion James .01 .05
191 Leon Durham .01 .05
192 Jesse Orosco .01 .05
193 Alvin Davis .01 .05
194 Gary Gaetti .02 .10
195 Fred McGriff .07 .20
196 Steve Lombardozzi .01 .05
197 Rance Mulliniks .01 .05
198 Rey Quinones .01 .05
199 Gary Carter .02 .10
200A Checklist 138-247 .01 .05
200B Checklist 134-239 .01 .05
201 Keith Moreland .01 .05
202 Ken Griffey .02 .10
203 Tommy Gregg .01 .05
204 Will Clark .07 .20
205 John Kruk .02 .10
206 Buddy Bell .02 .10
207 Von Hayes .01 .05
208 Tommy Herr .01 .05
209 Craig Reynolds .01 .05
210 Gary Pettis .01 .05
211 Harold Baines .02 .10
212 Vance Law .01 .05
213 Ken Gerhart .01 .05
214 Jim Gantner .01 .05
215 Chet Lemon .02 .10
216 Dwight Evans .05 .15
217 Don Mattingly .25 .60
218 Franklin Stubbs .01 .05
219 Pat Tabler .01 .05
220 Bo Jackson .07 .20
221 Tony Phillips .01 .05
222 Tim Wallach .01 .05
223 Ruben Sierra .02 .10
224 Steve Buechele .01 .05
225 Frank White .02 .10
226 Alfredo Griffin .01 .05
227 Greg Swindell .01 .05
228 Willie Randolph .02 .10
229 Mike Marshall .01 .05
230 Alan Trammell .02 .10
231 Eddie Murray .07 .20
232 Dale Sveum .01 .05
233 Dick Schofield .01 .05
234 Jose Oquendo .01 .05
235 Bill Doran .01 .05
236 Milt Thompson .01 .05
237 Marvell Wynne .01 .05
238 Bobby Bonilla .02 .10
239 Chris Speier .01 .05
240 Glenn Braggs .01 .05
241 Wally Backman .01 .05
242 Ryne Sandberg .15 .40
243 Phil Bradley .01 .05
244 Kelly Gruber .01 .05
245 Tom Brunansky .01 .05
246 Ron Oester .01 .05
247 Bobby Thigpen .01 .05
248 Fred Lynn .02 .10
249 Paul Molitor .02 .10
250 Darrell Evans .02 .10
251 Gary Ward .01 .05
252 Bruce Hurst .01 .05
253 Bob Welch .02 .10
254 Joe Carter .02 .10
255 Willie Wilson .02 .10
256 Mark McGwire .60 1.50
257 Mitch Webster .01 .05
258 Brian Downing .02 .10
259 Mike Stanley .01 .05
260 Carlton Fisk .05 .15
261 Billy Hatcher .01 .05
262 Glenn Wilson .01 .05
263 Ozzie Smith .10 .30
264 Randy Ready .01 .05
265 Kurt Stillwell .01 .05
266 David Palmer .01 .05
267 Mike Diaz .01 .05
268 Robby Thompson .01 .05
269 Andre Dawson .02 .10
270 Lee Guetterman .01 .05
271 Willie Upshaw .01 .05
272 Randy Bush .01 .05
273 Larry Sheets .01 .05
274 Rob Deer .01 .05
275 Kirk Gibson .07 .20
276 Marty Barrett .01 .05
277 Rickey Henderson .07 .20
278 Pedro Guerrero .02 .10
279 Brett Butler .02 .10
280 Kevin Seitzer .01 .05
281 Mike Davis .01 .05
282 Andres Galarraga .02 .10
283 Devon White .02 .10
284 Pete O'Brien .01 .05
285 Jerry Hairston .01 .05
286 Kevin Bass .01 .05
287 Carmelo Martinez .01 .05
288 Juan Samuel .01 .05
289 Kal Daniels .01 .05
290 Albert Hall .01 .05
291 Andy Van Slyke .05 .15
292 Lee Smith .02 .10
293 Vince Coleman .01 .05
294 Tom Niedenfuer .01 .05

295 Robin Yount .10 .30
296 Jeff M. Robinson .01 .05
297 Todd Benzinger RC .08 .25
298 Dave Winfield .02 .10
299 Mickey Hatcher .01 .05
300A Checklist 248-357 .01 .05
300B Checklist 240-345 .01 .05
301 Bud Black .01 .05
302 Jose Canseco .20 .50
303 Tom Foley .01 .05
304 Pete Incaviglia .01 .05
305 Bob Boone .02 .10
306 Bill Long .01 .05
307 Willie McGee .02 .10
308 Ken Caminiti RC .75 2.00
309 Darren Daulton .02 .10
310 Tracy Jones .01 .05
311 Greg Booker .01 .05
312 Mike LaValliere .01 .05
313 Chili Davis .02 .10
314 Glenn Hubbard .01 .05
315 Paul Noce .01 .05
316 Keith Hernandez .02 .10
317 Mark Langston .01 .05
318 Keith Atherton .01 .05
319 Tony Fernandez .01 .05
320 Kent Hrbek .02 .10
321 John Cerutti .01 .05
322 Mike Kingery .01 .05
323 Dave Magadan .01 .05
324 Rafael Palmeiro .15 .40
325 Jeff Dedmon .01 .05
326 Barry Bonds .75 2.00
327 Jeffrey Leonard .01 .05
328 Tim Flannery .01 .05
329 Dave Concepcion .02 .10
330 Mike Schmidt .20 .50
331 Bill Dawley .01 .05
332 Larry Andersen .01 .05
333 Jack Howell .01 .05
334 Ken Williams RC .01 .05
335 Bryn Smith .01 .05
336 Bill Ripken RC .08 .25
337 Greg Brock .01 .05
338 Mike Heath .01 .05
339 Mike Greenwell .01 .05
340 Claudell Washington .01 .05
341 Jose Gonzalez .01 .05
342 Mel Hall .01 .05
343 Jim Eisenreich .01 .05
344 Tony Bernazard .01 .05
345 Tim Raines .02 .10
346 Bob Brower .01 .05
347 Larry Parrish .01 .05
348 Thad Bosley .01 .05
349 Dennis Eckersley .05 .15
350 Cory Snyder .01 .05
351 Rick Cerone .01 .05
352 John Shelby .01 .05
353 Larry Herndon .01 .05
354 John Habyan .01 .05
355 Chuck Crim .01 .05
356 Gus Polidor .01 .05
357 Ken Dayley .01 .05
358 Danny Darwin .01 .05
359 Lance Parrish .02 .10
360 James Steels .01 .05
361 Al Pedrique .01 .05
362 Mike Aldrete .01 .05
363 Juan Castillo .01 .05
364 Len Dykstra .02 .10
365 Luis Quinones .01 .05
366 Jim Presley .01 .05
367 Lloyd Moseby .01 .05
368 Kirby Puckett .07 .20
369 Eric Davis .02 .10
370 Gary Redus .01 .05
371 Dave Schmidt .01 .05
372 Mark Clear .01 .05
373 Dave Bergman .01 .05
374 Charles Hudson .01 .05
375 Calvin Schiraldi .01 .05
376 Alex Trevino .01 .05
377 Tom Candiotti .01 .05
378 Steve Farr .01 .05
379 Mike Gallego .01 .05
380 Andy McGaffigan .01 .05
381 Kirk McCaskill .01 .05
382 Oddibe McDowell .01 .05
383 Floyd Bannister .01 .05
384 Denny Walling .01 .05
385 Don Carman .01 .05
386 Todd Worrell .01 .05
387 Eric Show .01 .05
388 Dave Parker .02 .10
389 Rick Mahler .01 .05
390 Mike Dunne .01 .05
391 Candy Maldonado .01 .05
392 Bob Dernier .01 .05
393 Dave Valle .01 .05
394 Ernie Whitt .01 .05
395 Juan Berenguer .01 .05
396 Mike Young .01 .05
397 Mike Felder .01 .05
398 Willie Hernandez .01 .05
399 Jim Rice .02 .10
400A Checklist 358-467 .01 .05
400B Checklist 346-451 .01 .05
401 Tommy John .02 .10
402 Brian Holton .01 .05
403 Carmen Castillo .01 .05
404 Jamie Quirk .01 .05
405 Dwayne Murphy .01 .05
406 Jeff Parrett .01 .05
407 Don Sutton .02 .10
408 Jerry Browne .01 .05
409 Jim Winn .01 .05
410 Dave Smith .01 .05
411 Shane Mack .01 .05
412 Greg Gross .01 .05
413 Nick Esasky .01 .05
414 Damaso Garcia .01 .05
415 Brian Fisher .01 .05
416 Brian Dayett .01 .05
417 Curt Ford .01 .05
418 Mark Williamson .01 .05
419 Bill Schroeder .01 .05
420 Mike Henneman RC .08 .25
421 John Marzano .01 .05
422 Ron Kittle .01 .05
423 Matt Young .01 .05
424 Steve Balboni .01 .05
425 Luis Polonia RC .08 .25
426 Randy St.Claire .01 .05
427 Greg Harris .01 .05
428 Johnny Ray .01 .05
429 Ray Searage .01 .05
430 Ricky Horton .01 .05
431 Gerald Young .01 .05
432 Rick Schu .01 .05
433 Paul O'Neill .05 .15
434 Rich Gossage .02 .10
435 John Cangelosi .01 .05
436 Mike LaCoss .01 .05
437 Gerald Perry .01 .05
438 Dave Martinez .01 .05
439 Darryl Strawberry .02 .10
440 John Moses .01 .05
441 Greg Gagne .01 .05
442 Jesse Barfield .02 .10
443 George Frazier .01 .05
444 Garth Iorg .01 .05
445 Ed Nunez .01 .05
446 Rick Aguilera .01 .05
447 Jerry Mumphrey .01 .05
448 Rafael Ramirez .01 .05
449 John Smiley RC .08 .25
450 Atlee Hammaker .01 .05
451 Lance McCullers .01 .05
452 Guy Hoffman .01 .05
453 Chris James .01 .05
454 Terry Pendleton .02 .10
455 Dave Meads .01 .05
456 Bill Buckner .02 .10
457 John Pawlowski .01 .05
458 Bob Sebra .01 .05
459 Jim Dwyer .01 .05
460 Jay Aldrich .01 .05
461 Frank Tanana .02 .10
462 Oil Can Boyd .01 .05
463 Dan Pasqua .01 .05
464 Tim Crews RC .08 .25
465 Andy Allanson .01 .05
466 Bill Pecota RC .02 .10
467 Steve Ontiveros .01 .05
468 Hubie Brooks .01 .05
469 Paul Kilgus .01 .05
470 Dale Mohorcic .01 .05
471 Dan Quisenberry .01 .05
472 Dave Stewart .02 .10
473 Dave Clark .01 .05
474 Joel Skinner .01 .05
475 Dave Anderson .01 .05
476 Dan Petry .01 .05
477 Carl Nichols .01 .05
478 Ernest Riles .01 .05
479 George Hendrick .02 .10
480 John Morris .01 .05
481 Manny Hernandez .01 .05
482 Jeff Stone .01 .05
483 Chris Brown .01 .05
484 Mike Bielecki .01 .05
485 Dave Dravecky .01 .05
486 Rick Manning .01 .05
487 Bill Almon .01 .05
488 Jim Sundberg .02 .10
489 Ken Phelps .01 .05
490 Tom Henke .01 .05
491 Dan Gladden .01 .05
492 Barry Larkin .05 .15
493 Fred Manrique .01 .05
494 Mike Griffin .01 .05
495 Mark Knudson .01 .05
496 Bill Madlock .02 .10
497 Tim Stoddard .01 .05
498 Sam Horn RC .02 .10
499 Tracy Woodson RC .02 .10
500A Checklist 468-577 .01 .05
500B Checklist 452-557 .01 .05
501 Ken Schrom .01 .05
502 Angel Salazar .01 .05
503 Eric Plunk .01 .05
504 Joe Hesketh .01 .05
505 Greg Minton .01 .05
506 Geno Petralli .01 .05
507 Bob James .01 .05
508 Robbie Wine .01 .05
509 Jeff Calhoun .01 .05
510 Steve Lake .01 .05
511 Mark Grant .01 .05
512 Frank Williams .01 .05
513 Jeff Blauser RC .08 .25
514 Bob Walk .01 .05
515 Craig Lefferts .01 .05
516 Manny Trillo .01 .05
517 Jerry Reed .01 .05
518 Rick Leach .01 .05
519 Mark Davidson .01 .05
520 Jeff Ballard .01 .05
521 Dave Stapleton .01 .05
522 Pat Sheridan .01 .05
523 Al Nipper .01 .05
524 Steve Trout .01 .05
525 Jeff Hamilton .01 .05
526 Tommy Hinzo .01 .05
527 Lonnie Smith .01 .05
528 Greg Cadaret .01 .05
529 Bob McClure UER .01 .05
(Rob on front)
530 Chuck Finley .02 .10
531 Jeff Russell .01 .05
532 Steve Lyons .01 .05
533 Terry Puhl .01 .05
534 Eric Nolte .01 .05
535 Kent Tekulve .01 .05
536 Pat Pacillo .01 .05
537 Charlie Puleo .01 .05
538 Tom Prince .01 .05
539 Greg Maddux .40 1.00
540 Jim Lindeman .01 .05
541 Pete Stanicek .01 .05
542 Steve Kiefer .01 .05
543A Jim Morrison ERR .05 .15
(No decimal before lifetime average)
543B Jim Morrison COR .01 .05
544 Spike Owen .01 .05
545 Jay Buhner RC .20 .50
546 Mike Devereaux RC .08 .25
547 Jerry Don Gleaton .01 .05
548 Jose Rijo .02 .10
549 Dennis Martinez .02 .10
550 Mike Loynd .01 .05
551 Darrell Miller .01 .05
552 Dave LaPoint .01 .05
553 John Tudor .02 .10
554 Rocky Childress .01 .05
555 Wally Ritchie .01 .05
556 Terry McGriff .01 .05
557 Dave Leiper .01 .05
558 Jeff D. Robinson .01 .05
559 Jose Uribe .01 .05
560 Ted Simmons .02 .10
561 Les Lancaster .01 .05
562 Keith A. Miller RC .08 .25
563 Harold Reynolds .02 .10
564 Gene Larkin RC .08 .25
565 Cecil Fielder .02 .10
566 Roy Smalley .01 .05
567 Duane Ward .01 .05
568 Bill Wilkinson .01 .05
569 Howard Johnson .02 .10
570 Frank DiPino .01 .05
571 Pete Smith RC .02 .10
572 Darnell Coles .01 .05
573 Don Robinson .01 .05
574 Rob Nelson UER .01 .05
(Career 0 RBI, but 1 RBI in '87)
575 Dennis Rasmussen .01 .05
576 Steve Jeltz UER .01 .05
(Photo actually Juan Samuel; Samuel noted for one batting glove and black bat)
577 Tom Pagnozzi RC .02 .10
578 Ty Gainey .01 .05
579 Gary Lucas .01 .05
580 Ron Hassey .01 .05
581 Herm Winningham .01 .05
582 Rene Gonzales RC .02 .10
583 Brad Komminsk .01 .05
584 Doyle Alexander .01 .05
585 Jeff Sellers .01 .05
586 Bill Gullickson .01 .05
587 Tim Belcher .01 .05
588 Doug Jones RC .08 .25
589 Melido Perez RC .08 .25
590 Rick Honeycutt .01 .05
591 Pascual Perez .01 .05
592 Curt Wilkerson .01 .05
593 Steve Howe .01 .05
594 John Davis .01 .05
595 Storm Davis .01 .05
596 Sammy Stewart .01 .05
597 Neil Allen .01 .05
598 Alejandro Pena .01 .05
599 Mark Thurmond .01 .05
600A Checklist 578-660 .01 .05
BC1-BC26
600B Checklist 558-660 .01 .05
601 Jose Mesa RC .08 .25
602 Don August .01 .05
603 Terry Leach SP .02 .10
604 Tom Newell .01 .05
605 Randall Byers SP .02 .10
606 Jim Gott .01 .05
607 Harry Spilman .01 .05
608 John Candelaria .01 .05
609 Mike Brumley .01 .05
610 Mickey Brantley .01 .05
611 Jose Nunez SP .02 .10
612 Tom Nieto .01 .05
613 Rick Reuschel .02 .10
614 Lee Mazzilli SP .02 .10
615 Scott Lusader .01 .05
616 Bobby Meacham .01 .05
617 Kevin McReynolds SP .02 .10
618 Gene Garber .01 .05
619 Barry Lyons SP .02 .10
620 Randy Myers .02 .10
621 Donnie Moore .01 .05
622 Domingo Ramos .01 .05
623 Ed Romero .01 .05
624 Greg Myers RC .08 .25
625 Ripken Family .15 .40
Cal Ripken Sr.
Cal Ripken Jr.
Billy Ripken
626 Pat Perry .01 .05
627 Andres Thomas SP .02 .10
628 Matt Williams SP RC .30 .75
629 Dave Hengel .01 .05
630 Jeff Musselman SP .02 .10
631 Tim Laudner .01 .05
632 Bob Ojeda SP .02 .10
633 Rafael Santana .01 .05
634 Wes Gardner .01 .05
635 Roberto Kelly SP RC .08 .25
636 Mike Flanagan SP .02 .10
637 Jay Bell RC .15 .40
638 Bob Melvin .01 .05
639 D.Berryhill RC UER .08 .25
Bats: Swithch
640 David Wells SP RC .40 1.00
641 Stan Musial PUZ .07 .20
642 Doug Sisk .01 .05
643 Keith Hughes .01 .05
644 Tom Glavine RC 1.00 2.50
645 Al Newman .01 .05
646 Scott Sanderson .01 .05
647 Scott Terry .01 .05
648 Tim Teufel SP .02 .10
649 Garry Templeton SP .02 .10
650 Manny Lee SP .02 .10
651 Roger McDowell SP .02 .10
652 Mookie Wilson SP .02 .10
653 David Cone SP .02 .10
654 Ron Gant SP RC .15 .40
655 Joe Price SP .02 .10
656 George Bell SP .02 .10
657 Gregg Jefferies SP RC .08 .25
658 Todd Stottlemyre SP RC .08 .25
659 Geronimo Berroa SP RC .08 .25
660 Jerry Royster SP .02 .10
XX Kirby Puckett .50 1.25
Blister Pack

1988 Donruss Rookies

The 1988 Donruss "The Rookies" set features 56 standard-size full-color cards plus a 15-piece puzzle of Stan Musial. This set was distributed exclusively in factory set form in a small, cellophane-wrapped, green and black through hobby dealers. Card fronts are similar in design to the 1988 Donruss regular issue except for the presence of "The Rookies" logo in the lower right corner and a green and black border instead of a blue and black border on the fronts. Extended Rookie Cards in this set include Brady Anderson, Edgar Martinez, and Walt Weiss. Notable early cards were issued of Roberto Alomar, Mark Grace and Jay Buhner.

COMP.FACT.SET (56) 4.00 10.00
1 Mark Grace .75 2.00
2 Mike Campbell .05 .15
3 Todd Frohwirth .05 .15
4 Dave Stapleton .05 .15
5 Shawn Abner .05 .15
6 Jose Cecena .05 .15
7 Dave Gallagher .05 .15
8 Mark Parent .05 .15
9 Cecil Espy XRC .05 .15
10 Pete Smith .05 .15
11 Jay Buhner .40 1.00
12 Pat Borders XRC .20 .50
13 Doug Jennings .05 .15
14 Brady Anderson XRC .30 .75
15 Pete Stanicek .05 .15
16 Roberto Kelly .20 .50
17 Jeff Treadway .05 .15
18 Walt Weiss XRC .30 .75
19 Paul Gibson .05 .15
20 Tim Crews .05 .15
21 Melido Perez .05 .15
22 Steve Peters .05 .15
23 Craig Worthington .05 .15
24 John Trautwein .05 .15
25 DeWayne Vaughn .05 .15
26 David Wells .60 1.50
27 Al Leiter .40 1.00
28 Tim Belcher .05 .15
29 Johnny Paredes .05 .15
30 Chris Sabo XRC .15 .40
31 Damon Berryhill .05 .15
32 Randy Milligan XRC .08 .25
33 Gary Thurman .05 .15
34 Kevin Elster .05 .15
35 Roberto Alomar 1.50 4.00
36 Edgar Martinez XRC 2.00 5.00
UER Photo actually Edwin Nunez
37 Todd Stottlemyre .05 .15
38 Joey Meyer .05 .15
39 Carl Nichols .05 .15
40 Jack McDowell .30 .75
41 Jose Bautista XRC .08 .25
42 Sil Campusano .05 .15
43 John Dopson .05 .15
44 Jody Reed .20 .50
45 Darrin Jackson XRC .08 .25
46 Mike Capel .05 .15
47 Ron Gant .30 .75
48 John Davis .05 .15
49 Kevin Coffman .05 .15
50 Cris Carpenter XRC .08 .25
51 Mackey Sasser .05 .15
52 Luis Alicea XRC .20 .50
53 Bryan Harvey XRC .10 .30
54 Steve Ellsworth .05 .15
55 Mike Macfarlane XRC .20 .50
56 Checklist 1-56 .05 .15

1989 Donruss

This set consists of 660 standard-size cards. The cards were primarily issued in 15-card wax packs, rack packs and hobby and retail factory sets. Each wax pack also contained a puzzle panel (featuring Warren Spahn this year). The wax packs were issued 36 packs to a box and 20 boxes to a case. The cards feature a distinctive black side border with an alternating coating. Subsets include Diamond Kings (1-27) and Rated Rookies (28-47). There are two variations that occur throughout most of the set. On the card backs "Denotes Led League" can be found with one asterisk to the left or with an asterisk on each side. On the card fronts the horizontal lines on the left and right borders can be glossy or non-glossy. Since both of these variation types are relatively minor and seem equally common, there is no premium value for either type. Rather than short-printing 26 cards in order to make room for printing the Bonus MVP's this year, Donruss apparently chose to double print 106 cards. These double prints are listed below by DP. Rookie Cards in this set include Sandy Alomar Jr., Brady Anderson, Dante Bichette, Craig Biggio, Ken Griffey Jr., Randy Johnson, Curt Schilling, Gary Sheffield and John Smoltz. Similar to the 1988 Donruss set, a special card was issued on blister packs, and features the card number as "Bonus Card".

COMPLETE SET (660) 10.00 25.00
COMP.FACT.SET (672) 10.00 25.00
1 Mike Greenwell DK .01 .05
2 Bobby Bonilla DK DP .02 .10
3 Pete Incaviglia DK .01 .05
4 Chris Sabo DK DP .02 .10
5 Robin Yount DK .15 .40
6 Tony Gwynn DK DP .05 .15
7 Carlton Fisk DK UER .05 .15
(OF on back)
8 Cory Snyder DK .01 .05
9 David Cone DK UER .02 .10
('hurdlers')
10 Kevin Seitzer DK .01 .05
11 Rick Reuschel DK .02 .10
12 Johnny Ray DK .01 .05
13 Dave Schmidt DK .01 .05
14 Andres Galarraga DK .02 .10
15 Kirk Gibson DK .02 .10
16 Fred McGriff DK .05 .15
17 Mark Grace DK .08 .25
18 Jeff M. Robinson DK .01 .05
19 Vince Coleman DK DP .01 .05
20 Dave Henderson DK .01 .05
21 Harold Reynolds DK .02 .10
22 Gerald Perry DK .01 .05
23 Frank Viola DK .02 .10
24 Steve Bedrosian DK .01 .05
25 Glenn Davis DK .01 .05
26 Don Mattingly DK UER .10 .30
(Doesn't mention Don's previous DK in 1985)
27 DK Checklist 1-26 DP .01 .05
28 S.Alomar Jr. RR RC .15 .40
29 Steve Searcy RR .01 .05
30 Cameron Drew RR .01 .05
31 Gary Sheffield RR RC .60 1.50
32 Erik Hanson RR RC .08 .25
33 Ken Griffey Jr. RR RC 3.00 8.00
34 Greg W. Harris RR RC .02 .10
35 Gregg Jefferies RR .01 .05
36 Luis Medina RR .01 .05
37 Carlos Quintana RR RC .02 .10
38 Felix Jose RR RC .02 .10
39 Cris Carpenter RR RC* .02 .10
40 Ron Jones RR .02 .10
41 Dave West RR RC .02 .10
42 R.Johnson RC RR UER .75 2.00
Card says born in 1964 he was born in 1963
43 Mike Harkey RR RC .02 .10
44 P.Harnisch RR DP RC .08 .25
45 Tom Gordon RR DP RC .20 .50
46 Gregg Olson RC RR DP .08 .25
47 Alex Sanchez RR DP .01 .05
48 Ruben Sierra .02 .10
49 Rafael Palmeiro .08 .25
50 Ron Gant .05 .15
51 Cal Ripken .30 .75
52 Wally Joyner .02 .10
53 Gary Carter .02 .10
54 Andy Van Slyke .05 .15
55 Robin Yount .15 .40
56 Pete Incaviglia .01 .05
57 Greg Brock .01 .05
58 Melido Perez .01 .05
59 Craig Lefferts .01 .05
60 Gary Pettis .01 .05
61 Danny Tartabull .01 .05
62 Guillermo Hernandez .01 .05
63 Ozzie Smith .15 .40
64 Gary Gaetti .02 .10
65 Mark Davis .01 .05
66 Lee Smith .02 .10
67 Dennis Eckersley .05 .15
68 Wade Boggs .05 .15
69 Mike Scott .02 .10
70 Fred McGriff .05 .15
71 Tom Browning .01 .05
72 Claudell Washington .01 .05
73 Mel Hall .01 .05
74 Don Mattingly .25 .60
75 Steve Bedrosian .01 .05
76 Juan Samuel .01 .05
77 Mike Scioscia .02 .10
78 Dave Righetti .02 .10
79 Alfredo Griffin .01 .05
80 Eric Davis UER .02 .10
(165 games in 1988, should be 135)
81 Juan Berenguer .01 .05
82 Todd Worrell .01 .05
83 Joe Carter .02 .10
84 Steve Sax .01 .05
85 Frank White .02 .10
86 John Kruk .02 .10
87 Rance Mulliniks .01 .05
88 Alan Ashby .01 .05
89 Charlie Leibrandt .01 .05
90 Frank Tanana .02 .10
91 Jose Canseco .08 .25
92 Barry Bonds .60 1.50
93 Harold Reynolds .02 .10
94 Mark McLemore .01 .05
95 Mark McGwire .40 1.00
96 Eddie Murray .08 .25
97 Tim Raines .02 .10
98 Robby Thompson .01 .05
99 Kevin McReynolds .01 .05
100 Checklist 28-137 .01 .05
101 Carlton Fisk .05 .15
102 Dave Martinez .01 .05
103 Glenn Braggs .01 .05
104 Dale Murphy .05 .15
105 Ryne Sandberg .15 .40
106 Dennis Martinez .02 .10
107 Pete O'Brien .01 .05
108 Dick Schofield .01 .05
109 Henry Cotto .01 .05
110 Mike Marshall .01 .05
111 Keith Moreland .01 .05
112 Tom Brunansky .01 .05
113 Kelly Gruber UER .01 .05
(Wrong birthdate)
114 Brook Jacoby .01 .05
115 Keith Brown .01 .05
116 Matt Nokes .01 .05
117 Keith Hernandez .02 .10
118 Bob Forsch .01 .05
119 Bert Blyleven UER .02 .10
(... 3000 strikeouts in 1987, should be 1986)
120 Willie Wilson .02 .10
121 Tommy Gregg .01 .05
122 Jim Rice .02 .10
123 Bob Knepper .01 .05
124 Danny Jackson .01 .05
125 Eric Plunk .01 .05
126 Brian Fisher .01 .05
127 Mike Pagliarulo .01 .05
128 Tony Gwynn .10 .30
129 Lance McCullers .01 .05
130 Andres Galarraga .02 .10
131 Jose Uribe .01 .05
132 Kirk Gibson UER .02 .10
(Wrong birthdate)
133 David Palmer .01 .05
134 R.J. Reynolds .01 .05
135 Greg Walker .01 .05
136 Kirk McCaskill UER .01 .05
(Wrong birthdate)
137 Shawon Dunston .01 .05
138 Andy Allanson .01 .05
139 Rob Murphy .01 .05
140 Mike Aldrete .01 .05
141 Terry Kennedy .01 .05
142 Scott Fletcher .01 .05
143 Steve Balboni .01 .05
144 Bret Saberhagen .02 .10
145 Ozzie Virgil .01 .05
146 Dale Sveum .01 .05
147 Darryl Strawberry .02 .10
148 Harold Baines .02 .10
149 George Bell .02 .10
150 Dave Parker .02 .10
151 Bobby Bonilla .02 .10
152 Mookie Wilson .02 .10
153 Ted Power .01 .05
154 Nolan Ryan .40 1.00
155 Jeff Reardon .02 .10
156 Tim Wallach .01 .05
157 Jamie Moyer .02 .10
158 Rich Gossage .02 .10
159 Dave Winfield .02 .10
160 Von Hayes .01 .05
161 Willie McGee .02 .10
162 Rich Gedman .01 .05
163 Tony Pena .01 .05
164 Mike Morgan .01 .05
165 Charlie Hough .02 .10
166 Mike Stanley .01 .05
167 Andre Dawson .02 .10
168 Joe Boever .01 .05
169 Pete Stanicek .01 .05
170 Bob Boone .02 .10
171 Ron Darling .02 .10
172 Bob Walk .01 .05
173 Rob Deer .01 .05
174 Steve Buechele .01 .05
175 Ted Higuera .01 .05
176 Ozzie Guillen .02 .10
177 Candy Maldonado .01 .05
178 Doyle Alexander .01 .05
179 Mark Gubicza .01 .05
180 Alan Trammell .02 .10
181 Vince Coleman .02 .10
182 Kirby Puckett .08 .25
183 Chris Brown .01 .05
184 Marty Barrett .01 .05
185 Stan Javier .01 .05
186 Mike Greenwell .01 .05
187 Billy Hatcher .01 .05
188 Jimmy Key .02 .10
189 Nick Esasky .01 .05
190 Don Slaught .01 .05
191 Cory Snyder .01 .05
192 John Candelaria .01 .05
193 Mike Schmidt .20 .50
194 Kevin Gross .01 .05
195 John Tudor .02 .10
196 Neil Allen .01 .05
197 Orel Hershiser .02 .10
198 Kal Daniels .01 .05
199 Kent Hrbek .02 .10
200 Checklist 138-247 .01 .05
201 Joe Magrane .01 .05
202 Scott Bailes .01 .05
203 Tim Belcher .01 .05
204 George Brett .25 .60
205 Benito Santiago .02 .10
206 Tony Fernandez .01 .05
207 Gerald Young .01 .05
208 Bo Jackson .08 .25
209 Chet Lemon .02 .10
210 Storm Davis .01 .05
211 Doug Drabek .01 .05
212 Mickey Brantley UER .01 .05
(Photo actually Nelson Simmons)
213 Devon White .02 .10
214 Dave Stewart .02 .10
215 Dave Schmidt .01 .05
216 Bryn Smith .01 .05
217 Brett Butler .02 .10
218 Bob Ojeda .01 .05
219 Steve Rosenberg .01 .05
220 Hubie Brooks .01 .05
221 B.J. Surhoff .02 .10
222 Rick Mahler .01 .05
223 Rick Sutcliffe .02 .10
224 Neal Heaton .01 .05
225 Mitch Williams .01 .05
226 Chuck Finley .02 .10
227 Mark Langston .01 .05
228 Jesse Orosco .01 .05
229 Ed Whitson .01 .05
230 Terry Pendleton .02 .10
231 Lloyd Moseby .01 .05
232 Greg Swindell .02 .10
233 John Franco .02 .10
234 Jack Morris .02 .10
235 Howard Johnson .02 .10
236 Glenn Davis .01 .05
237 Frank Viola .02 .10
238 Kevin Seitzer .01 .05
239 Gerald Perry .01 .05
240 Dwight Evans .05 .15
241 Jim Deshaies .01 .05
242 Bo Diaz .01 .05
243 Carney Lansford .02 .10
244 Mike LaValliere .01 .05
245 Rickey Henderson .08 .25
246 Roberto Alomar .08 .25
247 Jimmy Jones .01 .05
248 Pascual Perez .01 .05
249 Will Clark .05 .15
250 Fernando Valenzuela .02 .10
251 Shane Rawley .01 .05

252 Sid Bream .01 .05
253 Steve Lyons .01 .05
254 Brian Downing .02 .10
255 Mark Grace .08 .25
256 Tom Candiotti .01 .05
257 Barry Larkin .05 .15
258 Mike Krukow .01 .05
259 Billy Ripken .01 .05
260 Cecilio Guante .01 .05
261 Scott Bradley .01 .05
262 Floyd Bannister .01 .05
263 Pete Smith .01 .05
264 Jim Gantner UER .01 .05
(Wrong birthdate)
265 Roger McDowell .01 .05
266 Bobby Thigpen .01 .05
267 Jim Clancy .01 .05
268 Terry Steinbach .02 .10
269 Mike Dunne .01 .05
270 Dwight Gooden .02 .10
271 Mike Heath .01 .05
272 Dave Smith .01 .05
273 Keith Atherton .01 .05
274 Tim Burke .01 .05
275 Damon Berryhill .01 .05
276 Vance Law .01 .05
277 Rich Dotson .01 .05
278 Lance Parrish .02 .10
279 Denny Walling .01 .05
280 Roger Clemens .40 1.00
281 Greg Mathews .01 .05
282 Tom Niedenfuer .01 .05
283 Paul Kilgus .01 .05
284 Jose Guzman .01 .05
285 Calvin Schiraldi .01 .05
286 Charlie Puleo UER .01 .05
(Career ERA 4.24, should be 4.23)
287 Joe Orsulak .01 .05
288 Jack Howell .01 .05
289 Kevin Elster .01 .05
290 Jose Lind .01 .05
291 Paul Molitor .02 .10
292 Cecil Espy .01 .05
293 Bill Wegman .01 .05
294 Dan Pasqua .01 .05
295 Scott Garrelts UER .01 .05
(Wrong birthdate)
296 Walt Terrell .01 .05
297 Ed Hearn .01 .05
298 Lou Whitaker .02 .10
299 Ken Dayley .01 .05
300 Checklist 248-357 .01 .05
301 Tommy Herr .01 .05
302 Mike Brumley .01 .05
303 Ellis Burks .02 .10
304 Curt Young UER .01 .05
(Wrong birthdate)
305 Jody Reed .01 .05
306 Bill Doran .01 .05
307 David Wells .02 .10
308 Ron Robinson .01 .05
309 Rafael Santana .01 .05
310 Julio Franco .02 .10
311 Jack Clark .02 .10
312 Chris James .01 .05
313 Milt Thompson .01 .05
314 John Shelby .01 .05
315 Al Leiter .08 .25
316 Mike Davis .01 .05
317 Chris Sabo RC * .15 .40
318 Greg Gagne .01 .05
319 Jose Oquendo .01 .05
320 John Farrell .01 .05
321 Franklin Stubbs .01 .05
322 Kurt Stillwell .01 .05
323 Shawn Abner .01 .05
324 Mike Flanagan .01 .05
325 Kevin Bass .01 .05
326 Pat Tabler .01 .05
327 Mike Henneman .01 .05
328 Rick Honeycutt .01 .05
329 John Smiley .01 .05
330 Rey Quinones .01 .05
331 Johnny Ray .01 .05
332 Bob Welch .02 .10
333 Larry Sheets .01 .05
334 Jeff Parrett .01 .05
335 Rick Reuschel UER .02 .10
(For Don Robinson& should be Jeff)
336 Randy Myers .02 .10
337 Ken Williams .01 .05
338 Andy McGaffigan .01 .05
339 Joey Meyer .01 .05
340 Dion James .01 .05
341 Les Lancaster .01 .05
342 Tom Foley .01 .05
343 Geno Petralli .01 .05
344 Dan Petry .01 .05
345 Alvin Davis .01 .05
346 Mickey Hatcher .01 .05
347 Marvell Wynne .01 .05
348 Danny Cox .01 .05
349 Dave Stieb .02 .10
350 Jay Bell .02 .10
351 Jeff Treadway .01 .05
352 Luis Salazar .01 .05
353 Len Dykstra .02 .10
354 Juan Agosto .01 .05
355 Gene Larkin .01 .05
356 Steve Farr .01 .05
357 Paul Assenmacher .01 .05
358 Todd Benzinger .01 .05
359 Larry Andersen .01 .05
360 Paul O'Neill .05 .15
361 Ron Hassey .01 .05
362 Jim Gott .01 .05
363 Ken Phelps .01 .05
364 Tim Flannery .01 .05
365 Randy Ready .01 .05
366 Nelson Santovenia .01 .05
367 Kelly Downs .01 .05
368 Danny Heep .01 .05
369 Phil Bradley .01 .05
370 Jeff D. Robinson .01 .05
371 Ivan Calderon .01 .05
372 Mike Witt .01 .05
373 Greg Maddux .20 .50
374 Carmen Castillo .01 .05
375 Jose Rijo .02 .10
376 Joe Price .01 .05
377 Rene Gonzales .01 .05
378 Oddibe McDowell .01 .05
379 Jim Presley .01 .05
380 Brad Wellman .01 .05
381 Tom Glavine .08 .25
382 Dan Plesac .01 .05
383 Wally Backman .01 .05
384 Dave Gallagher .01 .05
385 Tom Henke .01 .05
386 Luis Polonia .01 .05
387 Junior Ortiz .01 .05
388 David Cone .02 .10
389 Dave Bergman .01 .05
390 Danny Darwin .01 .05
391 Dan Gladden .01 .05
392 John Dopson .01 .05
393 Frank DiPino .01 .05
394 Al Nipper .01 .05
395 Willie Randolph .02 .10
396 Don Carman .01 .05
397 Scott Terry .01 .05
398 Rick Cerone .01 .05
399 Tom Pagnozzi .01 .05
400 Checklist 358-467 .01 .05
401 Mickey Tettleton .01 .05
402 Curtis Wilkerson .01 .05
403 Jeff Russell .01 .05
404 Pat Perry .01 .05
405 Jose Alvarez RC .02 .10
406 Rick Schu .01 .05
407 Sherman Corbett .01 .05
408 Dave Magadan .01 .05
409 Bob Kipper .01 .05
410 Don August .01 .05
411 Bob Brower .01 .05
412 Chris Bosio .01 .05
413 Jerry Reuss .01 .05
414 Atlee Hammaker .01 .05
415 Jim Walewander .01 .05
416 Mike Macfarlane RC * .08 .25
417 Pat Sheridan .01 .05
418 Pedro Guerrero .02 .10
419 Allan Anderson .01 .05
420 Mark Parent .01 .05
421 Bob Stanley .01 .05
422 Mike Gallego .01 .05
423 Bruce Hurst .01 .05
424 Dave Meads .01 .05
425 Jesse Barfield .02 .10
426 Rob Dibble RC .15 .40
427 Joel Skinner .01 .05
428 Ron Kittle .01 .05
429 Rick Rhoden .01 .05
430 Bob Dernier .01 .05
431 Steve Jeltz .01 .05
432 Rick Dempsey .01 .05
433 Roberto Kelly .01 .05
434 Dave Anderson .01 .05
435 Herm Winningham .01 .05
436 Al Newman .01 .05
437 Jose DeLeon .01 .05
438 Doug Jones .01 .05
439 Brian Holton .01 .05
440 Jeff Montgomery .01 .05
441 Dickie Thon .01 .05
442 Cecil Fielder .02 .10
443 John Fishel .01 .05
444 Jerry Don Gleaton .01 .05
445 Paul Gibson .01 .05
446 Walt Weiss .01 .05
447 Glenn Wilson .01 .05
448 Mike Moore .01 .05
449 Chili Davis .02 .10
450 Dave Henderson .01 .05
451 Jose Bautista RC .02 .10
452 Rex Hudler .01 .05
453 Bob Brenly .01 .05
454 Mackey Sasser .01 .05
455 Daryl Boston .01 .05
456 Mike R. Fitzgerald .01 .05
457 Jeffrey Leonard .01 .05
458 Bruce Sutter .02 .10
459 Mitch Webster .01 .05
460 Joe Hesketh .01 .05
461 Bobby Witt .02 .10
462 Stu Cliburn .01 .05
463 Scott Bankhead .01 .05
464 Ramon Martinez RC .08 .25
465 Dave Leiper .01 .05
466 Luis Alicea RC * .08 .25
467 John Cerutti .01 .05
468 Ron Washington .01 .05
469 Jeff Reed .01 .05
470 Jeff M. Robinson .01 .05
471 Sid Fernandez .01 .05
472 Terry Puhl .01 .05
473 Charlie Lea .01 .05
474 Israel Sanchez .01 .05
475 Bruce Benedict .01 .05
476 Oil Can Boyd .01 .05
477 Craig Reynolds .01 .05
478 Frank Williams .01 .05
479 Greg Cadaret .01 .05
480 Randy Kramer .01 .05
481 Dave Eiland .01 .05
482 Eric Show .01 .05
483 Garry Templeton .02 .10
484 Wallace Johnson .01 .05
485 Kevin Mitchell .02 .10
486 Tim Crews .01 .05
487 Mike Maddux .01 .05
488 Dave LaPoint .01 .05
489 Fred Manrique .01 .05
490 Greg Minton .01 .05
491 Doug Dascenzo UER .01 .05
(Photo actually Damon Berryhill)
492 Willie Upshaw .01 .05
493 Jack Armstrong RC * .08 .25
494 Kirt Manwaring .01 .05
495 Jeff Ballard .01 .05
496 Jeff Kunkel .01 .05
497 Mike Campbell .01 .05
498 Gary Thurman .01 .05
499 Zane Smith .01 .05
500 Checklist 468-577 DP .01 .05
501 Mike Birkbeck .01 .05
502 Terry Leach .01 .05
503 Shawn Hillegas .01 .05
504 Manny Lee .01 .05
505 Doug Jennings .01 .05
506 Ken Oberkfell .01 .05
507 Tim Teufel .01 .05
508 Tom Brookens .01 .05
509 Rafael Ramirez .01 .05
510 Fred Toliver .01 .05
511 Brian Holman RC * .02 .10
512 Mike Bielecki .01 .05
513 Jeff Pico .01 .05
514 Charles Hudson .01 .05
515 Bruce Ruffin .01 .05
516 L.McWilliams UER .01 .05
New Richland, should be North Richland
517 Jeff Sellers .01 .05
518 John Costello .01 .05
519 Brady Anderson RC .15 .40
520 Craig McMurtry .01 .05
521 Ray Hayward DP .01 .05
522 Drew Hall DP .01 .05
523 Mark Lemke DP RC .15 .40
524 Oswald Peraza DP .01 .05
525 Bryan Harvey DP RC * .08 .25
526 Rick Aguilera DP .01 .05
527 Tom Prince DP .01 .05
528 Mark Clear DP .01 .05
529 Jerry Browne DP .01 .05
530 Juan Castillo DP .01 .05
531 Jack McDowell DP .02 .10
532 Chris Speier DP .01 .05
533 Darrell Evans DP .02 .10
534 Luis Aquino DP .01 .05
535 Eric King DP .01 .05
536 Ken Hill DP RC .08 .25
537 Randy Bush DP .01 .05
538 Shane Mack DP .01 .05
539 Tom Bolton DP .01 .05
540 Gene Nelson DP .01 .05
541 Wes Gardner DP .01 .05
542 Ken Caminiti DP .05 .15
543 Duane Ward DP .01 .05
544 Norm Charlton DP RC .08 .25
545 Hal Morris DP RC .08 .25
546 Rich Yett DP .01 .05
547 H.Meulens DP RC .02 .10
548 Greg A. Harris DP .01 .05
549 Darren Daulton DP .02 .10
(Posing as right-handed hitter)
550 Jeff Hamilton DP .01 .05
551 Luis Aguayo DP .01 .05
552 Tim Leary DP .01 .05
(Resembles M.Marshall)
553 Ron Oester DP .01 .05
554 S.Lombardozzi DP .01 .05
555 Tim Jones DP .01 .05
556 Bud Black DP .01 .05
557 Alejandro Pena DP .01 .05
558 Jose DeJesus DP .01 .05
559 D.Rasmussen DP .01 .05
560 Pat Borders DP RC* .08 .25
561 Craig Biggio DP RC 1.25 3.00
562 Luis DeLosSantos DP .01 .05
563 Fred Lynn DP .02 .10
564 Todd Burns DP .01 .05
565 Felix Fermin DP .01 .05
566 Darnell Coles DP .01 .05
567 Willie Fraser DP .01 .05
568 Glenn Hubbard DP .01 .05
569 Craig Worthington DP .01 .05
570 Johnny Paredes DP .01 .05
571 Don Robinson DP .01 .05
572 Barry Lyons DP .01 .05
573 Bill Long DP .01 .05
574 Tracy Jones DP .01 .05
575 Juan Nieves DP .01 .05
576 Andres Thomas DP .01 .05
577 Rolando Roomes DP .01 .05
578 Luis Rivera UER DP .01 .05
(Wrong birthdate)
579 Chad Kreuter DP RC .08 .25
580 Tony Armas DP .02 .10
581 Jay Buhner .02 .10
582 Ricky Horton DP .01 .05
583 Andy Hawkins DP .01 .05
584 Sil Campusano .01 .05
585 Dave Clark .01 .05
586 Van Snider DP .01 .05
587 Todd Frohwirth DP .01 .05
588 W.Spahn DP PUZ .05 .15
589 William Brennan .01 .05
590 German Gonzalez .01 .05
591 Ernie Whitt DP .01 .05
592 Jeff Blauser .01 .05
593 Spike Owen DP .01 .05
594 Matt Williams .08 .25
595 Lloyd McClendon DP .01 .05
596 Steve Ontiveros .01 .05
597 Scott Medvin .01 .05
598 Hipolito Pena DP .01 .05
599 Jerald Clark DP RC .02 .10
600A CL 578-660 DP .01 .05
635 Kurt Schilling
600B CL 578-660 DP .01 .05
635 Curt Schilling; MVP's not listed on checklist card
600C CL 578-660 DP .01 .05
635 Curt Schilling; MVP's listed following 660
601 Carmelo Martinez DP .01 .05
602 Mike LaCoss .01 .05
603 Mike Devereaux .01 .05
604 Alex Madrid DP .01 .05
605 Gary Redus DP .01 .05
606 Lance Johnson .01 .05
607 Terry Clark DP .01 .05
608 Manny Trillo DP .01 .05
609 Scott Jordan RC .08 .25
610 Jay Howell DP .01 .05
611 Francisco Melendez .01 .05
612 Mike Boddicker .01 .05
613 Kevin Brown DP .08 .25
614 Dave Valle .01 .05
615 Tim Laudner DP .01 .05
616 Andy Nezelek UER .01 .05
(Wrong birthdate)
617 Chuck Crim .01 .05
618 Jack Savage DP .01 .05
619 Adam Peterson .01 .05
620 Todd Stottlemyre .01 .05
621 Lance Blankenship RC .02 .10
622 Miguel Garcia DP .01 .05
623 Keith A. Miller DP .01 .05
624 Ricky Jordan DP RC* .08 .25
625 Ernest Riles DP .01 .05
626 John Moses DP .01 .05
627 Nelson Liriano DP .01 .05
628 Mike Smithson DP .01 .05
629 Scott Sanderson .01 .05
630 Dale Mohorcic .01 .05
631 Marvin Freeman DP .01 .05
632 Mike Young DP .01 .05
633 Dennis Lamp .01 .05
634 Dante Bichette DP RC .15 .40
635 Curt Schilling DP RC 1.50 4.00
636 Scott May DP .01 .05
637 Mike Schooler .01 .05
638 Rick Leach .01 .05
639 Tom Lampkin UER .01 .05
(Throws Left, should be Throws Right)
640 Brian Meyer .01 .05
641 Brian Harper .01 .05
642 John Smoltz RC .60 1.50
643 Jose Canseco .08 .25
(40/40 Club)
644 Bill Schroeder .01 .05
645 Edgar Martinez .08 .25
646 Dennis Cook RC .08 .25
647 Barry Jones .01 .05
648 Orel Hershiser .02 .10
(59 and Counting)
649 Rod Nichols .01 .05
650 Jody Davis .01 .05
651 Bob Milacki .01 .05
652 Mike Jackson .01 .05
653 Derek Lilliquist RC .02 .10
654 Paul Mirabella .01 .05
655 Mike Diaz .01 .05
656 Jeff Musselman .01 .05
657 Jerry Reed .01 .05
658 Kevin Blankenship .01 .05
659 Wayne Tolleson .01 .05
660 Eric Hetzel .01 .05
BC Jose Canseco .75 2.00
Blister Pack

1989 Donruss Rookies

The 1989 Donruss Rookies set contains 56 standard-size cards. The cards were distributed exclusively in factory set form in small, emerald green, cellophane-wrapped boxes through hobby dealers. The cards are almost identical in design to geular 1989 Donruss except for the green borders. Rookie Cards in this set include Jim Abbott, Steve Finley, Kenny Rogers and Deion Sanders. Ken Griffey Jr. and Randy Johnson are also featured on a card within the set.

COMP.FACT.SET (56) 6.00 15.00
1 Gary Sheffield .75 2.00
2 Gregg Jefferies .02 .10
3 Ken Griffey Jr. 4.00 10.00
4 Tom Gordon .08 .25
5 Billy Spiers RC .08 .25
6 Deion Sanders RC .60 1.50
7 Donn Pall .01 .05
8 Steve Carter .01 .05
9 Francisco Oliveras .01 .05
10 Steve Wilson RC .02 .10
11 Bob Geren RC .01 .05
12 Tony Castillo RC .02 .10
13 Kenny Rogers RC 1.00 2.50
14 Carlos Martinez RC .02 .10
15 Edgar Martinez .08 .25
16 Jim Abbott RC .40 1.00
17 Torey Lovullo RC .02 .10
18 Mark Carreon .01 .05
19 Geronimo Berroa .01 .05
20 Luis Medina .01 .05
21 Sandy Alomar Jr. .05 .15
22 Bob Milacki .01 .05
23 Joe Girardi RC .15 .40
24 German Gonzalez .01 .05
25 Craig Worthington .01 .05
26 Jerome Walton RC .08 .25
27 Gary Wayne .01 .05
28 Tim Jones .01 .05
29 Dante Bichette .05 .15
30 Alexis Infante RC .01 .05
31 Ken Hill .08 .25
32 Dwight Smith RC .08 .25
33 Luis de los Santos .01 .05
34 Eric Yelding .01 .05
35 Gregg Olson .08 .25
36 Phil Stephenson .01 .05
37 Ken Patterson .01 .05
38 Rick Wrona .01 .05
39 Mike Brumley .01 .05
40 Cris Carpenter .01 .05
41 Jeff Brantley RC .08 .25
42 Ron Jones .01 .05
43 Randy Johnson .75 2.00
44 Kevin Brown .08 .25
45 Ramon Martinez .02 .10
46 Greg W.Harris .01 .05
47 Steve Finley RC .30 .75
48 Randy Kramer .01 .05
49 Erik Hanson .02 .10
50 Matt Merullo .01 .05
51 Mike Devereaux .01 .05
52 Clay Parker .01 .05
53 Omar Vizquel RC .40 1.00
54 Derek Lilliquist .01 .05
55 Junior Felix .02 .10
56 Checklist 1-56 .01 .05

1990 Donruss

The 1990 Donruss set contains 716 standard-size cards. Cards were issued in wax packs and hobby and retail factory sets. The card fronts feature bright red borders. Subsets include Diamond Kings (1-27) and Rated Rookies (28-47). The set was the largest ever produced by Donruss, unfortunately it also had a large number of errors which were corrected after the cards were released. Most of these feature minor printing flaws and insignificant variations that collectors have found unworthy of price differentials. There are several double-printed cards indicated in our checklist with the set indicated with a "DP" coding. Rookie Cards of note include Juan Gonzalez, David Justice, John Olerud, Dean Palmer, Sammy Sosa, Larry Walker and Bernie Williams.

COMPLETE SET (716) 6.00 15.00
COMP.FACT.SET (728) 6.00 15.00
COMP.YAZ PUZZLE .40 1.00
1 Bo Jackson DK .05 .15
2 Steve Sax DK .01 .05
3A Ruben Sierra DK ERR .02 .10
(No small line on top border on card back)
3B Ruben Sierra DK COR .02 .10
4 Ken Griffey Jr. DK .15 .40
5 Mickey Tettleton DK .01 .05
6 Dave Stewart DK .01 .05
7 Jim Deshaies DK DP .01 .05
8 John Smoltz DK .08 .25
9 Mike Bielecki DK .01 .05
10A Brian Downing DK .05 .15
ERR (Reverse negative on card front)
10B Brian Downing DK COR .01 .05
11 Kevin Mitchell DK .01 .05
12 Kelly Gruber DK .01 .05
13 Joe Magrane DK .01 .05
14 John Franco DK .02 .10
15 Ozzie Guillen DK .02 .10
16 Lou Whitaker DK .02 .10
17 John Smiley DK .01 .05
18 Howard Johnson DK .01 .05
19 Willie Randolph DK .02 .10
20 Chris Bosio DK .01 .05
21 Tommy Herr DK DP .01 .05
22 Dan Gladden DK .01 .05
23 Ellis Burks DK .02 .10
24 Pete O'Brien DK .01 .05
25 Bryn Smith DK .01 .05
26 Ed Whitson DK DP .01 .05
27 DK Checklist 1-27 DP .01 .05
(Comments on Perez-Steele on back)
28 Robin Ventura RR .08 .25
29 Todd Zeile RR .02 .10
30 Sandy Alomar Jr. .02 .10
31 Kent Mercker RC .08 .25
32 B.McDonald RC UER .08 .25
Middle name Benard not Benjamin
33A J.Gonzalez ERR RC .75 2.00
Reverse negative
33B J.Gonzalez COR RC .40 1.00
34 Eric Anthony RC .02 .10
35 Mike Fetters RC .08 .25
36 Marquis Grissom RC .15 .40
37 Greg Vaughn RR .01 .05
38 Brian DuBois RC .02 .10
39 Steve Avery RR UER .01 .05
(Born in MI, not NJ)
40 Mark Gardner RC .02 .10
41 Andy Benes .02 .10
42 Delino DeShields RC .08 .25
43 Scott Coolbaugh RC .02 .10
44 Pat Combs DP .01 .05
45 Alex Sanchez DP .01 .05
46 Kelly Mann DP RC .02 .10
47 Julio Machado RC .02 .10
48 Pete Incaviglia .01 .05
49 Shawon Dunston .01 .05
50 Jeff Treadway .01 .05
51 Jeff Ballard .01 .05
52 Claudell Washington .01 .05
53 Juan Samuel .01 .05
54 John Smiley .01 .05
55 Rob Deer .01 .05
56 Geno Petralli .01 .05
57 Chris Bosio .01 .05
58 Carlton Fisk .05 .15
59 Kirt Manwaring .01 .05
60 Chet Lemon .01 .05
61 Bo Jackson .08 .25
62 Doyle Alexander .01 .05
63 Pedro Guerrero .01 .05
64 Allan Anderson .01 .05
65 Greg W. Harris .01 .05
66 Mike Greenwell .01 .05
67 Walt Weiss .01 .05
68 Wade Boggs .05 .15
69 Jim Clancy .01 .05
70 Junior Felix .01 .05
71 Barry Larkin .05 .15
72 Dave LaPoint .01 .05
73 Joel Skinner .01 .05
74 Jesse Barfield .01 .05
75 Tommy Herr .01 .05
76 Ricky Jordan .01 .05
77 Eddie Murray .08 .25
78 Steve Sax .01 .05
79 Tim Belcher .01 .05
80 Danny Jackson .01 .05
81 Kent Hrbek .02 .10
82 Milt Thompson .01 .05
83 Brook Jacoby .01 .05
84 Mike Marshall .01 .05
85 Kevin Seitzer .01 .05
86 Tony Gwynn .10 .30
87 Dave Stieb .02 .10
88 Dave Smith .01 .05
89 Bret Saberhagen .02 .10
90 Alan Trammell .02 .10
91 Tony Phillips .01 .05
92 Doug Drabek .01 .05
93 Jeffrey Leonard .01 .05
94 Wally Joyner .02 .10
95 Carney Lansford .02 .10
96 Cal Ripken .30 .75
97 Andres Galarraga .02 .10
98 Kevin Mitchell .01 .05
99 Howard Johnson .01 .05
100A Checklist 28-129 .01 .05
100B Checklist 28-125 .01 .05
101 Melido Perez .01 .05
102 Spike Owen .01 .05
103 Paul Molitor .02 .10
104 Geronimo Berroa .01 .05
105 Ryne Sandberg .15 .40
106 Bryn Smith .01 .05
107 Steve Buechele .01 .05
108 Jim Abbott .05 .15
109 Alvin Davis .01 .05
110 Lee Smith .02 .10
111 Roberto Alomar .05 .15
112 Rick Reuschel .01 .05
113A Kelly Gruber ERR .01 .05
(Born 2/22)
113B Kelly Gruber COR .01 .05
(Born 2/26; corrected in factory sets)
114 Joe Carter .02 .10
115 Jose Rijo .01 .05
116 Greg Minton .01 .05
117 Bob Ojeda .01 .05
118 Glenn Davis .01 .05
119 Jeff Reardon .02 .10
120 Kurt Stillwell .01 .05
121 John Smoltz .08 .25
122 Dwight Evans .05 .15
123 Eric Yelding RC .01 .05
124 John Franco .02 .10
125 Jose Canseco .05 .15
126 Barry Bonds .40 1.00
127 Lee Guetterman .01 .05
128 Jack Clark .02 .10
129 Dave Valle .01 .05
130 Hubie Brooks .01 .05
131 Ernest Riles .01 .05
132 Mike Morgan .01 .05
133 Steve Jeltz .01 .05
134 Jeff D. Robinson .01 .05
135 Ozzie Guillen .01 .05
136 Chili Davis .02 .10
137 Mitch Webster .01 .05
138 Jerry Browne .01 .05
139 Bo Diaz .01 .05
140 Robby Thompson .01 .05
141 Craig Worthington .01 .05
142 Julio Franco .02 .10
143 Brian Holman .01 .05
144 George Brett .25 .60
145 Tom Glavine .05 .15
146 Robin Yount .15 .40
147 Gary Carter .02 .10
148 Ron Kittle .01 .05
149 Tony Fernandez .01 .05
150 Dave Stewart .02 .10
151 Gary Gaetti .02 .10
152 Kevin Elster .01 .05
153 Gerald Perry .01 .05
154 Jesse Orosco .01 .05
155 Wally Backman .01 .05
156 Dennis Martinez .02 .10
157 Rick Sutcliffe .02 .10
158 Greg Maddux .15 .40
159 Andy Hawkins .01 .05
160 John Kruk .02 .10
161 Jose Oquendo .01 .05
162 John Dopson .01 .05
163 Joe Magrane .01 .05
164 Bill Ripken .01 .05
165 Fred Manrique .01 .05
166 Nolan Ryan UER .40 1.00
(Did not lead NL in K's in '89 as he was in AL in '89)
167 Damon Berryhill .01 .05
168 Dale Murphy .05 .15
169 Mickey Tettleton .01 .05
170A Kirk McCaskill ERR .01 .05
(Born 4/19)
170B Kirk McCaskill COR .01 .05
(Born 4/9; corrected in factory sets)
171 Dwight Gooden .02 .10
172 Jose Lind .01 .05
173 B.J. Surhoff .02 .10
174 Ruben Sierra .02 .10
175 Dan Plesac .01 .05
176 Dan Pasqua .01 .05
177 Kelly Downs .01 .05
178 Matt Nokes .01 .05
179 Luis Aquino .01 .05
180 Frank Tanana .01 .05
181 Tony Pena .01 .05
182 Dan Gladden .01 .05
183 Bruce Hurst .01 .05
184 Roger Clemens .40 1.00
185 Mark McGwire .40 1.00
186 Rob Murphy .01 .05
187 Jim Deshaies .01 .05
188 Fred McGriff .08 .25
189 Rob Dibble .02 .10
190 Don Mattingly .25 .60
191 Felix Fermin .01 .05
192 Roberto Kelly .01 .05
193 Dennis Cook .01 .05
194 Darren Daulton .02 .10
195 Alfredo Griffin .01 .05
196 Eric Plunk .01 .05
197 Orel Hershiser .02 .10
198 Paul O'Neill .05 .15
199 Randy Bush .01 .05
200A Checklist 130-231 .01 .05
200B Checklist 126-223 .01 .05
201 Ozzie Smith .15 .40
202 Pete O'Brien .01 .05
203 Jay Howell .01 .05

204 Mark Gubicza .01 .05
205 Ed Whitson .01 .05
206 George Bell .01 .05
207 Mike Scott .01 .05
208 Charlie Leibrandt .01 .05
209 Mike Heath .01 .05
210 Dennis Eckersley .02 .10
211 Mike LaValliere .01 .05
212 Darnell Coles .01 .05
213 Lance Parrish .01 .05
214 Mike Moore .01 .05
215 Steve Finley .02 .10
216 Tim Raines .02 .10
217A Scott Garrelts ERR (Born 10/20) .01 .05
217B Scott Garrelts COR (Born 10/30; corrected in factory sets) .01 .05
218 Kevin McReynolds .01 .05
219 Dave Gallagher .01 .05
220 Tim Wallach .01 .05
221 Chuck Crim .01 .05
222 Lonnie Smith .01 .05
223 Andre Dawson .02 .10
224 Nelson Santovenia .01 .05
225 Rafael Palmeiro .05 .15
226 Devon White .02 .10
227 Harold Reynolds .02 .10
228 Ellis Burks .05 .15
229 Mark Parent .01 .05
230 Will Clark .05 .15
231 Jimmy Key .02 .10
232 John Farrell .01 .05
233 Eric Davis .02 .10
234 Johnny Ray .01 .05
235 Darryl Strawberry .02 .10
236 Bill Doran .01 .05
237 Greg Gagne .01 .05
238 Jim Eisenreich .01 .05
239 Tommy Gregg .01 .05
240 Marty Barrett .01 .05
241 Rafael Ramirez .01 .05
242 Chris Sabo .01 .05
243 Dave Henderson .01 .05
244 Andy Van Slyke .05 .15
245 Alvaro Espinoza .01 .05
246 Garry Templeton .01 .05
247 Gene Harris .01 .05
248 Kevin Gross .01 .05
249 Brett Butler .02 .10
250 Willie Randolph .02 .10
251 Roger McDowell .01 .05
252 Rafael Belliard .01 .05
253 Steve Rosenberg .01 .05
254 Jack Howell .01 .05
255 Marvell Wynne .01 .05
256 Tom Candiotti .01 .05
257 Todd Benzinger .01 .05
258 Don Robinson .01 .05
259 Phil Bradley .01 .05
260 Cecil Espy .01 .05
261 Scott Bankhead .01 .05
262 Frank White .02 .10
263 Andres Thomas .01 .05
264 Glenn Braggs .01 .05
265 David Cone .02 .10
266 Bobby Thigpen .01 .05
267 Nelson Liriano .01 .05
268 Terry Steinbach .01 .05
269 Kirby Puckett UER (Back doesn't consider Joe Torre's .363 in '71) .08 .25
270 Gregg Jefferies .02 .10
271 Jeff Blauser .01 .05
272 Cory Snyder .01 .05
273 Roy Smith .01 .05
274 Tom Foley .01 .05
275 Mitch Williams .01 .05
276 Paul Kilgus .01 .05
277 Don Slaught .01 .05
278 Von Hayes .01 .05
279 Vince Coleman .01 .05
280 Mike Boddicker .01 .05
281 Ken Dayley .01 .05
282 Mike Devereaux .01 .05
283 Kenny Rogers .02 .10
284 Jeff Russell .01 .05
285 Jerome Walton .01 .05
286 Derek Lilliquist .01 .05
287 Joe Orsulak .01 .05
288 Dick Schofield .01 .05
289 Ron Darling .01 .05
290 Bobby Bonilla .02 .10
291 Jim Gantner .01 .05
292 Bobby Witt .01 .05
293 Greg Brock .01 .05
294 Ivan Calderon .01 .05
295 Steve Bedrosian .01 .05
296 Mike Henneman .01 .05
297 Tom Gordon .02 .10
298 Lou Whitaker .02 .10
299 Terry Pendleton .02 .10
300A Checklist 232-333 .01 .05
300B Checklist 224-321 .01 .05
301 Juan Berenguer .01 .05
302 Mark Davis .01 .05
303 Nick Esasky .01 .05
304 Rickey Henderson .08 .25
305 Rick Cerone .01 .05
306 Craig Biggio .08 .25
307 Duane Ward .01 .05
308 Tom Browning .01 .05
309 Walt Terrell .01 .05
310 Greg Swindell .01 .05
311 Dave Righetti .01 .05
312 Mike Maddux .01 .05
313 Len Dykstra .02 .10
314 Jose Gonzalez .01 .05
315 Steve Balboni .01 .05
316 Mike Scioscia .01 .05
317 Ron Oester .01 .05
318 Gary Wayne .01 .05
319 Todd Worrell .01 .05
320 Doug Jones .01 .05
321 Jeff Hamilton .01 .05
322 Danny Tartabull .01 .05
323 Chris James .01 .05
324 Mike Flanagan .01 .05
325 Gerald Young .01 .05
326 Bob Boone .02 .10
327 Frank Williams .01 .05
328 Dave Parker .02 .10
329 Sid Bream .01 .05
330 Mike Schooler .01 .05
331 Bert Blyleven .02 .10
332 Bob Welch .01 .05
333 Bob Milacki .01 .05
334 Tim Burke .01 .05
335 Jose Uribe .01 .05
336 Randy Myers .02 .10
337 Eric King .01 .05
338 Mark Langston .01 .05
339 Teddy Higuera .01 .05
340 Oddibe McDowell .01 .05
341 Lloyd McClendon .01 .05
342 Pascual Perez .01 .05
343 Kevin Brown UER (Signed is misspelled as signed on back) .02 .10
344 Chuck Finley .02 .10
345 Erik Hanson .01 .05
346 Rich Gedman .01 .05
347 Bip Roberts .01 .05
348 Matt Williams .02 .10
349 Tom Henke .01 .05
350 Brad Komminsk .01 .05
351 Jeff Reed .01 .05
352 Brian Downing .01 .05
353 Frank Viola .01 .05
354 Terry Puhl .01 .05
355 Brian Harper .01 .05
356 Steve Farr .01 .05
357 Joe Boever .01 .05
358 Danny Heep .01 .05
359 Larry Andersen .01 .05
360 Rolando Roomes .01 .05
361 Mike Gallego .01 .05
362 Bob Kipper .01 .05
363 Clay Parker .01 .05
364 Mike Pagliarulo .01 .05
365 Ken Griffey Jr. UER (Signed through 1990, should be 1991) .30 .75
366 Rex Hudler .01 .05
367 Pat Sheridan .01 .05
368 Kirk Gibson .02 .10
369 Jeff Parrett .01 .05
370 Bob Walk .01 .05
371 Ken Patterson .01 .05
372 Bryan Harvey .01 .05
373 Mike Bielecki .01 .05
374 Tom Magrann RC .01 .05
375 Rick Mahler .01 .05
376 Craig Lefferts .01 .05
377 Gregg Olson .02 .10
378 Jamie Moyer .02 .10
379 Randy Johnson .20 .50
380 Jeff Montgomery .02 .10
381 Marty Clary .01 .05
382 Bill Spiers .01 .05
383 Dave Magadan .01 .05
384 Greg Hibbard RC .02 .10
385 Ernie Whitt .01 .05
386 Rick Honeycutt .01 .05
387 Dave West .01 .05
388 Keith Hernandez .02 .10
389 Jose Alvarez .01 .05
390 Joey Belle .08 .25
391 Rick Aguilera .02 .10
392 Mike Fitzgerald .01 .05
393 Dwight Smith .01 .05
394 Steve Wilson .01 .05
395 Bob Geren .01 .05
396 Randy Ready .01 .05
397 Ken Hill .02 .10
398 Jody Reed .01 .05
399 Tom Brunansky .01 .05
400A Checklist 334-435 .01 .05
400B Checklist 322-419 .01 .05
401 Rene Gonzales .01 .05
402 Harold Baines .02 .10
403 Cecilio Guante .01 .05
404 Joe Girardi .05 .15
405A Sergio Valdez ERR RC (Card front shows black line crossing S in Sergio) .01 .05
405B Sergio Valdez COR .01 .05
406 Mark Williamson .01 .05
407 Glenn Hoffman .01 .05
408 Jeff Innis RC .01 .05
409 Randy Kramer .01 .05
410 Charlie O'Brien .01 .05
411 Charlie Hough .02 .10
412 Gus Polidor .01 .05
413 Ron Karkovice .01 .05
414 Trevor Wilson .01 .05
415 Kevin Ritz RC .01 .05
416 Gary Thurman .01 .05
417 Jeff M. Robinson .01 .05
418 Scott Terry .01 .05
419 Tim Laudner .01 .05
420 Dennis Rasmussen .01 .05
421 Luis Rivera .01 .05
422 Jim Corsi .01 .05
423 Dennis Lamp .01 .05
424 Ken Caminiti .02 .10
425 David Wells .02 .10
426 Norm Charlton .01 .05
427 Deion Sanders .08 .25
428 Dion James .01 .05
429 Chuck Cary .01 .05
430 Ken Howell .01 .05
431 Steve Lake .01 .05
432 Kal Daniels .01 .05
433 Lance McCullers .01 .05
434 Lenny Harris .01 .05
435 Scott Scudder .01 .05
436 Gene Larkin .01 .05
437 Dan Quisenberry .01 .05
438 Steve Olin RC .08 .25
439 Mickey Hatcher .01 .05
440 Willie Wilson .01 .05
441 Mark Grant .01 .05
442 Mookie Wilson .02 .10
443 Alex Trevino .01 .05
444 Pat Tabler .01 .05
445 Dave Bergman .01 .05
446 Todd Burns .01 .05
447 R.J. Reynolds .01 .05
448 Jay Buhner .02 .10
449 Lee Stevens .02 .10
450 Ron Hassey .01 .05
451 Bob Melvin .01 .05
452 Dave Martinez .01 .05
453 Greg Litton .01 .05
454 Mark Carreon .01 .05
455 Scott Fletcher .01 .05
456 Otis Nixon .01 .05
457 Tony Fossas RC .01 .05
458 John Russell .01 .05
459 Paul Assenmacher .01 .05
460 Zane Smith .01 .05
461 Jack Daugherty RC .01 .05
462 Rich Monteleone .01 .05
463 Greg Briley .01 .05
464 Mike Smithson .01 .05
465 Benito Santiago .02 .10
466 Jeff Brantley .01 .05
467 Jose Nunez .01 .05
468 Scott Bailes .01 .05
469 Ken Griffey Sr. .02 .10
470 Bob McClure .01 .05
471 Mackey Sasser .01 .05
472 Glenn Wilson .01 .05
473 Kevin Tapani RC .08 .25
474 Bill Buckner .01 .05
475 Ron Gant .02 .10
476 Kevin Romine .01 .05
477 Juan Agosto .01 .05
478 Herm Winningham .01 .05
479 Storm Davis .01 .05
480 Jeff King .01 .05
481 Kevin Mmahat RC .01 .05
482 Carmelo Martinez .01 .05
483 Omar Vizquel .08 .25
484 Jim Dwyer .01 .05
485 Bob Knepper .01 .05
486 Dave Anderson .01 .05
487 Ron Jones .01 .05
488 Jay Bell .02 .10
489 Sammy Sosa RC 1.00 2.50
490 Kent Anderson .01 .05
491 Domingo Ramos .01 .05
492 Dave Clark .01 .05
493 Tim Birtsas .01 .05
494 Ken Oberkfell .01 .05
495 Larry Sheets .01 .05
496 Jeff Kunkel .01 .05
497 Jim Presley .01 .05
498 Mike Macfarlane .01 .05
499 Pete Smith .01 .05
500A Checklist 436-537 DP .01 .05
500B Checklist 420-517 .01 .05
501 Gary Sheffield .08 .25
502 Terry Bross RC .01 .05
503 Jerry Kutzler RC .01 .05
504 Lloyd Moseby .01 .05
505 Curt Young .01 .05
506 Al Newman .01 .05
507 Keith Miller .01 .05
508 Mike Stanton RC .08 .25
509 Rich Yett .01 .05
510 Tim Drummond RC .01 .05
511 Joe Hesketh .01 .05
512 Rick Wrona .01 .05
513 Luis Salazar .01 .05
514 Hal Morris .01 .05
515 Terry Mulholland .01 .05
516 John Morris .01 .05
517 Carlos Quintana .01 .05
518 Frank DiPino .01 .05
519 Randy Milligan .01 .05
520 Chad Kreuter .01 .05
521 Mike Jeffcoat .01 .05
522 Mike Harkey .01 .05
523A Andy Nezelek ERR (Wrong birth year) .01 .05
523B Andy Nezelek COR (Finally corrected in factory sets) .05 .15
524 Dave Schmidt .01 .05
525 Tony Armas .01 .05
526 Barry Lyons .01 .05
527 Rick Reed RC .08 .25
528 Jerry Reuss .01 .05
529 Dean Palmer RC .08 .25
530 Jeff Peterek RC .01 .05
531 Carlos Martinez .01 .05
532 Atlee Hammaker .01 .05
533 Mike Brumley .01 .05
534 Terry Leach .01 .05
535 Doug Strange RC .01 .05
536 Jose DeLeon .01 .05
537 Shane Rawley .01 .05
538 Joey Cora .02 .10
539 Eric Hetzel .01 .05
540 Gene Nelson .01 .05
541 Wes Gardner .01 .05
542 Mark Portugal .01 .05
543 Al Leiter .08 .25
544 Jack Armstrong .01 .05
545 Greg Cadaret .01 .05
546 Rod Nichols .01 .05
547 Luis Polonia .01 .05
548 Charlie Hayes .01 .05
549 Dickie Thon .01 .05
550 Tim Crews .01 .05
551 Dave Winfield .02 .10
552 Mike Davis .01 .05
553 Ron Robinson .01 .05
554 Carmen Castillo .01 .05
555 John Costello .01 .05
556 Bud Black .01 .05
557 Rick Dempsey .01 .05
558 Jim Acker .01 .05
559 Eric Show .01 .05
560 Pat Borders .01 .05
561 Danny Darwin .01 .05
562 Rick Luecken RC .01 .05
563 Edwin Nunez .01 .05
564 Felix Jose .01 .05
565 John Cangelosi .01 .05
566 Bill Swift .01 .05
567 Bill Schroeder .01 .05
568 Stan Javier .01 .05
569 Jim Traber .01 .05
570 Wallace Johnson .01 .05
571 Donell Nixon .01 .05
572 Sid Fernandez .01 .05
573 Lance Johnson .01 .05
574 Andy McGaffigan .01 .05
575 Mark Knudson .01 .05
576 Tommy Greene RC .02 .10
577 Mark Grace .05 .15
578 Larry Walker RC .40 1.00
579 Mike Stanley .01 .05
580 Mike Witt DP .01 .05
581 Scott Bradley .01 .05
582 Greg A. Harris .01 .05
583A Kevin Hickey ERR .08 .25
583B Kevin Hickey COR .01 .05
584 Lee Mazzilli .01 .05
585 Jeff Pico .01 .05
586 Joe Oliver .01 .05
587 Willie Fraser DP .01 .05
588 Carl Yastrzemski Puzzle Card DP .08 .25
589 Kevin Bass DP .01 .05
590 John Moses DP .01 .05
591 Tom Pagnozzi DP .01 .05
592 Tony Castillo DP .01 .05
593 Jerald Clark DP .01 .05
594 Dan Schatzeder .01 .05
595 Luis Quinones DP .01 .05
596 Pete Harnisch DP .01 .05
597 Gary Redus .01 .05
598 Mel Hall .01 .05
599 Rick Schu .01 .05
600A Checklist 538-639 .01 .05
600B Checklist 518-617 .01 .05
601 Mike Kingery DP .01 .05
602 Terry Kennedy DP .01 .05
603 Mike Sharperson DP .01 .05
604 Don Carman DP .01 .05
605 Jim Gott .01 .05
606 Donn Pall DP .01 .05
607 Rance Mulliniks .01 .05
608 Curt Wilkerson DP .01 .05
609 Mike Felder DP .01 .05
610 G.Hernandez DP .01 .05
611 Candy Maldonado DP .01 .05
612 Mark Thurmond DP .01 .05
613 Rick Leach DP RC .01 .05
614 Jerry Reed DP .01 .05
615 Franklin Stubbs .01 .05
616 Billy Hatcher DP .01 .05
617 Don August DP .01 .05
618 Tim Teufel .01 .05
619 Shawn Hillegas DP .01 .05
620 Manny Lee .01 .05
621 Gary Ward DP .01 .05
622 Mark Guthrie DP RC .01 .05
623 Jeff Musselman DP .01 .05
624 Mark Lemke DP .01 .05
625 Fernando Valenzuela .02 .10
626 Paul Sorrento DP RC .08 .25
627 Glenallen Hill DP .01 .05
628 Les Lancaster DP .01 .05
629 Vance Law DP .01 .05
630 Randy Velarde DP .01 .05
631 Todd Frohwirth DP .01 .05
632 Willie McGee .02 .10
633 Dennis Boyd DP .01 .05
634 Cris Carpenter DP .01 .05
635 Brian Holton .01 .05
636 Tracy Jones DP .01 .05
637A Terry Steinbach AS (Recent Major League Performance) .01 .05
637B Terry Steinbach AS (All-Star Game Performance) .01 .05
638 Brady Anderson .02 .10
639A Jack Morris ERR (Card front shows black line crossing J in Jack) .02 .10
639B Jack Morris COR .02 .10
640 Jaime Navarro .01 .05
641 Darrin Jackson .01 .05
642 Mike Dyer RC .01 .05
643 Mike Schmidt .20 .50
644 Henry Cotto .01 .05
645 John Cerutti .01 .05
646 Francisco Cabrera .01 .05
647 Scott Sanderson .01 .05
648 Brian Meyer .01 .05
649 Ray Searage .01 .05
650A Bo Jackson AS (Recent Major League Performance) .08 .25
650B Bo Jackson AS (All-Star Game Performance) .08 .25
651 Steve Lyons .01 .05
652 Mike LaCoss .01 .05
653 Ted Power .01 .05
654A Howard Johnson AS (Recent Major League Performance) .01 .05
654B Howard Johnson AS (All-Star Game Performance) .01 .05
655 Mauro Gozzo RC .01 .05
656 Mike Blowers RC .02 .10
657 Paul Gibson .01 .05
658 Neal Heaton .01 .05
659 Nolan Ryan 5000K COR (Still an error as Ryan did not lead AL in K's in '75) .20 .50
659A Nolan Ryan 5000K (665 King of Kings back) ERR .60 1.50
660A Harold Baines AS (Black line through star on front; Recent Major League Performance) .30 .75
660B Harold Baines AS (Black line through star on front; All-Star Game Performance) .40 1.00
660C Harold Baines AS (Black line behind star on front; Recent Major League Performance) .08 .25
660D Harold Baines AS (Black line behind star on front; All-Star Game Performance) .01 .05
661 Gary Pettis .01 .05
662 Clint Zavaras RC .01 .05
663A Rick Reuschel AS (Recent Major League Performance) .01 .05
663B Rick Reuschel AS (All-Star Game Performance) .01 .05
664 Alejandro Pena .01 .05
665 N.Ryan KING COR .20 .50
665A Nolan Ryan KING (659 5000 K back) ERR .60 1.50
665C N.Ryan KING ERR No number on back in factory sets .30 .75
666 Ricky Horton .01 .05
667 Curt Schilling .40 1.00
668 Bill Landrum .01 .05
669 Todd Stottlemyre .02 .10
670 Tim Leary .01 .05
671 John Wetteland .08 .25
672 Calvin Schiraldi .01 .05
673A Ruben Sierra AS (Recent Major League Performance) .01 .05
673B Ruben Sierra AS (All-Star Game Performance) .01 .05
674A Pedro Guerrero AS (Recent Major League Performance) .01 .05
674B Pedro Guerrero AS (All-Star Game Performance) .01 .05
675 Ken Phelps .01 .05
676A Cal Ripken AS (All-Star Game Performance) .15 .40
676B Cal Ripken AS (Recent Major League Performance) .30 .75
677 Denny Walling .01 .05
678 Goose Gossage .02 .10
679 Gary Mielke RC .01 .05
680 Bill Bathe .01 .05
681 Tom Lawless .01 .05
682 Xavier Hernandez RC .01 .05
683A Kirby Puckett AS (Recent Major League Performance) .05 .15
683B Kirby Puckett AS (All-Star Game Performance) .05 .15
684 Mariano Duncan .01 .05
685 Ramon Martinez .01 .05
686 Tim Jones .01 .05
687 Tom Filer .01 .05
688 Steve Lombardozzi .01 .05
689 Bernie Williams RC .60 1.50
690 Chip Hale RC .01 .05
691 Beau Allred RC .01 .05
692A Ryne Sandberg AS (Recent Major League Performance) .08 .25
692B Ryne Sandberg AS (All-Star Game Performance) .08 .25
693 Jeff Huson RC .02 .10
694 Curt Ford .01 .05
695A Eric Davis AS (Recent Major League Performance) .01 .05
695B Eric Davis AS (All-Star Game Performance) .01 .05
696 Scott Lusader .01 .05
697A Mark McGwire AS (Recent Major League Performance) .20 .50
697B Mark McGwire AS (All-Star Game Performance) .20 .50
698 Steve Cummings RC .01 .05
699 George Canale RC .01 .05
700A Checklist 640-715 and BC1-BC26 .08 .25
700B Checklist 640-716 and BC1-BC26 .02 .10
700C Checklist 618-716 .01 .05
701A Julio Franco AS (Recent Major League Performance) .01 .05
701B Julio Franco AS (All-Star Game Performance) .01 .05
702 Dave Wayne Johnson RC .01 .05
703A Dave Stewart AS (Recent Major League Performance) .01 .05
703B Dave Stewart AS (All-Star Game Performance) .01 .05
704 Dave Justice RC .20 .50
705 Tony Gwynn AS (All-Star Game Performance) .05 .15
705A Tony Gwynn AS (Recent Major League Performance) .05 .15
706 Greg Myers .01 .05
707A Will Clark AS (Recent Major League Performance) .05 .15
707B Will Clark AS (All-Star Game Performance) .05 .15
708A Benito Santiago AS (Recent Major League Performance) .01 .05
708B Benito Santiago AS (All-Star Game Performance) .01 .05
709 Larry McWilliams .01 .05
710A Ozzie Smith AS (Recent Major League Performance) .08 .25
710B Ozzie Smith AS Perf .08 .25
711 John Olerud RC .20 .50
712A Wade Boggs AS (Recent Major League Performance) .02 .10
712B Wade Boggs AS (All-Star Game Performance) .02 .10
713 Gary Eave RC .01 .05
714 Bob Tewksbury .01 .05
715A Kevin Mitchell AS (Recent Major League Performance) .01 .05
715B Kevin Mitchell AS (All-Star Game Performance) .01 .05
716 B.Giamatti COMM In Memoriam .08 .25

1990 Donruss Rookies

The 1990 Donruss Rookies set marked the fifth consecutive year that Donruss issued a boxed set at season's end honoring the best rookies of the season. This set, which used the 1990 Donruss design but featured a green border, was issued exclusively through the Donruss dealer network to hobby dealers. This 56-card, standard size set came in its own box and the words "The Rookies" are featured prominently on the front of the cards. There are no notable Rookie Cards in this set.

COMP.FACT.SET (56) .75 2.00
1 Sandy Alomar Jr. UER (No stitches on baseball on Donruss logo on card front) .02 .10
2 John Olerud .20 .50
3 Pat Combs .01 .05
4 Brian DuBois .01 .05
5 Felix Jose .01 .05
6 Delino DeShields .08 .25
7 Mike Stanton .01 .05
8 Mike Munoz RC .01 .05
9 Craig Grebeck RC .02 .10
10 Joe Kraemer RC .01 .05
11 Jeff Huson .01 .05
12 Bill Sampen RC .01 .05
13 Brian Bohanon RC .02 .10
14 Dave Justice .20 .50
15 Robin Ventura .08 .25
16 Greg Vaughn .01 .05
17 Wayne Edwards RC .01 .05
18 Shawn Boskie RC .02 .10
19 Carlos Baerga RC .08 .25
20 Mark Gardner .01 .05
21 Kevin Appier .02 .10
22 Mike Harkey .01 .05
23 Tim Layana RC .01 .05
24 Glenallen Hill .01 .05
25 Jerry Kutzler .01 .05
26 Mike Blowers .02 .10
27 Scott Ruskin RC .01 .05
28 Dana Kiecker RC .01 .05
29 Willie Blair RC .02 .10
30 Ben McDonald .01 .05
31 Todd Zeile .02 .10
32 Scott Coolbaugh RC .01 .05
33 Xavier Hernandez .01 .05
34 Mike Hartley RC .01 .05
35 Kevin Tapani .08 .25
36 Kevin Wickander .01 .05
37 Carlos Hernandez RC .08 .25
38 Brian Traxler RC .02 .10
39 Marty Brown .01 .05
40 Scott Radinsky RC .02 .10
41 Julio Machado .01 .05
42 Steve Avery .01 .05
43 Mark Lemke .01 .05
44 Alan Mills RC .02 .10
45 Marquis Grissom .08 .25
46 Greg Olson (C) RC .02 .10
47 Dave Hollins RC .08 .25
48 Jerald Clark .01 .05
49 Eric Anthony .01 .05
50 Tim Drummond .01 .05
51 John Burkett .01 .05
52 Brent Knackert RC .02 .10
53 Jeff Shaw .01 .05
54 John Orton RC .02 .10
55 Terry Shumpert RC .01 .05
56 Checklist 1-56 .01 .05

1991 Donruss

The 1991 Donruss set was issued in two series of 386 and 384 for a total of 770 standard-size cards. This set marked the first time Donruss issued cards in multiple series. The second series was issued approximately three months after the first series was issued. Cards were issued in wax packs and factory sets. As a separate promotion, wax packs were also given away with six and 12-packs of Coke and Diet Coke. First series cards feature blue borders and second series green borders with some stripes and the players name in white against a red background. Subsets include Diamond Kings (1-27), Rated Rookies (28-47/413-432), AL All-Stars (48-56), MVP's (387-412) and NL All-Stars (433-441). There were also special cards to honor the award winners and the heroes of the World Series. On cards 60, 70, 127, 182, 239, 294, 355, 368, and 377, the border stripes are red and yellow. There are no notable Rookie Cards in this set.

COMPLETE SET (770) 3.00 8.00
COMP.FACT.w/LEAF PREV 4.00 10.00
COMP.FACT.w/STUD. PREV 4.00 10.00
COMP.STARGELL PUZZLE .40 1.00
1 Dave Stieb DK .01 .05
2 Craig Biggio DK .02 .10
3 Cecil Fielder DK .01 .05
4 Barry Bonds DK .20 .50
5 Barry Larkin DK .02 .10
6 Dave Parker DK .01 .05
7 Len Dykstra DK .01 .05
8 Bobby Thigpen DK .01 .05
9 Roger Clemens DK .15 .40
10 Ron Gant DK UER .02 .10
(No trademark on
team logo on back)
11 Delino DeShields DK .01 .05
12 Roberto Alomar DK UER .02 .10
No trademark on
team logo on back
13 Sandy Alomar Jr. DK .01 .05
14 Ryne Sandberg DK UER .08 .25
Was DK in '85, not
'83 as shown
15 Ramon Martinez DK .01 .05
16 Edgar Martinez DK .05 .15
17 Dave Magadan DK .01 .05
18 Matt Williams DK .01 .05
19 Rafael Palmeiro DK .02 .10
UER (No trademark on
team logo on back)
20 Bob Welch DK .01 .05
21 Dave Righetti DK .01 .05
22 Brian Harper DK .01 .05
23 Gregg Olson DK .01 .05
24 Kurt Stillwell DK .01 .05
25 Pedro Guerrero DK UER .01 .05
No trademark on
team logo on back
26 Chuck Finley DK UER .02 .10
(No trademark on
team logo on back)
27 DK Checklist 1-27 .01 .05
28 Tino Martinez RR .08 .25
29 Mark Lewis RR .01 .05
30 Bernard Gilkey RR .01 .05
31 Hensley Meulens RR .01 .05
32 Derek Bell RR .02 .10
33 Jose Offerman RR .01 .05
34 Terry Bross RR .01 .05
35 Leo Gomez RR .01 .05
36 Derrick May RR .01 .05
37 Kevin Morton RR RC .01 .05
38 Moises Alou RR .02 .10
39 Julio Valera RR .01 .05
40 Milt Cuyler RR .01 .05
41 Phil Plantier RR RC .08 .25
42 Scott Chiamparino RR .01 .05
43 Ray Lankford RR .02 .10
44 Mickey Morandini RR .01 .05
45 Dave Hansen RR .01 .05
46 Kevin Belcher RR RC .01 .05
47 Darrin Fletcher RR .01 .05
48 Steve Sax AS .01 .05
49 Ken Griffey Jr. AS .08 .25
50A J.Canseco AS ERR .02 .10
Team in stat box
should be AL, not A's
50B J.Canseco AS COR .05 .15
51 Sandy Alomar Jr. AS .01 .05
52 Cal Ripken AS .15 .40
53 Rickey Henderson AS .05 .15
54 Bob Welch AS .01 .05
55 Wade Boggs AS .02 .10
56 Mark McGwire AS .15 .40
57A Jack McDowell ERR .08 .25
(Career stats do
not include 1990)
57B Jack McDowell COR .20 .50
(Career stats do
not include 1990)
58 Jose Lind .01 .05
59 Alex Fernandez .01 .05
60 Pat Combs .01 .05
61 Mike Walker .01 .05
62 Juan Samuel .01 .05
63 Mike Blowers UER .01 .05
(Last line has
aseball, not baseball)
64 Mark Guthrie .01 .05
65 Mark Salas .01 .05
66 Tim Jones .01 .05
67 Tim Leary .01 .05
68 Andres Galarraga .02 .10
69 Bob Milacki .01 .05
70 Tim Belcher .01 .05
71 Todd Zeile .01 .05
72 Jerome Walton .01 .05
73 Kevin Seitzer .01 .05
74 Jerald Clark .01 .05
75 John Smoltz UER .05 .15
(Born in Detroit,
not Warren)
76 Mike Henneman .01 .05
77 Ken Griffey Jr. .20 .50
78 Jim Abbott .05 .15
79 Gregg Jefferies .01 .05
80 Kevin Reimer .01 .05
81 Roger Clemens .30 .75
82 Mike Fitzgerald .01 .05
83 Bruce Hurst UER .01 .05
(Middle name is
Lee, not Vee)
84 Eric Davis .02 .10
85 Paul Molitor .02 .10
86 Will Clark .05 .15
87 Mike Bielecki .01 .05
88 Bret Saberhagen .02 .10
89 Nolan Ryan .40 1.00
90 Bobby Thigpen .01 .05
91 Dickie Thon .01 .05
92 Duane Ward .01 .05
93 Luis Polonia .01 .05
94 Terry Kennedy .01 .05
95 Kent Hrbek .02 .10
96 Danny Jackson .01 .05
97 Sid Fernandez .01 .05
98 Jimmy Key .02 .10
99 Franklin Stubbs .01 .05
100 Checklist 28-103 .01 .05
101 R.J. Reynolds .01 .05
102 Dave Stewart .02 .10
103 Dan Pasqua .01 .05
104 Dan Plesac .01 .05
105 Mark McGwire .30 .75
106 John Farrell .01 .05
107 Don Mattingly .25 .60
108 Carlton Fisk .05 .15
109 Ken Oberkfell .01 .05
110 Darrel Akerfelds .01 .05
111 Gregg Olson .01 .05
112 Mike Scioscia .01 .05
113 Bryn Smith .01 .05
114 Bob Geren .01 .05
115 Tom Candiotti .01 .05
116 Kevin Tapani .01 .05
117 Jeff Treadway .01 .05
118 Alan Trammell .02 .10
119 Pete O'Brien UER .01 .05
(Blue shading goes
through stats)
120 Joel Skinner .01 .05
121 Mike LaValliere .01 .05
122 Dwight Evans .05 .15
123 Jody Reed .01 .05
124 Lee Guetterman .01 .05
125 Tim Burke .01 .05
126 Dave Johnson .01 .05
127 Fernando Valenzuela UER .02 .10
(Lower large stripe
in yellow instead
of blue)
128 Jose DeLeon .01 .05
129 Andre Dawson .02 .10
130 Gerald Perry .01 .05
131 Greg W. Harris .01 .05
132 Tom Glavine .05 .15
133 Lance McCullers .01 .05
134 Randy Johnson .10 .30
135 Lance Parrish UER .02 .10
(Born in McKeesport,
not Clairton)
136 Mackey Sasser .01 .05
137 Geno Petralli .01 .05
138 Dennis Lamp .01 .05
139 Dennis Martinez .02 .10
140 Mike Pagliarulo .01 .05
141 Hal Morris .01 .05
142 Dave Parker .02 .10
143 Brett Butler .02 .10
144 Paul Assenmacher .01 .05
145 Mark Gubicza .01 .05
146 Charlie Hough .02 .10
147 Sammy Sosa .08 .25
148 Randy Ready .01 .05
149 Kelly Gruber .01 .05
150 Devon White .02 .10
151 Gary Carter .02 .10
152 Gene Larkin .01 .05
153 Chris Sabo .01 .05
154 David Cone .02 .10
155 Todd Stottlemyre .01 .05
156 Glenn Wilson .01 .05
157 Bob Walk .01 .05
158 Mike Gallego .01 .05
159 Greg Hibbard .01 .05
160 Chris Bosio .01 .05
161 Mike Moore .01 .05
162 Jerry Browne UER .01 .05
(Born Christiansted,
should be St. Croix)
163 Steve Sax UER .01 .05
(No asterisk next to
his 1989 At Bats)
164 Melido Perez .01 .05
165 Danny Darwin .01 .05
166 Roger McDowell .01 .05
167 Bill Ripken .01 .05
168 Mike Sharperson .01 .05
169 Lee Smith .02 .10
170 Matt Nokes .01 .05
171 Jesse Orosco .01 .05
172 Rick Aguilera .02 .10
173 Jim Presley .01 .05
174 Lou Whitaker .02 .10
175 Harold Reynolds .02 .10
176 Brook Jacoby .01 .05
177 Wally Backman .01 .05
178 Wade Boggs .05 .15
179 Chuck Cary UER .01 .05
(Comma after DOB,
not on other cards)
180 Tom Foley .01 .05
181 Pete Harnisch .01 .05
182 Mike Morgan .01 .05
183 Bob Tewksbury .01 .05
184 Joe Girardi .01 .05
185 Storm Davis .01 .05
186 Ed Whitson .01 .05
187 Steve Avery UER .01 .05
(Born in New Jersey,
should be Michigan)
188 Lloyd Moseby .01 .05
189 Scott Bankhead .01 .05
190 Mark Langston .01 .05
191 Kevin McReynolds .01 .05
192 Julio Franco .02 .10
193 John Dopson .01 .05
194 Dennis Boyd .01 .05
195 Bip Roberts .01 .05
196 Billy Hatcher .01 .05
197 Edgar Diaz .01 .05
198 Greg Litton .01 .05
199 Mark Grace .05 .15
200 Checklist 104-179 .01 .05
201 George Brett .25 .60
202 Jeff Russell .01 .05
203 Ivan Calderon .01 .05
204 Ken Howell .01 .05
205 Tom Henke .01 .05
206 Bryan Harvey .01 .05
207 Steve Bedrosian .01 .05
208 Al Newman .01 .05
209 Randy Myers .01 .05
210 Daryl Boston .01 .05
211 Manny Lee .01 .05
212 Dave Smith .01 .05
213 Don Slaught .01 .05
214 Walt Weiss .01 .05
215 Donn Pall .01 .05
216 Jaime Navarro .01 .05
217 Willie Randolph .02 .10
218 Rudy Seanez .01 .05
219 Jim Leyritz .01 .05
220 Ron Karkovice .01 .05
221 Ken Caminiti .02 .10
222 Von Hayes .01 .05
223 Cal Ripken .30 .75
224 Lenny Harris .01 .05
225 Milt Thompson .01 .05
226 Alvaro Espinoza .01 .05
227 Chris James .01 .05
228 Dan Gladden .01 .05
229 Jeff Blauser .01 .05
230 Mike Heath .01 .05
231 Omar Vizquel .05 .15
232 Doug Jones .01 .05
233 Jeff King .01 .05
234 Luis Rivera .01 .05
235 Ellis Burks .02 .10
236 Greg Cadaret .01 .05
237 Dave Martinez .01 .05
238 Mark Williamson .01 .05
239 Stan Javier .01 .05
240 Ozzie Smith .15 .40
241 Shawn Boskie .01 .05
242 Tom Gordon .01 .05
243 Tony Gwynn .10 .30
244 Tommy Gregg .01 .05
245 Jeff M. Robinson .01 .05
246 Keith Comstock .01 .05
247 Jack Howell .01 .05
248 Keith Miller .01 .05
249 Bobby Witt .01 .05
250 Rob Murphy UER .01 .05
(Shown as on Reds
in '89 in stats,
should be Red Sox)
251 Spike Owen .01 .05
252 Garry Templeton .01 .05
253 Glenn Braggs .01 .05
254 Ron Robinson .01 .05
255 Kevin Mitchell .01 .05
256 Les Lancaster .01 .05
257 Mel Stottlemyre Jr. .01 .05
258 Kenny Rogers UER .02 .10
(IP listed as 171,
should be 172)
259 Lance Johnson .01 .05
260 John Kruk .02 .10
261 Fred McGriff .05 .15
262 Dick Schofield .01 .05
263 Trevor Wilson .01 .05
264 David West .01 .05
265 Scott Scudder .01 .05
266 Dwight Gooden .02 .10
267 Willie Blair .01 .05
268 Mark Portugal .01 .05
269 Doug Drabek .01 .05
270 Dennis Eckersley .02 .10
271 Eric King .01 .05
272 Robin Yount .15 .40
273 Carney Lansford .02 .10
274 Carlos Baerga .01 .05
275 Dave Righetti .02 .10
276 Scott Fletcher .01 .05
277 Eric Yelding .01 .05
278 Charlie Hayes .01 .05
279 Jeff Ballard .01 .05
280 Orel Hershiser .02 .10
281 Jose Oquendo .01 .05
282 Mike Witt .01 .05
283 Mitch Webster .01 .05
284 Greg Gagne .01 .05
285 Greg Olson .01 .05
286 Tony Phillips UER .01 .05
(Born 4/15
should be 4/25)
287 Scott Bradley .01 .05
288 Cory Snyder UER .01 .05
(In text, led is repeated
Inglewood is misspelled as Englewood)
289 Jay Bell UER .02 .10
(Born in Pensacola,
not Eglin AFB)
290 Kevin Romine .01 .05
291 Jeff D. Robinson .01 .05
292 Steve Frey UER .01 .05
(Bats left,
should be right)
293 Craig Worthington .01 .05
294 Tim Crews .01 .05
295 Joe Magrane .01 .05
296 Hector Villanueva .01 .05
297 Terry Shumpert .01 .05
298 Joe Carter .02 .10
299 Kent Mercker UER .01 .05
(IP listed as 53,
should be 52)
300 Checklist 180-255 .01 .05
301 Chet Lemon .01 .05
302 Mike Schooler .01 .05
303 Dante Bichette .02 .10
304 Kevin Elster .01 .05
305 Jeff Huson .01 .05
306 Greg A. Harris .01 .05
307 Marquis Grissom UER .02 .10
(Middle name Deon,
should be Dean)
308 Calvin Schiraldi .01 .05
309 Mariano Duncan .01 .05
310 Bill Spiers .01 .05
311 Scott Garrelts .01 .05
312 Mitch Williams .01 .05
313 Mike Macfarlane .01 .05
314 Kevin Brown .02 .10
315 Robin Ventura .02 .10
316 Darren Daulton .02 .10
317 Pat Borders .01 .05
318 Mark Eichhorn .01 .05
319 Jeff Brantley .01 .05
320 Shane Mack .01 .05
321 Rob Dibble .02 .10
322 John Franco .02 .10
323 Junior Felix .01 .05
324 Casey Candaele .01 .05
325 Bobby Bonilla .02 .10
326 Dave Henderson .01 .05
327 Wayne Edwards .01 .05
328 Mark Knudson .01 .05
329 Terry Steinbach .01 .05
330 Colby Ward UER RC .01 .05
(No comma between
city and state)
331 Oscar Azocar .01 .05
332 Scott Radinsky .01 .05
333 Eric Anthony .01 .05
334 Steve Lake .01 .05
335 Bob Melvin .01 .05
336 Kal Daniels .01 .05
337 Tom Pagnozzi .01 .05
338 Alan Mills .01 .05
339 Steve Olin .01 .05
340 Juan Berenguer .01 .05
341 Francisco Cabrera .01 .05
342 Dave Bergman .01 .05
343 Henry Cotto .01 .05
344 Sergio Valdez .01 .05
345 Bob Patterson .01 .05
346 John Marzano .01 .05
347 Dana Kiecker .01 .05
348 Dion James .01 .05
349 Hubie Brooks .01 .05
350 Bill Landrum .01 .05
351 Bill Sampen .01 .05
352 Greg Briley .01 .05
353 Paul Gibson .01 .05
354 Dave Eiland .01 .05
355 Steve Finley .02 .10
356 Bob Boone .02 .10
357 Steve Buechele .01 .05
358 Chris Hoiles .01 .05
359 Larry Walker .08 .25
360 Frank DiPino .01 .05
361 Mark Grant .01 .05
362 Dave Magadan .01 .05
363 Robby Thompson .01 .05
364 Lonnie Smith .01 .05
365 Steve Farr .01 .05
366 Dave Valle .01 .05
367 Tim Naehring .01 .05
368 Jim Acker .01 .05
369 Jeff Reardon UER .02 .10
(Born in Pittsfield,
not Dalton)
370 Tim Teufel .01 .05
371 Juan Gonzalez .08 .25
372 Luis Salazar .01 .05
373 Rick Honeycutt .01 .05
374 Greg Maddux .15 .40
375 Jose Uribe UER .01 .05
(Middle name Elta,
should be Alta)
376 Donnie Hill .01 .05
377 Don Carman .01 .05
378 Craig Grebeck .01 .05
379 Willie Fraser .01 .05
380 Glenallen Hill .01 .05
381 Joe Oliver .01 .05
382 Randy Bush .01 .05
383 Alex Cole .01 .05
384 Norm Charlton .01 .05
385 Gene Nelson .01 .05
386 Checklist 256-331 .01 .05
387 R. Henderson MVP .05 .15
388 Lance Parrish MVP .02 .10
389 Fred McGriff MVP .02 .10
390 Dave Parker MVP .01 .05
391 C. Maldonado MVP .01 .05
392 Ken Griffey Jr. MVP .08 .25
393 Gregg Olson MVP .01 .05
394 Rafael Palmeiro MVP .02 .10
395 Roger Clemens MVP .15 .40
396 George Brett MVP .08 .25
397 Cecil Fielder MVP .01 .05
398 Brian Harper MVP .01 .05
UER Major
League Performance,
should be Career
399 Bobby Thigpen MVP .01 .05
400 Roberto Kelly MVP .01 .05
UER (Second Base on
front and OF on back)
401 Danny Darwin MVP .01 .05
402 Dave Justice MVP .01 .05
403 Lee Smith MVP .01 .05
404 Ryne Sandberg MVP .08 .25
405 Eddie Murray MVP .05 .15
406 Tim Wallach MVP .01 .05
407 Kevin Mitchell MVP .01 .05
408 D. Strawberry MVP .01 .05
409 Joe Carter MVP .01 .05
410 Len Dykstra MVP .01 .05
411 Doug Drabek MVP .01 .05
412 Chris Sabo MVP .01 .05
413 Paul Marak RR RC .01 .05
414 Tim McIntosh RR .01 .05
415 Brian Barnes RR RC .02 .10
416 Eric Gunderson RR .01 .05
417 Mike Gardiner RR RC .01 .05
418 Steve Carter RR .01 .05
419 Gerald Alexander RR RC .01 .05
420 Rich Garces RR RC .02 .10
421 Chuck Knoblauch RR .02 .10
422 Scott Aldred RR .01 .05
423 W.Chamberlain RR RC .08 .25
424 Lance Dickson RR RC .02 .10
425 Greg Colbrunn RR RC .08 .25
426 Rich DeLucia RR UER RC .01 .05
(Misspelled Delucia
on card)
427 Jeff Conine RR RC .15 .40
428 Steve Decker RR RC .01 .05
429 Turner Ward RR RC .08 .25
430 Mo Vaughn RR .02 .10
431 Steve Chitren RR RC .01 .05
432 Mike Benjamin RR .01 .05
433 Ryne Sandberg AS .08 .25
434 Len Dykstra AS .01 .05
435 Andre Dawson AS .01 .05
436A Mike Scioscia AS .01 .05
(White star by name)
436B Mike Scioscia AS .01 .05
(Yellow star by name)
437 Ozzie Smith AS .08 .25
438 Kevin Mitchell AS .01 .05
439 Jack Armstrong AS .01 .05
440 Chris Sabo AS .01 .05
441 Will Clark AS .02 .10
442 Mel Hall .01 .05
443 Mark Gardner .01 .05
444 Mike Devereaux .01 .05
445 Kirk Gibson .02 .10
446 Terry Pendleton .02 .10
447 Mike Harkey .01 .05
448 Jim Eisenreich .01 .05
449 Benito Santiago .02 .10
450 Oddibe McDowell .01 .05
451 Cecil Fielder .02 .10
452 Ken Griffey Sr. .02 .10
453 Bert Blyleven .02 .10
454 Howard Johnson .01 .05
455 Monty Fariss UER .01 .05
(Misspelled Farris
on card)
456 Tony Pena .01 .05
457 Tim Raines .02 .10
458 Dennis Rasmussen .01 .05
459 Luis Quinones .01 .05
460 B.J. Surhoff .02 .10
461 Ernest Riles .01 .05
462 Rick Sutcliffe .02 .10
463 Danny Tartabull .01 .05
464 Pete Incaviglia .01 .05
465 Carlos Martinez .01 .05
466 Ricky Jordan .01 .05
467 John Cerutti .01 .05
468 Dave Winfield .02 .10
469 Francisco Oliveras .01 .05
470 Roy Smith .01 .05
471 Barry Larkin .05 .15
472 Ron Darling .01 .05
473 David Wells .02 .10
474 Glenn Davis .01 .05
475 Neal Heaton .01 .05
476 Ron Hassey .01 .05
477 Frank Thomas .08 .25
478 Greg Vaughn .01 .05
479 Todd Burns .01 .05
480 Candy Maldonado .01 .05
481 Dave LaPoint .01 .05
482 Alvin Davis .01 .05
483 Mike Scott .01 .05
484 Dale Murphy .05 .15
485 Ben McDonald .01 .05
486 Jay Howell .01 .05
487 Vince Coleman .01 .05
488 Alfredo Griffin .01 .05
489 Sandy Alomar Jr. .01 .05
490 Kirby Puckett .08 .25
491 Andres Thomas .01 .05
492 Jack Morris .02 .10
493 Matt Young .01 .05
494 Greg Myers .01 .05
495 Barry Bonds .40 1.00
496 Scott Cooper UER .01 .05
(No BA for 1990
and career)
497 Dan Schatzeder .01 .05
498 Jesse Barfield .01 .05
499 Jerry Goff .01 .05
500 Checklist 332-408 .01 .05
501 Anthony Telford RC .01 .05
502 Eddie Murray .08 .25
503 Omar Olivares RC .08 .25
504 Ryne Sandberg .15 .40
505 Jeff Montgomery .01 .05
506 Mark Parent .01 .05
507 Ron Gant .02 .10
508 Frank Tanana .01 .05
509 Jay Buhner .02 .10
510 Max Venable .01 .05
511 Wally Whitehurst .01 .05
512 Gary Pettis .01 .05
513 Tom Brunansky .01 .05
514 Tim Wallach .01 .05
515 Craig Lefferts .01 .05
516 Tim Layana .01 .05
517 Darryl Hamilton .01 .05
518 Rick Reuschel .01 .05
519 Steve Wilson .01 .05
520 Kurt Stillwell .01 .05
521 Rafael Palmeiro .05 .15
522 Ken Patterson .01 .05
523 Len Dykstra .02 .10
524 Tony Fernandez .01 .05
525 Kent Anderson .01 .05
526 Mark Leonard RC .01 .05
527 Allan Anderson .01 .05
528 Tom Browning .01 .05
529 Frank Viola .02 .10
530 John Olerud .02 .10
531 Juan Agosto .01 .05
532 Zane Smith .01 .05
533 Scott Sanderson .01 .05
534 Barry Jones .01 .05
535 Mike Felder .01 .05
536 Jose Canseco .05 .15
537 Felix Fermin .01 .05
538 Roberto Kelly .01 .05
539 Brian Holman .01 .05
540 Mark Davidson .01 .05
541 Terry Mulholland .01 .05
542 Randy Milligan .01 .05
543 Jose Gonzalez .01 .05
544 Craig Wilson RC .01 .05
545 Mike Hartley .01 .05
546 Greg Swindell .01 .05
547 Gary Gaetti .02 .10
548 Dave Justice .02 .10
549 Steve Searcy .01 .05
550 Erik Hanson .01 .05
551 Dave Stieb .01 .05
552 Andy Van Slyke .05 .15
553 Mike Greenwell .01 .05
554 Kevin Maas .01 .05
555 Delino DeShields .02 .10
556 Curt Schilling .08 .25
557 Ramon Martinez .01 .05
558 Pedro Guerrero .02 .10
559 Dwight Smith .01 .05
560 Mark Davis .01 .05
561 Shawn Abner .01 .05
562 Charlie Leibrandt .01 .05
563 John Shelby .01 .05
564 Bill Swift .01 .05
565 Mike Fetters .01 .05
566 Alejandro Pena .01 .05
567 Ruben Sierra .02 .10
568 Carlos Quintana .01 .05
569 Kevin Gross .01 .05
570 Derek Lilliquist .01 .05
571 Jack Armstrong .01 .05
572 Greg Brock .01 .05
573 Mike Kingery .01 .05
574 Greg Smith .01 .05
575 Brian McRae RC .08 .25
576 Jack Daugherty .01 .05
577 Ozzie Guillen .02 .10
578 Joe Boever .01 .05
579 Luis Sojo .01 .05
580 Chili Davis .02 .10
581 Don Robinson .01 .05
582 Brian Harper .01 .05
583 Paul O'Neill .05 .15
584 Bob Ojeda .01 .05
585 Mookie Wilson .02 .10
586 Rafael Ramirez .01 .05
587 Gary Redus .01 .05
588 Jamie Quirk .01 .05
589 Shawn Hillegas .01 .05
590 Tom Edens RC .01 .05
591 Joe Klink .01 .05
592 Charles Nagy .01 .05
593 Eric Plunk .01 .05
594 Tracy Jones .01 .05
595 Craig Biggio .05 .15
596 Jose DeJesus .01 .05
597 Mickey Tettleton .01 .05
598 Chris Gwynn .01 .05
599 Rex Hudler .01 .05
600 Checklist 409-506 .01 .05
601 Jim Gott .01 .05
602 Jeff Manto .01 .05
603 Nelson Liriano .01 .05
604 Mark Lemke .01 .05
605 Clay Parker .01 .05
606 Edgar Martinez .05 .15
607 Mark Whiten .01 .05
608 Ted Power .01 .05
609 Tom Bolton .01 .05
610 Tom Herr .01 .05
611 Andy Hawkins UER .01 .05
Pitched No-Hitter
on 7/1, not 7/2
612 Scott Ruskin .01 .05
613 Ron Kittle .01 .05
614 John Wetteland .02 .10
615 Mike Perez RC .02 .10
616 Dave Clark .01 .05
617 Brent Mayne .01 .05
618 Jack Clark .02 .10
619 Marvin Freeman .01 .05
620 Edwin Nunez .01 .05
621 Russ Swan .01 .05
622 Johnny Ray .01 .05
623 Charlie O'Brien .01 .05
624 Joe Bitker RC .01 .05
625 Mike Marshall .01 .05
626 Otis Nixon .01 .05
627 Andy Benes .01 .05
628 Ron Oester .01 .05
629 Ted Higuera .01 .05
630 Kevin Bass .01 .05
631 Damon Berryhill .01 .05
632 Bo Jackson .08 .25
633 Brad Arnsberg .01 .05
634 Jerry Willard .01 .05
635 Tommy Greene .01 .05
636 Bob MacDonald RC .01 .05
637 Kirk McCaskill .01 .05
638 John Burkett .01 .05
639 Paul Abbott RC .01 .05
640 Todd Benzinger .01 .05
641 Todd Hundley .01 .05
642 George Bell .01 .05
643 Javier Ortiz .01 .05
644 Sid Bream .01 .05
645 Bob Welch .01 .05
646 Phil Bradley .01 .05
647 Bill Krueger .01 .05
648 Rickey Henderson .08 .25
649 Kevin Wickander .01 .05
650 Steve Balboni .01 .05
651 Gene Harris .01 .05
652 Jim Deshaies .01 .05
653 Jason Grimsley .01 .05
654 Joe Orsulak .01 .05
655 Jim Poole .01 .05
656 Felix Jose .01 .05
657 Denis Cook .01 .05
658 Tom Brookens .01 .05
659 Junior Ortiz .01 .05
660 Jeff Parrett .01 .05
661 Jerry Don Gleaton .01 .05
662 Brent Knackert .01 .05
663 Rance Mulliniks .01 .05
664 John Smiley .01 .05
665 Larry Andersen .01 .05
666 Willie McGee .02 .10
667 Chris Nabholz .01 .05
668 Brady Anderson .02 .10
669 Darren Holmes UER RC .08 .25
19 CG's, should be 0)
670 Ken Hill .01 .05
671 Gary Varsho .01 .05
672 Bill Pecota .01 .05
673 Fred Lynn .01 .05
674 Kevin D. Brown .01 .05
675 Dan Petry .01 .05
676 Mike Jackson .01 .05
677 Wally Joyner .02 .10
678 Danny Jackson .01 .05
679 Bill Haselman RC .01 .05
680 Mike Boddicker .01 .05
681 Mel Rojas .01 .05
682 Roberto Alomar .05 .15
683 Dave Justice ROY .02 .10
684 Chuck Crim .01 .05
685 Matt Williams .02 .10
686 Shawon Dunston .01 .05
687 Jeff Schulz RC .01 .05
688 John Barfield .01 .05
689 Gerald Young .01 .05
690 Luis Gonzalez RC .20 .50
691 Frank Wills .01 .05
692 Chuck Finley .02 .10
693 S.Alomar Jr. ROY .01 .05
694 Tim Drummond .01 .05
695 Herm Winningham .01 .05
696 Darryl Strawberry .02 .10

697 Al Leiter .02 .10
698 Karl Rhodes .01 .05
699 Stan Belinda .01 .05
700 Checklist 507-604 .01 .05
701 Lance Blankenship .01 .05
702 Willie Stargell PUZ .05 .15
703 Jim Gantner .01 .05
704 Reggie Harris .01 .05
705 Rob Ducey .01 .05
706 Tim Hulett .01 .05
707 Atlee Hammaker .01 .05
708 Xavier Hernandez .01 .05
709 Chuck McElroy .01 .05
710 John Mitchell .01 .05
711 Carlos Hernandez .01 .05
712 Geronimo Pena .01 .05
713 Jim Neidlinger RC .01 .05
714 John Orton .01 .05
715 Terry Leach .01 .05
716 Mike Stanton .01 .05
717 Walt Terrell .01 .05
718 Luis Aquino .01 .05
719 Bud Black UER .01 .05
(Blue Jays uniform, but Giants logo)
720 Bob Kipper .01 .05
721 Jeff Gray RC .01 .05
722 Jose Rijo .01 .05
723 Curt Young .01 .05
724 Jose Vizcaino .01 .05
725 Randy Tomlin RC .02 .10
726 Junior Noboa .01 .05
727 Bob Welch CY .01 .05
728 Gary Ward .01 .05
729 Rob Deer UER .01 .05
(Brewers uniform, but Tigers logo)
730 David Segui .01 .05
731 Mark Carreon .01 .05
732 Vicente Palacios .01 .05
733 Sam Horn .01 .05
734 Howard Farmer .01 .05
735 Ken Dayley UER .01 .05
(Cardinals uniform, but Blue Jays logo)
736 Kelly Mann .01 .05
737 Joe Grahe RC .02 .10
738 Kelly Downs .01 .05
739 Jimmy Kremers .01 .05
740 Kevin Appier .02 .10
741 Jeff Reed .01 .05
742 Jose Rijo WS .01 .05
743 Dave Rohde .01 .05
744 Len Dykstra .05 .15
Dale Murphy
UER (No '91 Donruss logo on card front)
745 Paul Sorrento .01 .05
746 Thomas Howard .01 .05
747 Matt Stark RC .01 .05
748 Harold Baines .02 .10
749 Doug Dascenzo .01 .05
750 Doug Drabek CY .01 .05
751 Gary Sheffield .02 .10
752 Terry Lee RC .01 .05
753 Jim Vatcher RC .01 .05
754 Lee Stevens .01 .05
755 Randy Veres .01 .05
756 Bill Doran .01 .05
757 Gary Wayne .01 .05
758 Pedro Munoz RC .02 .10
759 Chris Hammond .01 .05
760 Checklist 605-702 .01 .05
761 R.Henderson MVP .05 .15
762 Barry Bonds MVP .20 .50
763 Billy Hatcher WS .01 .05
UER (Line 13, on should be one)
764 Julio Machado .01 .05
765 Jose Mesa .01 .05
766 Willie Randolph WS .01 .05
767 Scott Erickson .01 .05
768 Travis Fryman .02 .10
769 Rich Rodriguez RC .01 .05
770 Checklist 703-770/BC1-BC22 .01 .05

1991 Donruss Rookies

The 56-card 1991 Donruss Rookies set was issued exclusively in factory set form through hobby dealers. The cards measure the standard size and a mini puzzle featuring Hall of Famer Willie Stargell was included with the set. The fronts feature color action player photos, with white and red borders. Rookie Cards include Jeff Bagwell and Ivan Rodriguez.

COMP.FACT.SET (56) 2.00 5.00
1 Pat Kelly RC .02 .10
2 Rich DeLucia .02 .10
3 Wes Chamberlain .02 .10
4 Scott Leius .02 .10
5 Darryl Kile .08 .25
6 Milt Cuyler .02 .10
7 Todd Van Poppel RC .02 .10
8 Ray Lankford .08 .25
9 Brian R. Hunter RC .08 .25
10 Tony Perezchica .02 .10
11 Ced Landrum RC .02 .10
12 Dave Burba RC .08 .25
13 Ramon Garcia RC .02 .10
14 Ed Sprague .02 .10
15 Warren Newson RC .02 .10
16 Paul Faries RC .02 .10
17 Luis Gonzalez .20 .50
18 Charles Nagy .02 .10
19 Chris Hammond .02 .10
20 Frank Castillo RC .08 .25
21 Pedro Munoz .02 .10
22 Orlando Merced RC .02 .10
23 Jose Melendez RC .02 .10
24 Kirk Dressendorfer RC .02 .10
25 Heathcliff Slocumb RC .08 .25
26 Doug Simons RC .02 .10
27 Mike Timlin RC .08 .25
28 Jeff Fassero RC .08 .25
29 Mark Leiter RC .02 .10
30 Jeff Bagwell RC .60 1.50
31 Brian McRae .08 .25
32 Mark Whiten .02 .10
33 Ivan Rodriguez RC .75 2.00
34 Wade Taylor RC .02 .10
35 Darren Lewis .02 .10
36 Mo Vaughn .08 .25
37 Mike Remlinger .02 .10
38 Rick Wilkins RC .02 .10
39 Chuck Knoblauch .08 .25
40 Kevin Morton .02 .10
41 Carlos Rodriguez RC .02 .10
42 Mark Lewis .02 .10
43 Brent Mayne .02 .10
44 Chris Haney RC .02 .10
45 Denis Boucher RC .02 .10
46 Mike Gardiner .02 .10
47 Jeff Johnson RC .02 .10
48 Dean Palmer .08 .25
49 Chuck McElroy .02 .10
50 Chris Jones RC .02 .10
51 Scott Kamieniecki RC .02 .10
52 Al Osuna RC .02 .10
53 Rusty Meacham RC .02 .10
54 Chito Martinez RC .02 .10
55 Reggie Jefferson .02 .10
56 Checklist 1-56 .02 .10

1992 Donruss

The 1992 Donruss set contains 784 standard-size cards issued in two separate series of 396. Cards were issued in first and second series foil wrapped packs in addition to hobby and retail factory sets. One of 21 different puzzle panels featuring Hall of Famer Rod Carew was inserted into each pack. The basic card design features glossy color player photos with white borders. Two-toned blue stripes overlay the top and bottom of the picture. Subsets include Rated Rookies (1-20, 397-421), All-Stars (21-30/422-431) and Highlights (33, 94, 154, 215, 276, 434, 495, 555, 616, 677). The only notable Rookie Card in the set features Scott Brosius.

COMPLETE SET (784) 4.00 10.00
COMP.HOBBY SET (788) 4.00 10.00
COMP.RETAIL SET (788) 4.00 10.00
COMP. SERIES 1 (396) 2.00 5.00
COMP. SERIES 2 (388) 2.00 5.00
COMP.CAREW PUZZLE .40 1.00
1 Mark Wohlers RR .01 .05
2 Wil Cordero RR .01 .05
3 Kyle Abbott RR .01 .05
4 Dave Nilsson RR .01 .05
5 Kenny Lofton RR .05 .15
6 Luis Mercedes RR .01 .05
7 Roger Salkeld RR .01 .05
8 Eddie Zosky RR .01 .05
9 Todd Van Poppel RR .01 .05
10 Frank Seminara RR RC .02 .10
11 Andy Ashby RR .01 .05
12 Reggie Jefferson RR .01 .05
13 Ryan Klesko RR .02 .10
14 Carlos Garcia RR .01 .05
15 John Ramos RR .01 .05
16 Eric Karros RR .02 .10
17 Patrick Lennon RR .01 .05
18 Eddie Taubensee RR RC .08 .25
19 Roberto Hernandez RR .01 .05
20 D.J. Dozier RR .01 .05
21 Dave Henderson AS .01 .05
22 Cal Ripken AS .15 .40
23 Wade Boggs AS .02 .10
24 Ken Griffey Jr. AS .08 .25
25 Jack Morris AS .01 .05
26 Danny Tartabull AS .01 .05
27 Cecil Fielder AS .01 .05
28 Roberto Alomar AS .02 .10
29 Sandy Alomar Jr. AS .01 .05
30 Rickey Henderson AS .05 .15
31 Ken Hill .01 .05
32 John Habyan .01 .05
33 Otis Nixon HL .01 .05
34 Tim Wallach .01 .05
35 Cal Ripken .30 .75
36 Gary Carter .02 .10
37 Juan Agosto .01 .05
38 Doug Dascenzo .01 .05
39 Kirk Gibson .02 .10
40 Benito Santiago .02 .10
41 Otis Nixon .01 .05
42 Andy Allanson .01 .05
43 Brian Holman .01 .05
44 Dick Schofield .01 .05
45 Dave Magadan .01 .05
46 Rafael Palmeiro .05 .15
47 Jody Reed .01 .05
48 Ivan Calderon .01 .05
49 Greg W. Harris .01 .05
50 Chris Sabo .01 .05
51 Paul Molitor .02 .10
52 Robby Thompson .01 .05
53 Dave Smith .01 .05
54 Mark Davis .01 .05
55 Kevin Brown .02 .10
56 Donn Pall .01 .05
57 Len Dykstra .02 .10
58 Roberto Alomar .05 .15
59 Jeff D. Robinson .01 .05
60 Willie McGee .02 .10
61 Jay Buhner .02 .10
62 Mike Pagliarulo .01 .05
63 Paul O'Neill .05 .15
64 Hubie Brooks .01 .05
65 Kelly Gruber .01 .05
66 Ken Caminiti .02 .10
67 Gary Redus .01 .05
68 Harold Baines .02 .10
69 Charlie Hough .02 .10
70 B.J. Surhoff .02 .10
71 Walt Weiss .01 .05
72 Shawn Hillegas .01 .05
73 Roberto Kelly .01 .05
74 Jeff Ballard .01 .05
75 Craig Biggio .05 .15
76 Pat Combs .01 .05
77 Jeff M. Robinson .01 .05
78 Tim Belcher .01 .05
79 Cris Carpenter .01 .05
80 Checklist 1-79 .01 .05
81 Steve Avery .01 .05
82 Chris James .01 .05
83 Brian Harper .01 .05
84 Charlie Leibrandt .01 .05
85 Mickey Tettleton .01 .05
86 Pete O'Brien .01 .05
87 Danny Darwin .01 .05
88 Bob Walk .01 .05
89 Jeff Reardon .02 .10
90 Bobby Rose .01 .05
91 Danny Jackson .01 .05
92 John Morris .01 .05
93 Bud Black .01 .05
94 Tommy Greene HL .01 .05
95 Rick Aguilera .02 .10
96 Gary Gaetti .02 .10
97 David Cone .02 .10
98 John Olerud .02 .10
99 Joel Skinner .01 .05
100 Jay Bell .02 .10
101 Bob Milacki .01 .05
102 Norm Charlton .01 .05
103 Chuck Crim .01 .05
104 Terry Steinbach .01 .05
105 Juan Samuel .01 .05
106 Steve Howe .01 .05
107 Rafael Belliard .01 .05
108 Joey Cora .01 .05
109 Tommy Greene .01 .05
110 Gregg Olson .01 .05
111 Frank Tanana .01 .05
112 Lee Smith .02 .10
113 Greg A. Harris .01 .05
114 Dwayne Henry .01 .05
115 Chili Davis .02 .10
116 Kent Mercker .01 .05
117 Brian Barnes .01 .05
118 Rich DeLucia .01 .05
119 Andre Dawson .02 .10
120 Carlos Baerga .01 .05
121 Mike LaValliere .01 .05
122 Jeff Gray .01 .05
123 Bruce Hurst .01 .05
124 Alvin Davis .01 .05
125 John Candelaria .01 .05
126 Matt Nokes .01 .05
127 George Bell .01 .05
128 Bret Saberhagen .02 .10
129 Jeff Russell .01 .05
130 Jim Abbott .05 .15
131 Bill Gullickson .01 .05
132 Todd Zeile .01 .05
133 Dave Winfield .02 .10
134 Wally Whitehurst .01 .05
135 Matt Williams .02 .10
136 Tom Browning .01 .05
137 Marquis Grissom .02 .10
138 Erik Hanson .01 .05
139 Rob Dibble .02 .10
140 Don August .01 .05
141 Tom Henke .01 .05
142 Dan Pasqua .01 .05
143 George Brett .25 .60
144 Jerald Clark .01 .05
145 Robin Ventura .02 .10
146 Dale Murphy .05 .15
147 Dennis Eckersley .02 .10
148 Eric Yelding .01 .05
149 Mario Diaz .01 .05
150 Casey Candaele .01 .05
151 Steve Olin .01 .05
152 Luis Salazar .01 .05
153 Kevin Maas .01 .05
154 Nolan Ryan HL .20 .50
155 Barry Jones .01 .05
156 Chris Hoiles .01 .05
157 Bob Ojeda .01 .05
158 Pedro Guerrero .02 .10
159 Paul Assenmacher .01 .05
160 Checklist 80-157 .01 .05
161 Mike Macfarlane .01 .05
162 Craig Lefferts .01 .05
163 Brian Hunter .01 .05
164 Alan Trammell .02 .10
165 Ken Griffey Jr. .15 .40
166 Lance Parrish .02 .10
167 Brian Downing .01 .05
168 John Barfield .01 .05
169 Jack Clark .02 .10
170 Chris Nabholz .01 .05
171 Tim Teufel .01 .05
172 Chris Hammond .01 .05
173 Robin Yount .15 .40
174 Dave Righetti .02 .10
175 Joe Girardi .01 .05
176 Mike Boddicker .01 .05
177 Dean Palmer .02 .10
178 Greg Hibbard .01 .05
179 Randy Ready .01 .05
180 Devon White .02 .10
181 Mark Eichhorn .01 .05
182 Mike Felder .01 .05
183 Joe Klink .01 .05
184 Steve Bedrosian .01 .05
185 Barry Larkin .05 .15
186 John Franco .02 .10
187 Ed Sprague .01 .05
188 Mark Portugal .01 .05
189 Jose Lind .01 .05
190 Bob Welch .01 .05
191 Alex Fernandez .01 .05
192 Gary Sheffield .02 .10
193 Rickey Henderson .08 .25
194 Rod Nichols .01 .05
195 Scott Kamieniecki .01 .05
196 Mike Flanagan .01 .05
197 Steve Finley .02 .10
198 Darren Daulton .02 .10
199 Leo Gomez .01 .05
200 Mike Morgan .01 .05
201 Bob Tewksbury .01 .05
202 Sid Bream .01 .05
203 Sandy Alomar Jr. .01 .05
204 Greg Gagne .01 .05
205 Juan Berenguer .01 .05
206 Cecil Fielder .02 .10
207 Randy Johnson .08 .25
208 Tony Pena .01 .05
209 Doug Drabek .01 .05
210 Wade Boggs .05 .15
211 Bryan Harvey .01 .05
212 Jose Vizcaino .01 .05
213 Alonzo Powell .01 .05
214 Will Clark .05 .15
215 Rickey Henderson HL .05 .15
216 Jack Morris .02 .10
217 Junior Felix .01 .05
218 Vince Coleman .01 .05
219 Jimmy Key .02 .10
220 Alex Cole .01 .05
221 Bill Landrum .01 .05
222 Randy Milligan .01 .05
223 Jose Rijo .01 .05
224 Greg Vaughn .01 .05
225 Dave Stewart .02 .10
226 Lenny Harris .01 .05
227 Scott Sanderson .01 .05
228 Jeff Blauser .01 .05
229 Ozzie Guillen .02 .10
230 John Kruk .02 .10
231 Bob Melvin .01 .05
232 Milt Cuyler .01 .05
233 Felix Jose .01 .05
234 Ellis Burks .02 .10
235 Pete Harnisch .01 .05
236 Kevin Tapani .01 .05
237 Terry Pendleton .02 .10
238 Mark Gardner .01 .05
239 Harold Reynolds .02 .10
240 Checklist 158-237 .01 .05
241 Mike Harkey .01 .05
242 Felix Fermin .01 .05
243 Barry Bonds .40 1.00
244 Roger Clemens .20 .50
245 Dennis Rasmussen .01 .05
246 Jose DeLeon .01 .05
247 Orel Hershiser .02 .10
248 Mel Hall .01 .05
249 Rick Wilkins .01 .05
250 Tom Gordon .01 .05
251 Kevin Reimer .01 .05
252 Luis Polonia .01 .05
253 Mike Henneman .01 .05
254 Tom Pagnozzi .01 .05
255 Chuck Finley .02 .10
256 Mackey Sasser .01 .05
257 John Burkett .01 .05
258 Hal Morris .01 .05
259 Larry Walker .05 .15
260 Bill Swift .01 .05
261 Joe Oliver .01 .05
262 Julio Machado .01 .05
263 Todd Stottlemyre .01 .05
264 Matt Merullo .01 .05
265 Brent Mayne .01 .05
266 Thomas Howard .01 .05
267 Lance Johnson .01 .05
268 Terry Mulholland .01 .05
269 Rick Honeycutt .01 .05
270 Luis Gonzalez .02 .10
271 Jose Guzman .01 .05
272 Jimmy Jones .01 .05
273 Mark Lewis .01 .05
274 Rene Gonzales .01 .05
275 Jeff Johnson .01 .05
276 Dennis Martinez HL .01 .05
277 Delino DeShields .01 .05
278 Sam Horn .01 .05
279 Kevin Gross .01 .05
280 Jose Oquendo .01 .05
281 Mark Grace .05 .15
282 Mark Gubicza .01 .05
283 Fred McGriff .05 .15
284 Ron Gant .02 .10
285 Lou Whitaker .02 .10
286 Edgar Martinez .05 .15
287 Ron Tingley .01 .05
288 Kevin McReynolds .01 .05
289 Ivan Rodriguez .08 .25
290 Mike Gardiner .01 .05
291 Chris Haney .01 .05
292 Darrin Jackson .01 .05
293 Bill Doran .01 .05
294 Ted Higuera .01 .05
295 Jeff Brantley .01 .05
296 Les Lancaster .01 .05
297 Jim Eisenreich .01 .05
298 Ruben Sierra .02 .10
299 Scott Radinsky .01 .05
300 Jose DeJesus .01 .05
301 Mike Timlin .01 .05
302 Luis Sojo .01 .05
303 Kelly Downs .01 .05
304 Scott Bankhead .01 .05
305 Pedro Munoz .01 .05
306 Scott Scudder .01 .05
307 Kevin Elster .01 .05
308 Duane Ward .01 .05
309 Darryl Kile .02 .10
310 Orlando Merced .01 .05
311 Dave Henderson .01 .05
312 Tim Raines .02 .10
313 Mark Lee .01 .05
314 Mike Gallego .01 .05
315 Charles Nagy .01 .05
316 Jesse Barfield .01 .05
317 Todd Frohwirth .01 .05
318 Al Osuna .01 .05
319 Darrin Fletcher .01 .05
320 Checklist 238-316 .01 .05
321 David Segui .01 .05
322 Stan Javier .01 .05
323 Bryn Smith .01 .05
324 Jeff Treadway .01 .05
325 Mark Whiten .01 .05
326 Kent Hrbek .02 .10
327 Dave Justice .02 .10
328 Tony Phillips .01 .05
329 Rob Murphy .01 .05
330 Kevin Morton .01 .05
331 John Smiley .01 .05
332 Luis Rivera .01 .05
333 Wally Joyner .02 .10
334 Heathcliff Slocumb .01 .05
335 Rick Cerone .01 .05
336 Mike Remlinger .01 .05
337 Mike Moore .01 .05
338 Lloyd McClendon .01 .05
339 Al Newman .01 .05
340 Kirk McCaskill .01 .05
341 Howard Johnson .01 .05
342 Greg Myers .01 .05
343 Kal Daniels .01 .05
344 Bernie Williams .05 .15
345 Shane Mack .01 .05
346 Gary Thurman .01 .05
347 Dante Bichette .02 .10
348 Mark McGwire .25 .60
349 Travis Fryman .02 .10
350 Ray Lankford .02 .10
351 Mike Jeffcoat .01 .05
352 Jack McDowell .01 .05
353 Mitch Williams .01 .05
354 Mike Devereaux .01 .05
355 Andres Galarraga .02 .10
356 Henry Cotto .01 .05
357 Scott Bailes .01 .05
358 Jeff Bagwell .08 .25
359 Scott Leius .01 .05
360 Zane Smith .01 .05
361 Bill Pecota .01 .05
362 Tony Fernandez .01 .05
363 Glenn Braggs .01 .05
364 Bill Spiers .01 .05
365 Vicente Palacios .01 .05
366 Tim Burke .01 .05
367 Randy Tomlin .01 .05
368 Kenny Rogers .02 .10
369 Brett Butler .02 .10
370 Pat Kelly .01 .05
371 Bip Roberts .01 .05
372 Gregg Jefferies .01 .05
373 Kevin Bass .01 .05
374 Ron Karkovice .01 .05
375 Paul Gibson .01 .05
376 Bernard Gilkey .01 .05
377 Dave Gallagher .01 .05
378 Bill Wegman .01 .05
379 Pat Borders .01 .05
380 Ed Whitson .01 .05
381 Gilberto Reyes .01 .05
382 Russ Swan .01 .05
383 Andy Van Slyke .05 .15
384 Wes Chamberlain .01 .05
385 Steve Chitren .01 .05
386 Greg Olson .01 .05
387 Brian McRae .01 .05
388 Rich Rodriguez .01 .05
389 Steve Decker .01 .05
390 Chuck Knoblauch .02 .10
391 Bobby Witt .01 .05
392 Eddie Murray .08 .25
393 Juan Gonzalez .05 .15
394 Scott Ruskin .01 .05
395 Jay Howell .01 .05
396 Checklist 317-396 .01 .05
397 Royce Clayton RR .01 .05
398 John Jaha RR RC .08 .25
399 Dan Wilson RR .01 .05
400 Archie Corbin RR .01 .05
401 Barry Manuel RR .01 .05
402 Kim Batiste RR .01 .05
403 Pat Mahomes RR RC .08 .25
404 Dave Fleming RR .01 .05
405 Jeff Juden RR .01 .05
406 Jim Thome RR .08 .25
407 Sam Militello RR .01 .05
408 Jeff Nelson RR RC .15 .40
409 Anthony Young RR .01 .05
410 Tino Martinez RR .05 .15
411 Jeff Mutis RR .01 .05
412 Rey Sanchez RR RC .08 .25
413 Chris Gardner RR .01 .05
414 John Vander Wal RR .01 .05
415 Reggie Sanders RR .02 .10
416 Brian Williams RR RC .02 .10
417 Mo Sanford RR .01 .05
418 David Weathers RR RC .15 .40
419 Hector Fajardo RR RC .02 .10
420 Steve Foster RR .01 .05
421 Lance Dickson RR .01 .05
422 Andre Dawson AS .01 .05
423 Ozzie Smith AS .08 .25
424 Chris Sabo AS .01 .05
425 Tony Gwynn AS .05 .15
426 Tom Glavine AS .02 .10
427 Bobby Bonilla AS .01 .05
428 Will Clark AS .02 .10
429 Ryne Sandberg AS .08 .25
430 Benito Santiago AS .01 .05
431 Ivan Calderon AS .01 .05
432 Ozzie Smith .15 .40
433 Tim Leary .01 .05
434 Bret Saberhagen HL .01 .05
435 Mel Rojas .01 .05
436 Ben McDonald .01 .05
437 Tim Crews .01 .05
438 Rex Hudler .01 .05
439 Chico Walker .01 .05
440 Kurt Stillwell .01 .05
441 Tony Gwynn .10 .30
442 John Smoltz .05 .15
443 Lloyd Moseby .01 .05
444 Mike Schooler .01 .05
445 Joe Grahe .01 .05
446 Dwight Gooden .02 .10
447 Oil Can Boyd .01 .05
448 John Marzano .01 .05
449 Bret Barberie .01 .05
450 Mike Maddux .01 .05
451 Jeff Reed .01 .05
452 Dale Sveum .01 .05
453 Jose Uribe .01 .05
454 Bob Scanlan .01 .05
455 Kevin Appier .02 .10
456 Jeff Huson .01 .05
457 Ken Patterson .01 .05
458 Ricky Jordan .01 .05
459 Tom Candiotti .01 .05
460 Lee Stevens .01 .05
461 Rod Beck RC .08 .25
462 Dave Valle .01 .05
463 Scott Erickson .01 .05
464 Chris Jones .01 .05
465 Mark Carreon .01 .05
466 Rob Ducey .01 .05
467 Jim Corsi .01 .05
468 Jeff King .01 .05
469 Curt Young .01 .05
470 Bo Jackson .08 .25
471 Chris Bosio .01 .05
472 Jamie Quirk .01 .05
473 Jesse Orosco .01 .05
474 Alvaro Espinoza .01 .05
475 Joe Orsulak .01 .05
476 Checklist 397-477 .01 .05
477 Gerald Young .01 .05
478 Wally Backman .01 .05
479 Juan Bell .01 .05
480 Mike Scioscia .01 .05
481 Omar Olivares .01 .05
482 Francisco Cabrera .01 .05
483 Greg Swindell UER .01 .05
(Shown on Indians, but listed on Reds)
484 Terry Leach .01 .05
485 Tommy Gregg .01 .05
486 Scott Aldred .01 .05
487 Greg Briley .01 .05
488 Phil Plantier .01 .05
489 Curtis Wilkerson .01 .05
490 Tom Brunansky .01 .05
491 Mike Fetters .01 .05
492 Frank Castillo .01 .05
493 Joe Boever .01 .05
494 Kirt Manwaring .01 .05
495 Wilson Alvarez HL .01 .05
496 Gene Larkin .01 .05
497 Gary DiSarcina .01 .05
498 Frank Viola .02 .10
499 Manuel Lee .01 .05
500 Albert Belle .02 .10
501 Stan Belinda .01 .05
502 Dwight Evans .05 .15
503 Eric Davis .02 .10
504 Darren Holmes .01 .05
505 Mike Bordick .01 .05
506 Dave Hansen .01 .05
507 Lee Guetterman .01 .05
508 Keith Mitchell .01 .05
509 Melido Perez .01 .05
510 Dickie Thon .01 .05
511 Mark Williamson .01 .05
512 Mark Salas .01 .05
513 Milt Thompson .01 .05
514 Mo Vaughn .02 .10
515 Jim Deshaies .01 .05
516 Rich Garces .01 .05
517 Lonnie Smith .01 .05
518 Spike Owen .01 .05
519 Tracy Jones .01 .05
520 Greg Maddux .15 .40
521 Carlos Martinez .01 .05
522 Neal Heaton .01 .05
523 Mike Greenwell .01 .05
524 Andy Benes .01 .05
525 Jeff Schaefer UER .01 .05
(Photo actually Tino Martinez)
526 Mike Sharperson .01 .05
527 Wade Taylor .01 .05
528 Jerome Walton .01 .05
529 Storm Davis .01 .05
530 Jose Hernandez RC .08 .25
531 Mark Langston .01 .05
532 Rob Deer .01 .05
533 Geronimo Pena .01 .05
534 Juan Guzman .01 .05
535 Pete Schourek .01 .05
536 Todd Benzinger .01 .05
537 Billy Hatcher .01 .05
538 Tom Foley .01 .05
539 Dave Cochrane .01 .05
540 Mariano Duncan .01 .05
541 Edwin Nunez .01 .05
542 Rance Mulliniks .01 .05
543 Carlton Fisk .05 .15
544 Luis Aquino .01 .05
545 Ricky Bones .01 .05
546 Craig Grebeck .01 .05
547 Charlie Hayes .01 .05
548 Jose Canseco .05 .15
549 Andujar Cedeno .01 .05
550 Geno Petralli .01 .05
551 Javier Ortiz .01 .05
552 Rudy Seanez .01 .05
553 Rich Gedman .01 .05
554 Eric Plunk .01 .05
555 Nolan Ryan HL .15 .40
(With Rich Gossage)
556 Checklist 478-555 .01 .05
557 Greg Colbrunn .01 .05
558 Chito Martinez .01 .05
559 Darryl Strawberry .02 .10
560 Luis Alicea .01 .05
561 Dwight Smith .01 .05
562 Terry Shumpert .01 .05
563 Jim Vatcher .01 .05
564 Deion Sanders .05 .15
565 Walt Terrell .01 .05
566 Dave Burba .01 .05
567 Dave Howard .01 .05
568 Todd Hundley .01 .05
569 Jack Daugherty .01 .05
570 Scott Cooper .01 .05
571 Bill Sampen .01 .05
572 Jose Melendez .01 .05
573 Freddie Benavides .01 .05
574 Jim Gantner .01 .05
575 Trevor Wilson .01 .05
576 Ryne Sandberg .15 .40
577 Kevin Seitzer .01 .05
578 Gerald Alexander .01 .05
579 Mike Huff .01 .05
580 Von Hayes .01 .05

Card	Low	High
581 Derek Bell	.02	.10
582 Mike Stanley	.01	.05
583 Kevin Mitchell	.01	.05
584 Mike Jackson	.01	.05
585 Dan Gladden	.01	.05
586 Ted Power UER (Wrong year given for signing with Reds)	.01	.05
587 Jeff Innis	.01	.05
588 Bob MacDonald	.01	.05
589 Jose Tolentino	.01	.05
590 Bob Patterson	.01	.05
591 Scott Brosius RC	.15	.40
592 Frank Thomas	.08	.25
593 Darryl Hamilton	.01	.05
594 Kirk Dressendorfer	.01	.05
595 Jeff Shaw	.01	.05
596 Don Mattingly	.25	.60
597 Glenn Davis	.01	.05
598 Andy Mota	.01	.05
599 Jason Grimsley	.01	.05
600 Jim Poole	.01	.05
601 Jim Gott	.01	.05
602 Stan Royer	.01	.05
603 Marvin Freeman	.01	.05
604 Denis Boucher	.01	.05
605 Denny Neagle	.02	.10
606 Mark Lemke	.01	.05
607 Jerry Don Gleaton	.01	.05
608 Brent Knackert	.01	.05
609 Carlos Quintana	.01	.05
610 Bobby Bonilla	.02	.10
611 Joe Hesketh	.01	.05
612 Daryl Boston	.01	.05
613 Shawon Dunston	.01	.05
614 Danny Cox	.01	.05
615 Darren Lewis	.01	.05
616 Braves No-Hitter UER Kent Mercker (Misspelled Merker on card front) Alejandro Pena Mark Wohlers	.01	.05
617 Kirby Puckett	.08	.25
618 Franklin Stubbs	.01	.05
619 Chris Donnels	.01	.05
620 David Wells UER (Career Highlights in black not red)	.02	.10
621 Mike Aldrete	.01	.05
622 Bob Kipper	.01	.05
623 Anthony Telford	.01	.05
624 Randy Myers	.01	.05
625 Willie Randolph	.02	.10
626 Joe Slusarski	.01	.05
627 John Wetteland	.02	.10
628 Greg Cadaret	.01	.05
629 Tom Glavine	.05	.15
630 Wilson Alvarez	.01	.05
631 Wally Ritchie	.01	.05
632 Mike Mussina	.08	.25
633 Mark Leiter	.01	.05
634 Gerald Perry	.01	.05
635 Matt Young	.01	.05
636 Checklist 556-635	.01	.05
637 Scott Hemond	.01	.05
638 David West	.01	.05
639 Jim Clancy	.01	.05
640 Doug Piatt UER (Not born in 1955 as on card; incorrect info on How Acquired)	.01	.05
641 Omar Vizquel	.05	.15
642 Rick Sutcliffe	.02	.10
643 Glenallen Hill	.01	.05
644 Gary Varsho	.01	.05
645 Tony Fossas	.01	.05
646 Jack Howell	.01	.05
647 Jim Campanis	.01	.05
648 Chris Gwynn	.01	.05
649 Jim Leyritz	.01	.05
650 Chuck McElroy	.01	.05
651 Sean Berry	.01	.05
652 Donald Harris	.01	.05
653 Don Slaught	.01	.05
654 Rusty Meacham	.01	.05
655 Scott Terry	.01	.05
656 Ramon Martinez	.01	.05
657 Keith Miller	.01	.05
658 Ramon Garcia	.01	.05
659 Milt Hill	.01	.05
660 Steve Frey	.01	.05
661 Bob McClure	.01	.05
662 Ced Landrum	.01	.05
663 Doug Henry RC	.02	.10
664 Candy Maldonado	.01	.05
665 Carl Willis	.01	.05
666 Jeff Montgomery	.01	.05
667 Craig Shipley	.01	.05
668 Warren Newson	.01	.05
669 Mickey Morandini	.01	.05
670 Brook Jacoby	.01	.05
671 Ryan Bowen	.01	.05
672 Bill Krueger	.01	.05
673 Rob Mallicoat	.01	.05
674 Doug Jones	.01	.05
675 Scott Livingstone	.01	.05
676 Danny Tartabull	.01	.05
677 Joe Carter HL	.01	.05
678 Cecil Espy	.01	.05
679 Randy Velarde	.01	.05
680 Bruce Ruffin	.01	.05
681 Ted Wood	.01	.05
682 Dan Plesac	.01	.05
683 Eric Bullock	.01	.05
684 Junior Ortiz	.01	.05
685 Dave Hollins	.01	.05
686 Dennis Martinez	.02	.10
687 Larry Andersen	.01	.05
688 Doug Simons	.01	.05
689 Tim Spehr	.01	.05
690 Calvin Jones	.01	.05
691 Mark Guthrie	.01	.05
692 Alfredo Griffin	.01	.05
693 Joe Carter	.02	.10
694 Terry Mathews	.01	.05
695 Pascual Perez	.01	.05
696 Gene Nelson	.01	.05
697 Gerald Williams	.01	.05
698 Chris Cron	.01	.05
699 Steve Buechele	.01	.05
700 Paul McClellan	.01	.05
701 Jim Lindeman	.01	.05
702 Francisco Oliveras	.01	.05
703 Rob Maurer	.01	.05
704 Pat Hentgen	.01	.05
705 Jaime Navarro	.01	.05
706 Mike Magnante RC	.02	.10
707 Nolan Ryan	.40	1.00
708 Bobby Thigpen	.01	.05
709 John Cerutti	.01	.05
710 Steve Wilson	.01	.05
711 Hensley Meulens	.01	.05
712 Rheal Cormier	.01	.05
713 Scott Bradley	.01	.05
714 Mitch Webster	.01	.05
715 Roger Mason	.01	.05
716 Checklist 636-716	.01	.05
717 Jeff Fassero	.01	.05
718 Cal Eldred	.01	.05
719 Sid Fernandez	.01	.05
720 Bob Zupcic RC	.02	.10
721 Jose Offerman	.01	.05
722 Cliff Brantley	.01	.05
723 Ron Darling	.01	.05
724 Dave Stieb	.01	.05
725 Hector Villanueva	.01	.05
726 Mike Hartley	.01	.05
727 Arthur Rhodes	.01	.05
728 Randy Bush	.01	.05
729 Steve Sax	.01	.05
730 Dave Otto	.01	.05
731 John Wehner	.01	.05
732 Dave Martinez	.01	.05
733 Ruben Amaro	.01	.05
734 Billy Ripken	.01	.05
735 Steve Farr	.01	.05
736 Shawn Abner	.01	.05
737 Gil Heredia RC	.08	.25
738 Ron Jones	.01	.05
739 Tony Castillo	.01	.05
740 Sammy Sosa	.08	.25
741 Julio Franco	.02	.10
742 Tim Naehring	.01	.05
743 Steve Wapnick	.01	.05
744 Craig Wilson	.01	.05
745 Darrin Chapin	.01	.05
746 Chris George	.01	.05
747 Mike Simms	.01	.05
748 Rosario Rodriguez	.01	.05
749 Skeeter Barnes	.01	.05
750 Roger McDowell	.01	.05
751 Dann Howitt	.01	.05
752 Paul Sorrento	.01	.05
753 Braulio Castillo	.01	.05
754 Yorkis Perez	.01	.05
755 Willie Fraser	.01	.05
756 Jeremy Hernandez RC	.02	.10
757 Curt Schilling	.05	.15
758 Steve Lyons	.01	.05
759 Dave Anderson	.01	.05
760 Willie Banks	.01	.05
761 Mark Leonard	.01	.05
762 Jack Armstrong (Listed on Indians, but shown on Reds)	.01	.05
763 Scott Servais	.01	.05
764 Ray Stephens	.01	.05
765 Junior Noboa	.01	.05
766 Jim Olander	.01	.05
767 Joe Magrane	.01	.05
768 Lance Blankenship	.01	.05
769 Mike Humphreys	.01	.05
770 Jarvis Brown	.01	.05
771 Damon Berryhill	.01	.05
772 Alejandro Pena	.01	.05
773 Jose Mesa	.01	.05
774 Gary Cooper	.01	.05
775 Carney Lansford	.02	.10
776 Mike Bielecki Shown on Cubs, but listed on Braves	.01	.05
777 Charlie O'Brien	.01	.05
778 Carlos Hernandez	.01	.05
779 Howard Farmer	.01	.05
780 Mike Stanton	.01	.05
781 Reggie Harris	.01	.05
782 Xavier Hernandez	.01	.05
783 Bryan Hickerson RC	.02	.10
784 Checklist 717-784 and BC1-BC8	.01	.05

1992 Donruss Diamond Kings

These standard-size cards were randomly inserted in 1992 Donruss I foil packs (cards 1-13 and the checklist only) and in 1992 Donruss II foil packs (cards 14-26). The decision at the time to transform the popular Diamond King subset into an limieted distribution insert set created notable groups of supporters and dissenters. The attractive fronts feature player portraits by noted sports artist Dick Perez. The words "Donruss Diamond Kings" are superimposed at the card top in a gold-trimmed blue and black banner, with the player's name in a similarly designed black stripe at the card bottom. A very limited amount of 5" by 7" cards were produced. These issues were never formally released but these cards were intended to be premiums in retail products.

Card	Low	High
COMPLETE SET (27)	10.00	20.00
COMPLETE SERIES 1 (14)	8.00	16.00
COMPLETE SERIES 2 (13)	2.00	4.00
DK1 Paul Molitor	.30	.75
DK2 Will Clark	.50	1.25
DK3 Joe Carter	.30	.75
DK4 Julio Franco	.30	.75
DK5 Cal Ripken	2.50	6.00
DK6 Dave Justice	.30	.75
DK7 George Bell	.15	.40
DK8 Frank Thomas	.75	2.00
DK9 Wade Boggs	.50	1.25
DK10 Scott Sanderson	.15	.40
DK11 Jeff Bagwell	.75	2.00
DK12 John Kruk	.30	.75
DK13 Felix Jose	.15	.40
DK14 Harold Baines	.30	.75
DK15 Dwight Gooden	.30	.75
DK16 Brian McRae	.15	.40
DK17 Jay Bell	.30	.75
DK18 Brett Butler	.30	.75
DK19 Hal Morris	.15	.40
DK20 Mark Langston	.15	.40
DK21 Scott Erickson	.15	.40
DK22 Randy Johnson	.75	2.00
DK23 Greg Swindell	.15	.40
DK24 Dennis Martinez	.30	.75
DK25 Tony Phillips	.15	.40
DK26 Fred McGriff	.50	1.25
DK27 Checklist 1-26 DP (Dick Perez)	.15	.40

1992 Donruss Elite

These cards were random inserts in 1992 Donruss first and second series foil packs. Like the previous year, the cards were individually numbered of 10,000. Card fronts feature dramatic prismatic borders encasing a full color action or posed shot of the player. The numbering of the set is essentially a continuation of the series started the year before. Only 5,000 Ripken Signature Series cards were printed and only 7,500 Henderson Legends cards were printed. The complete set price does not include cards L2 and S2.

Card	Low	High
9 Wade Boggs	10.00	25.00
10 Joe Carter	6.00	15.00
11 Will Clark	10.00	25.00
12 Dwight Gooden	6.00	15.00
13 Ken Griffey Jr.	15.00	40.00
14 Tony Gwynn	10.00	25.00
15 Howard Johnson	6.00	15.00
16 Terry Pendleton	6.00	15.00
17 Kirby Puckett	10.00	25.00
18 Frank Thomas	10.00	25.00
L2 R.Henderson LGD/7500	10.00	25.00
S2 Cal Ripken AU/5000	150.00	250.00

1992 Donruss Rookies

After six years of issuing "The Rookies" as a 56-card boxed set, Donruss expanded it to a 132-card standard-size set and distributed the cards in hobby and retail foil packs. The card design is the same as the 1992 Donruss regular issue except that the two-tone blue color bars have been replaced by green, as in the previous six Donruss Rookies sets. The cards are arranged in alphabetical order and numbered on the back. Rookie Cards in this set include Jeff Kent, Manny Ramirez and Eric Young. In addition an early card of Pedro Martinez is featured.

Card	Low	High
COMPLETE SET (132)	4.00	10.00
1 Kyle Abbott	.01	.05
2 Troy Afenir	.01	.05
3 Rich Amaral RC	.02	.10
4 Ruben Amaro	.01	.05
5 Billy Ashley RC	.02	.10
6 Pedro Astacio RC	.08	.25
7 Jim Austin	.01	.05
8 Robert Ayrault	.01	.05
9 Kevin Baez	.01	.05
10 Esteban Beltre	.01	.05
11 Brian Bohanon	.01	.05
12 Kent Bottenfield RC	.08	.25
13 Jeff Branson	.01	.05
14 Brad Brink	.01	.05
15 John Briscoe	.01	.05
16 Doug Brocail RC	.02	.10
17 Rico Brogna	.01	.05
18 J.T. Bruett	.01	.05
19 Jacob Brumfield	.01	.05
20 Jim Bullinger	.01	.05
21 Kevin Campbell	.01	.05
22 Pedro Castellano RC	.02	.10
23 Mike Christopher	.01	.05
24 Archi Cianfrocco RC	.02	.10
25 Mark Clark RC	.02	.10
26 Craig Colbert	.01	.05
27 Victor Cole	.01	.05
28 Steve Cooke RC	.02	.10
29 Tim Costo	.01	.05
30 Chad Curtis RC	.08	.25
31 Doug Davis	.01	.05
32 Gary DiSarcina	.01	.05
33 John Doherty RC	.02	.10
34 Mike Draper	.01	.05
35 Monty Fariss	.01	.05
36 Bien Figueroa	.01	.05
37 John Flaherty	.01	.05
38 Tim Fortugno	.01	.05
39 Eric Fox RC	.02	.10
40 Jeff Frye RC	.02	.10
41 Ramon Garcia	.01	.05
42 Brent Gates RC	.02	.10
43 Tom Goodwin	.01	.05
44 Buddy Groom RC	.02	.10
45 Jeff Grotewold	.01	.05
46 Juan Guerrero	.01	.05
47 Johnny Guzman RC	.02	.10
48 Shawn Hare RC	.02	.10
49 Ryan Hawblitzel RC	.02	.10
50 Bert Heffernan	.01	.05
51 Butch Henry	.01	.05
52 Cesar Hernandez RC	.02	.10
53 Vince Horsman	.01	.05
54 Steve Hosey	.01	.05
55 Pat Howell	.01	.05
56 Peter Hoy	.01	.05
57 Jonathan Hurst RC	.02	.10
58 Mark Hutton RC	.02	.10
59 Shawn Jeter RC	.02	.10
60 Joel Johnston	.01	.05
61 Jeff Kent RC	1.00	2.50
62 Kurt Knudsen RC	.02	.10
63 Kevin Koslofski	.01	.05
64 Danny Leon	.01	.05
65 Jesse Levis	.01	.05
66 Tom Marsh	.01	.05
67 Ed Martel	.01	.05
68 Al Martin RC	.08	.25
69 Pedro Martinez	.75	2.00
70 Derrick May	.01	.05
71 Matt Maysey	.01	.05
72 Russ McGinnis	.01	.05
73 Tim McIntosh	.01	.05
74 Jim McNamara	.01	.05
75 Jeff McNeely	.01	.05
76 Rusty Meacham	.01	.05
77 Tony Menendez	.01	.05
78 Henry Mercedes	.01	.05
79 Paul Miller	.01	.05
80 Joe Millette	.01	.05
81 Blas Minor	.01	.05
82 Dennis Moeller	.01	.05
83 Raul Mondesi	.02	.10
84 Rob Natal	.01	.05
85 Troy Neel RC	.02	.10
86 David Nied RC	.02	.10
87 Jerry Nielson	.01	.05
88 Donovan Osborne	.01	.05
89 John Patterson RC	.02	.10
90 Roger Pavlik RC	.02	.10
91 Dan Peltier	.01	.05
92 Jim Pena	.01	.05
93 William Pennyfeather	.01	.05
94 Mike Perez	.01	.05
95 Hipolito Pichardo RC	.02	.10
96 Greg Pirkl RC	.02	.10
97 Harvey Pulliam	.01	.05
98 Manny Ramirez RC	1.50	4.00
99 Pat Rapp RC	.02	.10
100 Jeff Reboulet	.01	.05
101 Darren Reed	.01	.05
102 Shane Reynolds RC	.08	.25
103 Bill Risley	.01	.05
104 Ben Rivera	.01	.05
105 Henry Rodriguez	.01	.05
106 Rico Rossy	.01	.05
107 Johnny Ruffin	.01	.05
108 Steve Scarsone	.01	.05
109 Tim Scott	.01	.05
110 Steve Shifflett	.01	.05
111 Dave Silvestri	.01	.05
112 Matt Stairs RC	.08	.25
113 William Suero	.01	.05
114 Jeff Tackett	.01	.05
115 Eddie Taubensee	.02	.10
116 Rick Trlicek RC	.02	.10
117 Scooter Tucker	.01	.05
118 Shane Turner	.01	.05
119 Julio Valera	.01	.05
120 Paul Wagner RC	.02	.10
121 Tim Wakefield RC	1.25	3.00
122 Mike Walker	.01	.05
123 Bruce Walton	.01	.05
124 Lenny Webster	.01	.05
125 Bob Wickman	.08	.25
126 Mike Williams RC	.08	.25
127 Kerry Woodson	.01	.05
128 Eric Young RC	.08	.25
129 Kevin Young RC	.08	.25
130 Pete Young	.01	.05
131 Checklist 1-66	.01	.05
132 Checklist 67-132	.01	.05

1992 Donruss Rookies Phenoms

This 20-card standard size set features a selection young prospects. The first twelve cards were randomly inserted into 1992 Donruss The Rookies 12-card foil packs. The last eight were inserted one per 1992 Donruss Rookies 30-card jumbo pack. Each glossy card front features a black border surrounding a full color photo and gold foil type. One of only three MLB-licensed cards of Mike Piazza issued in 1992 is featured within this set.

Card	Low	High
COMP.FOIL SET (12)	15.00	30.00
COMP.JUMBO SET (8)	5.00	10.00
COMM.FOIL (BC1-BC12)	.40	1.00
COMMON (BC13-BC20)	.40	1.00
BC1 Moises Alou	.60	1.50
BC2 Bret Boone	.60	1.50
BC3 Jeff Conine	.60	1.50
BC4 Dave Fleming	.40	1.00
BC5 Tyler Green	.40	1.00
BC6 Eric Karros	.60	1.50
BC7 Pat Listach	.60	1.50
BC8 Kenny Lofton	.60	1.50
BC9 Mike Piazza	6.00	15.00
BC10 Tim Salmon	.60	1.50
BC11 Andy Stankiewicz	.40	1.00
BC12 Dan Walters	.40	1.00
BC13 Ramon Caraballo	.40	1.00
BC14 Brian Jordan	.60	1.50
BC15 Ryan Klesko	.60	1.50
BC16 Sam Militello	.40	1.00
BC17 Frank Seminara	.40	1.00
BC18 Salomon Torres	.40	1.00
BC19 John Valentin	.60	1.50
BC20 Wil Cordero	.40	1.00

1993 Donruss

The 792-card 1993 Donruss set was issued in two series, each with 396 standard-size cards. Cards were distributed in foil packs. The basic card fronts feature glossy color action photos with white borders. At the bottom of the picture, the team logo appears in a team color-coded diamond with the player's name in a color-coded bar extending to the right. A Rated Rookies (RR) subset, sprinkled throughout the set, spotlights 20 young prospects. There are no key Rookie Cards in this set.

Card	Low	High
COMPLETE SET (792)	12.00	30.00
COMP.SERIES 1 (396)	6.00	15.00
COMP.SERIES 2 (396)	6.00	15.00
1 Craig Lefferts	.02	.10
2 Kent Mercker	.02	.10
3 Phil Plantier	.02	.10
4 Alex Arias	.02	.10
5 Julio Valera	.02	.10
6 Dan Wilson	.07	.20
7 Frank Thomas	.20	.50
8 Eric Anthony	.02	.10
9 Derek Lilliquist	.02	.10
10 Rafael Bournigal	.02	.10
11 Manny Alexander RR	.02	.10
12 Bret Barberie	.02	.10
13 Mickey Tettleton	.02	.10
14 Anthony Young	.02	.10
15 Tim Spehr	.02	.10
16 Bob Ayrault	.02	.10
17 Bill Wegman	.02	.10
18 Jay Bell	.07	.20
19 Rick Aguilera	.02	.10
20 Todd Zeile	.02	.10
21 Steve Farr	.02	.10
22 Andy Benes	.02	.10
23 Lance Blankenship	.02	.10
24 Ted Wood	.02	.10
25 Omar Vizquel	.10	.30
26 Steve Avery	.02	.10
27 Brian Bohanon	.02	.10
28 Rick Wilkins	.02	.10
29 Devon White	.07	.20
30 Bobby Ayala RC	.02	.10
31 Leo Gomez	.02	.10
32 Mike Simms	.02	.10
33 Ellis Burks	.07	.20
34 Steve Wilson	.02	.10
35 Jim Abbott	.10	.30
36 Tim Wallach	.02	.10
37 Wilson Alvarez	.02	.10
38 Daryl Boston	.02	.10
39 Sandy Alomar Jr.	.02	.10
40 Mitch Williams	.02	.10
41 Rico Brogna	.02	.10
42 Gary Varsho	.02	.10
43 Kevin Appier	.07	.20
44 Eric Wedge RR RC	.02	.10
45 Dante Bichette	.07	.20
46 Jose Oquendo	.02	.10
47 Mike Trombley	.02	.10
48 Dan Walters	.02	.10
49 Gerald Williams	.02	.10
50 Bud Black	.02	.10
51 Bobby Witt	.02	.10
52 Mark Davis	.02	.10
53 Shawn Barton RC	.02	.10
54 Paul Assenmacher	.02	.10
55 Kevin Reimer	.02	.10
56 Billy Ashley RR	.02	.10
57 Eddie Zosky	.02	.10
58 Chris Sabo	.02	.10
59 Billy Ripken	.02	.10
60 Scooter Tucker	.02	.10
61 Tim Wakefield RR	.20	.50
62 Mitch Webster	.02	.10
63 Jack Clark	.07	.20
64 Mark Gardner	.02	.10
65 Lee Stevens	.02	.10
66 Todd Hundley	.02	.10
67 Bobby Thigpen	.02	.10
68 Dave Hollins	.02	.10
69 Jack Armstrong	.02	.10
70 Alex Cole	.02	.10
71 Mark Carreon	.02	.10
72 Todd Worrell	.02	.10
73 Steve Shifflett	.02	.10
74 Jerald Clark	.02	.10
75 Paul Molitor	.07	.20
76 Larry Carter RC	.02	.10
77 Rich Rowland RR	.02	.10
78 Damon Berryhill	.02	.10
79 Willie Banks	.02	.10
80 Hector Villanueva	.02	.10
81 Mike Gallego	.02	.10
82 Tim Belcher	.02	.10
83 Mike Bordick	.02	.10
84 Craig Biggio	.10	.30
85 Lance Parrish	.07	.20
86 Brett Butler	.07	.20
87 Mike Timlin	.02	.10
88 Brian Barnes	.02	.10
89 Brady Anderson	.07	.20
90 D.J. Dozier	.02	.10
91 Frank Viola	.07	.20
92 Darren Daulton	.07	.20
93 Chad Curtis	.02	.10
94 Zane Smith	.02	.10
95 George Bell	.02	.10
96 Rex Hudler	.02	.10
97 Mark Whiten	.02	.10
98 Tim Teufel	.02	.10
99 Kevin Ritz	.02	.10
100 Jeff Brantley	.02	.10
101 Jeff Conine	.07	.20
102 Vinny Castilla	.20	.50
103 Greg Vaughn	.02	.10
104 Steve Buechele	.02	.10
105 Darren Reed	.02	.10
106 Bip Roberts	.02	.10
107 John Habyan	.02	.10
108 Scott Servais	.02	.10
109 Walt Weiss	.02	.10
110 J.T. Snow RR RC	.10	.30
111 Jay Buhner	.07	.20
112 Darryl Strawberry	.07	.20
113 Roger Pavlik	.02	.10
114 Chris Nabholz	.02	.10
115 Pat Borders	.02	.10
116 Pat Howell	.02	.10
117 Gregg Olson	.02	.10
118 Curt Schilling	.07	.20
119 Roger Clemens	.40	1.00
120 Victor Cole	.02	.10
121 Gary DiSarcina	.02	.10
122 Gary Carter CL Kirt Manwaring	.02	.10
123 Steve Sax	.02	.10
124 Chuck Carr	.02	.10
125 Mark Lewis	.02	.10
126 Tony Gwynn	.25	.60
127 Travis Fryman	.07	.20
128 Dave Burba	.02	.10
129 Wally Joyner	.07	.20
130 John Smoltz	.10	.30
131 Cal Eldred	.02	.10
132 Roberto Alomar CL Devon White	.07	.20
133 Arthur Rhodes	.02	.10
134 Jeff Blauser	.02	.10
135 Scott Cooper	.02	.10
136 Doug Strange	.02	.10
137 Luis Sojo	.02	.10
138 Jeff Branson	.02	.10
139 Alex Fernandez	.02	.10
140 Ken Caminiti	.07	.20
141 Charles Nagy	.02	.10
142 Tom Candiotti	.02	.10
143 Willie Greene RR	.02	.10
144 John Vander Wal	.02	.10
145 Kurt Knudsen	.02	.10
146 John Franco	.07	.20
147 Eddie Pierce RC	.02	.10
148 Kim Batiste	.02	.10
149 Darren Holmes	.02	.10
150 Steve Cooke	.02	.10
151 Terry Jorgensen	.02	.10
152 Mark Clark	.02	.10
153 Randy Velarde	.02	.10
154 Greg W. Harris	.02	.10
155 Kevin Campbell	.02	.10
156 John Burkett	.02	.10
157 Kevin Mitchell	.02	.10
158 Deion Sanders	.10	.30
159 Jose Canseco	.10	.30
160 Jeff Hartsock	.02	.10
161 Tom Quinlan RC	.02	.10
162 Tim Pugh RC	.02	.10
163 Glenn Davis	.02	.10
164 Shane Reynolds	.02	.10
165 Jody Reed	.02	.10
166 Mike Sharperson	.02	.10
167 Scott Lewis	.02	.10
168 Dennis Martinez	.07	.20
169 Scott Radinsky	.02	.10
170 Dave Gallagher	.02	.10
171 Jim Thome	.10	.30
172 Terry Mulholland	.02	.10
173 Milt Cuyler	.02	.10
174 Bob Patterson	.02	.10
175 Jeff Montgomery	.02	.10
176 Tim Salmon RR	.10	.30
177 Franklin Stubbs	.02	.10
178 Donovan Osborne	.02	.10
179 Jeff Reboulet	.02	.10
180 Jeremy Hernandez	.02	.10
181 Charlie Hayes	.02	.10
182 Matt Williams	.07	.20
183 Mike Raczka	.02	.10
184 Francisco Cabrera	.02	.10
185 Rich DeLucia	.02	.10
186 Sammy Sosa	.20	.50
187 Ivan Rodriguez	.10	.30
188 Bret Boone RR	.07	.20
189 Juan Guzman	.02	.10
190 Tom Browning	.02	.10
191 Randy Milligan	.02	.10
192 Steve Finley	.07	.20
193 John Patterson RR	.02	.10
194 Kip Gross	.02	.10
195 Tony Fossas	.02	.10
196 Ivan Calderon	.02	.10
197 Junior Felix	.02	.10
198 Pete Schourek	.02	.10
199 Craig Grebeck	.02	.10
200 Juan Bell	.02	.10
201 Glenallen Hill	.02	.10
202 Danny Jackson	.02	.10
203 John Kiely	.02	.10
204 Bob Tewksbury	.02	.10
205 Kevin Koslofski	.02	.10
206 Craig Shipley	.02	.10
207 John Jaha	.02	.10
208 Royce Clayton	.02	.10
209 Mike Piazza RR	1.25	3.00
210 Ron Gant	.07	.20
211 Scott Erickson	.02	.10
212 Doug Dascenzo	.02	.10
213 Andy Stankiewicz	.02	.10
214 Geronimo Berroa	.02	.10
215 Dennis Eckersley	.07	.20
216 Al Osuna	.02	.10
217 Tino Martinez	.10	.30
218 Henry Rodriguez	.02	.10
219 Ed Sprague	.02	.10

220 Ken Hill .02 .10
221 Chito Martinez .02 .10
222 Bret Saberhagen .07 .20
223 Mike Greenwell .02 .10
224 Mickey Morandini .02 .10
225 Chuck Finley .07 .20
226 Denny Neagle .07 .20
227 Kirk McCaskill .02 .10
228 Rheal Cormier .02 .10
229 Paul Sorrento .02 .10
230 Darrin Jackson .02 .10
231 Rob Deer .02 .10
232 Bill Swift .02 .10
233 Kevin McReynolds .02 .10
234 Terry Pendleton .07 .20
235 Dave Nilsson .02 .10
236 Chuck McElroy .02 .10
237 Derek Parks .02 .10
238 Norm Charlton .02 .10
239 Matt Nokes .02 .10
240 Juan Guerrero .02 .10
241 Jeff Parrett .02 .10
242 Ryan Thompson RR .02 .10
243 Dave Fleming .02 .10
244 Dave Hansen .02 .10
245 Monty Fariss .02 .10
246 Archi Cianfrocco .02 .10
247 Pat Hentgen .02 .10
248 Bill Pecota .02 .10
249 Ben McDonald .02 .10
250 Cliff Brantley .02 .10
251 John Valentin .02 .10
252 Jeff King .02 .10
253 Reggie Williams .02 .10
254 Damon Berryhill CL .02 .10
Alex Arias
255 Ozzie Guillen .07 .20
256 Mike Perez .02 .10
257 Thomas Howard .02 .10
258 Kurt Stillwell .02 .10
259 Mike Henneman .02 .10
260 Steve Decker .02 .10
261 Brent Mayne .02 .10
262 Otis Nixon .02 .10
263 Mark Kiefer .02 .10
264 Don Mattingly CL .10 .30
Mike Bordick)
265 Richie Lewis RC .02 .10
266 Pat Gomez RC .02 .10
267 Scott Taylor .02 .10
268 Shawon Dunston .02 .10
269 Greg Myers .02 .10
270 Tim Costo .02 .10
271 Greg Hibbard .02 .10
272 Pete Harnisch .02 .10
273 Dave Mlicki .02 .10
274 Orel Hershiser .07 .20
275 Sean Berry RR .02 .10
276 Doug Simons .02 .10
277 John Doherty .02 .10
278 Eddie Murray .20 .50
279 Chris Haney .02 .10
280 Stan Javier .02 .10
281 Jaime Navarro .02 .10
282 Orlando Merced .02 .10
283 Kent Hrbek .07 .20
284 Bernard Gilkey .02 .10
285 Russ Springer .02 .10
286 Mike Maddux .02 .10
287 Eric Fox .02 .10
288 Mark Leonard .02 .10
289 Tim Leary .02 .10
290 Brian Hunter .02 .10
291 Donald Harris .02 .10
292 Bob Scanlan .02 .10
293 Turner Ward .02 .10
294 Hal Morris .02 .10
295 Jimmy Poole .02 .10
296 Doug Jones .02 .10
297 Tony Pena .02 .10
298 Ramon Martinez .02 .10
299 Tim Fortugno .02 .10
300 Marquis Grissom .07 .20
301 Lance Johnson .02 .10
302 Jeff Kent .20 .50
303 Reggie Jefferson .02 .10
304 Wes Chamberlain .02 .10
305 Shawn Hare .02 .10
306 Mike LaValliere .02 .10
307 Gregg Jefferies .02 .10
308 Troy Neel RR .02 .10
309 Pat Listach .02 .10
310 Geronimo Pena .02 .10
311 Pedro Munoz .02 .10
312 Guillermo Velasquez .02 .10
313 Roberto Kelly .02 .10
314 Mike Jackson .02 .10
315 Rickey Henderson .20 .50
316 Mark Lemke .02 .10
317 Erik Hanson .02 .10
318 Derrick May .02 .10
319 Geno Petralli .02 .10
320 Melvin Nieves RR .02 .10
321 Doug Linton .02 .10
322 Rob Dibble .07 .20
323 Chris Hoiles .02 .10
324 Jimmy Jones .02 .10
325 Dave Staton RR .02 .10
326 Pedro Martinez .40 1.00
327 Paul Quantrill .02 .10
328 Greg Colbrunn .02 .10
329 Hilly Hathaway RC .02 .10
330 Jeff Innis .02 .10
331 Ron Karkovice .02 .10
332 Keith Shepherd RC .02 .10
333 Alan Embree .02 .10
334 Paul Wagner .02 .10
335 Dave Haas .02 .10
336 Ozzie Canseco .02 .10
337 Bill Sampen .02 .10
338 Rich Rodriguez .02 .10
339 Dean Palmer .07 .20
340 Greg Litton .02 .10
341 Jim Tatum RR RC .02 .10
342 Todd Haney RC .02 .10
343 Larry Casian .02 .10
344 Ryne Sandberg .30 .75
345 Sterling Hitchcock RC .07 .20
346 Chris Hammond .02 .10
347 Vince Horsman .02 .10
348 Butch Henry .02 .10
349 Dann Howitt .02 .10
350 Roger McDowell .02 .10
351 Jack Morris .07 .20
352 Bill Krueger .02 .10
353 Cris Colon .02 .10
354 Joe Vitko .02 .10
355 Willie McGee .07 .20
356 Jay Baller .02 .10
357 Pat Mahomes .02 .10
358 Roger Mason .02 .10
359 Jerry Nielsen .02 .10
360 Tom Pagnozzi .02 .10
361 Kevin Baez .02 .10
362 Tim Scott .02 .10
363 Domingo Martinez RC .02 .10
364 Kirt Manwaring .02 .10
365 Rafael Palmeiro .10 .30
366 Ray Lankford .07 .20
367 Tim McIntosh .02 .10
368 Jessie Hollins .02 .10
369 Scott Leius .02 .10
370 Bill Doran .02 .10
371 Sam Militello .02 .10
372 Ryan Bowen .02 .10
373 Dave Henderson .02 .10
374 Dan Smith RR .02 .10
375 Steve Reed RR RC .02 .10
376 Jose Offerman .02 .10
377 Kevin Brown .07 .20
378 Darrin Fletcher .02 .10
379 Duane Ward .02 .10
380 Wayne Kirby RR .02 .10
381 Steve Scarsone .02 .10
382 Mariano Duncan .02 .10
383 Ken Ryan RC .02 .10
384 Lloyd McClendon .02 .10
385 Brian Holman .02 .10
386 Braulio Castillo .02 .10
387 Danny Leon .02 .10
388 Omar Olivares .02 .10
389 Kevin Wickander .02 .10
390 Fred McGriff .10 .30
391 Phil Clark .02 .10
392 Darren Lewis .02 .10
393 Phil Hiatt .02 .10
394 Mike Morgan .02 .10
395 Shane Mack .02 .10
396 Dennis Eckersley CL .07 .20
Art Kusnyer CO
397 David Segui .02 .10
398 Rafael Belliard .02 .10
399 Tim Naehring .02 .10
400 Frank Castillo .02 .10
401 Joe Grahe .02 .10
402 Reggie Sanders .07 .20
403 Roberto Hernandez .02 .10
404 Luis Gonzalez .07 .20
405 Carlos Baerga .02 .10
406 Carlos Hernandez .02 .10
407 Pedro Astacio RR .02 .10
408 Mel Rojas .02 .10
409 Scott Livingstone .02 .10
410 Chico Walker .02 .10
411 Brian McRae .02 .10
412 Ben Rivera .02 .10
413 Ricky Bones .02 .10
414 Andy Van Slyke .10 .30
415 Chuck Knoblauch .07 .20
416 Luis Alicea .02 .10
417 Bob Wickman .02 .10
418 Doug Brocail .02 .10
419 Scott Brosius .07 .20
420 Rod Beck .02 .10
421 Edgar Martinez .10 .30
422 Ryan Klesko .07 .20
423 Nolan Ryan .75 2.00
424 Rey Sanchez .02 .10
425 Roberto Alomar .10 .30
426 Barry Larkin .10 .30
427 Mike Mussina .10 .30
428 Jeff Bagwell .10 .30
429 Mo Vaughn .07 .20
430 Eric Karros .07 .20
431 John Orton .02 .10
432 Wil Cordero .02 .10
433 Jack McDowell .02 .10
434 Howard Johnson .02 .10
435 Albert Belle .07 .20
436 John Kruk .07 .20
437 Skeeter Barnes .02 .10
438 Don Slaught .02 .10
439 Rusty Meacham .02 .10
440 Tim Laker RR RC .02 .10
441 Robin Yount .30 .75
442 Brian Jordan .07 .20
443 Kevin Tapani .02 .10
444 Gary Sheffield .07 .20
445 Rich Monteleone .02 .10
446 Will Clark .10 .30
447 Jerry Browne .02 .10
448 Jeff Treadway .02 .10
449 Mike Schooler .02 .10
450 Mike Harkey .02 .10
451 Julio Franco .07 .20
452 Kevin Young RR .07 .20
453 Kelly Gruber .02 .10
454 Jose Rijo .02 .10
455 Mike Devereaux .02 .10
456 Andujar Cedeno .02 .10
457 Damion Easley RR .02 .10
458 Kevin Gross .02 .10
459 Matt Young .02 .10
460 Matt Stairs .02 .10
461 Luis Polonia .02 .10
462 Dwight Gooden .07 .20
463 Warren Newson .02 .10
464 Jose DeLeon .02 .10
465 Jose Mesa .02 .10
466 Danny Cox .02 .10
467 Dan Gladden .02 .10
468 Gerald Perry .02 .10
469 Mike Boddicker .02 .10
470 Jeff Gardner .02 .10
471 Doug Henry .02 .10
472 Mike Benjamin .02 .10
473 Dan Peltier RR .02 .10
474 Mike Stanton .02 .10
475 John Smiley .02 .10
476 Dwight Smith .02 .10
477 Jim Leyritz .02 .10
478 Dwayne Henry .02 .10
479 Mark McGwire .50 1.25
480 Pete Incaviglia .02 .10
481 Dave Cochrane .02 .10
482 Eric Davis .07 .20
483 John Olerud .07 .20
484 Kent Bottenfield .02 .10
485 Mark McLemore .02 .10
486 Dave Magadan .02 .10
487 John Marzano .02 .10
488 Ruben Amaro .02 .10
489 Rob Ducey .02 .10
490 Stan Belinda .02 .10
491 Dan Pasqua .02 .10
492 Joe Magrane .02 .10
493 Brook Jacoby .02 .10
494 Gene Harris .02 .10
495 Mark Leiter .02 .10
496 Bryan Hickerson .02 .10
497 Tom Gordon .02 .10
498 Pete Smith .02 .10
499 Chris Bosio .02 .10
500 Shawn Boskie .02 .10
501 Dave West .02 .10
502 Milt Hill .02 .10
503 Pat Kelly .02 .10
504 Joe Boever .02 .10
505 Terry Steinbach .02 .10
506 Butch Huskey RR .02 .10
507 David Valle .02 .10
508 Mike Scioscia .02 .10
509 Kenny Rogers .07 .20
510 Moises Alou .07 .20
511 David Wells .07 .20
512 Mackey Sasser .02 .10
513 Todd Frohwirth .02 .10
514 Ricky Jordan .02 .10
515 Mike Gardiner .02 .10
516 Gary Redus .02 .10
517 Gary Gaetti .07 .20
518 Checklist .02 .10
519 Carlton Fisk .10 .30
520 Ozzie Smith .30 .75
521 Rod Nichols .02 .10
522 Benito Santiago .07 .20
523 Bill Gullickson .02 .10
524 Robby Thompson .02 .10
525 Mike Macfarlane .02 .10
526 Sid Bream .02 .10
527 Darryl Hamilton .02 .10
528 Checklist .02 .10
529 Jeff Tackett .02 .10
530 Greg Olson .02 .10
531 Bob Zupcic .02 .10
532 Mark Grace .10 .30
533 Steve Frey .02 .10
534 Dave Martinez .02 .10
535 Robin Ventura .07 .20
536 Casey Candaele .02 .10
537 Kenny Lofton .07 .20
538 Jay Howell .02 .10
539 Fern.Ramsey RR RC .02 .10
540 Larry Walker .07 .20
541 Cecil Fielder .07 .20
542 Lee Guetterman .02 .10
543 Keith Miller .02 .10
544 Len Dykstra .07 .20
545 B.J. Surhoff .07 .20
546 Bob Walk .02 .10
547 Brian Harper .02 .10
548 Lee Smith .07 .20
549 Danny Tartabull .02 .10
550 Frank Seminara .02 .10
551 Henry Mercedes .02 .10
552 Dave Righetti .07 .20
553 Ken Griffey Jr. .30 .75
554 Tom Glavine .10 .30
555 Juan Gonzalez .07 .20
556 Jim Bullinger .02 .10
557 Derek Bell .02 .10
558 Cesar Hernandez .02 .10
559 Cal Ripken .60 1.50
560 Eddie Taubensee .02 .10
561 John Flaherty .02 .10
562 Todd Benzinger .02 .10
563 Hubie Brooks .02 .10
564 Delino DeShields .02 .10
565 Tim Raines .07 .20
566 Sid Fernandez .02 .10
567 Steve Olin .02 .10
568 Tommy Greene .02 .10
569 Buddy Groom .02 .10
570 Randy Tomlin .02 .10
571 Hipolito Pichardo .02 .10
572 Rene Arocha RR RC .07 .20
573 Mike Fetters .02 .10
574 Felix Jose .02 .10
575 Gene Larkin .02 .10
576 Bruce Hurst .02 .10
577 Bernie Williams .10 .30
578 Trevor Wilson .02 .10
579 Bob Welch .02 .10
580 David Justice .07 .20
581 Randy Johnson .20 .50
582 Jose Vizcaino .02 .10
583 Jeff Huson .02 .10
584 Rob Maurer RR .02 .10
585 Todd Stottlemyre .02 .10
586 Joe Oliver .02 .10
587 Bob Milacki .02 .10
588 Rob Murphy .02 .10
589 Greg Pirkl RR .02 .10
590 Lenny Harris .02 .10
591 Luis Rivera .02 .10
592 John Wetteland .07 .20
593 Mark Langston .02 .10
594 Bobby Bonilla .07 .20
595 Esteban Beltre .02 .10
596 Mike Hartley .02 .10
597 Felix Fermin .02 .10
598 Carlos Garcia .02 .10
599 Frank Tanana .02 .10
600 Pedro Guerrero .07 .20
601 Terry Shumpert .02 .10
602 Wally Whitehurst .02 .10
603 Kevin Seitzer .02 .10
604 Chris James .02 .10
605 Greg Gohr RR .02 .10
606 Mark Wohlers .02 .10
607 Kirby Puckett .20 .50
608 Greg Maddux .30 .75
609 Don Mattingly .50 1.25
610 Greg Cadaret .02 .10
611 Dave Stewart .07 .20
612 Mark Portugal .02 .10
613 Pete O'Brien .02 .10
614 Bob Ojeda .02 .10
615 Joe Carter .07 .20
616 Pete Young .02 .10
617 Sam Horn .02 .10
618 Vince Coleman .02 .10
619 Wade Boggs .10 .30
620 Todd Pratt RC .07 .20
621 Ron Tingley .02 .10
622 Doug Drabek .02 .10
623 Scott Hemond .02 .10
624 Tim Jones .02 .10
625 Dennis Cook .02 .10
626 Jose Melendez .02 .10
627 Mike Munoz .02 .10
628 Jim Pena .02 .10
629 Gary Thurman .02 .10
630 Charlie Leibrandt .02 .10
631 Scott Fletcher .02 .10
632 Andre Dawson .07 .20
633 Greg Gagne .02 .10
634 Greg Swindell .02 .10
635 Kevin Maas .02 .10
636 Xavier Hernandez .02 .10
637 Ruben Sierra .07 .20
638 Dmitri Young RR .07 .20
639 Harold Reynolds .07 .20
640 Tom Goodwin .02 .10
641 Todd Burns .02 .10
642 Jeff Fassero .02 .10
643 Dave Winfield .07 .20
644 Willie Randolph .07 .20
645 Luis Mercedes .02 .10
646 Dale Murphy .10 .30
647 Danny Darwin .02 .10
648 Dennis Moeller .02 .10
649 Chuck Crim .02 .10
650 Checklist .02 .10
651 Shawn Abner .02 .10
652 Tracy Woodson .02 .10
653 Scott Scudder .02 .10
654 Tom Lampkin .02 .10
655 Alan Trammell .07 .20
656 Cory Snyder .02 .10
657 Chris Gwynn .02 .10
658 Lonnie Smith .02 .10
659 Jim Austin .02 .10
660 Rob Picciolo CL .02 .10
661 Tim Hulett .02 .10
662 Marvin Freeman .02 .10
663 Greg A. Harris .02 .10
664 Heathcliff Slocumb .02 .10
665 Mike Butcher .02 .10
666 Steve Foster .02 .10
667 Donn Pall .02 .10
668 Darryl Kile .07 .20
669 Jesse Levis .02 .10
670 Jim Gott .02 .10
671 Mark Hutton RR .02 .10
672 Brian Drahman .02 .10
673 Chad Kreuter .02 .10
674 Tony Fernandez .02 .10
675 Jose Lind .02 .10
676 Kyle Abbott .02 .10
677 Dan Plesac .02 .10
678 Barry Bonds .60 1.50
679 Chili Davis .07 .20
680 Stan Royer .02 .10
681 Scott Kamieniecki .02 .10
682 Carlos Martinez .02 .10
683 Mike Moore .02 .10
684 Candy Maldonado .02 .10
685 Jeff Nelson .02 .10
686 Lou Whitaker .07 .20
687 Jose Guzman .02 .10
688 Manuel Lee .02 .10
689 Bob MacDonald .02 .10
690 Scott Bankhead .02 .10
691 Alan Mills .02 .10
692 Brian Williams .02 .10
693 Tom Brunansky .02 .10
694 Lenny Webster .02 .10
695 Greg Briley .02 .10
696 Paul O'Neill .10 .30
697 Joey Cora .02 .10
698 Charlie O'Brien .02 .10
699 Junior Ortiz .02 .10
700 Ron Darling .02 .10
701 Tony Phillips .02 .10
702 William Pennyfeather .02 .10
703 Mark Gubicza .02 .10
704 Steve Hosey RR .02 .10
705 Henry Cotto .02 .10
706 David Hulse RC .02 .10
707 Mike Pagliarulo .02 .10
708 Dave Stieb .02 .10
709 Melido Perez .02 .10
710 Jimmy Key .07 .20
711 Jeff Russell .02 .10
712 David Cone .07 .20
713 Russ Swan .02 .10
714 Mark Guthrie .02 .10
715 Checklist .02 .10
716 Al Martin RR .02 .10
717 Randy Knorr .02 .10
718 Mike Stanley .02 .10
719 Rick Sutcliffe .07 .20
720 Terry Leach .02 .10
721 Chipper Jones RR .20 .50
722 Jim Eisenreich .02 .10
723 Tom Henke .02 .10
724 Jeff Frye .02 .10
725 Harold Baines .07 .20
726 Scott Sanderson .02 .10
727 Tom Foley .02 .10
728 Bryan Harvey .02 .10
729 Tom Edens .02 .10
730 Eric Young .02 .10
731 Dave Weathers .02 .10
732 Spike Owen .02 .10
733 Scott Aldred .02 .10
734 Cris Carpenter .02 .10
735 Dion James .02 .10
736 Joe Girardi .02 .10
737 Nigel Wilson RR .02 .10
738 Scott Chiamparino .02 .10
739 Jeff Reardon .07 .20
740 Willie Blair .02 .10
741 Jim Corsi .02 .10
742 Ken Patterson .02 .10
743 Andy Ashby .02 .10
744 Rob Natal .02 .10
745 Kevin Bass .02 .10
746 Freddie Benavides .02 .10
747 Chris Donnels .02 .10
748 Kerry Woodson .02 .10
749 Calvin Jones .02 .10
750 Gary Scott .02 .10
751 Joe Orsulak .02 .10
752 Armando Reynoso .02 .10
753 Monty Fariss .02 .10
754 Billy Hatcher .02 .10
755 Denis Boucher .02 .10
756 Walt Weiss .02 .10
757 Mike Fitzgerald .02 .10
758 Rudy Seanez .02 .10
759 Bret Barberie .02 .10
760 Mo Sanford .02 .10
761 Pedro Castellano .02 .10
762 Chuck Carr .02 .10
763 Steve Howe .02 .10
764 Andres Galarraga .07 .20
765 Jeff Conine .07 .20
766 Ted Power .02 .10
767 Butch Henry .02 .10
768 Steve Decker .02 .10
769 Storm Davis .02 .10
770 Vinny Castilla .20 .50
771 Junior Felix .02 .10
772 Walt Terrell .02 .10
773 Brad Ausmus .20 .50
774 Jamie McAndrew .02 .10
775 Milt Thompson .02 .10
776 Charlie Hayes .02 .10
777 Jack Armstrong .02 .10
778 Dennis Rasmussen .02 .10
779 Darren Holmes .02 .10
780 Alex Arias .02 .10
781 Randy Bush .02 .10
782 Javy Lopez .10 .30
783 Dante Bichette .07 .20
784 John Johnstone RC .02 .10
785 Rene Gonzales .02 .10
786 Alex Cole .02 .10
787 Jeromy Burnitz RR .07 .20
788 Michael Huff .02 .10
789 Anthony Telford .02 .10
790 Jerald Clark .02 .10
791 Joel Johnston .02 .10
792 David Nied RR .02 .10

1993 Donruss Diamond Kings

These standard-size cards, commemorating Donruss' annual selection of the games top players, were randomly inserted in 1993 Donruss packs. The first 15 cards were available in the first series of the 1993 Donruss and cards 16-31 were inserted with the second series. The cards are gold-foil stamped and feature player portraits by noted sports artist Dick Perez. Card numbers 27-28 honor the first draft picks of the new Florida Marlins and Colorado Rockies franchises. Collectors 16 years of age and younger could enter Donruss' Diamond King contest by writing an essay of 75 words or less explaining who their favorite Diamond King player was and why. Winners were awarded one of 30 framed watercolors at the National Convention, held in Chicago, July 22-25, 1993.

COMPLETE SET (31) 12.00 30.00
COMPLETE SERIES 1 (15) 8.00 20.00
COMPLETE SERIES 2 (16) 4.00 10.00
DK1 Ken Griffey Jr. 2.00 5.00
DK2 Ryne Sandberg 2.00 5.00
DK3 Roger Clemens 2.50 6.00
DK4 Kirby Puckett 1.25 3.00
DK5 Bill Swift .25 .60
DK6 Larry Walker .50 1.25
DK7 Juan Gonzalez .50 1.25
DK8 Wally Joyner .50 1.25
DK9 Andy Van Slyke .75 2.00
DK10 Robin Ventura .50 1.25
DK11 Bip Roberts .25 .60
DK12 Roberto Kelly .25 .60
DK13 Carlos Baerga .25 .60
DK14 Orel Hershiser .50 1.25
DK15 Cecil Fielder .50 1.25
DK16 Robin Yount 2.00 5.00
DK17 Darren Daulton .50 1.25
DK18 Mark McGwire 3.00 8.00
DK19 Tom Glavine .75 2.00
DK20 Roberto Alomar .75 2.00
DK21 Gary Sheffield .50 1.25
DK22 Bob Tewksbury .25 .60
DK23 Brady Anderson .50 1.25
DK24 Craig Biggio .75 2.00
DK25 Eddie Murray 1.25 3.00
DK26 Luis Polonia .25 .60
DK27 Nigel Wilson .25 .60
DK28 David Nied .25 .60
DK29 Pat Listach ROY .25 .60
DK30 Eric Karros ROY .50 1.25
DK31 Checklist 1-31 .40 1.00

1993 Donruss Elite

The numbering on the 1993 Elite cards follows consecutively after that of the 1992 Elite series cards, and each of the 10,000 Elite cards is serially numbered. Cards 19-27 were random inserts in 1993 Donruss series I foil packs while cards 28-36 were inserted in series II packs. The backs of the Elite cards also carry the serial number ("X" of 10,000) as well as the card number. The Signature Series Will Clark card was randomly inserted in

1993 Donruss foil packs; he personally autographed 5,000 cards. Featuring a Dick Perez portrait, the ten thousand Legends Series cards honor Robin Yount for his 3,000th hit achievement.

19 Fred McGriff 10.00 25.00
20 Ryne Sandberg 15.00 40.00
21 Eddie Murray 10.00 25.00
22 Paul Molitor 6.00 15.00
23 Barry Larkin 10.00 25.00
24 Don Mattingly 20.00 50.00
25 Dennis Eckersley 6.00 15.00
26 Roberto Alomar 10.00 25.00
27 Edgar Martinez 10.00 25.00
28 Gary Sheffield 6.00 15.00
29 Darren Daulton 6.00 15.00
30 Larry Walker 6.00 15.00
31 Barry Bonds 20.00 50.00
32 Andy Van Slyke 10.00 25.00
33 Mark McGwire 20.00 50.00
34 Cecil Fielder 6.00 15.00
35 Dave Winfield 6.00 15.00
36 Juan Gonzalez 6.00 15.00
L3 Robin Yount Legend 10.00 25.00
S3 Will Clark AU/5000 20.00 50.00

1993 Donruss Elite Dominators

In a series of programs broadcast Dec. 8-13, 1993, on the Shop at Home cable network, viewers were offered the opportunity to purchase a factory-sealed box of either 1993 Donruss I or II, which included one Elite Dominator card produced especially for the promotion. The set retailed for 99.00 plus 6.00 for postage and handling. 5,000 serial-numbered sets were produced and half of the cards for Nolan Ryan, Juan Gonzalez, Paul Molitor, and Don Mattingly were signed by the player. The entire print run of 100,000 cards were reportedly purchased by the Shop at Home network and were to be offered periodically over the network. The production number, out of a total of 5,000 produced, is shown at the bottom.

COMP.UNSIG. SET (20) 160.00 300.00
1 Ryne Sandberg 8.00 20.00
2 Fred McGriff 2.50 6.00
3 Greg Maddux 10.00 25.00
4 Ron Gant 2.00 5.00
5 David Justice 3.00 8.00
6 Don Mattingly 8.00 20.00
7 Tim Salmon 5.00 12.00
8 Mike Piazza 20.00 40.00
9 John Olerud 2.00 5.00
10 Nolan Ryan 20.00 40.00
11 Juan Gonzalez 3.00 8.00
12 Ken Griffey Jr. 8.00 20.00
13 Frank Thomas 5.00 12.00
14 Tom Glavine 2.50 6.00
15 George Brett 8.00 20.00
16 Barry Bonds 8.00 20.00
17 Albert Belle 2.00 5.00
18 Paul Molitor 4.00 10.00
19 Cal Ripken 20.00 40.00
20 Roberto Alomar 3.00 8.00
AU6 Don Mattingly AU 20.00 50.00
AU10 Nolan Ryan AU 40.00 100.00
AU11 Juan Gonzalez AU 10.00 25.00
AU18 Paul Molitor AU 12.50 30.00

1993 Donruss Elite Supers

Sequentially numbered one through 5,000, these 20 oversized cards measure approximately 3 1/2" by 5" and have wide prismatic foil borders with an inner gray borders. The Elite Update set features all the players found in the regular Elite set, plus Nolan Ryan and Frank Thomas, whose cards replace numbers 19 and 20 from the earlier release, and an updated card of Barry Bonds in his Giants uniform. The backs carry the production number and the card number.

COMPLETE SET (20) 50.00 120.00
1 Fred McGriff 1.25 3.00
2 Ryne Sandberg 4.00 10.00
3 Eddie Murray 1.50 4.00
4 Paul Molitor 3.00 8.00
5 Barry Larkin 1.50 4.00
6 Don Mattingly 5.00 12.00
7 Dennis Eckersley 2.00 5.00
8 Roberto Alomar 1.50 4.00

9 Edgar Martinez 1.25 3.00
10 Gary Sheffield 2.00 5.00
11 Darren Daulton .75 2.00
12 Larry Walker 1.50 4.00
13 Barry Bonds 5.00 12.00
14 Andy Van Slyke .40 1.00
15 Mark McGwire 6.00 15.00
16 Cecil Fielder .75 2.00
17 Dave Winfield 2.00 5.00
18 Juan Gonzalez 1.50 4.00
19 Frank Thomas 4.00 10.00
20 Nolan Ryan 10.00 25.00

1994 Donruss

The 1994 Donruss set was issued in two separate series of 330 standard-size cards for a total of 660. Cards were issued in foil wrapped packs. The fronts feature borderless color player action photos on front. There are no notable Rookie Cards in this set.

COMPLETE SET (660) 12.00 30.00
COMP.SERIES 1 (330) 6.00 15.00
COMP.SERIES 2 (330) 6.00 15.00
1 Nolan Ryan 1.50 4.00
2 Mike Piazza .60 1.50
3 Moises Alou .10 .30
4 Ken Griffey Jr. .50 1.25
5 Gary Sheffield .10 .30
6 Roberto Alomar .20 .50
7 John Kruk .10 .30
8 Gregg Olson .05 .15
9 Gregg Jefferies .05 .15
10 Tony Gwynn .40 1.00
11 Chad Curtis .05 .15
12 Craig Biggio .20 .50
13 John Burkett .05 .15
14 Carlos Baerga .05 .15
15 Robin Yount .50 1.25
16 Dennis Eckersley .10 .30
17 Dwight Gooden .10 .30
18 Ryne Sandberg .50 1.25
19 Rickey Henderson .30 .75
20 Jack McDowell .05 .15
21 Jay Bell .10 .30
22 Kevin Brown .10 .30
23 Robin Ventura .10 .30
24 Paul Molitor .10 .30
25 David Justice .10 .30
26 Rafael Palmeiro .20 .50
27 Cecil Fielder .10 .30
28 Chuck Knoblauch .10 .30
29 Dave Hollins .05 .15
30 Jimmy Key .10 .30
31 Mark Langston .05 .15
32 Darryl Kile .10 .30
33 Ruben Sierra .10 .30
34 Ron Gant .10 .30
35 Ozzie Smith .50 1.25
36 Wade Boggs .20 .50
37 Marquis Grissom .10 .30
38 Will Clark .20 .50
39 Kenny Lofton .10 .30
40 Cal Ripken 1.00 2.50
41 Steve Avery .05 .15
42 Mo Vaughn .10 .30
43 Brian McRae .05 .15
44 Mickey Tettleton .05 .15
45 Barry Larkin .20 .50
46 Charlie Hayes .05 .15
47 Kevin Appier .10 .30
48 Robby Thompson .05 .15
49 Juan Gonzalez .10 .30
50 Paul O'Neill .20 .50
51 Marcos Armas .05 .15
52 Mike Butcher .05 .15
53 Ken Caminiti .10 .30
54 Pat Borders .05 .15
55 Pedro Munoz .05 .15
56 Tim Belcher .05 .15
57 Paul Assenmacher .05 .15
58 Damon Berryhill .05 .15
59 Ricky Bones .05 .15
60 Rene Arocha .05 .15
61 Shawn Boskie .05 .15
62 Pedro Astacio .05 .15
63 Frank Bolick .05 .15
64 Bud Black .05 .15
65 Sandy Alomar Jr. .05 .15
66 Rich Amaral .05 .15
67 Luis Aquino .05 .15
68 Kevin Baez .05 .15
69 Mike Devereaux .05 .15
70 Andy Ashby .05 .15
71 Larry Andersen .05 .15
72 Steve Cooke .05 .15
73 Mario Diaz .05 .15
74 Rob Deer .05 .15
75 Bobby Ayala .05 .15
76 Freddie Benavides .05 .15
77 Stan Belinda .05 .15
78 John Doherty .05 .15
79 Willie Banks .05 .15
80 Spike Owen .05 .15
81 Mike Bordick .05 .15
82 Chili Davis .10 .30
83 Luis Gonzalez .10 .30
84 Ed Sprague .05 .15
85 Jeff Reboulet .05 .15
86 Jason Bere .05 .15
87 Mark Hutton .05 .15
88 Jeff Blauser .05 .15
89 Cal Eldred .05 .15
90 Bernard Gilkey .05 .15
91 Frank Castillo .05 .15
92 Jim Gott .05 .15
93 Greg Colbrunn .05 .15
94 Jeff Brantley .05 .15
95 Jeremy Hernandez .05 .15
96 Norm Charlton .05 .15
97 Alex Arias .05 .15
98 John Franco .10 .30
99 Chris Hoiles .05 .15
100 Brad Ausmus .20 .50
101 Wes Chamberlain .05 .15
102 Mark Dewey .05 .15
103 Benji Gil .05 .15
104 John Dopson .05 .15
105 John Smiley .05 .15
106 David Nied .05 .15
107 George Brett .75 2.00
108 Kirk Gibson .10 .30
109 Larry Casian .05 .15
110 Ryne Sandberg CL .30 .75
111 Brent Gates .05 .15
112 Damion Easley .05 .15
113 Pete Harnisch .05 .15
114 Danny Cox .05 .15
115 Kevin Tapani .05 .15
116 Roberto Hernandez .05 .15
117 Domingo Jean .05 .15
118 Sid Bream .05 .15
119 Doug Henry .05 .15
120 Omar Olivares .05 .15
121 Mike Harkey .05 .15
122 Carlos Hernandez .05 .15
123 Jeff Fassero .05 .15
124 Dave Burba .05 .15
125 Wayne Kirby .05 .15
126 John Cummings .05 .15
127 Bret Barberie .05 .15
128 Todd Hundley .05 .15
129 Tim Hulett .05 .15
130 Phil Clark .05 .15
131 Danny Jackson .05 .15
132 Tom Foley .05 .15
133 Donald Harris .05 .15
134 Scott Fletcher .05 .15
135 Johnny Ruffin .05 .15
136 Jerald Clark .05 .15
137 Billy Brewer .05 .15
138 Dan Gladden .05 .15
139 Eddie Guardado .10 .30
140 Cal Ripken CL .30 .75
141 Scott Hemond .05 .15
142 Steve Frey .05 .15
143 Xavier Hernandez .05 .15
144 Mark Eichhorn .05 .15
145 Ellis Burks .10 .30
146 Jim Leyritz .05 .15
147 Mark Lemke .05 .15
148 Pat Listach .05 .15
149 Donovan Osborne .05 .15
150 Glenallen Hill .05 .15
151 Orel Hershiser .10 .30
152 Darrin Fletcher .05 .15
153 Royce Clayton .05 .15
154 Derek Lilliquist .05 .15
155 Mike Felder .05 .15
156 Jeff Conine .10 .30
157 Ryan Thompson .05 .15
158 Ben McDonald .05 .15
159 Ricky Gutierrez .05 .15
160 Terry Mulholland .05 .15
161 Carlos Garcia .05 .15
162 Tom Henke .05 .15
163 Mike Greenwell .05 .15
164 Thomas Howard .05 .15
165 Joe Girardi .05 .15
166 Hubie Brooks .05 .15
167 Greg Gohr .05 .15
168 Chip Hale .05 .15
169 Rick Honeycutt .05 .15
170 Hilly Hathaway .05 .15
171 Todd Jones .05 .15
172 Tony Fernandez .05 .15
173 Bo Jackson .30 .75
174 Bobby Munoz .05 .15
175 Greg McMichael .05 .15
176 Graeme Lloyd .05 .15
177 Tom Pagnozzi .05 .15
178 Derrick May .05 .15
179 Pedro Martinez .30 .75
180 Ken Hill .05 .15
181 Bryan Hickerson .05 .15
182 Jose Mesa .05 .15
183 Dave Fleming .05 .15
184 Henry Cotto .05 .15
185 Jeff Kent .20 .50
186 Mark McLemore .05 .15
187 Trevor Hoffman .20 .50
188 Todd Pratt .05 .15
189 Blas Minor .05 .15
190 Charlie Leibrandt .05 .15
191 Tony Pena .05 .15
192 Larry Luebbers RC .05 .15
193 Greg W. Harris .05 .15
194 David Cone .10 .30
195 Bill Gullickson .05 .15
196 Brian Harper .05 .15
197 Steve Karsay .05 .15
198 Greg Myers .05 .15
199 Mark Portugal .05 .15
200 Pat Hentgen .05 .15
201 Mike LaValliere .05 .15
202 Mike Stanley .05 .15
203 Kent Mercker .05 .15
204 Dave Nilsson .05 .15
205 Erik Pappas .05 .15
206 Mike Morgan .05 .15
207 Roger McDowell .05 .15
208 Mike Lansing .05 .15
209 Kirt Manwaring .05 .15
210 Randy Milligan .05 .15
211 Erik Hanson .05 .15
212 Orestes Destrade .05 .15
213 Mike Maddux .05 .15
214 Alan Mills .05 .15
215 Tim Mauser .05 .15
216 Ben Rivera .05 .15
217 Don Slaught .05 .15
218 Bob Patterson .05 .15
219 Carlos Quintana .05 .15
220 Tim Raines CL .05 .15
221 Hal Morris .05 .15
222 Darren Holmes .05 .15
223 Chris Gwynn .05 .15
224 Chad Kreuter .05 .15
225 Mike Hartley .05 .15
226 Scott Lydy .05 .15
227 Eduardo Perez .05 .15
228 Greg Swindell .05 .15
229 Al Leiter .10 .30
230 Scott Radinsky .05 .15
231 Bob Wickman .05 .15
232 Otis Nixon .05 .15
233 Kevin Reimer .05 .15
234 Geronimo Pena .05 .15
235 Kevin Roberson .05 .15
236 Jody Reed .05 .15
237 Kirk Rueter .05 .15
238 Willie McGee .10 .30
239 Charles Nagy .05 .15
240 Tim Leary .05 .15
241 Carl Everett .10 .30
242 Charlie O'Brien .05 .15
243 Mike Pagliarulo .05 .15
244 Kerry Taylor .05 .15
245 Kevin Stocker .05 .15
246 Joel Johnston .05 .15
247 Geno Petralli .05 .15
248 Jeff Russell .05 .15
249 Joe Oliver .05 .15
250 Roberto Mejia .05 .15
251 Chris Haney .05 .15
252 Bill Krueger .05 .15
253 Shane Mack .05 .15
254 Terry Steinbach .05 .15
255 Luis Polonia .05 .15
256 Eddie Taubensee .05 .15
257 Dave Stewart .10 .30
258 Tim Raines .10 .30
259 Bernie Williams .20 .50
260 John Smoltz .20 .50
261 Kevin Seitzer .05 .15
262 Bob Tewksbury .05 .15
263 Bob Scanlan .05 .15
264 Henry Rodriguez .05 .15
265 Tim Scott .05 .15
266 Scott Sanderson .05 .15
267 Eric Plunk .05 .15
268 Edgar Martinez .20 .50
269 Charlie Hough .10 .30
270 Joe Orsulak .05 .15
271 Harold Reynolds .10 .30
272 Tim Teufel .05 .15
273 Bobby Thigpen .05 .15
274 Randy Tomlin .05 .15
275 Gary Redus .05 .15
276 Ken Ryan .05 .15
277 Tim Pugh .05 .15
278 Jayhawk Owens .05 .15
279 Phil Hiatt .05 .15
280 Alan Trammell .10 .30
281 Dave McCarty .05 .15
282 Bob Welch .05 .15
283 J.T. Snow .10 .30
284 Brian Williams .05 .15
285 Devon White .10 .30
286 Steve Sax .05 .15
287 Tony Tarasco .05 .15
288 Bill Spiers .05 .15
289 Allen Watson .05 .15
290 Rickey Henderson CL .20 .50
291 Jose Vizcaino .05 .15
292 Darryl Strawberry .10 .30
293 John Wetteland .10 .30
294 Bill Swift .05 .15
295 Jeff Treadway .05 .15
296 Tino Martinez .20 .50
297 Richie Lewis .05 .15
298 Bret Saberhagen .10 .30
299 Arthur Rhodes .05 .15
300 Guillermo Velasquez .05 .15
301 Milt Thompson .05 .15
302 Doug Strange .05 .15
303 Aaron Sele .05 .15
304 Bip Roberts .05 .15
305 Bruce Ruffin .05 .15
306 Jose Lind .05 .15
307 David Wells .10 .30
308 Bobby Witt .05 .15
309 Mark Wohlers .05 .15
310 B.J. Surhoff .10 .30
311 Mark Whiten .05 .15
312 Turk Wendell .05 .15
313 Raul Mondesi .10 .30
314 Brian Turang RC .05 .15
315 Chris Hammond .05 .15
316 Tim Bogar .05 .15
317 Brad Pennington .05 .15
318 Tim Worrell .05 .15
319 Mitch Williams .05 .15
320 Rondell White .10 .30
321 Frank Viola .10 .30
322 Manny Ramirez .30 .75
323 Gary Wayne .05 .15
324 Mike Macfarlane .05 .15
325 Russ Springer .05 .15
326 Tim Wallach .05 .15
327 Salomon Torres .05 .15
328 Omar Vizquel .20 .50
329 Andy Tomberlin RC .05 .15
330 Chris Sabo .05 .15
331 Mike Mussina .20 .50
332 Andy Benes .05 .15
333 Darren Daulton .10 .30
334 Orlando Merced .05 .15
335 Mark McGwire .75 2.00
336 Dave Winfield .10 .30
337 Sammy Sosa .30 .75
338 Eric Karros .10 .30
339 Greg Vaughn .05 .15
340 Don Mattingly .75 2.00
341 Frank Thomas .30 .75
342 Fred McGriff .20 .50
343 Kirby Puckett .30 .75
344 Roberto Kelly .05 .15
345 Wally Joyner .10 .30
346 Andres Galarraga .10 .30
347 Bobby Bonilla .10 .30
348 Benito Santiago .10 .30
349 Barry Bonds .75 2.00
350 Delino DeShields .05 .15
351 Albert Belle .10 .30
352 Randy Johnson .30 .75
353 Tim Salmon .20 .50
354 John Olerud .10 .30
355 Dean Palmer .10 .30
356 Roger Clemens .60 1.50
357 Jim Abbott .20 .50
358 Mark Grace .20 .50
359 Ozzie Guillen .10 .30
360 Lou Whitaker .10 .30
361 Jose Rijo .05 .15
362 Jeff Montgomery .05 .15
363 Chuck Finley .10 .30
364 Tom Glavine .20 .50
365 Jeff Bagwell .20 .50
366 Joe Carter .10 .30
367 Ray Lankford .10 .30
368 Ramon Martinez .05 .15
369 Jay Buhner .10 .30
370 Matt Williams .10 .30
371 Larry Walker .10 .30
372 Jose Canseco .20 .50
373 Lenny Dykstra .10 .30
374 Bryan Harvey .05 .15
375 Andy Van Slyke .20 .50
376 Ivan Rodriguez .20 .50
377 Kevin Mitchell .05 .15
378 Travis Fryman .10 .30
379 Duane Ward .05 .15
380 Greg Maddux .50 1.25
381 Scott Servais .05 .15
382 Greg Olson .05 .15
383 Rey Sanchez .05 .15
384 Tom Kramer .05 .15
385 David Valle .05 .15
386 Eddie Murray .30 .75
387 Kevin Higgins .05 .15
388 Dan Wilson .05 .15
389 Todd Frohwirth .05 .15
390 Gerald Williams .05 .15
391 Hipolito Pichardo .05 .15
392 Pat Meares .05 .15
393 Luis Lopez .05 .15
394 Ricky Jordan .05 .15
395 Bob Walk .05 .15
396 Sid Fernandez .05 .15
397 Todd Worrell .05 .15
398 Darryl Hamilton .05 .15
399 Randy Myers .05 .15
400 Rod Brewer .05 .15
401 Lance Blankenship .05 .15
402 Steve Finley .10 .30
403 Phil Leftwich RC .05 .15
404 Juan Guzman .05 .15
405 Anthony Young .05 .15
406 Jeff Gardner .05 .15
407 Ryan Bowen .05 .15
408 Fernando Valenzuela .10 .30
409 David West .05 .15
410 Kenny Rogers .10 .30
411 Bob Zupcic .05 .15
412 Eric Young .05 .15
413 Bret Boone .10 .30
414 Danny Tartabull .05 .15
415 Bob MacDonald .05 .15
416 Ron Karkovice .05 .15
417 Scott Cooper .05 .15
418 Dante Bichette .10 .30
419 Tripp Cromer .05 .15
420 Billy Ashley .05 .15
421 Roger Smithberg .05 .15
422 Dennis Martinez .10 .30
423 Mike Blowers .05 .15
424 Darren Lewis .05 .15
425 Junior Ortiz .05 .15
426 Butch Huskey .05 .15
427 Jimmy Poole .05 .15
428 Walt Weiss .05 .15
429 Scott Bankhead .05 .15
430 Deion Sanders .20 .50
431 Scott Bullett .05 .15
432 Jeff Huson .05 .15
433 Tyler Green .05 .15
434 Billy Hatcher .05 .15
435 Bob Hamelin .05 .15
436 Reggie Sanders .10 .30
437 Scott Erickson .05 .15
438 Steve Reed .05 .15
439 Randy Velarde .05 .15
440 Tony Gwynn CL .20 .50
441 Terry Leach .05 .15
442 Danny Bautista .05 .15
443 Kent Hrbek .10 .30
444 Rick Wilkins .05 .15
445 Tony Phillips .05 .15
446 Dion James .05 .15
447 Joey Cora .05 .15
448 Andre Dawson .10 .30
449 Pedro Castellano .05 .15
450 Tom Gordon .05 .15
451 Rob Dibble .10 .30
452 Ron Darling .05 .15
453 Chipper Jones .30 .75
454 Joe Grahe .05 .15
455 Domingo Cedeno .05 .15
456 Tom Edens .05 .15
457 Mitch Webster .05 .15
458 Jose Bautista .05 .15
459 Troy O'Leary .05 .15
460 Todd Zeile .05 .15
461 Sean Berry .05 .15
462 Brad Holman RC .05 .15
463 Dave Martinez .05 .15
464 Mark Lewis .05 .15
465 Paul Carey .05 .15
466 Jack Armstrong .05 .15
467 David Telgheder .05 .15
468 Gene Harris .05 .15
469 Danny Darwin .05 .15
470 Kim Batiste .05 .15
471 Tim Wakefield .20 .50
472 Craig Lefferts .05 .15
473 Jacob Brumfield .05 .15
474 Lance Painter .05 .15
475 Milt Cuyler .05 .15
476 Melido Perez .05 .15
477 Derek Parks .05 .15
478 Gary DiSarcina .05 .15
479 Steve Bedrosian .05 .15
480 Eric Anthony .05 .15
481 Julio Franco .10 .30
482 Tommy Greene .05 .15
483 Pat Kelly .05 .15
484 Nate Minchey .05 .15
485 William Pennyfeather .05 .15
486 Harold Baines .10 .30
487 Howard Johnson .05 .15
488 Angel Miranda .05 .15
489 Scott Sanders .05 .15
490 Shawon Dunston .05 .15
491 Mel Rojas .05 .15
492 Jeff Nelson .05 .15
493 Archi Cianfrocco .05 .15
494 Al Martin .05 .15
495 Mike Gallego .05 .15
496 Mike Henneman .05 .15
497 Armando Reynoso .05 .15
498 Mickey Morandini .05 .15
499 Rick Renteria .05 .15
500 Rick Sutcliffe .10 .30
501 Bobby Jones .05 .15
502 Gary Gaetti .10 .30
503 Rick Aguilera .05 .15
504 Todd Stottlemyre .05 .15
505 Mike Mohler .05 .15
506 Mike Stanton .05 .15
507 Jose Guzman .05 .15
508 Kevin Rogers .05 .15
509 Chuck Carr .05 .15
510 Chris Jones .05 .15
511 Brent Mayne .05 .15
512 Greg Harris .05 .15
513 Dave Henderson .05 .15
514 Eric Hillman .05 .15
515 Dan Peltier .05 .15
516 Craig Shipley .05 .15
517 John Valentin .05 .15
518 Wilson Alvarez .05 .15
519 Andujar Cedeno .05 .15
520 Troy Neel .05 .15
521 Tom Candiotti .05 .15
522 Matt Mieske .05 .15
523 Jim Thome .20 .50
524 Lou Frazier .05 .15
525 Mike Jackson .05 .15
526 Pedro Martinez RC .05 .15
527 Roger Pavlik .05 .15
528 Kent Bottenfield .05 .15
529 Felix Jose .05 .15
530 Mark Guthrie .05 .15
531 Steve Farr .05 .15
532 Craig Paquette .05 .15
533 Doug Jones .05 .15
534 Luis Alicea .05 .15
535 Cory Snyder .05 .15
536 Paul Sorrento .05 .15
537 Nigel Wilson .05 .15
538 Jeff King .05 .15
539 Willie Greene .05 .15
540 Kirk McCaskill .05 .15
541 Al Osuna .05 .15
542 Greg Hibbard .05 .15
543 Brett Butler .10 .30
544 Jose Valentin .05 .15
545 Wil Cordero .05 .15
546 Chris Bosio .05 .15
547 Jamie Moyer .10 .30
548 Jim Eisenreich .05 .15
549 Vinny Castilla .10 .30
550 Dave Winfield CL .05 .15
551 John Roper .05 .15
552 Lance Johnson .05 .15
553 Scott Kamieniecki .05 .15
554 Mike Moore .05 .15
555 Steve Buechele .05 .15
556 Terry Pendleton .10 .30
557 Todd Van Poppel .05 .15
558 Rob Butler .05 .15
559 Zane Smith .05 .15
560 David Hulse .05 .15
561 Tim Costo .05 .15
562 John Habyan .05 .15
563 Terry Jorgensen .05 .15
564 Matt Nokes .05 .15
565 Kevin McReynolds .05 .15
566 Phil Plantier .05 .15
567 Chris Turner .05 .15
568 Carlos Delgado .20 .50
569 John Jaha .05 .15
570 Dwight Smith .05 .15
571 John Vander Wal .05 .15
572 Trevor Wilson .05 .15
573 Felix Fermin .05 .15
574 Marc Newfield .05 .15
575 Jeromy Burnitz .10 .30
576 Leo Gomez .05 .15
577 Curt Schilling .10 .30
578 Kevin Young .05 .15
579 Jerry Spradlin RC .05 .15
580 Curt Leskanic .05 .15
581 Carl Willis .05 .15
582 Alex Fernandez .05 .15
583 Mark Holzemer .05 .15
584 Domingo Martinez .05 .15
585 Pete Smith .05 .15
586 Brian Jordan .10 .30
587 Kevin Gross .05 .15
588 J.R. Phillips .05 .15
589 Chris Nabholz .05 .15
590 Bill Wertz .05 .15
591 Derek Bell .05 .15
592 Brady Anderson .10 .30
593 Matt Turner .05 .15
594 Pete Incaviglia .05 .15
595 Greg Gagne .05 .15
596 John Flaherty .05 .15
597 Scott Livingstone .05 .15
598 Rod Bolton .05 .15
599 Mike Perez .05 .15
600 Roger Clemens CL .30 .75
601 Tony Castillo .05 .15
602 Henry Mercedes .05 .15
603 Mike Fetters .05 .15
604 Rod Beck .05 .15
605 Damon Buford .05 .15
606 Matt Whiteside .05 .15
607 Shawn Green .30 .75
608 Midre Cummings .05 .15
609 Jeff McNeely .05 .15
610 Danny Sheaffer .05 .15
611 Paul Wagner .05 .15
612 Torey Lovullo .05 .15
613 Javier Lopez .10 .30
614 Mariano Duncan .05 .15
615 Doug Brocail .05 .15
616 Dave Hansen .05 .15
617 Ryan Klesko .10 .30
618 Eric Davis .10 .30
619 Scott Ruffcorn .05 .15
620 Mike Trombley .05 .15
621 Jaime Navarro .05 .15
622 Rheal Cormier .05 .15
623 Jose Offerman .05 .15
624 David Segui .05 .15
625 Robb Nen .10 .30
626 Dave Gallagher .05 .15
627 Julian Tavarez RC .10 .30
628 Chris Gomez .05 .15
629 Jeffrey Hammonds .05 .15
630 Scott Brosius .10 .30
631 Willie Blair .05 .15
632 Doug Drabek .05 .15
633 Bill Wegman .05 .15
634 Jeff McKnight .05 .15
635 Rich Rodriguez .05 .15
636 Steve Trachsel .05 .15
637 Buddy Groom .05 .15
638 Sterling Hitchcock .05 .15
639 Chuck McElroy .05 .15
640 Rene Gonzales .05 .15
641 Dan Plesac .05 .15
642 Jeff Branson .05 .15
643 Darrell Whitmore .05 .15
644 Paul Quantrill .05 .15
645 Rich Rowland .05 .15
646 Curtis Pride RC .10 .30
647 Erik Plantenberg RC .05 .15
648 Albie Lopez .05 .15
649 Rich Batchelor RC .05 .15
650 Lee Smith .10 .30
651 Cliff Floyd .10 .30
652 Pete Schourek .05 .15
653 Reggie Jefferson .05 .15
654 Bill Haselman .05 .15
655 Steve Hosey .05 .15
656 Mark Clark .05 .15
657 Mark Davis .05 .15
658 Dave Magadan .05 .15
659 Candy Maldonado .05 .15
660 Mark Langston CL .05 .15

1994 Donruss Diamond Kings

This 30-card standard-size set was split in two series. Cards 1-14 and 29 were randomly inserted in first series packs, while cards 15-28 and 30 were inserted in second series packs. With each series, the insertion rate was one in nine. The fronts feature full-bleed player portraits by noted sports artist Dick Perez. The cards are numbered on the back with the prefix DK.

COMPLETE SET (30) 25.00 50.00
*JUMBO DK's: .75X TO 2X BASIC DK'S
ONE JUMBO DK PER RETAIL BOX
DK1 Barry Bonds 2.50 6.00
DK2 Mo Vaughn .40 1.00
DK3 Steve Avery .20 .50
DK4 Tim Salmon .60 1.50
DK5 Rick Wilkins .20 .50
DK6 Brian Harper .20 .50
DK7 Andres Galarraga .40 1.00
DK8 Albert Belle .40 1.00
DK9 John Kruk .40 1.00
DK10 Ivan Rodriguez .60 1.50
DK11 Tony Gwynn 1.25 3.00
DK12 Brian McRae .20 .50
DK13 Bobby Bonilla .40 1.00
DK14 Ken Griffey Jr. 1.50 4.00
DK15 Mike Piazza 2.00 5.00
DK16 Don Mattingly 2.50 6.00
DK17 Barry Larkin .60 1.50
DK18 Ruben Sierra .40 1.00
DK19 Orlando Merced .20 .50
DK20 Greg Vaughn .20 .50
DK21 Gregg Jefferies .20 .50
DK22 Cecil Fielder .40 1.00
DK23 Moises Alou .40 1.00
DK24 John Olerud .40 1.00
DK25 Gary Sheffield .40 1.00
DK26 Mike Mussina .60 1.50
DK27 Jeff Bagwell .60 1.50
DK28 Frank Thomas 1.00 2.50
DK29 Dave Winfield .40 1.00
DK30 Checklist .20 .50

1994 Donruss Elite

This 12-card set was issued in two series of six. Using a continued numbering system from previous years, cards 37-42 were randomly inserted in first series foil packs with cards 43-48 a second series offering. The cards measure the standard size. Only 10,000 of each card were produced.

COMPLETE SET (12) 60.00 120.00
COMPLETE SERIES 1 (6) 30.00 60.00
COMPLETE SERIES 2 (6) 30.00 60.00
37 Frank Thomas 6.00 15.00
38 Tony Gwynn 6.00 15.00
39 Tim Salmon 6.00 15.00
40 Albert Belle 4.00 10.00
41 John Kruk 4.00 10.00
42 Juan Gonzalez 4.00 10.00
43 John Olerud 4.00 10.00

44 Barry Bonds 12.50 30.00
45 Ken Griffey Jr. 8.00 20.00
46 Mike Piazza 8.00 20.00
47 Jack McDowell 4.00 10.00
48 Andres Galarraga 4.00 10.00

1995 Donruss

The 1995 Donruss set consists of 550 standard-size cards. The first series had 330 cards while 220 cards comprised the second series. The fronts feature borderless color action player photos. A second, smaller color player photo in a homeplate shape with team color-coded borders appears in the lower left corner. There are no key Rookie Cards in this set. To preview the product prior to it's public release, Donruss printed up additional quantities of cards 5, 8, 20, 42, 55, 275, 331 and 340 and mailed them to dealers and hobby media.

COMPLETE SET (550) 12.00 30.00
COMP.SERIES 1 (330) 8.00 20.00
COMP.SERIES 2 (220) 4.00 10.00
1 David Justice .10 .30
2 Rene Arocha .05 .15
3 Sandy Alomar Jr. .05 .15
4 Luis Lopez .05 .15
5 Mike Piazza .50 1.25
6 Bobby Jones .05 .15
7 Damion Easley .05 .15
8 Barry Bonds .75 2.00
9 Mike Mussina .20 .50
10 Kevin Seitzer .05 .15
11 John Smiley .05 .15
12 Wm.VanLandingham .05 .15
13 Ron Darling .05 .15
14 Walt Weiss .05 .15
15 Mike Lansing .05 .15
16 Allen Watson .05 .15
17 Aaron Sele .05 .15
18 Randy Johnson .30 .75
19 Dean Palmer .10 .30
20 Jeff Bagwell .20 .50
21 Curt Schilling .10 .30
22 Darrell Whitmore .05 .15
23 Steve Trachsel .05 .15
24 Dan Wilson .05 .15
25 Steve Finley .10 .30
26 Bret Boone .10 .30
27 Charles Johnson .10 .30
28 Mike Stanton .05 .15
29 Ismael Valdes .05 .15
30 Salomon Torres .05 .15
31 Eric Anthony .05 .15
32 Spike Owen .05 .15
33 Joey Cora .05 .15
34 Robert Eenhoorn .05 .15
35 Rick White .05 .15
36 Omar Vizquel .20 .50
37 Carlos Delgado .10 .30
38 Eddie Williams .05 .15
39 Shawon Dunston .05 .15
40 Darrin Fletcher .05 .15
41 Leo Gomez .05 .15
42 Juan Gonzalez .10 .30
43 Luis Alicea .05 .15
44 Ken Ryan .05 .15
45 Lou Whitaker .10 .30
46 Mike Blowers .05 .15
47 Willie Blair .05 .15
48 Todd Van Poppel .05 .15
49 Roberto Alomar .20 .50
50 Ozzie Smith .50 1.25
51 Sterling Hitchcock .05 .15
52 Mo Vaughn .10 .30
53 Rick Aguilera .05 .15
54 Kent Mercker .05 .15
55 Don Mattingly .75 2.00
56 Bob Scanlan .05 .15
57 Wilson Alvarez .05 .15
58 Jose Mesa .05 .15
59 Scott Kamieniecki .05 .15
60 Todd Jones .05 .15
61 John Kruk .10 .30
62 Mike Stanley .05 .15
63 Tino Martinez .20 .50
64 Eddie Zambrano .05 .15
65 Todd Hundley .05 .15
66 Jamie Moyer .10 .30
67 Rich Amaral .05 .15
68 Jose Valentin .05 .15
69 Alex Gonzalez .05 .15
70 Kurt Abbott .05 .15
71 Delino DeShields .05 .15
72 Brian Anderson .05 .15
73 John Vander Wal .05 .15
74 Turner Ward .05 .15
75 Tim Raines .10 .30
76 Mark Acre .05 .15
77 Jose Offerman .05 .15
78 Jimmy Key .10 .30
79 Mark Whiten .05 .15
80 Mark Gubicza .05 .15
81 Darren Hall .05 .15
82 Travis Fryman .10 .30
83 Cal Ripken 1.00 2.50
84 Geronimo Berroa .05 .15
85 Bret Barberie .05 .15
86 Andy Ashby .05 .15
87 Steve Avery .05 .15
88 Rich Becker .05 .15
89 John Valentin .05 .15
90 Glenallen Hill .05 .15
91 Carlos Garcia .05 .15
92 Dennis Martinez .10 .30
93 Pat Kelly .05 .15
94 Orlando Miller .05 .15
95 Felix Jose .05 .15
96 Mike Kingery .05 .15
97 Jeff Kent .10 .30
98 Pete Incaviglia .05 .15
99 Chad Curtis .05 .15
100 Thomas Howard .05 .15
101 Hector Carrasco .05 .15
102 Tom Pagnozzi .05 .15
103 Danny Tartabull .05 .15
104 Donnie Elliott .05 .15
105 Danny Jackson .05 .15
106 Steve Dunn .05 .15
107 Roger Salkeld .05 .15
108 Jeff King .05 .15
109 Cecil Fielder .10 .30
110 Paul Molitor CL .05 .15
111 Denny Neagle .10 .30
112 Troy Neel .05 .15
113 Rod Beck .05 .15
114 Alex Rodriguez .75 2.00
115 Joey Eischen .05 .15
116 Tom Candiotti .05 .15
117 Ray McDavid .05 .15
118 Vince Coleman .05 .15
119 Pete Harnisch .05 .15
120 David Nied .05 .15
121 Pat Rapp .05 .15
122 Sammy Sosa .30 .75
123 Steve Reed .05 .15
124 Jose Oliva .05 .15
125 Ricky Bottalico .05 .15
126 Jose DeLeon .05 .15
127 Pat Hentgen .05 .15
128 Will Clark .20 .50
129 Mark Dewey .05 .15
130 Greg Vaughn .05 .15
131 Darren Dreifort .05 .15
132 Ed Sprague .05 .15
133 Lee Smith .10 .30
134 Charles Nagy .05 .15
135 Phil Plantier .05 .15
136 Jason Jacome .05 .15
137 Jose Lima .05 .15
138 J.R. Phillips .05 .15
139 J.T. Snow .10 .30
140 Michael Huff .05 .15
141 Billy Brewer .05 .15
142 Jeromy Burnitz .10 .30
143 Ricky Bones .05 .15
144 Carlos Rodriguez .05 .15
145 Luis Gonzalez .10 .30
146 Mark Lemke .05 .15
147 Al Martin .05 .15
148 Mike Bordick .05 .15
149 Robb Nen .10 .30
150 Wil Cordero .05 .15
151 Edgar Martinez .20 .50
152 Gerald Williams .05 .15
153 Esteban Beltre .05 .15
154 Mike Moore .05 .15
155 Mark Langston .05 .15
156 Mark Clark .05 .15
157 Bobby Ayala .05 .15
158 Rick Wilkins .05 .15
159 Bobby Munoz .05 .15
160 Brett Butler CL .05 .15
161 Scott Erickson .05 .15
162 Paul Molitor .10 .30
163 Jon Lieber .05 .15
164 Jason Grimsley .05 .15
165 Norberto Martin .05 .15
166 Javier Lopez .10 .30
167 Brian McRae .05 .15
168 Gary Sheffield .10 .30
169 Marcus Moore .05 .15
170 John Hudek .05 .15
171 Kelly Stinnett .05 .15
172 Chris Gomez .05 .15
173 Rey Sanchez .05 .15
174 Juan Guzman .05 .15
175 Chan Ho Park .10 .30
176 Terry Shumpert .05 .15
177 Steve Ontiveros .05 .15
178 Brad Ausmus .10 .30
179 Tim Davis .05 .15
180 Billy Ashley .05 .15
181 Vinny Castilla .10 .30
182 Bill Spiers .05 .15
183 Randy Knorr .05 .15
184 Brian Hunter .05 .15
185 Pat Meares .05 .15
186 Steve Buechele .05 .15
187 Kirt Manwaring .05 .15
188 Tim Naehring .05 .15
189 Matt Mieske .05 .15
190 Josias Manzanillo .05 .15
191 Greg McMichael .05 .15
192 Chuck Carr .05 .15
193 Midre Cummings .05 .15
194 Darryl Strawberry .10 .30
195 Greg Gagne .05 .15
196 Steve Cooke .05 .15
197 Woody Williams .05 .15
198 Ron Karkovice .05 .15
199 Phil Leftwich .05 .15
200 Jim Thome .20 .50
201 Brady Anderson .10 .30
202 Pedro A.Martinez .05 .15
203 Steve Karsay .05 .15
204 Reggie Sanders .10 .30
205 Bill Risley .05 .15
206 Jay Bell .10 .30
207 Kevin Brown .10 .30
208 Tim Scott .05 .15
209 Lenny Dykstra .10 .30
210 Willie Greene .05 .15
211 Jim Eisenreich .05 .15
212 Cliff Floyd .10 .30
213 Otis Nixon .05 .15
214 Eduardo Perez .05 .15
215 Manuel Lee .05 .15
216 Armando Benitez .05 .15
217 Dave McCarty .05 .15
218 Scott Livingstone .05 .15
219 Chad Kreuter .05 .15
220 Don Mattingly CL .40 1.00
221 Brian Jordan .10 .30
222 Matt Whiteside .05 .15
223 Jim Edmonds .20 .50
224 Tony Gwynn .40 1.00
225 Jose Lind .05 .15
226 Marvin Freeman .05 .15
227 Ken Hill .05 .15
228 David Hulse .05 .15
229 Joe Hesketh .05 .15
230 Roberto Petagine .05 .15
231 Jeffrey Hammonds .05 .15
232 John Jaha .05 .15
233 John Burkett .05 .15
234 Hal Morris .05 .15
235 Tony Castillo .05 .15
236 Ryan Bowen .05 .15
237 Wayne Kirby .05 .15
238 Brent Mayne .05 .15
239 Jim Bullinger .05 .15
240 Mike Lieberthal .10 .30
241 Barry Larkin .20 .50
242 David Segui .05 .15
243 Jose Bautista .05 .15
244 Hector Fajardo .05 .15
245 Orel Hershiser .10 .30
246 James Mouton .05 .15
247 Scott Leius .05 .15
248 Tom Glavine .20 .50
249 Danny Bautista .05 .15
250 Jose Mercedes .05 .15
251 Marquis Grissom .10 .30
252 Charlie Hayes .05 .15
253 Ryan Klesko .10 .30
254 Vicente Palacios .05 .15
255 Matias Carrillo .05 .15
256 Gary DiSarcina .05 .15
257 Kirk Gibson .10 .30
258 Garey Ingram .05 .15
259 Alex Fernandez .05 .15
260 John Mabry .05 .15
261 Chris Howard .05 .15
262 Miguel Jimenez .05 .15
263 Heathcliff Slocumb .05 .15
264 Albert Belle .10 .30
265 Dave Clark .05 .15
266 Joe Orsulak .05 .15
267 Joey Hamilton .05 .15
268 Mark Portugal .05 .15
269 Kevin Tapani .05 .15
270 Sid Fernandez .05 .15
271 Steve Dreyer .05 .15
272 Denny Hocking .05 .15
273 Troy O'Leary .05 .15
274 Milt Cuyler .05 .15
275 Frank Thomas .30 .75
276 Jorge Fabregas .05 .15
277 Mike Gallego .05 .15
278 Mickey Morandini .05 .15
279 Roberto Hernandez .05 .15
280 Henry Rodriguez .05 .15
281 Garret Anderson .10 .30
282 Bob Wickman .05 .15
283 Gar Finnvold .05 .15
284 Paul O'Neill .20 .50
285 Royce Clayton .05 .15
286 Chuck Knoblauch .10 .30
287 Johnny Ruffin .05 .15
288 Dave Nilsson .05 .15
289 David Cone .10 .30
290 Chuck McElroy .05 .15
291 Kevin Stocker .05 .15
292 Jose Rijo .05 .15
293 Sean Berry .05 .15
294 Ozzie Guillen .10 .30
295 Chris Hoiles .05 .15
296 Kevin Foster .05 .15
297 Jeff Frye .05 .15
298 Lance Johnson .05 .15
299 Mike Kelly .05 .15
300 Ellis Burks .10 .30
301 Roberto Kelly .05 .15
302 Dante Bichette .10 .30
303 Alvaro Espinoza .05 .15
304 Alex Cole .05 .15
305 Rickey Henderson .30 .75
306 Dave Weathers .05 .15
307 Shane Reynolds .05 .15
308 Bobby Bonilla .10 .30
309 Junior Felix .05 .15
310 Jeff Fassero .05 .15
311 Darren Lewis .05 .15
312 John Doherty .05 .15
313 Scott Servais .05 .15
314 Rick Helling .05 .15
315 Pedro Martinez .20 .50
316 Wes Chamberlain .05 .15
317 Bryan Eversgerd .05 .15
318 Trevor Hoffman .10 .30
319 John Patterson .05 .15
320 Matt Walbeck .05 .15
321 Jeff Montgomery .05 .15
322 Mel Rojas .05 .15
323 Eddie Taubensee .05 .15
324 Ray Lankford .10 .30
325 Jose Vizcaino .05 .15
326 Carlos Baerga .05 .15
327 Jack Voigt .05 .15
328 Julio Franco .10 .30
329 Brent Gates .05 .15
330 Kirby Puckett CL .20 .50
331 Greg Maddux .50 1.25
332 Jason Bere .05 .15
333 Bill Wegman .05 .15
334 Tuffy Rhodes .05 .15
335 Kevin Young .05 .15
336 Andy Benes .05 .15
337 Pedro Astacio .05 .15
338 Reggie Jefferson .05 .15
339 Tim Belcher .05 .15
340 Ken Griffey Jr. .50 1.25
341 Mariano Duncan .05 .15
342 Andres Galarraga .10 .30
343 Rondell White .10 .30
344 Cory Bailey .05 .15
345 Bryan Harvey .05 .15
346 John Franco .10 .30
347 Greg Swindell .05 .15
348 David West .05 .15
349 Fred McGriff .20 .50
350 Jose Canseco .20 .50
351 Orlando Merced .05 .15
352 Rheal Cormier .05 .15
353 Carlos Pulido .05 .15
354 Terry Steinbach .05 .15
355 Wade Boggs .20 .50
356 B.J. Surhoff .10 .30
357 Rafael Palmeiro .20 .50
358 Anthony Young .05 .15
359 Tom Brunansky .05 .15
360 Todd Stottlemyre .05 .15
361 Chris Turner .05 .15
362 Joe Boever .05 .15
363 Jeff Blauser .05 .15
364 Derek Bell .05 .15
365 Matt Williams .10 .30
366 Jeremy Hernandez .05 .15
367 Joe Girardi .05 .15
368 Mike Devereaux .05 .15
369 Jim Abbott .20 .50
370 Manny Ramirez .20 .50
371 Kenny Lofton .10 .30
372 Mark Smith .05 .15
373 Dave Fleming .05 .15
374 Dave Stewart .10 .30
375 Roger Pavlik .05 .15
376 Hipolito Pichardo .05 .15
377 Bill Taylor .05 .15
378 Robin Ventura .10 .30
379 Bernard Gilkey .05 .15
380 Kirby Puckett .30 .75
381 Steve Howe .05 .15
382 Devon White .10 .30
383 Roberto Mejia .05 .15
384 Darrin Jackson .05 .15
385 Mike Morgan .05 .15
386 Rusty Meacham .05 .15
387 Bill Swift .05 .15
388 Lou Frazier .05 .15
389 Andy Van Slyke .20 .50
390 Brett Butler .10 .30
391 Bobby Witt .05 .15
392 Jeff Conine .10 .30
393 Tim Hyers .05 .15
394 Terry Pendleton .10 .30
395 Ricky Jordan .05 .15
396 Eric Plunk .05 .15
397 Melido Perez .05 .15
398 Darryl Kile .10 .30
399 Mark McLemore .05 .15
400 Greg W.Harris .05 .15
401 Jim Leyritz .05 .15
402 Doug Strange .05 .15
403 Tim Salmon .20 .50
404 Terry Mulholland .05 .15
405 Robby Thompson .05 .15
406 Ruben Sierra .10 .30
407 Tony Phillips .05 .15
408 Moises Alou .10 .30
409 Felix Fermin .05 .15
410 Pat Listach .05 .15
411 Kevin Bass .05 .15
412 Ben McDonald .05 .15
413 Scott Cooper .05 .15
414 Jody Reed .05 .15
415 Deion Sanders .20 .50
416 Ricky Gutierrez .05 .15
417 Gregg Jefferies .05 .15
418 Jack McDowell .05 .15
419 Al Leiter .10 .30
420 Tony Longmire .05 .15
421 Paul Wagner .05 .15
422 Geronimo Pena .05 .15
423 Ivan Rodriguez .20 .50
424 Kevin Gross .05 .15
425 Kirk McCaskill .05 .15
426 Greg Myers .05 .15
427 Roger Clemens .60 1.50
428 Chris Hammond .05 .15
429 Randy Myers .05 .15
430 Roger Mason .05 .15
431 Bret Saberhagen .10 .30
432 Jeff Reboulet .05 .15
433 John Olerud .10 .30
434 Bill Gullickson .05 .15
435 Eddie Murray .30 .75
436 Pedro Munoz .05 .15
437 Charlie O'Brien .05 .15
438 Jeff Nelson .05 .15
439 Mike Macfarlane .05 .15
440 Don Mattingly CL .40 1.00
441 Derrick May .05 .15
442 John Roper .05 .15
443 Darryl Hamilton .05 .15
444 Dan Miceli .05 .15
445 Tony Eusebio .05 .15
446 Jerry Browne .05 .15
447 Wally Joyner .10 .30
448 Brian Harper .05 .15
449 Scott Fletcher .05 .15
450 Bip Roberts .10 .30
451 Pete Smith .05 .15
452 Chili Davis .10 .30
453 Dave Hollins .05 .15
454 Tony Pena .05 .15
455 Butch Henry .05 .15
456 Craig Biggio .20 .50
457 Zane Smith .05 .15
458 Ryan Thompson .05 .15
459 Mike Jackson .05 .15
460 Mark McGwire .75 2.00
461 John Smoltz .20 .50
462 Steve Scarsone .05 .15
463 Greg Colbrunn .05 .15
464 Shawn Green .10 .30
465 David Wells .10 .30
466 Jose Hernandez .05 .15
467 Chip Hale .05 .15
468 Tony Tarasco .05 .15
469 Kevin Mitchell .05 .15
470 Billy Hatcher .05 .15
471 Jay Buhner .10 .30
472 Ken Caminiti .10 .30
473 Tom Henke .05 .15
474 Todd Worrell .05 .15
475 Mark Eichhorn .05 .15
476 Bruce Ruffin .05 .15
477 Chuck Finley .10 .30
478 Marc Newfield .05 .15
479 Paul Shuey .05 .15
480 Bob Tewksbury .05 .15
481 Ramon J.Martinez .05 .15
482 Melvin Nieves .05 .15
483 Todd Zeile .05 .15
484 Benito Santiago .10 .30
485 Stan Javier .05 .15
486 Kirk Rueter .05 .15
487 Andre Dawson .10 .30
488 Eric Karros .10 .30
489 Dave Magadan .05 .15
490 Joe Carter CL .05 .15
491 Randy Velarde .05 .15
492 Larry Walker .10 .30
493 Cris Carpenter .05 .15
494 Tom Gordon .05 .15
495 Dave Burba .05 .15
496 Darren Bragg .05 .15
497 Darren Daulton .10 .30
498 Don Slaught .05 .15
499 Pat Borders .05 .15
500 Lenny Harris .05 .15
501 Joe Ausanio .05 .15
502 Alan Trammell .10 .30
503 Mike Fetters .05 .15
504 Scott Ruffcorn .05 .15
505 Rich Rowland .05 .15
506 Juan Samuel .05 .15
507 Bo Jackson .30 .75
508 Jeff Branson .05 .15
509 Bernie Williams .20 .50
510 Paul Sorrento .05 .15
511 Dennis Eckersley .10 .30
512 Pat Mahomes .05 .15
513 Rusty Greer .10 .30
514 Luis Polonia .05 .15
515 Willie Banks .05 .15
516 John Wetteland .10 .30
517 Mike LaValliere .05 .15
518 Tommy Greene .05 .15
519 Mark Grace .20 .50
520 Bob Hamelin .05 .15
521 Scott Sanderson .05 .15
522 Joe Carter .10 .30
523 Jeff Brantley .05 .15
524 Andrew Lorraine .05 .15
525 Rico Brogna .05 .15
526 Shane Mack .05 .15
527 Mark Wohlers .05 .15
528 Scott Sanders .05 .15
529 Chris Bosio .05 .15
530 Andujar Cedeno .05 .15
531 Kenny Rogers .10 .30
532 Doug Drabek .05 .15
533 Curt Leskanic .05 .15
534 Craig Shipley .05 .15
535 Craig Grebeck .05 .15
536 Cal Eldred .05 .15
537 Mickey Tettleton .05 .15
538 Harold Baines .10 .30
539 Tim Wallach .05 .15
540 Damon Buford .05 .15
541 Lenny Webster .05 .15
542 Kevin Appier .10 .30
543 Raul Mondesi .10 .30
544 Eric Young .05 .15
545 Russ Davis .05 .15
546 Mike Benjamin .05 .15
547 Mike Greenwell .05 .15
548 Scott Brosius .10 .30
549 Brian Dorsett .05 .15
550 Chili Davis CL .05 .15

1995 Donruss Diamond Kings

The 1995 Donruss Diamond King set consists of 29 standard-size cards that were randomly inserted in packs. The fronts feature water color player portraits by noted sports artist Dick Perez. The player's name and "Diamond Kings" are in gold foil. The backs have a dark blue border with a player photo and text. The cards are numbered on back with a DK prefix.

COMPLETE SET (29) 25.00 50.00
COMPLETE SERIES 1 (14) 10.00 20.00
COMPLETE SERIES 2 (15) 15.00 30.00
DK1 Frank Thomas 1.25 3.00
DK2 Jeff Bagwell .75 2.00
DK3 Chili Davis .50 1.25
DK4 Dante Bichette .50 1.25
DK5 Ruben Sierra .50 1.25
DK6 Jeff Conine .50 1.25
DK7 Paul O'Neill .75 2.00
DK8 Bobby Bonilla .50 1.25
DK9 Joe Carter .50 1.25
DK10 Moises Alou .50 1.25
DK11 Kenny Lofton .50 1.25
DK12 Matt Williams .50 1.25
DK13 Kevin Seitzer .25 .60
DK14 Sammy Sosa 1.25 3.00
DK15 Scott Cooper .25 .60
DK16 Raul Mondesi .50 1.25
DK17 Will Clark .75 2.00
DK18 Lenny Dykstra .50 1.25
DK19 Kirby Puckett 1.25 3.00
DK20 Hal Morris .25 .60
DK21 Travis Fryman .50 1.25
DK22 Greg Maddux 2.00 5.00
DK23 Rafael Palmeiro .75 2.00
DK24 Tony Gwynn 1.50 4.00
DK25 David Cone .50 1.25
DK26 Al Martin .25 .60
DK27 Ken Griffey Jr. 2.00 5.00
DK28 Gregg Jefferies .25 .60
DK29 Checklist .25 .60

1995 Donruss Elite

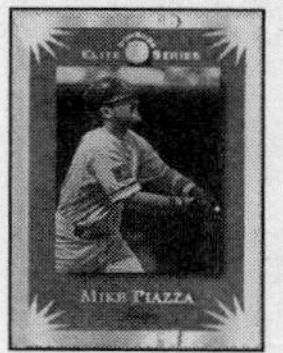

Randomly inserted one in every 210 Series 1 and 2 packs, this set consists of 12 standard-size cards that are numbered (49-60) based on where the previous year's set left off. The fronts contain an action photo surrounded by a marble border. Silver holographic foil borders the card on all four sides. Limited to 10,000, the backs are individually numbered, contain a small photo and write-up.

COMPLETE SET (12) 100.00 200.00
COMPLETE SERIES 1 (6) 50.00 100.00
COMPLETE SERIES 2 (6) 50.00 100.00
49 Jeff Bagwell 6.00 15.00
50 Paul O'Neill 6.00 15.00
51 Greg Maddux 10.00 25.00
52 Mike Piazza 10.00 25.00
53 Matt Williams 4.00 10.00
54 Ken Griffey 10.00 25.00
55 Frank Thomas 6.00 15.00
56 Barry Bonds 15.00 40.00
57 Kirby Puckett 6.00 15.00
58 Fred McGriff 6.00 15.00
59 Jose Canseco 6.00 15.00
60 Albert Belle 4.00 10.00

1996 Donruss

The 1996 Donruss set was issued in two series of 330 and 220 cards respectively, for a total of 550. The 12-card packs had a suggested retail price of $1.79. The full-bleed fronts feature full-color action photos with the player's name is in white ink in the upper right. The horizontal backs feature season and career stats, text, vital stats and another photo. Rookie Cards in this set include Mike Cameron.

COMPLETE SET (550) 16.00 40.00
COMP.SERIES 1 (330) 10.00 25.00
COMP.SERIES 2 (220) 6.00 15.00
1 Frank Thomas .30 .75
2 Jason Bates .10 .30
3 Steve Sparks .10 .30
4 Scott Servais .10 .30
5 Angelo Encarnacion RC .10 .30
6 Scott Sanders .10 .30
7 Billy Ashley .10 .30
8 Alex Rodriguez .60 1.50
9 Sean Bergman .10 .30
10 Brad Radke .10 .30
11 Andy Van Slyke .20 .50
12 Joe Girardi .10 .30
13 Mark Grudzielanek .10 .30
14 Rick Aguilera .10 .30
15 Randy Veres .10 .30
16 Tim Bogar .10 .30
17 Dave Veres .10 .30
18 Kevin Stocker .10 .30
19 Marquis Grissom .10 .30
20 Will Clark .20 .50
21 Jay Bell .10 .30
22 Allen Battle .10 .30
23 Frank Rodriguez .10 .30
24 Terry Steinbach .10 .30
25 Gerald Williams .10 .30
26 Sid Roberson .10 .30
27 Greg Zaun .10 .30
28 Ozzie Timmons .10 .30
29 Vaughn Eshelman .10 .30
30 Ed Sprague .10 .30
31 Gary DiSarcina .10 .30
32 Joe Boever .10 .30
33 Steve Avery .10 .30
34 Brad Ausmus .10 .30
35 Kirt Manwaring .10 .30
36 Gary Sheffield .10 .30
37 Jason Bere .10 .30
38 Jeff Manto .10 .30
39 David Cone .10 .30
40 Manny Ramirez .20 .50
41 Sandy Alomar Jr. .10 .30
42 Curtis Goodwin .10 .30
43 Tino Martinez .20 .50
44 Woody Williams .10 .30
45 Dean Palmer .10 .30
46 Hipolito Pichardo .10 .30
47 Jason Giambi .10 .30
48 Lance Johnson .10 .30
49 Bernard Gilkey .10 .30
50 Kirby Puckett .30 .75
51 Tony Fernandez .10 .30
52 Alex Gonzalez .10 .30
53 Bret Saberhagen .10 .30
54 Lyle Mouton .10 .30
55 Brian McRae .10 .30
56 Mark Gubicza .10 .30

1996 Donruss

57 Sergio Valdez .10 .30
58 Darrin Fletcher .10 .30
59 Steve Parris .10 .30
60 Johnny Damon .20 .50
61 Rickey Henderson .30 .75
62 Darrell Whitmore .10 .30
63 Roberto Petagine .10 .30
64 Trenidad Hubbard .10 .30
65 Heathcliff Slocumb .10 .30
66 Steve Finley .10 .30
67 Mariano Rivera .30 .75
68 Brian L.Hunter .10 .30
69 Jamie Moyer .10 .30
70 Ellis Burks .10 .30
71 Pat Kelly .10 .30
72 Mickey Tettleton .10 .30
73 Garret Anderson .10 .30
74 Andy Pettitte .20 .50
75 Glenallen Hill .10 .30
76 Brent Gates .10 .30
77 Lou Whitaker .10 .30
78 David Segui .10 .30
79 Dan Wilson .10 .30
80 Pat Listach .10 .30
81 Jeff Bagwell .20 .50
82 Ben McDonald .10 .30
83 John Valentin .10 .30
84 John Jaha .10 .30
85 Pete Schourek .10 .30
86 Bryce Florie .10 .30
87 Brian Jordan .10 .30
88 Ron Karkovice .10 .30
89 Al Leiter .10 .30
90 Tony Longmire .10 .30
91 Nelson Liriano .10 .30
92 David Bell .10 .30
93 Kevin Gross .10 .30
94 Tom Candiotti .10 .30
95 Dave Martinez .10 .30
96 Greg Myers .10 .30
97 Rheal Cormier .10 .30
98 Chris Hammond .10 .30
99 Randy Myers .10 .30
100 Bill Pulsipher .10 .30
101 Jason Isringhausen .10 .30
102 Dave Stevens .10 .30
103 Roberto Alomar .20 .50
104 Bob Higginson .10 .30
105 Eddie Murray .30 .75
106 Matt Walbeck .10 .30
107 Mark Wohlers .10 .30
108 Jeff Nelson .10 .30
109 Tom Goodwin .10 .30
110 Cal Ripken CL .50 1.25
111 Rey Sanchez .10 .30
112 Hector Carrasco .10 .30
113 B.J. Surhoff .10 .30
114 Dan Miceli .10 .30
115 Dean Hartgraves .10 .30
116 John Burkett .10 .30
117 Gary Gaetti .10 .30
118 Ricky Bones .10 .30
119 Mike Macfarlane .10 .30
120 Bip Roberts .10 .30
121 Dave Mlicki .10 .30
122 Chili Davis .10 .30
123 Mark Whiten .10 .30
124 Herbert Perry .10 .30
125 Butch Henry .10 .30
126 Derek Bell .10 .30
127 Al Martin .10 .30
128 John Franco .10 .30
129 W. VanLandingham .10 .30
130 Mike Bordick .10 .30
131 Mike Mordecai .10 .30
132 Robby Thompson .10 .30
133 Greg Colbrunn .10 .30
134 Domingo Cedeno .10 .30
135 Chad Curtis .10 .30
136 Jose Hernandez .10 .30
137 Scott Klingenbeck .10 .30
138 Ryan Klesko .10 .30
139 John Smiley .10 .30
140 Charlie Hayes .10 .30
141 Jay Buhner .10 .30
142 Doug Drabek .10 .30
143 Roger Pavlik .10 .30
144 Todd Worrell .10 .30
145 Cal Ripken 1.00 2.50
146 Steve Reed .10 .30
147 Chuck Finley .10 .30
148 Mike Blowers .10 .30
149 Orel Hershiser .10 .30
150 Allen Watson .10 .30
151 Ramon Martinez .10 .30
152 Melvin Nieves .10 .30
153 Tripp Cromer .10 .30
154 Yorkis Perez .10 .30
155 Stan Javier .10 .30
156 Mel Rojas .10 .30
157 Aaron Sele .10 .30
158 Eric Karros .10 .30
159 Robb Nen .10 .30
160 Raul Mondesi .10 .30
161 John Wetteland .10 .30
162 Tim Scott .10 .30
163 Kenny Rogers .10 .30
164 Melvin Bunch .10 .30
165 Rod Beck .10 .30
166 Andy Benes .10 .30
167 Lenny Dykstra .10 .30
168 Orlando Merced .10 .30
169 Tomas Perez .10 .30
170 Xavier Hernandez .10 .30
171 Ruben Sierra .10 .30
172 Alan Trammell .10 .30
173 Mike Fetters .10 .30
174 Wilson Alvarez .10 .30
175 Erik Hanson .10 .30
176 Travis Fryman .10 .30
177 Jim Abbott .20 .50
178 Bret Boone .10 .30
179 Sterling Hitchcock .10 .30
180 Pat Mahomes .10 .30
181 Mark Acre .10 .30
182 Charles Nagy .10 .30
183 Rusty Greer .10 .30
184 Mike Stanley .10 .30
185 Jim Bullinger .10 .30
186 Shane Andrews .10 .30
187 Brian Keyser .10 .30
188 Tyler Green .10 .30
189 Mark Grace .20 .50
190 Bob Hamelin .10 .30
191 Luis Ortiz .10 .30
192 Joe Carter .10 .30
193 Eddie Taubensee .10 .30
194 Brian Anderson .10 .30
195 Edgardo Alfonzo .10 .30
196 Pedro Munoz .10 .30
197 David Justice .10 .30
198 Trevor Hoffman .10 .30
199 Bobby Ayala .10 .30
200 Tony Eusebio .10 .30
201 Jeff Russell .10 .30
202 Mike Hampton .10 .30
203 Walt Weiss .10 .30
204 Joey Hamilton .10 .30
205 Roberto Hernandez .10 .30
206 Greg Vaughn .10 .30
207 Felipe Lira .10 .30
208 Harold Baines .10 .30
209 Tim Wallach .10 .30
210 Manny Alexander .10 .30
211 Tim Laker .10 .30
212 Chris Haney .10 .30
213 Brian Maxcy .10 .30
214 Eric Young .10 .30
215 Darryl Strawberry .10 .30
216 Barry Bonds .75 2.00
217 Tim Naehring .10 .30
218 Scott Brosius .10 .30
219 Reggie Sanders .10 .30
220 Eddie Murray CL .20 .50
221 Luis Alicea .10 .30
222 Albert Belle .10 .30
223 Benji Gil .10 .30
224 Dante Bichette .10 .30
225 Bobby Bonilla .10 .30
226 Todd Stottlemyre .10 .30
227 Jim Edmonds .10 .30
228 Todd Jones .10 .30
229 Shawn Green .10 .30
230 Javier Lopez .10 .30
231 Ariel Prieto .10 .30
232 Tony Phillips .10 .30
233 James Mouton .10 .30
234 Jose Oquendo .10 .30
235 Royce Clayton .10 .30
236 Chuck Carr .10 .30
237 Doug Jones .10 .30
238 Mark McLemore .10 .30
239 Bill Swift .10 .30
240 Scott Leius .10 .30
241 Russ Davis .10 .30
242 Ray Durham .10 .30
243 Matt Mieske .10 .30
244 Brent Mayne .10 .30
245 Thomas Howard .10 .30
246 Troy O'Leary .10 .30
247 Jacob Brumfield .10 .30
248 Mickey Morandini .10 .30
249 Todd Hundley .10 .30
250 Chris Bosio .10 .30
251 Omar Vizquel .20 .50
252 Mike Lansing .10 .30
253 John Mabry .10 .30
254 Mike Perez .10 .30
255 Delino DeShields .10 .30
256 Wil Cordero .10 .30
257 Mike James .10 .30
258 Todd Van Poppel .10 .30
259 Joey Cora .10 .30
260 Andre Dawson .10 .30
261 Jerry DiPoto .10 .30
262 Rick Krivda .10 .30
263 Glenn Dishman .10 .30
264 Mike Mimbs .10 .30
265 John Ericks .10 .30
266 Jose Canseco .20 .50
267 Jeff Branson .10 .30
268 Curt Leskanic .10 .30
269 Jon Nunnally .10 .30
270 Scott Stahoviak .10 .30
271 Jeff Montgomery .10 .30
272 Hal Morris .10 .30
273 Esteban Loaiza .10 .30
274 Rico Brogna .10 .30
275 Dave Winfield .10 .30
276 J.R. Phillips .10 .30
277 Todd Zeile .10 .30
278 Tom Pagnozzi .10 .30
279 Mark Lemke .10 .30
280 Dave Magadan .10 .30
281 Greg McMichael .10 .30
282 Mike Morgan .10 .30
283 Moises Alou .10 .30
284 Dennis Martinez .10 .30
285 Jeff Kent .10 .30
286 Mark Johnson .10 .30
287 Darren Lewis .10 .30
288 Brad Clontz .10 .30
289 Chad Fonville .10 .30
290 Paul Sorrento .10 .30
291 Lee Smith .10 .30
292 Tom Glavine .20 .50
293 Antonio Osuna .10 .30
294 Kevin Foster .10 .30
295 Sandy Martinez .10 .30
296 Mark Leiter .10 .30
297 Julian Tavarez .10 .30
298 Mike Kelly .10 .30
299 Joe Oliver .10 .30
300 John Flaherty .10 .30
301 Don Mattingly .75 2.00
302 Pat Meares .10 .30
303 John Doherty .10 .30
304 Joe Vitiello .10 .30
305 Vinny Castilla .10 .30
306 Jeff Brantley .10 .30
307 Mike Greenwell .10 .30
308 Midre Cummings .10 .30
309 Curt Schilling .10 .30
310 Ken Caminiti .10 .30
311 Scott Erickson .10 .30
312 Carl Everett .10 .30
313 Charles Johnson .10 .30
314 Alex Diaz .10 .30
315 Jose Mesa .10 .30
316 Mark Carreon .10 .30
317 Carlos Perez .10 .30
318 Ismael Valdes .10 .30
319 Frank Castillo .10 .30
320 Tom Henke .10 .30
321 Spike Owen .10 .30
322 Joe Orsulak .10 .30
323 Paul Menhart .10 .30
324 Pedro Borbon .10 .30
325 Paul Molitor CL .10 .30
326 Jeff Cirillo .10 .30
327 Edwin Hurtado .10 .30
328 Orlando Miller .10 .30
329 Steve Ontiveros .10 .30
330 Kirby Puckett CL .20 .50
331 Scott Bullett .10 .30
332 Andres Galarraga .10 .30
333 Cal Eldred .10 .30
334 Sammy Sosa .30 .75
335 Don Slaught .10 .30
336 Jody Reed .10 .30
337 Roger Cedeno .10 .30
338 Ken Griffey Jr. .50 1.25
339 Todd Hollandsworth .10 .30
340 Mike Trombley .10 .30
341 Gregg Jefferies .10 .30
342 Larry Walker .10 .30
343 Pedro Martinez .20 .50
344 Dwayne Hosey .10 .30
345 Terry Pendleton .10 .30
346 Pete Harnisch .10 .30
347 Tony Castillo .10 .30
348 Paul Quantrill .10 .30
349 Fred McGriff .20 .50
350 Ivan Rodriguez .20 .50
351 Butch Huskey .10 .30
352 Ozzie Smith .50 1.25
353 Marty Cordova .10 .30
354 John Wasdin .10 .30
355 Wade Boggs .20 .50
356 Dave Nilsson .10 .30
357 Rafael Palmeiro .20 .50
358 Luis Gonzalez .10 .30
359 Reggie Jefferson .10 .30
360 Carlos Delgado .10 .30
361 Orlando Palmeiro .10 .30
362 Chris Gomez .10 .30
363 John Smoltz .20 .50
364 Marc Newfield .10 .30
365 Matt Williams .10 .30
366 Jesus Tavarez .10 .30
367 Bruce Ruffin .10 .30
368 Sean Berry .10 .30
369 Randy Velarde .10 .30
370 Tony Pena .10 .30
371 Jim Thome .20 .50
372 Jeffrey Hammonds .10 .30
373 Bob Wolcott .10 .30
374 Juan Guzman .10 .30
375 Juan Gonzalez .10 .30
376 Michael Tucker .10 .30
377 Doug Johns .10 .30
378 Mike Cameron RC .25 .60
379 Ray Lankford .10 .30
380 Jose Parra .10 .30
381 Jimmy Key .10 .30
382 John Olerud .10 .30
383 Kevin Ritz .10 .30
384 Tim Raines .10 .30
385 Rich Amaral .10 .30
386 Keith Lockhart .10 .30
387 Steve Scarsone .10 .30
388 Cliff Floyd .10 .30
389 Rich Aude .10 .30
390 Hideo Nomo .30 .75
391 Geronimo Berroa .10 .30
392 Pat Rapp .10 .30
393 Dustin Hermanson .10 .30
394 Greg Maddux .50 1.25
395 Darren Daulton .10 .30
396 Kenny Lofton .10 .30
397 Ruben Rivera .10 .30
398 Billy Wagner .10 .30
399 Kevin Brown .10 .30
400 Mike Kingery .10 .30
401 Bernie Williams .20 .50
402 Otis Nixon .10 .30
403 Damion Easley .10 .30
404 Paul O'Neill .20 .50
405 Deion Sanders .20 .50
406 Dennis Eckersley .10 .30
407 Tony Clark .10 .30
408 Rondell White .10 .30
409 Luis Sojo .10 .30
410 David Hulse .10 .30
411 Shane Reynolds .10 .30
412 Chris Hoiles .10 .30
413 Lee Tinsley .10 .30
414 Scott Karl .10 .30
415 Ron Gant .10 .30
416 Brian Johnson .10 .30
417 Jose Oliva .10 .30
418 Jack McDowell .10 .30
419 Paul Molitor .10 .30
420 Ricky Bottalico .10 .30
421 Paul Wagner .10 .30
422 Terry Bradshaw .10 .30
423 Bob Tewksbury .10 .30
424 Mike Piazza .50 1.25
425 Luis Andujar .10 .30
426 Mark Langston .10 .30
427 Stan Belinda .10 .30
428 Kurt Abbott .10 .30
429 Shawon Dunston .10 .30
430 Bobby Jones .10 .30
431 Jose Vizcaino .10 .30
432 Matt Lawton RC .15 .40
433 Pat Hentgen .10 .30
434 Cecil Fielder .10 .30
435 Carlos Baerga .10 .30
436 Rich Becker .10 .30
437 Chipper Jones .30 .75
438 Bill Risley .10 .30
439 Kevin Appier .10 .30
440 Wade Boggs CL .10 .30
441 Jaime Navarro .10 .30
442 Barry Larkin .20 .50
443 Jose Valentin .10 .30
444 Bryan Rekar .10 .30
445 Rick Wilkins .10 .30
446 Quilvio Veras .10 .30
447 Greg Gagne .10 .30
448 Mark Kiefer .10 .30
449 Bobby Witt .10 .30
450 Andy Ashby .10 .30
451 Alex Ochoa .10 .30
452 Jorge Fabregas .10 .30
453 Gene Schall .10 .30
454 Ken Hill .10 .30
455 Tony Tarasco .10 .30
456 Donnie Wall .10 .30
457 Carlos Garcia .10 .30
458 Ryan Thompson .10 .30
459 Marvin Benard RC .15 .40
460 Jose Herrera .10 .30
461 Jeff Blauser .10 .30
462 Chris Hook .10 .30
463 Jeff Conine .10 .30
464 Devon White .10 .30
465 Danny Bautista .10 .30
466 Steve Trachsel .10 .30
467 C.J. Nitkowski .10 .30
468 Mike Devereaux .10 .30
469 David Wells .10 .30
470 Jim Eisenreich .10 .30
471 Edgar Martinez .20 .50
472 Craig Biggio .20 .50
473 Jeff Frye .10 .30
474 Karim Garcia .10 .30
475 Jimmy Haynes .10 .30
476 Darren Holmes .10 .30
477 Tim Salmon .20 .50
478 Randy Johnson .30 .75
479 Eric Plunk .10 .30
480 Scott Cooper .10 .30
481 Chan Ho Park .10 .30
482 Ray McDavid .10 .30
483 Mark Petkovsek .10 .30
484 Greg Swindell .10 .30
485 George Williams .10 .30
486 Yamil Benitez .10 .30
487 Tim Wakefield .10 .30
488 Kevin Tapani .10 .30
489 Derrick May .10 .30
490 Ken Griffey Jr. CL .30 .75
491 Derek Jeter .75 2.00
492 Jeff Fassero .10 .30
493 Benito Santiago .10 .30
494 Tom Gordon .10 .30
495 Jamie Brewington RC .10 .30
496 Vince Coleman .10 .30
497 Kevin Jordan .10 .30
498 Jeff King .10 .30
499 Mike Simms .10 .30
500 Jose Rijo .10 .30
501 Denny Neagle .10 .30
502 Jose Lima .10 .30
503 Kevin Seitzer .10 .30
504 Alex Fernandez .10 .30
505 Mo Vaughn .10 .30
506 Phil Nevin .10 .30
507 J.T. Snow .10 .30
508 Andujar Cedeno .10 .30
509 Ozzie Guillen .10 .30
510 Mark Clark .10 .30
511 Mark McGwire .75 2.00
512 Jeff Reboulet .10 .30
513 Armando Benitez .10 .30
514 LaTroy Hawkins .10 .30
515 Brett Butler .10 .30
516 Tavo Alvarez .10 .30
517 Chris Snopek .10 .30
518 Mike Mussina .20 .50
519 Darryl Kile .10 .30
520 Wally Joyner .10 .30
521 Willie McGee .10 .30
522 Kent Mercker .10 .30
523 Mike Jackson .10 .30
524 Troy Percival .10 .30
525 Tony Gwynn .40 1.00
526 Ron Coomer .10 .30
527 Darryl Hamilton .10 .30
528 Phil Plantier .10 .30
529 Norm Charlton .10 .30
530 Craig Paquette .10 .30
531 Dave Burba .10 .30
532 Mike Henneman .10 .30
533 Terrell Wade .10 .30
534 Eddie Williams .10 .30
535 Robin Ventura .10 .30
536 Chuck Knoblauch .10 .30
537 Les Norman .10 .30
538 Brady Anderson .10 .30
539 Roger Clemens .60 1.50
540 Mark Portugal .10 .30
541 Mike Matheny .10 .30
542 Jeff Parrett .10 .30
543 Roberto Kelly .10 .30
544 Damon Buford .10 .30
545 Chad Ogea .10 .30
546 Jose Offerman .10 .30
547 Brian Barber .10 .30
548 Danny Tartabull .10 .30
549 Duane Singleton .10 .30
550 Tony Gwynn CL .20 .50

1996 Donruss Diamond Kings

These 31 standard-size cards were randomly inserted into packs and issued in two series of 14 and 17 cards. They were inserted in first series packs at a ratio of approximately one every 60 packs. Second series cards were inserted one every 30 packs. The cards are sequentially numbered in the back lower right as "X" of 10,000. The fronts feature player portraits by noted sports artist Dick Perez. These cards are gold-foil stamped and the portraits are surrounded by gold-foil borders. The backs feature text about the player as well as a player photo. The cards are numbered on the back with a "DK" prefix.

COMPLETE SET (31) 100.00 250.00
COMPLETE SERIES 1 (14) 60.00 150.00
COMPLETE SERIES 2 (17) 40.00 100.00
1 Frank Thomas 5.00 12.00
2 Mo Vaughn 2.00 5.00
3 Manny Ramirez 3.00 8.00
4 Mark McGwire 12.50 30.00
5 Juan Gonzalez 2.00 5.00
6 Roberto Alomar 3.00 8.00
7 Tim Salmon 3.00 8.00
8 Barry Bonds 12.50 30.00
9 Tony Gwynn 6.00 15.00
10 Reggie Sanders 2.00 5.00
11 Larry Walker 2.00 5.00
12 Pedro Martinez 3.00 8.00
13 Jeff King 2.00 5.00
14 Mark Grace 3.00 8.00
15 Greg Maddux 6.00 15.00
16 Don Mattingly 10.00 25.00
17 Gregg Jefferies 1.50 4.00
18 Chad Curtis 1.50 4.00
19 Jason Isringhausen 1.50 4.00
20 B.J. Surhoff 1.50 4.00
21 Jeff Conine 1.50 4.00
22 Kirby Puckett 4.00 10.00
23 Derek Bell 1.50 4.00
24 Wally Joyner 1.50 4.00
25 Brian Jordan 1.50 4.00
26 Edgar Martinez 2.50 6.00
27 Hideo Nomo 4.00 10.00
28 Mike Mussina 2.50 6.00
29 Eddie Murray 4.00 10.00
30 Cal Ripken 12.50 30.00
31 Checklist 1.50 4.00

1996 Donruss Elite

Randomly inserted approximately one in Donruss packs, this 12-card standard-size set is continuously numbered (61-72) from the previous year. First series cards were inserted one every 40 packs. Second series cards were inserted one every 75 packs. The fronts contain an action photo surrounded by a silver border. Limited to 10,000 and sequentially numbered, the backs contain a small photo and write up.

COMPLETE SET (12) 45.00 110.00
COMPLETE SERIES 1 (6) 20.00 50.00
COMPLETE SERIES 2 (6) 25.00 60.00
61 Cal Ripken 12.50 30.00
62 Hideo Nomo 4.00 10.00
63 Reggie Sanders 1.50 4.00
64 Mo Vaughn 1.50 4.00
65 Tim Salmon 2.50 6.00
66 Chipper Jones 4.00 10.00
67 Manny Ramirez 2.50 6.00
68 Greg Maddux 6.00 15.00
69 Frank Thomas 4.00 10.00
70 Ken Griffey Jr. 6.00 15.00
71 Dante Bichette 1.50 4.00
72 Tony Gwynn 5.00 12.00

1997 Donruss

The 1997 Donruss set was issued in two separate series of 270 and 180 cards respectively. Both first series and Update cards were distributed in 10-card packs carrying a suggested retail price of $1.99 each. Card fronts feature color action player photos while the backs carry another color player photo with player information and career statistics. The following subsets are included within the set: Checklists (267-270/448-450), Rookies (353-397), Hit List (398-422), King of the Hill (423-437) and Interleague Showdown (438-447). Rookie Cards in this set include Jose Cruz Jr., Brian Giles and Hideki Irabu.

COMPLETE SET (450) 20.00 50.00
COMP. SERIES 1 (270) 10.00 25.00
COMPLETE UPDATE (180) 10.00 25.00
1 Juan Gonzalez .10 .30
2 Jim Edmonds .10 .30
3 Tony Gwynn .40 1.00
4 Andres Galarraga .10 .30
5 Joe Carter .10 .30
6 Raul Mondesi .10 .30
7 Greg Maddux .50 1.25
8 Travis Fryman .10 .30
9 Brian Jordan .10 .30
10 Henry Rodriguez .10 .30
11 Manny Ramirez .20 .50
12 Mark McGwire .75 2.00
13 Marc Newfield .10 .30
14 Craig Biggio .20 .50
15 Sammy Sosa .30 .75
16 Brady Anderson .10 .30
17 Wade Boggs .20 .50
18 Charles Johnson .10 .30
19 Matt Williams .10 .30
20 Denny Neagle .10 .30
21 Ken Griffey Jr. .50 1.25
22 Robin Ventura .10 .30
23 Barry Larkin .20 .50
24 Todd Zeile .10 .30
25 Chuck Knoblauch .10 .30
26 Todd Hundley .10 .30
27 Roger Clemens .60 1.50
28 Michael Tucker .10 .30
29 Rondell White .10 .30
30 Osvaldo Fernandez .10 .30
31 Ivan Rodriguez .20 .50
32 Alex Fernandez .10 .30
33 Jason Isringhausen .10 .30
34 Chipper Jones .30 .75
35 Paul O'Neill .20 .50
36 Hideo Nomo .30 .75
37 Roberto Alomar .20 .50
38 Derek Bell .10 .30
39 Paul Molitor .10 .30
40 Andy Benes .10 .30
41 Steve Trachsel .10 .30
42 J.T. Snow .10 .30
43 Jason Kendall .10 .30
44 Alex Rodriguez .50 1.25
45 Joey Hamilton .10 .30
46 Carlos Delgado .10 .30
47 Jason Giambi .10 .30
48 Larry Walker .10 .30
49 Derek Jeter .75 2.00
50 Kenny Lofton .10 .30
51 Devon White .10 .30
52 Matt Mieske .10 .30
53 Melvin Nieves .10 .30
54 Jose Canseco .20 .50
55 Tino Martinez .20 .50
56 Rafael Palmeiro .20 .50
57 Edgardo Alfonzo .10 .30
58 Jay Buhner .10 .30
59 Shane Reynolds .10 .30
60 Steve Finley .10 .30
61 Bobby Higginson .10 .30
62 Dean Palmer .10 .30
63 Terry Pendleton .10 .30
64 Marquis Grissom .10 .30
65 Mike Stanley .10 .30
66 Moises Alou .10 .30
67 Ray Lankford .10 .30
68 Marty Cordova .10 .30
69 John Olerud .10 .30
70 David Cone .10 .30
71 Benito Santiago .10 .30
72 Ryne Sandberg .50 1.25
73 Rickey Henderson .30 .75
74 Roger Cedeno .10 .30
75 Wilson Alvarez .10 .30
76 Tim Salmon .20 .50
77 Orlando Merced .10 .30
78 Vinny Castilla .10 .30
79 Ismael Valdes .10 .30
80 Dante Bichette .10 .30
81 Kevin Brown .10 .30
82 Andy Pettitte .20 .50
83 Scott Stahoviak .10 .30
84 Mickey Tettleton .10 .30
85 Jack McDowell .10 .30
86 Tom Glavine .20 .50
87 Gregg Jefferies .10 .30
88 Chili Davis .10 .30
89 Randy Johnson .30 .75
90 John Mabry .10 .30
91 Billy Wagner .10 .30
92 Jeff Cirillo .10 .30
93 Trevor Hoffman .10 .30
94 Juan Guzman .10 .30
95 Geronimo Berroa .10 .30
96 Bernard Gilkey .10 .30
97 Danny Tartabull .10 .30
98 Johnny Damon .20 .50
99 Charlie Hayes .10 .30
100 Reggie Sanders .10 .30
101 Robby Thompson .10 .30
102 Bobby Bonilla .10 .30
103 Reggie Jefferson .10 .30
104 John Smoltz .20 .50
105 Jim Thome .20 .50
106 Ruben Rivera .10 .30
107 Darren Oliver .10 .30
108 Mo Vaughn .10 .30
109 Roger Pavlik .10 .30
110 Terry Steinbach .10 .30
111 Jermaine Dye .10 .30
112 Mark Grudzielanek .10 .30
113 Rick Aguilera .10 .30
114 Jamey Wright .10 .30
115 Eddie Murray .30 .75
116 Brian L. Hunter .10 .30
117 Hal Morris .10 .30
118 Tom Pagnozzi .10 .30
119 Mike Mussina .20 .50
120 Mark Grace .20 .50
121 Cal Ripken 1.00 2.50
122 Tom Goodwin .10 .30
123 Paul Sorrento .10 .30
124 Jay Bell .10 .30
125 Todd Hollandsworth .10 .30
126 Edgar Martinez .20 .50
127 George Arias .10 .30
128 Greg Vaughn .10 .30
129 Roberto Hernandez .10 .30
130 Delino DeShields .10 .30
131 Bill Pulsipher .10 .30
132 Joey Cora .10 .30
133 Mariano Rivera .30 .75
134 Mike Piazza .50 1.25
135 Carlos Baerga .10 .30
136 Jose Mesa .10 .30
137 Will Clark .20 .50
138 Frank Thomas .30 .75
139 John Wetteland .10 .30
140 Shawn Estes .10 .30
141 Garret Anderson .10 .30
142 Andre Dawson .10 .30
143 Eddie Taubensee .10 .30
144 Ryan Klesko .10 .30
145 Rocky Coppinger .10 .30
146 Jeff Bagwell .20 .50
147 Donovan Osborne .10 .30
148 Greg Myers .10 .30
149 Brant Brown .10 .30
150 Kevin Elster .10 .30
151 Bob Wells .10 .30
152 Wally Joyner .10 .30
153 Rico Brogna .10 .30
154 Dwight Gooden .10 .30
155 Jermaine Allensworth .10 .30

156 Ray Durham .10 .30
157 Cecil Fielder .10 .30
158 John Burkett .10 .30
159 Gary Sheffield .10 .30
160 Albert Belle .10 .30
161 Tomas Perez .10 .30
162 David Doster .10 .30
163 John Valentin .10 .30
164 Danny Graves .10 .30
165 Jose Paniagua .10 .30
166 Brian Giles RC .60 1.50
167 Barry Bonds .75 2.00
168 Sterling Hitchcock .10 .30
169 Bernie Williams .20 .50
170 Fred McGriff .20 .50
171 George Williams .10 .30
172 Amaury Telemaco .10 .30
173 Ken Caminiti .10 .30
174 Ron Gant .10 .30
175 Dave Justice .10 .30
176 James Baldwin .10 .30
177 Pat Hentgen .10 .30
178 Ben McDonald .10 .30
179 Tim Naehring .10 .30
180 Jim Eisenreich .10 .30
181 Ken Hill .10 .30
182 Paul Wilson .10 .30
183 Marvin Benard .10 .30
184 Alan Benes .10 .30
185 Ellis Burks .10 .30
186 Scott Servais .10 .30
187 David Segui .10 .30
188 Scott Brosius .10 .30
189 Jose Offerman .10 .30
190 Eric Davis .10 .30
191 Brett Butler .10 .30
192 Curtis Pride .10 .30
193 Yamil Benitez .10 .30
194 Chan Ho Park .10 .30
195 Bret Boone .10 .30
196 Omar Vizquel .20 .50
197 Orlando Miller .10 .30
198 Ramon Martinez .10 .30
199 Harold Baines .10 .30
200 Eric Young .10 .30
201 Fernando Vina .10 .30
202 Alex Gonzalez .10 .30
203 Fernando Valenzuela .10 .30
204 Steve Avery .10 .30
205 Ernie Young .10 .30
206 Kevin Appier .10 .30
207 Randy Myers .10 .30
208 Jeff Suppan .10 .30
209 James Mouton .10 .30
210 Russ Davis .10 .30
211 Al Martin .10 .30
212 Troy Percival .10 .30
213 Al Leiter .10 .30
214 Dennis Eckersley .10 .30
215 Mark Johnson .10 .30
216 Eric Karros .10 .30
217 Royce Clayton .10 .30
218 Tony Phillips .10 .30
219 Tim Wakefield .10 .30
220 Alan Trammell .10 .30
221 Eduardo Perez .10 .30
222 Butch Huskey .10 .30
223 Tim Belcher .10 .30
224 Jamie Moyer .10 .30
225 F.P. Santangelo .10 .30
226 Rusty Greer .10 .30
227 Jeff Brantley .10 .30
228 Mark Langston .10 .30
229 Ray Montgomery .10 .30
230 Rich Becker .10 .30
231 Ozzie Smith .50 1.25
232 Rey Ordonez .10 .30
233 Ricky Otero .10 .30
234 Mike Cameron .10 .30
235 Mike Sweeney .10 .30
236 Mark Lewis .10 .30
237 Luis Gonzalez .10 .30
238 Marcus Jensen .10 .30
239 Ed Sprague .10 .30
240 Jose Valentin .10 .30
241 Jeff Frye .10 .30
242 Charles Nagy .10 .30
243 Carlos Garcia .10 .30
244 Mike Hampton .10 .30
245 B.J. Surhoff .10 .30
246 Wilton Guerrero .10 .30
247 Frank Rodriguez .10 .30
248 Gary Gaetti .10 .30
249 Lance Johnson .10 .30
250 Darren Bragg .10 .30
251 Darryl Hamilton .10 .30
252 John Jaha .10 .30
253 Craig Paquette .10 .30
254 Jaime Navarro .10 .30
255 Shawon Dunston .10 .30
256 Mark Loretta .10 .30
257 Tim Belk .10 .30
258 Jeff Darwin .10 .30
259 Ruben Sierra .10 .30
260 Chuck Finley .10 .30
261 Darryl Strawberry .10 .30
262 Shannon Stewart .10 .30
263 Pedro Martinez .20 .50
264 Neifi Perez .10 .30
265 Jeff Conine .10 .30
266 Orel Hershiser .10 .30
267 Eddie Murray CL .20 .50
268 Paul Molitor CL .10 .30
269 Barry Bonds CL .40 1.00
270 Mark McGwire CL .40 1.00
271 Matt Williams .10 .30
272 Todd Zeile .10 .30
273 Roger Clemens .60 1.50
274 Michael Tucker .10 .30
275 J.T. Snow .10 .30
276 Kenny Lofton .10 .30
277 Jose Canseco .20 .50
278 Marquis Grissom .10 .30
279 Moises Alou .10 .30
280 Benito Santiago .10 .30
281 Willie McGee .10 .30
282 Chili Davis .10 .30
283 Ron Coomer .10 .30
284 Orlando Merced .10 .30
285 Delino DeShields .10 .30
286 John Wetteland .10 .30
287 Darren Daulton .10 .30
288 Lee Stevens .10 .30
289 Albert Belle .10 .30
290 Sterling Hitchcock .10 .30
291 David Justice .10 .30
292 Eric Davis .10 .30
293 Brian Hunter .10 .30
294 Darryl Hamilton .10 .30
295 Steve Avery .10 .30
296 Joe Vitiello .10 .30
297 Jaime Navarro .10 .30
298 Eddie Murray .30 .75
299 Randy Myers .10 .30
300 Francisco Cordova .10 .30
301 Javier Lopez .10 .30
302 Geronimo Berroa .10 .30
303 Jeffrey Hammonds .10 .30
304 Deion Sanders .20 .50
305 Jeff Fassero .10 .30
306 Curt Schilling .10 .30
307 Robb Nen .10 .30
308 Mark McLemore .10 .30
309 Jimmy Key .10 .30
310 Quilvio Veras .10 .30
311 Bip Roberts .10 .30
312 Esteban Loaiza .10 .30
313 Andy Ashby .10 .30
314 Sandy Alomar Jr. .10 .30
315 Shawn Green .10 .30
316 Luis Castillo .10 .30
317 Benji Gil .10 .30
318 Otis Nixon .10 .30
319 Aaron Sele .10 .30
320 Brad Ausmus .10 .30
321 Troy O'Leary .10 .30
322 Terrell Wade .10 .30
323 Jeff King .10 .30
324 Kevin Seitzer .10 .30
325 Mark Wohlers .10 .30
326 Edgar Renteria .10 .30
327 Dan Wilson .10 .30
328 Brian McRae .10 .30
329 Rod Beck .10 .30
330 Julio Franco .10 .30
331 Dave Nilsson .10 .30
332 Glenallen Hill .10 .30
333 Kevin Elster .10 .30
334 Joe Girardi .10 .30
335 David Wells .10 .30
336 Jeff Blauser .10 .30
337 Darryl Kile .10 .30
338 Jeff Kent .10 .30
339 Jim Leyritz .10 .30
340 Todd Stottlemyre .10 .30
341 Tony Clark .10 .30
342 Chris Hoiles .10 .30
343 Mike Lieberthal .10 .30
344 Matt Lawton .10 .30
345 Alex Ochoa .10 .30
346 Chris Snopek .10 .30
347 Rudy Pemberton .10 .30
348 Eric Owens .10 .30
349 Joe Randa .10 .30
350 John Olerud .10 .30
351 Steve Karsay .10 .30
352 Mark Whiten .10 .30
353 Bob Abreu .20 .50
354 Bartolo Colon .10 .30
355 Vladimir Guerrero .30 .75
356 Darin Erstad .10 .30
357 Scott Rolen .20 .50
358 Andruw Jones .20 .50
359 Scott Spiezio .10 .30
360 Karim Garcia .10 .30
361 Hideki Irabu RC .15 .40
362 Nomar Garciaparra .50 1.25
363 Dmitri Young .10 .30
364 Bubba Trammell RC .15 .40
365 Kevin Orie .10 .30
366 Jose Rosado .10 .30
367 Jose Guillen .10 .30
368 Brooks Kieschnick .10 .30
369 Pokey Reese .10 .30
370 Glendon Rusch .10 .30
371 Jason Dickson .10 .30
372 Todd Walker .10 .30
373 Justin Thompson .10 .30
374 Todd Greene .10 .30
375 Jeff Suppan .10 .30
376 Trey Beamon .10 .30
377 Damon Mashore .10 .30
378 Wendell Magee .10 .30
379 S. Hasegawa RC .20 .50
380 Bill Mueller RC .50 1.25
381 Chris Widger .10 .30
382 Tony Graffanino .10 .30
383 Derrek Lee .20 .50
384 Brian Moehler RC .15 .40
385 Quinton McCracken .10 .30
386 Matt Morris .10 .30
387 Marvin Benard .10 .30
388 Deivi Cruz RC .15 .40
389 Javier Valentin .10 .30
390 Todd Dunwoody .10 .30
391 Derrick Gibson .10 .30
392 Raul Casanova .10 .30
393 George Arias .10 .30
394 Tony Womack RC .15 .40
395 Antone Williamson .10 .30
396 Jose Cruz Jr. RC .15 .40
397 Desi Relaford .10 .30
398 Frank Thomas HIT .20 .50
399 Ken Griffey Jr. HIT .30 .75
400 Cal Ripken HIT .50 1.25
401 Chipper Jones HIT .20 .50
402 Mike Piazza HIT .30 .75
403 Gary Sheffield HIT .10 .30
404 Alex Rodriguez HIT .30 .75
405 Wade Boggs HIT .10 .30
406 Juan Gonzalez HIT .10 .30
407 Tony Gwynn HIT .20 .50
408 Edgar Martinez HIT .10 .30
409 Jeff Bagwell HIT .10 .30
410 Larry Walker HIT .10 .30
411 Kenny Lofton HIT .10 .30
412 Manny Ramirez HIT .10 .30
413 Mark McGwire HIT .40 1.00
414 Roberto Alomar HIT .10 .30
415 Derek Jeter HIT .40 1.00
416 Brady Anderson HIT .10 .30
417 Paul Molitor HIT .10 .30
418 Dante Bichette HIT .10 .30
419 Jim Edmonds HIT .10 .30
420 Mo Vaughn HIT .10 .30
421 Barry Bonds HIT .40 1.00
422 Rusty Greer HIT .10 .30
423 Greg Maddux KING .30 .75
424 Andy Pettitte KING .10 .30
425 John Smoltz KING .10 .30
426 Randy Johnson KING .20 .50
427 Hideo Nomo KING .10 .30
428 Roger Clemens KING .30 .75
429 Tom Glavine KING .10 .30
430 Pat Hentgen KING .10 .30
431 Kevin Brown KING .10 .30
432 Mike Mussina KING .10 .30
433 Alex Fernandez KING .10 .30
434 Kevin Appier KING .10 .30
435 David Cone KING .10 .30
436 Jeff Fassero KING .10 .30
437 John Wetteland KING .10 .30
438 Barry Bonds IS .40 1.00
Ivan Rodriguez
439 Ken Griffey Jr. IS .30 .75
Andres Galarraga
440 Fred McGriff IS .10 .30
Rafael Palmeiro
441 Barry Larkin IS .20 .50
Jim Thome
442 Sammy Sosa IS .20 .50
Albert Belle
443 Bernie Williams IS .10 .30
Todd Hundley
444 Chuck Knoblauch IS .10 .30
Brian Jordan
445 Mo Vaughn IS .10 .30
Jeff Conine
446 Ken Caminiti IS .10 .30
Jason Giambi
447 Raul Mondesi IS .10 .30
Tim Salmon
448 Cal Ripken CL .50 1.25
449 Greg Maddux CL .30 .75
450 Ken Griffey Jr. CL .30 .75

1997 Donruss Diamond Kings

Randomly inserted in all first series packs at a rate of one in 45, this 10-card set commemorates the 15th anniversary of the annual art cards in Donruss baseball sets. Only 10,000 sets were produced each of which is sequentially numbered. Ten cards were printed with the number 1,982 representing the year the insert began and could be redeemed for an original piece of artwork by Diamond Kings artist Dan Gardiner. This was the first year Gardiner painted the Diamond King series.

COMPLETE SET (10) 60.00 120.00
*CANVAS: 1.25X TO 3X BASIC DK'S
CANVAS: RANDOM INS.IN SER.1 PACKS
CANVAS PRINT RUN 500 SERIAL #'d SETS
1 Ken Griffey Jr. 6.00 15.00
2 Cal Ripken 12.50 30.00
3 Mo Vaughn 1.50 4.00
4 Chuck Knoblauch 1.50 4.00
5 Jeff Bagwell 2.50 6.00
6 Henry Rodriguez 1.50 4.00
7 Mike Piazza 6.00 15.00
8 Ivan Rodriguez 2.50 6.00
9 Frank Thomas 4.00 10.00
10 Chipper Jones 4.00 10.00

1997 Donruss Elite Insert Promos

These 12 standard-size cards were issued by Pinnacle to promote their 1997 Donruss Elite Insert set. The fronts are the same as the regular 1997 Donruss Elite insert cards while the backs have a large sample card in black printed sideways on the card. The cards are also numbered promo/2500

COMPLETE SET (12) 40.00 100.00
1 Frank Thomas 3.00 8.00
2 Paul Molitor 2.50 6.00
3 Sammy Sosa 4.00 10.00
4 Barry Bonds 4.00 10.00
5 Chipper Jones 4.00 10.00
6 Alex Rodriguez 6.00 15.00
7 Ken Griffey Jr. 4.00 10.00
8 Jeff Bagwell 2.50 6.00
9 Cal Ripken 8.00 20.00
10 Mo Vaughn .75 2.00
11 Mike Piazza 6.00 15.00
12 Juan Gonzalez UER 2.00 5.00
name mispelled as Gonzales

1997 Donruss Elite Inserts

Randomly inserted in all first series packs, this 12-card set honors perennial all-star players of the League. The fronts feature Micro-etched color action player photos, while the backs carry player information. Only 2,500 of this set were produced

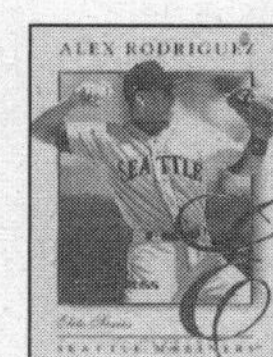

and are sequentially numbered.

COMPLETE SET (12) 100.00 250.00
1 Frank Thomas 6.00 15.00
2 Paul Molitor 2.50 6.00
3 Sammy Sosa 6.00 15.00
4 Barry Bonds 20.00 40.00
5 Chipper Jones 6.00 15.00
6 Alex Rodriguez 12.50 25.00
7 Ken Griffey Jr. 12.50 25.00
8 Jeff Bagwell 4.00 10.00
9 Cal Ripken 25.00 50.00
10 Mo Vaughn 2.50 6.00
11 Mike Piazza 12.50 25.00
12 Juan Gonzalez UER 2.50 6.00
name mispelled as Gonzales

1998 Donruss

The 1998 Donruss set was issued in two series (series one numbers 1-170, series two numbers 171-420) and was distributed in 10-card packs with a suggested retail price of $1.99. The fronts feature color player photos with player information on the backs. The set contains the topical subsets: Fan Club (156-165), Hit List (346-375), The Untouchables (376-385), Spirit of the Game (386-415) and Checklists (416-420). Each Fan Club card carried instructions on how the fan could vote for their favorite players to be included in the 1998 Donruss Update set. Rookie Cards include Kevin Millwood and Maggio Ordonez. Sadly, after an eighteen year run, this was the last Donruss set to be issued due to card manufacturer Pinnacle's bankruptcy in 1998. In 2001, however, Donruss/Playoff procured a license to produce baseball cards and the Donruss brand was reinstituted after a two year break.

COMPLETE SET (420) 20.00 50.00
COMP.SERIES 1 (170) 8.00 20.00
COMPLETE UPDATE (250) 12.50 30.00
1 Paul Molitor .08 .25
2 Juan Gonzalez .08 .25
3 Darryl Kile .08 .25
4 Randy Johnson .25 .60
5 Tom Glavine .15 .40
6 Pat Hentgen .08 .25
7 David Justice .08 .25
8 Kevin Brown .15 .40
9 Mike Mussina .15 .40
10 Ken Caminiti .08 .25
11 Todd Hundley .08 .25
12 Frank Thomas .25 .60
13 Ray Lankford .08 .25
14 Justin Thompson .08 .25
15 Jason Dickson .08 .25
16 Kenny Lofton .08 .25
17 Ivan Rodriguez .15 .40
18 Pedro Martinez .15 .40
19 Brady Anderson .08 .25
20 Barry Larkin .15 .40
21 Chipper Jones .25 .60
22 Tony Gwynn .30 .75
23 Roger Clemens .50 1.25
24 Sandy Alomar Jr. .08 .25
25 Tino Martinez .15 .40
26 Jeff Bagwell .15 .40
27 Shawn Estes .08 .25
28 Ken Griffey Jr. .40 1.00
29 Javier Lopez .08 .25
30 Denny Neagle .08 .25
31 Mike Piazza .40 1.00
32 Andres Galarraga .08 .25
33 Larry Walker .08 .25
34 Alex Rodriguez .40 1.00
35 Greg Maddux .40 1.00
36 Albert Belle .08 .25
37 Barry Bonds .60 1.50
38 Mo Vaughn .08 .25
39 Kevin Appier .08 .25
40 Wade Boggs .15 .40
41 Garret Anderson .08 .25
42 Jeffrey Hammonds .08 .25
43 Marquis Grissom .08 .25
44 Jim Edmonds .08 .25
45 Brian Jordan .08 .25
46 Raul Mondesi .08 .25
47 John Valentin .08 .25
48 Brad Radke .08 .25
49 Ismael Valdes .08 .25
50 Matt Stairs .08 .25
51 Matt Williams .08 .25
52 Reggie Jefferson .08 .25
53 Alan Benes .08 .25
54 Charles Johnson .08 .25
55 Chuck Knoblauch .08 .25
56 Edgar Martinez .15 .40
57 Nomar Garciaparra .40 1.00
58 Craig Biggio .15 .40
59 Bernie Williams .15 .40
60 David Cone .08 .25
61 Cal Ripken .75 2.00
62 Mark McGwire .60 1.50
63 Roberto Alomar .15 .40
64 Fred McGriff .15 .40
65 Eric Karros .08 .25
66 Robin Ventura .08 .25
67 Darin Erstad .08 .25
68 Michael Tucker .08 .25
69 Jim Thome .15 .40
70 Mark Grace .15 .40
71 Lou Collier .08 .25
72 Karim Garcia .08 .25
73 Alex Fernandez .08 .25
74 J.T. Snow .08 .25
75 Reggie Sanders .08 .25
76 John Smoltz .15 .40
77 Tim Salmon .15 .40
78 Paul O'Neill .15 .40
79 Vinny Castilla .08 .25
80 Rafael Palmeiro .15 .40
81 Jaret Wright .08 .25
82 Jay Buhner .08 .25
83 Brett Butler .08 .25
84 Todd Greene .08 .25
85 Scott Rolen .15 .40
86 Sammy Sosa .25 .60
87 Jason Giambi .08 .25
88 Carlos Delgado .08 .25
89 Deion Sanders .15 .40
90 Wilton Guerrero .08 .25
91 Andy Pettitte .15 .40
92 Brian Giles .08 .25
93 Dmitri Young .08 .25
94 Ron Coomer .08 .25
95 Mike Cameron .08 .25
96 Edgardo Alfonzo .08 .25
97 Jimmy Key .08 .25
98 Ryan Klesko .08 .25
99 Andy Benes .08 .25
100 Derek Jeter .60 1.50
101 Jeff Fassero .08 .25
102 Neifi Perez .08 .25
103 Hideo Nomo .25 .60
104 Andruw Jones .15 .40
105 Todd Helton .15 .40
106 Livan Hernandez .08 .25
107 Brett Tomko .08 .25
108 Shannon Stewart .08 .25
109 Bartolo Colon .08 .25
110 Matt Morris .08 .25
111 Miguel Tejada .25 .60
112 Pokey Reese .08 .25
113 Fernando Tatis .08 .25
114 Todd Dunwoody .08 .25
115 Jose Cruz Jr. .08 .25
116 Chan Ho Park .08 .25
117 Kevin Young .08 .25
118 Rickey Henderson .25 .60
119 Hideki Irabu .08 .25
120 Francisco Cordova .08 .25
121 Al Martin .08 .25
122 Tony Clark .08 .25
123 Curt Schilling .08 .25
124 Rusty Greer .08 .25
125 Jose Canseco .15 .40
126 Edgar Renteria .08 .25
127 Todd Walker .08 .25
128 Wally Joyner .08 .25
129 Bill Mueller .08 .25
130 Jose Guillen .08 .25
131 Manny Ramirez .15 .40
132 Bobby Higginson .08 .25
133 Kevin Orie .08 .25
134 Will Clark .15 .40
135 Dave Nilsson .08 .25
136 Jason Kendall .08 .25
137 Ivan Cruz .08 .25
138 Gary Sheffield .08 .25
139 Bubba Trammell .08 .25
140 Vladimir Guerrero .25 .60
141 Dennis Reyes .08 .25
142 Bobby Bonilla .08 .25
143 Ruben Rivera .08 .25
144 Ben Grieve .08 .25
145 Moises Alou .08 .25
146 Tony Womack .08 .25
147 Eric Young .08 .25
148 Paul Konerko .08 .25
149 Dante Bichette .08 .25
150 Joe Carter .08 .25
151 Rondell White .08 .25
152 Chris Holt .08 .25
153 Shawn Green .08 .25
154 Mark Grudzielanek .08 .25
UER back rudzielanek
155 Jermaine Dye .08 .25
156 Ken Griffey Jr. FC .25 .60
157 Frank Thomas FC .15 .40
158 Chipper Jones FC .15 .40
159 Mike Piazza FC .25 .60
160 Cal Ripken FC .40 1.00
161 Greg Maddux FC .25 .60
162 Juan Gonzalez FC .08 .25
163 Alex Rodriguez FC .25 .60
164 Mark McGwire FC .30 .75
165 Derek Jeter FC .30 .75
166 Larry Walker CL .08 .25
167 Tony Gwynn CL .15 .40
168 Tino Martinez CL .08 .25
169 Scott Rolen CL .08 .25
170 Nomar Garciaparra CL .25 .60
171 Mike Sweeney .08 .25
172 Dustin Hermanson .08 .25
173 Darren Dreifort .08 .25
174 Ron Gant .08 .25
175 Todd Hollandsworth .08 .25
176 John Jaha .08 .25
177 Kerry Wood .10 .30
178 Chris Stynes .08 .25
179 Kevin Elster .08 .25
180 Derek Bell .08 .25
181 Darryl Strawberry .08 .25
182 Damion Easley .08 .25
183 Jeff Cirillo .08 .25
184 John Thomson .08 .25
185 Dan Wilson .08 .25
186 Jay Bell .08 .25
187 Bernard Gilkey .08 .25
188 Marc Valdes .08 .25
189 Ramon Martinez .08 .25
190 Charles Nagy .08 .25
191 Derek Lowe .08 .25
192 Andy Benes .08 .25
193 Delino DeShields .08 .25
194 Ryan Jackson RC .08 .25
195 Kenny Lofton .08 .25
196 Chuck Knoblauch .08 .25
197 Andres Galarraga .08 .25
198 Jose Canseco .15 .40
199 John Olerud .08 .25
200 Lance Johnson .08 .25
201 Darryl Kile .08 .25
202 Luis Castillo .08 .25
203 Joe Carter .08 .25
204 Dennis Eckersley .08 .25
205 Steve Finley .08 .25
206 Esteban Loaiza .08 .25
207 R.Christenson RC UER .08 .25
birthdate says 1988
208 Deivi Cruz .08 .25
209 Mariano Rivera .25 .60
210 Mike Judd RC .10 .30
211 Billy Wagner .08 .25
212 Scott Spiezio .08 .25
213 Russ Davis .08 .25
214 Jeff Suppan .08 .25
215 Doug Glanville .08 .25
216 Dmitri Young .08 .25
217 Rey Ordonez .08 .25
218 Cecil Fielder .08 .25
219 Masato Yoshii RC .10 .30
220 Raul Casanova .08 .25
221 Rolando Arrojo RC .10 .30
222 Ellis Burks .08 .25
223 Butch Huskey .08 .25
224 Brian Hunter .08 .25
225 Marquis Grissom .08 .25
226 Kevin Brown .15 .40
227 Joe Randa .08 .25
228 Henry Rodriguez .08 .25
229 Omar Vizquel .15 .40
230 Fred McGriff .15 .40
231 Matt Williams .08 .25
232 Moises Alou .08 .25
233 Travis Fryman .08 .25
234 Wade Boggs .15 .40
235 Pedro Martinez .15 .40
236 Rickey Henderson .25 .60
237 Bubba Trammell .08 .25
238 Mike Caruso .08 .25
239 Wilson Alvarez .08 .25
240 Geronimo Berroa .08 .25
241 Eric Milton .08 .25
242 Scott Erickson .08 .25
243 Todd Erdos RC .08 .25
244 Bobby Hughes .08 .25
245 Dave Hollins .08 .25
246 Dean Palmer .08 .25
247 Carlos Baerga .08 .25
248 Jose Silva .08 .25
249 Jose Cabrera RC .08 .25
250 Tom Evans .08 .25
251 Marty Cordova .08 .25
252 Hanley Frias RC .08 .25
253 Javier Valentin .08 .25
254 Mario Valdez .08 .25
255 Joey Cora .08 .25
256 Mike Lansing .08 .25
257 Jeff Kent .08 .25
258 Dave Dellucci RC .20 .50
259 Curtis King RC .08 .25
260 David Segui .08 .25
261 Royce Clayton .08 .25
262 Jeff Blauser .08 .25
263 Manny Aybar RC .08 .25
264 Mike Cather RC .08 .25
265 Todd Zeile .08 .25
266 Richard Hidalgo .08 .25
267 Dante Powell .08 .25
268 Mike DeJean RC .08 .25
269 Ken Cloude .08 .25
270 Danny Klassen .08 .25
271 Sean Casey .08 .25
272 A.J. Hinch .08 .25
273 Rich Butler RC .08 .25
274 Ben Ford RC .08 .25
275 Billy McMillon .08 .25
276 Wilson Delgado .08 .25
277 Orlando Cabrera .08 .25
278 Geoff Jenkins .08 .25
279 Enrique Wilson .08 .25
280 Derrek Lee .15 .40
281 Marc Pisciotta RC .08 .25
282 Abraham Nunez .08 .25
283 Aaron Boone .08 .25
284 Brad Fullmer .08 .25
285 Rob Stanifer RC .08 .25
286 Preston Wilson .08 .25
287 Greg Norton .08 .25
288 Bobby Smith .08 .25
289 Josh Booty .08 .25
290 Russell Branyan .08 .25
291 Jeremi Gonzalez .08 .25
292 Michael Coleman .08 .25
293 Cliff Politte .08 .25
294 Eric Ludwick .08 .25
295 Rafael Medina .08 .25
296 Jason Varitek .25 .60
297 Ron Wright .08 .25
298 Mark Kotsay .08 .25
299 David Ortiz .30 .75
300 Frank Catalanotto RC .20 .50
301 Robinson Checo .08 .25
302 Kevin Millwood RC .30 .75
303 Jacob Cruz .08 .25
304 Javier Vazquez .08 .25
305 Magglio Ordonez RC 1.00 2.50
306 Kevin Witt .08 .25
307 Derrick Gibson .08 .25
308 Shane Monahan .08 .25
309 Brian Rose .08 .25
310 Bobby Estalella .08 .25
311 Felix Heredia .08 .25
312 Desi Relaford .08 .25
313 Esteban Yan RC .10 .30
314 Ricky Ledee .08 .25
315 Steve Woodard .08 .25
316 Pat Watkins .08 .25
317 Damian Moss .08 .25
318 Bob Abreu .08 .25
319 Jeff Abbott .08 .25
320 Miguel Cairo .08 .25
321 Rigo Beltran RC .08 .25
322 Tony Saunders .08 .25
323 Randall Simon .08 .25
324 Hiram Bocachica .08 .25
325 Richie Sexson .08 .25

326 Karim Garcia .08 .25
327 Mike Lowell RC .50 1.25
328 Pat Cline .08 .25
329 Matt Clement .08 .25
330 Scott Elarton .08 .25
331 Manuel Barrios RC .08 .25
332 Bruce Chen .08 .25
333 Juan Encarnacion .08 .25
334 Travis Lee .08 .25
335 Wes Helms .08 .25
336 Chad Fox RC .08 .25
337 Donnie Sadler .08 .25
338 Carlos Mendoza RC .08 .25
339 Damian Jackson .08 .25
340 Julio Ramirez RC .08 .25
341 John Halama RC .10 .30
342 Edwin Diaz .08 .25
343 Felix Martinez .08 .25
344 Eli Marrero .08 .25
345 Carl Pavano .08 .25
346 Vladimir Guerrero HL .15 .40
347 Barry Bonds HL .30 .75
348 Darin Erstad HL .08 .25
349 Albert Belle HL .08 .25
350 Kenny Lofton HL .08 .25
351 Mo Vaughn HL .08 .25
352 Jose Cruz Jr. HL .08 .25
353 Tony Clark HL .08 .25
354 Roberto Alomar HL .08 .25
355 Manny Ramirez HL .08 .25
356 Paul Molitor HL .08 .25
357 Jim Thome HL .08 .25
358 Tino Martinez HL .08 .25
359 Tim Salmon HL .08 .25
360 David Justice HL .08 .25
361 Raul Mondesi HL .08 .25
362 Mark Grace HL .08 .25
363 Craig Biggio HL .08 .25
364 Larry Walker HL .08 .25
365 Mark McGwire HL .30 .75
366 Juan Gonzalez HL .08 .25
367 Derek Jeter HL .30 .75
368 Chipper Jones HL .15 .40
369 Frank Thomas HL .15 .40
370 Alex Rodriguez HL .25 .60
371 Mike Piazza HL .25 .60
372 Tony Gwynn HL .15 .40
373 Jeff Bagwell HL .08 .25
374 N.Garciaparra HL .25 .60
375 Ken Griffey Jr. HL .25 .60
376 Livan Hernandez UN .08 .25
377 Chan Ho Park UN .08 .25
378 Mike Mussina UN .08 .25
379 Andy Pettitte UN .08 .25
380 Greg Maddux UN .25 .60
381 Hideo Nomo UN .15 .40
382 Roger Clemens UN .25 .60
383 Randy Johnson UN .15 .40
384 Pedro Martinez UN .15 .40
385 Jaret Wright UN .08 .25
386 Ken Griffey Jr. SG .25 .60
387 Todd Helton SG .08 .25
388 Paul Konerko SG .08 .25
389 Cal Ripken SG .40 1.00
390 Larry Walker SG .08 .25
391 Ken Caminiti SG .08 .25
392 Jose Guillen SG .08 .25
393 Jim Edmonds SG .08 .25
394 Barry Larkin SG .08 .25
395 Bernie Williams SG .08 .25
396 Tony Clark SG .08 .25
397 Jose Cruz Jr. SG .08 .25
398 Ivan Rodriguez SG .08 .25
399 Darin Erstad SG .08 .25
400 Scott Rolen SG .08 .25
401 Mark McGwire SG .30 .75
402 Andruw Jones SG .08 .25
403 Juan Gonzalez SG .08 .25
404 Derek Jeter SG .30 .75
405 Chipper Jones SG .15 .40
406 Greg Maddux SG .25 .60
407 Frank Thomas SG .15 .40
408 Alex Rodriguez SG .25 .60
409 Mike Piazza SG .25 .60
410 Tony Gwynn SG .15 .40
411 Jeff Bagwell SG .08 .25
412 N.Garciaparra SG .25 .60
413 Hideo Nomo SG .15 .40
414 Barry Bonds SG .30 .75
415 Ben Grieve SG .08 .25
416 Barry Bonds CL .30 .75
417 Mark McGwire CL .30 .75
418 Roger Clemens CL .25 .60
419 Livan Hernandez CL .08 .25
420 Ken Griffey Jr. CL .25 .60

1998 Donruss Diamond Kings

Randomly inserted in packs, this 20-card set features color player portraits of some of the greatest names in baseball. Only 9,500 sets were produced and are sequentially numbered. The first 500 of each card were printed on actual canvas card stock. In addition, a Frank Thomas sample card was created as a promo for the 1998 Donruss 1 product. The card was sent to all wholesale accounts along with the order forms for the product. The large "SAMPLE" stamp across the back of the card makes it easy to differentiate from Thomas' standard 1998 Diamond King insert card.

COMPLETE SET (20) 40.00 100.00
*CANVAS: 1.25X TO 3X BASIC DIAM.KINGS
CANVAS: RANDOM INSERTS IN PACKS
CANVAS PRINT RUN 500 SERIAL #'d SETS
1 Cal Ripken 8.00 20.00
2 Greg Maddux 4.00 10.00
3 Ivan Rodriguez 1.50 4.00
4 Tony Gwynn 3.00 8.00
5 Paul Molitor 1.00 2.50
6 Kenny Lofton 1.00 2.50
7 Andy Pettitte 1.50 4.00
8 Darin Erstad 1.00 2.50
9 Randy Johnson 2.50 6.00
10 Derek Jeter 6.00 15.00
11 Hideo Nomo 2.50 6.00
12 David Justice 1.00 2.50
13 Bernie Williams 1.50 4.00
14 Roger Clemens 5.00 12.00
15 Barry Larkin 1.50 4.00
16 Andruw Jones 1.50 4.00
17 Mike Piazza 4.00 10.00
18 Frank Thomas 2.50 6.00
19 Alex Rodriguez 4.00 10.00
20 Ken Griffey Jr. 4.00 10.00
S20 Frank Thomas Sample .75 2.00

1998 Donruss Elite Inserts

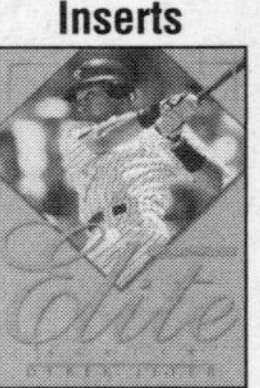

Continuing the popular tradition begun in 1991, Donruss again inserted Elite cards in their packs. These cards which have the work "Elite" written in big cursive letters on the bottom and a small player photo, were serially numbered to 2500 and has the "cream of the crop" of the baseball players. This set was designed to be the last time Donruss would issue Elite cards ending the succsessful eight year run. Itâ ™s interesting to note that unlike previous Elite inserts, the 1998 cards were not numbered in continuation of the Elite run.

COMPLETE SET (20) 125.00 300.00
1 Jeff Bagwell 3.00 8.00
2 Andruw Jones 3.00 8.00
3 Ken Griffey Jr. 8.00 20.00
4 Derek Jeter 12.50 30.00
5 Juan Gonzalez 2.00 5.00
6 Mark McGwire 12.50 30.00
7 Ivan Rodriguez 3.00 8.00
8 Paul Molitor 2.00 5.00
9 Hideo Nomo 5.00 12.00
10 Mo Vaughn 2.00 5.00
11 Chipper Jones 5.00 12.00
12 Nomar Garciaparra 8.00 20.00
13 Mike Piazza 8.00 20.00
14 Frank Thomas 5.00 12.00
15 Greg Maddux 8.00 20.00
16 Cal Ripken 15.00 40.00
17 Alex Rodriguez 8.00 20.00
18 Jose Cruz Jr. 2.00 5.00
19 Barry Bonds 12.50 30.00
20 Tony Gwynn 6.00 15.00

2001 Donruss

The 2001 Donruss product was released in early May, 2001. The 220-card base set was broken into tiers as follows: Base Veterans (1-150), short-printed Rated Rookies (151-200) serial numbered to 2001, and Fan Club cards (201-220) inserted approximatley one per box. Exchange cards with a redemption deadline of May 1st, 2003 was seeded into packs for card 156 Albert Pujols and 159 Ben Sheets. Each pack contained five cards, and a one card retro pack. Packs carried a suggested retail price of $1.99. Please note that 1999 Retro packs were inserted in Hobby packs, while 2000 Retro packs were inserted into Retail packs. One in every 720 packs contained an exchange card good for a complete set of 2001 Donruss Baseball's Best. One in every 72 packs contained and exchange card good for a complete set of 2001 Donruss the Rookies. The redemption deadline for both exchange cards was January 20th, 2002. The original exchange deadline was November 1st, 2001 but the manufacturer lengthened the redemption period.

COMP.SET w/o SP's (150) 10.00 25.00
COMMON CARD (1-150) .10 .30
COMMON (151-200) 3.00 8.00
COMMON (201-220) 1.00 2.50
1 Alex Rodriguez .50 1.25
2 Barry Bonds .75 2.00
3 Cal Ripken 1.00 2.50
4 Chipper Jones .30 .75
5 Derek Jeter .75 2.00
6 Troy Glaus .10 .30
7 Frank Thomas .30 .75
8 Greg Maddux .50 1.25
9 Ivan Rodriguez .20 .50
10 Jeff Bagwell .20 .50
11 Jose Canseco .20 .50
12 Todd Helton .20 .50
13 Ken Griffey Jr. .50 1.25
14 Manny Ramirez Sox .20 .50
15 Mark McGwire .75 2.00
16 Mike Piazza .50 1.25
17 Nomar Garciaparra .50 1.25
18 Pedro Martinez .20 .50
19 Randy Johnson .30 .75
20 Rick Ankiel .10 .30
21 Rickey Henderson .30 .75
22 Roger Clemens .60 1.50
23 Sammy Sosa .30 .75
24 Tony Gwynn .40 1.00
25 Vladimir Guerrero .30 .75
26 Eric Davis .10 .30
27 Roberto Alomar .10 .30
28 Mark Mulder .10 .30
29 Pat Burrell .10 .30
30 Harold Baines .10 .30
31 Carlos Delgado .10 .30
32 J.D. Drew .10 .30
33 Jim Edmonds .10 .30
34 Darin Erstad .10 .30
35 Jason Giambi .10 .30
36 Tom Glavine .20 .50
37 Juan Gonzalez .10 .30
38 Mark Grace .20 .50
39 Shawn Green .10 .30
40 Tim Hudson .10 .30
41 Andruw Jones .20 .50
42 David Justice .10 .30
43 Jeff Kent .10 .30
44 Barry Larkin .20 .50
45 Pokey Reese .10 .30
46 Mike Mussina .20 .50
47 Hideo Nomo .30 .75
48 Rafael Palmeiro .20 .50
49 Adam Piatt .10 .30
50 Scott Rolen .20 .50
51 Gary Sheffield .10 .30
52 Bernie Williams .20 .50
53 Bob Abreu .10 .30
54 Edgardo Alfonzo .10 .30
55 Jermaine Clark RC .20 .50
56 Albert Belle .10 .30
57 Craig Biggio .20 .50
58 Andres Galarraga .10 .30
59 Edgar Martinez .20 .50
60 Fred McGriff .20 .50
61 Magglio Ordonez .10 .30
62 Jim Thome .20 .50
63 Matt Williams .10 .30
64 Kerry Wood .10 .30
65 Moises Alou .10 .30
66 Brady Anderson .10 .30
67 Garret Anderson .10 .30
68 Tony Armas Jr. .10 .30
69 Tony Batista .10 .30
70 Jose Cruz Jr. .10 .30
71 Carlos Beltran .10 .30
72 Adrian Beltre .10 .30
73 Kris Benson .10 .30
74 Lance Berkman .10 .30
75 Kevin Brown .10 .30
76 Jay Buhner .10 .30
77 Jeromy Burnitz .10 .30
78 Ken Caminiti .10 .30
79 Sean Casey .10 .30
80 Luis Castillo .10 .30
81 Eric Chavez .10 .30
82 Jeff Cirillo .10 .30
83 Bartolo Colon .10 .30
84 David Cone .10 .30
85 Freddy Garcia .10 .30
86 Johnny Damon .20 .50
87 Ray Durham .10 .30
88 Jermaine Dye .10 .30
89 Juan Encarnacion .10 .30
90 Terrence Long .10 .30
91 Carl Everett .10 .30
92 Steve Finley .10 .30
93 Cliff Floyd .10 .30
94 Brad Fullmer .10 .30
95 Brian Giles .10 .30
96 Luis Gonzalez .10 .30
97 Rusty Greer .10 .30
98 Jeffrey Hammonds .10 .30
99 Mike Hampton .10 .30
100 Orlando Hernandez .10 .30
101 Richard Hidalgo .10 .30
102 Geoff Jenkins .10 .30
103 Jacque Jones .10 .30
104 Brian Jordan .10 .30
105 Gabe Kapler .10 .30
106 Eric Karros .10 .30
107 Jason Kendall .10 .30
108 Adam Kennedy .10 .30
109 Byung-Hyun Kim .10 .30
110 Ryan Klesko .10 .30
111 Chuck Knoblauch .10 .30
112 Paul Konerko .10 .30
113 Carlos Lee .10 .30
114 Kenny Lofton .10 .30
115 Javy Lopez .10 .30
116 Tino Martinez .20 .50
117 Ruben Mateo .10 .30
118 Kevin Millwood .10 .30
119 Ben Molina .10 .30
120 Raul Mondesi .10 .30
121 Trot Nixon .10 .30
122 John Olerud .10 .30
123 Paul O'Neill .20 .50
124 Chan Ho Park .10 .30
125 Andy Pettitte .20 .50
126 Jorge Posada .20 .50
127 Mark Quinn .10 .30
128 Aramis Ramirez .10 .30
129 Mariano Rivera .30 .75
130 Tim Salmon .20 .50
131 Curt Schilling .10 .30
132 Richie Sexson .10 .30
133 John Smoltz .20 .50
134 J.T. Snow .10 .30
135 Jay Payton .10 .30
136 Shannon Stewart .10 .30
137 B.J. Surhoff .10 .30
138 Mike Sweeney .10 .30
139 Fernando Tatis .10 .30
140 Miguel Tejada .10 .30
141 Jason Varitek .30 .75
142 Greg Vaughn .10 .30
143 Mo Vaughn .10 .30
144 Robin Ventura UER .10 .30
Listed as playing for Yankees last 2 years
Also Bat and Throw information is wrong
145 Jose Vidro .10 .30
146 Omar Vizquel .20 .50
147 Larry Walker .10 .30
148 David Wells .10 .30
149 Rondell White .10 .30
150 Preston Wilson .10 .30
151 Brent Abernathy RR 3.00 8.00
152 Cory Aldridge RR RC 3.00 8.00
153 Gene Altman RR RC 3.00 8.00
154 Josh Beckett RR 4.00 10.00
155 W. Betemit RR RC 4.00 10.00
156 A.Pujols RR/500 RC 125.00 250.00
157 Joe Crede RR 4.00 10.00
158 Jack Cust RR 3.00 8.00
159 Ben Sheets RR/500 15.00 40.00
160 Alex Escobar RR 3.00 8.00
161 A. Hernandez RR RC 3.00 8.00
162 Pedro Feliz RR 3.00 8.00
163 Nate Frese RR RC 3.00 8.00
164 Carlos Garcia RR RC 3.00 8.00
165 Marcus Giles RR 3.00 8.00
166 Alexis Gomez RR RC 3.00 8.00
167 Jason Hart RR 3.00 8.00
168 Eric Hinske RR RC 4.00 10.00
169 Cesar Izturis RR 3.00 8.00
170 Nick Johnson RR 3.00 8.00
171 Mike Young RR 4.00 10.00
172 B. Lawrence RR RC 3.00 8.00
173 Steve Lomasney RR 3.00 8.00
174 Nick Maness RR 3.00 8.00
175 Jose Mieses RR RC 3.00 8.00
176 Greg Miller RR RC 3.00 8.00
177 Eric Munson RR 3.00 8.00
178 Xavier Nady RR 3.00 8.00
179 Blaine Neal RR RC 3.00 8.00
180 Abraham Nunez RR 3.00 8.00
181 Jose Ortiz RR 3.00 8.00
182 Jeremy Owens RR RC 3.00 8.00
183 Pablo Ozuna RR 3.00 8.00
184 Corey Patterson RR 3.00 8.00
185 Carlos Pena RR 3.00 8.00
186 Wily Mo Pena RR 3.00 8.00
187 Timo Perez RR 3.00 8.00
188 A. Pettyjohn RR RC 3.00 8.00
189 Luis Rivas RR 3.00 8.00
190 J. Melian RR RC 3.00 8.00
191 Wilken Ruan RR RC 3.00 8.00
192 D. Sanchez RR RC 3.00 8.00
193 Alfonso Soriano RR 4.00 10.00
194 Rafael Soriano RR RC 3.00 8.00
195 Ichiro Suzuki RR RC 30.00 60.00
196 Billy Sylvester RR RC 3.00 8.00
197 Juan Uribe RR RC 4.00 10.00
198 Eric Valent RR 3.00 8.00
199 C.Valderrama RR RC 3.00 8.00
200 Matt White RR RC 3.00 8.00
201 Alex Rodriguez FC 2.50 6.00
202 Barry Bonds FC 4.00 10.00
203 Cal Ripken FC 5.00 12.00
204 Chipper Jones FC 1.50 4.00
205 Derek Jeter FC 4.00 10.00
206 Troy Glaus FC 1.00 2.50
207 Frank Thomas FC 1.50 4.00
208 Greg Maddux FC 2.50 6.00
209 Ivan Rodriguez FC 1.00 2.50
210 Jeff Bagwell FC 1.00 2.50
211 Todd Helton FC 1.00 2.50
212 Ken Griffey Jr. FC 2.50 6.00
213 Manny Ramirez Sox FC 1.00 2.50
214 Mark McGwire FC 4.00 10.00
215 Mike Piazza FC 2.50 6.00
216 Pedro Martinez FC 1.00 2.50
217 Sammy Sosa FC 1.50 4.00
218 Tony Gwynn FC 2.00 5.00
219 Vladimir Guerrero FC 1.50 4.00
220 Nomar Garciaparra FC 2.50 6.00
NNO BB Best Coupon .75 2.00
NNO The Rookies Coupon .20 .50

2001 Donruss Stat Line Career

Randomly inserted into 2001 Donruss packs, this 220-card insert parallels the 2001 Donruss base set. Each card is individually serial numbered to a career stat of the given players. Please note that the print runs are listed in our checklist. Exchange cards for Albert Pujols and Ben Sheets with a redemption deadline of May 1st, 2003 were seeded into packs. A special autographed version of Albert Pujols' Stat Line Career card was printed in response to an error in production whereby more Stat Line Career Pujols exchange cards were seeded into packs than the 154 copies intended for release. To honor their commitment to collectors redeeming the exchange card, Donruss had Pujols sign a special non-serial numbered version of the card and sent it out to collectors redeeming the exchange card. Cards with a print run of 25 or fewer are not priced due to market scarcity.

*1-150 P/R b/wn 251-400: 2.5X TO 6X
*1-150 P/R b/wn 201-250: 2.5X TO 6X
*1-150 P/R b/wn 151-200: 3X TO 8X
*1-150 P/R b/wn 121-150: 3X TO 8X
*1-150 P/R b/wn 81-120: 4X TO 10X
*1-150 P/R b/wn 66-80: 5X TO 12X
*1-150 P/R b/wn 51-65: 5X TO 12X
*1-150 P/R b/wn 36-50: 6X TO 15X
*1-150 P/R b/wn 26-35: 8X TO 20X
*201-220 P/R b/wn 251-400 .5X TO 1.2X
*201-220 P/R b/wn 201-250 .5X TO 1.2X
*201-220 P/R b/wn 151-200 .6X TO 1.5X
*201-220 P/R b/wn 121-150 .6X TO 1.5X
*201-220 P/R b/wn 81-120 .75X TO 2X
*201-220 P/R b/wn 36-50 1.25X TO 3X
151 B. Abernathy RR/22
152 Cory Aldridge RR/33 4.00 10.00
153 Gene Altman RR/351 .75 2.00
154 Josh Beckett RR/212 1.00 2.50
155 Wilson Betemit RR/15
156 Albert Pujols RR/154 125.00 200.00
156B Albert Pujols RR AU
157 Joe Crede RR/357 1.25 3.00
158 Jack Cust RR/66 2.00 5.00
159 Ben Sheets RR/159 6.00 15.00
159B Ben Sheets RR AU
160 Alex Escobar RR/45 3.00 8.00
161 A. Hernandez RR/86 2.00 5.00
162 Pedro Feliz RR/286 .75 2.00
163 Nate Frese RR/119 2.00 5.00
164 Carlos Garcia RR/106 2.00 5.00
165 Marcus Giles RR/320 .75 2.00
166 Alexis Gomez RR/34 4.00 10.00
167 Jason Hart RR/303 .75 2.00
168 Eric Hinske RR/332 1.00 2.50
169 Cesar Izturis RR/60 2.50 6.00
170 Nick Johnson RR/308 .75 2.00
171 Mike Young RR/37 5.00 12.00
172 B. Lawrence RR/281 .75 2.00
173 S. Lomasney RR/229 1.00 2.50
174 Nick Maness RR/25
175 Jose Mieses RR/265 .75 2.00
176 Greg Miller RR/328 .75 2.00
177 Eric Munson RR/3
178 Xavier Nady RR/1
179 Blaine Neal RR/296 .75 2.00
180 A. Nunez RR/38 3.00 8.00
181 Jose Ortiz RR/7
182 J. Owens RR/273 .75 2.00
183 Pablo Ozuna RR/333 .75 2.00
184 Corey Patterson RR/11
185 Carlos Pena RR/52 2.50 6.00
186 Wily Mo Pena RR/114 2.00 5.00
187 Timo Perez RR/49 3.00 8.00
188 A. Pettyjohn RR/20
189 Luis Rivas RR/310 .75 2.00
190 J. Melian RR/26 4.00 10.00
191 Wilken Ruan RR/215 1.00 2.50
192 D. Sanchez RR/19
193 A. Soriano RR/50 3.00 8.00
194 Rafael Soriano RR/13
195 Ichiro Suzuki RR/106 60.00 120.00
196 Billy Sylvester RR/11
197 Juan Uribe RR/157 1.25 3.00
198 Eric Valent RR/342 .75 2.00
199 Carlos Valderrama RR/13
200 Matt White RR/31 4.00 10.00

2001 Donruss Stat Line Season

Randomly inserted into 2001 Donruss packs, this 220-card insert parallels the 2001 Donruss base set. Each card is individually serial numbered to a season stat of the given players. Please note that the print runs are listed in our checklist. Exchange cards for Albert Pujols and Ben Sheets with a redemption deadline of May 1st, 2003 were seeded into packs. Autographed versions of Pujols and Sheets were made available due to an error in production whereby more than the stated amount of Stat Line Season cards for each player were produced. To honor their commitment to collectors - Donruss contracted with the two athletes to sign special non-serial numbered versions of their Stat Line Season card and sent them out to collectors that redeemed the exchange cards. Cards with a print run of 25 or fewer are not priced due to market scarcity.

*1-150 P/R b/wn 151-200: 3X TO 8X
*1-150 P/R b/wn 121-150: 3X TO 8X
*1-150 P/R b/wn 81-120: 4X TO 10X
*1-150 P/R b/wn 66-80: 5X TO 12X
*1-150 P/R b/wn 51-65: 5X TO 12X
*1-150 P/R b/wn 36-50: 6X TO 15X
*1-150 P/R b/wn 26-35: 8X TO 20X
*201-220 P/R b/wn 151-200 .6X TO 1.5X
*201-220 P/R b/wn 121-150 .6X TO 1.5X
*201-220 P/R b/wn 81-120 .75X TO 2X
*201-220 P/R b/wn 66-80 1X TO 2.5X
*201-220 P/R b/wn 36-50 1.25X TO 3X
*201-220 P/R b/wn 26-35 1.5X TO 4X
151 B. Abernathy RR/130 1.50 4.00
152 Cory Aldridge RR/100 2.00 5.00
153 Gene Altman RR/6
154 Josh Beckett RR/61 2.50 6.00
155 Wilson Betemit RR/89 6.00 15.00
156 Albert Pujols RR/17
156B Albert Pujols RR AU 500.00 800.00
157 Joe Crede RR/5
158 Jack Cust RR/131 1.50 4.00
159 Ben Sheets RR/8
159B Ben Sheets RR AU 30.00 60.00
160 Alex Escobar RR/126 1.50 4.00
161 Adrian Hernandez RR/8
162 Pedro Feliz RR/2
163 Nate Frese RR/126 1.50 4.00
164 Carlos Garcia RR/14
165 Marcus Giles RR/133 1.50 4.00
166 Alexis Gomez RR/117 2.00 5.00
167 Jason Hart RR/31 4.00 10.00
168 Eric Hinske RR/20
169 Cesar Izturis RR/95 2.00 5.00
170 Nick Johnson RR/145 1.50 4.00
171 Mike Young RR/155 2.00 5.00
172 B. Lawrence RR/165 1.25 3.00
173 Steve Lomasney RR/8
174 Nick Maness RR/127 1.50 4.00
175 Jose Mieses RR/17
176 Greg Miller RR/10
177 Eric Munson RR/1
178 Xavier Nady RR/1
179 Blaine Neal RR/65 2.50 6.00
180 A. Nunez RR/51 2.50 6.00
181 Jose Ortiz RR/9
182 Jeremy Owens RR/16
183 Pablo Ozuna RR/8
184 Corey Patterson RR/2
185 Carlos Pena RR/117 2.00 5.00
186 Wily Mo Pena RR/10
187 Timo Perez RR/14
188 A. Pettyjohn RR/68 2.00 5.00
189 Luis Rivas RR/18
190 J. Melian RR/73 2.00 5.00
191 Wilken Ruan RR/165 1.25 3.00
192 D.Sanchez RR/121 1.50 4.00
193 Alfonso Soriano RR/2
194 Rafael Soriano RR/90 2.00 5.00
195 Ichiro Suzuki RR/153 50.00 100.00
196 Billy Sylvester RR/16
197 Juan Uribe RR/22
198 Eric Valent RR/22
199 C.Valderrama RR/137 1.50 4.00
200 Matt White RR/126 1.50 4.00

2001 Donruss 1999 Retro

Inserted into hobby packs at one per hobby pack, this 100-card insert features cards that Donruss would have released in 1999 had they been producing baseball cards at the time. The set is broken into tiers as follows: Base Veterans (1-80), and Short-printed Prospects (81-100) serial numbered to 1999. Please note that these cards have a 2001 copyright, thus, are listed under the 2001 products.

COMPLETE SET (100) 75.00 150.00
COMP.SET w/o SP's (80) 20.00 50.00
COMMON CARD (1-80) .25 .60
COMMON CARD (81-100) 2.00 5.00
1 Ken Griffey Jr. 1.00 2.50
2 Nomar Garciaparra 1.00 2.50
3 Alex Rodriguez 1.00 2.50
4 Mark McGwire 1.50 4.00
5 Sammy Sosa .60 1.50
6 Chipper Jones .60 1.50
7 Mike Piazza 1.00 2.50
8 Barry Larkin .40 1.00
9 Andruw Jones .40 1.00
10 Albert Belle .25 .60
11 Jeff Bagwell .40 1.00
12 Tony Gwynn .75 2.00
13 Manny Ramirez .40 1.00
14 Mo Vaughn .25 .60
15 Barry Bonds 1.50 4.00
16 Frank Thomas .60 1.50
17 Vladimir Guerrero .60 1.50
18 Derek Jeter 1.50 4.00
19 Randy Johnson .60 1.50
20 Greg Maddux 1.00 2.50
21 Pedro Martinez .40 1.00
22 Cal Ripken 2.00 5.00
23 Ivan Rodriguez .40 1.00
24 Matt Williams .25 .60
25 Javy Lopez .25 .60
26 Tim Salmon .40 1.00
27 Raul Mondesi .25 .60
28 Todd Helton .40 1.00
29 Magglio Ordonez .25 .60
30 Sean Casey .25 .60
31 Jeromy Burnitz .25 .60
32 Jeff Kent .25 .60
33 Jim Edmonds .25 .60
34 Jim Thome .40 1.00
35 Dante Bichette .25 .60
36 Larry Walker .25 .60
37 Will Clark .40 1.00
38 Omar Vizquel .40 1.00
39 Mike Mussina .40 1.00
40 Eric Karros .25 .60
41 Kenny Lofton .25 .60
42 David Justice .25 .60
43 Craig Biggio .40 1.00
44 J.D. Drew .25 .60
45 Rickey Henderson .60 1.50
46 Bernie Williams .40 1.00
47 Brian Giles .25 .60
48 Paul O'Neill .40 1.00
49 Orlando Hernandez .25 .60
50 Jason Giambi .25 .60
51 Curt Schilling .25 .60
52 Scott Rolen .40 1.00
53 Mark Grace .40 1.00
54 Moises Alou .25 .60
55 Jason Kendall .25 .60
56 Ray Lankford .25 .60
57 Kerry Wood .25 .60
58 Gary Sheffield .25 .60
59 Ruben Mateo .25 .60
60 Darin Erstad .25 .60
61 Troy Glaus .25 .60
62 Jose Canseco .40 1.00
63 Wade Boggs .40 1.00
64 Tom Glavine .40 1.00
65 Gabe Kapler .25 .60
66 Juan Gonzalez .25 .60
67 Rafael Palmeiro .40 1.00
68 Richie Sexson .25 .60
69 Carl Everett .25 .60
70 David Wells .25 .60
71 Carlos Delgado .25 .60
72 Eric Davis .25 .60
73 Shawn Green .25 .60
74 Andres Galarraga .25 .60
75 Edgar Martinez .40 1.00
76 Roberto Alomar .40 1.00
77 John Olerud .25 .60
78 Luis Gonzalez .25 .60
79 Kevin Brown .25 .60
80 Roger Clemens 1.25 3.00
81 Josh Beckett SP 3.00 8.00
82 Alfonso Soriano SP 3.00 8.00
83 Alex Escobar SP 2.00 5.00
84 Pat Burrell SP 2.00 5.00
85 Eric Chavez SP 2.00 5.00
86 Erubiel Durazo SP 2.00 5.00
87 Abraham Nunez SP 2.00 5.00

88 Carlos Pena SP 2.00 5.00
89 Nick Johnson SP 2.00 5.00
90 Eric Munson SP 2.00 5.00
91 Corey Patterson SP 2.00 5.00
92 Wily Mo Pena SP 2.00 5.00
93 Rafael Furcal SP 2.00 5.00
94 Eric Valent SP 2.00 5.00
95 Mark Mulder SP 2.00 5.00
96 Chad Hutchinson SP 2.00 5.00
97 Freddy Garcia SP 2.00 5.00
98 Tim Hudson SP 2.00 5.00
99 Rick Ankiel SP 2.00 5.00
100 Kip Wells SP 2.00 5.00

2001 Donruss 1999 Retro Stat Line Career

Randomly inserted into 1999 Retro packs, this 100-card insert parallels the 1999 Retro base set. Each card is individually serial numbered to a career stat of the given players. Please note that the print runs are listed in our checklist. Cards with a print run of 25 or fewer are not priced due to market scarcity.

*1-80 P/R b/wn 251-400: 1.25X TO 3X
*1-80 P/R b/wn 201-250: 1.25X TO 3X
*1-80 P/R b/wn 151-200: 1.5X TO 4X
*1-80 P/R b/wn 121-150: 1.5X TO 4X
*1-80 P/R b/wn 81-120: 2X TO 5X
*1-80 P/R b/wn 66-80: 2.5X TO 6X
*1-80 P/R b/wn 51-65: 2.5X TO 6X
*1-80 P/R b/wn 36-50: 3X TO 8X
*1-80 P/R b/wn 26-35: 4X TO 10X
81 Josh Beckett/13
82 Alfonso Soriano/113 1.50 4.00
83 Alex Escobar/181 1.00 2.50
84 Pat Burrell/303 .75 2.00
85 Eric Chavez/314 .75 2.00
86 Erubiel Durazo/147 1.25 3.00
87 Abraham Nunez/106 1.50 4.00
88 Carlos Pena/46 2.50 6.00
89 Nick Johnson/259 .75 2.00
90 Eric Munson/392 .75 2.00
91 Corey Patterson/117 1.50 4.00
92 Wily Mo Pena/247 .75 2.00
93 Rafael Furcal/137 1.25 3.00
94 Eric Valent/53 2.00 5.00
95 Mark Mulder/340 .75 2.00
96 Chad Hutchinson/2
97 Freddy Garcia/397 .75 2.00
98 Tim Hudson/17
99 Rick Ankiel/222 .75 2.00
100 Kip Wells/371 .75 2.00

2001 Donruss 1999 Retro Stat Line Season

Randomly inserted into 1999 Retro packs, this 100-card insert parallels the 1999 Retro base set. Each card is individually serial numbered to a season stat of the given players. Please note that the print runs are listed in our checklist. Cards issued to a stated print run of 25 or fewer are not priced due to market scarcity.

*1-80 P/R b/wn 251-400: 1.25X TO 3X
*1-80 P/R b/wn 201-250: 1.25X TO 3X
*1-80 P/R b/wn 151-200: 1.5X TO 4X
*1-80 P/R b/wn 121-150: 1.5X TO 4X
*1-80 P/R b/wn 81-120: 2X TO 5X
*1-80 P/R b/wn 66-80: 2.5X TO 6X
*1-80 P/R b/wn 51-65: 2.5X TO 6X
*1-80 P/R b/wn 36-50: 3X TO 8X
*1-80 P/R b/wn 26-35: 4X TO 10X
81 Josh Beckett/178 1.00 2.50
82 Alfonso Soriano/7
83 Alex Escobar/27 3.00 8.00
84 Pat Burrell/7
85 Eric Chavez/33 3.00 8.00
86 Erubiel Durazo/19
87 Abraham Nunez/95 1.50 4.00
88 Carlos Pena/319 .75 2.00
89 Nick Johnson/17
90 Eric Munson/16
91 Corey Patterson/22
92 Wily Mo Pena/7
93 Rafael Furcal/88 1.50 4.00
94 Eric Valent/13
95 Mark Mulder/113 1.50 4.00
96 Chad Hutchinson/51 2.00 5.00
97 Freddy Garcia/10
98 Tim Hudson/152 1.00 2.50
99 Rick Ankiel/12
100 Kip Wells/135 1.00 2.50

2001 Donruss 1999 Retro Diamond Kings

Randomly inserted into 1999 Retro packs, this 5-card insert set features the "Diamond King" cards that Donruss would have produced had they been producing baseball cards in 1999. Each card is individually serial numbered to 2500.

COMPLETE SET (5) 30.00 60.00
*STUDIO: .75X TO 2X BASIC RETRO DK
STUDIO PRINT RUN 250 SERIAL #'d SETS

RANDOM INSERTS IN 1999 RETRO PACKS
1 Scott Rolen 4.00 10.00
2 Sammy Sosa 4.00 10.00
3 Juan Gonzalez 4.00 10.00
4 Ken Griffey Jr. 5.00 12.00
5 Derek Jeter 8.00 20.00

2001 Donruss 2000 Retro

Inserted into retail packs at one per retail pack, this 100-card insert features cards that Donruss would have released in 2000 had they been producing baseball cards at the time. The set is broken into tiers as follows: Base Veterans (1-80), and Short-printed Prospects (81-100) serial numbered to 2000. Please note that these cards have a 2001 copyright, thus, are listed under the 2001 products. Exchange cards originally intended for number 82 C.C. Sabathia and number 95 Ben Sheets were both issued in packs with an expiration date of 05/01/03. It's believed, however, two separate cards were made available for redemption card 95 . . . Ben Sheets and Ichiro Suzuki. It's not known at this time exactly which player was featured on the exchange card number 82.

COMPLETE SET (100) 125.00 250.00
COMP.SET w/o SP's (80) 40.00 80.00
COMMON CARD (1-80) .25 .60
COMMON CARD (81-100) 2.00 5.00
SP * 82/95 WERE AVAIL.ONLY VIA MAIL
1 Vladimir Guerrero .60 1.50
2 Alex Rodriguez 1.00 2.50
3 Ken Griffey Jr. 1.00 2.50
4 Nomar Garciaparra 1.00 2.50
5 Mike Piazza 1.00 2.50
6 Mark McGwire 1.50 4.00
7 Sammy Sosa .60 1.50
8 Chipper Jones .60 1.50
9 Jim Edmonds .25 .60
10 Tony Gwynn .75 2.00
11 Andruw Jones .40 1.00
12 Albert Belle .25 .60
13 Jeff Bagwell .40 1.00
14 Manny Ramirez .40 1.00
15 Mo Vaughn .25 .60
16 Barry Bonds 1.50 4.00
17 Frank Thomas .60 1.50
18 Ivan Rodriguez .40 1.00
19 Derek Jeter 1.50 4.00
20 Randy Johnson .60 1.50
21 Greg Maddux 1.00 2.50
22 Pedro Martinez .40 1.00
23 Cal Ripken 2.00 5.00
24 Mark Grace .40 1.00
25 Javy Lopez .25 .60
26 Ray Durham .25 .60
27 Todd Helton .40 1.00
28 Magglio Ordonez .25 .60
29 Sean Casey .25 .60
30 Darin Erstad .25 .60
31 Barry Larkin .40 1.00
32 Will Clark .40 1.00
33 Jim Thome .40 1.00
34 Dante Bichette .25 .60
35 Larry Walker .25 .60
36 Ken Caminiti .25 .60
37 Omar Vizquel .40 1.00
38 Miguel Tejada .25 .60
39 Eric Karros .25 .60
40 Gary Sheffield .25 .60
41 Jeff Cirillo .25 .60
42 Rondell White .25 .60
43 Rickey Henderson .60 1.50
44 Bernie Williams .40 1.00
45 Brian Giles .25 .60
46 Paul O'Neill .40 1.00
47 Orlando Hernandez .25 .60
48 Ben Grieve .25 .60
49 Jason Giambi .25 .60
50 Curt Schilling .25 .60
51 Scott Rolen .40 1.00
52 Bobby Abreu .25 .60
53 Jason Kendall .25 .60
54 Fernando Tatis .25 .60
55 Jeff Kent .25 .60
56 Mike Mussina .40 1.00
57 Troy Glaus .25 .60
58 Jose Canseco .40 1.00
59 Wade Boggs .40 1.00
60 Fred McGriff .25 .60
61 Juan Gonzalez .25 .60
62 Rafael Palmeiro .40 1.00
63 Rusty Greer .25 .60
64 Carl Everett .25 .60
65 David Wells .25 .60
66 Carlos Delgado .25 .60
67 Shawn Green .25 .60
68 David Justice .25 .60
69 Edgar Martinez .40 1.00
70 Andres Galarraga .25 .60
71 Roberto Alomar .40 1.00
72 Jermaine Dye .25 .60
73 John Olerud .25 .60
74 Luis Gonzalez .25 .60
75 Craig Biggio .40 1.00
76 Kevin Millwood .25 .60
77 Kevin Brown .25 .60
78 John Smoltz .40 1.00
79 Roger Clemens 1.25 3.00
80 Mike Hampton .25 .60
81 Tomas De La Rosa SP 2.00 5.00
82 C.C. Sabathia SP * 6.00 15.00
83 Ryan Christenson SP 2.00 5.00
84 Pedro Feliz SP 2.00 5.00
85 Jose Ortiz SP 2.00 5.00
86 Xavier Nady SP 2.00 5.00
87 Julio Zuleta SP 2.00 5.00
88 Jason Hart SP 2.00 5.00
89 Keith Ginter SP 2.00 5.00
90 Brent Abernathy SP 2.00 5.00
91 Timo Perez SP 2.00 5.00
92 Juan Pierre SP 2.00 5.00
93 Tike Redman SP 2.00 5.00
94 Mike Lamb SP 2.00 5.00
95A Ben Sheets SP * 6.00 15.00
95B Ichiro Suzuki SP * 20.00 50.00
96 Kazuhiro Sasaki SP 2.00 5.00
97 Barry Zito SP 3.00 8.00
98 Adam Bernero SP 2.00 5.00
99 Chad Durbin SP 2.00 5.00
100 Matt Ginter SP 2.00 5.00

2001 Donruss 2000 Retro Stat Line Career

Randomly inserted into 2000 Retro packs, this 100-card insert parallels the 2000 Retro base set. Each card is individually serial numbered to a career stat of the given players. Please note that the print runs are listed in our checklist. Cards issued to a stated print run of 25 or fewer are not priced due to market scarcity. Exchange cards were seeded into packs for cards 82 and 95. These cards were originally intended to be redeemed for C.C. Sabathia and Ben Sheets. It's since been discovered that Ichiro Suzuki cards were actually redeemed for card 95.

*1-80 P/R b/wn 251-400: 1.25X TO 3X
*1-80 P/R b/wn 201-250: 1.25X TO 3X
*1-80 P/R b/wn 151-200: 1.5X TO 4X
*1-80 P/R b/wn 121-150: 1.5X TO 4X
*1-80 P/R b/wn 81-120: 2X TO 5X
*1-80 P/R b/wn 66-80: 2.5X TO 6X
*1-80 P/R b/wn 51-65: 2.5X TO 6X
*1-80 P/R b/wn 36-50: 3X TO 8X
*1-80 P/R b/wn 26-35: 4X TO 10X
81 Tomas De La Rosa/76 2.00 5.00
82 C.C. Sabathia/6
83 Ryan Christenson/9
84 Pedro Feliz/45 2.00 5.00
85 Jose Ortiz/90 1.50 4.00
86 Xavier Nady/175 1.00 2.50
87 Julio Zuleta/295 .75 2.00
88 Jason Hart/19
89 Keith Ginter/188 1.00 2.50
90 Brent Abernathy/254 .75 2.00
91 Timo Perez/5
92 Juan Pierre/104 1.50 4.00
93 Tike Redman/151 1.00 2.50
94 Mike Lamb/240 .75 2.00
95 Ichiro Suzuki/159 10.00 25.00
96 Kazuhiro Sasaki/229 .75 2.00
97 Barry Zito/6
98 Adam Bernero/254 .75 2.00
99 Chad Durbin/3
100 Matt Ginter/300 .75 2.00

2001 Donruss 2000 Retro Stat Line Season

Randomly inserted into 2000 Retro packs, this 100-card insert parallels the 2000 Retro base set. Each card is individually serial numbered to a season stat of the given players. Please note that the print runs are listed in our checklist. Cards printed to a stated print run of 25 or fewer are not printed due to market scarcity. Exchange cards were seeded into packs for cards 82 and 95. These cards were originally intended to be redeemed for C.C. Sabathia and Ben Sheets. It's since been discovered that Ichiro Suzuki cards were actually redeemed for card 95.

*1-80 P/R b/wn 251-400: 1.25X TO 3X
*1-80 P/R b/wn 201-250: 1.25X TO 3X
*1-80 P/R b/wn 151-200: 1.5X TO 4X
*1-80 P/R b/wn 121-150: 1.5X TO 4X
*1-80 P/R b/wn 81-120: 2X TO 5X
*1-80 P/R b/wn 66-80: 2.5X TO 6X
*1-80 P/R b/wn 51-65: 2.5X TO 6X
*1-80 P/R b/wn 36-50: 3X TO 8X
*1-80 P/R b/wn 26-35: 4X TO 10X
81 Tomas De La Rosa/122 1.00 2.50
82 C.C. Sabathia/76 10.00 25.00
83 Ryan Christenson/56 2.00 5.00
84 Pedro Feliz/13
85 Jose Ortiz/107 1.50 4.00
86 Xavier Nady/23
87 Julio Zuleta/21
88 Jason Hart/168 1.00 2.50
89 Keith Ginter/13
90 Brent Abernathy/168 1.00 2.50
91 Timo Perez/4
92 Juan Pierre/187 1.00 2.50
93 Tike Redman/143 1.00 2.50
94 Mike Lamb/177 1.00 2.50
95 Ichiro Suzuki/8
96 Kazuhiro Sasaki/34 3.00 8.00
97 Barry Zito/97 1.50 4.00
98 Adam Bernero/80 2.00 5.00
99 Chad Durbin/3
100 Matt Ginter/66 2.00 5.00

2001 Donruss 2000 Retro Diamond Kings

Randomly inserted into 2000 Retro packs, this 5-card insert set features the "Diamond King" cards that Donruss would have produced had they been producing baseball cards in 2000. Each card is individually serial numbered to 2500. Card backs carry a "DK" prefix.

COMPLETE SET (5) 30.00 60.00
*STUDIO: .75X TO 2X BASIC RETRO DK
RANDOM IN 2000 RETRO RETAIL PACKS
STUDIO PRINT RUN 250 SERIAL #'d SETS
DK1 Frank Thomas 4.00 10.00
DK2 Greg Maddux 5.00 12.00
DK3 Alex Rodriguez 5.00 12.00
DK4 Jeff Bagwell 4.00 10.00
DK5 Manny Ramirez 4.00 10.00

2001 Donruss 2000 Retro Diamond Kings Studio Series Autograph

An exchange card for an Alex Rodriguez autograph with a redemption deadline of May 1st, 2003 was randomly inserted in 2001 Donruss retro 2000 retail packs. The card is a signed version of A-Rod's basic Diamond King Studio Series insert and only 250 serial numbered copies were produced.

DK3 Alex Rodriguez 150.00 250.00

2001 Donruss All-Time Diamond Kings

Randomly inserted into 2001 Donruss packs, this 10-card insert features some of the greatest players to have ever grace the front of a "Diamond Kings" card. Card backs carry a "ATDK" prefix. There were 2500 serial numbered sets produced. The Willie Mays and Hank Aaron cards both packed out as exchange cards with a redemption deadline of May 1st, 2003. The Mays card was originally intended to be card number ATDK-9 within this set, but was erroneously numbered ATDK-1 (the same number as the Frank Robinson card) when it was sent out by Donruss. Thus, this set has two card #1's and no card #9.

COMPLETE SET (10) 75.00 150.00
*STUDIO: 1X TO 2.5X BASIC ALL-TIME DK
STUDIO PRINT RUN 200 SERIAL #'d SETS
STUDIO CARDS ARE SERIAL #'d 51-250
ATDK1 Willie Mays 10.00 25.00
ATDK1 Frank Robinson 4.00 10.00
ATDK2 Harmon Killebrew 5.00 12.00
ATDK3 Mike Schmidt 8.00 20.00
ATDK4 Reggie Jackson 4.00 10.00
ATDK5 Nolan Ryan 15.00 40.00
ATDK6 George Brett 8.00 20.00
ATDK7 Tom Seaver 4.00 10.00
ATDK8 Hank Aaron 10.00 25.00
ATDK10 Stan Musial 8.00 20.00

2001 Donruss All-Time Diamond Kings Studio Series Autograph

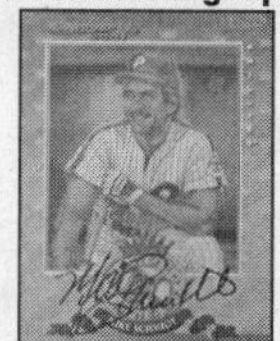

Randomly inserted into 2001 Donruss packs, this 10-card insert is a complete autographed parallel of the 2001 Donruss All-Time Diamond Kings. Card backs carry a "ATDK" prefix. Please note that the serial #ing for these cards is as follows: cards #'d 1/250 through 50/250 are from this Autograph set and cards #'d 51/250 to 250/250 are from the ATDK Studio Series (non-autographed set). Exchange cards with a redemption deadline of May 1st, 2003 were seeded into packs for Hank Aaron, Willie Mays and Nolan Ryan.

AU CARDS ARE #'d 1/250 TO 50/250

ATDK1 Willie Mays 150.00 250.00
ATDK1 Frank Robinson 40.00 80.00
ATDK2 Harmon Killebrew 60.00 120.00
ATDK3 Mike Schmidt 100.00 175.00
ATDK4 Reggie Jackson 60.00 120.00
ATDK5 Nolan Ryan 150.00 250.00
ATDK6 George Brett 125.00 200.00
ATDK7 Tom Seaver 50.00 100.00
ATDK8 Hank Aaron 150.00 250.00
ATDK10 Stan Musial 75.00 150.00

2001 Donruss Anniversary Originals Autograph

Each of these BGS graded cards were randomly inserted as box-toppers in boxes of 2001 Donruss. Unfortunately, exchange cards with a redemption deadline of May 1st, 2003 were seeded into packs for almost the entire set. Of the twelve cards featured in the set - only autograph cards for Tony Gwynn, David Justice and Ryne Sandberg actually made their way into packs. Since each card was signed to a different print run, we have included that information in our checklist.

82405 Cal Ripken/23
83277 Ryne Sandberg/24
83279 Cal Ripken/2
83586 Wade Boggs/25
83598 Tony Gwynn/24
84248 Don Mattingly/25
8736 Greg Maddux/25
8743 Rafael Palmeiro/250 30.00 60.00
87361 Barry Bonds/25
8834 Roberto Alomar/250 20.00 50.00
88644 Tom Glavine/250 30.00 60.00
8942 Randy Johnson/25
90704 David Justice/24

2001 Donruss Bat Kings

Randomly inserted into packs, this 10-card insert features swatches of actual game-used bat. Card backs carry a "BK" prefix. Each card is individually serial numbered to 200. An exchange card with a redemption deadline of May 1st, 2003 was seeded into packs for Hank Aaron.

BK1 Ivan Rodriguez 10.00 25.00
BK2 Tony Gwynn 15.00 40.00
BK3 Barry Bonds 40.00 80.00
BK4 Todd Helton 10.00 25.00
BK5 Troy Glaus 10.00 25.00
BK6 Mike Schmidt 30.00 60.00
BK7 Reggie Jackson 10.00 25.00
BK8 Harmon Killebrew 10.00 25.00
BK9 Frank Robinson 10.00 25.00
BK10 Hank Aaron 50.00 100.00

2001 Donruss Bat Kings Autograph

Randomly inserted into packs, this 10-card insert features swatches of actual game-used bat, as well as, an autograph from the depicted player. Card backs carry a "BK" prefix. Each card is individually serial numbered to 50. Exchange cards with a redemption deadline of May 1st, 2003 were seeded into packs for Barry Bonds, Troy Glaus, Todd Helton and Ivan Rodriguez. Unfortunately, Donruss was not able to get Barry Bonds to sign his Bat King cards - thus a non-autographed version of Bonds' card was sent out to collectors. Bonds did, however, agree to sign 100 of his vintage Donruss cards (1988 - 25 copies, 1989 -25 copies and 1990 - 50 copies). These 100 cards were stamped with a "Recollection Collection" logo and sent out to collectors - along with the unsigned Bonds Bat King card.

BK1 Ivan Rodriguez 60.00 120.00
BK2 Tony Gwynn 75.00 150.00
BK3 B.Bonds Bat NO AU 30.00 60.00
BK4 Todd Helton 50.00 100.00
BK5 Troy Glaus 50.00 100.00
BK6 Mike Schmidt 100.00 175.00
BK7 Reggie Jackson 60.00 120.00
BK8 Harmon Killebrew 60.00 120.00
BK9 Frank Robinson 150.00 250.00
BK10 Hank Aaron 175.00 300.00

2001 Donruss Diamond Kings Hawaii Promos

This card was given out to people who attended the 2001 Kit Young Hawaii Trade Conference. The card is gold-bordered and stamped with "Hawaii 2001" in gold lettering on the card front. Card back carries a "DK" prefix.

HDK1 Alex Rodriguez 4.00 10.00
Has 'Sample' stamped on back and '2001 Hawaii' stamp on card front.
HDK1 Alex Rodriguez 100.00 200.00
Has neither the 'Hawaii 2001' stamp or 'Sample' stamp on front.
HDK1 Alex Rodriguez 4.00 10.00
Does not have 'Sample' stamp on card back

2001 Donruss Diamond Kings

Randomly inserted into 2001 Donruss packs, this 20-card insert features players that are leaders on and off the baseball field. Card backs carry a "DK" prefix. Each card is individually serial numbered to 2500.

COMPLETE SET (20) 125.00 250.00
*STUDIO: .75X TO 2X BASIC DK
STUDIO NO AU PLAYER PRINT 250 #'d SETS
STUDIO AU PLAYER PRINT 200 #'d SETS
RANDOM INSERTS IN PACKS
DK1 Alex Rodriguez 5.00 12.00
DK2 Cal Ripken 10.00 25.00
DK3 Mark McGwire 8.00 20.00
DK4 Ken Griffey Jr. 5.00 12.00
DK5 Derek Jeter 8.00 20.00
DK6 Nomar Garciaparra 5.00 12.00
DK7 Mike Piazza 5.00 12.00
DK8 Roger Clemens 6.00 15.00
DK9 Greg Maddux 5.00 12.00
DK10 Chipper Jones 4.00 10.00
DK11 Tony Gwynn 4.00 10.00
DK12 Barry Bonds 8.00 20.00
DK13 Sammy Sosa 4.00 10.00
DK14 Vladimir Guerrero 4.00 10.00
DK15 Frank Thomas 4.00 10.00
DK16 Troy Glaus 4.00 10.00
DK17 Todd Helton 4.00 10.00
DK18 Ivan Rodriguez 4.00 10.00
DK19 Pedro Martinez 4.00 10.00
DK20 Carlos Delgado 4.00 10.00

2001 Donruss Diamond Kings Studio Series Autograph

Randomly inserted into 2001 Donruss packs, this 11-card insert is a partial parallel of the 2001 Diamond Kings insert. Each of these autographed cards were serial numbered to 50. Exchange cards with a redemption deadline of May 1st, 2003 were seeded into packs for Barry Bonds, Roger Clemens, Troy Glaus, Vladimir Guerrero, Todd Helton, Chipper Jones, Alex Rodriguez and Ivan Rodriguez.

DK1 Alex Rodriguez 150.00 250.00
DK2 Cal Ripken 175.00 300.00
DK8 Roger Clemens 125.00 200.00
DK9 Greg Maddux 125.00 200.00
DK10 Chipper Jones 60.00 120.00
DK11 Tony Gwynn 60.00 120.00
DK12 Barry Bonds
DK14 Vladimir Guerrero 60.00 120.00
DK16 Troy Glaus 50.00 100.00
DK17 Todd Helton 50.00 100.00
DK18 I. Rodriguez EXCH 60.00 120.00

2001 Donruss Diamond Kings Reprints

Randomly inserted into 2001 Donruss packs, this 20-card insert features reprints of past "Diamond King" cards. Card backs carry a "DKR" prefix. Print runs are listed in our checklist. An exchange card with a redemption deadline of May 1st, 2003 was seeded into packs for Will Clark.

COMPLETE SET (20)	100.00	200.00
DKR1 Rod Carew/1982	4.00	10.00
DKR2 Nolan Ryan/1982	10.00	25.00
DKR3 Tom Seaver/1982	4.00	10.00
DKR4 Carlton Fisk/1982	4.00	10.00
DKR5 R.Jackson/1983	4.00	10.00
DKR6 S. Carlton/1983	4.00	10.00
DKR7 Johnny Bench/1983	4.00	10.00
DKR8 Joe Morgan/1983	4.00	10.00
DKR9 Mike Schmidt/1984	8.00	20.00
DKR10 Wade Boggs/1984	4.00	10.00
DKR11 Cal Ripken/1985	10.00	25.00
DKR12 Tony Gwynn/1985	5.00	12.00
DKR13 A.Dawson/1986	4.00	10.00
DKR14 Ozzie Smith/1987	6.00	15.00
DKR15 George Brett/1987	8.00	20.00
DKR16 D.Winfield/1987	4.00	10.00
DKR17 Paul Molitor/1988	4.00	10.00
DKR18 Will Clark/1988	6.00	15.00
DKR19 Robin Yount/1989	4.00	10.00
DKR20 K.Griffey Jr./1989	6.00	15.00

2001 Donruss Diamond Kings Reprints Autographs

Randomly inserted into 2001 Donruss packs, this 20-card insert features autographed reprints of past "Diamond King" cards. Card backs carry a "DKR" prefix. Print runs are listed below. Exchange cards with a redemption deadline of May 1st, 2003 were seeded into packs for Wade Boggs, Rod Carew, Steve Carlton, Will Clark, Andre Dawson, Carlton Fisk, Cal Ripken, Nolan Ryan, Ozzie Smith, Dave Winfield and Robin Yount. Ken Griffey Jr. had a card issued serial #'d of 89 copies but he was the only player featured in the set to not sign any of his cards.

DKR1 Rod Carew/82	20.00	50.00
DKR2 Nolan Ryan/82	100.00	200.00
DKR3 Tom Seaver/82	40.00	80.00
DKR4 Carlton Fisk/82	20.00	50.00
DKR5 Reggie Jackson/83	40.00	80.00
DKR6 Steve Carlton/83	15.00	40.00
DKR7 Johnny Bench/83	40.00	80.00
DKR8 Joe Morgan/83	15.00	40.00
DKR9 Mike Schmidt/84	75.00	150.00
DKR10 Wade Boggs/84	20.00	50.00
DKR11 Cal Ripken/85	125.00	250.00
DKR12 Tony Gwynn/85	50.00	100.00
DKR13 Andre Dawson/86	15.00	40.00
DKR14 Ozzie Smith/87	50.00	100.00
DKR15 George Brett/87	75.00	150.00
DKR16 Dave Winfield/87	20.00	50.00
DKR17 Paul Molitor/88	15.00	40.00
DKR18 Will Clark/88	20.00	50.00
DKR19 Robin Yount/89	40.00	80.00
DKR20 Ken Griffey Jr. NO AU/89	15.00	40.00

2001 Donruss Elite Series

Randomly inserted into 2001 Donruss packs, this 20-card insert features many of the Major Leagues elite players. Card backs carry an "ES" prefix. Each card is individually serial numbered to 2500.

COMPLETE SET (20)	75.00	150.00
*DOMINATORS: 6X TO 15X BASIC ELITE		
DOMINATORS PRINT RUN 25 SERIAL #'d SETS		
RANDOM INSERTS IN PACKS		
ES1 Vladimir Guerrero	2.00	5.00
ES2 Cal Ripken	6.00	15.00
ES3 Greg Maddux	3.00	8.00
ES4 Alex Rodriguez	3.00	8.00
ES5 Barry Bonds	5.00	12.00
ES6 Chipper Jones	2.00	5.00
ES7 Derek Jeter	5.00	12.00
ES8 Ivan Rodriguez	1.50	4.00
ES9 Ken Griffey Jr.	3.00	8.00
ES10 Mark McGwire	5.00	12.00
ES11 Mike Piazza	3.00	8.00
ES12 Nomar Garciaparra	3.00	8.00
ES13 Pedro Martinez	1.50	4.00
ES14 Randy Johnson	2.00	5.00
ES15 Roger Clemens	4.00	10.00
ES16 Sammy Sosa	2.00	5.00
ES17 Tony Gwynn	2.50	6.00
ES18 Darin Erstad	1.50	4.00
ES19 Andruw Jones	1.50	4.00
ES20 Bernie Williams	1.50	4.00

2001 Donruss Jersey Kings

Randomly inserted into packs, this 10-card insert features swatches of actual game-used jerseys. Card

backs carry a "JK" prefix. Each card is individually serial numbered to 250. Chipper Jones and Ozzie Smith were available only via mail redemption. Exchange cards with a redemption deadline of May 1st, 2003 for "to be determined" players were seeded originally into packs and many months passed before Chipper Jones and Ozzie Smith were revealed as the players that would be used to fulfill these cards.

JK1 Vladimir Guerrero	10.00	25.00
JK2 Cal Ripken	60.00	120.00
JK3 Greg Maddux	20.00	50.00
JK4 Chipper Jones	10.00	25.00
JK5 Roger Clemens	30.00	60.00
JK6 George Brett	20.00	50.00
JK7 Tom Seaver	10.00	25.00
JK8 Nolan Ryan	60.00	120.00
JK9 Stan Musial	30.00	60.00
JK10 Ozzie Smith	15.00	40.00

2001 Donruss Jersey Kings Autograph

Randomly inserted into packs, this 10-card insert features swatches of actual game-used jerseys, as well as, an autograph from the depicted player. Card backs carry a "JK" prefix. Each card is individually serial numbered to 50. The following players players did not return their cards in time for inclusion in packs: Vladimir Guerrero, Cal Ripken, Chipper Jones, Roger Clemens, Nolan Ryan and Ozzie Smith. Exchange cards with a redemption deadline of May 1st, 2003 were seeded into packs for these players.

JK1 Vladimir Guerrero	75.00	150.00
JK2 Cal Ripken	175.00	300.00
JK3 Greg Maddux	125.00	200.00
JK4 Chipper Jones	75.00	150.00
JK5 Roger Clemens	125.00	200.00
JK6 George Brett	125.00	200.00
JK7 Tom Seaver	50.00	100.00
JK8 Nolan Ryan	150.00	250.00
JK9 Stan Musial	125.00	200.00
JK10 Ozzie Smith	75.00	150.00

2001 Donruss Longball Leaders

Randomly inserted into packs, this 20-card insert features some of the Major Leagues top power hitters. Card backs carry a "LL" prefix. Each card is individually serial numbered to 1000.

COMPLETE SET (20)	75.00	150.00
LL1 Vladimir Guerrero	3.00	8.00
LL2 Alex Rodriguez	5.00	12.00
LL3 Barry Bonds	8.00	20.00
LL4 Troy Glaus	1.50	4.00
LL5 Frank Thomas	3.00	8.00
LL6 Jeff Bagwell	2.00	5.00
LL7 Todd Helton	2.00	5.00
LL8 Ken Griffey Jr.	5.00	12.00
LL9 Manny Ramirez Sox	2.00	5.00
LL10 Mike Piazza	5.00	12.00
LL11 Sammy Sosa	3.00	8.00
LL12 Carlos Delgado	1.50	4.00
LL13 Jim Edmonds	1.50	4.00
LL14 Jason Giambi	1.50	4.00
LL15 David Justice	1.50	4.00
LL16 Rafael Palmeiro	2.00	5.00
LL17 Gary Sheffield	1.50	4.00
LL18 Jim Thome	2.00	5.00
LL19 Tony Batista	1.50	4.00
LL20 Richard Hidalgo	1.50	4.00

2001 Donruss Production Line

Randomly inserted into packs, this 60-card insert features some of the Major League's most feared hitters. Card backs carry a "PL" prefix. Each card is individually serial numbered to one of three offensive categories: OBP, SLG, and PI. Print runs are listed in our checklist.

COMPLETE SET (60)	200.00	400.00
COMMON SLG (21-40)	1.25	3.00
COMMON PI (41-60)	1.00	2.50
*DIE CUT OBP 1-20: .75X TO 2X BASIC PL		
*DIE CUT SLG 21-40: 1X TO 2.5X BASIC PL		
*DIE CUT PI 41-60: 1.25X TO 3X BASIC PL		
DIE CUT PRINT RUN 100 SERIAL #'d SETS		
PL1 J.Giambi OBP/476	1.50	4.00
PL2 C.Delgado OBP/470	1.50	4.00
PL3 Todd Helton OBP/463	2.50	6.00
PL4 M.Ramirez Sox OBP/457	2.50	6.00
PL5 Barry Bonds OBP/440	10.00	25.00
PL6 G.Sheffield OBP/438	1.50	4.00
PL7 F.Thomas OBP/436	4.00	10.00
PL8 N.Garciaparra OBP/434	6.00	15.00
PL9 Brian Giles OBP/432	1.50	4.00
PL10 E.Alfonzo OBP/425	1.50	4.00
PL11 Jeff Kent OBP/424	1.50	4.00
PL12 J.Bagwell OBP/424	2.50	6.00
PL13 E.Martinez OBP/423	2.50	6.00
PL14 A.Rodriguez OBP/420	6.00	15.00
PL15 L.Castillo OBP/418	1.50	4.00
PL16 Will Clark OBP/418	2.50	6.00
PL17 J.Posada OBP/417	2.50	6.00
PL18 Derek Jeter OBP/416	10.00	25.00
PL19 Bob Abreu OBP/416	1.50	4.00
PL20 M.Alou OBP/416	1.50	4.00
PL21 T.Helton SLG/698	2.00	5.00
PL22 M.Ramirez Sox SLG/697	2.00	5.00
PL23 B.Bonds SLG/688	8.00	20.00
PL24 C.Delgado SLG/664	1.25	3.00
PL25 V.Guerrero SLG/664	3.00	8.00
PL26 J.Giambi SLG/647	1.25	3.00
PL27 G.Sheffield SLG/643	1.25	3.00
PL28 R.Hidalgo SLG/636	1.25	3.00
PL29 S. Sosa SLG/634	3.00	8.00
PL30 F. Thomas SLG/625	3.00	8.00
PL31 M. Alou SLG/623	1.25	3.00
PL32 J.Bagwell SLG/615	2.00	5.00
PL33 M. Piazza SLG/614	5.00	12.00
PL34 A. Rodriguez SLG/606	5.00	12.00
PL35 Troy Glaus SLG/604	1.25	3.00
PL36 N.Garciaparra SLG/599	5.00	12.00
PL37 Jeff Kent SLG/596	1.25	3.00
PL38 Brian Giles SLG/594	1.25	3.00
PL39 G. Jenkins SLG/588	1.25	3.00
PL40 Carl Everett SLG/587	1.25	3.00
PL41 Todd Helton PI/1161	1.50	4.00
PL42 M. Ramirez Sox PI/1154	1.50	4.00
PL43 C. Delgado PI/1134	1.00	2.50
PL44 Barry Bonds PI/1128	6.00	15.00
PL45 J.Giambi PI/1123	1.00	2.50
PL46 G.Sheffield PI/1081	1.00	2.50
PL47 V.Guerrero PI/1074	2.50	6.00
PL48 F.Thomas PI/1061	2.50	6.00
PL49 S.Sosa PI/1040	2.50	6.00
PL50 Moises Alou PI/1039	1.00	2.50
PL51 Jeff Bagwell PI/1039	1.50	4.00
PL52 N.Garciaparra PI/1033	4.00	10.00
PL53 R.Hidalgo PI/1027	1.00	2.50
PL54 A.Rodriguez PI/1026	4.00	10.00
PL55 Brian Giles PI/1026	1.00	2.50
PL56 Jeff Kent PI/1020	1.00	2.50
PL57 Mike Piazza PI/1012	4.00	10.00
PL58 Troy Glaus PI/1008	1.00	2.50
PL59 E.Martinez PI/1002	1.50	4.00
PL60 J.Edmonds PI/994	1.50	4.00

2001 Donruss Recollection Autographs

Two different players signed cards for this program. Barry Bonds and Alex Rodriguez each signed 100 total cards.The Rodriguez cards were randomly inserted in packs as exchange cards and the Bonds cards were issued as concessionary cards for collectors that redeemed a Bat Kings Autograph Bonds. According to representatives at Donruss, Bonds refused to sign the memorabilia bat cards, but did approve signing these Recollection buybacks. The exchange deadline for the Rodriguez cards was May 1st, 2003. The Rodriguez exchange cards that went into packs were numbered RC1-RC4, but the actual autograph cards are not numbered as such. For simplicity's sake we have kept the original RC1-RC4 checklisting.

BB1 Barry Bonds 88/25		
BB2 Barry Bonds 89/25		
BB3 Barry Bonds 90/50		
RC1 Alex Rodriguez 97 Don Hit/10		
RC2 Alex Rodriguez 98 Don/20		
RC3 Alex Rodriguez 01 Retro/30	75.00	150.00
RC4 Alex Rodriguez 01 Don/40	75.00	150.00

2001 Donruss Rookie Reprints

Randomly inserted into packs, this 40-card insert features reprinted Donruss rookie cards from the 80's-90s. Card backs carry a "RR" prefix. Please note that there was an error in production, and there are two number 39's, no number 40. Print runs are listed in our checklist.

COMPLETE SET (40)	150.00	300.00
RR1 Cal Ripken/1982	10.00	25.00
RR2 Wade Boggs/1983	2.00	5.00
RR3 Tony Gwynn/1983	5.00	12.00
RR4 Ryne Sandberg/1983	6.00	15.00
RR5 Don Mattingly/1984	10.00	25.00
RR6 Joe Carter/1984	2.00	5.00
RR7 Roger Clemens/1985	8.00	20.00
RR8 Kirby Puckett/1985	3.00	8.00
RR9 Orel Hershiser/1985	2.00	5.00
RR10 A.Galarraga/1986	2.00	5.00
RR11 Jose Canseco/1986	2.00	5.00
RR12 Fred McGriff/1986	2.00	5.00
RR13 Paul O'Neill/1986	2.00	5.00
RR14 Mark McGwire/1987	8.00	20.00
RR15 Barry Bonds/1987	8.00	20.00
RR16 Kevin Brown/1987	2.00	5.00
RR17 David Cone/1987	2.00	5.00
RR18 R.Palmeiro/1987	2.00	5.00
RR19 Barry Larkin/1987	2.00	5.00
RR20 Bo Jackson/1987	3.00	8.00
RR21 Greg Maddux/1987	5.00	12.00
RR22 R. Alomar/1988	2.00	5.00
RR23 Mark Grace/1988	2.00	5.00
RR24 David Wells/1988	2.00	5.00
RR25 Tom Glavine/1988	2.00	5.00
RR26 Matt Williams/1988	2.00	5.00
RR27 Ken Griffey Jr./1989	5.00	12.00
RR28 R. Johnson/1989	3.00	8.00
RR29 Gary Sheffield/1989	2.00	5.00
RR30 Craig Biggio/1989	2.00	5.00
RR31 Curt Schilling/1989	2.00	5.00
RR32 Larry Walker/1990	2.00	5.00
RR33 B. Williams/1990	2.00	5.00
RR34 Sammy Sosa/1990	3.00	8.00
RR35 Juan Gonzalez/1990	2.00	5.00
RR36 David Justice/1990	2.00	5.00
RR37 I.Rodriguez/1991	2.00	5.00
RR38 Jeff Bagwell/1991	2.00	5.00
RR39 Jeff Kent/1992 UER Should have been RR40	2.00	5.00
RR39 M.Ramirez/1991	2.00	5.00

2001 Donruss Rookie Reprints Autograph

Randomly inserted into packs, this 26-card skip-numbered insert features autographed reprinted Donruss rookie cards from the 80's-90s. Card backs carry a "RR" prefix. Print runs are listed in our checklist. Nearly all of these cards packed out in the form of exchange cards - of which carried a May 1st, 2003 redemption deadline. Only autograph cards for Joe Carter, Tony Gwynn, David Justice, Greg Maddux and Ryne Sandberg actually made it into packs. Card RR24 was originally announced as a 1988 Donruss David Wells Reprint (with a print run of 88 copies) but due to contractual problems with the athlete the manufacturer substituted Diamondbacks outfielder Luis Gonzalez (reprinting 91 copies of his 1991 Donruss the Rookies RC).

RR1 Cal Ripken/82	125.00	200.00
RR2 W.Boggs/83 EXCH	30.00	60.00
RR3 Tony Gwynn/83	50.00	100.00
RR4 Ryne Sandberg/83	60.00	120.00
RR5 D.Mattingly/84 EXCH	60.00	120.00
RR6 Joe Carter/84	15.00	40.00
RR7 R.Clemens/85 EXCH	175.00	300.00
RR8 K.Puckett/85 EXCH	100.00	175.00
RR9 O.Hershiser/85 EXCH	30.00	60.00
RR10 A.Galarraga/86 EXCH	30.00	60.00
RR15 B.Bonds/87 EXCH	125.00	200.00
RR16 K. Brown/87 EXCH	15.00	40.00
RR17 D.Cone/87 EXCH	15.00	40.00
RR18 R.Palmeiro/87 EXCH	30.00	60.00
RR20 B.Jackson/87 EXCH	60.00	120.00
RR21 Greg Maddux/87	150.00	300.00
RR22 R.Alomar/88 EXCH	30.00	60.00
RR24 D.Wells/88 EXCH	15.00	40.00
RR25 T.Glavine/88 EXCH	20.00	50.00
RR28 R.Johnson/89 EXCH	100.00	175.00
RR29 G.Sheffield/89 EXCH	40.00	80.00
RR31 C.Schilling/89 EXCH	60.00	120.00
RR35 J.Gonzalez/90 EXCH	15.00	40.00
RR36 David Justice/90	15.00	40.00
RR37 I.Rodriguez/91 EXCH	30.00	60.00
RR39 M.Ramirez/92 EXCH	75.00	150.00

2001 Donruss Rookies

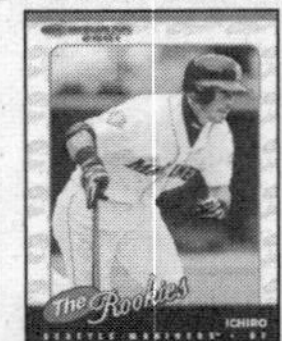

This 110-card redemption set was issued via coupons in the 2001 Donruss product. The coupons were issued in packs at a rate of 1:72 and were good for a complete factory sealed set of 2001 Donruss the Rookies. Collector's were to send the coupon along with $24.99 to Playoff by January 20th, 2002. The set also came with one additional Diamond King card (106-110).

COMP.FACT.SET (106)	60.00	100.00
COMP.SET w/o SP's (105)	40.00	80.00
R1 Adam Dunn	.30	.75
R2 Ryan Drese RC	.30	.75
R3 Bud Smith RC	.15	.40
R4 Tsuyoshi Shinjo RC	.30	.75
R5 Roy Oswalt	.40	1.00
R6 Wilmy Caceres RC	.20	.50
R7 Willie Harris RC	.20	.50
R8 Andres Torres RC	.15	.40
R9 Brandon Knight RC	.15	.40
R10 Horacio Ramirez RC	.30	.75
R11 Benito Baez RC	.15	.40
R12 Jeremy Affeldt RC	.20	.50
R13 Ryan Jensen RC	.20	.50
R14 Casey Fossum RC	.15	.40
R15 Ramon Vazquez RC	.20	.50
R16 Dustan Mohr RC	.20	.50
R17 Saul Rivera RC	.20	.50
R18 Zach Day RC	.20	.50
R19 Erik Hiljus RC	.15	.40
R20 Cesar Crespo RC	.15	.40
R21 Wilson Guzman RC	.20	.50
R22 Travis Hafner RC	2.00	5.00
R23 Grant Balfour RC	.15	.40
R24 Johnny Estrada RC	.30	.75
R25 Morgan Ensberg RC	.75	2.00
R26 Jack Wilson RC	.30	.75
R27 Aubrey Huff	.20	.50
R28 Endy Chavez RC	.30	.75
R29 Delvin James RC	.15	.40
R30 Michael Cuddyer	.15	.40
R31 Jason Michaels RC	.20	.50
R32 Martin Vargas RC	.20	.50
R33 Donaldo Mendez RC	.15	.40
R34 Jorge Julio RC	.20	.50
R35 T.Spooneybarger RC	.20	.50
R36 Kurt Ainsworth	.15	.40
R37 Josh Fogg RC	.20	.50
R38 Brian Reith RC	.15	.40
R39 Rick Bauer RC	.15	.40
R40 Tim Redding	.15	.40
R41 Erick Almonte RC	.15	.40
R42 Juan A.Pena RC	.15	.40
R43 Ken Harvey	.15	.40
R44 David Brous RC	.15	.40
R45 Kevin Olsen RC	.20	.50
R46 Henry Mateo RC	.15	.40
R47 Nick Neugebauer	.15	.40
R48 Mike Penney RC	.20	.50
R49 Jay Gibbons RC	.30	.75
R50 Tim Christman RC	.15	.40
R51 B.Duckworth RC	.15	.40
R52 Brett Jodie RC	.15	.40
R53 Christian Parker RC	.15	.40
R54 Carlos Hernandez	.15	.40
R55 Brandon Larson RC	.15	.40
R56 Nick Punto RC	.20	.50
R57 Elpidio Guzman RC	.15	.40
R58 Joe Beimel RC	.15	.40
R59 Junior Spivey RC	.30	.75
R60 Will Ohman RC	.20	.50
R61 Brandon Lyon RC	.15	.40
R62 Stubby Clapp RC	.15	.40
R63 J.Duchscherer RC	.20	.50
R64 Jimmy Rollins	.20	.50
R65 David Williams RC	.15	.40
R66 Craig Monroe RC	1.00	2.50
R67 Jose Acevedo RC	.15	.40
R68 Jason Jennings	.15	.40
R69 Josh Phelps	.15	.40
R70 Brian Roberts RC	.75	2.00
R71 Claudio Vargas RC	.15	.40
R72 Adam Johnson	.15	.40
R73 Bart Miadich RC	.15	.40
R74 Juan Rivera	.15	.40
R75 Brad Voyles RC	.15	.40
R76 Nate Cornejo	.15	.40
R77 Juan Moreno RC	.20	.50
R78 Brian Rogers RC	.15	.40
R79 R.Rodriguez RC	.20	.50
R80 Geronimo Gil RC	.15	.40
R81 Joe Kennedy RC	.30	.75
R82 Kevin Joseph RC	.20	.50
R83 Josue Perez RC	.20	.50
R84 Victor Zambrano RC	.30	.75
R85 Josh Towers RC	.30	.75
R86 Mike Rivera RC	.20	.50
R87 Mark Prior RC	2.00	5.00
R88 Juan Cruz RC	.20	.50
R89 Dewon Brazelton RC	.20	.50
R90 Angel Berroa RC	.30	.75
R91 Mark Teixeira RC	2.50	6.00
R92 Cody Ransom RC	.15	.40
R93 Angel Santos RC	.15	.40
R94 Corky Miller RC	.15	.40
R95 Brandon Berger RC	.15	.40
R96 Corey Patterson UPD	.15	.40
R97 A. Pujols UPD UER Homers and RBI Stats wrong	30.00	60.00
R98 Josh Beckett UPD	.30	.75
R99 C.C. Sabathia UPD	.20	.50
R100 A. Soriano UPD	.30	.75
R101 Ben Sheets UPD	.30	.75
R102 Rafael Soriano UPD	.20	.50
R103 Wilson Betemit UPD	.75	2.00
R104 Ichiro Suzuki UPD	6.00	15.00
R105 Jose Ortiz UPD	.15	.40

2001 Donruss Rookies Diamond Kings

Inserted one per Donruss Rookies set, these five cards feature some of the leading 2001 rookies in a special Diamond King format.

COMPLETE SET (5)	30.00	60.00
RDK1 C.C. Sabathia DK	3.00	8.00
RDK2 T.Shinjo DK	4.00	10.00
RDK3 Albert Pujols DK	30.00	60.00
RDK4 Roy Oswalt DK	4.00	10.00
RDK5 Ichiro Suzuki DK	10.00	25.00

2002 Donruss Samples

Issued one per sealed copy of Beckett Baseball Card Monthly issue number 204, this is a partial parallel to the 2002 Leaf Set. Only the first 150 cards of this set were issued in this format.

*SAMPLES: 1.5X TO 4X BASIC CARDS
ONE PER SEALED BBCM 204
*GOLD SAMPLES: 1.5X TO 4X LISTED PRICE

2002 Donruss

This 220 card set was issued in four card packs which had an SRP of $1.99 per pack and were issued 24 to a box and 20 boxes to a case. Cards numbered 151-200 featured leading rookie prospect and were inserted at stated odds of one in four. Card numbered 201-220 were Fan Club subset cards and were inserted at stated odds of one in eight.

COMPLETE SET (220)	60.00	150.00
COMP.SET w/o SP'S (150)	10.00	25.00
COMMON CARD (1-150)	.10	.30
COMMON CARD (151-200)	1.25	3.00
COMMON CARD (201-220)	.60	1.50
1 Alex Rodriguez	.50	1.25
2 Barry Bonds	.75	2.00
3 Derek Jeter	.75	2.00
4 Robert Fick	.10	.30
5 Juan Pierre	.10	.30
6 Torii Hunter	.10	.30
7 Todd Helton	.20	.50
8 Cal Ripken	1.00	2.50
9 Manny Ramirez	.20	.50
10 Johnny Damon	.20	.50
11 Mike Piazza	.50	1.25
12 Nomar Garciaparra	.50	1.25
13 Pedro Martinez	.20	.50
14 Brian Giles	.10	.30
15 Albert Pujols	.60	1.50
16 Roger Clemens	.60	1.50
17 Sammy Sosa	.30	.75
18 Vladimir Guerrero	.30	.75
19 Tony Gwynn	.40	1.00
20 Pat Burrell	.10	.30
21 Carlos Delgado	.10	.30
22 Tino Martinez	.20	.50
23 Jim Edmonds	.10	.30
24 Jason Giambi	.10	.30
25 Tom Glavine	.20	.50
26 Mark Grace	.20	.50
27 Tony Armas Jr.	.10	.30
28 Andruw Jones	.20	.50
29 Ben Sheets	.10	.30
30 Jeff Kent	.10	.30
31 Barry Larkin	.20	.50
32 Joe Mays	.10	.30
33 Mike Mussina	.20	.50
34 Hideo Nomo	.30	.75
35 Rafael Palmeiro	.20	.50
36 Scott Brosius	.10	.30
37 Scott Rolen	.20	.50
38 Gary Sheffield	.10	.30
39 Bernie Williams	.20	.50
40 Bob Abreu	.10	.30
41 Edgardo Alfonzo	.10	.30
42 C.C. Sabathia	.10	.30
43 Jeremy Giambi	.10	.30
44 Craig Biggio	.20	.50
45 Andres Galarraga	.10	.30
46 Edgar Martinez	.20	.50
47 Fred McGriff	.20	.50
48 Magglio Ordonez	.10	.30
49 Jim Thome	.20	.50
50 Matt Williams	.10	.30
51 Kerry Wood	.10	.30
52 Moises Alou	.10	.30
53 Brady Anderson	.10	.30
54 Garret Anderson	.10	.30
55 Juan Gonzalez	.10	.30
56 Bret Boone	.10	.30
57 Jose Cruz Jr.	.10	.30
58 Carlos Beltran	.10	.30
59 Adrian Beltre	.10	.30
60 Joe Kennedy	.10	.30
61 Lance Berkman	.10	.30
62 Kevin Brown	.10	.30
63 Tim Hudson	.10	.30
64 Jeromy Burnitz	.10	.30
65 Jarrod Washburn	.10	.30
66 Sean Casey	.10	.30
67 Eric Chavez	.10	.30
68 Bartolo Colon	.10	.30
69 Freddy Garcia	.10	.30
70 Jermaine Dye	.10	.30
71 Terrence Long	.10	.30
72 Cliff Floyd	.10	.30
73 Luis Gonzalez	.10	.30
74 Ichiro Suzuki	.60	1.50
75 Mike Hampton	.10	.30

76 Richard Hidalgo .10 .30
77 Geoff Jenkins .10 .30
78 Gabe Kapler .10 .30
79 Ken Griffey Jr. .50 1.25
80 Jason Kendall .10 .30
81 Josh Towers .10 .30
82 Ryan Klesko .10 .30
83 Paul Konerko .10 .30
84 Carlos Lee .10 .30
85 Kenny Lofton .10 .30
86 Josh Beckett .10 .30
87 Raul Mondesi .10 .30
88 Trot Nixon .10 .30
89 John Olerud .10 .30
90 Paul O'Neill .20 .50
91 Chan Ho Park .10 .30
92 Andy Pettitte .20 .50
93 Jorge Posada .20 .50
94 Mark Quinn .10 .30
95 Aramis Ramirez .10 .30
96 Curt Schilling .10 .30
97 Richie Sexson .10 .30
98 John Smoltz .20 .50
99 Wilson Betemit .10 .30
100 Shannon Stewart .10 .30
101 Alfonso Soriano .10 .30
102 Mike Sweeney .10 .30
103 Miguel Tejada .10 .30
104 Greg Vaughn .10 .30
105 Robin Ventura .10 .30
106 Jose Vidro .10 .30
107 Larry Walker .10 .30
108 Preston Wilson .10 .30
109 Corey Patterson .10 .30
110 Mark Mulder .10 .30
111 Tony Clark .10 .30
112 Roy Oswalt .10 .30
113 Jimmy Rollins .10 .30
114 Kazuhiro Sasaki .10 .30
115 Barry Zito .10 .30
116 Javier Vazquez .10 .30
117 Mike Cameron .10 .30
118 Phil Nevin .10 .30
119 Bud Smith .10 .30
120 Cristian Guzman .10 .30
121 Al Leiter .10 .30
122 Brad Radke .10 .30
123 Bobby Higginson .10 .30
124 Robert Person .10 .30
125 Adam Dunn .10 .30
126 Ben Grieve .10 .30
127 Rafael Furcal .10 .30
128 Jay Gibbons .10 .30
129 Paul LoDuca .10 .30
130 Wade Miller .10 .30
131 Tsuyoshi Shinjo .10 .30
132 Eric Milton .10 .30
133 Rickey Henderson .30 .75
134 Roberto Alomar .20 .50
135 Darin Erstad .10 .30
136 J.D. Drew .10 .30
137 Shawn Green .10 .30
138 Randy Johnson .30 .75
139 Austin Kearns .10 .30
140 Jose Canseco .20 .50
141 Jeff Bagwell .20 .50
142 Greg Maddux .50 1.25
143 Mark Buehrle .10 .30
144 Ivan Rodriguez .20 .50
145 Frank Thomas .30 .75
146 Rich Aurilia .10 .30
147 Troy Glaus .10 .30
148 Ryan Dempster .10 .30
149 Chipper Jones .30 .75
150 Matt Morris .10 .30
151 Marlon Byrd RR 1.25 3.00
152 Ben Howard RR RC 1.25 3.00
153 Brandon Backe RR RC 1.25 3.00
154 Jorge De La Rosa RR RC 1.25 3.00
155 Corky Miller RR 1.25 3.00
156 Dennis Tankersley RR 1.25 3.00
157 Kyle Kane RR RC 1.25 3.00
158 Justin Duchscherer RR 1.25 3.00
159 Brian Mallette RR RC 1.25 3.00
160 Chris Baker RR RC 1.25 3.00
161 Jason Lane RR 1.25 3.00
162 Hee Seop Choi RR 1.25 3.00
163 Juan Cruz RR 1.25 3.00
164 Rodrigo Rosario RR RC 1.25 3.00
165 Matt Guerrier RR 1.25 3.00
166 Anderson Machado RR RC 1.25 3.00
167 Geronimo Gil RR 1.25 3.00
168 Dewon Brazelton RR 1.25 3.00
169 Mark Prior RR 1.50 4.00
170 Bill Hall RR 1.25 3.00
171 Jorge Padilla RR RC 1.25 3.00
172 Jose Cueto RR 1.25 3.00
173 Allan Simpson RR RC 1.25 3.00
174 Doug Devore RR RC 1.25 3.00
175 Josh Pearce RR 1.25 3.00
176 Angel Berroa RR 1.25 3.00
177 Steve Bechler RR RC 1.25 3.00
178 Antonio Perez RR 1.25 3.00
179 Mark Teixeira RR 1.50 4.00
180 Erick Almonte RR 1.25 3.00
181 Orlando Hudson RR 1.25 3.00
182 Michael Rivera RR 1.25 3.00
183 Raul Chavez RR RC 1.25 3.00
184 Juan Pena RR 1.25 3.00
185 Travis Hughes RR RC 1.25 3.00
186 Ryan Ludwick RR 1.25 3.00
187 Ed Rogers RR 1.25 3.00
188 Andy Pratt RR RC 1.25 3.00
189 Nick Neugebauer RR 1.25 3.00
190 Tom Shearn RR RC 1.25 3.00
191 Eric Cyr RR 1.25 3.00
192 Victor Martinez RR 1.50 4.00
193 Brandon Berger RR 1.25 3.00
194 Erik Bedard RR 1.25 3.00
195 Fernando Rodney RR 1.25 3.00
196 Joe Thurston RR 1.25 3.00
197 John Buck RR 1.25 3.00
198 Jeff Deardorff RR 1.25 3.00
199 Ryan Jamison RR 1.25 3.00
200 Alfredo Amezaga RR 1.25 3.00
201 Luis Gonzalez FC .60 1.50
202 Roger Clemens FC 2.00 5.00
203 Barry Zito FC .60 1.50
204 Bud Smith FC .60 1.50
205 Magglio Ordonez FC .60 1.50
206 Kerry Wood FC .60 1.50
207 Freddy Garcia FC .60 1.50
208 Adam Dunn FC .60 1.50
209 Curt Schilling FC .60 1.50
210 Lance Berkman FC .60 1.50
211 Rafael Palmeiro FC .60 1.50
212 Ichiro Suzuki FC 2.00 5.00
213 Bob Abreu FC .60 1.50
214 Mark Mulder FC .60 1.50
215 Roy Oswalt FC .60 1.50
216 Mike Sweeney FC .60 1.50
217 Paul LoDuca FC .60 1.50
218 Aramis Ramirez FC .60 1.50
219 Randy Johnson FC 1.00 2.50
220 Albert Pujols FC 2.00 5.00

2002 Donruss Autographs

Inserted randomly in packs, these 19 cards feature signatures of players in the Fan Club subset. Since the cards have different stated print runs, we have listed those print runs in our checklist. Cards with a print run of 25 or fewer are not priced due to market scarcity.

201 Luis Gonzalez FC/25
202 Roger Clemens FC/25
203 Barry Zito FC/200 15.00 40.00
204 Bud Smith FC/200 10.00 25.00
205 Magglio Ordonez FC/200 10.00 25.00
206 Kerry Wood FC/200 15.00 40.00
207 Freddy Garcia FC/200 10.00 25.00
208 Adam Dunn FC/200 15.00 40.00
209 Curt Schilling FC/25
210 Lance Berkman FC/175 15.00 40.00
211 Rafael Palmeiro FC/25
213 Bob Abreu FC/200 10.00 25.00
214 Mark Mulder FC/200 10.00 25.00
215 Roy Oswalt FC/200 10.00 25.00
216 Mike Sweeney FC/200 10.00 25.00
217 Paul LoDuca FC/200 10.00 25.00
218 Aramis Ramirez FC/200 10.00 25.00
219 Randy Johnson FC/10
220 Albert Pujols FC/200 150.00 250.00

2002 Donruss Stat Line Career

Randomly inserted into packs, this is a parallel to the basic Donruss set. These cards feature cards printed on foil-board with silver holo-foil stamping. Each card has a stated print run to a unique career stat. Please note that is a card has a stated print run of 15 or less, no pricing is provided.

*1-150 P/R b/wn 251-400: 2.5X TO 6X
*1-150 P/R b/wn 201-250: 2.5X TO 6X
*1-150 P/R b/wn 151-200: 3X TO 8X
*1-150 P/R b/wn 121-150: 3X TO 8X
*1-150 P/R b/wn 81-120: 4X TO 10X
*1-150 P/R b/wn 66-80: 5X TO 12X
*1-150 P/R b/wn 51-65: 5X TO 12X
*1-150 P/R b/wn 36-50: 6X TO 15X
*201-220 P/R b/wn 251-400 .5X TO 1.2X
*201-220 P/R b/wn 201-250 .6X TO 1.5X
*201-220 P/R b/wn 151-200 .75X TO 2X
*201-220 P/R b/wn 121-150 1X TO 2.5X
*201-220 P/R b/wn 51-65 1.5X TO 4X
151 Marlon Byrd RR/232 1.00 2.50
152 Ben Howard RR/283 .75 2.00
153 Brandon Backe RR/94 2.00 5.00
154 Jorge De La Rosa RR/54 2.50 6.00
155 Corky Miller RR/184 1.25 3.00
156 Dennis Tankersley RR/253 .75 2.00
157 Kyle Kane RR/179 1.25 3.00
158 Justin Duchscherer RR/11
159 Brian Mallette RR/273 .75 2.00
160 Chris Baker RR/270 .75 2.00
161 Jason Lane RR/302 .75 2.00
162 Hee Seop Choi RR/286 .75 2.00
163 Juan Cruz RR/322 .75 2.00
164 Rodrigo Rosario RR/313 .75 2.00
165 Matt Guerrier RR/280 .75 2.00
166 Anderson Machado RR/252 .75 2.00
167 Geronimo Gil RR/293 .75 2.00
168 Dewon Brazelton RR/335 .75 2.00
169 Mark Prior RR/303 1.25 3.00
170 Bill Hall RR/373 .75 2.00
171 Jorge Padilla RR/273 .75 2.00
172 Jose Cueto RR/156 1.25 3.00
173 Allan Simpson RR/204 1.00 2.50
174 Doug Devore RR/287 .75 2.00
175 Josh Pearce RR/315 .75 2.00
176 Angel Berroa RR/268 .75 2.00
177 Steve Bechler RR/25
178 Antonio Perez RR/143 1.50 4.00
179 Mark Teixeira RR/165 2.00 5.00
180 Erick Almonte RR/4
181 Orlando Hudson RR/283 .75 2.00
182 Michael Rivera RR/333 .75 2.00
183 Raul Chavez RR/253 .75 2.00
184 Juan Pena RR/293 .75 2.00
185 Travis Hughes RR/174 1.25 3.00
186 Ryan Ludwick RR/264 .75 2.00
187 Ed Rogers RR/270 .75 2.00
188 Andy Pratt RR/203 1.00 2.50
189 Nick Neugebauer RR/11
190 Tom Shearn RR/251 .75 2.00
191 Eric Cyr RR/161 1.25 3.00
192 Victor Martinez RR/305 1.25 3.00
193 Brandon Berger RR/313 .75 2.00
194 Erik Bedard RR/279 .75 2.00
195 Fernando Rodney RR/309 .75 2.00
196 Joe Thurston RR/284 .75 2.00
197 John Buck RR/271 .75 2.00
198 Jeff Deardorff RR/201 1.00 2.50
199 Ryan Jamison RR/273 .75 2.00
200 Alfredo Amezaga RR/290 .75 2.00

2002 Donruss Stat Line Season

Randomly inserted into packs, this is a parallel to the basic Donruss set. These cards feature cards printed on foil-board with silver holo-foil stamping. Each card has a stated print run to a unique seasonal stat. Please note that is a card has a stated print run of 15 or less, no pricing is provided.

*1-150 P/R b/wn 151-200: 3X TO 8X
*1-150 P/R b/wn 121-150: 3X TO 8X
*1-150 P/R b/wn 81-120: 4X TO 10X
*1-150 P/R b/wn 66-80: 5X TO 12X
*1-150 P/R b/wn 51-65: 5X TO 12X
*1-150 P/R b/wn 36-50: 6X TO 15X
*1-150 P/R b/wn 26-35: 8X TO 20X
*201-220 P/R b/wn 81-120 1.25X TO 3X
*201-220 P/R b/wn 66-80 1.5X TO 4X
*201-220 P/R b/wn 51-65 1.5X TO 4X
*201-220 P/R b/wn 36-50 2X TO 5X
*201-220 P/R b/wn 26-35 2.5X TO 6X
151 Marlon Byrd RR/89 2.00 5.00
152 Ben Howard RR/29 4.00 10.00
153 Brandon Backe RR/39 3.00 8.00
154 Jorge De La Rosa RR/32 4.00 10.00
155 Corky Miller RR/7
156 Dennis Tankersley RR/30 4.00 10.00
157 Kyle Kane RR/75 2.50 6.00
158 Justin Duchscherer RR/20
159 Brian Mallette RR/94 2.00 5.00
160 Chris Baker RR/121 1.50 4.00
161 Jason Lane RR/38 3.00 8.00
162 Hee Seop Choi RR/45 3.00 8.00
163 Juan Cruz RR/39 3.00 8.00
164 Rodrigo Rosario RR/131 1.50 4.00
165 Matt Guerrier RR/118 2.00 5.00
166 Anderson Machado RR/36 3.00 8.00
167 Geronimo Gil RR/17
168 Dewon Brazelton RR/13
169 Mark Prior RR/14
170 Bill Hall RR/65 2.50 6.00
171 Jorge Padilla RR/66 2.50 6.00
172 Jose Cueto RR/62 2.50 6.00
173 Allan Simpson RR/77 2.50 6.00
174 Doug Devore RR/74 2.50 6.00
175 Josh Pearce RR/132 1.50 4.00
176 Angel Berroa RR/63 2.50 6.00
177 Steve Bechler RR/135 1.50 4.00
178 Antonio Perez RR/143 1.50 4.00
179 Mark Teixeira RR/20
180 Erick Almonte RR/8
181 Orlando Hudson RR/79 2.50 6.00
182 Michael Rivera RR/4
183 Raul Chavez RR/5
184 Juan Pena RR/106 2.00 5.00
185 Travis Hughes RR/86 2.00 5.00
186 Ryan Ludwick RR/103 2.00 5.00
187 Ed Rogers RR/54 2.50 6.00
188 Andy Pratt RR/132 1.50 4.00
189 Nick Neugebauer RR/5
190 Tom Shearn RR/136 1.50 4.00
191 Eric Cyr RR/131 1.50 4.00
192 Victor Martinez RR/57 4.00 10.00
193 Brandon Berger RR/16
194 Erik Bedard RR/137 1.50 4.00
195 Fernando Rodney RR/52 2.50 6.00
196 Joe Thurston RR/46 3.00 8.00
197 John Buck RR/73 2.50 6.00
198 Jeff Deardorff RR/100 2.00 5.00
199 Ryan Jamison RR/95 2.00 5.00
200 Alfredo Amezaga RR/37 3.00 8.00

2002 Donruss All-Time Diamond Kings

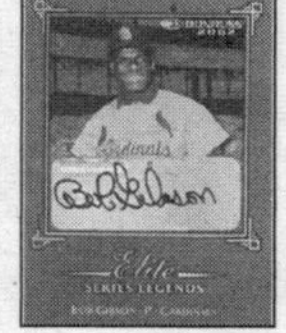

Randomly inserted in packs, these 10 cards feature legendary baseball superstars reproduced on conventional stock with bronze foil. These cards have a stated print run of 2,500 copies.

*STUDIO: 1X TO 2.5X BASIC ALL-TIME DK
STUDIO PRINT RUN 250 SERIAL #'d SETS
1 Ted Williams UER 6.00 15.00
Rogers Hornsby also won the triple crown twice
2 Cal Ripken 12.50 30.00
3 Lou Gehrig 6.00 15.00
4 Babe Ruth 10.00 25.00
5 Roberto Clemente 8.00 20.00
6 Don Mattingly 10.00 25.00
7 Kirby Puckett 4.00 10.00
8 Stan Musial 6.00 15.00
9 Yogi Berra 4.00 10.00
10 Ernie Banks 4.00 10.00

2002 Donruss Bat Kings

Randomly inserted in packs, these five cards feature a mix of active and retired superstars along with a sliver of each player's game-used bat. The active players have a stated print run of 250 copies while the retired players have a stated print run of 125 copies.

*STUDIO 1-3: .75X TO 2X BASIC BAT KING
STUDIO 1-3 PRINT RUN 50 SERIAL #'d SETS
STUDIO 4-5 PRINT RUN 25 SERIAL #'d SETS
RANDOM INSERTS IN PACKS
1 Jason Giambi 6.00 15.00
2 Alex Rodriguez 10.00 25.00
3 Mike Piazza 10.00 25.00
4 Roberto Clemente/125 50.00 100.00
5 Babe Ruth/125 100.00 200.00

2002 Donruss Diamond Kings Inserts

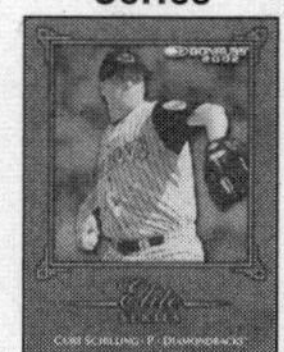

Randomly inserted in packs, these 20 cards feature leading players with silver foil stamping and stated sequential serial numbering to 2500.

*STUDIO: .75X TO 2X BASIC DK'S
STUDIO PRINT RUN 250 SERIAL #'d SETS
RANDOM INSERTS IN PACKS
1 Nomar Garciaparra 5.00 12.00
2 Shawn Green 4.00 10.00
3 Randy Johnson 4.00 10.00
4 Derek Jeter 8.00 20.00
5 Carlos Delgado 4.00 10.00
6 Roger Clemens 6.00 15.00
7 Jeff Bagwell 4.00 10.00
8 Vladimir Guerrero 4.00 10.00
9 Luis Gonzalez 4.00 10.00
10 Mike Piazza 5.00 12.00
11 Ichiro Suzuki 6.00 15.00
12 Pedro Martinez 4.00 10.00
13 Todd Helton 4.00 10.00
14 Sammy Sosa 4.00 10.00
15 Ivan Rodriguez 4.00 10.00
16 Barry Bonds 8.00 20.00
17 Albert Pujols 6.00 15.00
18 Jim Thome 4.00 10.00
19 Alex Rodriguez 5.00 12.00
20 Jason Giambi 4.00 10.00

2002 Donruss Elite Series

Randomly inserted in packs, these 20 cards feature some of today's most storied performers. These cards are printed on metalized film board and are sequentially numbered to 2,500.

1 Barry Bonds 5.00 12.00
2 Lance Berkman 1.50 4.00
3 Jason Giambi 1.50 4.00
4 Nomar Garciaparra 3.00 8.00
5 Curt Schilling 1.50 4.00
6 Vladimir Guerrero 2.00 5.00
7 Shawn Green 1.50 4.00
8 Jeff Bagwell 1.50 4.00
9 Troy Glaus 1.50 4.00
10 Manny Ramirez 1.50 4.00
11 Eric Chavez 1.50 4.00
12 Carlos Delgado 1.50 4.00
13 Mike Sweeney 1.50 4.00
14 Todd Helton 1.50 4.00
15 Luis Gonzalez 1.50 4.00
16 Enos Slaughter LGD 1.50 4.00
17 Frank Robinson LGD 1.50 4.00
18 Bob Gibson LGD 1.50 4.00
19 Warren Spahn LGD 1.50 4.00
20 Whitey Ford LGD 1.50 4.00

2002 Donruss Elite Series Signatures

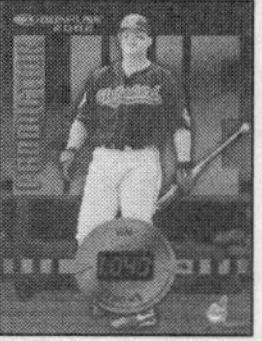

Randomly inserted in packs, these 18 cards feature players who signed cards for the 2002 Donruss Elite product. These cards have different print runs and we have notated that information in our checklist.

2 Lance Berkman/25
3 Jason Giambi/25
4 Nomar Garciaparra/25
5 Curt Schilling/25
6 Vladimir Guerrero/25
7 Shawn Green/25
8 Jeff Bagwell/25
9 Troy Glaus/25
10 Manny Ramirez/25
11 Eric Chavez/25
13 Mike Sweeney/25
14 Todd Helton/25
15 Luis Gonzalez/25
16 Enos Slaughter LGD/250 15.00 40.00
17 Frank Robinson LGD/250 15.00 40.00
18 Bob Gibson LGD/250 15.00 40.00
19 Warren Spahn LGD/250 30.00 60.00
20 Whitey Ford LGD/250 15.00 40.00

2002 Donruss Jersey Kings

Randomly inserted in packs, these 15 cards feature game-worn jersey swatches of a mix all-time greats and active superstars. The active players have a stated prinrt run of 250 serial numbered sets while the retired players have a stated print run of 125 sets.

*STUDIO 1-12: .75X TO 2X BASIC JSY KINGS
STUDIO 1-12 PRINT RUN 50 SERIAL #'d SETS
STUDIO 13-15 PRINT RUN 25 SERIAL #'d SETS
STUDIO 13-15 TOO SCARCE TO PRICE
RANDOM INSERTS IN PACKS
1 Alex Rodriguez 10.00 25.00
2 Jason Giambi 6.00 15.00
3 Carlos Delgado 6.00 15.00
4 Barry Bonds 15.00 40.00
5 Randy Johnson 10.00 25.00
6 Jim Thome 10.00 25.00
7 Shawn Green 6.00 15.00
8 Pedro Martinez 10.00 25.00
9 Jeff Bagwell 10.00 25.00
10 Vladimir Guerrero 10.00 25.00
11 Ivan Rodriguez 10.00 25.00
12 Nomar Garciaparra 10.00 25.00
13 Don Mattingly/125 15.00 40.00
14 Ted Williams/125 50.00 100.00
15 Lou Gehrig/125 125.00 200.00

2002 Donruss Longball Leaders

Randomly inserted in packs, these 20 cards feature the majors most powerful hitters and they are featured on metalized film board and have a stated print run of 1,000 sequentially numbered sets.

1 Barry Bonds 8.00 20.00
2 Sammy Sosa 3.00 8.00
3 Luis Gonzalez 1.50 4.00
4 Alex Rodriguez 5.00 12.00
5 Shawn Green 1.50 4.00
6 Todd Helton 2.00 5.00
7 Jim Thome 2.00 5.00
8 Rafael Palmeiro 2.00 5.00
9 Richie Sexson 1.50 4.00
10 Troy Glaus 1.50 4.00
11 Manny Ramirez 2.00 5.00
12 Phil Nevin 1.50 4.00
13 Jeff Bagwell 2.00 5.00
14 Carlos Delgado 1.50 4.00
15 Jason Giambi 1.50 4.00
16 Chipper Jones 3.00 8.00
17 Larry Walker 1.50 4.00
18 Albert Pujols 6.00 15.00
19 Brian Giles 1.50 4.00
20 Bret Boone 1.50 4.00

2002 Donruss Production Line

Randomly inserted in packs, these 60 cards feature the msot productive sluggers in three categories: On-Base Percentage, Slugging Percentage and OPS. Cards numbered 1-20 feature On-Base Percentage, while cards numbered 21-40 feature Slugging Percentage and cards numbered 41-60 feature OPS. Since all the cards have different stated print runs, we have listed that information next to the card in our checklist.

COMMON OBP (1-20) 1.50 4.00
COMMON SLG (21-40) 1.25 3.00
COMMON OPS (41-60) 1.00 2.50
*DIE CUT OBP 1-20: .75X TO 2X BASIC PL
*DIE CUT SLG 21-40: 1X TO 2.5X BASIC PL
*DIE CUT OPS 41-60: 1.25X TO 3X BASIC PL
DIE CUT PRINT RUN 100 SERIAL #'d SETS
DC's ARE 1ST 100 #'d OF EACH PLAYER
RANDOM INSERTS IN PACKS
1 Barry Bonds OBP/415 10.00 25.00
2 Jason Giambi OBP/377 1.50 4.00
3 Larry Walker OBP/349 1.50 4.00
4 Sammy Sosa OBP/337 4.00 10.00
5 Todd Helton OBP/332 2.50 6.00
6 Lance Berkman OBP/330 1.50 4.00
7 Luis Gonzalez OBP/329 1.50 4.00
8 Chipper Jones OBP/327 4.00 10.00
9 Edgar Martinez OBP/323 2.50 6.00
10 Gary Sheffield OBP/317 1.50 4.00
11 Jim Thome OBP/316 2.50 6.00
12 Roberto Alomar OBP/315 2.50 6.00
13 J.D. Drew OBP/314 1.50 4.00
14 Jim Edmonds OBP/310 1.50 4.00
15 Carlos Delgado OBP/308 1.50 4.00
16 Manny Ramirez OBP/305 2.50 6.00
17 Brian Giles OBP/304 1.50 4.00
18 Albert Pujols OBP/303 8.00 20.00
19 John Olerud OBP/301 1.50 4.00
20 Alex Rodriguez OBP/299 6.00 15.00
21 Barry Bonds SLG/763 8.00 20.00
22 Sammy Sosa SLG/637 4.00 10.00
23 Luis Gonzalez SLG/588 1.25 3.00
24 Todd Helton SLG/585 2.00 5.00
25 Larry Walker SLG/562 1.25 3.00
26 Jason Giambi SLG/560 1.25 3.00
27 Jim Thome SLG/524 2.00 5.00
28 Alex Rodriguez SLG/522 5.00 12.00
29 Lance Berkman SLG/520 1.25 3.00
30 J.D. Drew SLG/513 1.25 3.00
31 Albert Pujols SLG/510 6.00 15.00
32 Manny Ramirez SLG/509 2.00 5.00
33 Chipper Jones SLG/505 3.00 8.00
34 Shawn Green SLG/498 1.25 3.00
35 Brian Giles SLG/490 1.25 3.00
36 Juan Gonzalez SLG/490 1.25 3.00
37 Phil Nevin SLG/488 1.25 3.00
38 Gary Sheffield SLG/483 1.25 3.00
39 Bret Boone SLG/478 1.25 3.00
40 Cliff Floyd SLG/478 1.25 3.00
41 Barry Bonds OPS/1278 6.00 15.00
42 Sammy Sosa OPS/1074 4.00 10.00
43 Jason Giambi OPS/1037 1.00 2.50
44 Todd Helton OPS/1017 1.50 4.00
45 Luis Gonzalez OPS/1017 1.00 2.50
46 Larry Walker OPS/1011 1.00 2.50
47 Lance Berkman OPS/950 1.00 2.50
48 Jim Thome OPS/940 1.50 4.00
49 Chipper Jones OPS/932 2.50 6.00
50 J.D. Drew OPS/927 1.00 2.50
51 Alex Rodriguez OPS/921 4.00 10.00
52 Manny Ramirez OPS/914 1.50 4.00
53 Albert Pujols OPS/913 5.00 12.00
54 Gary Sheffield OPS/900 1.00 2.50
55 Brian Giles OPS/894 1.00 2.50
56 Phil Nevin OPS/876 1.00 2.50
57 Jim Edmonds OPS/874 1.00 2.50
58 Shawn Green OPS/870 1.00 2.50
59 Cliff Floyd OPS/868 1.00 2.50
60 Edgar Martinez OPS/866 1.50 4.00

2002 Donruss Recollection Autographs

Randomly inserted in packs, these 47 cards feature players who signed repurchased copies of their original cards for inclusion in the 2002 Donruss set. Since each player signed a different amount of cards, we have noted that information in our checklist. Please note that due to market scarcity, not all cards can be priced.

8 Gary Carter 87/100 10.00 25.00
9 Gary Carter 89/100 10.00 25.00
11 Joe Carter 87/45
13 Andre Dawson 81/50
14 Andre Dawson 83/50
16 Andre Dawson 87/45
17 Dennis Eckersley 81/45
24 Steve Garvey 87/75 15.00 40.00
46 Tom Seaver 87/60
47 Don Sutton 87/200 10.00 25.00

2002 Donruss Rookie Year Materials Bats

Randomly inserted into packs, these four cards feature a sliver of a game-used bat from the player's rookie season which includes silver holo-foil and are sequentially numbered a stated print run of 250 sequentially numbered sets.

1 Barry Bonds 40.00 80.00
2 Cal Ripken 30.00 60.00

3 Kirby Puckett 10.00 25.00
4 Johnny Bench 15.00 40.00

2002 Donruss Rookie Year Materials Bats ERA

These cards parallel the "Rookie Year Material Bats" insert set. These cards have gold holo-foil and have a stated print run sequentially numbered to the player's debut year. Since those years are all different, we have notated that information in our checklist.

1 Barry Bonds/86 75.00 150.00
2 Cal Ripken/81 60.00 120.00
3 Kirby Puckett/84 25.00 50.00
4 Johnny Bench/68 40.00 80.00

2002 Donruss Rookie Year Materials Jersey

Randomly inserted into packs, these four cards feature a swatch of a game-used jersey from the player's rookie season which includes silver holo-foil and are sequentially numbered a stated print run of either 250 or 50 sequentially numbered sets. The active players have the print run of 250 while the retired players have the print run of 50 sets.

1 Nomar Garciaparra 10.00 25.00
2 Randy Johnson 10.00 25.00
3 Ivan Rodriguez 10.00 25.00
4 Vladimir Guerrero 10.00 25.00
5 Stan Musial/50 40.00 80.00
6 Yogi Berra/50 40.00 80.00

2002 Donruss Rookie Year Materials Jersey Numbers

These cards parallel the "Rookie Year Material Jerseys" insert set. These cards have gold holo-foil and have a stated print run sequentially numbered to the player's jersey number his rookie season. We have notated that specific stated print information in our checklist.

1 Nomar Garciaparra/5
2 Randy Johnson/51
3 Ivan Rodriguez/7
4 Vladimir Guerrero/27
5 Stan Musial/6
6 Yogi Berra/35

2002 Donruss Rookies

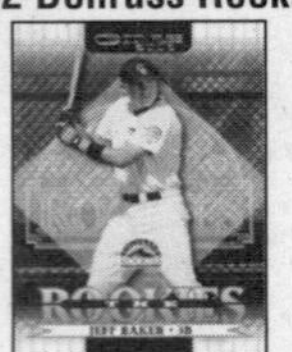

This 110 card set was released in December, 2002. These cards were issued in five card packs which came 24 packs to a box and 16 boxes to a case with an SRP of $3.29 per pack. This set features the top rookies and prospects of the 2002 season.

COMPLETE SET (110) 10.00 25.00
1 Kazuhisa Ishii RC .20 .50
2 P.J. Bevis RC .15 .40
3 Jason Simontacchi RC .15 .40
4 John Lackey .08 .25
5 Travis Driskill RC .15 .40
6 Carl Sadler RC .15 .40
7 Tim Kalita RC .15 .40
8 Nelson Castro RC .15 .40
9 Francis Beltran RC .15 .40
10 So Taguchi RC .20 .50
11 Ryan Bukvich RC .15 .40
12 Brian Fitzgerald RC .15 .40
13 Kevin Frederick RC .15 .40
14 Chone Figgins RC .60 1.50
15 Marlon Byrd .08 .25
16 Ron Calloway RC .15 .40
17 Jason Lane .15 .40
18 Satoru Komiyama RC .15 .40
19 John Ennis RC .15 .40
20 Juan Brito RC .15 .40
21 Gustavo Chacin RC .30 .75
22 Josh Bard RC .15 .40
23 Brett Myers .15 .40
24 Mike Smith RC .15 .40
25 Eric Hinske .08 .25
26 Jake Peavy .20 .50
27 Todd Donovan RC .15 .40
28 Luis Ugueto RC .15 .40
29 Corey Thurman RC .15 .40
30 Takahito Nomura RC .15 .40
31 Andy Shibilo RC .15 .40
32 Mike Crudale RC .15 .40
33 Earl Snyder RC .15 .40
34 Brian Tallet RC .15 .40
35 Miguel Asencio RC .15 .40
36 Felix Escalona RC .15 .40
37 Drew Henson .08 .25
38 Steve Kent RC .15 .40
39 Rene Reyes RC .15 .40
40 Edwin Almonte RC .15 .40
41 Chris Snelling RC .25 .60
42 Franklyn German RC .15 .40
43 Jeriome Robertson RC .15 .40
44 Colin Young RC .15 .40
45 Jeremy Lambert RC .15 .40
46 Kirk Saarloos RC .15 .40
47 Matt Childers RC .15 .40
48 Justin Wayne .08 .25
49 Jose Valverde RC .15 .40
50 Wily Mo Pena .15 .40
51 Victor Alvarez RC .15 .40
52 Julius Matos RC .15 .40
53 Aaron Cook RC .15 .40
54 Jeff Austin RC .15 .40
55 Adrian Burnside RC .15 .40
56 Brandon Puffer RC .15 .40
57 Jeremy Hill RC .15 .40
58 Jaime Cerda RC .15 .40
59 Aaron Guiel RC .15 .40
60 Ron Chiavacci .08 .25
61 Kevin Cash RC .15 .40
62 Elio Serrano RC .15 .40
63 Julio Mateo RC .15 .40
64 Cam Esslinger RC .15 .40
65 Ken Huckaby RC .15 .40
66 Will Nieves RC .15 .40
67 Luis Martinez RC .15 .40
68 Scotty Layfield RC .15 .40
69 Jeremy Guthrie RC .20 .50
70 Hansel Izquierdo RC .15 .40
71 Shane Nance RC .15 .40
72 Jeff Baker RC .40 1.00
73 Cliff Bartosh RC .15 .40
74 Mitch Wylie RC .15 .40
75 Oliver Perez RC .30 .75
76 Matt Thornton RC .15 .40
77 John Foster RC .15 .40
78 Joe Borchard .08 .25
79 Eric Junge RC .15 .40
80 Jorge Sosa RC .20 .50
81 Runelvys Hernandez RC .15 .40
82 Kevin Mench .08 .25
83 Ben Kozlowski RC .15 .40
84 Trey Hodges RC .15 .40
85 Reed Johnson RC .30 .75
86 Eric Eckenstahler RC .15 .40
87 Franklin Nunez RC .15 .40
88 Victor Martinez .30 .75
89 Kevin Gryboski RC .15 .40
90 Jason Jennings .08 .25
91 Jim Rushford RC .15 .40
92 Jeremy Ward RC .15 .40
93 Adam Walker RC .15 .40
94 Freddy Sanchez RC .75 2.00
95 Wilson Valdez RC .15 .40
96 Lee Gardner RC .15 .40
97 Eric Good RC .15 .40
98 Hank Blalock .20 .50
99 Mark Corey RC .15 .40
100 Jason Davis RC .15 .40
101 Mike Gonzalez RC .15 .40
102 David Ross RC .25 .60
103 Tyler Yates RC .15 .40
104 Cliff Lee RC 1.00 2.50
105 Mike Moriarty RC .15 .40
106 Josh Hancock RC .20 .50
107 Jason Beverlin RC .15 .40
108 Clay Condrey RC .15 .40
109 Shawn Sedlacek RC .15 .40
110 Sean Burroughs .08 .25

2002 Donruss Rookies Autographs

Randomly inserted into packs, this is a partial parallel to the Donruss Rookies set. Each players signed between 15 and 100 cards for insertion in this product and cards with a stated print run of 25 or fewer are not priced due to market scarcity.

1 Kazuhisa Ishii/25
2 P.J. Bevis/50 10.00 25.00
7 Tim Kalita/25
9 Francis Beltran/100 4.00 10.00
10 So Taguchi/15
13 Kevin Frederick/100 4.00 10.00
14 Chone Figgins/100 10.00 25.00
15 Marlon Byrd/100 4.00 10.00
17 Jason Lane/100 6.00 15.00
18 Satoru Komiyama/25
19 John Ennis/100 4.00 10.00
22 Josh Bard/100 4.00 10.00
25 Eric Hinske/100 4.00 10.00
28 Luis Ugueto/100 4.00 10.00
29 Corey Thurman/100 4.00 10.00
30 Takahito Nomura/100 10.00 25.00
33 Earl Snyder/100 4.00 10.00
34 Brian Tallet/100 4.00 10.00
36 Felix Escalona/25
37 Drew Henson/50 6.00 15.00
39 Rene Reyes/50 10.00 25.00
40 Edwin Almonte/50 10.00 25.00
41 Chris Snelling/50 12.50 30.00
42 Franklyn German/100 4.00 10.00
45 Jeremy Lambert/100 4.00 10.00
46 Kirk Saarloos/50 6.00 15.00
47 Matt Childers/100 4.00 10.00
50 Wily Mo Pena/100 6.00 15.00
51 Victor Alvarez/100 4.00 10.00
61 Kevin Cash/100 4.00 10.00
62 Elio Serrano/100 4.00 10.00
64 Cam Esslinger/100 4.00 10.00
69 Jeremy Guthrie/100 6.00 15.00
71 Shane Nance/100 4.00 10.00
72 Jeff Baker/100 10.00 25.00
75 Oliver Perez/25
76 Matt Thornton/100 4.00 10.00
78 Joe Borchard/100 4.00 10.00
79 Eric Junge/25
82 Kevin Mench/100 6.00 15.00
83 Ben Kozlowski/100 4.00 10.00
84 Trey Hodges/100 4.00 10.00
85 Reed Johnson/100 6.00 15.00
88 Victor Martinez/100 15.00 40.00
90 Jason Jennings/100 4.00 10.00
95 Wilson Valdez/100 4.00 10.00
97 Eric Good/100 4.00 10.00
98 Hank Blalock/100 6.00 15.00
104 Cliff Lee/100 20.00 50.00
110 Sean Burroughs/50 6.00 15.00

2002 Donruss Rookies Crusade

Randomly inserted into packs, these 50 cards, which were printed on metalized holo-foil board, were printed to a stated print run of 1500 serial numbered sets.

1 Corky Miller 1.50 4.00
2 Jack Cust 1.50 4.00
3 Erik Bedard 1.50 4.00
4 Andres Torres 1.50 4.00
5 Geronimo Gil 1.50 4.00
6 Rafael Soriano 1.50 4.00
7 Johnny Estrada 1.50 4.00
8 Steve Bechler 1.50 4.00
9 Adam Johnson 1.50 4.00
10 So Taguchi 1.50 4.00
11 Dee Brown 1.50 4.00
12 Kevin Frederick 1.50 4.00
13 Allan Simpson 1.50 4.00
14 Ricardo Rodriguez 1.50 4.00
15 Jason Hart 1.50 4.00
16 Matt Childers 1.50 4.00
17 Jason Jennings 1.50 4.00
18 Anderson Machado 1.50 4.00
19 Fernando Rodney 1.50 4.00
20 Brandon Larson 1.50 4.00
21 Satoru Komiyama 1.50 4.00
22 Francis Beltran 1.50 4.00
23 Joe Thurston 1.50 4.00
24 Josh Pearce 1.50 4.00
25 Carlos Hernandez 1.50 4.00
26 Ben Howard 1.50 4.00
27 Wilson Valdez 1.50 4.00
28 Victor Alvarez 1.50 4.00
29 Cesar Izturis 1.50 4.00
30 Endy Chavez 1.50 4.00
31 Michael Cuddyer 1.50 4.00
32 Bobby Hill 1.50 4.00
33 Willie Harris 1.50 4.00
34 Joe Crede 1.50 4.00
35 Jorge Padilla 1.50 4.00
36 Brandon Backe 1.50 4.00
37 Franklyn German 1.50 4.00
38 Xavier Nady 1.50 4.00
39 Raul Chavez 1.50 4.00
40 Shane Nance 1.50 4.00
41 Brandon Claussen 1.50 4.00
42 Tom Shearn 1.50 4.00
43 Freddy Sanchez 3.00 8.00
44 Chone Figgins 2.00 5.00
45 Cliff Lee 6.00 15.00
46 Brian Mallette 1.50 4.00
47 Mike Rivera 1.50 4.00
48 Elio Serrano 1.50 4.00
49 Rodrigo Rosario 1.50 4.00
50 Earl Snyder 1.50 4.00

2002 Donruss Rookies Crusade Autographs

These 49 cards basically parallel the Rookies Crusade set. These cards were issued to a stated print run of anywhere from 15 to 500 copies per. Cards with a print run of 25 or fewer are not priced due to market scarcity.

COMMON CARD p/r 300+ 4.00 10.00
COMMON ROOKIE p/r 300+ 4.00 10.00
COMMON CARD p/r 150-250 4.00 10.00
COMMON CARD p/r 100 4.00 10.00
1 Corky Miller/500 4.00 10.00
2 Jack Cust/500 4.00 10.00
3 Erik Bedard/100 4.00 10.00
4 Andres Torres/500 4.00 10.00
5 Geronimo Gil/500 4.00 10.00
6 Rafael Soriano/500 4.00 10.00
7 Johnny Estrada/400 4.00 10.00
8 Steve Bechler/500 4.00 10.00
9 Adam Johnson/500 4.00 10.00
10 So Taguchi/15
11 Dee Brown/500 4.00 10.00
12 Kevin Frederick/150 4.00 10.00
13 Allan Simpson/150 4.00 10.00
14 Ricardo Rodriguez/500 4.00 10.00
15 Jason Hart/500 4.00 10.00
16 Matt Childers/150 4.00 10.00
17 Jason Jennings/500 4.00 10.00
18 Anderson Machado/500 4.00 10.00
19 Fernando Rodney/500 4.00 10.00
20 Brandon Larson/400 4.00 10.00
21 Satoru Komiyama/25
22 Francis Beltran/500 4.00 10.00
23 Joe Thurston/500 4.00 10.00
24 Josh Pearce/500 4.00 10.00
25 Carlos Hernandez/500 4.00 10.00
26 Ben Howard/500 4.00 10.00
27 Wilson Valdez/500 4.00 10.00
28 Victor Alvarez/500 4.00 10.00
29 Cesar Izturis/500 4.00 10.00
30 Endy Chavez/500 4.00 10.00
31 Michael Cuddyer/375 4.00 10.00
32 Bobby Hill/250 4.00 10.00
33 Willie Harris/300 4.00 10.00
34 Joe Crede/100 4.00 10.00
35 Jorge Padilla/475 4.00 10.00
36 Brandon Backe/350 6.00 15.00
37 Franklyn German/500 4.00 10.00
38 Xavier Nady/500 4.00 10.00
39 Raul Chavez/500 4.00 10.00
40 Shane Nance/500 4.00 10.00
41 Brandon Claussen/150 4.00 10.00
42 Tom Shearn/500 4.00 10.00
44 Chone Figgins/500 6.00 15.00
45 Cliff Lee/500 15.00 40.00
46 Brian Mallette/150 4.00 10.00
47 Mike Rivera/400 4.00 10.00
48 Elio Serrano/500 4.00 10.00
49 Rodrigo Rosario/100 4.00 10.00
50 Earl Snyder/100 4.00 10.00

2002 Donruss Rookies Phenoms

Randomly inserted into packs, these 25 cards, which are set on shimmering double rainbow holo-foil board were sequentially numbered to 1000 serial numbered sets.

1 Kazuhisa Ishii 2.00 5.00
2 Eric Hinske 2.00 5.00
3 Jason Lane 2.00 5.00
4 Victor Martinez 3.00 8.00
5 Mark Prior 2.00 5.00
6 Antonio Perez 2.00 5.00
7 John Buck 2.00 5.00
8 Joe Borchard 2.00 5.00
9 Alexis Gomez 2.00 5.00
10 Sean Burroughs 2.00 5.00
11 Carlos Pena 2.00 5.00
12 Bill Hall 2.00 5.00
13 Alfredo Amezaga 2.00 5.00
14 Ed Rogers 2.00 5.00
15 Mark Teixeira 3.00 8.00
16 Chris Snelling 2.50 6.00
17 Nick Johnson 2.00 5.00
18 Angel Berroa 2.00 5.00
19 Orlando Hudson 2.00 5.00
20 Drew Henson 2.00 5.00
21 Austin Kearns 2.00 5.00
22 Dewon Brazelton 2.00 5.00
23 Dennis Tankersley 2.00 5.00
24 Josh Beckett 2.00 5.00
25 Marlon Byrd 2.00 5.00

2002 Donruss Rookies Phenoms Autographs

These cards parallel the Phenoms insert set. Each of these cards were issued to a stated print run of between 25 and 500 signed copies. As the Ishii was produced to a stated print run of 25 sets, no pricing is provided for that card.

COMMON CARD p/r 300+ 4.00 10.00
COMMON CARD p/r 150-250 4.00 10.00
1 Kazuhisa Ishii/25
2 Eric Hinske/500 4.00 10.00
3 Jason Lane/500 6.00 15.00
4 Victor Martinez/225 10.00 25.00
5 Mark Prior/100 10.00 235.00
6 Antonio Perez/500 4.00 10.00
7 John Buck/100 4.00 10.00
8 Joe Borchard/100 4.00 10.00
9 Alexis Gomez/400 4.00 10.00
10 Sean Burroughs/150 4.00 10.00
11 Carlos Pena/150 4.00 10.00
12 Bill Hall/200 6.00 15.00
13 Alfredo Amezaga/500 4.00 10.00
14 Ed Rogers/500 4.00 10.00
15 Mark Teixeira/100 15.00 40.00
16 Chris Snelling/100 8.00 20.00
17 Nick Johnson/250 6.00 15.00
18 Angel Berroa/500 4.00 10.00
19 Orlando Hudson/400 4.00 10.00
20 Drew Henson/500 4.00 10.00
21 Austin Kearns/75 4.00 10.00
22 Dewon Brazelton/350 4.00 10.00
23 Dennis Tankersley/100 4.00 10.00
24 Josh Beckett/125 10.00 25.00
25 Marlon Byrd/500 4.00 10.00

2003 Donruss Samples

Issued as a one per in an issue of Beckett Baseball Card Monthly, these cards previewed the 2003 Donruss set. These cards have the word sample printed in silver on the back.

*SAMPLES: 1.5X TO 4X BASIC CARDS
ONE PER BBCM MAGAZINE

2003 Donruss

This 400 card set was released in December, 2002. The set was issued in 13 card packs with an SRP of $2.29 which were packed 24 packs to a box and 20 boxes to a case. Subsets in this set include cards numbered Diamond Kings (1-20) and Rated Rookies (21-70). For the first time since Donruss/Playoff returned to card production, this was a baseball set without short printed base cards.

COMPLETE SET (400) 25.00 50.00
COMMON CARD (71-400) .10 .30
COMMON CARD (1-20) .20 .50
COMMON CARD (21-70) .20 .50
1 Vladimir Guerrero DK .30 .75
2 Derek Jeter DK .75 2.00
3 Adam Dunn DK .20 .50
4 Greg Maddux DK .50 1.25
5 Lance Berkman DK .20 .50
6 Ichiro Suzuki DK .60 1.50
7 Mike Piazza DK .50 1.25
8 Alex Rodriguez DK .50 1.25
9 Tom Glavine DK .20 .50
10 Randy Johnson DK .30 .75
11 Nomar Garciaparra DK .50 1.25
12 Jason Giambi DK .20 .50
13 Sammy Sosa DK .30 .75
14 Barry Zito DK .20 .50
15 Chipper Jones DK .30 .75
16 Magglio Ordonez DK .20 .50
17 Larry Walker DK .20 .50
18 Alfonso Soriano DK .20 .50
19 Curt Schilling DK .20 .50
20 Barry Bonds DK .75 2.00
21 Joe Borchard RR .20 .50
22 Chris Snelling RR .20 .50
23 Brian Tallet RR .20 .50
24 Cliff Lee RR .20 .50
25 Freddy Sanchez RR .20 .50
26 Chone Figgins RR .20 .50
27 Kevin Cash RR .20 .50
28 Josh Bard RR .20 .50
29 Jeriome Robertson RR .20 .50
30 Jeremy Hill RR .20 .50
31 Shane Nance RR .20 .50
32 Jake Peavy RR .20 .50
33 Trey Hodges RR .20 .50
34 Eric Eckenstahler RR .20 .50
35 Jim Rushford RR .20 .50
36 Oliver Perez RR .20 .50
37 Kirk Saarloos RR .20 .50
38 Hank Blalock RR .20 .50
39 Francisco Rodriguez RR .20 .50
40 Runelvys Hernandez RR .20 .50
41 Aaron Cook RR .20 .50
42 Josh Hancock RR .20 .50
43 P.J. Bevis RR .20 .50
44 Jon Adkins RR .20 .50
45 Tim Kalita RR .20 .50
46 Nelson Castro RR .20 .50
47 Colin Young RR .20 .50
48 Adrian Burnside RR .20 .50
49 Luis Martinez RR .20 .50
50 Pete Zamora RR .20 .50
51 Todd Donovan RR .20 .50
52 Jeremy Ward RR .20 .50
53 Wilson Valdez RR .20 .50
54 Eric Good RR .20 .50
55 Jeff Baker RR .20 .50
56 Mitch Wylie RR .20 .50
57 Ron Calloway RR .20 .50
58 Jose Valverde RR .20 .50
59 Jason Davis RR .20 .50
60 Scotty Layfield RR .20 .50
61 Matt Thornton RR .20 .50
62 Adam Walker RR .20 .50
63 Gustavo Chacin RR .20 .50
64 Ron Chiavacci RR .20 .50
65 Wiki Nieves RR .20 .50
66 Cliff Bartosh RR .20 .50
67 Mike Gonzalez RR .20 .50
68 Justin Wayne RR .20 .50
69 Eric Junge RR .20 .50
70 Ben Kozlowski RR .20 .50
71 Darin Erstad .10 .30
72 Garret Anderson .10 .30
73 Troy Glaus .10 .30
74 David Eckstein .10 .30
75 Adam Kennedy .10 .30
76 Kevin Appier .10 .30
77 Jarrod Washburn .10 .30
78 Scott Spiezio .10 .30
79 Tim Salmon .20 .50
80 Ramon Ortiz .10 .30
81 Bengie Molina .10 .30
82 Brad Fullmer .10 .30
83 Troy Percival .10 .30
84 David Segui .10 .30
85 Jay Gibbons .10 .30
86 Tony Batista .10 .30
87 Scott Erickson .10 .30
88 Jeff Conine .10 .30
89 Melvin Mora .10 .30
90 Buddy Groom .10 .30
91 Rodrigo Lopez .10 .30
92 Marty Cordova .10 .30
93 Geronimo Gil .10 .30
94 Kenny Lofton .10 .30
95 Shea Hillenbrand .10 .30
96 Manny Ramirez .20 .50
97 Pedro Martinez .20 .50
98 Nomar Garciaparra .50 1.25
99 Rickey Henderson .30 .75
100 Johnny Damon .20 .50
101 Trot Nixon .10 .30
102 Derek Lowe .10 .30
103 Hee Seop Choi .10 .30
104 Mark Teixeira .20 .50
105 Tim Wakefield .10 .30
106 Jason Varitek .30 .75
107 Frank Thomas .30 .75
108 Joe Crede .10 .30
109 Magglio Ordonez .10 .30
110 Ray Durham .10 .30
111 Mark Buehrle .10 .30
112 Paul Konerko .10 .30
113 Jose Valentin .10 .30
114 Carlos Lee .10 .30
115 Royce Clayton .10 .30
116 C.C. Sabathia .10 .30
117 Ellis Burks .10 .30
118 Omar Vizquel .20 .50
119 Jim Thome .20 .50
120 Matt Lawton .10 .30
121 Travis Fryman .10 .30
122 Earl Snyder .10 .30
123 Ricky Gutierrez .10 .30
124 Einar Diaz .10 .30
125 Danys Baez .10 .30
126 Robert Fick .10 .30
127 Bobby Higginson .10 .30
128 Steve Sparks .10 .30
129 Mike Rivera .10 .30
130 Wendell Magee .10 .30
131 Randall Simon .10 .30
132 Carlos Pena .10 .30
133 Mark Redman .10 .30
134 Juan Acevedo .10 .30
135 Mike Sweeney .10 .30
136 Aaron Guiel .10 .30
137 Carlos Beltran .10 .30
138 Joe Randa .10 .30
139 Paul Byrd .10 .30
140 Shawn Sedlacek .10 .30
141 Raul Ibanez .10 .30
142 Michael Tucker .10 .30
143 Torii Hunter .10 .30
144 Jacque Jones .10 .30
145 David Ortiz .30 .75
146 Corey Koskie .10 .30
147 Brad Radke .10 .30
148 Doug Mientkiewicz .10 .30
149 A.J. Pierzynski .10 .30
150 Dustan Mohr .10 .30
151 Michael Cuddyer .10 .30
152 Eddie Guardado .10 .30
153 Cristian Guzman .10 .30
154 Derek Jeter .75 2.00
155 Bernie Williams .20 .50
156 Roger Clemens .60 1.50
157 Mike Mussina .20 .50
158 Jorge Posada .20 .50
159 Alfonso Soriano .10 .30
160 Jason Giambi .10 .30
161 Robin Ventura .10 .30
162 Andy Pettitte .20 .50
163 David Wells .10 .30
164 Nick Johnson .10 .30
165 Jeff Weaver .10 .30
166 Raul Mondesi .10 .30
167 Rondell White .10 .30
168 Tim Hudson .10 .30
169 Barry Zito .10 .30
170 Mark Mulder .10 .30
171 Miguel Tejada .10 .30
172 Eric Chavez .10 .30
173 Billy Koch .10 .30
174 Jermaine Dye .10 .30
175 Scott Hatteberg .10 .30
176 Terrence Long .10 .30
177 David Justice .10 .30
178 Ramon Hernandez .10 .30
179 Ted Lilly .10 .30
180 Ichiro Suzuki .60 1.50
181 Edgar Martinez .20 .50
182 Mike Cameron .10 .30
183 John Olerud .10 .30
184 Bret Boone .10 .30
185 Dan Wilson .10 .30
186 Freddy Garcia .10 .30
187 Jamie Moyer .10 .30
188 Carlos Guillen .10 .30
189 Ruben Sierra .10 .30
190 Kazuhiro Sasaki .10 .30
191 Mark McLemore .10 .30
192 John Halama .10 .30
193 Joel Pineiro .10 .30
194 Jeff Cirillo .10 .30
195 Rafael Soriano .10 .30
196 Ben Grieve .10 .30
197 Aubrey Huff .10 .30
198 Steve Cox .10 .30

199 Toby Hall .10 .30
200 Randy Winn .10 .30
201 Brent Abernathy .10 .30
202 Chris Gomez .10 .30
203 John Flaherty .10 .30
204 Paul Wilson .10 .30
205 Chan Ho Park .10 .30
206 Alex Rodriguez .50 1.25
207 Juan Gonzalez .10 .30
208 Rafael Palmeiro .20 .50
209 Ivan Rodriguez .20 .50
210 Rusty Greer .10 .30
211 Kenny Rogers .10 .30
212 Ismael Valdes .10 .30
213 Frank Catalanotto .10 .30
214 Hank Blalock .10 .30
215 Michael Young .20 .50
216 Kevin Mench .10 .30
217 Herbert Perry .10 .30
218 Gabe Kapler .10 .30
219 Carlos Delgado .10 .30
220 Shannon Stewart .10 .30
221 Eric Hinske .10 .30
222 Roy Halladay .10 .30
223 Felipe Lopez .10 .30
224 Vernon Wells .10 .30
225 Josh Phelps .10 .30
226 Jose Cruz .10 .30
227 Curt Schilling .10 .30
228 Randy Johnson .30 .75
229 Luis Gonzalez .10 .30
230 Mark Grace .20 .50
231 Junior Spivey .10 .30
232 Tony Womack .10 .30
233 Matt Williams .10 .30
234 Steve Finley .10 .30
235 Byung-Hyun Kim .10 .30
236 Craig Counsell .10 .30
237 Greg Maddux .50 1.25
238 Tom Glavine .20 .50
239 John Smoltz .20 .50
240 Chipper Jones .30 .75
241 Gary Sheffield .10 .30
242 Andruw Jones .20 .50
243 Vinny Castilla .10 .30
244 Damian Moss .10 .30
245 Rafael Furcal .10 .30
246 Javy Lopez .10 .30
247 Kevin Millwood .10 .30
248 Kerry Wood .10 .30
249 Fred McGriff .20 .50
250 Sammy Sosa .30 .75
251 Alex Gonzalez .10 .30
252 Corey Patterson .10 .30
253 Moises Alou .10 .30
254 Juan Cruz .10 .30
255 Jon Lieber .10 .30
256 Matt Clement .10 .30
257 Mark Prior .20 .50
258 Ken Griffey Jr. .50 1.25
259 Barry Larkin .20 .50
260 Adam Dunn .10 .30
261 Sean Casey .10 .30
262 Jose Rijo .10 .30
263 Elmer Dessens .10 .30
264 Austin Kearns .10 .30
265 Corky Miller .10 .30
266 Todd Walker .10 .30
267 Chris Reitsma .10 .30
268 Ryan Dempster .10 .30
269 Aaron Boone .10 .30
270 Danny Graves .10 .30
271 Brandon Larson .10 .30
272 Larry Walker .10 .30
273 Todd Helton .20 .50
274 Juan Uribe .10 .30
275 Juan Pierre .10 .30
276 Mike Hampton .10 .30
277 Todd Zeile .10 .30
278 Todd Hollandsworth .10 .30
279 Jason Jennings .10 .30
280 Josh Beckett .10 .30
281 Mike Lowell .10 .30
282 Derrek Lee .20 .50
283 A.J. Burnett .10 .30
284 Luis Castillo .10 .30
285 Tim Raines .10 .30
286 Preston Wilson .10 .30
287 Juan Encarnacion .10 .30
288 Charles Johnson .10 .30
289 Jeff Bagwell .20 .50
290 Craig Biggio .20 .50
291 Lance Berkman .10 .30
292 Daryle Ward .10 .30
293 Roy Oswalt .10 .30
294 Richard Hidalgo .10 .30
295 Octavio Dotel .10 .30
296 Wade Miller .10 .30
297 Julio Lugo .10 .30
298 Billy Wagner .10 .30
299 Shawn Green .10 .30
300 Adrian Beltre .10 .30
301 Paul Lo Duca .10 .30
302 Eric Karros .10 .30
303 Kevin Brown .10 .30
304 Hideo Nomo .30 .75
305 Odalis Perez .10 .30
306 Eric Gagne .10 .30
307 Brian Jordan .10 .30
308 Cesar Izturis .10 .30
309 Mark Grudzielanek .10 .30
310 Kazuhisa Ishii .10 .30
311 Geoff Jenkins .10 .30
312 Richie Sexson .10 .30
313 Jose Hernandez .10 .30
314 Ben Sheets .10 .30
315 Ruben Quevedo .10 .30
316 Jeffrey Hammonds .10 .30
317 Alex Sanchez .10 .30
318 Eric Young .10 .30
319 Takahito Nomura .10 .30
320 Vladimir Guerrero .30 .75
321 Jose Vidro .10 .30
322 Orlando Cabrera .10 .30
323 Michael Barrett .10 .30
324 Javier Vazquez .10 .30
325 Tony Armas Jr. .10 .30
326 Andres Galarraga .10 .30
327 Tomo Ohka .10 .30
328 Bartolo Colon .10 .30
329 Fernando Tatis .10 .30
330 Brad Wilkerson .10 .30
331 Masato Yoshii .10 .30
332 Mike Piazza .50 1.25
333 Jeromy Burnitz .10 .30
334 Roberto Alomar .20 .50
335 Mo Vaughn .10 .30
336 Al Leiter .10 .30
337 Pedro Astacio .10 .30
338 Edgardo Alfonzo .10 .30
339 Armando Benitez .10 .30
340 Timo Perez .10 .30
341 Jay Payton .10 .30
342 Roger Cedeno .10 .30
343 Rey Ordonez .10 .30
344 Steve Trachsel .10 .30
345 Satoru Komiyama .10 .30
346 Scott Rolen .20 .50
347 Pat Burrell .10 .30
348 Bobby Abreu .10 .30
349 Mike Lieberthal .10 .30
350 Brandon Duckworth .10 .30
351 Jimmy Rollins .10 .30
352 Marlon Anderson .10 .30
353 Travis Lee .10 .30
354 Vicente Padilla .10 .30
355 Randy Wolf .10 .30
356 Jason Kendall .10 .30
357 Brian Giles .10 .30
358 Aramis Ramirez .10 .30
359 Pokey Reese .10 .30
360 Kip Wells .10 .30
361 Josh Fogg .10 .30
362 Mike Williams .10 .30
363 Jack Wilson .10 .30
364 Craig Wilson .10 .30
365 Kevin Young .10 .30
366 Ryan Klesko .10 .30
367 Phil Nevin .10 .30
368 Brian Lawrence .10 .30
369 Mark Kotsay .10 .30
370 Brett Tomko .10 .30
371 Trevor Hoffman .10 .30
372 Deivi Cruz .10 .30
373 Bubba Trammell .10 .30
374 Sean Burroughs .10 .30
375 Barry Bonds .75 2.00
376 Jeff Kent .10 .30
377 Rich Aurilia .10 .30
378 Tsuyoshi Shinjo .10 .30
379 Benito Santiago .10 .30
380 Kirk Rueter .10 .30
381 Livan Hernandez .10 .30
382 Russ Ortiz .10 .30
383 David Bell .10 .30
384 Jason Schmidt .10 .30
385 Reggie Sanders .10 .30
386 J.T. Snow .10 .30
387 Robb Nen .10 .30
388 Ryan Jensen .10 .30
389 Jim Edmonds .10 .30
390 J.D. Drew .10 .30
391 Albert Pujols .60 1.50
392 Fernando Vina .10 .30
393 Tino Martinez .20 .50
394 Edgar Renteria .10 .30
395 Matt Morris .10 .30
396 Woody Williams .10 .30
397 Jason Isringhausen .10 .30
398 Placido Polanco .10 .30
399 Eli Marrero .10 .30
400 Jason Simontacchi .10 .30

2003 Donruss Chicago Collection

These cards were distributed in March 2003 at the Chicago Sportsfest at the Donruss-Playoff corporate booth. Any collector that opened three Donruss/Playoff packs at the Donruss booth received one of these cards as a redemption for the wrappers. Only five serial-numbered sets were produced, thus the cards are too scarce to price. They can be easily identified by the large silver-foil "Chicago Collection" logo and serial-numbering stamped on the front of each card.

DISTRIBUTED AT CHICAGO SPORTSFEST
STATED PRINT RUN 5 SERIAL #'d SETS
NO PRICING DUE TO SCARCITY

2003 Donruss Stat Line Career

Randomly inserted into packs, this is a parallel to the 2003 Donruss set. Each card is printed to a number matching some career statistic and the cards are serial numbered to that amount. For those cards with a print run of 25 or fewer, no pricing is provided due to market scarcity.

*STAT LINE 1-20: 2.5X TO 6X BASIC
*21-70 P/R b/wn 251-400: 1.25X TO 3X
*21-70 P/R b/wn 201-250: 1.25X TO 3X
*21-70 P/R b/wn 151-200 1.5X TO 4X
*21-70 P/R b/wn 121-150: 2X TO 5X
*21-70 P/R b/wn 81-120: 2.5X TO 6X
*21-70 P/R b/wn 51-65: 3X TO 8X
*21-70 P/R b/wn 36-50: 4X TO 10X
*21-70 P/R b/wn 26-35: 5X TO 12X
*71-400 P/R b/wn 251-400: 2.5X TO 6X
*71-400 P/R b/wn 201-250: 2.5X TO 6X
*71-400 P/R b/wn 151-200 3X TO 8X
*71-400 P/R b/wn 121-150: 3X TO 8X
*71-400 P/R b/wn 81-120: 4X TO 10X
*71-400 P/R b/wn 66-80: 5X TO 12X
*71-400 P/R b/wn 51-65: 5X TO 12X
*71-400 P/R b/wn 36-50: 6X TO 15X
*71-400 P/R b/wn 26-35: 8X TO 20X
RANDOM INSERTS IN PACKS
SEE BECKETT.COM FOR FOR PRINT RUNS
NO PRICING ON QTY OF 25 OR LESS

2003 Donruss Stat Line Season

Randomly inserted into packs, this is a parallel to the 2003 Donruss set. Each card is printed to a number matching some seasonal statistic and the cards are serial numbered to that amount. For those cards with a print run of 25 or fewer, no pricing is provided due to market scarcity.

*1-20 P/R b/wn 121-150 3X TO 8X
*1-20 P/R b/wn 81-120 4X TO 10X
*1-20 P/R b/wn 66-80 5X TO 12X
*1-20 P/R b/wn 51-65 5X TO 12X
*1-20 P/R b/wn 36-50 6X TO 15X
*1-20 P/R b/wn 26-35 8X TO 20X
*21-70 P/R b/wn 81-120 2.5X TO 6X
*21-70 P/R b/wn 66-80 3X TO 8X
*21-70 P/R b/wn 51-65 3X TO 8X
*21-70 P/R b/wn 36-50 4X TO 10X
*21-70 P/R b/wn 26-35 5X TO 12X
*71-400 P/R b/wn 81-120 4X TO 10X
*71-400 P/R b/wn 66-80 5X TO 12X
*71-400 P/R b/wn 51-65 5X TO 12X
*71-400 P/R b/wn 36-50 6X TO 15X
*71-400 P/R b/wn 26-35 8X TO 20X
RANDOM INSERTS IN PACKS
SEE BECKETT.COM FOR PRINT RUNS
NO PRICING ON QTY OF 25 OR LESS

2003 Donruss All-Stars

Issued at a stated rate of one in 12 retail packs, these 10 cards feature players who are projected to be mainstays on the All-Star team.

1 Ichiro Suzuki 2.50 6.00
2 Alex Rodriguez 2.00 5.00
3 Nomar Garciaparra 2.00 5.00
4 Derek Jeter 3.00 8.00
5 Manny Ramirez 1.25 3.00
6 Barry Bonds 3.00 8.00
7 Adam Dunn 1.25 3.00
8 Mike Piazza 2.00 5.00
9 Sammy Sosa 1.25 3.00
10 Todd Helton 1.25 3.00

2003 Donruss Anniversary 1983

Issued at a stated rate of one in 12, this 20 card set features players who were among the most important players of that era. These cards use the 1983 Donruss design and photos.

1 Dale Murphy 1.25 3.00
2 Jim Palmer 1.25 3.00
3 Nolan Ryan 3.00 8.00
4 Ozzie Smith 2.00 5.00
5 Tom Seaver 1.25 3.00
6 Mike Schmidt 2.50 6.00
7 Steve Carlton 1.25 3.00
8 Robin Yount 1.25 3.00
9 Ryne Sandberg 2.00 5.00
10 Cal Ripken 4.00 10.00
11 Fernando Valenzuela 1.25 3.00
12 Andre Dawson 1.25 3.00
13 George Brett 2.50 6.00
14 Eddie Murray 1.25 3.00
15 Dave Winfield 1.25 3.00
16 Johnny Bench 1.25 3.00
17 Wade Boggs 1.25 3.00
18 Tony Gwynn 2.50 6.00
19 San Diego Chicken 1.25 3.00
20 Ty Cobb 2.00 5.00

2003 Donruss Bat Kings

Randomly inserted into packs, these 20 cards feature a game bat chip long with a reproduction of a previously used Diamond King card. Cards numbered 1 through 10 have a stated print run of 250 serial numbered sets while cards numbered 11 through 20 have a stated print run of 100 serial numbered sets.

1-10 PRINT RUN 250 SERIAL #'d SETS
11-20 PRINT RUN 100 SERIAL #'d SETS
*STUDIO 1-10: .75X TO 2X BASIC BAT KING
STUDIO 1-10 PRINT RUN 50 SERIAL #'d SETS
STUDIO 11-20 PRINT RUN 25 SERIAL #'d SETS
STUDIO 11-20 NO PRICING DUE TO SCARCITY
RANDOM INSERTS IN PACKS
1 Scott Rolen 99 DK/250 8.00 20.00
2 Frank Thomas 00 DK/250 8.00 20.00
3 Chipper Jones 01 DK/250 8.00 20.00
4 Ivan Rodriguez 01 DK/250 8.00 20.00
5 Stan Musial 01 ATDK/100 20.00 50.00
6 Nomar Garciaparra 02 DK/250 10.00 25.00
7 Vladimir Guerrero 03 DK/250 8.00 20.00
8 Adam Dunn 03 DK/250 6.00 15.00
9 Lance Berkman 03 DK/250 6.00 15.00
10 Magglio Ordonez 03 DK/250 6.00 15.00
11 Ernie Banks 02 ATDK/50
12 Manny Ramirez 95 DK/100 10.00 25.00
13 Mike Piazza 94 DK/100 15.00 40.00
14 Alex Rodriguez 97 DK/100 15.00 40.00
15 Todd Helton 97 RDK/100 10.00 25.00
16 Andre Dawson 85 DK/100 8.00 20.00
17 Cal Ripken 87 DK/100 40.00 80.00
18 Tony Gwynn 88 DK/100 12.50 30.00
19 Don Mattingly 02 ATDK/100 15.00 40.00
20 Ryne Sandberg 90 DK/100 30.00 60.00

2003 Donruss Diamond Kings Inserts

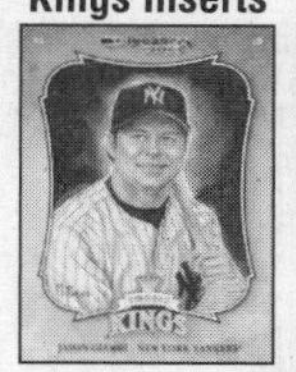

Randomly inserted into packs, these cards parallel the first 20 cards of the regular Donruss set except they are serial numbered to a stated print run of 2500 serial numbered sets. These cards can be easily seperated from the cards inserted into the regular packs as they were printed with a foil stamp.

*STUDIO: .75X TO 2X BASIC DK
STUDIO PRINT RUN 250 SERIAL #'d SETS
RANDOM INSERTS IN PACKS
1 Vladimir Guerrero 4.00 10.00
2 Derek Jeter 8.00 20.00
3 Adam Dunn 4.00 10.00
4 Greg Maddux 5.00 12.00
5 Lance Berkman 4.00 10.00
6 Ichiro Suzuki 6.00 15.00
7 Mike Piazza 5.00 12.00
8 Alex Rodriguez 5.00 12.00
9 Tom Glavine 4.00 10.00
10 Randy Johnson 4.00 10.00
11 Nomar Garciaparra 5.00 12.00
12 Jason Giambi 4.00 10.00
13 Sammy Sosa 4.00 10.00
14 Barry Zito 4.00 10.00
15 Chipper Jones 4.00 10.00
16 Magglio Ordonez 4.00 10.00
17 Larry Walker 4.00 10.00
18 Alfonso Soriano 4.00 10.00
19 Curt Schilling 4.00 10.00
20 Barry Bonds 8.00 20.00

2003 Donruss Elite Series

Randomly inserted into packs, this 15 card set, which is issued on metalized film board, features the elite 15 players in baseball. These cards were issued to a stated print run of 2500 serial numbered sets.

DOMINATORS PR.RUN 25 SERIAL #'d SETS
DOMINATORS NO PRICE DUE TO SCARCITY
RANDOM INSERTS IN PACKS
1 Alex Rodriguez 3.00 8.00
2 Barry Bonds 5.00 12.00
3 Ichiro Suzuki 4.00 10.00
4 Vladimir Guerrero 2.00 5.00
5 Randy Johnson 2.00 5.00
6 Pedro Martinez 1.50 4.00
7 Adam Dunn 1.50 4.00
8 Sammy Sosa 2.00 5.00
9 Jim Edmonds 1.50 4.00
10 Greg Maddux 3.00 8.00
11 Kazuhisa Ishii 1.50 4.00
12 Jason Giambi 1.50 4.00
13 Nomar Garciaparra 3.00 8.00
14 Tom Glavine 1.50 4.00
15 Todd Helton 1.50 4.00

2003 Donruss Gamers

Randomly inserted in DLP (Donruss/Leaf/Playoff) rookie packs, these 50 cards have game-worn memorabilia swatches of the featured players.

STATED PRINT RUN 500 SERIAL #'d SETS
*JSY NUM: .6X TO 1.5X BASIC
JSY NUM PRINT RUN 100 SERIAL #'d SETS
*POSITION: .6X TO 1.5X BASIC
POSITION PRINT RUN 100 SERIAL #'d SETS
PRIME PRINT RUN 25 SERIAL #'d SETS
NO PRIME PRICING DUE TO SCARCITY
REWARDS PRINT RUN 10 SERIAL #'d SETS
NO REWARDS PRICING DUE TO SCARCITY
RANDOM INSERTS IN DLP R/T PACKS
1 Nomar Garciaparra 6.00 15.00
2 Alex Rodriguez 4.00 10.00
3 Mike Piazza 4.00 10.00
4 Greg Maddux 4.00 10.00
5 Roger Clemens 6.00 15.00
6 Sammy Sosa 3.00 8.00
7 Randy Johnson 3.00 8.00
8 Albert Pujols 6.00 15.00
9 Alfonso Soriano 2.00 5.00
10 Chipper Jones 3.00 8.00
11 Mark Prior 3.00 8.00
12 Hideo Nomo 3.00 8.00
13 Adam Dunn 2.00 5.00
14 Juan Gonzalez 2.00 5.00
15 Vladimir Guerrero 3.00 8.00
16 Pedro Martinez 3.00 8.00
17 Jim Thome 3.00 8.00
18 Brandon Webb/200 4.00 10.00
19 Mike Mussina 3.00 8.00
20 Mark Teixeira 3.00 8.00
21 Barry Larkin 3.00 8.00
22 Ivan Rodriguez 3.00 8.00
23 Hank Blalock 2.00 5.00
24 Rafael Palmeiro 3.00 8.00
25 Curt Schilling 2.00 5.00
26 Troy Glaus 2.00 5.00
27 Bernie Williams 3.00 8.00
28 Scott Rolen 3.00 8.00
29 Torii Hunter 2.00 5.00
30 Nick Johnson 2.00 5.00
31 Kazuhisa Ishii 2.00 5.00
32 Shawn Green 2.00 5.00
33 Jeff Bagwell 3.00 8.00
34 Lance Berkman 2.00 5.00
35 Roy Oswalt 2.00 5.00
36 Kerry Wood 2.00 5.00
37 Todd Helton 3.00 8.00
38 Manny Ramirez 3.00 8.00
39 Andruw Jones 3.00 8.00
40 Frank Thomas 3.00 8.00
41 Gary Sheffield 2.00 5.00
42 Magglio Ordonez 2.00 5.00
43 Mike Sweeney 2.00 5.00
44 Carlos Beltran 2.00 5.00
45 Richie Sexson 2.00 5.00
46 Jeff Kent 2.00 5.00
47 Carlos Delgado 2.00 5.00
48 Vernon Wells 2.00 5.00
49 Dontrelle Willis 3.00 8.00
50 Jae Weong Seo 2.00 5.00

2003 Donruss Gamers Autographs

RANDOM INSERTS IN DLP R/T PACKS
PRINT RUNS B/WN 5-50 COPIES PER
NO PRICING ON QTY OF 25 OR LESS
2 Alex Rodriguez/5
3 Mike Piazza/5
4 Greg Maddux/5
5 Roger Clemens/5
7 Randy Johnson/5
8 Albert Pujols/5
9 Alfonso Soriano/5
10 Chipper Jones/10
11 Mark Prior/25
12 Hideo Nomo/5
13 Adam Dunn/25
14 Juan Gonzalez/25
15 Vladimir Guerrero/5
16 Pedro Martinez/5
18 Brandon Webb/25
19 Mike Mussina/5
20 Mark Teixeira/50 15.00 40.00
22 Ivan Rodriguez/5
23 Hank Blalock/50 12.50 30.00
24 Rafael Palmeiro/10
25 Curt Schilling/25
26 Troy Glaus/25
27 Bernie Williams/5
28 Scott Rolen/25
29 Torii Hunter/50 12.50 30.00
30 Nick Johnson/25
31 Kazuhisa Ishii/5
32 Shawn Green/5
33 Jeff Bagwell/5
34 Lance Berkman/10
35 Roy Oswalt/50 12.50 30.00
36 Kerry Wood/25
37 Todd Helton/10
39 Andruw Jones/25
40 Frank Thomas/10
41 Gary Sheffield/25
42 Magglio Ordonez/25
43 Mike Sweeney/50 12.50 30.00
44 Carlos Beltran/25
45 Richie Sexson/25
46 Jeff Kent/12
48 Vernon Wells/30 15.00 40.00
49 Dontrelle Willis/50 20.00 50.00
50 Jae Weong Seo/50 12.50 30.00

2003 Donruss Jersey Kings

Randomly inserted into packs, this set features cards which parallel previously issued Diamond King cards along with a game-worn jersey swatch. Cards were printed to a stated print run of either 100 or 250 serial numbered cards and we have put that information next to the player's name in our checklist.

*STUDIO 1-10: .75X TO 2X BASIC JSY KINGS
STUDIO 1-10 PRINT RUN 50 SERIAL #'d SETS
STUDIO 11-20 PRINT RUN 25 SERIAL #'d SETS
STUDIO 11-20 NO PRICE DUE TO SCARCITY
RANDOM INSERTS IN PACKS
1 Juan Gonzalez 99 DK/250 6.00 15.00
2 Greg Maddux 00 DK/250 8.00 20.00
3 Nomar Garciaparra 01 DK/250 10.00 25.00
4 Troy Glaus 01 DK/250 6.00 15.00
5 Reggie Jackson 01 ATDK/100 10.00 25.00
6 Alex Rodriguez 01 DK/250 10.00 25.00
7 Alfonso Soriano 03 DK/250 6.00 15.00
8 Curt Schilling 03 DK/250 6.00 15.00
9 Vladimir Guerrero 03 DK/250 6.00 15.00
10 Adam Dunn 03 DK/250 6.00 15.00
11 Mark Grace 88 DK/100 10.00 25.00
12 Roger Clemens 90 DK/100 15.00 40.00
13 Jeff Bagwell 91 DK/100 10.00 25.00
14 Tom Glavine 92 DK/100 10.00 25.00
15 Mike Piazza 94 DK/100 12.50 30.00
16 Rod Carew 82 DK/100 10.00 25.00
17 Rickey Henderson 82 DK/100 10.00 25.00
18 Mike Schmidt 83 DK/100 15.00 40.00
19 Cal Ripken 85 DK/100 40.00 80.00
20 Dale Murphy 86 DK/100 10.00 25.00

2003 Donruss Longball Leaders

Randomly inserted into packs, these 10 cards, honoring some of the leading home run hitters, were printed on metalized film board and were issued to a stated print run of 1000 serial numbered sets.

*SEASON SUM: 1.5X TO 4X BASIC LL
SEASON PRINT RUN BASED ON 02 HR'S
RANDOM INSERTS IN PACKS
1 Alex Rodriguez 5.00 12.00
2 Alfonso Soriano 2.00 5.00
3 Rafael Palmeiro 2.00 5.00
4 Jim Thome 2.00 5.00
5 Jason Giambi 2.00 5.00
6 Sammy Sosa 3.00 8.00
7 Barry Bonds 8.00 20.00
8 Lance Berkman 2.00 5.00
9 Shawn Green 2.00 5.00
10 Vladimir Guerrero 3.00 8.00

2003 Donruss Production Line

Randomly inserted into packs, these 30 cards feature players who excel in either on base percentage, slugging percentage, batting average or total bases. Each card is printed on metalized film board and was issued to that player's statistical information.

*DIE CUT OPS: 1.25X TO 3X BASIC PL
*DIE CUT OBP/SLG: 1X TO 2.5X BASIC PL
*DIE CUT AVG/TB: .75X TO 2X BASIC PL
DIE CUT PRINT RUN 100 SERIAL #'d SETS
RANDOM INSERTS IN PACKS
1 Alex Rodriguez OPS/1015 4.00 10.00
2 Jim Thome OPS/1122 1.50 4.00
3 Lance Berkman OPS/982 1.00 2.50

4 Barry Bonds OPS/1381 6.00 15.00
5 Sammy Sosa OPS/993 2.50 6.00
6 Vladimir Guerrero OPS/1010 2.50 6.00
7 Barry Bonds OBP/582 8.00 20.00
8 Jason Giambi OBP/435 1.25 3.00
9 Vladimir Guerrero OBP/417 3.00 8.00
10 Adam Dunn OBP/400 1.25 3.00
11 Chipper Jones OBP/435 3.00 8.00
12 Todd Helton OBP/429 2.00 5.00
13 Rafael Palmeiro SLG/571 2.00 5.00
14 Sammy Sosa SLG/594 3.00 8.00
15 Alex Rodriguez SLG/623 5.00 12.00
16 Larry Walker SLG/602 1.25 3.00
17 Lance Berkman SLG/578 1.25 3.00
18 Alfonso Soriano SLG/547 1.25 3.00
19 Ichiro Suzuki AVG/321 6.00 15.00
20 Mike Sweeney AVG/340 1.50 4.00
21 Manny Ramirez AVG/349 2.50 6.00
22 Larry Walker AVG/338 1.50 4.00
23 Barry Bonds AVG/370 10.00 25.00
24 Jim Edmonds AVG/311 1.50 4.00
25 Alfonso Soriano TB/381 1.50 4.00
26 Jason Giambi TB/335 1.50 4.00
27 Miguel Tejada TB/336 1.50 4.00
28 Brian Giles TB/309 1.50 4.00
29 Vladimir Guerrero TB/364 4.00 10.00
30 Pat Burrell TB/319 1.50 4.00

2003 Donruss Timber and Threads

Randomly inserted into packs, these 50 cards feature either a game-used jersey swatch or a game-use bat chip of the featured player. Since these cards have different stated print runs we have put that information next to the player's name in our checklist.

1 Al Kaline Bat/125 10.00 25.00
2 Alex Rodriguez Bat/350 8.00 20.00
3 Carlos Delgado Bat/250 4.00 10.00
4 Cliff Floyd Bat/250 4.00 10.00
5 Eddie Mathews Bat/125 10.00 25.00
6 Edgar Martinez Bat/125 10.00 25.00
7 Ernie Banks Bat/50 15.00 40.00
8 Ivan Rodriguez Bat/125 10.00 25.00
9 J.D. Drew Bat/125 6.00 15.00
10 Jorge Posada Bat/300 6.00 15.00
11 Lou Brock Bat/125 10.00 25.00
12 Mike Piazza Bat/125 10.00 25.00
13 Mike Schmidt Bat/125 15.00 40.00
14 Reggie Jackson Bat/125 10.00 25.00
15 Rickey Henderson Bat/125 10.00 25.00
16 Robin Yount Bat/125 10.00 25.00
17 Rod Carew Bat/125 10.00 25.00
18 Scott Rolen Bat/125 10.00 25.00
19 Shawn Green Bat/200 4.00 10.00
20 Willie Stargell Bat/125 10.00 25.00
21 Alex Rodriguez Jsy/175 12.50 30.00
22 Andruw Jones Jsy/275 6.00 15.00
23 Brooks Robinson Jsy/150 10.00 25.00
24 Chipper Jones Jsy/150 10.00 25.00
25 Greg Maddux Jsy/175 8.00 20.00
26 Hideo Nomo Jsy/300 15.00 40.00
27 Ivan Rodriguez Jsy/225 6.00 15.00
28 Jack Morris Jsy/150 6.00 15.00
29 J.D. Drew Jsy/150 6.00 15.00
30 Jeff Bagwell Jsy/500 6.00 15.00
31 Jim Thome Jsy/200 6.00 15.00
32 John Smoltz Jsy/175 6.00 15.00
33 John Olerud Jsy/450 4.00 10.00
34 Kerry Wood Jsy/200 4.00 10.00
35 Harmon Killebrew Jsy/50
36 Larry Walker Jsy/500 4.00 10.00
37 Magglio Ordonez Jsy/150 6.00 15.00
38 Manny Ramirez Jsy/500 6.00 15.00
39 Mike Piazza Jsy/300 6.00 15.00
40 Mike Sweeney Jsy/200 4.00 10.00
41 Nomar Garciaparra Jsy/200 10.00 25.00
42 Paul Konerko Jsy/500 4.00 10.00
43 Pedro Martinez Jsy/175 6.00 15.00
44 Randy Johnson Jsy/175 6.00 15.00
45 Roger Clemens Jsy/350 10.00 25.00
46 Shawn Green Jsy/250 4.00 10.00
47 Todd Helton Jsy/175 6.00 15.00
48 Tom Glavine Jsy/225 6.00 15.00
49 Tony Gwynn Jsy/150 10.00 25.00
50 Vladimir Guerrero Jsy/450 6.00 15.00

2003 Donruss Rookies

This 65-card set was released in December, 2003. This set was issued as part of the DLP (Donruss/Leaf/Playoff) Rookie Update product in which many of the products issued earlier in the year had Rookie Cards added. Each pack contained eight cards and were sold at an $5 SRP with 24 packs in a box and 12 boxes in a case. In this Rookies set, cards 1-60 feature Rookie Cards while cards numbered 61-65 feature some of the most important players who changed teams during the 2003 season. As mentioned cards from the following DLP products were inserted into these packs: Donruss, Donruss Champions, Donruss Classics, Donruss Diamond Kings, Donruss Elite, Donruss Signature, Donruss Team Heroes, Leaf, Leaf Certified Materials, Leaf Limited, Playoff Absolute Memorabilia, Playoff Prestige and Studio.

COMPLETE SET (65) 8.00 20.00
COMMON CARD (1-65) .07 .20
COMMON RC .08 .25
1 Jeremy Bonderman RC .75 2.00
2 Adam Loewen RC .20 .50
3 Dan Haren RC .20 .50
4 Jose Contreras RC .20 .50
5 Hideki Matsui RC .75 2.00
6 Arnie Munoz RC .08 .25
7 Miguel Cabrera .20 .50
8 Andrew Brown RC .15 .40
9 Josh Hall RC .08 .25
10 Josh Stewart RC .08 .25
11 Clint Barmes RC .30 .75
12 Luis Ayala RC .08 .25
13 Brandon Webb RC .60 1.50
14 Greg Aquino RC .08 .25
15 Chien-Ming Wang RC 2.00 5.00
16 Rickie Weeks RC .60 1.50
17 Edgar Gonzalez RC .08 .25
18 Dontrelle Willis .20 .50
19 Bo Hart RC .08 .25
20 Rosman Garcia RC .08 .25
21 Jeremy Griffiths RC .08 .25
22 Craig Brazell RC .08 .25
23 Daniel Cabrera RC .20 .50
24 Fernando Cabrera RC .08 .25
25 Termel Sledge RC .08 .25
26 Ramon Nivar RC .08 .25
27 Rob Hammock RC .08 .25
28 Francisco Rosario RC .08 .25
29 Cory Stewart RC .08 .25
30 Felix Sanchez RC .08 .25
31 Jorge Cordova RC .08 .25
32 Rocco Baldelli .07 .20
33 Beau Kemp RC .08 .25
34 Mike Nakamura RC .08 .25
35 Rett Johnson RC .08 .25
36 Guillermo Quiroz RC .08 .25
37 Hong-Chih Kuo RC .75 2.00
38 Ian Ferguson RC .08 .25
39 Franklin Perez RC .08 .25
40 Tim Olson RC .08 .25
41 Jerome Williams .07 .20
42 Rich Fischer RC .08 .25
43 Phil Seibel RC .08 .25
44 Aaron Looper RC .08 .25
45 Jae Weong Seo .07 .20
46 Chad Gaudin RC .08 .25
47 Matt Kata RC .08 .25
48 Ryan Wagner RC .08 .25
49 Michel Hernandez RC .08 .25
50 Diegomar Markwell RC .08 .25
51 Doug Waechter RC .15 .40
52 Mike Nicolas RC .08 .25
53 Prentice Redman RC .08 .25
54 Shane Bazzell RC .08 .25
55 Delmon Young RC 1.25 3.00
56 Brian Stokes RC .08 .25
57 Matt Bruback RC .08 .25
58 Nook Logan RC .15 .40
59 Oscar Villarreal RC .08 .25
60 Pete LaForest RC .08 .25
61 Shea Hillenbrand .07 .20
62 Aramis Ramirez .07 .20
63 Aaron Boone .07 .20
64 Roberto Alomar .10 .30
65 Rickey Henderson .20 .50

2003 Donruss Rookies Autographs

RANDOM INSERTS IN DLP R/T PACKS
PRINT RUNS B/WN 10-1000 COPIES PER
NO PRICING ON QTY OF 25 OR LESS
1 Jeremy Bonderman/50 20.00 50.00
2 Adam Loewen/500 6.00 15.00
3 Dan Haren/100 10.00 25.00
4 Jose Contreras/100 12.50 30.00
6 Arnie Munoz/584 4.00 10.00
7 Miguel Cabrera/50 20.00 50.00
8 Andrew Brown/584 6.00 15.00
9 Josh Hall/1000 4.00 10.00
10 Josh Stewart/300 4.00 10.00
11 Clint Barmes/129 6.00 15.00
12 Luis Ayala/1000 4.00 10.00
13 Brandon Webb/100 30.00 60.00
14 Greg Aquino/1000 4.00 10.00
15 Chien-Ming Wang/100 150.00 250.00
16 Rickie Weeks/10
17 Edgar Gonzalez/400 4.00 10.00
18 Dontrelle Willis/25
19 Bo Hart/150 4.00 10.00
20 Rosman Garcia/250 4.00 10.00
21 Jeremy Griffiths/812 4.00 10.00
22 Craig Brazell/205 4.00 10.00
23 Daniel Cabrera/383 10.00 25.00
24 Fernando Cabrera/1000 4.00 10.00
25 Termel Sledge/250 4.00 10.00
26 Ramon Nivar/100 4.00 10.00
27 Rob Hammock/201 4.00 10.00
28 Francisco Rosario/25
29 Cory Stewart/1000 4.00 10.00
30 Felix Sanchez/1000 4.00 10.00
31 Jorge Cordova/1000 4.00 10.00
32 Rocco Baldelli/25
33 Beau Kemp/1000 4.00 10.00
34 Mike Nakamura/1000 4.00 10.00
35 Rett Johnson/1000 4.00 10.00
36 Guillermo Quiroz/90 4.00 10.00
37 Hong-Chih Kuo/50 100.00 200.00
38 Ian Ferguson/1000 4.00 10.00
39 Franklin Perez/1000 4.00 10.00
40 Tim Olson/150 4.00 10.00
41 Jerome Williams/50 6.00 15.00
42 Rich Fischer/734 4.00 10.00
43 Phil Seibel/1000 4.00 10.00
44 Aaron Looper/513 4.00 10.00
45 Jae Weong Seo/50 10.00 25.00
46 Chad Gaudin/19
47 Matt Kata/203 4.00 10.00
48 Ryan Wagner/100 4.00 10.00
49 Michel Hernandez/41
50 Diegomar Markwell/1000 4.00 10.00
51 Doug Waechter/583 6.00 15.00
52 Mike Nicolas/1000 4.00 10.00
53 Prentice Redman/425 4.00 10.00
54 Shane Bazzell/1000 4.00 10.00
55 Delmon Young/75 100.00 200.00
56 Brian Stokes/1000 4.00 10.00
57 Matt Bruback/513 4.00 10.00
58 Nook Logan/150 6.00 15.00
59 Oscar Villarreal/150 6.00 15.00
60 Pete LaForest/250 4.00 10.00

2003 Donruss Rookies Stat Line Career

*SLC P/R b/wn 201+: 4X TO 10X
*SLC P/R b/wn 121-200: 5X TO 12X
*SLC P/R b/wn 81-120: 6X TO 15X
*SLC P/R b/wn 66-80: 8X TO 20X
*SLC P/R b/wn 51-65: 8X TO 20X
*SLC RC's P/R b/wn 201+: 4X TO 10X
*SLC RC's P/R b/wn 121-200: 4X TO 10X
*SLC RC's P/R b/wn 81-120: 4X TO 10X
*SLC RC's P/R b/wn 66-80: 5X TO 12X
*SLC RC's P/R b/wn 51-65: 5X TO 12X
*SLC RC's P/R b/wn 36-50: 6X TO 15X
*SLC RC's P/R b/wn 26-35: 8X TO 20X
RANDOM INSERTS IN DLP R/T PACKS
PRINT RUNS B/WN 1-245 COPIES PER
NO PRICING ON QTY OF 25 OR LESS
15 Chien-Ming Wang/212 30.00 60.00
37 Hong-Chih Kuo/45 30.00 60.00

2003 Donruss Rookies Stat Line Season

*SLS P/R b/wn 201+: 4X TO 10X
*SLS P/R b/wn 121-200: 5X TO 12X
*SLS P/R b/wn 66-80: 8X TO 20X
*SLS P/R b/wn 36-50: 10X TO 25X
*SLS P/R b/wn 26-35: 12.5X TO 30X
*SLS RC's P/R b/wn 81-120: 4X TO 10X
*SLS RC's P/R b/wn 66-80: 5X TO 12X
*SLS RC's P/R b/wn 51-65: 5X TO 12X
*SLS RC's P/R b/wn 36-50: 6X TO 15X
*SLS RC's P/R b/wn 26-35: 8X TO 20X
RANDOM INSERTS IN PACKS
PRINT RUNS B/WN 1-130 COPIES PER
NO PRICING ON QTY OF 25 OR LESS
15 Chien-Ming Wang/64 50.00 100.00

2003 Donruss Rookies Recollection Autographs

RANDOM INSERTS IN DLP R/T PACKS
PRINT RUNS B/WN 1-75 COPIES PER
NO PRICING ON QTY OF 5 OR LESS
1 Sandy Alomar Jr. 89 DR/2
2 Sandy Alomar Jr. 90 Black/5
3 Sandy Alomar Jr. 90 Blue/5
4 Jay Buhner 88 DR/5
5 Jose Canseco 86/1
6 Sid Fernandez 84/5
7 Jack McDowell 88/75 10.00 25.00
8 Paul O'Neill 86/5
9 Gary Sheffield 89/5
10 Ruben Sierra 86 DR/1
11 J.T. Snow 93/5
12 Robby Thompson 86 DR/5
13 Matt Williams 87 DR/5

2004 Donruss

This 400-card standard-size set was released in November, 2003. This set was issued in 10 card packs with an $1.99 SRP and those cards came 24 packs to a box and 16 boxes to a case. Please note the following subsets were issued as part of this product: Diamond King (1-25); Rated Rookies (26-70) and Team Checklists (371-400).

COMPLETE SET (400) 75.00 150.00
COMP.SET w/o SP's (300) 10.00 25.00
COMMON CARD (71-370) .10 .30
COMMON CARD (1-25/371-400) .75 2.00
COMMON CARD (26-70) .75 2.00
1-70/370-400 RANDOM INSERTS IN PACKS
1 Derek Jeter DK 1.50 4.00
2 Greg Maddux DK 1.25 3.00
3 Albert Pujols DK 1.50 4.00
4 Ichiro Suzuki DK 1.50 4.00
5 Alex Rodriguez DK 1.25 3.00
6 Roger Clemens DK 1.50 4.00
7 Andruw Jones DK .75 2.00
8 Barry Bonds DK 2.00 5.00
9 Jeff Bagwell DK .75 2.00
10 Randy Johnson DK .75 2.00
11 Scott Rolen DK .75 2.00
12 Lance Berkman DK .75 2.00
13 Barry Zito DK .75 2.00
14 Manny Ramirez DK .75 2.00
15 Carlos Delgado DK .75 2.00
16 Alfonso Soriano DK .75 2.00
17 Todd Helton DK .75 2.00
18 Mike Mussina DK .75 2.00
19 Austin Kearns DK .75 2.00
20 Nomar Garciaparra DK 1.25 3.00
21 Chipper Jones DK .75 2.00
22 Mark Prior DK .75 2.00
23 Jim Thome DK .75 2.00
24 Vladimir Guerrero DK .75 2.00
25 Pedro Martinez DK .75 2.00
26 Sergio Mitre RR .75 2.00
27 Adam Loewen RR .75 2.00
28 Alfredo Gonzalez RR .75 2.00
29 Miguel Ojeda RR .75 2.00
30 Rosman Garcia RR .75 2.00
31 Arnie Munoz RR .75 2.00
32 Andrew Brown RR .75 2.00
33 Josh Hall RR .75 2.00
34 Josh Stewart RR .75 2.00
35 Clint Barmes RR 1.25 3.00
36 Brandon Webb RR .75 2.00
37 Chien-Ming Wang RR 3.00 8.00
38 Edgar Gonzalez RR .75 2.00
39 Alejandro Machado RR .75 2.00
40 Jeremy Griffiths RR .75 2.00
41 Craig Brazell RR .75 2.00
42 Daniel Cabrera RR .75 2.00
43 Fernando Cabrera RR .75 2.00
44 Termel Sledge RR .75 2.00
45 Rob Hammock RR .75 2.00
46 Francisco Rosario RR .75 2.00
47 Francisco Cruceta RR .75 2.00
48 Rett Johnson RR .75 2.00
49 Guillermo Quiroz RR .75 2.00
50 Hong-Chih Kuo RR 1.25 3.00
51 Ian Ferguson RR .75 2.00
52 Tim Olson RR .75 2.00
53 Todd Wellemeyer RR .75 2.00
54 Rich Fischer RR .75 2.00
55 Phil Seibel RR .75 2.00
56 Joe Valentine RR .75 2.00
57 Matt Kata RR .75 2.00
58 Michael Hessman RR .75 2.00
59 Michel Hernandez RR .75 2.00
60 Doug Waechter RR .75 2.00
61 Prentice Redman RR .75 2.00
62 Nook Logan RR .75 2.00
63 Oscar Villarreal RR .75 2.00
64 Pete LaForest RR .75 2.00
65 Matt Bruback RR .75 2.00
66 Dan Haren RR .75 2.00
67 Greg Aquino RR .75 2.00
68 Lew Ford RR .75 2.00
69 Jeff Duncan RR .75 2.00
70 Ryan Wagner RR .75 2.00
71 Bengie Molina .10 .30
72 Brad Fullmer .10 .30
73 Darin Erstad .10 .30
74 David Eckstein .10 .30
75 Garret Anderson .10 .30
76 Jarrod Washburn .10 .30
77 Kevin Appier .10 .30
78 Scott Spiezio .10 .30
79 Tim Salmon .20 .50
80 Troy Glaus .10 .30
81 Troy Percival .10 .30
82 Jason Johnson .10 .30
83 Jay Gibbons .10 .30
84 Melvin Mora .10 .30
85 Sidney Ponson .10 .30
86 Tony Batista .10 .30
87 Bill Mueller .10 .30
88 Byung-Hyun Kim .10 .30
89 David Ortiz .30 .75
90 Derek Lowe .10 .30
91 Johnny Damon .20 .50
92 Casey Fossum .10 .30
93 Manny Ramirez .20 .50
94 Nomar Garciaparra .50 1.25
95 Pedro Martinez .20 .50
96 Todd Walker .10 .30
97 Trot Nixon .10 .30
98 Bartolo Colon .10 .30
99 Carlos Lee .10 .30
100 D'Angelo Jimenez .10 .30
101 Esteban Loaiza .10 .30
102 Frank Thomas .30 .75
103 Joe Crede .10 .30
104 Jose Valentin .10 .30
105 Magglio Ordonez .10 .30
106 Mark Buehrle .10 .30
107 Paul Konerko .10 .30
108 Brandon Phillips .10 .30
109 C.C Sabathia .10 .30
110 Ellis Burks .10 .30
111 Jeremy Guthrie .10 .30
112 Josh Bard .10 .30
113 Matt Lawton .10 .30
114 Milton Bradley .10 .30
115 Omar Vizquel .20 .50
116 Travis Hafner .10 .30
117 Bobby Higginson .10 .30
118 Carlos Pena .10 .30
119 Dmitri Young .10 .30
120 Eric Munson .10 .30
121 Jeremy Bonderman .10 .30
122 Nate Cornejo .10 .30
123 Omar Infante .10 .30
124 Ramon Santiago .10 .30
125 Angel Berroa .10 .30
126 Carlos Beltran .10 .30
127 Desi Relaford .10 .30
128 Jeremy Affeldt .10 .30
129 Joe Randa .10 .30
130 Ken Harvey .10 .30
131 Mike MacDougal .10 .30
132 Michael Tucker .10 .30
133 Mike Sweeney .10 .30
134 Raul Ibanez .10 .30
135 Runelvys Hernandez .10 .30
136 A.J. Pierzynski .10 .30
137 Brad Radke .10 .30
138 Corey Koskie .10 .30
139 Cristian Guzman .10 .30
140 Doug Mientkiewicz .10 .30
141 Dustan Mohr .10 .30
142 Jacque Jones .10 .30
143 Kenny Rogers .10 .30
144 Bobby Kielty .10 .30
145 Kyle Lohse .10 .30
146 Luis Rivas .10 .30
147 Torii Hunter .10 .30
148 Alfonso Soriano .10 .30
149 Andy Pettitte .20 .50
150 Bernie Williams .20 .50
151 David Wells .10 .30
152 Derek Jeter .60 1.50
153 Hideki Matsui .50 1.25
154 Jason Giambi .10 .30
155 Jorge Posada .20 .50
156 Jose Contreras .10 .30
157 Mike Mussina .20 .50
158 Nick Johnson .10 .30
159 Robin Ventura .10 .30
160 Roger Clemens .60 1.50
161 Barry Zito .10 .30
162 Chris Singleton .10 .30
163 Eric Byrnes .10 .30
164 Eric Chavez .10 .30
165 Erubiel Durazo .10 .30
166 Keith Foulke .10 .30
167 Mark Ellis .10 .30
168 Miguel Tejada .10 .30
169 Mark Mulder .10 .30
170 Ramon Hernandez .10 .30
171 Ted Lilly .10 .30
172 Terrence Long .10 .30
173 Tim Hudson .10 .30
174 Bret Boone .10 .30
175 Carlos Guillen .10 .30
176 Dan Wilson .10 .30
177 Edgar Martinez .20 .50
178 Freddy Garcia .10 .30
179 Gil Meche .10 .30
180 Ichiro Suzuki .60 1.50
181 Jamie Moyer .10 .30
182 Joel Pineiro .10 .30
183 John Olerud .10 .30
184 Mike Cameron .10 .30
185 Randy Winn .10 .30
186 Ryan Franklin .10 .30
187 Kazuhiro Sasaki .10 .30
188 Aubrey Huff .10 .30
189 Carl Crawford .10 .30
190 Joe Kennedy .10 .30
191 Marlon Anderson .10 .30
192 Rey Ordonez .10 .30
193 Rocco Baldelli .10 .30
194 Toby Hall .10 .30
195 Travis Lee .10 .30
196 Alex Rodriguez .50 1.25
197 Carl Everett .10 .30
198 Chan Ho Park .10 .30
199 Einar Diaz .10 .30
200 Hank Blalock .10 .30
201 Ismael Valdes .10 .30
202 Juan Gonzalez .10 .30
203 Mark Teixeira .20 .50
204 Mike Young .10 .30
205 Rafael Palmeiro .20 .50
206 Carlos Delgado .10 .30
207 Kelvim Escobar .10 .30
208 Eric Hinske .10 .30
209 Frank Catalanotto .10 .30
210 Josh Phelps .10 .30
211 Orlando Hudson .10 .30
212 Roy Halladay .10 .30
213 Shannon Stewart .10 .30
214 Vernon Wells .10 .30
215 Carlos Baerga .10 .30
216 Curt Schilling .10 .30
217 Junior Spivey .10 .30
218 Luis Gonzalez .10 .30
219 Lyle Overbay .10 .30
220 Mark Grace .20 .50
221 Matt Williams .10 .30
222 Randy Johnson .30 .75
223 Shea Hillenbrand .10 .30
224 Steve Finley .10 .30
225 Andruw Jones .20 .50
226 Chipper Jones .30 .75
227 Gary Sheffield .10 .30
228 Greg Maddux .50 1.25
229 Javy Lopez .10 .30
230 John Smoltz .20 .50
231 Marcus Giles .10 .30
232 Mike Hampton .10 .30
233 Rafael Furcal .10 .30
234 Robert Fick .10 .30
235 Russ Ortiz .10 .30
236 Alex Gonzalez .10 .30
237 Carlos Zambrano .10 .30
238 Corey Patterson .10 .30
239 Hee Seop Choi .10 .30
240 Kerry Wood .10 .30
241 Mark Bellhorn .10 .30
242 Mark Prior .20 .50
243 Moises Alou .10 .30
244 Sammy Sosa .30 .75
245 Aaron Boone .10 .30
246 Adam Dunn .10 .30
247 Austin Kearns .10 .30
248 Barry Larkin .20 .50
249 Felipe Lopez .10 .30
250 Jose Guillen .10 .30
251 Ken Griffey Jr. .50 1.25
252 Jason LaRue .10 .30
253 Scott Williamson .10 .30
254 Sean Casey .10 .30
255 Shawn Chacon .10 .30
256 Chris Stynes .10 .30
257 Jason Jennings .10 .30
258 Jay Payton .10 .30
259 Jose Hernandez .10 .30
260 Larry Walker .10 .30
261 Preston Wilson .10 .30
262 Ronnie Belliard .10 .30
263 Todd Helton .20 .50
264 A.J. Burnett .10 .30
265 Alex Gonzalez .10 .30
266 Brad Penny .10 .30
267 Derrek Lee .20 .50
268 Ivan Rodriguez .20 .50
269 Josh Beckett .10 .30
270 Juan Encarnacion .10 .30
271 Juan Pierre .10 .30
272 Luis Castillo .10 .30
273 Mike Lowell .10 .30
274 Todd Hollandsworth .10 .30
275 Billy Wagner .10 .30
276 Brad Ausmus .10 .30
277 Craig Biggio .20 .50
278 Jeff Bagwell .20 .50
279 Jeff Kent .10 .30
280 Lance Berkman .10 .30
281 Richard Hidalgo .10 .30
282 Roy Oswalt .10 .30
283 Wade Miller .10 .30
284 Adrian Beltre .10 .30
285 Brian Jordan .10 .30
286 Cesar Izturis .10 .30
287 Dave Roberts .10 .30
288 Eric Gagne .10 .30
289 Fred McGriff .20 .50
290 Hideo Nomo .30 .75
291 Kazuhisa Ishii .10 .30
292 Kevin Brown .10 .30
293 Paul Lo Duca .10 .30
294 Shawn Green .10 .30
295 Ben Sheets .10 .30
296 Geoff Jenkins .10 .30
297 Rey Sanchez .10 .30
298 Richie Sexson .10 .30
299 Wes Helms .10 .30
300 Brad Wilkerson .10 .30
301 Claudio Vargas .10 .30
302 Endy Chavez .10 .30
303 Fernando Tatis .10 .30
304 Javier Vazquez .10 .30
305 Jose Vidro .10 .30
306 Michael Barrett .10 .30
307 Orlando Cabrera .10 .30
308 Tony Armas Jr. .10 .30
309 Vladimir Guerrero .30 .75
310 Zach Day .10 .30
311 Al Leiter .10 .30
312 Cliff Floyd .10 .30
313 Jae Weong Seo .10 .30
314 Jeromy Burnitz .10 .30
315 Mike Piazza .50 1.25
316 Mo Vaughn .10 .30
317 Roberto Alomar .20 .50
318 Roger Cedeno .10 .30
319 Tom Glavine .20 .50
320 Jose Reyes .10 .30
321 Bobby Abreu .10 .30
322 Brett Myers .10 .30
323 David Bell .10 .30
324 Jim Thome .20 .50
325 Jimmy Rollins .10 .30
326 Kevin Millwood .10 .30
327 Marlon Byrd .10 .30
328 Mike Lieberthal .10 .30
329 Pat Burrell .10 .30
330 Randy Wolf .10 .30
331 Aramis Ramirez .10 .30
332 Brian Giles .10 .30
333 Jason Kendall .10 .30
334 Kenny Lofton .10 .30
335 Kip Wells .10 .30
336 Kris Benson .10 .30
337 Randall Simon .10 .30
338 Reggie Sanders .10 .30
339 Albert Pujols .60 1.50
340 Edgar Renteria .10 .30
341 Fernando Vina .10 .30
342 J.D. Drew .10 .30
343 Jim Edmonds .10 .30
344 Matt Morris .10 .30
345 Mike Matheny .10 .30
346 Scott Rolen .20 .50
347 Tino Martinez .20 .50
348 Woody Williams .10 .30
349 Brian Lawrence .10 .30
350 Mark Kotsay .10 .30
351 Mark Loretta .10 .30
352 Ramon Vazquez .10 .30
353 Rondell White .10 .30
354 Ryan Klesko .10 .30
355 Sean Burroughs .10 .30
356 Trevor Hoffman .10 .30
357 Xavier Nady .10 .30
358 Andres Galarraga .10 .30
359 Barry Bonds .75 2.00
360 Benito Santiago .10 .30
361 Deivi Cruz .10 .30
362 Edgardo Alfonzo .10 .30
363 J.T. Snow .10 .30
364 Jason Schmidt .10 .30
365 Kirk Rueter .10 .30
366 Kurt Ainsworth .10 .30
367 Marquis Grissom .10 .30
368 Ray Durham .10 .30
369 Rich Aurilia .10 .30
370 Tim Worrell .10 .30
371 Troy Glaus TC .75 2.00
372 Melvin Mora TC .75 2.00
373 Nomar Garciaparra TC 1.25 3.00
374 Magglio Ordonez TC .75 2.00
375 Omar Vizquel TC .75 2.00
376 Dmitri Young TC .75 2.00
377 Mike Sweeney TC .75 2.00
378 Torii Hunter TC .75 2.00
379 Derek Jeter TC 1.50 4.00

380 Barry Zito TC .75 2.00
381 Ichiro Suzuki TC 1.50 4.00
382 Rocco Baldelli TC .75 2.00
383 Alex Rodriguez TC 1.25 3.00
384 Carlos Delgado TC .75 2.00
385 Randy Johnson TC .75 2.00
386 Greg Maddux TC 1.25 3.00
387 Sammy Sosa TC .75 2.00
388 Ken Griffey Jr. TC 1.25 3.00
389 Todd Helton TC .75 2.00
390 Ivan Rodriguez TC .75 2.00
391 Jeff Bagwell TC .75 2.00
392 Hideo Nomo TC .75 2.00
393 Richie Sexson TC .75 2.00
394 Vladimir Guerrero TC .75 2.00
395 Mike Piazza TC 1.25 3.00
396 Jim Thome TC .75 2.00
397 Jason Kendall TC .75 2.00
398 Albert Pujols TC 1.50 4.00
399 Ryan Klesko TC .75 2.00
400 Barry Bonds TC 2.00 5.00

2004 Donruss Autographs

RANDOM INSERTS IN PACKS
#'d CARD PRINTS B/WN 5-141 COPIES PER
NO PRICING ON QTY OF 12 OR LESS
51 Ian Ferguson 4.00 10.00
73 Darin Erstad/5
106 Mark Buehrle/141 10.00 25.00
112 Josh Bard 4.00 10.00
123 Omar Infante 4.00 10.00
172 Terrence Long 4.00 10.00
188 Aubrey Huff/143 6.00 15.00
194 Toby Hall 4.00 10.00
217 Junior Spivey/132 4.00 10.00
234 Robert Fick 4.00 10.00
312 Cliff Floyd/12
349 Brian Lawrence 4.00 10.00

2004 Donruss Press Proofs Black

RANDOM INSERTS IN PACKS
STATED PRINT RUN 10 SERIAL #'d SETS
NO PRICING DUE TO SCARCITY

2004 Donruss Press Proofs Blue

*PP BLUE 71-370: 4X TO 10X BASIC
*PP BLUE 1-25/371-400: 1.5X TO 4X BASIC
*PP BLUE 26-70: .75X TO 2X BASIC
RANDOM INSERTS IN RETAIL PACKS
STATED PRINT RUN 100 SERIAL #'d SETS

2004 Donruss Press Proofs Gold

RANDOM INSERTS IN RETAIL PACKS
STATED PRINT RUN 25 SERIAL #'d SETS
NO PRICING DUE TO SCARCITY

2004 Donruss Press Proofs Red

*PP RED 71-370: 2.5X TO 6X BASIC
*PP RED 1-25/371-400: 1X TO 2.5X BASIC
*PP RED 26-70: .5X TO 1.2X BASIC
STATED ODDS 1:12 RETAIL

2004 Donruss Stat Line Career

*71-370 p/r 200-443 2.5X TO 6X
*71-370 p/r 121-200: 3X TO 8X
*71-370 p/r 81-120: 4X TO 10X
*71-370 p/r 66-80: 5X TO 12X
*71-370 p/r 51-65: 5X TO 12X
*71-370 p/r 36-50: 6X TO 15X
*71-370 p/r 26-35: 8X TO 20X
*1-25/371-400 p/r 200-500: 1X TO 2.5X
*1-25/371-400 p/r 121-200: 1.25X TO 3X
*1-25/371-400 p/r 81-120: 1.5X TO 4X
*1-25/371-400 p/r 66-80: 2X TO 5X
*1-25/371-400 p/r 51-65: 2X TO 5X
*1-25/371-400 p/r 36-50: 2.5X TO 6X
*1-25/371-400 p/r 26-35: 3X TO 8X
*26-70 p/r 200-491: .5X TO 1.2X
*26-70 p/r 121-200: .6X TO 1.5X
*26-70 p/r 81-120: .75X TO 2X
*26-70 p/r 66-80: 1X TO 2.5X
*26-70 p/r 51-65: 1X TO 2.5X
*26-70 p/r 36-50: 1.25X TO 3X
*26-70 p/r 26-35: 1.5X TO 4X
RANDOM INSERTS IN PACKS
PRINT RUNS B/WN 6-500 COPIES PER
NO PRICING ON QTY OF 25 OR LESS

2004 Donruss Stat Line Season

*71-370 p/r 121-193: 3X TO 8X
*71-370 p/r 81-120: 4X TO 10X
*71-370 p/r 66-80: 5X TO 12X
*71-370 p/r 51-65: 5X TO 12X
*71-370 p/r 36-50: 6X TO 15X
*71-370 p/r 26-35: 8X TO 20X
*1-25/371-400 p/r 201-225:1X TO 2.5X
*1-25/371-400 p/r 121-200: 1.25X TO 3X
*1-25/371-400 p/r 81-120: 1.5X TO 4X
*1-25/371-400 p/r 66-80: 2X TO 5X
*1-25/371-400 p/r 51-65: 2X TO 5X
*1-25/371-400 p/r 36-50: 2.5X TO 6X
*1-25/371-400 p/r 26-35: 3X TO 8X
*26-70 p/r 201-261: .5X TO 1.2X
*26-70 p/r 121-200: .6X TO 1.5X
*26-70 p/r 81-120: .75X TO 2X
*26-70 p/r 66-80: 1X TO 2.5X
*26-70 p/r 51-65: 1X TO 2.5X
*26-70 p/r 36-50: 1.25X TO 3X
*26-70 p/r 26-35: 1.5X TO 4X
RANDOM INSERTS IN PACKS
PRINT RUNS B/WN 1-261 COPIES PER
NO PRICING ON QTY OF 25 OR LESS

2004 Donruss All-Stars American League

STATED PRINT RUN 1000 SERIAL #'d SETS
*BLACK: .6X TO 1.5X BASIC
BLACK PRINT RUN 250 SERIAL #'d SETS
RANDOM INSERTS IN PACKS
1 Alex Rodriguez 3.00 8.00
2 Roger Clemens 4.00 10.00
3 Ichiro Suzuki 4.00 10.00
4 Barry Zito 1.25 3.00
5 Garret Anderson 1.25 3.00
6 Derek Jeter 4.00 10.00
7 Manny Ramirez 1.25 3.00
8 Pedro Martinez 1.25 3.00
9 Alfonso Soriano 1.25 3.00
10 Carlos Delgado 1.25 3.00

2004 Donruss All-Stars National League

STATED PRINT RUN 1000 SERIAL #'d SETS
*BLACK: .6X TO 1.5X BASIC
BLACK PRINT RUN 250 SERIAL #'d SETS
RANDOM INSERTS IN PACKS
1 Barry Bonds 5.00 12.00
2 Andruw Jones 1.25 3.00
3 Scott Rolen 1.25 3.00
4 Austin Kearns 1.25 3.00
5 Mark Prior 1.25 3.00
6 Vladimir Guerrero 2.00 5.00
7 Jeff Bagwell 1.25 3.00

8 Mike Piazza 3.00 8.00
9 Albert Pujols 4.00 10.00
10 Randy Johnson 2.00 5.00

2004 Donruss Bat Kings

1-4 PRINT RUN 250 SERIAL #'d SETS
5-8 PRINT RUN 100 SERIAL #'d SETS
*STUDIO 1-4: .75X TO 2X BASIC
STUDIO 1-4 PRINT RUN 50 SERIAL #'d SETS
STUDIO 5-8 PRINT RUN 25 SERIAL #'d SETS
STUDIO 5-8 NO PRICING DUE TO SCARCITY
RANDOM INSERTS IN PACKS
1 Alex Rodriguez 03 8.00 20.00
2 Albert Pujols 03 10.00 25.00
3 Chipper Jones 03 6.00 15.00
4 Lance Berkman 03 4.00 10.00
5 Cal Ripken 88 40.00 80.00
6 George Brett 87 15.00 40.00
7 Don Mattingly 89 15.00 40.00
8 Roberto Clemente 02 50.00 100.00

2004 Donruss Craftsmen

STATED PRINT RUN 2000 SERIAL #'d SETS
*BLACK: 1X TO 2.5X BASIC
BLACK PRINT RUN 275 SERIAL #'d SETS
*MASTER: 1.25X TO 3X BASIC
MASTER PRINT RUN 150 SERIAL #'d SETS
RANDOM INSERTS IN PACKS
1 Alex Rodriguez 2.00 5.00
2 Mark Prior .75 2.00
3 Ichiro Suzuki 2.50 6.00
4 Barry Bonds 3.00 8.00
5 Ken Griffey Jr. 2.00 5.00
6 Alfonso Soriano .75 2.00
7 Mike Piazza 2.00 5.00
8 Chipper Jones 1.25 3.00
9 Derek Jeter 2.50 6.00
10 Randy Johnson 1.25 3.00
11 Sammy Sosa 1.25 3.00
12 Roger Clemens 2.50 6.00
13 Nomar Garciaparra 2.00 5.00
14 Greg Maddux 2.00 5.00
15 Albert Pujols 2.50 6.00

2004 Donruss Diamond Kings Inserts

STATED PRINT RUN 2000 SERIAL #'d SETS
*BLACK: .75X TO 2X BASIC
BLACK PRINT RUN 100 SERIAL #'d SETS
*STUDIO: .6X TO 1.5X BASIC
STUDIO PRINT RUN 250 SERIAL #'d SETS
RANDOM INSERTS IN PACKS
1 Derek Jeter 5.00 12.00
2 Greg Maddux 4.00 10.00
3 Albert Pujols 5.00 12.00
4 Ichiro Suzuki 5.00 12.00
5 Alex Rodriguez 4.00 10.00
6 Roger Clemens 5.00 12.00
7 Andruw Jones 3.00 8.00
8 Barry Bonds 6.00 15.00
9 Jeff Bagwell 3.00 8.00
10 Randy Johnson 3.00 8.00
11 Scott Rolen 3.00 8.00
12 Lance Berkman 3.00 8.00
13 Barry Zito 3.00 8.00
14 Manny Ramirez 3.00 8.00
15 Carlos Delgado 3.00 8.00
16 Alfonso Soriano 3.00 8.00
17 Todd Helton 3.00 8.00
18 Mike Mussina 3.00 8.00
19 Austin Kearns 3.00 8.00
20 Nomar Garciaparra 4.00 10.00
21 Chipper Jones 3.00 8.00
22 Mark Prior 3.00 8.00
23 Jim Thome 3.00 8.00
24 Vladimir Guerrero 3.00 8.00
25 Pedro Martinez 3.00 8.00

2004 Donruss Elite Series

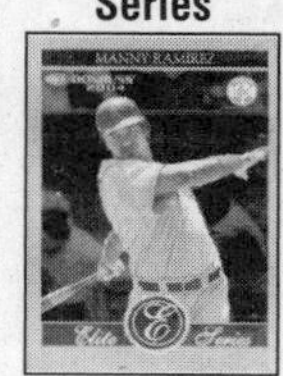

RANDOM INSERTS IN PACKS
STATED PRINT RUN 1500 SERIAL #'d SETS
*BLACK: 1X TO 2.5X BASIC
BLACK PRINT RUN 150 SERIAL #'d SETS
DOMINATORS PRINT 25 SERIAL #'d SETS
DOMINATORS NO PRICE DUE TO SCARCITY
RANDOM INSERTS IN PACKS
1 Albert Pujols 4.00 10.00
2 Barry Zito 1.25 3.00
3 Gary Sheffield 1.25 3.00
4 Mike Mussina 1.25 3.00
5 Lance Berkman 1.25 3.00
6 Alfonso Soriano 1.25 3.00
7 Randy Johnson 2.00 5.00
8 Nomar Garciaparra 3.00 8.00
9 Austin Kearns 1.25 3.00
10 Manny Ramirez 1.25 3.00
11 Mark Prior 1.25 3.00
12 Alex Rodriguez 3.00 8.00
13 Derek Jeter 4.00 10.00
14 Barry Bonds 5.00 12.00
15 Roger Clemens 4.00 10.00

2004 Donruss Inside View

RANDOM INSERTS IN PACKS
STATED PRINT RUN 1250 SERIAL #'d SETS
1 Derek Jeter 3.00 8.00
2 Greg Maddux 2.50 6.00
3 Albert Pujols 3.00 8.00
4 Ichiro Suzuki 3.00 8.00
5 Alex Rodriguez 2.50 6.00
6 Roger Clemens 3.00 8.00
7 Andruw Jones 1.00 2.50
8 Barry Bonds 4.00 10.00
9 Jeff Bagwell 1.00 2.50
10 Randy Johnson 1.50 4.00
11 Scott Rolen 1.00 2.50
12 Lance Berkman 1.00 2.50
13 Barry Zito 1.00 2.50
14 Manny Ramirez 1.00 2.50
15 Carlos Delgado 1.00 2.50
16 Alfonso Soriano 1.00 2.50
17 Todd Helton 1.00 2.50
18 Mike Mussina 1.00 2.50
19 Austin Kearns 1.00 2.50
20 Nomar Garciaparra 2.50 6.00
21 Chipper Jones 1.50 4.00
22 Mark Prior 1.00 2.50
23 Jim Thome 1.00 2.50
24 Vladimir Guerrero 1.50 4.00
25 Pedro Martinez 1.00 2.50

2004 Donruss Jersey Kings

1-6 PRINT RUN 250 SERIAL #'d SETS
7-12 PRINT RUN 100 SERIAL #'d SETS
*STUDIO 1-6: .75X TO 2X BASIC JSY KINGS
STUDIO 1-6 PRINT RUN 50 SERIAL #'d SETS
STUDIO 7-12 PRINT RUN 25 SERIAL #'d SETS
STUDIO 7-12 NO PRICING DUE TO SCARCITY
RANDOM INSERTS IN PACKS
1 Alfonso Soriano 03 4.00 10.00
2 Sammy Sosa 03 6.00 15.00
3 Roger Clemens 03 10.00 25.00
4 Nomar Garciaparra 03 8.00 20.00
5 Mark Prior 03 6.00 15.00
6 Vladimir Guerrero 03 6.00 15.00
7 Don Mattingly 89 15.00 40.00
8 Roberto Clemente 02 50.00 100.00
9 George Brett 87 15.00 40.00
10 Nolan Ryan 01 20.00 50.00
11 Cal Ripken 01 40.00 80.00
12 Mike Schmidt 01 15.00 40.00

2004 Donruss Longball Leaders

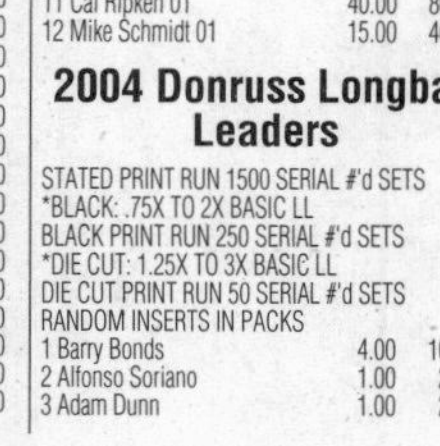

STATED PRINT RUN 1500 SERIAL #'d SETS
*BLACK: .75X TO 2X BASIC LL
BLACK PRINT RUN 250 SERIAL #'d SETS
*DIE CUT: 1.25X TO 3X BASIC LL
DIE CUT PRINT RUN 50 SERIAL #'d SETS
RANDOM INSERTS IN PACKS
1 Barry Bonds 4.00 10.00
2 Alfonso Soriano 1.00 2.50
3 Adam Dunn 1.00 2.50
4 Alex Rodriguez 2.50 6.00
5 Jim Thome 1.00 2.50
6 Garret Anderson 1.00 2.50
7 Juan Gonzalez 1.00 2.50
8 Jeff Bagwell 1.00 2.50
9 Gary Sheffield 1.00 2.50
10 Sammy Sosa 1.50 4.00

2004 Donruss Mound Marvels

STATED PRINT RUN 750 SERIAL #'d SETS
*BLACK: .75X TO 2X BASIC MM
BLACK PRINT RUN 175 SERIAL #'d SETS
RANDOM INSERTS IN PACKS
1 Mark Prior 1.25 3.00
2 Curt Schilling 1.25 3.00
3 Mike Mussina 1.25 3.00
4 Kevin Brown 1.25 3.00
5 Pedro Martinez 1.25 3.00
6 Mark Mulder 1.25 3.00
7 Kerry Wood 1.25 3.00
8 Greg Maddux 3.00 8.00
9 Kevin Millwood 1.25 3.00
10 Barry Zito 1.25 3.00
11 Roger Clemens 4.00 10.00
12 Randy Johnson 2.00 5.00
13 Hideo Nomo 2.00 5.00
14 Tim Hudson 1.25 3.00
15 Tom Glavine 1.25 3.00

2004 Donruss Power Alley Red

STATED PRINT RUN 2500 SERIAL #'d SETS
BLACK DC PRINT RUN 1 SERIAL #'d SET
BLACK DC NO PRICING DUE TO SCARCITY
*BLUE: .6X TO 1.5X BASIC RED
BLUE PRINT RUN 1000 SERIAL #'d SETS
*BLUE DC: 1.25X TO 3X BASIC RED
BLUE DC PRINT RUN 100 SERIAL #'d SETS
GREEN PRINT RUN 25 SERIAL #'d SETS
GREEN NO PRICING DUE TO SCARCITY
GREEN DC 5 SERIAL #'d SETS
GREEN DC NO PRICING DUE TO SCARCITY
*PURPLE: 1X TO 2.5X BASIC RED
PURPLE PRINT RUN 250 SERIAL #'d SETS
PURPLE DC PRINT RUN 25 SERIAL #'d SETS
PURPLE DC NO PRICING DUE TO SCARCITY
*RED DC: 1X TO 2.5X BASIC RED
RED DC PRINT RUN 250 SERIAL #'d SETS
*YELLOW: 1.25X TO 3X BASIC RED
YELLOW PRINT RUN 100 SERIAL #'d SETS
YELLOW DC PRINT RUN 10 SERIAL #'d SETS
YELLOW DC NO PRICING DUE TO SCARCITY
RANDOM INSERTS IN PACKS
1 Albert Pujols 2.50 6.00
2 Mike Piazza 2.00 5.00
3 Carlos Delgado .75 2.00
4 Barry Bonds 3.00 8.00
5 Jim Edmonds .75 2.00
6 Nomar Garciaparra 2.00 5.00
7 Alfonso Soriano .75 2.00
8 Alex Rodriguez 2.00 5.00
9 Lance Berkman .75 2.00
10 Scott Rolen .75 2.00
11 Manny Ramirez .75 2.00
12 Rafael Palmeiro .75 2.00
13 Sammy Sosa 1.25 3.00
14 Adam Dunn .75 2.00
15 Andruw Jones .75 2.00
16 Jim Thome .75 2.00
17 Jason Giambi .75 2.00
18 Jeff Bagwell .75 2.00
19 Juan Gonzalez .75 2.00
20 Austin Kearns .75 2.00

2004 Donruss Production Line Average

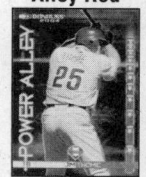

PRINT RUNS B/WN 300-359 COPIES PER
*BLACK: .75X TO 2X BASIC AVG
BLACK PRINT RUN 35 SERIAL #'d SETS
*DIE CUT: .5X TO 1.2X BASIC AVG
DIE CUT PRINT RUN 100 SERIAL #'d SETS
RANDOM INSERTS IN PACKS
1 Gary Sheffield/330 2.00 5.00
2 Ichiro Suzuki/312 6.00 15.00
3 Todd Helton/358 2.00 5.00
4 Manny Ramirez/325 2.00 5.00
5 Garret Anderson/315 2.00 5.00
6 Barry Bonds/341 8.00 20.00
7 Albert Pujols/359 6.00 15.00
8 Derek Jeter/324 6.00 15.00
9 Nomar Garciaparra/301 5.00 12.00
10 Hank Blalock/300 2.00 5.00

2004 Donruss Production Line OBP

PRINT RUNS B/WN 396-529 COPIES PER
*BLACK: 1X TO 2.5X BASIC OBP
BLACK PRINT RUN 40 SERIAL #'d SETS
*DIE CUT: .6X TO 1.5X BASIC OBP
DIE CUT PRINT RUN 100 SERIAL #'d SETS
RANDOM INSERTS IN PACKS
1 Todd Helton/458 1.50 4.00
2 Albert Pujols/439 5.00 12.00
3 Larry Walker/422 1.50 4.00
4 Barry Bonds/529 6.00 15.00
5 Chipper Jones/402 2.50 6.00
6 Manny Ramirez/427 1.50 4.00
7 Gary Sheffield/419 1.50 4.00
8 Lance Berkman/412 1.50 4.00
9 Alex Rodriguez/396 4.00 10.00
10 Jason Giambi/412 1.50 4.00

2004 Donruss Production Line OPS

PRINT RUNS B/WN 910-1278 COPIES PER
*BLACK: .75X TO 2X BASIC OPS
BLACK PRINT RUN 125 SERIAL #'d SETS
*DIE CUT: .75X TO 2X BASIC OPS
DIE CUT PRINT RUN 100 SERIAL #'d SETS
RANDOM INSERTS IN PACKS
1 Albert Pujols/1106 4.00 10.00
2 Barry Bonds/1278 5.00 12.00
3 Gary Sheffield/1023 1.25 3.00
4 Todd Helton/1088 1.25 3.00
5 Scott Rolen/910 1.25 3.00
6 Manny Ramirez/1014 1.25 3.00
7 Alex Rodriguez/995 3.00 8.00
8 Jim Thome/958 1.25 3.00
9 Jason Giambi/939 1.25 3.00
10 Frank Thomas/952 2.00 5.00

2004 Donruss Production Line Slugging

PRINT RUNS B/WN 541-749 COPIES PER
*BLACK: .75X TO 2X BASIC SLG
BLACK PRINT RUN 75 SERIAL #'d SETS
*DIE CUT: .6X TO 1.5X BASIC SLG
DIE CUT PRINT RUN 100 SERIAL #'d SETS
RANDOM INSERTS IN PACKS
1 Alex Rodriguez/600 4.00 10.00
2 Frank Thomas/562 2.50 6.00
3 Garret Anderson/541 1.50 4.00
4 Albert Pujols/667 5.00 12.00
5 Sammy Sosa/553 2.50 6.00
6 Gary Sheffield/604 1.50 4.00
7 Manny Ramirez/587 1.50 4.00
8 Jim Edmonds/617 1.50 4.00
9 Barry Bonds/749 6.00 15.00
10 Todd Helton/630 1.50 4.00

2004 Donruss Recollection Autographs

RANDOM INSERTS IN PACKS
PRINT RUNS B/WN 1-100 COPIES PER
NO PRICING ON QTY OF 50 OR LESS
27 John Candelaria 88 Black/83 6.00 15.00
39 Jack Clark 87/67 8.00 20.00
40 Jack Clark 88/75 6.00 15.00
69 Sid Fernandez 86/52 8.00 20.00
72 Sid Fernandez 88/58 8.00 20.00
83 George Foster 83/50 8.00 20.00
84 George Foster 84/70 8.00 20.00

85 George Foster 85/50 8.00 20.00
86 George Foster 86/83 6.00 15.00
91 Cliff Lee 03/100 4.00 10.00
92 Terrence Long 01/90 4.00 10.00
93 Melvin Mora 03/50 8.00 20.00
100 Jesse Orosco 86 Blue/65 5.00 12.00
102 Jesse Orosco 87 Blue/90 4.00 10.00
115 Jose Vidro 01/89 4.00 10.00

2004 Donruss Timber and Threads

STATED ODDS 1:40
*STUDIO: .75X TO 2X BASIC TT
STUDIO RANDOM INSERTS IN PACKS
STUDIO PRINT RUN 50 SERIAL #'d SETS
1 Adam Dunn Jsy 3.00 8.00
2 Alex Rodriguez Blue Jsy 6.00 15.00
3 Alex Rodriguez White Jsy 6.00 15.00
4 Andruw Jones Jsy 4.00 10.00
5 Austin Kearns Jsy 3.00 8.00
6 Carlos Beltran Jsy 3.00 8.00
7 Carlos Lee Jsy 3.00 8.00
8 Frank Thomas Jsy 4.00 10.00
9 Greg Maddux Jsy 4.00 10.00
10 Hideo Nomo Jsy 4.00 10.00
11 Jeff Bagwell Jsy 4.00 10.00
12 Lance Berkman Jsy 3.00 8.00
13 Magglio Ordonez Jsy 3.00 8.00
14 Mike Sweeney Jsy 3.00 8.00
15 Randy Johnson Jsy 4.00 10.00
16 Rocco Baldelli Jsy 3.00 8.00
17 Roger Clemens Jsy 6.00 15.00
18 Sammy Sosa Jsy 4.00 10.00
19 Shawn Green Jsy 3.00 8.00
20 Tom Glavine Jsy 4.00 10.00
21 Adam Dunn Bat 3.00 8.00
22 Andruw Jones Bat 4.00 10.00
23 Bobby Abreu Bat 3.00 8.00
24 Hank Blalock Bat 3.00 8.00
25 Ivan Rodriguez Bat 4.00 10.00
26 Jim Edmonds Bat 3.00 8.00
27 Josh Phelps Bat 3.00 8.00
28 Juan Gonzalez Bat 3.00 8.00
29 Lance Berkman Bat 3.00 8.00
30 Larry Walker Bat 3.00 8.00
31 Magglio Ordonez Bat 3.00 8.00
32 Manny Ramirez Bat 4.00 10.00
33 Mike Piazza Bat 4.00 10.00
34 Nomar Garciaparra Bat 6.00 15.00
35 Paul Lo Duca Bat 3.00 8.00
36 Roberto Alomar Bat 4.00 10.00
37 Rocco Baldelli Bat 3.00 8.00
38 Sammy Sosa Bat 4.00 10.00
39 Vernon Wells Bat 3.00 8.00
40 Vladimir Guerrero Bat 4.00 10.00

2004 Donruss Timber and Threads Autographs

RANDOM INSERTS IN PACKS
PRINT RUNS B/WN 5-50 COPIES PER
NO PRICING ON QTY OF 34 OR LESS
2 Alex Rodriguez Blue Jsy/5
5 Austin Kearns Jsy/19
6 Carlos Beltran Jsy/34
7 Carlos Lee Jsy/25
8 Frank Thomas Jsy/5
9 Greg Maddux Jsy/5
10 Hideo Nomo Jsy/5
11 Jeff Bagwell Jsy/5
12 Lance Berkman Jsy/5
13 Magglio Ordonez Jsy/30
14 Mike Sweeney Jsy/25
17 Roger Clemens Jsy/5
19 Shawn Green Jsy/5
20 Tom Glavine Jsy/5
21 Adam Dunn Bat/5
22 Andruw Jones Bat/5
23 Bobby Abreu Bat/50 10.00 25.00
24 Hank Blalock Bat/50 10.00 25.00
25 Ivan Rodriguez Bat/7
26 Jim Edmonds Bat/5
27 Josh Phelps Bat/50 10.00 25.00
28 Juan Gonzalez Bat/5
31 Magglio Ordonez Bat/30
32 Manny Ramirez Bat/5
35 Paul Lo Duca Bat/50 10.00 25.00
36 Roberto Alomar Bat/10
37 Rocco Baldelli Bat/15
40 Vladimir Guerrero Bat/50 30.00 60.00

2004 Donruss-Playoff Hawaii Fans of the Game Gandolfini

These cards, which were issued to select attendees of the 2004 Hawaii Trade Conference feature Sopranos star James Gandolfini. The cards were issued to promote the 2004 Donruss/Playoff initiative of having celebrity signatures within their 2004 products.

FG1 James Gandolfini/300
FG1A James Gandolfini AU/50

2005 Donruss

This 400-card set was released in November, 2004. The set was issued in 10-card packs with an $2 SRP which came 24 packs to a box and 16 boxes to a case. Subsets included: Diamond Kings (1-25), Rated Rookies (26-70), Team Checklists (371-400). All of these subets were issued at a stated rate of one in six.

COMPLETE SET (400) 75.00 150.00
COMP.SET w/o SP's (300) 10.00 25.00
COMMON CARD (71-3 .10 .30
COMMON (1-25/371-400) .75 2.00
COMMON CARD (26-70) .75 2.00
1-25 STATED ODDS 1:6
26-70 STATED ODDS 1:6
371-400 STATED ODDS 1:6
1 Garret Anderson DK .75 2.00
2 Vladimir Guerrero DK .75 2.00
3 Manny Ramirez DK .75 2.00
4 Kerry Wood DK .75 2.00
5 Sammy Sosa DK .75 2.00
6 Magglio Ordonez DK .75 2.00
7 Adam Dunn DK .75 2.00
8 Todd Helton DK .75 2.00
9 Josh Beckett DK .75 2.00
10 Miguel Cabrera DK .75 2.00
11 Lance Berkman DK .75 2.00
12 Carlos Beltran DK .75 2.00
13 Shawn Green DK .75 2.00
14 Roger Clemens DK 1.25 3.00
15 Mike Piazza DK .75 2.00
16 Alex Rodriguez DK 1.25 3.00
17 Derek Jeter DK 1.50 4.00
18 Mark Mulder DK .75 2.00
19 Jim Thome DK .75 2.00
20 Albert Pujols DK 1.50 4.00
21 Scott Rolen DK .75 2.00
22 Aubrey Huff DK .75 2.00
23 Alfonso Soriano DK .75 2.00
24 Hank Blalock DK .75 2.00
25 Vernon Wells DK .75 2.00
26 Kazuo Matsui RR 1.25 3.00
27 B.J. Upton RR 2.00 5.00
28 Charles Thomas RR .75 2.00
29 Akinori Otsuka RR 1.25 3.00
30 David Aardsma RR .75 2.00
31 Travis Blackley RR .75 2.00
32 Brad Halsey RR .75 2.00
33 David Wright RR 3.00 8.00
34 Kazuhito Tadano RR 1.25 3.00
35 Casey Kotchman RR 1.25 3.00
36 Khalil Greene RR 2.00 5.00
37 Adrian Gonzalez RR .75 2.00
38 Zack Greinke RR .75 2.00
39 Chad Cordero RR .75 2.00
40 Scott Kazmir RR 2.00 5.00
41 Jeremy Guthrie RR .75 2.00
42 Noah Lowry RR 1.25 3.00
43 Chase Utley RR 2.00 5.00
44 Billy Traber RR .75 2.00
45 Aarom Baldiris RR .75 2.00
46 Abe Alvarez RR .75 2.00
47 Angel Chavez RR .75 2.00
48 Joe Mauer RR 2.00 5.00
49 Joey Gathright RR 1.25 3.00
50 John Gall RR .75 2.00
51 Ronald Belisario RR .75 2.00
52 Ryan Wing RR .75 2.00
53 Scott Proctor RR .75 2.00
54 Yadier Molina RR 1.25 3.00
55 Carlos Hines RR .75 2.00
56 Frankie Francisco RR .75 2.00
57 Graham Koonce RR .75 2.00
58 Jake Woods RR .75 2.00
59 Jason Bartlett RR .75 2.00
60 Mike Rouse RR .75 2.00
61 Phil Stockman RR .75 2.00
62 Renyel Pinto RR .75 2.00
63 Roberto Novoa RR .75 2.00
64 Ryan Meaux RR .75 2.00
65 Dave Crouthers RR .75 2.00
66 Justin Knoedler RR .75 2.00
67 Justin Leone RR .75 2.00
68 Nick Regilio RR .75 2.00
69 Mike Gosling RR .75 2.00
70 Onil Joseph RR .75 2.00
71 Bartolo Colon .10 .30
72 Brad Fullmer .10 .30
73 Chone Figgins .10 .30
74 Darin Erstad .10 .30
75 Francisco Rodriguez .10 .30
76 Garret Anderson .10 .30
77 Jarrod Washburn .10 .30
78 John Lackey .10 .30
79 Jose Guillen .10 .30
80 Robb Quinlan .10 .30
81 Tim Salmon .20 .50
82 Troy Glaus .10 .30
83 Troy Percival .10 .30
84 Vladimir Guerrero .30 .75
85 Brandon Webb .10 .30
86 Casey Fossum .10 .30
87 Luis Gonzalez .10 .30
88 Randy Johnson .30 .75
89 Richie Sexson .10 .30
90 Robby Hammock .10 .30
91 Roberto Alomar .20 .50
92 Adam LaRoche .10 .30
93 Andruw Jones .20 .50
94 Bubba Nelson .10 .30
95 Chipper Jones .30 .75
96 J.D. Drew .10 .30
97 John Smoltz .20 .50
98 Johnny Estrada .10 .30
99 Marcus Giles .10 .30
100 Mike Hampton .10 .30
101 Nick Green .10 .30
102 Rafael Furcal .10 .30
103 Russ Ortiz .10 .30
104 Adam Loewen .10 .30
105 Brian Roberts .10 .30
106 Javy Lopez .10 .30
107 Jay Gibbons .10 .30
108 Larry Bigbie UER .10 .30
Player pictured is Brian Roberts
109 Luis Matos .10 .30
110 Melvin Mora .10 .30
111 Miguel Tejada .10 .30
112 Rafael Palmeiro .20 .50
113 Rodrigo Lopez .10 .30
114 Sidney Ponson .10 .30
115 Bill Mueller .10 .30
116 Byung-Hyun Kim .10 .30
117 Curt Schilling .20 .50
118 David Ortiz .30 .75
119 Derek Lowe .10 .30
120 Doug Mientkiewicz .10 .30
121 Jason Varitek .30 .75
122 Johnny Damon .20 .50
123 Keith Foulke .10 .30
124 Kevin Youkilis .10 .30
125 Manny Ramirez .20 .50
126 Orlando Cabrera .10 .30
127 Pedro Martinez .20 .50
128 Trot Nixon .10 .30
129 Aramis Ramirez .10 .30
130 Carlos Zambrano .10 .30
131 Corey Patterson .10 .30
132 Derrek Lee .20 .50
133 Greg Maddux .50 1.25
134 Kerry Wood .10 .30
135 Mark Prior .20 .50
136 Matt Clement .10 .30
137 Moises Alou .10 .30
138 Nomar Garciaparra .30 .75
139 Sammy Sosa .30 .75
140 Todd Walker .10 .30
141 Angel Guzman .10 .30
142 Billy Koch .10 .30
143 Carlos Lee .10 .30
144 Frank Thomas .30 .75
145 Magglio Ordonez .10 .30
146 Mark Buehrle .10 .30
147 Paul Konerko .10 .30
148 Wilson Valdez .10 .30
149 Adam Dunn .10 .30
150 Austin Kearns .10 .30
151 Barry Larkin .20 .50
152 Benito Santiago .10 .30
153 Jason LaRue .10 .30
154 Ken Griffey Jr. .50 1.25
155 Ryan Wagner .10 .30
156 Sean Casey .10 .30
157 Brandon Phillips .10 .30
158 Brian Tallet .10 .30
159 C.C. Sabathia .10 .30
160 Cliff Lee .10 .30
161 Jeremy Guthrie .10 .30
162 Jody Gerut .10 .30
163 Matt Lawton .10 .30
164 Omar Vizquel .20 .50
165 Travis Hafner .10 .30
166 Victor Martinez .10 .30
167 Charles Johnson .10 .30
168 Garrett Atkins .10 .30
169 Jason Jennings .10 .30
170 Jay Payton .10 .30
171 Jeromy Burnitz .10 .30
172 Joe Kennedy .10 .30
173 Larry Walker .20 .50
174 Preston Wilson .10 .30
175 Todd Helton .20 .50
176 Vinny Castilla .10 .30
177 Bobby Higginson .10 .30
178 Brandon Inge .10 .30
179 Carlos Guillen UER .10 .30
Photo is Alex Sanchez
180 Carlos Pena .10 .30
181 Craig Monroe .10 .30
182 Dmitri Young .10 .30
183 Eric Munson .10 .30
184 Fernando Vina .10 .30
185 Ivan Rodriguez .20 .50
186 Jeremy Bonderman .10 .30
187 Rondell White .10 .30
188 A.J. Burnett .10 .30
189 Dontrelle Willis .10 .30
190 Guillermo Mota .10 .30
191 Hee Seop Choi .10 .30
192 Jeff Conine .10 .30
193 Josh Beckett .10 .30
194 Juan Encarnacion .10 .30
195 Juan Pierre .10 .30
196 Luis Castillo .10 .30
197 Miguel Cabrera .20 .50
198 Mike Lowell .10 .30
199 Paul Lo Duca .10 .30
200 Andy Pettitte .20 .50
201 Brad Ausmus .10 .30
202 Carlos Beltran .10 .30
203 Chris Burke .10 .30
204 Craig Biggio .20 .50
205 Jeff Bagwell .20 .50
206 Jeff Kent .10 .30
207 Lance Berkman .10 .30
208 Morgan Ensberg .10 .30
209 Octavio Dotel .10 .30
210 Roger Clemens .50 1.25
211 Roy Oswalt .10 .30
212 Tim Redding .10 .30
213 Angel Berroa .10 .30
214 Juan Gonzalez .10 .30
215 Ken Harvey .10 .30
216 Mike Sweeney .10 .30
217 Adrian Beltre .10 .30
218 Brad Penny .10 .30
219 Eric Gagne .10 .30
220 Hideo Nomo .30 .75
221 Hong-Chih Kuo .10 .30
222 Jeff Weaver .10 .30
223 Kazuhisa Ishii .10 .30
224 Milton Bradley .10 .30
225 Shawn Green .10 .30
226 Steve Finley .10 .30
227 Danny Kolb .10 .30
228 Geoff Jenkins .10 .30
229 Junior Spivey .10 .30
230 Lyle Overbay .10 .30
231 Rickie Weeks .10 .30
232 Scott Podsednik .10 .30
233 Brad Radke .10 .30
234 Corey Koskie .10 .30
235 Cristian Guzman .10 .30
236 Dustan Mohr .10 .30
237 Eddie Guardado .10 .30
238 J.D. Durbin .10 .30
239 Jacque Jones .10 .30
240 Joe Nathan .10 .30
241 Johan Santana .30 .75
242 Lew Ford .10 .30
243 Michael Cuddyer .10 .30
244 Shannon Stewart .10 .30
245 Torii Hunter .10 .30
246 Brad Wilkerson .10 .30
247 Carl Everett .10 .30
248 Jeff Fassero .10 .30
249 Jose Vidro .10 .30
250 Livan Hernandez .10 .30
251 Michael Barrett .10 .30
252 Tony Batista .10 .30
253 Zach Day .10 .30
254 Al Leiter .10 .30
255 Cliff Floyd .10 .30
256 Jae Weong Seo .10 .30
257 John Olerud .10 .30
258 Jose Reyes .10 .30
259 Mike Cameron .10 .30
260 Mike Piazza .30 .75
261 Richard Hidalgo .10 .30
262 Tom Glavine .20 .50
263 Vance Wilson .10 .30
264 Alex Rodriguez .50 1.25
265 Armando Benitez .10 .30
266 Bernie Williams .20 .50
267 Bubba Crosby .10 .30
268 Chien-Ming Wang .50 1.25
269 Derek Jeter .60 1.50
270 Esteban Loaiza .10 .30
271 Gary Sheffield .10 .30
272 Hideki Matsui .50 1.25
273 Jason Giambi .10 .30
274 Javier Vazquez .10 .30
275 Jorge Posada .20 .50
276 Jose Contreras .10 .30
277 Kenny Lofton .10 .30
278 Kevin Brown .10 .30
279 Mariano Rivera .30 .75
280 Mike Mussina .20 .50
281 Barry Zito .10 .30
282 Bobby Crosby .10 .30
283 Eric Byrnes .10 .30
284 Eric Chavez .10 .30
285 Erubiel Durazo .10 .30
286 Jermaine Dye .10 .30
287 Mark Kotsay .10 .30
288 Mark Mulder .10 .30
289 Rich Harden .10 .30
290 Tim Hudson .10 .30
291 Billy Wagner .10 .30
292 Bobby Abreu .10 .30
293 Brett Myers .10 .30
294 Eric Milton .10 .30
295 Jim Thome .20 .50
296 Jimmy Rollins .10 .30
297 Kevin Millwood .10 .30
298 Marlon Byrd .10 .30
299 Mike Lieberthal .10 .30
300 Pat Burrell .10 .30
301 Randy Wolf .10 .30
302 Craig Wilson .10 .30
303 Jack Wilson .10 .30
304 Jacob Cruz .10 .30
305 Jason Bay .10 .30
306 Jason Kendall .10 .30
307 Jose Castillo .10 .30
308 Kip Wells .10 .30
309 Brian Giles .10 .30
310 Brian Lawrence .10 .30
311 Chris Oxspring .10 .30
312 David Wells .10 .30
313 Freddy Guzman .10 .30
314 Jake Peavy .10 .30
315 Mark Loretta .10 .30
316 Ryan Klesko .10 .30
317 Sean Burroughs .10 .30
318 Trevor Hoffman .10 .30
319 Xavier Nady .10 .30
320 A.J. Pierzynski .10 .30
321 Edgardo Alfonzo .10 .30
322 J.T. Snow .10 .30
323 Jason Schmidt .10 .30
324 Jerome Williams .10 .30
325 Kirk Rueter .10 .30
326 Bret Boone .10 .30
327 Bucky Jacobsen .10 .30
328 Edgar Martinez .20 .50
329 Freddy Garcia .10 .30
330 Ichiro Suzuki .60 1.50
331 Jamie Moyer .10 .30
332 Joel Pineiro .10 .30
333 Scott Spiezio .10 .30
334 Shigetoshi Hasegawa .10 .30
335 Albert Pujols .60 1.50
336 Edgar Renteria .10 .30
337 Jason Isringhausen .10 .30
338 Jim Edmonds .10 .30
339 Matt Morris .10 .30
340 Mike Matheny .10 .30
341 Reggie Sanders .10 .30
342 Scott Rolen .20 .50
343 Woody Williams .10 .30
344 Jeff Suppan .10 .30
345 Aubrey Huff .10 .30
346 Carl Crawford .10 .30
347 Chad Gaudin .10 .30
348 Delmon Young .20 .50
349 Dewon Brazelton .10 .30
350 Jose Cruz Jr. .10 .30
351 Rocco Baldelli .10 .30
352 Tino Martinez .20 .50
353 Toby Hall .10 .30
354 Alfonso Soriano .10 .30
355 Brian Jordan .10 .30
356 Francisco Cordero .10 .30
357 Hank Blalock .10 .30
358 Kenny Rogers .10 .30
359 Kevin Mench .10 .30
360 Laynce Nix .10 .30
361 Mark Teixeira .20 .50
362 Michael Young .10 .30
363 Alex S. Gonzalez .10 .30
364 Alexis Rios .10 .30
365 Carlos Delgado .10 .30
366 Eric Hinske .10 .30
367 Frank Catalanotto .10 .30
368 Josh Phelps .10 .30
369 Roy Halladay .10 .30
370 Vernon Wells .10 .30
371 Vladimir Guerrero TC .75 2.00
372 Randy Johnson TC .75 2.00
373 Chipper Jones TC .75 2.00
374 Miguel Tejada TC .75 2.00
375 Pedro Martinez TC .75 2.00
376 Sammy Sosa TC .75 2.00
377 Frank Thomas TC .75 2.00
378 Ken Griffey Jr. TC 1.25 3.00
379 Victor Martinez TC .75 2.00
380 Todd Helton TC .75 2.00
381 Ivan Rodriguez TC .75 2.00
382 Miguel Cabrera TC .75 2.00
383 Roger Clemens TC 1.25 3.00
384 Ken Harvey TC .75 2.00
385 Eric Gagne TC .75 2.00
386 Lyle Overbay TC .75 2.00
387 Shannon Stewart TC .75 2.00
388 Brad Wilkerson TC .75 2.00
389 Mike Piazza TC .75 2.00
390 Alex Rodriguez TC 1.25 3.00
391 Mark Mulder TC .75 2.00
392 Jim Thome TC .75 2.00
393 Jack Wilson TC .75 2.00
394 Khalil Greene TC .75 2.00
395 Jason Schmidt TC .75 2.00
396 Ichiro Suzuki TC 1.50 4.00
397 Albert Pujols TC 1.50 4.00
398 Rocco Baldelli TC .75 2.00
399 Alfonso Soriano TC .75 2.00
400 Vernon Wells TC .75 2.00

2005 Donruss 25th Anniversary

*25th ANN 71-370: 10X TO 25X BASIC
*25th ANN 1-25/371-400: 4X TO 10X BASIC
*25th ANN 26-70: 2X TO 5X BASIC
RANDOM INSERTS IN PACKS
STATED PRINT RUN 25 SERIAL #'d SETS

2005 Donruss Press Proofs Black

RANDOM INSERTS IN PACKS
STATED PRINT RUN 10 SERIAL #'d SETS
NO PRICING DUE TO SCARCITY

2005 Donruss Press Proofs Blue

*BLUE 71-370: 4X TO 10X BASIC
*BLUE 1-25/371-400: 1.5X TO 4X BASIC
*BLUE 26-70: .75X TO 2X BASIC
RANDOM INSERTS IN PACKS
STATED PRINT RUN 100 SERIAL #'d SETS

2005 Donruss Press Proofs Gold

*GOLD 71-370: 10X TO 25X BASIC
*GOLD 1-25/371-400: 4X TO 10X BASIC
*GOLD 26-70: 2X TO 5X BASIC
RANDOM INSERTS IN PACKS
STATED PRINT RUN 25 SERIAL #'d SETS

2005 Donruss Press Proofs Red

*RED 71-370: X TO X BASIC
*RED 1-25/371-400: 1X TO 2.5X BASIC
*RED 26-70: .5X TO 1.2X BASIC
RANDOM INSERTS IN PACKS
STATED PRINT RUN 200 SERIAL #'d SETS

2005 Donruss Stat Line Career

*71-370 p/r 200-394 2.5X TO 6X
*71-370 p/r 121-200: 3X TO 8X
*71-370 p/r 81-120: 4X TO 10X
*71-370 p/r 51-80: 5X TO 12X
*71-370 p/r 36-50: 6X TO 15X
*71-370 p/r 26-35: 8X TO 20X
*71-370 p/r 16-25: 10X TO 25X
*1-25/371-400 p/r 200-574:1X TO 2.5X
*1-25/371-400 p/r 121-200: 1.25X TO 3X
*1-25/371-400 p/r 81-120: 1.5X TO 4X
*1-25/371-400 p/r 51-80: 2X TO 5X
*1-25/371-400 p/r 36-50: 2.5X TO 6X
*1-25/371-400 p/r 26-35: 3X TO 8X
*26-70 p/r 200-263: .5X TO 1.2X
*26-70 p/r 121-200: .6X TO 1.5X
*26-70 p/r 81-120: .75X TO 2X
*26-70 p/r 51-80: 1X TO 2.5X
*26-70 p/r 36-50: 1.25X TO 3X
*26-70 p/r 26-35: 1.5X TO 4X
*26-70 p/r 16-25: 2X TO 5X
RANDOM INSERTS IN PACKS
PRINT RUNS B/WN 6-500 COPIES PER
NO PRICING ON QTY OF 15 OR LESS

2005 Donruss Stat Line Season

*71-370 p/r 121-158: 3X TO 8X
*71-370 p/r 81-120: 4X TO 10X
*71-370 p/r 51-80: 5X TO 12X
*71-370 p/r 36-50: 6X TO 15X
*71-370 p/r 26-35: 8X TO 20X
*71-370 p/r 16-25: 10X TO 25X
*1-25/371-400 p/r 81-120: 1.5X TO 4X
*1-25/371-400 p/r 51-80: 2X TO 5X
*1-25/371-400 p/r 36-50: 2.5X TO 6X
*1-25/371-400 p/r 26-35: 3X TO 8X
*1-25/371-400 p/r 16-25: 4X TO 10X
*26-70 p/r 121-200: .6X TO 1.5X
*26-70 p/r 81-120: .75X TO 2X
*26-70 p/r 51-80: 1X TO 2.5X
*26-70 p/r 36-50: 1.25X TO 3X
*26-70 p/r 26-35: 1.5X TO 4X
*26-70 p/r 16-25: 2X TO 5X
RANDOM INSERTS IN PACKS
PRINT RUNS B/WN 1-158 COPIES PER
NO PRICING ON QTY OF 15 OR LESS

2005 Donruss Autographs

RANDOM INSERTS IN PACKS
80 Robb Quinlan 4.00 10.00
101 Nick Green 4.00 10.00
141 Angel Guzman 4.00 10.00
148 Wilson Valdez 4.00 10.00
172 Joe Kennedy 4.00 10.00
178 Brandon Inge 6.00 15.00

181 Craig Monroe 4.00 10.00
263 Vance Wilson 4.00 10.00
304 Jacob Cruz 4.00 10.00
327 Bucky Jacobsen 4.00 10.00
344 Jeff Suppan 6.00 15.00

2005 Donruss '85 Reprints

RANDOM INSERTS IN PACKS
STATED PRINT RUN 1985 SERIAL #'d SETS
1 Eddie Murray 2.00 5.00
2 George Brett 3.00 8.00
3 Nolan Ryan 4.00 10.00
4 Mike Schmidt 4.00 10.00
5 Tony Gwynn 2.00 5.00
7 Cal Ripken 5.00 12.00
8 Dwight Gooden 1.25 3.00
9 Roger Clemens 3.00 8.00
10 Don Mattingly 3.00 8.00
11 Kirby Puckett 2.00 5.00
12 Orel Hershiser 1.25 3.00

2005 Donruss '85 Reprints Material

RANDOM INSERTS IN PACKS
STATED PRINT RUN 85 SERIAL #'d SETS
1 Eddie Murray Jsy 10.00 25.00
2 George Brett Jsy 15.00 40.00
3 Nolan Ryan Jkt 15.00 40.00
4 Mike Schmidt Jkt 15.00 40.00
5 Tony Gwynn Jsy 10.00 25.00
7 Cal Ripken Jsy 30.00 60.00
8 Dwight Gooden Jsy 6.00 15.00
9 Roger Clemens Jsy 15.00 40.00
10 Don Mattingly Jsy 15.00 40.00
11 Kirby Puckett Jsy 10.00 25.00
12 Orel Hershiser Jsy 6.00 15.00

2005 Donruss All-Stars AL

STATED PRINT RUN 1000 SERIAL #'d SETS
*GOLD: .75X TO 2X BASIC
GOLD PRINT RUN 100 SERIAL #'d SETS
RANDOM INSERTS IN PACKS
1 Alex Rodriguez 3.00 8.00
2 Alfonso Soriano 1.25 3.00
3 Curt Schilling 2.00 5.00
4 Derek Jeter 4.00 10.00
5 Hank Blalock 1.25 3.00
6 Hideki Matsui 3.00 8.00
7 Ichiro Suzuki 4.00 10.00
8 Ivan Rodriguez 2.00 5.00
9 Jason Giambi 1.25 3.00
10 Manny Ramirez 2.00 5.00
11 Mark Mulder 1.25 3.00
12 Michael Young 1.25 3.00
13 Tim Hudson 1.25 3.00
14 Victor Martinez 1.25 3.00
15 Vladimir Guerrero 2.00 5.00

2005 Donruss All-Stars NL

STATED PRINT RUN 1000 SERIAL #'d SETS
*GOLD: .75X TO 2X BASIC
GOLD PRINT RUN 100 SERIAL #'d SETS
RANDOM INSERTS IN PACKS
1 Albert Pujols 4.00 10.00
2 Ben Sheets 1.25 3.00
3 Edgar Renteria 1.25 3.00
4 Eric Gagne 1.25 3.00
5 Jack Wilson 1.25 3.00
6 Jason Schmidt 1.25 3.00
7 Jeff Kent 1.25 3.00
8 Jim Thome 2.00 5.00
9 Ken Griffey Jr. 3.00 8.00
10 Mike Piazza 2.00 5.00
11 Roger Clemens 3.00 8.00
12 Sammy Sosa 2.00 5.00
13 Scott Rolen 2.00 5.00
14 Sean Casey 1.25 3.00
15 Todd Helton 2.00 5.00

2005 Donruss Bat Kings

RANDOM INSERTS IN PACKS
PRINT RUNS B/WN 100-250 COPIES PER
1 Garret Anderson/250 3.00 8.00
2 Vladimir Guerrero/250 4.00 10.00
3 Cal Ripken/100 30.00 60.00
4 Manny Ramirez/250 4.00 10.00
5 Kerry Wood/250 3.00 8.00
6 Sammy Sosa/250 4.00 10.00
7 Magglio Ordonez/250 3.00 8.00
8 Adam Dunn/250 3.00 8.00
9 Todd Helton/250 4.00 10.00
10 Josh Beckett/250 3.00 8.00
11 Miguel Cabrera/250 4.00 10.00
12 Lance Berkman/250 3.00 8.00
13 Carlos Beltran/250 3.00 8.00
14 Shawn Green/250 3.00 8.00
15 Roger Clemens/100 8.00 20.00
16 Mike Piazza/250 4.00 10.00
17 Nolan Ryan/100 20.00 50.00
18 Mark Mulder/250 3.00 8.00
19 Jim Thome/250 4.00 10.00
20 Albert Pujols/250 8.00 20.00
21 Scott Rolen/250 4.00 10.00
22 Aubrey Huff/250 3.00 8.00
23 Alfonso Soriano/250 3.00 8.00

2005 Donruss Bat Kings Signatures

RANDOM INSERTS IN PACKS
PRINT RUNS B/WN 5-10 COPIES PER
NO PRICING DUE TO SCARCITY

2005 Donruss Craftsmen

STATED PRINT RUN 1000 SERIAL #'d SETS
*BLACK: 1.25X TO 3X BASIC
BLACK PRINT RUN 100 SERIAL #'d SETS
*MASTER: 1X TO 2.5X BASIC
MASTER PRINT RUN 250 SERIAL #'d SETS
MASTER BLACK PRINT RUN 10 #'d SETS
NO MASTER BLACK PRICING AVAILABLE
RANDOM INSERTS IN PACKS
1 Albert Pujols 2.50 6.00
2 Alex Rodriguez 2.00 5.00
3 Alfonso Soriano .75 2.00
4 Andruw Jones 1.25 3.00
5 Carlos Beltran .75 2.00
6 Derek Jeter 2.50 6.00
7 Greg Maddux 2.00 5.00
8 Hank Blalock .75 2.00
9 Ichiro Suzuki 2.50 6.00
10 Jeff Bagwell 1.25 3.00
11 Jim Thome 1.25 3.00
12 Josh Beckett .75 2.00
13 Ken Griffey Jr. 2.00 5.00
14 Manny Ramirez 1.25 3.00
15 Mark Mulder .75 2.00
16 Mark Prior 1.25 3.00
17 Mark Teixeira 1.25 3.00
18 Miguel Tejada .75 2.00
19 Mike Mussina 1.25 3.00
20 Mike Piazza 1.25 3.00
21 Nomar Garciaparra 1.25 3.00
22 Pedro Martinez 1.25 3.00
23 Rafael Palmeiro 1.25 3.00
24 Randy Johnson 1.25 3.00
25 Roger Clemens 2.00 5.00
26 Sammy Sosa 1.25 3.00
27 Scott Rolen 1.25 3.00
28 Tim Hudson .75 2.00
29 Vernon Wells .75 2.00
30 Vladimir Guerrero 1.25 3.00

2005 Donruss Diamond Kings Inserts

STATED PRINT RUN 2005 SERIAL #'d SETS
*STUDIO: 1X TO 2.5X BASIC
STUDIO PRINT RUN 250 SERIAL #'d SETS
*STUDIO BLACK: 1.25X TO 3X BASIC
STUDIO BLACK PRINT RUN 100 #'d SETS
RANDOM INSERTS IN PACKS
1 Garret Anderson .75 2.00
2 Vladimir Guerrero 1.25 3.00

3 Manny Ramirez 1.25 3.00
4 Kerry Wood .75 2.00
5 Sammy Sosa 1.25 3.00
6 Magglio Ordonez .75 2.00
7 Adam Dunn .75 2.00
8 Todd Helton 1.25 3.00
9 Josh Beckett .75 2.00
10 Miguel Cabrera 1.25 3.00
11 Lance Berkman .75 2.00
12 Carlos Beltran .75 2.00
13 Shawn Green .75 2.00
14 Roger Clemens 2.00 5.00
15 Mike Piazza 1.25 3.00
16 Alex Rodriguez 2.00 5.00
17 Derek Jeter 2.50 6.00
18 Mark Mulder .75 2.00
19 Jim Thome 1.25 3.00
20 Albert Pujols 2.50 6.00
21 Scott Rolen .75 2.00
22 Aubrey Huff .75 2.00
23 Alfonso Soriano .75 2.00
24 Hank Blalock .75 2.00
25 Vernon Wells .75 2.00

2005 Donruss Elite Series

STATED PRINT RUN 1500 SERIAL #'d SETS
*BLACK: .75X TO 2X BASIC
BLACK PRINT RUN 100 SERIAL #'d SETS
*DOMINATOR: .6X TO 1.5X BASIC
DOMINATOR PRINT RUN 250 #'d SETS
*DOM.BLACK: 1.5X TO 4X BASIC
DOM.BLACK PRINT RUN 25 #'d SETS
RANDOM INSERTS IN PACKS
1 Albert Pujols 4.00 10.00
2 Alex Rodriguez 3.00 8.00
3 Alfonso Soriano 1.25 3.00
4 Derek Jeter 4.00 10.00
5 Hank Blalock 1.25 3.00
6 Ichiro Suzuki 4.00 10.00
7 Ivan Rodriguez 2.00 5.00
8 Jim Thome 2.00 5.00
9 Ken Griffey Jr. 3.00 8.00
10 Manny Ramirez 2.00 5.00
11 Mark Mulder 1.25 3.00
12 Mark Prior 2.00 5.00
13 Michael Young 1.25 3.00
14 Miguel Cabrera 2.00 5.00
15 Miguel Tejada 1.25 3.00
16 Mike Piazza 2.00 5.00
17 Nomar Garciaparra 2.00 5.00
18 Rafael Palmeiro 2.00 5.00
19 Randy Johnson 2.00 5.00
20 Roger Clemens 3.00 8.00
21 Sammy Sosa 2.00 5.00
22 Scott Rolen 2.00 5.00
23 Tim Hudson 1.25 3.00
24 Todd Helton 2.00 5.00
25 Vladimir Guerrero 2.00 5.00

2005 Donruss Fans of the Game

COMPLETE SET (5) 4.00 10.00
RANDOM INSERTS IN PACKS
1 Jesse Ventura 1.25 3.00
2 John C. McGinley .75 2.00
3 Susie Essman .75 2.00
4 Dean Cain .75 2.00
5 Meat Loaf 1.25 3.00

2005 Donruss Fans of the Game Autographs

RANDOM INSERTS IN PACKS
SP PRINT RUNS PROVIDED BY DONRUSS
SP'S ARE NOT SERIAL-NUMBERED
1 Jesse Ventura 30.00 60.00
2 John C. McGinley SP/300 20.00 50.00
3 Susie Essman 20.00 50.00
4 Dean Cain SP/250 40.00 80.00
5 Meat Loaf 30.00 60.00

2005 Donruss Inside View

RANDOM INSERTS IN PACKS
NO PRICING DUE TO SCARCITY
NOT INTENDED FOR PUBLIC RELEASE
1 Alex Rodriguez
2 Austin Kearns
3 Barry Larkin
4 C.C. Sabathia
5 Carlos Delgado
6 Chipper Jones
7 Craig Biggio
8 Derek Jeter
9 Derrek Lee
10 Edgar Martinez
11 Garret Anderson
12 Hideo Nomo
13 Ichiro Suzuki
14 Javier Vazquez
15 Javy Lopez
16 Ken Griffey Jr.
17 Magglio Ordonez
18 Rafael Palmeiro
19 Rocco Baldelli
20 Torii Hunter

2005 Donruss Jersey Kings

RANDOM INSERTS IN PACKS
PRINT RUNS B/WN 100-250 COPIES PER
1 Garret Anderson/250 3.00 8.00
2 Vladimir Guerrero/250 4.00 10.00
3 Cal Ripken/100 30.00 60.00
4 Manny Ramirez/250 4.00 10.00
5 Kerry Wood/250 3.00 8.00
6 Sammy Sosa/250 4.00 10.00
7 Magglio Ordonez/250 3.00 8.00
8 Adam Dunn/250 3.00 8.00
9 Todd Helton/250 4.00 10.00
10 Josh Beckett/250 3.00 8.00
11 Miguel Cabrera/250 4.00 10.00
12 Lance Berkman/250 3.00 8.00
13 Carlos Beltran/250 3.00 8.00
14 Shawn Green/250 3.00 8.00
15 Roger Clemens/250 6.00 15.00
16 Mike Piazza/250 4.00 10.00
17 Nolan Ryan/100 20.00 50.00
18 Mark Mulder/250 3.00 8.00
19 Jim Thome/250 4.00 10.00
20 Albert Pujols/250 8.00 20.00
21 Scott Rolen/250 4.00 10.00
22 Aubrey Huff/250 3.00 8.00
23 Alfonso Soriano/250 3.00 8.00
24 Hank Blalock/250 3.00 8.00
25 Vernon Wells/250 3.00 8.00

2005 Donruss Jersey Kings Signatures

RANDOM INSERTS IN PACKS
PRINT RUNS B/WN 5-10 COPIES PER
NO PRICING DUE TO SCARCITY

2005 Donruss Longball Leaders

STATED PRINT RUN 1500 SERIAL #'d SETS
*BLACK: .75X TO 2X BASIC
BLACK PRINT RUN 250 SERIAL #'d SETS
*DIE CUT: 1.25X TO 3X BASIC
DIE CUT PRINT RUN 50 SERIAL #'d SETS
BLACK DC PRINT RUN 10 SERIAL #'d SETS
NO BLACK DC PRICING DUE TO SCARCITY
RANDOM INSERTS IN PACKS
1 Adam Dunn 1.00 2.50
2 Adrian Beltre 1.00 2.50
3 Albert Pujols 3.00 8.00
4 Alex Rodriguez 2.50 6.00
5 David Ortiz 1.50 4.00
6 Hank Blalock 1.00 2.50
7 J.D. Drew 1.00 2.50
8 Jeromy Burnitz 1.00 2.50
9 Jim Edmonds 1.00 2.50
10 Jim Thome 1.50 4.00
11 Manny Ramirez 1.50 4.00
12 Mark Teixeira 1.50 4.00
13 Moises Alou 1.00 2.50
14 Paul Konerko 1.00 2.50
15 Steve Finley 1.00 2.50

2005 Donruss Mound Marvels

STATED PRINT RUN 1000 SERIAL #'d SETS
BLACK PRINT RUN 10 SERIAL #'d SETS
NO BLACK PRICING DUE TO SCARCITY
RANDOM INSERTS IN PACKS
1 Curt Schilling 2.00 5.00
2 Dontrelle Willis 1.25 3.00
3 Eric Gagne 1.25 3.00
4 Greg Maddux 3.00 8.00
5 John Smoltz 2.00 5.00
6 Kenny Rogers 1.25 3.00
7 Kerry Wood 1.25 3.00
8 Mariano Rivera 2.00 5.00
9 Mark Mulder 1.25 3.00
10 Mark Prior 2.00 5.00
11 Mike Mussina 2.00 5.00
12 Pedro Martinez 2.00 5.00
13 Randy Johnson 2.00 5.00
14 Roger Clemens 3.00 8.00
15 Tim Hudson 1.25 3.00

2005 Donruss Power Alley Red

STATED PRINT RUN 2500 SERIAL #'d SETS
BLACK PRINT RUN 10 SERIAL #'d SETS
NO BLACK PRICING DUE TO SCARCITY
BLACK DC PRINT RUN 5 SERIAL #'d SETS
NO BLACK DC PRICING DUE TO SCARCITY
*BLUE: .6X TO 1.5X RED
BLUE PRINT RUN 1000 SERIAL #'d SETS
*BLUE DC: 1.25X TO 3X RED
BLUE DC PRINT RUN 100 SERIAL #'d SETS
*GREEN: 2.5X TO 6X RED
GREEN PRINT RUN 25 SERIAL #'d SETS
GREEN DC PRINT RUN 10 SERIAL #'d SETS
NO GREEN DC PRICING DUE TO SCARCITY
*PURPLE: 1X TO 2.5X RED
PURPLE PRINT RUN 250 SERIAL #'d SETS
*PURPLE DC: 1.5X TO 4X RED
PURPLE DC PRINT RUN 50 SERIAL #'d SETS
*RED DC: 1X TO 2.5X RED
RED DC PRINT RUN 250 SERIAL #'d SETS
*YELLOW: 1.25X TO 3X RED
YELLOW PRINT RUN 100 SERIAL #'d SETS
*YELLOW DC: 2.5X TO 6X RED
YELLOW DC PRINT RUN 25 #'d SETS
RANDOM INSERTS IN PACKS
1 Adam Dunn .75 2.00
2 Adrian Beltre .75 2.00
3 Albert Pujols 2.50 6.00
4 Alex Rodriguez 2.00 5.00
5 Alfonso Soriano .75 2.00
6 Gary Sheffield .75 2.00
7 Hank Blalock .75 2.00
8 Hideki Matsui 2.00 5.00
9 J.D. Drew .75 2.00
10 Jeromy Burnitz .75 2.00
11 Jim Edmonds .75 2.00
12 Jim Thome 1.25 3.00
13 Ken Griffey Jr. 2.00 5.00
14 Manny Ramirez 1.25 3.00
15 Mark Teixeira 1.25 3.00
16 Miguel Cabrera 1.25 3.00
17 Miguel Tejada .75 2.00
18 Mike Lowell .75 2.00
19 Mike Piazza 1.25 3.00
20 Moises Alou .75 2.00
21 Paul Konerko .75 2.00
22 Sammy Sosa 1.25 3.00
23 Scott Rolen 1.25 3.00
24 Todd Helton 1.25 3.00
25 Vladimir Guerrero 1.25 3.00

2005 Donruss Production Line BA

PRINT RUNS B/WN 324-372 COPIES PER
*BLACK: 1X TO 2.5X BASIC PL
BLACK PRINT RUN 25 SERIAL #'d SETS
*DIE CUT: .5X TO 1.2X BASIC PL
DIE CUT PRINT RUN 100 SERIAL #'d SETS
BLACK DC PRINT RUN 10 SERIAL #'d SETS
NO BLACK DC PRICING DUE TO SCARCITY
RANDOM INSERTS IN PACKS
1 Ichiro Suzuki/372 6.00 15.00

2 Ivan Rodriguez/334 3.00 8.00
3 Juan Pierre/326 2.00 5.00
4 Adrian Beltre/334 2.00 5.00
5 Albert Pujols/331 6.00 15.00
6 Mark Loretta/335 2.00 5.00
7 Melvin Mora/340 2.00 5.00
8 Sean Casey/324 2.00 5.00
9 Todd Helton/347 3.00 8.00
10 Vladimir Guerrero/337 3.00 8.00

2005 Donruss Production Line OBP

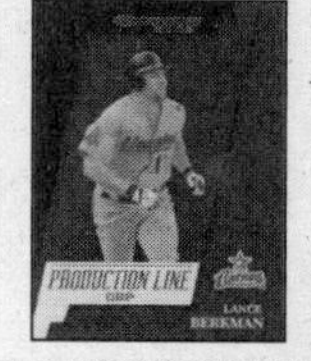

PRINT RUNS B/WN 397-469 COPIES PER
*BLACK: 1.25X TO 3X BASIC PL
BLACK PRINT RUN 25 SERIAL #'d SETS
*DIE CUT: .6X TO 1.5X BASIC PL
DIE CUT PRINT RUN 100 SERIAL #'d SETS
BLACK DC PRINT RUN 10 SERIAL #'d SETS
NO BLACK DC PRICING DUE TO SCARCITY
RANDOM INSERTS IN PACKS
1 Albert Pujols/415 5.00 12.00
2 Bobby Abreu/428 1.50 4.00
3 Lance Berkman/450 1.50 4.00
4 J.D. Drew/436 1.50 4.00
5 Jorge Posada/400 2.50 6.00
6 Ichiro Suzuki/414 5.00 12.00
7 Manny Ramirez/397 2.50 6.00
8 Melvin Mora/419 1.50 4.00
9 Todd Helton/469 2.50 6.00
10 Travis Hafner/410 1.50 4.00

2005 Donruss Production Line OPS

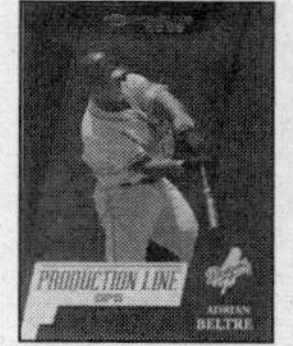

PRINT RUNS B/WN 977-1088 COPIES PER
*BLACK: 1X TO 2.5X BASIC PL
BLACK PRINT RUN 50 SERIAL #'d SETS
*DIE CUT: .75X TO 2X BASIC PL
DIE CUT PRINT RUN 100 SERIAL #'d SETS
*BLACK DC: 1.5X TO 4X BASIC PL
BLACK DC PRINT RUN 25 SERIAL #'d SETS
RANDOM INSERTS IN PACKS
1 Albert Pujols/1072 4.00 10.00
2 David Ortiz/983 2.00 5.00
3 Adrian Beltre/1017 1.25 3.00
4 J.D. Drew/1006 1.25 3.00
5 Jim Thome/977 2.00 5.00
6 Lance Berkman/1016 1.25 3.00
7 Manny Ramirez/1009 2.00 5.00
8 Scott Rolen/1007 2.00 5.00
9 Todd Helton/1088 2.00 5.00
10 Travis Hafner/993 1.25 3.00

2005 Donruss Production Line Slugging

PRINT RUNS B/WN 569-657 COPIES PER
*BLACK: .75X TO 2X BASIC PL
BLACK PRINT RUN 50 SERIAL #'d SETS
*DIE CUT: .6X TO 1.5X BASIC PL
DIE CUT PRINT RUN 100 SERIAL #'d SETS
*BLACK DC: 1.2X TO 3X BASIC PL
BLACK DC PRINT RUN 25 SERIAL #'d SETS
RANDOM INSERTS IN PACKS
1 Adrian Beltre/629 1.50 4.00
2 Albert Pujols/657 5.00 12.00
3 Todd Helton/620 2.50 6.00
4 J.D. Drew/569 1.50 4.00
5 Jim Edmonds/643 1.50 4.00
6 Jim Thome/581 2.50 6.00
7 Vladimir Guerrero/598 2.50 6.00
8 Manny Ramirez/613 2.50 6.00
9 Scott Rolen/598 2.50 6.00
10 Travis Hafner/583 1.50 4.00

2005 Donruss Recollection Autographs

RANDOM INSERTS IN PACKS
PRINT RUNS B/WN 1-5 COPIES PER
NO PRICING DUE TO SCARCITY

2005 Donruss Rookies

STATED ODDS 1:23
BLACK PRINT RUN 10 SERIAL #'d SETS
NO BLACK PRICING DUE TO SCARCITY
*BLUE: .5X TO 1.2X BASIC
BLUE PRINT RUN 100 SERIAL #'d SETS
*GOLD: 1.25X TO 3X BASIC
GOLD PRINT RUN 25 SERIAL #'d SETS
*RED: .4X TO 1X BASIC
RED PRINT RUN 200 SERIAL #'d SETS
PARALLELS RANDOM INSERTS IN PACKS

Card	Low	High
1 Fernando Nieve	1.25	3.00
2 Frankie Francisco	1.25	3.00
3 Jorge Vasquez	1.25	3.00
4 Travis Blackley	1.25	3.00
5 Joey Gathright	2.00	5.00
6 Kazuhito Tadano	2.00	5.00
7 Edwin Moreno	1.25	3.00
8 Lance Cormier	1.25	3.00
9 Justin Knoedler	1.25	3.00
10 Orlando Rodriguez	1.25	3.00
11 Renyel Pinto	1.25	3.00
12 Justin Leone	1.25	3.00
13 Dennis Sarfate	1.25	3.00
14 Sam Narron	1.25	3.00
15 Yadier Molina	2.00	5.00
16 Carlos Vasquez	1.25	3.00
17 Ryan Wing	1.25	3.00
18 Brad Halsey	1.25	3.00
19 Ryan Meaux	1.25	3.00
20 Michael Wuertz	1.25	3.00
21 Shawn Camp	1.25	3.00
22 Ruddy Yan	1.25	3.00
23 Don Kelly	1.25	3.00
24 Jake Woods	1.25	3.00
25 Colby Miller	1.25	3.00
26 Abe Alvarez	1.25	3.00
27 Mike Rouse	1.25	3.00
28 Phil Stockman	1.25	3.00
29 Kevin Cave	1.25	3.00
30 Chris Shelton	3.00	8.00
31 Tim Bittner	1.25	3.00
32 Mariano Gomez	1.25	3.00
33 Angel Chavez	1.25	3.00
34 Carlos Hines	1.25	3.00
35 Aarom Baldiris	1.25	3.00
36 Kazuo Matsui	2.00	5.00
37 Nick Regilio	1.25	3.00
38 Ivan Ochoa	1.25	3.00
39 Graham Koonce	1.25	3.00
40 Merkin Valdez	2.00	5.00
41 Greg Dobbs	1.25	3.00
42 Chris Oxspring	1.25	3.00
43 Dave Crouthers	1.25	3.00
44 Freddy Guzman	1.25	3.00
45 Akinori Otsuka	2.00	5.00
46 Jesse Crain	1.25	3.00
47 Casey Daigle	1.25	3.00
48 Roberto Novoa	1.25	3.00
49 Eddy Rodriguez	1.25	3.00
50 Jason Bartlett	1.25	3.00

2005 Donruss Rookies Stat Line Career

*SLC p/r 201-316: .4X TO 1X
*SLC p/r 121-200: .4X TO 1X
*SLC p/r 81-120: .5X TO 1.2X
*SLC p/r 51-80: .6X TO 1.5X
*SLC p/r 36-50: .75X TO 2X
*SLC p/r 26-35: 1X TO 2.5X
*SLC p/r 16-25: 1.25X TO 3X
RANDOM INSERTS IN DLP R/T PACKS
PRINT RUNS B/WN 1-316 COPIES PER
NO PRICING ON QTY OF 15 OR LESS

2005 Donruss Rookies Stat Line Season

*SLS p/r 121-200: .4X TO 1X
*SLS p/r 81-120: .5X TO 1.2X
*SLS p/r 51-80: .6X TO 1.5X
*SLS p/r 36-50: .75X TO 2X
*SLS p/r 26-35: 1X TO 2.5X

*SLS p/r 16-25: 1.25X TO 3X
RANDOM INSERTS IN DLP R/T PACKS
PRINT RUNS B/WN 1-188 COPIES PER
NO PRICING ON QTY OF 15 OR LESS

2005 Donruss Rookies Autographs

Card	Low	High
COMMON SP	4.00	10.00

RANDOM INSERTS IN PACKS
6/12/14/21/36/40-41/44-47 DO NOT EXIST
SP INFO PROVIDED BY DONRUSS

Card	Low	High
1 Fernando Nieve	3.00	8.00
2 Frankie Francisco	3.00	8.00
3 Jorge Vasquez	3.00	8.00
4 Travis Blackley	3.00	8.00
5 Joey Gathright	4.00	10.00
7 Edwin Moreno	3.00	8.00
8 Lance Cormier	3.00	8.00
9 Justin Knoedler	3.00	8.00
10 Orlando Rodriguez	3.00	8.00
11 Renyel Pinto	3.00	8.00
13 Dennis Sarfate	3.00	8.00
15 Yadier Molina	4.00	10.00
16 Carlos Vasquez		
17 Ryan Wing SP	4.00	10.00
18 Brad Halsey	4.00	10.00
19 Ryan Meaux	3.00	8.00
20 Michael Wuertz	3.00	8.00
22 Ruddy Yan	3.00	8.00
23 Don Kelly	3.00	8.00
24 Jake Woods	3.00	8.00
25 Colby Miller	3.00	8.00
26 Abe Alvarez	4.00	10.00
27 Mike Rouse SP	4.00	10.00
28 Phil Stockman	3.00	8.00
29 Kevin Cave	3.00	8.00
30 Chris Shelton SP	10.00	25.00
31 Tim Bittner	3.00	8.00
32 Mariano Gomez	3.00	8.00
33 Angel Chavez	3.00	8.00
34 Carlos Hines	3.00	8.00
35 Aarom Baldiris	3.00	8.00
37 Nick Regilio	3.00	8.00
38 Ivan Ochoa	3.00	8.00
39 Graham Koonce	3.00	8.00
42 Chris Oxspring	3.00	8.00
43 Dave Crouthers	3.00	8.00
48 Roberto Novoa	3.00	8.00
49 Eddy Rodriguez	3.00	8.00
50 Jason Bartlett	3.00	8.00

2005 Donruss Timber and Threads Bat

RANDOM INSERTS IN PACKS

Card	Low	High
1 Albert Pujols	6.00	15.00
2 Alfonso Soriano	3.00	8.00
3 Andre Dawson	3.00	8.00
4 Austin Kearns	3.00	8.00
5 Brad Penny	3.00	8.00
6 Carlos Beltran	3.00	8.00
7 Carlos Lee	3.00	8.00
8 Chipper Jones	4.00	10.00
9 Dale Murphy	4.00	10.00
10 Don Mattingly	8.00	20.00
11 Frank Thomas	4.00	10.00
12 Garret Anderson	3.00	8.00
13 Gary Carter	3.00	8.00
14 Hank Blalock	3.00	8.00
15 Jacque Jones	3.00	8.00
17 Jay Gibbons	3.00	8.00
18 Jeff Bagwell	4.00	10.00
20 Jermaine Dye	3.00	8.00
21 Jim Thome	4.00	10.00
22 Jose Vidro	3.00	8.00
23 Lance Berkman	3.00	8.00
24 Laynce Nix	3.00	8.00
25 Magglio Ordonez	3.00	8.00
26 Marcus Giles	3.00	8.00
27 Mark Prior	4.00	10.00
28 Mark Teixeira	4.00	10.00
29 Melvin Mora	3.00	8.00
30 Michael Young	3.00	8.00
31 Miguel Cabrera	4.00	10.00
32 Mike Lowell	3.00	8.00
33 Roy Oswalt	3.00	8.00
34 Sammy Sosa	4.00	10.00
35 Scott Rolen	4.00	10.00
36 Sean Burroughs	3.00	8.00
37 Sean Casey	3.00	8.00
38 Shannon Stewart	3.00	8.00
39 Torii Hunter	3.00	8.00
40 Travis Hafner	3.00	8.00

2005 Donruss Timber and Threads Bat Signature

RANDOM INSERTS IN PACKS
PRINT RUNS B/WN 5-10 COPIES PER
NO PRICING DUE TO SCARCITY

2005 Donruss Timber and Threads Combo

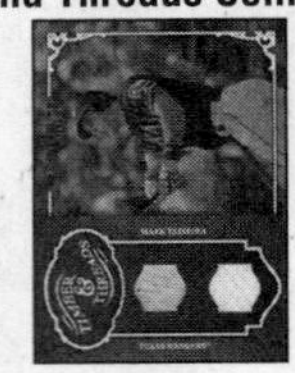

*COMBO: .6X TO 1.5X BAT
RANDOM INSERTS IN PACKS

2005 Donruss Timber and Threads Combo Signature

RANDOM INSERTS IN PACKS
PRINT RUNS B/WN 5-10 COPIES PER
NO PRICING DUE TO SCARCITY

2005 Donruss Timber and Threads Jersey

*JSY: .4X TO 1X BAT
RANDOM INSERTS IN PACKS

Card	Low	High
19 Jeremy Bonderman	3.00	8.00

2005 Donruss Timber and Threads Jersey Signature

RANDOM INSERTS IN PACKS
PRINT RUNS B/WN 5-10 COPIES PER
NO PRICING DUE TO SCARCITY

2001 Donruss Classics

This 200-card set was distributed in six-card packs with a suggested retail price of $11.99. The set features color photos of stars of the game from the past, present, and future highlighted with silver tint and foil. Cards 101-150 display color photos of rookies and are sequentially numbered to 585. Cards 151-200 consisting of retired players are sequentailly numbered to 1755 and are highlighted with gold tint and foil. Cards 162 (Sandy Koufax LGD) and 185 (Robin Roberts LGD) were not intended for public release but a handful of copies made their way into packs despite the manufacturers efforts to physically pull them from the production process. It's rumored that some Koufax cards were issued to dealers as sample cards along with wholesale order forms prior to the product's release but the scarcity of the card likely belies any truth to that statement. Due to their scarcity, the set is considered complete at 198 cards and pricing is unavailable on them individually.

Card	Low	High
COMP.SET w/o SP's (100)	10.00	25.00
COMMON CARD (1-100)	.25	.60
COMMON (101-150)	2.00	5.00
COMMON (151-200)	1.50	4.00
1 Alex Rodriguez	1.00	2.50
2 Barry Bonds	1.50	4.00
3 Cal Ripken	2.00	5.00
4 Chipper Jones	.60	1.50
5 Derek Jeter	1.50	4.00
6 Troy Glaus	.25	.60
7 Frank Thomas	.60	1.50
8 Greg Maddux	1.00	2.50
9 Ivan Rodriguez	.40	1.00
10 Jeff Bagwell	.40	1.00
11 Cliff Floyd	.25	.60
12 Todd Helton	.40	1.00
13 Ken Griffey Jr.	1.00	2.50
14 Manny Ramirez Sox	.40	1.00
15 Mark McGwire	1.50	4.00
16 Mike Piazza	1.00	2.50
17 Nomar Garciaparra	1.00	2.50
18 Pedro Martinez	.40	1.00
19 Randy Johnson	.60	1.50
20 Rick Ankiel	.25	.60
21 Rickey Henderson	.60	1.50
22 Roger Clemens	1.25	3.00
23 Sammy Sosa	.60	1.50
24 Tony Gwynn	.75	2.00
25 Vladimir Guerrero	.60	1.50
26 Kazuhiro Sasaki	.25	.60
27 Roberto Alomar	.40	1.00
28 Barry Zito	.40	1.00
29 Pat Burrell	.25	.60
30 Harold Baines	.25	.60
31 Carlos Delgado	.25	.60
32 J.D. Drew	.25	.60
33 Jim Edmonds	.25	.60
34 Darin Erstad	.25	.60
35 Jason Giambi	.25	.60
36 Tom Glavine	.40	1.00
37 Juan Gonzalez	.25	.60
38 Mark Grace	.40	1.00
39 Shawn Green	.25	.60
40 Tim Hudson	.25	.60
41 Andruw Jones	.40	1.00
42 Jeff Kent	.25	.60
43 Barry Larkin	.40	1.00
44 Rafael Furcal	.25	.60
45 Mike Mussina	.40	1.00
46 Hideo Nomo	.60	1.50
47 Rafael Palmeiro	.40	1.00
48 Scott Rolen	.40	1.00
49 Gary Sheffield	.25	.60
50 Bernie Williams	.40	1.00
51 Bob Abreu	.25	.60
52 Edgardo Alfonzo	.25	.60
53 Edgar Martinez	.40	1.00
54 Magglio Ordonez	.25	.60
55 Kerry Wood	.25	.60
56 Adrian Beltre	.25	.60
57 Lance Berkman	.25	.60
58 Kevin Brown	.25	.60
59 Sean Casey	.25	.60
60 Eric Chavez	.25	.60
61 Bartolo Colon	.25	.60
62 Johnny Damon	.40	1.00
63 Jermaine Dye	.25	.60
64 Juan Encarnacion	.25	.60
65 Carl Everett	.25	.60
66 Brian Giles	.25	.60
67 Mike Hampton	.25	.60
68 Richard Hidalgo	.25	.60
69 Geoff Jenkins	.25	.60
70 Jacque Jones	.25	.60
71 Jason Kendall	.25	.60
72 Ryan Klesko	.25	.60
73 Chan Ho Park	.25	.60
74 Richie Sexson	.25	.60
75 Mike Sweeney	.25	.60
76 Fernando Tatis	.25	.60
77 Miguel Tejada	.25	.60
78 Jose Vidro	.25	.60
79 Larry Walker	.25	.60
80 Preston Wilson	.25	.60
81 Craig Biggio	.40	1.00
82 Fred McGriff	.40	1.00
83 Jim Thome	.40	1.00
84 Garret Anderson	.25	.60
85 Russell Branyan	.25	.60
86 Tony Batista	.25	.60
87 Terrence Long	.25	.60
88 Brad Fullmer	.25	.60
89 Rusty Greer	.25	.60
90 Orlando Hernandez	.25	.60
91 Gabe Kapler	.25	.60
92 Paul Konerko	.25	.60
93 Carlos Lee	.25	.60
94 Kenny Lofton	.25	.60
95 Raul Mondesi	.25	.60
96 Jorge Posada	.40	1.00
97 Tim Salmon	.40	1.00
98 Greg Vaughn	.25	.60
99 Mo Vaughn	.25	.60
100 Omar Vizquel	.40	1.00
101 Aubrey Huff SP	2.00	5.00
102 Jimmy Rollins SP	2.00	5.00
103 Cory Aldridge SP RC	2.00	5.00
104 Wilmy Caceres SP RC	2.00	5.00
105 Josh Beckett SP	3.00	8.00
106 Wilson Betemit SP RC	3.00	8.00
107 Timo Perez SP	2.00	5.00
108 Albert Pujols SP RC	150.00	250.00
109 Bud Smith SP RC	2.00	5.00
110 Jack Wilson SP RC	3.00	8.00
111 Alex Escobar SP	2.00	5.00
112 J. Estrada SP RC	3.00	8.00
113 Pedro Feliz SP	2.00	5.00
114 Nate Frese SP RC	2.00	5.00
115 Carlos Garcia SP RC	2.00	5.00
116 Brandon Larson SP RC	2.00	5.00
117 Alexis Gomez SP RC	2.00	5.00
118 Jason Hart SP	2.00	5.00
119 Adam Dunn SP	3.00	8.00
120 Marcus Giles SP	2.00	5.00
121 C. Parker SP RC	2.00	5.00
122 J.Melian SP RC	2.00	5.00
123 Endy Chavez SP RC	2.00	5.00
124 A.Hernandez SP RC	2.00	5.00
125 Joe Kennedy SP RC	3.00	8.00
126 Jose Mieses SP RC	2.00	5.00
127 C.C. Sabathia SP	2.00	5.00
128 Eric Munson SP	2.00	5.00
129 Xavier Nady SP	2.00	5.00
130 H. Ramirez SP RC	3.00	8.00
131 Abraham Nunez SP	2.00	5.00
132 Jose Ortiz SP	2.00	5.00
133 Jeremy Owens SP RC	2.00	5.00
134 Claudio Vargas SP RC	2.00	5.00
135 Corey Patterson SP	2.00	5.00
136 Andres Torres SP RC	2.00	5.00
137 Ben Sheets SP	3.00	8.00
138 Joe Crede SP	3.00	8.00
139 A.Pettyjohn SP RC	2.00	5.00
140 E.Guzman SP RC	2.00	5.00
141 Jay Gibbons SP RC	3.00	8.00
142 Wilkin Ruan SP RC	2.00	5.00
143 Tsuyoshi Shinjo SP RC	3.00	8.00
144 Alfonso Soriano SP	3.00	8.00
145 Nick Johnson SP	2.00	5.00
146 Ichiro Suzuki SP RC	40.00	80.00
147 Juan Uribe SP RC	3.00	8.00
148 Jack Cust SP	2.00	5.00
149 C.Valderrama SP RC	2.00	5.00
150 Matt White SP RC	2.00	5.00
151 Hank Aaron LGD	4.00	10.00
152 Ernie Banks LGD	2.00	5.00
153 Johnny Bench LGD	2.00	5.00
154 George Brett LGD	4.00	10.00
155 Lou Brock LGD	2.00	5.00
156 Rod Carew LGD	2.00	5.00
157 Steve Carlton LGD	1.50	4.00
158 Bob Feller LGD	1.50	4.00
159 Bob Gibson LGD	2.00	5.00
160 Reggie Jackson LGD	2.00	5.00
161 Al Kaline LGD	2.00	5.00
162 Sandy Koufax LGD SP		
163 Don Mattingly LGD	4.00	10.00
164 Willie Mays LGD	4.00	10.00
165 Willie McCovey LGD	1.50	4.00
166 Joe Morgan LGD	1.50	4.00
167 Stan Musial LGD	3.00	8.00
168 Jim Palmer LGD	1.50	4.00
169 Brooks Robinson LGD	2.00	5.00
170 Frank Robinson LGD	2.00	5.00
171 Nolan Ryan LGD	5.00	12.00
172 Mike Schmidt LGD	4.00	10.00
173 Tom Seaver LGD	2.00	5.00
174 Warren Spahn LGD	2.00	5.00
175 Robin Yount LGD	2.00	5.00
176 Wade Boggs LGD	2.00	5.00
177 Ty Cobb LGD	3.00	8.00
178 Lou Gehrig LGD	4.00	10.00
179 Luis Aparicio LGD	1.50	4.00
180 Babe Ruth LGD	6.00	15.00
181 Ryne Sandberg LGD	4.00	10.00
182 Yogi Berra LGD	2.00	5.00
183 R.Clemente LGD	5.00	12.00
184 Eddie Murray LGD	2.00	5.00
185 Robin Roberts LGD SP		
186 Duke Snider LGD	2.00	5.00
187 Orlando Cepeda LGD	1.50	4.00
188 Billy Williams LGD	1.50	4.00
189 Juan Marichal LGD	1.50	4.00
190 Harmon Killebrew LGD	2.00	5.00
191 Kirby Puckett LGD	2.00	5.00
192 Carlton Fisk LGD	2.00	5.00
193 Dave Winfield LGD	1.50	4.00
194 Whitey Ford LGD	2.00	5.00
195 Paul Molitor LGD	1.50	4.00
196 Tony Perez LGD	1.50	4.00
197 Ozzie Smith LGD	3.00	8.00
198 Ralph Kiner LGD	2.00	5.00
199 Fergie Jenkins LGD	1.50	4.00
200 Phil Rizzuto LGD	2.00	5.00

2001 Donruss Classics Significant Signatures

Randomly inserted into packs at the rate of one in 18, this 83-card set is a partial parallel version of the base set. Each card is autographed and displays a rookie/prospect or retired player with platinum tint and holographic foil. Please note, the following cards packed out as redemption cards with an expiration date of September 10th, 2003: Hank Aaron, Luis Aparicio, Ernie Banks, Josh Beckett, Yogi Berra, Rod Carew, Steve Carlton, Orlando Cepeda, Adam Dunn, Johnny Estrada, Bob Feller, Carlton Fisk, Whitey Ford, Bob Gibson, Reggie Jackson, Nick Johnson, Juan Marichal, Willie Mays, Paul Molitor, Joe Morgan, Eddie Murray, Jim Palmer, Corey Patterson, Tony Perez, Kirby Puckett, Phil Rizzuto, Brooks Robinson, Frank Robinson, Nolan Ryan (Astros), C.C. Sabathia, Ryne Sandberg, Ron Santo, Mike Schmidt, Ben Sheets, Ozzie Smith, Billy Williams, Dave Winfield and Robin Yount. Exchange card 162 was originally intended to feature Sandy Koufax but in late 2002 representatives at Donruss switched the redemption to a Nolan Ryan Mets card (Ryan's basic card 171 in the set pictures him as a member of the Texas Rangers). In addition, exchange card 185 was originally intended to feature Robin Roberts but the redemption was switched in late 2002 to Ron Santo.

Card	Low	High
101 Aubrey Huff	4.00	10.00
103 Cory Aldridge	3.00	8.00
105 Josh Beckett SP	15.00	40.00
106 Wilson Betemit	10.00	25.00
107 Timo Perez	3.00	8.00
108 Albert Pujols	300.00	500.00
110 Jack Wilson	6.00	15.00
111 Alex Escobar	3.00	8.00
112 Johnny Estrada	6.00	15.00
113 Pedro Feliz	3.00	8.00
114 Nate Frese	4.00	10.00
115 Carlos Garcia	3.00	8.00
116 Brandon Larson	3.00	8.00
118 Jason Hart	3.00	8.00
119 Adam Dunn SP	10.00	25.00
120 Marcus Giles	4.00	10.00
121 Christian Parker	3.00	8.00
126 Jose Mieses	4.00	10.00
127 C.C.Sabathia SP	6.00	15.00
129 Xavier Nady	6.00	15.00
130 Horacio Ramirez	6.00	15.00
131 Abraham Nunez	3.00	8.00
132 Jose Ortiz	3.00	8.00
133 Jeremy Owens	4.00	10.00
134 Claudio Vargas	4.00	10.00
135 Corey Patterson SP	4.00	10.00
136 Andres Torres	3.00	8.00
137 Ben Sheets SP	10.00	25.00
138 Joe Crede	6.00	15.00
139 Adam Pettyjohn	3.00	8.00
140 Elpidio Guzman	3.00	8.00
141 Jay Gibbons	6.00	15.00
142 Wilkin Ruan	4.00	10.00
144 Alfonso Soriano SP	15.00	40.00
145 Nick Johnson SP	6.00	15.00
147 Juan Uribe	6.00	15.00
149 Carlos Valderrama	3.00	8.00
151 Hank Aaron SP	400.00	500.00
152 Ernie Banks	20.00	50.00
153 Johnny Bench SP	40.00	80.00
154 George Brett SP	75.00	150.00
155 Lou Brock	10.00	25.00
156 Rod Carew	10.00	25.00
157 Steve Carlton	8.00	20.00
158 Bob Feller	8.00	20.00
159 Bob Gibson	10.00	25.00
160 Reggie Jackson SP	40.00	80.00
161 Al Kaline	15.00	40.00
162 Nolan Ryan Astros SP	125.00	200.00
163 Don Mattingly	40.00	80.00
164 Willie Mays SP	125.00	200.00
165 Willie McCovey	10.00	25.00
166 Joe Morgan	8.00	20.00
167 Stan Musial SP	50.00	100.00
168 Jim Palmer	8.00	20.00
169 B. Robinson EXCH	10.00	25.00
170 Frank Robinson	10.00	25.00
171 Nolan Ryan Rangers SP	125.00	200.00
172 Mike Schmidt	40.00	80.00
173 Tom Seaver	15.00	40.00
174 Warren Spahn	20.00	50.00
175 Robin Yount SP	40.00	80.00
176 Wade Boggs SP	30.00	60.00
179 Luis Aparicio	8.00	20.00
181 Ryne Sandberg	30.00	60.00
182 Yogi Berra	15.00	40.00
184 Eddie Murray	30.00	60.00
185 Ron Santo	10.00	25.00
186 Duke Snider	10.00	25.00
187 Orlando Cepeda	8.00	20.00
188 Billy Williams	8.00	20.00
189 Juan Marichal	8.00	20.00
190 Harmon Killebrew	15.00	40.00
191 Kirby Puckett SP	75.00	150.00
192 Carlton Fisk	10.00	25.00
193 Dave Winfield SP	30.00	60.00
194 Whitey Ford	10.00	25.00
195 Paul Molitor SP	15.00	40.00
196 Tony Perez	8.00	20.00
197 Ozzie Smith SP	40.00	80.00
198 Ralph Kiner	10.00	25.00
199 Fergie Jenkins	8.00	20.00
200 Phil Rizzuto	15.00	40.00

2001 Donruss Classics Timeless Tributes

Randomly inserted in packs, this 198-card set is a parallel version of the base set featuring silver or gold holo-foil highlights. The cards are sequentially numbered to 100. Cards 162 and 185 were not intended for production due to contractual problems with the featured athletes (Sandy Koufax for card 162 and Robin Roberts for card 185). The manufacturer made the effort to pull and destroy all copies found within the print run during the packout process. A handful of copies of the basic versions of these cards have been confirmed to exist but pricing is unavailable due to lack of sales information.

*TRIBUTE 1-100: 2.5X TO 6X BASIC
*TRIBUTE 101-150: .5X TO 1.2X BASIC
*TRIBUTE 151-200: 1.25X TO 3X BASIC

Card	Low	High
108 Albert Pujols	100.00	200.00
146 Ichiro Suzuki	50.00	100.00

2001 Donruss Classics Benchmarks

Randomly inserted in hobby packs at the rate of one in 18 and in retail packs at the rate of one in 72, this 25-card set features color player photos with game-used bench swatches embedded in the cards. Hank Aaron, Willie Stargell and card BM19 were only available as exchange cards. Those cards could be redeemed until September 10, 2003.

CARDS 11, 19 AND 24 WERE EXCHANGE
NO EXCH.PRICING DUE TO SCARCITY
BM1 Todd Helton 6.00 15.00
BM2 Roberto Clemente 20.00 50.00
BM3 Mark McGwire 15.00 40.00
BM4 Barry Bonds 12.50 30.00
BM5 Bob Gibson 6.00 15.00
BM6 Ken Griffey Jr. 8.00 20.00
BM7 Frank Robinson 6.00 15.00
BM8 Greg Maddux 8.00 20.00
BM9 Reggie Jackson 6.00 15.00
BM10 Sammy Sosa 6.00 15.00
BM11 Willie Stargell
BM12 Vladimir Guerrero 6.00 15.00
BM13 Johnny Bench 6.00 15.00
BM14 Tony Gwynn 6.00 15.00
BM15 Mike Schmidt 10.00 25.00
BM16 Ivan Rodriguez 6.00 15.00
BM17 Jeff Bagwell 6.00 15.00
BM18 Cal Ripken 15.00 40.00
BM19 TBD EXCH
BM20 Kirby Puckett 6.00 15.00
BM21 Frank Thomas 6.00 15.00
BM22 Joe Morgan 4.00 10.00
BM23 Mike Piazza 8.00 20.00
BM24 Hank Aaron
BM25 Andruw Jones 6.00 15.00

2001 Donruss Classics Benchmarks Autographs

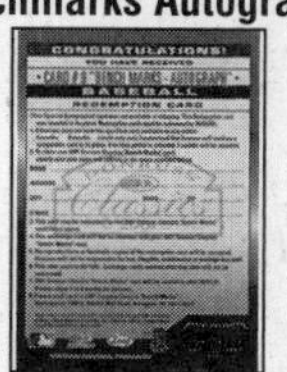

Randomly inserted in packs, this nine-card set is a partial parallel autographed version of the regular insert set. No autographed cards were seeded into packs. Rather, exchange cards with a redemption deadline of September 10th, 2003 were inserted in their place. According to the manufacturer, only 25 copies of each card were issued. The cards are not priced due to scarcity.

BM5 Bob Gibson
BM7 Frank Robinson
BM9 Reggie Jackson
BM12 Vladimir Guerrero
BM13 Johnny Bench
BM15 Mike Schmidt
BM20 Kirby Puckett
BM22 Joe Morgan
BM25 Andruw Jones

2001 Donruss Classics Combos

Randomly inserted in packs, this 45-card set features color action photos of baseball legends. Some cards consist of one player while others display a pairing of two great players. Each card has two or four swatches of game-worn/used memorabilia. One player cards are sequentially numbered to 100 while two player cards are sequentially numbered to 50. The following cards were issued in packs as exchange cards with a redemption deadline of Septemer 10th, 2003: Hank Aaron, Ernie Banks, Wade Boggs, Lou Brock, Steve Carlton, Andre Dawson, Don Mattingly, Jackie Robinson, Ryne Sandberg, Willie Stargell and Billy Williams. In addition, the following dual-player cards packed out as exchange cards (with the same redemption deadline as detailed above): Banks/Williams, Carlton/Schmidt, Clemente/Stargell, Dawson/Sandberg, Mattingly/Boggs, Musial/Brock and Robinson/Snider.

1 R.Clemente/100 75.00 150.00
2 Willie Stargell/100 15.00 40.00
3 Babe Ruth/100 250.00 400.00
4 Lou Gehrig/100 175.00 300.00
5 Hank Aaron/100 75.00 150.00
6 Eddie Mathews/100 20.00 50.00
7 Johnny Bench/100 20.00 50.00
8 Joe Morgan/100 10.00 25.00
9 Robin Yount/100 20.00 50.00
10 Paul Molitor/100 10.00 25.00
11 S.Carlton/85 EXCH 10.00 25.00
12 Mike Schmidt/85 40.00 80.00
13 Stan Musial/100 40.00 80.00
14 Lou Brock/100 15.00 40.00
15 Yogi Berra/100 30.00 60.00
16 Phil Rizzuto/100 20.00 50.00
17 Ernie Banks/85 30.00 60.00
18 B. Williams/85 EXCH 10.00 25.00
19 Don Mattingly/100 40.00 80.00
20 Wade Boggs/100 15.00 40.00
21 Jackie Robinson/100 75.00 150.00
22 Duke Snider/100 15.00 40.00
23 Frank Robinson/85 15.00 40.00
24 Brooks Robinson/85 15.00 40.00
25 Orlando Cepeda/100 10.00 25.00
26 Willie McCovey/100 10.00 25.00
27 Ryne Sandberg/100 40.00 80.00
28 Andre Dawson/100 10.00 25.00
29 H.Killebrew/100 20.00 50.00
30 Rod Carew/100 15.00 40.00
31 Roberto Clemente 125.00 200.00
Willie Stargell/50
32 Babe Ruth 600.00 1000.00
Lou Gehrig
33 Hank Aaron 75.00 150.00
Eddie Mathews
34 Johnny Bench 60.00 120.00
Joe Morgan
35 Robin Yount 60.00 120.00
Paul Molitor
36 Steve Carlton 75.00 150.00
Mike Schmidt/40
37 Stan Musial 75.00 150.00
Lou Brock/50
38 Yogi Berra 75.00 150.00
Phil Rizzuto/50
39 Ernie Banks 60.00 120.00
Billy Williams/40
40 Don Mattingly 75.00 150.00
Wade Boggs/50
41 Jackie Robinson Jacket-Jsy 125.00 200.00
Duke Snider Bat-Jsy/50
42 Brooks Robinson 50.00 100.00
Frank Robinson
43 Orlando Cepeda 50.00 100.00
Willie McCovey/50
44 Andre Dawson 75.00 150.00
Ryne Sandberg/50
45 Harmon Killebrew 60.00 120.00
Rod Carew

2001 Donruss Classics Combos Autograph

Randomly inserted in packs, this ten-card set is a partial parallel autographed version of the regular insert set. No autographed cards were seeded into packs. Rather, exchange cards with a redemption deadline of September 10th, 2003 were seeded in their place. Each actual single-player autograph card is serial numbered to 15 copies and dual-player card serial numbered to 10 copies.

CC11 Steve Carlton/15
CC12 Mike Schmidt/15
CC17 Ernie Banks/15
CC18 Billy Williams/15
CC23 Frank Robinson/15
CC24 Brooks Robinson/15
CC36 Steve Carlton
Mike Schmidt
CC39 Ernie Banks
Billy Williams
CC40 Don Mattingly
Wade Boggs/10
CC42 Brooks Robinson
Frank Robinson

2001 Donruss Classics Legendary Lumberjacks

Randomly inserted in hobby packs at the rate of one in 18 and in retail packs at the rate of one in 72, this 50-card set features color photos of the most skilled sluggers in Baseball. A swatch of a game-used bat was embedded in each card. The following cards packed out as exchange cards with a redemption deadline of September 10th, 2003: Hack Wilson, Hank Aaron, Ernie Banks, Nellie Fox, Jimmie Foxx, Rogers Horsnby, Roger Maris, Willie Stargell and Ted Williams.

STATED ODDS 1:18 HOBBY, 1:72 RETAIL
SP PRINT RUNS PROVIDED BY DONRUSS
SP'S ARE NOT SERIAL-NUMBERED
LL1 Hack Wilson SP/244 * 40.00 80.00
LL2 Chipper Jones 10.00 25.00
LL3 Rogers Hornsby SP/301 * 50.00 100.00
LL4 Nellie Fox SP/300 * 50.00 100.00
LL5 Ivan Rodriguez 6.00 15.00
LL6 Jimmie Foxx SP/300 * 60.00 120.00
LL7 Hank Aaron 20.00 50.00
LL8 Yogi Berra SP/400 *
LL9 Ernie Banks SP/300 * 30.00 60.00
LL10 George Brett 15.00 40.00
LL11 Ty Cobb SP/100 * 100.00 200.00
LL12 R. Clemente SP 100.00 200.00
LL13 Carlton Fisk 6.00 15.00
LL14 Reggie Jackson 6.00 15.00
LL15 Al Kaline 10.00 25.00
LL16 Harmon Killebrew 10.00 25.00
LL17 Ralph Kiner 6.00 15.00
LL18 Roger Maris SP/275 * 60.00 120.00
LL19 Eddie Mathews SP/400 *
LL20 Ted Williams SP/300 * 75.00 150.00
LL21 Willie McCovey 6.00 15.00
LL22 Eddie Murray 10.00 25.00
LL23 Joe Morgan SP/268 *
LL24 Frank Robinson 6.00 15.00
LL25 Tony Perez 4.00 10.00
LL26 Mike Schmidt 15.00 40.00
LL27 Ryne Sandberg 15.00 40.00
LL28 Duke Snider SP/300 *
LL29 Willie Stargell SP/500 *
LL30 Billy Williams 4.00 10.00
LL31 Dave Winfield 4.00 10.00
LL32 Robin Yount 10.00 25.00
LL33 Barry Bonds 20.00 50.00
LL34 Stan Musial SP/300 *
LL35 Johnny Bench SP/300 *
LL36 Orlando Cepeda 4.00 10.00
LL37 Todd Helton 6.00 15.00
LL38 Frank Thomas 10.00 25.00
LL39 Juan Gonzalez SP/400 *
LL40 Cal Ripken SP/500 *
LL41 Rafael Palmeiro 6.00 15.00
LL42 Troy Glaus SP/100 *
LL43 Vladimir Guerrero 10.00 25.00
LL44 Paul Molitor SP/400 *
LL45 Tony Gwynn 6.00 15.00
LL46 Rod Carew 6.00 15.00
LL47 Lou Brock 6.00 15.00
LL48 Wade Boggs 6.00 15.00
LL49 Babe Ruth SP/60 * 125.00 250.00
LL50 Lou Gehrig SP/100 * 100.00 200.00

2001 Donruss Classics Stadium Stars

Randomly inserted in hobby packs at the rate of one in 18 and in retail packs at the rate of one in 72, this 25-card set features color action player photos with swatches of stadium seats taken from some of the most heralded ballparks embedded in the cards. An exchange card with a redemption deadline of September 10th, 2003 was seeded into packs for Honus Wagner's card.

SS1 Babe Ruth SP 40.00 80.00
SS2 Cal Ripken 10.00 25.00
SS3 Brooks Robinson 4.00 10.00
SS4 Tony Gwynn SP 6.00 15.00
SS5 Ty Cobb 15.00 40.00
SS6 Vladimir Guerrero SP 6.00 15.00
SS7 Lou Gehrig SP 20.00 50.00
SS8 Nomar Garciaparra 6.00 15.00
SS9 Sammy Sosa SP 6.00 15.00
SS10 Reggie Jackson SP 6.00 15.00
SS11 Alex Rodriguez 6.00 15.00
SS12 Derek Jeter 10.00 25.00
SS13 Willie McCovey SP 4.00 10.00
SS14 Mark McGwire 10.00 25.00
SS15 Chipper Jones 4.00 10.00
SS16 Honus Wagner 10.00 25.00
SS17 Ken Griffey Jr. 6.00 15.00
SS18 Frank Robinson 4.00 10.00
SS19 Barry Bonds SP 10.00 25.00
SS20 Yogi Berra SP 6.00 15.00
SS21 Mike Piazza SP 6.00 15.00
SS22 Roger Clemens 6.00 15.00
SS23 Duke Snider SP 6.00 15.00
SS24 Frank Thomas 4.00 10.00
SS25 Andruw Jones 4.00 10.00

2001 Donruss Classics Timeless Treasures

Randomly inserted in hobby packs at the rate of one in 420, and in retail packs at the rate of one in 1680, this five-card set features pictures of great players with swatches of memorabilia from five famous events in baseball history.

TT1 M. McGwire Ball SP 125.00 200.00
TT2 Babe Ruth Seat 40.00 80.00
TT3 H. Killebrew Bat SP 20.00 50.00
TT4 Derek Jeter Base 20.00 50.00
TT5 Barry Bonds Ball SP 60.00 120.00

2002 Donruss Classics Samples

This partial parallel to the Donruss Classics set was issued as inserts in Beckett Baseball Card Monthly issue number 209. Only the first 100 cards of this set were created for this project.

*SAMPLES: .75X TO 2X BASIC CARDS
*GOLD: 1.5X TO 4X BASIC SAMPLES

2002 Donruss Classics

This 200 card standard-size was issued in June, 2002. An additional 25 update cards were seeded into Donruss the Rookies packs distributed in December, 2002. The basic set was released in six card packs which came in two nine-pack mini boxes per full box. The full boxes were issued four boxes to a case and had an SRP of $6 per pack. Cards 1-100 feature veteran active players, while cards 101-150 feature rookies and prospects and cards 151-200 feature retired greats. Cards numbered 101-200 were all printed to a stated print run of 1500 sets and were released two cards per mini-box (or 4 per full box of 18 packs). Update cards 201-225 were also serial-numbered to 1500.

COMP.SET w/o SP's (100) 10.00 25.00
COMMON CARD (1-100) .25 .60
COMMON (101-150/201-225) 1.50 4.00
COMMON CARD (151-200) 1.50 4.00
1 Alex Rodriguez 1.00 2.50
2 Barry Bonds 1.50 4.00
3 C.C. Sabathia .25 .60
4 Chipper Jones .60 1.50
5 Derek Jeter 1.50 4.00
6 Troy Glaus .25 .60
7 Frank Thomas .60 1.50
8 Greg Maddux 1.00 2.50
9 Ivan Rodriguez .40 1.00
10 Jeff Bagwell .40 1.00
11 Mark Buehrle .25 .60
12 Todd Helton .40 1.00
13 Ken Griffey Jr. 1.00 2.50
14 Manny Ramirez .40 1.00
15 Brad Penny .25 .60
16 Mike Piazza 1.00 2.50
17 Nomar Garciaparra 1.00 2.50
18 Pedro Martinez .40 1.00
19 Randy Johnson .60 1.50
20 Bud Smith .25 .60
21 Rickey Henderson .60 1.50
22 Roger Clemens 1.25 3.00
23 Sammy Sosa .60 1.50
24 Brandon Duckworth .25 .60
25 Vladimir Guerrero .60 1.50
26 Kazuhiro Sasaki .25 .60
27 Roberto Alomar .40 1.00
28 Barry Zito .25 .60
29 Rich Aurilia .25 .60
30 Ben Sheets .25 .60
31 Carlos Delgado .25 .60
32 J.D. Drew .25 .60
33 Jermaine Dye .25 .60
34 Darin Erstad .25 .60
35 Jason Giambi .25 .60
36 Tom Glavine .40 1.00
37 Juan Gonzalez .25 .60
38 Luis Gonzalez .25 .60
39 Shawn Green .25 .60
40 Tim Hudson .25 .60
41 Andruw Jones .40 1.00
42 Shannon Stewart .25 .60
43 Barry Larkin .40 1.00
44 Wade Miller .25 .60
45 Mike Mussina .40 1.00
46 Hideo Nomo .60 1.50
47 Rafael Palmeiro .40 1.00
48 Scott Rolen .40 1.00
49 Gary Sheffield .25 .60
50 Bernie Williams .40 1.00
51 Bob Abreu .25 .60
52 Javier Vazquez .25 .60
53 Edgar Martinez .40 1.00
54 Magglio Ordonez .25 .60
55 Kerry Wood .25 .60
56 Adrian Beltre .25 .60
57 Lance Berkman .25 .60
58 Kevin Brown .25 .60
59 Sean Casey .25 .60
60 Eric Chavez .25 .60
61 Robert Person .25 .60
62 Jeremy Giambi .25 .60
63 Freddy Garcia .25 .60
64 Alfonso Soriano .25 .60
65 Doug Davis .25 .60
66 Brian Giles .25 .60
67 Moises Alou .25 .60
68 Richard Hidalgo .25 .60
69 Paul LoDuca .25 .60
70 Aramis Ramirez .25 .60
71 Andres Galarraga .25 .60
72 Ryan Klesko .25 .60
73 Chan Ho Park .25 .60
74 Richie Sexson .25 .60
75 Mike Sweeney .25 .60
76 Aubrey Huff .25 .60
77 Miguel Tejada .25 .60
78 Jose Vidro .25 .60
79 Larry Walker .25 .60
80 Roy Oswalt .25 .60
81 Craig Biggio .40 1.00
82 Juan Pierre .25 .60
83 Jim Thome .40 1.00
84 Josh Towers .25 .60
85 Alex Escobar .25 .60
86 Cliff Floyd .25 .60
87 Terrence Long .25 .60
88 Curt Schilling .25 .60
89 Carlos Beltran .25 .60
90 Albert Pujols 1.25 3.00
91 Gabe Kapler .25 .60
92 Mark Mulder .25 .60
93 Carlos Lee .25 .60
94 Robert Fick .25 .60
95 Raul Mondesi .25 .60
96 Ichiro Suzuki 1.25 3.00
97 Adam Dunn .25 .60
98 Corey Patterson .25 .60
99 Tsuyoshi Shinjo .25 .60
100 Joe Mays .25 .60
101 Juan Cruz ROO 1.50 4.00
102 Marlon Byrd ROO 1.50 4.00
103 Luis Garcia ROO 1.50 4.00
104 Jorge Padilla ROO RC 1.50 4.00
105 Dennis Tankersley ROO 1.50 4.00
106 Josh Pearce ROO 1.50 4.00
107 Ramon Vazquez ROO 1.50 4.00
108 Chris Baker ROO RC 1.50 4.00
109 Eric Cyr ROO 1.50 4.00
110 Reed Johnson ROO RC 2.00 5.00
111 Ryan Jamison ROO 1.50 4.00
112 Antonio Perez ROO 1.50 4.00
113 Satoru Komiyama ROO RC 1.50 4.00
114 Austin Kearns ROO 1.50 4.00
115 Juan Pena ROO 1.50 4.00
116 Orlando Hudson ROO 1.50 4.00
117 Kazuhisa Ishii ROO RC 2.00 5.00
118 Erik Bedard ROO 1.50 4.00
119 Luis Ugueto ROO RC 1.50 4.00
120 Ben Howard ROO RC 1.50 4.00
121 Morgan Ensberg ROO 1.50 4.00
122 Doug Devore ROO RC 1.50 4.00
123 Josh Phelps ROO 1.50 4.00
124 Angel Berroa ROO 1.50 4.00
125 Ed Rogers ROO 1.50 4.00
126 Takahito Nomura ROO RC 1.50 4.00
127 John Ennis ROO RC 1.50 4.00
128 Bill Hall ROO 1.50 4.00
129 Dewon Brazelton ROO 1.50 4.00
130 Hank Blalock ROO 2.00 5.00
131 So Taguchi ROO RC 2.00 5.00
132 Jorge De La Rosa ROO RC 1.50 4.00
133 Matt Thornton ROO RC 1.50 4.00
134 Brandon Backe ROO RC 2.00 5.00
135 Jeff Deardorff ROO 1.50 4.00
136 Steve Smyth ROO 1.50 4.00
137 An. Machado ROO RC 1.50 4.00
138 John Buck ROO 1.50 4.00
139 Mark Prior ROO 2.00 5.00
140 Sean Burroughs ROO 1.50 4.00
141 Alex Herrera ROO 1.50 4.00
142 Francis Beltran ROO RC 1.50 4.00
143 Jason Romano ROO 1.50 4.00
144 Michael Cuddyer ROO 1.50 4.00
145 Steve Bechler ROO RC 1.50 4.00
146 Alfredo Amezaga ROO 1.50 4.00
147 Ryan Ludwick ROO 1.50 4.00
148 Martin Vargas ROO 1.50 4.00
149 Allan Simpson ROO RC 1.50 4.00
150 Mark Teixeira ROO 2.00 5.00
151 Dale Murphy LGD 2.00 5.00
152 Ernie Banks LGD 2.00 5.00
153 Johnny Bench LGD 2.00 5.00
154 George Brett LGD 3.00 8.00
155 Lou Brock LGD 2.00 5.00
156 Rod Carew LGD 2.00 5.00
157 Steve Carlton LGD 1.50 4.00
158 Joe Torre LGD 2.00 5.00
159 Dennis Eckersley LGD 1.50 4.00
160 Reggie Jackson LGD 2.00 5.00
161 Al Kaline LGD 2.00 5.00
162 Dave Parker LGD 1.50 4.00
163 Don Mattingly LGD 3.00 8.00
164 Tony Gwynn LGD 2.00 5.00
165 Willie McCovey LGD 1.50 4.00
166 Joe Morgan LGD 1.50 4.00
167 Stan Musial LGD 2.50 6.00
168 Jim Palmer LGD 1.50 4.00
169 Brooks Robinson LGD 2.00 5.00
170 Bo Jackson LGD 2.00 5.00
171 Nolan Ryan LGD 4.00 10.00
172 Mike Schmidt LGD 3.00 8.00
173 Tom Seaver LGD 2.00 5.00
174 Cal Ripken LGD 5.00 12.00
175 Robin Yount LGD 2.00 5.00
176 Wade Boggs LGD 2.00 5.00
177 Gary Carter LGD 1.50 4.00
178 Ron Santo LGD 2.00 5.00
179 Luis Aparicio LGD 1.50 4.00
180 Bobby Doerr LGD 2.00 5.00
181 Ryne Sandberg LGD 3.00 8.00
182 Yogi Berra LGD 2.00 5.00
183 Will Clark LGD 2.00 5.00
184 Eddie Murray LGD 2.00 5.00
185 Andre Dawson LGD 1.50 4.00
186 Duke Snider LGD 2.00 5.00
187 Orlando Cepeda LGD 1.50 4.00
188 Billy Williams LGD 1.50 4.00
189 Juan Marichal LGD 1.50 4.00
190 Harmon Killebrew LGD 2.00 5.00
191 Kirby Puckett LGD 2.00 5.00
192 Carlton Fisk LGD 2.00 5.00
193 Dave Winfield LGD 1.50 4.00
194 Alan Trammell LGD 1.50 4.00
195 Paul Molitor LGD 1.50 4.00
196 Tony Perez LGD 1.50 4.00
197 Ozzie Smith LGD 2.50 6.00
198 Ralph Kiner LGD 1.50 4.00
199 Fergie Jenkins LGD 1.50 4.00
200 Phil Rizzuto LGD 2.00 5.00
201 Oliver Perez ROO RC 2.00 5.00
202 Aaron Cook ROO RC 1.50 4.00
203 Eric Junge ROO RC 1.50 4.00
204 Freddy Sanchez ROO RC 2.00 5.00
205 Cliff Lee ROO RC 2.00 5.00
206 Run. Hernandez ROO RC 1.50 4.00
207 Chone Figgins ROO RC 2.00 5.00
208 Rodrigo Rosario ROO RC 1.50 4.00
209 Kevin Cash ROO RC 1.50 4.00
210 Josh Bard ROO RC 1.50 4.00
211 Felix Escalona ROO RC 1.50 4.00
212 Jer. Robertson ROO RC 1.50 4.00
213 J. Simontacchi ROO RC 1.50 4.00
214 Shane Nance ROO RC 1.50 4.00
215 Ben Kozlowski ROO RC 1.50 4.00
216 Brian Tallet ROO RC 1.50 4.00
217 Earl Snyder ROO RC 1.50 4.00
218 Andy Pratt ROO RC 1.50 4.00
219 Trey Hodges ROO RC 1.50 4.00
220 Kirk Saarloos ROO RC 1.50 4.00
221 Rene Reyes ROO RC 1.50 4.00
222 Joe Borchard ROO 1.50 4.00
223 Wilson Valdez ROO RC 1.50 4.00
224 Miguel Asencio ROO RC 1.50 4.00
225 Chris Snelling ROO RC 1.50 4.00

2002 Donruss Classics National

ISSUED AT '02 NATIONAL CONVENTION
STATED PRINT RUN 5 SERIAL #'d SETS
NO PRICING DUE TO SCARCITY

2002 Donruss Classics Significant Signatures

Cards checklisted 1-200 were randomly inserted in basic Donruss Classics packs. Cards 201-225 were randomly inserted in 2002 Donruss the Rookies packs in mid-December, 2002. This is a 202-card, skip-numbered, partial parallel to the Donruss Classics set. Each card has an autographed foil sticker attached to it and since each card has a different stated print run, we have notated that information next to the player's name. Cards with a print run of 25 or less are not priced due to market scarcity. A few signed signed cards were issued in "personal" form if the number of the signature had something important to their career.

1 Alex Rodriguez/15
3 C.C. Sabathia/20
4 Chipper Jones/15
6 Troy Glaus/25
7 Frank Thomas/15
8 Greg Maddux/15
9 Ivan Rodriguez/15
10 Jeff Bagwell/15
11 Mark Buehrle/25
12 Todd Helton/15
14 Manny Ramirez/15
15 Brad Penny/25
17 Nomar Garciaparra/15
18 Pedro Martinez/15
20 Bud Smith/25
21 Rickey Henderson/15
22 Roger Clemens/15
24 Brandon Duckworth/25
25 Vladimir Guerrero/25
27 Roberto Alomar/15
28 Barry Zito/25
29 Rich Aurilia/25
30 Ben Sheets/25
32 J.D. Drew/15
33 Jermaine Dye/25
34 Darin Erstad/15
35 Jason Giambi/15
36 Tom Glavine/15
37 Juan Gonzalez/15
38 Luis Gonzalez/15
40 Tim Hudson/25
41 Andruw Jones/15
42 Shannon Stewart/25
43 Barry Larkin/15
44 Wade Miller/25
45 Mike Mussina/15
47 Rafael Palmeiro/15
48 Scott Rolen/15
49 Gary Sheffield/15
50 Bernie Williams/15
51 Bobby Abreu/25
52 Javier Vazquez/25
53 Edgar Martinez/25
55 Kerry Wood/15
56 Adrian Beltre/25
57 Lance Berkman/25
58 Kevin Brown/15
59 Sean Casey/20
60 Eric Chavez/25
61 Robert Person/25
62 Jeremy Giambi/25
63 Freddy Garcia/25
64 Alfonso Soriano/25
65 Doug Davis/25
66 Brian Giles/13
67 Moises Alou/15
68 Richard Hidalgo/25
69 Paul LoDuca/25
70 Aramis Ramirez/25
71 Andres Galarraga/15
72 Ryan Klesko/20
74 Richie Sexson/25
75 Mike Sweeney/25
76 Aubrey Huff/25
77 Miguel Tejada/25
78 Jose Vidro/25
80 Roy Oswalt/25
81 Craig Biggio/15
82 Juan Pierre/25
84 Josh Towers/25
85 Alex Escobar/25
86 Cliff Floyd/25
87 Terrence Long/25
88 Curt Schilling/15
89 Carlos Beltran/25
90 Albert Pujols/25
91 Gabe Kapler/25
92 Mark Mulder/25
93 Carlos Lee/25
94 Robert Fick/25
97 Adam Dunn/6
98 Corey Patterson/25
100 Joe Mays/25
101 Juan Cruz ROO/400 4.00 10.00
102 Marlon Byrd ROO/500 4.00 10.00
103 Luis Garcia ROO/500 4.00 10.00
104 Jorge Padilla ROO/500 4.00 10.00
105 Dennis Tankersley ROO/250 6.00 15.00
106 Josh Pearce ROO/500 4.00 10.00
107 Ramon Vazquez ROO/500 4.00 10.00
108 Chris Baker ROO/500 4.00 10.00
109 Eric Cyr ROO/500 4.00 10.00
110 Reed Johnson ROO/500 6.00 15.00
111 Ryan Jamison ROO/500 4.00 10.00
112 Antonio Perez ROO/500 4.00 10.00
113 Satoru Komiyama ROO/50 15.00 40.00
114 Austin Kearns ROO/500 4.00 10.00
115 Juan Pena ROO/500 4.00 10.00
116 Orlando Hudson ROO/400 4.00 10.00
117 Kazuhisa Ishii ROO/50 15.00 40.00
118 Erik Bedard ROO/150 6.00 15.00
119 Luis Ugueto ROO/250 4.00 10.00
120 Ben Howard ROO/500 4.00 10.00
121 Morgan Ensberg ROO/500 6.00 15.00
122 Doug Devore ROO/500 4.00 10.00
123 Josh Phelps ROO/500 4.00 10.00
124 Angel Berroa ROO/500 4.00 10.00
125 Ed Rogers ROO/500 4.00 10.00
126 Takahito Nomura ROO/25
127 John Ennis ROO/500 4.00 10.00
128 Bill Hall ROO/400 6.00 15.00
129 Dewon Brazelton ROO/400 4.00 10.00
130 Hank Blalock ROO/100 6.00 15.00
131 So Taguchi ROO/150 12.50 30.00

132 Jorge De La Rosa ROO/500 4.00 10.00
133 Matt Thornton ROO/500 4.00 10.00
134 Brandon Backe ROO/500 6.00 15.00
135 Jeff Deardorff ROO/500 4.00 10.00
136 Steve Smyth ROO/400 4.00 10.00
137 Anderson Machado ROO/500 4.00 10.00
138 John Buck ROO/500 4.00 10.00
139 Mark Prior ROO/250 6.00 15.00
140 Sean Burroughs ROO/50 10.00 25.00
141 Alex Herrera ROO/500 4.00 10.00
142 Francis Beltran ROO/500 4.00 10.00
143 Jason Romano ROO/500 4.00 10.00
144 Michael Cuddyer ROO/400 4.00 10.00
145 Steve Bechler ROO/500 4.00 10.00
146 Alfredo Amezaga ROO/500 4.00 10.00
147 Ryan Ludwick ROO/500 20.00 50.00
148 Martin Vargas ROO/500 4.00 10.00
149 Allan Simpson ROO/500 4.00 10.00
150 Mark Teixeira ROO/200 15.00 40.00
151 Dale Murphy LGD/25
152 Ernie Banks LGD/25
153 Johnny Bench LGD/25
154 George Brett LGD/25
155 Lou Brock LGD/100 15.00 40.00
156 Rod Carew LGD/25
157 Steve Carlton LGD/125 10.00 25.00
158 Joe Torre LGD/25
159 Dennis Eckersley LGD/500 6.00 15.00
160 Reggie Jackson LGD/25
161 Al Kaline LGD/125 20.00 50.00
162 Dave Parker LGD/500 6.00 15.00
163 Don Mattingly LGD/50 50.00 100.00
164 Tony Gwynn LGD/25
165 Willie McCovey LGD/25
166 Joe Morgan LGD/25
167 Stan Musial LGD/25
168 Jim Palmer LGD/125 10.00 25.00
169 Brooks Robinson LGD/125 15.00 40.00
170 Bo Jackson LGD/25
171 Nolan Ryan LGD/25
172 Mike Schmidt LGD/25
173 Tom Seaver LGD/25
174 Cal Ripken LGD/25
175 Robin Yount LGD/25
176 Wade Boggs LGD/25
177 Gary Carter LGD/150 8.00 20.00
178 Ron Santo LGD/500 10.00 25.00
179 Luis Aparicio LGD/400 6.00 15.00
180 Bobby Doerr LGD/500 6.00 15.00
181 Ryne Sandberg LGD/25
182 Yogi Berra LGD/25
183 Will Clark LGD/50
184 Eddie Murray LGD/25
185 Andre Dawson LGD/200 8.00 20.00
186 Duke Snider LGD/25
187 Orlando Cepeda LGD/125 10.00 25.00
188 Billy Williams LGD/200 8.00 20.00
189 Juan Marichal LGD/500 6.00 15.00
190 Harmon Killebrew LGD/100 20.00 50.00
191 Kirby Puckett LGD/25
192 Carlton Fisk LGD/25
193 Dave Winfield LGD/25
194 Alan Trammell LGD/200 8.00 20.00
195 Paul Molitor LGD/25
196 Tony Perez LGD/150 8.00 20.00
197 Ozzie Smith LGD/25
198 Ralph Kiner LGD/125 10.00 25.00
199 Fergie Jenkins LGD/200 8.00 20.00
200 Phil Rizzuto LGD/125 15.00 40.00
201 Oliver Perez ROO/50 30.00 60.00
203 Eric Junge ROO/50 6.00 15.00
205 Cliff Lee ROO/100 30.00 60.00
207 Chone Figgins ROO/100 10.00 25.00
208 Rodrigo Rosario ROO/250 4.00 10.00
209 Kevin Cash ROO/100 4.00 10.00
210 Josh Bard ROO/100 4.00 10.00
211 Felix Escalona ROO/25
214 Shane Nance ROO/200 4.00 10.00
215 Ben Kozlowski ROO/200 4.00 10.00
216 Brian Tallet ROO/100 4.00 10.00
217 Earl Snyder ROO/100 4.00 10.00
218 Andy Pratt ROO/250 4.00 10.00
219 Trey Hodges ROO/250 4.00 10.00
220 Kirk Saarloos ROO/100 4.00 10.00
221 Rene Reyes ROO/50 6.00 15.00
222 Joe Borchard ROO/100 6.00 15.00
223 Wilson Valdez ROO/100 4.00 10.00
225 Chris Snelling ROO/100 8.00 20.00

2002 Donruss Classics Timeless Tributes

Cards 1-200 were randomly inserted in Donruss Classics packs and cards 201-225 in Donruss the Rookies packs. This is a parallel to the Donruss Classics set. The set is issued to a stated print run of 100 serial-numbered sets.

*TRIBUTE 1-100: 2.5X TO 6X BASIC
*TRIB.101-150/201-225: .6X TO 1.5X BASIC
*TRIB.151-200: 1.25X TO 3X BASIC

2002 Donruss Classics Classic Combos

Randomly inserted in packs, each of these 20 cards features two game-used pieces on them. Since each card is printed to a stated print run of 25 or less (which we have notated in our checklist), no pricing is provided for these cards.

1 Eddie Murray Jsy
Cal Ripken Jsy/25
2 George Brett Jsy
Bo Jackson Jsy/25
3 Ted Williams Bat
Jimmie Foxx Bat/25
4 Nolan Ryan Jsy
Steve Carlton Jsy/25
5 Mel Ott Jsy
Babe Ruth Jsy/15
6 Nolan Ryan Jsy
George Brett Jsy/25
7 Babe Ruth Bat
Ty Cobb Bat/15
8 Jackie Robinson Jsy
Duke Snider Jsy/15
9 Nolan Ryan Jsy
George Brett Jsy
Robin Yount Jsy
Orlando Cepeda Jsy/25
10 Rickey Henderson Bat
Ty Cobb Bat/25
11 Ted Williams Jsy
Tony Gwynn Jsy/15
12 Tony Gwynn Bat
Rickey Henderson Bat/25
13 Ty Cobb Bat
Tony Gwynn Bat/25
14 Dave Parker Jsy
Willie Stargell Jsy/25
15 Ted Williams Bat
Ty Cobb Bat/25
16 Jimmie Foxx Bat
Lou Gehrig Bat/15
17 Catfish Hunter Jsy
Reggie Jackson Jsy/25
18 Ted Williams Bat
Ty Cobb Bat
Jimmie Foxx Bat
Lou Gehrig Bat/15
19 Bobby Doerr Jsy
Ted Williams Jsy/15
20 Mike Schmidt Jsy
George Brett Jsy/25

2002 Donruss Classics Classic Singles

Randomly inserted into packs, these 30 cards feature both a veteran great as well as a game-used memorabilia piece. As these cards have varying print runs, we have notated that information next to the player's name as well as the information as to what memorabilia piece is used.

1 Cal Ripken Jsy/100 20.00 50.00
2 Eddie Murray Jsy/100 6.00 15.00
3 George Brett Jsy/100 10.00 25.00
4 Bo Jackson Jsy/100 6.00 15.00
5 Ted Williams Bat/50 50.00 100.00
6 Jimmie Foxx Sox Bat/50 40.00 80.00
7 Steve Carlton Jsy/50 6.00 15.00
8 Reg Jackson Yanks Jsy/100 6.00 15.00
9 Mel Ott Jsy/50 40.00 80.00
10 Catfish Hunter Jsy/100 6.00 15.00
11 Nolan Ryan Jsy/100 20.00 50.00
12 Rickey Henderson Jsy /100 6.00 15.00
13 Robin Yount Jsy/100 6.00 15.00
14 Orlando Cepeda Jsy/100 4.00 10.00
15 Ty Cobb Bat/50 75.00 150.00
16 Babe Ruth Bat/50 125.00 250.00
17 Dave Parker Jsy/100 4.00 10.00
18 Willie Stargell Jsy/100 6.00 15.00
19 Ernie Banks Bat/100 6.00 15.00
20 Mike Schmidt Jsy/100 10.00 25.00
21 Duke Snider Jsy/50 10.00 25.00
22 Jackie Robinson Jsy/50 50.00 100.00
23 Rickey Henderson Bat/100 6.00 15.00
24 Dale Murphy Bat/100 6.00 15.00
25 Lou Gehrig Bat/50 125.00 200.00
26 Jimmie Foxx A's Bat/50 40.00 80.00
27 Reggie Jackson A's Jsy/100 6.00 15.00
28 Tony Gwynn Bat/100 10.00 25.00
29 Bobby Doerr Jsy/100 4.00 10.00
30 Joe Torre Jsy/100 6.00 15.00

2002 Donruss Classics Legendary Hats

Randomly inserted into packs, this five-card set features not only a retired great but a game-worn swatch of a cap. Each card was printed to a stated print run of 50 serial numbered sets.

1 Don Mattingly 60.00 120.00
2 George Brett 60.00 120.00
3 Wade Boggs 20.00 50.00
4 Reggie Jackson 20.00 50.00
5 Ryne Sandberg 60.00 120.00

2002 Donruss Classics Legendary Leather

Randomly inserted into packs, this five-card set features not only a retired great but a game-worn swatch of a glove. Each card was printed to a stated print run of 50 serial numbered sets.

1 Don Mattingly Btg Glv 60.00 120.00
2 Wade Boggs Btg Glv 20.00 50.00
3 Tony Gwynn Fld Glv 50.00 100.00
4 Kirby Puckett Fld Glv 40.00 80.00
5 Mike Schmidt Fld Glv 60.00 120.00

2002 Donruss Classics Legendary Lumberjacks

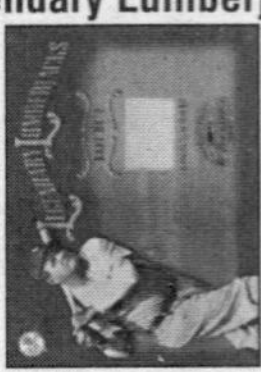

Randomly inserted in packs, this 35 card set features great players of the past along with a game-used bat piece. Since this set was printed to different amounts of cards printed, we have notated the stated print run information next to the player's name.

1 Don Mattingly/500 10.00 25.00
2 George Brett/400 10.00 25.00
3 Stan Musial/100 20.00 50.00
4 Lou Gehrig/50 125.00 200.00
5 Mike Piazza/500 6.00 15.00
6 Mel Ott/50 40.00 80.00
7 Ted Williams/50 50.00 100.00
8 Bo Jackson/500 6.00 15.00
9 Kirby Puckett/500 6.00 15.00
10 Rafael Palmeiro/500 6.00 15.00
11 Andre Dawson/500 4.00 10.00
12 Ozzie Smith/500 6.00 15.00
13 Paul Molitor/500 4.00 10.00
14 Babe Ruth/50 125.00 250.00
15 Carlton Fisk/500 6.00 15.00
16 Rickey Henderson/500 6.00 15.00
17 Gary Carter/500 4.00 10.00
18 Cal Ripken/100 15.00 40.00
19 Eddie Mathews/100 10.00 25.00
20 Luis Aparicio/500 4.00 10.00
21 Al Kaline/100 10.00 25.00
22 Eddie Murray/500 6.00 15.00
23 Yogi Berra/100 10.00 25.00
24 Alex Rodriguez/500 6.00 15.00
25 Tony Gwynn/500 6.00 15.00
26 Roberto Clemente/100 50.00 100.00
27 Mike Schmidt/400 10.00 25.00
28 Reggie Jackson/500 6.00 15.00
29 Ryne Sandberg/500 10.00 25.00
30 Joe Morgan/400 4.00 10.00
31 Joe Torre/500 6.00 15.00
32 Gary Sheffield/500 4.00 10.00
33 Nomar Garciaparra/500 6.00 15.00
34 Jeff Bagwell/500 6.00 15.00
35 Manny Ramirez/500 6.00 15.00

2002 Donruss Classics Legendary Spikes

Randomly inserted into packs, this five-card set features not only a retired great but a game-worn piece of a pair of spikes. Each card was printed to a stated print run of 50 serial numbered sets.

1 Don Mattingly 60.00 120.00
2 Eddie Murray 30.00 60.00
3 Paul Molitor 15.00 40.00
4 Harmon Killebrew 30.00 60.00
5 Mike Schmidt 60.00 120.00

2002 Donruss Classics New Millennium Classics

Randomly inserted into packs, these 60 cards feature both an active star as well as a game-used memorabilia piece. As these cards have varying print runs, we have notated that information next to the player's name as well as the information as to what memorabilia piece is used. The Ishii and Taguchi jersey cards were not ready as Donruss went to press and those cards were issued as exchange cards with an deadline of June 1, 2004 to redeem those cards.

*MULTI-COLOR PATCH: 1.25X TO 3X BASIC
1 Curt Schilling Jsy/500 3.00 8.00
2 Vladimir Guerrero Jsy/100 6.00 15.00
3 Jim Thome Jsy/500 4.00 10.00
4 Troy Glaus Jsy/400 3.00 8.00
5 Ivan Rodriguez Jsy/200 6.00 15.00
6 Todd Helton Jsy/400 4.00 10.00
7 Sean Casey Jsy/500 3.00 8.00
8 Scott Rolen Jsy/475 4.00 10.00
9 Ken Griffey Jr. Base/150 6.00 15.00
10 Hideo Nomo Jsy/100 10.00 25.00
11 Tom Glavine Jsy/350 4.00 10.00
12 Pedro Martinez Jsy/100 6.00 15.00
13 Cliff Floyd Jsy/500 3.00 8.00
14 Shawn Green Jsy/125 4.00 10.00
15 Rafael Palmeiro Jsy/250 4.00 10.00
16 Luis Gonzalez Jsy/100 4.00 10.00
17 Lance Berkman Jsy/100 4.00 10.00
18 Frank Thomas Jsy/500 4.00 10.00
19 Randy Johnson Jsy/400 4.00 10.00
20 Moises Alou Jsy/500 3.00 8.00
21 Chipper Jones Jsy/500 4.00 10.00
22 Larry Walker Jsy/300 3.00 8.00
23 Mike Sweeney Jsy/500 3.00 8.00
24 Juan Gonzalez Jsy/300 3.00 8.00
25 Roger Clemens Jsy/100 10.00 25.00
26 Albert Pujols Base/300 6.00 15.00
27 Magglio Ordonez Jsy/500 3.00 8.00
28 Alex Rodriguez Jsy/400 6.00 15.00
29 Jeff Bagwell Jsy/125 6.00 15.00
30 Kazuhiro Sasaki Jsy/500 3.00 8.00
31 Barry Larkin Jsy/300 4.00 10.00
32 Andruw Jones Jsy/350 4.00 10.00
33 Kerry Wood Jsy/200 4.00 10.00
34 Rickey Henderson Jsy/100 6.00 15.00
35 Greg Maddux Jsy/100 10.00 25.00
36 Brian Giles Jsy/400 3.00 8.00
37 Craig Biggio Jsy/100 6.00 15.00
38 Roberto Alomar Jsy/400 4.00 10.00
39 Mike Piazza Jsy/400 6.00 15.00
40 Bernie Williams Jsy/100 6.00 15.00
41 Ichiro Suzuki Ball/100 15.00 40.00
42 Kenny Lofton Jsy/450 3.00 8.00
43 Mark Mulder Jsy/500 3.00 8.00
44 Kazuhisa Ishii Jsy/100 6.00 15.00
45 Darin Erstad Jsy/500 3.00 8.00
46 Jose Vidro Jsy/500 3.00 8.00
47 Miguel Tejada Jsy/475 3.00 8.00
48 Roy Oswalt Jsy/500 3.00 8.00
49 So Taguchi Jsy/100 6.00 15.00
50 Barry Zito Jsy/500 3.00 8.00
51 Manny Ramirez Jsy/400 4.00 10.00
52 Nomar Garciaparra Jsy/400 6.00 15.00
53 C.C. Sabathia Jsy/500 3.00 8.00
54 Carlos Delgado Jsy/500 3.00 8.00
55 Gary Sheffield Jsy/500 3.00 8.00
56 J.D. Drew Jsy/500 3.00 8.00
57 Barry Bonds Ball/150 15.00 40.00
58 Derek Jeter Ball/150 15.00 40.00
59 Edgar Martinez Jsy/400 4.00 10.00
60 Sammy Sosa Ball/150 6.00 15.00

2002 Donruss Classics Timeless Treasures

Randomly inserted into packs, these 17 cards feature all-time greats along with key pieces of their memorabilia. These cards have different print runs which we have put next to their names. Those cards with a stated print run of 25 or less are not priced due to market scarcity.

1 Ted Williams .406 Avg Jsy/25
2 Ted Williams The Kid Jsy/10
3 Ted Williams Ballgame Jsy/10
4 Ted Williams Splinter Jsy/10
5 Ted Williams Crown Bat/42 50.00 100.00
6 Ted Williams Crown Bat/47 50.00 100.00
7 Ted Williams MVP Bat/46 50.00 100.00
8 Ted Williams MVP Bat/49 50.00 100.00
9 Ted Williams Jsy/9
10 Cal Ripken Iron Man Jsy/98 20.00 50.00
11 Cal Ripken ROY Jsy/82 40.00 80.00
12 Cal Ripken MVP Jsy/83 40.00 80.00
13 Cal Ripken MVP Jsy/91 40.00 80.00
14 Cal Ripken
Lou Gehrig Jsy/25
15 Cal Ripken 2131 Jsy/25
16 Cal Ripken 3000 Hits Jsy/25
17 Cal Ripken Jsy/8

2003 Donruss Classics Samples

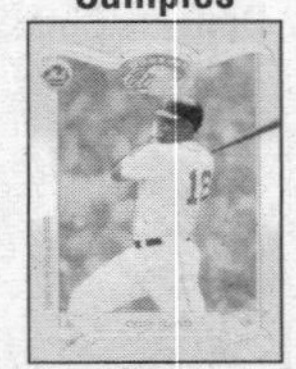

Inserted at a stated rate of one per sealed Beckett Baseball Collector Magazine, these cards parallel the basic Donruss Classic cards and can be differentiated by the word "Sample" printed in silver on the back.

*SAMPLES: 1.5X TO 4X BASIC CARDS
ONE PER SEALED BBC MAGAZINE
*GOLD: 1.5X TO 4X BASIC SAMPLES

2003 Donruss Classics

This 211-card set was released in two separate series. The primary Donruss Classics product - containing cards 1-200 from the basic set - was released in April, 2003. This set was issued in seven-card packs with an $6 SRP which were packed 18 to a box and 12 boxes to a case. Cards 201-211 were randomly seeded within packs of DLP Rookies and Traded of which was distributed in December, 2003. The first 100 cards feature active veterans, while cards 101-150 feature retired legends and cards 151-211 feature rookies and leading prospects. Please note that cards 101-200 were issued at a stated rate of one in nine and were issued to a stated print run of 1500 serial numbered sets. Cards 201-211 were serial-numbered to 1000 copies each.

COMP.LO SET w/o SP's (100) 10.00 25.00
COMMON CARD (1-100) .25 .60
COMMON CARD (101-150) 1.50 4.00
COMMON CARD (151-200) 1.50 4.00
COIMMON CARD (201-211) 1.50 4.00
1 Troy Glaus .25 .60
2 Barry Bonds 1.50 4.00
3 Miguel Tejada .25 .60
4 Randy Johnson .60 1.50
5 Eric Hinske .25 .60
6 Barry Zito .25 .60
7 Jason Jennings .25 .60
8 Derek Jeter 1.50 4.00
9 Vladimir Guerrero .60 1.50
10 Corey Patterson .25 .60
11 Manny Ramirez .40 1.00
12 Edgar Martinez .40 1.00
13 Roy Oswalt .25 .60
14 Andruw Jones .40 1.00
15 Alex Rodriguez 1.00 2.50
16 Mark Mulder .25 .60
17 Kazuhisa Ishii .25 .60
18 Gary Sheffield .25 .60
19 Jay Gibbons .25 .60
20 Roberto Alomar .40 1.00
21 A.J. Pierzynski .25 .60
22 Eric Chavez .25 .60
23 Roger Clemens 1.25 3.00
24 C.C. Sabathia .25 .60
25 Jose Vidro .25 .60
26 Shannon Stewart .25 .60
27 Mark Teixeira .40 1.00
28 Joe Thurston .25 .60
29 Josh Beckett .25 .60
30 Jeff Bagwell .40 1.00
31 Geronimo Gil .25 .60
32 Curt Schilling .25 .60
33 Frank Thomas .60 1.50
34 Lance Berkman .25 .60
35 Adam Dunn .25 .60
36 Christian Parker .25 .60
37 Jim Thome .40 1.00
38 Shawn Green .25 .60
39 Drew Henson .25 .60
40 Chipper Jones .60 1.50
41 Kevin Mench .25 .60
42 Hideo Nomo .60 1.50
43 Andres Galarraga .25 .60
44 Doug Davis .25 .60
45 Mark Prior .40 1.00
46 Sean Casey .25 .60
47 Magglio Ordonez .25 .60
48 Tom Glavine .40 1.00
49 Marlon Byrd .25 .60
50 Albert Pujols 1.25 3.00
51 Mark Buehrle .25 .60
52 Aramis Ramirez .25 .60
53 Pat Burrell .25 .60
54 Craig Biggio .40 1.00
55 Alfonso Soriano .25 .60
56 Kerry Wood .25 .60
57 Wade Miller .25 .60
58 Hank Blalock .25 .60
59 Cliff Floyd .25 .60
60 Jason Giambi .25 .60
61 Carlos Beltran .25 .60
62 Brian Roberts .25 .60
63 Paul Lo Duca .25 .60
64 Tim Redding .25 .60
65 Sammy Sosa .60 1.50
66 Joe Borchard .25 .60
67 Ryan Klesko .25 .60
68 Richie Sexson .25 .60
69 Carlos Lee .25 .60
70 Rickey Henderson .60 1.50
71 Brian Tallet .25 .60
72 Luis Gonzalez .25 .60
73 Satoru Komiyama .25 .60
74 Tim Hudson .25 .60
75 Ken Griffey Jr. 1.00 2.50
76 Adam Johnson .25 .60
77 Bobby Abreu .25 .60
78 Adrian Beltre .25 .60
79 Rafael Palmeiro .40 1.00
80 Ichiro Suzuki 1.25 3.00
81 Kenny Lofton .25 .60
82 Brian Giles .25 .60
83 Barry Larkin .40 1.00
84 Robert Fick .25 .60
85 Ben Sheets .25 .60
86 Scott Rolen .40 1.00
87 Nomar Garciaparra 1.00 2.50
88 Brandon Phillips .25 .60
89 Ben Kozlowski .25 .60
90 Bernie Williams .40 1.00
91 Pedro Martinez .40 1.00
92 Todd Helton .40 1.00
93 Jermaine Dye .25 .60
94 Carlos Delgado .25 .60
95 Mike Piazza 1.00 2.50
96 Junior Spivey .25 .60
97 Torii Hunter .25 .60
98 Mike Sweeney .25 .60
99 Ivan Rodriguez .40 1.00
100 Greg Maddux 1.00 2.50
101 Ernie Banks LGD 2.00 5.00
102 Steve Garvey LGD 1.50 4.00
103 George Brett LGD 3.00 8.00
104 Lou Brock LGD 2.00 5.00
105 Hoyt Wilhelm LGD 1.50 4.00
106 Steve Carlton LGD 1.50 4.00
107 Joe Torre LGD 1.50 4.00
108 Dennis Eckersley LGD 1.50 4.00
109 Reggie Jackson LGD 2.00 5.00
110 Al Kaline LGD 2.00 5.00
111 Harold Reynolds LGD 1.50 4.00
112 Don Mattingly LGD 3.00 8.00
113 Tony Gwynn LGD 2.00 5.00
114 Willie McCovey LGD 1.50 4.00
115 Joe Morgan LGD 1.50 4.00
116 Stan Musial LGD 2.50 6.00
117 Jim Palmer LGD 1.50 4.00
118 Brooks Robinson LGD 2.00 5.00
119 Don Sutton LGD 1.50 4.00
120 Nolan Ryan LGD 4.00 10.00
121 Mike Schmidt LGD 3.00 8.00
122 Tom Seaver LGD 2.00 5.00
123 Cal Ripken LGD 5.00 12.00
124 Robin Yount LGD 2.00 5.00
125 Bob Feller LGD 1.50 4.00
126 Joe Carter LGD 1.50 4.00
127 Jack Morris LGD 1.50 4.00
128 Luis Aparicio LGD 1.50 4.00
129 Bobby Doerr LGD 1.50 4.00
130 Dave Parker LGD 1.50 4.00
131 Yogi Berra LGD 2.00 5.00
132 Will Clark LGD 2.00 5.00
133 Fred Lynn LGD 1.50 4.00
134 Andre Dawson LGD 1.50 4.00
135 Duke Snider LGD 2.00 5.00
136 Orlando Cepeda LGD 1.50 4.00
137 Billy Williams LGD 1.50 4.00
138 Dale Murphy LGD 2.00 5.00
139 Harmon Killebrew LGD 2.00 5.00
140 Kirby Puckett LGD 2.00 5.00
141 Carlton Fisk LGD 2.00 5.00
142 Eric Davis LGD 1.50 4.00
143 Alan Trammell LGD 1.50 4.00
144 Paul Molitor LGD 1.50 4.00
145 Jose Canseco LGD 2.00 5.00
146 Ozzie Smith LGD 2.50 6.00
147 Ralph Kiner LGD 1.50 4.00
148 Dwight Gooden LGD 1.50 4.00
149 Phil Rizzuto LGD 2.00 5.00
150 Lenny Dykstra LGD 1.50 4.00
151 Adam LaRoche ROO 1.50 4.00
152 Tim Hummel ROO 1.50 4.00
153 Matt Kata ROO RC 1.50 4.00
154 Jeff Baker ROO 1.50 4.00
155 Josh Stewart ROO RC 1.50 4.00
156 Marshall McDougall ROO 1.50 4.00
157 Jhonny Peralta ROO 2.00 5.00
158 Mike Nicolas ROO RC 1.50 4.00
159 Jeremy Guthrie ROO 1.50 4.00
160 Craig Brazell ROO RC 1.50 4.00
161 Joe Valentine ROO RC 1.50 4.00
162 Buddy Hernandez ROO RC 1.50 4.00
163 Freddy Sanchez ROO 1.50 4.00
164 Shane Victorino ROO RC 2.50 6.00
165 Corwin Malone ROO 1.50 4.00
166 Jason Dubois ROO 1.50 4.00
167 Josh Wilson ROO 1.50 4.00
168 Tim Olson ROO RC 1.50 4.00
169 Cliff Bartosh ROO 1.50 4.00
170 Michael Hessman ROO RC 1.50 4.00
171 Ryan Church ROO 1.50 4.00
172 Garrett Atkins ROO 1.50 4.00
173 Jose Morban ROO 1.50 4.00
174 Ryan Cameron ROO RC 1.50 4.00
175 Todd Wellemeyer ROO RC 1.50 4.00
176 Travis Chapman ROO 1.50 4.00
177 Jason Anderson ROO 1.50 4.00
178 Adam Morrissey ROO 1.50 4.00
179 Jose Contreras ROO RC 2.00 5.00
180 Nic Jackson ROO 1.50 4.00
181 Rob Hammock ROO RC 1.50 4.00
182 Carlos Rivera ROO 1.50 4.00
183 Vinny Chulk ROO 1.50 4.00
184 Pete LaForest ROO RC 1.50 4.00
185 Jon Leicester ROO RC 1.50 4.00
186 Terrmel Sledge ROO RC 1.50 4.00
187 Jose Castillo ROO 1.50 4.00
188 Gerald Laird ROO 1.50 4.00
189 Nook Logan ROO RC 2.00 5.00
190 Clint Barmes ROO RC 1.25 3.00
191 Jesus Medrano ROO 1.50 4.00
192 Henri Stanley ROO 1.50 4.00
193 Hideki Matsui ROO RC 4.00 10.00
194 Walter Young ROO 1.50 4.00
195 Jon Adkins ROO 1.50 4.00
196 Tommy Whiteman ROO 1.50 4.00
197 Rob Bowen ROO 1.50 4.00
198 Brandon Webb ROO RC 4.00 10.00
199 Prentice Redman ROO RC 1.50 4.00
200 Jimmy Gobble ROO 1.50 4.00
201 J.Bonderman ROO RC 4.00 10.00
202 Adam Loewen ROO RC 2.00 5.00
203 Chien-Ming Wang ROO RC 12.50 30.00
204 Hong-Chih Kuo ROO RC 6.00 15.00
205 Ryan Wagner ROO RC 1.50 4.00
206 Dan Haren ROO RC 2.00 5.00
207 Dontrelle Willis ROO 2.00 5.00
208 Rickie Weeks ROO RC 3.00 8.00
209 Ramon Nivar ROO RC 1.50 4.00
210 Chad Gaudin ROO RC 1.50 4.00
211 Delmon Young ROO RC 6.00 15.00

2003 Donruss Classics Significant Signatures

Randomly inserted into packs, this is an almost complete parallel to the basic set. Please note, cards 201-211 were randomly inserted within packs of DLP Rookies and Traded. Each of the these cards feature an authentic "sticker" autograph of the featured player on them. Please note that these

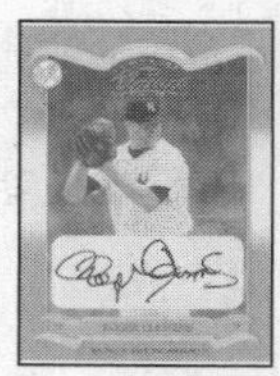

players signed a different amount of cards ranging between 5-500 copies per and that information is next to the player's name in our checklist. Please note that if the print run is 25 or fewer, no pricing is provided due to market scarcity. Also please note that Hoyt Wilhelm, since he had signed stickers, is able to have signed cards in this set despite having passed on the previous year.

1 Troy Glaus/10
3 Miguel Tejada/5
5 Eric Hinske/250 4.00 10.00
6 Barry Zito/25
7 Jason Jennings/250 4.00 10.00
9 Vladimir Guerrero/5
10 Corey Patterson/100 6.00 15.00
11 Manny Ramirez/5
12 Edgar Martinez/20
13 Roy Oswalt/100 10.00 25.00
14 Andruw Jones/10
15 Alex Rodriguez/5
16 Mark Mulder/100 10.00 25.00
17 Kazuhisa Ishii/5
18 Gary Sheffield/5
19 Jay Gibbons/250 4.00 10.00
20 Roberto Alomar/5
21 A.J. Pierzynski/75 10.00 25.00
22 Eric Chavez/20
23 Roger Clemens/5
24 C.C. Sabathia/5
25 Jose Vidro/75 6.00 15.00
26 Shannon Stewart/25
27 Mark Teixeira/50 15.00 40.00
29 Josh Beckett/5
31 Geronimo Gil/50 6.00 15.00
32 Curt Schilling/5
33 Frank Thomas/5
34 Lance Berkman/5
35 Adam Dunn/100 15.00 40.00
36 Christian Parker/250 4.00 10.00
37 Jim Thome/5
38 Shawn Green/5
39 Drew Henson/100 6.00 15.00
40 Chipper Jones/5
41 Kevin Mench/250 6.00 15.00
43 Andres Galarraga/5
44 Doug Davis/15
45 Mark Prior/50 12.50 30.00
46 Sean Casey/5
47 Magglio Ordonez/5
48 Tom Glavine/10
49 Marlon Byrd/10
50 Albert Pujols/10
51 Mark Buehrle/25
52 Aramis Ramirez/10
53 Pat Burrell/10
54 Craig Biggio/5
55 Alfonso Soriano/5
56 Kerry Wood/15
57 Wade Miller/200 4.00 10.00
58 Hank Blalock/50 10.00 25.00
59 Cliff Floyd/20
61 Carlos Beltran/20
62 Brian Roberts/250 10.00 25.00
63 Paul Lo Duca/100 10.00 25.00
64 Tim Redding/250 4.00 10.00
66 Joe Borchard/100 6.00 15.00
67 Ryan Klesko/20
68 Richie Sexson/20
69 Carlos Lee/25
70 Rickey Henderson/5
71 Brian Tallet/25
72 Luis Gonzalez/5
73 Satoru Komiyama/124 10.00 25.00
74 Tim Hudson/20
76 Adam Johnson/200 4.00 10.00
77 Bobby Abreu/10
78 Adrian Beltre/10
79 Rafael Palmeiro/5
81 Kenny Lofton/5
82 Brian Giles/25
83 Barry Larkin/5
84 Robert Fick/50 6.00 15.00
85 Ben Sheets/20
86 Scott Rolen/5
88 Brandon Phillips/250 4.00 10.00
89 Ben Kozlowski/150 4.00 10.00
90 Bernie Williams/5
91 Pedro Martinez/5
92 Todd Helton/5
93 Jermaine Dye/100 10.00 25.00
96 Junior Spivey/100 6.00 15.00
97 Torii Hunter/50 10.00 25.00
98 Mike Sweeney/25
99 Ivan Rodriguez/5
100 Greg Maddux/5
101 Ernie Banks LGD/5
102 Steve Garvey LGD/100 10.00 25.00
103 George Brett LGD/5
104 Lou Brock LGD/20
105 Hoyt Wilhelm LGD/25
106 Steve Carlton LGD/20
107 Joe Torre LGD/5
108 Dennis Eckersley LGD/50 15.00 40.00
109 Reggie Jackson LGD/5
110 Al Kaline LGD/20
111 Harold Reynolds LGD/50 15.00 40.00
112 Don Mattingly LGD/15
113 Tony Gwynn LGD/5
114 Willie McCovey LGD/5
115 Joe Morgan LGD/5
116 Stan Musial LGD/25
117 Jim Palmer LGD/20
118 Brooks Robinson LGD/20
119 Don Sutton LGD/100 10.00 25.00
120 Nolan Ryan LGD/50 150.00 250.00
121 Mike Schmidt LGD/15
122 Tom Seaver LGD/5
123 Cal Ripken LGD/50 150.00 250.00
124 Robin Yount LGD/5
125 Bob Feller LGD/25
126 Joe Carter LGD/100 10.00 25.00
127 Jack Morris LGD/100 10.00 25.00
128 Luis Aparicio LGD/50 15.00 40.00
129 Bobby Doerr LGD/25
130 Dave Parker LGD/10
131 Yogi Berra LGD/10
132 Will Clark LGD/20
133 Fred Lynn LGD/50 15.00 40.00
134 Andre Dawson LGD/50 15.00 40.00
135 Duke Snider LGD/5
136 Orlando Cepeda LGD/100 10.00 25.00
137 Billy Williams LGD/100 10.00 25.00
138 Dale Murphy LGD/20
139 Harmon Killebrew LGD/15
140 Kirby Puckett LGD/5
141 Carlton Fisk LGD/5
142 Eric Davis LGD/50 15.00 40.00
143 Alan Trammell LGD/50 15.00 40.00
144 Paul Molitor LGD/10
145 Jose Canseco LGD/15
146 Ozzie Smith LGD/5
147 Ralph Kiner LGD/20
148 Dwight Gooden LGD/50 15.00 40.00
149 Phil Rizzuto LGD/20
150 Lenny Dykstra LGD/50 15.00 40.00
151 Adam LaRoche ROO/250 4.00 10.00
152 Tim Hummel ROO/500 4.00 10.00
153 Matt Kata ROO/500 4.00 10.00
154 Jeff Baker ROO/500 4.00 10.00
155 Josh Stewart ROO/177 4.00 10.00
156 Marshall McDougall ROO/500 4.00 10.00
157 Jhonny Peralta ROO/500 6.00 15.00
158 Mike Nicolas ROO/500 4.00 10.00
159 Jeremy Guthrie ROO/500 4.00 10.00
160 Craig Brazell ROO/500 4.00 10.00
161 Joe Valentine ROO/172 4.00 10.00
162 Buddy Hernandez ROO/500 4.00 10.00
163 Freddy Sanchez ROO/500 6.00 15.00
164 Shane Victorino ROO/351 20.00 50.00
165 Corwin Malone ROO/500 4.00 10.00
166 Jason Dubois ROO/500 4.00 10.00
167 Josh Wilson ROO/500 4.00 10.00
168 Tim Olson ROO/500 4.00 10.00
169 Cliff Bartosh ROO/500 4.00 10.00
170 Michael Hessman ROO/427 4.00 10.00
171 Ryan Church ROO/500 6.00 15.00
172 Garrett Atkins ROO/500 4.00 10.00
173 Jose Morban ROO/500 4.00 10.00
174 Ryan Cameron ROO/500 4.00 10.00
175 Todd Wellemeyer ROO/500 4.00 10.00
176 Travis Chapman ROO/477 4.00 10.00
177 Jason Anderson ROO/500 6.00 15.00
178 Adam Morrissey ROO/500 4.00 10.00
179 Jose Contreras ROO/100 12.50 30.00
180 Nic Jackson ROO/500 4.00 10.00
181 Rob Hammock ROO/500 4.00 10.00
182 Carlos Rivera ROO/500 4.00 10.00
183 Vinny Chulk ROO/500 4.00 10.00
184 Pete LaForest ROO/177 4.00 10.00
185 John Leicester ROO/500 4.00 10.00
186 Termel Sledge ROO/500 4.00 10.00
187 Jose Castillo ROO/500 4.00 10.00
188 Gerald Laird ROO/500 4.00 10.00
189 Nook Logan ROO/427 6.00 15.00
190 Clint Barmes ROO/100 8.00 20.00
191 Jesus Medrano ROO/500 4.00 10.00
192 Henri Stanley ROO/500 4.00 10.00
194 Walter Young ROO/500 4.00 10.00
195 Jon Adkins ROO/500 4.00 10.00
196 Tommy Whiteman ROO/500 4.00 10.00
197 Rob Bowen ROO/500 4.00 10.00
198 Brandon Webb ROO/500 30.00 60.00
199 Prentice Redman ROO/127 4.00 10.00
200 Jimmy Gobble ROO/500 4.00 10.00
201 Jeremy Bonderman ROO/100 15.00 40.00
202 Adam Loewen ROO/100 10.00 25.00
203 Chien-Ming Wang ROO/50 150.00 250.00
204 Hong-Chih Kuo ROO/25
205 Ryan Wagner ROO/100 4.00 10.00
206 Dan Haren ROO/100 12.50 30.00
207 Dontrelle Willis ROO/25
208 Rickie Weeks ROO/10
209 Ramon Nivar ROO/100 4.00 10.00
210 Chad Gaudin ROO/25
211 Delmon Young ROO/25

2003 Donruss Classics Timeless Tributes

Randomly inserted into packs, this is a complete parallel of the basic Classics set. Please note, cards 201-211 were randomly inserted into packs of DLP Rookies and Traded. Each of these cards were issued to a stated print run of 100 serial numbered sets.

*TRIBUTE 1-100: 2.5X TO 6X BASIC
*TRIB.101-150: 1.25X TO 3X BASIC
*TRIBUTE 151-200: .6X TO 1.5X BASIC
*TRIBUTE 201-211: .6X TO 1.5X BASIC
203 Chien-Ming Wang ROO 30.00 60.00
204 Hong-Chih Kuo ROO 15.00 40.00

2003 Donruss Classics Classic Combos

Randomly inserted in packs, this 15 card set features two players along with game-used memorabilia of each player. We have noted the print run information next to the player's name in our checklist. Please note that if a card has a stated print run of 25 or fewer we have not priced the card due to market scarcity.

1 Babe Ruth Jsy 400.00 600.00
Lou Gehrig Jsy/50

2 Jackie Robinson Jsy 50.00 100.00
Pee Wee Reese Jsy/50
3 Bobby Doerr Jsy
Fred Lynn Jsy/25
4 Honus Wagner Seat 125.00 200.00
Roberto Clemente Jsy/50
5 Kirby Puckett Jsy
Torri Hunter Jsy/25
6 Ryne Sandberg Jsy
Sammy Sosa Jsy/25
7 Hideo Nomo Jsy
Kazuhisa Ishii Jsy/25
8 Mike Schmidt Jsy
Steve Carlton Jsy/25
9 Paul Molitor Jsy
Robin Yount Jsy/25
10 Duke Snider Jsy
Mike Piazza Jsy/25
11 Al Kaline Jsy
Ty Cobb Bat/25
12 Don Mattingly Jsy
Jason Giambi Jsy/25
13 Ozzie Smith Jsy
Stan Musial Jsy/25
14 Pedro Martinez Jsy
Roger Clemens Jsy/25
15 Thurman Munson Jsy
Yogi Berra Jsy/25

2003 Donruss Classics Classic Singles

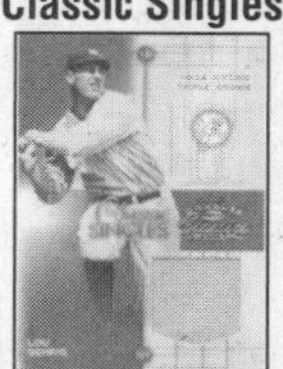

Randomly inserted into packs, this 30-card set features a mix of active and retired players along with a memorabilia piece about that player. We have noted the stated print run information next to the player's name in our checklist and if a card was issued to a stated print run of 25 or fewer, there is no pricing due to market scarcity.

1 Babe Ruth Jsy/100 250.00 400.00
2 Lou Gehrig Jsy/80 150.00 250.00
3 Jackie Robinson Jsy/80 50.00 100.00
4 Pee Wee Reese Jsy/25
5 Bobby Doerr Jsy/100 8.00 20.00
6 Fred Lynn Jsy/100 8.00 20.00
7 Honus Wagner Seat/100 20.00 50.00
8 Roberto Clemente Jsy/80 60.00 120.00
9 Kirby Puckett Jsy/100 15.00 40.00
10 Torii Hunter Jsy/100 6.00 15.00
11 Sammy Sosa Jsy/100 10.00 25.00
12 Ryne Sandberg Jsy/100 30.00 60.00
13 Hideo Nomo Jsy/50 60.00 120.00
14 Kazuhisa Ishii Jsy/50 10.00 25.00
15 Mike Schmidt Jsy/100 30.00 60.00
16 Steve Carlton Jsy/100 8.00 20.00
17 Robin Yount Jsy/100 15.00 40.00
18 Paul Molitor Jsy/100 8.00 20.00
19 Mike Piazza Jsy/100 10.00 25.00
20 Duke Snider Jsy/50 15.00 40.00
21 Al Kaline Jsy/50 30.00 60.00
22 Ty Cobb Bat/25
23 Don Mattingly Jsy/100 30.00 60.00
24 Jason Giambi Jsy/100 6.00 15.00
25 Stan Musial Jsy/25
26 Ozzie Smith Jsy/100 15.00 40.00
27 Roger Clemens Jsy/100 12.50 30.00
28 Pedro Martinez Jsy/100 8.00 20.00
29 Thurman Munson Jsy/50 30.00 60.00
30 Yogi Berra Jsy/25

2003 Donruss Classics Dress Code

Randomly inserted into pack, this 75-card set features anywhere from one to four swatches of game-worn/used materials. Each card was issued to different quantities and we have notated that information next to the card in our checklist.

1 Roger Clemens Yanks Jsy/500 6.00 15.00
2 Miguel Tejada Bat-Hat-Jsy/250 8.00 20.00
3 Vladimir Guerrero Jsy/425 4.00 10.00
4 Kazuhisa Ishii Jsy/250 3.00 8.00
5 Chipper Jones Jsy/425 4.00 10.00
6 Troy Glaus Jsy/425 3.00 8.00
7 Rafael Palmeiro Jsy/425 4.00 10.00
8 R.Henderson R.Sox Jsy/250 4.00 10.00
9 Pedro Martinez Jsy/425 4.00 10.00
10 Andruw Jones Jsy/425 4.00 10.00
11 Nomar Garciaparra Jsy/500 6.00 15.00
12 Carlos Delgado Jsy/500 3.00 8.00
13 R.Hend Padres Hat-Jsy/250 8.00 20.00
14 Kerry Wood Hat-Jsy/250 6.00 15.00
15 Lance Berkman Hat-Jsy/50 10.00 25.00
16 Tony Gwynn 40.00 80.00
Hat-Jsy-Pants-Shoe/100
17 Mark Mulder Jsy/425 3.00 8.00
18 Jim Thome Jsy/500 4.00 10.00
19 Mike Piazza Jsy/500 6.00 15.00
20 Mike Mussina Jsy/500 4.00 10.00
21 Luis Gonzalez Jsy/500 3.00 8.00
22 Ryan Klesko Jsy/500 3.00 8.00
23 Richie Sexson Jsy/500 3.00 8.00
24 Curt Schilling Jsy/200 3.00 8.00
25 Alex Rodriguez Rgr Jsy/500 6.00 15.00
26 Bernie Williams Jsy/425 4.00 10.00
27 Cal Ripken Jsy/500 15.00 40.00
28 C.C. Sabathia Jsy/500 3.00 8.00
29 Mike Piazza Bat-Jsy/200 15.00 40.00
30 R.Hend Mets Hat-Jsy/250 8.00 20.00
31 Torii Hunter Jsy/425 3.00 8.00
32 Mark Teixeira Jsy/425 4.00 10.00
33 Dale Murphy Bat-Jsy/300 6.00 15.00
34 Todd Helton Jsy/425 4.00 10.00
35 Eric Chavez Jsy/425 3.00 8.00
36 Vernon Wells Jsy/425 3.00 8.00
37 Jeff Bagwell Hat-Jsy/100 12.50 30.00
38 Nick Johnson Jsy/425 3.00 8.00
39 Tim Hudson Hat-Jsy/250 6.00 15.00
40 Shawn Green Jsy/425 3.00 8.00
41 Mark Buehrle Jsy/500 3.00 8.00
42 Garret Anderson Jsy/100 4.00 10.00
43 Alex Rodriguez M's Jsy/500 6.00 15.00
44 Jason Giambi Jsy/500 3.00 8.00
45 Carlos Beltran Jsy/500 3.00 8.00
46 Adam Dunn Hat-Jsy/100 8.00 20.00
47 Jorge Posada Jsy/425 4.00 10.00
48 Roy Oswalt Hat-Jsy/200 6.00 15.00
49 Rich Aurilia Jsy/500 3.00 8.00
50 Jason Jennings 8.00 20.00
Bat-Hat-Jsy-Shoe/250
51 Mark Prior 15.00 40.00
Fld Glv-Hat-Jsy-Shoe/250
52 Jim Edmonds Jsy/500 3.00 8.00
53 Fred McGriff Jsy/500 4.00 10.00
54 A.Soriano Jsy-Shoe/100 4.00 10.00
55 Jeff Kent Jsy/425 3.00 8.00
56 Hideo Nomo R.Sox Jsy/200 15.00 40.00
57 Manny Ramirez Jsy/425 4.00 10.00
58 Jose Canseco Bat-Jsy/350 6.00 15.00
59 Magglio Ordonez Jsy/500 3.00 8.00
60 Alan Trammell Bat-Jsy/250 6.00 15.00
61 Bobby Abreu Jsy/500 3.00 8.00
62 Rickey Henderson 8.00 20.00
A's Hat-Jsy/200
63 Josh Beckett Jsy/500 3.00 8.00
64 Barry Larkin Jsy/500 4.00 10.00
65 Randy Johnson Jsy/200 4.00 10.00
66 Juan Gonzalez Jsy/500 3.00 8.00
67 Barry Zito Hat-Jsy/125 8.00 20.00
68 Roger Clemens R.Sox Jsy/500 6.00 15.00
69 R.Henderson M's Hat-Jsy/100 12.50 30.00
70 Hideo Nomo Mets Jsy/100 30.00 60.00
71 Paul Konerko Jsy/400 3.00 8.00
72 Pat Burrell Jsy/100 4.00 10.00
73 Frank Thomas Jsy-Pants/500 6.00 15.00
74 Sammy Sosa Jsy/500 4.00 10.00
75 Greg Maddux Btg Glv-Jsy/50 40.00 80.00

2003 Donruss Classics Legendary Hats

Randomly inserted in packs, this five-card set features a game-worn hat swatch of the featured player. The Roberto Clemente card was issued to a stated print run of 80 serial numbered sets.

1 Roberto Clemente/80 50.00 100.00
2 Kirby Puckett 30.00 60.00
3 Mike Schmidt 60.00 120.00
4 Tony Gwynn 50.00 100.00
5 Rickey Henderson 30.00 60.00

2003 Donruss Classics Legendary Leather

Randomly inserted into packs, this five-card set features a game-used glove piece. Each of these cards were issued to a stated print run of 25 serial numbered sets and there is no pricing due to market scarcity.

1 Nolan Ryan Fld Glv/80 60.00 120.00
2 Jimmie Foxx Fld Glv
3 Steve Carlton Fld Glv
4 Don Mattingly Btg Glv
5 Mike Schmidt Btg Glv

2003 Donruss Classics Legendary Lumberjacks

Randomly inserted into packs, this 35-card set feature retired players along with a game-used bat swatch. These cards were issued to different stated print runs and we have notated that information next to their name in our checklist. Please note that for cards with a stated print run of 25 or fewer, there is no pricing due to market scarcity.

1 Babe Ruth/100 100.00 200.00
2 Lou Gehrig/80 75.00 150.00
3 George Brett/250 12.50 30.00
4 Duke Snider/250 10.00 25.00
5 Roberto Clemente/25
6 Ryne Sandberg/400 12.50 30.00
7 Robin Yount/300 8.00 20.00
8 Harmon Killebrew/250 10.00 25.00
9 Al Kaline/250 10.00 25.00
10 Eddie Mathews/225 10.00 25.00
11 Brooks Robinson/400 8.00 20.00
12 Stan Musial/11
13 Kirby Puckett/375 8.00 20.00
14 Jose Canseco/400 8.00 20.00
15 Nellie Fox/325 8.00 20.00
16 Don Mattingly/400 12.50 30.00
17 Joe Torre/250 6.00 15.00
18 Cal Ripken/250 20.00 50.00
19 Richie Ashburn/250 10.00 25.00
20 Mike Schmidt/250 12.50 30.00
21 Dale Murphy/250 10.00 25.00
22 Thurman Munson/400 8.00 20.00
23 Tony Gwynn/400 8.00 20.00
24 Orlando Cepeda/225 6.00 15.00
25 Ty Cobb/25
26 Paul Molitor/325 6.00 15.00
27 Ralph Kiner/200 6.00 15.00
28 Frank Robinson/225 10.00 25.00
29 Yogi Berra/50 30.00 60.00
30 Reggie Jackson/375 8.00 20.00
31 Rod Carew/325 8.00 20.00
32 Carlton Fisk/325 8.00 20.00
33 Rogers Hornsby/50 40.00 80.00
34 Mel Ott/125 15.00 40.00
35 Jimmie Foxx/50 40.00 80.00

2003 Donruss Classics Legendary Spikes

Randomly inserted into packs, this five-card set featureds game-used spike pieces of the featured players. These cards were issued to a stated print run of 50 serial numbered sets.

1 Kirby Puckett 30.00 60.00
2 Tony Gwynn 50.00 100.00
3 Don Mattingly 75.00 150.00
4 Frank Robinson 20.00 50.00
5 Gary Carter 15.00 40.00

2003 Donruss Classics Legends of the Fall

Randomly inserted into packs, this 10 card set featured players who were stars of at least one World Series they played in. Each of these cards were issued to a stated print run of 2500 serial numbered sets.

1 Reggie Jackson 1.50 4.00
2 Duke Snider 1.50 4.00
3 Roberto Clemente 5.00 12.00
4 Mel Ott 2.00 5.00
5 Yogi Berra 2.00 5.00
6 Jackie Robinson 2.00 5.00
7 Enos Slaughter 1.50 4.00
8 Willie Stargell 1.50 4.00
9 Bobby Doerr 1.50 4.00
10 Thurman Munson 2.00 5.00

2003 Donruss Classics Legends of the Fall Fabrics

Randomly inserted into packs, this is a parallel to the Legends of the Fall insert set. Each of these cards features a game-worn/used memorabilia swatch sequentially numbered to varying quantities. Please note that we have put that stated print run information next to the player's name in our checklist and if the print run is 25 or fewer, no pricing is provided due to market scarcity.

1 Reggie Jackson/100 10.00 25.00
2 Duke Snider/25
3 Roberto Clemente/50 75.00 150.00
4 Mel Ott/25
5 Yogi Berra/15
6 Jackie Robinson/50 50.00 100.00
7 Enos Slaughter/25
8 Willie Stargell/100 10.00 25.00
9 Bobby Doerr/100 8.00 20.00
10 Thurman Munson/25

2003 Donruss Classics Membership

Randomly inserted into packs, this 15-card set feature members of some of the most prestigious stat groups. Each of these cards were issued to a stated print run of 2500 serial numbered sets.

1 Babe Ruth 6.00 15.00
2 Steve Carlton 1.50 4.00
3 Honus Wagner 3.00 8.00
4 Warren Spahn 1.50 4.00
5 Eddie Mathews 2.00 5.00
6 Nolan Ryan 5.00 12.00
7 Rogers Hornsby 1.50 4.00
8 Ernie Banks 2.00 5.00
9 Harmon Killebrew 2.00 5.00
10 Tom Seaver 1.50 4.00
11 Jimmie Foxx 2.00 5.00
12 Ty Cobb 3.00 8.00
13 Frank Robinson 1.50 4.00
14 Mel Ott 2.00 5.00
15 Lou Gehrig 4.00 10.00

2003 Donruss Classics Membership VIP Memorabilia

Randomly inserted in packs, this is a parallel to the Membership insert set. Each of these cards feature a game worn/used memorabilia swatch. Each of these cards were issued to a varying sequential numbering and we have put that information next to the player's name in our checklist. Please note that if a card has a print run of 25 or fewer, no pricing is provided due to market scarcity.

1 Babe Ruth Bat/29
2 Steve Carlton Jsy/81 10.00 25.00
3 Honus Wagner Seat/14
4 Warren Spahn Jsy/61 30.00 60.00
5 Eddie Mathews Bat/67 30.00 60.00
6 Nolan Ryan Jsy/80 50.00 100.00
7 Rogers Hornsby Bat/31
8 Ernie Banks Jsy/70 30.00 60.00
9 Harmon Killebrew Jsy/71 30.00 60.00
10 Tom Seaver Jsy/81 15.00 40.00
11 Jimmie Foxx Bat/40 40.00 80.00
12 Ty Cobb Bat/21
13 Frank Robinson Jsy/71 20.00 50.00
14 Mel Ott Jsy/45 40.00 80.00
15 Lou Gehrig Bat/31

2003 Donruss Classics Timeless Treasures

Randomly inserted into packs, these five cards featured some of the game's most legendary players along with two swatches of game-worn/used material sequentially numbered to varying quantities. Please note that for cards with stated print runs of 25 or fewer, no pricing is provided due to market scarcity.

1 Stan Musial Jsy 75.00 150.00
Tony Gwynn Jsy/50
2 Alex Rodriguez Jsy
Cal Ripken Jsy/25
3 Roberto Clemente Jsy 75.00 150.00
Vladimir Guerrero Jsy/50
4 Ernie Banks Jsy
Sammy Sosa Jsy/25
5 Don Mattingly Jsy 60.00 120.00
Jason Giambi Jsy/50

2003 Donruss Classics Atlantic City National

Collectors who opened a stated number of Donruss Classic packs at the Donruss booth at the Atlantic

City National were rewarded with these cards. The fronts of these cards had a special Atlantic City embossed logo while the backs show serial numbering to five.

PRINT RUN 5 SERIAL #'d SETS

2004 Donruss Classics

This 213-card set was released in April, 2004. The set was issued in six card packs with an $6 SRP which came 18 packs to a box and 14 boxes to a case. The first 150 cards in this set are active veterans while cards 151-175 and 206-211 featured retired greats and cards number 176-205 feature leading prospects. All those cards were printed to a print run of 1999 serial numbered sets. The set closes with three cards featuring leading players who switched teams in the off-season and those cards were issued at a stated rate of one in 18.

COMP.SET w/o SP's (153) 10.00 25.00
COMMON CARD (1-150) .25 .60
COMMON (151-175/206-210) 1.50 4.00
COMMON CARD (176-205) 1.50 4.00
COMMON CARD (211-213) .40 1.00
1 Albert Pujols 1.25 3.00
2 Derek Jeter 1.25 3.00
3 Hank Blalock .25 .60
4 Shannon Stewart .25 .60
5 Jason Giambi .25 .60
6 Carlos Lee .25 .60
7 Trot Nixon .25 .60
8 Bret Boone .25 .60
9 Mark Mulder .25 .60
10 Mariano Rivera .60 1.50
11 Scott Podsednik .25 .60
12 Jim Edmonds .25 .60
13 Mike Lowell .25 .60
14 Robin Ventura .25 .60
15 Brian Giles .25 .60
16 Jose Vidro .25 .60
17 Manny Ramirez .40 1.00
18 Alex Rodriguez Rgr 1.00 2.50
19 Carlos Beltran .25 .60
20 Hideki Matsui 1.00 2.50
21 Johan Santana .60 1.50
22 Richie Sexson .25 .60
23 Chipper Jones .60 1.50
24 Steve Finley .25 .60
25 Mark Prior .40 1.00
26 Alexis Rios .25 .60
27 Rafael Palmeiro .40 1.00
28 Jorge Posada .40 1.00
29 Barry Zito .25 .60
30 Jamie Moyer .25 .60
31 Preston Wilson .25 .60
32 Miguel Cabrera .40 1.00
33 Pedro Martinez .40 1.00
34 Curt Schilling .40 1.00
35 Hee Seop Choi .25 .60
36 Dontrelle Willis .40 1.00
37 Rafael Soriano .25 .60
38 Richard Fischer .25 .60
39 Brian Tallet .25 .60
40 Jose Castillo .25 .60
41 Wade Miller .25 .60
42 Jose Contreras .25 .60
43 Runelvys Hernandez .25 .60
44 Joe Borchard .25 .60
45 Kazuhisa Ishii .25 .60
46 Jose Reyes .25 .60
47 Adam Dunn .25 .60
48 Randy Johnson .60 1.50
49 Brandon Phillips .25 .60
50 Scott Rolen .40 1.00
51 Ken Griffey Jr. 1.00 2.50
52 Tom Glavine .40 1.00
53 Cliff Lee .25 .60
54 Chien-Ming Wang 1.00 2.50
55 Roy Oswalt .25 .60
56 Austin Kearns .25 .60
57 Jhonny Peralta .25 .60
58 Greg Maddux Braves 1.00 2.50
59 Mark Grace .40 1.00
60 Jae Weong Seo .25 .60
61 Nic Jackson .25 .60
62 Roger Clemens 1.25 3.00
63 Jimmy Gobble .25 .60
64 Travis Hafner .25 .60
65 Paul Konerko .25 .60
66 Jerome Williams .25 .60
67 Ryan Klesko .25 .60
68 Alexis Gomez .25 .60
69 Omar Vizquel .40 1.00
70 Zach Day .25 .60
71 Rickey Henderson .60 1.50
72 Morgan Ensberg .25 .60
73 Josh Beckett .25 .60
74 Garrett Atkins .25 .60
75 Sean Casey .25 .60
76 Julio Franco .25 .60
77 Lyle Overbay .25 .60
78 Josh Phelps .25 .60
79 Juan Gonzalez .25 .60
80 Rich Harden .25 .60
81 Bernie Williams .40 1.00
82 Torii Hunter .25 .60
83 Angel Berroa .25 .60
84 Jody Gerut .25 .60
85 Roberto Alomar .40 1.00
86 Byung-Hyun Kim .25 .60
87 Jay Gibbons .25 .60
88 Chone Figgins .25 .60
89 Fred McGriff .40 1.00
90 Rich Aurilia .25 .60
91 Xavier Nady .25 .60
92 Marlon Byrd .25 .60
93 Mike Piazza 1.00 2.50
94 Vladimir Guerrero .60 1.50
95 Shawn Green .25 .60
96 Jeff Kent .25 .60
97 Ivan Rodriguez .40 1.00
98 Jay Payton .25 .60
99 Barry Larkin .40 1.00
100 Mike Sweeney .25 .60
101 Adrian Beltre .25 .60
102 Robby Hammock .25 .60
103 Orlando Hudson .25 .60
104 Mark Teixeira .40 1.00
105 Hong-Chih Kuo .25 .60
106 Eric Chavez .25 .60
107 Nick Johnson .25 .60
108 Jacque Jones .25 .60
109 Ken Harvey .25 .60
110 Aramis Ramirez .25 .60
111 Victor Martinez .25 .60
112 Joe Crede .25 .60
113 Jason Varitek .60 1.50
114 Troy Glaus .25 .60
115 Billy Wagner .25 .60
116 Kerry Wood .25 .60
117 Hideo Nomo .60 1.50
118 Brandon Webb .25 .60
119 Craig Biggio .40 1.00
120 Orlando Cabrera .25 .60
121 Sammy Sosa .60 1.50
122 Bobby Abreu .25 .60
123 Andruw Jones .40 1.00
124 Jeff Bagwell .40 1.00
125 Jim Thome .40 1.00
126 Javy Lopez .25 .60
127 Luis Castillo .25 .60
128 Todd Helton .40 1.00
129 Roy Halladay .25 .60
130 Mike Mussina .40 1.00
131 Eric Byrnes .25 .60
132 Eric Hinske .25 .60
133 Nomar Garciaparra 1.00 2.50
134 Edgar Martinez .40 1.00
135 Rocco Baldelli .25 .60
136 Miguel Tejada .25 .60
137 Alfonso Soriano Yanks .25 .60
138 Carlos Delgado .25 .60
139 Rafael Furcal .25 .60
140 Ichiro Suzuki 1.25 3.00
141 Aubrey Huff .25 .60
142 Garret Anderson .25 .60
143 Vernon Wells .25 .60
144 Maggio Ordonez .25 .60
145 Brett Myers .25 .60
146 Luis Gonzalez .25 .60
147 Lance Berkman .25 .60
148 Frank Thomas .60 1.50
149 Gary Sheffield .25 .60
150 Tim Hudson .25 .60
151 Duke Snider LGD 2.00 5.00
152 Carl Yastrzemski LGD 2.50 6.00
153 Whitey Ford LGD 2.00 5.00
154 Cal Ripken LGD 5.00 12.00
155 Dwight Gooden LGD 1.50 4.00
156 Warren Spahn LGD 2.00 5.00
157 Bob Gibson LGD 2.00 5.00
158 Don Mattingly LGD 4.00 10.00
159 Jack Morris LGD 1.50 4.00
160 Jim Bunning LGD 2.00 5.00
161 Fergie Jenkins LGD 1.50 4.00
162 Brooks Robinson LGD 2.00 5.00
163 George Kell LGD 1.50 4.00
164 Darryl Strawberry LGD 1.50 4.00
165 Robin Roberts LGD 1.50 4.00
166 Monte Irvin LGD 1.50 4.00
167 Ernie Banks LGD 2.00 5.00
168 Wade Boggs LGD 2.00 5.00
169 Gaylord Perry LGD 1.50 4.00
170 Keith Hernandez LGD 1.50 4.00
171 Lou Brock LGD 2.00 5.00
172 Frank Robinson LGD 2.00 5.00
173 Nolan Ryan LGD 4.00 10.00
174 Stan Musial LGD 2.50 6.00
175 Eddie Murray LGD 2.00 5.00
176 Byron Gettis ROO RC 1.50 4.00
177 Merkin Valdez ROO RC 2.00 5.00
178 Rickie Weeks ROO 1.50 4.00
179 Akinori Otsuka ROO RC 1.50 4.00
180 Brian Bruney ROO 1.50 4.00
181 Freddy Guzman ROO RC 2.00 5.00
182 Brendan Harris ROO 1.50 4.00
183 John Gall ROO RC 2.00 5.00
184 Jason Kubel ROO 2.00 5.00
185 Delmon Young ROO 2.00 5.00
186 Ryan Howard ROO UER 4.00 10.00
Stat headers are for a pitcher
187 Adam Loewen ROO 1.50 4.00
188 J.D. Durbin ROO 1.50 4.00
189 Dan Haren ROO 1.50 4.00
190 Dustin McGowan ROO 1.50 4.00
191 Chad Gaudin ROO 1.50 4.00
192 Preston Larrison ROO 1.50 4.00
193 Ramon Nivar ROO 1.50 4.00
194 Ronald Belisario ROO RC 1.50 4.00
195 Mike Gosling ROO RC 1.50 4.00
196 Kevin Youkilis ROO 1.50 4.00
197 Ryan Wagner ROO 1.50 4.00
198 Bubba Nelson ROO 1.50 4.00
199 Edwin Jackson ROO 1.50 4.00
200 Chris Burke ROO 1.50 4.00
201 Carlos Hines ROO RC 1.50 4.00
202 Greg Dobbs ROO RC 1.50 4.00
203 Jamie Brown ROO RC 1.50 4.00
204 Dave Crouthers ROO RC 1.50 4.00
205 Ian Snell ROO RC 2.00 5.00
206 Gary Carter LGD 1.50 4.00
207 Dale Murphy LGD 2.00 5.00
208 Ryne Sandberg LGD 3.00 8.00
209 Phil Niekro LGD 1.50 4.00
210 Don Sutton LGD 1.50 4.00
211 Alex Rodriguez Yanks SP 2.00 5.00
212 Alfonso Soriano Rgr SP .40 1.00
213 Greg Maddux Cubs SP 1.50 4.00

2004 Donruss Classics Significant Signatures Green

RANDOM INSERTS IN PACKS
PRINT RUNS B/WN 1-100 COPIES PER
NO PRICING ON QTY OF 15 OR LESS
3 Hank Blalock/25 10.00 25.00
4 Shannon Stewart/50 8.00 20.00

6 Carlos Lee/10
7 Trot Nixon/25 10.00 25.00
9 Mark Mulder/10
10 Mariano Rivera/5
12 Jim Edmonds/10
13 Mike Lowell/25 10.00 25.00
14 Robin Ventura/25 10.00 25.00
16 Jose Vidro/10
17 Manny Ramirez/5
18 Alex Rodriguez Rgr/1
19 Carlos Beltran/25 10.00 25.00
21 Johan Santana/50 12.50 30.00
22 Richie Sexson/5
23 Chipper Jones/1
24 Steve Finley/25 15.00 40.00
25 Mark Prior/5
26 Alexis Rios/100 6.00 15.00
27 Rafael Palmeiro/10
28 Jorge Posada/10
29 Barry Zito/10
30 Jamie Moyer/5
32 Miguel Cabrera/50 12.50 30.00
33 Pedro Martinez/1
34 Curt Schilling/1
36 Dontrelle Willis/25 15.00 40.00
37 Rafael Soriano/100 4.00 10.00
38 Richard Fischer/100 4.00 10.00
39 Brian Tallet/100 4.00 10.00
40 Jose Castillo/100 4.00 10.00
41 Wade Miller/25 6.00 15.00
42 Jose Contreras/10
43 Runelvys Hernandez/20 6.00 15.00
44 Joe Borchard/50 5.00 12.00
47 Adam Dunn/25 15.00 40.00
48 Randy Johnson/1
49 Brandon Phillips/50 5.00 12.00
50 Scott Rolen/10
52 Tom Glavine/5
53 Cliff Lee/50 5.00 12.00
54 Chien-Ming Wang/50 100.00 200.00
55 Roy Oswalt/10
56 Austin Kearns/10
57 Jhonny Peralta/100 6.00 15.00
58 Greg Maddux Braves/1
59 Mark Grace/5
60 Jae Weong Seo/50 8.00 20.00
61 Nic Jackson/100 4.00 10.00
62 Roger Clemens/1
63 Jimmy Gobble/45 5.00 12.00
64 Travis Hafner/50 8.00 20.00
65 Paul Konerko/10
66 Jerome Williams/50 5.00 12.00
67 Ryan Klesko/5
68 Alexis Gomez/50 5.00 12.00
70 Zach Day/50 5.00 12.00
72 Morgan Ensberg/50 8.00 20.00
73 Josh Beckett/5
74 Garrett Atkins/99 4.00 10.00
75 Sean Casey/10
76 Julio Franco/10
77 Lyle Overbay/50 4.00 10.00
78 Josh Phelps/25 6.00 15.00
79 Juan Gonzalez/25 10.00 25.00
80 Rich Harden/50 8.00 20.00
82 Torii Hunter/10
83 Angel Berroa/5
84 Jody Gerut/50 5.00 12.00
85 Roberto Alomar/5
87 Jay Gibbons/50 5.00 12.00
88 Chone Figgins/50 8.00 20.00
89 Fred McGriff/5
90 Rich Aurilia/10
91 Xavier Nady/5
92 Marlon Byrd/10
93 Mike Piazza/1
94 Vladimir Guerrero/5
95 Shawn Green/1
97 Ivan Rodriguez/5
98 Jay Payton/50 5.00 12.00
99 Barry Larkin/25 15.00 40.00
100 Mike Sweeney/1
101 Adrian Beltre/5
102 Robby Hammock/50 5.00 12.00
103 Orlando Hudson/50 5.00 12.00
104 Mark Teixeira/10
105 Hong-Chih Kuo/50 30.00 60.00
106 Eric Chavez/25 10.00 25.00
107 Nick Johnson/10
108 Jacque Jones/50 8.00 20.00
109 Ken Harvey/100 4.00 10.00
110 Aramis Ramirez/50 8.00 20.00
111 Victor Martinez/50 8.00 20.00
112 Joe Crede/50 8.00 20.00
113 Jason Varitek/25 20.00 50.00
114 Troy Glaus/10
116 Kerry Wood/5
117 Hideo Nomo/1
118 Brandon Webb/25 6.00 15.00
119 Craig Biggio/10
120 Orlando Cabrera/10
121 Sammy Sosa/21 50.00 100.00
122 Bobby Abreu/10
123 Andruw Jones/10
124 Jeff Bagwell/5
127 Luis Castillo/25 6.00 15.00
128 Todd Helton/1
130 Mike Mussina/1
131 Eric Byrnes/10
132 Eric Hinske/10
134 Edgar Martinez/25 20.00 50.00
135 Rocco Baldelli/10
136 Miguel Tejada/5
141 Aubrey Huff/5
142 Garret Anderson/5
143 Vernon Wells/10
144 Maggio Ordonez/10
145 Brett Myers/50 8.00 20.00
147 Lance Berkman/5
148 Frank Thomas/5
149 Gary Sheffield/25 15.00 40.00
150 Tim Hudson/10
151 Duke Snider LGD/25 20.00 50.00
152 Carl Yastrzemski LGD/5
153 Whitey Ford LGD/25 20.00 50.00
154 Cal Ripken LGD/5
155 Dwight Gooden LGD/50 10.00 25.00
156 Warren Spahn LGD/10
157 Bob Gibson LGD/5
158 Don Mattingly LGD/25 75.00 150.00
159 Jack Morris LGD/50 6.00 15.00
160 Jim Bunning LGD/50 30.00 60.00
161 Fergie Jenkins LGD/50 10.00 25.00
162 Brooks Robinson LGD/10
163 George Kell LGD/50 10.00 25.00
164 Darryl Strawberry LGD/50 10.00 25.00
165 Robin Roberts LGD/25 20.00 50.00
166 Monte Irvin LGD/25 12.50 30.00
167 Ernie Banks LGD/25 30.00 60.00
168 Wade Boggs LGD/25 30.00 60.00
169 Gaylord Perry LGD/50 6.00 15.00
170 Keith Hernandez LGD/50 10.00 25.00
171 Lou Brock LGD/10
172 Frank Robinson LGD/25 20.00 50.00
173 Nolan Ryan LGD/25 75.00 150.00
174 Stan Musial LGD/25 40.00 80.00
175 Eddie Murray LGD/25 50.00 100.00
176 Byron Gettis ROO/100 4.00 10.00
177 Merkin Valdez ROO/100 4.00 10.00
178 Rickie Weeks ROO/25 10.00 25.00
180 Brian Bruney ROO/100 4.00 10.00
181 Freddy Guzman ROO/100 4.00 10.00
182 Brendan Harris ROO/100 4.00 10.00
183 John Gall ROO/100 4.00 10.00
184 Jason Kubel ROO/100 4.00 10.00
185 Delmon Young ROO/50 20.00 50.00
186 Ryan Howard ROO/100 40.00 80.00
187 Adam Loewen ROO/100 4.00 10.00
188 J.D. Durbin ROO/100 4.00 10.00
189 Dan Haren ROO/100 4.00 10.00
190 Dustin McGowan ROO/100 4.00 10.00
191 Chad Gaudin ROO/100 4.00 10.00
192 Preston Larrison ROO/100 4.00 10.00
193 Ramon Nivar ROO/100 4.00 10.00
195 Mike Gosling ROO/100 4.00 10.00
196 Kevin Youkilis ROO/100 4.00 10.00
197 Ryan Wagner ROO/100 4.00 10.00
198 Bubba Nelson ROO/100 4.00 10.00
199 Edwin Jackson ROO/100 6.00 15.00
200 Chris Burke ROO/100 6.00 15.00
201 Carlos Hines ROO/100 4.00 10.00
202 Greg Dobbs ROO/50 5.00 12.00
203 Jamie Brown ROO/100 4.00 10.00
204 Dave Crouthers ROO/100
205 Ian Snell ROO/100 6.00 15.00
206 Gary Carter LGD/50 10.00 25.00
207 Dale Murphy LGD/50 15.00 40.00
208 Ryne Sandberg LGD/50 40.00 80.00
209 Phil Niekro LGD/50 15.00 40.00
210 Don Sutton LGD/50 10.00 25.00
211 Alex Rodriguez Yanks/1
213 Greg Maddux Cubs/1

2004 Donruss Classics Significant Signatures Platinum

RANDOM INSERTS IN PACKS
STATED PRINT RUN 1 SERIAL #'d SET
NO PRICING DUE TO SCARCITY

2004 Donruss Classics Significant Signatures Red

RANDOM INSERTS IN PACKS
PRINT RUNS B/WN 1-250 COPIES PER
NO PRICING ON QTY OF 15 OR LESS
3 Hank Blalock/50 8.00 20.00
4 Shannon Stewart/100 6.00 15.00
6 Carlos Lee/25 10.00 25.00
7 Trot Nixon/50 8.00 20.00
9 Mark Mulder/25 10.00 25.00
10 Mariano Rivera/5
12 Jim Edmonds/25 15.00 40.00
13 Mike Lowell/50 8.00 20.00
14 Robin Ventura/50 8.00 20.00
16 Jose Vidro/25 6.00 15.00
17 Manny Ramirez/5
18 Alex Rodriguez Rgr/5
19 Carlos Beltran/25 10.00 25.00
21 Johan Santana/100 10.00 25.00
22 Richie Sexson/10
23 Chipper Jones/5
24 Steve Finley/100 10.00 25.00
25 Mark Prior/10
26 Alexis Rios/250 6.00 15.00
27 Rafael Palmeiro/25 50.00 100.00
28 Jorge Posada/25 15.00 40.00
29 Barry Zito/10
30 Jamie Moyer/5
32 Miguel Cabrera/100 10.00 25.00
33 Pedro Martinez/5
34 Curt Schilling/5
36 Dontrelle Willis/100 10.00 25.00
37 Rafael Soriano/250 4.00 10.00
38 Richard Fischer/250 4.00 10.00
39 Brian Tallet/250 4.00 10.00
40 Jose Castillo/250 4.00 10.00
41 Wade Miller/92 4.00 10.00
42 Jose Contreras/25 10.00 25.00
43 Runelvys Hernandez/50 5.00 12.00
44 Joe Borchard/250 4.00 10.00
47 Adam Dunn/25 15.00 40.00
48 Randy Johnson/3
49 Brandon Phillips/70 4.00 10.00
50 Scott Rolen/25 15.00 40.00
52 Tom Glavine/10
53 Cliff Lee/100 4.00 10.00
54 Chien-Ming Wang/250 60.00 120.00
55 Roy Oswalt/25 10.00 25.00
56 Austin Kearns/25 6.00 15.00
57 Jhonny Peralta/250 6.00 15.00
58 Greg Maddux Braves/5
59 Mark Grace/5
60 Jae Weong Seo/100 6.00 15.00
61 Nic Jackson/250 4.00 10.00
62 Roger Clemens/1
63 Jimmy Gobble/200 4.00 10.00
64 Travis Hafner/100 6.00 15.00
65 Paul Konerko/25 15.00 40.00
66 Jerome Williams/250 4.00 10.00
67 Ryan Klesko/5
68 Alexis Gomez/100 4.00 10.00
70 Zach Day/100 4.00 10.00
72 Morgan Ensberg/100 6.00 15.00
73 Josh Beckett/5
74 Garrett Atkins/245 4.00 10.00
75 Sean Casey/10
76 Julio Franco/25 10.00 25.00
77 Lyle Overbay/250 4.00 10.00
78 Josh Phelps/50 5.00 12.00
79 Juan Gonzalez/25 10.00 25.00
80 Rich Harden/150 6.00 15.00
82 Torii Hunter/25 10.00 25.00
83 Angel Berroa/10
84 Jody Gerut/100 4.00 10.00
85 Roberto Alomar/10
87 Jay Gibbons/100 4.00 10.00
88 Chone Figgins/100 6.00 15.00
89 Fred McGriff/5
90 Rich Aurilia/50 6.00 15.00
91 Xavier Nady/10
92 Marlon Byrd/25 6.00 15.00
93 Mike Piazza/10
94 Vladimir Guerrero/10
95 Shawn Green/1
97 Ivan Rodriguez/10
98 Jay Payton/100 4.00 10.00
99 Barry Larkin/25 15.00 40.00
100 Mike Sweeney/1
101 Adrian Beltre/5
102 Robby Hammock/150 4.00 10.00
103 Orlando Hudson/100 4.00 10.00
104 Mark Teixeira/10
105 Hong-Chih Kuo/100 20.00 50.00
106 Eric Chavez/25 10.00 25.00
107 Nick Johnson/25 10.00 25.00
108 Jacque Jones/100 6.00 15.00
109 Ken Harvey/250 4.00 10.00
110 Aramis Ramirez/100 6.00 15.00
111 Victor Martinez/99 6.00 15.00
112 Joe Crede/250 6.00 15.00
113 Jason Varitek/25 20.00 50.00
114 Troy Glaus/25 15.00 40.00
116 Kerry Wood/10
117 Hideo Nomo/1
118 Brandon Webb/50 5.00 12.00
119 Craig Biggio/25 15.00 40.00
120 Orlando Cabrera/50 8.00 20.00
121 Sammy Sosa/25 50.00 100.00
122 Bobby Abreu/25 10.00 25.00
123 Andruw Jones/25 15.00 40.00
124 Jeff Bagwell/25 40.00 80.00
127 Luis Castillo/50 5.00 12.00
128 Todd Helton/5
130 Mike Mussina/5
131 Eric Byrnes/25 6.00 15.00
132 Eric Hinske/25 6.00 15.00
134 Edgar Martinez/50 20.00 50.00
135 Rocco Baldelli/25 10.00 25.00
136 Miguel Tejada/5
141 Aubrey Huff/5
142 Garret Anderson/5
143 Vernon Wells/25 10.00 25.00
144 Maggio Ordonez/25 15.00 40.00
145 Brett Myers/100 6.00 15.00
147 Lance Berkman/5
148 Frank Thomas/5
149 Gary Sheffield/50 12.50 30.00
150 Tim Hudson/25 15.00 40.00
151 Duke Snider LGD/50 15.00 40.00
152 Carl Yastrzemski LGD/10
153 Whitey Ford LGD/50 15.00 40.00
154 Cal Ripken LGD/10
155 Dwight Gooden LGD/100 8.00 20.00
156 Warren Spahn LGD/25 30.00 60.00
157 Bob Gibson LGD/15
158 Don Mattingly LGD/25 75.00 150.00
159 Jack Morris LGD/100 6.00 15.00
160 Jim Bunning LGD/100 15.00 40.00
161 Fergie Jenkins LGD/100 8.00 20.00
162 Brooks Robinson LGD/20 50.00 100.00
163 George Kell LGD/100 8.00 20.00
164 Darryl Strawberry LGD/100 8.00 20.00
165 Robin Roberts LGD/100 10.00 25.00
166 Monte Irvin LGD/100 8.00 20.00
167 Ernie Banks LGD/50 20.00 50.00
168 Wade Boggs LGD/50 20.00 50.00
169 Gaylord Perry LGD/100 6.00 15.00
170 Keith Hernandez LGD/100 8.00 20.00
171 Lou Brock LGD/25 20.00 50.00
172 Frank Robinson LGD/50 15.00 40.00
173 Nolan Ryan LGD/50 60.00 120.00
174 Stan Musial LGD/50 30.00 60.00
175 Eddie Murray LGD/50 40.00 80.00
176 Byron Gettis ROO/250 4.00 10.00
177 Merkin Valdez ROO/250 4.00 10.00
178 Rickie Weeks ROO/50 8.00 20.00
180 Brian Bruney ROO/250 4.00 10.00
181 Freddy Guzman ROO/250 4.00 10.00
182 Brendan Harris ROO/250 4.00 10.00
183 John Gall ROO/250 4.00 10.00
184 Jason Kubel ROO/250 4.00 10.00
185 Delmon Young ROO/100 20.00 50.00
186 Ryan Howard ROO/250 30.00 60.00
187 Adam Loewen ROO/250 4.00 10.00
188 J.D. Durbin ROO/250 4.00 10.00
189 Dan Haren ROO/250 4.00 10.00
190 Dustin McGowan ROO/250 4.00 10.00
191 Chad Gaudin ROO/250 4.00 10.00
192 Preston Larrison ROO/250 4.00 10.00
193 Ramon Nivar ROO/250 4.00 10.00
195 Mike Gosling ROO/250 4.00 10.00
196 Kevin Youkilis ROO/250 4.00 10.00
197 Ryan Wagner ROO/250 4.00 10.00
198 Bubba Nelson ROO/250 4.00 10.00
199 Edwin Jackson ROO/250 6.00 15.00
200 Chris Burke ROO/250 6.00 15.00
201 Carlos Hines ROO/250 4.00 10.00
202 Greg Dobbs ROO/100 4.00 10.00
203 Jamie Brown ROO/250 4.00 10.00
204 Dave Crouthers ROO/250 4.00 10.00
205 Ian Snell ROO/250 6.00 15.00
206 Gary Carter LGD/100 8.00 20.00
207 Dale Murphy LGD/50 15.00 40.00
208 Ryne Sandberg LGD/25 50.00 100.00
209 Phil Niekro LGD/100 10.00 25.00
210 Don Sutton LGD/100 8.00 20.00
211 Alex Rodriguez Yanks/5
213 Greg Maddux Cubs/5

2004 Donruss Classics Timeless Tributes Green

*GREEN 1-150: 3X TO 8X BASIC
*GREEN 151-175/206-210: 1.5X TO 4X BASIC
*GREEN 176-205: .75X TO 2X BASIC
*GREEN 211-213: 2X TO 5X BASIC
RANDOM INSERTS IN PACKS
STATED PRINT RUN 50 SERIAL #'d SETS

2004 Donruss Classics Timeless Tributes Platinum

RANDOM INSERTS IN PACKS
STATED PRINT RUN 1 SERIAL #'d SET
NO PRICING DUE TO SCARCITY

2004 Donruss Classics Timeless Tributes Red

*RED 1-150: 2.5X TO 6X BASIC
*RED 151-175/206-210: 1.25X TO 3X BASIC
*RED 176-205: .6X TO 1.5X BASIC
*RED 211-213: 1.5X TO 4X BASIC
RANDOM INSERTS IN PACKS
STATED PRINT RUN 100 SERIAL #'d SETS

2004 Donruss Classics Classic Combos Bat

RANDOM INSERTS IN PACKS
PRINT RUNS B/WN 25-50 COPIES PER
ALL CARDS FEATURE BAT-BAT COMBOS
1 Babe Ruth 200.00 350.00
Lou Gehrig/25
2 Roy Campanella 15.00 40.00
Pee Wee Reese/50
3 Ted Williams 125.00 200.00
Carl Yastrzemski/25
4 Roberto Clemente 75.00 150.00
Willie Stargell/25
5 Eddie Murray 40.00 80.00
Cal Ripken/50
6 Roger Maris 50.00 100.00
Yogi Berra/25
10 Nolan Ryan 20.00 50.00
Rod Carew/50
11 Don Mattingly 30.00 60.00
Rickey Henderson/50
15 Robin Yount 15.00 40.00

Paul Molitor/50
16 Mark Grace 15.00 40.00
Sammy Sosa/50
17 Ted Williams 75.00 150.00
Bobby Doerr/25
18 Reggie Jackson 15.00 40.00
Rod Carew/50

2004 Donruss Classics Classic Combos Jersey

PRINT RUNS B/WN
NO PRICING ON QTY OF 10 OR LESS
PRIME PRINT RUN 1 SERIAL #'d SET
NO PRIME PRICING DUE TO SCARCITY
RANDOM INSERTS IN PACKS
ALL ARE JSY-JSY COMBOS UNLESS NOTED
1 Babe Ruth Pants
Lou Gehrig Pants/15
2 Roy Campanella Pants 20.00 50.00
Pee Wee Reese/25
3 Ted Williams 175.00 300.00
Carl Yastrzemski/15
4 Roberto Clemente 75.00 150.00
Willie Stargell/25
5 Eddie Murray 60.00 120.00
Cal Ripken/25
6 Roger Maris 50.00 100.00
Yogi Berra/25
7 Stan Musial
Bob Gibson/10
8 Whitey Ford 20.00 50.00
Yogi Berra/25
9 Marty Marion 30.00 60.00
Stan Musial/25
10 Nolan Ryan 30.00 60.00
Rod Carew/25
11 Don Mattingly 30.00 60.00
Rickey Henderson/50
12 Jack Morris 10.00 25.00
Alan Trammell/50
13 Whitey Ford 20.00 50.00
Phil Rizzuto/25
14 Marty Marion 15.00 40.00
Red Schoendienst/25
15 Robin Yount 15.00 40.00
Paul Molitor/50
16 Mark Grace 15.00 40.00
Sammy Sosa/50
17 Ted Williams 150.00 250.00
Bobby Doerr/15
18 Reggie Jackson 15.00 40.00
Rod Carew/50

2004 Donruss Classics Classic Combos Quad

NO PRICING ON QTY OF 5 OR LESS
PRIME PRINT RUN 1 SERIAL #'d SET
NO PRIME PRICING DUE TO SCARCITY
RANDOM INSERTS IN PACKS
1 Babe Ruth Bat-Pants
Lou Gehrig Bat-Pants/5
2 Roy Campanella Bat-Pants 50.00 100.00
Pee Wee Reese Bat-Jsy/25
3 Ted Williams Bat-Jsy 250.00 400.00
Carl Yastrzemski Bat-Jsy/15
4 Roberto Clemente Bat-Jsy 175.00 300.00
Willie Stargell Bat-Jsy/25
5 Eddie Murray Bat-Jsy 125.00 200.00
Cal Ripken Bat-Jsy/25
6 Roger Maris Bat-Jsy 150.00 250.00
Yogi Berra Bat-Jsy/15
10 Nolan Ryan Bat-Jsy 60.00 120.00
Rod Carew Bat-Jsy/25
11 Don Mattingly Bat-Jsy 75.00 150.00
Rickey Henderson Bat-Jsy/25
15 Robin Yount Bat-Jsy 50.00 100.00
Paul Molitor Bat-Jsy/25
16 Mark Grace Bat-Jsy 50.00 100.00
Sammy Sosa Bat-Jsy/25
17 Ted Williams Bat-Jsy 175.00 300.00
Bobby Doerr Bat-Jsy/15
18 Reggie Jackson Bat-Jsy 40.00 80.00
Rod Carew Bat-Jsy/25

2004 Donruss Classics Classic Singles Bat

RANDOM INSERTS IN PACKS
PRINT RUNS B/WN 10-50 COPIES PER
NO PRICING ON QTY OF 10 OR LESS

1 Babe Ruth/15 250.00 400.00
2 Nolan Ryan/10
3 Stan Musial/25 20.00 50.00
4 Ted Williams/25 60.00 120.00
5 Lou Gehrig/25 75.00 150.00
6 Eddie Murray/50 12.50 30.00
7 Roy Campanella/50 12.50 30.00
8 Robin Yount/50 12.50 30.00
9 Roberto Clemente/25 50.00 100.00
10 Don Mattingly/50 20.00 50.00
12 Carl Yastrzemski/50 15.00 40.00
13 Mark Grace/50 10.00 25.00
15 Rickey Henderson/50 12.50 30.00
16 Reggie Jackson/50 10.00 25.00
17 Pee Wee Reese/50 10.00 25.00
20 Roger Maris/25 30.00 60.00
21 Cal Ripken/25 40.00 80.00
23 Willie Stargell/50 10.00 25.00
24 Paul Molitor/50 6.00 15.00
26 Alan Trammell/50 6.00 15.00
27 Sammy Sosa/50 12.50 30.00
28 Bobby Doerr/50 6.00 15.00
29 Rod Carew/50 10.00 25.00
30 Yogi Berra/25 15.00 40.00
32 George Brett/50 20.00 50.00

2004 Donruss Classics Classic Singles Jersey

PRINT RUNS B/WN 10-100 COPIES PER
NO PRICING ON QTY FO 10 OR LESS
PRIME PRINT RUN 1 SERIAL #'d SET
NO PRIME PRICING DUE TO SCARCITY
RANDOM INSERTS IN PACKS
1 Babe Ruth Pants/10
2 Nolan Ryan/50 20.00 50.00
3 Stan Musial/15 30.00 60.00
4 Ted Williams/10
5 Lou Gehrig Pants/10
6 Eddie Murray/100 8.00 20.00
7 Roy Campanella Pants/50 12.50 30.00
8 Robin Yount/100 8.00 20.00
9 Roberto Clemente/25 60.00 120.00
10 Don Mattingly/100 15.00 40.00
11 Bob Gibson/15 15.00 40.00
12 Carl Yastrzemski/50 15.00 40.00
13 Mark Grace/25 12.50 30.00
14 Jack Morris/100 4.00 10.00
15 Rickey Henderson/25 15.00 40.00
16 Reggie Jackson/50 10.00 25.00
17 Pee Wee Reese/25 12.50 30.00
18 Marty Marion/100 4.00 10.00
19 Tommy John/100 4.00 10.00
20 Roger Maris/25 30.00 60.00
21 Cal Ripken/25 60.00 120.00
22 Red Schoendienst/25 8.00 20.00
23 Willie Stargell/100 6.00 15.00
24 Paul Molitor/100 4.00 10.00
25 Whitey Ford/50 10.00 25.00
26 Alan Trammell/100 4.00 10.00
27 Sammy Sosa/50 8.00 20.00
28 Bobby Doerr/50 6.00 15.00
29 Rod Carew/100 6.00 15.00
30 Yogi Berra/15 20.00 50.00
31 Phil Rizzuto/25 12.50 30.00
32 George Brett/25 30.00 60.00

2004 Donruss Classics Classic Singles Jersey-Bat

PRINT RUNS B/WN 5-25 COPIES PER
NO PRICING ON QTY OF 10 OR LESS
PRIME PRINT RUN 1 SERIAL #'d SET
NO PRIME PRICING DUE TO SCARCITY
RANDOM INSERTS IN PACKS
ALL ARE JSY-BAT COMBOS UNLESS NOTED
1 Babe Ruth Pants/5
2 Nolan Ryan/25 30.00 60.00
3 Stan Musial/15 40.00 80.00
4 Ted Williams/10
5 Lou Gehrig Pants/10
6 Eddie Murray/25 20.00 50.00
7 Roy Campanella Pants/25 20.00 50.00
8 Robin Yount/25 20.00 50.00
9 Roberto Clemente/25 125.00 200.00
10 Don Mattingly/25 40.00 80.00
12 Carl Yastrzemski/25 30.00 60.00
13 Mark Grace/25 15.00 40.00
15 Rickey Henderson/25 20.00 50.00
16 Reggie Jackson/25 15.00 40.00
17 Pee Wee Reese/25 15.00 40.00
20 Roger Maris/15 60.00 120.00
21 Cal Ripken/25 75.00 150.00
23 Willie Stargell/25 15.00 40.00
24 Paul Molitor/25 10.00 25.00
26 Alan Trammell/25 10.00 25.00
27 Sammy Sosa/25 20.00 50.00
28 Bobby Doerr/25 10.00 25.00
29 Rod Carew/25 15.00 40.00
30 Yogi Berra/15 30.00 60.00
32 George Brett/25 40.00 80.00

2004 Donruss Classics Dress Code Bat

STATED PRINT RUN 50 SERIAL #'d SETS
S.STEWART PRINT 10 SERIAL #'d CARDS
*DC COMBO MTRL: .5X TO 1.2X BASIC
DC COMBO MTRL PRINT 50 SERIAL #'d SETS
DC COMBO MTRL STEWART 10 #'d CARDS
RANDOM INSERTS IN PACKS
NO S.STEWART PRICING DUE TO SCARCITY
1 Derek Jeter 15.00 40.00
2 Kerry Wood 4.00 10.00
3 Nomar Garciaparra 8.00 20.00
4 Jacque Jones 4.00 10.00
5 Mark Teixeira 6.00 15.00
6 Troy Glaus 4.00 10.00
7 Todd Helton 6.00 15.00
8 Miguel Tejada 4.00 10.00
9 Mike Piazza 8.00 20.00
11 Mike Sweeney 4.00 10.00
12 Albert Pujols 10.00 25.00
13 Rickey Henderson 6.00 15.00
14 Chipper Jones 6.00 15.00
15 Don Mattingly 20.00 50.00
16 Shawn Green 4.00 10.00
17 Mark Grace 6.00 15.00
18 Jason Giambi 4.00 10.00
19 Barry Zito 4.00 10.00
20 Sammy Sosa 6.00 15.00
22 Rafael Palmeiro 6.00 15.00
23 Frank Thomas 6.00 15.00
24 Manny Ramirez 6.00 15.00
25 Mike Mussina 6.00 15.00
26 Magglio Ordonez 4.00 10.00
27 Rocco Baldelli 4.00 10.00
28 Andruw Jones 6.00 15.00
29 Torii Hunter 4.00 10.00
30 Ivan Rodriguez 6.00 15.00
31 Jeff Bagwell 6.00 15.00
32 Mark Mulder 4.00 10.00
33 Trot Nixon 4.00 10.00
34 Cal Ripken 40.00 80.00
35 Dontrelle Willis 6.00 15.00
36 Hank Blalock 4.00 10.00
37 Brandon Webb 4.00 10.00
38 Miguel Cabrera 6.00 15.00
39 Hideo Nomo 6.00 15.00
40 Shannon Stewart/10
41 Tim Hudson 4.00 10.00
42 Pedro Martinez 6.00 15.00
43 Hee Seop Choi 4.00 10.00
44 Randy Johnson 6.00 15.00
45 Tony Gwynn 10.00 25.00
46 Mark Prior 6.00 15.00
47 Eric Chavez 4.00 10.00
48 Alex Rodriguez 6.00 15.00
50 Alfonso Soriano 4.00 10.00

2004 Donruss Classics Dress Code Combos Signature

PRINT RUNS B/WN 1-25 COPIES PER
NO PRICING ON QTY OF 10 OR LESS
PRIME PRINT RUN 1 SERIAL #'d SET
NO PRIME PRICING DUE TO SCARCITY
RANDOM INSERTS IN PACKS
2 Kerry Wood Jsy/5
4 Jacque Jones Jsy/25 10.00 25.00
5 Mark Teixeira Jsy/5
6 Troy Glaus Jsy/5
7 Todd Helton Jsy/5
8 Miguel Tejada Jsy/5
9 Mike Piazza Jsy/5
11 Mike Sweeney Jsy/5
13 Rickey Henderson Jsy/5
14 Chipper Jones Jsy/5
15 Don Mattingly Jsy/5
16 Shawn Green Jsy/1
17 Mark Grace Jsy/5
19 Barry Zito Jsy/5
20 Sammy Sosa Jsy/5
21 Jay Gibbons Jsy/25 10.00 25.00
22 Rafael Palmeiro Jsy/5
23 Frank Thomas Jsy/5
25 Mike Mussina Jsy/5
26 Magglio Ordonez Jsy/5
27 Rocco Baldelli Jsy/10
28 Andruw Jones Jsy/5
29 Torii Hunter Jsy/10
30 Ivan Rodriguez Jsy/5
31 Jeff Bagwell Jsy/5
32 Mark Mulder Jsy/25 10.00 25.00
33 Trot Nixon Jsy/25 10.00 25.00
34 Cal Ripken Jsy/5
35 Dontrelle Willis Jsy/25 15.00 40.00
36 Hank Blalock Jsy/10
37 Brandon Webb Jsy/10
38 Miguel Cabrera Jsy/25 15.00 40.00
39 Hideo Nomo Jsy/5
40 Shannon Stewart Jsy/25 10.00 25.00
41 Tim Hudson Jsy/10
42 Pedro Martinez Jsy/5
44 Randy Johnson Jsy/5
45 Tony Gwynn Jsy/5
46 Mark Prior Jsy/10
47 Eric Chavez Jsy/10
48 Alex Rodriguez Jsy/5
49 Johan Santana Jsy/25 15.00 40.00

2004 Donruss Classics Dress Code Jersey

STATED PRINT RUN 100 SERIAL #'d SETS
RIPKEN PRINT RUN 25 SERIAL #'d CARDS
*NUMBER: .4X TO 1X BASIC
*NUMBER RIPKEN: .15X TO .4X BASIC RIPKEN
NUMBER PRINT RUN 100 SERIAL #'d SETS
*PRIME: 1.5X TO 4X BASIC
*PRIME MATTINGLY: .75X TO 2X BASIC MATT
*PRIME RIPKEN: .6X TO 1.2X BASIC RIPKEN
PRIME PRINT RUN 25 SERIAL #'d SETS
PRIME SORIANO PRINT 12 #'d CARDS
NO PRIME SORIANO PRICING AVAILABLE
RANDOM INSERTS IN PACKS
1 Derek Jeter 12.50 30.00
2 Kerry Wood 3.00 8.00
3 Nomar Garciaparra 6.00 15.00
4 Jacque Jones 3.00 8.00
5 Mark Teixeira 4.00 10.00
6 Troy Glaus 3.00 8.00
7 Todd Helton 4.00 10.00
8 Miguel Tejada 3.00 8.00
9 Mike Piazza 6.00 15.00
11 Mike Sweeney 3.00 8.00
12 Albert Pujols 8.00 20.00
13 Rickey Henderson 4.00 10.00
14 Chipper Jones 4.00 10.00
15 Don Mattingly 15.00 40.00
16 Shawn Green 3.00 8.00
17 Mark Grace 4.00 10.00
18 Jason Giambi 3.00 8.00
19 Barry Zito 3.00 8.00
20 Sammy Sosa 4.00 10.00
21 Jay Gibbons 3.00 8.00
22 Rafael Palmeiro 4.00 10.00
23 Frank Thomas 4.00 10.00
24 Manny Ramirez 4.00 10.00
25 Mike Mussina 4.00 10.00
26 Magglio Ordonez 3.00 8.00
27 Rocco Baldelli 3.00 8.00
28 Andruw Jones 4.00 10.00
29 Torii Hunter 3.00 8.00
30 Ivan Rodriguez 4.00 10.00
31 Jeff Bagwell 4.00 10.00
32 Mark Mulder 3.00 8.00
33 Trot Nixon 3.00 8.00
34 Cal Ripken/25 60.00 120.00
35 Dontrelle Willis 4.00 10.00
36 Hank Blalock 3.00 8.00
37 Brandon Webb 3.00 8.00
38 Miguel Cabrera 4.00 10.00
39 Hideo Nomo 4.00 10.00
40 Shannon Stewart 3.00 8.00
41 Tim Hudson 3.00 8.00
42 Pedro Martinez 4.00 10.00
43 Hee Seop Choi 3.00 8.00
44 Randy Johnson 4.00 10.00
45 Tony Gwynn 8.00 20.00
46 Mark Prior 4.00 10.00
47 Eric Chavez 3.00 8.00
48 Alex Rodriguez 4.00 10.00
49 Johan Santana 4.00 10.00
50 Alfonso Soriano 3.00 8.00

2004 Donruss Classics Famous Foursomes

RANDOM INSERTS IN PACKS
STATED PRINT RUN 99 SERIAL #'d SETS
1 Roy Campanella 10.00 25.00
Pee Wee Reese
Jackie Robinson
Duke Snider
2 Stan Musial 10.00 25.00
Bob Gibson
Red Schoendienst
Ken Boyer

2004 Donruss Classics Famous Foursomes Jersey

STATED PRINT RUN 10 SERIAL #'d SETS
PRIME PRINT RUN 1 SERIAL #'d SET
NO PRIME PRICING DUE TO SCARCITY
RANDOM INSERTS IN PACKS
ALL ARE QUAD JSY CARDS UNLESS NOTED
1 Roy Campanella Pants
Pee Wee Reese
Jackie Robinson
Duke Snider
2 Stan Musial
Bob Gibson
Red Schoendienst
Ken Boyer

2004 Donruss Classics Legendary Hats Material

RANDOM INSERTS IN PACKS
PRINT RUNS B/WN 5-25 COPIES PER
NO PRICING ON QTY OF 10 OR LESS
1 Tony Gwynn/10
2 Mike Schmidt/25 40.00 80.00
6 George Brett/25 40.00 80.00
14 Cal Ripken/25 75.00 150.00
16 Kirby Puckett/25 20.00 50.00
20 Reggie Jackson Yanks/25 15.00 40.00
21 Roberto Clemente/5
22 Ernie Banks/25 20.00 50.00

29 Dave Winfield/25 10.00 25.00
40 Wade Boggs/25 15.00 40.00
42 Rickey Henderson A's/25 20.00 50.00
49 Reggie Jackson Angels/25 15.00 40.00
51 Rafael Palmeiro/25 15.00 40.00
52 Sammy Sosa/25 20.00 50.00
55 Steve Carlton/25 10.00 25.00
56 Rod Carew Angels/25 15.00 40.00
60 R.Henderson Angels/25 20.00 50.00

2004 Donruss Classics Legendary Jackets Material

RANDOM INSERTS IN PACKS
STATED PRINT RUN 100 SERIAL #'d SETS
2 Mike Schmidt 15.00 40.00
8 Reggie Jackson A's 6.00 15.00
17 Don Mattingly 15.00 40.00
32 Gary Carter 4.00 10.00
54 Nolan Ryan 20.00 50.00
56 Rod Carew Angels 6.00 15.00

2004 Donruss Classics Legendary Jerseys Material

PRINT RUNS B/WN 5-50 COPIES PER
NO PRICING ON QTY OF 10 OR LESS
PRIME PRINT RUN 1 SERIAL #'d SET
NO PRIME PRICING DUE TO SCARCITY
RANDOM INSERTS IN PACKS
1 Tony Gwynn/50 10.00 25.00
2 Mike Schmidt/25 30.00 60.00
3 Johnny Bench/50 10.00 25.00
4 Roger Maris Yanks/10
5 Ted Williams/10
6 George Brett/25 30.00 60.00
7 Carlton Fisk/50 10.00 25.00
8 Reggie Jackson A's/25 12.50 30.00
9 Joe Morgan/25 8.00 20.00
10 Bo Jackson/25 15.00 40.00
11 Stan Musial/10
12 Andre Dawson/50 6.00 15.00
13 R.Henderson Yanks/25 15.00 40.00
14 Cal Ripken/25 60.00 120.00
15 Dale Murphy/25 12.50 30.00
16 Kirby Puckett/50 12.50 30.00
17 Don Mattingly/50 20.00 50.00
18 Brooks Robinson/50 10.00 25.00
19 Orlando Cepeda/50 6.00 15.00
20 Reggie Jackson Yanks/25 12.50 30.00
21 Roberto Clemente/25 60.00 120.00
22 Ernie Banks/10
23 Frank Robinson/50 6.00 15.00
24 Harmon Killebrew/50 12.50 30.00
25 Willie Stargell/50 10.00 25.00
26 Al Kaline/15 20.00 50.00
27 Carl Yastrzemski/50 15.00 40.00
28 Duke Snider/10
29 Dave Winfield/50 6.00 15.00
30 Eddie Murray/50 12.50 30.00
31 Eddie Mathews/25 15.00 40.00
32 Gary Carter/50 6.00 15.00
33 Rod Carew Twins/25 12.50 30.00
35 Mel Ott/10
36 Paul Molitor/50 6.00 15.00
37 Thurman Munson/15 20.00 50.00
39 Robin Yount/50 12.50 30.00
40 Wade Boggs/50 10.00 25.00
41 Jackie Robinson/5
42 Rickey Henderson A's/25 15.00 40.00
44 Yogi Berra/15 20.00 50.00
46 Luis Aparicio/50 6.00 15.00
47 Phil Rizzuto/25 12.50 30.00
48 Roger Maris A's/25 30.00 60.00
49 Reggie Jackson Angels/50 10.00 25.00
50 Lou Gehrig/5
51 Rafael Palmeiro/50 10.00 25.00
52 Sammy Sosa/50 12.50 30.00
53 Roger Clemens/50 12.50 30.00
54 Nolan Ryan/50 20.00 50.00
55 Steve Carlton/50 6.00 15.00
56 Rod Carew Angels/50 10.00 25.00
57 Whitey Ford/25 12.50 30.00
59 Babe Ruth/5

2004 Donruss Classics Legendary Jerseys Material Number

*NUMBER p/r 50: .4X TO 1X BASIC p/r 50
*NUMBER p/r 25: .5X TO 1.2X BASIC p/r 50
*NUMBER p/r 25: .4X TO 1X BASIC p/r 25
*NUMBER p/r 15: .5X TO 1.2X BASIC p/r 25
*NUMBER p/r 15: .4X TO 1X BASIC p/r 15
RANDOM INSERTS IN PACKS
PRINT RUNS B/WN 3-50 COPIES PER
NO PRICNG ON QTY OF 10 OR LESS
45 Roy Campanella Pants/25 15.00 40.00
58 Fergie Jenkins Pants/25 8.00 20.00

2004 Donruss Classics Legendary Leather Material

RANDOM INSERTS IN PACKS
PRINT RUNS B/WN 5-25 COPIES PER
NO PRICING ON QTY OF 10 OR LESS
1 Tony Gwynn Fld Glv/10
2 Mike Schmidt Fld Glv/10
16 Kirby Puckett Fld Glv/25 20.00 50.00
17 Don Mattingly Btg Glv/10
29 Dave Winfield Fld Glv/10
32 Gary Carter Fld Glv/25 10.00 25.00
34 Jimmie Foxx Fld Glv/10
51 Rafael Palmeiro Fld Glv/25 15.00 40.00
52 Sammy Sosa Btg Glv/25 20.00 50.00
54 Nolan Ryan Fld Glv/5
55 Steve Carlton Fld Glv/25 10.00 25.00
58 Fergie Jenkins Fld Glv/25 10.00 25.00

2004 Donruss Classics Legendary Lumberjacks

STATED PRINT RUN 1000 SERIAL #'d SETS
*HATS: 1.5X TO 4X LUMBERJACKS
HATS PRINT RUN 50 SERIAL #'d SETS
*JACKETS: 1.5X TO 4X LUMBERJACKS
JACKET PRINT RUN 50 SERIAL #'d SETS
*JERSEYS: .6X TO 1.5X LUMBERJACKS
JERSEY PRINT RUN 500 SERIAL #'d SETS
*LEATHER: 1.2X TO 3X LUMBERJACKS
LEATHER PRINT RUN 100 SERIAL #'d SETS
*PANTS: 1.5X TO 4X LUMBERJACKS
PANTS PRINT RUN 50 SERIAL #'d SETS
*SPIKES: 1.25X TO 3X LUMBERJACKS
SPIKES PRINT RUN 100 SERIAL #'d SETS
RANDOM INSERTS IN PACKS
1 Tony Gwynn 2.00 5.00
2 Mike Schmidt 3.00 8.00
3 Johnny Bench 1.50 4.00
4 Roger Maris Yanks 1.50 4.00
5 Ted Williams 3.00 8.00
6 George Brett 3.00 8.00
7 Carlton Fisk 1.50 4.00
8 Reggie Jackson A's 1.50 4.00
9 Joe Morgan 1.00 2.50
10 Bo Jackson 1.50 4.00
11 Stan Musial 2.50 6.00
12 Andre Dawson 1.00 2.50
13 Rickey Henderson Yanks 1.50 4.00
14 Cal Ripken 5.00 12.00
15 Dale Murphy 1.50 4.00
16 Kirby Puckett 1.50 4.00
17 Don Mattingly 3.00 8.00
18 Brooks Robinson 1.50 4.00
19 Orlando Cepeda 1.00 2.50
20 Reggie Jackson Yanks 1.50 4.00
21 Roberto Clemente 4.00 10.00
22 Ernie Banks 1.50 4.00
23 Frank Robinson 1.00 2.50
24 Harmon Killebrew 1.50 4.00
25 Willie Stargell 1.50 4.00
26 Al Kaline 1.50 4.00
27 Carl Yastrzemski 2.50 6.00
28 Duke Snider 1.50 4.00
29 Dave Winfield 1.00 2.50
30 Eddie Murray 1.50 4.00
31 Eddie Mathews 1.50 4.00
32 Gary Carter 1.00 2.50
33 Rod Carew Twins 1.50 4.00
34 Jimmie Foxx 1.50 4.00
35 Mel Ott 1.50 4.00
36 Paul Molitor 1.00 2.50
37 Thurman Munson 1.50 4.00
38 Rogers Hornsby 1.50 4.00
39 Robin Yount 1.50 4.00

40 Wade Boggs 1.50 4.00
41 Jackie Robinson 1.50 4.00
42 Rickey Henderson A's 1.50 4.00
43 Ty Cobb 2.00 5.00
44 Yogi Berra 1.50 4.00
45 Roy Campanella 1.50 4.00
46 Luis Aparicio 1.00 2.50
47 Phil Rizzuto 1.50 4.00
48 Roger Maris A's 1.50 4.00
49 Reggie Jackson Angels 1.50 4.00
50 Lou Gehrig 2.50 6.00
51 Rafael Palmeiro 1.50 4.00
52 Sammy Sosa 1.50 4.00
53 Roger Clemens 3.00 8.00
54 Nolan Ryan 4.00 10.00
55 Steve Carlton 1.00 2.50
56 Rod Carew Angels 1.50 4.00
57 Whitey Ford 1.50 4.00
58 Fergie Jenkins 1.00 2.50
59 Babe Ruth 4.00 10.00
60 R.Henderson Angels 1.50 4.00

2004 Donruss Classics Legendary Lumberjacks Material

RANDOM INSERTS IN PACKS
PRINT RUNS B/WN 10-100 COPIES PER
NO PRICING ON QTY OF 10 OR LESS
1 Tony Gwynn/100 8.00 20.00
2 Mike Schmidt/100 10.00 25.00
3 Johnny Bench/100 6.00 15.00
4 Roger Maris Yanks/25 30.00 60.00
5 Ted Williams/25 60.00 120.00
6 George Brett/100 10.00 25.00
7 Carlton Fisk/100 6.00 15.00
8 Reggie Jackson A's/100 6.00 15.00
9 Joe Morgan/100 4.00 10.00
10 Bo Jackson/100 8.00 20.00
11 Stan Musial/25 20.00 50.00
12 Andre Dawson/100 4.00 10.00
13 R.Henderson Yanks/100 8.00 20.00
14 Cal Ripken/100 20.00 50.00
15 Dale Murphy/100 6.00 15.00
16 Kirby Puckett/100 8.00 20.00
17 Don Mattingly/100 10.00 25.00
18 Brooks Robinson/100 6.00 15.00
19 Orlando Cepeda/100 4.00 10.00
20 Reggie Jackson Yanks/100 6.00 15.00
21 Roberto Clemente/25 50.00 100.00
22 Ernie Banks/100 8.00 20.00
23 Frank Robinson/100 4.00 10.00
24 Harmon Killebrew/100 8.00 20.00
25 Willie Stargell/100 6.00 15.00
26 Al Kaline/100 8.00 20.00
27 Carl Yastrzemski/100 12.50 30.00
28 Duke Snider/10
29 Dave Winfield/100 4.00 10.00
30 Eddie Murray/100 8.00 20.00
31 Eddie Mathews/50 12.50 30.00
32 Gary Carter/100 4.00 10.00
33 Rod Carew Twins/100 6.00 15.00
34 Jimmie Foxx/10
35 Mel Ott/25 15.00 40.00
36 Paul Molitor/100 4.00 10.00
37 Thurman Munson/50 10.00 25.00
38 Rogers Hornsby/25 40.00 80.00
39 Robin Yount/100 8.00 20.00
40 Wade Boggs/100 6.00 15.00
42 Rickey Henderson A's/50 12.50 30.00
43 Ty Cobb/10
44 Yogi Berra/25 15.00 40.00
45 Roy Campanella/25 15.00 40.00
46 Luis Aparicio/100 4.00 10.00
48 Roger Maris A's/25 30.00 60.00
49 Reggie Jackson Angels/100 6.00 15.00
50 Lou Gehrig/25 125.00 200.00
51 Rafael Palmeiro/100 6.00 15.00
52 Sammy Sosa/100 8.00 20.00
56 Rod Carew Angels/100 6.00 15.00
59 Babe Ruth/10
60 R.Henderson Angels/100 8.00 20.00

2004 Donruss Classics Legendary Pants Material

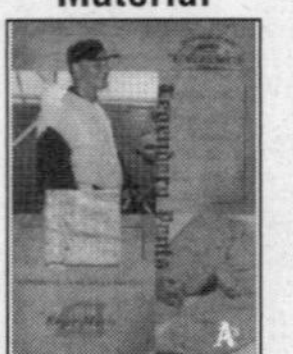

RANDOM INSERTS IN PACKS
PRINT RUNS B/WN 3-50 COPIES PER
NO PRICING ON QTY OF 10 OR LESS
1 Tony Gwynn/25 15.00 40.00
12 Andre Dawson/25 8.00 20.00
24 Harmon Killebrew/50 12.50 30.00
26 Al Kaline/50 12.50 30.00
35 Mel Ott/10
43 Ty Cobb/5
45 Roy Campanella/25 15.00 40.00
46 Luis Aparicio/50 6.00 15.00
47 Phil Rizzuto/50 10.00 25.00
48 Roger Maris A's/25 30.00 60.00
50 Lou Gehrig/4
51 Rafael Palmeiro/25 12.50 30.00
56 Rod Carew Angels/50 10.00 25.00
57 Whitey Ford/25 12.50 30.00
58 Fergie Jenkins/25 8.00 20.00
59 Babe Ruth/3

2004 Donruss Classics Legendary Spikes Material

RANDOM INSERTS IN PACKS
NO PRICING ON QTY OF 10 OR LESS
13 R.Henderson Yanks/25 20.00 50.00
17 Don Mattingly/50 40.00 80.00
29 Dave Winfield/50 8.00 20.00
42 Rickey Henderson A's/25 20.00 50.00
51 Rafael Palmeiro/25 15.00 40.00
52 Sammy Sosa/50 15.00 40.00
56 Rod Carew Angels/10
60 R.Henderson Angels/25 20.00 50.00

2004 Donruss Classics Membership

RANDOM INSERTS IN PACKS
STATED PRINT RUN 2499 SERIAL #'d SETS
1 Stan Musial 2.00 5.00
2 Ted Williams 2.50 6.00
3 Early Wynn .75 2.00
4 Roberto Clemente 3.00 8.00
5 Al Kaline 1.25 3.00
6 Bob Gibson 1.25 3.00
7 Lou Brock 1.25 3.00
8 Carl Yastrzemski 2.00 5.00
9 Gaylord Perry .75 2.00
10 Fergie Jenkins .75 2.00
11 Steve Carlton .75 2.00
12 Reggie Jackson 1.25 3.00
13 Rod Carew 1.25 3.00
14 Bert Blyleven .75 2.00
15 Mike Schmidt 2.50 6.00
16 Nolan Ryan 3.00 8.00
17 Robin Yount 1.25 3.00
18 George Brett 2.50 6.00
19 Eddie Murray 1.25 3.00
20 Tony Gwynn 1.50 4.00
21 Cal Ripken 4.00 10.00
22 Randy Johnson 1.25 3.00
23 Sammy Sosa 1.25 3.00
24 Rafael Palmeiro 1.25 3.00
25 Roger Clemens 2.50 6.00

2004 Donruss Classics Membership VIP Bat

RANDOM INSERTS IN PACKS
PRINT RUNS B/WN 10-25 COPIES PER
NO PRICING ON QTY OF 10 OR LESS
1 Stan Musial/25 20.00 50.00
2 Ted Williams/25 60.00 120.00
4 Roberto Clemente/25 50.00 100.00
5 Al Kaline/25 15.00 40.00
7 Lou Brock/25 12.50 30.00
8 Carl Yastrzemski/25 20.00 50.00
11 Steve Carlton/25 8.00 20.00
12 Reggie Jackson/25 12.50 30.00
13 Rod Carew/25 12.50 30.00
15 Mike Schmidt/25 30.00 60.00
16 Nolan Ryan/10
17 Robin Yount/25 15.00 40.00
18 George Brett/10
19 Eddie Murray/25 15.00 40.00
20 Tony Gwynn/25 15.00 40.00
21 Cal Ripken/10
22 Randy Johnson/25 15.00 40.00
23 Sammy Sosa/25 15.00 40.00
24 Rafael Palmeiro/25 12.50 30.00
25 Roger Clemens/25 15.00 40.00

2004 Donruss Classics Membership VIP Combos Material

PRINT RUNS B/WN 9-25 COPIES PER
NO PRICING ON QTY OF 10 OR LESS
PRIME PRINT RUN 1 SERIAL #'d SET
NO PRIME PRICING DUE TO SCARCITY
RANDOM INSERTS IN PACKS
1 Stan Musial Bat-Jsy/15 40.00 80.00
2 Ted Williams Bat-Jsy/9
4 Rob Clemente Bat-Jsy/25 125.00 200.00
5 Al Kaline Bat-Pants/25 20.00 50.00
7 Lou Brock Bat-Jsy/10
8 Carl Yastrzemski Bat-Jsy/25 30.00 60.00

10 F.Jenkins Fld Glv-Pants/25 10.00 25.00
11 Steve Carlton Bat-Jsy/25 10.00 25.00
12 Reggie Jackson Bat-Jsy/25 15.00 40.00
13 Rod Carew Bat-Pants/25 15.00 40.00
15 Mike Schmidt Bat-Jsy/25 40.00 80.00
16 Nolan Ryan Bat-Jsy/25 30.00 60.00
17 Robin Yount Bat-Jsy/25 20.00 50.00
18 George Brett Bat-Jsy/25 40.00 80.00
19 Eddie Murray Bat-Jsy/25 20.00 50.00
20 Tony Gwynn Bat-Jsy/25 30.00 60.00
21 Cal Ripken Bat-Jsy/25 75.00 150.00
22 Randy Johnson Bat-Jsy/25 20.00 50.00
23 Sammy Sosa Bat-Jsy/25 20.00 50.00
24 Rafael Palmeiro Bat-Jsy/25 15.00 40.00
25 Roger Clemens Bat-Jsy/25 20.00 50.00

2004 Donruss Classics Membership VIP Combos Signature

PRINT RUNS B/WN 1-50 COPIES PER
NO PRICING ON QTY OF 5 OR LESS
PRIME PRINT RUN 1 SERIAL #'d SET
NO PRIME PRICING DUE TO SCARCITY
RANDOM INSERTS IN PACKS
1 Stan Musial Jsy/5
5 Al Kaline Pants/25 60.00 120.00
6 Bob Gibson Jsy/5
7 Lou Brock Jsy/5
8 Carl Yastrzemski Jsy/5
9 Gaylord Perry Jsy/50 10.00 25.00
10 Fergie Jenkins Pants/50 15.00 40.00
11 Steve Carlton Jsy/25 20.00 50.00
12 Reggie Jackson Jsy/5
13 Rod Carew Pants/5
14 Bert Blyleven Jsy/50 10.00 25.00
16 Nolan Ryan Jsy/5
17 Robin Yount Jsy/5
18 George Brett Jsy/5
19 Eddie Murray Jsy/5
20 Tony Gwynn Jsy/5
21 Cal Ripken Jsy/5
22 Randy Johnson Jsy/5
23 Sammy Sosa Jsy/5
24 Rafael Palmeiro Jsy/5
25 Roger Clemens Jsy/1

2004 Donruss Classics Membership VIP Jersey

PRINT RUNS B/WN 9-25 COPIES PER
NO PRICING ON QTY OF 10 OR LESS
PRIME PRINT RUN 1 SERIAL #'d SET
NO PRIME PRICING DUE TO SCARCITY
RANDOM INSERTS IN PACKS
1 Stan Musial/15 30.00 60.00
2 Ted Williams/9
3 Early Wynn/10
4 Roberto Clemente/25 60.00 120.00
5 Al Kaline Pants/25 15.00 40.00
6 Bob Gibson/10
7 Lou Brock/10
8 Carl Yastrzemski/25 20.00 50.00
9 Gaylord Perry/25 8.00 20.00
10 Fergie Jenkins Pants/25 8.00 20.00
11 Steve Carlton/25 8.00 20.00
12 Reggie Jackson/25 12.50 30.00
13 Rod Carew/25 12.50 30.00
14 Bert Blyleven/25 8.00 20.00
15 Mike Schmidt/25 30.00 60.00
16 Nolan Ryan/25 30.00 60.00
17 Robin Yount/25 15.00 40.00
18 George Brett/25 30.00 60.00
19 Eddie Murray/25 15.00 40.00
20 Tony Gwynn/15 15.00 40.00
21 Cal Ripken/25 60.00 120.00
22 Randy Johnson/25 15.00 40.00
23 Sammy Sosa/25 15.00 40.00
24 Rafael Palmeiro/25 12.50 30.00
25 Roger Clemens/25 15.00 40.00

2004 Donruss Classics Membership VIP Signatures

RANDOM INSERTS IN PACKS
PRINT RUNS B/WN 1-50 COPIES PER
NO PRICING ON QTY OF 5 OR LESS
1 Stan Musial/5
5 Al Kaline/20 40.00 80.00
6 Bob Gibson/5

7 Lou Brock/5
8 Carl Yastrzemski/5
9 Gaylord Perry/50 6.00 15.00
10 Fergie Jenkins/50 10.00 25.00
11 Steve Carlton/20 12.50 30.00
12 Reggie Jackson/5
13 Rod Carew/5
14 Bert Blyleven/50 6.00 15.00
16 Nolan Ryan/5
17 Robin Yount/5
18 George Brett/5
19 Eddie Murray/5
20 Tony Gwynn/5
21 Cal Ripken/5
22 Randy Johnson/5
23 Sammy Sosa/5
24 Rafael Palmeiro/5
25 Roger Clemens/1

2004 Donruss Classics October Heroes

RANDOM INSERTS IN PACKS
STATED PRINT RUN 2499 SERIAL #'d SETS
1 Reggie Jackson 1.25 3.00
2 Bob Gibson 1.25 3.00
3 Carlton Fisk 1.25 3.00
4 Whitey Ford 1.25 3.00
5 George Brett 3.00 8.00
6 Roberto Clemente 3.00 8.00
7 Roy Campanella 1.25 3.00
8 Babe Ruth 3.00 8.00

2004 Donruss Classics October Heroes Bat

RANDOM INSERTS IN PACKS
PRINT RUNS B/WN 10-25 COPIES PER
NO PRICING OON QTY OF 10 OR LESS
1 Reggie Jackson/25 12.50 30.00
3 Carlton Fisk/25 12.50 30.00
5 George Brett/10
6 Roberto Clemente/25 50.00 100.00
7 Roy Campanella/25 15.00 40.00
8 Babe Ruth/10

2004 Donruss Classics October Heroes Combos Material

PRINT RUNS B/WN 3-25 COPIES PER
NO PRICING ON QTY OF 5 OR LESS
PRIME PRINT RUN 1 SERIAL #'d SET
NO PRIME PRICING DUE TO SCARCITY
RANDOM INSERTS IN PACKS
1 Reggie Jackson Bat-Hat/25 15.00 40.00
3 Carlton Fisk Bat-Jsy/25 15.00 40.00
5 George Brett Bat-Jsy/25 40.00 80.00
6 Roberto Clemente Bat-Jsy/5
7 R.Campanella Bat-Pants/25 20.00 50.00
8 Babe Ruth Bat-Pants/3

2004 Donruss Classics October Heroes Combos Signature

PRINT RUNS B/WN 5-50 COPIES PER
NO PRICING ON QTY OF 5 OR LESS
PRIME PRINT RUN 1 SERIAL #'d SET
NO PRIME PRICING DUE TO SCARCITY
RANDOM INSERTS IN PACKS
1 Reggie Jackson Bat/5
2 Bob Gibson Jsy/5
3 Carlton Fisk Jsy/5
4 Whitey Ford Jsy/50 30.00 60.00
5 George Brett Jsy/5

2004 Donruss Classics October Heroes Fabric

PRINT RUNS B/WN 5-25 COPIES PER
NO PRICING ON QTY OF 5 OR LESS
PRIME PRINT RUN 1 SERIAL #'d SET
NO PRIME PRICING DUE TO SCARCITY
RANDOM INSERTS IN PACKS
2 Bob Gibson Jsy/15 15.00 40.00
3 Carlton Fisk Jsy/25 12.50 30.00
4 Whitey Ford Jsy/25 12.50 30.00
5 George Brett Jsy/25 30.00 60.00
6 Roberto Clemente Jsy/5
7 Roy Campanella Pants/25 15.00 40.00
8 Babe Ruth Pants/5

2004 Donruss Classics October Heroes Signature

RANDOM INSERTS IN PACKS
PRINT RUNS B/WN 5-50 COPIES PER
NO PRICING ON QTY OF 5 OR LESS
1 Reggie Jackson/5
2 Bob Gibson/5

3 Carlton Fisk/5
4 Whitey Ford/50 15.00 40.00
5 George Brett/5

2004 Donruss Classics Team Colors Bat

RANDOM INSERTS IN PACKS
PRINT RUNS B/WN 10-50 COPIES PER
NO PRICING ON QTY OF 10 OR LESS
2 Steve Garvey/50 6.00 15.00
3 Eric Davis/25 12.50 30.00
4 Al Oliver/50 4.00 10.00
5 Nolan Ryan/10
6 Bobby Doerr/25 8.00 20.00
7 Paul Molitor/50 6.00 15.00
8 Dale Murphy/50 10.00 25.00
11 Jose Canseco/50 10.00 25.00
12 Jim Rice/50 6.00 15.00
13 Will Clark/50 20.00 50.00
14 Alan Trammell/50 6.00 15.00
16 Dwight Evans/50 10.00 25.00
18 Dave Parker Pirates/25 8.00 20.00
21 Andre Dawson Expos/50 6.00 15.00
22 Darryl Strawberry Dgr/50 6.00 15.00
23 George Foster/50 4.00 10.00
26 Bo Jackson/50 12.50 30.00
27 Cal Ripken/50 40.00 80.00
28 Deion Sanders/25 12.50 30.00
29 Don Mattingly/50 20.00 50.00
30 Mark Grace/50 10.00 25.00
31 Fred Lynn/50 4.00 10.00
33 Ernie Banks/25 15.00 40.00
34 Gary Carter/50 6.00 15.00
35 Roger Maris/25 30.00 60.00
36 Ron Santo/50 10.00 25.00
38 Tony Gwynn/50 10.00 25.00
40 Red Schoendienst/25 8.00 20.00
41 Steve Carlton/25 8.00 20.00
42 Wade Boggs/25 12.50 30.00
44 Luis Aparicio/25 8.00 20.00
46 Andre Dawson Cubs/25 8.00 20.00
48 Darryl Strawberry Mets/50 6.00 15.00
49 Dave Parker Reds/50 6.00 15.00

2004 Donruss Classics Team Colors Combos Material

STATED PRINT RUN 25 SERIAL #'d SETS
MARIS PRINT RUN 10 SERIAL #'d CARDS
NO MARIS PRICING DUE TO SCARCITY
PRIME PRINT RUN 1 SERIAL #'d SET
NO PRIME PRICING DUE TO SCARCITY
RANDOM INSERTS IN PACKS
2 Steve Garvey Bat-Jsy 10.00 25.00
3 Eric Davis Bat-Jsy 15.00 40.00
5 Nolan Ryan Bat-Jsy 30.00 60.00
6 Bobby Doerr Bat-Jsy 10.00 25.00
7 Paul Molitor Bat-Jsy 10.00 25.00
8 Dale Murphy Bat-Jsy 15.00 40.00
11 Jose Canseco Bat-Jsy 15.00 40.00
12 Jim Rice Bat-Jsy 10.00 25.00
13 Will Clark Bat-Jsy 40.00 80.00
14 Alan Trammell Bat-Jsy 10.00 25.00
16 Dwight Evans Bat-Jsy 15.00 40.00
18 Dave Parker Pirates Bat-Jsy 10.00 25.00
21 Andre Dawson Expos Bat-Jsy 10.00 25.00
22 Darryl Strawberry Dgr Bat-Jsy 10.00 25.00
23 George Foster Bat-Jsy 8.00 20.00
26 Bo Jackson Bat-Jsy 20.00 50.00
27 Cal Ripken Bat-Jsy 75.00 150.00
28 Deion Sanders Bat-Jsy 15.00 40.00
29 Don Mattingly Bat-Jsy 40.00 80.00
30 Mark Grace Bat-Jsy 15.00 40.00
33 Ernie Banks Bat-Jsy 20.00 50.00
34 Gary Carter Bat-Jacket 10.00 25.00
35 Roger Maris Bat-Jsy/10
38 Tony Gwynn Bat-Jsy 30.00 60.00
40 Red Schoendienst Bat-Jsy 10.00 25.00
41 Steve Carlton Bat-Jsy 10.00 25.00
42 Wade Boggs Bat-Jsy 15.00 40.00
44 Luis Aparicio Bat-Jsy 10.00 25.00
46 Andre Dawson Cubs Bat-Jsy 10.00 25.00
48 D.Strawberry Mets Bat-Jsy 10.00 25.00
49 Dave Parker Reds Bat-Jsy 10.00 25.00

2004 Donruss Classics Team Colors Combos Signature

PRINT RUNS B/WN 2-100 COPIES PER
NO PRICING ON QTY OF 10 OR LESS
PRIME PRINT RUN 1 SERIAL #'d SET
NO PRIME PRICING DUE TO SCARCITY
RANDOM INSERTS IN PACKS
1 L.Dykstra Mets Fld Glv/100 10.00 25.00
2 Steve Garvey Jsy/100 10.00 25.00
3 Eric Davis Jsy/100 15.00 40.00
4 Al Oliver Bat/100 10.00 25.00
5 Nolan Ryan Jsy/5
6 Bobby Doerr Jsy/100 10.00 25.00
7 Paul Molitor Jsy/10
8 Dale Murphy Jsy/10
9 Harold Baines Jsy/100 10.00 25.00
10 Dwight Gooden Jsy/100 10.00 25.00
11 Jose Canseco Jsy/10
12 Jim Rice Jsy/100 10.00 25.00
13 Will Clark Jsy/10
14 Alan Trammell Jsy/100 10.00 25.00
15 Lee Smith Jsy/100 10.00 25.00
16 Dwight Evans Jsy/100 15.00 40.00
17 Tony Oliva Jsy/100 10.00 25.00
18 Dave Parker Pirates Jsy/100 10.00 25.00
19 Jack Morris Jsy/100 10.00 25.00
20 Luis Tiant Jsy/100 10.00 25.00
21 Andre Dawson Expos Jsy/50 15.00 40.00
22 D.Strawberry Dgr Jsy/100 10.00 25.00
23 George Foster Jsy/100 10.00 25.00
24 Marty Marion Jsy/100 10.00 25.00
25 Dennis Eckersley Jsy/100 15.00 40.00
26 Bo Jackson Jsy/10
27 Cal Ripken Jsy/5
28 Deion Sanders Jsy/5
29 Don Mattingly Jacket/10
30 Mark Grace Jsy/10
31 Fred Lynn Jsy/100 10.00 25.00
32 Enos Slaughter Jsy/2
33 Ernie Banks Jsy/25 60.00 120.00
34 Gary Carter Jacket/50 15.00 40.00
36 Ron Santo Bat/25 20.00 50.00
37 Keith Hernandez Jsy/25 20.00 50.00
38 Tony Gwynn Jsy/5
39 Jim Palmer Jsy/50 15.00 40.00
40 Red Schoendienst Jsy/100 10.00 25.00
41 Steve Carlton Jsy/50 15.00 40.00
42 Wade Boggs Jsy/5
43 Tommy John Jsy/100 10.00 25.00
44 Luis Aparicio Jsy/100 10.00 25.00
45 Bob Feller Jsy/100 10.00 25.00
46 Andre Dawson Cubs Jsy/50 15.00 40.00
47 Bert Blyleven Jsy/100 10.00 25.00
48 D.Strawberry Mets Jsy/100 10.00 25.00
49 Dave Parker Reds Jsy/100 10.00 25.00
50 L.Dykstra Phils Btg Glv/30 20.00 50.00

2004 Donruss Classics Team Colors Jersey

PRINT RUNS B/WN 10-100 COPIES PER
NO PRICING ON QTY OF 10 OR LESS
PRIME PRINT RUN 1 SERIAL #'d SET
NO PRIME PRICING DUE TO SCARCITY
RANDOM INSERTS IN PACKS
1 L.Dykstra Mets Fld Glv/25 8.00 20.00
2 Steve Garvey/100 4.00 10.00
3 Eric Davis/25 12.50 30.00
5 Nolan Ryan/50 20.00 50.00
6 Bobby Doerr/25 8.00 20.00
7 Paul Molitor/100 4.00 10.00
8 Dale Murphy/50 10.00 25.00
9 Harold Baines/100 6.00 15.00
10 Dwight Gooden/50 6.00 15.00
11 Jose Canseco/100 6.00 15.00
12 Jim Rice/100 4.00 10.00
13 Will Clark/50 20.00 50.00
14 Alan Trammell/100 4.00 10.00
15 Lee Smith/100 4.00 10.00
16 Dwight Evans/50 10.00 25.00
17 Tony Oliva/100 4.00 10.00
18 Dave Parker Pirates/25 8.00 20.00
19 Jack Morris/100 4.00 10.00
20 Luis Tiant/100 4.00 10.00
21 Andre Dawson Expos/100 4.00 10.00
22 Darryl Strawberry Dgr/100 4.00 10.00
23 George Foster/100 4.00 10.00
24 Marty Marion/50 6.00 15.00
25 Dennis Eckersley/100 4.00 10.00
26 Bo Jackson/50 12.50 30.00
27 Cal Ripken/100 20.00 50.00
28 Deion Sanders/50 10.00 25.00
29 Don Mattingly Jacket/100 15.00 40.00
30 Mark Grace/50 10.00 25.00
31 Fred Lynn/50 6.00 15.00
32 Enos Slaughter/10
33 Ernie Banks/25 15.00 40.00
34 Gary Carter Jacket/100 4.00 10.00
35 Roger Maris/10
37 Keith Hernandez/25 8.00 20.00
38 Tony Gwynn/50 8.00 20.00
39 Jim Palmer/25 8.00 20.00

40 Red Schoendienst/25 8.00 20.00
41 Steve Carlton/25 8.00 20.00
42 Wade Boggs/25 12.50 30.00
43 Tommy John/100 4.00 10.00
44 Luis Aparicio/25 8.00 20.00
45 Bob Feller/10
46 Andre Dawson Cubs/25 8.00 20.00
47 Bert Blyleven/100 4.00 10.00
48 Darryl Strawberry Mets/100 4.00 10.00
49 Dave Parker Reds/100 4.00 10.00

2004 Donruss Classics Team Colors Signatures

RANDOM INSERTS IN PACKS
PRINT RUNS B/WN 1-50 COPIES PER
NO PRICING ON QTY OF 10 OR LESS
1 Len Dykstra Mets/50 10.00 25.00
2 Steve Garvey/50 10.00 25.00
3 Eric Davis/50 15.00 40.00
4 Al Oliver/50 6.00 15.00
5 Nolan Ryan/5
6 Bobby Doerr/50 10.00 25.00
7 Paul Molitor/5
8 Dale Murphy/5
9 Harold Baines/50 10.00 25.00
10 Dwight Gooden/50 10.00 25.00
11 Jose Canseco/5
12 Jim Rice/50 10.00 25.00
13 Will Clark/5
14 Alan Trammell/50 10.00 25.00
15 Lee Smith/50 10.00 25.00
16 Dwight Evans/50 15.00 40.00
17 Tony Oliva/50 10.00 25.00
18 Dave Parker Pirates/50 10.00 25.00
19 Jack Morris/50 6.00 15.00
20 Luis Tiant/50 6.00 15.00
21 Andre Dawson Expos/25 12.50 30.00
22 Darryl Strawberry Dgr/50 10.00 25.00
23 George Foster/50 6.00 15.00
24 Marty Marion/50 10.00 25.00
25 Dennis Eckersley/50 15.00 40.00
26 Bo Jackson/5
27 Cal Ripken/5
28 Deion Sanders/5
29 Don Mattingly/5
30 Mark Grace/5
31 Fred Lynn/50 6.00 15.00
32 Enos Slaughter/1
33 Ernie Banks/10
34 Gary Carter/20 12.50 30.00
36 Ron Santo/10
37 Keith Hernandez/25 12.50 30.00
38 Tony Gwynn/5
39 Jim Palmer/20 12.50 30.00
40 Red Schoendienst/50 10.00 25.00
41 Steve Carlton/20 12.50 30.00
42 Wade Boggs/5
43 Tommy John/50 6.00 15.00
44 Luis Aparicio/50 10.00 25.00
45 Bob Feller/50 10.00 25.00
46 Andre Dawson Cubs/25 12.50 30.00
47 Bert Blyleven/50 6.00 15.00
48 Darryl Strawberry Mets/50 10.00 25.00
49 Dave Parker Reds/50 10.00 25.00
50 Len Dykstra Phils/50 10.00 25.00

2004 Donruss Classics Timeless Triples

RANDOM INSERTS IN PACKS
STATED PRINT RUN 500 SERIAL #'d SETS
1 Ted Williams 5.00 12.00
Carl Yastrzemski
Carlton Fisk
2 Lou Gehrig 4.00 10.00
Roger Maris
Thurman Munson
3 Brooks Robinson 6.00 15.00
Frank Robinson
Cal Ripken
4 Roger Clemens 3.00 8.00
Andy Pettitte
Roy Oswalt
5 Greg Maddux 3.00 8.00
Mark Prior
Kerry Wood
6 Alex Rodriguez 6.00 15.00
Derek Jeter
Gary Sheffield

2004 Donruss Classics Timeless Triples Bat

RANDOM INSERTS IN PACKS
1 Ted Williams 150.00 250.00
Carl Yastrzemski
Carlton Fisk
2 Lou Gehrig 175.00 300.00
Roger Maris
Thurman Munson
3 Brooks Robinson 100.00 175.00
Frank Robinson
Cal Ripken

2004 Donruss Classics Timeless Triples Jersey

PRINT RUNS B/WN 10-25 COPIES PER
NO PRICING ON QTY OF 10 OR LESS
ALL ARE JSY SWATCHES UNLESS NOTED
GEHRIG IS PANTS SWATCH
PRIME PRINT RUN 1 SERIAL #'d SET
NO PRIME PRICING DUE TO SCARCITY
RANDOM INSERTS IN PACKS
1 Ted Williams
Carl Yastrzemski
Carlton Fisk/10
2 Lou Gehrig Pants
Roger Maris
Thurman Munson/10
3 Brooks Robinson 125.00 200.00
Frank Robinson
Cal Ripken/25

2005 Donruss Classics

This 242-card set was released in March, 2005. The set was issued in five card packs with a $6 SRP which came 18 packs to a box and 16 boxes to a case. The first 200 cards in the set features active veterans while cards 201-225 feature autographed Rookie Cards and cards 226 through 250 feature cards of retired supestars. Please note that cards 203, 209, 211, 212, 214, 216, 220 and 222 were never produced. The Rookie cards are signed and issued to a different amount of cards while the retired veterans were issued to a state print run of 1000 serial numbered sets.

COMP.SET w/o SP's (200) 15.00 40.00
COMMON CARD (1-200) .25 .60
AU 201-225 OVERALL AU-GU ODDS 1:6
AU 201-225 PRINT RUN B/WN 400-1500 PER
COMMON CARD (226-250) 1.50 4.00
226-250 OVERALL INSERT ODDS 1:2
226-250 PRINT RUN 1000 SERIAL #'d SETS
1 Scott Rolen .40 1.00
2 Derek Jeter 1.25 3.00
3 Jose Vidro .25 .60
4 Johnny Damon .40 1.00
5 Nomar Garciaparra .60 1.50
6 Jose Guillen .25 .60
7 Trot Nixon .40 1.00
8 Mark Loretta .25 .60
9 Jody Gerut .25 .60
10 Miguel Tejada .25 .60
11 Barry Larkin .40 1.00
12 Jeff Kent .25 .60
13 Carl Crawford .25 .60
14 Paul Konerko .25 .60
15 Jim Edmonds .25 .60
16 Garret Anderson .25 .60
17 Jay Gibbons .25 .60
18 Moises Alou .25 .60
19 Mike Lowell .25 .60
20 Mark Mulder .25 .60
21 Josh Beckett .25 .60
22 Tim Salmon .40 1.00
23 Shannon Stewart .25 .60
24 Miguel Cabrera .40 1.00
25 Jim Thome .40 1.00
26 Kevin Youkilis .25 .60
27 Justin Morneau .25 .60
28 Austin Kearns .25 .60
29 Cliff Lee .25 .60
30 Ken Griffey Jr. 1.00 2.50
31 Mike Piazza .60 1.50
32 Roy Halladay .25 .60
33 Larry Walker .40 1.00
34 David Ortiz .60 1.50
35 Dontrelle Willis .25 .60
36 Craig Wilson .25 .60
37 Jeff Suppan .25 .60
38 Curt Schilling .40 1.00
39 Larry Bigbie .25 .60
40 Rich Harden .25 .60
41 Victor Martinez .25 .60
42 Jorge Posada .40 1.00
43 Joey Gathright .25 .60
44 Adam Dunn .25 .60
45 Pedro Martinez .40 1.00
46 Dallas McPherson .25 .60
47 Tom Glavine .40 1.00
48 Torii Hunter .25 .60
49 Angel Berroa .25 .60
50 Mark Prior .40 1.00
51 Ichiro Suzuki 1.25 3.00
52 C.C. Sabathia .25 .60
53 Bobby Abreu .25 .60
54 Shigetoshi Hasegawa .25 .60
55 Brandon Webb .25 .60
56 Mark Buehrle .25 .60
57 Johan Santana .60 1.50
58 Francisco Rodriguez .25 .60
59 Roy Oswalt .25 .60
60 Mike Sweeney .25 .60
61 Jake Peavy .25 .60
62 Akinori Otsuka .25 .60
63 Dioner Navarro .25 .60
64 Kazuhito Tadano .25 .60
65 Ryan Wagner .25 .60
66 Abe Alvarez .25 .60
67 Mark Teixeira .40 1.00
68 Jermaine Dye .25 .60
69 Todd Walker .25 .60
70 Octavio Dotel .25 .60
71 Frank Thomas .60 1.50
72 Javy Lopez .25 .60
73 Scott Podsednik .25 .60
74 B.J. Upton .40 1.00
75 Barry Zito .25 .60
76 Raul Ibanez .25 .60
77 Orlando Cabrera .25 .60
78 Sean Burroughs .25 .60
79 Esteban Loaiza .25 .60
80 Jason Schmidt .25 .60
81 Vinny Castilla .25 .60
82 Shingo Takatsu .25 .60
83 Juan Pierre .25 .60
84 David Dellucci .25 .60
85 Travis Blackley .25 .60
86 Brad Penny .25 .60
87 Nick Johnson .25 .60
88 Brian Roberts .25 .60
89 Kazuo Matsui .25 .60
90 Mike Lieberthal .25 .60
91 Craig Biggio .40 1.00
92 Sean Casey .25 .60
93 Andy Pettitte .40 1.00
94 Milton Bradley .25 .60
95 Rocco Baldelli .25 .60
96 Adrian Gonzalez .25 .60
97 Chad Tracy .25 .60
98 Chad Cordero .25 .60
99 Albert Pujols 1.25 3.00
100 Jason Kubel .25 .60
101 Rafael Furcal .25 .60
102 Jack Wilson .25 .60
103 Eric Chavez .25 .60
104 Casey Kotchman .25 .60
105 Jeff Bagwell .40 1.00
106 Melvin Mora .25 .60
107 Bobby Crosby .25 .60
108 Preston Wilson .25 .60
109 Hank Blalock .25 .60
110 Vernon Wells .25 .60
111 Francisco Cordero .25 .60
112 Steve Finley .25 .60
113 Omar Vizquel .40 1.00
114 Eric Byrnes .25 .60
115 Tim Hudson .25 .60
116 Aramis Ramirez .25 .60
117 Lance Berkman .25 .60
118 Shea Hillenbrand .25 .60
119 Aubrey Huff .25 .60
120 Lew Ford .25 .60
121 Sammy Sosa .60 1.50
122 Marcus Giles .25 .60
123 Rickie Weeks .25 .60
124 Manny Ramirez .40 1.00
125 Jason Giambi .25 .60
126 Adam LaRoche .25 .60
127 Vladimir Guerrero .60 1.50
128 Ken Harvey .25 .60
129 Adrian Beltre .25 .60
130 Magglio Ordonez .25 .60
131 Greg Maddux 1.00 2.50
132 Russ Ortiz .25 .60
133 Jason Varitek .60 1.50
134 Kerry Wood .25 .60
135 Mike Mussina .40 1.00
136 Joe Nathan .25 .60
137 Troy Glaus .25 .60
138 Carlos Zambrano .25 .60
139 Ben Sheets .25 .60
140 Jae Weong Seo .25 .60
141 Derrek Lee .40 1.00
142 Carlos Beltran .25 .60
143 John Lackey .25 .60
144 Aaron Rowand .25 .60
145 Dewon Brazelton .25 .60
146 Jason Bay .25 .60
147 Alfonso Soriano .25 .60
148 Travis Hafner .25 .60
149 Ryan Church .25 .60
150 Bret Boone .25 .60
151 Bernie Williams .40 1.00
152 Wade Miller .25 .60
153 Zack Greinke .25 .60
154 Scott Kazmir .25 .60
155 Hideki Matsui 1.00 2.50
156 Livan Hernandez .25 .60
157 Jose Capellan .25 .60
158 David Wright 1.00 2.50
159 Chone Figgins .25 .60
160 Jeremy Reed .25 .60
161 J.D. Drew .25 .60
162 Hideo Nomo .60 1.50
163 Merkin Valdez .25 .60
164 Shawn Green .25 .60
165 Alexis Rios .25 .60
166 Johnny Estrada .25 .60
167 Danny Graves .25 .60
168 Carlos Lee .25 .60
169 John Van Benschoten .25 .60
170 Randy Johnson .60 1.50
171 Randy Wolf .25 .60
172 Luis Gonzalez .25 .60
173 Chipper Jones .60 1.50
174 Delmon Young .40 1.00
175 Edwin Jackson .25 .60
176 Carlos Delgado .25 .60
177 Matt Clement .25 .60
178 Jacque Jones .25 .60
179 Gary Sheffield .25 .60
180 Laynce Nix .25 .60
181 Tom Gordon .25 .60
182 Jose Castillo .25 .60
183 Andruw Jones .40 1.00
184 Brian Giles .25 .60
185 Paul Lo Duca .25 .60
186 Roger Clemens 1.00 2.50
187 Todd Helton .40 1.00
188 Keith Foulke .25 .60
189 Jeremy Bonderman .25 .60
190 Troy Percival .25 .60
191 Michael Young .25 .60
192 Carlos Guillen .25 .60
193 Rafael Palmeiro .40 1.00
194 Brett Myers .25 .60
195 Carl Pavano .25 .60
196 Alex Rodriguez 1.00 2.50
197 Lyle Overbay .25 .60
198 Ivan Rodriguez .40 1.00
199 Khalil Greene .40 1.00
200 Edgar Renteria .25 .60
201 Justin Verlander AU/400 RC 20.00 40.00
202 Miguel Negron AU/1300 RC 4.00 10.00
204 Paul Reynoso AU/1200 RC 3.00 8.00
205 Colter Bean AU/1200 RC 4.00 10.00
206 Raul Tablado AU/1200 RC 3.00 8.00
207 M.McLemore AU/1500 RC 3.00 8.00
208 Russ Rohlicek AU/1200 RC 3.00 8.00
210 Chris Seddon AU/785 RC 3.00 8.00
213 Mike Morse AU/1200 RC 4.00 10.00
215 R.Messenger AU/1200 RC 3.00 8.00
217 Carlos Ruiz AU/1200 RC 4.00 10.00
218 Chris Roberson AU/1200 RC 3.00 8.00
219 Ryan Speier AU/1200 RC 3.00 8.00
223 Dave Gassner AU/1200 RC 3.00 8.00
224 Sean Tracey AU/1200 RC 3.00 8.00
225 C.Rogowski AU/1500 RC 4.00 10.00
226 Billy Williams LGD 1.50 4.00
227 Ralph Kiner LGD 1.50 4.00
228 Ozzie Smith LGD 2.50 6.00
229 Rod Carew LGD 2.00 5.00
230 Nolan Ryan LGD 4.00 10.00
231 Fergie Jenkins LGD 1.50 4.00
232 Paul Molitor LGD 1.50 4.00
233 Carlton Fisk LGD 2.00 5.00
234 Rollie Fingers LGD 1.50 4.00
235 Lou Brock LGD 2.00 5.00
236 Gaylord Perry LGD 1.50 4.00
237 Don Mattingly LGD 3.00 8.00
238 Maury Wills LGD 1.50 4.00
239 Luis Aparicio LGD 1.50 4.00
240 George Brett LGD 3.00 8.00
241 Mike Schmidt LGD 3.00 8.00
242 Joe Morgan LGD 1.50 4.00
243 Dennis Eckersley LGD 1.50 4.00
244 Reggie Jackson LGD 2.00 5.00
245 Bobby Doerr LGD 1.50 4.00
246 Bob Feller LGD 2.00 5.00
247 Cal Ripken LGD 5.00 12.00
248 Harmon Killebrew LGD 2.00 5.00
249 Frank Robinson LGD 1.50 4.00
250 Stan Musial LGD 2.50 6.00

2005 Donruss Classics Significant Signatures Gold

*GOLD p/r 100: .5X TO 1.2X SILV p/r 200
*GOLD p/r 50: .6X TO 1.5X SILV p/r 200
*GOLD p/r 50: .5X TO 1.2X SILV p/r 100
*GOLD p/r 50: .5X TO 1.2X SILV p/r 50
OVERALL AU-GU ODDS 1:6
PRINT RUNS B/WN 1-100 COPIES PER
NO PRICING ON QTY OF 10 OR LESS

2005 Donruss Classics Significant Signatures Platinum

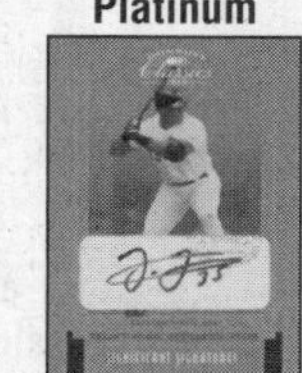

OVERALL AU-GU ODDS 1:6
STATED PRINT RUN 1 SERIAL #'d SET
NO PRICING DUE TO SCARCITY

2005 Donruss Classics Significant Signatures Silver

OVERALL AU-GU ODDS 1:6
PRINT RUNS B/WN 1-200 COPIES PER
1-200/226-250 NO PRICING ON 10 OR LESS
201-225 NO PRICING ON QTY OF 25
1 Scott Rolen/1
3 Jose Vidro/10
6 Jose Guillen/10
7 Trot Nixon/10
8 Mark Loretta/10
9 Jody Gerut/10
11 Barry Larkin/1
14 Paul Konerko/10
15 Jim Edmonds/1
16 Garret Anderson/10
17 Jay Gibbons/25 6.00 15.00
19 Mike Lowell/1
21 Josh Beckett/1
22 Tim Salmon/100 10.00 25.00
23 Shannon Stewart/10
24 Miguel Cabrera/10
26 Kevin Youkilis/25 6.00 15.00
28 Austin Kearns/10
29 Cliff Lee/200 4.00 10.00
32 Roy Halladay/1
34 David Ortiz/10
35 Dontrelle Willis/1
36 Craig Wilson/1
37 Jeff Suppan/200 6.00 15.00
38 Curt Schilling/1
39 Larry Bigbie/100 6.00 15.00
40 Rich Harden/100 6.00 15.00
41 Victor Martinez/25 10.00 25.00
43 Joey Gathright/100 4.00 10.00
44 Adam Dunn/5
45 Pedro Martinez/1
47 Tom Glavine/1
48 Torii Hunter/5
49 Angel Berroa/10
50 Mark Prior/1
52 C.C. Sabathia/10
54 Shigetoshi Hasegawa/10
55 Brandon Webb/10
56 Mark Buehrle/10
57 Johan Santana/10
58 Francisco Rodriguez/10
61 Jake Peavy/25 15.00 40.00
62 Akinori Otsuka/10
63 Dioner Navarro/100 6.00 15.00
64 Kazuhito Tadano/100 10.00 25.00
65 Ryan Wagner/50 5.00 12.00
66 Abe Alvarez/100 6.00 15.00
68 Jermaine Dye/25 10.00 25.00
69 Todd Walker/25 6.00 15.00
70 Octavio Dotel/25 10.00 25.00
71 Frank Thomas/1
73 Scott Podsednik/25 15.00 40.00
74 B.J. Upton/10
75 Barry Zito/1
76 Raul Ibanez/50 5.00 12.00
77 Orlando Cabrera/25 10.00 25.00
78 Sean Burroughs/10
79 Esteban Loaiza/50 8.00 20.00
82 Shingo Takatsu/10
84 David Dellucci/50 12.50 30.00
85 Travis Blackley/200 4.00 10.00
86 Brad Penny/25 6.00 15.00
87 Nick Johnson/10
88 Brian Roberts/100 6.00 15.00
90 Mike Lieberthal/25 10.00 25.00
91 Craig Biggio/1
92 Sean Casey/10
94 Milton Bradley/100 6.00 15.00
96 Adrian Gonzalez/200 6.00 15.00
97 Chad Tracy/100 4.00 10.00
98 Chad Cordero/100 6.00 15.00
99 Albert Pujols/1
100 Jason Kubel/200 4.00 10.00
101 Rafael Furcal/10
102 Jack Wilson/100 6.00 15.00
103 Eric Chavez/1
104 Casey Kotchman/100 6.00 15.00
105 Jeff Bagwell/1
106 Melvin Mora/100 6.00 15.00
107 Bobby Crosby/100 6.00 15.00
110 Vernon Wells/1
111 Francisco Cordero/50 8.00 20.00
112 Steve Finley/10
113 Omar Vizquel/10
114 Eric Byrnes/50 5.00 12.00
115 Tim Hudson/1
116 Aramis Ramirez/10
117 Lance Berkman/1
118 Shea Hillenbrand/25 10.00 25.00
119 Aubrey Huff/25 10.00 25.00
120 Lew Ford/25 6.00 15.00
121 Sammy Sosa/1
123 Rickie Weeks/10
124 Manny Ramirez/1
126 Adam LaRoche/25 6.00 15.00
128 Ken Harvey/50 5.00 12.00
129 Adrian Beltre/10
130 Magglio Ordonez/10
131 Greg Maddux/1
132 Russ Ortiz/25 6.00 15.00
134 Kerry Wood/1
135 Mike Mussina/1
136 Joe Nathan/100 10.00 25.00
138 Carlos Zambrano/25 15.00 40.00
139 Ben Sheets/10
140 Jae Weong Seo/10
141 Derrek Lee/10
143 John Lackey/200 6.00 15.00
145 Dewon Brazelton/200 4.00 10.00
146 Jason Bay/25 10.00 25.00
147 Alfonso Soriano/1
148 Travis Hafner/100 6.00 15.00
152 Wade Miller/50 5.00 12.00
154 Scott Kazmir/25 10.00 25.00
156 Livan Hernandez/25 10.00 25.00
157 Jose Capellan/10
158 David Wright/25 60.00 120.00
159 Chone Figgins/50 5.00 12.00
162 Hideo Nomo/1
163 Merkin Valdez/200 4.00 10.00
164 Shawn Green/1
165 Alexis Rios/50 8.00 20.00
166 Johnny Estrada/200 4.00 10.00
167 Danny Graves/50 5.00 12.00
168 Carlos Lee/25 10.00 25.00
170 Randy Johnson/1
171 Randy Wolf/25 10.00 25.00
173 Chipper Jones/1
174 Delmon Young/10
175 Edwin Jackson/25 6.00 15.00
177 Matt Clement/10
178 Jacque Jones/25 10.00 25.00
179 Gary Sheffield/1
180 Laynce Nix/200 4.00 10.00
181 Tom Gordon/25 10.00 25.00
182 Jose Castillo/100 4.00 10.00
185 Paul Lo Duca/10
186 Roger Clemens/1
187 Todd Helton/1
188 Keith Foulke/25 15.00 40.00
189 Jeremy Bonderman/50 8.00 20.00
190 Troy Percival/25 10.00 25.00
191 Michael Young/10
193 Rafael Palmeiro/1
194 Brett Myers/50 8.00 20.00
197 Lyle Overbay/25 6.00 15.00
200 Edgar Renteria/10
201 Justin Verlander/25
202 Miguel Negron/100 5.00 12.00
204 Paulino Reynoso/100 4.00 10.00
205 Colter Bean/100 5.00 12.00
206 Raul Tablado/100 4.00 10.00
207 Mark McLemore/100 4.00 10.00
208 Russ Rohlicek/100 4.00 10.00
210 Chris Seddon/100 4.00 10.00
213 Mike Morse/100 5.00 12.00
217 Carlos Ruiz/100 5.00 12.00
218 Chris Roberson/100 4.00 10.00
219 Ryan Speier/100 4.00 10.00
221 Ambiorix Burgos/100 4.00 10.00
223 Dave Gassner/100 4.00 10.00
224 Sean Tracey/100 4.00 10.00
225 Casey Rogowski/100 5.00 12.00
226 Billy Williams LGD/10
227 Ralph Kiner LGD/10
228 Ozzie Smith LGD/10
229 Rod Carew LGD/10
230 Nolan Ryan LGD/5
231 Fergie Jenkins LGD/10
232 Paul Molitor LGD/10
233 Carlton Fisk LGD/5
234 Rollie Fingers LGD/10
235 Lou Brock LGD/10
236 Gaylord Perry LGD/25 10.00 25.00
237 Don Mattingly LGD/5
238 Maury Wills LGD/10
239 Luis Aparicio LGD/10
240 George Brett LGD/5
241 Mike Schmidt LGD/5
243 Dennis Eckersley LGD/10
244 Reggie Jackson LGD/5
245 Bobby Doerr LGD/25 10.00 25.00
246 Bob Feller LGD/25 15.00 40.00
247 Cal Ripken LGD/5
248 Harmon Killebrew LGD/10
249 Frank Robinson LGD/10
250 Stan Musial LGD/5

2005 Donruss Classics Timeless Tributes Gold

*GOLD 1-200: 3X TO 8X BASIC
*GOLD 201-225: .25X TO .6X AU p/r 1200-1500
*GOLD 201-225: .25X TO .6X AU p/r 750-785
*GOLD 201-225: .2X TO .5X AU p/r 400
*GOLD 226-250: 1.5X TO 4X BASIC
OVERALL INSERT ODDS 1:2
STATED PRINT RUN 50 SERIAL #'d SETS
203 Agustin Montero 2.00 5.00
209 Geovany Soto 2.00 5.00
211 Enrique Gonzalez 2.50 6.00
212 Erick Threets 2.00 5.00
214 Wladimir Balentien 2.50 6.00
216 Ambiorix Concepcion 2.00 5.00
220 Ubaldo Jimenez 5.00 12.00
222 Mark Woodyard 2.00 5.00

2005 Donruss Classics Timeless Tributes Platinum

OVERALL INSERT ODDS 1:2
STATED PRINT RUN 1 SERIAL #'d SET
NO PRICING DUE TO SCARCITY

2005 Donruss Classics Timeless Tributes Silver

*SILV 1-200: 2X TO 5X BASIC
*SILV 201-225: .15X TO .4X AU p/r 1200-1500
*SILV 201-225: .15X TO .4X AU p/r 750-785
*SILV 201-225: .12X TO .3X AU p/r 400
*SILV 226-250: 1X TO 2.5X BASIC
OVERALL INSERT ODDS 1:2
STATED PRINT RUN 100 SERIAL #'d SETS
203 Agustin Montero 1.25 3.00
209 Geovany Soto 1.25 3.00
211 Enrique Gonzalez 1.50 4.00
212 Erick Threets 1.25 3.00
214 Wladimir Balentien 2.00 5.00
216 Ambiorix Concepcion 1.25 3.00
220 Ubaldo Jimenez 3.00 8.00
222 Mark Woodyard 1.25 3.00

2005 Donruss Classics Classic Combos

STATED PRINT RUN 400 SERIAL #'d SETS
*GOLD: 1.5X TO 4X BASIC
GOLD PRINT RUN 25 SERIAL #'d SETS
PLATINUM PRINT RUN 1 SERIAL #'d SET
NO PLATINUM PRICING DUE TO SCARCITY
OVERALL INSERT ODDS 1:2

33 Babe Ruth 6.00 15.00
Ted Williams
34 Roberto Clemente 5.00 12.00
Vladimir Guerrero
35 Willie Mays 4.00 10.00
Willie McCovey
36 Yogi Berra 2.00 5.00
Mike Piazza
37 Sandy Koufax 15.00 40.00
Nolan Ryan
38 Harmon Killebrew 4.00 10.00
Mike Schmidt
39 Whitey Ford 2.00 5.00
Randy Johnson
40 Cal Ripken 8.00 20.00
George Brett
41 Hank Aaron 4.00 10.00
Stan Musial
42 Carl Yastrzemski 3.00 8.00
Frank Robinson
43 Bob Feller 3.00 8.00
Roger Clemens
44 Bob Gibson 2.00 5.00
Tom Seaver
45 Roger Maris 2.00 5.00
Jim Thome
46 Albert Pujols 4.00 10.00
Don Mattingly
47 Duke Snider 2.00 5.00
Sammy Sosa
48 Rickey Henderson 2.00 5.00
Bo Jackson
49 Ernie Banks 2.00 5.00
Reggie Jackson
50 Burleigh Grimes 3.00 8.00
Greg Maddux

2005 Donruss Classics Classic Combos Bat

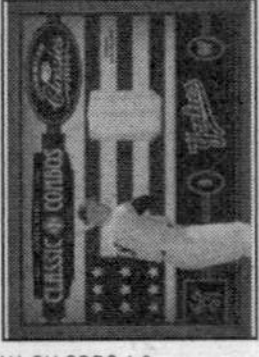

OVERALL AU-GU ODDS 1:6
STATED PRINT RUN 5 SERIAL #'d SETS
NO PRICING DUE TO SCARCITY

2005 Donruss Classics Classic Combos Jersey

PRINT RUNS B/WN 5-50 COPIES PER
NO PRICING ON QTY OF 10 OR LESS
PRIME PRINT RUNS B/WN 1-5 COPIES PER
NO PRIME PRICING DUE TO SCARCITY
OVERALL AU-GU ODDS 1:6

33 Babe Ruth
Ted Williams/5
34 Roberto Clemente
Vladimir Guerrero/5
35 Willie Mays
Willie McCovey/10
36 Yogi Berra
Mike Piazza/10
37 Sandy Koufax
Nolan Ryan/10
38 Harmon Killebrew 15.00 40.00
Mike Schmidt/50
39 Whitey Ford 12.50 30.00
Randy Johnson/25
40 Cal Ripken 40.00 80.00
George Brett/50
41 Hank Aaron
Stan Musial/10
43 Bob Feller Pants
Roger Clemens/10
45 Roger Maris 30.00 60.00
Jim Thome/25
46 Albert Pujols 20.00 50.00
Don Mattingly/50
47 Duke Snider 12.50 30.00
Sammy Sosa/25
48 Rickey Henderson 10.00 25.00
Bo Jackson/50
49 Ernie Banks
Reggie Jackson/10
50 Burleigh Grimes Pants
Greg Maddux/10

2005 Donruss Classics Classic Combos Materials

*MTL p/r 25: .5X TO 1.2X JSY p/r 50
PRINT RUNS B/WN 1-25 COPIES PER
NO PRICING ON QTY OF 10 OR LESS
ALL ARE BAT-JSY COMBOS UNLESS NOTED
PRIME PRINT RUN 5 SERIAL #'d SETS
NO PRIME PRICING DUE TO SCARCITY
OVERALL AU-GU ODDS 1:6

2005 Donruss Classics Classic Combos Materials HR

*MTL HR p/r 25: .5X TO 1.2X JSY p/r 50
OVERALL AU-GU ODDS 1:6
PRINT RUNS B/WN 1-25 COPIES PER
ALL ARE BAT-JSY COMBOS UNLESS NOTED
NO PRICING ON QTY OF 10 OR LESS

2005 Donruss Classics Classic Combos Signature

OVERALL AU-GU ODDS 1:6
STATED PRINT RUN 1 SERIAL #'d SET
NO PRICING DUE TO SCARCITY

2005 Donruss Classics Classic Combos Signature Bat

OVERALL AU-GU ODDS 1:6
STATED PRINT RUN 1 SERIAL #'d SET
NO PRICING DUE TO SCARCITY

2005 Donruss Classics Classic Combos Signature Jersey

PRINT RUNS B/WN 1-5 COPIES PER
NO PRICING DUE TO SCARCITY
PRIME PRINT RUN 1 SERIAL #'d SET
NO PRIME PRICING DUE TO SCARCITY
OVERALL AU-GU ODDS 1:6

35 Willie Mays
Willie McCovey/1
37 Sandy Koufax
Nolan Ryan/1
38 Harmon Killebrew
Mike Schmidt/5
39 Whitey Ford
Randy Johnson/1
40 Cal Ripken
George Brett/1
41 Hank Aaron
Stan Musial/1
42 Carl Yastrzemski
Frank Robinson/1
43 Bob Feller Pants
Roger Clemens/1
46 Albert Pujols
Don Mattingly/5
47 Duke Snider
Sammy Sosa/5
48 Rickey Henderson
Bo Jackson/1
49 Ernie Banks
Reggie Jackson/1

2005 Donruss Classics Classic Combos Signature Materials

STATED PRINT RUN 1 SERIAL #'d SET
ALL ARE BAT-JSY COMBOS UNLESS NOTED
HR PRINT RUN 1 SERIAL #'d SET
PRIME PRINT RUN 1 SERIAL #'d SET
OVERALL AU-GU ODDS 1:6
NO PRICING DUE TO SCARCITY

2005 Donruss Classics Classic Singles

STATED PRINT RUN 400 SERIAL #'d SETS
*GOLD: 1.5X TO 4X BASIC
GOLD PRINT RUN 25 SERIAL #'d SETS
PLATINUM PRINT RUN 1 SERIAL #'d SET
NO PLATINUM PRICING DUE TO SCARCITY
OVERALL INSERT ODDS 1:2

1 Hank Aaron 4.00 10.00
2 Tom Seaver 2.00 5.00
3 Harmon Killebrew 2.00 5.00
4 Paul Molitor 1.50 4.00
5 Brooks Robinson 2.00 5.00
6 Stan Musial 2.50 6.00
7 Bobby Doerr 1.50 4.00
8 Cal Ripken 8.00 20.00
9 Phil Niekro 1.50 4.00
10 Eddie Murray 2.00 5.00
11 Randy Johnson 2.00 5.00
12 Steve Carlton 1.50 4.00
13 Rickey Henderson 2.00 5.00
14 Ernie Banks 2.00 5.00
15 Curt Schilling 2.00 5.00
16 Whitey Ford 2.00 5.00
17 Al Kaline 2.00 5.00
18 Gary Carter 1.50 4.00
19 Robin Yount 2.00 5.00
20 Johnny Bench 2.00 5.00
21 Bob Feller 2.00 5.00
22 Jim Palmer 1.50 4.00
23 Don Mattingly 4.00 10.00
24 Willie Mays 4.00 10.00
25 Dave Righetti 1.50 4.00
26 Roger Clemens 3.00 8.00
27 Juan Marichal 1.50 4.00
28 Tony Gwynn 2.50 6.00
29 Nolan Ryan 5.00 12.00
30 Carlton Fisk 2.00 5.00
31 Greg Maddux 3.00 8.00
32 Sandy Koufax 15.00 40.00

2005 Donruss Classics Classic Singles Bat

*BAT p/r 50: .5X TO 1.2X JSY p/r 100
*BAT p/r 50: .4X TO 1X JSY p/r 50
*BAT p/r 50: .3X TO .8X JSY p/r 25
*BAT p/r 25: .6X TO 1.5X JSY p/r 100
*BAT p/r 25: .5X TO 1.2X JSY p/r 50
*BAT p/r 25: .4X TO 1X JSY p/r 25
OVERALL AU-GU ODDS 1:6
PRINT RUNS B/WN 25-50 COPIES PER

1 Hank Aaron/25 20.00 50.00
6 Stan Musial/25 12.50 30.00
17 Al Kaline/25 10.00 25.00
24 Willie Mays/25 20.00 50.00

2005 Donruss Classics Classic Singles Jersey

PRINT RUNS B/WN 10-100 COPIES PER
NO PRICING ON QTY OF 10
PRIME PRINT RUNS B/WN 1-5 COPIES PER
NO PRIME PRICING DUE TO SCARCITY
OVERALL AU-GU ODDS 1:6

1 Hank Aaron/10
2 Tom Seaver/25 8.00 20.00
3 Harmon Killebrew/25 10.00 25.00
4 Paul Molitor/50 4.00 10.00
5 Brooks Robinson/50 6.00 15.00
6 Stan Musial/10
7 Bobby Doerr Pants/100 3.00 8.00

8 Cal Ripken/25 40.00 80.00
9 Phil Niekro/50 4.00 10.00
10 Eddie Murray/50 8.00 20.00
11 Randy Johnson/100 6.00 15.00
12 Steve Carlton/25 5.00 12.00
13 Rickey Henderson/100 6.00 15.00
14 Ernie Banks/25 10.00 25.00
15 Curt Schilling/100 5.00 12.00
16 Whitey Ford/25 8.00 20.00
18 Gary Carter/100 3.00 8.00
19 Robin Yount/50 8.00 20.00
20 Johnny Bench/50 8.00 20.00
21 Bob Feller Pants/25 8.00 20.00
22 Jim Palmer/100 3.00 8.00
23 Don Mattingly/100 10.00 25.00
24 Willie Mays/25
25 Dave Righetti/50 4.00 10.00
26 Roger Clemens/25 10.00 25.00
27 Juan Marichal/50 4.00 10.00
28 Tony Gwynn/100 6.00 15.00
29 Nolan Ryan/50 15.00 40.00
30 Carlton Fisk/25 8.00 20.00
31 Greg Maddux/100 6.00 15.00
32 Sandy Koufax/25 75.00 150.00

2005 Donruss Classics Classic Singles Materials

*MTL p/r 25: .75X TO 2X JSY p/r 100
*MTL p/r 25: .6X TO 1.5X JSY p/r 50
*MTL p/r 25: .5X TO 1.2X JSY p/r 25
PRINT RUNS B/WN 10-25 COPIES PER
NO PRICING ON QTY OF 10
PRIME PRINT RUNS B/WN 1-5 COPIES PER
NO PRIME PRICING DUE TO SCARCITY
OVERALL AU-GU ODDS 1:6

2005 Donruss Classics Classic Singles Materials HR

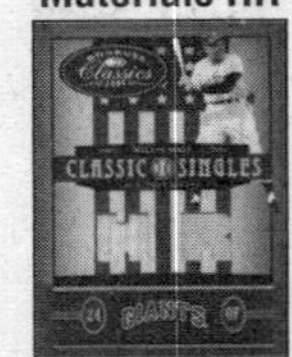

*MTL HR p/r 25: .75X TO 2X JSY p/r 100
*MTL HR p/r 25: .6X TO 1.5X JSY p/r 50
*MTL HR p/r 25: .5X TO 1.2X JSY p/r 25
OVERALL AU-GU ODDS 1:6
PRINT RUNS B/WN 10-25 COPIES PER
NO PRICING ON QTY OF 10

2005 Donruss Classics Classic Singles Signature

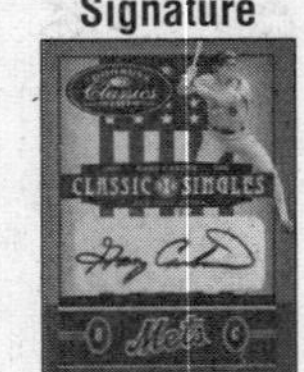

OVERALL AU-GU ODDS 1:6
PRINT RUNS B/WN 1-5 COPIES PER
NO PRICING DUE TO SCARCITY

2005 Donruss Classics Classic Singles Signature Bat

OVERALL AU-GU ODDS 1:6
PRINT RUNS B/WN 1-10 COPIES PER
NO PRICING DUE TO SCARCITY

2005 Donruss Classics Classic Singles Signature Jersey

PRINT RUNS B/WN 1-5 COPIES PER
PRIME PRINT RUN 1 SERIAL #'d SET
OVERALL AU-GU ODDS 1:6
NO PRICING DUE TO SCARCITY

2005 Donruss Classics Classic Singles Signature Materials

PRINT RUNS B/WN 1-10 COPIES PER
PRIME PRINT RUNS B/WN 1-5 COPIES PER
OVERALL AU-GU ODDS 1:6
NO PRICING DUE TO SCARCITY

2005 Donruss Classics Classic Singles Signature Materials HR

OVERALL AU-GU ODDS 1:6
PRINT RUNS B/WN 1-10 COPIES PER
NO PRICING DUE TO SCARCITY

2005 Donruss Classics Dress Code Bat

*BAT p/r 100: .3X TO .8X MTL p/r 100
*BAT p/r 50: .3X TO .8X MTL p/r 50
OVERALL AU-GU ODDS 1:6
PRINT RUNS B/WN 50-100 COPIES PER

14 Mark Prior/50 5.00 12.00

2005 Donruss Classics Dress Code Jersey Number

*JSY NBR p/r 38-57: .4X TO 1X MTL p/r 100
*JSY NBR p/r 38-57: .3X TO .8X MTL p/r 50
*JSY NBR p/r 20-34: .5X TO 1.2X MTL p/r 100
*JSY NBR p/r 15-17: .6X TO 1.5X MTL p/r 100
*JSY NBR p/r 15-17: .5X TO 1.2X MTL p/r 50
OVERALL AU-GU ODDS 1:6
PRINT RUNS B/WN 5-57 COPIES PER
NO PRICING ON QTY OF 13 OR LESS

12 Johan Santana/57 5.00 12.00
13 Mark Mulder/20 4.00 10.00
14 Mark Prior/22 6.00 15.00
20 Randy Johnson Pants/51 6.00 15.00
21 Roger Clemens/23 10.00 25.00
24 Tim Hudson/15 5.00 12.00

2005 Donruss Classics Dress Code Jersey Prime

*PRIME: .75X TO 2X MTL p/r 100
*PRIME: .6X TO 1.5X MTL p/r 50
OVERALL AU-GU ODDS 1:6
STATED PRINT RUN 25 SERIAL #'d SETS

3 Carl Crawford 6.00 15.00
12 Johan Santana 10.00 25.00

13 Mark Mulder 6.00 15.00
14 Mark Prior 10.00 25.00
20 Randy Johnson 12.50 30.00
21 Roger Clemens 15.00 40.00
24 Tim Hudson 6.00 15.00

2005 Donruss Classics Dress Code Materials

PRINT RUNS B/WN 5-100 COPIES PER
NO PRICING ON QTY OF 5
PRIME PRINT RUN 5 SERIAL #'d SETS
NO PRIME PRICING DUE TO SCARCITY
OVERALL AU-GU ODDS 1:6

1 Albert Pujols Bat-Jsy/100 10.00 25.00
2 Bernie Williams Bat-Jsy/50 6.00 15.00
4 C.Beltran Bat-Bat/Jsy/100 3.00 8.00
5 Chipper Jones Bat-Jsy/100 6.00 15.00
6 Curt Schilling Bat-Jsy/50 6.00 15.00
7 David Ortiz Bat-Hat/100 5.00 12.00
8 Hank Blalock Bat-Jsy/100 3.00 8.00
9 Hideki Matsui Bat-Jsy/100 15.00 40.00
10 Jim Edmonds Bat-Jsy/100 3.00 8.00
11 Jim Thome Jsy-Jsy/100 5.00 12.00
15 Mark Teixeira Bat-Jsy/100 5.00 12.00
16 Miguel Cabrera Jsy-Jsy/100 5.00 12.00
17 Miguel Tejada Bat-Jsy/100 3.00 8.00
18 Mike Piazza Bat-Jsy/100 6.00 15.00
19 Pedro Martinez Bat-Jsy/100 5.00 12.00
21 Roger Clemens Bat-Jsy/5
22 Sammy Sosa Bat-Jsy/100 6.00 15.00
23 Scott Rolen Bat-Jsy/100 5.00 12.00
25 Todd Helton Jsy-Jsy/50 6.00 15.00
26 Torii Hunter Bat-Jsy/100 3.00 8.00
27 Travis Hafner Jsy-Shoes/50 4.00 10.00
28 Vernon Wells Jsy-Jsy/50 4.00 10.00
29 Victor Martinez Jsy-Jsy/50 4.00 10.00
30 V.Guerrero Bat-Jsy/100 6.00 15.00

2005 Donruss Classics Dress Code Signature Bat

*BAT p/r 25: .4X TO 1X JSY p/r 25
OVERALL AU-GU ODDS 1:6
PRINT RUNS B/WN 1-25 COPIES PER
NO PRICING ON QTY OF 5 OR LESS

2005 Donruss Classics Dress Code Signature Jersey

PRINT RUNS B/WN 5-25 COPIES PER
NO PRICING ON QTY OF 10 OR LESS
PRIME PRINT RUNS B/WN 1-5 COPIES PER
NO PRIME PRICING DUE TO SCARCITY
OVERALL AU-GU ODDS 1:6

1 Albert Pujols/5
5 Chipper Jones/5
6 Curt Schilling/5
7 David Ortiz/25 30.00 60.00
8 Hank Blalock/25 12.50 30.00
10 Jim Edmonds/5
12 Johan Santana/25 20.00 50.00
14 Mark Prior/10
16 Miguel Cabrera/25 20.00 50.00
19 Pedro Martinez/5
20 Randy Johnson/5
21 Roger Clemens/5
22 Sammy Sosa/5
23 Scott Rolen/10
24 Tim Hudson/10
25 Todd Helton/5
26 Torii Hunter/25 12.50 30.00
27 Travis Hafner/25 12.50 30.00
28 Vernon Wells/25 12.50 30.00
29 Victor Martinez/25 12.50 30.00

2005 Donruss Classics Dress Code Signature Jersey Number

*NBR p/r 25: .4X TO 1X JSY p/r 25
OVERALL AU-GU ODDS 1:6
PRINT RUNS B/WN 1-25 COPIES PER
NO PRICING ON QTY OF 10 OR LESS

2005 Donruss Classics Dress Code Signature Materials

PRINT RUNS B/WN 1-5 COPIES PER
PRIME PRINT RUNS B/WN 1-5 COPIES PER
OVERALL AU-GU ODDS 1:6
NO PRICING DUE TO SCARCITY

2005 Donruss Classics Home Run Heroes

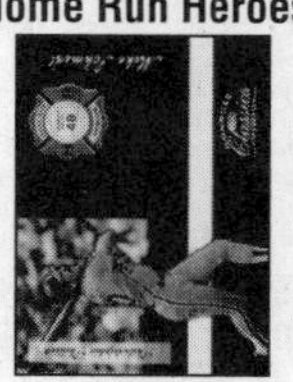

STATED PRINT RUN 1000 SERIAL #'d SETS
*GOLD: 1.5X TO 4X BASIC
GOLD PRINT RUN 50 SERIAL #'d SETS
PLATINUM PRINT RUN 1 SERIAL #'d SET
NO PLATINUM PRICING DUE TO SCARCITY
OVERALL INSERT ODDS 1:2
1 Mike Schmidt 2.50 6.00
2 Ken Griffey Jr. 2.00 5.00
3 Babe Ruth 2.50 6.00
4 Duke Snider 1.25 3.00
5 Johnny Bench 1.25 3.00
6 Stan Musial 1.50 4.00
7 Willie McCovey 1.25 3.00
8 Willie Stargell 1.25 3.00
9 Ted Williams 2.50 6.00
10 Frank Thomas 1.25 3.00
11 Gary Sheffield .75 2.00
12 Jim Thome 1.25 3.00
13 Harmon Killebrew 1.25 3.00
14 Ernie Banks 1.25 3.00
15 George Foster .75 2.00
16 Albert Pujols 2.50 6.00
17 Tony Perez .75 2.00
18 Richie Sexson .75 2.00
19 Juan Gonzalez .75 2.00
20 Frank Robinson .75 2.00
21 Sammy Sosa 1.25 3.00
22 Jeff Bagwell 1.25 3.00
23 Mark Teixeira 1.25 3.00
24 Willie Mays 2.50 6.00
25 Rafael Palmeiro 1.25 3.00
26 Billy Williams .75 2.00
27 Vladimir Guerrero 1.25 3.00
28 Gary Carter .75 2.00
29 Fred McGriff 1.25 3.00
30 Orlando Cepeda .75 2.00
31 Dave Winfield .75 2.00
32 Shawn Green .75 2.00
33 Jose Canseco 1.25 3.00
34 Hideki Matsui 2.50 6.00
35 Roger Maris 1.25 3.00
36 Andre Dawson .75 2.00
37 Paul Konerko .75 2.00
38 Darryl Strawberry .75 2.00
39 Dave Parker .75 2.00
40 Adam Dunn .75 2.00
41 Ralph Kiner .75 2.00
42 Miguel Tejada .75 2.00
43 Dale Murphy 1.25 3.00
44 Hank Aaron 2.50 6.00
45 Mike Piazza 1.25 3.00
46 Reggie Jackson 1.25 3.00
47 Adrian Beltre .75 2.00
48 Cal Ripken 5.00 12.00
49 Manny Ramirez 1.25 3.00
50 Alex Rodriguez 2.00 5.00

2005 Donruss Classics Home Run Heroes Bat

*BAT p/r 36-66: .4X TO 1X JSY p/r 38-66
*BAT p/r 36-66: .3X TO .8X JSY p/r 25
*BAT p/r 36-66: .4X TO 1X JSY p/r 38-66
*BAT p/r 19: .4X TO 1X JSY p/r 19
OVERALL AU-GU ODDS 1:6
PRINT RUNS B/WN 4-66 COPIES PER
NO PRICING ON QTY OF 14 OR LESS
3 Babe Ruth/25 125.00 200.00
6 Stan Musial/39 10.00 25.00

17 Tony Perez/24 5.00 12.00
20 Frank Robinson/49 4.00 10.00

2005 Donruss Classics Home Run Heroes Jersey HR

PRINT RUNS B/WN 1-66 COPIES PER
NO PRICING ON QTY OF 14 OR LESS
PRIME PRINT RUN 1 SERIAL #'d SET
NO PRIME PRICING DUE TO SCARCITY
OVERALL AU-GU ODDS 1:6
1 Mike Schmidt/48 12.50 30.00
3 Babe Ruth/25 175.00 300.00
4 Duke Snider Pants/14
5 Johnny Bench/45 8.00 20.00
6 Stan Musial/6
7 Willie McCovey/23 8.00 20.00
8 Willie Stargell/48 6.00 15.00
9 Ted Williams/43 30.00 60.00
10 Frank Thomas/43 6.00 15.00
11 Gary Sheffield/36 3.00 8.00
12 Jim Thome/47 5.00 12.00
13 Harmon Killebrew/49 8.00 20.00
14 Ernie Banks Pants/47 8.00 20.00
15 George Foster/25 5.00 12.00
16 Albert Pujols/46 15.00 40.00
18 Richie Sexson/45 3.00 8.00
19 Juan Gonzalez/47 3.00 8.00
20 Frank Robinson/1
21 Sammy Sosa/66 6.00 15.00
22 Jeff Bagwell/47 5.00 12.00
23 Mark Teixeira/38 5.00 12.00
24 Willie Mays/51 30.00 60.00
25 Rafael Palmeiro/47 5.00 12.00
26 Billy Williams/26 5.00 12.00
27 Vladimir Guerrero/44 6.00 15.00
28 Gary Carter/31 5.00 12.00
29 Fred McGriff/32 6.00 15.00
30 Orlando Cepeda Pants/46 4.00 10.00
31 Dave Winfield/34 5.00 12.00
32 Shawn Green/49 3.00 8.00
33 Jose Canseco/44 8.00 20.00
34 Hideki Matsui Pants/31 30.00 60.00
35 Roger Maris Pants/19 30.00 60.00
36 Andre Dawson/49 4.00 10.00
37 Paul Konerko/14
38 Darryl Strawberry/24 5.00 12.00
39 Dave Parker/34 5.00 12.00
40 Adam Dunn/46 3.00 8.00
42 Miguel Tejada/34 4.00 10.00
43 Dale Murphy/44 6.00 15.00
44 Hank Aaron/47 30.00 60.00
45 Mike Piazza/40 6.00 15.00
46 Reggie Jackson/39 6.00 15.00
47 Adrian Beltre/48 3.00 8.00
48 Cal Ripken/34 30.00 60.00
49 Manny Ramirez/43 5.00 12.00

2005 Donruss Classics Home Run Heroes Materials

*MTL p/r 36-66: .5X TO 1.2X JSY p/r 36-66
*MTL p/r 36-66: .4X TO 1X JSY p/r 25
*MTL p/r 23-34: .5X TO 1.2X JSY p/r 23-34
*MTL p/r 19: .5X TO 1.2X JSY p/r 19
PRINT RUNS B/WN 1-66 COPIES PER
NO PRICING ON QTY OF 14 OR LESS
PRIME PRINT RUN 1 SERIAL #'d SET
NO PRIME PRICING DUE TO SCARCITY
OVERALL AU-GU ODDS 1:6
3 Babe Ruth Bat-Jsy/25 250.00 400.00
17 Tony Perez Bat-Fld Glv/24 6.00 15.00

2005 Donruss Classics Home Run Heroes Signature

OVERALL AU-GU ODDS 1:6
PRINT RUNS B/WN 1-10 COPIES PER
NO PRICING DUE TO SCARCITY

2005 Donruss Classics Home Run Heroes Signature Materials

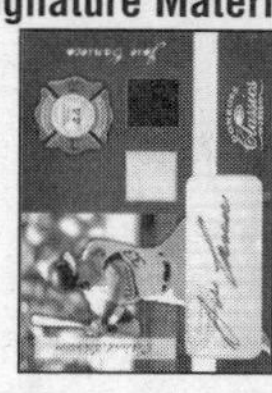

PRINT RUNS B/WN 1-10 COPIES PER
PRIME PRINT RUN 1 SERIAL #'d SET
OVERALL AU-GU ODDS 1:6
NO PRICING DUE TO SCARCITY

2005 Donruss Classics Legendary Lumberjacks Bat

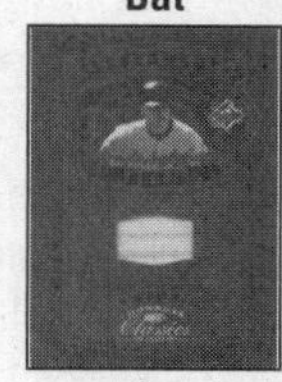

OVERALL AU-GU ODDS 1:6
PRINT RUNS B/WN 1-50 COPIES PER
NO PRICING ON QTY OF 6 OR LESS
1 Al Kaline/6
2 Babe Ruth/25 125.00 200.00
6 Brooks Robinson/50 6.00 15.00
7 Cal Ripken/50 20.00 50.00
8 Carlton Fisk/50 6.00 15.00
10 Don Mattingly/50 12.50 30.00
12 Eddie Murray/50 8.00 20.00
13 Ernie Banks/50 8.00 20.00
15 Frank Robinson/50 4.00 10.00
17 George Brett/50 12.50 30.00
19 Harmon Killebrew/50 8.00 20.00
21 Joe Morgan/50 4.00 10.00
22 Johnny Bench/50 8.00 20.00
24 Lou Brock/50 6.00 15.00
26 Mike Schmidt/50 12.50 30.00
28 Ozzie Smith/50 10.00 25.00
29 Paul Molitor/50 4.00 10.00
30 Pee Wee Reese/50 6.00 15.00
34 Reggie Jackson/50 6.00 15.00
35 Rickey Henderson/50 8.00 20.00
36 Roberto Clemente/50 40.00 80.00
37 Robin Yount/50 8.00 20.00
38 Rod Carew/50 6.00 15.00
39 Roger Maris/25 20.00 50.00
40 Stan Musial/25 12.50 30.00
42 Ted Williams/25 30.00 60.00
44 Tony Gwynn/50 8.00 20.00
45 Tony Perez/1
46 Wade Boggs/50 6.00 15.00
49 Willie McCovey/50 6.00 15.00
50 Yogi Berra/25 10.00 25.00

2005 Donruss Classics Legendary Lumberjacks Jersey

*JSY p/r 50: .4X TO 1X BAT p/r 50
*JSY p/r 25: .5X TO 1.2X BAT p/r 50
OVERALL AU-GU ODDS 1:6
PRINT RUNS B/WN 1-50 COPIES PER
NO PRICING ON QTY OF 10 OR LESS
3 Billy Williams/25 5.00 12.00
25 Maury Wills/25 5.00 12.00

2005 Donruss Classics Legendary Lumberjacks Jersey HR

*JSY HR p/r 25: .5X TO 1.2X BAT p/r 50
OVERALL AU-GU ODDS 1:6
PRINT RUNS B/WN 1-25 COPIES PER
NO PRICING ON QTY OF 10 OR LESS
45 Tony Perez/25 5.00 12.00

2005 Donruss Classics Legendary Lumberjacks Materials

*MTL p/r 44-50: .5X TO 1.2X BAT p/r 50
OVERALL AU-GU ODDS 1:6
PRINT RUNS B/WN - COPIES PER
NO PRICING ON QTY OF 10 OR LESS
*MTL p/r 25: .6X TO 1.5X BAT p/r 50
2 Babe Ruth Bat-Jsy/25 250.00 400.00

2005 Donruss Classics Legendary Players

STATED PRINT RUN 800 SERIAL #'d SETS
*GOLD: 1.25X TO 3X BASIC
GOLD PRINT RUN 75 SERIAL #'d SETS
PLATINUM PRINT RUN 1 SERIAL #'d SET
NO PLATINUM PRICING DUE TO SCARCITY
*LUMBERJACK: .6X TO 1.5X BASIC
LUMBERJACK PRINT RUN 400 #'d SETS
OVERALL INSERT ODDS 1:2
1 Al Kaline 1.25 3.00
2 Babe Ruth 2.50 6.00
3 Billy Williams .75 2.00
4 Bob Feller 1.25 3.00
5 Bob Gibson 1.25 3.00
6 Brooks Robinson 1.25 3.00
7 Cal Ripken 5.00 12.00
8 Carlton Fisk 1.25 3.00
9 Dennis Eckersley .75 2.00
10 Don Mattingly 2.50 6.00
11 Duke Snider 1.25 3.00
12 Eddie Murray 1.25 3.00
13 Ernie Banks 1.25 3.00
14 Fergie Jenkins .75 2.00
15 Frank Robinson .75 2.00
16 Gaylord Perry .75 2.00
17 George Brett 2.50 6.00
18 George Kell .75 2.00
19 Harmon Killebrew 1.25 3.00
20 Jim Palmer .75 2.00
21 Joe Morgan .75 2.00
22 Johnny Bench 1.25 3.00
23 Juan Marichal .75 2.00
24 Lou Brock 1.25 3.00
25 Maury Wills .75 2.00
26 Mike Schmidt 2.50 6.00
27 Nolan Ryan 3.00 8.00
28 Ozzie Smith 2.00 5.00
29 Paul Molitor .75 2.00
30 Pee Wee Reese 1.25 3.00
31 Phil Niekro .75 2.00
32 Phil Rizzuto 1.25 3.00
33 Ralph Kiner .75 2.00
34 Reggie Jackson 1.25 3.00
35 Rickey Henderson 1.25 3.00
36 Roberto Clemente 3.00 8.00
37 Robin Yount 1.25 3.00
38 Rod Carew 1.25 3.00
39 Roger Maris 1.25 3.00
40 Stan Musial 1.50 4.00
41 Steve Carlton .75 2.00
42 Ted Williams 2.50 6.00
43 Tom Seaver 1.25 3.00
44 Tony Gwynn 1.50 4.00
45 Tony Perez .75 2.00
46 Wade Boggs 1.25 3.00
47 Warren Spahn 1.25 3.00
48 Whitey Ford 1.25 3.00
49 Willie McCovey 1.25 3.00
50 Yogi Berra 1.25 3.00

2005 Donruss Classics Legendary Players Hat

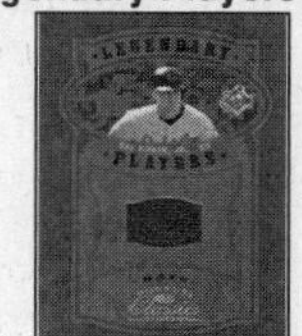

*HAT p/r 25: .4X TO 1X JSY NBR p/r 20-35
*HAT p/r 25: .3X TO .8X JSY NBR p/r 16-19
OVERALL AU-GU ODDS 1:6
PRINT RUNS B/WN 1-25 COPIES PER
NO PRICING ON QTY OF 10 OR LESS
13 Ernie Banks/25 10.00 25.00
17 George Brett/25 15.00 40.00
28 Ozzie Smith/25 12.50 30.00

2005 Donruss Classics Legendary Players Jacket

*JKT: .6X TO 1.5X JSY NBR p/r 72
*JKT: .5X TO 1.2X JSY NBR p/r 36-44

*JKT: .4X TO 1X JSY NBR p/r 20-34
OVERALL AU-GU ODDS 1:6
STATED PRINT RUN 25 SERIAL #'d SETS
7 Cal Ripken 40.00 80.00
34 Reggie Jackson 8.00 20.00
42 Ted Williams 40.00 80.00

2005 Donruss Classics Legendary Players Jersey Number

PRINT RUNS B/WN 1-72 COPIES PER
NO PRICING ON QTY OF 14 OR LESS
PRIME PRINT RUN 1 SERIAL #'d SET
NO PRIME PRICING DUE TO SCARCITY
OVERALL AU-GU ODDS 1:6
2 Babe Ruth/3
3 Billy Williams/26 5.00 12.00
4 Bob Feller/1
6 Brooks Robinson/5
7 Cal Ripken/8
8 Carlton Fisk/72 4.00 10.00
9 Dennis Eckersley/43 4.00 10.00
10 Don Mattingly/23 15.00 40.00
11 Duke Snider/4
12 Eddie Murray/33 10.00 25.00
13 Ernie Banks/14
16 Gaylord Perry/36 4.00 10.00
17 George Brett/5
19 Harmon Killebrew/3
20 Jim Palmer/22 5.00 12.00
21 Joe Morgan/1
22 Johnny Bench/5
23 Juan Marichal/27 5.00 12.00
24 Lou Brock/20 8.00 20.00
25 Maury Wills/30 5.00 12.00
26 Mike Schmidt/20 15.00 40.00
27 Nolan Ryan/34 20.00 50.00
28 Ozzie Smith/1
29 Paul Molitor/4
30 Pee Wee Reese/1
31 Phil Niekro/35 5.00 12.00
32 Phil Rizzuto Pants/1
34 Reggie Jackson/9
35 Rickey Henderson/24 10.00 25.00
36 Roberto Clemente/1
37 Robin Yount/19 12.50 30.00
38 Rod Carew/29 8.00 20.00
39 Roger Maris/9
40 Stan Musial/6
41 Steve Carlton/32 5.00 12.00
42 Ted Williams/9
43 Tom Seaver/41 6.00 15.00
44 Tony Gwynn/19 12.50 30.00
45 Tony Perez/24 5.00 12.00
46 Wade Boggs/26 8.00 20.00
47 Warren Spahn/24 8.00 20.00
48 Whitey Ford/16 10.00 25.00
49 Willie McCovey/44 6.00 15.00
50 Yogi Berra/8

2005 Donruss Classics Legendary Players Leather

*LTR p/r 25: .6X TO 1.5X JSY p/r 20-34
*LTR p/r 25: .5X TO 1.2X JSY p/r 16-19
OVERALL AU-GU ODDS 1:6
PRINT RUNS B/WN 10-25 COPIES PER
NO PRICING ON QTY OF 10
14 Fergie Jenkins Fld Glv/25 8.00 20.00

2005 Donruss Classics Legendary Players Pants

*PNTp/r24-25: .5X TO 1.2X JSY NUMp/r36-44
*PNTp/r24-25: .4X TO 1X JSY NUM p/r 20-34
*PNTp/r24-25: .3X TO .8X JSY NUM p/r 16-19
OVERALL AU-GU ODDS 1:6
PRINT RUNS B/WN 1-25 COPIES PER
NO PRICING ON QTY OF 10 OR LESS
4 Bob Feller/19 10.00 25.00
7 Cal Ripken/25 40.00 80.00
11 Duke Snider/25 8.00 20.00
14 Fergie Jenkins/25 5.00 12.00
22 Johnny Bench/25 10.00 25.00
28 Ozzie Smith/25 12.50 30.00
29 Paul Molitor/25 5.00 12.00
39 Roger Maris/25 20.00 50.00

2005 Donruss Classics Legendary Players Spikes

*SPK p/r 25: .5X TO 1.2X JSY NUM p/r 16-19
OVERALL AU-GU ODDS 1:6
PRINT RUNS B/WN 1-25 COPIES PER
NO PRICING ON QTY OF 10 OR LESS
15 Frank Robinson/25 8.00 20.00

2005 Donruss Classics Legendary Players Signature

OVERALL AU-GU ODDS 1:6
PRINT RUNS B/WN 1-10 COPIES PER
NO PRICING DUE TO SCARCITY

2005 Donruss Classics Membership

STATED PRINT RUN 1000 SERIAL #'d SETS
*GOLD: 1.5X TO 4X BASIC
GOLD PRINT RUN 50 SERIAL #'d SETS
PLATINUM PRINT RUN 1 SERIAL #'d SET
NO PLATINUM PRICING DUE TO SCARCITY
OVERALL INSERT ODDS 1:2
1 Bobby Doerr .75 2.00
2 Tom Seaver 1.25 3.00
3 Cal Ripken 5.00 12.00
4 Paul Molitor .75 2.00
5 Brooks Robinson 1.25 3.00
6 Al Kaline 1.25 3.00
7 Steve Carlton .75 2.00
8 Carl Yastrzemski 2.00 5.00
9 Bob Feller 1.25 3.00
10 Fred Lynn .75 2.00
11 Luis Aparicio .75 2.00
12 Hank Aaron 2.50 6.00
13 Willie Mays 2.50 6.00
14 Bob Gibson 1.25 3.00
15 Joe Morgan .75 2.00
16 Whitey Ford 1.25 3.00
17 Don Sutton .75 2.00
18 Harmon Killebrew 1.25 3.00
19 Tony Gwynn 1.50 4.00
20 Lou Brock 1.25 3.00
21 Dennis Eckersley .75 2.00
22 Jim Palmer .75 2.00
23 Don Mattingly 2.50 6.00
24 Carlton Fisk 1.25 3.00
25 Gaylord Perry .75 2.00
26 Mike Schmidt 2.50 6.00
27 Nolan Ryan 3.00 8.00
28 Sandy Koufax 8.00 20.00
29 Rod Carew 1.25 3.00
30 Maury Wills .75 2.00

2005 Donruss Classics Membership VIP Bat

*BAT p/r 25: .5X TO 1.2X JSY p/r 50
*BAT p/r 25: .4X TO 1X JSY p/r 25
OVERALL AU-GU ODDS 1:6
STATED PRINT RUN 25 SERIAL #'d SETS

1 Bobby Doerr 5.00 12.00
2 Tom Seaver 8.00 20.00
3 Cal Ripken 40.00 80.00
4 Paul Molitor 5.00 12.00
5 Brooks Robinson 8.00 20.00
6 Al Kaline 10.00 25.00
8 Carl Yastrzemski 8.00 20.00
12 Hank Aaron 20.00 50.00
13 Willie Mays 20.00 50.00
18 Harmon Killebrew 10.00 25.00

2005 Donruss Classics Membership VIP Jersey

PRINT RUNS B/WN 5-50 COPIES PER
NO PRICING ON QTY OF 10 OR LESS
PRIME PRINT RUN 1 SERIAL #'d SET
NO PRIME PRICING DUE TO SCARCITY
OVERALL AU-GU ODDS 1:6
1 Bobby Doerr Pants/10
2 Tom Seaver/10
3 Cal Ripken/10
4 Paul Molitor/10
5 Brooks Robinson/10
7 Steve Carlton/25 5.00 12.00
8 Carl Yastrzemski/10
9 Bob Feller Pants/10
10 Fred Lynn/25 5.00 12.00
11 Luis Aparicio/25 5.00 12.00
12 Hank Aaron/10
13 Willie Mays/10
14 Bob Gibson/5
15 Joe Morgan/25 5.00 12.00
16 Whitey Ford/10
17 Don Sutton/50 4.00 10.00
18 Harmon Killebrew/10
19 Tony Gwynn/50 8.00 20.00
20 Lou Brock/25 8.00 20.00
21 Dennis Eckersley/50 4.00 10.00
22 Jim Palmer/25 5.00 12.00
23 Don Mattingly/25 15.00 40.00
24 Carlton Fisk/25 8.00 20.00
25 Gaylord Perry/50 4.00 10.00
26 Mike Schmidt/50 12.50 30.00
27 Nolan Ryan/25 20.00 50.00
28 Sandy Koufax/5
29 Rod Carew/50 6.00 15.00
30 Maury Wills/10

2005 Donruss Classics Membership VIP Materials

*MTL p/r 25: .6X TO 1.5X JSY p/r 50
*MTL p/r 25: .5X TO 1.2X JSY p/r 25
PRINT RUNS B/WN 5-25 COPIES PER
NO PRICING ON QTY OF 10 OR LESS
PRIME PRINT RUN 1 SERIAL #'d SET
NO PRIME PRICING DUE TO SCARCITY
OVERALL AU-GU ODDS 1:6
1 Bobby Doerr Bat-Pants/25 6.00 15.00
2 Tom Seaver Bat-Jsy/25 10.00 25.00
3 Cal Ripken Bat-Jsy/25 50.00 100.00
4 Paul Molitor Bat-Jsy/25 6.00 15.00
5 Brooks Robinson Bat-Jsy/25 10.00 25.00
18 Harmon Killebrew Bat-Jsy/25 12.50 30.00

2005 Donruss Classics Membership VIP Materials Awards

OVERALL AU-GU ODDS 1:6
PRINT RUNS B/WN 5-10 COPIES PER
NO PRICING DUE TO SCARCITY

2005 Donruss Classics Membership VIP Materials HOF

OVERALL AU-GU ODDS 1:6
STATED PRINT RUN 10 SERIAL #'d SETS
NO PRICING DUE TO SCARCITY

2005 Donruss Classics Membership VIP Materials HR

*MTL HR p/r 37-49: .5X TO 1.2X JSY p/r 50
*MTL HR p/r 37-49: .4X TO 1X JSY p/r 25
*MTL HR p/r 21-35: .5X TO 1.2X JSY p/r 25
*MTL HR p/r 17: .75X TO 2X JSY p/r 50
OVERALL AU-GU ODDS 1:6
PRINT RUNS B/WN 6-49 COPIES PER
NO PRICING ON QTY OF 14 OR LESS
1 Bobby Doerr Jsy-Pants/27 6.00 15.00
3 Cal Ripken Jsy-Pants/34 40.00 80.00
4 Paul Molitor Bat-Jsy/22 6.00 15.00
8 Carl Yastrzemski Bat-Jsy/44 15.00 40.00
12 Hank Aaron Bat-Jsy/47 40.00 80.00
18 Harmon Killebrew Bat-Jsy/49 10.00 25.00

2005 Donruss Classics Membership VIP Materials Stats

OVERALL AU-GU ODDS 1:6
STATED PRINT RUN 10 SERIAL #'d SETS
NO PRICING DUE TO SCARCITY

2005 Donruss Classics Membership VIP Signature

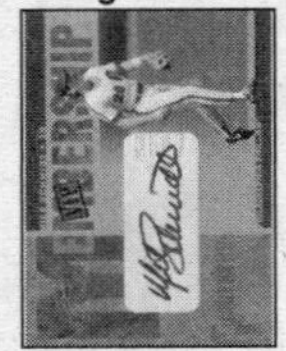

OVERALL AU-GU ODDS 1:6
PRINT RUNS B/WN 1-5 COPIES PER
NO PRICING DUE TO SCARCITY

2005 Donruss Classics Membership VIP Signature Bat

OVERALL AU-GU ODDS 1:6
PRINT RUNS B/WN 1-10 COPIES PER
NO PRICING DUE TO SCARCITY

2005 Donruss Classics Membership VIP Signature Jersey

PRINT RUNS B/WN 1-10 COPIES PER
PRIME PRINT RUN 1 SERIAL #'d SET
OVERALL AU-GU ODDS 1:6
NO PRICING DUE TO SCARCITY

2005 Donruss Classics Membership VIP Signature Materials

PRINT RUNS B/WN 1-25 COPIES PER
NO PRICING ON QTY OF 10 OR LESS
PRIME PRINT RUN 1 SERIAL #'d SET
NO PRIME PRICING DUE TO SCARCITY

OVERALL AU-GU ODDS 1:6
1 Bobby Doerr Bat-Pants/25 15.00 40.00
2 Tom Seaver Bat-Jsy/5
3 Cal Ripken Bat-Jsy/1
4 Paul Molitor Bat-Jsy/5
5 Brooks Robinson Bat-Jsy/5
7 Steve Carlton Bat-Jsy/5
8 Carl Yastrzemski Bat-Jsy/1
10 Fred Lynn Bat-Jsy/25 15.00 40.00
11 Luis Aparicio Bat-Jsy/25 15.00 40.00
12 Hank Aaron Bat-Jsy/5
13 Willie Mays Bat-Jsy/1
18 Harmon Killebrew Bat-Jsy/10
19 Tony Gwynn Bat-Jsy/10
20 Lou Brock Bat-Jsy/25 30.00 60.00
23 Don Mattingly Bat-Jsy/10
24 Carlton Fisk Bat-Jsy/5
27 Nolan Ryan Bat-Jsy/5
29 Rod Carew Bat-Jsy/5

2005 Donruss Classics Membership VIP Signature Materials Awards

OVERALL AU-GU ODDS 1:6
PRINT RUNS B/WN 1-10 COPIES PER
NO PRICING DUE TO SCARCITY

2005 Donruss Classics Membership VIP Signature Materials HOF

OVERALL AU-GU ODDS 1:6
PRINT RUNS B/WN 1-10 COPIES PER
NO PRICING DUE TO SCARCITY

2005 Donruss Classics Membership VIP Signature Materials HR

OVERALL AU-GU ODDS 1:6
PRINT RUNS B/WN 1-10 COPIES PER
NO PRICING DUE TO SCARCITY

2005 Donruss Classics Membership VIP Signature Materials Stats

OVERALL AU-GU ODDS 1:6
PRINT RUNS B/WN 5-10 COPIES PER
NO PRICING DUE TO SCARCITY

2005 Donruss Classics Stars of Summer

STATED PRINT RUN 1000 SERIAL #'d SETS
*GOLD: 1.5X TO 4X BASIC
GOLD PRINT RUN 50 SERIAL #'d SETS
PLATINUM PRINT RUN 1 SERIAL #'d SET
NO PLATINUM PRICING DUE TO SCARCITY
OVERALL INSERT ODDS 1:2

1 Andre Dawson .75 2.00
2 Bert Blyleven .75 2.00
3 Bill Madlock .75 2.00
4 Dale Murphy 1.25 3.00
5 Darryl Strawberry .75 2.00
6 Dave Parker .75 2.00
7 Dave Righetti .75 2.00
8 Dwight Evans 1.25 3.00
9 Dwight Gooden .75 2.00
10 Fred Lynn .75 2.00
11 George Foster .75 2.00
12 Harold Baines .75 2.00
13 Jack Morris .75 2.00
14 Jim Rice .75 2.00
15 Keith Hernandez .75 2.00
16 Kirk Gibson .75 2.00
17 Luis Aparicio .75 2.00
18 Mark Grace 1.25 3.00
19 Marty Marion .75 2.00
20 Orel Hershiser .75 2.00
21 Ron Guidry .75 2.00
22 Ron Santo 1.25 3.00
23 Steve Garvey .75 2.00
24 Tony Oliva .75 2.00
25 Will Clark 1.25 3.00

2005 Donruss Classics Stars of Summer Material

OVERALL AU-GU ODDS 1:6
PRINT RUNS B/WN 100-250 COPIES PER
1 Andre Dawson Jsy/250 3.00 8.00
2 Bert Blyleven Jsy/150 3.00 8.00
3 Bill Madlock Bat/250 3.00 8.00
4 Dale Murphy Jsy/250 5.00 12.00
5 Darryl Strawberry Jsy/250 3.00 8.00
6 Dave Parker Jsy/100 3.00 8.00
7 Dave Righetti Jsy/150 3.00 8.00
8 Dwight Evans Bat/250 5.00 12.00
9 Dwight Gooden Bat/150 3.00 8.00
10 Fred Lynn Jsy/100 3.00 8.00
11 George Foster Bat/250 3.00 8.00
12 Harold Baines Jsy/250 3.00 8.00
13 Jack Morris Jsy/100 3.00 8.00
14 Jim Rice Pants/250 3.00 8.00
15 Keith Hernandez Bat/100 3.00 8.00
16 Kirk Gibson Jsy/250 3.00 8.00
17 Luis Aparicio Bat/250 3.00 8.00
18 Mark Grace Bat/250 5.00 12.00
22 Ron Santo Bat/150 5.00 12.00
23 Steve Garvey Jsy/250 3.00 8.00
24 Tony Oliva Jsy/250 3.00 8.00
25 Will Clark Bat/250 5.00 12.00

2005 Donruss Classics Stars of Summer Signature

*SIG p/r 50: .4X TO 1X MTL SIG p/r 100
*SIG p/r 50: .3X TO .8X MTL SIG p/r 50
*SIG p/r 50: .25X TO .6X MTL SIG p/r 25
*SIG p/r 25: .4X TO 1X MTL SIG p/r 50
*SIG p/r 25: .3X TO .8X MTL SIG p/r 25
OVERALL AU-GU ODDS 1:6
PRINT RUNS B/WN 10-100 COPIES PER
NO PRICING ON QTY OF 10
5 Darryl Strawberry/100 6.00 15.00
19 Marty Marion/50 8.00 20.00
21 Ron Guidry/25 15.00 40.00

2005 Donruss Classics Stars of Summer Signature Material

OVERALL AU-GU ODDS 1:6
PRINT RUNS B/WN 25-100 COPIES PER
1 Andre Dawson Jsy/100 8.00 20.00
2 Bert Blyleven Jsy/50 10.00 25.00
3 Bill Madlock Bat/100 8.00 20.00
4 Dale Murphy Jsy/25 20.00 50.00
6 Dave Parker Jsy/50 10.00 25.00
7 Dave Righetti Jsy/50 10.00 25.00
8 Dwight Evans Jsy/50 15.00 40.00
9 Dwight Gooden Bat/25 12.50 30.00
10 Fred Lynn Jsy/100 8.00 20.00
11 George Foster Bat/50 10.00 25.00
12 Harold Baines Jsy/100 8.00 20.00
13 Jack Morris Jsy/100 8.00 20.00
14 Jim Rice Pants/50 10.00 25.00
15 Keith Hernandez Jsy/50 10.00 25.00
16 Kirk Gibson Jsy/25 12.50 30.00
17 Luis Aparicio Bat/50 10.00 25.00
18 Mark Grace Bat/25 20.00 50.00
22 Ron Santo Bat/50 15.00 40.00
23 Steve Garvey Jsy/50 10.00 25.00
24 Tony Oliva Jsy/50 10.00 25.00
25 Will Clark Bat/25 20.00 50.00

2005 Donruss Classics Team Colors

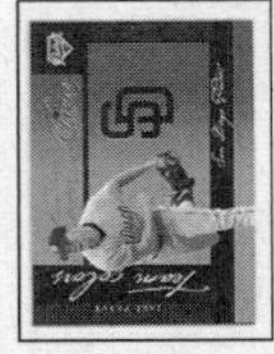

STATED PRINT RUN 800 SERIAL #'d SETS
*GOLD: 1.5X TO 4X BASIC
GOLD PRINT RUN 50 SERIAL #'d SETS
PLATINUM PRINT RUN 1 SERIAL #'d SET
NO PLATINUM PRICING DUE TO SCARCITY
OVERALL INSERT ODDS 1:2
1 Adam Dunn .75 2.00
2 Albert Pujols 2.50 6.00
3 Andruw Jones 1.25 3.00
4 Aramis Ramirez .75 2.00
5 Aubrey Huff .75 2.00
6 Bobby Abreu .75 2.00
7 Cal Ripken 5.00 12.00
8 Carlos Lee .75 2.00
9 Craig Biggio 1.25 3.00
10 Derrek Lee 1.25 3.00
11 Garret Anderson .75 2.00
12 Gary Carter .75 2.00
13 Geoff Jenkins .75 2.00
14 Greg Maddux 2.00 5.00
15 Hank Blalock .75 2.00
16 Hideki Matsui 2.00 5.00
17 Jake Peavy .75 2.00
18 Jim Edmonds .75 2.00
19 Jim Palmer .75 2.00
20 Jose Guillen .75 2.00
21 Jose Vidro .75 2.00
22 Juan Pierre .75 2.00
23 Lew Ford .75 2.00
24 Lyle Overbay .75 2.00
25 Manny Ramirez 1.25 3.00
26 Mark Loretta .75 2.00
27 Mark Teixeira 1.25 3.00
28 Melvin Mora .75 2.00
29 Michael Young .75 2.00
30 Miguel Cabrera 1.25 3.00
31 Mike Lowell .75 2.00
32 Mike Mussina 1.25 3.00
33 Milton Bradley .75 2.00
34 Randy Johnson 1.25 3.00
35 Roger Clemens 2.00 5.00
36 Sean Casey .75 2.00
37 Shawn Green .75 2.00
38 Steve Carlton .75 2.00
39 Todd Helton 1.25 3.00
40 Travis Hafner .75 2.00

2005 Donruss Classics Team Colors Bat

OVERALL AU-GU ODDS 1:6
STATED PRINT RUN 100 SERIAL #'d SETS
1 Adam Dunn 2.50 6.00
2 Albert Pujols 8.00 20.00
3 Andruw Jones 4.00 10.00
4 Aramis Ramirez 2.50 6.00
7 Cal Ripken 15.00 40.00
9 Craig Biggio 4.00 10.00
10 Derrek Lee 4.00 10.00
11 Garret Anderson 2.50 6.00
12 Gary Carter 2.50 6.00
15 Hank Blalock 2.50 6.00
16 Hideki Matsui 15.00 40.00
18 Jim Edmonds 2.50 6.00
21 Jose Vidro 2.50 6.00
22 Juan Pierre 2.50 6.00
23 Lew Ford 2.50 6.00
27 Mark Teixeira 4.00 10.00
28 Melvin Mora 2.50 6.00
29 Michael Young 2.50 6.00
30 Miguel Cabrera 4.00 10.00
31 Mike Lowell 2.50 6.00
36 Sean Casey 2.50 6.00
37 Shawn Green 2.50 6.00

2005 Donruss Classics Team Colors Jersey Prime

*JSY PRIME p/r 25: 1X TO 2.5X BAT p/r 100
OVERALL AU-GU ODDS 1:6

PRINT RUNS B/WN 5-25 COPIES PER
NO PRICING ON QTY OF 5
5 Aubrey Huff/25 5.00 12.00
6 Bobby Abreu/25 5.00 12.00
8 Carlos Lee/25 5.00 12.00
13 Geoff Jenkins/25 5.00 12.00
24 Lyle Overbay/25 5.00 12.00
32 Mike Mussina/25 8.00 20.00
34 Randy Johnson/25 10.00 25.00
35 Roger Clemens/25 15.00 40.00
38 Steve Carlton/25 5.00 12.00
39 Todd Helton/25 8.00 20.00
40 Travis Hafner/25 5.00 12.00

2005 Donruss Classics Team Colors Materials

*MTL p/r 100: .5X TO 1.2X BAT p/r 100
*MTL p/r 50: .6X TO 1.5X BAT p/r 100
PRINT RUNS B/WN 25-100 COPIES PER
PRIME PRINT RUN 5 SERIAL #'d SETS
NO PRIME PRICING DUE TO SCARCITY
OVERALL AU-GU ODDS 1:6
6 Bobby Abreu Jsy-Jsy/100 3.00 8.00
8 Carlos Lee Jsy-Jsy/100 3.00 8.00
13 Geoff Jenkins Jsy-Pants/100 3.00 8.00
19 Jim Palmer Jsy-Pants/25 5.00 12.00
25 Manny Ramirez Jsy-Jsy/100 5.00 12.00
39 Todd Helton Jsy-Jsy/50 6.00 15.00

2005 Donruss Classics Team Colors Signature

*SIG p/r 25: .3X TO .8X SIG JSY p/r 25
OVERALL AU-GU ODDS 1:6
PRINT RUNS B/WN 1-25 COPIES PER
NO PRICING ON QTY OF 10 OR LESS
17 Jake Peavy/25 15.00 40.00
20 Jose Guillen/25 10.00 25.00
26 Mark Loretta/25 6.00 15.00
33 Milton Bradley/25 10.00 25.00

2005 Donruss Classics Team Colors Signature Bat

*SIG BAT p/r 25: .4X TO 1X SIG JSY p/r 25
OVERALL AU-GU ODDS 1:6
PRINT RUNS B/WN 5-25 COPIES PER
NO PRICING ON QTY OF 10 OR LESS
10 Derrek Lee/25 20.00 50.00

2005 Donruss Classics Team Colors Signature Jersey

PRINT RUNS B/WN 1-25 COPIES PER
NO PRICING ON QTY OF 10 OR LESS
PRIME PRINT RUN 1 SERIAL #'d SET
NO PRIME PRICING DUE TO SCARCITY
OVERALL AU-GU ODDS 1:6
1 Adam Dunn/25 20.00 50.00
2 Albert Pujols/1
4 Aramis Ramirez/25 12.50 30.00
5 Aubrey Huff/25 12.50 30.00

7 Cal Ripken/1
8 Carlos Lee/25 12.50 30.00
9 Craig Biggio/10
11 Garret Anderson/25 12.50 30.00
12 Gary Carter/25 12.50 30.00
14 Greg Maddux/1
15 Hank Blalock/25 12.50 30.00
18 Jim Edmonds/10
19 Jim Palmer/10
21 Jose Vidro/25 12.50 30.00
23 Lew Ford/25 8.00 20.00
24 Lyle Overbay/25 8.00 20.00
25 Manny Ramirez/1
28 Melvin Mora/25 12.50 30.00
29 Michael Young/25 12.50 30.00
30 Miguel Cabrera/10
32 Mike Mussina/1
34 Randy Johnson/1
35 Roger Clemens/1
36 Sean Casey/10
37 Shawn Green/5
38 Steve Carlton/10
39 Todd Helton/5
40 Travis Hafner/25 12.50 30.00

2005 Donruss Classics Team Colors Signature Materials

*SIG MTL p/r 25: .5X TO 1.2X SIG JSY p/r 25
PRINT RUNS B/WN 5-25 COPIES PER
NO PRICING ON QTY OF 10 OR LESS
PRIME PRINT RUN 1 SERIAL #'d SET
NO PRIME PRICING DUE TO SCARCITY
OVERALL AU-GU ODDS 1:6

1997 Donruss Elite

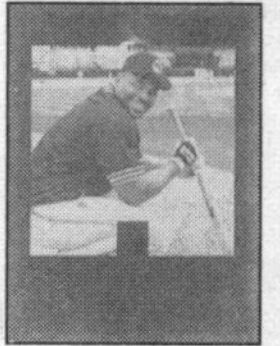

The 1997 Donruss Elite set was issued in one series totalling 150 cards. The product was distributed exclusively to hobby dealers around February, 1997. Each foil-wrapped pack contained eight cards and carried a suggested retail price of $3.49. Player selection was limited to the top stars (plus three player checklist cards) and card design is very similar to the Donruss Elite hockey set that was released one year earlier. Strangely enough, the backs only provide career statistics neglecting statistics from the previous season.

COMPLETE SET (150) 10.00 25.00
1 Juan Gonzalez .15 .40
2 Alex Rodriguez .60 1.50
3 Frank Thomas .40 1.00
4 Greg Maddux .60 1.50
5 Ken Griffey Jr. .60 1.50
6 Cal Ripken 1.25 3.00
7 Mike Piazza .60 1.50
8 Chipper Jones .40 1.00
9 Albert Belle .15 .40
10 Andruw Jones .25 .60
11 Vladimir Guerrero .40 1.00
12 Mo Vaughn .15 .40
UER front Gonzales
13 Ivan Rodriguez .25 .60
14 Andy Pettitte .25 .60
15 Tony Gwynn .50 1.25
16 Barry Bonds 1.00 2.50
17 Jeff Bagwell .25 .60
18 Manny Ramirez .25 .60
19 Kenny Lofton .15 .40
20 Roberto Alomar .25 .60
21 Mark McGwire 1.00 2.50
22 Ryan Klesko .15 .40
23 Tim Salmon .25 .60
24 Derek Jeter 1.00 2.50
25 Eddie Murray .40 1.00
26 Jermaine Dye .15 .40
27 Ruben Rivera .15 .40
28 Jim Edmonds .15 .40
29 Mike Mussina .25 .60
30 Randy Johnson .40 1.00
31 Sammy Sosa .40 1.00
32 Hideo Nomo .40 1.00
33 Chuck Knoblauch .15 .40
34 Paul Molitor .15 .40
35 Rafael Palmeiro .25 .60
36 Brady Anderson .15 .40
37 Will Clark .25 .60
38 Craig Biggio .25 .60
39 Jason Giambi .15 .40
40 Roger Clemens .75 2.00
41 Jay Buhner .15 .40
42 Edgar Martinez .25 .60
43 Gary Sheffield .15 .40
44 Fred McGriff .25 .60
45 Bobby Bonilla .15 .40
46 Tom Glavine .25 .60
47 Wade Boggs .25 .60
48 Jeff Conine .15 .40
49 John Smoltz .25 .60
50 Jim Thome .25 .60
51 Billy Wagner .25 .60
52 Jose Canseco .25 .60
53 Javy Lopez .15 .40
54 Cecil Fielder .15 .40
55 Garret Anderson .15 .40
56 Alex Ochoa .15 .40
57 Scott Rolen .25 .60
58 Darin Erstad .15 .40
59 Rey Ordonez .15 .40
60 Dante Bichette .15 .40
61 Joe Carter .15 .40
62 Moises Alou .15 .40
63 Jason Isringhausen .15 .40
64 Karim Garcia .15 .40
65 Brian Jordan .15 .40
66 Ruben Sierra .15 .40
67 Todd Hollandsworth .15 .40
68 Paul Wilson .15 .40
69 Ernie Young .15 .40
70 Ryne Sandberg .60 1.50
71 Raul Mondesi .15 .40
72 George Arias .15 .40
73 Ray Durham .15 .40
74 Dean Palmer .15 .40
75 Shawn Green .15 .40
76 Eric Young .15 .40
77 Jason Kendall .15 .40
78 Greg Vaughn .15 .40
79 Terrell Wade .15 .40
80 Bill Pulsipher .15 .40
81 Bobby Higginson .15 .40
82 Mark Grudzielanek .15 .40
83 Ken Caminiti .15 .40
84 Todd Greene .15 .40
85 Carlos Delgado .15 .40
86 Mark Grace .25 .60
87 Rondell White .15 .40
88 Barry Larkin .25 .60
89 J.T. Snow .15 .40
90 Alex Gonzalez .15 .40
91 Raul Casanova .15 .40
92 Marc Newfield .15 .40
93 Jermaine Allensworth .15 .40
94 John Mabry .15 .40
95 Kirby Puckett .40 1.00
96 Travis Fryman .15 .40
97 Kevin Brown .15 .40
98 Andres Galarraga .15 .40
99 Marty Cordova .15 .40
100 Henry Rodriguez .15 .40
101 Sterling Hitchcock .15 .40
102 Trey Beamon .15 .40
103 Brett Butler .15 .40
104 Rickey Henderson .40 1.00
105 Tino Martinez .25 .60
106 Kevin Appier .15 .40
107 Brian Hunter .15 .40
108 Eric Karros .15 .40
109 Andre Dawson .15 .40
110 Darryl Strawberry .15 .40
111 James Baldwin .15 .40
112 Chad Mottola .15 .40
113 Dave Nilsson .15 .40
114 Carlos Baerga .15 .40
115 Chan Ho Park .15 .40
116 John Jaha .15 .40
117 Alan Benes .15 .40
118 Mariano Rivera .40 1.00
119 Ellis Burks .15 .40
120 Tony Clark .15 .40
121 Todd Walker .15 .40
122 Dwight Gooden .15 .40
123 Ugueth Urbina .15 .40
124 David Cone .15 .40
125 Ozzie Smith .60 1.50
126 Kimera Bartee .15 .40
127 Rusty Greer .15 .40
128 Pat Hentgen .15 .40
129 Charles Johnson .15 .40
130 Quinton McCracken .15 .40
131 Troy Percival .15 .40
132 Shane Reynolds .15 .40
133 Charles Nagy .15 .40
134 Tom Goodwin .15 .40
135 Ron Gant .15 .40
136 Dan Wilson .15 .40
137 Matt Williams .15 .40
138 LaTroy Hawkins .15 .40
139 Kevin Seitzer .15 .40
140 Michael Tucker .15 .40
141 Todd Hundley .15 .40
142 Alex Fernandez .15 .40
143 Marquis Grissom .15 .40
144 Steve Finley .15 .40
145 Curtis Pride .15 .40
146 Derek Bell .15 .40
147 Butch Huskey .15 .40
148 Dwight Gooden CL .15 .40
149 Al Leiter CL .15 .40
150 Hideo Nomo CL .15 .40

1997 Donruss Elite Gold Stars

Randomly seeded into one in every nine packs, cards from this set parallel the 150-card base issue. The distinctive gold foil fronts easily differentiate them from their silver-foiled base-issue brethren. The following cards were erroneously printed with a silver (rather than gold) logo on front: 6, 15, 25, 32, 42, 47, 57, 60, 69 and 70. Corrected gold logo versions of these cards do exist but are in far shorter supply though secondary market trading values remain similar due to general indifference. The set is considered complete with the erroneous silver logo cards.

*STARS: 4X TO 10X BASIC CARDS

1997 Donruss Elite Leather and Lumber

This ten-card insert set features color action veteran player photos printed on two unique materials. The fronts display a player image on real wood card stock with the end of a baseball bat as background. The backs carry another player photo printed on genuine leather card stock with a baseball and glove as background. Only 500 of each card was produced and are sequentially numbered.

COMPLETE SET (10) 15.00 40.00
1 Ken Griffey Jr. 15.00 40.00
2 Alex Rodriguez 15.00 40.00
3 Frank Thomas 10.00 25.00
4 Chipper Jones 10.00 25.00
5 Ivan Rodriguez 6.00 15.00
6 Cal Ripken 30.00 80.00
7 Barry Bonds 25.00 60.00
8 Chuck Knoblauch 4.00 10.00
9 Manny Ramirez 6.00 15.00
10 Mark McGwire 25.00 60.00

1997 Donruss Elite Passing the Torch

This 12-card insert set features eight players on four double-sided cards. A color portrait of a superstar veteran is displayed on one side with a gold foil background, and a portrait of a rising young star is printed on the flipside. Each of the eight players also has his own card to round out the 12-card set. Only 1500 of this set were produced and are sequentially numbered. However, only 1,350 of each card are available without autographs.

COMPLETE SET (12) 100.00 250.00
1 Cal Ripken 15.00 40.00
2 Alex Rodriguez 8.00 20.00
3 Cal Ripken 20.00 50.00
Alex Rodriguez
4 Kirby Puckett 5.00 12.00
5 Andruw Jones 3.00 8.00
6 Kirby Puckett 4.00 10.00
Andruw Jones
7 Cecil Fielder 2.00 5.00
8 Frank Thomas 5.00 12.00
9 Cecil Fielder 4.00 10.00
Frank Thomas
10 Ozzie Smith 8.00 20.00
11 Derek Jeter 12.50 30.00
12 Ozzie Smith 12.50 30.00
Derek Jeter

1997 Donruss Elite Passing the Torch Autographs

This 12-card set consists of the first 150 sets of the regular "Passing the Torch" set with each card displaying an authentic player autograph. The set features a double front design which captures eight of the league's top superstars, alternating one of four different megastars on the flipside. An individual card for each of the eight players rounds out the set. Each set is sequentially numbered to 150.

1 Cal Ripken 175.00 300.00
2 Alex Rodriguez 175.00 300.00
3 Cal Ripken 500.00 800.00
Alex Rodriguez
4 Kirby Puckett 60.00 120.00
5 Andruw Jones 50.00 100.00
6 Kirby Puckett 100.00 175.00
Andruw Jones
7 Cecil Fielder 20.00 50.00
8 Frank Thomas 50.00 100.00
9 Cecil Fielder 60.00 120.00
Frank Thomas
10 Ozzie Smith 75.00 150.00
11 Derek Jeter 175.00 300.00
12 Ozzie Smith 200.00 350.00
Derek Jeter

1997 Donruss Elite Turn of the Century

This 20-card set showcases the stars of the next millennium and features a color player image on a silver-and-black background. The backs display another player photo with a short paragraph about the player. Only 3,500 of this set were produced and

are sequentially numbered, but the first 500 sets were devoted to the TOC Die Cuts parallel.

COMPLETE SET (20) 50.00 120.00
*DIE CUTS: 1.25X TO 3X BASIC TURN CENT.
DC STATED PRINT RUN 500 SERIAL #'d SETS
RANDOM INSERTS IN PACKS
1 Alex Rodriguez 6.00 15.00
2 Andruw Jones 2.50 6.00
3 Chipper Jones 4.00 10.00
4 Todd Walker 1.50 4.00
5 Scott Rolen 2.50 6.00
6 Trey Beamon 1.50 4.00
7 Derek Jeter 10.00 25.00
8 Darin Erstad 1.50 4.00
9 Tony Clark 1.50 4.00
10 Todd Greene 1.50 4.00
11 Jason Giambi 1.50 4.00
12 Justin Thompson 1.50 4.00
13 Ernie Young 1.50 4.00
14 Jason Kendall 1.50 4.00
15 Alex Ochoa 1.50 4.00
16 Brooks Kieschnick 1.50 4.00
17 Bobby Higginson 1.50 4.00
18 Ruben Rivera 1.50 4.00
19 Chan Ho Park 1.50 4.00
20 Chad Mottola 1.50 4.00
P5 Scott Rolen PROMO .75 2.00
P7 Derek Jeter PROMO 1.25 3.00
P20 Chad Mottola PROMO .40 1.00

1998 Donruss Elite

The 1998 Donruss Elite set was issued in one series totalling 150 cards and distributed in five-card packs with a suggested retail price of $3.99. The fronts feature color player action photos. The backs carry player information. The set contains the topical subset: Generations (118-147). A special embossed Frank Thomas autograph card (parallel to basic issue card number two, except, of course, for Thomas' signature) was available to lucky collectors who pulled a Back to the Future Frank Thomas/David Ortiz card serial numbered between 1 and 100 and redeemed it to Donruss/Leaf.

COMPLETE SET (150) 10.00 25.00
1 Ken Griffey Jr. .50 1.25
2 Frank Thomas .30 .75
3 Alex Rodriguez .50 1.25
4 Mike Piazza .50 1.25
5 Greg Maddux .50 1.25
6 Cal Ripken 1.00 2.50
7 Chipper Jones .30 .75
8 Derek Jeter .75 2.00
9 Tony Gwynn .40 1.00
10 Andruw Jones .20 .50
11 Juan Gonzalez .10 .30
12 Jeff Bagwell .20 .50
13 Mark McGwire .75 2.00
14 Roger Clemens .60 1.50
15 Albert Belle .10 .30
16 Barry Bonds .75 2.00
17 Kenny Lofton .10 .30
18 Ivan Rodriguez .20 .50
19 Manny Ramirez .20 .50
20 Jim Thome .20 .50
21 Chuck Knoblauch .10 .30
22 Paul Molitor .10 .30
23 Barry Larkin .20 .50
24 Andy Pettitte .20 .50
25 John Smoltz .20 .50
26 Randy Johnson .30 .75
27 Bernie Williams .20 .50
28 Larry Walker .10 .30
29 Mo Vaughn .10 .30
30 Bobby Higginson .10 .30
31 Edgardo Alfonzo .10 .30
32 Justin Thompson .10 .30
33 Jeff Suppan .10 .30
34 Roberto Alomar .20 .50
35 Hideo Nomo .30 .75
36 Rusty Greer .10 .30
37 Tim Salmon .20 .50
38 Jim Edmonds .10 .30
39 Gary Sheffield .10 .30
40 Ken Caminiti .10 .30
41 Sammy Sosa .30 .75
42 Tony Womack .10 .30
43 Matt Williams .10 .30
44 Andres Galarraga .10 .30
45 Garret Anderson .10 .30
46 Rafael Palmeiro .20 .50
47 Mike Mussina .20 .50
48 Craig Biggio .20 .50
49 Wade Boggs .20 .50
50 Tom Glavine .20 .50
51 Jason Giambi .10 .30
52 Will Clark .20 .50
53 David Justice .10 .30
54 Sandy Alomar Jr. .10 .30
55 Edgar Martinez .20 .50
56 Brady Anderson .10 .30
57 Eric Young .10 .30
58 Ray Lankford .10 .30
59 Kevin Brown .20 .50
60 Raul Mondesi .10 .30
61 Bobby Bonilla .10 .30
62 Javier Lopez .10 .30
63 Fred McGriff .20 .50
64 Rondell White .10 .30
65 Todd Hundley .10 .30
66 Mark Grace .20 .50
67 Alan Benes .10 .30
68 Jeff Abbott .10 .30
69 Bob Abreu .10 .30
70 Deion Sanders .20 .50
71 Tino Martinez .20 .50
72 Shannon Stewart .10 .30
73 Homer Bush .10 .30
74 Carlos Delgado .10 .30
75 Raul Ibanez .10 .30
76 Hideki Irabu .10 .30
77 Jose Cruz Jr. .10 .30
78 Tony Clark .10 .30
79 Wilton Guerrero .10 .30
80 Vladimir Guerrero .30 .75
81 Scott Rolen .20 .50
82 Nomar Garciaparra .50 1.25
83 Darin Erstad .10 .30
84 Chan Ho Park .10 .30
85 Mike Cameron .10 .30
86 Todd Walker .10 .30
87 Todd Dunwoody .10 .30
88 Neifi Perez .10 .30
89 Brett Tomko .10 .30
90 Jose Guillen .10 .30
91 Matt Morris .10 .30
92 Bartolo Colon .10 .30
93 Jaret Wright .10 .30
94 Shawn Estes .10 .30
95 Livan Hernandez .10 .30
96 Bobby Estalella .10 .30
97 Ben Grieve .10 .30
98 Paul Konerko .10 .30
99 David Ortiz .40 1.00
100 Todd Helton .20 .50
101 Juan Encarnacion .10 .30
102 Bubba Trammell .10 .30
103 Miguel Tejada .30 .75
104 Jacob Cruz .10 .30
105 Todd Greene .10 .30
106 Kevin Orie .10 .30
107 Mark Kotsay .10 .30
108 Fernando Tatis .10 .30
109 Jay Payton .10 .30
110 Pokey Reese .10 .30
111 Derrek Lee .20 .50
112 Richard Hidalgo .10 .30
113 Ricky Ledee .10 .30
UER front Rickey
114 Lou Collier .10 .30
115 Ruben Rivera .10 .30
116 Shawn Green .10 .30
117 Moises Alou .10 .30
118 Ken Griffey Jr. GEN .30 .75
119 Frank Thomas GEN .20 .50
120 Alex Rodriguez GEN .30 .75
121 Mike Piazza GEN .30 .75
122 Greg Maddux GEN .30 .75
123 Cal Ripken GEN .50 1.25
124 Chipper Jones GEN .20 .50
125 Derek Jeter GEN .40 1.00
126 Tony Gwynn GEN .20 .50
127 Andruw Jones GEN .10 .30
128 Juan Gonzalez GEN .10 .30
129 Jeff Bagwell GEN .10 .30
130 Mark McGwire GEN .40 1.00
131 Roger Clemens GEN .30 .75
132 Albert Belle GEN .10 .30
133 Barry Bonds GEN .40 1.00
134 Kenny Lofton GEN .10 .30
135 Ivan Rodriguez GEN .10 .30
136 Manny Ramirez GEN .20 .50
137 Jim Thome GEN .10 .30
138 C.Knoblauch GEN .10 .30
139 Paul Molitor GEN .10 .30
140 Barry Larkin GEN .10 .30
141 Mo Vaughn GEN .10 .30
142 Hideki Irabu GEN .10 .30
143 Jose Cruz Jr. GEN .10 .30
144 Tony Clark GEN .10 .30
145 V.Guerrero GEN .20 .50
146 Scott Rolen GEN .10 .30
147 N.Garciaparra GEN .30 .75
148 Nomar Garciaparra CL .30 .75
149 Larry Walker CL .10 .30
150 Tino Martinez CL .10 .30
AU2 F.Thomas AUTO/100 40.00 80.00

1998 Donruss Elite Aspirations

Randomly inserted in packs, this 150-card set is parallel to the base set. Only 750 of this set were produced and are sequentially numbered.

*ASPIRATION: 3X TO 8X BASIC CARDS

1998 Donruss Elite Status

Randomly inserted in packs, this 150-card set is parallel to the base set. Only 100 of this set were produced and are serially numbered.

*STATUS: 10X TO 25X BASIC

1998 Donruss Elite Back to the Future

Randomly inserted in packs, this eight-card set is double-sided and features color images of top veteran and new players on a tile background. Only 1,500 of each card were produced and sequentially numbered but the first 100 #'d cards were devoted to the Back to the Future Autograph parallel set.

COMPLETE SET (8) 50.00 120.00
1 Cal Ripken 12.50 30.00
Paul Konerko
2 Jeff Bagwell 2.50 6.00
Todd Helton
3 Eddie Mathews 4.00 10.00
Chipper Jones
4 Juan Gonzalez 1.50 4.00
Ben Grieve
5 Hank Aaron 6.00 15.00
Jose Cruz Jr.
6 Frank Thomas 5.00 12.00
David Ortiz
1-100
7 Nolan Ryan 15.00 40.00
Greg Maddux
8 Alex Rodriguez 6.00 15.00
Nomar Garciaparra

1998 Donruss Elite Back to the Future Autographs

Randomly inserted in packs, this seven-card set is a parallel version of the the regular 1998 Donruss Elite Back to the Future insert set and contains the first 100 cards of the regular set signed by both pictured players. Card number six does not exist. Cal Ripken did not sign card number 1 along with Paul Konerko. Ripken eventually signed 200 separate cards. One hundred special redemptions (rather bland black and white text-based cards) were issued for the Ripken card and randomly seeded into packs. In addition, lucky collectors that pulled one of the first 100 serial numbered Back to the Future Konerko autograph cards could exchange it for a Ripken autograph AND still receive their Konerko autograph back. The first 100 of each card were autographed by both players pictured on the card. There is no autographed card number six. Due to problems in obtaining Frank Thomas' autograph prior to the shipping deadline for the parallel signed Back to the Future cards, the manufacturer was forced to make the first 100 serial numbered cards of card number 6 a redemption for a special Frank Thomas autographed card (a basic 1998 Donruss Elite Thomas card, embossed with a special stamp and signed by Thomas on front). Due to Pinnacle's bankruptcy, the exchange program was abruptly halted in late 1998. Prior to this, the serial numbered 1-100 Thomas/Ortiz cards traded for as much as $300. After this date, the premiums disappeared entirely.

1A Cal Ripken 15.00 40.00
Paul Konerko Redeemed/100
Redeemed card signed only by Konerko
1B C. Ripken AU/200 125.00 200.00
Redeemed card signed only by Ripken
2 Jeff Bagwell 75.00 150.00
Todd Helton
3 Eddie Mathews 150.00 250.00
Chipper Jones
4 Juan Gonzalez 50.00 100.00
Ben Grieve
5 Hank Aaron 150.00 250.00
Jose Cruz Jr.
7 Nolan Ryan 800.00 1200.00
Greg Maddux
8 Alex Rodriguez 400.00 600.00
Nomar Garciaparra

1998 Donruss Elite Craftsmen

Randomly inserted in packs, this 30-card set features color photos of players who are the best at what they do. Only 3,500 of this set were produced and are sequentially numbered.

COMPLETE SET (30) 60.00 150.00
*MASTER: 2.5X TO 6X BASIC CRAFTSMEN
MASTER PRINT RUN 100 SERIAL #'d SETS
RANDOM INSERTS IN PACKS
1 Ken Griffey Jr. 4.00 10.00
2 Frank Thomas 2.50 6.00
3 Alex Rodriguez 4.00 10.00
4 Cal Ripken 8.00 20.00
5 Greg Maddux 4.00 10.00
6 Mike Piazza 4.00 10.00
7 Chipper Jones 2.50 6.00
8 Derek Jeter 6.00 15.00
9 Tony Gwynn 3.00 8.00
10 Nomar Garciaparra 4.00 10.00
11 Scott Rolen 1.50 4.00
12 Jose Cruz Jr. 1.00 2.50
13 Tony Clark 1.00 2.50
14 Vladimir Guerrero 2.50 6.00
15 Todd Helton 1.50 4.00
16 Ben Grieve 1.00 2.50
17 Andruw Jones 1.50 4.00
18 Jeff Bagwell 1.50 4.00
19 Mark McGwire 6.00 15.00
20 Juan Gonzalez 1.00 2.50
21 Roger Clemens 5.00 12.00
22 Albert Belle 1.00 2.50
23 Barry Bonds 6.00 15.00
24 Kenny Lofton 1.00 2.50
25 Ivan Rodriguez 1.50 4.00
26 Paul Molitor 1.00 2.50
27 Barry Larkin UER 1.50 4.00
His team was midentified as the Cardinals
28 Mo Vaughn 1.00 2.50
29 Larry Walker 1.00 2.50
30 Tino Martinez 1.50 4.00

1998 Donruss Elite Prime Numbers Samples

Promotional samples were created for all 36 Prime Numbers inserts and distributed one per wholesale dealer order form. The cards are identical to regular Prime Numbers inserts except for the large "SAMPLE" text running diagonally across the backs and lack of serial numbering.

COMPLETE SET (36) 140.00 350.00
1A Ken Griffey Jr. 2 5.00 12.00
1B Ken Griffey Jr. 9 5.00 12.00
1C Ken Griffey Jr. 4 5.00 12.00
2A Frank Thomas 4 2.50 6.00
2B Frank Thomas 5 2.50 6.00
2C Frank Thomas 6 2.50 6.00
3A Mark McGwire 3 6.00 15.00
3B Mark McGwire 8 6.00 15.00
3C Mark McGwire 7 6.00 15.00
4A Cal Ripken 5 8.00 20.00
4B Cal Ripken 1 8.00 20.00
4C Cal Ripken 7 8.00 20.00
5A Mike Piazza 5 6.00 15.00
5B Mike Piazza 7 6.00 15.00
5C Mike Piazza 6 6.00 15.00
6A Chipper Jones 4 4.00 10.00
6B Chipper Jones 8 4.00 10.00
6C Chipper Jones 9 4.00 10.00
7A Tony Gwynn 3 4.00 10.00
7B Tony Gwynn 7 4.00 10.00
7C Tony Gwynn 2 4.00 10.00
8A Barry Bonds 3 4.00 10.00
8B Barry Bonds 7 4.00 10.00
8C Barry Bonds 4 4.00 10.00
9A Jeff Bagwell 4 2.50 6.00
9B Jeff Bagwell 2 2.50 6.00
9C Jeff Bagwell 5 2.50 6.00
10A Juan Gonzalez 5 2.00 5.00
10B Juan Gonzalez 8 2.00 5.00
10C Juan Gonzalez 9 2.00 5.00
11A Alex Rodriguez 5 6.00 15.00
11B Alex Rodriguez 3 6.00 15.00
11C Alex Rodriguez 4 6.00 15.00
12A Kenny Lofton 3 1.50 4.00
12B Kenny Lofton 5 1.50 4.00
12C Kenny Lofton 4 1.50 4.00

1998 Donruss Elite Prime Numbers

Randomly inserted in packs, this 36-card set features three cards each of 12 top players in the league printed with three different numerical backgrounds (of which form a statistical benchmark when placed together). The total number of each card produced depended on the player's particular statistic. Print runs are included below in parentheses at the end of each card description.

1A Ken Griffey Jr. 2 (94) 20.00 50.00
1B Ken Griffey Jr. 9 (204) 10.00 25.00
1C Ken Griffey Jr. 4 (290) 8.00 20.00
2A Frank Thomas 4 (56) 15.00 40.00
2B Frank Thomas 5 (406) 4.00 10.00
2C Frank Thomas 6 (450) 4.00 10.00
3A Mark McGwire 3 (87) 40.00 100.00
3B Mark McGwire 8 (307) 15.00 40.00
3C Mark McGwire 7 (380) 15.00 40.00
4A Cal Ripken 5 (17) 150.00 400.00
4B Cal Ripken 1 (507) 12.50 30.00
4C Cal Ripken 7 (510) 12.50 30.00
5A Mike Piazza 5 (76) 20.00 50.00
5B Mike Piazza 7 (506) 6.00 15.00
5C Mike Piazza 6 (570) 6.00 15.00
6A Chipper Jones 4 (89) 12.50 30.00
6B Chipper Jones 8 (409) 4.00 10.00
6C Chipper Jones 9 (480) 4.00 10.00
7A Tony Gwynn 3 (72) 15.00 40.00
7B Tony Gwynn 7 (302) 6.00 15.00
7C Tony Gwynn 2 (370) 6.00 15.00
8A Barry Bonds 3 (74) 30.00 80.00
8B Barry Bonds 7 (304) 12.50 30.00
8C Barry Bonds 4 (370) 12.50 30.00
9A Jeff Bagwell 4 (25) 25.00 60.00
9B Jeff Bagwell 2 (405) 2.50 6.00
9C Jeff Bagwell 5 (420) 2.50 6.00
10A Juan Gonzalez 5 (89) 6.00 15.00
10B J.Gonzalez 8 (509) 2.00 5.00
10C J.Gonzalez 9 (580) 2.00 5.00
11A Alex Rodriguez 5 (34) 30.00 80.00
11B A.Rodriguez 3 (504) 6.00 15.00
11C A.Rodriguez 4 (530) 6.00 15.00
12A Kenny Lofton 3 (54) 8.00 20.00
12B Kenny Lofton 5 (304) 2.00 5.00
12C Kenny Lofton 4 (350) 2.00 5.00

1998 Donruss Elite Prime Numbers Die Cuts

Randomly inserted in packs, this 36-card set is a die-cut parallel version to the regular Donruss Elite Prime Numbers set. Print runs are included below in parentheses at the end of each card description. Cards printed in quantites of 10 or less are identified in the checklist but not priced below.

1A Ken Griffey Jr. 2 (200) 10.00 25.00
1B Ken Griffey Jr. 9 (90) 20.00 50.00
1C Ken Griffey Jr. 4 (4)
2A Frank Thomas 4 (400) 4.00 10.00
2B Frank Thomas 5 (50) 15.00 40.00
2C Frank Thomas 6 (6)
3A Mark McGwire 3 (300) 15.00 40.00
3B Mark McGwire 8 (80) 40.00 100.00
3C Mark McGwire 7 (7)
4A Cal Ripken 5 (500) 12.50 30.00
4B Cal Ripken 1 (10)
4C Cal Ripken 7 (7)
5A Mike Piazza 5 (500) 6.00 15.00
5B Mike Piazza 7 (70) 20.00 50.00
5C Mike Piazza 6 (6)
6A Chipper Jones 4 (400) 4.00 10.00
6B Chipper Jones 8 (80) 12.50 30.00
7A Tony Gwynn 3 (300) 6.00 15.00
7B Tony Gwynn 7 (70) 15.00 40.00
7C Tony Gwynn 2 (2)
8A Barry Bonds 3 (300) 12.50 30.00
8B Barry Bonds 7 (70) 30.00 80.00
8C Barry Bonds 4 (4)
9A Jeff Bagwell 4 (400) 2.50 6.00
9B Jeff Bagwell 2 (20) 30.00 80.00
9C Jeff Bagwell 5 (5)
10A J.Gonzalez 5 (500) 2.00 5.00
10B Juan Gonzalez 8 (80) 6.00 15.00
10C Juan Gonzalez 9 (9)
11A A.Rodriguez 5 (500) 6.00 15.00
11B Alex Rodriguez 3 (30) 40.00 100.00
11C Alex Rodriguez 4 (4)
12A Kenny Lofton 3 (300) 2.00 5.00
12B Kenny Lofton 5 (50) 8.00 20.00
12C Kenny Lofton 4 (4)

2001 Donruss Elite

This 200-card hobby only set was distributed in May, 2001 in five-card packs with a suggested retail price of $3.99 and features color photos of some of Baseball's finest players and hot rookies. The low series rookie cards are sequentially numbered to 1000 with the first 100 labeled "Turn of the Century." Cards 201-250 were issued as exchange coupons for unspecified rookies and prospects and randomly seeded into packs at a rate of 1:14. Specific players for each exchange card were announced on Donruss' website in late October, 2001 (and about 15 players were dropped and updated with new players about a month later). The deadline to redeem the coupons was originally 11/01/01 but it was extended to January 20th, 2002. Each coupon carried a cost of $5.99 to redeem. In April of 2002 representatives at Donruss-Playoff released explicit quantities for each of these exchange cards, of which ranged from as few as 377 to as many as 556. All of these cards are actually serial-numbered "XXX/1000" on back but were mailed out in non-sequential order, thus cards serial-numbered as high as 900/1000 etc are in existence but it doesn't mean that 900+ copies were distributed. When the January 20th deadline passed, according to representatives at Donruss-Playoff, the remaining cards were destroyed. Please see our checklist for specific quantities of each card produced.

COMP.SET w/o SP's (150) 10.00 25.00
COMMON CARD (1-150) .10 .30
COMMON (151-200) 3.00 8.00
COMMON CARD (201-250) 4.00 10.00
1 Alex Rodriguez .50 1.25
2 Barry Bonds .75 2.00
3 Cal Ripken 1.00 2.50
4 Chipper Jones .30 .75
5 Derek Jeter .75 2.00
6 Troy Glaus .10 .30
7 Frank Thomas .30 .75
8 Greg Maddux .50 1.25
9 Ivan Rodriguez .20 .50
10 Jeff Bagwell .20 .50
11 Jose Canseco .20 .50
12 Todd Helton .20 .50
13 Ken Griffey Jr. .50 1.25
14 Manny Ramirez Sox .20 .50
15 Mark McGwire .75 2.00
16 Mike Piazza .50 1.25
17 Nomar Garciaparra .50 1.25
18 Pedro Martinez .20 .50
19 Randy Johnson .30 .75
20 Rick Ankiel .10 .30
21 Rickey Henderson .30 .75
22 Roger Clemens .60 1.50
23 Sammy Sosa .30 .75
24 Tony Gwynn .40 1.00
25 Vladimir Guerrero .30 .75
26 Eric Davis .10 .30
27 Roberto Alomar .20 .50
28 Mark Mulder .10 .30
29 Pat Burrell .10 .30
30 Harold Baines .10 .30
31 Carlos Delgado .10 .30
32 J.D. Drew .10 .30
33 Jim Edmonds .10 .30
34 Darin Erstad .10 .30
35 Jason Giambi .10 .30
36 Tom Glavine .20 .50
37 Juan Gonzalez .10 .30
38 Mark Grace .20 .50
39 Shawn Green .10 .30
40 Tim Hudson .10 .30
41 Andruw Jones .20 .50
42 David Justice .10 .30
43 Jeff Kent .10 .30
44 Barry Larkin .20 .50
45 Pokey Reese .10 .30
46 Mike Mussina .20 .50
47 Hideo Nomo .30 .75
48 Rafael Palmeiro .20 .50
49 Adam Piatt .10 .30
50 Scott Rolen .20 .50
51 Gary Sheffield .10 .30
52 Bernie Williams .20 .50
53 Bob Abreu .10 .30
54 Edgardo Alfonzo .10 .30
55 Jermaine Clark RC .30 .75
56 Albert Belle .10 .30
57 Craig Biggio .20 .50
58 Andres Galarraga .10 .30
59 Edgar Martinez .20 .50
60 Fred McGriff .20 .50
61 Magglio Ordonez .10 .30
62 Jim Thome .20 .50
63 Matt Williams .10 .30
64 Kerry Wood .10 .30
65 Moises Alou .10 .30
66 Brady Anderson .10 .30
67 Garret Anderson .10 .30
68 Tony Armas Jr. .10 .30
69 Tony Batista .10 .30
70 Jose Cruz Jr. .10 .30
71 Carlos Beltran .10 .30
72 Adrian Beltre .10 .30
73 Kris Benson .10 .30
74 Lance Berkman .10 .30
75 Kevin Brown .10 .30
76 Jay Buhner .10 .30
77 Jeromy Burnitz .10 .30
78 Ken Caminiti .10 .30
79 Sean Casey .10 .30
80 Luis Castillo .10 .30
81 Eric Chavez .10 .30
82 Jeff Cirillo .10 .30
83 Bartolo Colon .10 .30
84 David Cone .10 .30
85 Freddy Garcia .10 .30
86 Johnny Damon .20 .50
87 Ray Durham .10 .30
88 Jermaine Dye .10 .30
89 Juan Encarnacion .10 .30
90 Terrence Long .10 .30
91 Carl Everett .10 .30
92 Steve Finley .10 .30
93 Cliff Floyd .10 .30
94 Brad Fullmer .10 .30
95 Brian Giles .10 .30
96 Luis Gonzalez .10 .30
97 Rusty Greer .10 .30
98 Jeffrey Hammonds .10 .30
99 Mike Hampton .10 .30
100 Orlando Hernandez .10 .30
101 Richard Hidalgo .10 .30
102 Geoff Jenkins .10 .30
103 Jacque Jones .10 .30
104 Brian Jordan .10 .30
105 Gabe Kapler .10 .30
106 Eric Karros .10 .30
107 Jason Kendall .10 .30
108 Adam Kennedy .10 .30
109 Byung-Hyun Kim .10 .30
110 Ryan Klesko .10 .30
111 Chuck Knoblauch .10 .30
112 Paul Konerko .10 .30
113 Carlos Lee .10 .30
114 Kenny Lofton .10 .30
115 Javy Lopez .10 .30
116 Tino Martinez .20 .50
117 Ruben Mateo .10 .30
118 Kevin Millwood .10 .30
119 Ben Molina .10 .30
120 Raul Mondesi .10 .30
121 Trot Nixon .10 .30
122 John Olerud .10 .30
123 Paul O'Neill .20 .50
124 Chan Ho Park .10 .30
125 Andy Pettitte .20 .50
126 Jorge Posada .20 .50
127 Mark Quinn .10 .30
128 Aramis Ramirez .10 .30
129 Mariano Rivera .30 .75
130 Tim Salmon .20 .50
131 Curt Schilling .10 .30
132 Richie Sexson .10 .30
133 John Smoltz .20 .50
134 J.T. Snow .10 .30
135 Jay Payton .10 .30
136 Shannon Stewart .10 .30
137 B.J. Surhoff .10 .30
138 Mike Sweeney .10 .30
139 Fernando Tatis .10 .30
140 Miguel Tejada .10 .30
141 Jason Varitek .30 .75
142 Greg Vaughn .10 .30
143 Mo Vaughn .10 .30
144 Robin Ventura UER .10 .30
Listed as playing for Yankees last 2 years, Also Bat and Throw information is wrong
145 Jose Vidro .10 .30
146 Omar Vizquel .20 .50
147 Larry Walker .10 .30
148 David Wells .10 .30
149 Rondell White .10 .30
150 Preston Wilson .10 .30
151 Brent Abernathy SP RC 3.00 8.00
152 Cory Aldridge SP RC 3.00 8.00
153 Gene Altman SP RC 3.00 8.00
154 Josh Beckett SP 4.00 10.00
155 Wilson Betemit SP RC 4.00 10.00
156 Albert Pujols SP RC 275.00 400.00
157 Joe Crede SP 4.00 10.00
158 Jack Cust SP 3.00 8.00
159 Ben Sheets SP 4.00 10.00
160 Alex Escobar SP 3.00 8.00
161 A. Hernandez SP RC 3.00 8.00
162 Pedro Feliz SP 3.00 8.00
163 Nate Frese SP RC 3.00 8.00
164 Carlos Garcia SP RC 3.00 8.00
165 Marcus Giles SP 3.00 8.00
166 Alexis Gomez SP RC 3.00 8.00
167 Jason Hart SP 3.00 8.00
168 Aubrey Huff SP 3.00 8.00
169 Cesar Izturis SP 3.00 8.00
170 Nick Johnson SP 3.00 8.00
171 Jack Wilson SP RC 4.00 10.00
172 B.Lawrence SP RC 3.00 8.00
173 C. Parker SP RC 3.00 8.00
174 Nick Maness SP RC 3.00 8.00
175 Jose Mieses SP RC 3.00 8.00
176 Greg Miller SP RC 3.00 8.00
177 Eric Munson SP 3.00 8.00
178 Xavier Nady SP 3.00 8.00
179 Blaine Neal SP RC 3.00 8.00
180 Abraham Nunez SP 3.00 8.00
181 Jose Ortiz SP 3.00 8.00
182 Jeremy Owens SP RC 3.00 8.00
183 Jay Gibbons SP RC 4.00 10.00
184 Corey Patterson SP 3.00 8.00
185 Carlos Pena SP 3.00 8.00
186 C.C. Sabathia SP 3.00 8.00
187 Timo Perez SP 3.00 8.00
188 A. Pettyjohn SP RC 3.00 8.00
189 D. Mendez SP RC 3.00 8.00
190 J. Melian SP RC 3.00 8.00
191 Wilkin Ruan SP RC 3.00 8.00
192 D. Sanchez SP RC 3.00 8.00
193 Alfonso Soriano SP 4.00 10.00
194 Rafael Soriano SP RC 3.00 8.00
195 Ichiro Suzuki SP RC 75.00 125.00
196 Billy Sylvester SP RC 3.00 8.00
197 Juan Uribe SP RC 4.00 10.00
198 T. Shinjo SP RC 4.00 10.00
199 C. Valderrama SP RC 3.00 8.00
200 Matt White SP RC 3.00 8.00
201 Adam Dunn/468 6.00 15.00
202 Joe Kennedy/465 XRC 6.00 15.00
203 Mike Rivera/427 XRC 4.00 10.00
204 Erick Almonte/401 XRC 4.00 10.00
205 Bran Duckworth EXCH 4.00 10.00
206 Victor Martinez/410 XRC 75.00 125.00
207 Rick Bauer/390 XRC 4.00 10.00
208 Jeff Deardorff/396 XRC 4.00 10.00
209 Antonio Perez/448 XRC 6.00 15.00
210 Bill Hall/404 XRC 15.00 40.00
211 D. Tankersley EXCH 4.00 10.00
212 Jeremy Affeldt/386 XRC 4.00 10.00
213 Junior Spivey/377 XRC 6.00 15.00
214 Casey Fossum/393 XRC 4.00 10.00
215 Brandon Lyon/402 XRC 4.00 10.00
216 Angel Santos/408 XRC 4.00 10.00
217 Cody Ransom/404 XRC 4.00 10.00
218 Jason Lane/424 XRC 6.00 15.00
219 David Williams/408 XRC 4.00 10.00
220 Alex Herrera/405 XRC 4.00 10.00
221 Ryan Drese/378 XRC 6.00 15.00
222 Travis Hafner/419 XRC 30.00 60.00
223 Bud Smith/468 XRC 4.00 10.00
224 Johnny Estrada/415 XRC 6.00 15.00
225 R. Rodriguez EXCH 4.00 10.00
226 Brandon Berger/428 XRC 4.00 10.00
227 Claudio Vargas/395 XRC 4.00 10.00
228 Luis Garcia/438 XRC 4.00 10.00
229 Marlon Byrd/452 XRC 4.00 10.00
230 Hee Seop Choi/479 XRC 6.00 15.00
231 Corky Miller/431 XRC 4.00 10.00
232 J. Duchscherer EXCH 4.00 10.00
233 T. Spooneybarger EXCH 4.00 10.00
234 Roy Oswalt/427 6.00 15.00
235 Willie Harris/418 XRC 4.00 10.00
236 Josh Towers/437 XRC 6.00 15.00
237 Juan A.Pena/400 XRC 4.00 10.00
238 A. Amezaga EXCH 4.00 10.00
239 Geronimo Gil/396 XRC 4.00 10.00
240 Juan Cruz/489 XRC 4.00 10.00
241 Ed Rogers/429 XRC 4.00 10.00
242 Joe Thurston/420 XRC 4.00 10.00
243 O.Hudson EXCH 6.00 15.00
244 John Buck/416 XRC 6.00 15.00
245 Martin Vargas/400 XRC 4.00 10.00
246 David Brous/399 XRC 4.00 10.00
247 D. Brazelton EXCH 4.00 10.00
248 Mark Prior/556 XRC 15.00 40.00
249 Angel Berroa/420 XRC 6.00 15.00
250 Mark Teixeira/543 XRC 20.00 50.00

2001 Donruss Elite Aspirations

Randomly inserted in packs at the rate of one in 62, this 200-card set is a parallel version of the base set printed on holo-foil board with red foil and red tint. Each card was sequentially numbered to the remaining number after subtracting the player's jersey number from 100. Cards with a print run of 25 or fewer are not priced due to market scarcity.

*1-150 PRINT RUN b/wn 81-100: 4X TO 10X
*1-150 PRINT RUN b/wn 66-80: 5X TO 12X
*1-150 PRINT RUN b/wn 51-65: 5X TO 12X
*1-150 PRINT RUN b/wn 36-50: 6X TO 15X
*1-150 PRINT RUN b/wn 26-35: 8X TO 20X
COMMON (151-200) p/r 81-100 1.50 4.00
MINOR 151-200 p/r 81-100 2.50 6.00
UNLISTED 151-200 p/r 81-100 6.00 15.00
MINOR 151-200 p/r 66-80 3.00 8.00
SEMISTARS 151-200 p/r 66-80 5.00 12.00
UNLISTED 151-200 p/r 66-80 8.00 20.00
MINOR 151-200 p/r 51-65 4.00 10.00
UNLISTED 151-200 p/r 51-65 10.00 25.00
COMMON (151-200) p/r 36-50 3.00 8.00
MINOR 151-200 p/r 36-50 5.00 12.00
SEMISTARS 151-200 p/r 36-50 8.00 20.00
UNLISTED 151-200 p/r 36-50 12.50 30.00
COMMON (151-200) p/r 26-35 4.00 10.00
MINOR 151-200 p/r 26-35 6.00 15.00
UNLISTED 151-200 p/r 26-35 15.00 40.00
UNLISTED 151-200 p/r 21-25 20.00 50.00
MINOR 151-200 p/r 16-20 10.00 25.00
RANDOM INSERTS IN PACKS
SEE BECKETT.COM FOR PRINT RUNS
PRINTS b/wn 1-15 TOO SCARCE TO PRICE
RC'S OF 25 OR LESS TOO SCARCE TO PRICE

2001 Donruss Elite Status

Randomly inserted in packs at the rate of one in 163, this 200-card set is a parallel version of the base set printed on holo-foil board with gold foil and gold tint. Each card is sequentially numbered to the player's jersey number. Cards issued to a stated print run of 25 or fewer are not priced due to market scarcity.

*1-150 PRINT RUN b/wn 81-100: 4X TO 10X
*1-150 PRINT RUN b/wn 66-80: 5X TO 12X
*1-150 PRINT RUN b/wn 51-65: 5X TO 12X
*1-150 PRINT RUN b/wn 36-50: 6X TO 15X
*1-150 PRINT RUN b/wn 26-35: 8X TO 20X
*1-150 PRINT RUN b/wn 21-25: 10X TO 25X
*1-150 PRINT RUN b/wn 16-20: 12.5X TO 30X
MINOR 151-200 p/r 81-100 2.50 6.00
COMMON (151-200) p/r 66-80 2.00 5.00
MINOR 151-200 p/r 66-80 3.00 8.00
UNLISTED 151-200 p/r 66-80 8.00 20.00
COMMON (151-200) p/r 51-65 2.50 6.00
MINOR 151-200 p/r 51-65 4.00 10.00
SEMISTARS 151-200 p/r 51-65 6.00 15.00
UNLISTED 151-200 p/r 51-65 10.00 25.00
MINOR 151-200 p/r 36-50 5.00 12.00
SEMISTARS 151-200 p/r 36-50 8.00 20.00
MINOR 151-200 p/r 21-25 8.00 20.00
UNLISTED 151-200 p/r 21-25 20.00 50.00
MINOR 151-200 p/r 16-20 10.00 25.00
SEMISTARS 151-200 p/r 16-20 15.00 40.00
UNLISTED 151-200 p/r 16-20 25.00 60.00
RANDOM INSERTS IN PACKS
SEE BECKETT.COM FOR PRINT RUNS
PRINTS b/wn 1-15 TOO SCARCE TO PRICE

2001 Donruss Elite Extra Edition Autographs

These certified autograph cards were made available as a compensation by Donruss-Playoff to collectors for autograph exchange cards that the manufacturer was unable to fulfill in the 2001 season. Each card is serial-numbered of 100 on front. Unlike most Donruss-Playoff autograph cards from 2001, the athletes signed the actual card rather than signing a sticker (of which was then affixed to the card at a later date). The cards first started to appear on the secondary market in April, 2002 but are catalogued as 2001 cards to avoid confusion for collectors looking to reference them.

234 Roy Oswalt 30.00 60.00
238 Alfredo Amezaga 6.00 15.00
241 Ed Rogers 6.00 15.00

2001 Donruss Elite Turn of the Century Autographs

Randomly inserted in packs, these 50 cards feature prospects who signed their cards for the Donruss Elite product. Each card had a stated print run of 100 sets though they are cumulatively serial-numbered to 1000 (only the first 100 numbered copies of each card Turn of the Century Autographs - the last 900 numbered copies of each card are basic Elite cards). Some players did not return their cards in time for inclusion in the product and these cards had an redemption deadline of May 1, 2003. Cards number 195 and 198 at first were not believed to exist, but subsequently were issued without autographs.

151 Brent Abernathy 6.00 15.00
152 Cory Aldridge 4.00 10.00
153 Gene Altman 4.00 10.00
154 Josh Beckett 40.00 80.00
155 Wilson Betemit 20.00 50.00
156 Albert Pujols 900.00 1200.00
157 Joe Crede 15.00 40.00
158 Jack Cust 6.00 15.00
159 Ben Sheets 15.00 40.00
160 Alex Escobar 6.00 15.00
161 Adrian Hernandez 4.00 10.00
162 Pedro Feliz 6.00 15.00
163 Nate Frese 6.00 15.00
164 Carlos Garcia 4.00 10.00
165 Marcus Giles 10.00 25.00
166 Alexis Gomez 4.00 10.00
167 Jason Hart 6.00 15.00
168 Aubrey Huff 10.00 25.00
169 Cesar Izturis 6.00 15.00
170 Nick Johnson 10.00 25.00
171 Jack Wilson 10.00 25.00
172 Brian Lawrence 6.00 15.00
173 Christian Parker 4.00 10.00
174 Nick Maness 6.00 15.00
175 Jose Mieses 6.00 15.00
176 Greg Miller 4.00 10.00
177 Eric Munson 6.00 15.00
178 Xavier Nady 15.00 40.00
179 Blaine Neal 4.00 10.00
180 Abraham Nunez 6.00 15.00
181 Jose Ortiz 6.00 15.00
182 Jeremy Owens 6.00 15.00
183 Jay Gibbons 10.00 25.00
184 Corey Patterson 6.00 15.00
185 Carlos Pena 6.00 15.00
186 C.C. Sabathia 10.00 25.00
187 Timo Perez 6.00 15.00
188 Adam Pettyjohn 4.00 10.00
189 Donaldo Mendez 4.00 10.00
190 Jackson Melian 4.00 10.00
191 Wilkin Ruan 6.00 15.00
192 Duaner Sanchez 4.00 10.00
193 Alfonso Soriano 15.00 40.00
194 Rafael Soriano 6.00 15.00
195 Ichiro Suzuki NO AU
196 Billy Sylvester 4.00 10.00
197 Juan Uribe 10.00 25.00
198 Tsuyoshi Shinjo NO AU
199 Carlos Valderrama 4.00 10.00
200 Matt White 6.00 15.00

2001 Donruss Elite Back 2 Back Jacks

Randomly inserted in packs, this double-sided 45-card set features color photos of one or two players with game-used bat pieces embedded in the cards. Cards with single players are sequentially numbered to 100 while those with doubles were numbered to 50. Exchange cards with a redemption deadline of May 1st, 2003 were seeded into packs for Eddie Mathews, Frank Thomas, Mathews/Glaus combo and F.Robinson/Thomas combo.

BB1 Ernie Banks SP/75 10.00 25.00
BB2 Ryne Sandberg SP/75 20.00 50.00
BB3 Babe Ruth 100.00 200.00
BB4 Lou Gehrig 75.00 150.00
BB5 Eddie Mathews 10.00 25.00
BB6 Troy Glaus SP/50 10.00 25.00
BB7 Don Mattingly SP/50 30.00 60.00
BB8 Todd Helton 10.00 25.00
BB9 Wade Boggs 10.00 25.00
BB10 Tony Gwynn 10.00 25.00
BB11 Robin Yount 10.00 25.00
BB12 Paul Molitor SP/50 10.00 25.00
BB13 Mike Schmidt SP/50 20.00 50.00
BB14 Scott Rolen SP/75 10.00 25.00
BB15 Reggie Jackson 10.00 25.00
BB16 Dave Winfield 6.00 15.00
BB17 J. Bench SP/50 15.00 40.00
BB18 Joe Morgan 6.00 15.00
BB19 B. Robinson SP/50 15.00 40.00
BB20 Cal Ripken 20.00 50.00
BB21 Ty Cobb 60.00 120.00
BB22 Al Kaline SP/50 15.00 40.00
BB23 F. Robinson SP/50 15.00 40.00
BB24 Frank Thomas 10.00 25.00
BB25 Roberto Clemente 50.00 100.00
BB26 V. Guerrero SP/50 15.00 40.00
BB27 H.Killebrew SP/50 15.00 40.00
BB28 Kirby Puckett 10.00 25.00
BB29 Yogi Berra SP/75 15.00 40.00
BB30 Phil Rizzuto SP/75 15.00 40.00
BB31 Ernie Banks 50.00 100.00
Ryne Sandberg
BB32 Babe Ruth 250.00 400.00
Lou Gehrig
BB33 Eddie Mathews 30.00 60.00
Troy Glaus
BB34 Don Mattingly 50.00 100.00
Todd Helton
BB35 Wade Boggs 40.00 80.00
Tony Gwynn
BB36 Robin Yount 30.00 60.00
Paul Molitor

BB37 Mike Schmidt 50.00 100.00
Scott Rolen
BB38 Reggie Jackson 15.00 40.00
Dave Winfield
BB39 Johnny Bench 30.00 60.00
Joe Morgan
BB40 Brooks Robinson 60.00 120.00
Cal Ripken
BB41 Ty Cobb 100.00 200.00
Al Kaline
BB42 Frank Robinson 30.00 60.00
Frank Thomas
BB43 Roberto Clemente 60.00 120.00
Vladimir Guerrero
BB44 Harmon Killebrew 30.00 60.00
Kirby Puckett
BB45 Yogi Berra
Phil Rizzuto SP/25

2001 Donruss Elite Back 2 Back Jacks Autograph

Randomly inserted in packs, this 16-card set is a partial parallel autographed version of the regular insert set. Almost every card in the set packed out as an exchange card with a redemption deadline of May 1st, 2003. Only Johnny Bench, Al Kaline and Harmon Killebrew signed cards in time to be seeded directly into packs. Cards with a print run of 25 copies are not priced due to scarcity.

BB1 Ernie Banks/25
BB2 Ryne Sandberg/25
BB6 Troy Glaus/50 40.00 80.00
BB7 Don Mattingly/50 100.00 200.00
BB12 Paul Molitor/50 30.00 60.00
BB13 Mike Schmidt/50 60.00 120.00
BB14 Scott Rolen/25
BB17 Johnny Bench/50 60.00 120.00
BB19 Brooks Robinson/50 40.00 80.00
BB22 Al Kaline/50 60.00 120.00
BB23 Frank Robinson/50 40.00 80.00
BB26 Vladimir Guerrero/50 60.00 120.00
BB27 Harmon Killebrew/50 60.00 120.00
BB29 Yogi Berra/25
BB30 Phil Rizzuto/25
BB45 Yogi Berra
Phil Rizzuto/25

2001 Donruss Elite Passing the Torch

Randomly inserted in packs, this 24-card set features color action photos of legendary players and up-and-coming phenoms printed on holo-foil board. Cards with single players were sequentially numbered to 1000 while those with two players were numbered to 500.

PT1 Stan Musial 5.00 12.00
PT2 Tony Gwynn 4.00 10.00
PT3 Willie Mays 6.00 15.00
PT4 Barry Bonds 8.00 20.00
PT5 Mike Schmidt 6.00 15.00
PT6 Scott Rolen 2.00 5.00
PT7 Cal Ripken 10.00 25.00
PT8 Alex Rodriguez 5.00 12.00
PT9 Hank Aaron 6.00 15.00
PT10 Andruw Jones 2.00 5.00
PT11 Nolan Ryan 8.00 20.00
PT12 Pedro Martinez 2.00 5.00
PT13 Wade Boggs 2.00 5.00
PT14 Nomar Garciaparra 5.00 12.00
PT15 Don Mattingly 6.00 15.00
PT16 Todd Helton 2.00 5.00
PT17 Stan Musial 8.00 20.00
Tony Gwynn
PT18 Willie Mays 10.00 25.00
Barry Bonds
PT19 Mike Schmidt 8.00 20.00
Scott Rolen
PT20 Cal Ripken 15.00 40.00
Alex Rodriguez
PT21 Hank Aaron 10.00 25.00
Andruw Jones
PT22 Nolan Ryan 12.50 30.00
Pedro Martinez
PT23 Wade Boggs 8.00 20.00
Nomar Garciaparra
PT24 Don Mattingly 8.00 20.00
Todd Helton

2001 Donruss Elite Passing the Torch Autographs

Randomly inserted in packs, this 22-card set is a partial autographed parallel version of the regular insert set printed on double-sided holo-foil board. Cards with single players were sequentially numbered to 100 while those with dual players were numbered to 50. Nearly all of these cards were not available in time for insertion into packs and collectors had until May 1st, 2003 to redeem them. Wade Boggs, Todd Helton, Stan Musial and Nolan Ryan were the only players to return their cards in

time for them to be seeded into packs. Cards PT22, PT23 and PT24 were actually 2001 Donruss Elite football exchange cards that were erroneously placed into baseball packs. To honor their commitment to collectors that pulled these cards - the manufacturer created three additional dual autograph baseball cards. These cards are tagged in our checklist with an "FB" status to indicate their origin. The set contains two separate cards numbered PT22 because of this same football snafu - whereby it's theorized that the baseball was originally intended to be complete at 22 cards. The three additional football exchange cards expanded the set to 25 cards and also created two separate PT22 cards.

PT1 Stan Musial 60.00 120.00
PT2 Tony Gwynn 40.00 80.00
PT3 Willie Mays 175.00 300.00
PT4 Barry Bonds 175.00 300.00
PT5 Mike Schmidt 60.00 120.00
PT6 Scott Rolen 30.00 60.00
PT7 Cal Ripken 125.00 200.00
PT8 Alex Rodriguez 125.00 200.00
PT9 Hank Aaron 175.00 300.00
PT10 Andruw Jones 30.00 60.00
PT11 Nolan Ryan 75.00 150.00
PT12 P.Martinez EXCH 75.00 150.00
PT13 Wade Boggs 30.00 60.00
PT14 N.Garciaparra EXCH 60.00 120.00
PT15 Don Mattingly 60.00 120.00
PT16 Todd Helton 30.00 60.00
PT17 Stan Musial 125.00 200.00
Tony Gwynn
PT18 Willie Mays 900.00 1200.00
Barry Bonds
PT19 Mike Schmidt 125.00 200.00
Scott Rolen
PT20 Cal Ripken 500.00 800.00
Alex Rodriguez
PT21 Hank Aaron 250.00 400.00
Andruw Jones
PT22A Nolan Ryan 400.00 600.00
Roger Clemens FB
PT22B Nolan Ryan 250.00 400.00
Pedro Martinez BB
PT23 Wade Boggs 175.00 300.00
Nomar Garciaparra FB
PT24 Don Mattingly 150.00 250.00
Todd Helton FB

2001 Donruss Elite Primary Colors Red

Randomly inserted in packs, this 40-card set features color action player images with the initials "PC" on a red background. The cards are sequentially numbered to 975. A die-cut holo-foil parallel version of this set was produced and sequentially numbered to 25. A Blue parallel version numbered to 200 and a Yellow one numbered to 25 were also printed. Holo-foil, die-cut parallel versions of both of these sets were produced with the Blue sequentially numbered to 50 and the Yellow to 75.

COMPLETE SET (40) 200.00 400.00
*BLUE: .6X TO 1.5X BASIC RED
BLUE PRINT RUN 200 SERIAL #'d SETS
*BLUE DIE CUT: 1.25X TO 3X BASIC RED
BLUE DC PRINT RUN 50 SERIAL #'d SETS
*RED DIE CUT: 2X TO 5X BASIC RED
RED DC PRINT RUN 25 SERIAL #'d SETS
*YELLOW: 2X TO 5X BASIC RED
YELLOW PRINT RUN 25 SERIAL #'d SETS
*YELLOW DIE CUT: 1X TO 2.5X BASIC RED
YELLOW DC PRINT RUN 75 SERIAL #'d SETS
RANDOM INSERTS IN PACKS
PC1 Alex Rodriguez 6.00 15.00
PC2 Barry Bonds 8.00 20.00
PC3 Cal Ripken 12.50 30.00
PC4 Chipper Jones 4.00 10.00
PC5 Derek Jeter 10.00 25.00
PC6 Troy Glaus 2.00 5.00
PC7 Frank Thomas 4.00 10.00
PC8 Greg Maddux 6.00 15.00
PC9 Ivan Rodriguez 2.50 6.00
PC10 Jeff Bagwell 2.50 6.00
PC11 Todd Helton 2.50 6.00
PC12 Ken Griffey Jr. 6.00 15.00
PC13 Manny Ramirez Sox 2.50 6.00
PC14 Mark McGwire 10.00 25.00
PC15 Mike Piazza 6.00 15.00
PC16 Nomar Garciaparra 6.00 15.00
PC17 Pedro Martinez 2.50 6.00
PC18 Randy Johnson 4.00 10.00
PC19 Rick Ankiel 2.00 5.00
PC20 Roger Clemens 8.00 20.00
PC21 Sammy Sosa 4.00 10.00
PC22 Tony Gwynn 5.00 12.00
PC23 Vladimir Guerrero 4.00 10.00
PC24 Carlos Delgado 2.00 5.00
PC25 Jason Giambi 2.00 5.00
PC26 Andruw Jones 2.50 6.00
PC27 Bernie Williams 2.50 6.00
PC28 Roberto Alomar 2.50 6.00
PC29 Shawn Green 2.00 5.00
PC30 Barry Larkin 2.50 6.00
PC31 Scott Rolen 2.50 6.00
PC32 Gary Sheffield 2.00 5.00
PC33 Rafael Palmeiro 2.50 6.00
PC34 Albert Belle 2.00 5.00
PC35 Magglio Ordonez 2.00 5.00
PC36 Jim Thome 2.50 6.00
PC37 Jim Edmonds 2.00 5.00
PC38 Darin Erstad 2.00 5.00
PC39 Kris Benson 2.00 5.00
PC40 Sean Casey 2.00 5.00

2001 Donruss Elite Prime Numbers

Randomly inserted in packs at the rate of one in 84, this 30-card set features color action images of 10 stellar performers. Each player has three cards highlighted by a single digit from his high average. The cards are sequentially numbered to the base total of the digit displayed.

PN1A Alex Rodriguez/300 8.00 20.00
PN1B Alex Rodriguez/50 20.00 50.00
PN1C Alex Rodriguez/8
PN2A Ken Griffey Jr./400 8.00 20.00
PN2B Ken Griffey Jr./30 25.00 60.00
PN2C Ken Griffey Jr./8
PN3A Mark McGwire/500 12.50 30.00
PN3B Mark McGwire/50 30.00 80.00
PN3C Mark McGwire/4
PN4A Cal Ripken/400 15.00 40.00
PN4B Cal Ripken/10
PN4C Cal Ripken/7
PN5A Derek Jeter/300 12.50 30.00
PN5B Derek Jeter/20 60.00 150.00
PN5C Derek Jeter/2
PN6A Mike Piazza/300 8.00 20.00
PN6B Mike Piazza/60 15.00 40.00
PN6C Mike Piazza/2
PN7A N.Garciaparra/300 8.00 20.00
PN7B N.Garciaparra/70 12.50 30.00
PN7C Nomar Garciaparra/2
PN8A Sammy Sosa/300 6.00 15.00
PN8B Sammy Sosa/80 10.00 25.00
PN8C Sammy Sosa/6
PN9A V.Guerrero/300 5.00 12.00
PN9B V.Guerrero/40 12.50 30.00
PN9C Vladimir Guerrero/5
PN10A Tony Gwynn/300 6.00 15.00
PN10B Tony Gwynn/90 8.00 20.00
PN10C Tony Gwynn/4

2001 Donruss Elite Throwback Threads

Randomly inserted into packs, this 45-card set features past and present greats with swatches of game-worn jerseys displayed on the cards. Cards with single players are sequentially numbered to 100 while those with doubles are numbered to 50. Exchange cards with a redemption deadline of May 1st, 2003 were seeded into packs for Ernie Banks, Lou Brock, Pedro Martinez, Ozzie Smith and Frank Thomas. In addition, exchange cards packed out for the following dual-player cards: Brock/Ozzie, Banks/Sandberg, F.Robinson/Thomas and Clemens/Pedro. Pricing is not available for cards with a print run of 25 copies due to scarcity.

TT1 Stan Musial SP/75 30.00 60.00
TT2 Tony Gwynn SP/75 15.00 40.00
TT3 Willie McCovey 6.00 15.00
TT4 Barry Bonds 20.00 50.00
TT5 Babe Ruth 175.00 300.00
TT6 Lou Gehrig 150.00 250.00
TT7 Mike Schmidt SP/75 20.00 50.00
TT8 Scott Rolen 10.00 25.00
TT9 H.Killebrew SP/75 15.00 40.00
TT10 Kirby Puckett 10.00 25.00
TT11 Al Kaline SP/75 15.00 40.00
TT12 Eddie Mathews 15.00 40.00
TT13 Hank Aaron SP/75 40.00 80.00
TT14 Andruw Jones SP/50 15.00 40.00
TT15 Lou Brock 10.00 25.00
TT16 Ozzie Smith 10.00 25.00
TT17 Ernie Banks SP/75
TT18 Ryne Sandberg 20.00 50.00
TT19 Roberto Clemente 50.00 100.00
TT20 V. Guerrero SP/50 15.00 40.00
TT21 F.Robinson SP/50 15.00 40.00
TT22 Frank Thomas SP/50 15.00 40.00
TT23 B.Robinson SP/50 15.00 40.00
TT24 Cal Ripken 20.00 50.00
TT25 Roger Clemens 10.00 25.00
TT26 Pedro Martinez 10.00 25.00
TT27 Reggie Jackson 10.00 25.00
TT28 Dave Winfield 6.00 15.00
TT29 Don Mattingly SP/50 30.00 60.00
TT30 Todd Helton 10.00 25.00
TT32 Willie McCovey 50.00 100.00
Barry Bonds
TT33 Babe Ruth 350.00 600.00
Lou Gehrig
TT34 Mike Schmidt
Scott Rolen SP/25
TT35 Harmon Killebrew 40.00 80.00
Kirby Puckett
TT36 Al Kaline 50.00 100.00
Eddie Mathews
TT37 Hank Aaron 60.00 120.00
Andruw Jones
TT38 Lou Brock 40.00 80.00
Ozzie Smith
TT39 Ernie Banks
Ryne Sandberg SP/25
TT40 Roberto Clemente 60.00 120.00
Vladimir Guerrero
TT41 Frank Robinson 30.00 60.00
Frank Thomas
TT42 Brooks Robinson 50.00 100.00
Cal Ripken
TT43 Roger Clemens 40.00 80.00
Pedro Martinez
TT44 Reggie Jackson 15.00 40.00
Dave Winfield
TT45 Don Mattingly 40.00 80.00
Todd Helton

2001 Donruss Elite Throwback Threads Autographs

Randomly inserted in packs, this 15-card set is a partial parallel autographed version of the regular insert set. Exchange cards with a May 1st, 2003 redemption deadline were seeded into packs for almost the entire set. Only Al Kaline, Harmon Killebrew and Stan Musial managed to return their cards in time for packout. 2001 Donruss Elite football exchange cards were erroneously seeded into baseball packs for cards TT21 and TT22. Those cards have an "FB" tag added to their listing to denote their origins. The quantity for Ernie Banks signed cards was never revealed by the manufacturer.

TT1 Stan Musial/25
TT2 Tony Gwynn/25
TT7 Mike Schmidt/25
TT9 Harmon Killebrew/25
TT11 Al Kaline/25
TT13 Hank Aaron/25
TT14 Andruw Jones/50 40.00 80.00
TT17 Ernie Banks/25
TT20 Vladimir Guerrero/50 50.00 100.00
TT21 Frank Robinson/50 FB 40.00 80.00
TT22 Frank Thomas/50 FB 50.00 100.00
TT23 Brooks Robinson/50 40.00 80.00
TT29 Don Mattingly/50 75.00 150.00
TT31 Stan Musial
Tony Gwynn/25
TT34 Mike Schmidt
Scott Rolen/25
TT39 Ernie Banks
Ryne Sandberg/25

2001 Donruss Elite Title Waves

Randomly inserted in packs, this 30-card set features the game's most decorated performers highlighted in five different title-winning categories and sequentially numbered to the year they won the title.

COMPLETE SET (30) 125.00 250.00
*HOLO: 1.5X TO 4X BASIC WAVES
HOLO-FOIL PRINT RUN 100 SERIAL #'d SETS
RANDOM INSERTS IN PACKS
TW1 Tony Gwynn/1994 3.00 8.00
TW2 Todd Helton/2000 1.50 4.00
TW3 N.Garciaparra/2000 4.00 10.00
TW4 Frank Thomas/1997 2.50 6.00
TW5 Alex Rodriguez/1996 4.00 10.00
TW6 Jeff Bagwell/1994 1.50 4.00
TW7 Mark McGwire/1998 6.00 15.00
TW8 Sammy Sosa/2000 2.50 6.00
TW9 Ken Griffey Jr./1997 4.00 10.00
TW10 Albert Belle/1995 1.25 3.00
TW11 Barry Bonds/1993 6.00 15.00
TW12 Jose Canseco/1991 1.50 4.00
TW13 M.Ramirez Sox/1999 1.50 4.00
TW14 Sammy Sosa/1998 2.50 6.00
TW15 A.Galarraga/1996 1.25 3.00
TW16 Todd Helton/2000 1.50 4.00
TW17 Ken Griffey Jr./1997 4.00 10.00
TW18 Jeff Bagwell/1994 1.50 4.00
TW19 Mike Piazza/1995 4.00 10.00
TW20 A.Rodriguez/1995 4.00 10.00
TW21 Jason Giambi/2000 1.25 3.00
TW22 I.Rodriguez/1999 1.50 4.00
TW23 Greg Maddux/1997 4.00 10.00
TW24 P.Martinez/1994 1.50 4.00
TW25 Derek Jeter/2000 6.00 15.00
TW26 B.Williams/1998 1.50 4.00
TW27 R.Clemens/1999 5.00 12.00
TW28 Chipper Jones/1995 2.50 6.00
TW29 M.McGwire/1990 6.00 15.00
TW30 Cal Ripken/1983 8.00 20.00

2002 Donruss Elite Samples

Issued one per sealed copy of Beckett Baseball Card Monthly issue number 207, this is a partial parallel to the 2002 Donruss Elite Set. Only the first 100 cards of this set were issued in this format.

*SAMPLES: 1.5X TO 4X BASIC CARDS
ONE PER SEALED BBCM 207
*GOLD: 4X TO 10X BASIC SAMPLES
GOLD 10% OF PRESS RUN

2002 Donruss Elite

This 268-card set highlights baseball's premier performers. The standard-size set is made up of 100 veteran players, 50 STAR veteran subset cards and 50 rookie players. The fronts feature full color action shots. The STAR subset cards (101-150) were seeded into packs at a rate of 1:10. The rookie cards (151-200) are sequentially numbered to 1500 but only 1350 of each were actually produced. The first 150 of each rookie card is die-cut and labeled "Turn of the Century" with varying quantities of some autographed. These cards were issued in 5 card packs with a $3.99 SRP which came 20 packs to a box and 20 boxes to a case. Cards 256, 263 and 267-271 were never released.

COMP.LO SET w/o SP's (100) 8.00 20.00
COMMON CARD (1-100) .10 .30
COMMON CARD (101-150) .75 2.00
COMMON CARD (151-200) 2.00 5.00
COMMON CARD (201-275) 2.00 5.00
1 Vladimir Guerrero .30 .75
2 Bernie Williams .20 .50
3 Ichiro Suzuki .60 1.50
4 Roger Clemens .60 1.50
5 Greg Maddux .50 1.25
6 Fred McGriff .20 .50
7 Jermaine Dye .10 .30
8 Ken Griffey Jr. .50 1.25
9 Todd Helton .20 .50
10 Torii Hunter .10 .30
11 Pat Burrell .10 .30
12 Chipper Jones .30 .75
13 Ivan Rodriguez .20 .50
14 Roy Oswalt .10 .30
15 Shannon Stewart .10 .30
16 Magglio Ordonez .10 .30
17 Lance Berkman .10 .30
18 Mark Mulder .10 .30
19 Al Leiter .10 .30
20 Sammy Sosa .30 .75
21 Scott Rolen .20 .50
22 Aramis Ramirez .10 .30
23 Alfonso Soriano .10 .30
24 Phil Nevin .10 .30
25 Barry Bonds .75 2.00
26 Joe Mays .10 .30
27 Jeff Kent .10 .30
28 Mark Quinn .10 .30
29 Adrian Beltre .10 .30
30 Freddy Garcia .10 .30
31 Pedro Martinez .20 .50
32 Darryl Kile .10 .30
33 Mike Cameron .10 .30
34 Frank Catalanotto .10 .30
35 Jose Vidro .10 .30
36 Jim Thome .20 .50
37 Javy Lopez .10 .30
38 Paul Konerko .10 .30
39 Jeff Bagwell .20 .50
40 Curt Schilling .10 .30
41 Miguel Tejada .10 .30
42 Jim Edmonds .10 .30
43 Ellis Burks .10 .30
44 Mark Grace .20 .50
45 Robb Nen .10 .30
46 Jeff Conine .10 .30
47 Derek Jeter .75 2.00
48 Mike Lowell .10 .30
49 Javier Vazquez .10 .30
50 Manny Ramirez .20 .50
51 Bartolo Colon .10 .30
52 Carlos Beltran .10 .30
53 Tim Hudson .10 .30
54 Rafael Palmeiro .20 .50
55 Jimmy Rollins .10 .30
56 Andruw Jones .20 .50
57 Orlando Cabrera .10 .30
58 Dean Palmer .10 .30
59 Bret Boone .10 .30
60 Carlos Febles .10 .30
61 Ben Grieve .10 .30
62 Richie Sexson .10 .30
63 Alex Rodriguez .50 1.25
64 Juan Pierre .10 .30
65 Bobby Higginson .10 .30
66 Barry Zito .10 .30
67 Raul Mondesi .10 .30
68 Albert Pujols .60 1.50
69 Omar Vizquel .20 .50
70 Bobby Abreu .10 .30
71 Corey Koskie .10 .30
72 Tom Glavine .20 .50
73 Paul LoDuca .10 .30
74 Terrence Long .10 .30
75 Matt Morris .10 .30
76 Andy Pettitte .20 .50
77 Rich Aurilia .10 .30
78 Todd Walker .10 .30
79 John Olerud UER .10 .30
Career Header stats are those for a pitcher
80 Mike Sweeney .10 .30
81 Ray Durham .10 .30
82 Fernando Vina .10 .30
83 Nomar Garciaparra .50 1.25
84 Mariano Rivera .30 .75
85 Mike Piazza .50 1.25
86 Mark Buehrle .10 .30
87 Adam Dunn .10 .30
88 Luis Gonzalez .10 .30
89 Richard Hidalgo .10 .30
90 Brad Radke .10 .30
91 Russ Ortiz .10 .30
92 Brian Giles .10 .30
93 Billy Wagner .10 .30
94 Cliff Floyd .10 .30
95 Eric Milton .10 .30
96 Bud Smith .10 .30
97 Wade Miller .10 .30
98 Jon Lieber .10 .30
99 Derrek Lee .20 .50
100 Jose Cruz Jr. .10 .30
101 Dmitri Young STAR .75 2.00
102 Mo Vaughn STAR .75 2.00
103 Tino Martinez STAR 1.25 3.00
104 Larry Walker STAR .75 2.00
105 Chuck Knoblauch STAR .75 2.00
106 Troy Glaus STAR .75 2.00
107 Jason Giambi STAR .75 2.00
108 Travis Fryman STAR .75 2.00
109 Josh Beckett STAR .75 2.00
110 Edgar Martinez STAR 1.25 3.00
111 Tim Salmon STAR 1.25 3.00
112 C.C. Sabathia STAR .75 2.00
113 Randy Johnson STAR 2.00 5.00
114 Juan Gonzalez STAR .75 2.00
115 Carlos Delgado STAR .75 2.00
116 Hideo Nomo STAR 2.00 5.00
117 Kerry Wood STAR .75 2.00
118 Brian Jordan STAR .75 2.00
119 Carlos Pena STAR .75 2.00
120 Roger Cedeno STAR .75 2.00
121 Chan Ho Park STAR .75 2.00
122 Rafael Furcal STAR .75 2.00
123 Frank Thomas STAR 2.00 5.00
124 Mike Mussina STAR 1.25 3.00
125 Rickey Henderson STAR 2.00 5.00
126 Sean Casey STAR .75 2.00
127 Barry Larkin STAR 1.25 3.00
128 Kazuhiro Sasaki STAR .75 2.00
129 Moises Alou STAR .75 2.00
130 Jeff Cirillo STAR .75 2.00
131 Jason Kendall STAR .75 2.00
132 Gary Sheffield STAR .75 2.00
133 Ryan Klesko STAR .75 2.00
134 Kevin Brown STAR .75 2.00
135 Darin Erstad STAR .75 2.00
136 Roberto Alomar STAR 1.25 3.00
137 Brad Fullmer STAR .75 2.00
138 Eric Chavez STAR .75 2.00
139 Ben Sheets STAR .75 2.00
140 Trot Nixon STAR .75 2.00
141 Garret Anderson STAR .75 2.00
142 Shawn Green STAR .75 2.00
143 Troy Percival STAR .75 2.00
144 Craig Biggio STAR 1.25 3.00
145 Jorge Posada STAR 1.25 3.00
146 J.D. Drew STAR .75 2.00
147 Johnny Damon STAR 1.25 3.00
148 Jeromy Burnitz STAR .75 2.00
149 Robin Ventura STAR .75 2.00
150 Aaron Sele STAR .75 2.00
151 Cam Esslinger ROO RC 2.00 5.00
152 Ben Howard ROO RC 2.00 5.00
153 Brandon Backe ROO RC 3.00 8.00
154 Jorge De La Rosa ROO RC 2.00 5.00
155 Austin Kearns ROO 2.00 5.00
156 Carlos Zambrano ROO 2.00 5.00
157 Kyle Kane ROO RC 2.00 5.00
158 So Taguchi ROO RC 3.00 8.00
159 Brian Mallette ROO RC 2.00 5.00
160 Brett Jodie ROO 2.00 5.00
161 Elio Serrano ROO RC 2.00 5.00
162 Joe Thurston ROO 2.00 5.00
163 Kevin Olsen ROO 2.00 5.00
164 Rodrigo Rosario ROO RC 2.00 5.00
165 Matt Guerrier ROO 2.00 5.00
166 And. Machado ROO RC 2.00 5.00
167 Bert Snow ROO 2.00 5.00
168 Franklyn German ROO RC 2.00 5.00
169 Brandon Claussen ROO 2.00 5.00
170 Jason Romano ROO 2.00 5.00
171 Jorge Padilla ROO RC 2.00 5.00
172 Jose Cueto ROO 2.00 5.00
173 Allan Simpson ROO RC 2.00 5.00
174 Doug Devore ROO RC 2.00 5.00
175 Justin Duchscherer ROO 2.00 5.00
176 Josh Pearce ROO 2.00 5.00
177 Steve Bechler ROO RC 2.00 5.00
178 Josh Phelps ROO 2.00 5.00
179 Juan Diaz ROO 2.00 5.00
180 Victor Alvarez ROO RC 2.00 5.00
181 Ramon Vazquez ROO 2.00 5.00
182 Mike Rivera ROO 2.00 5.00
183 Kazuhisa Ishii ROO RC 3.00 8.00
184 Henry Mateo ROO 2.00 5.00
185 Travis Hughes ROO RC 2.00 5.00
186 Zach Day ROO 2.00 5.00
187 Brad Voyles ROO 2.00 5.00
188 Sean Douglass ROO 2.00 5.00
189 Nick Neugebauer ROO 2.00 5.00
190 Tom Shearn ROO RC 2.00 5.00
191 Eric Cyr ROO 2.00 5.00
192 Adam Johnson ROO 2.00 5.00
193 Michael Cuddyer ROO 2.00 5.00
194 Erik Bedard ROO 2.00 5.00
195 Mark Ellis ROO 2.00 5.00
196 Carlos Hernandez ROO 2.00 5.00
197 Deivis Santos ROO 2.00 5.00
198 Morgan Ensberg ROO 2.00 5.00
199 Ryan Jamison ROO 2.00 5.00
200 Cody Ransom ROO 2.00 5.00
201 Chris Snelling ROO RC 2.00 5.00
202 Satoru Komiyama ROO RC 2.00 5.00

203 Jas. Simontacchi ROO RC 2.00 5.00
204 Tim Kalita ROO RC 2.00 5.00
205 Run. Hernandez ROO RC 2.00 5.00
206 Kirk Saarloos ROO RC 2.00 5.00
207 Aaron Cook ROO RC 2.00 5.00
208 Luis Ugueto ROO RC 2.00 5.00
209 Gustavo Chacin ROO RC 3.00 8.00
210 Francis Beltran ROO RC 2.00 5.00
211 Takahito Nomura ROO RC 2.00 5.00
212 Oliver Perez ROO RC 4.00 10.00
213 Miguel Asencio ROO RC 2.00 5.00
214 Rene Reyes ROO RC 2.00 5.00
215 Jeff Baker ROO RC 3.00 8.00
216 Jon Adkins ROO RC 2.00 5.00
217 Carlos Rivera ROO RC 2.00 5.00
218 Corey Thurman ROO RC 2.00 5.00
219 Earl Snyder ROO RC 2.00 5.00
220 Felix Escalona ROO RC 2.00 5.00
221 Jeremy Guthrie ROO RC 2.00 5.00
222 Josh Hancock ROO RC 2.50 6.00
223 Ben Kozlowski ROO RC 2.00 5.00
224 Eric Good ROO RC 2.00 5.00
225 Eric Junge ROO RC 2.00 5.00
226 Andy Pratt ROO RC 2.00 5.00
227 Matt Thornton ROO RC 2.00 5.00
228 Jorge Sosa ROO RC 3.00 8.00
229 Mike Smith ROO RC 2.00 5.00
230 Mitch Wylie ROO RC 2.00 5.00
231 John Ennis ROO RC 2.00 5.00
232 Reed Johnson ROO RC 3.00 8.00
233 Joe Borchard ROO 2.00 5.00
234 Ron Calloway ROO RC 2.00 5.00
235 Brian Tallet ROO RC 2.00 5.00
236 Chris Baker ROO RC 2.00 5.00
237 Cliff Lee ROO RC 5.00 12.00
238 Matt Childers ROO RC 2.00 5.00
239 Freddy Sanchez ROO RC 4.00 10.00
240 Chone Figgins ROO RC 3.00 8.00
241 Kevin Cash ROO RC 2.00 5.00
242 Josh Bard ROO RC 2.00 5.00
243 Jer. Robertson ROO RC 2.00 5.00
244 Jeremy Hill ROO RC 2.00 5.00
245 Shane Nance ROO RC 2.00 5.00
246 Wes Obermueller ROO RC 2.00 5.00
247 Trey Hodges ROO RC 2.00 5.00
248 Eric Eckenstahler ROO RC 2.00 5.00
249 Jim Rushford ROO RC 2.00 5.00
250 Jose Castillo ROO RC 6.00 15.00
251 Garrett Atkins ROO RC 6.00 15.00
252 Alexis Rios ROO RC 35.00 60.00
253 Ryan Church ROO RC 3.00 8.00
254 Jimmy Gobble ROO RC 2.00 5.00
255 Corwin Malone ROO RC 2.00 5.00
256 Nic Jackson ROO RC 2.00 5.00
257 Tommy Whiteman ROO RC 2.00 5.00
258 Mario Ramos ROO RC 2.00 5.00
260 Rob Bowen ROO RC 2.00 5.00
261 Josh Wilson ROO RC 2.00 5.00
262 Tim Hummel ROO RC 2.00 5.00
264 Gerald Laird ROO RC 3.00 8.00
265 Vinny Chulk ROO RC 2.00 5.00
266 Jesus Medrano ROO RC 2.00 5.00
272 Adam LaRoche ROO RC 20.00 50.00
273 Adam Morrissey ROO RC 2.00 5.00
274 Henri Stanley ROO RC 2.00 5.00
275 Walter Young ROO RC 3.00 8.00

2002 Donruss Elite Aspirations

Randomly inserted into packs, this 200-card set is a parallel to the base set. The cards are standard-size and die-cut on holo-foil board with blue tint and blue foil stamping sequentially numbered to the featured player's jersey number. Due to market scarcity, cards with a print run of less than 25 are not priced.

*1-100 PRINT RUN b/wn 26-35 8X TO 20X
*1-100 PRINT RUN b/wn 36-50 6X TO 15X
*1-100 PRINT RUN b/wn 51-65 5X TO 12X
*1-100 PRINT RUN b/wn 66-80 5X TO 12X
*101-150 PRINT RUN b/wn 26-35 1.25X TO 3X
*101-150 PRINT RUN b/wn 36-50 1X TO 2.5X
*101-150 PRINT RUN b/wn 51-65 .75X TO 2X
UNLISTED 151-200 p/r 81-99 6.00 15.00
COMMON (151-200) p/r 66-80 3.00 8.00
SEMIS 151-200 p/r 66-80 5.00 12.00
UNLISTED 151-200 p/r 66-80 8.00 20.00
COMMON (151-200) p/r 51-65 4.00 10.00
SEMIS 151-200 p/r 51-65 6.00 15.00
UNLISTED 151-200 p/r 51-65 10.00 25.00
COMMON (151-200) p/r 36-50 5.00 12.00
SEMIS 151-200 p/r 36-50 5.00 20.00
UNLISTED 151-200 p/r 36-50 12.50 30.00
COMMON (151-200) p/r 26-35 6.00 15.00
SEMIS 151-200 p/r 26-35 10.00 25.00
UNLISTED 151-200 p/r 26-35 15.00 40.00
RANDOM INSERTS IN PACKS
SEE BECKETT.COM FOR PRINT RUNS
NO PRICING ON QUANTITIES OF 25 OR LESS

2002 Donruss Elite Status

Randomly inserted into packs, this 200-card set is a parallel to the base set. The cards are die-cut on holo-foil board with platinum tint and platinum foil stamping sequentially numbered to the remaining number out of 100 as reduced from the Donruss Elite Aspirations parallel (of which was serial numbered to the featured player's jersey number). We have listed the stated print run next to the player's name in our checklist. Cards with a stated print run of 25 or fewer are not printed due to market scarcity.

*1-100 PRINT RUN b/wn 36-50 6X TO 15X
*1-100 PRINT RUN b/wn 51-65 5X TO 12X
*1-100 PRINT RUN b/wn 66-80 5X TO 12X
*1-100 PRINT RUN b/wn 81-98 4X TO 10X
*101-150 PRINT RUN b/wn 36-50 1X TO 2.5X
*101-150 PRINT RUN b/wn 51-65 .75X TO 2X
*101-150 PRINT RUN b/wn 66-80 .75X TO 2X
*101-150 PRINT RUN b/wn 81-99 .6X TO 1.5X
COMMON (151-200) p/r 81-99 2.50 6.00
SEMIS 151-200 p/r 81-99 4.00 10.00
UNLISTED 151-200 p/r 81-99 6.00 15.00
COMMON (151-200) p/r 66-80 3.00 8.00
SEMIS 151-200 p/r 66-80 5.00 12.00
UNLISTED 151-200 p/r 66-80 8.00 20.00
COMMON (151-200) p/r 51-65 4.00 10.00
SEMIS 151-200 p/r 51-65 6.00 15.00
UNLISTED 151-200 p/r 51-65 10.00 25.00
COMMON (151-200) p/r 36-50 5.00 12.00
SEMIS 151-200 p/r 36-50 8.00 20.00
UNLISTED 151-200 p/r 36-50 12.50 30.00
COMMON (151-200) p/r 26-35 6.00 15.00
SEMIS 151-200 p/r 26-35 10.00 25.00
UNLISTED 151-200 p/r 26-35 15.00 40.00
RANDOM INSERTS IN PACKS
SEE BECKETT.COM FOR PRINT RUNS
NO PRICING ON QUANTITIES OF 25 OR LESS

2002 Donruss Elite Turn of the Century

Randomly inserted in packs of Elite and Donruss the Rookies, these 71 cards partially parallel the prospect cards in 2002 Donruss Elite. Cards checklisted between 151-200 were distributed in Elite packs and 201-275 in Donruss the Rookies packs. The Turn of the Century parallels are easily identified from basic issue cards by their rounded corners. It's important to note that Turn of the Centruy cards were cumulatively serial-numbered, intermingling the basic Elite cards and the Turn of the Century Autograph cards. For example, card 201 Chris Snelling features serial numbering to 1000. The first 100 numbered copies were devoted to the Turn of the Century sets with Snelling signing cards "1 of 1000" through "50 of 1000". The last 900 numbered cards are his basic Elite Rookie Card. Some players signed all of their Turn of the Century cards and others signed none. We have notated the stated print run next to the player's name in our checklist and cards with a print run of less than 25 are not priced due to market scarcity.

*TOC p/r 100-150: .6X TO 1.5X BASIC
*TOC p/r 50-75: .75X TO 2X BASIC
151-200 RANDOM INSERTS IN ELITE PACKS
201-275 RANDOM IN DON.ROOKIES UPDATE
CARDS DISPLAY CUMULATIVE PRINT RUNS
SEE BECKETT.COM FOR PRINT RUNS
PRINT RUNS B/WN 25-150 COPIES PER
151-200 DIE CUTS ARE 1ST 150 #'d OF 1500
201-275 DIE CUTS ARE 1ST 100 #'d OF 1000
SKIP-NUMBERED 72-CARD SET
NO PRICING ON QTY OF 25 OR LESS
252 Alexis Rios/100 50.00 100.00

2002 Donruss Elite Turn of the Century Autographs

Randomly inserted into packs of Elite and Donruss the Rookies, these 95 cards basically parallel the prospect cards in 2002 Donruss Elite. Cards 151-200 were distributed in Elite packs and cards 201-275 in Donruss the Rookies. These cards are all signed by the featured player and we have notated the stated print run information next to the player's name in our checklist. Please note, the cards are serial numbered cumulatively out of 1,500 for cards 151-200 and 1,000 for cards 201-275 - intermingling the basic issue Elite set, the Turn of the Century parallel die cuts and the Turn of the Century Autographs. Actual print runs for the autographs are listed below.

151 Cam Esslinger/150 6.00 15.00
152 Ben Howard/150 6.00 15.00
153 Brandon Backe/150 10.00 25.00
154 Jorge De La Rosa/100 6.00 15.00
155 Austin Kearns/150 6.00 15.00
156 Carlos Zambrano/100 10.00 25.00
157 Kyle Kane/100 6.00 15.00
158 So Taguchi/125 10.00 25.00
159 Brian Mallette/100 6.00 15.00
160 Brett Jodie/100 6.00 15.00
161 Elio Serrano/150 6.00 15.00
162 Tom Shearn/150 6.00 15.00
163 Kevin Olsen/150 6.00 15.00
164 Rodrigo Rosario/150 6.00 15.00
165 Matt Guerrier/100 6.00 15.00
166 Anderson Machado/150 6.00 15.00
167 Bert Snow/150 6.00 15.00
168 Franklyn German/100 6.00 15.00
169 Brandon Claussen/100 6.00 15.00
170 Jason Romano/150 6.00 15.00
171 Jorge Padilla/100 6.00 15.00
172 Jose Cueto/100 6.00 15.00
173 Allan Simpson/150 6.00 15.00
174 Doug Devore/150 6.00 15.00
175 Justin Duchscherer/150 12.50 30.00
176 Josh Pearce/100 6.00 15.00
177 Steve Bechler/100 6.00 15.00
178 Josh Phelps/100 6.00 15.00
179 Juan Diaz/150 6.00 15.00
180 Victor Alvarez/100 6.00 15.00
181 Ramon Vazquez/150 6.00 15.00
182 Michael Rivera/100 6.00 15.00
183 Kazuhisa Ishii/25
184 Henry Mateo/100 6.00 15.00
185 Travis Hughes/150 6.00 15.00
186 Zach Day/100 6.00 15.00
187 Brad Voyles/150 6.00 15.00
188 Sean Douglass/150 6.00 15.00
189 Nick Neugebauer/50 10.00 25.00
190 Tom Shearn/150 6.00 15.00
191 Eric Cyr/150 6.00 15.00
192 Adam Johnson/25
193 Michael Cuddyer/100 6.00 15.00
194 Erik Bedard/150 6.00 15.00
195 Mark Ellis/125 6.00 15.00
197 Deivis Santos/150 6.00 15.00
198 Morgan Ensberg/100 6.00 15.00
199 Ryan Jamison/150 6.00 15.00
201 Chris Snelling/50 15.00 40.00
202 Satoru Komiyama/25
204 Tim Kalita/25
206 Kirk Saarloos/50 10.00 25.00
208 Luis Ugueto/25
210 Francis Beltran/25
211 Takahito Nomura/25
212 Oliver Perez/25
214 Rene Reyes/25
215 Jeff Baker/100 15.00 40.00
216 Jon Adkins/100 6.00 15.00
217 Carlos Rivera/100 6.00 15.00
218 Corey Thurman/25
219 Earl Snyder/25
220 Felix Escalona/25
221 Jeremy Guthrie/100 10.00 25.00
223 Ben Kozlowski/100 6.00 15.00
224 Eric Good/100 6.00 15.00
225 Eric Junge/25
226 Andy Pratt/25
227 Matt Thornton/25
231 John Ennis/25
232 Reed Johnson/25
233 Joe Borchard/25
235 Brian Tallet/25
236 Chris Baker/25
237 Cliff Lee/25
238 Matt Childers/25
240 Chone Figgins/100 15.00 40.00
241 Kevin Cash/100 6.00 15.00
242 Josh Bard/25
245 Shane Nance/25
247 Trey Hodges/100 6.00 15.00
251 Garrett Atkins/100 20.00 50.00
253 Ryan Church/100 15.00 40.00
254 Jimmy Gobble/100 6.00 15.00
255 Corwin Malone/100 6.00 15.00
258 Tommy Whiteman/100 6.00 15.00
259 Mario Ramos/100 6.00 15.00
260 Rob Bowen/100 6.00 15.00
261 Josh Wilson/100 6.00 15.00
262 Tim Hummel/100 6.00 15.00
264 Gerald Laird/100 10.00 25.00
266 Jesus Medrano/100 6.00 15.00
272 Adam LaRoche/100 60.00 120.00
273 Adam Morrissey/100 6.00 15.00
274 Henri Stanley/100 6.00 15.00

2002 Donruss Elite All-Star Salutes

Randomly inserted into packs, this 25-card insert set spotlights on the most heralded players. The fronts of the standard-size cards feature full color action shots set on metalized film board with foil and is sequentially numbered to the year the featured player shined in the All-Star Game.

COMPLETE SET (25) 75.00 150.00
*CENTURY: 1.25X TO 3X BASIC AS SALUTE
CENTURY PRINT RUN 100 SERIAL #'d SETS
1 Ichiro Suzuki/2001 5.00 12.00
2 Tony Gwynn/2001 3.00 8.00
3 Magglio Ordonez/2001 1.50 4.00
4 Cal Ripken/2001 8.00 20.00
5 Roger Clemens/1998 5.00 12.00
6 Kazuhiro Sasaki/2001 1.50 4.00
7 Freddy Garcia/2001 1.50 4.00
8 Luis Gonzalez/2001 1.50 4.00
9 Lance Berkman/2001 1.50 4.00
10 Derek Jeter/2000 6.00 15.00
11 Chipper Jones/2000 2.50 6.00
12 Randy Johnson/2000 2.50 6.00
13 Andruw Jones/2000 1.50 4.00
14 Pedro Martinez/1999 1.50 4.00
15 Jim Thome/1999 1.50 4.00
16 Rafael Palmeiro/1999 1.50 4.00
17 Barry Larkin/1999 1.50 4.00
18 Ivan Rodriguez/1998 1.50 4.00
19 Omar Vizquel/1998 1.50 4.00
20 Edgar Martinez/1997 1.50 4.00
21 Larry Walker/1997 1.50 4.00
22 Javy Lopez/1997 1.50 4.00
23 Mariano Rivera/1997 2.50 6.00
24 Frank Thomas/1995 2.50 6.00
25 Greg Maddux/1994 4.00 10.00

2002 Donruss Elite Back 2 Back Jacks

Randomly inserted into pack, this 30-card insert set showcases both retired and present-day stars. The standard-size fronts are full color action shots that are featured with one or two swatches of game-used bats. Cards featuring one player have a stated print run of 150 sets while cards featuring two players have a stated print run of 75 sets.

1 Ivan Rodriguez 15.00 40.00
Alex Rodriguez
2 Kirby Puckett 20.00 50.00
Dave Winfield
3 Ted Williams 50.00 100.00
Nomar Garciaparra
4 Jeff Bagwell 20.00 50.00
Craig Biggio
5 Eddie Murray 50.00 100.00
Cal Ripken
6 Andruw Jones 20.00 50.00
Chipper Jones
7 Roberto Clemente 60.00 120.00
Willie Stargell
8 Lou Gehrig 100.00 200.00
Don Mattingly
9 Larry Walker 20.00 50.00
Todd Helton
10 Manny Ramirez 20.00 50.00
Trot Nixon
11 Ivan Rodriguez 10.00 25.00
12 Alex Rodriguez 10.00 25.00
13 Kirby Puckett 15.00 40.00
14 Dave Winfield 10.00 25.00
15 Ted Williams 50.00 100.00
16 Nomar Garciaparra 10.00 25.00
17 Jeff Bagwell 10.00 25.00
18 Craig Biggio 10.00 25.00
19 Eddie Murray 15.00 40.00
20 Cal Ripken 20.00 50.00
21 Andruw Jones 10.00 25.00
22 Chipper Jones 10.00 25.00
23 Roberto Clemente 50.00 100.00
24 Willie Stargell 10.00 25.00
25 Lou Gehrig 75.00 150.00
26 Don Mattingly 15.00 40.00
27 Larry Walker 6.00 15.00
28 Todd Helton 10.00 25.00
29 Manny Ramirez 10.00 25.00
30 Trot Nixon 6.00 15.00

2002 Donruss Elite Back to the Future

Randomly inserted into packs, this 22-card insert set matches both current and future stars on the fronts and backs respectively. The standard-size card fronts/backs feature full color action shots on metalized film board. 500 serial-numbered copies of each dual-player card were produced and 1000 serial-numbered copies of each single-player card were produced. Card number 6 was originally intended to feature Cardinals rookie So Taguchi paired up with Jim Edmonds and card number 20 was to feature Taguchi by himself, but both cards were pulled from the set before production was finalized, thus this set is complete at 22 cards. Cards featuring one player had a stated print run of 1000 sets and cards featuring two players had a stated print run of 500 sets.

1 Scott Rolen 2.50 6.00
Marlon Byrd
2 Joe Crede 1.50 4.00
Frank Thomas
3 Lance Berkman 2.50 6.00
Jeff Bagwell
4 Marcus Giles 2.50 6.00
Chipper Jones
5 Shawn Green 2.00 5.00
Paul LoDuca
7 Kerry Wood 2.00 5.00
Juan Cruz
8 Vladimir Guerrero 2.50 6.00
Orlando Cabrera
9 Scott Rolen 1.50 4.00
10 Marlon Byrd 1.50 4.00
11 Frank Thomas 2.00 5.00
12 Joe Crede 1.50 4.00
13 Jeff Bagwell 1.50 4.00
14 Lance Berkman 1.50 4.00
15 Chipper Jones 2.00 5.00
16 Marcus Giles 1.50 4.00
17 Shawn Green 1.50 4.00
18 Paul LoDuca 1.50 4.00
19 Jim Edmonds 1.50 4.00
21 Kerry Wood 1.50 4.00
22 Juan Cruz 1.50 4.00
23 Vladimir Guerrero 2.00 5.00
24 Orlando Cabrera 1.50 4.00

2002 Donruss Elite Back to the Future Threads

Randomly inserted into packs, this 24-card insert set is a parallel to Donruss Elite Back to the Future. It matches both current and future stars on the fronts and backs respectively. The standard-size card fronts/backs feature full color action shots on metalized film board. The fronts differ by offering one or two swatches of game-worn jerseys. Autograph exchange cards for the Edmonds/Taguchi dual card and So Taguchi's stand alone card were seeded into packs. Please note that only Taguchi was contracted to sign the Edmonds/Taguchi combo card. Both cards had a redemption deadline of October 10th, 2003. Cards featuring one player had a stated print run of 100 sets and cards featuring two players have a stated print run of 50 sets.

1 Scott Rolen Jsy 15.00 40.00
Marlon Byrd Jsy
2 Frank Thomas Jsy 6.00 15.00
Joe Crede Hat
3 Jeff Bagwell Jsy 15.00 40.00
Lance Berkman Jsy
4 Chipper Jones Jsy 15.00 40.00
Marcus Giles Jsy
5 Shawn Green Jsy 10.00 25.00
Paul LoDuca Jsy
6 So Taguchi Jsy AU 20.00 50.00
Jim Edmonds Jsy
7 Kerry Wood Jsy 10.00 25.00
Juan Cruz Jsy
8 Vladimir Guerrero Jsy 15.00 40.00
Orlando Cabrera Jsy
9 Scott Rolen 10.00 25.00
10 Marlon Byrd 6.00 15.00
11 Frank Thomas 15.00 40.00
12 Joe Crede Shoes 6.00 15.00
13 Jeff Bagwell 10.00 25.00
14 Lance Berkman 6.00 15.00
15 Chipper Jones 15.00 40.00
16 Marcus Giles 6.00 15.00
17 Shawn Green 6.00 15.00
18 Paul LoDuca 6.00 15.00
19 Jim Edmonds 6.00 15.00
20 So Taguchi AU 15.00 40.00
21 Kerry Wood 6.00 15.00
22 Juan Cruz 6.00 15.00
23 Vladimir Guerrero 15.00 40.00
24 Orlando Cabrera 6.00 15.00

2002 Donruss Elite Career Best

Randomly inserted into packs, this 40-card insert set spotlights on players who established career statistical highs in 2001. Each card is serial numbered to a specific statistical achievement and the cards were randomly seeded into packs. The standard-size card fronts feature color action shots on metalized film board with silver holo-foil stamping. Cards with a stated print run of less than 25 copies are not priced due to market scarcity.

1 Albert Pujols OPS/1013 5.00 12.00
2 Alex Rodriguez HR/52 10.00 25.00
3 Alex Rodriguez RBI/135 8.00 20.00
4 Andruw Jones RBI/104 3.00 8.00
5 Barry Bonds HR/73 15.00 40.00
6 Barry Bonds OPS/1379 6.00 15.00
7 Barry Bonds BB/177 12.50 30.00
8 C.C. Sabathia K/171 3.00 8.00
9 Carlos Beltran OPS/876 1.50 4.00
10 Chipper Jones BA/330 3.00 8.00
11 Derek Jeter SB/900 6.00 15.00
12 Eric Chavez RBI/114 3.00 8.00
13 Frank Catalanotto BA/330 2.00 5.00
14 Ichiro Suzuki OPS/838 5.00 12.00
15 Ichiro Suzuki RUN/127 10.00 25.00
16 Ichiro Suzuki 3B/8
17 J.D. Drew HR/27 12.50 30.00
18 J.D. Drew OPS/1027 1.50 4.00
19 Jason Giambi SLG/660 1.50 4.00
20 Jim Thome HR/49 12.50 30.00
21 Jim Thome SLG/624 1.50 4.00
22 Jorge Posada RBI/95 6.00 15.00
23 Jose Cruz Jr. SLG/856 1.50 4.00
24 Kazuhiro Sasaki SV/45 12.50 30.00
25 Kerry Wood ERA/336 2.00 5.00
26 Lance Berkman OPS/1050 1.50 4.00
27 Magglio Ordonez OB/382 2.00 5.00
28 Mark Mulder ERA/345 2.00 5.00
29 Pat Burrell HR/27 12.50 30.00
30 Pat Burrell SLG/469 2.00 5.00
31 Randy Johnson K/372 3.00 8.00
32 Randy Johnson WIN/21
33 Richie Sexson SLG/547 1.50 4.00
34 Roberto Alomar OPS/956 1.50 4.00
35 Sammy Sosa RBI/160 5.00 12.00
36 Sammy Sosa OPS/1174 2.50 6.00
37 Shawn Green RBI/125 3.00 8.00
38 Tsuyoshi Shinjo RUN/10
39 Trot Nixon HIT/150 3.00 8.00
40 Troy Glaus RBI/108 3.00 8.00

2002 Donruss Elite Passing the Torch

Randomly inserted into packs, this 24-card insert set presents baseball legends and rising stars on double-sided holo-foil board. The front/back of these standard-size cards feature color photos of the players. 500 serial-numbered copies of each dual-player card were produced. 1000 serial-numbered copies of single player card were produced.

COMPLETE SET (24) 125.00 250.00
1 Fergie Jenkins 3.00 8.00
Mark Prior
2 Nolan Ryan 12.50 30.00
Roy Oswalt
3 Ozzie Smith 6.00 15.00
J.D. Drew
4 George Brett 10.00 25.00
Carlos Beltran
5 Kirby Puckett 4.00 10.00
Michael Cuddyer
6 Johnny Bench 4.00 10.00
Adam Dunn
7 Duke Snider 4.00 10.00
Paul LoDuca
8 Tony Gwynn 6.00 15.00
Xavier Nady
9 Fergie Jenkins 2.00 5.00
10 Mark Prior 2.00 5.00
11 Nolan Ryan 8.00 20.00
12 Roy Oswalt 2.00 5.00
13 Ozzie Smith 5.00 12.00
14 J.D. Drew 2.00 5.00
15 George Brett 8.00 20.00
16 Carlos Beltran 2.00 5.00
17 Kirby Puckett 3.00 8.00
18 Michael Cuddyer 2.00 5.00
19 Johnny Bench 3.00 8.00
20 Adam Dunn 2.00 5.00
21 Duke Snider 2.00 5.00
22 Paul LoDuca 2.00 5.00
23 Tony Gwynn 4.00 10.00
24 Xavier Nady 2.00 5.00

2002 Donruss Elite Passing the Torch Autographs

Randomly inserted into packs, this 24-card autograph set is a parallel to the Donruss Elite Passing the Torch insert set. It presents baseball legends and rising stars on double-sided holo-foil board. The front/back of these standard-size cards also feature color photos of the players, but differ by using color highlight overlays. We have notated the stated print runs next to the player's name in our checklist.

1 Fergie Jenkins 30.00 60.00
Mark Prior/50
2 Nolan Ryan 100.00 200.00
Roy Oswalt/50
3 Ozzie Smith 60.00 120.00
J.D. Drew/50
4 George Brett
Carlos Beltran/25
5 Kirby Puckett 60.00 120.00
Michael Cuddyer/50
6 Johnny Bench 50.00 100.00
Adam Dunn/50
7 Duke Snider 50.00 100.00
Paul LoDuca/50
8 Tony Gwynn 50.00 100.00
Xavier Nady/50
9 Fergie Jenkins/50 20.00 50.00
10 Mark Prior/100 10.00 25.00
11 Nolan Ryan/100 60.00 120.00
12 Roy Oswalt/100 10.00 25.00
13 Ozzie Smith/25
14 J.D. Drew/100 10.00 25.00
15 George Brett/25
16 Carlos Beltran/100 10.00 25.00
17 Kirby Puckett/25
18 Michael Cuddyer/100 10.00 25.00
19 Johnny Bench/100 30.00 60.00
20 Adam Dunn/50 30.00 60.00
21 Duke Snider/100 15.00 40.00
22 Paul LoDuca/100 10.00 25.00
23 Tony Gwynn/100 30.00 60.00
24 Xavier Nady/100 10.00 25.00

2002 Donruss Elite Recollection Autographs

Randomly inserted into packs, these 23 cards featured signed copies of the player's 2001 Donruss Elite card. We have notated the stated print run next to the player's name and cards with a stated print run of 25 or less are not priced due to market scarcity.

1 Jeremy Affeldt 01/25
2 Alfredo Amezaga 01/50 8.00 20.00

3 Angel Berroa 01/25
4 Dewon Brazelton 01/25
5 John Buck 01/25
6 Marlon Byrd 01/25
7 Juan Cruz 01/25
8 Brandon Duckworth 01/10
9 Brandon Duckworth 01/15
10 Casey Fossum 01/25
11 Luis Garcia 01/25
12 Tony Gwynn 01/10
13 Bill Hall 01/25
14 Orlando Hudson 01/50 8.00 20.00
15 Ryan Klesko 01/5
16 Jason Lane 01/24
17 Corky Miller 01/25
18 Roy Oswalt 01/25
19 Antonio Perez 01/50 8.00 20.00
20 Mark Prior 01/25
21 Mike Rivera 01/50 8.00 20.00
22 Mark Teixeira 01/25
23 Claudio Vargas 01/50 8.00 20.00
24 Martin Vargas 01/50 8.00 20.00

2002 Donruss Elite Throwback Threads

Randomly inserted into packs, this 64-card insert set offers standard-size cards that display one or two swatches of game-used jerseys from retired legends or current stars. The card front/back features a white border background with color action shots. Card number 28 (intended to be a Rickey Henderson Red Sox card) does not exist in unsigned form. The legendary speedster signed all 100 copies produced and this card can be referenced in the Throwback Threads Autographs parallel set. Cards featuring one player have a stated print run of 100 sets while cards featuring two players have a stated print run of 50 sets.

1 Ted Williams 50.00 100.00
Manny Ramirez
2 Carlton Fisk 15.00 40.00
Mike Piazza
3 Bo Jackson 40.00 80.00
George Brett
4 Curt Schilling 20.00 50.00
Randy Johnson
5 Don Mattingly 150.00 250.00
Lou Gehrig
6 Bernie Williams 20.00 50.00
Dave Winfield
7 Rickey Henderson 20.00 50.00
Rickey Henderson
8 Robin Yount 20.00 50.00
Paul Molitor
9 Stan Musial 40.00 80.00
J.D. Drew
10 Andre Dawson 30.00 60.00
Ryne Sandberg
11 Babe Ruth 250.00 400.00
Reggie Jackson
12 Brooks Robinson 50.00 100.00
Cal Ripken
13 Ted Williams 50.00 100.00
Nomar Garciaparra
14 Jackie Robinson 40.00 80.00
Shawn Green
15 Cal Ripken 50.00 100.00
Tony Gwynn
16 Ted Williams 40.00 80.00
17 Manny Ramirez 10.00 25.00
18 Carlton Fisk Red Sox 15.00 40.00
19 Mike Piazza 10.00 25.00
20 Bo Jackson 15.00 40.00
21 George Brett 15.00 40.00
22 Curt Schilling 6.00 15.00
23 Randy Johnson 10.00 25.00
24 Don Mattingly 15.00 40.00
25 Lou Gehrig 100.00 200.00
26 Bernie Williams 10.00 25.00
27 Dave Winfield 10.00 25.00
29 Rickey Henderson Mariners 10.00 25.00
30 Robin Yount 15.00 40.00
31 Paul Molitor 10.00 25.00
32 Stan Musial 30.00 60.00
33 J.D. Drew 6.00 15.00
34 Andre Dawson 10.00 25.00
35 Ryne Sandberg 20.00 50.00
36 Babe Ruth 175.00 300.00
37 Reggie Jackson 15.00 40.00
38 Brooks Robinson 15.00 40.00
39 Cal Ripken Running 40.00 80.00
40 Nomar Garciaparra
41 Jackie Robinson 40.00 80.00
42 Shawn Green 6.00 15.00
43 Pedro Martinez Grey 10.00 25.00
44 Nolan Ryan Astros 30.00 60.00
45 Kazuhiro Sasaki 6.00 15.00
46 Tony Gwynn 15.00 40.00
47 Carlton Fisk White Sox 15.00 40.00
48 Cal Ripken Batting 40.00 80.00
49 Rod Carew Angels 15.00 40.00
50 Nolan Ryan Rangers 30.00 60.00
51 Alex Rodriguez 10.00 25.00
52 Greg Maddux 10.00 25.00
53 Pedro Martinez White 10.00 25.00
54 Rickey Henderson Padres 10.00 25.00
55 Rod Carew Twins 15.00 40.00
56 Roberto Clemente 50.00 100.00
57 Hideo Nomo 10.00 25.00
58 Rickey Henderson Mets 10.00 25.00
59 Dave Parker 10.00 25.00
60 Eddie Mathews 15.00 40.00
61 Eddie Murray 15.00 40.00
62 Nolan Ryan Angels 30.00 60.00
63 Tom Seaver 15.00 40.00
64 Roger Clemens 15.00 40.00
65 Rickey Henderson A's 10.00 25.00

2002 Donruss Elite Throwback Threads Autographs

Randomly inserted in packs, these cards partially parallel the Throwback Threads insert set. Other than the Rickey Henderson card, all these cards have stated print runs of 25 or less and we have notated that information in our checklist. Also, due to market scarcity, no pricing is provided for these cards.

17 Manny Ramirez/10
18 Carlton Fisk Red Sox/15
20 Bo Jackson/10
21 George Brett/5
22 Curt Schilling/10
24 Don Mattingly/20
26 Bernie Williams/5
27 Dave Winfield/10
28 R.Henderson/100 75.00 150.00
30 Robin Yount/10
31 Paul Molitor/15
32 Stan Musial/10
33 J.D. Drew/25
34 Andre Dawson/15
35 Ryne Sandberg/20
37 Reggie Jackson/10
43 Pedro Martinez/10
44 Nolan Ryan Astros/10
46 Tony Gwynn/10
47 Carlton Fisk White Sox/10
49 Rod Carew Angels/10
50 Nolan Ryan Rangers/10
51 Alex Rodriguez/10
52 Greg Maddux/10
55 Rod Carew Twins/10
59 Dave Parker/25
61 Eddie Murray/10
62 Nolan Ryan Angels/10
63 Tom Seaver/15

2003 Donruss Elite

This 200 card set was released in June, 2003. The first 180 cards consist of veterans while the final 20 cards are either rookies or leading prospects. This product was issued in five card packs which came 20 packs to a box and 20 boxes to a case with an $5 SRP. The final 20 cards consist of rookies and leading prospects, which were randomly inserted into packs and printed to a stated print run of 1750 serial numbered sets.

COMP.SET w/o SP's (180) 8.00 20.00
COMMON CARD (1-180) .10 .30
COMMON CARD (181-200) 1.50 4.00
1 Darin Erstad .10 .30
2 David Eckstein .10 .30
3 Garret Anderson .10 .30
4 Jarrod Washburn .10 .30
5 Tim Salmon .20 .50
6 Troy Glaus .10 .30
7 Marty Cordova .10 .30
8 Melvin Mora .10 .30
9 Rodrigo Lopez .10 .30
10 Tony Batista .10 .30
11 Derek Lowe .10 .30
12 Johnny Damon .20 .50
13 Manny Ramirez .20 .50
14 Nomar Garciaparra .50 1.25
15 Pedro Martinez .20 .50
16 Shea Hillenbrand .10 .30
17 Carlos Lee .10 .30
18 Joe Crede .10 .30
19 Frank Thomas .30 .75
20 Magglio Ordonez .10 .30
21 Mark Buehrle .10 .30
22 Paul Konerko .10 .30
23 C.C. Sabathia .10 .30
24 Ellis Burks .10 .30
25 Omar Vizquel .20 .50
26 Brian Tallet .10 .30
27 Bobby Higginson .10 .30
28 Carlos Pena .10 .30
29 Mark Redman .10 .30
30 Steve Sparks .10 .30
31 Carlos Beltran .10 .30
32 Joe Randa .10 .30
33 Mike Sweeney .10 .30
34 Raul Ibanez .10 .30
35 Runelvys Hernandez .10 .30
36 Brad Radke .10 .30
37 Corey Koskie .10 .30
38 Cristian Guzman .10 .30
39 David Ortiz .30 .75
40 Doug Mientkiewicz .10 .30
41 Jacque Jones .10 .30
42 Torii Hunter .10 .30
43 Alfonso Soriano .10 .30
44 Andy Pettitte .20 .50
45 Bernie Williams .20 .50
46 David Wells .10 .30
47 Derek Jeter .75 2.00
48 Jason Giambi .10 .30
49 Jeff Weaver .10 .30
50 Jorge Posada .20 .50
51 Mike Mussina .20 .50
52 Roger Clemens .60 1.50
53 Barry Zito .10 .30
54 Eric Chavez .10 .30
55 Jermaine Dye .10 .30
56 Mark Mulder .10 .30
57 Miguel Tejada .10 .30
58 Tim Hudson .10 .30
59 Bret Boone .10 .30
60 Chris Snelling .10 .30
61 Edgar Martinez .20 .50
62 Freddy Garcia .10 .30
63 Ichiro Suzuki .60 1.50
64 Jamie Moyer .10 .30
65 John Olerud .10 .30
66 Kazuhiro Sasaki .10 .30
67 Aubrey Huff .10 .30
68 Joe Kennedy .10 .30
69 Paul Wilson .10 .30
70 Alex Rodriguez .50 1.25
71 Chan Ho Park .10 .30
72 Hank Blalock .10 .30
73 Juan Gonzalez .10 .30
74 Kevin Mench .10 .30
75 Rafael Palmeiro .20 .50
76 Carlos Delgado .10 .30
77 Eric Hinske .10 .30
78 Josh Phelps .10 .30
79 Roy Halladay .10 .30
80 Shannon Stewart .10 .30
81 Vernon Wells .10 .30
82 Curt Schilling .10 .30
83 Junior Spivey .10 .30
84 Luis Gonzalez .10 .30
85 Mark Grace .20 .50
86 Randy Johnson .30 .75
87 Steve Finley .10 .30
88 Andruw Jones .20 .50
89 Chipper Jones .30 .75
90 Gary Sheffield .10 .30
91 Greg Maddux .50 1.25
92 John Smoltz .20 .50
93 Corey Patterson .10 .30
94 Kerry Wood .10 .30
95 Mark Prior .20 .50
96 Moises Alou .10 .30
97 Sammy Sosa .30 .75
98 Adam Dunn .10 .30
99 Austin Kearns .10 .30
100 Barry Larkin .20 .50
101 Ken Griffey Jr. .50 1.25
102 Sean Casey .10 .30
103 Jason Jennings .10 .30
104 Jay Payton .10 .30
105 Larry Walker .10 .30
106 Todd Helton .20 .50
107 A.J. Burnett .10 .30
108 Josh Beckett .10 .30
109 Juan Encarnacion .10 .30
110 Mike Lowell .10 .30
111 Craig Biggio .20 .50
112 Daryle Ward .10 .30
113 Jeff Bagwell .20 .50
114 Lance Berkman .10 .30
115 Roy Oswalt .10 .30
116 Jason Lane .10 .30
117 Adrian Beltre .10 .30
118 Hideo Nomo .30 .75
119 Kazuhisa Ishii .10 .30
120 Kevin Brown .10 .30
121 Odalis Perez .10 .30
122 Paul Lo Duca .10 .30
123 Shawn Green .10 .30
124 Ben Sheets .10 .30
125 Jeffrey Hammonds .10 .30
126 Jose Hernandez .10 .30
127 Richie Sexson .10 .30
128 Bartolo Colon .10 .30
129 Brad Wilkerson .10 .30
130 Javier Vazquez .10 .30
131 Jose Vidro .10 .30
132 Michael Barrett .10 .30
133 Vladimir Guerrero .30 .75
134 Al Leiter .10 .30
135 Mike Piazza .50 1.25
136 Mo Vaughn .10 .30
137 Pedro Astacio .10 .30
138 Roberto Alomar .20 .50
139 Pat Burrell .10 .30
140 Vicente Padilla .10 .30
141 Jimmy Rollins .10 .30
142 Bobby Abreu .10 .30
143 Marlon Byrd .10 .30
144 Brian Giles .10 .30
145 Jason Kendall .10 .30
146 Aramis Ramirez .10 .30
147 Josh Fogg .10 .30
148 Ryan Klesko .10 .30
149 Phil Nevin .10 .30
150 Sean Burroughs .10 .30
151 Mark Kotsay .10 .30
152 Barry Bonds .75 2.00
153 Damian Moss .10 .30
154 Jason Schmidt .10 .30
155 Benito Santiago .10 .30
156 Rich Aurilia .10 .30
157 Scott Rolen .20 .50
158 J.D. Drew .10 .30
159 Jim Edmonds .10 .30
160 Matt Morris .10 .30
161 Tino Martinez .20 .50
162 Albert Pujols .60 1.50
163 Russ Ortiz .10 .30
164 Rey Ordonez .10 .30
165 Paul Byrd .10 .30
166 Kenny Lofton .10 .30
167 Kenny Rogers .10 .30
168 Rickey Henderson .30 .75
169 Fred McGriff .20 .50
170 Charles Johnson .10 .30
171 Mike Hampton .10 .30
172 Jim Thome .20 .50
173 Travis Hafner .10 .30
174 Ivan Rodriguez .20 .50
175 Ray Durham .10 .30
176 Jeremy Giambi .10 .30
177 Jeff Kent .10 .30
178 Cliff Floyd .10 .30
179 Kevin Millwood .10 .30
180 Tom Glavine .20 .50
181 Hideki Matsui ROO RC 4.00 10.00
182 Jose Contreras ROO RC 2.00 5.00
183 Termel Sledge ROO RC 1.50 4.00
184 Lew Ford ROO RC 2.00 5.00
185 Jhonny Peralta ROO 2.00 5.00
186 Alexis Rios ROO 3.00 8.00
187 Jeff Baker ROO 1.50 4.00
188 Jeremy Guthrie ROO 1.50 4.00
189 Jose Castillo ROO 1.50 4.00
190 Garrett Atkins ROO 1.50 4.00
191 Jer. Bonderman ROO RC 2.50 6.00
192 Adam LaRoche ROO 1.50 4.00
193 Vinny Chulk ROO 1.50 4.00
194 Walter Young ROO 1.50 4.00
195 Jimmy Gobble ROO 1.50 4.00
196 Prentice Redman ROO RC 1.50 4.00
197 Jason Anderson ROO 1.50 4.00
198 Nic Jackson ROO 1.50 4.00
199 Travis Chapman ROO 1.50 4.00
200 Shane Victorino ROO RC 2.50 6.00

2003 Donruss Elite Aspirations

*1-180 PRINT RUN b/wn 36-50 6X TO 15X
*1-180 PRINT RUN b/wn 51-65: 5X TO 12X
*1-180 PRINT RUN b/wn 66-80 5X TO 12X
*1-180 PRINT RUN b/wn 81-99 4X TO 10X
COMMON (181-200) p/r 81-99 2.50 6.00
SEMIS 181-200 p/r 81-99 4.00 10.00
COMMON (181-200) p/r 51-65 4.00 10.00
SEMIS 181-200 p/r 51-65 6.00 15.00
COMMON (181-200) p/r 36-50 4.00 10.00
COMMON (181-200) p/r 26-35 5.00 12.00
SEMIS 181-200 p/r 26-35 8.00 20.00
RANDOM INSERTS IN PACKS
SEE BECKETT.COM FOR PRINT RUNS
NO PRICING ON QTY OF 25 OR LESS

2003 Donruss Elite Aspirations Gold

RANDOM INSERTS IN PACKS
STATED PRINT RUN 1 SERIAL #'d SET
NO PRICING DUE TO SCARCITY

2003 Donruss Elite Atlantic City National

Collectors who opened Donruss Elite product while at the Donruss corporate booth at the 2003 Atlantic City National were eligible to receive these specially produced cards. The fronts of these cards have special stamping with the Atlantic City National logo and the backs are serially numbered to a stated print run of five copies. Due to market scarcity, no pricing is provided for these cards.

PRINT RUN 5 SERIAL #'d SETS

2003 Donruss Elite Status

*1-180 PRINT RUN b/wn 26-35: 8X TO 20X
*1-180 PRINT RUN b/wn 36-50: 6X TO 15X
*1-180 PRINT RUN b/wn 51-65: 5X TO 12X
*1-180 PRINT RUN b/wn 66-80: 5X TO 12X
*1-180 PRINT RUN b/wn 81-99: 4X TO 10X
COMMON (181-200) p/r 66-80 3.00 8.00
COMMON (181-200) p/r 51-65 4.00 10.00
COMMON (181-200) p/r 36-50 4.00 10.00
RANDOM INSERTS IN PACKS
NO PRICING ON QTY OF 25 OR LESS

2003 Donruss Elite Status Gold

RANDOM INSERTS IN PACKS
STATED PRINT RUN 24 SERIAL #'d SETS
NO PRICING DUE TO SCARCITY

2003 Donruss Elite Turn of the Century Autographs

Randomly inserted into packs, this is a partial parallel to the Donruss Elite set and features just the rookie cards with the exception of Hideki Matsui who was under an exclusive contract to Upper Deck. These cards are signed by the player and were issued to a stated print run of 50 serial numbered sets.

182 Jose Contreras ROO 15.00 40.00
183 Termel Sledge ROO 6.00 15.00
184 Lew Ford ROO 10.00 25.00
185 Jhonny Peralta ROO 15.00 40.00
186 Alexis Rios ROO 15.00 40.00
187 Jeff Baker ROO 6.00 15.00
188 Jeremy Guthrie ROO 6.00 15.00
189 Jose Castillo ROO 6.00 15.00
190 Garrett Atkins ROO 6.00 15.00
191 Jeremy Bonderman ROO 40.00 80.00
192 Adam LaRoche ROO 6.00 15.00
193 Vinny Chulk ROO 6.00 15.00
194 Walter Young ROO 6.00 15.00
195 Jimmy Gobble ROO 6.00 15.00
196 Prentice Redman ROO 6.00 15.00
197 Jason Anderson ROO 6.00 15.00
198 Nic Jackson ROO 6.00 15.00
199 Travis Chapman ROO 6.00 15.00
200 Shane Victorino ROO 40.00 80.00

2003 Donruss Elite All-Time Career Best

STATED ODDS 1:9
*PARALLEL 1-25 p/r 211-239: 1X TO 2.5X
*PARALLEL 1-25 p/r 105-140: 1.25X TO 3X
*PARALLEL 1-25 p/r 53-60: 2X TO 5X
*PARALLEL 1-25 p/r 39-49: 2.5X TO 6X
*PARALLEL 1-25 p/r 29-31: 3X TO 8X
*PARALLEL 26-50 p/r 393: .6X TO 1.5X
*PARALLEL 26-50 p/r 130-137: 1X TO 2.5X
*PARALLEL 26-50 p/r 55-66: 1.5X TO 4X
*PARALLEL 26-50 p/r 37-49: 2X TO 5X
*PARALLEL 26-50 p/r 35: 2.5X TO 6X
PARALLEL RANDOM INSERTS IN PACKS
PARALLEL PRINTS B/WN 1-393 COPIES PER
NO PARALLEL PRICING ON QTY OF 25 OR LESS
1 Babe Ruth 5.00 12.00
2 Ty Cobb 3.00 8.00
3 Jackie Robinson 1.50 4.00
4 Lou Gehrig 3.00 8.00
5 Thurman Munson 1.50 4.00
6 Nolan Ryan 5.00 12.00
7 Mike Schmidt 3.00 8.00
8 Don Mattingly 3.00 8.00
9 Yogi Berra 1.50 4.00
10 Rod Carew 1.25 3.00
11 Reggie Jackson 1.50 4.00
12 Al Kaline 1.50 4.00
13 Harmon Killebrew 1.50 4.00
14 Eddie Mathews 1.50 4.00
15 Stan Musial 2.50 6.00
16 Jim Palmer 1.25 3.00
17 Phil Rizzuto 1.25 3.00
18 Brooks Robinson 1.25 3.00
19 Tom Seaver 1.25 3.00
20 Robin Yount 1.50 4.00
21 Carlton Fisk 1.25 3.00
22 Dale Murphy 1.25 3.00
23 Cal Ripken 5.00 12.00
24 Tony Gwynn 2.00 5.00
25 Andre Dawson 1.25 3.00
26 Derek Jeter 4.00 10.00
27 Ken Griffey Jr. 2.50 6.00
28 Albert Pujols 3.00 8.00
29 Sammy Sosa 1.50 4.00
30 Jason Giambi 1.25 3.00
31 Randy Johnson 1.50 4.00
32 Greg Maddux 2.50 6.00
33 Rickey Henderson 1.50 4.00
34 Pedro Martinez 1.25 3.00
35 Jeff Bagwell 1.25 3.00
36 Alex Rodriguez 2.50 6.00
37 Vladimir Guerrero 1.50 4.00
38 Chipper Jones 1.50 4.00
39 Shawn Green 1.25 3.00
40 Tom Glavine 1.25 3.00
41 Curt Schilling 1.25 3.00
42 Todd Helton 1.25 3.00
43 Roger Clemens 3.00 8.00
44 Lance Berkman 1.25 3.00
45 Nomar Garciaparra 2.50 6.00

2003 Donruss Elite All-Time Career Best Materials

Randomly inserted into packs, this is a parallel to the All-Time Career Best insert set. Each of these cards feature not only the player but also a piece of game-used memorabilia from their career. We have printed what type of material as well as the stated print run next to the player's name in our checklist. Please note that for cards with a stated print run of 25 or fewer, there is no pricing due to market scarcity.

*MULTI-COLOR PATCH: 1.5X TO 4X HI COL
1 Babe Ruth Bat/25
2 Ty Cobb Bat/25
3 Jackie Robinson Jkt/50 40.00 80.00
4 Lou Gehrig Bat/100 75.00 150.00
5 Thurman Munson Bat/200 10.00 25.00
6 Nolan Ryan Jkt/400 20.00 50.00
7 Mike Schmidt Jkt/400 15.00 40.00
8 Don Mattingly Hat/250 15.00 40.00
9 Yogi Berra Bat/100 12.50 30.00
10 Rod Carew Bat/400 6.00 15.00
11 Reggie Jackson Bat/400 6.00 15.00
12 Al Kaline Bat/400 8.00 20.00
13 Harmon Killebrew Pants/400 8.00 20.00
14 Eddie Mathews Bat/200 10.00 25.00
15 Stan Musial Bat/100 20.00 50.00
16 Jim Palmer Jsy/200 8.00 20.00
17 Phil Rizzuto Bat/400 6.00 15.00
18 Brooks Robinson Bat/400 6.00 15.00
19 Tom Seaver Jsy/400 6.00 15.00
20 Robin Yount Bat/400 8.00 20.00
21 Carlton Fisk Bat/400 6.00 15.00
22 Dale Murphy Bat/400 6.00 15.00
23 Cal Ripken Bat/400 15.00 40.00
24 Tony Gwynn Pants/400 6.00 15.00
25 Andre Dawson Bat/400 4.00 10.00
26 Derek Jeter Base/400 8.00 20.00
27 Ken Griffey Jr. Base/400 6.00 15.00
28 Albert Pujols Base/400 6.00 15.00
29 Sammy Sosa Bat/400 4.00 10.00
30 Jason Giambi Bat/400 3.00 8.00
31 Randy Johnson Jsy/400 4.00 10.00
32 Greg Maddux Jsy/400 4.00 10.00
33 Rickey Henderson Bat/400 4.00 10.00
34 Pedro Martinez Jsy/400 4.00 10.00
35 Jeff Bagwell Pants/400 4.00 10.00
36 Alex Rodriguez Bat/400 6.00 15.00
37 Vladimir Guerrero Bat/400 4.00 10.00
38 Chipper Jones Bat/400 4.00 10.00
39 Shawn Green Bat/400 3.00 8.00
40 Tom Glavine Jsy/400 4.00 10.00
41 Curt Schilling Jsy/400 3.00 8.00
42 Todd Helton Bat/400 4.00 10.00
43 Roger Clemens Jsy/400 8.00 20.00
44 Lance Berkman Bat/400 3.00 8.00
45 Nomar Garciaparra Bat/400 6.00 15.00

2003 Donruss Elite All-Time Career Best Materials Parallel

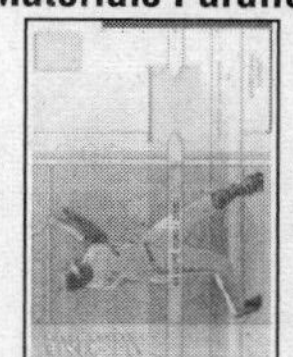

RANDOM INSERTS IN PACKS
PRINT RUNS B/WN 1-393 COPIES PER
NO PRICING ON QTY OF 25 OR LESS
1 Babe Ruth Bat/60 75.00 150.00
2 Ty Cobb Bat/24
3 Jackie Robinson Jkt/19
4 Lou Gehrig Bat/49 75.00 150.00
5 Thurman Munson Bat/105 15.00 40.00
6 Nolan Ryan Jkt/22
7 Mike Schmidt Jkt/48 40.00 80.00
8 Don Mattingly Hat/53 40.00 80.00
9 Yogi Berra Bat/30 30.00 60.00
10 Rod Carew Bat/239 6.00 15.00
11 Reggie Jackson Bat/39 15.00 40.00
12 Al Kaline Bat/29 30.00 60.00
13 Harmon Killebrew Pants/140 10.00 25.00
14 Eddie Mathews Bat/31 30.00 60.00
15 Stan Musial Bat/39 50.00 100.00
16 Jim Palmer Jsy/23
17 Phil Rizzuto Bat/10
18 Brooks Robinson Bat/118 10.00 25.00
19 Tom Seaver Jsy/7
20 Robin Yount Bat/49 20.00 50.00
21 Carlton Fisk Bat/107 10.00 25.00
22 Dale Murphy Bat/44 15.00 40.00
23 Cal Ripken Bat/211 20.00 50.00
24 Tony Gwynn Pants/220 8.00 20.00
25 Andre Dawson Bat/49 10.00 25.00
26 Derek Jeter Base/24
27 Ken Griffey Jr. Base/56 15.00 40.00
28 Albert Pujols Base/37 20.00 50.00
29 Sammy Sosa Bat/66 10.00 25.00
30 Jason Giambi Bat/137 4.00 10.00
31 Randy Johnson Jsy/12
32 Greg Maddux Jsy/20
33 Rickey Henderson Bat/130 6.00 15.00

34 Pedro Martinez Jsy/23
35 Jeff Bagwell Pants/47 10.00 25.00
36 Alex Rodriguez Bat/393 6.00 15.00
37 Vladimir Guerrero Bat/44 15.00 40.00
38 Chipper Jones Bat/45 15.00 40.00
39 Shawn Green Bat/49 6.00 15.00
40 Tom Glavine Jsy/22
41 Curt Schilling Jsy/35 6.00 15.00
42 Todd Helton Bat/59 10.00 25.00
43 Roger Clemens Jsy/4
44 Lance Berkman Bat/55 6.00 15.00
45 Nomar Garciaparra Bat/35 40.00 80.00

2003 Donruss Elite Back to Back Jacks

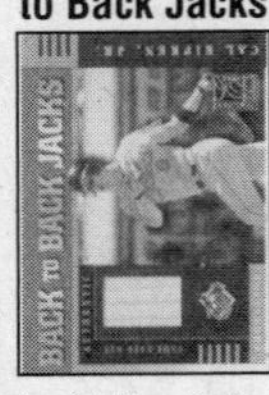

Randomly inserted into packs, these 50 cards feature game use bat pieces on them. These cards were issued to different print runs depending on what the card number is and we have notated that information in our headers to this set.

1-25 PRINT RUN 250 SERIAL #'d SETS
26-35 PRINT RUN 125 SERIAL #'d SETS
36-40 PRINT RUN 100 SERIAL #'d SETS
41-45 PRINT RUN 75 SERIAL #'d SETS
46-50 PRINT RUN 50 SERIAL #'d SETS
1 Adam Dunn 3.00 8.00
2 Alex Rodriguez 6.00 15.00
3 Alfonso Soriano 3.00 8.00
4 Andruw Jones 4.00 10.00
5 Chipper Jones 4.00 10.00
6 Jason Giambi 3.00 8.00
7 Jeff Bagwell 4.00 10.00
8 Jim Thome 4.00 10.00
9 Juan Gonzalez 3.00 8.00
10 Lance Berkman 3.00 8.00
11 Magglio Ordonez 3.00 8.00
12 Manny Ramirez 4.00 10.00
13 Miguel Tejada 3.00 8.00
14 Mike Piazza 6.00 15.00
15 Nomar Garciaparra 6.00 15.00
16 Rafael Palmeiro 4.00 10.00
17 Rickey Henderson 4.00 10.00
18 Sammy Sosa 4.00 10.00
19 Scott Rolen 4.00 10.00
20 Shawn Green 3.00 8.00
21 Todd Helton 4.00 10.00
22 Vladimir Guerrero 4.00 10.00
23 Ivan Rodriguez 4.00 10.00
24 Eric Chavez 3.00 8.00
25 Larry Walker 3.00 8.00
26 Garret Anderson 8.00 20.00
Troy Glaus
27 Adam Dunn 8.00 20.00
Austin Kearns
28 Alex Rodriguez 12.50 30.00
Rafael Palmeiro
29 Miguel Tejada 8.00 20.00
Eric Chavez
30 Magglio Ordonez 10.00 25.00
Frank Thomas
31 Lance Berkman 8.00 20.00
Jeff Bagwell
32 Nomar Garciaparra 15.00 40.00
Manny Ramirez
33 Vladimir Guerrero 10.00 25.00
Jose Vidro
34 Mike Piazza 10.00 25.00
Roberto Alomar
35 Todd Helton 8.00 20.00
Larry Walker
36 Babe Ruth 75.00 150.00
37 Cal Ripken 40.00 80.00
38 Don Mattingly 20.00 50.00
39 Kirby Puckett 10.00 25.00
40 Roberto Clemente 50.00 100.00
41 Alfonso Soriano 12.50 30.00
Phil Rizzuto
42 Sammy Sosa 15.00 40.00
Andre Dawson
43 Ozzie Smith 30.00 60.00
Scott Rolen
44 Don Mattingly 30.00 60.00
Jason Giambi
45 Rickey Henderson 75.00 150.00
Ty Cobb
46 Joe Morgan 30.00 60.00
Johnny Bench
47 Cal Ripken 75.00 150.00
Brooks Robinson
48 George Brett 50.00 100.00
Bo Jackson
49 Babe Ruth 250.00 400.00
Lou Gehrig
50 Yogi Berra 40.00 80.00
Thurman Munson

2003 Donruss Elite Back to the Future

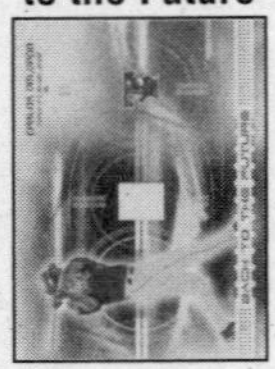

1-10 PRINT RUN 1000 SERIAL #'d SETS
11-15 PRINT RUN 500 SERIAL #'d SETS
RANDOM INSERTS IN PACKS
1 Kerry Wood 1.50 4.00
2 Mark Prior 1.50 4.00
3 Magglio Ordonez 1.50 4.00
4 Joe Borchard 1.50 4.00
5 Lance Berkman 1.50 4.00
6 Jason Lane 1.50 4.00
7 Rafael Palmeiro 1.50 4.00
8 Mark Teixeira 1.50 4.00
9 Carlos Delgado 1.50 4.00
10 Josh Phelps 1.50 4.00
11 Kerry Wood 2.50 6.00
Mark Prior
12 Magglio Ordonez 2.50 6.00
Joe Borchard
13 Lance Berkman 2.50 6.00
Jason Lane
14 Rafael Palmeiro 2.50 6.00
Mark Teixeira
15 Carlos Delgado 2.50 6.00
John Phelps

2003 Donruss Elite Back to the Future Threads

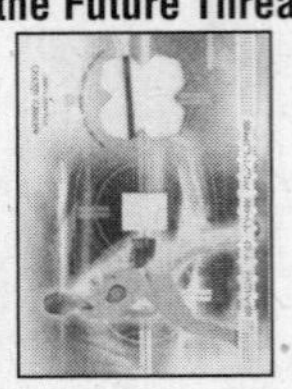

*MULTI-COLOR PATCH: .75X TO 2X HI COL
1-10 PRINT RUN 250 SERIAL #'d SETS
11-15 PRINT RUN 125 SERIAL #'d SETS
RANDOM INSERTS IN PACKS
1 Kerry Wood 3.00 8.00
2 Mark Prior 4.00 10.00
3 Magglio Ordonez 3.00 8.00
4 Joe Borchard 3.00 8.00
5 Lance Berkman 3.00 8.00
6 Jason Lane 3.00 8.00
7 Rafael Palmeiro 4.00 10.00
8 Mark Teixeira 4.00 10.00
9 Carlos Delgado 3.00 8.00
10 Josh Phelps 3.00 8.00
11 Kerry Wood 6.00 15.00
Mark Prior
12 Magglio Ordonez 6.00 15.00
Joe Borchard
13 Lance Berkman 6.00 15.00
Jason Lane
14 Rafael Palmeiro 6.00 15.00
Mark Teixeira
15 Carlos Delgado 6.00 15.00
John Phelps

2003 Donruss Elite Career Bests

RANDOM INSERTS IN PACKS
PRINT RUNS B/WN 4-417 COPIES PER
NO PRICING ON QTY OF 25 OR LESS
1 Randy Johnson WIN/24
2 Curt Schilling WIN/23
3 Garret Anderson 2B/56 4.00 10.00
4 Andruw Jones BB/83 4.00 10.00
5 Kerry Wood CG/4
6 Magglio Ordonez HR/38 5.00 12.00
7 Magglio Ordonez RBI/135 2.50 6.00
8 Adam Dunn HR/26 6.00 15.00
9 Roy Oswalt WIN/19
10 Lance Berkman HR/42 5.00 12.00
11 Lance Berkman RBI/128 2.50 6.00
12 Shawn Green OBP/385 2.00 5.00
13 Alfonso Soriano HR/39 5.00 12.00
14 Alfonso Soriano AVG/300 2.00 5.00
15 Jason Giambi RUN/120 2.50 6.00
16 Derek Jeter SB/32 25.00 60.00
17 Vladimir Guerrero SB/40 8.00 20.00
18 Vladimir Guerrero OBP/417 3.00 8.00
19 Barry Zito WIN/23
20 Miguel Tejada HR/34 6.00 15.00
21 Barry Bonds BB/198 10.00 25.00
22 Barry Bonds AVG/370 8.00 20.00
23 Ichiro Suzuki OBP/388 6.00 15.00
24 Alex Rodriguez HR/57 12.50 30.00
25 Alex Rodriguez RBI/142 8.00 20.00

2003 Donruss Elite Career Bests Materials

RANDOM INSERTS IN PACKS
STATED PRINT RUN 500 SERIAL #'d SETS
1 Randy Johnson WIN Jsy 4.00 10.00
2 Curt Schilling WIN Jsy 3.00 8.00
3 Garret Anderson 2B Bat 3.00 8.00
4 Andruw Jones BB Bat 4.00 10.00
5 Kerry Wood CG Shoe 4.00 10.00
6 Magglio Ordonez HR Bat 3.00 8.00
7 Magglio Ordonez RBI Bat 3.00 8.00
8 Adam Dunn HR Bat 3.00 8.00
9 Roy Oswalt WIN Jsy 3.00 8.00
10 Lance Berkman HR Bat 3.00 8.00
11 Lance Berkman RBI Bat 3.00 8.00
12 Shawn Green OBP Bat 3.00 8.00
13 Alfonso Soriano HR Bat 3.00 8.00
14 Alfonso Soriano AVG Bat 3.00 8.00
15 Jason Giambi RUN Bat 3.00 8.00
16 Derek Jeter SB Base 8.00 20.00
17 Vladimir Guerrero SB Bat 4.00 10.00
18 Vladimir Guerrero OBP Bat 4.00 10.00
19 Barry Zito WIN Jsy 3.00 8.00
20 Miguel Tejada HR Bat 3.00 8.00
21 Barry Bonds BB Base 8.00 20.00
22 Barry Bonds AVG Base 8.00 20.00
23 Ichiro Suzuki OBP Base 10.00 25.00
24 Alex Rodriguez HR Jsy 6.00 15.00
25 Alex Rodriguez RBI Jsy 6.00 15.00

2003 Donruss Elite Career Bests Materials Autographs

RANDOM INSERTS IN PACKS
PRINT RUNS B/WN 5-250 COPIES PER
NO PRICING ON QTY OF 25 OR LESS
1 Roy Oswalt WIN Jsy/5
2 Curt Schilling WIN Jsy/5
3 Garret Anderson 2B Bat/75 20.00 50.00
4 Andruw Jones BB Bat/10
5 Kerry Wood CG Shoe/15
6 Magglio Ordonez HR Bat/10
7 Magglio Ordonez RBI Bat/10
8 Adam Dunn HR Bat/100 30.00 60.00
9 Roy Oswalt WIN Jsy/250 15.00 40.00
10 Lance Berkman HR Bat/25
11 Lance Berkman RBI Bat/25
13 Alfonso Soriano HR Bat/5
14 Alfonso Soriano AVG Bat/5
17 Vlad Guerrero SB Bat/50 50.00 100.00
18 Vlad Guerrero OBP Bat/50 50.00 100.00
19 Barry Zito WIN Jsy/75 30.00 60.00
20 Miguel Tejada HR Bat/25
24 Alex Rodriguez HR Jsy/5
25 Alex Rodriguez RBI Jsy/5

2003 Donruss Elite Highlights

RANDOM INSERTS IN PACKS
STATED PRINT RUN 500 SERIAL #'d SETS
1 Sammy Sosa 500 HR 3.00 8.00
2 Rafael Palmeiro 500 HR 3.00 8.00
3 Hideki Matsui Debut 4.00 10.00
4 Jose Contreras Debut 3.00 8.00
5 Kevin Millwood No-Hit 2.00 5.00

2003 Donruss Elite Highlights Autographs

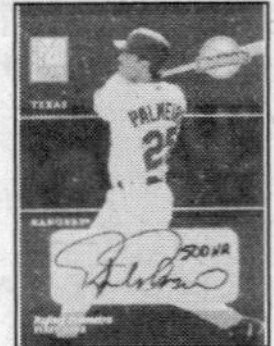

RANDOM INSERTS IN PACKS
STATED PRINT RUN 50 SERIAL #'d SETS
2 Rafael Palmeiro 500 HR 50.00 100.00
4 Jose Contreras Debut 15.00 40.00

2003 Donruss Elite Passing the Torch

1-10 PRINT RUN 1000 SERIAL #'d SETS
11-15 PRINT RUN 500 SERIAL #'d SETS
RANDOM INSERTS IN PACKS
1 Stan Musial 4.00 10.00
2 Jim Edmonds 1.50 4.00
3 Dale Murphy 2.50 6.00
4 Andruw Jones 2.50 6.00
5 Roger Clemens 5.00 12.00
6 Mark Prior 2.50 6.00
7 Tom Seaver 2.50 6.00
8 Tom Glavine 2.50 6.00
9 Mike Schmidt 5.00 12.00
10 Pat Burrell 1.50 4.00
11 Stan Musial 6.00 15.00
Jim Edmonds
12 Dale Murphy 4.00 10.00
Andruw Jones
13 Roger Clemens 6.00 15.00
Mark Prior
14 Tom Seaver 4.00 10.00
Tom Glavine
15 Mike Schmidt 8.00 20.00
Pat Burrell

2003 Donruss Elite Passing the Torch Autographs

Randomly inserted into packs, these cards feature the continuation of the popular Passing the Torch Autograph insert set. The first 10 cards feature individual autographs while the final five cards feature dual autographs of the players.

1-10 PRINT RUN 50 SERIAL #'d SETS
11-15 PRINT RUN 25 SERIAL #'d SETS
NO 11-15 PRICING DUE TO SCARCITY
RANDOM INSERTS IN PACKS
1 Stan Musial 60.00 120.00
2 Jim Edmonds 40.00 80.00
3 Dale Murphy 40.00 80.00
4 Andruw Jones 40.00 80.00
5 Roger Clemens 100.00 200.00
6 Mark Prior 20.00 50.00
7 Tom Seaver 40.00 80.00
8 Tom Glavine 40.00 80.00
9 Mike Schmidt 75.00 150.00
10 Pat Burrell 20.00 50.00
11 Stan Musial
Jim Edmonds
12 Dale Murphy
Andruw Jones
13 Roger Clemens
Mark Prior
14 Tom Seaver
Tom Glavine
15 Mike Schmidt
Pat Burrell

2003 Donruss Elite Recollection Autographs

Randomly inserted into packs, these 65 cards feature cards prepared for previous Donruss Elite products and they feature both autographs and a recollection collection stamp on all the cards. Please note that we have notated the stated print run next to the player's name and specific card in our checklist. For cards with print runs of 25 or fewer, no pricing is available due to market scarcity.

1 Jeremy Affeldt 01/75 4.00 10.00
2 Erick Almonte 01/75 4.00 10.00
3 Jeff Bagwell 02/1
4 Adrian Beltre 02/36 10.00 25.00
5 Adrian Beltre 02 Asp/5
6 Adrian Beltre 02 Sta/3
7 Brandon Berger 01/83 4.00 10.00
8 Angel Berroa 01/28 10.00 25.00
9 John Buck 01/25
10 Mark Buehrle 02/23
11 Marlon Byrd 01/24
12 Jose Castillo 02/23
13 Jeff Deardorff 01/53 4.00 10.00
14 Ryan Drese 01/100 6.00 15.00
15 J.D. Drew 01/15
16 J.D. Drew 02/10
17 J.D. Drew 02 CB/5
18 Jim Edmonds 01/15
19 Jim Edmonds 02/5
20 Jim Edmonds 02 BTF/5
21 Luis Garcia 01/28 6.00 15.00
22 Geronimo Gil 01/75 4.00 10.00
23 Mark Grace 02/2
24 Shawn Green 01/2
25 Shawn Green 02/2
26 Shawn Green 02 BTF/2
27 Shawn Green 02 CB/2
28 Travis Hafner 01 Black/52 20.00 50.00
29 Travis Hafner 01 Blue/23
30 Bill Hall 01/27 10.00 25.00
31 Orlando Hudson 01 Black/12
32 Orlando Hudson 01 Blue /13
33 Tim Hudson 01/25
34 Tim Hudson 02/25
35 Gerald Laird 02/46 6.00 15.00
36 Jason Lane 01/27 10.00 25.00
37 Adam LaRoche 02/25
38 Cliff Lee 01/25
39 Kenny Lofton 01/25
40 Greg Maddux 01/5
41 Greg Maddux 01 TW/5
42 Greg Maddux 02/10
43 Greg Maddux 02 AS/5
44 Victor Martinez 01/52 60.00 120.00
45 Corky Miller 01/25
46 Roy Oswalt 01 Black/61 6.00 15.00
47 Roy Oswalt 01 Blue/9
48 Roy Oswalt 02/24
49 Mark Prior 01/10
50 Mike Rivera 01/3
51 Ricardo Rodriguez 01/75 4.00 10.00
52 Freddy Sanchez 02/25
53 Gary Sheffield 01/25
54 Gary Sheffield 02/14
55 Bud Smith 01/50 6.00 15.00
56 Bud Smith 02/28 6.00 15.00
57 Chris Snelling 02/25
58 Junior Spivey 01/45 6.00 15.00
59 Tim Spooneybarger 01/100 4.00 10.00
60 Shannon Stewart 01/24
61 Shannon Stewart 02/35 10.00 25.00
62 Dennis Tankersley 01/15
63 Mark Teixeira 01/19
64 Claudio Vargas 01/51 4.00 10.00
65 Martin Vargas 01/10

2003 Donruss Elite Throwback Threads

Randomly inserted into packs, these 100 cards feature not only the player's featured but also a game-worn uniform piece from during their career. Please note that the final 10 cards in the checklist feature either two different pieces from a player's career or two pieces from players who have something in common.

1-45 PRINT RUN 250 SERIAL #'d SETS
46-75 PRINT RUN 125 SERIAL #'d SETS
76-90 PRINT RUN 100 SERIAL #'d SETS
91-95 PRINT RUN 75 SERIAL #'d SETS
96-100 PRINT RUN RUN 50 SERIAL #'d SETS
*MULTI-COLOR PATCH: .75X TO 2X HI COL
1 Randy Johnson D'backs 4.00 10.00
2 Randy Johnson M's 4.00 10.00
3 Roger Clemens Yanks 10.00 25.00
4 Roger Clemens Red Sox 10.00 25.00
5 Manny Ramirez 4.00 10.00
6 Greg Maddux 6.00 15.00
7 Jason Giambi Yanks 3.00 8.00
8 Jason Giambi A's 3.00 8.00
9 Alex Rodriguez Rgr 6.00 15.00
10 Alex Rodriguez M's 6.00 15.00
11 Miguel Tejada 3.00 8.00
12 Alfonso Soriano 3.00 8.00
13 Nomar Garciaparra 6.00 15.00
14 Pedro Martinez Red Sox 4.00 10.00
15 Pedro Martinez Expos 4.00 10.00
16 Andruw Jones 4.00 10.00
17 Chipper Jones 4.00 10.00
18 Barry Zito 3.00 8.00
19 Mark Mulder 3.00 8.00
20 Lance Berkman 3.00 8.00
21 Magglio Ordonez 3.00 8.00
22 Mike Piazza Mets 6.00 15.00
23 Mike Piazza Dodgers 6.00 15.00
24 Rickey Henderson Padres 4.00 10.00
25 Rickey Henderson Mets 4.00 10.00
26 Rickey Henderson M's 4.00 10.00
27 Sammy Sosa 4.00 10.00
28 Shawn Green 3.00 8.00
29 Troy Glaus 3.00 8.00
30 Vladimir Guerrero 4.00 10.00
31 Adam Dunn 3.00 8.00
32 Jeff Bagwell 4.00 10.00
33 Curt Schilling 3.00 8.00
34 Hideo Nomo Dodgers 15.00 40.00
35 Hideo Nomo Red Sox 15.00 40.00
36 Hideo Nomo Mets 15.00 40.00
37 Kerry Wood 3.00 8.00
38 Mark Prior 4.00 10.00
39 Roberto Alomar 4.00 10.00
40 Todd Helton 4.00 10.00
41 Jim Thome 4.00 10.00
42 Rafael Palmeiro 4.00 10.00
43 Juan Gonzalez 3.00 8.00
44 Vernon Wells 3.00 8.00
45 Torii Hunter 3.00 8.00
46 Randy Johnson D'backs 10.00 25.00
Randy Johnson M's
47 Roger Clemens Yankees 20.00 50.00
Roger Clemens Red Sox
48 Jason Giambi Yankees 8.00 20.00
Jason Giambi A's
49 Alex Rodriguez Rangers 15.00 40.00
Alex Rodriguez M's
50 Pedro Martinez Red Sox 10.00 25.00
Pedro Martinez Expos
51 Mike Piazza Mets 15.00 40.00
Mike Piazza Dodgers
52 Rickey Henderson A's 10.00 25.00
Rickey Henderson M's
53 Rickey Henderson Padres 10.00 25.00
Rickey Henderson Mets
54 Rickey Henderson Angels 10.00 25.00
Rickey Henderson Padres
55 Hideo Nomo Dodgers 20.00 50.00
Hideo Nomo Red Sox
56 Randy Johnson D'backs 10.00 25.00
Randy Johnson Expos
57 Randy Johnson 10.00 25.00
Curt Schilling
58 Alfonso Soriano 8.00 20.00
Jason Giambi
59 Barry Zito 8.00 20.00
Mark Mulder
60 Andruw Jones 10.00 25.00
Chipper Jones
61 Greg Maddux 30.00 60.00
Tom Glavine
62 Lance Berkman 10.00 25.00
Jeff Bagwell
63 Roger Clemens 12.50 30.00
Mark Prior
64 Alex Rodriguez 12.50 30.00
Rafael Palmeiro
65 Jim Thome 10.00 25.00
Roberto Alomar
66 Mike Piazza 10.00 25.00
Roberto Alomar
67 Sammy Sosa 10.00 25.00
Mark Grace
68 Todd Helton 10.00 25.00
Larry Walker
69 Adam Dunn 8.00 20.00
Austin Kearns
70 Alex Rodriguez 10.00 25.00
Ivan Rodriguez
71 Bobby Abreu 8.00 20.00
Marlon Byrd
72 Miguel Tejada 8.00 20.00
Eric Chavez
73 Greg Maddux 15.00 40.00
John Smoltz
74 Kerry Wood 4.00 10.00
Mark Prior
75 Barry Zito 8.00 20.00
Tim Hudson
76 Babe Ruth 250.00 400.00
77 Ty Cobb 60.00 120.00
78 Jackie Robinson 50.00 100.00
79 Lou Gehrig 100.00 200.00
80 Thurman Munson 20.00 50.00
81 Nolan Ryan Astros 20.00 50.00
82 Don Mattingly 15.00 40.00
83 Mike Schmidt 15.00 40.00
84 Reggie Jackson 10.00 25.00
85 George Brett 15.00 40.00
86 Cal Ripken 30.00 60.00
87 Tony Gwynn 10.00 25.00
88 Yogi Berra 10.00 25.00
89 Stan Musial 20.00 50.00
90 Jim Palmer 8.00 20.00
91 Thurman Munson 30.00 60.00
Jorge Posada
92 Dale Murphy 30.00 60.00
Chipper Jones
93 Don Mattingly 40.00 80.00
Jason Giambi
94 Andre Dawson 15.00 40.00
Sammy Sosa
95 Nolan Ryan 40.00 80.00
Mark Prior
96 Babe Ruth 300.00 500.00
Lou Gehrig
97 Tom Seaver 30.00 60.00
Joe Morgan
98 Harmon Killebrew 30.00 60.00
Rod Carew
99 Nolan Ryan Rangers 60.00 120.00
Nolan Ryan Angels
100 Reggie Jackson Yankees 30.00 60.00
Reggie Jackson A's

2003 Donruss Elite Throwback Threads Autographs

Randomly inserted into packs, this is a quasi-parallel to the Throwback Threads insert set. These cards were signed by the player featured and issued to stated print runs of between five and 75 copies per. Please note that if a player signed 25 or fewer copies, there is no pricing due to market scarcity.

3 Roger Clemens Yanks/15
4 Roger Clemens Red Sox/5
6 Greg Maddux/5
9 Alex Rodriguez Rgr/5
10 Alex Rodriguez M's/5
12 Alfonso Soriano/5
14 Pedro Martinez Red Sox/5
15 Pedro Martinez Expos/5
16 Andruw Jones/25
17 Chipper Jones/20
18 Barry Zito/25
19 Mark Mulder/10
20 Lance Berkman/25
21 Magglio Ordonez/15
24 Rickey Henderson Padres/10
25 Rickey Henderson Mets/5
26 Rickey Henderson M's/5
27 Sammy Sosa/15
29 Troy Glaus/15
30 Vladimir Guerrero/50 50.00 100.00
31 Adam Dunn/50 50.00 100.00
37 Kerry Wood/50 50.00 100.00
38 Mark Prior/75 30.00 60.00
39 Roberto Alomar/50 50.00 100.00
40 Todd Helton/15
41 Jim Thome/25
45 Torii Hunter/25
81 Nolan Ryan Angels/25
82 Don Mattingly/25
83 Mike Schmidt/25
84 Reggie Jackson/25
85 George Brett/15
86 Cal Ripken/15
87 Tony Gwynn/25
88 Yogi Berra/25
89 Stan Musial/25
90 Jim Palmer/25

2003 Donruss Elite Throwback Threads Prime

1-45 PRINT RUN 25 SERIAL #'d SETS
46-75 PRINT RUN 15 SERIAL #'d SETS
76-95 PRINT RUN 10 SERIAL #'d SETS
96-100 PRINT RUN 5 SERIAL #'d SETS

2003 Donruss Elite Extra Edition

These cards were also inserted as part of the overall DLP Rookie/Traded Packs. Each of these cards feature Rookie Cards and are all issued to a stated print run of 900 serial numbered sets. Please note that cards numbered 42, 51, 54 and 56 do not exist for this set.

1 Adam Loewen RC 2.00 5.00
2 Brandon Webb RC 4.00 10.00
3 Chien-Ming Wang RC 15.00 40.00
4 Hong-Chih Kuo RC 8.00 20.00
5 Clint Barmes RC 2.00 5.00
6 Guillermo Quiroz RC 1.50 4.00
7 Edgar Gonzalez RC 1.50 4.00
8 Todd Wellemeyer RC 2.00 5.00
9 Alfredo Gonzalez RC 1.50 4.00
10 Craig Brazell RC 1.50 4.00
11 Tim Olson RC 1.50 4.00
12 Rich Fischer RC 1.50 4.00
13 Daniel Cabrera RC 2.00 5.00
14 Francisco Rosario RC 1.50 4.00
15 Francisco Cruceta RC 1.50 4.00
16 Alejandro Machado RC 1.50 4.00
17 Andrew Brown RC 2.00 5.00
18 Rob Hammock RC 1.50 4.00
19 Arnie Munoz RC 1.50 4.00
20 Felix Sanchez RC 1.50 4.00
21 Nook Logan RC 2.00 5.00
22 Cory Stewart RC 1.50 4.00
23 Michel Hernandez RC 1.50 4.00
24 Rett Johnson RC 1.50 4.00
25 Josh Hall RC 1.50 4.00
26 Doug Waechter RC 2.00 5.00
27 Matt Kata RC 1.50 4.00
28 Dan Haren RC 2.00 5.00
29 Dontrelle Willis 2.00 5.00
30 Ramon Nivar RC 1.50 4.00
31 Chad Gaudin RC 1.50 4.00
32 Rickie Weeks RC 4.00 10.00
33 Ryan Wagner RC 1.50 4.00
34 Kevin Correia RC 1.50 4.00
35 Bo Hart RC 1.50 4.00
36 Oscar Villarreal RC 1.50 4.00
37 Josh Willingham RC 3.00 8.00
38 Jeff Duncan RC 1.50 4.00
39 David DeJesus RC 2.00 5.00
40 Dustin McGowan RC 2.00 5.00
41 Preston Larrison RC 2.00 5.00
43 Kevin Youkilis RC 3.00 8.00
44 Bubba Nelson RC 2.00 5.00
45 Chris Burke RC 2.00 5.00
46 J.D. Durbin RC 1.50 4.00
47 Ryan Howard RC 20.00 50.00
48 Jason Kubel RC 2.00 5.00
49 Brendan Harris RC 2.00 5.00
50 Brian Bruney RC 2.00 5.00
52 Byron Gettis RC 1.50 4.00
53 Edwin Jackson RC 2.00 5.00
55 Daniel Garcia RC 1.50 4.00
57 Chad Cordero RC 3.00 8.00
58 Delmon Young RC 10.00 25.00

2003 Donruss Elite Extra Edition Aspirations

*ASP P/R b/wn 51-65: 1X TO 2.5X
*ASP RC's P/R b/wn 81-120: .6X TO 1.5X
*ASP RC's P/R b/wn 66-80: .75X TO 2X
*ASP RC's P/R b/wn 51-65: .75X TO 2X
*ASP RC's P/R b/wn 36-50: 1X TO 2.5X
*ASP RC's P/R b/wn 26-35: 1.25X TO 3X
RANDOM INSERTS IN DLP R/T PACKS
PRINT RUNS B/WN 24-98 COPIES PER
NO PRICING ON QTY OF 25 OR LESS
CARDS 42/51/54/56 DO NOT EXIST
4 Hong-Chih Kuo/32 50.00 100.00
32 Rickie Weeks/89 12.50 30.00
47 Ryan Howard/43 75.00 150.00
58 Delmon Young/70 15.00 40.00

2003 Donruss Elite Extra Edition Aspirations Gold

RANDOM INSERTS IN DLP R/T PACKS
STATED PRINT RUN 1 SERIAL #'d SET
NO PRICING DUE TO SCARCITY
CARDS 42/51/54/56 DO NOT EXIST

2003 Donruss Elite Extra Edition Status

*STATUS P/R b/wn 26-35: 1.5X TO 4X
*STATUS RC's P/R b/wn 66-80: .75X TO 2X
*STATUS RC's P/R b/wn 51-65: .75X TO 2X
*STATUS RC's P/R b/wn 36-50: 1X TO 2.5X
*STATUS RC's P/R b/wn 26-35: 1.25X TO 3X
RANDOM INSERTS IN DLP R/T PACKS
PRINT RUNS B/WN 2-76 COPIES PER
NO PRICING ON QTY OF 25 OR LESS
CARDS 42/51/54/56 DO NOT EXIST
3 Chien-Ming Wang/76 40.00 80.00
4 Hong-Chih Kuo/68 30.00 60.00
47 Ryan Howard/57 75.00 150.00

2003 Donruss Elite Extra Edition Status Gold

RANDOM INSERTS IN DLP R/T PACKS
STATED PRINT RUN 24 SERIAL #'d SETS
NO PRICING DUE TO SCARCITY
CARDS 42/51/54/56 DO NOT EXIST

2003 Donruss Elite Extra Edition Turn of the Century

*TOC P/R b/wn 66-80: .75X TO 2X
*TOC RC's P/R b/wn 66-80: .75X TO 2X
RANDOM INSERTS IN DLP R/T PACKS
PRINT RUNS B/WN 75-100 COPIES PER

2003 Donruss Elite Extra Edition Turn of the Century Autographs

RANDOM INSERTS IN DLP R/T PACKS
STATED PRINT RUN 100 SERIAL #'d SETS
CARDS 29/32/34 PRINT RUN 25 #'d SETS
NO PRICING ON QTY OF 25 OR LESS
1 Adam Loewen 10.00 25.00
2 Brandon Webb 100.00 175.00
3 Chien-Ming Wang 175.00 300.00
4 Hong-Chih Kuo 100.00 200.00
5 Clint Barmes 4.00 10.00
6 Guillermo Quiroz 4.00 10.00
7 Edgar Gonzalez 4.00 10.00
8 Todd Wellemeyer 4.00 10.00
9 Alfredo Gonzalez 4.00 10.00
10 Craig Brazell 4.00 10.00
11 Tim Olson 4.00 10.00
12 Rich Fischer 4.00 10.00
13 Daniel Cabrera 15.00 40.00
14 Francisco Rosario 4.00 10.00
15 Francisco Cruceta 4.00 10.00
16 Alejandro Machado 4.00 10.00
17 Andrew Brown 6.00 15.00
18 Rob Hammock 4.00 10.00
19 Arnie Munoz 4.00 10.00
20 Felix Sanchez 4.00 10.00
21 Nook Logan 6.00 15.00
22 Cory Stewart 4.00 10.00
23 Michel Hernandez 4.00 10.00
24 Rett Johnson 4.00 10.00
25 Josh Hall 4.00 10.00
26 Doug Waechter 6.00 15.00
27 Matt Kata 4.00 10.00
28 Dan Haren 20.00 50.00
29 Dontrelle Willis/25
30 Ramon Nivar 4.00 10.00
31 Chad Gaudin 4.00 10.00
32 Rickie Weeks/25
33 Ryan Wagner 4.00 10.00
34 Kevin Correia/25
35 Bo Hart 4.00 10.00
36 Oscar Villarreal 6.00 15.00
37 Josh Willingham 15.00 40.00
38 Jeff Duncan 4.00 10.00
40 Dustin McGowan 6.00 15.00
41 Preston Larrison 4.00 10.00
43 Kevin Youkilis 50.00 100.00
44 Bubba Nelson 4.00 10.00
45 Chris Burke 15.00 40.00
46 J.D. Durbin 4.00 10.00
47 Ryan Howard 300.00 500.00
48 Jason Kubel 15.00 40.00
49 Brendan Harris 6.00 15.00
50 Brian Bruney 6.00 15.00
52 Byron Gettis 4.00 10.00
53 Edwin Jackson 6.00 15.00
55 Daniel Garcia 4.00 10.00
58 Delmon Young 150.00 300.00

2004 Donruss Elite

This 205 card set was released in May, 2004. The set was issued in five card packs with an $5 SRP which came 20 packs to a box and 12 boxes to a case. The first 150 cards of this set featured veterans while cards numbered 151 through 180 featured rookie cards printed to varying print runs. We have notated those specfic print runs next to the players name in our checklist. Cards numbered 181 through 200 feature retired greats which were randomly inserted into packs and those cards were issued to a stated print run of 1000 serial numbered sets. Please note, that although there is two separate numberings (including 201-205) for the Fans of the Game insert set, we have moved those cards into an insert set listing. Card number 169 was not issued.

COMP.SET w/o SP's (150) 10.00 25.00
COMMON CARD 1-150 .10 .30
COMMON AUTO (151-180) 3.00 8.00
COMMON CARD (181-200) 1.25 3.00
CARD NUMBER 169 DOES NOT EXIST
1 Troy Glaus .10 .30
2 Darin Erstad .10 .30
3 Garret Anderson .10 .30
4 Tim Salmon .20 .50
5 Bartolo Colon .10 .30
6 Jose Guillen .10 .30
7 Miguel Tejada .10 .30
8 Adam Loewen .10 .30
9 Jay Gibbons .10 .30
10 Melvin Mora .10 .30
11 Javy Lopez .10 .30
12 Pedro Martinez .20 .50
13 Curt Schilling .20 .50
14 David Ortiz .30 .75
15 Keith Foulke .10 .30
16 Nomar Garciaparra .50 1.25
17 Magglio Ordonez .10 .30
18 Frank Thomas .30 .75
19 Carlos Lee .10 .30
20 Paul Konerko .10 .30
21 Mark Buehrle .10 .30
22 Jody Gerut .10 .30
23 Victor Martinez .10 .30
24 C.C. Sabathia .10 .30
25 Ellis Burks .10 .30
26 Bobby Higginson .10 .30
27 Jeremy Bonderman .10 .30
28 Fernando Vina .10 .30
29 Carlos Pena .10 .30
30 Dmitri Young .10 .30
31 Carlos Beltran .10 .30
32 Benito Santiago .10 .30
33 Mike Sweeney .10 .30
34 Angel Berroa .10 .30
35 Runelvys Hernandez .10 .30
36 Johan Santana .30 .75
37 Doug Mientkiewicz .10 .30
38 Shannon Stewart .10 .30
39 Torii Hunter .10 .30
40 Derek Jeter .60 1.50
41 Jason Giambi .10 .30
42 Bernie Williams .20 .50
43 Alfonso Soriano .10 .30
44 Gary Sheffield .10 .30
45 Mike Mussina .20 .50
46 Jorge Posada .20 .50
47 Hideki Matsui .50 1.25
48 Kevin Brown .10 .30
49 Javier Vazquez .10 .30
50 Mariano Rivera .30 .75
51 Eric Chavez .10 .30
52 Tim Hudson .10 .30
53 Mark Mulder .10 .30
54 Barry Zito .10 .30
55 Ichiro Suzuki .60 1.50
56 Edgar Martinez .20 .50
57 Bret Boone .10 .30
58 John Olerud .10 .30
59 Scott Spiezio .10 .30
60 Aubrey Huff .10 .30
61 Rocco Baldelli .10 .30
62 Jose Cruz Jr. .10 .30
63 Delmon Young .20 .50
64 Mark Teixeira .20 .50
65 Hank Blalock .10 .30
66 Michael Young .10 .30
67 Alex Rodriguez .50 1.25
68 Carlos Delgado .10 .30
69 Eric Hinske .10 .30
70 Roy Halladay .10 .30
71 Vernon Wells .10 .30
72 Randy Johnson .30 .75
73 Richie Sexson .10 .30
74 Brandon Webb .10 .30
75 Luis Gonzalez .10 .30
76 Steve Finley .10 .30
77 Chipper Jones .30 .75
78 Andruw Jones .20 .50
79 Marcus Giles .10 .30
80 Rafael Furcal .10 .30
81 J.D. Drew .10 .30
82 Sammy Sosa .30 .75
83 Kerry Wood .10 .30
84 Mark Prior .20 .50
85 Derrek Lee .20 .50
86 Moises Alou .10 .30
87 Corey Patterson .10 .30
88 Ken Griffey Jr. .50 1.25
89 Austin Kearns .10 .30
90 Adam Dunn .10 .30
91 Barry Larkin .20 .50
92 Todd Helton .20 .50
93 Larry Walker .10 .30
94 Preston Wilson .10 .30
95 Charles Johnson .10 .30
96 Luis Castillo .10 .30
97 Josh Beckett .10 .30
98 Mike Lowell .10 .30
99 Miguel Cabrera .20 .50
100 Juan Pierre .10 .30
101 Dontrelle Willis .20 .50
102 Andy Pettitte .20 .50
103 Wade Miller .10 .30
104 Jeff Bagwell .20 .50
105 Craig Biggio .20 .50
106 Lance Berkman .10 .30
107 Jeff Kent .10 .30
108 Roy Oswalt .10 .30
109 Hideo Nomo .30 .75
110 Adrian Beltre .10 .30
111 Paul Lo Duca .10 .30
112 Shawn Green .10 .30
113 Fred McGriff .20 .50
114 Eric Gagne .10 .30
115 Geoff Jenkins .10 .30
116 Rickie Weeks .10 .30
117 Scott Podsednik .10 .30
118 Nick Johnson .10 .30
119 Orlando Cabrera .10 .30
120 Jose Vidro .10 .30
121 Kazuo Matsui RC .60 1.50
122 Tom Glavine .20 .50
123 Al Leiter .10 .30
124 Mike Piazza .50 1.25
125 Jose Reyes .10 .30
126 Mike Cameron .10 .30
127 Pat Burrell .10 .30
128 Jim Thome .20 .50
129 Mike Lieberthal .10 .30
130 Bobby Abreu .10 .30
131 Kip Wells .10 .30
132 Jack Wilson .10 .30
133 Pokey Reese .10 .30
134 Brian Giles .10 .30
135 Sean Burroughs .10 .30
136 Ryan Klesko .10 .30
137 Trevor Hoffman .10 .30
138 Jason Schmidt .10 .30
139 J.T. Snow .10 .30
140 A.J. Pierzynski .10 .30
141 Ray Durham .10 .30
142 Jim Edmonds .10 .30
143 Albert Pujols .60 1.50
144 Edgar Renteria .10 .30
145 Scott Rolen .20 .50
146 Matt Morris .10 .30
147 Ivan Rodriguez .20 .50
148 Vladimir Guerrero .30 .75
149 Greg Maddux .50 1.25
150 Kevin Millwood .10 .30
151 Hector Gimenez AU/750 RC 3.00 8.00
152 Willy Taveras AU/750 RC 8.00 20.00
153 Ruddy Yan AU/750 3.00 8.00
154 Graham Koonce AU/750 3.00 8.00
155 Jose Capellan AU/750 RC 3.00 8.00
156 Onil Joseph AU/750 RC 3.00 8.00
157 John Gall AU/1000 RC 3.00 8.00
158 Carlos Hines AU/750 RC 3.00 8.00
159 Jerry Gil AU/750 RC 3.00 8.00
160 Mike Gosling AU/750 RC 3.00 8.00
161 Jason Frasor AU/750 RC 3.00 8.00
162 Justin Knoedler AU/750 RC 3.00 8.00
163 Merkin Valdez AU/500 RC 3.00 8.00
164 Angel Chavez AU/1000 RC 3.00 8.00
165 Ivan Ochoa AU/750 RC 3.00 8.00
166 Greg Dobbs AU/750 RC 3.00 8.00
167 Ronald Belisario AU/750 RC 3.00 8.00
168 Aarom Baldiris AU/750 RC 3.00 8.00
170 Dave Crouthers AU/750 RC 3.00 8.00
171 Freddy Guzman AU/750 RC 3.00 8.00
172 Akinori Otsuka AU/250 RC 12.50 30.00
173 Ian Snell AU/750 RC 6.00 15.00
174 Nick Regilio AU/1000 RC 3.00 8.00
175 Jamie Brown AU/750 RC 3.00 8.00
176 Jerome Gamble AU/750 RC 3.00 8.00
177 Roberto Novoa AU/1000 RC 3.00 8.00
178 Sean Henn AU/1000 RC 3.00 8.00
179 Ramon Ramirez AU/1000 RC 3.00 8.00
180 Jason Bartlett AU/1000 RC 4.00 10.00
181 Bob Gibson RET 1.50 4.00
182 Cal Ripken RET 4.00 10.00
183 Carl Yastrzemski RET 2.00 5.00
184 Dale Murphy RET 1.50 4.00
185 Don Mattingly RET 2.50 6.00
186 Eddie Murray RET 1.50 4.00
187 George Brett RET 2.50 6.00
188 Jackie Robinson RET 1.50 4.00
189 Jim Palmer RET 1.25 3.00
190 Lou Gehrig RET 2.00 5.00
191 Mike Schmidt RET 2.50 6.00
192 Ozzie Smith RET 2.00 5.00
193 Nolan Ryan RET 3.00 8.00
194 Reggie Jackson RET 1.50 4.00
195 Roberto Clemente RET 3.00 8.00
196 Robin Yount RET 1.50 4.00
197 Stan Musial RET 2.00 5.00
198 Ted Williams RET 2.50 6.00
199 Tony Gwynn RET 1.50 4.00
200 Ty Cobb RET 1.50 4.00

2004 Donruss Elite Aspirations

*1-150 PRINT RUN b/wn 81-99: 4X TO 10X
*1-150 PRINT RUN b/wn 66-80: 5X TO 12X
*1-150 PRINT RUN b/wn 51-65: 5X TO 12X
*1-150 PRINT RUN b/wn 36-50: 6X TO 15X
*1-150 PRINT RUN b/wn 26-35: 8X TO 20X
*1-150 PRINT RUN b/wn 16-25: 10X TO 25X
*151-180 P/R 81-99: .3X TO .8X AU 750+
*151-180 P/R 66-80: .4X TO 1X AU 750+
*151-180 P/R 51-65: .4X TO 1X AU 750+
*151-180 P/R 36-50: .5X TO 1.2X AU 750+
*151-180 P/R 26-35: .6X TO 1.5X AU 750+
*151-180 P/R 81-99: .2X TO .5X AU 250
*181-200 P/R b/wn 81-99: 1.25X TO 3X
*181-200 P/R b/wn 66-80: 1.5X TO 4X
*181-200 P/R b/wn 51-65: 1.5X TO 4X
RANDOM INSERTS IN PACKS
PRINT RUNS B/WN 19-99 COPIES PER
1-150/181-200 NO PRICING ON 15 OR LESS
151-180 NO PRICING ON 25 OR LESS
121 Kazuo Matsui/75 6.00 15.00
169 Kazuo Matsui ROO/75 6.00 15.00

2004 Donruss Elite Status

*1-150 PRINT RUN b/wn 66-80: 5X TO 12X
*1-150 PRINT RUN b/wn 51-65: 5X TO 12X
*1-150 PRINT RUN b/wn 36-50: 6X TO 15X
*1-150 PRINT RUN b/wn 26-35: 8X TO 20X
*1-150 PRINT RUN b/wn 16-25: 10X TO 25X
*151-180 P/R 81: .3X TO .8X AU 750+
*151-180 P/R 66-80: .4X TO 1X AU 750+
*151-180 P/R 51-65: .4X TO 1X AU 750+
*151-180 P/R 36-50: .5X TO 1.2X AU 750+
*181-200 P/R b/wn 36-50: 2X TO 5X
*181-200 P/R b/wn 26-35: 2.5X TO 6X
*181-200 P/R b/wn 16-25: 3X TO 8X
RANDOM INSERTS IN PACKS
PRINT RUNS B/WN 1-81 COPIES PER
1-120/122-50/181-200 NO PRICE 15 OR LESS
121/151-180 NO PRICING ON 25 OR LESS

2004 Donruss Elite Status Gold

*GOLD 1-120/122-150: 10X TO 25X BASIC
*GOLD 181-200: 3X TO 8X BASIC
RANDOM INSERTS IN PACKS
STATED PRINT RUN 24 SERIAL #'d SETS
121/151-180 NO PRICING DUE TO SCARCITY

2004 Donruss Elite Turn of the Century

*TOC 1-120/122-150: 1.5X TO 4X BASIC
*TOC 121: 1.25X TO 3X BASIC
1-150 PRINT RUN 750 SERIAL #'d SETS
*TOC 181-200: .75X TO 2X BASIC
181-200 PRINT RUN 250 SERIAL #'d SETS
RANDOM INSERTS IN PACKS
CARDS 151-180 DO NOT EXIST

2004 Donruss Elite Back 2 Back Jacks

RANDOM INSERTS IN PACKS
SINGLE PRINT RUNS B/WN 25-125 PER
DUAL PRINT RUNS B/WN 25-50 PER
1 Albert Pujols/125 6.00 15.00
2 Alex Rodriguez Rgr/125 4.00 10.00
3 Alfonso Soriano/125 3.00 8.00
4 Andruw Jones/125 4.00 10.00
5 Chipper Jones/125 4.00 10.00
6 Derek Jeter/125 8.00 20.00
7 Frank Thomas/125 4.00 10.00
8 Miguel Cabrera/125 4.00 10.00
9 Jason Giambi/125 3.00 8.00
10 Jim Thome/125 4.00 10.00
11 Mike Piazza/125 4.00 10.00
12 Nomar Garciaparra/25 10.00 25.00
13 Sammy Sosa/125 4.00 10.00
14 Shawn Green/125 3.00 8.00
15 Vladimir Guerrero/125 4.00 10.00
16 Andruw Jones / Chipper Jones/50 10.00 25.00
17 Alfonso Soriano / Derek Jeter/50 15.00 40.00
18 Jeff Bagwell / Lance Berkman/50 10.00 25.00
19 Alex Rodriguez / Rafael Palmeiro/50 10.00 25.00
20 Adam Dunn / Austin Kearns/25 8.00 20.00
21 Al Kaline/100 6.00 15.00
22 Babe Ruth/50 100.00 175.00
23 Cal Ripken/100 15.00 40.00
24 Dale Murphy/100 6.00 15.00
25 Don Mattingly/100 6.00 15.00
26 George Brett/100 6.00 15.00
27 Lou Gehrig/100 50.00 100.00
28 Mike Schmidt/100 6.00 15.00
29 Roberto Clemente/100 30.00 60.00
30 Roy Campanella/100 6.00 15.00
31 Babe Ruth / Roger Maris /25 150.00 250.00
32 Harmon Killebrew / Kirby Puckett /50 15.00 40.00
33 Paul Molitor / Robin Yount /50 10.00 25.00
34 Reggie Jackson / Reggie Jackson /50 10.00 25.00
35 Lou Gehrig / Ty Cobb /50 125.00 200.00
36 Don Mattingly / Jason Giambi /50 12.50 30.00
37 Ted Williams / Nomar Garciaparra /50 40.00 80.00
38 Andre Dawson / Sammy Sosa /50 10.00 25.00
39 Dale Murphy / Chipper Jones /50 10.00 25.00
40 Stan Musial / Jim Edmonds /50 12.50 30.00

2004 Donruss Elite Back 2 Back Jacks Combos

*COMBO 1-15: .75X TO 2X B2B p/r 125
*COMBO 1-15: .4X TO 1X B2B p/r 25
*COMBO 16-20: .6X TO 1.5X B2B p/r 50
*COMBO 16-20: .5X TO 1.2X B2B p/r 25
*COMBO 21-30 p/r 50:.6X TO 1.5X BTBp/r100
*COMBO 21-30 p/r 25: 1X TO 2.5X BTB p/r 100
*COMBO 21-30 p/r 25: .6X TO 1.5X BTB p/r 50
*COMBO 31-40 p/r 25: .6X TO 1.5X B2B p/r 50
RANDOM INSERTS IN PACKS
SINGLE PRINT RUNS B/WN 25-50 PER
DUAL PRINT RUNS B/WN 10-25 PER
NO PRICING ON QTY OF 10 OR LESS
12 N.Garciaparra Bat-Jsy/50 10.00 25.00
22 Babe Ruth Bat-Jsy/25 250.00 400.00
27 Lou Gehrig Bat-Jsy/25 150.00 250.00
35 Lou Gehrig Bat-Jsy / Ty Cobb Bat-Jsy/25 250.00 400.00
37 Ted Williams Bat-Jsy / Nomar Garciaparra Bat-Jsy/25 75.00 150.00

2004 Donruss Elite Back to the Future

1-6 PRINT RUN 500 SERIAL #'d SETS
6-9 PRINT RUN 250 SERIAL #'d SETS
*BLACK 1-6: 1X TO 2.5X BASIC
*BLACK 7-9: 1.25X TO 3X BASIC
BLACK 1-6 PRINT RUN 50 SERIAL #'d SETS
BLACK 7-9 PRINT RUN 25 SERIAL #'d SETS
*GOLD 1-6: .6X TO 1.5X BASIC
*GOLD 7-9: .75X TO 2X BASIC
GOLD 1-6 PRINT RUN 100 SERIAL #'d SETS
GOLD 7-9 PRINT RUN 50 SERIAL #'d SETS
*RED 1-6: .5X TO 1.2X BASIC
*RED 7-9: .5X TO 1.2X BASIC
RED 1-6 PRINT RUN 250 SERIAL #'d SETS
RED 7-9 PRINT RUN 125 SERIAL #'d SETS
RANDOM INSERTS IN PACKS
1 Tim Hudson 1.25 3.00
2 Rich Harden 1.25 3.00
3 Alex Rodriguez Rgr 2.50 6.00
4 Hank Blalock 1.25 3.00
5 Sammy Sosa 1.50 4.00
6 Hee Seop Choi 1.25 3.00
7 Tim Hudson / Rich Harden 1.50 4.00
8 Alex Rodriguez / Hank Blalock 3.00 8.00
9 Sammy Sosa / Hee Seop Choi 2.00 5.00

2004 Donruss Elite Back to the Future Bats

1-6 PRINT RUN 200 SERIAL #'d SETS
8-9 PRINT RUN 100 SERIAL #'d SETS
RANDOM INSERTS IN PACKS
1 Tim Hudson 2.50 6.00
3 Alex Rodriguez Rgr 4.00 10.00
4 Hank Blalock 2.50 6.00
5 Sammy Sosa 3.00 8.00
6 Hee Seop Choi 2.50 6.00
8 Alex Rodriguez 6.00 15.00
Hank Blalock
9 Sammy Sosa 5.00 12.00
Hee Seop Choi

2004 Donruss Elite Back to the Future Jerseys

1-6 PRINT RUN 200 SERIAL #'d SETS
7-9 PRINT RUN 100 SERIAL #'d SETS
*PRIME: 1.25X TO 3X BASIC
PRIME 1-6 PRINT RUN 50 SERIAL #'d SETS
PRIME 7-9 PRINT RUN 25 SERIAL #'d SETS
RANDOM INSERTS IN PACKS
1 Tim Hudson 2.50 6.00
2 Rich Harden 2.50 6.00
3 Alex Rodriguez Rgr 4.00 10.00
4 Hank Blalock 2.50 6.00
5 Sammy Sosa 3.00 8.00
6 Hee Seop Choi 2.50 6.00
7 Tim Hudson 4.00 10.00
Rich Harden
8 Alex Rodriguez 6.00 15.00
Hank Blalock
9 Sammy Sosa 5.00 12.00
Hee Seop Choi

2004 Donruss Elite Career Best

STATED PRINT RUN 1000 SERIAL #'d SETS
*BLACK: 1.25X TO 3X BASIC
BLACK PRINT RUN 100 SERIAL #'d SETS
*GOLD p/r 220-390: 1X TO 2.5X BASIC
*GOLD p/r 130-193: 1X TO 2.5X BASIC
*GOLD p/r 113-116: 1.25X TO 3X BASIC
*GOLD p/r 40-57: 2X TO 5X BASIC
*GOLD p/r 23-33: 3X TO 8X BASIC
*GOLD p/r 18-20: 4X TO 10X BASIC
GOLD PRINT RUNS B/WN 14-393 PER
NO GOLD PRICING ON QTY OF 14 OR LESS
RANDOM INSERTS IN PACKS
1 Albert Pujols 1.50 4.00
2 Alex Rodriguez Rgr 1.25 3.00
3 Alfonso Soriano .60 1.50
4 Andruw Jones .75 2.00
5 Barry Zito .60 1.50
6 Cal Ripken 3.00 8.00
7 Chipper Jones .75 2.00
8 Curt Schilling .60 1.50
9 Derek Jeter 1.50 4.00
10 Don Mattingly 2.00 5.00
11 Dontrelle Willis .75 2.00
12 Doc Gooden .75 2.00
13 Eddie Murray 1.00 2.50
14 Frank Thomas .75 2.00
15 Gary Sheffield .60 1.50
16 George Brett 2.00 5.00
17 Greg Maddux 1.25 3.00
18 Hideo Nomo .75 2.00
19 Ichiro Suzuki 1.50 4.00
20 Ivan Rodriguez .75 2.00
21 Jason Giambi .60 1.50
22 Jeff Bagwell .75 2.00
23 Jim Thome .75 2.00
24 Kerry Wood .60 1.50
25 Lance Berkman .60 1.50
26 Magglio Ordonez .60 1.50
27 Mark Prior .75 2.00
28 Mike Piazza 1.25 3.00
29 Mike Schmidt 2.00 5.00
30 Nomar Garciaparra .75 2.00
31 Pedro Martinez .75 2.00
32 Randy Johnson .75 2.00
33 Roger Clemens 1.25 3.00
34 Sammy Sosa .75 2.00
35 Tony Gwynn 1.25 3.00

2004 Donruss Elite Career Best Bats

PRINT RUNS B/WN 100-200 COPIES PER
*COMBO p/r 50: 1X TO 2.5X BASIC p/r 200
*COMBO p/r 50: .75X TO 2X BASIC p/r 100
*COMBO p/r 25: 1.25X TO 3X BASIC p/r 200
COMBO PRINT RUNS B/WN 25-50 PER
RANDOM INSERTS IN PACKS
1 Albert Pujols/200 6.00 15.00
2 Alex Rodriguez Rgr/200 4.00 10.00
3 Alfonso Soriano/200 2.50 6.00
4 Andruw Jones/200 3.00 8.00
5 Barry Zito/200 2.50 6.00
6 Cal Ripken/200 15.00 40.00
7 Chipper Jones/200 3.00 8.00
8 Curt Schilling/200 2.50 6.00
9 Derek Jeter/200 6.00 15.00
10 Don Mattingly/200 6.00 15.00
11 Dontrelle Willis/100 4.00 10.00
12 Doc Gooden/200 3.00 8.00
13 Eddie Murray/200 4.00 10.00
14 Frank Thomas/200 3.00 8.00
15 Gary Sheffield/200 2.50 6.00
16 George Brett/200 6.00 15.00
17 Greg Maddux/100 5.00 12.00
18 Hideo Nomo/100 4.00 10.00
20 Ivan Rodriguez/200 3.00 8.00
21 Jason Giambi/200 2.50 6.00
22 Jeff Bagwell/200 3.00 8.00
23 Jim Thome/200 3.00 8.00
24 Kerry Wood/100 3.00 8.00
25 Lance Berkman/200 2.50 6.00
26 Magglio Ordonez/200 2.50 6.00
27 Mark Prior/100 4.00 10.00
28 Mike Piazza/200 4.00 10.00
29 Mike Schmidt/200 6.00 15.00
30 Nomar Garciaparra/200 4.00 10.00
31 Pedro Martinez/200 3.00 8.00
32 Randy Johnson/200 3.00 8.00
33 Roger Clemens/200 6.00 15.00
34 Sammy Sosa/200 3.00 8.00
35 Tony Gwynn/200 6.00 15.00

2004 Donruss Elite Career Best Jerseys

PRINT RUNS B/WN 50-200 COPIES PER
*PRIME p/r 50: 1.25X TO 3X BASIC p/r 200
*PRIME p/r 25: 1.5X TO 4X BASIC p/r 200
*PRIME p/r 25: 1X TO 2.5X BASIC p/r 100
*PRIME p/r 25: 1X TO 2.5X BASIC p/r 50
PRIME PRINT RUNS B/WN 25-50 COPIES PER
RANDOM INSERTS IN PACKS
1 Albert Pujols/200 6.00 15.00
2 Alex Rodriguez/200 4.00 10.00
3 Alfonso Soriano/200 2.50 6.00
4 Andruw Jones/200 3.00 8.00
5 Barry Zito/200 2.50 6.00
6 Cal Ripken/50 30.00 60.00
7 Chipper Jones/200 3.00 8.00
8 Curt Schilling/200 2.50 6.00
9 Derek Jeter/200 6.00 15.00
10 Don Mattingly/50 12.50 30.00
11 Dontrelle Willis/200 3.00 8.00
12 Doc Gooden/200 3.00 8.00
13 Eddie Murray/200 4.00 10.00
14 Frank Thomas/200 3.00 8.00
15 Gary Sheffield/200 2.50 6.00
16 George Brett/50 12.50 30.00
17 Greg Maddux/200 4.00 10.00
18 Hideo Nomo/200 4.00 10.00
20 Ivan Rodriguez/200 3.00 8.00
21 Jason Giambi/200 2.50 6.00
22 Jeff Bagwell/200 3.00 8.00
23 Jim Thome/200 3.00 8.00
24 Kerry Wood/200 2.50 6.00
25 Lance Berkman/200 2.50 6.00
26 Magglio Ordonez/200 2.50 6.00
27 Mark Prior/200 3.00 8.00
28 Mike Piazza/200 4.00 10.00
29 Mike Schmidt/100 10.00 25.00
30 Nomar Garciaparra/200 4.00 10.00
31 Pedro Martinez/200 3.00 8.00
32 Randy Johnson/200 3.00 8.00
33 Roger Clemens/200 6.00 15.00
34 Sammy Sosa/200 3.00 8.00
35 Tony Gwynn/50 10.00 25.00

2004 Donruss Elite Fans of the Game

RANDOM INSERTS IN PACKS
201 James Gandolfini 1.25 3.00
202 Freddy Adu 1.25 3.00
203 Summer Sanders .75 2.00
204 Janet Evans .75 2.00
205 Brandi Chastain 1.25 3.00

2004 Donruss Elite Fans of the Game Autographs

This five card insert set, which was randomly inserted into packs, was the lead-off insert of

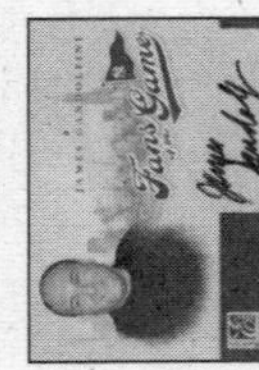

inserting autograph cards of living celebrities from other fields into major sport mainstream packs. Among the players in these packs were teenage soccer sensation Freddy Adu and star of Television show "The Sopranos" James Gandolfini.

RANDOM INSERTS IN PACKS
SP PRINT RUNS PROVIDED BY DONRUSS
SP'S ARE NOT SERIAL-NUMBERED
201 James Gandolfini 30.00 60.00
202 Freddy Adu 20.00 50.00
203 Summer Sanders SP/250 20.00 50.00
204 Janet Evans SP/250 15.00 40.00
205 Brandi Chastain SP/250 20.00 50.00

2004 Donruss Elite Passing the Torch

1-30 PRINT RUN 1000 SERIAL #'d SETS
31-45 PRINT RUN 500 SERIAL #'d SETS
*BLACK 1-30: .75X TO 2X BASIC
*BLACK 31-45: 1X TO 2.5X BASIC
BLACK 1-30 PRINT RUN 100 #'d SETS
BLACK 31-45 PRINT RUN 50 #'d SETS
*BLUE 1-30: .6X TO 1.5X BASIC
*BLUE 31-45: .6X TO 1.5X BASIC
BLUE 1-30 PRINT RUN 250 #'d SETS
BLUE 31-45 PRINT RUN 125 #'d SETS
*GOLD 1-30: 1.25X TO 3X BASIC
*GOLD 31-45: 1.5X TO 4X BASIC
GOLD 1-30 PRINT RUN 50 #'d SETS
GOLD 31-45 PRINT RUN 25 #'d SETS
*GREEN 1-30: .5X TO 1.2X BASIC
*GREEN 31-45: .5X TO 1.2X BASIC
GREEN 1-30 PRINT RUN 500 #'d SETS
GREEN 31-45 PRINT RUN 250 #'d SETS
RANDOM INSERTS IN PACKS
1 Whitey Ford 1.50 4.00
2 Andy Pettitte 1.25 3.00
3 Willie McCovey 1.25 3.00
4 Will Clark 1.50 4.00
5 Stan Musial 2.50 6.00
6 Albert Pujols 2.50 6.00
7 Andre Dawson 1.25 3.00
8 Vladimir Guerrero 1.25 3.00
9 Dale Murphy 1.50 4.00
10 Chipper Jones 1.25 3.00
11 Joe Morgan 1.25 3.00
12 Barry Larkin 1.50 4.00
13 Catfish Hunter 1.50 4.00
14 Tim Hudson 1.00 2.50
15 Jim Rice 1.25 3.00
16 Manny Ramirez 1.25 3.00
17 Greg Maddux 2.00 5.00
18 Mark Prior 1.25 3.00
19 Don Mattingly 3.00 8.00
20 Jason Giambi 1.00 2.50
21 Roy Campanella 1.50 4.00
22 Mike Piazza 2.00 5.00
23 Ozzie Smith 2.50 6.00
24 Scott Rolen 1.25 3.00
25 Roger Clemens 2.50 6.00
26 Mike Mussina 1.25 3.00
27 Babe Ruth 3.00 8.00
28 Roger Maris 1.50 4.00
29 Nolan Ryan 4.00 10.00
30 Roy Oswalt 1.00 2.50
31 Whitey Ford 2.00 5.00
Andy Pettitte
32 Willie McCovey 2.00 5.00
Will Clark
33 Stan Musial 3.00 8.00
Albert Pujols
34 Andre Dawson 2.00 5.00
Vladimir Guerrero
35 Dale Murphy 2.00 5.00
Chipper Jones
36 Joe Morgan 2.00 5.00
Barry Larkin
37 Catfish Hunter 2.00 5.00
Tim Hudson
38 Jim Rice 2.00 5.00
Manny Ramirez
39 Greg Maddux 2.50 6.00
Mark Prior
40 Don Mattingly 4.00 10.00
Jason Giambi
41 Roy Campanella 2.50 6.00
Mike Piazza
42 Ozzie Smith 3.00 8.00
Scott Rolen
43 Roger Clemens 3.00 8.00
Mike Mussina
44 Babe Ruth 4.00 10.00
Roger Maris
45 Nolan Ryan 5.00 12.00
Roy Oswalt

2004 Donruss Elite Passing the Torch Autographs

RANDOM INSERTS IN PACKS
SINGLE PRINT RUNS B/WN 5-50 PER
DUAL PRINT RUNS B/WN 1-5 COPIES PER

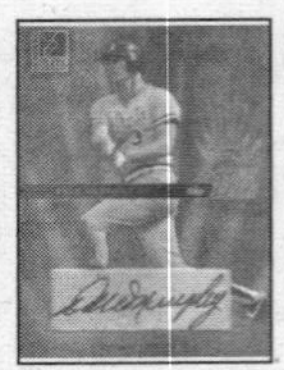

NO PRICING ON QTY OF 10 OR LESS
1 Whitey Ford/10
3 Willie McCovey/10
4 Will Clark/15 75.00 150.00
6 Stan Musial/10
7 Andre Dawson/50 8.00 20.00
8 Vladimir Guerrero/5
9 Dale Murphy/50 10.00 25.00
10 Chipper Jones/5
11 Joe Morgan/15 15.00 40.00
12 Barry Larkin/10
14 Tim Hudson/15 30.00 60.00
15 Jim Rice/50 8.00 20.00
16 Manny Ramirez/5
17 Greg Maddux/5
18 Mark Prior/15 20.00 50.00
19 Don Mattingly/10
22 Mike Piazza/5
23 Ozzie Smith/5
24 Scott Rolen/15 30.00 60.00
25 Roger Clemens/5
26 Mike Mussina/5
29 Nolan Ryan/10
30 Roy Oswalt/50 8.00 20.00
32 Willie McCovey
Will Clark/5
33 Stan Musial
Albert Pujols/5
34 Andre Dawson
Vladimir Guerrero/5
35 Dale Murphy
Chipper Jones/5
36 Joe Morgan
Barry Larkin/5
38 Jim Rice
Manny Ramirez/5
39 Greg Maddux
Mark Prior/5
42 Ozzie Smith
Scott Rolen/5
43 Roger Clemens
Mike Mussina/5
44 Babe Ruth
Roger Maris/1
45 Nolan Ryan
Roy Oswalt/5

2004 Donruss Elite Passing the Torch Bats

1-30 PRINT RUNS B/WN 25-200 COPIES PER
31-45 PRINT RUNS B/WN 25-50 COPIES PER
RANDOM INSERTS IN PACKS
2 Andy Pettitte/200 3.00 8.00
3 Willie McCovey/100 4.00 10.00
4 Will Clark/100 6.00 15.00
5 Stan Musial/100 12.50 30.00
6 Albert Pujols/200 6.00 15.00
7 Andre Dawson/100 4.00 10.00
8 Vladimir Guerrero/200 3.00 8.00
9 Dale Murphy/100 6.00 15.00
10 Chipper Jones/200 3.00 8.00
11 Joe Morgan/200 3.00 8.00
12 Barry Larkin/200 3.00 8.00
14 Tim Hudson/200 2.50 6.00
15 Jim Rice/200 3.00 8.00
16 Manny Ramirez/200 3.00 8.00
17 Greg Maddux/200 4.00 10.00
18 Mark Prior/200 3.00 8.00
19 Don Mattingly/100 8.00 20.00
20 Jason Giambi/200 2.50 6.00
21 Roy Campanella/50 12.50 30.00
22 Mike Piazza/200 4.00 10.00
23 Ozzie Smith/200 6.00 15.00
24 Scott Rolen/200 3.00 8.00
25 Roger Clemens/200 6.00 15.00
26 Mike Mussina/200 3.00 8.00
27 Babe Ruth/25 100.00 200.00
28 Roger Maris/50 20.00 50.00
29 Nolan Ryan/100 10.00 25.00
30 Roy Oswalt/200 2.50 6.00
32 Willie McCovey 10.00 25.00
Will Clark /50
33 Stan Musial 20.00 50.00
Albert Pujols /50
34 Andre Dawson 10.00 25.00
Vladimir Guerrero /50
35 Dale Murphy 10.00 25.00
Chipper Jones /50
36 Joe Morgan 10.00 25.00
Barry Larkin /50
38 Jim Rice 10.00 25.00
Manny Ramirez /50
39 Greg Maddux 15.00 40.00
Mark Prior /50
40 Don Mattingly 15.00 40.00
Jason Giambi /50
41 Roy Campanella 15.00 40.00
Mike Piazza /25
42 Ozzie Smith 12.50 30.00
Scott Rolen /50
43 Roger Clemens 12.50 30.00
Mike Mussina /50
44 Babe Ruth 150.00 250.00
Roger Maris /25
45 Nolan Ryan 15.00 40.00
Roy Oswalt /50

2004 Donruss Elite Passing the Torch Jerseys

1-30 PRINT RUNS B/WN 25-200 COPIES PER
31-45 PRINT RUNS B/WN 25-50 COPIES PER
RANDOM INSERTS IN PACKS
1 Whitey Ford/100 6.00 15.00
2 Andy Pettitte/200 3.00 8.00
3 Willie McCovey/100 4.00 10.00
4 Will Clark/100 6.00 15.00
5 Stan Musial/100 12.50 30.00
6 Albert Pujols/200 6.00 15.00
7 Andre Dawson/200 3.00 8.00
8 Vladimir Guerrero/200 3.00 8.00
9 Dale Murphy/100 6.00 15.00
10 Chipper Jones/200 3.00 8.00
11 Joe Morgan/100 4.00 10.00
12 Barry Larkin/200 3.00 8.00
13 Catfish Hunter/100 6.00 15.00
14 Tim Hudson/200 2.50 6.00
15 Jim Rice/200 3.00 8.00
16 Manny Ramirez/200 3.00 8.00
18 Mark Prior/200 3.00 8.00
19 Don Mattingly/100 10.00 25.00
20 Jason Giambi/200 2.50 6.00
21 Roy Campanella/50 12.50 30.00
22 Mike Piazza/200 4.00 10.00
23 Ozzie Smith/100 8.00 20.00
24 Scott Rolen/200 3.00 8.00
25 Roger Clemens/200 6.00 15.00
26 Mike Mussina/200 3.00 8.00
27 Babe Ruth/25 250.00 400.00
28 Roger Maris/50 30.00 60.00
29 Nolan Ryan/100 12.50 30.00
30 Roy Oswalt/200 2.50 6.00
31 Whitey Ford 10.00 25.00
Andy Pettitte/50
32 Willie McCovey 10.00 25.00
Will Clark/50
33 Stan Musial 20.00 50.00
Albert Pujols/50
34 Andre Dawson 10.00 25.00
Vladimir Guerrero/50
35 Dale Murphy 10.00 25.00
Chipper Jones/50
36 Joe Morgan 10.00 25.00
Barry Larkin/50
37 Catfish Hunter 10.00 25.00
Tim Hudson/50
38 Jim Rice 10.00 25.00
Manny Ramirez/50
40 Don Mattingly 15.00 40.00
Jason Giambi/50
41 Roy Campanella 20.00 50.00
Mike Piazza/25
42 Ozzie Smith 12.50 30.00
Scott Rolen/50
43 Roger Clemens 12.50 30.00
Mike Mussina/50
44 Babe Ruth
Roger Maris/25
45 Nolan Ryan 20.00 50.00
Roy Oswalt/50

2004 Donruss Elite Recollection Autographs

RANDOM INSERTS IN PACKS
PRINT RUNS B/WN 1-95 COPIES PER
NO PRICING ON QTY OF 14 OR LESS
1 Jeremy Affeldt 01/25 8.00 20.00
2 Erick Almonte 01/26 6.00 15.00
3 Rich Aurilia 02/2
4 Jeff Baker 02/25 15.00 40.00
5 Brandon Berger 01/25 6.00 15.00
6 Marlon Byrd 01/24 8.00 20.00
7 Juan Cruz 01/5
8 Ryan Drese 02/45 6.00 15.00
9 Brandon Duckworth 01/16 6.00 15.00
10 Casey Fossum 01/23 8.00 20.00
11 Geronimo Gil 01/25 6.00 15.00
12 Mark Grace 02/2
13 Jeremy Guthrie 02/25 8.00 20.00
14 Nic Jackson 02/95 4.00 10.00
15 Barry Larkin 01 PCRD/4
16 Greg Maddux 01 Ser/1
17 Antonio Perez 01/3
18 Mark Prior 01/14
19 Ivan Rodriguez 01 Ser/3
20 Ivan Rodriguez 01 SerDom/3
21 Ricardo Rodriguez 01/25 6.00 15.00
22 Ruben Sierra 97 GS/1
23 Bud Smith 01/25 6.00 15.00
24 Sammy Sosa 01/1
25 Junior Spivey 01/20 8.00 20.00
26 Tim Spooneybarger 01/25 6.00 15.00
27 Mark Teixeira 01/6
28 Martin Vargas 01/37 4.00 10.00

2004 Donruss Elite Team

STATED PRINT RUN 1500 SERIAL #'d SETS
*BLACK: 1X TO 2.5X BASIC
BLACK PRINT RUN 150 SERIAL #'d SETS
*GOLD: .75X TO 2X BASIC
GOLD PRINT RUN 250 SERIAL #'d SETS
RANDOM INSERTS IN PACKS
1 Cal Ripken 4.00 10.00
Eddie Murray
Jim Palmer
2 Derek Jeter 2.00 5.00
Roger Clemens
Bernie Williams
Andy Pettitte
3 Johnny Bench 2.00 5.00
Tony Perez
George Foster
Dave Concepcion
4 Josh Beckett 1.00 2.50
Dontrelle Willis
Ivan Rodriguez
5 Randy Johnson 1.00 2.50
Curt Schilling
Luis Gonzalez
Mark Grace
6 Derek Jeter 2.00 5.00
Wade Boggs
Darryl Strawberry
7 Chipper Jones 2.00 5.00
Tom Glavine
Greg Maddux
Ryan Klesko
8 Doc Gooden 1.00 2.50
Gary Carter
Darryl Strawberry
9 Jackie Robinson 1.25 3.00
Roy Campanella
Duke Snider
10 Phil Rizzuto 1.25 3.00
Yogi Berra
Whitey Ford
11 Stan Musial 2.00 5.00
Red Schoendienst
Marty Marion
Enos Slaughter

2004 Donruss Elite Team Bats

RANDOM INSERTS IN PACKS
STATED PRINT RUN 100 SERIAL #'d SETS
2 Derek Jeter 15.00 40.00
Roger Clemens
Bernie Williams
Andy Pettitte
3 Johnny Bench 20.00 50.00
Tony Perez
George Foster
Dave Concepcion
4 Josh Beckett 6.00 15.00
Dontrelle Willis
Ivan Rodriguez
5 Randy Johnson 10.00 25.00
Curt Schilling
Luis Gonzalez
Mark Grace
6 Derek Jeter 12.50 30.00
Wade Boggs
Darryl Strawberry
7 Chipper Jones 12.50 30.00
Tom Glavine
Greg Maddux
Ryan Klesko
8 Doc Gooden 6.00 15.00
Gary Carter
Darryl Strawberry

2004 Donruss Elite Team Jerseys

RANDOM INSERTS IN PACKS
STATED PRINT RUN 100 SERIAL #'d SETS
JACKIE/CAMPY/SNIDER PRINT 50 #'d CARDS
ROY CAMPANELLA SWATCH IS PANTS
1 Cal Ripken 30.00 60.00
Eddie Murray
Jim Palmer
2 Derek Jeter 15.00 40.00
Roger Clemens
Bernie Williams

Andy Pettitte
4 Josh Beckett 6.00 15.00
Dontrelle Willis
Ivan Rodriguez
5 Randy Johnson 10.00 25.00
Curt Schilling
Luis Gonzalez
Mark Grace
6 Derek Jeter 12.50 30.00
Wade Boggs
Darryl Strawberry
7 Chipper Jones 12.50 30.00
Tom Glavine
Greg Maddux
Ryan Klesko
9 Jackie Robinson 40.00 80.00
Roy Campanella Pants
Duke Snider/50
10 Phil Rizzuto 15.00 40.00
Yogi Berra
Whitey Ford
11 Stan Musial 30.00 60.00
Red Schoendienst
Marty Marion
Enos Slaughter

2004 Donruss Elite Throwback Threads

1-20 PRINT RUN 150 SERIAL #'d SETS
21-30 PRINT RUN 75 SERIAL #'d SETS
RUTH 31 PRINT RUN 50 #'d CARDS
32-50 PRINT RUN 100 SERIAL #'d SETS
RUTH/GEHRIG 51 PRINT 25 #'d CARDS
52-60 PRINT RUN 50 SERIAL #'d SETS
*PRIME 1-20: 1.5X TO 4X BASIC 1-20
*PRIME 21-30: 1X TO 2.5X BASIC 21-30
*PRIME 31-50: 1.25X TO 3X BASIC 31-50
PRIME SINGLE PRINTS B/WN 10-25 PER
PRIME DUAL PRINTS B/WN 5-15 PER
NO PRIME PRICING ON QTY OF 10 OR LESS
RANDOM INSERTS IN PACKS
CARD NUMBER 3 DOES NOT EXIST
1 Albert Pujols/150 6.00 15.00
2 Alex Rodriguez Rgr/150 4.00 10.00
4 Chipper Jones/150 3.00 8.00
5 Derek Jeter/150 6.00 15.00
6 Greg Maddux/150 4.00 10.00
7 Hideo Nomo/150 4.00 10.00
8 Miguel Cabrera/150 3.00 8.00
9 Ivan Rodriguez/150 3.00 8.00
10 Jason Giambi/150 2.50 6.00
11 Jeff Bagwell/150 3.00 8.00
12 Lance Berkman/150 2.50 6.00
13 Mark Prior/150 3.00 8.00
14 Mike Piazza/150 4.00 10.00
15 Nomar Garciaparra/150 4.00 10.00
16 Pedro Martinez/150 3.00 8.00
17 Randy Johnson/150 3.00 8.00
18 Sammy Sosa/150 3.00 8.00
19 Shawn Green/150 2.50 6.00
20 Vladimir Guerrero/150 3.00 8.00
21 Adam Dunn 6.00 15.00
Austin Kearns /75
22 Barry Zito 6.00 15.00
Mark Mulder /75
23 Curt Schilling 6.00 15.00
Curt Schilling /75
24 Derek Jeter 12.50 30.00
Jason Giambi /75
25 Dontrelle Willis 8.00 20.00
Josh Beckett /75
26 Frank Thomas 8.00 20.00
Magglio Ordonez /75
27 Jim Thome 8.00 20.00
Jim Thome /75
28 Kerry Wood 6.00 15.00
Mark Prior /75
29 Hank Blalock 8.00 20.00
Mark Teixeira /75
30 Albert Pujols 15.00 40.00
Scott Rolen /75
31 Babe Ruth/50 200.00 300.00
32 Cal Ripken/100 20.00 50.00
33 Carl Yastrzemski/100 10.00 25.00
34 Deion Sanders/100 6.00 15.00
35 Don Mattingly/100 10.00 25.00
36 George Brett/100 10.00 25.00
37 Jim Palmer/100 4.00 10.00
38 Kirby Puckett/100 6.00 15.00
39 Lou Gehrig/100 125.00 200.00
40 Mark Grace/100 6.00 15.00
41 Mike Schmidt/100 10.00 25.00
42 Nolan Ryan/100 12.50 30.00
43 Ozzie Smith/100 8.00 20.00
44 Reggie Jackson/100 6.00 15.00
45 Rickey Henderson/100 6.00 15.00
46 Roberto Clemente/100 40.00 80.00
47 Roger Clemens/100 8.00 20.00
48 Roger Maris/100 20.00 50.00
49 Roy Campanella Pants/100 10.00 25.00
50 Tony Gwynn/100 8.00 20.00
51 Babe Ruth 300.00 500.00
Lou Gehrig /25
52 Cal Ripken 30.00 60.00
Eddie Murray /50
53 Ted Williams 50.00 100.00
Carl Yastrzemski /50
54 Andre Dawson 8.00 20.00
Gary Carter /50
55 Reggie Jackson 10.00 25.00
Rod Carew /50
56 Derek Jeter 20.00 50.00
Phil Rizzuto /50
57 Nolan Ryan 20.00 50.00
Roy Oswalt /50
58 Roger Clemens 12.50 30.00
Mike Mussina /50
59 Albert Pujols 20.00 50.00
Stan Musial /50
60 Nomar Garciaparra 50.00 100.00
Ted Williams /50

2004 Donruss Elite Throwback Threads Autographs

STATED PRINT RUN 25 SERIAL #'d SETS
PRIME PRINT RUNS B/WN 5-10 COPIES PER
NO PRIME PRICING DUE TO SCARCITY
RANDOM INSERTS IN PACKS
9 Ivan Rodriguez/25 40.00 80.00
13 Mark Prior/25 20.00 50.00
18 Sammy Sosa/25 50.00 100.00
35 Don Mattingly/25 75.00 150.00
37 Jim Palmer/25 20.00 50.00

2004 Donruss Elite Extra Edition

This 286-card set was released in December, 2004. The set was issued in five card packs with an $6 SRP which came 12 packs to a box and 32 boxes to case. Cards numbered 1-150 featured active veterans while cards numbered 206 through 215 feature retired players and cards 216 through 355 are all Rookie Cards including many players drafted in 2004. This is the set in which Donruss had the right to picture any player drafted and later signed from the 2004 amateur draft. Each company, which the exception of Topps (who signs their players individually), was allowed to have one product with a full run of 2004 amateur draft in it. This was Donruss' product for that purpose.

COMP.SET w/o SP's (150) 10.00 25.00
COMMON CARD (1-150) .10 .30
COMMON CARD (206-215) 1.25 3.00
206-215 RANDOM INSERTS IN PACKS
206-215 PRINT RUN 1000 SERIAL #'d SETS
COMMON NO AU (234-254) 1.50 4.00
NO AU 234-254 RANDOM IN PACKS
NO AU 234-254 PRINT RUN 1000 #'d SETS
216-355 OVERALL AU-GU ODDS 1:4
216-355 PRINT RUNS B/WN 260-1617 PER
DO NOT EXIST: 151-205/232/236-238/240
DO NOT EXIST: 241/245/248-249/251/255
DO NOT EXIST: 274/339
1 Troy Glaus .10 .30
2 John Lackey .10 .30
3 Garret Anderson .10 .30
4 Francisco Rodriguez .10 .30
5 Casey Kotchman .10 .30
6 Jose Guillen .10 .30
7 Miguel Tejada .10 .30
8 Rafael Palmeiro .20 .50
9 Jay Gibbons .10 .30
10 Melvin Mora .10 .30
11 Javy Lopez .10 .30
12 Pedro Martinez .20 .50
13 Curt Schilling .20 .50
14 David Ortiz .30 .75
15 Manny Ramirez .20 .50
16 Nomar Garciaparra .50 1.25
17 Magglio Ordonez .10 .30
18 Frank Thomas .30 .75
19 Esteban Loaiza .10 .30
20 Paul Konerko .10 .30
21 Mark Buehrle .10 .30
22 Jody Gerut .10 .30
23 Victor Martinez .10 .30
24 C.C. Sabathia .10 .30
25 Travis Hafner .10 .30
26 Cliff Lee .10 .30
27 Jeremy Bonderman .10 .30
28 Dallas McPherson .10 .30
29 Jermaine Dye .10 .30
30 Carlos Guillen .10 .30
31 Carlos Beltran .10 .30
32 Ken Harvey .10 .30
33 Mike Sweeney .10 .30
34 Angel Berroa .10 .30
35 Joe Nathan .10 .30
36 Johan Santana .30 .75
37 Jacque Jones .10 .30
38 Shannon Stewart .10 .30
39 Torii Hunter .10 .30
40 Derek Jeter .60 1.50
41 Jason Giambi .10 .30
42 Danny Graves .10 .30
43 Alfonso Soriano .10 .30
44 Gary Sheffield .10 .30
45 Mike Mussina .20 .50
46 Jorge Posada .20 .50
47 Hideki Matsui .50 1.25
48 Francisco Cordero .10 .30
49 Javier Vazquez .10 .30
50 Mariano Rivera .30 .75
51 Eric Chavez .10 .30
52 Tim Hudson .10 .30
53 Mark Mulder .10 .30
54 Barry Zito .10 .30
55 Ichiro Suzuki .60 1.50
56 Edgar Martinez .20 .50
57 Bret Boone .10 .30
58 Lew Ford .10 .30
59 B.J. Upton .20 .50
60 Aubrey Huff .10 .30
61 Rocco Baldelli .10 .30
62 Carl Crawford .10 .30
63 Delmon Young .20 .50
64 Mark Teixeira .20 .50
65 Hank Blalock .10 .30
66 Michael Young .10 .30
67 Alex Rodriguez .50 1.25
68 Carlos Delgado .10 .30
69 Milton Bradley .10 .30
70 Roy Halladay .10 .30
71 Vernon Wells .10 .30
72 Randy Johnson .30 .75
73 Bobby Crosby .10 .30
74 Lyle Overbay .10 .30
75 Luis Gonzalez .10 .30
76 Steve Finley .10 .30
77 Chipper Jones .30 .75
78 Andruw Jones .20 .50
79 Marcus Giles .10 .30
80 Rafael Furcal .10 .30
81 J.D. Drew .10 .30
82 Sammy Sosa .30 .75
83 Kerry Wood .20 .50
84 Mark Prior .20 .50
85 Derrek Lee .20 .50
86 Moises Alou .10 .30
87 Carlos Zambrano .10 .30
88 Ken Griffey Jr. .50 1.25
89 Austin Kearns .10 .30
90 Adam Dunn .10 .30
91 Barry Larkin .20 .50
92 Todd Helton .20 .50
93 Larry Walker Cards .20 .50
94 Preston Wilson .10 .30
95 Sean Casey .10 .30
96 Luis Castillo .10 .30
97 Josh Beckett .10 .30
98 Mike Lowell .10 .30
99 Miguel Cabrera .20 .50
100 Brad Penny .10 .30
101 Dontrelle Willis .20 .50
102 Andy Pettitte .20 .50
103 Wade Miller .10 .30
104 Jeff Bagwell .20 .50
105 Craig Biggio .20 .50
106 Lance Berkman .20 .50
107 Jeff Kent .10 .30
108 Roy Oswalt .10 .30
109 Hideo Nomo .30 .75
110 Adrian Beltre .10 .30
111 Paul Lo Duca .10 .30
112 Shawn Green .10 .30
113 Roger Clemens .75 2.00
114 Eric Gagne .10 .30
115 Danny Kolb .10 .30
116 Rickie Weeks .10 .30
117 Scott Podsednik .10 .30
118 Livan Hernandez .10 .30
119 Orlando Cabrera .10 .30
120 Jose Vidro .10 .30
121 David Wright .75 2.00
122 Tom Glavine .20 .50
123 Al Leiter .10 .30
124 Mike Piazza .50 1.25
125 Jose Reyes .10 .30
126 Richard Hidalgo .10 .30
127 Eric Milton .10 .30
128 Jim Thome .20 .50
129 Mike Lieberthal .10 .30
130 Bobby Abreu .10 .30
131 Kip Wells .10 .30
132 Jack Wilson .10 .30
133 Jason Bay .10 .30
134 Brian Giles .10 .30
135 Sean Burroughs .10 .30
136 Khalil Greene .20 .50
137 Jake Peavy .10 .30
138 Jason Schmidt .10 .30
139 J.T. Snow .10 .30
140 Craig Wilson .10 .30
141 Chase Utley .20 .50
142 Jim Edmonds .10 .30
143 Albert Pujols .60 1.50
144 Edgar Renteria .10 .30
145 Scott Rolen .20 .50
146 Matt Morris .10 .30
147 Ivan Rodriguez .20 .50
148 Vladimir Guerrero .30 .75
149 Greg Maddux .50 1.25
150 Ben Sheets .10 .30
206 Will Clark RET 1.50 4.00
207 Nolan Ryan RET 3.00 8.00
208 Bob Feller RET 1.25 3.00
209 Red Schoendienst RET 1.25 3.00
210 Brooks Robinson RET 1.50 4.00
211 Al Kaline RET 1.50 4.00
212 Ozzie Smith RET 2.00 5.00
213 Maury Wills RET 1.25 3.00
214 Steve Carlton RET 1.25 3.00
215 Duke Snider RET 1.50 4.00
216 Scott Lewis AU/603 RC 8.00 20.00
217 Josh Johnson AU/597 RC 4.00 10.00
218 Jeff Fiorentino AU/597 RC 5.00 12.00
219 Grant Hansen AU/599 RC 3.00 8.00
220 Yov Gallardo AU/803 RC 30.00 50.00
221 Eddie Prasch AU/603 RC 4.00 10.00
222 Danny Hill AU/603 RC 3.00 8.00
223 Chuck Lofgren AU/803 RC 6.00 15.00
224 Blake Johnson AU/811 RC 4.00 10.00
225 Cory Dunlap AU/599 RC 6.00 15.00
226 Carlos Vasquez AU/869 RC 3.00 8.00
227 Jesse Crain AU/1000 RC 3.00 8.00
228 Yhency Brazoban AU/1000 3.00 8.00
229 Abe Alvarez AU/1000 RC 3.00 8.00
230 Scott Kazmir AU/350 RC 15.00 40.00
231 J.A. Happ AU/1195 RC 4.00 10.00
233 Mark Jecmen AU/1047 RC 3.00 8.00
234 Kameron Loe/1000 RC 2.00 5.00
235 Ervin Santana/1000 RC 3.00 8.00
239 Josh Karp/1000 RC 1.50 4.00
242 Alberto Callaspo/1000 RC 2.00 5.00
243 Jesse Hoover AU/1191 RC 4.00 10.00
246 Just Hoyman AU/1124 RC 4.00 10.00
247 Juan Cedeno/1000 RC 1.50 4.00
250 Jake Dittler/1000 RC 1.50 4.00
252 Ben Zobrist AU/1178 RC 8.00 20.00
253 Jeff Salazar/1000 RC 2.00 5.00
254 Fausto Carmona/1000 RC 8.00 20.00
256 Jor Vasquez AU/1000 RC 3.00 8.00
257 Raf Gonzalez AU/603 RC 3.00 8.00
258 Andrew Dobies AU/601 RC 10.00 25.00
259 Colby Miller AU/997 RC 3.00 8.00
260 K.C. Herren AU/735 RC 3.00 8.00
261 Ryan Meaux AU/546 RC 3.00 8.00
262 Dust Pedroia AU/1114 RC 50.00 100.00
263 Fern Nieve AU/1000 RC 3.00 8.00
264 Mar Gomez AU/1000 RC 3.00 8.00
265 Eric Campbell AU/260 RC 70.00 120.00
266 Billy Killian AU/703 RC 4.00 10.00
267 Mike Rouse AU/999 RC 3.00 8.00
268 Kyle Bono AU/1203 RC 3.00 8.00
269 M.Einertson AU/1047 RC 6.00 15.00
270 Scott Proctor AU/1000 RC 3.00 8.00
271 Tim Bittner AU/1000 RC 3.00 8.00
272 Christian Garcia AU/799 RC 4.00 10.00
273 Yadier Molina AU/1000 RC 8.00 20.00
275 C.Thomas AU/907 RC 3.00 8.00
276 Trav Blackley AU/1000 RC 3.00 8.00
277 F.Francisco AU/1000 RC 3.00 8.00
278 Dion Navarro AU/1000 RC 3.00 8.00
279 Joey Gathright AU/1000 RC 3.00 8.00
280 Kaz Tadano AU/1000 RC 4.00 10.00
281 Matt Bush AU/1100 RC 6.00 15.00
282 David Haehnel AU/865 RC 4.00 10.00
283 Tommy Hottovy AU/825 RC 4.00 10.00
284 Chris Carter AU/973 RC 10.00 25.00
285 Mark Rogers AU/578 RC 8.00 20.00
286 Jeremy Sowers AU/537 RC 15.00 30.00
287 Homer Bailey AU/1571 RC 15.00 40.00
288 Mike Butia AU/825 RC 3.00 8.00
289 Chris Nelson AU/465 RC 15.00 30.00
290 T.Diamond AU/1055 RC 6.00 15.00
291 Neil Walker AU/1343 RC 8.00 20.00
292 Sean Gamble AU/1229 RC 3.00 8.00
293 Bill Bray AU/1073 RC 3.00 8.00
294 Reid Brignac AU/522 RC 30.00 60.00
295 R.Klosterman AU/865 RC 3.00 8.00
296 David Purcey AU/1485 RC 3.00 8.00
297 Scott Elbert AU/1617 RC 8.00 20.00
298 Josh Fields AU/961 RC 15.00 30.00
299 Chris Lambert AU/954 RC 4.00 10.00
300 Trevor Plouffe AU/1329 RC 4.00 10.00
301 Greg Golson AU/1334 RC 4.00 10.00
302 Josh Baker AU/525 RC 3.00 8.00
303 Philip Hughes AU/1485 RC 20.00 50.00
304 Matt Macri AU/979 RC 4.00 10.00
305 Kyle Waldrop AU/823 RC 6.00 15.00
306 Rich Robnett AU/1575 RC 4.00 10.00
307 T.Tankersley AU/1073 RC 4.00 10.00
308 Blake DeWitt AU/1562 RC 8.00 20.00
309 Daryl Jones AU/575 RC 12.50 30.00
310 Eric Hurley AU/1021 RC 10.00 25.00
311 J.P. Howell AU/1453 RC 4.00 10.00
312 Zach Jackson AU/1069 RC 3.00 8.00
313 Justin Orenduff AU/473 RC 12.50 30.00
314 Tyler Lumsden AU/473 RC 4.00 10.00
315 Matt Fox AU/473 RC 4.00 10.00
316 Danny Putnam AU/473 RC 4.00 10.00
317 Jon Poterson AU/464 RC 6.00 10.00
318 Gio Gonzalez AU/473 RC 10.00 25.00
319 Jay Rainville AU/823 RC 10.00 25.00
320 Huston Street AU/709 RC 10.00 25.00
321 Jeff Marquez AU/493 RC 4.00 10.00
322 Eric Beattie AU/930 RC 4.00 10.00
323 B.Szymanski AU/1327 RC 4.00 10.00
324 Seth Smith AU/1065 RC 4.00 10.00
325 Rob Johnson AU/790 RC 4.00 10.00
326 Wes Whisler AU/473 RC 4.00 10.00
327 Billy Buckner AU/673 RC 4.00 10.00
328 Jon Zeringue AU/473 RC 3.00 8.00
329 Curtis Thigpen AU/673 RC 12.50 30.00
330 Donny Lucy AU/573 RC 3.00 8.00
331 Mike Ferris AU/558 RC 4.00 10.00
332 A.Swarzak AU/370 RC 10.00 25.00
333 Jason Jaramillo AU/573 RC 4.00 10.00
334 Hunter Pence AU/672 RC 60.00 120.00
335 Mike Rozier AU/628 RC 4.00 10.00
336 Kurt Suzuki AU/473 RC 6.00 15.00
337 Jason Vargas AU/621 RC 8.00 20.00
338 Brian Bixler AU/665 RC 10.00 25.00
340 Dexter Fowler AU/623 RC 30.00 60.00
341 Mark Trumbo AU/1321 RC 6.00 15.00
342 Jeff Frazier AU/423 RC 4.00 10.00
343 Steve Register AU/673 RC 3.00 8.00
344 M.Schlact AU/477 RC 4.00 10.00
345 Garrett Mock AU/471 RC 4.00 10.00
346 Eric Haberer AU/473 RC 4.00 10.00
347 M.Tuiasosopo AU/473 RC 10.00 25.00
348 Jason Windsor AU/473 RC 10.00 25.00
349 Grant Johnson AU/815 RC 4.00 10.00
350 J.C. Holt AU/673 RC 4.00 10.00
351 Joe Bauserman AU/472 RC 4.00 10.00
352 Jamar Walton AU/481 RC 4.00 10.00
353 Eric Patterson AU/1571 RC 6.00 15.00
354 Tyler Johnson AU/775 RC 6.00 15.00
355 Nick Adenhart AU/653 RC 50.00 100.00

2004 Donruss Elite Extra Edition Aspirations

*1-150 p/r 81-99: 4X TO 10X
*1-150 p/r 51-80: 5X TO 12X
*1-150 p/r 36-50: 6X TO 15X
*1-150 p/r 26-35: 8X TO 20X
*1-150 p/r 16-25: 10X TO 25X
*206-215 p/r 26-35: 1.25X TO 3X
*206-215 p/r 51-80: 1.5X TO 4X
*216-355 p/r 51-80: .6X TO 1.5X NO AU
*216-355 p/r 36-50: .75X TO 2X NO AU
*216-355p/r81-99: .3X TO .8X AUp/r803-1617
*216-355p/r81-99: .25X TO .6X AU p/r522-799
*216-355p/r81-99: .2X TO .5X AU p/r 350-493
*216-355p/r51-80: .4X TO 1X AU p/r 803-1617
*216-355p/r51-80: .3X TO .8X AU p/r 522-799
*216-355p/r51-80: .25X TO .6X AUp/r350-493
*216-355 p/r 51-80: .15X TO .4X AU p/r 260
*216-355p/r36-50:.5X TO 1.2X AUp/r803-1617
*216-355 p/r 36-50: .4X TO 1X AU p/r 522-799
*216-355p/r36-50: .3X TO .8X AU p/r 350-493
*216-355 p/r 26-35: .4X TO 1X AU p/r 350-493
RANDOM INSERTS IN PACKS
PRINT RUNS B/WN 4-99 COPIES PER
NO PRICING ON QTY OF 13 OR LESS
230 Scott Kazmir ROO/43 12.50 30.00
254 Fausto Carmona ROO/50 20.00 50.00
262 Dustin Pedroia ROO/88 20.00 50.00
274 Justin Leone ROO/75 3.00 8.00
303 Philip Hughes DP/75 12.50 30.00
334 Hunter Pence DP/92 40.00 80.00
340 Dexter Fowler DP/75 10.00 25.00
347 Matt Tuiasosopo DP/79 8.00 20.00
355 Nick Adenhart DP/50 20.00 50.00

2004 Donruss Elite Extra Edition Aspirations Gold

*ASP.GOLD 1-150: 10X TO 25X
*ASP.GOLD 206-215: 3X TO 8X
RANDOM INSERTS IN PACKS
STATED PRINT RUN 25 SERIAL #'d SETS
216-355 NO PRICING DUE TO SCARCITY

2004 Donruss Elite Extra Edition Status

*1-150 p/r 51-80: 5X TO 12X
*1-150 p/r 36-50: 6X TO 15X
*1-150 p/r 26-35: 8X TO 20X
*1-150 p/r 16-25: 10X TO 25X
*206-215 p/r 26-35: 2.5X TO 6X
*206-215 p/r 16-25: 3X TO 8X
*216-355 p/r 36-50: .75X TO 2X NO AU
*216-355p/r81-96: .3X TO .8X AUp/r803-1617
*216-355p/r51-80: .4X TO 1X AU p/r 803-1617
*216-355p/r51-80: .3X TO .8X AU p/r 522-799
*216-355p/r51-80: .25X TO .6X AUp/r350-493
*216-355p/r36-50:.5X TO 1.2X AUp/r803-1617
*216-355 p/r 36-50: .4X TO 1X AU p/r 522-799
*216-355p/r36-50: .3X TO .8X AU p/r 350-493
*216-355p/r26-35:.6X TO 1.5X AUp/r803-1617
*216-355p/r26-35: .5X TO 1.2X AU p/r 522-799
*216-355 p/r 26-35: .4X TO 1X AU p/r 350-493
*216-355 p/r 26-35: .25X TO .6X AU p/r 260
RANDOM INSERTS IN PACKS
PRINT RUNS B/WN 1-96 COPIES PER
1-215 NO PRICING ON QTY OF 15 OR LESS
216-355 NO PRICING ON QTY 25 OR LESS
220 Yovani Gallardo ROO/96 12.50 30.00
230 Scott Kazmir ROO/57 12.50 30.00
274 Justin Leone ROO/26 5.00 12.00
355 Nick Adenhart DP/50 20.00 50.00

2004 Donruss Elite Extra Edition Status Gold

RANDOM INSERTS IN PACKS
STATED PRINT RUN 10 SERIAL #'d SETS
NO PRICING DUE TO SCARCITY

2004 Donruss Elite Extra Edition Turn of the Century

*1-150: 2.5X TO 6X BASIC
1-150 PRINT RUN 250 SERIAL #'d SETS
*206-215: 1.25X TO 3X BASIC
*216-355: .5X TO 1.2X NO AU p/r 1000
*216-355: .3X TO .8X AU p/r 803-1617
*216-355: .25X TO .6X AU p/r 522-799
*216-355: .2X TO .5X AU p/r 350-493
*216-355: .12X TO .3X AU p/r 260
206-355 PRINT RUN 100 SERIAL #'d SETS
RANDOM INSERTS IN PACKS
220 Yovani Gallardo ROO 12.50 30.00
230 Scott Kazmir ROO 8.00 20.00
262 Dustin Pedroia ROO 20.00 50.00
274 Justin Leone ROO 2.50 6.00
303 Philip Hughes DP 10.00 25.00
334 Hunter Pence DP 60.00 120.00
347 Matt Tuiasosopo DP 4.00 10.00
355 Nick Adenhart DP 12.50 30.00

2004 Donruss Elite Extra Edition Signature

*216-355 p/r 50: 1X TO 2.5X AU p/r 803-1617
OVERALL AU-GU ODDS 1:4
PRINT RUNS B/WN 1-50 #'d COPIES PER
NO PRICING ON QTY OF 10 OR LESS
132 Jack Wilson/25 12.50 30.00
133 Jason Bay/25 12.50 30.00
234 Kameron Loe ROO/50 10.00 25.00
235 Ervin Santana ROO/50 20.00 50.00
239 Josh Karp ROO/50 8.00 20.00
247 Juan Cedeno ROO/50 8.00 20.00
253 Jeff Salazar ROO/50 10.00 25.00
254 Fausto Carmona ROO/50 75.00 150.00

2004 Donruss Elite Extra Edition Signature Aspirations

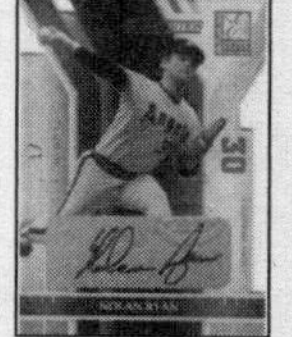

*216-355 p/r 100: .6X TO 1.5X p/r 803-1617
*216-355 p/r 100: .6X TO 1.5X p/r 522-799
*216-355 p/r 100: .5X TO 1.2X p/r 350-493
*216-355 p/r 49-50: 1.25X TO 3X p/r 803-1617
*216-355 p/r 49-50: 1X TO 2.5X p/r 522-799
*216-355 p/r 49-50: .75X TO 2X p/r 350-493
OVERALL AU-GU ODDS 1:4
PRINT RUNS B/WN 1-100 COPIES PER
NO PRICING ON QTY OF 10 OR LESS
220 Yovani Gallardo ROO/50 75.00 150.00
274 Justin Leone ROO/50 10.00 25.00
281 Matt Bush DP/100 12.50 30.00
303 Philip Hughes DP/100 20.00 50.00
334 Hunter Pence DP/50 150.00 350.00
340 Dexter Fowler DP/50 40.00 80.00
347 Matt Tuiasosopo DP/100 20.00 40.00
355 Nick Adenhart DP/100 50.00 100.00

2004 Donruss Elite Extra Edition Signature Aspirations Gold

OVERALL AU-GU ODDS 1:4
PRINT RUNS B/WN 1-25 COPIES PER
NO PRICING DUE TO SCARCITY

2004 Donruss Elite Extra Edition Signature Status

*216-355 p/r 50: 1.25X TO 3X p/r 803-1617
*216-355 p/r 50: 1X TO 2.5X p/r 522-799
*216-355 p/r 50: .75X TO 2X p/r 350-493
*216-355 p/r 50: .5X TO 1.2X p/r 260
OVERALL AU-GU ODDS 1:4
PRINT RUNS B/WN 1-50 COPIES PER
NO PRICING ON QTY OF 25 OR LESS
281 Matt Bush DP/50 15.00 40.00
289 Chris Nelson DP/50 30.00 60.00
303 Philip Hughes DP/50 50.00 100.00
308 Blake DeWitt DP/50 15.00 40.00
318 Gio Gonzalez DP/50 20.00 50.00
334 Hunter Pence DP/50 90.00 150.00
340 Dexter Fowler DP/50 40.00 80.00
347 Matt Tuiasosopo DP/50 30.00 60.00
355 Nick Adenhart DP/50 60.00 120.00

2004 Donruss Elite Extra Edition Signature Status Gold

OVERALL AU-GU ODDS 1:4
PRINT RUNS B/WN 1-10 COPIES PER
NO PRICING DUE TO SCARCITY

2004 Donruss Elite Extra Edition Signature Turn of the Century

*216-355p/r150-250: .6X TO 1.5X p/r803-1617
*216-355p/r150-250: .5X TO 1.2X p/r 522-799
*216-355p/r150-250: .4X TO 1X p/r 350-493
*216-355 p/r 100: .75X TO 2X p/r 803-1617
*216-355 p/r 100: .6X TO 1.5X p/r 522-799
*216-355 p/r 100: .5X TO 1.2X p/r 350-493
*216-355 p/r 50: .75X TO 2X p/r 350-493
OVERALL AU-GU ODDS 1:4
PRINT RUNS B/WN 1-250 COPIES PER
NO PRICING ON QTY OF 25 OR LESS
220 Yovani Gallardo ROO/100 70.00 120.00
274 Justin Leone ROO/100 6.00 15.00
281 Matt Bush DP/250 8.00 20.00
285 Mark Rogers DP/100 12.50 30.00
287 Homer Bailey DP/250 20.00 50.00
303 Philip Hughes DP/250 50.00 100.00
308 Blake DeWitt DP/250 10.00 25.00
310 Eric Hurley DP/250 12.50 30.00
334 Hunter Pence DP/200 75.00 150.00
340 Dexter Fowler DP/250 20.00 50.00
347 Matt Tuiasosopo DP/250 15.00 30.00
355 Nick Adenhart DP/100 50.00 100.00

2004 Donruss Elite Extra Edition Back to Back Picks Signature

OVERALL AU-GU ODDS 1:4
1-10 PRINT RUNS B/WN 10-50 COPIES PER
11-20 PRINT RUNS B/WN 100-250 PER
NO PRICING ON QTY OF 10 OR LESS
1 Delmon Young 30.00 60.00
Rickie Weeks/25
2 George Brett
Mike Schmidt/10
3 Adam Dunn 30.00 60.00
Austin Kearns/25
4 Bubba Crosby
Lance Berkman/10
5 Michael Young 30.00 60.00
Vernon Wells/25
6 Brian Roberts 15.00 40.00
Larry Bigbie/50
7 Ron Cey 20.00 50.00
Steve Garvey/50
8 Bill Madlock 40.00 80.00
Dave Parker/50
9 Derrek Lee 30.00 60.00
Torii Hunter
Trot Nixon/50
10 Barry Zito
Ben Sheets
Brett Myers/10
11 Chris Nelson 25.00 60.00
Matt Bush
Reid Brignac/250
12 B.J. Szymanski 15.00 40.00
Greg Golson
Jeff Frazier/250
13 Mark Trumbo 40.00 80.00
Nick Adenhart
Tyler Johnson/100
14 Chris Carter 15.00 40.00
Danny Putnam
Mark Jecmen/100
15 Billy Killian 15.00 40.00
Daryl Jones
Matt Bush/100
16 Blake DeWitt 12.50 30.00
Justin Orenduff
Scott Elbert/250
17 Jay Rainville 20.00 50.00
Kyle Waldrop
Trevor Plouffe/250
18 Jeff Marquez 20.00 50.00
Jon Poterson
Philip Hughes/100
19 Gio Gonzalez 20.00 50.00
Tyler Lumsden
Wes Whisler/100
20 Curtis Thigpen 12.50 30.00
David Purcey
Zach Jackson/100

2004 Donruss Elite Extra Edition Career Best All-Stars

RANDOM INSERTS IN PACKS
STATED PRINT RUN 500 SERIAL #'d SETS
1 Randy Johnson 1.50 4.00
2 David Ortiz 1.50 4.00
3 Edgar Renteria 1.25 3.00
4 Victor Martinez 1.25 3.00
5 Albert Pujols 3.00 8.00
6 Hideki Matsui 2.50 6.00
7 Mariano Rivera 1.50 4.00
8 Carlos Zambrano 1.25 3.00
9 Hank Blalock 1.25 3.00
10 Michael Young 1.25 3.00
11 Mike Piazza 2.50 6.00
12 Alfonso Soriano 1.25 3.00
13 Carl Crawford 1.25 3.00
14 Scott Rolen 1.50 4.00
15 Vladimir Guerrero 1.50 4.00
16 Lance Berkman 1.25 3.00
17 Todd Helton 1.50 4.00
18 Curt Schilling 1.50 4.00
19 Francisco Cordero 1.25 3.00
20 Mark Mulder 1.25 3.00
21 Sammy Sosa 1.50 4.00
22 Roger Clemens 4.00 10.00
23 Miguel Cabrera 1.50 4.00
24 Manny Ramirez 1.50 4.00
25 Jim Thome 1.50 4.00

2004 Donruss Elite Extra Edition Career Best All-Stars Jersey

STATED PRINT RUN 50 SERIAL #'d SETS
*PRIME p/r 25: .75X TO 2X BASIC
PRIME PRINT RUN B/WN 5-25 COPIES PER
NO PRIME PRICING ON QTY OF 5
OVERALL AU-GU ODDS 1:4
1 Randy Johnson 6.00 15.00
2 David Ortiz 6.00 15.00
3 Edgar Renteria 4.00 10.00
4 Victor Martinez 4.00 10.00
5 Albert Pujols 10.00 25.00
6 Hideki Matsui 12.50 30.00
7 Mariano Rivera 6.00 15.00
8 Carlos Zambrano 4.00 10.00
9 Hank Blalock 4.00 10.00
10 Michael Young 4.00 10.00
11 Mike Piazza 8.00 20.00
12 Alfonso Soriano 4.00 10.00
13 Carl Crawford 4.00 10.00
14 Scott Rolen 6.00 15.00
15 Vladimir Guerrero 6.00 15.00
16 Lance Berkman 4.00 10.00
17 Todd Helton 6.00 15.00
18 Curt Schilling 6.00 15.00
19 Francisco Cordero 4.00 10.00
20 Mark Mulder 4.00 10.00
21 Sammy Sosa 6.00 15.00
22 Roger Clemens 8.00 20.00
23 Miguel Cabrera 6.00 15.00
24 Manny Ramirez 6.00 15.00
25 Jim Thome 6.00 15.00

2004 Donruss Elite Extra Edition Career Best All-Stars Signature Jersey Gold

PRINT RUNS B/WN 1-25 COPIES PER
NO PRICING ON QTY OF 10 OR LESS
SIG BLACK PRINT RUN B/WN 1-5 PER
NO SIG BLACK PRICING DUE TO SCARCITY
SIG GOLD PRINT RUN B/WN 1-10 PER
NO SIG GOLD PRICING DUE TO SCARCITY
SIG JSY PRIME PRINT RUN B/WN 1-10 PER
NO SIG JSY PRIME PRICING AVAILABLE
OVERALL AU-GU ODDS 1:4
1 Randy Johnson/1
2 David Ortiz/25 40.00 80.00
3 Edgar Renteria/25 15.00 40.00
4 Victor Martinez/25 15.00 40.00
5 Albert Pujols/1
8 Carlos Zambrano/25 15.00 40.00
9 Hank Blalock/10
10 Michael Young/25 15.00 40.00
11 Mike Piazza/1
12 Alfonso Soriano/5
13 Carl Crawford/25 15.00 40.00
16 Lance Berkman/5
17 Todd Helton/5
18 Curt Schilling/1
19 Francisco Cordero/25 10.00 25.00
20 Mark Mulder/10
21 Sammy Sosa/1
22 Roger Clemens/1
23 Miguel Cabrera/10
24 Manny Ramirez/1

2004 Donruss Elite Extra Edition Draft Class

RANDOM INSERTS IN PACKS
STATED PRINT RUN 500 SERIAL #'d SETS
1 Johnny Bench 6.00 15.00
Nolan Ryan
2 Bert Blyleven 1.50 4.00
Dwight Evans
3 Jim Rice 1.25 3.00
Keith Hernandez
4 Dennis Eckersley 1.50 4.00
Gary Carter
5 Fred Lynn 1.50 4.00
Robin Yount
6 Andre Dawson 1.25 3.00
Lee Smith
7 Alan Trammell 1.25 3.00
Jack Morris
8 Harold Baines 1.25 3.00
Paul Molitor
9 Cal Ripken 6.00 15.00
Kirk Gibson
10 Don Mattingly 3.00 8.00
Orel Hershiser
11 Darryl Strawberry 1.25 3.00
Eric Davis
12 Dwight Gooden 1.50 4.00
Jose Canseco
13 Rafael Palmeiro 1.50 4.00
Randy Johnson
14 Curt Schilling 1.50 4.00
Gary Sheffield
15 Mike Piazza 2.50 6.00
Robin Ventura
16 Frank Thomas 1.50 4.00
Jeff Bagwell
17 Chipper Jones 1.50 4.00
Mike Mussina
18 Garret Anderson 1.50 4.00
Jorge Posada
19 Scott Rolen 1.50 4.00
Torii Hunter
20 Kerry Wood 1.50 4.00
Todd Helton
21 Eric Chavez 1.25 3.00
Roy Oswalt
22 Johnny Estrada 1.25 3.00
Vernon Wells
23 Lance Berkman 1.25 3.00
Tim Hudson
24 Mark Buehrle 1.25 3.00
Mark Mulder
25 C.C. Sabathia 1.25 3.00
Sean Burroughs
26 Albert Pujols 3.00 8.00
Barry Zito
27 Rich Harden 1.25 3.00
Rocco Baldelli
28 Bobby Crosby 1.50 4.00
Mark Teixeira
29 Casey Kotchman 1.25 3.00
Mark Prior
30 Dewon Brazelton 1.25 3.00
Jeremy Bonderman
31 J.C. Holt 2.00 5.00
Jon Zeringue
32 Kyle Bono 2.00 5.00
Matt Fox
33 Dexter Fowler 2.50 6.00
Mike Rozier
34 Huston Street 1.50 4.00
J.P. Howell
35 Grant Johnson 2.00 5.00
Matt Macri
36 Eric Beattie 2.00 5.00
Jeff Frazier
37 Jason Windsor 2.50 6.00
Kurt Suzuki
38 Josh Fields 4.00 10.00
Matt Tuiasosopo
39 Joe Bauserman 2.00 5.00
K.C. Herren
40 Chris Lambert 2.00 5.00
Eric Haberer

2004 Donruss Elite Extra Edition Draft Class Signature

OVERALL AU-GU ODDS 1:4
1-30 PRINT RUNS B/WN 5-50 COPIES PER
31-40 PRINT RUNS B/WN 100-250 PER
NO PRICING ON QTY OF 10 OR LESS
1 Johnny Bench
Nolan Ryan/10
2 Bert Blyleven 20.00 50.00
Dwight Evans/50
3 Jim Rice 15.00 40.00

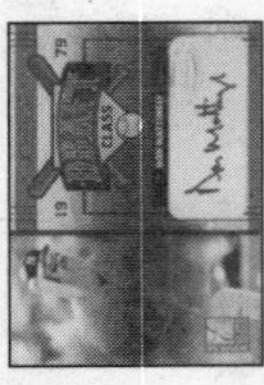

Keith Hernandez/50
4 Dennis Eckersley 30.00 60.00
Gary Carter/25
5 Fred Lynn
Robin Yount/10
6 Andre Dawson 15.00 40.00
Lee Smith/50
7 Alan Trammell 15.00 40.00
Jack Morris/50
8 Harold Baines 20.00 50.00
Paul Molitor/25
9 Cal Ripken
Kirk Gibson/10
10 Don Mattingly
Orel Hershiser/10
11 Darryl Strawberry 15.00 40.00
Eric Davis/50
12 Dwight Gooden 30.00 60.00
Jose Canseco/25
13 Rafael Palmeiro
Randy Johnson/5
14 Curt Schilling
Gary Sheffield/5
15 Mike Piazza
Robin Ventura/5
16 Frank Thomas
Jeff Bagwell/10
17 Chipper Jones
Mike Mussina/10
18 Garret Anderson
Jorge Posada/10
20 Kerry Wood
Todd Helton/5
21 Eric Chavez 20.00 50.00
Roy Oswalt/25
22 Johnny Estrada 20.00 50.00
Vernon Wells/25
23 Lance Berkman
Tim Hudson/10
24 Mark Buehrle
Mark Mulder/10
25 C.C. Sabathia 10.00 25.00
Sean Burroughs/50
26 Albert Pujols
Barry Zito/5
28 Bobby Crosby 30.00 60.00
Mark Teixeira/25
29 Casey Kotchman 20.00 50.00
Mark Prior/25
30 Dewon Brazelton 15.00 40.00
Jeremy Bonderman/50
31 J.C. Holt 10.00 25.00
Jon Zeringue/100
32 Kyle Bono 8.00 20.00
Matt Fox/100
33 Dexter Fowler 15.00 40.00
Mike Rozier/250
34 Huston Street 10.00 25.00
J.P. Howell/100
35 Grant Johnson 8.00 20.00
Matt Macri/100
36 Eric Beattie 8.00 20.00
Jeff Frazier/100
37 Jason Windsor 10.00 25.00
Kurt Suzuki/100
38 Josh Fields 20.00 50.00
Matt Tuiasosopo/100
39 Joe Bauserman 8.00 20.00
K.C. Herren/100
40 Chris Lambert 8.00 20.00
Eric Haberer/100

2004 Donruss Elite Extra Edition Passing the Torch

RANDOM INSERTS IN PACKS
STATED PRINT RUN 500 SERIAL #'d SETS
1 Dennis Eckersley 1.50 4.00
Huston Street
2 Matt Bush 2.00 5.00
Tony Gwynn
3 Homer Bailey 4.00 10.00
Tom Seaver
4 Bob Feller 2.50 6.00
Jeremy Sowers
5 Josh Fields 2.50 6.00
Robin Ventura
6 Nolan Ryan 4.00 10.00
Thomas Diamond
7 Eric Patterson 3.00 8.00
Ryne Sandberg
8 Richie Robnett 2.00 5.00
Rickey Henderson
9 Mike Ferris 2.50 6.00
Stan Musial
10 Bobby Doerr 6.00 15.00
Dustin Pedroia

2004 Donruss Elite Extra Edition Passing the Torch Autograph Gold

PRINT RUNS B/WN 5-25 COPIES PER
BLACK PRINT RUNS B/WN 5-10 PER
OVERALL AU-GU ODDS 1:4
NO PRICING DUE TO SCARCITY
1 Dennis Eckersley
Huston Street/10
2 Matt Bush
Tony Gwynn/25
3 Homer Bailey
Tom Seaver/5
4 Bob Feller
Jeremy Sowers/25
5 Josh Fields
Robin Ventura/10
6 Nolan Ryan
Thomas Diamond/5
7 Eric Patterson
Ryne Sandberg/5
8 Richie Robnett
Rickey Henderson/5
9 Mike Ferris
Stan Musial/10
10 Bobby Doerr
Dustin Pedroia/25

2004 Donruss Elite Extra Edition Round Numbers

RANDOM INSERTS IN PACKS
STATED PRINT RUN 500 SERIAL #'d SETS
1 Ozzie Smith 2.50 6.00
2 Derek Jeter 3.00 8.00
3 Alex Rodriguez 2.50 6.00
4 Paul Molitor 1.25 3.00
5 George Brett 3.00 8.00
6 Delmon Young 1.50 4.00
7 Dontrelle Willis 1.50 4.00
8 Gary Carter 1.25 3.00
9 Reggie Jackson 1.50 4.00
10 Andre Dawson 1.25 3.00
11 Neil Walker 2.50 6.00
12 Laynce Nix 1.25 3.00
13 Matt Bush 2.50 5.00
14 Lyle Overbay 1.25 3.00
15 Carlos Beltran 1.25 3.00
16 Todd Helton 1.50 4.00
17 Mark Grace 1.50 4.00
18 Fred Lynn 1.25 3.00
19 Robin Yount 1.50 4.00
20 Mike Schmidt 3.00 8.00
21 Roger Clemens 4.00 10.00
22 Will Clark 1.50 4.00
23 Don Mattingly 3.00 8.00
24 Blake DeWitt 3.00 8.00
25 Rafael Palmeiro 1.50 4.00
26 Wade Boggs 1.50 4.00
27 Mark Rogers 2.00 5.00
28 Billy Buckner 2.00 5.00
29 Jeff Baker 1.25 3.00
30 Nolan Ryan 4.00 10.00
31 Mike Piazza 2.50 6.00
32 Alexis Rios 1.25 3.00
33 Eddie Murray 1.50 4.00
34 Jose Canseco 1.50 4.00
35 Mike Mussina 1.50 4.00
36 Eric Beattie 2.00 5.00
37 Keith Hernandez 1.25 3.00
38 Michael Young 1.25 3.00
39 Dwight Evans 1.50 4.00
40 Scott Elbert 4.00 10.00
41 Adrian Gonzalez 1.25 3.00
42 Johnny Bench 1.50 4.00
43 Dennis Eckersley 1.50 4.00
44 Dale Murphy 1.50 4.00
45 Ryne Sandberg 3.00 8.00
46 David Wright 2.00 5.00
47 Hank Blalock 1.25 3.00
48 Orel Hershiser 1.25 3.00
49 Sean Casey 1.25 3.00
50 Albert Pujols 3.00 8.00

2004 Donruss Elite Extra Edition Round Numbers Signature

OVERALL AU-GU ODDS 1:4
PRINT RUNS B/WN 5-250 COPIES PER
NO PRICING ON QTY OF 10 OR LESS
1 Ozzie Smith/25 40.00 80.00
4 Paul Molitor/25 10.00 25.00
5 George Brett/5
6 Delmon Young/50 12.50 30.00
7 Dontrelle Willis/25 15.00 40.00
8 Gary Carter/50 8.00 20.00
9 Reggie Jackson/5
10 Andre Dawson/50 8.00 20.00
11 Neil Walker/250 8.00 20.00
12 Laynce Nix/50 5.00 12.00
13 Matt Bush/100 12.50 30.00
14 Lyle Overbay/50 5.00 12.00
15 Carlos Beltran/25 10.00 25.00
16 Todd Helton/5
17 Mark Grace/25 15.00 40.00
18 Fred Lynn/50 5.00 12.00
19 Robin Yount/5
20 Mike Schmidt/25 50.00 100.00
21 Roger Clemens/5
22 Will Clark/20 15.00 40.00
23 Don Mattingly/25 50.00 100.00
24 Blake DeWitt/250 6.00 15.00
25 Rafael Palmeiro/5
26 Wade Boggs/5
27 Mark Rogers/100 12.50 30.00
28 Billy Buckner/100 6.00 15.00
29 Jeff Baker/6
30 Nolan Ryan/10
31 Mike Piazza/5
32 Alexis Rios/50 8.00 20.00
33 Eddie Murray/5
34 Jose Canseco/25 15.00 40.00
35 Mike Mussina/5
36 Eric Beattie/100 6.00 15.00
37 Keith Hernandez/50 8.00 20.00
38 Michael Young/50 8.00 20.00
39 Dwight Evans/50 12.50 30.00
40 Scott Elbert/250 12.50 30.00
41 Adrian Gonzalez/50 5.00 12.00
42 Johnny Bench/5
43 Dennis Eckersley/50 12.50 30.00
44 Dale Murphy/50 12.50 30.00
45 Ryne Sandberg/5
46 David Wright/25 50.00 100.00
47 Hank Blalock/25 8.00 20.00
48 Orel Hershiser/5
49 Sean Casey/25 8.00 20.00
50 Albert Pujols/5

2004 Donruss Elite Extra Edition Throwback Threads

OVERALL AU-GU ODDS 1:4
1 Roger Maris 30.00 60.00
2 Ted Williams 40.00 80.00
3 Cal Ripken 40.00 80.00
4 Duke Snider 10.00 25.00
5 George Brett 15.00 40.00

2004 Donruss Elite Extra Edition Throwback Threads Autograph

OVERALL AU-GU ODDS 1:4
PRINT RUNS B/WN 5-10 COPIES PER
NO PRICING DUE TO SCARCITY
3 Cal Ripken/8
4 Duke Snider/10
5 George Brett/5

2004 Donruss Elite Ripken World Series

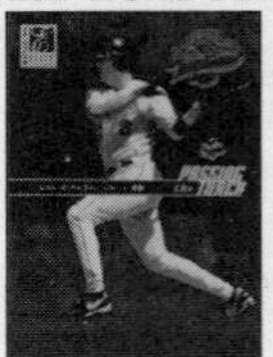

These standard-size cards were issued as part of a special promotion for the 2004 Cal Ripken League World Series. Each of these cards issued have a special 2004 Cal Ripken World Series logo embossed on the card. Although representatives at Donruss had no specific record of which regular Elite cards were stamped for this promotion they did issue a special Passing the Torch set for the project.

COMPLETE SET
RWS1 Babe Ruth
Cal Ripken
RWS2 Cal Ripken
Billy Ripken
RWS2A Cal Ripken AU
Billy Ripken
RWS2B Cal Ripken
Billy Ripken AU

2005 Donruss Elite

This 200-card set was released in May, 2005. The set was issued in five-card packs with an $5 SRP which were issued 20 packs to a box and 12 boxes to a case. Cards numbered 1-150 feature active veterans while cards numbered 151 through 170 feature retired greats and cards numbered 171-200 (with the exception of 188 and 189) feature autographed Rookie Cards. Cards numbered 151 through 170 were issued to a stated print run of

1250 serial numbered sets and were randomly inserted into packs. Cards numbered 171 through 200 were issued to varying print runs which have been notated in our checklist.

COMP.SET w/o SP's (150) 10.00 25.00
COMMON CARD (1-150) .10 .30
COMMON CARD (151-170) 1.25 3.00
COMMON CARD (188-189) 1.25 3.00
171-200: OVERALL AU-GU ODDS 3 PER BOX
171-200 PRINT RUNS B/WN 500-1500 PER
CARD 185 DOES NOT EXIST
1 Bartolo Colon .10 .30
2 Casey Kotchman .10 .30
3 Chone Figgins .10 .30
4 Darin Erstad .10 .30
5 Garret Anderson .10 .30
6 Jose Guillen .10 .30
7 Vladimir Guerrero .30 .75
8 Luis Gonzalez .10 .30
9 Randy Johnson .30 .75
10 Troy Glaus .10 .30
11 Andruw Jones .20 .50
12 Chipper Jones .30 .75
13 J.D. Drew .10 .30
14 John Smoltz .20 .50
15 Johnny Estrada .10 .30
16 Marcus Giles .10 .30
17 Rafael Furcal .10 .30
18 Javy Lopez .10 .30
19 Jay Gibbons .10 .30
20 Melvin Mora .10 .30
21 Miguel Tejada .20 .50
22 Rafael Palmeiro .20 .50
23 Sidney Ponson .10 .30
24 Curt Schilling .20 .50
25 David Ortiz .30 .75
26 Derek Lowe .10 .30
27 Jason Varitek .30 .75
28 Johnny Damon .20 .50
29 Manny Ramirez .20 .50
30 Pedro Martinez .20 .50
31 Aramis Ramirez .10 .30
32 Carlos Zambrano .10 .30
33 Corey Patterson .10 .30
34 Derrek Lee .20 .50
35 Greg Maddux .50 1.25
36 Kerry Wood .10 .30
37 Mark Prior .20 .50
38 Moises Alou .10 .30
39 Nomar Garciaparra .30 .75
40 Sammy Sosa .30 .75
41 Carlos Lee .10 .30
42 Frank Thomas .30 .75
43 Jermaine Dye .10 .30
44 Magglio Ordonez .10 .30
45 Mark Buehrle .10 .30
46 Paul Konerko .10 .30
47 Adam Dunn .10 .30
48 Austin Kearns .10 .30
49 Barry Larkin .20 .50
50 Ken Griffey Jr. .50 1.25
51 Sean Casey .10 .30
52 C.C. Sabathia .10 .30
53 Cliff Lee .10 .30
54 Travis Hafner .10 .30
55 Victor Martinez .10 .30
56 Jeromy Burnitz .10 .30
57 Preston Wilson .10 .30
58 Todd Helton .20 .50
59 Brandon Inge .10 .30
60 Ivan Rodriguez .20 .50
61 Jeremy Bonderman .10 .30
62 Troy Percival .10 .30
63 Dontrelle Willis .10 .30
64 Josh Beckett .10 .30
65 Juan Pierre .10 .30
66 Miguel Cabrera .20 .50
67 Mike Lowell .10 .30
68 Paul Lo Duca .10 .30
69 Andy Pettitte .20 .50
70 Brad Ausmus .10 .30
71 Carlos Beltran .10 .30
72 Craig Biggio .20 .50
73 Jeff Bagwell .20 .50
74 Lance Berkman .10 .30
75 Roger Clemens .50 1.25
76 Roy Oswalt .10 .30
77 Juan Gonzalez .10 .30
78 Mike Sweeney .10 .30
79 Zack Greinke .10 .30
80 Adrian Beltre .10 .30
81 Hideo Nomo .30 .75
82 Jeff Kent .10 .30
83 Milton Bradley .10 .30
84 Shawn Green .10 .30
85 Steve Finley .10 .30
86 Ben Sheets .10 .30
87 Lyle Overbay .10 .30
88 Scott Podsednik .10 .30
89 Lew Ford .10 .30
90 Shannon Stewart .10 .30
91 Torii Hunter .10 .30
92 David Wright .50 1.25
93 Jose Reyes .10 .30
94 Kazuo Matsui .10 .30
95 Mike Piazza .30 .75
96 Tom Glavine .20 .50
97 Alex Rodriguez .50 1.25
98 Bernie Williams .20 .50
99 Derek Jeter .60 1.50
100 Gary Sheffield .10 .30
101 Hideki Matsui .50 1.25
102 Jason Giambi .10 .30
103 Kevin Brown .10 .30
104 Mike Mussina .20 .50
105 Barry Zito .10 .30
106 Bobby Crosby .10 .30
107 Eric Chavez .10 .30
108 Jason Kendall .10 .30
109 Mark Mulder .10 .30
110 Bobby Abreu .10 .30
111 Jim Thome .20 .50
112 Kevin Millwood .10 .30
113 Pat Burrell .10 .30
114 Craig Wilson .10 .30
115 Jack Wilson .10 .30
116 Jason Bay .10 .30
117 Brian Giles .10 .30
118 Khalil Greene .20 .50
119 Mark Loretta .10 .30
120 Ryan Klesko .10 .30
121 Sean Burroughs .10 .30
122 Edgardo Alfonzo .10 .30
123 J.T. Snow .10 .30
124 Jason Schmidt .10 .30
125 Omar Vizquel .20 .50
126 Ichiro Suzuki .60 1.50
127 Jamie Moyer .10 .30
128 Bret Boone .10 .30
129 Richie Sexson .10 .30
130 Albert Pujols .60 1.50
131 Edgar Renteria .10 .30
132 Jeff Suppan .10 .30
133 Jim Edmonds .10 .30
134 Larry Walker .20 .50
135 Scott Rolen .20 .50
136 Aubrey Huff .10 .30
137 B.J. Upton .10 .30
138 Carl Crawford .10 .30
139 Rocco Baldelli .10 .30
140 Alfonso Soriano .10 .30
141 Hank Blalock .10 .30
142 Kenny Rogers .10 .30
143 Laynce Nix .10 .30
144 Mark Teixeira .20 .50
145 Michael Young .10 .30
146 Carlos Delgado .10 .30
147 Eric Hinske .10 .30
148 Roy Halladay .10 .30
149 Vernon Wells .10 .30
150 Jose Vidro .10 .30
151 Bob Gibson RET 1.50 4.00
152 Brooks Robinson RET 1.50 4.00
153 Cal Ripken RET 3.00 8.00
154 Carl Yastrzemski RET 1.50 4.00
155 Don Mattingly RET 2.00 5.00
156 Eddie Murray RET 1.50 4.00
157 Ernie Banks RET 1.50 4.00
158 Frank Robinson RET 1.25 3.00
159 George Brett RET 2.00 5.00
160 Harmon Killebrew RET 1.50 4.00
161 Johnny Bench RET 1.50 4.00
162 Mike Schmidt RET 2.00 5.00
163 Nolan Ryan RET 2.50 6.00
164 Paul Molitor RET 1.25 3.00
165 Stan Musial RET 1.50 4.00
166 Steve Carlton RET 1.25 3.00
167 Tony Gwynn RET 1.50 4.00
168 Warren Spahn RET 1.50 4.00
169 Willie Mays RET 2.00 5.00
170 Willie McCovey RET 1.50 4.00
171 Miguel Negron AU/1500 RC 4.00 10.00
172 Mike Morse AU/1000 RC 4.00 10.00
173 W.Balentien AU/1500 RC 10.00 25.00
174 A.Concepcion AU/651 RC 3.00 8.00
175 Ubaldo Jimenez AU/500 RC 8.00 20.00
176 Justin Verlander AU/500 RC 20.00 40.00
177 Ryan Speier AU/1000 RC 3.00 8.00
178 Geovany Soto AU/500 RC 30.00 60.00
179 M.McLemore AU/1200 RC 3.00 8.00
180 Ambiorix Burgos AU/599 RC 3.00 8.00
181 C.Roberson AU/1000 RC 3.00 8.00
182 Colter Bean AU/625 RC 4.00 10.00
183 Erick Threets AU/500 RC 3.00 8.00
184 Carlos Ruiz AU/1000 RC 4.00 10.00
186 J.Gothreaux AU/1000 RC 3.00 8.00
187 L.Hernandez AU/1000 RC 3.00 8.00
188 Agustin Montero/1000 RC 1.25 3.00
189 Paulino Reynoso/1000 RC 1.25 3.00
190 Garrett Jones AU/500 RC 3.00 8.00
191 S.Thompson AU/500 RC 3.00 8.00
192 Matt Lindstrom AU/1500 RC 3.00 8.00
193 Nate McLouth AU/500 RC 8.00 20.00
194 Luke Scott AU/671 RC 10.00 25.00
195 John Hattig AU/1500 RC 3.00 8.00
196 Jason Hammel AU/1500 RC 3.00 8.00
197 Danny Rueckel AU/671 RC 3.00 8.00
198 Justin Wechsler AU/500 RC 3.00 8.00
199 Chris Resop AU/500 RC 4.00 10.00
200 Jeff Miller AU/500 RC 3.00 8.00

2005 Donruss Elite Aspirations

*1-150 p/r 81-99: 4X TO 10X
*1-150 p/r 51-80: 5X TO 12X
*1-150 p/r 36-50: 6X TO 15X
*1-150 p/r 16-25: 10X TO 25X
*151-170 p/r 51-80: 1.25X TO 3X
*151-170 p/r 36-50: 1.5X TO 4X
*171-200 p/r 81-99: .25X TO .6X AU 1000+
*171-200 p/r 51-80: .3X TO .8X AU 1000+
*171-200 p/r 36-50: .4X TO 1X AU 1000+
*171-200 p/r 26-35: .5X TO 1.2X AU 1000+
COMMON (171-200) p/r 26-35 4.00 10.00
*171-200 p/r 51-80: .3X TO .8X AU 500-671
*171-200 p/r 36-50: .4X TO 1X AU 500-671
*171-200 p/r 26-35: .5X TO 1.2X AU 500-671
*188-189 p/r 36-50: 1X TO 2.5X BASIC
RANDOM INSERTS IN PACKS
PRINT RUNS B/WN 15-99 COPIES PER
NO PRICING ON QTY OF 15
153 Cal Ripken RET/92 15.00 40.00

2005 Donruss Elite Status

*1-150 p/r 51-80: 5X TO 12X
*1-150 p/r 36-50: 6X TO 15X
*1-150 p/r 26-35: 8X TO 20X
*1-150 p/r 16-25: 10X TO 25X
*151-170 p/r 36-50: 1.5X TO 4X
*151-170 p/r 26-35: 2X TO 5X
*151-170 p/r 16-25: 2.5X TO 6X
*171-200 p/r 51-80: .3X TO .8X AU 1000+
*171-200 p/r 36-50: .4X TO 1X AU 1000+
COMMON (171-200) p/r 51-80 2.50 6.00
*171-200 p/r 81-99: .25X TO .6X AU 500-671
*171-200 p/r 51-80: .3X TO .8X AU 500-671
*171-200 p/r 36-50: .4X TO 1X AU 500-671
*171-200 p/r 26-35: .5X TO 1.2X AU 500-671
*188-189 p/r 51-80: .75X TO 2X BASIC
*188-189 p/r 36-50: 1X TO 2.5X BASIC
RANDOM INSERTS IN PACKS
PRINT RUNS B/WN 1-81 COPIES PER
NO PRICING ON QTY OF 15 OR LESS

2005 Donruss Elite Status Gold

*GOLD 1-150: 10X TO 25X BASIC
*GOLD 151-170: 2.5X TO 6X BASIC
RANDOM INSERTS IN PACKS
STATED PRINT RUN 24 SERIAL #'d SETS
171-200 NO PRICING DUE TO SCARCITY
153 Cal Ripken RET 60.00 120.00

2005 Donruss Elite Turn of the Century

*TOC 1-150: 1.5X TO 4X BASIC
1-150 PRINT RUN 750 SERIAL #'d SETS
*TOC 151-170: .6X TO 1.5X BASIC
151-170 PRINT RUN 250 SERIAL #'d SETS
COMMON CARD (171-200) 1.25 3.00
*TOC 171-200: .15X TO .4X AU 1000+
*TOC 171-200: .15X TO .4X AU 500-671
*TOC 188-189: .4X TO 1X BASIC 1000
171-200 PRINT RUN 500 SERIAL #'d SETS
RANDOM INSERTS IN PACKS

2005 Donruss Elite Back 2 Back Jacks

1-30 PRINT RUNS B/WN 25-200 COPIES PER
31-36 PRINT RUN 50 SERIAL #'d SETS
OVERALL AU-GU ODDS THREE PER BOX
1 Adam Dunn/200 2.50 6.00
3 Albert Pujols/100 6.00 15.00
4 Babe Ruth/50 100.00 175.00
5 Cal Ripken/100 12.50 30.00
6 David Ortiz/200 3.00 8.00
7 Eddie Murray/150 4.00 10.00
8 Ernie Banks/50 6.00 15.00
9 Frank Robinson/50 4.00 10.00
10 Gary Sheffield/200 2.50 6.00
11 George Foster/125 3.00 8.00
12 Don Mattingly/100 6.00 15.00
13 Hideki Matsui/25 12.50 30.00
14 Jason Giambi/50 4.00 10.00
16 Jim Rice/125 3.00 8.00
17 Jim Thome/200 3.00 8.00
18 Johnny Bench/125 5.00 12.00
19 Lance Berkman/200 2.50 6.00
20 Manny Ramirez/200 3.00 8.00
21 Mike Piazza/200 3.00 8.00
22 Mike Schmidt/125 6.00 15.00
23 Rafael Palmeiro/200 3.00 8.00
24 Reggie Jackson/125 4.00 10.00
25 Sammy Sosa/100 4.00 10.00
26 Scott Rolen/200 3.00 8.00
27 Stan Musial/125 6.00 15.00
28 Willie Mays/50 20.00 50.00
29 Kirk Gibson/125 3.00 8.00
30 Will Clark/125 4.00 10.00
31 Willie Mays 30.00 60.00
Sammy Sosa/50
32 Eddie Murray 6.00 15.00
Mike Piazza/50
33 Mike Schmidt 15.00 40.00
Jim Thome/50
34 Rafael Palmeiro 6.00 15.00
Kirk Gibson/50
35 Jim Rice 6.00 15.00
Manny Ramirez/50
36 Adrian Beltre 6.00 15.00
Will Clark/50
37 Reggie Jackson 6.00 15.00
David Ortiz/50
38 Johnny Bench 8.00 20.00
Adam Dunn/50

2005 Donruss Elite Back 2 Back Jacks Combos

*1-30 p/r 100: .6X TO 1.5X B2B p/r 200
*1-30 p/r 100: .5X TO 1.2X B2B p/r 100
*1-30 p/r 50: .75X TO 2X B2B p/r 150-200
*1-30 p/r 50: .6X TO 1.5X B2B p/r 100-125
*1-30 p/r 50: .5X TO 1.2X B2B p/r 50
*1-30 p/r 25: .5X TO 1.2X B2B p/r 25
1-30 PRINT RUNS B/WN 25-100 COPIES PER
*31-36 p/r 50: .5X TO 1.2X B2B p/r 50
*31-36 p/r 25: .6X TO 1.5X B2B p/r 50
31-36 PRINT RUNS B/WN 10-50 COPIES PER
31-36 ARE ALL DUAL BAT-JSY COMBOS
OVERALL AU-GU ODDS THREE PER BOX
2 Adrian Beltre Bat-Jsy/100 4.00 10.00
4 Babe Ruth Bat-Pants/25 250.00 400.00
15 Jim Edmonds Bat-Jsy/100 4.00 10.00
40 Cal Ripken Bat-Jsy 60.00 120.00
Albert Pujols Bat-Jsy/25

2005 Donruss Elite Career Best

STATED PRINT RUN 1500 SERIAL #'d SETS
*BLACK: 1X TO 2.5X BASIC
BLACK PRINT RUN 150 SERIAL #'d SETS
*BLUE: .75X TO 2X BASIC
BLUE PRINT RUN 250 SERIAL #'d SETS
*GOLD: .6X TO 1.5X BASIC
GOLD PRINT RUN 500 SERIAL #'d SETS
RANDOM INSERTS IN PACKS
1 Adam Dunn .60 1.50
2 Adrian Beltre .60 1.50
3 Albert Pujols 1.50 4.00
4 Andruw Jones .75 2.00
5 Ben Sheets .60 1.50
6 Bo Jackson 1.00 2.50
7 Brooks Robinson 1.00 2.50
8 Cal Ripken 3.00 8.00
9 Dale Murphy 1.00 2.50
10 Don Mattingly 2.00 5.00
11 Eddie Murray 1.00 2.50
12 George Brett 2.00 5.00
13 Hank Blalock .60 1.50
14 Ichiro Suzuki 1.50 4.00
15 Jim Thome .75 2.00
16 Kerry Wood .60 1.50
17 Lance Berkman .60 1.50
18 Mark Prior .75 2.00
19 Mark Teixeira .75 2.00
20 Mike Schmidt 2.00 5.00
21 Pedro Martinez .75 2.00
22 Randy Johnson .75 2.00
23 Rickey Henderson 1.00 2.50
24 Sammy Sosa .75 2.00
25 Tony Gwynn 1.25 3.00

2005 Donruss Elite Career Best Bats

*BAT p/r 150-250: .4X TO 1X JSY p/r 150-250
*BAT p/r 150-250: .3X TO .8X JSY p/r 100
*BAT p/r 150-250: .25X TO .6X JSY p/r 50
*BAT p/r 100: .5X TO 1.2X JSY p/r 150-250
*BAT p/r 100: .4X TO 1X JSY p/r 100
OVERALL AU-GU ODDS THREE PER BOX
PRINT RUNS B/WN 50-250 COPIES PER

2005 Donruss Elite Career Best Jerseys

OVERALL AU-GU ODDS THREE PER BOX
PRINT RUNS B/WN 50-250 COPIES PER
1 Adam Dunn/250 2.50 6.00
2 Adrian Beltre/250 2.50 6.00
3 Albert Pujols/250 6.00 15.00
4 Andruw Jones/250 3.00 8.00
5 Ben Sheets/250 2.50 6.00
6 Bo Jackson/250 4.00 10.00
7 Brooks Robinson/50 5.00 12.00
8 Cal Ripken/150 10.00 25.00
9 Dale Murphy/100 4.00 10.00
10 Don Mattingly/150 5.00 12.00
11 Eddie Murray/100 5.00 12.00
12 George Brett/100 6.00 15.00
13 Hank Blalock/250 2.50 6.00
15 Jim Thome/250 3.00 8.00
16 Kerry Wood/250 2.50 6.00
17 Lance Berkman/250 2.50 6.00
18 Mark Prior/250 3.00 8.00
19 Mark Teixeira/250 3.00 8.00
20 Mike Schmidt/100 6.00 15.00
21 Pedro Martinez/250 3.00 8.00
22 Randy Johnson/100 4.00 10.00
23 Rickey Henderson/50 6.00 15.00
24 Sammy Sosa/250 3.00 8.00
25 Tony Gwynn/250 4.00 10.00

2005 Donruss Elite Career Best Combos

*COMBO p/r 150: .5X TO 1.2X JSY p/r 150-250
*COMBO p/r 125: .6X TO 1.5X JSY p/r 150-250
*COMBO p/r 25: 1X TO 2.5X JSY p/r 150-250
*COMBO p/r 25: .75X TO 2X JSY p/r 100
*COMBO p/r 25: .6X TO 1.5X JSY p/r 50
OVERALL AU-GU ODDS THREE PER BOX
PRINT RUNS B/WN 25-150 COPIES PER

2005 Donruss Elite Face 2 Face

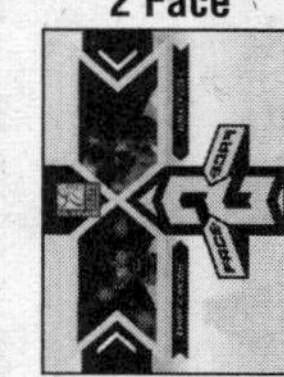

STATED PRINT RUN 1500 SERIAL #'d SETS
*BLACK: .6X TO 1.5X BASIC
BLACK PRINT RUN 500 SERIAL #'d SETS
*GOLD: 1X TO 2.5X BASIC
GOLD PRINT RUN 100 SERIAL #'d SETS
*RED: .5X TO 1.2X BASIC
RED PRINT RUN 750 SERIAL #'d SETS
RANDOM INSERTS IN PACKS
1 Roger Clemens 1.25 3.00
Scott Rolen
2 Greg Maddux 1.25 3.00
Jeff Bagwell
3 Mark Prior .75 2.00
Mike Piazza
4 Mike Mussina .75 2.00
Ivan Rodriguez
5 Josh Beckett .75 2.00
Sammy Sosa
6 Roy Oswalt .75 2.00
Miguel Cabrera
7 Roger Clemens 1.50 4.00
Albert Pujols
8 Pedro Martinez .75 2.00
Vladimir Guerrero
9 Randy Johnson .75 2.00
Jim Edmonds
10 Curt Schilling 1.50 4.00
Derek Jeter
11 Kerry Wood .60 1.50
Lance Berkman
12 Tim Hudson .60 1.50
Garret Anderson
13 Pedro Martinez .75 2.00
Gary Sheffield
14 Barry Zito .60 1.50
Magglio Ordonez
15 Kerry Wood .60 1.50
Shawn Green
16 Mike Mussina .75 2.00
Miguel Tejada
17 Randy Johnson 1.50 4.00
Albert Pujols
18 Nolan Ryan 2.50 6.00
George Brett
19 Tom Seaver 2.00 5.00
Mike Schmidt
20 Jim Palmer .75 2.00
Harmon Killebrew

2005 Donruss Elite Face 2 Face Bats

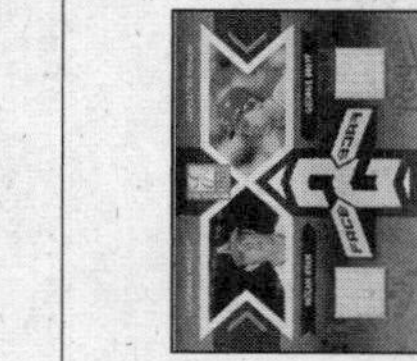

*BAT p/r 150: .4X TO 1X JSY p/r 200
*BAT p/r 150: .3X TO .8X JSY p/r 75
*BAT p/r 150: .25X TO .6X JSY p/r 50
*BAT p/r 100: .5X TO 1.2X JSY p/r 200
*BAT p/r 100: .25X TO .6X JSY p/r 25
*BAT p/r 50: .6X TO 1.5X JSY p/r 200
*BAT p/r 50: .5X TO 1.2X JSY p/r 75
*BAT p/r 25: .75X TO 2X JSY p/r 200
OVERALL AU-GU ODDS THREE PER BOX
PRINT RUNS B/WN 25-150 COPIES PER
9 Randy Johnson 6.00 15.00
Jim Edmonds/50

2005 Donruss Elite Face 2 Face Jerseys

OVERALL AU-GU ODDS THREE PER BOX
PRINT RUNS B/WN 25-200 COPIES PER
1 Roger Clemens 4.00 10.00
Scott Rolen/200
2 Greg Maddux 5.00 12.00
Jeff Bagwell/75
3 Mark Prior 4.00 10.00
Mike Piazza/200
4 Mike Mussina 4.00 10.00
Ivan Rodriguez/200
5 Josh Beckett 4.00 10.00
Sammy Sosa/200
6 Roy Oswalt 4.00 10.00
Miguel Cabrera/200
7 Roger Clemens 10.00 25.00
Albert Pujols/200
8 Pedro Martinez 5.00 12.00
Vladimir Guerrero/75
11 Kerry Wood 3.00 8.00
Lance Berkman/200
12 Tim Hudson 4.00 10.00
Garret Anderson/75
13 Pedro Martinez 5.00 12.00
Gary Sheffield/75
14 Barry Zito 3.00 8.00
Magglio Ordonez/200
15 Kerry Wood 3.00 8.00
Shawn Green/200
16 Mike Mussina 4.00 10.00
Miguel Tejada/200
17 Randy Johnson 10.00 25.00
Albert Pujols/75
18 Nolan Ryan 30.00 60.00
George Brett/25
19 Tom Seaver 10.00 25.00
Mike Schmidt/50
20 Jim Palmer 10.00 25.00
Harmon Killebrew/25

2005 Donruss Elite Face 2 Face Combos

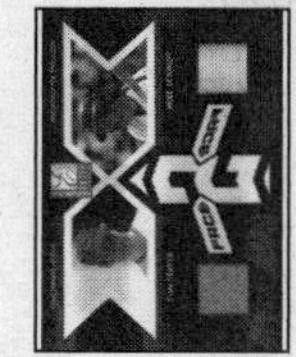

*COMBO p/r 250: .4X TO 1X JSY p/r 200
*COMBO p/r 75-100: .5X TO 1.2X JSY p/r 200
*COMBO p/r 75-100: .4X TO 1X JSY p/r 75
*COMBO p/r 50: .4X TO 1X JSY p/r 50
*COMBO p/r 25: .4X TO 1X JSY p/r 25
OVERALL AU-GU ODDS THREE PER BOX
PRINT RUNS B/WN 25-250 COPIES PER

2005 Donruss Elite Passing the Torch

1-30 PRINT RUN 1000 SERIAL #'d SETS
31-45 PRINT RUN 500 SERIAL #'d SETS
*BLACK 1-30: 1.25X TO 3X BASIC
*BLACK 31-45: 1.5X TO 4X BASIC
BLACK 1-30 PRINT RUN 50 #'d SETS
BLACK 31-45 PRINT RUN 25 #'d SETS
*GOLD 1-30: .75X TO 2X BASIC

*GOLD 31-45: 1X TO 2.5X BASIC
GOLD 1-30 PRINT RUN 100 #'d SETS
GOLD 31-45 PRINT RUN 50 #'d SETS
*GREEN 1-30: .6X TO 1.5X BASIC
*GREEN 31-45: .6X TO 1.5X BASIC
GREEN 1-30 PRINT RUN 250 #'d SETS
GREEN 31-45 PRINT RUN 125 #'d SETS
*RED 1-30: .5X TO 1.2X BASIC
*RED 31-45: .5X TO 1.2X BASIC
RED 1-30 PRINT RUN 500 #'d SETS
RED 31-45 PRINT RUN 250 #'d SETS
RANDOM INSERTS IN PACKS
1 Adrian Beltre 1.00 2.50
2 Albert Pujols 2.50 6.00
3 Alex Rodriguez 2.00 5.00
4 Andruw Jones 1.25 3.00
5 Babe Ruth 3.00 8.00
6 Ben Sheets 1.00 2.50
7 Brooks Robinson 1.50 4.00
8 Cal Ripken 5.00 12.00
9 Carl Yastrzemski 2.50 6.00
10 Dale Murphy 1.50 4.00
11 David Ortiz 1.25 3.00
12 Derek Jeter 2.50 6.00
13 Don Mattingly 3.00 8.00
14 George Brett 3.00 8.00
15 Greg Maddux 2.00 5.00
16 Hank Blalock 1.00 2.50
17 Jeff Bagwell 1.25 3.00
18 Johnny Bench 1.50 4.00
19 Magglio Ordonez 1.00 2.50
20 Mark Prior 1.25 3.00
21 Mark Teixeira 1.25 3.00
22 Miguel Cabrera 1.25 3.00
23 Mike Schmidt 3.00 8.00
24 Nolan Ryan 4.00 10.00
25 Pedro Martinez 1.25 3.00
26 Sammy Sosa 1.25 3.00
27 Scott Rolen 1.25 3.00
28 Tom Seaver 1.50 4.00
29 Vladimir Guerrero 1.25 3.00
30 Willie Mays 3.00 8.00
31 Carlton Fisk 2.00 5.00
Magglio Ordonez
32 Nolan Ryan 5.00 12.00
Ben Sheets
33 Babe Ruth 4.00 10.00
Alex Rodriguez
34 Cal Ripken 6.00 15.00
B.J. Upton
35 Willie Mays 4.00 10.00
Andruw Jones
36 George Brett 4.00 10.00
Hank Blalock
37 Greg Maddux 2.50 6.00
Whitey Ford
38 Harmon Killebrew 2.00 5.00
Adrian Beltre
39 Tom Seaver 2.00 5.00
Mark Prior
40 Don Mattingly 4.00 10.00
Mark Teixeira
41 Stan Musial 3.00 8.00
Carlos Beltran
42 Dale Murphy 2.00 5.00
Lance Berkman
43 Willie McCovey 2.00 5.00
Jeff Bagwell
44 Andre Dawson 2.00 5.00
Miguel Cabrera
45 Brooks Robinson 2.00 5.00
Scott Rolen

2005 Donruss Elite Passing the Torch Autographs

1-30 SINGLE PRINT RUNS B/WN 5-100 PER
31-45 DUAL PRINT RUNS B/WN 5-25 PER
NO PRICING ON QTY OF 10 OR LESS
1 Adrian Beltre/75 6.00 15.00
2 Albert Pujols/5
6 Ben Sheets/75 6.00 15.00
7 Brooks Robinson/100 10.00 25.00
8 Cal Ripken/10
9 Carl Yastrzemski/5
10 Dale Murphy/100 10.00 25.00
13 Don Mattingly/25 20.00 50.00
14 George Brett/5
16 Hank Blalock/25 10.00 25.00
17 Jeff Bagwell/5
18 Johnny Bench/25 20.00 50.00
19 Magglio Ordonez/75 6.00 15.00
20 Mark Prior/25 12.50 30.00
21 Mark Teixeira/75 10.00 25.00
22 Miguel Cabrera/75 10.00 25.00
23 Mike Schmidt/25 30.00 60.00
24 Nolan Ryan/10
25 Pedro Martinez/5
26 Sammy Sosa/5
27 Scott Rolen/25 15.00 40.00
28 Tom Seaver/25 20.00 50.00
30 Willie Mays/10
31 Carlton Fisk 30.00 60.00
Magglio Ordonez/25
32 Nolan Ryan 125.00 200.00
Ben Sheets/25
34 Cal Ripken
B.J. Upton/5
36 George Brett
Hank Blalock/5
38 Harmon Killebrew
Adrian Beltre/10
39 Tom Seaver
Mark Prior/10
40 Don Mattingly
Mark Teixeira/10
43 Willie McCovey
Jeff Bagwell/5
44 Andre Dawson 30.00 60.00
Miguel Cabrera/25
45 Brooks Robinson 40.00 80.00
Scott Rolen/25

2005 Donruss Elite Passing the Torch Bats

*1-30 p/r 150-250: .4X TO 1X JSY p/r 150-250
*1-30 p/r 150-250: .25X TO .6X JSY p/r 50
*1-30 p/r 150-250: .2X TO .5X JSY p/r 25
*1-30 p/r 50: .6X TO 1.5X JSY p/r 150-250
*1-30 p/r 50: .4X TO 1X JSY p/r 50
*1-30 p/r 50: .3X TO .8X JSY p/r 25
1-30 PRINT RUNS B/WN 25-250 PER
*31-45 p/r 150-250: .4X TO 1X JSY p/r 150
*31-45 p/r 150-250: .3X TO .8X JSY p/r 100
*31-45 p/r 150-250: .25X TO .6X JSY p/r 50
*31-45 p/r 150-250: .2X TO .5X JSY p/r 25
*31-45 p/r 50: .6X TO 1.5X JSY p/r 150
*31-45 p/r 50: .4X TO 1X JSY p/r 50
*31-45 p/r 25: .5X TO 1.2X JSY p/r 50
*31-45 p/r 25: .4X TO 1X JSY p/r 25
31-45 PRINT RUNS B/WN 25-250 PER
OVERALL AU-GU ODDS THREE PER BOX
5 Babe Ruth/25 125.00 200.00

2005 Donruss Elite Passing the Torch Jerseys

31-45 PRINT RUNS B/WN 25-150 PER
OVERALL AU-GU ODDS THREE PER BOX
1 Adrian Beltre/250 2.50 6.00
2 Albert Pujols/250 6.00 15.00
4 Andruw Jones/250 3.00 8.00
5 Babe Ruth Pants/25 150.00 250.00
6 Ben Sheets/250 2.50 6.00
7 Brooks Robinson/25 6.00 15.00
8 Cal Ripken/250 10.00 25.00
9 Carl Yastrzemski Pants/50 6.00 15.00
10 Dale Murphy/250 3.00 8.00
11 David Ortiz/250 3.00 8.00
13 Don Mattingly/150 5.00 12.00
14 George Brett/50 8.00 20.00
15 Greg Maddux/250 4.00 10.00
16 Hank Blalock/250 2.50 6.00
17 Jeff Bagwell/250 3.00 8.00
18 Johnny Bench Pants/150 4.00 10.00
19 Magglio Ordonez/250 2.50 6.00
20 Mark Prior/250 3.00 8.00
21 Mark Teixeira/250 3.00 8.00
22 Miguel Cabrera/250 3.00 8.00
23 Mike Schmidt/150 5.00 12.00
24 Nolan Ryan/50 10.00 25.00
25 Pedro Martinez/250 3.00 8.00
26 Sammy Sosa/250 3.00 8.00
27 Scott Rolen/250 3.00 8.00
28 Tom Seaver/50 5.00 12.00
29 Vladimir Guerrero/250 3.00 8.00
30 Willie Mays/25 30.00 60.00
31 Carlton Fisk 5.00 12.00
Magglio Ordonez/50
32 Nolan Ryan 15.00 40.00
Ben Sheets/50
34 Cal Ripken 30.00 60.00
B.J. Upton/50
35 Willie Mays 30.00 60.00
Andruw Jones/50
36 George Brett 10.00 25.00
Hank Blalock/50
37 Greg Maddux 15.00 40.00
Whitey Ford/25
38 Harmon Killebrew 8.00 20.00
Adrian Beltre/50
39 Tom Seaver 8.00 20.00
Mark Prior/25
40 Don Mattingly 8.00 20.00
Mark Teixeira/100
41 Stan Musial Pants 12.50 30.00
Carlos Beltran/25
42 Dale Murphy 4.00 10.00
Lance Berkman/150
43 Willie McCovey 6.00 15.00
Jeff Bagwell/50
44 Andre Dawson 4.00 10.00
Miguel Cabrera/150
45 Brooks Robinson 8.00 20.00
Scott Rolen/25

2005 Donruss Elite Teams

STATED PRINT RUN 1500 SERIAL #'d SETS
*BLACK: .75X TO 2X BASIC
BLACK PRINT RUN 250 SERIAL #'d SETS
*BLUE: .4X TO 1X BASIC
BLUE PRINT RUN 1000 SERIAL #'d SETS
*GOLD: 1.25X TO 3X BASIC
GOLD PRINT RUN 100 SERIAL #'d SETS
*GREEN: .5X TO 1.2X BASIC
GREEN PRINT RUN 750 SERIAL #'d SETS

*RED: .6X TO 1.5X BASIC
RED PRINT RUN 500 SERIAL #'d SETS
RANDOM INSERTS IN PACKS
1 Manny Ramirez 2.00 5.00
Pedro Martinez
David Ortiz
2 Albert Pujols 2.00 5.00
Scott Rolen
Jim Edmonds
3 Roger Clemens 2.00 5.00
Jeff Bagwell
Lance Berkman
Craig Biggio
4 Miguel Cabrera 1.00 2.50
Josh Beckett
Mike Lowell
5 Kerry Wood 2.00 5.00
Mark Prior
Sammy Sosa
Greg Maddux
6 Adrian Beltre 1.00 2.50
Shawn Green
Hideo Nomo
Kazuhisa Ishii
7 Cal Ripken 4.00 10.00
Eddie Murray
Jim Palmer
8 George Brett 2.00 5.00
Bo Jackson
Frank White
9 Roger Clemens 2.00 5.00
Mike Mussina
Alfonso Soriano
Bernie Williams
10 Tom Glavine 2.00 5.00
Greg Maddux
Ryan Klesko
David Justice

2005 Donruss Elite Teams Bats

*BAT p/r 100: .5X TO 1.2X JSY p/r 150
*BAT p/r 100: .3X TO .8X JSY p/r 50
*BAT p/r 50: .6X TO 1.5X JSY p/r 150
*BAT p/r 50: .4X TO 1X JSY p/r 50
OVERALL AU-GU ODDS THREE PER BOX
PRINT RUNS B/WN 50-100 COPIES PER
8 George Brett 12.50 30.00
Bo Jackson
Frank White/100

2005 Donruss Elite Teams Jerseys

OVERALL AU-GU ODDS THREE PER BOX
PRINT RUNS B/WN 50-150 COPIES PER
1 Manny Ramirez 6.00 15.00
Pedro Martinez
David Ortiz/150
2 Albert Pujols 12.50 30.00
Scott Rolen
Jim Edmonds/150
3 Roger Clemens 10.00 25.00
Jeff Bagwell
Lance Berkman
Craig Biggio/150
4 Miguel Cabrera 6.00 15.00
Josh Beckett
Mike Lowell/50
5 Kerry Wood 12.50 30.00
Mark Prior
Sammy Sosa
Greg Maddux/150
6 Adrian Beltre 10.00 25.00
Shawn Green
Hideo Nomo
Kazuhisa Ishii/50
7 Cal Ripken 20.00 50.00
Eddie Murray
Jim Palmer/100
9 Roger Clemens 10.00 25.00
Mike Mussina
Alfonso Soriano
Bernie Williams/100
10 Tom Glavine 15.00 40.00
Greg Maddux
Ryan Klesko
David Justice/100

2005 Donruss Elite Throwback Threads

1-40 PRINT RUNS B/WN 10-200 PER
1-40 NO PRICING ON QTY OF 10
41-60 PRINT RUNS B/WN 5-150 PER
41-60 NO PRICING ON QTY OF 5
OVERALL AU-GU ODDS THREE PER BOX
1 Albert Pujols/200 6.00 15.00
2 Babe Ruth Pants/25 150.00 250.00
3 Bert Blyleven/200 2.50 6.00
4 Bobby Doerr Pants/200 2.50 6.00
5 Brooks Robinson/25 6.00 15.00
6 Cal Ripken/150 10.00 25.00
7 Carl Yastrzemski Pants/150 5.00 12.00
8 Dale Murphy/150 3.00 8.00
9 Dennis Eckersley/50 4.00 10.00
10 Don Mattingly/200 5.00 12.00
11 Don Sutton/100 3.00 8.00
12 Duke Snider Pants/25 6.00 15.00
13 Early Wynn/50 4.00 10.00
14 Eddie Murray/100 5.00 12.00
15 George Brett/25 10.00 25.00
16 Greg Maddux/150 4.00 10.00
17 Harmon Killebrew/100 5.00 12.00
18 Hoyt Wilhelm/150 2.50 6.00
19 Jim Edmonds/200 2.50 6.00
20 Jim Palmer/25 5.00 12.00
21 Lou Boudreau/50 4.00 10.00
22 Lou Brock/100 4.00 10.00
23 Miguel Cabrera/200 3.00 8.00
24 Mike Mussina/150 3.00 8.00
25 Mike Piazza/150 3.00 8.00
26 Mike Schmidt/150 5.00 12.00
27 Nolan Ryan/50 10.00 25.00
28 Phil Niekro/100 3.00 8.00
29 Randy Johnson/150 3.00 8.00
30 Rickey Henderson/150 4.00 10.00
31 Sammy Sosa/150 3.00 8.00
32 Scott Rolen/200 3.00 8.00
33 Stan Musial/10
34 Steve Carlton/100 3.00 8.00
35 Ted Williams/25 50.00 100.00
36 Tommy John/150 2.50 6.00
37 Vladimir Guerrero/200 3.00 8.00
38 Whitey Ford/25 6.00 15.00
39 Willie Mays/50 20.00 50.00
40 Willie McCovey/150 3.00 8.00
41 Babe Ruth Pants
Don Mattingly/25
42 Whitey Ford 15.00 40.00
Roger Clemens/25
43 Stan Musial
Jim Edmonds/5
44 Ted Williams 60.00 120.00
Tony Gwynn/25
45 Willie Mays Pants 30.00 60.00
Miguel Cabrera/25
46 Lou Brock 5.00 12.00
Rickey Henderson/100
47 Brooks Robinson 30.00 60.00
George Brett/25
48 Willie McCovey 8.00 20.00
David Ortiz/25
49 Bo Jackson 4.00 10.00
Deion Sanders/150
50 Nolan Ryan 12.50 30.00
Curt Schilling/100
51 Don Sutton 6.00 15.00
Greg Maddux/100
52 Harmon Killebrew 5.00 12.00
Rafael Palmeiro/100
53 Dale Murphy 4.00 10.00
Dwight Evans/150
54 Steve Carlton 8.00 20.00
Randy Johnson/25
55 Carl Yastrzemski 8.00 20.00
Vladimir Guerrero/50
56 Eddie Murray 5.00 12.00
Mike Piazza/100
57 Johnny Bench 6.00 15.00
Ivan Rodriguez/50
58 Jim Palmer 5.00 12.00
Tim Hudson/50
59 Cal Ripken 20.00 50.00
Hank Blalock/50
60 Jim Rice 5.00 12.00
Manny Ramirez/100

2005 Donruss Elite Throwback Threads Prime

*1-40 p/r 25: 1.5X TO 4X TT p/r 150-200
*1-40 p/r 25: 1.25X TO 3X TT p/r 100
*1-40 p/r 25: 1X TO 2.5X TT p/r 50
*1-40 p/r 25: .75X TO 2X TT p/r 25
1-40 PRINT RUNS B/WN 5-25 COPIES PER
*41-60 p/r 25: 2X TO 5X TT p/r 150-200
*41-60 p/r 25: 1.5X TO 4X TT p/r 100
*41-60 p/r 25: 1.25X TO 3X TT p/r 50
*41-60 p/r 25: 1X TO 2.5X TT p/r 25
41-60 PRINT RUNS B/WN 1-25 COPIES PER
OVERALL AU-GU ODDS THREE PER BOX
NO PRICING ON QTY OF 10 OR LESS
59 Cal Ripken 60.00 120.00
Hank Blalock/25

2005 Donruss Elite Throwback Threads Autographs

PRINT RUNS B/WN 5-100 COPIES PER
NO PRICING ON QTY OF 10 OR LESS
PRIME PRINT RUNS B/WN 1-10 PER
NO PRIME PRICING DUE TO SCARCITY
OVERALL AU-GU ODDS THREE PER BOX
3 Bert Blyleven/100 8.00 20.00
4 Bobby Doerr Pants/100 8.00 20.00
5 Brooks Robinson/50 15.00 40.00
6 Cal Ripken/5
8 Dale Murphy/100 12.50 30.00
9 Dennis Eckersley/75 10.00 25.00
10 Don Mattingly/25 40.00 80.00
11 Don Sutton/50 10.00 25.00
12 Duke Snider/10
15 George Brett/5
17 Harmon Killebrew/75 15.00 40.00
19 Jim Edmonds/5
20 Jim Palmer/75 8.00 20.00
22 Lou Brock Jkt/75 12.50 30.00
23 Miguel Cabrera/75 12.50 30.00
24 Mike Mussina/5
26 Mike Schmidt/5
27 Nolan Ryan/5
32 Scott Rolen/5
33 Stan Musial/5
38 Whitey Ford/5
39 Willie Mays/5
40 Willie McCovey/25 20.00 50.00

2007 Donruss Elite Extra Edition *

This 142-card set was released in December, 2007. This set marked the return of Donruss to producing baseball cards. The set was issued in five-card packs which came 20 packs to a box and 20 boxes to a case. Cards numbered 1-55 and 91-92 feature leading prospects while cards numbered 56-76 feature mainly football coaches with a few basketball coaches included and cards numbered 77-90 honor retired greats from a mix of sports. Cards numbered 93-142 are signed cards of some of the leading prospects in the set. All of those signed cards were issued to a stated print run of between 374 and 999 copies. A few players did not return their signatures in time for pack out and those cards could be redeemed until July 1, 2009.

COMP.SET w/o AU's (92) 8.00 20.00
COMMON CARD (1-92) .20 .50
COMMON AU (92-142) 4.00 10.00
OVERALL AUTO/MEM ODDS 1:5
AU PRINT RUNS B/WN 374-999 COPIES PER
EXCHANGE DEADLINE 07/01/2009
1 Andrew Brackman .60 1.50
2 Austin Gallagher .20 .50
3 Brett Cecil .20 .50
4 Darwin Barney .50 1.25
5 David Price 1.00 2.50
6 J. P. Arencibia .20 .50
7 Josh Donaldson .20 .50
8 Brandon Hicks .20 .50
9 Brian Rike .20 .50
10 Bryan Morris .20 .50
11 Cale Iorg .20 .50
12 Casey Weathers .20 .50
13 Corey Kluber .20 .50
14 Daniel Moskos .20 .50
15 Danny Payne .20 .50
16 David Kopp .20 .50
17 Dellin Betances .60 1.50
18 Derrick Robinson .20 .50
19 Drew Stubbs .20 .50
20 Eric Eiland .20 .50
21 Francisco Pena .20 .50
22 Greg Reynolds .20 .50
23 Jeff Samardzija 1.25 3.00
24 Jess Todd .20 .50
25 John Tolisano .20 .50
26 Jordan Zimmerman UER .30 .75
Last name misspelled
27 Julian Sampson .20 .50
28 Luke Hochevar .50 1.25
29 Mat Latos .20 .50
30 Matt Mangini .20 .50
31 Matt Spencer .30 .75
32 Matthew Sweeney .50 1.25
33 Max Scherzer .75 2.00
34 Mitch Canham .20 .50
35 Nick Schmidt .20 .50
36 Paul Kelly .20 .50
37 Ryan Pope .30 .75
38 Sam Runion .20 .50
39 Steven Souza .20 .50
40 Travis Mattair .20 .50
41 Trystan Magnuson .20 .50
42 Will Middlebrooks .30 .75
43 Zack Cozart .30 .75
44 James Adkins .20 .50
45 Cory Luebke .20 .50
46 Aaron Poreda .20 .50
47 Clayton Mortensen .20 .50
48 Bradley Suttle .30 .75
49 Tony Butler .30 .75
50 Zach Britton .20 .50
51 Scott Cousins .20 .50
52 Wendell Fairley .50 1.25
53 Eric Sogard .20 .50
54 Jonathan Lucroy .30 .75
55 Lars Davis .20 .50
56 Demetris Nichols .20 .50
57 Aaron Gray .20 .50
58 Daequan Cook .20 .50
59 Derrick Byars .20 .50
60 Reyshawn Terry .20 .50
61 Taurean Green .20 .50
62 Don Haskins .20 .50
63 Jerry Tarkanian .20 .50
64 Rick Majerus .20 .50
65 Rollie Massimino .20 .50
66 Ara Parseghian .20 .50
67 Dale Brown .20 .50
68 Dean Smith .20 .50
69 Eddie Sutton .20 .50
70 Frank Broyles .20 .50
71 Gene Keady .20 .50
72 Jim Boeheim .20 .50
73 Norm Stewart .20 .50
74 Steve Spurrier .20 .50
75 Tom Osborne .20 .50
76 Vince Dooley .20 .50
77 Jennie Finch .50 1.25
78 Amanda Beard .20 .50
79 Mike Powell .20 .50
80 Rebecca Lobo .20 .50
81 Brandi Chastain .20 .50
82 Clint Dolezel .20 .50
83 Elvin Hayes .20 .50
84 Cobi Jones .20 .50
85 Bill Walton .20 .50
86 Sidney Moncrief .20 .50
87 Dominique Wilkins .20 .50
88 Summer Sanders .20 .50
89 Michelle Akers .20 .50
90 Muggsy Bogues .20 .50
91 Charlie Culberson .60 1.50
92 Jacob Smolinski .20 .50
93 Blake Beaven AU/719 6.00 15.00
94 Brad Chalk AU/613 4.00 10.00
95 Brett Anderson AU/549 10.00 25.00
96 Chris Withrow AU/700 4.00 10.00
97 Clay Fuller AU/674 4.00 10.00
98 Damon Sublett AU/674 5.00 12.00
99 Devin Mesoraco AU/674 4.00 10.00
100 Drew Cumberland AU/744 4.00 10.00
101 Jack McGeary AU/674 4.00 10.00
102 Jake Arrieta AU/949 6.00 15.00
103 James Simmons AU/624 EXCH 4.00 10.00
104 Jarrod Parker AU/499 15.00 40.00
105 Jason Dominguez AU/744 4.00 10.00
106 Jason Heyward AU/750 30.00 60.00
107 Joe Savery AU/750 5.00 12.00
108 Jon Gilmore AU/819 4.00 10.00
109 Jordan Walden AU/794 10.00 25.00
110 Josh Smoker AU/719 4.00 10.00
111 Josh Vitters AU/769 10.00 25.00
112 Julio Borbon AU/594 4.00 10.00
113 Justin Jackson AU/850 4.00 10.00
114 Kellen Kulbacki AU/549 4.00 10.00
115 Kevin Ahrens AU/794 5.00 12.00
116 Kyle Lotzkar AU/611 4.00 10.00
117 Madison Bumgarner AU/794 12.50 30.00
118 Matt Dominguez AU/769 6.00 15.00
119 Matt LaPorta AU/594 30.00 60.00
120 Matt Wieters AU/799 75.00 150.00
121 Michael Burgess AU/672 10.00 25.00
122 Michael Main AU/794 5.00 12.00
123 Mike Moustakas AU/999 30.00 60.00
124 Nathan Vineyard AU/700 5.00 12.00
125 Neil Ramirez AU/774 6.00 15.00
126 Nick Hagadone AU/544 6.00 15.00
127 Pete Kozma AU/719 4.00 10.00
128 Phillippe Aumont AU/674 15.00 40.00
129 Preston Mattingly AU/519 4.00 10.00
130 Mystery EXCH 40.00 80.00
131 Ross Detwiler AU/650 5.00 12.00
132 Tim Alderson AU/719 8.00 20.00
133 Todd Frazier AU/774 5.00 12.00
134 Wes Roemer AU/694 4.00 10.00
135 Ben Revere AU/700 6.00 15.00
136 Chris Davis AU/374 EXCH 50.00 100.00
137 Alando Tucker AU/494 4.00 10.00
138 Bryan Anderson AU/474 EXCH 4.00 10.00
139 Marc Gasol AU/474 EXCH 4.00 10.00
140 Stephane Lasme AU/674 4.00 10.00
141 Austin Jackson AU/794 30.00 60.00
142 Beau Mills AU/624 EXCH 8.00 20.00

2007 Donruss Elite Extra Edition Aspirations *

*ASP 1-92: 3X TO 8X BASIC
OVERALL INSERT ODDS 1:4
STATED PRINT RUN 100 SER.#'d SETS
23 Jeff Samardzija 8.00 20.00
33 Max Scherzer 30.00 60.00
92 Jacob Smolinski 1.50 4.00
93 Blake Beaven 1.50 4.00
94 Brad Chalk 1.50 4.00
95 Brett Anderson 2.50 6.00
96 Chris Withrow 1.50 4.00
97 Clay Fuller 1.50 4.00
98 Damon Sublett 2.50 6.00
99 Devin Mesoraco 1.50 4.00
100 Drew Cumberland 1.50 4.00
101 Jack McGeary 2.00 5.00
102 Jake Arrieta 1.50 4.00
103 James Simmons 1.50 4.00
104 Jarrod Parker 8.00 20.00
105 Jason Dominguez 1.50 4.00
106 Jason Heyward 10.00 25.00
107 Joe Savery 2.00 5.00
108 Jon Gilmore 2.00 5.00
109 Jordan Walden 2.50 6.00
110 Josh Smoker 2.50 6.00
111 Josh Vitters 10.00 25.00
112 Julio Borbon 2.00 5.00
113 Justin Jackson 1.50 4.00
114 Kellen Kulbacki 2.00 5.00
115 Kevin Ahrens 2.00 5.00
116 Kyle Lotzkar 1.50 4.00
117 Madison Bumgarner 8.00 20.00
118 Matt Dominguez 6.00 15.00
119 Matt LaPorta 10.00 25.00
120 Matt Wieters 15.00 40.00
121 Michael Burgess 6.00 15.00
122 Michael Main 2.00 5.00
123 Mike Moustakas 10.00 25.00
124 Nathan Vineyard 2.00 5.00
125 Neil Ramirez 1.50 4.00

126 Nick Hagadone 2.50 6.00
127 Pete Kozma 1.50 4.00
128 Phillippe Aumont 5.00 12.00
129 Preston Mattingly 4.00 10.00
131 Ross Detwiler 2.50 6.00
132 Tim Alderson 2.50 6.00
133 Todd Frazier 2.00 5.00
134 Wes Roemer 1.50 4.00
135 Ben Revere 2.50 6.00
136 D.J. Strawberry 2.00 5.00
137 Alando Tucker 1.50 4.00
138 Jared Jordan 1.50 4.00
139 Marc Gasol 1.50 4.00
140 Stephane Lasme 1.50 4.00
141 Austin Jackson 10.00 25.00
142 Beau Mills 4.00 10.00

2007 Donruss Elite Extra Edition Status *

*STATUS 1-92: 4X TO 10X BASIC
OVERALL INSERT ODDS 1:4
STATED PRINT RUN 50 SER.#'d SETS
93 Blake Beaven 2.00 5.00
94 Brad Chalk 2.00 5.00
95 Brett Anderson 3.00 8.00
96 Chris Withrow 2.00 5.00
97 Clay Fuller 2.00 5.00
98 Damon Sublett 3.00 8.00
99 Devin Mesoraco 2.50 6.00
100 Drew Cumberland 2.00 5.00
101 Jack McGeary 2.50 6.00
102 Jake Arrieta 2.00 5.00
103 James Simmons 2.00 5.00
104 Jarrod Parker 10.00 25.00
105 Jason Dominguez 2.00 5.00
106 Jason Heyward 12.50 30.00
107 Joe Savery 2.00 5.00
108 Jon Gilmore 2.00 5.00
109 Jordan Walden 3.00 8.00
110 Josh Smoker 3.00 8.00
111 Josh Vitters 12.50 30.00
112 Julio Borbon 2.50 6.00
113 Justin Jackson 2.00 5.00
114 Kellen Kulbacki 2.50 6.00
115 Kevin Ahrens 2.00 5.00
116 Kyle Lotzkar 2.00 5.00
117 Madison Bumgarner 10.00 25.00
118 Matt Dominguez 8.00 20.00
119 Matt LaPorta 12.50 30.00
120 Matt Wieters 12.50 30.00
121 Michael Burgess 8.00 20.00
122 Michael Main 2.50 6.00
123 Mike Moustakas 12.50 30.00
124 Nathan Vineyard 2.50 6.00
125 Neil Ramirez 2.00 5.00
126 Nick Hagadone 3.00 8.00
127 Pete Kozma 2.00 5.00
128 Phillippe Aumont 6.00 15.00
129 Preston Mattingly 5.00 12.00
131 Ross Detwiler 3.00 8.00
132 Tim Alderson 3.00 8.00
133 Todd Frazier 2.50 6.00
134 Wes Roemer 2.00 5.00
135 Ben Revere 3.00 8.00
136 D.J. Strawberry 2.50 6.00
137 Alando Tucker 2.00 5.00
138 Jared Jordan 2.00 5.00
139 Marc Gasol 2.00 5.00
140 Stephane Lasme 2.00 5.00
141 Austin Jackson 12.50 30.00
142 Beau Mills 5.00 12.00

2007 Donruss Elite Extra Edition Status Gold *

OVERALL INSERT ODDS 1:4
STATED PRINT RUN 25 SER.#'d SETS
NO PRICING DUE TO SCARCITY

2007 Donruss Elite Extra Edition Signature Aspirations *

OVERALL AU/MEM ODDS 1:5
PRINT RUNS B/WN 5-100 COPIES PER
NO PRICING ON QTY 25 OR LESS
EXCHANGE DEADLINE 07/01/2007
1 Andrew Brackman/100 12.50 30.00
2 Austin Gallagher/100 12.50 30.00
3 Brett Cecil /100 10.00 25.00
4 Danny Worth/100 EXCH 6.00 15.00
5 David Price/100 75.00 150.00
6 J. P. Arencibia/100 EXCH 6.00 15.00
7 Josh Donaldson/100 20.00 50.00
8 Brandon Hicks/100 4.00 10.00
9 Brian Rike/100 4.00 10.00
10 Bryan Morris/100 8.00 20.00
11 Cale Iorg/100 12.50 30.00
12 Casey Weathers/100 6.00 15.00
13 Corey Kluber/100 4.00 10.00
14 Daniel Moskos/100 4.00 10.00
15 Danny Payne/50 6.00 15.00
16 David Kopp/36 6.00 15.00
17 Dellin Betances/50 30.00 60.00
18 Derrick Robinson/100 4.00 10.00
19 Drew Stubbs/100 12.50 30.00
20 Eric Eiland/100 4.00 10.00
21 Francisco Pena/100 8.00 20.00
22 Greg Reynolds/100 4.00 10.00
23 Jeff Samardzija/15
24 Jess Todd/50 12.50 30.00
25 John Tolisano/100 4.00 10.00
26 Jordan Zimmerman/75 UER 10.00 25.00
Last name misspelled
27 Julian Sampson/50 4.00 10.00
28 Luke Hochevar/25
29 Mat Latos/34 30.00 60.00
30 Matt Mangini/80 10.00 25.00
31 Matt Spencer/30 6.00 15.00
32 Matthew Sweeney/100 EXCH 8.00 20.00
34 Mitch Canham/25
35 Nick Schmidt/25
36 Paul Kelly/100 4.00 10.00
37 Ryan Pope/100 12.50 30.00
38 Sam Runion/50 6.00 15.00
39 Steven Souza/100 6.00 15.00
40 Travis Mattair/50 6.00 15.00
41 Trystan Magnuson/50 4.00 10.00
42 Will Middlebrooks/25
43 Zack Cozart/25
44 James Adkins/100 10.00 25.00
45 Cory Luebke/100 4.00 10.00
46 Aaron Poreda/100 6.00 15.00
47 Clayton Mortensen/100 6.00 15.00
48 Bradley Suttle/100 12.50 30.00
49 Tony Butler/100 4.00 10.00
50 Zach Britton/100 4.00 10.00
51 Scott Cousins /50 6.00 15.00
52 Wendell Fairley/100 8.00 20.00
53 Eric Sogard/100 4.00 10.00
54 Jonathan Lucroy/100 6.00 15.00
55 Lars Davis/100 4.00 10.00
56 Tony Thomas/100 EXCH 4.00 10.00
57 Aaron Gray/100 4.00 10.00
58 Daequan Cook/50 10.00 25.00
59 Nick Noonan/100 EXCH 4.00 10.00
60 Henry Sosa/100 EXCH 4.00 10.00
61 Taurean Green/75 4.00 10.00
62 Don Haskins/100 4.00 10.00
63 Jerry Tarkanian/50 5.00 12.00
64 Rick Majerus/100 4.00 10.00
65 Rollie Massimino/5 EXCH
66 Ara Parseghian/100 12.50 30.00
67 Dale Brown/25
68 Dean Smith/5 EXCH
69 Eddie Sutton/50 5.00 12.00
70 Frank Broyles/100 5.00 12.00
71 Gene Keady/50 4.00 10.00
72 Jim Boeheim/100 5.00 12.00
73 Corey Brown/5 EXCH
74 Steve Spurrier/25
75 Tom Osborne/100 12.50 30.00
76 Vince Dooley/50 10.00 25.00
77 Jennie Finch/50 40.00 80.00
78 Amanda Beard/5
79 Mike Powell/100 6.00 15.00
80 Rebecca Lobo/100 6.00 15.00
81 Brandi Chastain/50 20.00 50.00
82 Clint Dolezel/100 4.00 10.00
83 Elvin Hayes/100 4.00 10.00
84 Cobi Jones/100 6.00 15.00
85 Bill Walton/100 6.00 15.00
86 Sidney Moncrief/50 5.00 12.00
87 Dominique Wilkins/50 10.00 25.00
88 Summer Sanders/50 10.00 25.00
89 Michelle Akers/100 8.00 20.00
90 Muggsy Bogues/100 4.00 10.00
91 Charlie Culberson/100 15.00 40.00
92 Jacob Smolinski/100 8.00 20.00
93 Blake Beaven/100 10.00 25.00
94 Brad Chalk/100 4.00 10.00
95 Brett Anderson/100 12.50 30.00
96 Chris Withrow/100 6.00 15.00
97 Clay Fuller/100 5.00 12.00
98 Damon Sublett/50 10.00 25.00
99 Devin Mesoraco/100 6.00 15.00
100 Drew Cumberland/100 5.00 12.00
101 Jack McGeary/100 4.00 10.00
102 Jake Arrieta/100 6.00 15.00
103 James Simmons/50 EXCH 4.00 10.00
104 Jarrod Parker/50 40.00 80.00
105 Jason Dominguez/100 5.00 12.00
106 Jason Heyward/100 60.00 120.00
107 Joe Savery/100 5.00 12.00
108 Jon Gilmore/100 5.00 12.00
109 Jordan Walden/50 20.00 50.00
110 Josh Smoker/100 12.50 30.00
111 Josh Vitters/100 30.00 60.00
112 Julio Borbon/100 5.00 12.00
113 Justin Jackson/50 6.00 15.00
114 Kellen Kulbacki/100 6.00 15.00
115 Kevin Ahrens/50 10.00 25.00
116 Kyle Lotzkar/100 5.00 12.00
117 Madison Bumgarner/50 30.00 60.00
118 Matt Dominguez/50 30.00 60.00
119 Matt LaPorta/100 60.00 120.00
120 Matt Wieters/50 150.00 250.00
121 Michael Burgess/50 15.00 40.00
122 Michael Main/50 12.50 30.00
123 Mike Moustakas/100 75.00 150.00
124 Nathan Vineyard/100 5.00 12.00
125 Neil Ramirez/100 6.00 15.00
126 Nick Hagadone/50 10.00 25.00
127 Pete Kozma/100 10.00 25.00
128 Phillippe Aumont/100 40.00 80.00
129 Preston Mattingly/50 6.00 15.00
131 Ross Detwiler/100 6.00 15.00
132 Tim Alderson/100 15.00 40.00
133 Todd Frazier/50 12.50 30.00
134 Wes Roemer/100 5.00 12.00
135 Ben Revere/100 10.00 25.00
136 Chris Davis/50 EXCH 100.00 200.00
137 Alando Tucker/50 5.00 12.00
138 Bryan Anderson/50 EXCH 4.00 10.00
139 Marc Gasol/50 EXCH 4.00 10.00
140 Stephane Lasme/100 4.00 10.00
141 Austin Jackson/50 60.00 120.00
142 Beau Mills/50 EXCH 6.00 15.00

2007 Donruss Elite Extra Edition Signature Status *

OVERALL AU/MEM ODDS 1:5
PRINT RUNS B/WN 1-50 COPIES PER
NO PRICING ON QTY 25 OR LESS
EXCHANGE DEADLINE 07/01/2007
1 Andrew Brackman/50 75.00 150.00
2 Austin Gallagher/50 20.00 50.00
3 Brett Cecil /50 20.00 50.00
4 Danny Worth/50 EXCH 8.00 20.00
5 David Price/50 150.00 250.00
6 J. P. Arencibia/50 EXCH 10.00 25.00
7 Josh Donaldson/50 30.00 60.00
8 Brandon Hicks/50 6.00 15.00
9 Brian Rike/50 6.00 15.00
10 Bryan Morris/50 12.50 30.00
11 Cale Iorg/50 12.50 30.00
12 Casey Weathers/50 10.00 25.00
13 Corey Kluber/50 6.00 15.00
14 Daniel Moskos/50 6.00 15.00
15 Danny Payne/25
16 David Kopp/25
17 Dellin Betances/25
18 Derrick Robinson/50 6.00 15.00
19 Drew Stubbs/50 15.00 40.00
20 Eric Eiland/50 6.00 15.00
21 Francisco Pena/50 12.50 30.00
22 Greg Reynolds/50 6.00 15.00
23 Jeff Samardzija/10
24 Jess Todd/25
25 John Tolisano/50 6.00 15.00
26 Jordan Zimmerman/25 UER
Last name misspelled
27 Julian Sampson/25
28 Luke Hochevar/10
29 Mat Latos/25
30 Matt Mangini/50 15.00 40.00
31 Matt Spencer/15
32 Matthew Sweeney/50 EXCH 12.50 30.00
33 Max Scherzer/12
34 Mitch Canham/10
35 Nick Schmidt/10
36 Paul Kelly/50 6.00 15.00
37 Ryan Pope/50 20.00 50.00
38 Sam Runion/25
39 Steven Souza/50 10.00 25.00
40 Travis Mattair/25
41 Trystan Magnuson/25
42 Will Middlebrooks/10
43 Zack Cozart/10
44 James Adkins/50 6.00 15.00
45 Cory Luebke/50 6.00 15.00
46 Aaron Poreda/50 10.00 25.00
47 Clayton Mortensen/50 10.00 25.00
48 Bradley Suttle/50 20.00 50.00
49 Tony Butler/50 6.00 15.00
50 Zach Britton/50 6.00 15.00
51 Scott Cousins /19
52 Wendell Fairley/50 10.00 25.00
53 Eric Sogard/50 6.00 15.00
54 Jonathan Lucroy/50 10.00 25.00
55 Lars Davis/50 6.00 15.00
56 Tony Thomas/50 EXCH 6.00 15.00
57 Aaron Gray/50 6.00 15.00
58 Daequan Cook/25
59 Nick Noonan/50 EXCH 6.00 15.00
60 Henry Sosa/50 EXCH 6.00 15.00
61 Taurean Green/29 6.00 15.00
62 Don Haskins/50 6.00 15.00
63 Jerry Tarkanian/25
64 Rick Majerus/50 6.00 15.00
65 Rollie Massimino/1 EXCH
66 Ara Parseghian/50 20.00 50.00
67 Dale Brown/10
68 Dean Smith/1 EXCH
69 Eddie Sutton/25
70 Frank Broyles/50 8.00 20.00
71 Gene Keady/25
72 Jim Boeheim/50 8.00 20.00
73 Corey Brown/1 EXCH
74 Steve Spurrier/10
75 Tom Osborne/50 20.00 50.00
76 Vince Dooley/25
77 Jennie Finch/25
78 Amanda Beard/5
79 Mike Powell/50 10.00 25.00
80 Rebecca Lobo/50 10.00 25.00
81 Brandi Chastain/25
82 Clint Dolezel/50 6.00 15.00
83 Elvin Hayes/50 6.00 15.00
84 Cobi Jones/50 10.00 25.00
85 Bill Walton/50 10.00 25.00
86 Sidney Moncrief/25
87 Dominique Wilkins/25
88 Summer Sanders/25
89 Michelle Akers/50 12.50 30.00
90 Muggsy Bogues/50 6.00 15.00
91 Charlie Culberson/50 30.00 60.00
92 Jacob Smolinski/50 12.50 30.00
93 Blake Beaven/50 12.50 30.00
94 Brad Chalk/50 6.00 15.00
95 Brett Anderson/50 15.00 40.00
96 Chris Withrow/50 10.00 25.00
97 Clay Fuller/50 8.00 20.00
98 Damon Sublett/25
99 Devin Mesoraco/50 10.00 25.00
100 Drew Cumberland/50 8.00 20.00
101 Jack McGeary/50 6.00 15.00
102 Jake Arrieta/50 10.00 25.00
103 James Simmons/25 EXCH
104 Jarrod Parker/25
105 Jason Dominguez/50 8.00 20.00
106 Jason Heyward/50 90.00 150.00
107 Joe Savery/50 8.00 20.00
108 Jon Gilmore/50 8.00 20.00
109 Jordan Walden/25
110 Josh Smoker/50 15.00 40.00
111 Josh Vitters/50 50.00 100.00
112 Julio Borbon/50 8.00 20.00
113 Justin Jackson/25
114 Kellen Kulbacki/50 10.00 25.00
115 Kevin Ahrens/25
116 Kyle Lotzkar/50 6.00 15.00
117 Madison Bumgarner/25
118 Matt Dominguez/25
119 Matt LaPorta/50 100.00 150.00
120 Matt Wieters/25
121 Michael Burgess/25
122 Michael Main/25
123 Mike Moustakas/50 150.00 250.00
124 Nathan Vineyard/50 8.00 20.00
125 Neil Ramirez/50 10.00 25.00
126 Nick Hagadone/25
127 Pete Kozma/50 10.00 25.00
128 Phillippe Aumont/50 60.00 120.00
129 Preston Mattingly/25
131 Ross Detwiler/50 15.00 40.00
132 Tim Alderson/50 30.00 60.00
133 Todd Frazier/50 15.00 40.00
134 Wes Roemer/50 6.00 15.00
135 Ben Revere/50 15.00 40.00
136 Chris Davis/25 EXCH
137 Alando Tucker/25
138 Bryan Anderson/25 EXCH
139 Marc Gasol/25 EXCH
140 Stephane Lasme/50 6.00 15.00
141 Austin Jackson/25
142 Beau Mills/25 EXCH

2007 Donruss Elite Extra Edition Signature Status Black *

OVERALL AUTO/MEM ODDS 1:5
STATED PRINT RUN 1 SER.#'d SET
NO PRICING DUE TO SCARCITY
EXCHANGE DEADLINE 07/01/2009

2007 Donruss Elite Extra Edition Signature Status Gold *

OVERALL AUTO/MEM ODDS 1:5
STATED PRINT RUN 5 SER.#'d SETS
NO PRICING DUE TO SCARCITY
EXCHANGE DEADLINE 07/01/2009

2007 Donruss Elite Extra Edition Signature Turn of the Century *

OVERALL AU/MEM ODDS 1:5
PRINT RUNS B/WN 10-500 COPIES PER
NO PRICING ON QTY 25 OR LESS
EXCHANGE DEADLINE 07/01/2007
1 Andrew Brackman/500 12.50 30.00
2 Austin Gallagher/500 10.00 25.00
3 Brett Cecil /500 8.00 20.00
4 Danny Worth/500 EXCH 4.00 10.00
5 David Price/500 30.00 60.00
6 J. P. Arencibia/500 EXCH 5.00 12.00
7 Josh Donaldson/500 4.00 10.00
8 Brandon Hicks/419 4.00 10.00
9 Brian Rike/500 5.00 12.00
10 Bryan Morris/500 5.00 12.00
11 Cale Iorg/397 4.00 10.00
12 Casey Weathers/500 4.00 10.00
13 Corey Kluber/419 4.00 10.00
14 Daniel Moskos/500 4.00 10.00
15 Danny Payne/394 4.00 10.00
16 David Kopp/449 4.00 10.00
17 Dellin Betances/494 12.50 30.00
18 Derrick Robinson/500 4.00 10.00
19 Drew Stubbs/494 8.00 20.00
20 Eric Eiland/419 4.00 10.00
21 Francisco Pena/396 6.00 15.00
22 Greg Reynolds/500 4.00 10.00
23 Jeff Samardzija/219 20.00 50.00
24 Jess Todd/394 8.00 20.00
25 John Tolisano/419 4.00 10.00
26 Jordan Zimmerman/469 UER 4.00 10.00
Last name misspelled
27 Julian Sampson/494 4.00 10.00
28 Luke Hochevar/158 12.50 30.00
29 Mat Latos/499 8.00 20.00
30 Matt Mangini/500 4.00 10.00
31 Matt Spencer/500 4.00 10.00
32 Matthew Sweeney/500 EXCH 6.00 15.00
33 Max Scherzer/250 40.00 80.00
34 Mitch Canham/209 5.00 12.00
35 Nick Schmidt/409 4.00 10.00
36 Paul Kelly/500 4.00 10.00
37 Ryan Pope/500 6.00 15.00
38 Sam Runion/494 5.00 12.00
39 Steven Souza/500 6.00 15.00
40 Travis Mattair/494 4.00 10.00
41 Trystan Magnuson/246 4.00 10.00
42 Will Middlebrooks/409 10.00 25.00
43 Zack Cozart/409 4.00 10.00
44 James Adkins/500 4.00 10.00
45 Cory Luebke/469 4.00 10.00
46 Aaron Poreda/500 4.00 10.00
47 Clayton Mortensen/500 4.00 10.00
48 Bradley Suttle/500 6.00 15.00
49 Tony Butler/419 4.00 10.00
50 Zach Britton/437 4.00 10.00
51 Scott Cousins/500 4.00 10.00
52 Wendell Fairley/500 6.00 15.00
53 Eric Sogard/500 4.00 10.00
54 Jonathan Lucroy/500 5.00 12.00
55 Lars Davis/500 4.00 10.00
56 Tony Thomas/300 EXCH 4.00 10.00
57 Aaron Gray/500 4.00 10.00
58 Daequan Cook/494 4.00 10.00
59 Nick Noonan/300 EXCH 4.00 10.00
60 Henry Sosa/300 EXCH 5.00 12.00
61 Taurean Green/500 4.00 10.00
62 Don Haskins/194 5.00 12.00
63 Jerry Tarkanian/144 5.00 12.00
64 Rick Majerus/194 5.00 12.00
65 Rollie Massimino/10 EXCH
66 Ara Parseghian/69 10.00 25.00
67 Dale Brown/89 6.00 15.00
68 Dean Smith/10 EXCH
69 Eddie Sutton/144 6.00 15.00
70 Frank Broyles/69 6.00 15.00
71 Gene Keady/144 4.00 10.00
72 Jim Boeheim/19
73 Corey Brown/10 EXCH
74 Steve Spurrier/59 30.00 60.00
75 Tom Osborne/320 10.00 25.00
76 Vince Dooley/91 6.00 15.00
77 Jennie Finch/119 15.00 40.00
78 Amanda Beard/13
79 Mike Powell/119 10.00 25.00
80 Rebecca Lobo/234 5.00 12.00
81 Brandi Chastain/94 6.00 15.00
82 Clint Dolezel/243 4.00 10.00
83 Elvin Hayes/344 4.00 10.00
84 Cobi Jones/247 6.00 15.00
85 Bill Walton/19
86 Sidney Moncrief/169 4.00 10.00
87 Dominique Wilkins/20
88 Summer Sanders/169 6.00 15.00
89 Michelle Akers/344 6.00 15.00
90 Muggsy Bogues/94 5.00 12.00
91 Charlie Culberson/500 6.00 15.00
92 Jacob Smolinski/500 5.00 12.00
93 Blake Beaven/100 10.00 25.00
94 Brad Chalk/100 5.00 12.00
95 Brett Anderson/145 12.50 30.00
96 Chris Withrow/168 6.00 15.00
97 Clay Fuller/145 5.00 12.00
98 Damon Sublett/220 10.00 25.00
99 Devin Mesoraco/145 5.00 12.00
100 Drew Cumberland/125 5.00 12.00
101 Jack McGeary/145 4.00 10.00
102 Jake Arrieta/145 6.00 15.00
103 James Simmons/100 EXCH 5.00 12.00
104 Jarrod Parker/55 40.00 80.00
105 Jason Dominguez/100 5.00 12.00
106 Jason Heyward/100 30.00 60.00
107 Joe Savery/119 6.00 15.00
108 Jon Gilmore/145 5.00 12.00
109 Jordan Walden/100 12.50 30.00
110 Josh Smoker/200 8.00 20.00
111 Josh Vitters/150 20.00 50.00
112 Julio Borbon/100 5.00 12.00
113 Justin Jackson/100 5.00 12.00
114 Kellen Kulbacki/145 6.00 15.00
115 Kevin Ahrens/100 8.00 20.00
116 Kyle Lotzkar/100 5.00 12.00
117 Madison Bumgarner/100 40.00 80.00
118 Matt Dominguez/100 20.00 50.00
119 Matt LaPorta/100 30.00 60.00
120 Matt Wieters/100 125.00 175.00
121 Michael Burgess/100 12.50 30.00
122 Michael Main/100 6.00 15.00
123 Mike Moustakas/345 30.00 60.00
124 Nathan Vineyard/119 6.00 15.00
125 Neil Ramirez/145 6.00 15.00
126 Nick Hagadone/100 8.00 20.00
127 Pete Kozma/100 5.00 12.00
128 Phillippe Aumont/120 20.00 50.00
129 Preston Mattingly/100 5.00 12.00
131 Ross Detwiler/119 10.00 25.00
132 Tim Alderson/100 15.00 40.00
133 Todd Frazier/145 12.50 30.00
134 Wes Roemer/100 5.00 12.00
135 Ben Revere/119 10.00 25.00
136 Chris Davis/100 EXCH 75.00 150.00
137 Alando Tucker/100 4.00 10.00
138 Bryan Anderson/100 EXCH 4.00 10.00
139 Tommy Hunter/100 EXCH 4.00 10.00
140 Stephane Lasme/145 5.00 12.00
141 Austin Jackson/100 50.00 100.00
142 Beau Mills/100 EXCH 12.50 30.00

2007 Donruss Elite Extra Edition College Ties *

STATED PRINT RUN 1500 SER.#'d SETS
*GOLD: .6X TO 1.5X BASIC
GOLD PRINT RUN 500 SER.#'d SETS
*RED: 1X TO 2.5X BASIC
RED PRINT RUN 100 SER.#'d SETS
OVERALL INSERT ODDS 1:4
1 Daniel Moskos .75 2.00
David Kopp
2 Nick Schmidt .75 2.00
Jess Todd
3 J.P. Arencibia .75 2.00
Julio Borbon
4 David Price 1.50 4.00
Casey Weathers
5 Taurean Green 1.25 3.00
Matt LaPorta
6 Jennie Finch 1.50 4.00
Amanda Beard
7 Jim Boeheim .75 2.00
Demetris Nichols
8 Danny Payne 1.50 4.00
Matt Wieters
9 Darwin Barney .75 2.00
Mitch Canham
10 Luke Hochevar .75 2.00
James Adkins
11 Daequan Cook .75 2.00
Cory Luebke
12 D. J. Strawberry .75 2.00
Brett Cecil

2007 Donruss Elite Extra Edition College Ties Autographs *

OVERALL AUTO/MEM ODDS 1:5
PRINT RUNS B/WN 50-100 COPIES PER
EXCHANGE DEADLINE 07/01/2009
1 Daniel Moskos 6.00 15.00
David Kopp
2 Nick Schmidt 6.00 15.00
Jess Todd
3 J.P. Arencibia 10.00 25.00
Julio Borbon EXCH
4 David Price 20.00 50.00
Casey Weathers
5 Taurean Green 12.50 30.00
Matt LaPorta
6 Jennie Finch 125.00 200.00
Amanda Beard
7 Jim Boeheim 6.00 15.00
Demetris Nichols EXCH
8 Danny Payne 15.00 40.00
Matt Wieters
9 Darwin Barney 6.00 15.00
Mitch Canham EXCH
10 Luke Hochevar 15.00 40.00
James Adkins
11 Daequan Cook 10.00 25.00
Cory Luebke
12 D. J. Strawberry 6.00 15.00
Brett Cecil EXCH

2007 Donruss Elite Extra Edition College Ties Jerseys *

OVERALL AUTO/MEM ODDS 1:5
PRINT RUNS B/WN 50-500 COPIES PER
1 Daniel Moskos 4.00 10.00
David Kopp/75
6 Jennie Finch 6.00 15.00
Amanda Beard/50
9 Darwin Barney 3.00 8.00
Mitch Canham/500

2007 Donruss Elite Extra Edition College Ties Jerseys Prime *

OVERALL AUTO/MEM ODDS 1:5
PRINT RUNS B/WN 5-50 COPIES PER
NO PRICING ON QTY 25 OR LESS
1 Daniel Moskos
David Kopp/5
6 Jennie Finch
Amanda Beard/25
9 Darwin Barney 4.00 10.00
Mitch Canham/50

2007 Donruss Elite Extra Edition Collegiate Patches *

OVERALL AUTO/MEM ODDS 1:5
PRINT RUNS B/WN 25-250 COPIES PER
NO PRICING ON QTY 25 OR LESS
EXCHANGE DEADLINE 07/01/2009
1 Amanda Beard/100 20.00 50.00
2 Ara Parseghian/25 15.00 40.00
4 Burt Reynolds/25
5 Dale Brown/25 8.00 20.00
6 Dean Smith/250 EXCH 30.00 60.00
7 Eddie Sutton/250 10.00 25.00
8 Frank Broyles/250 6.00 15.00
9 Gene Keady/250 10.00 25.00
10 Jennie Finch/249 30.00 60.00
11 Jim Boeheim/250 8.00 20.00
12 Sheryl Swoopes/250 10.00 25.00
13 Norm Stewart/250 EXCH 15.00 40.00
14 Rebecca Lobo/250 10.00 25.00
15 Ron Howard/25
16 Steve Spurrier South Carolina/100
17 Tom Osborne/249 20.00 50.00
18 Vince Dooley/250 6.00 15.00
19 Josh Donaldson/250 6.00 15.00
20 Cobi Jones/97 15.00 40.00
21 Bill Walton/250 15.00 40.00
22 Sidney Moncrief/250 6.00 15.00
23 Dominique Wilkins/100 10.00 25.00
24 Steve Spurrier Florida/100
25 Drew Stubbs/250 8.00 20.00
26 Andrew Brackman/250 10.00 25.00
27 Casey Weathers/250 10.00 25.00
28 Daniel Moskos/250 6.00 15.00
29 David Price/250 30.00 60.00
30 Greg Reynolds/250 6.00 15.00
31 J. P. Arencibia/249 10.00 25.00
32 Jeff Samardzija/150 30.00 60.00
33 Julio Borbon/250 6.00 15.00
34 Luke Hochevar/100 12.50 30.00
35 Matt LaPorta/250 40.00 80.00
36 Matt Mangini/250 6.00 15.00
37 Matt Wieters/250 EXCH 40.00 80.00
38 Max Scherzer/182 20.00 50.00
39 Mitch Canham/250 6.00 15.00
40 Nick Schmidt/250 8.00 20.00
41 James Adkins/250 6.00 15.00
42 Tony Thomas/250 EXCH 6.00 15.00
43 Aaron Gray/250 6.00 15.00
44 Daequan Cook/250 6.00 15.00
45 Tommy Hunter/250 EXCH 8.00 20.00
46 Rick Majeras/250 EXCH 6.00 15.00
47 Taurean Green/250 6.00 15.00
48 Summer Sanders/250 10.00 25.00
49 Bobby Hurley/250 EXCH 8.00 20.00
50 Muggsy Bogues/250 10.00 25.00
51 Jerry Tarkanian/250 6.00 15.00
52 Cale Iorg/250 6.00 15.00
53 Lynette Woodard/249 6.00 15.00
54 Nick Hagadone/250 6.00 15.00
55 Trystan Magnuson/248 6.00 15.00
64 Matt Spencer/249 6.00 15.00
65 Corey Brown/250 EXCH 6.00 15.00
67 Connie Mack III/100 6.00 15.00
68 Mike Powell/99 12.50 30.00

2007 Donruss Elite Extra Edition School Colors *

OVERALL INSERT ODDS 1:4
STATED PRINT RUN 1500 SER.#'d SETS
1 David Price 1.50 4.00
2 Daniel Moskos .75 2.00
3 Greg Reynolds .75 2.00
4 Matt LaPorta 1.25 3.00
5 Matt Wieters 2.50 6.00
6 Luke Hochevar .75 2.00
7 Max Scherzer .75 2.00
8 Alando Tucker .75 2.00
9 Daequan Cook .75 2.00
10 Eddie Sutton .75 2.00
11 Dean Smith .75 2.00
12 Steve Spurrier .75 2.00
13 Tom Osborne .75 2.00
14 Don Haskins .75 2.00
15 Jerry Tarkanian .75 2.00
16 Rick Majerus .75 2.00
17 Rollie Massimino .75 2.00
18 Ara Parseghian .75 2.00
19 Dale Brown .75 2.00
20 Frank Broyles .75 2.00
21 Gene Keady .75 2.00
22 Jim Boeheim .75 2.00
23 Norm Stewart .75 2.00
24 Vince Dooley .75 2.00
25 Bill Walton .75 2.00
26 Nick Schmidt .75 2.00
27 Burt Reynolds .75 2.00
28 Ron Howard .75 2.00
29 Beau Mills .75 2.00
30 James Simmons .75 2.00
31 Joe Savery .75 2.00
32 Ross Detwiler .75 2.00
33 J. P. Arencibia .75 2.00
34 Drew Stubbs .75 2.00

2007 Donruss Elite Extra Edition School Colors Autographs *

OVERALL AUTO/MEM ODDS 1:5
PRINT RUNS B/WN 10-50 COPIES PER
NO PRICING ON QTY 25 OR LESS
EXCHANGE DEADLINE 07/01/2009
1 David Price/50 30.00 60.00
2 Daniel Moskos/50 6.00 15.00
3 Greg Reynolds/50 6.00 15.00
4 Matt LaPorta/50 40.00 80.00
5 Matt Wieters/50 75.00 150.00
6 Luke Hochevar/50 10.00 25.00
7 Max Scherzer/50 75.00 150.00
8 Alando Tucker/50 6.00 15.00
9 Daequan Cook/50 6.00 15.00
10 Eddie Sutton/25
11 Dean Smith/25 EXCH
12 Steve Spurrier/25
13 Tom Osborne/25
14 Don Haskins/25

15 Jerry Tarkanian/25
16 Rick Majerus/25
17 Rollie Massimino/25 EXCH
18 Ara Parseghian/25
19 Dale Brown/25
20 Frank Broyles/25
21 Gene Keady/25
22 Jim Boeheim/25
23 Norm Stewart/25 EXCH
24 Vince Dooley/25
25 Bill Walton/25
26 Nick Schmidt/50 6.00 15.00
27 Burt Reynolds/10
28 Ron Howard/10
29 Beau Mills/50 EXCH 10.00 25.00
30 James Simmons/50 EXCH 6.00 15.00
31 Joe Savery/50 6.00 15.00
32 Ross Detwiler/50 10.00 25.00
33 J. P. Arencibia/50 EXCH 10.00 25.00
34 Drew Stubbs/50 6.00 15.00

2007 Donruss Elite Extra Edition Throwback Threads *

OVERALL AUTO/MEM ODDS 1:5
PRINT RUNS B/WN 44-500 COPIES PER
1 Brandi Chastain/500 6.00 15.00
2 Amanda Beard/44 10.00 25.00
3 Drew Stubbs/500 3.00 8.00
4 Drew Cumberland/500 3.00 8.00
5 Clint Dolezel/500 3.00 8.00
6 Mat Latos/500 3.00 8.00
7 Brett Cecil/500 3.00 8.00
8 Vince Dooley/500 3.00 8.00
9 Brett Anderson/500 3.00 8.00
10 Casey Weathers/75 4.00 10.00
11 Daniel Moskos/500 3.00 8.00
12 Darwin Barney/500 3.00 8.00
13 Kellen Kulbacki/500 3.00 8.00
14 Matt Dominguez/500 3.00 8.00
15 Matt Mangini/500 3.00 8.00
16 Mitch Canham/500 3.00 8.00
18 Will Middlebrooks/500 3.00 8.00
19 Mike Powell/500 3.00 8.00
20 Steve Spurrier/500 4.00 10.00
21 Dale Brown/500 3.00 8.00
22 Don Haskins/500 3.00 8.00
23 Nick Schmidt/500 3.00 8.00
24 Zack Cozart/500 3.00 8.00

2007 Donruss Elite Extra Edition Throwback Threads Prime *

*PRIME: .75X TO 2X BASIC
OVERALL AUTO/MEM ODDS 1:5
PRINT RUNS B/WN 3-50 COPIES PER
NO PRICING ON QTY 25 OR LESS
8 Vince Dooley/7
10 Casey Weathers/3
21 Dale Brown/5

2007 Donruss Elite Extra Edition Throwback Threads Autographs *

OVERALL AUTO/MEM ODDS 1:5
PRINT RUNS B/WN 50-100 COPIES PER
EXCHANGE DEADLINE 07/01/2009
1 Brandi Chastain/100 15.00 40.00
2 Amanda Beard/50 40.00 80.00
3 Drew Stubbs/100 20.00 50.00
4 Drew Cumberland/100 6.00 15.00
5 Clint Dolezel/100 6.00 15.00
6 Mat Latos/100 12.50 30.00
8 Vince Dooley/50 10.00 25.00
9 Brett Anderson/100 10.00 25.00
10 Casey Weathers/100 10.00 25.00
11 Daniel Moskos/100 6.00 15.00
12 Josh Vitters/100 EXCH 12.50 30.00
13 Kellen Kulbacki/100 6.00 15.00
14 Matt Dominguez/100 20.00 50.00
15 Matt Mangini/100 10.00 25.00
16 Mitch Canham/100 6.00 15.00
18 Will Middlebrooks/100 6.00 15.00
19 Mike Powell/100 15.00 40.00
20 Steve Spurrier/50 30.00 60.00
21 Dale Brown/50 6.00 15.00
22 Don Haskins/100 12.50 30.00
23 Nick Schmidt/100 6.00 15.00
24 Zack Cozart/100 6.00 15.00

2007 Donruss Elite Extra Edition Throwback Threads Autographs Prime *

OVERALL AUTO/MEM ODDS 1:5
PRINT RUNS B/WN 1-25 COPIES PER
NO PRICING DUE TO SCARCITY
EXCHANGE DEADLINE 07/01/2009

2008 Donruss Elite Extra Edition

This set was released on November 26, 2008. The base set consists of 199 cards.

COMP.SET w/o AU's (100) 10.00 25.00
COMMON CARD (1-100) .20 .50
COMMON AU (101-200) 3.00 8.00
RANDOM INSERTS IN PACKS
PRINT RUNS B/WN 99-1495
EXCH DEADLINE 5/26/2010
1 Aaron Cunningham .20 .50
2 Aaron Pribanic .20 .50
3 Aaron Shafer .20 .50
4 Adam Mills .20 .50
5 Adam Moore .20 .50
6 Beamer Weems .20 .50
7 Beau Mills .20 .50
8 Blake Tekotte .30 .75
9 Bobby Lanigan .20 .50
10 Brad Hand .20 .50
11 Brandon Crawford .30 .75
12 Brandon Waring .60 1.50
13 Brent Morel .20 .50
14 Brett Jacobson .20 .50
15 Caleb Gindl .20 .50
16 Carlos Peguero .20 .50
17 Charlie Blackmon .20 .50
18 Charlie Furbush .20 .50
19 Chris Davis .50 1.25
20 Chris Valaika .20 .50
21 Clark Murphy .30 .75
22 Clayton Cook .30 .75
23 Cody Adams .30 .75
24 Cody Satterwhite .30 .75
25 Cole St. Clair .20 .50
26 Corey Young .20 .50
27 Curtis Petersen .20 .50
28 Danny Rams .30 .75
29 Dennis Raben .30 .75
30 Derek Norris .20 .50
31 Tyson Brummett .20 .50
32 Dusty Coleman .20 .50
33 Edgar Olmos .20 .50
34 Engel Beltre .60 1.50
35 Eric Beaulac .20 .50
36 Geison Aguasviva .20 .50
37 Gerardo Parra .20 .50
38 Graham Hicks .30 .75
39 Greg Halman .60 1.50
40 Hector Gomez .50 1.25
41 J.D. Alfaro .20 .50
42 Jack Egbert .30 .75
43 James Darnell .20 .50
44 Jay Austin .30 .75
45 Jeremy Beckham .30 .75
46 Jeremy Farrell .20 .50
47 Jeremy Hamilton .20 .50
48 Jericho Jones .20 .50
49 Jesse Darcy .20 .50
50 Jeudy Valdez .30 .75
51 Jharmidy De Jesus .20 .50
52 Joba Chamberlain .60 1.50
53 Johnny Giavotella .20 .50
54 Jon Mark Owings .30 .75
55 Jordan Meaker .30 .75
56 Jose Duran .30 .75
57 Josh Harrison .30 .75
58 Josh Lindblom .30 .75
59 Josh Reddick .60 1.50
60 Juan Carlos Sulbaran .20 .50
61 Justin Bristow .20 .50
62 Kenny Gilbert .20 .50
63 Kirk Nieuwenhuis .20 .50
64 Kyle Hudson .20 .50
65 Kyle Russell .20 .50
66 Kyle Weiland .50 1.25
67 L. J. Hoes .50 1.25
68 Mark Cohoon .30 .75
69 Mark Sobolewski .50 1.25
70 Mat Gamel .30 .75
71 Matt Harrison .20 .50
72 Max Ramirez .20 .50
73 Tony Delmonico .30 .75
74 Mike Stanton .60 1.50
75 Mitch Abeita .20 .50
76 Neftali Feliz .30 .75
77 Neftali Soto .30 .75
78 Niko Vasquez .50 1.25
79 Omar Aguilar .30 .75
80 Petey Paramore .30 .75
81 Ray Kruml .20 .50
82 Rolando Gomez .30 .75
83 Ryan Chaffee .30 .75
84 Ryan Pressly .20 .50
85 Sam Freeman .50 1.25
86 Sawyer Carroll .30 .75
87 Scott Green .20 .50
88 Sean Ratliff .20 .50
89 Shane Peterson .30 .75
90 T.J. Steele .30 .75
91 Tim Federowicz .30 .75
92 Tyler Chatwood .20 .50
93 Tyler Cline .20 .50
94 Tyler Ladendorf .30 .75
95 Tyler Yockey .20 .50
96 Wilmer Flores .60 1.50
97 Wilson Ramos .50 1.25
98 Zach McAllister .30 .75
99 Zachary Stewart .20 .50
100 Zeke Spruill .50 1.25
101 Adrian Nieto AU/521 4.00 10.00
102 Alan Horne AU/349 6.00 15.00
103 Andrew Cashner AU/685 4.00 10.00
104 Anthony Hewitt AU/920 6.00 15.00
105 Brad Holt AU/432 8.00 20.00
106 Bryan Petersen AU/319 3.00 8.00
107 Bryan Price AU/572 3.00 8.00
108 Bud Norris AU/1095 3.00 8.00
109 Carlos Gutierrez AU/202 5.00 12.00
110 Chase D'Arnaud AU/1218 3.00 8.00
111 Chris Johnson AU/99 EXCH 8.00 20.00
112 Christian Friedrich AU/402 3.00 8.00
113 Christian Marrero AU/662 4.00 10.00
114 Clayton Conner AU/819 3.00 8.00
115 Cole Rohrbough AU/719 4.00 10.00
116 Collin DeLome AU/819 4.00 10.00
117 Daniel Cortes AU/680 5.00 12.00
118 Daniel Schlereth AU/570 3.00 8.00
119 Denny Almonte AU/821 3.00 8.00
120 Allan Dykstra AU/1069 8.00 20.00
121 Dominic Brown AU/996 8.00 20.00
122 Evan Fredrickson AU/922 3.00 8.00
123 Gordon Beckham AU/710 20.00 50.00
124 Greg Veloz AU/819 3.00 8.00
125 Ike Davis AU/995 8.00 20.00
126 Isaac Galloway AU/1099 4.00 10.00
127 Jacob Jefferies AU/819 3.00 8.00
128 Michael Kohn AU/199 3.00 8.00
129 Jared Goedert AU/819 3.00 8.00
130 Jason Knapp AU/999 5.00 12.00
131 Jhoulys Chacin AU/821 10.00 25.00
132 Jordy Mercer AU/483 3.00 8.00
133 Jorge Bucardo AU/819 3.00 8.00
134 Jose Ceda AU/1470 3.00 8.00
135 Jose Martinez AU/868 4.00 10.00
136 Josh Roenicke AU/829 4.00 10.00
137 Juan Francisco AU/1495 5.00 12.00
138 Justin Parker AU/719 4.00 10.00
139 Kyle Ginley AU/819 3.00 8.00
140 Lance Lynn AU/570 6.00 15.00
141 Logan Forsythe AU/162
142 Logan Morrison AU/360 40.00 80.00
143 Logan Schafer AU/793 4.00 10.00
144 Lorenzo Cain AU/817 3.00 8.00
145 Lucas Duda AU/124 8.00 20.00
146 Matt Mitchell AU/719 3.00 8.00
147 Danny Espinosa AU/443 3.00 8.00
148 Michael Taylor AU/720 12.50 30.00
149 Michel Inoa AU/1199 12.50 30.00
150 Mike Montgomery AU/922 5.00 12.00
151 Cord Phelps AU/693 5.00 12.00
152 Pablo Sandoval AU/819 10.00 25.00
153 Quincy Latimore AU/819 4.00 10.00
154 R. J. Seidel AU/819 3.00 8.00
155 Rayner Contreras AU/1349 3.00 8.00
156 Rick Porcello AU/1299 30.00 60.00
157 Robert Hernandez AU/859 3.00 8.00
158 Ryan Kalish AU/1129 5.00 12.00
159 Ryan Perry AU/745 5.00 12.00
160 Shelby Ford AU/819 3.00 8.00
161 Shooter Hunt AU/397 8.00 20.00
162 Tyler Kolodny AU/819 4.00 10.00
163 Tyler Sample AU/619 4.00 10.00
164 Tyson Ross AU/999 4.00 10.00
166 Waldis Joaquin AU/819 3.00 8.00
167 Welington Castillo AU/1319 3.00 8.00
168 Wilin Rosario AU/1099 4.00 10.00
169 Xavier Avery AU/199 10.00 25.00
170 Zach Collier AU/217 10.00 25.00
171 Zach Putnam AU/444 6.00 15.00
172 Anthony Gose AU/519 4.00 10.00
173 Roger Kieschnick AU/569 10.00 25.00
174 Andrew Liebel AU/219 5.00 12.00
175 Tim Murphy AU/244 4.00 10.00
176 Vance Worley AU/219 8.00 20.00
177 Buster Posey AU/934 30.00 60.00
178 Kenn Kasparek AU/694 3.00 8.00
179 J.P. Ramirez AU/719 5.00 12.00
180 Evan Bigley AU/819 3.00 8.00
181 Trey Haley AU/719 3.00 8.00
182 Robbie Grossman AU/719 5.00 12.00
183 Jordan Danks AU/254 EXCH 6.00 15.00
184 Brett Hunter AU/269 4.00 10.00
185 Rafael Rodriguez AU/999 12.50 30.00
186 Yeicok Calderon AU/819 5.00 12.00
187 Gustavo Pierre AU/719 4.00 10.00
188 Will Smith AU/719 4.00 10.00
189 Daniel Thomas AU/719 3.00 8.00
190 Carson Blair AU/719 4.00 10.00
191 Chris Hicks AU/719 3.00 8.00
192 Rashun Dixon AU/199 EXCH 10.00 25.00
193 Marcus Lemon AU/199 5.00 12.00
194 Kyle Nicholson AU/719 3.00 8.00
195 Mike Cisco AU/719 4.00 10.00
196 Jarek Cunningham AU/719 4.00 10.00
197 Cat Osterman AU/719 12.50 30.00
198 Derrick Rose AU/99 75.00 150.00
199 Michael Beasley AU/99 40.00 80.00
200 O.J. Mayo AU/99 40.00 80.00

2008 Donruss Elite Extra Edition Aspirations

*ASP 1-100: 2.5X TO 6X BASIC
RANDOM INSERTS IN PACKS
STATED PRINT RUN 150 SER.#'d SETS
101 Adrian Nieto 2.00 5.00
102 Alan Horne 1.25 3.00
103 Andrew Cashner 1.25 3.00
104 Anthony Hewitt 1.25 3.00
105 Brad Holt 1.25 3.00
106 Bryan Petersen 1.25 3.00
107 Bryan Price 1.25 3.00
108 Bud Norris 1.25 3.00
109 Carlos Gutierrez 3.00 8.00
110 Chase D'Arnaud 1.25 3.00
111 Chris Johnson 2.00 5.00
112 Christian Friedrich 3.00 8.00
113 Christian Marrero 2.00 5.00
114 Clayton Conner 1.25 3.00
115 Cole Rohrbough 1.25 3.00
116 Collin DeLome 2.00 5.00
117 Daniel Cortes 3.00 8.00
118 Daniel Schlereth 1.25 3.00
119 Denny Almonte 1.25 3.00
120 Allan Dykstra 1.25 3.00
121 Dominic Brown 5.00 12.00
122 Evan Fredrickson 1.25 3.00
123 Gordon Beckham 3.00 8.00
124 Greg Veloz 1.25 3.00
125 Ike Davis 1.25 3.00
126 Isaac Galloway 2.00 5.00
127 Jacob Jefferies 1.25 3.00
128 Michael Kohn 1.25 3.00
129 Jared Goedert 1.25 3.00
130 Jason Knapp 1.25 3.00
131 Jhoulys Chacin 6.00 15.00
132 Jordy Mercer 1.25 3.00
133 Jorge Bucardo 1.25 3.00
134 Jose Ceda 1.25 3.00
135 Jose Martinez 1.25 3.00
136 Josh Roenicke 1.25 3.00
137 Juan Francisco 6.00 15.00
138 Justin Parker 1.25 3.00
139 Kyle Ginley 1.25 3.00
140 Lance Lynn 2.00 5.00
141 Logan Forsythe 1.25 3.00
142 Logan Morrison 5.00 12.00
143 Logan Schafer 1.25 3.00
144 Lorenzo Cain 1.25 3.00
145 Lucas Duda 2.00 5.00
146 Matt Mitchell 1.25 3.00
147 Danny Espinosa 1.25 3.00
148 Michael Taylor 3.00 8.00
149 Michel Inoa 3.00 8.00
150 Mike Montgomery 1.25 3.00
151 Cord Phelps 1.25 3.00
152 Pablo Sandoval 1.25 3.00
153 Quincy Latimore 1.25 3.00
154 R. J. Seidel 1.25 3.00
155 Rayner Contreras 1.25 3.00
156 Rick Porcello 5.00 12.00
157 Robert Hernandez 1.25 3.00
158 Ryan Kalish 1.25 3.00
159 Ryan Perry 2.00 5.00
160 Shelby Ford 2.00 5.00
161 Shooter Hunt 1.25 3.00
162 Tyler Kolodny 3.00 8.00
163 Tyler Sample 1.25 3.00
164 Tyson Ross 2.00 5.00
166 Waldis Joaquin 1.25 3.00
167 Welington Castillo 1.25 3.00
168 Wilin Rosario 1.25 3.00
169 Xavier Avery 3.00 8.00
170 Zach Collier 2.00 5.00
171 Zach Putnam 1.25 3.00
172 Anthony Gose 1.25 3.00
173 Roger Kieschnick 2.00 5.00
174 Andrew Liebel 1.25 3.00
175 Tim Murphy 1.25 3.00
176 Vance Worley 1.25 3.00
177 Buster Posey 4.00 10.00
178 Kenn Kasparek 3.00 8.00
179 J.P. Ramirez 1.25 3.00
180 Evan Bigley 1.25 3.00
181 Trey Haley 1.25 3.00
182 Robbie Grossman 2.00 5.00
183 Jordan Danks 3.00 8.00
184 Brett Hunter 1.25 3.00
185 Rafael Rodriguez 3.00 8.00
186 Yeicok Calderon 1.25 3.00
187 Gustavo Pierre 1.25 3.00
188 Will Smith 1.25 3.00
189 Daniel Thomas 1.25 3.00
190 Carson Blair 1.25 3.00
191 Chris Hicks 1.25 3.00
192 Rashun Dixon 1.25 3.00
193 Marcus Lemon 1.25 3.00
194 Kyle Nicholson 1.25 3.00
195 Mike Cisco 1.25 3.00
196 Jarek Cunningham 1.25 3.00
197 Cat Osterman 4.00 10.00
198 Derrick Rose 6.00 15.00
199 Michael Beasley 6.00 15.00
200 O.J. Mayo 3.00 8.00

2008 Donruss Elite Extra Edition Status

*STATUS 1-100: 4X TO 10X BASIC
*STATUS 101-200: .6X TO 1.5X ASP
RANDOM INSERTS IN PACKS
STATED PRINT RUN 50 SER.#'d SETS
101 Adrian Nieto 3.00 8.00
102 Alan Horne 2.00 5.00
103 Andrew Cashner 2.00 5.00
104 Anthony Hewitt 2.00 5.00
105 Brad Holt 2.00 5.00
106 Bryan Petersen 2.00 5.00
107 Bryan Price 2.00 5.00
108 Bud Norris 2.00 5.00
109 Carlos Gutierrez 5.00 12.00
110 Chase D'Arnaud 2.00 5.00
111 Chris Johnson 3.00 8.00
112 Christian Friedrich 5.00 12.00
113 Christian Marrero 3.00 8.00
114 Clayton Conner 2.00 5.00
115 Cole Rohrbough 2.00 5.00
116 Collin DeLome 3.00 8.00
117 Daniel Cortes 5.00 12.00
118 Daniel Schlereth 2.00 5.00
119 Denny Almonte 2.00 5.00
120 Allan Dykstra 2.00 5.00
121 Dominic Brown 8.00 20.00
122 Evan Fredrickson 2.00 5.00
123 Gordon Beckham 5.00 12.00
124 Greg Veloz 2.00 5.00
125 Ike Davis 2.00 5.00
126 Isaac Galloway 3.00 8.00
127 Jacob Jefferies 2.00 5.00
128 Michael Kohn 2.00 5.00
129 Jared Goedert 2.00 5.00
130 Jason Knapp 2.00 5.00
131 Jhoulys Chacin 10.00 25.00
132 Jordy Mercer 2.00 5.00
133 Jorge Bucardo 2.00 5.00
134 Jose Ceda 2.00 5.00
135 Jose Martinez 2.00 5.00
136 Josh Roenicke 2.00 5.00
137 Juan Francisco 1.50 4.00
138 Justin Parker 2.00 5.00
139 Kyle Ginley 2.00 5.00
140 Lance Lynn 3.00 8.00
141 Logan Forsythe 2.00 5.00
142 Logan Morrison 8.00 20.00
143 Logan Schafer 2.00 5.00
144 Lorenzo Cain 2.00 5.00
145 Lucas Duda 3.00 8.00
146 Matt Mitchell 2.00 5.00
147 Danny Espinosa 2.00 5.00
148 Michael Taylor 5.00 12.00
149 Michel Inoa 5.00 12.00
150 Mike Montgomery 2.00 5.00
151 Cord Phelps 2.00 5.00
152 Pablo Sandoval 2.00 5.00
153 Quincy Latimore 2.00 5.00
154 R. J. Seidel 2.00 5.00
155 Rayner Contreras 2.00 5.00
156 Rick Porcello 8.00 20.00
157 Robert Hernandez 2.00 5.00
158 Ryan Kalish 2.00 5.00
159 Ryan Perry 3.00 8.00
160 Shelby Ford 3.00 8.00
161 Shooter Hunt 2.00 5.00
162 Tyler Kolodny 5.00 12.00
163 Tyler Sample 2.00 5.00
164 Tyson Ross 3.00 8.00
166 Waldis Joaquin 2.00 5.00
167 Welington Castillo 2.00 5.00
168 Wilin Rosario 2.00 5.00
169 Xavier Avery 5.00 12.00
170 Zach Collier 3.00 8.00
171 Zach Putnam 2.00 5.00
172 Anthony Gose 2.00 5.00
173 Roger Kieschnick 3.00 8.00
174 Andrew Liebel 2.00 5.00
175 Tim Murphy 2.00 5.00
176 Vance Worley 2.00 5.00
177 Buster Posey 6.00 15.00
178 Kenn Kasparek 5.00 12.00
179 J.P. Ramirez 2.00 5.00
180 Evan Bigley 2.00 5.00
181 Trey Haley 2.00 5.00
182 Robbie Grossman 3.00 8.00
183 Jordan Danks 5.00 12.00
184 Brett Hunter 2.00 5.00
185 Rafael Rodriguez 5.00 12.00
186 Yeicok Calderon 2.00 5.00
187 Gustavo Pierre 2.00 5.00
188 Will Smith 2.00 5.00
189 Daniel Thomas 2.00 5.00
190 Carson Blair 2.00 5.00
191 Chris Hicks 2.00 5.00
192 Rashun Dixon 2.00 5.00
193 Marcus Lemon 2.00 5.00
194 Kyle Nicholson 2.00 5.00
195 Mike Cisco 2.00 5.00
196 Jarek Cunningham 2.00 5.00
197 Cat Osterman 6.00 15.00
198 Derrick Rose 10.00 25.00
199 Michael Beasley 10.00 25.00
200 O.J. Mayo 5.00 12.00

2008 Donruss Elite Extra Edition Status Gold

RANDOM INSERTS IN PACKS
STATED PRINT RUN 25 SER.#'d SETS
NO PRICING DUE TO SCARCITY

2008 Donruss Elite Extra Edition Signature Aspirations

OVERALL AUTO/MEM ODDS 1:5
PRINT RUN B/WN 5-100 COPIES PER
NO PRICING ON QTY 25 OR LESS
EXCH DEADLINE 5/26/2010
1 Aaron Cunningham/50 6.00 15.00
2 Aaron Pribanic/100 5.00 12.00
3 Aaron Shafer/100 4.00 10.00
4 Adam Mills/100 4.00 10.00
5 Adam Moore/100 5.00 12.00
6 Beamer Weems/100 4.00 10.00
7 Beau Mills/50 6.00 15.00
8 Blake Tekotte/25
9 Bobby Lanigan/100 4.00 10.00
10 Brad Hand/50 5.00 12.00
11 Brandon Crawford/50 8.00 20.00
12 Brandon Waring/100 10.00 25.00
13 Brent Morel/100 10.00 25.00
14 Brett Jacobson/100 5.00 12.00
15 Caleb Gindl/100 8.00 20.00
16 Carlos Peguero/100 4.00 10.00
17 Charlie Blackmon/50 4.00 10.00
18 Charlie Furbush/100 5.00 12.00
19 Chris Davis/100 12.50 30.00
20 Chris Valaika/100 8.00 20.00
21 Clark Murphy/50 10.00 25.00
22 Clayton Cook/100 4.00 10.00
23 Cody Adams/50 4.00 10.00
24 Cody Satterwhite/50 10.00 25.00
25 Cole St. Clair/100 5.00 12.00
26 Corey Young/100 4.00 10.00
27 Curtis Petersen/100 4.00 10.00
28 Danny Rams/100 5.00 12.00
29 Dennis Raben/50 8.00 20.00
30 Derek Norris/50 5.00 12.00
31 Tyson Brummett/100 4.00 10.00
32 Dusty Coleman/50 5.00 12.00
33 Edgar Olmos/100 4.00 10.00
34 Engel Beltre/5
35 Eric Beaulac/100 4.00 10.00
36 Geison Aguasviva/100 4.00 10.00
37 Gerardo Parra/100 5.00 12.00
38 Graham Hicks/100 4.00 10.00
39 Greg Halman/100 15.00 40.00
40 Hector Gomez/100 5.00 12.00
41 J.D. Alfaro/100 4.00 10.00
42 Jack Egbert/100 4.00 10.00
43 James Darnell/50 6.00 15.00
44 Jay Austin/50 5.00 12.00
45 Jeremy Beckham/100 EXCH 6.00 15.00
46 Jeremy Farrell/100 4.00 10.00
47 Jeremy Hamilton/100 4.00 10.00
48 Jericho Jones/100 6.00 15.00
49 Jesse Darcy/100 5.00 12.00
50 Jeudy Valdez/100 4.00 10.00
51 Jharmidy De Jesus/50 12.50 30.00
52 Joba Chamberlain/25
53 Johnny Giavotella/100 4.00 10.00
54 Jon Mark Owings/100 5.00 12.00
55 Jordan Meaker/100 4.00 10.00
56 Jose Duran/100 12.50 30.00
57 Josh Harrison/100 5.00 12.00
58 Josh Lindblom/50 4.00 10.00
59 Josh Reddick/100 12.50 30.00
60 Juan Carlos Sulbaran/100 5.00 12.00
61 Justin Bristow/100 4.00 10.00
62 Kenny Gilbert/100 4.00 10.00
63 Kirk Nieuwenhuis/100 4.00 10.00
64 Kyle Hudson/50 5.00 12.00
65 Kyle Russell/50 5.00 12.00
66 Kyle Weiland/50 5.00 12.00
67 L. J. Hoes/50 5.00 12.00
68 Mark Cohoon/100 5.00 12.00
69 Mark Sobolewski/100 15.00 40.00
70 Mat Gamel/50 30.00 60.00
71 Matt Harrison/100 4.00 10.00
72 Max Ramirez/100 8.00 20.00
73 Tony Delmonico/50 6.00 15.00
74 Mike Stanton/25
75 Mitch Abeita/100 4.00 10.00
76 Neftali Feliz/50 30.00 60.00
77 Neftali Soto/50 20.00 50.00
78 Niko Vasquez/50 6.00 15.00
79 Omar Aguilar/100 5.00 12.00
80 Petey Paramore/100 4.00 10.00
81 Ray Kruml/100 5.00 12.00
82 Rolando Gomez/50 4.00 10.00
83 Ryan Chaffee/100 5.00 12.00
84 Ryan Pressly/100 4.00 10.00
85 Sam Freeman/100 5.00 12.00
86 Sawyer Carroll/100 4.00 10.00
87 Scott Green/100 6.00 15.00
88 Sean Ratliff/100 8.00 20.00
89 Shane Peterson/50 8.00 20.00
90 T.J. Steele/50 8.00 20.00
91 Tim Federowicz/100 6.00 15.00
92 Tyler Chatwood/50 4.00 10.00
93 Tyler Cline/100 4.00 10.00
94 Tyler Ladendorf/50 5.00 12.00
95 Tyler Yockey/100 6.00 15.00
96 Wilmer Flores/50 EXCH 40.00 80.00
97 Wilson Ramos/100 6.00 15.00
98 Zach McAllister/100 6.00 15.00
99 Zachary Stewart/100 5.00 12.00
100 Zeke Spruill/50 EXCH 5.00 12.00
101 Adrian Nieto/25
102 Alan Horne/100 10.00 25.00
103 Andrew Cashner/25
104 Anthony Hewitt/25
105 Brad Holt/25
106 Bryan Petersen/50 4.00 10.00
107 Bryan Price/25
108 Bud Norris/50 4.00 10.00
109 Carlos Gutierrez/25
110 Chase D'Arnaud/25
111 Chris Johnson/25
112 Christian Friedrich/25
113 Christian Marrero/50 5.00 12.00
114 Clayton Conner/50 4.00 10.00
115 Cole Rohrbough/25
116 Collin DeLome/50 6.00 15.00
117 Daniel Cortes/25
118 Daniel Schlereth/25
119 Denny Almonte/50 4.00 10.00
120 Allan Dykstra/25
121 Dominic Brown/50 10.00 25.00
122 Evan Fredrickson/25
123 Gordon Beckham/25
124 Greg Veloz/50 4.00 10.00
125 Ike Davis/25
126 Isaac Galloway/25
127 Jacob Jefferies/50 4.00 10.00
128 Michael Kohn/25
129 Jared Goedert/50 4.00 10.00
130 Jason Knapp/50 6.00 15.00
131 Jhoulys Chacin/50 20.00 50.00
132 Jordy Mercer/75 4.00 10.00
133 Jorge Bucardo/50 4.00 10.00
134 Jose Ceda/100 5.00 12.00
135 Jose Martinez/75 5.00 12.00
136 Josh Roenicke/50 5.00 12.00
137 Juan Francisco/100 EXCH 10.00 25.00
138 Justin Parker/25
139 Kyle Ginley/50 4.00 10.00
140 Lance Lynn/25
141 Logan Forsythe/10
142 Logan Morrison/25
143 Logan Schafer/50 5.00 12.00
144 Lorenzo Cain/50 4.00 10.00
145 Lucas Duda/20
146 Matt Mitchell/25
147 Danny Espinosa/25
148 Michael Taylor/50 15.00 40.00
149 Michel Inoa/25
150 Mike Montgomery/25
151 Cord Phelps/25
152 Pablo Sandoval/50 15.00 40.00
153 Quincy Latimore/50 5.00 12.00
154 R. J. Seidel/50 4.00 10.00
155 Rayner Contreras/100 4.00 10.00
156 Rick Porcello/25
157 Robert Hernandez/50 4.00 10.00
158 Ryan Kalish/50 6.00 15.00
159 Ryan Perry/25
160 Shelby Ford/50 4.00 10.00
161 Shooter Hunt/25
162 Tyler Kolodny/50 10.00 25.00
163 Tyler Sample/25
164 Tyson Ross/25
166 Waldis Joaquin/50 4.00 10.00
167 Welington Castillo/50 4.00 10.00
168 Wilin Rosario/25
169 Xavier Avery/25
170 Zach Collier/25
171 Zach Putnam/25
172 Anthony Gose/25
173 Roger Kieschnick/50 20.00 50.00
174 Andrew Liebel/25
175 Tim Murphy/25
176 Vance Worley/25
177 Buster Posey/25
178 Kenn Kasparek/25
179 J.P. Ramirez/25
180 Evan Bigley/50 6.00 15.00
181 Trey Haley/25
182 Robbie Grossman/25
183 Jordan Danks/25 EXCH
184 Brett Hunter/25
185 Rafael Rodriguez/25
186 Yeicok Calderon/50 6.00 15.00
187 Gustavo Pierre/25
188 Will Smith/25
189 Daniel Thomas/25
190 Carson Blair/25
191 Chris Hicks/25
192 Rashun Dixon/10 EXCH
193 Marcus Lemon/25
194 Kyle Nicholson/25
195 Mike Cisco/25
196 Jarek Cunningham/25
197 Cat Osterman/10
198 Derrick Rose/10
199 Michael Beasley/10
200 O.J. Mayo/25

2008 Donruss Elite Extra Edition Signature Status

OVERALL AUTO/MEM ODDS 1:5
PRINT RUN B/WN 5-50 COPIES PER
NO PRICING ON QTY 25 OR LESS
EXCH DEADLINE 5/26/2010
1 Aaron Cunningham/25
2 Aaron Pribanic/50 5.00 12.00
3 Aaron Shafer/50 4.00 10.00
4 Adam Mills/50 4.00 10.00

5 Adam Moore/50 5.00 12.00
6 Beamer Weems/50 4.00 10.00
7 Beau Mills/25
8 Blake Tekotte/10
9 Bobby Lanigan/50 4.00 10.00
10 Brad Hand/10
11 Brandon Crawford/25
12 Brandon Waring/50 10.00 25.00
13 Brent Morel/50 10.00 25.00
14 Brett Jacobson/50 5.00 12.00
15 Caleb Gindl/50 8.00 20.00
16 Carlos Peguero/50 4.00 10.00
17 Charlie Blackmon/25
18 Charlie Furbush/50 5.00 12.00
19 Chris Davis/50 12.50 30.00
20 Chris Valaika/50 8.00 20.00
21 Clark Murphy/25
22 Clayton Cook/50 4.00 10.00
23 Cody Adams/25
24 Cody Satterwhite/25
25 Cole St. Clair/50 5.00 12.00
26 Corey Young/50 4.00 10.00
27 Curtis Petersen/50 4.00 10.00
28 Danny Rams/50 5.00 12.00
29 Dennis Raben/25
30 Derek Norris/25
31 Tyson Brummett/50 5.00 12.00
32 Dusty Coleman/25
33 Edgar Olmos/50 4.00 10.00
34 Engel Beltre/5
35 Eric Beaulac/50 4.00 10.00
36 Geison Aguasviva/50 4.00 10.00
37 Gerardo Parra/50 5.00 12.00
38 Graham Hicks/50 4.00 10.00
39 Greg Halman/50 15.00 40.00
40 Hector Gomez/50 5.00 12.00
41 J.D. Alfaro/50 4.00 10.00
42 Jack Egbert/50 5.00 12.00
43 James Darnell/25
44 Jay Austin/25
45 Jeremy Beckham/50 EXCH 6.00 15.00
46 Jeremy Farrell/50 4.00 10.00
47 Jeremy Hamilton/50 4.00 10.00
48 Jericho Jones/50 6.00 15.00
49 Jesse Darcy/50 5.00 12.00
50 Jeudy Valdez/50 4.00 10.00
51 Jharmidy De Jesus/25
52 Joba Chamberlain/10
53 Johnny Giavotella/50 4.00 10.00
54 Jon Mark Owings/50 5.00 12.00
55 Jordan Meaker/50 4.00 10.00
56 Jose Duran/50 12.50 30.00
57 Josh Harrison/50 5.00 12.00
58 Josh Lindblom/25
59 Josh Reddick/50 12.50 30.00
60 Juan Carlos Sulbaran/50 5.00 12.00
61 Justin Bristow/50 4.00 10.00
62 Kenny Gilbert/50 4.00 10.00
63 Kirk Nieuwenhuis/50 4.00 10.00
64 Kyle Hudson/25
65 Kyle Russell/25
66 Kyle Weiland/25
67 L. J. Hoes/25
68 Mark Cohoon/50 5.00 12.00
69 Mark Sobolewski/50 15.00 40.00
70 Mat Gamel/25
71 Matt Harrison/50 4.00 10.00
72 Max Ramirez/50 8.00 20.00
73 Tony Delmonico/25
74 Mike Stanton/10
75 Mitch Abeita/50 4.00 10.00
76 Neftali Feliz/25
77 Neftali Soto/25
78 Niko Vasquez/25
79 Omar Aguilar/50 5.00 12.00
80 Petey Paramore/50 4.00 10.00
81 Ray Kruml/50 5.00 12.00
82 Rolando Gomez/25
83 Ryan Chaffee/50 5.00 12.00
84 Ryan Pressly/50 4.00 10.00
85 Sam Freeman/50 5.00 12.00
86 Sawyer Carroll/50 4.00 10.00
87 Scott Green/50 6.00 15.00
88 Sean Ratliff/50 8.00 20.00
89 Shane Peterson/25
90 T.J. Steele/25
91 Tim Federowicz/50 6.00 15.00
92 Tyler Chatwood/25
93 Tyler Cline/50 4.00 10.00
94 Tyler Ladendorf/25
95 Tyler Yockey/50 6.00 15.00
96 Wilmer Flores/25 EXCH
97 Wilson Ramos/50 6.00 15.00
98 Zach McAllister/50 6.00 15.00
99 Zachary Stewart/50 5.00 12.00
100 Zeke Spruill/25 EXCH
101 Adrian Nieto/10
102 Alan Horne/25
103 Andrew Cashner/10
104 Anthony Hewitt/10
105 Brad Holt/10
106 Bryan Petersen/25
107 Bryan Price/10
108 Bud Norris/25
109 Carlos Gutierrez/10
110 Chase D'Arnaud/10
111 Chris Johnson/10
112 Christian Friedrich/10
113 Christian Marrero/10
114 Clayton Conner/25
115 Cole Rohrbough/10
116 Collin DeLome/25
117 Daniel Cortes/10
118 Daniel Schlereth/10
119 Denny Almonte/25
120 Allan Dykstra/10
121 Dominic Brown/10
122 Evan Fredrickson/10
123 Gordon Beckham/10
124 Greg Veloz/25
125 Ike Davis/10
126 Isaac Galloway/10
127 Jacob Jefferies/25
128 Michael Kohn/10
129 Jared Goedert/25
130 Jason Knapp/10
131 Jhoulys Chacin/25
132 Jordy Mercer/40 5.00 12.00
133 Jorge Bucardo/25
134 Jose Ceda/50 5.00 12.00
135 Jose Martinez/50 5.00 12.00
136 Josh Roenicke/25
137 Juan Francisco/25
138 Justin Parker/10
139 Kyle Ginley/25
140 Lance Lynn/10
141 Logan Forsythe/10
142 Logan Morrison/10
143 Logan Schafer/10
144 Lorenzo Cain/25
145 Lucas Duda/25
146 Matt Mitchell/10
147 Danny Espinosa/10
148 Michael Taylor/25
149 Michel Inoa/10
150 Mike Montgomery/10
151 Cord Phelps/10
152 Pablo Sandoval/25
153 Quincy Latimore/25
154 R. J. Seidel/25
155 Rayner Contreras/25
156 Rick Porcello/10
157 Robert Hernandez/25
158 Ryan Kalish/25
159 Ryan Perry/10
160 Shelby Ford/25
161 Shooter Hunt/10
162 Tyler Kolodny/25
163 Tyler Sample/10
164 Tyson Ross/10
166 Waldis Joaquin/25
167 Welington Castillo/25
168 Wilin Rosario/10
169 Xavier Avery/10
170 Zach Collier/10
171 Zach Putnam/10
172 Anthony Gose/10
173 Roger Kieschnick/25
174 Andrew Liebel/10
175 Tim Murphy/10
176 Vance Worley/10
177 Buster Posey/10
178 Kenn Kasparek/10
179 J.P. Ramirez/10
180 Evan Bigley/25
181 Trey Haley/10
182 Robbie Grossman/10
183 Jordan Danks/10 EXCH
184 Brett Hunter/10
185 Rafael Rodriguez/10
186 Yeicok Calderon/25
187 Gustavo Pierre/10
188 Will Smith/10
189 Daniel Thomas/10
190 Carson Blair/10
191 Chris Hicks/10
192 Rashun Dixon/10 EXCH
193 Marcus Lemon/10
194 Kyle Nicholson/10
195 Mike Cisco/10
196 Jarek Cunningham/10
197 Cat Osterman/10
198 Derrick Rose/10
199 Michael Beasley/10
200 O.J. Mayo/10

2008 Donruss Elite Extra Edition Signature Status Black

OVERALL AUTO/MEM ODDS 1:5
STATED PRINT RUN 1 SER.#'d SET
NO PRICING DUE TO SCARCITY
EXCH DEADLINE 5/26/2010

2008 Donruss Elite Extra Edition Signature Status Gold

OVERALL AUTO/MEM ODDS 1:5
STATED PRINT RUN 5 SER.#'d SETS
NO PRICING DUE TO SCARCITY
EXCH DEADLINE 5/26/2010

2008 Donruss Elite Extra Edition Signature Turn of the Century

OVERALL AUTO/MEM ODDS 1:5
PRINT RUNS B/WN 8-999 COPIES PER
EXCH DEADLINE 5/26/2010
1 Aaron Cunningham/150 5.00 12.00
2 Aaron Pribanic/269 4.00 10.00
3 Aaron Shafer/117 4.00 10.00
4 Adam Mills/841 3.00 8.00
5 Adam Moore/844 4.00 10.00
6 Beamer Weems/844 3.00 8.00
7 Beau Mills/64 6.00 15.00
8 Blake Tekotte/194 4.00 10.00
9 Bobby Lanigan/594 3.00 8.00
10 Brad Hand/447 4.00 10.00
11 Brandon Crawford/718 4.00 10.00
12 Brandon Waring/369 6.00 15.00
13 Brent Morel/269 8.00 20.00
14 Brett Jacobson/488 4.00 10.00
15 Caleb Gindl/245 6.00 15.00
16 Carlos Peguero/344 3.00 8.00
17 Charlie Blackmon/122 3.00 8.00
18 Charlie Furbush/469 4.00 10.00
19 Chris Davis/399 10.00 25.00
20 Chris Valaika/309 6.00 15.00
21 Clark Murphy/644 6.00 15.00
22 Clayton Cook/844 3.00 8.00
23 Cody Adams/447 3.00 8.00
24 Cody Satterwhite/322 6.00 15.00
25 Cole St. Clair/342 4.00 10.00
26 Corey Young/594 3.00 8.00
27 Curtis Petersen/199 3.00 8.00
28 Danny Rams/594 4.00 10.00
29 Dennis Raben/172 6.00 15.00
30 Derek Norris/744 3.00 8.00
31 Tyson Brummett/919 3.00 8.00
32 Dusty Coleman/719 3.00 8.00
33 Edgar Olmos/594 3.00 8.00
34 Engel Beltre/8
35 Eric Beaulac/594 3.00 8.00
36 Geison Aguasviva/368 3.00 8.00
37 Gerardo Parra/421 4.00 10.00
38 Graham Hicks/594 3.00 8.00
39 Greg Halman/429 12.50 30.00
40 Hector Gomez/320 4.00 10.00
41 J.D. Alfaro/790 3.00 8.00
42 Jack Egbert/844 3.00 8.00
43 James Darnell/89 5.00 12.00
44 Jay Austin/207 4.00 10.00
45 Jeremy Beckham/199 EXCH 5.00 12.00
46 Jeremy Farrell/844 3.00 8.00
47 Jeremy Hamilton/844 3.00 8.00
48 Jericho Jones/844 5.00 12.00
49 Jesse Darcy/594 4.00 10.00
50 Jeudy Valdez/374 3.00 8.00
51 Jharmidy De Jesus/269 10.00 25.00
52 Joba Chamberlain/39 30.00 60.00
53 Johnny Giavotella/844 3.00 8.00
54 Jon Mark Owings/844 4.00 10.00
55 Jordan Meaker/844 3.00 8.00
56 Jose Duran/262 10.00 25.00
57 Josh Harrison/844 4.00 10.00
58 Josh Lindblom/131 3.00 8.00
59 Josh Reddick/320 10.00 25.00
60 Juan Carlos Sulbaran/844 4.00 10.00
61 Justin Bristow/594 3.00 8.00
62 Kenny Gilbert/842 3.00 8.00
63 Kirk Nieuwenhuis/844 3.00 8.00
64 Kyle Hudson/419 4.00 10.00
65 Kyle Russell/594 4.00 10.00
66 Kyle Weiland/394 4.00 10.00
67 L. J. Hoes/494 5.00 12.00
68 Mark Cohoon/844 4.00 10.00
69 Mark Sobolewski/269 12.50 30.00
70 Mat Gamel/145 20.00 50.00
71 Matt Harrison/244 3.00 8.00
72 Max Ramirez/604 5.00 12.00
73 Tony Delmonico/744 5.00 12.00
74 Mike Stanton/100 40.00 80.00
75 Mitch Abeita/769 3.00 8.00
76 Neftali Feliz/999 12.50 30.00
77 Neftali Soto/645 10.00 25.00
78 Niko Vasquez/494 5.00 12.00
79 Omar Aguilar/594 4.00 10.00
80 Petey Paramore/519 3.00 8.00
81 Ray Kruml/844 4.00 10.00
82 Rolando Gomez/544 3.00 8.00
83 Ryan Chaffee/594 4.00 10.00
84 Ryan Pressly/844 3.00 8.00
85 Sam Freeman/819 4.00 10.00
86 Sawyer Carroll/544 3.00 8.00
87 Scott Green/294 5.00 12.00
88 Sean Ratliff/544 6.00 15.00
89 Shane Peterson/132 6.00 15.00
90 T.J. Steele/122 6.00 15.00
91 Tim Federowicz/844 5.00 12.00
92 Tyler Chatwood/257 3.00 8.00
93 Tyler Cline/594 3.00 8.00
94 Tyler Ladendorf/227 4.00 10.00
95 Tyler Yockey/844 5.00 12.00
96 Wilmer Flores/99 EXCH 30.00 60.00
97 Wilson Ramos/745 5.00 12.00
98 Zach McAllister/844 5.00 12.00
99 Zachary Stewart/594 4.00 10.00
100 Zeke Spruill/99 EXCH 5.00 12.00
101 Adrian Nieto/50 10.00 25.00
102 Alan Horne/125 10.00 25.00
103 Andrew Cashner/50 5.00 12.00
104 Anthony Hewitt/50 8.00 20.00
105 Brad Holt/50 10.00 25.00
106 Bryan Petersen/100 4.00 10.00
107 Bryan Price/50 4.00 10.00
108 Bud Norris/100 4.00 10.00
109 Carlos Gutierrez/50 6.00 15.00
110 Chase D'Arnaud/50 4.00 10.00
111 Chris Johnson/50 8.00 20.00
112 Christian Friedrich/50 10.00 25.00
113 Christian Marrero/100 5.00 12.00
114 Clayton Conner/100 4.00 10.00
115 Cole Rohrbough/50 10.00 25.00
116 Collin DeLome/50 6.00 15.00
117 Daniel Cortes/50 8.00 20.00
118 Daniel Schlereth/50 4.00 10.00
119 Denny Almonte/100 4.00 10.00
120 Allan Dykstra/50 12.50 30.00
121 Dominic Brown/100 10.00 25.00
122 Evan Fredrickson/50 4.00 10.00
123 Gordon Beckham/50 40.00 80.00
124 Greg Veloz/100 4.00 10.00
125 Ike Davis/50 10.00 25.00
126 Isaac Galloway/50 12.50 30.00
127 Jacob Jefferies/50 4.00 10.00
128 Michael Kohn/40 4.00 10.00
129 Jared Goedert/100 4.00 10.00
130 Jason Knapp/125 6.00 15.00
131 Jhoulys Chacin/50 20.00 50.00
132 Jordy Mercer/50 5.00 12.00
133 Jorge Bucardo/100 4.00 10.00
134 Jose Ceda/250 4.00 10.00
135 Jose Martinez/100 4.00 10.00
136 Josh Roenicke/100 5.00 12.00
137 Juan Francisco/250 10.00 25.00
138 Justin Parker/50 5.00 12.00
139 Kyle Ginley/100 4.00 10.00
140 Lance Lynn/50 10.00 25.00
141 Logan Forsythe/100
142 Logan Morrison/50 60.00 120.00
143 Logan Schafer/125 5.00 12.00
144 Lorenzo Cain/100 4.00 10.00
145 Lucas Duda/50
146 Matt Mitchell/50 4.00 10.00
147 Danny Espinosa/50 4.00 10.00
148 Michael Taylor/100 15.00 40.00
149 Michel Inoa/50 30.00 60.00
150 Mike Montgomery/50 10.00 25.00
151 Cord Phelps/50 6.00 15.00
152 Pablo Sandoval/100 15.00 40.00
153 Quincy Latimore/100 5.00 12.00
154 R. J. Seidel/100 4.00 10.00
155 Rayner Contreras/250 4.00 10.00
156 Rick Porcello/100 60.00 120.00
157 Robert Hernandez/100 4.00 10.00
158 Ryan Kalish/100 6.00 15.00
159 Ryan Perry/50 12.50 30.00
160 Shelby Ford/100 4.00 10.00
161 Shooter Hunt/50 15.00 40.00
162 Tyler Kolodny/100 10.00 25.00
163 Tyler Sample/50 5.00 12.00
164 Tyson Ross/50 5.00 12.00
166 Waldis Joaquin/100 4.00 10.00
167 Welington Castillo/100 4.00 10.00
168 Wilin Rosario/50 8.00 20.00
169 Xavier Avery/50 15.00 40.00
170 Zach Collier/50 12.50 30.00
171 Zach Putnam/50 10.00 25.00
172 Anthony Gose/50 12.50 30.00
173 Roger Kieschnick/50 20.00 50.00
174 Andrew Liebel/50 6.00 15.00
175 Tim Murphy/50 5.00 12.00
176 Vance Worley/50 10.00 25.00
177 Buster Posey/50 50.00 100.00
178 Kenn Kasparek/50 4.00 10.00
179 J.P. Ramirez/50 10.00 25.00
180 Evan Bigley/100 6.00 15.00
181 Trey Haley/50 6.00 15.00
182 Robbie Grossman/50 10.00 25.00
183 Jordan Danks/40 EXCH 10.00 25.00
184 Brett Hunter/50 5.00 12.00
185 Rafael Rodriguez/50 30.00 60.00
186 Yeicok Calderon/100 6.00 15.00
187 Gustavo Pierre/50 6.00 15.00
188 Will Smith/50 5.00 12.00
189 Daniel Thomas/50 4.00 10.00
190 Carson Blair/50 10.00 25.00
191 Chris Hicks/50 6.00 15.00
192 Rashun Dixon/25 EXCH
193 Marcus Lemon/40 6.00 15.00
194 Kyle Nicholson/50 10.00 25.00
195 Mike Cisco/50 5.00 12.00
196 Jarek Cunningham/50 5.00 12.00
197 Cat Osterman/50 20.00 50.00
198 Derrick Rose/25
199 Michael Beasley/25
200 O.J. Mayo/25

2008 Donruss Elite Extra Edition College Ties Green

STATED PRINT RUN 1500 SER.#'d SETS
*GOLD: .75X TO 2X BASIC
OVERALL INSERT ODDS 1:2
GOLD PRINT RUN 100 SER.#'d SETS
*RED: 1.2X TO 3X BASIC
OVERALL INSERT ODDS 1:2
RED PRINT RUN 50 SER.#'d SETS
1 Cord Phelps#[Sean Ratliff .75 2.00
2 Ryan Perry#[T.J. Steele 1.25 3.00
3 Mitch Abeita#[Aaron Pribanic .75 2.00
4 Ryan Perry#[Daniel Schlereth 1.25 3.00
5 Daniel Schlereth#[T.J. Steele 1.25 3.00
6 Matt Mangini#[Jordy Mercer .75 2.00
7 Blake Tekotte#[Mark Sobolewski .75 2.00
8 Nick Schmidt#[Logan Forsythe .75 2.00
9 Matt Wieters#[Charlie Blackmon 2.00 5.00
10 Mitch Abeita#[Joba Chamberlain 1.50 4.00
11 Andrew Cashner#[Andrew Walker .75 2.00
12 Sawyer Carroll#[Scott Green .75 2.00
13 Taylor Teagarden#[Kyle Russell .75 2.00
14 Carlos Gutierrez#[Dennis Raben 1.25 3.00
15 Lance Lynn#[Cody Satterwhite .75 2.00
16 Jordan Danks#[Cat Osterman 1.25 3.00
17 Dusty Coleman#[Aaron Shafer .75 2.00
18 Joba Chamberlain#[Aaron Pribanic 1.50 4.00
19 Bryan Price#[Cole St. Clair .75 2.00
20 Cat Osterman#[Kenn Kasparek 1.25 3.00
21 Jose Duran#[Brandon Hicks .75 2.00
22 Roger Kieschnick#[Zachary Stewart .75 2.00
23 Shane Peterson#[Danny Espinosa 1.25 3.00
24 David Price#[Brett Jacobson .50 1.25
25 Joe Savery#[Bryan Price .75 2.00
26 Petey Paramore#[Ike Davis .75 2.00
27 Brent Morel#[Logan Schafer .75 2.00
28 Dennis Raben#[Mark Sobolewski .75 2.00
29 Andrew Liebel#[Shane Peterson 1.25 3.00
30 Buster Posey#[Tony Thomas 2.00 5.00
31 Joe Savery#[Cole St. Clair .75 2.00
32 Cat Osterman#[Bradley Suttle .75 2.00
33 Dennis Raben#[Blake Tekotte 1.25 3.00
34 Carlos Gutierrez#[Mark Sobolewski 1.25 3.00
35 Carlos Gutierrez#[Blake Tekotte 1.25 3.00

2008 Donruss Elite Extra Edition College Ties Autographs

OVERALL AUTO/MEM ODDS 1:5
PRINT RUNS B/N 20-44 COPIES PER
NO PRICING ON QTY 25 OR LESS
EXCH DEADLINE 5/26/2010
1 Cord Phelps
Sean Ratliff/25
2 Ryan Perry
T.J. Steele/25
3 Mitch Abeita
Aaron Pribanic/25
4 Ryan Perry
Daniel Schlereth/25
5 Daniel Schlereth
T.J. Steele/25
7 Blake Tekotte
Mark Sobolewski/25
8 Nick Schmidt
Logan Forsythe/25
9 Matt Wieters
Charlie Blackmon/25
10 Mitch Abeita
Joba Chamberlain/25
11 Andrew Cashner
Andrew Walker/25
12 Sawyer Carroll
Scott Green/25
13 Taylor Teagarden
Kyle Russell/25
14 Carlos Gutierrez
Dennis Raben/25
15 Lance Lynn
Cody Satterwhite/25
16 Jordan Danks
Cat Osterman/25 EXCH
17 Dusty Coleman
Aaron Shafer/25
18 Joba Chamberlain
Aaron Pribanic/25
19 Bryan Price
Cole St. Clair/25
20 Cat Osterman
Kenn Kasparek/25
21 Jose Duran
Brandon Hicks/25
22 Roger Kieschnick
Zachary Stewart/25
23 Shane Peterson
Danny Espinosa/25
24 David Price 20.00 50.00
Brett Jacobson/44
25 Joe Savery
Bryan Price/25
26 Petey Paramore
Ike Davis/25
27 Brent Morel
Logan Schafer/25
28 Dennis Raben
Mark Sobolewski/25
29 Andrew Liebel
Shane Peterson/25
30 Buster Posey
Tony Thomas/20
31 Joe Savery
Cole St. Clair/25
32 Cat Osterman
Bradley Suttle/25
33 Dennis Raben
Blake Tekotte/25
34 Carlos Gutierrez
Mark Sobolewski/25
35 Carlos Gutierrez
Blake Tekotte/25

2008 Donruss Elite Extra Edition College Ties Jerseys

OVERALL AU/MEM ODDS 1:5
PRINT RUNS B/WN 100-500 COPIES PER
6 Matt Mangini#[Jordy Mercer/500 3.00 8.00
8 Nick Schmidt#[Logan Forsythe/500 3.00 8.00
11 Andrew Cashner#[Andrew Walker/500 3.00 8.00
15 Lance Lynn#[Cody Satterwhite/500 3.00 8.00
16 Jordan Danks#[Cat Osterman/100 5.00 12.00
20 Cat Osterman#[Kenn Kasparek/100 6.00 15.00
21 Jose Duran#[Brandon Hicks/100 4.00 10.00
30 Buster Posey#[Tony Thomas/500 6.00 15.00
32 Cat Osterman#[Bradley Suttle/500

2008 Donruss Elite Extra Edition College Ties Jerseys Prime

OVERALL AU/MEM ODDS 1:5
STATED PRINT RUN 25 SER.#'d SETS
NO PRICING DUE TO SCARCITY
6 Matt Mangini#[Jordy Mercer/25
8 Nick Schmidt#[Logan Forsythe/25
11 Andrew Cashner#[Andrew Walker/25
15 Lance Lynn#[Cody Satterwhite/25
21 Jose Duran#[Brandon Hicks/25
30 Buster Posey#[Tony Thomas/25

2008 Donruss Elite Extra Edition Collegiate Patches Autographs

OVERALL AUTO/MEM ODDS 1:5
PRINT RUNS B/WN 20-255 COPIES PER
NO PRICING ON QTY 25 OR LESS
EXCH DEADLINE 5/26/2010
1 Ryan Patterson/250 6.00 15.00
2 Mark Melancon/250 8.00 20.00
3 Buster Posey/250 40.00 80.00
4 O.J. Mayo/50
5 Gordon Beckham/250 40.00 80.00
6 Josh Roenicke/250 5.00 12.00
7 Michael Beasley/100
8 Jack Egbert/249 6.00 15.00
9 Matt Wieters/25
10 Joba Chamberlain/20
11 Tyson Brummett/250 4.00 10.00
12 Ike Davis/250 10.00 25.00
13 Andrew Cashner/250 5.00 12.00
14 Charlie Furbush/250 5.00 12.00
15 Ryan Perry/248 4.00 10.00
16 Sean Doolittle/250 12.50 30.00
17 Alan Horne/250 EXCH 8.00 20.00
18 Daniel Schlereth/250 8.00 20.00
19 Carlos Gutierrez/249 8.00 20.00
20 Shooter Hunt/250 10.00 25.00
21 Cat Osterman/250 20.00 50.00
22 Lance Lynn/249 8.00 20.00
23 Byron Wiley/248 4.00 10.00
24 Brad Mills/249 6.00 15.00
25 Bryan Price/249 6.00 15.00
26 Logan Forsythe/249 8.00 20.00
27 Brian Duensing/50
28 Tyson Ross/255 5.00 12.00
29 Shane Peterson/250 6.00 15.00
30 Josh Lindblom/249 6.00 15.00
31 Aaron Shafer/250 8.00 20.00
32 Dennis Raben/250 6.00 15.00
33 Cody Satterwhite/250 8.00 20.00
34 James Darnell/250 8.00 20.00
35 Charlie Blackmon/240 5.00 12.00
36 Blake Wood/250 4.00 10.00
37 Jordan Danks/250 EXCH 5.00 12.00
38 Jordy Mercer/247 4.00 10.00
39 Roger Kieschnick/250 4.00 10.00
40 Zachary Stewart/250 6.00 15.00
41 Daniel McCutchen/250 5.00 12.00
42 Brent Morel/250 6.00 15.00
43 Kyle Hudson/249 5.00 12.00
44 Tim Murphy/250 4.00 10.00
45 Petey Paramore/250 5.00 12.00
46 Kyle Russell/250 4.00 10.00
47 Logan Schafer/250 6.00 15.00
48 Andrew Liebel/248 6.00 15.00
49 Aaron Pribanic/250 5.00 12.00
50 Scott Green/250 4.00 10.00
51 Blake Tekotte/248 6.00 15.00
52 Vance Worley/250 6.00 15.00
53 Taylor Teagarden/250 8.00 20.00
54 Cord Phelps/250 5.00 12.00
55 Kyle Weiland/250 6.00 15.00
56 Allan Dykstra/250 5.00 12.00
57 Danny Espinosa/250 5.00 12.00
58 James Caan/30
59 Zach Putnam/244 4.00 10.00
60 Mark Sobolewski/250 10.00 25.00
61 Regis Philbin/50 50.00 100.00
62 Randy Couture/50 50.00 100.00
63 Jose Duran/250 5.00 12.00
64 Lucas Duda/249 6.00 15.00
65 Ashley Judd/29

2008 Donruss Elite Extra Edition School Colors

OVERALL INSERT ODDS 1:2
STATED PRINT RUN 1500 SER.#'d SET
1 T.J. Steele 1.25 3.00
2 Brett Jacobson .50 1.25
3 Buster Posey 3.00 8.00
4 O.J. Mayo 1.25 3.00
5 Gordon Beckham 1.50 4.00
6 Sean Ratliff .75 2.00
7 Michael Beasley 1.25 3.00
8 Jose Duran .75 2.00
9 Derrick Rose 1.25 3.00
10 Joba Chamberlain 2.50 6.00
11 Sam Freeman 1.25 3.00
12 Ike Davis .75 2.00
13 Andrew Cashner .75 2.00
14 Chase D'Arnaud .75 2.00
15 Ryan Perry 1.25 3.00
16 Blake Tekotte 1.25 3.00
17 Cole St. Clair .75 2.00
18 Daniel Schlereth .75 2.00
19 Carlos Gutierrez 1.25 3.00
20 Shooter Hunt .75 2.00
21 Zach Putnam .75 2.00
22 Lance Lynn .75 2.00
23 Mitch Abeita .75 2.00
24 Jordan Danks 1.25 3.00
25 Bryan Price .75 2.00
26 Logan Forsythe .75 2.00
27 Brandon Crawford 1.25 3.00
28 Tyson Ross .75 2.00
29 Shane Peterson 1.25 3.00
30 Josh Lindblom .75 2.00
31 Aaron Shafer .75 2.00
32 Dennis Raben 1.25 3.00
33 Cody Satterwhite .75 2.00
34 James Darnell .75 2.00
35 Charlie Blackmon .75 2.00
36 Sawyer Carroll .75 2.00
37 Cat Osterman 2.00 5.00
38 Jordy Mercer .75 2.00
39 Roger Kieschnick .75 2.00
40 Zachary Stewart .75 2.00
41 Kyle Weiland 2.00 5.00
42 Brent Morel .75 2.00
43 Lucas Duda .75 2.00
44 Tim Murphy .75 2.00
45 Petey Paramore .75 2.00
46 Kyle Russell .75 2.00
47 Logan Schafer .75 2.00
48 Andrew Liebel .75 2.00

49 Aaron Pribanic .75 2.00
50 Scott Green .75 2.00

2008 Donruss Elite Extra Edition School Colors Autographs

OVERALL AUTO/MEM ODDS 1:5
PRINT RUNS B/WN 25-50 COPIES PER
NO PRICING ON QTY 25 OR LESS
EXCH DEADLINE 5/26/2010
1 T.J. Steele/25
2 Brett Jacobson/25
3 Buster Posey/50 40.00 80.00
4 O.J. Mayo/25
5 Gordon Beckham/50 30.00 60.00
6 Sean Ratliff/25
7 Michael Beasley/25
8 Jose Duran/50 4.00 10.00
9 Derrick Rose/25
10 Joba Chamberlain/25
11 Sam Freeman/25
12 Ike Davis/50 12.50 30.00
13 Andrew Cashner/50 5.00 12.00
14 Chase D'Arnaud/50 5.00 12.00
15 Ryan Perry/50 4.00 10.00
16 Blake Tekotte/50 4.00 10.00
17 Cole St. Clair/25
18 Daniel Schlereth/50 4.00 10.00
19 Carlos Gutierrez/25
20 Shooter Hunt/25
21 Zach Putnam/25
22 Lance Lynn/50 10.00 25.00
23 Mitch Abeita/25
24 Jordan Danks/25 EXCH
25 Bryan Price/50 5.00 12.00
26 Logan Forsythe/25
27 Brandon Crawford/25
28 Tyson Ross/25
29 Shane Peterson/25
30 Josh Lindblom/25
31 Aaron Shafer/50 4.00 10.00
32 Dennis Raben/50 6.00 15.00
33 Cody Satterwhite/50 20.00 50.00
34 James Darnell/25
35 Charlie Blackmon/50 5.00 12.00
36 Sawyer Carroll/25
37 Cat Osterman/25
38 Jordy Mercer/25
39 Roger Kieschnick/25
40 Zachary Stewart/25
41 Kyle Weiland/25
42 Brent Morel/50 4.00 10.00
43 Lucas Duda/25
44 Tim Murphy/25
45 Petey Paramore/50
46 Kyle Russell/50 8.00 20.00
47 Logan Schafer/50 4.00 10.00
48 Andrew Liebel/25
49 Aaron Pribanic/25
50 Scott Green/25

2008 Donruss Elite Extra Edition School Colors Materials

OVERALL AU/MEM ODDS 1:5
STATED PRINT RUN 100 SER.#'d SETS
3 Buster Posey 6.00 15.00
4 O.J. Mayo 6.00 15.00
5 Gordon Beckham 6.00 15.00
7 Michael Beasley 6.00 15.00
8 Jose Duran 4.00 10.00
9 Derrick Rose 6.00 15.00
13 Andrew Cashner 4.00 10.00
33 Cody Satterwhite 6.00 15.00
37 Cat Osterman 8.00 20.00

2008 Donruss Elite Extra Edition School Colors Materials Prime

OVERALL AU/MEM ODDS 1:5
STATED PRINT RUN 25 SER.#'d SETS
NO PRICING DUE TO SCARCITY

2008 Donruss Elite Extra Edition Throwback Threads

OVERALL AU/MEM ODDS 1:5
PRINT RUNS B/WN 15-500 COPIES PER
NO PRICING ON QTY 25 OR LESS
1 Rick Porcello/500 5.00 12.00
2 Gordon Beckham/500 5.00 12.00
3 Andrew Cashner/500 3.00 8.00
5 Xavier Avery/15
6 Cody Satterwhite/500 6.00 15.00
8 Logan Morrison/25
9 Jose Duran/500 3.00 8.00
10 Derrick Rose/500 6.00 15.00
11 Michael Beasley/500 10.00 25.00
12 O.J. Mayo/400 5.00 12.00
13 Buster Posey/250 10.00 25.00
15 Luis Exposito/25
20 Cat Osterman/100 6.00 15.00
24 Tim Alderson/500 3.00 8.00
25 Michael Burgess/500 3.00 8.00

2008 Donruss Elite Extra Edition Throwback Threads Prime

OVERALL AU/MEM ODDS 1:5
PRINT RUNS B/WN 1-50 COPIES PER
NO PRICING ON QTY 10 OR LESS
1 Rick Porcello/10
2 Gordon Beckham/10
3 Andrew Cashner/10
6 Cody Satterwhite/10
9 Jose Duran/10
10 Derrick Rose/10
11 Michael Beasley/10
12 O.J. Mayo/10
13 Buster Posey/10
21 Mark Melancon/1
24 Tim Alderson/50 6.00 15.00
25 Michael Burgess/50 6.00 15.00

2008 Donruss Elite Extra Edition Throwback Threads Autographs

OVERALL AUTO/MEM ODDS 1:5
PRINT RUNS B/WN 4-100 COPIES PER
NO PRICING ON QTY 25 OR LESS
EXCH DEADLINE 5/26/2010
1 Rick Porcello/100 40.00 80.00
2 Gordon Beckham/100 40.00 80.00
3 Andrew Cashner/100 10.00 25.00
5 Xavier Avery/35 20.00 50.00
6 Cody Satterwhite/100
8 Logan Morrison/25
9 Jose Duran/100 10.00 25.00
10 Derrick Rose/25
11 Michael Beasley/25
12 O.J. Mayo/25
13 Buster Posey/100 40.00 80.00
15 Luis Exposito/25
20 Cat Osterman/50 30.00 60.00
21 Mark Melancon/4
22 Madison Bumgarner/4
23 Nick Hagadone/15
24 Tim Alderson/40 10.00 25.00
25 Michael Burgess/5

2008 Donruss Elite Extra Edition Throwback Threads Autographs Prime

OVERALL AUTO/MEM ODDS 1:5
PRINT RUNS B/WN 1-25 COPIES PER
NO PRICING DUE TO SCARCITY
EXCH DEADLINE 5/26/2010
1 Rick Porcello/10
2 Gordon Beckham/10
3 Andrew Cashner/10
6 Cody Satterwhite/25
9 Jose Duran/10
10 Derrick Rose/10
11 Michael Beasley/10
12 O.J. Mayo/10
13 Buster Posey/10
15 Luis Exposito/1
20 Cat Osterman/5
21 Mark Melancon/1
22 Madison Bumgarner/1
24 Tim Alderson/10
25 Michael Burgess/5

1997 Donruss Signature

Distributed in five-card packs with one authentic autographed card per pack, this 100-card set was issued in two series. However, these regular cards were issued with both series and one could make sets from either series. These packs carried a suggested retail price of $14.99. The fronts feature color player photos with player information on the backs. The only Rookie Cards of note in this set are Jose Cruz Jr. and Mark Kotsay.

COMPLETE SET (100) 25.00 50.00
1 Mark McGwire 1.25 3.00
2 Kenny Lofton .20 .50
3 Tony Gwynn .60 1.50
4 Tony Clark .20 .50
5 Tim Salmon .30 .75
6 Ken Griffey Jr. .75 2.00
7 Mike Piazza .75 2.00
8 Greg Maddux .75 2.00
9 Roberto Alomar .30 .75
10 Andres Galarraga .20 .50
11 Roger Clemens 1.00 2.50
12 Bernie Williams .30 .75
13 Rondell White .20 .50
14 Kevin Appier .20 .50
15 Ray Lankford .20 .50
16 Frank Thomas .50 1.25
17 Will Clark .30 .75
18 Chipper Jones .50 1.25
19 Jeff Bagwell .30 .75
20 Manny Ramirez .30 .75
21 Ryne Sandberg .75 2.00
22 Paul Molitor .20 .50
23 Gary Sheffield .20 .50
24 Jim Edmonds .20 .50
25 Barry Larkin .30 .75
26 Rafael Palmeiro .30 .75
27 Alan Benes .20 .50
28 Dave Justice .20 .50
29 Randy Johnson .50 1.25
30 Barry Bonds 1.25 3.00
31 Mo Vaughn .20 .50
32 Michael Tucker .20 .50
33 Larry Walker .20 .50
34 Tino Martinez .30 .75
35 Jose Guillen .20 .50
36 Carlos Delgado .20 .50
37 Jason Dickson .20 .50
38 Tom Glavine .30 .75
39 Raul Mondesi .20 .50
40 Jose Cruz Jr. RC .20 .50
41 Johnny Damon .30 .75
42 Mark Grace .30 .75
43 Juan Gonzalez .20 .50
44 Vladimir Guerrero .50 1.25
45 Kevin Brown .20 .50
46 Justin Thompson .20 .50
47 Eric Young .20 .50
48 Ron Coomer .20 .50
49 Mark Kotsay RC .50 1.25
50 Scott Rolen .30 .75
51 Derek Jeter 1.25 3.00
52 Jim Thome .30 .75
53 Fred McGriff .30 .75
54 Albert Belle .20 .50
55 Garret Anderson .20 .50
56 Wilton Guerrero .20 .50
57 Jose Canseco .30 .75
58 Cal Ripken 1.50 4.00
59 Sammy Sosa .50 1.25
60 Dmitri Young .20 .50
61 Alex Rodriguez .75 2.00
62 Javier Lopez .20 .50
63 Sandy Alomar Jr. .20 .50
64 Joe Carter .20 .50
65 Dante Bichette .20 .50
66 Al Martin .20 .50
67 Darin Erstad .20 .50
68 Pokey Reese .20 .50
69 Brady Anderson .20 .50
70 Andruw Jones .30 .75
71 Ivan Rodriguez .30 .75
72 Nomar Garciaparra .75 2.00
73 Moises Alou .20 .50
74 Andy Pettitte .30 .75
75 Jay Buhner .20 .50
76 Craig Biggio .30 .75
77 Wade Boggs .30 .75
78 Shawn Estes .20 .50
79 Neifi Perez .20 .50
80 Rusty Greer .20 .50
81 Pedro Martinez .30 .75
82 Mike Mussina .30 .75
83 Jason Giambi .30 .75
84 Hideo Nomo .50 1.25
85 Todd Hundley .20 .50
86 Deion Sanders .30 .75
87 Mike Cameron .20 .50
88 Bobby Bonilla .20 .50
89 Todd Greene .20 .50
90 Kevin Orie .20 .50
91 Ken Caminiti .20 .50
92 Chuck Knoblauch .20 .50
93 Matt Morris .20 .50
94 Matt Williams .20 .50
95 Pat Hentgen .20 .50
96 John Smoltz .30 .75
97 Edgar Martinez .30 .75
98 Jason Kendall .20 .50
99 Ken Griffey Jr. CL .50 1.25
100 Frank Thomas CL .30 .75

1997 Donruss Signature Platinum Press Proofs

Randomly inserted in packs, this set is a holo foil parallel version of the base set. Only 150 of this set were produced. Each card is numbered "1 of 150" on the back. Some cards were mistakenly printed with the "1 of 150 backs" but did not have the platinum press proof front. These cards are valued at approximately the same price as the values below.

*STARS: 10X TO 25X BASIC CARDS
*ROOKIES: 4X TO 10X BASIC CARDS

1997 Donruss Signature Autographs

Inserted one per pack, this 117-card set features color player autographed photos. The first 100 cards each player signed were blue, sequentially numbered to 100, and designated as "Century Marks." The next 100 cards signed were green, sequentially numbered 101-1100, and designated as "Millenium Marks." Player autographs surpassing 1100 were red and were not numbered. Some autographed signature cards were not available at first and were designated by blank-backed redemption cards which could be redeemed by mail for the player's autograph card. The cards are checklisted below in alphabetical order. Asterisk cards were found in both Series A and B. Print runs for how many cards each player signed is noted next to the players name. Exchange cards for Raul Mondesi and Edgar Renteria were seeded into packs. Notable cards of players in their Rookie Card seasons include Brian Giles and Miguel Tejada. The Miguel Tejada and David Ortiz cards were signed in either black or blue ink. At this time, there is no price differential for either version of these cards.

1 Jeff Abbott/3900 2.00 5.00
2 Bob Abreu/3900 6.00 15.00
3 Edgardo Alfonzo/3900 2.00 5.00
4 Roberto Alomar/150 * 20.00 50.00
5 Sandy Alomar Jr./1400 6.00 15.00
6 Moises Alou/900 6.00 15.00
7 Garret Anderson/3900 4.00 10.00
8 Andy Ashby/3900 2.00 5.00
9 Trey Beamon/3900 2.00 5.00
10 Alan Benes/3900 2.00 5.00
11 Geronimo Berroa/3900 2.00 5.00
12 Wade Boggs/150 * 60.00 120.00
13 Kevin Brown C/3900 2.00 5.00
14 Brett Butler/1400 6.00 15.00
15 Mike Cameron/3900 4.00 10.00
16 Giovanni Carrara/2900 2.00 5.00
17 Luis Castillo/3900 4.00 10.00
18 Tony Clark/3900 2.00 5.00
19 Will Clark/1400 8.00 20.00
20 Lou Collier/3900 2.00 5.00
21 Bartolo Colon/3900 4.00 10.00
22 Ron Coomer/3900 2.00 5.00
23 Marty Cordova/3900 2.00 5.00
24 Jacob Cruz/3900 * 2.00 5.00
25 Jose Cruz Jr./900 * 3.00 8.00
26 Russ Davis/3900 2.00 5.00
27 Jason Dickson/3900 2.00 5.00
28 Todd Dunwoody/3900 2.00 5.00
29 Jermaine Dye/3900 4.00 10.00
30 Jim Edmonds/3900 6.00 15.00
31 Darin Erstad/900 * 4.00 10.00
32 Bobby Estalella/3900 2.00 5.00
33 Shawn Estes/3900 2.00 5.00
34 Jeff Fassero/3900 2.00 5.00
35 Andres Galarraga/900 6.00 15.00
36 Karim Garcia/3900 2.00 5.00
37 Derrick Gibson/3900 2.00 5.00
38 Brian Giles/3900 6.00 15.00
39 Tom Glavine/150 40.00 80.00
40 Rick Gorecki/900 3.00 8.00
41 Shawn Green/1900 6.00 15.00
42 Todd Greene/3900 2.00 5.00
43 Rusty Greer/3900 4.00 10.00
44 Ben Grieve/3900 2.00 5.00
45 M.Grudzielanek/3900 4.00 10.00
46 V.Guerrero/1900 * 15.00 40.00
47 Wilton Guerrero/2150 2.00 5.00
48 Jose Guillen/2900 4.00 10.00
49 J.Hammonds/2150 2.00 5.00
50 Todd Helton/1400 10.00 25.00
51 T.Hollandsworth/2900 2.00 5.00
52 Trenidad Hubbard/900 3.00 8.00
53 Todd Hundley/1400 3.00 8.00
54 Bobby Jones/3900 2.00 5.00
55 Brian Jordan/1400 6.00 15.00
56 David Justice/900 6.00 15.00
57 Eric Karros/650 6.00 15.00
58 Jason Kendall/3900 4.00 10.00
59 Jimmy Key/3900 4.00 10.00
60 B.Kieschnick/3900 2.00 5.00
61 Ryan Klesko/225 15.00 40.00
62 Paul Konerko/3900 6.00 15.00
63 Mark Kotsay/2400 6.00 15.00
64 Ray Lankford/3900 4.00 10.00
65 Barry Larkin/150 * 20.00 50.00
66 Derrek Lee/3900 6.00 15.00
67 Esteban Loaiza/3900 2.00 5.00
68 Javier Lopez/1400 6.00 15.00
69 Edgar Martinez/150 * 12.50 30.00
70 Pedro Martinez/900 30.00 60.00
71 Rafael Medina/3900 2.00 5.00
72 Raul Mondesi/650 6.00 15.00
73 Matt Morris/3900 4.00 10.00
74 Paul O'Neill/900 10.00 25.00
75 Kevin Orie/3900 2.00 5.00
76 David Ortiz/3900 20.00 50.00
77 Rafael Palmeiro/900 20.00 50.00
78 Jay Payton/3900 2.00 5.00
79 Neifi Perez/3900 2.00 5.00
80 Manny Ramirez/900 20.00 50.00
81 Joe Randa/3900 4.00 10.00
82 Pokey Reese/3900 4.00 10.00
83 Edgar Renteria SP 10.00 25.00
84 Dennis Reyes/3900 2.00 5.00
85 Henry Rodriguez/3900 2.00 5.00
86 Scott Rolen/1900 * 6.00 15.00
87 Kirk Rueter/2900 2.00 5.00
88 Ryne Sandberg/400 30.00 60.00
89 Dwight Smith/2900 2.00 5.00
90 J.T. Snow/900 4.00 10.00
91 Scott Spiezio/3900 2.00 5.00
92 Shannon Stewart/2900 4.00 10.00
93 Jeff Suppan/1900 4.00 10.00
94 Mike Sweeney/3900 4.00 10.00
95 Miguel Tejada/3900 6.00 15.00
96 Justin Thompson/2400 2.00 5.00
97 Brett Tomko/3900 2.00 5.00
98 Bubba Trammell/3900 3.00 8.00
99 Michael Tucker/3900 4.00 10.00
100 Javier Valentin/3900 2.00 5.00
101 Mo Vaughn/150 * 15.00 40.00
102 Robin Ventura/1400 6.00 15.00
103 Terrell Wade/3900 2.00 5.00
104 Billy Wagner/3900 6.00 15.00
105 Larry Walker/900 12.50 30.00
106 Todd Walker/2400 2.00 5.00
107 Rondell White/3900 2.00 5.00
108 Kevin Wickander/900 2.00 5.00
109 Chris Widger/3900 2.00 5.00
110 Matt Williams/150 * 12.50 30.00
111 A.Williamson/3900 2.00 5.00
112 Dan Wilson/3900 2.00 5.00
113 Tony Womack/3900 3.00 8.00
114 Jaret Wright/3900 3.00 8.00
115 Dmitri Young/3900 4.00 10.00
116 Eric Young/3900 2.00 5.00
117 Kevin Young/3900 2.00 5.00
NNO F.Thomas Sample .75 2.00
Fascimile Autograph

1997 Donruss Signature Autographs Century

Randomly inserted in packs, this set, identified with blue card fronts, features the first 100 cards signed by each player. The cards are sequentially numbered. Raul Mondesi, Eddie Murray, Edgar Renteria and Jim Thome were seeded in packs as exchange cards. The cards are checklisted below in alphabetical order. A number of Nomar Garciaparra Century marks were lost or destroyed during packaging and only 62 of these cards were inserted into packs.

1 Jeff Abbott 12.50 30.00
2 Bob Abreu 40.00 80.00
3 Edgardo Alfonzo 20.00 50.00
4 Roberto Alomar * 40.00 80.00
5 Sandy Alomar Jr. 20.00 50.00
6 Moises Alou 20.00 50.00
7 Garret Anderson 20.00 50.00
8 Andy Ashby 12.50 30.00
9 Jeff Bagwell 75.00 150.00
10 Trey Beamon 12.50 30.00
11 Albert Belle 20.00 50.00
12 Alan Benes 12.50 30.00
13 Geronimo Berroa 12.50 30.00
14 Wade Boggs * 50.00 100.00
15 Barry Bonds 225.00 350.00
16 Bobby Bonilla * 20.00 50.00
17 Kevin Brown 20.00 50.00
18 Kevin Brown C 12.50 30.00
19 Jay Buhner 20.00 50.00
20 Brett Butler 20.00 50.00
21 Mike Cameron 20.00 50.00
22 Giovanni Carrara 12.50 30.00
23 Luis Castillo 20.00 50.00
24 Tony Clark 12.50 30.00
25 Will Clark 40.00 80.00
26 Roger Clemens * 175.00 300.00
27 Lou Collier 12.50 30.00
28 Bartolo Colon 20.00 50.00
29 Ron Coomer 20.00 50.00
30 Marty Cordova 12.50 30.00
31 Jacob Cruz * 12.50 30.00
32 Jose Cruz Jr. * 12.50 30.00
33 Russ Davis 12.50 30.00
34 Jason Dickson 12.50 30.00
35 Todd Dunwoody 12.50 30.00
36 Jermaine Dye 20.00 50.00
37 Jim Edmonds 60.00 120.00
38 Darin Erstad * 20.00 50.00
39 Bobby Estalella 12.50 30.00
40 Shawn Estes 12.50 30.00
41 Jeff Fassero 12.50 30.00
42 Andres Galarraga 20.00 50.00
43 Karim Garcia 12.50 30.00
44 N. Garciaparra SP62 * 125.00 200.00
45 Derrick Gibson 12.50 30.00
46 Brian Giles 30.00 60.00
47 Tom Glavine 50.00 100.00
48 Juan Gonzalez 20.00 50.00
49 Rick Gorecki 12.50 30.00
50 Shawn Green 40.00 80.00
51 Todd Greene 12.50 30.00
52 Rusty Greer 20.00 50.00
53 Ben Grieve 12.50 30.00
54 Mark Grudzielanek 20.00 50.00
55 Vladimir Guerrero * 75.00 150.00
56 Wilton Guerrero 12.50 30.00
57 Jose Guillen 20.00 50.00
58 Tony Gwynn * 60.00 120.00
59 Jeffrey Hammonds 12.50 30.00
60 Todd Helton 40.00 80.00
61 Todd Hollandsworth 12.50 30.00
62 Trenidad Hubbard 12.50 30.00
63 Todd Hundley 12.50 30.00
64 Derek Jeter * 250.00 400.00
65 Andruw Jones * 50.00 100.00
66 Bobby Jones 12.50 30.00
67 Chipper Jones * 200.00 300.00
68 Brian Jordan 20.00 50.00
69 David Justice 20.00 50.00
70 Eric Karros 20.00 50.00
71 Jason Kendall 20.00 50.00
72 Jimmy Key 20.00 50.00
73 Brooks Kieschnick 12.50 30.00
74 Ryan Klesko 20.00 50.00
75 Chuck Knoblauch * 20.00 50.00
76 Paul Konerko 40.00 80.00
77 Mark Kotsay 20.00 50.00
78 Ray Lankford 20.00 50.00
79 Barry Larkin * 40.00 80.00
80 Derrek Lee 40.00 80.00
81 Esteban Loaiza 12.50 30.00
82 Javier Lopez 20.00 50.00
83 Greg Maddux * 175.00 300.00
84 Edgar Martinez * 50.00 100.00
85 Pedro Martinez 75.00 150.00
86 Tino Martinez * 75.00 150.00
87 Rafael Medina 12.50 30.00
88 Raul Mondesi 20.00 50.00
89 Matt Morris 20.00 50.00
90 Eddie Murray EXCH* 60.00 120.00
91 Mike Mussina 40.00 80.00
92 Paul O'Neill 40.00 80.00
93 Kevin Orie 12.50 30.00
94 David Ortiz 400.00 600.00
95 Rafael Palmeiro 50.00 100.00
96 Jay Payton 12.50 30.00
97 Neifi Perez 12.50 30.00
98 Andy Pettitte * 50.00 100.00
99 Manny Ramirez 60.00 120.00
100 Joe Randa 20.00 50.00
101 Pokey Reese 20.00 50.00
102 Edgar Renteria 40.00 80.00
103 Dennis Reyes 12.50 30.00
104 Cal Ripken 200.00 350.00
105 Alex Rodriguez 600.00 800.00
106 Henry Rodriguez 12.50 30.00
107 Ivan Rodriguez 50.00 100.00
108 Scott Rolen * 40.00 80.00
109 Kirk Rueter 12.50 30.00
110 Ryne Sandberg 90.00 150.00
111 Gary Sheffield * 40.00 80.00
112 Dwight Smith 12.50 30.00
113 J.T. Snow 20.00 50.00
114 Scott Spiezio 12.50 30.00
115 Shannon Stewart 20.00 50.00
116 Jeff Suppan 20.00 50.00
117 Mike Sweeney 20.00 50.00
118 Miguel Tejada 75.00 150.00
119 Frank Thomas 50.00 100.00
120 Jim Thome 50.00 100.00
121 Justin Thompson 12.50 30.00
122 Brett Tomko 12.50 30.00
123 Bubba Trammell 12.50 30.00
124 Michael Tucker 20.00 50.00
125 Javier Valentin 12.50 30.00
126 Mo Vaughn * 20.00 50.00
127 Robin Ventura 20.00 50.00
128 Terrell Wade 12.50 30.00
129 Billy Wagner 40.00 80.00
130 Larry Walker 60.00 120.00
131 Todd Walker 12.50 30.00
132 Rondell White 20.00 50.00
133 Kevin Wickander 12.50 30.00
134 Chris Widger 12.50 30.00
135 Bernie Williams 60.00 120.00
136 Matt Williams * 40.00 80.00
137 Antone Williamson 12.50 30.00
138 Dan Wilson 12.50 30.00
139 Tony Womack 12.50 30.00
140 Jaret Wright 12.50 30.00
141 Dmitri Young 20.00 50.00
142 Eric Young 12.50 30.00
143 Kevin Young 12.50 30.00

1997 Donruss Signature Autographs Millennium

Randomly inserted in packs, this set, identified with green card fronts, features the second group of 100 cards signed by each player. The cards are sequentially numbered 101-1,100 (except for some shortprinted cards in quantities of 400, 650 or 900) and are checklisted in alphabetical order. It has been noted that there are some cards in circulation that lack serial numbering. Edgar Renteria was seeded into packs as an exchange card and has been verified by representatives at Donruss as being a short-print. Eddie Murray, Raul Mondesi and Jim Thome were also exchange cards.

1 Jeff Abbott 3.00 8.00
2 Bob Abreu 10.00 25.00
3 Edgardo Alfonzo 3.00 8.00
4 Roberto Alomar * 10.00 25.00
5 Sandy Alomar Jr. 6.00 15.00
6 Moises Alou 6.00 15.00
7 Garret Anderson 6.00 15.00
8 Andy Ashby 3.00 8.00
9 Jeff Bagwell/400 30.00 60.00
10 Trey Beamon 3.00 8.00
11 Albert Belle/400 10.00 25.00
12 Alan Benes 3.00 8.00
13 Geronimo Berroa 3.00 8.00
14 Wade Boggs * 15.00 40.00
15 Barry Bonds/400 100.00 175.00
16 Bobby Bonilla/900 * 6.00 15.00
17 Kevin Brown/900 6.00 15.00
18 Kevin Brown C 3.00 8.00
19 Jay Buhner/900 6.00 15.00
20 Brett Butler 6.00 15.00
21 Mike Cameron 6.00 15.00
22 Giovanni Carrara 3.00 8.00
23 Luis Castillo 6.00 15.00
24 Tony Clark 3.00 8.00
25 Will Clark 10.00 25.00
26 Roger Clemens/400 * 60.00 120.00
27 Lou Collier 3.00 8.00
28 Bartolo Colon 6.00 15.00
29 Ron Coomer 3.00 8.00
30 Marty Cordova 3.00 8.00
31 Jacob Cruz 3.00 8.00
32 Jose Cruz Jr. * 4.00 10.00
33 Russ Davis 3.00 8.00
34 Jason Dickson 3.00 8.00
35 Todd Dunwoody 3.00 8.00
36 Jermaine Dye 6.00 15.00
37 Jim Edmonds 10.00 25.00
38 Darin Erstad * 6.00 15.00
39 Bobby Estalella 3.00 8.00
40 Shawn Estes 3.00 8.00
41 Jeff Fassero 3.00 8.00
42 Andres Galarraga 6.00 15.00
43 Karim Garcia 3.00 8.00
44 N.Garciaparra/650 * 50.00 100.00
45 Derrick Gibson 3.00 8.00
46 Brian Giles 10.00 25.00
47 Tom Glavine 15.00 40.00
48 Juan Gonzalez/900 6.00 15.00
49 Rick Gorecki 3.00 8.00
50 Shawn Green 10.00 25.00
51 Todd Greene 3.00 8.00
52 Rusty Greer 6.00 15.00
53 Ben Grieve 3.00 8.00
54 Mark Grudzielanek 6.00 15.00
55 Vladimir Guerrero * 20.00 50.00
56 Wilton Guerrero 3.00 8.00
57 Jose Guillen 6.00 15.00
58 Tony Gwynn/900 * 15.00 40.00
59 Jeffrey Hammonds 3.00 8.00

60 Todd Helton	10.00	25.00
61 Todd Hundley	3.00	8.00
62 Todd Hollandsworth	3.00	8.00
63 Trenidad Hubbard	3.00	8.00
64 Derek Jeter/400 *	100.00	175.00
65 Andruw Jones/900 *	15.00	40.00
66 Bobby Jones	3.00	8.00
67 Chipper Jones/900 *	20.00	50.00
68 Brian Jordan	6.00	15.00
69 David Justice	6.00	15.00
70 Eric Karros	6.00	15.00
71 Jason Kendall	3.00	8.00
72 Jimmy Key	6.00	15.00
73 Brooks Kieschnick	3.00	8.00
74 Ryan Klesko	6.00	15.00
75 C.Knoblauch/900 *	6.00	15.00
76 Paul Konerko	10.00	25.00
77 Mark Kotsay	8.00	20.00
78 Ray Lankford	6.00	15.00
79 Barry Larkin *	10.00	25.00
80 Derrek Lee	10.00	25.00
81 Esteban Loaiza	3.00	8.00
82 Javier Lopez	6.00	15.00
83 Greg Maddux/400 *	60.00	120.00
84 Edgar Martinez *	15.00	40.00
85 Pedro Martinez	30.00	60.00
86 Tino Martinez/900 *	30.00	60.00
87 Rafael Medina	3.00	8.00
88 Raul Mondesi	6.00	15.00
89 Matt Morris	6.00	15.00
90 Eddie Murray/900 *	30.00	60.00
91 Mike Mussina/900	10.00	25.00
92 Paul O'Neill	10.00	25.00
93 Kevin Orie	3.00	8.00
94 David Ortiz	40.00	80.00
95 Rafael Palmeiro	20.00	50.00
96 Jay Payton	3.00	8.00
97 Neifi Perez	3.00	8.00
98 Andy Pettitte/900 *	12.50	30.00
99 Manny Ramirez	20.00	50.00
100 Joe Randa	6.00	15.00
101 Pokey Reese	6.00	15.00
102 Edgar Renteria SP	10.00	25.00
103 Dennis Reyes	3.00	8.00
104 Cal Ripken/400	75.00	150.00
105 Alex Rodriguez/400	75.00	150.00
106 Henry Rodriguez	3.00	8.00
107 Ivan Rodriguez/900	15.00	40.00
108 Scott Rolen *	10.00	25.00
109 Kirk Rueter	3.00	8.00
110 Ryne Sandberg	20.00	50.00
111 Gary Sheffield/400 *	15.00	40.00
112 Dwight Smith	3.00	8.00
113 J.T. Snow	6.00	15.00
114 Scott Spiezio	3.00	8.00
115 Shannon Stewart	6.00	15.00
116 Jeff Suppan	6.00	15.00
117 Mike Sweeney	6.00	15.00
118 Miguel Tejada	10.00	25.00
119 Frank Thomas/400	30.00	60.00
120 Jim Thome/900	15.00	40.00
121 Justin Thompson	3.00	8.00
122 Brett Tomko	3.00	8.00
123 Bubba Trammell	4.00	10.00
124 Michael Tucker	6.00	15.00
125 Javier Valentin	3.00	8.00
126 Mo Vaughn *	6.00	15.00
127 Robin Ventura	6.00	15.00
128 Terrell Wade	3.00	8.00
129 Billy Wagner	10.00	25.00
130 Larry Walker	10.00	25.00
131 Todd Walker	3.00	8.00
132 Rondell White	6.00	15.00
133 Kevin Wickander	3.00	8.00
134 Chris Widger	3.00	8.00
135 Bernie Williams/400	60.00	120.00
136 Matt Williams *	10.00	25.00
137 Antone Williamson	3.00	8.00
138 Dan Wilson	3.00	8.00
139 Tony Womack	4.00	10.00
140 Jaret Wright	4.00	10.00
141 Dmitri Young	6.00	15.00
142 Eric Young	3.00	8.00
143 Kevin Young	3.00	8.00

1997 Donruss Signature Notable Nicknames

Randomly inserted in packs, this 10-card set features photos of players with notable nicknames. Only 200 of this serial numbered set were produced. The cards are unnumbered and checklisted in alphabetical order. Roger Clemens signed a good deal of his cards without using his "Rocket" nickname. In addition, some Frank Thomas cards have been seen signed without "The Big Hurt" nickname. There is no difference in value between the two versions.

1 Ernie Banks Mr. Cub	125.00	200.00
2 Tony Clark The Tiger	60.00	100.00
3 Roger Clemens The Rocket	400.00	600.00
4 Reggie Jackson Mr. October	125.00	200.00
5 Randy Johnson The Big Unit	300.00	500.00
6 Stan Musial The Man	150.00	250.00
7 Ivan Rodriguez Pudge	125.00	200.00
9 Frank Thomas The Big Hurt	125.00	200.00
10 Mo Vaughn The Hit Dog	70.00	120.00
11 Billy Wagner The Kid	90.00	150.00

1997 Donruss Signature Significant Signatures

Randomly inserted in packs, this 22-card set features photos with autographs of legendary Hall of Fame players. Only 2000 of each card was produced and serially numbered. The cards are checklisted below in alphabetical order. Reggie Jackson signed his cards in 2 different color inks. The cards he signed in silver are in shorter supply and are valued higher.

1 Ernie Banks	20.00	50.00
2 Johnny Bench	15.00	40.00
3 Yogi Berra	15.00	40.00
4 George Brett	30.00	60.00
5 Lou Brock	8.00	20.00
6 Rod Carew	12.50	30.00
7 Steve Carlton	10.00	25.00
8 Larry Doby	30.00	60.00
9 Carlton Fisk	10.00	25.00
10 Bob Gibson	10.00	25.00
11 Reggie Jackson	15.00	40.00
11A R.Jackson Silver Ink	100.00	200.00
12 Al Kaline	15.00	40.00
13 Harmon Killebrew	15.00	40.00
14 Don Mattingly	20.00	50.00
15 Stan Musial	20.00	50.00
16 Jim Palmer	10.00	25.00
17 Brooks Robinson	8.00	20.00
18 Frank Robinson	10.00	25.00
19 Mike Schmidt	20.00	50.00
20 Tom Seaver	15.00	40.00
21 Duke Snider	10.00	25.00
22 Carl Yastrzemski	20.00	50.00

1998 Donruss Signature

The 140-card 1998 Donruss Signature set was distributed in five-card packs with one authentic autographed card per pack and a suggested retail price of $14.99. The fronts feature color action player photos in white borders. The backs carry player information and career statistics. Due to Pinnacle's bankruptcy, these cards were later released by Playoff. This set was released in very late December, 1998. Notable Rookie Cards in this set include J.D. Drew, Troy Glaus, Orlando Hernandez, Gabe Kapler, Kevin Millwood and Magglio Ordonez.

COMPLETE SET (140)	20.00	50.00
1 David Justice	.15	.40
2 Derek Jeter	1.00	2.50
3 Nomar Garciaparra	.60	1.50
4 Ryan Klesko	.15	.40
5 Jeff Bagwell	.25	.60
6 Dante Bichette	.15	.40
7 Ivan Rodriguez	.25	.60
8 Albert Belle	.15	.40
9 Cal Ripken	1.25	3.00
10 Craig Biggio	.25	.60
11 Barry Larkin	.25	.60
12 Jose Guillen	.15	.40
13 Will Clark	.25	.60
14 J.T. Snow	.15	.40
15 Chuck Knoblauch	.15	.40
16 Todd Walker	.15	.40
17 Scott Rolen	.25	.60
18 Rickey Henderson	.40	1.00
19 Juan Gonzalez	.15	.40
20 Justin Thompson	.15	.40
21 Roger Clemens	.75	2.00
22 Ray Lankford	.15	.40
23 Jose Cruz Jr.	.15	.40
24 Ken Griffey Jr.	.60	1.50
25 Andruw Jones	.25	.60
26 Darin Erstad	.15	.40
27 Jim Thome	.25	.60
28 Wade Boggs	.25	.60
29 Ken Caminiti	.15	.40
30 Todd Hundley	.15	.40
31 Mike Piazza	.60	1.50
32 Sammy Sosa	.40	1.00
33 Larry Walker	.15	.40
34 Matt Williams	.15	.40
35 Frank Thomas	.40	1.00
36 Gary Sheffield	.15	.40
37 Alex Rodriguez	.60	1.50
38 Hideo Nomo	.40	1.00
39 Kenny Lofton	.15	.40
40 John Smoltz	.25	.60
41 Mo Vaughn	.15	.40
42 Edgar Martinez	.25	.60
43 Paul Molitor	.15	.40
44 Rafael Palmeiro	.25	.60
45 Barry Bonds	1.00	2.50
46 Vladimir Guerrero	.40	1.00
47 Carlos Delgado	.15	.40
48 Bobby Higginson	.15	.40
49 Greg Maddux	.60	1.50
50 Jim Edmonds	.15	.40
51 Randy Johnson	.40	1.00
52 Mark McGwire	1.00	2.50
53 Rondell White	.15	.40
54 Raul Mondesi	.15	.40
55 Manny Ramirez	.25	.60
56 Pedro Martinez	.25	.60
57 Tim Salmon	.25	.60
58 Moises Alou	.15	.40
59 Fred McGriff	.25	.60
60 Garret Anderson	.15	.40
61 Sandy Alomar Jr.	.15	.40
62 Chan Ho Park	.15	.40
63 Mark Kotsay	.15	.40
64 Mike Mussina	.25	.60
65 Tom Glavine	.25	.60
66 Tony Clark	.15	.40
67 Mark Grace	.25	.60
68 Tony Gwynn	.50	1.25
69 Tino Martinez	.25	.60
70 Kevin Brown	.25	.60
71 Todd Greene	.15	.40
72 Andy Pettitte	.25	.60
73 Livan Hernandez	.15	.40
74 Curt Schilling	.15	.40
75 Andres Galarraga	.15	.40
76 Rusty Greer	.15	.40
77 Jay Buhner	.15	.40
78 Bobby Bonilla	.15	.40
79 Chipper Jones	.40	1.00
80 Eric Young	.15	.40
81 Jason Giambi	.15	.40
82 Javy Lopez	.15	.40
83 Roberto Alomar	.25	.60
84 Bernie Williams	.25	.60
85 A.J. Hinch	.15	.40
86 Kerry Wood	.20	.50
87 Juan Encarnacion	.15	.40
88 Brad Fullmer	.15	.40
89 Ben Grieve	.15	.40
90 Magglio Ordonez RC	2.00	5.00
91 Todd Helton	.25	.60
92 Richard Hidalgo	.15	.40
93 Paul Konerko	.15	.40
94 Aramis Ramirez	.15	.40
95 Ricky Ledee	.15	.40
96 Derrek Lee	.25	.60
97 Travis Lee	.15	.40
98 Matt Anderson RC	.15	.40
99 Jaret Wright	.15	.40
100 David Ortiz	.50	1.25
101 Carl Pavano	.15	.40
102 O.Hernandez RC	.75	2.00
103 Fernando Tatis	.15	.40
104 Miguel Tejada	.40	1.00
105 Rolando Arrojo RC	.25	.60
106 Kevin Millwood RC	.60	1.50
107 Ken Griffey Jr. CL	.40	1.00
108 Frank Thomas CL	.25	.60
109 Cal Ripken CL	.60	1.50
110 Greg Maddux CL	.40	1.00
111 John Olerud	.15	.40
112 David Cone	.15	.40
113 Vinny Castilla	.15	.40
114 Jason Kendall	.15	.40
115 Brian Jordan	.15	.40
116 Hideki Irabu	.15	.40
117 Bartolo Colon	.15	.40
118 Greg Vaughn	.15	.40
119 David Segui	.15	.40
120 Bruce Chen	.15	.40
121 Julio Ramirez RC	.15	.40
122 Troy Glaus RC	1.50	4.00
123 Jeremy Giambi RC	.25	.60
124 Ryan Minor RC	.15	.40
125 Richie Sexson	.15	.40
126 Dermal Brown	.15	.40
127 Adrian Beltre	.15	.40
128 Eric Chavez	.15	.40
129 J.D. Drew RC	1.25	3.00
130 Gabe Kapler RC	.40	1.00
131 Masato Yoshii RC	.25	.60
132 Mike Lowell RC	1.00	2.50
133 Jim Parque RC	.25	.60
134 Roy Halladay	.15	.40
135 Carlos Lee RC	1.25	3.00
136 Jin Ho Cho RC	.15	.40
137 Michael Barrett	.15	.40
138 F.Seguignol RC	.15	.40
139 Odalis Perez RC UER Back pictures John Rocker	.60	1.50
140 Mark McGwire CL	.50	1.25

1998 Donruss Signature Proofs

Randomly inserted in packs, this 140-card set is a holo-foil treated parallel version of the base set. Only 150 sets were produced and numbered "1 of 150."

*STARS: 6X TO 15X BASIC CARDS
*RC's: 2X TO 5X BASIC CARDS

1998 Donruss Signature Autographs

Inserted one per pack, this 98-card set features color action player images on a red foil background with the player's autograph in the lower portion of the card. The numbers following the player's name in our checklist indicate how many cards that player signed. The first 100 cards signed by each player are blue, sequentially-numbered and designated as "Century Marks." The next 1,000 signed are green, sequentially numbered and designated as "Millennium Marks." The cards are unnumbered and checklisted below in alphabetical order. An unnumbered Travis Lee sample card was distributed many months prior to the product's release. It's important to note that sample card features a facsimile autograph of Lee's.

1 Roberto Alomar/150	15.00	40.00
2 Sandy Alomar Jr./700	3.00	8.00
3 Moises Alou/900	6.00	15.00
4 Gabe Alvarez/2900	2.00	5.00
5 Wilson Alvarez/1600	2.00	5.00
6 Jay Bell/1500	2.00	5.00
7 Adrian Beltre/1900	6.00	15.00
8 Andy Benes/2600	2.00	5.00
9 Aaron Boone/3400	6.00	15.00
10 Russell Branyan/1650	2.00	5.00
11 Orlando Cabrera/3100	6.00	15.00
12 Mike Cameron/1150	2.00	5.00
13 Joe Carter/400	6.00	15.00
14 Sean Casey/2275	6.00	15.00
15 Bruce Chen/150	6.00	15.00
16 Tony Clark/2275	2.00	5.00
17 Will Clark/1400	8.00	20.00
18 Matt Clement/1400	6.00	15.00
19 Pat Cline/1400	2.00	5.00
20 Ken Cloude/3400	2.00	5.00
21 Michael Coleman/2800	2.00	5.00
22 David Cone/25		
23 Jeff Conine/1400	6.00	15.00
24 Jacob Cruz/3200	2.00	5.00
25 Russ Davis/3500	2.00	5.00
26 Jason Dickson/1400	2.00	5.00
27 Todd Dunwoody/3500	2.00	5.00
28 Juan Encarnacion/3400	6.00	15.00
29 Darin Erstad/700	6.00	15.00
30 Bobby Estalella/3400	2.00	5.00
31 Jeff Fassero/3400	2.00	5.00
32 John Franco/1800	6.00	15.00
33 Brad Fullmer/3100	2.00	5.00
34 Jason Giambi/3100	8.00	20.00
35 Derrick Gibson/1200	2.00	5.00
36 Todd Greene/1400	2.00	5.00
37 Ben Grieve/1400	2.00	5.00
38 M.Grudzielanek/3200	2.00	5.00
39 V.Guerrero/2100	12.50	30.00
40 Wilton Guerrero/1900	2.00	5.00
41 Jose Guillen/2400	6.00	15.00
42 Todd Helton/1300	10.00	25.00
43 Richard Hidalgo/3400	2.00	5.00
44 A.J. Hinch/2900	2.00	5.00
45 Butch Huskey/1900	2.00	5.00
46 Raul Ibanez/3300	2.00	5.00
47 Damian Jackson/900	3.00	8.00
48 Geoff Jenkins/3100	6.00	15.00
49 Eric Karros/650	6.00	15.00
50 Ryan Klesko/400	6.00	15.00
51 Mark Kotsay/3600	6.00	15.00
52 Ricky Ledee/2200	2.00	5.00
53 Derrek Lee/3400	10.00	25.00
54 Travis Lee/150	6.00	15.00
55 Javier Lopez/650	6.00	15.00
56 Mike Lowell/3500	6.00	15.00
57 Greg Maddux/12		
58 Eli Marrero/3400	2.00	5.00
59 Al Martin/1300	2.00	5.00
60 Rafael Medina/1400	2.00	5.00
61 Scott Morgan/900	3.00	8.00
62 Abraham Nunez/3500	2.00	5.00
63 Paul O'Neill/1000	10.00	25.00
64 Luis Ordaz/2700	2.00	5.00
65 Magglio Ordonez/3200	8.00	20.00
66 Kevin Orie/1350	2.00	5.00
67 David Ortiz/3400	12.50	30.00
68 Rafael Palmeiro/1000	20.00	50.00
69 Carl Pavano/2600	6.00	15.00
70 Neifi Perez/3300	2.00	5.00
71 Dante Powell/3050	2.00	5.00
72 Aramis Ramirez/2800	6.00	15.00
73 Mariano Rivera/900	30.00	60.00
74 Felix Rodriguez/1400	2.00	5.00
75 Henry Rodriguez/3400	2.00	5.00
76 Scott Rolen/1900	10.00	25.00
77 Brian Rose/1400	2.00	5.00
78 Curt Schilling/900	20.00	50.00
79 Richie Sexson/3500	6.00	15.00
80 Randall Simon/3500	2.00	5.00
81 J.T. Snow/400	6.00	15.00
82 Jeff Suppan/1400	2.00	5.00
83 Fernando Tatis/3900	2.00	5.00
84 Miguel Tejada/3800	8.00	20.00
85 Brett Tomko/3400	2.00	5.00
86 Bubba Trammell/3900	2.00	5.00
87 Ismael Valdes/1900	2.00	5.00
88 Robin Ventura/1400	6.00	15.00
89 Billy Wagner/3900	10.00	25.00
90 Todd Walker/1900	6.00	15.00
91 Daryle Ward/400	3.00	8.00
92 Rondell White/3400	6.00	15.00
93 A.Williamson/3350	2.00	5.00
94 Dan Wilson/2400	2.00	5.00
95 Enrique Wilson/3400	2.00	5.00
96 Preston Wilson/2100	6.00	15.00
97 Tony Womack/3500	2.00	5.00
98 Kerry Wood/3400	8.00	20.00
NNO Travis Lee Sample Facsimile Autograph	.40	1.00

1998 Donruss Signature Autographs Century

Randomly inserted in packs, this 122-card set is a sequentially numbered, blue parallel version of the Signature Autographs insert set and features the first 100 cards signed by each pictured player. The cards are unnumbered and checklisted in alphabetical order.

1 Roberto Alomar	60.00	120.00
2 Sandy Alomar Jr.	12.50	30.00
3 Moises Alou	20.00	50.00
4 Gabe Alvarez	12.50	30.00
5 Wilson Alvarez	12.50	30.00
6 Brady Anderson	20.00	50.00
7 Jay Bell	20.00	50.00
8 Albert Belle	20.00	50.00
9 Adrian Beltre	20.00	50.00
10 Andy Benes	12.50	30.00
11 Wade Boggs	50.00	100.00
12 Barry Bonds	225.00	350.00
13 Aaron Boone	20.00	50.00
14 Russell Branyan	12.50	30.00
15 Jay Buhner	20.00	50.00
16 Ellis Burks	20.00	50.00
17 Orlando Cabrera	20.00	50.00
18 Mike Cameron	20.00	50.00
19 Ken Caminiti	50.00	100.00
20 Joe Carter	20.00	50.00
21 Sean Casey	20.00	50.00
22 Bruce Chen	12.50	30.00
23 Tony Clark	12.50	30.00
24 Will Clark	40.00	80.00
25 Roger Clemens	175.00	300.00
26 Matt Clement	20.00	50.00
27 Pat Cline	12.50	30.00
28 Ken Cloude	12.50	30.00
29 Michael Coleman	12.50	30.00
30 David Cone	40.00	80.00
31 Jeff Conine	20.00	50.00
32 Jacob Cruz	12.50	30.00
33 Jose Cruz Jr.	12.50	30.00
34 Russ Davis	12.50	30.00
35 Jason Dickson	12.50	30.00
36 Todd Dunwoody	12.50	30.00
37 Scott Elarton	12.50	30.00
38 Darin Erstad	20.00	50.00
39 Bobby Estalella	12.50	30.00
40 Jeff Fassero	12.50	30.00
41 John Franco	20.00	50.00
42 Brad Fullmer	12.50	30.00
43 Andres Galarraga	20.00	50.00
44 Nomar Garciaparra	60.00	120.00
45 Jason Giambi	40.00	80.00
46 Derrick Gibson	12.50	30.00
47 Tom Glavine	50.00	100.00
48 Juan Gonzalez	20.00	50.00
49 Todd Greene	12.50	30.00
50 Ben Grieve	12.50	30.00
51 Mark Grudzielanek	12.50	30.00
52 Vladimir Guerrero	75.00	150.00
53 Wilton Guerrero	12.50	30.00
54 Jose Guillen	20.00	50.00
55 Tony Gwynn	60.00	120.00
56 Todd Helton	40.00	80.00
57 Richard Hidalgo	12.50	30.00
58 A.J. Hinch	12.50	30.00
59 Butch Huskey	12.50	30.00
60 Raul Ibanez	12.50	30.00
61 Damian Jackson	12.50	30.00
62 Geoff Jenkins	20.00	50.00
63 Derek Jeter	300.00	500.00
64 Randy Johnson	150.00	250.00
65 Chipper Jones	250.00	350.00
66 Eric Karros/50	20.00	50.00
67 Ryan Klesko	20.00	50.00
68 Chuck Knoblauch	20.00	50.00
69 Mark Kotsay	20.00	50.00
70 Ricky Ledee	12.50	30.00
71 Derrek Lee	40.00	80.00
72 Travis Lee	12.50	30.00
73 Javier Lopez	20.00	50.00
74 Mike Lowell	50.00	100.00
75 Greg Maddux	350.00	500.00
76 Eli Marrero	12.50	30.00
77 Al Martin	12.50	30.00
78 Rafael Medina	12.50	30.00
79 Paul Molitor	20.00	50.00
80 Scott Morgan	12.50	30.00
81 Mike Mussina	40.00	80.00
82 Abraham Nunez	12.50	30.00
83 Paul O'Neill	40.00	80.00
84 Luis Ordaz	12.50	30.00
85 Magglio Ordonez	40.00	80.00
86 Kevin Orie	12.50	30.00
87 David Ortiz	50.00	100.00
88 Rafael Palmeiro	60.00	120.00
89 Carl Pavano	20.00	50.00
90 Neifi Perez	12.50	30.00
91 Andy Pettitte	50.00	100.00
92 Aramis Ramirez	40.00	80.00
93 Cal Ripken	200.00	350.00
94 Mariano Rivera	60.00	120.00
95 Alex Rodriguez	250.00	400.00
96 Felix Rodriguez	12.50	30.00
97 Henry Rodriguez	12.50	30.00
98 Ivan Rodriguez	50.00	100.00
99 Scott Rolen	40.00	80.00
100 Brian Rose	12.50	30.00
101 Curt Schilling	50.00	100.00
102 Richie Sexson	20.00	50.00
103 Randall Simon	12.50	30.00
104 J.T. Snow	20.00	50.00
105 Darryl Strawberry	125.00	200.00
106 Jeff Suppan	20.00	50.00
107 Fernando Tatis	12.50	30.00
108 Brett Tomko	12.50	30.00
109 Bubba Trammell	12.50	30.00
110 Ismael Valdes	12.50	30.00
111 Robin Ventura	20.00	50.00
112 Billy Wagner	40.00	80.00
113 Todd Walker	20.00	50.00
114 Daryle Ward	12.50	30.00
115 Rondell White	20.00	50.00
116 Matt Williams/80	40.00	80.00
117 Antone Williamson	12.50	30.00
118 Dan Wilson	12.50	30.00
119 Enrique Wilson	12.50	30.00
120 Preston Wilson	20.00	50.00
121 Tony Womack	12.50	30.00
122 Kerry Wood	60.00	120.00

1998 Donruss Signature Autographs Millennium

Randomly inserted in packs, this 125-card set is a sequentially numbered, green foil parallel version of the Signature Autographs insert set and features the next 1,000 cards signed by each pictured player after the initial 100. In numerous cases, players signed less than 1,000 cards. Print runs for these short-prints are specified after the player's name in the checklist. The cards are unnumbered and checklisted below in alphabetical order.

1 Roberto Alomar	10.00	25.00
2 Sandy Alomar Jr.	3.00	8.00
3 Moises Alou	6.00	15.00
4 Gabe Alvarez	3.00	8.00
5 Wilson Alvarez	3.00	8.00
6 Brady Anderson/800	6.00	15.00
7 Jay Bell	6.00	15.00
8 Albert Belle/400	10.00	25.00
9 Adrian Beltre	6.00	15.00
10 Andy Benes	3.00	8.00
11 Wade Boggs/900	12.50	30.00
12 Barry Bonds/400	100.00	175.00
13 Aaron Boone	6.00	15.00
14 Russell Branyan	3.00	8.00
15 Jay Buhner/400	15.00	40.00
16 Ellis Burks/900	6.00	15.00
17 Orlando Cabrera	6.00	15.00
18 Mike Cameron	6.00	15.00
19 Ken Caminiti/900	15.00	40.00
20 Joe Carter	6.00	15.00
21 Sean Casey	6.00	15.00
22 Bruce Chen	3.00	8.00
23 Tony Clark	3.00	8.00
24 Will Clark	10.00	25.00
25 Roger Clemens/400	75.00	150.00
26 Matt Clement/900	6.00	15.00
27 Pat Cline	3.00	8.00
28 Ken Cloude	3.00	8.00
29 Michael Coleman	3.00	8.00
30 David Cone	6.00	15.00
31 Jeff Conine	6.00	15.00
32 Jacob Cruz	3.00	8.00
33 Jose Cruz Jr./850	3.00	8.00
34 Russ Davis/950	3.00	8.00
35 Jason Dickson/950	3.00	8.00
36 Todd Dunwoody	3.00	8.00
37 Scott Elarton/900	3.00	8.00
38 Juan Encarnacion	6.00	15.00
39 Darin Erstad	6.00	15.00
40 Bobby Estalella	3.00	8.00
41 Jeff Fassero	3.00	8.00
42 John Franco/950	6.00	15.00
43 Brad Fullmer	3.00	8.00
44 Andres Galarraga/900	6.00	15.00
45 Nomar Garciaparra/400	40.00	80.00
46 Jason Giambi	10.00	25.00
47 Derrick Gibson	3.00	8.00
48 Tom Glavine/700	15.00	40.00
49 Juan Gonzalez	6.00	15.00
50 Todd Greene	3.00	8.00
51 Ben Grieve	3.00	8.00
52 Mark Grudzielanek	3.00	8.00
53 Vladimir Guerrero	12.50	30.00
54 Wilton Guerrero	3.00	8.00
55 Jose Guillen	6.00	15.00
56 Tony Gwynn/900	15.00	40.00
57 Todd Helton	8.00	20.00
58 Richard Hidalgo	3.00	8.00
59 A.J. Hinch	3.00	8.00
60 Butch Huskey	3.00	8.00
61 Raul Ibanez	3.00	8.00
62 Damian Jackson	3.00	8.00
63 Geoff Jenkins	6.00	15.00
64 Derek Jeter/400	100.00	175.00
65 Randy Johnson/800	40.00	80.00
66 Chipper Jones/900	30.00	60.00
67 Eric Karros	6.00	15.00
68 Ryan Klesko	6.00	15.00
69 Chuck Knoblauch/900	6.00	15.00
70 Mark Kotsay	6.00	15.00
71 Ricky Ledee	3.00	8.00
72 Derrek Lee	10.00	25.00
73 Travis Lee	3.00	8.00
74 Javier Lopez/800	6.00	15.00
75 Mike Lowell	12.50	30.00
76 Greg Maddux/400	60.00	120.00
77 Eli Marrero	3.00	8.00
78 Al Martin/950	3.00	8.00
79 Rafael Medina/850	3.00	8.00
80 Paul Molitor/900	6.00	15.00
81 Scott Morgan	3.00	8.00
82 Mike Mussina/900	10.00	25.00
83 Abraham Nunez	3.00	8.00
84 Paul O'Neill/900	10.00	25.00
85 Luis Ordaz	3.00	8.00
86 Magglio Ordonez	15.00	40.00
87 Kevin Orie	3.00	8.00
88 David Ortiz	15.00	40.00
89 Rafael Palmeiro/900	20.00	50.00
90 Carl Pavano	6.00	15.00
91 Neifi Perez	3.00	8.00
92 Andy Pettitte/900	15.00	40.00
93 Dante Powell/950	3.00	8.00
94 Aramis Ramirez	10.00	25.00
95 Cal Ripken/375	75.00	150.00
96 Mariano Rivera	30.00	60.00
97 Alex Rodriguez/350	75.00	150.00
98 Felix Rodriguez	3.00	8.00
99 Henry Rodriguez	3.00	8.00
100 Ivan Rodriguez	15.00	40.00
101 Scott Rolen	10.00	25.00
102 Brian Rose	3.00	8.00
103 Curt Schilling	20.00	50.00
104 Richie Sexson	6.00	15.00
105 Randall Simon	3.00	8.00

106 J.T. Snow 6.00 15.00
107 Darryl Strawberry/900 12.50 30.00
108 Jeff Suppan 6.00 15.00
109 Fernando Tatis 3.00 8.00
110 Miguel Tejada 15.00 40.00
111 Brett Tomko 3.00 8.00
112 Bubba Trammell 3.00 8.00
113 Ismael Valdes 3.00 8.00
114 Robin Ventura 6.00 15.00
115 Billy Wagner/900 10.00 25.00
116 Todd Walker 6.00 15.00
117 Daryle Ward 3.00 8.00
118 Rondell White 6.00 15.00
119 Matt Williams/820 10.00 25.00
120 Antone Williamson 3.00 8.00
121 Dan Wilson 3.00 8.00
122 Enrique Wilson 3.00 8.00
123 Preston Wilson/400 15.00 40.00
124 Tony Womack 3.00 8.00
125 Kerry Wood 8.00 20.00

1998 Donruss Signature Significant Signatures

Randomly inserted in packs, this 18-card set features color photos with autographs of some of baseball's all-time great players. Only 2,000 of this sequentially-numbered set were produced. Sandy Koufax was on the original checklist but his cards were not returned in time for the pack out. Thus, officials at Donruss made the Billy Williams card an exchange card. Each collector that pulled a Billy Williams card could send it in to Donruss for a Koufax card. In addition, the signed Williams card was sent back too. Special exchange cards were created for Nolan Ryan and Ozzie Smith. The cards were randomly seeded into packs and then redeemed to Donruss for the real autograph cards. The exchange deadline for cards R1-R3 was December 31st, 1999. All three "R-Series" exchange cards (Ryan, Koufax and Smith) feature refractive, shiny fronts whereas the other cards seeded in packs are printed on basic foilboard. For pricing on these R1-R3 cards, please see the 1998 Donruss Signature Significant Signatures Refractors listing. At some point in time after the product's release, non-refractive versions of the Koufax (#'d of 2000), Ozzie (#'[d of 2000) and Ryan (#'d of 1000) cards made their way into the secondary market. Each card features a different card front image than the Refractor versions (most notably with Koufax wearing a Brooklyn cap). Representatives at Donruss-Playoff were unable to provide us with information on this matter given that the company was technically owned by Pinnacle in 1998 and then purchased out of bankruptcy in 2001 by the new Donruss-Playoff Corporation. The Catfish Hunter card was signed in either blue or blank ink. Only 1,000 serial #'d copies of Phil Rizzuto's card were produced.

KOUFAX NOT MEANT FOR PUBLIC RELEASE
OZZIE NOT MEANT FOR PUBLIC RELEASE
RYAN NOT MEANT FOR PUBLIC RELEASE
1 Ernie Banks/2000 20.00 50.00
2 Yogi Berra/2000 20.00 50.00
3 George Brett/2000 20.00 50.00
4 Catfish Hunter/2000 20.00 50.00
5 Al Kaline/2000 12.50 30.00
6 Harmon Killebrew/2000 15.00 40.00
7 Ralph Kiner/2000 10.00 25.00
9 Eddie Mathews/2000 20.00 50.00
10 Don Mattingly/2000 30.00 60.00
11 Willie McCovey/2000 10.00 25.00
12 Stan Musial/2000 30.00 60.00
13 Phil Rizzuto/1000 15.00 40.00
14 Nolan Ryan No Auto 6.00 15.00
15 Ozzie Smith No Auto 2.00 5.00
16 Duke Snider/2000 10.00 25.00
17 Don Sutton/2000 10.00 25.00
18 Billy Williams/2000 10.00 25.00
18A Billy Williams No Auto 2.00 5.00
SP Nolan Ryan/1000 40.00 80.00
NNO S.Koufax Brooklyn/2000 90.00 150.00
NNO Ozzie Smith/2000 15.00 40.00

1998 Donruss Signature Significant Signatures Refractors

AVAILABLE VIA MAIL EXCHANGE
STATED PRINT RUN 2000 SERIAL #'d SETS
R1 Nolan Ryan 40.00 80.00
R2 Ozzie Smith 20.00 50.00
R3 Sandy Koufax LA 175.00 250.00

2001 Donruss Signature

This 311 card set was issued 25 cards to a "gift" box. The 25 card boxes had a SRP of $49.99 per box and the boxes were issued eight to a mini case. Cards numbered from 111 through 165 were inserted at an approximate rate of one per box and were serial numbered to 330. Cards numbered 166 to 311 were issued at an approximate rate of two per box and were serial numbered to 800.

COMP.SET w/o SP'S (110) 20.00 50.00
COMMON CARD (1-110) .40 1.00
COMMON (111-165) 4.00 10.00
COMMON AU RC (111-165) 4.00 10.00
COMMON NO AU (111-165) 3.00 8.00
COMMON (166-311) 2.00 5.00
COMMON RC (166-311) 2.00 5.00
1 Alex Rodriguez 1.50 4.00
2 Barry Bonds 2.50 6.00
3 Cal Ripken 3.00 8.00
4 Chipper Jones 1.00 2.50
5 Derek Jeter 2.50 6.00
6 Troy Glaus .40 1.00
7 Frank Thomas 1.00 2.50
8 Greg Maddux 1.50 4.00
9 Ivan Rodriguez .60 1.50
10 Jeff Bagwell .60 1.50
11 John Olerud .40 1.00
12 Todd Helton .60 1.50
13 Ken Griffey Jr. 1.50 4.00
14 Manny Ramirez Sox .60 1.50
15 Mark McGwire 2.50 6.00
16 Mike Piazza 1.50 4.00
17 Nomar Garciaparra 1.50 4.00
18 Moises Alou .40 1.00
19 Aramis Ramirez .40 1.00
20 Curt Schilling .40 1.00
21 Pat Burrell .40 1.00
22 Doug Mientkiewicz .40 1.00
23 Carlos Delgado .40 1.00
24 J.D. Drew .40 1.00
25 Cliff Floyd .40 1.00
26 Freddy Garcia .40 1.00
27 Roberto Alomar .60 1.50
28 Barry Zito .60 1.50
29 Juan Encarnacion .40 1.00
30 Paul Konerko .40 1.00
31 Mark Mulder .40 1.00
32 Andy Pettitte .60 1.50
33 Jim Edmonds .40 1.00
34 Darin Erstad .40 1.00
35 Jason Giambi .40 1.00
36 Tom Glavine .60 1.50
37 Juan Gonzalez .40 1.00
38 Fred McGriff .60 1.50
39 Shawn Green .40 1.00
40 Tim Hudson .40 1.00
41 Andruw Jones .60 1.50
42 Jeff Kent .40 1.00
43 Barry Larkin .60 1.50
44 Brad Radke .40 1.00
45 Mike Mussina .60 1.50
46 Hideo Nomo 1.00 2.50
47 Rafael Palmeiro .60 1.50
48 Scott Rolen .60 1.50
49 Gary Sheffield .40 1.00
50 Bernie Williams .60 1.50
51 Bob Abreu .40 1.00
52 Edgardo Alfonzo .40 1.00
53 Edgar Martinez .60 1.50
54 Magglio Ordonez .40 1.00
55 Kerry Wood .40 1.00
56 Adrian Beltre .40 1.00
57 Lance Berkman .40 1.00
58 Kevin Brown 1.00 2.50
59 Sean Casey .40 1.00
60 Eric Chavez .40 1.00
61 Bartolo Colon .40 1.00
62 Sammy Sosa 1.00 2.50
63 Jermaine Dye .40 1.00
64 Tony Gwynn 1.25 3.00
65 Carl Everett .40 1.00
66 Brian Giles .40 1.00
67 Mike Hampton .40 1.00
68 Richard Hidalgo .40 1.00
69 Geoff Jenkins .40 1.00
70 Tony Clark .40 1.00
71 Roger Clemens 2.00 5.00
72 Ryan Klesko .40 1.00
73 Chan Ho Park .40 1.00
74 Richie Sexson .40 1.00
75 Mike Sweeney .40 1.00
76 Kazuhiro Sasaki .40 1.00
77 Miguel Tejada .40 1.00
78 Jose Vidro .40 1.00
79 Larry Walker .40 1.00
80 Preston Wilson .40 1.00
81 Craig Biggio .60 1.50
82 Andres Galarraga .40 1.00
83 Jim Thome .60 1.50
84 Vladimir Guerrero 1.00 2.50
85 Rafael Furcal .40 1.00
86 Cristian Guzman .40 1.00
87 Terrence Long .40 1.00
88 Bret Boone .40 1.00
89 Wade Miller .40 1.00
90 Eric Milton .40 1.00
91 Gabe Kapler .40 1.00
92 Johnny Damon .60 1.50
93 Carlos Lee .40 1.00
94 Kenny Lofton .40 1.00
95 Raul Mondesi .40 1.00
96 Jorge Posada .60 1.50
97 Mark Grace .60 1.50
98 Robert Fick .40 1.00
99 Joe Mays .40 1.00
100 Aaron Sele .40 1.00
101 Ben Grieve .40 1.00
102 Luis Gonzalez .40 1.00
103 Ray Durham .40 1.00
104 Mark Quinn .40 1.00
105 Jose Canseco .60 1.50
106 David Justice .40 1.00
107 Pedro Martinez .60 1.50
108 Randy Johnson 1.00 2.50
109 Phil Nevin .40 1.00
110 Rickey Henderson 1.00 2.50
111 Alex Escobar AU 4.00 10.00
112 J.Estrada AU RC 6.00 15.00
113 Pedro Feliz AU 4.00 10.00
114 Nate Frese AU RC 4.00 10.00
115 R. Rodriguez AU RC 4.00 10.00
116 B.Larson AU RC 4.00 10.00
117 Alexis Gomez AU RC 4.00 10.00
118 Jason Hart AU 4.00 10.00
119 C.C. Sabathia AU 6.00 15.00
120 Endy Chavez AU RC 4.00 10.00
121 C.Parker AU RC 4.00 10.00
122 Jackson Melian RC 3.00 8.00
123 Joe Kennedy AU RC 6.00 15.00
124 A.Hernandez AU RC 4.00 10.00
125 Cesar Izturis AU 4.00 10.00
126 Jose Mieses AU RC 4.00 10.00
127 Roy Oswalt AU 15.00 40.00
128 Eric Munson AU 4.00 10.00
129 Xavier Nady AU 6.00 15.00
130 H.Ramirez AU RC 6.00 15.00
131 Abraham Nunez AU 4.00 10.00
132 Jose Ortiz AU 4.00 10.00
133 Jeremy Owens AU RC 4.00 10.00
134 Claudio Vargas AU RC 4.00 10.00
135 Corey Patterson AU 4.00 10.00
136 Carlos Pena 3.00 8.00
137 Bud Smith AU RC 4.00 10.00
138 Adam Dunn AU 10.00 25.00
139 A.Pettyjohn AU RC 4.00 10.00
140 E.Guzman AU RC 4.00 10.00
141 Jay Gibbons AU RC 6.00 15.00
142 Wilkin Ruan AU RC 4.00 10.00
143 Tsuyoshi Shinjo RC 4.00 10.00
144 Alfonso Soriano AU 10.00 25.00
145 Marcus Giles AU 6.00 15.00
146 Ichiro Suzuki RC 40.00 80.00
147 Juan Uribe AU RC 6.00 15.00
148 David Williams AU RC 4.00 10.00
149 C. Valderrama AU RC 4.00 10.00
150 Matt White AU RC 4.00 10.00
151 Albert Pujols AU RC 400.00 800.00
152 D.Mendez AU RC 4.00 10.00
153 Cory Aldridge AU RC 4.00 10.00
154 B. Duckworth AU RC 4.00 10.00
155 Josh Beckett AU 12.50 30.00
156 W.Betemit AU RC 10.00 25.00
157 Ben Sheets AU 10.00 25.00
158 Andres Torres AU RC 4.00 10.00
159 Aubrey Huff AU 6.00 15.00
160 Jack Wilson AU RC 6.00 15.00
161 Rafael Soriano AU RC 4.00 10.00
162 Nick Johnson AU 6.00 15.00
163 Carlos Garcia AU RC 4.00 10.00
164 Josh Towers AU RC 6.00 15.00
165 J.Michaels AU RC 4.00 10.00
166 Ryan Drese RC 3.00 8.00
167 Dewon Brazelton RC 2.00 5.00
168 Kevin Olsen RC 2.00 5.00
169 Benito Baez RC 2.00 5.00
170 Mark Prior RC 10.00 25.00
171 Wilmy Caceres RC 2.00 5.00
172 Mark Teixeira RC 10.00 25.00
173 Willie Harris RC 2.00 5.00
174 Mike Koplove RC 2.00 5.00
175 Brandon Knight RC 2.00 5.00
176 John Grabow RC 2.00 5.00
177 Jeremy Affeldt RC 2.00 5.00
178 Brandon Inge 2.00 5.00
179 Casey Fossum RC 2.00 5.00
180 Scott Stewart RC 2.00 5.00
181 Luke Hudson RC 2.00 5.00
182 Ken Vining RC 2.00 5.00
183 Toby Hall 2.00 5.00
184 Eric Knott RC 2.00 5.00
185 Kris Foster RC 2.00 5.00
186 David Brous RC 2.00 5.00
187 Roy Smith RC 2.00 5.00
188 Grant Balfour RC 2.00 5.00
189 Jeremy Fikac RC 2.00 5.00
190 Morgan Ensberg RC 3.00 8.00
191 Ryan Freel RC 3.00 8.00
192 Ryan Jensen RC 2.00 5.00
193 Lance Davis RC 2.00 5.00
194 Delvin James RC 2.00 5.00
195 Timo Perez 2.00 5.00
196 Michael Cuddyer 2.00 5.00
197 Bob File RC 2.00 5.00
198 Martin Vargas RC 2.00 5.00
199 Kris Keller RC 2.00 5.00
200 T.Spooneybarger RC 2.00 5.00
201 Adam Everett 2.00 5.00
202 Josh Fogg RC 2.00 5.00
203 Kip Wells 2.00 5.00
204 Rick Bauer RC 2.00 5.00
205 Brent Abernathy 2.00 5.00
206 Erick Almonte RC 2.00 5.00
207 Pedro Santana RC 2.00 5.00
208 Ken Harvey 2.00 5.00
209 Jerrod Riggan RC 2.00 5.00
210 Nick Punto RC 2.00 5.00
211 Steve Green RC 2.00 5.00
212 Nick Neugebauer 2.00 5.00
213 Chris George 2.00 5.00
214 Mike Penney RC 2.00 5.00
215 Bret Prinz RC 2.00 5.00
216 Tim Christman RC 2.00 5.00
217 Sean Douglass RC 2.00 5.00
218 Brett Jodie RC 2.00 5.00
219 Juan Diaz RC 2.00 5.00
220 Carlos Hernandez 2.00 5.00
221 Alex Cintron 2.00 5.00
222 Juan Cruz RC 2.00 5.00
223 Larry Bigbie 2.00 5.00
224 Junior Spivey RC 3.00 8.00
225 Luis Rivas 2.00 5:00
226 Brandon Lyon RC 2.00 5.00
227 Tony Cogan RC 2.00 5.00
228 J.Duchscherer RC 2.00 5.00
229 Tike Redman 2.00 5.00
230 Jimmy Rollins 2.00 5.00
231 Scott Podsednik RC 8.00 20.00
232 Jose Acevedo RC 2.00 5.00
233 Luis Pineda RC 2.00 5.00
234 Josh Phelps 2.00 5.00
235 Paul Phillips RC 2.00 5.00
236 Brian Roberts RC 3.00 8.00
237 O.Woodards RC 2.00 5.00
238 Bart Miadich RC 2.00 5.00
239 Les Walrond RC 2.00 5.00
240 Brad Voyles RC 2.00 5.00
241 Joe Crede 3.00 8.00
242 Juan Moreno RC 2.00 5.00
243 Matt Ginter 2.00 5.00
244 Brian Rogers RC 2.00 5.00
245 Pablo Ozuna 2.00 5.00
246 Geronimo Gil RC 2.00 5.00
247 Mike Maroth RC 3.00 8.00
248 Josue Perez RC 2.00 5.00
249 Dee Brown 2.00 5.00
250 Victor Zambrano RC 3.00 8.00
251 Nick Maness RC 2.00 5.00
252 Kyle Lohse RC 3.00 8.00
253 Greg Miller RC 2.00 5.00
254 Henry Mateo RC 2.00 5.00
255 Duaner Sanchez RC 2.00 5.00
256 Rob MacKowiak RC 3.00 8.00
257 Steve Lomasney 2.00 5.00
258 Angel Santos RC 2.00 5.00
259 Winston Abreu RC 2.00 5.00
260 Brandon Berger RC 2.00 5.00
261 Tomas De La Rosa 2.00 5.00
262 Ramon Vazquez RC 2.00 5.00
263 Mickey Callaway RC 2.00 5.00
264 Corky Miller RC 2.00 5.00
265 Keith Ginter 2.00 5.00
266 Cody Ransom RC 2.00 5.00
267 Doug Nickle RC 2.00 5.00
268 Derrick Lewis RC 2.00 5.00
269 Eric Hinske RC 3.00 8.00
270 Travis Phelps RC 2.00 5.00
271 Eric Valent 2.00 5.00
272 Michael Rivera RC 2.00 5.00
273 Esix Snead RC 2.00 5.00
274 Troy Mattes RC 2.00 5.00
275 Jermaine Clark RC 2.00 5.00
276 Nate Cornejo 2.00 5.00
277 George Perez RC 2.00 5.00
278 Juan Rivera 2.00 5.00
279 Justin Atchley RC 2.00 5.00
280 Adam Johnson 2.00 5.00
281 Gene Altman RC 2.00 5.00
282 Jason Jennings 2.00 5.00
283 Scott MacRae RC 2.00 5.00
284 Craig Monroe RC 3.00 8.00
285 Bert Snow RC 2.00 5.00
286 Stubby Clapp RC 2.00 5.00
287 Jack Cust 2.00 5.00
288 Will Ohman RC 2.00 5.00
289 Wily Mo Pena 2.00 5.00
290 Joe Beimel RC 2.00 5.00
291 Jason Karnuth RC 2.00 5.00
292 Bill Ortega RC 2.00 5.00
293 Nate Teut RC 2.00 5.00
294 Erik Hiljus RC 2.00 5.00
295 Jason Smith RC 2.00 5.00
296 Juan A.Pena RC 2.00 5.00
297 David Espinosa 2.00 5.00
298 Tim Redding 2.00 5.00
299 Brian Lawrence RC 2.00 5.00
300 Brian Reith RC 2.00 5.00
301 Chad Durbin 2.00 5.00
302 Kurt Ainsworth 2.00 5.00
303 Blaine Neal RC 2.00 5.00
304 Jorge Julio RC 2.00 5.00
305 Adam Bernero 2.00 5.00
306 Travis Hafner RC 8.00 20.00
307 Dustan Mohr RC 2.00 5.00
308 Cesar Crespo RC 2.00 5.00
309 Billy Sylvester RC 2.00 5.00
310 Zach Day RC 2.00 5.00
311 Angel Berroa RC 3.00 8.00

2001 Donruss Signature Proofs

Randomly inserted in gift boxes, these 311 cards parallel the Donruss Signature set. Cards numbered 1-110 were issued to a print run of 175 sets while cards numbered 111-311 were issued to a print run of 25 sets. Please note that all cards numbered between 111 and 165 were autographed in addition to a few other scattered cards throughout the set. Due to market scarcity, no pricing is provided for cards numbered 111-311.

*PROOFS 1-110: 1.5X TO 4X BASIC
111 Alex Escobar AU
112 Johnny Estrada AU
113 Pedro Feliz AU
114 Nate Frese AU
115 Ricardo Rodriguez AU
116 Brandon Larson AU
117 Alexis Gomez AU
118 Jason Hart AU
119 C.C. Sabathia AU
120 Endy Chavez AU
121 Christian Parker AU
122 Jackson Melian
123 Joe Kennedy AU
124 Adrian Hernandez AU
125 Cesar Izturis AU
126 Jose Mieses AU
127 Roy Oswalt AU
128 Eric Munson AU
129 Xavier Nady AU
130 Horacio Ramirez AU
131 Abraham Nunez AU
132 Jose Ortiz AU
133 Jeremy Owens AU
134 Claudio Vargas AU
135 Corey Patterson AU
136 Carlos Pena AU
137 Bud Smith AU
138 Adam Dunn AU
139 Adam Pettyjohn AU
140 Elpidio Guzman AU
141 Jay Gibbons AU
142 Wilkin Ruan AU
143 Tsuyoshi Shinjo
144 Alfonso Soriano AU
145 Marcus Giles AU
146 Ichiro Suzuki
147 Juan Uribe AU
148 David Williams AU
149 Carlos Valderrama AU
150 Matt White AU
151 Albert Pujols AU
152 Donaldo Mendez AU
153 Cory Aldridge AU
154 Brandon Duckworth AU
155 Josh Beckett AU
156 Wilson Betemit AU
157 Ben Sheets AU
158 Andres Torres AU
159 Aubrey Huff AU
160 Jack Wilson AU
161 Rafael Soriano AU
162 Nick Johnson AU
163 Carlos Garcia AU
164 Josh Towers AU
165 Jason Michaels AU
167 Dewon Brazelton AU
172 Mark Teixeira AU
179 Casey Fossum AU
194 Delvin James AU
196 Michael Cuddyer AU
222 Juan Cruz AU
241 Joe Crede AU
249 Dee Brown AU
265 Keith Ginter AU
269 Eric Hinske AU
271 Eric Valent AU
280 Adam Johnson AU
282 Jason Jennings AU
287 Jack Cust AU
289 Wily Mo Pena AU
297 David Espinosa AU
311 Angel Berroa AU

2001 Donruss Signature Award Winning Signatures

Randomly inserted in gift boxes, these cards feature signature from various players who won awards and the cards have stated print runs to that year they won an award. Please see our checklist for specific print run information.

1 Jeff Bagwell/94 50.00 100.00
2 Carlos Beltran/99 10.00 25.00
3 Johnny Bench/68 50.00 100.00
4 Yogi Berra/55 30.00 60.00
5 Craig Biggio/97 20.00 50.00
6 Barry Bonds/93 100.00 175.00
7 Rod Carew/77 40.00 80.00
8 Orlando Cepeda/67 12.50 30.00
9 Andre Dawson/77 12.50 30.00
10 D.Eckersley CY/92 12.50 30.00
11 D.Eckersley MVP/92 12.50 30.00
12 Whitey Ford/61 30.00 60.00
13 Jason Giambi/100 10.00 25.00
14 Bob Gibson/68 20.00 50.00
15 Juan Gonzalez/96 10.00 25.00
16 Orel Hershiser/88 15.00 40.00
17 Al Kaline/67 50.00 100.00
18 Fred Lynn/75 MVP 12.50 30.00
19 Fred Lynn/75 ROY 12.50 30.00
20 Jim Palmer/76 12.50 30.00
21 Cal Ripken/83 75.00 150.00
22 Phil Rizzuto/50 20.00 50.00
23 Brooks Robinson/64 20.00 50.00
24 Scott Rolen/97 15.00 40.00
25 Ryne Sandberg/84 60.00 120.00
26 Warren Spahn/57 30.00 60.00
27 Frank Thomas/94 20.00 50.00
28 Billy Williams/61 12.50 30.00
29 Kerry Wood/98 15.00 40.00
30 Robin Yount/89 40.00 80.00

2001 Donruss Signature Award Winning Signatures Masters Series

Randomly inserted in gift boxes, these cards feature various award winners who signed cards relating to various awards they won during their career.

1 Jeff Bagwell
2 Carlos Beltran 10.00 25.00
3 Johnny Bench
4 Yogi Berra
5 Craig Biggio 20.00 50.00
6 Barry Bonds
7 Rod Carew
8 Orlando Cepeda 10.00 25.00
9 Andre Dawson 10.00 25.00
10 Dennis Eckersley CY 10.00 25.00
11 Dennis Eckersley MVP 10.00 25.00
12 Whitey Ford 40.00 80.00
13 Jason Giambi
14 Bob Gibson 15.00 40.00
15 Juan Gonzalez
16 Orel Hershiser 50.00 100.00
17 Al Kaline 40.00 80.00
18 Fred Lynn MVP 10.00 25.00
19 Fred Lynn ROY 10.00 25.00
20 Jim Palmer 10.00 25.00
21 Cal Ripken
22 Phil Rizzuto 15.00 40.00
23 Brooks Robinson 15.00 40.00
24 Scott Rolen 15.00 40.00
25 Ryne Sandberg
26 Warren Spahn 30.00 60.00
27 Frank Thomas
28 Billy Williams 10.00 25.00
29 Kerry Wood 15.00 40.00
30 Robin Yount

2001 Donruss Signature Century Marks

Randomly inserted in gift boxes, these 48 cards feature signed cards of the featured players to various amounts. Please see our checklist to get the specific information on how many cards each player signed for this part of the promotion.

1 Brent Abernathy/184 4.00 10.00
2 Roberto Alomar/102 15.00 40.00
3 Rick Ankiel/119 10.00 25.00
4 Lance Berkman/121 10.00 25.00
5 Mark Buehrle/224 10.00 25.00
6 Wilmy Caceres/194 4.00 10.00
7 Eric Chavez/170 6.00 15.00
8 Joe Crede/154 10.00 25.00
9 Jack Cust/178 4.00 10.00
10 B. Duckworth/183 4.00 10.00
11 David Espinosa/199 4.00 10.00
12 Johnny Estrada/198 6.00 15.00
13 Pedro Feliz/180 4.00 10.00
14 Robert Fick/232 4.00 10.00
15 Cliff Floyd/146 6.00 15.00
16 Casey Fossum/100 4.00 10.00
17 Jay Gibbons/175 6.00 15.00
18 Keith Ginter/163 4.00 10.00
19 Troy Glaus/144 10.00 25.00
20 Luis Gonzalez/101 6.00 15.00
21 Vladimir Guerrero/187 15.00 40.00
22 Richard Hidalgo/173 4.00 10.00
23 Tim Hudson/145 10.00 25.00
24 Adam Johnson/130 4.00 10.00
25 Gabe Kapler/150 6.00 15.00
26 Joe Kennedy/219 6.00 15.00
27 Ryan Klesko/176 6.00 15.00
28 Carlos Lee/179 6.00 15.00
29 Terrence Long/180 4.00 10.00
30 Edgar Martinez/110 15.00 40.00
31 Joe Mays/209 4.00 10.00
32 Greg Miller/194 4.00 10.00
33 Wade Miller/180 4.00 10.00
34 Mark Mulder/203 6.00 15.00
35 Xavier Nady/180 6.00 15.00
36 Magglio Ordonez/104 6.00 15.00
37 Jose Ortiz/187 4.00 10.00
38 Roy Oswalt/192 15.00 40.00
39 Wily Mo Pena/203 6.00 15.00
40 Brad Penny/198 4.00 10.00
41 Aramis Ramirez/241 6.00 15.00
42 Luis Rivas/163 4.00 10.00
43 Alex Rodriguez/110 75.00 150.00
44 Scott Rolen/106 10.00 25.00
45 Mike Sweeney/99 6.00 15.00
46 Eric Valent/163 4.00 10.00
47 Kip Wells/223 4.00 10.00
48 Kerry Wood/109 10.00 25.00

2001 Donruss Signature Century Marks Masters Series

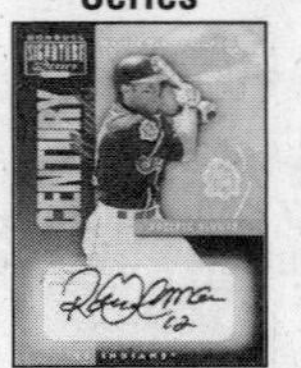

Randomly inserted in packs, these cards were signed by the players.

1 Brent Abernathy 4.00 10.00
2 Roberto Alomar 20.00 50.00
3 Rick Ankiel 10.00 25.00
4 Lance Berkman 10.00 25.00
5 Mark Buehrle 10.00 25.00
6 Wilmy Caceres 4.00 10.00
7 Eric Chavez 6.00 15.00
8 Joe Crede 10.00 25.00
9 Jack Cust 4.00 10.00
10 Brandon Duckworth 4.00 10.00
11 David Espinosa 4.00 10.00
12 Johnny Estrada 6.00 15.00
13 Pedro Feliz 4.00 10.00
14 Robert Fick 4.00 10.00
15 Cliff Floyd 6.00 15.00
16 Casey Fossum 4.00 10.00
17 Jay Gibbons 6.00 15.00
18 Keith Ginter 4.00 10.00
19 Troy Glaus 15.00 40.00
20 Luis Gonzalez
21 Vladimir Guerrero
22 Richard Hidalgo 4.00 10.00
23 Tim Hudson 10.00 25.00
24 Adam Johnson 4.00 10.00
25 Gabe Kapler 6.00 15.00
26 Joe Kennedy 6.00 15.00
27 Ryan Klesko 6.00 15.00
28 Carlos Lee 6.00 15.00
29 Terrence Long 4.00 10.00
30 Edgar Martinez 15.00 40.00
31 Joe Mays 4.00 10.00
32 Greg Miller 4.00 10.00
33 Wade Miller 4.00 10.00
34 Mark Mulder 6.00 15.00
35 Xavier Nady 6.00 15.00
36 Magglio Ordonez 6.00 15.00
37 Jose Ortiz 4.00 10.00

38 Roy Oswalt 15.00 40.00
39 Wily Mo Pena 6.00 15.00
40 Brad Penny 4.00 10.00
41 Aramis Ramirez 6.00 15.00
42 Luis Rivas 4.00 10.00
43 Alex Rodriguez
44 Scott Rolen
45 Mike Sweeney 6.00 15.00
46 Eric Valent 4.00 10.00
47 Kip Wells 4.00 10.00
48 Kerry Wood

2001 Donruss Signature Milestone Marks

Randomly inserted in gift boxes, these 36 cards feature players autographs on a card related to specific highlights from each player's career. Since each player signed a different number of cards, please see our checklist for more detailed information on how many of each card was signed.

1 Ernie Banks/285 20.00 50.00
2 Yogi Berra/120 30.00 60.00
3 Wade Boggs/98 60.00 120.00
4 Barry Bonds/55 100.00 175.00
5 G. Brett 3000 Hits/27
6 George Brett 1500 RBI/23
7 Lou Brock/83 12.50 30.00
8 Rod Carew/110 20.00 50.00
9 Steve Carlton/75 8.00 20.00
10 Gary Carter/213 8.00 20.00
11 Bobby Doerr/192 8.00 20.00
12 Bob Feller/202 8.00 20.00
13 Whitey Ford/186 12.50 30.00
14 Steve Garvey/175 8.00 20.00
15 Tony Gwynn/99 30.00 60.00
16 Fergie Jenkins/149 8.00 20.00
17 Al Kaline/149 30.00 60.00
18 Harmon Killebrew/127 20.00 50.00
19 Ralph Kiner/105 8.00 20.00
20 Willie McCovey/20
21 Paul Molitor/96 20.00 50.00
22 E. Murray 3000 Hits/46 75.00 150.00
23 Eddie Murray 1500 RBI/17
24 Stan Musial/109 40.00 80.00
25 Phil Niekro/300 8.00 20.00
26 Tony Perez/146 8.00 20.00
27 Cal Ripken/25
28 Frank Robinson/136 12.50 30.00
29 M. Schmidt 500 HR/40
30 Mike Schmidt 1500 RBI/23
31 Enos Slaughter/117 12.50 30.00
32 Warren Spahn/300 20.00 50.00
33 Alan Trammell/154 8.00 20.00
34 Hoyt Wilhelm/227 12.50 30.00
35 D.Winfield Padres/31
36 Dave Winfield Yankees/15

2001 Donruss Signature Milestone Marks Masters Series

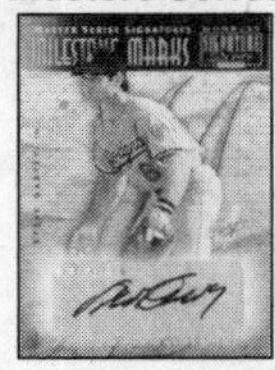

Randomly inserted in packs, these cards were signed by the players. Card number one does not exist for this set.

1 Does Not Exist
2 Yogi Berra
3 Wade Boggs
4 Barry Bonds
5 George Brett 3000 Hits
6 George Brett 1500 RBI
7 Lou Brock 12.50 30.00
8 Rod Carew
9 Steve Carlton 12.50 20.00
10 Gary Carter 12.50 20.00
11 Bobby Doerr 12.50 20.00
12 Bob Feller 12.50 20.00
13 Whitey Ford 40.00 80.00
14 Steve Garvey 12.50 20.00
15 Tony Gwynn
16 Fergie Jenkins 12.50 20.00
17 Al Kaline 50.00 100.00
18 Harmon Killebrew 40.00 80.00
19 Ralph Kiner 12.50 20.00
20 Willie McCovey
21 Paul Molitor 40.00 80.00
22 Eddie Murray 3000 Hits
23 Eddie Murray 1500 RBI
24 Stan Musial
25 Phil Niekro 12.50 20.00
26 Tony Perez 12.50 20.00
27 Cal Ripken
28 Frank Robinson 12.50 30.00
29 Mike Schmidt 500 HR
30 Mike Schmidt 1500 RBI
31 Enos Slaughter 12.50 30.00
32 Warren Spahn
33 Alan Trammell 12.50 20.00
34 Hoyt Wilhelm 12.50 30.00
35 Dave Winfield Padres
36 Dave Winfield Yankees

2001 Donruss Signature Notable Nicknames

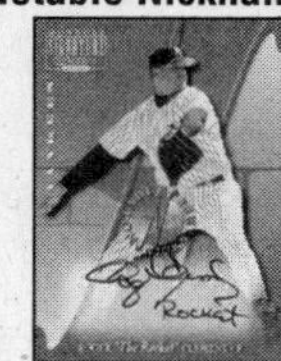

Randomly inserted in gift boxes, these 18 cards feature players along with their nickname. Each player signed 100 of these cards for inclusion in this product.

1 Ernie Banks Mr. Cub 60.00 120.00
2 Orlando Cepeda Baby Bull 30.00 60.00
3 Will Clark The Thrill 50.00 100.00
4 Roger Clemens The Rocket 300.00 500.00
5 Andre Dawson The Hawk 30.00 60.00
6 Bob Feller Rapid Robert 30.00 60.00
7 Carlton Fisk Pudge 50.00 100.00
8 Andres Galarraga Big Cat 50.00 100.00
9 Luis Gonzalez 4 30.00 60.00
10 Reggie Jackson Mr. October 60.00 120.00
11 Harmon Killebrew Killer 60.00 120.00
12 Stan Musial The Man 75.00 150.00
13 Brooks Robinson Hoover 50.00 100.00
14 Nolan Ryan The Express 250.00 400.00
15 Ryne Sandberg Ryno 125.00 200.00
16 Enos Slaughter Country 50.00 100.00
17 Duke Snider 4 50.00 100.00
18 Frank Thomas MVP 60.00 120.00

2001 Donruss Signature Notable Nicknames Masters Series

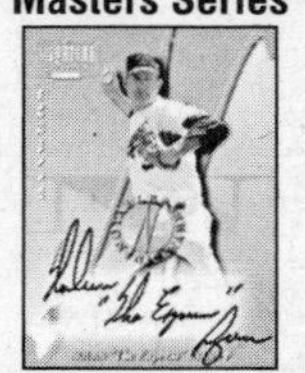

Randomly inserted into gift boxes, these 18 cards featured signed cards of star players along with their nicknames.

1 Ernie Banks Mr. Cub 75.00 150.00
2 Orlando Cepeda Baby Bull 40.00 80.00
3 Will Clark The Thrill 75.00 150.00
4 Roger Clemens The Rocket
5 Andre Dawson The Hawk 40.00 80.00
6 Bob Feller Rapid Robert 40.00 80.00
7 Carlton Fisk Pudge 60.00 120.00
8 Andres Galarraga Big Cat 60.00 120.00
9 Luis Gonzalez 4 40.00 80.00
10 Reggie Jackson Mr. October
11 Harmon Killebrew Killer 75.00 150.00
12 Stan Musial The Man
13 Brooks Robinson Hoover 60.00 120.00
14 Nolan Ryan The Express 300.00 500.00
15 Ryne Sandberg Rhino 175.00 300.00
16 Enos Slaughter Country 60.00 120.00
17 Duke Snider 4
18 Frank Thomas MVP

2001 Donruss Signature Stats

Randomly inserted into gift boxes, these 52 cards feature players who signed cards relating to a key stat in their career. Since each card is signed to a different amount, please see our checklist for specific information about each card.

1 Roberto Alomar/120 15.00 40.00
2 Moises Alou/124 6.00 15.00
3 Luis Aparicio/313 6.00 15.00
4 Lance Berkman/297 10.00 25.00
5 Wade Boggs/51 75.00 150.00
6 Lou Brock/118 10.00 25.00
7 Gary Carter/32
8 Joe Carter/121 6.00 15.00
9 Sean Casey/103 6.00 15.00
10 Darin Erstad/100 6.00 15.00
11 Bob Feller/26
12 Cliff Floyd/45 6.00 15.00
13 Whitey Ford/72 30.00 60.00
14 Andres Galarraga/150 6.00 15.00
15 Bob Gibson/112 10.00 25.00
16 Brian Giles/123 6.00 15.00
17 Troy Glaus/102 10.00 25.00
18 Luis Gonzalez/114 6.00 15.00
19 Vladimir Guerrero/131 15.00 40.00
20 Tony Gwynn/17
21 Richard Hidalgo/314 4.00 10.00
22 Bo Jackson/32
23 Fergie Jenkins/25
24 Randy Johnson/20
25 Al Kaline/128 30.00 60.00
26 Gabe Kapler/302 6.00 15.00
27 Ralph Kiner/54 15.00 40.00
28 Ryan Klesko/23
29 Carlos Lee/261 6.00 15.00
30 Kenny Lofton/210 10.00 25.00
31 Edgar Martinez/145 15.00 40.00
32 Joe Mays/115 4.00 10.00
33 Paul Molitor/41 30.00 60.00
34 Mark Mulder/88 10.00 25.00
35 Phil Niekro/23
36 Magglio Ordonez/126 6.00 15.00
37 Rafael Palmeiro/47 30.00 60.00
38 Jim Palmer/23
39 Chan Ho Park/18
40 Kirby Puckett/31
41 Manny Ramirez/45 40.00 80.00
42 Alex Rodriguez/132 75.00 150.00
43 Ivan Rodriguez/113 15.00 40.00
44 Curt Schilling/15
45 Tom Seaver/25
46 Shannon Stewart/319 6.00 15.00
47 Mike Sweeney/144 6.00 15.00
48 Miguel Tejada/115 10.00 25.00
49 Joe Torre/230 15.00 40.00
50 Javier Vazquez/405 6.00 15.00
51 Jose Vidro/330 4.00 10.00
52 Hoyt Wilhelm/243 10.00 25.00

2001 Donruss Signature Stats Masters Series

Randomly inserted into gift boxes, these 52 cards featured signed cards of star players along with information about a key stat.

1 Roberto Alomar 30.00 60.00
2 Moises Alou 6.00 15.00
3 Luis Aparicio 6.00 15.00
4 Lance Berkman 10.00 25.00
5 Wade Boggs
6 Lou Brock 40.00 80.00
7 Gary Carter 6.00 15.00
8 Joe Carter 6.00 15.00
9 Sean Casey 6.00 15.00
10 Darin Erstad 30.00 60.00
11 Bob Feller 6.00 15.00
12 Cliff Floyd 6.00 15.00
13 Whitey Ford 40.00 80.00
14 Andres Galarraga 30.00 60.00
15 Bob Gibson 20.00 50.00
16 Brian Giles 6.00 15.00
17 Troy Glaus 12.50 30.00
18 Luis Gonzalez
19 Vladimir Guerrero
20 Tony Gwynn
21 Richard Hidalgo 4.00 10.00
22 Bo Jackson 40.00 80.00
23 Fergie Jenkins 6.00 15.00
24 Randy Johnson
25 Al Kaline 40.00 80.00
26 Gabe Kapler 6.00 15.00
27 Ralph Kiner 10.00 25.00
28 Ryan Klesko 6.00 15.00
29 Carlos Lee 6.00 15.00
30 Kenny Lofton 10.00 25.00
31 Edgar Martinez 20.00 50.00
32 Joe Mays 4.00 10.00
33 Paul Molitor
34 Mark Mulder 6.00 15.00
35 Phil Niekro 6.00 15.00
36 Magglio Ordonez 6.00 15.00
37 Rafael Palmeiro
38 Jim Palmer 15.00 40.00
39 Chan Ho Park 125.00 200.00
40 Kirby Puckett
41 Manny Ramirez
42 Alex Rodriguez
43 Ivan Rodriguez
44 Curt Schilling 30.00 60.00
45 Tom Seaver
46 Shannon Stewart 6.00 15.00
47 Mike Sweeney 6.00 15.00
48 Miguel Tejada 6.00 15.00
49 Joe Torre 50.00 100.00
50 Javier Vazquez 6.00 15.00
51 Jose Vidro 4.00 10.00
52 Hoyt Wilhelm

2001 Donruss Signature Team Trademarks

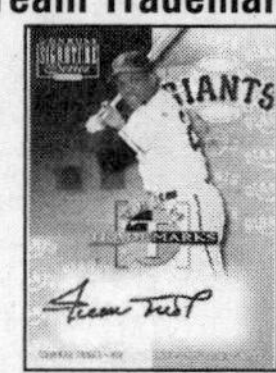

Randomly inserted in gift boxes, these 58 cards feature signed cards of a player as well as information about the team they played for. Since each player signed a different amount of cards for this promotion, we have included detailed information in our checklist.

1 Rick Ankiel/179 10.00 25.00
2 Ernie Banks/180 30.00 60.00
3 Johnny Bench/20
4 Yogi Berra/124 30.00 60.00
5 Wade Boggs/89 60.00 120.00
6 Barry Bonds/77 100.00 175.00
7 Lou Brock/29
8 Steve Carlton/174 6.00 15.00
9 Sean Casey/123 6.00 15.00
10 Orlando Cepeda/100 6.00 15.00
11 Roger Clemens RS/30
12 Roger Clemens Yankees/21
13 Andre Dawson/176 6.00 15.00
14 Bobby Doerr/193 10.00 25.00
15 Whitey Ford/94 20.00 50.00
17 Steve Garvey/182 6.00 15.00
18 Bob Gibson/98 15.00 40.00
19 Juan Gonzalez/70 20.00 50.00
20 Shawn Green/109 10.00 25.00
21 Orel Hershiser/210 20.00 50.00
22 Reggie Jackson/73 40.00 80.00
23 Fergie Jenkins/213 6.00 15.00
24 Chipper Jones/74 40.00 80.00
25 Pedro Martinez/27
26 Don Mattingly/72 75.00 150.00
27 Willie Mays/197 75.00 150.00
28 Willie McCovey/26 40.00 80.00
29 Joe Morgan/33
30 Eddie Murray/45 60.00 120.00
31 Stan Musial/65 50.00 100.00
32 Mike Mussina Balt./85 40.00 80.00
33 M.Mussina Yanks/95 40.00 80.00
34 Phil Niekro/187 6.00 15.00
35 Rafael Palmeiro/99 20.00 50.00
36 Jim Palmer/142 6.00 15.00
37 Tony Perez/73 6.00 15.00
38 Manny Ramirez Sox/57 30.00 60.00
39 Cal Ripken/47 150.00 300.00
40 Phil Rizzuto/98 20.00 50.00
41 Brooks Robinson/146 10.00 25.00
42 F.Robinson Orioles/118 10.00 25.00
43 F.Robinson Reds/116 10.00 25.00
44 Alex Rodriguez/100 75.00 150.00
45 Ivan Rodriguez/62 40.00 80.00
46 Scott Rolen/39
47 Nolan Ryan/153 75.00 150.00
48 Ryne Sandberg/52 75.00 150.00
49 Curt Schilling/63 15.00 40.00
50 Mike Schmidt/107 50.00 100.00
51 Tom Seaver/25
52 Gary Sheffield/194 10.00 25.00
53 Enos Slaughter/215 10.00 25.00
54 Duke Snider/47 40.00 80.00
55 Warren Spahn/140 15.00 40.00
56 Joe Torre/90 30.00 60.00
57 Billy Williams/194 6.00 15.00
58 Kerry Wood/52 30.00 60.00

2001 Donruss Signature Team Trademarks Masters Series

Randomly inserted into gift boxes, these 56 cards featured signed cards of star players along with information about the team they played for. Card number 27 does not exist in this set.

1 Rick Ankiel
2 Does Not Exist
3 Johnny Bench
4 Yogi Berra
5 Wade Boggs
6 Barry Bonds
7 Lou Brock
8 Steve Carlton 6.00 15.00
9 Sean Casey
10 Orlando Cepeda 6.00 15.00
11 Roger Clemens Red Sox
12 Roger Clemens Yankees
13 Andre Dawson 6.00 15.00
14 Bobby Doerr 6.00 15.00
15 Whitey Ford
16 Nomar Garciaparra 60.00 120.00
17 Steve Garvey 6.00 15.00
18 Bob Gibson 30.00 60.00
19 Juan Gonzalez
20 Shawn Green
21 Orel Hershiser 40.00 80.00
22 Reggie Jackson
23 Fergie Jenkins 6.00 15.00
24 Chipper Jones
25 Pedro Martinez
26 Don Mattingly 75.00 150.00
27 Does Not Exist
28 Willie McCovey
29 Joe Morgan
30 Eddie Murray
31 Stan Musial
32 Mike Mussina Orioles
33 Mike Mussina Yankees
34 Phil Niekro 6.00 15.00
35 Rafael Palmeiro
36 Jim Palmer 10.00 25.00
37 Tony Perez 6.00 15.00
38 Manny Ramirez Sox
39 Cal Ripken
40 Phil Rizzuto 20.00 50.00
41 Brooks Robinson 20.00 50.00
42 Frank Robinson Orioles 40.00 80.00
43 Frank Robinson Reds
44 Alex Rodriguez
45 Ivan Rodriguez
46 Scott Rolen
47 Nolan Ryan 75.00 150.00
48 Ryne Sandberg
49 Curt Schilling 15.00 40.00
50 Mike Schmidt
51 Tom Seaver 30.00 60.00
52 Gary Sheffield 8.00 20.00
53 Enos Slaughter 8.00 20.00
54 Duke Snider
55 Warren Spahn 20.00 50.00
56 Joe Torre
57 Billy Williams 6.00 15.00
58 Kerry Wood

2003 Donruss Signature

This 150 card set was released in August, 2003. This set was issued in four card packs issued in a special "box". These pack/boxes had a $50 SRP. Cards numbered 1-100 feature veterans in team alphabetical order while cards numbered 111 through 150 feature rookies. Unlike most Donruss/Playoff products, these rookie cards were not shortprinted.

COMMON CARD (1-100) .40 1.00
COMMON CARD (101-150) .40 1.00
1 Garret Anderson .40 1.00
2 Tim Salmon .60 1.50
3 Troy Glaus .40 1.00
4 Curt Schilling .40 1.00
5 Luis Gonzalez .40 1.00
6 Mark Grace .60 1.50
7 Matt Williams .40 1.00
8 Randy Johnson 1.00 2.50
9 Andruw Jones .60 1.50
10 Chipper Jones 1.00 2.50
11 Gary Sheffield .40 1.00
12 Greg Maddux 1.50 4.00
13 Johnny Damon .60 1.50
14 Manny Ramirez .60 1.50
15 Nomar Garciaparra 1.50 4.00
16 Pedro Martinez .60 1.50
17 Corey Patterson .40 1.00
18 Kerry Wood .40 1.00
19 Mark Prior .60 1.50
20 Sammy Sosa 1.00 2.50
21 Bartolo Colon .40 1.00
22 Frank Thomas 1.00 2.50
23 Magglio Ordonez .40 1.00
24 Paul Konerko .40 1.00
25 Adam Dunn .40 1.00
26 Austin Kearns .40 1.00
27 Barry Larkin .60 1.50
28 Ken Griffey Jr. 1.50 4.00
29 C.C. Sabathia .40 1.00
30 Omar Vizquel .60 1.50
31 Larry Walker .40 1.00
32 Todd Helton .60 1.50
33 Ivan Rodriguez .60 1.50
34 Josh Beckett .40 1.00
35 Craig Biggio .60 1.50
36 Jeff Bagwell .60 1.50
37 Jeff Kent .40 1.00
38 Lance Berkman .40 1.00
39 Richard Hidalgo .40 1.00
40 Roy Oswalt .40 1.00
41 Carlos Beltran .40 1.00
42 Mike Sweeney .40 1.00
43 Runelvys Hernandez .40 1.00
44 Hideo Nomo 1.00 2.50
45 Kazuhisa Ishii .40 1.00
46 Paul Lo Duca .40 1.00
47 Shawn Green .40 1.00
48 Ben Sheets .40 1.00
49 Richie Sexson .40 1.00
50 A.J. Pierzynski .40 1.00
51 Torii Hunter .40 1.00
52 Javier Vazquez .40 1.00
53 Jose Vidro .40 1.00
54 Vladimir Guerrero 1.00 2.50
55 Cliff Floyd .40 1.00
56 David Cone .40 1.00
57 Mike Piazza 1.50 4.00
58 Roberto Alomar .60 1.50
59 Tom Glavine .60 1.50
60 Alfonso Soriano .60 1.50
61 Derek Jeter 2.50 6.00
62 Drew Henson .40 1.00
63 Jason Giambi .40 1.00
64 Mike Mussina .60 1.50
65 Nick Johnson .40 1.00
66 Roger Clemens 2.00 5.00
67 Barry Zito .40 1.00
68 Eric Chavez .40 1.00
69 Mark Mulder .40 1.00
70 Miguel Tejada .40 1.00
71 Tim Hudson .40 1.00
72 Bobby Abreu .40 1.00
73 Jim Thome .60 1.50
74 Kevin Millwood .40 1.00
75 Pat Burrell .40 1.00
76 Brian Giles .40 1.00
77 Jason Kendall .40 1.00
78 Kenny Lofton .40 1.00
79 Phil Nevin .40 1.00
80 Ryan Klesko .40 1.00
81 Andres Galarraga .40 1.00
82 Barry Bonds 2.50 6.00
83 Rich Aurilia .40 1.00
84 Edgar Martinez .60 1.50
85 Freddy Garcia .40 1.00
86 Ichiro Suzuki 2.00 5.00
87 Albert Pujols 2.00 5.00
88 Jim Edmonds .40 1.00
89 Scott Rolen .60 1.50
90 So Taguchi .40 1.00
91 Rocco Baldelli .40 1.00
92 Alex Rodriguez 1.50 4.00
93 Hank Blalock .40 1.00
94 Juan Gonzalez .40 1.00
95 Mark Teixeira .60 1.50
96 Rafael Palmeiro .60 1.50
97 Carlos Delgado .40 1.00
98 Eric Hinske .40 1.00
99 Roy Halladay .40 1.00
100 Vernon Wells .40 1.00
101 Hideki Matsui ROO RC 4.00 10.00
102 Jose Contreras ROO RC 1.00 2.50
103 Jer. Bonderman ROO RC 3.00 8.00
104 Bernie Castro ROO RC .40 1.00
105 Alfredo Gonzalez ROO RC .40 1.00
106 Arnie Munoz ROO RC .40 1.00
107 Andrew Brown ROO RC .60 1.50
108 Josh Hall ROO RC .40 1.00
109 Josh Stewart ROO RC .40 1.00
110 Clint Barmes ROO RC 1.25 3.00
111 Brandon Webb ROO RC 3.00 8.00
112 Chien-Ming Wang ROO RC 5.00 12.00
113 Edgar Gonzalez ROO RC .40 1.00
114 Al. Machado ROO RC .40 1.00
115 Jeremy Griffiths ROO RC .40 1.00
116 Craig Brazell ROO RC .40 1.00
117 Shane Bazzell ROO RC .40 1.00
118 Fernando Cabrera ROO RC .40 1.00
119 Termel Sledge ROO RC .40 1.00
120 Rob Hammock ROO RC .40 1.00
121 Francisco Rosario ROO RC .40 1.00
122 Francisco Cruceta ROO RC .40 1.00
123 Rett Johnson ROO RC .40 1.00
124 Guillermo Quiroz ROO RC .40 1.00
125 Hong-Chih Kuo ROO RC 3.00 8.00
126 Ian Ferguson ROO RC .40 1.00
127 Tim Olson ROO RC .40 1.00
128 Todd Wellemeyer ROO RC .40 1.00
129 Rich Fischer ROO RC .40 1.00
130 Phil Seibel ROO RC .40 1.00
131 Joe Valentine ROO RC .40 1.00
132 Matt Kata ROO RC .40 1.00
133 Michael Hessman ROO RC .40 1.00
134 Michel Hernandez ROO RC .40 1.00
135 Doug Waechter ROO RC .60 1.50
136 Prentice Redman ROO RC .40 1.00
137 Nook Logan ROO RC .60 1.50
138 Oscar Villarreal ROO RC .40 1.00
139 Pete LaForest ROO RC .40 1.00
140 Matt Bruback ROO RC .40 1.00
141 Dontrelle Willis ROO 1.00 2.50
142 Greg Aquino ROO RC .40 1.00
143 Lew Ford ROO RC .60 1.50
144 Jeff Duncan ROO RC .40 1.00
145 Dan Haren ROO RC 1.00 2.50
146 Miguel Ojeda ROO RC .40 1.00
147 Rosman Garcia ROO RC .40 1.00
148 Felix Sanchez ROO RC .40 1.00
149 Jon Leicester ROO RC .40 1.00
150 Roger Deago ROO RC .40 1.00

2003 Donruss Signature Century Proofs

*CENTURY 1-100: 2X TO 5X BASIC
*CENTURY 101-150: 1X TO 2.5X BASIC
RANDOM INSERTS IN PACKS
STATED PRINT RUN 100 SERIAL #'d SETS
112 Chien-Ming Wang ROO 30.00 60.00
125 Hong-Chih Kuo ROO 15.00 40.00

2003 Donruss Signature Decade Proofs

RANDOM INSERTS IN PACKS
STATED PRINT RUN 10 SERIAL #'d SETS
NO PRICING DUE TO SCARCITY

2003 Donruss Signature Autographs

Randomly inserted into packs; these 50 cards parallel the basic set and feature autographs of the featured players. The first 47 of these cards (checklisted from 1-102) are not serial numbered but we are giving print run information in our checklist provided by Donruss/Playoff. Cards 151-153 were distributed as random inserts within packs of DLP Rookies and Traded and each is serial numbered to 200. No pricing is provided for cards

with print runs of 28 or fewer due to scarcity.

1 Garret Anderson	6.00	15.00
6 Mark Grace SP/141	15.00	40.00
7 Matt Williams	10.00	25.00
8 Randy Johnson SP/50	40.00	80.00
10 Chipper Jones SP/50	40.00	80.00
12 Greg Maddux SP/25		
14 Manny Ramirez SP/50	20.00	50.00
16 Pedro Martinez SP/5		
27 Barry Larkin SP/159	15.00	40.00
32 Todd Helton SP/5		
33 Ivan Rodriguez SP/50	20.00	50.00
36 Jeff Bagwell SP/25		
38 Lance Berkman SP/75	10.00	25.00
39 Richard Hidalgo	4.00	10.00
40 Roy Oswalt SP/150	10.00	25.00
42 Mike Sweeney	6.00	15.00
44 Hideo Nomo SP/25		
45 Kazuhisa Ishii SP/25		
50 A.J. Pierzynski	6.00	15.00
51 Torii Hunter	6.00	15.00
53 Jose Vidro	6.00	15.00
54 Vladimir Guerrero	15.00	40.00
55 Cliff Floyd	6.00	15.00
56 David Cone SP/35	10.00	25.00
57 Mike Piazza SP/5		
58 Roberto Alomar SP/50	15.00	40.00
62 Drew Henson SP/28		
64 Mike Mussina SP/5		
65 Nick Johnson	6.00	15.00
67 Barry Zito SP/150	6.00	15.00
68 Eric Chavez	6.00	15.00
69 Mark Mulder SP/50	10.00	25.00
72 Bobby Abreu	6.00	15.00
78 Kenny Lofton SP/229	10.00	25.00
80 Ryan Klesko SP/150	6.00	15.00
81 Andres Galarraga	6.00	15.00
83 Rich Aurilia SP/122	4.00	10.00
84 Edgar Martinez	15.00	40.00
88 Jim Edmonds SP/25		
89 Scott Rolen SP/200	10.00	25.00
90 So Taguchi SP/220	6.00	15.00
92 Alex Rodriguez SP/25		
95 Mark Teixeira SP/150	10.00	25.00
96 Rafael Palmeiro SP/25		
100 Vernon Wells	6.00	15.00
102 Jose Contreras ROO	8.00	20.00
141 D.Willis ROO SP/150	15.00	40.00
151 Delmon Young ROO	60.00	120.00
152 Rickie Weeks ROO	20.00	50.00
153 Edwin Jackson ROO	6.00	15.00

2003 Donruss Signature Autographs Century

1-RANDOM INSERTS IN PACKS
151-154 RANDOM IN DLP R/T PACKS
1-102 PRINT RUN 100 SERIAL #'d SETS
151-154 PRINT RUN 21 SERIAL #'d SETS
NO PRICING ON QTY OF 25 OR LESS
CARD 154 IS NOT SIGNED

1 Garret Anderson	10.00	25.00
7 Matt Williams	15.00	40.00
27 Barry Larkin	15.00	40.00
39 Richard Hidalgo	6.00	15.00
42 Mike Sweeney	10.00	25.00
50 A.J. Pierzynski	10.00	25.00
51 Torii Hunter	10.00	25.00
53 Jose Vidro	6.00	15.00
54 Vladimir Guerrero	15.00	40.00
55 Cliff Floyd	10.00	25.00
62 Drew Henson	6.00	15.00
65 Nick Johnson	10.00	25.00
69 Mark Mulder	10.00	25.00
72 Bobby Abreu	10.00	25.00
78 Kenny Lofton	15.00	40.00
81 Andres Galarraga	10.00	25.00
84 Edgar Martinez	15.00	40.00
89 Scott Rolen	15.00	40.00
90 So Taguchi	10.00	25.00
100 Vernon Wells	10.00	25.00
102 Jose Contreras ROO	12.50	30.00
151 Delmon Young ROO/21		
152 Rickie Weeks ROO/21		
153 Edwin Jackson ROO/21		

2003 Donruss Signature Autographs Decade

1-102 RANDOM INSERTS IN PACKS
151-154 RANDOM IN DLP R/T PACKS
STATED PRINT RUN 10 SERIAL #'d SETS
NO PRICING DUE TO SCARCITY
CARD 154 IS NOT SIGNED

2003 Donruss Signature Autographs Notations

Randomly inserted into packs, these cards feature not only authentic autographs from the featured player but also a special "notation" next to their name in the checklist. Since each card has a different print run we have put that information next to the card in our checklist. Please note that for cards with print runs of 30 or fewer, no pricing is provided.

1A Garret Anderson #16/75	10.00	25.00
1B Garret Anderson 7-27-94/45	12.50	30.00
1C Garret Anderson WSC 02/75	10.00	25.00
6 Mark Grace Amazing/5		
7A Matt Williams #9/250	10.00	25.00
7B Matt Williams 01 WS/50	20.00	50.00
10A Chipper Jones 96-01 AS/25		
10B Chipper Jones MVP 99/25		
32 Todd Helton 02 AS/15		
33 Ivan Rodriguez #7/5		
36 Jeff Bagwell Baggy/5		
38A Lance Berkman #17/15		
38B Lance Berkman #22/5		
38C Lance Berkman #27/1		
38D Lance Berkman 02/1		
38E Lance Berkman Rice Owls/5		
38F Lance Berkman Rice Univ./5		
38G Lance Berkman William/1		
40 Roy Oswalt #44/25		
45 Kazuhisa Ishii #17/35	12.50	30.00
50 A.J. Pierzynski 02 AS/200	6.00	15.00
51A Torii Hunter 02 AS/25		
51B Torii Hunter #48/20		
53A Jose Vidro #3/40	8.00	20.00
53B Jose Vidro AS 00/15		
53C Jose Vidro 2X AS/6		
55 Cliff Floyd #30/5		
57A Mike Piazza #31/5		
57B Mike Piazza ROY 93/1		
62A Drew Henson UM #7/2		
62B Drew Henson QB #7/24		
62C Drew Henson DH #7/73	6.00	15.00
68A Eric Chavez #3/50	12.50	30.00
68B Eric Chavez Chavy/25		
69 Mark Mulder MSU/30		
78 Kenny Lofton #7/150	10.00	25.00
80 Ryan Klesko #30/75	10.00	25.00
83 Rich Aurilia #35/61	8.00	20.00
84A Edgar Martinez #11/250	10.00	25.00
84B E.Martinez BT 92-95/60	20.00	50.00
92A Alex Rodriguez #3/5		
92B Alex Rodriguez WCS 93/5		
92C Alex Rodriguez Westminster/1		
96 Rafael Palmeiro 500 HR/25		
100 Vernon Wells #10/75	10.00	25.00

2003 Donruss Signature Autographs Notations Century

RANDOM INSERTS IN PACKS
STATED PRINT RUN 100 SERIAL #'d SETS

1A Garret Anderson #16	10.00	25.00
1B Garret Anderson 7-27-94	10.00	25.00
7A Matt Williams #9	15.00	40.00
7B Matt Williams 01 WS	15.00	40.00
50 A.J. Pierzynski 02 AS	10.00	25.00
68A Eric Chavez #3	10.00	25.00
78 Kenny Lofton #7	15.00	40.00
84A Edgar Martinez #11	15.00	40.00

2003 Donruss Signature Autographs Notations Decade

RANDOM INSERTS IN PACKS
STATED PRINT RUN 10 SERIAL #'d SETS
NO PRICING DUE TO SCARCITY

2003 Donruss Signature Cuts

Randomly inserted into packs, these 15 cards feature "cut" signatures from the featured player. Each of these cards have different print runs and we have notated that print run information in our checklist. Please note for cards with 25 or fewer

copies, no pricing is provided.

4 Curt Schilling/7		
8 Randy Johnson/40	40.00	80.00
10 Chipper Jones/9		
33 Ivan Rodriguez/122	15.00	40.00
54 Vladimir Guerrero/34	20.00	50.00
58 Roberto Alomar/100	15.00	40.00
59 Tom Glavine/9		
64 Mike Mussina/82	20.00	50.00
66 Roger Clemens/9		
73 Jim Thome/127	15.00	40.00
80 Ryan Klesko/35	12.50	30.00
81 Andres Galarraga/51	12.50	30.00
89 Scott Rolen/36	20.00	50.00
94 Juan Gonzalez/9		
96 Rafael Palmeiro/13		

2003 Donruss Signature Cuts Decade

RANDOM INSERTS IN PACKS
STATED PRINT RUN 10 SERIAL #'d SETS
NO PRICING DUE TO SCARCITY

2003 Donruss Signature Authentic Cuts

Randomly inserted into packs, these three cards feature cut signatures of the most legendary players in baseball history. We have notated the print run next to the player's name in our checklist and due to market scarcity, no pricing is provided for these cards.

1 Ty Cobb/3
2 Babe Ruth/1
3 Lou Gehrig/1

2003 Donruss Signature INKredible Three

Randomly inserted into packs, these five cards feature three signatures on each card from players with a common team allegiance. Each of these cards were issued to a stated print run of 50 serial numbered sets.

1 Barry Zito	150.00	250.00
Mark Mulder		
Tim Hudson		
2 Greg Maddux	250.00	400.00
Chipper Jones		
Andruw Jones		
3 Kerry Wood	125.00	250.00
Mark Prior		
Ernie Banks		
4 Kirby Puckett	150.00	300.00
Harmon Killebrew		
Torii Hunter		
5 Vladimir Guerrero	90.00	150.00
Jose Vidro		
Javier Vazquez		

2003 Donruss Signature INKredible Four

Randomly inserted into packs, these 10 cards feature four signatures from players with a common team allegiance. Each of these cards were issued to a stated print run of 25 serial numbered sets and no pricing is provided due to market scarcity.

1 Jeff Bagwell
Craig Biggio
Lance Berkman
Roy Oswalt
2 Mike Schmidt
Steve Carlton
Pat Burrell
Jim Thome
3 Carlos Lee
Magglio Ordonez
Frank Thomas
Mark Buehrle
4 Brooks Robinson
Frank Robinson
Cal Ripken
Jim Palmer
5 Pedro Martinez
Manny Ramirez
Rickey Henderson
Bobby Doerr
6 Mike Sweeney
Carlos Beltran
Bo Jackson
George Brett
7 Randy Johnson
Curt Schilling
Mark Grace
Junior Spivey
8 Dwight Gooden
Lenny Dykstra
Tom Glavine
Roberto Alomar
9 Alex Rodriguez
Rafael Palmeiro
Nolan Ryan
Ferguson Jenkins
10 Roberto Alomar
Joe Carter
Ryan Klesko
Tony Gwynn

2003 Donruss Signature INKredible Six

Randomly inserted into packs, these five cards feature six signatures on each card with a common thread tying together all the players. Each of these cards were issued to a stated print run of 10 serial numbered sets and no pricing is provided due to market scarcity.

1 Adam Dunn
Tom Seaver
Johnny Bench
Austin Kearns
Joe Morgan
Barry Larkin
2 Albert Pujols
Stan Musial
Jim Edmonds
Scott Rolen
Lou Brock
Ozzie Smith
3 Andre Dawson
Ernie Banks
Mark Prior
Ryne Sandberg
Kerry Wood
Mark Grace
4 Yogi Berra
Whitey Ford
Rickey Henderson
Don Mattingly
Phil Rizzuto
Reggie Jackson
5 Alex Rodriguez
Roger Clemens
Hideo Nomo
George Brett
Don Mattingly
Nolan Ryan

2003 Donruss Signature Legends of Summer

Randomly inserted into packs, these 40 cards feature some of the best retired players. Each of these cards were issued to a stated print run of 250 serial numbered sets.

*CENTURY: .6X TO 1.5X BASIC
CENTURY PRINT RUN 100 SERIAL #'d SETS
DECADE PRINT RUN 10 SERIAL #'d SETS
NO DECADE PRICING DUE TO SCARCITY
RANDOM INSERTS IN PACKS

1 Al Kaline	3.00	8.00
2 Alan Trammell	2.00	5.00
3 Andre Dawson	2.00	5.00
4 Babe Ruth	6.00	15.00
5 Billy Williams	2.00	5.00
6 Bo Jackson	3.00	8.00
7 Bob Feller	2.00	5.00
8 Bobby Doerr	2.00	5.00
9 Brooks Robinson	2.00	5.00
10 Dale Murphy	2.00	5.00
11 Dennis Eckersley	2.00	5.00
12 Don Mattingly	5.00	12.00
13 Duke Snider	2.00	5.00
14 Eric Davis	2.00	5.00
15 Frank Robinson	2.00	5.00
16 Fred Lynn	2.00	5.00
17 Gary Carter	2.00	5.00
18 Harmon Killebrew	3.00	8.00
19 Jack Morris	2.00	5.00
20 Jim Palmer	2.00	5.00
21 Jim Abbott	2.00	5.00
22 Joe Morgan	2.00	5.00
23 Joe Torre	2.00	5.00
24 Johnny Bench	3.00	8.00
25 Jose Canseco	2.00	5.00
26 Kirby Puckett	3.00	8.00
27 Lenny Dykstra	2.00	5.00
28 Lou Brock	2.00	5.00
29 Ralph Kiner	2.00	5.00
30 Mike Schmidt	5.00	12.00
31 Nolan Ryan Rgr	6.00	15.00
32 Nolan Ryan Angels	6.00	15.00
33 Orel Hershiser	2.00	5.00
34 Phil Rizzuto	2.00	5.00
35 Orlando Cepeda	2.00	5.00
36 Ryne Sandberg	5.00	12.00
37 Stan Musial	4.00	10.00
38 Steve Garvey	2.00	5.00
39 Tony Perez	2.00	5.00
40 Ty Cobb	4.00	10.00

2003 Donruss Signature Legends of Summer Autographs

Randomly inserted into packs, this is a partial parallel of the Legends of Summer set. A few cards were issued in smaller quantities and we have notated that information (as provided by Donruss/Playoff) in our checklist.

1 Al Kaline	10.00	25.00
2 Alan Trammell	6.00	15.00
3 Andre Dawson	6.00	15.00
5 Billy Williams	6.00	15.00
6 Bo Jackson SP/100	30.00	60.00
7 Bob Feller	6.00	15.00
8 Bobby Doerr	6.00	15.00
9 Brooks Robinson	10.00	25.00
10 Dale Murphy SP/75	15.00	40.00
11 Dennis Eckersley	6.00	15.00
12 Don Mattingly SP/50	50.00	100.00
13 Duke Snider SP/225	10.00	25.00
14 Eric Davis	6.00	15.00
15 Frank Robinson	6.00	15.00
16 Fred Lynn	6.00	15.00
17 Gary Carter	6.00	15.00
18 Harmon Killebrew SP/171	10.00	25.00
19 Jack Morris	6.00	15.00
20 Jim Palmer	6.00	15.00
21 Jim Abbott	6.00	15.00
22 Joe Morgan SP/125	10.00	25.00
23 Joe Torre	6.00	15.00
24 Johnny Bench SP/75	15.00	40.00
25 Jose Canseco SP/75	15.00	40.00
26 Kirby Puckett SP/75	50.00	100.00
27 Lenny Dykstra	6.00	15.00
28 Lou Brock	10.00	25.00
29 Ralph Kiner	6.00	15.00
30 Mike Schmidt SP/75	40.00	80.00
31 Nolan Ryan Rgr SP/75	75.00	150.00
33 Orel Hershiser	10.00	25.00
34 Phil Rizzuto	10.00	25.00
35 Orlando Cepeda	6.00	15.00
36 Ryne Sandberg SP/75	40.00	80.00
37 Stan Musial SP/200	30.00	60.00
38 Steve Garvey	6.00	15.00
39 Tony Perez	6.00	15.00

2003 Donruss Signature Legends of Summer Autographs Century

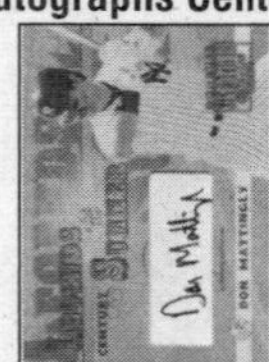

RANDOM INSERTS IN PACKS
STATED PRINT RUN 100 SERIAL #'d SETS

1 Al Kaline	15.00	40.00
2 Alan Trammell	10.00	25.00
3 Andre Dawson	10.00	25.00
5 Billy Williams	10.00	25.00
6 Bo Jackson	30.00	60.00
7 Bob Feller	10.00	25.00
8 Bobby Doerr	10.00	25.00
9 Brooks Robinson	15.00	40.00
11 Dennis Eckersley	10.00	25.00
12 Don Mattingly	40.00	80.00
14 Eric Davis	10.00	25.00
15 Frank Robinson	10.00	25.00
16 Fred Lynn	10.00	25.00
17 Gary Carter	10.00	25.00
19 Jack Morris	10.00	25.00
20 Jim Palmer	10.00	25.00
21 Jim Abbott	10.00	25.00
23 Joe Torre	10.00	25.00
27 Lenny Dykstra	10.00	25.00
28 Lou Brock	15.00	40.00
29 Ralph Kiner	10.00	25.00
33 Orel Hershiser	40.00	80.00
34 Phil Rizzuto	15.00	40.00
35 Orlando Cepeda	10.00	25.00
36 Ryne Sandberg	40.00	80.00
37 Stan Musial	30.00	60.00
38 Steve Garvey	10.00	25.00
39 Tony Perez	10.00	25.00

2003 Donruss Signature Legends of Summer Autographs Decade

RANDOM INSERTS IN PACKS
STATED PRINT RUN 10 SERIAL #'d SETS
NO PRICING DUE TO SCARCITY

2003 Donruss Signature Legends of Summer Autographs Notations

This parallel to the Legends of Summer insert set features not only authentic autographs from some of the featured players but also special notations added by the player. Since there are varying print runs on these cards we have provided that information next to the player's name in our checklist. Please note that cards with a print run of 25 or fewer are not priced due to market scarcity.

1A Al Kaline #6/200	10.00	25.00
1B Al Kaline HOF '80/200	10.00	25.00
1C Al Kaline Mr. Tiger/200	10.00	25.00
2 A.Trammell 84 WS MVP/250	6.00	15.00
3A Andre Dawson #8/165	6.00	15.00
3B Andre Dawson 87 MVP/250	6.00	15.00
5B Billy Williams 61 ROY/250	6.00	15.00
5C Billy Williams 87 HOF/150	6.00	15.00
7A Bob Feller #19/250	6.00	15.00
7B Bob Feller HOF 62/250	6.00	15.00
7C Bob Feller Triple Crown/200		
8A Bobby Doerr #1/250	6.00	15.00
8B Bobby Doerr HOF 86/250	6.00	15.00
8C Bobby Doerr MVP 44/250	6.00	15.00
9A B.Robinson 64 MVP/150	10.00	25.00
9B B.Robinson 70 WS MVP/50	20.00	50.00
10A Dale Murphy MVP 82/50	20.00	50.00
10B Dale Murphy MVP 83/50	20.00	50.00
11A D.Eckersley 92 CY/250	6.00	15.00
11B D.Eckersley 92 CY-MVP/250	6.00	15.00
11C D.Eckersley 92 MVP/250	6.00	15.00
13 Duke Snider HOF 80/25		
14A Eric Davis #44/250	6.00	15.00
14B Eric Davis 87 AS/150	6.00	15.00
14C Eric Davis 90 WS/200	6.00	15.00
16A Fred Lynn 75 MVP-ROY/240	6.00	15.00
16B Fred Lynn 75-83 AS/250	6.00	15.00
17 Gary Carter The Kid/5		
18A H.Killebrew #3/75	15.00	40.00
18B H.Killebrew 69 MVP/50	20.00	50.00
18C H.Killebrew 573 HR/50	20.00	50.00
18D H.Killebrew HOF 84/125	15.00	40.00
19A J.Morris 91 WS MVP/250	6.00	15.00
19B Jack Morris 92 WS/250	6.00	15.00
20A Jim Palmer 73 CY/190	6.00	15.00
20B Jim Palmer 75 CY/140	6.00	15.00
20C Jim Palmer 76 CY/50	12.50	30.00
21A Jim Abbott 4-8-89/200	6.00	15.00
21B Jim Abbott 9-4-93/100	10.00	25.00
21C Jim Abbott 6-15-99/75	10.00	25.00
21D Jim Abbott U of Mich/50	12.50	30.00
21E Jim Abbott Yanks/25		
24A Johnny Bench #5/20		
24B Johnny Bench HOF/1		
24C Johnny Bench HOF 89/5		
24D Johnny Bench MVP 70/1		
24E Johnny Bench MVP 72/1		
27 Lenny Dykstra 86 WS/226	6.00	15.00
28A Lou Brock SB 938/25		
28B Lou Brock HOF 85/50	20.00	50.00
29A Ralph Kiner #4/150	6.00	15.00
29B Ralph Kiner 48-53 AS/25		
29C Ralph Kiner HOF/200	6.00	15.00
29D Ralph Kiner HOF 75/100	10.00	25.00
31 Nolan Ryan Rgr 5714 SO/25		
35A O.Cepeda Baby Bull/75	20.00	50.00
35B O.Cepeda MVP 67/40	12.50	30.00
35C O.Cepeda 58 ROY/40	12.50	30.00
35D O.Cepeda 67 WS/40	12.50	30.00
35E O.Cepeda 68 WS/40	12.50	30.00
36A Ryne Sandberg #23/5		
36B Ryne Sandberg Cubs/20		
36C Ryne Sandberg 84 MVP/25		
38A Steve Garvey #6/150	6.00	15.00
38B Steve Garvey 74 MVP/25		
38C Steve Garvey 78 AS MVP/50	12.50	30.00
38D Steve Garvey 81 WS/75	10.00	25.00
39A Tony Perez #24/250	6.00	15.00
39B Tony Perez HOF 02/175	6.00	15.00
39C Tony Perez WS 75/125	10.00	25.00
39D Tony Perez WS 76/75	10.00	25.00

2003 Donruss Signature Legends of Summer Autographs Notations Century

RANDOM INSERTS IN PACKS
STATED PRINT RUN 100 SERIAL #'d SETS
1A Al Kaline #6 15.00 40.00
1B Al Kaline HOF 80 15.00 40.00
1C Al Kaline Mr. Tiger 15.00 40.00
2 Alan Trammell 84 WS MVP 10.00 25.00
3A Andre Dawson #8 10.00 25.00
3B Andre Dawson 87 MVP 10.00 25.00
5A Billy Williams #26 10.00 25.00
5B Billy Williams 61 ROY 10.00 25.00
5C Billy Williams 87 HOF 10.00 25.00
7A Bob Feller #19 10.00 25.00
7B Bob Feller HOF 62 10.00 25.00
7C Bob Feller Triple Crown 10.00 25.00
8A Bobby Doerr #1 10.00 25.00
8B Bobby Doerr HOF 86 10.00 25.00
8C Bobby Doerr MVP 44 10.00 25.00
11A Dennis Eckersley 92 CY 10.00 25.00
11B D.Eckersley 92 CY-MVP 10.00 25.00
11C Dennis Eckersley 92 MVP 10.00 25.00
14A Eric Davis #44 10.00 25.00
14B Eric Davis 87 AS 10.00 25.00
14C Eric Davis 90 WS 10.00 25.00
16A Fred Lynn 75 MVP-ROY 10.00 25.00
16B Fred Lynn 75-83 AS 10.00 25.00
19A Jack Morris 91 WS MVP 10.00 25.00
19B Jack Morris 92 WS 10.00 25.00
20A Jim Palmer 73 CY 10.00 25.00
20B Jim Palmer 75 CY 10.00 25.00
20C Jim Palmer 76 CY 10.00 25.00
21A Jim Abbott 4-8-89 10.00 25.00
21B Jim Abbott 9-4-93 10.00 25.00
21C Jim Abbott 6-15-99 10.00 25.00
21D Jim Abbott U of Mich 10.00 25.00
21E Jim Abbott Yanks 10.00 25.00
27 Lenny Dykstra 86 WS 10.00 25.00
29A Ralph Kiner #4 10.00 25.00
29B Ralph Kiner 48-53 AS 10.00 25.00
29C Ralph Kiner HOF 10.00 25.00
29D Ralph Kiner HOF 75 10.00 25.00
38A Steve Garvey #6 10.00 25.00
38B Steve Garvey 74 MVP 10.00 25.00
38C Steve Garvey 78 AS MVP 10.00 25.00
38D Steve Garvey 81 WS 10.00 25.00
39A Tony Perez #24 10.00 25.00
39B Tony Perez HOF 02 10.00 25.00
39C Tony Perez WS 75 10.00 25.00
39D Tony Perez WS 76 10.00 25.00

2003 Donruss Signature Legends of Summer Autographs Notations Decade

RANDOM INSERTS IN PACKS
STATED PRINT RUN 10 SERIAL #'d SETS
NO PRICING DUE TO SCARCITY

2003 Donruss Signature Notable Nicknames

Randomly inserted into packs, these 20 cards players who are commonly known by a nickname. Each of these cards were issued to a stated print run of 750 serial numbered sets.

*CENTURY: .6X TO 1.5X BASIC
CENTURY PRINT RUN 100 SERIAL #'d SETS
DECADE PRINT RUN 10 SERIAL #'d SETS
NO DECADE PRICING DUE TO SCARCITY
RANDOM INSERTS IN PACKS
1 Andre Dawson 2.00 5.00
2 Torii Hunter 2.00 5.00
3 Brooks Robinson 2.00 5.00
4 Carlton Fisk 2.00 5.00
5 Mike Mussina 2.00 5.00
6 Don Mattingly 5.00 12.00
7 Duke Snider 2.00 5.00
8 Eric Davis 2.00 5.00
9 Frank Thomas 2.50 6.00
10 Randy Johnson 2.50 6.00
11 Lenny Dykstra 2.00 5.00
12 Ivan Rodriguez 2.00 5.00
13 Nolan Ryan 6.00 15.00
14 Phil Rizzuto 2.00 5.00
15 Reggie Jackson 2.00 5.00
16 Roger Clemens 5.00 12.00
17 Ryne Sandberg 5.00 12.00
18 Stan Musial 4.00 10.00
19 Luis Gonzalez 2.00 5.00
20 Will Clark 2.00 5.00

2003 Donruss Signature Notable Nicknames Century

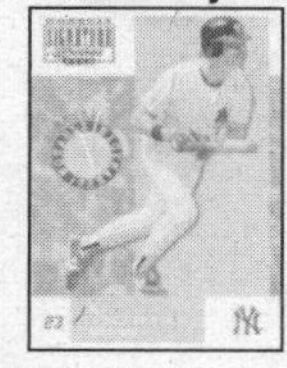

RANDOM INSERTS IN PACKS
STATED PRINT RUN 100 SERIAL #'d SETS

2003 Donruss Signature Notable Nicknames Decade

STATED PRINT RUN 10 SERIAL #'d SETS
NO PRICING DUE TO SCARCITY

2003 Donruss Signature Notable Nicknames Autographs

Randomly inserted in packs, these cards parallel the regular Notable Nickname set but also include an authentic autograph from the featured player as well as his nickname. Most of these cards were issued to a stated print run of 100 copies but a few were issued in smaller quantities and that information is notated in our checklist. For those cards with a print run of 25 or fewer, no pricing is provided due to market scarcity.

1 Andre Dawson 20.00 50.00
2 Torii Hunter 20.00 50.00
3 Brooks Robinson 40.00 80.00
4 Carlton Fisk 40.00 80.00
5 Mike Mussina 50.00 100.00
6 Don Mattingly 75.00 150.00
7 Duke Snider 40.00 80.00
8 Eric Davis/40 40.00 80.00
9 Frank Thomas 50.00 100.00
10 Randy Johnson 60.00 120.00
11 Lenny Dykstra 12.50 30.00
12 Ivan Rodriguez/75 40.00 80.00
13 Nolan Ryan/15
14 Phil Rizzuto 40.00 80.00
15 Reggie Jackson 40.00 80.00
16 Roger Clemens 125.00 200.00
17 Ryne Sandberg 50.00 100.00
18 Stan Musial 60.00 120.00
19 Luis Gonzalez 20.00 50.00
20 Will Clark 40.00 80.00

2003 Donruss Signature Notable Nicknames Autographs Decade

RANDOM INSERTS IN PACKS
STATED PRINT RUN 10 SERIAL #'d SETS
NO PRICING DUE TO SCARCITY

2003 Donruss Signature Player Collection Autographs

Randomly inserted in packs, these cards feature authentic autographs on "player collection" cards. Since each of these cards were issued to a different print run, we have noted that information next to the player's name in our checklist.

1 Roberto Alomar/75 15.00 40.00
2 Adrian Beltre/104 10.00 25.00
3 Lance Berkman/50 20.00 50.00
4 Craig Biggio Btg/26
5 Craig Biggio Fldg/26
6 Joe Borchard/53 8.00 20.00
7 Roger Clemens Pitch/9
8 Roger Clemens Stretch/4
9 J.D. Drew/52 12.50 30.00
10 Jim Edmonds/52 20.00 50.00
11 Tony Gwynn/11
12 Todd Helton/50 20.00 50.00
13 Jason Jennings/49 8.00 20.00
14 Andruw Jones Away/25
15 Andruw Jones Home/25
16 Chipper Jones/51 30.00 60.00
17 Paul Konerko/26
18 Paul Lo Duca/227 6.00 15.00
19 Magglio Ordonez/102 10.00 25.00
20 Roy Oswalt/10
21 Rafael Palmeiro/25
22 Mark Prior/27 20.00 50.00
23 Cal Ripken/22
24 Alex Rodriguez M's/24
25 Alex Rodriguez Rgr/25
26 Ivan Rodriguez/52 20.00 50.00
27 Richie Sexson/50 12.50 30.00
28 Alfonso Soriano/11
29A Matt Williams/19
29B Matt Williams/483 10.00 25.00

2003 Donruss Signature Team Trademarks

Randomly inserted into packs, these cards feature the term "team trademark" on the card. Each of these cards were issued to a stated print run of 500 serial numbered sets.

*CENTURY: .75X TO 2X BASIC
CENTURY PRINT RUN 100 SERIAL #'d SETS
DECADE PRINT RUN 10 SERIAL #'d SETS
NO DECADE PRICING DUE TO SCARCITY
RANDOM INSERTS IN PACKS
1 Adam Dunn 1.50 4.00
2 Andre Dawson 1.50 4.00
3 Babe Ruth 5.00 12.00
4 Barry Bonds 5.00 12.00
5 Brooks Robinson 1.50 4.00
6 Cal Ripken 6.00 15.00
7 Derek Jeter 5.00 12.00
8 Don Mattingly 4.00 10.00
9 Frank Robinson 1.50 4.00
10 Fred Lynn 1.50 4.00
11 Gary Carter 1.50 4.00
12 George Brett 4.00 10.00
13 Greg Maddux 3.00 8.00
14 Ichiro Suzuki 4.00 10.00
15 Jim Palmer 1.50 4.00
16 Jose Contreras 2.00 5.00
17 Kerry Wood 1.50 4.00
18 Lou Gehrig 3.00 8.00
19 Magglio Ordonez 1.50 4.00
20 Mark Grace 1.50 4.00
21 Mike Schmidt 4.00 10.00
22 Nolan Ryan Rgr 5.00 12.00
23 Nolan Ryan Astros 5.00 12.00
24 Reggie Jackson 1.50 4.00
25 Rickey Henderson 2.00 5.00
26 Roberto Clemente 4.00 10.00
27 Roger Clemens Sox 4.00 10.00
28 Roger Clemens Yanks 4.00 10.00
29 Ryne Sandberg 4.00 10.00
30 Sammy Sosa 2.00 5.00
31 Stan Musial 3.00 8.00
32 Steve Carlton 1.50 4.00
33 Tim Hudson 1.50 4.00
34 Tom Glavine 1.50 4.00
35 Tom Seaver 1.50 4.00
36 Tony Gwynn 2.50 6.00
37 Torii Hunter 1.50 4.00
38 Ty Cobb 3.00 8.00
39 Vladimir Guerrero 2.00 5.00
40 Will Clark 1.50 4.00

2003 Donruss Signature Team Trademarks Autographs

Randomly inserted into packs, these cards partially parallel the Team Trademark insert set. Each of these cards feature an authentic autograph from the featured player. Since there are some different print runs we have notated that information in our checklist next to the player's name. For those cards with print runs of 25 or fewer, no pricing is provided due to market scarcity.

1 Adam Dunn/50 20.00 50.00
2 Andre Dawson/250 6.00 15.00
5 Brooks Robinson/250 10.00 25.00
6 Cal Ripken/50 125.00 200.00
8 Don Mattingly/75 50.00 100.00
10 Fred Lynn/250 6.00 15.00
11 Gary Carter/250 6.00 15.00
12 George Brett/50 60.00 120.00
13 Greg Maddux/50 60.00 120.00
16 Jose Contreras/250 8.00 20.00
17 Kerry Wood/50 20.00 50.00
19 Magglio Ordonez/75 10.00 25.00
20 Mark Grace/25
23 Nolan Ryan Astros/50 75.00 150.00
24 Reggie Jackson/75 15.00 40.00
25 Rickey Henderson/50 50.00 100.00
27 Roger Clemens Sox/50 75.00 150.00
28 Roger Clemens Yanks/50 75.00 150.00
29 Ryne Sandberg/100 40.00 80.00
31 Stan Musial/200 30.00 60.00
32 Steve Carlton/150 6.00 15.00
33 Tim Hudson/100 15.00 40.00
34 Tom Glavine/50 20.00 50.00
35 Tom Seaver/50 20.00 50.00
36 Tony Gwynn/50 40.00 80.00
37 Torii Hunter/250 6.00 15.00
39 Vladimir Guerrero/250 10.00 25.00
40 Will Clark/125 15.00 40.00

2003 Donruss Signature Team Trademarks Autographs Century

RANDOM INSERTS IN PACKS
STATED PRINT RUN 100 SERIAL #'d SETS
1 Andre Dawson 10.00 25.00
5 Brooks Robinson 15.00 40.00
9 Frank Robinson 10.00 25.00
10 Fred Lynn 10.00 25.00
11 Gary Carter 10.00 25.00
15 Jim Palmer 10.00 25.00
16 Jose Contreras 12.50 30.00
20 Mark Grace 30.00 60.00
29 Ryne Sandberg 40.00 80.00
31 Stan Musial 30.00 60.00
32 Steve Carlton 10.00 25.00
34 Tom Glavine 15.00 40.00
37 Torii Hunter 10.00 25.00
39 Vladimir Guerrero 15.00 40.00

2003 Donruss Signature Team Trademarks Autographs Decade

RANDOM INSERTS IN PACKS
STATED PRINT RUN 10 SERIAL #'d SETS
NO PRICING DUE TO SCARCITY

2003 Donruss Signature Team Trademarks Autographs Notations

Randomly inserted into packs, these cards feature not only authentic autographs from the featured player as well as a special notation added to that autographs. Each of these cards have varying print runs and we have added that information in our checklist next to the player's name. For those cards with a stated print run of 25 or fewer copies, no pricing is provided due to market scarcity.

2A Andre Dawson #10/250 6.00 15.00
2B Andre Dawson ROY 77/150 6.00 15.00
5A B.Robinson 64 MVP/75 20.00 50.00
5B B.Robinson 70 WS MVP/125 15.00 40.00
10A Fred Lynn 75-83 AS/50 12.50 30.00
11 Gary Carter The Kid/25
12 George Brett #5/25
15A Jim Palmer 73 CY/32 12.50 30.00
15B Jim Palmer 75 CY/128 10.00 25.00
15C Jim Palmer 76 CY/150 6.00 15.00
17 Kerry Wood ROY 98/25
24A Reggie Jackson #44/5
24B Reggie Jackson 99/20
29A Ryne Sandberg #23/40 60.00 120.00
29B Ryne Sandberg Cubs/5
29C Ryne Sandberg 84 MVP/55 50.00 100.00
32A Steve Carlton 72 CY/50 12.50 30.00
32B Steve Carlton 77 CY/50 12.50 30.00
32C Steve Carlton 80 CY/50 12.50 30.00
32D Steve Carlton 82 CY/50 12.50 30.00
33A Tim Hudson Black Angus/5
33B Tim Hudson Huddy/50 20.00 50.00
37A Torii Hunter #48/20
40A Will Clark 89 MVP/52 40.00 80.00
40B Will Clark 89 WS/52 40.00 80.00

2003 Donruss Signature Team Trademarks Autographs Notations Century

RANDOM INSERTS IN PACKS
STATED PRINT RUN 100 SERIAL #'d SETS
2A Andre Dawson #10 10.00 25.00
2B Andre Dawson ROY 77 10.00 25.00
10A Fred Lynn 75-83 AS 10.00 25.00
10B Fred Lynn 75 MVP-ROY 10.00 25.00
15A Jim Palmer 73 CY 10.00 25.00
15B Jim Palmer 75 CY 10.00 25.00
15C Jim Palmer 76 CY 10.00 25.00

2003 Donruss Signature Team Trademarks Autographs Notations Decade

RANDOM INSERTS IN PACKS
STATED PRINT RUN 10 SERIAL #'d SETS
NO PRICING DUE TO SCARCITY

2005 Donruss Signature

This 159-card set was released in November, 2005. The set was issued in five-card packs with an $10 SRP which came four packs to a box and four boxes to a case. Cards numbered 1-150 feature a mix of current stars, prospects and retired stars while cards numbered 151 through 159 feature two or more rookies or prospects with common teams and those cards were issued at different stated odds which we have notated in our set detail.

COMMON CARD (1-150) .75 2.00
COMMON RC (1-150) .75 2.00
151-156 DUAL AU STATED ODDS 1:14
157-158 TRIPLE AU STATED ODDS 1:51
159 QUAD AU STATED ODDS 1:626
151-159 TIER 1 QTY B/WN 1-50 PER
151-159 TIER 2 QTY B/WN 51-100 PER
151-159 TIER 3 QTY B/WN 101-250 PER
151-159 TIER 4 QTY B/WN 251-800 PER
151-159 TIER 6 QTY B/WN 1201-2000 PER
151-159 ARE NOT SERIAL-NUMBERED
151-159 QTY INFO PROVIDED BY DONRUSS
155-156 NOT PRICED DUE TO SCARCITY
1 Scot Shields .75 2.00
2 Tim Salmon 1.25 3.00
3 Chone Figgins .75 2.00
4 Dallas McPherson .75 2.00
5 John Lackey .75 2.00
6 Ervin Santana .75 2.00
7 Casey Kotchman .75 2.00
8 Steve Finley .75 2.00
9 Brandon Webb .75 2.00
10 Chad Tracy .75 2.00
11 Russ Ortiz .75 2.00
12 Alex Cintron .75 2.00
13 Marcus Giles .75 2.00
14 Ichiro Suzuki 2.50 6.00
15 Tadahito Iguchi RC 2.00 5.00
16 Chipper Jones 1.25 3.00
17 Cal Ripken 5.00 12.00
18 Rick Dempsey .75 2.00
19 Adam Loewen .75 2.00
20 Eric Byrnes .75 2.00
21 Luis Matos .75 2.00
22 Miguel Tejada .75 2.00
23 Brooks Robinson 1.25 3.00
24 Kevin Youkilis .75 2.00
25 Keith Foulke .75 2.00
26 Trot Nixon .75 2.00
27 Edgar Renteria .75 2.00
28 Luis Tiant .75 2.00
29 Todd Walker .75 2.00
30 Mark Grace 1.25 3.00
31 Steve Stone .75 2.00
32 Ron Santo 1.25 3.00
33 Michael Wuertz .75 2.00
34 Russ Rohlicek RC .75 2.00
35 Ryne Sandberg 2.50 6.00
36 Andre Dawson .75 2.00
37 Aramis Ramirez .75 2.00
38 Derrek Lee 1.25 3.00
39 Paulino Reynoso RC .75 2.00
40 Jose Contreras .75 2.00
41 Freddy Garcia .75 2.00
42 Mark Buehrle .75 2.00
43 Bubba Nelson .75 2.00
44 Eric Davis .75 2.00
45 Adam Dunn .75 2.00
46 Travis Hafner .75 2.00
47 Larry Bigbie .75 2.00
48 Todd Helton 1.25 3.00
49 Chris Shelton 1.25 3.00
50 Willie Mays 2.00 5.00
51 Craig Monroe .75 2.00
52 Ivan Rodriguez 1.25 3.00
53 Miguel Cabrera 1.25 3.00
54 Chris Resop RC .75 2.00
55 Paul Lo Duca .75 2.00
56 Luke Scott RC 1.50 4.00
57 Brandon Backe .75 2.00
58 Mark McLemore RC .75 2.00
59 Devon Lowery RC .75 2.00
60 Jeremy Affeldt .75 2.00
61 Duke Snider 1.25 3.00
62 Johnny Podres .75 2.00
63 Rickie Weeks .75 2.00
64 Ben Sheets .75 2.00
65 Carlos Lee .75 2.00
66 Lew Ford .75 2.00
67 Travis Bowyer RC .75 2.00
68 Garrett Jones RC .75 2.00
69 Joe Nathan .75 2.00
70 Kent Hrbek .75 2.00
71 J.D. Durbin .75 2.00
72 Shannon Stewart .75 2.00
73 Torii Hunter .75 2.00
74 Kirby Puckett 1.25 3.00
75 Danny Graves .75 2.00
76 Jae Weong Seo .75 2.00
77 Matt Lindstrom RC .75 2.00
78 Dwight Gooden .75 2.00
79 Carlos Beltran .75 2.00
80 Mike Piazza 1.25 3.00
81 Tom Gordon .75 2.00
82 Adam LaRoche .75 2.00
83 Dave Righetti .75 2.00
84 Joe Pepitone .75 2.00
85 Gary Sheffield .75 2.00
86 Jim Leyritz .75 2.00
87 Rich Gossage .75 2.00
88 Don Larsen .75 2.00
89 Bernie Williams 1.25 3.00
90 Jorge Posada 1.25 3.00
91 Octavio Dotel .75 2.00
92 Rollie Fingers .75 2.00
93 Dennis Eckersley .75 2.00
94 Rich Harden .75 2.00
95 Art Howe .75 2.00
96 Jose Canseco 1.25 3.00
97 Barry Zito .75 2.00
98 Eric Chavez .75 2.00
99 Rickey Henderson 1.25 3.00
100 Chris Roberson RC .75 2.00
101 Eude Brito RC .75 2.00
102 Randy Wolf .75 2.00
103 Mike Lieberthal .75 2.00
104 John Kruk .75 2.00
105 Lenny Dykstra .75 2.00
106 Carlos Ruiz RC .75 2.00
107 Bobby Abreu .75 2.00
108 Bill Madlock .75 2.00
109 Mike Johnston .75 2.00
110 Ian Snell .75 2.00
111 Freddy Sanchez .75 2.00
112 Jose Castillo .75 2.00
113 Jeff Miller RC .75 2.00
114 John Candelaria .75 2.00
115 Jason Bay .75 2.00
116 Mark Loretta .75 2.00
117 Sean Thompson RC .75 2.00
118 Akinori Otsuka .75 2.00
119 Omar Vizquel 1.25 3.00
120 Will Clark 1.25 3.00
121 Clint Nageotte .75 2.00
122 J.J. Putz .75 2.00
123 Raul Ibanez .75 2.00
124 Wladimir Balentien RC 1.25 3.00
125 Jamie Moyer .75 2.00
126 Adrian Beltre .75 2.00
127 Richie Sexson .75 2.00
128 Edgar Martinez 1.25 3.00
129 Jeff Suppan .75 2.00
130 Marty Marion .75 2.00
131 Keith Hernandez .75 2.00
132 Ozzie Smith 1.25 3.00
133 Mark Mulder .75 2.00
134 Lee Smith .75 2.00
135 Jim Edmonds .75 2.00
136 Nomar Garciaparra 1.25 3.00
137 Delmon Young 1.25 3.00
138 Jason Hammel RC .75 2.00
139 Agustin Montero RC .75 2.00
140 Francisco Cordero .75 2.00
141 Michael Young .75 2.00
142 Al Oliver .75 2.00
143 David Dellucci .75 2.00
144 Nolan Ryan 3.00 8.00
145 Rafael Palmeiro 1.25 3.00
146 Alexis Rios .75 2.00
147 Jose Guillen .75 2.00
148 Danny Rueckel RC .75 2.00
149 Jose Vidro .75 2.00
150 Preston Wilson .75 2.00
151 Rickie Weeks 60.00 100.00
Prince Fielder RC T3
152 Hayden Penn RC 8.00 20.00
Adam Loewen T4
153 Akinori Otsuka 10.00 25.00
Keiichi Yabu RC T4
154 Brandon McCarthy RC 12.50 30.00
Anibal Sanchez RC T6
155 Norihiro Nakamura RC
Keiichi Yabu T1/35 *
156 Mike Morse RC
Yuniesky Betancourt RC T1/49 *
157 Jeff Niemann RC 15.00 40.00
Justin Verlander RC
Phil Humber RC T4
158 Wladimir Balentien 12.50 30.00
Ambiorix Concepcion RC
Miguel Negron RC T2/77 *
159 Justin Verlander 50.00 100.00
Jeff Niemann
Tony Pena RC
Ubaldo Jimenez RC T2/74 *

2005 Donruss Signature Century Proofs Gold

*GOLD: 1.5X TO 4X BASIC
RANDOM INSERTS IN PACKS
STATED PRINT RUN 25 SERIAL #'d SETS
NO RC PRICING DUE TO SCARCITY

2005 Donruss Signature Century Proofs Platinum

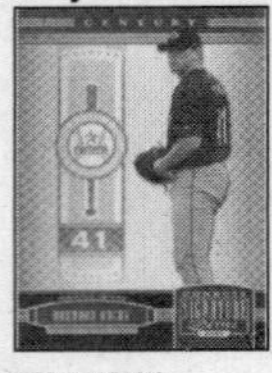

RANDOM INSERTS IN PACKS
STATED PRINT RUN 10 SERIAL #'d SETS
NO PRICING DUE TO SCARCITY

2005 Donruss Signature Century Proofs Silver

*SILVER: 1X TO 2.5X BASIC
*SILVER: 1X TO 2.5X BASIC RC
RANDOM INSERTS IN PACKS
STATED PRINT RUN 75 SERIAL #'d SETS

2005 Donruss Signature Autograph Gold MS

*GOLD p/r 25-50: .6X TO 1.5X SILV T5-T6
*GOLD p/r 25-50: .6X TO 1.5X SILV T4
*GOLD p/r 25-50: .6X TO 1.5X SILV T3
*GOLD p/r 25-50: .5X TO 1.2X SILV T2
*GOLD p/r 25-50: 1X TO 1X SILV T1
RANDOM INSERTS IN PACKS
PRINT RUNS B/WN 3-50 COPIES PER
NO PRICING ON QTY OF 21 OR LESS
NO RC YR PRICING ON QTY OF 25 OR LESS
17 Cal Ripken/50 60.00 120.00
21 Luis Matos/50 6.00 15.00
49 Chris Shelton/43 12.50 30.00
88 Don Larsen/25 10.00 25.00
93 Dennis Eckersley/50 10.00 25.00
110 Ian Snell/34 6.00 15.00
142 Al Oliver/25 10.00 25.00
143 David Dellucci/25 10.00 25.00

2005 Donruss Signature Autograph Platinum MS

*PLAT p/r 25: .6X TO 1.5X SILV T5-T6
*PLAT p/r 25: .6X TO 1.5X SILV T4
*PLAT p/r 25: .6X TO 1.5X SILV T3
*PLAT p/r 25: .5X TO 1.2X SILV T2
*PLAT p/r 25: .4X TO 1X SILV T1
RANDOM INSERTS IN PACKS
PRINT RUNS B/WN 1-25 COPIES PER
NO PRICING ON QTY OF 22 OR LESS
NO RC YR PRICING DUE TO SCARCITY
17 Cal Ripken/25 75.00 150.00

2005 Donruss Signature Autograph Silver

STATED ODDS 1:2
TIER 1 QTY B/WN 1-50 COPIES PER
TIER 2 QTY B/WN 51-100 COPIES PER
TIER 3 QTY B/WN 101-250 COPIES PER
TIER 4 QTY B/WN 251-800 COPIES PER
TIER 5 QTY B/WN 801-1200 COPIES PER
TIER 6 QTY B/WN 1201-2000 COPIES PER
CARDS ARE NOT SERIAL-NUMBERED
PRINT RUN INFO PROVIDED BY DONRUSS
NO PRICING ON QTY OF 21 OR LESS
1 Scot Shields T6 4.00 10.00
2 Tim Salmon T4 6.00 15.00
3 Chone Figgins T3 6.00 15.00
4 Dallas McPherson T3 4.00 10.00
5 John Lackey T3 6.00 15.00
6 Ervin Santana T1/25 * 10.00 25.00
8 Steve Finley T1/14 *
9 Brandon Webb T5 4.00 10.00
10 Chad Tracy T4 4.00 10.00
11 Russ Ortiz T4 4.00 10.00
12 Alex Cintron T4 4.00 10.00
16 Chipper Jones T1/15 *
17 Cal Ripken T5 50.00 100.00
18 Rick Dempsey T6 4.00 10.00
19 Adam Loewen T5 4.00 10.00
20 Eric Byrnes T4 4.00 10.00
24 Kevin Youkilis T6 4.00 10.00
25 Keith Foulke T5 6.00 15.00
26 Trot Nixon T4 6.00 15.00
27 Edgar Renteria T4 6.00 15.00
28 Luis Tiant T3 6.00 15.00
29 Todd Walker T5 4.00 10.00
30 Mark Grace T4 10.00 25.00
31 Steve Stone T3 6.00 15.00
32 Ron Santo T3 10.00 25.00
33 Michael Wuertz T3 4.00 10.00
34 Russ Rohlicek T2/60 * 5.00 12.00
35 Ryne Sandberg T4 20.00 50.00
36 Andre Dawson T1/11 *
39 Paulino Reynoso T2/86 * 5.00 12.00
40 Jose Contreras T1/19 *
43 Bubba Nelson T3 4.00 10.00
47 Larry Bigbie T2/92 * 8.00 20.00
53 Miguel Cabrera T4 10.00 25.00
54 Chris Resop T4 3.00 8.00
56 Luke Scott T3 8.00 20.00
58 Mark McLemore T1/43 * 6.00 15.00
59 Devon Lowery T4 3.00 8.00
61 Duke Snider T4 10.00 25.00
62 Johnny Podres T2/99 * 8.00 20.00
63 Rickie Weeks T4 6.00 15.00
64 Ben Sheets T4 6.00 15.00
66 Lew Ford T5 4.00 10.00
67 Travis Bowyer T5 3.00 8.00
68 Garrett Jones T4 3.00 8.00
69 Joe Nathan T4 6.00 15.00
70 Kent Hrbek T4 6.00 15.00
71 J.D. Durbin T1/39 * 6.00 15.00
75 Danny Graves T5 4.00 10.00
76 Jae Weong Seo T4 6.00 15.00
77 Matt Lindstrom T4 3.00 8.00
79 Carlos Beltran T1/37 * 10.00 25.00
81 Tom Gordon T5 4.00 10.00
82 Adam LaRoche T2/53 * 8.00 20.00
83 Dave Righetti T4 6.00 15.00
84 Joe Pepitone T3 6.00 15.00
85 Gary Sheffield T3 10.00 25.00
86 Jim Leyritz T2/93 * 8.00 20.00
87 Rich Gossage T2/65 * 8.00 20.00
91 Octavio Dotel T4 4.00 10.00
92 Rollie Fingers T4 6.00 15.00
94 Rich Harden T3 6.00 15.00
96 Jose Canseco T1/8 *
97 Barry Zito T1/26 * 10.00 25.00
100 Chris Roberson T4 3.00 8.00
101 Eude Brito T4 3.00 8.00
102 Randy Wolf T4 4.00 10.00
103 Mike Lieberthal T4 6.00 15.00
104 John Kruk T3 6.00 15.00
105 Lenny Dykstra T1/21 *
106 Carlos Ruiz T1/11 *
109 Mike Johnston T3 4.00 10.00
112 Jose Castillo T1/20 *
113 Jeff Miller T1/49 * 6.00 15.00
114 John Candelaria T1/43 * 10.00 25.00
116 Mark Loretta T5 4.00 10.00
117 Sean Thompson T3 4.00 10.00
118 Akinori Otsuka T2/52 * 8.00 20.00
119 Omar Vizquel T2/100 * 12.50 30.00
121 Clint Nageotte T5 4.00 10.00
122 J.J. Putz T6 4.00 10.00
123 Raul Ibanez T6 4.00 10.00
124 Wladimir Balentien T4 5.00 12.00
125 Jamie Moyer T4 6.00 15.00
129 Jeff Suppan T6 4.00 10.00
130 Marty Marion T5 6.00 15.00
131 Keith Hernandez T4 6.00 15.00
132 Ozzie Smith T2/94 * 20.00 50.00
133 Mark Mulder T3 6.00 15.00
134 Lee Smith T1/6 *
137 Delmon Young T2/99 * 12.50 30.00
138 Jason Hammel T2/57 * 5.00 12.00
139 Agustin Montero T3 4.00 10.00
140 Francisco Cordero T3 4.00 10.00
141 Michael Young T1/6 *
142 Al Oliver T1/7 *
144 Nolan Ryan T2/62 * 50.00 100.00
145 Rafael Palmeiro T1/6 *
146 Alexis Rios T3 6.00 15.00
147 Jose Guillen T6 4.00 10.00
148 Danny Rueckel T4 3.00 8.00
149 Jose Vidro T1/18 *

2005 Donruss Signature Autograph Silver Notation

*NT T4: .5X TO 1.2X SILV T5-T6
*NT T3: .5X TO 1.2X SILV T5-T6
*NT T2: .6X TO 1.5X SILV T4
*NT T1 p/r 25-41: .75X TO 2X SILV T4
RANDOM INSERTS IN PACKS
TIER 1 QTY B/WN 1-50 COPIES PER
TIER 2 QTY B/WN 51-100 COPIES PER
TIER 3 QTY B/WN 101-250 COPIES PER
TIER 4 QTY B/WN 251-800 COPIES PER
CARDS ARE NOT SERIAL-NUMBERED
PRINT RUN INFO PROVIDED BY DONRUSS
NO PRICING ON QTY OF 24 OR LESS
17 Cal Ripken T1/25 * 75.00 150.00
105 Lenny Dykstra T1/41 * 12.50 30.00

2005 Donruss Signature Autograph Material Bat Gold

*BAT p/r 25-50: .6X TO 1.5X SILV T5-T6
*BAT p/r 25-50: .6X TO 1.5X SILV T3
*BAT p/r 25-50: .5X TO 1.2X SILV T2
RANDOM INSERTS IN PACKS
PRINT RUNS B/WN 1-50 COPIES PER
NO PRICING ON QTY OF 15 OR LESS
7 Casey Kotchman/25 10.00 25.00
24 Kevin Youkilis/25 6.00 15.00
65 Carlos Lee/25 10.00 25.00
108 Bill Madlock/50 10.00 25.00
111 Freddy Sanchez/42 6.00 15.00

2005 Donruss Signature Autograph Material Bat Platinum

*BAT p/r 25: .6X TO 1.5X SILV T3
*BAT p/r 25: .5X TO 1.2X SILV T2
RANDOM INSERTS IN PACKS
PRINT RUNS B/WN 1-25 COPIES PER
NO PRICING ON QTY OF 21 OR LESS
108 Bill Madlock/25 10.00 25.00
111 Freddy Sanchez/25 6.00 15.00

2005 Donruss Signature Autograph Material Bat Silver

*BAT T1 p/r 50: .6X TO 1.5X SILV T3
RANDOM INSERTS IN PACKS
TIER 1 QTY B/WN 1-50 COPIES PER
TIER 3 QTY B/WN 101-250 COPIES PER
CARDS ARE NOT SERIAL-NUMBERED
PRINT RUN INFO PROVIDED BY DONRUSS
NO PRICING ON QTY OF 22 OR LESS
108 Bill Madlock T3 6.00 15.00
119 Omar Vizquel T3 10.00 25.00

2005 Donruss Signature Autograph Material Button Platinum

RANDOM INSERTS IN PACKS
PRINT RUNS B/WN 1-6 COPIES PER
NO PRICING DUE TO SCARCITY

2005 Donruss Signature Autograph Material Jersey Silver

*JSY T3: .4X TO 1X SILV T4 10.00 25.00
*JSY T2: .5X TO 1.2X SILV T4 10.00 25.00
*JSY T1 p/r 36-50: .6X TO 1.5X SILV T5-T6
TIER 1 QTY B/WN 1-50 COPIES PER
TIER 2 QTY B/WN 51-100 COPIES PER
TIER 3 QTY B/WN 101-250 COPIES PER
CARDS ARE NOT SERIAL-NUMBERED
PRINT RUN INFO PROVIDED BY DONRUSS
NO PRICING ON QTY OF 22 OR LESS
21 Luis Matos T3 4.00 10.00
60 Jeremy Affeldt Pants T1/36 * 6.00 15.00
93 Dennis Eckersley T1/50 * 10.00 25.00

2005 Donruss Signature Autograph Material Jersey Number Platinum

*JSY NP p/r 25: .6X TO 1.5X SILV T5-T6
*JSY NP p/r 25: .6X TO 1.5X SILV T4
RANDOM INSERTS IN PACKS
PRINT RUNS B/WN 1-25 COPIES PER
NO PRICING ON QTY OF 14 OR LESS

21 Luis Matos/25 6.00 15.00
57 Brandon Backe/25 6.00 15.00
93 Dennis Eckersley/25 10.00 25.00

2005 Donruss Signature Autograph Material Jersey Position Gold

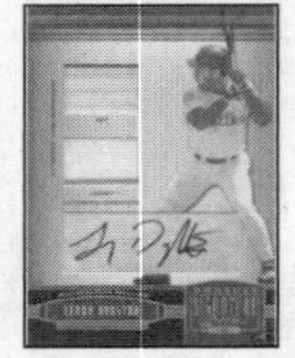

*JSY JP p/r 25-50: .6X TO 1.5X SILV T5-T6
*JSY JP p/r 25-50: .6X TO 1.5X SILV T4
RANDOM INSERTS IN PACKS
PRINT RUNS B/WN 1-50 COPIES PER
NO PRICING ON QTY OF 10 OR LESS
21 Luis Matos/50 6.00 15.00
57 Brandon Backe/50 6.00 15.00
93 Dennis Eckersley/50 10.00 25.00

2005 Donruss Signature Autograph Material Combo Gold

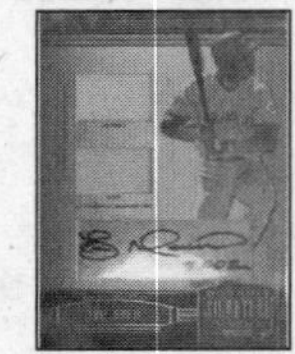

*COMBO p/r 25-46: .75X TO 2X SILV T4
RANDOM INSERTS IN PACKS
PRINT RUNS B/WN 1-46 COPIES PER
NO PRICING ON QTY OF 10 OR LESS
17 C.Ripken Bat-Pants/46 75.00 150.00

2005 Donruss Signature Autograph Material Combo Platinum

RANDOM INSERTS IN PACKS
PRINT RUNS B/WN 1-25 COPIES PER
NO PRICING ON QTY OF 10 OR LESS
44 Eric Davis Bat-Jsy/25 40.00 80.00
50 Willie Mays Bat-Jsy/25 75.00 150.00
78 D.Gooden Bat-Jsy/25 12.50 30.00

2005 Donruss Signature Autograph Material Combo Silver

*COMBO p/r 50: .75X TO 2X SILV T4
RANDOM INSERTS IN PACKS
TIER 1 QTY B/WN 1-50 COPIES PER
TIER 2 QTY B/WN 51-100 COPIES PER
CARDS ARE NOT SERIAL-NUMBERED
PRINT RUN INFO PROVIDED BY DONRUSS
NO PRICING ON QTY OF 22 OR LESS
17 C.Rip Bat-Pants T2/100 * 60.00 120.00

2005 Donruss Signature Club Autograph Barrel

RANDOM INSERTS IN PACKS
PRINT RUNS B/WN 1-4 COPIES PER
CARDS ARE NOT SERIAL-NUMBERED
PRINT RUN INFO PROVIDED BY DONRUSS
NO PRICING DUE TO SCARCITY

2005 Donruss Signature Club Autograph Bat

STATED ODDS 1:20
TIER 1 QTY B/WN 1-50 COPIES PER

TIER 2 QTY B/WN 51-100 COPIES PER
TIER 3 QTY B/WN 101-250 COPIES PER
TIER 4 QTY B/WN 251-800 COPIES PER
CARDS ARE NOT SERIAL-NUMBERED
PRINT RUN INFO PROVIDED BY DONRUSS
NO PRICING ON QTY OF 2
1 Paul O'Neill T1/32 * 15.00 40.00
2 Alan Trammell T2/70 * 8.00 20.00
3 Barry Larkin T3 10.00 25.00
4 Carlton Fisk T1/34 * 15.00 40.00
5 Dale Murphy T2/100 * 12.50 30.00
6 Frank Thomas T3 15.00 40.00
7 Magglio Ordonez T4 6.00 15.00
8 Mark Teixeira T2/100 * 12.50 30.00
10 Omar Vizquel T4 10.00 25.00
11 Steve Garvey T4 6.00 15.00
12 Willie Mays T1/2 *

2005 Donruss Signature Hall of Fame

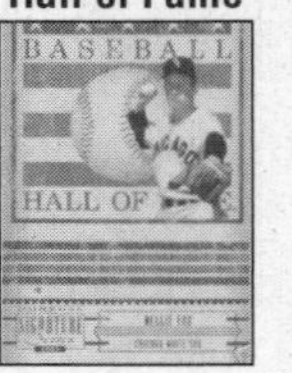

STATED ODDS 1:3
1 Al Kaline 3.00 8.00
2 Billy Williams 1.50 4.00
3 Bobby Doerr 1.50 4.00
4 Gaylord Perry 1.50 4.00
5 George Brett 4.00 10.00
6 Hank Aaron 4.00 10.00
7 Mike Schmidt 4.00 10.00
8 Nolan Ryan 5.00 12.00
9 Robin Roberts 1.50 4.00
10 Phil Niekro 1.50 4.00
11 Phil Rizzuto 2.00 5.00
12 Ralph Kiner 2.00 5.00
13 Rod Carew 2.00 5.00
14 Ryne Sandberg 4.00 10.00
15 Stan Musial 3.00 8.00
16 Steve Carlton 1.50 4.00
17 Tom Seaver 2.00 5.00
18 Willie McCovey 2.00 5.00
19 Willie Mays 4.00 10.00
20 Duke Snider 2.00 5.00
21 Rollie Fingers 1.50 4.00
22 Monte Irvin 1.50 4.00
23 Ozzie Smith 3.00 8.00
24 Johnny Bench 3.00 8.00
25 Luis Aparicio 1.50 4.00
26 Whitey Ford 2.00 5.00
27 Orlando Cepeda 1.50 4.00
28 Jim Bunning 1.50 4.00
29 Earl Weaver 1.50 4.00
30 Frank Robinson 1.50 4.00
31 Babe Ruth Yanks 4.00 10.00
32 Yogi Berra 3.00 8.00
33 Wade Boggs 2.00 5.00
34 Ted Williams 4.00 10.00
35 Roberto Clemente 5.00 12.00
36 Nellie Fox 2.00 5.00
37 Joe Morgan 1.50 4.00
38 Harmon Killebrew 3.00 8.00
39 Carlton Fisk 2.00 5.00
40 Babe Ruth Sox 4.00 10.00

2005 Donruss Signature Hall of Fame Material Bat

*BAT T3: .4X TO 1X JSY T4
*BAT T3: .4X TO 1X JSY T3
STATED ODDS 1:20
TIER 2 QTY B/WN 51-100 COPIES PER
TIER 3 QTY B/WN 101-250 COPIES PER
TIER 4 QTY B/WN 251-800 COPIES PER
TIER 5 QTY B/WN 801-1200 COPIES PER
CARDS ARE NOT SERIAL-NUMBERED
PRINT RUN INFO PROVIDED BY DONRUSS
31 Babe Ruth Yanks T3 90.00 150.00
33 Wade Boggs T4 4.00 10.00
35 Roberto Clemente T5 15.00 40.00
40 Babe Ruth Sox T2/55 *

2005 Donruss Signature Hall of Fame Material Jersey

STATED ODDS 1:21
TIER 1 QTY B/WN 1-50 COPIES PER
TIER 2 QTY B/WN 51-100 COPIES PER
TIER 3 QTY B/WN 101-250 COPIES PER
TIER 4 QTY B/WN 251-800 COPIES PER
CARDS ARE NOT SERIAL-NUMBERED

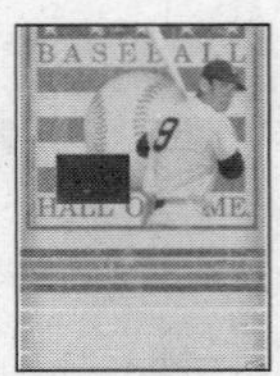

PRINT RUN INFO PROVIDED BY DONRUSS
NO PRICING ON QTY OF 17 OR LESS
2 Billy Williams T1/25 * 5.00 12.00
3 Bobby Doerr T2/100 * 4.00 10.00
4 Gaylord Perry T3 3.00 8.00
6 Hank Aaron T3 10.00 25.00
8 Nolan Ryan T1/30 * 20.00 50.00
10 Phil Niekro T3 3.00 8.00
11 Phil Rizzuto T3 4.00 10.00
13 Rod Carew T3 4.00 10.00
14 Ryne Sandberg T1/11 *
15 Stan Musial T2/66 * 8.00 20.00
16 Steve Carlton Pants T3 3.00 8.00
18 Willie McCovey T1/17 *
19 Willie Mays Pants T4 10.00 25.00
21 Rollie Fingers T1/33 * 5.00 12.00
23 Ozzie Smith T1/47 * 8.00 20.00
24 J.Bench Pants T2/51 * 6.00 15.00
26 Whitey Ford T1/13 *
34 Ted Williams Jkt T4 15.00 40.00

2005 Donruss Signature Hall of Fame Material Combo

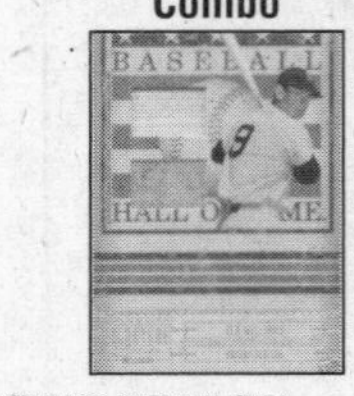

*COMBO T3: .6X TO 1.5X JSY T4
*COMBO T3: .6X TO 1.5X JSY T3
STATED ODDS 1:49
TIER 2 QTY B/WN 51-100 COPIES PER
TIER 3 QTY B/WN 101-250 COPIES PER
CARDS ARE NOT SERIAL-NUMBERED
PRINT RUN INFO PROVIDED BY DONRUSS
31 B.Ruth Yank Bat-Jsy T2/79 * 200.00 300.00

2005 Donruss Signature Hall of Fame Autograph

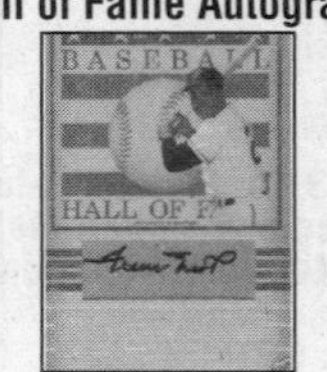

STATED ODDS 1:16
TIER 1 QTY B/WN 1-50 COPIES PER
TIER 2 QTY B/WN 51-100 COPIES PER
TIER 3 QTY B/WN 101-250 COPIES PER
TIER 4 QTY B/WN 251-800 COPIES PER
CARDS ARE NOT SERIAL-NUMBERED
PRINT RUN INFO PROVIDED BY DONRUSS
NO PRICING ON QTY OF 22 OR LESS
1 Al Kaline T2/82 * 15.00 40.00
2 Billy Williams T1/42 * 10.00 25.00
3 Bobby Doerr T1/25 * 10.00 25.00
4 Gaylord Perry T3 6.00 15.00
5 George Brett T1/2 *
6 Hank Aaron T1/5 *
7 Mike Schmidt T1/4 *
8 Nolan Ryan T1/25 * 60.00 120.00
9 Robin Roberts T4 6.00 15.00
11 Phil Rizzuto T3 10.00 25.00
12 Ralph Kiner T1/3 *
13 Rod Carew T1/4 *
14 Ryne Sandberg T2/55 * 30.00 60.00
15 Stan Musial T2/56 * 30.00 60.00
16 Steve Carlton T1/5 *
17 Tom Seaver T1/10 *
18 Willie McCovey T3 10.00 25.00
19 Willie Mays T1/2 *
20 Duke Snider T4 10.00 25.00
21 Rollie Fingers T4 6.00 15.00
22 Monte Irvin T4 6.00 15.00
23 Ozzie Smith T4 15.00 40.00
24 Johnny Bench T3 15.00 40.00
25 Luis Aparicio T1/1 *
26 Whitey Ford T1/6 *
27 Orlando Cepeda T1/30 * 10.00 25.00
28 Jim Bunning T1/25 * 15.00 40.00
29 Earl Weaver T1/22 *
30 Frank Robinson T1/1 *

2005 Donruss Signature Hall of Fame Autograph MS

*AUTO MS p/r 25: .6X TO 1.5X AUTO T4
*AUTO MS p/r 25: .6X TO 1.5X AUTO T3
*AUTO MS p/r 25: .5X TO 1.2X AUTO T2
*AUTO MS p/r 25: .4X TO 1X AUTO T1
RANDOM INSERTS IN PACKS
PRINT RUNS B/WN 1-25 COPIES PER
NO PRICING ON QTY OF 23 OR LESS
26 Whitey Ford/25 15.00 40.00
29 Earl Weaver/25 10.00 25.00

2005 Donruss Signature Hall of Fame Autograph Material Bat

STATED ODDS 1:63
TIER 1 QTY B/WN 1-50 COPIES PER
TIER 2 QTY B/WN 51-100 COPIES PER
CARDS ARE NOT SERIAL-NUMBERED
PRINT RUN INFO PROVIDED BY DONRUSS
NO PRICING ON QTY OF 10 OR LESS
12 Ralph Kiner T2/97 * 12.50 30.00
25 Luis Aparicio T2/100 * 8.00 20.00
33 Wade Boggs T2/56 * 12.50 30.00

2005 Donruss Signature Hall of Fame Autograph Material Jersey

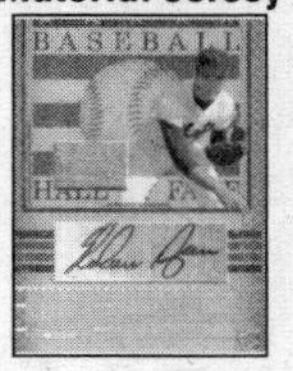

*AU JSY T2: .5X TO 1.2X AU T4
*AU JSY T2: .5X TO 1.2X AU T3
*AU JSY T1: .6X TO 1.5X AU T3
*AU JSY T1: .5X TO 1.2X AU T2
*AU JSY T1: .4X TO 1X AU T1
TIER 1 QTY B/WN 1-50 COPIES PER
TIER 2 QTY B/WN 51-100 COPIES PER
CARDS ARE NOT SERIAL-NUMBERED
PRINT RUN INFO PROVIDED BY DONRUSS
NO PRICING ON QTY OF 20 OR LESS
6 Hank Aaron T1/25 * 125.00 200.00
16 Steve Carlton Pants T1/25 * 10.00 25.00
17 Tom Seaver T1/25 * 15.00 40.00
26 Whitey Ford T1/33 * 15.00 40.00

2005 Donruss Signature Hall of Fame Autograph Material Combo

*AU COM T2: .6X TO 1.5X AU T3
*AU COM T2: .5X TO 1.2X AU T2
*AU COM T1: .75X TO 2X AU T3
TIER 1 QTY B/WN 1-50 COPIES PER
TIER 2 QTY B/WN 51-100 COPIES PER
CARDS ARE NOT SERIAL-NUMBERED
PRINT RUN INFO PROVIDED BY DONRUSS
NO PRICING ON QTY OF 20 OR LESS
6 Hank Aaron Bat-Jsy T1/50 * 125.00 200.00
16 S.Carlton Bat-Pants T1/50 * 12.50 30.00
17 T.Seaver Jsy-Pants T1/50 * 20.00 50.00

2005 Donruss Signature HOF Combos Autograph

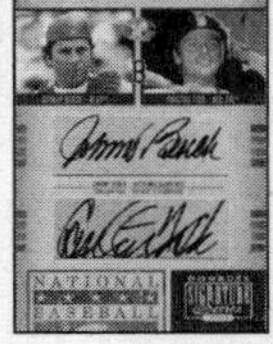

STATED ODDS 1:41
TIER 1 QTY B/WN 1-50 COPIES PER
TIER 2 QTY B/WN 51-100 COPIES PER
TIER 3 QTY B/WN 101-250 COPIES PER
CARDS ARE NOT SERIAL-NUMBERED
PRINT RUN INFO PROVIDED BY DONRUSS
NO PRICING ON QTY OF 10
41 Harmon Killebrew 50.00 100.00
Rod Carew T1/25 *
42 Ryne Sandberg 40.00 80.00
Wade Boggs T2/100 *
43 Nolan Ryan 75.00 150.00
George Brett T1/36 *
44 Steve Carlton 20.00 50.00
Phil Rizzuto T2/100 *
45 Tom Seaver 20.00 50.00
Rollie Fingers T2/100 *
46 Jim Palmer 20.00 50.00
Joe Morgan T1/25 *
47 Bobby Doerr 15.00 40.00
Willie McCovey T2/51 *
48 Luis Aparicio 40.00 80.00
Harmon Killebrew T1/25 *
49 Al Kaline 40.00 80.00
Duke Snider T1/25 *
50 Jim Palmer 20.00 50.00
Frank Robinson T1/25 *
51 Bobby Doerr 30.00 60.00
Carlton Fisk T1/25 *
52 Johnny Bench 40.00 80.00
Joe Morgan T1/25 *
53 Duke Snider 20.00 50.00
Don Sutton T2/100 *
54 Whitey Ford 30.00 60.00
Phil Rizzuto T2/57 *
55 Johnny Bench 40.00 80.00
Carlton Fisk T1/25 *
56 Willie Mays
Duke Snider T1/10 *
57 Whitey Ford 30.00 60.00
Steve Carlton T1/25 *
58 Jim Palmer 30.00 60.00
Tom Seaver T1/32 *
59 Reggie Jackson 40.00 80.00
Rollie Fingers T1/49 *
60 Duke Snider 50.00 100.00
Stan Musial T3

2005 Donruss Signature HOF Trios Autograph

STATED ODDS 1:80
TIER 1 QTY B/WN 1-50 COPIES PER
TIER 2 QTY B/WN 51-100 COPIES PER
CARDS ARE NOT SERIAL-NUMBERED
PRINT RUN INFO PROVIDED BY DONRUSS
NO PRICING ON QTY OF 15
61 Billy Williams 60.00 120.00
Fergie Jenkins
Ryne Sandberg T2/100 *
62 Tony Perez
Joe Morgan
Johnny Bench T2/61 *
63 Rod Carew
Gaylord Perry
Fergie Jenkins T1/25 *
64 Bobby Doerr 50.00 100.00
Joe Morgan
Ryne Sandberg T2/63 *
65 Luis Aparicio 50.00 100.00
Phil Rizzuto
Ozzie Smith T1/50 *
66 Wade Boggs
George Brett
Mike Schmidt T1/25 *
67 Frank Robinson 50.00 100.00
Reggie Jackson
Ralph Kiner T1/25 *
68 Gaylord Perry 40.00 80.00
Fergie Jenkins
Bob Gibson T1/50 *
69 Ozzie Smith 75.00 150.00
Stan Musial
Bob Gibson T2/100 *
70 Willie Mays
Juan Marichal
Willie McCovey T1/15 *

2005 Donruss Signature HOF Quads Autograph

STATED ODDS 1:147
TIER 1 QTY B/WN 1-50 COPIES PER
TIER 2 QTY B/WN 51-100 COPIES PER
CARDS ARE NOT SERIAL-NUMBERED
PRINT RUN INFO PROVIDED BY DONRUSS
NO PRICING ON QTY OF 15
71 Gaylord Perry 40.00 80.00
Juan Marichal
Monte Irvin
Willie McCovey T2/85 *
72 Mike Schmidt
Robin Roberts
Jim Bunning
Steve Carlton T1/38 *
73 Juan Marichal
Willie Mays
Willie McCovey
Gaylord Perry T1/15 *
74 Lou Brock 50.00 100.00
Monte Irvin
Ralph Kiner
Billy Williams T1/41 *
75 Bob Gibson 60.00 120.00
Fergie Jenkins
Gaylord Perry
Tom Seaver T1/50 *
76 Nolan Ryan 125.00 200.00
Steve Carlton
Tom Seaver
Don Sutton T1/50 *

2005 Donruss Signature HOF Six Autograph

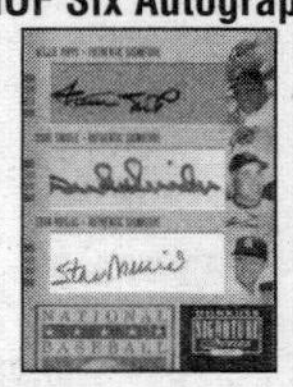

STATED ODDS 1:579
TIER 1 QTY B/WN 1-50 COPIES PER
CARDS ARE NOT SERIAL-NUMBERED
PRINT RUN INFO PROVIDED BY DONRUSS
NO PRICING ON QTY OF 5 OR LESS
77 Willie Mays
Duke Snider
Stan Musial
Al Kaline
Harmon Killebrew
Frank Robinson T1/5 *
78 Bob Gibson
Willie McCovey
Billy Williams
Juan Marichal
Don Sutton
Gaylord Perry T1/25 *
79 Nolan Ryan
George Brett
Johnny Bench
Carlton Fisk
Mike Schmidt
Tom Seaver T1/25 *
80 Eddie Murray
Carl Yastrzemski
Robin Yount
Hoyt Wilhelm
Dave Winfield
Lou Brock T1/1 *
81 Eddie Murray
Robin Yount
Ernie Banks
Kirby Puckett
Dave Winfield
Brooks Robinson T1/1 *
82 Eddie Murray
Ernie Banks
Brooks Robinson
Kirby Puckett
Dave Winfield
Red Schoendienst T1/3 *

2005 Donruss Signature INKcredible Combos

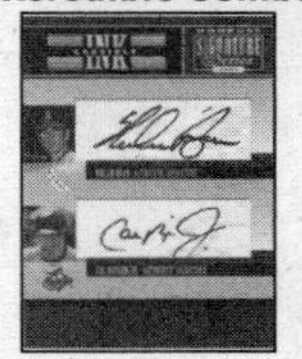

STATED ODDS 1:7
TIER 1 QTY B/WN 1-50 COPIES PER
TIER 2 QTY B/WN 51-100 COPIES PER
TIER 3 QTY B/WN 101-250 COPIES PER
TIER 4 QTY B/WN 251-800 COPIES PER
CARDS ARE NOT SERIAL-NUMBERED
PRINT RUN INFO PROVIDED BY DONRUSS
NO PRICING ON QTY OF 21 OR LESS
1 Troy Percival 12.50 30.00
Francisco Rodriguez T3
2 Scot Shields 8.00 20.00
Francisco Rodriguez T3
3 Scot Shields 6.00 15.00
Troy Percival T4
5 Adam LaRoche
Chipper Jones T1/1 *
6 Rickie Weeks 12.50 30.00
Paul Molitor T1/28 *
7 Ozzie Smith 30.00 60.00
Marty Marion T2/100 *
8 Jeff Suppan 6.00 15.00
{Mark Mulder T4
9 Ron Cey 30.00 60.00
Ron Santo T1/25 *
10 Greg Maddux
Mark Prior T1/11 *
11 Steve Garvey 15.00 40.00
Don Sutton T2/100 *
12 Cal Ripken 50.00 100.00
Billy Ripken T4
13 Jim Palmer 10.00 25.00
Rick Dempsey T2/100 *
14 Jeff Bagwell
Craig Biggio T1/3 *
15 Mark Loretta 4.00 10.00
Sean Burroughs T4
16 David Ortiz
Jason Varitek T1/3 *
17 Brett Myers 5.00 12.00
Randy Wolf T3
18 Andruw Jones
Chipper Jones T1/5 *
19 Justin Morneau 12.50 30.00
Kent Hrbek T1/36 *
20 Frank Thomas 30.00 60.00
Paul Konerko T1/50 *
21 Luis Aparicio 10.00 25.00
Minnie Minoso T4
22 Cal Ripken 75.00 150.00
Tony Gwynn T2/100 *
23 Cal Ripken
Roger Clemens T1/4 *
24 Jose Guillen 6.00 15.00
Tim Salmon T4
25 Kevin Youkilis 6.00 15.00
Dallas McPherson T4
26 Esteban Loaiza 6.00 15.00
Jose Guillen T4
27 Nolan Ryan
Roger Clemens T1/4 *
28 Nolan Ryan
Cal Ripken T1/21 *
29 Chan Ho Park
Jae Weong Seo T1/1 *
30 Nolan Ryan
Randy Johnson T1/29 *
31 Lew Ford 5.00 12.00
Jason Kubel T3
32 Danny Graves 5.00 12.00
Matt Lindstrom T3
33 Tim Salmon 12.50 30.00
Garret Anderson T3
34 Clint Nageotte 4.00 10.00
J.J. Putz T4

2005 Donruss Signature INKcredible Trios

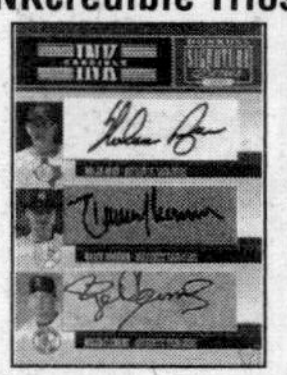

STATED ODDS 1:23
TIER 1 QTY B/WN 1-50 COPIES PER
TIER 2 QTY B/WN 51-100 COPIES PER
TIER 3 QTY B/WN 101-250 COPIES PER
TIER 4 QTY B/WN 251-800 COPIES PER
CARDS ARE NOT SERIAL-NUMBERED
PRINT RUN INFO PROVIDED BY DONRUSS
NO PRICING ON QTY OF 16 OR LESS
35 Scot Shields 15.00 40.00
Troy Percival
Francisco Rodriguez T3
36 Barry Zito 60.00 120.00
Mark Mulder
Tim Hudson T1/37 *
37 Mike Mussina
Mariano Rivera
Jorge Posada T1/1 *
38 Roy Halladay 20.00 50.00
Vernon Wells
Alexis Rios T1/39 *
39 Greg Maddux
Mark Grace
Ryne Sandberg T1/25 *
40 Duke Snider 30.00 60.00
Johnny Podres
Maury Wills T2/100 *
41 Josh Beckett
Dontrelle Willis
Miguel Cabrera T1/2 *
42 Keith Hernandez 20.00 50.00
Lenny Dykstra
Jesse Orosco T2/80 *
43 Esteban Loaiza 15.00 40.00
Jose Guillen
Marlon Byrd T4
44 Cal Ripken 75.00 150.00
Jim Palmer
Rick Dempsey T2/80 *
45 Brett Myers 15.00 40.00
Randy Wolf
Mike Lieberthal T3
46 Jacque Jones 15.00 40.00
Lew Ford
Jason Kubel T2/91 *
47 Randy Jones 50.00 100.00
Ozzie Smith
Rollie Fingers T1/36 *
48 Ron Guidry 20.00 50.00
Rich Gossage
Luis Tiant T3
49 Ron Guidry 20.00 50.00
Rich Gossage
Dave Righetti T3
50 Ozzie Smith 125.00 200.00
Cal Ripken
Alan Trammell T2/99 *
51 Wade Boggs 75.00 150.00
Ryne Sandberg
Tony Gwynn T2/95 *
52 Earl Weaver 75.00 150.00
Cal Ripken
Frank Robinson T1/38 *
53 Harmon Killebrew 60.00 120.00
Rod Carew
Kent Hrbek T1/28 *
54 Minnie Minoso 40.00 80.00
Luis Aparicio
Carlton Fisk T1/25 *
55 Jeff Bagwell
Craig Biggio
Lance Berkman T1/5 *
56 Nolan Ryan
Randy Johnson
Roger Clemens T1/4 *
57 Hideo Nomo
Shigetoshi Hasegawa
Akinori Otsuka T1/16 *
58 David Ortiz
Jason Varitek
Manny Ramirez T1/1 *

2005 Donruss Signature INKcredible Quads

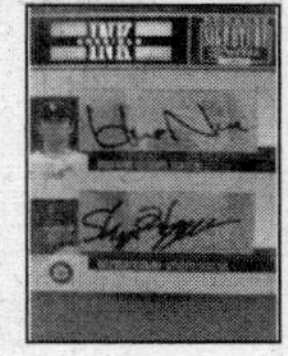

STATED ODDS 1:105
TIER 1 QTY B/WN 1-50 COPIES PER
TIER 2 QTY B/WN 51-100 COPIES PER
TIER 3 QTY B/WN 101-250 COPIES PER
CARDS ARE NOT SERIAL-NUMBERED
PRINT RUN INFO PROVIDED BY DONRUSS
NO PRICING ON QTY OF 11 OR LESS
59 Michael Young
Bobby Crosby
Mike Morse
Orlando Cabrera T1/1 *
60 Jose Guillen 30.00 60.00
Esteban Loaiza
Marlon Byrd
Junior Spivey T3
61 Marlon Byrd 30.00 60.00
Jose Guillen
Livan Hernandez
Esteban Loaiza T3
62 Alfonso Soriano
David Dellucci
Mark Teixeira
Michael Young T1/50 *
63 Dwight Evans 60.00 120.00
Jim Rice
Luis Tiant
Carlton Fisk T2/73 *
64 Phil Rizzuto
Whitey Ford
Don Mattingly
Ron Guidry T1/25 *
65 Hideo Nomo 200.00 350.00
Shigetoshi Hasegawa
So Taguchi
Akinori Otsuka T1/45 *
66 Shigetoshi Hasegawa
Akinori Otsuka
Shingo Takatsu
Keiichi Yabu T1/11 *

2005 Donruss Signature INKcredible Six

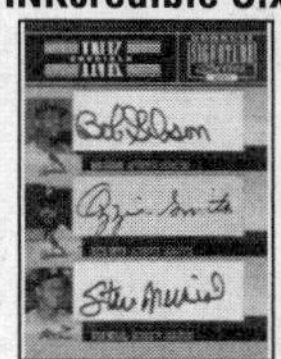

STATED ODDS 1:188
TIER 1 QTY B/WN 1-50 COPIES PER
TIER 2 QTY B/WN 51-100 COPIES PER
TIER 3 QTY B/WN 101-250 COPIES PER
CARDS ARE NOT SERIAL-NUMBERED
PRINT RUN INFO PROVIDED BY DONRUSS
NO PRICING ON QTY OF 1
67 Bob Gibson 150.00 250.00
Ozzie Smith
Stan Musial
Lou Brock
Red Schoendienst
Marty Marion T3
68 Livan Hernandez 50.00 100.00
Jose Guillen
Esteban Loaiza
Jose Vidro
Marlon Byrd
Junior Spivey T2/70 *
69 Cal Ripken
Wade Boggs
Tony Gwynn
Ryne Sandberg
Don Mattingly
Ozzie Smith T1/25 *
70 Hideo Nomo
Kazuhisa Ishii
Shigetoshi Hasegawa
So Taguchi
Akinori Otsuka
Shingo Takatsu T1/1 *
71 Shigetoshi Hasegawa
So Taguchi
Akinori Otsuka
Shingo Takatsu
Keiichi Yabu
Hideo Nomo T1/1 *
72 Hideo Nomo
Shigetoshi Hasegawa
So Taguchi
Akinori Otsuka
Shingo Takatsu
Norihiro Nakamura T1/1 *
73 Andruw Jones
Albert Pujols
Derrek Lee
Adam Dunn
Morgan Ensberg
Aramis Ramirez T1/1 *

2005 Donruss Signature K-Force

STATED ODDS 1:7
1 Nolan Ryan 5.00 12.00
2 Steve Carlton 1.50 4.00
3 Roger Clemens 3.00 8.00
4 Randy Johnson 3.00 8.00
5 Tom Seaver 2.00 5.00
6 Don Sutton 1.50 4.00
7 Gaylord Perry 1.50 4.00
8 Fergie Jenkins 1.50 4.00
9 Bob Gibson 2.00 5.00
10 Greg Maddux 3.00 8.00
11 David Cone 1.50 4.00
12 Bob Feller 1.50 4.00
13 Johan Santana 2.00 5.00
14 Roy Halladay 1.50 4.00
15 Juan Marichal 1.50 4.00

2005 Donruss Signature K-Force Autograph

RANDOM INSERTS IN PACKS
TIER 1 QTY B/WN 1-50 COPIES PER
TIER 2 QTY B/WN 51-100 COPIES PER
TIER 3 QTY B/WN 101-250 COPIES PER
CARDS ARE NOT SERIAL-NUMBERED
PRINT RUN INFO PROVIDED BY DONRUSS
NO PRICING ON QTY OF 20 OR LESS
1 Nolan Ryan T3 40.00 80.00
2 Steve Carlton T1/33 * 10.00 25.00
3 Roger Clemens T1/1 *
4 Randy Johnson T1/5 *
5 Tom Seaver T1/5 *
6 Don Sutton T3 6.00 15.00
7 Gaylord Perry T2/75 * 8.00 20.00
8 Fergie Jenkins T2/55 * 8.00 20.00
9 Bob Gibson T1/20 *
10 Greg Maddux T1/25 * 50.00 100.00
11 David Cone T3 6.00 15.00
12 Bob Feller T1/39 * 10.00 25.00
13 Johan Santana T2/55 * 12.50 30.00
14 Roy Halladay T1/11 *
15 Juan Marichal T3 6.00 15.00

2005 Donruss Signature K-Force Autograph MS

*AU MS p/r 25: .6X TO 1.5X AU T3
*AU MS p/r 25: .5X TO 1.2X AU T2
*AU MS p/r 25: .4X TO 1X AU T1
RANDOM INSERTS IN PACKS
PRINT RUNS B/WN 1-25 COPIES PER
NO PRICING ON QTY OF 20 OR LESS

2005 Donruss Signature K-Force Autograph Material

*AU MAT T3: .4X TO 1X AU T3
*AU MAT T3: .25X TO .6X AU T1
*AU MAT T2: .5X TO 1.2X AU T3
*AU MAT T1: .5X TO 1.2X AU T2
*AU MAT T1: .4X TO 1X AU T1
STATED ODDS 1:54
TIER 1 QTY B/WN 1-50 COPIES PER
TIER 2 QTY B/WN 51-100 COPIES PER
TIER 3 QTY B/WN 101-250 COPIES PER
CARDS ARE NOT SERIAL-NUMBERED
PRINT RUN INFO PROVIDED BY DONRUSS
NO PRICING ON QTY OF 7 OR LESS
9 Bob Gibson Jsy T1/41 * 15.00 40.00

2005 Donruss Signature Milestone Marks

STATED ODDS 1:10
CARD 8 DOES NOT EXIST
1 Duke Snider 2.00 5.00
2 Nolan Ryan 5.00 12.00
3 Gaylord Perry 1.50 4.00
4 Johnny Bench 3.00 8.00
5 Willie McCovey 2.00 5.00
6 Stan Musial 3.00 8.00
7 Randy Johnson 3.00 8.00
9 Gary Carter 1.50 4.00
10 Tony Gwynn 3.00 8.00

2005 Donruss Signature Milestone Marks Autograph

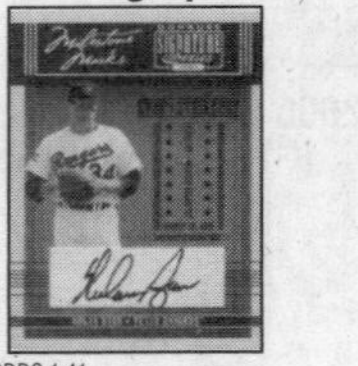

STATED ODDS 1:41
TIER 1 QTY B/WN 1-50 COPIES PER
TIER 3 QTY B/WN 101-250 COPIES PER
CARDS ARE NOT SERIAL-NUMBERED
PRINT RUN INFO PROVIDED BY DONRUSS
NO PRICING ON QTY OF 6 OR LESS
1 Duke Snider T3 10.00 25.00
2 Nolan Ryan T3 40.00 80.00
3 Gaylord Perry T3 6.00 15.00
The milestone mark celebrated was when Perry was a Mariner
4 Johnny Bench T3 12.50 30.00
5 Willie McCovey T1/44 * 15.00 40.00
6 Stan Musial T3 20.00 50.00
9 Gary Carter T1/1 *
10 Tony Gwynn T1/6 *

2005 Donruss Signature Milestone Marks Autograph MS

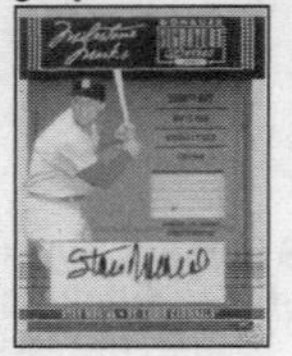

*AU MS: .6X TO 1.5X AU T3
*AU MS: .4X TO 1X AU T1
RANDOM INSERTS IN PACKS
PRINT RUNS B/WN 20-25 COPIES PER
NO PRICING ON QTY OF 20
10 Tony Gwynn/25 20.00 50.00

2005 Donruss Signature Milestone Marks Autograph Material Bat

*AU BAT T1 p/r 25: .6X TO 1.5X AU T3
STATED ODDS 1:1524
TIER 1 QTY B/WN 1-50 COPIES PER
CARDS ARE NOT SERIAL-NUMBERED
PRINT RUN INFO PROVIDED BY DONRUSS
NO PRICING ON QTY OF 5

2005 Donruss Signature Milestone Marks Autograph Material Jersey

*AU JSY T3: .4X TO 1X AU T3
*AU JSY T2: .3X TO .8X AU T1
STATED ODDS 1:134
TIER 1 QTY B/WN 1-50 COPIES PER
TIER 2 QTY B/WN 51-100 COPIES PER
TIER 3 QTY B/WN 101-250 COPIES PER
CARDS ARE NOT SERIAL-NUMBERED
PRINT RUN INFO PROVIDED BY DONRUSS
NO PRICING ON QTY OF 21
10 Tony Gwynn T2/75 * 15.00 40.00

2005 Donruss Signature Milestone Marks Autograph Material Combo

STATED ODDS 1:210
TIER 1 QTY B/WN 1-50 COPIES PER
TIER 3 QTY B/WN 101-250 COPIES PER
CARDS ARE NOT SERIAL-NUMBERED
PRINT RUN INFO PROVIDED BY DONRUSS
NO PRICING ON QTY OF 17 OR LESS
7 R.John Fld Glv-Jsy T1/25 * 40.00 80.00
10 T.Gwynn Jsy-Pants T3 15.00 40.00

2005 Donruss Signature Notable Nicknames 01

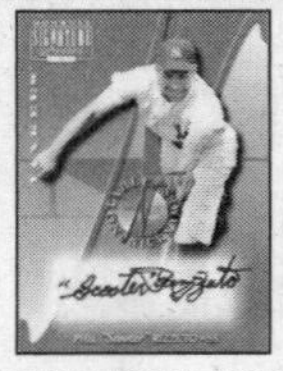

STATED PRINT RUN 100 SERIAL #'d SETS
NON #'d MASTER SERIES CARDS ISSUED
NO MAST.SER.PRICING DUE TO SCARCITY
RANDOM INSERTS IN PACKS
I-ROD AUTO IS NOT NOTATED
OZZIE AUTO IS NOT NOTATED
GM Greg Maddux Bulldog 250.00 400.00
IR Ivan Rodriguez Pudge 30.00 60.00
OS Ozzie Smith Wizard
PR Phil Rizzuto Scooter 30.00 60.00

2005 Donruss Signature Recollection Autographs

STATED ODDS 1:116
NO PRICING DUE TO SCARCITY

2005 Donruss Signature Stamps Material Centennial

PRINT RUNS B/WN 40-100 COPIES PER
*PRO BALL: .4X TO 1X CENTENNIAL
PRO BALL PRINT RUNS B/WN 40-100 PER
RANDOM INSERTS IN PACKS
1 Babe Ruth Pants/40
2 Cal Ripken Pants/50 20.00 50.00
5 Harmon Killebrew Bat/70 6.00 15.00
8 Adrian Beltre Shoes/100 4.00 10.00
10 Cal Ripken Pants/50 20.00 50.00
11 Jim Thorpe Jsy/68 90.00 150.00
12 Willie Mays Jsy/100 20.00 50.00
13 Roger Maris Pants/100 20.00 50.00

2005 Donruss Signature Stamps Autograph Centennial

PRINT RUNS B/WN 3-81 COPIES PER
*PRO BALL: .4X TO 1X CENTENNIAL
PRO BALL PRINT RUNS B/WN 3-81 PER
RANDOM INSERTS IN PACKS
NO PRICING ON QTY OF 17 OR LESS
2 Cal Ripken/50 75.00 150.00
3 Sandy Koufax/17
4 Duke Snider/81 12.50 30.00
5 Harmon Killebrew/5
6 Orlando Cepeda/48 10.00 25.00
7 Don Larsen/50 10.00 25.00
8 Adrian Beltre/5
9 Jim Palmer/3
10 Cal Ripken/50 75.00 150.00

2005 Donruss Signature Stamps Autograph Material Centennial

PRINT RUNS B/WN 2-50 COPIES PER
*PRO BALL: .4X TO 1X CENTENNIAL
PRO BALL PRINT RUNS B/WN 1-50 PER
RANDOM INSERTS IN PACKS
NO PRICING ON QTY OF 20 OR LESS
1 Babe Ruth Jsy/2
2 Cal Ripken Pants/50 75.00 150.00
3 Sandy Koufax Jsy/10
5 Harmon Killebrew Bat/33 15.00 40.00
8 Adrian Beltre Shoes/20
10 Cal Ripken Pants/50 75.00 150.00

2005 Donruss Signature Stamps Centennial Autograph

RANDOM INSERTS IN PACKS
PRINT RUNS B/WN 1-2 COPIES PER
NO PRICING DUE TO SCARCITY

2005 Donruss Signature Stars Autograph

STATED ODDS 1:47
TIER 1 QTY B/WN 1-50 COPIES PER
TIER 2 QTY B/WN 51-100 COPIES PER
TIER 3 QTY B/WN 101-250 COPIES PER
CARDS ARE NOT SERIAL-NUMBERED
PRINT RUN INFO PROVIDED BY DONRUSS
1 Mark Teixeira T1/42 * 15.00 40.00
2 Scott Rolen T3 10.00 25.00
3 Roy Oswalt T2/85 * 8.00 20.00
5 Morgan Ensberg T3 6.00 15.00
6 Mark Grace T2/86 * 12.50 30.00
7 Gary Sheffield T2/82 * 12.50 30.00
8 Sean Casey T3 6.00 15.00
10 Ryne Sandberg T3 20.00 50.00

2005 Donruss Signature Stars Autograph MS

*AU MS p/r 25: .6X TO 1.5X AU T3
*AU MS p/r 25: .5X TO 1.2X AU T2
*AU MS p/r 25: .4X TO 1X AU T1
RANDOM INSERTS IN PACKS
PRINT RUNS B/WN 1-25 COPIES PER
NO PRICING ON QTY OF 5 OR LESS
14 Barry Larkin/25 15.00 40.00

2005 Donruss Signature Stars Autograph Material Bat

*AU BAT T3: .3X TO .8X AU T2
*AU BAT T2: .3X TO .8X AU T1
STATED ODDS 1:35
TIER 1 QTY B/WN 1-50 COPIES PER
TIER 2 QTY B/WN 51-100 COPIES PER
TIER 3 QTY B/WN 101-250 COPIES PER
CARDS ARE NOT SERIAL-NUMBERED
PRINT RUN INFO PROVIDED BY DONRUSS
NO PRICING ON QTY OF 9
4 Hideo Nomo T1/36 * 175.00 300.00
11 Stan Musial T1/38 * 40.00 80.00
12 Joe Torre T1/44 * 15.00 40.00
13 Wade Boggs T1/40 * 15.00 40.00
14 Barry Larkin T3 10.00 25.00
15 Dale Murphy T2/100 * 12.50 30.00

2005 Donruss Signature Stars Autograph Material Jersey

*AU JSY T3: .4X TO 1X AU T3
*AU JSY T2: .5X TO 1.2X AU T3
*AU JSY T1: .5X TO 1.2X AU T2
STATED ODDS 1:64
TIER 1 QTY B/WN 1-50 COPIES PER
TIER 2 QTY B/WN 51-100 COPIES PER
TIER 3 QTY B/WN 101-250 COPIES PER
CARDS ARE NOT SERIAL-NUMBERED
PRINT RUN INFO PROVIDED BY DONRUSS
NO PRICING ON QTY OF 19 OR LESS
4 Hideo Nomo Pants T1/50 * 175.00 300.00
11 Stan Musial T1/44 * 40.00 80.00
12 Joe Torre T1/50 * 15.00 40.00
15 Dale Murphy T3 10.00 25.00

2005 Donruss Signature Stats Autograph

STATED ODDS 1:102
TIER 1 QTY B/WN 1-50 COPIES PER
TIER 3 QTY B/WN 101-250 COPIES PER
CARDS ARE NOT SERIAL-NUMBERED
PRINT RUN INFO PROVIDED BY DONRUSS
NO PRICING ON QTY OF 16 OR LESS
1 Tony Gwynn T1/6 *
2 Johan Santana T1/13 *
3 Orel Hershiser T1/16 *
4 Alfonso Soriano T3 6.00 15.00
5 Don Mattingly T1/6 *
6 Curt Schilling T1/2 *
8 Victor Martinez T1/9 *
9 Miguel Cabrera T3 10.00 25.00
10 Mark Teixeira T1/41 * 15.00 40.00

2005 Donruss Signature Stats Autograph MS

*AU MS p/r 25: .6X TO 1.5X AU T3
*AU MS p/r 25: .4X TO 1X AU T1
RANDOM INSERTS IN PACKS
PRINT RUNS B/WN 1-25 COPIES PER
NO PRICING ON QTY OF 15 OR LESS
1 Tony Gwynn/25 20.00 50.00
2 Johan Santana/25 15.00 40.00
3 Orel Hershiser/25 10.00 25.00
5 Don Mattingly/25 40.00 80.00
8 Victor Martinez/25 10.00 25.00

2005 Donruss Signature Stats Autograph Material Bat

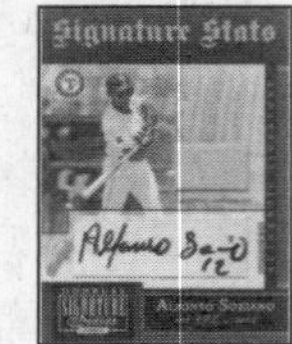

*AU BAT T4: .3X TO .8X AU T3
*AU BAT T3: .25X TO .6X AU T1
RANDOM INSERTS IN PACKS
TIER 1 QTY B/WN 1-50 COPIES PER
TIER 3 QTY B/WN 101-250 COPIES PER
TIER 4 QTY B/WN 251-800 COPIES PER
CARDS ARE NOT SERIAL-NUMBERED
PRINT RUN INFO PROVIDED BY DONRUSS
NO PRICING ON QTY OF 15
5 Don Mattingly T1/25 * 40.00 80.00

2005 Donruss Signature Stats Autograph Material Jersey

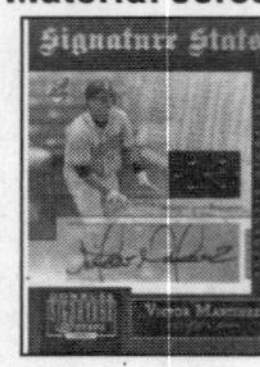

STATED ODDS 1:238
TIER 1 QTY B/WN 1-50 COPIES PER
TIER 2 QTY B/WN 51-100 COPIES PER
CARDS ARE NOT SERIAL-NUMBERED
PRINT RUN INFO PROVIDED BY DONRUSS
NO PRICING ON QTY OF 17 OR LESS
1 Tony Gwynn T1/25 * 20.00 50.00
2 Johan Santana T2/100 * 12.50 30.00
3 Orel Hershiser T1/25 * 10.00 25.00
8 Victor Martinez T1/25 * 10.00 25.00

2005 Donruss Signature Stats Autograph Material Combo

*AU COM T1: .75X TO 2X AU T3
STATED ODDS 1:186
TIER 1 QTY B/WN 1-50 COPIES PER
TIER 3 QTY B/WN 101-250 COPIES PER
CARDS ARE NOT SERIAL-NUMBERED
PRINT RUN INFO PROVIDED BY DONRUSS
NO PRICING ON QTY OF 14 OR LESS
1 T.Gwynn Jsy-Pants T3 15.00 40.00

2008 Donruss Threads

This set was released on October 22, 2008. The base set consists of 184 cards.

COMP.SET w/o AU's (100) 10.00 25.00
COMMON CARD (1-50) .15 .40
COMMON CARD (51-100) .30 .75
COMMON AUTO (101-184) 3.00 8.00
AUTOS RANDOMLY INSERTED
AU PRINT RUN B/WN 99-199 COPIES
EXCHANGE DEADLINE 4/22/2010
1 Hank Aaron .75 2.00
2 Dale Murphy .25 .60
3 Brooks Robinson .25 .60
4 Cal Ripken Jr. 1.50 4.00
5 Eddie Murray .40 1.00
6 Carl Yastrzemski .60 1.50
7 Carlton Fisk .25 .60
8 Wade Boggs .25 .60
9 Joe Jackson 1.25 3.00
10 Johnny Pesky .15 .40
11 Jim Rice .15 .40
12 Fred Lynn .15 .40
13 Duke Snider .25 .60
14 Carl Erskine .15 .40
15 Ernie Banks .40 1.00
16 Ryne Sandberg .75 2.00
17 Don Sutton .15 .40
18 Luis Aparicio .15 .40
19 Tom Seaver .25 .60
20 Tony Perez .25 .60
21 Pete Rose 1.25 3.00
22 Bob Feller .25 .60
23 Al Kaline .40 1.00
24 Mark Fidrych .15 .40
25 Kirk Gibson .15 .40
26 Alan Trammell .15 .40
27 George Brett .75 2.00
28 Steve Garvey .15 .40
29 Robin Yount .40 1.00
30 Harmon Killebrew .40 1.00
31 Paul Molitor .40 1.00
32 Gary Carter .25 .60
33 George Bush .60 1.50
34 Don Larsen .15 .40
35 Don Mattingly .75 2.00
36 Reggie Jackson .40 1.00
37 Tim Raines .15 .40
38 Mike Schmidt .60 1.50
39 Steve Carlton .25 .60
40 Tony Gwynn .40 1.00
41 Juan Marichal .25 .60
42 Willie Mays .75 2.00
43 Willie McCovey .25 .60
44 Will Clark .25 .60
45 Bob Gibson .25 .60
46 Dennis Eckersley .15 .40
47 Red Schoendienst .15 .40
48 Stan Musial .60 1.50
49 Nolan Ryan 1.00 2.50
50 Frank Howard .15 .40
51 Austin Romine .50 1.25
52 Chris Carter .50 1.25
53 Jordan Schafer .30 .75
54 Michael Burgess .50 1.25
55 John Raynor .30 .75
56 Lars Anderson .75 2.00
57 Josh Reddick .30 .75
58 Luis Esposito .30 .75
59 Aneury Rodriguez .75 2.00
60 Nick Weglarz .30 .75
61 Hector Gomez .30 .75
62 Jon Still .30 .75
63 Brandon Hamilton .50 1.25
64 Bud Norris .30 .75
65 Danny Duffy .50 1.25
66 Jovan Rosa .50 1.25
67 Sean O'Sullivan .30 .75
68 Edilio Colina .30 .75
69 Ryan Patterson .30 .75
70 Brent Brewer .30 .75
71 David Bromberg .30 .75
72 Bryan Petersen .50 1.25
73 Lucas Duda .50 1.25
74 Ruben Tejada .50 1.25
75 Andrew Lambo .75 2.00
76 Jeff Corsaletti .30 .75
77 Alexis Oliveras .30 .75
78 Fernando Garcia .30 .75
79 Jairo Heredia .30 .75
80 Jesus Montero .30 .75
81 Jose Tabata .30 .75
82 Carlos Gonzalez .50 1.25
83 Patrick Ryan .30 .75
84 Sean Doolittle .30 .75
85 Carlos Carrasco .50 1.25
86 Luis Cruz .50 1.25
87 Yefri Carvajal .30 .75
88 Stolmy Pimentel .30 .75
89 Wilber Bucardo .30 .75
90 Angel Villalona .75 2.00
91 Madison Bumgarner .75 2.00
92 Danny Carroll .30 .75
93 Juan Ramirez .30 .75
94 Lou Marson .30 .75
95 Josh Vitters .50 1.25
96 Desmond Jennings .50 1.25
97 Abraham Almonte .30 .75
98 Mat Gamel .50 1.25
99 Andrew LeFave .30 .75
100 Elvis Andrus .50 1.25
101 Emilio Bonifacio AU/1874 3.00 8.00
102 Wilin Rosario AU/999 4.00 10.00
103 Carlos Peguero AU/465 8.00 20.00
104 Tyler Flowers AU/999 10.00 25.00
105 Tyler Henson AU/999 4.00 10.00
106 Nevin Griffith AU/999 3.00 8.00
107 Caleb Gindl AU/465 5.00 12.00
108 Jose Ceda AU/999 3.00 8.00
109 Brandon Waring AU/465 6.00 15.00
110 Neftali Soto AU/500 10.00 25.00
111 Ryan Miller AU/999 3.00 8.00
112 Jack Egbert AU/999 3.00 8.00
113 Juan Silverio AU/999 5.00 12.00
114 Jhoulys Chacin AU/1999 6.00 15.00
115 Charlie Furbush AU/465 4.00 10.00
116 Hector Correa AU/999 3.00 8.00
117 Brad James AU/1999 3.00 8.00
119 Keaton Hayenga AU/999 4.00 10.00
120 Brent Fisher AU/1058 3.00 8.00
121 Juan Francisco AU/999 8.00 20.00
122 Andrew Romine AU/875 3.00 8.00
123 Mason Tobin AU/999 3.00 8.00
124 Anel De Los Santos AU/999 3.00 8.00
125 Andrew Walker AU/99 EXCH 6.00 15.00
126 Alfredo Silverio AU/999 3.00 8.00
127 Mario Martinez AU/1375 5.00 12.00
128 Taylor Green AU/999 4.00 10.00
129 D.J. Jones AU/399 4.00 10.00
130 Wilson Ramos AU/999 4.00 10.00
131 Trevor Reckling AU/875 4.00 10.00
132 Engel Beltre AU/465 8.00 20.00
133 Scott Moviel AU/1000 4.00 10.00
134 Josh Tomlin AU/875 3.00 8.00
135 Dominic Brown AU/999 6.00 15.00
136 Neftali Feliz AU/465 12.50 30.00
137 Brian Friday AU/1249 3.00 8.00
138 Drew Miller AU/1999 3.00 8.00
139 Steve Garrison AU/1999 3.00 8.00
140 Mike McBryde AU/950 3.00 8.00
141 Brian Duensing AU/575 3.00 8.00
142 Greg Halman AU/465 12.50 30.00
143 Jharmidy De Jesus AU/465 8.00 20.00
144 Mike Stanton AU/465 20.00 50.00
145 Wilmer Flores AU/99 EXCH 50.00 100.00
146 Heath Rollins AU/999 3.00 8.00
147 Alex Cobb AU/999 3.00 8.00
148 Omar Poveda AU/999 3.00 8.00
149 Yohermyn Chavez AU/999 4.00 10.00
150 Gerardo Parra AU/999 3.00 8.00
151 Clayton Conner AU/240 4.00 10.00
152 Tyler Kolodny AU/280 6.00 15.00
153 Ryan Kalish AU/240 10.00 25.00
154 Rick Porcello AU/240 40.00 80.00
155 Shane Peterson AU/240 5.00 12.00
156 Tyler Ladendorf AU/269 4.00 10.00
157 Josh Lindblom AU/240 5.00 12.00
158 Tyler Chatwood AU/240 6.00 15.00
159 Logan Morrison AU/240 30.00 60.00
160 Collin DeLome AU/240 6.00 15.00
161 Daniel Cortes AU/240 6.00 15.00
162 Chris Johnson AU/280 EXCH 20.00 50.00
163 Matt Mitchell AU/240 5.00 12.00
164 Denny Almonte AU/280 6.00 15.00
165 Greg Veloz AU/250 8.00 20.00
166 R. J. Seidel AU/240 5.00 12.00
167 Xavier Avery AU/250 8.00 20.00
168 Quincy Latimore AU/240 6.00 15.00
169 Aaron Shafer AU/280 EXCH 5.00 12.00
170 Rayner Contreras AU/270 5.00 12.00
171 Waldis Joaquin AU/280 5.00 12.00
172 Jorge Bucardo AU/280 5.00 12.00
173 James Darnell AU/280 6.00 15.00
174 Logan Forsythe AU/239 6.00 15.00
175 Kyle Ginley AU/240 5.00 12.00
176 Ike Davis AU/250 10.00 25.00
177 Max Ramirez AU/244 6.00 15.00
178 Chris Davis AU/250 12.50 30.00
180 Jay Austin AU/240 5.00 12.00
181 Brad Holt AU/240 10.00 25.00
182 Carlos Gutierrez AU/270 6.00 15.00
183 Christian Friedrich AU/270 EXCH 5.00 12.00
184 Zach Collier AU/280 10.00 25.00
186 Robert Hernandez AU/269 6.00 15.00
187 Christian Marrero AU/280 6.00 15.00

2008 Donruss Threads Century Proof Gold

*GOLD 1-50: 3X TO 8X BASIC
*GOLD 51-100: 3X TO 8X BASIC
*GOLD 101-150: 1.2X TO 3X GREEN
RANDOM INSERTS IN PACKS
STATED PRINT RUN 50 SER.#'d SETS

2008 Donruss Threads Century Proof Green

*GRN 1-50: 1X TO 2.5X BASIC
*GRN 51-100: 1X TO 2.5X BASIC
RANDOM INSERTS IN PACKS
STATED PRINT RUN 250 SER.#'d SETS
101 Emilio Bonifacio .75 2.00
102 Wilin Rosario 1.00 2.50
103 Carlos Peguero .75 2.00
104 Tyler Flowers 2.00 5.00
105 Tyler Henson 1.00 2.50
106 Nevin Griffith .75 2.00
107 Caleb Gindl .75 2.00
108 Jose Ceda .75 2.00
109 Brandon Waring 2.00 5.00
110 Neftali Soto 2.00 5.00
111 Ryan Miller .75 2.00
112 Jack Egbert .75 2.00
113 Juan Silverio 1.25 3.00
114 Jhoulys Chacin 2.50 6.00
115 Charlie Furbush 1.00 2.50
116 Hector Correa .75 2.00
117 Brad James .75 2.00
119 Keaton Hayenga 1.00 2.50
120 Brent Fisher .75 2.00
121 Juan Francisco 1.25 3.00
122 Andrew Romine .75 2.00
123 Mason Tobin .75 2.00

124 Anel De Los Santos .75 2.00
125 Andrew Walker .75 2.00
126 Alfredo Silverio .75 2.00
127 Mario Martinez 1.50 4.00
128 Taylor Green 1.00 2.50
129 D.J. Jones 1.00 2.50
130 Wilson Ramos 1.00 2.50
131 Trevor Reckling 1.00 2.50
132 Engel Beltre 1.00 2.50
133 Scott Moviel 1.00 2.50
134 Josh Tomlin .75 2.00
135 Dominic Brown 1.50 4.00
136 Neftali Feliz 2.50 6.00
137 Brian Friday .75 2.00
138 Drew Miller .75 2.00
139 Steve Garrison .75 2.00
140 Mike McBryde .75 2.00
141 Brian Duensing .75 2.00
142 Greg Halman 2.50 6.00
143 Jharmidy De Jesus 2.00 5.00
144 Mike Stanton 2.50 6.00
145 Wilmer Flores 3.00 8.00
146 Heath Rollins .75 2.00
147 Alex Cobb .75 2.00
148 Omar Poveda .75 2.00
149 Yohermyn Chavez 1.00 2.50
150 Gerardo Parra .75 2.00

2008 Donruss Threads Century Proof Platinum

RANDOM INSERTS IN PACKS
STATED PRINT RUN 25 SER.#'d SETS
NO PRICING DUE TO SCARCITY

2008 Donruss Threads Century Proof Silver

*SILVER 1-50: 1.5X TO 4X BASIC
*SILVER 51-100: 1.5X TO 4X BASIC
*SILVER 101-150: .6X TO 1.5X GREEN
RANDOM INSERTS IN PACKS
STATED PRINT RUN 100 SER.#'d SETS

2008 Donruss Threads Baseball Americana

RANDOM INSERTS IN PACKS
STATED PRINT RUN 500 SER.#'d SETS
1 Bud Abbott 1.25 3.00
2 Lou Costello 1.25 3.00
3 Don Mattingly 2.50 6.00
4 Eddie Murray 1.25 3.00
5 Ryne Sandberg 2.00 5.00
6 Pete Rose 4.00 10.00
7 Cal Ripken Jr. 4.00 10.00
8 Ernie Banks 2.00 5.00
9 George Brett 2.50 6.00
10 Mike Schmidt 2.00 5.00
11 Johnny Bench 1.50 4.00
12 Carlton Fisk 1.50 4.00
13 Tony Gwynn 1.50 4.00
14 Hank Aaron 2.00 5.00
15 Willie Mays 2.00 5.00
16 Joe Jackson 4.00 10.00
17 Ted Williams 2.00 5.00
18 Stan Musial 2.00 5.00
19 Nolan Ryan 3.00 8.00
20 Bob Feller 1.50 4.00
21 Kurt Russell 1.25 3.00
22 Burt Lancaster 1.25 3.00
23 Tab Hunter 1.25 3.00
24 Gary Cooper 1.25 3.00
25 Tony Curtis 1.25 3.00
26 John Cusack 1.25 3.00
27 Bernie Mac 1.25 3.00
28 Regis Philbin 1.25 3.00
29 Marcia Gay Harden 1.25 3.00
30 Albert Brooks 1.25 3.00
31 Billy Dee Williams 1.25 3.00
32 Esther Williams 1.25 3.00
33 Betty Garrett 1.25 3.00
34 Karen Allen 1.25 3.00
35 Ed Asner 1.25 3.00
36 Robert Wagner 1.25 3.00
37 Gary Coleman 1.25 3.00
38 Ed McMahon 1.25 3.00
39 Rob Schneider 1.25 3.00
40 Lori Petty 1.25 3.00
41 Bob Gibson 1.50 4.00
42 Dennis Eckersley 1.50 4.00
43 Carl Yastrzemski 1.50 4.00
44 Don Drysdale 1.50 4.00
45 Satchel Paige 2.00 5.00
46 Casey Stengel 1.50 4.00
47 Eddie Mathews 1.50 4.00
48 Early Wynn 1.50 4.00
49 Marilyn Monroe 2.50 6.00
50 George Bush 2.50 6.00

2008 Donruss Threads Baseball Americana Materials

RANDOM INSERTS IN PACKS
PRINT RUNS B/WN 1-500 PER
NO PRICING ON QTY 25 OR LESS
1 Bud Abbott/500 6.00 15.00
2 Lou Costello/250 8.00 20.00
3 Don Mattingly/100 6.00 15.00
4 Eddie Murray/150 5.00 12.00
5 Ryne Sandberg/25
6 Pete Rose/250 20.00 50.00
7 Cal Ripken Jr./100 20.00 50.00
8 Ernie Banks/1
9 George Brett/75 6.00 15.00
10 Mike Schmidt/100 6.00 15.00
11 Johnny Bench/50 12.50 30.00
12 Carlton Fisk/75 4.00 10.00
13 Tony Gwynn/250 3.00 8.00
14 Hank Aaron/5
15 Willie Mays/15
17 Ted Williams/100 20.00 50.00
18 Stan Musial/25
19 Nolan Ryan/100 10.00 25.00
20 Bob Feller/5
21 Kurt Russell/500 3.00 8.00
22 Burt Lancaster/500 4.00 10.00
24 Gary Cooper/500 6.00 15.00
25 Tony Curtis/500 3.00 8.00
26 John Cusack/500 4.00 10.00
27 Bernie Mac/250 5.00 12.00
33 Betty Garrett/250 3.00 8.00
35 Ed Asner/500 3.00 8.00
36 Robert Wagner/500 3.00 8.00
38 Ed McMahon/500 3.00 8.00
39 Rob Schneider/350 3.00 8.00
40 Lori Petty/100 3.00 8.00
41 Bob Gibson/100 3.00 8.00
42 Dennis Eckersley/100 4.00 10.00
43 Carl Yastrzemski/100 3.00 8.00
44 Don Drysdale/100 5.00 12.00
45 Satchel Paige/100 15.00 40.00
46 Casey Stengel/500 6.00 15.00
47 Eddie Mathews/100 8.00 20.00
48 Early Wynn/100 4.00 10.00
49 Marilyn Monroe/250 20.00 50.00
50 George Bush/500 6.00 15.00

2008 Donruss Threads Baseball Americana Materials Position

RANDOM INSERTS IN PACKS
PRINT RUNS B/WN 1-250 PER
NO PRICING ON QTY 25 OR LESS
1 Bud Abbott/200 6.00 15.00
2 Lou Costello/100 8.00 20.00
3 Don Mattingly/50 8.00 20.00
4 Eddie Murray/50 6.00 15.00
5 Ryne Sandberg/25
6 Pete Rose/100 20.00 50.00
7 Cal Ripken Jr./25
8 Ernie Banks/1
9 George Brett/75 6.00 15.00
10 Mike Schmidt/100 6.00 15.00
11 Johnny Bench/25
12 Carlton Fisk/75 4.00 10.00
13 Tony Gwynn/100 4.00 10.00
14 Hank Aaron/5
15 Willie Mays/100
17 Ted Williams/50 30.00 60.00
18 Stan Musial/25
19 Nolan Ryan/50 12.50 30.00
20 Bob Feller/5
21 Kurt Russell/250 3.00 8.00
22 Burt Lancaster/250 4.00 10.00
24 Gary Cooper/250 6.00 15.00
25 Tony Curtis/250 3.00 8.00
26 John Cusack/250 4.00 10.00
27 Bernie Mac/100 5.00 12.00
29 Marcia Gay Harden/100 3.00 8.00
33 Betty Garrett/100 3.00 8.00
35 Ed Asner/250 3.00 8.00
36 Robert Wagner/250 3.00 8.00
38 Ed McMahon/250 3.00 8.00
39 Rob Schneider/250 3.00 8.00
40 Lori Petty/100 3.00 8.00
41 Bob Gibson/100 3.00 8.00
42 Dennis Eckersley/100 4.00 10.00
43 Carl Yastrzemski/100 3.00 8.00
44 Don Drysdale/100 5.00 12.00
45 Satchel Paige/100 15.00 40.00
46 Casey Stengel/250 6.00 15.00
47 Eddie Mathews/100 8.00 20.00
48 Early Wynn/100 4.00 10.00
49 Marilyn Monroe/250 20.00 50.00
50 George Bush/250 6.00 15.00

2008 Donruss Threads Baseball Americana Signatures Materials

RANDOM INSERTS IN PACKS
PRINT RUNS B/WN 3-100 COPIES
NO PRICING ON QTY 25 OR LESS
3 Don Mattingly/25
4 Eddie Murray/25
5 Ryne Sandberg/5
6 Pete Rose/50 100.00 200.00
7 Cal Ripken Jr./25
8 Ernie Banks/3
9 George Brett/5
10 Mike Schmidt/25
11 Johnny Bench/25 30.00 60.00
12 Carlton Fisk/50 10.00 25.00
13 Tony Gwynn/50 15.00 40.00
14 Hank Aaron/25
15 Willie Mays/25
18 Stan Musial/25
19 Nolan Ryan/25
20 Bob Feller/10
26 John Cusack/50 40.00 80.00
27 Bernie Mac/100 60.00 120.00
28 Regis Philbin/10
29 Marcia Gay Harden/50 12.50 30.00
41 Bob Gibson/50 12.50 30.00
42 Dennis Eckersley/25
43 Carl Yastrzemski/25
50 George Bush/25

2008 Donruss Threads Bats

RANDOM INSERTS IN PACKS
PRINT RUNS B/WN 1-500 PER
NO PRICING ON QTY 20 OR LESS
1 Hank Aaron/100 10.00 25.00
9 Joe Jackson/100 250.00 400.00
25 Kirk Gibson/10
28 Steve Garvey/20
31 Paul Molitor/1
35 Don Mattingly/250 5.00 12.00
36 Reggie Jackson/500 4.00 10.00
38 Mike Schmidt/500 5.00 12.00
39 Steve Carlton/3
42 Willie Mays/50 10.00 25.00
52 Chris Carter/500 3.00 8.00
53 Jordan Schafer/500 3.00 8.00
54 Michael Burgess/500 3.00 8.00
70 Brent Brewer/500 3.00 8.00
81 Jose Tabata/500 3.00 8.00
84 Sean Doolittle/500 3.00 8.00
92 Danny Carroll/500 3.00 8.00
96 Desmond Jennings/500 3.00 8.00
128 Taylor Green/500 3.00 8.00
142 Greg Halman/500 3.00 8.00
143 Jharmidy De Jesus/500 3.00 8.00

2008 Donruss Threads Century Collection Materials

RANDOM INSERTS IN PACKS
PRINT RUNS B/WN 10-100 PER
NO MAYS PRICING AVAILABLE
1 Cal Ripken Jr./100 12.50 30.00
2 Ryne Sandberg/75 6.00 15.00
3 Pete Rose/100 20.00 50.00
4 Fred Lynn/100 3.00 8.00
5 Tom Seaver/100 3.00 8.00
6 George Brett/50 10.00 25.00
7 Don Mattingly/75 6.00 15.00
8 Mike Schmidt/100 6.00 15.00
9 Tony Gwynn/100 4.00 10.00
10 Willie Mays/10
11 Nolan Ryan/100 8.00 20.00
12 Dale Murphy/100 6.00 15.00
13 Pete Rose/100 20.00 50.00
15 Dave Winfield/100 3.00 8.00
16 Paul Molitor/100 3.00 8.00
17 Barry Larkin/100 4.00 10.00
18 Kirk Gibson/100 5.00 12.00
19 Pete Rose/100 20.00 50.00
20 Steve Garvey/100 5.00 12.00
21 Wade Boggs/100 3.00 8.00
22 Ted Williams/100 15.00 40.00
23 Steve Carlton/100 3.00 8.00
24 Robin Yount/100 4.00 10.00
25 Luis Aparicio/100 3.00 8.00
26 Jim Rice/100 3.00 8.00
27 Jim Palmer/100 3.00 8.00
28 Harmon Killebrew/100 5.00 12.00
29 Gaylord Perry/100 3.00 8.00
30 Gary Carter/100 4.00 10.00
31 Eddie Murray/50 4.00 10.00
32 Don Drysdale/100 4.00 10.00
33 Satchel Paige/100 15.00 40.00
34 Casey Stengel/100 6.00 15.00
35 Eddie Mathews/100 8.00 20.00
36 Dennis Eckersley/100 3.00 8.00
37 Carlton Fisk/100 4.00 10.00
38 Carl Yastrzemski/100 4.00 10.00
39 Early Wynn/100 4.00 10.00
40 Lefty Grove/50 75.00 150.00

2008 Donruss Threads Century Collection Materials Prime

RANDOM INSERTS IN PACKS
PRINT RUNS B/WN 3-10 COPIES PER
NO PRICING DUE TO SCARCITY
1 Cal Ripken Jr./10
2 Ryne Sandberg/10
3 Pete Rose/10
4 Fred Lynn/10
5 Tom Seaver/10
6 George Brett/10
7 Don Mattingly/10
8 Mike Schmidt/10
9 Tony Gwynn/10
10 Willie Mays/5
11 Nolan Ryan/10
12 Dale Murphy/10
13 Pete Rose/10
15 Dave Winfield/10
16 Paul Molitor/10
17 Barry Larkin/10
19 Pete Rose/10
21 Wade Boggs/10
22 Ted Williams/5
23 Steve Carlton/10
24 Robin Yount/10
25 Luis Aparicio/3
26 Jim Rice/10
27 Jim Palmer/10
28 Harmon Killebrew/10
29 Gaylord Perry/10
30 Gary Carter/10
31 Eddie Murray/10
32 Don Drysdale/10
33 Satchel Paige/10
34 Casey Stengel/10
35 Eddie Mathews/10
36 Dennis Eckersley/10
37 Carlton Fisk/10
38 Carl Yastrzemski/3
39 Early Wynn/10

2008 Donruss Threads Century Legends

RANDOM INSERTS IN PACKS
*CENTURY PROOF: .75X TO 2X BASIC
CENTRUY RANDOMLY INSERTED
CENTURY PRINT RUN 100 SER.#'d SETS
1 Stan Musial 2.00 5.00
2 Willie Mays 2.00 5.00
3 Hank Aaron 2.00 5.00
4 Ted Williams 2.00 5.00
5 Whitey Ford .75 2.00
6 Bob Gibson .75 2.00
7 Joe Jackson 3.00 8.00
8 Duke Snider 1.25 3.00
9 Ernie Banks 1.25 3.00
10 Bob Feller .75 2.00
11 Nolan Ryan 2.50 6.00
12 Mike Schmidt 1.50 4.00
13 Carl Yastrzemski 1.25 3.00
14 Pete Rose 3.00 8.00
15 Harmon Killebrew 1.25 3.00

2008 Donruss Threads Century Legends Materials

RANDOM INSERTS IN PACKS
PRINT RUNS B/WN 1-100 COPIES
NO PRICING ON QTY 25 OR LESS
1 Stan Musial/25
2 Willie Mays/10
4 Ted Williams/50 20.00 50.00
5 Whitey Ford/1
6 Bob Gibson/50 5.00 12.00
9 Ernie Banks/10
10 Bob Feller/10
11 Nolan Ryan/100 6.00 15.00
12 Mike Schmidt/100 6.00 15.00
13 Carl Yastrzemski/100 5.00 12.00
14 Pete Rose/100 20.00 50.00
15 Harmon Killebrew/100 5.00 12.00

2008 Donruss Threads Century Legends Materials Prime

RANDOM INSERTS IN PACKS
PRINT RUNS B/WN 1-25 COPIES PER
NO PRICING DUE TO SCARCITY
1 Stan Musial/1
2 Willie Mays/5
4 Ted Williams/5
5 Whitey Ford/1
6 Bob Gibson/3
9 Ernie Banks/10
11 Nolan Ryan/10
12 Mike Schmidt/25
13 Carl Yastrzemski/1
14 Pete Rose/25
15 Harmon Killebrew/1

2008 Donruss Threads Century Stars Materials

RANDOM INSERTS IN PACKS
PRINT RUNS B/WN 50-100 PER
1 Carlton Fisk/100 4.00 10.00
2 Harmon Killebrew/100 3.00 8.00
3 Ryne Sandberg/50 15.00 40.00
4 Cal Ripken Jr./100 15.00 40.00
5 Mike Schmidt/100 6.00 15.00
6 Tony Gwynn/100 3.00 8.00
7 Pete Rose/100 20.00 50.00
9 Dale Murphy/100 3.00 8.00
10 Steve Carlton/100 3.00 8.00
11 Bob Gibson/100 3.00 8.00
12 Nolan Ryan/100 8.00 20.00
13 Robin Yount/100 3.00 8.00
14 Paul Molitor/100 3.00 8.00
15 Kirk Gibson/50 3.00 8.00

2008 Donruss Threads Century Stars Materials Prime

RANDOM INSERTS IN PACKS
PRINT RUNS B/WN 1-10 COPIES PER
NO PRICING DUE TO SCARCITY
1 Carlton Fisk/10
2 Harmon Killebrew/1
3 Ryne Sandberg/10
4 Cal Ripken Jr./10
5 Mike Schmidt/10
6 Tony Gwynn/10
7 Pete Rose/10
9 Dale Murphy/10
10 Steve Carlton/10
11 Bob Gibson/1
12 Nolan Ryan/10
13 Robin Yount/10
15 Kirk Gibson/10

2008 Donruss Threads College Greats

RANDOM INSERTS IN PACKS
1 Tom Seaver 1.50 4.00
2 Reggie Jackson 1.50 4.00
3 Frank Howard 1.00 2.50
4 Dave Winfield 1.00 2.50
5 Paul Molitor 1.00 2.50
6 Barry Larkin 1.00 2.50
7 Kirk Gibson 1.00 2.50
8 Robin Roberts 1.00 2.50
9 Will Clark 1.50 4.00
10 Bob Gibson 1.50 4.00
11 Steve Garvey 1.00 2.50
12 Fred Lynn 1.00 2.50

2008 Donruss Threads College Greats Signatures

RANDOM INSERTS IN PACKS
PRINT RUNS B/WN 5-50 COPIES PER
NO PRICING ON QTY 25 OR LESS
1 Tom Seaver/25
2 Reggie Jackson/25
3 Frank Howard/50 10.00 25.00
4 Dave Winfield/25
5 Paul Molitor/25
6 Barry Larkin/10 30.00 60.00
7 Kirk Gibson/5
8 Robin Roberts/40 10.00 25.00
9 Will Clark/25
10 Bob Gibson/50 12.50 30.00
11 Steve Garvey/20
12 Fred Lynn/50 10.00 25.00

2008 Donruss Threads College Greats Signatures Combos

RANDOM INSERTS IN PACKS
STATED PRINT RUN 25 SER.#'d SETS
NO PRICING DUE TO SCARCITY
1 Dave Winfield
Paul Molitor
2 Kirk Gibson
Steve Garvey
3 Tom Seaver
Fred Lynn
4 Kirk Gibson
Robin Roberts
5 Steve Garvey
Robin Roberts

2008 Donruss Threads Diamond Kings

RANDOM INSERTS IN PACKS
*GOLD: .6X TO 1.5X BASIC
GOLD RANDOMLY INSERTED
GOLD PRINT RUN 100 SER.#'d SETS
FRM.BLK.RANDOMLY INSERTED
FRM.BLK.PRINT RUN 10 SER.#'d SETS
NO FRM.BLK PRINCING AVAILABLE
*FRM.BLUE: .75X TO 2X BASIC
FRM.BLUE RANDOMLY INSERTS
FRM.BLUE PRINT RUN 50 SER.#'d SETS
FRM.GRN.RANDOMLY INSERTED
FRM.GRN.PRINT RUN 25 SER.#'d SETS
NO FRM.GRN PRINCING AVAILABLE
*FRM.RED: .6X TO 1.5X BASIC
FRM.RED RANDOMLY INSERTS
FRM.RED PRINT RUN 100 SER.#'d SETS
PLAT.RANDOMLY INSERTED
PLAT.PRINT RUN 25 SER.#'d SETS
NO PLAT.PRINCING AVAILABLE
*SILVER: .5X TO 1.2X BASIC
SILVER RANDOMLY INSERTS
SILVER PRINT RUN 250 SER.#'d SETS
1 Jordan Schafer 1.00 2.50
2 Nolan Reimold 1.00 2.50
3 Matt McBride 1.00 2.50
4 Lars Anderson 1.25 3.00
5 Blake Wood 1.00 2.50
6 Josh Vitters 1.00 2.50
7 Chris Valaika 1.00 2.50
8 Mark Melancon 1.00 2.50
9 Drew Stubbs 1.00 2.50
10 Rick Porcello 2.50 6.00
11 Anthony Rizzo 1.00 2.50
12 Jon Jay 1.00 2.50
13 Clay Fuller 1.00 2.50
14 Damon Sublett 1.00 2.50
15 Brett Anderson 1.00 2.50
16 Matt Spencer 1.00 2.50
17 Drew Cumberland 1.00 2.50
18 Tim Alderson 1.00 2.50
19 Madison Bumgarner 1.00 2.50
20 Jess Todd 1.00 2.50
21 Michael Hollimon 1.00 2.50
22 Taylor Teagarden 1.00 2.50
23 Daniel McCutchen 1.00 2.50
24 Trystan Magnuson 1.00 2.50
25 Michael Burgess 1.00 2.50
26 Hank Aaron 2.50 6.00
27 Cal Ripken Jr. 3.00 8.00
28 Jim Palmer 1.00 2.50
29 Bobby Doerr 1.00 2.50
30 Duke Snider 1.25 3.00
31 Rod Carew 1.00 2.50
32 Ernie Banks 1.50 4.00
33 Ryne Sandberg 2.50 6.00
34 Billy Williams 1.00 2.50
35 Fergie Jenkins 1.00 2.50
36 Pete Rose 3.00 8.00
37 George Kell 1.00 2.50
38 George Brett 2.50 6.00
39 Reggie Jackson 1.25 3.00
40 Don Mattingly 2.50 6.00
41 Phil Niekro 1.00 2.50
42 Whitey Ford 1.25 3.00
43 Yogi Berra 1.50 4.00
44 Mike Schmidt 2.00 5.00
45 Tony Gwynn 1.50 4.00
46 Willie Mays 2.50 6.00
47 Gaylord Perry 1.00 2.50
48 Stan Musial 2.00 5.00
49 Lou Brock 1.25 3.00
50 Nolan Ryan 2.50 6.00
51 Joe Jackson 3.00 8.00
52 Gordon Beckham 2.50 6.00
56 Pete Rose 3.00 8.00
57 Rick Porcello 2.50 6.00
58 Nolan Ryan 2.50 6.00

2008 Donruss Threads Diamond Kings Materials

RANDOM INSERTS IN PACKS
PRINT RUNS B/WN 1-250 PER
NO PRICING ON QTY 25 OR LESS
1 Jordan Schafer/250 3.00 8.00
6 Josh Vitters/250 3.00 8.00
8 Mark Melancon/125 3.00 8.00
9 Drew Stubbs/250 3.00 8.00
10 Rick Porcello/250 5.00 12.00
13 Clay Fuller/250 3.00 8.00
14 Damon Sublett/250 5.00 12.00
15 Brett Anderson/250 3.00 8.00
16 Matt Spencer/250 3.00 8.00
17 Drew Cumberland/250 3.00 8.00
18 Tim Alderson/250 3.00 8.00
19 Madison Bumgarner/125 6.00 15.00
20 Jess Todd/250 3.00 8.00
24 Trystan Magnuson/250 3.00 8.00
25 Michael Burgess/250 3.00 8.00
26 Hank Aaron/10
27 Cal Ripken Jr./200 12.50 30.00
28 Jim Palmer/50 5.00 12.00
29 Bobby Doerr/5
31 Rod Carew/5
32 Ernie Banks/1
33 Ryne Sandberg/50 12.50 30.00
36 Pete Rose/250 20.00 50.00
38 George Brett/75 8.00 20.00
39 Reggie Jackson/5
40 Don Mattingly/150 10.00 25.00
42 Whitey Ford/5
43 Yogi Berra/25
44 Mike Schmidt/75 8.00 20.00
45 Tony Gwynn/250 5.00 12.00
46 Willie Mays/50 20.00 50.00
48 Stan Musial/25
49 Lou Brock/100 6.00 15.00
50 Nolan Ryan/50 12.50 30.00
51 Joe Jackson/25
56 Pete Rose/100 20.00 50.00
57 Rick Porcello/100 5.00 12.00
58 Nolan Ryan/50 12.50 30.00

2008 Donruss Threads Diamond Kings Materials Prime

RANDOM INSERTS IN PACKS
PRINT RUNS B/WN 1-25 COPIES PER
NO PRICING DUE TO SCARCITY

2008 Donruss Threads Diamond Kings Signatures

RANDOM INSERTS IN PACKS
PRINT RUNS B/WN 5-500 COPIES PER
NO PRICING ON QTY 25 OR LESS
1 Jordan Schafer/199 5.00 12.00
2 Nolan Reimold/500 4.00 10.00
3 Matt McBride /500 4.00 10.00
4 Lars Anderson/474 15.00 40.00
5 Blake Wood/500 4.00 10.00
6 Josh Vitters/10
7 Chris Valaika/500 5.00 12.00
8 Mark Melancon/238 6.00 15.00
9 Drew Stubbs/465 4.00 10.00
10 Rick Porcello/300 30.00 60.00
11 Anthony Rizzo/500 6.00 15.00
12 Jon Jay/10
14 Damon Sublett/14
15 Brett Anderson/315 4.00 10.00
18 Tim Alderson/215 5.00 12.00
19 Madison Bumgarner/223 10.00 25.00
21 Michael Hollimon/500 4.00 10.00
22 Taylor Teagarden/475 4.00 10.00
23 Daniel McCutchen/500 4.00 10.00
24 Trystan Magnuson/215 4.00 10.00
25 Michael Burgess/182 5.00 12.00
26 Hank Aaron/5
27 Cal Ripken Jr./5
28 Jim Palmer/100 8.00 20.00
29 Bobby Doerr/250 6.00 15.00
30 Duke Snider/50 15.00 40.00
31 Rod Carew/5
32 Ernie Banks/5
33 Ryne Sandberg/5
34 Billy Williams/5
35 Fergie Jenkins/100 8.00 20.00
36 Pete Rose/50 90.00 150.00
37 George Kell/5
38 George Brett/5
39 Reggie Jackson/25
40 Don Mattingly/25
41 Phil Niekro/50 10.00 25.00
42 Whitey Ford/100 20.00 50.00
43 Yogi Berra/5
44 Mike Schmidt/25
45 Tony Gwynn/5
46 Willie Mays/5
47 Gaylord Perry/150 5.00 12.00
48 Stan Musial/25
49 Lou Brock/50 10.00 25.00
50 Nolan Ryan/25
56 Pete Rose/25
57 Rick Porcello/25
58 Nolan Ryan/25

2008 Donruss Threads Diamond Kings Signatures Materials

RANDOM INSERTS IN PACKS
PRINT RUNS B/WN 5-100 COPIES PER
NO PRICING ON MOST DUE TO SCARICTY
1 Jordan Schafer/25
6 Josh Vitters/10
8 Mark Melancon/10
9 Drew Stubbs/25
10 Rick Porcello/25 60.00 120.00
14 Damon Sublett/25
15 Brett Anderson/25
18 Tim Alderson/25
19 Madison Bumgarner/25
24 Trystan Magnuson/25
25 Michael Burgess/25
26 Hank Aaron/5
27 Cal Ripken Jr./25
28 Jim Palmer/25
29 Bobby Doerr/5
31 Rod Carew/5
32 Ernie Banks/5
33 Ryne Sandberg/5
34 Billy Williams/5
36 Pete Rose/25 125.00 250.00
38 George Brett/5
39 Reggie Jackson/10
40 Don Mattingly/25
42 Whitey Ford/5
43 Yogi Berra/5
44 Mike Schmidt/25
45 Tony Gwynn/25
48 Stan Musial/15
49 Lou Brock/100 12.50 30.00
50 Nolan Ryan/25
56 Pete Rose/25 125.00 250.00
57 Rick Porcello/25 60.00 120.00
58 Nolan Ryan/10

2008 Donruss Threads Diamond Kings Signatures Materials Prime

RANDOM INSERTS IN PACKS
PRINT RUNS B/WN 1-10 COPIES PER
NO PRICING DUE TO SCARCITY
6 Josh Vitters/5
8 Mark Melancon/2
9 Drew Stubbs/10
10 Rick Porcello/10
15 Brett Anderson/10
18 Tim Alderson/10
19 Madison Bumgarner/1
24 Trystan Magnuson/10
25 Michael Burgess/10
26 Hank Aaron/5
27 Cal Ripken Jr./10
28 Jim Palmer/10
31 Rod Carew/5
32 Ernie Banks/3
33 Ryne Sandberg/5
34 Billy Williams/5
36 Pete Rose/10
38 George Brett/5
39 Reggie Jackson/1
40 Don Mattingly/10
42 Whitey Ford/5

44 Mike Schmidt/10
45 Tony Gwynn/10
49 Lou Brock/5
50 Nolan Ryan/10
56 Pete Rose/10
57 Rick Porcello/10
58 Nolan Ryan/5

2008 Donruss Threads Dynasty

RANDOM INSERTS IN PACKS
*CENTURY PROOF: .75X TO 2X BASIC
CENTRUY RANDOMLY INSERTED
CENTURY PRINT RUN 100 SER.#'d SETS
1 Cal Ripken Jr./Jim Palmer/Eddie Murray 2.50 6.00
2 Johnny Bench/Pete Rose/Joe Morgan 3.00 8.00
3 Juan Marichal/Willie Mays/Willie McCovey 2.00 5.00

2008 Donruss Threads Dynasty Materials

RANDOM INSERTS IN PACKS
PRINT RUN B/WN 50-100 COPIES PER
1 Cal Ripken Jr./Jim Palmer/Eddie Murray/50 12.50 30.00
2 Johnny Bench/Pete Rose/Joe Morgan/100 40.00 80.00

2008 Donruss Threads Dynasty Materials Prime

RANDOM INSERTS IN PACKS
STATED PRINT RUN 10 SER.#'d SETS
NO PRICING DUE TO SCARCITY

2008 Donruss Threads Generations

RANDOM INSERTS IN PACKS
*CENTURY PROOF: .75X TO 2X BASIC
CENTURY RANDOMLY INSERTED
CENTURY PRINT RUN 100 SER.#'d SETS
1 Hank Aaron 2.50 6.00
Dale Murphy
2 Eddie Murray 3.00 8.00
Cal Ripken Jr.
3 Ernie Banks 3.00 8.00
Ryne Sandberg
4 Willie Mays 2.50 6.00
Willie McCovey
5 Rod Carew 2.00 5.00
Paul Molitor

2008 Donruss Threads Generations Materials

RANDOM INSERTS IN PACKS
PRINT RUNS B/WN 10-100 COPIES PER
NO PRICING ON QTY 15 OR LESS
1 Hank Aaron
Dale Murphy
10
2 Eddie Murray 15.00 40.00
Cal Ripken Jr.
100
3 Ernie Banks
Ryne Sandberg
15
4 Willie Mays
Willie McCovey
10

2008 Donruss Threads Generations Materials Prime

RANDOM INSERTS IN PACKS
PRINT RUN B/WN 5-10 COPIES PER
NO PRICING DUE TO SCARCITY

2008 Donruss Threads Jerseys

RANDOM INSERTS IN PACKS
PRINT RUNS B/WN 5-500 PER
NO PRICING ON QTY 25 OR LESS
1 Hank Aaron/10
2 Dale Murphy/350 5.00 12.00
3 Brooks Robinson/250 5.00 12.00
4 Cal Ripken Jr./350 6.00 15.00
5 Eddie Murray/250 3.00 8.00
6 Carl Yastrzemski/400 3.00 8.00
7 Carlton Fisk/150 3.00 8.00
8 Wade Boggs/500 3.00 8.00
11 Jim Rice/350 3.00 8.00
12 Fred Lynn/350 3.00 8.00
15 Ernie Banks/10
16 Ryne Sandberg/150 5.00 12.00
18 Luis Aparicio/200 3.00 8.00
19 Tom Seaver/350 3.00 8.00
21 Pete Rose/100 20.00 50.00
22 Bob Feller/15
22 Bob Feller/15
25 Kirk Gibson/250 3.00 8.00
26 Alan Trammell/250 3.00 8.00
27 George Brett/250 5.00 12.00
28 Steve Garvey/150 4.00 10.00
29 Robin Yount/500 4.00 10.00
30 Harmon Killebrew/150 5.00 12.00
31 Paul Molitor/300 3.00 8.00
32 Gary Carter/450 3.00 8.00
33 George Bush/500 6.00 15.00
35 Don Mattingly/150 6.00 15.00
36 Reggie Jackson/350 3.00 8.00
38 Mike Schmidt/350 4.00 10.00
39 Steve Carlton/250 4.00 10.00
40 Tony Gwynn/500 3.00 8.00
42 Willie Mays/5
43 Willie McCovey/500 3.00 8.00
44 Will Clark/500 3.00 8.00
45 Bob Gibson/100 4.00 10.00
46 Dennis Eckersley/500 3.00 8.00
47 Red Schoendienst/300 4.00 10.00
48 Stan Musial/25
49 Nolan Ryan/250 8.00 20.00
54 Michael Burgess/500 3.00 8.00
55 John Raynor/50 4.00 10.00
58 Luis Exposito/100 4.00 10.00
91 Madison Bumgarner/100 5.00 12.00
95 Josh Vitters/500 3.00 8.00
104 Tyler Flowers/95 4.00 10.00
105 Tyler Henson/50 3.00 8.00
146 Heath Rollins/90 3.00 8.00
147 Alex Cobb/95 3.00 8.00

2008 Donruss Threads Jerseys Prime

RANDOM INSERTS IN PACKS
PRINT RUN B/WN 1-25 COPIES PER
NO PRICING DUE TO SCARCITY

2008 Donruss Threads Signatures Gold

RANDOM INSERTS IN PACKS
PRINT RUNS B/WN 10-999 COPIES PER
NO PRICING ON QTY 25 OR LESS
1 Hank Aaron/10
2 Dale Murphy/10
3 Brooks Robinson/50 10.00 25.00
4 Cal Ripken Jr./50 50.00 100.00
5 Eddie Murray/25
6 Carl Yastrzemski/50 20.00 50.00
7 Carlton Fisk/50 12.50 30.00
8 Wade Boggs/10
10 Johnny Pesky/100 5.00 12.00
11 Jim Rice/100 10.00 25.00
12 Fred Lynn/50 5.00 12.00
13 Duke Snider/50 12.50 30.00
14 Carl Erskine/75 5.00 12.00
15 Ernie Banks/10
16 Ryne Sandberg/50 20.00 50.00
17 Don Sutton/100 5.00 12.00
18 Luis Aparicio/50 5.00 12.00
19 Tom Seaver/50 15.00 40.00
20 Tony Perez/25
21 Pete Rose/75 90.00 150.00
22 Bob Feller/100 12.50 30.00
23 Al Kaline/50 12.50 30.00
24 Mark Fidrych/100 6.00 15.00
25 Kirk Gibson/10
26 Alan Trammell/75 5.00 12.00
27 George Brett/10
28 Steve Garvey/45 10.00 25.00
29 Robin Yount/50 15.00 40.00
30 Harmon Killebrew/10
31 Paul Molitor/50 6.00 15.00
32 Gary Carter/50 10.00 25.00
33 George Bush/25
34 Don Larsen/50 8.00 20.00
35 Don Mattingly/50 12.50 30.00
36 Reggie Jackson/50 12.50 30.00
37 Tim Raines/25
38 Mike Schmidt/50 20.00 50.00
39 Steve Carlton/50 20.00 50.00
40 Tony Gwynn/50 15.00 40.00
41 Juan Marichal/50 10.00 25.00
42 Willie Mays/50 75.00 150.00
43 Willie McCovey/50 15.00 40.00
44 Will Clark/15
45 Bob Gibson/50 8.00 20.00
46 Dennis Eckersley/50 6.00 15.00
47 Red Schoendienst/100 8.00 20.00
48 Stan Musial/50 40.00 80.00
49 Nolan Ryan/50 40.00 80.00
50 Frank Howard/75 6.00 15.00
51 Austin Romine/725 5.00 12.00
52 Chris Carter/499 8.00 20.00
53 Jordan Schafer/275 5.00 12.00
54 Michael Burgess/25
55 John Raynor/575 4.00 10.00
56 Lars Anderson/499 15.00 40.00
57 Josh Reddick/499 12.50 30.00
58 Luis Exposito/971 4.00 10.00
59 Aneury Rodriguez/975 4.00 10.00
60 Nick Weglarz/999 4.00 10.00
61 Hector Gomez/499 5.00 12.00
62 Jon Still/775 4.00 10.00
63 Brandon Hamilton/972 4.00 10.00
64 Bud Norris/499 4.00 10.00
65 Danny Duffy/499 8.00 20.00
66 Jovan Rosa/973 4.00 10.00
67 Sean O'Sullivan/499 4.00 10.00
68 Edilio Colina/975 4.00 10.00
69 Ryan Patterson/775 4.00 10.00
70 Brent Brewer/470 5.00 12.00
71 David Bromberg/999 4.00 10.00
72 Bryan Petersen/475 4.00 10.00
73 Lucas Duda/250 6.00 15.00
74 Ruben Tejada/999 5.00 12.00
75 Andrew Lambo/25
76 Jeff Corsaletti/975 4.00 10.00
77 Alexis Oliveras/975 4.00 10.00
78 Fernando Garcia/975 4.00 10.00
79 Jairo Heredia/999 4.00 10.00
80 Jesus Montero/975 12.50 30.00
81 Jose Tabata/975 4.00 10.00
82 Carlos Gonzalez/975 4.00 10.00
83 Patrick Ryan/499 4.00 10.00
84 Sean Doolittle/249 10.00 25.00
85 Carlos Carrasco/999 4.00 10.00
86 Luis Cruz/975 4.00 10.00
87 Yefri Carvajal/999 4.00 10.00
88 Stolmy Pimentel/975 4.00 10.00
89 Wilber Bucardo/420 4.00 10.00
90 Angel Villalona/25
91 Madison Bumgarner/250 10.00 25.00
92 Danny Carroll/999 4.00 10.00
93 Juan Ramirez/999 4.00 10.00
94 Lou Marson/725 5.00 12.00
95 Josh Vitters/25
96 Desmond Jennings/749 4.00 10.00
97 Abraham Almonte/975 4.00 10.00
98 Mat Gamel/25
99 Andrew LeFave/975 4.00 10.00
100 Elvis Andrus/749 5.00 12.00
101 Emilio Bonifacio/100 4.00 10.00
102 Wilin Rosario/100 5.00 12.00
103 Carlos Peguero/25
104 Tyler Flowers/100 20.00 50.00
105 Tyler Henson/100 4.00 10.00
106 Nevin Griffith/100 4.00 10.00
107 Caleb Gindl/25
108 Jose Ceda/100 4.00 10.00
109 Brandon Waring/25
110 Neftali Soto/100 20.00 50.00
111 Ryan Miller/100 4.00 10.00
112 Jack Egbert/100 6.00 15.00
113 Juan Silverio/100 6.00 15.00
114 Jhoulys Chacin/100 15.00 40.00
115 Charlie Furbush/25
116 Hector Correa/100 4.00 10.00
117 Brad James/100 4.00 10.00
119 Keaton Hayenga/100 4.00 10.00
120 Brent Fisher/100 4.00 10.00
121 Juan Francisco/100 8.00 20.00
122 Andrew Romine/100 4.00 10.00
123 Mason Tobin/100 4.00 10.00
124 Anel De Los Santos/100 4.00 10.00
125 Andrew Walker/25
126 Alfredo Silverio/100 4.00 10.00
127 Mario Martinez/100 5.00 12.00
128 Taylor Green/100 5.00 12.00
129 D.J. Jones/100 4.00 10.00
130 Wilson Ramos/100 5.00 12.00
131 Trevor Reckling/100 8.00 20.00
132 Engel Beltre/25
133 Scott Moviel/100 4.00 10.00
134 Josh Tomlin/100 4.00 10.00
135 Dominic Brown/100 12.50 30.00
136 Neftali Feliz/25
137 Brian Friday/100 4.00 10.00
138 Drew Miller/100 4.00 10.00
139 Steve Garrison/100 4.00 10.00
140 Mike McBryde/100 4.00 10.00
141 Brian Duensing/100 4.00 10.00
142 Greg Halman/25
143 Jharmidy De Jesus/25
144 Mike Stanton/25
145 Wilmer Flores/25
146 Heath Rollins/100 4.00 10.00
147 Alex Cobb/100 4.00 10.00
148 Omar Poveda/100 4.00 10.00
149 Yohermyn Chavez/100 4.00 10.00
150 Gerardo Parra/100 6.00 15.00

2008 Donruss Threads Signatures Platinum

RANDOM INSERTS IN PACKS
PRINT RUNS B/WN 5-25 COPIES PER
NO PRICING DUE TO SCARCITY

1941 Double Play

The cards in this 75-card set measure approximately 2 1/2" by 3 1/8" was a blank-backed issue distributed by Gum Products. It consists of 75 numbered cards (two consecutive numbers per card), each depicting two players in sepia tone photographs. Cards 81-100 contain action poses, and the last 50 numbers of the set are slightly harder to find. Cards that have been cut in half to form "singles" have a greatly reduced value. These cards have a value from five to ten percent of the uncut strips and are very difficult to sell. The player on the left has an odd number and the other player has an even number. We are using only the odd numbers to identify these panels. Each penny pack contained two cards and they were issued 100 packs to a box.

COMPLETE SET (150) 3000.00 5000.00
COMMON PAIRS (1-100) 15.00 25.00
COMMON (101-150) 18.00 30.00
WRAPPER (1-CENT) 400.00 500.00
1 Larry French 35.00 60.00
Vance Page XRC
3 Billy Herman 30.00 50.00
Stan Hack
5 Lonny Frey 25.00 40.00
Johnny VanderMeer XRC
7 Paul Derringer 25.00 40.00
Bucky Walters
9 Frank McCormick 15.00 25.00
Billy Werber
11 Johnny Ripple 30.00 50.00
Ernie Lombardi
13 Alex Kampouris 15.00 25.00
Whitlow Wyatt
15 Mickey Owen 30.00 50.00
Paul Waner
17 Cookie Lavagetto 18.00 30.00
Pete Reiser XRC
19 James Wasdell XRC 18.00 30.00
Dolph Camilli
21 Dixie Walker 30.00 50.00
Joe Medwick
23 Pee Wee Reese XRC 125.00 200.00
Kirby Higbe XRC
25 Harry Danning 15.00 25.00
Cliff Melton
27 Harry Gumbert 15.00 25.00
Burgess Whitehead
29 Joe Orengo XRC 15.00 25.00
Joe Moore
31 Mel Ott 60.00 100.00
Norman Young
33 Lee Handley 30.00 50.00
Arky Vaughan
35 Bob Klinger 15.00 25.00
Stanley Brown XRC
37 Terry Moore XRC 18.00 30.00
Gus Mancuso
39 Johnny Mize XRC 90.00 150.00
Enos Slaughter XRC
41 Johnny Cooney 15.00 25.00
Sibby Sisti XRC
43 Max West 15.00 25.00
Carvel Rowell XRC
45 Danny Litwhiler XRC 15.00 25.00
Merrill May
47 Frank Hayes 15.00 25.00
Al Brancato XRC
49 Bob Johnson 18.00 30.00
Bill Nagel XRC
51 Buck Newsom 60.00 100.00
Hank Greenberg
53 Barney McCosky 45.00 75.00
Charlie Gehringer
55 Pinky Higgins 18.00 30.00
Dick Bartell
57 Ted Williams 300.00 500.00
Jim Tabor
59 Joe Cronin 125.00 200.00
Jimmy Foxx
61 Lefty Gomez 150.00 250.00
Phil Rizzuto XRC
63 Joe DiMaggio 450.00 750.00
Charley Keller
65 Red Rolfe 60.00 100.00
Bill Dickey
67 Joe Gordon XRC 60.00 100.00
Red Ruffing
69 Mike Tresh XRC 35.00 60.00
Luke Appling
71 Moose Solters 15.00 25.00
Johnny Rigney XRC
73 Buddy Meyer 18.00 30.00
Ben Chapman
75 Cecil Travis 18.00 30.00
George Case
77 Joe Krakauskas 75.00 125.00
Bob Feller
79 Ken Keltner XRC 18.00 30.00
Hal Trosky
81 Ted Williams 350.00 600.00
Joe Cronin
83 Joe Gordon XRC 25.00 40.00
Charlie Keller
85 Hank Greenberg 125.00 200.00
Red Ruffing
87 Hal Trosky 18.00 30.00
George Case
89 Mel Ott 60.00 100.00
Burgess Whitehead
91 Harry Danning 15.00 25.00
Harry Gumbert
93 Norman Young 15.00 25.00
Cliff Melton
95 Jimmy Ripple 18.00 30.00
Bucky Walters
97 Stan Hack 18.00 30.00
Bob Klinger
99 Johnny Mize XRC 40.00 75.00
Dan Litwhiler XRC
101 Dom Dallessandro XRC 18.00 30.00
Augie Galan
103 Bill Lee 25.00 40.00
Phil Cavarretta
105 Lefty Grove 90.00 150.00
Bobby Doerr
107 Frank Pytlak 35.00 60.00
Dom DiMaggio XRC
109 Jerry Priddy XRC 25.00 40.00
Johnny Murphy
111 Tommy Henrich 30.00 50.00
Marius Russo XRC
113 Frank Crosetti 30.00 50.00
Johnny Sturm XRC
115 Ival Goodman 18.00 30.00
Myron McCormick XRC
117 Eddie Joost 18.00 30.00
Ernie Koy XRC
119 Lloyd Waner 35.00 60.00
Hank Majeski XRC
121 Buddy Hassett 18.00 30.00
Eugene Moore
123 Nick Etten XRC 18.00 30.00
Johnny Rizzo
125 Sam Chapman 18.00 30.00
Wally Moses
127 Johnny Babich 18.00 30.00
Dick Siebert
129 Nelson Potter XRC 18.00 30.00
Benny McCoy XRC
131 Clarence Campbell XRC 45.00 75.00
Lou Boudreau XRC
133 Rollie Hemsley 25.00 40.00
Mel Harder
135 Gerald Walker 18.00 30.00
Joe Heving
137 Johnny Rucker 18.00 30.00
Ace Adams XRC
139 Morris Arnovich 60.00 100.00
Carl Hubbell
141 Lew Riggs 45.00 75.00
Leo Durocher
143 Fred Fitzsimmons 18.00 30.00
Joe Vosmik
145 Frank Crespi XRC 18.00 30.00
Jim Brown
147 Don Heffner 18.00 30.00
Harlond Clift XRC
149 Debs Garms 25.00 40.00
Elbie Fletcher

1997 E-X2000

This 100-card set (produced by Fleer/SkyBox) was distributed in two-card foil packs with a suggested retail price of $3.99. An oversized Alex Rodriguez card shipped in its own holder was mailed to dealers who ordered E-X 2000 cases. They are numbered out of 3,000 and priced below. Also priced below is the redemption card for a baseball signed by Rodriguez. 100 of these cards were produced and the redemption deadline was May 1, 1998.

COMPLETE SET (100) 30.00 80.00
1 Jim Edmonds .30 .75
2 Darin Erstad .30 .75
3 Eddie Murray .75 2.00
4 Roberto Alomar .50 1.25
5 Brady Anderson .30 .75
6 Mike Mussina .50 1.25
7 Rafael Palmeiro .50 1.25
8 Cal Ripken 2.50 6.00
9 Steve Avery .30 .75
10 Nomar Garciaparra 1.25 3.00
11 Mo Vaughn .30 .75
12 Albert Belle .30 .75
13 Mike Cameron .30 .75
14 Ray Durham .30 .75
15 Frank Thomas .75 2.00
16 Robin Ventura .30 .75
17 Manny Ramirez .50 1.25
18 Jim Thome .50 1.25
19 Matt Williams .30 .75
20 Tony Clark .30 .75
21 Travis Fryman .30 .75
22 Bob Higginson .30 .75
23 Kevin Appier .30 .75
24 Johnny Damon .50 1.25
25 Jermaine Dye .30 .75
26 Jeff Cirillo .30 .75
27 Ben McDonald .30 .75
28 Chuck Knoblauch .30 .75
29 Paul Molitor .30 .75
30 Todd Walker .30 .75
31 Wade Boggs .50 1.25
32 Cecil Fielder .30 .75
33 Derek Jeter 2.00 5.00
34 Andy Pettitte .50 1.25
35 Ruben Rivera .30 .75
36 Bernie Williams .50 1.25
37 Jose Canseco .50 1.25
38 Mark McGwire 2.00 5.00
39 Jay Buhner .30 .75
40 Ken Griffey Jr. 1.25 3.00
41 Randy Johnson .75 2.00
42 Edgar Martinez .50 1.25
43 Alex Rodriguez 1.25 3.00
44 Dan Wilson .30 .75
45 Will Clark .50 1.25
46 Juan Gonzalez .30 .75
47 Ivan Rodriguez .50 1.25
48 Joe Carter .30 .75
49 Roger Clemens 1.50 4.00
50 Juan Guzman .30 .75
51 Pat Hentgen .30 .75
52 Tom Glavine .50 1.25
53 Andruw Jones .50 1.25
54 Chipper Jones .75 2.00
55 Ryan Klesko .30 .75
56 Kenny Lofton .30 .75
57 Greg Maddux 1.25 3.00
58 Fred McGriff .50 1.25
59 John Smoltz .50 1.25
60 Mark Wohlers .30 .75
61 Mark Grace .50 1.25
62 Ryne Sandberg 1.25 3.00
63 Sammy Sosa .75 2.00
64 Barry Larkin .50 1.25
65 Deion Sanders .50 1.25
66 Reggie Sanders .30 .75
67 Dante Bichette .30 .75
68 Ellis Burks .30 .75
69 Andres Galarraga .30 .75
70 Moises Alou .30 .75
71 Kevin Brown .30 .75
72 Cliff Floyd .30 .75
73 Edgar Renteria .30 .75
74 Gary Sheffield .30 .75
75 Bob Abreu .50 1.25
76 Jeff Bagwell .50 1.25
77 Craig Biggio .50 1.25
78 Todd Hollandsworth .30 .75
79 Eric Karros .30 .75
80 Raul Mondesi .30 .75
81 Hideo Nomo .75 2.00
82 Mike Piazza 1.25 3.00
83 Vladimir Guerrero .75 2.00
84 Henry Rodriguez .30 .75
85 Todd Hundley .30 .75
86 Alex Ochoa .30 .75
87 Rey Ordonez .30 .75
88 Gregg Jefferies .30 .75
89 Scott Rolen .50 1.25
90 Jermaine Allensworth .30 .75
91 Jason Kendall .30 .75
92 Ken Caminiti .30 .75
93 Tony Gwynn 1.00 2.50
94 Rickey Henderson .75 2.00
95 Barry Bonds 2.00 5.00
96 J.T. Snow .30 .75
97 Dennis Eckersley .30 .75
98 Ron Gant .30 .75
99 Brian Jordan .30 .75
100 Ray Lankford .30 .75
101 Checklist .30 .75
102 Checklist .30 .75
P43 Alex Rodriguez .60 1.50
Three card promo strip
S43 Alex Rodriguez Sample/3000 4.00 10.00
NNO A.Rod AU Ball/100 6.00 15.00

1997 E-X2000 Credentials

Randomly inserted in packs at the approximate rate of one in 60, this 100-card set is parallel to the base set with an etched holofoil border. 299 serial-numbered sets were issued.

*STARS: 3X TO 8X BASIC CARDS

1997 E-X2000 Essential Credentials

Randomly inserted in packs at the rate of one in 200, this 100-card set is parallel to the base set with an etched refractive holographic foil border. 99 serial-numbered sets were issued.

*STARS: 8X TO 20X BASIC CARDS

1997 E-X2000 A Cut Above

Randomly inserted in packs at the rate of one in 288, this 10-card set features color images of "power hitters" on a holographic foil, die-cut sawblade background.

COMPLETE SET (10) 125.00 250.00
1 Frank Thomas 8.00 20.00
2 Ken Griffey Jr. 12.50 30.00
3 Alex Rodriguez 12.50 30.00
4 Albert Belle 3.00 8.00
5 Juan Gonzalez 3.00 8.00
6 Mark McGwire 20.00 50.00
7 Mo Vaughn 3.00 8.00
8 Manny Ramirez 5.00 12.00
9 Barry Bonds 20.00 50.00
10 Fred McGriff 5.00 12.00

1997 E-X2000 Emerald Autographs

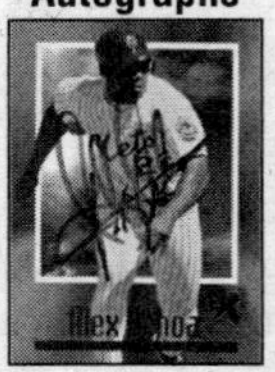

This six-card set features autographed color player photos of some of the hottest young stars in baseball. In addition to an authentic black-ink autograph, each card is embossed with a SkyBox logo about the size of a quarter. These cards were obtained by exchanging a redemption card by mail before the May 1, 1998, deadline.

*EXCH.CARDS: .1X TO .25X BASIC AUTO
2 Darin Erstad 6.00 15.00
30 Todd Walker 6.00 15.00
43 Alex Rodriguez 75.00 150.00
78 Todd Hollandsworth 6.00 15.00
86 Alex Ochoa 6.00 15.00
89 Scott Rolen 10.00 25.00

1997 E-X2000 Hall or Nothing

Randomly inserted in packs at the rate of one in 20, this 20-card set features color images of future Cooperstown Hall of Fame candidates printed on 30-pt. acrylic card stock with etched copper foil borders and gold foil stamping.

COMPLETE SET (20) 50.00 120.00
1 Frank Thomas 2.00 5.00
2 Ken Griffey Jr. 3.00 8.00
3 Eddie Murray 2.00 5.00
4 Cal Ripken 6.00 15.00
5 Ryne Sandberg 3.00 8.00
6 Wade Boggs 1.25 3.00
7 Roger Clemens 4.00 10.00
8 Tony Gwynn 2.50 6.00
9 Alex Rodriguez 3.00 8.00
10 Mark McGwire 5.00 12.00
11 Barry Bonds 5.00 12.00
12 Greg Maddux 3.00 8.00
13 Juan Gonzalez .75 2.00
14 Albert Belle .75 2.00
15 Mike Piazza 3.00 8.00
16 Jeff Bagwell 1.25 3.00
17 Dennis Eckersley .75 2.00
18 Mo Vaughn .75 2.00
19 Roberto Alomar 1.25 3.00
20 Kenny Lofton .75 2.00

1997 E-X2000 Star Date 2000

Randomly inserted in packs at the rate of one in nine, this 15-card set features color images of young star players printed on holographic foil with swirls of spot glitter coating.

COMPLETE SET (15) 12.50 30.00
1 Alex Rodriguez 2.00 5.00
2 Andruw Jones .75 2.00
3 Andy Pettitte .75 2.00
4 Brooks Kieschnick .50 1.25
5 Chipper Jones 1.25 3.00
6 Darin Erstad .50 1.25
7 Derek Jeter 3.00 8.00
8 Jason Kendall .50 1.25
9 Jermaine Dye .50 1.25
10 Neifi Perez .50 1.25
11 Scott Rolen .75 2.00
12 Todd Hollandsworth .50 1.25
13 Todd Walker .50 1.25
14 Tony Clark .50 1.25
15 Vladimir Guerrero 1.25 3.00

1998 E-X2001 Rodriguez Hawaii XIII Promo

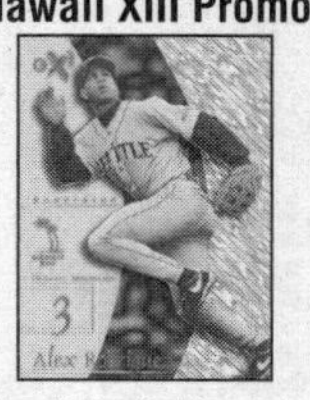

This card was distributed to industry leaders at the 13th Annual Hawaii Trade Show in late February, 1998. It previewed the upcoming 1998 E-X2001 baseball release. A small gold foil "Hawaii XIII" stamp with a palm tree on the left-hand side of the card front distinguishes the card. According to informed sources, Fleer/SkyBox produced approximately 200 of these cards.

NNO Alex Rodriguez	10.00	25.00

1998 E-X2001

The 1998 E-X2001 set (made by Fleer/SkyBox) was issued in one series totalling 100 cards and distributed exclusively to hobby outlets. Cards were issued in two-card packs carrying a $3.99 suggested retail price. The cards are stunningly attractive, featuring full color action shots printed on clear acetate stock with sparkling foil backgrounds. An unnumbered Kerry Wood exchange card was randomly seeded into 1 in every 50 packs (the same pull rate as any other basic issue card). Unlike the acetate stock basic cards, this Wood exchange card was printed on paper stock and could be redeemed until March 31st, 1999 for a real E-X2001 acetate stock Wood card (number 101). In addition, an Alex Rodriguez sample card was issued a few months prior to the product's release. This sample card was distributed to dealers and hobby media to preview the upcoming release. The card is identical to a standard Alex Rodriguez E-X2001 except for the text "PROMOTIONAL SAMPLE" printed diagonally across the card back. There are no key Rookie Cards in this set.

COMPLETE SET (100)	30.00	80.00
1 Alex Rodriguez	1.25	3.00
2 Barry Bonds	2.00	5.00
3 Greg Maddux	1.25	3.00
4 Roger Clemens	1.50	4.00
5 Juan Gonzalez	.30	.75
6 Chipper Jones	.75	2.00
7 Derek Jeter	2.00	5.00
8 Frank Thomas	.75	2.00
9 Cal Ripken	2.50	6.00
10 Ken Griffey Jr.	1.25	3.00
11 Mark McGwire	2.00	5.00
12 Hideo Nomo	.75	2.00
13 Tony Gwynn	1.00	2.50
14 Ivan Rodriguez	.50	1.25
15 Mike Piazza	1.25	3.00
16 Roberto Alomar	.50	1.25
17 Jeff Bagwell	.50	1.25
18 Andruw Jones	.50	1.25
19 Albert Belle	.30	.75
20 Mo Vaughn	.30	.75
21 Kenny Lofton	.30	.75
22 Gary Sheffield	.30	.75
23 Tony Clark	.20	.50
24 Mike Mussina	.50	1.25
25 Barry Larkin	.50	1.25
26 Moises Alou	.30	.75
27 Brady Anderson	.30	.75
28 Andy Pettitte	.50	1.25
29 Sammy Sosa	.75	2.00
30 Raul Mondesi	.30	.75
31 Andres Galarraga	.30	.75
32 Chuck Knoblauch	.30	.75
33 Jim Thome	.50	1.25
34 Craig Biggio	.50	1.25
35 Jay Buhner	.30	.75
36 Rafael Palmeiro	.50	1.25
37 Curt Schilling	.30	.75
38 Tino Martinez	.50	1.25
39 Pedro Martinez	.50	1.25
40 Jose Canseco	.50	1.25
41 Jeff Cirillo	.20	.50
42 Dean Palmer	.30	.75
43 Tim Salmon	.50	1.25
44 Jason Giambi	.30	.75
45 Bobby Higginson	.30	.75
46 Jim Edmonds	.30	.75
47 David Justice	.30	.75
48 John Olerud	.30	.75
49 Ray Lankford	.30	.75
50 Al Martin	.20	.50
51 Mike Lieberthal	.30	.75
52 Henry Rodriguez	.20	.50
53 Edgar Renteria	.30	.75
54 Eric Karros	.30	.75
55 Marquis Grissom	.30	.75
56 Wilson Alvarez	.20	.50
57 Darryl Kile	.20	.50
58 Jeff King	.20	.50
59 Shawn Estes	.20	.50
60 Tony Womack	.20	.50
61 Willie Greene	.20	.50
62 Ken Caminiti	.30	.75
63 Vinny Castilla	.30	.75
64 Mark Grace	.50	1.25
65 Ryan Klesko	.30	.75
66 Robin Ventura	.30	.75
67 Todd Hundley	.20	.50
68 Travis Fryman	.30	.75
69 Edgar Martinez	.50	1.25
70 Matt Williams	.30	.75
71 Paul Molitor	.30	.75
72 Kevin Brown	.50	1.25
73 Randy Johnson	.75	2.00
74 Bernie Williams	.50	1.25
75 Manny Ramirez	.50	1.25
76 Fred McGriff	.50	1.25
77 Tom Glavine	.50	1.25
78 Carlos Delgado	.30	.75
79 Larry Walker	.30	.75
80 Hideki Irabu	.20	.50
81 Ryan McGuire	.20	.50
82 Justin Thompson	.20	.50
83 Kevin Orie	.20	.50
84 Jon Nunnally	.20	.50
85 Mark Kotsay	.20	.50
86 Todd Walker	.20	.50
87 Jason Dickson	.20	.50
88 Fernando Tatis	.20	.50
89 Karim Garcia	.20	.50
90 Ricky Ledee	.20	.50
91 Paul Konerko	.30	.75
92 Jaret Wright	.20	.50
93 Darin Erstad	.30	.75
94 Livan Hernandez	.30	.75
95 Nomar Garciaparra	1.25	3.00
96 Jose Cruz Jr.	.20	.50
97 Scott Rolen	.50	1.25
98 Ben Grieve	.20	.50
99 Vladimir Guerrero	.75	2.00
100 Travis Lee	.20	.50
101 Kerry Wood	1.50	4.00
NNO Kerry Wood	.75	2.00
NNO A.Rodriguez Sample	.60	1.50

1998 E-X2001 Essential Credentials Future

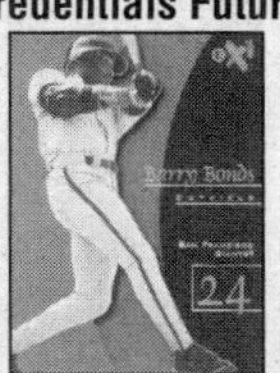

These cards were randomly inserted in E-X2001 packs. For this parallel version, the amount of cards produced is inverse to the card number. Each card is individually serial numbered on the lower edge of the card back. For conveniece, the amount of each player produced is listed next to their listing. Cards between 76 and 100 are not priced due to scarcity.

1 Alex Rodriguez (100)	25.00	60.00
2 Barry Bonds (99)	40.00	100.00
3 Greg Maddux (98)	25.00	60.00
4 Roger Clemens (97)	30.00	80.00
5 Juan Gonzalez (96)	10.00	25.00
6 Chipper Jones (95)	15.00	40.00
7 Derek Jeter (94)	40.00	100.00
8 Frank Thomas (93)	15.00	40.00
9 Cal Ripken (92)	50.00	120.00
10 Ken Griffey Jr. (91)	25.00	60.00
11 Mark McGwire (90)	40.00	100.00
12 Hideo Nomo (89)	15.00	40.00
13 Tony Gwynn (88)	20.00	50.00
14 Ivan Rodriguez (87)	10.00	25.00
15 Mike Piazza (86)	25.00	60.00
16 Roberto Alomar (85)	10.00	25.00
17 Jeff Bagwell (84)	10.00	25.00
18 Andruw Jones (83)	10.00	25.00
19 Albert Belle (82)	10.00	25.00
20 Mo Vaughn (81)	10.00	25.00
21 Kenny Lofton (80)	10.00	25.00
22 Gary Sheffield (79)	10.00	25.00
23 Tony Clark (78)	6.00	15.00
24 Mike Mussina (77)	10.00	25.00
25 Barry Larkin (76)	10.00	25.00
26 Moises Alou (75)	10.00	25.00
27 Brady Anderson (74)	10.00	25.00
28 Andy Pettitte (73)	10.00	25.00
29 Sammy Sosa (72)	15.00	40.00
30 Raul Mondesi (71)	10.00	25.00
31 Andres Galarraga (70)	10.00	25.00
32 Chuck Knoblauch (69)	8.00	20.00
33 Jim Thome (68)	12.50	30.00
34 Craig Biggio (67)	12.50	30.00
35 Jay Buhner (66)	8.00	20.00
36 Rafael Palmeiro (65)	12.50	30.00
37 Curt Schilling (64)	8.00	20.00
38 Tino Martinez (63)	12.50	30.00
39 Pedro Martinez (62)	12.50	30.00
40 Jose Canseco (61)	12.50	30.00
41 Jeff Cirillo (60)	5.00	12.00
42 Dean Palmer (59)	8.00	20.00
43 Tim Salmon (58)	12.50	30.00
44 Jason Giambi (57)	8.00	20.00
45 Bobby Higginson (56)	8.00	20.00
46 Jim Edmonds (55)	8.00	20.00
47 David Justice (54)	8.00	20.00
48 John Olerud (53)	8.00	20.00
49 Ray Lankford (52)	8.00	20.00
50 Al Martin (51)	5.00	12.00
51 Mike Lieberthal (50)	10.00	25.00
52 Henry Rodriguez (49)	6.00	15.00
53 Edgar Renteria (48)	10.00	25.00
54 Eric Karros (47)	10.00	25.00
55 Marquis Grissom (46)	10.00	25.00
56 Wilson Alvarez (45)	6.00	15.00
57 Darryl Kile (44)	10.00	25.00
58 Jeff King (43)	6.00	15.00
59 Shawn Estes (42)	6.00	15.00
60 Tony Womack (41)	6.00	15.00
61 Willie Greene (40)	6.00	15.00
62 Ken Caminiti (39)	10.00	25.00
63 Vinny Castilla (38)	10.00	25.00
64 Mark Grace (37)	15.00	40.00
65 Ryan Klesko (36)	10.00	25.00
66 Robin Ventura (35)	15.00	40.00
67 Todd Hundley (34)	12.50	30.00
68 Travis Fryman (33)	15.00	40.00
69 Edgar Martinez (32)	20.00	50.00
70 Matt Williams (31)	15.00	40.00
71 Paul Molitor (30)	15.00	40.00
72 Kevin Brown (29)	20.00	50.00
73 Randy Johnson (28)	30.00	80.00
74 Bernie Williams (27)	20.00	50.00
75 Manny Ramirez (26)	20.00	50.00
76 Fred McGriff (25)		
77 Tom Glavine (24)		
78 Carlos Delgado (23)		
79 Larry Walker (22)		
80 Hideki Irabu (21)		
81 Ryan McGuire (20)		
82 Justin Thompson (19)		
83 Kevin Orie (18)		
84 Jon Nunnally (17)		
85 Mark Kotsay (16)		
86 Todd Walker (15)		
87 Jason Dickson (14)		
88 Fernando Tatis (13)		
89 Karim Garcia (12)		
90 Ricky Ledee (11)		
91 Paul Konerko (10)		
92 Jaret Wright (9)		
93 Darin Erstad (8)		
94 Livan Hernandez (7)		
95 Nomar Garciaparra (6)		
96 Jose Cruz Jr. (5)		
97 Scott Rolen (4)		
98 Ben Grieve (3)		
99 Vladimir Guerrero (2)		
100 Travis Lee (1)		

1998 E-X2001 Essential Credentials Now

These cards were randomly inserted in E-X2001 packs. For this parallel version, the amount of cards produced is equal to their card number. Each card in individually serial numbered on the lower edge of the card back. Again like in the Essential Credentials Future, we have put the amount of cards produced next to the players name. Cards numbered between 1 and 25 are not priced due to scarcity.

1 Alex Rodriguez (1)		
2 Barry Bonds (2)		
3 Greg Maddux (3)		
4 Roger Clemens (4)		
5 Juan Gonzalez (5)		
6 Chipper Jones (6)		
7 Derek Jeter (7)		
8 Frank Thomas (8)		
9 Cal Ripken (9)		
10 Ken Griffey Jr. (10)		
11 Mark McGwire (11)		
12 Hideo Nomo (12)		
13 Tony Gwynn (13)		
14 Ivan Rodriguez (14)		
15 Mike Piazza (15)		
16 Roberto Alomar (16)		
17 Jeff Bagwell (17)		
18 Andruw Jones (18)		
19 Albert Belle (19)		
20 Mo Vaughn (20)		
21 Kenny Lofton (21)		
22 Gary Sheffield (22)		
23 Tony Clark (23)		
24 Mike Mussina (24)		
25 Barry Larkin (25)		
26 Moises Alou (26)	15.00	40.00
27 Brady Anderson (27)	15.00	40.00
28 Andy Pettitte (28)	20.00	50.00
29 Sammy Sosa (29)	40.00	80.00
30 Raul Mondesi (30)	15.00	40.00
31 Andres Galarraga (31)	15.00	40.00
32 Chuck Knoblauch (32)	15.00	40.00
33 Jim Thome (33)	20.00	50.00
34 Craig Biggio (34)	20.00	50.00
35 Jay Buhner (35)	15.00	40.00
36 Rafael Palmeiro (36)	15.00	40.00
37 Curt Schilling (37)	10.00	25.00
38 Tino Martinez (38)	15.00	40.00
39 Pedro Martinez (39)	15.00	40.00
40 Jose Canseco (40)	15.00	40.00
41 Jeff Cirillo (41)	6.00	15.00
42 Dean Palmer (42)	10.00	25.00
43 Tim Salmon (43)	15.00	40.00
44 Jason Giambi (44)	10.00	25.00
45 Bobby Higginson (45)	10.00	25.00
46 Jim Edmonds (46)	10.00	25.00
47 David Justice (47)	10.00	25.00
48 John Olerud (48)	10.00	25.00
49 Ray Lankford (49)	10.00	25.00
50 Al Martin (50)	6.00	15.00
51 Mike Lieberthal (51)	8.00	20.00
52 Henry Rodriguez (52)	5.00	12.00
53 Edgar Renteria (53)	8.00	20.00
54 Eric Karros (54)	8.00	20.00
55 Marquis Grissom (55)	8.00	20.00
56 Wilson Alvarez (56)	5.00	12.00
57 Darryl Kile (57)	8.00	20.00
58 Jeff King (58)	5.00	12.00
59 Shawn Estes (59)	5.00	12.00
60 Tony Womack (60)	5.00	12.00
61 Willie Greene (61)	5.00	12.00
62 Ken Caminiti (62)	8.00	20.00
63 Vinny Castilla (63)	8.00	20.00
64 Mark Grace (64)	10.00	25.00
65 Ryan Klesko (65)	8.00	20.00
66 Robin Ventura (66)	8.00	20.00
67 Todd Hundley (67)	5.00	12.00
68 Travis Fryman (68)	8.00	20.00
69 Edgar Martinez (69)	10.00	25.00
70 Matt Williams (70)	8.00	20.00
71 Paul Molitor (71)	6.00	15.00
72 Kevin Brown (72)	10.00	25.00
73 Randy Johnson (73)	15.00	40.00
74 Bernie Williams (74)	10.00	25.00
75 Manny Ramirez (75)	15.00	40.00
76 Fred McGriff (76)	10.00	25.00
77 Tom Glavine (77)	10.00	25.00
78 Carlos Delgado (78)	6.00	15.00
79 Larry Walker (79)	6.00	15.00
80 Hideki Irabu (80)	4.00	10.00
81 Ryan McGuire (81)	4.00	10.00
82 Justin Thompson (82)	4.00	10.00
83 Kevin Orie (83)	4.00	10.00
84 Jon Nunnally (84)	4.00	10.00
85 Mark Kotsay (85)	6.00	15.00
86 Todd Walker (86)	4.00	10.00
87 Jason Dickson (87)	4.00	10.00
88 Fernando Tatis (88)	4.00	10.00
89 Karim Garcia (89)	4.00	10.00
90 Ricky Ledee (90)	4.00	10.00
91 Paul Konerko (91)	6.00	15.00
92 Jaret Wright (92)	4.00	10.00
93 Darin Erstad (93)	6.00	15.00
94 Livan Hernandez (94)	6.00	15.00
95 N.Garciaparra (95)	25.00	60.00
96 Jose Cruz Jr. (96)	4.00	10.00
97 Scott Rolen (97)	10.00	25.00
98 Ben Grieve (98)	4.00	10.00
99 Vladimir Guerrero (99)	15.00	40.00
100 Travis Lee (100)	4.00	10.00

1998 E-X2001 Cheap Seat Treats

Randomly inserted in packs at a rate of one in 24, this 20-card set is an insert to the SkyBox E-X2001 brand. Each die-cut card is shaped like a folding chair with silver foil stamping and features a color player photo of some of today's greatest sluggers.

COMPLETE SET (20)	40.00	100.00
1 Frank Thomas	3.00	8.00
2 Ken Griffey Jr.	5.00	12.00
3 Mark McGwire	8.00	20.00
4 Tino Martinez	2.00	5.00
5 Larry Walker	1.25	3.00
6 Juan Gonzalez	1.25	3.00
7 Mike Piazza	5.00	12.00
8 Jeff Bagwell	2.00	5.00
9 Tony Clark	.75	2.00
10 Albert Belle	1.25	3.00
11 Andres Galarraga	1.25	3.00
12 Jim Thome	2.00	5.00
13 Mo Vaughn	1.25	3.00
14 Barry Bonds	8.00	20.00
15 Vladimir Guerrero	3.00	8.00
16 Scott Rolen	2.00	5.00
17 Travis Lee	.75	2.00
18 David Justice	1.25	3.00
19 Jose Cruz Jr.	.75	2.00
20 Andruw Jones	2.00	5.00

1998 E-X2001 Destination Cooperstown

Randomly inserted in packs at a rate of one in 720, this 15-card set is an insert to the SkyBox E-X2001 brand. Each card is designed to resemble a luggage destination tag including a piece of string tied to a hole at the top of each card and honors future Hall-of Famers with color player photos. The cards also provide the featured player's name, team, and position.

1 Alex Rodriguez	15.00	40.00
2 Frank Thomas	10.00	25.00
3 Cal Ripken	30.00	80.00
4 Roger Clemens	20.00	50.00
5 Greg Maddux	15.00	40.00
6 Chipper Jones	10.00	25.00
7 Ken Griffey Jr.	15.00	40.00
8 Mark McGwire	25.00	60.00
9 Tony Gwynn	12.50	30.00
10 Mike Piazza	15.00	40.00
11 Jeff Bagwell	6.00	15.00
12 Jose Cruz Jr.	4.00	10.00
13 Derek Jeter	25.00	60.00
14 Hideo Nomo	15.00	40.00
15 Ivan Rodriguez	6.00	15.00

1998 E-X2001 Signature 2001

Randomly inserted in packs at a rate of one in 60, this 17-card set is an insert to the SkyBox E-X2001 brand. The exclusive insert features color action photos and autographs signed by some of MLB's brightest young stars.

1 Ricky Ledee	4.00	10.00
2 Derrick Gibson	4.00	10.00
3 Mark Kotsay	6.00	15.00
4 Kevin Millwood	10.00	25.00
5 Brad Fullmer	4.00	10.00
6 Todd Walker	6.00	15.00
7 Ben Grieve	4.00	10.00
8 Tony Clark	4.00	10.00
9 Jaret Wright	4.00	10.00
10 Randall Simon	4.00	10.00
11 Paul Konerko	10.00	25.00
12 Todd Helton	10.00	25.00
13 David Ortiz	15.00	40.00
14 Alex Gonzalez	4.00	10.00
15 Bobby Estalella	4.00	10.00
16 Alex Rodriguez SP	60.00	120.00
17 Mike Lowell	12.50	30.00

1998 E-X2001 Star Date 2001

Randomly inserted in packs at a rate of one in 12, this 15-card set is an insert to the SkyBox E-X2001 brand. The fronts feature a background of space-age graphics and gold-foil stamping on plastic stock. The color action photos showcase some of the hottest up-and-coming stars in the MLB.

COMPLETE SET (15)	6.00	15.00
1 Travis Lee	.40	1.00
2 Jose Cruz Jr.	.40	1.00
3 Paul Konerko	.40	1.00
4 Bobby Estalella	.40	1.00
5 Magglio Ordonez	1.25	3.00
6 Juan Encarnacion	.40	1.00
7 Richard Hidalgo	.40	1.00
8 Abraham Nunez	.40	1.00
9 Sean Casey	.40	1.00
10 Todd Helton	.60	1.50
11 Brad Fullmer	.40	1.00
12 Ben Grieve	.40	1.00
13 Livan Hernandez	.40	1.00
14 Jaret Wright	.40	1.00
15 Todd Dunwoody	.40	1.00

1999 E-X Century

This 120-card set features color action player photos silhouetted on extra thick transparent plastic card stock. Each pack contained three cards and carried a suggested retail price of $5.99. The set contains a 30-card Rookie short-printed subset (91-120) with an insertion rate of 1:2 packs. A promotional sample card featuring Ben Grieve was distributed to dealer accounts and hobby media shortly before the product's national release. This card can be easily identified by the "PROMOTIONAL SAMPLE" text running across the back. Notable Rookie Cards include Pat Burrell.

COMPLETE SET (120)	30.00	80.00
COMP.SET w/o SP's (90)	15.00	40.00
COMMON CARD (1-90)	.20	.50
COMMON SP (91-120)	.40	1.00
1 Scott Rolen	.50	1.25
2 Nomar Garciaparra	1.25	3.00
3 Mike Piazza	1.25	3.00
4 Tony Gwynn	1.00	2.50
5 Sammy Sosa	1.25	3.00
6 Alex Rodriguez	1.25	3.00
7 Vladimir Guerrero	.75	2.00
8 Chipper Jones	.75	2.00
9 Derek Jeter	2.00	5.00
10 Kerry Wood	.30	.75
11 Juan Gonzalez	.30	.75
12 Frank Thomas	.75	2.00
13 Mo Vaughn	.30	.75
14 Greg Maddux	1.25	3.00
15 Jeff Bagwell	.50	1.25
16 Mark McGwire	2.00	5.00
17 Ken Griffey Jr.	1.25	3.00
18 Roger Clemens	1.50	4.00
19 Cal Ripken	2.50	6.00
20 Travis Lee	.20	.50
21 Todd Helton	.50	1.25
22 Darin Erstad	.30	.75
23 Pedro Martinez	.50	1.25
24 Barry Bonds	2.00	5.00
25 Andruw Jones	.50	1.25
26 Larry Walker	.30	.75
27 Albert Belle	.30	.75
28 Ivan Rodriguez	.50	1.25
29 Magglio Ordonez	.30	.75
30 Andres Galarraga	.30	.75
31 Mike Mussina	.50	1.25
32 Randy Johnson	.75	2.00
33 Tom Glavine	.50	1.25
34 Barry Larkin	.50	1.25
35 Jim Thome	.50	1.25
36 Gary Sheffield	.30	.75
37 Bernie Williams	.50	1.25
38 Carlos Delgado	.30	.75
39 Rafael Palmeiro	.50	1.25
40 Edgar Renteria	.30	.75
41 Brad Fullmer	.20	.50
42 David Wells	.30	.75
43 Dante Bichette	.30	.75
44 Jaret Wright	.20	.50
45 Ricky Ledee	.20	.50
46 Ray Lankford	.30	.75
47 Mark Grace	.50	1.25
48 Jeff Cirillo	.20	.50
49 Rondell White	.30	.75
50 Jeromy Burnitz	.30	.75
51 Sean Casey	.30	.75
52 Rolando Arrojo	.20	.50
53 Jason Giambi	.30	.75
54 John Olerud	.30	.75
55 Will Clark	.50	1.25
56 Raul Mondesi	.30	.75
57 Scott Brosius	.30	.75
58 Bartolo Colon	.30	.75
59 Steve Finley	.30	.75
60 Javy Lopez	.30	.75
61 Tim Salmon	.50	1.25
62 Roberto Alomar	.50	1.25
63 Vinny Castilla	.30	.75
64 Craig Biggio	.50	1.25
65 Jose Guillen	.30	.75
66 Greg Vaughn	.20	.50
67 Jose Canseco	.50	1.25
68 Shawn Green	.30	.75
69 Curt Schilling	.30	.75
70 Orlando Hernandez	.30	.75
71 Jose Cruz Jr.	.20	.50
72 Alex Gonzalez	.20	.50
73 Tino Martinez	.50	1.25
74 Todd Hundley	.20	.50
75 Brian Giles	.30	.75
76 Cliff Floyd	.30	.75
77 Paul O'Neill	.50	1.25
78 Ken Caminiti	.30	.75
79 Ron Gant	.30	.75
80 Juan Encarnacion	.20	.50
81 Ben Grieve	.20	.50
82 Brian Jordan	.30	.75
83 Rickey Henderson	.75	2.00
84 Tony Clark	.20	.50
85 Shannon Stewart	.30	.75
86 Robin Ventura	.30	.75
87 Todd Walker	.20	.50
88 Kevin Brown	.50	1.25
89 Moises Alou	.30	.75
90 Manny Ramirez	.50	1.25
91 Gabe Alvarez SP	.40	1.00
92 Jeremy Giambi SP	.40	1.00
93 Adrian Beltre SP	.40	1.00
94 George Lombard SP	.40	1.00
95 Ryan Minor SP	.40	1.00
96 Kevin Witt SP	.40	1.00
97 Scott Hunter SP RC	.40	1.00
98 Carlos Guillen SP	.40	1.00
99 Derrick Gibson SP	.40	1.00
100 Trot Nixon SP	.40	1.00
101 Troy Glaus SP	.40	1.00
102 Armando Rios SP	.40	1.00
103 Preston Wilson SP	.40	1.00
104 Pat Burrell SP RC	1.25	3.00
105 J.D. Drew SP	.40	1.00
106 Bruce Chen SP	.40	1.00
107 Matt Clement SP	.40	1.00
108 Carlos Beltran SP	.40	1.00
109 Carlos Febles SP	.40	1.00
110 Rob Fick SP	.40	1.00
111 Russell Branyan SP	.40	1.00
112 R.Brown SP RC	.40	1.00
113 Corey Koskie SP	.40	1.00
114 M.Encarnacion SP RC	.40	1.00
115 Peter Tucci SP	.40	1.00
116 Eric Chavez SP	.40	1.00
117 Gabe Kapler SP	.40	1.00
118 Marlon Anderson SP	.40	1.00
119 A.J. Burnett SP RC	.60	1.50
120 Ryan Bradley SP	.40	1.00
P81 Ben Grieve Sample	.40	1.00

1999 E-X Century Essential Credentials Future

Randomly inserted into packs, this 120-card set is a sequentially numbered gold foil parallel version of the E-X Century base set. The print run for each card follows the player's name in the checklist below.

1 Scott Rolen (120)	8.00	20.00
2 N.Garciaparra (119)	20.00	50.00
3 Mike Piazza (118)	20.00	50.00
4 Tony Gwynn (117)	15.00	40.00
5 Sammy Sosa (116)	8.00	20.00
6 Alex Rodriguez (115)	20.00	50.00
7 Vladimir Guerrero (114)	8.00	20.00
8 Chipper Jones (113)	8.00	20.00
9 Derek Jeter (112)	30.00	80.00
10 Kerry Wood (111)	6.00	15.00
11 Juan Gonzalez (110)	6.00	15.00
12 Frank Thomas (109)	8.00	20.00
13 Mo Vaughn (108)	6.00	15.00
14 Greg Maddux (107)	20.00	50.00
15 Jeff Bagwell (106)	8.00	20.00
16 Mark McGwire (105)	30.00	80.00
17 Ken Griffey Jr. (104)	20.00	50.00
18 Roger Clemens (103)	25.00	60.00
19 Cal Ripken (102)	40.00	100.00
20 Travis Lee (101)	5.00	12.00
21 Todd Helton (100)	8.00	20.00
22 Darin Erstad (99)	5.00	12.00
23 Pedro Martinez (98)	8.00	20.00
24 Barry Bonds (97)	40.00	100.00
25 Andruw Jones (96)	8.00	20.00
26 Larry Walker (95)	5.00	12.00
27 Albert Belle (94)	5.00	12.00
28 Ivan Rodriguez (93)	8.00	20.00

29 Magglio Ordonez (92) 5.00 12.00
30 Andres Galarraga (91) 5.00 12.00
31 Mike Mussina (90) 8.00 20.00
32 Randy Johnson (89) 12.50 30.00
33 Tom Glavine (88) 8.00 20.00
34 Barry Larkin (87) 8.00 20.00
35 Jim Thome (86) 8.00 20.00
36 Gary Sheffield (85) 5.00 12.00
37 Bernie Williams (84) 8.00 20.00
38 Carlos Delgado (83) 5.00 12.00
39 Rafael Palmeiro (82) 8.00 20.00
40 Edgar Renteria (81) 5.00 12.00
41 Brad Fullmer (80) 4.00 10.00
42 David Wells (79) 5.00 12.00
43 Dante Bichette (78) 5.00 12.00
44 Jaret Wright (77) 4.00 10.00
45 Ricky Ledee (76) 4.00 10.00
46 Ray Lankford (75) 5.00 12.00
47 Mark Grace (74) 8.00 20.00
48 Jeff Cirillo (73) 4.00 10.00
49 Rondell White (72) 5.00 12.00
50 Jeromy Burnitz (71) 5.00 12.00
51 Sean Casey (70) 6.00 15.00
52 Rolando Arrojo (69) 5.00 12.00
53 Jason Giambi (68) 6.00 15.00
54 John Olerud (67) 6.00 15.00
55 Will Clark (66) 10.00 25.00
56 Raul Mondesi (65) 6.00 15.00
57 Scott Brosius (64) 6.00 15.00
58 Bartolo Colon (63) 6.00 15.00
59 Steve Finley (62) 6.00 15.00
60 Javy Lopez (61) 6.00 15.00
61 Tim Salmon (60) 10.00 25.00
62 Roberto Alomar (59) 10.00 25.00
63 Vinny Castilla (58) 6.00 15.00
64 Craig Biggio (57) 10.00 25.00
65 Jose Guillen (56) 6.00 15.00
66 Greg Vaughn (55) 5.00 12.00
67 Jose Canseco (54) 10.00 25.00
68 Shawn Green (53) 6.00 15.00
69 Curt Schilling (52) 6.00 15.00
70 O.Hernandez (51) 6.00 15.00
71 Jose Cruz Jr. (50) 5.00 12.00
72 Alex Gonzalez (49) 5.00 12.00
73 Tino Martinez (48) 12.50 30.00
74 Todd Hundley (47) 5.00 12.00
75 Brian Giles (46) 8.00 20.00
76 Cliff Floyd (45) 8.00 20.00
77 Paul O'Neill (44) 12.50 30.00
78 Ken Caminiti (43) 8.00 20.00
79 Ron Gant (42) 8.00 20.00
80 Juan Encarnacion (41) 5.00 12.00
81 Ben Grieve (40) 5.00 12.00
82 Brian Jordan (39) 8.00 20.00
83 Rickey Henderson (38) 20.00 50.00
84 Tony Clark (37) 5.00 12.00
85 Shannon Stewart (36) 8.00 20.00
86 Robin Ventura (35) 10.00 25.00
87 Todd Walker (34) 6.00 15.00
88 Kevin Brown (33) 15.00 40.00
89 Moises Alou (32) 10.00 25.00
90 Manny Ramirez (31) 15.00 40.00
91 Gabe Alvarez (30) 6.00 15.00
92 Jeremy Giambi (29) 6.00 15.00
93 Adrian Beltre (28) 10.00 25.00
94 George Lombard (27) 6.00 15.00
95 Ryan Minor (26) 6.00 15.00
96 Kevin Witt (25)
97 Scott Hunter (24)
98 Carlos Guillen (23)
99 Derrick Gibson (22)
100 Trot Nixon (21)
101 Troy Glaus (20)
102 Armando Rios (19)
103 Preston Wilson (18)
104 Pat Burrell (17)
105 J.D. Drew (16)
106 Bruce Chen (15)
107 Matt Clement (14)
108 Carlos Beltran (13)
109 Carlos Febles (12)
110 Rob Fick (11)
111 Russell Branyan (10)
112 Roosevelt Brown (9)
113 Corey Koskie (8)
114 Mario Encarnacion (7)
115 Peter Tucci (6)
116 Eric Chavez (5)
117 Gabe Kapler (4)
118 Marlon Anderson (3)
119 A.J. Burnett (2)
120 Ryan Bradley (1)

1999 E-X Century Essential Credentials Now

Randomly inserted into packs, this 120-card set is a silver foil parallel version of the E-X Century base set. Each card is sequentially numbered to the pictured player's card number and follows the player's name in the checklist below.

1 Scott Rolen (1)
2 Nomar Garciaparra (2)
3 Mike Piazza (3)
4 Tony Gwynn (4)
5 Sammy Sosa (5)
6 Alex Rodriguez (6)
7 Vladimir Guerrero (7)
8 Chipper Jones (8)
9 Derek Jeter (9)
10 Kerry Wood (10)
11 Juan Gonzalez (11)
12 Frank Thomas (12)
13 Mo Vaughn (13)
14 Greg Maddux (14)
15 Jeff Bagwell (15)
16 Mark McGwire (16)
17 Ken Griffey Jr. (17)
18 Roger Clemens (18)
19 Cal Ripken (19)
20 Travis Lee (20)
21 Todd Helton (21)
22 Darin Erstad (22)
23 Pedro Martinez (23)
24 Barry Bonds (24)
25 Andruw Jones (25)
26 Larry Walker (26) 15.00 40.00
27 Albert Belle (27) 15.00 40.00
28 Ivan Rodriguez (28) 20.00 50.00
29 Magglio Ordonez (29) 15.00 40.00
30 Andres Galarraga (30) 15.00 40.00
31 Mike Mussina (31) 20.00 50.00
32 Randy Johnson (32) 25.00 60.00
33 Tom Glavine (33) 20.00 50.00
34 Barry Larkin (34) 20.00 50.00
35 Jim Thome (35) 20.00 50.00
36 Gary Sheffield (36) 8.00 20.00
37 Bernie Williams (37) 12.50 30.00
38 Carlos Delgado (38) 8.00 20.00
39 Rafael Palmeiro (39) 12.50 30.00
40 Edgar Renteria (40) 8.00 20.00
41 Brad Fullmer (41) 5.00 12.00
42 David Wells (42) 8.00 20.00
43 Dante Bichette (43) 8.00 20.00
44 Jaret Wright (44) 5.00 12.00
45 Ricky Ledee (45) 5.00 12.00
46 Ray Lankford (46) 8.00 20.00
47 Mark Grace (47) 12.50 30.00
48 Jeff Cirillo (48) 5.00 12.00
49 Rondell White (49) 8.00 20.00
50 Jeromy Burnitz (50) 8.00 20.00
51 Sean Casey (51) 6.00 15.00
52 Rolando Arrojo (52) 5.00 12.00
53 Jason Giambi (53) 6.00 15.00
54 John Olerud (54) 6.00 15.00
55 Will Clark (55) 10.00 25.00
56 Raul Mondesi (56) 6.00 15.00
57 Scott Brosius (57) 6.00 15.00
58 Bartolo Colon (58) 6.00 15.00
59 Steve Finley (59) 6.00 15.00
60 Javy Lopez (60) 6.00 15.00
61 Tim Salmon (61) 10.00 25.00
62 Roberto Alomar (62) 10.00 25.00
63 Vinny Castilla (63) 6.00 15.00
64 Craig Biggio (64) 10.00 25.00
65 Jose Guillen (65) 6.00 15.00
66 Greg Vaughn (66) 5.00 12.00
67 Jose Canseco (67) 10.00 25.00
68 Shawn Green (68) 6.00 15.00
69 Curt Schilling (69) 6.00 15.00
70 O.Hernandez (70) 6.00 15.00
71 Jose Cruz Jr. (71) 4.00 10.00
72 Alex Gonzalez (72) 4.00 10.00
73 Tino Martinez (73) 8.00 20.00
74 Todd Hundley (74) 4.00 10.00
75 Brian Giles (75) 5.00 12.00
76 Cliff Floyd (76) 5.00 12.00
77 Paul O'Neill (77) 8.00 20.00
78 Ken Caminiti (78) 5.00 12.00
79 Ron Gant (79) 5.00 12.00
80 Juan Encarnacion (80) 4.00 10.00
81 Ben Grieve (81) 4.00 10.00
82 Brian Jordan (82) 5.00 12.00
83 Rickey Henderson (83) 12.50 30.00
84 Tony Clark (84) 4.00 10.00
85 Shannon Stewart (85) 5.00 12.00
86 Robin Ventura (86) 5.00 12.00
87 Todd Walker (87) 4.00 10.00
88 Kevin Brown (88) 8.00 20.00
89 Moises Alou (89) 5.00 12.00
90 Manny Ramirez (90) 8.00 20.00
91 Gabe Alvarez (91) 4.00 10.00
92 Jeremy Giambi (92) 4.00 10.00
93 Adrian Beltre (93) 5.00 12.00
94 George Lombard (94) 4.00 10.00
95 Ryan Minor (95) 4.00 10.00
96 Kevin Witt (96) 4.00 10.00
97 Scott Hunter (97) 4.00 10.00
98 Carlos Guillen (98) 5.00 12.00
99 Derrick Gibson (99) 4.00 10.00
100 Trot Nixon (100) 5.00 12.00
101 Troy Glaus (101) 6.00 15.00
102 Armando Rios (102) 2.50 6.00
103 Preston Wilson (103) 4.00 10.00
104 Pat Burrell (104) 20.00 50.00
105 J.D. Drew (105) 4.00 10.00
106 Bruce Chen (106) 2.50 6.00
107 Matt Clement (107) 4.00 10.00
108 Carlos Beltran (108) 6.00 15.00
109 Carlos Febles (109) 2.50 6.00
110 Rob Fick (110) 2.50 6.00
111 Russell Branyan (111) 2.50 6.00
112 R.Brown (112) 2.50 6.00
113 Corey Koskie (113) 2.50 6.00
114 M.Encarnacion (114) 2.50 6.00
115 Peter Tucci (115) 2.50 6.00
116 Eric Chavez (116) 4.00 10.00
117 Gabe Kapler (117) 4.00 10.00
118 M.Anderson (118) 2.50 6.00
119 A.J. Burnett (119) 10.00 25.00
120 Ryan Bradley (120) 2.50 6.00

1999 E-X Century Authen-Kicks

Randomly inserted into packs, this nine-card set features color cut-outs of top young players with swatches of their game-worn shoes embedded in the cards beside black-and-white head shots of the players in the background. The print run for each card follows the player's name in our checklist.

B1/R1 AU PRINT RUN 8 #'d OF EACH
NO B1/R1 PRICING DUE TO SCARCITY
1 J.D. Drew/160 10.00 25.00
2 Travis Lee/175 6.00 15.00
3 Kevin Millwood/165 10.00 25.00
4 Bruce Chen/205 6.00 15.00
5 Troy Glaus/205 15.00 40.00
6 Todd Helton/205 15.00 40.00
7 Ricky Ledee/180 6.00 15.00
8 Scott Rolen/205 15.00 40.00
9 Jeremy Giambi/205 6.00 15.00
B1 J.D. Drew Black AU/8
R1 J.D. Drew Red AU/8

1999 E-X Century E-X Quisite

Randomly inserted into packs at the rate of one in 18, this 15-card set features color cut-outs of top young players printed on cards with an unique interior die-cut design.

COMPLETE SET (15) 15.00 40.00
1 Troy Glaus .60 1.50
2 J.D. Drew .60 1.50
3 Pat Burrell 1.50 4.00
4 Russell Branyan .60 1.50
5 Kerry Wood 1.00 2.50
6 Eric Chavez .60 1.50
7 Ben Grieve .60 1.50
8 Gabe Kapler .60 1.50
9 Adrian Beltre .60 1.50
10 Todd Helton 1.50 4.00
11 Roosevelt Brown .60 1.50
12 Marlon Anderson .60 1.50
13 Jeremy Giambi .60 1.50
14 Magglio Ordonez 1.00 2.50
15 Travis Lee .60 1.50

1999 E-X Century Favorites for Fenway '99

Randomly inserted into packs at the rate of one in 36, this 20-card set features color cut-outs of All-Star Game starters silhouetted in front of The Green Monster, Fenway Park.

COMPLETE SET (20) 150.00 300.00
1 Mo Vaughn 1.50 4.00
2 Nomar Garciaparra 6.00 15.00
3 Frank Thomas 4.00 10.00
4 Ken Griffey Jr. 6.00 15.00
5 Roger Clemens 8.00 20.00
6 Alex Rodriguez 6.00 15.00
7 Derek Jeter 10.00 25.00
8 Juan Gonzalez 1.50 4.00
9 Cal Ripken 12.50 30.00
10 Ivan Rodriguez 2.50 6.00
11 J.D. Drew 2.00 5.00
12 Barry Bonds 10.00 25.00
13 Tony Gwynn 5.00 12.00
14 Vladimir Guerrero 4.00 10.00
15 Chipper Jones 4.00 10.00
16 Kerry Wood 1.50 4.00
17 Mike Piazza 6.00 15.00
18 Sammy Sosa 6.00 15.00
19 Scott Rolen 2.50 6.00
20 Mark McGwire 10.00 25.00

1999 E-X Century Milestones of the Century

Randomly inserted into packs, this 10-card set features color action photos of players with top statistical performances from the 1998 season printed on a multi-layered card design. Each card is sequentially numbered to the pictured player's 1998 statistical performance and follows the player's name in our checklist.

1 Kerry Wood/20
2 Mark McGwire/70 60.00 120.00
3 Sammy Sosa/66 15.00 40.00
4 Ken Griffey Jr./350 12.50 30.00
5 Roger Clemens/98 30.00 60.00
6 Cal Ripken/17
7 Alex Rodriguez/40 40.00 80.00
8 Barry Bonds/400 15.00 40.00
9 N.Y. Yankees/114 40.00 80.00
10 Travis Lee/98 2.00 5.00

2000 E-X

The 2000 E-X product was released in June, 2000 as a 90-card set. The set featured 60-player cards and

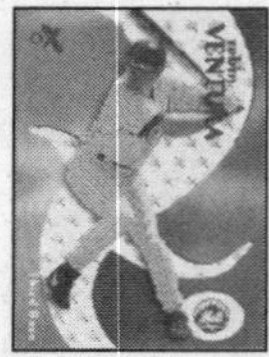

30-short printed prospect cards. Each of the prospect cards were individually serial numbered to 3499. Each pack contained three cards and carried a suggested retail price of $3.99.

COMPLETE SET (90) 40.00 100.00
COMP.SET w/o SP's (60) 8.00 20.00
COMMON CARD (1-60) .15 .40
COMMON PROS (61-90) 1.50 4.00
1 Alex Rodriguez .60 1.50
2 Jeff Bagwell .25 .60
3 Mike Piazza .60 1.50
4 Tony Gwynn .50 1.25
5 Ken Griffey Jr. .60 1.50
6 Juan Gonzalez .15 .40
7 Vladimir Guerrero .40 1.00
8 Cal Ripken 1.25 3.00
9 Mo Vaughn .15 .40
10 Chipper Jones .40 1.00
11 Derek Jeter 1.00 2.50
12 Nomar Garciaparra .60 1.50
13 Mark McGwire 1.00 2.50
14 Sammy Sosa .40 1.00
15 Pedro Martinez .25 .60
16 Greg Maddux .60 1.50
17 Frank Thomas .40 1.00
18 Shawn Green .15 .40
19 Carlos Beltran .15 .40
20 Roger Clemens .75 2.00
21 Randy Johnson .40 1.00
22 Bernie Williams .25 .60
23 Carlos Delgado .15 .40
24 Manny Ramirez .25 .60
25 Freddy Garcia .15 .40
26 Barry Bonds 1.00 2.50
27 Tim Hudson .15 .40
28 Larry Walker .15 .40
29 Raul Mondesi .15 .40
30 Ivan Rodriguez .25 .60
31 Magglio Ordonez .15 .40
32 Scott Rolen .25 .60
33 Mike Mussina .25 .60
34 J.D. Drew .15 .40
35 Tom Glavine .25 .60
36 Barry Larkin .25 .60
37 Jim Thome .25 .60
38 Erubiel Durazo .15 .40
39 Curt Schilling .15 .40
40 Orlando Hernandez .15 .40
41 Rafael Palmeiro .25 .60
42 Gabe Kapler .15 .40
43 Mark Grace .25 .60
44 Jeff Cirillo .15 .40
45 Jeromy Burnitz .15 .40
46 Sean Casey .15 .40
47 Kevin Millwood .15 .40
48 Vinny Castilla .15 .40
49 Jose Canseco .25 .60
50 Roberto Alomar .25 .60
51 Craig Biggio .25 .60
52 Preston Wilson .15 .40
53 Jeff Weaver .15 .40
54 Robin Ventura .15 .40
55 Ben Grieve .15 .40
56 Troy Glaus .15 .40
57 Jacque Jones .15 .40
58 Brian Giles .15 .40
59 Kevin Brown .15 .40
60 Todd Helton .25 .60
61 Ben Petrick PROS 1.50 4.00
62 C.Hermansen PROS 1.50 4.00
63 Kevin Barker PROS 1.50 4.00
64 Matt LeCroy PROS 1.50 4.00
65 Brad Penny PROS 1.50 4.00
66 D.T. Cromer PROS 1.50 4.00
67 Steve Lomasney PROS 1.50 4.00
68 Cole Liniak PROS 1.50 4.00
69 B.J. Ryan PROS 1.50 4.00
70 Wilton Veras PROS 1.50 4.00
71 A.McNeal PROS RC 1.50 4.00
72 Nick Johnson PROS 1.50 4.00
73 Adam Piatt PROS 1.50 4.00
74 Adam Kennedy PROS 1.50 4.00
75 Cesar King PROS 1.50 4.00
76 Peter Bergeron PROS 1.50 4.00
77 Rob Bell PROS 1.50 4.00
78 Wily Pena PROS 1.50 4.00
79 Ruben Mateo PROS 1.50 4.00
80 Kip Wells PROS 1.50 4.00
81 Alex Escobar PROS 1.50 4.00
82 Danys Baez PROS RC 1.50 4.00
83 Travis Dawkins PROS 1.50 4.00
84 Mark Quinn PROS 1.50 4.00
85 Jimmy Anderson PROS 1.50 4.00
86 Rick Ankiel PROS 1.50 4.00
87 Alfonso Soriano PROS 2.00 5.00
88 Pat Burrell PROS 1.50 4.00
89 Eric Munson PROS 1.50 4.00
90 Josh Beckett PROS 2.00 5.00

2000 E-X Essential Credentials Future

Randomly inserted into packs, this 90-card insert is a complete parallel of the E-X base set. Print runs for each of these cards are provided after the player's name in our checklist.

1 Alex Rodriguez (60) 30.00 80.00
2 Jeff Bagwell (59) 12.50 30.00
3 Mike Piazza (58) 30.00 80.00
4 Tony Gwynn (57) 25.00 60.00
5 Ken Griffey Jr. (56) 30.00 80.00
6 Juan Gonzalez (55) 12.50 30.00
7 Vladimir Guerrero (54) 15.00 40.00
8 Cal Ripken (53) 60.00 150.00
9 Mo Vaughn (52) 12.50 30.00
10 Chipper Jones (51) 15.00 40.00
11 Derek Jeter (50) 50.00 120.00
12 N.Garciaparra (49) 30.00 80.00
13 Mark McGwire (48) 50.00 120.00
14 Sammy Sosa (47) 15.00 40.00
15 Pedro Martinez (46) 15.00 40.00
16 Greg Maddux (45) 30.00 80.00
17 Frank Thomas (44) 15.00 40.00
18 Shawn Green (43) 8.00 20.00
19 Carlos Beltran (42) 8.00 20.00
20 Roger Clemens (41) 40.00 100.00
21 Randy Johnson (40) 15.00 40.00
22 Bernie Williams (39) 15.00 40.00
23 Carlos Delgado (38) 8.00 20.00
24 Manny Ramirez (37) 15.00 40.00
25 Freddy Garcia (36) 8.00 20.00
26 Barry Bonds (35) 60.00 150.00
27 Tim Hudson (34) 15.00 40.00
28 Larry Walker (33) 15.00 40.00
29 Raul Mondesi (32) 15.00 40.00
30 Ivan Rodriguez (31) 20.00 50.00
31 Magglio Ordonez (30) 15.00 40.00
32 Scott Rolen (29) 20.00 50.00
33 Mike Mussina (28) 20.00 50.00
34 J.D. Drew (27) 15.00 40.00
35 Tom Glavine (26) 20.00 50.00
36 Barry Larkin (25)
37 Jim Thome (24)
38 Erubiel Durazo (23)
39 Curt Schilling (22)
40 O.Hernandez (21)
41 Rafael Palmeiro (20)
42 Gabe Kapler (19)
43 Mark Grace (18)
44 Jeff Cirillo (17)
45 Jeromy Burnitz (16)
46 Sean Casey (15)
47 Kevin Millwood (14)
48 Vinny Castilla (13)
49 Jose Canseco (12)
50 Roberto Alomar (11)
51 Craig Biggio (10)
52 Preston Wilson (9)
53 Jeff Weaver (8)
54 Robin Ventura (7)
55 Ben Grieve (6)
56 Troy Glaus (5)
57 Jacque Jones (4)
58 Brian Giles (3)
59 Kevin Brown (2)
60 Todd Helton (1)
61 Ben Petrick (30) 10.00 25.00
62 Chad Hermansen (29) 10.00 25.00
63 Kevin Barker (28) 10.00 25.00
64 Matt LeCroy (27) 10.00 25.00
65 Brad Penny (26) 10.00 25.00
66 D.T. Cromer (25)
67 Steve Lomasney (24)
68 Cole Liniak (23)
69 B.J. Ryan (22)
70 Wilton Veras (21)
71 Aaron McNeal (20)
72 Nick Johnson (19)
73 Adam Piatt (18)
74 Adam Kennedy (17)
75 Cesar King (16)
76 Peter Bergeron (15)
77 Rob Bell (14)
78 Wily Pena (13)
79 Ruben Mateo (12)
80 Kip Wells (11)
81 Alex Escobar (10)
82 Danys Baez (9)
83 Travis Dawkins (8)
84 Mark Quinn (7)
85 Jimmy Anderson (6)
86 Rick Ankiel (5)
87 Alfonso Soriano (4)
88 Pat Burrell (3)
89 Eric Munson (2)
90 Josh Beckett (1)

2000 E-X Essential Credentials Now

Randomly inserted into packs, this 90-card insert is a complete parallel of the E-X base set. Print runs for each of these cards are provided after the player's name in our checklist.

1 Alex Rodriguez (1)
2 Jeff Bagwell (2)
3 Mike Piazza (3)
4 Tony Gwynn (4)
5 Ken Griffey Jr. (5)
6 Juan Gonzalez (6)
7 Vladimir Guerrero (7)
8 Cal Ripken (8)
9 Mo Vaughn (9)
10 Chipper Jones (10)
11 Derek Jeter (11)
12 Nomar Garciaparra (12)
13 Mark McGwire (13)
14 Sammy Sosa (14)
15 Pedro Martinez (15)
16 Greg Maddux (16)
17 Frank Thomas (17)
18 Shawn Green (18)
19 Carlos Beltran (19)
20 Roger Clemens (20)
21 Randy Johnson (21)
22 Bernie Williams (22)
23 Carlos Delgado (23)
24 Manny Ramirez (24)
25 Freddy Garcia (25)
26 Barry Bonds (26) 60.00 150.00
27 Tim Hudson (27)
28 Larry Walker (28) 15.00 40.00
29 Raul Mondesi (29) 15.00 40.00
30 Ivan Rodriguez (30) 25.00 60.00
31 Magglio Ordonez (31) 15.00 40.00
32 Scott Rolen (32) 20.00 50.00
33 Mike Mussina (33) 20.00 50.00
34 J.D. Drew (34) 15.00 40.00
35 Tom Glavine (35) 20.00 50.00
36 Barry Larkin (36) 12.50 30.00
37 Jim Thome (37) 12.50 30.00
38 Erubiel Durazo (38) 8.00 20.00
39 Curt Schilling (39) 10.00 25.00
40 O.Hernandez (40) 10.00 25.00
41 Rafael Palmeiro (41) 12.50 30.00
42 Gabe Kapler (42) 10.00 25.00
43 Mark Grace (43) 12.50 30.00
44 Jeff Cirillo (44) 8.00 20.00
45 Jeromy Burnitz (45) 10.00 25.00
46 Sean Casey (46) 10.00 25.00
47 Kevin Millwood (47) 10.00 25.00
48 Vinny Castilla (48) 10.00 25.00
49 Jose Canseco (49) 12.50 30.00
50 Roberto Alomar (50) 12.50 30.00
51 Craig Biggio (51) 10.00 25.00
52 Preston Wilson (52) 8.00 20.00
53 Jeff Weaver (53) 6.00 15.00
54 Robin Ventura (54) 8.00 20.00
55 Ben Grieve (55) 6.00 15.00
56 Troy Glaus (56) 8.00 20.00
57 Jacque Jones (57) 8.00 20.00
58 Brian Giles (58) 8.00 20.00
59 Kevin Brown (59) 10.00 25.00
60 Todd Helton (60) 10.00 25.00
61 Ben Petrick (1)
62 Chad Hermansen (2)
63 Kevin Barker (3)
64 Matt LeCroy (4)
65 Brad Penny (5)
66 D.T. Cromer (6)
67 Steve Lomasney (7)
68 Cole Liniak (8)
69 B.J. Ryan (9)
70 Wilton Veras (10)
71 Aaron McNeal (11)
72 Nick Johnson (12)
73 Adam Piatt (13)
74 Adam Kennedy (14)
75 Cesar King (15)
76 Peter Bergeron (16)
77 Rob Bell (17)
78 Wily Pena (18)
79 Ruben Mateo (19)
80 Kip Wells (20)
81 Alex Escobar (21)
82 Danys Baez (22)
83 Travis Dawkins (23)
84 Mark Quinn (24)
85 Jimmy Anderson (25)
86 Rick Ankiel (26) 20.00 50.00
87 Alfonso Soriano (27) 25.00 60.00
88 Pat Burrell (28) 25.00 60.00
89 Eric Munson (29) 20.00 50.00
90 Josh Beckett (30) 25.00 60.00

2000 E-X E-Xceptional Red

Randomly inserted into packs, this 15-card insert features some of the hottest major league ballplayers. Each card is individually numbered to 1999. Card backs carry a "XC" prefix.

COMPLETE SET (15) 60.00 150.00
*BLUE: 1.25X TO 3X RED 2.50 6.00
BLUE PRINT RUN 250 SERIAL #'d SETS 2.50 6.00
*GREEN: .6X TO 1.5X RED 2.50 6.00
GREEN PRINT RUN 999 SERIAL #'d SETS 2.50 6.00
RANDOM INSERTS IN PACKS
XC1 Ken Griffey Jr. 4.00 10.00
XC2 Derek Jeter 6.00 15.00
XC3 Nomar Garciaparra 4.00 10.00
XC4 Mark McGwire 6.00 15.00
XC5 Sammy Sosa 2.50 6.00
XC6 Mike Piazza 4.00 10.00
XC7 Alex Rodriguez 4.00 10.00
XC8 Cal Ripken 8.00 20.00
XC9 Chipper Jones 2.50 6.00
XC10 Pedro Martinez 1.50 4.00
XC11 Jeff Bagwell 1.50 4.00
XC12 Greg Maddux 4.00 10.00
XC13 Roger Clemens 5.00 12.00
XC14 Tony Gwynn 3.00 8.00
XC15 Frank Thomas 2.50 6.00

2000 E-X E-Xciting

Randomly inserted into packs at one in 24, this 10-card insert set features some of the most exciting players in modern major league baseball. Card backs carry a "XT" prefix.

COMPLETE SET (10)	25.00	60.00
XT1 Mark McGwire	4.00	10.00
XT2 Ken Griffey Jr.	2.50	6.00
XT3 Randy Johnson	1.50	4.00
XT4 Sammy Sosa	1.50	4.00
XT5 Manny Ramirez	1.00	2.50
XT6 Jose Canseco	1.00	2.50
XT7 Derek Jeter	4.00	10.00
XT8 Scott Rolen	1.00	2.50
XT9 Juan Gonzalez	.60	1.50
XT10 Barry Bonds	4.00	10.00

2000 E-X E-Xplosive

Randomly inserted into packs, this 20-card set features some of the most explosive players in major league baseball. Each card is individually serial numbered to 2499. Card backs carry a "XP" prefix.

COMPLETE SET (20)	80.00	200.00
XP1 Tony Gwynn	3.00	8.00
XP2 Alex Rodriguez	4.00	10.00
XP3 Pedro Martinez	1.50	4.00
XP4 Sammy Sosa	1.50	4.00
XP5 Cal Ripken	8.00	20.00
XP6 Adam Piatt	1.50	4.00
XP7 Pat Burrell	1.50	4.00
XP8 J.D. Drew	1.50	4.00
XP9 Mike Piazza	4.00	10.00
XP10 Shawn Green	1.50	4.00
XP11 Troy Glaus	1.50	4.00
XP12 Randy Johnson	1.50	4.00
XP13 Juan Gonzalez	1.50	4.00
XP14 Chipper Jones	1.50	4.00
XP15 Ivan Rodriguez	1.50	4.00
XP16 Nomar Garciaparra	4.00	10.00
XP17 Ken Griffey Jr.	4.00	10.00
XP18 Nick Johnson	1.50	4.00
XP19 Mark McGwire	6.00	15.00
XP20 Frank Thomas	1.50	4.00

2000 E-X Generation E-X

Randomly inserted into packs at one in eight, this15-card insert set features some of the hottest young talent in major league baseball. Card backs carry a "GX" prefix.

COMPLETE SET (15)	20.00	50.00
GX1 Rick Ankiel	1.50	4.00
GX2 Josh Beckett	1.25	3.00
GX3 Carlos Beltran	.60	1.50
GX4 Pat Burrell	1.25	3.00
GX5 Freddy Garcia	1.25	3.00
GX6 Alex Rodriguez	2.50	6.00
GX7 Derek Jeter	4.00	10.00
GX8 Tim Hudson	1.25	3.00
GX9 Shawn Green	1.25	3.00
GX10 Eric Munson	1.25	3.00
GX11 Adam Piatt	1.50	4.00
GX12 Adam Kennedy	.60	1.50
GX13 Nick Johnson	1.25	3.00
GX14 Alfonso Soriano	1.25	3.00
GX15 Nomar Garciaparra	2.50	6.00

2000 E-X Genuine Coverage

Randomly inserted into packs at one in 144, this 10-card insert set features swatches from actual game-used jerseys. Cards are numbered based on each player's actual uniform number.

2 Derek Jeter	12.50	30.00
3 Alex Rodriguez	6.00	15.00
8 Cal Ripken	12.50	30.00
10 Chipper Jones	6.00	15.00
11 Edgar Martinez	6.00	15.00
25 Barry Bonds	10.00	25.00
35 Mike Mussina		
43 Raul Mondesi	4.00	10.00
47 Tom Glavine	6.00	15.00
52 Tim Hudson	4.00	10.00

2001 E-X

The 2001 E-X product was released in mid-May, 2001, and featured a 130-card base set that was broken into tiers as follows: Base Veterans (1-100), and Rookies/Prospects (101-130) (individually serial numbered). Each pack contained 5 cards, and carried a suggested retail price of $4.99. An additional ten cards (131-140) featuring a selection of top prospects was distributed in late December, 2001 within Fleer Platinum RC packs. Each of these cards is serial-numbered to 499 copies.

COMP.SET w/o SP's (100)	10.00	25.00
COMMON CARD (1-100)	.20	.50
COMMON (101-130)	3.00	8.00
COMMON (131-140)	3.00	8.00
1 Jason Kendall	.20	.50
2 Derek Jeter	1.25	3.00
3 Greg Vaughn	.20	.50
4 Eric Chavez	.20	.50
5 Nomar Garciaparra	.75	2.00
6 Roberto Alomar	.30	.75
7 Barry Larkin	.30	.75
8 Matt Lawton	.20	.50
9 Larry Walker	.20	.50
10 Chipper Jones	.50	1.25
11 Scott Rolen	.30	.75
12 Carlos Lee	.20	.50
13 Adrian Beltre	.20	.50
14 Ben Grieve	.20	.50
15 Mike Sweeney	.20	.50
16 John Olerud	.20	.50
17 Gabe Kapler	.20	.50
18 Brian Giles	.20	.50
19 Luis Gonzalez	.20	.50
20 Sammy Sosa	.50	1.25
21 Roger Clemens	1.00	2.50
22 Vladimir Guerrero	.50	1.25
23 Ken Griffey Jr.	.75	2.00
24 Mark McGwire	1.25	3.00
25 Orlando Hernandez	.20	.50
26 Shannon Stewart	.20	.50
27 Fred McGriff	.30	.75
28 Lance Berkman	.20	.50
29 Carlos Delgado	.20	.50
30 Mike Piazza	.75	2.00
31 Juan Encarnacion	.20	.50
32 David Justice	.20	.50
33 Greg Maddux	.75	2.00
34 Frank Thomas	.50	1.25
35 Jason Giambi	.20	.50
36 Ruben Mateo	.20	.50
37 Todd Helton	.30	.75
38 Jim Edmonds	.20	.50
39 Steve Finley	.20	.50
40 Tom Glavine	.30	.75
41 Mo Vaughn	.20	.50
42 Phil Nevin	.20	.50
43 Richie Sexson	.20	.50
44 Craig Biggio	.30	.75
45 Kerry Wood	.20	.50
46 Pat Burrell	.20	.50
47 Edgar Martinez	.30	.75
48 Jim Thome	.30	.75
49 Jeff Bagwell	.30	.75
50 Bernie Williams	.30	.75
51 Andruw Jones	.30	.75
52 Gary Sheffield	.20	.50
53 Johnny Damon	.30	.75
54 Rondell White	.20	.50
55 J.D. Drew	.20	.50
56 Tony Batista	.20	.50
57 Paul Konerko	.20	.50
58 Rafael Palmeiro	.30	.75
59 Cal Ripken	1.50	4.00
60 Darin Erstad	.20	.50
61 Ivan Rodriguez	.30	.75
62 Barry Bonds	1.25	3.00
63 Edgardo Alfonzo	.20	.50
64 Ellis Burks	.20	.50
65 Mike Lieberthal	.20	.50
66 Robin Ventura	.20	.50
67 Richard Hidalgo	.20	.50
68 Magglio Ordonez	.20	.50
69 Kazuhiro Sasaki	.20	.50
70 Miguel Tejada	.20	.50
71 David Wells	.20	.50
72 Troy Glaus	.20	.50
73 Jose Vidro	.20	.50
74 Shawn Green	.20	.50
75 Barry Zito	.30	.75
76 Jermaine Dye	.20	.50
77 Geoff Jenkins	.20	.50
78 Jeff Kent	.20	.50
79 Al Leiter	.20	.50
80 Deivi Cruz	.20	.50
81 Eric Karros	.20	.50
82 Albert Belle	.20	.50
83 Pedro Martinez	.30	.75
84 Raul Mondesi	.20	.50
85 Preston Wilson	.20	.50
86 Rafael Furcal	.20	.50
87 Rick Ankiel	.20	.50
88 Randy Johnson	.50	1.25
89 Kevin Brown	.20	.50
90 Sean Casey	.20	.50
91 Mike Mussina	.30	.75
92 Alex Rodriguez	.75	2.00
93 Andres Galarraga	.20	.50
94 Juan Gonzalez	.20	.50
95 Manny Ramirez Sox	.30	.75
96 Mark Grace	.30	.75
97 Carl Everett	.20	.50
98 Tony Gwynn	.60	1.50
99 Mike Hampton	.20	.50
100 Ken Caminiti	.20	.50
101 Jason Hart/1749	3.00	8.00
102 Corey Patterson/1199	3.00	8.00
103 Timo Perez/1999	3.00	8.00
104 Marcus Giles/1999	3.00	8.00
105 I. Suzuki/1999 RC	20.00	50.00
106 Aubrey Huff/1499	3.00	8.00
107 Joe Crede/1999	4.00	10.00
108 Larry Barnes/1499	3.00	8.00
109 Esix Snead/1999 RC	3.00	8.00
110 Kenny Kelly/2249	3.00	8.00
111 Justin Miller/2249	3.00	8.00
112 Jack Cust/1999	3.00	8.00
113 Xavier Nady/999	3.00	8.00
114 Eric Munson/1499	3.00	8.00
115 E. Guzman/1749 RC	3.00	8.00
116 Juan Pierre/2189	3.00	8.00
117 W. Abreu/1749 RC	3.00	8.00
118 Keith Ginter/1999	3.00	8.00
119 Jace Brewer/2699	3.00	8.00
120 P. Crawford/2249	3.00	8.00
121 Jason Tyner/2249	3.00	8.00
122 Tike Redman/1999	3.00	8.00
123 John Riedling/2499	3.00	8.00
124 Jose Ortiz/1499	3.00	8.00
125 O. Mairena/2499	3.00	8.00
126 Eric Byrnes/2249	3.00	8.00
127 Brian Cole/999	3.00	8.00
128 Adam Piatt/2249	3.00	8.00
129 Nate Rolison/2499	3.00	8.00
130 Keith McDonald/2249	3.00	8.00
131 Albert Pujols/499 RC	200.00	300.00
132 Bud Smith/499 RC	3.00	8.00
133 T.Shinjo/499 RC	5.00	12.00
134 W.Betemit/499 RC	5.00	12.00
135 A.Hernandez/499 RC	3.00	8.00
136 J.Melian/499 RC	3.00	8.00
137 Jay Gibbons/499 RC	5.00	12.00
138 J.Estrada/499 RC	5.00	12.00
139 M.Ensberg/499 RC	5.00	12.00
140 Drew Henson/499 RC	5.00	12.00
NNO Derek Jeter Base Inks AU/500	75.00	150.00
MM2 Derek Jeter Monumental Moments	5.00	12.00
NNO Derek Jeter Monumental Moments AU/96	60.00	120.00

2001 E-X Prospect Autographs

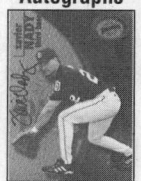

Randomly inserted into packs, this 29-card insert is actually an autographed parallel of cards 101-130 in the 2001 E-X base set (with exception of card 105). Please note that the print runs are listed below for each card.

101 Jason Hart/250	4.00	10.00
102 Corey Patterson/800	4.00	10.00
103 Timo Perez/1000	4.00	10.00
104 Marcus Giles/500	6.00	15.00
106 Aubrey Huff/500	6.00	15.00
107 Joe Crede/500	10.00	25.00
108 Larry Barnes/500	4.00	10.00
109 Esix Snead/500	4.00	10.00
110 Kenny Kelly/250	4.00	10.00
111 Justin Miller/250	4.00	10.00
112 Jack Cust/1000	4.00	10.00
113 Xavier Nady/1000	4.00	10.00
114 Eric Munson/1500	4.00	10.00
115 Elpidio Guzman/250	4.00	10.00
116 Juan Pierre/810	6.00	15.00
117 Winston Abreu/250	4.00	10.00
118 Keith Ginter/500	4.00	10.00
119 Jace Brewer/300	4.00	10.00
120 Paxton Crawford/250	4.00	10.00
121 Jason Tyner/250	4.00	10.00
122 Tike Redman/250	4.00	10.00
123 John Riedling/250	4.00	10.00
124 Jose Ortiz/500	4.00	10.00
125 Oswaldo Mairena/500	4.00	10.00
126 Eric Byrnes/250	4.00	10.00
127 Brian Cole/2000	6.00	15.00
128 Adam Piatt/250	4.00	10.00
129 Nate Rolison/500	4.00	10.00
130 Keith McDonald/250	4.00	10.00

2001 E-X Essential Credentials

Randomly inserted into packs, this 130-card insert is a complete parallel of the 2001 E-X base set. Please note that cards 1-100 are individually serial numbered to 299, while cards 101-130 are serial numbered to 29.

COMMON CARD (1-100)	2.00	5.00
*STARS 1-100: 5X TO 12X BASIC CARDS		
COMMON (101-130)	6.00	15.00

2001 E-X Behind the Numbers Game Jersey

Randomly inserted into packs at one in 33, this 44-card insert set features game used jersey swatches for some of the greatest players of all-time. Card backs carry a "BH" prefix.

BH1 Johnny Bench	6.00	15.00
BH2 Wade Boggs	6.00	15.00
BH3 George Brett	10.00	25.00
BH4 Lou Brock	6.00	15.00
BH5 Rollie Fingers	4.00	10.00
BH6 Carlton Fisk	6.00	15.00
BH7 Reggie Jackson	6.00	15.00
BH8 Al Kaline	6.00	15.00
BH9 Willie Mays		
BH10 Willie McCovey	4.00	10.00
BH11 Paul Molitor	4.00	10.00
BH12 Eddie Murray	6.00	15.00
BH13 Jim Palmer	4.00	10.00
BH14 Ozzie Smith	6.00	15.00
BH15 Nolan Ryan	20.00	50.00
BH16 Mike Schmidt	10.00	25.00
BH17 Tom Seaver	6.00	15.00
BH18 Dave Winfield	4.00	10.00
BH19 Ted Williams	50.00	100.00
BH20 Robin Yount	6.00	15.00
BH21 Brady Anderson	4.00	10.00
BH22 Rick Ankiel	4.00	10.00
BH23 Albert Belle	4.00	10.00
BH24 Adrian Beltre	4.00	10.00
BH25 Barry Bonds	15.00	40.00
BH26 Eric Chavez	4.00	10.00
BH27 J.D. Drew	4.00	10.00
BH28 Darin Erstad	4.00	10.00
BH29 Troy Glaus	4.00	10.00
BH30 Mark Grace	6.00	15.00
BH31 Ben Grieve	4.00	10.00
BH32 Tony Gwynn	8.00	20.00
BH33 Todd Helton	6.00	15.00
BH34 Derek Jeter	15.00	40.00
BH35 Jeff Kent	4.00	10.00
BH36 Jason Kendall	4.00	10.00
BH37 Greg Maddux	8.00	20.00
BH38 John Olerud	4.00	10.00
BH39 Cal Ripken	15.00	40.00
BH40 Chipper Jones	6.00	15.00
BH41 John Smoltz	6.00	15.00
BH42 Frank Thomas	6.00	15.00
BH43 Robin Ventura	4.00	10.00
BH44 Bernie Williams	6.00	15.00

2001 E-X Behind the Numbers Game Jersey Autograph

Randomly inserted into packs, this 42-card insert is a partial parallel of the 2001 E-X Behind the Numbers insert. Each card in this set is autographed, and the stated print run for each card is listed below for your convenience.

1 Brady Anderson/9		
2 Rick Ankiel/66	15.00	40.00
3 Albert Belle/88	20.00	50.00
4 Adrian Beltre/29	20.00	50.00
5 Johnny Bench/5		
6 Wade Boggs/26	50.00	100.00
7 Barry Bonds/25		
8 George Brett/5		
9 Lou Brock/20		
10 Eric Chavez/3		
11 J.D. Drew/7		
12 Darin Erstad/17		
13 Rollie Fingers/34	20.00	50.00
14 Carlton Fisk/27	50.00	100.00
15 Troy Glaus/25		
16 Mark Grace/17		
17 Ben Grieve/14		
18 Tony Gwynn/19		
19 Todd Helton/17		
20 Reggie Jackson/44	50.00	100.00
21 Derek Jeter/2		
22 Chipper Jones/10		
23 Al Kaline/6		
24 Jason Kendall/18		
25 Jeff Kent/21		
26 Greg Maddux/31	175.00	300.00
27 Willie McCovey/44	40.00	80.00
28 Paul Molitor/4		
29 Eddie Murray/33	50.00	100.00
30 John Olerud/5		
31 Jim Palmer/22		
32 Cal Ripken/8		
33 Nolan Ryan/34	175.00	300.00
34 Mike Schmidt/20		
35 Tom Seaver/41	50.00	100.00
36 Ozzie Smith/1		
37 John Smoltz/29	40.00	80.00
38 Frank Thomas/35	50.00	100.00
39 Robin Ventura/4		
40 Bernie Williams/51	50.00	100.00
41 Dave Winfield/31	50.00	100.00
42 Robin Yount/19		

2001 E-X Extra Innings

Randomly inserted into retail packs at one in 20, this 10-card insert set features players that keep on going long after 9-innings. Card backs carry an "XI" prefix.

COMPLETE SET (10)	50.00	100.00
XI1 Mark McGwire	5.00	12.00
XI2 Sammy Sosa	2.00	5.00
XI3 Chipper Jones	2.00	5.00
XI4 Mike Piazza	3.00	8.00
XI5 Cal Ripken	6.00	15.00
XI6 Ken Griffey Jr.	3.00	8.00
XI7 Alex Rodriguez	3.00	8.00
XI8 Vladimir Guerrero	2.00	5.00
XI9 Nomar Garciaparra	3.00	8.00
XI10 Derek Jeter	5.00	12.00

2001 E-X Wall of Fame

Randomly inserted into packs at one in 24, this 30-card insert features swatches of the outfield walls used in Major League ballparks. Please note that the cards are not numbered, and are listed below in alphabetical order for convenience.

1 Jeff Bagwell	4.00	10.00
2 Barry Bonds	10.00	25.00
3 Pat Burrell	3.00	8.00
4 Roger Clemens	6.00	15.00
5 Nomar Garciaparra	6.00	15.00
6 Jason Giambi	3.00	8.00
7 Troy Glaus	3.00	8.00
8 Juan Gonzalez	3.00	8.00
9 Ken Griffey Jr.	6.00	15.00
10 Vladimir Guerrero	4.00	10.00
11 Tony Gwynn	6.00	15.00
12 Todd Helton	4.00	10.00
13 Geoff Jenkins	3.00	8.00
14 Derek Jeter	10.00	25.00
15 Andruw Jones	4.00	10.00
16 Chipper Jones	4.00	10.00
17 Jason Kendall	3.00	8.00
18 Greg Maddux	4.00	10.00
19 Pedro Martinez	4.00	10.00
20 Mark McGwire	15.00	40.00
21 Paul Molitor	3.00	8.00
22 Mike Piazza	4.00	10.00
23 Manny Ramirez Sox	4.00	10.00
24 Cal Ripken	15.00	40.00
25 Alex Rodriguez	6.00	15.00
26 Ivan Rodriguez	4.00	10.00
27 Scott Rolen	4.00	10.00
28 Sammy Sosa	4.00	10.00
29 Frank Thomas	4.00	10.00
30 Robin Yount	4.00	10.00

2002 E-X

This 139 card set was issued in May, 2002. It was released in four card packs which came 24 packs to a box and four boxes to a case. The price for hobby packs (which had many more inserts) was $5 per pack and the retail packs were $3 per pack. The first 100 cards featured veterans while the last 40 cards featured rookies and prospects. Cards numbered 101 through 125 were printed to specific serial numbers while cards 126-140 were issued at a stated rate of one in 24 hobby or retail packs. Though the set is checklisted 1-140, card 133 does not exist. It was originally intended to feature Yankees prospect Drew Henson, but Fleer's exclusive contract with the ballplayer expired two weeks prior to the release of E-X.

COMP.SET w/o SP's (100)	10.00	25.00
COMMON CARD (1-100)	.20	.50
COMMON CARD (101-120)	2.00	5.00
COMMON CARD (121-125)	2.00	5.00
COMMON CARD (126-140)	2.00	5.00
1 Alex Rodriguez	.75	2.00
2 Albert Pujols	1.00	2.50
3 Ken Griffey Jr.	.75	2.00
4 Vladimir Guerrero	.50	1.25
5 Sammy Sosa	.50	1.25
6 Ichiro Suzuki	1.00	2.50
7 Jorge Posada	.30	.75
8 Matt Williams	.20	.50
9 Adrian Beltre	.20	.50
10 Pat Burrell	.20	.50
11 Roger Cedeno	.20	.50
12 Tony Clark	.20	.50
13 Steve Finley	.20	.50
14 Rafael Furcal	.20	.50
15 Rickey Henderson	.50	1.25
16 Richard Hidalgo	.20	.50
17 Jason Kendall	.20	.50
18 Tino Martinez	.30	.75
19 Scott Rolen	.30	.75
20 Shannon Stewart	.20	.50
21 Jose Vidro	.20	.50
22 Preston Wilson	.20	.50
23 Raul Mondesi	.20	.50
24 Lance Berkman	.20	.50
25 Rick Ankiel	.20	.50
26 Kevin Brown	.20	.50
27 Jeromy Burnitz	.20	.50
28 Jeff Cirillo	.20	.50
29 Carl Everett	.20	.50
30 Eric Chavez	.20	.50
31 Freddy Garcia	.20	.50
32 Mark Grace	.30	.75
33 David Justice	.20	.50
34 Fred McGriff	.30	.75
35 Mike Mussina	.30	.75
36 John Olerud	.20	.50
37 Magglio Ordonez	.20	.50
38 Curt Schilling	.20	.50
39 Aaron Sele	.20	.50
40 Robin Ventura	.20	.50
41 Adam Dunn	.20	.50
42 Jeff Bagwell	.30	.75
43 Barry Bonds	1.25	3.00
44 Roger Clemens	1.00	2.50
45 Cliff Floyd	.20	.50
46 Jason Giambi	.20	.50
47 Juan Gonzalez	.20	.50
48 Luis Gonzalez	.20	.50
49 Cristian Guzman	.20	.50
50 Todd Helton	.30	.75
51 Derek Jeter	1.25	3.00
52 Rafael Palmeiro	.30	.75
53 Mike Sweeney	.20	.50
54 Ben Grieve	.20	.50
55 Phil Nevin	.20	.50
56 Mike Piazza	.75	2.00
57 Moises Alou	.20	.50
58 Ivan Rodriguez	.30	.75
59 Manny Ramirez	.30	.75
60 Brian Giles	.20	.50
61 Jim Thome	.30	.75
62 Larry Walker	.20	.50
63 Bobby Abreu	.20	.50
64 Troy Glaus	.20	.50
65 Garret Anderson	.20	.50
66 Roberto Alomar	.30	.75
67 Bret Boone	.20	.50
68 Marty Cordova	.20	.50
69 Craig Biggio	.30	.75
70 Omar Vizquel	.30	.75
71 Jermaine Dye	.20	.50
72 Darin Erstad	.20	.50
73 Carlos Delgado	.20	.50
74 Nomar Garciaparra	.75	2.00
75 Greg Maddux	.75	2.00
76 Tom Glavine	.30	.75
77 Frank Thomas	.50	1.25
78 Shawn Green	.20	.50
79 Bobby Higginson	.20	.50
80 Jeff Kent	.20	.50
81 Chuck Knoblauch	.20	.50
82 Paul Konerko	.20	.50
83 Carlos Lee	.20	.50
84 Jon Lieber	.20	.50
85 Paul LoDuca	.20	.50
86 Mike Lowell	.20	.50
87 Edgar Martinez	.30	.75
88 Doug Mientkiewicz	.20	.50
89 Pedro Martinez	.30	.75
90 Randy Johnson	.50	1.25
91 Aramis Ramirez	.20	.50
92 J.D. Drew	.20	.50
93 Chris Richard	.20	.50
94 Jimmy Rollins	.20	.50
95 Ryan Klesko	.20	.50
96 Gary Sheffield	.20	.50
97 Chipper Jones	.50	1.25
98 Greg Vaughn	.20	.50
99 Mo Vaughn	.20	.50
100 Bernie Williams	.30	.75
101 John Foster NT/2999 RC	2.00	5.00
102 J. DeLaRosa NT/2999 RC	2.00	5.00
103 Ed. Almonte NT/2999 RC	2.00	5.00
104 Chris Booker NT/2999 RC	2.00	5.00
105 Victor Alvarez NT/2999 RC	2.00	5.00
106 Cliff Bartosh NT/2999 RC	2.00	5.00
107 Felix Escalona NT/2999 RC	2.00	5.00
108 C. Thurman NT/2999 RC	2.00	5.00
109 Kazuhisa Ishii NT/2999 RC	3.00	8.00
110 Mig. Asencio NT/2999 RC	2.00	5.00
111 P.J. Bevis NT/2499 RC	2.00	5.00
112 Gus. Chacin NT/2499 RC	3.00	8.00
113 Steve Kent NT/2499 RC	2.00	5.00
114 Tak. Nomura NT/2499 RC	2.00	5.00
115 Adam Walker NT/2499 RC	2.00	5.00
116 So Taguchi NT/2499 RC	3.00	8.00
117 Reed Johnson NT/2499 RC	3.00	8.00
118 Rod Rosario NT/2499 RC	2.00	5.00
119 Luis Martinez NT/2499 RC	2.00	5.00
120 Sat Komiyama NT/2499 RC	2.00	5.00
121 Sean Burroughs NT/1999	2.00	5.00
122 Hank Blalock NT/1999	3.00	8.00
123 Marlon Byrd NT/1999	2.00	5.00
124 Nick Johnson NT/1999	2.00	5.00
125 Mark Teixeira NT/1999	3.00	8.00
126 David Espinosa NT	2.00	5.00
127 Adrian Burnside NT RC	2.00	5.00
128 Mark Corey NT RC	2.00	5.00
129 Matt Thornton NT RC	2.00	5.00
130 Dane Sardinha NT	2.00	5.00
131 Juan Rivera NT	2.00	5.00
132 Austin Kearns NT	2.00	5.00
134 Ben Broussard NT	2.00	5.00
135 Orlando Hudson NT	2.00	5.00
136 Carlos Pena NT	2.00	5.00
137 Kenny Kelly NT	2.00	5.00
138 Bill Hall NT	2.00	5.00
139 Ron Chiavacci NT	2.00	5.00
140 Mark Prior NT	2.00	5.00

2002 E-X Essential Credentials Future

Randomly inserted in packs, these 125 cards have two distinct patterns of serial numbering. Cards numbered 1 through 60 are inversely numbered and have a game used piece on them while cards numbered 61 through 125 are also inversley numbered.

1 Alex Rodriguez Jsy/60 30.00 60.00
2 Albert Pujols Base/59 30.00 60.00
3 Ken Griffey Jr. Base/58 30.00 60.00
4 Vladimir Guerrero Base/57 15.00 40.00
5 Sammy Sosa Base/56 15.00 40.00
6 Ichiro Suzuki Base/55
7 Jorge Posada Bat/54 12.50 30.00
8 Matt Williams Bat/53 10.00 25.00
9 Adrian Beltre Bat/52 10.00 25.00
10 Pat Burrell Bat/51 10.00 25.00
11 Roger Cedeno Bat/50 10.00 25.00
12 Tony Clark Bat/49 10.00 25.00
13 Steve Finley Bat/48 12.50 30.00
14 Rafael Furcal Bat/47 12.50 30.00
15 Rickey Henderson Bat/46 20.00 50.00
16 Richard Hidalgo Bat/45 10.00 25.00
17 Jason Kendall Bat/44 12.50 30.00
18 Tino Martinez Bat/43 15.00 40.00
19 Scott Rolen Bat/42 15.00 40.00
20 Shannon Stewart Bat/41 12.50 30.00
21 Jose Vidro Bat/40 10.00 25.00
22 Preston Wilson Bat/39 12.50 30.00
23 Raul Mondesi Bat/38 12.50 30.00
24 Lance Berkman Bat/37 12.50 30.00
25 Rick Ankiel Jsy/36 10.00 25.00
26 Kevin Brown Jsy/35 15.00 40.00
27 Jeromy Burnitz Bat/34 15.00 40.00
28 Jeff Cirillo Jsy/33 12.50 30.00
29 Carl Everett Jsy/32 15.00 40.00
30 Eric Chavez Bat/31 15.00 40.00
31 Freddy Garcia Jsy/30 15.00 40.00
32 Mark Grace Jsy/29 20.00 50.00
33 David Justice Jsy/28 15.00 40.00
34 Fred McGriff Jsy/27 20.00 50.00
35 Mike Mussina Jsy/26
36 John Olerud Jsy/25
37 Magglio Ordonez Jsy/24
38 Curt Schilling Jsy/23
39 Aaron Sele Jsy/22
40 Robin Ventura Jsy/21
41 Adam Dunn Bat/20
42 Jeff Bagwell Jsy/19
43 Barry Bonds Pants/18
44 Roger Clemens Bat/17
45 Cliff Floyd Bat/16
46 Jason Giambi Base/15
47 Juan Gonzalez Jsy/14
48 Luis Gonzalez Base/13
49 Cristian Guzman Bat/12
50 Todd Helton Base/11
51 Derek Jeter Bat/10
52 Rafael Palmeiro Bat/9
53 Mike Sweeney Bat/8
54 Ben Grieve Jsy/7
55 Phil Nevin Bat/6
56 Mike Piazza Base/5
57 Moises Alou Bat/4
58 Ivan Rodriguez Jsy/3
59 Manny Ramirez Base/2
60 Brian Giles Bat/1
61 Jim Thome/125 5.00 12.00
62 Larry Walker/124 3.00 8.00
63 Bobby Abreu/123 3.00 8.00
64 Troy Glaus/122 3.00 8.00
65 Garret Anderson/121 3.00 8.00
66 Roberto Alomar/120 5.00 12.00
67 Bret Boone/119 3.00 8.00
68 Marty Cordova/118 3.00 8.00
69 Craig Biggio/117 5.00 12.00
70 Omar Vizquel/116 5.00 12.00
71 Jermaine Dye/115 3.00 8.00
72 Darin Erstad/114 3.00 8.00
73 Carlos Delgado/113 3.00 8.00
74 Nomar Garciaparra/112 12.50 30.00
75 Greg Maddux/111 12.50 30.00
76 Tom Glavine/110 5.00 12.00
77 Frank Thomas/109 8.00 20.00
78 Shawn Green/108 3.00 8.00
79 Bobby Higginson/107 3.00 8.00
80 Jeff Kent/106 3.00 8.00
81 Chuck Knoblauch/105 3.00 8.00
82 Paul Konerko/104 3.00 8.00
83 Carlos Lee/103 3.00 8.00
84 Jon Lieber/102 3.00 8.00
85 Paul LoDuca/101 3.00 8.00
86 Mike Lowell/100 3.00 8.00
87 Edgar Martinez/99 5.00 12.00
88 Doug Mientkiewicz/98 3.00 8.00
89 Pedro Martinez/97 5.00 12.00
90 Randy Johnson/96 8.00 20.00
91 Aramis Ramirez/95 3.00 8.00
92 J.D. Drew/94 3.00 8.00
93 Chris Richard/93 3.00 8.00
94 Jimmy Rollins/92 3.00 8.00
95 Ryan Klesko/91 3.00 8.00
96 Gary Sheffield/90 3.00 8.00
97 Chipper Jones/89 8.00 20.00
98 Greg Vaughn/88 3.00 8.00
99 Mo Vaughn/87 3.00 8.00
100 Bernie Williams/86 5.00 12.00
101 John Foster NT/85 3.00 8.00
102 Jorge De La Rosa NT/84 3.00 8.00
103 Edwin Almonte NT/83 3.00 8.00
104 Chris Booker NT/82 3.00 8.00
105 Victor Alvarez NT/81 3.00 8.00
106 Cliff Bartosh NT/80 4.00 10.00
107 Felix Escalona NT/79 4.00 10.00
108 Corey Thurman NT/78 4.00 10.00
109 Kazuhisa Ishii NT/77 6.00 15.00
110 Miguel Asencio NT/76 4.00 10.00
111 P.J. Bevis NT/75 4.00 10.00
112 Gustavo Chacin NT/74 10.00 25.00
113 Steve Kent NT/73 4.00 10.00
114 Takahito Nomura NT/72 4.00 10.00
115 Adam Walker NT/71 4.00 10.00
116 So Taguchi NT/70 6.00 15.00
117 Reed Johnson NT/69 6.00 15.00
118 Rodrigo Rosario NT/68 4.00 10.00
119 Luis Martinez NT/67 4.00 10.00
120 Satoru Komiyama NT/66 4.00 10.00
121 Sean Burroughs NT/65 5.00 12.00
122 Hank Blalock NT/64 8.00 20.00
123 Marlon Byrd NT/63 5.00 12.00
124 Nick Johnson NT/62 5.00 12.00
125 Mark Teixeira NT/61 12.50 30.00

2002 E-X Essential Credentials Now

Randomly inserted in packs, these 125 cards are printed to a stated print run matching their card number. In addition, the first 60 cards of the set have a game-used piece mounted to the card.

1 Alex Rodriguez Jsy/1
2 Albert Pujols Base/2
3 Ken Griffey Jr. Base/3
4 Vladimir Guerrero Base/4
5 Sammy Sosa Base/5
6 Ichiro Suzuki Base/6
7 Jorge Posada Bat/7
8 Matt Williams Bat/8
9 Adrian Beltre Bat/9
10 Pat Burrell Bat/10
11 Roger Cedeno Bat/11
12 Tony Clark Bat/12
13 Steve Finley Bat/13
14 Rafael Furcal Bat/14
15 Rickey Henderson Bat/15
16 Richard Hidalgo Bat/16
17 Jason Kendall Bat/17
18 Tino Martinez Bat/18
19 Scott Rolen Bat/19
20 Shannon Stewart Bat/20
21 Jose Vidro Bat/21
22 Preston Wilson Bat/22
23 Raul Mondesi Bat/23
24 Lance Berkman Bat/24
25 Rick Ankiel Jsy/25
26 Kevin Brown Jsy/26 15.00 40.00
27 Jeromy Burnitz Bat/27 15.00 40.00
28 Jeff Cirillo Jsy/28 12.50 30.00
29 Carl Everett Jsy/29 15.00 40.00
30 Eric Chavez Bat/30 15.00 40.00
31 Freddy Garcia Jsy/31 15.00 40.00
32 Mark Grace Jsy/32 20.00 50.00
33 David Justice Jsy/33 15.00 40.00
34 Fred McGriff Jsy/34 20.00 50.00
35 Mike Mussina Jsy/35
36 John Olerud Jsy/36 12.50 30.00
37 Magglio Ordonez Jsy/37 12.50 30.00
38 Curt Schilling Jsy/38 12.50 30.00
39 Aaron Sele Jsy/39 10.00 25.00
40 Robin Ventura Jsy/40 12.50 30.00
41 Adam Dunn Bat/41 12.50 30.00
42 Jeff Bagwell Jsy/42 15.00 40.00
43 Barry Bonds Pants/43 60.00 120.00
44 Roger Clemens Bat/44 50.00 100.00
45 Cliff Floyd Bat/45 12.50 30.00
46 Jason Giambi Base/46 12.50 30.00
47 Juan Gonzalez Jsy/47 12.50 30.00
48 Luis Gonzalez Base/48 12.50 30.00
49 Cristian Guzman Bat/49 10.00 25.00
50 Todd Helton Base/50 15.00 40.00
51 Derek Jeter Bat/51 60.00 120.00
52 Rafael Palmeiro Bat/52 12.50 30.00
53 Mike Sweeney Bat/53 10.00 25.00
54 Ben Grieve Jsy/54 8.00 20.00
55 Phil Nevin Bat/55 10.00 25.00
56 Mike Piazza Base/56 30.00 60.00
57 Moises Alou Bat/57 10.00 25.00
58 Ivan Rodriguez Jsy/58 12.50 30.00
59 Manny Ramirez Base/59 12.50 30.00
60 Brian Giles Bat/60 10.00 25.00
61 Jim Thome/61 8.00 20.00
62 Larry Walker/62 5.00 12.00
63 Bobby Abreu/63 5.00 12.00
64 Troy Glaus/64 5.00 12.00
65 Garret Anderson/65 5.00 12.00
66 Roberto Alomar/66 6.00 15.00
67 Bret Boone/67 4.00 10.00
68 Marty Cordova/68 4.00 10.00
69 Craig Biggio/69 6.00 15.00
70 Omar Vizquel/70 6.00 15.00
71 Jermaine Dye/71 4.00 10.00
72 Darin Erstad/72 4.00 10.00
73 Carlos Delgado/73 4.00 10.00
74 Nomar Garciaparra/74 15.00 40.00
75 Greg Maddux/75 15.00 40.00
76 Tom Glavine/76 6.00 15.00
77 Frank Thomas/77 10.00 25.00
78 Shawn Green/78 4.00 10.00
79 Bobby Higginson/79 4.00 10.00
80 Jeff Kent/80 4.00 10.00
81 Chuck Knoblauch/81 3.00 8.00
82 Paul Konerko/82 3.00 8.00
83 Carlos Lee/83 3.00 8.00
84 Jon Lieber/84 3.00 8.00
85 Paul LoDuca/85 3.00 8.00
86 Mike Lowell/86 3.00 8.00
87 Edgar Martinez/87 5.00 12.00
88 Doug Mientkiewicz/88 3.00 8.00
89 Pedro Martinez/89 5.00 12.00
90 Randy Johnson/90 8.00 20.00
91 Aramis Ramirez/91 3.00 8.00
92 J.D. Drew/92 3.00 8.00
93 Chris Richard/93 3.00 8.00
94 Jimmy Rollins/94 3.00 8.00
95 Ryan Klesko/95 3.00 8.00
96 Gary Sheffield/96 3.00 8.00
97 Chipper Jones/97 8.00 20.00
98 Greg Vaughn/98 3.00 8.00
99 Mo Vaughn/99 3.00 8.00
100 Bernie Williams/100 5.00 12.00
101 John Foster NT/101 3.00 8.00
102 Jorge De La Rosa NT/102 3.00 8.00
103 Edwin Almonte NT/103 3.00 8.00
104 Chris Booker NT/104 3.00 8.00
105 Victor Alvarez NT/105 3.00 8.00
106 Cliff Bartosh NT/106 3.00 8.00
107 Felix Escalona NT/107 3.00 8.00
108 Corey Thurman NT/108 3.00 8.00
109 Kazuhisa Ishii NT/109 5.00 12.00
110 Miguel Asencio NT/110 3.00 8.00
111 P.J. Bevis NT/111 3.00 8.00
112 Gustavo Chacin NT/112 8.00 20.00
113 Steve Kent NT/113 3.00 8.00
114 Takahito Nomura NT/114 3.00 8.00
115 Adam Walker NT/115 3.00 8.00
116 So Taguchi NT/116 5.00 12.00
117 Reed Johnson NT/117 5.00 12.00
118 Rodrigo Rosario NT/118 3.00 8.00
119 Luis Martinez NT/119 3.00 8.00
120 Satoru Komiyama NT/120 3.00 8.00
121 Sean Burroughs NT/121 3.00 8.00
122 Hank Blalock NT/122 5.00 12.00
123 Marlon Byrd NT/123 3.00 8.00
124 Nick Johnson NT/124 3.00 8.00
125 Mark Teixeira NT/125 8.00 20.00

2002 E-X Behind the Numbers

Inserted at stated odds of one in eight hobby and one in 12 retail, these 35 cards pays tribute to special numbers for hitters and pitchers.

COMPLETE SET (35) 50.00 120.00
1 Ichiro Suzuki 3.00 8.00
2 Jason Giambi 1.00 2.50
3 Mike Piazza 2.50 6.00
4 Brian Giles 1.00 2.50
5 Barry Bonds 4.00 10.00
6 Pedro Martinez 1.00 2.50
7 Nomar Garciaparra 2.50 6.00
8 Randy Johnson 1.50 4.00
9 Craig Biggio 1.00 2.50
10 Manny Ramirez 1.00 2.50
11 Mike Mussina 1.00 2.50
12 Kerry Wood 1.00 2.50
13 Jim Edmonds 1.00 2.50
14 Ivan Rodriguez 1.00 2.50
15 Jeff Bagwell 1.00 2.50
16 Roger Clemens 3.00 8.00
17 Chipper Jones 1.50 4.00
18 Shawn Green 1.00 2.50
19 Albert Pujols 3.00 8.00
20 Andruw Jones 1.00 2.50
21 Luis Gonzalez 1.00 2.50
22 Todd Helton 1.00 2.50
23 Jorge Posada 1.00 2.50
24 Scott Rolen 1.00 2.50
25 Ben Sheets 1.00 2.50
26 Alfonso Soriano 1.00 2.50
27 Greg Maddux 2.50 6.00
28 Gary Sheffield 1.00 2.50
29 Barry Zito 1.00 2.50
30 Alex Rodriguez 2.50 6.00
31 Larry Walker 1.00 2.50
32 Derek Jeter 4.00 10.00
33 Ken Griffey Jr. 2.50 6.00
34 Vladimir Guerrero 1.50 4.00
35 Sammy Sosa 1.50 4.00

2002 E-X Behind the Numbers Game Jersey

This partial parallel, issued at a stated rate of one in 24 hobby packs and one in 130 retail packs, features not only the Behind the Numbers insert card but a swatch of game used memorabilia.

1 Jeff Bagwell 6.00 15.00
2 Craig Biggio Jsy/Pants 6.00 15.00
3 Barry Bonds SP/50
4 Roger Clemens 10.00 25.00
5 Jim Edmonds 4.00 10.00
6 Brian Giles 4.00 10.00
7 Luis Gonzalez 4.00 10.00
8 Shawn Green 4.00 10.00
9 Todd Helton 6.00 15.00
10 Derek Jeter SP 15.00 40.00
11 Randy Johnson SP 6.00 15.00
12 Andruw Jones 6.00 15.00
13 Chipper Jones 6.00 15.00
14 Greg Maddux 6.00 15.00
15 Pedro Martinez 6.00 15.00
16 Mike Mussina 6.00 15.00
17 Mike Piazza Pants 6.00 15.00
18 Jorge Posada 6.00 15.00
19 Manny Ramirez 6.00 15.00
20 Alex Rodriguez 8.00 20.00
21 Ivan Rodriguez 6.00 15.00
22 Scott Rolen 6.00 15.00
23 Alfonso Soriano SP 8.00 20.00
24 Barry Zito 4.00 10.00

2002 E-X Behind the Numbers Game Jersey Dual

Randomly inserted in packs, these seven cards feature two swatches of jerseys from players who wear the same uniform number. These cards have a stated print run of 25 serial number sets and there is no pricing due to scarcity.

1 Craig Biggio
Ivan Rodriguez
2 Barry Bonds

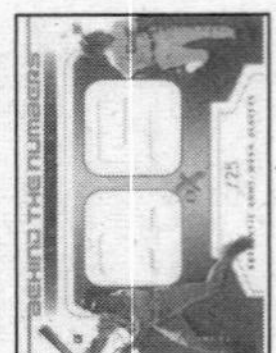

Andruw Jones
3 Jim Edmonds
Shawn Green
4 Brian Giles
Manny Ramirez
5 Greg Maddux
Mike Piazza
6 Scott Rolen
Todd Helton
7 Alfonso Soriano
Larry Walker

2002 E-X Barry Bonds 4X MVP

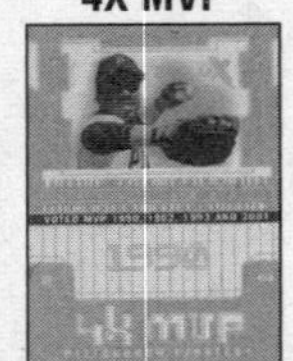

Randomly inserted in packs, these four cards have a stated print run to the years in which Barry Bonds won the MVP award.

COMMON CARD (1-4) 4.00 10.00

2002 E-X Game Essentials

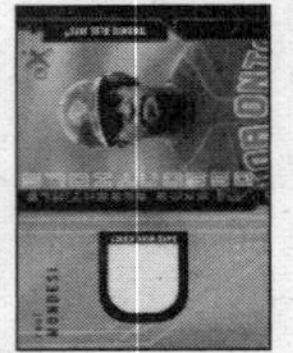

Randomly inserted in packs, these 35 cards feature players along with a piece of their game-used gear.

*PATCH PREMIUM: 1.5X TO 3X LISTED PRICE
1 Carlos Beltran Jsy 4.00 10.00
2 Barry Bonds Btg Glv SP
3 Barry Bonds Wristband SP
4 Kevin Brown Pants 4.00 10.00
5 Jeromy Burnitz Jsy 4.00 10.00
6 Carlos Delgado Bat 4.00 10.00
7 Jason Hart Bat SP
8 Rickey Henderson Bat 6.00 15.00
9 Rickey Henderson Jsy 6.00 15.00
10 Drew Henson Bat 4.00 10.00
11 Drew Henson Cleat 4.00 10.00
12 Drew Henson Fld Glv 6.00 15.00
13 Derek Jeter Cleat 20.00 50.00
14 Jason Kendall Jsy 4.00 10.00
15 Jeff Kent Jsy SP
16 Barry Larkin Fld Glv 10.00 25.00
17 Javy Lopez Jsy 4.00 10.00
18 Raul Mondesi Btg Glv 6.00 15.00
19 Raul Mondesi Jsy 4.00 10.00
20 Rafael Palmeiro Bat 6.00 15.00
21 Rafael Palmeiro Pants 6.00 15.00
22 Adam Piatt Jsy 4.00 10.00
23 Brad Radke Jsy 4.00 10.00
24 Cal Ripken Jsy 15.00 40.00
25 Mariano Rivera Jsy 6.00 15.00
26 Alex Rodriguez Btg Glv 10.00 25.00
27 Alex Rodriguez Cleat SP
28 Ivan Rodriguez Cleat SP
29 Kazuhiro Sasaki Jsy 4.00 10.00
30 J.T. Snow Jsy SP
31 Mo Vaughn Jsy 4.00 10.00
32 Robin Ventura Btg Glv 6.00 15.00
33 Robin Ventura Jsy 4.00 10.00
34 Jose Vidro Jsy 4.00 10.00
35 Matt Williams Jsy 4.00 10.00

2002 E-X HardWear

Inserted in packs at stated odds of one in 72 hobby and one in 216 retail, these 10 cards feature players who play the game with proper aggressiveness.

COMPLETE SET (10) 40.00 100.00
1 Ivan Rodriguez 3.00 8.00
2 Mike Piazza 5.00 12.00
3 Derek Jeter 8.00 20.00
4 Barry Bonds 8.00 20.00
5 Todd Helton 3.00 8.00
6 Roberto Alomar 3.00 8.00
7 Albert Pujols 6.00 15.00
8 Ichiro Suzuki 6.00 15.00
9 Ken Griffey Jr. 5.00 12.00
10 Jason Giambi 3.00 8.00

2002 E-X Hit and Run

Inserted at stated odds of one in 12 hobby and one in 72 retail, these 30 cards feature players who do the best job of hitting a baseball.

COMPLETE SET (30) 40.00 100.00
1 Adam Dunn 1.00 2.50
2 Derek Jeter 4.00 10.00
3 Frank Thomas 1.50 4.00
4 Albert Pujols 3.00 8.00
5 J.D. Drew 1.00 2.50
6 Richard Hidalgo 1.00 2.50
7 John Olerud 1.00 2.50
8 Roberto Alomar 1.00 2.50
9 Pat Burrell 1.00 2.50
10 Darin Erstad 1.00 2.50
11 Mark Grace 1.00 2.50
12 Chipper Jones 1.50 4.00
13 Jose Vidro 1.00 2.50
14 Cliff Floyd 1.00 2.50
15 Mo Vaughn 1.00 2.50
16 Nomar Garciaparra 2.50 6.00
17 Ivan Rodriguez 1.00 2.50
18 Luis Gonzalez 1.00 2.50
19 Jason Giambi 1.00 2.50
20 Bernie Williams 1.00 2.50
21 Mike Piazza 2.50 6.00
22 Barry Bonds 4.00 10.00
23 Jose Ortiz 1.00 2.50
24 Magglio Ordonez 1.00 2.50
25 Troy Glaus 1.00 2.50
26 Alex Rodriguez 2.50 6.00
27 Ichiro Suzuki 3.00 8.00
28 Sammy Sosa 1.50 4.00
29 Ken Griffey Jr. 2.50 6.00
30 Vladimir Guerrero 1.50 4.00

2002 E-X Hit and Run Game Base

Inserted in packs at stated odds of one in 120 hobby and one in 360 retail, this 10-card partial parallel set to the Hit and Run set includes a game base piece.

1 J.D. Drew 3.00 8.00
2 Adam Dunn 3.00 8.00
3 Jason Giambi 3.00 8.00
4 Troy Glaus 3.00 8.00
5 Ken Griffey Jr. 6.00 15.00
6 Vladimir Guerrero 4.00 10.00
7 Albert Pujols 6.00 15.00
8 Sammy Sosa 4.00 10.00
9 Ichiro Suzuki 6.00 15.00
10 Bernie Williams 4.00 10.00

2002 E-X Hit and Run Game Bat

Inserted in packs at a stated rate of one in 24 hobby and one in 130 retail packs, this 19-card partial parallel set features not only players from the Hit and Run insert set but a game bat sliver attached to the card.

1 Roberto Alomar 5.00 12.00
2 J.D. Drew 3.00 8.00
3 Darin Erstad 3.00 8.00
4 Cliff Floyd 3.00 8.00
5 Nomar Garciaparra 10.00 25.00
6 Luis Gonzalez 3.00 8.00
7 Richard Hidalgo 3.00 8.00
8 Derek Jeter 12.50 30.00
9 Chipper Jones 5.00 12.00
10 John Olerud 3.00 8.00
11 Magglio Ordonez 3.00 8.00
12 Jose Ortiz 3.00 8.00
13 Mike Piazza 6.00 15.00
14 Alex Rodriguez 8.00 20.00
15 Ivan Rodriguez 5.00 12.00
16 Frank Thomas 5.00 12.00
17 Mo Vaughn 3.00 8.00
18 Jose Vidro 3.00 8.00
19 Bernie Williams 5.00 12.00

2002 E-X Hit and Run Game Bat and Base

Inserted in packs at a stated rate of one in 240 hobby and one in 720 retail packs, these eight cards are a partial parallel to the Hit and Run insert set. These cards feature both a piece of a game bat and a base used by the featured players.

1 Roberto Alomar 6.00 15.00

2 Barry Bonds SP
3 Nomar Garciaparra 15.00 40.00
4 Derek Jeter 20.00 50.00
5 Chipper Jones 10.00 25.00
6 Mike Piazza 12.50 30.00
7 Alex Rodriguez 15.00 40.00
8 Mo Vaughn 6.00 15.00

2002 E-X Derek Jeter 4X Champ

Randomly inserted in packs, these four cards honor the four years that Fleer representative Derek Jeter was on a World Series Champion. These cards have a stated print run of the season in which Jeter finished as a champion.

COMMON CARD (1-4) 4.00 10.00

2003 E-X

This 102 card set was issued in October, 2003. This set was issued in three card packs which had an $6 SRP and were issued 20 packs to a box and 12 boxes to a case. The first 72 cards featured common veterans while cards 73 through 82 feature shorter printed veterans and cards numbered 83 through 86 feature 2003 rookies and cards numbered 87 through 102 feature Rookie Cards of the player.

COMP.SET w/o SP's (72) 15.00 40.00
COMMON CARD (1-72) .20 .50
COMMON CARD (73-82) 1.50 4.00
COMMON CARD (83-86) 1.50 4.00
COMMON CARD (87-102) 1.50 4.00
1 Troy Glaus .20 .50
2 Darin Erstad .20 .50
3 Garret Anderson .20 .50
4 Curt Schilling .20 .50
5 Randy Johnson .50 1.25
6 Luis Gonzalez .20 .50
7 Greg Maddux .75 2.00
8 Chipper Jones .50 1.25
9 Andruw Jones .30 .75
10 Melvin Mora .20 .50
11 Jay Gibbons .20 .50
12 Nomar Garciaparra .75 2.00
13 Pedro Martinez .30 .75
14 Manny Ramirez .30 .75
15 Sammy Sosa .50 1.25
16 Kerry Wood .20 .50
17 Magglio Ordonez .20 .50
18 Frank Thomas .50 1.25
19 Roberto Alomar .30 .75
20 Barry Larkin .30 .75
21 Adam Dunn .20 .50
22 Austin Kearns .20 .50
23 Omar Vizquel .30 .75
24 Larry Walker .20 .50
25 Todd Helton .30 .75
26 Preston Wilson .20 .50
27 Dmitri Young .20 .50
28 Ivan Rodriguez .30 .75
29 Mike Lowell .20 .50
30 Jeff Kent .20 .50
31 Jeff Bagwell .30 .75
32 Roy Oswalt .20 .50
33 Craig Biggio .30 .75
34 Mike Sweeney .20 .50
35 Carlos Beltran .20 .50
36 Shawn Green .20 .50
37 Kazuhisa Ishii .20 .50
38 Richie Sexson .20 .50
39 Torii Hunter .20 .50
40 Jacque Jones .20 .50
41 Jose Vidro .20 .50
42 Vladimir Guerrero .50 1.25
43 Mike Piazza .75 2.00
44 Tom Glavine .30 .75
45 Roger Clemens 1.00 2.50
46 Jason Giambi .20 .50
47 Bernie Williams .30 .75
48 Alfonso Soriano .20 .50
49 Mike Mussina .30 .75
50 Barry Zito .20 .50
51 Miguel Tejada .20 .50
52 Eric Chavez .20 .50
53 Eric Byrnes .20 .50
54 Jim Thome .30 .75
55 Kevin Millwood .20 .50
56 Brian Giles .20 .50
57 Xavier Nady .20 .50
58 Barry Bonds 1.25 3.00
59 Bret Boone .20 .50

60 Edgar Martinez .30 .75
61 Kazuhiro Sasaki .20 .50
62 Edgar Renteria .20 .50
63 J.D. Drew .20 .50
64 Scott Rolen .30 .75
65 Jim Edmonds .20 .50
66 Aubrey Huff .20 .50
67 Alex Rodriguez .75 2.00
68 Juan Gonzalez .20 .50
69 Hank Blalock .20 .50
70 Mark Teixeira .30 .75
71 Carlos Delgado .20 .50
72 Vernon Wells .20 .50
73 Shea Hillenbrand SP 1.50 4.00
74 Gary Sheffield SP 1.50 4.00
75 Mark Prior SP 2.00 5.00
76 Ken Griffey Jr. SP 5.00 12.00
77 Lance Berkman SP 1.50 4.00
78 Hideo Nomo SP 6.00 15.00
79 Derek Jeter SP 8.00 20.00
80 Ichiro Suzuki SP 6.00 15.00
81 Albert Pujols SP 6.00 15.00
82 Rafael Palmeiro SP 2.00 5.00
83 Jose Reyes ROO SP 1.50 4.00
84 Rocco Baldelli ROO SP 1.50 4.00
85 Hee Seop Choi ROO SP 1.50 4.00
86 Dontrelle Willis ROO SP 2.00 5.00
87 Robb Hammock ROO SP RC 1.50 4.00
88 Brandon Webb ROO SP RC 4.00 10.00
89 Matt Kata ROO SP RC 1.50 4.00
90 T.Wellemeyer ROO SP RC 1.50 4.00
91 Fran Cruceta ROO SP RC 1.50 4.00
92 Clint Barmes ROO SP RC 1.50 4.00
93 Jer Bonderman ROO SP RC 5.00 12.00
94 David Matranga ROO SP RC 1.50 4.00
95 Ryan Wagner ROO SP RC 1.50 4.00
96 Jeremy Griffiths ROO SP RC 1.50 4.00
97 Hideki Matsui ROO SP RC 6.00 15.00
98 Jose Contreras ROO SP RC 2.00 5.00
99 C.Wang ROO SP RC 8.00 20.00
100 Bo Hart ROO SP RC 1.50 4.00
101 Danny Haren ROO SP RC 2.00 5.00
102 Rickie Weeks ROO SP RC 3.00 8.00

2003 E-X Essential Credentials Future

*EC FUTURE 1-22: 4X TO 10X BASIC
*EC FUTURE 23-52: 5X TO 12X BASIC
*EC FUTURE 53-67: 6X TO 15X BASIC
*EC FUTURE 68-72: 8X TO 20X BASIC
*EC FUTURE 73-77: 1.5X TO 4X BASIC
RANDOM INSERTS IN PACKS
PRINT RUNS B/WN 1-102 COPIES PER
78-102 NOT PRICED DUE TO SCARCITY

2003 E-X Essential Credentials Now

*EC NOW 26-30: 10X TO 25X BASIC
*EC NOW 31-35: 8X TO 20X BASIC
*EC NOW 36-50: 6X TO 15X BASIC
*EC NOW 51-72: 5X TO 12X BASIC
*EC NOW 73-80: .75X TO 2X BASIC
*EC NOW 81-82: .6X TO 1.5X BASIC
*EC NOW 83-102: .75X TO 2X BASIC
*EC NOW 83-102: .75X TO 2X BASIC RC'S
RANDOM INSERTS IN PACKS
PRINT RUNS B/WN 1-102 COPIES PER
1-25 NO PRICING DUE TO SCARCITY
99 Chien-Ming Wang ROO/99 30.00 60.00

2003 E-X Behind the Numbers

STATED ODDS 1:80
1 Derek Jeter 8.00 20.00
2 Alex Rodriguez 5.00 12.00
3 Randy Johnson 3.00 8.00
4 Chipper Jones 3.00 8.00
5 Jim Thome 3.00 8.00
6 Alfonso Soriano 2.00 5.00
7 Adam Dunn 2.00 5.00
8 Nomar Garciaparra 5.00 12.00
9 Roger Clemens 6.00 15.00
10 Gary Sheffield 2.00 5.00
11 Vladimir Guerrero 3.00 8.00
12 Greg Maddux 5.00 12.00
13 Sammy Sosa 3.00 8.00
14 Mike Piazza 5.00 12.00
15 Troy Glaus 2.00 5.00

2003 E-X Behind the Numbers Game Jersey 500

PRINT RUN 500 SERIAL #'d SETS
*BTN 199: .5X TO 1.2X BTN 500
BTN 199 PRINT RUN 199 #'d SETS
*BTN 99 MULTI-PATCH: 1.25X TO 3X BTN 500
*BTN 99 ONE COLOR: .75X TO 2X BTN 500
BTN 99 PRINT RUN 99 #'d SETS
BTN 99 ARE MOSTLY PATCH CARDS
RANDOM INSERTS IN PACKS
AD Adam Dunn 2.00 5.00
AR Alex Rodriguez 5.00 12.00
AS Alfonso Soriano 2.00 5.00
BM Brett Myers 2.00 5.00
BZ Barry Zito 2.00 5.00
CJ Chipper Jones 3.00 8.00
DJ Derek Jeter 8.00 20.00
DW Dontrelle Willis 3.00 8.00
GM Greg Maddux 4.00 10.00
GS Gary Sheffield 2.00 5.00
HB Hank Blalock 2.00 5.00
JT Jim Thome 3.00 8.00
LB Lance Berkman 2.00 5.00
MB Marlon Byrd 2.00 5.00
MP Mike Piazza 4.00 10.00
NG Nomar Garciaparra 5.00 12.00
RA Roberto Alomar 3.00 8.00
RB Rocco Baldelli 2.00 5.00
RC Roger Clemens 5.00 12.00
RJ Randy Johnson 3.00 8.00
RP Rafael Palmeiro 3.00 8.00
SS Sammy Sosa 3.00 8.00
TG Troy Glaus 2.00 5.00
TGL Tom Glavine 3.00 8.00
VG Vladimir Guerrero 3.00 8.00

2003 E-X Behind the Numbers Game Jersey Autographs

Please note there is no expiration date to redeem the Marlon Byrd autographs.
RANDOM INSERTS IN PACKS
PRINT RUNS B/WN 5-35 COPIES PER
DW Dontrelle Willis/35 30.00 60.00
HB Hank Blalock/29
MB Marlon Byrd/29
RB Rocco Baldelli/5

2003 E-X Behind the Numbers Game Jersey Number

RANDOM INSERTS IN PACKS
PRINT RUNS B/WN 2-75 COPIES PER
NO PRICING ON QTY OF 25 OR LESS
AD Adam Dunn/44 8.00 20.00
AR Alex Rodriguez/3
AS Alfonso Soriano/12
BM Brett Myers/39 6.00 15.00
BZ Barry Zito/75 4.00 10.00
CJ Chipper Jones/10
DJ Derek Jeter/2
DW Dontrelle Willis/35 10.00 25.00
GM Greg Maddux/31 15.00 40.00
GS Gary Sheffield/11
HB Hank Blalock/9
JT Jim Thome/25
LB Lance Berkman/17
MB Marlon Byrd/29 8.00 20.00
MP Mike Piazza/31 15.00 40.00
NG Nomar Garciaparra/5
RA Roberto Alomar/12
RB Rocco Baldelli/5
RC Roger Clemens/22
RJ Randy Johnson/51 6.00 15.00
RP Rafael Palmeiro/25
SS Sammy Sosa/21
TG Troy Glaus/25
TGL Tom Glavine/47 8.00 20.00
VG Vladimir Guerrero/27 10.00 25.00

2003 E-X Diamond Essentials

STATED ODDS 1:480
NO MORE THAN 30 SETS PRODUCED
PRINT RUN INFO PROVIDED BY FLEER

NO PRICING DUE TO SCARCITY
1 Randy Johnson
2 Ichiro Suzuki
3 Albert Pujols
4 Barry Bonds
5 Hideki Matsui
6 Derek Jeter
7 Chipper Jones
8 Sammy Sosa
9 Jeff Bagwell
10 Mike Piazza
11 Pedro Martinez
12 Mark Prior
13 Jason Giambi
14 Jose Reyes
15 Alfonso Soriano

2003 E-X Diamond Essentials Autographs

Please note there is no scheduled expiration date to redeem these Albert Pujols autographs.
RANDOM INSERTS IN PACKS
PRINT RUNS B/WN 100-299 COPIES PER
AP Albert Pujols/100
DW Dontrelle Willis/265 10.00 25.00
RB Rocco Baldelli/299 6.00 15.00
RW Ryan Wagner/199 6.00 15.00

2003 E-X Diamond Essentials Game Jersey 345

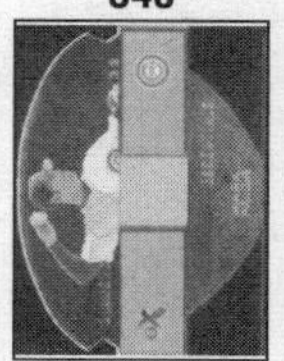

STATED PRINT RUN 345 SERIAL #'d SETS
*DE 245: .5X TO 1.2X DE 345
DE 245 PRINT RUN 245 #'d SETS
*DE 145: .6X TO 1.5X DE 345
DE 145 PRINT RUN 145 #'d SETS
*DE 55 MULTI-PATCH: 1.25X TO 3X DE 345
*DE 55 ONE COLOR: 1X TO 2.5X DE 345
DE 55 PRINT RUN 55 #'d SETS
DE 55 ARE MOSTLY PATCH CARDS
DE 5 PRINT RUN 5 #'d SETS
NO DE 5 PRICING DUE TO SCARCITY
CJ Chipper Jones 3.00 8.00
DJ Derek Jeter 8.00 20.00
JB Jeff Bagwell 3.00 8.00
JG Jason Giambi 2.00 5.00
JR Jose Reyes 2.00 5.00
MP Mike Piazza 5.00 12.00
MP Mark Prior 3.00 8.00
PM Pedro Martinez 3.00 8.00
RJ Randy Johnson 3.00 8.00
SS Sammy Sosa 3.00 8.00

2003 E-X Emerald Essentials

STATED ODDS 1:240
NO PRICING DUE TO SCARCITY
1 Austin Kearns
2 Alfonso Soriano
3 Miguel Tejada
4 Troy Glaus
5 Adam Dunn
6 Hideo Nomo
7 Kerry Wood
8 Nomar Garciaparra
9 Roger Clemens
10 Derek Jeter

2003 E-X Emerald Essentials Autographs

Please note that there is no expiration date to redeem the Marlon Byrd autographs.
RANDOM INSERTS IN PACKS
PRINT RUNS B/WN 29-299 COPIES PER

BW Brandon Webb/299 40.00 80.00
HB Hank Blalock/29 6.00 15.00
MB Marlon Byrd/29

2003 E-X Emerald Essentials Game Jersey 375

STATED PRINT RUN 375 SERIAL #'d SETS
*EE 250: .5X TO 1.2X EE 375
EE 250 PRINT RUN 250 #'d SETS
*EE 175: .6X TO 1.5X EE 375
EE 175 PRINT RUN 175 #'d SETS
*EE 60 SWATCH: 1X TO 2.5X EE 375
*EE 60 MULTI-PATCH: 1.25X TO 3X EE 375
EE 60 PRINT RUN 60 #'d SETS
ABOUT HALF OF EE 60'S ARE PATCH CARDS
EE 15 PRINT RUN 15 #'d SETS
NO EE 15 PRICING DUE TO SCARCITY
AD Adam Dunn 2.00 5.00
AK Austin Kearns 2.00 5.00
AR Alex Rodriguez 5.00 12.00
AS Alfonso Soriano 2.00 5.00
HN Hideo Nomo 6.00 15.00
KW Kerry Wood 2.00 5.00
MT Miguel Tejada 2.00 5.00
NG Nomar Garciaparra 5.00 12.00
RC Roger Clemens 5.00 12.00
TG Troy Glaus 2.00 5.00

2003 E-X X-tra Innings

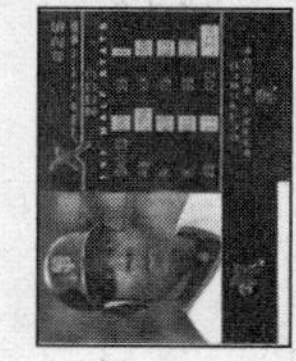

STATED ODDS 1:32
1 Ichiro Suzuki 4.00 10.00
2 Albert Pujols 4.00 10.00
3 Barry Bonds 5.00 12.00
4 Jason Giambi 1.50 4.00
5 Pedro Martinez 2.00 5.00
6 Mark Prior 2.00 5.00
7 Derek Jeter 5.00 12.00
8 Curt Schilling 1.50 4.00
9 Jeff Bagwell 2.00 5.00
10 Alex Rodriguez 3.00 8.00

2004 E-X

This 65-card set was released in late August, 2004. The set was issued in seven -card packs with an $200 SRP which came 12 "packs" to a case. The first 40-cards of this set featured veterans while the final 25 cards feature Rookie Cards and leading prospects which were inserted at a stated rate of one per pack. Those cards (41-65) were issued to a stated print run of 350 serial numbered sets with the first 150 of those cards being die-cut.

COMMON CARD (1-40) .75 2.00
COMMON CARD (41-65) 2.00 5.00
SEE PARALLEL SET FOR DIE CUT PRICES
1 Vladimir Guerrero 1.25 3.00
2 Randy Johnson 1.25 3.00
3 Chipper Jones 1.25 3.00
4 Miguel Tejada .75 2.00
5 Pedro Martinez 1.25 3.00
6 Nomar Garciaparra 2.00 5.00
7 Sammy Sosa 1.25 3.00
8 Greg Maddux 2.00 5.00
9 Frank Thomas 1.25 3.00
10 Ken Griffey Jr. 2.00 5.00
11 Omar Vizquel 1.25 3.00
12 Todd Helton 1.25 3.00
13 Ivan Rodriguez 1.25 3.00
14 Miguel Cabrera 1.25 3.00
15 Dontrelle Willis 1.25 3.00
16 Jeff Bagwell 1.25 3.00
17 Roger Clemens 2.50 6.00
18 Carlos Beltran .75 2.00
19 Hideo Nomo 1.25 3.00
20 Scott Podsednik .75 2.00
21 Torii Hunter .75 2.00
22 Jose Vidro .75 2.00
23 Mike Piazza 2.00 5.00
24 Hideki Matsui 2.00 5.00
25 Alex Rodriguez 2.00 5.00
26 Derek Jeter 2.50 6.00
27 Tim Hudson .75 2.00
28 Jim Thome 1.25 3.00
29 Craig Wilson .75 2.00
30 Brian Giles .75 2.00
31 Jason Schmidt .75 2.00
32 Ichiro Suzuki 2.50 6.00
33 Scott Rolen 1.25 3.00
34 Albert Pujols 2.50 6.00
35 Rocco Baldelli .75 2.00
36 Alfonso Soriano .75 2.00
37 Carlos Delgado .75 2.00
38 Curt Schilling 1.25 3.00
39 Mark Prior 1.25 3.00
40 Josh Beckett .75 2.00
41 Merkin Valdez ROO RC 3.00 8.00
42 Akinori Otsuka ROO RC 2.00 5.00
43 Ian Snell ROO RC 3.00 8.00
44 Kaz Matsui ROO RC 3.00 8.00
45 Jason Bartlett ROO RC 3.00 8.00
46 Dennis Sarfate ROO RC 2.00 5.00
47 Sean Henn ROO RC 2.00 5.00
48 David Aardsma ROO RC 3.00 8.00
49 Casey Kotchman ROO 2.00 5.00
50 John Gall ROO RC 3.00 8.00
51 William Bergolla ROO RC 2.00 5.00
52 Angel Chavez ROO RC 2.00 5.00
53 Hector Gimenez ROO RC 2.00 5.00
54 Aaron Baldiris ROO RC 3.00 8.00
55 Justin Leone ROO RC 3.00 8.00
56 Onil Joseph ROO RC 2.00 5.00
57 Freddy Guzman ROO RC 2.00 5.00
58 Andres Blanco ROO RC 2.00 5.00
59 Greg Dobbs ROO RC 2.00 5.00
60 Joe Mauer ROO 2.50 6.00
61 Luis Gonzalez ROO RC 2.00 5.00
62 Chris Saenz ROO RC 2.00 5.00
63 Zack Greinke ROO 2.00 5.00
64 Jose Capellan ROO RC 3.00 8.00
65 Brad Halsey ROO RC 3.00 8.00

2004 E-X Die Cuts

*DIE CUTS 41-65: .5X TO 1.2X BASIC
41-65 OVERALL ODDS ONE PER PACK
STATED PRINT RUN 150 SERIAL #'d SETS
DIE CUTS ARE 1ST 150 SERIAL #'d COPIES

2004 E-X Essential Credentials Future

*FUTURE p/r 51-65: 1.5X TO 4X BASIC
*FUTURE p/r 36-50: 2X TO 5X BASIC
*FUTURE p/r 26-35: 2.5X TO 6X BASIC
OVERALL PARALLEL ODDS 1:3
PRINT RUNS B/WN 1-65 COPIES PER
NO PRICING ON QTY OF 25 OR LESS

2004 E-X Essential Credentials Now

*NOW p/r 51-65: .75X TO 2X BASIC
*NOW p/r 41-50: 1X TO 2.5X BASIC
*NOW p/r
*NOW p/r 26-35: 2.5X TO 6X BASIC
*NOW p/r 16-25: 3X TO 8X BASIC
OVERALL PARALLEL ODDS 1:3
PRINT RUNS B/WN 1-65 COPIES PER
NO PRICING ON QTY OF 14 OR LESS

2004 E-X Check Mates

OVERALL AUTO ODDS ONE PER PACK
PRINT RUNS B/WN 1-25 COPIES PER
NO PRICING ON QTY OF 1 COPY PER
EXCHANGE DEADLINE INDEFINITE
APSM Albert Pujols 300.00 400.00
Stan Musial/25
BRLG Babe Ruth
Lou Gehrig/1
CYDS Carl Yastrzemski
Duke Snider/25
EBRS Ernie Banks 125.00 200.00
Ryne Sandberg/25
EMRP Eddie Murray 90.00 150.00
Rafael Palmeiro/25
HWTC Honus Wagner
Ty Cobb/1
MRPM Manny Ramirez
Pedro Martinez/25
RJDM Reggie Jackson 150.00 250.00
Don Mattingly/25
RJGM Randy Johnson
Greg Maddux/25
RYKP Robin Yount
Kirby Puckett/25
WBTG Wade Boggs 100.00 175.00
Tony Gwynn/25
YBJB Yogi Berra
Johnny Bench/25

2004 E-X Classic ConnExions Game Used Double

STATED PRINT RUN 22 SERIAL #'d SETS
DOUBLE EMERALD PRINT RUN 1 #'d SET
NO DOUBLE EMERALD PRICING AVAILABLE
OVERALL GU ODDS ONE PER PACK
BRJF Babe Ruth Bat 150.00 250.00
Jimmie Foxx Bat
CRBR Cal Ripken Jsy 75.00 150.00
Brooks Robinson Bat
CRNR Cal Ripken Jsy 75.00 150.00
Nolan Ryan Jsy
CRRY Cal Ripken Jsy 60.00 120.00
Robin Yount Jsy
DMRJ Don Mattingly Jsy 40.00 80.00
Reggie Jackson Jsy
DMTM Don Mattingly Jsy 50.00 100.00
Thurman Munson Jsy
DWCY Dave Winfield Jsy 20.00 50.00
Carl Yastrzemski Jsy
EMCR Eddie Murray Jsy 75.00 150.00
Cal Ripken Jsy
EMRJ Eddie Murray Jsy 30.00 60.00
Reggie Jackson Jsy
HKAK Harmon Killebrew Pants 30.00 60.00
Al Kaline Pants
HWHG Hack Wilson Bat 50.00 100.00
Hank Greenberg Bat
JBCF Johnny Bench Jsy 30.00 60.00
Carlton Fisk Pants
JCRH Jose Canseco Jsy 30.00 60.00
Rickey Henderson Jsy
KPDM Kirby Puckett Jsy 40.00 80.00
Don Mattingly Jsy
LBRC Lou Brock Jsy 15.00 40.00
Rod Carew Jsy
MSEM Mike Schmidt Jsy 75.00 150.00
Eddie Mathews Pants
NRTS Nolan Ryan Jsy 60.00 120.00
Tom Seaver Jsy
PMRY Paul Molitor Jsy 30.00 60.00
Robin Yount Jsy
RCRJ Rod Carew Jsy 15.00 40.00
Reggie Jackson Jsy
RHLB Rickey Henderson Jsy 30.00 60.00
Lou Brock Jsy
RMBR Roger Maris Bat 175.00 300.00
Babe Ruth Bat
TGRH Tony Gwynn Jsy 40.00 80.00
Rickey Henderson Jsy
TWCY Ted Williams Bat 125.00 200.00
Carl Yastrzemski Bat
WBCY Wade Boggs Bat 30.00 60.00
Carl Yastrzemski Jsy
WBDM Wade Boggs Jsy 30.00 60.00
Don Mattingly Jsy
WBTG Wade Boggs Bat 30.00 60.00
Tony Gwynn Jsy
WMWS Willie McCovey Bat 15.00 40.00
Willie Stargell Bat
WSWF Warren Spahn Jsy 30.00 60.00
Whitey Ford Pants
YBRC Yogi Berra Bat 30.00 60.00
Roy Campanella Bat

2004 E-X Classic ConnExions Game Used Triple

STATED PRINT RUN 13 SERIAL #'d SETS
TRIPLE EMERALD PRINT RUN 1 #'d SET
NO TRIPLE EMERALD PRICING AVAILABLE
OVERALL GU ODDS ONE PER PACK
B = BAT, J = JSY, P = PANTS
BCB Yogi Berra Bat
Roy Campanella Bat
Johnny Bench Jsy
BCH Lou Brock Jsy
Rod Carew Jsy

Rickey Henderson Jsy
BGM Wade Boggs Bat
Tony Gwynn Jsy
Don Mattingly Jsy
KKY Harmon Killebrew Pants
Al Kaline Pants
Carl Yastrzemski Jsy
MMJ Don Mattingly Jsy
Thurman Munson Jsy
Reggie Jackson Jsy
RFG Babe Ruth Bat
Jimmie Foxx Bat
Hank Greenberg Bat
RMR Brooks Robinson Bat
Eddie Murray Jsy
Cal Ripken Jsy
SMR Mike Schmidt Jsy
Eddie Mathews Pants
Cal Ripken Jsy
WRF Ted Williams Bat
Babe Ruth Bat
Jimmie Foxx Bat
WYB Ted Williams Bat
Carl Yastrzemski Jsy
Wade Boggs Bat

2004 E-X Clearly Authentics Black Patch

*3-COLOR PATCHES: ADD 20% PREMIUM
*4-COLOR PATCHES: ADD 50% PREMIUM
*5-COLOR PATCHES: ADD 100% PREMIUM
*JSY TAG PATCHES: ADD 100% PREMIUM
OVERALL GU ODDS ONE PER PACK
STATED PRINT RUN 75 SERIAL #'d SETS

AD Adam Dunn	6.00	15.00
AJ Andruw Jones	8.00	20.00
AP Albert Pujols	20.00	50.00
AR Alex Rodriguez	15.00	40.00
AS Alfonso Soriano	6.00	15.00
BG Brian Giles	6.00	15.00
BZ Barry Zito	6.00	15.00
CJ Chipper Jones	10.00	25.00
CR Cal Ripken	40.00	80.00
CS Curt Schilling	8.00	20.00
DM Don Mattingly	20.00	50.00
DW Dontrelle Willis	8.00	20.00
EG Eric Gagne	6.00	15.00
EM Eddie Murray	15.00	40.00
FT Frank Thomas	10.00	25.00
GM Greg Maddux	12.50	30.00
HB Hank Blalock	6.00	15.00
HM Hideki Matsui	30.00	60.00
HN Hideo Nomo	15.00	40.00
IR Ivan Rodriguez	8.00	20.00
JB Jeff Bagwell	8.00	20.00
JB2 Josh Beckett	6.00	15.00
JG2 Jason Giambi	6.00	15.00
JT Jim Thome	8.00	20.00
KM Kaz Matsui	10.00	25.00
KW Kerry Wood	6.00	15.00
LB Lance Berkman	6.00	15.00
MC Miguel Cabrera	8.00	20.00
MO Magglio Ordonez	6.00	15.00
MP Mark Prior	8.00	20.00
MP2 Mike Piazza	15.00	40.00
MR Manny Ramirez	8.00	20.00
MT Mark Teixeira	8.00	20.00
MT2 Miguel Tejada	6.00	15.00
OS Ozzie Smith	15.00	40.00
PB Pat Burrell	6.00	15.00
PM Paul Molitor	6.00	15.00
PR Pedro Martinez	8.00	20.00
RB Rocco Baldelli	6.00	15.00
RC Roger Clemens	15.00	40.00
RC2 Rod Carew	10.00	25.00
RH Rickey Henderson	12.50	30.00
RJ Randy Johnson	10.00	25.00
RP Rafael Palmeiro	8.00	20.00
RW Rickie Weeks	6.00	15.00
SG Shawn Green	6.00	15.00
SR Scott Rolen	8.00	20.00
SS Sammy Sosa	10.00	25.00
TG Troy Glaus	6.00	15.00
TG2 Tony Gwynn	15.00	40.00
TH Todd Helton	8.00	20.00
TH2 Torii Hunter	6.00	15.00
TH3 Tim Hudson	6.00	15.00
VG Vladimir Guerrero	10.00	25.00

2004 E-X Clearly Authentics Bronze Jersey-Patch

*BRONZE JSY-PATCH: .6X TO 1.5X BASIC
*3-COLOR PATCHES: ADD 20% PREMIUM
*4-COLOR PATCHES: ADD 50% PREMIUM
*5-COLOR PATCHES: ADD 100% PREMIUM
*JSY TAG PATCHES: ADD 100% PREMIUM
OVERALL GU ODDS ONE PER PACK
STATED PRINT RUN 35 SERIAL #'d SETS

CY Carl Yastrzemski	25.00	60.00
RJ2 Reggie Jackson	15.00	40.00

2004 E-X Clearly Authentics Burgundy Triple Patch

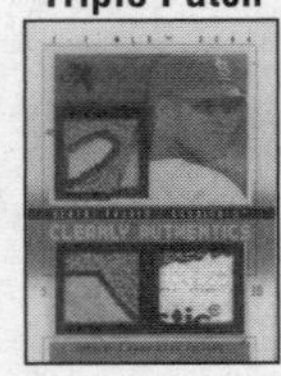

OVERALL GU ODDS ONE PER PACK
STATED PRINT RUN 13 SERIAL #'d SETS
NO PRICING DUE TO SCARCITY

2004 E-X Clearly Authentics Pewter Bat-Patch

*PEWTER BAT-PATCH: .6X TO 1.5X BASIC
*3-COLOR PATCHES: ADD 20% PREMIUM
*4-COLOR PATCHES: ADD 50% PREMIUM
*5-COLOR PATCHES: ADD 100% PREMIUM
*JSY TAG PATCHES: ADD 100% PREMIUM
OVERALL GU ODDS ONE PER PACK
STATED PRINT RUN 44 SERIAL #'d SETS

CY Carl Yastrzemski	25.00	60.00
RJ2 Reggie Jackson	15.00	40.00

2004 E-X Clearly Authentics Royal Blue Bat-Jersey-Patch

OVERALL GU ODDS ONE PER PACK
STATED PRINT RUN 8 SERIAL #'d SETS
NO PRICING DUE TO SCARCITY

2004 E-X Clearly Authentics Tan Double Patch

*TAN DOUBLE PATCH: .75X TO 2X BASIC
*3-COLOR PATCHES: ADD 20% PREMIUM
*4-COLOR PATCHES: ADD 50% PREMIUM
*5-COLOR PATCHES: ADD 100% PREMIUM
*JSY TAG PATCHES: ADD 100% PREMIUM
OVERALL GU ODDS ONE PER PACK
STATED PRINT RUN 22 SERIAL #'d SETS

CY Carl Yastrzemski	30.00	80.00
RJ2 Reggie Jackson	20.00	50.00

2004 E-X Clearly Authentics Turquoise Nameplate

OVERALL GU ODDS ONE PER PACK
PRINT RUNS B/WN 4-11 COPIES PER
NO PRICING DUE TO SCARCITY

2004 E-X Clearly Authentics Double MLB Logo

OVERALL GU ODDS ONE PER PACK
STATED PRINT RUN 1 SERIAL #'d SET
NO PRICING DUE TO SCARCITY
AJCJ Andruw Jones
Chipper Jones
APSR Albert Pujols
Scott Rolen

ASAR Alfonso Soriano
Alex Rodriguez
BZTH Barry Zito
Tim Hudson
CSPM Curt Schilling
Pedro Martinez
FTMO Frank Thomas
Magglio Ordonez
GMMP Greg Maddux
Mark Prior
GMRC Greg Maddux
Roger Clemens
HBMT Hank Blalock
Mark Teixeira
HMJG Hideki Matsui
Jason Giambi
HNEG Hideo Nomo
Eric Gagne
HNHM Hideo Nomo
Hideki Matsui
IRMP Ivan Rodriguez
Mike Piazza
JTPB Jim Thome
Pat Burrell
KWMP Kerry Wood
Mark Prior
LBJB Lance Berkman
Jeff Bagwell
MGRP Mark Grace
Rafael Palmeiro
MRVG Manny Ramirez
Vladimir Guerrero
RJRC Randy Johnson
Roger Clemens
TGVG Troy Glaus
Vladimir Guerrero

2004 E-X Clearly Authentics Signature Black Jersey

*3-COLOR PATCHES: ADD 20% PREMIUM
*4-COLOR PATCHES: ADD 50% PREMIUM
*5-COLOR PATCHES: ADD 100% PREMIUM
*JSY TAG PATCHES: ADD 100% PREMIUM
OVERALL AUTO ODDS ONE PER PACK
PRINT RUNS B/WN 17-50 COPIES PER
EXCHANGE DEADLINE INDEFINITE

AP Albert Pujols/50	150.00	250.00
BW Bernie Williams/42	20.00	50.00
BZ Barry Zito/18	15.00	40.00
CJ Chipper Jones/50	30.00	60.00
DW Dontrelle Willis/50	15.00	40.00
FT Frank Thomas/50	20.00	50.00
GM Greg Maddux/37		
GS Gary Sheffield/50	15.00	40.00
HB Hank Blalock/50	10.00	25.00
IR Ivan Rodriguez/50	20.00	50.00
JB Josh Beckett/50	15.00	40.00
JD J.D. Drew/50	10.00	25.00
KW Kerry Wood/34	20.00	50.00
MC Miguel Cabrera/50	15.00	40.00
MP1 Mike Piazza/37	60.00	120.00
MR1 Manny Ramirez/50	30.00	60.00
MR2 Mariano Rivera/50	40.00	80.00
PM Pedro Martinez/23	60.00	120.00
RC Roger Clemens/50	75.00	150.00
RJ Randy Johnson/17	60.00	120.00
RO Roy Oswalt/49	10.00	25.00
RP Rafael Palmeiro/43	30.00	60.00
TG Troy Glaus/50	15.00	40.00
TH Todd Helton/50	15.00	40.00
VG Vladimir Guerrero/50	30.00	60.00

2004 E-X Clearly Authentics Signature Burgundy Button

OVERALL AUTO ODDS ONE PER PACK
STATED PRINT RUN 6 SERIAL #'d SETS
NO PRICING DUE TO SCARCITY
EXCHANGE DEADLINE INDEFINITE

2004 E-X Clearly Authentics Signature Emerald MLB Logo

OVERALL AUTO ODDS ONE PER PACK
STATED PRINT RUN 1 SERIAL #'d SET

NO PRICING DUE TO SCARCITY
EXCHANGE DEADLINE INDEFINITE

2004 E-X Clearly Authentics Signature Pewter Jersey

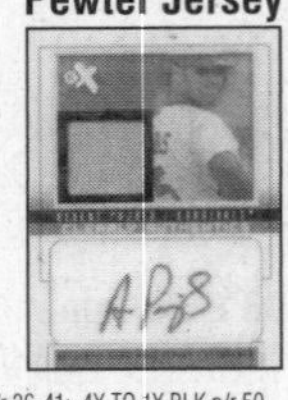

*PTR p/r 36-41: .4X TO 1X BLK p/r 50
*PTR p/r 20-27: .5X TO 1.2X BLK p/r 50
*3-COLOR PATCHES: ADD 20% PREMIUM
*4-COLOR PATCHES: ADD 50% PREMIUM
*5-COLOR PATCHES: ADD 100% PREMIUM
*JSY TAG PATCHES: ADD 100% PREMIUM
OVERALL AUTO ODDS ONE PER PACK
PRINT RUNS B/WN 7-41 COPIES PER
NO PRICING ON QTY OF 10 OR LESS

2004 E-X Clearly Authentics Signature Tan Patch

*TAN p/r 75: .4X TO .1X BLK p/r 18
*TAN p/r 42-51: .6X TO 1.5X BLK p/r 42-50
*TAN p/r 42-51: .4X TO 1X BLK p/r 23
*TAN p/r 42-51: .4X TO 1X BLK p/r 17
*TAN p/r 21-35: .6X TO 1.5X BLK p/r 37-50
*TAN p/r 21-35: .5X TO 1.2X BLK p/r 34
*TAN p/r 17: .75X TO 2X BLK p/r 50
*3-COLOR PATCHES: ADD 20% PREMIUM
*4-COLOR PATCHES: ADD 50% PREMIUM
*5-COLOR PATCHES: ADD 100% PREMIUM
*JSY TAG PATCHES: ADD 100% PREMIUM
OVERALL AUTO ODDS ONE PER PACK
PRINT RUNS B/WN 5-75 COPIES PER
NO PRICING ON QTY OF 11 OR LESS
EXCHANGE DEADLINE INDEFINITE

RC Roger Clemens/22	100.00	200.00

2004 E-X ConnExions Dual Autograph

OVERALL AUTO ODDS ONE PER PACK
PRINT RUNS B/WN 25-50 COPIES PER
EXCHANGE DEADLINE INDEFINITE

ABCB Adrian Beltre / Carlos Beltran/25	30.00	60.00
BBMW Bill Buckner / Mookie Wilson/50	30.00	60.00
BDMT Bucky Dent / Mike Torrez/50	20.00	50.00
BGMG Brian Giles / Marcus Giles/25	30.00	60.00
BJDS Bo Jackson / Deion Sanders/25		
BZTH Barry Zito / Tim Hudson/25	40.00	80.00
CKJM Casey Kotchman / Joe Mauer/50	25.00	60.00
CLMO Carlos Lee / Magglio Ordonez/25	30.00	60.00
CWJW Craig Wilson / Jack Wilson/25	20.00	50.00
DWMC Dontrelle Willis / Miguel Cabrera/25	40.00	80.00
EGBW Eric Gagne / Billy Wagner/25		
JDTN Johnny Damon / Trot Nixon/25	50.00	100.00
JNPN Joe Niekro / Phil Niekro/50	20.00	50.00
KGDE Kirk Gibson / Dennis Eckersley/25	40.00	80.00
MTHB Mark Teixeira / Hank Blalock/25	40.00	80.00
MYKG Michael Young / Khalil Greene/50	40.00	80.00
RWDY Rickie Weeks / Delmon Young/25	40.00	80.00

SPLO Scott Podsednik / Lyle Overbay/25	40.00	80.00
SSTH Shannon Stewart / Torii Hunter/25	30.00	60.00

2004 E-X Double Barrel

OVERALL GU ODDS ONE PER PACK
STATED PRINT RUN 1 SERIAL #'d SET
NO PRICING DUE TO SCARCITY
AJCJ Andruw Jones
Chipper Jones
AKAD Austin Kearns
Adam Dunn
BWGS Bernie Williams
Gary Sheffield
DMRJ Don Mattingly
Reggie Jackson
IRAR Ivan Rodriguez
Alex Rodriguez
KMHM Kaz Matsui
Hideki Matsui
KPTH Kirby Puckett
Torii Hunter
LBJB Lance Berkman
Jeff Bagwell
MPGC Mike Piazza
Gary Carter
MRSS Manny Ramirez
Sammy Sosa
MTHB Mark Teixeira
Hank Blalock
RCOC Roberto Clemente
Orlando Cepeda
RJCS Randy Johnson
Curt Schilling
RPJT Rafael Palmeiro
Jim Thome
TGVG Troy Glaus
Vladimir Guerrero
TWCY Ted Williams
Carl Yastrzemski
WBTG Wade Boggs
Tony Gwynn
WSWM Willie Stargell
Willie McCovey

2004 E-X Signings of the Times Best Year

OVERALL AUTO ODDS ONE PER PACK
PRINT RUNS B/WN 48-94 COPIES PER
EXCHANGE DEADLINE INDEFINITE

BJ Bo Jackson Jsy/89	30.00	60.00
CY Carl Yastrzemski Bat/67	40.00	80.00
DM Don Mattingly Jsy/85	40.00	80.00
DS Duke Snider Bat/55	20.00	50.00
DS2 Deion Sanders Jsy/92	30.00	60.00
EB Ernie Banks Bat/58	40.00	80.00
EM Eddie Murray Jsy/83	30.00	60.00
GB George Brett Jsy/80	50.00	100.00
JB Johnny Bench Jsy/72	30.00	60.00
JC Jose Canseco Jsy/88	15.00	40.00
KP Kirby Puckett Bat/88	50.00	100.00
MS Mike Schmidt Jsy/80	50.00	100.00
NR Nolan Ryan Jsy/73	75.00	150.00
OS Ozzie Smith Jsy/87	30.00	60.00
RH Rickey Henderson Jsy/90	40.00	80.00
RJ Reggie Jackson Jsy/73	30.00	60.00
RS Ryne Sandberg Bat/90	40.00	80.00
RY Robin Yount Jsy/82		
SM Stan Musial Bat/48	40.00	80.00
TG Tony Gwynn Jsy/94	30.00	60.00
TS Tom Seaver Jsy/69	20.00	50.00
WB Wade Boggs Bat/87	15.00	40.00
WC Will Clark Jsy/91	15.00	40.00
YB Yogi Berra Bat/54	40.00	80.00

2004 E-X Signings of the Times Debut Year

*DEBUT p/r 66-89: .4X TO 1X BEST p/r 69-94
*DEBUT p/r 41-61: .4X TO 1X BEST p/r 48-58
OVERALL AUTO ODDS ONE PER PACK
PRINT RUNS B/WN 41-89 COPIES PER
EXCHANGE DEADLINE INDEFINITE

2004 E-X Signings of the Times Emerald

OVERALL AUTO ODDS ONE PER PACK
STATED PRINT RUN 1 SERIAL #'d SET

NO PRICING DUE TO SCARCITY
EXCHANGE DEADLINE INDEFINITE

2004 E-X Signings of the Times HOF Year

*HOF p/r 69-99: .4X TO 1X BEST p/r 67-82
*HOF p/r 69-99: .6X TO .8X BEST p/r 48-58
OVERALL AUTO ODDS ONE PER PACK
PRINT RUNS B/WN 1-99 COPIES PER
NO PRICING ON QTY OF 3 OR LESS
EXCHANGE DEADLINE INDEFINITE

CY Carl Yastrzemski Bat/89	30.00	80.00
DS Duke Snider Bat/80	15.00	40.00
EB Ernie Banks Bat/77	25.00	60.00
EM Eddie Murray Jsy/3		
GB George Brett Jsy/99	40.00	100.00
JB Johnny Bench Jsy/89	25.00	60.00
KP Kirby Puckett Bat/1		
MS Mike Schmidt Jsy/95	40.00	100.00
NR Nolan Ryan Jsy/99	60.00	150.00
OS Ozzie Smith Jsy/2		
RJ Reggie Jackson Jsy/93	25.00	60.00
RY Robin Yount Jsy/99		
SM Stan Musial Bat/69	25.00	60.00
TS Tom Seaver Jsy/92	20.00	50.00
YB Yogi Berra Bat/72	25.00	60.00

2004 E-X Signings of the Times Pewter

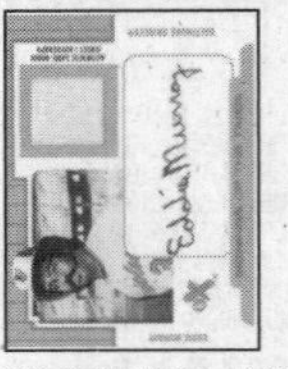

*PTR p/r 36-60: .5X TO 1.2X BEST p/r 83-92
*PTR p/r 36-60: .4X TO 1X BEST p/r 48
*PTR p/r 21-33: .6X TO 1.5X BEST p/r 85-94
*PTR p/r 21-33: .5X TO 1.2X BEST p/r 54-58
OVERALL AUTO ODDS ONE PER PACK
PRINT RUNS B/WN 21-60 COPIES PER

1947-66 Exhibits

This grouping encompasses a wide time span but displays a common design. The following players have been illegally reprinted in mass quantities on a thinner-than-original cardboard which is also characterized by a dark gray back: Aaron, Ford, Fox, Hodges, Elston Howard, Mantle, Mays, Musial, Newcombe, Reese, Spahn, and Ted Williams. Each card measures 3 3/8" by 5 3/8". In the checklist below SIG refers to signature and SCR refers to script name on card. The abbreviations POR (portrait), BAT (batting), and FIE (fielding) are also used below. There are many levels of scarcity within this "set," essentially based on which year(s) the player's card was printed. The Mickey Mantle portrait card, for example, was only printed in 1966, the last year of production. Those scarce cards which were only produced one or two years are noted parenthetically below by the last two digits of the year(s) of issue. Cards which seem to be especially difficult to obtain are the ones produced only in 1966 which are the aforementioned Mantle Portrait, Ford, Kranepool, Richardson, Skowron (White Sox), Ward and Yastrzemski. Some leading exhibit experts believe that the salutation and these cards should be checklisted together because of the long printing history of some of the salutations.

COMPLETE SET (321)	3500.00	7000.00
1 Hank Aaron (has been reprinted)	20.00	50.00
2A Joe Adcock SCR	2.50	6.00
2B Joe Adcock SIG	2.50	6.00
3 Max Alvis 66	20.00	50.00
4A Johnny Antonelli (Braves)	2.50	6.00
4B Johnny Antonelli (Giants)	2.50	6.00
5A Luis Aparicio POR	3.00	8.00
5B Luis Aparicio BAT 64	30.00	60.00
6 Luke Appling	3.00	8.00
7A Richie Ashburn	20.00	50.00

(Phillies)
7B Ritchie Ashburn 5.00 12.00
(sic, Richie)
7C Richie Ashburn 30.00 60.00
(Cubs) 61
8 Bob Aspromonte 64/66 2.50 6.00
9 Toby Atwell 2.50 6.00
10A Ed Bailey 61 5.00 12.00
(Cincinnati cap)
10B Ed Bailey (no cap) 2.50 6.00
11 Gene Baker 2.50 6.00
12A Ernie Banks SCR 15.00 40.00
12B Ernie Banks SIG 8.00 20.00
12C Ernie Banks POR 15.00 40.00
64/66
13 Steve Barber 64/66 2.50 6.00
14 Earl Battey 64/66 2.50 6.00
15 Matt Batts 3.00 8.00
16A Hank Bauer 2.50 6.00
(New York cap)
16B Hank Bauer 61 15.00 40.00
(plain cap)
17 Frank Baumholtz 2.50 6.00
18 Gene Bearden 2.50 6.00
19 Joe Beggs 47 10.00 25.00
20A Yogi Berra 5.00 12.00
20B Larry Yogi Berra 20.00 50.00
64/66
21 Steve Bilko 2.50 6.00
22A Ewell Blackwell 3.00 8.00
(foot up)
22B Ewell Blackwell POR 2.00 6.00
23A Don Blasingame 2.50 6.00
(St. Louis cap)
23B Don Blasingame 3.00 8.00
(plain cap)
24 Ken Boyer 64/66 10.00 25.00
25 Ralph Branca 2.50 6.00
26 Jackie Brandt 61 30.00 60.00
27 Harry Brecheen 2.50 6.00
28 Tom Brewer 61 20.00 50.00
29 Lou Brissie 2.50 6.00
30 Bill Bruton 2.50 6.00
31A Lew Burdette 2.50 6.00
(side view)
31B Lew Burdette 12.50 30.00
(facing) 64
32 Johnny Callison 64/66 3.00 8.00
33 Roy Campanella 20.00 50.00
34A Chico Carrasquel 2.50 6.00
(White Sox)
34B Chico Carrasquel 8.00 20.00
(plain cap)
35 George Case 47 10.00 25.00
36 Hugh Casey 5.00 12.00
37 Norm Cash 64/66 8.00 20.00
38A Orlando Cepeda POR 8.00 20.00
60/61
38B Orlando Cepeda BAT 8.00 20.00
64/66
39A Bob Cerv 60 2.50 6.00
(A's uniform)
39B Bob Cerv 61 20.00 50.00
(plain uniform)
40 Dean Chance 64/66 2.50 6.00
41 Spud Chandler 47 10.00 25.00
42 Tom Cheney 64/66 2.50 6.00
43 Bubba Church 2.00 6.00
44 Roberto Clemente 60.00 120.00
45A Rocky Colavito POR 60.00 120.00
61
45B Rocky Colavito BAT 12.50 30.00
64/66
46 Choo Choo Coleman 64 12.50 30.00
47 Gordy Coleman 66 20.00 50.00
48 Jerry Coleman 2.50 6.00
49 Mort Cooper 47 12.50 30.00
50 Walker Cooper 2.50 6.00
51 Roger Craig 64/66 5.00 12.00
52 Delmar Crandall 2.50 6.00
53A Joe Cunningham POR 3.00 8.00
64/66
53B Joe Cunningham BAT 30.00 60.00
61
54 Guy Curtwright 47 10.00 25.00
(sic, Curtright)
55 Bud Daley 61 20.00 50.00
56A Alvin Dark 5.00 12.00
(Boston cap)
56B Alvin Dark 2.50 6.00
(New York cap)
56C Alvin Dark (Cubs) 60 15.00 40.00
57 Murray Dickson 2.50 6.00
58 Bob Dillinger 5.00 12.00
59 Dom DiMaggio 5.00 12.00
60 Joe Dobson 2.50 6.00
61 Larry Doby 2.50 6.00
62 Bobby Doerr 5.00 12.00
63A Dick Donovan 2.50 6.00
(Braves, plain cap)
63B Dick Donovan 2.50 6.00
(White Sox)
64 Walter Dropo 2.50 6.00
65A Don Drysdale Portrait 20.00 50.00
(circa 1960-61)
65B Don Drysdale Glove at Waist 20.00 50.00
(circa 1964-66)
66 Luke Easter 2.50 6.00
67 Bruce Edwards 5.00 12.00
68 Del Ennis 2.50 6.00
69 Al Evans 2.50 6.00
70 Walter Evers 2.50 6.00
71A Ferris Fain FIE 5.00 12.00
71B Ferris Fain POR 2.50 6.00
72 Dick Farrell 64/66 2.50 6.00
73A Whitey Ford 5.00 12.00
(has been reprinted)
(no glove, throwing)
73B Whitey Ford POR 66 150.00 300.00
73C Ed Whitey Ford 20.00 50.00
(glove on shoulder)
64/66
74 Dick Fowler 2.50 6.00
75 Nelson Fox 8.00 20.00
(has been reprinted)
76 Tito Francona 64/66 2.50 6.00
77 Bob Friend 2.50 6.00
78 Carl Furillo 10.00 25.00
79 Augie Galan 10.00 25.00
80 Jim Gentile 64/66 2.50 6.00
81 Tony Gonzalez 64/66 2.50 6.00
82A Billy Goodman FIE 2.50 6.00
(fielding)
82B Billy Goodman BAT 10.00 25.00
60/61
83 Ted Greengrass 5.00 12.00
(sic, Jim)
84 Dick Groat 2.50 6.00
85 Steve Gromek 5.00 12.00
86 Johnny Groth 2.50 6.00
87 Orval Grove 47 10.00 25.00
88A Frank Gustine 2.50 6.00
(Pirates)
88B Frank Gustine(Cubs) 2.50 6.00
89 Berthold Haas 10.00 25.00
90 Grady Hatton 2.50 6.00
91 Jim Hegan 2.50 6.00
92 Tommy Henrich 2.50 6.00
93 Ray Herbert 66 20.00 50.00
94 Gene Hermanski 5.00 12.00
95 Whitey Herzog 60/61 5.00 12.00
96 Kirby Higbe 47 10.00 25.00
97 Chuck Hinton 64/66 2.50 6.00
98 Don Hoak 64 12.50 30.00
99A Gil Hodges 5.00 12.00
(Brooklyn cap)
(has been reprinted)
99B Gil Hodges 10.00 25.00
(Los Angeles cap)
100 Johnny Hopp 47 10.00 25.00
101 Elston Howard 2.50 6.00
(has been reprinted)
102 Frank Howard 64/66 8.00 20.00
103 Ken Hubbs 64 60.00 120.00
104 Tex Hughson 47 10.00 25.00
105 Fred Hutchinson 50 5.00 12.00
106 Monte Irvin 5.00 12.00
107 Joey Jay 64/66 2.50 6.00
108 Jackie Jensen 60 30.00 60.00
109 Sam Jethroe 3.00 8.00
110 Bill Johnson 50 3.00 8.00
111 Walter Judnich 47 10.00 25.00
112A Al Kaline SCR 10.00 25.00
(kneeling)
112B Al Kaline SIG POR 8.00 20.00
113 George Kell 5.00 12.00
114 Charley Keller 5.00 12.00
115 Alex Kellner 2.50 6.00
116 Kenn Keltner 10.00 25.00
(sic, Ken)
117A Harmon Killebrew 20.00 50.00
pinstripes, batting)
60/61
117B Harmon Killibrew 30.00 60.00
(sic, Killebrew)
POR 66
117C Harmon Killebrew 12.50 30.00
(throwing) 64/66
118 Ellis Kinder 2.50 6.00
119 Ralph Kiner 5.00 12.00
120 Billy Klaus 60 20.00 50.00
121A Ted Kluszewski(Reds) 10.00 25.00
121B Ted Kluszewski 10.00 25.00
(Pirates)
121C Ted Kluszewski 30.00 60.00
(plain uniform) 60/61
122 Don Kolloway 50 5.00 12.00
123 Jim Konstanty 3.00 8.00
124 Sandy Koufax 64/66 60.00 120.00
125 Ed Kranepool 66 125.00 250.00
126A Tony Kubek 2.50 6.00
(dark background)
126B Tony Kubek 2.50 6.00
(light background)
127A Harvey Kuenn 60 5.00 12.00
(Detroit)
127B Harvey Kuenn 61 20.00 50.00
(plain uniform)
127C Harvey Kuenn 5.00 12.00
(San Francisco) 64/66
128 Whitey Kurowski 50 10.00 25.00
129 Eddie Lake 47 10.00 25.00
130 Jim Landis 64/66 2.50 6.00
131 Don Larsen 2.50 6.00
132A Bob Lemon 3.00 8.00
(left arm not shown)
132B Bob Lemon 30.00 60.00
(left arm extended)
133 Buddy Lewis 47 10.00 25.00
134 Johnny Lindell 50 10.00 25.00
135 Phil Linz 66 20.00 50.00
136 Don Lock 66 20.00 50.00
137 Whitey Lockman 2.50 6.00
138 Johnny Logan 2.50 6.00
139A Dale Long (Pirates) 2.50 6.00
139B Dale Long (Cubs) 61 20.00 50.00
140 Ed Lopat 2.50 6.00
141A Harry Lowery 5.00 12.00
(sic, Lowrey)
141B Harry Lowrey 2.50 6.00
142 Sal Maglie 2.50 6.00
143 Art Mahaffey 64/66 2.50 6.00
144 Hank Majeski 2.50 6.00
145 Frank Malzone 2.00 6.00
146A Mickey Mantle Batting at Waist
White Outline 75.00 150.00
146B Mickey Mantle Batting at Waist
No White Outline 125.00 250.00
146C Mickey Mantle Batting
Full (circa 1964-66) 75.00 150.00
146D Mickey Mantle Portrait
(circa 1966) 350.00 700.00
147 Marty Marion 2.50 6.00
148 Roger Maris 64/66 30.00 60.00
149 Willard Marshall 2.50 6.00
150A Ed Mathews SCR 8.00 20.00
(sic, Mathews)
150B Eddie Mathews SIG 12.50 30.00
151 Ed Mayo 2.50 6.00
152A Willie Mays Batting 20.00 50.00
(New York)
Card has been reprinted
152B Willie Mays 20.00 50.00
(San Francisco)
153A Bill Mazeroski POR 6.00 15.00
60/61
153B Bill Mazeroski BAT 6.00 15.00
64/66
154 Ken McBride 64/66 2.50 6.00
155A Barney McCaskey 12.50 30.00
(sic, McCosky)
155B Barney McCoskey 40.00 80.00
(sic, McCosky)
156 Lindy McDaniel 60/61 2.50 6.00
157 Gil McDougald 2.50 6.00
158 Albert Mele 20.00 50.00
159 Sam Mele 5.00 12.00
160A Minnie Minoso 2.50 6.00
(White Sox)
160B Minnie Minoso 5.00 12.00
(Cleveland)
161 Dale Mitchell 2.50 6.00
162 Wally Moon 2.50 6.00
163 Don Mueller 12.50 30.00
164A Stan Musial 20.00 50.00
(three bats, kneeling)
(has been reprinted)
164B Stan Musial BAT 64 75.00 150.00
165 Charles Neal 64 12.50 30.00
166A Don Newcombe 5.00 12.00
(shaking hands)
166B Don Newcombe 2.50 6.00
(Brooklyn cap)
(has been reprinted)
166C Don Newcombe 8.00 20.00
(plain cap)
167 Hal Newhouser 5.00 12.00
168 Ron Northey 47 12.50 30.00
169 Bill O'Dell 64/66 2.50 6.00
170 Joe Page 50 10.00 25.00
171 Satchel Paige 60.00 120.00
172 Milt Pappas 64/66 2.50 6.00
173 Camilo Pascual 64/66 2.50 6.00
174 Albie Pearson 66 20.00 50.00
175 Johnny Pesky 2.50 6.00
176 Gary Peters 66 20.00 50.00
177 Dave Philley 2.50 6.00
178 Billy Pierce 60/61 2.50 6.00
179 Jimmy Piersall 66 40.00 80.00
180 Vada Pinson 64/66 8.00 20.00
181 Bob Porterfield 2.50 6.00
182 Boog Powell 66 60.00 120.00
183 Vic Raschi 2.50 6.00
184A Harold Peewee Reese 8.00 20.00
(ball visible along
bottom border)
184B Harold Peewee Reese 8.00 20.00
(ball not visible)
(has been reprinted)
185 Del Rice 2.50 6.00
186 Bobby Richardson 66 150.00 300.00
187A Phil Rizzuto 8.00 20.00
(small photo)
187B Phil Rizzuto 5.00 12.00
(larger photo)
188A Robin Roberts SIG 5.00 12.00
188B Robin Roberts SCR 6.00 15.00
189 Brooks Robinson 20.00 50.00
190 Eddie Robinson POR 2.50 6.00
191 Floyd Robinson 66 20.00 50.00
192 Frankie Robinson 20.00 50.00
64/66
193 Jackie Robinson 30.00 60.00
194 Preacher Roe 2.50 6.00
195 Bob Rogers 66 20.00 50.00
(sic, Rodgers)
196 Richard Rollins 66 20.00 50.00
197 Pete Runnels 64 12.50 30.00
198 John Sain 2.50 6.00
199 Ron Santo 64/66 10.00 25.00
200 Henry Sauer 2.50 6.00
201A Carl Sawatski 2.50 6.00
(Milwaukee cap)
201B Carl Sawatski 2.50 6.00
(Philadelphia cap)
201C Carl Sawatski 61 12.50 30.00
(plain cap)
202 Johnny Schmitz 3.00 8.00
203A Red Schoendeinst 12.50 30.00
(one foot shown
catching)
(sic, Schoendienst)
203B Red Schoendeinst 20.00 50.00
(both feet shown
catching)
(sic, Schoendienst)
203C Red Schoendinst BAT 5.00 12.00
(sic, Schoendienst)
204A Herb Score 5.00 12.00
(Cleveland cap)
204B Herb Score 61 20.00 50.00
(plain cap)
205 Andy Seminick 2.50 6.00
206 Rip Sewell 47 12.50 30.00
207 Norm Siebern 2.50 6.00
208A Roy Sievers 51 30.00 60.00
(Browns)
208B Roy Sievers 2.50 6.00
(Senators)
dark background)
208C Roy Sievers 2.50 6.00
(Senators)
light background)
208D Roy Sievers 61 20.00 50.00
(plain uniform)
209 Curt Simmons 2.50 6.00
210 Dick Sisler 2.50 6.00
211A Bill Skowron 2.50 6.00
(New York)
211B Bill Moose Skowron 125.00 250.00
(White Sox) 66
212 Enos Slaughter 5.00 12.00
213A Duke Snider 8.00 20.00
(Brooklyn)
213B Duke Snider 12.50 30.00
(Los Angeles)
214A Warren Spahn 5.00 12.00
(Boston)
(has been reprinted)
214B Warren Spahn 10.00 25.00
(Milwaukee)
215 Stanley Spence 10.00 25.00
216A Ed Stanky 2.50 6.00
(plain uniform)
216B Ed Stanky (Giants) 2.50 6.00
217A Vern Stephens 2.50 6.00
(Browns)
217B Vern Stephens 3.00 8.00
(Red Sox)
218 Ed Stewart 2.50 6.00
219 Snuffy Stirnweiss 12.50 30.00
220 George Birdie Tebbets 12.50 30.00
221A Frankie Thomas BAT 20.00 50.00
(Bob Skinner picture)
59
221B Frank Thomas (Cubs) 20.00 50.00
60/61
222 Lee Thomas 64/66 2.50 6.00
223 Bobby Thomson 5.00 12.00
224A Earl Torgeson 2.50 6.00
(Braves)
224B Earl Torgeson 60/61 2.50 6.00
(plain uniform)
225 Gus Triandos 60/61 5.00 12.00
226 Virgil Trucks 2.50 6.00
227 Johnny Vandermeer 47 30.00 60.00
228 Emil Verban 12.50 30.00
229A Mickey Vernon 2.50 6.00
(throwing)
229B Mickey Vernon BAT 2.50 6.00
230 Bill Voiselle 47 12.50 30.00
231 Leon Wagner 64/66 2.50 6.00
232A Eddie Waitkus BAT 2.50 6.00
(Cub uniform)
232B Eddie Waitkus BAT 2.50 6.00
(plain uniform)
232C Eddie Waitkus POR 20.00 50.00
(Phillies uniform)
233 Dick Wakefield 2.50 6.00
234 Harry Walker 30.00 60.00
235 Bucky Walters 5.00 12.00
236 Pete Ward 66 100.00 200.00
237 Herman Wehmeier 2.50 6.00
238A Vic Wertz (Tigers) 2.50 6.00
238B Vic Wertz(Red Sox) 2.50 6.00
239 Wally Westlake 2.50 6.00
240 Wes Westrum 20.00 50.00
241 Billy Williams 64/66 20.00 50.00
242 Maurice Wills 64/66 10.00 25.00
243A Gene Woodling SCR 2.50 6.00
243B Gene Woodling SIG 2.50 6.00
244 Taffy Wright 47 10.00 25.00
245 Carl Yastrzemski 66 200.00 400.00
246 Al Zarilla 51 5.00 12.00
247A Gus Zernial SCR 2.50 6.00
247B Gus Zernial SIG 2.50 6.00

2006 Exquisite Collection

COMMON AU RC (1-90) 8.00 20.00
ISSUED AS EXCH CARDS IN VARIOUS
2006 UPPER DECK PRODUCTS
1-90 PRINT RUN 55 SER.#'d SETS
91-100 PRINT RUN 10 SER.#'d SETS
1-90 FEATURE ROOKIE LOGOS
NO PRICING ON 91-100 DUE TO SCARCITY
1 Melky Cabrera AU (RC)
Jeremy Hermida AU (RC)
2 Craig Hansen AU (RC) 10.00 25.00
Fausto Carmona AU (RC)
3 Andre Ethier AU (RC) 8.00 20.00
Jason Kubel AU (RC)
4 Chad Billingsley AU (RC) 10.00 25.00
Boof Bonser AU (RC)
5 Jeremy Sowers AU (RC) 20.00 50.00
Fausto Carmona AU (RC)
6 Josh Willingham AU (RC) 10.00 25.00
Ronny Paulino AU (RC)
7 Takashi Saito AU RC 20.00 50.00
Andre Ethier AU (RC)
8 Cole Hamels AU (RC) 50.00 100.00
James Shields AU RC
9 Chris Denorfia AU (RC) 10.00 25.00
Carlos Quentin AU (RC)
10 Jason Hammel AU (RC) 10.00 25.00
James Shields AU RC
11 Dan Uggla AU (RC) 15.00 40.00
Ian Kinsler AU (RC)
12 Jeremy Accardo AU RC 15.00 40.00
Matt Cain AU (RC)
13 Jeremy Sowers AU (RC) 10.00 25.00
Paul Maholm AU (RC)
14 Cole Hamels AU (RC) 20.00 50.00
Jeremy Sowers AU (RC)
15 Francisco Liriano AU (RC) 15.00 40.00
Boof Bonser AU (RC)
16 Justin Verlander AU (RC) 40.00 80.00
Joel Zumaya AU (RC)
17 Hanley Ramirez AU (RC) 30.00 60.00
Stephen Drew AU (RC)
18 Alay Soler AU RC 10.00 25.00
Brian Bannister AU (RC)
19 Dave Gassner AU (RC) 10.00 25.00
Boof Bonser AU (RC)
20 Angel Pagan AU (RC) 20.00 50.00
Ryan Theroit AU (RC)
21 Dan Uggla AU (RC) 12.50 30.00
Jeremy Hermida AU (RC)
22 Mike Pelfrey AU RC
Chad Billingsley AU (RC)
23 Fausto Carmona AU (RC) 40.00 80.00
Cole Hamels AU (RC)
24 Takashi Saito AU RC 60.00 120.00
Hong-Chin Kuo AU (RC)
25 Paul Maholm AU (RC) 8.00 20.00
Sean Marshall AU (RC)
26 Howie Kendrick AU (RC) 12.50 30.00
Dan Uggla AU (RC)
27 Josh Johnson AU (RC) 10.00 25.00
Yusmeiro Petit AU (RC)
28 Matt Cain AU (RC)
Mike Pelfrey AU RC
29 Russell Martin AU (RC) 40.00 80.00
Andre Ethier AU (RC)
30 Francisco Liriano AU (RC) 20.00 50.00
Jered Weaver AU (RC)
31 Cole Hamels AU (RC) 12.50 30.00
Zach Jackson AU (RC)
32 Jonathan Papelbon AU (RC) 20.00 50.00
Craig Hansen AU RC
33 Mike Pelfrey AU RC
Alay Soler AU RC
34 Chris Denorfia AU (RC) 12.50 30.00
Jeremy Hermida AU (RC)
35 Josh Willingham AU (RC) 10.00 25.00
Cody Ross AU (RC)
36 Stephen Drew AU (RC) 20.00 50.00
Jered Weaver AU (RC)
37 Melky Cabrera AU (RC)
Wil Nieves AU (RC)
38 Scott Dunn AU (RC) 10.00 25.00
James Shields AU RC
39 Howie Kendrick AU (RC) 20.00 50.00
Kendry Morales AU (RC)
40 Paul Maholm AU (RC) 10.00 25.00
Matt Capps AU (RC)
41 Ian Kinsler AU (RC) 10.00 25.00
Howie Kendrick AU (RC)
42 Matt Cain AU (RC) 20.00 50.00
Alay Soler AU RC
43 Andre Ethier AU (RC)
Melky Cabrera AU (RC)
44 Justin Verlander AU (RC) 20.00 50.00
Jeremy Sowers AU (RC)
45 Howie Kendrick AU (RC)
Jered Weaver AU (RC)
46 Hanley Ramirez AU (RC) 20.00 50.00
Josh Willingham AU (RC)
47 Hanley Ramirez AU (RC) 15.00 40.00
Jeremy Hermida AU (RC)
48 Dan Uggla AU (RC) 12.50 30.00
Josh Willingham AU (RC)
49 Alay Soler AU RC 15.00 40.00
Cole Hamels AU (RC)
50 Jason Kubel AU (RC) 10.00 25.00
Boof Bonser AU (RC)
51 Mike Jacobs AU (RC) 10.00 25.00
Kendry Morales AU (RC)
52 Takashi Saito AU RC 20.00 50.00
Jonathan Papelbon AU (RC)
53 Jonathan Papelbon AU (RC) 40.00 80.00
Justin Verlander AU (RC)
54 Andre Ethier AU (RC) 20.00 50.00
Chad Billingsley AU (RC)
55 Jeremy Hermida AU (RC) 12.50 30.00
Tony Gwynn Jr. AU (RC)
56 Ryan Zimmerman AU (RC) 40.00 80.00
Stephen Drew AU (RC)
57 Tony Gwynn Jr. AU (RC) 12.50 30.00
Josh Barfield AU (RC)
58 Clay Hensley AU (RC) 10.00 25.00
Mike Thompson AU RC
59 Justin Verlander AU (RC) 20.00 50.00
Josh Johnson AU (RC)
60 Justin Verlander AU (RC)
Jered Weaver AU (RC)
61 Tony Gwynn Jr. AU (RC)
Melky Cabrera AU (RC)
62 Tony Gwynn Jr. AU (RC) 12.50 30.00
Andre Ethier AU (RC)
63 Stephen Drew AU (RC) 20.00 50.00
Carlos Quentin AU (RC)
64 Conor Jackson AU (RC) 20.00 50.00
Carlos Quentin AU (RC)
65 Ryan Zimmerman AU (RC) 30.00 60.00
Brendan Harris AU (RC)
66 Takashi Saito AU RC 20.00 50.00
Russell Martin AU (RC)
67 Mike Jacobs AU (RC) 12.50 30.00
Josh Willingham AU (RC)
68 Mike Jacobs AU (RC) 15.00 40.00
Hanley Ramiez AU (RC)
69 Mike Pelfrey AU RC
Justin Verlander AU (RC)
70 Mike Pelfrey AU RC
Jonathan Papelbon AU (RC)
71 Craig Hansen AU RC 20.00 50.00
Cole Hamels AU (RC)
72 Hanley Ramirez AU (RC) 12.50 30.00
Freddie Bynum AU (RC)
73 Tony Gwynn Jr. AU (RC)
Choo Freeman AU (RC)
74 Fernando Nieve AU (RC) 8.00 20.00
Taylor Buchholz AU (RC)
75 Adam Wainwright AU (RC) 15.00 40.00
Josh Johnson AU (RC)
76 Josh Willingham AU (RC) 20.00 50.00
Russell Martin AU (RC)
77 Russell Martin AU (RC) 15.00 40.00
Wil Nieves AU (RC)
78 Ben Johnson AU (RC) 8.00 20.00
Mike Thompson AU RC
79 Zach Jackson AU (RC) 8.00 20.00
Ben Hendrickson AU (RC)
80 Jonathan Papelbon AU (RC) 30.00 60.00
Joel Zumaya AU (RC)
81 Ben Hendrickson AU (RC) 10.00 25.00
Jose Capellan AU (RC)
82 Joey Devine AU RC 10.00 25.00
Ken Ray AU RC
83 Mike Pelfrey AU RC
Anderson Hernandez AU (RC)
84 Kelly Shoppach AU (RC) 20.00 50.00
Russell Martin AU (RC)
85 Alay Soler AU RC 8.00 20.00
Josh Johnson AU (RC)
86 Alay Soler AU RC 10.00 25.00
Craig Hansen AU RC
87 Craig Hansen AU RC 20.00 50.00
Chad Billingsley AU (RC)
88 Chad Billingsley AU (RC) 20.00 50.00
Matt Cain AU (RC)
89 Francisco Liriano AU (RC) 15.00 40.00
Craig Hansen AU RC
90 Conor Jackson AU (RC) 12.50 30.00
Mike Jacobs AU (RC)
91 Ken Griffey Jr. AU
92 Derek Jeter AU
93 Albert Pujols AU
94 Roger Clemens AU
95 Jim Thome AU
96 Howie Kendrick AU (RC)
97 Francisco Liriano AU (RC)
98 Jered Weaver AU (RC)
99 Justin Verlander AU (RC)
100 Stephen Drew AU (RC)

2006 Exquisite Collection Gold

*GOLD 1-90: .5X TO 1.2X BASIC
ISSUED AS EXCH CARDS IN VARIOUS
2006 UPPER DECK PRODUCTS
1-90 PRINT RUN 30 SER.#'d SETS
91-100 PRINT RUN 5 SER.#'d SETS
NO PRICING ON 91-100 DUE TO SCARCITY

2006 Exquisite Collection Platinum

ISSUED AS EXCH CARDS IN VARIOUS
2006 UPPER DECK PRODUCTS
STATED PRINT RUN 1 SER.#'d SET
NO PRICING DUE TO SCARCITY

2006 Exquisite Collection Cuts

ISSUED AS EXCH CARDS IN VARIOUS
2006 UPPER DECK PRODUCTS
PRINT RUNS B/WN 25-65 COPIES PER
AC Al Campanis/65 40.00 80.00
BD Bill Dickey/65 75.00 150.00
BG Burleigh Grimes/65 60.00 120.00
BH Billy Herman/65 50.00 100.00
CG Charlie Gehringer/65 50.00 100.00
CH Carl Hubbell/65 60.00 120.00
DC Dolph Camilli/65 50.00 100.00
DD Dizzy Dean/30
EA Earl Averill/65 50.00 100.00
EM Eddie Mathews/65 75.00 150.00
ER Edd Roush/65 50.00 100.00
GE George Selkirk/65 75.00 150.00
GH Gabby Hartnett/25
GS George Sisler/65 200.00 250.00
HG Hank Greenberg/65 125.00 250.00
JC Joe Cronin/65 50.00 100.00
JD Joe DiMaggio/25
JM Johnny Mize/65 50.00 100.00
LA Luke Appling/65 50.00 100.00
LB Lou Boudreau/65 50.00 100.00
LG Lefty Gomez/65 60.00 120.00
MC Max Carey/65 60.00 120.00
PW Pee Wee Reese/65
RR Red Ruffing/52
RS Ray Schalk/30
SC Stan Coveleski/65 50.00 100.00
VW Vic Wertz/65 50.00 100.00
WG Warren Giles/65 60.00 120.00
WH Waite Hoyt/65 50.00 100.00
WS Warren Spahn/65 60.00 120.00

2006 Exquisite Collection Cuts Dual

ISSUED AS EXCH CARDS IN VARIOUS
2006 UPPER DECK PRODUCTS
STATED PRINT RUN 5 SER.#'d SETS
NO PRICING DUE TO SCARCITY
1 Lou Gehrig
Babe Ruth
2 Joe DiMaggio
Mel Ott
3 Joe DiMaggio
Lou Gehrig
4 Gil Hodges
Pee Wee Reese
5 Honus Wagner
Roberto Clemente
6 Cy Young
Ted Williams

2006 Exquisite Collection Endorsed Emblems

ISSUED AS EXCH CARDS IN VARIOUS
2006 UPPER DECK PRODUCTS
STATED PRINT RUN 25 SER.#'d SETS

AB A.J. Burnett
AD Adam Dunn 20.00 50.00
AJ Andruw Jones 30.00 60.00
AR Alex Rios 30.00 60.00
BJ B.J. Upton 20.00 50.00
BR Brian Roberts 30.00 60.00
BS Ben Sheets 30.00 60.00
CB Craig Biggio 60.00 120.00
CC Chris Carpenter
CL Carlos Lee
CU Chase Utley 30.00 60.00
CZ Carlos Zambrano
DJ Derek Jeter
DL Derrek Lee 50.00 100.00
DO David Ortiz
FH Felix Hernandez
FL Francisco Liriano 50.00 100.00
HR Hanley Ramirez
HS Huston Street 20.00 50.00
JB Jason Bay
JM Joe Mauer 50.00 100.00
JO Jonathan Papelbon 100.00 150.00
JP Jake Peavy 50.00 100.00
JR Jose Reyes
JS Jeremy Sowers 20.00 50.00
JT Jim Thome 60.00 120.00
JU Justin Morneau 30.00 60.00
JU2 Justin Morneau 30.00 60.00
JV Justin Verlander 50.00 100.00
JW Jered Weaver 30.00 60.00
KG Ken Griffey Jr. 125.00 250.00
KG2 Ken Griffey Jr. 125.00 250.00
KG3 Ken Griffey Jr. 125.00 250.00
KH Khalil Greene 30.00 60.00
MC Miguel Cabrera 100.00 150.00
MG Marcus Giles 20.00 50.00
MH Matt Holliday 30.00 60.00
MI Miguel Tejada
MT Mark Teixeira 20.00 50.00
MY Michael Young 20.00 50.00
NS Nick Swisher 30.00 60.00
RO Roy Oswalt
RW Rickie Weeks 30.00 60.00
SD Stephen Drew 60.00 120.00
SK Scott Kazmir
SM John Smoltz 100.00 150.00
TH Travis Hafner 50.00 100.00
TI Tadahito Iguchi
TR Trevor Hoffman 50.00 100.00
VM Victor Martinez

2006 Exquisite Collection Endorsements

ISSUED AS EXCH CARDS IN VARIOUS
2006 UPPER DECK PRODUCTS
STATED PRINT RUN 40 SER.#'d SETS

AP Albert Pujols
AS Alay Soler 15.00 40.00
BF Bob Feller 20.00 50.00
BJ B.J. Upton 20.00 50.00
BR Brooks Robinson 30.00 60.00
CC Chris Carpenter 30.00 60.00
CF Carlton Fisk 30.00 60.00
CH Cole Hamels 30.00 60.00
CJ Chipper Jones 60.00 120.00
CR Cal Ripken Jr. 75.00 150.00
DJ Derek Jeter
DO David Ortiz 40.00 80.00
DW Dontrelle Willis 20.00 50.00
FH Felix Hernandez 50.00 100.00
FL Francisco Liriano 15.00 40.00
FR Frank Robinson 30.00 60.00
GP Gaylord Perry 15.00 40.00
HA Craig Hansen
HK Howie Kendrick 30.00 60.00
JB Johnny Bench 30.00 60.00
JD Johnny Damon
JM Joe Mauer 30.00 60.00
JO Jonathan Papelbon 30.00 60.00
JP Jake Peavy 30.00 60.00
JR Jose Reyes 60.00 120.00
JS Jeremy Sowers 20.00 50.00
JT Jim Thome
JV Justin Verlander 30.00 60.00
JW Jered Weaver 20.00 50.00
KG Ken Griffey Jr. 90.00 150.00
KG2 Ken Griffey Jr. 90.00 150.00
MC Miguel Cabrera 30.00 60.00
MS Mike Schmidt
MT Mark Teixeira 20.00 50.00
NR Nolan Ryan 100.00 200.00
PM Paul Molitor 15.00 40.00
RC Roger Clemens 60.00 120.00
RJ Reggie Jackson 40.00 80.00
RO Roy Oswalt 30.00 60.00
RS Ryne Sandberg 40.00 80.00
RZ Ryan Zimmerman 30.00 60.00
SD Stephen Drew 30.00 60.00
SK Scott Kazmir 15.00 40.00
SM Stan Musial 40.00 80.00
TG Tony Gwynn
TH Travis Hafner 30.00 60.00
TI Tadahito Iguchi 30.00 60.00
VG Vladimir Guerrero 40.00 80.00
VM Victor Martinez 15.00 40.00
WC Will Clark 15.00 40.00

2006 Exquisite Collection Ensemble Dual Patches

ISSUED AS EXCH CARDS IN VARIOUS
2006 UPPER DECK PRODUCTS
STATED PRINT RUN 25 SER.#'d SETS
NO PRICING DUE TO SCARCITY

2006 Exquisite Collection Ensemble Endorsements Dual

ISSUED AS EXCH CARDS IN VARIOUS
2006 UPPER DECK PRODUCTS
STATED PRINT RUN 20 SER.#'d SETS
NO PRICING DUE TO SCARCITY

2006 Exquisite Collection Ensemble Endorsements Triple

ISSUED AS EXCH CARDS IN VARIOUS
2006 UPPER DECK PRODUCTS
STATED PRINT RUN 15 SER.#'d SETS
NO PRICING DUE TO SCARCITY

2006 Exquisite Collection Ensemble Endorsements Quad

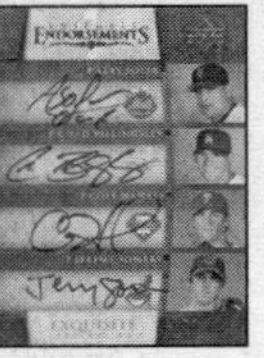

ISSUED AS EXCH CARDS IN VARIOUS
2006 UPPER DECK PRODUCTS
STATED PRINT RUN 10 SER.#'d SETS
NO PRICING DUE TO SCARCITY

2006 Exquisite Collection Ensemble Triple Patches

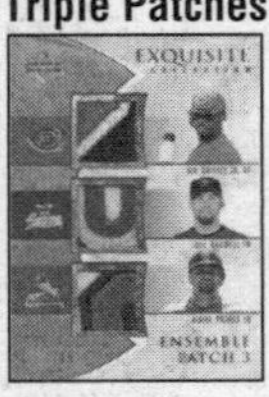

ISSUED AS EXCH CARDS IN VARIOUS
2006 UPPER DECK PRODUCTS
STATED PRINT RUN 15 SER.#'d SETS
NO PRICING DUE TO SCARCITY

2006 Exquisite Collection Ensemble Quad Patches

ISSUED AS EXCH CARDS IN VARIOUS
2006 UPPER DECK PRODUCTS
STATED PRINT RUN 10 SER.#'d SETS
NO PRICING DUE TO SCARCITY

2006 Exquisite Collection Legends Memorabilia

ISSUED AS EXCH CARDS IN VARIOUS
2006 UPPER DECK PRODUCTS
STATED PRINT RUN 15 SER.#'d SETS
PLAT.ISSUED AS EXCH CARDS IN VARIOUS
2006 UPPER DECK PRODUCTS
PLATINUM PRINT RUN 1 SER.#'d SET
NO PLATINUM PRICING DUE TO SCARCITY

AK Al Kaline 20.00 50.00
BD Bill Dickey 40.00 80.00
BD2 Bill Dickey 40.00 80.00
BM Bill Mazeroski 30.00 60.00
BM2 Bill Mazeroski 30.00 60.00
BR Babe Ruth 900.00 1200.00
BR2 Babe Ruth 900.00 1200.00
CF Carlton Fisk 20.00 50.00
CR Cal Ripken Jr. 30.00 60.00
CR2 Cal Ripken Jr. 30.00 60.00
CR3 Cal Ripken Jr. 30.00 60.00
DM Don Mattingly 60.00 120.00
FR Frank Robinson 20.00 50.00
JB Johnny Bench 20.00 50.00
JB2 Johnny Bench 20.00 50.00
JC Joe Cronin 20.00 50.00
JD Joe DiMaggio 150.00 250.00
JD2 Joe DiMaggio 150.00 250.00
JF Jimmie Foxx 200.00 300.00
JM Joe Morgan 20.00 50.00
LG Lou Gehrig 300.00 500.00
LG2 Lou Gehrig 300.00 500.00
MO Mel Ott 100.00 175.00
MS Mike Schmidt 20.00 50.00
NR Nolan Ryan 75.00 150.00
NR2 Nolan Ryan 75.00 150.00
OC Orlando Cepeda 20.00 50.00
RC Roberto Clemente 250.00 300.00
RC2 Roberto Clemente 250.00 300.00
RH Rogers Hornsby 75.00 150.00
RH2 Rogers Hornsby 75.00 150.00
RJ Reggie Jackson 40.00 80.00
RJ2 Reggie Jackson 40.00 80.00
RO Brooks Robinson 20.00 50.00
RS Ryne Sandberg 40.00 80.00
SM Stan Musial 40.00 80.00
TG Tony Gwynn 30.00 60.00
TG2 Tony Gwynn 30.00 60.00
TM Thurman Munson 75.00 150.00
TM2 Thurman Munson 75.00 150.00
TW Ted Williams 150.00 250.00
WB Wade Boggs 40.00 80.00

2006 Exquisite Collection Material Cuts

ISSUED AS EXCH CARDS IN VARIOUS
2006 UPPER DECK PRODUCTS
STATED PRINT RUN 2 SER.#'d SETS
NO PRICING DUE TO SCARCITY

2006 Exquisite Collection Maximum Patch

ISSUED AS EXCH CARDS IN VARIOUS
2006 UPPER DECK PRODUCTS
STATED PRINT RUN 25 SER.#'d SETS
PRICING FOR NON-LOGO PATCHES

AD Adam Dunn 40.00 80.00
AP Albert Pujols 150.00 250.00
AS Alfonso Soriano 40.00 80.00
CA Carl Crawford 40.00 80.00
CB Carlos Beltran 50.00 100.00
CC Chris Carpenter 75.00 150.00
CD Carlos Delgado 40.00 80.00
CJ Chipper Jones 75.00 150.00
CR Craig Biggio 50.00 100.00
CS Curt Schilling 40.00 80.00
CU Chase Utley
CZ Carlos Zambrano
DJ Derek Jeter 300.00 400.00
DL Derrek Lee
DO David Ortiz 60.00 120.00
FH Felix Hernandez 75.00 150.00
FL Francisco Liriano 40.00 80.00
FT Frank Thomas 75.00 150.00
JF Jeff Francoeur
JG Jason Giambi 100.00 200.00
JM Justin Morneau
JO Jonathan Papelbon 40.00 80.00
JP Jake Peavy 40.00 80.00
JR Jose Reyes
JS Johan Santana
JT Jim Thome 40.00 80.00
JV Justin Verlander 40.00 80.00
JW Jered Weaver 40.00 80.00
KG Ken Griffey Jr. 90.00 150.00
MC Miguel Cabrera 40.00 80.00
MI Miguel Tejada 40.00 80.00
MT Mark Teixeira 40.00 80.00
MY Michael Young
PF Prince Fielder 40.00 80.00
PM Pedro Martinez 50.00 100.00
RH Ryan Howard
TG Troy Glaus 40.00 80.00
TH Todd Helton 40.00 80.00
TO Tom Glavine
TR Travis Hafner
VG Vladimir Guerrero 40.00 80.00
VM Victor Martinez 40.00 80.00

2006 Exquisite Collection Memorabilia

ISSUED AS EXCH CARDS IN VARIOUS
2006 UPPER DECK PRODUCTS
STATED PRINT RUN 45 SER.#'d SETS
MEM.1 ISSUED AS EXCH CARD IN VARIOUS
2006 UPPER DECK PRODUCTS
MEM.1 PRINT RUN 1 SER.#'d SET
NO MEM.1 PRICING DUE TO SCARCITY
*GOLD: .5X TO 1.2X BASIC
GOLD ISSUED AS EXCH CARD IN VARIOUS
2006 UPPER DECK PRODUCTS
GOLD PRINT RUN 25 SER.#'d SETS
PLAT.ISSUED AS EXCH CARD IN VARIOUS
2006 UPPER DECK PRODUCTS
PLAT.PRINT RUN 15 SER.#'d SETS
NO PLAT.PRICING DUE TO SCARCITY

AD Adam Dunn 6.00 15.00
AD2 Adam Dunn 6.00 15.00
AJ Andruw Jones 10.00 25.00
AJ2 Andruw Jones 10.00 25.00
AP Albert Pujols 20.00 50.00
AP2 Albert Pujols 20.00 50.00
AR Alex Rodriguez 20.00 50.00
AS Alfonso Soriano 6.00 15.00
AS2 Alfonso Soriano 6.00 15.00
BR Babe Ruth 350.00 450.00
BR2 Babe Ruth 350.00 450.00
BZ Barry Zito 10.00 25.00
BZ2 Barry Zito 10.00 25.00
CB Carlos Beltran 10.00 25.00
CB2 Carlos Beltran 10.00 25.00
CF Carlton Fisk 10.00 25.00
CF2 Carlton Fisk 10.00 25.00
CJ Chipper Jones 15.00 40.00
CJ2 Chipper Jones 15.00 40.00
CR Cal Ripken Jr. 20.00 50.00
CR2 Cal Ripken Jr. 20.00 50.00
CR3 Cal Ripken Jr. 20.00 50.00
CS Curt Schilling 6.00 15.00
CU Chase Utley 15.00 40.00
CU2 Chase Utley 15.00 40.00
CY Carl Yastrzemski 10.00 25.00
CY2 Carl Yastrzemski 10.00 25.00
DA Daisuke Matsuzaka 150.00 250.00
DJ Derek Jeter 30.00 60.00
DJ2 Derek Jeter 30.00 60.00
DL Derrek Lee 10.00 25.00
DM Don Mattingly 20.00 50.00
DO David Ortiz 10.00 25.00
DO2 David Ortiz 10.00 25.00
FL Francisco Liriano 10.00 25.00
FL2 Francisco Liriano 10.00 25.00
GM Greg Maddux 10.00 25.00
GM2 Greg Maddux 10.00 25.00
HO Ryan Howard 10.00 25.00
HO2 Ryan Howard 10.00 25.00
IS Ichiro Suzuki 200.00 250.00
JA Jason Bay 6.00 15.00
JA2 Jason Bay 6.00 15.00
JB Jeff Bagwell 10.00 25.00
JB2 Jeff Bagwell 10.00 25.00
JD Joe DiMaggio 125.00 200.00
JM Joe Mauer 10.00 25.00
JP Jake Peavy 6.00 15.00
JP2 Jake Peavy 6.00 15.00
JS Johan Santana 10.00 25.00
JS2 Johan Santana 10.00 25.00
JT Jim Thome 10.00 25.00
JT2 Jim Thome 10.00 25.00
JV Justin Verlander 15.00 40.00
JV2 Justin Verlander 15.00 40.00
JW Jered Weaver 6.00 15.00
JW2 Jered Weaver 6.00 15.00
KG Ken Griffey Jr. 15.00 40.00
KG2 Ken Griffey Jr. 15.00 40.00
KG3 Ken Griffey Jr. 15.00 40.00
KJ Kenji Johjima 15.00 40.00
KJ2 Kenji Johjima 15.00 40.00
MA Manny Ramirez 10.00 25.00
MA2 Manny Ramirez 10.00 25.00
MA3 Manny Ramirez 10.00 25.00
MC Miguel Cabrera 10.00 25.00
MC2 Miguel Cabrera 10.00 25.00
MI Miguel Tejada 6.00 15.00
MI2 Miguel Tejada 6.00 15.00
MR Mariano Rivera 15.00 40.00
MR2 Mariano Rivera 15.00 40.00
MS Mike Schmidt 10.00 25.00
MS2 Mike Schmidt 10.00 25.00
MT Mark Teixeira 6.00 15.00
NR Nolan Ryan 20.00 50.00
NR2 Nolan Ryan 20.00 50.00
PE Pedro Martinez 15.00 40.00
PF Prince Fielder 10.00 25.00
PF2 Prince Fielder 10.00 25.00
PM Paul Molitor 6.00 15.00
PM2 Paul Molitor 6.00 15.00
RC Roger Clemens 15.00 40.00
RC2 Roger Clemens 15.00 40.00
RC3 Roger Clemens 15.00 40.00
RE Reggie Jackson 15.00 40.00
RE2 Reggie Jackson 15.00 40.00
RH Roy Halladay 6.00 15.00
RH2 Roy Halladay 6.00 15.00
RJ Randy Johnson 10.00 25.00
RO Roy Oswalt 6.00 15.00
RO2 Roy Oswalt 6.00 15.00
RY Robin Yount 15.00 40.00
RY2 Robin Yount 15.00 40.00
SM Stan Musial 20.00 50.00
SM2 Stan Musial 20.00 50.00
TG Tony Gwynn 20.00 50.00
TH Travis Hafner 6.00 15.00
VG Vladimir Guerrero 10.00 25.00
VG2 Vladimir Guerrero 10.00 25.00
WB Wade Boggs 10.00 25.00

2006 Exquisite Collection Patch

ISSUED AS EXCH CARDS IN VARIOUS
2006 UPPER DECK PRODUCTS
STATED PRINT RUN 25 SER.#'d SETS
NO PRICING ON MOST DUE TO SCARCITY
PATCH 1 ISSUED AS EXCH IN VARIOUS
2006 UPPER DECK PRODUCTS
PATCH 1 PRINT RUN 1 SER.#'d SET
NO PATCH 1 PRICING DUE TO SCARCITY
*PATCH 10: .5X TO 1.2X BASIC
PATCH 10 ISSUED AS EXCH IN VARIOUS
2006 UPPER DECK PRODUCTS
PATCH 10 PRINT RUN 10 SER.#'d SETS
PRICING IS FOR NON-LOGO PATCHES

AD Adam Dunn 15.00 40.00
AD2 Adam Dunn 15.00 40.00
AJ Andruw Jones 20.00 50.00
AJ2 Andruw Jones 20.00 50.00
AP Albert Pujols 75.00 150.00
AP2 Albert Pujols 75.00 150.00
AR Alex Rodriguez
AS Alfonso Soriano 30.00 60.00
AS2 Alfonso Soriano 30.00 60.00
BR Babe Ruth
BR2 Babe Ruth
BZ Barry Zito 15.00 40.00
BZ2 Barry Zito 15.00 40.00
CB Carlos Beltran 30.00 60.00
CB2 Carlos Beltran 30.00 60.00
CF Carlton Fisk 20.00 50.00
CF2 Carlton Fisk 20.00 50.00
CJ Chipper Jones 50.00 100.00
CJ2 Chipper Jones 50.00 100.00
CR Cal Ripken Jr. 75.00 150.00
CR2 Cal Ripken Jr. 75.00 150.00
CR3 Cal Ripken Jr. 75.00 150.00
CS Curt Schilling 20.00 50.00
CU Chase Utley 30.00 60.00
CU2 Chase Utley 30.00 60.00
CY Carl Yastrzemski
CY2 Carl Yastrzemski
DA Daisuke Matsuzaka
DJ Derek Jeter 100.00 200.00
DJ2 Derek Jeter 100.00 200.00
DL Derrek Lee 20.00 50.00
DM Don Mattingly 60.00 120.00
DO David Ortiz 30.00 60.00
DO2 David Ortiz 30.00 60.00
FL Francisco Liriano 20.00 50.00
FL2 Francisco Liriano 20.00 50.00
GM Greg Maddux 40.00 80.00
GM2 Greg Maddux 40.00 80.00
HO Ryan Howard 50.00 100.00
HO2 Ryan Howard 50.00 100.00
IS Ichiro Suzuki
JA Jason Bay 20.00 50.00
JA2 Jason Bay 20.00 50.00
JB Jeff Bagwell
JB2 Jeff Bagwell
JD Joe DiMaggio
JM Joe Mauer 40.00 80.00
JP Jake Peavy 30.00 60.00
JP2 Jake Peavy 30.00 60.00
JS Johan Santana 30.00 60.00
JS2 Johan Santana 30.00 60.00
JT Jim Thome 20.00 50.00
JT2 Jim Thome 20.00 50.00
JV Justin Verlander 20.00 50.00
JV2 Justin Verlander 20.00 50.00
JW Jered Weaver 30.00 60.00
JW2 Jered Weaver 30.00 60.00
KG Ken Griffey Jr. 75.00 150.00
KG2 Ken Griffey Jr. 75.00 150.00
KG3 Ken Griffey Jr. 75.00 150.00
KJ Kenji Johjima 30.00 60.00
KJ2 Kenji Johjima 30.00 60.00
MA Manny Ramirez 30.00 60.00
MA2 Manny Ramirez 30.00 60.00
MA3 Manny Ramirez 30.00 60.00
MC Miguel Cabrera 30.00 60.00
MC2 Miguel Cabrera 30.00 60.00
MI Miguel Tejada 20.00 50.00
MI2 Miguel Tejada 20.00 50.00
MR Mariano Rivera 40.00 80.00
MR2 Mariano Rivera 40.00 80.00
MS Mike Schmidt 20.00 50.00
MS2 Mike Schmidt 20.00 50.00
MT Mark Teixeira 20.00 50.00
NR Nolan Ryan 60.00 120.00
NR2 Nolan Ryan 60.00 120.00
PE Pedro Martinez 20.00 50.00
PF Prince Fielder 30.00 60.00
PF2 Prince Fielder 30.00 60.00
PM Paul Molitor
PM2 Paul Molitor
RC Roger Clemens 40.00 80.00
RC2 Roger Clemens 40.00 80.00
RC3 Roger Clemens 40.00 80.00
RE Reggie Jackson 20.00 50.00
RE2 Reggie Jackson 20.00 50.00
RH Roy Halladay 30.00 60.00
RH2 Roy Halladay 30.00 60.00
RJ Randy Johnson 20.00 50.00
RO Roy Oswalt 20.00 50.00
RO2 Roy Oswalt 20.00 50.00
RY Robin Yount 40.00 80.00
RY2 Robin Yount 40.00 80.00
SM Stan Musial
SM2 Stan Musial
TG Tony Gwynn 50.00 100.00
TH Travis Hafner 20.00 50.00
VG Vladimir Guerrero 30.00 60.00
VG2 Vladimir Guerrero 30.00 60.00
WB Wade Boggs 20.00 50.00

2006 Exquisite Collection Signature Patch

ISSUED AS EXCH CARDS IN VARIOUS
2006 UPPER DECK PRODUCTS
STATED PRINT RUN 30 SER.#'d SETS
NO PRICING ON MANY DUE TO SCARCITY

AB A.J. Burnett
AD Adam Dunn 20.00 50.00
AJ Andruw Jones 40.00 80.00
AR Alex Rios 30.00 60.00
BJ B.J. Upton 30.00 60.00
BR Brian Roberts 20.00 50.00
BS Ben Sheets
CB Craig Biggio 60.00 120.00
CC Chris Carpenter 40.00 80.00
CL Carlos Lee 20.00 50.00
CU Chase Utley 50.00 100.00
CZ Carlos Zambrano 20.00 50.00
DJ Derek Jeter 275.00 350.00
DL Derrek Lee 60.00 120.00
DO David Ortiz
FH Felix Hernandez 100.00 200.00
FL Francisco Liriano
HR Hanley Ramirez
HS Huston Street
JB Jason Bay
JM Joe Mauer
JO Jonathan Papelbon
JP Jake Peavy 30.00 60.00
JR Jose Reyes 100.00 200.00
JS Jeremy Sowers 30.00 60.00
JT Jim Thome
JU Justin Morneau 40.00 80.00
JU2 Justin Morneau 40.00 80.00
JV Justin Verlander
JW Jered Weaver 30.00 60.00
KG Ken Griffey Jr.
KG2 Ken Griffey Jr.
KG3 Ken Griffey Jr.
KH Khalil Greene 60.00 120.00
MC Miguel Cabrera 40.00 80.00
MG Marcus Giles 30.00 60.00
MH Matt Holliday 50.00 100.00
MI Miguel Tejada
MT Mark Teixeira 20.00 50.00
MY Michael Young 20.00 50.00
NS Nick Swisher 30.00 60.00
RO Roy Oswalt 20.00 50.00
RW Rickie Weeks 30.00 60.00
SD Stephen Drew 40.00 80.00
SK Scott Kazmir 40.00 80.00
SM John Smoltz
TH Travis Hafner 60.00 120.00
TI Tadahito Iguchi 30.00 60.00
TR Trevor Hoffman
VM Victor Martinez 30.00 60.00

2006 Exquisite Collection Signature Patch Dual

ISSUED AS EXCH CARDS IN VARIOUS
2006 UPPER DECK PRODUCTS
STATED PRINT RUN 1 SER.#'d SET
NO PRICING DUE TO SCARCITY

2006 Exquisite Collection Signature Patch Triple

ISSUED AS EXCH CARDS IN VARIOUS
2006 UPPER DECK PRODUCTS
STATED PRINT RUN 1 SER.#'d SET
NO PRICING DUE TO SCARCITY

2007 Exquisite Collection Rookie Signatures

This 191-card set was released in January, 2008. The set was issued in six-card packs (which were actually small boxes which came five boxes to a case. The first 100 cards in this set feature veterans while cards 101-191 feature signed 2007 rookies. A few of the cards in that range also have game-used relic pieces as a part of the card. All the cards from 101-191 were issued to stated print runs between 125 and 235 serial numbered copies. The specific print run for each card in notated in our checklist. In addition, a few players did not return their signatures in time for pack out and those cards could be redeemed until December 28, 2009.

COMMON CARD (1-100) 1.50 4.00
ONE BASE CARD PER PACK
1-100 PRINT RUN 99 SER.#'d SETS
COMMON AU RC (101-191) 4.00 10.00
OVERALL FIVE AUTOS PER PACK
AU RC SER.#'d B/WN 150-235 PER
COMMON JSY AU RC (101-191) 6.00 15.00
OVERALL FIVE AUTOS PER PACK
JSY AU RC SER.#'d B/WN 125-199 PER
EXCHANGE DEADLINE 12/28/2009

1 Ichiro Suzuki 6.00 15.00
2 Alex Rodriguez 6.00 15.00
3 David Wright 6.00 15.00
4 Ryan Howard 6.00 15.00
5 Ken Griffey Jr. 6.00 15.00
6 Derek Jeter 8.00 20.00
7 Vladimir Guerrero 4.00 10.00
8 Roger Clemens 5.00 12.00
9 Greg Maddux 6.00 15.00
10 Johan Santana 2.50 6.00
11 Nomar Garciaparra 4.00 10.00
12 Carlos Beltran 1.50 4.00
13 Carlos Delgado 1.50 4.00
14 Manny Ramirez 2.50 6.00
15 John Lackey 1.50 4.00
16 David Ortiz 4.00 10.00
17 Curt Schilling 2.50 6.00
18 Cal Ripken Jr. 12.00 30.00
19 Albert Pujols 6.00 15.00
20 Frank Thomas 4.00 10.00
21 Chris Carpenter 1.50 4.00
22 Prince Fielder 4.00 10.00
23 Justin Morneau 1.50 4.00
24 Joe Mauer 2.50 6.00
25 Torii Hunter 1.50 4.00
26 Jake Peavy 1.50 4.00
27 Roy Oswalt 1.50 4.00
28 Craig Biggio 2.50 6.00
29 Lance Berkman 1.50 4.00
30 Carlos Zambrano 1.50 4.00
31 Derrek Lee 1.50 4.00
32 Aramis Ramirez 1.50 4.00
33 Noah Lowry 1.50 4.00
34 Magglio Ordonez 1.50 4.00
35 Ivan Rodriguez 2.50 6.00
36 Johnny Damon 2.50 6.00
37 Justin Verlander 4.00 10.00
38 John Smoltz 2.50 6.00
39 Chipper Jones 4.00 10.00
40 Jeff Francoeur 4.00 10.00
41 Hanley Ramirez 2.50 6.00
42 Miguel Cabrera 2.50 6.00
43 Josh Beckett 2.50 6.00
44 Cole Hamels 4.00 10.00
45 Chase Utley 4.00 10.00
46 Grady Sizemore 2.50 6.00
47 Travis Hafner 1.50 4.00
48 Victor Martinez 1.50 4.00
49 Russell Martin 1.50 4.00
50 Jason Varitek 4.00 10.00
51 Hideki Matsui 4.00 10.00
52 Carl Crawford 1.50 4.00
53 Scott Kazmir 2.50 6.00
54 Miguel Tejada 1.50 4.00
55 Erik Bedard 1.50 4.00
56 Carlos Lee 1.50 4.00
57 Sammy Sosa 4.00 10.00
58 Mark Teixeira 2.50 6.00
59 Michael Young 1.50 4.00
60 Jim Thome 2.50 6.00
61 Paul Konerko 1.50 4.00
62 Jermaine Dye 1.50 4.00
63 Mark Teahen 1.50 4.00
64 Felix Hernandez 2.50 6.00
65 Andruw Jones 2.50 6.00
66 Pedro Martinez 2.50 6.00
67 Randy Johnson 4.00 10.00
68 Ryan Zimmerman 4.00 10.00
69 Matt Holliday 4.00 10.00
70 Todd Helton 2.50 6.00
71 Brian Bannister 1.50 4.00
72 Jeremy Bonderman 1.50 4.00
73 Adam Dunn 1.50 4.00
74 Aaron Harang 1.50 4.00
75 Jason Bay 1.50 4.00
76 Adam LaRoche 1.50 4.00
77 Freddy Sanchez 1.50 4.00
78 Dan Uggla 2.50 6.00
79 Joe Nathan 1.50 4.00
80 Brad Penny 1.50 4.00
81 Takashi Saito 1.50 4.00
82 Jimmy Rollins 1.50 4.00
83 Jose Reyes 4.00 10.00
84 Jered Weaver 2.50 6.00
85 Chien-Ming Wang 6.00 15.00
86 Jonathan Papelbon 4.00 10.00
87 Mariano Rivera 4.00 10.00
88 Eric Byrnes 1.50 4.00
89 Nick Markakis 2.50 6.00
90 Brian Roberts 1.50 4.00
91 Omar Vizquel 2.50 6.00
92 Vernon Wells 1.50 4.00
93 Dan Haren 1.50 4.00
94 Ben Sheets 1.50 4.00
95 B.J. Upton 1.50 4.00
96 Adrian Gonzalez 1.50 4.00
97 J.J. Hardy 1.50 4.00
98 Mike Piazza 4.00 10.00
99 Roy Halladay 1.50 4.00
100 Alfonso Soriano 1.50 4.00
101 Sean Henn AU/235 (RC) 4.00 10.00
102 Sean White AU/235 RC 4.00 10.00
103 Mike Schultz AU/234 RC 4.00 10.00
104 Michael Bourn AU/234 (RC) 4.00 10.00
105 Matt Chico AU/235 (RC) 4.00 10.00
106 Matt Lindstrom AU/235 (RC) 4.00 10.00
107 Connor Robertson AU/235 RC 4.00 10.00
108 Jay Marshall AU/235 RC 4.00 10.00
109 Jared Burton AU/235 RC 4.00 10.00
110 Juan Perez AU/235 RC 4.00 10.00
111 Scott Moore AU/235 (RC) 4.00 10.00
112 Brad Salmon AU/235 RC 4.00 10.00
113 Danny Putnam AU/235 (RC) 4.00 10.00
114 Kelvin Jimenez AU/235 RC 4.00 10.00
115 Dennis Dove AU/235 (RC) 4.00 10.00
116 Yoel Hernandez AU/234 RC 4.00 10.00
117 Devern Hansack AU/235 RC 4.00 10.00
118 Mike Rabelo AU/235 RC 4.00 10.00
119 Miguel Montero AU/235 (RC) 4.00 10.00
120 Kevin Cameron AU/235 RC 4.00 10.00
121 Joseph Bisenius AU/235 RC 4.00 10.00
122 Ryan Z. Braun AU/234 RC 4.00 10.00
123 Levale Speigner AU/235 RC 4.00 10.00
124 Lee Gardner AU/235 (RC) 4.00 10.00
125 Ryan Rowland-Smith AU/234 RC 4.00 10.00
126 Zack Segovia AU/235 (RC) 4.00 10.00
127 Rick Vanden Hurk AU/235 RC 4.00 10.00
128 Dallas Braden AU/235 RC 4.00 10.00
129 Rocky Cherry AU/234 RC 4.00 10.00
130 Andy Gonzalez AU/235 RC 4.00 10.00
131 Neal Musser AU/235 RC 4.00 10.00
132 Garrett Jones AU/235 (RC) 4.00 10.00
133 Ben Francisco AU/235 (RC) 4.00 10.00
134 Jon Coutlangus AU/235 (RC) 4.00 10.00
135 A.J. Murray AU/235 RC 4.00 10.00
136 Brett Carroll AU/235 RC 4.00 10.00
137 John Danks AU/235 RC 4.00 10.00
138 Kyle Kendrick AU/235 RC 6.00 15.00
139 Joaquin Arias AU/235 (RC) 4.00 10.00
140 Matt Brown AU/235 RC 4.00 10.00
141 Kurt Suzuki AU/150 (RC) 10.00 25.00
142 Curtis Thigpen AU/150 (RC) 4.00 10.00
143 Jerry Owens AU/150 (RC) 4.00 10.00
144 Billy Butler AU/150 (RC) 15.00 40.00
145 Kei Igawa AU/150 RC 15.00 40.00
146 Mike Fontenot AU/150 (RC) 6.00 15.00
147 Brandon Wood AU/150 (RC) 10.00 25.00
148 Alexi Casilla AU/150 RC 4.00 10.00
149 Jeff Baker AU/150 (RC) 4.00 10.00
150 Brian Barden AU/150 RC 4.00 10.00
151 Chris Stewart AU/150 RC 4.00 10.00
152 Jon Knott AU/150 (RC) 4.00 10.00
153 Chase Wright AU/150 RC 6.00 15.00
154 Chase Headley AU/150 (RC) 10.00 25.00
155 Jesse Litsch Jsy AU/199 RC 6.00 15.00
156 Tyler Clippard AU/150 (RC) 6.00 15.00
157 Matt DeSalvo AU/150 (RC) 4.00 10.00
158 Kory Casto AU/150 (RC) 4.00 10.00
159 Jarrod Saltalamacchia Jsy AU/199 (RC) 8.00 20.00
160 Glen Perkins AU/150 (RC) 4.00 10.00
161 Ryan Braun Jsy AU/199 RC 40.00 80.00
162 Justin Upton Jsy AU/199 RC 50.00 100.00
163 Tim Lincecum Jsy AU/199 RC 75.00 150.00
164 Fred Lewis AU/150 (RC) 6.00 15.00
165 Alex Gordon Jsy AU/199 RC 30.00 60.00
166 Akinori Iwamura Jsy AU/199 RC 10.00 25.00
167 Delmon Young Jsy AU/199 (RC) 12.50 30.00
168 Troy Tulowitzki Jsy AU/199 (RC) 50.00 100.00
169 Daisuke Matsuzaka Jsy AU/199 RC 250.00 350.00
170 Josh Hamilton Jsy AU/199 (RC) 50.00 100.00
171 Kevin Kouzmanoff Jsy AU/199 (RC) 6.00 15.00
172 Hunter Pence Jsy AU/199 (RC) 40.00 80.00
173 Felix Pie Jsy AU/199 (RC) 6.00 15.00
174 Andrew Miller Jsy AU/199 RC 15.00 40.00
175 Yovani Gallardo Jsy AU/199 (RC) 15.00 40.00
176 Ryan Sweeney Jsy AU/199 (RC) 6.00 15.00
177 Josh Fields Jsy AU/199 (RC) 8.00 20.00
178 Mark Reynolds Jsy AU/199 RC 30.00 60.00
180 Homer Bailey AU/150 (RC) 10.00 25.00
182 Joba Chamberlain AU/150 RC 125.00 250.00
184 Travis Metcalf AU/125 RC 8.00 20.00
185 Kevin Slowey Jsy AU/199 (RC) 12.50 30.00
186 Phil Hughes AU/150 (RC) 30.00 60.00
187 Micah Owings AU/150 (RC) 10.00 25.00
188 Joe Smith AU/150 RC 4.00 10.00
189 Joakim Soria Jsy AU/199 RC 10.00 25.00
190 Adam Lind Jsy AU/199 (RC) 6.00 15.00
191 Andy LaRoche Jsy AU/199 (RC) 8.00 20.00
192 Brandon Morrow Jsy AU/175 RC 10.00 25.00
193 Carlos Gomez Jsy AU/125 RC 15.00 40.00
194 Yunel Escobar AU/150 (RC) 12.50 30.00

2007 Exquisite Collection Rookie Signatures Gold

*1-100 GOLD: .6X TO 1.5X BASIC
ONE BASE OR BASE PARALLEL PER PACK
1-100 PRINT RUN 75 SER.#'d SETS
*101-191 AU GOLD: .6X TO 1.5X BASIC
OVERALL FIVE AUTOS PER PACK
101-191 AU SER.#'d B/WN 25-75 PER
NO PRICING ON QTY 25 OR LESS
*101-191 JSY AU GOLD: .6X TO 1.5X BASIC
101-191 JSY AU SER.#'d B/WN 50-99 PER
EXCHANGE DEADLINE 12/28/2009
169 Daisuke Matsuzaka Jsy AU/99 300.00 400.00

2007 Exquisite Collection Rookie Signatures Gold Spectrum Patches

OVERALL FIVE AUTOS PER PACK
STATED PRINT RUN 1 SER.#'d SET
NO PRICING DUE TO SCARCITY
EXCHANGE DEADLINE 12/28/2009

2007 Exquisite Collection Rookie Signatures Silver Spectrum

ONE BASE OR BASE PARALLEL PER PACK
1-100 STATED PRINT RUN 1 SER.#'d SET
OVERALL AU ODDS FIVE PER PACK
101-191 AU PRINT RUN 1 SER.#'d SET
101-191 JSY AU PRINT RUN 25 SER.#'d SETS
NO PRICING DUE TO SCARCITY
EXCHANGE DEADLINE 12/28/2009

2007 Exquisite Collection Rookie Signatures All Rookie Team Autographs

OVERALL FIVE AUTOS PER PACK
STATED PRINT RUN 20 SER.#'d SETS
NO PRICING DUE TO SCARCITY
COPPER SPEC.PRINT RUN 1 SER.#'d SET
NO COPPER SPEC PRICING AVAILABLE
GOLD SPEC. PRINT RUN 5 SER.#'d SETS
NO GOLD SPEC PRICING AVAILABLE
SILVER INK PRINT RUN 1 SER.#'d SET
NO SILVER INK PRICING AVAILABLE
SILVER SPEC PRINT RUN 15 SER.#'d SETS
NO SILVER SPEC PRICING AVAILABLE
EXCHANGE DEADLINE 12/28/2009

2007 Exquisite Collection Rookie Signatures Cal Ripken Jr. All Rookie Team Autographs

OVERALL FIVE AUTOS PER PACK
STATED PRINT RUN 8 SER.#'d SETS
NO PRICING DUE TO SCARCITY
SILVER SPEC PRINT RUN 1 SER.#'d SET
NO SILVER SPEC PRICING AVAILABLE
RAR1 Cal Ripken Jr.
Akinori Iwamura
RAR2 Cal Ripken Jr.
Alex Gordon
RAR3 Cal Ripken Jr.
Andrew Miller
RAR4 Cal Ripken Jr.
Andy LaRoche
RAR5 Cal Ripken Jr.
Billy Butler
RAR6 Cal Ripken Jr.
Brandon Wood
RAR7 Cal Ripken Jr.
Chase Headley
RAR8 Cal Ripken Jr.
Curtis Thigpen
RAR9 Cal Ripken Jr.
Don Kelly
RAR10 Cal Ripken Jr.
Felix Pie
RAR11 Cal Ripken Jr.
Fred Lewis
RAR12 Cal Ripken Jr.
Homer Bailey
RAR13 Cal Ripken Jr.
Hunter Pence
RAR14 Cal Ripken Jr.
Jeff Baker
RAR15 Cal Ripken Jr.
Jon Knott
RAR16 Cal Ripken Jr.
Josh Fields
RAR17 Cal Ripken Jr.
Josh Hamilton
RAR18 Cal Ripken Jr.
Kevin Kouzmanoff
RAR19 Cal Ripken Jr.
Mark Reynolds
RAR20 Cal Ripken Jr.
Mike Fontenot
RAR21 Cal Ripken Jr.
Phil Hughes
RAR22 Cal Ripken Jr.
Ryan Braun
RAR23 Cal Ripken Jr.
Tim Lincecum
RAR24 Cal Ripken Jr.
Tony Abreu
RAR25 Cal Ripken Jr.
Travis Buck
RAR26 Cal Ripken Jr.
Travis Metcalf
RAR27 Cal Ripken Jr.
Troy Tulowitzki
RAR28 Cal Ripken Jr.
Yovani Gallardo
RAR29 Cal Ripken Jr.
Joba Chamberlain
RAR30 Cal Ripken Jr.
Kyle Kendrick

2007 Exquisite Collection Rookie Signatures College Ties Autographs

OVERALL FIVE AUTOS PER PACK
PRINT RUNS B/WN 10-25 COPIES PER
NO PRICING DUE TO SCARCITY
GOLD PRINT RUN 2 SER.#'d SETS
NO GOLD PRICING AVAILABLE
SILVER SPEC PRINT RUN 1 SER.#'d SET
NO SILVER SPEC PRICING AVAILABLE
EXCHANGE DEADLINE 12/28/2009

2007 Exquisite Collection Rookie Signatures Common Ground Signatures

OVERALL FIVE AUTOS PER PACK
STATED PRINT RUN 25 SER.#'d SETS
NO PRICING DUE TO SCARCITY
GOLD PRINT RUN 2 SER.#'d SETS
NO GOLD PRICING AVAILABLE
SILVER SPEC PRINT RUN 1 SER.#'d SET
NO SILVER SPEC PRICING AVAILABLE
EXCHANGE DEADLINE 12/28/2009

2007 Exquisite Collection Rookie Signatures Common Numbers

OVERALL FIVE AUTOS PER PACK
PRINT RUNS B/WN 2-60 COPIES PER
NO PRICING ON QTY 25 OR LESS
GOLD SPEC. PRINT RUN 1 SER.#'d SET
NO GOLD SPEC PRICING AVAILABLE
SILVER SPEC PRINT RUN 2 SER.#'d SETS
NO SILVER SPEC PRICING AVAILABLE
EXCHANGE DEADLINE 12/28/2009
BB Jason Bay 10.00 25.00
Jeremy Bonderman/38
BC Ryan Z. Braun 6.00 15.00
Matt Chico/47
BR Ryan Braun
Cal Ripken Jr./8
CP Manny Corpas 6.00 15.00
Glen Perkins/60
EC Yunel Escobar
Tyler Clippard/19
EH Andre Ethier
Chase Headley/16
FR Josh Fields 8.00 20.00
Mark Reynolds/27
GH Yovani Gallardo 8.00 20.00
Philip Humber/49
GO Alex Gordon
Jerry Owens/7
GS Jose Garcia 8.00 20.00
Kevin Slowey/59
LC Adam LaRoche
Alexi Casilla/25
LT Derrek Lee
Jim Thome/25
MB Nick Markakis
Billy Butler/21
MS Andrew Miller 10.00 25.00
Joakim Soria/48
PB Hunter Pence
Michael Bourn/9
RJ Hanley Ramirez
Derek Jeter/2
TJ Troy Tulowitzki -
Derek Jeter/2
VG Jamie Vermilyea 6.00 15.00
Sean Gallagher/36
VT Justin Verlander 60.00 120.00
Frank Thomas/35
WL Josh Willingham
Fred Lewis/14

2007 Exquisite Collection Rookie Signatures Derek Jeter All Rookie Team Autographs

OVERALL FIVE AUTOS PER PACK
STATED PRINT RUN 2 SER.#'d SETS
NO PRICING DUE TO SCARCITY
SILVER SPEC PRINT RUN 1 SER.#'d SET
NO SILVER SPEC PRICING AVAILABLE
JAR1 Derek Jeter/Adam Lind
JAR2 Derek Jeter/Akinori Iwamura
JAR3 Derek Jeter/Alex Gordon
JAR4 Derek Jeter/Alexi Casilla
JAR5 Derek Jeter/Andrew Miller
JAR6 Derek Jeter/Billy Butler
JAR7 Derek Jeter/Brandon Morrow
JAR8 Derek Jeter/Carlos Gomez
JAR9 Derek Jeter/Chase Wright
JAR10 Derek Jeter/Delmon Young
JAR11 Derek Jeter/Devern Hansack
JAR12 Derek Jeter/Felix Pie
JAR13 Derek Jeter/Fred Lewis
JAR14 Derek Jeter/Homer Bailey
JAR15 Derek Jeter/Hunter Pence
JAR16 Derek Jeter/Jeff Baker
JAR17 Derek Jeter/Joe Smith
JAR18 Derek Jeter/Josh Hamilton
JAR19 Derek Jeter/Kei Igawa
JAR20 Derek Jeter/Kevin Kouzmanoff
JAR21 Derek Jeter/Kevin Slowey
JAR22 Derek Jeter/Kyle Kendrick
JAR23 Derek Jeter/Mark Reynolds
JAR24 Derek Jeter/Matt Chico
JAR25 Derek Jeter/Matt DeSalvo
JAR26 Derek Jeter/Micah Owings
JAR27 Derek Jeter/Mike Fontenot
JAR28 Derek Jeter/Phil Hughes
JAR29 Derek Jeter/Ryan Braun
JAR30 Derek Jeter/Sean Henn
JAR31 Derek Jeter/Tim Lincecum
JAR32 Derek Jeter/Tony Abreu
JAR33 Derek Jeter/Travis Metcalf
JAR34 Derek Jeter/Troy Tulowitzki
JAR35 Derek Jeter/Tyler Clippard

2007 Exquisite Collection Rookie Signatures Draft Choice Autographs

OVERALL FIVE AUTOS PER PACK
STATED PRINT RUN 20 SER.#'d SETS
NO PRICING DUE TO SCARCITY
COPPER SPEC.PRINT RUN 1 SER.#'d SET
NO COPPER SPEC PRICING AVAILABLE
GOLD SPEC. PRINT RUN 5 SER.#'d SETS
NO GOLD SPEC PRICING AVAILABLE
SILVER INK PRINT RUN 15 SER.#'d SETS
NO SILVER INK PRICING AVAILABLE
SILVER SPEC PRINT RUN 15 SER.#'d SETS
NO SILVER SPEC PRICING AVAILABLE
EXCHANGE DEADLINE 12/28/2009

2007 Exquisite Collection Rookie Signatures Draft Duals Autographs

OVERALL FIVE AUTOS PER PACK
STATED PRINT RUN 25 SER.#'d SETS
NO PRICING DUE TO SCARCITY
GOLD PRINT RUN 2 SER.#'d SETS
NO GOLD PRICING AVAILABLE
SILVER SPEC PRINT RUN 1 SER.#'d SET
NO SILVER SPEC PRICING AVAILABLE
EXCHANGE DEADLINE 12/28/2009

2007 Exquisite Collection Rookie Signatures Dual Signatures

OVERALL FIVE AUTOS PER PACK
PRINT RUNS B/WN 10-35 COPIES PER
NO PRICING ON QTY 10 OR LESS
GOLD #'d B/WN 5-25 COPIES PER
NO GOLD PRICING AVAILABLE
SILVER SPEC. #'d B/WN 1-10 COPIES PER
NO SILVER SPEC PRICING AVAILABLE
EXCHANGE DEADLINE 12/28/2009
AC Andrew Miller 30.00 60.00
Cameron Maybin/35
AD Alexi Casilla 6.00 15.00
Don Kelly/35
AJ Aaron Harang 10.00 25.00
Jeff Keppinger/35
AM Joaquin Arias 6.00 15.00
Travis Metcalf/35
BB Ryan Braun 20.00 50.00
Ryan Z. Braun/35
BC Jared Burton 6.00 15.00
Jon Coutlangus/35
BG Jason Bay 6.00 15.00
Tom Gorzelanny/35
BH Brian Burres 6.00 15.00
Ramon Hernandez/35
BI Ryan Braun 30.00 60.00
Akinori Iwamura/35
BJ Bill Hall 6.00 15.00
Johnny Estrada/35
BK Chad Billingsley 20.00 50.00
Hong-Chih Kuo/35
BL Homer Bailey 20.00 50.00
Tim Lincecum/35
BR Brian Barden 20.00 50.00
Mark Reynolds/35
BW Billy Butler 12.50 30.00
Brandon Wood/35
CC Curtis Granderson 30.00 60.00
Cameron Maybin/35
CD Matt Chico 6.00 15.00
Matt DeSalvo/35
CH Joba Chamberlain 125.00 200.00
Phil Hughes/35
CJ Alexi Casilla 6.00 15.00
Garrett Jones/35
CK Cesar Jimenez 6.00 15.00
Kelvin Jimenez/35
CY Carl Crawford 10.00 25.00
Delmon Young/35
DH J.D. Durbin 6.00 15.00
Yoel Hernandez/35
DM Doug Slaten 6.00 15.00
Mike Schultz/35
DO Stephen Drew 10.00 25.00
Micah Owings/35
DW Matt DeSalvo 6.00 15.00
Chase Wright/35
FE Mike Fontenot 6.00 15.00
Mark Ellis/35
FL Prince Fielder 30.00 60.00
Carlos Lee/35
GB Alex Gordon 30.00 60.00
Ryan Braun/35
GC Sean Gallagher 6.00 15.00
Rocky Cherry/35
GG Jose Garcia 6.00 15.00
Lee Gardner/35
GJ Vladimir Guerrero 30.00 60.00
Andruw Jones/35
GK Adrian Gonzalez 10.00 25.00
Casey Kotchman/35
GL Jose Garcia 6.00 15.00
Matt Lindstrom/35
GM Gustavo Molina 6.00 15.00
Miguel Montero/35
GP Carlos Gomez 10.00 25.00
Felix Pie/35
GR Ken Griffey Jr.
Cal Ripken Jr./10
GV Lee Gardner 6.00 15.00
Rick Vanden Hurk/35
HA Homer Bailey 15.00 40.00
Aaron Harang/35
HB Yoel Hernandez 6.00 15.00
Joseph Bisenius/35
HC Sean Henn 6.00 15.00
Tyler Clippard/35
HD Sean Henn 6.00 15.00
Matt DeSalvo/35
HE Ramon Hernandez 6.00 15.00
Johnny Estrada/35
HG Josh Hamilton 40.00 80.00
Curtis Granderson/35
HH Justin Hampson 6.00 15.00
Chase Headley/35
HK Phil Hughes 40.00 80.00
Hong-Chih Kuo/35
HL Phil Hughes 50.00 100.00
Tim Lincecum/35
HM Cole Hamels 20.00 50.00
Andrew Miller/35
HP Homer Bailey 30.00 60.00
Phil Hughes/35
IC Kei Igawa 15.00 40.00
Tyler Clippard/35
IH Kei Igawa 20.00 50.00
Phil Hughes/35
JE Kelly Johnson 15.00 40.00
Yunel Escobar/35
JJ James Shields 6.00 15.00
Juan Salas/35
KB Ian Kinsler 10.00 25.00
Hank Blalock/35
KH Kevin Kouzmanoff 6.00 15.00
Chase Headley/35
KK Howie Kendrick 12.50 30.00
Casey Kotchman/35
KW Howie Kendrick 12.50 30.00
Brandon Wood/35
LA Andy LaRoche 10.00 25.00
Tony Abreu/35
LB Fred Lewis 6.00 15.00
Michael Bourn/35
LE John Lackey 10.00 25.00
Kelvim Escobar/35
LH Jon Lester 12.50 30.00
Devern Hansack/35
LO Tim Lincecum 40.00 80.00
Roy Oswalt/35
LP Carlos Lee 30.00 60.00
Hunter Pence/35
LS Jesse Litsch 6.00 15.00
Kevin Slowey/35
ME Brian McCann 12.50 30.00
Yunel Escobar/35
MH Nick Markakis 40.00 80.00
Josh Hamilton/35
MM Russell Martin 12.50 30.00
Brian McCann/35
MO Andrew Miller 12.50 30.00
Micah Owings/35
MS John Maine 10.00 25.00
Joe Smith/35
NT Nick Swisher 12.50 30.00
Travis Buck/35
OC Micah Owings 12.50 30.00
Matt Chico/35
PH Hunter Pence 40.00 80.00
Josh Hamilton/35
PM Corey Patterson 12.50 30.00
Nick Markakis/35
PO Felix Pie 6.00 15.00
Jerry Owens/35
RB Mark Reynolds 20.00 50.00
Ryan Braun/35
RJ Cal Ripken Jr.
Derek Jeter/10
RM Connor Robertson 6.00 15.00
Jay Marshall/35
RO Mark Reynolds 12.50 30.00
Micah Owings/35
RU Hanley Ramirez 12.50 30.00
Dan Uggla/35
RZ Aramis Ramirez 20.00 50.00
Carlos Zambrano/35
SA Joakim Soria 6.00 15.00
Jeremy Accardo/35
SB Joakim Soria 6.00 15.00
Ryan Z. Braun/35
SG Joe Smith 10.00 25.00
Carlos Gomez/35
SM Kurt Suzuki 6.00 15.00
Gustavo Molina/35
SO Ryan Sweeney 6.00 15.00
Jerry Owens/35
SR Chris Stewart 6.00 15.00
Mike Rabelo/35
SS Joe Smith 6.00 15.00
Kevin Slowey/35
ST Sean Henn 6.00 15.00
Tyler Clippard/35
TB Troy Tulowitzki 20.00 50.00
Jeff Baker/35
TE Yunel Escobar 10.00 25.00
Ryan Theriot/35
TF Ryan Theriot 20.00 50.00
Mike Fontenot/35
TJ Curtis Thigpen 6.00 15.00
Garrett Jones/35
TL Curtis Thigpen 6.00 15.00
Adam Lind/35
TR Travis Hafner 15.00 40.00
Ryan Garko/35
TT Frank Thomas 60.00 120.00
Jim Thome/35
TV Travis Hafner 15.00 40.00
Victor Martinez/35
VL Rick Vanden Hurk 6.00 15.00
Matt Lindstrom/35
VM Justin Verlander 20.00 50.00
Andrew Miller/35
WI Chase Wright 15.00 40.00
Kei Igawa/35
YT Yovani Gallardo 20.00 50.00
Tim Lincecum/35
ZB Ryan Zimmerman 30.00 60.00
Ryan Braun/35
ZG Ryan Zimmerman 20.00 50.00
Alex Gordon/35

2007 Exquisite Collection Rookie Signatures Endorsements Signatures

OVERALL FIVE AUTOS PER PACK
STATED PRINT RUN 50 SER.#'d SETS
GOLD PRINT RUN 15 SER.#'d SETS
NO GOLD PRICING AVAILABLE
SILVER SPEC PRINT RUN 1 SER.#'d SET
NO SILVER SPEC PRICING AVAILABLE
EXCHANGE DEADLINE 12/28/2009
AC Alexi Casilla 4.00 10.00
AE Andre Ethier 6.00 15.00
AL Adam Lind 6.00 15.00
BH Brendan Harris 6.00 15.00
BO Jeremy Bonderman 10.00 25.00
CP Corey Patterson 4.00 10.00
DH Dan Haren 4.00 10.00
DL Derrek Lee 10.00 25.00
DM David Murphy 4.00 10.00
DU Dan Uggla 4.00 10.00
FL Fred Lewis 6.00 15.00
FP Felix Pie 6.00 15.00
GP Glen Perkins 4.00 10.00
HB Homer Bailey 10.00 25.00
HP Hunter Pence 30.00 60.00
HR Hanley Ramirez 10.00 25.00
JB Jason Bay 6.00 15.00
JF Josh Fields 4.00 10.00
JL Jon Lester 6.00 15.00
JP Jonathan Papelbon 10.00 25.00
JS James Shields 4.00 10.00
JV Justin Verlander 15.00 40.00
KI Kei Igawa 15.00 40.00
KS Kevin Slowey 6.00 15.00
LG Luis Gonzalez 6.00 15.00
MH Matt Holliday 15.00 40.00
MO Micah Owings 6.00 15.00
NS Nick Swisher 6.00 15.00
PF Prince Fielder 30.00 60.00
RB Ryan Braun 30.00 60.00
RM Russell Martin 10.00 25.00
RS Ryan Sweeney 4.00 10.00
RT Ryan Theriot 6.00 15.00
RZ Ryan Zimmerman 15.00 40.00
SM Joe Smith 6.00 15.00
TH Travis Hafner 10.00 25.00
TL Tim Lincecum 30.00 60.00
TT Troy Tulowitzki 15.00 40.00
VM Victor Martinez 10.00 25.00
YE Yunel Escobar 10.00 25.00

2007 Exquisite Collection Rookie Signatures Ensemble Quad Signatures

OVERALL FIVE AUTOS PER PACK
STATED PRINT RUN 15 SER.#'d SETS
NO PRICING DUE TO SCARCITY
GOLD SPEC. PRINT RUN 1 SER.#'d SET
NO GOLD SPEC PRICING AVAILABLE
SILVER SPEC PRINT RUN 4 SER.#'d SETS
NO SILVER SPEC PRICING AVAILABLE
EXCHANGE DEADLINE 12/28/2009

2007 Exquisite Collection Rookie Signatures Ensemble Triple Signatures

OVERALL FIVE AUTOS PER PACK
PRINT RUNS B/WN 10-35 COPIES PER
NO PRICING ON QTY 10 OR LESS
GOLD SPEC. PRINT RUN 3 SER.#'d SETS
NO GOLD SPEC PRICING AVAILABLE
SILVER SPEC PRINT RUN 1 SER.#'d SET
NO SILVER SPEC PRICING AVAILABLE
EXCHANGE DEADLINE 12/28/2009
BGL Ryan Braun 50.00 100.00
Alex Gordon
Andy LaRoche/35
BLG Michael Bourn 12.50 30.00
Fred Lewis
Carlos Gomez/35
BTY Ryan Braun 50.00 100.00
Troy Tulowitzki
Delmon Young/35
BWL Billy Butler 30.00 60.00
Brandon Wood
Adam Lind/35
CSP Joba Chamberlain 100.00 200.00
Joakim Soria
Glen Perkins/35
FCE Mike Fontenot 20.00 50.00
Alexi Casilla
Yunel Escobar/35
GFC Sean Gallagher 12.50 30.00
Mike Fontenot
Rocky Cherry/35
GIB Alex Gordon 60.00 120.00
Akinori Iwamura
Ryan Braun/35
GJR Ken Griffey Jr.
Derek Jeter
Cal Ripken Jr./10
HHD Phil Hughes
Sean Henn
Matt DeSalvo/35
IGR Akinori Iwamura 50.00 100.00
Alex Gordon
Mark Reynolds/35
KHH Kevin Kouzmanoff
Chase Headley
Justin Hampson/35
LHB Tim Lincecum 60.00 120.00
Phil Hughes
Homer Bailey/35
LLT Adam Lind 12.50 30.00
Jesse Litsch
Curtis Thigpen/35
MKI Andrew Miller 30.00 60.00
Kyle Kendrick
Kei Igawa/35
PHY Hunter Pence 50.00 100.00
Josh Hamilton
Delmon Young/35
SHG Joakim Soria 12.50 30.00
Justin Hampson
Sean Gallagher/35
SMA Jarrod Saltalamacchia 15.00 40.00
David Murphy
Joaquin Arias/35
UBB Justin Upton 60.00 120.00
Travis Buck
Billy Butler/35
WCD Chase Wright
Tyler Clippard
Matt DeSalvo/35

2007 Exquisite Collection Rookie Signatures First Signs Autographs

OVERALL FIVE AUTOS PER PACK
STATED PRINT RUN 20 SER.#'d SETS
NO PRICING DUE TO SCARCITY
COPPER SPEC.PRINT RUN 1 SER.#'d SET
NO COPPER SPEC PRICING AVAILABLE
GOLD SPEC. PRINT RUN 5 SER.#'d SETS
NO GOLD SPEC PRICING AVAILABLE
SILVER INK PRINT RUN 1 SER.#'d SET
NO SILVER INK PRICING AVAILABLE
SILVER SPEC PRINT RUN 15 SER.#'d SETS
NO SILVER SPEC PRICING AVAILABLE
EXCHANGE DEADLINE 12/28/2009

2007 Exquisite Collection Rookie Signatures Futures Autographs

OVERALL FIVE AUTOS PER PACK
STATED PRINT RUN 20 SER.#'d SETS
NO PRICING DUE TO SCARCITY
GOLD SPEC. PRINT RUN 1 SER.#'d SET
NO GOLD SPEC PRICING AVAILABLE
SILVER SPEC PRINT RUN 5 SER.#'d SETS
NO SILVER SPEC PRICING AVAILABLE
EXCHANGE DEADLINE 12/28/2009

2007 Exquisite Collection Rookie Signatures Game Dated Debut Signatures

OVERALL FIVE AUTOS PER PACK
STATED PRINT RUN 20 SER.#'d SETS
NO PRICING DUE TO SCARCITY
GOLD PRINT RUN 5 SER.#'d SETS
NO GOLD SPEC PRICING AVAILABLE
SILVER INK PRINT RUN 1 SER.#'d SET
NO SILVER INK PRICING AVAILABLE
SILVER SPEC PRINT RUN 15 SER.#'d SETS
NO SILVER SPEC PRICING AVAILABLE
EXCHANGE DEADLINE 12/28/2009

2007 Exquisite Collection Rookie Signatures Imagery Autographs

OVERALL FIVE AUTOS PER PACK
STATED PRINT RUN 25 SER.#'d SETS
NO PRICING ON MOST DUE TO SCARCITY
EACG VERSION PRICED EQUALLY
GOLD PRINT RUN 10 SER.#'d SETS
NO GOLD PRICING AVAILABLE
SILVER INK PRINT RUN 1 SER.#'d SET
NO SILVER INK PRICING AVAILABLE
SILVER SPEC PRINT RUN 1 SER.#'d SET
NO SILVER SPEC PRICING AVAILABLE
EXCHANGE DEADLINE 12/28/2009
AC Alexi Casilla
AG Alex Gordon 20.00 50.00
AG2 Alex Gordon 20.00 50.00
AL Adam Lind 10.00 25.00
AL2 Adam Lind 10.00 25.00
BB Billy Butler
BH Bill Hall
BO Michael Bourn 6.00 15.00
BO2 Michael Bourn 6.00 15.00
BR Ryan Z. Braun
BS Brian Stokes
CG Carlos Gomez 12.50 30.00
CG2 Carlos Gomez 12.50 30.00
CG3 Carlos Gomez 12.50 30.00
CH Chase Headley
CT Curtis Thigpen
CW Chase Wright
CZ Carlos Zambrano
DD Dennis Dove
DH Devern Hansack
DM David Murphy 10.00 25.00
DM2 David Murphy 10.00 25.00
FL Fred Lewis 6.00 15.00
FL2 Fred Lewis 6.00 15.00
FL3 Fred Lewis 6.00 15.00
FP Felix Pie 6.00 15.00
FP2 Felix Pie 6.00 15.00
GJ Garrett Jones
GM Gustavo Molina
GP Glen Perkins
HA Justin Hampson
HB Homer Bailey
HP Hunter Pence
HR Hanley Ramirez
JB Jason Bay 6.00 15.00
JB2 Jason Bay 6.00 15.00
JF Josh Fields 6.00 15.00
JF2 Josh Fields 6.00 15.00
JF3 Josh Fields 6.00 15.00
JH Josh Hamilton 10.00 25.00
JH2 Josh Hamilton 10.00 25.00
JL Jesse Litsch
JO Jerry Owens
JS James Shields
JU Justin Upton
JW Josh Willingham 6.00 15.00
JW2 Josh Willingham 6.00 15.00
KE Kyle Kendrick 10.00 25.00
KE2 Kyle Kendrick 10.00 25.00
KI Kei Igawa
KK Kevin Kouzmanoff 6.00 15.00
KK2 Kevin Kouzmanoff 6.00 15.00
KK3 Kevin Kouzmanoff 6.00 15.00
KS Kevin Slowey 6.00 15.00
KS2 Kevin Slowey 6.00 15.00
LA Andy LaRoche
MB Matt Brown
MD Matt DeSalvo
MF Mike Fontenot 6.00 15.00
MF2 Mike Fontenot 6.00 15.00
MF3 Mike Fontenot 6.00 15.00
MH Matt Holliday 20.00 50.00
MH2 Matt Holliday 20.00 50.00
MO Micah Owings 10.00 25.00
MO2 Micah Owings 10.00 25.00
MR Mark Reynolds 10.00 25.00
MR2 Mark Reynolds 10.00 25.00
MT Miguel Tejada
NM Nick Markakis
RB Ryan Braun 20.00 50.00
RB2 Ryan Braun 20.00 50.00
RC Rocky Cherry
RM Russell Martin 20.00 50.00
RM2 Russell Martin 20.00 50.00
RS Ryan Sweeney 6.00 15.00
RS2 Ryan Sweeney 6.00 15.00
RV Rick Vanden Hurk
RZ Ryan Zimmerman 20.00 50.00
RZ2 Ryan Zimmerman 20.00 50.00
SA Jarrod Saltalamacchia
SG Sean Gallagher
SH Sean Henn
SM Joe Smith 6.00 15.00
SM2 Joe Smith 6.00 15.00
TA Tony Abreu
TB Travis Buck 6.00 15.00
TB2 Travis Buck 6.00 15.00
TC Tyler Clippard
TG Tom Gorzelanny
TH Travis Hafner 6.00 15.00
TH2 Travis Hafner 6.00 15.00
TM Travis Metcalf
VM Victor Martinez 6.00 15.00
VM2 Victor Martinez 6.00 15.00
VM3 Victor Martinez 6.00 15.00
YE Yunel Escobar 12.50 30.00
YE2 Yunel Escobar 12.50 30.00
YG Yovani Gallardo
YH Yoel Hernandez
ZS Zack Segovia

2007 Exquisite Collection Rookie Signatures Ken Griffey Jr. All Rookie Team Autographs

OVERALL FIVE AUTOS PER PACK
STATED PRINT RUN 3 SER.#'d SETS
NO PRICING DUE TO SCARCITY
SILVER SPEC PRINT RUN 1 SER.#'d SET
NO SILVER SPEC PRICING AVAILABLE
GAR1 Ken Griffey Jr.
Adam Lind
GAR2 Ken Griffey Jr.
Akinori Iwamura
GAR3 Ken Griffey Jr.
Alex Gordon
GAR4 Ken Griffey Jr.
Andrew Miller
GAR5 Ken Griffey Jr.
Andy LaRoche
GAR6 Ken Griffey Jr.
Brandon Morrow
GAR7 Ken Griffey Jr.
Brandon Wood
GAR8 Ken Griffey Jr.
Carlos Gomez
GAR9 Ken Griffey Jr.
Chase Headley
GAR10 Ken Griffey Jr.
Delmon Young
GAR11 Ken Griffey Jr.
Felix Pie
GAR12 Ken Griffey Jr.
Fred Lewis
GAR13 Ken Griffey Jr.
Homer Bailey
GAR14 Ken Griffey Jr.
Hunter Pence
GAR15 Ken Griffey Jr.
Jerry Owens
GAR16 Ken Griffey Jr.
Joe Smith
GAR17 Ken Griffey Jr.
Jon Coutlangus
GAR18 Ken Griffey Jr.
Jon Knott
GAR19 Ken Griffey Jr.
Josh Fields
GAR20 Ken Griffey Jr.
Josh Hamilton
GAR21 Ken Griffey Jr.
Justin Hampson
GAR22 Ken Griffey Jr.
Justin Upton
GAR23 Ken Griffey Jr.
Kei Igawa
GAR24 Ken Griffey Jr.
Kevin Kouzmanoff
GAR25 Ken Griffey Jr.
Mark Reynolds
GAR26 Ken Griffey Jr.
Matt Chico
GAR27 Ken Griffey Jr.
Michael Bourn
GAR28 Ken Griffey Jr.
Mike Fontenot
GAR29 Ken Griffey Jr.
Phil Hughes
GAR30 Ken Griffey Jr.
Ryan Braun
GAR31 Ken Griffey Jr.
Tony Abreu
GAR32 Ken Griffey Jr.
Travis Buck
GAR33 Ken Griffey Jr.
Travis Metcalf
GAR34 Ken Griffey Jr.
Troy Tulowitzki
GAR35 Ken Griffey Jr.
Yovani Gallardo

2007 Exquisite Collection Rookie Signatures Phenoms Autographs

OVERALL FIVE AUTOS PER PACK
STATED PRINT RUN 20 SER.#'d SETS
NO PRICING DUE TO SCARCITY
GOLD PRINT RUN 15 SER.#'d SETS
NO GOLD PRICING AVAILABLE
SILVER INK PRINT RUN 1 SER.#'d SET
NO SILVER INK PRICING AVAILABLE
SILVER SPEC PRINT RUN 15 SER.#'d SETS
NO SILVER SPEC PRICING AVAILABLE
EXCHANGE DEADLINE 12/28/2009

2007 Exquisite Collection Rookie Signatures Reflections Autographs

OVERALL FIVE AUTOS PER PACK
PRINT RUNS B/WN 10-40 COPIES PER
NO PRICING QTY OF 20 OR LESS
GOLD #'d B/WN 5-20 COPIES PER
NO GOLD PRICING AVAILABLE
SILVER INK #'d B/WN 5-20 COPIES PER
NO SILVER INK PRICING AVAILABLE
SILVER SPEC #'d B/WN 1-10 COPIES PER
NO SILVER SPEC PRICING AVAILABLE
AB Alex Gordon 20.00 50.00
Billy Butler/40
AC Joaquin Arias 6.00 15.00
Alexi Casilla/40
AH Aaron Harang 20.00 50.00
Homer Bailey/40
AJ Andrew Miller 10.00 25.00
Jeremy Sowers/40
BA Matt Brown 6.00 15.00
Tony Abreu/40
BB Brian Bannister 6.00 15.00
Boof Bonser/40
BD Brian Bannister 6.00 15.00
John Danks/40
BG Ryan Braun 30.00 60.00
Alex Gordon/40
BH Josh Barfield 10.00 25.00
Travis Hafner/40
BJ Brad Salmon 10.00 25.00
Jared Burton/40
BL Michael Bourn 10.00 25.00
Fred Lewis/40
BS Joseph Bisenius 6.00 15.00
Zack Segovia/40
BT Brian Bannister 10.00 25.00
Mark Teahen/40
BV Jeremy Bonderman 15.00 40.00
Justin Verlander/40
BW Matt Brown 10.00 25.00
Brandon Wood/40
CG Carl Crawford 10.00 25.00
Carlos Gomez/40
CH Kevin Cameron 6.00 15.00
Justin Hampson/40
CK Curtis Thigpen 10.00 25.00
Kurt Suzuki/40
CR Cal Ripken Jr.
Ryan Braun/10
CS Rocky Cherry 6.00 15.00
Joakim Soria/40
DC Matt DeSalvo 6.00 15.00
Matt Chico/40
DH J.D. Durbin 6.00 15.00
Yoel Hernandez/40
DO John Danks 6.00 15.00
Micah Owings/40
DS J.D. Durbin 10.00 25.00
Zack Segovia/40
EC Yunel Escobar 6.00 15.00
Alexi Casilla/40
EL Andre Ethier 6.00 15.00
Fred Lewis/40
EP Mark Ellis 10.00 25.00
Danny Putnam/40
FM Josh Fields 6.00 15.00
Travis Metcalf/40
FO Prince Fielder 30.00 60.00
David Ortiz/40
FY Felix Hernandez 12.50 30.00
Yovani Gallardo/40
GA Glen Perkins 6.00 15.00
Alexi Casilla/40
GB Jeremy Guthrie 10.00 25.00
Brian Burres/40
GC Sean Gallagher 6.00 15.00
Rocky Cherry/40
GG Jeremy Guthrie 6.00 15.00
Tom Gorzelanny/40
GK Alex Gordon 20.00 50.00
Kevin Kouzmanoff/40
GL Lee Gardner 6.00 15.00
Matt Lindstrom/40
GM Gustavo Molina 6.00 15.00
Miguel Montero/40
GT Ken Griffey Jr.
Frank Thomas/20
GV Jose Garcia 6.00 15.00
Rick Vanden Hurk/40
HB Phil Hughes 20.00 50.00
Homer Bailey/40
HC Justin Hampson 6.00 15.00
Jon Coutlangus/40
HD Huston Street 6.00 15.00
Dallas Braden/40
HG Rich Hill 10.00 25.00
Sean Gallagher/40
HH Phil Hughes 20.00 50.00
Sean Henn/40
HK Chase Headley 6.00 15.00
Kevin Kouzmanoff/40
HM Cole Hamels 20.00 50.00
Andrew Miller/40
HP Josh Hamilton 20.00 50.00
Hunter Pence/40
HT Homer Bailey 20.00 50.00
Tim Lincecum/40
HW Jeremy Hermida 6.00 15.00
Josh Willingham/40
IM Kei Igawa 20.00 50.00
Andrew Miller/40
JC James Shields 15.00 40.00
Chad Billingsley/40
JD Kelvin Jimenez 6.00 15.00
Dennis Dove/40
JE Kelly Johnson 15.00 40.00
Yunel Escobar/40
JJ Josh Fields 10.00 25.00
Jerry Owens/40
JK Jarrod Saltalamacchia 10.00 25.00
Kurt Suzuki/40
JL Reed Johnson 6.00 15.00
Adam Lind/40
JM John Danks 6.00 15.00
Matt Chico/40
JR Derek Jeter
Cal Ripken Jr./10
KC Kelvin Jimenez 10.00 25.00
Cesar Jimenez/40
KG Kurt Suzuki 6.00 15.00
Gustavo Molina/40
LA Andy LaRoche 10.00 25.00
Tony Abreu/40
LB Adam Lind 6.00 15.00
Jeff Baker/40
LH Jon Lester 30.00 60.00
Cole Hamels/40
LL Jesse Litsch 10.00 25.00
Adam Lind/40
LO Fred Lewis 6.00 15.00
Jerry Owens/40
MA Mark Ellis 6.00 15.00
Alexi Casilla/40
MB Jay Marshall 6.00 15.00
Dallas Braden/40
MG Nick Markakis 12.50 30.00
Jeremy Guthrie/40
MJ Matt Holliday 20.00 50.00
Jason Bay/40
MK Nick Markakis 10.00 25.00
Jon Knott/40
MM Russell Martin 12.50 30.00
Brian McCann/40
MR Jay Marshall 10.00 25.00
Connor Robertson/40
MS Russell Martin 12.50 30.00
Kurt Suzuki/40
NR Neal Musser 10.00 25.00
Ryan Z. Braun/40
OB Micah Owings 6.00 15.00
Homer Bailey/40
PB Danny Putnam 6.00 15.00
Travis Buck/40
PC Glen Perkins 6.00 15.00
Matt Chico/40
PD Glen Perkins 6.00 15.00
Matt DeSalvo/40
PG Felix Pie 12.50 30.00
Carlos Gomez/40
PO Felix Pie 6.00 15.00
Jerry Owens/40
PR Phil Hughes
Roger Clemens/10
RB Mark Reynolds 20.00 50.00
Ryan Braun/40
RC Ryan Braun 15.00 40.00
Chase Headley/40
RM Mike Rabelo 6.00 15.00
Gustavo Molina/40
RR Ryan Z. Braun 20.00 50.00
Ryan Braun/40
SB Joakim Soria 6.00 15.00
Ryan Z. Braun/40
SG Ben Sheets 20.00 50.00
Yovani Gallardo/40
SH Joe Smith 10.00 25.00
Justin Hampson/40
SM Jarrod Saltalamacchia 10.00 25.00
David Murphy/40
SP Kevin Slowey 10.00 25.00
Glen Perkins/40
SR Kurt Suzuki 6.00 15.00
Shawn Riggans/40
SS Joe Smith 6.00 15.00
Kevin Slowey/40
ST Sean Henn 6.00 15.00
Tyler Clippard/40
TJ Curtis Thigpen 6.00 15.00
Garrett Jones/40
TR Curtis Thigpen 6.00 15.00
Shawn Riggans/40
TS Mark Teahen 6.00 15.00
Angel Sanchez/40
VG Rick Vanden Hurk 6.00 15.00
Lee Gardner/40
WD Chase Wright 6.00 15.00
John Danks/40
WH Josh Willingham 10.00 25.00
Bill Hall/40
ZY Zack Segovia 6.00 15.00
Yoel Hernandez/40

2007 Exquisite Collection Rookie Signatures Retro Rookie Duals Autographs

OVERALL FIVE AUTOS PER PACK
PRINT RUNS B/WN 3-15 COPIES PER
NO PRICING DUE TO SCARCITY
GOLD PRINT RUN 2 SER.#'d SETS
NO GOLD PRICING AVAILABLE
SILVER SPEC PRINT RUN 1 SER.#'d SET
NO SILVER SPEC PRICING AVAILABLE
EXCHANGE DEADLINE 12/28/2009

2007 Exquisite Collection Rookie Signatures Rookie Biography Autographs

OVERALL FIVE AUTOS PER PACK
STATED PRINT RUN 20 SER.#'d SETS
NO PRICING DUE TO SCARCITY
BLUE SPEC PRINT RUN 1 SER.#'d SET
NO BLUE SPEC PRICING AVAILABLE
GOLD PRINT RUN 15 SER.#'d SETS
NO GOLD PRICING AVAILABLE
GOLD SPEC. PRINT RUN 1 SER.#'d SET
NO GOLD SPEC PRICING AVAILABLE
SILVER INK PRINT RUN 1 SER.#'d SET
NO SILVER INK PRICING AVAILABLE
SILVER SPEC PRINT RUN 10 SER.#'d SETS
NO SILVER SPEC PRICING AVAILABLE
EXCHANGE DEADLINE 12/28/2009

2007 Exquisite Collection Rookie Signatures Rookie Heroes Autographs

OVERALL FIVE AUTOS PER PACK
STATED PRINT RUN 25 SER.#'d SETS
EACH VERSION PRICED EQUALLY
*GOLD: .6X TO 1.5X BASIC
GOLD PRINT RUN 15 SER.#'d SETS
GOLD SPEC. PRINT RUN 1 SER.#'d SET
NO GOLD SPEC PRICING AVAILABLE
SILVER INK PRINT RUN 1 SER.#'d SET
NO SILVER INK PRICING AVAILABLE
*SILVER SPEC: .75X TO 2X BASIC
SILVER SPEC PRINT RUN 10 SER.#'d SETS
EXCHANGE DEADLINE 12/28/2009
AI1 Akinori Iwamura 10.00 25.00
AI2 Akinori Iwamura 10.00 25.00
AI3 Akinori Iwamura 10.00 25.00
AI4 Akinori Iwamura 10.00 25.00
AI5 Akinori Iwamura 10.00 25.00
AM1 Andrew Miller 10.00 25.00
AM2 Andrew Miller 10.00 25.00
AM3 Andrew Miller 10.00 25.00
AM4 Andrew Miller 10.00 25.00
AM5 Andrew Miller 10.00 25.00
BB1 Billy Butler 10.00 25.00
BB2 Billy Butler 10.00 25.00
BB3 Billy Butler 10.00 25.00
BB4 Billy Butler 10.00 25.00
BB5 Billy Butler 10.00 25.00
CG1 Carlos Gomez 10.00 25.00
CG2 Carlos Gomez 10.00 25.00
CG3 Carlos Gomez 10.00 25.00
CG4 Carlos Gomez 10.00 25.00
CG5 Carlos Gomez 10.00 25.00
FL1 Fred Lewis 6.00 15.00
FL2 Fred Lewis 6.00 15.00
FL3 Fred Lewis 6.00 15.00
FL4 Fred Lewis 6.00 15.00
FL5 Fred Lewis 6.00 15.00
FP1 Felix Pie 6.00 15.00
FP2 Felix Pie 6.00 15.00
FP3 Felix Pie 6.00 15.00
FP4 Felix Pie 6.00 15.00
FP5 Felix Pie 6.00 15.00
HB1 Homer Bailey 6.00 15.00
HB2 Homer Bailey 6.00 15.00
HB3 Homer Bailey 6.00 15.00
HB4 Homer Bailey 6.00 15.00
HB5 Homer Bailey 6.00 15.00
HP1 Hunter Pence 15.00 40.00
HP2 Hunter Pence 15.00 40.00
HP3 Hunter Pence 15.00 40.00
HP4 Hunter Pence 15.00 40.00
HP5 Hunter Pence 15.00 40.00
JD1 John Danks 6.00 15.00
JD2 John Danks 6.00 15.00
JD3 John Danks 6.00 15.00
JD4 John Danks 6.00 15.00
JD5 John Danks 6.00 15.00
JS1 Jarrod Saltalamacchia 6.00 15.00
JS2 Jarrod Saltalamacchia 6.00 15.00
JS3 Jarrod Saltalamacchia 6.00 15.00
JS4 Jarrod Saltalamacchia 6.00 15.00
JS5 Jarrod Saltalamacchia 6.00 15.00
KE1 Kyle Kendrick 10.00 25.00
KE2 Kyle Kendrick 10.00 25.00
KE3 Kyle Kendrick 10.00 25.00
KE4 Kyle Kendrick 10.00 25.00
KE5 Kyle Kendrick 10.00 25.00
KK1 Kevin Kouzmanoff 6.00 15.00
KK2 Kevin Kouzmanoff 6.00 15.00
KK3 Kevin Kouzmanoff 6.00 15.00
KK4 Kevin Kouzmanoff 6.00 15.00
KK5 Kevin Kouzmanoff 6.00 15.00
KS1 Kevin Slowey 6.00 15.00
KS2 Kevin Slowey 6.00 15.00
KS3 Kevin Slowey 6.00 15.00
KS4 Kevin Slowey 6.00 15.00
KS5 Kevin Slowey 6.00 15.00
MR1 Mark Reynolds 40.00 80.00
MR2 Mark Reynolds 40.00 80.00
MR3 Mark Reynolds 40.00 80.00
MR4 Mark Reynolds 40.00 80.00
MR5 Mark Reynolds 40.00 80.00
RB1 Ryan Braun 30.00 60.00
RB2 Ryan Braun 30.00 60.00
RB3 Ryan Braun 30.00 60.00
RB4 Ryan Braun 30.00 60.00
RB5 Ryan Braun 30.00 60.00
SO1 Joakim Soria 6.00 15.00
SO2 Joakim Soria 6.00 15.00
SO3 Joakim Soria 6.00 15.00
SO4 Joakim Soria 6.00 15.00
SO5 Joakim Soria 6.00 15.00
TB1 Travis Buck 6.00 15.00
TB2 Travis Buck 6.00 15.00
TB3 Travis Buck 6.00 15.00
TB4 Travis Buck 6.00 15.00
TB5 Travis Buck 6.00 15.00
TL1 Tim Lincecum 50.00 100.00
TL2 Tim Lincecum 50.00 100.00
TL3 Tim Lincecum 50.00 100.00
TL4 Tim Lincecum 50.00 100.00
TL5 Tim Lincecum 50.00 100.00
TT1 Troy Tulowitzki 30.00 60.00
TT2 Troy Tulowitzki 30.00 60.00
TT3 Troy Tulowitzki 30.00 60.00
TT4 Troy Tulowitzki 30.00 60.00
TT5 Troy Tulowitzki 30.00 60.00
YE1 Yunel Escobar 10.00 25.00
YE2 Yunel Escobar 10.00 25.00
YE3 Yunel Escobar 10.00 25.00
YE4 Yunel Escobar 10.00 25.00
YE5 Yunel Escobar 10.00 25.00

2007 Exquisite Collection Rookie Signatures Signature Materials

OVERALL FIVE AUTOS PER PACK
PRINT RUNS B/WN 25-85 COPIES PER
NO PRICING ON QTY 25 OR LESS
*GOLD: X TO X BASIC
GOLD SER.#'d B/WN 15-50 COPIES PER
NO PRICING ON QTY 15 OR LESS
GOLD SPEC. PRINT RUN 1 SER.#'d SET
NO GOLD SPEC PRICING AVAILABLE
SILVER SPEC #'d B/WN 10-25 COPIES PER
NO SILVER SPEC PRICING AVAILABLE
EXCHANGE DEADLINE 12/28/2009
AD Adam Dunn/85 10.00 25.00
AG Adrian Gonzalez/85 5.00 12.00
AH Aaron Harang/85 5.00 12.00
AR Aramis Ramirez/85 6.00 15.00
BA Bronson Arroyo/85 5.00 12.00
BH Bill Hall/85 6.00 15.00
BL Joe Blanton/85 5.00 12.00
BO Jeremy Bonderman/85 10.00 25.00
BR Brian Roberts/85 6.00 15.00
BS Ben Sheets/85 5.00 12.00
BU B.J. Upton/85 5.00 12.00
CC Carl Crawford/85 6.00 15.00
CH Cole Hamels/85 15.00 40.00
CL Carlos Lee/85 5.00 12.00
CR Cal Ripken Jr./85 60.00 120.00
CZ Carlos Zambrano/85 10.00 25.00
DH Dan Haren/85 6.00 15.00
DJ Derek Jeter/25
DL Derrek Lee/85 10.00 25.00
DU Dan Uggla/85 5.00 12.00
DW Dontrelle Willis/85 10.00 25.00
FH Felix Hernandez/85 15.00 40.00
FT Frank Thomas/85 30.00 60.00
HA Travis Hafner/85 10.00 25.00
HK Howie Kendrick/85 10.00 25.00
HR Hanley Ramirez/85 15.00 40.00
HS Huston Street/85 5.00 12.00

IK Ian Kinsler/85 5.00 12.00
JB Jason Bay/85 6.00 15.00
JM John Maine/85 6.00 15.00
JO Josh Barfield/85 5.00 12.00
JP Jonathan Papelbon/85 15.00 40.00
JV Justin Verlander/85 10.00 25.00
JW Josh Willingham/85 5.00 12.00
KG Ken Griffey Jr./25
LS Luke Scott/85 5.00 12.00
MC Matt Cain/85 6.00 15.00
MO Justin Morneau/85 10.00 25.00
MT Mark Teixeira/85 10.00 25.00
NM Nick Markakis/85 10.00 25.00
NS Nick Swisher/85 6.00 15.00
PF Prince Fielder/85 20.00 50.00
RC Roger Clemens/25
RH Rich Harden/85 5.00 12.00
RM Russell Martin/85 10.00 25.00
RW Rickie Weeks/85 6.00 15.00
RZ Ryan Zimmerman/85 12.50 30.00
SD Stephen Drew/85 10.00 25.00
TH Torii Hunter/85 6.00 15.00
VM Victor Martinez/85 6.00 15.00

2007 Exquisite Collection Rookie Signatures The Future Autographs

OVERALL FIVE AUTOS PER PACK
STATED PRINT RUN 20 SER.#'d SETS
NO PRICING DUE TO SCARCITY
GOLD PRINT RUN 15 SER.#'d SETS
NO GOLD PRICING AVAILABLE
SILVER INK PRINT RUN 1 SER.#'d SET
NO SILVER INK PRICING AVAILABLE
SILVER SPEC PRINT RUN 1 SER.#'d SET
NO SILVER SPEC PRICING AVAILABLE
EXCHANGE DEADLINE 12/28/2009

2007 Exquisite Collection Rookie Signatures The Next Generation Signatures

OVERALL FIVE AUTOS PER PACK
STATED PRINT RUN 20 SER.#'d SETS
NO PRICING DUE TO SCARCITY
GOLD PRINT RUN 15 SER.#'d SETS
NO GOLD PRICING AVAILABLE
SILVER INK PRINT RUN 1 SER.#'d SET
NO SILVER INK PRICING AVAILABLE
SILVER SPEC PRINT RUN 1 SER.#'d SET
NO SILVER SPEC PRICING AVAILABLE
EXCHANGE DEADLINE 12/28/2009

1993 Finest

This 199-card standard-size single series set is widely recognized as one of the most important issues of the 1990's. The Finest brand was Topps first attempt at the super-premium card market. Production was announced at 4,000 cases and cards were distributed exclusively through hobby dealers in the fall of 1993. This was the first time in the history of the hobby that a major manufacturer publicly released production figures. Cards were issued in seven-card foil fin-wrapped packs that carried a suggested retail price of $3.99. The product was a smashing success upon release with pack prices immediately soaring well above suggested retail prices. The popularity of the product has continued to grow throughout the years as it's place in hobby lore is now well soldified. The cards have silver-blue metallic finishes on their fronts and feature color player action photos. The set's title appears at the top, and the player's name is shown at the bottom. J.T. Snow is the only Rookie Card of note in this set.

COMPLETE SET (199) 75.00 150.00
1 David Justice 1.00 2.50
2 Lou Whitaker 1.00 2.50
3 Bryan Harvey .60 1.50
4 Carlos Garcia .60 1.50
5 Sid Fernandez .60 1.50
6 Brett Butler 1.00 2.50
7 Scott Cooper .60 1.50
8 B.J. Surhoff 1.00 2.50
9 Steve Finley 1.00 2.50
10 Curt Schilling 1.00 2.50
11 Jeff Bagwell 1.50 4.00
12 Alex Cole .60 1.50
13 John Olerud 1.00 2.50
14 John Smiley .60 1.50
15 Bip Roberts .60 1.50
16 Albert Belle 1.00 2.50
17 Duane Ward .60 1.50
18 Alan Trammell 1.00 2.50
19 Andy Benes .60 1.50
20 Reggie Sanders 1.00 2.50
21 Todd Zeile .60 1.50
22 Rick Aguilera .60 1.50
23 Dave Hollins .60 1.50
24 Jose Rijo .60 1.50
25 Matt Williams 1.00 2.50
26 Sandy Alomar Jr. .60 1.50
27 Alex Fernandez .60 1.50
28 Ozzie Smith 4.00 10.00
29 Ramon Martinez .60 1.50
30 Bernie Williams 1.50 4.00
31 Gary Sheffield 1.00 2.50
32 Eric Karros 1.00 2.50
33 Frank Viola 1.00 2.50
34 Kevin Young 1.00 2.50
35 Ken Hill .60 1.50
36 Tony Fernandez .60 1.50
37 Tim Wakefield 2.50 6.00
38 John Kruk 1.00 2.50
39 Chris Sabo .60 1.50
40 Marquis Grissom 1.00 2.50
41 Glenn Davis .60 1.50
42 Jeff Montgomery .60 1.50
43 Kenny Lofton 1.00 2.50
44 John Burkett .60 1.50
45 Darryl Hamilton .60 1.50
46 Jim Abbott 1.50 4.00
47 Ivan Rodriguez 1.50 4.00
48 Eric Young .60 1.50
49 Mitch Williams .60 1.50
50 Harold Reynolds 1.00 2.50
51 Brian Harper .60 1.50
52 Rafael Palmeiro 1.50 4.00
53 Bret Saberhagen 1.00 2.50
54 Jeff Conine 1.00 2.50
55 Ivan Calderon .60 1.50
56 Juan Guzman .60 1.50
57 Carlos Baerga .60 1.50
58 Charles Nagy .60 1.50
59 Wally Joyner 1.00 2.50
60 Charlie Hayes .60 1.50
61 Shane Mack .60 1.50
62 Pete Harnisch .60 1.50
63 George Brett 6.00 15.00
64 Lance Johnson .60 1.50
65 Ben McDonald .60 1.50
66 Bobby Bonilla 1.00 2.50
67 Terry Steinbach .60 1.50
68 Ron Gant 1.00 2.50
69 Doug Jones .60 1.50
70 Paul Molitor 1.00 2.50
71 Brady Anderson 1.00 2.50
72 Chuck Finley 1.00 2.50
73 Mark Grace 1.50 4.00
74 Mike Devereaux .60 1.50
75 Tony Phillips .60 1.50
76 Chuck Knoblauch 1.00 2.50
77 Tony Gwynn 3.00 8.00
78 Kevin Appier 1.00 2.50
79 Sammy Sosa 2.50 6.00
80 Mickey Tettleton .60 1.50
81 Felix Jose .60 1.50
82 Mark Langston .60 1.50
83 Gregg Jefferies .60 1.50
84 Andre Dawson AS 1.00 2.50
85 Greg Maddux AS 4.00 10.00
86 Rickey Henderson AS 2.50 6.00
87 Tom Glavine AS 1.50 4.00
88 Roberto Alomar AS 1.50 4.00
89 Darryl Strawberry AS 1.00 2.50
90 Wade Boggs AS 1.50 4.00
91 Bo Jackson AS 2.50 6.00
92 Mark McGwire AS 6.00 15.00
93 Robin Ventura AS 1.00 2.50
94 Joe Carter AS 1.00 2.50
95 Lee Smith AS 1.00 2.50
96 Cal Ripken AS 8.00 20.00
97 Larry Walker AS 1.00 2.50
98 Don Mattingly AS 6.00 15.00
99 Jose Canseco AS 1.50 4.00
100 Dennis Eckersley AS 1.00 2.50
101 Terry Pendleton AS 1.00 2.50
102 Frank Thomas AS 2.50 6.00
103 Barry Bonds AS 6.00 15.00
104 Roger Clemens AS 5.00 12.00
105 Ryne Sandberg AS 4.00 10.00
106 Fred McGriff AS 1.50 4.00
107 Nolan Ryan AS 10.00 25.00
108 Will Clark AS 1.50 4.00
109 Pat Listach AS .60 1.50
110 Ken Griffey Jr. AS 4.00 10.00
111 Cecil Fielder AS 1.00 2.50
112 Kirby Puckett AS 2.50 6.00
113 Dwight Gooden AS 1.00 2.50
114 Barry Larkin AS 1.50 4.00
115 David Cone AS 1.00 2.50
116 Juan Gonzalez AS 1.00 2.50
117 Kent Hrbek 1.00 2.50
118 Tim Wallach .60 1.50
119 Craig Biggio 1.50 4.00
120 Roberto Kelly .60 1.50
121 Gregg Olson .60 1.50
122 Eddie Murray UER 2.50 6.00
122 career strikeouts should be 1224
123 Wil Cordero .60 1.50
124 Jay Buhner 1.00 2.50
125 Carlton Fisk 1.50 4.00
126 Eric Davis 1.00 2.50
127 Doug Drabek .60 1.50
128 Ozzie Guillen 1.00 2.50
129 John Wetteland 1.00 2.50
130 Andres Galarraga 1.00 2.50
131 Ken Caminiti 1.00 2.50
132 Tom Candiotti .60 1.50
133 Pat Borders .60 1.50
134 Kevin Brown 1.00 2.50
135 Travis Fryman 1.00 2.50
136 Kevin Mitchell .60 1.50
137 Greg Swindell .60 1.50
138 Benito Santiago 1.00 2.50
139 Reggie Jefferson .60 1.50
140 Chris Bosio .60 1.50
141 Deion Sanders 1.50 4.00
142 Scott Erickson .60 1.50
143 Howard Johnson .60 1.50
144 Orestes Destrade .60 1.50
145 Jose Guzman .60 1.50
146 Chad Curtis .60 1.50
147 Cal Eldred .60 1.50
148 Willie Greene .60 1.50
149 Tommy Greene .60 1.50
150 Erik Hanson .60 1.50
151 Bob Welch .60 1.50
152 John Jaha .60 1.50
153 Harold Baines 1.00 2.50
154 Randy Johnson 2.50 6.00
155 Al Martin .60 1.50
156 J.T. Snow RC 1.50 4.00
157 Mike Mussina 1.50 4.00
158 Ruben Sierra 1.00 2.50
159 Dean Palmer 1.00 2.50
160 Steve Avery .60 1.50
161 Julio Franco 1.00 2.50
162 Dave Winfield 1.00 2.50
163 Tim Salmon 1.50 4.00
164 Tom Henke .60 1.50
165 Mo Vaughn 1.00 2.50
166 John Smoltz 1.50 4.00
167 Danny Tartabull .60 1.50
168 Delino DeShields .60 1.50
169 Charlie Hough 1.00 2.50
170 Paul O'Neill 1.50 4.00
171 Darren Daulton 1.00 2.50
172 Jack McDowell .60 1.50
173 Junior Felix .60 1.50
174 Jimmy Key 1.00 2.50
175 George Bell .60 1.50
176 Mike Stanton .60 1.50
177 Len Dykstra 1.00 2.50
178 Norm Charlton .60 1.50
179 Eric Anthony .60 1.50
180 Rob Dibble 1.00 2.50
181 Otis Nixon .60 1.50
182 Randy Myers .60 1.50
183 Tim Raines 1.00 2.50
184 Orel Hershiser 1.00 2.50
185 Andy Van Slyke 1.50 4.00
186 Mike Lansing RC 1.00 2.50
187 Ray Lankford 1.00 2.50
188 Mike Morgan .60 1.50
189 Moises Alou 1.00 2.50
190 Edgar Martinez 1.50 4.00
191 John Franco 1.00 2.50
192 Robin Yount 4.00 10.00
193 Bob Tewksbury .60 1.50
194 Jay Bell 1.00 2.50
195 Luis Gonzalez 1.00 2.50
196 Dave Fleming .60 1.50
197 Mike Greenwell .60 1.50
198 David Nied .60 1.50
199 Mike Piazza 6.00 15.00

1993 Finest Refractors

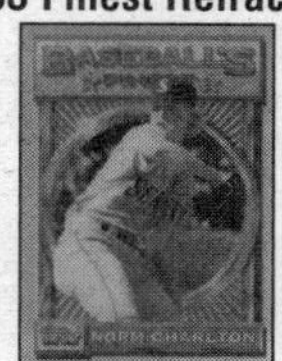

Randomly inserted in packs at a rate of one in 18, these 199 standard-size cards are identical to the regular-issue 1993 Topps Finest except that their fronts have been laminated with a plastic diffraction grating that gives the card a colorful 3-D appearance. Because of the known production numbers, these cards are believed to have a print run of 241 of each card. It is believed that there might be short printed cards in this set. Topps, however, has never publicly released any verification of shortprinted singles, but some of the singles are accepted as being tough to find due to poor regional distribution and hoarding. Due to their high value, these cards are extremely condition sensitive, with much attention paid to centering and minor scratches on the card fronts.

28 Ozzie Smith 60.00 120.00
41 Glenn Davis* 60.00 120.00
47 Ivan Rodriguez * 75.00 150.00
63 George Brett 125.00 200.00
77 Tony Gwynn 60.00 120.00
79 Sammy Sosa * 100.00 200.00
81 Felix Jose* 40.00 80.00
85 Greg Maddux AS 100.00 200.00
88 Roberto Alomar AS 40.00 80.00
91 Bo Jackson AS 50.00 100.00
92 Mark McGwire AS 175.00 300.00
96 Cal Ripken AS 200.00 400.00
98 Don Mattingly AS 125.00 250.00
99 Jose Canseco AS 40.00 80.00
102 Frank Thomas AS 150.00 300.00
103 Barry Bonds AS 250.00 400.00
104 Roger Clemens AS 125.00 200.00
105 Ryne Sandberg AS 75.00 150.00
107 Nolan Ryan AS 300.00 500.00
108 Will Clark AS 40.00 80.00
110 Ken Griffey Jr. AS 200.00 400.00
112 Kirby Puckett AS 60.00 120.00
114 Barry Larkin AS 40.00 80.00
116 Juan Gonzalez AS * 150.00 250.00
122 Eddie Murray UER 60.00 120.00
122 career strikeouts should be 1224
154 Randy Johnson 75.00 150.00
157 Mike Mussina 40.00 80.00
192 Robin Yount 60.00 120.00
199 Mike Piazza 100.00 200.00

1993 Finest Jumbos

These oversized (approximately 4" by 6") cards were inserted one per sealed box of 1993 Topps Finest packs and feature reproductions of 33 players from that set's All-Star subset (84-116). Some hobby dealers believe because of the known production numbers that slightly less than 1,500 of each of these cards were produced.

*STARS: 1X TO 2.5X BASIC CARDS

1994 Finest Pre-Production

This 40-card preview standard-size set is identical in design to the basic Finest set. Cards were randomly inserted at a rate of one in 36 in second series Topps packs and three cards were issued with each Topps factory set. The card numbers on back correspond to those of the regular issue. The only way to distinguish between the preview and basic cards is "Pre-Production" in small red letters on back.

COMPLETE SET (40) 75.00 150.00
22P Deion Sanders 5.00 12.00
23P Jose Offerman 2.00 5.00
26P Alex Fernandez 2.00 5.00
31P Steve Finley 3.00 8.00
35P Andres Galarraga 3.00 8.00
43P Reggie Sanders 3.00 8.00
47P Dave Hollins 2.00 5.00
52P David Cone 3.00 8.00
59P Dante Bichette 3.00 8.00
61P Orlando Merced 2.00 5.00
62P Brian McRae 2.00 5.00
66P Mike Mussina 5.00 12.00
76P Mike Stanley 2.00 5.00
78P Mark McGwire 20.00 50.00
79P Pat Listach 2.00 5.00
82P Dwight Gooden 3.00 8.00
84P Phil Plantier 2.00 5.00
90P Jeff Russell 2.00 5.00
92P Gregg Jefferies 2.00 5.00
93P Jose Guzman 2.00 5.00
100P John Smoltz 5.00 12.00
102P Jim Thome 5.00 12.00
121P Moises Alou 3.00 8.00
125P Devon White 3.00 8.00
126P Ivan Rodriguez 5.00 12.00
130P Dave Magadan 2.00 5.00
136P Ozzie Smith 12.50 30.00
141P Chris Hoiles 2.00 5.00
149P Jim Abbott 5.00 12.00
151P Bill Swift 2.00 5.00
154P Edgar Martinez 5.00 12.00
157P J.T. Snow 3.00 8.00
159P Alan Trammell 3.00 8.00
163P Roberto Kelly 2.00 5.00
166P Scott Erickson 2.00 5.00
168P Scott Cooper 2.00 5.00
169P Rod Beck 2.00 5.00
177P Dean Palmer 3.00 8.00
182P Todd Van Poppel 2.00 5.00
185P Paul Sorrento 2.00 5.00

1994 Finest

The 1994 Topps Finest baseball set consists of two series of 220 cards each, for a total of 440 standard-size cards. Each series includes 40 special design Finest cards: 20 top 1993 rookies (1-20), 20 top 1994 rookies (421-440) and 40 top veterans (201-240). It's believed that these subset cards are in slightly shorter supply than the basic issue cards, but the manufacturer has never confirmed this. These glossy and metallic cards have a color photo on front with green and gold borders. A color photo on back is accompanied by statistics and a "Finest Moment" note. Some series 2 packs contained either one or two series 1 cards. The only notable Rookie Card is Chan Ho Park.

COMPLETE SET (440) 50.00 120.00
COMP. SERIES 1 (220) 25.00 60.00
COMP. SERIES 2 (220) 25.00 60.00
1 Mike Piazza FIN 2.50 6.00
2 Kevin Stocker FIN .30 .75
3 Greg McMichael FIN .30 .75
4 Jeff Conine FIN .50 1.25
5 Rene Arocha FIN .30 .75
6 Aaron Sele FIN .30 .75
7 Brent Gates FIN .30 .75
8 Chuck Carr FIN .30 .75
9 Kirk Rueter FIN .30 .75
10 Mike Lansing FIN .30 .75
11 Al Martin FIN .30 .75
12 Jason Bere FIN .30 .75
13 Troy Neel FIN .30 .75
14 Armando Reynoso FIN .30 .75
15 Jeromy Burnitz FIN .50 1.25
16 Rich Amaral FIN .30 .75
17 David McCarty FIN .30 .75
18 Tim Salmon FIN .75 2.00
19 Steve Cooke FIN .30 .75
20 Wil Cordero FIN .30 .75
21 Kevin Tapani .30 .75
22 Deion Sanders .75 2.00
23 Jose Offerman .30 .75
24 Mark Langston .30 .75
25 Ken Hill .30 .75
26 Alex Fernandez .30 .75
27 Jeff Blauser .30 .75
28 Royce Clayton .30 .75
29 Brad Ausmus .75 2.00
30 Ryan Bowen .30 .75
31 Steve Finley .50 1.25
32 Charlie Hayes .30 .75
33 Jeff Kent .75 2.00
34 Mike Henneman .30 .75
35 Andres Galarraga .50 1.25
36 Wayne Kirby .30 .75
37 Joe Oliver .30 .75
38 Terry Steinbach .30 .75
39 Ryan Thompson .30 .75
40 Luis Alicea .30 .75
41 Randy Velarde .30 .75
42 Bob Tewksbury .30 .75
43 Reggie Sanders .50 1.25
44 Brian Williams .30 .75
45 Joe Orsulak .30 .75
46 Jose Lind .30 .75
47 Dave Hollins .30 .75
48 Graeme Lloyd .30 .75
49 Jim Gott .30 .75
50 Andre Dawson .50 1.25
51 Steve Buechele .30 .75
52 David Cone .50 1.25
53 Ricky Gutierrez .30 .75
54 Lance Johnson .30 .75
55 Tino Martinez .75 2.00
56 Phil Hiatt .30 .75
57 Carlos Garcia .30 .75
58 Danny Darwin .30 .75
59 Dante Bichette .50 1.25
60 Scott Kamieniecki .30 .75
61 Orlando Merced .30 .75
62 Brian McRae .30 .75
63 Pat Kelly .30 .75
64 Tom Henke .30 .75
65 Jeff King .30 .75
66 Mike Mussina .75 2.00
67 Tim Pugh .30 .75
68 Robby Thompson .30 .75
69 Paul O'Neill .75 2.00
70 Hal Morris .30 .75
71 Ron Karkovice .30 .75
72 Joe Girardi .30 .75
73 Eduardo Perez .30 .75
74 Raul Mondesi .50 1.25
75 Mike Gallego .30 .75
76 Mike Stanley .30 .75
77 Kevin Roberson .30 .75
78 Mark McGwire 3.00 8.00
79 Pat Listach .30 .75
80 Eric Davis .50 1.25
81 Mike Bordick .30 .75
82 Dwight Gooden .50 1.25
83 Mike Moore .30 .75
84 Phil Plantier .30 .75
85 Darren Lewis .30 .75
86 Rick Wilkins .30 .75
87 Darryl Strawberry .50 1.25
88 Rob Dibble .50 1.25
89 Greg Vaughn .30 .75
90 Jeff Russell .30 .75
91 Mark Lewis .30 .75
92 Gregg Jefferies .30 .75
93 Jose Guzman .30 .75
94 Kenny Rogers .50 1.25
95 Mark Lemke .30 .75
96 Mike Morgan .30 .75
97 Andujar Cedeno .30 .75
98 Orel Hershiser .50 1.25
99 Greg Swindell .30 .75
100 John Smoltz .75 2.00
101 Pedro A.Martinez RC .30 .75
102 Jim Thome .75 2.00
103 David Segui .30 .75
104 Charles Nagy .30 .75
105 Shane Mack .30 .75
106 John Jaha .30 .75
107 Tom Candiotti .30 .75
108 David Wells .50 1.25
109 Bobby Jones .30 .75
110 Bob Hamelin .30 .75
111 Bernard Gilkey .30 .75
112 Chili Davis .50 1.25
113 Todd Stottlemyre .30 .75
114 Derek Bell .30 .75
115 Mark McLemore .30 .75
116 Mark Whiten .30 .75
117 Mike Devereaux .30 .75
118 Terry Pendleton .50 1.25
119 Pat Meares .30 .75
120 Pete Harnisch .30 .75
121 Moises Alou .50 1.25
122 Jay Buhner .50 1.25
123 Wes Chamberlain .30 .75
124 Mike Perez .30 .75
125 Devon White .50 1.25
126 Ivan Rodriguez .75 2.00
127 Don Slaught .30 .75
128 John Valentin .30 .75
129 Jaime Navarro .30 .75
130 Dave Magadan .30 .75
131 Brady Anderson .50 1.25
132 Juan Guzman .30 .75
133 John Wetteland .50 1.25
134 Dave Stewart .50 1.25
135 Scott Servais .30 .75
136 Ozzie Smith 2.00 5.00
137 Darrin Fletcher .30 .75
138 Jose Mesa .30 .75
139 Wilson Alvarez .30 .75
140 Pete Incaviglia .30 .75
141 Chris Hoiles .30 .75
142 Darryl Hamilton .30 .75
143 Chuck Finley .50 1.25
144 Archi Cianfrocco .30 .75
145 Bill Wegman .30 .75
146 Joey Cora .30 .75
147 Darrell Whitmore .30 .75
148 David Hulse .30 .75
149 Jim Abbott .75 2.00
150 Curt Schilling .50 1.25
151 Bill Swift .30 .75
152 Tommy Greene .30 .75
153 Roberto Mejia .30 .75
154 Edgar Martinez .75 2.00
155 Roger Pavlik .30 .75
156 Randy Tomlin .30 .75
157 J.T. Snow .50 1.25
158 Bob Welch .30 .75
159 Alan Trammell .50 1.25
160 Ed Sprague .30 .75
161 Ben McDonald .30 .75
162 Derrick May .30 .75
163 Roberto Kelly .30 .75
164 Bryan Harvey .30 .75
165 Ron Gant .50 1.25
166 Scott Erickson .30 .75
167 Anthony Young .30 .75
168 Scott Cooper .30 .75
169 Rod Beck .30 .75
170 John Franco .50 1.25
171 Gary DiSarcina .30 .75
172 Dave Fleming .30 .75
173 Wade Boggs .75 2.00
174 Kevin Appier .50 1.25
175 Jose Bautista .30 .75
176 Wally Joyner .50 1.25
177 Dean Palmer .50 1.25
178 Tony Phillips .30 .75
179 John Smiley .30 .75
180 Charlie Hough .50 1.25
181 Scott Fletcher .30 .75
182 Todd Van Poppel .30 .75
183 Mike Blowers .30 .75
184 Willie McGee .50 1.25
185 Paul Sorrento .30 .75
186 Eric Young .30 .75
187 Bret Barberie .30 .75
188 Manuel Lee .30 .75
189 Jeff Branson .30 .75
190 Jim Deshaies .30 .75
191 Ken Caminiti .50 1.25
192 Tim Raines .50 1.25
193 Joe Grahe .30 .75
194 Hipolito Pichardo .30 .75
195 Denny Neagle .50 1.25
196 Jeff Gardner .30 .75
197 Mike Benjamin .30 .75
198 Milt Thompson .30 .75
199 Bruce Ruffin .30 .75
200 Chris Hammond UER .30 .75
(Back of card has Mariners; should be Marlins)
201 Tony Gwynn FIN 1.50 4.00
202 Robin Ventura FIN .50 1.25
203 Frank Thomas FIN 1.25 3.00
204 Kirby Puckett FIN 1.25 3.00
205 Roberto Alomar FIN .75 2.00
206 Dennis Eckersley FIN .50 1.25
207 Joe Carter FIN .50 1.25
208 Albert Belle FIN .50 1.25
209 Greg Maddux FIN 2.00 5.00
210 Ryne Sandberg FIN 2.00 5.00
211 Juan Gonzalez FIN .50 1.25
212 Jeff Bagwell FIN .75 2.00
213 Randy Johnson FIN 1.25 3.00
214 Matt Williams FIN .50 1.25
215 Dave Winfield FIN .50 1.25
216 Larry Walker FIN .50 1.25
217 Roger Clemens FIN 2.50 6.00
218 Kenny Lofton FIN .50 1.25
219 Cecil Fielder FIN .50 1.25
220 Darren Daulton FIN .50 1.25
221 John Olerud FIN .50 1.25
222 Jose Canseco FIN .75 2.00
223 Rickey Henderson FIN 1.25 3.00
224 Fred McGriff FIN .75 2.00
225 Gary Sheffield FIN .50 1.25
226 Jack McDowell FIN .30 .75
227 Rafael Palmeiro FIN .75 2.00
228 Travis Fryman FIN .50 1.25
229 Marquis Grissom FIN .50 1.25
230 Barry Bonds FIN 3.00 8.00
231 Carlos Baerga FIN .30 .75
232 Ken Griffey Jr. FIN 2.00 5.00
233 David Justice FIN .50 1.25
234 Bobby Bonilla FIN .50 1.25
235 Cal Ripken FIN 4.00 10.00
236 Sammy Sosa FIN 1.25 3.00
237 Len Dykstra FIN .50 1.25
238 Will Clark FIN .75 2.00
239 Paul Molitor FIN .50 1.25
240 Barry Larkin FIN .75 2.00
241 Bo Jackson 1.25 3.00
242 Mitch Williams .30 .75
243 Ron Darling .30 .75
244 Darryl Kile .50 1.25
245 Geronimo Berroa .30 .75
246 Gregg Olson .30 .75
247 Brian Harper .30 .75
248 Rheal Cormier .30 .75
249 Rey Sanchez .30 .75
250 Jeff Fassero .30 .75
251 Sandy Alomar Jr. .30 .75
252 Chris Bosio .30 .75
253 Andy Stankiewicz .30 .75
254 Harold Baines .50 1.25
255 Andy Ashby .30 .75
256 Tyler Green .30 .75
257 Kevin Brown .50 1.25
258 Mo Vaughn .50 1.25
259 Mike Harkey .30 .75
260 Dave Henderson .30 .75
261 Kent Hrbek .50 1.25
262 Darrin Jackson .30 .75
263 Bob Wickman .30 .75
264 Spike Owen .30 .75
265 Todd Jones .30 .75
266 Pat Borders .30 .75
267 Tom Glavine .75 2.00
268 Dave Nilsson .30 .75
269 Rich Batchelor .30 .75
270 Delino DeShields .30 .75
271 Felix Fermin .30 .75
272 Orestes Destrade .30 .75
273 Mickey Morandini .30 .75
274 Otis Nixon .30 .75
275 Ellis Burks .50 1.25
276 Greg Gagne .30 .75
277 John Doherty .30 .75
278 Julio Franco .50 1.25
279 Bernie Williams .75 2.00
280 Rick Aguilera .30 .75
281 Mickey Tettleton .30 .75
282 David Nied .30 .75
283 Johnny Ruffin .30 .75
284 Dan Wilson .30 .75
285 Omar Vizquel .75 2.00
286 Willie Banks .30 .75
287 Erik Pappas .30 .75
288 Cal Eldred .30 .75
289 Bobby Witt .30 .75
290 Luis Gonzalez .50 1.25
291 Greg Pirkl .30 .75
292 Alex Cole .30 .75
293 Ricky Bones .30 .75
294 Denis Boucher .30 .75
295 John Burkett .30 .75
296 Steve Trachsel .30 .75
297 Ricky Jordan .30 .75
298 Mark Dewey .30 .75
299 Jimmy Key .50 1.25
300 Mike Macfarlane .30 .75

301 Tim Belcher .30 .75
302 Carlos Reyes .30 .75
303 Greg A. Harris .30 .75
304 Brian Anderson RC .50 1.25
305 Terry Mulholland .30 .75
306 Felix Jose .30 .75
307 Darren Holmes .30 .75
308 Jose Rijo .30 .75
309 Paul Wagner .30 .75
310 Bob Scanlan .30 .75
311 Mike Jackson .30 .75
312 Jose Vizcaino .30 .75
313 Rob Butler .30 .75
314 Kevin Seitzer .30 .75
315 Geronimo Pena .30 .75
316 Hector Carrasco .30 .75
317 Eddie Murray 1.25 3.00
318 Roger Salkeld .30 .75
319 Todd Hundley .30 .75
320 Danny Jackson .30 .75
321 Kevin Young .30 .75
322 Mike Greenwell .30 .75
323 Kevin Mitchell .30 .75
324 Chuck Knoblauch .50 1.25
325 Danny Tartabull .30 .75
326 Vince Coleman .30 .75
327 Marvin Freeman .30 .75
328 Andy Benes .30 .75
329 Mike Kelly .30 .75
330 Karl Rhodes .30 .75
331 Allen Watson .30 .75
332 Damion Easley .30 .75
333 Reggie Jefferson .30 .75
334 Kevin McReynolds .30 .75
335 Arthur Rhodes .30 .75
336 Brian R. Hunter .30 .75
337 Tom Browning .30 .75
338 Pedro Munoz .30 .75
339 Billy Ripken .30 .75
340 Gene Harris .30 .75
341 Fernando Vina .30 .75
342 Sean Berry .30 .75
343 Pedro Astacio .30 .75
344 B.J. Surhoff .50 1.25
345 Doug Drabek .30 .75
346 Jody Reed .30 .75
347 Ray Lankford .50 1.25
348 Steve Farr .30 .75
349 Eric Anthony .30 .75
350 Pete Smith .30 .75
351 Lee Smith .50 1.25
352 Mariano Duncan .30 .75
353 Doug Strange .30 .75
354 Tim Bogar .30 .75
355 Dave Weathers .30 .75
356 Eric Karros .50 1.25
357 Randy Myers .30 .75
358 Chad Curtis .30 .75
359 Steve Avery .30 .75
360 Brian Jordan .50 1.25
361 Tim Wallach .30 .75
362 Pedro Martinez 1.25 3.00
363 Bip Roberts .30 .75
364 Lou Whitaker .50 1.25
365 Luis Polonia .30 .75
366 Benito Santiago .50 1.25
367 Brett Butler .50 1.25
368 Shawon Dunston .30 .75
369 Kelly Stinnett RC .50 1.25
370 Chris Turner .30 .75
371 Ruben Sierra .50 1.25
372 Greg A. Harris .30 .75
373 Xavier Hernandez .30 .75
374 Howard Johnson .30 .75
375 Duane Ward .30 .75
376 Roberto Hernandez .30 .75
377 Scott Leius .30 .75
378 Dave Valle .30 .75
379 Sid Fernandez .30 .75
380 Doug Jones .30 .75
381 Zane Smith .30 .75
382 Craig Biggio .75 2.00
383 Rick White RC .30 .75
384 Tom Pagnozzi .30 .75
385 Chris James .30 .75
386 Bret Boone .50 1.25
387 Jeff Montgomery .30 .75
388 Chad Kreuter .30 .75
389 Greg Hibbard .30 .75
390 Mark Grace .75 2.00
391 Phil Leftwich RC .30 .75
392 Don Mattingly 3.00 8.00
393 Ozzie Guillen .50 1.25
394 Gary Gaetti .50 1.25
395 Erik Hanson .30 .75
396 Scott Brosius .50 1.25
397 Tom Gordon .30 .75
398 Bill Gullickson .30 .75
399 Matt Mieske .30 .75
400 Pat Hentgen .30 .75
401 Walt Weiss .30 .75
402 Greg Blosser .30 .75
403 Stan Javier .30 .75
404 Doug Henry .30 .75
405 Ramon Martinez .30 .75
406 Frank Viola .50 1.25
407 Mike Hampton .50 1.25
408 Andy Van Slyke .75 2.00
409 Bobby Ayala .30 .75
410 Todd Zeile .30 .75
411 Jay Bell .50 1.25
412 Dennis Martinez .50 1.25
413 Mark Portugal .30 .75
414 Bobby Munoz .30 .75
415 Kirt Manwaring .30 .75
416 John Kruk .50 1.25
417 Trevor Hoffman .75 2.00
418 Chris Sabo .30 .75
419 Bret Saberhagen .50 1.25
420 Chris Nabholz .30 .75
421 James Mouton FIN .30 .75
422 Tony Tarasco FIN .30 .75
423 Carlos Delgado FIN .75 2.00
424 Rondell White FIN .50 1.25
425 Javier Lopez FIN .50 1.25
426 Chan Ho Park FIN RC .75 2.00
427 Cliff Floyd FIN .50 1.25
428 Dave Staton FIN .30 .75
429 J.R. Phillips FIN .30 .75
430 Manny Ramirez FIN 1.25 3.00
431 Kurt Abbott FIN RC .30 .75
432 Melvin Nieves FIN .30 .75
433 Alex Gonzalez FIN .30 .75
434 Rick Helling FIN .30 .75
435 Danny Bautista FIN .30 .75
436 Matt Walbeck FIN .30 .75
437 Ryan Klesko FIN .50 1.25
438 Steve Karsay FIN .30 .75
439 Salomon Torres FIN .30 .75
440 Scott Ruffcorn FIN .30 .75

1994 Finest Refractors

The 1994 Topps Finest Refractors baseball set consists of two series of 220 cards each, for a total of 440 cards. These special cards were inserted at a rate of one in every nine packs. They are identical to the basic Finest card except for a more intense luster and 3-D appearance.

*STARS: 2.5X TO 6X BASIC CARDS
*ROOKIES: 1.5X TO 4X BASIC CARDS

1994 Finest Jumbos

Inserted one per Finest box, this 80-card over-sized set (3 1/2" by 5") was issued in two series of 40. Each of the 80 cards is identical in design to the special "Finest" cards from the basic Finest set except for the size. The "Finest" subset was designated to showcase top rookies, prospects and veterans. The card numbering is the same as the corresponding basic issue cards. Hence, the first series comprises of cards 1-20 and 201-220. The second series is cards 221-240 and 421-440.

*JUMBOS: 1.25X TO 3X BASIC CARDS

1995 Finest

Consisting of 330 standard-size cards, this set (produced by Topps) was issued in series of 220 and 110. A protective film, designed to keep the card from scratching and to maintain original gloss, covers the front. With the Finest logo at the top, a silver baseball diamond design surrounded by green (field) form the background to an action photo. Horizontally designed backs have a photo to the right with statistical information to the left. A Finest Moment, or career highlight, is also included. Rookie Cards in this set include Bobby Higginson and Hideo Nomo.

COMPLETE SET (330) 25.00 60.00
COMP. SERIES 1 (220) 20.00 50.00
COMP. SERIES 2 (110) 6.00 15.00
1 Raul Mondesi .40 1.00
2 Kurt Abbott .20 .50
3 Chris Gomez .20 .50
4 Manny Ramirez .60 1.50
5 Rondell White .40 1.00
6 William VanLandingham .20 .50
7 Jon Lieber .20 .50
8 Ryan Klesko .40 1.00
9 John Hudek .20 .50
10 Joey Hamilton .20 .50
11 Bob Hamelin .20 .50
12 Brian Anderson .20 .50
13 Mike Lieberthal .40 1.00
14 Rico Brogna .20 .50
15 Rusty Greer .40 1.00
16 Carlos Delgado .40 1.00
17 Jim Edmonds .60 1.50
18 Steve Trachsel .20 .50
19 Matt Walbeck .20 .50
20 Armando Benitez .20 .50
21 Steve Karsay .20 .50
22 Jose Oliva .20 .50
23 Cliff Floyd .40 1.00
24 Kevin Foster .20 .50
25 Javier Lopez .40 1.00
26 Jose Valentin .20 .50
27 James Mouton .20 .50
28 Hector Carrasco .20 .50
29 Orlando Miller .20 .50
30 Garret Anderson .40 1.00
31 Marvin Freeman .20 .50
32 Brett Butler .40 1.00
33 Roberto Kelly .20 .50
34 Rod Beck .20 .50
35 Jose Rijo .20 .50
36 Edgar Martinez .60 1.50
37 Jim Thome .60 1.50
38 Rick Wilkins .20 .50
39 Wally Joyner .40 1.00
40 Wil Cordero .20 .50
41 Tommy Greene .20 .50
42 Travis Fryman .40 1.00
43 Don Slaught .20 .50
44 Brady Anderson .40 1.00
45 Matt Williams .40 1.00
46 Rene Arocha .20 .50
47 Rickey Henderson 1.00 2.50
48 Mike Mussina .60 1.50
49 Greg McMichael .20 .50
50 Jody Reed .20 .50
51 Tino Martinez .60 1.50
52 Dave Clark .20 .50
53 John Valentin .20 .50
54 Bret Boone .40 1.00
55 Walt Weiss .20 .50
56 Kenny Lofton .40 1.00
57 Scott Leius .20 .50
58 Eric Karros .40 1.00
59 John Olerud .40 1.00
60 Chris Hoiles .20 .50
61 Sandy Alomar Jr. .20 .50
62 Tim Wallach .20 .50
63 Cal Eldred .20 .50
64 Tom Glavine .60 1.50
65 Mark Grace .60 1.50
66 Rey Sanchez .20 .50
67 Bobby Ayala .20 .50
68 Dante Bichette .40 1.00
69 Andres Galarraga .40 1.00
70 Chuck Carr .20 .50
71 Bobby Witt .20 .50
72 Steve Avery .20 .50
73 Bobby Jones .20 .50
74 Delino DeShields .20 .50
75 Kevin Tapani .20 .50
76 Randy Johnson 1.00 2.50
77 David Nied .20 .50
78 Pat Hentgen .20 .50
79 Tim Salmon .60 1.50
80 Todd Zeile .20 .50
81 John Wetteland .40 1.00
82 Albert Belle .40 1.00
83 Ben McDonald .20 .50
84 Bobby Munoz .20 .50
85 Bip Roberts .20 .50
86 Mo Vaughn .40 1.00
87 Chuck Finley .40 1.00
88 Chuck Knoblauch .40 1.00
89 Frank Thomas 1.00 2.50
90 Danny Tartabull .20 .50
91 Dean Palmer .40 1.00
92 Len Dykstra .40 1.00
93 J.R. Phillips .20 .50
94 Tom Candiotti .20 .50
95 Marquis Grissom .40 1.00
96 Barry Larkin .60 1.50
97 Bryan Harvey .20 .50
98 David Justice .40 1.00
99 David Cone .40 1.00
100 Wade Boggs .60 1.50
101 Jason Bere .20 .50
102 Hal Morris .20 .50
103 Fred McGriff .60 1.50
104 Bobby Bonilla .40 1.00
105 Jay Buhner .40 1.00
106 Allen Watson .20 .50
107 Mickey Tettleton .20 .50
108 Kevin Appier .40 1.00
109 Ivan Rodriguez .60 1.50
110 Carlos Garcia .20 .50
111 Andy Benes .20 .50
112 Eddie Murray 1.00 2.50
113 Mike Piazza 1.50 4.00
114 Greg Vaughn .20 .50
115 Paul Molitor .40 1.00
116 Terry Steinbach .20 .50
117 Jeff Bagwell .60 1.50
118 Ken Griffey Jr. 1.50 4.00
119 Gary Sheffield .40 1.00
120 Cal Ripken 3.00 8.00
121 Jeff Kent .40 1.00
122 Jay Bell .40 1.00
123 Will Clark .60 1.50
124 Cecil Fielder .40 1.00
125 Alex Fernandez .20 .50
126 Don Mattingly 2.50 6.00
127 Reggie Sanders .40 1.00
128 Moises Alou .40 1.00
129 Craig Biggio .60 1.50
130 Eddie Williams .20 .50
131 John Franco .40 1.00
132 John Kruk .40 1.00
133 Jeff King .20 .50
134 Royce Clayton .20 .50
135 Doug Drabek .20 .50
136 Ray Lankford .40 1.00
137 Roberto Alomar .60 1.50
138 Todd Hundley .20 .50
139 Alex Cole .20 .50
140 Shawon Dunston .20 .50
141 John Roper .20 .50
142 Mark Langston .20 .50
143 Tom Pagnozzi .20 .50
144 Wilson Alvarez .20 .50
145 Scott Cooper .20 .50
146 Kevin Mitchell .20 .50
147 Mark Whiten .20 .50
148 Jeff Conine .40 1.00
149 Chili Davis .40 1.00
150 Luis Gonzalez .40 1.00
151 Juan Guzman .20 .50
152 Mike Greenwell .20 .50
153 Mike Henneman .20 .50
154 Rick Aguilera .20 .50
155 Dennis Eckersley .40 1.00
156 Darrin Fletcher .20 .50
157 Darren Lewis .20 .50
158 Juan Gonzalez .40 1.00
159 Dave Hollins .20 .50
160 Jimmy Key .40 1.00
161 Roberto Hernandez .20 .50
162 Randy Myers .20 .50
163 Joe Carter .40 1.00
164 Darren Daulton .40 1.00
165 Mike Macfarlane .20 .50
166 Bret Saberhagen .20 .50
167 Kirby Puckett 1.00 2.50
168 Lance Johnson .20 .50
169 Mark McGwire 2.50 6.00
170 Jose Canseco .60 1.50
171 Mike Stanley .20 .50
172 Lee Smith .40 1.00
173 Robin Ventura .40 1.00
174 Greg Gagne .20 .50
175 Brian McRae .20 .50
176 Mike Bordick .20 .50
177 Rafael Palmeiro .60 1.50
178 Kenny Rogers .40 1.00
179 Chad Curtis .20 .50
180 Devon White .40 1.00
181 Paul O'Neill .60 1.50
182 Ken Caminiti .40 1.00
183 Dave Nilsson .20 .50
184 Tim Naehring .20 .50
185 Roger Clemens 2.00 5.00
186 Otis Nixon .20 .50
187 Tim Raines .40 1.00
188 Denny Martinez .40 1.00
189 Pedro Martinez .60 1.50
190 Jim Abbott .60 1.50
191 Ryan Thompson .20 .50
192 Barry Bonds 2.50 6.00
193 Joe Girardi .20 .50
194 Steve Finley .40 1.00
195 John Jaha .20 .50
196 Tony Gwynn 1.25 3.00
197 Sammy Sosa 1.00 2.50
198 John Burkett .20 .50
199 Carlos Baerga .20 .50
200 Ramon Martinez .20 .50
201 Aaron Sele .20 .50
202 Eduardo Perez .20 .50
203 Alan Trammell .40 1.00
204 Orlando Merced .20 .50
205 Deion Sanders .60 1.50
206 Robb Nen .40 1.00
207 Jack McDowell .20 .50
208 Ruben Sierra .40 1.00
209 Bernie Williams .60 1.50
210 Kevin Seitzer .20 .50
211 Charles Nagy .20 .50
212 Tony Phillips .20 .50
213 Greg Maddux 1.50 4.00
214 Jeff Montgomery .20 .50
215 Larry Walker .40 1.00
216 Andy Van Slyke .60 1.50
217 Ozzie Smith 1.50 4.00
218 Geronimo Pena .20 .50
219 Gregg Jefferies .20 .50
220 Lou Whitaker .40 1.00
221 Chipper Jones 1.00 2.50
222 Benji Gil .20 .50
223 Tony Phillips .20 .50
224 Trevor Wilson .20 .50
225 Tony Tarasco .20 .50
226 Roberto Petagine .20 .50
227 Mike Macfarlane .20 .50
228 Hideo Nomo RCUER 4.00 10.00
(In 3rd line agianst)
229 Mark McLemore .20 .50
230 Ron Gant .40 1.00
231 Andujar Cedeno .20 .50
232 Mike Mimbs RC .20 .50
233 Jim Abbott .60 1.50
234 Ricky Bones .20 .50
235 Marty Cordova .20 .50
236 Mark Johnson RC .50 1.25
237 Marquis Grissom .40 1.00
238 Tom Henke .20 .50
239 Terry Pendleton .40 1.00
240 John Wetteland .40 1.00
241 Lee Smith .40 1.00
242 Jaime Navarro .20 .50
243 Luis Alicea .20 .50
244 Scott Cooper .20 .50
245 Gary Gaetti .40 1.00
246 Edgardo Alfonzo UER .20 .50
(Incomplete career BA)
247 Brad Clontz .20 .50
248 Dave Mlicki .20 .50
249 Dave Winfield .40 1.00
250 Mark Grudzielanek RC .75 2.00
251 Alex Gonzalez .20 .50
252 Kevin Brown .40 1.00
253 Esteban Loaiza .20 .50
254 Vaughn Eshelman .20 .50
255 Bill Swift .20 .50
256 Brian McRae .20 .50
257 Bobby Higginson RC .75 2.00
258 Jack McDowell .20 .50
259 Scott Stahoviak .20 .50
260 Jon Nunnally .20 .50
261 Charlie Hayes .20 .50
262 Jacob Brumfield .20 .50
263 Chad Curtis .20 .50
264 Heathcliff Slocumb .20 .50
265 Mark Whiten .20 .50
266 Mickey Tettleton .20 .50
267 Jose Mesa .20 .50
268 Doug Jones .20 .50
269 Trevor Hoffman .40 1.00
270 Paul Sorrento .20 .50
271 Shane Andrews .20 .50
272 Brett Butler .40 1.00
273 Curtis Goodwin .20 .50
274 Larry Walker .40 1.00
275 Phil Plantier .20 .50
276 Ken Hill .20 .50
277 Vinny Castilla UER .40 1.00
Rockies spelled Rockie
278 Billy Ashley .20 .50
279 Derek Jeter 2.50 6.00
280 Bob Tewksbury .20 .50
281 Jose Offerman .20 .50
282 Glenallen Hill .20 .50
283 Tony Fernandez .20 .50
284 Mike Devereaux .20 .50
285 John Burkett .20 .50
286 Geronimo Berroa .20 .50
287 Quilvio Veras .20 .50
288 Jason Bates .20 .50
289 Lee Tinsley .20 .50
290 Derek Bell .20 .50
291 Jeff Fassero .20 .50
292 Ray Durham .40 1.00
293 Chad Ogea .20 .50
294 Bill Pulsipher .20 .50
295 Phil Nevin .40 1.00
296 Carlos Perez RC .50 1.25
297 Roberto Kelly .20 .50
298 Tim Wakefield .40 1.00
299 Jeff Manto .20 .50
300 Brian Hunter .20 .50
301 C.J. Nitkowski .20 .50
302 Dustin Hermanson .20 .50
303 John Mabry .20 .50
304 Orel Hershiser .40 1.00
305 Ron Villone .20 .50
306 Sean Bergman .20 .50
307 Tom Goodwin .20 .50
308 Al Reyes .20 .50
309 Todd Stottlemyre .20 .50
310 Rich Becker .20 .50
311 Joey Cora .20 .50
312 Ed Sprague .20 .50
313 John Smoltz UER .60 1.50
(3rd line; from spelled as form)
314 Frank Castillo .20 .50
315 Chris Hammond .20 .50
316 Ismael Valdes .20 .50
317 Pete Harnisch .20 .50
318 Bernard Gilkey .20 .50
319 John Kruk .40 1.00
320 Marc Newfield .20 .50
321 Brian Johnson .20 .50
322 Mark Portugal .20 .50
323 David Hulse .20 .50
324 Luis Ortiz UER .20 .50
(Below spelled beloe)
325 Mike Benjamin .20 .50
326 Brian Jordan .40 1.00
327 Shawn Green .40 1.00
328 Joe Oliver .20 .50
329 Felipe Lira .20 .50
330 Andre Dawson .40 1.00

1995 Finest Refractors

This set is a parallel to the basic Finest set, including the use of protective coating, the difference can be found in the refractive sheen. The cards were inserted at a rate of one in 12 packs.

*STARS: 4X TO 10X BASIC CARDS
*ROOKIES: 3X TO 8X BASIC CARDS

1995 Finest Flame Throwers

Randomly inserted in first series packs at a rate of 1:48, this nine-card set showcases strikeout leaders who bring on the heat. With a protective coating, a player photo is superimposed over a fiery orange background.

COMPLETE SET (9) 15.00 40.00
FT1 Jason Bere 1.25 3.00
FT2 Roger Clemens 12.50 30.00
FT3 Juan Guzman 1.25 3.00
FT4 John Hudek 1.25 3.00
FT5 Randy Johnson 6.00 15.00
FT6 Pedro Martinez 4.00 10.00
FT7 Jose Rijo 1.25 3.00
FT8 Bret Saberhagen 2.50 6.00
FT9 John Wetteland 2.50 6.00

1995 Finest Power Kings

Randomly inserted in series one packs at a rate of one in 24, Power Kings is an 18-card set highlighting top sluggers. With a protective coating, the fronts feature chromium technology that allows the player photo to be further enhanced as if to jump out from a blue lightning bolt background.

COMPLETE SET (18) 60.00 150.00
PK1 Bob Hamelin 1.00 2.50
PK2 Raul Mondesi 2.00 5.00
PK3 Ryan Klesko 2.00 5.00
PK4 Carlos Delgado 2.00 5.00
PK5 Manny Ramirez 3.00 8.00
PK6 Mike Piazza 8.00 20.00
PK7 Jeff Bagwell 3.00 8.00
PK8 Mo Vaughn 2.00 5.00
PK9 Frank Thomas 5.00 12.00
PK10 Ken Griffey Jr. 8.00 20.00
PK11 Albert Belle 2.00 5.00
PK12 Sammy Sosa 5.00 12.00
PK13 Dante Bichette 2.00 5.00
PK14 Gary Sheffield 2.00 5.00
PK15 Matt Williams 2.00 5.00
PK16 Fred McGriff 2.00 5.00
PK17 Barry Bonds 12.50 30.00
PK18 Cecil Fielder 2.00 5.00

1995 Finest Bronze

Available exclusively direct from Topps, this six-card set features 1994 league leaders. The fronts feature chromium metallized graphics, mounted on bronze and factory sealed in clear resin. The cards are numbered on the back "X of 6."

COMPLETE SET (6) 40.00 80.00
1 Matt Williams 3.00 8.00
2 Tony Gwynn 10.00 25.00
3 Jeff Bagwell 6.00 15.00
4 Ken Griffey Jr. 12.50 30.00
5 Paul O'Neill 2.00 5.00
6 Frank Thomas 6.00 15.00

1996 Finest

The 1996 Finest set (produced by Topps) was issued in two series of 191 cards and 168 cards respectively, for a total of 359 cards. The six-card foil packs originally retailed for $5.00 each. A protective film, designed to keep the card from scratching and to maintain original gloss, covers the front. This product provides collectors with the opportunity to complete a number of sets within sets, each with a different degree of insertion. Each card is numbered twice to indicate the set count and the theme count. Series 1 set covers four distinct themes: Finest Phenoms, Finest Intimidators, Finest Gamers and Finest Sterling. Within the first three themes, some players will be common (bronze trim), some uncommon (silver) and some rare (gold). Finest Sterling consists of star players included within one of the other three themes, but featured with a new design and different photography. The breakdown for the player selection of common, uncommon and rare cards is completely random. There are 110 common, 55 uncommon (1:4 packs) and 25 rare cards (1:24 packs). Series 2 covers four distict themes also with common, uncommon and rare cards seeded at the same ratio. The four themes are: Finest Franchises which features 36 team leaders and bonafide superstars, Finest Additions which features 47 players who have switched teams in '96, Finest Prodigies which features 45 best up-and-coming players, and Finest Sterling with 39 top stars. In addition to the cards' special borders, each card will also have either "common," "uncommon", or "rare" written within the numbering box on the card backs to let collectors know which type of card they hold.

COMP.BRONZE SER.1 (110) 10.00 25.00
COMP.BRONZE SER.2 (110) 10.00 25.00
COMMON BRONZE .20 .50
COMMON GOLD 2.00 5.00
COMMON G RC 2.00 5.00
COMMON SILVER 1.00 2.50
B5 Roberto Hernandez B .20 .50
B8 Terry Pendleton B .20 .50
B12 Ken Caminiti B .20 .50
B15 Dan Miceli B .20 .50
B16 Chipper Jones B .50 1.25
B17 John Wetteland B .20 .50
B19 Tim Naehring B .20 .50
B21 Eddie Murray B .50 1.25
B23 Kevin Appier B .20 .50
B24 Ken Griffey Jr. B .75 2.00
B26 Brian McRae B .20 .50
B27 Pedro Martinez B .30 .75
B28 Brian Jordan B .20 .50
B29 Mike Fetters B .20 .50
B30 Carlos Delgado B .20 .50
B31 Shane Reynolds B .20 .50
B32 Terry Steinbach B .20 .50
B34 Mark Leiter B .20 .50
B36 David Segui B .20 .50
B40 Fred McGriff B .30 .75
B44 Glenallen Hill B .20 .50
B45 Brady Anderson B .20 .50
B47 Jim Thome B .30 .75
B48 Frank Thomas B .50 1.25
B49 Chuck Knoblauch B .20 .50
B50 Len Dykstra B .20 .50
B53 Tom Pagnozzi B .20 .50
B55 Ricky Bones B .20 .50
B56 David Justice B .20 .50
B57 Steve Avery B .20 .50
B58 Robby Thompson B .20 .50
B61 Tony Gwynn B .60 1.50
B63 Denny Neagle B .20 .50
B67 Robin Ventura B .20 .50
B70 Kevin Seitzer B .20 .50
B71 Ramon Martinez B .20 .50
B75 Brian L.Hunter B .20 .50
B76 Alan Benes B .20 .50
B80 Ozzie Guillen B .20 .50
B82 Benji Gil B .20 .50
B85 Todd Hundley B .20 .50
B87 Pat Hentgen B .20 .50
B89 Chuck Finley B .20 .50
B92 Derek Jeter B 1.25 3.00
B93 Paul O'Neill B .30 .75
B94 Darrin Fletcher B .20 .50
B96 Delino DeShields B .20 .50
B97 Tim Salmon B .30 .75

B98 John Olerud B .20 .50
B101 Tim Wakefield B .20 .50
B103 Dave Stevens B .20 .50
B104 Orlando Merced B .20 .50
B106 Jay Bell B .20 .50
B107 John Burkett B .20 .50
B108 Chris Hoiles B .20 .50
B110 Dave Nilsson B .20 .50
B111 Rod Beck B .20 .50
B113 Mike Piazza B .75 2.00
B114 Mark Langston B .20 .50
B116 Rico Brogna B .20 .50
B118 Tom Goodwin B .20 .50
B119 Bryan Rekar B .20 .50
B120 David Cone B .20 .50
B122 Andy Pettitte B .30 .75
B123 Chili Davis B .20 .50
B124 John Smoltz B .30 .75
B125 H.Slocumb B .20 .50
B126 Dante Bichette B .20 .50
B128 Alex Gonzalez B .20 .50
B129 Jeff Montgomery B .20 .50
B131 Denny Martinez B .20 .50
B132 Mel Rojas B .20 .50
B133 Derek Bell B .20 .50
B134 Trevor Hoffman B .20 .50
B136 Darren Daulton B .20 .50
B137 Pete Schourek B .20 .50
B138 Phil Nevin B .20 .50
B139 Andres Galarraga B .20 .50
B140 Chad Fonville B .20 .50
B144 J.T. Snow B .20 .50
B146 Barry Bonds B 1.25 3.00
B147 Orel Hershiser B .20 .50
B148 Quilvio Veras B .20 .50
B149 Will Clark B .30 .75
B150 Jose Rijo B .20 .50
B152 Travis Fryman B .20 .50
B154 Alex Fernandez B .20 .50
B155 Wade Boggs B .30 .75
B156 Troy Percival B .20 .50
B157 Moises Alou B .20 .50
B158 Javy Lopez B .20 .50
B159 Jason Giambi B .20 .50
B162 Mark McGwire B 1.25 3.00
B163 Eric Karros B .20 .50
B166 Mickey,Tettleton B .20 .50
B167 Barry Larkin B .30 .75
B169 Ruben Sierra B .20 .50
B170 Bill Swift B .20 .50
B172 Chad Curtis B .20 .50
B173 Dean Palmer B .20 .50
B175 Bobby Bonilla B .20 .50
B176 Greg Colbrunn B .20 .50
B177 Jose Mesa B .20 .50
B178 Mike Greenwell B .20 .50
B181 Doug Drabek B .20 .50
B183 Wilson Alvarez B .20 .50
B184 Marty Cordova B .20 .50
B185 Hal Morris B .20 .50
B187 Carlos Garcia B .20 .50
B190 Marquis Grissom B .20 .50
B193 Will Clark B .30 .75
B194 Paul Molitor B .20 .50
B195 Kenny Rogers B .20 .50
B196 Reggie Sanders B .20 .50
B199 Raul Mondesi B .20 .50
B200 Lance Johnson B .20 .50
B201 Alvin Morman B .20 .50
B203 Jack McDowell B .20 .50
B204 Randy Myers B .20 .50
B205 Harold Baines B .20 .50
B206 Marty Cordova B .20 .50
B207 Rich Hunter B RC .20 .50
B208 Al Leiter B .20 .50
B209 Greg Gagne B .20 .50
B210 Ben McDonald B .20 .50
B212 Terry Adams B .20 .50
B213 Paul Sorrento B .20 .50
B214 Albert Belle B .20 .50
B215 Mike Blowers B .20 .50
B216 Jim Edmonds B .20 .50
B217 Felipe Crespo B .20 .50
B219 Shawon Dunston B .20 .50
B220 Jimmy Haynes B .20 .50
B221 Jose Canseco B .30 .75
B222 Eric Davis B .20 .50
B224 Tim Raines B .20 .50
B225 Tony Phillips B .20 .50
B226 Charlie Hayes B .20 .50
B227 Eric Owens B .20 .50
B228 Roberto Alomar B .30 .75
B233 Kenny Lofton B .20 .50
B236 Mark McGwire B 1.25 3.00
B237 Jay Buhner B .20 .50
B238 Craig Biggio B .30 .75
B240 Barry Bonds B 1.25 3.00
B244 Ron Gant B .20 .50
B245 Paul Wilson B .20 .50
B246 T.Hollandsworth B .20 .50
B247 Todd Zeile B .20 .50
B248 David Justice B .20 .50
B250 Moises Alou B .20 .50
B251 Bob Wolcott B .20 .50
B252 David Wells B .20 .50
B253 Juan Gonzalez B .20 .50
B254 Andres Galarraga B .20 .50
B255 Dave Hollins B .20 .50
B257 Sammy Sosa B .50 1.25
B258 Ivan Rodriguez B .30 .75
B259 Bip Roberts B .20 .50
B260 Tino Martinez B .30 .75
B262 Mike Stanley B .20 .50
B264 Butch Huskey B .20 .50
B265 Jeff Conine B .20 .50
B267 Mark Grace B .30 .75
B268 Jason Schmidt B .30 .75
B269 Otis Nixon B .20 .50
B271 Kirby Puckett B .50 1.25
B273 Andy Benes B .20 .50
B275 Mike Piazza B .75 2.00
B276 Rey Ordonez B .20 .50
B278 Gary Gaetti B .20 .50
B280 Robin Ventura B .20 .50
B281 Cal Ripken B 1.50 4.00
B282 Carlos Baerga B .20 .50
B283 Roger Cedeno B .20 .50
B285 Terrell Wade B .20 .50
B286 Kevin Brown B .20 .50
B287 Rafael Palmeiro B .30 .75
B288 Mo Vaughn B .20 .50
B292 Bob Tewksbury B .20 .50
B297 T.J. Mathews B .20 .50
B298 Manny Ramirez B .30 .75
B299 Jeff Bagwell B .30 .75
B301 Wade Boggs B .30 .75
B303 Steve Gibralter B .20 .50
B304 B.J. Surhoff B .20 .50
B306 Royce Clayton B .20 .50
B307 Sal Fasano B .20 .50
B309 Gary Sheffield B .20 .50
B310 Ken Hill B .20 .50
B311 Joe Girardi B .20 .50
B312 Matt Lawton B RC .20 .50
B314 Julio Franco B .20 .50
B315 Joe Carter B .20 .50
B316 Brooks Kieschnick B .20 .50
B318 H.Slocumb B .20 .50
B319 Barry Larkin B .30 .75
B320 Tony Gwynn B .60 1.50
B322 Frank Thomas B .50 1.25
B323 Edgar Martinez B .30 .75
B325 Henry Rodriguez B .20 .50
B326 Marvin Benard B RC .20 .50
B329 Ugueth Urbina B .20 .50
B331 Roger Salkeld B .20 .50
B332 Edgar Renteria B .20 .50
B333 Ryan Klesko B .20 .50
B334 Ray Lankford B .20 .50
B336 Justin Thompson B .20 .50
B339 Mark Clark B .20 .50
B340 Ruben Rivera B .20 .50
B342 Matt Williams B .20 .50
B343 F.Cordova B RC .20 .50
B344 Cecil Fielder B .20 .50
B348 Mark Grudzielanek B .20 .50
B349 Ron Coomer B .20 .50
B351 Rich Aurilia B RC .20 .50
B352 Jose Herrera B .20 .50
B356 Tony Clark B .20 .50
B358 Dan Naulty B .20 .50
B359 Checklist B .20 .50
G4 Marty Cordova G 2.00 5.00
G6 Tony Gwynn G 6.00 15.00
G9 Albert Belle G 2.00 5.00
G18 Kirby Puckett G 5.00 12.00
G20 Karim Garcia G 2.00 5.00
G25 Cal Ripken G 15.00 40.00
G33 Hideo Nomo G 5.00 12.00
G39 Ryne Sandberg G 8.00 20.00
G42 Jeff Bagwell G 1.50 4.00
G51 Jason Isringhausen G 2.00 5.00
G64 Mo Vaughn G 2.00 5.00
G66 Dante Bichette G 2.00 5.00
G74 Mark McGwire G 12.50 30.00
G81 Kenny Lofton G 2.00 5.00
G83 Jim Edmonds G 2.00 5.00
G90 Mike Mussina G 3.00 8.00
G100 Jeff Conine G 2.00 5.00
G102 Johnny Damon G 3.00 8.00
G105 Barry Bonds G 12.50 30.00
G117 Jose Canseco G 3.00 8.00
G135 Ken Griffey Jr. G 8.00 20.00
G141 Chipper Jones G 5.00 12.00
G145 Greg Maddux G 8.00 20.00
G164 Jay Buhner G 2.00 5.00
G186 Frank Thomas G 5.00 12.00
G191 Checklist G 2.00 5.00
G192 Chipper Jones G 5.00 12.00
G197 Roberto Alomar G 3.00 8.00
G198 Dennis Eckersley G 2.00 5.00
G202 George Arias G 2.00 5.00
G232 Hideo Nomo G 5.00 12.00
G243 Chris Snopek G 2.00 5.00
G249 Tim Salmon G 3.00 8.00
G266 Matt Williams G 2.00 5.00
G270 Randy Johnson G 5.00 12.00
G279 Paul Molitor G 2.00 5.00
G290 Cecil Fielder G 2.00 5.00
G294 L.Hernandez G RC 4.00 10.00
G300 Marty Janzen G RC 2.00 5.00
G308 Ron Gant G 2.00 5.00
G321 Ryan Klesko G 2.00 5.00
G324 Jermaine Dye G 2.00 5.00
G330 Jason Giambi G 2.00 5.00
G335 Edgar Martinez G 3.00 8.00
G338 Rey Ordonez G 2.00 5.00
G347 Sammy Sosa G 5.00 12.00
G354 Juan Gonzalez G 2.00 5.00
G355 Craig Biggio G 3.00 8.00
S1 Greg Maddux S UER 4.00 10.00
95 stats listed as Mariners
S2 Bernie Williams S 1.50 4.00
S3 Ivan Rodriguez S 1.50 4.00
S7 Barry Larkin S 1.50 4.00
S10 Ray Lankford S 1.00 2.50
S11 Mike Piazza S 4.00 10.00
S13 Larry Walker S 1.00 2.50
S14 Matt Williams S 1.00 2.50
S22 Tim Salmon S 1.50 4.00
S35 Edgar Martinez S 1.50 4.00
S37 Gregg Jefferies S 1.00 2.50
S38 Bill Pulsipher S 1.00 2.50
S41 Shawn Green S 1.00 2.50
S43 Jim Abbott S 1.50 4.00
S46 Roger Clemens S 5.00 12.00
S52 Rondell White S 1.00 2.50
S54 Dennis Eckersley S 1.00 2.50
S59 Hideo Nomo S 2.50 6.00
S60 Gary Sheffield S 1.00 2.50
S62 Will Clark S 1.50 4.00
S65 Bret Boone S 1.00 2.50
S68 Rafael Palmeiro S 1.50 4.00
S69 Carlos Baerga S 1.00 2.50
S72 Tom Glavine S 1.50 4.00
S73 Garret Anderson S 1.00 2.50
S77 Randy Johnson S 2.50 6.00
S78 Jeff King S 1.00 2.50
S79 Kirby Puckett S 2.50 6.00
S84 Cecil Fielder S 1.00 2.50
S86 Reggie Sanders S 1.00 2.50
S88 Ryan Klesko S 1.00 2.50
S91 John Valentin S 1.00 2.50
S95 Manny Ramirez S 1.50 4.00
S99 Vinny Castilla S 1.00 2.50
S109 Carlos Perez S 1.00 2.50
S112 Craig Biggio S 1.50 4.00
S115 Juan Gonzalez S 1.00 2.50
S121 Ray Durham S 1.00 2.50
S127 C.J. Nitkowski S 1.00 2.50
S130 Raul Mondesi S 1.00 2.50
S142 Lee Smith S 1.00 2.50
S143 Joe Carter S 1.00 2.50
S151 Mo Vaughn S 1.00 2.50
S153 Frank Rodriguez S 1.00 2.50
S160 Steve Finley S 1.00 2.50
S161 Jeff Bagwell S 1.50 4.00
S165 Cal Ripken S 8.00 20.00
S168 Lyle Mouton S 1.00 2.50
S171 Sammy Sosa S 2.50 6.00
S174 John Franco S 1.00 2.50
S179 Greg Vaughn S 1.00 2.50
S180 Mark Wohlers S 1.00 2.50
S182 Paul O'Neill S 1.50 4.00
S188 Albert Belle S 1.00 2.50
S189 Mark Grace S 1.50 4.00
S211 Ernie Young S 1.00 2.50
S218 Fred McGriff S 1.50 4.00
S223 Kimera Bartee S 1.00 2.50
S229 Rickey Henderson S 2.50 6.00
S230 Sterling Hitchcock S 1.00 2.50
S231 Bernard Gilkey S 1.00 2.50
S234 Ryne Sandberg S 4.00 10.00
S235 Greg Maddux S 4.00 10.00
S239 Todd Stottlemyre S 1.00 2.50
S241 Jason Kendall S 1.00 2.50
S242 Paul O'Neill S 1.50 4.00
S256 Devon White S 1.00 2.50
S261 Chuck Knoblauch S 1.00 2.50
S263 Wally Joyner S 1.00 2.50
S272 Andy Fox S 1.00 2.50
S274 Sean Berry S 1.00 2.50
S277 Benito Santiago S 1.00 2.50
S284 Chad Mottola S 1.00 2.50
S289 Dante Bichette S 1.00 2.50
S291 Dwight Gooden S 1.00 2.50
S293 Kevin Mitchell S 1.00 2.50
S295 Russ Davis S 1.00 2.50
S296 Chan Ho Park S 1.00 2.50
S302 Larry Walker S 1.00 2.50
S305 Ken Griffey Jr. S 4.00 10.00
S313 Billy Wagner S 1.00 2.50
S317 Mike Grace S RC 1.00 2.50
S327 Kenny Lofton S 1.00 2.50
S328 Derek Bell S 1.00 2.50
S337 Gary Sheffield S 1.00 2.50
S341 Mark Grace S 1.50 4.00
S345 Andres Galarraga S 1.00 2.50
S346 Brady Anderson S 1.00 2.50
S350 Derek Jeter S 5.00 12.00
S353 Jay Buhner S 1.00 2.50
S357 Tino Martinez S 1.50 4.00

1996 Finest Refractors

This 359-card set is parallel to the basic 1996 Finest set. The first 191 cards are parallel to the regular Series 1 with the second 168 cards parallel to regular Series 2. The word "refractor" is printed above the numbers on the card backs. The rate of insertion is one in 12 for a Bronze refractor (common), one in 48 for a Silver refractor (uncommon), and one in 288 for a Gold refractor (rare).

*BRONZE STARS: 4X to 10X BASIC CARDS
*GOLD STARS: .75X TO 2X BASIC CARDS
*SILVER STARS: 1.25X TO 3X BASIC CARDS

1996 Finest Landmark

This four-card limited edition medallion set came with a Certificate of Authenticity and was produced by Topps. Only 2,000 sets were made. The fronts feature color action player photos on a gold ball and star metallic background. The backs carry player biographical and career information including batting records.

COMPLETE SET (4) 40.00 100.00
1 Greg Maddux 12.50 30.00
2 Albert Belle 4.00 10.00
3 Cal Ripken 25.00 60.00
4 Eddie Murray 6.00 15.00

1997 Finest Promos

This five-card set features one promo card for each of the five themes found in the 1997 Finest Series I set. The fronts, backs, and card numbers are identical to the regular set with the exception of the words, "Promotional Sample Not for Resale" printed in red across the back. The cards are checklisted below according to their numbers in the regular set.

COMPLETE SET (5) 3.20 8.00
1 Barry Bonds C .60 1.50
15 Derek Jeter C 1.25 3.00
30 Mark McGwire C 1.00 2.50
143 Hideo Nomo U .40 1.00
159 Jeff Bagwell R .60 1.50

1997 Finest

The 1997 Finest set (produced by Topps) was issued in two series of 175 cards each and was distributed in six-card packs with a suggested retail price of $5.00. The fronts feature a borderless action player photo while the backs carry player information with another player photo. Series one is divided into five distinct themes: Finest Hurlers (top pitchers), Finest Blue Chips (up-and-coming future stars), Finest Power (long-ball hitters), Finest Warriors (superstar players), and Finest Masters (hottest players). Series two is also divided into five distinct themes: Finest Power (power hitters and pitchers), Finest Masters (top players), Finest Blue Chips (top new players), Finest Competitors (hottest players), and Finest Acquisitions (latest trades and new signings). All five themes of each series have common cards (1-100 and 176-275) designated with bronze trim, uncommon (101-150 and 276-325) with silver trim and an insertion rate of one in four for both series, and rare (151-175 and 326-350) with gold trim and an insertion rate of one in 24 for both series. The cards are numbered on the backs within the whole set and within the theme set. Notable Rookie Cards include Brian Giles.

COMP.BRONZE SER.1 (100) 12.50 30.00
COMP.BRONZE SER.2 (100) 12.50 30.00
COM.BRON.(1-100/176-275) .20 .50
COMP.SILVER SER.1 (50)
COMP.SILVER SER.2 (50)
COM.SILV.(101-150/276-325) .75 2.00
COMP.GOLD SER.1 (25)
COMP.GOLD SER.2 (25)
COM.GOLD (151-175/326-350) 2.00 5.00
BICHETTE/JETER BOTH NUMBERED 155
BICHETTE UER SHOULD BE NUMBER 5
1 Barry Bonds B 1.25 3.00
2 Ryne Sandberg B .75 2.00
3 Brian Jordan B .20 .50
4 Rocky Coppinger B .20 .50
5 Dante Bichette B UER .20 .50
Card is erroneously numbered 155
6 Al Martin B .20 .50
7 Charles Nagy B .20 .50
8 Otis Nixon B .20 .50
9 Mark Johnson B .20 .50
10 Jeff Bagwell B .30 .75
11 Ken Hill B .20 .50
12 Willie Adams B .20 .50
13 Raul Mondesi B .20 .50
14 Reggie Sanders B .20 .50
15 Derek Jeter B 1.25 3.00
16 Jermaine Dye B .20 .50
17 Edgar Renteria B .20 .50
18 Travis Fryman B .20 .50
19 Roberto Hernandez B .20 .50
20 Sammy Sosa B .50 1.25
21 Garret Anderson B .20 .50
22 Rey Ordonez B .20 .50
23 Glenallen Hill B .20 .50
24 Dave Nilsson B .20 .50
25 Kevin Brown B .20 .50
26 Brian McRae B .20 .50
27 Joey Hamilton B .20 .50
28 Jamey Wright B .20 .50
29 Frank Thomas B .50 1.25
30 Mark McGwire B 1.25 3.00
31 Ramon Martinez B .20 .50
32 Jaime Bluma B .20 .50
33 Frank Rodriguez B .20 .50
34 Andy Benes B .20 .50
35 Jay Buhner B .20 .50
36 Justin Thompson B .20 .50
37 Darin Erstad B .20 .50
38 Gregg Jefferies B .20 .50
39 Jeff D'Amico B .20 .50
40 Pedro Martinez B .30 .75
41 Nomar Garciaparra B .75 2.00
42 Jose Valentin B .20 .50
43 Pat Hentgen B .20 .50
44 Will Clark B .30 .75
45 Bernie Williams B .30 .75
46 Luis Castillo B .20 .50
47 B.J. Surhoff B .20 .50
48 Greg Gagne B .20 .50
49 Pete Schourek B .20 .50
50 Mike Piazza B .75 2.00
51 Dwight Gooden B .20 .50
52 Javy Lopez B .20 .50
53 Chuck Finley B .20 .50
54 James Baldwin B .20 .50
55 Jack McDowell B .20 .50
56 Royce Clayton B .20 .50
57 Carlos Delgado B .20 .50
58 Neifi Perez B .20 .50
59 Eddie Taubensee B .20 .50
60 Rafael Palmeiro B .30 .75
61 Marty Cordova B .20 .50
62 Wade Boggs B .30 .75
63 Rickey Henderson B .50 1.25
64 Mike Hampton B .20 .50
65 Troy Percival B .20 .50
66 Barry Larkin B .30 .75
67 J.Allensworth B .20 .50
68 Mark Clark B .20 .50
69 Mike Lansing B .20 .50
70 Mark Grudzielanek B .20 .50
71 Todd Stottlemyre B .20 .50
72 Juan Guzman B .20 .50
73 John Burkett B .20 .50
74 Wilson Alvarez B .20 .50
75 Ellis Burks B .20 .50
76 Bobby Higginson B .20 .50
77 Ricky Bottalico B .20 .50
78 Omar Vizquel B .30 .75
79 Paul Sorrento B .20 .50
80 Denny Neagle B .20 .50
81 Roger Pavlik B .20 .50
82 Mike Lieberthal B .20 .50
83 Devon White B .20 .50
84 John Olerud B .20 .50
85 Kevin Appier B .20 .50
86 Joe Girardi B .20 .50
87 Paul O'Neill B .30 .75
88 Mike Sweeney B .20 .50
89 John Smiley B .20 .50
90 Ivan Rodriguez B .30 .75
91 Randy Myers B .20 .50
92 Bip Roberts B .20 .50
93 Jose Mesa B .20 .50
94 Paul Wilson B .20 .50
95 Mike Mussina B .30 .75
96 Ben McDonald B .20 .50
97 John Mabry B .20 .50
98 Tom Goodwin B .20 .50
99 Edgar Martinez B .30 .75
100 Andruw Jones B .30 .75
101 Jose Canseco S 1.25 3.00
102 Billy Wagner S .75 2.00
103 Dante Bichette S .75 2.00
104 Curt Schilling S .75 2.00
105 Dean Palmer S .75 2.00
106 Larry Walker S .75 2.00
107 Bernie Williams S 1.25 3.00
108 Chipper Jones S 2.00 5.00
109 Gary Sheffield S .75 2.00
110 Randy Johnson S 2.00 5.00
111 Roberto Alomar S 1.25 3.00
112 Todd Walker S .75 2.00
113 Sandy Alomar Jr. S .75 2.00
114 John Jaha S .75 2.00
115 Ken Caminiti S UER .75 2.00
Card is numbered 135
116 Ryan Klesko S .75 2.00
117 Mariano Rivera S 2.00 5.00
118 Jason Giambi S .75 2.00
119 Lance Johnson S .75 2.00
120 Robin Ventura S .75 2.00
121 Todd Hollandsworth S .75 2.00
122 Johnny Damon S 1.25 3.00
123 W. VanLandingham S .75 2.00
124 Jason Kendall S .75 2.00
125 Vinny Castilla S .75 2.00
126 Harold Baines S .75 2.00
127 Joe Carter S .75 2.00
128 Craig Biggio S 1.25 3.00
129 Tony Clark S .75 2.00
130 Ron Gant S .75 2.00
131 David Segui S .75 2.00
132 Steve Trachsel S .75 2.00
133 Scott Rolen S 1.25 3.00
134 Mike Stanley S .75 2.00
135 Cal Ripken S 6.00 15.00
136 John Smoltz S 1.25 3.00
137 Bobby Jones S .75 2.00
138 Manny Ramirez S 1.25 3.00
139 Ken Griffey Jr. S 3.00 8.00
140 Chuck Knoblauch S .75 2.00
141 Mark Grace S 1.25 3.00
142 Chris Snopek S .75 2.00
143 Hideo Nomo S 2.00 5.00
144 Tim Salmon S 1.25 3.00
145 David Cone S .75 2.00
146 Eric Young S .75 2.00
147 Jeff Brantley S .75 2.00
148 Jim Thome S 1.25 3.00
149 Trevor Hoffman S .75 2.00
150 Juan Gonzalez S .75 2.00
151 Mike Piazza G 8.00 20.00
152 Ivan Rodriguez G 3.00 8.00
153 Mo Vaughn G 2.00 5.00
154 Brady Anderson G 2.00 5.00
155 Mark McGwire G 12.50 30.00
156 Rafael Palmeiro G 3.00 8.00
157 Barry Larkin G 3.00 8.00
158 Greg Maddux G 8.00 20.00
159 Jeff Bagwell G 3.00 8.00
160 Frank Thomas G 5.00 12.00
161 Ken Caminiti G 2.00 5.00
162 Andruw Jones G 3.00 8.00
163 Dennis Eckersley G 2.00 5.00
164 Jeff Conine G 2.00 5.00
165 Jim Edmonds G 2.00 5.00
166 Derek Jeter G 12.50 30.00
167 Vladimir Guerrero G 5.00 12.00
168 Sammy Sosa G 5.00 12.00
169 Tony Gwynn G 6.00 15.00
170 Andres Galarraga G 2.00 5.00
171 Todd Hundley G 2.00 5.00
172 Jay Buhner G UER 2.00 5.00
Card is numbered 164
173 Paul Molitor G 2.00 5.00
174 Kenny Lofton G 2.00 5.00
175 Barry Bonds G 12.50 30.00
176 Gary Sheffield B .20 .50
177 Dmitri Young B .20 .50
178 Jay Bell B .20 .50
179 David Wells B .20 .50
180 Walt Weiss B .20 .50
181 Paul Molitor B .20 .50
182 Jose Guillen B .20 .50
183 Al Leiter B .20 .50
184 Mike Fetters B .20 .50
185 Mark Langston B .20 .50
186 Fred McGriff B .30 .75
187 Darrin Fletcher B .20 .50
188 Brant Brown B .20 .50
189 Geronimo Berroa B .20 .50
190 Jim Thome B .30 .75
191 Jose Vizcaino B .20 .50
192 Andy Ashby B .20 .50
193 Rusty Greer B .20 .50
194 Brian Hunter B .20 .50
195 Chris Hoiles B .20 .50
196 Orlando Merced B .20 .50
197 Brett Butler B .20 .50
198 Derek Bell B .20 .50
199 Bobby Bonilla B .20 .50
200 Alex Ochoa B .20 .50
201 Wally Joyner B .20 .50
202 Mo Vaughn B .20 .50
203 Doug Drabek B .20 .50
204 Tino Martinez B .30 .75
205 Roberto Alomar B .30 .75
206 Brian Giles B RC 1.25 3.00
207 Todd Worrell B .20 .50
208 Alan Benes B .20 .50
209 Jim Leyritz B .20 .50
210 Darryl Hamilton B .20 .50
211 Jimmy Key B .20 .50
212 Juan Gonzalez B .20 .50
213 Vinny Castilla B .20 .50
214 Chuck Knoblauch B .20 .50
215 Tony Phillips B .20 .50
216 Jeff Cirillo B .20 .50
217 Carlos Garcia B .20 .50
218 Brooks Kieschnick B .20 .50
219 Marquis Grissom B .20 .50
220 Dan Wilson B .20 .50
221 Greg Vaughn B .20 .50
222 John Wetteland B .20 .50
223 Andres Galarraga B .20 .50
224 Ozzie Guillen B .20 .50
225 Kevin Elster B .20 .50
226 Bernard Gilkey B .20 .50
227 Mike Macfarlane B .20 .50
228 Heathcliff Slocumb B .20 .50
229 Wendell Magee Jr. B .20 .50
230 Carlos Baerga B .20 .50
231 Kevin Seitzer B .20 .50
232 Henry Rodriguez B .20 .50
233 Roger Clemens B 1.00 2.50
234 Mark Wohlers B .20 .50
235 Eddie Murray B .50 1.25
236 Todd Zeile B .20 .50
237 J.T. Snow B .20 .50
238 Ken Griffey Jr. B .75 2.00
239 Sterling Hitchcock B .20 .50
240 Albert Belle B .20 .50
241 Terry Steinbach B .20 .50
242 Robb Nen B .20 .50
243 Mark McLemore B .20 .50
244 Jeff King B .20 .50
245 Tony Clark B .20 .50
246 Tim Salmon B .30 .75
247 Benito Santiago B .20 .50
248 Robin Ventura B .20 .50
249 Bubba Trammell B RC .20 .50
250 Chili Davis B .20 .50
251 John Valentin B .20 .50
252 Cal Ripken B 1.50 4.00
253 Matt Williams B .20 .50
254 Jeff Kent B .20 .50
255 Eric Karros B .20 .50
256 Ray Lankford B .20 .50
257 Ed Sprague B .20 .50
258 Shane Reynolds B .20 .50
259 Jaime Navarro B .20 .50
260 Eric Davis B .20 .50
261 Orel Hershiser B .20 .50
262 Mark Grace B .30 .75
263 Rod Beck B .20 .50
264 Ismael Valdes B .20 .50
265 Manny Ramirez B .30 .75
266 Ken Caminiti B .20 .50
267 Tim Naehring B .20 .50
268 Jose Rosado B .20 .50
269 Greg Colbrunn B .20 .50
270 Dean Palmer B .20 .50
271 David Justice B .20 .50
272 Scott Spiezio B .20 .50
273 Chipper Jones B .50 1.25
274 Mel Rojas B .20 .50
275 Bartolo Colon B .20 .50
276 Darin Erstad S .75 2.00
277 Sammy Sosa S 2.00 5.00
278 Rafael Palmeiro S 1.25 3.00
279 Frank Thomas S 2.00 5.00
280 Ruben Rivera S .75 2.00
281 Hal Morris S .75 2.00
282 Jay Buhner S .75 2.00
283 Kenny Lofton S .75 2.00
284 Jose Canseco S 1.25 3.00
285 Alex Fernandez S .75 2.00
286 Todd Helton S 2.00 5.00
287 Andy Pettitte S 1.25 3.00
288 John Franco S .75 2.00
289 Ivan Rodriguez S 1.25 3.00
290 Ellis Burks S .75 2.00
291 Julio Franco S .75 2.00
292 Mike Piazza S 3.00 8.00
293 Brian Jordan S .75 2.00
294 Greg Maddux S 3.00 8.00
295 Bob Abreu S 1.25 3.00
296 Rondell White S .75 2.00
297 Moises Alou S .75 2.00
298 Tony Gwynn S 2.50 6.00
299 Deion Sanders S 1.25 3.00
300 Jeff Montgomery S .75 2.00
301 Ray Durham S .75 2.00
302 John Wasdin S .75 2.00
303 Ryne Sandberg S 3.00 8.00
304 Delino DeShields S .75 2.00
305 Mark McGwire S 5.00 12.00
306 Andruw Jones S 1.25 3.00
307 Kevin Orie S .75 2.00
308 Matt Williams S .75 2.00
309 Karim Garcia S .75 2.00
310 Derek Jeter S 5.00 12.00
311 Mo Vaughn S .75 2.00
312 Brady Anderson S .75 2.00
313 Barry Bonds S 5.00 12.00
314 Steve Finley S .75 2.00
315 Vladimir Guerrero S 2.00 5.00
316 Matt Morris S .75 2.00
317 Tom Glavine S 1.25 3.00
318 Jeff Bagwell S 1.25 3.00
319 Albert Belle S .75 2.00
320 Hideki Irabu S RC .75 2.00
321 Andres Galarraga S .75 2.00
322 Cecil Fielder S .75 2.00
323 Barry Larkin S 1.25 3.00
324 Todd Hundley S .75 2.00
325 Fred McGriff S 1.25 3.00
326 Gary Sheffield G 2.00 5.00
327 Craig Biggio G 3.00 8.00
328 Raul Mondesi G 2.00 5.00
329 Edgar Martinez G 3.00 8.00
330 Chipper Jones G 5.00 12.00
331 Bernie Williams G 3.00 8.00
332 Juan Gonzalez G 2.00 5.00
333 Ron Gant G 2.00 5.00
334 Cal Ripken G 15.00 40.00
335 Larry Walker G 2.00 5.00
336 Matt Williams G 2.00 5.00

Card	Low	High
337 Jose Cruz Jr. G RC	2.00	5.00
338 Joe Carter G	2.00	5.00
339 Wilton Guerrero G	2.00	5.00
340 Cecil Fielder G	2.00	5.00
341 Todd Walker G	2.00	5.00
342 Ken Griffey Jr. G	8.00	20.00
343 Ryan Klesko G	2.00	5.00
344 Roger Clemens G	10.00	25.00
345 Hideo Nomo G	5.00	12.00
346 Dante Bichette G	2.00	5.00
347 Albert Belle G	2.00	5.00
348 Randy Johnson G	5.00	12.00
349 Manny Ramirez G	3.00	8.00
350 John Smoltz G	3.00	8.00

1997 Finest Embossed

This 150-card set is parallel to regular set numbers 101-175 of Finest Series 1 and 276-350 of Finest Series 2. There is an embossed version of cards 101-150 and 276-325 with an insertion rate of one in 16 for each series. There is an embossed die-cut version of cards 151-175 and 326-350 with an insertion rate of one in 96 packs for each series.

*SILV.STARS: .60X TO 1.5X BASIC CARD
*SILVER ROOKIES: .5X TO 1.25X BASIC
*GOLD STARS: .75X TO 2X BASIC CARD
*GOLD ROOKIES: .5X TO 1.2X BASIC CARD

1997 Finest Embossed Refractors

This 150-card set is a parallel version of the regular Finest Embossed set and is similar in design. The difference is found in the refractive quality of the cards.

*SILVER STARS: 2.5X TO 6X BASIC CARDS
*SILVER ROOKIES: 2X TO 5X BASIC CARDS
*SER.1 GOLD STARS: 2X TO 5X BASIC
*SER.2 GOLD STARS: 2X TO 5X BASIC
*SER.2 GOLD RC'S: 1.25X TO 3X BASIC

1997 Finest Refractors

This 350-card set is parallel and similar in design to the regular Finest set. The distinction is in the refractive quality of the card. Cards 1-100 and 176-275 have an insertion rate of one in 12 in each series packs. Cards 101-150 and 276-325 have an insertion rate of one in 48 in each series packs. Cards 151-175 and 326-350 have an insertion rate of one in 288.

*BRONZE STARS: 4X TO 10X BASIC CARD
*BRONZE RC'S: 1.25X TO 3X BASIC CARD
*SILVER STARS: 1.25X TO 3X BASIC CARD
*SILVER ROOKIES: 1X TO 2.5X BASIC CARD
*GOLD STARS: 1.25X TO 3X BASIC CARD
*GOLD ROOKIES: .75X TO 2X BASIC CARD

1998 Finest Pre-Production

These five cards tagged with a "PP" prefix were created so collectors and dealers could get an early look about the 1998 Finest set.

Card	Low	High
COMPLETE SET (5)	4.00	10.00
PP1 Nomar Garciaparra	1.00	2.50
PP2 Mark McGwire	1.00	2.50
PP3 Ivan Rodriguez	.60	1.50
PP4 Ken Griffey Jr	1.00	2.50
PP5 Roger Clemens	1.00	2.50

1998 Finest

This 275-card set (produced by Topps) was distributed in first and second series six-card packs with a suggested retail price of $5. Series one contains cards 1-150 and series two contains cards 151-275. Each card features action color player photos printed on 26 pt. card stock with each postion identified by a different card design. The backs carry player information and career statistics.

Card	Low	High
COMPLETE SET (275)	20.00	50.00
COMP.SERIES 1 (150)	10.00	25.00
COMP.SERIES 2 (125)	10.00	25.00
1 Larry Walker	.15	.40
2 Andruw Jones	.25	.60
3 Ramon Martinez	.08	.25
4 Geronimo Berroa	.08	.25
5 David Justice	.15	.40
6 Rusty Greer	.15	.40
7 Chad Ogea	.08	.25
8 Tom Goodwin	.08	.25
9 Tino Martinez	.25	.60
10 Jose Guillen	.15	.40
11 Jeffrey Hammonds	.08	.25
12 Brian McRae	.08	.25
13 Jeremi Gonzalez	.08	.25
14 Craig Counsell	.08	.25
15 Mike Piazza	.60	1.50
16 Greg Maddux	.60	1.50
17 Todd Greene	.08	.25
18 Rondell White	.15	.40
19 Kirk Rueter	.08	.25
20 Tony Clark	.08	.25
21 Brad Radke	.15	.40
22 Jaret Wright	.08	.25
23 Carlos Delgado	.15	.40
24 Dustin Hermanson	.08	.25
25 Gary Sheffield	.15	.40
26 Jose Canseco	.25	.60
27 Kevin Young	.15	.40
28 David Wells	.15	.40
29 Mariano Rivera	.40	1.00
30 Reggie Sanders	.15	.40
31 Mike Cameron	.08	.25
32 Bobby Witt	.08	.25
33 Kevin Orie	.08	.25
34 Royce Clayton	.08	.25
35 Edgar Martinez	.25	.60
36 Neifi Perez	.08	.25
37 Kevin Appier	.15	.40
38 Darryl Hamilton	.08	.25
39 Michael Tucker	.08	.25
40 Roger Clemens	.75	2.00
41 Carl Everett	.15	.40
42 Mike Sweeney	.15	.40
43 Pat Meares	.08	.25
44 Brian Giles	.15	.40
45 Matt Morris	.15	.40
46 Jason Dickson	.08	.25
47 Rich Loiselle RC	.15	.40
48 Joe Girardi	.08	.25
49 Steve Trachsel	.08	.25
50 Ben Grieve	.08	.25
51 Brian Johnson	.08	.25
52 Hideki Irabu	.08	.25
53 J.T. Snow	.15	.40
54 Mike Hampton	.15	.40
55 Dave Nilsson	.08	.25
56 Alex Fernandez	.08	.25
57 Brett Tomko	.08	.25
58 Wally Joyner	.15	.40
59 Kelvim Escobar	.08	.25
60 Roberto Alomar	.25	.60
61 Todd Jones	.08	.25
62 Paul O'Neill	.25	.60
63 Jamie Moyer	.15	.40
64 Mark Wohlers	.08	.25
65 Jose Cruz Jr.	.08	.25
66 Troy Percival	.15	.40
67 Rick Reed	.08	.25
68 Will Clark	.25	.60
69 Jamey Wright	.08	.25
70 Mike Mussina	.25	.60
71 David Cone	.15	.40
72 Ryan Klesko	.15	.40
73 Scott Hatteberg	.08	.25
74 James Baldwin	.08	.25
75 Tony Womack	.08	.25
76 Carlos Perez	.08	.25
77 Charles Nagy	.08	.25
78 Jeromy Burnitz	.15	.40
79 Shane Reynolds	.08	.25
80 Cliff Floyd	.15	.40
81 Jason Kendall	.15	.40
82 Chad Curtis	.08	.25
83 Matt Karchner	.08	.25
84 Ricky Bottalico	.08	.25
85 Sammy Sosa	.40	1.00
86 Javy Lopez	.15	.40
87 Jeff Kent	.15	.40
88 Shawn Green	.15	.40
89 Joey Cora	.08	.25
90 Tony Gwynn	.50	1.25
91 Bob Tewksbury	.08	.25
92 Derek Jeter	1.00	2.50
93 Eric Davis	.15	.40
94 Jeff Fassero	.08	.25
95 Denny Neagle	.08	.25
96 Ismael Valdes	.08	.25
97 Tim Salmon	.25	.60
98 Mark Grudzielanek	.08	.25
99 Curt Schilling	.15	.40
100 Ken Griffey Jr.	.60	1.50
101 Edgardo Alfonzo	.08	.25
102 Vinny Castilla	.15	.40
103 Jose Rosado	.08	.25
104 Scott Erickson	.08	.25
105 Alan Benes	.08	.25
106 Shannon Stewart	.15	.40
107 Delino DeShields	.08	.25
108 Mark Loretta	.08	.25
109 Todd Hundley	.08	.25
110 Chuck Knoblauch	.15	.40
111 Todd Helton	.25	.60
112 F.P. Santangelo	.08	.25
113 Jeff Cirillo	.08	.25
114 Omar Vizquel	.25	.60
115 John Valentin	.08	.25
116 Damion Easley	.08	.25
117 Matt Lawton	.08	.25
118 Jim Thome	.25	.60
119 Sandy Alomar Jr.	.08	.25
120 Albert Belle	.15	.40
121 Chris Stynes	.08	.25
122 Butch Huskey	.08	.25
123 Shawn Estes	.08	.25
124 Terry Adams	.08	.25
125 Ivan Rodriguez	.25	.60
126 Ron Gant	.15	.40
127 John Mabry	.08	.25
128 Jeff Shaw	.08	.25
129 Jeff Montgomery	.08	.25
130 Justin Thompson	.08	.25
131 Livan Hernandez	.15	.40
132 Ugueth Urbina	.08	.25
133 Scott Servais	.08	.25
134 Troy O'Leary	.08	.25
135 Cal Ripken	1.25	3.00
136 Quilvio Veras	.08	.25
137 Pedro Astacio	.08	.25
138 Willie Greene	.08	.25
139 Lance Johnson	.08	.25
140 Nomar Garciaparra	.60	1.50
141 Jose Offerman	.08	.25
142 Scott Rolen	.25	.60
143 Derek Bell	.08	.25
144 Johnny Damon	.25	.60
145 Mark McGwire	1.00	2.50
146 Chan Ho Park	.15	.40
147 Edgar Renteria	.15	.40
148 Eric Young	.08	.25
149 Craig Biggio	.25	.60
150 Checklist (1-150)	.08	.25
151 Frank Thomas	.40	1.00
152 John Wetteland	.15	.40
153 Mike Lansing	.08	.25
154 Pedro Martinez	.25	.60
155 Rico Brogna	.08	.25
156 Kevin Brown	.25	.60
157 Alex Rodriguez	.60	1.50
158 Wade Boggs	.25	.60
159 Richard Hidalgo	.08	.25
160 Mark Grace	.25	.60
161 Jose Mesa	.08	.25
162 John Olerud	.15	.40
163 Tim Belcher	.08	.25
164 Chuck Finley	.15	.40
165 Brian Hunter	.08	.25
166 Joe Carter	.15	.40
167 Stan Javier	.08	.25
168 Jay Bell	.15	.40
169 Ray Lankford	.15	.40
170 John Smoltz	.25	.60
171 Ed Sprague	.08	.25
172 Jason Giambi	.15	.40
173 Todd Walker	.08	.25
174 Paul Konerko	.15	.40
175 Rey Ordonez	.08	.25
176 Dante Bichette	.15	.40
177 Bernie Williams	.25	.60
178 Jon Nunnally	.08	.25
179 Rafael Palmeiro	.25	.60
180 Jay Buhner	.15	.40
181 Devon White	.15	.40
182 Jeff D'Amico	.08	.25
183 Walt Weiss	.15	.40
184 Scott Spiezio	.08	.25
185 Moises Alou	.15	.40
186 Carlos Baerga	.08	.25
187 Todd Zeile	.15	.40
188 Gregg Jefferies	.08	.25
189 Mo Vaughn	.15	.40
190 Terry Steinbach	.08	.25
191 Ray Durham	.15	.40
192 Robin Ventura	.15	.40
193 Jeff Reed	.08	.25
194 Ken Caminiti	.15	.40
195 Eric Karros	.15	.40
196 Wilson Alvarez	.08	.25
197 Gary Gaetti	.15	.40
198 Andres Galarraga	.15	.40
199 Alex Gonzalez	.08	.25
200 Garret Anderson	.15	.40
201 Andy Benes	.08	.25
202 Harold Baines	.15	.40
203 Ron Coomer	.08	.25
204 Dean Palmer	.15	.40
205 Reggie Jefferson	.08	.25
206 John Burkett	.08	.25
207 Jermaine Allensworth	.08	.25
208 Bernard Gilkey	.08	.25
209 Jeff Bagwell	.25	.60
210 Kenny Lofton	.15	.40
211 Bobby Jones	.08	.25
212 Bartolo Colon	.15	.40
213 Jim Edmonds	.15	.40
214 Pat Hentgen	.08	.25
215 Matt Williams	.15	.40
216 Bob Abreu	.15	.40
217 Jorge Posada	.25	.60
218 Marty Cordova	.08	.25
219 Ken Hill	.08	.25
220 Steve Finley	.15	.40
221 Jeff King	.08	.25
222 Quinton McCracken	.08	.25
223 Matt Stairs	.08	.25
224 Darin Erstad	.15	.40
225 Fred McGriff	.25	.60
226 Marquis Grissom	.15	.40
227 Doug Glanville	.08	.25
228 Tom Glavine	.25	.60
229 John Franco	.15	.40
230 Darren Bragg	.08	.25
231 Barry Larkin	.25	.60
232 Trevor Hoffman	.15	.40
233 Brady Anderson	.15	.40
234 Al Martin	.08	.25
235 B.J. Surhoff	.15	.40
236 Ellis Burks	.15	.40
237 Randy Johnson	.40	1.00
238 Mark Clark	.08	.25
239 Tony Saunders	.08	.25
240 Hideo Nomo	.40	1.00
241 Brad Fullmer	.08	.25
242 Chipper Jones	.40	1.00
243 Jose Valentin	.08	.25
244 Manny Ramirez	.25	.60
245 Derrek Lee	.25	.60
246 Jimmy Key	.15	.40
247 Tim Naehring	.08	.25
248 Bobby Higginson	.15	.40
249 Charles Johnson	.15	.40
250 Chili Davis	.15	.40
251 Tom Gordon	.08	.25
252 Mike Lieberthal	.15	.40
253 Billy Wagner	.15	.40
254 Juan Guzman	.08	.25
255 Todd Stottlemyre	.08	.25
256 Brian Jordan	.15	.40
257 Barry Bonds	1.00	2.50
258 Dan Wilson	.08	.25
259 Paul Molitor	.15	.40
260 Juan Gonzalez	.15	.40
261 Francisco Cordova	.08	.25
262 Cecil Fielder	.15	.40
263 Travis Lee	.08	.25
264 Kevin Tapani	.08	.25
265 Raul Mondesi	.15	.40
266 Travis Fryman	.15	.40
267 Armando Benitez	.08	.25
268 Pokey Reese	.08	.25
269 Rick Aguilera	.08	.25
270 Andy Pettitte	.25	.60
271 Jose Vizcaino	.08	.25
272 Kerry Wood	.20	.50
273 Vladimir Guerrero	.40	1.00
274 John Smiley	.08	.25
275 Checklist (151-275)	.08	.25

1998 Finest No-Protectors

Randomly inserted in retail packs at the rate of one in two and one in every HTA pack, this 275-card set is parallel to the base set only without the Finest Protector covering and features double-sided Finest technology.

Card	Low	High
COMPLETE SET (275)	175.00	350.00
COMP. SERIES 1 (150)	100.00	200.00
COMP. SERIES 2 (125)	75.00	150.00

*STARS: 2X TO 4X BASIC CARDS

1998 Finest Oversize

These sixteen 3" by 5" cards were inserted one every three hobby boxes. Though not actually on the cards, first series cards have been assigned an A prefix and second series a B prefix to clarify our listing. The cards are parallel to the regular Finest cards except numbering "of 8". They were issued as chiptoppers in the boxes.

Card	Low	High
COMPLETE SERIES 1 (8)	50.00	120.00
COMPLETE SERIES 2 (8)	30.00	80.00

*REFRACTORS: .75X TO 2X BASIC OVERSIZE
REF.ODDS 1:6 HOBBY/HTA BOXES

Card	Low	High
A1 Mark McGwire	6.00	15.00
A2 Cal Ripken	8.00	20.00
A3 Nomar Garciaparra	4.00	10.00
A4 Mike Piazza	4.00	10.00
A5 Greg Maddux	4.00	10.00
A6 Jose Cruz Jr.	.60	1.50
A7 Roger Clemens	5.00	12.00
A8 Ken Griffey Jr.	4.00	10.00
B1 Frank Thomas	2.50	6.00
B2 Bernie Williams	1.50	4.00
B3 Randy Johnson	2.50	6.00
B4 Chipper Jones	2.50	6.00
B5 Manny Ramirez	1.50	4.00
B6 Barry Bonds	6.00	15.00
B7 Juan Gonzalez	1.00	2.50
B8 Jeff Bagwell	1.50	4.00

1998 Finest Refractors

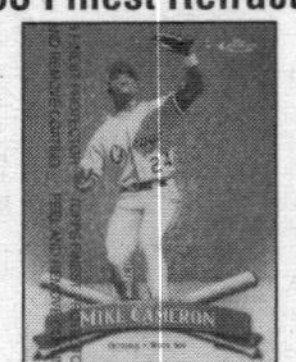

Randomly inserted in retail packs at the rate of one in 12 and in HTA packs at the rate of one in five, this 275-card set is parallel to the base set. The difference is found in the refractive quality of the card.

*STARS: 5X TO 12X BASIC CARDS

1998 Finest Centurions

Randomly inserted in Series one hobby packs at a rate of 1:153 and Home Team Advantage packs at a rate of 1:71, cards from this 20-card set feature action color photos of top players who will lead the game into the next century. Each card is sequentially numbered on back to 500. Unfortunately, an unknown quantity of unnumbered Centurions made their way into the secondary market in 1999. Itâ ™s believed that these cards were quality control extras. To further compound this situation, some unscrupulous parties attempted to serial-number the cards. The fake cards have flat gold foil numbering. The real cards have bright foil numbering.

Card	Low	High
COMPLETE SET (20)	40.00	100.00

*REF: 2X TO 5X BASIC CENTURIONS
SER.1 REF.ODDS 1:1020 HOBBY, 1:471 HTA
REFRACTOR PR.RUN 75 SERIAL #'d SETS

Card	Low	High
C1 Andruw Jones	1.25	3.00
C2 Vladimir Guerrero	2.00	5.00
C3 Nomar Garciaparra	3.00	8.00
C4 Scott Rolen	1.25	3.00
C5 Ken Griffey Jr.	3.00	8.00
C6 Jose Cruz Jr.	.50	1.25
C7 Barry Bonds	5.00	12.00
C8 Mark McGwire	5.00	12.00
C9 Juan Gonzalez	.75	2.00
C10 Jeff Bagwell	1.25	3.00
C11 Frank Thomas	2.00	5.00
C12 Paul Konerko	.75	2.00
C13 Alex Rodriguez	3.00	8.00
C14 Mike Piazza	3.00	8.00
C15 Travis Lee	.50	1.25
C16 Chipper Jones	2.00	5.00
C17 Larry Walker	.75	2.00
C18 Mo Vaughn	.75	2.00
C19 Livan Hernandez	.75	2.00
C20 Jaret Wright	.50	1.25

1998 Finest The Man

Randomly inserted in packs at a rate of one in 119, this 20-card set is an insert to the 1998 Finest base set. The entire set is sequentially numbered to 500.

Card	Low	High
COMPLETE SET (20)	150.00	400.00

*REF: 1X TO 2.5X BASIC THE MAN
REF.SER.2 ODDS 1:793
REFRACTOR PR.RUN 75 SERIAL #'d SETS

Card	Low	High
TM1 Ken Griffey Jr.	10.00	25.00
TM2 Barry Bonds	15.00	40.00
TM3 Frank Thomas	6.00	15.00
TM4 Chipper Jones	6.00	15.00
TM5 Cal Ripken	20.00	50.00
TM6 Nomar Garciaparra	10.00	25.00
TM7 Mark McGwire	15.00	40.00
TM8 Mike Piazza	10.00	25.00
TM9 Derek Jeter	15.00	40.00
TM10 Alex Rodriguez	10.00	25.00
TM11 Jose Cruz Jr.	1.50	4.00
TM12 Larry Walker	2.50	6.00
TM13 Jeff Bagwell	4.00	10.00
TM14 Tony Gwynn	8.00	20.00
TM15 Travis Lee	1.50	4.00
TM16 Juan Gonzalez	2.50	6.00
TM17 Scott Rolen	4.00	10.00
TM18 Randy Johnson	6.00	15.00
TM19 Roger Clemens	12.50	30.00
TM20 Greg Maddux	10.00	25.00

1998 Finest Mystery Finest 1

Randomly inserted in first series hobby packs at the rate of one in 36 and Home Team Advantage packs at the rate of one in 15, cards from this 50-card set feature color action photos of 20 top players on double-sided cards. Each player is matched with three different players on the opposite side or another photo of himself. Each side is covered with the Finest opaque protector.

*REFRACTOR: 1X TO 2.5X BASIC MYSTERY
REF.SER.1 ODDS 1:144 HOBBY, 1:64 HTA

Card	Low	High
M1 Frank Thomas Ken Griffey Jr.	6.00	15.00
M2 Frank Thomas Mike Piazza	4.00	10.00
M3 Frank Thomas Mark McGwire	10.00	25.00
M4 Frank Thomas Frank Thomas	4.00	10.00
M5 Ken Griffey Jr. Mike Piazza	6.00	15.00
M6 Ken Griffey Jr. Mark McGwire	10.00	25.00
M7 Ken Griffey Jr. Ken Griffey Jr.	6.00	15.00
M8 Mike Piazza Mark McGwire	10.00	25.00
M9 Mike Piazza Mike Piazza	8.00	20.00
M10 Mark McGwire Mark McGwire	12.50	30.00
M11 Nomar Garciaparra Jose Cruz Jr.	6.00	15.00
M12 Nomar Garciaparra Derek Jeter	8.00	20.00
M13 Nomar Garciaparra Andruw Jones	6.00	15.00
M14 Nomar Garciaparra Nomar Garciaparra	8.00	20.00
M15 Jose Cruz Jr. Derek Jeter	10.00	25.00
M16 Jose Cruz Jr. Andruw Jones	2.50	6.00
M17 Jose Cruz Jr. Jose Cruz Jr.	1.50	4.00
M18 Derek Jeter Andruw Jones	10.00	25.00
M19 Derek Jeter Derek Jeter	12.50	30.00
M20 Andruw Jones Andruw Jones	2.50	6.00
M21 Cal Ripken Tony Gwynn	10.00	25.00
M22 Cal Ripken Barry Bonds	12.50	30.00
M23 Cal Ripken Greg Maddux	12.50	30.00
M24 Cal Ripken Cal Ripken	15.00	40.00
M25 Tony Gwynn Barry Bonds	12.50	30.00
M26 Tony Gwynn Greg Maddux	6.00	15.00
M27 Tony Gwynn Tony Gwynn	6.00	15.00
M28 Barry Bonds Greg Maddux	12.50	30.00
M29 Barry Bonds Barry Bonds	12.50	30.00
M30 Greg Maddux Greg Maddux	8.00	20.00
M31 Juan Gonzalez Larry Walker	1.50	4.00
M32 Juan Gonzalez Andres Galarraga	1.50	4.00
M33 Juan Gonzalez Chipper Jones	4.00	10.00
M34 Juan Gonzalez Juan Gonzalez	1.50	4.00
M35 Larry Walker Andres Galarraga	1.50	4.00
M36 Larry Walker Chipper Jones	4.00	10.00
M37 Larry Walker Larry Walker -	1.50	4.00
M38 Andres Galarraga Chipper Jones	4.00	10.00
M39 Andres Galarraga Andres Galarraga	1.50	4.00
M40 Chipper Jones Chipper Jones	4.00	10.00
M41 Gary Sheffield Sammy Sosa	4.00	10.00
M42 Gary Sheffield Jeff Bagwell	2.50	6.00
M43 Gary Sheffield Tino Martinez	2.50	6.00
M44 Gary Sheffield Gary Sheffield	1.50	4.00
M45 Sammy Sosa Jeff Bagwell	8.00	20.00
M46 Sammy Sosa Tino Martinez	4.00	10.00
M47 Sammy Sosa Sammy Sosa	4.00	10.00
M48 Jeff Bagwell Tino Martinez	2.50	6.00
M49 Jeff Bagwell Jeff Bagwell	2.50	6.00
M50 Tino Martinez Tino Martinez	2.50	6.00

1998 Finest Mystery Finest 2

Randomly inserted in second series hobby packs at the rate of one in 36 and Home Team Advantage packs at the rate of one in 15, cards from this 50-card set feature color action photos of 20 top players on double-sided cards. Each player is matched with three different players on the opposite side or another photo of himself. Each side is covered with the Finest opaque protector.

Card	Low	High
COMPLETE SET (40)	125.00	300.00

*REFRACTOR: 1X TO 2.5X BASIC MYSTERY
REF.SER.2 ODDS 1:144

Card	Low	High
M1 Nomar Garciaparra Frank Thomas	4.00	10.00
M2 Nomar Garciaparra Albert Belle	4.00	10.00
M3 Nomar Garciaparra Scott Rolen	6.00	15.00
M4 Frank Thomas Albert Belle	4.00	10.00
M5 Frank Thomas Scott Rolen	4.00	10.00
M6 Albert Belle Scott Rolen	2.50	6.00
M7 Ken Griffey Jr. Jose Cruz Jr.	6.00	15.00
M8 Ken Griffey Jr. Alex Rodriguez	6.00	15.00
M9 Ken Griffey Jr. Roger Clemens	8.00	20.00
M10 Jose Cruz Jr. Alex Rodriguez	6.00	15.00
M11 Jose Cruz Jr. Roger Clemens	8.00	20.00
M12 Alex Rodriguez Roger Clemens	6.00	15.00
M13 Mike Piazza Barry Bonds	12.50	30.00
M14 Mike Piazza Derek Jeter	10.00	25.00
M15 Mike Piazza Bernie Williams	6.00	15.00
M16 Barry Bonds	12.50	30.00

Derek Jeter
M17 Barry Bonds 6.00 15.00
Bernie Williams
M18 Deter Jeter 10.00 25.00
Bernie Williams
M19 Mark McGwire 10.00 25.00
Jeff Bagwell
M20 Mark McGwire 10.00 25.00
Mo Vaughn
M21 Mark McGwire 10.00 25.00
Jim Thome
M22 Jeff Bagwell 2.50 6.00
Mo Vaughn
M23 Jeff Bagwell 2.50 6.00
Jim Thome
M24 Mo Vaughn 2.50 6.00
Jim Thome
M25 Juan Gonzalez 1.50 4.00
Travis Lee
M26 Juan Gonzalez 1.50 4.00
Ben Grieve
M27 Juan Gonzalez 2.50 6.00
Fred McGriff
M28 Travis Lee 1.50 4.00
Ben Grieve
M29 Travis Lee 2.50 6.00
Fred McGriff
M30 Ben Grieve 2.50 6.00
Fred McGriff
M31 Albert Belle 1.50 4.00
Albert Belle
M32 Scott Rolen 2.50 6.00
Scott Rolen
M33 Alex Rodriguez 8.00 20.00
Alex Rodriguez
M34 Roger Clemens 8.00 20.00
Roger Clemens
M35 Bernie Williams 2.50 6.00
Bernie Williams
M36 Mo Vaughn 1.50 4.00
Mo Vaughn
M37 Jim Thome 2.50 6.00
Jim Thome
M38 Travis Lee 1.50 4.00
Travis Lee
M39 Fred McGriff 2.50 6.00
Fred McGriff
M40 Ben Grieve 1.50 4.00
Ben Grieve

1998 Finest Mystery Finest Oversize

One of these three different cards was randomly seeded as chiptoppers (lying on top of the packs, but within the sealed box) at a rate of 1:6 series two Home Team Collector boxes. Besides the obvious difference in size, these cards are also numbered differently than the standard-sized cards, but beyond that they're essentially straight parallels of their standard sized siblings.

COMPLETE SET (3) 15.00 40.00
SER.2 STATED ODDS 1:6 HTA BOXES
*REFRACTOR: .75X TO 2X OVERSIZE
SER.2 REF.STATED ODDS 1:12 HTA BOXES
1 Ken Griffey Jr. 4.00 10.00
Alex Rodriguez
2 Derek Jeter 6.00 15.00
Bernie Williams
3 Mark McGwire 6.00 15.00
Jeff Bagwell

1998 Finest Power Zone

Randomly inserted in series one hobby packs at the rate of one in 72 and in series one Home Team Advantage packs at the rate of one in 32, this 20-card set features color action photos of top players printed with new "Flop Inks" technology which actually changes the color of the card when it is held at different angles.

COMPLETE SET (20) 80.00 200.00
P1 Ken Griffey Jr. 8.00 20.00
P2 Jeff Bagwell 3.00 8.00
P3 Jose Cruz Jr. 1.25 3.00
P4 Barry Bonds 12.50 30.00
P5 Mark McGwire 12.50 30.00
P6 Jim Thome 3.00 8.00
P7 Mo Vaughn 2.00 5.00
P8 Gary Sheffield 2.00 5.00
P9 Andres Galarraga 2.00 5.00
P10 Nomar Garciaparra 8.00 20.00
P11 Rafael Palmeiro 3.00 8.00
P12 Sammy Sosa 5.00 12.00
P13 Jay Buhner 2.00 5.00
P14 Tony Clark 1.25 3.00
P15 Mike Piazza 8.00 20.00
P16 Larry Walker 2.00 5.00
P17 Albert Belle 2.00 5.00
P18 Tino Martinez 3.00 8.00
P19 Juan Gonzalez 2.00 5.00
P20 Frank Thomas 5.00 12.00

1998 Finest Stadium Stars

Randomly inserted in packs at a rate of one in 72, this 24-card set features a selection of the majors top hitters set against an attractive foil-glowing stadium background.

COMPLETE SET (24) 125.00 300.00
SS1 Ken Griffey Jr. 8.00 20.00
SS2 Alex Rodriguez 8.00 20.00
SS3 Mo Vaughn 2.00 5.00
SS4 Nomar Garciaparra 8.00 20.00
SS5 Frank Thomas 5.00 12.00
SS6 Albert Belle 2.00 5.00

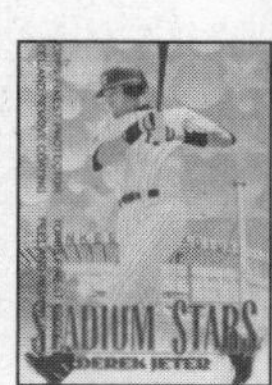

SS7 Derek Jeter 12.50 30.00
SS8 Chipper Jones 5.00 12.00
SS9 Cal Ripken 15.00 40.00
SS10 Jim Thome 3.00 8.00
SS11 Mike Piazza 8.00 20.00
SS12 Juan Gonzalez 2.00 5.00
SS13 Jeff Bagwell 3.00 8.00
SS14 Sammy Sosa 5.00 12.00
SS15 Jose Cruz Jr. 1.25 3.00
SS16 Gary Sheffield 2.00 5.00
SS17 Larry Walker 2.00 5.00
SS18 Tony Gwynn 6.00 15.00
SS19 Mark McGwire 12.50 30.00
SS20 Barry Bonds 12.50 30.00
SS21 Tino Martinez 3.00 8.00
SS22 Manny Ramirez 3.00 8.00
SS23 Ken Caminiti 2.00 5.00
SS24 Andres Galarraga 2.00 5.00

1999 Finest Pre-Production

This six-card set was issued to preview the 1999 Finest set. Six of the more popular players in baseball today were picked to represent the players in the set. The cards are numbered with a "PP" prefix.

COMPLETE SET (6) 3.20 8.00
PP1 Darin Erstad .75 2.00
PP2 Javy Lopez .75 2.00
PP3 Vinny Castilla .40 1.00
PP4 Jim Thome .60 1.50
PP5 Tino Martinez .40 1.00
PP6 Mark Grace .75 2.00

1999 Finest

This 300-card set (produced by Topps) was distributed in first and second series six-card packs with a suggested retail price of $5. The fronts feature color action player photos printed on 27 pt. card stock using Chromium technology. The backs carry player information. The set includes the following subsets: Gems (101-120), Sensations (121-130) Rookies (131-150/277-299), Sterling (251-265) and Gamers (266-276). Card number 300 is a special Hank Aaron/Mark McGwire tribute. Cards numbered from 101 through 150 and 251 through 300 were short printed and seeded at a rate of one per hobby, one per retail and two per Home Team Advantage pack. Notable Rookie Cards include Pat Burrell, Sean Burroughs, Nick Johnson, Austin Kearns, Corey Patterson and Alfonso Soriano.

COMPLETE SET (300) 30.00 80.00
COMP.SERIES 1 (150) 15.00 40.00
COMP.SERIES 2 (150) 15.00 40.00
COMP.SER.1 w/o SP's (100) 6.00 15.00
COMP.SER.2 w/o SP's (100) 6.00 15.00
COMMON (1-100/151-250) .15 .40
COMMON (101-150/251-300) .20 .50
1 Darin Erstad .15 .40
2 Javy Lopez .15 .40
3 Vinny Castilla .15 .40
4 Jim Thome .25 .60
5 Tino Martinez .25 .60
6 Mark Grace .25 .60
7 Shawn Green .15 .40
8 Dustin Hermanson .15 .40
9 Kevin Young .15 .40
10 Tony Clark .15 .40
11 Scott Brosius .15 .40
12 Craig Biggio .25 .60
13 Brian McRae .15 .40
14 Chan Ho Park .15 .40
15 Manny Ramirez .25 .60
16 Chipper Jones .40 1.00
17 Rico Brogna .15 .40
18 Quinton McCracken .15 .40
19 J.T. Snow .15 .40
20 Tony Gwynn .50 1.25
21 Juan Guzman .15 .40
22 John Valentin .15 .40
23 Rick Helling .15 .40
24 Sandy Alomar Jr. .15 .40
25 Frank Thomas .40 1.00
26 Jorge Posada .25 .60
27 Dmitri Young .15 .40
28 Rick Reed .15 .40
29 Kevin Tapani .15 .40
30 Troy Glaus .25 .60
31 Kenny Rogers .15 .40
32 Jeromy Burnitz .15 .40
33 Mark Grudzielanek .15 .40
34 Mike Mussina .25 .60
35 Scott Rolen .25 .60
36 Neifi Perez .15 .40
37 Brad Radke .15 .40
38 Darryl Strawberry .15 .40
39 Robb Nen .15 .40
40 Moises Alou .15 .40
41 Eric Young .15 .40
42 Livan Hernandez .15 .40
43 John Wetteland .15 .40
44 Matt Lawton .15 .40
45 Ben Grieve .15 .40
46 Fernando Tatis .15 .40
47 Travis Fryman .15 .40
48 David Segui .15 .40
49 Bob Abreu .15 .40
50 Nomar Garciaparra .60 1.50
51 Paul O'Neill .25 .60
52 Jeff King .15 .40
53 Francisco Cordova .15 .40
54 John Olerud .15 .40
55 Vladimir Guerrero .40 1.00
56 Fernando Vina .15 .40
57 Shane Reynolds .15 .40
58 Chuck Finley .15 .40
59 Rondell White .15 .40
60 Greg Vaughn .15 .40
61 Ryan Minor .15 .40
62 Tom Gordon .15 .40
63 Damion Easley .15 .40
64 Ray Durham .15 .40
65 Orlando Hernandez .15 .40
66 Bartolo Colon .15 .40
67 Jaret Wright .15 .40
68 Royce Clayton .15 .40
69 Tim Salmon .25 .60
70 Mark McGwire 1.00 2.50
71 Alex Gonzalez .15 .40
72 Tom Glavine .25 .60
73 David Justice .15 .40
74 Omar Vizquel .25 .60
75 Juan Gonzalez .15 .40
76 Bobby Higginson .15 .40
77 Todd Walker .15 .40
78 Dante Bichette .15 .40
79 Kevin Millwood .15 .40
80 Roger Clemens .75 2.00
81 Kerry Wood .15 .40
82 Cal Ripken 1.25 3.00
83 Jay Bell .15 .40
84 Barry Bonds 1.00 2.50
85 Alex Rodriguez .60 1.50
86 Doug Glanville .15 .40
87 Jason Kendall .15 .40
88 Sean Casey .15 .40
89 Aaron Sele .15 .40
90 Derek Jeter 1.00 2.50
91 Andy Ashby .15 .40
92 Rusty Greer .15 .40
93 Rod Beck .15 .40
94 Matt Williams .15 .40
95 Mike Piazza .60 1.50
96 Wally Joyner .15 .40
97 Barry Larkin .25 .60
98 Eric Milton .15 .40
99 Gary Sheffield .15 .40
100 Greg Maddux .60 1.50
101 Ken Griffey Jr. GEM 1.00 2.50
102 Frank Thomas GEM .60 1.50
103 N.Garciaparra GEM 1.00 2.50
104 Mark McGwire GEM 1.50 4.00
105 Alex Rodriguez GEM 1.00 2.50
106 Tony Gwynn GEM .75 2.00
107 Juan Gonzalez GEM .25 .60
108 Jeff Bagwell GEM .40 1.00
109 Sammy Sosa GEM .60 1.50
110 V.Guerrero GEM .60 1.50
111 Roger Clemens GEM 1.25 3.00
112 Barry Bonds GEM 1.50 4.00
113 Darin Erstad GEM .25 .60
114 Mike Piazza GEM 1.00 2.50
115 Derek Jeter GEM 1.50 4.00
116 Chipper Jones GEM .60 1.50
117 Larry Walker GEM .25 .60
118 Scott Rolen GEM .40 1.00
119 Cal Ripken GEM 2.00 5.00
120 Greg Maddux GEM 1.00 2.50
121 Troy Glaus SENS .40 1.00
122 Ben Grieve SENS .20 .50
123 Ryan Minor SENS .20 .50
124 Kerry Wood SENS .25 .60
125 Travis Lee SENS .20 .50
126 Adrian Beltre SENS .25 .60
127 Brad Fullmer SENS .20 .50
128 Aramis Ramirez SENS .25 .60
129 Eric Chavez SENS .25 .60
130 Todd Helton SENS .40 1.00
131 Pat Burrell RC 1.25 3.00
132 Ryan Mills RC .20 .50
133 Austin Kearns RC 1.25 3.00
134 Josh McKinley RC .20 .50
135 Adam Everett RC .40 1.00
136 Marlon Anderson .20 .50
137 Bruce Chen .20 .50
138 Matt Clement .25 .60
139 Alex Gonzalez .20 .50
140 Roy Halladay .25 .60
141 Calvin Pickering .20 .50
142 Randy Wolf .20 .50
143 Ryan Anderson .20 .50
144 Ruben Mateo .20 .50
145 Alex Escobar RC .25 .60
146 Jeremy Giambi .20 .50
147 Lance Berkman .25 .60
148 Michael Barrett .20 .50
149 Preston Wilson .25 .60
150 Gabe Kapler .25 .60
151 Roger Clemens .75 2.00
152 Jay Buhner .15 .40
153 Brad Fullmer .15 .40
154 Ray Lankford .15 .40
155 Jim Edmonds .15 .40
156 Jason Giambi .15 .40
157 Bret Boone .15 .40
158 Jeff Cirillo .15 .40
159 Rickey Henderson .40 1.00
160 Edgar Martinez .25 .60
161 Ron Gant .15 .40
162 Mark Kotsay .15 .40
163 Trevor Hoffman .15 .40
164 Jason Schmidt .15 .40
165 Brett Tomko .15 .40
166 David Ortiz .40 1.00
167 Dean Palmer .15 .40
168 Hideki Irabu .15 .40
169 Mike Cameron .15 .40
170 Pedro Martinez .25 .60
171 Tom Goodwin .15 .40
172 Brian Hunter .15 .40
173 Al Leiter .15 .40
174 Charles Johnson .15 .40
175 Curt Schilling .15 .40
176 Robin Ventura .15 .40
177 Travis Lee .15 .40
178 Jeff Shaw .15 .40
179 Ugueth Urbina .15 .40
180 Roberto Alomar .25 .60
181 Cliff Floyd .15 .40
182 Adrian Beltre .15 .40
183 Tony Womack .15 .40
184 Brian Jordan .15 .40
185 Randy Johnson .40 1.00
186 Mickey Morandini .15 .40
187 Todd Hundley .15 .40
188 Jose Valentin .15 .40
189 Eric Davis .15 .40
190 Ken Caminiti .15 .40
191 David Wells .15 .40
192 Ryan Klesko .15 .40
193 Garret Anderson .15 .40
194 Eric Karros .15 .40
195 Ivan Rodriguez .25 .60
196 Aramis Ramirez .15 .40
197 Mike Lieberthal .15 .40
198 Will Clark .25 .60
199 Rey Ordonez .15 .40
200 Ken Griffey Jr. .60 1.50
201 Jose Guillen .15 .40
202 Scott Erickson .15 .40
203 Paul Konerko .15 .40
204 Johnny Damon .25 .60
205 Larry Walker .15 .40
206 Denny Neagle .15 .40
207 Jose Offerman .15 .40
208 Andy Pettitte .25 .60
209 Bobby Jones .15 .40
210 Kevin Brown .25 .60
211 John Smoltz .25 .60
212 Henry Rodriguez .15 .40
213 Tim Belcher .15 .40
214 Carlos Delgado .15 .40
215 Andruw Jones .25 .60
216 Andy Benes .15 .40
217 Fred McGriff .25 .60
218 Edgar Renteria .15 .40
219 Miguel Tejada .15 .40
220 Bernie Williams .25 .60
221 Justin Thompson .15 .40
222 Marty Cordova .15 .40
223 Delino DeShields .15 .40
224 Ellis Burks .15 .40
225 Kenny Lofton .15 .40
226 Steve Finley .15 .40
227 Eric Chavez .15 .40
228 Jose Cruz Jr. .15 .40
229 Marquis Grissom .15 .40
230 Jeff Bagwell .25 .60
231 Jose Canseco .25 .60
232 Edgardo Alfonzo .15 .40
233 Richie Sexson .15 .40
234 Jeff Kent .15 .40
235 Rafael Palmeiro .25 .60
236 David Cone .15 .40
237 Gregg Jefferies .15 .40
238 Mike Lansing .15 .40
239 Mariano Rivera .40 1.00
240 Albert Belle .15 .40
241 Chuck Knoblauch .15 .40
242 Derek Bell .15 .40
243 Pat Hentgen .15 .40
244 Andres Galarraga .15 .40
245 Mo Vaughn .15 .40
246 Wade Boggs .25 .60
247 Devon White .15 .40
248 Todd Helton .25 .60
249 Raul Mondesi .15 .40
250 Sammy Sosa .40 1.00
251 Nomar Garciaparra ST 1.00 2.50
252 Mark McGwire ST 1.50 4.00
253 Alex Rodriguez ST 1.00 2.50
254 Juan Gonzalez ST .20 .50
255 Vladimir Guerrero ST .60 1.50
256 Ken Griffey Jr. ST 1.00 2.50
257 Mike Piazza ST 1.00 2.50
258 Derek Jeter ST 1.50 4.00
259 Albert Belle ST .20 .50
260 Greg Vaughn ST .20 .50
261 Sammy Sosa ST .60 1.50
262 Greg Maddux ST 1.00 2.50
263 Frank Thomas ST .60 1.50
264 Mark Grace ST .40 1.00
265 Ivan Rodriguez ST .40 1.00
266 Roger Clemens GM 1.25 3.00
267 Mo Vaughn GM .25 .60
268 Jim Thome GM .40 1.00
269 Darin Erstad GM .25 .60
270 Chipper Jones GM .60 1.50
271 Larry Walker GM .25 .60
272 Cal Ripken GM 2.00 5.00
273 Scott Rolen GM .40 1.00
274 Randy Johnson GM .60 1.50
275 Tony Gwynn GM .75 2.00
276 Barry Bonds GM 1.50 4.00
277 Sean Burroughs RC .40 1.00
278 J.M. Gold RC .20 .50
279 Carlos Lee .25 .60
280 George Lombard .20 .50
281 Carlos Beltran .40 1.00
282 Fernando Seguignol .20 .50
283 Eric Chavez .25 .60
284 Carlos Pena RC .30 .75
285 Corey Patterson RC .60 1.50
286 Alfonso Soriano RC 3.00 8.00
287 Nick Johnson RC .60 1.50
288 Jorge Toca RC .25 .60
289 A.J. Burnett RC .60 1.50
290 Andy Brown RC .20 .50
291 D.Mientkiewicz RC .40 1.00
292 Bobby Seay RC .20 .50
293 Chip Ambres RC .20 .50
294 C.C. Sabathia RC 1.50 4.00
295 Choo Freeman RC .25 .60
296 Eric Valent RC .25 .60
297 Matt Belisle RC .20 .50
298 Jason Tyner RC .20 .50
299 Masao Kida RC .25 .60
300 Hank Aaron 1.25 3.00
Mark McGwire

1999 Finest Gold Refractors

This 300-card set is a die-cut gold foil parallel version of the base set. Only 100 serially numbered sets were produced. Cards were randomly inserted in hobby and retail packs. Series one packs were at the rate of one in 82 and HTA packs at a rate of one in 38. Series 2 packs were at the rate of one in 57 and HTA packs at a rate of one in 26.

*STARS 1-100/151-250: 10X TO 25X BASIC
*STARS 101-150/251-300: 6X TO 15X BAS.
*ROOKIES: 4X TO 10X BASIC

1999 Finest Refractors

Randomly inserted in series one and two packs at the rate of one in 12 hobby/retail and one in five HTA, this 300-card set is a parallel version of the base set and is similar in design. The difference is found in the refractive quality of the card.

*STARS 1-100/151-250: 3X TO 8X BASIC
*STARS 101-150/251-300: 2X TO 5X BASIC
*ROOKIES: 1.5X TO 4X BASIC

1999 Finest Aaron Award Contenders

Randomly inserted into Series two packs at different rates depending on the player, this nine-card set features color action photos of players vying for the Hank Aaron Award.

COMPLETE SET (9) 30.00 60.00
HA1 SER.2 ODDS 1:216, 1:108 HTA
HA2 SER.2 ODDS 1:108, 1:54 HTA
HA3 SER.2 ODDS 1:72, 1:36 HTA
HA4 SER.2 ODDS 1:54, 1:27 HTA
HA5 SER.2 ODDS 1:43, 1:21 HTA
HA6 SER.2 ODDS 1:36, 1:18 HTA
HA7 SER.2 ODDS 1:31, 1:15 HTA
HA8 SER.2 ODDS 1:27, 1:13 HTA
HA9 SER.2 ODDS 1:24, 1:12 HTA
*REFRACTORS: 1.5X TO 4X BASIC AARON AW
REF HA1 SER.2 ODDS 1:1728, 1:864 HTA
REF HA2 SER.2 ODDS 1:864, 1:432 HTA
REF HA3 SER.2 ODDS 1:576, 1:288 HTA
REF HA4 SER.2 ODDS 1:432, 1:216 HTA
REF HA5 SER.2 ODDS 1:344, 1:172 HTA
REF HA6 SER.2 ODDS 1:288, 1:144 HTA
REF HA7 SER.2 ODDS 1:248, 1:124 HTA
REF HA8 SER.2 ODDS 1:216, 1:108 HTA
REF HA9 SER.2 ODDS 1:192, 1:96 HTA
HA1 Juan Gonzalez 2.00 5.00
HA2 Vladimir Guerrero 4.00 10.00
HA3 Nomar Garciaparra 5.00 12.00
HA4 Albert Belle 2.00 5.00
HA5 Frank Thomas 2.00 5.00
HA6 Sammy Sosa 2.00 5.00
HA7 Alex Rodriguez 2.00 5.00
HA8 Ken Griffey Jr. 1.50 4.00
HA9 Mark McGwire 2.00 5.00

1999 Finest Complements

Randomly inserted into Series two packs at the rate of one in 56, this seven-card set features color action photos of 14 stars who complement each other's skills and share a common bond paired together on cards printed with advanced "Split Screen" technology which combines Refractor and Non-Refractor technology on the same card. Each card has three variations as follows: 1) Non-Refractor/Refractor, 2) Refractor/Non-Refractor, and 3) Refractor/Refractor.

COMPLETE SET (7) 25.00 50.00
RIGHT/LEFT REF.VARIATIONS EQUAL VALUE
*DUAL REF: 1.25X TO 3X BASIC COMP.
DUAL REF.SER.2 ODDS 1:168, 1:81 HTA
C1 Mike Piazza 2.50 6.00
Ivan Rodriguez
C2 Tony Gwynn 2.00 5.00
Wade Boggs
C3 Kerry Wood 3.00 8.00
Roger Clemens
C4 Juan Gonzalez 1.50 4.00
Sammy Sosa
C5 Derek Jeter 4.00 10.00
Nomar Garciaparra
C6 Mark McGwire 4.00 10.00
Frank Thomas
C7 Vladimir Guerrero 1.50 4.00
Andruw Jones

1999 Finest Double Feature

Randomly inserted into Series two packs at the rate of one in 56, this seven-card set features color photos of fourteen paired teammates printed on cards using Split Screen technology combining Refractor and Non-Refractor technology on the same card. There are three different versions of each card as follows: 1) Non-Refractor/Refractor, 2) Refractor/Non-Refractor, and 3) Refractor/Refractor.

COMPLETE SET (7) 20.00 40.00
RIGHT/LEFT REF.VARIATIONS EQUAL VALUE
*DUAL REF: 1.25X TO 3X BASIC DOUB.FEAT.
*DUAL REF BURRELL: 1.25X TO 3X HI COLUMN
DUAL REF.SER.2 ODDS 1:168, 1:81 HTA
DF1 Ken Griffey Jr. 2.50 6.00
Alex Rodriguez
DF2 Chipper Jones 1.50 4.00
Andruw Jones
DF3 Darin Erstad .60 1.50
Mo Vaughn
DF4 Craig Biggio 1.00 2.50
Jeff Bagwell
DF5 Ben Grieve .60 1.50
Eric Chavez
DF6 Albert Belle 5.00 12.00
Cal Ripken
DF7 Scott Rolen 1.25 3.00
Pat Burrell

1999 Finest Franchise Records

Randomly inserted into Series two packs at the rate of one in 129, this ten-card set features color action photos of all-time and single-season franchise statistic holders. A refractive parallel version of this set was also produced and inserted in Series two packs at the rate of one in 378.

COMPLETE SET (10) 75.00 150.00
*REFRACTORS: .75X TO 2X BASIC FRAN.REC.
REF.SER.2 ODDS 1:378, 1:189 HTA
FR1 Frank Thomas 4.00 10.00
FR2 Ken Griffey Jr. 6.00 15.00
FR3 Mark McGwire 10.00 25.00
FR4 Juan Gonzalez 1.50 4.00
FR5 Nomar Garciaparra 6.00 15.00
FR6 Mike Piazza 6.00 15.00
FR7 Cal Ripken 12.50 30.00
FR8 Sammy Sosa 4.00 10.00
FR9 Barry Bonds 10.00 25.00
FR10 Tony Gwynn 5.00 12.00

1999 Finest Future's Finest

Randomly inserted into Series two packs at the rate of one in 171, this 10-card set features color photos of top young stars printed on card stock using Refractive Finest technology. The cards are sequentially numbered to 500.

COMPLETE SET (10) 50.00 100.00
FF1 Pat Burrell 6.00 15.00
FF2 Troy Glaus 4.00 10.00
FF3 Eric Chavez 4.00 10.00
FF4 Ryan Anderson 4.00 10.00
FF5 Ruben Mateo 4.00 10.00

FF6 Gabe Kapler	4.00	10.00
FF7 Alex Gonzalez	4.00	10.00
FF8 Michael Barrett	4.00	10.00
FF9 Adrian Beltre	4.00	10.00
FF10 Fernando Seguignol	4.00	10.00

1999 Finest Leading Indicators

Randomly inserted in Series one packs at the rate of one in 24, this 10-card set features color action photos highlighting the 1998 home run totals of superstar players and printed on cards using a heat-sensitvie, thermal-ink technology. When a collector touched the baseball field background in left, center, or right field, the heat from his finger revealed the pictured player's '98 home run totals in that direction.

COMPLETE SET (10)	20.00	50.00
L1 Mark McGwire	4.00	10.00
L2 Sammy Sosa	1.50	4.00
L3 Ken Griffey Jr.	2.50	6.00
L4 Greg Vaughn	.60	1.50
L5 Albert Belle	.60	1.50
L6 Juan Gonzalez	.60	1.50
L7 Andres Galarraga	.60	1.50
L8 Alex Rodriguez	2.50	6.00
L9 Barry Bonds	4.00	10.00
L10 Jeff Bagwell	1.00	2.50

1999 Finest Milestones

Randomly inserted into packs at the rate of one in 29, this 40-card set features color photos of players who have the highest statistics in four categories: Hits, Home Runs, RBI's and Doubles. The cards are printed with Refractor technology and sequentially numbered based on the category as follows: Hits to 3,000, Home Runs to 500, RBIs to 1,400, and Doubles to 500.

M1 Tony Gwynn HIT	2.00	5.00
M2 Cal Ripken HIT	5.00	12.00
M3 Wade Boggs HIT	1.00	2.50
M4 Ken Griffey Jr. HIT	2.50	6.00
M5 Frank Thomas HIT	1.50	4.00
M6 Barry Bonds HIT	4.00	10.00
M7 Travis Lee HIT	.60	1.50
M8 Alex Rodriguez HIT	2.50	6.00
M9 Derek Jeter HIT	4.00	10.00
M10 V.Guerrero HIT	1.50	4.00
M11 Mark McGwire HR	12.50	30.00
M12 Ken Griffey Jr. HR	8.00	20.00
M13 Vladimir Guerrero HR	5.00	12.00
M14 Alex Rodriguez HR	8.00	20.00
M15 Barry Bonds HR	12.50	30.00
M16 Sammy Sosa HR	5.00	12.00
M17 Albert Belle HR	2.00	5.00
M18 Frank Thomas HR	5.00	12.00
M19 Jose Canseco HR	3.00	8.00
M20 Mike Piazza HR	8.00	20.00
M21 Jeff Bagwell RBI	1.50	4.00
M22 Barry Bonds RBI	6.00	15.00
M23 Ken Griffey Jr. RBI	4.00	10.00
M24 Albert Belle RBI	1.00	2.50
M25 Juan Gonzalez RBI	1.00	2.50
M26 Vinny Castilla RBI	1.00	2.50
M27 Mark McGwire RBI	6.00	15.00
M28 Alex Rodriguez RBI	4.00	10.00
M29 N.Garciaparra RBI	4.00	10.00
M30 Frank Thomas RBI	2.50	6.00
M31 Barry Bonds 2B	12.50	30.00
M32 Albert Belle 2B	2.00	5.00
M33 Ben Grieve 2B	2.00	5.00
M34 Craig Biggio 2B	3.00	8.00
M35 Vladimir Guerrero 2B	5.00	12.00
M36 N.Garciaparra 2B	8.00	20.00
M37 Alex Rodriguez 2B	8.00	20.00
M38 Derek Jeter 2B	12.50	30.00
M39 Ken Griffey Jr. 2B	8.00	20.00
M40 Brad Fullmer 2B	2.00	5.00

1999 Finest Peel and Reveal Sparkle

Randomly inserted in Series one packs at the rate of one in 30, this 20-card set features color action player images on a sparkle background. This set was considered Common and the protective coating had to be peeled from the card front and back to reveal the level.

COMPLETE SET (20)	60.00	120.00
*HYPERPLAID: .6X TO 1.5X SPARKLE		
HYPERPLAID SER.1 ODDS 1:60 H/R,1:30 HTA		
*STADIUM STARS: 1.25X TO 3X SPARKLE		
STAD.STAR SER.1 ODDS 1:120 H/R, 1:60 HTA		
1 Kerry Wood	.75	2.00
2 Mark McGwire	5.00	12.00
3 Sammy Sosa	2.00	5.00
4 Ken Griffey Jr.	3.00	8.00
5 Nomar Garciaparra	3.00	8.00
6 Greg Maddux	3.00	8.00
7 Derek Jeter	5.00	12.00
8 Andres Galarraga	.75	2.00
9 Alex Rodriguez	3.00	8.00
10 Frank Thomas	2.00	5.00
11 Roger Clemens	4.00	10.00
12 Juan Gonzalez	.75	2.00
13 Ben Grieve	.75	2.00
14 Jeff Bagwell	1.25	3.00
15 Todd Helton	1.25	3.00
16 Chipper Jones	2.00	5.00
17 Barry Bonds	5.00	12.00
18 Travis Lee	.75	2.00
19 Vladimir Guerrero	2.00	5.00
20 Pat Burrell	1.50	4.00

1999 Finest Prominent Figures

Randomly inserted in Series one packs with various insertion rates, this 50-card set features color action photos of ten superstars in each of five statistical categories and printed with refractor technology. The categories are: Home Runs (with an insertion rate of 1:1,749) and sequentially numbered to 70, Slugging Percentage (1:145) numbered to 847, Batting Average (1:289) numbered to 424, Runs Batted In (1:644) numbered to 190, and Total Bases (1:268) numbered to 457.

PF1 Mark McGwire HR	40.00	100.00
PF2 Sammy Sosa HR	15.00	40.00
PF3 Ken Griffey Jr. HR	25.00	60.00
PF4 Mike Piazza HR	25.00	60.00
PF5 Juan Gonzalez HR	6.00	15.00
PF6 Greg Vaughn HR	6.00	15.00
PF7 Alex Rodriguez HR	25.00	60.00
PF8 Manny Ramirez HR	10.00	25.00
PF9 Jeff Bagwell HR	10.00	25.00
PF10 Andres Galarraga HR	6.00	15.00
PF11 Mark McGwire SLG	8.00	20.00
PF12 Sammy Sosa SLG	3.00	8.00
PF13 Juan Gonzalez SLG	1.25	3.00
PF14 Ken Griffey Jr. SLG	5.00	12.00
PF15 Barry Bonds SLG	8.00	20.00
PF16 Greg Vaughn SLG	1.25	3.00
PF17 Larry Walker SLG	1.25	3.00
PF18 A.Galarraga SLG	1.25	3.00
PF19 Jeff Bagwell SLG	2.00	5.00
PF20 Albert Belle SLG	1.25	3.00
PF21 Tony Gwynn BAT	1.25	3.00
PF22 Mike Piazza BAT	6.00	15.00
PF23 Larry Walker BAT	1.50	4.00
PF24 Alex Rodriguez BAT	6.00	15.00
PF25 John Olerud BAT	1.50	4.00
PF26 Frank Thomas BAT	4.00	10.00
PF27 Bernie Williams BAT	2.50	6.00
PF28 Chipper Jones BAT	4.00	10.00
PF29 Jim Thome BAT	2.50	6.00
PF30 Barry Bonds BAT	10.00	25.00
PF31 Juan Gonzalez RBI	2.50	6.00
PF32 Sammy Sosa RBI	6.00	15.00
PF33 Mark McGwire RBI	15.00	40.00
PF34 Albert Belle RBI	2.50	6.00
PF35 Ken Griffey Jr. RBI	10.00	25.00
PF36 Jeff Bagwell RBI	4.00	10.00
PF37 Chipper Jones RBI	6.00	15.00
PF38 Vinny Castilla RBI	2.50	6.00
PF39 Alex Rodriguez RBI	10.00	25.00
PF40 A.Galarraga RBI	2.50	6.00
PF41 Sammy Sosa TB	4.00	10.00
PF42 Mark McGwire TB	10.00	25.00
PF43 Albert Belle TB	1.50	4.00
PF44 Ken Griffey Jr. TB	6.00	15.00
PF45 Jeff Bagwell TB	2.50	6.00
PF46 Juan Gonzalez TB	1.50	4.00
PF47 Barry Bonds TB	10.00	25.00
PF48 V.Guerrero TB	4.00	10.00
PF49 Larry Walker TB	1.50	4.00
PF50 Alex Rodriguez TB	6.00	15.00

1999 Finest Split Screen

Randomly inserted in Series one packs at the rate of one in 28, this 14-card set features action color photos of two players paired together on the same card and printed using a special refractor and non-refractor technology. Each card was printed with right/left refractor variations.

COMPLETE SET (14)	50.00	100.00
RIGHT/LEFT REF.VARIATIONS EQUAL VALUE		
*DUAL REF: 1.25X TO 3X BASIC SCREEN		
DUAL REF.SER.1 ODDS 1:82 H/R, 1:42 HTA		
SS1 Mark McGwire Sammy Sosa	4.00	10.00
SS2 Ken Griffey Jr. Alex Rodriguez	2.50	6.00
SS3 Nomar Garciaparra Derek Jeter	4.00	10.00
SS4 Barry Bonds Albert Belle	4.00	10.00
SS5 C.Ripken REF/T.Gwynn	5.00	12.00
SS6 Manny Ramirez Juan Gonzalez	1.00	2.50
SS7 Frank Thomas Andres Galarraga	1.50	4.00
SS8 Scott Rolen Chipper Jones	1.50	4.00
SS9 Ivan Rodriguez Mike Piazza	2.50	6.00
SS10 Kerry Wood Roger Clemens	3.00	8.00
SS11 Greg Maddux Tom Glavine	2.50	6.00
SS12 Troy Glaus Eric Chavez	1.00	2.50
SS13 Ben Grieve Todd Helton	1.00	2.50
SS14 Travis Lee Pat Burrell	1.25	3.00

1999 Finest Team Finest Blue

Randomly inserted in Series one and Series two packs at the rate of one in 82 first series and one in 57 second series. Also distributed in HTA packs at a rate of one in 38 first series and one in 26 second series. This 20-card set features color action player images printed using prismatic Chromium technology with blue highlights and is sequentially numbered to 1500. Cards 1-10 were distributed in first series packs and 11-20 in second series packs.

COMP.BLUE SET (20)	75.00	150.00
*BLUE REF: .75X TO 2X BASIC BLUE		
BLUE REF.SER.1 ODDS 1:816 HOB, 1:377 HTA		
BLUE REF.SER.2 ODDS 1:571 HOB, 1:263 HTA		
BLUE REF.PRINT RUN 150 SERIAL #'d SETS		
*RED: .5X TO 1.2X BASIC BLUE		
RED SER.2 ODDS 1:18 HTA		
RED SER.1 ODDS 1:25 HTA		
RED PRINT RUN 500 SERIAL #'d SETS		
*RED REF: 2.5X TO 6X BASIC BLUE		
RED REF.SER.1 ODDS 1:254 HTA		
RED REF.SER.2 ODDS 1:184 HTA		
RED REF.PRINT RUN 50 SERIAL #'d SETS		
*GOLD: .6X TO 1.5X BASIC BLUE		
GOLD SER.1 ODDS 1:51 HTA		
GOLD SER.2 ODDS 1:37 HTA		
GOLD PRINT RUN 250 SERIAL #'d SETS		
*GOLD REF: 4X TO 10X BASIC BLUE		
GOLD REF.SER.1 ODDS 1:510 HTA		
GOLD REF.SER.2 ODDS 1:369 HTA		
GOLD REF.PRINT RUN 25 SERIAL #'d SETS		
TF1 Greg Maddux	2.50	6.00
TF2 Mark McGwire	4.00	10.00
TF3 Sammy Sosa	1.50	4.00
TF4 Juan Gonzalez	.75	2.00
TF5 Alex Rodriguez	2.50	6.00
TF6 Travis Lee	.75	2.00
TF7 Roger Clemens	3.00	8.00
TF8 Darin Erstad	.75	2.00
TF9 Todd Helton	1.00	2.50
TF10 Mike Piazza	2.50	6.00
TF11 Kerry Wood	.75	2.00
TF12 Ken Griffey Jr.	2.50	6.00
TF13 Frank Thomas	1.50	4.00
TF14 Jeff Bagwell	1.00	2.50
TF15 Nomar Garciaparra	2.50	6.00
TF16 Derek Jeter	4.00	10.00
TF17 Chipper Jones	1.50	4.00
TF18 Barry Bonds	4.00	10.00
TF19 Tony Gwynn	2.00	5.00
TF20 Ben Grieve	.75	2.00

2000 Finest Pre-Production

This five card standard-size set was issued to preview what the 2000 Finest set would look like. It was issued to the dealers and hobby media on Topps' mailing list several weeks before the release of 2000 Finest. The cards can be differentiated from the regular Finest cards by the "PP" numbering on the back.

COMPLETE SET (5)	3.20	6.00
PP1 Brian Jordan	.20	.50
PP2 Bernie Williams	.40	1.00
PP3 Pat Burrell	.20	.50
PP4 Corey Myers	.20	.50
PP5 Derek Jeter GEM	1.60	4.00

2000 Finest

Produced by Topps, the 2000 Finest Series one product was released in April, 2000 as a 147-card set. The Finest Series two product was released in July, 2000 as a 140-card set. Each hobby and retail pack contained six cards and carried a suggested retail price of $4.99. Each HTA pack contained 13 cards and carried a suggested retail price of $10.00. The set includes 179-player cards, 20 first series Rookie Cards (cards 101-120) each serial numbered

to 2000 and 20 second series Rookie Cards (cards 247-266) each serial numbered to 3000, 15 Features subset cards (cards 121-135), 10 Counterparts subset cards (numbers 267-276), and 20 Gems subset cards (numbers 136-145 and 277-286). The set also includes two versions of card number 146 Ken Griffey Jr. wearing his Reds uniform (a portrait and action shot). Rookie Cards were seeded at a rate of 1:23 hobby/retail packs and 1:6 HTA packs. Features and Counterparts subset cards were inserted one every eight hobby and retail packs and one every three HTA packs. Gems subset cards were inserted one every 24 hobby and retail packs and one every nine HTA packs. Finally, 20 "Graded Gems" exchange cards were randomly seeded into packs (10 per series). The lucky handful of collectors that found these cards could send them into Topps for a complete Gems subset, each of which was professionally graded "Gem Mint 10" by PSA.

COMP.SERIES 1 w/o SP's (100)	10.00	25.00
COMP.SERIES 2 w/o SP's (100)	10.00	25.00
COMMON (1-100/147-246)	.15	.40
COMMON (101-120)	2.00	5.00
COMMON (121-135)	.60	1.50
COMMON (136-145/277-286)	.75	2.00
COMMON (247-266)	2.00	5.00
COMMON (267-276)	.40	1.00
1 Nomar Garciaparra	.60	1.50
2 Chipper Jones	.40	1.00
3 Erubiel Durazo	.15	.40
4 Robin Ventura	.25	.60
5 Garret Anderson	.15	.40
6 Dean Palmer	.15	.40
7 Mariano Rivera	.40	1.00
8 Rusty Greer	.15	.40
9 Jim Thome	.25	.60
10 Jeff Bagwell	.25	.60
11 Jason Giambi	.15	.40
12 Jeromy Burnitz	.15	.40
13 Mark Grace	.25	.60
14 Russ Ortiz	.15	.40
15 Kevin Brown	.25	.60
16 Kevin Millwood	.15	.40
17 Scott Williamson	.15	.40
18 Orlando Hernandez	.15	.40
19 Todd Walker	.15	.40
20 Carlos Beltran	.15	.40
21 Ruben Rivera	.15	.40
22 Curt Schilling	.15	.40
23 Brian Giles	.15	.40
24 Eric Karros	.15	.40
25 Preston Wilson	.15	.40
26 Al Leiter	.15	.40
27 Juan Encarnacion	.15	.40
28 Tim Salmon	.25	.60
29 B.J. Surhoff	.15	.40
30 Bernie Williams	.25	.60
31 Lee Stevens	.15	.40
32 Pokey Reese	.15	.40
33 Mike Sweeney	.15	.40
34 Corey Koskie	.15	.40
35 Roberto Alomar	.25	.60
36 Tim Hudson	.15	.40
37 Tom Glavine	.25	.60
38 Jeff Kent	.15	.40
39 Mike Lieberthal	.15	.40
40 Barry Larkin	.25	.60
41 Paul O'Neill	.25	.60
42 Rico Brogna	.15	.40
43 Brian Daubach	.15	.40
44 Rich Aurilia	.15	.40
45 Vladimir Guerrero	.40	1.00
46 Luis Castillo	.15	.40
47 Bartolo Colon	.15	.40
48 Kevin Appier	.15	.40
49 Mo Vaughn	.15	.40
50 Alex Rodriguez	.60	1.50
51 Randy Johnson	.40	1.00
52 Kris Benson	.15	.40
53 Tony Clark	.15	.40
54 Chad Allen	.15	.40
55 Larry Walker	.15	.40
56 Freddy Garcia	.15	.40
57 Paul Konerko	.15	.40
58 Edgardo Alfonzo	.15	.40
59 Brady Anderson	.15	.40
60 Derek Jeter	1.00	2.50
61 John Smoltz	.25	.60
62 Doug Glanville	.15	.40
63 Shannon Stewart	.15	.40
64 Greg Maddux	.60	1.50
65 Mark McGwire	1.00	2.50
66 Gary Sheffield	.15	.40
67 Kevin Young	.15	.40
68 Tony Gwynn	.50	1.25
69 Rey Ordonez	.15	.40
70 Cal Ripken	1.25	3.00
71 Todd Helton	.25	.60
72 Brian Jordan	.15	.40
73 Jose Canseco	.25	.60
74 Luis Gonzalez	.15	.40
75 Barry Bonds	1.00	2.50
76 Jermaine Dye	.15	.40
77 Jose Offerman	.15	.40
78 Magglio Ordonez	.15	.40
79 Fred McGriff	.25	.60
80 Ivan Rodriguez	.25	.60
81 Josh Hamilton	.75	2.00
82 Vernon Wells	.15	.40
83 Mark Mulder	.15	.40
84 John Patterson	.15	.40
85 Nick Johnson	.15	.40
86 Pablo Ozuna	.15	.40
87 A.J. Burnett	.15	.40
88 Jack Cust	.15	.40
89 Adam Piatt	.15	.40
90 Rob Ryan	.15	.40
91 Sean Burroughs	.15	.40
92 D'Angelo Jimenez	.15	.40
93 Chad Hermansen	.15	.40
94 Robert Fick	.15	.40
95 Ruben Mateo	.15	.40
96 Alex Escobar	.15	.40
97 Wily Pena	.15	.40
98 Corey Patterson	.15	.40
99 Eric Munson	.15	.40
100 Pat Burrell	.15	.40
101 Michael Tejera RC	2.00	5.00
102 Bobby Bradley RC	2.00	5.00
103 Larry Bigbie RC	3.00	8.00
104 B.J. Garbe RC	2.00	5.00
105 Josh Kalinowski RC	2.00	5.00
106 Brett Myers RC	3.00	8.00
107 Chris Mears RC	2.00	5.00
108 Aaron Rowand RC	4.00	10.00
109 Corey Myers RC	2.00	5.00
110 John Sneed RC	2.00	5.00
111 Ryan Christianson RC	2.00	5.00
112 Kyle Snyder	2.00	5.00
113 Mike Paradis	2.00	5.00
114 Chance Caple RC	2.00	5.00
115 Ben Christensen RC	2.00	5.00
116 Brad Baker RC	2.00	5.00
117 Rob Purvis RC	2.00	5.00
118 Rick Asadoorian RC	2.00	5.00
119 Ruben Salazar RC	2.00	5.00
120 Julio Zuleta RC	2.00	5.00
121 Alex Rodriguez Ken Griffey Jr.	1.00	2.50
122 Nomar Garciaparra Derek Jeter	1.25	3.00
123 Mark Mcgwire Sammy Sosa	1.50	4.00
124 Randy Johnson Pedro Martinez	1.00	2.50
125 Ivan Rodriguez Mike Piazza	1.00	2.50
126 Manny Ramirez Roberto Alomar	.60	1.50
127 Chipper Jones Andruw Jones	1.00	2.50
128 Cal Ripken Tony Gwynn	2.00	5.00
129 Jeff Bagwell Craig Biggio	.60	1.50
130 Barry Bonds Vladimir Guerrero	1.50	4.00
131 Nick Johnson Alfonso Soriano	1.00	2.50
132 Josh Hamilton Pat Burrell	4.00	10.00
133 Corey Patterson Ruben Mateo	.60	1.50
134 Larry Walker Todd Helton	.60	1.50
135 Rey Ordonez Edgardo Alfonzo	.60	1.50
136 Derek Jeter GEM	3.00	8.00
137 Alex Rodriguez GEM	2.00	5.00
138 Chipper Jones GEM	2.00	5.00
139 Mike Piazza GEM	2.00	5.00
140 Mark McGwire GEM	3.00	8.00
141 Ivan Rodriguez GEM	1.25	3.00
142 Cal Ripken GEM	4.00	10.00
143 V.Guerrero GEM	2.00	5.00
144 Randy Johnson GEM	2.00	5.00
145 Jeff Bagwell GEM	1.25	3.00
146 K.Griffey Jr. ACTION	.60	1.50
146A Ken Griffey Jr. PORT	.60	1.50
147 Andruw Jones	.25	.60
148 Kerry Wood	.15	.40
149 Jim Edmonds	.15	.40
150 Pedro Martinez	.25	.60
151 Warren Morris	.15	.40
152 Trevor Hoffman	.15	.40
153 Ryan Klesko	.15	.40
154 Andy Pettitte	.25	.60
155 Frank Thomas	.40	1.00
156 Damion Easley	.15	.40
157 Cliff Floyd	.15	.40
158 Ben Davis	.15	.40
159 John Valentin	.15	.40
160 Rafael Palmeiro	.25	.60
161 Andy Ashby	.15	.40
162 J.D. Drew	.15	.40
163 Jay Bell	.15	.40
164 Adam Kennedy	.15	.40
165 Manny Ramirez	.25	.60
166 John Halama	.15	.40
167 Octavio Dotel	.15	.40
168 Darin Erstad	.15	.40
169 Jose Lima	.15	.40
170 Andres Galarraga	.15	.40
171 Scott Rolen	.25	.60
172 Delino DeShields	.15	.40
173 J.T. Snow	.15	.40
174 Tony Womack	.15	.40
175 John Olerud	.15	.40
176 Jason Kendall	.15	.40
177 Carlos Lee	.15	.40
178 Eric Milton	.15	.40
179 Jeff Cirillo	.15	.40
180 Gabe Kapler	.15	.40
181 Greg Vaughn	.15	.40
182 Denny Neagle	.15	.40
183 Tino Martinez	.25	.60
184 Doug Mientkiewicz	.15	.40
185 Juan Gonzalez	.15	.40
186 Ellis Burks	.15	.40
187 Mike Hampton	.15	.40
188 Royce Clayton	.15	.40
189 Mike Mussina	.25	.60
190 Carlos Delgado	.15	.40
191 Ben Grieve	.15	.40
192 Fernando Tatis	.15	.40
193 Matt Williams	.15	.40
194 Rondell White	.15	.40
195 Shawn Green	.15	.40
196 Hideki Irabu	.15	.40
197 Troy Glaus	.15	.40
198 Roger Cedeno	.15	.40
199 Ray Lankford	.15	.40
200 Sammy Sosa	.40	1.00
201 Kenny Lofton	.15	.40
202 Edgar Martinez	.25	.60
203 Mark Kotsay	.15	.40
204 David Wells	.15	.40
205 Craig Biggio	.25	.60
206 Ray Durham	.15	.40
207 Troy O'Leary	.15	.40
208 Rickey Henderson	.40	1.00
209 Bob Abreu	.15	.40
210 Neifi Perez	.15	.40
211 Carlos Febles	.15	.40
212 Chuck Knoblauch	.15	.40
213 Moises Alou	.15	.40
214 Omar Vizquel	.25	.60
215 Vinny Castilla	.15	.40
216 Javy Lopez	.15	.40
217 Johnny Damon	.25	.60
218 Roger Clemens	.75	2.00
219 Miguel Tejada	.15	.40
220 Carl Everett	.15	.40
221 Matt Lawton	.15	.40
222 Albert Belle	.15	.40
223 Adrian Beltre	.15	.40
224 Dante Bichette	.15	.40
225 Raul Mondesi	.15	.40
226 Mike Piazza	.60	1.50
227 Brad Penny	.15	.40
228 Kip Wells	.15	.40
229 Adam Everett	.15	.40
230 Eddie Yarnall	.15	.40
231 Matt LeCroy	.15	.40
232 Jason Tyner	.15	.40
233 Rick Ankiel	.15	.40
234 Lance Berkman	.15	.40
235 Rafael Furcal	.15	.40
236 Dee Brown	.15	.40
237 Gookie Dawkins	.15	.40
238 Eric Valent	.15	.40
239 Peter Bergeron	.15	.40
240 Alfonso Soriano	.40	1.00
241 Adam Dunn	.40	1.00
242 Jorge Toca	.15	.40
243 Ryan Anderson	.15	.40
244 Jason Dellaero	.15	.40
245 Jason Grilli	.15	.40
246 Milton Bradley	.15	.40
247 Scott Downs RC	2.00	5.00
248 Keith Reed RC	2.00	5.00
249 Edgar Cruz RC	2.00	5.00
250 Wes Anderson RC	2.00	5.00
251 Lyle Overbay RC	3.00	8.00
252 Mike Lamb RC	3.00	8.00
253 Vince Faison RC	2.00	5.00
254 Chad Alexander	2.00	5.00
255 Chris Wakeland RC	2.00	5.00
256 Aaron McNeal RC	2.00	5.00
257 Tomo Ohka RC	2.00	5.00
258 Ty Howington RC	2.00	5.00
259 Javier Colina RC	2.00	5.00
260 Jason Jennings	2.00	5.00
261 Ramon Santiago RC	2.00	5.00
262 Johan Santana RC	40.00	80.00
263 Quincy Foster RC	2.00	5.00
264 Junior Brignac RC	2.00	5.00
265 Rico Washington RC	2.00	5.00
266 Scott Sobkowiak RC	2.00	5.00
267 Pedro Martinez Rick Ankiel	.60	1.50
268 Manny Ramirez Vladimir Guerrero	1.00	2.50
269 A.J.Burnett Mark Mulder	.40	1.00
270 Mike Piazza Eric Munson	1.00	2.50
271 Josh Hamilton Corey Patterson	1.25	3.00
272 Ken Griffey Jr. Sammy Sosa	.75	2.00
273 Derek Jeter Alfonso Soriano	1.50	4.00
274 Mark McGwire Pat Burrell	1.50	4.00
275 Chipper Jones Cal Ripken	1.50	4.00
276 Nomar Garciaparra Alex Rodriguez	1.00	2.50
277 Pedro Martinez GEM	1.25	3.00
278 Tony Gwynn GEM	1.50	4.00
279 Barry Bonds GEM	3.00	8.00
280 Juan Gonzalez GEM	.75	2.00
281 Larry Walker GEM	.75	2.00
282 N.Garciaparra GEM	2.00	5.00
283 Ken Griffey Jr. GEM	2.00	5.00
284 Manny Ramirez GEM	1.25	3.00
285 Shawn Green GEM	.75	2.00
286 Sammy Sosa GEM	2.00	5.00
NNO Graded Gems Ser.1 EXCH/10		
NNO Graded Gems Ser.2 EXCH/10		

2000 Finest Gold Refractors

Randomly inserted in packs, this 287-card set parallels the base set. The set includes 179-player cards, 40 Rookie Cards (numbers 101-120 and 247-266) each serial numbered to 100, 15 Features subset cards (numbers 121-135), 10 Counterparts subset cards (numbers 267-276), and 20 Gems subset cards (numbers 136-145 and 277-286). The set also includes two versions of card number 146 Ken Griffey Jr. wearing his Reds uniform (a portrait and action shot). Rookie/Veteran Cards were seeded at a rate of 1:240 hobby/retail packs and TBD HTA packs. Features and Counterparts subset cards were inserted one every 960 hobby and retail packs and one every 400 HTA packs. Gems subset cards were inserted one every 2880 hobby and retail packs and one every 1200 HTA packs. All cards are featured on gold die-cut technology.

*STARS 1-100/146-246: 20X TO 50X BASIC
*ROOKIES 101-120: 2.5X TO 6X BASIC

*ROOKIES 247-266: 2.5X TO 6X BASIC
*FEATURES 121-135: 4X TO 10X BASIC
*GEMS 136-145/277-286: 4X TO 10X BASIC
*COUNTER 267-276: 4X TO 10X BASIC

2000 Finest Refractors

Randomly inserted in packs, this 146-card set parallels the base set. The set includes 179-player cards, 40 Rookie Cards (numbers 101-120 serial numbered to 500 and and 247-266 serial-numbered to 1,000), 15 Features subset cards (numbers 121-135), 10 Counterparts subset cards (numbers 267-276), and 20 Gems subset cards (numbers 136-145 and 277-286). The set also includes two versions of card number 146 Ken Griffey Jr. wearing his Reds uniform (a portrait and action shot). Rookie/Veteran Cards were seeded at a rate of 1:24 hobby/retail packs and 1:6 HTA packs. Features and Counterparts subset cards were inserted one every 96 hobby and retail packs and one every 40 HTA packs. Gems subset cards were inserted one every 288 hobby and retail packs and one every 120 HTA packs.

*STARS 1-100/146-246: 6X TO 15X BASIC
*ROOKIES 101-120: 1X TO 2.5X BASIC
*FEATURES 121-135: 1.5X TO 4X BASIC
*GEMS 136-145/277-286: 1.5X TO 4X BASIC
*ROOKIES 247-266: 1X TO 2.5X BASIC RC'S
*COUNTER 267-276: 1.5X TO 4X BASIC

2000 Finest Gems Oversize

Randomly inserted as a "box-topper", this 20-card oversized set features some of the best players in major league baseball. Please note that cards 1-10 were inserted into series one boxes, and cards 11-20 were inserted into series two boxes.

COMPLETE SERIES 1 (10)	30.00	60.00
COMPLETE SERIES 2 (10)	20.00	50.00
*REF: .4X TO 1X BASIC GEMS OVERSIZE	1.50	4.00
REFRACTORS ONE PER HTA CHIP-TOPPER		
1 Derek Jeter	4.00	10.00
2 Alex Rodriguez	2.50	6.00
3 Chipper Jones	1.50	4.00
4 Mike Piazza	2.50	6.00
5 Mark McGwire	4.00	10.00
6 Ivan Rodriguez	1.00	2.50
7 Cal Ripken	5.00	12.00
8 Vladimir Guerrero	1.50	4.00
9 Randy Johnson	1.50	4.00
10 Jeff Bagwell	1.00	2.50
11 Nomar Garciaparra	2.50	6.00
12 Ken Griffey Jr.	2.50	6.00
13 Manny Ramirez	1.00	2.50
14 Shawn Green	.60	1.50
15 Sammy Sosa	1.50	4.00
16 Pedro Martinez	1.00	2.50
17 Tony Gwynn	2.00	5.00
18 Barry Bonds	4.00	10.00
19 Juan Gonzalez	.60	1.50
20 Larry Walker	.60	1.50

2000 Finest Ballpark Bounties

Randomly inserted into first and second series packs at one in 24 hobby/retail and 1:12 HTA, this insert set features 30 MLB players who are "wanted" for their pure talent. Card backs carry a "BB" prefix. Please note that cards 1-15 were inserted into series one packs, while cards 16-30 were inserted into series two packs.

COMPLETE SERIES 1 (15)	30.00	80.00
COMPLETE SERIES 2 (15)	40.00	100.00
BB1 Chipper Jones	2.00	5.00
BB2 Mike Piazza	3.00	8.00
BB3 Vladimir Guerrero	2.00	5.00
BB4 Sammy Sosa	2.00	5.00
BB5 Nomar Garciaparra	3.00	8.00
BB6 Manny Ramirez	1.25	3.00
BB7 Jeff Bagwell	1.25	3.00
BB8 Scott Rolen	1.25	3.00
BB9 Carlos Beltran	.75	2.00
BB10 Pedro Martinez	1.25	3.00
BB11 Greg Maddux	3.00	8.00
BB12 Josh Hamilton	2.00	5.00
BB13 Adam Piatt	.75	2.00
BB14 Pat Burrell	.75	2.00
BB15 Alfonso Soriano	2.00	5.00
BB16 Alex Rodriguez	3.00	8.00
BB17 Derek Jeter	5.00	12.00
BB18 Cal Ripken	6.00	15.00
BB19 Larry Walker	.75	2.00
BB20 Barry Bonds	5.00	12.00
BB21 Ken Griffey Jr.	3.00	8.00
BB22 Mark McGwire	5.00	12.00
BB23 Ivan Rodriguez	1.25	3.00
BB24 Andruw Jones	1.25	3.00
BB25 Todd Helton	1.25	3.00
BB26 Randy Johnson	2.00	5.00
BB27 Ruben Mateo	.75	2.00
BB28 Corey Patterson	.75	2.00
BB29 Sean Burroughs	.75	2.00
BB30 Eric Munson	.75	2.00

2000 Finest Dream Cast

Randomly inserted into series two packs at one in 36 hobby/retail packs and one in 13 HTA packs, this 10-card insert set features players that have skills people dream about having. Card backs carry a "DC" prefix.

COMPLETE SET (10)	40.00	100.00
DC1 Mark McGwire	6.00	15.00
DC2 Roberto Alomar	1.50	4.00
DC3 Chipper Jones	2.50	6.00
DC4 Derek Jeter	6.00	15.00
DC5 Barry Bonds	6.00	15.00
DC6 Ken Griffey Jr.	4.00	10.00
DC7 Sammy Sosa	2.50	6.00
DC8 Mike Piazza	4.00	10.00
DC9 Pedro Martinez	1.50	4.00
DC10 Randy Johnson	2.50	6.00

2000 Finest For the Record

Randomly inserted in first series packs at a rate of 1:71 hobby or retail and 1:33 HTA, this insert set features 30 serial-numbered cards. Each player has three versions that are sequentially numbered to the distance of the left, center, and right field walls of their home ballpark. Card backs carry a "FR" prefix.

FR1A Derek Jeter/318	12.50	30.00
FR1B Derek Jeter/408	12.50	30.00
FR1C Derek Jeter/314	12.50	30.00
FR2A Mark McGwire/330	12.50	30.00
FR2B Mark McGwire/402	12.50	30.00
FR2C Mark McGwire/330	12.50	30.00
FR3A Ken Griffey Jr./331	6.00	15.00
FR3B Ken Griffey Jr./405	6.00	15.00
FR3C Ken Griffey Jr./327	6.00	15.00
FR4A Alex Rodriguez/331	8.00	20.00
FR4B Alex Rodriguez/405	8.00	20.00
FR4C Alex Rodriguez/327	8.00	20.00
FR5A N.Garciaparra/310	6.00	15.00
FR5B N.Garciaparra/390	6.00	15.00
FR5C N.Garciaparra/302	6.00	15.00
FR6A Cal Ripken/333	15.00	40.00
FR6B Cal Ripken/410	15.00	40.00
FR6C Cal Ripken/318	15.00	40.00
FR7A Sammy Sosa/355	4.00	10.00
FR7B Sammy Sosa/400	4.00	10.00
FR7C Sammy Sosa/353	4.00	10.00
FR8A Manny Ramirez/325	4.00	10.00
FR8B Manny Ramirez/410	4.00	10.00
FR8C Manny Ramirez/325	4.00	10.00
FR9A Mike Piazza/338	6.00	15.00
FR9B Mike Piazza/410	6.00	15.00
FR9C Mike Piazza/338	6.00	15.00
FR10A Chipper Jones/335	4.00	10.00
FR10B Chipper Jones/401	4.00	10.00
FR10C Chipper Jones/330	4.00	10.00

2000 Finest Going the Distance

Randomly inserted in first series hobby and retail packs at one in 24 and HTA packs at a rate of one in 12, this 12-card insert set features some of the best hitters in major league baseball. Card backs carry a "GTD" prefix.

COMPLETE SET (12)	30.00	80.00
GTD1 Tony Gwynn	2.00	5.00
GTD2 Alex Rodriguez	2.50	6.00
GTD3 Derek Jeter	4.00	10.00
GTD4 Chipper Jones	1.50	4.00
GTD5 Nomar Garciaparra	2.50	6.00
GTD6 Sammy Sosa	1.50	4.00
GTD7 Ken Griffey Jr.	2.50	6.00
GTD8 Vladimir Guerrero	1.50	4.00
GTD9 Mark McGwire	4.00	10.00
GTD10 Mike Piazza	2.50	6.00
GTD11 Manny Ramirez	1.00	2.50
GTD12 Cal Ripken	5.00	12.00

2000 Finest Moments

Randomly inserted into series two hobby and retail packs at one in nine, and HTA packs at one in four, this four-card insert features great moments from the 1999 baseball season. Card backs carry a "FM" prefix.

COMPLETE SET (4)	2.50	6.00
*REFRACTORS: .75X TO 2X BASIC MOMENTS		
SER.2 REF.ODDS 1:20 H/R 1:9 HTA		
FM1 Chipper Jones	.60	1.50
FM2 Ivan Rodriguez	.40	1.00
FM3 Tony Gwynn	.75	2.00
FM4 Wade Boggs	.60	1.50

2000 Finest Moments Refractors Autograph

Randomly inserted into series two hobby/retail packs at one in 425, and in HTA packs at one in 196, this four-card set is a complete parallel of the Finest Moments insert. This set is autographed by the player depicted on the card. Card backs carry a "FM" prefix.

FM1 Chipper Jones	20.00	50.00
FM2 Ivan Rodriguez	15.00	40.00
FM3 Tony Gwynn	20.00	50.00
FM4 Wade Boggs	15.00	40.00

2001 Finest

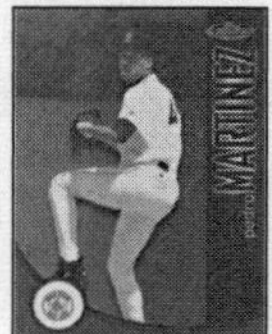

This 140-card set was distributed in six-card hobby packs with a suggested retail price of $6. Printed on 27 pt. card stock, the set features color action photos of 100 veteran players, 30 draft picks and prospects printed with the "Rookie Card" logo and sequentially numbered to 999, and 10 standout veterans sequentially numbered to 1999.

COMP.SET w/o SP's	10.00	25.00
COMMON CARD (1-110)	.15	.40
COMMON SP	4.00	10.00
COMMON (111-140)	4.00	10.00
1 Mike Piazza SP	8.00	20.00
2 Andruw Jones	.25	.60
3 Jason Giambi	.15	.40
4 Fred McGriff	.25	.60
5 Vladimir Guerrero SP	4.00	10.00
6 Adrian Gonzalez	.15	.40
7 Pedro Martinez	.25	.60
8 Mike Lieberthal	.15	.40
9 Warren Morris	.15	.40
10 Juan Gonzalez	.15	.40
11 Jose Canseco	.25	.60
12 Jose Valentin	.15	.40
13 Jeff Cirillo	.15	.40
14 Pokey Reese	.15	.40
15 Scott Rolen	.25	.60
16 Greg Maddux	.60	1.50
17 Carlos Delgado	.15	.40
18 Rick Ankiel	.15	.40
19 Steve Finley	.15	.40
20 Shawn Green	.15	.40
21 Orlando Cabrera	.15	.40
22 Roberto Alomar	.25	.60
23 John Olerud	.15	.40
24 Albert Belle	.15	.40
25 Edgardo Alfonzo	.15	.40
26 Rafael Palmeiro	.25	.60
27 Mike Sweeney	.15	.40
28 Bernie Williams	.25	.60
29 Larry Walker	.15	.40
30 Barry Bonds SP	10.00	25.00
31 Orlando Hernandez	.15	.40
32 Randy Johnson	.40	1.00
33 Shannon Stewart	.15	.40
34 Mark Grace	.25	.60
35 Alex Rodriguez SP	10.00	25.00
36 Tino Martinez	.25	.60
37 Carlos Febles	.15	.40
38 Al Leiter	.15	.40
39 Omar Vizquel	.25	.60
40 Chuck Knoblauch	.15	.40
41 Tim Salmon	.25	.60
42 Brian Jordan	.15	.40
43 Edgar Renteria	.15	.40
44 Preston Wilson	.15	.40
45 Mariano Rivera	.40	1.00
46 Gabe Kapler	.15	.40
47 Jason Kendall	.15	.40
48 Rickey Henderson	.40	1.00
49 Luis Gonzalez	.15	.40
50 Tom Glavine	.25	.60
51 Jeromy Burnitz	.15	.40
52 Garret Anderson	.15	.40
53 Craig Biggio	.25	.60
54 Vinny Castilla	.15	.40
55 Jeff Kent	.15	.40
56 Gary Sheffield	.15	.40
57 Jorge Posada	.25	.60
58 Sean Casey	.15	.40
59 Johnny Damon	.25	.60
60 Dean Palmer	.15	.40
61 Todd Helton	.25	.60
62 Barry Larkin	.25	.60
63 Robin Ventura	.15	.40
64 Kenny Lofton	.15	.40
65 Sammy Sosa SP	4.00	10.00
66 Rafael Furcal	.15	.40
67 Jay Bell	.15	.40
68 J.T. Snow	.15	.40
69 Jose Vidro	.15	.40
70 Ivan Rodriguez	.25	.60
71 Jermaine Dye	.15	.40
72 Chipper Jones SP	4.00	10.00
73 Fernando Vina	.15	.40
74 Ben Grieve	.15	.40
75 Mark McGwire SP	10.00	25.00
76 Matt Williams	.15	.40
77 Mark Grudzielanek	.15	.40
78 Mike Hampton	.15	.40
79 Brian Giles	.15	.40
80 Tony Gwynn	.50	1.25
81 Carlos Beltran	.15	.40
82 Ray Durham	.15	.40
83 Brad Radke	.15	.40
84 David Justice	.15	.40
85 Frank Thomas	.40	1.00
86 Todd Zeile	.15	.40
87 Pat Burrell	.15	.40
88 Jim Thome	.25	.60
89 Greg Vaughn	.15	.40
90 Ken Griffey Jr. SP	6.00	15.00
91 Mike Mussina	.25	.60
92 Magglio Ordonez	.15	.40
93 Bob Abreu	.15	.40
94 Alex Gonzalez	.15	.40
95 Kevin Brown	.15	.40
96 Jay Buhner	.15	.40
97 Roger Clemens	.75	2.00
98 Nomar Garciaparra SP	6.00	15.00
99 Derrek Lee	.25	.60
100 Derek Jeter SP	10.00	25.00
101 Adrian Beltre	.15	.40
102 Geoff Jenkins	.15	.40
103 Javy Lopez	.15	.40
104 Raul Mondesi	.15	.40
105 Troy Glaus	.15	.40
106 Jeff Bagwell	.25	.60
107 Eric Karros	.15	.40
108 Mo Vaughn	.15	.40
109 Cal Ripken	1.25	3.00
110 Manny Ramirez Sox	.25	.60
111 Scott Heard PROS	4.00	10.00
112 L. Montanez PROS RC	4.00	10.00
113 Ben Diggins PROS	4.00	10.00
114 Shaun Boyd PROS RC	4.00	10.00
115 Sean Burnett PROS	4.00	10.00
116 Carmen Cali PROS RC	4.00	10.00
117 D.Thompson PROS	4.00	10.00
118 D.Parrish PROS RC	4.00	10.00
119 D.Rich PROS RC	4.00	10.00
120 Chad Petty PROS RC	4.00	10.00
121 S.Smyth PROS RC	4.00	10.00
122 John Lackey PROS	4.00	10.00
123 M.Galante PROS RC	4.00	10.00
124 D.Borrell PROS RC	4.00	10.00
125 Bob Keppel PROS RC	4.00	10.00
126 J.Wayne PROS RC	4.00	10.00
127 J.R. House PROS	4.00	10.00
128 Brian Sellier PROS RC	4.00	10.00
129 Dan Moylan PROS RC	4.00	10.00
130 Scott Pratt PROS RC	4.00	10.00
131 Victor Hall PROS RC	4.00	10.00
132 Joel Pineiro PROS	4.00	10.00
133 J.Axelson PROS RC	4.00	10.00
134 Jose Reyes PROS RC	90.00	150.00
135 G. Runser PROS RC	4.00	10.00
136 B. Hebson PROS RC	4.00	10.00
137 S.Serrano PROS RC	4.00	10.00
138 K. Joseph PROS RC	4.00	10.00
139 J. Richardson PROS RC	4.00	10.00
140 M. Fischer PROS RC	4.00	10.00

2001 Finest Refractors

This 140-card set is a parallel version of the base set and is distinguished by the refractive quality of the cards. The 100 veteran cards are sequentially numbered to 499, the 30 draft picks and prospects to 241, and the 10 standout veterans to 399.

*1-110 REF: 4X TO 10X BASIC 1-110
*SP REF: .5X TO 1.2X BASIC SP
*111-140 REF: .75X TO 2X BASIC 111-140

2001 Finest All-Stars

Randomly inserted in packs at the rate of one in five, this 10-card set features color photos of the preeminent players at their respective positions. A refractive parallel version of this insert set was also produced and inserted in packs at the rate of one in 20.

COMPLETE SET (10)	30.00	60.00
*REF: 1X TO 2.5X BASIC ALL-STARS		
REFRACTOR ODDS 1:40 HOBBY, 1:20 HTA		
FAS1 Mark McGwire	4.00	10.00
FAS2 Derek Jeter	4.00	10.00
FAS3 Alex Rodriguez	2.50	6.00
FAS4 Chipper Jones	1.50	4.00
FAS5 Nomar Garciaparra	2.50	6.00
FAS6 Sammy Sosa	1.50	4.00
FAS7 Mike Piazza	2.50	6.00
FAS8 Barry Bonds	4.00	10.00
FAS9 Vladimir Guerrero	1.50	4.00
FAS10 Ken Griffey Jr.	2.50	6.00

2001 Finest Autographs

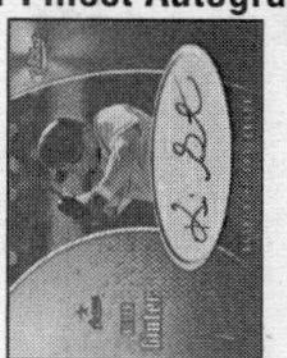

Randomly inserted in packs at the rate of one in 22, this 29-card set features autographed color photos of players who made the moments. All of these cards are refractors and carry the Topps "Certified Autograph" stamp and the Topps "Genuine Issue" sticker.

FAAG Adrian Gonzalez	6.00	15.00
FAAH Adam Hyzdu	4.00	10.00
FAAK Adam Kennedy	6.00	15.00
FAAP Albert Pujols	200.00	350.00
FABD Ben Diggins	4.00	10.00
FABM Ben Molina	6.00	15.00
FABS Ben Sheets	10.00	25.00
FABZ Barry Zito	10.00	25.00
FABKC Brian Cole	4.00	10.00
FACD Chad Durham	4.00	10.00
FACP Carlos Pena	4.00	10.00
FADK Dave Krynzel	4.00	10.00
FADCP Corey Patterson	4.00	10.00
FAJC Joe Crede	10.00	25.00
FAJH Jason Hart	4.00	10.00
FAJM Justin Morneau	50.00	80.00
FAJO Jose Ortiz	4.00	10.00
FAJP Jay Payton	4.00	10.00
FAJHH Josh Hamilton	15.00	40.00
FAJRH J.R. House	4.00	10.00
FAKG Keith Ginter	4.00	10.00
FAKM Kevin Mench	6.00	15.00
FAMB Milton Bradley	6.00	15.00
FAMQ Mark Quinn	4.00	10.00
FAMR Mark Redman	4.00	10.00
FARF Rafael Furcal	6.00	15.00
FASB Sean Burnett	4.00	10.00
FATF Troy Farnsworth	4.00	10.00
FATL Terrence Long	4.00	10.00

2001 Finest Moments

Randomly inserted in packs at the rate of one in 12, this 25-card set features color photos of players involved in great moments from the 2000 season plus both active and retired 3000 Hit Club members. A refractive parallel version of this set was also produced with an insertion rate of 1:40.

COMPLETE SET (25)	60.00	120.00
*REF: .75X TO 2X BASIC MOMENTS		
REFRACTOR ODDS 1:40 HOBBY, 1:20 HTA		
FM1 Pat Burrell	1.00	2.50
FM2 Adam Kennedy	1.00	2.50
FM3 Mike Lamb	1.00	2.50
FM4 Rafael Furcal	1.00	2.50
FM5 Terrence Long	1.00	2.50
FM6 Jay Payton	1.00	2.50
FM7 Mark Quinn	1.00	2.50
FM8 Ben Molina	1.00	2.50
FM9 Kazuhiro Sasaki	1.00	2.50
FM10 Mark Redman	1.00	2.50
FM11 Barry Bonds	6.00	15.00
FM12 Alex Rodriguez	4.00	10.00
FM13 Roger Clemens	5.00	12.00
FM14 Jim Edmonds	1.00	2.50
FM15 Jason Giambi	1.00	2.50
FM16 Todd Helton	1.50	4.00
FM17 Troy Glaus	1.00	2.50
FM18 Carlos Delgado	1.00	2.50
FM19 Darin Erstad	1.00	2.50
FM20 Cal Ripken	8.00	20.00
FM21 Paul Molitor	1.00	2.50
FM22 Robin Yount	2.50	6.00
FM23 George Brett	5.00	12.00
FM24 Dave Winfield	1.00	2.50
FM25 Eddie Murray	2.50	6.00

2001 Finest Moments Refractors Autograph

Randomly inserted in packs at the rate of one in 250, this 10-card set features autographed player photos with the Topps "Certified Autograph" stamp and the

Topps "Genuine Issue" sticker printed on these refractive cards. Exchange cards with a redemption deadline of April 30, 2003 were seeded into packs for Cal Ripken, Eddie Murray and Robin Yount.

FMABB Barry Bonds	100.00	175.00
FMACR Cal Ripken	75.00	150.00
FMADW Dave Winfield	15.00	40.00
FMAEM Eddie Murray	30.00	60.00
FMAGB George Brett	60.00	120.00
FMAJG Jason Giambi	15.00	40.00
FMAPM Paul Molitor	15.00	40.00
FMARY Robin Yount	30.00	60.00
FMATG Troy Glaus	15.00	40.00
FMATH Todd Helton	15.00	40.00

2001 Finest Origins

Randomly inserted in packs at the rate of one in seven, this 15-card set features some of today's best ballplayers who didn't make the 1993 Finest cut. These cards are printed in the 1993 classic Finest card design. A refractive parallel version of this set was also produced with an insertion rate of 1:40.

COMPLETE SET (15)	20.00	40.00
*REF: 1X TO 2.5X BASIC ORIGINS		
REFRACTOR ODDS 1:40 HOBBY, 1:20 HTA		
FO1 Derek Jeter	5.00	12.00
FO2 Jason Kendall	.75	2.00
FO3 Jose Vidro	.75	2.00
FO4 Preston Wilson	.75	2.00
FO5 Jim Edmonds	.75	2.00
FO6 Vladimir Guerrero	2.00	5.00
FO7 Andruw Jones	1.25	3.00
FO8 Scott Rolen	1.25	3.00
FO9 Edgardo Alfonzo	.75	2.00
FO10 Mike Sweeney	.75	2.00
FO11 Alex Rodriguez	3.00	8.00
FO12 Jermaine Dye	.75	2.00
FO13 Charles Johnson	.75	2.00
FO14 Darren Dreifort	.75	2.00
FO15 Neifi Perez	.75	2.00

2002 Finest

This 110 card set was issued in five card pack with an SRP of $6 per pack which were packed six per mini box with three mini boxes per full box and twelve boxes per case. Cards number 101 through 110 are Rookie Cards which were all autographed by the featured player. One of these autograph cards were inserted into each six pack mini box.

COMP.SET w/o SP's (100)	10.00	25.00
COMMON CARD (1-100)	.20	.50
COMMON CARD (101-110)	4.00	10.00
1 Mike Mussina	.30	.75
2 Steve Sparks	.20	.50
3 Randy Johnson	.50	1.25
4 Orlando Cabrera	.20	.50
5 Jeff Kent	.20	.50
6 Carlos Delgado	.20	.50
7 Ivan Rodriguez	.30	.75
8 Jose Cruz	.20	.50
9 Jason Giambi	.20	.50
10 Brad Penny	.20	.50
11 Moises Alou	.20	.50
12 Mike Piazza	.75	2.00
13 Ben Grieve	.20	.50
14 Derek Jeter	1.25	3.00
15 Roy Oswalt	.20	.50
16 Pat Burrell	.20	.50
17 Preston Wilson	.20	.50
18 Kevin Brown	.20	.50
19 Barry Bonds	1.25	3.00
20 Phil Nevin	.20	.50
21 Aramis Ramirez	.20	.50
22 Carlos Beltran	.20	.50
23 Chipper Jones	.50	1.25
24 Curt Schilling	.20	.50
25 Jorge Posada	.30	.75
26 Alfonso Soriano	.20	.50
27 Cliff Floyd	.20	.50
28 Rafael Palmeiro	.30	.75
29 Terrence Long	.20	.50
30 Ken Griffey Jr.	.75	2.00
31 Jason Kendall	.20	.50
32 Jose Vidro	.20	.50
33 Jermaine Dye	.20	.50
34 Bobby Higginson	.20	.50
35 Albert Pujols	1.00	2.50
36 Miguel Tejada	.20	.50
37 Jim Edmonds	.20	.50
38 Barry Zito	.20	.50

39 Jimmy Rollins .20 .50
40 Rafael Furcal .20 .50
41 Omar Vizquel .30 .75
42 Kazuhiro Sasaki .20 .50
43 Brian Giles .20 .50
44 Darin Erstad .20 .50
45 Mariano Rivera .50 1.25
46 Troy Percival .20 .50
47 Mike Sweeney .20 .50
48 Vladimir Guerrero .50 1.25
49 Troy Glaus .20 .50
50 So Taguchi RC 1.00 2.50
51 Edgardo Alfonzo .20 .50
52 Roger Clemens 1.00 2.50
53 Eric Chavez .20 .50
54 Alex Rodriguez .75 2.00
55 Cristian Guzman .20 .50
56 Jeff Bagwell .30 .75
57 Bernie Williams .30 .75
58 Kerry Wood .20 .50
59 Ryan Klesko .20 .50
60 Ichiro Suzuki 1.00 2.50
61 Larry Walker .20 .50
62 Nomar Garciaparra .75 2.00
63 Craig Biggio .30 .75
64 J.D. Drew .20 .50
65 Juan Pierre .20 .50
66 Roberto Alomar .30 .75
67 Luis Gonzalez .20 .50
68 Bud Smith .20 .50
69 Magglio Ordonez .20 .50
70 Scott Rolen .30 .75
71 Tsuyoshi Shinjo .20 .50
72 Paul Konerko .20 .50
73 Garret Anderson .20 .50
74 Tim Hudson .20 .50
75 Adam Dunn .20 .50
76 Gary Sheffield .20 .50
77 Johnny Damon Sox .30 .75
78 Todd Helton .30 .75
79 Geoff Jenkins .20 .50
80 Shawn Green .20 .50
81 C.C. Sabathia .20 .50
82 Kazuhisa Ishii RC UER 1.00 2.50
2001 ERA is incorrect
83 Rich Aurilia .20 .50
84 Mike Hampton .20 .50
85 Ben Sheets .20 .50
86 Andruw Jones .30 .75
87 Richie Sexson .20 .50
88 Jim Thome .30 .75
89 Sammy Sosa .50 1.25
90 Greg Maddux .75 2.00
91 Pedro Martinez .30 .75
92 Jeromy Burnitz .20 .50
93 Raul Mondesi .20 .50
94 Bret Boone .20 .50
95 Jerry Hairston .20 .50
96 Mike Rivera .20 .50
97 Juan Cruz .20 .50
98 Morgan Ensberg .20 .50
99 Nathan Haynes .20 .50
100 Xavier Nady .20 .50
101 Nic Jackson FY AU RC 4.00 10.00
102 Mauricio Lara FY AU RC 4.00 10.00
103 Freddy Sanchez FY AU RC 12.50 30.00
104 Clint Nageotte FY AU RC 4.00 10.00
105 Beltran Perez FY AU RC 4.00 10.00
106 Garrett Gentry FY AU RC 4.00 10.00
107 Chad Qualls FY AU RC 4.00 10.00
108 Jason Bay FY AU RC 15.00 40.00
109 Michael Hill FY AU RC 4.00 10.00
110 Brian Tallet FY AU RC 4.00 10.00

2002 Finest Refractors

Inserted in packs at stated odds of one in two mini boxes, these cards parallel the 2002 Finest set. These cards have the patented topps "refractor" sheen and have a stated print run of 499 serial numbered sets.

*REFRACTORS 1-100: 2.5X TO 6X BASIC
*REF.RC'S 1-100: 1.5X TO 4X BASIC
101 Nic Jackson FY 2.00 5.00
102 Mauricio Lara FY 2.00 5.00
103 Freddy Sanchez FY 5.00 12.00
104 Clint Nageotte FY 3.00 8.00
105 Beltran Perez FY 2.00 5.00
106 Garett Gentry FY 2.00 5.00
107 Chad Qualls FY 3.00 8.00
108 Jason Bay FY 8.00 20.00
109 Michael Hill FY 2.00 5.00
110 Brian Tallet FY 2.00 5.00

2002 Finest X-Fractors

Inserted at a rate of one in three mini boxes, these cards parallel the Finest set. These cards have a uniquely patterned finest design and are printed to a stated print run of 299 serial numbered sets.

*XF 1-100: 3X TO 8X BASIC
*XF RC'S 1-100: 2X TO 5X BASIC
*XF 101-110: .5X TO 1.2X REFRACTOR

2002 Finest X-Fractors Protectors

Inserted at a rate of one in seven mini boxes, these cards parallel the Finest set. These cards have a uniquely patterned finest design and were created with a "finest protector" and are printed to a stated print run of 99 serial numbered sets.

*XF PROT. 1-100: 6X TO 15X BASIC
*XF PROT.RC'S 1-100: 4X TO 10X BASIC
*XF PROT 101-110: .75X TO 2X REFRACTOR

2002 Finest Bat Relics

Inserted at a stated rate of one in 12 mini boxes these 15 cards feature a bat slice from the featured player.

FBRAJ Andruw Jones 6.00 15.00
FBRAP Albert Pujols 8.00 20.00
FBRAR Alex Rodriguez 6.00 15.00
FBRAS Alfonso Soriano 4.00 10.00
FBRBB Barry Bonds 10.00 25.00
FBRBO Bret Boone 4.00 10.00
FBRBW Bernie Williams 6.00 15.00
FBRCJ Chipper Jones 6.00 15.00
FBRIR Ivan Rodriguez 6.00 15.00
FBRLG Luis Gonzalez 4.00 10.00
FBRMP Mike Piazza 6.00 15.00
FBRNG Nomar Garciaparra 6.00 15.00
FBRTG Tony Gwynn 6.00 15.00
FBRTH Todd Helton 6.00 15.00
FBRTS Tsuyoshi Shinjo 4.00 10.00

2002 Finest Jersey Relics

Inserted at a stated rate of one in four mini boxes, these 24 cards feature the player photo along with a game-used jersey swatch.

FJRAJ Andruw Jones 6.00 15.00
FJRAR Alex Rodriguez 6.00 15.00
FJRBB Barry Bonds 10.00 25.00
FJRBO Bret Boone 4.00 10.00
FJRCD Carlos Delgado 4.00 10.00
FJRCJ Chipper Jones 6.00 15.00
FJRCS Curt Schilling 4.00 10.00
FJRFT Frank Thomas 6.00 15.00
FJRGM Greg Maddux 6.00 15.00
FJRHN Hideo Nomo 6.00 15.00
FJRIR Ivan Rodriguez 6.00 15.00
FJRJB Jeff Bagwell 6.00 15.00
FJRLG Luis Gonzalez 4.00 10.00
FJRLW Larry Walker 4.00 10.00
FJRMG Mark Grace 6.00 15.00
FJRMP Mike Piazza 6.00 15.00
FJRPM Pedro Martinez 6.00 15.00
FJRRA Roberto Alomar 6.00 15.00
FJRRH Rickey Henderson 6.00 15.00
FJRRP Rafael Palmeiro 6.00 15.00
FJRSG Shawn Green 4.00 10.00
FJRTG Tony Gwynn 6.00 15.00
FJRTH Todd Helton 6.00 15.00
FJRTS Tsuyoshi Shinjo 4.00 10.00

2002 Finest Moments Autographs

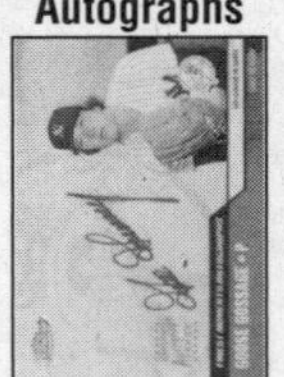

Inserted at a stated rate of one in three mini boxes, these cards feature leading retired players who signed cards honoring their greatest career moment.

FMABG Bob Gibson 10.00 25.00
FMABR Bobby Richardson 6.00 15.00
FMABT Bobby Thomson 6.00 15.00
FMADL Don Larsen 6.00 15.00
FMADM Don Mattingly 40.00 80.00
FMAFJ Fergie Jenkins 6.00 15.00
FMAGG Goose Gossage 10.00 25.00
FMAGP Gaylord Perry 6.00 15.00
FMAJB Jim Bunning 10.00 25.00
FMAJS Johnny Sain 6.00 15.00
FMALA Luis Aparicio 6.00 15.00
FMAMS Mike Schmidt 40.00 80.00
FMARS Red Schoendienst 6.00 15.00
FMAYB Yogi Berra 20.00 50.00
FMABRO Brooks Robinson 10.00 25.00

2003 Finest

This 110 card set was released in May, 2003. This product was issued in six pack mini-boxes with an SRP of $36. The first 100 cards are veterans while the final 10 cards featured autographed cards of leading rookies and prospects. Those cards (101-110) were issued at a stated rate of one in four mini boxes.

COMP.SET w/o SP's (100) 10.00 25.00
COMMON CARD (1-100) .20 .50
COMMON CARD (101-110) 6.00 15.00
1 Sammy Sosa .50 1.25
2 Paul Konerko .20 .50
3 Todd Helton .30 .75
4 Mike Lowell .20 .50
5 Lance Berkman .20 .50
6 Kazuhisa Ishii .20 .50
7 A.J. Pierzynski .20 .50
8 Jose Vidro .20 .50
9 Roberto Alomar .30 .75
10 Derek Jeter 1.25 3.00
11 Barry Zito .20 .50
12 Jimmy Rollins .20 .50
13 Brian Giles .20 .50
14 Ryan Klesko .20 .50
15 Rich Aurilia .20 .50
16 Jim Edmonds .20 .50
17 Aubrey Huff .20 .50
18 Ivan Rodriguez .30 .75
19 Eric Hinske .20 .50
20 Barry Bonds 1.25 3.00
21 Darin Erstad .20 .50
22 Curt Schilling .20 .50
23 Andruw Jones .30 .75
24 Jay Gibbons .20 .50
25 Nomar Garciaparra .75 2.00
26 Kerry Wood .20 .50
27 Magglio Ordonez .20 .50
28 Austin Kearns .20 .50
29 Jason Jennings .20 .50
30 Jason Giambi .20 .50
31 Tim Hudson .20 .50
32 Edgar Martinez .30 .75
33 Carl Crawford .20 .50
34 Hee Seop Choi .20 .50
35 Vladimir Guerrero .50 1.25
36 Jeff Kent .20 .50
37 John Smoltz .30 .75
38 Frank Thomas .50 1.25
39 Cliff Floyd .20 .50
40 Mike Piazza .75 2.00
41 Mark Prior .30 .75
42 Tim Salmon .30 .75
43 Shawn Green .20 .50
44 Bernie Williams .30 .75
45 Jim Thome .30 .75
46 John Olerud .20 .50
47 Orlando Hudson .20 .50
48 Mark Teixeira .30 .75
49 Gary Sheffield .20 .50
50 Ichiro Suzuki 1.00 2.50
51 Tom Glavine .30 .75
52 Torii Hunter .20 .50
53 Craig Biggio .30 .75
54 Carlos Beltran .30 .75
55 Bartolo Colon .20 .50
56 Jorge Posada .30 .75
57 Pat Burrell .20 .50
58 Edgar Renteria .20 .50
59 Rafael Palmeiro .30 .75
60 Alfonso Soriano .20 .50
61 Brandon Phillips .20 .50
62 Luis Gonzalez .20 .50
63 Manny Ramirez .30 .75
64 Garret Anderson .20 .50
65 Ken Griffey Jr. .75 2.00
66 A.J. Burnett .20 .50
67 Mike Sweeney .20 .50
68 Doug Mientkiewicz .20 .50
69 Eric Chavez .20 .50
70 Adam Dunn .20 .50
71 Shea Hillenbrand .20 .50
72 Troy Glaus .20 .50
73 Rodrigo Lopez .20 .50
74 Moises Alou .20 .50
75 Chipper Jones .50 1.25
76 Bobby Abreu .20 .50
77 Mark Mulder .20 .50
78 Kevin Brown .20 .50
79 Josh Beckett .20 .50
80 Larry Walker .20 .50
81 Randy Johnson .50 1.25
82 Greg Maddux .75 2.00
83 Johnny Damon .30 .75
84 Omar Vizquel .30 .75
85 Jeff Bagwell .30 .75
86 Carlos Pena .20 .50
87 Roy Oswalt .20 .50
88 Richie Sexson .20 .50
89 Roger Clemens 1.00 2.50
90 Miguel Tejada .20 .50
91 Vicente Padilla .20 .50
92 Phil Nevin .20 .50
93 Edgardo Alfonzo .20 .50
94 Bret Boone .20 .50
95 Albert Pujols 1.00 2.50
96 Carlos Delgado .20 .50
97 Jose Contreras RC .75 2.00
98 Scott Rolen .30 .75
99 Pedro Martinez .30 .75
100 Alex Rodriguez .75 2.00
101 Adam LaRoche AU 6.00 15.00
102 Andy Marte AU RC 25.00 50.00
103 Daryl Clark AU RC 4.00 10.00
104 J.D. Durbin AU RC 4.00 10.00
105 Craig Brazell AU RC 4.00 10.00
106 Brian Burgamy AU RC 4.00 10.00
107 Tyler Johnson AU RC 4.00 10.00
108 Joey Gomes AU RC 4.00 10.00
109 Bryan Bullington AU RC 6.00 15.00
110 Byron Gettis AU RC 4.00 10.00

2003 Finest Refractors

This is a complete parallel of the basic Finest set. Cards numbered 1-100 were issued at a stated rate of one per mini-box and cards numbered 101-110 were issued at a stated rate of one every 34 mini-boxes.

*REFRACTORS 1-100: 2X TO 5X BASIC
*REFRACTOR RC'S 1-100: 1.25X TO 3X BASIC
*REFRACTORS 101-110: .75X TO 2X BASIC

2003 Finest X-Fractors

Inserted at a stated rate of one in seven mini-boxes, this is a parallel to the Finest set. These cards were issued to a stated print run of 99 serial numbered sets.

*X-FRACTORS 1-100: 6X TO 15X BASIC
*X-FRACTOR RC'S 1-100: 4X TO 10X BASIC
*X-FRACTORS 101-110: 1X TO 2.5X BASIC

2003 Finest Uncirculated Gold X-Fractors

Issued as a box topper for the big box which contained all the mini-boxes, this is a parallel to the basic set. These cards are sealed in plastic holders and were issued to a stated print run of 199 serial numbered sets.

*GOLD X-F 1-100: 5X TO 12X BASIC
*GOLD X-F RC'S 1-100: 3X TO 8X BASIC
*GOLD X-F 101-110: .75X TO 2X BASIC

2003 Finest Bat Relics

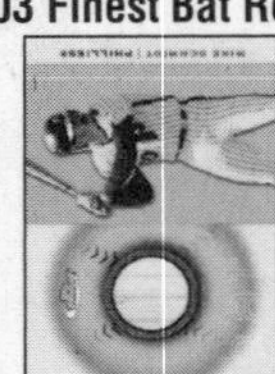

These cards were inserted at different rates depending on what group the bat relic belonged to. We have notated what group the player belonged to next to their name in our checklist.

GROUP A STATED ODDS 1:104 MINI-BOXES
GROUP B STATED ODDS 1:32 MINI-BOXES
GROUP C STATED ODDS 1:29 MINI-BOXES
GROUP D STATED ODDS 1:42 MINI-BOXES
GROUP E STATED ODDS 1:40 MINI-BOXES
GROUP F STATED ODDS 1:23 MINI-BOXES
GROUP G STATED ODDS 1:18 MINI-BOXES
GROUP H STATED ODDS 1:24 MINI-BOXES
GROUP I STATED ODDS 1:12 MINI-BOXES
GROUP J STATED ODDS 1:22 MINI-BOXES
GROUP K STATED ODDS 1:21 MINI-BOXES
AD Adam Dunn H 3.00 8.00
AK Austin Kearns F 3.00 8.00
AP Albert Pujols I 6.00 15.00
AR Alex Rodriguez E 6.00 15.00
AS Alfonso Soriano H 3.00 8.00
BB Barry Bonds F 8.00 20.00
CJ Chipper Jones G 6.00 15.00
CR Cal Ripken B 15.00 40.00
DM Dale Murphy I 4.00 10.00
GM Greg Maddux F 6.00 15.00
IR Ivan Rodriguez G 4.00 10.00
JB Jeff Bagwell D 4.00 10.00
JT Jim Thome D 4.00 10.00
KP Kirby Puckett K 6.00 15.00
LB Lance Berkman C 3.00 8.00
MP Mike Piazza E 6.00 15.00
MR Manny Ramirez I 4.00 10.00
MS Mike Schmidt C 10.00 25.00
MT Miguel Tejada I 3.00 8.00
NG Nomar Garciaparra A 10.00 25.00
PM Paul Molitor C 3.00 8.00
RC Rod Carew K 4.00 10.00
RCL Roger Clemens J 6.00 15.00
RH Rickey Henderson B 6.00 15.00
RP Rafael Palmeiro J 4.00 10.00
TH Todd Helton B 4.00 10.00
WB Wade Boggs G 4.00 10.00

2003 Finest Moments Refractors Autographs

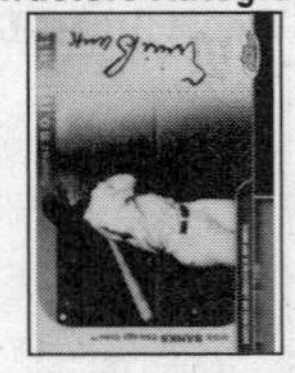

Inserted at different odds depening on whether the card was issued as part of group A or group B, this 12 card set features authentic signatures of baseball legends. Johnny Sain did not return his card in time for inclusion in this product and the exchange cards could be redeemed until April 30th, 2005.

GROUP A STATED ODDS 1:113 MINI-BOXES
GROUP B STATED ODDS 1:5 MINI-BOXES
DL Don Larsen B 6.00 15.00
EB Ernie Banks A 30.00 60.00
GC Gary Carter B 6.00 15.00
GF George Foster B 6.00 15.00
GG Goose Gossage B 6.00 15.00
GP Gaylord Perry B 6.00 15.00
JP Jim Palmer B 6.00 15.00
JS Johnny Sain B 6.00 15.00
KH Keith Hernandez B 6.00 15.00
LB Lou Brock B 10.00 25.00
OC Orlando Cepeda B 6.00 15.00
PB Paul Blair B 6.00 15.00
WMA Willie Mays A 100.00 200.00

2003 Finest Uniform Relics

These 22 cards were inserted in different odds depending on what group the player belonged to. We have notated what group the player belonged to next to their name in our checklist.

GROUP A STATED ODDS 1:28 MINI-BOXES
GROUP B STATED ODDS 1:11 MINI-BOXES
GROUP C STATED ODDS 1:11 MINI-BOXES
GROUP D STATED ODDS 1:10 MINI-BOXES
GROUP E STATED ODDS 1:19 MINI-BOXES
GROUP F STATED ODDS 1:12 MINI-BOXES
GROUP G STATED ODDS 1:34 MINI-BOXES
GROUP H STATED ODDS 1:17 MINI-BOXES
AD Adam Dunn B 3.00 8.00
AJ Andruw Jones H 4.00 10.00
AP Albert Pujols D 6.00 15.00
AR Alex Rodriguez F 6.00 15.00
AS Alfonso Soriano A 3.00 8.00
BB Barry Bonds D 8.00 20.00
CJ Chipper Jones B 6.00 15.00
CS Curt Schilling B 3.00 8.00
EC Eric Chavez B 3.00 8.00
GM Greg Maddux C 6.00 15.00
LG Luis Gonzalez D 3.00 8.00
LW Larry Walker C 3.00 8.00
MM Mark Mulder C 3.00 8.00
MP Mike Piazza C 6.00 15.00
MR Manny Ramirez E 4.00 10.00
MSW Mike Sweeney F 3.00 8.00
RJ Randy Johnson H 6.00 15.00
RO Roy Oswalt G 3.00 8.00
RP Rafael Palmeiro E 4.00 10.00
SS Sammy Sosa D 6.00 15.00
TH Todd Helton F 4.00 10.00
WM Willie Mays A 20.00 50.00

2004 Finest

This 122 card set was released in May, 2004. The set was issued in 30-card packs with a $40 SRP. Those packs were issued three to a box and 12 boxes to a case. The first 100 cards in this set feature veterans while cards 101-110 feature veteran players with a game-used jersey swatch on the card and cards 111-122 feature autograph rookie cards. Please note that David Murphy and Lastings Milledge did not sign their cards in time for pack out and those cards could be redeemed until April 30, 2006. In addition, troubled Marlins prospect Jeff Allison also had an exchange card with a 4/30/06 redemption deadline seeded into packs, but Topps was unable to fulfill the redemption and sent 2004 Topps World Series Highlights Autographs Bobby Thomson cards in their place.

COMP.SET w/o SP's (100) 10.00 25.00
COMMON CARD (1-100) .20 .50
COMMON CARD (101-110) 3.00 8.00
101-110 STATED ODDS 1:7 MINI-BOXES
COMMON CARD (111-122) 4.00 10.00
111-122 STATED ODDS 1:3 MINI-BOXES
EXCHANGE DEADLINE 04/30/06
CARD 112 EXCH UNABLE TO BE FULFILLED
04 WS HL B.THOMSON AU SENT INSTEAD
1 Juan Pierre .20 .50
2 Derek Jeter 1.00 2.50
3 Garret Anderson .20 .50
4 Javy Lopez .20 .50
5 Corey Patterson .20 .50
6 Todd Helton .30 .75
7 Roy Oswalt .20 .50
8 Shawn Green .20 .50
9 Vladimir Guerrero .50 1.25
10 Jorge Posada .30 .75
11 Jason Kendall .20 .50
12 Scott Rolen .30 .75
13 Randy Johnson .50 1.25
14 Bill Mueller .20 .50
15 Magglio Ordonez .20 .50
16 Larry Walker .20 .50
17 Lance Berkman .20 .50
18 Richie Sexson .20 .50
19 Orlando Cabrera .20 .50
20 Alfonso Soriano .20 .50
21 Kevin Millwood .20 .50
22 Edgar Martinez .30 .75
23 Aubrey Huff .20 .50
24 Carlos Delgado .20 .50
25 Vernon Wells .20 .50
26 Mark Teixeira .30 .75
27 Troy Glaus .20 .50
28 Jeff Kent .20 .50
29 Hideo Nomo .50 1.25
30 Torii Hunter .20 .50
31 Hank Blalock .20 .50
32 Brandon Webb .20 .50
33 Tony Batista .20 .50
34 Bret Boone .20 .50
35 Ryan Klesko .20 .50
36 Barry Zito .20 .50
37 Edgar Renteria .20 .50
38 Geoff Jenkins .20 .50
39 Jeff Bagwell .30 .75
40 Dontrelle Willis .30 .75
41 Adam Dunn .20 .50
42 Mark Buehrle .20 .50
43 Esteban Loaiza .20 .50
44 Angel Berroa .20 .50
45 Ivan Rodriguez .30 .75
46 Jose Vidro .20 .50
47 Mark Mulder .20 .50
48 Roger Clemens 1.00 2.50
49 Jim Edmonds .20 .50
50 Eric Gagne .20 .50
51 Marcus Giles .20 .50
52 Curt Schilling .30 .75
53 Ken Griffey Jr. .75 2.00
54 Jason Schmidt .20 .50
55 Miguel Tejada .20 .50
56 Dmitri Young .20 .50
57 Mike Lowell .20 .50
58 Mike Sweeney .20 .50
59 Scott Podsednik .20 .50
60 Miguel Cabrera .30 .75
61 Johan Santana .50 1.25
62 Bernie Williams .30 .75
63 Eric Chavez .20 .50
64 Bobby Abreu .20 .50
65 Brian Giles .20 .50
66 Michael Young .20 .50
67 Paul Lo Duca .20 .50
68 Austin Kearns .20 .50
69 Jody Gerut .20 .50
70 Kerry Wood .20 .50
71 Luis Matos .20 .50
72 Greg Maddux .75 2.00
73 Alex Rodriguez Yanks .75 2.00
74 Mike Lieberthal .20 .50
75 Jim Thome .30 .75
76 Javier Vazquez .20 .50
77 Bartolo Colon .20 .50
78 Manny Ramirez .30 .75
79 Jacque Jones .20 .50
80 Johnny Damon .30 .75
81 Carlos Beltran .20 .50
82 C.C. Sabathia .20 .50
83 Preston Wilson .20 .50
84 Luis Castillo .20 .50
85 Kevin Brown .20 .50
86 Shannon Stewart .20 .50
87 Cliff Floyd .20 .50
88 Mike Mussina .30 .75
89 Rafael Furcal .20 .50
90 Roy Halladay .20 .50
91 Frank Thomas .50 1.25
92 Melvin Mora .20 .50
93 Andruw Jones .30 .75
94 Luis Gonzalez .20 .50
95 David Ortiz .50 1.25
96 Gary Sheffield .20 .50
97 Tim Hudson .20 .50
98 Phil Nevin .20 .50
99 Ichiro Suzuki 1.00 2.50
100 Albert Pujols 1.00 2.50
101 Nomar Garciaparra SR Jsy 6.00 15.00
102 Sammy Sosa SR Jsy 4.00 10.00
103 Josh Beckett SR Jsy 3.00 8.00
104 Jason Giambi SR Jsy 3.00 8.00
105 Rocco Baldelli SR Jsy 3.00 8.00
106 Jose Reyes SR Jsy 3.00 8.00
107 Chipper Jones SR Jsy 4.00 10.00
108 Pedro Martinez SR Jsy 4.00 10.00
109 Mike Piazza SR Jsy 6.00 15.00
110 Mark Prior SR Jsy 4.00 10.00
111 Craig Ansman AU RC 4.00 10.00
113 David Murphy AU RC 4.00 10.00
114 Jason Hirsh AU RC 10.00 25.00
115 Matt Moses AU RC 6.00 15.00
116 Estee Harris AU RC 6.00 15.00
117 Logan Kensing AU RC 4.00 10.00
118 L.Milledge AU RC 20.00 50.00
119 Merkin Valdez AU RC 4.00 10.00
120 Travis Blackley AU RC 4.00 10.00

121 Vito Chiaravalloti AU RC 4.00 10.00
122 Dioner Navarro AU RC 4.00 10.00

2004 Finest Gold Refractors

*GOLD REF 1-100: 6X TO 15X BASIC
1-100 STATED ODDS 1:11
*GOLD REF 101-110: 1.25X TO 3X BASIC
101-110 STATED ODDS 1:102
*GOLD REF 111-122: 2X TO 4X BASIC
111-122 STATED ODDS 1:85
STATED PRINT RUN 50 SERIAL #'d SETS
EXCHANGE DEADLINE 04/30/06
118 L.Milledge AU 150.00 250.00

2004 Finest Refractors

*REFRACTORS 1-100: 2X TO 5X BASIC
1-100 APPX.ODDS 3 IN EVERY 4 MINI-BOXES
*REFRACTORS 101-110: .5X TO 1.2X BASIC
101-110 STATED ODDS 1:26 MINI-BOXES
*REFRACTORS 111-122: .6X TO 1.5X BASIC
111-122 STATED ODDS 1:22 MINI-BOXES
EXCHANGE DEADLINE 04/30/06
118 Lastings Milledge AU 30.00 60.00

2004 Finest Uncirculated Gold X-Fractors

*GOLD X-F 1-100: 4X TO 10X BASIC
*GOLD X-F 101-110: .75X TO 2X BASIC
*GOLD X-F 111-122: 1X TO 2.5X BASIC
ONE PER BASIC SEALED BOX
STATED PRINT RUN 139 SERIAL #'d SETS
EXCHANGE DEADLINE 04/30/06
118 L.Milledge AU 60.00 120.00

2004 Finest Moments Autographs

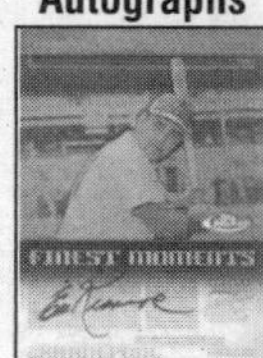

GROUP A ODDS 1:86 MINI-BOXES
GROUP B ODDS 1:102 MINI-BOXES
GROUP C ODDS 1:5 MINI-BOXES
DS Duke Snider A 15.00 40.00
EK Ed Kranepool C 4.00 10.00
GS George Foster C 4.00 10.00
JA Jim Abbott A 10.00 25.00
JP Johnny Podres C 4.00 10.00
LD Lenny Dykstra C 4.00 10.00
OC Orlando Cepeda C 4.00 10.00
RY Robin Yount A 20.00 50.00
VB Vida Blue C 4.00 10.00
WM Willie Mays B 75.00 150.00

2004 Finest Relics

GROUP A ODDS 1:3 MINI-BOXES
GROUP B ODDS 1:4 MINI-BOXES
AB Angel Berroa Bat B 3.00 8.00
AD Adam Dunn Jsy A 3.00 8.00
AG Adrian Gonzalez Bat A 3.00 8.00
AJ Andruw Jones Bat A 4.00 10.00
AP Andy Pettitte Uni B 4.00 10.00
AP1 Albert Pujols Uni A 8.00 20.00
AP2 Albert Pujols Bat A 8.00 20.00
AR1 A.Rodriguez Rgr Jsy A 6.00 15.00
AR2 A.Rodriguez Yanks Jsy A 10.00 25.00
AS Alfonso Soriano Bat A 3.00 8.00
BM1 B.Myers Arm Down Jsy A 3.00 8.00
BM2 B.Myers Arm Up Jsy A 3.00 8.00
BW Bernie Williams Bat B 4.00 10.00
BZ Barry Zito Jsy A 3.00 8.00
CCS C.C. Sabathia Jsy A 3.00 8.00
CG Cristian Guzman Jsy A 3.00 8.00
CS Curt Schilling Jsy A 3.00 8.00
DE Darin Erstad Bat A 3.00 8.00
DL Derek Lowe Uni A 3.00 8.00
DW Dontrelle Willis Uni B 4.00 10.00
DY Delmon Young Bat B 4.00 10.00
EC Eric Chavez Uni B 3.00 8.00
FT Frank Thomas Jsy A 4.00 10.00
GM Greg Maddux Jsy A 6.00 15.00
GS Gary Sheffield Bat A 3.00 8.00
HB1 Hank Blalock Bat A 3.00 8.00
HB2 Hank Blalock Jsy B 3.00 8.00
IR1 I.Rodriguez Running Jsy A 4.00 10.00
IR2 I.Rodriguez w/Glove Jsy A 4.00 10.00
IR3 Ivan Rodriguez Bat B 4.00 10.00
JB Jeff Bagwell Jsy A 4.00 10.00
JL Javy Lopez Jsy A 3.00 8.00
JP Juan Pierre Bat A 3.00 8.00
JPB1 Josh Beckett Jsy A 3.00 8.00
JR1 Jose Reyes White Jsy A 3.00 8.00
JR2 Jose Reyes Bat A 3.00 8.00
JR3 Jose Reyes Black Jsy B 3.00 8.00
JS John Smoltz Uni A 4.00 10.00
JT Jim Thome Jsy A 4.00 10.00
KI Kazuhisa Ishii Jsy A 3.00 8.00
KM Kevin Millwood Jsy A 3.00 8.00
KS Kazuhiro Sasaki Jsy A 3.00 8.00
KW1 Kerry Wood Jsy A 3.00 8.00
KW2 Kerry Wood Bat A 3.00 8.00
LB1 Lance Berkman Bat A 3.00 8.00
LB2 Lance Berkman Jsy A 3.00 8.00
LG Luis Gonzalez Jsy A 3.00 8.00
LW Larry Walker Jsy A 3.00 8.00
MB Marlon Byrd Jsy A 3.00 8.00
MC Miguel Cabrera Bat B 4.00 10.00
ML1 Mike Lowell Grey Jsy A 3.00 8.00
ML2 Mike Lowell Black Jsy B 3.00 8.00
MM Mark Mulder Uni B 3.00 8.00
MO1 Magglio Ordonez Jsy A 3.00 8.00
MO2 Magglio Ordonez Bat A 3.00 8.00
MP Mark Prior Bat A 4.00 10.00
MR Mariano Rivera Uni A 4.00 10.00
MT1 Miguel Tejada Bat A 3.00 8.00
MT2 Miguel Tejada Uni A 3.00 8.00
NG Nomar Garciaparra Bat A 6.00 15.00
PB Pat Burrell Jsy A 3.00 8.00
PW Preston Wilson Bat A 3.00 8.00
RB1 R.Baldelli Bat Down Jsy B 3.00 8.00
RB3 R.Baldelli Bat on Ball Jsy B 3.00 8.00
RH Rich Harden Uni B 3.00 8.00
RJ Randy Johnson Jsy A 4.00 10.00
RP1 Rafael Palmeiro Bat A 4.00 10.00
RP2 Rafael Palmeiro Uni A 4.00 10.00
RP3 Rafael Palmeiro Jsy B 4.00 10.00
SB Sean Burroughs Bat A 3.00 8.00
SG Shawn Green Jsy A 3.00 8.00
SR Scott Rolen Bat A 4.00 10.00
SS Sammy Sosa Bat A 4.00 10.00
TG Troy Glaus Bat A 3.00 8.00
TH Tim Hudson Uni B 3.00 8.00
TH1 Todd Helton Bat A 4.00 10.00
TH2 Todd Helton Jsy A 4.00 10.00
TKH1 Torii Hunter Bat A 3.00 8.00
TKH2 Torii Hunter Jsy B 3.00 8.00
VG Vladimir Guerrero Jsy B 4.00 10.00
VW Vernon Wells Jsy A 3.00 8.00

2005 Finest

This 166-card set was released in May, 2005. The set was issued in three "mini-boxes" which contained 30 total cards (or 10 cards per mini-box). These "full boxes" came eight to a case. Cards numbered 1 through 140 featured active veterans while cards numbered 141 through 156 feature signed Rookie Cards which were issued to a varying print run amount and are noted in our checklist. Cards numbers 157 through 166 feature retired stars.

COMP.SET w/o SP's (150) 40.00 80.00
COMMON CARD (1-140) .20 .50
COMMON CARD (157-166) .40 1.00
AU p/r 970 ODDS 1:3 MINI BOXES
AU p/r 970 PRINT RUN 970 #'d SETS
AU p/r 375 ODDS 1:41 MINI BOXES
AU p/r 375 PRINT RUN 375 #'d SETS
OVERALL PLATE ODDS 1:51 MINI BOX
OVERALL AU PLATE ODDS 1:478 MINI BOX
PLATE PRINT RUN 1 SET PER COLOR
BLACK-CYAN-MAGENTA-YELLOW ISSUED
NO PLATE PRICING DUE TO SCARCITY
1 Alexis Rios .20 .50
2 Hank Blalock .20 .50
3 Bobby Abreu .20 .50
4 Curt Schilling .30 .75
5 Albert Pujols 1.00 2.50
6 Aaron Rowand .20 .50
7 B.J. Upton .20 .50
8 Andruw Jones .30 .75
9 Jeff Francis .20 .50
10 Sammy Sosa .50 1.25
11 Aramis Ramirez .20 .50
12 Carl Pavano .20 .50
13 Bartolo Colon .20 .50
14 Greg Maddux .75 2.00
15 Scott Kazmir .20 .50
16 Melvin Mora .20 .50
17 Brandon Backe .20 .50
18 Bobby Crosby .20 .50
19 Carlos Lee .20 .50
20 Carl Crawford .20 .50
21 Brian Giles .20 .50
22 Jeff Bagwell .30 .75
23 J.D. Drew .20 .50
24 C.C. Sabathia .20 .50
25 Alfonso Soriano .20 .50
26 Chipper Jones .50 1.25
27 Austin Kearns .20 .50
28 Carlos Delgado .20 .50
29 Jack Wilson .20 .50
30 Dmitri Young .20 .50
31 Carlos Guillen .20 .50
32 Jim Thome .30 .75
33 Eric Chavez .20 .50
34 Jason Schmidt .20 .50
35 Brad Radke .20 .50
36 Frank Thomas .50 1.25
37 Darin Erstad .20 .50
38 Javier Vazquez .20 .50
39 Garret Anderson .20 .50
40 David Ortiz .50 1.25
41 Javy Lopez .20 .50
42 Geoff Jenkins .20 .50
43 Jose Vidro .20 .50
44 Aubrey Huff .20 .50
45 Bernie Williams .30 .75
46 Dontrelle Willis .20 .50
47 Jim Edmonds .20 .50
48 Ivan Rodriguez .30 .75
49 Gary Sheffield .20 .50
50 Alex Rodriguez .75 2.00
51 John Buck .20 .50
52 Andy Pettitte .30 .75
53 Ichiro Suzuki 1.00 2.50
54 Johnny Estrada .20 .50
55 Jake Peavy .20 .50
56 Carlos Zambrano .20 .50
57 Jose Reyes .20 .50
58 Bret Boone .20 .50
59 Jason Bay .20 .50
60 David Wright .75 2.00
61 Jeromy Burnitz .20 .50
62 Corey Patterson .20 .50
63 Juan Pierre .20 .50
64 Zack Greinke .20 .50
65 Mike Lowell .20 .50
66 Ken Griffey Jr. .75 2.00
67 Marcus Giles .20 .50
68 Edgar Renteria .20 .50
69 Ken Harvey .20 .50
70 Pedro Martinez .30 .75
71 Johnny Damon .30 .75
72 Lyle Overbay .20 .50
73 Mike Maroth .20 .50
74 Jorge Posada .30 .75
75 Carlos Beltran .30 .75
76 Mark Buehrle .20 .50
77 Khalil Greene .30 .75
78 Josh Beckett .20 .50
79 Mark Loretta .20 .50
80 Rafael Palmeiro .30 .75
81 Justin Morneau .20 .50
82 Rocco Baldelli .20 .50
83 Ben Sheets .20 .50
84 Kerry Wood .20 .50
85 Miguel Tejada .30 .75
86 Magglio Ordonez .30 .75
87 Livan Hernandez .20 .50
88 Kazuo Matsui .20 .50
89 Manny Ramirez .30 .75
90 Hideki Matsui .75 2.00
91 Jeff Kent .20 .50
92 Matt Lawton .20 .50
93 Richie Sexson .20 .50
94 Mike Mussina .30 .75
95 Adam Dunn .30 .75
96 Johan Santana .50 1.25
97 Nomar Garciaparra .50 1.25
98 Michael Young .20 .50
99 Victor Martinez .20 .50
100 Barry Bonds 1.25 3.00
101 Oliver Perez .20 .50
102 Randy Johnson .50 1.25
103 Mark Mulder .20 .50
104 Pat Burrell .20 .50
105 Mike Sweeney .20 .50
106 Mark Teixeira .30 .75
107 Paul Lo Duca .20 .50
108 Jon Lieber .20 .50
109 Mike Piazza .50 1.25
110 Roger Clemens .75 2.00
111 Rafael Furcal .20 .50
112 Troy Glaus .20 .50
113 Miguel Cabrera .30 .75
114 Randy Wolf .20 .50
115 Lance Berkman .30 .75
116 Mark Prior .30 .75
117 Rich Harden .20 .50
118 Preston Wilson .20 .50
119 Roy Oswalt .20 .50
120 Luis Gonzalez .20 .50
121 Ronnie Belliard .20 .50
122 Sean Casey .20 .50
123 Barry Zito .20 .50
124 Larry Walker .30 .75
125 Derek Jeter 1.00 2.50
126 Tim Hudson .20 .50
127 Tom Glavine .30 .75
128 Scott Rolen .30 .75
129 Torii Hunter .20 .50
130 Paul Konerko .20 .50
131 Shawn Green .20 .50
132 Travis Hafner .20 .50
133 Vernon Wells .20 .50
134 Sidney Ponson .20 .50
135 Vladimir Guerrero .50 1.25
136 Mark Kotsay .20 .50
137 Todd Helton .30 .75
138 Adrian Beltre .20 .50
139 Wily Mo Pena .20 .50
140 Joe Mauer .50 1.25
141 Brian Stavisky AU/970 RC 4.00 10.00
142 Nate McLouth AU/970 RC 6.00 15.00
143 Glen Perkins AU/375 RC 8.00 20.00
144 Chip Cannon AU/970 RC 8.00 20.00
145 Shane Costa AU/970 RC 4.00 10.00
146 W.Swackhamer AU/970 RC 4.00 10.00
147 Kelvin Melillo AU/970 RC 6.00 15.00
148 Billy Butler AU/970 RC 25.00 50.00
149 Landon Powell AU/970 RC 6.00 15.00
150 Scott Mathieson AU/970 RC 4.00 10.00
151 Chris Roberson AU/970 4.00 10.00
152 Chad Orvella AU/375 RC 6.00 15.00
153 Eric Nielsen AU/970 RC 4.00 10.00
154 Matt Campbell AU/970 RC 4.00 10.00
155 Mike Rogers AU/970 RC 4.00 10.00
156 Melky Cabrera AU/970 RC 20.00 40.00
157 Nolan Ryan RET 2.00 5.00
158 Bo Jackson RET .75 2.00
159 Wade Boggs RET .60 1.50
160 Andre Dawson RET .40 1.00
161 Dave Winfield RET .40 1.00
162 Reggie Jackson RET .60 1.50
163 David Justice RET .75 2.00
164 Dale Murphy RET .60 1.50
165 Paul O'Neill RET .60 1.50
166 Tom Seaver RET .60 1.50

2005 Finest Refractors

*REF 1-140: 1.5X TO 4X BASIC
*REF 157-166: 1X TO 2.5X BASIC
1-140/157-166 ODDS ONE PER MINI BOX
COMMON AUTO (141-156) 4.00 10.00
*REF AU 141-156: .4X TO 1X p/r 970
*REF AU 141-156: .3X TO .8X p/r 375
AU 141-156 ODDS 1:5 MINI BOX
STATED PRINT RUN 399 SERIAL #'d SETS
148 Billy Butler AU 30.00 60.00

2005 Finest Refractors Black

*REF BLACK 1-140: 4X TO 10X BASIC
*REF BLACK 157-166: 2.5X TO 6X BASIC
1-140/157-166 ODDS 1:2 MINI BOX
COMMON AUTO (141-156) 10.00 25.00
*REF BLK AU 141-156: .6X TO 1.5X p/r 970
*REF BLK AU 141-156: .5X TO 1.2X p/r 375
AU 141-156 ODDS 1:19 MINI BOX
STATED PRINT RUN 99 SERIAL #'d SETS
148 Billy Butler AU 75.00 150.00

2005 Finest Refractors Blue

*REF BLUE 1-140: 1.5X TO 4X BASIC
*REF BLUE 157-166: 1X TO 2.5X BASIC
1-140/157-166 ODDS ONE PER MINI BOX
COMMON AUTO (141-156) 4.00 10.00
*REF BLUE AU 141-156: .4X TO 1X p/r 970
*REF BLUE AU 141-156: .3X TO .8X p/r 375
AU 141-156 ODDS 1:7 MINI BOX
STATED PRINT RUN 299 SERIAL #'d SETS
148 Billy Butler AU 30.00 60.00

2005 Finest Refractors Gold

*REF GOLD 1-140: 5X TO 12X BASIC
*REF GOLD 157-166: 3X TO 8X BASIC
1-140/157-166 ODDS 1:5 MINI BOX
COMMON AUTO (141-156) 15.00 40.00
*REF GOLD AU 141-156: 1X TO 2.5X p/r 970
*REF GOLD AU 141-156: .75X TO 2X p/r 375
AU 141-156 ODDS 1:39 MINI BOX
STATED PRINT RUN 49 SERIAL #'d SETS
53 Ichiro Suzuki 15.00 40.00
90 Hideki Matsui 15.00 40.00
100 Barry Bonds 30.00 60.00
125 Derek Jeter 20.00 50.00
148 Billy Butler AU 125.00 250.00
157 Nolan Ryan RET 20.00 50.00

2005 Finest Refractors Green

*REF GREEN 1-140: 2X TO 5X BASIC
*REF GREEN 157-166: 1.25X TO 3X BASIC
1-140/157-166 ODDS ONE PER MINI BOX
COMMON AUTO (141-156) 5.00 12.00
*REF GRN AU 141-156: .4X TO 1X p/r 970
*REF GRN AU 141-156: .3X TO 8X p/r 375
AU 141-156 ODDS 1:10 MINI BOX
STATED PRINT RUN 199 SERIAL #'d SETS
148 Billy Butler AU 30.00 60.00

2005 Finest Refractors White Framed

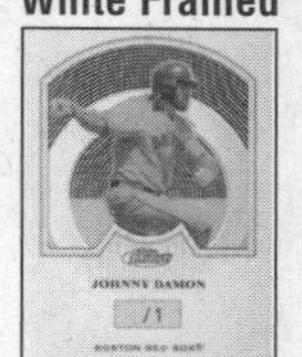

1-140/157-166 ODDS 1:202 MINI BOX
AU 141-165 ODDS 1:1914 MINI BOX
STATED PRINT RUN 1 SERIAL #'d SET
NO PRICING DUE TO SCARCITY

2005 Finest SuperFractors

1-140/157-166 ODDS 1:202 MINI BOX
AU 141-165 ODDS 1:1914 MINI BOX
STATED PRINT RUN 1 SERIAL #'d SET
NO PRICING DUE TO SCARCITY

2005 Finest X-Fractors

*XF 1-140: 2X TO 5X BASIC
*XF 157-166: 1.25X TO 3X BASIC
1-140/157-166 ODDS ONE PER MINI BOX
COMMON AUTO (141-156) 4.00 10.00
*XF AU 141-156: .4X TO 1X p/r 970
*XF AU 141-156: .3X TO 8X p/r 375
AU 141-156 ODDS 1:8 MINI BOX
STATED PRINT RUN 250 SERIAL #'d SETS
148 Billy Butler AU 30.00 60.00

2005 Finest X-Fractors Black

*XF BLACK 1-140: 8X TO 20X BASIC
*XF BLACK 157-166: 5X TO 12X BASIC
1-140/157-166 ODDS 1:8 MINI BOX
AU 141-156 ODDS 1:76 MINI BOX
STATED PRINT RUN 25 SERIAL #'d SETS
AU 141-156 NO PRICING DUE TO SCARCITY
53 Ichiro Suzuki 30.00 60.00
90 Hideki Matsui 20.00 50.00
100 Barry Bonds 60.00 120.00
125 Derek Jeter 40.00 80.00
157 Nolan Ryan RET 40.00 80.00

2005 Finest X-Fractors Blue

*XF BLUE 1-140: 2.5X TO 6X BASIC
*XF BLUE 157-166: 1.5X TO 4X BASIC
1-140/157-166 ODDS 1:2 MINI BOX
COMMON AUTO (141-156) 6.00 15.00
*XF BLUE AU 141-156: .5X TO 1.2X p/r 970
*XF BLUE AU 141-156: .4X TO 1X p/r 375
AU 141-156 ODDS 1:13 MINI BOX
STATED PRINT RUN 150 SERIAL #'d SETS
148 Billy Butler AU 40.00 80.00

2005 Finest X-Fractors Gold

1-140/157-166 ODDS 1:20 MINI BOX
AU 141-156 ODDS 1:190 MINI BOX
STATED PRINT RUN 10 SERIAL #'d SETS
NO PRICING DUE TO SCARCITY

2005 Finest X-Fractors Green

*XF GREEN 1-140: 5X TO 12X BASIC
*XF GREEN 157-166: 3X TO 8X BASIC
1-140/157-166 ODDS 1:2 MINI BOX
COMMON AUTO (141-156) 12.50 30.00
*XF GRN AU 141-156: .75X TO 2X p/r 970
*XF GRN AU 141-156: .6X TO 1.5X p/r 375
AU 141-156 ODDS 1:38 MINI BOX
STATED PRINT RUN 50 SERIAL #'d SETS
148 Billy Butler AU 100.00 200.00

2005 Finest X-Fractors White Framed

1-140/157-166 ODDS 1:202 MINI BOX
AU 141-165 ODDS 1:1914 MINI BOX
STATED PRINT RUN 1 SERIAL #'d SET
NO PRICING DUE TO SCARCITY

2005 Finest A-Rod Moments

COMMON CARD (1-49) 3.00 8.00
ONE PER MASTER BOX
STATED PRINT RUN 190 SERIAL #'d SETS

2005 Finest A-Rod Moments Autographs

COMMON CARD (1-49) 90.00 180.00
APPROXIMATE ODDS 1:15 MASTER BOXES
STATED PRINT RUN 13 SERIAL #'d SETS

2005 Finest Autograph Refractors

GROUP A ODDS 1:435 MINI BOX
GROUP B ODDS 1:13 MINI BOX
GROUP C ODDS 1:32 MINI BOX
GROUP D ODDS 1:15 MINI BOX
GROUP A PRINT RUN 70 CARDS
GROUP A CARD IS NOT SERIAL-NUMBERED
GROUP A PRINT RUN PROVIDED BY TOPPS
OVERALL PLATE ODDS 1:513 MINI BOX
PLATE PRINT RUN 1 SET PER COLOR
BLACK-CYAN-MAGENTA-YELLOW ISSUED
NO PLATE PRICING DUE TO SCARCITY
SUPERFRACTOR ODDS 1:2051 MINI BOX
SUPERFRACTOR PRINT RUN 1 #'d SET
NO SUPERFRACTOR PRICING AVAILABLE
*X-FRACTOR: 1.25X TO 3X BASIC D
*X-FRACTOR: .75X TO 2X BASIC C
*X-FRACTOR: .6X TO 1.5X BASIC B
*X-FRACTOR: .6X TO 1.5X BASIC A
X-FRACTOR ODDS 1:81 MINI BOX
X-FRACTOR PRINT RUN 25 SERIAL #'d SETS
EXCHANGE DEADLINE 04/30/07
AS Alfonso Soriano B 10.00 25.00
BB Barry Bonds A/70 * 200.00 350.00
CB Carlos Beltran B EXCH 10.00 25.00
DO David Ortiz B 20.00 50.00
DW David Wright C 30.00 60.00
EC Eric Chavez B 10.00 25.00
EG Eric Gagne B 15.00 40.00
GS Gary Sheffield C 10.00 25.00
JB Jason Bay B 10.00 25.00
JE Johnny Estrada B 6.00 15.00
JS Johan Santana B 30.00 60.00
JST Jacob Stevens D 4.00 10.00
KM Kevin Millar B 15.00 40.00
MB Milton Bradley B 6.00 15.00
MR Mariano Rivera B 30.00 60.00

2005 Finest Moments Autograph Gold Refractors

STATED ODDS 1:305 MINI BOX
PEDRO PRINT RUN 50 SERIAL #'d CARDS
SCHILLING PRINT RUN 50 CARDS
SCHILLING IS NOT SERIAL-NUMBERED
SCHILLING QTY PROVIDED BY TOPPS
CS Curt Schilling/50 * 100.00 175.00
PM Pedro Martinez/50 50.00 100.00

2005 Finest Two of a Kind Autograph

STATED ODDS 1:9568 MINI BOX
STATED PRINT RUN 13 SERIAL #'d SETS
NO PRICING DUE TO SCARCITY
RB Alex Rodriguez
Ernie Banks

2006 Finest

This 155-card set was released in May, 2006. The set was issued in an "mini-box" form. There were three mini-boxes in a full box and each mini-box contained 30 cards. The SRP for an individual mini-box was $50 and there were eight full boxes in a case. Cards numbered 1-130 feature veterans while cards cards 131-155 feature 2006 rookies. Cards numbered 141 through 155 were all signed and all of those cards were issued to a stated print run of 963 signed copies.

COMP.SET w/o AU's (140) 30.00 60.00
COMMON CARD (1-131) .20 .50
COMMON ROOKIE (132-140) .30 .75
COMMON AUTO (141-155) 4.00 10.00
141-155 AU ODDS 1:4 MINI BOX
141-155 AU PRINT RUN 963 SETS
141-155 AU's NOT SERIAL NUMBERED
PRINT RUN INFO PROVIDED BY TOPPS
1-140 PLATES RANDOM INSERTS IN PACKS
AU 141-155 PLATE ODDS 1:792 MINI BOX
PLATE PRINT RUN 1 SET PER COLOR
BLACK-CYAN-MAGENTA-YELLOW ISSUED
NO PLATE PRICING DUE TO SCARCITY
1 Vladimir Guerrero .50 1.25
2 Troy Glaus .20 .50
3 Andruw Jones .30 .75
4 Miguel Tejada .20 .50
5 Manny Ramirez .30 .75
6 Curt Schilling .30 .75
7 Mark Prior .30 .75
8 Kerry Wood .20 .50
9 Tadahito Iguchi .20 .50
10 Freddy Garcia .20 .50
11 Ryan Howard .75 2.00
12 Mark Buehrle .20 .50
13 Wily Mo Pena .20 .50
14 C.C. Sabathia .20 .50
15 Garret Anderson .20 .50
16 Shawn Green .20 .50
17 Rafael Furcal .20 .50
18 Jeff Francoeur .50 1.25
19 Ken Griffey Jr. .75 2.00
20 Derrek Lee .20 .50
21 Paul Konerko .20 .50
22 Rickie Weeks .20 .50
23 Magglio Ordonez .20 .50
24 Juan Pierre .20 .50
25 Felix Hernandez .30 .75
26 Roger Clemens 1.00 2.50
27 Zack Greinke .20 .50
28 Johan Santana .30 .75
29 Jose Reyes .50 1.25
30 Bobby Crosby .20 .50
31 Jason Schmidt .20 .50
32 Khalil Greene .30 .75
33 Richie Sexson .20 .50
34 Mark Mulder .20 .50
35 Mark Teixeira .30 .75
36 Nick Johnson .20 .50
37 Vernon Wells .20 .50
38 Scott Kazmir .30 .75
39 Jim Edmonds .30 .75
40 Adrian Beltre .20 .50
41 Dan Johnson .20 .50
42 Carlos Lee .20 .50
43 Lance Berkman .20 .50
44 Josh Beckett .20 .50
45 Morgan Ensberg .20 .50
46 Garrett Atkins .20 .50
47 Chase Utley .50 1.25
48 Joe Mauer .20 .50
49 Travis Hafner .20 .50
50 Alex Rodriguez .75 2.00
51 Austin Kearns .20 .50
52 Scott Podsednik .20 .50
53 Jose Contreras .20 .50
54 Greg Maddux .75 2.00
55 Hideki Matsui .75 2.00
56 Matt Clement .20 .50
57 Javy Lopez .20 .50
58 Tim Hudson .20 .50
59 Luis Gonzalez .20 .50
60 Bartolo Colon .20 .50
61 Marcus Giles .20 .50
62 Justin Morneau .20 .50
63 Nomar Garciaparra .50 1.25
64 Robinson Cano .30 .75
65 Ervin Santana .20 .50
66 Brady Clark .20 .50
67 Edgar Renteria .20 .50
68 Jon Garland .20 .50
69 Felipe Lopez .20 .50
70 Ivan Rodriguez .30 .75
71 Dontrelle Willis .20 .50
72 Carlos Guillen .20 .50
73 J.D. Drew .20 .50
74 Rich Harden .20 .50
75 Albert Pujols 1.00 2.50
76 Livan Hernandez .20 .50
77 Roy Halladay .20 .50
78 Hank Blalock .20 .50
79 David Wright .75 2.00
80 Jimmy Rollins .30 .75
81 John Smoltz .30 .75
82 Miguel Cabrera .30 .75
83 David DeJesus .20 .50
83 Zach Duke .20 .50
84 Torii Hunter .20 .50
85 Adam Dunn .20 .50
86 Randy Johnson .50 1.25
87 Roy Oswalt .20 .50
88 Bobby Abreu .20 .50
89 Rocco Baldelli .20 .50
90 Ichiro Suzuki .75 2.00
91 Jorge Cantu .20 .50
92 Jack Wilson .20 .50
93 Jose Vidro .20 .50
94 Kevin Millwood .20 .50
95 David Ortiz .50 1.25
96 Victor Martinez .20 .50
97 Jeremy Bonderman .20 .50
98 Todd Helton .30 .75
99 Carlos Beltran .30 .75
100 Barry Bonds 1.25 3.00
101 Jeff Kent .20 .50
102 Mike Sweeney .20 .50
103 Ben Sheets .20 .50
104 Melvin Mora .20 .50
105 Gary Sheffield .20 .50
106 Craig Wilson .20 .50
107 Chris Carpenter .20 .50
108 Michael Young .20 .50
109 Gustavo Chacin .20 .50
110 Chipper Jones .50 1.25
111 Mark Loretta .20 .50
112 Andy Pettitte .30 .75
113 Carlos Delgado .20 .50
114 Pat Burrell .20 .50
115 Jason Bay .20 .50
116 Brian Roberts .20 .50
117 Joe Crede .20 .50
118 Jake Peavy .20 .50
119 Aubrey Huff .20 .50
120 Pedro Martinez .30 .75
121 Jorge Posada .30 .75
122 Barry Zito .20 .50
123 Scott Rolen .30 .75
124 Brett Myers .20 .50
125 Derek Jeter 1.25 3.00
126 Eric Chavez .20 .50
127 Carl Crawford .20 .50
128 Jim Thome .30 .75
129 Johnny Damon .30 .75
130 Alfonso Soriano .30 .75
131 Clint Barmes .20 .50
132 Dustin Nippert (RC) .30 .75
133 Hanley Ramirez (RC) .75 2.00
134 Matt Capps (RC) .30 .75
135 Miguel Perez (RC) .30 .75
136 Tom Gorzelanny (RC) .30 .75
137 Charlton Jimerson (RC) .30 .75
138 Bryan Bullington (RC) .30 .75
139 Kenji Johjima RC 1.50 4.00
140 Craig Hansen RC 1.25 3.00
141 Craig Breslow AU/963 RC * 4.00 10.00
142 Adam Wainwright AU/963 (RC) * 6.00 15.00
143 Joey Devine AU/963 RC * 4.00 10.00
144 Hong-Chih Kuo AU/963 (RC) * 20.00 50.00
145 Jason Botts AU/963 (RC) * 4.00 10.00
146 Josh Johnson AU/963 (RC) * 8.00 20.00
147 Jason Bergmann AU/963 RC * 4.00 10.00
148 Scott Olsen AU/963 (RC) * 6.00 15.00
149 Darrell Rasner AU/963 (RC) * 4.00 10.00
150 Dan Ortmeier AU/963 (RC) * 4.00 10.00
151 Chuck James AU/963 (RC) * 6.00 15.00
152 Ryan Garko AU/963 (RC) * 4.00 10.00
153 Nelson Cruz AU/963 (RC) * 4.00 10.00
154 Anthony Lerew AU/963 (RC) * 4.00 10.00
155 Francisco Liriano AU/963 (RC) * 20.00 50.00

2006 Finest Refractors

*REF 1-131: 1.5X TO 4X BASIC
*REF 132-140: 1.5X TO 4X BASIC
1-140 ODDS ONE PER MINI BOX
*REF AU 141-155: .4X TO 1X BASIC AU
AU 141-155 ODDS 1:8 MINI BOX
STATED PRINT RUN 399 SERIAL #'d SETS

2006 Finest Refractors Black

*REF BLACK 1-131: 4X TO 10X BASIC
*REF BLACK 132-140: 4X TO 10X BASIC
1-140 ODDS 1:4 MINI BOX
*REF BLK AU 141-155: .6X TO 1.5X BASIC AU
AU 141-155 ODDS 1:32 MINI BOX
STATED PRINT RUN 99 SERIAL #'d SETS

2006 Finest Refractors Blue

*REF BLUE 1-131: 1.5X TO 4X BASIC
*REF BLUE 132-140: 1.5X TO 4X BASIC
1-140 ODDS 1:2 MINI BOX
*REF BLUE AU 141-155: .4X TO 1X BASIC AU
AU 141-155 ODDS 1:11 MINI BOX
STATED PRINT RUN 299 SERIAL #'d SETS

2006 Finest Refractors Gold

*REF GOLD 1-131: 5X TO 12X BASIC
*REF GOLD 132-140: 5X TO 12X BASIC
1-140 ODDS 1:7 MINI BOX
*REF GOLD AU 141-155: 1X TO 2.5X BASIC AU
AU 141-155 ODDS 1:64 MINI BOX
STATED PRINT RUN 49 SERIAL #'d SETS

2006 Finest Refractors Green

*REF GREEN 1-131: 2X TO 5X BASIC
*REF GREEN 132-140: 2X TO 5X BASIC
1-140 ODDS 1:2 MINI BOX
*REF GRN AU 141-155: .4X TO 1X BASIC AU
AU 141-155 ODDS 1:16 MINI BOX
STATED PRINT RUN 199 SERIAL #'d SETS

2006 Finest Refractors White Framed

1-140 ODDS 1:340 MINI BOX
AU 141-155 ODDS 1:3342 MINI BOX
STATED PRINT RUN 1 SERIAL #'d SET
NO PRICING DUE TO SCARCITY

2006 Finest SuperFractors

1-140 ODDS 1:340 MINI BOX
AU 141-155 ODDS 1:3342 MINI BOX
STATED PRINT RUN 1 SERIAL #'d SET
NO PRICING DUE TO SCARCITY

2006 Finest X-Fractors

*XF 1-131: 2X TO 5X BASIC
*XF 132-140: 2X TO 5X BASIC
1-140 ODDS 1:2 MINI BOX
*XF AU 141-155: .4X TO 1X BASIC AU
AU 141-155 ODDS 1:13 MINI BOX
STATED PRINT RUN 250 SERIAL #'d SETS

2006 Finest X-Fractors Black

*XF BLACK 1-131: 8X TO 20X BASIC
1-140 ODDS 1:14 MINI BOX
NO XF BLACK 132-140 PRICING
AU 141-155 ODDS 1:125 MINI BOX
STATED PRINT RUN 25 SERIAL #'d SETS
NO XF BLACK AU PRICING

2006 Finest X-Fractors Blue

*XF BLUE 1-131: 2.5X TO 6X BASIC
*XF BLUE 132-140: 2.5X TO 6X BASIC
1-140 ODDS 1:3 MINI BOX
*XF BLUE AU 141-155: .5X TO 1.2X BASIC AU
AU 141-155 ODDS 1:21 MINI BOX
STATED PRINT RUN 150 SERIAL #'d SETS

2006 Finest X-Fractors Gold

1-140 ODDS 1:34 MINI BOX
AU 141-155 ODDS 1:314 MINI BOX
STATED PRINT RUN 10 SERIAL #'d SETS
NO PRICING DUE TO SCARCITY

2006 Finest X-Fractors Green

*XF GREEN 1-131: 5X TO 12X BASIC
*XF GREEN 132-140: 5X TO 12X BASIC
1-140 ODDS 1:7 MINI BOX
*XF GREEN AU 141-155: .75X TO 2X BASIC AU
AU 141-155 ODDS 1:63 MINI BOX
STATED PRINT RUN 50 SERIAL #'d SETS

2006 Finest X-Fractors White Framed

1-140 ODDS 1:340 MINI BOX
AU 141-155 ODDS 1:3342 MINI BOX
STATED PRINT RUN 1 SERIAL #'d SET
NO PRICING DUE TO SCARCITY

2006 Finest Autograph Refractors

GROUP A ODDS 1:22 MINI BOX
GROUP B ODDS 1:8 MINI BOX
GROUP C ODDS 1:214 MINI BOX
GROUP A PRINT RUN 720 CARDS
GROUP B PRINT RUN 470 CARDS
GROUP C PRINT RUN 220 CARDS
CARDS ARE NOT SERIAL NUMBERED
PRINT RUN INFO PROVIDED BY TOPPS
OVERALL PLATE ODDS 1:654 MINI BOX
PLATE PRINT RUN 1 SET PER COLOR
BLACK-CYAN-MAGENTA-YELLOW ISSUED
NO PLATE PRICING DUE TO SCARCITY
SUPERFRACTOR ODDS 1:2751 MINI BOX
SUPERFRACTOR PRINT RUN 1 #'d SET
NO SUPERFRACTOR PRICING AVAILABLE
*GROUP A-B XF: .75X TO 2X BASIC
*GROUP C XF: 1X TO 2X BASIC
X-FRACTOR ODDS 1:104 MINI BOX
X-FRACTOR PRINT RUN 25 SERIAL #'d SETS
X-F JOHJIMA PRICING NOT AVAILABLE
APPROX. 10 PERCENT OF D.LEE ARE EXCH
EXCHANGE DEADLINE 04/30/08
AJ Andruw Jones B/470 * 15.00 40.00
AR Alex Rodriguez C/220 * 100.00 175.00
CJ Chipper Jones B/470 * 20.00 50.00
CW Craig Wilson B/470 * 4.00 10.00
DL Derrek Lee A/720 * 10.00 25.00
DW David Wright B/470 * 30.00 60.00
DWI Dontrelle Willis B/470 * 6.00 15.00
EC Eric Chavez A/720 * 6.00 15.00
GS Gary Sheffield B/470 * 10.00 25.00
JB Jason Bay B/470 * 6.00 15.00
JG Jose Guillen B/470 * 4.00 10.00
KJ Kenji Johjima B/470 * 50.00 100.00
MC Miguel Cabrera B/470 * 10.00 25.00
MG Marcus Giles B/470 * 6.00 15.00
RC Robinson Cano B/470 * 15.00 40.00
RH Rich Harden B/470 * 6.00 15.00
RO Roy Oswalt B/470 * 6.00 15.00
VG Vladimir Guerrero A/720 * 15.00 40.00

2006 Finest Bonds Moments Refractors

COMMON CARD (M1-M25) 3.00 8.00
STATED ODDS 1:2 MASTER BOX
STATED PRINT RUN 425 SERIAL #'d SETS
*REF GOLD: .5X TO 1.25X BASIC
REF.GOLD STATED ODDS 1:4 MASTER BOX
REF.GOLD PRINT RUN 199 SERIAL #'d SETS

2006 Finest Bonds Moments Refractors Gold Autographs

STATED ODDS 1:316 MASTER BOX
STATED PRINT RUN 2 SERIAL #'d SETS
NO PRICING DUE TO SCARCITY

2006 Finest Mantle Moments

COMMON CARD (M1-M20) 2.50 6.00
STATED ODDS 1:3 MINI BOX
STATED PRINT RUN 850 SERIAL #'d SETS
PRINTING PLATES RANDOM IN PACKS
PLATE PRINT RUN 1 SET PER COLOR
BLACK-CYAN-MAGENTA-YELLOW ISSUED
NO PLATE PRICING DUE TO SCARCITY
*REF: .5X TO 1.25X BASIC
REF ODDS 1:6 MINI BOX
REF PRINT RUN 399 SERIAL #'d SETS
*REF BLACK: 1.25X TO 3X BASIC
REF BLACK ODDS 1:24 MINI BOX
REF BLACK PRINT RUN 99 SERIAL #'d SETS
*REF BLUE: .6X TO 1.5X BASIC
REF BLUE ODDS 1:8 MINI BOX
REF BLUE PRINT RUN 299 SERIAL #'d SETS
*REF GOLD: 2.5X TO 6X BASIC
REF GOLD ODDS 1:49 MINI BOX
REF GOLD PRINT RUN 49 SERIAL #'d SETS
*REF GREEN: .75X TO 2X BASIC
REF GREEN ODDS 1:12 MINI BOX
REF GREEN PRINT RUN 199 SERIAL #'d SETS
REF WHITE FRAME ODDS 1:2482 MINI BOX
REF WHITE FRAME PRINT RUN 1 #'d SET
NO REF WF PRICING DUE TO SCARCITY
SUPERFRACTORS ODDS 1:2482 MINI BOX
SUPERFRACTORS PRINT RUN 1 #'d SET
NO SF PRICING DUE TO SCARCITY
*X-FRAC: .6X TO 1.5X BASIC
X-FRAC ODDS 1:10 MINI BOX
X-FRAC PRINT RUN 250 SERIAL #'d SETS
*X-FRAC BLACK: 3X TO 8X BASIC
X-FRAC BLACK ODDS 1:95 MINI BOX
X-FRAC BLACK PRINT RUN 25 #'d SETS
*X-FRAC BLUE: .75X TO 2X BASIC
X-FRAC BLUE ODDS 1:16 MINI BOX
X-FRAC BLUE PRINT RUN 150 #'d SETS
*X-FRAC GOLD: 8X TO 20X BASIC
X-FRAC GOLD ODDS 1:238 MINI BOX
X-FRAC GOLD PRINT RUN 10 SERIAL #'d SETS
*X-FRAC GREEN: 2.5X TO 6X BASIC
X-FRAC GREEN ODDS 1:48 MINI BOX
X-FRAC GREEN PRINT RUN 50 #'d SETS
X-FRAC WF ODDS 1:2482 MINI BOX
X-FRAC WF PRINT RUN 1 SERIAL #'d SET
NO X-F WF PRICING DUE TO SCARCITY

2006 Finest Mantle Moments Cut Signatures

STATED ODDS 1:23,555 MINI BOX
STATED PRINT RUN 1 SERIAL #'d SET
NO PRICING DUE TO SCARCITY

2007 Finest

This 166-card set was released in March, 2007. The set was issued in five-card packs, which were issued six packs per mini box (which had an $50 SRP) and those mini-boxes were issued three per master box and eight master boxes per case. Cards numbered 1-135 feature veterans while cards numbered 135-150 were 2007 rookies and cards numbered 151-166 feature 2007 signed rookies. The signed rookie cards were issued at a stated rate of one in three mini-boxes.

COMP.SET w/o AU's (150) 30.00 60.00
COMMON CARD (1-135) .15 .40
COMMON ROOKIE (136-150) .40 1.00
151-166 AU ODDS 1:3 MINI BOX
1-150 PLATE ODDS 1:96 MINI BOX
AU 151-166 PLATE ODDS 1:909 MINI BOX
PLATE PRINT RUN 1 SET PER COLOR
BLACK-CYAN-MAGENTA-YELLOW ISSUED
NO PLATE PRICING DUE TO SCARCITY
EXCHANGE DEADLINE 02/28/09
1 David Wright .60 1.50
2 Jered Weaver .25 .60
3 Chipper Jones .40 1.00
4 Magglio Ordonez .15 .40
5 Ben Sheets .15 .40
6 Nick Johnson .15 .40
7 Melvin Mora .15 .40
8 Chien-Ming Wang .60 1.50
9 Andre Ethier .25 .60
10 Carlos Beltran .15 .40
11 Ryan Zimmerman .40 1.00
12 Troy Glaus .15 .40
13 Hanley Ramirez .25 .60
14 Mark Buehrle .15 .40
15 Dan Uggla .25 .60
16 Richie Sexson .15 .40
17 Scott Kazmir .25 .60
18 Garrett Atkins .15 .40
19 Matt Cain .25 .60
20 Jorge Posada .25 .60
21 Brett Myers .15 .40
22 Jeff Francoeur .40 1.00
23 Scott Rolen .25 .60
24 Derrek Lee .15 .40
25 Manny Ramirez .25 .60
26 Johnny Damon .25 .60

27 Mark Teixeira .25 .60
28 Mark Prior .25 .60
29 Victor Martinez .15 .40
30 Greg Maddux .60 1.50
31 Prince Fielder .40 1.00
32 Jeremy Bonderman .15 .40
33 Paul LoDuca .15 .40
34 Brandon Webb .15 .40
35 Robinson Cano .25 .60
36 Josh Beckett .25 .60
37 David DeJesus .15 .40
38 Kenny Rogers .15 .40
39 Jim Thome .25 .60
40 Brian McCann .15 .40
41 Lance Berkman .15 .40
42 Adam Dunn .15 .40
43 Rocco Baldelli .15 .40
44 Brian Roberts .15 .40
45 Vladimir Guerrero .40 1.00
46 Dontrelle Willis .15 .40
47 Eric Chavez .15 .40
48 Carlos Zambrano .15 .40
49 Ivan Rodriguez .25 .60
50 Alex Rodriguez .60 1.50
51 Curt Schilling .25 .60
52 Carlos Delgado .15 .40
53 Matt Holliday .40 1.00
54 Mark Teahen .15 .40
55 Frank Thomas .40 1.00
56 Grady Sizemore .25 .60
57 Aramis Ramirez .15 .40
58 Rafael Furcal .15 .40
59 David Ortiz .40 1.00
60 Paul Konerko .15 .40
61 Barry Zito .15 .40
62 Travis Hafner .15 .40
63 Nick Swisher .15 .40
64 Johan Santana .25 .60
65 Miguel Tejada .15 .40
66 Carl Crawford .15 .40
67 Kenji Johjima .40 1.00
68 Derek Jeter 1.00 2.50
69 Francisco Liriano .75 2.00
70 Ken Griffey Jr. .60 1.50
71 Pat Burrell .15 .40
72 Adrian Gonzalez .15 .40
73 Miguel Cabrera .25 .60
74 Albert Pujols .75 2.00
75 Justin Verlander .40 1.00
76 Carlos Lee .15 .40
77 John Smoltz .25 .60
78 Orlando Hudson .15 .40
79 Joe Mauer .25 .60
80 Freddy Sanchez .15 .40
81 Bobby Abreu .15 .40
82 Pedro Martinez .25 .60
83 Vernon Wells .15 .40
84 Justin Morneau .15 .40
85 Bill Hall .15 .40
86 Jason Schmidt .15 .40
87 Michael Young .15 .40
88 Tadahito Iguchi .15 .40
89 Kevin Millwood .15 .40
90 Randy Johnson .40 1.00
91 Roy Halladay .15 .40
92 Mike Lowell .15 .40
93 Jake Peavy .15 .40
94 Jason Varitek .40 1.00
95 Todd Helton .25 .60
96 Mark Loretta .15 .40
97 Gary Matthews Jr. .15 .40
98 Ryan Howard .60 1.50
99 Jose Reyes .15 .40
100 Chris Carpenter .15 .40
101 Hideki Matsui .40 1.00
102 Brian Giles .15 .40
103 Torii Hunter .15 .40
104 Rich Harden .15 .40
105 Ichiro Suzuki .60 1.50
106 Chase Utley .40 1.00
107 Nick Markakis .25 .60
108 Marcus Giles .15 .40
109 Gary Sheffield .15 .40
110 Jim Edmonds .25 .60
111 Brandon Phillips .15 .40
112 Roy Oswalt .15 .40
113 Jeff Kent .15 .40
114 Jason Bay .15 .40
115 Raul Ibanez .15 .40
116 Stephen Drew .25 .60
117 Hank Blalock .15 .40
118 Tom Glavine .25 .60
119 Andruw Jones .25 .60
120 Alfonso Soriano .15 .40
121 Mariano Rivera .40 1.00
122 Garret Anderson .15 .40
123 Erik Bedard UER .15 .40
Name misspelled Erick
124 Huston Street .15 .40
125 Austin Kearns .15 .40
126 Jermaine Dye .15 .40
127 C.C. Sabathia .15 .40
128 Joe Nathan .15 .40
129 Craig Monroe .15 .40
130 Aubrey Huff .15 .40
131 Billy Wagner .15 .40
132 Jorge Cantu .15 .40
133 Trevor Hoffman .15 .40
134 Ronnie Belliard .15 .40
135 B.J. Ryan .15 .40
136 Adam Lind (RC) .40 1.00
137 Hector Gimenez (RC) .40 1.00
138 Shawn Riggans UER (RC) .40 1.00
Name misspelled Riggins
139 Joaquin Arias (RC) .40 1.00
140 Drew Anderson RC .40 1.00
141 Mike Rabelo RC .40 1.00
142 Chris Narveson (RC) .40 1.00
143 Ryan Feierabend (RC) .40 1.00
144 Vinny Rottino (RC) .40 1.00
145 Jon Knott (RC) .40 1.00
146 Oswaldo Navarro RC .40 1.00
147 Brian Stokes (RC) .40 1.00
148 Glen Perkins (RC) .40 1.00
149 Mitch Maier RC .40 1.00
150 Delmon Young (RC) UER 1.00 2.50
Listed as born in the wrong city
151 Andrew Miller AU RC 15.00 40.00
152 Troy Tulowitzki AU (RC) 12.50 30.00
153 Philip Humber AU (RC) 6.00 15.00
154 Kevin Kouzmanoff AU (RC) 6.00 15.00
155 Michael Bourn AU (RC) 4.00 10.00
156 Miguel Montero AU (RC) EXCH 4.00 10.00
157 David Murphy AU (RC) 4.00 10.00
158 Ryan Sweeney AU (RC) 4.00 10.00
159 Jeff Baker AU (RC) 4.00 10.00
160 Jeff Salazar AU (RC) 4.00 10.00
161 Jose Garcia AU RC EXCH 4.00 10.00
162 Josh Fields AU (RC) 4.00 10.00
163 Delwyn Young AU (RG) 4.00 10.00
164 Fred Lewis AU (RC) 4.00 10.00
165 Scott Moore AU (RC) 4.00 10.00
166 Chris Stewart AU RC 4.00 10.00

2007 Finest Refractors

*REF 1-135: .5X TO 1.2X BASIC
*REF 136-150: .5X TO 1.2X BASIC
1-150 ODDS TWO PER MINI BOX
*REF AU 151-166: .4X TO 1X BASIC AU
AU 151-166 ODDS 1:10 MINI BOX
AU 151-166 PRINT RUN 399 SER.#'d SETS
EXCHANGE DEADLINE 02/28/09

2007 Finest Refractors Black

*REF BLACK 1-135: 4X TO 10X BASIC
*REF BLACK 136-150: 2.5X TO 6X BASIC
1-150 ODDS 1:4 MINI BOX
*REF BLK AU 151-166: 1X TO 2.5X BASIC AU
AU 151-166 ODDS 1:37 MINI BOX
STATED PRINT RUN 99 SERIAL #'d SETS
EXCHANGE DEADLINE 02/28/09
8 Chien-Ming Wang 20.00 50.00
55 Frank Thomas 8.00 20.00
70 Ken Griffey Jr. 12.50 30.00
101 Hideki Matsui 6.00 15.00
105 Ichiro Suzuki 10.00 25.00
150 Delmon Young 4.00 10.00
151 Andrew Miller AU 75.00 150.00
153 Philip Humber AU 10.00 25.00
159 Jeff Baker AU 5.00 12.00
160 Jeff Salazar AU 5.00 12.00
164 Fred Lewis AU 12.50 30.00

2007 Finest Refractors Blue

*REF BLUE 1-135: 1.5X TO 4X BASIC
*REF BLUE 136-150: 1X TO 2.5X BASIC
1-150 ODDS ONE PER MINI BOX
1-150 PRINT RUN 399 SER.#'d SETS
*REF BLUE AU 151-166: .5X TO 1.2X BASIC AU
AU 151-166 ODDS 1:13 MINI BOX
AU 151-166 PRINT RUN 299 SER.#'d SETS
EXCHANGE DEADLINE 02/28/09
8 Chien-Ming Wang 6.00 15.00

2007 Finest Refractors Gold

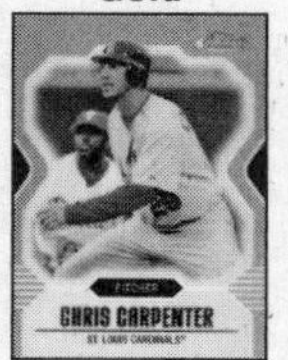

*REF GOLD 1-135: 5X TO 12X BASIC
*REF GOLD 136-150: 4X TO 10X BASIC
1-150 ODDS 1:8 MINI BOX
1-150 PRINT RUN 50 SER.#'d SETS
*REF GOLD AU 151-166: 1.25X TO 3X BASIC AU
AU 151-166 ODDS 1:74 MINI BOX
AU 151-166 PRINT RUN 49 SER.#'d SETS
EXCHANGE DEADLINE 02/28/09
3 Chipper Jones 10.00 25.00
8 Chien-Ming Wang 30.00 60.00
25 Manny Ramirez 4.00 10.00
30 Greg Maddux 15.00 40.00
55 Frank Thomas 20.00 50.00
68 Derek Jeter 40.00 80.00
70 Ken Griffey Jr. 30.00 60.00
74 Albert Pujols 20.00 50.00
79 Joe Mauer 5.00 12.00
99 Jose Reyes 8.00 20.00
101 Hideki Matsui 10.00 25.00
105 Ichiro Suzuki 20.00 50.00
121 Mariano Rivera 12.50 30.00
151 Andrew Miller AU 150.00 250.00
155 Michael Bourn AU 15.00 40.00
156 Miguel Montero AU EXCH 15.00 40.00
158 Ryan Sweeney AU 15.00 40.00
162 Josh Fields AU 15.00 40.00
164 Fred Lewis AU 15.00 40.00
165 Scott Moore AU 15.00 40.00

2007 Finest Refractors Green

*REF GREEN 1-135: 2X TO 5X BASIC
*REF GREEN 136-150: 1.25X TO 3X BASIC
1-150 ODDS 1:2 MINI BOX
*REF GRN AU 151-166: .6X TO 1.5X BASIC AU
AU 151-166 ODDS 1:19 MINI BOX
STATED PRINT RUN 199 SERIAL #'d SETS
EXCHANGE DEADLINE 02/28/09
8 Chien-Ming Wang 10.00 25.00
70 Ken Griffey Jr. 6.00 15.00
101 Hideki Matsui 4.00 10.00

2007 Finest SuperFractors

1-150 ODDS 1:385 MINI BOX
AU 151-166 ODDS 1:3582 MINI BOX
STATED PRINT RUN 1 SERIAL #'d SET
NO PRICING DUE TO SCARCITY
EXCHANGE DEADLINE 02/28/09

2007 Finest X-Fractors

*XF 1-135: 8X TO 20X BASIC
1-150 ODDS 1:16 MINI BOX
AU 151-166 ODDS 1:144 MINI BOX
STATED PRINT RUN 25 SER.#'d SETS
NO ROOKIE PRICING AVAILABLE
EXCHANGE DEADLINE 02/28/09
3 Chipper Jones 12.50 30.00
8 Chien-Ming Wang 60.00 120.00
25 Manny Ramirez 5.00 12.00
30 Greg Maddux 20.00 50.00
50 Alex Rodriguez 20.00 50.00
55 Frank Thomas 30.00 60.00
68 Derek Jeter 50.00 100.00
70 Ken Griffey Jr. 40.00 80.00
74 Albert Pujols 30.00 60.00
79 Joe Mauer 6.00 15.00
99 Jose Reyes 10.00 25.00
101 Hideki Matsui 12.50 30.00
105 Ichiro Suzuki 30.00 60.00
121 Mariano Rivera 15.00 40.00

2007 Finest X-Fractors White Framed

1-150 ODDS 1:385 MINI BOX
AU 151-166 ODDS 1:3582 MINI BOX
STATED PRINT RUN 1 SERIAL #'d SET
NO PRICING DUE TO SCARCITY
EXCHANGE DEADLINE 02/28/09

2007 Finest Mantle Cut Signature

STATED ODDS 1:11,400 MINI BOX
STATED PRINT RUN 1 SER.#'d SET
NO PRICING DUE TO SCARCITY
STATED PLATE ODDS 1:11,400 MINI BOX
PLATE PRINT RUN 1 SET PER COLOR
BLACK-CYAN-MAGENTA-YELLOW ISSUED
NO PLATE PRICING DUE TO SCARCITY

2007 Finest Rookie Finest Moments

STATED ODDS 2 PER MINI BOX
PRINTING PLATE ODDS 1:289 MINI BOX
PLATE PRINT RUN 1 SET PER COLOR
BLACK-CYAN-MAGENTA-YELLOW ISSUED
NO PLATE PRICING DUE TO SCARCITY
*REF: .6X TO 1.5X BASIC
REFRACTOR ODDS 1 PER MINI BOX
*REF BLACK: 2.5X TO 6X BASIC
REF BLACK ODDS 1:12 MINI BOX
REF BLACK PRINT RUN 99 SER.#'d SETS
*REF BLUE: 1X TO 2.5X BASIC
REF BLUE ODDS 1:4 MINI BOX
REF BLUE PRINT RUN 299 SER.#'d SETS
*REF GOLD: 5X TO 12X BASIC
REF GOLD ODDS 1:23 MINI BOX
REF GOLD PRINT RUN 50 SER.#'d SETS
*REF GREEN: 1.25X TO 3X BASIC
REF GREEN ODDS 1:6 MINI BOX
REF GREEN PRINT RUN 199 SER.#'d SETS
SUPERFRACTOR ODDS 1:1156 MINI BOX
SUPERFRACTOR PRINT RUN 1 SER.#'d SET
NO SUPERFRACTOR PRICING AVAILABLE
*X-FRACTOR: 8X TO 20X BASIC
X-FRACTOR ODDS 1:46 MINI BOX
X-FRACTOR PRINT RUN 25 SER.#'d SETS
X-F WHITE ODDS 1:1156 MINI BOX
X-F WHITE PRINT RUN 1 SER.#'d SET
NO X-F WHITE PRICING AVAILABLE
AD Adam Dunn .25 .60
AE Andre Ethier .40 1.00
AJ Andruw Jones .40 1.00
AP Albert Pujols 1.25 3.00
AR Alex Rodriguez 1.00 2.50
AS Anibal Sanchez .25 .60
AW Adam Wainwright .25 .60
CB Carlos Beltran .25 .60
CC Carl Crawford .25 .60
CH Cole Hamels .60 1.50
CJ Chipper Jones .60 1.50
CQ Carlos Quentin .25 .60
DJ Derek Jeter 1.50 4.00
DL Derrek Lee .25 .60
DO David Ortiz .60 1.50
DU Dan Uggla .40 1.00
DW David Wright 1.00 2.50
FL Francisco Liriano .60 1.50
HM Hideki Matsui .60 1.50
HR Hanley Ramirez .60 1.50
IK Ian Kinsler .25 .60
IS Ichiro Suzuki 1.00 2.50
JB Jason Bay .25 .60
JH Jason Hirsh .25 .60
JM Joe Mauer .40 1.00
JP Jonathan Papelbon .60 1.50
JR Jose Reyes .25 .60
JS Jeremy Sowers .25 .60
JV Justin Verlander .60 1.50
JW Jered Weaver .40 1.00
KG Ken Griffey Jr. 1.00 2.50
KJ Kenji Johjima .60 1.50
MC Miguel Cabrera .40 1.00
MK Matt Kemp .25 .60
MN Mike Napoli .25 .60
MP Mike Piazza .60 1.50
MR Manny Ramirez .40 1.00
MT Miguel Tejada .25 .60
NC Nelson Cruz .25 .60
NG Nomar Garciaparra .60 1.50
NM Nick Markakis .60 1.50
PF Prince Fielder .60 1.50
RH Ryan Howard 1.00 2.50
RM Russ Martin .25 .60
SD Stephen Drew .40 1.00
VG Vladimir Guerrero .60 1.50
DWW Dontrelle Willis .25 .60
JBA Josh Barfield .25 .60
JST Brian Stokes .25 .60
MCA Melky Cabrera .25 .60

2007 Finest Rookie Finest Moments Autographs

STATED ODDS 1:5 MINI BOX
PRINTING PLATE ODDS 1:482 MINI BOX
PLATE PRINT RUN 1 SET PER COLOR
BLACK-CYAN-MAGENTA-YELLOW ISSUED
NO PLATE PRICING DUE TO SCARCITY
REFRACTOR ODDS 1:77 MINI BOX
REFRACTOR PRINT RUN 25 #'d SETS
NO REFRACTOR PRICING AVAILABLE
SUPERFRACTOR ODDS 1:1975 MINI BOX
NO SUPERFRACTOR PRICING AVAILABLE
SUPERFRACTOR PRINT RUN 1 #'d SET
AR Alex Rodriguez 50.00 100.00
AS Anibal Sanchez 3.00 8.00
AW Adam Wainwright 10.00 25.00
BP Brandon Phillips 3.00 8.00
BW Brad Wilkerson 3.00 8.00
CH Cole Hamels 12.50 30.00
CJ Chuck James 4.00 10.00
CQ Carlos Quentin 6.00 15.00
DO David Ortiz 20.00 50.00
DU Dan Uggla 8.00 20.00
DW David Wright 30.00 60.00
DWW Dontrelle Willis 6.00 15.00
DY Delmon Young 10.00 25.00
ES Ervin Santana 3.00 8.00
FC Fausto Carmona 10.00 25.00
HR Hanley Ramirez 6.00 15.00
JM Justin Morneau 10.00 25.00
JN Joe Nathan 3.00 8.00
JP Jonathan Papelbon 12.50 30.00
LM Lastings Milledge 6.00 15.00
MC Melky Cabrera 15.00 40.00
MN Mike Napoli 3.00 8.00
MTC Matt Cain 6.00 15.00
RC Robinson Cano 15.00 40.00
RH Rich Hill 10.00 25.00
RH Ryan Howard 40.00 80.00
RM Russ Martin 6.00 15.00
RZ Ryan Zimmerman 12.50 30.00
TH Travis Hafner 6.00 15.00
YP Yusmeiro Petit 3.00 8.00

2007 Finest Rookie Finest Moments Autographs Dual

STATED ODDS 1:32 MINI BOX
STATED PRINT RUN 74 SER.#'d SETS
REFRACTOR ODDS 1:93 MINI BOX
REFRACTOR PRINT RUN 25 #'d SETS
NO REFRACTOR PRICING AVAILABLE
REF GOLD ODDS 1:2387 MINI BOX
REF GOLD PRINT RUN 1 #'d SET
NO REF GOLD PRICING AVAILABLE
EXCHANGE DEADLINE 02/28/09
BM Jason Bay 20.00 50.00
Justin Morneau
CC Eric Chavez 20.00 50.00
Miguel Cabrera
CK Nelson Cruz 10.00 25.00
Matt Kemp
CR Matt Cain 15.00 40.00
Anthony Reyes
CY Robinson Cano 15.00 40.00
Michael Young
HJ Rich Hill 15.00 40.00
Josh Johnson
HM Cole Hamels 20.00 50.00
Brett Myers
HR Travis Hafner 20.00 50.00
Manny Ramirez
JH Chuck James 15.00 40.00
Cole Hamels
MC Lastings Milledge 15.00 40.00
Melky Cabrera
MG Russ Martin 8.00 20.00
Ryan Garko
MK Lastings Milledge 10.00 25.00
Matt Kemp
MN Kendry Morales 8.00 20.00
Mike Napoli
MNA Russ Martin 10.00 25.00
Mike Napoli
OP Roy Oswalt 15.00 40.00
Mark Prior
PO Yusmeiro Petit 8.00 20.00
Scott Olsen
PP Jonathan Papelbon 50.00 100.00
Dustin Pedroia
RP Mariano Rivera 75.00 150.00
Jorge Posada
RU Hanley Ramirez 15.00 40.00
Dan Uggla
UG Dan Uggla 8.00 20.00
Marcus Giles
US Dan Uggla 10.00 25.00
Anibal Sanchez
UW Chase Utley 50.00 100.00
David Wright EXCH
VE Justin Verlander 20.00 50.00
Hanley Ramirez
WW Chien-Ming Wang 150.00 300.00
Brandon Webb
ZC Joel Zumaya 8.00 20.00
Fausto Carmona

2007 Finest Rookie Photo Variation

STATED ODDS 1:5 MINI BOX
STATED PRINT RUN 439 SER.#'d SETS
*REF: .75X TO 2X BASIC
REFRACTOR ODDS 1:13 MINI BOX
REFRACTOR PRINT RUN 149 #'d SETS
REF GOLD ODDS 1:1975 MINI BOX
REF GOLD PRINT RUN 1 SER.#'d SET
NO REF GOLD PRICING AVAILABLE
*X-FRACTOR: 2X TO 5X BASIC
X-FRACTOR ODDS 1:39 MINI BOX
X-FRACTOR PRINT RUN 50 SER.#'d SETS
136 Adam Lind Bat Up .75 2.00
136 Adam Lind Bat Out .75 2.00
137 Hector Gimenez Posed .75 2.00
137 Hector Gimenez Batting .75 2.00
138 Shawn Riggans w/Bat .75 2.00
138 Shawn Riggans w/Glove .75 2.00
139 Joaquin Arias w/Bat .75 2.00
139 Joaquin Arias Throw .75 2.00
140 Drew Anderson Run Away .75 2.00
140 Drew Anderson w/Glove .75 2.00
141 Mike Rabelo Bat Shoulder .75 2.00
141 Mike Rabelo Bat Up .75 2.00
142 Chris Narveson Portrait .75 2.00
142 Chris Narveson w/Glove .75 2.00
143 Ryan Feierabend Catch .75 2.00
143 Ryan Feierabend Pitch .75 2.00
144 Vinny Rottino Swing .75 2.00
144 Vinny Rottino Field .75 2.00
145 Jon Knott Run .75 2.00
145 Jon Knott w/Bat .75 2.00
146 Oswaldo Navarro Posed .75 2.00
146 Oswaldo Navarro Swing .75 2.00
147 Brian Stokes Windup .75 2.00
147 Brian Stokes Throw .75 2.00
148 Glen Perkins Windup .75 2.00
148 Glen Perkins w/Jacket .75 2.00
149 Mitch Maier In OF .75 2.00
149 Mitch Maier On Deck .75 2.00
150 Delmon Young Running 2.00 5.00
150 Delmon Young Portrait 2.00 5.00

2007 Finest Rookie Redemption

This 10-card set was announced during the year as new 2007 rookies made an impact in the majors. These cards, which were inserted at a stated rate of one in three mini-boxes, could be redeemed until December 31, 2007.

COMPLETE SET (10) 150.00 250.00
STATED ODDS 1:3 MINI BOX
REDEEMABLE FOR 07 RC LOGO PLAYER
EXCHANGE DEADLINE 12/30/07
1 Hideki Okajima 3.00 8.00
2 Elijah Dukes 2.00 5.00
3 Akinori Iwamura 3.00 8.00
4 Tim Lincecum 8.00 20.00
5 Daisuke Matsuzaka 5.00 12.00
6 Ryan Braun 5.00 12.00
7 Daisuke Matsuzaka 4.00 10.00
Hideki Okajima
8 Justin Upton 5.00 12.00
9 Philip Hughes 4.00 10.00
10 Joba Chamberlain AU 60.00 120.00

2007 Finest Ryan Howard Finest Moments

COMMON CARD 1.50 4.00
STATED ODDS 2 PER HOWARD BOX LOADER
STATED PRINT RUN 459 SER.#'d SETS
*REF: .6X TO 1.5X BASIC
REFRACTOR ODDS 1:3 BOXES
REFRACTOR PRINT RUN 149 SER.#'d SETS
REF GOLD ODDS 1:329 BOXES
REF GOLD PRINT RUN 1 SER.#'d SET
NO REF GOLD PRICING AVAILABLE
*X-FRACTOR: .75X TO 2X BASIC
X-FRACTOR ODDS 1:7 BOXES
X-FRACTOR PRINT RUN 50 SER.#'d SETS

2008 Finest

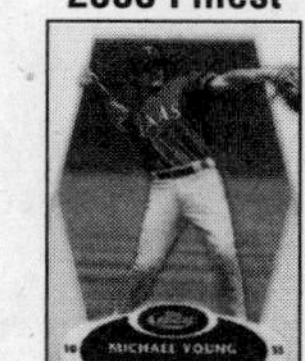

COMP.SET w/o AUs (150) 40.00 80.00
COMMON CARD (1-125) .15 .40
COMMON RC (126-150) .75 2.00
COMMON AU RC (151-166) 4.00 10.00
151-166 AU ODDS 1:3 MINI BOX
1-150 PLATE ODDS 1:82 MINI BOX
AU 151-166 PLATE ODDS 1:775 MINI BOX
PLATE PRINT RUN 1 SET PER COLOR
BLACK-CYAN-MAGENTA-YELLOW ISSUED
NO PLATE PRICING DUE TO SCARCITY
1 Daisuke Matsuzaka .75 2.00
2 Justin Upton .40 1.00
3 Andruw Jones .15 .40
4 John Lackey .15 .40
5 Brandon Phillips .15 .40
6 Ryan Zimmerman .25 .60
7 Tim Lincecum .40 1.00
8 Johnny Damon .25 .60
9 Garrett Atkins .15 .40
10 Magglio Ordonez .25 .60
11 Tom Gorzelany .15 .40

12 Eric Chavez .15 .40
13 Troy Tulowitzki .25 .60
14 Mike Lowell .15 .40
15 Brandon Webb .25 .60
16 Chipper Jones .50 1.25
17 Alex Gordon .40 1.00
18 Ken Griffey Jr. .60 1.50
19 Roy Oswalt .15 .40
20 Miguel Cabrera .25 .60
21 Chase Utley .40 1.00
22 Scott Kazmir .25 .60
23 Kenji Johjima .15 .40
24 Frank Thomas .40 1.00
25 Ryan Braun .50 1.25
26 Carlos Pena .40 1.00
27 Robinson Cano .25 .60
28 Ben Sheets .25 .60
29 Russell Martin .15 .40
30 Joe Mauer .25 .60
31 Gary Sheffield .15 .40
32 Carlos Zambrano .15 .40
33 Jermaine Dye .15 .40
34 Dan Uggla .25 .60
35 Erik Bedard .15 .40
36 Tim Hudson .15 .40
37 David Ortiz .40 1.00
38 Tom Glavine .25 .60
39 Adrian Gonzalez .25 .60
40 Jorge Posada .25 .60
41 Noah Lowry .15 .40
42 Vernon Wells .15 .40
43 Johan Santana .25 .60
44 Dmitri Young .15 .40
45 Manny Ramirez .40 1.00
46 Jim Edmonds .25 .60
47 Roy Halladay .15 .40
48 Delmon Young .25 .60
49 Nick Swisher .15 .40
50 David Wright .50 1.25
51 Paul Konerko .15 .40
52 Curt Schilling .25 .60
53 Torii Hunter .15 .40
54 Gary Matthews .15 .40
55 Derrek Lee .25 .60
56 John Smoltz .40 1.00
57 Adam Dunn .15 .40
58 C.C Sabathia .15 .40
59 Chris Young .15 .40
60 Jake Peavy .25 .60
61 Joba Chamberlain .50 1.25
62 Jason Bay .15 .40
63 Chris Carpenter .15 .40
64 Jimmy Rollins .25 .60
65 Grady Sizemore .25 .60
66 Joe Blanton .15 .40
67 Justin Morneau .15 .40
68 Lance Berkman .25 .60
69 Jeff Francis .15 .40
70 Nick Markakis .25 .60
71 Orlando Cabrera .15 .40
72 Barry Zito .15 .40
73 Eric Byrnes .15 .40
74 Brian McCann .25 .60
75 Albert Pujols .60 1.50
76 Josh Beckett .25 .60
77 Jim Thome .25 .60
78 Fausto Carmona .15 .40
79 Brad Hawpe .15 .40
80 Prince Fielder .40 1.00
81 Justin Verlander .25 .60
82 Billy Butler .15 .40
83 J.J. Hardy .15 .40
84 Hideki Matsui .40 1.00
85 Matt Holliday .25 .60
86 Bobby Crosby .15 .40
87 Orlando Hudson .15 .40
88 Ichiro Suzuki .60 1.50
89 Troy Glaus .25 .60
90 Hanley Ramirez .40 1.00
91 Carlos Beltran .15 .40
92 Mark Buehrle .15 .40
93 Andy Pettitte .25 .60
94 Mark Teixeira .25 .60
95 Curtis Granderson .15 .40
96 Cole Hamels .40 1.00
97 Jarrod Saltalamacchia .15 .40
98 Carl Crawford .15 .40
99 Dontrelle Willis .15 .40
100 Alex Rodriguez .60 1.50
101 Brad Penny .15 .40
102 Michael Young .15 .40
103 Greg Maddux .50 1.25
104 Brian Roberts .25 .60
105 Hunter Pence .40 1.00
106 Aaron Harang .15 .40
107 Ivan Rodriguez .25 .60
108 Dan Haren .15 .40
109 Freddy Sanchez .15 .40
110 Alfonso Soriano .25 .60
111 Hank Blalock .15 .40
112 Chien- Ming Wang .60 1.50
113 Carlos Delgado .15 .40
114 Aramis Ramirez .15 .40
115 Jose Reyes .25 .60
116 Victor Martinez .15 .40
117 Carlos Lee .15 .40
118 Jeff Kent .15 .40
119 Miguel Tejada .15 .40
120 Vladimir Guerrero .40 1.00
121 Travis Hafner .15 .40
122 Todd Helton .25 .60
123 Chris Young .15 .40
124 Derek Jeter 1.00 2.50
125 Ryan Howard .50 1.25
126 Alberto Gonzalez RC 1.25 3.00
127 Felipe Paulino RC 1.25 3.00
128 Donny Lucy (RC) .75 2.00
129 Nick Blackburn RC 1.25 3.00
130 Luke Hochevar RC 2.00 5.00
131 Bronson Sardinha (RC) .75 2.00
132 Heath Phillips RC 1.25 3.00
133 Bryan Bullington (RC) .75 2.00
134 Jeff Clement (RC) .75 2.00
135 Josh Banks (RC) .75 2.00
136 Emilio Bonifacio RC 1.25 3.00
137 Ryan Hanigan RC 1.25 3.00
138 Erick Threets (RC) .75 2.00
139 Seth Smith (RC) .75 2.00
140 Billy Buckner (RC) .75 2.00
141 Bill Murphy (RC) .75 2.00
142 Radhames Liz RC 1.25 3.00
143 Joey Votto (RC) 2.00 5.00
144 Mel Stocker RC .75 2.00
145 Dan Meyer (RC) .75 2.00
146 Rob Johnson (RC) .75 2.00
147 Josh Newman RC 1.25 3.00
148 Dan Giese (RC) .75 2.00
149 Luis Mendoza (RC) .75 2.00
150 Wladimir Balentien (RC) .75 2.00
151 Brandon Jones AU RC 4.00 10.00
152 Rich Thompson AU RC 4.00 10.00
153 Chin-Lung Hu AU RC 15.00 40.00
154 Chris Seddon AU (RC) 4.00 10.00
155 Steve Pearce AU RC 6.00 15.00
156 Lance Broadway AU (RC) 4.00 10.00
157 Nyjer Morgan AU (RC) 4.00 10.00
158 Jonathan Meloan AU RC 4.00 10.00
159 Josh Anderson AU (RC) 4.00 10.00
160 Clay Buchholz AU (RC) 15.00 40.00
161 Joe Koshansky AU (RC) 4.00 10.00
162 Clint Sammons AU (RC) 4.00 10.00
163 Daric Barton AU (RC) 5.00 12.00
164 Ross Detwiler AU RC 5.00 12.00
165 Sam Fuld AU RC 4.00 10.00
166 Justin Ruggiano AU RC 4.00 10.00

2008 Finest Refractors

*REF VET: 1X TO 2.5X BASIC
*REF RC: .5X TO 1.2X BASIC RC
1-150 REF.RANDOMLY INSERTED
*REF AU: .4X TO 1X BASIC AU
151-166 ODDS 1:7 MINI PACKS
151-166 PRINT RUN 499 SER.#'d SETS

2008 Finest Refractors Black

*BLACK VET: 4X TO 10X BASIC
*BLACK RC: 1X TO 2.5X BASIC RC
1-150 ODDS 1:4 MINI BOXES
1-150 PRINT RUN 99 SER.#'d SETS
*REF AU: .6X TO 1.5X BASIC AU
151-166 ODDS 1:32 MINI PACKS
151-166 PRINT RUN 99 SER.#'d SETS
153 Chin-Lung Hu AU 75.00 150.00
164 Ross Detwiler AU 10.00 25.00

2008 Finest Refractors Blue

*BLUE VET: 1.5X TO 4X BASIC
*BLUE RC: .6X TO 1.5X BASIC RC
1-150 ODDS 1:2 MINI BOXES
1-150 PRINT RUN 299 SER.#'d SETS
*REF AU: .5X TO 1.2X BASIC AU
151-166 ODDS 1:8 MINI PACKS
151-166 PRINT RUN 399 SER.#'d SETS
153 Chin-Lung Hu AU 30.00 60.00

2008 Finest Refractors Gold

*GOLD VET: 6X TO 15X BASIC
*GOLD RC: 2X TO 5X BASIC RC
1-150 ODDS 1:7 MINI BOXES
1-150 PRINT RUN 50 SER.#'d SETS
*REF AU: 1X TO 2.5X BASIC AU
151-166 ODDS 1:64 MINI PACKS
151-166 PRINT RUN 50 SER.#'d SETS
24 Frank Thomas 20.00 50.00
75 Albert Pujols 15.00 40.00
88 Ichiro Suzuki 15.00 40.00
100 Alex Rodriguez 15.00 40.00
103 Greg Maddux 20.00 50.00
124 Derek Jeter 30.00 60.00
126 Alberto Gonzalez 10.00 25.00
129 Nick Blackburn 20.00 50.00
132 Heath Phillips 6.00 15.00
134 Jeff Clement 15.00 40.00
147 Josh Newman 6.00 15.00
148 Dan Giese 6.00 15.00
150 Wladimir Balentien 6.00 15.00
153 Chin-Lung Hu AU 100.00 200.00
160 Clay Buchholz AU 40.00 80.00
163 Daric Barton AU 15.00 40.00
164 Ross Detwiler AU 15.00 40.00

2008 Finest Refractors Green

*GREEN VET: 2X TO 5X BASIC
*GREEN RC: .75X TO 2X BASIC RC
1-150 ODDS 1:2 MINI BOXES
1-150 PRINT RUN 199 SER.#'d SETS
*REF AU: .5X TO 1.2X BASIC AU
151-166 ODDS 1:16 MINI PACKS
151-166 PRINT RUN 199 SER.#'d SETS
153 Chin-Lung Hu AU 40.00 80.00

2008 Finest Refractors Red

1-150 ODDS 1:14 MINI BOXES
151-166 AU ODDS 1:128 MINI BOXES
STATED PRINT RUN 25 SER.#'d SETS
NO PRICING DUE TO SCARCITY

2008 Finest X-Fractors White Framed

1-150 ODDS 1:327 MINI BOXES
151-166 AU ODDS 1:2036 MINI BOXES
STATED PRINT RUN 1 SER.#'d SET
NO PRICING DUE TO SCARCITY

2008 Finest Finest Moments

*REF: .6X TO 1.5X BASIC
REF.RANDOMLY INSERTED
STATED ODDS XX PER MINI BOX
*BLACK REF: 1.5X TO 4X BASIC
BLACK ODDS 1:10 MINI BOXES
BLACK PRINT RUN 99 SER.#'d SETS
*BLUE REF: .75X TO 2X BASIC
BLUE ODDS 1:4 MINI BOXES
BLUE PRINT RUN 399 SER.#'d SETS
*GOLD REF: 2.5X TO 6X BASIC
GOLD ODDS 1:20 MINI BOXES
GOLD PRINT RUN 50 SER.#'d SETS
*GREEN REF: 1X TO 2.5X BASIC
GREEN ODDS 1:5 MINI BOXES
GREEN PRINT RUN 199 SER.#'d SETS
PRINTING PLATE ODDS 1:245 MINI BOXES
PLATE PRINT RUN 1 SET PER COLOR
BLACK-CYAN-MAGENTA-YELLOW ISSUED
NO PLATE PRICING DUE TO SCARCITY
AG Adrian Gonzalez .60 1.50
AP Andy Pettitte .60 1.50
APU Albert Pujols 1.50 4.00
AR Alex Rodriguez 1.50 4.00
AS Andy Sonnanstine .40 1.00
BP Brandon Phillips .40 1.00
BPB Brian Bannister .40 1.00
BW Brandon Webb .60 1.50
CB Clay Buchholz 1.00 2.50
CF Chone Figgins .40 1.00
CG Curtis Granderson .40 1.00
CH Cole Hamels 1.00 2.50
CP Carlos Pena 1.00 2.50
CS C.C. Sabathia .40 1.00
DH Dan Haren .40 1.00
DJ Derek Jeter 2.50 6.00
DL Derrek Lee .60 1.50
DO David Ortiz 1.00 2.50
DW David Wright 1.25 3.00
EB Eric Byrnes .40 1.00
FC Fausto Carmona .40 1.00
FH Felix Hernandez .60 1.50
FT Frank Thomas 1.00 2.50
HP Hunter Pence 1.00 2.50
HR Hanley Ramirez 1.00 2.50
IS Ichiro Suzuki 1.50 4.00
ISS Ichiro Suzuki 1.50 4.00
JAS Johan Santana .60 1.50
JMC Miguel Cabrera .60 1.50
JR Jose Reyes .60 1.50
JS John Smoltz 1.00 2.50
JSA Jarrod Saltalamacchia .40 1.00
JT Jim Thome .60 1.50
JV Justin Verlander .60 1.50
MB Mark Buehrle .40 1.00
ME Mark Ellis .40 1.00
MH Matt Holliday .60 1.50
MR Mark Reynolds .40 1.00
PF Prince Fielder 1.00 2.50
PM Pedro Martinez .60 1.50
RA Rick Ankiel .40 1.00
RB Ryan Braun 1.25 3.00
RH Ryan Howard 1.25 3.00
ROH Roy Halladay .40 1.00
SS Sammy Sosa .60 1.50
TG Tom Glavine .60 1.50
TH Trevor Hoffman .40 1.00
TOH Todd Helton .60 1.50
TT Troy Tulowitzki .60 1.50
VG Vladimir Guerrero 1.00 2.50

2008 Finest Finest Moments Refractors Red

STATED ODDS 1:39 MINI BOXES
STATED PRINT RUN 25 SER.#'d SETS
NO PRICING DUE TO SCARCITY

2008 Finest Finest Moments X-Fractors White Framed

STATED ODDS 1:982 MINI BOXES
STATED PRINT RUN 1 SER.#'d SET
NO PRICING DUE TO SCARCITY

2008 Finest Finest Moments Autographs

GROUP A ODDS 1:5 MINI BOXES
GROUP B ODDS 1:282 MINI BOXES
AR Alex Rios A 6.00 15.00
AS Andy Sonnanstine A 3.00 8.00
BP Brandon Phillips A 6.00 15.00
BPB Brian Bannister A 6.00 15.00
CG Curtis Granderson A 10.00 25.00
CH Cole Hamels A 12.50 30.00
CMW Chien-Ming Wang A 40.00 80.00
DW David Wright A 20.00 50.00
FC Fausto Carmona A 6.00 15.00
HR Hanley Ramirez A 10.00 25.00
JA Jeremy Accardo A 3.00 8.00
JC Jack Cust A 3.00 8.00
JD Justin Duchscherer A 6.00 15.00
JH Josh Hamilton A 20.00 50.00
JMC Miguel Cabrera A 10.00 25.00
JR Jose Reyes A 15.00 40.00
JS Jarrod Saltalamacchia A 3.00 8.00
ME Mark Ellis A 3.00 8.00
MR Mark Reynolds A 6.00 15.00
NM Nick Markakis A 10.00 25.00
PH Phil Hughes A 15.00 40.00
RB Ryan Braun A 12.50 30.00
RH Ryan Howard B 30.00 60.00
RZ Ryan Zimmerman A 10.00 25.00
VG Vladimir Guerrero A 12.50 30.00

2008 Finest Finest Moments Autographs Refractors Red

STATED ODDS 1:79 MINI BOXES
STATED PRINT RUN 25 SER.#'d SETS
NO PRICING DUE TO SCARCITY

2008 Finest Finest Moments Autographs X-Fractors White Framed

STATED ODDS 1:3260 MINI BOXES
STATED PRINT RUN 1 SER.#'d SET
NO PRICING DUE TO SCARCITY

2008 Finest Rookie Redemption

STATED ODDS 1:3 MINI BOXES
EXCHANGE DEADLINE 4/30/2009
1 Johnny Cueto EXCH 6.00 15.00
2 Jay Bruce AU EXCH 20.00 50.00
3 Kosuke Fukudome EXCH 5.00 12.00
4 Jeff Samardzija EXCH 5.00 12.00
5 Chris Davis EXCH 4.00 10.00
6 Justin Masterson EXCH 4.00 10.00
7 Clayton Kershaw EXCH 4.00 10.00
8 Daniel Murphy EXCH 6.00 15.00
9 Denard Span EXCH 4.00 10.00
10 Jed Lowrie AU EXCH 12.50 30.00

2008 Finest Topps Team Favorites

COMPLETE SET (8) 5.00 12.00
RANDOM INSERTS IN PACKS
*REF: .5X TO 1.2X BASIC
REF.ODDS 1:4 MINI BOXES
AS Alfonso Soriano 1.00 2.50
BC Bobby Crosby .60 1.50
DW David Wright 2.00 5.00
EC Eric Chavez .60 1.50
FP Felix Pie .60 1.50
JR Jose Reyes 1.00 2.50
MC Melky Cabrera .60 1.50
RC Robinson Cano 1.00 2.50

2008 Finest Topps Team Favorites Autographs

STATED PRINT RUN 100 SER.#'d SETS
AS Alfonso Soriano 20.00 50.00
BC Bobby Crosby 6.00 15.00
DW David Wright 40.00 80.00
EC Eric Chavez 6.00 15.00
FP Felix Pie 6.00 15.00
JR Jose Reyes 20.00 50.00
MC Melky Cabrera 10.00 25.00
RC Robinson Cano 15.00 40.00

2008 Finest Topps Team Favorites Autographs Refractors Red

STATED ODDS 1:164 MINI BOXES
STATED PRINT RUN 25 SER.#'d SETS
NO PRICING DUE TO SCARCITY

2008 Finest Topps Team Favorites Autographs X-Fractors White Framed

STATED ODDS 1:4092 MINI BOXES
STATED PRINT RUN 1 SER.#'d SET
NO PRICING DUE TO SCARCITY

2008 Finest Topps Team Favorites Dual

COMPLETE SET (4) 3.00 8.00
RANDOM INSERTS IN PACKS
*REF: .5X TO 1.2X BASIC
REF.RANDOMLY INSERTED
CC Melky Cabrera 1.00 2.50
Robinson Cano
EB Eric Chavez .60 1.50
Bobby Crosby
RW Jose Reyes 2.00 5.00
David Wright
SP Alfonso Soriano 1.00 2.50
Felix Pie

2008 Finest Topps Team Favorites Dual Autographs

STATED ODDS 1:166 MINI BOXES
STATED PRINT RUN 74 SER.#'d SETS
CC Melky Cabrera 20.00 50.00
Robinson Cano
EB Eric Chavez 12.50 30.00
Bobby Crosby
RW Jose Reyes 75.00 150.00
David Wright
SP Alfonso Soriano 20.00 50.00
Felix Pie

2008 Finest Topps Team Favorites Dual Autographs Refractors

STATED ODDS 1:164 MINI BOXES
STATED PRINT RUN 25 SER.#'d SETS
NO PRICING DUE TO SCARCITY

2008 Finest Topps Team Favorites Dual Autographs X-Fractors White Framed

STATED ODDS 1:4092 MINI BOXES
STATED PRINT RUN 1 SER.#'d SET
NO PRICING DUE TO SCARCITY

2008 Finest Topps Team Favorites Dual Autographs Cuts

STATED ODDS 1:9821 MINI BOXES
STATED PRINT RUN 1 SER.#'d SET
NO PRICING DUE TO SCARCITY
MC Mickey Mantle
Robinson Cano
MD Mickey Mantle
Johnny Damon
MM Mickey Mantle
Melky Cabrera
MP Mickey Mantle
Jorge Posada
MR Mickey Mantle
Mariano Rivera

2008 Finest Topps TV Autographs

STATED ODDS 1:11 MINI BOXES
RM Alan 4.00 10.00
RGF Felicia 4.00 10.00
RGH Hollie 4.00 10.00
RGR Rachael 4.00 10.00
RGLS Lindsey/Stephanie 4.00 10.00

2008 Finest Topps TV Autographs Red Ink

RANDOM INSERTS IN PACKS
PRINT RUNS B/WN 5-10 COPIES PER
NO PRICING DUE TO SCARCITY

2008 Finest Topps TV Autographs Refractors

STATED ODDS 1:392 MINI BOXES
STATED PRINT RUN 1 SER.#'d SET
NO PRICING DUE TO SCARCITY

2002 Flair

This 138 card set was issued in April, 2002. These cards were issued in five card packs which came 20 boxes to a case with a cost of $7 per pack. Each unopened box also contained a "Sweet Swatch" box topper. The last 38 cards in the set are are future fame cards featuring leading prospects in the game. These cards have a stated print run of 1750 serial numbered sets.

COMP.SET w/o SP's (100) 10.00 25.00
COMMON CARD (1-100) .20 .50
COMMON CARD (101-138) 2.00 5.00
1 Scott Rolen .30 .75
2 Derek Jeter 1.25 3.00
3 Sean Casey .20 .50
4 Hideo Nomo .50 1.25
5 Craig Biggio .30 .75
6 Randy Johnson .50 1.25
7 J.D. Drew .20 .50
8 Greg Maddux .75 2.00
9 Paul LoDuca .20 .50
10 John Olerud .20 .50
11 Barry Larkin .30 .75
12 Mark Grace .30 .75
13 Jimmy Rollins .20 .50
14 Todd Helton .30 .75
15 Jim Edmonds .20 .50
16 Roy Oswalt .20 .50
17 Phil Nevin .20 .50
18 Tim Salmon .30 .75
19 Magglio Ordonez .20 .50
20 Roger Clemens 1.00 2.50
21 Raul Mondesi .20 .50
22 Edgar Martinez .30 .75
23 Pedro Martinez .30 .75
24 Edgardo Alfonzo .20 .50
25 Bernie Williams .30 .75
26 Gary Sheffield .20 .50
27 D'Angelo Jimenez .20 .50
28 Toby Hall .20 .50
29 Joe Mays .20 .50
30 Alfonso Soriano .20 .50
31 Mike Piazza .75 2.00
32 Lance Berkman .20 .50
33 Jim Thome .30 .75
34 Ben Sheets .20 .50
35 Brandon Inge .20 .50
36 Luis Gonzalez .20 .50
37 Jeff Kent .20 .50
38 Ben Grieve .20 .50
39 Carlos Delgado .20 .50
40 Pat Burrell .20 .50
41 Mark Buehrle .20 .50
42 Cristian Guzman .20 .50
43 Shawn Green .20 .50
44 Nomar Garciaparra .75 2.00
45 Carlos Beltran .20 .50
46 Troy Glaus .20 .50
47 Paul Konerko .20 .50
48 Moises Alou .20 .50
49 Kerry Wood .20 .50
50 Jose Vidro .20 .50
51 Juan Encarnacion .20 .50
52 Bobby Abreu .20 .50
53 C.C. Sabathia .20 .50
54 Alex Rodriguez .75 2.00
55 Albert Pujols 1.00 2.50
56 Bret Boone .20 .50
57 Orlando Hernandez .20 .50
58 Jason Kendall .20 .50
59 Tim Hudson .20 .50
60 Darin Erstad .20 .50
61 Mike Mussina .30 .75
62 Ken Griffey Jr. .75 2.00
63 Adrian Beltre .20 .50
64 Jeff Bagwell .30 .75
65 Vladimir Guerrero .50 1.25
66 Mike Sweeney .20 .50
67 Sammy Sosa .50 1.25
68 Andruw Jones .30 .75
69 Richie Sexson .20 .50
70 Matt Morris .20 .50
71 Ivan Rodriguez .30 .75
72 Shannon Stewart .20 .50
73 Barry Bonds 1.25 3.00
74 Matt Williams .20 .50
75 Jason Giambi .20 .50
76 Brian Giles .20 .50
77 Cliff Floyd .20 .50
78 Tino Martinez .30 .75
79 Juan Gonzalez .20 .50
80 Frank Thomas .50 1.25
81 Ichiro Suzuki 1.00 2.50
82 Barry Zito .20 .50
83 Chipper Jones .50 1.25
84 Adam Dunn .20 .50
85 Kazuhiro Sasaki .20 .50
86 Mark Quinn .20 .50
87 Rafael Palmeiro .30 .75
88 Jeromy Burnitz .20 .50
89 Curt Schilling .20 .50
90 Chris Richard .20 .50
91 Jon Lieber .20 .50
92 Doug Mientkiewicz .20 .50
93 Roberto Alomar .30 .75
94 Rich Aurilia .20 .50
95 Eric Chavez .20 .50
96 Larry Walker .20 .50
97 Manny Ramirez .30 .75
98 Tony Clark .20 .50
99 Tsuyoshi Shinjo .20 .50
100 Josh Beckett .20 .50
101 Dewon Brazelton FF 2.00 5.00
102 Jeremy Lambert FF RC 2.00 5.00
103 Andres Torres FF 2.00 5.00
104 Matt Childers FF RC 2.00 5.00
105 Wilson Betemit FF 2.00 5.00
106 Willie Harris FF 2.00 5.00
107 Drew Henson FF 2.00 5.00
108 Rafael Soriano FF 2.00 5.00
109 Carlos Valderrama FF 2.00 5.00
110 Victor Martinez FF 3.00 8.00
111 Juan Rivera FF 2.00 5.00
112 Felipe Lopez FF 2.00 5.00
113 Brandon Duckworth FF 2.00 5.00
114 Jeremy Owens FF 2.00 5.00
115 Aaron Cook FF RC 2.00 5.00
116 Derrick Lewis FF 2.00 5.00
117 Mark Teixeira FF 3.00 8.00
118 Ken Harvey FF 2.00 5.00
119 Tim Spooneybarger FF 2.00 5.00
120 Bill Hall FF 2.00 5.00
121 Adam Pettyjohn FF 2.00 5.00
122 Ramon Castro FF 2.00 5.00
123 Marlon Byrd FF 2.00 5.00
124 Matt White FF 2.00 5.00
125 Eric Cyr FF 2.00 5.00
126 Morgan Ensberg FF 2.00 5.00
127 Horacio Ramirez FF 2.00 5.00
128 Ron Calloway FF RC 2.00 5.00
129 Nick Punto FF 2.00 5.00
130 Joe Kennedy FF 2.00 5.00
131 So Taguchi FF RC 3.00 8.00
132 Austin Kearns FF 2.00 5.00
133 Mark Prior FF 3.00 8.00
134 Kazuhisa Ishii FF RC 3.00 8.00
135 Steve Torrealba FF 2.00 5.00
136 Adam Walker FF RC 2.00 5.00
137 Travis Hafner FF 2.00 5.00
138 Zach Day FF 2.00 5.00

2002 Flair Collection

Randomly inserted into packs, this is a parallel set to the basic Flair set. These cards are serial numbered to 175 for the lower number cards and to 50 for the future fame set.

*COLLECTION 1-100: 3X TO 8X BASIC
*COLLECTION 101-138: 1X TO 2.5X BASIC

2002 Flair Jersey Heights

This 25-card set features game-used jersey swatches from a selection of major league stars. The cards were seeded into packs at a rate of 1:18 hobby and 1:100 retail. Though the cards are not serial-numbered in any way, representatives at Fleer confirmed that the following players were produced in slightly lower quantities: Barry Bonds, Roger Clemens, J.D. Drew; Greg Maddux and Alex Rodriguez. In addition, based upon analysis of secondary market trading volume by our staff, the following cards are perceived to be in greater supply: Jeff Bagwell, Jim Edmonds, Randy Johnson, Chipper Jones, Ivan Rodriguez, Curt Schilling and Larry Walker.

1 Edgardo Alfonzo 3.00 8.00
2 Jeff Bagwell * 3.00 8.00
3 Craig Biggio 3.00 8.00
4 Barry Bonds SP 10.00 25.00
5 Sean Casey 3.00 8.00
6 Roger Clemens SP 10.00 25.00
7 Carlos Delgado 3.00 8.00
8 J.D. Drew SP 3.00 8.00
9 Jim Edmonds * 3.00 8.00
10 Nomar Garciaparra 8.00 20.00
11 Shawn Green 3.00 8.00
12 Todd Helton 3.00 8.00
13 Derek Jeter * 10.00 25.00
14 Randy Johnson * 4.00 10.00
15 Chipper Jones * 4.00 10.00
16 Barry Larkin 3.00 8.00
17 Greg Maddux SP 6.00 15.00
18 Pedro Martinez 3.00 8.00
19 Rafael Palmeiro 3.00 8.00
20 Mike Piazza 6.00 15.00
21 Manny Ramirez 3.00 8.00
22 Alex Rodriguez SP 6.00 15.00
23 Ivan Rodriguez * 3.00 8.00
24 Curt Schilling * 3.00 8.00
25 Larry Walker * 3.00 8.00

2002 Flair Jersey Heights Dual Swatch

Randomly inserted in packs, these 12 cards features not only two players (usually teammates) with something in common but also a jersey swatch from each player featured. These cards have a stated print run of 100 serial numbered sets.

1 Randy Johnson 15.00 40.00
Curt Schilling
2 Pedro Martinez 40.00 80.00
Nomar Garciaparra
3 Edgardo Alfonzo 15.00 40.00
Mike Piazza
4 Derek Jeter 40.00 80.00
Roger Clemens
5 Greg Maddux 15.00 40.00
Chipper Jones
6 Jim Edmonds 10.00 25.00
J.D. Drew
7 Jeff Bagwell 15.00 40.00
Craig Biggio
8 Rafael Palmeiro 15.00 40.00
Ivan Rodriguez
9 Carlos Delgado 10.00 25.00
Shawn Green
10 Todd Helton 15.00 40.00
Larry Walker
11 Sean Casey 15.00 40.00
Barry Larkin
12 Alex Rodriguez 15.00 40.00
Manny Ramirez

2002 Flair Jersey Heights Hot Numbers Patch

Randomly inserted into packs, these 24 cards feature a jersey patch from the featured player. These cards have a stated print run of 100 serial numbered sets.

1 Edgardo Alfonzo 10.00 25.00
2 Jeff Bagwell 15.00 40.00
3 Craig Biggio 15.00 40.00
4 Sean Casey 10.00 25.00
5 Roger Clemens
6 Carlos Delgado 10.00 25.00
7 J.D. Drew 10.00 25.00
8 Jim Edmonds 10.00 25.00
9 Nomar Garciaparra 40.00 80.00
10 Shawn Green 10.00 25.00
11 Todd Helton 15.00 40.00
12 Derek Jeter 40.00 80.00
13 Randy Johnson 15.00 40.00
14 Chipper Jones 15.00 40.00
15 Barry Larkin 15.00 40.00
16 Greg Maddux 30.00 60.00
17 Pedro Martinez 15.00 40.00
18 Rafael Palmeiro 15.00 40.00
19 Mike Piazza 30.00 60.00
20 Manny Ramirez 15.00 40.00
21 Alex Rodriguez 30.00 60.00
22 Ivan Rodriguez 15.00 40.00
23 Curt Schilling 10.00 25.00
24 Larry Walker 10.00 25.00

2002 Flair Power Tools Bats

This 28-card set features game-used bat chips from a selection of major league stars. The cards were seeded into packs at a rate of 1:19 hobby and 1:123 retail. Though not serial-numbered, the following players were reported by Fleer as being short prints: Jeff Bagwell, Pat Burrell, J.D. Drew, Rafael Palmeiro, Scott Rolen, Reggie Sanders and Jim Thome. All of these cards are immeasurably tougher to pull from packs than others from this set. Please refer to our checklist for specific print run quantities on these short prints. In addition, based on market research by our staff, the following players appear to be in greater supply than other cards from this set: Bret Boone, Ivan Rodriguez and Tsuyoshi Shinjo.

1 Roberto Alomar 3.00 8.00
2 Jeff Bagwell SP/150 6.00 15.00
3 Craig Biggio 3.00 8.00
4 Barry Bonds 8.00 20.00
5 Bret Boone * 3.00 8.00
6 Pat Burrell SP/225 6.00 15.00
7 Eric Chavez 3.00 8.00
8 J.D. Drew SP/150 6.00 15.00
9 Jim Edmonds 3.00 8.00
10 Juan Gonzalez 3.00 8.00
11 Luis Gonzalez 3.00 8.00
12 Shawn Green 3.00 8.00
13 Derek Jeter 8.00 20.00
14 Doug Mientkiewicz 3.00 8.00
15 Magglio Ordonez 3.00 8.00
16 Rafael Palmeiro SP/100 6.00 15.00
17 Mike Piazza 6.00 15.00
18 Alex Rodriguez 6.00 15.00
19 Ivan Rodriguez * 3.00 8.00
20 Scott Rolen SP/42
21 Reggie Sanders SP/120 6.00 15.00
22 Gary Sheffield 3.00 8.00
23 Tsuyoshi Shinjo * 3.00 8.00
24 Miguel Tejada 3.00 8.00
25 Frank Thomas 4.00 10.00
26 Jim Thome SP/225 6.00 15.00
27 Larry Walker 3.00 8.00
28 Bernie Williams 3.00 8.00

2002 Flair Power Tools Dual Bats

Randomly inserted into packs, these 15 cards feature not only two players but bat chips from each of the featured players. A few cards were issued in lesser quantity and we have notated those cards along with the stated print run in our checklist. Please note that these cards are not serial numbered.

*GOLD: 1X TO 2.5X BASIC DUAL BAT
GOLD RANDOM INSERTS IN PACKS
GOLD PRINT RUN 50 SERIAL #'d SETS
GOLD CARDS 7 AND 13 DO NOT EXIST

1 Eric Chavez 6.00 15.00
Miguel Tejada
2 Barry Bonds 12.50 30.00
Tsuyoshi Shinjo
3 Jim Edmonds 6.00 15.00
J.D. Drew
4 Jeff Bagwell 10.00 25.00
Craig Biggio
5 Bernie Williams 15.00 40.00
Derek Jeter
6 Roberto Alomar 10.00 25.00
Mike Piazza
7 Sean Casey
Jim Thome SP/40
8 Pat Burrell 6.00 15.00
Scott Rolen
9 Gary Sheffield 6.00 15.00
Shawn Green
10 Ivan Rodriguez 10.00 25.00
Alex Rodriguez
11 Juan Gonzalez 6.00 15.00
Rafael Palmeiro
12 Magglio Ordonez 8.00 20.00
Frank Thomas
13 Larry Walker 6.00 15.00
Todd Helton SP/225
14 Luis Gonzalez 6.00 15.00
Reggie Sanders
15 Doug Mientkiewicz 6.00 15.00
Bret Boone

2002 Flair Sweet Swatch

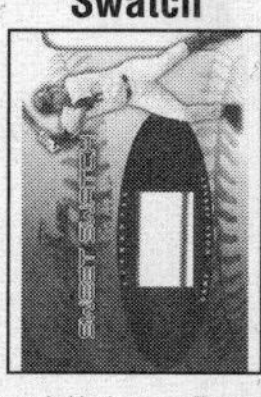

Issued one per hobby box as a "box-topper", these cards feature a larger jersey swatch from the featured players. Each player was issued to a different print run and we have notated the stated print run in our checklist.

1 Jeff Bagwell/490 6.00 15.00
2 Josh Beckett/500 6.00 15.00
3 Darin Erstad/525 6.00 15.00
4 Freddy Garcia/620 6.00 15.00
5 Brian Giles Pants/445 6.00 15.00
6 Juan Gonzalez/505 6.00 15.00
7 Mark Grace/795 6.00 15.00
8 Derek Jeter/525 15.00 40.00
9 Jason Kendall/990 6.00 15.00
10 Paul LoDuca/440 6.00 15.00
11 Greg Maddux/475 6.00 15.00
12 Magglio Ordonez/495 6.00 15.00
13 Rafael Palmeiro/535 6.00 15.00
14 Mike Piazza/1000 6.00 15.00
15 Alex Rodriguez/550 10.00 25.00
16 Ivan Rodriguez/475 6.00 15.00
17 Tim Salmon/465 6.00 15.00
18 Kazuhiro Sasaki/770 6.00 15.00
19 Alfonso Soriano/775 6.00 15.00
20 Larry Walker/430 6.00 15.00
21 Ted Williams/250 75.00 150.00

2002 Flair Sweet Swatch Bat Autograph

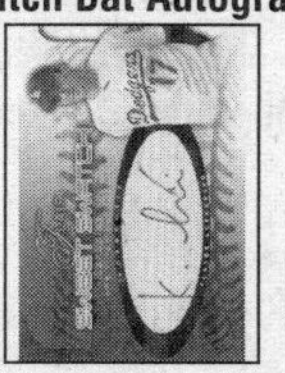

Randomly inserted as hobby box toppers, these cards feature not only a bat chip from the featured player but also an autograph. Each card was printed to a different amount and we have notated that stated print run information next to the player's name in our checklist. Some of the Drew Henson cards and all of the Derek Jeter cards were issued as exchange cards and those cards could be redeemed until April 30th, 2003.

GOLD PARALLELS RANDOM BOX-TOPPERS
GOLD PRINT RUN 15 SERIAL #'d SETS
GOLD NOT PRICED DUE TO SCARCITY

1 Barry Bonds/35 150.00 250.00
2 Dewon Brazelton/185 8.00 20.00
3 Marlon Byrd/185 8.00 20.00
4 Ron Cey/285 10.00 25.00
5 David Espinosa/485 8.00 20.00
6 Drew Henson/785 8.00 20.00
7 Kazuhisa Ishii/335 15.00 40.00
8 Derek Jeter/375 75.00 150.00
9 Al Kaline/285 30.00 60.00
10 Don Mattingly/85 100.00 200.00
11 Paul Molitor/85 20.00 50.00
12 Dale Murphy/285 40.00 80.00
13 Tony Perez/115 10.00 25.00
14 Mark Prior/285 10.00 25.00
15 Albert Pujols/50
16 Brooks Robinson/185 15.00 40.00
17 Dane Sardinha/485 8.00 20.00
18 Ben Sheets/85 20.00 50.00
19 Ozzie Smith/185 50.00 100.00
20 So Taguchi/335 15.00 40.00
21 Mark Teixeira/185 20.00 50.00
22 Maury Wills/285 10.00 25.00

2002 Flair Sweet Swatch Patch

This 20-card over-sized set is a premium parallel version of the basic Sweet Swatch inserts. The cards were randomly seeded exclusively into hobby boxes as box-toppers. Unlike the basic cards, each of these parallels features a piece of jersey patch (often with very colorful pieces of the player's name or a team logo taken from their game used jersey). Each card was serial-numbered by hand. In general, between 50-80 copies of each card were produced, but please reference our checklist for specific quantities. Ted Williams (15 copies) and Derek Jeter (20 copies) are the scarcest cards in this set. Also, Pirates outfielder Brian Giles was the only player to have a basic Sweet Swatch card that was NOT featured in this Patch parallel because Fleer used a pair of his game-used pants for the basic card (thus no patch swatches were available).

*PREMIUM PATCHES: 2X LISTED PRICES
1 OF 1 PARALLEL RANDOM BOX-TOPPER
NO 1 OF 1 PRICING DUE TO SCARCITY

1 Jeff Bagwell/45 30.00 60.00
2 Josh Beckett/60 15.00 40.00
3 Darin Erstad/50 15.00 40.00
4 Freddy Garcia/50 15.00 40.00
5 Juan Gonzalez/55 15.00 40.00
6 Mark Grace/75 30.00 60.00
7 Derek Jeter/20
8 Jason Kendall/120 10.00 25.00
9 Paul LoDuca/50 15.00 40.00
10 Greg Maddux/50 50.00 100.00
11 Magglio Ordonez/55 15.00 40.00
12 Rafael Palmeiro/60 30.00 60.00
13 Mike Piazza/95 40.00 80.00
14 Alex Rodriguez/50 50.00 100.00
15 Ivan Rodriguez/50 30.00 60.00
16 Tim Salmon/40 30.00 60.00
17 Kazuhiro Sasaki/80 15.00 40.00
18 Alfonso Soriano/35 15.00 40.00
19 Larry Walker/60 15.00 40.00
20 Ted Williams/15

2003 Flair

This 135 card set was issued in two separate releases. The primary Flair product was released in June, 2003. These cards were issued in five card packs with an $6 SRP which came 20 packs to a box and 12 boxes to a case. Cards numbered 1-90 feature veterans while cards numbered 91-125 feature rookies. The cards 91 through 125 were issued to a stated print run of 500 serial numbered sets. Cards 126-135 were randomly seeded into packs of Fleer Rookies and Greats of which was distributed in December, 2003. Each of these update cards featured a top prospect and was serial numbered to 500 copies.

COMP.LO SET w/o SP's (90) 10.00 25.00
COMMON CARD (1-90) .20 .50
COMMON CARD (91-135) 1.50 4.00
1 Hideo Nomo .50 1.25
2 Derek Jeter 1.25 3.00
3 Junior Spivey .20 .50
4 Rich Aurilia .20 .50
5 Luis Gonzalez .20 .50
6 Sean Burroughs .20 .50
7 Pedro Martinez .30 .75
8 Randy Winn .20 .50
9 Carlos Delgado .20 .50
10 Pat Burrell .20 .50
11 Barry Larkin .30 .75
12 Roberto Alomar .30 .75
13 Tony Batista .20 .50
14 Barry Bonds 1.25 3.00
15 Craig Biggio .30 .75
16 Ivan Rodriguez .30 .75
17 Javier Vazquez .20 .50
18 Joe Borchard .20 .50
19 Josh Phelps .20 .50
20 Omar Vizquel .30 .75
21 Tom Glavine .30 .75
22 Darin Erstad .20 .50
23 Hee Seop Choi .20 .50
24 Roger Clemens 1.00 2.50
25 Michael Cuddyer .20 .50
26 Mike Sweeney .20 .50
27 Phil Nevin .20 .50
28 Torii Hunter .20 .50
29 Vladimir Guerrero .50 1.25
30 Ellis Burks .20 .50
31 Jimmy Rollins .20 .50
32 Ken Griffey Jr. .75 2.00
33 Magglio Ordonez .20 .50
34 Mark Prior .30 .75
35 Mike Lieberthal .20 .50
36 Jorge Posada .30 .75
37 Rodrigo Lopez .20 .50
38 Todd Helton .30 .75
39 Adam Kennedy .20 .50
40 Curt Schilling .20 .50
41 Jim Thome .30 .75
42 Josh Beckett .20 .50
43 Carlos Pena .20 .50
44 Jason Kendall .20 .50
45 Sammy Sosa .50 1.25
46 Scott Rolen .30 .75
47 Alex Rodriguez .75 2.00
48 Aubrey Huff .20 .50
49 Bobby Abreu .20 .50
50 Jeff Kent .20 .50
51 Joe Randa .20 .50
52 Lance Berkman .20 .50
53 Orlando Cabrera .20 .50
54 Richie Sexson .20 .50
55 Albert Pujols .75 2.00
56 Alfonso Soriano .20 .50
57 Greg Maddux .75 2.00
58 Jason Giambi .20 .50
59 Jeff Bagwell .30 .75
60 Kerry Wood .20 .50
61 Manny Ramirez .30 .75
62 Eric Chavez .20 .50
63 Preston Wilson .20 .50
64 Shawn Green .20 .50
65 Shea Hillenbrand .20 .50
66 Austin Kearns .20 .50
67 Cliff Floyd .20 .50
68 Edgardo Alfonzo .20 .50
69 J.D. Drew .20 .50
70 Larry Walker .20 .50
71 Mike Piazza .75 2.00
72 Andruw Jones .30 .75
73 Ben Grieve .20 .50
74 Eric Hinske .20 .50
75 Geoff Jenkins .20 .50
76 Kazuhiro Sasaki .20 .50
77 Matt Morris .20 .50
78 Miguel Tejada .20 .50
79 Aramis Ramirez .20 .50
80 Troy Glaus .20 .50
81 Ichiro Suzuki .75 2.00
82 Mark Teixeira .30 .75
83 Nomar Garciaparra .75 2.00
84 Chipper Jones .50 1.25
85 Frank Thomas .50 1.25
86 Paul Lo Duca .20 .50
87 Bernie Williams .30 .75
88 Adam Dunn .20 .50
89 Randy Johnson .50 1.25
90 Barry Zito .20 .50
91 Lew Ford FF RC 2.50 6.00
92 Joe Valentine FF RC 1.50 4.00
93 Jhonny Peralta FF 2.50 6.00
94 Hideki Matsui FF RC 6.00 15.00
95 Francisco Rosario FF RC 1.50 4.00
96 Adam LaRoche FF 1.50 4.00
97 Josh Hall FF RC 1.50 4.00
98 Chien-Ming Wang FF RC 15.00 40.00
99 Josh Willingham FF RC 3.00 8.00
100 Guillermo Quiroz FF RC 1.50 4.00
101 Termel Sledge FF RC 1.50 4.00
102 Prentice Redman FF RC 1.50 4.00
103 Matt Bruback FF RC 1.50 4.00
104 Alejandro Machado FF RC 1.50 4.00
105 Shane Victorino FF RC 3.00 8.00
106 Chris Waters FF RC 1.50 4.00
107 Jose Contreras FF RC 2.50 6.00
108 Pete LaForest FF RC 1.50 4.00
109 Nook Logan FF RC 2.50 6.00
110 Hector Luna FF RC 1.50 4.00
111 Daniel Cabrera FF RC 2.50 6.00
112 Matt Kata FF RC 1.50 4.00
113 Rontrez Johnson FF RC 1.50 4.00
114 Josh Stewart FF RC 1.50 4.00
115 Michael Hessman FF RC 1.50 4.00
116 Felix Sanchez FF RC 1.50 4.00
117 Michel Hernandez FF RC 1.50 4.00
118 Arnaldo Munoz FF RC 1.50 4.00
119 Ian Ferguson FF RC 1.50 4.00
120 Clint Barmes FF RC 1.50 4.00
121 Brian Stokes FF RC 1.50 4.00
122 Craig Brazell FF RC 1.50 4.00
123 John Webb FF 1.50 4.00
124 Tim Olson FF RC 1.50 4.00
125 Jeremy Bonderman FF RC 5.00 12.00
126 Jeff Duncan RC 1.50 4.00
127 Rickie Weeks RC 3.00 8.00
128 Brandon Webb RC 4.00 10.00
129 Robby Hammock RC 1.50 4.00
130 Jon Leicester RC 1.50 4.00
131 Ryan Wagner RC 1.50 4.00
132 Bo Hart RC 1.50 4.00
133 Edwin Jackson RC 2.50 6.00
134 Sergio Mitre RC 2.50 6.00
135 Delmon Young RC 12.50 30.00

2003 Flair Collection Row 1

*ROW 1 1-90: 1.25X TO 3X BASIC
*ROW 1 91-125: .4X TO 1X BASIC
RANDOM INSERTS IN PACKS
STATED PRINT RUN 150 SERIAL #'d SETS
98 Chien-Ming Wang FF 20.00 50.00

2003 Flair Collection Row 2

RANDOM INSERTS IN PACKS
STATED PRINT RUN 25 SERIAL #'d SETS
NO PRICING DUE TO SCARCITY

2003 Flair Diamond Cuts Jersey

Issued at a stated rate of one in 10, these 15 cards feature jersey swatches from some of baseball's leading players.

STATED ODDS 1:10
*GOLD: 1X TO 2.5X BASIC
GOLD RANDOM INSERTS IN PACKS
GOLD PRINT RUN 100 SERIAL #'d SETS
AR Alex Rodriguez 4.00 10.00
AS Alfonso Soriano 2.00 5.00
BZ Barry Zito 2.00 5.00
CJ Chipper Jones 3.00 8.00
DJ Derek Jeter 6.00 15.00
GM Greg Maddux 4.00 10.00
JD J.D. Drew 2.00 5.00
MP Mike Piazza 4.00 10.00
PB Pat Burrell 2.00 5.00
RA Roberto Alomar 3.00 8.00
RC Roger Clemens 4.00 10.00
RO Roy Oswalt 2.00 5.00
SR Scott Rolen 3.00 8.00
TG Troy Glaus 2.00 5.00
VG Vladimir Guerrero 3.00 8.00

2003 Flair Hot Numbers Patch

Randomly inserted into packs, these 15 cards feature game-used "patch pieces" from leading baseball players. Each of these cards were issued to a stated print run of 100 serial numbered sets.

AR Alex Rodriguez 15.00 40.00
AS Alfonso Soriano 10.00 25.00
BZ Barry Zito 10.00 25.00
CJ Chipper Jones 12.50 30.00
DJ Derek Jeter 25.00 60.00
GM Greg Maddux 15.00 40.00
JD J.D. Drew 10.00 25.00
MP Mike Piazza 15.00 40.00
PB Pat Burrell 10.00 25.00
RA Roberto Alomar 12.50 30.00
RC Roger Clemens
RO Roy Oswalt 10.00 25.00
SR Scott Rolen 12.50 30.00
TG Troy Glaus 10.00 25.00
VG Vladimir Guerrero 12.50 30.00

2003 Flair Hot Numbers Dual Patch

Randomly inserted into packs, these cards feature two "patch" swatches from leading baseball players. Each of these cards were issued to a stated print run of 25 serial numbered sets and no pricing is available due to market scarcity.

ARVG Alex Rodriguez
Vladimir Guerrero
ASDJ Alfonso Soriano
Derek Jeter
ASRA Alfonso Soriano
Roberto Alomar
CJPB Chipper Jones
Pat Burrell
DJAR Derek Jeter
Alex Rodriguez
JDSR J.D. Drew
Scott Rolen
PBJD Pat Burrell
J.D. Drew
RAMP Roberto Alomar
Mike Piazza
SRCJ Scott Rolen
Chipper Jones
VGMP Vladimir Guerrero
Mike Piazza

2003 Flair Power Tools Bats

Randomly inserted into packs, these 18 cards feature game-used bat chips from leading players. Each of these cards were issued to a stated print run of 500 serial numbered sets.

*GOLD: .6X TO 1.5X BASIC
GOLD PRINT RUN 100 SERIAL #'d SETS
RANDOM INSERTS IN PACKS
AD Adam Dunn 3.00 8.00
AJ Andruw Jones 4.00 10.00
AK Austin Kearns 3.00 8.00
AR Alex Rodriguez 6.00 15.00
AS Alfonso Soriano 3.00 8.00
BW Bernie Williams 4.00 10.00
DJ Derek Jeter 8.00 20.00
HSC Hee-Seop Choi 3.00 8.00
JB Jeff Bagwell 4.00 10.00
JGI Jason Giambi 3.00 8.00
JGO Juan Gonzalez 3.00 8.00
JT Jim Thome 4.00 10.00
LB Lance Berkman 3.00 8.00
MP Mike Piazza 6.00 15.00
MT Miguel Tejada 3.00 8.00

NG Nomar Garciaparra 6.00 15.00
SR Scott Rolen 4.00 10.00
SS Sammy Sosa 4.00 10.00

2003 Flair Power Tools Dual Bats

Randomly inserted into packs, these cards feature two "game-used" bat chips of the featured players. Each of these cards were issued to a stated print run of 200 serial numbered sets.

ADAK Adam Dunn 6.00 15.00
Austin Kearns
ARNG Alex Rodriguez 12.50 30.00
Nomar Garciaparra
DJAS Derek Jeter 15.00 40.00
Alfonso Soriano
JGBW Jason Giambi 8.00 20.00
Bernie Williams
JGMP Jason Giambi 10.00 25.00
Mike Piazza
JTSS Jim Thome 8.00 20.00
Sammy Sosa
LBJB Lance Berkman 8.00 20.00
Jeff Bagwell
MTAR Miguel Tejada 8.00 20.00
Alex Rodriguez
NBDJ Nomar Garciaparra 15.00 40.00
Derek Jeter

2003 Flair Sweet Swatch Autos Jumbo

Randomly inserted in jumbo packs, these seven cards feature authentic autographs from leading players. There are three different varieties of Derek Jeter autographs. Please note that we have put the stated serial numbered print run next to the player's name in our checklist.

GOLD PRINT RUN 25 SERIAL #'d SETS
NO GOLD PRICING DUE TO SCARCITY
MASTERPIECE PRINT 1 SERIAL #'d SET
NO M'PIECE PRICING DUE TO SCARCITY
RANDOM INSERTS IN JUMBO PACKS
AD Adam Dunn/218 20.00 50.00
DJ Derek Jeter/312 60.00 120.00
DJA Derek Jeter/30
DJW Derek Jeter/50
JB Jeff Bagwell/218 20.00 50.00
RJ Randy Johnson/218 40.00 80.00
TG Troy Glaus/116 20.00 50.00

2003 Flair Sweet Swatch Jersey

Randomly inserted into packs, these 18 cards feature game-used jersey swatches from some of baseball's star players.

*JUMBO 50: 1X TO 2.5X BASIC
JUMBO 50 PRINT RUN 50 SERIAL #'d SETS
*JUMBO 150: .6X TO 1.5X BASIC
JUMBO 150 PRINT RUN 150 SERIAL #'d SETS
JUMBO MASTERPIECE 1 SERIAL #'d SET
NO JUMBO M'PIECE PRICING AVAILABLE
JUMBOS RANDOM IN JUMBO PACKS
SSAD Adam Dunn 3.00 8.00
SSAR Alex Rodriguez 6.00 15.00
SSAS Alfonso Soriano 3.00 8.00
SSBW Bernie Williams 4.00 10.00
SSCJ Chipper Jones 4.00 10.00
SSDJ Derek Jeter 8.00 20.00
SSHN Hideo Nomo 6.00 15.00
SSJG Jason Giambi 3.00 8.00
SSKS Kazuhiro Sasaki 3.00 8.00
SSLB Lance Berkman 3.00 8.00
SSMP Mark Prior 4.00 10.00
SSMT Miguel Tejada 3.00 8.00
SSNG Nomar Garciaparra 6.00 15.00
SSPM Pedro Martinez 4.00 10.00
SSRC Roger Clemens 6.00 15.00
SSRJ Randy Johnson 4.00 10.00
SSSS Sammy Sosa 4.00 10.00
SSVG Vladimir Guerrero 4.00 10.00

2003 Flair Sweet Swatch Jersey Jumbo

Inserted at a stated rate of one per jumbo pack, these 18 cards feature jersey swatches from some of baseball's leading players.

ADSSJ Adam Dunn/1090 3.00 8.00

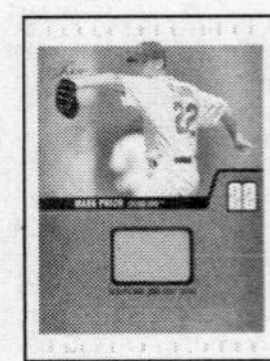

ARSSJ Alex Rodriguez/55 15.00 40.00
ASSSJ Alfonso Soriano/57
BWSSJ Bernie Williams/1420 4.00 10.00
CJSSJ Chipper Jones/80 10.00 25.00
DJSSJ Derek Jeter/47 20.00 50.00
HNSSJ Hideo Nomo/970 4.00 10.00
JGSSJ Jason Giambi/350 4.00 10.00
KSSSJ Kazuhiro Sasaki/505 4.00 10.00
LBSSJ Lance Berkman/1465 3.00 8.00
MPSSJ Mark Prior/1195 4.00 10.00
MTSSJ Miguel Tejada/518 4.00 10.00
NGSSJ Nomar Garciaparra/727 8.00 20.00
PMSSJ Pedro Martinez/1480 4.00 10.00
RCSSJ Roger Clemens/97 12.50 30.00
RJSSJ Randy Johnson/274 6.00 15.00
SSSSJ Sammy Sosa/279 6.00 15.00
VGSSJ Vladimir Guerrero/46 15.00 40.00

2003 Flair Sweet Swatch Jersey Dual Jumbo

Randomly inserted into jumbo packs, these eight cards feature two jersey swatches from some of baseball's leading players. Each of these cards were issued to a stated print run of 25 serial numbered sets and no pricing is available due to market scarcity.

ADLB Adam Dunn
Lance Berkman
DJBW Derek Jeter
Bernie Williams
JGAS Jason Giambi
Alfonso Soriano
KSHN Kazuhiro Sasaki
Hideo Nomo
MTAR Miguel Tejada
Alex Rodriguez
NMPM Nomar Garciaparra
Pedro Martinez
RJMP Randy Johnson
Mark Prior
VGCJ Vladimir Guerrero
Chipper Jones

2003 Flair Sweet Swatch Patch

Randomly inserted into packs, these 18 cards feature patches from some of baseball's superstars. Each of these cards were issued to a stated print run of 50 serial numbered sets.

SSPAD Adam Dunn
SSPAR Alex Rodriguez 20.00 50.00
SSPAS Alfonso Soriano 12.50 30.00
SSPBW Bernie Williams 15.00 40.00
SSPCJ Chipper Jones 15.00 40.00
SSPDJ Derek Jeter 30.00 80.00
SSPHN Hideo Nomo 15.00 40.00
SSPJG Jason Giambi 12.50 30.00
SSPKS Kazuhiro Sasaki 12.50 30.00
SSPLB Lance Berkman 12.50 30.00
SSPMP Mark Prior 15.00 40.00
SSPMT Miguel Tejada 12.50 30.00
SSPNG Nomar Garciaparra 20.00 50.00
SSPPM Pedro Martinez 15.00 40.00
SSPRC Roger Clemens 25.00 60.00
SSPRJ Randy Johnson 15.00 40.00
SSPSS Sammy Sosa 15.00 40.00
SSPVG Vladimir Guerrero 15.00 40.00

2003 Flair Sweet Swatch Patch Jumbo

Randomly inserted in jumbo packs, these 18 cards feature patch pieces of leading players. Each of these cards were produced to differing print runs and we have notated the print run next to the player's name in our checklist. If any card was issued to a stated print run of 25 or fewer cards, there is no pricing due to market scarcity.

ADSSPE Adam Dunn/130 12.50 30.00
ARSSPE Alex Rodriguez/298 20.00 50.00
ASSSPE Alfonso Soriano/28
BWSSPE Bernie Williams/123 15.00 40.00
CJSSPE Chipper Jones/284 12.50 30.00
DJSSPE Derek Jeter/35
HNSSPE Hideo Nomo/114 25.00 60.00
JGSSPE Jason Giambi/26
KSSSPE Kazuhiro Sasaki/90 12.50 30.00
LBSSPE Lance Berkman/287 10.00 25.00
MPSSPE Mark Prior/290 12.50 30.00
MTSSPE Miguel Tejada/183 10.00 25.00
NGSSPE Nomar Garciaparra/124 20.00 50.00
PMSSPE Pedro Martinez/185 12.50 30.00
RCSSPE Roger Clemens/1
RJSSPE Randy Johnson/46 20.00 50.00
SSSSPE Sammy Sosa/190 12.50 30.00
VGSSPE Vladimir Guerrero/290 12.50 30.00

2003 Flair Wave of the Future Memorabilia

Randomly inserted into packs, these six cards feature not only some of the up and coming young prospects but also an game-used memorabilia piece. Each of these cards were issued to a stated print run of 500 serial numbered sets.

*GOLD: .6X TO 1.5X BASIC
GOLD PRINT RUN 100 SERIAL #'d SETS
RANDOM INSERTS IN PACKS
AH Aubrey Huff Bat 3.00 8.00
AK Austin Kearns Jsy 3.00 8.00
CC Carl Crawford Bat 3.00 8.00
HB Hank Blalock Bat 3.00 8.00
JP Josh Phelps Jsy 3.00 8.00
SB Sean Burroughs Jsy 3.00 8.00

2004 Flair

This 82 card set was released in April, 2004. It was issued in 12-card hobby packs with an $120 SRP packs (little boxes) which were packed 12 to a case. This set was also issued in four-card retail packs with an $3 SRP. The retail packs were issued 24 packs to a box and 20 boxes to a case. The first 60 cards in this set feature veterans while the final 22 cards feature leading rookies and prospects entering the 2004 season. The final 22 cards were issued at a stated rate of one per hobby pack and one in 200 retail packs and were issued to a stated print run of 799 serial numbered sets.

COMMON CARD (61-82) 1.50 4.00
1 Brandon Webb .60 1.50
2 Todd Helton .75 2.00
3 Jeff Bagwell .75 2.00
4 Shawn Green .60 1.50
5 Vladimir Guerrero 1.25 3.00
6 Tom Glavine .75 2.00
7 Jason Giambi .60 1.50
8 Barry Zito .60 1.50
9 Jason Kendall .60 1.50
10 Carlos Delgado .60 1.50
11 Curt Schilling .75 2.00
12 Ken Griffey Jr. 2.00 5.00
13 Mike Piazza 2.00 5.00
14 Alfonso Soriano .60 1.50
15 Albert Pujols 2.50 6.00
16 Chipper Jones 1.25 3.00
17 Alex Rodriguez 2.00 5.00
18 Miguel Tejada .60 1.50
19 Pedro Martinez .75 2.00
20 Mark Prior .75 2.00
21 Magglio Ordonez .60 1.50
22 Scott Podsednik .60 1.50
23 Shannon Stewart .60 1.50
24 Rocco Baldelli .60 1.50
25 Darin Erstad .60 1.50
26 Omar Vizquel .75 2.00
27 Angel Berroa .60 1.50
28 Jose Vidro .60 1.50
29 Rich Harden .60 1.50
30 Andruw Jones .75 2.00
31 Troy Glaus .60 1.50
32 Sammy Sosa 1.25 3.00
33 Dontrelle Willis .75 2.00
34 Ivan Rodriguez .75 2.00
35 Nomar Garciaparra 2.00 5.00
36 Josh Beckett .60 1.50
37 Jose Reyes .60 1.50
38 Scott Rolen .75 2.00
39 Greg Maddux 2.00 5.00
40 Andy Pettitte .75 2.00
41 Jason Schmidt .60 1.50
42 Edgar Martinez .75 2.00
43 Manny Ramirez .75 2.00
44 Torii Hunter .60 1.50
45 Mark Teixeira .75 2.00
46 Hideo Nomo 1.25 3.00
47 Brian Giles .60 1.50
48 Adam Dunn .60 1.50
49 Fernando Vina .60 1.50
50 Hideki Matsui 2.00 5.00
51 Jim Thome .75 2.00
52 Hank Blalock .60 1.50
53 Miguel Cabrera .75 2.00
54 Randy Johnson 1.25 3.00
55 Javy Lopez .60 1.50
56 Frank Thomas 1.25 3.00
57 Roger Clemens 2.50 6.00
58 Marlon Byrd .60 1.50
59 Derek Jeter 2.50 6.00
60 Ichiro Suzuki 2.50 6.00
61 Kaz Matsui C04 RC 2.00 5.00
62 Chad Bentz C04 RC 1.50 4.00
63 Greg Dobbs C04 RC 1.50 4.00
64 John Gall C04 RC 2.00 5.00
65 Cory Sullivan C04 RC 1.50 4.00
66 Hector Gimenez C04 RC 1.50 4.00
67 Graham Koonce C04 1.50 4.00
68 Jason Bartlett C04 RC 2.00 5.00
69 Angel Chavez C04 RC 1.50 4.00
70 Ronny Cedeno C04 RC 2.00 5.00
71 Don Kelly C04 RC 1.50 4.00
72 Ivan Ochoa C04 RC 1.50 4.00
73 Ruddy Yan C04 1.50 4.00
74 Mike Gosling C04 RC 1.50 4.00
75 Alfredo Simon C04 RC 1.50 4.00
76 Jerome Gamble C04 RC 1.50 4.00
77 Chris Aguila C04 RC 1.50 4.00
78 Mike Rouse C04 RC 1.50 4.00
79 Justin Leone C04 RC 2.00 5.00
80 Merkin Valdez C04 RC 2.00 5.00
81 Aaron Baldiris C04 RC 2.00 5.00
82 Chris Shelton C04 RC 2.00 5.00

2004 Flair Collection Row 1

*ROW 1 1-60: 1.25X TO 3X BASIC
*ROW 1 61-82: .6X TO 1.5X BASIC
OVERALL PARALLEL ODDS 1:6 HOBBY
ROW 1 STATED ODDS 1:55 RETAIL
STATED PRINT RUN 100 SERIAL #'d SETS
61 Kaz Matsui C04 3.00 8.00

2004 Flair Collection Row 2

OVERALL PARALLEL ODDS 1:6 HOBBY
STATED PRINT RUN 1 SERIAL #'d SET
NO PRICING DUE TO SCARCITY

2004 Flair Autograph

PRINT RUNS B/WN 60-280 COPIES PER
*CROWN: .4X TO 1X p/r 122-280
*CROWN: .4X TO 1X p/r 60-96
CROWN PRINT RUN 100 SERIAL #'d SETS
MASTERPIECE PRINT RUN 1 SER.#'d SET
NO M'PIECE PRICING DUE TO SCARCITY
*PARCHMENT: .75X TO 2X p/r 122-280
*PARCHMENT: .6X TO 1.5X p/r 60-96
PARCHMENT PRINT RUN 25 SER.#'d SETS
NO RC YR PARCHMENT PRICING AVAIL.
PLATINUM PRINT RUN 10 SERIAL #'d SETS
NO PLATINUM PRICING DUE TO SCARCITY
OVERALL AU ODDS 1:1 HOBBY
OVERALL AU-GU ODDS 1:24 RETAIL
AB1 Aarom Baldiris/180 4.00 10.00
AB2 Angel Berroa/178 4.00 10.00
AJ Andruw Jones/163 10.00 25.00
ALR Adam LaRoche/280 4.00 10.00
AR Alexis Rios/185 6.00 15.00
BC Bobby Crosby/87 10.00 25.00
BN Bubba Nelson/185 4.00 10.00
BW Brandon Webb/122 4.00 10.00
CMW Chien-Ming Wang/178 75.00 150.00
CP Corey Patterson/172 4.00 10.00
CS Chris Shelton/170 8.00 20.00
DH Dan Haren/95 4.00 10.00
DW Dontrelle Willis/73 15.00 40.00
DY Delmon Young/177 10.00 25.00
EJ Edwin Jackson/193 4.00 10.00
GA Garrett Atkins/193 4.00 10.00
GK Graham Koonce/175 4.00 10.00
GS Grady Sizemore/197 15.00 40.00
JB1 Jason Bartlett/95 6.00 15.00
JB2 Josh Beckett/65 15.00 40.00
JE Jim Edmonds/73 15.00 40.00
JG John Gall/94 6.00 15.00
JL Josh Labandeira/166 4.00 10.00
JP Juan Pierre/94 6.00 15.00
JUL Justin Leone/180 6.00 15.00
JV Javier Vazquez/187 6.00 15.00
KG Khalil Greene/195 10.00 25.00
KWO Kerry Wood/73 15.00 40.00
MC Miguel Cabrera/172 10.00 25.00
MM Mike Mussina/69 15.00 40.00
MN Michael Nakamura/180 4.00 10.00
MP Mark Prior/60 12.50 30.00
MR Mike Rouse/195 4.00 10.00
MV Merkin Valdez/179 4.00 10.00
RB Rocco Baldelli/180 6.00 15.00
RH Ryan Howard/185 30.00 60.00
RM Ryan Meaux/180 4.00 10.00
RW1 Ryan Wagner/175 4.00 10.00
RW2 Rickie Weeks/169 6.00 15.00
SP Scott Podsednik/96 15.00 40.00

2004 Flair Autograph Die Cut

OVERALL AU ODDS 1:1 HOBBY
PRINT RUNS B/WN 10-113 COPIES PER
NO PRICING ON QTY OF 19 OR LESS
AB1 Aarom Baldiris/17
AB2 Angel Berroa/17
ALR Adam LaRoche/10
BC Bobby Crosby/102 10.00 25.00
BN Bubba Nelson/10
BW Brandon Webb/10
CMW Chien-Ming Wang/17
CP Corey Patterson/16
CS Chris Shelton/17
DH Dan Haren/10
DW Dontrelle Willis/10
EJ Edwin Jackson/16
GA Garrett Atkins/10
JB1 Jason Bartlett/113 6.00 15.00
JG John Gall/94 6.00 15.00
JL Josh Labandeira/19
JP Juan Pierre/80 10.00 25.00
KG Khalil Greene/10
MC Miguel Cabrera/14
MN Michael Nakamura/10
RH Ryan Howard/10
RM Ryan Meaux/10
RW1 Ryan Wagner/16
RW2 Rickie Weeks/16
SP Scott Podsednik/84 15.00 40.00

2004 Flair Cuts and Glory 100

STATED PRINT RUN 100 SERIAL #'d SETS
*CUTS/GLORY 50: .5X TO 1X BASIC
CUTS/GLORY 50 PRINT RUN 50 #'d SETS
CUTS/GLORY 15 PRINT RUN 15 #'d SETS
C/G 15 NO PRICING DUE TO SCARCITY
CUTS/GLORY 3 PRINT RUN 3 #'d SETS
C/G 3 NO PRICING DUE TO SCARCITY
CUTS/GLORY 1 PRINT RUN 1 #'d SETS
C/G 1 NO PRICING DUE TO SCARCITY
OVERALL AU ODDS 1:1 HOBBY
OVERALL AU-GU ODDS 1:24 RETAIL
EXCHANGE DEADLINE INDEFINITE
AD Adam Dunn 15.00 40.00
AK Austin Kearns 6.00 15.00
AP Albert Pujols 150.00 250.00
CD Carlos Delgado 15.00 40.00
CJ Chipper Jones 30.00 60.00
EG Eric Gagne 15.00 40.00
EM Edgar Martinez 15.00 40.00
FT Frank Thomas 30.00 60.00
GA Garret Anderson 10.00 25.00
GM Greg Maddux EXCH 50.00 100.00
HB Hank Blalock 10.00 25.00
JR Jose Reyes 10.00 25.00
LG Luis Gonzalez 10.00 25.00
MB Marlon Byrd 6.00 15.00
MO Magglio Ordonez 10.00 25.00
MT Mark Teixeira 15.00 40.00
RH Ricky Henderson 40.00 80.00
RJ Randy Johnson 30.00 60.00
SR Scott Rolen 15.00 40.00
TH Torii Hunter 10.00 25.00
VG Vladimir Guerrero 20.00 50.00

2004 Flair Diamond Cuts Game Used Blue

STATED PRINT RUN 250 SERIAL #'d SETS
*BLUE DC: 1X TO 2.5X BLUE
BLUE DC PRINT RUN 25 SERIAL #'d SETS
*COPPER: .6X TO 1.5X BLUE
COPPER PRINT RUN 75 SERIAL #'d SETS
COPPER DC PRINT RUN 8 SERIAL #'d SETS
NO COPPER DC PRICING DUE TO SCARCITY
*GOLD p/r 38-55: 1.25X TO 3X BLUE
*GOLD p/r 21-35: 1.5X TO 4X BLUE
GOLD PRINT RUNS B/WN 2-55 COPIES PER
NO GOLD PRICING ON QTY OF 10 OR LESS
GOLD DC PRINT RUN 3 SERIAL #'d SETS
NO GOLD DC PRICING DUE TO SCARCITY
*PEWTER: .5X TO 1.2X BLUE
PEWTER PRINT RUN 125 SERIAL #'d SETS
PEWTER DC PRINT RUN 13 SER.#'d SETS
NO PEWTER DC PRICING DUE TO SCARCITY
*PLATINUM p/r 36-43: 1.25X TO 3X BLUE
*PLATINUM p/r 21-29: 1.5X TO 4X BLUE
*PLATINUM p/r 16-18: 2X TO 5X BLUE
PLAT.PRINT RUNS B/WN 5-43 COPIES PER
NO PLAT.PRICING ON QTY OF 14 OR LESS
PLATINUM DC PRINT RUN 1 SERIAL #'d SET
NO PLATINUM DC PRICING DUE TO SCARCITY
PURPLE PRINT RUN 1 SERIAL #'d SET
NO PURPLE PRICING DUE TO SCARCITY
*RED: .4X TO 1X BLUE
RED PRINT RUN 175 SERIAL #'d SETS
RED DC: 1.25X TO 3X BLUE
RED DC PRINT RUN 18 SERIAL #'d SETS
*SILVER: 1.25X TO 3X BLUE
SILVER PRINT RUN 50 SERIAL #'d SETS
SILVER DC PRINT RUN 5 SERIAL #'d SETS
NO SILVER DC PRICING DUE TO SCARCITY
OVERALL GU ODDS 3 PER HOBBY PACK
ALL ARE JERSEY CARDS UNLESS NOTED
AJ Andruw Jones 3.00 8.00
ALP Albert Pujols 6.00 15.00
ANP Andy Pettitte 3.00 8.00
CJ Chipper Jones 3.00 8.00
CS Curt Schilling 3.00 8.00
DJ Derek Jeter 6.00 15.00
DW Dontrelle Willis 3.00 8.00
HB Hank Blalock 2.00 5.00
HM Hideki Matsui Base 6.00 15.00
IS Ichiro Suzuki Base 6.00 15.00
JB Josh Beckett 2.00 5.00
JR Jose Reyes 2.00 5.00
MAP Mark Prior 3.00 8.00
MIP Mike Piazza 5.00 12.00
MT Mark Teixeira 3.00 8.00
NG Nomar Garciaparra 5.00 12.00
PM Pedro Martinez 3.00 8.00
RC Roger Clemens 6.00 15.00
SR Scott Rolen 3.00 8.00
SS Sammy Sosa 3.00 8.00

2004 Flair Diamond Cuts Game Used Dual Gold

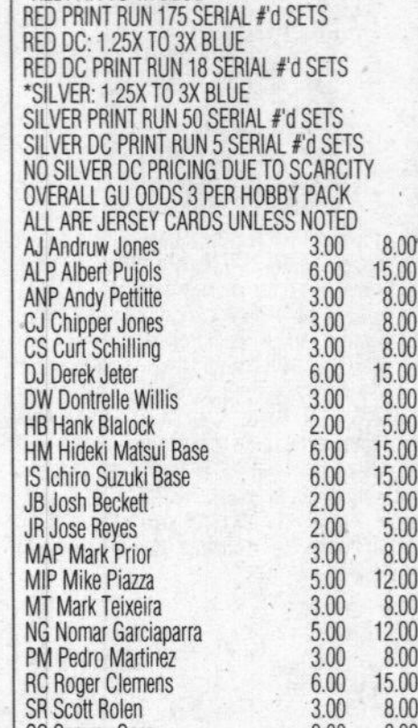

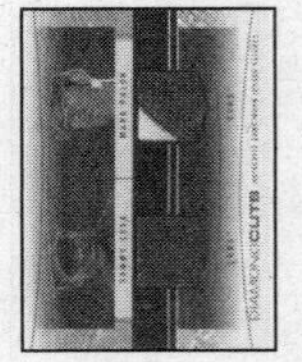

OVERALL GU ODDS 3 PER HOBBY PACK
STATED PRINT RUN 10 SERIAL #'d SETS
NO PRICING DUE TO SCARCITY
CJAJ Chipper Jones
Andruw Jones
CSPM Curt Schilling
Pedro Martinez
HBMT Hank Blalock
Mark Teixeira
ISHM Ichiro Suzuki
(Hideki Matsui
JBDW Josh Beckett
Dontrelle Willis
JRMP Jose Reyes
Mike Piazza
NGDJ Nomar Garciaparra
Derek Jeter
RCAP Roger Clemens
Andy Pettitte
SRAP Scott Rolen
Albert Pujols
SSMP Sammy Sosa
Mark Prior

2004 Flair Hot Numbers

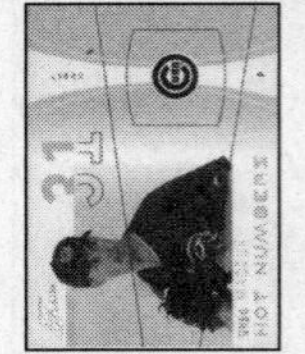

STATED ODDS 1:16 RETAIL
STATED PRINT RUN 500 SERIAL #'d SETS
*GOLD p/r 51-75: .75X TO 2X BASIC
*GOLD p/r 38-48: 1X TO 2.5X BASIC
*GOLD p/r 21-35: 1.25X TO 3X BASIC
*GOLD p/r 17: 1.5X TO 4X BASIC
GOLD ODDS 1:275 RETAIL
GOLD PRINT RUNS B/WN 2-75 COPIES PER
NO GOLD PRICING ON QTY OF 13 OR LESS
1 Chipper Jones 2.00 5.00
2 Derek Jeter 4.00 10.00
3 Alex Rodriguez 3.00 8.00
4 Torii Hunter 1.50 4.00
5 Nomar Garciaparra 3.00 8.00
6 Troy Glaus 1.50 4.00
7 Tom Glavine 2.00 5.00
8 Albert Pujols 4.00 10.00
9 Kerry Wood 1.50 4.00
10 Hideo Nomo 2.00 5.00
11 Rocco Baldelli 1.50 4.00
12 Mark Prior 2.00 5.00
13 Hank Blalock 1.50 4.00
14 Mark Teixeira 2.00 5.00
15 Curt Schilling 2.00 5.00
16 Randy Johnson 2.00 5.00
17 Barry Larkin 2.00 5.00
18 Vladimir Guerrero 2.00 5.00
19 Brandon Webb 1.50 4.00
20 Todd Helton 2.00 5.00
21 Jeff Bagwell 2.00 5.00
22 Barry Zito 1.50 4.00
23 Sammy Sosa 2.00 5.00
24 Pedro Martinez 2.00 5.00
25 Jim Thome 2.00 5.00
26 Frank Thomas 2.00 5.00

27 Greg Maddux 3.00 8.00
28 Jason Giambi 1.50 4.00
29 Manny Ramirez 2.00 5.00
30 Josh Beckett 1.50 4.00
31 Mike Piazza 3.00 8.00
32 Hideki Matsui 3.00 8.00
33 Ichiro Suzuki 4.00 10.00
34 Ken Griffey Jr. 3.00 8.00
35 Mike Mussina 2.00 5.00

2004 Flair Hot Numbers Game Used Blue

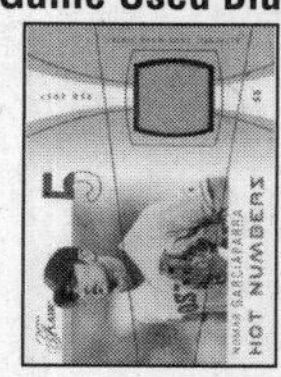

STATED PRINT RUN 250 SERIAL #'d SETS
*BLUE DC: 1X TO 2.5X BLUE
BLUE DC PRINT RUN 25 SERIAL #'d SETS
COPPER: .6X TO 1.5X BLUE
COPPER PRINT RUN 75 SERIAL #'d SETS
COPPER DC PRINT RUN 8 SERIAL #'d SETS
NO COPPER DC PRICING DUE TO SCARCITY
*GOLD p/r 38-55: 1.25X TO 3X BLUE
*GOLD p/r 21-35: 1.5X TO 4X BLUE
*GOLD p/r 17: 2X TO 5X BLUE
GOLD PRINT RUNS B/WN 2-55 COPIES PER
NO GOLD PRICING ON QTY OF 13 OR LESS
GOLD DC PRINT RUN 3 SERIAL #'d SETS
NO GOLD DC PRICING DUE TO SCARCITY
*PEWTER: .5X TO 1.2X BLUE
PEWTER PRINT RUN 125 SERIAL #'d SETS
PEWTER DC PRINT RUN 13 SER.#'d SETS
NO PEWTER DC PRICING DUE TO SCARCITY
*PLATINUM p/r 37-47: 1.25X TO 3X BLUE
*PLATINUM p/r 25-33: 1.5X TO 4X BLUE
*PLATINUM p/r 16-18: 2X TO 5X BLUE
PLAT.PRINT RUNS B/WN 2-47 COPIES PER
NO PLAT.PRICING ON QTY OF 14 OR LESS
PLATINUM DC PRINT RUN 1 SERIAL #'d SET
NO PLAT.DC PRICING DUE TO SCARCITY
PURPLE PRINT RUN 1 SERIAL #'d SET
NO PURPLE PRICING DUE TO SCARCITY
*RED: .4X TO 1X BLUE
RED PRINT RUN 175 SERIAL #'d SETS
*RED DC: 1.25X TO 3X BLUE
RED DC PRINT RUN 18 SERIAL #'d SETS
*SILVER: 1.25X TO 3X BLUE
SILVER PRINT RUN 50 SERIAL #'d SETS
SILVER DC PRINT RUN 5 SERIAL #'d SETS
NO SILVER DC PRICING DUE TO SCARCITY
OVERALL GU ODDS 3 PER HOBBY PACK
AP Albert Pujols 6.00 15.00
AR Alex Rodriguez 6.00 15.00
BL Barry Larkin 3.00 8.00
BW Brandon Webb 2.00 5.00
CJ Chipper Jones 3.00 8.00
CS Curt Schilling 3.00 8.00
DJ Derek Jeter 6.00 15.00
FT Frank Thomas 3.00 8.00
GM Greg Maddux 5.00 12.00
HB Hank Blalock 2.00 5.00
HN Hideo Nomo 3.00 8.00
JEB Jeff Bagwell 3.00 8.00
JG Jason Giambi 2.00 5.00
JOB Josh Beckett 2.00 5.00
JT Jim Thome 3.00 8.00
KW Kerry Wood 2.00 5.00
MAP Mark Prior 3.00 8.00
MIP Mike Piazza 5.00 12.00
MM Mike Mussina 3.00 8.00
MR Manny Ramirez 3.00 8.00
MT Mark Teixeira 3.00 8.00
NG Nomar Garciaparra 5.00 12.00
PM Pedro Martinez 3.00 8.00
RB Rocco Baldelli 2.00 5.00
RJ Randy Johnson 3.00 8.00
SS Sammy Sosa 3.00 8.00
TH Todd Helton 3.00 8.00
TOG Tom Glavine 3.00 8.00
TRG Troy Glaus 2.00 5.00
VG Vladimir Guerrero 3.00 8.00

2004 Flair Lettermen

OVERALL GU ODDS 3 PER HOBBY PACK
PRINT RUNS B/WN 4-11 COPIES PER
NO PRICING DUE TO SCARCITY
AP Albert Pujols/6
AR Alex Rodriguez/9
DW Dontrelle Willis/5
HB Hank Blalock/7
HN Hideo Nomo/4
JB Josh Beckett/7
JT Jim Thome/5
MP Mark Prior/5
MT Mark Teixeira/8
NG Nomar Garciaparra/11
PM Pedro Martinez/8
RB Rocco Baldelli/8
SS Sammy Sosa/4
TH Torii Hunter/6
VG Vladimir Guerrero/8

2004 Flair Power Tools Game Used Blue

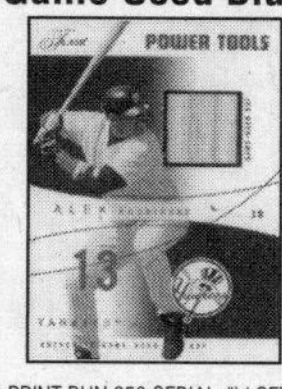

STATED PRINT RUN 250 SERIAL #'d SETS
*BLUE DC: 1X TO 2.5X BLUE
BLUE DC PRINT RUN 25 SERIAL #'d SETS
*COPPER: .75X TO 2X BLUE
COPPER PRINT RUN 75 SERIAL #'d SETS
COPPER DC PRINT RUN 8 SERIAL #'d SETS
NO COPPER DC PRICING DUE TO SCARCITY
*GOLD p/r 44: 1.5X TO 4X BLUE
*GOLD p/r 20-31: 2X TO 5X BLUE
GOLD PRINT RUNS B/WN 2-44 COPIES PER
NO GOLD PRICING ON QTY OF 13 OR LESS
GOLD DC PRINT RUN 3 SERIAL #'d SETS
NO GOLD DC PRICING DUE TO SCARCITY
*PEWTER: .75X TO 2X BLUE
PEWTER PRINT RUN 125 SERIAL #'d SETS
PEWTER DC 13 SERIAL #'d SETS
NO PEWTER DC PRICING DUE TO SCARCITY
*PLATINUM p/r 37-47: 1.5X TO 4X BLUE
*PLATINUM p/r 25-30: 2X TO 5X BLUE
PLAT.PRINT RUN B/WN 10-47 COPIES PER
NO PLAT.PRICING ON QTY OF 11 OR LESS
PLATINUM DC PRINT RUN 1 SERIAL #'d SET
NO PLAT.DC PRICING DUE TO SCARCITY
PURPLE PRINT RUN 1 SERIAL #'d SET
NO PURPLE PRICING DUE TO SCARCITY
*RED: .4X TO 1X BLUE
RED PRINT RUN 175 SERIAL #'d SETS
*RED DC: 1.25X TO 3X BLUE
RED DC PRINT RUN 18 SERIAL #'d SETS
*SILVER: 1X TO 2.5X BLUE
SILVER PRINT RUN 50 SERIAL #'d SETS
SILVER DC PRINT RUN 5 SERIAL #'d SETS
NO SILVER DC PRICING DUE TO SCARCITY
OVERALL GU ODDS 3 PER HOBBY PACK
AD Adam Dunn 2.00 5.00
AP Albert Pujols 6.00 15.00
AR Alex Rodriguez 6.00 15.00
AS Alfonso Soriano 2.00 5.00
CJ Chipper Jones 3.00 8.00
DJ Derek Jeter 6.00 15.00
JG Jason Giambi 2.00 5.00
JP Jorge Posada 3.00 8.00
JT Jim Thome 3.00 8.00
MP Mike Piazza 5.00 12.00
MR Manny Ramirez 3.00 8.00
NG Nomar Garciaparra 5.00 12.00
RB Rocco Baldelli 2.00 5.00
SS Sammy Sosa 3.00 8.00
VG Vladimir Guerrero 3.00 8.00

2004 Flair Significant Cuts

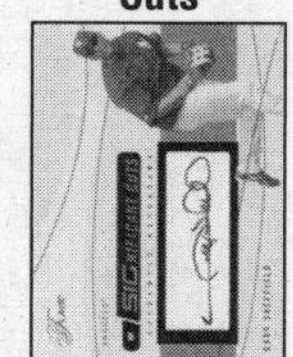

OVERALL AU ODDS 1:1 HOBBY
PRINT RUNS B/WN 1-200 COPIES PER
NO PRICING ON QTY OF 10 OR LESS
AP1 Andy Pettitte/50 30.00 60.00
AP2 Albert Pujols/20
BL Barry Larkin/75 15.00 40.00
BR Babe Ruth/1
BT Bill Terry/3
CG Charlie Gehringer/2
CJ Chipper Jones/22
CR Cal Ripken/25 150.00 250.00
DE Dennis Eckersley/75 15.00 40.00
DM Don Mattingly/25 60.00 120.00
ES Enos Slaughter/3
FF Frankie Frisch/1
GS Gary Sheffield/50 15.00 40.00
IR Ivan Rodriguez/50 20.00 50.00
JB1 Josh Beckett/10
JB2 Johnny Bench/25 30.00 60.00
JR Jose Reyes/25 12.50 30.00
JS John Smoltz/75 30.00 60.00
MR Mariano Rivera/50 40.00 80.00
MS Mike Schmidt/25 75.00 150.00
MT Miguel Tejada/25 20.00 50.00
NR Nolan Ryan/25 100.00 175.00
PM Paul Molitor/75 10.00 25.00
RA Roberto Alomar/50 15.00 40.00
RH Roy Halladay/50 10.00 25.00
RP Rafael Palmeiro/25 30.00 60.00
TC Ty Cobb/3
VC Vince Carter/200 20.00 40.00

2005 Flair

COMMON CARD (1-50) .60 1.50
COMMON CARD (51-80) 1.50 4.00
51-80 ODDS 1:1 HOBBY, 1:130 RETAIL
51-80 PRINT RUN 699 SERIAL #'d SETS
COMMON CARD (81-90) 1.50 4.00
81-90 ODDS 1:2 HOBBY, 1:240 RETAIL
81-90 PRINT RUN 699 SERIAL #'d SETS
1 Curt Schilling .75 2.00
2 Jim Thome .75 2.00
3 Miguel Cabrera .75 2.00
4 Randy Johnson 1.25 3.00
5 David Ortiz 1.25 3.00
6 Vladimir Guerrero 1.25 3.00
7 Nomar Garciaparra 1.25 3.00
8 Ivan Rodriguez .75 2.00
9 Jason Schmidt .60 1.50
10 Khalil Greene .75 2.00
11 Jose Vidro .60 1.50
12 Lyle Overbay .60 1.50
13 Todd Helton .75 2.00
14 Vernon Wells .60 1.50
15 B.J. Upton .60 1.50
16 Hideki Matsui 2.00 5.00
17 Pedro Martinez .75 2.00
18 Victor Martinez .60 1.50
19 Adam Dunn .60 1.50
20 Andruw Jones .75 2.00
21 Jeff Bagwell .75 2.00
22 Mike Sweeney .60 1.50
23 Mike Piazza 1.25 3.00
24 Ben Sheets .60 1.50
25 Adrian Beltre .60 1.50
26 Chipper Jones 1.25 3.00
27 Greg Maddux 2.00 5.00
28 Manny Ramirez .75 2.00
29 Roger Clemens 2.00 5.00
30 Johan Santana 1.25 3.00
31 Derek Jeter 2.50 6.00
32 Jason Bay .60 1.50
33 Ken Griffey Jr. 2.00 5.00
34 Miguel Tejada .60 1.50
35 Richie Sexson .60 1.50
36 Scott Rolen .75 2.00
37 Alfonso Soriano .60 1.50
38 Ichiro Suzuki 2.50 6.00
39 Sammy Sosa 1.25 3.00
40 Barry Zito .60 1.50
41 Kaz Matsui .60 1.50
42 Mark Teixeira .75 2.00
43 Carlos Beltran .60 1.50
44 Mark Prior .75 2.00
45 Travis Hafner .60 1.50
46 Alex Rodriguez 2.00 5.00
47 Lew Ford .60 1.50
48 Albert Pujols 2.50 6.00
49 Frank Thomas 1.25 3.00
50 Juan Pierre .60 1.50
51 David Aardsma C05 1.50 4.00
52 J.D. Durbin C05 1.50 4.00
53 Zack Greinke C05 1.50 4.00
54 Dioner Navarro C05 1.50 4.00
55 Edwin Encarnacion C05 1.50 4.00
56 Luis Hernandez C05 RC 1.50 4.00
57 Jeff Baker C05 1.50 4.00
58 Victor Diaz C05 1.50 4.00
59 Joey Gathright C05 1.50 4.00
60 Casey Kotchman C05 1.50 4.00
61 David Wright C05 3.00 8.00
62 Jon Knott C05 1.50 4.00
63 Charlton Jimerson C05 1.50 4.00
64 Nick Swisher C05 1.50 4.00
65 Ryan Raburn C05 1.50 4.00
66 Josh Kroeger C05 1.50 4.00
67 Kelly Johnson C05 1.50 4.00
68 Justin Verlander C05 RC 3.00 8.00
69 Taylor Buchholz C05 1.50 4.00
70 Ubaldo Jimenez C05 RC 4.00 10.00
71 Russ Adams C05 1.50 4.00
72 Ronny Cedeno C05 1.50 4.00
73 Bobby Jenks C05 1.50 4.00
74 Dan Meyer C05 1.50 4.00
75 Jeff Francis C05 1.50 4.00
76 Scott Kazmir C05 1.50 4.00
77 Sean Burnett C05 1.50 4.00
78 Jose Lopez C05 1.50 4.00
79 Andres Blanco C05 1.50 4.00
80 Gavin Floyd C05 1.50 4.00
81 Tom Seaver RET 2.00 5.00
82 Steve Carlton RET 1.50 4.00
83 Al Kaline RET 2.00 5.00
84 Cal Ripken RET 6.00 15.00
85 Willie McCovey RET 2.00 5.00
86 Johnny Bench RET 2.00 5.00
87 Nolan Ryan RET 4.00 10.00
88 Mike Schmidt RET 3.00 8.00
89 Carlton Fisk RET 2.00 5.00
90 Don Mattingly RET 3.00 8.00

2005 Flair Row 1

*ROW 1 1-50: 1.25X TO 3X BASIC
*ROW 1 51-80: .6X TO 1.5X BASIC
*ROW 1 81-90: 1X TO 2.5X BASIC
OVERALL PARALLEL ODDS 1:6 H, 1:55 R
STATED PRINT RUN 100 SERIAL #'d SETS

2005 Flair Row 2

OVERALL PARALLEL ODDS 1:6 HOBBY
STATED PRINT RUN 1 SERIAL #'d SET
NO PRICING DUE TO SCARCITY

2005 Flair Cuts and Glory Jersey

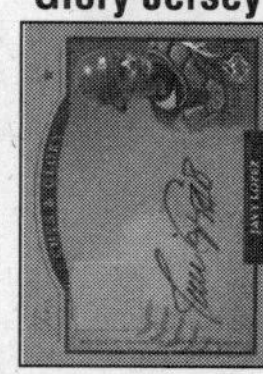

STATED PRINT RUN 100 SERIAL #'d SETS
LOGO PRINT RUN 1 SERIAL #'d SET
NO LOGO PRICING DUE TO SCARCITY
PATCH-JSY PRINT RUN 15 #'d SETS
NO PATCH-JSY PRICING DUE TO SCARCITY
OVERALL AU ODDS 1:1 H, AU-GU 1:24 R
BS Ben Sheets 10.00 25.00
CC Carl Crawford 10.00 25.00
HA Hank Aaron
JB Johnny Bench 30.00 60.00
JL Javy Lopez 10.00 25.00
JP Josh Phelps 6.00 15.00
SS Shannon Stewart 10.00 25.00

2005 Flair Cuts and Glory Patch

*PATCH: .6X TO 1.5X JSY
OVERALL AU ODDS 1:1 H, AU-GU 1:24 R
STATED PRINT RUN 50 SERIAL #'d SETS
HA Hank Aaron 175.00 300.00

2005 Flair Diamond Cuts Jersey

STATED PRINT RUN 150 SERIAL #'d SETS
*BLUE FOIL: .4X TO 1X BASIC
BLUE FOIL ODDS 1:48 RETAIL
BLUE FOIL CARDS ARE NOT SERIAL #'d
*DIE CUT: .5X TO 1.2X BASIC
DIE CUT PRINT RUN 75 SERIAL #'d SETS
*PATCH: 1X TO 2.5X BASIC
PATCH PRINT RUN 50 SERIAL #'d SETS
*PATCH DIE CUT: 1.5X TO 4X BASIC
PATCH DC PRINT RUN 25 SERIAL #'d SETS
PATCH MLB LOGO PRINT RUN 1 #'d SET
NO PATCH MLB LOGO PRICING AVAILABLE
PATCH SUPER PRINT RUN 20 #'d SETS
NO PATCH SUPER PRICING AVAILABLE
PATCH SUPER DC PRINT RUN 10 #'d SETS
NO PATCH SUPER DC PRICING AVAILABLE
OVERALL GU ODDS 2:1 HOBBY
AD Adam Dunn Jsy 3.00 8.00
Austin Kearns
AJ Andruw Jones Jsy 3.00 8.00
Chipper Jones
AK Austin Kearns Jsy 3.00 8.00
Adam Dunn
AP Albert Pujols Jsy 6.00 15.00
Scott Rolen
AS Alfonso Soriano Jsy 3.00 8.00
Hank Blalock
BU B.J. Upton Jsy 3.00 8.00
Hideo Nomo
CB Carlos Beltran Jsy 3.00 8.00
Pedro Martinez
CJ Chipper Jones Jsy 4.00 10.00
Andruw Jones
CS Curt Schilling Jsy 3.00 8.00
Randy Johnson
DO David Ortiz Jsy 3.00 8.00
Manny Ramirez
GS Gary Sheffield Jsy 3.00 8.00
Hideki Matsui
HB Hank Blalock Jsy 3.00 8.00
Alfonso Soriano
HM Hideki Matsui Jsy 10.00 25.00
Gary Sheffield
HN Hideo Nomo Jsy 4.00 10.00
B.J. Upton
JB Jeff Bagwell Jsy 3.00 8.00
Roger Clemens
JT Jim Thome Jsy 3.00 8.00
Mike Piazza
KW Kerry Wood Jsy 3.00 8.00
Mark Prior
MC Miguel Cabrera Jsy 3.00 8.00
Todd Helton
MP Mike Piazza Jsy 4.00 10.00
Jim Thome
MP2 Mark Prior Jsy 3.00 8.00
Kerry Wood
MR Manny Ramirez Jsy 3.00 8.00
David Ortiz
MT Mark Teixeira Jsy 3.00 8.00
Victor Martinez
PM Pedro Martinez Jsy 3.00 8.00
Carlos Beltran
RC Roger Clemens Jsy 4.00 10.00
Jeff Bagwell
RJ Randy Johnson Jsy 4.00 10.00
Curt Schilling
SR Scott Rolen Jsy 3.00 8.00
Albert Pujols
SS Sammy Sosa Jsy 4.00 10.00
Vladimir Guerrero
TH Todd Helton Jsy 3.00 8.00
Miguel Cabrera
VG Vladimir Guerrero Jsy 4.00 10.00
Sammy Sosa
VM Victor Martinez Jsy 3.00 8.00
Mark Teixeira

2005 Flair Diamond Cuts Dual Jersey

STATED PRINT RUN 99 SERIAL #'d SETS
*DIE CUT: .5X TO 1.2X BASIC
DIE CUT PRINT RUN 50 SERIAL #'d SETS
PATCH PRINT RUN 15 SERIAL #'d SETS
NO PATCH PRICING DUE TO SCARCITY
PATCH DIE CUT PRINT RUN 5 #'d SETS
NO PATCH DC PRICING DUE TO SCARCITY
OVERALL GU ODDS 2:1 HOBBY
BC Jeff Bagwell 6.00 15.00
Roger Clemens
BM Carlos Beltran 4.00 10.00
Pedro Martinez
BS Hank Blalock 4.00 10.00
Alfonso Soriano
CH Miguel Cabrera 4.00 10.00
Todd Helton
DK Adam Dunn 4.00 10.00
Austin Kearns
JJ Chipper Jones 6.00 15.00
Andruw Jones
JS Randy Johnson 6.00 15.00
Curt Schilling
MS Hideki Matsui 12.50 30.00
Gary Sheffield
MT Victor Martinez 4.00 10.00
Mark Teixeira
NU Hideo Nomo 6.00 15.00
B.J. Upton
OR David Ortiz 4.00 10.00
Manny Ramirez
PR Albert Pujols 10.00 25.00
Scott Rolen
PT Mike Piazza 6.00 15.00
Jim Thome
PW Mark Prior 4.00 10.00
Kerry Wood
SG Sammy Sosa 6.00 15.00
Vladimir Guerrero

2005 Flair Dynasty Cornerstones Signatures

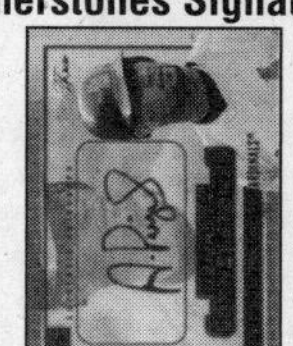

OVERALL AU ODDS 1:1 HOBBY
PRINT RUNS B/WN 3-75 COPIES PER
NO PRICING ON QTY OF 16 OR LESS
AP Albert Pujols/3
DG Dwight Gooden/25 10.00 25.00
DO David Ortiz/75 20.00 50.00
DS Darryl Strawberry/16
JB Jeremy Bonderman/75 10.00 25.00
JV Jason Varitek/75 30.00 60.00
JV2 Justin Verlander/75 15.00 40.00
SM Stan Musial/3
TS Tom Seaver/3

2005 Flair Dynasty Cornerstones Dual Signatures

OVERALL AU ODDS 1:1 HOBBY
PRINT RUNS B/WN 2-30 COPIES PER
NO PRICING ON QTY OF 15 OR LESS
BV Jeremy Bonderman 40.00 80.00
Justin Verlander/30
GS Dwight Gooden
Darryl Strawberry/15
PM Albert Pujols
Stan Musial/2
PS Mike Piazza
Tom Seaver/3
VO Jason Varitek
David Ortiz/2

2005 Flair Dynasty Foundations

STATED PRINT RUN 500 SERIAL #'d SETS
*GOLD p/r 61-98: .75X TO 2X BASIC
GOLD PRINT RUNS B/WN 1-98 COPIES PER
NO GOLD PRICING ON QTY OF 1
OVERALL ODDS 1:25 RETAIL
1 Vladimir Guerrero 4.00 10.00
Garret Anderson
Darin Erstad
Rod Carew
Nolan Ryan
2 Cal Ripken 6.00 15.00
Miguel Tejada
Javy Lopez
Jim Palmer
Brooks Robinson
3 Manny Ramirez 3.00 8.00
Ted Williams
David Ortiz
Johnny Damon
Carl Yastrzemski
4 Sammy Sosa 3.00 8.00
Ernie Banks
Ryne Sandberg
Greg Maddux
Mark Prior
5 Adam Dunn 2.00 5.00
Austin Kearns
Joe Morgan
Johnny Bench
Tony Perez
6 Victor Martinez 2.00 5.00
Travis Hafner
C.C. Sabathia
Larry Doby
Bob Feller
7 Todd Helton 2.50 6.00
Garrett Atkins
Preston Wilson
Aaron Miles
Matt Holliday
8 Miguel Cabrera 2.00 5.00
Josh Beckett
Dontrelle Willis
Juan Pierre
Al Leiter
9 Jeff Bagwell 3.00 8.00
Lance Berkman
Craig Biggio
Roger Clemens
Roy Oswalt
10 Geoff Jenkins 2.00 5.00
Paul Molitor
Ben Sheets
Lyle Overbay
Robin Yount
11 Johan Santana 2.00 5.00
Harmon Killebrew
Torii Hunter
Shannon Stewart
Lew Ford
12 Mike Piazza 4.00 10.00
Tom Seaver
Nolan Ryan
Pedro Martinez
Tom Glavine
13 Barry Zito 2.00 5.00
Eric Chavez
Reggie Jackson
Bobby Crosby
Dennis Eckersley
14 Jim Thome 3.00 8.00
Bobby Abreu
Gavin Floyd
Robin Roberts
Mike Schmidt
15 Craig Wilson 2.00 5.00
Jack Wilson
Jason Bay
Willie Stargell
Bill Mazeroski
16 Jason Schmidt 2.00 5.00
Juan Marichal
Willie McCovey
Orlando Cepeda
Ray Durham
17 Scott Rolen 3.00 8.00
Albert Pujols
Jim Edmonds
Mark Mulder
Stan Musial
18 B.J. Upton 1.50 4.00
Carl Crawford
Scott Kazmir
Aubrey Huff
Rocco Baldelli
19 Alfonso Soriano 4.00 10.00
Mark Teixeira
Hank Blalock
Nolan Ryan
Michael Young
20 Orlando Hudson 1.50 4.00
Vernon Wells
Alexis Rios
Paul Molitor
Roy Halladay

2005 Flair Dynasty Foundations Level 1 Jersey

OVERALL AU-GU ODDS 1:24 RETAIL
STATED PRINT RUN 150 SERIAL #'d SETS
ACTUAL PRINT RUNS B/WN 140-150 PER
*PATCH: 1X TO 2.5X BASIC

PATCH ODDS OVERALL GU 2:1 HOBBY
PATCH PRINT RUN 99 SERIAL #'d SETS
ACTUAL PATCH PRINT B/WN 98-99 PER
BR David Ortiz Jsy 3.00 8.00
Manny Ramirez
Ted Williams
Johnny Damon
Carl Yastrzemski
CI Victor Martinez Jsy 3.00 8.00
Travis Hafner
C.C. Sabathia
Larry Doby
Bob Feller
CR1 Adam Dunn Jsy 3.00 8.00
Austin Kearns
Joe Morgan
Johnny Bench
Tony Perez/140 UER
CR2 Todd Helton Jsy 3.00 8.00
Garrett Atkins
Preston Wilson
Aaron Miles
Matt Holliday
FM Miguel Cabrera Jsy 3.00 8.00
Josh Beckett
Dontrelle Willis
Juan Pierre
Al Leiter/140 UER
HA Jeff Bagwell Jsy 3.00 8.00
Lance Berkman
Craig Biggio
Roger Clemens
Roy Oswalt/146 UER
LA Vladimir Guerrero Jsy 4.00 10.00
Garret Anderson
Darin Erstad
Rod Carew
Nolan Ryan
MB Lyle Overbay Jsy 3.00 8.00
Geoff Jenkins
Paul Molitor
Ben Sheets
Robin Yount
MT Johan Santana Jsy 4.00 10.00
Harmon Killebrew
Torii Hunter
Shannon Stewart
Lew Ford
NM Mike Piazza Jsy 4.00 10.00
Tom Seaver
Nolan Ryan
Pedro Martinez
Tom Glavine
OA Barry Zito Jsy 3.00 8.00
Eric Chavez
Reggie Jackson
Bobby Crosby
Dennis Eckersley
PP Jim Thome Jsy 3.00 8.00
Bobby Abreu
Gavin Floyd
Robin Roberts
Mike Schmidt
PT Jason Bay Jsy 3.00 8.00
Craig Wilson
Jack Wilson
Willie Stargell
Bill Mazeroski
SC Albert Pujols Jsy 6.00 15.00
Scott Rolen
Jim Edmonds
Mark Mulder
Stan Musial
SG Jason Schmidt Jsy 3.00 8.00
Juan Marichal
Willie McCovey
Orlando Cepeda
Ray Durham
TD B.J. Upton Jsy 3.00 8.00
Carl Crawford
Scott Kazmir
Aubrey Huff
Rocco Baldelli
TR Michael Young Jsy 3.00 8.00
Alfonso Soriano
Mark Teixeira
Hank Blalock
Nolan Ryan

2005 Flair Dynasty Foundations Level 2 Jersey

STATED PRINT RUN 150 SERIAL #'d SETS
*PATCH: 1X TO 2.5X BASIC
PATCH PRINT RUN 50 SERIAL #'d SETS
OVERALL GU ODDS 2:1 HOBBY
BR Manny Ramirez Jsy 4.00 10.00
David Ortiz Jsy
Ted Williams
Johnny Damon
Carl Yastrzemski
CI Victor Martinez Jsy 4.00 10.00
Travis Hafner Jsy
C.C. Sabathia
Larry Doby
Bob Feller
CR1 Adam Dunn Jsy 4.00 10.00
Austin Kearns Jsy
Joe Morgan
Johnny Bench
Tony Perez
CR2 Todd Helton Jsy 5.00 12.00
Preston Wilson Jsy
Garrett Atkins
Aaron Miles
Matt Holliday
FM Miguel Cabrera Jsy 4.00 10.00
Juan Pierre Jsy
Josh Beckett
Dontrelle Willis
Al Leiter
HA Jeff Bagwell Jsy 4.00 10.00
Lance Berkman Jsy
Craig Biggio
Roger Clemens
Roy Oswalt
LA Vladimir Guerrero Jsy 6.00 15.00
Garret Anderson Jsy
Darin Erstad
Rod Carew
Nolan Ryan
MT Johan Santana Jsy 6.00 15.00
Torii Hunter Jsy
Harmon Killebrew
Shannon Stewart
Lew Ford
NM Mike Piazza Jsy 6.00 15.00
Tom Glavine Jsy
Tom Seaver
Nolan Ryan
Pedro Martinez
OA Barry Zito Jsy 4.00 10.00
Eric Chavez Jsy
Reggie Jackson
Bobby Crosby
Dennis Eckersley
PP Jim Thome Jsy 4.00 10.00
Bobby Abreu Jsy
Gavin Floyd
Robin Roberts
Mike Schmidt
SC Scott Rolen Jsy 10.00 25.00
Albert Pujols Jsy
Jim Edmonds
Mark Mulder
Stan Musial
TD B.J. Upton Jsy 4.00 10.00
Scott Kazmir Jsy
Carl Crawford
Aubrey Huff
Rocco Baldelli
TR Mark Teixeira Jsy 4.00 10.00
Michael Young Jsy
Alfonso Soriano
Hank Blalock
Nolan Ryan

2005 Flair Dynasty Foundations Level 3 Jersey

OVERALL GU ODDS 2:1 HOBBY
STATED PRINT RUN 99 SERIAL #'d SETS
CR1 Adam Dunn Jsy 6.00 15.00
Austin Kearns Jsy
Joe Morgan Jsy
Johnny Bench
Tony Perez
FM Miguel Cabrera Jsy 6.00 15.00
Josh Beckett Jsy
Juan Pierre Jsy
Dontrelle Willis
Al Leiter
HA Jeff Bagwell Jsy 12.50 30.00
Lance Berkman Jsy
Roger Clemens Jsy
Craig Biggio
Roy Oswalt
LA Vladimir Guerrero Jsy 10.00 25.00
Garret Anderson Jsy
Darin Erstad Jsy
Rod Carew
Nolan Ryan
MT Johan Santana Jsy 10.00 25.00
Torii Hunter Jsy
Shannon Stewart Jsy
Harmon Killebrew
Lew Ford
NM Mike Piazza Jsy 10.00 25.00
Pedro Martinez Jsy
Tom Glavine Jsy
Tom Seaver
Nolan Ryan
SC Scott Rolen Jsy 20.00 50.00
Albert Pujols Jsy
Jim Edmonds Jsy
Mark Mulder
Stan Musial
TR Alfonso Soriano Jsy 6.00 15.00
Mark Teixeira Jsy
Michael Young Jsy
Hank Blalock
Nolan Ryan

2005 Flair Dynasty Foundations Level 3 Patch

*PATCH: 1X TO 2.5X L3 JSY
OVERALL GU ODDS 2:1 HOBBY

STATED PRINT RUN 25 SERIAL #'d SETS
TD B.J. Upton Patch
Scott Kazmir Patch
Aubrey Huff Patch
Carl Crawford
Rocco Baldelli

2005 Flair Dynasty Foundations Level 4 Jersey

STATED PRINT RUN 40 SERIAL #'d SETS
PATCH PRINT RUN 15 SERIAL #'d SETS
NO PATCH PRICING DUE TO SCARCITY
OVERALL GU ODDS 2:1 HOBBY
CR1 Adam Dunn Jsy 15.00 40.00
Austin Kearns Jsy
Joe Morgan Jsy
Johnny Bench Jsy
Tony Perez
FM Miguel Cabrera Jsy 10.00 25.00
Josh Beckett Jsy
Dontrelle Willis Jsy
Juan Pierre Jsy
Al Leiter
HA Jeff Bagwell Jsy 15.00 40.00
Lance Berkman Jsy
Roger Clemens Jsy
Roy Oswalt Jsy
Craig Biggio
LA Vladimir Guerrero Jsy
Garret Anderson Jsy
Darin Erstad Jsy
Nolan Ryan Jsy
Rod Carew
NM Mike Piazza Jsy 30.00 60.00
Nolan Ryan Jsy
Pedro Martinez Jsy
Tom Glavine Jsy
Tom Seaver
SC Scott Rolen Jsy 30.00 60.00
Albert Pujols Jsy
Jim Edmonds Jsy
Mark Mulder Jsy
Stan Musial
TD B.J. Upton Jsy
Scott Kazmir Jsy
Aubrey Huff Jsy
Rocco Baldelli Jsy
Carl Crawford
TR Alfonso Soriano Jsy 15.00 40.00
Mark Teixeira Jsy
Nolan Ryan Jsy
Michael Young Jsy
Hank Blalock

2005 Flair Dynasty Foundations Level 5 Jersey

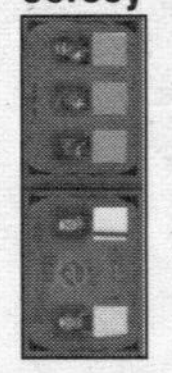

STATED PRINT RUN 25 SERIAL #'d SETS
MLB LOGO PRINT RUN 1 SERIAL #'d SET
NO MLB LOGO PRICING DUE TO SCARCITY
PATCH PRINT RUN 9 SERIAL #'d SETS
NO PATCH PRICING DUE TO SCARCITY
OVERALL GU ODDS 2:1 HOBBY
FM Miguel Cabrera Jsy 15.00 40.00
Josh Beckett Jsy
Dontrelle Willis Jsy
Juan Pierre Jsy
Al Leiter Jsy
HA Jeff Bagwell Jsy
Lance Berkman Jsy
Craig Biggio Jsy
Roger Clemens Jsy
Roy Oswalt Jsy
LA Vladimir Guerrero Jsy 40.00 80.00
Garret Anderson Jsy
Darin Erstad Jsy
Rod Carew Jsy
Nolan Ryan Jsy
NM Mike Piazza Jsy 75.00 150.00
Tom Seaver Jsy
Nolan Ryan Jsy
Pedro Martinez Jsy
Tom Glavine Jsy
TR Alfonso Soriano Jsy 40.00 80.00
Mark Teixeira Jsy
Hank Blalock Jsy
Nolan Ryan Jsy
Michael Young Jsy

2005 Flair Head of the Class Triple Jersey

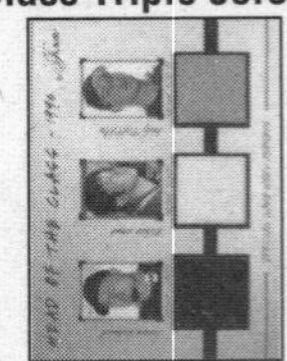

PRINT RUNS B/WN 1-99 COPIES PER
NO PRICING ON QTY OF 3 OR LESS
LOGO PRINT RUN 1 SERIAL #'d SET
NO LOGO PRICING DUE TO SCARCITY
OVERALL GU ODDS 2:1 HOBBY
AGJ Bobby Abreu 6.00 15.00
Vladimir Guerrero
Andruw Jones/96
BGB Carlos Beltran 6.00 15.00
Troy Glaus
Adrian Beltre/98
BMK Hank Blalock
Victor Martinez
Austin Kearns/2
BSO Josh Beckett
Ben Sheets
Roy Oswalt/1
BTR Jeff Bagwell 6.00 15.00
Jim Thome
Ivan Rodriguez/91
CGB Miguel Cabrera
Khalil Greene
Jason Bay/3
GBH Eric Gagne 6.00 15.00
AJ Burnett
Tim Hudson/99
JDR Chipper Jones 6.00 15.00
Carlos Delgado
Manny Ramirez/93
OHS David Ortiz 6.00 15.00
Torii Hunter
Richie Sexson/97
SNP Jason Schmidt 10.00 25.00
Hideo Nomo
Andy Pettite/95
TMR Mark Teixeira
Hideki Matsui
Jose Reyes/3

2005 Flair Head of the Class Triple Patch

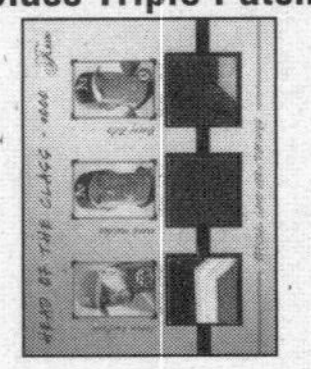

*PATCH: 1.25X TO 3X BASIC p/r 91-99
OVERALL GU ODDS 2:1 HOBBY
STATED PRINT RUN 33 SERIAL #'d SETS
BMK Hank Blalock 20.00 50.00
Victor Martinez
Austin Kearns
CGB Miguel Cabrera 20.00 50.00
Khalil Greene
Jason Bay
SMZ Johan Santana 20.00 50.00
Mark Mulder
Barry Zito

2005 Flair Letterman

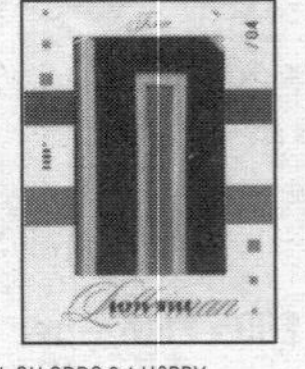

OVERALL GU ODDS 2:1 HOBBY
PRINT RUNS B/WN 4-8 COPIES PER
NO PRICING DUE TO SCARCITY
AP Albert Pujols/6
CJ Chipper Jones/6
CM Miguel Cabrera/7
CR Cal Ripken/6
GM Greg Maddux/6
HN Hideo Nomo/4
KW Kerry Wood/4
MP Mike Piazza/5
VG Vladimir Guerrero/8

2005 Flair Significant Signings Blue

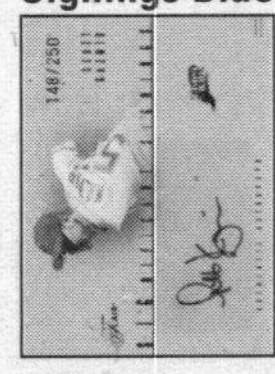

PRINT RUNS B/WN 4-250 COPIES PER
NO PRICING ON QTY OF 20 OR LESS
JSY TAG OVERALL AU ODDS 1:1 HOBBY
JSY TAG PRINT RUN 1 SERIAL #'d SET
NO JSY TAG PRICING DUE TO SCARCITY
PATCH PRINT RUN 15 SERIAL #'d SETS
ACTUAL HAFNER PATCH QTY 8 COPIES
NO PATCH PRICING DUE TO SCARCITY
OVERALL AU ODDS 1:1 H, AU-GU 1:24 R
AB Adrian Beltre/30 10.00 25.00
BC Bobby Crosby/93 6.00 15.00
BU B.J. Upton/250 6.00 15.00
CB Carlos Beltran/4
CK Casey Kotchman/250 6.00 15.00
CR Cal Ripken/16
DM Don Mattingly/103 30.00 60.00
DW David Wright/250 20.00 50.00
GF Gavin Floyd/221 4.00 10.00
JB Jason Bay/250 6.00 15.00
JM Justin Morneau/225 6.00 15.00
JP Jake Peavy UER 200/198 * 10.00 25.00
JR Jeremy Reed/250 4.00 10.00
KW Kerry Wood/200 10.00 25.00
LF Lew Ford/230 4.00 10.00
MC Miguel Cabrera/250 10.00 25.00
MS Mike Schmidt/20
MT Mark Teixeira/160 10.00 25.00
NR Nolan Ryan/92 50.00 100.00
PM Pedro Martinez/101 40.00 80.00
RC Roger Clemens UER 43/33 * 75.00 150.00
SC Steve Carlton/59 8.00 20.00
SK Scott Kazmir/250 8.00 20.00
TH T.Hafner UER 250/249 * 6.00 15.00
VM Victor Martinez/224 6.00 15.00
ZG Zack Greinke/250 4.00 10.00

2005 Flair Significant Signings Die Cut Silver

*DC SIL: .5X TO 1.2X BLUE p/r 160-250
*DC SIL: .5X TO 1.2X BLUE p/r 92-101
*DC SIL: .4X TO 1X BLUE p/r 43-59
*DC SIL: .3X TO .8X BLUE p/r 30
OVERALL AU ODDS 1:1 HOBBY
STATED PRINT RUN 50 SERIAL #'d SETS
CB Carlos Beltran 8.00 20.00
CR Cal Ripken 100.00 175.00
MS Mike Schmidt 40.00 80.00

2005 Flair Significant Signings Jersey Gold

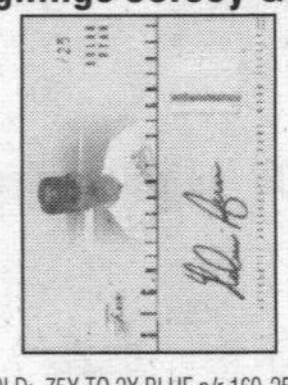

*JSY GOLD: .75X TO 2X BLUE p/r 160-250
*JSY GOLD: .75X TO 2X BLUE p/r 92-103
OVERALL AU ODDS 1:1 H, AU-GU 1:24 R
STATED PRINT RUN 25 SERIAL #'d SETS
ACTUAL CLEMENS PRINT RUN 6 COPIES
NO PRICING ON CLEMENS
KG Khalil Greene 20.00 50.00
KW Kerry Wood 20.00 50.00
MS Mike Schmidt
NR Nolan Ryan 75.00 150.00
PM Pedro Martinez 60.00 120.00
RC Roger Clemens/6 UER *

2005 Flair Significant Signings Dual

STATED PRINT RUN 40 SERIAL #'d SETS
ACTUAL UPTON/KAZMIR QTY 33 COPIES
JSY PRINT RUN 15 SERIAL #'d SETS
NO JSY PRICING DUE TO SCARCITY
PATCH PRINT RUN 5 SERIAL #'d SETS
NO PATCH PRICING DUE TO SCARCITY
OVERALL AU ODDS 1:1 HOBBY
BR Adrian Beltre 20.00 50.00
Jeremy Reed
CF Steve Carlton 20.00 50.00
Gavin Floyd
FM Lew Ford 20.00 50.00
Justin Morneau
MH Victor Martinez 20.00 50.00
Travis Hafner
RC Nolan Ryan
Roger Clemens
SR Mike Schmidt 150.00 250.00
Cal Ripken
UK B.J. Upton 20.00 50.00
Scott Kazmir/33 UER

2003 Flair Greats

This 133 card set was released in December, 2002. These cards were issued in five card packs with an SRP of $6. These cards were issued in 20 pack boxes which came 12 boxes to a case. Cards numbered 96 through 133 were inserted four per special home team boxes which also had 20 packs in a box but only had 4 boxes to a case. A promo card of Al Kaline was also issued before the product was issued and we have placed that card at the end of our set listings.

COMP.SET w/o SP's (95) 15.00 40.00
COMMON CARD (1-95) .40 1.00
COMMON CARD (96-133) 2.00 5.00
1 Ozzie Smith 1.50 4.00
2 Red Schoendienst .40 1.00
3 Harmon Killebrew 1.00 2.50
4 Ralph Kiner .40 1.00
5 Johnny Bench 1.00 2.50
6 Al Kaline 1.00 2.50
7 Bobby Doerr .40 1.00
8 Cal Ripken 3.00 8.00
9 Enos Slaughter .40 1.00
10 Phil Rizzuto .60 1.50
11 Luis Aparicio .40 1.00
12 Pee Wee Reese .60 1.50
13 Richie Ashburn .60 1.50
14 Ernie Banks 1.00 2.50
15 Earl Weaver .40 1.00
16 Whitey Ford .60 1.50
17 Brooks Robinson .60 1.50
18 Lou Boudreau .40 1.00
19 Robin Yount 1.00 2.50
20 Mike Schmidt 2.00 5.00
21 Bob Lemon .40 1.00
22 Stan Musial 1.50 4.00
23 Joe Morgan .40 1.00
24 Early Wynn .40 1.00
25 Willie Stargell .60 1.50
26 Yogi Berra 1.00 2.50
27 Juan Marichal .40 1.00
28 Rick Ferrell .40 1.00
29 Rod Carew .60 1.50
30 Jim Bunning .40 1.00
31 Ferguson Jenkins .40 1.00
32 Steve Carlton .40 1.00
33 Larry Doby .40 1.00
34 Nolan Ryan 2.50 6.00
35 Phil Niekro UER .40 1.00
Career win total in blurb is wrong
36 Billy Williams .40 1.00
37 Hal Newhouser .40 1.00
38 Bob Feller .40 1.00
39 Lou Brock .60 1.50
40 Monte Irvin .40 1.00
41 Eddie Mathews 1.00 2.50
42 Rollie Fingers .40 1.00
43 Gaylord Perry .40 1.00
44 Reggie Jackson .60 1.50
45 Bob Gibson .60 1.50
46 Robin Roberts .60 1.50
47 Tom Seaver .60 1.50
48 Willie McCovey .40 1.00
49 Hoyt Wilhelm .40 1.00
50 George Kell .40 1.00
51 Warren Spahn .60 1.50
52 Catfish Hunter .60 1.50
53 Dom DiMaggio .40 1.00
54 Joe Medwick .40 1.00
55 Johnny Pesky .40 1.00
56 Steve Garvey .40 1.00
57 Harry Heilmann .40 1.00
58 Dave Winfield .40 1.00
59 Andre Dawson .40 1.00
60 Jimmie Foxx 1.00 2.50
61 Buddy Bell .40 1.00
62 Gabby Hartnett .40 1.00
63 Babe Ruth 3.00 8.00
64 Dizzy Dean .60 1.50
65 Hank Greenberg 1.00 2.50
66 Don Drysdale .60 1.50
67 Gary Carter .40 1.00
68 Wade Boggs .60 1.50
69 Tony Perez .40 1.00
70 Mickey Cochrane .60 1.50
71 Bill Dickey .60 1.50
72 George Brett 2.00 5.00
73 Honus Wagner 1.00 2.50
74 George Sisler .40 1.00
75 Walter Johnson 1.00 2.50
76 Ron Santo .60 1.50
77 Roy Campanella 1.00 2.50
78 Roger Maris 1.00 2.50
79 Kirby Puckett 1.00 2.50
80 Alan Trammell .40 1.00
81 Don Mattingly 2.00 5.00
82 Ty Cobb 1.25 3.00
83 Lou Gehrig 2.00 5.00
84 Jackie Robinson 1.00 2.50
85 Billy Martin .60 1.50
86 Paul Molitor .40 1.00
87 Duke Snider .60 1.50
88 Thurman Munson 1.00 2.50
89 Luke Appling .40 1.00
90 Ernie Lombardi .40 1.00
91 Rube Waddell .40 1.00
92 Travis Jackson .40 1.00
93 Joe Sewell .40 1.00
94 King Kelly .60 1.50
95 Heinie Manush .40 1.00
96 Bobby Doerr HT 2.00 5.00
97 Johnny Pesky HT 2.00 5.00
98 Wade Boggs HT 3.00 8.00
99 Tony Conigliaro HT 3.00 8.00
100 Carlton Fisk HT 3.00 8.00
101 Rico Petrocelli HT 2.00 5.00
102 Jim Rice HT 2.00 5.00
103 Al Lopez HT 2.00 5.00
104 Pee Wee Reese HT 3.00 8.00
105 Tommy Lasorda HT 2.00 5.00
106 Gil Hodges HT 3.00 8.00
107 Jackie Robinson HT 3.00 8.00
108 Duke Snider HT 3.00 8.00

109 Don Drysdale HT	3.00	8.00
110 Steve Garvey HT	2.00	5.00
111 Hoyt Wilhelm HT	2.00	5.00
112 Juan Marichal HT	2.00	5.00
113 Monte Irvin HT	2.00	5.00
114 Willie McCovey HT	2.00	5.00
115 Travis Jackson HT	2.00	5.00
116 Bobby Bonds HT	2.00	5.00
117 Orlando Cepeda HT	2.00	5.00
118 Whitey Ford HT	3.00	8.00
119 Phil Rizzuto HT	3.00	8.00
120 Reggie Jackson HT	3.00	8.00
121 Yogi Berra HT	3.00	8.00
122 Roger Maris HT	3.00	8.00
123 Don Mattingly HT	8.00	20.00
124 Babe Ruth HT	6.00	15.00
125 Dave Winfield HT	2.00	5.00
126 Bob Gibson HT	3.00	8.00
127 Enos Slaughter HT	2.00	5.00
128 Joe Medwick HT	2.00	5.00
129 Lou Brock HT	3.00	8.00
130 Ozzie Smith HT	4.00	10.00
131 Stan Musial HT	4.00	10.00
132 Steve Carlton HT	2.00	5.00
133 Dizzy Dean HT	3.00	8.00
P6 Al Kaline Promotional Sample	.75	2.00

2003 Flair Greats Ballpark Heroes

Issued at a stated rate of one in 10, these nine cards feature some of baseball's greatest players.

1 Nolan Ryan	2.50	6.00
2 Babe Ruth	3.00	8.00
3 Honus Wagner	1.00	2.50
4 Ty Cobb	1.50	4.00
5 Ernie Banks	1.00	2.50
6 Mike Schmidt	2.00	5.00
7 Duke Snider	1.00	2.50
8 Cal Ripken	3.00	8.00
9 Stan Musial	1.50	4.00

2003 Flair Greats Bat Rack Classics Quads

Randomly inserted into packs, these five cards feature game-used bat chips from four players all on the same card. These cards were issued to a stated print run of 150 serial numbered sets.

1 Don Mattingly Joe Morgan Cal Ripken Brooks Robinson	60.00	120.00
2 Eddie Murray Eddie Mathews Reggie Jackson Willie McCovey	30.00	60.00
3 Tony Perez Don Mattingly Hank Greenberg Willie Stargell	40.00	80.00
4 Ryne Sandberg Ron Santo Billy Williams Andre Dawson	30.00	60.00
5 Dave Winfield Cal Ripken Paul Molitor Robin Yount	40.00	80.00

2003 Flair Greats Bat Rack Classics Trios

Randomly inserted into packs, these five cards feature game-used bat chips from three players all on the same card. These cards were issued to a stated print run of 300 serial numbered sets.

1 Tommy Agee Jerry Grote Bud Harrelson	10.00	25.00
2 Johnny Bench Joe Morgan Tony Perez	15.00	40.00
3 Hank Greenberg Harry Heilman George Kell	20.00	50.00
4 Reggie Jackson Don Mattingly Dave Winfield	20.00	50.00
5 Eddie Mathews Paul Molitor Robin Yount	15.00	40.00
6 Eddie Murray Cal Ripken Brooks Robinson	40.00	80.00
7 Dave Parker Willie Stargell	10.00	25.00
8 Ryne Sandberg Ron Santo Billy Williams	20.00	50.00

2003 Flair Greats Classic Numbers

Inserted into packs at a stated rate of one in 20, these 13 cards feature some of the most famous uniform numbers ever.

1 Jackie Robinson	2.50	6.00
2 Willie McCovey	1.50	4.00
3 Brooks Robinson	1.50	4.00
4 Reggie Jackson	1.50	4.00
5 Ozzie Smith	4.00	10.00
6 Johnny Bench	2.50	6.00
7 Yogi Berra	2.50	6.00
8 Cal Ripken	8.00	20.00
9 George Brett	5.00	12.00
10 Thurman Munson	2.50	6.00
11 Joe Morgan	1.50	4.00
12 Nolan Ryan	6.00	15.00
13 Steve Carlton	1.50	4.00

2003 Flair Greats Classic Numbers Game Used

Inserted at stated odds of one in 24 hobby packs and one in 27 home team packs, these 11 cards feature game-worn material from 11 of the players from the Classic Numbers set. A few players were issued in shorter supply and we have notated that information along with their announced print run information next to the player's name in our checklist.

PATCH RANDOM INSERTS IN PACKS
PATCH PRINT RUN 25 SERIAL #'d SETS
NO PATCH PRICING DUE TO SCARCITY

1 Johnny Bench Jsy	8.00	20.00
2 Yogi Berra Pants SP/75	10.00	25.00
3 George Brett Jsy	10.00	25.00
4 Steve Carlton Jsy	8.00	20.00
5 Willie McCovey Jsy SP/125	6.00	15.00
6 Joe Morgan Pants SP/200	6.00	15.00
7 Thurman Munson Pants	12.50	30.00
8 Cal Ripken Jsy	12.50	30.00
9 Nolan Ryan Jsy	20.00	50.00
10 Ryne Sandberg Jsy	10.00	25.00
11 Ozzie Smith Jsy	8.00	20.00

2003 Flair Greats Classic Numbers Game Used Dual

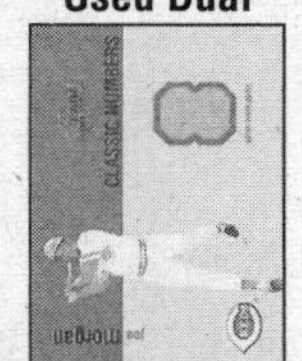

Randomly inserted into packs, these eight cards feature two players along with game-worn swatches of each of these players. Each of these cards was issued to a stated print run of 250 serial numbered sets.

1 Johnny Bench Jsy Thurman Munson Pants	15.00	40.00
2 Yogi Berra Pants Thurman Munson Pants	15.00	40.00
3 Yogi Berra Pants Cal Ripken Jsy	30.00	60.00
4 George Brett Jsy Nolan Ryan Jsy	40.00	80.00
5 Willie McCovey Jsy Johnny Bench Jsy	10.00	25.00
6 Joe Morgan Pants Ryne Sandberg Jsy	15.00	40.00
7 Cal Ripken Pants Ozzie Smith Jsy	30.00	60.00
8 Nolan Ryan Jsy Steve Carlton Jsy	30.00	60.00

2003 Flair Greats Cut of History Autographs

Randomly inserted into packs, these cards feature authentic autographs of the featured player. These cards were issued to different print runs and we have notated that information in our checklist.

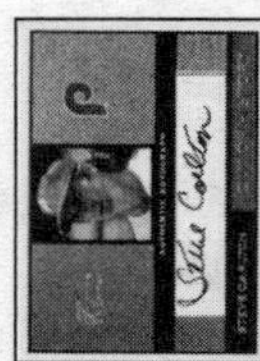

1 Johnny Bench/161	30.00	60.00
2 Steve Carlton/506	10.00	25.00
3 Dom DiMaggio/402	20.00	50.00
4 Tony Kubek/161	20.00	50.00
5 Cal Ripken/155	100.00	175.00
6 Alan Trammell/211	10.00	25.00

2003 Flair Greats Cut of History Game Used

Issued at a stated rate of one in ten packs, these 27 cards feature game-used pieces of 27 of baseball's all time greats. A few players were issued in smaller quantity and we have notated that information along with their stated print run next to their name in our checklist.

1 Luis Aparicio Jsy	3.00	8.00
2 Frank Baker Bat SP/50	20.00	50.00
3 Buddy Bell Bat	3.00	8.00
4 Wade Boggs Jsy SP/250	8.00	20.00
5 Steve Carlton Pants	3.00	8.00
6 Gary Carter Jsy	3.00	8.00
7 Dennis Eckersley Jsy	3.00	8.00
8 Hank Greenberg Bat SP/100	20.00	50.00
9 Catfish Hunter Jsy SP/200	8.00	20.00
10 Reggie Jackson Bat	4.00	10.00
11 Ferguson Jenkins Pants	3.00	8.00
12 Roger Maris Jsy SP/250	30.00	60.00
13 Billy Martin Pants	4.00	10.00
14 Willie McCovey Pants	3.00	8.00
15 Joe Medwick Bat	8.00	20.00
16 Eddie Murray Jsy	4.00	10.00
17 Graig Nettles Bat	3.00	8.00
18 Phil Niekro Pants	3.00	8.00
19 Paul O'Neill Jsy	4.00	10.00
20 Jim Palmer Pants	3.00	8.00
21 Kirby Puckett Bat	4.00	10.00
22 Cal Ripken Pants	10.00	25.00
23 Tom Seaver Pants	4.00	10.00
24A Alan Trammell Bat	3.00	8.00
24B Alan Trammell Jsy	3.00	8.00
25 Hoyt Wilhelm Jsy	3.00	8.00
26 Early Wynn Jsy	3.00	8.00

2003 Flair Greats Cut of History Game Used Gold

This set parallels the Cut of History Game Used set. Each of these cards were issued to a stated print run of 100 serial numbered sets.

*GOLD: .75X TO 2X BASIC
*GOLD: .5X TO 1.2X BASIC SP'S
RANDOM INSERTS IN PACKS
STATED PRINT RUN 100 SERIAL #'d SETS

2003 Flair Greats of the Grain

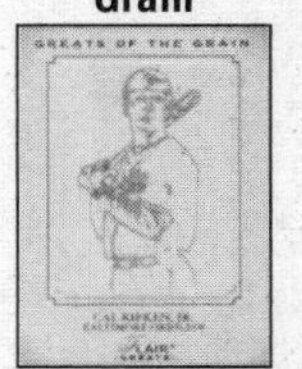

Randomly inserted into packs, these nine cards feature all-time greats laser etched on to a wood swatch. These cards were issued to a stated print run of 50 serial numbered sets. Please note that these cards do not contain game-used wood on them.

1 George Brett	40.00	80.00
2 Ty Cobb	40.00	80.00
3 Lou Gehrig	30.00	60.00
4 Eddie Mathews	30.00	60.00
5 Don Mattingly	40.00	80.00
6 Stan Musial	40.00	80.00
7 Cal Ripken	50.00	100.00
8 Babe Ruth	50.00	100.00
9 Mike Schmidt	40.00	80.00

2003 Flair Greats Hall of Fame Postmark

Randomly inserted into packs, these cards honor the day that Ozzie Smith was inducted into the Hall of Fame. Some of these cards were autographed and we have noted the print run for both of these cards in our checklist.

1 Ozzie Smith/2002	10.00	25.00
2 Ozzie Smith AU/202	50.00	100.00

2003 Flair Greats Home Team Cuts Game Used

These cards were issued at an overall rate of one in 20 for both single or dual game used cards in the home team boxes. A few cards were issued in smaller quantities than the others and we have notated that information in our checklist.

1 Wade Boggs Jsy SP/250	8.00	20.00
2 Bobby Bonds Bat	4.00	10.00
3 Carlton Fisk Jsy	6.00	15.00
4 Steve Garvey Jsy	4.00	10.00
5 Reggie Jackson Bat	6.00	15.00
6 Tom Lasorda Jsy SP/150	6.00	15.00
7 Juan Marichal Pants	4.00	10.00
8 Roger Maris Jsy SP/150	30.00	80.00
9 Billy Martin Pants	6.00	15.00
10 Willie McCovey Pants SP/200	6.00	15.00
11 Joe Medwick Bat SP/250	10.00	25.00
12 P.Reese Pants SP/75	8.00	20.00
13 Jim Rice Bat	4.00	10.00
14 R.Schoendienst Pants SP/200	6.00	15.00
15 Ozzie Smith Bat	8.00	20.00
16 Duke Snider Pants	6.00	15.00
17 Dave Winfield Bat	4.00	10.00

2003 Flair Greats Home Team Cuts Game Used Dual

These cards were issued at an overall rate of one in 20 for both single or dual game used cards in the home team boxes. A few cards were issued in smaller quantities than the others and we have notated that information in our checklist.

1 Bobby Bonds Bat Willie McCovey Pants/100	15.00	40.00
2 Carlton Fisk Jsy Jim Rice Bat/100	12.50	30.00
3 Billy Martin Pants Reggie Jackson Bat/175	12.50	30.00
4 Pee Wee Reese Pants Duke Snider Pants/100	12.50	30.00
5 Red Schoendienst Pants Joe Medwick Bat/125	10.00	25.00

2003 Flair Greats Sweet Swatch Classic Bat

Randomly inserted into jumbo packs, these 12 cards feature game-used bat pieces of the featured players. Each player was issued to a different print run and we have notated that information in our checklist.

1 Johnny Bench/175	10.00	25.00
2 George Brett/320	15.00	40.00
3 Jose Canseco/175	10.00	25.00
4 Orlando Cepeda/165	8.00	20.00
5 Andre Dawson/310	6.00	15.00
6 Reggie Jackson/155	10.00	25.00
7 Eddie Mathews/185	10.00	25.00
8 Don Mattingly/340	15.00	40.00
9 Willie McCovey/155	8.00	20.00
10 Kirby Puckett/165	10.00	25.00
11 Pee Wee Reese/165	10.00	25.00
12 Cal Ripken/305	20.00	50.00

2003 Flair Greats Sweet Swatch Classic Bat Image

These four cards partially parallel the sweet swatch classic bat insert set. Each of these cards were issued to a stated print run of less than 50 copies.

1 Johnny Bench/36	40.00	80.00
2 Tony Kubek/35	30.00	60.00
3 Cal Ripken/42	75.00	150.00
4 Alan Trammell/44	30.00	60.00

2003 Flair Greats Sweet Swatch Classic Bat Image Autographs

These four cards partially parallel the sweet swatch classic bat insert image set along with the player's autograph. Each of these cards were issued to a stated print run of 40 serial numbered sets.

1 Johnny Bench	60.00	120.00
2 Tony Kubek	50.00	100.00
3 Cal Ripken	150.00	250.00
4 Alan Trammell	40.00	80.00

2003 Flair Greats Sweet Swatch Classic Jersey

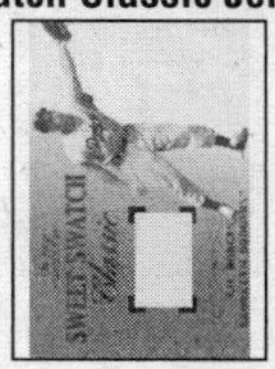

Randomly inserted into jumbo packs, these 72 cards feature game-used jersey swatches of the featured players. Each player was issued to a different print run and we have notated that information in our checklist.

1 Johnny Bench Jsy/410	8.00	20.00
2 George Brett Jsy/384	15.00	40.00
3 Jose Canseco Jsy/1329	6.00	15.00
4 Jerry Coleman Jsy/528	8.00	20.00
5 Andre Dawson Jsy/335	8.00	20.00
6 Carlton Fisk Jsy/1200	6.00	15.00
7 Gil Hodges Jsy/545	8.00	20.00
8 Juan Marichal Jsy/385	8.00	20.00
9 Don Mattingly Jsy/880	10.00	25.00
10 Paul Molitor Jsy/592	8.00	20.00
11 Jim Palmer Jsy/335	8.00	20.00
12 Kirby Puckett Jsy/445	8.00	20.00
13 Cal Ripken Jsy/557	15.00	40.00
14 Nolan Ryan Jsy/590	20.00	50.00
15 Ryne Sandberg Jsy/374	12.50	30.00
17 Robin Yount Jsy/340	8.00	20.00
19 Tom Seaver Jsy/385	8.00	20.00

2003 Flair Greats Sweet Swatch Classic Patch

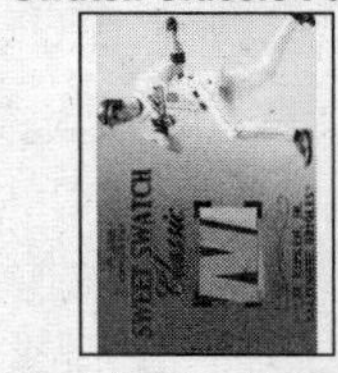

This 16 card set partially parallels the sweet swatch classic jersey set. Each of these cards feature a game-used patch piece and we have notated the stated print run in our checklist.

PATCH MASTERPIECE PRINT RUN 1 #'d SET
NO PATCH MP PRICING DUE TO SCARCITY

1 Johnny Bench/59	40.00	80.00
2 George Brett/53	75.00	150.00
3 Jose Canseco/177	30.00	60.00
4 Jerry Coleman/37	20.00	50.00
5 Andre Dawson/58	20.00	50.00
6 Carlton Fisk/51	40.00	80.00
7 Juan Marichal/48	20.00	50.00
8 Don Mattingly/106	60.00	120.00
9 Paul Molitor/96	30.00	60.00
10 Jim Palmer/63	30.00	60.00
11 Kirby Puckett/72	40.00	80.00
12 Cal Ripken/69	75.00	150.00
13 Nolan Ryan/60	75.00	150.00
14 Ryne Sandberg/40	75.00	150.00
15 Tom Seaver/66	30.00	60.00
16 Robin Yount/66	40.00	80.00

1997 Flair Showcase Rodriguez Sample Strip

This three-card unperforated strip was distributed to dealers and hobby media a few months prior to the release of 1997 Flair Showcase. The strip contains parallel versions of three different Alex Rodriguez cards later issued in packs. The cards on this promotional strip are identical to the standard Rodriguez Flair Showcase cards except for the text "PROMOTIONAL SAMPLE" written diagonally across the front and back.

NNO Alex Rodriguez Promo Strip
Row 2, Row 1, Row 0

1997 Flair Showcase Row 2

The 1997 Flair Showcase set (produced by Fleer) was issued in one series totalling 540 cards and was distributed in five-card packs with a suggested retail price of $4.99. Three groups of 60 cards were inserted at different rates: Cards numbered from one through 60 were inserted 1.5 cards per pack, cards numbered from 61 through 120 were inserted one every 1.5 packs and cards numbered from 61 through 120 were inserted at a rate of one per pack. This hobby exclusive set is divided into three 180-card sets (Row 2/Style, Row 1/Grace, and Row 0/Showcase) and features holographic foil fronts with an action photo of the player silhouetted over a larger black-and-white head-shot image in the background. The thick card stock is laminated with a shiny glossy coating for a super-premium "feel." Also inserted one in every pack was a Million Dollar Moments card. Rookie Cards include Brian Giles. Finally, 25 serial-numbered Alex Rodriguez Emerald Exchange cards (good for a signed Rodriguez glove) were randomly seeded into packs. The card fronts were very similar in design to the regular Row 2 Rodriguez, except for green foil accents. The card back, however, consisted entirely of text explaining prize guidelines. The deadline to exchange the card was 8/1/98.

COMPLETE SET (180)	40.00	80.00
COMMON CARD (1-60)	.20	.50
ROW 2 1-60 ODDS 1.5:1		
COMMON (61-120)	.30	.75
ROW 2 61-120 ODDS 1:1.5		
COMMON (121-180)	.25	.60
ROW 2 121-180 STATED ODDS 1:1		
A.ROD GLOVE EXCH RANDOM IN PACKS		
A.ROD GLOVE EXCH.DEADLINE: 8/1/98		
1 Andruw Jones	.30	.75
2 Derek Jeter	1.25	3.00
3 Alex Rodriguez	.75	2.00
4 Paul Molitor	.20	.50
5 Jeff Bagwell	.30	.75
6 Scott Rolen	.30	.75
7 Kenny Lofton	.20	.50
8 Cal Ripken	1.50	4.00
9 Brady Anderson	.20	.50
10 Chipper Jones	.50	1.25
11 Todd Greene	.20	.50
12 Todd Walker	.20	.50
13 Billy Wagner	.20	.50
14 Craig Biggio	.30	.75
15 Kevin Orie	.20	.50
16 Hideo Nomo	.50	1.25
17 Kevin Appier	.20	.50
18 B.Trammell RC	.20	.50
19 Juan Gonzalez	.20	.50
20 Randy Johnson	.50	1.25
21 Roger Clemens	1.00	2.50
22 Johnny Damon	.30	.75
23 Ryne Sandberg	.75	2.00
24 Ken Griffey Jr.	.75	2.00
25 Barry Bonds	1.25	3.00
26 Nomar Garciaparra	.75	2.00
27 Vladimir Guerrero	.50	1.25
28 Ron Gant	.20	.50
29 Joe Carter	.20	.50
30 Tim Salmon	.30	.75
31 Mike Piazza	.75	2.00
32 Barry Larkin	.30	.75
33 Manny Ramirez	.30	.75
34 Sammy Sosa	.50	1.25
35 Frank Thomas	.50	1.25
36 Melvin Nieves	.20	.50
37 Tony Gwynn	.60	1.50
38 Gary Sheffield	.20	.50
39 Darin Erstad	.20	.50
40 Ken Caminiti	.20	.50
41 Jermaine Dye	.20	.50
42 Mo Vaughn	.20	.50
43 Raul Mondesi	.20	.50
44 Greg Maddux	.75	2.00
45 Chuck Knoblauch	.20	.50
46 Andy Pettitte	.30	.75
47 Deion Sanders	.30	.75
48 Albert Belle	.20	.50
49 Jamey Wright	.20	.50
50 Rey Ordonez	.20	.50
51 Bernie Williams	.30	.75
52 Mark McGwire	1.25	3.00
53 Mike Mussina	.30	.75
54 Bob Abreu	.30	.75
55 Reggie Sanders	.20	.50
56 Brian Jordan	.20	.50
57 Ivan Rodriguez	.30	.75
58 Roberto Alomar	.30	.75
59 Tim Naehring	.20	.50
60 Edgar Renteria	.20	.50
61 Dean Palmer	.30	.75
62 Benito Santiago	.30	.75
63 David Cone	.30	.75
64 Carlos Delgado	.30	.75

65 Brian Giles RC	.75	2.00
66 Alex Ochoa	.30	.75
67 Rondell White	.30	.75
68 Robin Ventura	.30	.75
69 Eric Karros	.30	.75
70 Jose Valentin	.30	.75
71 Rafael Palmeiro	.50	1.25
72 Chris Snopek	.30	.75
73 David Justice	.30	.75
74 Tom Glavine	.50	1.25
75 Rudy Pemberton	.30	.75
76 Larry Walker	.30	.75
77 Jim Thome	.50	1.25
78 Charles Johnson	.30	.75
79 Dante Powell	.30	.75
80 Derrek Lee	.50	1.25
81 Jason Kendall	.30	.75
82 Todd Hollandsworth	.30	.75
83 Bernard Gilkey	.30	.75
84 Mel Rojas	.30	.75
85 Dmitri Young	.30	.75
86 Bret Boone	.30	.75
87 Pat Hentgen	.30	.75
88 Bobby Bonilla	.30	.75
89 John Wetteland	.30	.75
90 Todd Hundley	.30	.75
91 Wilton Guerrero	.30	.75
92 Geronimo Berroa	.30	.75
93 Al Martin	.30	.75
94 Danny Tartabull	.30	.75
95 Brian McRae	.30	.75
96 Steve Finley	.30	.75
97 Todd Stottlemyre	.30	.75
98 John Smoltz	.50	1.25
99 Matt Williams	.30	.75
100 Eddie Murray	.75	2.00
101 Henry Rodriguez	.30	.75
102 Marty Cordova	.30	.75
103 Juan Guzman	.30	.75
104 Chili Davis	.30	.75
105 Eric Young	.30	.75
106 Jeff Abbott	.30	.75
107 Shannon Stewart	.30	.75
108 Rocky Coppinger	.30	.75
109 Jose Canseco	.50	1.25
110 Dante Bichette	.30	.75
111 Dwight Gooden	.30	.75
112 Scott Brosius	.30	.75
113 Steve Avery	.30	.75
114 Andres Galarraga	.30	.75
115 Sandy Alomar Jr.	.30	.75
116 Ray Lankford	.30	.75
117 Jorge Posada	.50	1.25
118 Ryan Klesko	.30	.75
119 Jay Buhner	.30	.75
120 Jose Guillen	.30	.75
121 Paul O'Neill	.40	1.00
122 Jimmy Key	.25	.60
123 Hal Morris	.25	.60
124 Travis Fryman	.25	.60
125 Jim Edmonds	.25	.60
126 Jeff Cirillo	.25	.60
127 Fred McGriff	.40	1.00
128 Alan Benes	.25	.60
129 Derek Bell	.25	.60
130 Tony Graffanino	.25	.60
131 Shawn Green	.25	.60
132 Denny Neagle	.25	.60
133 Alex Fernandez	.25	.60
134 Mickey Morandini	.25	.60
135 Royce Clayton	.25	.60
136 Jose Mesa	.25	.60
137 Edgar Martinez	.40	1.00
138 Curt Schilling	.25	.60
139 Lance Johnson	.25	.60
140 Andy Benes	.25	.60
141 Charles Nagy	.25	.60
142 Mariano Rivera	.60	1.50
143 Mark Wohlers	.25	.60
144 Ken Hill	.25	.60
145 Jay Bell	.25	.60
146 Bob Higginson	.25	.60
147 Mark Grudzielanek	.25	.60
148 Ray Durham	.25	.60
149 John Olerud	.25	.60
150 Joey Hamilton	.25	.60
151 Trevor Hoffman	.25	.60
152 Dan Wilson	.25	.60
153 J.T. Snow	.25	.60
154 Marquis Grissom	.25	.60
155 Yamil Benitez	.25	.60
156 Rusty Greer	.25	.60
157 Darryl Kile	.25	.60
158 Ismael Valdes	.25	.60
159 Jeff Conine	.25	.60
160 Darren Daulton	.25	.60
161 Chan Ho Park	.25	.60
162 Troy Percival	.25	.60
163 Wade Boggs	.40	1.00
164 Dave Nilsson	.25	.60
165 Vinny Castilla	.25	.60
166 Kevin Brown	.25	.60
167 Dennis Eckersley	.25	.60
168 Wendell Magee Jr.	.25	.60
169 John Jaha	.25	.60
170 Garret Anderson	.25	.60
171 Jason Giambi	.25	.60
172 Mark Grace	.40	1.00
173 Tony Clark	.25	.60
174 Moises Alou	.25	.60
175 Brett Butler	.25	.60
176 Cecil Fielder	.25	.60
177 Chris Widger	.25	.60
178 Doug Drabek	.25	.60
179 Ellis Burks	.25	.60
180 S. Hasegawa RC	.40	1.00
NNO A.Rod. Glove/25	.75	2.00

1997 Flair Showcase Row 1

Randomly inserted in packs at various rates: Cards number 1 through 60 at a rate of one in 2.5 packs, cards numbered 61 through 120 at a rate of one every two packs and cards numbered from 121 through 180 at a rate of one every three packs. This 180-card Grace set is parallel to the base Flair Showcase Row 2 (Style) set and features holographic foil fronts with an action photo of the player silhouetted over a larger color head-shot image in the background.

*STARS 1-60: .75X TO 2X ROW 2
*STARS 61-120: .4X TO 1X ROW 2
*ROOKIES 61-120: .5X TO 1.25X ROW 2
*ROOKIES 61-120: .5X TO 1.25X ROW 2

1997 Flair Showcase Row 0

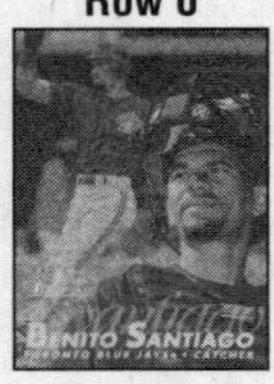

Randomly inserted in various rates depending on the card number: Cards numbered one through 60 were inserted one every 24 packs, cards numbered 61 through 120 at a rate of one per 12 and cards numbered 121 through 180 at a rate of one every five packs. This 180-card Showcase set is parallel to the base Flair Showcase Row 2 (Style) set and features holographic foil fronts with a head-shot image of the player silhouetted over a larger player action-shot in the background.

*STARS 1-60: 4X TO 10X ROW 2
*STARS 61-120: 1.25X TO 3X ROW 2
*ROOKIES 61-120: 1.5X TO 4X ROW 2
*STARS 121-180: 1X TO 2.5X ROW 2

1997 Flair Showcase Legacy Collection Row 2

Randomly inserted in packs at a rate of one in 30 (cumulatively between all three rows of Legacy), this 180-card set is parallel to the regular set. Only 100 sequentially numbered sets were produced, each featuring an "alternate" player photo printed on a matte finish/foil stamped card.

*LC ROW 2 1-60: 25X TO 60X BASIC
*LC ROW 2 61-120: 15X TO 40X BASIC
*LC ROW 2 RC'S 61-120: 12.5X TO 30X BASIC
*LC ROW 2 121-180: 20X TO 50X BASIC

1997 Flair Showcase Legacy Collection Row 1

Randomly inserted in packs at a rate of one in 30 (cumulatively between all three rows of Legacy), this 180-card set is parallel to the regular set. Only 100 sequentially numbered sets were produced, each featuring an "alternate" player photo printed on a matte finish/foil stamped card.

*LC ROW 1 1-60: 25X TO 60X BASIC
*LC ROW 1 61-120: 15X TO 40X BASIC
*LC ROW 1 RC'S 61-120: 12.5X TO 30X BASIC
*LC ROW 1 121-180: 20X TO 50X BASIC

1997 Flair Showcase Legacy Collection Row 0

Randomly inserted in packs at a rate of one in 30 (cumulatively between all three rows of Legacy), this 180-card set is parallel to the regular set. Only 100 sequentially numbered sets were produced, each featuring an "alternate" player photo printed on a matte finish/foil stamped card.

*LC ROW 0 1-60: 25X TO 60X BASIC
*LC ROW 0 61-120: 15X TO 40X BASIC
*LC ROW 0 RC'S 61-120: 12.5X TO 30X BASIC
*LC ROW 0 121-180: 20X TO 50X BASIC

1997 Flair Showcase Diamond Cuts

Randomly inserted in packs at a rate of one in 20, this 20-card set features color images of baseball's brightest stars silhouetted on a holofoil-stamped die-cut diamond-design background.

COMPLETE SET (20)	60.00	150.00
1 Jeff Bagwell	1.50	4.00
2 Albert Belle	1.00	2.50
3 Ken Caminiti	1.00	2.50
4 Juan Gonzalez	1.00	2.50
5 Ken Griffey Jr.	4.00	10.00
6 Tony Gwynn	3.00	8.00
7 Todd Hundley	1.50	4.00
8 Andruw Jones	1.50	4.00
9 Chipper Jones	2.50	6.00
10 Greg Maddux	4.00	10.00
11 Mark McGwire	6.00	15.00
12 Mike Piazza	4.00	10.00
13 Derek Jeter	6.00	15.00
14 Manny Ramirez	1.50	4.00
15 Cal Ripken	8.00	20.00
16 Alex Rodriguez	4.00	10.00
17 Frank Thomas	2.50	6.00
18 Mo Vaughn	1.00	2.50
19 Bernie Williams	1.50	4.00
20 Matt Williams	1.50	4.00

1997 Flair Showcase Hot Gloves

Randomly inserted in packs at a rate of one in 90, this 15-card set features color images of baseball's top glovemen silhouetted against a die-cut flame and glove background with temperature-sensitive inks.

1 Roberto Alomar	5.00	12.00
2 Barry Bonds	20.00	50.00
3 Juan Gonzalez	3.00	8.00
4 Ken Griffey Jr.	12.50	30.00
5 Marquis Grissom	4.00	10.00
6 Derek Jeter	20.00	50.00
7 Chipper Jones	8.00	20.00
8 Barry Larkin	5.00	12.00
9 Kenny Lofton	3.00	8.00
10 Greg Maddux	12.50	30.00
11 Mike Piazza	12.50	30.00
12 Cal Ripken	25.00	60.00
13 Alex Rodriguez	12.50	30.00
14 Ivan Rodriguez	5.00	12.00
15 Frank Thomas	8.00	20.00

1997 Flair Showcase Wave of the Future

Randomly inserted in packs at a rate of one in four, this 27-card set features color images of top rookies silhouetted against a background of an embossed wave design with simulated sand.

COMPLETE SET (27)	15.00	40.00
COMMON RC YR	.40	1.00
STATED ODDS 1:4		
1 Todd Greene	.40	1.00
2 Andruw Jones	.75	2.00
3 Randall Simon	.60	1.50
4 Wady Almonte	.40	1.00
5 Pat Cline	.40	1.00
6 Jeff Abbott	.40	1.00
7 Justin Towle	.40	1.00
8 Richie Sexson	.60	1.50
9 Bubba Trammell	.60	1.50
10 Bob Abreu	.75	2.00
11 David Arias-Ortiz	5.00	12.00
12 Todd Walker	.40	1.00
13 Orlando Cabrera	1.50	4.00
14 Vladimir Guerrero	1.25	3.00
15 Ricky Ledee	.60	1.50
16 Jorge Posada	.75	2.00
17 Ruben Rivera	.40	1.00
18 Scott Spiezio	.40	1.00
19 Scott Rolen	.75	2.00
20 Emil Brown	.40	1.00
21 Jose Guillen	.60	1.50
22 T.J. Staton	.40	1.00
23 Eli Marrero	.40	1.00
24 Fernando Tatis	.40	1.00
25 Ryan Jones	.40	1.00
WF1 Hideki Irabu	.60	1.50
WF2 Jose Cruz Jr.	.60	1.50

1998 Flair Showcase Ripken Sample Strip

This four-card unperforated strip was distributed to dealers and hobby media a few months prior to the release of 1998 Flair Showcase. The strip contains parallel versions of four different Cal Ripken cards later issued in packs. The cards on this promotional strip are identical to the standard Ripken Flair Showcase cards except for the text "PROMOTIONAL SAMPLE" written diagonally across the front and back.

NNO Cal Ripken Promo Strip	1.25	3.00
Row 3 Cal Ripken Flair		
Row 2 Cal Ripken Style		
Row 1 Cal Ripken Grace		
Row 0 Cal Ripken Showcase		

1998 Flair Showcase Row 3

This set (produced by Fleer) was issued in five card packs which retailed for $4.99 per pack and were released in July, 1998. Each player was featured in four rows with Row 3 being the easiest to obtain from opening packs. This 120 card set features two photos of the player on the front. The Row 3 cards were inserted in different ratios depending on which numbers they are. The complete odds are listed below for each group of 30 cards. Cards numbered 1-30 were seeded one every 9/10th of a pack; cards numbered 31-60 were seeded one every 1.1 packs; cards numbered 61-90 were seeded one every 1.5 packs and cards 91-120 were seeded one every two packs. Rookie Cards include Magglio Ordonez.

COMPLETE SET (120)	30.00	60.00
COMMON CARD (1-30)	.20	.50
COMMON CARD (31-60)	.20	.50
COMMON CARD (61-90)	.25	.60
COMMON CARD (91-120)	.30	.75
1 Ken Griffey Jr.	.75	2.00
2 Travis Lee	.20	.50
3 Frank Thomas	.50	1.25
4 Ben Grieve	.20	.50
5 Nomar Garciaparra	.75	2.00
6 Jose Cruz Jr.	.20	.50
7 Alex Rodriguez	.75	2.00
8 Cal Ripken	1.50	4.00
9 Mark McGwire	1.25	3.00
10 Chipper Jones	.50	1.25
11 Paul Konerko	.20	.50
12 Todd Helton	.30	.75
13 Greg Maddux	.75	2.00
14 Derek Jeter	1.25	3.00
15 Jaret Wright	.20	.50
16 Livan Hernandez	.20	.50
17 Mike Piazza	.75	2.00
18 Juan Encarnacion	.20	.50
19 Tony Gwynn	.60	1.50
20 Scott Rolen	.30	.75
21 Roger Clemens	1.00	2.50
22 Tony Clark	.20	.50
23 Albert Belle	.20	.50
24 Mo Vaughn	.20	.50
25 Andruw Jones	.30	.75
26 Jason Dickson	.20	.50
27 Fernando Tatis	.20	.50
28 Ivan Rodriguez	.30	.75
29 Ricky Ledee	.20	.50
30 Darin Erstad	.20	.50
31 Brian Rose	.20	.50
32 Magglio Ordonez RC	2.50	6.00
33 Larry Walker	.20	.50
34 Bobby Higginson	.20	.50
35 Chili Davis	.20	.50
36 Barry Bonds	1.25	3.00
37 Vladimir Guerrero	.50	1.25
38 Jeff Bagwell	.30	.75
39 Kenny Lofton	.20	.50
40 Ryan Klesko	.20	.50
41 Mike Cameron	.20	.50
42 Charles Johnson	.20	.50
43 Andy Pettitte	.30	.75
44 Juan Gonzalez	.20	.50
45 Tim Salmon	.30	.75
46 Hideki Irabu	.20	.50
47 Paul Molitor	.20	.50
48 Edgar Renteria	.20	.50
49 Manny Ramirez	.30	.75
50 Jim Edmonds	.20	.50
51 Bernie Williams	.30	.75
52 Roberto Alomar	.30	.75
53 David Justice	.20	.50
54 Rey Ordonez	.20	.50
55 Ken Caminiti	.20	.50
56 Jose Guillen	.20	.50
57 Randy Johnson	.50	1.25
58 Brady Anderson	.20	.50
59 Hideo Nomo	.50	1.25
60 Tino Martinez	.30	.75
61 John Smoltz	.40	1.00
62 Joe Carter	.25	.60
63 Matt Williams	.25	.60
64 Robin Ventura	.25	.60
65 Barry Larkin	.40	1.00
66 Dante Bichette	.25	.60
67 Travis Fryman	.25	.60
68 Gary Sheffield	.25	.60
69 Eric Karros	.25	.60
70 Matt Stairs	.25	.60
71 Al Martin	.25	.60
72 Jay Buhner	.25	.60
73 Ray Lankford	.25	.60
74 Carlos Delgado	.25	.60
75 Edgardo Alfonzo	.25	.60
76 Rondell White	.25	.60
77 Chuck Knoblauch	.25	.60
78 Raul Mondesi	.25	.60
79 Johnny Damon	.40	1.00
80 Matt Morris	.25	.60
81 Tom Glavine	.40	1.00
82 Kevin Brown	.40	1.00
83 Garret Anderson	.25	.60
84 Mike Mussina	.40	1.00
85 Pedro Martinez	.40	1.00
86 Craig Biggio	.40	1.00
87 Darryl Kile	.25	.60
88 Rafael Palmeiro	.40	1.00
89 Jim Thome	.40	1.00
90 Andres Galarraga	.25	.60
91 Sammy Sosa	.50	1.25
92 Willie Greene	.30	.75
93 Vinny Castilla	.30	.75
94 Justin Thompson	.30	.75
95 Jeff King	.30	.75
96 Jeff Cirillo	.30	.75
97 Mark Grudzielanek	.30	.75
98 Brad Radke	.30	.75
99 John Olerud	.30	.75
100 Curt Schilling	.30	.75
101 Steve Finley	.30	.75
102 J.T. Snow	.30	.75
103 Edgar Martinez	.50	1.25
104 Wilson Alvarez	.30	.75
105 Rusty Greer	.30	.75
106 Pat Hentgen	.30	.75
107 David Cone	.30	.75
108 Fred McGriff	.50	1.25
109 Jason Giambi	.30	.75
110 Tony Womack	.30	.75
111 Bernard Gilkey	.30	.75
112 Alan Benes	.30	.75
113 Mark Grace	.50	1.25
114 Reggie Sanders	.30	.75
115 Moises Alou	.30	.75
116 John Jaha	.30	.75
117 Henry Rodriguez	.30	.75
118 Dean Palmer	.30	.75
119 Mike Lieberthal	.30	.75
120 Shawn Estes	.30	.75

1998 Flair Showcase Row 2

These Row 2 cards are parallel to regular base set. Similar to the other rows there is different pull ratios for each group of 30 cards as follows. Cards numbered 1 through 30 are seeded one every two packs; cards numbered from 31 through 60 are seeded one every 2.5 packs; cards numbered from 61 through 90 are seeded one every four packs and cards numbered from 91-120 are seeded one every 3.5 packs.

COMPLETE SET (120)	40.00	100.00

*STARS 1-30: .6X TO 1.5X ROW 3
*STARS 31-60: .5X TO 1.25X ROW 3
*STARS 61-90: .6X TO 1.5X ROW 3
*STARS 91-120: .5X TO 1.25X ROW 3

1998 Flair Showcase Row 1

These Row 1 cards are parallel to regular base set. Similar to the other rows there is different pull ratios for each group of 30 cards as follows. Cards numbered from 1 through 30 are inserted one every 16 packs; cards numbered from 31 through 60 are inserted one every 24 packs; cards numbered from 61 through 90 are inserted one every six packs and cards numbered from 91 through 120 are inserted one every 10 packs.

*STARS 1-30: 2X TO 5X ROW 3
*STARS 31-60: 2.5X TO 6X ROW 3
*ROOKIES 31-60: 2.5X TO 6X ROW 3
*STARS 61-90: .75X TO 2X ROW 3
*STARS 91-120: 1X TO 2.5X ROW 3

1998 Flair Showcase Row 0

These Row 0 cards are parallel to regular base set. These cards are serial numbered and get more plentiful as they are numbered higher in the set. Serial numbering is as follows: Cards numbered from 1 through 30 are serial numbered to 250, cards numbered from 31 through 60 are serial numbered to 500, cards numbered from 61 through 90 are serial numbered to 1000 and cards numbered 91 through 120 are serial numbered to 2000.

*STARS 1-30: 6X TO 15X ROW 3
*STARS 31-60: 5X TO 12X ROW 3
*ROOKIES 31-60: 5X TO 12X ROW 3
*STARS 61-90: 3X TO 8X ROW 3
*STARS 91-120: 1.5X TO 4X ROW 3

1998 Flair Showcase Legacy Collection Row 3

Yet another parallel version of the Flair Showcase set, these cards are serial numbered to 100 each.

*STARS 1-30: 12.5X TO 30X BASIC ROW 3
*STARS 31-60: 12.5X TO 30X BASIC ROW 3
*ROOKIES 31-60: 8X TO 20X BASIC ROW 3
*STARS 61-90: 8X TO 20X ROW 3
*STARS 91-120: 8X TO 20X BASIC ROW 3

1998 Flair Showcase Legacy Collection Row 2

Yet another parallel version of the Flair Showcase set, these cards are serial numbered to 100 each.

*STARS 1-30: 12.5X TO 30X BASIC ROW 3
*STARS 31-60: 12.5X TO 30X BASIC ROW 3
*ROOKIES 31-60: 8X TO 20X BASIC ROW 2
*STARS 61-90: 8X TO 20X ROW 3
*STARS 91-120: 8X TO 20X BASIC ROW 3

1998 Flair Showcase Legacy Collection Row 1

Yet another parallel version of the Flair Showcase set, these cards are serial numbered to 100 each.

*STARS 1-30: 12.5X TO 30X BASIC ROW 3
*STARS 31-60: 12.5X TO 30X BASIC ROW 3
*ROOKIES 31-60: 8X TO 20X BASIC ROW 1
*STARS 61-90: 8X TO 20X ROW 3
*STARS 91-120: 8X TO 20X BASIC ROW 3

1998 Flair Showcase Legacy Collection Row 0

Yet another parallel version of the Flair Showcase set, these cards are serial numbered to 100 each.

*STARS 1-30: 12.5X TO 30X BASIC ROW 3
*STARS 31-60: 12.5X TO 30X BASIC ROW 3
*ROOKIES 31-60: 8X TO 20X BASIC ROW 3
*STARS 61-90: 8X TO 20X ROW 3
*STARS 91-120: 8X TO 20X BASIC ROW 3

1998 Flair Showcase Perfect 10

Sequentially numbered to 10, this 10-card insert features color player photography using silk-screen technology. While no pricing is available due to scarcity, we provide a checklist for identification purposes.

1 Ken Griffey Jr.
2 Cal Ripken
3 Frank Thomas
4 Mike Piazza
5 Greg Maddux
6 Nomar Garciaparra
7 Mark McGwire
8 Scott Rolen
9 Alex Rodriguez
10 Roger Clemens

1998 Flair Showcase Wave of the Future

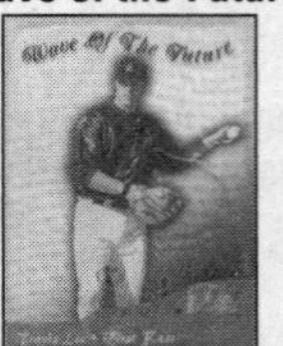

Randomly inserted in packs at a rate of one in 20, this 12-card insert feature color action photography on cards filled with vegetable oil and sparkles in an attempt to mimic ocean waters.

COMPLETE SET (12)	10.00	25.00
1 Travis Lee	.75	2.00
2 Todd Helton	1.25	3.00
3 Ben Grieve	.75	2.00
4 Juan Encarnacion	.75	2.00
5 Brad Fullmer	.75	2.00
6 Ruben Rivera	.75	2.00
7 Paul Konerko	.75	2.00
8 Derrek Lee	1.25	3.00
9 Mike Lowell	3.00	8.00
10 Magglio Ordonez	1.50	4.00
11 Rich Butler	.75	2.00
12 Eli Marrero	.75	2.00

1999 Flair Showcase Samples

These sample cards were distributed to dealers and hobby media as a complete set in a three-card clear

cello-wrapped pack several weeks prior to the national release of 1999 Flair Showcase. Company spokesperson Scott Rolen was the only player featured. Each card is parallel to it's accompanying basic issue card except for the text "PROMOTIONAL SAMPLE" running diagonally across the front and back.

COMPLETE SET (3) 1.20 3.00
COMMON ROLEN (1-3) .40 1.00

1999 Flair Showcase Row 3

This 144-card set was distributed in five-card packs with a suggested retail price of $4.99 and features two color player photos on the front with full rainbow holofoil, silver foil and embossing. This base set is considered the "Power" level. The set was broken into three separate tiers of 28 card subsets as follows: Cards numbered from 1 through 48 were seeded one every .9 packs; cards numbered 49 through 96 were seeded one every 1.1 packs and cards numbered 97 through 144 were seeded one every 1.2 packs. Rookie Cards include Pat Burrell.

COMPLETE SET (144) 25.00 60.00
COMMON CARD (1-48) .20 .50
COMMON CARD (49-96) .20 .50
COMMON CARD (97-144) .25 .60
1 Mark McGwire 1.25 3.00
2 Sammy Sosa .50 1.25
3 Ken Griffey Jr. .75 2.00
4 Chipper Jones .50 1.25
5 Ben Grieve .20 .50
6 J.D. Drew .20 .50
7 Jeff Bagwell .30 .75
8 Cal Ripken 1.50 4.00
9 Tony Gwynn .60 1.50
10 Nomar Garciaparra .75 2.00
11 Travis Lee .20 .50
12 Troy Glaus UER .30 .75
Spelled Tony on back
13 Mike Piazza .75 2.00
14 Alex Rodriguez .75 2.00
15 Kevin Brown .30 .75
16 Darin Erstad .20 .50
17 Scott Rolen .30 .75
18 Micah Bowie RC .20 .50
19 Juan Gonzalez .20 .50
20 Kerry Wood .20 .50
21 Roger Clemens 1.00 2.50
22 Derek Jeter 1.25 3.00
23 Pat Burrell RC 1.25 3.00
24 Tim Salmon .30 .75
25 Barry Bonds 1.25 3.00
26 Roosevelt Brown RC .20 .50
27 Vladimir Guerrero .50 1.25
28 Randy Johnson .50 1.25
29 Mo Vaughn .20 .50
30 Fernando Seguignol .20 .50
31 Greg Maddux .75 2.00
32 Tony Clark .20 .50
33 Eric Chavez .20 .50
34 Kris Benson .20 .50
35 Frank Thomas .50 1.25
36 Mario Encarnacion RC .20 .50
37 Gabe Kapler .20 .50
38 Jeremy Giambi .20 .50
39 Peter Tucci .20 .50
40 Manny Ramirez .30 .75
41 Albert Belle .20 .50
42 Warren Morris .20 .50
43 Michael Barrett .20 .50
44 Andruw Jones .30 .75
45 Carlos Delgado .20 .50
46 Jaret Wright .20 .50
47 Juan Encarnacion .20 .50
48 Scott Hunter RC .20 .50
49 Tino Martinez .30 .75
50 Craig Biggio .30 .75
51 Jim Thome .30 .75
52 Vinny Castilla .20 .50
53 Tom Glavine .30 .75
54 Bob Higginson .20 .50
55 Moises Alou .20 .50
56 Robin Ventura .20 .50
57 Bernie Williams .30 .75
58 Pedro Martinez .30 .75
59 Greg Vaughn .20 .50
60 Ray Lankford .20 .50
61 Jose Canseco .30 .75
62 Ivan Rodriguez .30 .75
63 Shawn Green .20 .50
64 Rafael Palmeiro .30 .75
65 Ellis Burks .20 .50
66 Jason Kendall .20 .50
67 David Wells .20 .50
68 Rondell White .20 .50
69 Gary Sheffield .20 .50
70 Ken Caminiti .20 .50
71 Cliff Floyd .20 .50
72 Larry Walker .20 .50
73 Bartolo Colon .20 .50
74 Barry Larkin .30 .75
75 Calvin Pickering .20 .50
76 Jim Edmonds .20 .50
77 Henry Rodriguez .20 .50
78 Roberto Alomar .30 .75
79 Andres Galarraga .20 .50
80 Richie Sexson .20 .50
81 Todd Helton .30 .75
82 Damion Easley .20 .50
83 Livan Hernandez .20 .50
84 Carlos Beltran .30 .75
85 Todd Hundley .20 .50
86 Todd Walker .20 .50
87 Scott Brosius .20 .50
88 Bob Abreu .20 .50
89 Corey Koskie .20 .50
90 Ruben Rivera .20 .50
91 Edgar Renteria .20 .50
92 Quinton McCracken .20 .50
93 Bernard Gilkey .20 .50
94 Shannon Stewart .20 .50
95 Dustin Hermanson .20 .50
96 Mike Caruso .20 .50
97 Alex Gonzalez .25 .60
98 Raul Mondesi .25 .60
99 David Cone .25 .60
100 Curt Schilling .25 .60
101 Brian Giles .25 .60
102 Edgar Martinez .40 1.00
103 Rolando Arrojo .25 .60
104 Derek Bell .25 .60
105 Denny Neagle .25 .60
106 Marquis Grissom .25 .60
107 Bret Boone .25 .60
108 Mike Mussina .40 1.00
109 John Smoltz .40 1.00
110 Brett Tomko .25 .60
111 David Justice .25 .60
112 Andy Pettitte .40 1.00
113 Eric Karros .25 .60
114 Dante Bichette .25 .60
115 Jeromy Burnitz .25 .60
116 Paul Konerko .25 .60
117 Steve Finley .25 .60
118 Ricky Ledee .25 .60
119 Edgardo Alfonzo .25 .60
120 Dean Palmer .25 .60
121 Rusty Greer .25 .60
122 Luis Gonzalez .25 .60
123 Randy Winn .25 .60
124 Jeff Kent .25 .60
125 Doug Glanville .25 .60
126 Justin Thompson .25 .60
127 Bret Saberhagen .25 .60
128 Wade Boggs .40 1.00
129 Al Leiter .25 .60
130 Paul O'Neill .40 1.00
131 Chan Ho Park .25 .60
132 Johnny Damon .40 1.00
133 Darryl Kile .25 .60
134 Reggie Sanders .25 .60
135 Kevin Millwood .25 .60
136 Charles Johnson .25 .60
137 Ray Durham .25 .60
138 Rico Brogna .25 .60
139 Matt Williams .25 .60
140 Sandy Alomar Jr. .25 .60
141 Jeff Cirillo .25 .60
142 Devon White .25 .60
143 Andy Benes .25 .60
144 Mike Stanley .25 .60

1999 Flair Showcase Row 2

This 144-card set is parallel to the Row 1 or base set and features two action player photos with embossed jersey-like background printed on full rainbow holofoil cards. This set is called the "Passion" level. Seeding rates are as follows, cards numbered one through 48 are seeded one every three packs; cards numbered 49 through 96 are seeded one every 1.33 packs and cards numbered 97-144 are seeded one every two packs.

COMPLETE SET (144)
*STARS 1-48: 1X TO 2.5X ROW 3
*ROOKIES 1-48: 1.25X TO 3X ROW 3
*STARS 49-96: .5X TO 1.25X ROW 3
*STARS 97-144: .5X TO 1.25X ROW 3

1999 Flair Showcase Row 1

This 144-card set is parallel to the base set and features three photos of the same player on a plastic laminate individual numbered card. Cards 1-48 are serially numbered to 1500; Cards 49-96 to 3000; Cards 97-144 to 6000. This set is the "Showcase" level.

*STARS 1-48: 4X TO 10X ROW 3
*ROOKIES 1-48: 4X TO 10X ROW 3
*STARS 49-96: 2.5X TO 6X ROW 3
*STARS 97-144: 1.25X TO 3X ROW 3

1999 Flair Showcase Legacy Collection

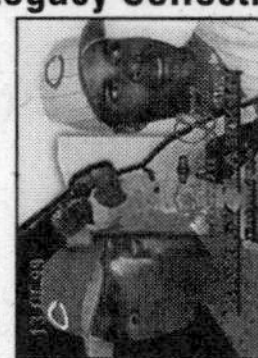

Randomly inserted in packs, this set is a blue foil parallel version of the regular Flair Showcase set. Only 99 sequentially numbered sets were produced for each Row. Similar to the regular Showcase set, each player has three different cards. Therefore, in actuality, 297 cards of each player were produced.

*STARS 1-48: 12.5X TO 30X ROW 3
*ROOKIES 1-48: 8X TO 20X ROW 3
*STARS 49-96: 12.5X TO 30X ROW 3
*STARS 97-144: 10X TO 25X ROW 3

1999 Flair Showcase Masterpiece

Randomly inserted into packs, three versions of this 144-card set were created as exclusive one of one parallels. Only one of each card was printed with purple foil stamping on the fronts and "The Only 1 of 1 Masterpiece" printed on the backs. No pricing is available due to scarcity.

PRINT RUN 1 SERIAL #'d SET FOR EACH ROW
NOT PRICED DUE TO SCARCITY

1999 Flair Showcase Measure of Greatness

Randomly inserted into packs, this 15-card set features color photos of superstars who are closing in on milestones of all-time great players. Only 500 serial-numbered cards were produced.

COMPLETE SET (15) 200.00 400.00
1 Roger Clemens 12.50 30.00
2 Nomar Garciaparra 10.00 25.00
3 Juan Gonzalez 2.50 6.00
4 Ken Griffey Jr. 10.00 25.00
5 Vladimir Guerrero 6.00 15.00
6 Tony Gwynn 8.00 20.00
7 Derek Jeter 15.00 40.00
8 Chipper Jones 6.00 15.00
9 Mark McGwire 15.00 40.00
10 Mike Piazza 10.00 25.00
11 Manny Ramirez 4.00 10.00
12 Cal Ripken 20.00 50.00
13 Alex Rodriguez 10.00 25.00
14 Sammy Sosa 6.00 15.00
15 Frank Thomas 6.00 15.00

1999 Flair Showcase Wave of the Future

Randomly inserted into packs, this 15-card set features color photos of young stars. Each card is serially numbered to 1000.

COMPLETE SET (15) 50.00 100.00
1 Kerry Wood 2.00 5.00
2 Ben Grieve 2.00 5.00
3 J.D. Drew 2.00 5.00
4 Juan Encarnacion 2.00 5.00
5 Travis Lee 2.00 5.00
6 Todd Helton 3.00 8.00
7 Troy Glaus 3.00 8.00
8 Ricky Ledee 2.00 5.00
9 Eric Chavez 2.00 5.00
10 Ben Davis 2.00 5.00
11 George Lombard 2.00 5.00
12 Jeremy Giambi 2.00 5.00
13 Roosevelt Brown 2.00 5.00
14 Pat Burrell 6.00 15.00
15 Preston Wilson 2.00 5.00

2006 Flair Showcase

This 200-card set was released in August, 2006. The set was issued in five-card hobby packs, which came 18 packs to a box and 16 boxes to a case, with

an $4.99 SRP. Cards numbered 101-150, which were titled Field Box, were issued at a stated rate of one per four hobby and one per eight retail packs. Cards numbered 151-200,which were titled Suite Level, were issued at a stated rate of on per eight hobby packs and one per sixteen retail packs.

COMP.SET w/o SP's (100) 15.00 40.00
101-150 STATED ODDS 1:4 H, 1:8 R
151-200 STATED ODDS 1:8 H, 1:16 R
PLATE ODDS: 1-2 PER HOBBY CASE
PLATE PRINT RUN 1 SET PER COLOR
BLACK-CYAN-MAGENTA-YELLOW ISSUED
NO PLATE PRICING DUE TO SCARCITY
1 Jeremy Hermida UD (RC) .40 1.00
2 Albert Pujols UD 1.50 4.00
3 Ryan Shealy UD (RC) .40 1.00
4 Mark Prior UD .50 1.25
5 Chuck James UD (RC) .60 1.50
6 Shawn Green UD .30 .75
7 Rickie Weeks UD .30 .75
8 Roy Halladay UD .30 .75
9 Luis Gonzalez UD .30 .75
10 David Ortiz UD .75 2.00
11 Josh Beckett UD .30 .75
12 Gary Sheffield UD .30 .75
13 Jose Reyes UD .75 2.00
14 Brandon Watson UD (RC) .40 1.00
15 Tadahito Iguchi UD .30 .75
16 Rich Harden UD .30 .75
17 Skip Schumaker UD (RC) .40 1.00
18 Vladimir Guerrero UD .75 2.00
19 Chris Carpenter UD .30 .75
20 Brian Roberts UD .30 .75
21 Roy Oswalt UD .30 .75
22 Ben Johnson UD (RC) .40 1.00
23 Todd Helton UD .50 1.25
24 Wil Nieves UD (RC) .40 1.00
25 Michael Young UD .30 .75
26 A.J. Burnett UD .30 .75
27 J.D. Drew UD .30 .75
28 Adrian Beltre UD .30 .75
29 Tim Hudson UD .30 .75
30 Jake Peavy UD .30 .75
31 Magglio Ordonez UD .30 .75
32 Brad Wilkerson UD .30 .75
33 Ryan Freel UD .30 .75
34 Javier Vazquez UD .30 .75
35 Tom Glavine UD .50 1.25
36 Jason Bergmann UD RC .40 1.00
37 Marcus Giles UD .30 .75
38 Jim Thome UD .50 1.25
39 Ichiro Suzuki UD 1.25 3.00
40 Jeff Harris UD RC .30 .75
41 Miguel Cabrera UD .50 1.25
42 Nomar Garciaparra UD .75 2.00
43 Brian Giles UD .30 .75
44 Jeremy Accardo UD RC .40 1.00
45 Taylor Buchholz UD (RC) .60 1.50
46 Mike Jacobs UD (RC) .40 1.00
47 Chris Denorfia UD (RC) .40 1.00
48 Ian Rodriguez UD .50 1.25
49 Mike Piazza UD .75 2.00
50 Curt Schilling UD .50 1.25
51 Kelly Shoppach UD (RC) .40 1.00
52 Jason Kubel UD (RC) .40 1.00
53 Craig Biggio UD .50 1.25
54 Livan Hernandez UD .30 .75
55 Joe Mauer UD .50 1.25
56 Scott Feldman UD RC .40 1.00
57 Garrett Anderson UD .30 .75
58 Steve Stemle UD RC .40 1.00
59 Boof Bonser UD (RC) .40 1.00
60 Jose Guillen UD .30 .75
61 Rafael Furcal UD .30 .75
62 John Van Benschoten UD (RC) .40 1.00
63 Dontrelle Willis UD .30 .75
64 Jose Vidro UD .30 .75
65 David Wright UD 1.25 3.00
66 Alfonso Soriano UD .30 .75
67 Scott Podsednik UD .30 .75
68 Felix Hernandez UD .50 1.25
69 Richie Sexson UD .30 .75
70 Jeff Francoeur UD .75 2.00
71 Conor Jackson UD .50 1.25
72 Javy Lopez UD .30 .75
73 Jonathan Papelbon UD (RC) 2.00 5.00
74 Frank Thomas UD .75 2.00
75 Greg Maddux UD 1.25 3.00
76 Josh Rupe UD (RC) .40 1.00
77 Eric Chavez UD .30 .75
78 Ben Sheets UD .30 .75
79 Chase Utley UD .75 2.00
80 Derrek Lee UD .30 .75
81 Manny Ramirez UD .50 1.25
82 Pedro Martinez UD .50 1.25
83 Hideki Matsui UD .75 2.00
84 Jeremy Bonderman UD .30 .75
85 Ronny Cedeno UD .30 .75
86 Trevor Hoffman UD .30 .75
87 Mark Buehrle UD .30 .75
88 Jason Bay UD .30 .75
89 Reggie Sanders UD .30 .75
90 Brian Anderson UD (RC) .40 1.00
91 Travis Hafner UD .30 .75
92 Carlos Beltran UD .30 .75
93 Cody Ross UD (RC) .40 1.00
94 Melvin Mora UD .30 .75
95 Chris Duffy UD .30 .75
96 Vernon Wells UD .30 .75
97 Bartolo Colon UD .30 .75
98 Aubrey Huff UD .30 .75
99 Paul Konerko UD .30 .75
100 Cesar Izturis UD .30 .75
101 Josh Willingham FB (RC) .75 2.00
102 Matt Cain FB (RC) 1.25 3.00
103 Macay McBride FB (RC) .75 2.00
104 Jeff Mathis FB .75 2.00

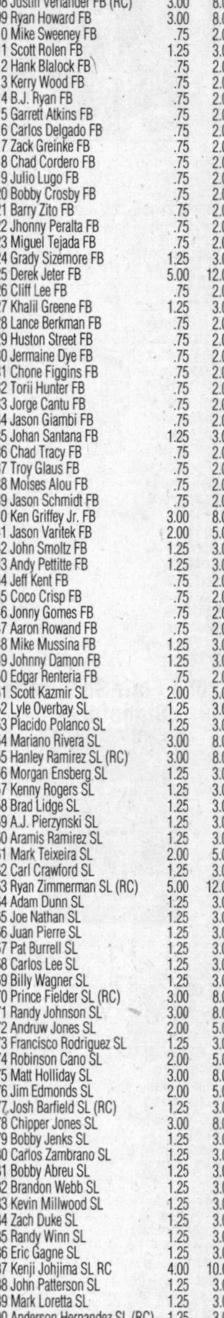

105 Alex Rodriguez FB 3.00 8.00
106 Justin Morneau FB .75 2.00
107 Felipe Lopez FB .75 2.00
108 Justin Verlander FB (RC) 3.00 8.00
109 Ryan Howard FB 3.00 8.00
110 Mike Sweeney FB .75 2.00
111 Scott Rolen FB 1.25 3.00
112 Hank Blalock FB .75 2.00
113 Kerry Wood FB .75 2.00
114 B.J. Ryan FB .75 2.00
115 Garrett Atkins FB .75 2.00
116 Carlos Delgado FB .75 2.00
117 Zack Greinke FB .75 2.00
118 Chad Cordero FB .75 2.00
119 Julio Lugo FB .75 2.00
120 Bobby Crosby FB .75 2.00
121 Barry Zito FB .75 2.00
122 Jhonny Peralta FB .75 2.00
123 Miguel Tejada FB .75 2.00
124 Grady Sizemore FB 1.25 3.00
125 Derek Jeter FB 5.00 12.00
126 Cliff Lee FB .75 2.00
127 Khalil Greene FB 1.25 3.00
128 Lance Berkman FB .75 2.00
129 Huston Street FB .75 2.00
130 Jermaine Dye FB .75 2.00
131 Chone Figgins FB .75 2.00
132 Torii Hunter FB .75 2.00
133 Jorge Cantu FB .75 2.00
134 Jason Giambi FB .75 2.00
135 Johan Santana FB 1.25 3.00
136 Chad Tracy FB .75 2.00
137 Troy Glaus FB .75 2.00
138 Moises Alou FB .75 2.00
139 Jason Schmidt FB .75 2.00
140 Ken Griffey Jr. FB 3.00 8.00
141 Jason Varitek FB 2.00 5.00
142 John Smoltz FB 1.25 3.00
143 Andy Pettitte FB 1.25 3.00
144 Jeff Kent FB .75 2.00
145 Coco Crisp FB .75 2.00
146 Jonny Gomes FB .75 2.00
147 Aaron Rowand FB .75 2.00
148 Mike Mussina FB 1.25 3.00
149 Johnny Damon FB 1.25 3.00
150 Edgar Renteria FB .75 2.00
151 Scott Kazmir SL 2.00 5.00
152 Lyle Overbay SL 1.25 3.00
153 Placido Polanco SL 1.25 3.00
154 Mariano Rivera SL 3.00 8.00
155 Hanley Ramirez SL (RC) 3.00 8.00
156 Morgan Ensberg SL 1.25 3.00
157 Kenny Rogers SL 1.25 3.00
158 Brad Lidge SL 1.25 3.00
159 A.J. Pierzynski SL 1.25 3.00
160 Aramis Ramirez SL 1.25 3.00
161 Mark Teixeira SL 2.00 5.00
162 Carl Crawford SL 1.25 3.00
163 Ryan Zimmerman SL (RC) 5.00 12.00
164 Adam Dunn SL 1.25 3.00
165 Joe Nathan SL 1.25 3.00
166 Juan Pierre SL 1.25 3.00
167 Pat Burrell SL 1.25 3.00
168 Carlos Lee SL 1.25 3.00
169 Billy Wagner SL 1.25 3.00
170 Prince Fielder SL (RC) 3.00 8.00
171 Randy Johnson SL 3.00 8.00
172 Andruw Jones SL 2.00 5.00
173 Francisco Rodriguez SL 1.25 3.00
174 Robinson Cano SL 2.00 5.00
175 Matt Holliday SL 3.00 8.00
176 Jim Edmonds SL 2.00 5.00
177 Josh Barfield SL (RC) 1.25 3.00
178 Chipper Jones SL 3.00 8.00
179 Bobby Jenks SL 1.25 3.00
180 Carlos Zambrano SL 1.25 3.00
181 Bobby Abreu SL 1.25 3.00
182 Brandon Webb SL 1.25 3.00
183 Kevin Millwood SL 1.25 3.00
184 Zach Duke SL 1.25 3.00
185 Randy Winn SL 1.25 3.00
186 Eric Gagne SL 1.25 3.00
187 Kenji Johjima SL RC 4.00 10.00
188 John Patterson SL 1.25 3.00
189 Mark Loretta SL 1.25 3.00
190 Anderson Hernandez SL (RC) 1.25 3.00
191 Chris Resop SL (RC) 1.25 3.00
192 Ian Kinsler SL (RC) 2.00 5.00
193 Francisco Liriano SL (RC) 4.00 10.00
194 Noah Lowry SL 1.25 3.00
195 Brett Myers SL 1.25 3.00
196 Rocco Baldelli SL 1.25 3.00
197 Cliff Floyd SL 1.25 3.00
198 Sean Casey SL 1.25 3.00
199 Geoff Jenkins SL 1.25 3.00
200 Clint Barmes SL 1.25 3.00

2006 Flair Showcase Legacy Blue

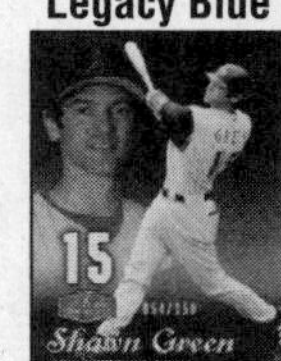

*BLUE 1-100: 1.5X TO 4X BASIC
*BLUE 1-100: 1.25X TO 3X BASIC RC's
*BLUE 101-150: .6X TO 1.5X BASIC
*BLUE 151-200: .4X TO 1X BASIC
STATED ODDS 1:18 HOBBY
STATED PRINT RUN 150 SERIAL #'d SETS
73 Jonathan Papelbon UD 4.00 10.00
108 Justin Verlander FB 3.00 8.00
163 Ryan Zimmerman SL 5.00 12.00
170 Prince Fielder SL 3.00 8.00
187 Kenji Johjima SL 4.00 10.00
193 Francisco Liriano SL 4.00 10.00

2006 Flair Showcase Legacy Emerald

*EMERALD 1-100: 1.5X TO 4X BASIC
*EMERALD 1-100: 1.25X TO 3X BASIC RC's

*EMERALD 101-150: .6X TO 1.5X BASIC
*EMERALD 151-200: .4X TO 1X BASIC
STATED ODDS 1:18 HOBBY
STATED PRINT RUN 150 SERIAL #'d SETS
73 Jonathan Papelbon UD 4.00 10.00
108 Justin Verlander FB 3.00 8.00
163 Ryan Zimmerman SL 5.00 12.00
170 Prince Fielder SL 3.00 8.00
187 Kenji Johjima SL 4.00 10.00
193 Francisco Liriano SL 4.00 10.00

2006 Flair Showcase Autographics

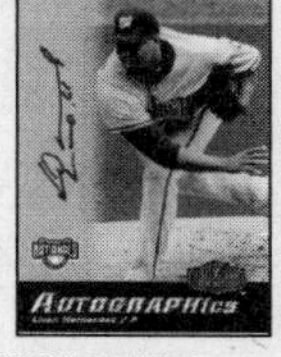

STATED ODDS 1:36 H, 1:576 R
SP PRINT RUNS PROVIDED BY UD
SP'S ARE NOT SERIAL-NUMBERED
NO SP PRICING ON QTY OF 46 OR LESS
PLATE ODDS: 1-2 PER HOBBY CASE
PLATE PRINT RUN 1 SET PER COLOR
BLACK-CYAN-MAGENTA-YELLOW-ISSUED
PLATES DO NOT FEATURE AUTOS
NO PLATE PRICING DUE TO SCARCITY
AH Aaron Harang 6.00 15.00
AR Aaron Rowand 6.00 15.00
BA Bronson Arroyo 10.00 25.00
BC Brandon Claussen 4.00 10.00
BO Jeremy Bonderman 6.00 15.00
CA Carl Crawford 6.00 15.00
CC Coco Crisp 8.00 20.00
CH Chad Cordero 4.00 10.00
CI Cesar Izturis 4.00 10.00
CL Cliff Lee 4.00 10.00
CO Craig Counsell 6.00 15.00
CU Chase Utley SP/100 * 20.00 50.00
DL Derrek Lee SP/43 *
GC Gustavo Chacin 4.00 10.00
HB Hank Blalock 6.00 15.00
JB Jason Bay 6.00 15.00
JG Jose Guillen 4.00 10.00
JH Jhonny Peralta 6.00 15.00
JK Jason Kendall SP/46 *
JM Justin Morneau 6.00 15.00
JP Joel Pineiro 4.00 10.00
JV Javier Vazquez 6.00 15.00
KG Ken Griffey Jr. 40.00 80.00
LH Livan Hernandez 4.00 10.00
MK Mark Kotsay 4.00 10.00
MT Mark Teixeira SP/25 *
OV Omar Vizquel 10.00 25.00
RA Aramis Ramirez 6.00 15.00
RO Roy Oswalt 6.00 15.00
RZ Ryan Zimmerman 15.00 40.00
SC Sean Casey 6.00 15.00
TH Travis Hafner 6.00 15.00
WP Wily Mo Pena 6.00 15.00
XN Xavier Nady 4.00 10.00

2006 Flair Showcase Fresh Ink

STATED ODDS 1:36 H, 1:576 R
SP PRINT RUNS PROVIDED BY UD
SP'S ARE NOT SERIAL-NUMBERED
NO SP PRICING ON QTY OF 43
PLATE ODDS: 1-2 PER HOBBY CASE
PLATE PRINT RUN 1 SET PER COLOR
BLACK-CYAN-MAGENTA-YELLOW ISSUED
PLATES DO NOT FEATURE AUTOS
NO PLATE PRICING DUE TO SCARCITY
BC Bobby Crosby 6.00 15.00
BM Brandon McCarthy 4.00 10.00
BR Brian Roberts 6.00 15.00
CB Clint Barmes 4.00 10.00
CC Chris Carpenter SP/43 *
CK Casey Kotchman 4.00 10.00
CS Chris Shelton 6.00 15.00
DD David DeJesus 4.00 10.00
DH Danny Haren 4.00 10.00
DW Dontrelle Willis 6.00 15.00
ES Ervin Santana 6.00 15.00
GA Garrett Atkins 4.00 10.00
GF Gavin Floyd 4.00 10.00
HA Rich Harden 6.00 15.00
HS Huston Street 6.00 15.00
JB Joe Blanton 4.00 10.00
JG Jonny Gomes 4.00 10.00
JM Joe Mauer SP/43 *
JR Jose Reyes SP/43 *
JS Johan Santana 15.00 40.00
KG Khalil Greene 10.00 25.00
KY Kevin Youkilis 6.00 15.00

MA Matt Cain 10.00 25.00
MC Miguel Cabrera 10.00 25.00
MT Mark Teahen 4.00 10.00
MY Michael Young SP/100 * 10.00 25.00
NL Noah Lowry 6.00 15.00
OP Odalis Perez 4.00 10.00
RE Jeremy Reed 4.00 10.00
RH Rich Hill 10.00 25.00
SK Scott Kazmir 8.00 20.00
TI Tadahito Iguchi 15.00 40.00
VM Victor Martinez 6.00 15.00
WR David Wright SP/100 * 30.00 60.00
ZG Zack Greinke 4.00 10.00

2006 Flair Showcase Hot Gloves

STATED ODDS 1:108 H, 1:576 R
STATED PRINT RUN B/WN 125-150 SETS
PRINT RUN INFO PROVIDED BY UD
CARDS ARE NOT SERIAL-NUMBERED
PLATE ODDS: 1-2 PER HOBBY CASE
PLATE PRINT RUN 1 SET PER COLOR
BLACK-CYAN-MAGENTA-YELLOW ISSUED
NO PLATE PRICING DUE TO SCARCITY
1 Derrek Lee 8.00 20.00
2 Andruw Jones 12.50 30.00
3 Bobby Abreu 8.00 20.00
4 Luis Castillo 8.00 20.00
5 Mike Matheny 8.00 20.00
6 Cesar Izturis 8.00 20.00
7 Craig Biggio 12.50 30.00
8 Darin Erstad 8.00 20.00
9 Derek Jeter 30.00 60.00
10 Eric Chavez 8.00 20.00
11 Greg Maddux 20.00 50.00
12 Ichiro Suzuki 30.00 60.00
13 Ivan Rodriguez 12.50 30.00
14 J.T. Snow 8.00 20.00
15 Jim Edmonds 12.50 30.00
16 Steve Finley 8.00 20.00
17 Kenny Rogers 8.00 20.00
18 Jason Varitek 12.50 30.00
19 Ken Griffey Jr. 30.00 60.00
20 Mark Teixeira 8.00 20.00
21 Orlando Hudson 8.00 20.00
22 Mike Hampton 8.00 20.00
23 Mike Mussina 12.50 30.00
24 Vernon Wells 8.00 20.00
25 Omar Vizquel 12.50 30.00
26 Alex Rodriguez 30.00 60.00
27 Mike Cameron 8.00 20.00
28 Scott Rolen 12.50 30.00
29 Todd Helton 12.50 30.00
30 Torii Hunter 8.00 20.00

2006 Flair Showcase Hot Numbers

STATED ODDS 1:6 H, 1:36 R
PLATE ODDS: 1-2 PER HOBBY CASE
PLATE PRINT RUN 1 SET PER COLOR
BLACK-CYAN-MAGENTA-YELLOW ISSUED
NO PLATE PRICING DUE TO SCARCITY
1 Albert Pujols 3.00 8.00
2 Alex Rodriguez 2.50 6.00
3 Andruw Jones 1.00 2.50
4 Bobby Abreu .60 1.50
5 Chipper Jones 1.50 4.00
6 Curt Schilling 1.00 2.50
7 David Ortiz 1.50 4.00
8 David Wright 2.50 6.00
9 Derek Jeter 4.00 10.00
10 Derrek Lee .60 1.50
11 Eric Gagne .60 1.50
12 Greg Maddux 2.50 6.00
13 Hideki Matsui 1.50 4.00
14 Ichiro Suzuki 2.50 6.00
15 Ivan Rodriguez 1.00 2.50
16 Johan Santana 1.00 2.50
17 Johnny Damon 1.00 2.50
18 Ken Griffey Jr. 2.50 6.00
19 Manny Ramirez 1.00 2.50
20 Mark Prior 1.00 2.50
21 Mark Teixeira 1.00 2.50
22 Miguel Cabrera 1.00 2.50
23 Miguel Tejada .60 1.50
24 Pedro Martinez 1.00 2.50
25 Randy Johnson 1.50 4.00
26 Rickie Weeks .60 1.50
27 Roger Clemens 3.00 8.00
28 Todd Helton 1.00 2.50
29 Torii Hunter .60 1.50
30 Vladimir Guerrero 1.50 4.00

2006 Flair Showcase Lettermen

RANDOM INSERTS IN HOBBY PACKS
PRINT RUNS B/WN 3-9 #'d COPIES PER
NO PRICING DUE TO SCARCITY
AJ Andruw Jones/5
AP Albert Pujols/6
AR Aramis Ramirez/7
AS Alfonso Soriano/7

BA Bobby Abreu/5
BR Brian Roberts/7
CB Carlos Beltran/7
CD Carlos Delgado/7
CJ Craig Biggio/6
DL Derrek Lee/3
DO David Ortiz/5
EC Eric Chavez/6
ED Jim Edmonds/7
GM Greg Maddux/6
GR Khalil Greene/6
IR Ivan Rodriguez/9
JM Joe Mauer/5
JO Chipper Jones/5
JP Jake Peavy/5
JS Johan Santana/7
JT Jim Thome/5
KG Ken Griffey Jr./7
LG Luis Gonzalez/8
MC Miguel Cabrera/7
MT Mark Teixeira/8
MY Michael Young/5
PM Pedro Martinez/8
RH Roy Halladay/8
SM John Smoltz/6
SR Scott Rolen/5
TE Miguel Tejada/6
TH Todd Helton/6
TO Torii Hunter/6
VG Vladimir Guerrero/8
WI Dontrelle Willis/6
WR David Wright/6

2006 Flair Showcase Signatures

RANDOM INSERTS IN HOBBY PACKS
STATED PRINT RUN 35 SERIAL #'d SETS
NO PRICING DUE TO SCARCITY
PLATE ODDS: 1-2 PER HOBBY CASE
PLATE PRINT RUN 1 SET PER COLOR
BLACK-CYAN-MAGENTA-YELLOW ISSUED
PLATES DO NOT FEATURE AUTOS
NO PLATE PRICING DUE TO SCARCITY
AH Aaron Harang
AR Aaron Rowand
BA Bronson Arroyo
BC Brandon Claussen
BL Joe Blanton
BM Brandon McCarthy
BR Brian Roberts
BY Bobby Crosby
CA Matt Cain
CB Clint Barmes
CC Craig Counsell
CD Chad Cordero
CH Chris Carpenter
CI Cesar Izturis
CK Casey Kotchman
CL Cliff Lee
CO Coco Crisp
CS Chris Shelton
CU Chase Utley
CW Carl Crawford
DD David DeJesus
DH Danny Haren
DL Derrek Lee
DW Dontrelle Willis
ES Ervin Santana
GA Garrett Atkins
GC Gustavo Chacin
GF Gavin Floyd
GO Jonny Gomes
GR Khalil Greene
HA Rich Harden
HB Hank Blalock
HO Ryan Howard
HS Huston Street
JA Jason Bay
JE Jeremy Bonderman
JG Jose Guillen
JK Jason Kendall
JM Justin Morneau
JP Jake Peavy
JR Jose Reyes
JS Johan Santana
KG Ken Griffey Jr.
KY Kevin Youkilis
LH Livan Hernandez
MA Joe Mauer
MC Miguel Cabrera
MK Mark Kotsay
MT Mark Teixeira
MY Michael Young
NL Noah Lowry
OP Odalis Perez
OV Omar Vizquel
PE Jhonny Peralta
PF Prince Fielder
PI Joel Pineiro
RA Aramis Ramirez
RE Jeremy Reed
RH Rich Hill
RO Roy Oswalt
RY Roy Halladay
RZ Ryan Zimmerman
SC Sean Casey
SK Scott Kazmir
TE Mark Teahen
TH Travis Hafner
TI Tadahito Iguchi
VA Javier Vazquez
VM Victor Martinez
WM Wily Mo Pena
WR David Wright
XN Xavier Nady
YB Yuniesky Betancourt
ZG Zack Greinke

2006 Flair Showcase Stitches

OVERALL GU ODDS 1:9 H, 1:18 R
AB Adrian Beltre Jsy 3.00 8.00
AD Adam Dunn Jsy 3.00 8.00
AJ Andruw Jones Jsy 4.00 10.00
AN Andy Pettitte Jsy 4.00 10.00
AP Albert Pujols Pants 8.00 20.00
AR Aramis Ramirez Jsy 3.00 8.00
AS Alfonso Soriano Jsy 3.00 8.00
BA Bobby Abreu Jsy 3.00 8.00
BC Bobby Crosby Jsy 3.00 8.00
BG Brian Giles Jsy 3.00 8.00
BO Jeremy Bonderman Jsy 3.00 8.00
BR Brian Roberts Jsy 3.00 8.00
BS Ben Sheets Jsy 3.00 8.00
BZ Barry Zito Jsy 3.00 8.00
CA Carl Crawford Jsy 3.00 8.00
CB Carlos Beltran Jsy 3.00 8.00
CC C.C. Sabathia Jsy 3.00 8.00
CD Carlos Delgado Jsy 3.00 8.00
CJ Chipper Jones Jsy 4.00 10.00
CL Carlos Lee Jsy 3.00 8.00
CO Michael Collins Jsy 3.00 8.00
CS Curt Schilling Jsy 4.00 10.00
DJ Derek Jeter Pants 8.00 20.00
DL Derrek Lee Jsy 3.00 8.00
DM Daisuke Matsuzaka Jsy 20.00 50.00
DO David Ortiz Jsy 4.00 10.00
DR J.D. Drew Jsy 3.00 8.00
DW Dontrelle Willis Jsy 3.00 8.00
EC Eric Chavez Jsy 3.00 8.00
EG Eric Gagne Jsy 3.00 8.00
FG Freddy Garcia Jsy 3.00 8.00
FR Francisco Rodriguez Jsy 3.00 8.00
FT Frank Thomas Jsy 4.00 10.00
GM Greg Maddux Jsy 4.00 10.00
GR Khalil Greene Jsy 3.00 8.00
GS Gary Sheffield Jsy 3.00 8.00
HA J.J. Hardy Jsy 3.00 8.00
HB Hank Blalock Jsy 3.00 8.00
HO Trevor Hoffman Jsy 3.00 8.00
HU Tim Hudson Jsy 3.00 8.00
IR Ivan Rodriguez Jsy 4.00 10.00
JA Jason Schmidt Jsy 3.00 8.00
JC Jorge Cantu Jsy 3.00 8.00
JD Johnny Damon Jsy 4.00 10.00
JE Jim Edmonds Jsy 3.00 8.00
JG Jason Giambi Jsy 3.00 8.00
JJ Jacque Jones Jsy 3.00 8.00
JK Jeff Kent Jsy 3.00 8.00
JL Javy Lopez Jsy 3.00 8.00
JM Joe Mauer Jsy 4.00 10.00
JO Josh Beckett Jsy 3.00 8.00
JP Jake Peavy Jsy 3.00 8.00
JR Jose Reyes Jsy 3.00 8.00
JS Johan Santana Jsy 4.00 10.00
JT Jim Thome Jsy 4.00 10.00
JU Juan Uribe Jsy 3.00 8.00
JV Jason Varitek Jsy 4.00 10.00
KE Kevin Millwood Jsy 3.00 8.00
KG Ken Griffey Jr. Jsy 6.00 15.00
KM Kazuo Matsui Jsy 3.00 8.00
KW Kerry Wood Jsy 3.00 8.00
LB Lance Berkman Jsy 3.00 8.00
LG Luis Gonzalez Jsy 3.00 8.00
MA Moises Alou Jsy 3.00 8.00
MB Mark Buehrle Jsy 3.00 8.00
MC Miguel Cabrera Jsy 4.00 10.00
MH Matt Holliday Jsy 4.00 10.00
MI Mike Piazza Jsy 4.00 10.00
MM Mike Mussina Jsy 4.00 10.00
MP Mark Prior Jsy 3.00 8.00
MR Manny Ramirez Jsy 4.00 10.00
MT Mark Teixeira Jsy 3.00 8.00
MY Michael Young Jsy 3.00 8.00
OV Omar Vizquel Jsy 4.00 10.00
PL Paul Lo Duca Jsy 3.00 8.00
PM Pedro Martinez Jsy 4.00 10.00
PW Preston Wilson Jsy 3.00 8.00
RB Rocco Baldelli Jsy 3.00 8.00
RC Robinson Cano Jsy 6.00 15.00
RE Jeremy Reed Jsy 3.00 8.00
RF Rafael Furcal Jsy 3.00 8.00
RH Roy Halladay Jsy 3.00 8.00
RI Rich Harden Jsy 3.00 8.00
RJ Randy Johnson Jsy 4.00 10.00
RS Richie Sexson Jsy 3.00 8.00
RW Rickie Weeks Jsy 3.00 8.00
SK Scott Kazmir Jsy 3.00 8.00
SM John Smoltz Jsy 4.00 10.00
SR Scott Rolen Jsy 4.00 10.00
SW Mike Sweeney Jsy 3.00 8.00
TE Miguel Tejada Jsy 3.00 8.00
TG Tom Glavine Jsy 4.00 10.00
TH Todd Helton Jsy 4.00 10.00
TN Trot Nixon Jsy 3.00 8.00
TO Torii Hunter Jsy 3.00 8.00
TR Travis Hafner Jsy 3.00 8.00
VG Vladimir Guerrero Jsy 4.00 10.00
VW Vernon Wells Jsy 3.00 8.00
WR David Wright Jsy 4.00 10.00

2006 Flair Showcase Wave of the Future

STATED ODDS 1:3 H, 1:36 R
PLATE ODDS: 1-2 PER HOBBY CASE
PLATE PRINT RUN 1 SET PER COLOR
BLACK-CYAN-MAGENTA-YELLOW ISSUED
NO PLATE PRICING DUE TO SCARCITY
1 Jeremy Hermida .40 1.00
2 Kelly Shoppach .40 1.00
3 Adam Wainwright .40 1.00
4 Ryan Zimmerman 2.50 6.00
5 Josh Willingham .40 1.00
6 Brandon McCarthy .40 1.00
7 Conor Jackson .60 1.50
8 Grady Sizemore .60 1.50
9 Curtis Granderson .40 1.00
10 Jose Capellan .40 1.00
11 Mike Jacobs .40 1.00
12 Gavin Floyd .40 1.00
13 Hanley Ramirez 1.00 2.50
14 Jason Kubel .40 1.00
15 Nate McLouth .40 1.00
16 Felix Hernandez .60 1.50
17 Jeff Francoeur 1.00 2.50
18 Wil Nieves .40 1.00
19 Cody Ross .40 1.00
20 Justin Verlander 1.50 4.00
21 Ben Johnson .40 1.00
22 Guillermo Quiroz .40 1.00
23 Jonathan Papelbon 2.00 5.00
24 Prince Fielder 1.50 4.00
25 Rickie Weeks .40 1.00
26 Robinson Cano .60 1.50
27 Kenji Johjima 2.00 5.00
28 Anderson Hernandez .40 1.00
29 Yuniesky Betancourt .40 1.00
30 Zach Duke .40 1.00

2006 Flair Showcase World Baseball Classic

STATED ODDS 1:8 H, 1:36 R
PLATE ODDS: 1-2 PER HOBBY CASE
PLATE PRINT RUN 1 SET PER COLOR
BLACK-CYAN-MAGENTA-YELLOW ISSUED
NO PLATE PRICING DUE TO SCARCITY
1 Adam Stern .75 2.00
2 Jason Bay .75 2.00
3 Wei Wang .75 2.00
4 Yung Chi Chen 2.50 6.00
5 Pedro Lazo 1.25 3.00
6 Yoandy Garlobo .75 2.00
7 Ormari Romero .75 2.00
8 Frederich Cepeda .75 2.00
9 Yulieski Gourriel .75 2.00
10 Yadel Marti .75 2.00
11 David Ortiz 1.25 3.00
12 Albert Pujols 3.00 8.00
13 Adrian Beltre .75 2.00
14 Alberto Castillo .75 2.00
15 Odalis Perez .75 2.00
16 Jason Grilli .75 2.00
17 Daisuke Matsuzaka 8.00 20.00
18 Sadaharu Oh 6.00 15.00
19 Nobuhiko Matsunaka 2.00 5.00
20 Ichiro Suzuki 3.00 8.00
21 Akinori Otsuka 2.00 5.00
22 Koji Uehara 2.00 5.00
23 Kosuke Fukudome 2.00 5.00
24 Daisuke Matsuzaka 8.00 20.00
25 Ichiro Suzuki 3.00 8.00
26 Seung Yeop Lee 1.25 3.00
27 Seung Yeop Lee 1.25 3.00
28 Jong Beom Lee .75 2.00
29 Jae Seo .75 2.00
30 Chan Ho Park .75 2.00
31 Hee Seop Choi .75 2.00
32 Jorge Cantu .75 2.00
33 Oliver Perez .75 2.00
34 Vinny Castilla .75 2.00
35 Esteban Loaiza .75 2.00
36 Shairon Martis .75 2.00
37 Bernie Williams 1.25 3.00
38 Javier Vazquez .75 2.00
39 Carlos Beltran .75 2.00
40 Bernie Williams 1.25 3.00
41 Roger Clemens 3.00 8.00
42 Ken Griffey Jr. 3.00 8.00
43 Alex Rodriguez 3.00 8.00
44 Derrek Lee .75 2.00
45 Derek Jeter 4.00 10.00
46 Chipper Jones 2.00 5.00
47 Miguel Cabrera 1.25 3.00
48 Francisco Rodriguez .75 2.00
49 Victor Martinez .75 2.00
50 Freddy Garcia .75 2.00

1959 Fleer Ted Williams

The cards in this 80-card set measure 2 1/2" by 3 1/2". The 1959 Fleer set, with a catalog designation of R418-1, portrays the life of Ted Williams. The wording of the wrapper, "Baseball's Greatest Series," has led to speculation that Fleer contemplated

similar sets honoring other baseball immortals, but chose to develop instead the format of the 1960 and 1961 issues. These packs contained either six or eight cards. The packs cost a nickel and were packed 24 to a box which were packed 24 to a case. Card number 68, which was withdrawn early in production, is considered scarce and has even been counterfeited; the fake has a rosy coloration and a cross-hatch pattern visible over the picture area. The card numbering is arranged essentially in chronological order.

COMPLETE SET (80) 900.00 1500.00
WRAPPER (6-CARD) 100.00 125.00
WRAPPER (8-CARD) 100.00 150.00
1 Ted Williams 60.00 100.00
The Early Years
Choosing up sides
on the sandlots
2 Ted Williams 60.00 100.00
Babe Ruth
Meeting boyhood idol
Babe Ruth
3 Ted Williams 7.50 15.00
Practice Makes Perfect
At plate practicing on the sandlots
4 Ted Williams 7.50 15.00
Learns Fine Points
Sliding at Herbert Hoover High
5 Ted Williams 7.50 15.00
Ted's Fame Spreads
At plate at Herbert Hoover High
6 Ted Williams 12.50 25.00
Ted Turns Pro
Portrait
San Diego Padres
PCL League
uniform)
7 Ted Williams 7.50 15.00
From Mound to Plate
At plate
San Diego Padres, PCL
8 Ted Williams 7.50 15.00
1937 First Full Season
Making a leaping catch
9 Ted Williams 10.00 20.00
Eddie Collins
First Step to Majors
10 Ted Williams 7.50 15.00
Gunning as Pastime
Wearing hunting gear, taking aim
11 Ted Williams 20.00 40.00
Jimmie Foxx
First Spring Training
12 Ted Williams 10.00 20.00
Burning Up Minors
Pitching for Minneapolis
American Association
13 Ted Williams 7.50 15.00
1939 Shows Will Stay
Follow-through
14 Ted Williams 7.50 15.00
Outstanding Rookie '39
Follow-through
15 Ted Williams 10.00 20.00
Licks Sophomore Jinx
Sliding into third base
for a triple
16 Ted Williams 7.50 15.00
1941 Greatest Year
Follow-through at plate
17 Ted Williams 20.00 40.00
How Ted Hit .400
Youthful Williams
as he looked in '41
18 Ted Williams 10.00 20.00
1941 All Star Hero
Crossing plate
after home run
19 Ted Williams 7.50 15.00
Wins Triple Crown
Crossing plate at Fenway Park
20 Ted Williams 7.50 15.00
On to Naval Training
In training plane
at Amherst College
21 Ted Williams 7.50 15.00
Honors for Williams
Receiving 1942 Sporting News POY
22 Ted Williams 7.50 15.00
1944 Ted Solos
In cockpit at
Pensacola, FL Navy Air Station
23 Ted Williams 7.50 15.00
Williams Wins Wings
Wearing Naval
Aviation Cadet uniform
24 Ted Williams 7.50 15.00
1945 Sharpshooter
Taking Naval eye test
25 Ted Williams 7.50 15.00
1945 Ted Discharged
In cockpit, giving
the thumbs up
26 Ted Williams 7.50 15.00
Off to Flying Start
In batters box
spring training, 1946
27 Ted Williams 7.50 15.00
7/9/46 One Man Show
Riding blooper pitch out of park
28 Ted Williams 7.50 15.00
The Williams Shift
Diagram of Cleveland Indians
position shift to defense Williams
29 Ted Williams 10.00 20.00
Ted Hits for Cycle
Close-up of follow through
30 Ted Williams 7.50 15.00
Beating Williams Shift
Crossing plate after home run
31 Ted Williams 10.00 20.00
Sox Lose Series
Sliding across plate
Sept. 14, 1946
32 Ted Williams 7.50 15.00
Joseph Cashman
Most Valuable Player
Receiving MVP Award
33 Ted Williams 7.50 15.00
Another Triple Crown
Famous Williams' Grip
34 Ted Williams 7.50 15.00
Runs Scored Record
Sliding into 2nd base
in 1947 AS Game
35 Ted Williams 7.50 15.00
Sox Miss Pennant
Checking weight on
new 36 oz. hickory bat
36 Ted Williams 7.50 15.00
Banner Year for Ted
Bunting down the
3rd base line
37 Ted Williams 7.50 15.00
1949 Sox Miss Again
Two moods: grim and determined
smiling and happy
38 Ted Williams 7.50 15.00
1949 Power Rampage
Full shot of his
batting follow through
39 Ted Williams 12.50 25.00
Joe Cronin
Eddie Collins
1950 Great Start
Signing $125,000 contract
40 Ted Williams 7.50 15.00
Ted Crashes into Wall
Making catch in
1950 All Star game
and crashing into wall
41 Ted Williams 7.50 15.00
1950 Ted Recovers
Recuperating from elbow operation
in hospital
42 Ted Williams 7.50 15.00
Tom Yawkey
Slowed by Injury
43 Ted Williams 7.50 15.00
Double Play Lead
Leaping high to
make great catch
44 Ted Williams 7.50 15.00
Back to Marines
Hanging up number 9
prior to leaving for Marines
45 Ted Williams 7.50 15.00
Farewell to Baseball
Honored at Fenway Park
prior to return to service
46 Ted Williams 7.50 15.00
Ready for Combat
Drawing jet pilot equipment
in Willow Grove
47 Ted Williams 7.50 15.00
Ted Crash Lands Jet
In flying gear
and jet he crash landed in
48 Ted Williams 10.00 20.00
Ford Frick
1953 Ted Returns
Throwing out 1st ball
at All-Star Game in Cincinnati
49 Ted Williams 7.50 15.00
Smash Return
Giving his arm
whirlpool treatment
50 Ted Williams 12.50 25.00
1954 Spring Injury
Full batting pose at plate
51 Ted Williams 7.50 15.00
Ted is Patched Up
In first workout after
fractured collar bone
52 Ted Williams 10.00 20.00
1954 Ted's Comeback
Hitting a home run
against Detroit
53 Ted Williams 7.50 15.00
Comeback is Success
Beating catcher's
tag at home plate
54 Ted Williams 7.50 15.00
Ted Hooks Big One
With prize catch
1235 lb. black marlin
55 Ted Williams 10.00 20.00
Joe Cronin
Retirement 'No Go'
Returning from retirement
56 Ted Williams 7.50 15.00
2,000th Hit
8/11/55
57 Ted Williams 10.00 20.00
400th Homer
In locker room
58 Ted Williams 7.50 15.00
Williams Hits .388
Four-picture sequence
of his batting swing
59 Ted Williams 7.50 15.00
Hot September for Ted
Full shot of follow through
at plate
60 Ted Williams 7.50 15.00
More Records for Ted
Swinging and missing
61 Ted Williams 10.00 20.00
1957 Outfielder
Warming up prior
to ball game
62 Ted Williams 7.50 15.00
1958 Sixth Batting Title
Slamming pitch into stands
63 Ted Williams 50.00 80.00
Ted's All-Star Record
Portrait and facsimile autograph
64 Ted Williams 7.50 15.00

Barbara Williams
Daughter and Daddy
In uniform holding his daughter
65 Ted Williams 10.00 20.00
1958 August 30
Determination on face
connecting with ball
66 Ted Williams 7.50 15.00
1958 Powerhouse
Stance and follow through
in batters box
67 Ted Williams 20.00 40.00
Sam Snead
Two Famous Fishermen
testing fishing equipment
68 Ted Williams 400.00 700.00
Bucky Harris
Ted Signs for 1959 SP
signing contract
69 Ted Williams 7.50 15.00
A Future Ted Williams
With eager, young newcomer
70 Ted Williams 20.00 40.00
Jim Thorpe
at Sportsmen's Show
71 Ted Williams 7.50 15.00
Hitting Fund. 1
Proper gripping of
a baseball bat
72 Ted Williams 7.50 15.00
Hitting Fund. 2
Checking his swing
73 Ted Williams 7.50 15.00
Hitting Fund. 3
Stance and follow-through
74 Ted Williams 7.50 15.00
Here's How
Demonstrating in locker room
an aspect of hitting
75 Ted Williams 30.00 50.00
Eddie Collins
Babe Ruth
Williams' Value to Sox
76 Ted Williams 7.50 15.00
On Base Record
Awaiting intentional walk
to first base
77 Ted Williams 7.50 15.00
Ted Relaxes
Displaying bonefish
which he caught
78 Ted Williams 7.50 15.00
Rep. Joe Martin
Justice Earl Warren
Honors for Williams
Clark Griffith Memorial Award
79 Ted Williams 12.50 25.00
Where Ted Stands
Wielding giant eight foot bat
when honored as modern-day Paul Bunyan
80 Ted Williams 20.00 40.00
Ted's Goals for 1959
Admiring his portrait

1960 Fleer

The cards in this 79-card set measure 2 1/2" by 3 1/2". The cards from the 1960 Fleer series of Baseball Greats are sometimes mistaken for 1930s cards by collectors not familiar with this set. The cards each contain a tinted photo of a baseball immortal, and were issued in one series. There are no known scarcities, although a number 80 card (Pepper Martin reverse with Eddie Collins, Joe Tinker or Lefty Grove obverse) exists (this is not considered part of the set). The catalog designation for 1960 Fleer is R418-2. The cards were printed on a 96-card sheet with 17 double prints. These are noted in the checklist below by DP. On the sheet the second Eddie Collins card is typically found in the number 80 position. According to correspondence sent from Fleers at the time -- no card 80 was issued because of contract problems. Some cards have been discovered with wrong backs. The cards were issued in nickel packs which were packed 24 to a box.

COMPLETE SET (79) 300.00 600.00
WRAPPER 50.00 100.00
1 Napoleon Lajoie DP 12.50 30.00
2 Christy Mathewson 6.00 15.00
3 Babe Ruth 50.00 100.00
4 Carl Hubbell 3.00 8.00
5 Grover C. Alexander 3.00 8.00
6 Walter Johnson DP 4.00 10.00
7 Chief Bender 1.50 4.00
8 Roger Bresnahan 1.50 4.00
9 Mordecai Brown 1.50 4.00
10 Tris Speaker 3.00 8.00
11 Arky Vaughan DP 1.50 4.00
12 Zach Wheat 1.50 4.00
13 George Sisler 1.50 4.00
14 Connie Mack 3.00 8.00
15 Clark Griffith 1.50 4.00
16 Lou Boudreau DP 3.00 8.00
17 Ernie Lombardi 1.50 4.00
18 Heinie Manush 1.50 4.00
19 Marty Marion 2.50 6.00
20 Eddie Collins DP 1.50 4.00
21 Rabbit Maranville DP 1.50 4.00
22 Joe Medwick 1.50 4.00
23 Ed Barrow 1.50 4.00
24 Mickey Cochrane 2.50 6.00
25 Jimmy Collins 1.50 4.00
26 Bob Feller DP 6.00 15.00
27 Luke Appling 2.50 6.00
28 Lou Gehrig 40.00 80.00
29 Gabby Hartnett 1.50 4.00
30 Chuck Klein 1.50 4.00
31 Tony Lazzeri DP 2.50 6.00
32 Al Simmons 1.50 4.00
33 Wilbert Robinson 1.50 4.00
34 Sam Rice 1.50 4.00
35 Herb Pennock 1.50 4.00
36 Mel Ott DP 3.00 8.00
37 Lefty O'Doul 1.50 4.00
38 Johnny Mize 3.00 8.00
39 Edmund (Bing) Miller 1.50 4.00
40 Joe Tinker 1.50 4.00
41 Frank Baker DP 1.50 4.00
42 Ty Cobb 30.00 60.00
43 Paul Derringer 1.50 4.00
44 Cap Anson 1.50 4.00
45 Jim Bottomley 1.50 4.00
46 Eddie Plank DP 1.50 4.00
47 Denton (Cy) Young 4.00 10.00
48 Hack Wilson 2.50 6.00
49 Ed Walsh UER 1.50 4.00
(Photo actually
Ed Walsh Jr.)
50 Frank Chance 1.50 4.00
51 Dazzy Vance DP 1.50 4.00
52 Bill Terry 2.50 6.00
53 Jimmie Foxx 4.00 10.00
54 Lefty Gomez 3.00 8.00
55 Branch Rickey 1.50 4.00
56 Ray Schalk DP 1.50 4.00
57 Johnny Evers 1.50 4.00
58 Charley Gehringer 2.50 6.00
59 Burleigh Grimes 1.50 4.00
60 Lefty Grove 3.00 8.00
61 Rube Waddell DP 1.50 4.00
62 John(Honus) Wagner 6.00 15.00
63 Red Ruffing 1.50 4.00
64 Kenesaw M. Landis 1.50 4.00
65 Harry Heilmann 1.50 4.00
66 John McGraw DP 1.50 4.00
67 Hughie Jennings 1.50 4.00
68 Hal Newhouser 2.50 6.00
69 Waite Hoyt 1.50 4.00
70 Bobo Newsom 1.50 4.00
71 Earl Averill DP 1.50 4.00
72 Ted Williams 40.00 80.00
73 Warren Giles 2.50 6.00
74 Ford Frick 2.50 6.00
75 Kiki Cuyler 1.50 4.00
76 Paul Waner DP 2.50 6.00
77 Pie Traynor 1.50 4.00
78 Lloyd Waner 1.50 4.00
79 Ralph Kiner 4.00 10.00
80A Pepper Martin SP 1250.00 2500.00
Eddie Collins
pictured on obverse
80B Pepper Martin SP 1000.00 2000.00
Lefty Grove
pictured on obverse
80C Pepper Martin SP 1000.00 2000.00
Joe Tinker on Front

1961 Fleer

The cards in this 154-card set measure 2 1/2" by 3 1/2". In 1961, Fleer continued its Baseball Greats format by issuing this series of cards. The set was released in two distinct series, 1-88 and 89-154 (of which the latter is more difficult to obtain). The players within each series are conveniently numbered in alphabetical order. The catalog number for this set is F418-3. In each first series pack Fleer inserted a Major League team decal and a pennant sticker honoring past World Series winners. The cards were issued in nickel packs which were issued 24 to a box.

COMPLETE SET (154) 600.00 1200.00
COMMON CARD (1-88) 1.25 3.00
COMMON CARD (89-154) 3.00 8.00
WRAPPER (5-CENT) 50.00 100.00
1 Frank Baker CL 20.00 50.00
Ty Cobb
Zack Wheat
2 Grover C. Alexander 2.50 6.00
3 Nick Altrock 1.25 3.00
4 Cap Anson 1.50 4.00
5 Earl Averill 1.50 4.00
6 Frank Baker 1.50 4.00
7 Dave Bancroft 1.50 4.00
8 Chief Bender 1.50 4.00
9 Jim Bottomley 1.50 4.00
10 Roger Bresnahan 1.50 4.00
11 Mordecai Brown 1.50 4.00
12 Max Carey 1.50 4.00
13 Jack Chesbro 1.50 4.00
14 Ty Cobb 20.00 50.00
15 Mickey Cochrane 1.50 4.00
16 Eddie Collins 2.50 6.00
17 Earle Combs 1.50 4.00
18 Charles Comiskey 1.50 4.00
19 Kiki Cuyler 1.50 4.00
20 Paul Derringer 1.25 3.00
21 Howard Ehmke 1.25 3.00
22 Billy Evans UMP 1.50 4.00
23 Johnny Evers 1.50 4.00
24 Urban Faber 1.50 4.00
25 Bob Feller 5.00 12.00
26 Wes Ferrell 1.25 3.00
27 Lew Fonseca 1.25 3.00
28 Jimmie Foxx 2.50 6.00
29 Ford Frick 1.25 3.00
30 Frankie Frisch 1.50 4.00
31 Lou Gehrig 40.00 80.00
32 Charley Gehringer 1.50 4.00
33 Warren Giles 1.25 3.00
34 Lefty Gomez 1.50 4.00
35 Goose Goslin 1.50 4.00
36 Clark Griffith 1.50 4.00
37 Burleigh Grimes 1.50 4.00
38 Lefty Grove 2.50 6.00
39 Chick Hafey 1.50 4.00
40 Jesse Haines 1.50 4.00
41 Gabby Hartnett 1.50 4.00
42 Harry Heilmann 1.50 4.00
43 Rogers Hornsby 2.50 6.00
44 Waite Hoyt 1.50 4.00
45 Carl Hubbell 2.50 6.00
46 Miller Huggins 1.50 4.00
47 Hughie Jennings 1.50 4.00
48 Ban Johnson 1.50 4.00
49 Walter Johnson 5.00 12.00
50 Ralph Kiner 2.50 6.00
51 Chuck Klein 1.50 4.00
52 Johnny Kling 1.25 3.00
53 Kenesaw M. Landis 1.50 4.00
54 Tony Lazzeri 1.50 4.00
55 Ernie Lombardi 1.50 4.00
56 Dolf Luque 1.25 3.00
57 Heinie Manush 1.50 4.00
58 Marty Marion 1.25 3.00
59 Christy Mathewson 5.00 12.00
60 John McGraw 1.50 4.00
61 Joe Medwick 1.50 4.00
62 Edmund (Bing) Miller 1.25 3.00
63 Johnny Mize 1.50 4.00
64 John Mostil 1.25 3.00
65 Art Nehf 1.25 3.00
66 Hal Newhouser 1.50 4.00
67 Bobo Newsom 1.25 3.00
68 Mel Ott 2.50 6.00
69 Allie Reynolds 1.25 3.00
70 Sam Rice 1.50 4.00
71 Eppa Rixey 1.50 4.00
72 Edd Roush 1.50 4.00
73 Schoolboy Rowe 1.25 3.00
74 Red Ruffing 1.50 4.00
75 Babe Ruth 60.00 120.00
76 Joe Sewell 1.50 4.00
77 Al Simmons 1.50 4.00
78 George Sisler 1.50 4.00
79 Tris Speaker 1.50 4.00
80 Fred Toney 1.25 3.00
81 Dazzy Vance 1.50 4.00
82 Hippo Vaughn 1.25 3.00
83 Ed Walsh 1.50 4.00
84 Lloyd Waner 1.50 4.00
85 Paul Waner 1.50 4.00
86 Zack Wheat 1.50 4.00
87 Hack Wilson 1.50 4.00
88 Jimmy Wilson 1.25 3.00
89 George Sisler CL 30.00 60.00
Pie Traynor
90 Babe Adams 3.00 8.00
91 Dale Alexander 3.00 8.00
92 Jim Bagby 3.00 8.00
93 Ossie Bluege 3.00 8.00
94 Lou Boudreau 4.00 10.00
95 Tommy Bridges 3.00 8.00
96 Donie Bush 3.00 8.00
97 Dolph Camilli 3.00 8.00
98 Frank Chance 4.00 10.00
99 Jimmy Collins 4.00 10.00
100 Stan Coveleskie 4.00 10.00
101 Hugh Critz 3.00 8.00
102 Alvin Crowder 3.00 8.00
103 Joe Dugan 3.00 8.00
104 Bibb Falk 3.00 8.00
105 Rick Ferrell 4.00 10.00
106 Art Fletcher 3.00 8.00
107 Dennis Galehouse 3.00 8.00
108 Chick Galloway 3.00 8.00
109 Mule Haas 3.00 8.00
110 Stan Hack 3.00 8.00
111 Bump Hadley 3.00 8.00
112 Billy Hamilton 4.00 10.00
113 Joe Hauser 3.00 8.00
114 Babe Herman 3.00 8.00
115 Travis Jackson 4.00 10.00
116 Eddie Joost 3.00 8.00
117 Addie Joss 4.00 10.00
118 Joe Judge 3.00 8.00
119 Joe Kuhel 3.00 8.00
120 Napoleon Lajoie 5.00 12.00
121 Dutch Leonard 3.00 8.00
122 Ted Lyons 4.00 10.00
123 Connie Mack 5.00 12.00
124 Rabbit Maranville 4.00 10.00
125 Fred Marberry 3.00 8.00
126 Joe McGinnity 4.00 10.00
127 Oscar Melillo 3.00 8.00
128 Ray Mueller 3.00 8.00
129 Kid Nichols 4.00 10.00
130 Lefty O'Doul 4.00 10.00
131 Bob O'Farrell 3.00 8.00
132 Roger Peckinpaugh 3.00 8.00
133 Herb Pennock 4.00 10.00
134 George Pipgras 3.00 8.00
135 Eddie Plank 4.00 10.00
136 Ray Schalk 4.00 10.00
137 Hal Schumacher 3.00 8.00
138 Luke Sewell 3.00 8.00
139 Bob Shawkey 3.00 8.00
140 Riggs Stephenson 3.00 8.00
141 Billy Sullivan 3.00 8.00
142 Bill Terry 5.00 12.00
143 Joe Tinker 4.00 10.00
144 Pie Traynor 4.00 10.00
145 Hal Trosky 3.00 8.00
146 George Uhle 3.00 8.00
147 Johnny VanderMeer 4.00 10.00
148 Arky Vaughan 4.00 10.00
149 Rube Waddell 4.00 10.00
150 Honus Wagner 20.00 50.00
151 Dixie Walker 3.00 8.00
152 Ted Williams 60.00 120.00
153 Cy Young 15.00 40.00
154 Ross Youngs 15.00 40.00

1963 Fleer

The Fleer set of current baseball players was marketed in 1963 in a gum card-style waxed wrapper package which contained a cherry cookie instead of gum. The five cent packs were packaged 24 to a box. The cards were printed in sheets of 66 with the scarce card of Joe Adcock (number 46) replaced by the unnumbered checklist card for the final press run. The complete set price includes the checklist card. The catalog designation for this set is R418-4. The key Rookie Card in this set is Maury Wills. The set is basically arranged numerically in alphabetical order by teams which are also in alphabetical order.

COMPLETE SET (67) 1000.00 2000.00
WRAPPER (5-CENT) 50.00 100.00
1 Steve Barber 10.00 25.00
2 Ron Hansen 6.00 15.00
3 Milt Pappas 8.00 20.00
4 Brooks Robinson 50.00 100.00
5 Willie Mays 100.00 200.00
6 Lou Clinton 6.00 15.00
7 Bill Monbouquette 6.00 15.00
8 Carl Yastrzemski 50.00 100.00
9 Ray Herbert 6.00 15.00
10 Jim Landis 6.00 15.00
11 Dick Donovan 6.00 15.00
12 Tito Francona 6.00 15.00
13 Jerry Kindall 6.00 15.00
14 Frank Lary 8.00 20.00
15 Dick Howser 8.00 20.00
16 Jerry Lumpe 6.00 15.00
17 Norm Siebern 6.00 15.00
18 Don Lee 6.00 15.00
19 Albie Pearson 8.00 20.00
20 Bob Rodgers 8.00 20.00
21 Leon Wagner 6.00 15.00
22 Jim Kaat 10.00 25.00
23 Vic Power 8.00 20.00
24 Rich Rollins 8.00 20.00
25 Bobby Richardson 10.00 25.00
26 Ralph Terry 8.00 20.00
27 Tom Cheney 6.00 15.00
28 Chuck Cottier 6.00 15.00
29 Jimmy Piersall 8.00 20.00
30 Dave Stenhouse 6.00 15.00
31 Glen Hobbie 6.00 15.00
32 Ron Santo 10.00 25.00
33 Gene Freese 6.00 15.00
34 Vada Pinson 10.00 25.00
35 Bob Purkey 6.00 15.00
36 Joe Amalfitano 6.00 15.00
37 Bob Aspromonte 6.00 15.00
38 Dick Farrell 6.00 15.00
39 Al Spangler 6.00 15.00
40 Tommy Davis 8.00 20.00
41 Don Drysdale 40.00 80.00
42 Sandy Koufax 100.00 200.00
43 Maury Wills RC 50.00 100.00
44 Frank Bolling 6.00 15.00
45 Warren Spahn 40.00 80.00
46 Joe Adcock SP 75.00 150.00
47 Roger Craig 8.00 20.00
48 Al Jackson 8.00 20.00
49 Rod Kanehl 8.00 20.00
50 Ruben Amaro 6.00 15.00
51 Johnny Callison 8.00 20.00
52 Clay Dalrymple 6.00 15.00
53 Don Demeter 6.00 15.00
54 Art Mahaffey 6.00 15.00
55 Smoky Burgess 8.00 20.00
56 Roberto Clemente 100.00 200.00
57 Roy Face 8.00 20.00
58 Vern Law 8.00 20.00
59 Bill Mazeroski 12.50 30.00
60 Ken Boyer 10.00 25.00
61 Bob Gibson 40.00 80.00
62 Gene Oliver 6.00 15.00
63 Bill White 8.00 20.00
64 Orlando Cepeda 12.50 30.00
65 Jim Davenport 6.00 15.00
66 Billy O'Dell 10.00 25.00
NNO Checklist card 250.00 500.00

1981 Fleer

This issue of cards marks Fleer's first modern era entry into the current player baseball card market since 1963. Unopened packs contained 17 cards as well as a piece of gum. Unopened boxes contained 38 packs. As a matter of fact, the boxes actually told the retailer there was extra profit as they were charged as if there were 36 packs in the box. These cards were packed 20 boxes to a case. Cards are grouped in team order and teams are ordered based upon their standings from the 1980 season with the World Series champion Philadelphia Phillies starting off the set. Cards 638-660 feature specials and checklists. The cards of pitchers in this set erroneously show a heading (on the card backs) of "Batting Record" over their career pitching statistics. There were three distinct printings: the two following the primary run were designed to correct numerous errors. The variations caused by these multiple printings are noted in the checklist below (P1, P2, or P3). The Craig Nettles variation was corrected before the end of the first printing and thus is not included in the complete set consideration due to scarcity. The key Rookie Cards in this set are Danny Ainge, Harold Baines, Kirk Gibson, Jeff Reardon, and Fernando Valenzuela, whose first name was erroneously spelled Fernand on the card front.

COMPLETE SET (660) 15.00 40.00
1 Pete Rose UER 1.25 3.00
270 hits in 63
should be 170
2 Larry Bowa .08 .25
3 Manny Trillo .02 .10
4 Bob Boone .08 .25
5 Mike Schmidt 1.00 2.50
See also 640A
6 Steve Carlton P1 .20 .50
Golden Arm
Back 1066 Cardinals
Number on back 6
6B Steve Carlton P2 .60 1.50
Pitcher of Year
Back 1066 Cardinals
6C Steve Carlton P3 .75 2.00
1966 Cardinals
7 Tug McGraw .08 .25
See 657A
8 Larry Christenson .02 .10
9 Bake McBride .08 .25
10 Greg Luzinski .08 .25
11 Ron Reed .02 .10
12 Dickie Noles .02 .10
13 Keith Moreland RC .02 .10
14 Bob Walk RC .20 .50
15 Lonnie Smith .08 .25
16 Dick Ruthven .02 .10
17 Sparky Lyle .08 .25
18 Greg Gross .02 .10
19 Garry Maddox .02 .10
20 Nino Espinosa .02 .10
21 George Vukovich RC .02 .10
22 John Vukovich .02 .10
23 Ramon Aviles .02 .10
24A Kevin Saucier P1 .02 .10
Name on back Ken
24B Kevin Saucier P2 .02 .10
Name on back Ken
24C Kevin Saucier P3 .20 .50
Name on back Kevin
25 Randy Lerch .02 .10
26 Del Unser .02 .10
27 Tim McCarver .08 .25
28 George Brett 1.00 2.50
See also 655A
29 Willie Wilson .08 .25
See also 653A
30 Paul Splittorff .02 .10
31 Dan Quisenberry .02 .10
32A Amos Otis P1 .08 .25
(Batting Pose
Outfield
32 on back
32B Amos Otis P2 .08 .25
Series Starter
483 on back
33 Steve Busby .02 .10
34 U.L. Washington .02 .10
35 Dave Chalk .02 .10
36 Darrell Porter .02 .10
37 Marty Pattin .02 .10
38 Larry Gura .02 .10
39 Renie Martin .02 .10
40 Rich Gale .02 .10
41A Hal McRae P1 .20 .50
(Royals on front
in black letters
41B Hal McRae P2 .08 .25
(Royals on front
in blue letters
42 Dennis Leonard .02 .10
43 Willie Aikens .02 .10
44 Frank White .08 .25
45 Clint Hurdle .02 .10
46 John Wathan .02 .10
47 Pete LaCock .02 .10
48 Rance Mulliniks .02 .10
49 Jeff Twitty RC .02 .10
50 Jamie Quirk .02 .10
51 Art Howe .02 .10
52 Ken Forsch .02 .10
53 Vern Ruhle .02 .10
54 Joe Niekro .02 .10
55 Frank LaCorte .02 .10
56 J.R. Richard .08 .25
57 Nolan Ryan 2.00 5.00
58 Enos Cabell .02 .10
59 Cesar Cedeno .08 .25
60 Jose Cruz .08 .25
61 Bill Virdon MG .02 .10
62 Terry Puhl .02 .10
63 Joaquin Andujar .08 .25
64 Alan Ashby .02 .10
65 Joe Sambito .02 .10
66 Denny Walling .02 .10
67 Jeff Leonard .08 .25
68 Luis Pujols .02 .10
69 Bruce Bochy .02 .10
70 Rafael Landestoy .02 .10
71 Dave Smith RC .20 .50
72 Danny Heep RC .02 .10
73 Julio Gonzalez .02 .10
74 Craig Reynolds .02 .10
75 Gary Woods .02 .10
76 Dave Bergman .02 .10
77 Randy Niemann .02 .10
78 Joe Morgan .20 .50
79 Reggie Jackson .40 1.00
See also 650A
80 Bucky Dent .08 .25
81 Tommy John .08 .25
82 Luis Tiant .08 .25
83 Rick Cerone .02 .10
84 Dick Howser MG .02 .10
85 Lou Piniella .08 .25
86 Ron Davis .02 .10
87A Graig Nettles ERR 2.00 5.00
Name on back spelled Craig
87B Graig Nettles COR .08 .25
Graig
88 Ron Guidry .08 .25
89 Rich Gossage .08 .25
90 Rudy May .02 .10
91 Gaylord Perry .08 .25
92 Eric Soderholm .02 .10
93 Bob Watson .02 .10
94 Bobby Murcer .08 .25
95 Bobby Brown .02 .10
96 Jim Spencer .02 .10
97 Tom Underwood .02 .10
98 Oscar Gamble .02 .10
99 Johnny Oates .08 .25
100 Fred Stanley .02 .10
101 Ruppert Jones .02 .10
102 Dennis Werth RC .02 .10
103 Joe Lefebvre RC .02 .10
104 Brian Doyle .02 .10
105 Aurelio Rodriguez .02 .10
106 Doug Bird .02 .10
107 Mike Griffin RC .05 .15
108 Tim Lollar RC .02 .10
109 Willie Randolph .08 .25
110 Steve Garvey .20 .50
111 Reggie Smith .08 .25
112 Don Sutton .08 .25
113 Burt Hooton .02 .10
114A Dave Lopes P1 .20 .50
Small hand on back
114B Dave Lopes P2 .08 .25
No hand
115 Dusty Baker .08 .25
116 Tom Lasorda MG .20 .50
117 Bill Russell .08 .25
118 Jerry Reuss UER .02 .10
Home omitted
119 Terry Forster .08 .25
120A Bob Welch P1 .08 .25
(Name on back is Bob
120B Bob Welch P2 .08 .25
Name on back is Robert
121 Don Stanhouse .02 .10
122 Rick Monday .08 .25
123 Derrel Thomas .02 .10
124 Joe Ferguson .02 .10
125 Rick Sutcliffe .08 .25
126A Ron Cey P1 .08 .25
Small hand on back
126B Ron Cey P2 .08 .25
No hand
127 Dave Goltz .02 .10
128 Jay Johnstone .02 .10
129 Steve Yeager .08 .25
130 Gary Weiss RC .02 .10
131 Mike Scioscia RC .60 1.50
132 Vic Davalillo .02 .10
133 Doug Rau .02 .10
134 Pepe Frias .02 .10
135 Mickey Hatcher .02 .10
136 Steve Howe RC .20 .50
137 Robert Castillo RC .02 .10
138 Gary Thomasson .02 .10
139 Rudy Law .02 .10
140 Fernando Valenzuela RC 2.00 5.00
UER Misspelled Fernand on card
141 Manny Mota .08 .25
142 Gary Carter .20 .50
143 Steve Rogers .08 .25
144 Warren Cromartie .02 .10
145 Andre Dawson .20 .50
146 Larry Parrish .02 .10
147 Rowland Office .02 .10
148 Ellis Valentine .02 .10
149 Dick Williams MG .02 .10
150 Bill Gullickson RC .20 .50
151 Elias Sosa .02 .10
152 John Tamargo .02 .10
153 Chris Speier .02 .10
154 Ron LeFlore .08 .25
155 Rodney Scott .02 .10
156 Stan Bahnsen .02 .10
157 Bill Lee .08 .25
158 Fred Norman .02 .10
159 Woodie Fryman .02 .10
160 David Palmer .02 .10
161 Jerry White .02 .10
162 Roberto Ramos RC .02 .10
163 John D'Acquisto .02 .10
164 Tommy Hutton .02 .10
165 Charlie Lea RC .02 .10
166 Scott Sanderson .02 .10
167 Ken Macha .02 .10
168 Tony Bernazard .02 .10
169 Jim Palmer .20 .50
170 Steve Stone .02 .10
171 Mike Flanagan .02 .10
172 Al Bumbry .02 .10
173 Doug DeCinces .02 .10
174 Scott McGregor .02 .10
175 Mark Belanger .02 .10
176 Tim Stoddard .02 .10
177A Rick Dempsey P1 .08 .25
Small hand on front
177B Rick Dempsey P2 .02 .10
No hand
178 Earl Weaver MG .08 .25
179 Tippy Martinez .02 .10
180 Dennis Martinez .08 .25
181 Sammy Stewart .02 .10
182 Rich Dauer .02 .10
183 Lee May .02 .10
184 Eddie Murray .60 1.50
185 Benny Ayala .02 .10
186 John Lowenstein .02 .10
187 Gary Roenicke .02 .10
188 Ken Singleton .08 .25
189 Dan Graham .02 .10
190 Terry Crowley .02 .10
191 Kiko Garcia .02 .10
192 Dave Ford RC .02 .10
193 Mark Corey .02 .10
194 Lenn Sakata .02 .10
195 Doug DeCinces .02 .10
196 Johnny Bench .40 1.00
197 Dave Concepcion .08 .25
198 Ray Knight .08 .25
199 Ken Griffey .08 .25
200 Tom Seaver .40 1.00
201 Dave Collins .02 .10
202A George Foster P1 .20 .50
Slugger
Number on back 216
202B George Foster P2 .20 .50
Slugger
Number on back 202
203 Junior Kennedy .02 .10
204 Frank Pastore .02 .10
205 Dan Driessen .02 .10
206 Hector Cruz .02 .10
207 Paul Moskau .02 .10
208 Charlie Leibrandt RC .20 .50
209 Harry Spilman .02 .10
210 Joe Price RC .02 .10
211 Tom Hume .02 .10
212 Joe Nolan RC .02 .10
213 Doug Bair .02 .10

214 Mario Soto .08 .25
215A Bill Bonham P1 .20 .50
(Small hand on back)
215B Bill Bonham P2 .02 .10
(No hand)
216 George Foster SLG .08 .25
(See 202)
217 Paul Householder RC .02 .10
218 Ron Oester .02 .10
219 Sam Mejias .02 .10
220 Sheldon Burnside RC .02 .10
221 Carl Yastrzemski .60 1.50
222 Jim Rice .08 .25
223 Fred Lynn .08 .25
224 Carlton Fisk .20 .50
225 Rick Burleson .02 .10
226 Dennis Eckersley .20 .50
227 Butch Hobson .02 .10
228 Tom Burgmeier .02 .10
229 Garry Hancock .02 .10
230 Don Zimmer MG .08 .25
231 Steve Renko .02 .10
232 Dwight Evans .20 .50
233 Mike Torrez .02 .10
234 Bob Stanley .02 .10
235 Jim Dwyer .02 .10
236 Dave Stapleton RC .02 .10
237 Glenn Hoffman RC .02 .10
238 Jerry Remy .02 .10
239 Dick Drago .02 .10
240 Bill Campbell .02 .10
241 Tony Perez .20 .50
242 Phil Niekro .08 .25
243 Dale Murphy .20 .50
244 Bob Horner .08 .25
245 Jeff Burroughs .08 .25
246 Rick Camp .02 .10
247 Bobby Cox MG .08 .25
248 Bruce Benedict .02 .10
249 Gene Garber .02 .10
250 Jerry Royster .02 .10
251A Gary Matthews P1 .20 .50
Small hand on back
251B Gary Matthews P2 .08 .25
No hand
252 Chris Chambliss .08 .25
253 Luis Gomez .02 .10
254 Bill Nahorodny .02 .10
255 Doyle Alexander .02 .10
256 Brian Asselstine .02 .10
257 Biff Pocoroba .02 .10
258 Mike Lum .02 .10
259 Charlie Spikes .02 .10
260 Glenn Hubbard .02 .10
261 Tommy Boggs .02 .10
262 Al Hrabosky UER .08 .25
Card lists him as 5' 1"
263 Rick Matula .02 .10
264 Preston Hanna .02 .10
265 Larry Bradford .02 .10
266 Rafael Ramirez RC .02 .10
267 Larry McWilliams .02 .10
268 Rod Carew .20 .50
269 Bobby Grich .08 .25
270 Carney Lansford .08 .25
271 Don Baylor .08 .25
272 Joe Rudi .08 .25
273 Dan Ford .02 .10
274 Jim Fregosi MG .02 .10
275 Dave Frost .02 .10
276 Frank Tanana .08 .25
277 Dickie Thon .02 .10
278 Jason Thompson .02 .10
279 Rick Miller .02 .10
280 Bert Campaneris .08 .25
281 Tom Donohue .02 .10
282 Brian Downing .08 .25
283 Fred Patek .02 .10
284 Bruce Kison .02 .10
285 Dave LaRoche .02 .10
286 Don Aase .02 .10
287 Jim Barr .02 .10
288 Alfredo Martinez RC .02 .10
289 Larry Harlow .02 .10
290 Andy Hassler .02 .10
291 Dave Kingman .08 .25
292 Bill Buckner .08 .25
293 Rick Reuschel .08 .25
294 Bruce Sutter .20 .50
295 Jerry Martin .02 .10
296 Scot Thompson .02 .10
297 Ivan DeJesus .02 .10
298 Steve Dillard .02 .10
299 Dick Tidrow .02 .10
300 Randy Martz RC .02 .10
301 Lenny Randle .02 .10
302 Lynn McGlothen .02 .10
303 Cliff Johnson .02 .10
304 Tim Blackwell .02 .10
305 Dennis Lamp .02 .10
306 Bill Caudill .02 .10
307 Carlos Lezcano RC .02 .10
308 Jim Tracy RC .40 1.00
309 Doug Capilla UER .02 .10
Cubs on front but
Braves on back
310 Willie Hernandez .02 .10
311 Mike Vail .02 .10
312 Mike Krukow RC .02 .10
313 Barry Foote .02 .10
314 Larry Biittner .02 .10
315 Mike Tyson .02 .10
316 Lee Mazzilli .08 .25
317 John Stearns .02 .10
318 Alex Trevino .02 .10
319 Craig Swan .02 .10
320 Frank Taveras .02 .10
321 Steve Henderson .02 .10
322 Neil Allen .02 .10
323 Mark Bomback RC .02 .10
324 Mike Jorgensen .02 .10
325 Joe Torre MG .08 .25
326 Elliott Maddox .02 .10
327 Pete Falcone .02 .10
328 Ray Burris .02 .10
329 Claudell Washington .02 .10
330 Doug Flynn .02 .10
331 Joel Youngblood .02 .10
332 Bill Almon RC .02 .10
333 Tom Hausman .02 .10
334 Pat Zachry .02 .10
335 Jeff Reardon RC .40 1.00
336 Wally Backman RC .20 .50
337 Dan Norman .02 .10
338 Jerry Morales .02 .10
339 Ed Farmer .02 .10
340 Bob Molinaro .02 .10
341 Todd Cruz .02 .10
342A Britt Burns P1 .20 .50
Small hand on front
342B Britt Burns RC .08 .25
(P2 No hand)
343 Kevin Bell .02 .10
344 Tony LaRussa MG .08 .25
345 Steve Trout .02 .10
346 Harold Baines RC .75 2.00
347 Richard Wortham .02 .10
348 Wayne Nordhagen .02 .10
349 Mike Squires .02 .10
350 Lamar Johnson .02 .10
351 Rickey Henderson 1.25 3.00
Most Stolen Bases AL
352 Francisco Barrios .02 .10
353 Thad Bosley .02 .10
354 Chet Lemon .08 .25
355 Bruce Kimm .02 .10
356 Richard Dotson RC .02 .10
357 Jim Morrison .02 .10
358 Mike Proly .02 .10
359 Greg Pryor .02 .10
360 Dave Parker .08 .25
361 Omar Moreno .02 .10
362A Kent Tekulve P1 .02 .10
Back 1071 Waterbury
and 1078 Pirates
362B Kent Tekulve P2 .02 .10
1971 Waterbury and
1978 Pirates
363 Willie Stargell .20 .50
364 Phil Garner .08 .25
365 Ed Ott .02 .10
366 Don Robinson .02 .10
367 Chuck Tanner MG .02 .10
368 Jim Rooker .02 .10
369 Dale Berra .02 .10
370 Jim Bibby .02 .10
371 Steve Nicosia .02 .10
372 Mike Easler .02 .10
373 Bill Robinson .02 .10
374 Lee Lacy .02 .10
375 John Candelaria .08 .25
376 Manny Sanguillen .08 .25
377 Rick Rhoden .02 .10
378 Grant Jackson .02 .10
379 Tim Foli .02 .10
380 Rod Scurry RC .02 .10
381 Bill Madlock .08 .25
382A Kurt Bevacqua .08 .25
P1 ERR
P on cap backwards
382B Kurt Bevacqua P2 .02 .10
COR
383 Bert Blyleven .08 .25
384 Eddie Solomon .02 .10
385 Enrique Romo .02 .10
386 John Milner .02 .10
387 Mike Hargrove .08 .25
388 Jorge Orta .02 .10
389 Toby Harrah .08 .25
390 Tom Veryzer .02 .10
391 Miguel Dilone .02 .10
392 Dan Spillner .02 .10
393 Jack Brohamer .02 .10
394 Wayne Garland .02 .10
395 Sid Monge .02 .10
396 Rick Waits .02 .10
397 Joe Charboneau RC .40 1.00
398 Gary Alexander .02 .10
399 Jerry Dybzinski RC .02 .10
400 Mike Stanton RC .02 .10
401 Mike Paxton .02 .10
402 Gary Gray RC .02 .10
403 Rick Manning .02 .10
404 Bo Diaz .02 .10
405 Ron Hassey .02 .10
406 Ross Grimsley .02 .10
407 Victor Cruz .02 .10
408 Len Barker .08 .25
409 Bob Bailor .02 .10
410 Otto Velez .02 .10
411 Ernie Whitt .02 .10
412 Jim Clancy .02 .10
413 Barry Bonnell .02 .10
414 Dave Stieb .08 .25
415 Damaso Garcia RC .02 .10
416 John Mayberry .02 .10
417 Roy Howell .02 .10
418 Danny Ainge RC 1.25 3.00
419A Jesse Jefferson P1 .02 .10
Back says Pirates
419B Jesse Jefferson P2 .02 .10
Back says Pirates
419C Jesse Jefferson P3 .20 .50
Back says Blue Jays
420 Joey McLaughlin .02 .10
421 Lloyd Moseby RC .20 .50
422 Alvis Woods .02 .10
423 Garth Iorg .02 .10
424 Doug Ault .02 .10
425 Ken Schrom RC .02 .10
426 Mike Willis .02 .10
427 Steve Braun .02 .10
428 Bob Davis .02 .10
429 Jerry Garvin .02 .10
430 Alfredo Griffin .02 .10
431 Bob Mattick MG RC .02 .10
432 Vida Blue .08 .25
433 Jack Clark .08 .25
434 Willie McCovey .20 .50
435 Mike Ivie .02 .10
436A Darrel Evans P1 ERR .20 .50
(Name on front Darrel)
436B Darrell Evans P2 COR .20 .50
Name on front Darrell
437 Terry Whitfield .02 .10
438 Rennie Stennett .02 .10
439 John Montefusco .02 .10
440 Jim Wohlford .02 .10
441 Bill North .02 .10
442 Milt May .02 .10
443 Max Venable RC .02 .10
444 Ed Whitson .02 .10
445 Al Holland RC .02 .10
446 Randy Moffitt .02 .10
447 Bob Knepper .02 .10
448 Gary Lavelle .02 .10
449 Greg Minton .02 .10
450 Johnnie LeMaster .02 .10
451 Larry Herndon .02 .10
452 Rich Murray RC .02 .10
453 Joe Pettini RC .02 .10
454 Allen Ripley .02 .10
455 Dennis Littlejohn .02 .10
456 Tom Griffin .02 .10
457 Alan Hargesheimer RC .02 .10
458 Joe Strain .02 .10
459 Steve Kemp .02 .10
460 Sparky Anderson MG .08 .25
461 Alan Trammell .20 .50
462 Mark Fidrych .08 .25
463 Lou Whitaker .20 .50
464 Dave Rozema .02 .10
465 Milt Wilcox .02 .10
466 Champ Summers .02 .10
467 Lance Parrish .08 .25
468 Dan Petry .02 .10
469 Pat Underwood .02 .10
470 Rick Peters RC .02 .10
471 Al Cowens .02 .10
472 John Wockenfuss .02 .10
473 Tom Brookens .02 .10
474 Richie Hebner .02 .10
475 Jack Morris .20 .50
476 Jim Lentine RC .02 .10
477 Bruce Robbins .02 .10
478 Mark Wagner .02 .10
479 Tim Corcoran .02 .10
480A Stan Papi P1 .08 .25
Front as Pitcher
480B Stan Papi P2 .02 .10
Front as Shortstop
481 Kirk Gibson RC 2.00 5.00
482 Dan Schatzeder .02 .10
483A Amos Otis P1 .08 .25
See card 32
483B Amos Otis P2 .08 .25
See card 32
484 Dave Winfield .20 .50
485 Rollie Fingers .08 .25
486 Gene Richards .02 .10
487 Randy Jones .02 .10
488 Ozzie Smith 1.25 3.00
489 Gene Tenace .08 .25
490 Bill Fahey .02 .10
491 John Curtis .02 .10
492 Dave Cash .02 .10
493A Tim Flannery P1 .08 .25
Batting right
493B Tim Flannery P2 .02 .10
Batting left
494 Jerry Mumphrey .02 .10
495 Bob Shirley .02 .10
496 Steve Mura .02 .10
497 Eric Rasmussen .02 .10
498 Broderick Perkins .02 .10
499 Barry Evans RC .02 .10
500 Chuck Baker .02 .10
501 Luis Salazar RC .20 .50
502 Gary Lucas RC .02 .10
503 Mike Armstrong RC .02 .10
504 Jerry Turner .02 .10
505 Dennis Kinney RC .02 .10
506 Willie Montanez UER .02 .10
Spelled Willy on card front
507 Gorman Thomas .08 .25
508 Ben Oglivie .08 .25
509 Larry Hisle .02 .10
510 Sal Bando .08 .25
511 Robin Yount .60 1.50
512 Mike Caldwell .02 .10
513 Sixto Lezcano .02 .10
514A Bill Travers P1 ERR .08 .25
Jerry Augustine
with Augustine back
514B Bill Travers P2 COR .02 .10
515 Paul Molitor .40 1.00
516 Moose Haas .02 .10
517 Bill Castro .02 .10
518 Jim Slaton .02 .10
519 Lary Sorensen .02 .10
520 Bob McClure .02 .10
521 Charlie Moore .02 .10
522 Jim Gantner .02 .10
523 Reggie Cleveland .02 .10
524 Don Money .02 .10
525 Bill Travers .02 .10
526 Buck Martinez .02 .10
527 Dick Davis .02 .10
528 Ted Simmons .08 .25
529 Garry Templeton .08 .25
530 Ken Reitz .02 .10
531 Tony Scott .02 .10
532 Ken Oberkfell .02 .10
533 Bob Sykes .02 .10
534 Keith Smith .02 .10
535 John Littlefield RC .02 .10
536 Jim Kaat .08 .25
537 Bob Forsch .02 .10
538 Mike Phillips .02 .10
539 Terry Landrum RC .02 .10
540 Leon Durham RC .20 .50
541 Terry Kennedy .02 .10
542 George Hendrick .08 .25
543 Dane Iorg .02 .10
544 Mark Littell .02 .10
545 Keith Hernandez .08 .25
546 Silvio Martinez .02 .10
547A Don Hood P1 ERR .08 .25
Pete Vuckovich
with Vuckovich back
547B Don Hood P2 COR .02 .10
548 Bobby Bonds .08 .25
549 Mike Ramsey RC .05 .15
550 Tom Herr .02 .10
551 Roy Smalley .02 .10
552 Jerry Koosman .08 .25
553 Ken Landreaux .02 .10
554 John Castino .02 .10
555 Doug Corbett RC .02 .10
556 Bombo Rivera .02 .10
557 Ron Jackson .02 .10
558 Butch Wynegar .02 .10
559 Hosken Powell .02 .10
560 Pete Redfern .02 .10
561 Roger Erickson .02 .10
562 Glenn Adams .02 .10
563 Rick Sofield .02 .10
564 Geoff Zahn .02 .10
565 Pete Mackanin .02 .10
566 Mike Cubbage .02 .10
567 Darrell Jackson .02 .10
568 Dave Edwards .02 .10
569 Rob Wilfong .02 .10
570 Sal Butera RC .02 .10
571 Jose Morales .02 .10
572 Rick Langford .02 .10
573 Mike Norris .02 .10
574 Rickey Henderson 2.50 6.00
575 Tony Armas .08 .25
576 Dave Revering .02 .10
577 Jeff Newman .02 .10
578 Bob Lacey .02 .10
579 Brian Kingman .02 .10
580 Mitchell Page .02 .10
581 Billy Martin MG .20 .50
582 Rob Picciolo .02 .10
583 Mike Heath .02 .10
584 Mickey Klutts .02 .10
585 Orlando Gonzalez .02 .10
586 Mike Davis RC .20 .50
587 Wayne Gross .02 .10
588 Matt Keough .02 .10
589 Steve McCatty .02 .10
590 Dwayne Murphy .02 .10
591 Mario Guerrero .02 .10
592 Dave McKay RC .02 .10
593 Jim Essian .02 .10
594 Dave Heaverlo .02 .10
595 Maury Wills MG .08 .25
596 Juan Beniquez .02 .10
597 Rodney Craig .02 .10
598 Jim Anderson .02 .10
599 Floyd Bannister .02 .10
600 Bruce Bochte .02 .10
601 Julio Cruz .02 .10
602 Ted Cox .02 .10
603 Dan Meyer .02 .10
604 Larry Cox .02 .10
605 Bill Stein .02 .10
606 Steve Garvey .20 .50
Most Hits NL
607 Dave Roberts .02 .10
608 Leon Roberts .02 .10
609 Reggie Walton RC .02 .10
610 Dave Edler RC .02 .10
611 Larry Milbourne .02 .10
612 Kim Allen RC .02 .10
613 Mario Mendoza .02 .10
614 Tom Paciorek .02 .10
615 Glenn Abbott .02 .10
616 Joe Simpson .02 .10
617 Mickey Rivers .02 .10
618 Jim Kern .02 .10
619 Jim Sundberg .08 .25
620 Richie Zisk .02 .10
621 Jon Matlack .02 .10
622 Ferguson Jenkins .08 .25
623 Pat Corrales MG .02 .10
624 Ed Figueroa .02 .10
625 Buddy Bell .08 .25
626 Al Oliver .08 .25
627 Doc Medich .02 .10
628 Bump Wills .02 .10
629 Rusty Staub .08 .25
630 Pat Putnam .02 .10
631 John Grubb .02 .10
632 Danny Darwin .02 .10
633 Ken Clay .02 .10
634 Jim Norris .02 .10
635 John Butcher RC .02 .10
636 Dave Roberts .02 .10
637 Billy Sample .02 .10
638 Carl Yastrzemski .60 1.50
639 Cecil Cooper .08 .25
640 Mike Schmidt P1 1.00 2.50
Portrait
Third Base
number on back 5
640B Mike Schmidt P2 1.00 2.50
1980 Home Run King
640 on back
641A CL: Phils/Royals P1 .08 .25
41 is Hal McRae
641B CL: Phils/Royals P2 .08 .25
41 is Hal McRae
Double Threat
642 CL: Astros/Yankees .02 .10
643 CL: Expos/Dodgers .02 .10
644A CL: Reds/Orioles P1 .08 .25
202 is George Foster
Joe Nolan pitcher
should be catcher
644B CL: Reds/Orioles P2 .08 .25
202 is Foster Slugger
Joe Nolan pitcher
should be catcher
645 Pete Rose .60 1.50
Larry Bowa
Mike Schmidt
Triple Threat P1
No number on back
645B Pete Rose 1.00 2.50
Larry Bowa
Mike Schmidt
Triple Threat P2
Back numbered 645
646 CL: Braves/Red Sox .02 .10
647 CL: Cubs/Angels .02 .10
648 CL: Mets/White Sox .02 .10
649 CL: Indians/Pirates .02 .10
650 Reggie Jackson .40 1.00
Mr. Baseball P1
Number on back 79
650B Reggie Jackson .20 .50
Mr. Baseball P2
Number on back 650
651 CL: Giants/Blue Jays .02 .10
652A CL:Tigers/Padres P1 .08 .25
483 is listed
652B CL:Tigers/Padres P2 .08 .25
483 is deleted
653A Willie Wilson P1 .08 .25
Most Hits Most Runs
Number on back 29
653B Willie Wilson P2 .08 .25
Most Hits Most Runs
Number on back 653
654A Checklist Brewers .08 .25
Cards P1
514 Jerry Augustine
547 Pete Vuckovich
654B Checklist Brewers .08 .25
Cards P2
514 Billy Travers
547 Don Hood
655 George Brett P1 1.00 2.50
.390 Average
Number on back 28
655B George Brett P2 1.00 2.50
.390 Average
Number on back 655
656 CL:Twins/Oakland A's .08 .25
657A Tug McGraw P1 .08 .25
Game Saver
Number on back 7
657B Tug McGraw P2 .08 .25
Game Saver
Number on back 657
658 CL: Rangers/Mariners .02 .10
659A Checklist P1 .02 .10
of Special Cards
Last lines on front
Wilson Most Hits
659B Checklist P2 .02 .10
of Special Cards
Last lines on front
Otis Series Starter
660 Steve Carlton P1 .20 .50
Golden Arm
(Number on back 660
Back 1066 Cardinals
660B Steve Carlton P2 .75 2.00
Golden Arm
1966 Cardinals

1982 Fleer

The 1982 Fleer set contains 660-card standard-size cards, of which are grouped in team order based upon standings from the previous season. Cards numbered 628 through 646 are special cards highlighting some of the stars and leaders of the 1981 season. The last 14 cards in the set (647-660) are checklist cards. The backs feature player statistics and a full-color team logo in the upper right-hand corner of each card. The complete set price below does not include any of the more valuable variation cards listed. Fleer was not allowed to insert bubble gum or other confectionary products into these packs; therefore logo stickers were included in these 15-card packs. Those 15-card packs with an SRP of 30 cents were packed 36 packs to a box and 20 boxes to a case. Notable Rookie Cards in this set include Cal Ripken Jr., Lee Smith, and Dave Stewart.

COMPLETE SET (660) 20.00 50.00
1 Dusty Baker .07 .20
2 Robert Castillo .02 .10
3 Ron Cey .07 .20
4 Terry Forster .07 .20
5 Steve Garvey .07 .20
6 Dave Goltz .02 .10
7 Pedro Guerrero .07 .20
8 Burt Hooton .02 .10
9 Steve Howe .02 .10
10 Jay Johnstone .02 .10
11 Ken Landreaux .02 .10
12 Dave Lopes .07 .20
13 Mike A. Marshall RC .20 .50
14 Bobby Mitchell .02 .10
15 Rick Monday .07 .20
16 Tom Niedenfuer RC .20 .50
17 Ted Power RC .05 .15
18 Jerry Reuss UER .02 .10
19 Ron Roenicke .02 .10
20 Bill Russell .07 .20
21 Steve Sax RC .40 1.00
22 Mike Scioscia .07 .20
23 Reggie Smith .07 .20
24 Dave Stewart RC .60 1.50
25 Rick Sutcliffe .07 .20
26 Derrel Thomas .02 .10
27 Fernando Valenzuela .30 .75
28 Bob Welch .07 .20
29 Steve Yeager .07 .20
30 Bobby Brown .02 .10
31 Rick Cerone .02 .10
32 Ron Davis .02 .10
33 Bucky Dent .07 .20
34 Barry Foote .02 .10
35 George Frazier .02 .10
36 Oscar Gamble .02 .10
37 Rich Gossage .07 .20
38 Ron Guidry .07 .20
39 Reggie Jackson .15 .40
40 Tommy John .07 .20
41 Rudy May .02 .10
42 Larry Milbourne .02 .10
43 Jerry Mumphrey .02 .10
44 Bobby Murcer .07 .20
45 Gene Nelson .02 .10
46 Graig Nettles .07 .20
47 Johnny Oates .07 .20
48 Lou Piniella .07 .20
49 Willie Randolph .07 .20
50 Rick Reuschel .07 .20
51 Dave Revering .02 .10
52 Dave Righetti RC .60 1.50
53 Aurelio Rodriguez .02 .10
54 Bob Watson .02 .10
55 Dennis Werth .02 .10
56 Dave Winfield .07 .20
57 Johnny Bench .30 .75
58 Bruce Berenyi .02 .10
59 Larry Biittner .02 .10
60 Scott Brown .02 .10
61 Dave Collins .02 .10
62 Geoff Combe .02 .10
63 Dave Concepcion .07 .20
64 Dan Driessen .02 .10
65 Joe Edelen .02 .10
66 George Foster .07 .20
67 Ken Griffey .07 .20
68 Paul Householder .02 .10
69 Tom Hume .02 .10
70 Junior Kennedy .02 .10
71 Ray Knight .07 .20
72 Mike LaCoss .02 .10
73 Rafael Landestoy .02 .10
74 Charlie Leibrandt .02 .10
75 Sam Mejias .02 .10
76 Paul Moskau .02 .10
77 Joe Nolan .02 .10
78 Mike O'Berry .02 .10
79 Ron Oester .02 .10
80 Frank Pastore .02 .10
81 Joe Price .02 .10
82 Tom Seaver .30 .75
83 Mario Soto .07 .20
84 Mike Vail .02 .10
85 Tony Armas .07 .20
86 Shooty Babitt .02 .10
87 Dave Beard .02 .10
88 Rick Bosetti .02 .10
89 Keith Drumwright .02 .10
90 Wayne Gross .02 .10
91 Mike Heath .02 .10
92 Rickey Henderson 1.00 2.50
93 Cliff Johnson .02 .10
94 Jeff Jones .02 .10
95 Matt Keough .02 .10
96 Brian Kingman .02 .10
97 Mickey Klutts .02 .10
98 Rick Langford .02 .10
99 Steve McCatty .02 .10
100 Dan McKay .02 .10
101 Dwayne Murphy .02 .10
102 Jeff Newman .02 .10
103 Mike Norris .02 .10
104 Bob Owchinko .02 .10
105 Mitchell Page .02 .10
106 Rob Picciolo .02 .10
107 Jim Spencer .02 .10
108 Fred Stanley .02 .10
109 Tom Underwood .02 .10
110 Joaquin Andujar .07 .20
111 Steve Braun .02 .10
112 Bob Forsch .02 .10
113 George Hendrick .07 .20
114 Keith Hernandez .07 .20
115 Tom Herr .07 .20
116 Dane Iorg .02 .10
117 Jim Kaat .07 .20
118 Tito Landrum .02 .10
119 Sixto Lezcano .02 .10
120 Mark Littell .02 .10
121 John Martin RC .05 .15
122 Silvio Martinez .02 .10
123 Ken Oberkfell .02 .10
124 Darrell Porter .02 .10
125 Mike Ramsey .02 .10
126 Orlando Sanchez .02 .10
127 Bob Shirley .02 .10
128 Lary Sorensen .02 .10
129 Bruce Sutter .15 .40
130 Bob Sykes .02 .10
131 Garry Templeton .07 .20
132 Gene Tenace .07 .20
133 Jerry Augustine .02 .10
134 Sal Bando .07 .20
135 Mark Brouhard .02 .10
136 Mike Caldwell .02 .10
137 Reggie Cleveland .02 .10
138 Cecil Cooper .07 .20
139 Jamie Easterly .02 .10
140 Marshall Edwards .02 .10
141 Rollie Fingers .07 .20
142 Jim Gantner .02 .10
143 Moose Haas .02 .10
144 Larry Hisle .02 .10
145 Roy Howell .02 .10
146 Rickey Keeton .02 .10
147 Randy Lerch .02 .10
148 Paul Molitor .07 .20
149 Don Money .02 .10
150 Charlie Moore .02 .10
151 Ben Oglivie .07 .20
152 Ted Simmons .07 .20
153 Jim Slaton .02 .10
154 Gorman Thomas .07 .20
155 Robin Yount .50 1.25
156 Pete Vuckovich .02 .10
(Should precede Yount
in the team order)
157 Benny Ayala .02 .10
158 Mark Belanger .02 .10
159 Al Bumbry .02 .10
160 Terry Crowley .02 .10
161 Rich Dauer .02 .10
162 Doug DeCinces .02 .10
163 Rick Dempsey .02 .10
164 Jim Dwyer .02 .10
165 Mike Flanagan .02 .10
166 Dave Ford .02 .10
167 Dan Graham .02 .10
168 Wayne Krenchicki .02 .10
169 John Lowenstein .02 .10
170 Dennis Martinez .07 .20
171 Tippy Martinez .02 .10
172 Scott McGregor .02 .10
173 Jose Morales .02 .10
174 Eddie Murray .30 .75
175 Jim Palmer .07 .20
176 Cal Ripken RC 10.00 25.00
Fleer Ripken cards from 1982
through 1993 erroneously have 22
games played in 1981;not 23.
177 Gary Roenicke .02 .10
178 Lenn Sakata .02 .10
179 Ken Singleton .07 .20
180 Sammy Stewart .02 .10
181 Tim Stoddard .02 .10
182 Steve Stone .02 .10

Card	Low	High
183 Stan Bahnsen	.02	.10
184 Ray Burris	.02	.10
185 Gary Carter	.07	.20
186 Warren Cromartie	.02	.10
187 Andre Dawson	.07	.20
188 Terry Francona RC	1.25	3.00
189 Woodie Fryman	.02	.10
190 Bill Gullickson	.02	.10
191 Grant Jackson	.02	.10
192 Wallace Johnson	.02	.10
193 Charlie Lea	.02	.10
194 Bill Lee	.07	.20
195 Jerry Manuel	.02	.10
196 Brad Mills	.02	.10
197 John Milner	.02	.10
198 Rowland Office	.02	.10
199 David Palmer	.02	.10
200 Larry Parrish	.02	.10
201 Mike Phillips	.02	.10
202 Tim Raines	.15	.40
203 Bobby Ramos	.02	.10
204 Jeff Reardon	.07	.20
205 Steve Rogers	.07	.20
206 Scott Sanderson	.02	.10
207 Rodney Scott UER (Photo actually Tim Raines)	.15	.40
208 Elias Sosa	.02	.10
209 Chris Speier	.02	.10
210 Tim Wallach RC	.40	1.00
211 Jerry White	.02	.10
212 Alan Ashby	.02	.10
213 Cesar Cedeno	.07	.20
214 Jose Cruz	.07	.20
215 Kiko Garcia	.02	.10
216 Phil Garner	.07	.20
217 Danny Heep	.02	.10
218 Art Howe	.02	.10
219 Bob Knepper	.02	.10
220 Frank LaCorte	.02	.10
221 Joe Niekro	.02	.10
222 Joe Pittman	.02	.10
223 Terry Puhl	.02	.10
224 Luis Pujols	.02	.10
225 Craig Reynolds	.02	.10
226 J.R. Richard	.07	.20
227 Dave Roberts	.02	.10
228 Vern Ruhle	.02	.10
229 Nolan Ryan	1.50	4.00
230 Joe Sambito	.02	.10
231 Tony Scott	.02	.10
232 Dave Smith	.02	.10
233 Harry Spilman	.02	.10
234 Don Sutton	.07	.20
235 Dickie Thon	.02	.10
236 Denny Walling	.02	.10
237 Gary Woods	.02	.10
238 Luis Aguayo	.02	.10
239 Ramon Aviles	.02	.10
240 Bob Boone	.07	.20
241 Larry Bowa	.07	.20
242 Warren Brusstar	.02	.10
243 Steve Carlton	.15	.40
244 Larry Christenson	.02	.10
245 Dick Davis	.02	.10
246 Greg Gross	.02	.10
247 Sparky Lyle	.07	.20
248 Garry Maddox	.02	.10
249 Gary Matthews	.07	.20
250 Bake McBride	.07	.20
251 Tug McGraw	.07	.20
252 Keith Moreland	.02	.10
253 Dickie Noles	.02	.10
254 Mike Proly	.02	.10
255 Ron Reed	.02	.10
256 Pete Rose	1.00	2.50
257 Dick Ruthven	.02	.10
258 Mike Schmidt	.75	2.00
259 Lonnie Smith	.02	.10
260 Manny Trillo	.02	.10
261 Del Unser	.02	.10
262 George Vukovich	.02	.10
263 Tom Brookens	.02	.10
264 George Cappuzzello	.02	.10
265 Marty Castillo	.02	.10
266 Al Cowens	.02	.10
267 Kirk Gibson	.30	.75
268 Richie Hebner	.02	.10
269 Ron Jackson	.02	.10
270 Lynn Jones	.02	.10
271 Steve Kemp	.02	.10
272 Rick Leach	.02	.10
273 Aurelio Lopez	.02	.10
274 Jack Morris	.07	.20
275 Kevin Saucier	.02	.10
276 Lance Parrish	.07	.20
277 Rick Peters	.02	.10
278 Dan Petry	.02	.10
279 Dave Rozema	.02	.10
280 Stan Papi	.02	.10
281 Dan Schatzeder	.02	.10
282 Champ Summers	.02	.10
283 Alan Trammell	.07	.20
284 Lou Whitaker	.07	.20
285 Milt Wilcox	.02	.10
286 John Wockenfuss	.02	.10
287 Gary Allenson	.02	.10
288 Tom Burgmeier	.02	.10
289 Bill Campbell	.02	.10
290 Mark Clear	.02	.10
291 Steve Crawford	.02	.10
292 Dennis Eckersley	.15	.40
293 Dwight Evans	.15	.40
294 Rich Gedman	.20	.50
295 Garry Hancock	.02	.10
296 Glenn Hoffman	.02	.10
297 Bruce Hurst	.02	.10
298 Carney Lansford	.07	.20
299 Rick Miller	.02	.10
300 Reid Nichols	.02	.10
301 Bob Ojeda RC	.20	.50
302 Tony Perez	.15	.40
303 Chuck Rainey	.02	.10
304 Jerry Remy	.02	.10
305 Jim Rice	.07	.20
306 Joe Rudi	.07	.20
307 Bob Stanley	.02	.10
308 Dave Stapleton	.02	.10
309 Frank Tanana	.07	.20
310 Mike Torrez	.02	.10
311 John Tudor	.07	.20
312 Carl Yastrzemski	.50	1.25
313 Buddy Bell	.07	.20
314 Steve Comer	.02	.10
315 Danny Darwin	.02	.10
316 John Ellis	.02	.10
317 John Grubb	.02	.10
318 Rick Honeycutt	.02	.10
319 Charlie Hough	.07	.20
320 Ferguson Jenkins	.07	.20
321 John Henry Johnson	.02	.10
322 Jim Kern	.02	.10
323 Jon Matlack	.02	.10
324 Doc Medich	.02	.10
325 Mario Mendoza	.02	.10
326 Al Oliver	.07	.20
327 Pat Putnam	.02	.10
328 Mickey Rivers	.02	.10
329 Leon Roberts	.02	.10
330 Billy Sample	.02	.10
331 Bill Stein	.02	.10
332 Jim Sundberg	.07	.20
333 Mark Wagner	.02	.10
334 Bump Wills	.02	.10
335 Bill Almon	.02	.10
336 Harold Baines	.07	.20
337 Ross Baumgarten	.02	.10
338 Tony Bernazard	.02	.10
339 Britt Burns	.02	.10
340 Richard Dotson	.02	.10
341 Jim Essian	.02	.10
342 Ed Farmer	.02	.10
343 Carlton Fisk	.15	.40
344 Kevin Hickey RC	.05	.15
345 LaMarr Hoyt	.02	.10
346 Lamar Johnson	.02	.10
347 Jerry Koosman	.07	.20
348 Rusty Kuntz	.02	.10
349 Dennis Lamp	.02	.10
350 Ron LeFlore	.07	.20
351 Chet Lemon	.07	.20
352 Greg Luzinski	.07	.20
353 Bob Molinaro	.02	.10
354 Jim Morrison	.02	.10
355 Wayne Nordhagen	.02	.10
356 Greg Pryor	.02	.10
357 Mike Squires	.02	.10
358 Steve Trout	.02	.10
359 Alan Bannister	.02	.10
360 Len Barker	.02	.10
361 Bert Blyleven	.07	.20
362 Joe Charboneau	.07	.20
363 John Denny	.02	.10
364 Bo Diaz	.02	.10
365 Miguel Dilone	.02	.10
366 Jerry Dybzinski	.02	.10
367 Wayne Garland	.02	.10
368 Mike Hargrove	.02	.10
369 Toby Harrah	.07	.20
370 Ron Hassey	.02	.10
371 Von Hayes RC	.20	.50
372 Pat Kelly	.02	.10
373 Duane Kuiper	.02	.10
374 Rick Manning	.02	.10
375 Sid Monge	.02	.10
376 Jorge Orta	.02	.10
377 Dave Rosello	.02	.10
378 Dan Spillner	.02	.10
379 Mike Stanton	.02	.10
380 Andre Thornton	.02	.10
381 Tom Veryzer	.02	.10
382 Rick Waits	.02	.10
383 Doyle Alexander	.02	.10
384 Vida Blue	.07	.20
385 Fred Breining	.02	.10
386 Enos Cabell	.02	.10
387 Jack Clark	.07	.20
388 Darrell Evans	.07	.20
389 Tom Griffin	.02	.10
390 Larry Herndon	.02	.10
391 Al Holland	.02	.10
392 Gary Lavelle	.02	.10
393 Johnnie LeMaster	.02	.10
394 Jerry Martin	.02	.10
395 Milt May	.02	.10
396 Greg Minton	.02	.10
397 Joe Morgan	.07	.20
398 Joe Pettini	.02	.10
399 Allen Ripley	.02	.10
400 Billy Smith	.02	.10
401 Rennie Stennett	.02	.10
402 Ed Whitson	.02	.10
403 Jim Wohlford	.02	.10
404 Willie Aikens	.02	.10
405 George Brett	.75	2.00
406 Ken Brett	.02	.10
407 Dave Chalk	.02	.10
408 Rich Gale	.02	.10
409 Cesar Geronimo	.02	.10
410 Larry Gura	.02	.10
411 Clint Hurdle	.02	.10
412 Mike Jones	.02	.10
413 Dennis Leonard	.02	.10
414 Renie Martin	.02	.10
415 Lee May	.02	.10
416 Hal McRae	.07	.20
417 Darryl Motley	.02	.10
418 Rance Mulliniks	.02	.10
419 Amos Otis	.07	.20
420 Ken Phelps	.02	.10
421 Jamie Quirk	.02	.10
422 Dan Quisenberry	.02	.10
423 Paul Splittorff	.02	.10
424 U.L. Washington	.02	.10
425 John Wathan	.02	.10
426 Frank White	.07	.20
427 Willie Wilson	.07	.20
428 Brian Asselstine	.02	.10
429 Bruce Benedict	.02	.10
430 Tommy Boggs	.02	.10
431 Larry Bradford	.02	.10
432 Rick Camp	.02	.10
433 Chris Chambliss	.07	.20
434 Gene Garber	.02	.10
435 Preston Hanna	.02	.10
436 Bob Horner	.07	.20
437 Glenn Hubbard	.02	.10
438A Al Hrabosky ERR (Height 5'1 All on reverse)	3.00	8.00
438B Al Hrabosky ERR (Height 5'1)	.15	.40
438C Al Hrabosky (Height 5'10)	.07	.20
439 Rufino Linares	.02	.10
440 Rick Mahler	.02	.10
441 Ed Miller	.02	.10
442 John Montefusco	.02	.10
443 Dale Murphy	.15	.40
444 Phil Niekro	.07	.20
445 Gaylord Perry	.07	.20
446 Biff Pocoroba	.02	.10
447 Rafael Ramirez	.02	.10
448 Jerry Royster	.02	.10
449 Claudell Washington	.02	.10
450 Don Aase	.02	.10
451 Don Baylor	.07	.20
452 Juan Beniquez	.02	.10
453 Rick Burleson	.02	.10
454 Bert Campaneris	.07	.20
455 Rod Carew	.15	.40
456 Bob Clark	.02	.10
457 Brian Downing	.07	.20
458 Dan Ford	.02	.10
459 Ken Forsch	.02	.10
460A Dave Frost (5 mm space before ERA)	.07	.20
460B Dave Frost (1 mm space)	.02	.10
461 Bobby Grich	.07	.20
462 Larry Harlow	.02	.10
463 John Harris	.02	.10
464 Andy Hassler	.02	.10
465 Butch Hobson	.02	.10
466 Jesse Jefferson	.02	.10
467 Bruce Kison	.02	.10
468 Fred Lynn	.07	.20
469 Angel Moreno	.07	.20
470 Ed Ott	.02	.10
471 Fred Patek	.02	.10
472 Steve Renko	.02	.10
473 Mike Witt	.20	.50
474 Geoff Zahn	.02	.10
475 Gary Alexander	.02	.10
476 Dale Berra	.02	.10
477 Kurt Bevacqua	.02	.10
478 Jim Bibby	.02	.10
479 John Candelaria	.02	.10
480 Victor Cruz	.02	.10
481 Mike Easler	.02	.10
482 Tim Foli	.02	.10
483 Lee Lacy	.02	.10
484 Vance Law	.02	.10
485 Bill Madlock	.07	.20
486 Willie Montanez	.02	.10
487 Omar Moreno	.02	.10
488 Steve Nicosia	.02	.10
489 Dave Parker	.07	.20
490 Tony Pena	.07	.20
491 Pascual Perez	.07	.20
492 Johnny Ray RC	.20	.50
493 Rick Rhoden	.02	.10
494 Bill Robinson	.02	.10
495 Don Robinson	.02	.10
496 Enrique Romo	.02	.10
497 Rod Scurry	.02	.10
498 Eddie Solomon	.02	.10
499 Willie Stargell	.15	.40
500 Kent Tekulve	.02	.10
501 Jason Thompson	.02	.10
502 Glenn Abbott	.02	.10
503 Jim Anderson	.02	.10
504 Floyd Bannister	.02	.10
505 Bruce Bochte	.02	.10
506 Jeff Burroughs	.02	.10
507 Bryan Clark RC	.05	.15
508 Ken Clay	.02	.10
509 Julio Cruz	.02	.10
510 Dick Drago	.02	.10
511 Gary Gray	.02	.10
512 Dan Meyer	.02	.10
513 Jerry Narron	.02	.10
514 Tom Paciorek	.02	.10
515 Casey Parsons	.02	.10
516 Lenny Randle	.02	.10
517 Shane Rawley	.02	.10
518 Joe Simpson	.02	.10
519 Richie Zisk	.02	.10
520 Neil Allen	.02	.10
521 Bob Bailor	.02	.10
522 Hubie Brooks	.02	.10
523 Mike Cubbage	.02	.10
524 Pete Falcone	.02	.10
525 Doug Flynn	.02	.10
526 Tom Hausman	.02	.10
527 Ron Hodges	.02	.10
528 Randy Jones	.02	.10
529 Mike Jorgensen	.02	.10
530 Dave Kingman	.07	.20
531 Ed Lynch	.02	.10
532 Mike G. Marshall	.02	.10
533 Lee Mazzilli	.07	.20
534 Dyar Miller	.02	.10
535 Mike Scott	.07	.20
536 Rusty Staub	.07	.20
537 John Stearns	.02	.10
538 Craig Swan	.07	.20
539 Frank Taveras	.02	.10
540 Alex Trevino	.02	.10
541 Ellis Valentine	.02	.10
542 Mookie Wilson	.07	.20
543 Joel Youngblood	.02	.10
544 Pat Zachry	.02	.10
545 Glenn Adams	.02	.10
546 Fernando Arroyo	.02	.10
547 John Verhoeven	.02	.10
548 Sal Butera	.02	.10
549 John Castino	.02	.10
550 Don Cooper	.02	.10
551 Doug Corbett	.02	.10
552 Dave Engle	.02	.10
553 Roger Erickson	.02	.10
554 Danny Goodwin	.02	.10
555A Darrell Jackson (Black cap)	.15	.40
555B Darrell Jackson (Red cap with T)	.07	.20
555C Darrell Jackson (Red cap, no emblem)	1.25	3.00
556 Pete Mackanin	.02	.10
557 Jack O'Connor	.02	.10
558 Hosken Powell	.02	.10
559 Pete Redfern	.02	.10
560 Roy Smalley	.02	.10
561 Chuck Baker UER (Shortshop on front)	.02	.10
562 Gary Ward	.02	.10
563 Rob Wilfong	.02	.10
564 Al Williams	.02	.10
565 Butch Wynegar	.02	.10
566 Randy Bass	.20	.50
567 Juan Bonilla RC	.05	.15
568 Danny Boone	.02	.10
569 John Curtis	.02	.10
570 Juan Eichelberger	.02	.10
571 Barry Evans	.02	.10
572 Tim Flannery	.02	.10
573 Ruppert Jones	.02	.10
574 Terry Kennedy	.02	.10
575 Joe Lefebvre	.02	.10
576A John Littlefield ERR (Left handed; reverse negative)	50.00	100.00
576B John Littlefield COR (Right handed)	.07	.20
577 Gary Lucas	.02	.10
578 Steve Mura	.02	.10
579 Broderick Perkins	.02	.10
580 Gene Richards	.02	.10
581 Luis Salazar	.02	.10
582 Ozzie Smith	.60	1.50
583 John Urrea	.02	.10
584 Chris Welsh	.02	.10
585 Rick Wise	.02	.10
586 Doug Bird	.02	.10
587 Tim Blackwell	.02	.10
588 Bobby Bonds	.07	.20
589 Bill Buckner	.07	.20
590 Bill Caudill	.02	.10
591 Hector Cruz	.02	.10
592 Jody Davis	.02	.10
593 Ivan DeJesus	.02	.10
594 Steve Dillard	.02	.10
595 Leon Durham	.02	.10
596 Rawly Eastwick	.07	.20
597 Steve Henderson	.02	.10
598 Mike Krukow	.02	.10
599 Mike Lum	.02	.10
600 Randy Martz	.02	.10
601 Jerry Morales	.02	.10
602 Ken Reitz	.02	.10
603 Lee Smith RC ERR (Cubs logo reversed)	.75	2.00
603B Lee Smith COR	2.50	6.00
604 Dick Tidrow	.02	.10
605 Jim Tracy	.07	.20
606 Mike Tyson	.02	.10
607 Ty Waller	.02	.10
608 Danny Ainge	.07	.20
609 Jorge Bell RC	.40	1.00
610 Mark Bomback	.02	.10
611 Barry Bonnell	.02	.10
612 Jim Clancy	.02	.10
613 Damaso Garcia	.02	.10
614 Jerry Garvin	.02	.10
615 Alfredo Griffin	.02	.10
616 Garth Iorg	.02	.10
617 Luis Leal	.02	.10
618 Ken Macha	.02	.10
619 John Mayberry	.02	.10
620 Joey McLaughlin	.02	.10
621 Lloyd Moseby	.02	.10
622 Dave Stieb	.07	.20
623 Jackson Todd	.02	.10
624 Willie Upshaw	.20	.50
625 Otto Velez	.02	.10
626 Ernie Whitt	.02	.10
627 Alvis Woods	.02	.10
628 All Star Game Cleveland, Ohio	.07	.20
629 Frank White Bucky Dent	.07	.20
630 Dan Driessen Dave Concepcion George Foster	.07	.20
631 Bruce Sutter Top NL Relief Pitcher	.07	.20
632 Steve Carlton Carlton Fisk	.07	.20
633 Carl Yastrzemski 3000th Game	.30	.75
634 Johnny Bench Tom Seaver	.30	.75
635 Fernando Valenzuela Gary Carter	.02	.10
636A Fernando Valenzuela: NL SO King 'he' NL	.15	.40
636B Fernando Valenzuela NL SO King 'the' NL	.15	.40
637 Mike Schmidt Home Run King	.30	.75
638 Gary Carter Dave Parker	.02	.10
639 Perfect Game UER Len Barker Bo Diaz (Catcher actually Ron Hassey)	.07	.20
640 Pete Rose Pete Rose Jr.	.30	.75
641 Lonnie Smith Mike Schmidt Steve Carlton	.30	.75
642 Fred Lynn Dwight Evans	.15	.40
643 Rickey Henderson Most Hits and Runs	.50	1.25
644 Rollie Fingers Most Saves AL	.07	.20
645 Tom Seaver Most 1981 Wins	.07	.20
646 Yankee Powerhouse Reggie Jackson Dave Winfield (Comma on back after outfielder)	.07	.20
646B Yankee Powerhouse Reggie Jackson Dave Winfield (No comma)	.07	.20
647 CL: Yankees/Dodgers	.02	.10
648 CL: A's/Reds	.02	.10
649 CL: Cards/Brewers	.02	.10
650 CL: Expos/Orioles	.02	.10
651 CL: Astros/Phillies	.02	.10
652 CL: Tigers/Red Sox	.02	.10
653 CL: Rangers/White Sox	.02	.10
654 CL: Giants/Indians	.02	.10
655 CL: Royals/Braves	.02	.10
656 CL: Angels/Pirates	.02	.10
657 CL: Mariners/Mets	.02	.10
658 CL: Padres/Twins	.02	.10
659 CL: Blue Jays/Cubs	.02	.10
660 Specials Checklist	.02	.10

1983 Fleer

In 1983, for the third straight year, Fleer produced a baseball series of 660 standard-size cards. Of these, 1-628 are player cards, 629-646 are special cards, and 647-660 are checklist cards. The player cards are again ordered alphabetically within team and teams seeded in descending order based upon the previous season's standings. The front of each card has a colorful team logo at bottom left and the player's name and position at lower right. The reverses are done in shades of brown on white. Wax packs consisted of 15 cards plus logo stickers in a 38-pack box. Notable Rookie Cards include Wade Boggs, Tony Gwynn and Ryne Sandberg.

Card	Low	High
COMPLETE SET (660)	30.00	60.00
1 Joaquin Andujar	.07	.20
2 Doug Bair	.02	.10
3 Steve Braun	.02	.10
4 Glenn Brummer	.02	.10
5 Bob Forsch	.02	.10
6 David Green RC	.20	.50
7 George Hendrick	.07	.20
8 Keith Hernandez	.07	.20
9 Tom Herr	.07	.20
10 Dane Iorg	.02	.10
11 Jim Kaat	.07	.20
12 Jeff Lahti	.02	.10
13 Tito Landrum	.02	.10
14 Dave LaPoint	.02	.10
15 Willie McGee RC	.60	1.50
16 Steve Mura	.02	.10
17 Ken Oberkfell	.02	.10
18 Darrell Porter	.02	.10
19 Mike Ramsey	.02	.10
20 Gene Roof	.02	.10
21 Lonnie Smith	.02	.10
22 Ozzie Smith	.50	1.25
23 John Stuper	.02	.10
24 Bruce Sutter	.15	.40
25 Gene Tenace	.07	.20
26 Jerry Augustine	.02	.10
27 Dwight Bernard	.02	.10
28 Mark Brouhard	.02	.10
29 Mike Caldwell	.02	.10
30 Cecil Cooper	.07	.20
31 Jamie Easterly	.02	.10
32 Marshall Edwards	.02	.10
33 Rollie Fingers	.07	.20
34 Jim Gantner	.02	.10
35 Moose Haas	.02	.10
36 Roy Howell	.02	.10
37 Pete Ladd	.02	.10
38 Bob McClure	.02	.10
39 Doc Medich	.02	.10
40 Paul Molitor	.07	.20
41 Don Money	.02	.10
42 Charlie Moore	.02	.10
43 Ben Oglivie	.07	.20
44 Ed Romero	.02	.10
45 Ted Simmons	.07	.20
46 Jim Slaton	.02	.10
47 Don Sutton	.07	.20
48 Gorman Thomas	.07	.20
49 Pete Vuckovich	.02	.10
50 Ned Yost	.02	.10
51 Robin Yount	.50	1.25
52 Benny Ayala	.02	.10
53 Bob Bonner	.02	.10
54 Al Bumbry	.02	.10
55 Terry Crowley	.02	.10
56 Storm Davis RC	.20	.50
57 Rich Dauer	.02	.10
58 Rick Dempsey UER (Posing batting lefty)	.02	.10
59 Jim Dwyer	.02	.10
60 Mike Flanagan	.02	.10
61 Dan Ford	.02	.10
62 Glenn Gulliver	.02	.10
63 John Lowenstein	.02	.10
64 Dennis Martinez	.07	.20
65 Tippy Martinez	.02	.10
66 Scott McGregor	.02	.10
67 Eddie Murray	.30	.75
68 Joe Nolan	.02	.10
69 Jim Palmer	.07	.20
70 Cal Ripken	2.50	6.00
71 Gary Roenicke	.02	.10
72 Lenn Sakata	.02	.10
73 Ken Singleton	.07	.20
74 Sammy Stewart	.02	.10
75 Tim Stoddard	.02	.10
76 Don Aase	.02	.10
77 Don Baylor	.07	.20
78 Juan Beniquez	.02	.10
79 Bob Boone	.07	.20
80 Rick Burleson	.02	.10
81 Rod Carew	.15	.40
82 Bobby Clark	.02	.10
83 Doug Corbett	.02	.10
84 John Curtis	.02	.10
85 Doug DeCinces	.02	.10
86 Brian Downing	.07	.20
87 Joe Ferguson	.02	.10
88 Tim Foli	.02	.10
89 Ken Forsch	.02	.10
90 Dave Goltz	.02	.10
91 Bobby Grich	.07	.20
92 Andy Hassler	.02	.10
93 Reggie Jackson	.15	.40
94 Ron Jackson	.02	.10
95 Tommy John	.07	.20
96 Bruce Kison	.02	.10
97 Fred Lynn	.07	.20
98 Ed Ott	.02	.10
99 Steve Renko	.02	.10
100 Luis Sanchez	.02	.10
101 Rob Wilfong	.02	.10
102 Mike Witt	.02	.10
103 Geoff Zahn	.02	.10
104 Willie Aikens	.02	.10
105 Mike Armstrong	.02	.10
106 Vida Blue	.07	.20
107 Bud Black RC	.20	.50
108 George Brett	.75	2.00
109 Bill Castro	.02	.10
110 Onix Concepcion	.02	.10
111 Dave Frost	.02	.10
112 Cesar Geronimo	.02	.10
113 Larry Gura	.02	.10
114 Steve Hammond	.02	.10
115 Don Hood	.02	.10
116 Dennis Leonard	.02	.10
117 Jerry Martin	.02	.10
118 Lee May	.02	.10
119 Hal McRae	.07	.20
120 Amos Otis	.07	.20
121 Greg Pryor	.02	.10
122 Dan Quisenberry	.07	.20
123 Don Slaught RC	.20	.50
124 Paul Splittorff	.02	.10
125 U.L. Washington	.02	.10
126 John Wathan	.02	.10
127 Frank White	.07	.20
128 Willie Wilson	.07	.20
129 Steve Bedrosian UER (Height 6'33)	.02	.10
130 Bruce Benedict	.02	.10
131 Tommy Boggs	.02	.10
132 Brett Butler	.07	.20
133 Rick Camp	.02	.10
134 Chris Chambliss	.07	.20
135 Ken Dayley	.02	.10
136 Gene Garber	.02	.10
137 Terry Harper	.02	.10
138 Bob Horner	.07	.20
139 Glenn Hubbard	.02	.10
140 Rufino Linares	.02	.10
141 Rick Mahler	.02	.10
142 Dale Murphy	.15	.40
143 Phil Niekro	.07	.20
144 Pascual Perez	.02	.10
145 Biff Pocoroba	.02	.10
146 Rafael Ramirez	.02	.10
147 Jerry Royster	.02	.10
148 Ken Smith	.02	.10
149 Bob Walk	.02	.10
150 Claudell Washington	.02	.10
151 Bob Watson	.02	.10
152 Larry Whisenton	.02	.10
153 Porfirio Altamirano	.02	.10
154 Marty Bystrom	.02	.10
155 Steve Carlton	.15	.40
156 Larry Christenson	.02	.10
157 Ivan DeJesus	.02	.10
158 John Denny	.02	.10
159 Bob Dernier	.02	.10
160 Bo Diaz	.02	.10
161 Ed Farmer	.02	.10
162 Greg Gross	.02	.10
163 Mike Krukow	.02	.10
164 Garry Maddox	.02	.10
165 Gary Matthews	.07	.20
166 Tug McGraw	.07	.20
167 Bob Molinaro	.02	.10
168 Sid Monge	.02	.10
169 Ron Reed	.02	.10
170 Bill Robinson	.02	.10
171 Pete Rose	1.00	2.50
172 Dick Ruthven	.02	.10
173 Mike Schmidt	.75	2.00
174 Manny Trillo	.02	.10
175 Ozzie Virgil	.02	.10
176 George Vukovich	.02	.10
177 Gary Allenson	.02	.10
178 Luis Aponte	.02	.10
179 Wade Boggs RC	4.00	10.00
180 Tom Burgmeier	.02	.10
181 Mark Clear	.02	.10
182 Dennis Eckersley	.15	.40
183 Dwight Evans	.15	.40
184 Rich Gedman	.02	.10
185 Glenn Hoffman	.02	.10
186 Bruce Hurst	.02	.10
187 Carney Lansford	.07	.20
188 Rick Miller	.02	.10
189 Reid Nichols	.02	.10
190 Bob Ojeda	.02	.10
191 Tony Perez	.15	.40
192 Chuck Rainey	.02	.10
193 Jerry Remy	.02	.10
194 Jim Rice	.07	.20
195 Bob Stanley	.02	.10
196 Dave Stapleton	.02	.10
197 Mike Torrez	.02	.10
198 John Tudor	.07	.20
199 Julio Valdez	.02	.10
200 Carl Yastrzemski	.50	1.25
201 Dusty Baker	.07	.20
202 Joe Beckwith	.02	.10
203 Greg Brock	.02	.10
204 Ron Cey	.07	.20
205 Terry Forster	.07	.20
206 Steve Garvey	.07	.20
207 Pedro Guerrero	.07	.20
208 Burt Hooton	.02	.10
209 Steve Howe	.02	.10
210 Ken Landreaux	.02	.10
211 Mike Marshall	.02	.10
212 Candy Maldonado RC	.20	.50
213 Rick Monday	.07	.20
214 Tom Niedenfuer	.02	.10
215 Jorge Orta	.02	.10
216 Jerry Reuss UER	.02	.10
217 Ron Roenicke	.02	.10
218 Vicente Romo	.02	.10
219 Bill Russell	.07	.20
220 Steve Sax	.07	.20

221 Mike Scioscia .07 .20
222 Dave Stewart .07 .20
223 Derrel Thomas .02 .10
224 Fernando Valenzuela .07 .20
225 Bob Welch .07 .20
226 Ricky Wright .02 .10
227 Steve Yeager .07 .20
228 Bill Almon .02 .10
229 Harold Baines .07 .20
230 Salome Barojas .02 .10
231 Tony Bernazard .02 .10
232 Britt Burns .02 .10
233 Richard Dotson .02 .10
234 Ernesto Escarrega .02 .10
235 Carlton Fisk .15 .40
236 Jerry Hairston .02 .10
237 Kevin Hickey .02 .10
238 LaMarr Hoyt .02 .10
239 Steve Kemp .02 .10
240 Jim Kern .02 .10
241 Ron Kittle RC .40 1.00
242 Jerry Koosman .07 .20
243 Dennis Lamp .02 .10
244 Rudy Law .02 .10
245 Vance Law .02 .10
246 Ron LeFlore .07 .20
247 Greg Luzinski .07 .20
248 Tom Paciorek .02 .10
249 Aurelio Rodriguez .02 .10
250 Mike Squires .02 .10
251 Steve Trout .02 .10
252 Jim Barr .02 .10
253 Dave Bergman .02 .10
254 Fred Breining .02 .10
255 Bob Brenly .02 .10
256 Jack Clark .07 .20
257 Chili Davis .07 .20
258 Darrell Evans .07 .20
259 Alan Fowlkes .02 .10
260 Rich Gale .02 .10
261 Atlee Hammaker .02 .10
262 Al Holland .02 .10
263 Duane Kuiper .02 .10
264 Bill Laskey .02 .10
265 Gary Lavelle .02 .10
266 Johnnie LeMaster .02 .10
267 Renie Martin .02 .10
268 Milt May .02 .10
269 Greg Minton .02 .10
270 Joe Morgan .07 .20
271 Tom O'Malley .02 .10
272 Reggie Smith .07 .20
273 Guy Sularz .02 .10
274 Champ Summers .02 .10
275 Max Venable .02 .10
276 Jim Wohlford .02 .10
277 Ray Burris .02 .10
278 Gary Carter .07 .20
279 Warren Cromartie .02 .10
280 Andre Dawson .07 .20
281 Terry Francona .07 .20
282 Doug Flynn .02 .10
283 Woodie Fryman .02 .10
284 Bill Gullickson .02 .10
285 Wallace Johnson .02 .10
286 Charlie Lea .02 .10
287 Randy Lerch .02 .10
288 Brad Mills .02 .10
289 Dan Norman .02 .10
290 Al Oliver .07 .20
291 David Palmer .02 .10
292 Tim Raines .07 .20
293 Jeff Reardon .07 .20
294 Steve Rogers .07 .20
295 Scott Sanderson .02 .10
296 Dan Schatzeder .02 .10
297 Bryn Smith .02 .10
298 Chris Speier .02 .10
299 Tim Wallach .07 .20
300 Jerry White .02 .10
301 Joel Youngblood .02 .10
302 Ross Baumgarten .02 .10
303 Dale Berra .02 .10
304 John Candelaria .02 .10
305 Dick Davis .02 .10
306 Mike Easler .02 .10
307 Richie Hebner .02 .10
308 Lee Lacy .02 .10
309 Bill Madlock .07 .20
310 Larry McWilliams .02 .10
311 John Milner .02 .10
312 Omar Moreno .02 .10
313 Jim Morrison .02 .10
314 Steve Nicosia .02 .10
315 Dave Parker .07 .20
316 Tony Pena .02 .10
317 Johnny Ray .02 .10
318 Rick Rhoden .02 .10
319 Don Robinson .02 .10
320 Enrique Romo .02 .10
321 Manny Sarmiento .02 .10
322 Rod Scurry .02 .10
323 Jimmy Smith .02 .10
324 Willie Stargell .15 .40
325 Jason Thompson .02 .10
326 Kent Tekulve .02 .10
327A Tom Brookens .02 .10
(Short .375-inch brown box shaded in on card back)
327B Tom Brookens .02 .10
(Longer 1.25-inch brown box shaded in on card back)
328 Enos Cabell .02 .10
329 Kirk Gibson .07 .20
330 Larry Herndon .02 .10
331 Mike Ivie .02 .10
332 Howard Johnson RC .40 1.00
333 Lynn Jones .02 .10
334 Rick Leach .02 .10
335 Chet Lemon .07 .20
336 Jack Morris .07 .20
337 Lance Parrish .07 .20
338 Larry Pashnick .02 .10
339 Dan Petry .02 .10
340 Dave Rozema .02 .10
341 Dave Rucker .02 .10
342 Elias Sosa .02 .10
343 Dave Tobik .02 .10
344 Alan Trammell .07 .20
345 Jerry Turner .02 .10
346 Jerry Ujdur .02 .10
347 Pat Underwood .02 .10
348 Lou Whitaker .07 .20
349 Milt Wilcox .02 .10
350 Glenn Wilson .20 .50
351 John Wockenfuss .02 .10
352 Kurt Bevacqua .02 .10
353 Juan Bonilla .02 .10
354 Floyd Chiffer .02 .10
355 Luis DeLeon .02 .10
356 Dave Dravecky RC .40 1.00
357 Dave Edwards .02 .10
358 Juan Eichelberger .02 .10
359 Tim Flannery .02 .10
360 Tony Gwynn RC 5.00 12.00
361 Ruppert Jones .02 .10
362 Terry Kennedy .02 .10
363 Joe Lefebvre .02 .10
364 Sixto Lezcano .02 .10
365 Tim Lollar .02 .10
366 Gary Lucas .02 .10
367 John Montefusco .02 .10
368 Broderick Perkins .02 .10
369 Joe Pittman .02 .10
370 Gene Richards .02 .10
371 Luis Salazar .02 .10
372 Eric Show RC .20 .50
373 Garry Templeton .07 .20
374 Chris Welsh .02 .10
375 Alan Wiggins .02 .10
376 Rick Cerone .02 .10
377 Dave Collins .02 .10
378 Roger Erickson .02 .10
379 George Frazier .02 .10
380 Oscar Gamble .02 .10
381 Rich Gossage .07 .20
382 Ken Griffey .07 .20
383 Ron Guidry .07 .20
384 Dave LaRoche .02 .10
385 Rudy May .02 .10
386 John Mayberry .02 .10
387 Lee Mazzilli .07 .20
388 Mike Morgan .02 .10
389 Jerry Mumphrey .02 .10
390 Bobby Murcer .07 .20
391 Graig Nettles .07 .20
392 Lou Piniella .07 .20
393 Willie Randolph .07 .20
394 Shane Rawley .02 .10
395 Dave Righetti .07 .20
396 Andre Robertson .02 .10
397 Roy Smalley .02 .10
398 Dave Winfield .07 .20
399 Butch Wynegar .02 .10
400 Chris Bando .02 .10
401 Alan Bannister .02 .10
402 Len Barker .02 .10
403 Tom Brennan .02 .10
404 Carmelo Castillo .02 .10
405 Miguel Dilone .02 .10
406 Jerry Dybzinski .02 .10
407 Mike Fischlin .02 .10
408 Ed Glynn UER .02 .10
(Photo actually Bud Anderson)
409 Mike Hargrove .02 .10
410 Toby Harrah .07 .20
411 Ron Hassey .02 .10
412 Von Hayes .02 .10
413 Rick Manning .02 .10
414 Bake McBride .07 .20
415 Larry Milbourne .02 .10
416 Bill Nahorodny .02 .10
417 Jack Perconte .02 .10
418 Lary Sorensen .02 .10
419 Dan Spillner .02 .10
420 Rick Sutcliffe .07 .20
421 Andre Thornton .02 .10
422 Rick Waits .02 .10
423 Eddie Whitson .02 .10
424 Jesse Barfield .07 .20
425 Barry Bonnell .02 .10
426 Jim Clancy .02 .10
427 Damaso Garcia .02 .10
428 Jerry Garvin .02 .10
429 Alfredo Griffin .02 .10
430 Garth Iorg .02 .10
431 Roy Lee Jackson .02 .10
432 Luis Leal .02 .10
433 Buck Martinez .02 .10
434 Joey McLaughlin .02 .10
435 Lloyd Moseby .02 .10
436 Rance Mulliniks .02 .10
437 Dale Murray .02 .10
438 Wayne Nordhagen .02 .10
439 Geno Petralli .20 .50
440 Hosken Powell .02 .10
441 Dave Stieb .07 .20
442 Willie Upshaw .02 .10
443 Ernie Whitt .02 .10
444 Alvis Woods .02 .10
445 Alan Ashby .02 .10
446 Jose Cruz .07 .20
447 Kiko Garcia .02 .10
448 Phil Garner .07 .20
449 Danny Heep .02 .10
450 Art Howe .02 .10
451 Bob Knepper .02 .10
452 Alan Knicely .02 .10
453 Ray Knight .07 .20
454 Frank LaCorte .02 .10
455 Mike LaCoss .02 .10
456 Randy Moffitt .02 .10
457 Joe Niekro .02 .10
458 Terry Puhl .02 .10
459 Luis Pujols .02 .10
460 Craig Reynolds .02 .10
461 Bert Roberge .02 .10
462 Vern Ruhle .02 .10
463 Nolan Ryan 1.50 4.00
464 Joe Sambito .02 .10
465 Tony Scott .02 .10
466 Dave Smith .02 .10
467 Harry Spilman .02 .10
468 Dickie Thon .02 .10
469 Denny Walling .02 .10
470 Larry Andersen .02 .10
471 Floyd Bannister .02 .10
472 Jim Beattie .02 .10
473 Bruce Bochte .02 .10
474 Manny Castillo .02 .10
475 Bill Caudill .02 .10
476 Bryan Clark .02 .10
477 Al Cowens .07 .20
478 Julio Cruz .02 .10
479 Todd Cruz .02 .10
480 Gary Gray .02 .10
481 Dave Henderson .02 .10
482 Mike Moore RC .20 .50
483 Gaylord Perry .07 .20
484 Dave Revering .02 .10
485 Joe Simpson .02 .10
486 Mike Stanton .02 .10
487 Rick Sweet .02 .10
488 Ed VandeBerg .02 .10
489 Richie Zisk .02 .10
490 Doug Bird .02 .10
491 Larry Bowa .07 .20
492 Bill Buckner .07 .20
493 Bill Campbell .02 .10
494 Jody Davis .02 .10
495 Leon Durham .02 .10
496 Steve Henderson .02 .10
497 Willie Hernandez .02 .10
498 Ferguson Jenkins .07 .20
499 Jay Johnstone .02 .10
500 Junior Kennedy .02 .10
501 Randy Martz .02 .10
502 Jerry Morales .02 .10
503 Keith Moreland .02 .10
504 Dickie Noles .02 .10
505 Mike Proly .02 .10
506 Allen Ripley .02 .10
507 R.Sandberg RC UER 4.00 10.00
Should say High School in Spokane, Washington
508 Lee Smith .15 .40
509 Pat Tabler .02 .10
510 Dick Tidrow .02 .10
511 Bump Wills .02 .10
512 Gary Woods .02 .10
513 Tony Armas .07 .20
514 Dave Beard .02 .10
515 Jeff Burroughs .02 .10
516 John D'Acquisto .02 .10
517 Wayne Gross .02 .10
518 Mike Heath .02 .10
519 R.Henderson UER .60 1.50
Brock record listed as 120 steals
520 Cliff Johnson .02 .10
521 Matt Keough .02 .10
522 Brian Kingman .02 .10
523 Rick Langford .02 .10
524 Dave Lopes .07 .20
525 Steve McCatty .02 .10
526 Dave McKay .02 .10
527 Dan Meyer .02 .10
528 Dwayne Murphy .02 .10
529 Jeff Newman .02 .10
530 Mike Norris .02 .10
531 Bob Owchinko .02 .10
532 Joe Rudi .07 .20
533 Jimmy Sexton .02 .10
534 Fred Stanley .02 .10
535 Tom Underwood .02 .10
536 Neil Allen .02 .10
537 Wally Backman .02 .10
538 Bob Bailor .02 .10
539 Hubie Brooks .02 .10
540 Carlos Diaz RC .08 .25
541 Pete Falcone .02 .10
542 George Foster .07 .20
543 Ron Gardenhire .02 .10
544 Brian Giles .02 .10
545 Ron Hodges .02 .10
546 Randy Jones .02 .10
547 Mike Jorgensen .02 .10
548 Dave Kingman .07 .20
549 Ed Lynch .02 .10
550 Jesse Orosco .02 .10
551 Rick Ownbey .02 .10
552 Charlie Puleo .02 .10
553 Gary Rajsich .02 .10
554 Mike Scott .07 .20
555 Rusty Staub .07 .20
556 John Stearns .02 .10
557 Craig Swan .02 .10
558 Ellis Valentine .02 .10
559 Tom Veryzer .02 .10
560 Mookie Wilson .07 .20
561 Pat Zachry .02 .10
562 Buddy Bell .07 .20
563 John Butcher .02 .10
564 Steve Comer .02 .10
565 Danny Darwin .02 .10
566 Bucky Dent .07 .20
567 John Grubb .02 .10
568 Rick Honeycutt .02 .10
569 Dave Hostetler .02 .10
570 Charlie Hough .07 .20
571 Lamar Johnson .02 .10
572 Jon Matlack .02 .10
573 Paul Mirabella .02 .10
574 Larry Parrish .02 .10
575 Mike Richardt .02 .10
576 Mickey Rivers .02 .10
577 Billy Sample .02 .10
578 Dave Schmidt .02 .10
579 Bill Stein .02 .10
580 Jim Sundberg .07 .20
581 Frank Tanana .07 .20
582 Mark Wagner .02 .10
583 George Wright RC .20 .50
584 Johnny Bench .30 .75
585 Bruce Berenyi .02 .10
586 Larry Biittner .02 .10
587 Cesar Cedeno .07 .20
588 Dave Concepcion .07 .20
589 Dan Driessen .02 .10
590 Greg Harris .02 .10
591 Ben Hayes .02 .10
592 Paul Householder .02 .10
593 Tom Hume .02 .10
594 Wayne Krenchicki .02 .10
595 Rafael Landestoy .02 .10
596 Charlie Leibrandt .02 .10
597 Eddie Milner .02 .10
598 Ron Oester .02 .10
599 Frank Pastore .02 .10
600 Joe Price .02 .10
601 Tom Seaver .30 .75
602 Bob Shirley .02 .10
603 Mario Soto .07 .20
604 Alex Trevino .02 .10
605 Mike Vail .02 .10
606 Duane Walker .02 .10
607 Tom Brunansky .07 .20
608 Bobby Castillo .02 .10
609 John Castino .02 .10
610 Ron Davis .02 .10
611 Lenny Faedo .02 .10
612 Terry Felton .02 .10
613 Gary Gaetti RC .40 1.00
614 Mickey Hatcher .02 .10
615 Brad Havens .02 .10
616 Kent Hrbek .07 .20
617 Randy Johnson .02 .10
618 Tim Laudner .02 .10
619 Jeff Little .02 .10
620 Bobby Mitchell .02 .10
621 Jack O'Connor .02 .10
622 John Pacella .02 .10
623 Pete Redfern .02 .10
624 Jesus Vega .02 .10
625 Frank Viola RC .60 1.50
626 Ron Washington .02 .10
627 Gary Ward .02 .10
628 Al Williams .02 .10
629 Carl Yastrzemski .30 .75
Dennis Eckersley
Mark Clear
630 Gaylord Perry .02 .10
Terry Bulling 5/6/82
631 Dave Concepcion .07 .20
Manny Trillo
632 Robin Yount .30 .75
Buddy Bell
633 Dave Winfield .02 .10
Kent Hrbek
634 Willie Stargell .30 .75
Pete Rose
635 Toby Harrah .07 .20
Andre Thornton
636 Ozzie Smith .30 .75
Lonnie Smith
637 Bo Diaz .02 .10
Gary Carter
638 Carlton Fisk .07 .20
Gary Carter
639 Rickey Henderson IA .30 .75
640 Ben Oglivie .15 .40
Reggie Jackson
641 Joel Youngblood .02 .10
August 4, 1982
642 Ron Hassey .07 .20
Len Barker
643 Black and Blue .07 .20
Vida Blue
644 Black and Blue .02 .10
Bud Black
645 Reggie Jackson Power .07 .20
646 Rickey Henderson Speed .30 .75
647 CL: Cards/Brewers .02 .10
648 CL: Orioles/Angels .02 .10
649 CL: Royals/Braves .02 .10
650 CL: Phillies/Red Sox .02 .10
651 CL: Dodgers/White Sox .02 .10
652 CL: Giants/Expos .02 .10
653 CL: Pirates/Tigers .02 .10
654 CL: Padres/Yankees .02 .10
655 CL: Indians/Blue Jays .02 .10
656 CL: Astros/Mariners .02 .10
657 CL: Cubs/A's .02 .10
658 CL: Mets/Rangers .02 .10
659 CL: Reds/Twins .02 .10
660 CL: Specials/Teams .02 .10

1984 Fleer

The 1984 Fleer card 660-card standard-size set featured fronts with full-color team logos along with the player's name and position and the Fleer identification. Wax packs again consisted of 15 cards plus logo stickers. The set features many imaginative photos, several multi-player cards, and many more action shots than the 1983 card set. The backs are quite similar to the 1983 backs except that blue rather than brown ink is used. The player cards are alphabetized within team and the teams are ordered by their 1983 season finish and won-lost record. Specials (626-646) and checklist cards (647-660) make up the end of the set. The key Rookie Cards in this set are Don Mattingly, Darryl Strawberry and Andy Van Slyke.

COMPLETE SET (660) 25.00 50.00
1 Mike Boddicker .05 .15
2 Al Bumbry .05 .15
3 Todd Cruz .05 .15
4 Rich Dauer .05 .15
5 Storm Davis .05 .15
6 Rick Dempsey .05 .15
7 Jim Dwyer .05 .15
8 Mike Flanagan .05 .15
9 Dan Ford .05 .15
10 John Lowenstein .05 .15
11 Dennis Martinez .15 .40
12 Tippy Martinez .05 .15
13 Scott McGregor .05 .15
14 Eddie Murray .60 1.50
15 Joe Nolan .05 .15
16 Jim Palmer .15 .40
17 Cal Ripken 4.00 10.00
18 Gary Roenicke .05 .15
19 Lenn Sakata .05 .15
20 John Shelby .05 .15
21 Ken Singleton .15 .40
22 Sammy Stewart .05 .15
23 Tim Stoddard .05 .15
24 Marty Bystrom .05 .15
25 Steve Carlton .30 .75
26 Ivan DeJesus .05 .15
27 John Denny .05 .15
28 Bob Dernier .05 .15
29 Bo Diaz .05 .15
30 Kiko Garcia .05 .15
31 Greg Gross .05 .15
32 Kevin Gross RC .20 .50
33 Von Hayes .05 .15
34 Willie Hernandez .05 .15
35 Al Holland .05 .15
36 Charles Hudson .05 .15
37 Joe Lefebvre .05 .15
38 Sixto Lezcano .05 .15
39 Garry Maddox .05 .15
40 Gary Matthews .15 .40
41 Len Matuszek .05 .15
42 Tug McGraw .15 .40
43 Joe Morgan .15 .40
44 Tony Perez .30 .75
45 Ron Reed .05 .15
46 Pete Rose 2.00 5.00
47 Juan Samuel RC .40 1.00
48 Mike Schmidt 1.50 4.00
49 Ozzie Virgil .05 .15
50 Juan Agosto .05 .15
51 Harold Baines .15 .40
52 Floyd Bannister .05 .15
53 Salome Barojas .05 .15
54 Britt Burns .05 .15
55 Julio Cruz .05 .15
56 Richard Dotson .05 .15
57 Jerry Dybzinski .05 .15
58 Carlton Fisk .30 .75
59 Scott Fletcher .05 .15
60 Jerry Hairston .05 .15
61 Kevin Hickey .05 .15
62 Marc Hill .05 .15
63 LaMarr Hoyt .05 .15
64 Ron Kittle .05 .15
65 Jerry Koosman .15 .40
66 Dennis Lamp .05 .15
67 Rudy Law .05 .15
68 Vance Law .05 .15
69 Greg Luzinski .15 .40
70 Tom Paciorek .05 .15
71 Mike Squires .05 .15
72 Dick Tidrow .05 .15
73 Greg Walker .20 .50
74 Glenn Abbott .05 .15
75 Howard Bailey .05 .15
76 Doug Bair .05 .15
77 Juan Berenguer .05 .15
78 Tom Brookens .15 .40
79 Enos Cabell .05 .15
80 Kirk Gibson .60 1.50
81 John Grubb .05 .15
82 Larry Herndon .15 .40
83 Wayne Krenchicki .05 .15
84 Rick Leach .05 .15
85 Chet Lemon .15 .40
86 Aurelio Lopez .05 .15
87 Jack Morris .15 .40
88 Lance Parrish .30 .75
89 Dan Petry .15 .40
90 Dave Rozema .05 .15
91 Alan Trammell .15 .40
92 Lou Whitaker .15 .40
93 Milt Wilcox .05 .15
94 Glenn Wilson .15 .40
95 John Wockenfuss .05 .15
96 Dusty Baker .15 .40
97 Joe Beckwith .05 .15
98 Greg Brock .05 .15
99 Jack Fimple .05 .15
100 Pedro Guerrero .15 .40
101 Rick Honeycutt .05 .15
102 Burt Hooton .05 .15
103 Steve Howe .05 .15
104 Ken Landreaux .05 .15
105 Mike Marshall .05 .15
106 Rick Monday .15 .40
107 Jose Morales .05 .15
108 Tom Niedenfuer .05 .15
109 Alejandro Pena RC .40 1.00
110 Jerry Reuss UER .05 .15
111 Bill Russell .15 .40
112 Steve Sax .05 .15
113 Mike Scioscia .15 .40
114 Derrel Thomas .05 .15
115 Fernando Valenzuela .15 .40
116 Bob Welch .15 .40
117 Steve Yeager .15 .40
118 Pat Zachry .05 .15
119 Don Baylor .15 .40
120 Bert Campaneris .15 .40
121 Rick Cerone .05 .15
122 Ray Fontenot .05 .15
123 George Frazier .05 .15
124 Oscar Gamble .05 .15
125 Rich Gossage .15 .40
126 Ken Griffey .15 .40
127 Ron Guidry .15 .40
128 Jay Howell .05 .15
129 Steve Kemp .05 .15
130 Matt Keough .05 .15
131 Don Mattingly RC 8.00 20.00
132 John Montefusco .05 .15
133 Omar Moreno .05 .15
134 Dale Murray .05 .15
135 Graig Nettles .15 .40
136 Lou Piniella .15 .40
137 Willie Randolph .15 .40
138 Shane Rawley .05 .15
139 Dave Righetti .15 .40
140 Andre Robertson .05 .15
141 Bob Shirley .05 .15
142 Roy Smalley .05 .15
143 Dave Winfield .15 .40
144 Butch Wynegar .05 .15
145 Jim Acker .05 .15
146 Doyle Alexander .05 .15
147 Jesse Barfield .15 .40
148 Jorge Bell .15 .40
149 Barry Bonnell .05 .15
150 Jim Clancy .05 .15
151 Dave Collins .05 .15
152 Tony Fernandez RC .40 1.00
153 Damaso Garcia .05 .15
154 Dave Geisel .05 .15
155 Jim Gott .05 .15
156 Alfredo Griffin .05 .15
157 Garth Iorg .05 .15
158 Roy Lee Jackson .05 .15
159 Cliff Johnson .05 .15
160 Luis Leal .05 .15
161 Buck Martinez .05 .15
162 Joey McLaughlin .05 .15
163 Randy Moffitt .05 .15
164 Lloyd Moseby .05 .15
165 Rance Mulliniks .05 .15
166 Jorge Orta .05 .15
167 Dave Stieb .15 .40
168 Willie Upshaw .05 .15
169 Ernie Whitt .05 .15
170 Len Barker .05 .15
171 Steve Bedrosian .05 .15
172 Bruce Benedict .05 .15
173 Brett Butler .15 .40
174 Rick Camp .05 .15
175 Chris Chambliss .15 .40
176 Ken Dayley .05 .15
177 Pete Falcone .05 .15
178 Terry Forster .15 .40
179 Gene Garber .05 .15
180 Terry Harper .05 .15
181 Bob Horner .15 .40
182 Glenn Hubbard .05 .15
183 Randy Johnson .05 .15
184 Craig McMurtry .05 .15
185 Donnie Moore .05 .15
186 Dale Murphy .30 .75
187 Phil Niekro .15 .40
188 Pascual Perez .05 .15
189 Biff Pocoroba .05 .15
190 Rafael Ramirez .05 .15
191 Jerry Royster .05 .15
192 Claudell Washington .05 .15
193 Bob Watson .05 .15
194 Jerry Augustine .05 .15
195 Mark Brouhard .05 .15
196 Mike Caldwell .05 .15
197 Tom Candiotti RC .40 1.00
198 Cecil Cooper .15 .40
199 Rollie Fingers .15 .40
200 Jim Gantner .05 .15
201 Bob L. Gibson RC .08 .25
202 Moose Haas .05 .15
203 Roy Howell .05 .15
204 Pete Ladd .05 .15
205 Rick Manning .05 .15
206 Bob McClure .05 .15
207 Paul Molitor UER .15 .40
('83 stats should say .270 BA and 608 AB)
208 Don Money .05 .15
209 Charlie Moore .05 .15
210 Ben Oglivie .15 .40
211 Chuck Porter .05 .15
212 Ed Romero .05 .15
213 Ted Simmons .15 .40
214 Jim Slaton .05 .15
215 Don Sutton .15 .40
216 Tom Tellmann .05 .15
217 Pete Vuckovich .05 .15
218 Ned Yost .05 .15
219 Robin Yount 1.00 2.50
220 Alan Ashby .05 .15
221 Kevin Bass .05 .15
222 Jose Cruz .15 .40
223 Bill Dawley .05 .15
224 Frank DiPino .05 .15
225 Bill Doran RC .20 .50
226 Phil Garner .15 .40
227 Art Howe .05 .15
228 Bob Knepper .05 .15
229 Ray Knight .15 .40
230 Frank LaCorte .05 .15
231 Mike LaCoss .05 .15
232 Mike Madden .05 .15
233 Jerry Mumphrey .05 .15
234 Joe Niekro .05 .15
235 Terry Puhl .05 .15
236 Luis Pujols .05 .15
237 Craig Reynolds .05 .15
238 Vern Ruhle .05 .15
239 Nolan Ryan 3.00 8.00
240 Mike Scott .15 .40
241 Tony Scott .05 .15
242 Dave Smith .05 .15
243 Dickie Thon .05 .15
244 Denny Walling .05 .15
245 Dale Berra .05 .15
246 Jim Bibby .05 .15
247 John Candelaria .05 .15
248 Jose DeLeon RC .20 .50
249 Mike Easler .05 .15
250 Cecilio Guante .05 .15
251 Richie Hebner .05 .15
252 Lee Lacy .05 .15
253 Bill Madlock .15 .40
254 Milt May .05 .15
255 Lee Mazzilli .15 .40
256 Larry McWilliams .05 .15
257 Jim Morrison .05 .15
258 Dave Parker .15 .40
259 Tony Pena .05 .15
260 Johnny Ray .05 .15
261 Rick Rhoden .05 .15
262 Don Robinson .05 .15
263 Manny Sarmiento .05 .15
264 Rod Scurry .05 .15
265 Kent Tekulve .05 .15
266 Gene Tenace .15 .40
267 Jason Thompson .05 .15
268 Lee Tunnell .05 .15
269 Marvell Wynne .20 .50
270 Ray Burris .05 .15
271 Gary Carter .15 .40
272 Warren Cromartie .05 .15
273 Andre Dawson .15 .40
274 Doug Flynn .05 .15
275 Terry Francona .15 .40
276 Bill Gullickson .15 .40
277 Bob James .05 .15
278 Charlie Lea .05 .15
279 Bryan Little .05 .15
280 Al Oliver .15 .40
281 Tim Raines .15 .40
282 Bobby Ramos .05 .15
283 Jeff Reardon .15 .40
284 Steve Rogers .15 .40
285 Scott Sanderson .05 .15

286 Dan Schatzeder .05 .15
287 Bryn Smith .05 .15
288 Chris Speier .05 .15
289 Manny Trillo .05 .15
290 Mike Vail .05 .15
291 Tim Wallach .05 .15
292 Chris Welsh .05 .15
293 Jim Wohlford .05 .15
294 Kurt Bevacqua .05 .15
295 Juan Bonilla .05 .15
296 Bobby Brown .05 .15
297 Luis DeLeon .05 .15
298 Dave Dravecky .05 .15
299 Tim Flannery .05 .15
300 Steve Garvey .15 .40
301 Tony Gwynn 2.50 6.00
302 Andy Hawkins .05 .15
303 Ruppert Jones .05 .15
304 Terry Kennedy .05 .15
305 Tim Lollar .05 .15
306 Gary Lucas .05 .15
307 Kevin McReynolds RC .40 1.00
308 Sid Monge .05 .15
309 Mario Ramirez .05 .15
310 Gene Richards .05 .15
311 Luis Salazar .05 .15
312 Eric Show .05 .15
313 Elias Sosa .05 .15
314 Garry Templeton .15 .40
315 Mark Thurmond .05 .15
316 Ed Whitson .05 .15
317 Alan Wiggins .05 .15
318 Neil Allen .05 .15
319 Joaquin Andujar .15 .40
320 Steve Braun .05 .15
321 Glenn Brummer .05 .15
322 Bob Forsch .05 .15
323 David Green .05 .15
324 George Hendrick .15 .40
325 Tom Herr .05 .15
326 Dane Iorg .05 .15
327 Jeff Lahti .05 .15
328 Dave LaPoint .05 .15
329 Willie McGee .15 .40
330 Ken Oberkfell .05 .15
331 Darrell Porter .05 .15
332 Jamie Quirk .05 .15
333 Mike Ramsey .05 .15
334 Floyd Rayford .05 .15
335 Lonnie Smith .05 .15
336 Ozzie Smith 1.00 2.50
337 John Stuper .05 .15
338 Bruce Sutter .30 .75
339 Andy Van Slyke RC 1.00 2.50
UER Batting and throwing
both wrong on card back
340 Dave Von Ohlen .05 .15
341 Willie Aikens .05 .15
342 Mike Armstrong .05 .15
343 Bud Black .05 .15
344 George Brett 1.50 4.00
345 Onix Concepcion .05 .15
346 Keith Creel .05 .15
347 Larry Gura .05 .15
348 Don Hood .05 .15
349 Dennis Leonard .05 .15
350 Hal McRae .15 .40
351 Amos Otis .15 .40
352 Gaylord Perry .15 .40
353 Greg Pryor .05 .15
354 Dan Quisenberry .05 .15
355 Steve Renko .05 .15
356 Leon Roberts .05 .15
357 Pat Sheridan .05 .15
358 Joe Simpson .05 .15
359 Don Slaught .15 .40
360 Paul Splittorff .05 .15
361 U.L. Washington .05 .15
362 John Wathan .05 .15
363 Frank White .15 .40
364 Willie Wilson .15 .40
365 Jim Barr .05 .15
366 Dave Bergman .05 .15
367 Fred Breining .05 .15
368 Bob Brenly .05 .15
369 Jack Clark .15 .40
370 Chili Davis .15 .40
371 Mark Davis .05 .15
372 Darrell Evans .15 .40
373 Atlee Hammaker .05 .15
374 Mike Krukow .05 .15
375 Duane Kuiper .05 .15
376 Bill Laskey .05 .15
377 Gary Lavelle .05 .15
378 Johnnie LeMaster .05 .15
379 Jeff Leonard .05 .15
380 Randy Lerch .05 .15
381 Renie Martin .05 .15
382 Andy McGaffigan .05 .15
383 Greg Minton .05 .15
384 Tom O'Malley .05 .15
385 Max Venable .05 .15
386 Brad Wellman .05 .15
387 Joel Youngblood .05 .15
388 Gary Allenson .05 .15
389 Luis Aponte .05 .15
390 Tony Armas .15 .40
391 Doug Bird .05 .15
392 Wade Boggs 1.50 4.00
393 Dennis Boyd .15 .40
394 Mike G. Brown UER .08 .25
(shown with record
of 31-104)
395 Mark Clear .05 .15
396 Dennis Eckersley .30 .75
397 Dwight Evans .30 .75
398 Rich Gedman .05 .15
399 Glenn Hoffman .05 .15
400 Bruce Hurst .05 .15
401 John Henry Johnson .05 .15
402 Ed Jurak .05 .15
403 Rick Miller .05 .15
404 Jeff Newman .05 .15
405 Reid Nichols .05 .15
406 Bob Ojeda .05 .15
407 Jerry Remy .05 .15
408 Jim Rice .15 .40
409 Bob Stanley .05 .15
410 Dave Stapleton .05 .15
411 John Tudor .15 .40
412 Carl Yastrzemski .60 1.50
413 Buddy Bell .15 .40
414 Larry Biittner .05 .15
415 John Butcher .05 .15
416 Danny Darwin .05 .15
417 Bucky Dent .15 .40
418 Dave Hostetler .05 .15
419 Charlie Hough .15 .40
420 Bobby Johnson .05 .15
421 Odell Jones .05 .15
422 Jon Matlack .05 .15
423 Pete O'Brien RC .20 .50
424 Larry Parrish .05 .15
425 Mickey Rivers .05 .15
426 Billy Sample .05 .15
427 Dave Schmidt .05 .15
428 Mike Smithson .05 .15
429 Bill Stein .05 .15
430 Dave Stewart .15 .40
431 Jim Sundberg .15 .40
432 Frank Tanana .15 .40
433 Dave Tobik .05 .15
434 Wayne Tolleson .05 .15
435 George Wright .05 .15
436 Bill Almon .05 .15
437 Keith Atherton .05 .15
438 Dave Beard .05 .15
439 Tom Burgmeier .05 .15
440 Jeff Burroughs .05 .15
441 Chris Codiroli .05 .15
442 Tim Conroy .05 .15
443 Mike Davis .05 .15
444 Wayne Gross .05 .15
445 Garry Hancock .05 .15
446 Mike Heath .05 .15
447 Rickey Henderson 1.00 2.50
448 Donnie Hill .05 .15
449 Bob Kearney .05 .15
450 Bill Krueger RC .08 .25
451 Rick Langford .05 .15
452 Carney Lansford .15 .40
453 Dave Lopes .15 .40
454 Steve McCatty .05 .15
455 Dan Meyer .05 .15
456 Dwayne Murphy .05 .15
457 Mike Norris .05 .15
458 Ricky Peters .05 .15
459 Tony Phillips RC .40 1.00
460 Tom Underwood .05 .15
461 Mike Warren .05 .15
462 Johnny Bench .60 1.50
463 Bruce Berenyi .05 .15
464 Dann Bilardello .05 .15
465 Cesar Cedeno .15 .40
466 Dave Concepcion .15 .40
467 Dan Driessen .05 .15
468 Nick Esasky .05 .15
469 Rich Gale .05 .15
470 Ben Hayes .05 .15
471 Paul Householder .05 .15
472 Tom Hume .05 .15
473 Alan Knicely .05 .15
474 Eddie Milner .05 .15
475 Ron Oester .05 .15
476 Kelly Paris .05 .15
477 Frank Pastore .05 .15
478 Ted Power .05 .15
479 Joe Price .05 .15
480 Charlie Puleo .05 .15
481 Gary Redus RC .20 .50
482 Bill Scherrer .05 .15
483 Mario Soto .15 .40
484 Alex Trevino .05 .15
485 Duane Walker .05 .15
486 Larry Bowa .15 .40
487 Warren Brusstar .05 .15
488 Bill Buckner .15 .40
489 Bill Campbell .05 .15
490 Ron Cey .15 .40
491 Jody Davis .05 .15
492 Leon Durham .05 .15
493 Mel Hall .15 .40
494 Ferguson Jenkins .15 .40
495 Jay Johnstone .05 .15
496 Craig Lefferts RC .08 .25
497 Carmelo Martinez .05 .15
498 Jerry Morales .05 .15
499 Keith Moreland .05 .15
500 Dickie Noles .05 .15
501 Mike Proly .05 .15
502 Chuck Rainey .05 .15
503 Dick Ruthven .05 .15
504 Ryne Sandberg 2.50 6.00
505 Lee Smith .15 .40
506 Steve Trout .05 .15
507 Gary Woods .05 .15
508 Juan Beniquez .05 .15
509 Bob Boone .15 .40
510 Rick Burleson .05 .15
511 Rod Carew .30 .75
512 Bobby Clark .05 .15
513 John Curtis .05 .15
514 Doug DeCinces .05 .15
515 Brian Downing .15 .40
516 Tim Foli .05 .15
517 Ken Forsch .05 .15
518 Bobby Grich .15 .40
519 Andy Hassler .05 .15
520 Reggie Jackson .30 .75
521 Ron Jackson .05 .15
522 Tommy John .15 .40
523 Bruce Kison .05 .15
524 Steve Lubratich .05 .15
525 Fred Lynn .15 .40
526 Gary Pettis .05 .15
527 Luis Sanchez .05 .15
528 Daryl Sconiers .05 .15
529 Ellis Valentine .05 .15
530 Rob Wilfong .05 .15
531 Mike Witt .05 .15
532 Geoff Zahn .05 .15
533 Bud Anderson .05 .15
534 Chris Bando .05 .15
535 Alan Bannister .05 .15
536 Bert Blyleven .15 .40
537 Tom Brennan .05 .15
538 Jamie Easterly .05 .15
539 Juan Eichelberger .05 .15
540 Jim Essian .05 .15
541 Mike Fischlin .05 .15
542 Julio Franco .15 .40
543 Mike Hargrove .05 .15
544 Toby Harrah .15 .40
545 Ron Hassey .05 .15
546 Neal Heaton .05 .15
547 Bake McBride .15 .40
548 Broderick Perkins .05 .15
549 Lary Sorensen .05 .15
550 Dan Spillner .05 .15
551 Rick Sutcliffe .15 .40
552 Pat Tabler .05 .15
553 Gorman Thomas .15 .40
554 Andre Thornton .05 .15
555 George Vukovich .05 .15
556 Darrell Brown .05 .15
557 Tom Brunansky .05 .15
558 Randy Bush .05 .15
559 Bobby Castillo .05 .15
560 John Castino .05 .15
561 Ron Davis .05 .15
562 Dave Engle .05 .15
563 Lenny Faedo .05 .15
564 Pete Filson .05 .15
565 Gary Gaetti .30 .75
566 Mickey Hatcher .05 .15
567 Kent Hrbek .15 .40
568 Rusty Kuntz .05 .15
569 Tim Laudner .05 .15
570 Rick Lysander .05 .15
571 Bobby Mitchell .05 .15
572 Ken Schrom .05 .15
573 Ray Smith .05 .15
574 Tim Teufel RC .20 .50
575 Frank Viola .30 .75
576 Gary Ward .05 .15
577 Ron Washington .05 .15
578 Len Whitehouse .05 .15
579 Al Williams .05 .15
580 Bob Bailor .05 .15
581 Mark Bradley .05 .15
582 Hubie Brooks .05 .15
583 Carlos Diaz .05 .15
584 George Foster .15 .40
585 Brian Giles .05 .15
586 Danny Heep .05 .15
587 Keith Hernandez .15 .40
588 Ron Hodges .05 .15
589 Scott Holman .05 .15
590 Dave Kingman .15 .40
591 Ed Lynch .05 .15
592 Jose Oquendo RC .20 .50
593 Jesse Orosco .05 .15
594 Junior Ortiz .05 .15
595 Tom Seaver .60 1.50
596 Doug Sisk .05 .15
597 Rusty Staub .15 .40
598 John Stearns .05 .15
599 Darryl Strawberry RC 2.00 5.00
600 Craig Swan .05 .15
601 Walt Terrell .05 .15
602 Mike Torrez .05 .15
603 Mookie Wilson .15 .40
604 Jamie Allen .05 .15
605 Jim Beattie .05 .15
606 Tony Bernazard .05 .15
607 Manny Castillo .05 .15
608 Bill Caudill .05 .15
609 Bryan Clark .05 .15
610 Al Cowens .05 .15
611 Dave Henderson .15 .40
612 Steve Henderson .05 .15
613 Orlando Mercado .05 .15
614 Mike Moore .05 .15
615 Ricky Nelson UER .05 .15
(Jamie Nelson's
stats on back)
616 Spike Owen RC .20 .50
617 Pat Putnam .05 .15
618 Ron Roenicke .05 .15
619 Mike Stanton .05 .15
620 Bob Stoddard .05 .15
621 Rick Sweet .05 .15
622 Roy Thomas .05 .15
623 Ed VandeBerg .05 .15
624 Matt Young RC .20 .50
625 Richie Zisk .05 .15
626 Fred Lynn IA .15 .40
627 Manny Trillo IA .05 .15
628 Steve Garvey IA .15 .40
629 Rod Carew IA .15 .40
630 Wade Boggs IA .60 1.50
631 Tim Raines IA .15 .40
632 Al Oliver IA .15 .40
633 Steve Sax IA .15 .40
634 Dickie Thon IA .05 .15
635 Dan Quisenberry .05 .15
Tippy Martinez
636 Joe Morgan .60 1.50
Pete Rose
Tony Perez
637 Lance Parrish .30 .75
Bob Boone
638 George Brett .75 2.00
Gaylord Perry
639 Dave Righetti .30 .75
Mike Warren
Bob Forsch
640 Johnny Bench .60 1.50
Carl Yastrzemski
641 Gaylord Perry IA .05 .15
642 Steve Carlton IA .15 .40
643 Joe Altobelli MG .05 .15
Paul Owens MG
644 Rick Dempsey WS .05 .15
645 Mike Boddicker WS .05 .15
646 Scott McGregor WS .05 .15
647 CL: Orioles/Royals .05 .15
Joe Altobelli MG
648 CL: Phillies/Giants .05 .15
Paul Owens MG
649 CL: White Sox/Red Sox .30 .75
Tony LaRussa MG
650 CL: Tigers/Rangers .30 .75
Sparky Anderson MG
651 CL: Dodgers/A's .30 .75
Tommy Lasorda MG
652 CL: Yankees/Reds .30 .75
Billy Martin MG
653 CL: Blue Jays/Cubs .15 .40
Bobby Cox MG
654 CL: Braves/Angels .30 .75
Joe Torre MG
655 CL: Brewers/Indians .05 .15
Rene Lachemann MG
656 CL: Astros/Twins .05 .15
Bob Lillis MG
657 CL: Pirates/Mets .05 .15
Chuck Tanner MG
658 CL: Expos/Mariners .05 .15
Bill Virdon MG
659 CL: Padres/Specials .15 .40
Dick Williams MG
660 CL: Cardinals/Teams .30 .75
Whitey Herzog MG

1984 Fleer Update

This set was Fleer's first update set and portrayed players with their proper team for the current year and rookies who were not in their regular issue. Like the Topps Traded sets of the time, the Fleer Update sets were distributed in factory set form through hobby dealers only. The set was quite popular with collectors, and, apparently, the print run was relatively short, as the set was quickly in short supply and exhibited a rapid and dramatic price increase in the mid to late 1980's. The cards are numbered on the back with a U prefix and placed in alphabetical order by player name. The key (extended) Rookie Cards in this set are Roger Clemens, John Franco, Dwight Gooden, Jimmy Key, Mark Langston, Kirby Puckett, and Bret Saberhagen. Collectors are urged to be careful if purchasing single cards of Clemens, Darling, Gooden, Puckett, Rose, or Saberhagen as these specific cards have been illegally reprinted. These fakes are blurry when compared to the real cards and have noticeably different printing dot patterns under 8X or greater magnification..

COMP.FACT.SET (132) 175.00 300.00
1 Willie Aikens .40 1.00
2 Luis Aponte .40 1.00
3 Mark Bailey .40 1.00
4 Bob Bailor .40 1.00
5 Dusty Baker .60 1.50
6 Steve Balboni .40 1.00
7 Alan Bannister .40 1.00
8 Marty Barrett XRC .75 2.00
9 Dave Beard .40 1.00
10 Joe Beckwith .40 1.00
11 Dave Bergman .40 1.00
12 Tony Bernazard .40 1.00
13 Bruce Bochte .40 1.00
14 Barry Bonnell .40 1.00
15 Phil Bradley .75 2.00
16 Fred Breining .40 1.00
17 Mike C. Brown .40 1.00
18 Bill Buckner .60 1.50
19 Ray Burris .40 1.00
20 John Butcher .40 1.00
21 Brett Butler .60 1.50
22 Enos Cabell .40 1.00
23 Bill Campbell .40 1.00
24 Bill Caudill .40 1.00
25 Bobby Clark .40 1.00
26 Bryan Clark .40 1.00
27 Roger Clemens XRC 60.00 120.00
28 Jaime Cocanower .40 1.00
29 Ron Darling XRC 2.00 5.00
30 Alvin Davis XRC .75 2.00
31 Bob Dernier .40 1.00
32 Carlos Diaz .40 1.00
33 Mike Easler .40 1.00
34 Dennis Eckersley 1.00 2.50
35 Jim Essian .40 1.00
36 Darrell Evans .60 1.50
37 Mike Fitzgerald .40 1.00
38 Tim Foli .40 1.00
39 John Franco XRC 2.00 5.00
40 George Frazier .40 1.00
41 Rich Gale .40 1.00
42 Barbaro Garbey .40 1.00
43 Dwight Gooden XRC 8.00 20.00
44 Rich Gossage .60 1.50
45 Wayne Gross .40 1.00
46 Mark Gubicza XRC .75 2.00
47 Jackie Gutierrez .40 1.00
48 Toby Harrah .60 1.50
49 Ron Hassey .40 1.00
50 Richie Hebner .40 1.00
51 Willie Hernandez .40 1.00
52 Ed Hodge .40 1.00
53 Ricky Horton .40 1.00
54 Art Howe .40 1.00
55 Dane Iorg .40 1.00
56 Brook Jacoby .75 2.00
57 Dion James XRC .40 1.00
58 Mike Jeffcoat XRC .40 1.00
59 Ruppert Jones .40 1.00
60 Bob Kearney .40 1.00
61 Jimmy Key XRC 2.00 5.00
62 Dave Kingman .60 1.50
63 Brad Komminsk XRC .40 1.00
64 Jerry Koosman .60 1.50
65 Wayne Krenchicki .40 1.00
66 Rusty Kuntz .40 1.00
67 Frank LaCorte .40 1.00
68 Dennis Lamp .40 1.00
69 Tito Landrum .40 1.00
70 Mark Langston XRC 2.00 5.00
71 Rick Leach .40 1.00
72 Craig Lefferts .40 1.00
73 Gary Lucas .40 1.00
74 Jerry Martin .40 1.00
75 Carmelo Martinez .40 1.00
76 Mike Mason XRC .40 1.00
77 Gary Matthews .60 1.50
78 Andy McGaffigan .40 1.00
79 Joey McLaughlin .40 1.00
80 Joe Morgan .60 1.50
81 Darryl Motley .40 1.00
82 Graig Nettles .60 1.50
83 Phil Niekro .60 1.50
84 Ken Oberkfell .40 1.00
85 Al Oliver .60 1.50
86 Jorge Orta .40 1.00
87 Amos Otis .60 1.50
88 Bob Owchinko .40 1.00
89 Dave Parker .60 1.50
90 Jack Perconte .40 1.00
91 Tony Perez 1.00 2.50
92 Gerald Perry .75 2.00
93 Kirby Puckett XRC 30.00 60.00
94 Shane Rawley .40 1.00
95 Floyd Rayford .40 1.00
96 Ron Reed .40 1.00
97 R.J. Reynolds .40 1.00
98 Gene Richards .40 1.00
99 Jose Rijo XRC 2.00 5.00
100 Jeff D. Robinson .40 1.00
101 Ron Romanick .40 1.00
102 Pete Rose 5.00 12.00
103 Bret Saberhagen XRC 4.00 10.00
104 Scott Sanderson .40 1.00
105 Dick Schofield XRC .75 2.00
106 Tom Seaver 1.50 4.00
107 Jim Slaton .40 1.00
108 Mike Smithson .40 1.00
109 Lary Sorensen .40 1.00
110 Tim Stoddard .40 1.00
111 Jeff Stone XRC .40 1.00
112 Champ Summers .40 1.00
113 Jim Sundberg .60 1.50
114 Rick Sutcliffe .60 1.50
115 Craig Swan .40 1.00
116 Derrel Thomas .40 1.00
117 Gorman Thomas .60 1.50
118 Alex Trevino .40 1.00
119 Manny Trillo .40 1.00
120 John Tudor .60 1.50
121 Tom Underwood .40 1.00
122 Mike Vail .40 1.00
123 Tom Waddell .40 1.00
124 Gary Ward .40 1.00
125 Terry Whitfield .40 1.00
126 Curtis Wilkerson .40 1.00
127 Frank Williams .40 1.00
128 Glenn Wilson .60 1.50
129 John Wockenfuss .40 1.00
130 Ned Yost .40 1.00
131 Mike Young XRC .40 1.00
132 Checklist 1-132 .40 1.00

1985 Fleer

The 1985 Fleer set consists of 660 standard-size cards. Wax packs contained 15 cards plus logo stickers. Card fronts feature a full color photo, team logo along with the player's name and position. The borders enclosing the photo are color-coded to correspond to the player's team. The cards are ordered alphabetically within team. The teams are ordered based on their respective performance during the prior year. Subsets include Specials (626-643) and Major League Prospects (644-653). The black and white photo on the reverse is included for the third straight year. Rookie Cards include Roger Clemens, Eric Davis, Shawon Dunston, John Franco, Dwight Gooden, Orel Hershiser, Jimmy Key, Mark Langston, Terry Pendleton, Kirby Puckett and Bret Saberhagen

COMPLETE SET (660) 30.00 60.00
COMP.FACT.SET (660) 50.00 100.00
1 Doug Bair .05 .15
2 Juan Berenguer .05 .15
3 Dave Bergman .05 .15
4 Tom Brookens .05 .15
5 Marty Castillo .05 .15
6 Darrell Evans .15 .40
7 Barbaro Garbey .05 .15
8 Kirk Gibson .15 .40
9 John Grubb .05 .15
10 Willie Hernandez .05 .15
11 Larry Herndon .05 .15
12 Howard Johnson .15 .40
13 Ruppert Jones .05 .15
14 Rusty Kuntz .05 .15
15 Chet Lemon .15 .40
16 Aurelio Lopez .05 .15
17 Sid Monge .05 .15
18 Jack Morris .15 .40
19 Lance Parrish .15 .40
20 Dan Petry .05 .15
21 Dave Rozema .05 .15
22 Bill Scherrer .05 .15
23 Alan Trammell .15 .40
24 Lou Whitaker .15 .40
25 Milt Wilcox .05 .15
26 Kurt Bevacqua .05 .15
27 Greg Booker .05 .15
28 Bobby Brown .05 .15
29 Luis DeLeon .05 .15
30 Dave Dravecky .05 .15
31 Tim Flannery .05 .15
32 Steve Garvey .15 .40
33 Rich Gossage .15 .40
34 Tony Gwynn 1.00 2.50
35 Greg Harris .05 .15
36 Andy Hawkins .05 .15
37 Terry Kennedy .05 .15
38 Craig Lefferts .05 .15
39 Tim Lollar .05 .15
40 Carmelo Martinez .05 .15
41 Kevin McReynolds .15 .40
42 Graig Nettles .15 .40
43 Luis Salazar .05 .15
44 Eric Show .05 .15
45 Garry Templeton .15 .40
46 Mark Thurmond .05 .15
47 Ed Whitson .05 .15
48 Alan Wiggins .05 .15
49 Rich Bordi .05 .15
50 Larry Bowa .15 .40
51 Warren Brusstar .05 .15
52 Ron Cey .15 .40
53 Henry Cotto RC .08 .25
54 Jody Davis .05 .15
55 Bob Dernier .05 .15
56 Leon Durham .05 .15
57 Dennis Eckersley .30 .75
58 George Frazier .05 .15
59 Richie Hebner .05 .15
60 Dave Lopes .15 .40
61 Gary Matthews .15 .40
62 Keith Moreland .05 .15
63 Rick Reuschel .15 .40
64 Dick Ruthven .05 .15
65 Ryne Sandberg 1.00 2.50
66 Scott Sanderson .05 .15
67 Lee Smith .15 .40
68 Tim Stoddard .05 .15
69 Rick Sutcliffe .15 .40
70 Steve Trout .05 .15
71 Gary Woods .05 .15
72 Wally Backman .05 .15
73 Bruce Berenyi .05 .15
74 Hubie Brooks UER .05 .15
(Kelvin Chapman's
stats on card back)
75 Kelvin Chapman .05 .15
76 Ron Darling .15 .40
77 Sid Fernandez .15 .40
78 Mike Fitzgerald .05 .15
79 George Foster .15 .40
80 Brent Gaff .05 .15
81 Ron Gardenhire .05 .15
82 Dwight Gooden RC 1.25 3.00
83 Tom Gorman .05 .15
84 Danny Heep .05 .15
85 Keith Hernandez .15 .40
86 Ray Knight .15 .40
87 Ed Lynch .05 .15
88 Jose Oquendo .05 .15
89 Jesse Orosco .05 .15
90 Rafael Santana .05 .15
91 Doug Sisk .05 .15
92 Rusty Staub .15 .40
93 Darryl Strawberry .50 1.25
94 Walt Terrell .05 .15
95 Mookie Wilson .15 .40
96 Jim Acker .05 .15
97 Willie Aikens .05 .15
98 Doyle Alexander .05 .15
99 Jesse Barfield .15 .40
100 George Bell .15 .40
101 Jim Clancy .05 .15
102 Dave Collins .05 .15
103 Tony Fernandez .15 .40
104 Damaso Garcia .05 .15
105 Jim Gott .05 .15
106 Alfredo Griffin .05 .15
107 Garth Iorg .05 .15
108 Roy Lee Jackson .05 .15
109 Cliff Johnson .05 .15
110 Jimmy Key RC .40 1.00
111 Dennis Lamp .05 .15
112 Rick Leach .05 .15
113 Luis Leal .05 .15
114 Buck Martinez .05 .15
115 Lloyd Moseby .05 .15
116 Rance Mulliniks .05 .15
117 Dave Stieb .15 .40
118 Willie Upshaw .05 .15
119 Ernie Whitt .05 .15
120 Mike Armstrong .05 .15
121 Don Baylor .15 .40
122 Marty Bystrom .05 .15
123 Rick Cerone .05 .15
124 Joe Cowley .05 .15
125 Brian Dayett .05 .15
126 Tim Foli .05 .15
127 Ray Fontenot .05 .15
128 Ken Griffey .15 .40
129 Ron Guidry .15 .40
130 Toby Harrah .15 .40
131 Jay Howell .05 .15
132 Steve Kemp .05 .15
133 Don Mattingly 2.00 5.00
134 Bobby Meacham .05 .15
135 John Montefusco .05 .15
136 Omar Moreno .05 .15
137 Dale Murray .05 .15
138 Phil Niekro .15 .40
139 Mike Pagliarulo .05 .15
140 Willie Randolph .15 .40
141 Dennis Rasmussen .05 .15
142 Dave Righetti .15 .40
143 Jose Rijo RC .40 1.00
144 Andre Robertson .05 .15
145 Bob Shirley .05 .15
146 Dave Winfield .15 .40
147 Butch Wynegar .05 .15
148 Gary Allenson .05 .15
149 Tony Armas .15 .40
150 Marty Barrett .05 .15
151 Wade Boggs .50 1.25
152 Dennis Boyd .05 .15
153 Bill Buckner .15 .40
154 Mark Clear .05 .15
155 Roger Clemens RC 8.00 20.00
156 Steve Crawford .05 .15
157 Mike Easler .05 .15
158 Dwight Evans .30 .75
159 Rich Gedman .05 .15
160 Jackie Gutierrez .15 .40
(Wade Boggs
shown on deck)
161 Bruce Hurst .05 .15
162 John Henry Johnson .05 .15
163 Rick Miller .05 .15
164 Reid Nichols .05 .15
165 Al Nipper .05 .15
166 Bob Ojeda .05 .15
167 Jerry Remy .05 .15
168 Jim Rice .15 .40
169 Bob Stanley .05 .15
170 Mike Boddicker .05 .15
171 Al Bumbry .05 .15
172 Todd Cruz .05 .15
173 Rich Dauer .05 .15

174 Storm Davis .05 .15
175 Rick Dempsey .05 .15
176 Jim Dwyer .05 .15
177 Mike Flanagan .05 .15
178 Dan Ford .05 .15
179 Wayne Gross .05 .15
180 John Lowenstein .05 .15
181 Dennis Martinez .15 .40
182 Tippy Martinez .05 .15
183 Scott McGregor .05 .15
184 Eddie Murray .50 1.25
185 Joe Nolan .05 .15
186 Floyd Rayford .05 .15
187 Cal Ripken 2.00 5.00
188 Gary Roenicke .05 .15
189 Lenn Sakata .05 .15
190 John Shelby .05 .15
191 Ken Singleton .15 .40
192 Sammy Stewart .05 .15
193 Bill Swaggerty .05 .15
194 Tom Underwood .05 .15
195 Mike Young .05 .15
196 Steve Balboni .05 .15
197 Joe Beckwith .05 .15
198 Bud Black .05 .15
199 George Brett 1.25 3.00
200 Onix Concepcion .05 .15
201 Mark Gubicza RC .20 .50
202 Larry Gura .05 .15
203 Mark Huismann .05 .15
204 Dane Iorg .05 .15
205 Danny Jackson .05 .15
206 Charlie Leibrandt .05 .15
207 Hal McRae .15 .40
208 Darryl Motley .05 .15
209 Jorge Orta .05 .15
210 Greg Pryor .05 .15
211 Dan Quisenberry .05 .15
212 Bret Saberhagen RC .60 1.50
213 Pat Sheridan .05 .15
214 Don Slaught .05 .15
215 U.L. Washington .05 .15
216 John Wathan .05 .15
217 Frank White .15 .40
218 Willie Wilson .15 .40
219 Neil Allen .05 .15
220 Joaquin Andujar .15 .40
221 Steve Braun .05 .15
222 Danny Cox .05 .15
223 Bob Forsch .05 .15
224 David Green .05 .15
225 George Hendrick .15 .40
226 Tom Herr .05 .15
227 Ricky Horton .05 .15
228 Art Howe .05 .15
229 Mike Jorgensen .05 .15
230 Kurt Kepshire .05 .15
231 Jeff Lahti .05 .15
232 Tito Landrum .05 .15
233 Dave LaPoint .05 .15
234 Willie McGee .15 .40
235 Tom Nieto .05 .15
236 Terry Pendleton RC .40 1.00
237 Darrell Porter .05 .15
238 Dave Rucker .05 .15
239 Lonnie Smith .05 .15
240 Ozzie Smith .75 2.00
241 Bruce Sutter .15 .40
242 Andy Van Slyke UER .30 .75
(Bats Right,
Throws Left)
243 Dave Von Ohlen .05 .15
244 Larry Andersen .05 .15
245 Bill Campbell .05 .15
246 Steve Carlton .15 .40
247 Tim Corcoran .05 .15
248 Ivan DeJesus .05 .15
249 John Denny .05 .15
250 Bo Diaz .05 .15
251 Greg Gross .05 .15
252 Kevin Gross .05 .15
253 Von Hayes .05 .15
254 Al Holland .05 .15
255 Charles Hudson .05 .15
256 Jerry Koosman .15 .40
257 Joe Lefebvre .05 .15
258 Sixto Lezcano .05 .15
259 Garry Maddox .05 .15
260 Len Matuszek .05 .15
261 Tug McGraw .15 .40
262 Al Oliver .15 .40
263 Shane Rawley .05 .15
264 Juan Samuel .05 .15
265 Mike Schmidt 1.25 3.00
266 Jeff Stone RC .05 .15
267 Ozzie Virgil .05 .15
268 Glenn Wilson .05 .15
269 John Wockenfuss .05 .15
270 Darrell Brown .05 .15
271 Tom Brunansky .05 .15
272 Randy Bush .05 .15
273 John Butcher .05 .15
274 Bobby Castillo .05 .15
275 Ron Davis .05 .15
276 Dave Engle .05 .15
277 Pete Filson .05 .15
278 Gary Gaetti .15 .40
279 Mickey Hatcher .05 .15
280 Ed Hodge .05 .15
281 Kent Hrbek .15 .40
282 Houston Jimenez .05 .15
283 Tim Laudner .05 .15
284 Rick Lysander .05 .15
285 Dave Meier .05 .15
286 Kirby Puckett RC 6.00 15.00
287 Pat Putnam .05 .15
288 Ken Schrom .05 .15
289 Mike Smithson .05 .15
290 Tim Teufel .05 .15
291 Frank Viola .15 .40
292 Ron Washington .05 .15
293 Don Aase .05 .15
294 Juan Beniquez .05 .15
295 Bob Boone .15 .40
296 Mike C. Brown .05 .15
297 Rod Carew .30 .75
298 Doug Corbett .05 .15
299 Doug DeCinces .05 .15
300 Brian Downing .15 .40
301 Ken Forsch .05 .15
302 Bobby Grich .15 .40
303 Reggie Jackson .30 .75
304 Tommy John .15 .40
305 Curt Kaufman .05 .15
306 Bruce Kison .05 .15
307 Fred Lynn .15 .40
308 Gary Pettis .05 .15
309 Ron Romanick .05 .15
310 Luis Sanchez .05 .15
311 Dick Schofield .05 .15
312 Daryl Sconiers .05 .15
313 Jim Slaton .05 .15
314 Derrel Thomas .05 .15
315 Rob Wilfong .05 .15
316 Mike Witt .05 .15
317 Geoff Zahn .05 .15
318 Len Barker .05 .15
319 Steve Bedrosian .05 .15
320 Bruce Benedict .05 .15
321 Rick Camp .05 .15
322 Chris Chambliss .15 .40
323 Jeff Dedmon .05 .15
324 Terry Forster .15 .40
325 Gene Garber .05 .15
326 Albert Hall .05 .15
327 Terry Harper .05 .15
328 Bob Horner .15 .40
329 Glenn Hubbard .05 .15
330 Randy Johnson .05 .15
331 Brad Komminsk .05 .15
332 Rick Mahler .05 .15
333 Craig McMurtry .05 .15
334 Donnie Moore .05 .15
335 Dale Murphy .30 .75
336 Ken Oberkfell .05 .15
337 Pascual Perez .05 .15
338 Gerald Perry .05 .15
339 Rafael Ramirez .05 .15
340 Jerry Royster .05 .15
341 Alex Trevino .05 .15
342 Claudell Washington .05 .15
343 Alan Ashby .05 .15
344 Mark Bailey .05 .15
345 Kevin Bass .05 .15
346 Enos Cabell .05 .15
347 Jose Cruz .15 .40
348 Bill Dawley .05 .15
349 Frank DiPino .05 .15
350 Bill Doran .05 .15
351 Phil Garner .15 .40
352 Bob Knepper .05 .15
353 Mike LaCoss .05 .15
354 Jerry Mumphrey .05 .15
355 Joe Niekro .05 .15
356 Terry Puhl .05 .15
357 Craig Reynolds .05 .15
358 Vern Ruhle .05 .15
359 Nolan Ryan 2.50 6.00
360 Joe Sambito .05 .15
361 Mike Scott .15 .40
362 Dave Smith .05 .15
363 Julio Solano .05 .15
364 Dickie Thon .05 .15
365 Denny Walling .05 .15
366 Dave Anderson .05 .15
367 Bob Bailor .05 .15
368 Greg Brock .05 .15
369 Carlos Diaz .05 .15
370 Pedro Guerrero .15 .40
371 Orel Hershiser RC 1.25 3.00
372 Rick Honeycutt .05 .15
373 Burt Hooton .05 .15
374 Ken Howell .05 .15
375 Ken Landreaux .05 .15
376 Candy Maldonado .05 .15
377 Mike Marshall .05 .15
378 Tom Niedenfuer .05 .15
379 Alejandro Pena .05 .15
380 Jerry Reuss UER .05 .15
381 R.J. Reynolds .05 .15
382 German Rivera .05 .15
383 Bill Russell .15 .40
384 Steve Sax .05 .15
385 Mike Scioscia .15 .40
386 Franklin Stubbs .05 .15
387 Fernando Valenzuela .15 .40
388 Bob Welch .15 .40
389 Terry Whitfield .05 .15
390 Steve Yeager .15 .40
391 Pat Zachry .05 .15
392 Fred Breining .05 .15
393 Gary Carter .15 .40
394 Andre Dawson .15 .40
395 Miguel Dilone .05 .15
396 Dan Driessen .05 .15
397 Doug Flynn .05 .15
398 Terry Francona .15 .40
399 Bill Gullickson .05 .15
400 Bob James .05 .15
401 Charlie Lea .05 .15
402 Bryan Little .05 .15
403 Gary Lucas .05 .15
404 David Palmer .05 .15
405 Tim Raines .15 .40
406 Mike Ramsey .05 .15
407 Jeff Reardon .15 .40
408 Steve Rogers .15 .40
409 Dan Schatzeder .05 .15
410 Bryn Smith .05 .15
411 Mike Stenhouse .05 .15
412 Tim Wallach .15 .40
413 Jim Wohlford .05 .15
414 Bill Almon .05 .15
415 Keith Atherton .05 .15
416 Bruce Bochte .05 .15
417 Tom Burgmeier .05 .15
418 Ray Burris .05 .15
419 Bill Caudill .05 .15
420 Chris Codiroli .05 .15
421 Tim Conroy .05 .15
422 Mike Davis .05 .15
423 Jim Essian .05 .15
424 Mike Heath .05 .15
425 Rickey Henderson .60 1.50
426 Donnie Hill .05 .15
427 Dave Kingman .15 .40
428 Bill Krueger .05 .15
429 Carney Lansford .15 .40
430 Steve McCatty .05 .15
431 Joe Morgan .15 .40
432 Dwayne Murphy .05 .15
433 Tony Phillips .05 .15
434 Lary Sorensen .05 .15
435 Mike Warren .05 .15
436 Curt Young .05 .15
437 Luis Aponte .05 .15
438 Chris Bando .05 .15
439 Tony Bernazard .05 .15
440 Bert Blyleven .15 .40
441 Brett Butler .15 .40
442 Ernie Camacho .05 .15
443 Joe Carter .50 1.25
444 Carmelo Castillo .05 .15
445 Jamie Easterly .05 .15
446 Steve Farr RC .20 .50
447 Mike Fischlin .05 .15
448 Julio Franco .15 .40
449 Mel Hall .05 .15
450 Mike Hargrove .05 .15
451 Neal Heaton .05 .15
452 Brook Jacoby .05 .15
453 Mike Jeffcoat .05 .15
454 Don Schulze .05 .15
455 Roy Smith .05 .15
456 Pat Tabler .05 .15
457 Andre Thornton .05 .15
458 George Vukovich .05 .15
459 Tom Waddell .05 .15
460 Jerry Willard .05 .15
461 Dale Berra .05 .15
462 John Candelaria .05 .15
463 Jose DeLeon .05 .15
464 Doug Frobel .05 .15
465 Cecilio Guante .05 .15
466 Brian Harper .05 .15
467 Lee Lacy .05 .15
468 Bill Madlock .15 .40
469 Lee Mazzilli .15 .40
470 Larry McWilliams .05 .15
471 Jim Morrison .05 .15
472 Tony Pena .05 .15
473 Johnny Ray .05 .15
474 Rick Rhoden .05 .15
475 Don Robinson .05 .15
476 Rod Scurry .05 .15
477 Kent Tekulve .05 .15
478 Jason Thompson .05 .15
479 John Tudor .15 .40
480 Lee Tunnell .05 .15
481 Marvell Wynne .05 .15
482 Salome Barojas .05 .15
483 Dave Beard .05 .15
484 Jim Beattie .05 .15
485 Barry Bonnell .05 .15
486 Phil Bradley .20 .50
487 Al Cowens .05 .15
488 Alvin Davis RC .20 .50
489 Dave Henderson .05 .15
490 Steve Henderson .05 .15
491 Bob Kearney .05 .15
492 Mark Langston RC .40 1.00
493 Larry Milbourne .05 .15
494 Paul Mirabella .05 .15
495 Mike Moore .05 .15
496 Edwin Nunez .05 .15
497 Spike Owen .05 .15
498 Jack Perconte .05 .15
499 Ken Phelps .05 .15
500 Jim Presley .20 .50
501 Mike Stanton .05 .15
502 Bob Stoddard .05 .15
503 Gorman Thomas .15 .40
504 Ed VandeBerg .05 .15
505 Matt Young .05 .15
506 Juan Agosto .05 .15
507 Harold Baines .15 .40
508 Floyd Bannister .05 .15
509 Britt Burns .05 .15
510 Julio Cruz .05 .15
511 Richard Dotson .05 .15
512 Jerry Dybzinski .05 .15
513 Carlton Fisk .30 .75
514 Scott Fletcher .05 .15
515 Jerry Hairston .05 .15
516 Marc Hill .05 .15
517 LaMarr Hoyt .05 .15
518 Ron Kittle .05 .15
519 Rudy Law .05 .15
520 Vance Law .05 .15
521 Greg Luzinski .15 .40
522 Gene Nelson .05 .15
523 Tom Paciorek .05 .15
524 Ron Reed .05 .15
525 Bert Roberge .05 .15
526 Tom Seaver .30 .75
527 Roy Smalley .05 .15
528 Dan Spillner .05 .15
529 Mike Squires .05 .15
530 Greg Walker .05 .15
531 Cesar Cedeno .15 .40
532 Dave Concepcion .15 .40
533 Eric Davis RC 1.25 3.00
534 Nick Esasky .05 .15
535 Tom Foley .05 .15
536 John Franco UER RC .40 1.00
(Koufax misspelled
as Kofax on back)
537 Brad Gulden .05 .15
538 Tom Hume .05 .15
539 Wayne Krenchicki .05 .15
540 Andy McGaffigan .05 .15
541 Eddie Milner .05 .15
542 Ron Oester .05 .15
543 Bob Owchinko .05 .15
544 Dave Parker .15 .40
545 Frank Pastore .05 .15
546 Tony Perez .30 .75
547 Ted Power .05 .15
548 Joe Price .05 .15
549 Gary Redus .05 .15
550 Pete Rose 1.50 4.00
551 Jeff Russell .05 .15
552 Mario Soto .15 .40
553 Jay Tibbs .05 .15
554 Duane Walker .05 .15
555 Alan Bannister .05 .15
556 Buddy Bell .15 .40
557 Danny Darwin .05 .15
558 Charlie Hough .15 .40
559 Bobby Jones .05 .15
560 Odell Jones .05 .15
561 Jeff Kunkel .05 .15
562 Mike Mason RC .08 .25
563 Pete O'Brien .05 .15
564 Larry Parrish .05 .15
565 Mickey Rivers .05 .15
566 Billy Sample .05 .15
567 Dave Schmidt .05 .15
568 Donnie Scott .05 .15
569 Dave Stewart .15 .40
570 Frank Tanana .15 .40
571 Wayne Tolleson .05 .15
572 Gary Ward .05 .15
573 Curtis Wilkerson .05 .15
574 George Wright .05 .15
575 Ned Yost .05 .15
576 Mark Brouhard .05 .15
577 Mike Caldwell .05 .15
578 Bobby Clark .05 .15
579 Jaime Cocanower .05 .15
580 Cecil Cooper .15 .40
581 Rollie Fingers .15 .40
582 Jim Gantner .05 .15
583 Moose Haas .05 .15
584 Dion James .05 .15
585 Pete Ladd .05 .15
586 Rick Manning .05 .15
587 Bob McClure .05 .15
588 Paul Molitor .15 .40
589 Charlie Moore .05 .15
590 Ben Oglivie .15 .40
591 Chuck Porter .05 .15
592 Randy Ready RC .08 .25
593 Ed Romero .05 .15
594 Bill Schroeder .05 .15
595 Ray Searage .05 .15
596 Ted Simmons .15 .40
597 Jim Sundberg .15 .40
598 Don Sutton .15 .40
599 Tom Tellmann .05 .15
600 Rick Waits .05 .15
601 Robin Yount .75 2.00
602 Dusty Baker .15 .40
603 Bob Brenly .05 .15
604 Jack Clark .15 .40
605 Chili Davis .15 .40
606 Mark Davis .05 .15
607 Dan Gladden RC .20 .50
608 Atlee Hammaker .05 .15
609 Mike Krukow .05 .15
610 Duane Kuiper .05 .15
611 Bob Lacey .05 .15
612 Bill Laskey .05 .15
613 Gary Lavelle .05 .15
614 Johnnie LeMaster .05 .15
615 Jeff Leonard .05 .15
616 Randy Lerch .05 .15
617 Greg Minton .05 .15
618 Steve Nicosia .05 .15
619 Gene Richards .05 .15
620 Jeff D. Robinson .05 .15
621 Scot Thompson .05 .15
622 Manny Trillo .05 .15
623 Brad Wellman .05 .15
624 Frank Williams .05 .15
625 Joel Youngblood .05 .15
626 Cal Ripken IA 1.25 3.00
627 Mike Schmidt IA .50 1.25
628 Sparky Anderson IA .15 .40
629 Dave Winfield .15 .40
Rickey Henderson
630 Mike Schmidt .75 2.00
Ryne Sandberg
631 Darryl Strawberry .50 1.25
Gary Carter
Steve Garvey
Ozzie Smith
632 Gary Carter .05 .15
Charlie Lea
633 Steve Garvey .15 .40
Rich Gossage
634 Dwight Gooden .50 1.25
Juan Samuel
635 Willie Upshaw IA .05 .15
636 Lloyd Moseby IA .05 .15
637 HOLLAND .05 .15
Al Holland
638 TUNNELL .05 .15
Lee Tunnell
639 Reggie Jackson IA .15 .40
640 Pete Rose .50 1.25
4000th Hit IA
641 Cal Ripken Jr. 1.25 3.00
Cal Ripken Sr.
642 Cubs Division Champs .15 .40
643 Two Perfect Games .15 .40
and One No-Hitter:
Mike Witt
David Palmer
Jack Morris
644 Willie Lozado RC .05 .15
Vic Mata RC
645 Kelly Gruber RC .20 .50
Randy O'Neal RC
646 Jose Roman RC .05 .15
Joel Skinner
647 Steve Kiefer RC .40 1.00
Danny Tartabull RC
648 Rob Deer RC .20 .50
Alejandro Sanchez RC
649 Billy Hatcher RC .40 1.00
Shawon Dunston RC
650 Ron Robinson .05 .15
Mike Bielecki RC
651 Zane Smith RC .20 .50
Paul Zuvella RC
652 Joe Hesketh RC .20 .50
Glenn Davis RC
653 John Russell RC .05 .15
Steve Jeltz RC
654 CL: Tigers/Padres .05 .15
and Cubs/Mets
655 CL: Blue Jays/Yankees .05 .15
and Red Sox/Orioles
656 CL: Royals/Cardinals .05 .15
and Phillies/Twins
657 CL: Angels/Braves .05 .15
and Astros/Dodgers
658 CL: Expos/A's .05 .15
and Indians/Pirates
659 CL: Mariners/White Sox .05 .15
and Reds/Rangers
660 CL: Brewers/Giants .05 .15
and Special Cards

1985 Fleer Update

This 132-card standard-size update set was issued in factory set form exclusively through hobby dealers. Design is identical to the regular-issue 1985 Fleer cards except for the U prefixed card numbers on back. Cards are ordered alphabetically by the player's name. This set features the extended Rookie Cards of Vince Coleman, Darren Daulton, Ozzie Guillen and Mickey Tettleton.

COMP.FACT.SET (132) 3.00 8.00
1 Don Aase .05 .15
2 Bill Almon .05 .15
3 Dusty Baker .15 .40
4 Dale Berra .05 .15
5 Karl Best .05 .15
6 Tim Birtsas .05 .15
7 Vida Blue .15 .40
8 Rich Bordi .05 .15
9 Daryl Boston XRC .08 .25
10 Hubie Brooks .05 .15
11 Chris Brown XRC .08 .25
12 Tom Browning XRC .20 .50
13 Al Bumbry .05 .15
14 Tim Burke .05 .15
15 Ray Burris .05 .15
16 Jeff Burroughs .05 .15
17 Ivan Calderon XRC .20 .50
18 Jeff Calhoun .05 .15
19 Bill Campbell .05 .15
20 Don Carman .05 .15
21 Gary Carter .15 .40
22 Bobby Castillo .05 .15
23 Bill Caudill .05 .15
24 Rick Cerone .05 .15
25 Jack Clark .15 .40
26 Pat Clements .05 .15
27 Stu Cliburn .05 .15
28 Vince Coleman XRC .40 1.00
29 Dave Collins .05 .15
30 Fritz Connally .05 .15
31 Henry Cotto .08 .25
32 Danny Darwin .05 .15
33 Darren Daulton XRC .40 1.00
34 Jerry Davis .05 .15
35 Brian Dayett .05 .15
36 Ken Dixon .05 .15
37 Tommy Dunbar .05 .15
38 Mariano Duncan XRC .20 .50
39 Bob Fallon .05 .15
40 Brian Fisher XRC .08 .25
41 Mike Fitzgerald .05 .15
42 Ray Fontenot .05 .15
43 Greg Gagne XRC .20 .50
44 Oscar Gamble .05 .15
45 Jim Gott .05 .15
46 David Green .05 .15
47 Alfredo Griffin .05 .15
48 Ozzie Guillen XRC 2.00 5.00
49 Toby Harrah .15 .40
50 Ron Hassey .05 .15
51 Rickey Henderson 1.00 2.50
52 Steve Henderson .05 .15
53 George Hendrick .15 .40
54 Teddy Higuera XRC .20 .50
55 Al Holland .05 .15
56 Burt Hooton .05 .15
57 Jay Howell .05 .15
58 LaMarr Hoyt .05 .15
59 Tim Hulett XRC .08 .25
60 Bob James .05 .15
61 Cliff Johnson .05 .15
62 Howard Johnson .15 .40
63 Ruppert Jones .05 .15
64 Steve Kemp .05 .15
65 Bruce Kison .05 .15
66 Mike LaCoss .05 .15
67 Lee Lacy .05 .15
68 Dave LaPoint .05 .15
69 Gary Lavelle .05 .15
70 Vance Law .05 .15
71 Manny Lee XRC .08 .25
72 Sixto Lezcano .05 .15
73 Tim Lollar .05 .15
74 Urbano Lugo .05 .15
75 Fred Lynn .15 .40
76 Steve Lyons XRC .20 .50
77 Mickey Mahler .05 .15
78 Ron Mathis .05 .15
79 Len Matuszek .05 .15
80 O.McDowell XRC UER .20 .50
Part of bio
actually Roger's
81 R.McDowell XRC UER .20 .50
Part of bio
actually Oddibe's
82 Donnie Moore .05 .15
83 Ron Musselman .05 .15
84 Al Oliver .15 .40
85 Joe Orsulak XRC .20 .50
86 Dan Pasqua XRC .20 .50
87 Chris Pittaro .05 .15
88 Rick Reuschel .15 .40
89 Earnie Riles .05 .15
90 Jerry Royster .05 .15
91 Dave Rozema .05 .15
92 Dave Rucker .05 .15
93 Vern Ruhle .05 .15
94 Mark Salas .05 .15
95 Luis Salazar .05 .15
96 Joe Sambito .05 .15
97 Billy Sample .05 .15
98 Alejandro Sanchez XRC .08 .25
99 Calvin Schiraldi XRC .20 .50
100 Rick Schu .05 .15
101 Larry Sheets XRC .08 .25
102 Ron Shephard .05 .15
103 Nelson Simmons .05 .15
104 Don Slaught .05 .15
105 Roy Smalley .05 .15
106 Lonnie Smith .05 .15
107 Nate Snell .05 .15
108 Lary Sorensen .05 .15
109 Chris Speier .05 .15
110 Mike Stenhouse .05 .15
111 Tim Stoddard .05 .15
112 John Stuper .05 .15
113 Jim Sundberg .15 .40
114 Bruce Sutter .15 .40
115 Don Sutton .15 .40
116 Bruce Tanner .05 .15
117 Kent Tekulve .05 .15
118 Walt Terrell .05 .15
119 Mickey Tettleton XRC .20 .50
120 Rich Thompson .05 .15
121 Louis Thornton .05 .15
122 Alex Trevino .05 .15
123 John Tudor .15 .40
124 Jose Uribe .05 .15
125 Dave Valle XRC .20 .50
126 Dave Von Ohlen .05 .15
127 Curt Wardle .05 .15
128 U.L. Washington .05 .15
129 Ed Whitson .05 .15
130 Herm Winningham .05 .15
131 Rich Yett .05 .15
132 Checklist U1-U132 .05 .15

1986 Fleer

The 1986 Fleer set consists of 660-card standard-size cards. Wax packs included 15 cards plus logo stickers. Card fronts feature dark blue borders (resulting in extremely condition sensitive cards commonly found with chipped edges), a team logo along with the player's name and position. The player cards are alphabetized within team and the teams are ordered by their 1985 season finish and won-lost record. Subsets include Specials (626-643) and Major League Prospects (644-653). The Dennis and Tippy Martinez cards were apparently switched in the set numbering, as their adjacent numbers (279 and 280) were reversed on the Orioles checklist card. The set includes the Rookie Cards of Rick Aguilera, Jose Canseco, Darren Daulton, Len Dykstra, Cecil Fielder, Andres Galarraga and Paul O'Neill.

COMPLETE SET (660) 15.00 40.00
COMP.FACT.SET (660) 15.00 40.00
1 Steve Balboni .05 .15
2 Joe Beckwith .05 .15
3 Buddy Biancalana .05 .15
4 Bud Black .05 .15
5 George Brett .75 2.00
6 Onix Concepcion .05 .15
7 Steve Farr .05 .15
8 Mark Gubicza .05 .15
9 Dane Iorg .05 .15
10 Danny Jackson .05 .15
11 Lynn Jones .05 .15
12 Mike Jones .05 .15
13 Charlie Leibrandt .05 .15
14 Hal McRae .08 .25
15 Omar Moreno .05 .15
16 Darryl Motley .05 .15
17 Jorge Orta .05 .15
18 Dan Quisenberry .05 .15
19 Bret Saberhagen .08 .25
20 Pat Sheridan .05 .15
21 Lonnie Smith .05 .15
22 Jim Sundberg .08 .25
23 John Wathan .05 .15
24 Frank White .08 .25
25 Willie Wilson .08 .25
26 Joaquin Andujar .08 .25
27 Steve Braun .05 .15
28 Bill Campbell .05 .15
29 Cesar Cedeno .08 .25
30 Jack Clark .08 .25
31 Vince Coleman RC .40 1.00
32 Danny Cox .05 .15
33 Ken Dayley .05 .15
34 Ivan DeJesus .05 .15
35 Bob Forsch .05 .15
36 Brian Harper .05 .15
37 Tom Herr .05 .15
38 Ricky Horton .05 .15
39 Kurt Kepshire .05 .15
40 Jeff Lahti .05 .15
41 Tito Landrum .05 .15
42 Willie McGee .08 .25
43 Tom Nieto .05 .15
44 Terry Pendleton .08 .25
45 Darrell Porter .05 .15
46 Ozzie Smith .50 1.25
47 John Tudor .08 .25
48 Andy Van Slyke .20 .50
49 Todd Worrell RC .20 .50
50 Jim Acker .05 .15
51 Doyle Alexander .05 .15
52 Jesse Barfield .08 .25
53 George Bell .08 .25
54 Jeff Burroughs .05 .15
55 Bill Caudill .05 .15
56 Jim Clancy .05 .15
57 Tony Fernandez .05 .15
58 Tom Filer .05 .15
59 Damaso Garcia .05 .15
60 Tom Henke .08 .25
61 Garth Iorg .05 .15
62 Cliff Johnson .05 .15
63 Jimmy Key .08 .25
64 Dennis Lamp .05 .15
65 Gary Lavelle .05 .15
66 Buck Martinez .05 .15
67 Lloyd Moseby .05 .15

68 Rance Mulliniks .05 .15
69 Al Oliver .08 .25
70 Dave Stieb .08 .25
71 Louis Thornton .05 .15
72 Willie Upshaw .05 .15
73 Ernie Whitt .05 .15
74 Rick Aguilera RC .20 .50
75 Wally Backman .05 .15
76 Gary Carter .08 .25
77 Ron Darling .08 .25
78 Len Dykstra RC .60 1.50
79 Sid Fernandez .05 .15
80 George Foster .08 .25
81 Dwight Gooden .30 .75
82 Tom Gorman .05 .15
83 Danny Heep .05 .15
84 Keith Hernandez .08 .25
85 Howard Johnson .08 .25
86 Ray Knight .08 .25
87 Terry Leach .05 .15
88 Ed Lynch .05 .15
89 Roger McDowell RC .20 .50
90 Jesse Orosco .05 .15
91 Tom Paciorek .05 .15
92 Ronn Reynolds .05 .15
93 Rafael Santana .05 .15
94 Doug Sisk .05 .15
95 Rusty Staub .08 .25
96 Darryl Strawberry .20 .50
97 Mookie Wilson .08 .25
98 Neil Allen .05 .15
99 Don Baylor .08 .25
100 Dale Berra .05 .15
101 Rich Bordi .05 .15
102 Marty Bystrom .05 .15
103 Joe Cowley .05 .15
104 Brian Fisher RC .05 .15
105 Ken Griffey .08 .25
106 Ron Guidry .08 .25
107 Ron Hassey .05 .15
108 R.Henderson UER .30 .75
SB Record of 120, sic
109 Don Mattingly 1.00 2.50
110 Bobby Meacham .05 .15
111 John Montefusco .05 .15
112 Phil Niekro .08 .25
113 Mike Pagliarulo .05 .15
114 Dan Pasqua .05 .15
115 Willie Randolph .08 .25
116 Dave Righetti .08 .25
117 Andre Robertson .05 .15
118 Billy Sample .05 .15
119 Bob Shirley .05 .15
120 Ed Whitson .05 .15
121 Dave Winfield .08 .25
122 Butch Wynegar .05 .15
123 Dave Anderson .05 .15
124 Bob Bailor .05 .15
125 Greg Brock .05 .15
126 Enos Cabell .05 .15
127 Bobby Castillo .05 .15
128 Carlos Diaz .05 .15
129 Mariano Duncan RC .20 .50
130 Pedro Guerrero .08 .25
131 Orel Hershiser .30 .75
132 Rick Honeycutt .05 .15
133 Ken Howell .05 .15
134 Ken Landreaux .05 .15
135 Bill Madlock .08 .25
136 Candy Maldonado .05 .15
137 Mike Marshall .05 .15
138 Len Matuszek .05 .15
139 Tom Niedenfuer .05 .15
140 Alejandro Pena .05 .15
141 Jerry Reuss .05 .15
142 Bill Russell .08 .25
143 Steve Sax .05 .15
144 Mike Scioscia .08 .25
145 Fernando Valenzuela .08 .25
146 Bob Welch .08 .25
147 Terry Whitfield .05 .15
148 Juan Beniquez .05 .15
149 Bob Boone .08 .25
150 John Candelaria .05 .15
151 Rod Carew .20 .50
152 Stu Cliburn .05 .15
153 Doug DeCinces .05 .15
154 Brian Downing .08 .25
155 Ken Forsch .05 .15
156 Craig Gerber .05 .15
157 Bobby Grich .08 .25
158 George Hendrick .08 .25
159 Al Holland .05 .15
160 Reggie Jackson .20 .50
161 Ruppert Jones .05 .15
162 Urbano Lugo .05 .15
163 Kirk McCaskill RC .20 .50
164 Donnie Moore .05 .15
165 Gary Pettis .05 .15
166 Ron Romanick .05 .15
167 Dick Schofield .05 .15
168 Daryl Sconiers .05 .15
169 Jim Slaton .05 .15
170 Don Sutton .08 .25
171 Mike Witt .05 .15
172 Buddy Bell .08 .25
173 Tom Browning .05 .15
174 Dave Concepcion .08 .25
175 Eric Davis .30 .75
176 Bo Diaz .05 .15
177 Nick Esasky .05 .15
178 John Franco .08 .25
179 Tom Hume .05 .15
180 Wayne Krenchicki .05 .15
181 Andy McGaffigan .05 .15
182 Eddie Milner .05 .15
183 Ron Oester .05 .15
184 Dave Parker .08 .25
185 Frank Pastore .05 .15
186 Tony Perez .20 .50
187 Ted Power .05 .15
188 Joe Price .05 .15
189 Gary Redus .05 .15
190 Ron Robinson .05 .15
191 Pete Rose 1.00 2.50
192 Mario Soto .08 .25
193 John Stuper .05 .15
194 Jay Tibbs .05 .15
195 Dave Van Gorder .05 .15
196 Max Venable .05 .15
197 Juan Agosto .05 .15
198 Harold Baines .08 .25
199 Floyd Bannister .05 .15
200 Britt Burns .05 .15
201 Julio Cruz .05 .15
202 Joel Davis .05 .15
203 Richard Dotson .05 .15
204 Carlton Fisk .20 .50
205 Scott Fletcher .05 .15
206 Ozzie Guillen RC .75 2.00
207 Jerry Hairston .05 .15
208 Tim Hulett .05 .15
209 Bob James .05 .15
210 Ron Kittle .05 .15
211 Rudy Law .05 .15
212 Bryan Little .05 .15
213 Gene Nelson .05 .15
214 Reid Nichols .05 .15
215 Luis Salazar .05 .15
216 Tom Seaver .20 .50
217 Dan Spillner .05 .15
218 Bruce Tanner .05 .15
219 Greg Walker .05 .15
220 Dave Wehrmeister .05 .15
221 Juan Berenguer .05 .15
222 Dave Bergman .05 .15
223 Tom Brookens .05 .15
224 Darrell Evans .08 .25
225 Barbaro Garbey .05 .15
226 Kirk Gibson .08 .25
227 John Grubb .05 .15
228 Willie Hernandez .05 .15
229 Larry Herndon .05 .15
230 Chet Lemon .08 .25
231 Aurelio Lopez .05 .15
232 Jack Morris .08 .25
233 Randy O'Neal .05 .15
234 Lance Parrish .08 .25
235 Dan Petry .05 .15
236 Alejandro Sanchez .05 .15
237 Bill Scherrer .05 .15
238 Nelson Simmons .05 .15
239 Frank Tanana .08 .25
240 Walt Terrell .05 .15
241 Alan Trammell .08 .25
242 Lou Whitaker .08 .25
243 Milt Wilcox .05 .15
244 Hubie Brooks .05 .15
245 Tim Burke .05 .15
246 Andre Dawson .08 .25
247 Mike Fitzgerald .05 .15
248 Terry Francona .08 .25
249 Bill Gullickson .05 .15
250 Joe Hesketh .05 .15
251 Bill Laskey .05 .15
252 Vance Law .05 .15
253 Charlie Lea .05 .15
254 Gary Lucas .05 .15
255 David Palmer .05 .15
256 Tim Raines .08 .25
257 Jeff Reardon .08 .25
258 Bert Roberge .05 .15
259 Dan Schatzeder .05 .15
260 Bryn Smith .05 .15
261 Randy St.Claire .05 .15
262 Scot Thompson .05 .15
263 Tim Wallach .05 .15
264 U.L. Washington .05 .15
265 Mitch Webster .05 .15
266 Herm Winningham .05 .15
267 Floyd Youmans .05 .15
268 Don Aase .05 .15
269 Mike Boddicker .05 .15
270 Rich Dauer .05 .15
271 Storm Davis .05 .15
272 Rick Dempsey .05 .15
273 Ken Dixon .05 .15
274 Jim Dwyer .05 .15
275 Mike Flanagan .05 .15
276 Wayne Gross .05 .15
277 Lee Lacy .05 .15
278 Fred Lynn .08 .25
279 Tippy Martinez .05 .15
280 Dennis Martinez .08 .25
281 Scott McGregor .05 .15
282 Eddie Murray .30 .75
283 Floyd Rayford .05 .15
284 Cal Ripken 1.25 3.00
285 Gary Roenicke .05 .15
286 Larry Sheets .05 .15
287 John Shelby .05 .15
288 Nate Snell .05 .15
289 Sammy Stewart .05 .15
290 Alan Wiggins .05 .15
291 Mike Young .05 .15
292 Alan Ashby .05 .15
293 Mark Bailey .05 .15
294 Kevin Bass .05 .15
295 Jeff Calhoun .05 .15
296 Jose Cruz .08 .25
297 Glenn Davis .08 .25
298 Bill Dawley .05 .15
299 Frank DiPino .05 .15
300 Bill Doran .05 .15
301 Phil Garner .08 .25
302 Jeff Heathcock .05 .15
303 Charlie Kerfeld .05 .15
304 Bob Knepper .05 .15
305 Ron Mathis .05 .15
306 Jerry Mumphrey .05 .15
307 Jim Pankovits .05 .15
308 Terry Puhl .05 .15
309 Craig Reynolds .05 .15
310 Nolan Ryan 1.50 4.00
311 Mike Scott .08 .25
312 Dave Smith .05 .15
313 Dickie Thon .05 .15
314 Denny Walling .05 .15
315 Kurt Bevacqua .05 .15
316 Al Bumbry .05 .15
317 Jerry Davis .05 .15
318 Luis DeLeon .05 .15
319 Dave Dravecky .05 .15
320 Tim Flannery .05 .15
321 Steve Garvey .08 .25
322 Rich Gossage .08 .25
323 Tony Gwynn .50 1.25
324 Andy Hawkins .05 .15
325 LaMarr Hoyt .05 .15
326 Roy Lee Jackson .05 .15
327 Terry Kennedy .05 .15
328 Craig Lefferts .05 .15
329 Carmelo Martinez .05 .15
330 Lance McCullers .05 .15
331 Kevin McReynolds .05 .15
332 Graig Nettles .08 .25
333 Jerry Royster .05 .15
334 Eric Show .05 .15
335 Tim Stoddard .05 .15
336 Garry Templeton .08 .25
337 Mark Thurmond .05 .15
338 Ed Wojna .05 .15
339 Tony Armas .08 .25
340 Marty Barrett .05 .15
341 Wade Boggs .20 .50
342 Dennis Boyd .05 .15
343 Bill Buckner .08 .25
344 Mark Clear .05 .15
345 Roger Clemens 2.00 5.00
346 Steve Crawford .05 .15
347 Mike Easler .05 .15
348 Dwight Evans .20 .50
349 Rich Gedman .05 .15
350 Jackie Gutierrez .05 .15
351 Glenn Hoffman .05 .15
352 Bruce Hurst .05 .15
353 Bruce Kison .05 .15
354 Tim Lollar .05 .15
355 Steve Lyons .05 .15
356 Al Nipper .05 .15
357 Bob Ojeda .05 .15
358 Jim Rice .08 .25
359 Bob Stanley .05 .15
360 Mike Trujillo .05 .15
361 Thad Bosley .05 .15
362 Warren Brusstar .05 .15
363 Ron Cey .08 .25
364 Jody Davis .05 .15
365 Bob Dernier .05 .15
366 Shawon Dunston .08 .25
367 Leon Durham .05 .15
368 Dennis Eckersley .20 .50
369 Ray Fontenot .05 .15
370 George Frazier .05 .15
371 Billy Hatcher .05 .15
372 Dave Lopes .08 .25
373 Gary Matthews .08 .25
374 Ron Meridith .05 .15
375 Keith Moreland .05 .15
376 Reggie Patterson .05 .15
377 Dick Ruthven .05 .15
378 Ryne Sandberg .60 1.50
379 Scott Sanderson .05 .15
380 Lee Smith .08 .25
381 Lary Sorensen .05 .15
382 Chris Speier .05 .15
383 Rick Sutcliffe .08 .25
384 Steve Trout .05 .15
385 Gary Woods .05 .15
386 Bert Blyleven .08 .25
387 Tom Brunansky .08 .25
388 Randy Bush .05 .15
389 John Butcher .05 .15
390 Ron Davis .05 .15
391 Dave Engle .05 .15
392 Frank Eufemia .05 .15
393 Pete Filson .05 .15
394 Gary Gaetti .08 .25
395 Greg Gagne .05 .15
396 Mickey Hatcher .05 .15
397 Kent Hrbek .08 .25
398 Tim Laudner .05 .15
399 Rick Lysander .05 .15
400 Dave Meier .05 .15
401 Kirby Puckett UER .75 2.00
Card has him in NL,
should be AL
402 Mark Salas .05 .15
403 Ken Schrom .05 .15
404 Roy Smalley .05 .15
405 Mike Smithson .05 .15
406 Mike Stenhouse .05 .15
407 Tim Teufel .05 .15
408 Frank Viola .08 .25
409 Ron Washington .08 .25
410 Keith Atherton .05 .15
411 Dusty Baker .08 .25
412 Tim Birtsas .05 .15
413 Bruce Bochte .05 .15
414 Chris Codiroli .05 .15
415 Dave Collins .05 .15
416 Mike Davis .05 .15
417 Alfredo Griffin .05 .15
418 Mike Heath .05 .15
419 Steve Henderson .05 .15
420 Donnie Hill .05 .15
421 Jay Howell .05 .15
422 Tommy John .08 .25
423 Dave Kingman .08 .25
424 Bill Krueger .05 .15
425 Rick Langford .05 .15
426 Carney Lansford .08 .25
427 Steve McCatty .05 .15
428 Dwayne Murphy .05 .15
429 Steve Ontiveros RC .05 .15
430 Tony Phillips .08 .25
431 Jose Rijo .08 .25
432 Mickey Tettleton RC .20 .50
433 Luis Aguayo .05 .15
434 Larry Andersen .05 .15
435 Steve Carlton .08 .25
436 Don Carman .05 .15
437 Tim Corcoran .05 .15
438 Darren Daulton RC .40 1.00
439 John Denny .05 .15
440 Tom Foley .05 .15
441 Greg Gross .05 .15
442 Kevin Gross .05 .15
443 Von Hayes .05 .15
444 Charles Hudson .05 .15
445 Garry Maddox .05 .15
446 Shane Rawley .05 .15
447 Dave Rucker .05 .15
448 John Russell .05 .15
449 Juan Samuel .05 .15
450 Mike Schmidt .75 2.00
451 Rick Schu .05 .15
452 Dave Shipanoff .05 .15
453 Dave Stewart .08 .25
454 Jeff Stone .05 .15
455 Kent Tekulve .05 .15
456 Ozzie Virgil .05 .15
457 Glenn Wilson .05 .15
458 Jim Beattie .05 .15
459 Karl Best .05 .15
460 Barry Bonnell .05 .15
461 Phil Bradley .05 .15
462 Ivan Calderon RC .20 .50
463 Al Cowens .05 .15
464 Alvin Davis .05 .15
465 Dave Henderson .05 .15
466 Bob Kearney .05 .15
467 Mark Langston .08 .25
468 Bob Long .05 .15
469 Mike Moore .05 .15
470 Edwin Nunez .05 .15
471 Spike Owen .05 .15
472 Jack Perconte .05 .15
473 Jim Presley .05 .15
474 Donnie Scott .05 .15
475 Bill Swift .05 .15
476 Danny Tartabull .08 .25
477 Gorman Thomas .08 .25
478 Roy Thomas .05 .15
479 Ed VandeBerg .05 .15
480 Frank Wills .05 .15
481 Matt Young .05 .15
482 Ray Burris .05 .15
483 Jaime Cocanower .05 .15
484 Cecil Cooper .08 .25
485 Danny Darwin .05 .15
486 Rollie Fingers .08 .25
487 Jim Gantner .05 .15
488 Bob L. Gibson .05 .15
489 Moose Haas .05 .15
490 Teddy Higuera RC .20 .50
491 Paul Householder .05 .15
492 Pete Ladd .05 .15
493 Rick Manning .05 .15
494 Bob McClure .05 .15
495 Paul Molitor .08 .25
496 Charlie Moore .05 .15
497 Ben Oglivie .08 .25
498 Randy Ready .05 .15
499 Earnie Riles .05 .15
500 Ed Romero .05 .15
501 Bill Schroeder .05 .15
502 Ray Searage .05 .15
503 Ted Simmons .08 .25
504 Pete Vuckovich .05 .15
505 Rick Waits .05 .15
506 Robin Yount .50 1.25
507 Len Barker .05 .15
508 Steve Bedrosian .05 .15
509 Bruce Benedict .05 .15
510 Rick Camp .05 .15
511 Rick Cerone .05 .15
512 Chris Chambliss .08 .25
513 Jeff Dedmon .05 .15
514 Terry Forster .08 .25
515 Gene Garber .05 .15
516 Terry Harper .05 .15
517 Bob Horner .08 .25
518 Glenn Hubbard .05 .15
519 Joe Johnson .05 .15
520 Brad Komminsk .05 .15
521 Rick Mahler .05 .15
522 Dale Murphy .20 .50
523 Ken Oberkfell .05 .15
524 Pascual Perez .05 .15
525 Gerald Perry .05 .15
526 Rafael Ramirez .05 .15
527 Steve Shields .05 .15
528 Zane Smith .05 .15
529 Bruce Sutter .08 .25
530 Milt Thompson RC .20 .50
531 Claudell Washington .05 .15
532 Paul Zuvella .05 .15
533 Vida Blue .08 .25
534 Bob Brenly .05 .15
535 Chris Brown RC .05 .15
536 Chili Davis .08 .25
537 Mark Davis .05 .15
538 Rob Deer .05 .15
539 Dan Driessen .05 .15
540 Scott Garrelts .05 .15
541 Dan Gladden .05 .15
542 Jim Gott .05 .15
543 David Green .05 .15
544 Atlee Hammaker .05 .15
545 Mike Jeffcoat .05 .15
546 Mike Krukow .05 .15
547 Dave LaPoint .05 .15
548 Jeff Leonard .05 .15
549 Greg Minton .05 .15
550 Alex Trevino .05 .15
551 Manny Trillo .05 .15
552 Jose Uribe .05 .15
553 Brad Wellman .05 .15
554 Frank Williams .05 .15
555 Joel Youngblood .05 .15
556 Alan Bannister .05 .15
557 Glenn Brummer .05 .15
558 Steve Buechele RC .20 .50
559 Jose Guzman RC .05 .15
560 Toby Harrah .08 .25
561 Greg Harris .05 .15
562 Dwayne Henry .05 .15
563 Burt Hooton .05 .15
564 Charlie Hough .08 .25
565 Mike Mason .05 .15
566 Oddibe McDowell .05 .15
567 Dickie Noles .05 .15
568 Pete O'Brien .05 .15
569 Larry Parrish .05 .15
570 Dave Rozema .05 .15
571 Dave Schmidt .05 .15
572 Don Slaught .05 .15
573 Wayne Tolleson .05 .15
574 Duane Walker .05 .15
575 Gary Ward .05 .15
576 Chris Welsh .05 .15
577 Curtis Wilkerson .05 .15
578 George Wright .05 .15
579 Chris Bando .05 .15
580 Tony Bernazard .05 .15
581 Brett Butler .08 .25
582 Ernie Camacho .05 .15
583 Joe Carter .08 .25
584 Carmen Castillo .05 .15
585 Jamie Easterly .05 .15
586 Julio Franco .08 .25
587 Mel Hall .05 .15
588 Mike Hargrove .05 .15
589 Neal Heaton .05 .15
590 Brook Jacoby .05 .15
591 Otis Nixon RC .40 1.00
592 Jerry Reed .05 .15
593 Vern Ruhle .05 .15
594 Pat Tabler .05 .15
595 Rich Thompson .05 .15
596 Andre Thornton .05 .15
597 Dave Von Ohlen .05 .15
598 George Vukovich .05 .15
599 Tom Waddell .05 .15
600 Curt Wardle .05 .15
601 Jerry Willard .05 .15
602 Bill Almon .05 .15
603 Mike Bielecki .05 .15
604 Sid Bream .05 .15
605 Mike C. Brown .05 .15
606 Pat Clements .05 .15
607 Jose DeLeon .05 .15
608 Denny Gonzalez .05 .15
609 Cecilio Guante .05 .15
610 Steve Kemp .05 .15
611 Sammy Khalifa .05 .15
612 Lee Mazzilli .08 .25
613 Larry McWilliams .05 .15
614 Jim Morrison .05 .15
615 Joe Orsulak RC .20 .50
616 Tony Pena .05 .15
617 Johnny Ray .05 .15
618 Rick Reuschel .08 .25
619 R.J. Reynolds .05 .15
620 Rick Rhoden .05 .15
621 Don Robinson .05 .15
622 Jason Thompson .05 .15
623 Lee Tunnell .05 .15
624 Jim Winn .05 .15
625 Marvell Wynne .05 .15
626 Dwight Gooden IA .20 .50
627 Don Mattingly IA .50 1.25
628 Pete Rose 4192 .20 .50
629 Rod Carew 3000 Hits .08 .25
630 Tom Seaver .08 .25
Phil Niekro
631 Don Baylor Ouch .08 .25
632 Darryl Strawberry .08 .25
Tim Raines
633 Cal Ripken .60 1.50
Alan Trammell
634 Wade Boggs .40 1.00
George Brett
635 Bob Horner .20 .50
Dale Murphy
636 Willie McGee .08 .25
Vince Coleman
637 Vince Coleman IA .08 .25
638 Pete Rose .30 .75
Dwight Gooden
639 Wade Boggs .50 1.25
Don Mattingly
640 Dale Murphy .20 .50
Steve Garvey
Dave Parker
641 Fernando Valenzuela .20 .50
Dwight Gooden
642 Jimmy Key .08 .25
Dave Stieb
643 Carlton Fisk .08 .25
Rich Gedman
644 Gene Walter RC .75 2.00
Benito Santiago RC
645 Mike Woodard RC .05 .15
Colin Ward RC
646 Kal Daniels RC 1.50 4.00
Paul O'Neill RC
647 Andres Galarraga RC .60 1.50
Fred Toliver RC
648 Bob Kipper RC .05 .15
Curt Ford RC
649 Jose Canseco RC 3.00 8.00
Eric Plunk RC
650 Mark McLemore RC .40 1.00
Gus Polidor RC
651 Rob Woodward RC .05 .15
Mickey Brantley RC
652 Billy Joe Robidoux RC .05 .15
Mark Funderburk RC
653 Cecil Fielder RC .75 2.00
Cory Snyder
654 CL: Royals/Cardinals .05 .15
Blue Jays/Mets
655 CL: Yankees/Dodgers .05 .15
Angels/Reds UER
(168 Darly Sconiers)
656 CL: White Sox/Tigers .05 .15
Expos/Orioles
(279 Dennis&
280 Tippy)
657 CL: Astros/Padres .05 .15
Red Sox/Cubs
658 CL: Twins/A's .05 .15
Phillies/Mariners
659 CL: Brewers/Braves .05 .15
Giants/Rangers
660 CL: Indians/Pirates .05 .15
Special Cards

1986 Fleer Update

This 132-card standard-size set was distributed in factory set form through hobby dealers. These sets were distributed in 50-set cases. In addition to the complete set of 132 cards, the box also contains 25 Team Logo Stickers.The card fronts look very similar to the 1986 Fleer regular issue. These cards are just as condition sensitive with most cards having chipped edges straight out of the box. The cards are numbered (with a U prefix) alphabetically according to player's last name. The extended Rookie Cards in this set include Barry Bonds, Bobby Bonilla, Will Clark, Wally Joyner and John Kruk.

COMP.FACT.SET (132) 12.00 30.00
1 Mike Aldrete XRC .05 .15
2 Andy Allanson XRC .05 .15
3 Neil Allen .05 .15
4 Joaquin Andujar .08 .25
5 Paul Assenmacher XRC .20 .50
6 Scott Bailes XRC .05 .15
7 Jay Baller XRC .05 .15
8 Scott Bankhead .05 .15
9 Bill Bathe XRC .05 .15
10 Don Baylor .08 .25
11 Billy Beane XRC .40 1.00
12 Steve Bedrosian .05 .15
13 Juan Beniquez .05 .15
14 Barry Bonds XRC 6.00 15.00
15 Bobby Bonilla XRC .40 1.00
UER Wrong birthday
16 Rich Bordi .05 .15
17 Bill Campbell .05 .15
18 Tom Candiotti .05 .15
19 John Cangelosi XRC .20 .50
20 Jose Canseco UER 1.50 4.00
(Headings on back
for a pitcher)
21 Chuck Cary XRC .05 .15
22 Juan Castillo XRC .05 .15
23 Rick Cerone .05 .15
24 John Cerutti XRC .05 .15
25 Will Clark XRC .75 2.00
26 Mark Clear .05 .15
27 Darnell Coles .05 .15
28 Dave Collins .05 .15
29 Tim Conroy .05 .15
30 Ed Correa XRC .05 .15
31 Joe Cowley .05 .15
32 Bill Dawley .05 .15
33 Rob Deer .05 .15
34 John Denny .05 .15
35 Jim Deshaies XRC .05 .15
36 Doug Drabek XRC .40 1.00
37 Mike Easler .05 .15
38 Mark Eichhorn XRC .05 .15
39 Dave Engle .05 .15
40 Mike Fischlin .05 .15
41 Scott Fletcher .05 .15
42 Terry Forster .08 .25
43 Terry Francona .08 .25
44 Andres Galarraga .60 1.50
45 Lee Guetterman XRC .05 .15
46 Bill Gullickson .05 .15
47 Jackie Gutierrez .05 .15
48 Moose Haas .05 .15
49 Billy Hatcher .05 .15
50 Mike Heath .05 .15
51 Guy Hoffman .05 .15
52 Tom Hume .05 .15
53 Pete Incaviglia XRC .20 .50
54 Dane Iorg .05 .15
55 Chris James XRC .05 .15
56 Stan Javier XRC .20 .50
57 Tommy John .08 .25
58 Tracy Jones XRC .05 .15
59 Wally Joyner XRC .40 1.00
60 Wayne Krenchicki .05 .15
61 John Kruk XRC .60 1.50
62 Mike LaCoss .05 .15
63 Pete Ladd .05 .15
64 Dave LaPoint .05 .15
65 Mike LaValliere XRC .20 .50
66 Rudy Law .05 .15
67 Dennis Leonard .05 .15
68 Steve Lombardozzi XRC .05 .15
69 Aurelio Lopez .05 .15
70 Mickey Mahler .05 .15
71 Candy Maldonado .05 .15
72 Roger Mason XRC .05 .15
73 Greg Mathews XRC .05 .15
74 Andy McGaffigan .05 .15
75 Joel McKeon .05 .15
76 Kevin Mitchell XRC .40 1.00
77 Bill Mooneyham XRC .05 .15
78 Omar Moreno .05 .15
79 Jerry Mumphrey .05 .15
80 Al Newman XRC .08 .25
81 Phil Niekro .08 .25
82 Randy Niemann .05 .15
83 Juan Nieves XRC .05 .15
84 Bob Ojeda .05 .15
85 Rick Ownbey .05 .15
86 Tom Paciorek .05 .15
87 David Palmer .05 .15
88 Jeff Parrett XRC .05 .15
89 Pat Perry XRC .05 .15
90 Dan Plesac XRC .05 .15
91 Darrell Porter .05 .15
92 Luis Quinones XRC .05 .15
93 Rey Quinones XRC .05 .15
UER Misspelled Quinonez
94 Gary Redus .05 .15
95 Jeff Reed .05 .15
96 Bip Roberts XRC .20 .50
97 Billy Joe Robidoux .05 .15
98 Gary Roenicke .05 .15
99 Ron Roenicke .05 .15
100 Angel Salazar .05 .15
101 Joe Sambito .05 .15
102 Billy Sample .05 .15
103 Dave Schmidt .05 .15
104 Ken Schrom .05 .15
105 Ruben Sierra XRC .60 1.50
106 Ted Simmons .08 .25
107 Sammy Stewart .05 .15
108 Kurt Stillwell XRC .05 .15
109 Dale Sveum XRC .05 .15
110 Tim Teufel .05 .15
111 Bob Tewksbury XRC .20 .50
112 Andres Thomas XRC .05 .15
113 Jason Thompson .05 .15
114 Milt Thompson .20 .50
115 Robby Thompson XRC .20 .50
116 Jay Tibbs .05 .15
117 Fred Toliver .05 .15
118 Wayne Tolleson .05 .15
119 Alex Trevino .05 .15
120 Manny Trillo .05 .15
121 Ed VandeBerg .05 .15
122 Ozzie Virgil .05 .15
123 Tony Walker XRC .05 .15

124 Gene Walter .05 .15
125 Duane Ward XRC .20 .50
126 Jerry Willard .05 .15
127 Mitch Williams XRC .20 .50
128 Reggie Williams XRC .05 .15
129 Bobby Witt XRC .20 .50
130 Marvell Wynne .05 .15
131 Steve Yeager .08 .25
132 Checklist 1-132 .05 .15

1987 Fleer

This set consists of 660 standard-size cards. Cards were primarily issued in 17-card wax packs, rack packs and hobby and retail factory sets. The wax packs were packed 36 to a box and 20 boxes to a case. The rack packs were packed 24 to a box and 3 boxes to a case and had 51 regular cards and three sticker card per pack. Card fronts feature a distinctive light blue and white blended border encasing a color photo. Cards are again organized numerically by teams with team ordering based on the previous seasons record. The last 36 cards in the set consist of Specials (625-643), Rookie Pairs (644-653), and checklists (654-660). The key Rookie Cards in this set are Barry Bonds, Bobby Bonilla, Will Clark, Chuck Finley, Bo Jackson, Wally Joyner, John Kruk, Barry Larkin and Devon White.

COMPLETE SET (660) 20.00 40.00
COMP.FACT.SET (672) 25.00 50.00
1 Rick Aguilera .05 .15
2 Richard Anderson .05 .15
3 Wally Backman .05 .15
4 Gary Carter .08 .25
5 Ron Darling .08 .25
6 Len Dykstra .08 .25
7 Kevin Elster RC .20 .50
8 Sid Fernandez .05 .15
9 Dwight Gooden .15 .40
10 Ed Hearn RC .05 .15
11 Danny Heep .05 .15
12 Keith Hernandez .08 .25
13 Howard Johnson .08 .25
14 Ray Knight .08 .25
15 Lee Mazzilli .08 .25
16 Roger McDowell .05 .15
17 Kevin Mitchell RC .50 1.25
18 Randy Niemann .05 .15
19 Bob Ojeda .05 .15
20 Jesse Orosco .05 .15
21 Rafael Santana .05 .15
22 Doug Sisk .05 .15
23 Darryl Strawberry .08 .25
24 Tim Teufel .05 .15
25 Mookie Wilson .08 .25
26 Tony Armas .08 .25
27 Marty Barrett .05 .15
28 Don Baylor .08 .25
29 Wade Boggs .15 .40
30 Oil Can Boyd .05 .15
31 Bill Buckner .08 .25
32 Roger Clemens 1.25 3.00
33 Steve Crawford .05 .15
34 Dwight Evans .15 .40
35 Rich Gedman .05 .15
36 Dave Henderson .05 .15
37 Bruce Hurst .05 .15
38 Tim Lollar .05 .15
39 Al Nipper .05 .15
40 Spike Owen .05 .15
41 Jim Rice .08 .25
42 Ed Romero .05 .15
43 Joe Sambito .05 .15
44 Calvin Schiraldi .05 .15
45 Tom Seaver UER .15 .40
Lifetime saves total 0, should be 1
46 Jeff Sellers .05 .15
47 Bob Stanley .05 .15
48 Sammy Stewart .05 .15
49 Larry Andersen .05 .15
50 Alan Ashby .05 .15
51 Kevin Bass .05 .15
52 Jeff Calhoun .05 .15
53 Jose Cruz .08 .25
54 Danny Darwin .05 .15
55 Glenn Davis .05 .15
56 Jim Deshaies RC .08 .25
57 Bill Doran .05 .15
58 Phil Garner .08 .25
59 Billy Hatcher .05 .15
60 Charlie Kerfeld .05 .15
61 Bob Knepper .05 .15
62 Dave Lopes .08 .25
63 Aurelio Lopez .05 .15
64 Jim Pankovits .05 .15
65 Terry Puhl .05 .15
66 Craig Reynolds .05 .15
67 Nolan Ryan 1.25 3.00
68 Mike Scott .08 .25
69 Dave Smith .05 .15
70 Dickie Thon .05 .15
71 Tony Walker .05 .15
72 Denny Walling .05 .15
73 Bob Boone .08 .25
74 Rick Burleson .05 .15
75 John Candelaria .05 .15
76 Doug Corbett .05 .15
77 Doug DeCinces .05 .15
78 Brian Downing .08 .25
79 Chuck Finley RC .50 1.25
80 Terry Forster .08 .25
81 Bob Grich .08 .25
82 George Hendrick .08 .25
83 Jack Howell .05 .15
84 Reggie Jackson .15 .40
85 Ruppert Jones .05 .15
86 Wally Joyner RC .50 1.25
87 Gary Lucas .05 .15
88 Kirk McCaskill .05 .15
89 Donnie Moore .05 .15
90 Gary Pettis .05 .15
91 Vern Ruhle .05 .15
92 Dick Schofield .05 .15
93 Don Sutton .08 .25
94 Rob Wilfong .05 .15
95 Mike Witt .05 .15
96 Doug Drabek RC .50 1.25
97 Mike Easler .05 .15
98 Mike Fischlin .05 .15
99 Brian Fisher .05 .15
100 Ron Guidry .08 .25
101 Rickey Henderson .25 .60
102 Tommy John .08 .25
103 Ron Kittle .05 .15
104 Don Mattingly .75 2.00
105 Bobby Meacham .05 .15
106 Joe Niekro .05 .15
107 Mike Pagliarulo .05 .15
108 Dan Pasqua .05 .15
109 Willie Randolph .08 .25
110 Dennis Rasmussen .05 .15
111 Dave Righetti .08 .25
112 Gary Roenicke .05 .15
113 Rod Scurry .05 .15
114 Bob Shirley .05 .15
115 Joel Skinner .05 .15
116 Tim Stoddard .05 .15
117 Bob Tewksbury RC .20 .50
118 Wayne Tolleson .05 .15
119 Claudell Washington .05 .15
120 Dave Winfield .08 .25
121 Steve Buechele .05 .15
122 Ed Correa .05 .15
123 Scott Fletcher .05 .15
124 Jose Guzman .05 .15
125 Toby Harrah .08 .25
126 Greg Harris .05 .15
127 Charlie Hough .08 .25
128 Pete Incaviglia RC .20 .50
129 Mike Mason .05 .15
130 Oddibe McDowell .05 .15
131 Dale Mohorcic .05 .15
132 Pete O'Brien .05 .15
133 Tom Paciorek .05 .15
134 Larry Parrish .05 .15
135 Geno Petralli .05 .15
136 Darrell Porter .05 .15
137 Jeff Russell .05 .15
138 Ruben Sierra RC .75 2.00
139 Don Slaught .05 .15
140 Gary Ward .05 .15
141 Curtis Wilkerson .05 .15
142 Mitch Williams RC .20 .50
143 Bobby Witt RC UER .20 .50
(Tulsa misspelled as
Tusla; ERA should
be 6.43, not .643)
144 Dave Bergman .05 .15
145 Tom Brookens .05 .15
146 Bill Campbell .05 .15
147 Chuck Cary .05 .15
148 Darnell Coles .05 .15
149 Dave Collins .05 .15
150 Darrell Evans .08 .25
151 Kirk Gibson .08 .25
152 John Grubb .05 .15
153 Willie Hernandez .05 .15
154 Larry Herndon .05 .15
155 Eric King .05 .15
156 Chet Lemon .08 .25
157 Dwight Lowry .05 .15
158 Jack Morris .08 .25
159 Randy O'Neal .05 .15
160 Lance Parrish .08 .25
161 Dan Petry .05 .15
162 Pat Sheridan .05 .15
163 Jim Slaton .05 .15
164 Frank Tanana .08 .25
165 Walt Terrell .05 .15
166 Mark Thurmond .05 .15
167 Alan Trammell .08 .25
168 Lou Whitaker .08 .25
169 Luis Aguayo .05 .15
170 Steve Bedrosian .05 .15
171 Don Carman .05 .15
172 Darren Daulton .08 .25
173 Greg Gross .05 .15
174 Kevin Gross .05 .15
175 Von Hayes .05 .15
176 Charles Hudson .05 .15
177 Tom Hume .05 .15
178 Steve Jeltz .05 .15
179 Mike Maddux RC .05 .15
180 Shane Rawley .05 .15
181 Gary Redus .05 .15
182 Ron Roenicke .05 .15
183 Bruce Ruffin RC .08 .25
184 John Russell .05 .15
185 Juan Samuel .05 .15
186 Dan Schatzeder .05 .15
187 Mike Schmidt .60 1.50
188 Rick Schu .05 .15
189 Jeff Stone .05 .15
190 Kent Tekulve .05 .15
191 Milt Thompson .05 .15
192 Glenn Wilson .05 .15
193 Buddy Bell .08 .25
194 Tom Browning .05 .15
195 Sal Butera .05 .15
196 Dave Concepcion .08 .25
197 Kal Daniels .05 .15
198 Eric Davis .15 .40
199 John Denny .05 .15
200 Bo Diaz .05 .15
201 Nick Esasky .05 .15
202 John Franco .08 .25
203 Bill Gullickson .05 .15
204 Barry Larkin RC 1.25 3.00
205 Eddie Milner .05 .15
206 Rob Murphy .05 .15
207 Ron Oester .05 .15
208 Dave Parker .08 .25
209 Tony Perez .15 .40
210 Ted Power .05 .15
211 Joe Price .05 .15
212 Ron Robinson .05 .15
213 Pete Rose .75 2.00
214 Mario Soto .08 .25
215 Kurt Stillwell .05 .15
216 Max Venable .05 .15
217 Chris Welsh .05 .15
218 Carl Willis RC .08 .25
219 Jesse Barfield .08 .25
220 George Bell .08 .25
221 Bill Caudill .05 .15
222 John Cerutti .05 .15
223 Jim Clancy .05 .15
224 Mark Eichhorn .05 .15
225 Tony Fernandez .05 .15
226 Damaso Garcia .05 .15
227 Kelly Gruber ERR .05 .15
(Wrong birth year)
228 Tom Henke .05 .15
229 Garth Iorg .05 .15
230 Joe Johnson .05 .15
231 Cliff Johnson .05 .15
232 Jimmy Key .08 .25
233 Dennis Lamp .05 .15
234 Rick Leach .05 .15
235 Buck Martinez .05 .15
236 Lloyd Moseby .05 .15
237 Rance Mulliniks .05 .15
238 Dave Stieb .08 .25
239 Willie Upshaw .05 .15
240 Ernie Whitt .05 .15
241 Andy Allanson RC .05 .15
242 Scott Bailes .05 .15
243 Chris Bando .05 .15
244 Tony Bernazard .05 .15
245 John Butcher .05 .15
246 Brett Butler .08 .25
247 Ernie Camacho .05 .15
248 Tom Candiotti .05 .15
249 Joe Carter .08 .25
250 Carmen Castillo .05 .15
251 Julio Franco .08 .25
252 Mel Hall .05 .15
253 Brook Jacoby .05 .15
254 Phil Niekro .08 .25
255 Otis Nixon .05 .15
256 Dickie Noles .05 .15
257 Bryan Oelkers .05 .15
258 Ken Schrom .05 .15
259 Don Schulze .05 .15
260 Cory Snyder .05 .15
261 Pat Tabler .05 .15
262 Andre Thornton .05 .15
263 Rich Yett .05 .15
264 Mike Aldrete .05 .15
265 Juan Berenguer .05 .15
266 Vida Blue .08 .25
267 Bob Brenly .05 .15
268 Chris Brown .05 .15
269 Will Clark RC 1.25 3.00
270 Chili Davis .08 .25
271 Mark Davis .05 .15
272 Kelly Downs RC .08 .25
273 Scott Garrelts .05 .15
274 Dan Gladden .05 .15
275 Mike Krukow .05 .15
276 Randy Kutcher .05 .15
277 Mike LaCoss .05 .15
278 Jeff Leonard .05 .15
279 Candy Maldonado .05 .15
280 Roger Mason .05 .15
281 Bob Melvin .05 .15
282 Greg Minton .05 .15
283 Jeff D. Robinson .05 .15
284 Harry Spilman .05 .15
285 Robby Thompson RC .20 .50
286 Jose Uribe .05 .15
287 Frank Williams .05 .15
288 Joel Youngblood .05 .15
289 Jack Clark .08 .25
290 Vince Coleman .05 .15
291 Tim Conroy .05 .15
292 Danny Cox .05 .15
293 Ken Dayley .05 .15
294 Curt Ford .05 .15
295 Bob Forsch .05 .15
296 Tom Herr .05 .15
297 Ricky Horton .05 .15
298 Clint Hurdle .05 .15
299 Jeff Lahti .05 .15
300 Steve Lake .05 .15
301 Tito Landrum .05 .15
302 Mike LaValliere RC .20 .50
303 Greg Mathews .05 .15
304 Willie McGee .08 .25
305 Jose Oquendo .05 .15
306 Terry Pendleton .08 .25
307 Pat Perry .05 .15
308 Ozzie Smith .40 1.00
309 Ray Soff .05 .15
310 John Tudor .08 .25
311 Andy Van Slyke UER .15 .40
(Bats R, Throws L)
312 Todd Worrell .05 .15
313 Dann Bilardello .05 .15
314 Hubie Brooks .05 .15
315 Tim Burke .05 .15
316 Andre Dawson .08 .25
317 Mike Fitzgerald .05 .15
318 Tom Foley .05 .15
319 Andres Galarraga .08 .25
320 Joe Hesketh .05 .15
321 Wallace Johnson .05 .15
322 Wayne Krenchicki .05 .15
323 Vance Law .05 .15
324 Dennis Martinez .08 .25
325 Bob McClure .05 .15
326 Andy McGaffigan .05 .15
327 Al Newman RC .05 .15
328 Tim Raines .08 .25
329 Jeff Reardon .08 .25
330 Luis Rivera RC .08 .25
331 Bob Sebra .05 .15
332 Bryn Smith .05 .15
333 Jay Tibbs .05 .15
334 Tim Wallach .05 .15
335 Mitch Webster .05 .15
336 Jim Wohlford .05 .15
337 Floyd Youmans .05 .15
338 Chris Bosio RC .20 .50
339 Glenn Braggs RC .08 .25
340 Rick Cerone .05 .15
341 Mark Clear .05 .15
342 Bryan Clutterbuck .05 .15
343 Cecil Cooper .08 .25
344 Rob Deer .05 .15
345 Jim Gantner .05 .15
346 Ted Higuera .05 .15
347 John Henry Johnson .05 .15
348 Tim Leary .05 .15
349 Rick Manning .05 .15
350 Paul Molitor .08 .25
351 Charlie Moore .05 .15
352 Juan Nieves .05 .15
353 Ben Oglivie .08 .25
354 Dan Plesac .05 .15
355 Ernest Riles .05 .15
356 Billy Joe Robidoux .05 .15
357 Bill Schroeder .05 .15
358 Dale Sveum .05 .15
359 Gorman Thomas .08 .25
360 Bill Wegman .05 .15
361 Robin Yount .40 1.00
362 Steve Balboni .05 .15
363 Scott Bankhead .05 .15
364 Buddy Biancalana .05 .15
365 Bud Black .05 .15
366 George Brett .60 1.50
367 Steve Farr .05 .15
368 Mark Gubicza .05 .15
369 Bo Jackson RC 3.00 8.00
370 Danny Jackson .05 .15
371 Mike Kingery RC .08 .25
372 Rudy Law .05 .15
373 Charlie Leibrandt .05 .15
374 Dennis Leonard .05 .15
375 Hal McRae .08 .25
376 Jorge Orta .05 .15
377 Jamie Quirk .05 .15
378 Dan Quisenberry .05 .15
379 Bret Saberhagen .08 .25
380 Angel Salazar .05 .15
381 Lonnie Smith .05 .15
382 Jim Sundberg .08 .25
383 Frank White .08 .25
384 Willie Wilson .08 .25
385 Joaquin Andujar .08 .25
386 Doug Bair .05 .15
387 Dusty Baker .08 .25
388 Bruce Bochte .05 .15
389 Jose Canseco .60 1.50
390 Chris Codiroli .05 .15
391 Mike Davis .05 .15
392 Alfredo Griffin .05 .15
393 Moose Haas .05 .15
394 Donnie Hill .05 .15
395 Jay Howell .05 .15
396 Dave Kingman .08 .25
397 Carney Lansford .08 .25
398 Dave Leiper .05 .15
399 Bill Mooneyham .05 .15
400 Dwayne Murphy .05 .15
401 Steve Ontiveros .05 .15
402 Tony Phillips .05 .15
403 Eric Plunk .05 .15
404 Jose Rijo .08 .25
405 Terry Steinbach RC .50 1.25
406 Dave Stewart .08 .25
407 Mickey Tettleton .05 .15
408 Dave Von Ohlen .05 .15
409 Jerry Willard .05 .15
410 Curt Young .05 .15
411 Bruce Bochy .05 .15
412 Dave Dravecky .05 .15
413 Tim Flannery .05 .15
414 Steve Garvey .08 .25
415 Rich Gossage .08 .25
416 Tony Gwynn .40 1.00
417 Andy Hawkins .05 .15
418 LaMarr Hoyt .05 .15
419 Terry Kennedy .05 .15
420 John Kruk RC .75 2.00
421 Dave LaPoint .05 .15
422 Craig Lefferts .05 .15
423 Carmelo Martinez .05 .15
424 Lance McCullers .05 .15
425 Kevin McReynolds .05 .15
426 Graig Nettles .08 .25
427 Bip Roberts RC .20 .50
428 Jerry Royster .05 .15
429 Benito Santiago .08 .25
430 Eric Show .05 .15
431 Bob Stoddard .05 .15
432 Garry Templeton .08 .25
433 Gene Walter .05 .15
434 Ed Whitson .05 .15
435 Marvell Wynne .05 .15
436 Dave Anderson .05 .15
437 Greg Brock .05 .15
438 Enos Cabell .05 .15
439 Mariano Duncan .05 .15
440 Pedro Guerrero .08 .25
441 Orel Hershiser .15 .40
442 Rick Honeycutt .05 .15
443 Ken Howell .05 .15
444 Ken Landreaux .05 .15
445 Bill Madlock .08 .25
446 Mike Marshall .05 .15
447 Len Matuszek .05 .15
448 Tom Niedenfuer .05 .15
449 Alejandro Pena .05 .15
450 Dennis Powell .05 .15
451 Jerry Reuss .05 .15
452 Bill Russell .08 .25
453 Steve Sax .05 .15
454 Mike Scioscia .08 .25
455 Franklin Stubbs .05 .15
456 Alex Trevino .05 .15
457 Fernando Valenzuela .08 .25
458 Ed VandeBerg .05 .15
459 Bob Welch .08 .25
460 Reggie Williams .05 .15
461 Don Aase .05 .15
462 Juan Beniquez .05 .15
463 Mike Boddicker .05 .15
464 Juan Bonilla .05 .15
465 Rich Bordi .05 .15
466 Storm Davis .05 .15
467 Rick Dempsey .05 .15
468 Ken Dixon .05 .15
469 Jim Dwyer .05 .15
470 Mike Flanagan .05 .15
471 Jackie Gutierrez .05 .15
472 Brad Havens .05 .15
473 Lee Lacy .05 .15
474 Fred Lynn .08 .25
475 Scott McGregor .05 .15
476 Eddie Murray .25 .60
477 Tom O'Malley .05 .15
478 Cal Ripken Jr. 1.00 2.50
479 Larry Sheets .05 .15
480 John Shelby .05 .15
481 Nate Snell .05 .15
482 Jim Traber .05 .15
483 Mike Young .05 .15
484 Neil Allen .05 .15
485 Harold Baines .08 .25
486 Floyd Bannister .05 .15
487 Daryl Boston .05 .15
488 Ivan Calderon .05 .15
489 John Cangelosi .05 .15
490 Steve Carlton .08 .25
491 Joe Cowley .05 .15
492 Julio Cruz .05 .15
493 Bill Dawley .05 .15
494 Jose DeLeon .05 .15
495 Richard Dotson .05 .15
496 Carlton Fisk .15 .40
497 Ozzie Guillen .15 .40
498 Jerry Hairston .05 .15
499 Ron Hassey .05 .15
500 Tim Hulett .05 .15
501 Bob James .05 .15
502 Steve Lyons .05 .15
503 Joel McKeon .05 .15
504 Gene Nelson .05 .15
505 Dave Schmidt .05 .15
506 Ray Searage .05 .15
507 Bobby Thigpen RC .20 .50
508 Greg Walker .05 .15
509 Jim Acker .05 .15
510 Doyle Alexander .05 .15
511 Paul Assenmacher .20 .50
512 Bruce Benedict .05 .15
513 Chris Chambliss .08 .25
514 Jeff Dedmon .05 .15
515 Gene Garber .05 .15
516 Ken Griffey .08 .25
517 Terry Harper .05 .15
518 Bob Horner .08 .25
519 Glenn Hubbard .05 .15
520 Rick Mahler .05 .15
521 Omar Moreno .05 .15
522 Dale Murphy .15 .40
523 Ken Oberkfell .05 .15
524 Ed Olwine .05 .15
525 David Palmer .05 .15
526 Rafael Ramirez .05 .15
527 Billy Sample .05 .15
528 Ted Simmons .08 .25
529 Zane Smith .05 .15
530 Bruce Sutter .08 .25
531 Andres Thomas .05 .15
532 Ozzie Virgil .05 .15
533 Allan Anderson RC .05 .15
534 Keith Atherton .05 .15
535 Billy Beane .08 .25
536 Bert Blyleven .08 .25
537 Tom Brunansky .05 .15
538 Randy Bush .05 .15
539 George Frazier .05 .15
540 Gary Gaetti .08 .25
541 Greg Gagne .05 .15
542 Mickey Hatcher .05 .15
543 Neal Heaton .05 .15
544 Kent Hrbek .08 .25
545 Roy Lee Jackson .05 .15
546 Tim Laudner .05 .15
547 Steve Lombardozzi .05 .15
548 Mark Portugal RC .20 .50
549 Kirby Puckett .40 1.00
550 Jeff Reed .05 .15
551 Mark Salas .05 .15
552 Roy Smalley .05 .15
553 Mike Smithson .05 .15
554 Frank Viola .08 .25
555 Thad Bosley .05 .15
556 Ron Cey .08 .25
557 Jody Davis .05 .15
558 Ron Davis .05 .15
559 Bob Dernier .05 .15
560 Frank DiPino .05 .15
561 Shawon Dunston UER .05 .15
(Wrong birth year
listed on card back)
562 Leon Durham .05 .15
563 Dennis Eckersley .15 .40
564 Terry Francona .08 .25
565 Dave Gumpert .05 .15
566 Guy Hoffman .05 .15
567 Ed Lynch .05 .15
568 Gary Matthews .08 .25
569 Keith Moreland .05 .15
570 Jamie Moyer RC .75 2.00
571 Jerry Mumphrey .05 .15
572 Ryne Sandberg .50 1.25
573 Scott Sanderson .05 .15
574 Lee Smith .08 .25
575 Chris Speier .05 .15
576 Rick Sutcliffe .08 .25
577 Manny Trillo .05 .15
578 Steve Trout .05 .15
579 Karl Best .05 .15
580 Scott Bradley .05 .15
581 Phil Bradley .05 .15
582 Mickey Brantley .05 .15
583 Mike G. Brown P .05 .15
584 Alvin Davis .05 .15
585 Lee Guetterman .05 .15
586 Mark Huismann .05 .15
587 Bob Kearney .05 .15
588 Pete Ladd .05 .15
589 Mark Langston .05 .15
590 Mike Moore .05 .15
591 Mike Morgan .05 .15
592 John Moses .05 .15
593 Ken Phelps .05 .15
594 Jim Presley .05 .15
595 Rey Quinones UER .05 .15
(Quinonez on front)
596 Harold Reynolds .08 .25
597 Billy Swift .05 .15
598 Danny Tartabull .05 .15
599 Steve Yeager .08 .25
600 Matt Young .05 .15
601 Bill Almon .05 .15
602 Rafael Belliard RC .20 .50
603 Mike Bielecki .05 .15
604 Barry Bonds RC 6.00 15.00
605 Bobby Bonilla RC .50 1.25
606 Sid Bream .05 .15
607 Mike C. Brown .05 .15
608 Pat Clements .05 .15
609 Mike Diaz .05 .15
610 Cecilio Guante .05 .15
611 Barry Jones .05 .15
612 Bob Kipper .05 .15
613 Larry McWilliams .05 .15
614 Jim Morrison .05 .15
615 Joe Orsulak .05 .15
616 Junior Ortiz .05 .15
617 Tony Pena .05 .15
618 Johnny Ray .05 .15
619 Rick Reuschel .08 .25
620 R.J. Reynolds .05 .15
621 Rick Rhoden .05 .15
622 Don Robinson .05 .15
623 Bob Walk .05 .15
624 Jim Winn .05 .15
625 Pete Incaviglia .30 .75
Jose Canseco
626 Don Sutton .08 .25
Phil Niekro
627 Dave Righetti .05 .15
Don Aase
628 Wally Joyner .30 .75
Jose Canseco
629 Gary Carter .15 .40
Sid Fernandez
Dwight Gooden
Keith Hernandez
Darryl Strawberry
630 Mike Scott .05 .15
Mike Krukow
631 Fernando Valenzuela .05 .15
John Franco
632 Bob Horner 4 Homers .05 .15
633 Jose Canseco .30 .75
Jim Rice
Kirby Puckett
634 Gary Carter .25 .60
Roger Clemens
635 Steve Carlton 4000K's .08 .25
636 Glenn Davis .25 .60
Eddie Murray
637 Wade Boggs .08 .25
Keith Hernandez
638 Don Mattingly .40 1.00
Darryl Strawberry
639 Dave Parker .25 .60
Ryne Sandberg
640 Dwight Gooden .25 .60
Roger Clemens
641 Mike Witt .05 .15
Charlie Hough
642 Juan Samuel .08 .25
Tim Raines
643 Harold Baines .08 .25
Jesse Barfield
644 Dave Clark RC .20 .50
Greg Swindell RC
645 Ron Karkovice RC .20 .50
Russ Morman RC
646 Devon White RC .50 1.25
Willie Fraser RC
647 Mike Stanley RC .20 .50
Jerry Browne RC
648 Dave Magadan RC .20 .50
Phil Lombardi RC
649 Jose Gonzalez RC .08 .25
Ralph Bryant RC
650 Jimmy Jones RC .08 .25
Randy Asadoor RC
651 Tracy Jones RC .08 .25
Marvin Freeman RC
652 John Stefero .20 .50
Kevin Seitzer RC
653 Rob Nelson RC .08 .25
Steve Fireovid RC
654 CL: Mets/Red Sox .05 .15
Astros/Angels
655 CL: Yankees/Rangers .05 .15
Tigers/Phillies
656 CL: Reds/Blue Jays .05 .15
Indians/Giants
ERR (230/231 wrong)
657 CL: Cardinals/Expos .05 .15
Brewers/Royals
658 CL: A's/Padres .05 .15
Dodgers/Orioles
659 CL: White Sox/Braves .05 .15
Twins/Cubs
660 CL: Mariners/Pirates .05 .15
Special Cards
ER (580/581 wrong)

1987 Fleer Glossy

This set parallels the regular 1987 Fleer issue and signified a short-lived three year run of Glossy parallel cards likely produced in response to Topps' run of Tiffany parallel sets. The cards were issued in a special tin which also included a glossy version of the World Series set. These 672 standard-size are differentiated only by the gloss on the front. This set was produced in fairly large quantities, although still significantly less than regular issue cards. According to widely held beliefs in the hobby, somewhere between 75 and 100 thousand of these sets were produced.

COMP.FACT.SET (672) 40.00 80.00
*STARS: .5X TO 1.2X BASIC CARDS
*ROOKIES: .5X TO 1.2X BASIC CARDS
FACTORY SET PRICE IS FOR SEALED SETS
OPENED SETS SELL FOR 50-60% OF SEALED
604 Barry Bonds 6.00 15.00

1987 Fleer Update

This 132-card standard-size set was distributed exclusively in factory set form through hobby dealers. In addition to the complete set of 132 cards, the box also contained 25 Team Logo stickers. The cards look very similar to the 1987 Fleer regular issue except for the U-prefixed numbering on back. Cards are ordered alphabetically according to player's last name. The key extended Rookie Cards in this set are Ellis Burks, Greg Maddux, Fred McGriff and Matt Williams. In addition an early card of legendary slugger Mark McGwire highlights this set.

COMP.FACT.SET (132)	5.00	12.00
1 Scott Bankhead	.02	.10
2 Eric Bell	.05	.15
3 Juan Beniquez	.02	.10
4 Juan Berenguer	.02	.10
5 Mike Birkbeck	.05	.15
6 Randy Bockus	.02	.10
7 Rod Booker	.02	.10
8 Thad Bosley	.02	.10
9 Greg Brock	.02	.10
10 Bob Brower	.02	.10
11 Chris Brown	.02	.10
12 Jerry Browne	.05	.15
13 Ralph Bryant	.02	.10
14 DeWayne Buice	.02	.10
15 Ellis Burks XRC	.30	.75
16 Casey Candaele	.02	.10
17 Steve Carlton	.05	.15
18 Juan Castillo	.05	.15
19 Chuck Crim	.02	.10
20 Mark Davidson	.02	.10
21 Mark Davis	.02	.10
22 Storm Davis	.02	.10
23 Bill Dawley	.02	.10
24 Andre Dawson	.05	.15
25 Brian Dayett	.02	.10
26 Rick Dempsey	.02	.10
27 Ken Dowell	.02	.10
28 Dave Dravecky	.02	.10
29 Mike Dunne	.02	.10
30 Dennis Eckersley	.08	.25
31 Cecil Fielder	.05	.15
32 Brian Fisher	.02	.10
33 Willie Fraser	.05	.15
34 Ken Gerhart	.02	.10
35 Jim Gott	.02	.10
36 Dan Gladden	.02	.10
37 Mike Greenwell XRC	.10	.30
38 Cecilio Guante	.02	.10
39 Albert Hall	.02	.10
40 Atlee Hammaker	.02	.10
41 Mickey Hatcher	.02	.10
42 Mike Heath	.02	.10
43 Neal Heaton	.02	.10
44 Mike Henneman XRC	.10	.30
45 Guy Hoffman	.02	.10
46 Charles Hudson	.02	.10
47 Chuck Jackson	.02	.10
48 Mike Jackson XRC	.10	.30
49 Reggie Jackson	.08	.25
50 Chris James	.02	.10
51 Dion James	.02	.10
52 Stan Javier	.02	.10
53 Stan Jefferson	.02	.10
54 Jimmy Jones	.05	.15
55 Tracy Jones	.02	.10
56 Terry Kennedy	.02	.10
57 Mike Kingery	.05	.15
58 Ray Knight	.05	.15
59 Gene Larkin XRC	.10	.30
60 Mike LaValliere	.10	.30
61 Jack Lazorko	.02	.10
62 Terry Leach	.02	.10
63 Rick Leach	.02	.10
64 Craig Lefferts	.02	.10
65 Jim Lindeman	.05	.15
66 Bill Long	.02	.10
67 Mike Loynd XRC	.05	.15
68 Greg Maddux XRC	3.00	8.00
69 Bill Madlock	.05	.15
70 Dave Magadan	.10	.30
71 Joe Magrane XRC	.05	.15
72 Fred Manrique	.02	.10
73 Mike Mason	.02	.10
74 Lloyd McClendon XRC	.10	.30
75 Fred McGriff	.40	1.00
76 Mark McGwire	2.00	5.00
77 Mark McLemore	.05	.15
78 Kevin McReynolds	.02	.10
79 Dave Meads	.02	.10
80 Greg Minton	.02	.10
81 John Mitchell XRC	.05	.15
82 Kevin Mitchell	.08	.25
83 John Morris	.02	.10
84 Jeff Musselman	.02	.10
85 Randy Myers XRC	.30	.75
86 Gene Nelson	.02	.10
87 Joe Niekro	.02	.10
88 Tom Nieto	.02	.10
89 Reid Nichols	.02	.10
90 Matt Nokes XRC	.10	.30
91 Dickie Noles	.02	.10
92 Edwin Nunez	.02	.10
93 Jose Nunez XRC	.02	.10
94 Paul O'Neill	.15	.40
95 Jim Paciorek	.02	.10
96 Lance Parrish	.05	.15
97 Bill Pecota XRC	.05	.15
98 Tony Pena	.02	.10
99 Luis Polonia XRC	.10	.30
100 Randy Ready	.02	.10
101 Jeff Reardon	.05	.15
102 Gary Redus	.02	.10
103 Rick Rhoden	.02	.10
104 Wally Ritchie	.02	.10
105 Jeff M. Robinson UER (Wrong Jeff's stats on back)	.02	.10
106 Mark Salas	.02	.10
107 Dave Schmidt	.02	.10
108 Kevin Seitzer UER (Wrong birth year)	.10	.30
109 John Shelby	.02	.10
110 John Smiley XRC	.10	.30
111 Lary Sorensen	.02	.10
112 Chris Speier	.02	.10
113 Randy St.Claire	.02	.10
114 Jim Sundberg	.05	.15
115 B.J. Surhoff XRC	.30	.75
116 Greg Swindell	.10	.30
117 Danny Tartabull	.02	.10
118 Dorn Taylor	.02	.10
119 Lee Tunnell	.02	.10
120 Ed VandeBerg	.02	.10
121 Andy Van Slyke	.08	.25
122 Gary Ward	.02	.10
123 Devon White	.30	.75
124 Alan Wiggins	.02	.10
125 Bill Wilkinson	.02	.10
126 Jim Winn	.02	.10
127 Frank Williams	.02	.10
128 Ken Williams XRC	.02	.10
129 Matt Williams XRC	.60	1.50
130 Herm Winningham	.02	.10
131 Matt Young	.02	.10
132 Checklist 1-132	.02	.10

1987 Fleer Update Glossy

This set parallels the regular Fleer Update issue. The cards were issued in a special tin. These 132 standard-size are differentiated only by the gloss on the front. This set was produced in fairly large quantities, although still significantly less than regular issue cards. Similar to the regular Glossy set -- it is believed that between 75 and 100 thousand of these sets were produced.

COMP.FACT.SET (132)	6.00	15.00
*STARS: .4X TO 1X BASIC CARDS		
*ROOKIES: .4X TO 1X BASIC CARDS		

1987 Fleer Hottest Stars

This 44-card boxed standard-size set was produced by Fleer for distribution by Revco stores all over the country. The cards feature full color fronts and red, white, and black backs. The card fronts are easily distinguished by their solid red outside borders and and white and blue inner borders framing the player's picture. The box for the cards proclaims "1987 Limited Edition Baseball's Hottest Stars" and is styled in the same manner and color scheme as the cards themselves. The checklist for the set is given on the back of the set box. The card numbering is in alphabetical order by player's name. An early card of Barry Bonds highlights this set.

COMP.FACT.SET (44)	15.00	40.00
1 Joaquin Andujar	.02	.10
2 Harold Baines	.05	.15
3 Kevin Bass	.02	.10
4 Don Baylor	.05	.15
5 Barry Bonds	8.00	20.00
6 George Brett	.40	1.00
7 Tom Brunansky	.02	.10
8 Brett Butler	.05	.15
9 Jose Canseco	.40	1.00
10 Roger Clemens	1.25	3.00
11 Ron Darling	.02	.10
12 Eric Davis	.08	.25
13 Andre Dawson	.05	.15
14 Doug DeCinces	.02	.10
15 Leon Durham	.02	.10
16 Mark Eichhorn	.02	.10
17 Scott Garrelts	.02	.10
18 Dwight Gooden	.08	.25
19 Dave Henderson	.02	.10
20 Rickey Henderson	.15	.40
21 Keith Hernandez	.05	.15
22 Ted Higuera	.02	.10
23 Bob Horner	.05	.15
24 Pete Incaviglia	.05	.15
25 Wally Joyner	.08	.25
26 Mark Langston	.02	.10
27 Don Mattingly UER (Pirates logo on back)	.50	1.25
28 Dale Murphy	.08	.25
29 Kirk McCaskill	.02	.10
30 Willie McGee	.05	.15
31 Dave Righetti	.02	.10
32 Pete Rose	.50	1.25
33 Bruce Ruffin	.02	.10
34 Steve Sax	.02	.10
35 Mike Schmidt	.40	1.00
36 Larry Sheets	.02	.10
37 Eric Show	.02	.10
38 Dave Smith	.02	.10
39 Cory Snyder	.02	.10
40 Frank Tanana	.05	.15
41 Alan Trammell	.05	.15
42 Reggie Williams	.02	.10
43 Mookie Wilson	.05	.15
44 Todd Worrell	.05	.15

1988 Fleer

This set consists of 660 standard-size cards. Cards were primarily issued in 15-card wax packs and hobby and retail factory sets. Each wax pack contained one of 26 different "Stadium Card" stickers. Card fronts feature a distinctive white background with red and blue diagonal stripes across the card. As in years past cards are organized numerically by teams and team order is based upon the previous season's record. Subsets include Specials (622-640), Rookie Pairs (641-653), and checklists (654-660). Rookie Cards in this set include Jay Bell, Ellis Burks, Ken Caminiti, Ron Gant, Tom Glavine, Mark Grace, Edgar Martinez, Jack McDowell and Matt Williams.

COMPLETE SET (660)	6.00	15.00
COMP.RETAIL SET (660)	6.00	15.00
COMP.HOBBY SET (672)	6.00	15.00
1 Keith Atherton	.02	.10
2 Don Baylor	.05	.15
3 Juan Berenguer	.02	.10
4 Bert Blyleven	.05	.15
5 Tom Brunansky	.02	.10
6 Randy Bush	.02	.10
7 Steve Carlton	.05	.15
8 Mark Davidson	.02	.10
9 George Frazier	.02	.10
10 Gary Gaetti	.05	.15
11 Greg Gagne	.02	.10
12 Dan Gladden	.02	.10
13 Kent Hrbek	.05	.15
14 Gene Larkin RC	.15	.40
15 Tim Laudner	.02	.10
16 Steve Lombardozzi	.02	.10
17 Al Newman	.02	.10
18 Joe Niekro	.02	.10
19 Kirby Puckett	.10	.30
20 Jeff Reardon	.05	.15
21A Dan Schatzeder ERR (Misspelled Schatzader on both sides of the card)	.05	.15
21B Dan Schatzeder COR	.02	.10
22 Roy Smalley	.02	.10
23 Mike Smithson	.02	.10
24 Les Straker	.02	.10
25 Frank Viola	.05	.15
26 Jack Clark	.05	.15
27 Vince Coleman	.02	.10
28 Danny Cox	.02	.10
29 Bill Dawley	.02	.10
30 Ken Dayley	.02	.10
31 Doug DeCinces	.02	.10
32 Curt Ford	.02	.10
33 Bob Forsch	.02	.10
34 David Green	.02	.10
35 Tom Herr	.02	.10
36 Ricky Horton	.02	.10
37 Lance Johnson RC	.15	.40
38 Steve Lake	.02	.10
39 Jim Lindeman	.02	.10
40 Joe Magrane RC	.15	.40
41 Greg Mathews	.02	.10
42 Willie McGee	.05	.15
43 John Morris	.02	.10
44 Jose Oquendo	.02	.10
45 Tony Pena	.02	.10
46 Terry Pendleton	.05	.15
47 Ozzie Smith	.20	.50
48 John Tudor	.05	.15
49 Lee Tunnell	.02	.10
50 Todd Worrell	.02	.10
51 Doyle Alexander	.02	.10
52 Dave Bergman	.02	.10
53 Tom Brookens	.02	.10
54 Darrell Evans	.05	.15
55 Kirk Gibson	.10	.30
56 Mike Heath	.02	.10
57 Mike Henneman RC	.15	.40
58 Willie Hernandez	.02	.10
59 Larry Herndon	.02	.10
60 Eric King	.02	.10
61 Chet Lemon	.05	.15
62 Scott Lusader	.02	.10
63 Bill Madlock	.05	.15
64 Jack Morris	.05	.15
65 Jim Morrison	.02	.10
66 Matt Nokes RC	.15	.40
67 Dan Petry	.02	.10
68A Jeff M. Robinson ERR, Stats for Jeff D. Robinson on card back Born 12-13-60	.07	.20
68B Jeff M. Robinson COR, Born 12-14-61	.02	.10
69 Pat Sheridan	.02	.10
70 Nate Snell	.02	.10
71 Frank Tanana	.05	.15
72 Walt Terrell	.02	.10
73 Mark Thurmond	.02	.10
74 Alan Trammell	.05	.15
75 Lou Whitaker	.05	.15
76 Mike Aldrete	.02	.10
77 Bob Brenly	.02	.10
78 Will Clark	.10	.30
79 Chili Davis	.05	.15
80 Kelly Downs	.02	.10
81 Dave Dravecky	.02	.10
82 Scott Garrelts	.02	.10
83 Atlee Hammaker	.02	.10
84 Dave Henderson	.02	.10
85 Mike Krukow	.02	.10
86 Mike LaCoss	.02	.10
87 Craig Lefferts	.02	.10
88 Jeff Leonard	.02	.10
89 Candy Maldonado	.02	.10
90 Eddie Milner	.02	.10
91 Bob Melvin	.02	.10
92 Kevin Mitchell	.05	.15
93 Jon Perlman	.05	.15
94 Rick Reuschel	.05	.15
95 Don Robinson	.02	.10
96 Chris Speier	.02	.10
97 Harry Spilman	.02	.10
98 Robby Thompson	.02	.10
99 Jose Uribe	.02	.10
100 Mark Wasinger	.02	.10
101 Matt Williams RC	.60	1.50
102 Jesse Barfield	.05	.15
103 George Bell	.05	.15
104 Juan Beniquez	.02	.10
105 John Cerutti	.02	.10
106 Jim Clancy	.02	.10
107 Rob Ducey	.02	.10
108 Mark Eichhorn	.02	.10
109 Tony Fernandez	.02	.10
110 Cecil Fielder	.05	.15
111 Kelly Gruber	.02	.10
112 Tom Henke	.02	.10
113A Garth Iorg ERR (Misspelled Iorq on card front)	.07	.20
113B Garth Iorg COR	.02	.10
114 Jimmy Key	.05	.15
115 Rick Leach	.02	.10
116 Manny Lee	.02	.10
117 Nelson Liriano	.02	.10
118 Fred McGriff	.10	.30
119 Lloyd Moseby	.02	.10
120 Rance Mulliniks	.02	.10
121 Jeff Musselman	.02	.10
122 Jose Nunez	.02	.10
123 Dave Stieb	.05	.15
124 Willie Upshaw	.02	.10
125 Duane Ward	.02	.10
126 Ernie Whitt	.02	.10
127 Rick Aguilera	.02	.10
128 Wally Backman	.02	.10
129 Mark Carreon RC	.05	.15
130 Gary Carter	.05	.15
131 David Cone	.05	.15
132 Ron Darling	.02	.10
133 Len Dykstra	.05	.15
134 Sid Fernandez	.02	.10
135 Dwight Gooden	.05	.15
136 Keith Hernandez	.05	.15
137 Gregg Jefferies RC	.15	.40
138 Howard Johnson	.05	.15
139 Terry Leach	.02	.10
140 Barry Lyons	.02	.10
141 Dave Magadan	.02	.10
142 Roger McDowell	.02	.10
143 Kevin McReynolds	.02	.10
144 Keith A. Miller RC	.15	.40
145 John Mitchell RC	.05	.15
146 Randy Myers	.05	.15
147 Bob Ojeda	.02	.10
148 Jesse Orosco	.02	.10
149 Rafael Santana	.02	.10
150 Doug Sisk	.02	.10
151 Darryl Strawberry	.05	.15
152 Tim Teufel	.02	.10
153 Gene Walter	.02	.10
154 Mookie Wilson	.05	.15
155 Jay Aldrich	.02	.10
156 Chris Bosio	.02	.10
157 Glenn Braggs	.02	.10
158 Greg Brock	.02	.10
159 Juan Castillo	.02	.10
160 Mark Clear	.02	.10
161 Cecil Cooper	.05	.15
162 Chuck Crim	.02	.10
163 Rob Deer	.02	.10
164 Mike Felder	.02	.10
165 Jim Gantner	.02	.10
166 Ted Higuera	.02	.10
167 Steve Kiefer	.02	.10
168 Rick Manning	.02	.10
169 Paul Molitor	.05	.15
170 Juan Nieves	.02	.10
171 Dan Plesac	.02	.10
172 Earnest Riles	.02	.10
173 Bill Schroeder	.02	.10
174 Steve Stanicek	.02	.10
175 B.J. Surhoff	.05	.15
176 Dale Sveum	.02	.10
177 Bill Wegman	.02	.10
178 Robin Yount	.20	.50
179 Hubie Brooks	.02	.10
180 Tim Burke	.02	.10
181 Casey Candaele	.02	.10
182 Mike Fitzgerald	.02	.10
183 Tom Foley	.02	.10
184 Andres Galarraga	.05	.15
185 Neal Heaton	.02	.10
186 Wallace Johnson	.02	.10
187 Vance Law	.02	.10
188 Dennis Martinez	.05	.15
189 Bob McClure	.02	.10
190 Andy McGaffigan	.02	.10
191 Reid Nichols	.02	.10
192 Pascual Perez	.02	.10
193 Tim Raines	.05	.15
194 Jeff Reed	.02	.10
195 Bob Sebra	.02	.10
196 Bryn Smith	.02	.10
197 Randy St.Claire	.02	.10
198 Tim Wallach	.02	.10
199 Mitch Webster	.02	.10
200 Herm Winningham	.02	.10
201 Floyd Youmans	.02	.10
202 Brad Arnsberg	.02	.10
203 Rick Cerone	.02	.10
204 Pat Clements	.02	.10
205 Henry Cotto	.02	.10
206 Mike Easler	.02	.10
207 Ron Guidry	.05	.15
208 Bill Gullickson	.02	.10
209 Rickey Henderson	.10	.30
210 Charles Hudson	.02	.10
211 Tommy John	.05	.15
212 Roberto Kelly RC	.15	.40
213 Ron Kittle	.02	.10
214 Don Mattingly	.40	1.00
215 Bobby Meacham	.02	.10
216 Mike Pagliarulo	.02	.10
217 Dan Pasqua	.02	.10
218 Willie Randolph	.05	.15
219 Rick Rhoden	.02	.10
220 Dave Righetti	.05	.15
221 Jerry Royster	.02	.10
222 Tim Stoddard	.02	.10
223 Wayne Tolleson	.02	.10
224 Gary Ward	.02	.10
225 Claudell Washington	.02	.10
226 Dave Winfield	.05	.15
227 Buddy Bell	.05	.15
228 Tom Browning	.02	.10
229 Dave Concepcion	.05	.15
230 Kal Daniels	.02	.10
231 Eric Davis	.05	.15
232 Bo Diaz	.02	.10
233 Nick Esasky (Has a dollar sign before '87 SB totals)	.02	.10
234 John Franco	.05	.15
235 Guy Hoffman	.02	.10
236 Tom Hume	.02	.10
237 Tracy Jones	.02	.10
238 Bill Landrum	.02	.10
239 Barry Larkin	.07	.20
240 Terry McGriff	.02	.10
241 Rob Murphy	.02	.10
242 Ron Oester	.02	.10
243 Dave Parker	.05	.15
244 Pat Perry	.02	.10
245 Ted Power	.02	.10
246 Dennis Rasmussen	.02	.10
247 Ron Robinson	.02	.10
248 Kurt Stillwell	.02	.10
249 Jeff Treadway RC	.15	.40
250 Frank Williams	.02	.10
251 Steve Balboni	.02	.10
252 Bud Black	.02	.10
253 Thad Bosley	.02	.10
254 George Brett	.30	.75
255 John Davis	.02	.10
256 Steve Farr	.02	.10
257 Gene Garber	.02	.10
258 Jerry Don Gleaton	.02	.10
259 Mark Gubicza	.02	.10
260 Bo Jackson	.10	.30
261 Danny Jackson	.02	.10
262 Ross Jones	.02	.10
263 Charlie Leibrandt	.02	.10
264 Bill Pecota RC	.05	.15
265 Melido Perez RC	.15	.40
266 Jamie Quirk	.02	.10
267 Dan Quisenberry	.02	.10
268 Bret Saberhagen	.05	.15
269 Angel Salazar	.02	.10
270 Kevin Seitzer UER (Wrong birth year)	.05	.15
271 Danny Tartabull	.02	.10
272 Gary Thurman	.02	.10
273 Frank White	.05	.15
274 Willie Wilson	.05	.15
275 Tony Bernazard	.02	.10
276 Jose Canseco	.30	.75
277 Mike Davis	.02	.10
278 Storm Davis	.02	.10
279 Dennis Eckersley	.07	.20
280 Alfredo Griffin	.02	.10
281 Rick Honeycutt	.02	.10
282 Jay Howell	.02	.10
283 Reggie Jackson	.07	.20
284 Dennis Lamp	.02	.10
285 Carney Lansford	.05	.15
286 Mark McGwire	1.00	2.50
287 Dwayne Murphy	.02	.10
288 Gene Nelson	.02	.10
289 Steve Ontiveros	.02	.10
290 Tony Phillips	.02	.10
291 Eric Plunk	.02	.10
292 Luis Polonia RC	.15	.40
293 Rick Rodriguez	.02	.10
294 Terry Steinbach	.05	.15
295 Dave Stewart	.05	.15
296 Curt Young	.02	.10
297 Luis Aguayo	.02	.10
298 Steve Bedrosian	.02	.10
299 Jeff Calhoun	.02	.10
300 Don Carman	.02	.10
301 Todd Frohwirth	.02	.10
302 Greg Gross	.02	.10
303 Kevin Gross	.02	.10
304 Von Hayes	.02	.10
305 Keith Hughes	.02	.10
306 Mike Jackson RC	.15	.40
307 Chris James	.02	.10
308 Steve Jeltz	.02	.10
309 Mike Maddux	.02	.10
310 Lance Parrish	.05	.15
311 Shane Rawley	.02	.10
312 Wally Ritchie	.02	.10
313 Bruce Ruffin	.02	.10
314 Juan Samuel	.02	.10
315 Mike Schmidt	.30	.75
316 Rick Schu	.02	.10
317 Jeff Stone	.02	.10
318 Kent Tekulve	.02	.10
319 Milt Thompson	.02	.10
320 Glenn Wilson	.02	.10
321 Rafael Belliard	.02	.10
322 Barry Bonds	1.00	2.50
323 Bobby Bonilla UER (Wrong birth year)	.05	.15
324 Sid Bream	.02	.10
325 John Cangelosi	.02	.10
326 Mike Diaz	.02	.10
327 Doug Drabek	.02	.10
328 Mike Dunne	.02	.10
329 Brian Fisher	.02	.10
330 Brett Gideon	.02	.10
331 Terry Harper	.02	.10
332 Bob Kipper	.02	.10
333 Mike LaValliere	.02	.10
334 Jose Lind RC	.15	.40
335 Junior Ortiz	.02	.10
336 Vicente Palacios	.02	.10
337 Bob Patterson	.02	.10
338 Al Pedrique	.02	.10
339 R.J. Reynolds	.02	.10
340 John Smiley RC	.15	.40
341 Andy Van Slyke UER (Wrong batting and throwing listed)	.07	.20
342 Bob Walk	.02	.10
343 Marty Barrett	.02	.10
344 Todd Benzinger RC	.15	.40
345 Wade Boggs	.07	.20
346 Tom Bolton	.02	.10
347 Oil Can Boyd	.02	.10
348 Ellis Burks RC	.20	.50
349 Roger Clemens	.60	1.50
350 Steve Crawford	.02	.10
351 Dwight Evans	.07	.20
352 Wes Gardner	.02	.10
353 Rich Gedman	.02	.10
354 Mike Greenwell	.02	.10
355 Sam Horn RC	.05	.15
356 Bruce Hurst	.02	.10
357 John Marzano	.02	.10
358 Al Nipper	.02	.10
359 Spike Owen	.02	.10
360 Jody Reed RC	.15	.40
361 Jim Rice	.05	.15
362 Ed Romero	.02	.10
363 Kevin Romine	.02	.10
364 Joe Sambito	.02	.10
365 Calvin Schiraldi	.02	.10
366 Jeff Sellers	.02	.10
367 Bob Stanley	.02	.10
368 Scott Bankhead	.02	.10
369 Phil Bradley	.02	.10
370 Scott Bradley	.02	.10
371 Mickey Brantley	.02	.10
372 Mike Campbell	.02	.10
373 Alvin Davis	.02	.10
374 Lee Guetterman	.02	.10
375 Dave Hengel	.02	.10
376 Mike Kingery	.02	.10
377 Mark Langston	.02	.10
378 Edgar Martinez RC	2.00	5.00
379 Mike Moore	.02	.10
380 Mike Morgan	.02	.10
381 John Moses	.02	.10
382 Donell Nixon	.02	.10
383 Edwin Nunez	.02	.10
384 Ken Phelps	.02	.10
385 Jim Presley	.02	.10
386 Rey Quinones	.02	.10
387 Jerry Reed	.02	.10
388 Harold Reynolds	.05	.15
389 Dave Valle	.02	.10
390 Bill Wilkinson	.02	.10
391 Harold Baines	.05	.15
392 Floyd Bannister	.02	.10
393 Daryl Boston	.02	.10
394 Ivan Calderon	.02	.10
395 Jose DeLeon	.02	.10
396 Richard Dotson	.02	.10
397 Carlton Fisk	.07	.20
398 Ozzie Guillen	.05	.15
399 Ron Hassey	.02	.10
400 Donnie Hill	.02	.10
401 Bob James	.02	.10
402 Dave LaPoint	.02	.10
403 Bill Lindsey	.02	.10
404 Bill Long	.02	.10
405 Steve Lyons	.02	.10
406 Fred Manrique	.02	.10
407 Jack McDowell RC	.20	.50
408 Gary Redus	.02	.10
409 Ray Searage	.02	.10
410 Bobby Thigpen	.02	.10
411 Greg Walker	.02	.10
412 Ken Williams RC	.02	.10
413 Jim Winn	.02	.10
414 Jody Davis	.02	.10
415 Andre Dawson	.05	.15
416 Brian Dayett	.02	.10
417 Bob Dernier	.02	.10
418 Frank DiPino	.02	.10
419 Shawon Dunston	.02	.10
420 Leon Durham	.02	.10
421 Les Lancaster	.02	.10
422 Ed Lynch	.02	.10
423 Greg Maddux	.60	1.50
424 Dave Martinez	.02	.10
425A Keith Moreland ERR (Photo actually Jody Davis)	.60	1.50
425B Keith Moreland COR (Bat on shoulder)	.05	.15
426 Jamie Moyer	.05	.15
427 Jerry Mumphrey	.02	.10
428 Paul Noce	.02	.10
429 Rafael Palmeiro	.25	.60
430 Wade Rowdon	.02	.10
431 Ryne Sandberg	.25	.60
432 Scott Sanderson	.02	.10
433 Lee Smith	.05	.15
434 Jim Sundberg	.05	.15
435 Rick Sutcliffe	.05	.15
436 Manny Trillo	.02	.10
437 Juan Agosto	.02	.10
438 Larry Andersen	.02	.10
439 Alan Ashby	.02	.10
440 Kevin Bass	.02	.10
441 Ken Caminiti RC	1.25	3.00
442 Rocky Childress	.02	.10
443 Jose Cruz	.05	.15
444 Danny Darwin	.02	.10
445 Glenn Davis	.02	.10
446 Jim Deshaies	.02	.10
447 Bill Doran	.02	.10
448 Ty Gainey	.02	.10
449 Billy Hatcher	.02	.10
450 Jeff Heathcock	.02	.10
451 Bob Knepper	.02	.10
452 Rob Mallicoat	.02	.10
453 Dave Meads	.02	.10
454 Craig Reynolds	.02	.10
455 Nolan Ryan	.60	1.50
456 Mike Scott	.05	.15
457 Dave Smith	.02	.10
458 Denny Walling	.02	.10
459 Robbie Wine	.02	.10
460 Gerald Young	.02	.10
461 Bob Brower	.02	.10
462A Jerry Browne ERR (Photo actually Bob Brower, white player)	.60	1.50

462B Jerry Browne COR .05 .15
(Black player)
463 Steve Buechele .02 .10
464 Edwin Correa .02 .10
465 Cecil Espy RC .02 .10
466 Scott Fletcher .02 .10
467 Jose Guzman .02 .10
468 Greg Harris .02 .10
469 Charlie Hough .05 .15
470 Pete Incaviglia .02 .10
471 Paul Kilgus .02 .10
472 Mike Loynd .02 .10
473 Oddibe McDowell .02 .10
474 Dale Mohorcic .02 .10
475 Pete O'Brien .02 .10
476 Larry Parrish .02 .10
477 Geno Petralli .02 .10
478 Jeff Russell .02 .10
479 Ruben Sierra .05 .15
480 Mike Stanley .02 .10
481 Curtis Wilkerson .02 .10
482 Mitch Williams .02 .10
483 Bobby Witt .02 .10
484 Tony Armas .05 .15
485 Bob Boone .05 .15
486 Bill Buckner .05 .15
487 DeWayne Buice .02 .10
488 Brian Downing .05 .15
489 Chuck Finley .05 .15
490 Willie Fraser UER .02 .10
(Wrong bio stats,
for George Hendrick)
491 Jack Howell .02 .10
492 Ruppert Jones .02 .10
493 Wally Joyner .05 .15
494 Jack Lazorko .02 .10
495 Gary Lucas .02 .10
496 Kirk McCaskill .02 .10
497 Mark McLemore .02 .10
498 Darrell Miller .02 .10
499 Greg Minton .02 .10
500 Donnie Moore .02 .10
501 Gus Polidor .02 .10
502 Johnny Ray .02 .10
503 Mark Ryal .02 .10
504 Dick Schofield .02 .10
505 Don Sutton .05 .15
506 Devon White .05 .15
507 Mike Witt .02 .10
508 Dave Anderson .02 .10
509 Tim Belcher .02 .10
510 Ralph Bryant .02 .10
511 Tim Crews RC .15 .40
512 Mike Devereaux RC .15 .40
513 Mariano Duncan .02 .10
514 Pedro Guerrero .05 .15
515 Jeff Hamilton .02 .10
516 Mickey Hatcher .02 .10
517 Brad Havens .02 .10
518 Orel Hershiser .05 .15
519 Shawn Hillegas .02 .10
520 Ken Howell .02 .10
521 Tim Leary .02 .10
522 Mike Marshall .02 .10
523 Steve Sax .02 .10
524 Mike Scioscia .05 .15
525 Mike Sharperson .02 .10
526 John Shelby .02 .10
527 Franklin Stubbs .02 .10
528 Fernando Valenzuela .05 .15
529 Bob Welch .05 .15
530 Matt Young .02 .10
531 Jim Acker .02 .10
532 Paul Assenmacher .02 .10
533 Jeff Blauser RC .15 .40
534 Joe Boever .02 .10
535 Martin Clary .02 .10
536 Kevin Coffman .02 .10
537 Jeff Dedmon .02 .10
538 Ron Gant RC .20 .50
539 Tom Glavine RC 1.50 4.00
540 Ken Griffey .05 .15
541 Albert Hall .02 .10
542 Glenn Hubbard .02 .10
543 Dion James .02 .10
544 Dale Murphy .07 .20
545 Ken Oberkfell .02 .10
546 David Palmer .02 .10
547 Gerald Perry .02 .10
548 Charlie Puleo .02 .10
549 Ted Simmons .05 .15
550 Zane Smith .02 .10
551 Andres Thomas .02 .10
552 Ozzie Virgil .02 .10
553 Don Aase .02 .10
554 Jeff Ballard .02 .10
555 Eric Bell .02 .10
556 Mike Boddicker .02 .10
557 Ken Dixon .02 .10
558 Jim Dwyer .02 .10
559 Ken Gerhart .02 .10
560 Rene Gonzales RC .05 .15
561 Mike Griffin .02 .10
562 John Habyan UER .02 .10
(Misspelled Hayban on
both sides of card)
563 Terry Kennedy .02 .10
564 Ray Knight .05 .15
565 Lee Lacy .02 .10
566 Fred Lynn .05 .15
567 Eddie Murray .10 .30
568 Tom Niedenfuer .02 .10
569 Bill Ripken RC .15 .40
570 Cal Ripken .50 1.25
571 Dave Schmidt .02 .10
572 Larry Sheets .02 .10
573 Pete Stanicek .02 .10
574 Mark Williamson .02 .10
575 Mike Young .02 .10
576 Shawn Abner .02 .10
577 Greg Booker .02 .10
578 Chris Brown .02 .10
579 Keith Comstock .02 .10
580 Joey Cora RC .15 .40
581 Mark Davis .02 .10
582 Tim Flannery .07 .20
(With surfboard)
583 Goose Gossage .05 .15
584 Mark Grant .02 .10
585 Tony Gwynn .20 .50
586 Andy Hawkins .02 .10
587 Stan Jefferson .02 .10
588 Jimmy Jones .02 .10
589 John Kruk .05 .15
590 Shane Mack .02 .10
591 Carmelo Martinez .02 .10
592 Lance McCullers UER .02 .10
(6'11 tall)
593 Eric Nolte .02 .10
594 Randy Ready .02 .10
595 Luis Salazar .02 .10
596 Benito Santiago .05 .15
597 Eric Show .02 .10
598 Garry Templeton .05 .15
599 Ed Whitson .02 .10
600 Scott Bailes .02 .10
601 Chris Bando .02 .10
602 Jay Bell RC .20 .50
603 Brett Butler .05 .15
604 Tom Candiotti .02 .10
605 Joe Carter .05 .15
606 Carmen Castillo .02 .10
607 Brian Dorsett .02 .10
608 John Farrell RC .02 .10
609 Julio Franco .05 .15
610 Mel Hall .02 .10
611 Tommy Hinzo .02 .10
612 Brook Jacoby .02 .10
613 Doug Jones RC .15 .40
614 Ken Schrom .02 .10
615 Cory Snyder .02 .10
616 Sammy Stewart .02 .10
617 Greg Swindell .02 .10
618 Pat Tabler .02 .10
619 Ed VandeBerg .02 .10
620 Eddie Williams RC .05 .15
621 Rich Yett .02 .10
622 Wally Joyner .05 .15
Cory Snyder
623 George Bell .02 .10
Pedro Guerrero
624 Mark McGwire .60 1.50
Jose Canseco
625 Dave Righetti .02 .10
Dan Plesac
626 Bret Saberhagen .05 .15
Mike Witt
Jack Morris
627 John Franco .02 .10
Steve Bedrosian
628 Ozzie Smith .10 .30
Ryne Sandberg
629 Mark McGwire HL .50 1.25
630 Mike Greenwell .10 .30
Ellis Burks
Todd Benzinger
631 Tony Gwynn .07 .20
Tim Raines
632 Mike Scott .05 .15
Orel Hershiser
633 Pat Tabler .50 1.25
Mark McGwire
634 Tony Gwynn .07 .20
Vince Coleman
635 Tony Fernandez .20 .50
Cal Ripken
Alan Trammell
636 Mike Schmidt .10 .30
Gary Carter
637 Darryl Strawberry .05 .15
Eric Davis
638 Matt Nokes .07 .20
Kirby Puckett
639 Keith Hernandez .05 .15
Dale Murphy
640 Billy Ripken .30 .75
Cal Ripken
641 Mark Grace RC 1.25 3.00
Darrin Jackson
642 Damon Berryhill RC .15 .40
Jeff Montgomery RC
643 Felix Fermin .05 .15
Jesse Reid RC
644 Greg Myers .15 .40
Greg Tabor RC
645 Joey Meyer .05 .15
Jim Eppard RC
646 Adam Peterson RC .15 .40
Randy Velarde RC
647 Pete Smith .15 .40
Chris Gwynn RC
648 Tom Newell .05 .15
Greg Jelks RC
649 Mario Diaz .05 .15
Clay Parker RC
650 Jack Savage .05 .15
Todd Simmons RC
651 John Burkett .15 .40
Kirt Manwaring RC
652 Dave Otto .20 .50
Walt Weiss RC
653 Jeff King .15 .40
Randell Byers RC
654 CL: Twins/Cards .02 .10
Tigers/Giants UER
(90 Bob Melvin,
91 Eddie Milner)
655 CL: Blue Jays/Mets .02 .10
Brewers/Expos UER
(Mets listed before
Blue Jays on card)
656 CL: Yankees/Reds .02 .10
Royals/A's
657 CL: Phillies/Pirates .02 .10
Red Sox/Mariners
658 CL: White Sox/Cubs .02 .10
Astros/Rangers
659 CL: Angels/Dodgers .02 .10
Braves/Orioles
660 CL: Padres/Indians .02 .10
Rookies/Specials

1988 Fleer Glossy

This 660 card set is a parallel to the regular Fleer issue. The cards are the same as the regular issue except for the glossy sheen on the front. The cards (along with the 12-card World Series insert set) were issued in a factory tin distributed exclusively through hobby dealers. Since many dealers had problems selling their 1987 sets, production was reduced for the 1988 issues. It is believed that

between 40 and 60 thousand of these sets were produced,

COMP.FACT.SET (672) 10.00 25.00
*STARS: .6X TO 1.5X BASIC CARDS
*ROOKIES: .75X TO 2X BASIC CARDS

1988 Fleer Update

This 132-card standard-size set was distributed exclusively in factory set form in a red, white and blue, cellophane-wrapped box through hobby dealers. In addition to the complete set of 132 cards, the box also contained 25 Team Logo stickers. The cards look very similar to the 1988 Fleer regular issue except for the U-prefixed numbering on back. Cards are ordered alphabetically by player's last name. This was the first Fleer Update set to adopt the Fleer "alphabetical within team" numbering system. The key extended Rookie Cards in this set are Roberto Alomar, Craig Biggio Al Leiter, John Smoltz and David Wells.

COMP.FACT.SET (132) 4.00 10.00
1 Jose Bautista XRC .08 .25
2 Joe Orsulak .02 .10
3 Doug Sisk .02 .10
4 Craig Worthington .02 .10
5 Mike Boddicker .02 .10
6 Rick Cerone .02 .10
7 Larry Parrish .02 .10
8 Lee Smith .07 .20
9 Mike Smithson .02 .10
10 John Trautwein .02 .10
11 Sherman Corbett .02 .10
12 Chili Davis .07 .20
13 Jim Eppard .02 .10
14 Bryan Harvey XRC .20 .50
15 John Davis .02 .10
16 Dave Gallagher .02 .10
17 Ricky Horton .02 .10
18 Dan Pasqua .02 .10
19 Melido Perez .02 .10
20 Jose Segura .02 .10
21 Andy Allanson .02 .10
22 Jon Perlman .02 .10
23 Domingo Ramos .02 .10
24 Rick Rodriguez .02 .10
25 Willie Upshaw .02 .10
26 Paul Gibson .02 .10
27 Don Heinkel .02 .10
28 Ray Knight .07 .20
29 Gary Pettis .02 .10
30 Luis Salazar .02 .10
31 Mike Macfarlane XRC .20 .50
32 Jeff Montgomery .20 .50
33 Ted Power .02 .10
34 Israel Sanchez .02 .10
35 Kurt Stillwell .02 .10
36 Pat Tabler .02 .10
37 Don August .02 .10
38 Darryl Hamilton XRC .20 .50
39 Jeff Leonard .02 .10
40 Joey Meyer .02 .10
41 Allan Anderson .02 .10
42 Brian Harper .02 .10
43 Tom Herr .02 .10
44 Charlie Lea .02 .10
45 John Moses .02 .10
(Listed as Hohn on
checklist card)
46 John Candelaria .02 .10
47 Jack Clark .07 .20
48 Richard Dotson .02 .10
49 Al Leiter XRC .40 1.00
50 Rafael Santana .02 .10
51 Don Slaught .02 .10
52 Todd Burns .02 .10
53 Dave Henderson .02 .10
54 Doug Jennings .02 .10
55 Dave Parker .07 .20
56 Walt Weiss .30 .75
57 Bob Welch .07 .20
58 Henry Cotto .02 .10
59 Mario Diaz UER .02 .10
(Listed as Marion
on card front)
60 Mike Jackson .07 .20
61 Bill Swift .02 .10
62 Jose Cecena .02 .10
63 Ray Hayward .02 .10
64 Jim Steels UER .02 .10
(Listed as Jim Steele
on card back)
65 Pat Borders XRC .20 .50
66 Sil Campusano .02 .10
67 Mike Flanagan .02 .10
68 Todd Stottlemyre XRC .20 .50
69 David Wells XRC .60 1.50
70 Jose Alvarez XRC .08 .25
71 Paul Runge .02 .10
72 Cesar Jimenez .02 .10
(Card was intended
for German Jiminez&
it's his photo)
73 Pete Smith .02 .10
74 John Smoltz XRC 1.50 4.00
75 Damon Berryhill .08 .25
76 Goose Gossage .07 .20
77 Mark Grace .75 2.00
78 Darrin Jackson .08 .25
79 Vance Law .02 .10
80 Jeff Pico .02 .10
81 Gary Varsho .02 .10
82 Tim Birtsas .02 .10
83 Rob Dibble XRC .30 .75
84 Danny Jackson .02 .10
85 Paul O'Neill .10 .30
86 Jose Rijo .07 .20
87 Chris Sabo XRC .30 .75
88 John Fishel .02 .10
89 Craig Biggio XRC 2.00 5.00
90 Terry Puhl .02 .10
91 Rafael Ramirez .02 .10
92 Louie Meadows .02 .10
93 Kirk Gibson .20 .50
94 Alfredo Griffin .02 .10
95 Jay Howell .02 .10
96 Jesse Orosco .02 .10
97 Alejandro Pena .02 .10
98 Tracy Woodson XRC .08 .25
99 John Dopson .02 .10
100 Brian Holman XRC .08 .25
101 Rex Hudler .02 .10
102 Jeff Parrett .02 .10
103 Nelson Santovenia .02 .10
104 Kevin Elster .02 .10
105 Jeff Innis .02 .10
106 Mackey Sasser XRC .20 .50
107 Phil Bradley .02 .10
108 Danny Clay .02 .10
109 Greg A.Harris .02 .10
110 Ricky Jordan XRC .20 .50
111 David Palmer .02 .10
112 Jim Gott .02 .10
113 Tommy Gregg UER .02 .10
(Photo actually
Randy Milligan)
114 Barry Jones .02 .10
115 Randy Milligan XRC .08 .25
116 Luis Alicea XRC .20 .50
117 Tom Brunansky .02 .10
118 John Costello .02 .10
119 Jose DeLeon .02 .10
120 Bob Horner .07 .20
121 Scott Terry .02 .10
122 Roberto Alomar XRC .75 2.00
123 Dave Leiper .02 .10
124 Keith Moreland .02 .10
125 Mark Parent .02 .10
126 Dennis Rasmussen .02 .10
127 Randy Bockus .02 .10
128 Brett Butler .07 .20
129 Donell Nixon .02 .10
130 Earnest Riles .02 .10
131 Roger Samuels .02 .10
132 Checklist U1-U132 .02 .10

1988 Fleer Update Glossy

This 132 card set is a parallel to the regular Fleer Update issue. Except for a glossy sheen on the front, the cards are identical to the regular Fleer issue. The cards were issued through hobby dealers in a special tin box. The cards are not as plentiful as the regular Fleer update set. Similar to the regular Glossy set, it is believed that between 40 and 60 thousand of these sets were produced.

COMP.FACT.SET (132) 10.00 25.00
*STARS: .75X TO 2X BASIC CARDS
*ROOKIES: .75X TO 2X BASIC CARDS

1989 Fleer

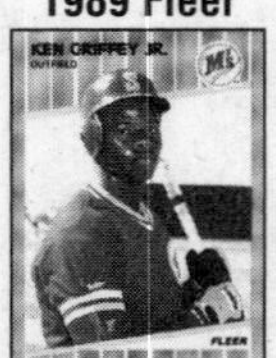

This set consists of 660 standard-size cards. Cards were primarily issued in 15-card wax packs, rack packs and hobby and retail factory sets. Card fronts feature a distinctive gray border background with white and yellow trim. Cards are again organized alphabetically within teams and teams ordered by previous season record. The last 33 cards in the set consist of Specials (628-639), Rookie Pairs (640-653), and checklists (654-660). Approximately half of the California Angels players have white rather than yellow halos. Certain Oakland A's player cards have red instead of green lines for front photo borders. Checklist cards are available either with or without positions listed for each player. Rookie Cards in this set include Craig Biggio, Ken Griffey Jr., Randy Johnson, Gary Sheffield, and John Smoltz. An interesting variation was discovered in late 1999 by Beckett Grading Services on the Randy Johnson RC (card number 381). It seems the most common version features a crudely-blacked out image of an outfield billboard. A scarcer version clearly reveals the words "Marlboro" on the billboard. A value for this variation is not provided due to scarcity. One of the hobby's most notorious errors and variations hails from this product. Card number 616, Billy Ripken, was originally published with a four-letter word imprinted on the bat. Needless to say, this caused quite a stir in 1989 and the card was quickly reprinted. Because of this, several different variations were printed with the final solution (and the most common version of this card) being a black box covering the bat knob. The first variation is still actively sought after in the hobby and the other versions are still sought after by collectors seeking a "master" set.

COMPLETE SET (660) 6.00 15.00
COMP.FACT.SET (672) 6.00 15.00
1 Don Baylor .02 .10
2 Lance Blankenship RC .02 .10
3 Todd Burns UER .01 .05
(Wrong birthdate;
before/after All-Star
stats missing)
4 Greg Cadaret UER .01 .05
(All-Star Break stats
show 3 losses, should be 2
5 Jose Canseco .08 .25
6 Storm Davis .01 .05
7 Dennis Eckersley .05 .15
8 Mike Gallego .01 .05
9 Ron Hassey .01 .05
10 Dave Henderson .01 .05
11 Rick Honeycutt .01 .05
12 Glenn Hubbard .01 .05
13 Stan Javier .01 .05
14 Doug Jennings .01 .05
15 Felix Jose RC .02 .10
16 Carney Lansford .02 .10
17 Mark McGwire .40 1.00
18 Gene Nelson .01 .05
19 Dave Parker .02 .10
20 Eric Plunk .01 .05
21 Luis Polonia .01 .05
22 Terry Steinbach .02 .10
23 Dave Stewart .02 .10
24 Walt Weiss .01 .05
25 Bob Welch .02 .10
26 Curt Young .01 .05
27 Rick Aguilera .01 .05
28 Wally Backman .01 .05
29 Mark Carreon UER .01 .05
(After All-Star Break
batting 7.14)
30 Gary Carter .02 .10
31 David Cone .02 .10
32 Ron Darling .02 .10
33 Len Dykstra .02 .10
34 Kevin Elster .01 .05
35 Sid Fernandez .01 .05
36 Dwight Gooden .02 .10
37 Keith Hernandez .02 .10
38 Gregg Jefferies .01 .05
39 Howard Johnson .02 .10
40 Terry Leach .01 .05
41 Dave Magadan UER .01 .05
(Bio says 15 doubles,
should be 13)
42 Bob McClure .01 .05
43 Roger McDowell UER .01 .05
(Led Mets with 58,
should be 62)
44 Kevin McReynolds .01 .05
45 Keith A. Miller .01 .05
46 Randy Myers .02 .10
47 Bob Ojeda .01 .05
48 Mackey Sasser .01 .05
49 Darryl Strawberry .02 .10
50 Tim Teufel .01 .05
51 Dave West RC .02 .10
52 Mookie Wilson .02 .10
53 Dave Anderson .01 .05
54 Tim Belcher .01 .05
55 Mike Davis .01 .05
56 Mike Devereaux .01 .05
57 Kirk Gibson .02 .10
58 Alfredo Griffin .01 .05
59 Chris Gwynn .01 .05
60 Jeff Hamilton .01 .05
61A Danny Heep ERR .08 .25
Lake Hills
61B Danny Heep COR .01 .05
San Antonio
62 Orel Hershiser .02 .10
63 Brian Holton .01 .05
64 Jay Howell .01 .05
65 Tim Leary .01 .05
66 Mike Marshall .01 .05
67 Ramon Martinez RC .08 .25
68 Jesse Orosco .01 .05
69 Alejandro Pena .01 .05
70 Steve Sax .01 .05
71 Mike Scioscia .02 .10
72 Mike Sharperson .01 .05
73 John Shelby .01 .05
74 Franklin Stubbs .01 .05
75 John Tudor .02 .10
76 Fernando Valenzuela .02 .10
77 Tracy Woodson .01 .05
78 Marty Barrett .01 .05
79 Todd Benzinger .01 .05
80 Mike Boddicker UER .01 .05
(Rochester in '76,
should be '78)
81 Wade Boggs .05 .15
82 Oil Can Boyd .01 .05
83 Ellis Burks .02 .10
84 Rick Cerone .01 .05
85 Roger Clemens .40 1.00
86 Steve Curry .01 .05
87 Dwight Evans .05 .15
88 Wes Gardner .01 .05
89 Rich Gedman .01 .05
90 Mike Greenwell .01 .05
91 Bruce Hurst .01 .05
92 Dennis Lamp .01 .05
93 Spike Owen .01 .05
94 Larry Parrish UER .01 .05
(Before All-Star Break
batting 1.90)
95 Carlos Quintana RC .02 .10
96 Jody Reed .01 .05
97 Jim Rice .02 .10
98A Kevin Romine ERR .08 .25
(Photo actually
Randy Kutcher batting)
98B Kevin Romine COR .01 .05
(Arms folded)
99 Lee Smith .02 .10
100 Mike Smithson .01 .05
101 Bob Stanley .01 .05
102 Allan Anderson .01 .05
103 Keith Atherton .01 .05
104 Juan Berenguer .01 .05
105 Bert Blyleven .02 .10
106 Eric Bullock UER .01 .05
Bats/Throws Right,
should be Left
107 Randy Bush .01 .05
108 John Christensen .01 .05
109 Mark Davidson .01 .05
110 Gary Gaetti .02 .10
111 Greg Gagne .01 .05
112 Dan Gladden .01 .05
113 German Gonzalez .01 .05
114 Brian Harper .01 .05
115 Tom Herr .01 .05
116 Kent Hrbek .02 .10
117 Gene Larkin .01 .05
118 Tim Laudner .01 .05
119 Charlie Lea .01 .05
120 Steve Lombardozzi .01 .05
121A John Moses ERR .08 .25
Tempe
121B John Moses COR .01 .05
Phoenix
122 Al Newman .01 .05
123 Mark Portugal .01 .05
124 Kirby Puckett .08 .25
125 Jeff Reardon .02 .10
126 Fred Toliver .01 .05
127 Frank Viola .02 .10
128 Doyle Alexander .01 .05
129 Dave Bergman .01 .05
130A Tom Brookens ERR .30 .75
(Mike Heath back)
130B Tom Brookens COR .01 .05
131 Paul Gibson .01 .05
132A Mike Heath ERR .30 .75
(Tom Brookens back)
132B Mike Heath COR .01 .05
133 Don Heinkel .01 .05
134 Mike Henneman .01 .05
135 Guillermo Hernandez .01 .05
136 Eric King .01 .05
137 Chet Lemon .02 .10
138 Fred Lynn UER .02 .10
'74 and '75 stats missing
139 Jack Morris .02 .10
140 Matt Nokes .01 .05
141 Gary Pettis .01 .05
142 Ted Power .01 .05
143 Jeff M. Robinson .01 .05
144 Luis Salazar .01 .05
145 Steve Searcy .01 .05
146 Pat Sheridan .01 .05
147 Frank Tanana .02 .10
148 Alan Trammell .02 .10
149 Walt Terrell .01 .05
150 Jim Walewander .01 .05
151 Lou Whitaker .02 .10
152 Tim Birtsas .01 .05
153 Tom Browning .01 .05
154 Keith Brown .01 .05
155 Norm Charlton RC .08 .25
156 Dave Concepcion .02 .10
157 Kal Daniels .01 .05
158 Eric Davis .02 .10
159 Bo Diaz .01 .05
160 Rob Dibble RC .15 .40
161 Nick Esasky .01 .05
162 John Franco .02 .10
163 Danny Jackson .01 .05
164 Barry Larkin .05 .15
165 Rob Murphy .01 .05
166 Paul O'Neill .05 .15
167 Jeff Reed .01 .05
168 Jose Rijo .02 .10
169 Ron Robinson .01 .05
170 Chris Sabo RC .15 .40
171 Candy Sierra .01 .05
172 Van Snider .01 .05
173A Jeff Treadway 10.00 25.00
(Target registration
mark above head
on front in
light blue)
173B Jeff Treadway .01 .05
(No target on front)
174 Frank Williams UER .01 .05
(After All-Star Break
stats are jumbled)
175 Herm Winningham .01 .05
176 Jim Adduci .01 .05
177 Don August .01 .05
178 Mike Birkbeck .01 .05
179 Chris Bosio .01 .05
180 Glenn Braggs .01 .05
181 Greg Brock .01 .05
182 Mark Clear .01 .05
183 Chuck Crim .01 .05
184 Rob Deer .01 .05
185 Tom Filer .01 .05
186 Jim Gantner .01 .05
187 Darryl Hamilton RC .08 .25
188 Ted Higuera .01 .05
189 Odell Jones .01 .05
190 Jeffrey Leonard .01 .05
191 Joey Meyer .01 .05
192 Paul Mirabella .01 .05
193 Paul Molitor .02 .10
194 Charlie O'Brien .01 .05
195 Dan Plesac .01 .05
196 Gary Sheffield RC .60 1.50
197 B.J. Surhoff .02 .10
198 Dale Sveum .01 .05
199 Bill Wegman .01 .05
200 Robin Yount .15 .40
201 Rafael Belliard .01 .05
202 Barry Bonds .60 1.50
203 Bobby Bonilla .02 .10
204 Sid Bream .01 .05
205 Benny Distefano .01 .05
206 Doug Drabek .01 .05
207 Mike Dunne .01 .05
208 Felix Fermin .01 .05
209 Brian Fisher .01 .05
210 Jim Gott .01 .05
211 Bob Kipper .01 .05
212 Dave LaPoint .01 .05
213 Mike LaValliere .01 .05
214 Jose Lind .01 .05
215 Junior Ortiz .01 .05
216 Vicente Palacios .01 .05
217 Tom Prince .01 .05
218 Gary Redus .01 .05
219 R.J. Reynolds .01 .05
220 Jeff D. Robinson .01 .05
221 John Smiley .01 .05
222 Andy Van Slyke .05 .15
223 Bob Walk .01 .05
224 Glenn Wilson .01 .05

225 Jesse Barfield .02 .10
226 George Bell .02 .10
227 Pat Borders RC .08 .25
228 John Cerutti .01 .05
229 Jim Clancy .01 .05
230 Mark Eichhorn .01 .05
231 Tony Fernandez .01 .05
232 Cecil Fielder .02 .10
233 Mike Flanagan .01 .05
234 Kelly Gruber .01 .05
235 Tom Henke .01 .05
236 Jimmy Key .02 .10
237 Rick Leach .01 .05
238 Manny Lee UER .01 .05
(Bio says regular
shortstop, sic,
Tony Fernandez)
239 Nelson Liriano .01 .05
240 Fred McGriff .05 .15
241 Lloyd Moseby .01 .05
242 Rance Mulliniks .01 .05
243 Jeff Musselman .01 .05
244 Dave Stieb .02 .10
245 Todd Stottlemyre .01 .05
246 Duane Ward .01 .05
247 David Wells .02 .10
248 Ernie Whitt UER .01 .05
(HR total 21,
should be 121)
249 Luis Aguayo .01 .05
250A Neil Allen ERR .30 .75
Sarasota, FL
250B Neil Allen COR .01 .05
Syosset, NY
251 John Candelaria .01 .05
252 Jack Clark .02 .10
253 Richard Dotson .01 .05
254 Rickey Henderson .08 .25
255 Tommy John .02 .10
256 Roberto Kelly .01 .05
257 Al Leiter .08 .25
258 Don Mattingly .25 .60
259 Dale Mohorcic .01 .05
260 Hal Morris RC .08 .25
261 Scott Nielsen .01 .05
262 Mike Pagliarulo UER .01 .05
(Wrong birthdate)
263 Hipolito Pena .01 .05
264 Ken Phelps .01 .05
265 Willie Randolph .02 .10
266 Rick Rhoden .01 .05
267 Dave Righetti .02 .10
268 Rafael Santana .01 .05
269 Steve Shields .01 .05
270 Joel Skinner .01 .05
271 Don Slaught .01 .05
272 Claudell Washington .01 .05
273 Gary Ward .01 .05
274 Dave Winfield .02 .10
275 Luis Aquino .01 .05
276 Floyd Bannister .01 .05
277 George Brett .25 .60
278 Bill Buckner .02 .10
279 Nick Capra .01 .05
280 Jose DeJesus .01 .05
281 Steve Farr .01 .05
282 Jerry Don Gleaton .01 .05
283 Mark Gubicza .01 .05
284 Tom Gordon RC UER .20 .50
(16.2 innings in '88,
should be 15.2)
285 Bo Jackson .08 .25
286 Charlie Leibrandt .01 .05
287 Mike Macfarlane RC .08 .25
288 Jeff Montgomery .01 .05
289 Bill Pecota UER .01 .05
(Photo actually
Brad Wellman)
290 Jamie Quirk .01 .05
291 Bret Saberhagen .02 .10
292 Kevin Seitzer .01 .05
293 Kurt Stillwell .01 .05
294 Pat Tabler .01 .05
295 Danny Tartabull .01 .05
296 Gary Thurman .01 .05
297 Frank White .02 .10
298 Willie Wilson .02 .10
299 Roberto Alomar .08 .25
300 S.Alomar Jr. RC UER .15 .40
Wrong birthdate, says
6/16/66, should say
6/18/66
301 Chris Brown .01 .05
302 Mike Brumley UER .01 .05
(133 hits in '88,
should be 134)
303 Mark Davis .01 .05
304 Mark Grant .01 .05
305 Tony Gwynn .10 .30
306 Greg W. Harris RC .02 .10
307 Andy Hawkins .01 .05
308 Jimmy Jones .01 .05
309 John Kruk .02 .10
310 Dave Leiper .01 .05
311 Carmelo Martinez .01 .05
312 Lance McCullers .01 .05
313 Keith Moreland .01 .05
314 Dennis Rasmussen .01 .05
315 Randy Ready UER .01 .05
(1214 games in '88,
should be 114)
316 Benito Santiago .02 .10
317 Eric Show .01 .05
318 Todd Simmons .01 .05
319 Garry Templeton .02 .10
320 Dickie Thon .01 .05
321 Ed Whitson .01 .05
322 Marvell Wynne .01 .05
323 Mike Aldrete .01 .05
324 Brett Butler .02 .10
325 Will Clark UER .05 .15
(Three consecutive
100 RBI seasons)
326 Kelly Downs UER .01 .05
('88 stats missing)
327 Dave Dravecky .01 .05
328 Scott Garrelts .01 .05
329 Atlee Hammaker .01 .05
330 Charlie Hayes RC .08 .25
331 Mike Krukow .01 .05
332 Craig Lefferts .01 .05
333 Candy Maldonado .01 .05
334 Kirt Manwaring UER .01 .05
(Bats Rights)
335 Bob Melvin .01 .05
336 Kevin Mitchell .02 .10
337 Donell Nixon .01 .05
338 Tony Perezchica .01 .05
339 Joe Price .01 .05
340 Rick Reuschel .02 .10
341 Earnest Riles .01 .05
342 Don Robinson .01 .05
343 Chris Speier .01 .05
344 Robby Thompson UER .01 .05
(West Plam Beach)
345 Jose Uribe .01 .05
346 Matt Williams .08 .25
347 Trevor Wilson RC .02 .10
348 Juan Agosto .01 .05
349 Larry Andersen .01 .05
350A Alan Ashby ERR .75 2.00
(Throws Rig)
350B Alan Ashby COR .01 .05
351 Kevin Bass .01 .05
352 Buddy Bell .02 .10
353 Craig Biggio RC 1.00 2.50
354 Danny Darwin .01 .05
355 Glenn Davis .01 .05
356 Jim Deshaies .01 .05
357 Bill Doran .01 .05
358 John Fishel .01 .05
359 Billy Hatcher .01 .05
360 Bob Knepper .01 .05
361 L.Meadows UER .01 .05
Bio says 10 EBH's
and 6 SB's in '88,
should be 3 and 4
362 Dave Meads .01 .05
363 Jim Pankovits .01 .05
364 Terry Puhl .01 .05
365 Rafael Ramirez .01 .05
366 Craig Reynolds .01 .05
367 Mike Scott .02 .10
(Card number listed
as 368 on Astros CL)
368 Nolan Ryan .40 1.00
(Card number listed
as 367 on Astros CL)
369 Dave Smith .01 .05
370 Gerald Young .01 .05
371 Hubie Brooks .01 .05
372 Tim Burke .01 .05
373 John Dopson .01 .05
374 Mike R. Fitzgerald .01 .05
375 Tom Foley .01 .05
376 Andres Galarraga UER .02 .10
(Home: Caracus)
377 Neal Heaton .01 .05
378 Joe Hesketh .01 .05
379 Brian Holman RC .02 .10
380 Rex Hudler .01 .05
381 R.Johnson RC UER .75 2.00
Innings for '85 and
'86 shown as 27 and
120, should be 27.1
and 119.2
381B R.Johnson Marlboro ERR 10.00 25.00
382 Wallace Johnson .01 .05
383 Tracy Jones .01 .05
384 Dave Martinez .01 .05
385 Dennis Martinez .02 .10
386 Andy McGaffigan .01 .05
387 Otis Nixon .01 .05
388 Johnny Paredes .01 .05
389 Jeff Parrett .01 .05
390 Pascual Perez .01 .05
391 Tim Raines .02 .10
392 Luis Rivera .01 .05
393 Nelson Santovenia .01 .05
394 Bryn Smith .01 .05
395 Tim Wallach .01 .05
396 Andy Allanson UER .01 .05
1214 hits in '88,
should be 114
397 Rod Allen .01 .05
398 Scott Bailes .01 .05
399 Tom Candiotti .01 .05
400 Joe Carter .02 .10
401 Carmen Castillo UER .01 .05
(After All-Star Break
batting 2.50)
402 Dave Clark UER .01 .05
(Card front shows
position as Rookie;
after All-Star Break
batting 3.14)
403 John Farrell UER .01 .05
(Typo in runs
allowed in '88)
404 Julio Franco .02 .10
405 Don Gordon .01 .05
406 Mel Hall .01 .05
407 Brad Havens .01 .05
408 Brook Jacoby .01 .05
409 Doug Jones .01 .05
410 Jeff Kaiser .01 .05
411 Luis Medina .01 .05
412 Cory Snyder .01 .05
413 Greg Swindell .01 .05
414 Ron Tingley UER .01 .05
(Hit HR in first ML
at-bat, should be
first AL at-bat)
415 Willie Upshaw .01 .05
416 Ron Washington .01 .05
417 Rich Yett .01 .05
418 Damon Berryhill .01 .05
419 Mike Bielecki .01 .05
420 Doug Dascenzo .01 .05
421 Jody Davis UER .01 .05
(Braves stats for
'88 missing)
422 Andre Dawson .02 .10
423 Frank DiPino .01 .05
424 Shawon Dunston .01 .05
425 Rich Gossage .02 .10
426 Mark Grace UER .08 .25
(Minor League stats
for '88 missing)
427 Mike Harkey RC .02 .10
428 Darrin Jackson .02 .10
429 Les Lancaster .01 .05
430 Vance Law .01 .05
431 Greg Maddux .20 .50
432 Jamie Moyer .02 .10
433 Al Nipper .01 .05
434 Rafael Palmeiro UER .08 .25
170 hits in '88,
should be 178
435 Pat Perry .01 .05
436 Jeff Pico .01 .05
437 Ryne Sandberg .15 .40
438 Calvin Schiraldi .01 .05
439 Rick Sutcliffe .02 .10
440A Manny Trillo ERR .75 2.00
(Throws Rig)
440B Manny Trillo COR .01 .05
441 Gary Varsho UER .01 .05
(Wrong birthdate;
.303 should be .302;
11/28 should be 9/19)
442 Mitch Webster .01 .05
443 Luis Alicea RC .08 .25
444 Tom Brunansky .01 .05
445 Vince Coleman UER .01 .05
Third straight with 83
should be fourth straight with 81
446 John Costello UER .01 .05
(Home California,
should be New York)
447 Danny Cox .01 .05
448 Ken Dayley .01 .05
449 Jose DeLeon .01 .05
450 Curt Ford .01 .05
451 Pedro Guerrero .02 .10
452 Bob Horner .02 .10
453 Tim Jones .01 .05
454 Steve Lake .01 .05
455 Joe Magrane UER .01 .05
(Des Moines,IO)
456 Greg Mathews .01 .05
457 Willie McGee .02 .10
458 Larry McWilliams .01 .05
459 Jose Oquendo .01 .05
460 Tony Pena .01 .05
461 Terry Pendleton .02 .10
462 Steve Peters UER .01 .05
(Lives in Harrah,
not Harah)
463 Ozzie Smith .15 .40
464 Scott Terry .01 .05
465 Denny Walling .01 .05
466 Todd Worrell .01 .05
467 Tony Armas UER .02 .10
(Before All-Star Break
batting 2.39)
468 Dante Bichette RC .15 .40
469 Bob Boone .02 .10
470 Terry Clark .01 .05
471 Stu Cliburn .01 .05
472 Mike Cook UER .01 .05
(TM near Angels logo
missing from front)
473 Sherman Corbett .01 .05
474 Chili Davis .02 .10
475 Brian Downing .02 .10
476 Jim Eppard .01 .05
477 Chuck Finley .02 .10
478 Willie Fraser .01 .05
479 Bryan Harvey UER RC .08 .25
ML record shows 0-0,
should be 7-5
480 Jack Howell .01 .05
481 Wally Joyner UER .02 .10
(Yorba Linda, GA)
482 Jack Lazorko .01 .05
483 Kirk McCaskill .01 .05
484 Mark McLemore .01 .05
485 Greg Minton .01 .05
486 Dan Petry .01 .05
487 Johnny Ray .01 .05
488 Dick Schofield .01 .05
489 Devon White .02 .10
490 Mike Witt .01 .05
491 Harold Baines .02 .10
492 Daryl Boston .01 .05
493 Ivan Calderon UER .01 .05
('80 stats shifted)
494 Mike Diaz .01 .05
495 Carlton Fisk .05 .15
496 Dave Gallagher .01 .05
497 Ozzie Guillen .02 .10
498 Shawn Hillegas .01 .05
499 Lance Johnson .01 .05
500 Barry Jones .01 .05
501 Bill Long .01 .05
502 Steve Lyons .01 .05
503 Fred Manrique .01 .05
504 Jack McDowell .02 .10
505 Donn Pall .01 .05
506 Kelly Paris .01 .05
507 Dan Pasqua .01 .05
508 Ken Patterson .01 .05
509 Melido Perez .01 .05
510 Jerry Reuss .01 .05
511 Mark Salas .01 .05
512 Bobby Thigpen UER .01 .05
('86 ERA 4.69,
should be 4.68)
513 Mike Woodard .01 .05
514 Bob Brower .01 .05
515 Steve Buechele .01 .05
516 Jose Cecena .01 .05
517 Cecil Espy .01 .05
518 Scott Fletcher .01 .05
519 Cecilio Guante .01 .05
('87 Yankee stats
are off-centered)
520 Jose Guzman .01 .05
521 Ray Hayward .01 .05
522 Charlie Hough .02 .10
523 Pete Incaviglia .01 .05
524 Mike Jeffcoat .01 .05
525 Paul Kilgus .01 .05
526 Chad Kreuter RC .08 .25
527 Jeff Kunkel .01 .05
528 Oddibe McDowell .01 .05
529 Pete O'Brien .01 .05
530 Geno Petralli .01 .05
531 Jeff Russell .01 .05
532 Ruben Sierra .02 .10
533 Mike Stanley .02 .10
534A Ed VandeBerg ERR .75 2.00
(Throws Lef)
534B Ed VandeBerg COR .01 .05
535 Curtis Wilkerson ERR .01 .05
(Pitcher headings
at bottom)
536 Mitch Williams .01 .05
537 Bobby Witt UER .01 .05
('85 ERA .643,
should be 6.43)
538 Steve Balboni .01 .05
539 Scott Bankhead .01 .05
540 Scott Bradley .01 .05
541 Mickey Brantley .01 .05
542 Jay Buhner .02 .10
543 Mike Campbell .01 .05
544 Darnell Coles .01 .05
545 Henry Cotto .01 .05
546 Alvin Davis .01 .05
547 Mario Diaz .01 .05
548 Ken Griffey Jr. RC 4.00 10.00
549 Erik Hanson RC .08 .25
550 Mike Jackson UER .01 .05
(Lifetime ERA 3.345,
should be 3.45)
551 Mark Langston .01 .05
552 Edgar Martinez .08 .25
553 Bill McGuire .01 .05
554 Mike Moore .01 .05
555 Jim Presley .01 .05
556 Rey Quinones .01 .05
557 Jerry Reed .01 .05
558 Harold Reynolds .02 .10
559 Mike Schooler .01 .05
560 Bill Swift .01 .05
561 Dave Valle .01 .05
562 Steve Bedrosian .01 .05
563 Phil Bradley .01 .05
564 Don Carman .01 .05
565 Bob Dernier .01 .05
566 Marvin Freeman .01 .05
567 Todd Frohwirth .01 .05
568 Greg Gross .01 .05
569 Kevin Gross .01 .05
570 Greg A. Harris .01 .05
571 Von Hayes .01 .05
572 Chris James .01 .05
573 Steve Jeltz .01 .05
574 Ron Jones UER .02 .10
(Led IL in '88 with
85, should be 75)
575 Ricky Jordan RC .08 .25
576 Mike Maddux .01 .05
577 David Palmer .01 .05
578 Lance Parrish .02 .10
579 Shane Rawley .01 .05
580 Bruce Ruffin .01 .05
581 Juan Samuel .01 .05
582 Mike Schmidt .20 .50
583 Kent Tekulve .01 .05
584 Milt Thompson UER .01 .05
(19 hits in '88,
should be 109)
585 Jose Alvarez RC .02 .10
586 Paul Assenmacher .01 .05
587 Bruce Benedict .01 .05
588 Jeff Blauser .01 .05
589 Terry Blocker .01 .05
590 Ron Gant .02 .10
591 Tom Glavine .08 .25
592 Tommy Gregg .01 .05
593 Albert Hall .01 .05
594 Dion James .01 .05
595 Rick Mahler .01 .05
596 Dale Murphy .05 .15
597 Gerald Perry .01 .05
598 Charlie Puleo .01 .05
599 Ted Simmons .02 .10
600 Pete Smith .01 .05
601 Zane Smith .01 .05
602 John Smoltz RC .60 1.50
603 Bruce Sutter .02 .10
604 Andres Thomas .01 .05
605 Ozzie Virgil .01 .05
606 Brady Anderson RC .15 .40
607 Jeff Ballard .01 .05
608 Jose Bautista RC .02 .10
609 Ken Gerhart .01 .05
610 Terry Kennedy .01 .05
611 Eddie Murray .08 .25
612 Carl Nichols UER .01 .05
(Before All-Star Break
batting 1.88)
613 Tom Niedenfuer .01 .05
614 Joe Orsulak .01 .05
615 Oswald Peraza UER .01 .05
(Shown as Oswaldo)
616A Bill Ripken ERR 6.00 15.00
(Rick Face written
on knob of bat)
616B Bill Ripken 60.00 120.00
(Bat knob
whited out)
616C Bill Ripken 10.00 25.00
(Words on bat knob
scribbled out in White)
616D Bill Ripken 6.00 15.00
Words on Bat
covered by black scribble
616E Bill Ripken DP 2.00 5.00
(Black box covering
bat knob)
617 Cal Ripken .30 .75
618 Dave Schmidt .01 .05
619 Rick Schu .01 .05
620 Larry Sheets .01 .05
621 Doug Sisk .01 .05
622 Pete Stanicek .01 .05
623 Mickey Tettleton .01 .05
624 Jay Tibbs .01 .05
625 Jim Traber .01 .05
626 Mark Williamson .01 .05
627 Craig Worthington .01 .05
628 Jose Canseco 40/40 .08 .25
629 Tom Browning Perfect .01 .05
630 Roberto Alomar .08 .25
Sandy Alomar Jr. UER
(Names on card listed
in wrong order)
631 Will Clark .05 .15
Rafael Palmeiro UER
(Gallaraga, sic;
Clark 3 consecutive
100 RBI seasons;
third with 102 RBI's)
632 Darryl Strawberry .02 .10
Will Clark UER (Homeruns
should be two words)
633 Wade Boggs .02 .10
Carney Lansford UER
(Boggs hit .366 in
'86, should be '88)
634 Jose Canseco .30 .75
Terry Steinbach
Mark McGwire
635 Mark Davis .01 .05
Dwight Gooden
636 Danny Jackson .01 .05
David Cone UER
Hersheiser, sic
637 Chris Sabo .02 .10
Bobby Bonilla UER
Bobby Bonds, sic
638 Andres Galarraga UER .01 .05
(Misspelled Gallaraga
on card back)
Gerald Perry
639 Kirby Puckett .05 .15
Eric Davis
640 Steve Wilson .01 .05
Cameron Drew
641 Kevin Brown .08 .25
Kevin Reimer
642 Brad Pounders RC .02 .10
Jerald Clark
643 Mike Capel .01 .05
Drew Hall
644 Joe Girardi RC .15 .40
Rolando Roomes
645 Lenny Harris RC .08 .25
Marty Brown
646 Luis De Los Santos .01 .05
Jim Campbell
647 Randy Kramer .01 .05
Miguel Garcia
648 Torey Lovullo RC .02 .10
Robert Palacios
649 Jim Corsi .01 .05
Bob Milacki
650 Grady Hall .01 .05
Mike Rochford
651 Terry Taylor RC .02 .10
Vance Lovelace
652 Ken Hill RC .08 .25
Dennis Cook
653 Scott Service .01 .05
Shane Turner
654 CL: Oakland/Mets .01 .05
Dodgers/Red Sox
(10 Henderson;
68 Jess Orosco)
655A CL: Twins/Tigers ERR .01 .05
Reds/Brewers
(179 Boslo and
Twins/Tigers positions
listed)
655B CL: Twins/Tigers COR .01 .05
Reds/Brewers
(179 Boslo but
Twins/Tigers positions
not listed)
656 CL: Pirates/Blue Jays .01 .05
Yankees/Royals
(225 Jess Barfield)
657 CL: Padres/Giants .01 .05
Astros/Expos
(367/368 wrong)
658 CL: Indians/Cubs .01 .05
Cardinals/Angels
(449 Deleon)
659 CL: White Sox/Rangers .01 .05
Mariners/Phillies
660 CL: Braves/Orioles .01 .05
Specials/Checklists
(632 hyphenated diff-
erently and 650 Hali;
595 Rich Mahler;
619 Rich Schu)

1989 Fleer Glossy

This 660 card set turned out to be the final parallel glossy issue for Fleer. These cards are identical to the regular Fleer cards except for the glossy sheen on the front. As many dealers did not order this product, this set is considerably scarcer than the regular 1989 Fleer set and the preceding years of Glossy parallels. Unlike the previous two seasons, the update set was not issued in Glossy form. It is estimated that Fleer made approximately 30,000 of these sets. The Ken Griffey Jr. card from this set is regarded as one of the most important early parallels in hobby history and is more often than not found with poor centering.

COMP.FACT.SET (672) 50.00 100.00
*STARS: 2X TO 5X BASIC CARDS
*ROOKIES: 2X TO 5X BASIC CARDS

1989 Fleer Update

The 1989 Fleer Update set contains 132 standard-size cards. The cards were distributed exclusively in factory set form in grey and white, cellophane wrapped boxes through hobby dealers. The cards are identical in design to regular issue 1989 Fleer cards except for the U-prefixed numbering on back. The set numbering is in team order with players within teams ordered alphabetically. The set includes special cards for Nolan Ryan's 5,000th strikeout and Mike Schmidt's retirement. Rookie

Cards include Kevin Appier, Joey (Albert) Belle, Deion Sanders, Greg Vaughn, Robin Ventura and Todd Zeile.

COMP.FACT.SET (132) 2.00 5.00
1 Phil Bradley .01 .05
2 Mike Devereaux .01 .05
3 Steve Finley RC .30 .75
4 Kevin Hickey .01 .05
5 Brian Holton .01 .05
6 Bob Milacki .01 .05
7 Randy Milligan .01 .05
8 John Dopson .01 .05
9 Nick Esasky .01 .05
10 Rob Murphy .01 .05
11 Jim Abbott RC .40 1.00
12 Bert Blyleven .02 .10
13 Jeff Manto RC .02 .10
14 Bob McClure .01 .05
15 Lance Parrish .02 .10
16 Lee Stevens RC .08 .25
17 Claudell Washington .01 .05
18 Mark Davis RC .08 .25
19 Eric King .01 .05
20 Ron Kittle .01 .05
21 Matt Merullo .01 .05
22 Steve Rosenberg .01 .05
23 Robin Ventura RC .30 .75
24 Keith Atherton .01 .05
25 Joey Belle RC .40 1.00
26 Jerry Browne .01 .05
27 Felix Fermin .01 .05
28 Brad Komminsk .01 .05
29 Pete O'Brien .01 .05
30 Mike Brumley .01 .05
31 Tracy Jones .01 .05
32 Mike Schwabe .01 .05
33 Gary Ward .01 .05
34 Frank Williams .01 .05
35 Kevin Appier RC .20 .50
36 Bob Boone .02 .10
37 Luis DeLosSantos .01 .05
38 Jim Eisenreich .01 .05
39 Jaime Navarro RC .02 .10
40 Bill Spiers RC .08 .25
41 Greg Vaughn RC .15 .40
42 Randy Veres .01 .05
43 Wally Backman .01 .05
44 Shane Rawley .01 .05
45 Steve Balboni .01 .05
46 Jesse Barfield .02 .10
47 Alvaro Espinoza .01 .05
48 Bob Geren RC .01 .05
49 Mel Hall .01 .05
50 Andy Hawkins .01 .05
51 Hensley Meulens RC .02 .10
52 Steve Sax .01 .05
53 Deion Sanders RC .60 1.50
54 Rickey Henderson .08 .25
55 Mike Moore .01 .05
56 Tony Phillips .01 .05
57 Greg Briley .02 .10
58 Gene Harris RC .02 .10
59 Randy Johnson 1.00 2.50
60 Jeffrey Leonard .01 .05
61 Dennis Powell .01 .05
62 Omar Vizquel RC .40 1.00
63 Kevin Brown .08 .25
64 Julio Franco .02 .10
65 Jamie Moyer .02 .10
66 Rafael Palmeiro .08 .25
67 Nolan Ryan .60 1.50
68 Francisco Cabrera RC .02 .10
69 Junior Felix RC .02 .10
70 Al Leiter .08 .25
71 Alex Sanchez RC .01 .05
72 Geronimo Berroa .01 .05
73 Derek Lilliquist RC .02 .10
74 Lonnie Smith .01 .05
75 Jeff Treadway .01 .05
76 Paul Kilgus .01 .05
77 Lloyd McClendon .01 .05
78 Scott Sanderson .01 .05
79 Dwight Smith RC .08 .25
80 Jerome Walton RC .08 .25
81 Mitch Williams .01 .05
82 Steve Wilson .01 .05
83 Todd Benzinger .01 .05
84 Ken Griffey Sr. .02 .10
85 Rick Mahler .01 .05
86 Rolando Roomes .01 .05
87 Scott Scudder RC .02 .10
88 Jim Clancy .01 .05
89 Rick Rhoden .01 .05
90 Dan Schatzeder .01 .05
91 Mike Morgan .01 .05
92 Eddie Murray .08 .25
93 Willie Randolph .02 .10
94 Ray Searage .01 .05
95 Mike Aldrete .01 .05
96 Kevin Gross .01 .05
97 Mark Langston .01 .05
98 Spike Owen .01 .05
99 Zane Smith .01 .05
100 Don Aase .01 .05
101 Barry Lyons .01 .05
102 Juan Samuel .01 .05
103 Wally Whitehurst RC .02 .10
104 Dennis Cook .01 .05
105 Len Dykstra .02 .10
106 Charlie Hayes .08 .25
107 Tommy Herr .01 .05
108 Ken Howell .01 .05
109 John Kruk .02 .10
110 Roger McDowell .01 .05
111 Terry Mulholland .01 .05
112 Jeff Parrett .01 .05
113 Neal Heaton .01 .05

114 Jeff King .01 .05
115 Randy Kramer .01 .05
116 Bill Landrum .01 .05
117 Cris Carpenter RC .02 .10
118 Frank DiPino .01 .05
119 Ken Hill .08 .25
120 Dan Quisenberry .01 .05
121 Milt Thompson .01 .05
122 Todd Zeile RC .15 .40
123 Jack Clark .02 .10
124 Bruce Hurst .01 .05
125 Mark Parent .01 .05
126 Bip Roberts .01 .05
127 Jeff Brantley RC UER .08 .25
(Photo actually Joe Kmak)
128 Terry Kennedy .01 .05
129 Mike LaCoss .01 .05
130 Greg Litton .01 .05
131 Mike Schmidt .30 .75
132 Checklist 1-132 .01 .05

1990 Fleer

The 1990 Fleer set contains 660 standard-size cards. Cards were primarily issued in wax packs, cello packs, rack packs and hobby and retail factory sets. Card fronts feature white outer borders with ribbon-like, colored inner borders. The set is again ordered numerically by teams based upon the previous season's record. Subsets include Decade Greats (621-630), Superstar Combinations (631-639), Rookie Prospects (640-653) and checklists (654-660). Rookie Cards of note include Moises Alou, Juan Gonzalez, David Justice, Sammy Sosa and Larry Walker.

COMPLETE SET (660) 6.00 15.00
COMP.RETAIL SET (660) 6.00 15.00
COMP.HOBBY SET (672) 6.00 15.00
1 Lance Blankenship .01 .05
2 Todd Burns .01 .05
3 Jose Canseco .05 .15
4 Jim Corsi .01 .05
5 Storm Davis .01 .05
6 Dennis Eckersley .02 .10
7 Mike Gallego .01 .05
8 Ron Hassey .01 .05
9 Dave Henderson .01 .05
10 Rickey Henderson .08 .25
11 Rick Honeycutt .01 .05
12 Stan Javier .01 .05
13 Felix Jose .01 .05
14 Carney Lansford .02 .10
15 Mark McGwire UER .40 1.00
(1989 runs listed as 4, should be 74)
16 Mike Moore .01 .05
17 Gene Nelson .01 .05
18 Dave Parker .02 .10
19 Tony Phillips .01 .05
20 Terry Steinbach .01 .05
21 Dave Stewart .02 .10
22 Walt Weiss .01 .05
23 Bob Welch .01 .05
24 Curt Young .01 .05
25 Paul Assenmacher .01 .05
26 Damon Berryhill .01 .05
27 Mike Bielecki .01 .05
28 Kevin Blankenship .01 .05
29 Andre Dawson .02 .10
30 Shawon Dunston .01 .05
31 Joe Girardi .05 .15
32 Mark Grace .05 .15
33 Mike Harkey .01 .05
34 Paul Kilgus .01 .05
35 Les Lancaster .01 .05
36 Vance Law .01 .05
37 Greg Maddux .15 .40
38 Lloyd McClendon .01 .05
39 Jeff Pico .01 .05
40 Ryne Sandberg .15 .40
41 Scott Sanderson .01 .05
42 Dwight Smith .01 .05
43 Rick Sutcliffe .02 .10
44 Jerome Walton .01 .05
45 Mitch Webster .01 .05
46 Curt Wilkerson .01 .05
47 Dean Wilkins RC .01 .05
48 Mitch Williams .01 .05
49 Steve Wilson .01 .05
50 Steve Bedrosian .01 .05
51 Mike Benjamin RC .02 .10
52 Jeff Brantley .01 .05
53 Brett Butler .02 .10
54 Will Clark UER .02 .10
(Did You Know says first in runs, should say tied for first)
55 Kelly Downs .01 .05
56 Scott Garrelts .01 .05
57 Atlee Hammaker .01 .05
58 Terry Kennedy .01 .05
59 Mike LaCoss .01 .05
60 Craig Lefferts .01 .05
61 Greg Litton .01 .05
62 Candy Maldonado .01 .05
63 Kirt Manwaring UER .01 .05
(No '88 Phoenix stats as noted in box)
64 Randy McCament RC .01 .05
65 Kevin Mitchell .01 .05
66 Donell Nixon .01 .05
67 Ken Oberkfell .01 .05
68 Rick Reuschel .01 .05
69 Ernest Riles .01 .05
70 Don Robinson .01 .05
71 Pat Sheridan .01 .05
72 Chris Speier .01 .05
73 Robby Thompson .01 .05
74 Jose Uribe .01 .05
75 Matt Williams .02 .10
76 George Bell .01 .05
77 Pat Borders .01 .05
78 John Cerutti .01 .05
79 Junior Felix .01 .05
80 Tony Fernandez .01 .05
81 Mike Flanagan .01 .05
82 Mauro Gozzo RC .01 .05
83 Kelly Gruber .01 .05
84 Tom Henke .01 .05
85 Jimmy Key .02 .10
86 Manny Lee .01 .05
87 Nelson Liriano UER .01 .05
(Should say led the IL instead of led the TL)
88 Lee Mazzilli .01 .05
89 Fred McGriff .08 .25
90 Lloyd Moseby .01 .05
91 Rance Mulliniks .01 .05
92 Alex Sanchez .01 .05
93 Dave Stieb .02 .10
94 Todd Stottlemyre .02 .10
95 Duane Ward UER .01 .05
(Double line of '87 Syracuse stats)
96 David Wells .02 .10
97 Ernie Whitt .01 .05
98 Frank Wills .01 .05
99 Mookie Wilson .02 .10
100 Kevin Appier .02 .10
101 Luis Aquino .01 .05
102 Bob Boone .02 .10
103 George Brett .25 .60
104 Jose DeJesus .01 .05
105 Luis De Los Santos .01 .05
106 Jim Eisenreich .01 .05
107 Steve Farr .01 .05
108 Tom Gordon .02 .10
109 Mark Gubicza .01 .05
110 Bo Jackson .08 .25
111 Terry Leach .01 .05
112 Charlie Leibrandt .01 .05
113 Rick Luecken RC .01 .05
114 Mike Macfarlane .01 .05
115 Jeff Montgomery .02 .10
116 Bret Saberhagen .02 .10
117 Kevin Seitzer .01 .05
118 Kurt Stillwell .01 .05
119 Pat Tabler .01 .05
120 Danny Tartabull .01 .05
121 Gary Thurman .01 .05
122 Frank White .02 .10
123 Willie Wilson .01 .05
124 Matt Winters RC .01 .05
125 Jim Abbott .05 .15
126 Tony Armas .01 .05
127 Dante Bichette .02 .10
128 Bert Blyleven .02 .10
129 Chili Davis .02 .10
130 Brian Downing .01 .05
131 Mike Fetters RC .08 .25
132 Chuck Finley .02 .10
133 Willie Fraser .01 .05
134 Bryan Harvey .01 .05
135 Jack Howell .01 .05
136 Wally Joyner .02 .10
137 Jeff Manto .01 .05
138 Kirk McCaskill .01 .05
139 Bob McClure .01 .05
140 Greg Minton .01 .05
141 Lance Parrish .01 .05
142 Dan Petry .01 .05
143 Johnny Ray .01 .05
144 Dick Schofield .01 .05
145 Lee Stevens .02 .10
146 Claudell Washington .01 .05
147 Devon White .02 .10
148 Mike Witt .01 .05
149 Roberto Alomar .05 .15
150 Sandy Alomar Jr. .02 .10
151 Andy Benes .02 .10
152 Jack Clark .02 .10
153 Pat Clements .01 .05
154 Joey Cora .02 .10
155 Mark Davis .01 .05
156 Mark Grant .01 .05
157 Tony Gwynn .10 .30
158 Greg W. Harris .01 .05
159 Bruce Hurst .01 .05
160 Darrin Jackson .01 .05
161 Chris James .01 .05
162 Carmelo Martinez .01 .05
163 Mike Pagliarulo .01 .05
164 Mark Parent .01 .05
165 Dennis Rasmussen .01 .05
166 Bip Roberts .01 .05
167 Benito Santiago .02 .10
168 Calvin Schiraldi .01 .05
169 Eric Show .01 .05
170 Garry Templeton .01 .05
171 Ed Whitson .01 .05
172 Brady Anderson .02 .10
173 Jeff Ballard .01 .05
174 Phil Bradley .01 .05
175 Mike Devereaux .01 .05
176 Steve Finley .02 .10
177 Pete Harnisch .01 .05
178 Kevin Hickey .01 .05
179 Brian Holton .01 .05
180 Ben McDonald RC .08 .25
181 Bob Melvin .01 .05
182 Bob Milacki .01 .05
183 Randy Milligan UER .01 .05
(Double line of '87 stats)
184 Gregg Olson .02 .10
185 Joe Orsulak .01 .05
186 Bill Ripken .01 .05
187 Cal Ripken .30 .75
188 Dave Schmidt .01 .05
189 Larry Sheets .01 .05
190 Mickey Tettleton .01 .05
191 Mark Thurmond .01 .05
192 Jay Tibbs .01 .05
193 Jim Traber .01 .05
194 Mark Williamson .01 .05
195 Craig Worthington .01 .05
196 Don Aase .01 .05
197 Blaine Beatty RC .01 .05
198 Mark Carreon .01 .05
199 Gary Carter .02 .10
200 David Cone .02 .10
201 Ron Darling .01 .05
202 Kevin Elster .01 .05
203 Sid Fernandez .01 .05
204 Dwight Gooden .02 .10
205 Keith Hernandez .02 .10
206 Jeff Innis RC .01 .05
207 Gregg Jefferies .02 .10
208 Howard Johnson .01 .05
209 Barry Lyons UER .01 .05
(Double line of '87 stats)
210 Dave Magadan .01 .05
211 Kevin McReynolds .01 .05
212 Jeff Musselman .01 .05
213 Randy Myers .02 .10
214 Bob Ojeda .01 .05
215 Juan Samuel .01 .05
216 Mackey Sasser .01 .05
217 Darryl Strawberry .02 .10
218 Tim Teufel .01 .05
219 Frank Viola .01 .05
220 Juan Agosto .01 .05
221 Larry Andersen .01 .05
222 Eric Anthony RC .02 .10
223 Kevin Bass .01 .05
224 Craig Biggio .08 .25
225 Ken Caminiti .02 .10
226 Jim Clancy .01 .05
227 Danny Darwin .01 .05
228 Glenn Davis .01 .05
229 Jim Deshaies .01 .05
230 Bill Doran .01 .05
231 Bob Forsch .01 .05
232 Brian Meyer .01 .05
233 Terry Puhl .01 .05
234 Rafael Ramirez .01 .05
235 Rick Rhoden .01 .05
236 Dan Schatzeder .01 .05
237 Mike Scott .01 .05
238 Dave Smith .01 .05
239 Alex Trevino .01 .05
240 Glenn Wilson .01 .05
241 Gerald Young .01 .05
242 Tom Brunansky .01 .05
243 Cris Carpenter .01 .05
244 Alex Cole RC .02 .10
245 Vince Coleman .01 .05
246 John Costello .01 .05
247 Ken Dayley .01 .05
248 Jose DeLeon .01 .05
249 Frank DiPino .01 .05
250 Pedro Guerrero .01 .05
251 Ken Hill .02 .10
252 Joe Magrane .01 .05
253 Willie McGee UER .02 .10
(No decimal point before 353)
254 John Morris .01 .05
255 Jose Oquendo .01 .05
256 Tony Pena .01 .05
257 Terry Pendleton .02 .10
258 Ted Power .01 .05
259 Dan Quisenberry .01 .05
260 Ozzie Smith .15 .40
261 Scott Terry .01 .05
262 Milt Thompson .01 .05
263 Denny Walling .01 .05
264 Todd Worrell .01 .05
265 Todd Zeile .02 .10
266 Marty Barrett .01 .05
267 Mike Boddicker .01 .05
268 Wade Boggs .05 .15
269 Ellis Burks .05 .15
270 Rick Cerone .01 .05
271 Roger Clemens .40 1.00
272 John Dopson .01 .05
273 Nick Esasky .01 .05
274 Dwight Evans .05 .15
275 Wes Gardner .01 .05
276 Rich Gedman .01 .05
277 Mike Greenwell .01 .05
278 Danny Heep .01 .05
279 Eric Hetzel .01 .05
280 Dennis Lamp .01 .05
281 Rob Murphy UER .01 .05
('89 stats say Reds, should say Red Sox)
282 Joe Price .01 .05
283 Carlos Quintana .01 .05
284 Jody Reed .01 .05
285 Luis Rivera .01 .05
286 Kevin Romine .01 .05
287 Lee Smith .02 .10
288 Mike Smithson .01 .05
289 Bob Stanley .01 .05
290 Harold Baines .02 .10
291 Kevin Brown .02 .10
292 Steve Buechele .01 .05
293 Scott Coolbaugh RC .01 .05
294 Jack Daugherty RC .01 .05
295 Cecil Espy .01 .05
296 Julio Franco .02 .10
297 Juan Gonzalez RC .40 1.00
298 Cecilio Guante .01 .05
299 Drew Hall .01 .05
300 Charlie Hough .02 .10
301 Pete Incaviglia .01 .05
302 Mike Jeffcoat .01 .05
303 Chad Kreuter .01 .05
304 Jeff Kunkel .01 .05
305 Rick Leach .01 .05
306 Fred Manrique .01 .05
307 Jamie Moyer .02 .10
308 Rafael Palmeiro .05 .15
309 Geno Petralli .01 .05
310 Kevin Reimer .01 .05
311 Kenny Rogers .02 .10
312 Jeff Russell .01 .05
313 Nolan Ryan .40 1.00
314 Ruben Sierra .02 .10
315 Bobby Witt .01 .05
316 Chris Bosio .01 .05
317 Glenn Braggs UER .01 .05
(Stats say 111 K's, but bio says 117 K's)
318 Greg Brock .01 .05
319 Chuck Crim .01 .05
320 Rob Deer .01 .05
321 Mike Felder .01 .05
322 Tom Filer .01 .05
323 Tony Fossas RC .01 .05
324 Jim Gantner .01 .05
325 Darryl Hamilton .01 .05
326 Teddy Higuera .01 .05
327 Mark Knudson .01 .05
328 Bill Krueger UER .01 .05
('86 stats missing)
329 Tim McIntosh RC .02 .10
330 Paul Molitor .02 .10
331 Jaime Navarro .01 .05
332 Charlie O'Brien .01 .05
333 Jeff Peterek RC .01 .05
334 Dan Plesac .01 .05
335 Jerry Reuss .01 .05
336 Gary Sheffield UER .08 .25
337 Bill Spiers .01 .05
338 B.J. Surhoff .02 .10
339 Greg Vaughn .01 .05
340 Robin Yount .15 .40
341 Hubie Brooks .01 .05
342 Tim Burke .01 .05
343 Mike Fitzgerald .01 .05
344 Tom Foley .01 .05
345 Andres Galarraga .02 .10
346 Damaso Garcia .01 .05
347 Marquis Grissom RC .15 .40
348 Kevin Gross .01 .05
349 Joe Hesketh .01 .05
350 Jeff Huson RC .01 .05
351 Wallace Johnson .01 .05
352 Mark Langston .01 .05
353A Dave Martinez .75 2.00
(Yellow on front)
353B Dave Martinez .01 .05
(Red on front)
354 Dennis Martinez UER .02 .10
('87 ERA is 616, should be 6.16)
355 Andy McGaffigan .01 .05
356 Otis Nixon .01 .05
357 Spike Owen .01 .05
358 Pascual Perez .01 .05
359 Tim Raines .02 .10
360 Nelson Santovenia .01 .05
361 Bryn Smith .01 .05
362 Zane Smith .01 .05
363 Larry Walker RC .40 1.00
364 Tim Wallach .01 .05
365 Rick Aguilera .02 .10
366 Allan Anderson .01 .05
367 Wally Backman .01 .05
368 Doug Baker .01 .05
369 Juan Berenguer .01 .05
370 Randy Bush .01 .05
371 Carmelo Castillo .01 .05
372 Mike Dyer RC .01 .05
373 Gary Gaetti .02 .10
374 Greg Gagne .01 .05
375 Dan Gladden .01 .05
376 G.Gonzalez UER .01 .05
Bio says 31 saves in '88, but stats say 30
377 Brian Harper .01 .05
378 Kent Hrbek .02 .10
379 Gene Larkin .01 .05
380 Tim Laudner UER .01 .05
(No decimal point before '85 BA of 238)
381 John Moses .01 .05
382 Al Newman .01 .05
383 Kirby Puckett .08 .25
384 Shane Rawley .01 .05
385 Jeff Reardon .02 .10
386 Roy Smith .01 .05
387 Gary Wayne .01 .05
388 Dave West .01 .05
389 Tim Belcher .01 .05
390 Tim Crews UER .01 .05
(Stats say 163 IP for '83, but bio says 136)
391 Mike Davis .01 .05
392 Rick Dempsey .01 .05
393 Kirk Gibson .02 .10
394 Jose Gonzalez .01 .05
395 Alfredo Griffin .01 .05
396 Jeff Hamilton .01 .05
397 Lenny Harris .01 .05
398 Mickey Hatcher .01 .05
399 Orel Hershiser .02 .10
400 Jay Howell .01 .05
401 Mike Marshall .01 .05
402 Ramon Martinez .01 .05
403 Mike Morgan .01 .05
404 Eddie Murray .08 .25
405 Alejandro Pena .01 .05
406 Willie Randolph .02 .10
407 Mike Scioscia .01 .05
408 Ray Searage .01 .05
409 Fernando Valenzuela .02 .10
410 Jose Vizcaino RC .08 .25
411 John Wetteland .08 .25
412 Jack Armstrong .01 .05
413 Todd Benzinger UER .01 .05
(Bio says .323 at Pawtucket, but stats say .321)
414 Tim Birtsas .01 .05
415 Tom Browning .01 .05
416 Norm Charlton .01 .05
417 Eric Davis .02 .10
418 Rob Dibble .02 .10
419 John Franco .02 .10
420 Ken Griffey Sr. .02 .10
421 Chris Hammond RC .02 .10
(No 1989 used for Did Not Play stat, actually did play for Nashville in 1989)
422 Danny Jackson .01 .05
423 Barry Larkin .05 .15
424 Tim Leary .01 .05
425 Rick Mahler .01 .05
426 Joe Oliver .01 .05
427 Paul O'Neill .05 .15
428 Luis Quinones UER .01 .05
('86-'88 stats are omitted from card but included in totals)
429 Jeff Reed .01 .05
430 Jose Rijo .01 .05
431 Ron Robinson .01 .05
432 Rolando Roomes .01 .05
433 Chris Sabo .01 .05
434 Scott Scudder .01 .05
435 Herm Winningham .01 .05
436 Steve Balboni .01 .05
437 Jesse Barfield .01 .05
438 Mike Blowers RC .02 .10
439 Tom Brookens .01 .05
440 Greg Cadaret .01 .05
441 Alvaro Espinoza UER .01 .05
(Career games say 218, should be 219)
442 Bob Geren .01 .05
443 Lee Guetterman .01 .05
444 Mel Hall .01 .05
445 Andy Hawkins .01 .05
446 Roberto Kelly .01 .05
447 Don Mattingly .25 .60
448 Lance McCullers .01 .05
449 Hensley Meulens .01 .05
450 Dale Mohorcic .01 .05
451 Clay Parker .01 .05
452 Eric Plunk .01 .05
453 Dave Righetti .01 .05
454 Deion Sanders .08 .25
455 Steve Sax .01 .05
456 Don Slaught .01 .05
457 Walt Terrell .01 .05
458 Dave Winfield .02 .10
459 Jay Bell .02 .10
460 Rafael Belliard .01 .05
461 Barry Bonds .40 1.00
462 Bobby Bonilla .02 .10
463 Sid Bream .01 .05
464 Benny Distefano .01 .05
465 Doug Drabek .01 .05
466 Jim Gott .01 .05
467 Billy Hatcher UER .01 .05
(.1 hits for Cubs in 1984)
468 Neal Heaton .01 .05
469 Jeff King .01 .05
470 Bob Kipper .01 .05
471 Randy Kramer .01 .05
472 Bill Landrum .01 .05
473 Mike LaValliere .01 .05
474 Jose Lind .01 .05
475 Junior Ortiz .01 .05
476 Gary Redus .01 .05
477 Rick Reed RC .08 .25
478 R.J. Reynolds .01 .05
479 Jeff D. Robinson .01 .05
480 John Smiley .01 .05
481 Andy Van Slyke .05 .15
482 Bob Walk .01 .05
483 Andy Allanson .01 .05
484 Scott Bailes .01 .05
485 Joey Belle UER .08 .25
(Has Jay Bell Did You Know)
Later changed his name to Albert
486 Bud Black .01 .05
487 Jerry Browne .01 .05
488 Tom Candiotti .01 .05
489 Joe Carter .02 .10
490 Dave Clark .01 .05
(No '84 stats)
491 John Farrell .01 .05
492 Felix Fermin .01 .05
493 Brook Jacoby .01 .05
494 Dion James .01 .05
495 Doug Jones .01 .05
496 Brad Komminsk .01 .05
497 Rod Nichols .01 .05
498 Pete O'Brien .01 .05
499 Steve Olin RC .02 .10
500 Jesse Orosco .01 .05
501 Joel Skinner .01 .05
502 Cory Snyder .01 .05
503 Greg Swindell .01 .05
504 Rich Yett .01 .05
505 Scott Bankhead .01 .05
506 Scott Bradley .01 .05
507 Greg Briley UER .01 .05
(28 SB's in bio, but 27 in stats)
508 Jay Buhner .02 .10
509 Darnell Coles .01 .05
510 Keith Comstock .01 .05
511 Henry Cotto .01 .05
512 Alvin Davis .01 .05
513 Ken Griffey Jr. .30 .75
514 Erik Hanson .01 .05
515 Gene Harris .01 .05
516 Brian Holman .01 .05
517 Mike Jackson .01 .05
518 Randy Johnson .20 .50
519 Jeffrey Leonard .01 .05
520 Edgar Martinez .05 .15
521 Dennis Powell .01 .05
522 Jim Presley .01 .05
523 Jerry Reed .01 .05
524 Harold Reynolds .02 .10
525 Mike Schooler .01 .05
526 Bill Swift .01 .05
527 Dave Valle .01 .05
528 Omar Vizquel .08 .25
529 Ivan Calderon .01 .05
530 Carlton Fisk UER .05 .15
(Bellow Falls, should be Bellows Falls)
531 Scott Fletcher .01 .05
532 Dave Gallagher .01 .05
533 Ozzie Guillen .02 .10
534 Greg Hibbard RC .02 .10
535 Shawn Hillegas .01 .05
536 Lance Johnson .01 .05
537 Eric King .01 .05
538 Ron Kittle .01 .05
539 Steve Lyons .01 .05
540 Carlos Martinez .01 .05
541 Tom McCarthy .01 .05
542 Matt Merullo .01 .05
(Had 5 ML runs scored entering '90, not 6)
543 Donn Pall UER .01 .05
(Stats say pro career began in '85, bio says '88)
544 Dan Pasqua .01 .05
545 Ken Patterson .01 .05
546 Melido Perez .01 .05
547 Steve Rosenberg .01 .05
548 Sammy Sosa RC 1.00 2.50
549 Bobby Thigpen .01 .05
550 Robin Ventura .08 .25
551 Greg Walker .01 .05
552 Don Carman .01 .05
553 Pat Combs .01 .05
(6 walks for Phillies in '89 in stats, brief bio says 4)
554 Dennis Cook .01 .05
555 Darren Daulton .02 .10
556 Len Dykstra .02 .10
557 Curt Ford .01 .05
558 Charlie Hayes .01 .05
559 Von Hayes .01 .05
560 Tommy Herr .01 .05
561 Ken Howell .01 .05
562 Steve Jeltz .01 .05
563 Ron Jones .01 .05
564 Ricky Jordan UER .01 .05
(Duplicate line of statistics on back)
565 John Kruk .02 .10
566 Steve Lake .01 .05
567 Roger McDowell .01 .05
568 Terry Mulholland UER .01 .05
(Did You Know refers to Dave Magadan)
569 Dwayne Murphy .01 .05
570 Jeff Parrett .01 .05
571 Randy Ready .01 .05
572 Bruce Ruffin .01 .05
573 Dickie Thon .01 .05
574 Jose Alvarez UER .01 .05
('78 and '79 stats are reversed)
575 Geronimo Berroa .01 .05
576 Jeff Blauser .01 .05
577 Joe Boever .01 .05
578 Marty Clary UER .01 .05
(No comma between city and state)
579 Jody Davis .01 .05
580 Mark Eichhorn .01 .05
581 Darrell Evans .02 .10
582 Ron Gant .02 .10
583 Tom Glavine .05 .15
584 Tommy Greene RC .02 .10
585 Tommy Gregg .01 .05
586 Dave Justice RC UER .20 .50
(Actually had 16 2B in Sumter in '86)
587 Mark Lemke .01 .05
588 Derek Lilliquist .01 .05
589 Oddibe McDowell .01 .05
590 Kent Mercker UER RC .01 .05
(Bio says 2.75 ERA, stats say 2.68 ERA)
591 Dale Murphy .05 .15
592 Gerald Perry .01 .05
593 Lonnie Smith .01 .05
594 Pete Smith .01 .05
595 John Smoltz .08 .25
596 Mike Stanton RC UER .08 .25
(No comma between city and state)
597 Andres Thomas .01 .05
598 Jeff Treadway .01 .05
599 Doyle Alexander .01 .05
600 Dave Bergman .01 .05
601 Brian DuBois RC .01 .05
602 Paul Gibson .01 .05
603 Mike Heath .01 .05
604 Mike Henneman .01 .05
605 Guillermo Hernandez .01 .05
606 Shawn Holman RC .01 .05
607 Tracy Jones .01 .05
608 Chet Lemon .01 .05
609 Fred Lynn .01 .05
610 Jack Morris .02 .10
611 Matt Nokes .01 .05
612 Gary Pettis .01 .05
613 Kevin Ritz RC .01 .05
614 Jeff M. Robinson .01 .05
('88 stats are not in line)
615 Steve Searcy .01 .05
616 Frank Tanana .01 .05
617 Alan Trammell .02 .10
618 Gary Ward .01 .05
619 Lou Whitaker .02 .10
620 Frank Williams .01 .05
621A George Brett '80 .75 2.00
ERR (Had 10 .390 hitting seasons)
621B George Brett '80 .10 .30
COR
622 Fern.Valenzuela '81 .01 .05
623 Dale Murphy '82 .05 .15
624A Cal Ripken '83 ERR 2.00 5.00
(Misspelled Ripkin on card back)
624B Cal Ripken '83 COR .15 .40
625 Ryne Sandberg '84 .08 .25
626 Don Mattingly '85 .07 .20
627 Roger Clemens '86 .20 .50
628 George Bell '87 .01 .05
629 J.Canseco '88 UER .02 .10
Reggie won MVP in '83, should say '73
630A Will Clark '89 ERR .40 1.00
(32 total bases on card back)
630B Will Clark '89 COR .05 .15
(321 total bases; technically still an error, listing only 24 runs)
631 Mark Davis .01 .05
Mitch Williams
632 Wade Boggs .02 .10
Mike Greenwell
633 Mark Gubicza .01 .05
Jeff Russell
634 Tony Fernandez .08 .25
Cal Ripken

635 Kirby Puckett .05 .15
Bo Jackson
636 Nolan Ryan .15 .40
Mike Scott
637 Will Clark .02 .10
Kevin Mitchell
638 Don Mattingly .10 .30
Mark McGwire
639 Howard Johnson .08 .25
Ryne Sandberg
640 Rudy Seanez RC .02 .10
Colin Charland RC
641 George Canale RC .08 .25
Kevin Maas RC
642 Kelly Mann RC .08 .25
Dave Hansen RC
643 Greg Smith RC .02 .10
Stu Tate RC
644 Tom Drees RC .02 .10
Dann Howitt RC
645 Mike Roesler RC .02 .10
Derrick May RC
646 Scott Hemond RC .02 .10
Mark Gardner RC
647 John Orton RC .02 .10
Scott Leius RC
648 Rich Monteleone RC .02 .10
Dana Williams RC
649 Mike Huff RC .02 .10
Steve Frey RC
650 Chuck McElroy .30 .75
Moises Alou RC
651 Bobby Rose RC .08 .25
Mike Hartley RC
652 Matt Kinzer RC .02 .10
Wayne Edwards RC
653 Delino DeShields RC .08 .25
Jason Grimsley RC
654 CL: A's/Cubs .01 .05
Giants/Blue Jays
655 CL: Royals/Angels .01 .05
Padres/Orioles
656 CL: Mets/Astros .01 .05
Cards/Red Sox
657 CL: Rangers/Brewers .01 .05
Expos/Twins
658 CL: Dodgers/Reds .01 .05
Yankees/Pirates
659 CL: Indians/Mariners .01 .05
White Sox/Phillies
660A CL: Braves/Tigers .01 .05
Specials/Checklists
(Checklist-660 in smaller print on card front)
660B CL: Braves/Tigers .01 .05
Specials/Checklists
(Checklist-660 in normal print on card front)

1990 Fleer Update

The 1990 Fleer Update set contains 132 standard-size cards. This set marked the seventh consecutive year Fleer issued an end of season Update set. The set was issued exclusively as a boxed set through hobby dealers. The set is checklisted alphabetically by team for each league and then alphabetically within each team. The fronts are styled the same as the 1990 Fleer regular issue set. The backs are numbered with the prefix "U" for Update. Rookie Cards in this set include Travis Fryman, Todd Hundley, John Olerud and Frank Thomas.

COMP.FACT.SET (132) 1.50 4.00
1 Steve Avery .01 .05
2 Francisco Cabrera .01 .05
3 Nick Esasky .01 .05
4 Jim Kremers RC .01 .05
5 Greg Olson (C) RC .02 .10
6 Jim Presley .01 .05
7 Shawn Boskie RC .02 .10
8 Joe Kraemer RC .01 .05
9 Luis Salazar .01 .05
10 Hector Villanueva RC .01 .05
11 Glenn Braggs .01 .05
12 Mariano Duncan .01 .05
13 Billy Hatcher .01 .05
14 Tim Layana RC .01 .05
15 Hal Morris .01 .05
16 Javier Ortiz RC .01 .05
17 Dave Rohde RC .01 .05
18 Eric Yelding RC .01 .05
19 Hubie Brooks .01 .05
20 Kal Daniels .01 .05
21 Dave Hansen RC .01 .05
22 Mike Hartley .01 .05
23 Stan Javier .01 .05
24 Jose Offerman RC .08 .25
25 Juan Samuel .01 .05
26 Dennis Boyd .01 .05
27 Delino DeShields .08 .25
28 Steve Frey .01 .05
29 Mark Gardner .01 .05
30 Chris Nabholz RC .02 .10
31 Bill Sampen RC .01 .05
32 Dave Schmidt .01 .05
33 Daryl Boston .01 .05
34 Chuck Carr RC .02 .10
35 John Franco .02 .10
36 Todd Hundley RC .08 .25
37 Julio Machado RC .01 .05
38 Alejandro Pena .01 .05
39 Darren Reed RC .01 .05
40 Kelvin Torve .01 .05
41 Darrel Akerfelds .01 .05
42 Jose DeJesus .01 .05
43 Dave Hollins UER RC .08 .25
(Misspelled Dane on card back)
44 Carmelo Martinez .01 .05
45 Brad Moore .01 .05
46 Dale Murphy .05 .15
47 Wally Backman .01 .05
48 Stan Belinda RC .02 .10
49 Bob Patterson .01 .05
50 Ted Power .01 .05
51 Don Slaught .01 .05
52 Geronimo Pena RC .02 .10
53 Lee Smith .02 .10
54 John Tudor .01 .05
55 Joe Carter .02 .10
56 Thomas Howard .01 .05
57 Craig Lefferts .01 .05
58 Rafael Valdez RC .01 .05
59 Dave Anderson .01 .05
60 Kevin Bass .01 .05
61 John Burkett .01 .05
62 Gary Carter .02 .10
63 Rick Parker RC .01 .05
64 Trevor Wilson .01 .05
65 Chris Hoiles RC .08 .25
66 Tim Hulett .01 .05
67 Dave Wayne Johnson RC .01 .05
68 Curt Schilling .40 1.00
69 David Segui RC .15 .40
70 Tom Brunansky .01 .05
71 Greg A. Harris .01 .05
72 Dana Kiecker RC .01 .05
73 Tim Naehring RC .02 .10
74 Tony Pena .01 .05
75 Jeff Reardon .02 .10
76 Jerry Reed .01 .05
77 Mark Eichhorn .01 .05
78 Mark Langston .01 .05
79 John Orton .01 .05
80 Luis Polonia .01 .05
81 Dave Winfield .02 .10
82 Cliff Young RC .01 .05
83 Wayne Edwards RC .01 .05
84 Alex Fernandez RC .08 .25
85 Craig Grebeck RC .02 .10
86 Scott Radinsky RC .02 .10
87 Frank Thomas RC .75 2.00
88 Beau Allred RC .01 .05
89 Sandy Alomar Jr. .02 .10
90 Carlos Baerga RC .08 .25
91 Kevin Bearse RC .01 .05
92 Chris James .01 .05
93 Candy Maldonado .01 .05
94 Jeff Manto .01 .05
95 Cecil Fielder .02 .10
96 Travis Fryman RC .15 .40
97 Lloyd Moseby .01 .05
98 Edwin Nunez .01 .05
99 Tony Phillips .01 .05
100 Larry Sheets .01 .05
101 Mark Davis .01 .05
102 Storm Davis .01 .05
103 Gerald Perry .01 .05
104 Terry Shumpert RC .01 .05
105 Edgar Diaz RC .01 .05
106 Dave Parker .02 .10
107 Tim Drummond RC .01 .05
108 Junior Ortiz .01 .05
109 Park Pittman RC .01 .05
110 Kevin Tapani RC .08 .25
111 Oscar Azocar RC .01 .05
112 Jim Leyritz RC .08 .25
113 Kevin Maas .02 .10
114 Alan Mills RC .02 .10
115 Matt Nokes .01 .05
116 Pascual Perez .01 .05
117 Ozzie Canseco .01 .05
118 Scott Sanderson .01 .05
119 Tino Martinez .20 .50
120 Jeff Schaefer RC .01 .05
121 Matt Young .01 .05
122 Brian Bohanon RC .02 .10
123 Jeff Huson .01 .05
124 Ramon Manon RC .01 .05
125 Gary Mielke UER RC .01 .05
(Shown as Blue Jay on front)
126 Willie Blair RC .02 .10
127 Glenallen Hill .01 .05
128 John Olerud RC UER .20 .50
(Listed as throwing right, should be left)
129 Luis Sojo RC .01 .05
130 Mark Whiten RC .08 .25
131 Nolan Ryan .40 1.00
132 Checklist U1-U132 .01 .05

1991 Fleer

The 1991 Fleer set consists of 720 standard-size cards. Cards were primarily issued in wax packs, cello packs and factory sets. This set does not have what had been a Fleer tradition in prior years, the two-player Rookie Cards and there are less two-player special cards than in prior years. The design features bright yellow borders with the information in black indicating name, position, and team. The set is again ordered numerically by teams, followed by combination cards, rookie prospect pairs, and checklists. There are no notable Rookie Cards in this set. A number of the cards in the set can be found with photos cropped (very slightly) differently as Fleer used two separate printers in their attempt to maximize production.

COMPLETE SET (720) 3.00 8.00
COMP.RETAIL SET (732) 4.00 10.00
COMP.HOBBY SET (732) 4.00 10.00
1 Troy Afenir RC .01 .05
2 Harold Baines .02 .10
3 Lance Blankenship .01 .05
4 Todd Burns .01 .05
5 Jose Canseco .05 .15
6 Dennis Eckersley .02 .10
7 Mike Gallego .01 .05
8 Ron Hassey .01 .05
9 Dave Henderson .01 .05
10 Rickey Henderson .08 .25
11 Rick Honeycutt .01 .05
12 Doug Jennings .01 .05
13 Joe Klink .01 .05
14 Carney Lansford .02 .10
15 Darren Lewis .01 .05
16 Willie McGee UER .02 .10
(Height 6'11)
17 Mark McGwire UER .30 .75
(183 extra base hits in 1987)
18 Mike Moore .01 .05
19 Gene Nelson .01 .05
20 Dave Otto .01 .05
21 Jamie Quirk .01 .05
22 Willie Randolph .02 .10
23 Scott Sanderson .01 .05
24 Terry Steinbach .01 .05
25 Dave Stewart .02 .10
26 Walt Weiss .01 .05
27 Bob Welch .01 .05
28 Curt Young .01 .05
29 Wally Backman .01 .05
30 Stan Belinda UER .01 .05
(Born in Huntington, should be State College)
31 Jay Bell .02 .10
32 Rafael Belliard .01 .05
33 Barry Bonds .40 1.00
34 Bobby Bonilla .02 .10
35 Sid Bream .01 .05
36 Doug Drabek .01 .05
37 Carlos Garcia RC .02 .10
38 Neal Heaton .01 .05
39 Jeff King .01 .05
40 Bob Kipper .01 .05
41 Bill Landrum .01 .05
42 Mike LaValliere .01 .05
43 Jose Lind .01 .05
44 Carmelo Martinez .01 .05
45 Bob Patterson .01 .05
46 Ted Power .01 .05
47 Gary Redus .01 .05
48 R.J. Reynolds .01 .05
49 Don Slaught .01 .05
50 John Smiley .01 .05
51 Zane Smith .01 .05
52 Randy Tomlin RC .02 .10
53 Andy Van Slyke .05 .15
54 Bob Walk .01 .05
55 Jack Armstrong .01 .05
56 Todd Benzinger .01 .05
57 Glenn Braggs .01 .05
58 Keith Brown .01 .05
59 Tom Browning .01 .05
60 Norm Charlton .01 .05
61 Eric Davis .02 .10
62 Rob Dibble .02 .10
63 Bill Doran .01 .05
64 Mariano Duncan .01 .05
65 Chris Hammond .01 .05
66 Billy Hatcher .01 .05
67 Danny Jackson .01 .05
68 Barry Larkin .05 .15
69 Tim Layana UER .01 .05
(Black line over made in first text line)
70 Terry Lee RC .01 .05
71 Rick Mahler .01 .05
72 Hal Morris .01 .05
73 Randy Myers .01 .05
74 Ron Oester .01 .05
75 Joe Oliver .01 .05
76 Paul O'Neill .05 .15
77 Luis Quinones .01 .05
78 Jeff Reed .01 .05
79 Jose Rijo .01 .05
80 Chris Sabo .01 .05
81 Scott Scudder .01 .05
82 Herm Winningham .01 .05
83 Larry Andersen .01 .05
84 Marty Barrett .01 .05
85 Mike Boddicker .01 .05
86 Wade Boggs .05 .15
87 Tom Bolton .01 .05
88 Tom Brunansky .01 .05
89 Ellis Burks .02 .10
90 Roger Clemens .30 .75
91 Scott Cooper .01 .05
92 John Dopson .01 .05
93 Dwight Evans .05 .15
94 Wes Gardner .01 .05
95 Jeff Gray RC .01 .05
96 Mike Greenwell .01 .05
97 Greg A. Harris .01 .05
98 Daryl Irvine RC .01 .05
99 Dana Kiecker .01 .05
100 Randy Kutcher .01 .05
101 Dennis Lamp .01 .05
102 Mike Marshall .01 .05
103 John Marzano .01 .05
104 Rob Murphy .01 .05
105 Tim Naehring .01 .05
106 Tony Pena .01 .05
107 Phil Plantier RC .08 .25
108 Carlos Quintana .01 .05
109 Jeff Reardon .02 .10
110 Jerry Reed .01 .05
111 Jody Reed .01 .05
112 Luis Rivera UER .01 .05
(Born 1/3/84)
113 Kevin Romine .01 .05
114 Phil Bradley .01 .05
115 Ivan Calderon .01 .05
116 Wayne Edwards .01 .05
117 Alex Fernandez .01 .05
118 Carlton Fisk .05 .15
119 Scott Fletcher .01 .05
120 Craig Grebeck .01 .05
121 Ozzie Guillen .02 .10
122 Greg Hibbard .01 .05
123 Lance Johnson UER .01 .05
(Born Cincinnati, should be Lincoln Heights)
124 Barry Jones .01 .05
125 Ron Karkovice .01 .05
126 Eric King .01 .05
127 Steve Lyons .01 .05
128 Carlos Martinez .01 .05
129 Jack McDowell UER .01 .05
(Stanford misspelled as Standford on back)
130 Donn Pall .01 .05
(No dots over any i's in text)
131 Dan Pasqua .01 .05
132 Ken Patterson .01 .05
133 Melido Perez .01 .05
134 Adam Peterson .01 .05
135 Scott Radinsky .01 .05
136 Sammy Sosa .08 .25
137 Bobby Thigpen .01 .05
138 Frank Thomas .08 .25
139 Robin Ventura .02 .10
140 Daryl Boston .01 .05
141 Chuck Carr .01 .05
142 Mark Carreon .01 .05
143 David Cone .02 .10
144 Ron Darling .01 .05
145 Kevin Elster .01 .05
146 Sid Fernandez .01 .05
147 John Franco .02 .10
148 Dwight Gooden .02 .10
149 Tom Herr .01 .05
150 Todd Hundley .01 .05
151 Gregg Jefferies .01 .05
152 Howard Johnson .01 .05
153 Dave Magadan .01 .05
154 Kevin McReynolds .01 .05
155 Keith Miller UER .01 .05
(Text says Rochester in '87, stats say Tidewater, mixed up with other Keith Miller)
156 Bob Ojeda .01 .05
157 Tom O'Malley .01 .05
158 Alejandro Pena .01 .05
159 Darren Reed .01 .05
160 Mackey Sasser .01 .05
161 Darryl Strawberry .02 .10
162 Tim Teufel .01 .05
163 Kelvin Torve .01 .05
164 Julio Valera .01 .05
165 Frank Viola .02 .10
166 Wally Whitehurst .01 .05
167 Jim Acker .01 .05
168 Derek Bell .02 .10
169 George Bell .01 .05
170 Willie Blair .01 .05
171 Pat Borders .01 .05
172 John Cerutti .01 .05
173 Junior Felix .01 .05
174 Tony Fernandez .01 .05
175 Kelly Gruber UER .01 .05
(Born in Houston, should be Bellaire)
176 Tom Henke .01 .05
177 Glenallen Hill .01 .05
178 Jimmy Key .02 .10
179 Manny Lee .01 .05
180 Fred McGriff .05 .15
181 Rance Mulliniks .01 .05
182 Greg Myers .01 .05
183 John Olerud UER .02 .10
(Listed as throwing right, should be left)
184 Luis Sojo .01 .05
185 Dave Stieb .01 .05
186 Todd Stottlemyre .01 .05
187 Duane Ward .01 .05
188 David Wells .01 .05
189 Mark Whiten .01 .05
190 Ken Williams .01 .05
191 Frank Wills .01 .05
192 Mookie Wilson .02 .10
193 Don Aase .01 .05
194 Tim Belcher UER .01 .05
(Born Sparta, Ohio, should say Mt. Gilead)
195 Hubie Brooks .01 .05
196 Dennis Cook .01 .05
197 Tim Crews .01 .05
198 Kal Daniels .01 .05
199 Kirk Gibson .02 .10
200 Jim Gott .01 .05
201 Alfredo Griffin .01 .05
202 Chris Gwynn .01 .05
203 Dave Hansen .01 .05
204 Lenny Harris .01 .05
205 Mike Hartley .01 .05
206 Mickey Hatcher .01 .05
207 Carlos Hernandez .01 .05
208 Orel Hershiser .02 .10
209 Jay Howell UER .01 .05
(No 1982 Yankee stats)
210 Mike Huff .01 .05
211 Stan Javier .01 .05
212 Ramon Martinez .01 .05
213 Mike Morgan .01 .05
214 Eddie Murray .08 .25
215 Jim Neidlinger RC .01 .05
216 Jose Offerman .01 .05
217 Jim Poole .01 .05
218 Juan Samuel .01 .05
219 Mike Scioscia .01 .05
220 Ray Searage .01 .05
221 Mike Sharperson .01 .05
222 Fernando Valenzuela .02 .10
223 Jose Vizcaino .01 .05
224 Mike Aldrete .01 .05
225 Scott Anderson RC .01 .05
226 Dennis Boyd .01 .05
227 Tim Burke .01 .05
228 Delino DeShields .02 .10
229 Mike Fitzgerald .01 .05
230 Tom Foley .01 .05
231 Steve Frey .01 .05
232 Andres Galarraga .02 .10
233 Mark Gardner .01 .05
234 Marquis Grissom .02 .10
235 Kevin Gross .01 .05
(No date given for first Expos win)
236 Drew Hall .01 .05
237 Dave Martinez .01 .05
238 Dennis Martinez .02 .10
239 Dale Mohorcic .01 .05
240 Chris Nabholz .01 .05
241 Otis Nixon .01 .05
242 Junior Noboa .01 .05
243 Spike Owen .01 .05
244 Tim Raines .02 .10
245 Mel Rojas UER .01 .05
(Stats show 3.60 ERA, bio says 3.19 ERA)
246 Scott Ruskin .01 .05
247 Bill Sampen .01 .05
248 Nelson Santovenia .01 .05
249 Dave Schmidt .01 .05
250 Larry Walker .08 .25
251 Tim Wallach .01 .05
252 Dave Anderson .01 .05
253 Kevin Bass .01 .05
254 Steve Bedrosian .01 .05
255 Jeff Brantley .01 .05
256 John Burkett .01 .05
257 Brett Butler .02 .10
258 Gary Carter .02 .10
259 Will Clark .05 .15
260 Steve Decker RC .02 .10
261 Kelly Downs .01 .05
262 Scott Garrelts .01 .05
263 Terry Kennedy .01 .05
264 Mike LaCoss .01 .05
265 Mark Leonard RC .01 .05
266 Greg Litton .01 .05
267 Kevin Mitchell .01 .05
268 Randy O'Neal .01 .05
269 Rick Parker .01 .05
270 Rick Reuschel .01 .05
271 Ernest Riles .01 .05
272 Don Robinson .01 .05
273 Robby Thompson .01 .05
274 Mark Thurmond .01 .05
275 Jose Uribe .01 .05
276 Matt Williams .02 .10
277 Trevor Wilson .01 .05
278 Gerald Alexander RC .01 .05
279 Brad Arnsberg .01 .05
280 Kevin Belcher RC .01 .05
281 Joe Bitker RC .01 .05
282 Kevin Brown .02 .10
283 Steve Buechele .01 .05
284 Jack Daugherty .01 .05
285 Julio Franco .02 .10
286 Juan Gonzalez .08 .25
287 Bill Haselman RC .01 .05
288 Charlie Hough .02 .10
289 Jeff Huson .01 .05
290 Pete Incaviglia .01 .05
291 Mike Jeffcoat .01 .05
292 Jeff Kunkel .01 .05
293 Gary Mielke .01 .05
294 Jamie Moyer .02 .10
295 Rafael Palmeiro .05 .15
296 Geno Petralli .01 .05
297 Gary Pettis .01 .05
298 Kevin Reimer .01 .05
299 Kenny Rogers .02 .10
300 Jeff Russell .01 .05
301 John Russell .01 .05
302 Nolan Ryan .40 1.00
303 Ruben Sierra .02 .10
304 Bobby Witt .01 .05
305 Jim Abbott UER .05 .15
(Text on back states he won Sullivan Award (outstanding amateur athlete) in 1989;should be '88)
306 Kent Anderson .01 .05
307 Dante Bichette .02 .10
308 Bert Blyleven .02 .10
309 Chili Davis .02 .10
310 Brian Downing .01 .05
311 Mark Eichhorn .01 .05
312 Mike Fetters .01 .05
313 Chuck Finley .02 .10
314 Willie Fraser .01 .05
315 Bryan Harvey .01 .05
316 Donnie Hill .01 .05
317 Wally Joyner .02 .10
318 Mark Langston .01 .05
319 Kirk McCaskill .01 .05
320 John Orton .01 .05
321 Lance Parrish .02 .10
322 Luis Polonia UER .01 .05
(1984 Madfison, should be Madison)
323 Johnny Ray .01 .05
324 Bobby Rose .01 .05
325 Dick Schofield .01 .05
326 Rick Schu .01 .05
327 Lee Stevens .01 .05
328 Devon White .02 .10
329 Dave Winfield .02 .10
330 Cliff Young .01 .05
331 Dave Bergman .01 .05
332 Phil Clark RC .02 .10
333 Darnell Coles .01 .05
334 Milt Cuyler .01 .05
335 Cecil Fielder .02 .10
336 Travis Fryman .02 .10
337 Paul Gibson .01 .05
338 Jerry Don Gleaton .01 .05
339 Mike Heath .01 .05
340 Mike Henneman .01 .05
341 Chet Lemon .01 .05
342 Lance McCullers .01 .05
343 Jack Morris .02 .10
344 Lloyd Moseby .01 .05
345 Edwin Nunez .01 .05
346 Clay Parker .01 .05
347 Dan Petry .01 .05
348 Tony Phillips .01 .05
349 Jeff M. Robinson .01 .05
350 Mark Salas .01 .05
351 Mike Schwabe .01 .05
352 Larry Sheets .01 .05
353 John Shelby .01 .05
354 Frank Tanana .01 .05
355 Alan Trammell .02 .10
356 Gary Ward .01 .05
357 Lou Whitaker .02 .10
358 Beau Allred .01 .05
359 Sandy Alomar Jr. .01 .05
360 Carlos Baerga .01 .05
361 Kevin Bearse .01 .05
362 Tom Brookens .01 .05
363 Jerry Browne UER .01 .05
(No dot over i in first text line)
364 Tom Candiotti .01 .05
365 Alex Cole .01 .05
366 John Farrell UER .01 .05
(Born in Neptune, should be Monmouth)
367 Felix Fermin .01 .05
368 Keith Hernandez .02 .10
369 Brook Jacoby .01 .05
370 Chris James .01 .05
371 Dion James .01 .05
372 Doug Jones .01 .05
373 Candy Maldonado .01 .05
374 Steve Olin .01 .05
375 Jesse Orosco .01 .05
376 Rudy Seanez .01 .05
377 Joel Skinner .01 .05
378 Cory Snyder .01 .05
379 Greg Swindell .01 .05
380 Sergio Valdez .01 .05
381 Mike Walker .01 .05
382 Colby Ward RC .01 .05
383 Turner Ward RC .08 .25
384 Mitch Webster .01 .05
385 Kevin Wickander .01 .05
386 Darrel Akerfelds .01 .05
387 Joe Boever .01 .05
388 Rod Booker .01 .05
389 Sil Campusano .01 .05
390 Don Carman .01 .05
391 Wes Chamberlain RC .08 .25
392 Pat Combs .01 .05
393 Darren Daulton .02 .10
394 Jose DeJesus .01 .05
395A Len Dykstra .02 .10
Name spelled Lenny on back
395B Len Dykstra .02 .10
Name spelled Len on back
396 Jason Grimsley .01 .05
397 Charlie Hayes .01 .05
398 Von Hayes .01 .05
399 David Hollins UER .01 .05
(Atl-bats& should say at-bats)
400 Ken Howell .01 .05
401 Ricky Jordan .01 .05
402 John Kruk .02 .10
403 Steve Lake .01 .05
404 Chuck Malone .01 .05
405 Roger McDowell UER .01 .05
(Says Phillies is saves, should say in)
406 Chuck McElroy .01 .05
407 Mickey Morandini .01 .05
408 Terry Mulholland .01 .05
409 Dale Murphy .05 .15
410A Randy Ready ERR .01 .05
(No Brewers stats listed for 1983)
410B Randy Ready COR .01 .05
411 Bruce Ruffin .01 .05
412 Dickie Thon .01 .05
413 Paul Assenmacher .01 .05
414 Damon Berryhill .01 .05
415 Mike Bielecki .01 .05
416 Shawn Boskie .01 .05
417 Dave Clark .01 .05
418 Doug Dascenzo .01 .05
419A Andre Dawson ERR .02 .10
(No stats for 1976)
419B Andre Dawson COR .02 .10
420 Shawon Dunston .01 .05
421 Joe Girardi .01 .05
422 Mark Grace .05 .15
423 Mike Harkey .01 .05
424 Les Lancaster .01 .05
425 Bill Long .01 .05
426 Greg Maddux .15 .40
427 Derrick May .01 .05
428 Jeff Pico .01 .05
429 Domingo Ramos .01 .05
430 Luis Salazar .01 .05
431 Ryne Sandberg .15 .40
432 Dwight Smith .01 .05
433 Greg Smith .01 .05
434 Rick Sutcliffe .02 .10
435 Gary Varsho .01 .05
436 Hector Villanueva .01 .05
437 Jerome Walton .01 .05
438 Curtis Wilkerson .01 .05
439 Mitch Williams .01 .05
440 Steve Wilson .01 .05
441 Marvell Wynne .01 .05
442 Scott Bankhead .01 .05
443 Scott Bradley .01 .05
444 Greg Briley .01 .05
445 Mike Brumley UER .01 .05
(Text 40 SB's in 1988, stats say 41)
446 Jay Buhner .02 .10
447 Dave Burba RC .08 .25
448 Henry Cotto .01 .05
449 Alvin Davis .01 .05
450 Ken Griffey Jr. .20 .50
(Bat around .300)
450A Ken Griffey Jr. .40 1.00
(Bat .300)
451 Erik Hanson .01 .05
452 Gene Harris UER .01 .05
(63 career runs, should be 73)
453 Brian Holman .01 .05
454 Mike Jackson .01 .05
455 Randy Johnson .10 .30
456 Jeffrey Leonard .01 .05
457 Edgar Martinez .05 .15
458 Tino Martinez .08 .25
459 Pete O'Brien UER .01 .05
(1987 BA .266, should be .286)
460 Harold Reynolds .02 .10
461 Mike Schooler .01 .05
462 Bill Swift .01 .05
463 David Valle .01 .05
464 Omar Vizquel .05 .15
465 Matt Young .01 .05
466 Brady Anderson .02 .10
467 Jeff Ballard UER .01 .05
(Missing top of right parenthesis after

Saberhagen in last text line)
468 Juan Bell .01 .05
469A Mike Devereaux .02 .10
(First line of text ends with six)
469B Mike Devereaux .02 .10
(First line of text ends with runs)
470 Steve Finley .02 .10
471 Dave Gallagher .01 .05
472 Leo Gomez .01 .05
473 Rene Gonzales .01 .05
474 Pete Harnisch .01 .05
475 Kevin Hickey .01 .05
476 Chris Hoiles .01 .05
477 Sam Horn .01 .05
478 Tim Hulett .01 .05
(Photo shows National League sliding into second base)
479 Dave Johnson .01 .05
480 Ron Kittle UER .01 .05
(Edmonton misspelled as Edmundton)
481 Ben McDonald .01 .05
482 Bob Melvin .01 .05
483 Bob Milacki .01 .05
484 Randy Milligan .01 .05
485 John Mitchell .01 .05
486 Gregg Olson .01 .05
487 Joe Orsulak .01 .05
488 Joe Price .01 .05
489 Bill Ripken .01 .05
490 Cal Ripken .30 .75
491 Curt Schilling .08 .25
492 David Segui .01 .05
493 Anthony Telford RC .01 .05
494 Mickey Tettleton .01 .05
495 Mark Williamson .01 .05
496 Craig Worthington .01 .05
497 Juan Agosto .01 .05
498 Eric Anthony .01 .05
499 Craig Biggio .05 .15
500 Ken Caminiti UER .02 .10
(Born 4/4, should be 4/21)
501 Casey Candaele .01 .05
502 Andujar Cedeno .01 .05
503 Danny Darwin .01 .05
504 Mark Davidson .01 .05
505 Glenn Davis .01 .05
506 Jim Deshaies .01 .05
507 Luis Gonzalez RC .20 .50
508 Bill Gullickson .01 .05
509 Xavier Hernandez .01 .05
510 Brian Meyer .01 .05
511 Ken Oberkfell .01 .05
512 Mark Portugal .01 .05
513 Rafael Ramirez .01 .05
514 Karl Rhodes .01 .05
515 Mike Scott .01 .05
516 Mike Simms RC .01 .05
517 Dave Smith .01 .05
518 Franklin Stubbs .01 .05
519 Glenn Wilson .01 .05
520 Eric Yelding UER .01 .05
(Text has 63 steals, stats have 64, which is correct)
521 Gerald Young .01 .05
522 Shawn Abner .01 .05
523 Roberto Alomar .05 .15
524 Andy Benes .01 .05
525 Joe Carter .02 .10
526 Jack Clark .02 .10
527 Joey Cora .01 .05
528 Paul Faries RC .01 .05
529 Tony Gwynn .10 .30
530 Atlee Hammaker .01 .05
531 Greg W. Harris .01 .05
532 Thomas Howard .01 .05
533 Bruce Hurst .01 .05
534 Craig Lefferts .01 .05
535 Derek Lilliquist .01 .05
536 Fred Lynn .01 .05
537 Mike Pagliarulo .01 .05
538 Mark Parent .01 .05
539 Dennis Rasmussen .01 .05
540 Bip Roberts .01 .05
541 Richard Rodriguez RC .01 .05
542 Benito Santiago .02 .10
543 Calvin Schiraldi .01 .05
544 Eric Show .01 .05
545 Phil Stephenson .01 .05
546 Garry Templeton UER .01 .05
(Born 3/24/57; should be 3/24/56)
547 Ed Whitson .01 .05
548 Eddie Williams .01 .05
549 Kevin Appier .02 .10
550 Luis Aquino .01 .05
551 Bob Boone .02 .10
552 George Brett .25 .60
553 Jeff Conine RC .15 .40
554 Steve Crawford .01 .05
555 Mark Davis .01 .05
556 Storm Davis .01 .05
557 Jim Eisenreich .01 .05
558 Steve Farr .01 .05
559 Tom Gordon .01 .05
560 Mark Gubicza .01 .05
561 Bo Jackson .08 .25
562 Mike Macfarlane .01 .05
563 Brian McRae RC .08 .25
564 Jeff Montgomery .01 .05
565 Bill Pecota .01 .05
566 Gerald Perry .01 .05
567 Bret Saberhagen .02 .10
568 Jeff Schulz RC .01 .05
569 Kevin Seitzer .01 .05
570 Terry Shumpert .01 .05
571 Kurt Stillwell .01 .05
572 Danny Tartabull .01 .05
573 Gary Thurman .01 .05
574 Frank White .02 .10
575 Willie Wilson .01 .05
576 Chris Bosio .01 .05
577 Greg Brock .01 .05
578 George Canale .01 .05
579 Chuck Crim .01 .05
580 Rob Deer .01 .05
581 Edgar Diaz .01 .05
582 Tom Edens RC .01 .05
583 Mike Felder .01 .05
584 Jim Gantner .01 .05
585 Darryl Hamilton .01 .05
586 Ted Higuera .01 .05
587 Mark Knudson .01 .05
588 Bill Krueger .01 .05
589 Tim McIntosh .01 .05
590 Paul Mirabella .01 .05
591 Paul Molitor .02 .10
592 Jaime Navarro .01 .05
593 Dave Parker .02 .10
594 Dan Plesac .01 .05
595 Ron Robinson .01 .05
596 Gary Sheffield .02 .10
597 Bill Spiers .01 .05
598 B.J. Surhoff .02 .10
599 Greg Vaughn .01 .05
600 Randy Veres .01 .05
601 Robin Yount .15 .40
602 Rick Aguilera .02 .10
603 Allan Anderson .01 .05
604 Juan Berenguer .01 .05
605 Randy Bush .01 .05
606 Carmelo Castillo .01 .05
607 Tim Drummond .01 .05
608 Scott Erickson .01 .05
609 Gary Gaetti .02 .10
610 Greg Gagne .01 .05
611 Dan Gladden .01 .05
612 Mark Guthrie .01 .05
613 Brian Harper .01 .05
614 Kent Hrbek .02 .10
615 Gene Larkin .01 .05
616 Terry Leach .01 .05
617 Nelson Liriano .01 .05
618 Shane Mack .01 .05
619 John Moses .01 .05
620 Pedro Munoz RC .02 .10
621 Al Newman .01 .05
622 Junior Ortiz .01 .05
623 Kirby Puckett .08 .25
624 Roy Smith .01 .05
625 Kevin Tapani .01 .05
626 Gary Wayne .01 .05
627 David West .01 .05
628 Cris Carpenter .01 .05
629 Vince Coleman .01 .05
630 Ken Dayley .01 .05
631A Jose DeLeon ERR .01 .05
(missing '79 Bradenton stats)
631B Jose DeLeon COR .01 .05
(with '79 Bradenton stats)
632 Frank DiPino .01 .05
633 Bernard Gilkey .01 .05
634A Pedro Guerrero ERR .02 .10
634B Pedro Guerrero COR .02 .10
635 Ken Hill .01 .05
636 Felix Jose .01 .05
637 Ray Lankford .02 .10
638 Joe Magrane .01 .05
639 Tom Niedenfuer .01 .05
640 Jose Oquendo .01 .05
641 Tom Pagnozzi .01 .05
642 Terry Pendleton .02 .10
643 Mike Perez RC .02 .10
644 Bryn Smith .01 .05
645 Lee Smith .02 .10
646 Ozzie Smith .15 .40
647 Scott Terry .01 .05
648 Bob Tewksbury .01 .05
649 Milt Thompson .01 .05
650 John Tudor .01 .05
651 Denny Walling .01 .05
652 Craig Wilson RC .01 .05
653 Todd Worrell .01 .05
654 Todd Zeile .01 .05
655 Oscar Azocar .01 .05
656 Steve Balboni UER .01 .05
(Born 1/5/57, should be 1/16)
657 Jesse Barfield .01 .05
658 Greg Cadaret .01 .05
659 Chuck Cary .01 .05
660 Rick Cerone .01 .05
661 Dave Eiland .01 .05
662 Alvaro Espinoza .01 .05
663 Bob Geren .01 .05
664 Lee Guetterman .01 .05
665 Mel Hall .01 .05
666 Andy Hawkins .01 .05
667 Jimmy Jones .01 .05
668 Roberto Kelly .01 .05
669 Dave LaPoint UER .01 .05
(No '81 Brewers stats, totals also are wrong)
670 Tim Leary .01 .05
671 Jim Leyritz .01 .05
672 Kevin Maas .01 .05
673 Don Mattingly .25 .60
674 Matt Nokes .01 .05
675 Pascual Perez .01 .05
676 Eric Plunk .01 .05
677 Dave Righetti .02 .10
678 Jeff D. Robinson .01 .05
679 Steve Sax .01 .05
680 Mike Witt .01 .05
681 Steve Avery UER .01 .05
(Born in New Jersey, should say Michigan)
682 Mike Bell RC .01 .05
683 Jeff Blauser .01 .05
684 F.Cabrera UER .01 .05
Born 10/16, should say 10/10
685 Tony Castillo .01 .05
686 Marty Clary UER .01 .05
(Shown pitching righty, but bio has left)
687 Nick Esasky .01 .05
688 Ron Gant .02 .10
689 Tom Glavine .05 .15
690 Mark Grant .01 .05
691 Tommy Gregg .01 .05
692 Dwayne Henry .01 .05
693 Dave Justice .02 .10
694 Jimmy Kremers .01 .05
695 Charlie Leibrandt .01 .05
696 Mark Lemke .01 .05
697 Oddibe McDowell .01 .05
698 Greg Olson .01 .05
699 Jeff Parrett .01 .05
700 Jim Presley .01 .05
701 Victor Rosario RC .01 .05
702 Lonnie Smith .01 .05
703 Pete Smith .01 .05
704 John Smoltz .05 .15
705 Mike Stanton .01 .05
706 Andres Thomas .01 .05
707 Jeff Treadway .01 .05
708 Jim Vatcher RC .01 .05
709 Ryne Sandberg .08 .25
Cecil Fielder
710 Barry Bonds .40 1.00
Ken Griffey Jr.
711 Bobby Bonilla .02 .10
Barry Larkin
712 Bobby Thigpen .01 .05
John Franco
713 Andre Dawson .08 .25
Ryne Sandberg UER
(Ryno misspelled Rhino)
714 CL:A's/Pirates .01 .05
Reds/Red Sox
715 CL:White Sox/Mets .01 .05
Blue Jays/Dodgers
716 CL:Expos/Giants .01 .05
Rangers/Angels
717 CL:Tigers/Indians .01 .05
Phillies/Cubs
718 CL:Mariners/Orioles .01 .05
Astros/Padres
719 CL:Royals/Brewers .01 .05
Twins/Cardinals
720 CL:Yankees/Braves .01 .05
Superstars/Specials

1991 Fleer Update

The 1991 Fleer Update set contains 132 standard-size cards. The cards were distributed exclusively in factory set form through hobby dealers. Card design is identical to regular issue 1991 Fleer cards with the notable bright yellow borders except for the U-prefixed numbering on back. The cards are ordered alphabetically by team. The key Rookie Cards in this set are Jeff Bagwell and Ivan Rodriguez.

COMP.FACT.SET (132) 2.00 5.00
1 Glenn Davis .01 .05
2 Dwight Evans .05 .15
3 Jose Mesa .01 .05
4 Jack Clark .02 .10
5 Danny Darwin .01 .05
6 Steve Lyons .01 .05
7 Mo Vaughn .02 .10
8 Floyd Bannister .01 .05
9 Gary Gaetti .02 .10
10 Dave Parker .02 .10
11 Joey Cora .01 .05
12 Charlie Hough .02 .10
13 Matt Merullo .01 .05
14 Warren Newson RC .01 .05
15 Tim Raines .02 .10
16 Albert Belle .02 .10
17 Glenallen Hill .01 .05
18 Shawn Hillegas .01 .05
19 Mark Lewis .01 .05
20 Charles Nagy .01 .05
21 Mark Whiten .01 .05
22 John Cerutti .01 .05
23 Rob Deer .01 .05
24 Mickey Tettleton .01 .05
25 Warren Cromartie .01 .05
26 Kirk Gibson .02 .10
27 David Howard RC .01 .05
28 Brent Mayne .01 .05
29 Dante Bichette .02 .10
30 Mark Lee RC .01 .05
31 Julio Machado .01 .05
32 Edwin Nunez .01 .05
33 Willie Randolph .02 .10
34 Franklin Stubbs .01 .05
35 Bill Wegman .01 .05
36 Chili Davis .02 .10
37 Chuck Knoblauch .02 .10
38 Scott Leius .01 .05
39 Jack Morris .02 .10
40 Mike Pagliarulo .01 .05
41 Lenny Webster .01 .05
42 John Habyan .01 .05
43 Steve Howe .01 .05
44 Jeff Johnson RC .01 .05
45 Scott Kamieniecki RC .01 .05
46 Pat Kelly RC .01 .05
47 Hensley Meulens .01 .05
48 Wade Taylor RC .01 .05
49 Bernie Williams .08 .25
50 Kirk Dressendorfer RC .01 .05
51 Ernest Riles .01 .05
52 Rich DeLucia RC .01 .05
53 Tracy Jones .01 .05
54 Bill Krueger .01 .05
55 Alonzo Powell RC .01 .05
56 Jeff Schaefer .01 .05
57 Russ Swan .01 .05
58 John Barfield .01 .05
59 Rich Gossage .02 .10
60 Jose Guzman .01 .05
61 Dean Palmer .02 .10
62 Ivan Rodriguez RC .75 2.00
63 Roberto Alomar .05 .15
64 Tom Candiotti .01 .05
65 Joe Carter .02 .10
66 Ed Sprague .01 .05
67 Pat Tabler .01 .05
68 Mike Timlin RC .02 .10
69 Devon White .02 .10
70 Rafael Belliard .01 .05
71 Juan Berenguer .01 .05
72 Sid Bream .01 .05
73 Marvin Freeman .01 .05
74 Kent Mercker .01 .05
75 Otis Nixon .01 .05
76 Terry Pendleton .02 .10
77 George Bell .01 .05
78 Danny Jackson .01 .05
79 Chuck McElroy .01 .05
80 Gary Scott RC .01 .05
81 Heathcliff Slocumb RC .02 .10
82 Dave Smith .01 .05
83 Rick Wilkins RC .01 .05
84 Freddie Benavides RC .01 .05
85 Ted Power .01 .05
86 Mo Sanford RC .01 .05
87 Jeff Bagwell RC .60 1.50
88 Steve Finley .02 .10
89 Pete Harnisch .01 .05
90 Darryl Kile .02 .10
91 Brett Butler .02 .10
92 John Candelaria .01 .05
93 Gary Carter .02 .10
94 Kevin Gross .01 .05
95 Bob Ojeda .01 .05
96 Darryl Strawberry .02 .10
97 Ivan Calderon .01 .05
98 Ron Hassey .01 .05
99 Gilberto Reyes .01 .05
100 Hubie Brooks .01 .05
101 Rick Cerone .01 .05
102 Vince Coleman .01 .05
103 Jeff Innis .01 .05
104 Pete Schourek RC .01 .05
105 Andy Ashby RC .08 .25
106 Wally Backman .01 .05
107 Darrin Fletcher .01 .05
108 Tommy Greene .01 .05
109 John Morris .01 .05
110 Mitch Williams .01 .05
111 Lloyd McClendon .01 .05
112 Orlando Merced RC .01 .05
113 Vicente Palacios .01 .05
114 Gary Varsho .01 .05
115 John Wehner RC .01 .05
116 Rex Hudler .01 .05
117 Tim Jones .01 .05
118 Geronimo Pena .01 .05
119 Gerald Perry .01 .05
120 Larry Andersen .01 .05
121 Jerald Clark .01 .05
122 Scott Coolbaugh .01 .05
123 Tony Fernandez .01 .05
124 Darrin Jackson .01 .05
125 Fred McGriff .05 .15
126 Jose Mota RC .01 .05
127 Tim Teufel .01 .05
128 Bud Black .01 .05
129 Mike Felder .01 .05
130 Willie McGee .02 .10
131 Dave Righetti .02 .10
132 Checklist U1-U132 .01 .05

1992 Fleer

The 1992 Fleer set contains 720 standard-size cards issued in one comprehensive series. The cards were distributed in plastic wrapped packs, 35-card cello packs, 42-card rack packs and factory sets. The card fronts shade from metallic pale green to white as one moves down the face. The team logo and player's name appear to the right of the picture, running the length of the card. The cards are ordered alphabetically within and according to teams for each league with AL preceding NL. Topical subsets feature Major League Prospects (652-680), Record Setters (681-687), League Leaders (688-697), Super Star Specials (698-707) and Pro Visions (708-713). Rookie Cards include Scott Brosius and Vinny Castilla.

COMPLETE SET (720) 4.00 10.00
COMP.HOBBY SET (732) 8.00 20.00
COMP.RETAIL SET (732) 8.00 20.00
1 Brady Anderson .02 .10
2 Jose Bautista .02 .10
3 Juan Bell .02 .10
4 Glenn Davis .02 .10
5 Mike Devereaux .02 .10
6 Dwight Evans .05 .15
7 Mike Flanagan .02 .10
8 Leo Gomez .02 .10
9 Chris Hoiles .02 .10
10 Sam Horn .02 .10
11 Tim Hulett .02 .10
12 Dave Johnson .02 .10
13 Chito Martinez .02 .10
14 Ben McDonald .02 .10
15 Bob Melvin .02 .10
16 Luis Mercedes .02 .10
17 Jose Mesa .02 .10
18 Bob Milacki .02 .10
19 Randy Milligan .02 .10
20 Mike Mussina UER .08 .25
(Card back refers to him as Jeff)
21 Gregg Olson .02 .10
22 Joe Orsulak .02 .10
23 Jim Poole .02 .10
24 Arthur Rhodes .02 .10
25 Billy Ripken .02 .10
26 Cal Ripken .30 .75
27 David Segui .02 .10
28 Roy Smith .02 .10
29 Anthony Telford .02 .10
30 Mark Williamson .02 .10
31 Craig Worthington .02 .10
32 Wade Boggs .05 .15
33 Tom Bolton .02 .10
34 Tom Brunansky .02 .10
35 Ellis Burks .02 .10
36 Jack Clark .02 .10
37 Roger Clemens .20 .50
38 Danny Darwin .02 .10
39 Mike Greenwell .02 .10
40 Joe Hesketh .02 .10
41 Daryl Irvine .02 .10
42 Dennis Lamp .02 .10
43 Tony Pena .02 .10
44 Phil Plantier .02 .10
45 Carlos Quintana .02 .10
46 Jeff Reardon .02 .10
47 Jody Reed .02 .10
48 Luis Rivera .02 .10
49 Mo Vaughn .02 .10
50 Jim Abbott .05 .15
51 Kyle Abbott .02 .10
52 Ruben Amaro .02 .10
53 Scott Bailes .02 .10
54 Chris Beasley .02 .10
55 Mark Eichhorn .02 .10
56 Mike Fetters .02 .10
57 Chuck Finley .02 .10
58 Gary Gaetti .02 .10
59 Dave Gallagher .02 .10
60 Donnie Hill .02 .10
61 Bryan Harvey UER .02 .10
(Lee Smith led the Majors with 47 saves)
62 Wally Joyner .02 .10
63 Mark Langston .02 .10
64 Kirk McCaskill .02 .10
65 John Orton .02 .10
66 Lance Parrish .02 .10
67 Luis Polonia .02 .10
68 Bobby Rose .02 .10
69 Dick Schofield .02 .10
70 Luis Sojo .02 .10
71 Lee Stevens .02 .10
72 Dave Winfield .02 .10
73 Cliff Young .02 .10
74 Wilson Alvarez .02 .10
75 Esteban Beltre .02 .10
76 Joey Cora .02 .10
77 Brian Drahman .02 .10
78 Alex Fernandez .02 .10
79 Carlton Fisk .05 .15
80 Scott Fletcher .02 .10
81 Craig Grebeck .02 .10
82 Ozzie Guillen .02 .10
83 Greg Hibbard .02 .10
84 Charlie Hough .02 .10
85 Mike Huff .02 .10
86 Bo Jackson .08 .25
87 Lance Johnson .02 .10
88 Ron Karkovice .02 .10
89 Jack McDowell .02 .10
90 Matt Merullo .02 .10
91 Warren Newson .02 .10
92 Donn Pall UER .02 .10
(Called Dunn on card back)
93 Dan Pasqua .02 .10
94 Ken Patterson .02 .10
95 Melido Perez .02 .10
96 Scott Radinsky .02 .10
97 Tim Raines .02 .10
98 Sammy Sosa .08 .25
99 Bobby Thigpen .02 .10
100 Frank Thomas .08 .25
101 Robin Ventura .02 .10
102 Mike Aldrete .02 .10
103 Sandy Alomar Jr. .02 .10
104 Carlos Baerga .02 .10
105 Albert Belle .02 .10
106 Willie Blair .02 .10
107 Jerry Browne .02 .10
108 Alex Cole .02 .10
109 Felix Fermin .02 .10
110 Glenallen Hill .02 .10
111 Shawn Hillegas .02 .10
112 Chris James .02 .10
113 Reggie Jefferson .02 .10
114 Doug Jones .02 .10
115 Eric King .02 .10
116 Mark Lewis .02 .10
117 Carlos Martinez .02 .10
118 Charles Nagy UER .02 .10
(Throws right, but card says left)
119 Rod Nichols .02 .10
120 Steve Olin .02 .10
121 Jesse Orosco .02 .10
122 Rudy Seanez .02 .10
123 Joel Skinner .02 .10
124 Greg Swindell .02 .10
125 Jim Thome .08 .25
126 Mark Whiten .02 .10
127 Scott Aldred .02 .10
128 Andy Allanson .02 .10
129 John Cerutti .02 .10
130 Milt Cuyler .02 .10
131 Mike Dalton .02 .10
132 Rob Deer .02 .10
133 Cecil Fielder .02 .10
134 Travis Fryman .02 .10
135 Dan Gakeler .02 .10
136 Paul Gibson .02 .10
137 Bill Gullickson .02 .10
138 Mike Henneman .02 .10
139 Pete Incaviglia .02 .10
140 Mark Leiter .02 .10
141 Scott Livingstone .02 .10
142 Lloyd Moseby .02 .10
143 Tony Phillips .02 .10
144 Mark Salas .02 .10
145 Frank Tanana .02 .10
146 Walt Terrell .02 .10
147 Mickey Tettleton .02 .10
148 Alan Trammell .02 .10
149 Lou Whitaker .02 .10
150 Kevin Appier .02 .10
151 Luis Aquino .02 .10
152 Todd Benzinger .02 .10
153 Mike Boddicker .02 .10
154 George Brett .25 .60
155 Storm Davis .02 .10
156 Jim Eisenreich .02 .10
157 Kirk Gibson .02 .10
158 Tom Gordon .02 .10
159 Mark Gubicza .02 .10
160 David Howard .02 .10
161 Mike Macfarlane .02 .10
162 Brent Mayne .02 .10
163 Brian McRae .02 .10
164 Jeff Montgomery .02 .10
165 Bill Pecota .02 .10
166 Harvey Pulliam .02 .10
167 Bret Saberhagen .02 .10
168 Kevin Seitzer .02 .10
169 Terry Shumpert .02 .10
170 Kurt Stillwell .02 .10
171 Danny Tartabull .02 .10
172 Gary Thurman .02 .10
173 Dante Bichette .02 .10
174 Kevin D. Brown .02 .10
175 Chuck Crim .02 .10
176 Jim Gantner .02 .10
177 Darryl Hamilton .02 .10
178 Ted Higuera .02 .10
179 Darren Holmes .02 .10
180 Mark Lee .02 .10
181 Julio Machado .02 .10
182 Paul Molitor .02 .10
183 Jaime Navarro .02 .10
184 Edwin Nunez .02 .10
185 Dan Plesac .02 .10
186 Willie Randolph .02 .10
187 Ron Robinson .02 .10
188 Gary Sheffield .02 .10
189 Bill Spiers .02 .10
190 B.J. Surhoff .02 .10
191 Dale Sveum .02 .10
192 Greg Vaughn .02 .10
193 Bill Wegman .02 .10
194 Robin Yount .15 .40
195 Rick Aguilera .02 .10
196 Allan Anderson .02 .10
197 Steve Bedrosian .02 .10
198 Randy Bush .02 .10
199 Larry Casian .02 .10
200 Chili Davis .02 .10
201 Scott Erickson .02 .10
202 Greg Gagne .02 .10
203 Dan Gladden .02 .10
204 Brian Harper .02 .10
205 Kent Hrbek .02 .10
206 C.Knoblauch UER .02 .10
Career hit total of 59 is wrong
207 Gene Larkin .02 .10
208 Terry Leach .02 .10
209 Scott Leius .02 .10
210 Shane Mack .02 .10
211 Jack Morris .02 .10
212 Pedro Munoz .02 .10
213 Denny Neagle .02 .10
214 Al Newman .02 .10
215 Junior Ortiz .02 .10
216 Mike Pagliarulo .02 .10
217 Kirby Puckett .08 .25
218 Paul Sorrento .02 .10
219 Kevin Tapani .02 .10
220 Lenny Webster .02 .10
221 Jesse Barfield .02 .10
222 Greg Cadaret .02 .10
223 Dave Eiland .02 .10
224 Alvaro Espinoza .02 .10
225 Steve Farr .02 .10
226 Bob Geren .02 .10
227 Lee Guetterman .02 .10
228 John Habyan .02 .10
229 Mel Hall .02 .10
230 Steve Howe .02 .10
231 Mike Humphreys .02 .10
232 Scott Kamieniecki .02 .10
233 Pat Kelly .02 .10
234 Roberto Kelly .02 .10
235 Tim Leary .02 .10
236 Kevin Maas .02 .10
237 Don Mattingly .25 .60
238 Hensley Meulens .02 .10
239 Matt Nokes .02 .10
240 Pascual Perez .02 .10
241 Eric Plunk .02 .10
242 John Ramos .02 .10
243 Scott Sanderson .02 .10
244 Steve Sax .02 .10
245 Wade Taylor .02 .10
246 Randy Velarde .02 .10
247 Bernie Williams .05 .15
248 Troy Afenir .02 .10
249 Harold Baines .02 .10
250 Lance Blankenship .02 .10
251 Mike Bordick .02 .10
252 Jose Canseco .05 .15
253 Steve Chitren .02 .10
254 Ron Darling .02 .10
255 Dennis Eckersley .02 .10
256 Mike Gallego .02 .10
257 Dave Henderson .02 .10
258 R.Henderson UER .08 .25
Wearing 24 on front and 22 on back
259 Rick Honeycutt .02 .10
260 Brook Jacoby .02 .10
261 Carney Lansford .02 .10
262 Mark McGwire .25 .60
263 Mike Moore .02 .10
264 Gene Nelson .02 .10
265 Jamie Quirk .02 .10
266 Joe Slusarski .02 .10
267 Terry Steinbach .02 .10
268 Dave Stewart .02 .10
269 Todd Van Poppel .02 .10
270 Walt Weiss .02 .10
271 Bob Welch .02 .10
272 Curt Young .02 .10
273 Scott Bradley .02 .10
274 Greg Briley .02 .10
275 Jay Buhner .02 .10
276 Henry Cotto .02 .10
277 Alvin Davis .02 .10
278 Rich DeLucia .02 .10
279 Ken Griffey Jr. .15 .40
280 Erik Hanson .02 .10
281 Brian Holman .02 .10
282 Mike Jackson .02 .10
283 Randy Johnson .08 .25
284 Tracy Jones .02 .10

285 Bill Krueger .02 .10
286 Edgar Martinez .05 .15
287 Tino Martinez .05 .15
288 Rob Murphy .02 .10
289 Pete O'Brien .02 .10
290 Alonzo Powell .02 .10
291 Harold Reynolds .02 .10
292 Mike Schooler .02 .10
293 Russ Swan .02 .10
294 Bill Swift .02 .10
295 Dave Valle .02 .10
296 Omar Vizquel .05 .15
297 Gerald Alexander .02 .10
298 Brad Arnsberg .02 .10
299 Kevin Brown .02 .10
300 Jack Daugherty .02 .10
301 Mario Diaz .02 .10
302 Brian Downing .02 .10
303 Julio Franco .02 .10
304 Juan Gonzalez .05 .15
305 Rich Gossage .02 .10
306 Jose Guzman .02 .10
307 Jose Hernandez RC .08 .25
308 Jeff Huson .02 .10
309 Mike Jeffcoat .02 .10
310 Terry Mathews .02 .10
311 Rafael Palmeiro .05 .15
312 Dean Palmer .02 .10
313 Geno Petralli .02 .10
314 Gary Pettis .02 .10
315 Kevin Reimer .02 .10
316 Ivan Rodriguez .08 .25
317 Kenny Rogers .02 .10
318 Wayne Rosenthal .02 .10
319 Jeff Russell .02 .10
320 Nolan Ryan .40 1.00
321 Ruben Sierra .02 .10
322 Jim Acker .02 .10
323 Roberto Alomar .05 .15
324 Derek Bell .02 .10
325 Pat Borders .02 .10
326 Tom Candiotti .02 .10
327 Joe Carter .02 .10
328 Rob Ducey .02 .10
329 Kelly Gruber .02 .10
330 Juan Guzman .02 .10
331 Tom Henke .02 .10
332 Jimmy Key .02 .10
333 Manny Lee .02 .10
334 Al Leiter .02 .10
335 Bob MacDonald .02 .10
336 Candy Maldonado .02 .10
337 Rance Mulliniks .02 .10
338 Greg Myers .02 .10
339 John Olerud UER .02 .10
(1991 BA has .256, but text says .258)
340 Ed Sprague .02 .10
341 Dave Stieb .02 .10
342 Todd Stottlemyre .02 .10
343 Mike Timlin .02 .10
344 Duane Ward .02 .10
345 David Wells .02 .10
346 Devon White .02 .10
347 Mookie Wilson .02 .10
348 Eddie Zosky .02 .10
349 Steve Avery .02 .10
350 Mike Bell .02 .10
351 Rafael Belliard .02 .10
352 Juan Berenguer .02 .10
353 Jeff Blauser .02 .10
354 Sid Bream .02 .10
355 Francisco Cabrera .02 .10
356 Marvin Freeman .02 .10
357 Ron Gant .02 .10
358 Tom Glavine .05 .15
359 Brian Hunter .02 .10
360 Dave Justice .02 .10
361 Charlie Leibrandt .02 .10
362 Mark Lemke .02 .10
363 Kent Mercker .02 .10
364 Keith Mitchell .02 .10
365 Greg Olson .02 .10
366 Terry Pendleton .02 .10
367 Armando Reynoso RC .08 .25
368 Deion Sanders .05 .15
369 Lonnie Smith .02 .10
370 Pete Smith .02 .10
371 John Smoltz .05 .15
372 Mike Stanton .02 .10
373 Jeff Treadway .02 .10
374 Mark Wohlers .02 .10
375 Paul Assenmacher .02 .10
376 George Bell .02 .10
377 Shawn Boskie .02 .10
378 Frank Castillo .02 .10
379 Andre Dawson .02 .10
380 Shawon Dunston .02 .10
381 Mark Grace .05 .15
382 Mike Harkey .02 .10
383 Danny Jackson .02 .10
384 Les Lancaster .02 .10
385 Ced Landrum .02 .10
386 Greg Maddux .15 .40
387 Derrick May .02 .10
388 Chuck McElroy .02 .10
389 Ryne Sandberg .15 .40
390 Heathcliff Slocumb .02 .10
391 Dave Smith .02 .10
392 Dwight Smith .02 .10
393 Rick Sutcliffe .02 .10
394 Hector Villanueva .02 .10
395 Chico Walker .02 .10
396 Jerome Walton .02 .10
397 Rick Wilkins .02 .10
398 Jack Armstrong .02 .10
399 Freddie Benavides .02 .10
400 Glenn Braggs .02 .10
401 Tom Browning .02 .10
402 Norm Charlton .02 .10
403 Eric Davis .02 .10
404 Rob Dibble .02 .10
405 Bill Doran .02 .10
406 Mariano Duncan .02 .10
407 Kip Gross .02 .10
408 Chris Hammond .02 .10
409 Billy Hatcher .02 .10
410 Chris Jones .02 .10
411 Barry Larkin .05 .15
412 Hal Morris .02 .10
413 Randy Myers .02 .10
414 Joe Oliver .02 .10
415 Paul O'Neill .05 .15
416 Ted Power .02 .10
417 Luis Quinones .02 .10
418 Jeff Reed .02 .10
419 Jose Rijo .02 .10
420 Chris Sabo .02 .10
421 Reggie Sanders .02 .10
422 Scott Scudder .02 .10
423 Glenn Sutko .02 .10
424 Eric Anthony .02 .10
425 Jeff Bagwell .08 .25
426 Craig Biggio .05 .15
427 Ken Caminiti .02 .10
428 Casey Candaele .02 .10
429 Mike Capel .02 .10
430 Andujar Cedeno .02 .10
431 Jim Corsi .02 .10
432 Mark Davidson .02 .10
433 Steve Finley .02 .10
434 Luis Gonzalez .02 .10
435 Pete Harnisch .02 .10
436 Dwayne Henry .02 .10
437 Xavier Hernandez .02 .10
438 Jimmy Jones .02 .10
439 Darryl Kile .02 .10
440 Rob Mallicoat .02 .10
441 Andy Mota .02 .10
442 Al Osuna .02 .10
443 Mark Portugal .02 .10
444 Scott Servais .02 .10
445 Mike Simms .02 .10
446 Gerald Young .02 .10
447 Tim Belcher .02 .10
448 Brett Butler .02 .10
449 John Candelaria .02 .10
450 Gary Carter .02 .10
451 Dennis Cook .02 .10
452 Tim Crews .02 .10
453 Kal Daniels .02 .10
454 Jim Gott .02 .10
455 Alfredo Griffin .02 .10
456 Kevin Gross .02 .10
457 Chris Gwynn .02 .10
458 Lenny Harris .02 .10
459 Orel Hershiser .02 .10
460 Jay Howell .02 .10
461 Stan Javier .02 .10
462 Eric Karros .02 .10
463 Ramon Martinez UER .02 .10
(Card says bats right, should be left)
464 Roger McDowell UER .02 .10
(Wins add up to 54, totals have 51)
465 Mike Morgan .02 .10
466 Eddie Murray .08 .25
467 Jose Offerman .02 .10
468 Bob Ojeda .02 .10
469 Juan Samuel .02 .10
470 Mike Scioscia .02 .10
471 Darryl Strawberry .02 .10
472 Bret Barberie .02 .10
473 Brian Barnes .02 .10
474 Eric Bullock .02 .10
475 Ivan Calderon .02 .10
476 Delino DeShields .02 .10
477 Jeff Fassero .02 .10
478 Mike Fitzgerald .02 .10
479 Steve Frey .02 .10
480 Andres Galarraga .02 .10
481 Mark Gardner .02 .10
482 Marquis Grissom .02 .10
483 Chris Haney .02 .10
484 Barry Jones .02 .10
485 Dave Martinez .02 .10
486 Dennis Martinez .02 .10
487 Chris Nabholz .02 .10
488 Spike Owen .02 .10
489 Gilberto Reyes .02 .10
490 Mel Rojas .02 .10
491 Scott Ruskin .02 .10
492 Bill Sampen .02 .10
493 Larry Walker .05 .15
494 Tim Wallach .02 .10
495 Daryl Boston .02 .10
496 Hubie Brooks .02 .10
497 Tim Burke .02 .10
498 Mark Carreon .02 .10
499 Tony Castillo .02 .10
500 Vince Coleman .02 .10
501 David Cone .02 .10
502 Kevin Elster .02 .10
503 Sid Fernandez .02 .10
504 John Franco .02 .10
505 Dwight Gooden .02 .10
506 Todd Hundley .02 .10
507 Jeff Innis .02 .10
508 Gregg Jefferies .02 .10
509 Howard Johnson .02 .10
510 Dave Magadan .02 .10
511 Terry McDaniel .02 .10
512 Kevin McReynolds .02 .10
513 Keith Miller .02 .10
514 Charlie O'Brien .02 .10
515 Mackey Sasser .02 .10
516 Pete Schourek .02 .10
517 Julio Valera .02 .10
518 Frank Viola .02 .10
519 Wally Whitehurst .02 .10
520 Anthony Young .02 .10
521 Andy Ashby .02 .10
522 Kim Batiste .02 .10
523 Joe Boever .02 .10
524 Wes Chamberlain .02 .10
525 Pat Combs .02 .10
526 Danny Cox .02 .10
527 Darren Daulton .02 .10
528 Jose DeJesus .02 .10
529 Len Dykstra .02 .10
530 Darrin Fletcher .02 .10
531 Tommy Greene .02 .10
532 Jason Grimsley .02 .10
533 Charlie Hayes .02 .10
534 Von Hayes .02 .10
535 Dave Hollins .02 .10
536 Ricky Jordan .02 .10
537 John Kruk .02 .10
538 Jim Lindeman .02 .10
539 Mickey Morandini .02 .10
540 Terry Mulholland .02 .10
541 Dale Murphy .05 .15
542 Randy Ready .02 .10
543 Wally Ritchie UER .02 .10
(Letters in data are cut off on card)
544 Bruce Ruffin .02 .10
545 Steve Searcy .02 .10
546 Dickie Thon .02 .10
547 Mitch Williams .02 .10
548 Stan Belinda .02 .10
549 Jay Bell .02 .10
550 Barry Bonds .40 1.00
551 Bobby Bonilla .02 .10
552 Steve Buechele .02 .10
553 Doug Drabek .02 .10
554 Neal Heaton .02 .10
555 Jeff King .02 .10
556 Bob Kipper .02 .10
557 Bill Landrum .02 .10
558 Mike LaValliere .02 .10
559 Jose Lind .02 .10
560 Lloyd McClendon .02 .10
561 Orlando Merced .02 .10
562 Bob Patterson .02 .10
563 Joe Redfield .02 .10
564 Gary Redus .02 .10
565 Rosario Rodriguez .02 .10
566 Don Slaught .02 .10
567 John Smiley .02 .10
568 Zane Smith .02 .10
569 Randy Tomlin .02 .10
570 Andy Van Slyke .05 .15
571 Gary Varsho .02 .10
572 Bob Walk .02 .10
573 John Wehner UER .02 .10
(Actually played for Carolina in 1991, not Cards)
574 Juan Agosto .02 .10
575 Cris Carpenter .02 .10
576 Jose DeLeon .02 .10
577 Rich Gedman .02 .10
578 Bernard Gilkey .02 .10
579 Pedro Guerrero .02 .10
580 Ken Hill .02 .10
581 Rex Hudler .02 .10
582 Felix Jose .02 .10
583 Ray Lankford .02 .10
584 Omar Olivares .02 .10
585 Jose Oquendo .02 .10
586 Tom Pagnozzi .02 .10
587 Geronimo Pena .02 .10
588 Mike Perez .02 .10
589 Gerald Perry .02 .10
590 Bryn Smith .02 .10
591 Lee Smith .02 .10
592 Ozzie Smith .15 .40
593 Scott Terry .02 .10
594 Bob Tewksbury .02 .10
595 Milt Thompson .02 .10
596 Todd Zeile .02 .10
597 Larry Andersen .02 .10
598 Oscar Azocar .02 .10
599 Andy Benes .02 .10
600 Ricky Bones .02 .10
601 Jerald Clark .02 .10
602 Pat Clements .02 .10
603 Paul Faries .02 .10
604 Tony Fernandez .02 .10
605 Tony Gwynn .10 .30
606 Greg W. Harris .02 .10
607 Thomas Howard .02 .10
608 Bruce Hurst .02 .10
609 Darrin Jackson .02 .10
610 Tom Lampkin .02 .10
611 Craig Lefferts .02 .10
612 Jim Lewis RC .02 .10
613 Mike Maddux .02 .10
614 Fred McGriff .05 .15
615 Jose Melendez .02 .10
616 Jose Mota .02 .10
617 Dennis Rasmussen .02 .10
618 Bip Roberts .02 .10
619 Rich Rodriguez .02 .10
620 Benito Santiago .02 .10
621 Craig Shipley .02 .10
622 Tim Teufel .02 .10
623 Kevin Ward .02 .10
624 Ed Whitson .02 .10
625 Dave Anderson .02 .10
626 Kevin Bass .02 .10
627 Rod Beck RC .15 .40
628 Bud Black .02 .10
629 Jeff Brantley .02 .10
630 John Burkett .02 .10
631 Will Clark .05 .15
632 Royce Clayton .02 .10
633 Steve Decker .02 .10
634 Kelly Downs .02 .10
635 Mike Felder .02 .10
636 Scott Garrelts .02 .10
637 Eric Gunderson .02 .10
638 Bryan Hickerson RC .02 .10
639 Darren Lewis .02 .10
640 Greg Litton .02 .10
641 Kirt Manwaring .02 .10
642 Paul McClellan .02 .10
643 Willie McGee .02 .10
644 Kevin Mitchell .02 .10
645 Francisco Oliveras .02 .10
646 Mike Remlinger .02 .10
647 Dave Righetti .02 .10
648 Robby Thompson .02 .10
649 Jose Uribe .02 .10
650 Matt Williams .02 .10
651 Trevor Wilson .02 .10
652 T.Goodwin MLP UER .02 .10
Timed in 3.5, should be be timed
653 Terry Bross MLP .02 .10
654 M.Christopher MLP .02 .10
655 Kenny Lofton MLP .05 .15
656 Chris Cron MLP .02 .10
657 Willie Banks MLP .02 .10
658 Pat Rice MLP .02 .10
659A R.Maurer MLP ERR .30 .75
Name misspelled as Mauer on card front
659B R.Maurer MLP COR .02 .10
660 Don Harris MLP .02 .10
661 Henry Rodriguez MLP .02 .10
662 Cliff Brantley MLP .02 .10
663 M.Linskey MLP UER .02 .10
220 pounds in data, 200 in text
664 Gary DiSarcina MLP .02 .10
665 Gil Heredia RC .08 .25
666 Vinny Castilla RC .40 1.00
667 Paul Abbott MLP .02 .10
668 M.Fariss MLP UER .02 .10
Called Paul on back
669 Jarvis Brown MLP .02 .10
670 Wayne Kirby RC .02 .10
671 Scott Brosius RC .15 .40
672 Bob Hamelin MLP .02 .10
673 Joel Johnston MLP .02 .10
674 Tim Spehr MLP .02 .10
675A J.Gardner MLP ERR .30 .75
P on front, should be SS
675B Jeff Gardner MLP COR .02 .10
676 Rico Rossy MLP .02 .10
677 R.Hernandez MLP RC .02 .10
678 Ted Wood MLP .02 .10
679 Cal Eldred MLP .02 .10
680 Sean Berry MLP .02 .10
681 Rickey Henderson RS .05 .15
682 Nolan Ryan RS .20 .50
683 Dennis Martinez RS .02 .10
684 Wilson Alvarez RS .02 .10
685 Joe Carter RS .02 .10
686 Dave Winfield RS .02 .10
687 David Cone RS .02 .10
688 Jose Canseco LL UER .02 .10
(Text on back has 42 stolen bases in 88; should be 40)
689 Howard Johnson LL .02 .10
690 Julio Franco LL .02 .10
691 Terry Pendleton LL .02 .10
692 Cecil Fielder LL .02 .10
693 Scott Erickson LL .02 .10
694 Tom Glavine LL .02 .10
695 Dennis Martinez LL .02 .10
696 Bryan Harvey LL .02 .10
697 Lee Smith LL .02 .10
698 Roberto Alomar .02 .10
Sandy Alomar Jr.
699 Bobby Bonilla .02 .10
Will Clark
700 Mark Wohlers .02 .10
Kent Mercker
Alejandro Pena
701 Stacy Jones .05 .15
Bo Jackson
Gregg Olson
Frank Thomas
702 Paul Molitor .02 .10
Brett Butler
703 Cal Ripken .15 .40
Joe Carter
704 Barry Larkin .05 .15
Kirby Puckett
705 Mo Vaughn .02 .10
Cecil Fielder
706 Ramon Martinez .02 .10
Ozzie Guillen
707 Harold Baines .02 .10
Wade Boggs
708 Robin Yount PV .08 .25
709 K.Griffey Jr. PV UER .08 .25
Missing quotations on back; BA has .322, but was actually .327
710 Nolan Ryan PV .20 .50
711 Cal Ripken PV .15 .40
712 Frank Thomas PV .05 .15
713 Dave Justice PV .02 .10
714 Checklist 1-101 .02 .10
715 Checklist 102-194 .02 .10
716 Checklist 195-296 .02 .10
717 Checklist 297-397 .02 .10
718 Checklist 398-494 .02 .10
719 Checklist 495-596 .02 .10
720A CL 597-720 ERR .02 .10
659 Rob Mauer
720B CL 597-720 COR .02 .10
659 Rob Maurer

1992 Fleer Update

The 1992 Fleer Update set contains 132 standard-size cards. Cards were distributed exclusively in factory sets through hobby dealers. Factory sets included a four-card, black-bordered "92 Headliners" insert set for a total of 136 cards. Due to lackluster retail response for previous Fleer Update sets, wholesale orders for this product were low, resulting in a short print run. As word got out that the cards were in short supply, the secondary market prices soared soon after release. The basic card design is identical to the regular issue 1992 Fleer cards except for the U-prefixed numbering on back. The cards are checklisted alphabetically within and according to teams for each league with AL preceding NL. Rookie Cards in this set include Jeff Kent and Mike Piazza. The Piazza card is widely recognized as one of the more desirable singles issued in the 1990's.

COMP.FACT.SET (136) 30.00 60.00
COMPLETE SET (132) 30.00 60.00
1 Todd Frohwirth .20 .50
2 Alan Mills .20 .50
3 Rick Sutcliffe .40 1.00
4 John Valentin RC .60 1.50
5 Frank Viola .40 1.00
6 Bob Zupcic RC .20 .50
7 Mike Butcher .20 .50
8 Chad Curtis RC .60 1.50
9 Damion Easley RC .60 1.50
10 Tim Salmon .60 1.50
11 Julio Valera .20 .50
12 George Bell .20 .50
13 Roberto Hernandez .20 .50
14 Shawn Jeter RC .20 .50
15 Thomas Howard .20 .50
16 Jesse Levis .20 .50
17 Kenny Lofton .60 1.50
18 Paul Sorrento .20 .50
19 Rico Brogna .20 .50
20 John Doherty RC .20 .50
21 Dan Gladden .20 .50
22 Buddy Groom RC .20 .50
23 Shawn Hare RC .20 .50
24 John Kiely .20 .50
25 Kurt Knudsen .20 .50
26 Gregg Jefferies .20 .50
27 Wally Joyner .40 1.00
28 Kevin Koslofski .20 .50
29 Kevin McReynolds .20 .50
30 Rusty Meacham .20 .50
31 Keith Miller .20 .50
32 Hipolito Pichardo RC .20 .50
33 Jim Austin .20 .50
34 Scott Fletcher .20 .50
35 John Jaha RC .60 1.50
36 Pat Listach RC .60 1.50
37 Dave Nilsson .20 .50
38 Kevin Seitzer .20 .50
39 Tom Edens .20 .50
40 Pat Mahomes RC .60 1.50
41 John Smiley .20 .50
42 Charlie Hayes .20 .50
43 Sam Militello .20 .50
44 Andy Stankiewicz .20 .50
45 Danny Tartabull .20 .50
46 Bob Wickman 1.00 2.50
47 Jerry Browne .20 .50
48 Kevin Campbell .20 .50
49 Vince Horsman .20 .50
50 Troy Neel RC .20 .50
51 Ruben Sierra .40 1.00
52 Bruce Walton .20 .50
53 Willie Wilson .20 .50
54 Bret Boone .60 1.50
55 Dave Fleming .20 .50
56 Kevin Mitchell .20 .50
57 Jeff Nelson RC 1.00 2.50
58 Shane Turner .20 .50
59 Jose Canseco .60 1.50
60 Jeff Frye RC .20 .50
61 Danny Leon .20 .50
62 Roger Pavlik RC .20 .50
63 David Cone .40 1.00
64 Pat Hentgen .20 .50
65 Randy Knorr .20 .50
66 Jack Morris .40 1.00
67 Dave Winfield .40 1.00
68 David Nied RC .20 .50
69 Otis Nixon .20 .50
70 Alejandro Pena .20 .50
71 Jeff Reardon .40 1.00
72 Alex Arias RC .20 .50
73 Jim Bullinger .20 .50
74 Mike Morgan .20 .50
75 Rey Sanchez RC .60 1.50
76 Bob Scanlan .20 .50
77 Sammy Sosa 1.50 4.00
78 Scott Bankhead .20 .50
79 Tim Belcher .20 .50
80 Steve Foster .20 .50
81 Willie Greene .20 .50
82 Bip Roberts .20 .50
83 Scott Ruskin .20 .50
84 Greg Swindell .20 .50
85 Juan Guerrero .20 .50
86 Butch Henry .20 .50
87 Doug Jones .20 .50
88 Brian Williams RC .20 .50
89 Tom Candiotti .20 .50
90 Eric Davis .40 1.00
91 Carlos Hernandez .20 .50
92 Mike Piazza RC 10.00 25.00
93 Mike Sharperson .20 .50
94 Eric Young RC .60 1.50
95 Moises Alou .40 1.00
96 Greg Colbrunn .20 .50
97 Wil Cordero .20 .50
98 Ken Hill .20 .50
99 John Vander Wal RC .60 1.50
100 John Wetteland .40 1.00
101 Bobby Bonilla .40 1.00
102 Eric Hillman RC .20 .50
103 Pat Howell .20 .50
104 Jeff Kent RC 6.00 15.00
105 Dick Schofield .20 .50
106 Ryan Thompson RC .20 .50
107 Chico Walker .20 .50
108 Juan Bell .20 .50
109 Mariano Duncan .20 .50
110 Jeff Grotewold .20 .50
111 Ben Rivera .20 .50
112 Curt Schilling .60 1.50
113 Victor Cole .20 .50
114 Al Martin RC .60 1.50
115 Roger Mason .20 .50
116 Blas Minor .20 .50
117 Tim Wakefield RC 4.00 10.00
118 Mark Clark RC .20 .50
119 Rheal Cormier .20 .50
120 Donovan Osborne .20 .50
121 Todd Worrell .20 .50
122 Jeremy Hernandez RC .20 .50
123 Randy Myers .20 .50
124 Frank Seminara RC .20 .50
125 Gary Sheffield .40 1.00
126 Dan Walters .20 .50
127 Steve Hosey .20 .50
128 Mike Jackson .20 .50
129 Jim Pena .20 .50
130 Cory Snyder .20 .50
131 Bill Swift .20 .50
132 Checklist U1-U132 .20 .50

1993 Fleer

The 720-card 1993 Fleer baseball set contains two series of 360 standard-size cards. Cards were distributed in plastic wrapped packs, cello packs, jumbo packs and rack packs. For the first time in years, Fleer did not issue a factory set. In fact, Fleer

discontinued issuing factory sets from 1993 through 1998. The cards are checklisted below alphabetically within and according to teams for each league with NL preceding AL. Topical subsets include League Leaders (344-348/704-708), Round Trippers (349-353/709-713), and Super Star Specials (354-357/714-717). Each series concludes with checklists (358-360/718-720). There are no key Rookie Cards in this set.

COMPLETE SET (720) 20.00 40.00
COMP.SERIES 1 (360) 10.00 20.00
COMP.SERIES 2 (360) 10.00 20.00
1 Steve Avery .02 .10
2 Sid Bream .02 .10
3 Ron Gant .07 .20
4 Tom Glavine .10 .30
5 Brian Hunter .02 .10
6 Ryan Klesko .07 .20
7 Charlie Leibrandt .02 .10
8 Kent Mercker .02 .10
9 David Nied .02 .10
10 Otis Nixon .02 .10
11 Greg Olson .02 .10
12 Terry Pendleton .07 .20
13 Deion Sanders .10 .30
14 John Smoltz .10 .30
15 Mike Stanton .02 .10
16 Mark Wohlers .02 .10
17 Paul Assenmacher .02 .10
18 Steve Buechele .02 .10
19 Shawon Dunston .02 .10
20 Mark Grace .10 .30
21 Derrick May .02 .10
22 Chuck McElroy .02 .10
23 Mike Morgan .02 .10
24 Rey Sanchez .02 .10
25 Ryne Sandberg .30 .75
26 Bob Scanlan .02 .10
27 Sammy Sosa .20 .50
28 Rick Wilkins .02 .10
29 Bobby Ayala RC .02 .10
30 Tim Belcher .02 .10
31 Jeff Branson .02 .10
32 Norm Charlton .02 .10
33 Steve Foster .02 .10
34 Willie Greene .02 .10
35 Chris Hammond .02 .10
36 Milt Hill .02 .10
37 Hal Morris .02 .10
38 Joe Oliver .02 .10
39 Paul O'Neill .10 .30
40 Tim Pugh RC .02 .10
41 Jose Rijo .02 .10
42 Bip Roberts .02 .10
43 Chris Sabo .02 .10
44 Reggie Sanders .07 .20
45 Eric Anthony .02 .10
46 Jeff Bagwell .10 .30
47 Craig Biggio .10 .30
48 Joe Boever .02 .10
49 Casey Candaele .02 .10
50 Steve Finley .07 .20
51 Luis Gonzalez .07 .20
52 Pete Harnisch .02 .10
53 Xavier Hernandez .02 .10
54 Doug Jones .02 .10
55 Eddie Taubensee .02 .10
56 Brian Williams .02 .10
57 Pedro Astacio .02 .10
58 Todd Benzinger .02 .10
59 Brett Butler .07 .20
60 Tom Candiotti .02 .10
61 Lenny Harris .02 .10
62 Carlos Hernandez .02 .10
63 Orel Hershiser .07 .20
64 Eric Karros .07 .20
65 Ramon Martinez .02 .10
66 Jose Offerman .02 .10
67 Mike Scioscia .02 .10
68 Mike Sharperson .02 .10
69 Eric Young .02 .10
70 Moises Alou .07 .20
71 Ivan Calderon .02 .10
72 Archi Cianfrocco .02 .10
73 Wil Cordero .02 .10
74 Delino DeShields .02 .10
75 Mark Gardner .02 .10
76 Ken Hill .02 .10
77 Tim Laker RC .02 .10
78 Chris Nabholz .02 .10
79 Mel Rojas .02 .10
80 John Vander Wal UER .02 .10
(Misspelled Vander Wall in letters on back)
81 Larry Walker .07 .20
82 Tim Wallach .02 .10
83 John Wetteland .07 .20
84 Bobby Bonilla .07 .20
85 Daryl Boston .02 .10
86 Sid Fernandez .02 .10
87 Eric Hillman .02 .10
88 Todd Hundley .02 .10
89 Howard Johnson .02 .10
90 Jeff Kent .20 .50
91 Eddie Murray .20 .50
92 Bill Pecota .02 .10
93 Bret Saberhagen .07 .20
94 Dick Schofield .02 .10
95 Pete Schourek .02 .10
96 Anthony Young .02 .10
97 Ruben Amaro .02 .10
98 Juan Bell .02 .10
99 Wes Chamberlain .02 .10
100 Darren Daulton .07 .20
101 Mariano Duncan .02 .10
102 Mike Hartley .02 .10
103 Ricky Jordan .02 .10

104 John Kruk .07 .20
105 Mickey Morandini .02 .10
106 Terry Mulholland .02 .10
107 Ben Rivera .02 .10
108 Curt Schilling .07 .20
109 Keith Shepherd RC .02 .10
110 Stan Belinda .02 .10
111 Jay Bell .07 .20
112 Barry Bonds .60 1.50
113 Jeff King .02 .10
114 Mike LaValliere .02 .10
115 Jose Lind .02 .10
116 Roger Mason .02 .10
117 Orlando Merced .02 .10
118 Bob Patterson .02 .10
119 Don Slaught .02 .10
120 Zane Smith .02 .10
121 Randy Tomlin .02 .10
122 Andy Van Slyke .10 .30
123 Tim Wakefield .20 .50
124 Rheal Cormier .02 .10
125 Bernard Gilkey .02 .10
126 Felix Jose .02 .10
127 Ray Lankford .07 .20
128 Bob McClure .02 .10
129 Donovan Osborne .02 .10
130 Tom Pagnozzi .02 .10
131 Geronimo Pena .02 .10
132 Mike Perez .02 .10
133 Lee Smith .07 .20
134 Bob Tewksbury .02 .10
135 Todd Worrell .02 .10
136 Todd Zeile .02 .10
137 Jerald Clark .02 .10
138 Tony Gwynn .25 .60
139 Greg W. Harris .02 .10
140 Jeremy Hernandez .02 .10
141 Darrin Jackson .02 .10
142 Mike Maddux .02 .10
143 Fred McGriff .10 .30
144 Jose Melendez .02 .10
145 Rich Rodriguez .02 .10
146 Frank Seminara .02 .10
147 Gary Sheffield .07 .20
148 Kurt Stillwell .02 .10
149 Dan Walters .02 .10
150 Rod Beck .02 .10
151 Bud Black .02 .10
152 Jeff Brantley .02 .10
153 John Burkett .02 .10
154 Will Clark .10 .30
155 Royce Clayton .02 .10
156 Mike Jackson .02 .10
157 Darren Lewis .02 .10
158 Kirt Manwaring .02 .10
159 Willie McGee .07 .20
160 Cory Snyder .02 .10
161 Bill Swift .02 .10
162 Trevor Wilson .02 .10
163 Brady Anderson .07 .20
164 Glenn Davis .02 .10
165 Mike Devereaux .02 .10
166 Todd Frohwirth .02 .10
167 Leo Gomez .02 .10
168 Chris Hoiles .02 .10
169 Ben McDonald .02 .10
170 Randy Milligan .02 .10
171 Alan Mills .02 .10
172 Mike Mussina .10 .30
173 Gregg Olson .02 .10
174 Arthur Rhodes .02 .10
175 David Segui .02 .10
176 Ellis Burks .07 .20
177 Roger Clemens .40 1.00
178 Scott Cooper .02 .10
179 Danny Darwin .02 .10
180 Tony Fossas .02 .10
181 Paul Quantrill .02 .10
182 Jody Reed .02 .10
183 John Valentin .02 .10
184 Mo Vaughn .07 .20
185 Frank Viola .07 .20
186 Bob Zupcic .02 .10
187 Jim Abbott .10 .30
188 Gary DiSarcina .02 .10
189 Damion Easley .02 .10
190 Junior Felix .02 .10
191 Chuck Finley .07 .20
192 Joe Grahe .02 .10
193 Bryan Harvey .02 .10
194 Mark Langston .02 .10
195 John Orton .02 .10
196 Luis Polonia .02 .10
197 Tim Salmon .10 .30
198 Luis Sojo .02 .10
199 Wilson Alvarez .02 .10
200 George Bell .02 .10
201 Alex Fernandez .02 .10
202 Craig Grebeck .02 .10
203 Ozzie Guillen .07 .20
204 Lance Johnson .02 .10
205 Ron Karkovice .02 .10
206 Kirk McCaskill .02 .10
207 Jack McDowell .02 .10
208 Scott Radinsky .02 .10
209 Tim Raines .07 .20
210 Frank Thomas .20 .50
211 Robin Ventura .07 .20
212 Sandy Alomar Jr. .02 .10
213 Carlos Baerga .02 .10
214 Dennis Cook .02 .10
215 Thomas Howard .02 .10
216 Mark Lewis .02 .10
217 Derek Lilliquist .02 .10
218 Kenny Lofton .07 .20
219 Charles Nagy .02 .10
220 Steve Olin .02 .10
221 Paul Sorrento .02 .10
222 Jim Thome .10 .30
223 Mark Whiten .02 .10
224 Milt Cuyler .02 .10
225 Rob Deer .02 .10
226 John Doherty .02 .10
227 Cecil Fielder .07 .20
228 Travis Fryman .07 .20
229 Mike Henneman .02 .10
230 John Kiely UER .02 .10
(Card has batting stats of Pat Kelly)
231 Kurt Knudsen .02 .10
232 Scott Livingstone .02 .10
233 Tony Phillips .02 .10
234 Mickey Tettleton .02 .10
235 Kevin Appier .07 .20
236 George Brett .50 1.25
237 Tom Gordon .02 .10
238 Gregg Jefferies .02 .10
239 Wally Joyner .07 .20
240 Kevin Koslofski .02 .10
241 Mike Macfarlane .02 .10
242 Brian McRae .02 .10
243 Rusty Meacham .02 .10
244 Keith Miller .02 .10
245 Jeff Montgomery .02 .10
246 Hipolito Pichardo .02 .10
247 Ricky Bones .02 .10
248 Cal Eldred .02 .10
249 Mike Fetters .02 .10
250 Darryl Hamilton .02 .10
251 Doug Henry .02 .10
252 John Jaha .02 .10
253 Pat Listach .02 .10
254 Paul Molitor .07 .20
255 Jaime Navarro .02 .10
256 Kevin Seitzer .02 .10
257 B.J. Surhoff .07 .20
258 Greg Vaughn .02 .10
259 Bill Wegman .02 .10
260 Robin Yount .30 .75
261 Rick Aguilera .02 .10
262 Chili Davis .07 .20
263 Scott Erickson .02 .10
264 Greg Gagne .02 .10
265 Mark Guthrie .02 .10
266 Brian Harper .02 .10
267 Kent Hrbek .07 .20
268 Terry Jorgensen .02 .10
269 Gene Larkin .02 .10
270 Scott Leius .02 .10
271 Pat Mahomes .02 .10
272 Pedro Munoz .02 .10
273 Kirby Puckett .20 .50
274 Kevin Tapani .02 .10
275 Carl Willis .02 .10
276 Steve Farr .02 .10
277 John Habyan .02 .10
278 Mel Hall .02 .10
279 Charlie Hayes .02 .10
280 Pat Kelly .02 .10
281 Don Mattingly .50 1.25
282 Sam Militello .02 .10
283 Matt Nokes .02 .10
284 Melido Perez .02 .10
285 Andy Stankiewicz .02 .10
286 Danny Tartabull .02 .10
287 Randy Velarde .02 .10
288 Bob Wickman .02 .10
289 Bernie Williams .10 .30
290 Lance Blankenship .02 .10
291 Mike Bordick .02 .10
292 Jerry Browne .02 .10
293 Dennis Eckersley .07 .20
294 Rickey Henderson .20 .50
295 Vince Horsman .02 .10
296 Mark McGwire .50 1.25
297 Jeff Parrett .02 .10
298 Ruben Sierra .07 .20
299 Terry Steinbach .02 .10
300 Walt Weiss .02 .10
301 Bob Welch .02 .10
302 Willie Wilson .02 .10
303 Bobby Witt .02 .10
304 Bret Boone .07 .20
305 Jay Buhner .07 .20
306 Dave Fleming .02 .10
307 Ken Griffey Jr. .30 .75
308 Erik Hanson .02 .10
309 Edgar Martinez .10 .30
310 Tino Martinez .10 .30
311 Jeff Nelson .02 .10
312 Dennis Powell .02 .10
313 Mike Schooler .02 .10
314 Russ Swan .02 .10
315 Dave Valle .02 .10
316 Omar Vizquel .10 .30
317 Kevin Brown .07 .20
318 Todd Burns .02 .10
319 Jose Canseco .10 .30
320 Julio Franco .07 .20
321 Jeff Frye .02 .10
322 Juan Gonzalez .07 .20
323 Jose Guzman .02 .10
324 Jeff Huson .02 .10
325 Dean Palmer .07 .20
326 Kevin Reimer .02 .10
327 Ivan Rodriguez .10 .30
328 Kenny Rogers .07 .20
329 Dan Smith .02 .10
330 Roberto Alomar .10 .30
331 Derek Bell .02 .10
332 Pat Borders .02 .10
333 Joe Carter .07 .20
334 Kelly Gruber .02 .10
335 Tom Henke .02 .10
336 Jimmy Key .07 .20
337 Manuel Lee .02 .10
338 Candy Maldonado .02 .10
339 John Olerud .07 .20
340 Todd Stottlemyre .02 .10
341 Duane Ward .02 .10
342 Devon White .07 .20
343 Dave Winfield .07 .20
344 Edgar Martinez LL .07 .20
345 Cecil Fielder LL .02 .10
346 Kenny Lofton LL .02 .10
347 Jack Morris LL .02 .10
348 Roger Clemens LL .20 .50
349 Fred McGriff RT .07 .20
350 Barry Bonds RT .30 .75
351 Gary Sheffield RT .02 .10
352 Darren Daulton RT .02 .10
353 Dave Hollins RT .02 .10
354 Pedro Martinez .20 .50
Ramon Martinez
355 Ivan Rodriguez .10 .30
Kirby Puckett
356 Ryne Sandberg .20 .50
Gary Sheffield
357 Roberto Alomar .07 .20
Chuck Knoblauch
Carlos Baerga
358 Checklist 1-120 .02 .10
359 Checklist 121-240 .02 .10
360 Checklist 241-360 .02 .10
361 Rafael Belliard .02 .10
362 Damon Berryhill .02 .10
363 Mike Bielecki .02 .10
364 Jeff Blauser .02 .10
365 Francisco Cabrera .02 .10
366 Marvin Freeman .02 .10
367 David Justice .07 .20
368 Mark Lemke .02 .10
369 Alejandro Pena .02 .10
370 Jeff Reardon .07 .20
371 Lonnie Smith .02 .10
372 Pete Smith .02 .10
373 Shawn Boskie .02 .10
374 Jim Bullinger .02 .10
375 Frank Castillo .02 .10
376 Doug Dascenzo .02 .10
377 Andre Dawson .07 .20
378 Mike Harkey .02 .10
379 Greg Hibbard .02 .10
380 Greg Maddux .30 .75
381 Ken Patterson .02 .10
382 Jeff D. Robinson .02 .10
383 Luis Salazar .02 .10
384 Dwight Smith .02 .10
385 Jose Vizcaino .02 .10
386 Scott Bankhead .02 .10
387 Tom Browning .02 .10
388 Darnell Coles .02 .10
389 Rob Dibble .07 .20
390 Bill Doran .02 .10
391 Dwayne Henry .02 .10
392 Cesar Hernandez .02 .10
393 Roberto Kelly .02 .10
394 Barry Larkin .10 .30
395 Dave Martinez .02 .10
396 Kevin Mitchell .02 .10
397 Jeff Reed .02 .10
398 Scott Ruskin .02 .10
399 Greg Swindell .02 .10
400 Dan Wilson .07 .20
401 Andy Ashby .02 .10
402 Freddie Benavides .02 .10
403 Dante Bichette .07 .20
404 Willie Blair .02 .10
405 Denis Boucher .02 .10
406 Vinny Castilla .20 .50
407 Braulio Castillo .02 .10
408 Alex Cole .02 .10
409 Andres Galarraga .07 .20
410 Joe Girardi .02 .10
411 Butch Henry .02 .10
412 Darren Holmes .02 .10
413 Calvin Jones .02 .10
414 Steve Reed RC .02 .10
415 Kevin Ritz .02 .10
416 Jim Tatum RC .02 .10
417 Jack Armstrong .02 .10
418 Bret Barberie .02 .10
419 Ryan Bowen .02 .10
420 Cris Carpenter .02 .10
421 Chuck Carr .02 .10
422 Scott Chiamparino .02 .10
423 Jeff Conine .07 .20
424 Jim Corsi .02 .10
425 Steve Decker .02 .10
426 Chris Donnels .02 .10
427 Monty Fariss .02 .10
428 Bob Natal .02 .10
429 Pat Rapp .02 .10
430 Dave Weathers .02 .10
431 Nigel Wilson .02 .10
432 Ken Caminiti .07 .20
433 Andujar Cedeno .02 .10
434 Tom Edens .02 .10
435 Juan Guerrero .02 .10
436 Pete Incaviglia .02 .10
437 Jimmy Jones .02 .10
438 Darryl Kile .07 .20
439 Rob Murphy .02 .10
440 Al Osuna .02 .10
441 Mark Portugal .02 .10
442 Scott Servais .02 .10
443 John Candelaria .02 .10
444 Tim Crews .02 .10
445 Eric Davis .07 .20
446 Tom Goodwin .02 .10
447 Jim Gott .02 .10
448 Kevin Gross .02 .10
449 Dave Hansen .02 .10
450 Jay Howell .02 .10
451 Roger McDowell .02 .10
452 Bob Ojeda .02 .10
453 Henry Rodriguez .02 .10
454 Darryl Strawberry .07 .20
455 Mitch Webster .02 .10
456 Steve Wilson .02 .10
457 Brian Barnes .02 .10
458 Sean Berry .02 .10
459 Jeff Fassero .02 .10
460 Darrin Fletcher .02 .10
461 Marquis Grissom .07 .20
462 Dennis Martinez .07 .20
463 Spike Owen .02 .10
464 Matt Stairs .02 .10
465 Sergio Valdez .02 .10
466 Kevin Bass .02 .10
467 Vince Coleman .02 .10
468 Mark Dewey .02 .10
469 Kevin Elster .02 .10
470 Tony Fernandez .02 .10
471 John Franco .07 .20
472 Dave Gallagher .02 .10
473 Paul Gibson .02 .10
474 Dwight Gooden .07 .20
475 Lee Guetterman .02 .10
476 Jeff Innis .02 .10
477 Dave Magadan .02 .10
478 Charlie O'Brien .02 .10
479 Willie Randolph .07 .20
480 Mackey Sasser .02 .10
481 Ryan Thompson .02 .10
482 Chico Walker .02 .10
483 Kyle Abbott .02 .10
484 Bob Ayrault .02 .10
485 Kim Batiste .02 .10
486 Cliff Brantley .02 .10
487 Jose DeLeon .02 .10
488 Len Dykstra .07 .20
489 Tommy Greene .02 .10
490 Jeff Grotewold .02 .10
491 Dave Hollins .02 .10
492 Danny Jackson .02 .10
493 Stan Javier .02 .10
494 Tom Marsh .02 .10
495 Greg Mathews .02 .10
496 Dale Murphy .10 .30
497 Todd Pratt RC .07 .20
498 Mitch Williams .02 .10
499 Danny Cox .02 .10
500 Doug Drabek .02 .10
501 Carlos Garcia .02 .10
502 Lloyd McClendon .02 .10
503 Denny Neagle .07 .20
504 Gary Redus .02 .10
505 Bob Walk .02 .10
506 John Wehner .02 .10
507 Luis Alicea .02 .10
508 Mark Clark .02 .10
509 Pedro Guerrero .07 .20
510 Rex Hudler .02 .10
511 Brian Jordan .07 .20
512 Omar Olivares .02 .10
513 Jose Oquendo .02 .10
514 Gerald Perry .02 .10
515 Bryn Smith .02 .10
516 Craig Wilson .02 .10
517 Tracy Woodson .02 .10
518 Larry Andersen .02 .10
519 Andy Benes .02 .10
520 Jim Deshaies .02 .10
521 Bruce Hurst .02 .10
522 Randy Myers .02 .10
523 Benito Santiago .07 .20
524 Tim Scott .02 .10
525 Tim Teufel .02 .10
526 Mike Benjamin .02 .10
527 Dave Burba .02 .10
528 Craig Colbert .02 .10
529 Mike Felder .02 .10
530 Bryan Hickerson .02 .10
531 Chris James .02 .10
532 Mark Leonard .02 .10
533 Greg Litton .02 .10
534 Francisco Oliveras .02 .10
535 John Patterson .02 .10
536 Jim Pena .02 .10
537 Dave Righetti .07 .20
538 Robby Thompson .02 .10
539 Jose Uribe .02 .10
540 Matt Williams .07 .20
541 Storm Davis .02 .10
542 Sam Horn .02 .10
543 Tim Hulett .02 .10
544 Craig Lefferts .02 .10
545 Chito Martinez .02 .10
546 Mark McLemore .02 .10
547 Luis Mercedes .02 .10
548 Bob Milacki .02 .10
549 Joe Orsulak .02 .10
550 Billy Ripken .02 .10
551 Cal Ripken Jr. .60 1.50
552 Rick Sutcliffe .07 .20
553 Jeff Tackett .02 .10
554 Wade Boggs .10 .30
555 Tom Brunansky .02 .10
556 Jack Clark .07 .20
557 John Dopson .02 .10
558 Mike Gardiner .02 .10
559 Mike Greenwell .02 .10
560 Greg A. Harris .02 .10
561 Billy Hatcher .02 .10
562 Joe Hesketh .02 .10
563 Tony Pena .02 .10
564 Phil Plantier .02 .10
565 Luis Rivera .02 .10
566 Herm Winningham .02 .10
567 Matt Young .02 .10
568 Bert Blyleven .07 .20
569 Mike Butcher .02 .10
570 Chuck Crim .02 .10
571 Chad Curtis .02 .10
572 Tim Fortugno .02 .10
573 Steve Frey .02 .10
574 Gary Gaetti .07 .20
575 Scott Lewis .02 .10
576 Lee Stevens .02 .10
577 Ron Tingley .02 .10
578 Julio Valera .02 .10
579 Shawn Abner .02 .10
580 Joey Cora .02 .10
581 Chris Cron .02 .10
582 Carlton Fisk .10 .30
583 Roberto Hernandez .02 .10
584 Charlie Hough .07 .20
585 Terry Leach .02 .10
586 Donn Pall .02 .10
587 Dan Pasqua .02 .10
588 Steve Sax .02 .10
589 Bobby Thigpen .02 .10
590 Albert Belle .07 .20
591 Felix Fermin .02 .10
592 Glenallen Hill .02 .10
593 Brook Jacoby .02 .10
594 Reggie Jefferson .02 .10
595 Carlos Martinez .02 .10
596 Jose Mesa .02 .10
597 Rod Nichols .02 .10
598 Junior Ortiz .02 .10
599 Eric Plunk .02 .10
600 Ted Power .02 .10
601 Scott Scudder .02 .10
602 Kevin Wickander .02 .10
603 Skeeter Barnes .02 .10
604 Mark Carreon .02 .10
605 Dan Gladden .02 .10
606 Bill Gullickson .02 .10
607 Chad Kreuter .02 .10
608 Mark Leiter .02 .10
609 Mike Munoz .02 .10
610 Rich Rowland .02 .10
611 Frank Tanana .02 .10
612 Walt Terrell .02 .10
613 Alan Trammell .07 .20
614 Lou Whitaker .07 .20
615 Luis Aquino .02 .10
616 Mike Boddicker .02 .10
617 Jim Eisenreich .02 .10
618 Mark Gubicza .02 .10
619 David Howard .02 .10
620 Mike Magnante .02 .10
621 Brent Mayne .02 .10
622 Kevin McReynolds .02 .10
623 Ed Pierce RC .02 .10
624 Bill Sampen .02 .10
625 Steve Shifflett .02 .10
626 Gary Thurman .02 .10
627 Curt Wilkerson .02 .10
628 Chris Bosio .02 .10
629 Scott Fletcher .02 .10
630 Jim Gantner .02 .10
631 Dave Nilsson .02 .10
632 Jesse Orosco .02 .10
633 Dan Plesac .02 .10
634 Ron Robinson .02 .10
635 Bill Spiers .02 .10
636 Franklin Stubbs .02 .10
637 Willie Banks .02 .10
638 Randy Bush .02 .10
639 Chuck Knoblauch .07 .20
640 Shane Mack .02 .10
641 Mike Pagliarulo .02 .10
642 Jeff Reboulet .02 .10
643 John Smiley .02 .10
644 Mike Trombley .02 .10
645 Gary Wayne .02 .10
646 Lenny Webster .02 .10
647 Tim Burke .02 .10
648 Mike Gallego .02 .10
649 Dion James .02 .10
650 Jeff Johnson .02 .10
651 Scott Kamieniecki .02 .10
652 Kevin Maas .02 .10
653 Rich Monteleone .02 .10
654 Jerry Nielsen .02 .10
655 Scott Sanderson .02 .10
656 Mike Stanley .02 .10
657 Gerald Williams .02 .10
658 Curt Young .02 .10
659 Harold Baines .07 .20
660 Kevin Campbell .02 .10
661 Ron Darling .02 .10
662 Kelly Downs .02 .10
663 Eric Fox .02 .10
664 Dave Henderson .02 .10
665 Rick Honeycutt .02 .10
666 Mike Moore .02 .10
667 Jamie Quirk .02 .10
668 Jeff Russell .02 .10
669 Dave Stewart .07 .20
670 Greg Briley .02 .10
671 Dave Cochrane .02 .10
672 Henry Cotto .02 .10
673 Rich DeLucia .02 .10
674 Brian Fisher .02 .10
675 Mark Grant .02 .10
676 Randy Johnson .20 .50
677 Tim Leary .02 .10
678 Pete O'Brien .02 .10
679 Lance Parrish .07 .20
680 Harold Reynolds .07 .20
681 Shane Turner .02 .10
682 Jack Daugherty .02 .10
683 David Hulse RC .02 .10
684 Terry Mathews .02 .10
685 Al Newman .02 .10
686 Edwin Nunez .02 .10
687 Rafael Palmeiro .10 .30
688 Roger Pavlik .02 .10
689 Geno Petralli .02 .10
690 Nolan Ryan .75 2.00
691 David Cone .07 .20
692 Alfredo Griffin .02 .10
693 Juan Guzman .02 .10
694 Pat Hentgen .02 .10
695 Randy Knorr .02 .10
696 Bob MacDonald .02 .10
697 Jack Morris .07 .20
698 Ed Sprague .02 .10
699 Dave Stieb .02 .10
700 Pat Tabler .02 .10
701 Mike Timlin .02 .10
702 David Wells .07 .20
703 Eddie Zosky .02 .10
704 Gary Sheffield LL .02 .10
705 Darren Daulton LL .02 .10
706 Marquis Grissom LL .02 .10
707 Greg Maddux LL .20 .50
708 Bill Swift LL .02 .10
709 Juan Gonzalez RT .02 .10
710 Mark McGwire RT .25 .60
711 Cecil Fielder RT .02 .10
712 Albert Belle RT .07 .20
713 Joe Carter RT .02 .10
714 Cecil Fielder SS .10 .30
Frank Thomas
715 Larry Walker SS .07 .20
Darren Daulton
716 Edgar Martinez SS .07 .20
Robin Ventura
717 Roger Clemens SS .20 .50
Dennis Eckersley
718 Checklist 361-480 .02 .10
719 Checklist 481-600 .02 .10
720 Checklist 601-720 .02 .10

1993 Fleer Final Edition

This 300-card standard-size set was issued exclusively in factory set form (along with ten Diamond Tribute inserts) to update and feature rookies not in the regular 1993 Fleer set. The cards are identical in design to regular issue 1993 Fleer cards except for the F-prefixed numbering. Cards are ordered alphabetically within teams with NL preceding AL. The set closes with checklist cards (298-300). The only key Rookie Card in this set features Jim Edmonds.

COMP.FACT.SET (310) 4.00 10.00
COMPLETE SET (300) 3.00 8.00
1 Steve Bedrosian .02 .10
2 Jay Howell .02 .10
3 Greg Maddux .30 .75
4 Greg McMichael RC .05 .15
5 Tony Tarasco RC .05 .15
6 Jose Bautista .02 .10
7 Jose Guzman .02 .10
8 Greg Hibbard .02 .10
9 Candy Maldonado .02 .10
10 Randy Myers .02 .10
11 Matt Walbeck RC .15 .40
12 Turk Wendell .02 .10
13 Willie Wilson .02 .10
14 Greg Cadaret .02 .10
15 Roberto Kelly .02 .10
16 Randy Milligan .02 .10
17 Kevin Mitchell .02 .10
18 Jeff Reardon .07 .20
19 John Roper .02 .10
20 John Smiley .02 .10
21 Andy Ashby .02 .10
22 Dante Bichette .07 .20
23 Willie Blair .02 .10
24 Pedro Castellano .02 .10
25 Vinny Castilla .20 .50
26 Jerald Clark .02 .10
27 Alex Cole .02 .10
28 Scott Fredrickson RC .05 .15
29 Jay Gainer RC .05 .15
30 Andres Galarraga .07 .20
31 Joe Girardi .02 .10
32 Ryan Hawblitzel .02 .10
33 Charlie Hayes .02 .10
34 Darren Holmes .02 .10
35 Chris Jones .02 .10
36 David Nied .02 .10
37 J.Owens RC .05 .15
38 Lance Painter RC .15 .40
39 Jeff Parrett .02 .10
40 Steve Reed .02 .10
41 Armando Reynoso .02 .10
42 Bruce Ruffin .02 .10
43 Danny Sheaffer RC .05 .15
44 Keith Shepherd .02 .10
45 Jim Tatum .02 .10
46 Gary Wayne .02 .10
47 Eric Young .02 .10
48 Luis Aquino .02 .10
49 Alex Arias .02 .10
50 Jack Armstrong .02 .10
51 Bret Barberie .02 .10
52 Geronimo Berroa .02 .10
53 Ryan Bowen .02 .10
54 Greg Briley .02 .10
55 Cris Carpenter .02 .10
56 Chuck Carr .02 .10
57 Jeff Conine .07 .20
58 Jim Corsi .02 .10
59 Orestes Destrade .02 .10
60 Junior Felix .02 .10
61 Chris Hammond .02 .10
62 Bryan Harvey .02 .10
63 Charlie Hough .07 .20
64 Joe Klink .02 .10
65 Richie Lewis RC UER .05 .15
(Refers to place of birth and residence as Illinois instead of Indiana)
66 Mitch Lyden RC .05 .15
67 Bob Natal .02 .10
68 Scott Pose RC .05 .15
69 Rich Renteria .02 .10
70 Benito Santiago .07 .20
71 Gary Sheffield .07 .20
72 Matt Turner RC .05 .15
73 Walt Weiss .02 .10
74 Darrell Whitmore RC .05 .15
75 Nigel Wilson .02 .10
76 Kevin Bass .02 .10
77 Doug Drabek .02 .10
78 Tom Edens .02 .10
79 Chris James .02 .10
80 Greg Swindell .02 .10
81 Omar Daal RC .05 .15
82 Raul Mondesi .07 .20
83 Jody Reed .02 .10
84 Cory Snyder .02 .10
85 Rick Trlicek .02 .10
86 Tim Wallach .02 .10
87 Todd Worrell .02 .10
88 Tavo Alvarez .02 .10
89 Frank Bolick .02 .10
90 Kent Bottenfield .02 .10
91 Greg Colbrunn .02 .10
92 Cliff Floyd .07 .20
93 Lou Frazier RC .05 .15
94 Mike Gardiner .02 .10
95 Mike Lansing RC .15 .40
96 Bill Risley .02 .10
97 Jeff Shaw .02 .10
98 Kevin Baez .02 .10
99 Tim Bogar RC .05 .15
100 Jeromy Burnitz .07 .20
101 Mike Draper .02 .10
102 Darrin Jackson .02 .10
103 Mike Maddux .02 .10
104 Joe Orsulak .02 .10
105 Doug Saunders RC .05 .15
106 Frank Tanana .02 .10
107 Dave Telgheder RC .05 .15
108 Larry Andersen .02 .10
109 Jim Eisenreich .02 .10
110 Pete Incaviglia .02 .10
111 Danny Jackson .02 .10
112 David West .02 .10
113 Al Martin .02 .10
114 Blas Minor .02 .10
115 Dennis Moeller .02 .10
116 William Pennyfeather .02 .10
117 Rich Robertson RC .05 .15
118 Ben Shelton .02 .10
119 Lonnie Smith .02 .10
120 Freddie Toliver .02 .10
121 Paul Wagner .02 .10
122 Kevin Young .07 .20
123 Rene Arocha RC .15 .40
124 Gregg Jefferies .02 .10
125 Paul Kilgus .02 .10
126 Les Lancaster .02 .10
127 Joe Magrane .02 .10
128 Rob Murphy .02 .10

129 Erik Pappas .02 .10
130 Stan Royer .02 .10
131 Ozzie Smith .30 .75
132 Tom Urbani RC .05 .15
133 Mark Whiten .02 .10
134 Derek Bell .02 .10
135 Doug Brocail .02 .10
136 Phil Clark .02 .10
137 Mark Ettles RC .05 .15
138 Jeff Gardner .02 .10
139 Pat Gomez RC .05 .15
140 Ricky Gutierrez .02 .10
141 Gene Harris .02 .10
142 Kevin Higgins .02 .10
143 Trevor Hoffman .20 .50
144 Phil Plantier .02 .10
145 Kerry Taylor RC .05 .15
146 Guillermo Velasquez .02 .10
147 Wally Whitehurst .02 .10
148 Tim Worrell RC .15 .40
149 Todd Benzinger .02 .10
150 Barry Bonds .60 1.50
151 Greg Brummett RC .05 .15
152 Mark Carreon .02 .10
153 Dave Martinez .02 .10
154 Jeff Reed .02 .10
155 Kevin Rogers .02 .10
156 Harold Baines .07 .20
157 Damon Buford .02 .10
158 Paul Carey RC .05 .15
159 Jeffrey Hammonds .02 .10
160 Jamie Moyer .07 .20
161 Sherman Obando RC .05 .15
162 John O'Donoghue RC .05 .15
163 Brad Pennington .02 .10
164 Jim Poole .02 .10
165 Harold Reynolds .07 .20
166 Fernando Valenzuela .07 .20
167 Jack Voigt RC .05 .15
168 Mark Williamson .02 .10
169 Scott Bankhead .02 .10
170 Greg Blosser .02 .10
171 Jim Byrd RC .05 .15
172 Ivan Calderon .02 .10
173 Andre Dawson .07 .20
174 Scott Fletcher .02 .10
175 Jose Melendez .02 .10
176 Carlos Quintana .02 .10
177 Jeff Russell .02 .10
178 Aaron Sele .02 .10
179 Rod Correia RC .05 .15
180 Chili Davis .07 .20
181 Jim Edmonds RC 1.25 3.00
182 Rene Gonzales .02 .10
183 Hilly Hathaway RC .05 .15
184 Torey Lovullo .02 .10
185 Greg Myers .02 .10
186 Gene Nelson .02 .10
187 Troy Percival .10 .30
188 Scott Sanderson .02 .10
189 Darryl Scott RC .05 .15
190 J.T. Snow RC .25 .60
191 Russ Springer .02 .10
192 Jason Bere .02 .10
193 Rodney Bolton .02 .10
194 Ellis Burks .07 .20
195 Bo Jackson .20 .50
196 Mike LaValliere .02 .10
197 Scott Ruffcorn .02 .10
198 Jeff Schwarz .02 .10
199 Jerry DiPoto .02 .10
200 Alvaro Espinoza .02 .10
201 Wayne Kirby .02 .10
202 Tom Kramer RC .05 .15
203 Jesse Levis .02 .10
204 Manny Ramirez .30 .75
205 Jeff Treadway .02 .10
206 Bill Wertz RC .05 .15
207 Cliff Young .02 .10
208 Matt Young .02 .10
209 Kirk Gibson .07 .20
210 Greg Gohr .02 .10
211 Bill Krueger .02 .10
212 Bob MacDonald .02 .10
213 Mike Moore .02 .10
214 David Wells .07 .20
215 Billy Brewer .02 .10
216 David Cone .07 .20
217 Greg Gagne .02 .10
218 Mark Gardner .02 .10
219 Chris Haney .02 .10
220 Phil Hiatt .02 .10
221 Jose Lind .02 .10
222 Juan Bell .02 .10
223 Tom Brunansky .02 .10
224 Mike Ignasiak .02 .10
225 Joe Kmak .02 .10
226 Tom Lampkin .02 .10
227 Graeme Lloyd RC .15 .40
228 Carlos Maldonado .02 .10
229 Matt Mieske .02 .10
230 Angel Miranda .02 .10
231 Troy O'Leary RC .15 .40
232 Kevin Reimer .02 .10
233 Larry Casian .02 .10
234 Jim Deshaies .02 .10
235 Eddie Guardado RC .25 .60
236 Chip Hale .02 .10
237 Mike Maksudian RC .05 .15
238 David McCarty .02 .10
239 Pat Meares RC .15 .40
240 George Tsamis RC .05 .15
241 Dave Winfield .07 .20
242 Jim Abbott .10 .30
243 Wade Boggs .10 .30
244 Andy Cook RC .05 .15
245 Russ Davis RC .05 .15
246 Mike Humphreys .02 .10
247 Jimmy Key .07 .20
248 Jim Leyritz .02 .10
249 Bobby Munoz .02 .10
250 Paul O'Neill .10 .30
251 Spike Owen .02 .10
252 Dave Silvestri .02 .10
253 Marcos Armas RC .05 .15
254 Brent Gates .02 .10
255 Rich Gossage .07 .20
256 Scott Lydy RC .05 .15
257 Henry Mercedes .05 .15
258 Mike Mohler RC .15 .40
259 Troy Neel .02 .10
260 Edwin Nunez .02 .10
261 Craig Paquette .02 .10
262 Kevin Seitzer .02 .10
263 Rich Amaral .02 .10
264 Mike Blowers .02 .10
265 Chris Bosio .02 .10
266 Norm Charlton .02 .10
267 Jim Converse RC .05 .15
268 John Cummings RC .05 .15
269 Mike Felder .02 .10
270 Mike Hampton .07 .20
271 Bill Haselman .02 .10
272 Dwayne Henry .02 .10
273 Greg Litton .02 .10
274 Mackey Sasser .02 .10
275 Lee Tinsley .02 .10
276 David Wainhouse .02 .10
277 Jeff Bronkey .02 .10
278 Benji Gil .02 .10
279 Tom Henke .02 .10
280 Charlie Leibrandt .02 .10
281 Robb Nen .07 .20
282 Bill Ripken .02 .10
283 Jon Shave RC .05 .15
284 Doug Strange .02 .10
285 Matt Whiteside RC .05 .15
286 Scott Brow RC .05 .15
287 Willie Canate RC .05 .15
288 Tony Castillo .02 .10
289 Domingo Cedeno RC .05 .15
290 Darnell Coles .02 .10
291 Danny Cox .02 .10
292 Mark Eichhorn .02 .10
293 Tony Fernandez .02 .10
294 Al Leiter .07 .20
295 Paul Molitor .07 .20
296 Dave Stewart .07 .20
297 Woody Williams RC .25 .60
298 Checklist F1-F100 .02 .10
299 Checklist F101-F200 .02 .10
300 Checklist F201-F300 .02 .10

1994 Fleer

The 1994 Fleer baseball set consists of 720 standard-size cards. Cards were distributed in hobby, retail, and jumbo packs. The cards are numbered on the back, grouped alphabetically within teams, and checklisted below alphabetically according to teams for each league with AL preceding NL. The set closes with a Superstar Specials (706-713) subset. There are no key Rookie Cards in this set.

COMPLETE SET (720) 25.00 50.00
1 Brady Anderson .10 .30
2 Harold Baines .10 .30
3 Mike Devereaux .05 .15
4 Todd Frohwirth .05 .15
5 Jeffrey Hammonds .05 .15
6 Chris Hoiles .05 .15
7 Tim Hulett .05 .15
8 Ben McDonald .05 .15
9 Mark McLemore .05 .15
10 Alan Mills .05 .15
11 Jamie Moyer .10 .30
12 Mike Mussina .20 .50
13 Gregg Olson .05 .15
14 Mike Pagliarulo .05 .15
15 Brad Pennington .05 .15
16 Jim Poole .05 .15
17 Harold Reynolds .10 .30
18 Arthur Rhodes .05 .15
19 Cal Ripken Jr. 1.00 2.50
20 David Segui .05 .15
21 Rick Sutcliffe .10 .30
22 Fernando Valenzuela .10 .30
23 Jack Voigt .05 .15
24 Mark Williamson .05 .15
25 Scott Bankhead .05 .15
26 Roger Clemens .60 1.50
27 Scott Cooper .05 .15
28 Danny Darwin .05 .15
29 Andre Dawson .10 .30
30 Rob Deer .05 .15
31 John Dopson .05 .15
32 Scott Fletcher .05 .15
33 Mike Greenwell .05 .15
34 Greg A. Harris .05 .15
35 Billy Hatcher .05 .15
36 Bob Melvin .05 .15
37 Tony Pena .05 .15
38 Paul Quantrill .05 .15
39 Carlos Quintana .05 .15
40 Ernest Riles .05 .15
41 Jeff Russell .05 .15
42 Ken Ryan .05 .15
43 Aaron Sele .05 .15
44 John Valentin .05 .15
45 Mo Vaughn .10 .30
46 Frank Viola .10 .30
47 Bob Zupcic .05 .15
48 Mike Butcher .05 .15
49 Rod Correia .05 .15
50 Chad Curtis .05 .15
51 Chili Davis .10 .30
52 Gary DiSarcina .05 .15
53 Damion Easley .05 .15
54 Jim Edmonds .30 .75
55 Chuck Finley .10 .30
56 Steve Frey .05 .15
57 Rene Gonzales .05 .15
58 Joe Grahe .05 .15
59 Hilly Hathaway .05 .15
60 Stan Javier .05 .15
61 Mark Langston .05 .15
62 Phil Leftwich RC .05 .15
63 Torey Lovullo .05 .15
64 Joe Magrane .05 .15
65 Greg Myers .05 .15
66 Ken Patterson .05 .15
67 Eduardo Perez .05 .15
68 Luis Polonia .05 .15
69 Tim Salmon .20 .50
70 J.T. Snow .10 .30
71 Ron Tingley .05 .15
72 Julio Valera .05 .15
73 Wilson Alvarez .05 .15
74 Tim Belcher .05 .15
75 George Bell .05 .15
76 Jason Bere .05 .15
77 Rod Bolton .05 .15
78 Ellis Burks .10 .30
79 Joey Cora .05 .15
80 Alex Fernandez .05 .15
81 Craig Grebeck .05 .15
82 Ozzie Guillen .10 .30
83 Roberto Hernandez .05 .15
84 Bo Jackson .30 .75
85 Lance Johnson .05 .15
86 Ron Karkovice .05 .15
87 Mike LaValliere .05 .15
88 Kirk McCaskill .05 .15
89 Jack McDowell .05 .15
90 Warren Newson .05 .15
91 Dan Pasqua .05 .15
92 Scott Radinsky .05 .15
93 Tim Raines .10 .30
94 Steve Sax .05 .15
95 Jeff Schwarz .05 .15
96 Frank Thomas .30 .75
97 Robin Ventura .10 .30
98 Sandy Alomar Jr. .05 .15
99 Carlos Baerga .05 .15
100 Albert Belle .10 .30
101 Mark Clark .05 .15
102 Jerry DiPoto .05 .15
103 Alvaro Espinoza .05 .15
104 Felix Fermin .05 .15
105 Jeremy Hernandez .05 .15
106 Reggie Jefferson .05 .15
107 Wayne Kirby .05 .15
108 Tom Kramer .05 .15
109 Mark Lewis .05 .15
110 Derek Lilliquist .05 .15
111 Kenny Lofton .10 .30
112 Candy Maldonado .05 .15
113 Jose Mesa .05 .15
114 Jeff Mutis .05 .15
115 Charles Nagy .05 .15
116 Bob Ojeda .05 .15
117 Junior Ortiz .05 .15
118 Eric Plunk .05 .15
119 Manny Ramirez .30 .75
120 Paul Sorrento .05 .15
121 Jim Thome .20 .50
122 Jeff Treadway .05 .15
123 Bill Wertz .05 .15
124 Skeeter Barnes .05 .15
125 Milt Cuyler .05 .15
126 Eric Davis .10 .30
127 John Doherty .05 .15
128 Cecil Fielder .10 .30
129 Travis Fryman .10 .30
130 Kirk Gibson .10 .30
131 Dan Gladden .05 .15
132 Greg Gohr .05 .15
133 Chris Gomez .05 .15
134 Bill Gullickson .05 .15
135 Mike Henneman .05 .15
136 Kurt Knudsen .05 .15
137 Chad Kreuter .05 .15
138 Bill Krueger .05 .15
139 Scott Livingstone .05 .15
140 Bob MacDonald .05 .15
141 Mike Moore .05 .15
142 Tony Phillips .05 .15
143 Mickey Tettleton .05 .15
144 Alan Trammell .10 .30
145 David Wells .10 .30
146 Lou Whitaker .10 .30
147 Kevin Appier .10 .30
148 Stan Belinda .05 .15
149 George Brett .75 2.00
150 Billy Brewer .05 .15
151 Hubie Brooks .05 .15
152 David Cone .10 .30
153 Gary Gaetti .10 .30
154 Greg Gagne .05 .15
155 Tom Gordon .05 .15
156 Mark Gubicza .05 .15
157 Chris Gwynn .05 .15
158 John Habyan .05 .15
159 Chris Haney .05 .15
160 Phil Hiatt .05 .15
161 Felix Jose .05 .15
162 Wally Joyner .10 .30
163 Jose Lind .05 .15
164 Mike Macfarlane .05 .15
165 Mike Magnante .05 .15
166 Brent Mayne .05 .15
167 Brian McRae .05 .15
168 Kevin McReynolds .05 .15
169 Keith Miller .05 .15
170 Jeff Montgomery .05 .15
171 Hipolito Pichardo .05 .15
172 Rico Rossy .05 .15
173 Juan Bell .05 .15
174 Ricky Bones .05 .15
175 Cal Eldred .05 .15
176 Mike Fetters .05 .15
177 Darryl Hamilton .05 .15
178 Doug Henry .05 .15
179 Mike Ignasiak .05 .15
180 John Jaha .05 .15
181 Pat Listach .05 .15
182 Graeme Lloyd .05 .15
183 Matt Mieske .05 .15
184 Angel Miranda .05 .15
185 Jaime Navarro .05 .15
186 Dave Nilsson .05 .15
187 Troy O'Leary .05 .15
188 Jesse Orosco .05 .15
189 Kevin Reimer .05 .15
190 Kevin Seitzer .05 .15
191 Bill Spiers .05 .15
192 B.J. Surhoff .10 .30
193 Dickie Thon .05 .15
194 Jose Valentin .05 .15
195 Greg Vaughn .05 .15
196 Bill Wegman .05 .15
197 Robin Yount .50 1.25
198 Rick Aguilera .05 .15
199 Willie Banks .05 .15
200 Bernardo Brito .05 .15
201 Larry Casian .05 .15
202 Scott Erickson .05 .15
203 Eddie Guardado .10 .30
204 Mark Guthrie .05 .15
205 Chip Hale .05 .15
206 Brian Harper .05 .15
207 Mike Hartley .05 .15
208 Kent Hrbek .10 .30
209 Terry Jorgensen .05 .15
210 Chuck Knoblauch .10 .30
211 Gene Larkin .05 .15
212 Shane Mack .05 .15
213 David McCarty .05 .15
214 Pat Meares .05 .15
215 Pedro Munoz .05 .15
216 Derek Parks .05 .15
217 Kirby Puckett .30 .75
218 Jeff Reboulet .05 .15
219 Kevin Tapani .05 .15
220 Mike Trombley .05 .15
221 George Tsamis .05 .15
222 Carl Willis .05 .15
223 Dave Winfield .10 .30
224 Jim Abbott .20 .50
225 Paul Assenmacher .05 .15
226 Wade Boggs .20 .50
227 Russ Davis .05 .15
228 Steve Farr .05 .15
229 Mike Gallego .05 .15
230 Paul Gibson .05 .15
231 Steve Howe .05 .15
232 Dion James .05 .15
233 Domingo Jean .05 .15
234 Scott Kamieniecki .05 .15
235 Pat Kelly .05 .15
236 Jimmy Key .10 .30
237 Jim Leyritz .05 .15
238 Kevin Maas .05 .15
239 Don Mattingly .75 2.00
240 Rich Monteleone .05 .15
241 Bobby Munoz .05 .15
242 Matt Nokes .05 .15
243 Paul O'Neill .20 .50
244 Spike Owen .05 .15
245 Melido Perez .05 .15
246 Lee Smith .10 .30
247 Mike Stanley .05 .15
248 Danny Tartabull .05 .15
249 Randy Velarde .05 .15
250 Bob Wickman .05 .15
251 Bernie Williams .20 .50
252 Mike Aldrete .05 .15
253 Marcos Armas .05 .15
254 Lance Blankenship .05 .15
255 Mike Bordick .05 .15
256 Scott Brosius .10 .30
257 Jerry Browne .05 .15
258 Ron Darling .05 .15
259 Kelly Downs .05 .15
260 Dennis Eckersley .10 .30
261 Brent Gates .05 .15
262 Rich Gossage .10 .30
263 Scott Hemond .05 .15
264 Dave Henderson .05 .15
265 Rick Honeycutt .05 .15
266 Vince Horsman .05 .15
267 Scott Lydy .05 .15
268 Mark McGwire .75 2.00
269 Mike Mohler .05 .15
270 Troy Neel .05 .15
271 Edwin Nunez .05 .15
272 Craig Paquette .05 .15
273 Ruben Sierra .10 .30
274 Terry Steinbach .05 .15
275 Todd Van Poppel .05 .15
276 Bob Welch .05 .15
277 Bobby Witt .05 .15
278 Rich Amaral .05 .15
279 Mike Blowers .05 .15
280 Bret Boone UER .10 .30
(Name spelled Brett on front)
281 Chris Bosio .05 .15
282 Jay Buhner .10 .30
283 Norm Charlton .05 .15
284 Mike Felder .05 .15
285 Dave Fleming .05 .15
286 Ken Griffey Jr. .50 1.25
287 Erik Hanson .05 .15
288 Bill Haselman .05 .15
289 Brad Holman RC .05 .15
290 Randy Johnson .30 .75
291 Tim Leary .05 .15
292 Greg Litton .05 .15
293 Dave Magadan .05 .15
294 Edgar Martinez .20 .50
295 Tino Martinez .20 .50
296 Jeff Nelson .05 .15
297 Erik Plantenberg RC .05 .15
298 Mackey Sasser .05 .15
299 Brian Turang RC .05 .15
300 Dave Valle .05 .15
301 Omar Vizquel .20 .50
302 Brian Bohanon .05 .15
303 Kevin Brown .10 .30
304 Jose Canseco UER .20 .50
(Back mentions 1991 as his 40/40 MVP season; should be '88)
305 Mario Diaz .05 .15
306 Julio Franco .10 .30
307 Juan Gonzalez .10 .30
308 Tom Henke .05 .15
309 David Hulse .05 .15
310 Manuel Lee .05 .15
311 Craig Lefferts .05 .15
312 Charlie Leibrandt .05 .15
313 Rafael Palmeiro .20 .50
314 Dean Palmer .10 .30
315 Roger Pavlik .05 .15
316 Dan Peltier .05 .15
317 Gene Petralli .05 .15
318 Gary Redus .05 .15
319 Ivan Rodriguez .20 .50
320 Kenny Rogers .10 .30
321 Nolan Ryan 1.25 3.00
322 Doug Strange .05 .15
323 Matt Whiteside .05 .15
324 Roberto Alomar .20 .50
325 Pat Borders .05 .15
326 Joe Carter .10 .30
327 Tony Castillo .05 .15
328 Darnell Coles .05 .15
329 Danny Cox .05 .15
330 Mark Eichhorn .05 .15
331 Tony Fernandez .05 .15
332 Alfredo Griffin .05 .15
333 Juan Guzman .05 .15
334 Rickey Henderson .30 .75
335 Pat Hentgen .05 .15
336 Randy Knorr .05 .15
337 Al Leiter .10 .30
338 Paul Molitor .10 .30
339 Jack Morris .10 .30
340 John Olerud .10 .30
341 Dick Schofield .05 .15
342 Ed Sprague .05 .15
343 Dave Stewart .10 .30
344 Todd Stottlemyre .05 .15
345 Mike Timlin .05 .15
346 Duane Ward .05 .15
347 Turner Ward .05 .15
348 Devon White .10 .30
349 Woody Williams .10 .30
350 Steve Avery .05 .15
351 Steve Bedrosian .05 .15
352 Rafael Belliard .05 .15
353 Damon Berryhill .05 .15
354 Jeff Blauser .05 .15
355 Sid Bream .05 .15
356 Francisco Cabrera .05 .15
357 Marvin Freeman .05 .15
358 Ron Gant .10 .30
359 Tom Glavine .20 .50
360 Jay Howell .05 .15
361 David Justice .10 .30
362 Ryan Klesko .10 .30
363 Mark Lemke .05 .15
364 Javier Lopez .10 .30
365 Greg Maddux .50 1.25
366 Fred McGriff .20 .50
367 Greg McMichael .05 .15
368 Kent Mercker .05 .15
369 Otis Nixon .05 .15
370 Greg Olson .05 .15
371 Bill Pecota .05 .15
372 Terry Pendleton .10 .30
373 Deion Sanders .20 .50
374 Pete Smith .05 .15
375 John Smoltz .20 .50
376 Mike Stanton .05 .15
377 Tony Tarasco .05 .15
378 Mark Wohlers .05 .15
379 Jose Bautista .05 .15
380 Shawn Boskie .05 .15
381 Steve Buechele .05 .15
382 Frank Castillo .05 .15
383 Mark Grace .20 .50
384 Jose Guzman .05 .15
385 Mike Harkey .05 .15
386 Greg Hibbard .05 .15
387 Glenallen Hill .05 .15
388 Steve Lake .05 .15
389 Derrick May .05 .15
390 Chuck McElroy .05 .15
391 Mike Morgan .05 .15
392 Randy Myers .05 .15
393 Dan Plesac .05 .15
394 Kevin Roberson .05 .15
395 Rey Sanchez .05 .15
396 Ryne Sandberg .50 1.25
397 Bob Scanlan .05 .15
398 Dwight Smith .05 .15
399 Sammy Sosa .30 .75
400 Jose Vizcaino .05 .15
401 Rick Wilkins .05 .15
402 Willie Wilson .05 .15
403 Eric Yelding .05 .15
404 Bobby Ayala .05 .15
405 Jeff Branson .05 .15
406 Tom Browning .05 .15
407 Jacob Brumfield .05 .15
408 Tim Costo .05 .15
409 Rob Dibble .10 .30
410 Willie Greene .05 .15
411 Thomas Howard .05 .15
412 Roberto Kelly .05 .15
413 Bill Landrum .05 .15
414 Barry Larkin .20 .50
415 Larry Luebbers RC .05 .15
416 Kevin Mitchell .05 .15
417 Hal Morris .05 .15
418 Joe Oliver .05 .15
419 Tim Pugh .05 .15
420 Jeff Reardon .10 .30
421 Jose Rijo .05 .15
422 Bip Roberts .05 .15
423 John Roper .05 .15
424 Johnny Ruffin .05 .15
425 Chris Sabo .05 .15
426 Juan Samuel .05 .15
427 Reggie Sanders .10 .30
428 Scott Service .05 .15
429 John Smiley .05 .15
430 Jerry Spradlin RC .05 .15
431 Kevin Wickander .05 .15
432 Freddie Benavides .05 .15
433 Dante Bichette .10 .30
434 Willie Blair .05 .15
435 Daryl Boston .05 .15
436 Kent Bottenfield .05 .15
437 Vinny Castilla .10 .30
438 Jerald Clark .05 .15
439 Alex Cole .05 .15
440 Andres Galarraga .10 .30
441 Joe Girardi .05 .15
442 Greg W. Harris .05 .15
443 Charlie Hayes .05 .15
444 Darren Holmes .05 .15
445 Chris Jones .05 .15
446 Roberto Mejia .05 .15
447 David Nied .05 .15
448 Jayhawk Owens .05 .15
449 Jeff Parrett .05 .15
450 Steve Reed .05 .15
451 Armando Reynoso .05 .15
452 Bruce Ruffin .05 .15
453 Mo Sanford .05 .15
454 Danny Sheaffer .05 .15
455 Jim Tatum .05 .15
456 Gary Wayne .05 .15
457 Eric Young .05 .15
458 Luis Aquino .05 .15
459 Alex Arias .05 .15
460 Jack Armstrong .05 .15
461 Bret Barberie .05 .15
462 Ryan Bowen .05 .15
463 Chuck Carr .05 .15
464 Jeff Conine .10 .30
465 Henry Cotto .05 .15
466 Orestes Destrade .05 .15
467 Chris Hammond .05 .15
468 Bryan Harvey .05 .15
469 Charlie Hough .10 .30
470 Joe Klink .05 .15
471 Richie Lewis .05 .15
472 Bob Natal .05 .15
473 Pat Rapp .05 .15
474 Rich Renteria .05 .15
475 Rich Rodriguez .05 .15
476 Benito Santiago .10 .30
477 Gary Sheffield .10 .30
478 Matt Turner .05 .15
479 David Weathers .05 .15
480 Walt Weiss .05 .15
481 Darrell Whitmore .05 .15
482 Eric Anthony .05 .15
483 Jeff Bagwell .20 .50
484 Kevin Bass .05 .15
485 Craig Biggio .20 .50
486 Ken Caminiti .10 .30
487 Andujar Cedeno .05 .15
488 Chris Donnels .05 .15
489 Doug Drabek .05 .15
490 Steve Finley .10 .30
491 Luis Gonzalez .10 .30
492 Pete Harnisch .05 .15
493 Xavier Hernandez .05 .15
494 Doug Jones .05 .15
495 Todd Jones .05 .15
496 Darryl Kile .10 .30
497 Al Osuna .05 .15
498 Mark Portugal .05 .15
499 Scott Servais .05 .15
500 Greg Swindell .05 .15
501 Eddie Taubensee .05 .15
502 Jose Uribe .05 .15
503 Brian Williams .05 .15
504 Billy Ashley .05 .15
505 Pedro Astacio .05 .15
506 Brett Butler .10 .30
507 Tom Candiotti .05 .15
508 Omar Daal .05 .15
509 Jim Gott .05 .15
510 Kevin Gross .05 .15
511 Dave Hansen .05 .15
512 Carlos Hernandez .05 .15
513 Orel Hershiser .10 .30
514 Eric Karros .10 .30
515 Pedro Martinez .30 .75
516 Ramon Martinez .05 .15
517 Roger McDowell .05 .15
518 Raul Mondesi .10 .30
519 Jose Offerman .05 .15
520 Mike Piazza .60 1.50
521 Jody Reed .05 .15
522 Henry Rodriguez .05 .15
523 Mike Sharperson .05 .15
524 Cory Snyder .05 .15
525 Darryl Strawberry .10 .30
526 Rick Trlicek .05 .15
527 Tim Wallach .05 .15
528 Mitch Webster .05 .15
529 Steve Wilson .05 .15
530 Todd Worrell .05 .15
531 Moises Alou .10 .30
532 Brian Barnes .05 .15
533 Sean Berry .05 .15
534 Greg Colbrunn .05 .15
535 Delino DeShields .05 .15
536 Jeff Fassero .05 .15
537 Darrin Fletcher .05 .15
538 Cliff Floyd .10 .30
539 Lou Frazier .05 .15
540 Marquis Grissom .10 .30
541 Butch Henry .05 .15
542 Ken Hill .05 .15
543 Mike Lansing .05 .15
544 Brian Looney RC .05 .15
545 Dennis Martinez .10 .30
546 Chris Nabholz .05 .15
547 Randy Ready .05 .15
548 Mel Rojas .05 .15
549 Kirk Rueter .05 .15
550 Tim Scott .05 .15
551 Jeff Shaw .05 .15
552 Tim Spehr .05 .15
553 John Vander Wal .05 .15
554 Larry Walker .10 .30
555 John Wetteland .10 .30
556 Rondell White .10 .30
557 Tim Bogar .05 .15
558 Bobby Bonilla .10 .30
559 Jeromy Burnitz .10 .30
560 Sid Fernandez .05 .15
561 John Franco .10 .30
562 Dave Gallagher .05 .15
563 Dwight Gooden .10 .30
564 Eric Hillman .05 .15
565 Todd Hundley .05 .15
566 Jeff Innis .05 .15
567 Darrin Jackson .05 .15
568 Howard Johnson .05 .15
569 Bobby Jones .05 .15
570 Jeff Kent .20 .50
571 Mike Maddux .05 .15
572 Jeff McKnight .05 .15
573 Eddie Murray .30 .75
574 Charlie O'Brien .05 .15
575 Joe Orsulak .05 .15
576 Bret Saberhagen .10 .30
577 Pete Schourek .05 .15
578 Dave Telgheder .05 .15
579 Ryan Thompson .05 .15
580 Anthony Young .05 .15
581 Ruben Amaro .05 .15
582 Larry Andersen .05 .15
583 Kim Batiste .05 .15
584 Wes Chamberlain .05 .15
585 Darren Daulton .10 .30

586 Mariano Duncan .05 .15
587 Lenny Dykstra .10 .30
588 Jim Eisenreich .05 .15
589 Tommy Greene .05 .15
590 Dave Hollins .05 .15
591 Pete Incaviglia .05 .15
592 Danny Jackson .05 .15
593 Ricky Jordan .05 .15
594 John Kruk .10 .30
595 Roger Mason .05 .15
596 Mickey Morandini .05 .15
597 Terry Mulholland .05 .15
598 Todd Pratt .05 .15
599 Ben Rivera .05 .15
600 Curt Schilling .10 .30
601 Kevin Stocker .05 .15
602 Milt Thompson .05 .15
603 David West .05 .15
604 Mitch Williams .05 .15
605 Jay Bell .10 .30
606 Dave Clark .05 .15
607 Steve Cooke .05 .15
608 Tom Foley .05 .15
609 Carlos Garcia .05 .15
610 Joel Johnston .05 .15
611 Jeff King .05 .15
612 Al Martin .05 .15
613 Lloyd McClendon .05 .15
614 Orlando Merced .05 .15
615 Blas Minor .05 .15
616 Denny Neagle .10 .30
617 Mark Petkovsek RC .05 .15
618 Tom Prince .05 .15
619 Don Slaught .05 .15
620 Zane Smith .05 .15
621 Randy Tomlin .05 .15
622 Andy Van Slyke .20 .50
623 Paul Wagner .05 .15
624 Tim Wakefield .20 .50
625 Bob Walk .05 .15
626 Kevin Young .05 .15
627 Luis Alicea .05 .15
628 Rene Arocha .05 .15
629 Rod Brewer .05 .15
630 Rheal Cormier .05 .15
631 Bernard Gilkey .05 .15
632 Lee Guetterman .05 .15
633 Gregg Jefferies .05 .15
634 Brian Jordan .10 .30
635 Les Lancaster .05 .15
636 Ray Lankford .10 .30
637 Rob Murphy .05 .15
638 Omar Olivares .05 .15
639 Jose Oquendo .05 .15
640 Donovan Osborne .05 .15
641 Tom Pagnozzi .05 .15
642 Erik Pappas .05 .15
643 Geronimo Pena .05 .15
644 Mike Perez .05 .15
645 Gerald Perry .05 .15
646 Ozzie Smith .50 1.25
647 Bob Tewksbury .05 .15
648 Allen Watson .05 .15
649 Mark Whiten .05 .15
650 Tracy Woodson .05 .15
651 Todd Zeile .05 .15
652 Andy Ashby .05 .15
653 Brad Ausmus .20 .50
654 Billy Bean .05 .15
655 Derek Bell .05 .15
656 Andy Benes .05 .15
657 Doug Brocail .05 .15
658 Jarvis Brown .05 .15
659 Archi Cianfrocco .05 .15
660 Phil Clark .05 .15
661 Mark Davis .05 .15
662 Jeff Gardner .05 .15
663 Pat Gomez .05 .15
664 Ricky Gutierrez .05 .15
665 Tony Gwynn .40 1.00
666 Gene Harris .05 .15
667 Kevin Higgins .05 .15
668 Trevor Hoffman .20 .50
669 Pedro Martinez RC .05 .15
670 Tim Mauser .05 .15
671 Melvin Nieves .05 .15
672 Phil Plantier .05 .15
673 Frank Seminara .05 .15
674 Craig Shipley .05 .15
675 Kerry Taylor .05 .15
676 Tim Teufel .05 .15
677 Guillermo Velasquez .05 .15
678 Wally Whitehurst .05 .15
679 Tim Worrell .05 .15
680 Rod Beck .05 .15
681 Mike Benjamin .05 .15
682 Todd Benzinger .05 .15
683 Bud Black .05 .15
684 Barry Bonds .75 2.00
685 Jeff Brantley .05 .15
686 Dave Burba .05 .15
687 John Burkett .05 .15
688 Mark Carreon .05 .15
689 Will Clark .20 .50
690 Royce Clayton .05 .15
691 Bryan Hickerson .05 .15
692 Mike Jackson .05 .15
693 Darren Lewis .05 .15
694 Kirt Manwaring .05 .15
695 Dave Martinez .05 .15
696 Willie McGee .10 .30
697 John Patterson .05 .15
698 Jeff Reed .05 .15
699 Kevin Rogers .05 .15
700 Scott Sanderson .05 .15
701 Steve Scarsone .05 .15
702 Billy Swift .05 .15
703 Robby Thompson .05 .15
704 Matt Williams .10 .30
705 Trevor Wilson .05 .15
706 Fred McGriff .10 .30
Ron Gant
David Justice
707 John Olerud .10 .30
Paul Molitor
708 Mike Mussina .10 .30
Jack McDowell
709 Lou Whitaker .10 .30
Alan Trammell
710 Rafael Palmeiro .10 .30
Juan Gonzalez
711 Brett Butler .20 .50
Tony Gwynn
712 Kirby Puckett .20 .50
Chuck Knoblauch
713 Mike Piazza .30 .75
Eric Karros
714 Checklist 1 .05 .15
715 Checklist 2 .05 .15
716 Checklist 3 .05 .15
717 Checklist 4 .05 .15
718 Checklist 5 .05 .15
719 Checklist 6 .05 .15
720 Checklist 7 .05 .15
P69 Tim Salmon Promo .40 1.00

1994 Fleer Update

This 200-card standard-size set highlights traded players in their new uniforms and promising young rookies. The Update set was exclusively distributed in factory set form through hobby dealers. Each hobby case contained 20 cases. A ten card Diamond Tribute set was included in each factory set for a total of 210 cards. The cards are numbered on the back, grouped alphabetically by team by league with AL preceding NL. Key Rookie Cards include Chan Ho Park and Alex Rodriguez.

COMP.FACT.SET (210) 25.00 50.00
1 Mark Eichhorn .08 .25
2 Sid Fernandez .08 .25
3 Leo Gomez .08 .25
4 Mike Oquist .08 .25
5 Rafael Palmeiro .30 .75
6 Chris Sabo .08 .25
7 Dwight Smith .08 .25
8 Lee Smith .20 .50
9 Damon Berryhill .08 .25
10 Wes Chamberlain .08 .25
11 Gar Finnvold .08 .25
12 Chris Howard .08 .25
13 Tim Naehring .08 .25
14 Otis Nixon .08 .25
15 Brian Anderson RC .20 .50
16 Jorge Fabregas .08 .25
17 Rex Hudler .08 .25
18 Bo Jackson .50 1.25
19 Mark Leiter .08 .25
20 Spike Owen .08 .25
21 Harold Reynolds .20 .50
22 Chris Turner .08 .25
23 Dennis Cook .08 .25
24 Jose DeLeon .08 .25
25 Julio Franco .20 .50
26 Joe Hall .08 .25
27 Darrin Jackson .08 .25
28 Dane Johnson .08 .25
29 Norberto Martin .08 .25
30 Scott Sanderson .08 .25
31 Jason Grimsley .08 .25
32 Dennis Martinez .20 .50
33 Jack Morris .20 .50
34 Eddie Murray .50 1.25
35 Chad Ogea .08 .25
36 Tony Pena .08 .25
37 Paul Shuey .08 .25
38 Omar Vizquel .30 .75
39 Danny Bautista .08 .25
40 Tim Belcher .08 .25
41 Joe Boever .08 .25
42 Storm Davis .08 .25
43 Junior Felix .08 .25
44 Mike Gardiner .08 .25
45 Buddy Groom .08 .25
46 Juan Samuel .08 .25
47 Vince Coleman .08 .25
48 Bob Hamelin .08 .25
49 Dave Henderson .08 .25
50 Rusty Meacham .08 .25
51 Terry Shumpert .08 .25
52 Jeff Bronkey .08 .25
53 Alex Diaz .08 .25
54 Brian Harper .08 .25
55 Jose Mercedes .08 .25
56 Jody Reed .08 .25
57 Bob Scanlan .08 .25
58 Turner Ward .08 .25
59 Rich Becker .08 .25
60 Alex Cole .08 .25
61 Denny Hocking .08 .25
62 Scott Leius .08 .25
63 Pat Mahomes .08 .25
64 Carlos Pulido .08 .25
65 Dave Stevens .08 .25
66 Matt Walbeck .08 .25
67 Xavier Hernandez .08 .25
68 Sterling Hitchcock .08 .25
69 Terry Mulholland .08 .25
70 Luis Polonia .08 .25
71 Gerald Williams .08 .25
72 Mark Acre RC .08 .25
73 Geronimo Berroa .08 .25
74 Rickey Henderson .50 1.25
75 Stan Javier .08 .25
76 Steve Karsay .08 .25
77 Carlos Reyes .08 .25
78 Bill Taylor RC .20 .50
79 Eric Anthony .08 .25
80 Bobby Ayala .08 .25
81 Tim Davis .08 .25
82 Felix Fermin .08 .25
83 Reggie Jefferson .08 .25
84 Keith Mitchell .08 .25
85 Bill Risley .08 .25
86 Alex Rodriguez RC 12.50 30.00
87 Roger Salkeld .08 .25
88 Dan Wilson .08 .25
89 Cris Carpenter .08 .25
90 Will Clark .30 .75
91 Jeff Frye .08 .25
92 Rick Helling .08 .25
93 Chris James .08 .25
94 Oddibe McDowell .08 .25
95 Billy Ripken .08 .25
96 Carlos Delgado .30 .75
97 Alex Gonzalez .08 .25
98 Shawn Green .50 1.25
99 Darren Hall .08 .25
100 Mike Huff .08 .25
101 Mike Kelly .08 .25
102 Roberto Kelly .08 .25
103 Charlie O'Brien .08 .25
104 Jose Oliva .08 .25
105 Gregg Olson .08 .25
106 Willie Banks .08 .25
107 Jim Bullinger .08 .25
108 Chuck Crim .08 .25
109 Shawon Dunston .08 .25
110 Karl Rhodes .08 .25
111 Steve Trachsel .08 .25
112 Anthony Young .08 .25
113 Eddie Zambrano .08 .25
114 Bret Boone .20 .50
115 Jeff Brantley .08 .25
116 Hector Carrasco .08 .25
117 Tony Fernandez .08 .25
118 Tim Fortugno .08 .25
119 Erik Hanson .08 .25
120 Chuck McElroy .08 .25
121 Deion Sanders .30 .75
122 Ellis Burks .20 .50
123 Marvin Freeman .08 .25
124 Mike Harkey .08 .25
125 Howard Johnson .08 .25
126 Mike Kingery .08 .25
127 Nelson Liriano .08 .25
128 Marcus Moore .08 .25
129 Mike Munoz .08 .25
130 Kevin Ritz .08 .25
131 Walt Weiss .08 .25
132 Kurt Abbott RC .08 .25
133 Jerry Browne .08 .25
134 Greg Colbrunn .08 .25
135 Jeremy Hernandez .08 .25
136 Dave Magadan .08 .25
137 Kurt Miller .08 .25
138 Robb Nen .20 .50
139 Jesus Tavarez RC .08 .25
140 Sid Bream .08 .25
141 Tom Edens .08 .25
142 Tony Eusebio .08 .25
143 John Hudek RC .08 .25
144 Brian L. Hunter .08 .25
145 Orlando Miller .08 .25
146 James Mouton .08 .25
147 Shane Reynolds .08 .25
148 Rafael Bournigal .08 .25
149 Delino DeShields .08 .25
150 Garey Ingram RC .08 .25
151 Chan Ho Park RC .30 .75
152 Wil Cordero .08 .25
153 Pedro Martinez .50 1.25
154 Randy Milligan .08 .25
155 Lenny Webster .08 .25
156 Rico Brogna .08 .25
157 Josias Manzanillo .08 .25
158 Kevin McReynolds .08 .25
159 Mike Remlinger .08 .25
160 David Segui .08 .25
161 Pete Smith .08 .25
162 Kelly Stinnett RC .20 .50
163 Jose Vizcaino .08 .25
164 Billy Hatcher .08 .25
165 Doug Jones .08 .25
166 Mike Lieberthal .20 .50
167 Tony Longmire .08 .25
168 Bobby Munoz .08 .25
169 Paul Quantrill .08 .25
170 Heathcliff Slocumb .08 .25
171 Fernando Valenzuela .20 .50
172 Mark Dewey .08 .25
173 Brian R. Hunter .08 .25
174 Jon Lieber .20 .50
175 Ravelo Manzanillo .08 .25
176 Dan Miceli .08 .25
177 Rick White .08 .25
178 Bryan Eversgerd .08 .25
179 John Habyan .08 .25
180 Terry McGriff .08 .25
181 Vicente Palacios .08 .25
182 Rich Rodriguez .08 .25
183 Rick Sutcliffe .20 .50
184 Donnie Elliott .08 .25
185 Joey Hamilton .08 .25
186 Tim Hyers RC .08 .25
187 Luis Lopez .08 .25
188 Ray McDavid .08 .25
189 Bip Roberts .08 .25
190 Scott Sanders .08 .25
191 Eddie Williams .08 .25
192 Steve Frey .08 .25
193 Pat Gomez .08 .25
194 Rich Monteleone .08 .25
195 Mark Portugal .08 .25
196 Darryl Strawberry .20 .50
197 Salomon Torres .08 .25
198 W.VanLandingham RC .08 .25
199 Checklist .08 .25
200 Checklist .08 .25

1995 Fleer

The 1995 Fleer set consists of 600 standard-size cards issued as one series. Each pack contained at least one insert card with some 'Hot Packs' containing nothing but insert cards. Full-bleed fronts have two player photos and, atypical of baseball cards fronts, biographical information such as height, weight, etc. The backgrounds are multi-colored. The backs are horizontal and contain year-by-year statistics along with a photo. There was a different design for each of baseball's six divisions. The checklist is arranged alphabetically by teams within each league with AL preceding NL. To preview the product prior to it's public release, Fleer printed up additional quantities of cards 26, 78, 155, 235, 285, 351, 509 and 514 and mailed them to dealers and hobby media.

COMPLETE SET (600) 20.00 50.00
1 Brady Anderson .10 .30
2 Harold Baines .10 .30
3 Damon Buford .05 .15
4 Mike Devereaux .05 .15
5 Mark Eichhorn .05 .15
6 Sid Fernandez .05 .15
7 Leo Gomez .05 .15
8 Jeffrey Hammonds .05 .15
9 Chris Hoiles .05 .15
10 Rick Krivda .05 .15
11 Ben McDonald .05 .15
12 Mark McLemore .05 .15
13 Alan Mills .05 .15
14 Jamie Moyer .10 .30
15 Mike Mussina .20 .50
16 Mike Oquist .05 .15
17 Rafael Palmeiro .20 .50
18 Arthur Rhodes .05 .15
19 Cal Ripken Jr. 1.00 2.50
20 Chris Sabo .05 .15
21 Lee Smith .10 .30
22 Jack Voigt .05 .15
23 Damon Berryhill .05 .15
24 Tom Brunansky .05 .15
25 Wes Chamberlain .05 .15
26 Roger Clemens .60 1.50
27 Scott Cooper .05 .15
28 Andre Dawson .10 .30
29 Gar Finnvold .05 .15
30 Tony Fossas .05 .15
31 Mike Greenwell .05 .15
32 Joe Hesketh .05 .15
33 Chris Howard .05 .15
34 Chris Nabholz .05 .15
35 Tim Naehring .05 .15
36 Otis Nixon .05 .15
37 Carlos Rodriguez .05 .15
38 Rich Rowland .05 .15
39 Ken Ryan .05 .15
40 Aaron Sele .05 .15
41 John Valentin .05 .15
42 Mo Vaughn .10 .30
43 Frank Viola .10 .30
44 Danny Bautista .05 .15
45 Joe Boever .05 .15
46 Milt Cuyler .05 .15
47 Storm Davis .05 .15
48 John Doherty .05 .15
49 Junior Felix .05 .15
50 Cecil Fielder .10 .30
51 Travis Fryman .10 .30
52 Mike Gardiner .05 .15
53 Kirk Gibson .10 .30
54 Chris Gomez .05 .15
55 Buddy Groom .05 .15
56 Mike Henneman .05 .15
57 Chad Kreuter .05 .15
58 Mike Moore .05 .15
59 Tony Phillips .05 .15
60 Juan Samuel .05 .15
61 Mickey Tettleton .05 .15
62 Alan Trammell .10 .30
63 David Wells .10 .30
64 Lou Whitaker .10 .30
65 Jim Abbott .20 .50
66 Joe Ausanio .05 .15
67 Wade Boggs .20 .50
68 Mike Gallego .05 .15
69 Xavier Hernandez .05 .15
70 Sterling Hitchcock .05 .15
71 Steve Howe .05 .15
72 Scott Kamieniecki .05 .15
73 Pat Kelly .05 .15
74 Jimmy Key .10 .30
75 Jim Leyritz .05 .15
76 Don Mattingly UER .75 2.00
Photo is a reversed negative
77 Terry Mulholland .05 .15
78 Paul O'Neill .20 .50
79 Melido Perez .05 .15
80 Luis Polonia .05 .15
81 Mike Stanley .05 .15
82 Danny Tartabull .05 .15
83 Randy Velarde .05 .15
84 Bob Wickman .05 .15
85 Bernie Williams .20 .50
86 Gerald Williams .05 .15
87 Roberto Alomar .20 .50
88 Pat Borders .05 .15
89 Joe Carter .10 .30
90 Tony Castillo .05 .15
91 Brad Cornett RC .05 .15
92 Carlos Delgado .10 .30
93 Alex Gonzalez .05 .15
94 Shawn Green .10 .30
95 Juan Guzman .05 .15
96 Darren Hall .05 .15
97 Pat Hentgen .05 .15
98 Mike Huff .05 .15
99 Randy Knorr .05 .15
100 Al Leiter .10 .30
101 Paul Molitor .10 .30
102 John Olerud .10 .30
103 Dick Schofield .05 .15
104 Ed Sprague .05 .15
105 Dave Stewart .10 .30
106 Todd Stottlemyre .05 .15
107 Devon White .10 .30
108 Woody Williams .10 .30
109 Wilson Alvarez .05 .15
110 Paul Assenmacher .05 .15
111 Jason Bere .05 .15
112 Dennis Cook .05 .15
113 Joey Cora .05 .15
114 Jose DeLeon .05 .15
115 Alex Fernandez .05 .15
116 Julio Franco .10 .30
117 Craig Grebeck .05 .15
118 Ozzie Guillen .10 .30
119 Roberto Hernandez .05 .15
120 Darrin Jackson .05 .15
121 Lance Johnson .05 .15
122 Ron Karkovice .05 .15
123 Mike LaValliere .05 .15
124 Norberto Martin .05 .15
125 Kirk McCaskill .05 .15
126 Jack McDowell .05 .15
127 Tim Raines .10 .30
128 Frank Thomas .30 .75
129 Robin Ventura .10 .30
130 Sandy Alomar Jr. .05 .15
131 Carlos Baerga .05 .15
132 Albert Belle .10 .30
133 Mark Clark .05 .15
134 Alvaro Espinoza .05 .15
135 Jason Grimsley .05 .15
136 Wayne Kirby .05 .15
137 Kenny Lofton .10 .30
138 Albie Lopez .05 .15
139 Dennis Martinez .10 .30
140 Jose Mesa .05 .15
141 Eddie Murray .30 .75
142 Charles Nagy .05 .15
143 Tony Pena .05 .15
144 Eric Plunk .05 .15
145 Manny Ramirez .20 .50
146 Jeff Russell .05 .15
147 Paul Shuey .05 .15
148 Paul Sorrento .05 .15
149 Jim Thome .20 .50
150 Omar Vizquel .20 .50
151 Dave Winfield .10 .30
152 Kevin Appier .10 .30
153 Billy Brewer .05 .15
154 Vince Coleman .05 .15
155 David Cone .10 .30
156 Gary Gaetti .10 .30
157 Greg Gagne .05 .15
158 Tom Gordon .05 .15
159 Mark Gubicza .05 .15
160 Bob Hamelin .05 .15
161 Dave Henderson .05 .15
162 Felix Jose .05 .15
163 Wally Joyner .10 .30
164 Jose Lind .05 .15
165 Mike Macfarlane .05 .15
166 Mike Magnante .05 .15
167 Brent Mayne .05 .15
168 Brian McRae .05 .15
169 Rusty Meacham .05 .15
170 Jeff Montgomery .05 .15
171 Hipolito Pichardo .05 .15
172 Terry Shumpert .05 .15
173 Michael Tucker .05 .15
174 Ricky Bones .05 .15
175 Jeff Cirillo .05 .15
176 Alex Diaz .05 .15
177 Cal Eldred .05 .15
178 Mike Fetters .05 .15
179 Darryl Hamilton .05 .15
180 Brian Harper .05 .15
181 John Jaha .05 .15
182 Pat Listach .05 .15
183 Graeme Lloyd .05 .15
184 Jose Mercedes .05 .15
185 Matt Mieske .05 .15
186 Dave Nilsson .05 .15
187 Jody Reed .05 .15
188 Bob Scanlan .05 .15
189 Kevin Seitzer .05 .15
190 Bill Spiers .05 .15
191 B.J. Surhoff .10 .30
192 Jose Valentin .05 .15
193 Greg Vaughn .05 .15
194 Turner Ward .05 .15
195 Bill Wegman .05 .15
196 Rick Aguilera .05 .15
197 Rich Becker .05 .15
198 Alex Cole .05 .15
199 Marty Cordova .05 .15
200 Steve Dunn .05 .15
201 Scott Erickson .05 .15
202 Mark Guthrie .05 .15
203 Chip Hale .05 .15
204 LaTroy Hawkins .05 .15
205 Denny Hocking .05 .15
206 Chuck Knoblauch .10 .30
207 Scott Leius .05 .15
208 Shane Mack .05 .15
209 Pat Mahomes .05 .15
210 Pat Meares .05 .15
211 Pedro Munoz .05 .15
212 Kirby Puckett .30 .75
213 Jeff Reboulet .05 .15
214 Dave Stevens .05 .15
215 Kevin Tapani .05 .15
216 Matt Walbeck .05 .15
217 Carl Willis .05 .15
218 Brian Anderson .05 .15
219 Chad Curtis .05 .15
220 Chili Davis .10 .30
221 Gary DiSarcina .05 .15
222 Damion Easley .05 .15
223 Jim Edmonds .20 .50
224 Chuck Finley .10 .30
225 Joe Grahe .05 .15
226 Rex Hudler .05 .15
227 Bo Jackson .30 .75
228 Mark Langston .05 .15
229 Phil Leftwich .05 .15
230 Mark Leiter .05 .15
231 Spike Owen .05 .15
232 Bob Patterson .05 .15
233 Troy Percival .10 .30
234 Eduardo Perez .05 .15
235 Tim Salmon .20 .50
236 J.T. Snow .10 .30
237 Chris Turner .05 .15
238 Mark Acre .05 .15
239 Geronimo Berroa .05 .15
240 Mike Bordick .05 .15
241 John Briscoe .05 .15
242 Scott Brosius .10 .30
243 Ron Darling .05 .15
244 Dennis Eckersley .10 .30
245 Brent Gates .05 .15
246 Rickey Henderson .30 .75
247 Stan Javier .05 .15
248 Steve Karsay .05 .15
249 Mark McGwire .75 2.00
250 Troy Neel .05 .15
251 Steve Ontiveros .05 .15
252 Carlos Reyes .05 .15
253 Ruben Sierra .10 .30
254 Terry Steinbach .05 .15
255 Bill Taylor .05 .15
256 Todd Van Poppel .05 .15
257 Bobby Witt .05 .15
258 Rich Amaral .05 .15
259 Eric Anthony .05 .15
260 Bobby Ayala .05 .15
261 Mike Blowers .05 .15
262 Chris Bosio .05 .15
263 Jay Buhner .10 .30
264 John Cummings .05 .15
265 Tim Davis .05 .15
266 Felix Fermin .05 .15
267 Dave Fleming .05 .15
268 Goose Gossage .10 .30
269 Ken Griffey Jr. .50 1.25
270 Reggie Jefferson .05 .15
271 Randy Johnson .30 .75
272 Edgar Martinez .20 .50
273 Tino Martinez .20 .50
274 Greg Pirkl .05 .15
275 Bill Risley .05 .15
276 Roger Salkeld .05 .15
277 Luis Sojo .05 .15
278 Mac Suzuki .05 .15
279 Dan Wilson .05 .15
280 Kevin Brown .10 .30
281 Jose Canseco .20 .50
282 Cris Carpenter .05 .15
283 Will Clark .20 .50
284 Jeff Frye .05 .15
285 Juan Gonzalez .10 .30
286 Rick Helling .05 .15
287 Tom Henke .05 .15
288 David Hulse .05 .15
289 Chris James .05 .15
290 Manuel Lee .05 .15
291 Oddibe McDowell .05 .15
292 Dean Palmer .10 .30
293 Roger Pavlik .05 .15
294 Bill Ripken .05 .15
295 Ivan Rodriguez .20 .50
296 Kenny Rogers .10 .30
297 Doug Strange .05 .15
298 Matt Whiteside .05 .15
299 Steve Avery .05 .15
300 Steve Bedrosian .05 .15
301 Rafael Belliard .05 .15
302 Jeff Blauser .05 .15
303 Dave Gallagher .05 .15
304 Tom Glavine .20 .50
305 David Justice .10 .30
306 Mike Kelly .05 .15
307 Roberto Kelly .05 .15
308 Ryan Klesko .10 .30
309 Mark Lemke .05 .15
310 Javier Lopez .10 .30
311 Greg Maddux .50 1.25
312 Fred McGriff .20 .50
313 Greg McMichael .05 .15
314 Kent Mercker .05 .15
315 Charlie O'Brien .05 .15
316 Jose Oliva .05 .15
317 Terry Pendleton .10 .30
318 John Smoltz .20 .50
319 Mike Stanton .05 .15
320 Tony Tarasco .05 .15
321 Terrell Wade .05 .15
322 Mark Wohlers .05 .15
323 Kurt Abbott .05 .15
324 Luis Aquino .05 .15
325 Bret Barberie .05 .15
326 Ryan Bowen .05 .15
327 Jerry Browne .05 .15
328 Chuck Carr .05 .15
329 Matias Carrillo .05 .15
330 Greg Colbrunn .05 .15
331 Jeff Conine .10 .30
332 Mark Gardner .05 .15
333 Chris Hammond .05 .15
334 Bryan Harvey .05 .15
335 Richie Lewis .05 .15
336 Dave Magadan .05 .15
337 Terry Mathews .05 .15
338 Robb Nen .10 .30
339 Yorkis Perez .05 .15
340 Pat Rapp .05 .15
341 Benito Santiago .10 .30
342 Gary Sheffield .10 .30
343 Dave Weathers .05 .15
344 Moises Alou .10 .30
345 Sean Berry .05 .15
346 Wil Cordero .05 .15
347 Joey Eischen .05 .15
348 Jeff Fassero .05 .15
349 Darrin Fletcher .05 .15
350 Cliff Floyd .10 .30
351 Marquis Grissom .10 .30
352 Butch Henry .05 .15
353 Gil Heredia .05 .15
354 Ken Hill .05 .15
355 Mike Lansing .05 .15
356 Pedro Martinez .20 .50
357 Mel Rojas .05 .15
358 Kirk Rueter .05 .15
359 Tim Scott .05 .15
360 Jeff Shaw .05 .15
361 Larry Walker .10 .30
362 Lenny Webster .05 .15
363 John Wetteland .10 .30
364 Rondell White .10 .30
365 Bobby Bonilla .10 .30
366 Rico Brogna .05 .15
367 Jeromy Burnitz .10 .30
368 John Franco .10 .30
369 Dwight Gooden .10 .30
370 Todd Hundley .05 .15
371 Jason Jacome .05 .15
372 Bobby Jones .05 .15
373 Jeff Kent .10 .30
374 Jim Lindeman .05 .15
375 Josias Manzanillo .05 .15
376 Roger Mason .05 .15
377 Kevin McReynolds .05 .15
378 Joe Orsulak .05 .15
379 Bill Pulsipher .05 .15

380 Bret Saberhagen	.10	.30
381 David Segui	.05	.15
382 Pete Smith	.05	.15
383 Kelly Stinnett	.05	.15
384 Ryan Thompson	.05	.15
385 Jose Vizcaino	.05	.15
386 Toby Borland	.05	.15
387 Ricky Bottalico	.05	.15
388 Darren Daulton	.10	.30
389 Mariano Duncan	.05	.15
390 Lenny Dykstra	.10	.30
391 Jim Eisenreich	.05	.15
392 Tommy Greene	.05	.15
393 Dave Hollins	.05	.15
394 Pete Incaviglia	.05	.15
395 Danny Jackson	.05	.15
396 Doug Jones	.05	.15
397 Ricky Jordan	.05	.15
398 John Kruk	.10	.30
399 Mike Lieberthal	.10	.30
400 Tony Longmire	.05	.15
401 Mickey Morandini	.05	.15
402 Bobby Munoz	.05	.15
403 Curt Schilling	.10	.30
404 Heathcliff Slocumb	.05	.15
405 Kevin Stocker	.05	.15
406 Fernando Valenzuela	.10	.30
407 David West	.05	.15
408 Willie Banks	.05	.15
409 Jose Bautista	.05	.15
410 Steve Buechele	.05	.15
411 Jim Bullinger	.05	.15
412 Chuck Crim	.05	.15
413 Shawon Dunston	.05	.15
414 Kevin Foster	.05	.15
415 Mark Grace	.20	.50
416 Jose Hernandez	.05	.15
417 Glenallen Hill	.05	.15
418 Brooks Kieschnick	.05	.15
419 Derrick May	.05	.15
420 Randy Myers	.05	.15
421 Dan Plesac	.05	.15
422 Karl Rhodes	.05	.15
423 Rey Sanchez	.05	.15
424 Sammy Sosa	.30	.75
425 Steve Trachsel	.05	.15
426 Rick Wilkins	.05	.15
427 Anthony Young	.05	.15
428 Eddie Zambrano	.05	.15
429 Bret Boone	.10	.30
430 Jeff Branson	.05	.15
431 Jeff Brantley	.05	.15
432 Hector Carrasco	.05	.15
433 Brian Dorsett	.05	.15
434 Tony Fernandez	.05	.15
435 Tim Fortugno	.05	.15
436 Erik Hanson	.05	.15
437 Thomas Howard	.05	.15
438 Kevin Jarvis	.05	.15
439 Barry Larkin	.20	.50
440 Chuck McElroy	.05	.15
441 Kevin Mitchell	.05	.15
442 Hal Morris	.05	.15
443 Jose Rijo	.05	.15
444 John Roper	.05	.15
445 Johnny Ruffin	.05	.15
446 Deion Sanders	.20	.50
447 Reggie Sanders	.10	.30
448 Pete Schourek	.05	.15
449 John Smiley	.05	.15
450 Eddie Taubensee	.05	.15
451 Jeff Bagwell	.20	.50
452 Kevin Bass	.05	.15
453 Craig Biggio	.20	.50
454 Ken Caminiti	.10	.30
455 Andujar Cedeno	.05	.15
456 Doug Drabek	.05	.15
457 Tony Eusebio	.05	.15
458 Mike Felder	.05	.15
459 Steve Finley	.10	.30
460 Luis Gonzalez	.10	.30
461 Mike Hampton	.10	.30
462 Pete Harnisch	.05	.15
463 John Hudek	.05	.15
464 Todd Jones	.05	.15
465 Darryl Kile	.10	.30
466 James Mouton	.05	.15
467 Shane Reynolds	.05	.15
468 Scott Servais	.05	.15
469 Greg Swindell	.05	.15
470 Dave Veres RC	.15	.40
471 Brian Williams	.05	.15
472 Jay Bell	.10	.30
473 Jacob Brumfield	.05	.15
474 Dave Clark	.05	.15
475 Steve Cooke	.05	.15
476 Midre Cummings	.05	.15
477 Mark Dewey	.05	.15
478 Tom Foley	.05	.15
479 Carlos Garcia	.05	.15
480 Jeff King	.05	.15
481 Jon Lieber	.05	.15
482 Ravelo Manzanillo	.05	.15
483 Al Martin	.05	.15
484 Orlando Merced	.05	.15
485 Danny Miceli	.05	.15
486 Denny Neagle	.10	.30
487 Lance Parrish	.10	.30
488 Don Slaught	.05	.15
489 Zane Smith	.05	.15
490 Andy Van Slyke	.20	.50
491 Paul Wagner	.05	.15
492 Rick White	.05	.15
493 Luis Alicea	.05	.15
494 Rene Arocha	.05	.15
495 Rheal Cormier	.05	.15
496 Bryan Eversgerd	.05	.15
497 Bernard Gilkey	.05	.15
498 John Habyan	.05	.15
499 Gregg Jefferies	.05	.15
500 Brian Jordan	.10	.30
501 Ray Lankford	.10	.30
502 John Mabry	.05	.15
503 Terry McGriff	.05	.15
504 Tom Pagnozzi	.05	.15
505 Vicente Palacios	.05	.15
506 Geronimo Pena	.05	.15
507 Gerald Perry	.05	.15
508 Rich Rodriguez	.05	.15
509 Ozzie Smith	.50	1.25
510 Bob Tewksbury	.05	.15
511 Allen Watson	.05	.15
512 Mark Whiten	.05	.15
513 Todd Zeile	.05	.15
514 Dante Bichette	.10	.30
515 Willie Blair	.05	.15
516 Ellis Burks	.10	.30
517 Marvin Freeman	.05	.15
518 Andres Galarraga	.10	.30
519 Joe Girardi	.05	.15
520 Greg W. Harris	.05	.15
521 Charlie Hayes	.05	.15
522 Mike Kingery	.05	.15
523 Nelson Liriano	.05	.15
524 Mike Munoz	.05	.15
525 David Nied	.05	.15
526 Steve Reed	.05	.15
527 Kevin Ritz	.05	.15
528 Bruce Ruffin	.05	.15
529 John Vander Wal	.05	.15
530 Walt Weiss	.05	.15
531 Eric Young	.05	.15
532 Billy Ashley	.05	.15
533 Pedro Astacio	.05	.15
534 Rafael Bournigal	.05	.15
535 Brett Butler	.10	.30
536 Tom Candiotti	.05	.15
537 Omar Daal	.05	.15
538 Delino DeShields	.05	.15
539 Darren Dreifort	.05	.15
540 Kevin Gross	.05	.15
541 Orel Hershiser	.10	.30
542 Garey Ingram	.05	.15
543 Eric Karros	.10	.30
544 Ramon Martinez	.05	.15
545 Raul Mondesi	.10	.30
546 Chan Ho Park	.10	.30
547 Mike Piazza	.50	1.25
548 Henry Rodriguez	.05	.15
549 Rudy Seanez	.05	.15
550 Ismael Valdes	.05	.15
551 Tim Wallach	.05	.15
552 Todd Worrell	.05	.15
553 Andy Ashby	.05	.15
554 Brad Ausmus	.10	.30
555 Derek Bell	.05	.15
556 Andy Benes	.05	.15
557 Phil Clark	.05	.15
558 Donnie Elliott	.05	.15
559 Ricky Gutierrez	.05	.15
560 Tony Gwynn	.40	1.00
561 Joey Hamilton	.05	.15
562 Trevor Hoffman	.10	.30
563 Luis Lopez	.05	.15
564 Pedro A. Martinez	.05	.15
565 Tim Mauser	.05	.15
566 Phil Plantier	.05	.15
567 Bip Roberts	.05	.15
568 Scott Sanders	.05	.15
569 Craig Shipley	.05	.15
570 Jeff Tabaka	.05	.15
571 Eddie Williams	.05	.15
572 Rod Beck	.05	.15
573 Mike Benjamin	.05	.15
574 Barry Bonds	.75	2.00
575 Dave Burba	.05	.15
576 John Burkett	.05	.15
577 Mark Carreon	.05	.15
578 Royce Clayton	.05	.15
579 Steve Frey	.05	.15
580 Bryan Hickerson	.05	.15
581 Mike Jackson	.05	.15
582 Darren Lewis	.05	.15
583 Kirt Manwaring	.05	.15
584 Rich Monteleone	.05	.15
585 John Patterson	.05	.15
586 J.R. Phillips	.05	.15
587 Mark Portugal	.05	.15
588 Joe Rosselli	.05	.15
589 Darryl Strawberry	.10	.30
590 Bill Swift	.05	.15
591 Robby Thompson	.05	.15
592 W.VanLandingham	.05	.15
593 Matt Williams	.10	.30
594 Checklist	.05	.15
595 Checklist	.05	.15
596 Checklist	.05	.15
597 Checklist	.05	.15
598 Checklist	.05	.15
599 Checklist	.05	.15
600 Checklist	.05	.15

1995 Fleer All-Fleer

This nine-card standard-size set was available through a 1995 Fleer wrapper offer. Nine of the leading players for each position are featured in this set. The wrapper redemption offer expired on September 30, 1995. The fronts feature the player's photo covering most of the card with a small section on the right set off for the words "All Fleer 9" along with the playerâ ™s name. The backs feature player information as to why they are among the best in the game.

COMPLETE SET (9)	4.00	10.00
1 Mike Piazza	.50	1.25
2 Frank Thomas	.30	.75
3 Roberto Alomar	.20	.50
4 Cal Ripken	1.00	2.50
5 Matt Williams	.10	.30
6 Barry Bonds	.75	2.00
7 Ken Griffey Jr.	.50	1.25
8 Tony Gwynn	.40	1.00
9 Greg Maddux	.50	1.25

1995 Fleer All-Rookies

This nine-card standard-size set was available through a Rookie Exchange redemption card randomly inserted in packs. The redemption

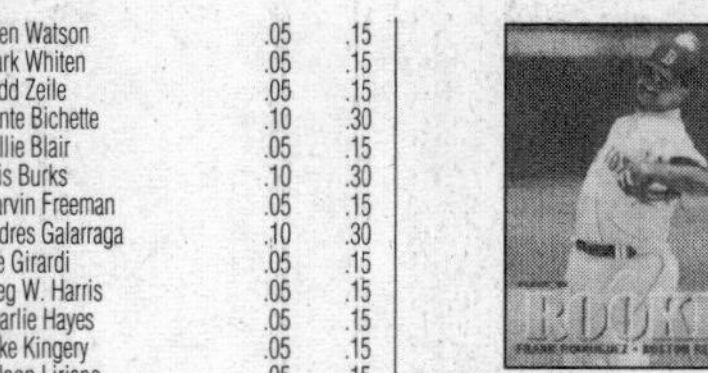

deadline was 9/30/95. This set features players who made their major league debut in 1995. The fronts have an action photo with a grainy background. The player's name and team are in gold foil at the bottom. Horizontal backs have a player photo the left and minor league highlights to the right.

COMPLETE SET (9)	1.25	3.00
M1 Edgardo Alfonzo	.08	.25
M2 Jason Bates	.08	.25
M3 Brian Boehringer	.08	.25
M4 Darren Bragg	.08	.25
M5 Brad Clontz	.08	.25
M6 Jim Dougherty	.08	.25
M7 Todd Hollandsworth	.08	.25
M8 Rudy Pemberton	.08	.25
M9 Frank Rodriguez	.08	.25
NNO Exp. All-Rookie Exch.	.08	.25

1995 Fleer All-Stars

Randomly inserted in all pack types at a rate of one in three, this 25-card standard-size set showcases those that participated in the 1994 mid-season classic held in Pittsburgh. Horizontally designed, the fronts contain photos of American League stars with the back protraying the National League player from the same position. On each side, the 1994 All-Star Game logo appears in gold foil as does either the A.L. or N.L. logo in silver foil.

COMPLETE SET (25)	4.00	10.00
1 Ivan Rodriguez Mike Piazza	.60	1.50
2 Frank Thomas Gregg Jefferies	.40	1.00
3 Robert Alomar Mariano Duncan	.25	.60
4 Wade Boggs Matt Williams	.25	.60
5 Cal Ripken Jr. Ozzie Smith	1.25	3.00
6 Joe Carter Barry Bonds	1.00	2.50
7 Ken Griffey Jr. Tony Gwynn	.60	1.50
8 Kirby Puckett David Justice	.40	1.00
9 Jimmy Key Greg Maddux	.60	1.50
10 Chuck Knoblauch Wil Cordero	.15	.40
11 Scott Cooper Ken Caminiti	.15	.40
12 Will Clark Carlos Garcia	.25	.60
13 Paul Molitor Jeff Bagwell	.25	.60
14 Travis Fryman Craig Biggio	.25	.60
15 Mickey Tettleton Fred McGriff	.25	.60
16 Kenny Lofton Moises Alou	.15	.40
17 Albert Belle Marquis Grissom	.15	.40
18 Paul O'Neill Dante Bichette	.25	.60
19 David Cone Ken Hill	.15	.40
20 Mike Mussina Doug Drabek	.25	.60
21 Randy Johnson John Hudek	.40	1.00
22 Pat Hentgen Danny Jackson	.07	.20
23 Wilson Alvarez Rod Beck	.07	.20
24 Lee Smith Randy Myers	.15	.40
25 Jason Bere Doug Jones	.07	.20

1995 Fleer Award Winners

Randomly inserted in all pack types at a rate of one in 24, this six card standard-size set highlights the major award winners of 1994. Card fronts feature action photos that are full-bleed on the right border and have gold border on the left. Within the gold border are the player's name and Fleer Award Winner. The backs contain a photo with text that references 1994 accomplishments.

COMPLETE SET (6)	2.00	5.00
1 Frank Thomas	.50	1.25
2 Jeff Bagwell	.30	.75
3 David Cone	.20	.50
4 Greg Maddux	.75	2.00
5 Bob Hamelin	.08	.25
6 Raul Mondesi	.20	.50

1995 Fleer League Leaders

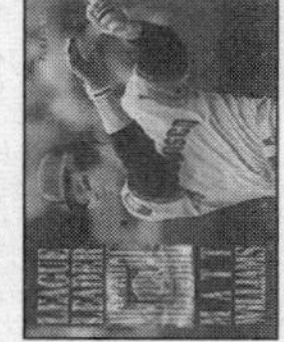

Randomly inserted in all pack types at a rate of one in 12, this 10-card standard-size set features 1994 American and National League leaders in various categories. The horizontal cards have player photos on front and back. The back also has a brief write-up concerning the accomplishment.

COMPLETE SET (10)	3.00	8.00
1 Paul O'Neill	.30	.75
2 Ken Griffey Jr.	.75	2.00
3 Kirby Puckett	.50	1.25
4 Jimmy Key	.20	.50
5 Randy Johnson	.50	1.25
6 Tony Gwynn	.60	1.50
7 Matt Williams	.20	.50
8 Jeff Bagwell	.30	.75
9 Greg Maddux Ken Hill	.75	2.00
10 Andy Benes	.08	.25

1995 Fleer Lumber Company

Randomly inserted in retail packs at a rate of one in 24, this standard-size set highlights 10 of the game's top sluggers. Full-bleed card fronts feature an action photo with the Lumber Company logo, which includes the player's name, toward the bottom of the photo. Card backs have a player photo and woodgrain background with a write-up that highlights individual achievements.

COMPLETE SET (10)	12.50	30.00
1 Jeff Bagwell	1.00	2.50
2 Albert Belle	.60	1.50
3 Barry Bonds	4.00	10.00
4 Jose Canseco	1.00	2.50
5 Joe Carter	.60	1.50
6 Ken Griffey Jr.	2.50	6.00
7 Fred McGriff	1.00	2.50
8 Kevin Mitchell	.30	.75
9 Frank Thomas	1.50	4.00
10 Matt Williams	.60	1.50

1995 Fleer Major League Prospects

Randomly inserted in all pack types at a rate of one in six, this 10-card standard-size set spotlights major league hopefuls. Card fronts feature a player photo with the words "Major League Prospects" serving as part of the background. The player's name and team appear in silver foil at the bottom. The backs have a photo and a write-up on his minor league career.

COMPLETE SET (10)	4.00	10.00
1 Garret Anderson	.20	.50
2 James Baldwin	.08	.25
3 Alan Benes	.08	.25
4 Armando Benitez	.08	.25
5 Ray Durham	.20	.50
6 Brian L. Hunter	.08	.25
7 Derek Jeter	1.50	4.00
8 Charles Johnson	.20	.50
9 Orlando Miller	.08	.25
10 Alex Rodriguez	1.50	4.00

1995 Fleer Pro-Visions

Randomly inserted in all pack types at a rate of one in nine, this six card standard-size set features top players illustrated by Wayne Anthony Still. The colorful artwork on front features the player in a surrealistic setting. The backs offer write-up on the player's previous season.

COMPLETE SET (6)	1.25	3.00
1 Mike Mussina	.20	.50
2 Raul Mondesi	.10	.30
3 Jeff Bagwell	.20	.50
4 Greg Maddux	.50	1.25
5 Tim Salmon	.20	.50
6 Manny Ramirez	.20	.50

1995 Fleer Rookie Sensations

Randomly inserted in 18-card packs, this 20-card standard-size set features top rookies from the 1994 season. The fronts have full-bleed color photos with the team and player's name in gold foil along the right edge. The backs also have full-bleed color photos along with player information.

COMPLETE SET (20)	15.00	40.00
1 Kurt Abbott	.75	2.00
2 Rico Brogna	.75	2.00
3 Hector Carrasco	.75	2.00
4 Kevin Foster	.75	2.00
5 Chris Gomez	.75	2.00
6 Darren Hall	.75	2.00
7 Bob Hamelin	.75	2.00
8 Joey Hamilton	.75	2.00
9 John Hudek	.75	2.00
10 Ryan Klesko	1.50	4.00
11 Javier Lopez	1.50	4.00
12 Matt Mieske	.75	2.00
13 Raul Mondesi	1.50	4.00
14 Manny Ramirez	2.00	5.00
15 Shane Reynolds	.75	2.00
16 Bill Risley	.75	2.00
17 Johnny Ruffin	.75	2.00
18 Steve Trachsel	.75	2.00
19 W.VanLandingham	.75	2.00
20 Rondell White	1.50	4.00

1995 Fleer Team Leaders

Randomly inserted in 12-card hobby packs at a rate of one in 24, this 28-card standard-size set features top players from each team. Each team is represented with card the has the team's leading hitter on one side with the leading pitcher on the other side. The team logo, "Team Leaders" and the player's name are gold foil stamped on front and back.

COMPLETE SET (28)	50.00	100.00
1 Cal Ripken Jr. Mike Mussina	10.00	25.00
2 Mo Vaughn Roger Clemens	6.00	15.00
3 Tim Salmon Chuck Finley	2.00	5.00
4 Frank Thomas Jack McDowell	3.00	8.00
5 Albert Belle Dennis Martinez	1.25	3.00
6 Cecil Fielder Mike Moore	1.25	3.00
7 Bob Hamelin David Cone	1.25	3.00
8 Greg Vaughn Ricky Bones	.60	1.50
9 Kirby Puckett Rick Aguilera	3.00	8.00
10 Don Mattingly Jimmy Key	8.00	20.00
11 Ruben Sierra Dennis Eckersley	1.25	3.00
12 Ken Griffey Jr. Randy Johnson	5.00	12.00
13 Jose Canseco Kenny Rogers	2.00	5.00
14 Joe Carter Pat Hentgen	1.25	3.00
15 David Justice Greg Maddux	5.00	12.00
16 Sammy Sosa Steve Trachsel	3.00	8.00
17 Kevin Mitchell Jose Rijo	.60	1.50
18 Dante Bichette Bruce Ruffin	1.25	3.00
19 Jeff Conine Robb Nen	1.25	3.00
20 Jeff Bagwell Doug Drabek	2.00	5.00
21 Mike Piazza Ramon Martinez	5.00	12.00
22 Moises Alou Ken Hill	1.25	3.00
23 Bobby Bonilla Bret Saberhagen	1.25	3.00
24 Darren Daulton Danny Jackson	1.25	3.00
25 Jay Bell Zane Smith	1.25	3.00
26 Gregg Jefferies Bob Tewksbury	.60	1.50
27 Tony Gwynn Andy Benes	4.00	10.00
28 Matt Williams Rod Beck	1.25	3.00

1995 Fleer Update

This 200-card standard-size set features many players who were either rookies in 1995 or played for new teams. These cards were issued in either 12-card packs with a suggested retail price of $1.49 or 18-card packs that had a suggested retail price of $2.29. Each Fleer Update pack included one card from several insert sets produced with this product. Hot packs featuring only these insert cards were included one every 72 packs. The full-bleed fronts have two player photos and, atypical of baseball card fronts, biographical information such as height, weight, etc. The backgrounds are multi-colored. The backs are horizontal, have yearly statistics, a photo, and are numbered with the prefix "U". The checklist is arranged alphabetically by team within each leagueâ ™s divisions. Key Rookie Cards in this set include Bobby Higginson and Hideo Nomo.

COMPLETE SET (200)	6.00	15.00
1 Manny Alexander	.02	.10
2 Bret Barberie	.02	.10
3 Armando Benitez	.02	.10
4 Kevin Brown	.07	.20
5 Doug Jones	.02	.10
6 Sherman Obando	.02	.10
7 Andy Van Slyke	.10	.30
8 Stan Belinda	.02	.10
9 Jose Canseco	.10	.30
10 Vaughn Eshelman	.02	.10
11 Mike Macfarlane	.02	.10
12 Troy O'Leary	.02	.10
13 Steve Rodriguez	.02	.10
14 Lee Tinsley	.02	.10
15 Tim Vanegmond	.02	.10
16 Mark Whiten	.02	.10
17 Sean Bergman	.02	.10
18 Chad Curtis	.02	.10
19 John Flaherty	.02	.10
20 Bob Higginson RC	.30	.75
21 Felipe Lira	.02	.10
22 Shannon Penn	.02	.10
23 Todd Steverson	.02	.10
24 Sean Whiteside	.02	.10
25 Tony Fernandez	.02	.10
26 Jack McDowell	.02	.10
27 Andy Pettitte	.10	.30
28 John Wetteland	.07	.20
29 David Cone	.07	.20
30 Mike Timlin	.02	.10
31 Duane Ward	.02	.10
32 Jim Abbott	.10	.30
33 James Baldwin	.02	.10
34 Mike Devereaux	.02	.10
35 Ray Durham	.07	.20
36 Tim Fortugno	.02	.10
37 Scott Ruffcorn	.02	.10
38 Chris Sabo	.02	.10
39 Paul Assenmacher	.02	.10
40 Bud Black	.02	.10
41 Orel Hershiser	.07	.20
42 Julian Tavarez	.02	.10
43 Dave Winfield	.07	.20
44 Pat Borders	.02	.10
45 Melvin Bunch RC	.02	.10
46 Tom Goodwin	.02	.10
47 Jon Nunnally	.02	.10
48 Joe Randa	.07	.20
49 Dilson Torres RC	.02	.10
50 Joe Vitiello	.02	.10
51 David Hulse	.02	.10
52 Scott Karl	.02	.10
53 Mark Kiefer	.02	.10
54 Derrick May	.02	.10
55 Joe Oliver	.02	.10
56 Al Reyes RC	.02	.10
57 Steve Sparks RC	.15	.40
58 Jerald Clark	.02	.10
59 Eddie Guardado	.02	.10
60 Kevin Maas	.02	.10
61 David McCarty	.02	.10
62 Brad Radke RC	.30	.75
63 Scott Stahoviak	.02	.10
64 Garret Anderson	.07	.20
65 Shawn Boskie	.02	.10
66 Mike James	.02	.10
67 Tony Phillips	.02	.10
68 Lee Smith	.07	.20
69 Mitch Williams	.02	.10
70 Jim Corsi	.02	.10
71 Mark Harkey	.02	.10
72 Dave Stewart	.07	.20
73 Todd Stottlemyre	.02	.10
74 Joey Cora	.02	.10
75 Chad Kreuter	.02	.10
76 Jeff Nelson	.02	.10
77 Alex Rodriguez	.50	1.25
78 Ron Villone	.02	.10
79 Bob Wells RC	.15	.40
80 Jose Alberro RC	.02	.10
81 Terry Burrows	.02	.10
82 Kevin Gross	.02	.10
83 Wilson Heredia	.02	.10
84 Mark McLemore	.02	.10
85 Otis Nixon	.02	.10
86 Jeff Russell	.02	.10
87 Mickey Tettleton	.02	.10
88 Bob Tewksbury	.02	.10

89 Pedro Borbon .02 .10
90 Marquis Grissom .07 .20
91 Chipper Jones .20 .50
92 Mike Mordecai .02 .10
93 Jason Schmidt .20 .50
94 John Burkett .02 .10
95 Andre Dawson .07 .20
96 Matt Dunbar RC .02 .10
97 Charles Johnson .07 .20
98 Terry Pendleton .07 .20
99 Rich Scheid .02 .10
100 Quilvio Veras .02 .10
101 Bobby Witt .02 .10
102 Eddie Zosky .02 .10
103 Shane Andrews .02 .10
104 Reid Cornelius .02 .10
105 Chad Fonville RC .02 .10
106 Mark Grudzielanek RC .30 .75
107 Roberto Kelly .02 .10
108 Carlos Perez RC .15 .40
109 Tony Tarasco .02 .10
110 Brett Butler .07 .20
111 Carl Everett .07 .20
112 Pete Harnisch .02 .10
113 Doug Henry .02 .10
114 Kevin Lomon RC .02 .10
115 Blas Minor .02 .10
116 Dave Mlicki .02 .10
117 Ricky Otero RC .02 .10
118 Norm Charlton .02 .10
119 Tyler Green .02 .10
120 Gene Harris .02 .10
121 Charlie Hayes .02 .10
122 Gregg Jefferies .02 .10
123 Michael Mimbs RC .02 .10
124 Paul Quantrill .02 .10
125 Frank Castillo .02 .10
126 Brian McRae .02 .10
127 Jaime Navarro .02 .10
128 Mike Perez .02 .10
129 Tanyon Sturtze .02 .10
130 Ozzie Timmons .02 .10
131 John Courtright .02 .10
132 Ron Gant .07 .20
133 Xavier Hernandez .02 .10
134 Brian Hunter .02 .10
135 Benito Santiago .07 .20
136 Pete Smith .02 .10
137 Scott Sullivan .02 .10
138 Derek Bell .02 .10
139 Doug Brocail .02 .10
140 Ricky Gutierrez .02 .10
141 Pedro A.Martinez .02 .10
142 Orlando Miller .02 .10
143 Phil Plantier .02 .10
144 Craig Shipley .02 .10
145 Rich Aude .02 .10
146 J.Christiansen RC .02 .10
147 Freddy Adrian Garcia RC .02 .10
148 Jim Gott .02 .10
149 Mark Johnson RC .15 .40
150 Esteban Loaiza .02 .10
151 Dan Plesac .02 .10
152 Gary Wilson RC .02 .10
153 Allen Battle .02 .10
154 Terry Bradshaw .02 .10
155 Scott Cooper .02 .10
156 Tripp Cromer .02 .10
157 John Frascatore RC .02 .10
158 John Habyan .02 .10
159 Tom Henke .02 .10
160 Ken Hill .02 .10
161 Danny Jackson .02 .10
162 Donovan Osborne .02 .10
163 Tom Urbani .02 .10
164 Roger Bailey .02 .10
165 Jorge Brito RC .02 .10
166 Vinny Castilla .07 .20
167 Darren Holmes .02 .10
168 Roberto Mejia .02 .10
169 Bill Swift .02 .10
170 Mark Thompson .02 .10
171 Larry Walker .07 .20
172 Greg Hansell .02 .10
173 Dave Hansen .02 .10
174 Carlos Hernandez .02 .10
175 Hideo Nomo RC .75 2.00
176 Jose Offerman .02 .10
177 Antonio Osuna .02 .10
178 Reggie Williams .02 .10
179 Todd Williams .02 .10
180 Andres Berumen .02 .10
181 Ken Caminiti .07 .20
182 Andujar Cedeno .02 .10
183 Steve Finley .07 .20
184 Bryce Florie .02 .10
185 Dustin Hermanson .02 .10
186 Ray Holbert .02 .10
187 Melvin Nieves .02 .10
188 Roberto Petagine .02 .10
189 Jody Reed .02 .10
190 Fernando Valenzuela .07 .20
191 Brian Williams .02 .10
192 Mark Dewey .02 .10
193 Glenallen Hill .02 .10
194 Chris Hook RC .02 .10
195 Terry Mulholland .02 .10
196 Steve Scarsone .02 .10
197 Trevor Wilson .02 .10
198 Checklist .02 .10
199 Checklist .02 .10
200 Checklist .02 .10

1995 Fleer Update Diamond Tribute

This 10-card standard-size set featuring some of baseball's leading stars were inserted at a stated rate of one in five packs. The cards are numbered in the lower right with an "X" of 10.

COMPLETE SET (10) 3.00 8.00
1 Jeff Bagwell .20 .50
2 Albert Belle .10 .30
3 Barry Bonds .75 2.00
4 David Cone .10 .30
5 Dennis Eckersley .10 .30
6 Ken Griffey Jr. .50 1.25
7 Rickey Henderson .30 .75
8 Greg Maddux .50 1.25
9 Frank Thomas .30 .75
10 Matt Williams .10 .30

1995 Fleer Update Headliners

Inserted one every three packs, this 20-card standard-size set features various major league stars. The cards are numbered in the lower left as "X" of 20.

COMPLETE SET (20) 5.00 12.00
1 Jeff Bagwell .20 .50
2 Albert Belle .10 .30
3 Barry Bonds .75 2.00
4 Jose Canseco .20 .50
5 Joe Carter .10 .30
6 Will Clark .20 .50
7 Roger Clemens .60 1.50
8 Lenny Dykstra .10 .30
9 Cecil Fielder .10 .30
10 Juan Gonzalez .10 .30
11 Ken Griffey Jr. .50 1.25
12 Kenny Lofton .10 .30
13 Greg Maddux .50 1.25
14 Fred McGriff .20 .50
15 Mike Piazza .50 1.25
16 Kirby Puckett .30 .75
17 Tim Salmon .20 .50
18 Frank Thomas .30 .75
19 Mo Vaughn .10 .30
20 Matt Williams .10 .30

1995 Fleer Update Rookie Update

Inserted one in every four packs, this 10-card standard-size set features some of 1995's best rookies. The cards are numbered as "X of 10". Chipper Jones and Hideo Nomo are among the players included in this set.

COMPLETE SET (10) 5.00 10.00
1 Shane Andrews .08 .25
2 Ray Durham .20 .50
3 Shawn Green .20 .50
4 Charles Johnson .20 .50
5 Chipper Jones .60 1.50
6 Esteban Loaiza .08 .25
7 Hideo Nomo .75 2.00
8 Jon Nunnally .08 .25
9 Alex Rodriguez 1.50 4.00
10 Julian Tavarez .08 .25

1995 Fleer Update Smooth Leather

Inserted one every five jumbo packs, this 10-card standard-size set features many leading defensive wizards. The card fronts feature a player photo. Underneath the player photo, is his name along with the words "smooth leather" on the bottom. The right corner features a glove. All of this information as well as the "Fleer 95" logo is in gold print. All of this is on a card with a special leather-like coating. The back features a photo as well as fielding information. The cards are numbered in the lower left as "X of 10" and are sequenced in alphabetical order.

COMPLETE SET (10) 10.00 25.00
1 Roberto Alomar .60 1.50
2 Barry Bonds 2.50 6.00
3 Ken Griffey Jr. 1.50 4.00
4 Marquis Grissom .40 1.00
5 Darren Lewis .20 .50
6 Kenny Lofton .40 1.00
7 Don Mattingly 2.50 6.00
8 Cal Ripken 3.00 8.00
9 Ivan Rodriguez .60 1.50
10 Matt Williams .40 1.00

1995 Fleer Update Soaring Stars

This nine-card standard-size set was inserted one every 36 packs. The fronts feature the player's photo set against a prismatic background of baseballs. The player's name, the "Soaring Stars" logo as well as a star are all printed in gold foil at the bottom. The back has a player photo, his name as well as some career information. The cards are numbered in the upper right "X of 9" and are sequenced in alphabetical order.

COMPLETE SET (9) 10.00 25.00
1 Moises Alou UER 1.00 2.50
(says .399 BA in 1994)
2 Jason Bere .50 1.25
3 Jeff Conine 1.00 2.50
4 Cliff Floyd 1.00 2.50
5 Pat Hentgen .50 1.25
6 Kenny Lofton 1.00 2.50
7 Raul Mondesi 1.00 2.50
8 Mike Piazza 4.00 10.00
9 Tim Salmon 1.50 4.00

1996 Fleer

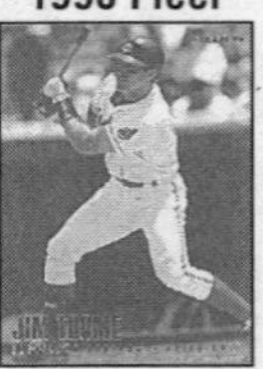

The 1996 Fleer baseball set consists of 600 standard-size cards issued in one series. Cards were issued in 11-card packs with a suggested retail price of $1.49. Borderless fronts are matte-finished and have full-color action shots with the player's name, team and position stamped in gold foil. Backs contain a biography and career stats on the top and a full-color head shot with a 1995 synopsis on the bottom. The matte finish on the cards was designed so collectors could have an easier surface for cards to be autographed. Fleer included in each pack a "Thanks a Million" scratch-off game card redeemable for instant-win prizes and a chance to bat for a million-dollar prize in a Major League park. Rookie Cards in this set include Matt Lawton and Mike Sweeney. A Cal Ripken promo was distributed to dealers and hobby media to preview the set.

COMPLETE SET (600) 40.00 80.00
1 Manny Alexander .10 .30
2 Brady Anderson .10 .30
3 Harold Baines .10 .30
4 Armando Benitez .10 .30
5 Bobby Bonilla .10 .30
6 Kevin Brown .10 .30
7 Scott Erickson .10 .30
8 Curtis Goodwin .10 .30
9 Jeffrey Hammonds .10 .30
10 Jimmy Haynes .10 .30
11 Chris Hoiles .10 .30
12 Doug Jones .10 .30
13 Rick Krivda .10 .30
14 Jeff Manto .10 .30
15 Ben McDonald .10 .30
16 Jamie Moyer .10 .30
17 Mike Mussina .20 .50
18 Jesse Orosco .10 .30
19 Rafael Palmeiro .20 .50
20 Cal Ripken 1.00 2.50
21 Rick Aguilera .10 .30
22 Luis Alicea .10 .30
23 Stan Belinda .10 .30
24 Jose Canseco .20 .50
25 Roger Clemens .60 1.50
26 Vaughn Eshelman .10 .30
27 Mike Greenwell .10 .30
28 Erik Hanson .10 .30
29 Dwayne Hosey .10 .30
30 Mike Macfarlane UER .10 .30
31 Tim Naehring .10 .30
32 Troy O'Leary .10 .30
33 Aaron Sele .10 .30
34 Zane Smith .10 .30
35 Jeff Suppan .10 .30
36 Lee Tinsley .10 .30
37 John Valentin .10 .30
38 Mo Vaughn .10 .30
39 Tim Wakefield .10 .30
40 Jim Abbott .20 .50
41 Brian Anderson .10 .30
42 Garret Anderson .10 .30
43 Chili Davis .10 .30
44 Gary DiSarcina .10 .30
45 Damion Easley .10 .30
46 Jim Edmonds .10 .30
47 Chuck Finley .10 .30
48 Todd Greene .10 .30
49 Mike Harkey .10 .30
50 Mike James .10 .30
51 Mark Langston .10 .30
52 Greg Myers .10 .30
53 Orlando Palmeiro .10 .30
54 Bob Patterson .10 .30
55 Troy Percival .10 .30
56 Tony Phillips .10 .30
57 Tim Salmon .20 .50
58 Lee Smith .10 .30
59 J.T. Snow .10 .30
60 Randy Velarde .10 .30
61 Wilson Alvarez .10 .30
62 Luis Andujar .10 .30
63 Jason Bere .10 .30
64 Ray Durham .10 .30
65 Alex Fernandez .10 .30
66 Ozzie Guillen .10 .30
67 Roberto Hernandez .10 .30
68 Lance Johnson .10 .30
69 Matt Karchner .10 .30
70 Ron Karkovice .10 .30
71 Norberto Martin .10 .30
72 Dave Martinez .10 .30
73 Kirk McCaskill .10 .30
74 Lyle Mouton .10 .30
75 Tim Raines .10 .30
76 Mike Sirotka RC .10 .30
77 Frank Thomas .30 .75
78 Larry Thomas .10 .30
79 Robin Ventura .10 .30
80 Sandy Alomar Jr. .10 .30
81 Paul Assenmacher .10 .30
82 Carlos Baerga .10 .30
83 Albert Belle .10 .30
84 Mark Clark .10 .30
85 Alan Embree .10 .30
86 Alvaro Espinoza .10 .30
87 Orel Hershiser .10 .30
88 Ken Hill .10 .30
89 Kenny Lofton .10 .30
90 Dennis Martinez .10 .30
91 Jose Mesa .10 .30
92 Eddie Murray .30 .75
93 Charles Nagy .10 .30
94 Chad Ogea .10 .30
95 Tony Pena .10 .30
96 Herb Perry .10 .30
97 Eric Plunk .10 .30
98 Jim Poole .10 .30
99 Manny Ramirez .20 .50
100 Paul Sorrento .10 .30
101 Julian Tavarez .10 .30
102 Jim Thome .20 .50
103 Omar Vizquel .20 .50
104 Dave Winfield .10 .30
105 Danny Bautista .10 .30
106 Joe Boever .10 .30
107 Chad Curtis .10 .30
108 John Doherty .10 .30
109 Cecil Fielder .10 .30
110 John Flaherty .10 .30
111 Travis Fryman .10 .30
112 Chris Gomez .10 .30
113 Bob Higginson .10 .30
114 Mark Lewis .10 .30
115 Jose Lima .10 .30
116 Felipe Lira .10 .30
117 Brian Maxcy .10 .30
118 C.J. Nitkowski .10 .30
119 Phil Plantier .10 .30
120 Clint Sodowsky .10 .30
121 Alan Trammell .10 .30
122 Lou Whitaker .10 .30
123 Kevin Appier .10 .30
124 Johnny Damon .20 .50
125 Gary Gaetti .10 .30
126 Tom Goodwin .10 .30
127 Tom Gordon .10 .30
128 Mark Gubicza .10 .30
129 Bob Hamelin .10 .30
130 David Howard .10 .30
131 Jason Jacome .10 .30
132 Wally Joyner .10 .30
133 Keith Lockhart .10 .30
134 Brent Mayne .10 .30
135 Jeff Montgomery .10 .30
136 Jon Nunnally .10 .30
137 Juan Samuel .10 .30
138 Mike Sweeney RC .40 1.00
139 Michael Tucker .10 .30
140 Joe Vitiello .10 .30
141 Ricky Bones .10 .30
142 Chuck Carr .10 .30
143 Jeff Cirillo .10 .30
144 Mike Fetters .10 .30
145 Darryl Hamilton .10 .30
146 David Hulse .10 .30
147 John Jaha .10 .30
148 Scott Karl .10 .30
149 Mark Kiefer .10 .30
150 Pat Listach .10 .30
151 Mark Loretta .10 .30
152 Mike Matheny .10 .30
153 Matt Mieske .10 .30
154 Dave Nilsson .10 .30
155 Joe Oliver .10 .30
156 Al Reyes .10 .30
157 Kevin Seitzer .10 .30
158 Steve Sparks .10 .30
159 B.J. Surhoff .10 .30
160 Jose Valentin .10 .30
161 Greg Vaughn .10 .30
162 Fernando Vina .10 .30
163 Rich Becker .10 .30
164 Ron Coomer .10 .30
165 Marty Cordova .10 .30
166 Chuck Knoblauch .10 .30
167 Matt Lawton RC .20 .50
168 Pat Meares .10 .30
169 Paul Molitor .10 .30
170 Pedro Munoz .10 .30
171 Jose Parra .10 .30
172 Kirby Puckett .30 .75
173 Brad Radke .10 .30
174 Jeff Reboulet .10 .30
175 Rich Robertson .10 .30
176 Frank Rodriguez .10 .30
177 Scott Stahoviak .10 .30
178 Dave Stevens .10 .30
179 Matt Walbeck .10 .30
180 Wade Boggs .20 .50
181 David Cone .10 .30
182 Tony Fernandez .10 .30
183 Joe Girardi .10 .30
184 Derek Jeter .75 2.00
185 Scott Kamieniecki .10 .30
186 Pat Kelly .10 .30
187 Jim Leyritz .10 .30
188 Tino Martinez .20 .50
189 Don Mattingly .75 2.00
190 Jack McDowell .10 .30
191 Jeff Nelson .10 .30
192 Paul O'Neill .20 .50
193 Melido Perez .10 .30
194 Andy Pettitte .20 .50
195 Mariano Rivera .30 .75
196 Ruben Sierra .10 .30
197 Mike Stanley .10 .30
198 Darryl Strawberry .10 .30
199 John Wetteland .10 .30
200 Bob Wickman .10 .30
201 Bernie Williams .20 .50
202 Mark Acre .10 .30
203 Geronimo Berroa .10 .30
204 Mike Bordick .10 .30
205 Scott Brosius .10 .30
206 Dennis Eckersley .10 .30
207 Brent Gates .10 .30
208 Jason Giambi .10 .30
209 Rickey Henderson .30 .75
210 Jose Herrera .10 .30
211 Stan Javier .10 .30
212 Doug Johns .10 .30
213 Mark McGwire .75 2.00
214 Steve Ontiveros .10 .30
215 Craig Paquette .10 .30
216 Ariel Prieto .10 .30
217 Carlos Reyes .10 .30
218 Terry Steinbach .10 .30
219 Todd Stottlemyre .10 .30
220 Danny Tartabull .10 .30
221 Todd Van Poppel .10 .30
222 John Wasdin .10 .30
223 George Williams .10 .30
224 Steve Wojciechowski .10 .30
225 Rich Amaral .10 .30
226 Bobby Ayala .10 .30
227 Tim Belcher .10 .30
228 Andy Benes .10 .30
229 Chris Bosio .10 .30
230 Darren Bragg .10 .30
231 Jay Buhner .10 .30
232 Norm Charlton .10 .30
233 Vince Coleman .10 .30
234 Joey Cora .10 .30
235 Russ Davis .10 .30
236 Alex Diaz .10 .30
237 Felix Fermin .10 .30
238 Ken Griffey Jr. .50 1.25
239 Sterling Hitchcock .10 .30
240 Randy Johnson .30 .75
241 Edgar Martinez .20 .50
242 Bill Risley .10 .30
243 Alex Rodriguez .60 1.50
244 Luis Sojo .10 .30
245 Dan Wilson .10 .30
246 Bob Wolcott .10 .30
247 Will Clark .20 .50
248 Jeff Frye .10 .30
249 Benji Gil .10 .30
250 Juan Gonzalez .10 .30
251 Rusty Greer .10 .30
252 Kevin Gross .10 .30
253 Roger McDowell .10 .30
254 Mark McLemore .10 .30
255 Otis Nixon .10 .30
256 Luis Ortiz .10 .30
257 Mike Pagliarulo .10 .30
258 Dean Palmer .10 .30
259 Roger Pavlik .10 .30
260 Ivan Rodriguez .20 .50
261 Kenny Rogers .10 .30
262 Jeff Russell .10 .30
263 Mickey Tettleton .10 .30
264 Bob Tewksbury .10 .30
265 Dave Valle .10 .30
266 Matt Whiteside .10 .30
267 Roberto Alomar .20 .50
268 Joe Carter .10 .30
269 Tony Castillo .10 .30
270 Domingo Cedeno .10 .30
271 Tim Crabtree UER .10 .30
272 Carlos Delgado .10 .30
273 Alex Gonzalez .10 .30
274 Shawn Green .10 .30
275 Juan Guzman .10 .30
276 Pat Hentgen .10 .30
277 Al Leiter .10 .30
278 Sandy Martinez .10 .30
279 Paul Menhart .10 .30
280 John Olerud .10 .30
281 Paul Quantrill .10 .30
282 Ken Robinson .10 .30
283 Ed Sprague .10 .30
284 Mike Timlin .10 .30
285 Steve Avery .10 .30
286 Rafael Belliard .10 .30
287 Jeff Blauser .10 .30
288 Pedro Borbon .10 .30
289 Brad Clontz .10 .30
290 Mike Devereaux .10 .30
291 Tom Glavine .20 .50
292 Marquis Grissom .10 .30
293 Chipper Jones .30 .75
294 David Justice .10 .30
295 Mike Kelly .10 .30
296 Ryan Klesko .10 .30
297 Mark Lemke .10 .30
298 Javier Lopez .10 .30
299 Greg Maddux .50 1.25
300 Fred McGriff .20 .50
301 Greg McMichael .10 .30
302 Kent Mercker .10 .30
303 Mike Mordecai .10 .30
304 Charlie O'Brien .10 .30
305 Eduardo Perez .10 .30
306 Luis Polonia .10 .30
307 Jason Schmidt .20 .50
308 John Smoltz .20 .50
309 Terrell Wade .10 .30
310 Mark Wohlers .10 .30
311 Scott Bullett .10 .30
312 Jim Bullinger .10 .30
313 Larry Casian .10 .30
314 Frank Castillo .10 .30
315 Shawon Dunston .10 .30
316 Kevin Foster .10 .30
317 Matt Franco .10 .30
318 Luis Gonzalez .10 .30
319 Mark Grace .20 .50
320 Jose Hernandez .10 .30
321 Mike Hubbard .10 .30
322 Brian McRae .10 .30
323 Randy Myers .10 .30
324 Jaime Navarro .10 .30
325 Mark Parent .10 .30
326 Mike Perez .10 .30
327 Rey Sanchez .10 .30
328 Ryne Sandberg .50 1.25
329 Scott Servais .10 .30
330 Sammy Sosa .30 .75
331 Ozzie Timmons .10 .30
332 Steve Trachsel .10 .30
333 Todd Zeile .10 .30
334 Bret Boone .10 .30
335 Jeff Branson .10 .30
336 Jeff Brantley .10 .30
337 Dave Burba .10 .30
338 Hector Carrasco .10 .30
339 Mariano Duncan .10 .30
340 Ron Gant .10 .30
341 Lenny Harris .10 .30
342 Xavier Hernandez .10 .30
343 Thomas Howard .10 .30
344 Mike Jackson .10 .30
345 Barry Larkin .20 .50
346 Darren Lewis .10 .30
347 Hal Morris .10 .30
348 Eric Owens .10 .30
349 Mark Portugal .10 .30
350 Jose Rijo .10 .30
351 Reggie Sanders .10 .30
352 Benito Santiago .10 .30
353 Pete Schourek .10 .30
354 John Smiley .10 .30
355 Eddie Taubensee .10 .30
356 Jerome Walton .10 .30
357 David Wells .10 .30
358 Roger Bailey .10 .30
359 Jason Bates .10 .30
360 Dante Bichette .10 .30
361 Ellis Burks .10 .30
362 Vinny Castilla .10 .30
363 Andres Galarraga .10 .30
364 Darren Holmes .10 .30
365 Mike Kingery .10 .30
366 Curt Leskanic .10 .30
367 Quinton McCracken .10 .30
368 Mike Munoz .10 .30
369 David Nied .10 .30
370 Steve Reed .10 .30
371 Bryan Rekar .10 .30
372 Kevin Ritz .10 .30
373 Bruce Ruffin .10 .30
374 Bret Saberhagen .10 .30
375 Bill Swift .10 .30
376 John Vander Wal .10 .30
377 Larry Walker .10 .30
378 Walt Weiss .10 .30
379 Eric Young .10 .30
380 Kurt Abbott .10 .30
381 Alex Arias .10 .30
382 Jerry Browne .10 .30
383 John Burkett .10 .30
384 Greg Colbrunn .10 .30
385 Jeff Conine .10 .30
386 Andre Dawson .10 .30
387 Chris Hammond .10 .30
388 Charles Johnson .10 .30
389 Terry Mathews .10 .30
390 Robb Nen .10 .30
391 Joe Orsulak .10 .30
392 Terry Pendleton .10 .30
393 Pat Rapp .10 .30
394 Gary Sheffield .10 .30
395 Jesus Tavarez .10 .30
396 Marc Valdes .10 .30
397 Quilvio Veras .10 .30
398 Randy Veres .10 .30
399 Devon White .10 .30
400 Jeff Bagwell .20 .50
401 Derek Bell .10 .30
402 Craig Biggio .20 .50
403 John Cangelosi .10 .30
404 Jim Dougherty .10 .30
405 Doug Drabek .10 .30
406 Tony Eusebio .10 .30
407 Ricky Gutierrez .10 .30
408 Mike Hampton .10 .30
409 Dean Hartgraves .10 .30
410 John Hudek .10 .30
411 Brian L. Hunter .10 .30
412 Todd Jones .10 .30
413 Darryl Kile .10 .30
414 Dave Magadan .10 .30
415 Derrick May .10 .30
416 Orlando Miller .10 .30
417 James Mouton .10 .30
418 Shane Reynolds .10 .30
419 Greg Swindell .10 .30
420 Jeff Tabaka .10 .30
421 Dave Veres .10 .30
422 Billy Wagner .10 .30
423 Donne Wall .10 .30
424 Rick Wilkins .10 .30
425 Billy Ashley .10 .30
426 Mike Blowers .10 .30
427 Brett Butler .10 .30
428 Tom Candiotti .10 .30
429 Juan Castro .10 .30
430 John Cummings .10 .30
431 Delino DeShields .10 .30
432 Joey Eischen .10 .30
433 Chad Fonville .10 .30
434 Greg Gagne .10 .30
435 Dave Hansen .10 .30
436 Carlos Hernandez .10 .30
437 Todd Hollandsworth .10 .30
438 Eric Karros .10 .30
439 Roberto Kelly .10 .30
440 Ramon Martinez .10 .30
441 Raul Mondesi .10 .30
442 Hideo Nomo .30 .75
443 Antonio Osuna .10 .30
444 Chan Ho Park .10 .30
445 Mike Piazza .50 1.25
446 Felix Rodriguez .10 .30
447 Kevin Tapani .10 .30
448 Ismael Valdes .10 .30
449 Todd Worrell .10 .30
450 Moises Alou .10 .30
451 Shane Andrews .10 .30
452 Yamil Benitez .10 .30
453 Sean Berry .10 .30
454 Wil Cordero .10 .30

455 Jeff Fassero	.10	.30
456 Darrin Fletcher	.10	.30
457 Cliff Floyd	.10	.30
458 Mark Grudzielanek	.10	.30
459 Gil Heredia	.10	.30
460 Tim Laker	.10	.30
461 Mike Lansing	.10	.30
462 Pedro J.Martinez	.20	.50
463 Carlos Perez	.10	.30
464 Curtis Pride	.10	.30
465 Mel Rojas	.10	.30
466 Kirk Rueter	.10	.30
467 F.P. Santangelo	.10	.30
468 Tim Scott	.10	.30
469 David Segui	.10	.30
470 Tony Tarasco	.10	.30
471 Rondell White	.10	.30
472 Edgardo Alfonzo	.10	.30
473 Tim Bogar	.10	.30
474 Rico Brogna	.10	.30
475 Damon Buford	.10	.30
476 Paul Byrd	.10	.30
477 Carl Everett	.10	.30
478 John Franco	.10	.30
479 Todd Hundley	.10	.30
480 Butch Huskey	.10	.30
481 Jason Isringhausen	.10	.30
482 Bobby Jones	.10	.30
483 Chris Jones	.10	.30
484 Jeff Kent	.10	.30
485 Dave Mlicki	.10	.30
486 Robert Person	.10	.30
487 Bill Pulsipher	.10	.30
488 Kelly Stinnett	.10	.30
489 Ryan Thompson	.10	.30
490 Jose Vizcaino	.10	.30
491 Howard Battle	.10	.30
492 Toby Borland	.10	.30
493 Ricky Bottalico	.10	.30
494 Darren Daulton	.10	.30
495 Lenny Dykstra	.10	.30
496 Jim Eisenreich	.10	.30
497 Sid Fernandez	.10	.30
498 Tyler Green	.10	.30
499 Charlie Hayes	.10	.30
500 Gregg Jefferies	.10	.30
501 Kevin Jordan	.10	.30
502 Tony Longmire	.10	.30
503 Tom Marsh	.10	.30
504 Michael Mimbs	.10	.30
505 Mickey Morandini	.10	.30
506 Gene Schall	.10	.30
507 Curt Schilling	.10	.30
508 Heathcliff Slocumb	.10	.30
509 Kevin Stocker	.10	.30
510 Andy Van Slyke	.20	.50
511 Lenny Webster	.10	.30
512 Mark Whiten	.10	.30
513 Mike Williams	.10	.30
514 Jay Bell	.10	.30
515 Jacob Brumfield	.10	.30
516 Jason Christiansen	.10	.30
517 Dave Clark	.10	.30
518 Midre Cummings	.10	.30
519 Angelo Encarnacion	.10	.30
520 John Ericks	.10	.30
521 Carlos Garcia	.10	.30
522 Mark Johnson	.10	.30
523 Jeff King	.10	.30
524 Nelson Liriano	.10	.30
525 Esteban Loaiza	.10	.30
526 Al Martin	.10	.30
527 Orlando Merced	.10	.30
528 Dan Miceli	.10	.30
529 Ramon Morel	.10	.30
530 Denny Neagle	.10	.30
531 Steve Parris	.10	.30
532 Dan Plesac	.10	.30
533 Don Slaught	.10	.30
534 Paul Wagner	.10	.30
535 John Wehner	.10	.30
536 Kevin Young	.10	.30
537 Allen Battle	.10	.30
538 David Bell	.10	.30
539 Alan Benes	.10	.30
540 Scott Cooper	.10	.30
541 Tripp Cromer	.10	.30
542 Tony Fossas	.10	.30
543 Bernard Gilkey	.10	.30
544 Tom Henke	.10	.30
545 Brian Jordan	.10	.30
546 Ray Lankford	.10	.30
547 John Mabry	.10	.30
548 T.J. Mathews	.10	.30
549 Mike Morgan	.10	.30
550 Jose Oliva	.10	.30
551 Jose Oquendo	.10	.30
552 Donovan Osborne	.10	.30
553 Tom Pagnozzi	.10	.30
554 Mark Petkovsek	.10	.30
555 Danny Sheaffer	.10	.30
556 Ozzie Smith	.50	1.25
557 Mark Sweeney	.10	.30
558 Allen Watson	.10	.30
559 Andy Ashby	.10	.30
560 Brad Ausmus	.10	.30
561 Willie Blair	.10	.30
562 Ken Caminiti	.10	.30
563 Andujar Cedeno	.10	.30
564 Glenn Dishman	.10	.30
565 Steve Finley	.10	.30
566 Bryce Florie	.10	.30
567 Tony Gwynn	.40	1.00
568 Joey Hamilton	.10	.30
569 Dustin Hermanson	.10	.30
570 Trevor Hoffman	.10	.30
571 Brian Johnson	.10	.30
572 Marc Kroon	.10	.30
573 Scott Livingstone	.10	.30
574 Marc Newfield	.10	.30
575 Melvin Nieves	.10	.30
576 Jody Reed	.10	.30
577 Bip Roberts	.10	.30
578 Scott Sanders	.10	.30
579 Fernando Valenzuela	.10	.30
580 Eddie Williams	.10	.30
581 Rod Beck	.10	.30
582 Marvin Benard RC	.10	.30
583 Barry Bonds	.75	2.00
584 Jamie Brewington RC	.10	.30
585 Mark Carreon	.10	.30
586 Royce Clayton	.10	.30
587 Shawn Estes	.10	.30
588 Glenallen Hill	.10	.30
589 Mark Leiter	.10	.30
590 Kirt Manwaring	.10	.30
591 David McCarty	.10	.30
592 Terry Mulholland	.10	.30
593 John Patterson	.10	.30
594 J.R. Phillips	.10	.30
595 Deion Sanders	.20	.50
596 Steve Scarsone	.10	.30
597 Robby Thompson	.10	.30
598 Sergio Valdez	.10	.30
599 W.Van Landingham	.10	.30
600 Matt Williams	.10	.30
P20 Cal Ripken Promo	1.25	3.00

1996 Fleer Tiffany

The Tiffany Collection is a 600-card parallel set that has a special UV coating that replaces the matte finish of the regular cards and silver holographic foil that takes the place of gold foil for lettering. These cards were inserted in regular packs at one card per pack.

*STARS: 2X TO 5X BASIC CARDS
*ROOKIES: 4X TO 10X BASIC CARDS

1996 Fleer Checklists

Checklist cards were seeded one per six regular packs and have glossy, borderless fronts with full-color shots of the Major League's best. "Checklist" and the player's name are stamped in gold foil. Backs list the entire rundown of '96 Fleer cards printed in black type on a white background.

COMPLETE SET (10)	1.50	4.00
1 Barry Bonds	.40	1.00
2 Ken Griffey Jr.	.25	.60
3 Chipper Jones	.15	.40
4 Greg Maddux	.25	.60
5 Mike Piazza	.25	.60
6 Manny Ramirez	.08	.25
7 Cal Ripken	.50	1.25
8 Frank Thomas	.15	.40
9 Mo Vaughn	.05	.15
10 Matt Williams	.05	.15

1996 Fleer Golden Memories

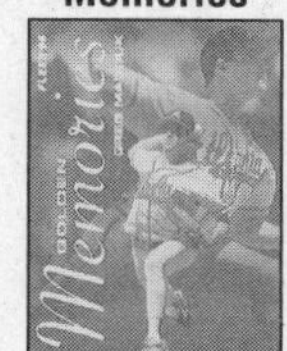

Randomly inserted at a rate of one in 10 regular packs, this 10-card standard-size set features important highlights of the 1995 season. Fronts have two action shots, one serving as a background, the other a full-color cutout. "Golden Memories" and player's name are printed vertically in white type. Backs contain a biography, player close-up and career statistics.

COMPLETE SET (10)	3.00	8.00
1 Albert Belle	.15	.40
2 Barry Bonds Sammy Sosa	.40	1.00
3 Greg Maddux	.60	1.50
4 Edgar Martinez	.25	.60
5 Ramon Martinez	.15	.40
6 Mark McGwire	1.00	2.50
7 Eddie Murray	.40	1.00
8 Cal Ripken	1.25	3.00
9 Frank Thomas	.40	1.00
10 Alan Trammell Lou Whitaker	.15	.40

1996 Fleer Lumber Company

This retail-exclusive 12-card set was inserted one in every nine packs and features RBI and HR power hitters. The fronts display a color action player cut-out on a wood background with embossed printing. The backs carry a player photo and information about the player.

COMPLETE SET (12)	10.00	25.00
1 Albert Belle	.40	1.00
2 Dante Bichette	.40	1.00
3 Barry Bonds	2.50	6.00
4 Ken Griffey Jr.	1.50	4.00
5 Mark McGwire	2.50	6.00
6 Mike Piazza	1.50	4.00
7 Manny Ramirez	.60	1.50
8 Tim Salmon	.60	1.50
9 Sammy Sosa	1.00	2.50
10 Frank Thomas	1.00	2.50
11 Mo Vaughn	.40	1.00
12 Matt Williams	.40	1.00

1996 Fleer Postseason Glory

Randomly inserted in regular packs at a rate of one in five, this five-card standard-size set highlights great moments of the 1996 Divisional, League Championship and World Series games. Horizontal, white-bordered fronts feature a player in three full-color action cutouts with black strips on top and bottom. "Post-Season Glory" appears on top and the player's name is printed in silver hologram foil. White-bordered backs are split between a full-color player close-up and a description of his post-season play printed in white type on a black background.

COMPLETE SET (5)	.75	2.00
1 Tom Glavine	.08	.25
2 Ken Griffey Jr.	.25	.60
3 Orel Hershiser	.05	.15
4 Randy Johnson	.15	.40
5 Jim Thome	.08	.25

1996 Fleer Prospects

Randomly inserted at a rate of one in six regular packs, this ten-card standard-size set focuses on players moving up through the farm system. Borderless fronts have full-color head shots on one-color backgrounds. "Prospect" and the player's name are stamped in silver hologram foil. Backs feature a full-color action shot with a synopsis of talent printed in a green box.

COMPLETE SET (10)	1.50	4.00
1 Yamil Benitez	.20	.50
2 Roger Cedeno	.20	.50
3 Tony Clark	.20	.50
4 Micah Franklin	.20	.50
5 Karim Garcia	.20	.50
6 Todd Greene	.20	.50
7 Alex Ochoa	.20	.50
8 Ruben Rivera	.20	.50
9 Chris Snopek	.20	.50
10 Shannon Stewart	.40	1.00

1996 Fleer Road Warriors

Randomly inserted in regular packs at a rate of one in 13, this 10-card standard-size set focuses on players who thrive on the road. Fronts feature a full-color player cutout set against a winding rural highway background. "Road Warriors" is printed in reverse type with a hazy white border and the player's name is printed in white type underneath. Backs include the player's road stats, biography and a close-up shot.

COMPLETE SET (10)	5.00	12.00
1 Derek Bell	.20	.50
2 Tony Gwynn	.60	1.50
3 Greg Maddux	.75	2.00
4 Mark McGwire	1.25	3.00
5 Mike Piazza	.75	2.00
6 Manny Ramirez	.30	.75
7 Tim Salmon	.30	.75
8 Frank Thomas	.50	1.25
9 Mo Vaughn	.20	.50
10 Matt Williams	.20	.50

1996 Fleer Rookie Sensations

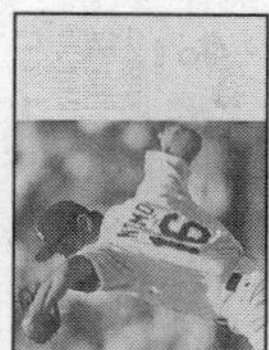

Randomly inserted at a rate of one in 11 regular packs, this 15-card standard-size set highlights 1995's best rookies. Borderless, horizontal fronts have a full-color action shot and a silver hologram strip containing the player's name and team logo. Horizontal backs have full-color head shots with a player profile all printed on a white background.

COMPLETE SET (15)	6.00	15.00
1 Garret Anderson	.50	1.25
2 Marty Cordova	.50	1.25
3 Johnny Damon	.75	2.00
4 Ray Durham	.50	1.25
5 Carl Everett	.50	1.25
6 Shawn Green	.50	1.25
7 Brian L.Hunter	.50	1.25
8 Jason Isringhausen	.50	1.25
9 Charles Johnson	.50	1.25
10 Chipper Jones	1.25	3.00
11 John Mabry	.50	1.25
12 Hideo Nomo	1.25	3.00
13 Troy Percival	.50	1.25
14 Andy Pettitte	.75	2.00
15 Quilvio Veras	.50	1.25

1996 Fleer Smoke 'n Heat

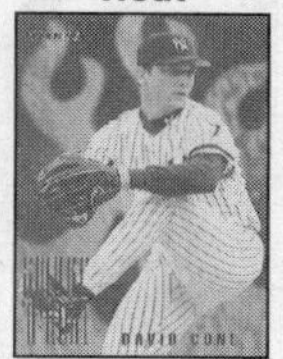

Randomly inserted at a rate of one in nine regular packs, this 10-card standard-size set celebrates the pitchers with rifle arms and a high strikeout count. Fronts feature a full-color player cutout set against a red flame background. "Smoke 'n Heat" and the player's name are printed in gold type. Backs feature the pitcher's 1995 numbers, a biography and career stats along with a full-color close-up.

COMPLETE SET (10)	2.50	6.00
1 Kevin Appier	.20	.50
2 Roger Clemens	1.00	2.50
3 David Cone	.20	.50
4 Chuck Finley	.20	.50
5 Randy Johnson	.50	1.25
6 Greg Maddux	.75	2.00
7 Pedro Martinez	.30	.75
8 Hideo Nomo	.50	1.25
9 John Smoltz	.30	.75
10 Todd Stottlemyre	.20	.50

1996 Fleer Team Leaders

This hobby-exclusive 28-card set was randomly inserted one in every nine packs and features statistical and inspirational leaders. The fronts display color action player cut-out on a foil background of the team name and logo. The backs carry a player portrait and player information.

COMPLETE SET (28)	25.00	60.00
1 Cal Ripken	4.00	10.00
2 Mo Vaughn	.50	1.25
3 Jim Edmonds	.50	1.25
4 Frank Thomas	1.25	3.00
5 Kenny Lofton	.50	1.25
6 Travis Fryman	.50	1.25
7 Gary Gaetti	.50	1.25
8 B.J. Surhoff	.50	1.25
9 Kirby Puckett	1.25	3.00
10 Don Mattingly	3.00	8.00
11 Mark McGwire	3.00	8.00
12 Ken Griffey Jr.	2.00	5.00
13 Juan Gonzalez	.50	1.25
14 Joe Carter	.50	1.25
15 Greg Maddux	2.00	5.00
16 Sammy Sosa	1.25	3.00
17 Barry Larkin	.75	2.00
18 Dante Bichette	.50	1.25
19 Jeff Conine	.50	1.25
20 Jeff Bagwell	.75	2.00
21 Mike Piazza	2.00	5.00
22 Rondell White	.50	1.25
23 Rico Brogna	.50	1.25
24 Darren Daulton	.50	1.25
25 Jeff King	.50	1.25
26 Ray Lankford	.50	1.25
27 Tony Gwynn	1.50	4.00
28 Barry Bonds	3.00	8.00

1996 Fleer Tomorrow's Legends

Randomly inserted in regular packs at a rate of one in 13, this 10-card set focuses on young talent with bright futures. Multicolored fronts have four panels of art that serve as a background and a full-color player cutout. "Tomorrow's Legends" and player's name are printed in white type at the bottom. Backs include the player's '95 stats, biography and a full-color close-up shot.

COMPLETE SET (10)	4.00	10.00
1 Garret Anderson	.30	.75
2 Jim Edmonds	.30	.75
3 Brian L.Hunter	.30	.75
4 Jason Isringhausen	.30	.75
5 Charles Johnson	.30	.75
6 Chipper Jones	.75	2.00
7 Ryan Klesko	.30	.75
8 Hideo Nomo	.75	2.00
9 Manny Ramirez	.50	1.25
10 Rondell White	.30	.75

1996 Fleer Zone

This 12-card set was randomly inserted one in every 90 packs and features "unstoppable" hitters and "unhittable" pitchers. The fronts display a color action player cut-out printed on holographic foil. The backs carry a player portrait with information as to why they were selected for this set.

COMPLETE SET (12)	40.00	100.00
1 Albert Belle	1.25	3.00
2 Barry Bonds	8.00	20.00
3 Ken Griffey Jr.	5.00	12.00
4 Tony Gwynn	4.00	10.00
5 Randy Johnson	3.00	8.00
6 Kenny Lofton	1.25	3.00
7 Greg Maddux	5.00	12.00
8 Edgar Martinez	2.00	5.00
9 Mike Piazza	5.00	12.00
10 Frank Thomas	3.00	8.00
11 Mo Vaughn	1.25	3.00
12 Matt Williams	1.25	3.00

1996 Fleer Update

The 1996 Fleer Update set was issued in one series totalling 250 cards. The 11-card packs retailed for $1.49 each. The fronts feature color action player photos. The backs carry complete player stats and a "Did you know?" fact. The cards are grouped alphabetically within teams and checklisted below alphabetically according to teams for each league with AL preceding NL. The set contains the subset: Encore (U211-U245). Notable Rookie Cards include Tony Batista, Mike Cameron, Matt Mantei and Chris Singleton.

COMPLETE SET (250)	12.50	30.00
U1 Roberto Alomar	.20	.50
U2 Mike Devereaux	.10	.30
U3 Scott McClain RC	.10	.30
U4 Roger McDowell	.10	.30
U5 Kent Mercker	.10	.30
U6 Jimmy Myers RC	.10	.30
U7 Randy Myers	.10	.30
U8 B.J. Surhoff	.10	.30
U9 Tony Tarasco	.10	.30
U10 David Wells	.10	.30
U11 Wil Cordero	.10	.30
U12 Tom Gordon	.10	.30
U13 Reggie Jefferson	.10	.30
U14 Jose Malave	.10	.30
U15 Kevin Mitchell	.10	.30
U16 Jamie Moyer	.10	.30
U17 Heathcliff Slocumb	.10	.30
U18 Mike Stanley	.10	.30
U19 George Arias	.10	.30
U20 Jorge Fabregas	.10	.30
U21 Don Slaught	.10	.30
U22 Randy Velarde	.10	.30
U23 Harold Baines	.10	.30
U24 Mike Cameron RC	.30	.75
U25 Darren Lewis	.10	.30
U26 Tony Phillips	.10	.30
U27 Bill Simas	.10	.30
U28 Chris Snopek	.10	.30
U29 Kevin Tapani	.10	.30
U30 Danny Tartabull	.10	.30
U31 Julio Franco	.10	.30
U32 Jack McDowell	.10	.30
U33 Kimera Bartee	.10	.30
U34 Mark Lewis	.10	.30
U35 Melvin Nieves	.10	.30
U36 Mark Parent	.10	.30
U37 Eddie Williams	.10	.30
U38 Tim Belcher	.10	.30
U39 Sal Fasano	.10	.30
U40 Chris Haney	.10	.30
U41 Mike Macfarlane	.10	.30
U42 Jose Offerman	.10	.30
U43 Joe Randa	.10	.30
U44 Bip Roberts	.10	.30
U45 Chuck Carr	.10	.30
U46 Bobby Hughes	.10	.30
U47 Graeme Lloyd	.10	.30
U48 Ben McDonald	.10	.30
U49 Kevin Wickander	.10	.30
U50 Rick Aguilera	.10	.30
U51 Mike Durant	.10	.30
U52 Chip Hale	.10	.30
U53 LaTroy Hawkins	.10	.30
U54 Dave Hollins	.10	.30
U55 Roberto Kelly	.10	.30
U56 Paul Molitor	.10	.30
U57 Dan Naulty	.10	.30
U58 Mariano Duncan	.10	.30
U59 Andy Fox	.10	.30
U60 Joe Girardi	.10	.30
U61 Dwight Gooden	.10	.30
U62 Jimmy Key	.10	.30
U63 Matt Luke	.10	.30
U64 Tino Martinez	.20	.50
U65 Jeff Nelson	.10	.30
U66 Tim Raines	.10	.30
U67 Ruben Rivera	.10	.30
U68 Kenny Rogers	.10	.30
U69 Gerald Williams	.10	.30
U70 Tony Batista RC	.30	.75
U71 Allen Battle	.10	.30
U72 Jim Corsi	.10	.30
U73 Steve Cox	.10	.30
U74 Pedro Munoz	.10	.30
U75 Phil Plantier	.10	.30
U76 Scott Spiezio	.10	.30
U77 Ernie Young	.10	.30
U78 Russ Davis	.10	.30
U79 Sterling Hitchcock	.10	.30
U80 Edwin Hurtado	.10	.30
U81 Raul Ibanez RC	.40	1.00
U82 Mike Jackson	.10	.30
U83 Ricky Jordan	.10	.30
U84 Paul Sorrento	.10	.30
U85 Doug Strange	.10	.30
U86 M.Brandenburg RC	.10	.30
U87 Damon Buford	.10	.30
U88 Kevin Elster	.10	.30
U89 Darryl Hamilton	.10	.30
U90 Ken Hill	.10	.30
U91 Ed Vosberg	.10	.30
U92 Craig Worthington	.10	.30
U93 Tilson Brito RC	.10	.30
U94 Giovanni Carrara RC	.10	.30
U95 Felipe Crespo	.10	.30
U96 Erik Hanson	.10	.30
U97 Marty Janzen RC	.10	.30
U98 Otis Nixon	.10	.30
U99 Charlie O'Brien	.10	.30
U100 Robert Perez	.10	.30
U101 Paul Quantrill	.10	.30
U102 Bill Risley	.10	.30
U103 Juan Samuel	.10	.30
U104 Jermaine Dye	.10	.30
U105 W.Monds RC	.10	.30
U106 Dwight Smith	.10	.30
U107 Jerome Walton	.10	.30
U108 Terry Adams	.10	.30
U109 Leo Gomez	.10	.30
U110 Robin Jennings	.10	.30
U111 Doug Jones	.10	.30
U112 Brooks Kieschnick	.10	.30
U113 Dave Magadan	.10	.30
U114 Jason Maxwell RC	.10	.30
U115 Rodney Myers RC	.10	.30
U116 Eric Anthony	.10	.30
U117 Vince Coleman	.10	.30
U118 Eric Davis	.10	.30
U119 Steve Gibralter	.10	.30
U120 Curtis Goodwin	.10	.30
U121 Willie Greene	.10	.30
U122 Mike Kelly	.10	.30
U123 Marcus Moore	.10	.30
U124 Chad Mottola	.10	.30
U125 Chris Sabo	.10	.30
U126 Roger Salkeld	.10	.30
U127 Pedro Castellano	.10	.30
U128 Trenidad Hubbard	.10	.30
U129 Jayhawk Owens	.10	.30
U130 Jeff Reed	.10	.30
U131 Kevin Brown	.10	.30
U132 Al Leiter	.10	.30
U133 Matt Mantei RC	.20	.50
U134 Dave Weathers	.10	.30
U135 Devon White	.10	.30
U136 Bob Abreu	.30	.75
U137 Sean Berry	.10	.30
U138 Doug Brocail	.10	.30
U139 Richard Hidalgo	.10	.30
U140 Alvin Morman	.10	.30
U141 Mike Blowers	.10	.30
U142 Roger Cedeno	.10	.30
U143 Greg Gagne	.10	.30
U144 Karim Garcia	.10	.30
U145 Wilton Guerrero RC	.10	.30
U146 Israel Alcantara RC	.10	.30
U147 Omar Daal	.10	.30
U148 Ryan McGuire	.10	.30
U149 Sherman Obando	.10	.30
U150 Jose Paniagua	.10	.30
U151 Henry Rodriguez	.10	.30
U152 Andy Stankiewicz	.10	.30
U153 Dave Veres	.10	.30
U154 Juan Acevedo	.10	.30
U155 Mark Clark	.10	.30
U156 Bernard Gilkey	.10	.30
U157 Pete Harnisch	.10	.30
U158 Lance Johnson	.10	.30
U159 Brent Mayne	.10	.30
U160 Rey Ordonez	.10	.30
U161 Kevin Roberson	.10	.30
U162 Paul Wilson	.10	.30
U163 David Doster RC	.10	.30
U164 Mike Grace RC	.10	.30
U165 Rich Hunter RC	.10	.30
U166 Pete Incaviglia	.10	.30
U167 Mike Lieberthal	.10	.30
U168 Terry Mulholland	.10	.30
U169 Ken Ryan	.10	.30
U170 Benito Santiago	.10	.30
U171 Kevin Sefcik RC	.10	.30
U172 Lee Tinsley	.10	.30
U173 Todd Zeile	.10	.30

U174 F.Cordova RC	.20	.50
U175 Danny Darwin	.10	.30
U176 Charlie Hayes	.10	.30
U177 Jason Kendall	.10	.30
U178 Mike Kingery	.10	.30
U179 Jon Lieber	.10	.30
U180 Zane Smith	.10	.30
U181 Luis Alicea	.10	.30
U182 Cory Bailey	.10	.30
U183 Andy Benes	.10	.30
U184 Pat Borders	.10	.30
U185 Mike Busby RC	.10	.30
U186 Royce Clayton	.10	.30
U187 Dennis Eckersley	.10	.30
U188 Gary Gaetti	.10	.30
U189 Ron Gant	.10	.30
U190 Aaron Holbert	.10	.30
U191 Willie McGee	.10	.30
U192 Miguel Mejia RC	.10	.30
U193 Jeff Parrett	.10	.30
U194 Todd Stottlemyre	.10	.30
U195 Sean Bergman	.10	.30
U196 Archi Cianfrocco	.10	.30
U197 Rickey Henderson	.30	.75
U198 Wally Joyner	.10	.30
U199 Craig Shipley	.10	.30
U200 Bob Tewksbury	.10	.30
U201 Tim Worrell	.10	.30
U202 Rich Aurilia RC	.20	.50
U203 Doug Creek	.10	.30
U204 Shawon Dunston	.10	.30
U205 O.Fernandez RC	.10	.30
U206 Mark Gardner	.10	.30
U207 Stan Javier	.10	.30
U208 Marcus Jensen	.10	.30
U209 Chris Singleton RC	.20	.50
U210 Allen Watson	.10	.30
U211 Jeff Bagwell ENC	.20	.50
U212 Derek Bell ENC	.10	.30
U213 Albert Belle ENC	.10	.30
U214 Wade Boggs ENC	.20	.50
U215 Barry Bonds ENC	.75	2.00
U216 Jose Canseco ENC	.20	.50
U217 Marty Cordova ENC	.10	.30
U218 Jim Edmonds ENC	.10	.30
U219 Cecil Fielder ENC	.10	.30
U220 A.Galarraga ENC	.10	.30
U221 Juan Gonzalez ENC	.10	.30
U222 Mark Grace ENC	.20	.50
U223 Ken Griffey Jr. ENC	.50	1.25
U224 Tony Gwynn ENC	.40	1.00
U225 J. Isringhausen ENC	.10	.30
U226 Derek Jeter ENC	.75	2.00
U227 Randy Johnson ENC	.30	.75
U228 Chipper Jones ENC	.30	.75
U229 Ryan Klesko ENC	.10	.30
U230 Barry Larkin ENC	.20	.50
U231 Kenny Lofton ENC	.10	.30
U232 Greg Maddux ENC	.50	1.25
U233 Raul Mondesi ENC	.10	.30
U234 Hideo Nomo ENC	.30	.75
U235 Mike Piazza ENC	.50	1.25
U236 Manny Ramirez ENC	.20	.50
U237 Cal Ripken ENC	.60	1.50
U238 Tim Salmon ENC	.20	.50
U239 Ryne Sandberg ENC	.50	1.25
U240 Reggie Sanders ENC	.10	.30
U241 Gary Sheffield ENC	.10	.30
U242 Sammy Sosa ENC	.30	.75
U243 Frank Thomas ENC	.30	.75
U244 Mo Vaughn ENC	.10	.30
U245 Matt Williams ENC	.10	.30
U246 Barry Bonds CL	.40	1.00
U247 Ken Griffey Jr. CL	.30	.75
U248 Rey Ordonez CL	.10	.30
U249 Ryne Sandberg CL	.30	.75
U250 Frank Thomas CL	.20	.50

1996 Fleer Update Tiffany

Inserted one per pack, these 250 cards parallel the basic Fleer Update cards. Unlike the basic cards, Tiffany inserts feature a layer of UV coating and a special logo on each card front.

COMPLETE SET (250)	50.00	120.00

*STARS: 1.25X TO 3X BASIC CARDS
*ROOKIES: 2X TO 5X BASIC CARDS

1996 Fleer Update Diamond Tribute

Randomly inserted in packs at a rate of one in 100, this 10-card set spotlights future Hall of Famers with holographic foils in a diamond design.

COMPLETE SET (10)	60.00	150.00
1 Wade Boggs	2.50	6.00
2 Barry Bonds	10.00	25.00
3 Ken Griffey Jr.	6.00	15.00
4 Tony Gwynn	5.00	12.00
5 Rickey Henderson	4.00	10.00
6 Greg Maddux	6.00	15.00
7 Eddie Murray	4.00	10.00
8 Cal Ripken	12.50	30.00
9 Ozzie Smith	6.00	15.00
10 Frank Thomas	4.00	10.00

1996 Fleer Update Headliners

Randomly inserted exclusively in retail packs at a rate of one in 20, cards from this 20-card set feature raised textured printing. The fronts carry color action player photos with the word "headliner" running continuously across the background.

COMPLETE SET (20)	15.00	40.00
1 Roberto Alomar	.50	1.25
2 Jeff Bagwell	.50	1.25
3 Albert Belle	.30	.75
4 Barry Bonds	2.00	5.00
5 Cecil Fielder	.30	.75
6 Juan Gonzalez	.30	.75
7 Ken Griffey Jr.	1.25	3.00
8 Tony Gwynn	1.00	2.50
9 Randy Johnson	.75	2.00
10 Chipper Jones	.75	2.00
11 Ryan Klesko	.30	.75
12 Kenny Lofton	.30	.75
13 Greg Maddux	1.25	3.00
14 Hideo Nomo	.75	2.00
15 Mike Piazza	1.25	3.00
16 Manny Ramirez	.50	1.25
17 Cal Ripken	2.50	6.00
18 Tim Salmon	.50	1.25
19 Frank Thomas	.75	2.00
20 Matt Williams	.30	.75

1996 Fleer Update New Horizons

Randomly inserted in hobby packs only at a rate of one in five, this 20-card set features 1996 rookies and prospects. The fronts carry player action color photos printed on foil cards. The backs display a player portrait and information about the player.

COMPLETE SET (20)	6.00	15.00
1 Bob Abreu	.60	1.50
2 George Arias	.20	.50
3 Tony Batista	.40	1.00
4 Steve Cox	.20	.50
5 Jermaine Dye	.20	.50
6 Andy Fox	.20	.50
7 Mike Grace	.20	.50
8 Todd Greene	.20	.50
9 Wilton Guerrero	.20	.50
10 Richard Hidalgo	.20	.50
11 Raul Ibanez	.40	1.00
12 Robin Jennings	.20	.50
13 Marcus Jensen	.20	.50
14 Jason Kendall	.20	.50
15 Jason Maxwell	.20	.50
16 Ryan McGuire	.20	.50
17 Miguel Mejia	.20	.50
18 Wonderful Monds	.20	.50
19 Rey Ordonez	.20	.50
20 Paul Wilson	.20	.50

1996 Fleer Update Smooth Leather

Randomly inserted in packs at a rate of one in five, this 10-card set features defensive stars. The fronts display color player photos and gold foil printing. The backs carry a player portrait and information about why the player was selected for this set.

COMPLETE SET (10)	4.00	10.00
1 Roberto Alomar	.25	.60
2 Barry Bonds	1.00	2.50
3 Will Clark	.25	.60
4 Ken Griffey Jr.	.60	1.50
5 Kenny Lofton	.15	.40
6 Greg Maddux	.60	1.50
7 Raul Mondesi	.15	.40
8 Rey Ordonez	.15	.40
9 Cal Ripken	1.25	3.00
10 Matt Williams	.15	.40

1996 Fleer Update Soaring Stars

Randomly inserted in packs at a rate of one in 11, this 10-card set features 10 of the hottest young players. The fronts carry color player cut-outs on a background of soaring baseballs in etched foil. The backs display another player photo on the same

background with player information.

COMPLETE SET (10)	10.00	25.00
1 Jeff Bagwell	.50	1.25
2 Barry Bonds	2.00	5.00
3 Juan Gonzalez	.30	.75
4 Ken Griffey Jr.	1.25	3.00
5 Chipper Jones	.75	2.00
6 Greg Maddux	1.25	3.00
7 Mike Piazza	1.25	3.00
8 Manny Ramirez	.50	1.25
9 Frank Thomas	.75	2.00
10 Matt Williams	.30	.75

1997 Fleer

The 1997 Fleer set was issued in two series totaling 761 cards and distributed in 10-card packs with a suggested retail price of $1.49. The fronts feature color action player photos with a matte finish and gold foil printing. The backs carry another player photo with player information and career statistics. Cards 491-500 are a Checklist subset of Series one and feature black-and-white or sepia tone photos of big-name players. Series two contains the following subsets: Encore (696-720) which are redesigned cards of the big-name players from Series one, and Checklists (721-748). Cards 749 and 750 are expansion team logo cards with the insert checklists on the backs. Many dealers believe that cards numbered 751-761 were shortprinted. An Andruw Jones autographed Circa card numbered to 200 was also randomly inserted into packs. Rookie Cards in this set include Jose Cruz Jr., Brian Giles and Fernando Tatis.

COMPLETE SET (761)	70.00	140.00
COMP. SERIES 1 (500)	30.00	60.00
COMP. SERIES 2 (261)	40.00	80.00
COMMON CARD (1-750)	.10	.30
COMMON CARD (751-761)	.20	.50
1 Roberto Alomar	.20	.50
2 Brady Anderson	.10	.30
3 Bobby Bonilla	.10	.30
4 Rocky Coppinger	.10	.30
5 Cesar Devarez	.10	.30
6 Scott Erickson	.10	.30
7 Jeffrey Hammonds	.10	.30
8 Chris Hoiles	.10	.30
9 Eddie Murray	.30	.75
10 Mike Mussina	.20	.50
11 Randy Myers	.10	.30
12 Rafael Palmeiro	.20	.50
13 Cal Ripken	1.00	2.50
14 B.J. Surhoff	.10	.30
15 David Wells	.10	.30
16 Todd Zeile	.10	.30
17 Darren Bragg	.10	.30
18 Jose Canseco	.20	.50
19 Roger Clemens	.60	1.50
20 Wil Cordero	.10	.30
21 Jeff Frye	.10	.30
22 Nomar Garciaparra	.50	1.25
23 Tom Gordon	.10	.30
24 Mike Greenwell	.10	.30
25 Reggie Jefferson	.10	.30
26 Jose Malave	.10	.30
27 Tim Naehring	.10	.30
28 Troy O'Leary	.10	.30
29 Heathcliff Slocumb	.10	.30
30 Mike Stanley	.10	.30
31 John Valentin	.10	.30
32 Mo Vaughn	.10	.30
33 Tim Wakefield	.10	.30
34 Garret Anderson	.10	.30
35 George Arias	.10	.30
36 Shawn Boskie	.10	.30
37 Chili Davis	.10	.30
38 Jason Dickson	.10	.30
39 Gary DiSarcina	.10	.30
40 Jim Edmonds	.10	.30
41 Darin Erstad	.10	.30
42 Jorge Fabregas	.10	.30
43 Chuck Finley	.10	.30
44 Todd Greene	.10	.30
45 Mike Holtz	.10	.30
46 Rex Hudler	.10	.30
47 Mike James	.10	.30
48 Mark Langston	.10	.30
49 Troy Percival	.10	.30
50 Tim Salmon	.20	.50
51 Jeff Schmidt	.10	.30
52 J.T. Snow	.10	.30
53 Randy Velarde	.10	.30
54 Wilson Alvarez	.10	.30
55 Harold Baines	.10	.30
56 James Baldwin	.10	.30
57 Jason Bere	.10	.30
58 Mike Cameron	.10	.30
59 Ray Durham	.10	.30
60 Alex Fernandez	.10	.30
61 Ozzie Guillen	.10	.30
62 Roberto Hernandez	.10	.30
63 Ron Karkovice	.10	.30
64 Darren Lewis	.10	.30
65 Dave Martinez	.10	.30
66 Lyle Mouton	.10	.30
67 Greg Norton	.10	.30
68 Tony Phillips	.10	.30
69 Chris Snopek	.10	.30
70 Kevin Tapani	.10	.30
71 Danny Tartabull	.10	.30
72 Frank Thomas	.30	.75
73 Robin Ventura	.10	.30
74 Sandy Alomar Jr.	.10	.30
75 Albert Belle	.10	.30
76 Mark Carreon	.10	.30
77 Julio Franco	.10	.30
78 Brian Giles RC	.60	1.50
79 Orel Hershiser	.10	.30
80 Kenny Lofton	.10	.30
81 Dennis Martinez	.10	.30
82 Jack McDowell	.10	.30
83 Jose Mesa	.10	.30
84 Charles Nagy	.10	.30
85 Chad Ogea	.10	.30
86 Eric Plunk	.10	.30
87 Manny Ramirez	.20	.50
88 Kevin Seitzer	.10	.30
89 Julian Tavarez	.10	.30
90 Jim Thome	.20	.50
91 Jose Vizcaino	.10	.30
92 Omar Vizquel	.20	.50
93 Brad Ausmus	.10	.30
94 Kimera Bartee	.10	.30
95 Raul Casanova	.10	.30
96 Tony Clark	.10	.30
97 John Cummings	.10	.30
98 Travis Fryman	.10	.30
99 Bob Higginson	.10	.30
100 Mark Lewis	.10	.30
101 Felipe Lira	.10	.30
102 Phil Nevin	.10	.30
103 Melvin Nieves	.10	.30
104 Curtis Pride	.10	.30
105 A.J. Sager	.10	.30
106 Ruben Sierra	.10	.30
107 Justin Thompson	.10	.30
108 Alan Trammell	.10	.30
109 Kevin Appier	.10	.30
110 Tim Belcher	.10	.30
111 Jaime Bluma	.10	.30
112 Johnny Damon	.20	.50
113 Tom Goodwin	.10	.30
114 Chris Haney	.10	.30
115 Keith Lockhart	.10	.30
116 Mike Macfarlane	.10	.30
117 Jeff Montgomery	.10	.30
118 Jose Offerman	.10	.30
119 Craig Paquette	.10	.30
120 Joe Randa	.10	.30
121 Bip Roberts	.10	.30
122 Jose Rosado	.10	.30
123 Mike Sweeney	.10	.30
124 Michael Tucker	.10	.30
125 Jeromy Burnitz	.10	.30
126 Jeff Cirillo	.10	.30
127 Jeff D'Amico	.10	.30
128 Mike Fetters	.10	.30
129 John Jaha	.10	.30
130 Scott Karl	.10	.30
131 Jesse Levis	.10	.30
132 Mark Loretta	.10	.30
133 Mike Matheny	.10	.30
134 Ben McDonald	.10	.30
135 Matt Mieske	.10	.30
136 Marc Newfield	.10	.30
137 Dave Nilsson	.10	.30
138 Jose Valentin	.10	.30
139 Fernando Vina	.10	.30
140 Bob Wickman	.10	.30
141 Gerald Williams	.10	.30
142 Rick Aguilera	.10	.30
143 Rich Becker	.10	.30
144 Ron Coomer	.10	.30
145 Marty Cordova	.10	.30
146 Roberto Kelly	.10	.30
147 Chuck Knoblauch	.10	.30
148 Matt Lawton	.10	.30
149 Pat Meares	.10	.30
150 Travis Miller	.10	.30
151 Paul Molitor	.10	.30
152 Greg Myers	.10	.30
153 Dan Naulty	.10	.30
154 Kirby Puckett	.30	.75
155 Brad Radke	.10	.30
156 Frank Rodriguez	.10	.30
157 Scott Stahoviak	.10	.30
158 Dave Stevens	.10	.30
159 Matt Walbeck	.10	.30
160 Todd Walker	.10	.30
161 Wade Boggs	.20	.50
162 David Cone	.10	.30
163 Mariano Duncan	.10	.30
164 Cecil Fielder	.10	.30
165 Joe Girardi	.10	.30
166 Dwight Gooden	.10	.30
167 Charlie Hayes	.10	.30
168 Derek Jeter	.75	2.00
169 Jimmy Key	.10	.30
170 Jim Leyritz	.10	.30
171 Tino Martinez	.20	.50
172 Ramiro Mendoza RC	.10	.30
173 Jeff Nelson	.10	.30
174 Paul O'Neill	.20	.50
175 Andy Pettitte	.20	.50
176 Mariano Rivera	.30	.75
177 Ruben Rivera	.10	.30
178 Kenny Rogers	.10	.30
179 Darryl Strawberry	.10	.30
180 John Wetteland	.10	.30
181 Bernie Williams	.20	.50
182 Willie Adams	.10	.30
183 Tony Batista	.10	.30
184 Geronimo Berroa	.10	.30
185 Mike Bordick	.10	.30
186 Scott Brosius	.10	.30
187 Bobby Chouinard	.10	.30
188 Jim Corsi	.10	.30
189 Brent Gates	.10	.30
190 Jason Giambi	.10	.30
191 Jose Herrera	.10	.30
192 Damon Mashore	.10	.30
193 Mark McGwire	.75	2.00
194 Mike Mohler	.10	.30
195 Scott Spiezio	.10	.30
196 Terry Steinbach	.10	.30
197 Bill Taylor	.10	.30
198 John Wasdin	.10	.30
199 Steve Wojciechowski	.10	.30
200 Ernie Young	.10	.30
201 Rich Amaral	.10	.30
202 Jay Buhner	.10	.30
203 Norm Charlton	.10	.30
204 Joey Cora	.10	.30
205 Russ Davis	.10	.30
206 Ken Griffey Jr.	.50	1.25
207 Sterling Hitchcock	.10	.30
208 Brian Hunter	.10	.30
209 Raul Ibanez	.10	.30
210 Randy Johnson	.30	.75
211 Edgar Martinez	.20	.50
212 Jamie Moyer	.10	.30
213 Alex Rodriguez	.50	1.25
214 Paul Sorrento	.10	.30
215 Matt Wagner	.10	.30
216 Bob Wells	.10	.30
217 Dan Wilson	.10	.30
218 Damon Buford	.10	.30
219 Will Clark	.20	.50
220 Kevin Elster	.10	.30
221 Juan Gonzalez	.10	.30
222 Rusty Greer	.10	.30
223 Kevin Gross	.10	.30
224 Darryl Hamilton	.10	.30
225 Mike Henneman	.10	.30
226 Ken Hill	.10	.30
227 Mark McLemore	.10	.30
228 Darren Oliver	.10	.30
229 Dean Palmer	.10	.30
230 Roger Pavlik	.10	.30
231 Ivan Rodriguez	.20	.50
232 Mickey Tettleton	.10	.30
233 Bobby Witt	.10	.30
234 Jacob Brumfield	.10	.30
235 Joe Carter	.10	.30
236 Tim Crabtree	.10	.30
237 Carlos Delgado	.10	.30
238 Huck Flener	.10	.30
239 Alex Gonzalez	.10	.30
240 Shawn Green	.10	.30
241 Juan Guzman	.10	.30
242 Pat Hentgen	.10	.30
243 Marty Janzen	.10	.30
244 Sandy Martinez	.10	.30
245 Otis Nixon	.10	.30
246 Charlie O'Brien	.10	.30
247 John Olerud	.10	.30
248 Robert Perez	.10	.30
249 Ed Sprague	.10	.30
250 Mike Timlin	.10	.30
251 Steve Avery	.10	.30
252 Jeff Blauser	.10	.30
253 Brad Clontz	.10	.30
254 Jermaine Dye	.10	.30
255 Tom Glavine	.20	.50
256 Marquis Grissom	.10	.30
257 Andruw Jones	.20	.50
258 Chipper Jones	.30	.75
259 David Justice	.10	.30
260 Ryan Klesko	.10	.30
261 Mark Lemke	.10	.30
262 Javier Lopez	.10	.30
263 Greg Maddux	.50	1.25
264 Fred McGriff	.20	.50
265 Greg McMichael	.10	.30
266 Denny Neagle	.10	.30
267 Terry Pendleton	.10	.30
268 Eddie Perez	.10	.30
269 John Smoltz	.20	.50
270 Terrell Wade	.10	.30
271 Mark Wohlers	.10	.30
272 Terry Adams	.10	.30
273 Brant Brown	.10	.30
274 Leo Gomez	.10	.30
275 Luis Gonzalez	.10	.30
276 Mark Grace	.20	.50
277 Tyler Houston	.10	.30
278 Robin Jennings	.10	.30
279 Brooks Kieschnick	.10	.30
280 Brian McRae	.10	.30
281 Jaime Navarro	.10	.30
282 Ryne Sandberg	.50	1.25
283 Scott Servais	.10	.30
284 Sammy Sosa	.30	.75
285 Dave Swartzbaugh	.10	.30
286 Amaury Telemaco	.10	.30
287 Steve Trachsel	.10	.30
288 Pedro Valdes	.10	.30
289 Turk Wendell	.10	.30
290 Bret Boone	.10	.30
291 Jeff Branson	.10	.30
292 Jeff Brantley	.10	.30
293 Eric Davis	.10	.30
294 Willie Greene	.10	.30
295 Thomas Howard	.10	.30
296 Barry Larkin	.20	.50
297 Kevin Mitchell	.10	.30
298 Hal Morris	.10	.30
299 Chad Mottola	.10	.30
300 Joe Oliver	.10	.30
301 Mark Portugal	.10	.30
302 Roger Salkeld	.10	.30
303 Reggie Sanders	.10	.30
304 Pete Schourek	.10	.30
305 John Smiley	.10	.30
306 Eddie Taubensee	.10	.30
307 Dante Bichette	.10	.30
308 Ellis Burks	.10	.30
309 Vinny Castilla	.10	.30
310 Andres Galarraga	.10	.30
311 Curt Leskanic	.10	.30
312 Quinton McCracken	.10	.30
313 Neifi Perez	.10	.30
314 Jeff Reed	.10	.30
315 Steve Reed	.10	.30
316 Armando Reynoso	.10	.30
317 Kevin Ritz	.10	.30
318 Bruce Ruffin	.10	.30
319 Larry Walker	.10	.30
320 Walt Weiss	.10	.30
321 Jamey Wright	.10	.30
322 Eric Young	.10	.30
323 Kurt Abbott	.10	.30
324 Alex Arias	.10	.30
325 Kevin Brown	.10	.30
326 Luis Castillo	.10	.30
327 Greg Colbrunn	.10	.30
328 Jeff Conine	.10	.30
329 Andre Dawson	.10	.30
330 Charles Johnson	.10	.30
331 Al Leiter	.10	.30
332 Ralph Milliard	.10	.30
333 Robb Nen	.10	.30
334 Pat Rapp	.10	.30
335 Edgar Renteria	.10	.30
336 Gary Sheffield	.10	.30
337 Devon White	.10	.30
338 Bob Abreu	.20	.50
339 Jeff Bagwell	.20	.50
340 Derek Bell	.10	.30
341 Sean Berry	.10	.30
342 Craig Biggio	.20	.50
343 Doug Drabek	.10	.30
344 Tony Eusebio	.10	.30
345 Ricky Gutierrez	.10	.30
346 Mike Hampton	.10	.30
347 Brian Hunter	.10	.30
348 Todd Jones	.10	.30
349 Darryl Kile	.10	.30
350 Derrick May	.10	.30
351 Orlando Miller	.10	.30
352 James Mouton	.10	.30
353 Shane Reynolds	.10	.30
354 Billy Wagner	.10	.30
355 Donne Wall	.10	.30
356 Mike Blowers	.10	.30
357 Brett Butler	.10	.30
358 Roger Cedeno	.10	.30
359 Chad Curtis	.10	.30
360 Delino DeShields	.10	.30
361 Greg Gagne	.10	.30
362 Karim Garcia	.10	.30
363 Wilton Guerrero	.10	.30
364 Todd Hollandsworth	.10	.30
365 Eric Karros	.10	.30
366 Ramon Martinez	.10	.30
367 Raul Mondesi	.10	.30
368 Hideo Nomo	.30	.75
369 Antonio Osuna	.10	.30
370 Chan Ho Park	.10	.30
371 Mike Piazza	.50	1.25
372 Ismael Valdes	.10	.30
373 Todd Worrell	.10	.30
374 Moises Alou	.10	.30
375 Shane Andrews	.10	.30
376 Yamil Benitez	.10	.30
377 Jeff Fassero	.10	.30
378 Darrin Fletcher	.10	.30
379 Cliff Floyd	.10	.30
380 Mark Grudzielanek	.10	.30
381 Mike Lansing	.10	.30
382 Barry Manuel	.10	.30
383 Pedro Martinez	.20	.50
384 Henry Rodriguez	.10	.30
385 Mel Rojas	.10	.30
386 F.P. Santangelo	.10	.30
387 David Segui	.10	.30
388 Ugueth Urbina	.10	.30
389 Rondell White	.10	.30
390 Edgardo Alfonzo	.10	.30
391 Carlos Baerga	.10	.30
392 Mark Clark	.10	.30
393 Alvaro Espinoza	.10	.30
394 John Franco	.10	.30
395 Bernard Gilkey	.10	.30
396 Pete Harnisch	.10	.30
397 Todd Hundley	.10	.30
398 Butch Huskey	.10	.30
399 Jason Isringhausen	.10	.30
400 Lance Johnson	.10	.30
401 Bobby Jones	.10	.30
402 Alex Ochoa	.10	.30
403 Rey Ordonez	.10	.30
404 Robert Person	.10	.30
405 Paul Wilson	.10	.30
406 Matt Beech	.10	.30
407 Ron Blazier	.10	.30
408 Ricky Bottalico	.10	.30
409 Lenny Dykstra	.10	.30
410 Jim Eisenreich	.10	.30
411 Bobby Estalella	.10	.30
412 Mike Grace	.10	.30
413 Gregg Jefferies	.10	.30
414 Mike Lieberthal	.10	.30
415 Wendell Magee	.10	.30
416 Mickey Morandini	.10	.30
417 Ricky Otero	.10	.30
418 Scott Rolen	.20	.50
419 Ken Ryan	.10	.30
420 Benito Santiago	.10	.30
421 Curt Schilling	.10	.30
422 Kevin Sefcik	.10	.30
423 Jermaine Allensworth	.10	.30
424 Trey Beamon	.10	.30
425 Jay Bell	.10	.30
426 Francisco Cordova	.10	.30
427 Carlos Garcia	.10	.30
428 Mark Johnson	.10	.30
429 Jason Kendall	.10	.30
430 Jeff King	.10	.30
431 Jon Lieber	.10	.30
432 Al Martin	.10	.30
433 Orlando Merced	.10	.30
434 Ramon Morel	.10	.30
435 Matt Ruebel	.10	.30
436 Jason Schmidt	.10	.30
437 Marc Wilkins	.10	.30
438 Alan Benes	.10	.30
439 Andy Benes	.10	.30
440 Royce Clayton	.10	.30
441 Dennis Eckersley	.10	.30
442 Gary Gaetti	.10	.30
443 Ron Gant	.10	.30
444 Aaron Holbert	.10	.30
445 Brian Jordan	.10	.30
446 Ray Lankford	.10	.30
447 John Mabry	.10	.30
448 T.J. Mathews	.10	.30
449 Willie McGee	.10	.30
450 Donovan Osborne	.10	.30
451 Tom Pagnozzi	.10	.30
452 Ozzie Smith	.50	1.25
453 Todd Stottlemyre	.10	.30
454 Mark Sweeney	.10	.30
455 Dmitri Young	.10	.30
456 Andy Ashby	.10	.30
457 Ken Caminiti	.10	.30
458 Archi Cianfrocco	.10	.30
459 Steve Finley	.10	.30

460 John Flaherty .10 .30
461 Chris Gomez .10 .30
462 Tony Gwynn .40 1.00
463 Joey Hamilton .10 .30
464 Rickey Henderson .30 .75
465 Trevor Hoffman .10 .30
466 Brian Johnson .10 .30
467 Wally Joyner .10 .30
468 Jody Reed .10 .30
469 Scott Sanders .10 .30
470 Bob Tewksbury .10 .30
471 Fernando Valenzuela .10 .30
472 Greg Vaughn .10 .30
473 Tim Worrell .10 .30
474 Rich Aurilia .10 .30
475 Rod Beck .10 .30
476 Marvin Benard .10 .30
477 Barry Bonds .75 2.00
478 Jay Canizaro .10 .30
479 Shawon Dunston .10 .30
480 Shawn Estes .10 .30
481 Mark Gardner .10 .30
482 Glenallen Hill .10 .30
483 Stan Javier .10 .30
484 Marcus Jensen .10 .30
485 Bill Mueller RC .50 1.25
486 Wm. VanLandingham .10 .30
487 Allen Watson .10 .30
488 Rick Wilkins .10 .30
489 Matt Williams .10 .30
490 Desi Wilson .10 .30
491 Albert Belle CL .10 .30
492 Ken Griffey Jr. CL .30 .75
493 Andruw Jones CL .10 .30
494 Chipper Jones CL .20 .50
495 Mark McGwire CL .40 1.00
496 Paul Molitor CL .10 .30
497 Mike Piazza CL .30 .75
498 Cal Ripken CL .50 1.25
499 Alex Rodriguez CL .30 .75
500 Frank Thomas CL .20 .50
501 Kenny Lofton .10 .30
502 Carlos Perez .10 .30
503 Tim Raines .10 .30
504 Danny Patterson .10 .30
505 Derrick May .10 .30
506 Dave Hollins .10 .30
507 Felipe Crespo .10 .30
508 Brian Banks .10 .30
509 Jeff Kent .10 .30
510 Bubba Trammell RC .15 .40
511 Robert Person .10 .30
512 David Arias-Ortiz RC 15.00 40.00
513 Ryan Jones .10 .30
514 David Justice .10 .30
515 Will Cunnane .10 .30
516 Russ Johnson .10 .30
517 John Burkett .10 .30
518 Robinson Checo RC .10 .30
519 Ricardo Rincon RC .10 .30
520 Woody Williams .10 .30
521 Rick Helling .10 .30
522 Jorge Posada .20 .50
523 Kevin Orie .10 .30
524 Fernando Tatis RC .10 .30
525 Jermaine Dye .10 .30
526 Brian Hunter .10 .30
527 Greg McMichael .10 .30
528 Matt Wagner .10 .30
529 Richie Sexson .10 .30
530 Scott Ruffcorn .10 .30
531 Luis Gonzalez .10 .30
532 Mike Johnson RC .10 .30
533 Mark Petkovsek .10 .30
534 Doug Drabek .10 .30
535 Jose Canseco .20 .50
536 Bobby Bonilla .10 .30
537 J.T. Snow .10 .30
538 Shawon Dunston .10 .30
539 John Ericks .10 .30
540 Terry Steinbach .10 .30
541 Jay Bell .10 .30
542 Joe Borowski RC .15 .40
543 David Wells .10 .30
544 Justin Towle RC .10 .30
545 Mike Blowers .10 .30
546 Shannon Stewart .10 .30
547 Rudy Pemberton .10 .30
548 Bill Swift .10 .30
549 Osvaldo Fernandez .10 .30
550 Eddie Murray .30 .75
551 Don Wengert .10 .30
552 Brad Ausmus .10 .30
553 Carlos Garcia .10 .30
554 Jose Guillen .10 .30
555 Rheal Cormier .10 .30
556 Doug Brocail .10 .30
557 Rex Hudler .10 .30
558 Armando Benitez .10 .30
559 Eli Marrero .10 .30
560 Ricky Ledee RC .15 .40
561 Bartolo Colon .10 .30
562 Quilvio Veras .10 .30
563 Alex Fernandez .10 .30
564 Darren Dreifort .10 .30
565 Benji Gil .10 .30
566 Kent Mercker .10 .30
567 Glendon Rusch .10 .30
568 Ramon Tatis RC .10 .30
569 Roger Clemens .60 1.50
570 Mark Lewis .10 .30
571 Emil Brown RC .10 .30
572 Jaime Navarro .10 .30
573 Sherman Obando .10 .30
574 John Wasdin .10 .30
575 Calvin Maduro .10 .30
576 Todd Jones .10 .30
577 Orlando Merced .10 .30
578 Cal Eldred .10 .30
579 Mark Gubicza .10 .30
580 Michael Tucker .10 .30
581 Tony Saunders RC .10 .30
582 Garvin Alston .10 .30
583 Joe Roa .10 .30
584 Brady Raggio RC .10 .30
585 Jimmy Key .10 .30
586 Marc Sagmoen RC .10 .30
587 Jim Bullinger .10 .30
588 Yorkis Perez .10 .30
589 Jose Cruz Jr. RC .15 .40
590 Mike Stanton .10 .30
591 Deivi Cruz RC .15 .40
592 Steve Karsay .10 .30
593 Mike Trombley .10 .30
594 Doug Glanville .10 .30
595 Scott Sanders .10 .30
596 Thomas Howard .10 .30
597 T.J. Staton RC .10 .30
598 Garrett Stephenson .10 .30
599 Rico Brogna .10 .30
600 Albert Belle .10 .30
601 Jose Vizcaino .10 .30
602 Chili Davis .10 .30
603 Shane Mack .10 .30
604 Jim Eisenreich .10 .30
605 Todd Zeile .10 .30
606 Brian Boehringer RC .10 .30
607 Paul Shuey .10 .30
608 Kevin Tapani .10 .30
609 John Wetteland .10 .30
610 Jim Leyritz .10 .30
611 Ray Montgomery RC .10 .30
612 Doug Bochtler .10 .30
613 Wady Almonte RC .10 .30
614 Danny Tartabull .10 .30
615 Orlando Miller .10 .30
616 Bobby Ayala .10 .30
617 Tony Graffanino .10 .30
618 Marc Valdes .10 .30
619 Ron Villone .10 .30
620 Derrek Lee .20 .50
621 Greg Colbrunn .10 .30
622 Felix Heredia RC .15 .40
623 Carl Everett .10 .30
624 Mark Thompson .10 .30
625 Jeff Granger .10 .30
626 Damian Jackson .10 .30
627 Mark Leiter .10 .30
628 Chris Holt .10 .30
629 Dario Veras RC .10 .30
630 Dave Burba .10 .30
631 Darryl Hamilton .10 .30
632 Mark Acre .10 .30
633 F.Hernandez RC .10 .30
634 Terry Mulholland .10 .30
635 Dustin Hermanson .10 .30
636 Delino DeShields .10 .30
637 Steve Avery .10 .30
638 Tony Womack RC .15 .40
639 Mark Whiten .10 .30
640 Marquis Grissom .10 .30
641 Xavier Hernandez .10 .30
642 Eric Davis .10 .30
643 Bob Tewksbury .10 .30
644 Dante Powell .10 .30
645 Carlos Castillo RC .10 .30
646 Chris Widger .10 .30
647 Moises Alou .10 .30
648 Pat Listach .10 .30
649 Edgar Ramos RC .10 .30
650 Deion Sanders .20 .50
651 John Olerud .10 .30
652 Todd Dunwoody .10 .30
653 Randall Simon RC .15 .40
654 Dan Carlson .10 .30
655 Matt Williams .10 .30
656 Jeff King .10 .30
657 Luis Alicea .10 .30
658 Brian Moehler RC .15 .40
659 Ariel Prieto .10 .30
660 Kevin Elster .10 .30
661 Mark Hutton .10 .30
662 Aaron Sele .10 .30
663 Graeme Lloyd .10 .30
664 John Burke .10 .30
665 Mel Rojas .10 .30
666 Sid Fernandez .10 .30
667 Pedro Astacio .10 .30
668 Jeff Abbott .10 .30
669 Darren Daulton .10 .30
670 Mike Bordick .10 .30
671 Sterling Hitchcock .10 .30
672 Damion Easley .10 .30
673 Armando Reynoso .10 .30
674 Pat Cline .10 .30
675 Orlando Cabrera RC .30 .75
676 Alan Embree .10 .30
677 Brian Bevil .10 .30
678 David Weathers .10 .30
679 Cliff Floyd .10 .30
680 Joe Randa .10 .30
681 Bill Haselman .10 .30
682 Jeff Fassero .10 .30
683 Matt Morris .10 .30
684 Mark Portugal .10 .30
685 Lee Smith .10 .30
686 Pokey Reese .10 .30
687 Benito Santiago .10 .30
688 Brian Johnson .10 .30
689 Brent Brede RC .10 .30
690 S.Hasegawa RC .20 .50
691 Julio Santana .10 .30
692 Steve Kline .10 .30
693 Julian Tavarez .10 .30
694 John Hudek .10 .30
695 Manny Alexander .10 .30
696 Roberto Alomar ENC .10 .30
697 Jeff Bagwell ENC .10 .30
698 Barry Bonds ENC .40 1.00
699 Ken Caminiti ENC .10 .30
700 Juan Gonzalez ENC .10 .30
701 Ken Griffey Jr. ENC .30 .75
702 Tony Gwynn ENC .20 .50
703 Derek Jeter ENC .40 1.00
704 Andruw Jones ENC .20 .50
705 Chipper Jones ENC .20 .50
706 Barry Larkin ENC .10 .30
707 Greg Maddux ENC .30 .75
708 Mark McGwire ENC .40 1.00
709 Paul Molitor ENC .10 .30
710 Hideo Nomo ENC .10 .30
711 Andy Pettitte ENC .10 .30
712 Mike Piazza ENC .30 .75
713 Manny Ramirez ENC .20 .50
714 Cal Ripken ENC .50 1.25
715 Alex Rodriguez ENC .30 .75
716 Ryne Sandberg ENC .30 .75
717 John Smoltz ENC .10 .30
718 Frank Thomas ENC .20 .50
719 Mo Vaughn ENC .10 .30
720 Bernie Williams ENC .10 .30
721 Tim Salmon CL .10 .30
722 Greg Maddux CL .30 .75
723 Cal Ripken CL .50 1.25
724 Mo Vaughn CL .10 .30
725 Ryne Sandberg CL .30 .75
726 Frank Thomas CL .20 .50
727 Barry Larkin CL .10 .30
728 Manny Ramirez CL .10 .30
729 Andres Galarraga CL .10 .30
730 Tony Clark CL .10 .30
731 Gary Sheffield CL .10 .30
732 Jeff Bagwell CL .10 .30
733 Kevin Appier CL .10 .30
734 Mike Piazza CL .30 .75
735 Jeff Cirillo CL .10 .30
736 Paul Molitor CL .10 .30
737 Henry Rodriguez CL .10 .30
738 Todd Hundley CL .10 .30
739 Derek Jeter CL .40 1.00
740 Mark McGwire CL .40 1.00
741 Curt Schilling CL .10 .30
742 Jason Kendall CL .10 .30
743 Tony Gwynn CL .20 .50
744 Barry Bonds CL .40 1.00
745 Ken Griffey Jr. CL .30 .75
746 Brian Jordan CL .10 .30
747 Juan Gonzalez CL .10 .30
748 Joe Carter CL .10 .30
749 Ariz. Diamondbacks CL Inserts .10 .30
750 Tampa Bay Devil Rays CL Inserts .10 .30
751 Hideki Irabu RC .30 .75
752 Jeremi Gonzalez RC .20 .50
753 Mario Valdez RC .20 .50
754 Aaron Boone .30 .75
755 Brett Tomko .20 .50
756 Jaret Wright RC .30 .75
757 Ryan McGuire .20 .50
758 Jason McDonald .20 .50
759 Adrian Brown RC .20 .50
760 Keith Foulke RC .75 2.00
761 Bonus Checklist .20 .50
P489 M.Williams Promo .40 1.00
NNO Andruw Jones Circa AU/200 10.00 25.00

1997 Fleer Tiffany

Randomly inserted in series one and two packs at a rate of one in 20, this 751-card set is a parallel version of the regular set featuring a glossy holographic design, foil stamping, and UV coating.

*TIFFANY 1-750: 10X TO 25X BASIC CARDS
*TIFFANY RC's 1-750: 6X TO 15X BASIC
*TIFFANY 751-761: 4X TO 10X BASIC
*TIFFANY 751-761: 3X TO 8X BASIC RC'S
512 David Arias-Ortiz 175.00 300.00
675 Orlando Cabrera 5.00 12.00
760 Keith Foulke 6.00 15.00

1997 Fleer Bleacher Blasters

Randomly inserted in Fleer series two retail packs only at a rate of one in 36, this 10-card set features color action photos of power hitters who reach the bleachers with great frequency.

COMPLETE SET (10) 40.00 80.00
1 Albert Belle 1.00 2.50
2 Barry Bonds 6.00 15.00
3 Juan Gonzalez 1.00 2.50
4 Ken Griffey Jr. 4.00 10.00
5 Mark McGwire 6.00 15.00
6 Mike Piazza 4.00 10.00
7 Alex Rodriguez 4.00 10.00
8 Frank Thomas 2.50 6.00
9 Mo Vaughn 1.00 2.50
10 Matt Williams 1.00 2.50

1997 Fleer Decade of Excellence

Randomly inserted in Fleer Series two hobby packs only at a rate of one in 36, this 12-card set spotlights players who started their major league careers no later than 1987. The set features photos of these players from the 1987 season in the 1987 Fleer Baseball card design.

COMPLETE SET (12) 30.00 60.00
*RARE TRAD: 2X TO 5X BASIC DECADE
RARE TRAD.STATED ODDS 1:360 HOBBY
1 Wade Boggs 1.25 3.00
2 Barry Bonds 5.00 12.00
3 Roger Clemens 4.00 10.00
4 Tony Gwynn 2.50 6.00
5 Rickey Henderson 2.00 5.00
6 Greg Maddux 3.00 8.00
7 Mark McGwire 5.00 12.00
8 Paul Molitor .75 2.00
9 Eddie Murray 2.00 5.00
10 Cal Ripken 6.00 15.00
11 Ryne Sandberg 3.00 8.00
12 Matt Williams .75 2.00

1997 Fleer Diamond Tribute

Randomly inserted in Fleer Series two packs at a rate of one in 288, this 12-card set features color action images of Baseball's top players on a dazzling foil background.

1 Albert Belle 3.00 8.00
2 Barry Bonds 20.00 50.00
3 Juan Gonzalez 3.00 8.00
4 Ken Griffey Jr. 12.50 30.00
5 Tony Gwynn 10.00 25.00
6 Greg Maddux 12.50 30.00
7 Mark McGwire 20.00 50.00
8 Eddie Murray 8.00 20.00
9 Mike Piazza 12.50 30.00
10 Cal Ripken 25.00 60.00
11 Alex Rodriguez 12.50 30.00
12 Frank Thomas 8.00 20.00

1997 Fleer Golden Memories

Randomly inserted in first series packs at a rate of one in 16, this ten-card set commemorates major achievements by individual players from the 1996 season. The fronts feature color player images on a background of the top portion of the sun and its rays. The backs carry player information.

COMPLETE SET (10) 4.00 10.00
1 Barry Bonds 1.25 3.00
2 Dwight Gooden .20 .50
3 Todd Hundley .20 .50
4 Mark McGwire 1.25 3.00
5 Paul Molitor .20 .50
6 Eddie Murray .50 1.25
7 Hideo Nomo .50 1.25
8 Mike Piazza .75 2.00
9 Cal Ripken 1.50 4.00
10 Ozzie Smith .75 2.00

1997 Fleer Goudey Greats

Randomly inserted in Fleer Series two packs at a rate of one in eight, this 15-card set features color player photos of today's stars on cards styled and sized to resemble the 1933 Goudey Baseball card set.

COMPLETE SET (15) 6.00 15.00
*FOIL CARDS: 6X TO 15X BASIC GOUDEY
FOIL SER.2 STATED ODDS 1:800
1 Barry Bonds 1.25 3.00
2 Ken Griffey Jr. .75 2.00
3 Tony Gwynn .60 1.50
4 Derek Jeter 1.25 3.00
5 Chipper Jones .50 1.25
6 Kenny Lofton .20 .50
7 Greg Maddux .75 2.00
8 Mark McGwire 1.25 3.00
9 Eddie Murray .50 1.25
10 Mike Piazza .75 2.00
11 Cal Ripken 1.50 4.00
12 Alex Rodriguez .75 2.00
13 Ryne Sandberg .75 2.00
14 Frank Thomas .50 1.25
15 Mo Vaughn .20 .50

1997 Fleer Headliners

Randomly inserted in Fleer Series two packs at a rate of one in two, this 20-card set features color action photos of top players who make headlines for their teams. The backs carry player information.

COMPLETE SET (20) 4.00 10.00
1 Jeff Bagwell .10 .30
2 Albert Belle .07 .20
3 Barry Bonds .50 1.25
4 Ken Caminiti .07 .20
5 Juan Gonzalez .07 .20
6 Ken Griffey Jr. .30 .75

7 Tony Gwynn .25 .60
8 Derek Jeter .50 1.25
9 Andruw Jones .10 .30
10 Chipper Jones .20 .50
11 Greg Maddux .30 .75
12 Mark McGwire .50 1.25
13 Paul Molitor .07 .20
14 Eddie Murray .20 .50
15 Mike Piazza .30 .75
16 Cal Ripken .60 1.50
17 Alex Rodriguez .30 .75
18 Ryne Sandberg .30 .75
19 John Smoltz .10 .30
20 Frank Thomas .20 .50

1997 Fleer Lumber Company

Randomly inserted exclusively in Fleer Series one retail packs, this 18-card set features a selection of the game's top sluggers. The innovative design displays pure die-cut circular borders, simulating the effect of a cut tree.

COMPLETE SET (18) 50.00 120.00
1 Brady Anderson 1.25 3.00
2 Jeff Bagwell 2.00 5.00
3 Albert Belle 1.25 3.00
4 Barry Bonds 8.00 20.00
5 Jay Buhner 1.25 3.00
6 Ellis Burks 1.25 3.00
7 Andres Galarraga 1.25 3.00
8 Juan Gonzalez 1.25 3.00
9 Ken Griffey Jr. 5.00 12.00
10 Todd Hundley 1.25 3.00
11 Ryan Klesko 1.25 3.00
12 Mark McGwire 8.00 20.00
13 Mike Piazza 5.00 12.00
14 Alex Rodriguez 5.00 12.00
15 Gary Sheffield 1.25 3.00
16 Sammy Sosa 3.00 8.00
17 Frank Thomas 3.00 8.00
18 Mo Vaughn 1.25 3.00

1997 Fleer New Horizons

Randomly inserted in Fleer Series two packs at a rate of one in four, this 15-card set features borderless color action photos of Rookies and prospects. The backs carry player information.

COMPLETE SET (15) 3.00 8.00
1 Bob Abreu .30 .75
2 Jose Cruz Jr. .25 .60
3 Darin Erstad .20 .50
4 Nomar Garciaparra .75 2.00
5 Vladimir Guerrero .50 1.25
6 Wilton Guerrero .20 .50
7 Jose Guillen .20 .50
8 Hideki Irabu .50 1.25
9 Andruw Jones .30 .75
10 Kevin Orie .20 .50
11 Scott Rolen .30 .75
12 Scott Spiezio .20 .50
13 Bubba Trammell .25 .60
14 Todd Walker .20 .50
15 Dmitri Young .20 .50

1997 Fleer Night and Day

Randomly inserted in Fleer Series one packs at a rate of one in 240, this ten-card set features color action player photos of superstars who excel in day games, night games, or both and are printed on lenticular 3D cards. The backs carry player information.

COMPLETE SET (10) 60.00 150.00
1 Barry Bonds 12.50 30.00
2 Ellis Burks 2.00 5.00
3 Juan Gonzalez 2.00 5.00
4 Ken Griffey Jr. 8.00 20.00
5 Mark McGwire 12.50 30.00
6 Mike Piazza 8.00 20.00
7 Manny Ramirez 3.00 8.00
8 Alex Rodriguez 8.00 20.00
9 John Smoltz 3.00 8.00
10 Frank Thomas 5.00 12.00

1997 Fleer Rookie Sensations

Randomly inserted in Fleer Series one packs at a rate of one in six, this 20-card set honors the top rookies from the 1996 season and the 1997 season rookies/prospects. The fronts feature color action

player images on a multi-color swirling background. The backs carry a paragraph with information about the player.

COMPLETE SET (20) 8.00 20.00
1 Jermaine Allensworth .30 .75
2 James Baldwin .30 .75
3 Alan Benes .30 .75
4 Jermaine Dye .30 .75
5 Darin Erstad .30 .75
6 Todd Hollandsworth .30 .75
7 Derek Jeter 2.00 5.00
8 Jason Kendall .30 .75
9 Alex Ochoa .30 .75
10 Rey Ordonez .30 .75
11 Edgar Renteria .30 .75
12 Bob Abreu .50 1.25
13 Nomar Garciaparra 1.25 3.00
14 Wilton Guerrero .30 .75
15 Andruw Jones .50 1.25
16 Wendell Magee .30 .75
17 Neifi Perez .30 .75
18 Scott Rolen .50 1.25
19 Scott Spiezio .30 .75
20 Todd Walker .30 .75

1997 Fleer Soaring Stars

Randomly inserted in Fleer Series two packs at a rate of one in 12, this 12-card set features color action photos of players who enjoyed a meteoric rise to stardom and have all the skills to stay there. The player's image is set on a background of twinkling stars.

COMPLETE SET (12) 12.50 30.00
*GLOWING: 4X TO 10X BASIC SOARING
GLOWING: RANDOM INSERTS IN SER.2 PACKS
LAST 20% OF PRINT RUN WAS GLOWING
1 Albert Belle .25 .60
2 Barry Bonds 1.50 4.00
3 Juan Gonzalez .25 .60
4 Ken Griffey Jr. 1.00 2.50
5 Derek Jeter 1.50 4.00
6 Andruw Jones .40 1.00
7 Chipper Jones .60 1.50
8 Greg Maddux 1.00 2.50
9 Mark McGwire 1.50 4.00
10 Mike Piazza 1.00 2.50
11 Alex Rodriguez 1.00 2.50
12 Frank Thomas .60 1.50

1997 Fleer Team Leaders

Randomly inserted in Fleer Series one packs at a rate of one in 20, this 28-card set honors statistical or inspirational leaders from each team on a die-cut card. The fronts feature color action player images with the player's face in the background. The backs carry a paragraph with information about the player.

COMPLETE SET (28) 40.00 100.00
1 Cal Ripken 6.00 15.00
2 Mo Vaughn .75 2.00
3 Jim Edmonds .75 2.00
4 Frank Thomas 2.00 5.00
5 Albert Belle .75 2.00
6 Bob Higginson .75 2.00
7 Kevin Appier .75 2.00
8 John Jaha .75 2.00
9 Paul Molitor .75 2.00
10 Andy Pettitte 1.25 3.00
11 Mark McGwire 5.00 12.00
12 Ken Griffey Jr. 3.00 8.00
13 Juan Gonzalez .75 2.00
14 Pat Hentgen .75 2.00
15 Chipper Jones 2.00 5.00
16 Mark Grace 1.25 3.00
17 Barry Larkin 1.25 3.00
18 Ellis Burks .75 2.00
19 Gary Sheffield .75 2.00
20 Jeff Bagwell 1.25 3.00
21 Mike Piazza 3.00 8.00
22 Henry Rodriguez .75 2.00
23 Todd Hundley .75 2.00
24 Curt Schilling .75 2.00
25 Jeff King .75 2.00
26 Brian Jordan .75 2.00
27 Tony Gwynn 2.50 6.00
28 Barry Bonds 5.00 12.00

1997 Fleer Zone

Randomly inserted in Fleer Series one hobby packs only at a rate of one in 80, this 20-card set features color player images of some of the 1996 season's unstoppable hitters and unhittable pitchers on a holographic card. The backs carry another color photo with a paragraph about the player.

COMPLETE SET (20)	80.00	200.00
1 Jeff Bagwell	2.50	6.00
2 Albert Belle	1.50	4.00
3 Barry Bonds	10.00	25.00
4 Ken Caminiti	1.50	4.00
5 Andres Galarraga	1.50	4.00
6 Juan Gonzalez	1.50	4.00
7 Ken Griffey Jr.	6.00	15.00
8 Tony Gwynn	5.00	12.00
9 Chipper Jones	4.00	10.00
10 Greg Maddux	6.00	15.00
11 Mark McGwire	10.00	25.00
12 Dean Palmer	1.50	4.00
13 Andy Pettitte	2.50	6.00
14 Mike Piazza	6.00	15.00
15 Alex Rodriguez	6.00	15.00
16 Gary Sheffield	1.50	4.00
17 John Smoltz	2.50	6.00
18 Frank Thomas	4.00	10.00
19 Jim Thome	2.50	6.00
20 Matt Williams	1.50	4.00

2001 Fleer Autographics

Randomly inserted into packs of Fleer Focus (1:72 w/memorabilia), Fleer Triple Crown (1:72 w/memorabilia cards), Ultra (1:48 w/memorabilia cards), 2002 Fleer Platinum Rack Packs (on average 1:6 racks contains an Autographics card) and 2002 Fleer Genuine (1:18 Hobby Direct box and 1:30 Hobby Distributor box), this insert set features authentic autographs from modern stars and prospects. The cards are designed horizontally with a full color player image at the side allowing plenty of room for the player's autograph. Card backs are unnumbered and feature Fleer's certificate of authenticity. Cards are checklisted alphabetically by player's last name and abbreviations indicating which brands each card was distributed in follows the player name. The brand legend is as follows: FC = Fleer Focus, TC = Fleer Triple Crown, UL = Ultra.

FC SUFFIX ON FOCUS DISTRIBUTION
FS SUFFIX ON SHOWCASE DISTRIBUTION
FP'02 SUFFIX ON ULTRA DISTRIBUTION
GN SUFFIX ON GENUINE DISTRIBUTION
PM SUFFIX ON PREMIUM DISTRIBUTION
TC SUFFIX ON TRIPLE CROWN DISTRIBUTION
UL SUFFIX ON ULTRA DISTRIBUTION

1 Roberto Alomar FC-FS-GN-PM-TC-UL	10.00	25.00
2 Jimmy Anderson TC-UL	4.00	10.00
3 Ryan Anderson TC	4.00	10.00
4 Rick Ankiel FC-FS-GN-PM-TC	10.00	25.00
5 Albert Belle FC-FS-GN	6.00	15.00
6 Carlos Beltran FS-GN	6.00	15.00
7 Adrian Beltre FC-FS-GN-PM-TC	6.00	15.00
8 Peter Bergeron GN-PM-TC	4.00	10.00
9 Lance Berkman FC-GN-TC-UL	10.00	25.00
10 Barry Bonds FC-GN-TC-UL	100.00	175.00
11 Milton Bradley FS-GN-TC	6.00	15.00
12 Ryan Bradley GN'02	4.00	10.00
13 Dee Brown FS-GN-PM-TC-FP'02	4.00	10.00
14 Roosevelt Brown TC-UL	4.00	10.00
15 Jeromy Burnitz FC-FS-GN-PM-UL	6.00	15.00
16 Pat Burrell FC-FS-GN-PM-TC-UL	6.00	15.00
17 Alex Cabrera UL	10.00	25.00
18 Sean Casey FC-FS-GN-PM-TC	6.00	15.00
19 Eric Chavez FC-GN-PM-TC-UL	6.00	15.00
20 Giuseppe Chiaramonte TC	4.00	10.00
21 Joe Crede FS-PM-TC-UL-FP'02	10.00	25.00
22 Jose Cruz Jr. FS-GN-PM-TC	4.00	10.00
23 Johnny Damon GN-PM-UL	15.00	40.00
24 Carlos Delgado FC-GN-TC-UL	6.00	15.00
25 Ryan Dempster FS-GN-TC-FP'02	4.00	10.00
26 J.D. Drew FC-FS-GN-PM	6.00	15.00
27 Adam Dunn FS-TC-UL-FP'02	10.00	25.00
28 Erubiel Durazo FS-GN	4.00	10.00
29 Jermaine Dye FC-FS-GN-PM	6.00	15.00
30 David Eckstein FS-TC	15.00	40.00
31 Jim Edmonds FC-GN-PM-TC-UL	10.00	25.00
32 Alex Escobar FS-GN-PM	4.00	10.00
33 Seth Etherton FS-GN	4.00	10.00
34 Adam Everett FS-GN	4.00	10.00
35 Carlos Febles FS-GN	4.00	10.00
36 Troy Glaus FC-FS-GN-PM-TC	10.00	25.00
37 Chad Green TC-UL	4.00	10.00
38 Ben Grieve FC-FS-GN	4.00	10.00
39 Wilton Guerrero GN'02	4.00	10.00
40 Tony Gwynn FC-GN-PM-TC	20.00	50.00
41 Toby Hall FS-GN	4.00	10.00
42 Todd Helton FS-GN-PM-TC	10.00	25.00
43 Chad Hermansen GN-PM-TC	4.00	10.00
44 Dustin Hermanson PM-UL	4.00	10.00
45 Shea Hillenbrand FS-GN-PM-TC	6.00	15.00
46 Aubrey Huff FS-GN-PM-TC	4.00	10.00
47 Derek Jeter GN-PM	60.00	120.00
48 D'Angelo Jimenez FS	4.00	10.00
49 Randy Johnson FC-GN-TC-UL	40.00	80.00
50 Chipper Jones FC-GN-PMTC	20.00	50.00
51 Cesar King GN	4.00	10.00
52 Paul Konerko FS-GN-PM-FP'02	10.00	25.00
53 Corey Koskie GN'02	6.00	15.00
54 Mike Lamb FC-FS-GN-TC	4.00	10.00
55 Matt Lawton FS-GN	4.00	10.00
56 Corey Lee GN-TC-UL	4.00	10.00
57 Derrek Lee FS-GN-PM-UL	10.00	25.00
58 Mike Lieberthal FC-FS-GN-PM	6.00	15.00
59 Cole Liniak		
60 Steve Lomasney TC	4.00	10.00
61 Terrence Long FC-GN-PM-TC-UL	4.00	10.00
62 Mike Lowell FS-GN	6.00	15.00
63 Julio Lugo FS-GN-PM-TC-UL	4.00	10.00
64 Greg Maddux FC-GN	40.00	80.00
65 Jason Marquis FS-GN-TC	6.00	15.00
66 Edgar Martinez FC-FS-GN-UL	15.00	40.00
67 Justin Miller GN-UL	4.00	10.00
68 Kevin Millwood FC-FS-GN-PM	6.00	15.00
69 Eric Milton FS-GN-PM	4.00	10.00
70 Bengie Molina FS-GN-TC	4.00	10.00
71 Mike Mussina FC-FS-GN-PM-TC	10.00	25.00
72 David Ortiz GN'02	12.50	30.00
73 Russ Ortiz FS-PM-UL	4.00	10.00
74 Pablo Ozuna GN-PM-TC-UL	4.00	10.00
75 Corey Patterson FC-FS-GN-PM-TC	4.00	10.00
76 Carl Pavano PM	6.00	15.00
77 Jay Payton FC-FS-GN-PM-TC	4.00	10.00
78 Wily Pena TC	6.00	15.00
79 Josh Phelps TC	4.00	10.00
80 Adam Piatt FS-GN-TC-UL-FP'02	4.00	10.00
81 Juan Pierre FC-FS-GN	6.00	15.00
82 Brad Radke FC-FS-GN-PM-FP'02	6.00	15.00
83 Mark Redman UL	4.00	10.00
84 Matt Riley GN-TC	4.00	10.00
85 Cal Ripken GN-PM	75.00	150.00
86 John Rocker FS-GN	10.00	25.00
87 Alex Rodriguez FS-GN-TC	60.00	120.00
88 Scott Rolen FC-FS-GN-PM	10.00	25.00
89 Alex Sanchez PM-TC	4.00	10.00
90 Fernando Seguignol GN'02	4.00	10.00
91 Richie Sexson FS-GN-PM-UL	6.00	15.00
92 Gary Sheffield FC-FS-GN-PM-TC-UL	10.00	25.00
93 Alfonso Soriano GN-PM-TC-UL	10.00	25.00
94 Dernell Stenson GN-PM	6.00	15.00
95 Garrett Stephenson PM	4.00	10.00
96 Shannon Stewart FS-GN-PM-TC	6.00	15.00
97 Fernando Tatis FC-GN-TC	4.00	10.00
98 Miguel Tejada FS-FP'02	10.00	25.00
99 Jorge Toca GN-PM	4.00	10.00
100 Robin Ventura FC-FS-GN-PM	6.00	15.00
101 Jose Vidro FS-GN-PM-TC-UL-FP'02	4.00	10.00
102 Billy Wagner FS-PM	10.00	25.00
103 Kip Wells FS-GN	4.00	10.00
104 Vernon Wells GN-PM-UL	6.00	15.00
105 Rondell White FS-GN	6.00	15.00
106 Bernie Williams FP'02	40.00	80.00
107 Scott Williamson GN	4.00	10.00
108 Preston Wilson FS-GN-TC-UL	6.00	15.00
109 Kerry Wood FC-FS-GN-PM-TC-FP'02	10.00	25.00
110 Jamey Wright GN-UL	4.00	10.00
111 Julio Zuleta FS-GN-PM-TC-UL	4.00	10.00

2001 Fleer Autographics Gold

Randomly inserted into a selection of Fleer products, this set is a complete parallel of the Autographics insert. These cards were produced with gold foil stamping on front and are individually serial numbered to 50. Corey Koskie was released exclusively in 2002 Fleer Platinum rack packs.

*GOLD: .75X TO 2X BASIC AUTOS

2001 Fleer Autographics Silver

Randomly inserted into a selection of Fleer products, this set is a complete parallel of the Autographics insert. These cards were produced with silver foil stamping on front and are individually serial numbered to 250. Corey Koskie was distributed exclusively in 2002 Fleer Platinum rack packs.

*SILVER: .6X TO 1.5X BASIC AUTOS

2001 Fleer Feel the Game

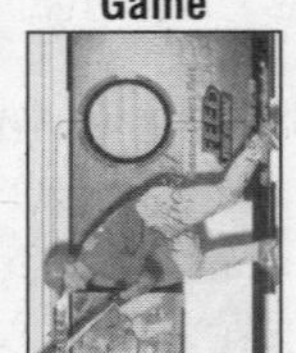

This insert set features game-used bat cards of major league stars. The cards were distributed across several different Fleer products issued in 2001. Please note that the cards are listed below in alphabetical order for convience. Cards with "FC" listed after the players name were inserted into Fleer Focus packs (one Autographic or Feel Game in every 72 packs), "TC" listed after the players name were inserted into packs of Fleer Triple Crown (one Feel Game, Autographic or Crown of Gold in every 72 packs), while cards with "UL" after their name were inserted into Ultra packs (one Autographic or Feel Game in every 48 packs).

*GOLD: 1.25X TO 2.5X BASIC FEEL GAME
GOLD PRINT RUN 50 SERIAL #'d SETS

1 Moises Alou Bat FC-UL	4.00	10.00
2 Brady Anderson Bat FC-UL	4.00	10.00
3 Adrian Beltre Bat TC-UL	4.00	10.00
4 Dante Bichette Bat FC-TC	4.00	10.00
5 Roger Cedeno BatTC	4.00	10.00
6 Ben Davis Bat TC	4.00	10.00
7 Carlos Delgado Bat TC-UL	4.00	10.00
8 J.D. Drew Bat Bat TC-UL	4.00	10.00
9 Jermaine Dye Bat FC-UL	4.00	10.00
10 Jason Giambi Bat TC-UL	4.00	10.00
11 Brian Giles Bat FC-TC	4.00	10.00
12 Juan Gonzalez Bat FC-TC	4.00	10.00
13 Rickey Henderson BatFC	6.00	15.00
14 Richard Hidalgo BatTC-UL	4.00	10.00
15 Chipper Jones Bat TC-UL	6.00	15.00
16 Eric Karros Bat TC-UL	4.00	10.00
17 Javy Lopez Bat FC-TC	4.00	10.00
18 Tino Martinez BatFC-TC	6.00	15.00
19 Raul Mondesi Bat TC-UL	4.00	10.00
20 Phil Nevin Bat FC-TC	4.00	10.00
21 Chan Ho Park Bat TC-UL	4.00	10.00
22 Ivan Rodriguez Bat TC-UL	6.00	15.00
23 Matt Stairs Bat FC-UL	4.00	10.00
24 Shannon Stewart BatFC-TC	4.00	10.00
25 Frank Thomas Bat TC-UL	6.00	15.00
26 Jose Vidro Bat FC-TC-UL	4.00	10.00
27 Matt Williams Bat TC-UL	4.00	10.00
28 Preston Wilson Bat TC-UL	4.00	10.00

2002 Fleer

This 540 card set was issued in May, 2002. These cards were issued in 10 card packs which came packed 24 packs to a box and 10 boxes to a case and had an SRP of $2 per pack. Cards number 432 through 491 featured players who switched teams in the off season while cards 492 through 531 featured leading prospects and cards numbered 532 through 540 feature photos of important ballparks along with checklists on the back.

COMPLETE SET (540)	30.00	80.00
COMMON CARD (1-540)	.08	.25
COMMON CARD (492-531)	.20	.50
1 Darin Erstad FP	.08	.25
2 Randy Johnson FP	.25	.60
3 Chipper Jones FP	.25	.60
4 Jay Gibbons FP	.08	.25
5 Nomar Garciaparra FP	.40	1.00
6 Sammy Sosa FP	.25	.60
7 Frank Thomas FP	.25	.60
8 Ken Griffey Jr. FP	.40	1.00
9 Jim Thome FP	.15	.40
10 Todd Helton FP	.15	.40
11 Jeff Weaver FP	.08	.25
12 Cliff Floyd FP	.08	.25
13 Jeff Bagwell FP	.15	.40
14 Mike Sweeney FP	.08	.25
15 Adrian Beltre FP	.08	.25
16 Richie Sexson FP	.08	.25
17 Brad Radke FP	.08	.25
18 Vladimir Guerrero FP	.25	.60
19 Mike Piazza FP	.40	1.00
20 Derek Jeter FP	.50	1.25
21 Eric Chavez FP	.08	.25
22 Pat Burrell FP	.08	.25
23 Brian Giles FP	.08	.25
24 Trevor Hoffman FP	.08	.25
25 Barry Bonds FP	.40	1.00
26 Ichiro Suzuki FP	.40	1.00
27 Albert Pujols FP	.40	1.00
28 Ben Grieve FP	.08	.25
29 Alex Rodriguez FP	.40	1.00
30 Carlos Delgado FP	.08	.25
31 Miguel Tejada	.15	.40
32 Todd Hollandsworth	.08	.25
33 Marlon Anderson	.08	.25
34 Kerry Robinson	.08	.25
35 Chris Richard	.08	.25
36 Jamey Wright	.08	.25
37 Ray Lankford	.15	.40
38 Mike Bordick	.15	.40
39 Danny Graves	.08	.25
40 A.J. Pierzynski	.15	.40
41 Shannon Stewart	.15	.40
42 Tony Armas Jr.	.08	.25
43 Brad Ausmus	.15	.40
44 Alfonso Soriano	.15	.40
45 Junior Spivey	.08	.25
46 Brent Mayne	.08	.25
47 Jim Thome	.25	.60
48 Dan Wilson	.08	.25
49 Geoff Jenkins	.08	.25
50 Kris Benson	.08	.25
51 Rafael Furcal	.15	.40
52 Wiki Gonzalez	.08	.25
53 Jeff Kent	.15	.40
54 Curt Schilling	.15	.40
55 Ken Harvey	.08	.25
56 Roosevelt Brown	.08	.25
57 David Segui	.08	.25
58 Mario Valdez	.08	.25
59 Adam Dunn	.15	.40
60 Bob Howry	.08	.25
61 Michael Barrett	.08	.25
62 Garret Anderson	.15	.40
63 Kelvim Escobar	.08	.25
64 Ben Grieve	.08	.25
65 Randy Johnson	.40	1.00
66 Jose Offerman	.08	.25
67 Jason Kendall	.15	.40
68 Joel Pineiro	.08	.25
69 Alex Escobar	.08	.25
70 Chris George	.08	.25
71 Bobby Higginson	.15	.40
72 Nomar Garciaparra	.60	1.50
73 Pat Burrell	.15	.40
74 Lee Stevens	.08	.25
75 Felipe Lopez	.08	.25
76 Al Leiter	.15	.40
77 Jim Edmonds	.15	.40
78 Al Levine	.08	.25
79 Raul Mondesi	.15	.40
80 Jose Valentin	.08	.25
81 Matt Clement	.15	.40
82 Richard Hidalgo	.08	.25
83 Jamie Moyer	.15	.40
84 Brian Schneider	.08	.25
85 John Franco	.15	.40
86 Brian Buchanan	.08	.25
87 Roy Oswalt	.15	.40
88 Johnny Estrada	.08	.25
89 Marcus Giles	.15	.40
90 Carlos Valderrama	.08	.25
91 Mark Mulder	.15	.40
92 Mark Grace	.25	.60
93 Andy Ashby	.08	.25
94 Woody Williams	.08	.25
95 Ben Petrick	.08	.25
96 Roy Halladay	.15	.40
97 Fred McGriff	.25	.60
98 Shawn Green	.15	.40
99 Todd Hundley	.08	.25
100 Carlos Febles	.08	.25
101 Jason Marquis	.08	.25
102 Mike Redmond	.08	.25
103 Shane Halter	.08	.25
104 Trot Nixon	.15	.40
105 Jeremy Giambi	.08	.25
106 Carlos Delgado	.15	.40
107 Richie Sexson	.15	.40
108 Russ Ortiz	.08	.25
109 David Ortiz	.40	1.00
110 Curtis Leskanic	.08	.25
111 Jay Payton	.08	.25
112 Travis Phelps	.08	.25
113 J.T. Snow	.15	.40
114 Edgar Renteria	.15	.40
115 Freddy Garcia	.15	.40
116 Cliff Floyd	.15	.40
117 Charles Nagy	.08	.25
118 Tony Batista	.08	.25
119 Rafael Palmeiro	.25	.60
120 Darren Dreifort	.08	.25
121 Warren Morris	.08	.25
122 Augie Ojeda	.08	.25
123 Rusty Greer	.15	.40
124 Esteban Yan	.08	.25
125 Corey Patterson	.08	.25
126 Matt Ginter	.08	.25
127 Matt Lawton	.08	.25
128 Miguel Batista	.08	.25
129 Randy Winn	.08	.25
130 Eric Milton	.08	.25
131 Jack Wilson	.08	.25
132 Sean Casey	.15	.40
133 Mike Sweeney	.15	.40
134 Jason Tyner	.08	.25
135 Carlos Hernandez	.08	.25
136 Shea Hillenbrand	.15	.40
137 Shawn Wooten	.08	.25
138 Peter Bergeron	.08	.25
139 Travis Lee	.08	.25
140 Craig Wilson	.08	.25
141 Carlos Guillen	.15	.40
142 Chipper Jones	.40	1.00
143 Gabe Kapler	.15	.40
144 Raul Ibanez	.08	.25
145 Eric Chavez	.15	.40
146 D'Angelo Jimenez	.08	.25
147 Chad Hermansen	.08	.25
148 Joe Kennedy	.08	.25
149 Mariano Rivera	.40	1.00
150 Jeff Bagwell	.25	.60
151 Joe McEwing	.08	.25
152 Ronnie Belliard	.08	.25
153 Desi Relaford	.08	.25
154 Vinny Castilla	.15	.40
155 Tim Hudson	.15	.40
156 Wilton Guerrero	.08	.25
157 Raul Casanova	.08	.25
158 Edgardo Alfonzo	.08	.25
159 Derrek Lee	.25	.60
160 Phil Nevin	.15	.40
161 Roger Clemens	.75	2.00
162 Jason LaRue	.08	.25
163 Brian Lawrence	.08	.25
164 Adrian Beltre	.15	.40
165 Troy Glaus	.15	.40
166 Jeff Weaver	.08	.25
167 B.J. Surhoff	.15	.40
168 Eric Byrnes	.08	.25
169 Mike Sirotka	.08	.25
170 Bill Haselman	.08	.25
171 Javier Vazquez	.15	.40
172 Sidney Ponson	.08	.25
173 Adam Everett	.08	.25
174 Bubba Trammell	.08	.25
175 Robb Nen	.15	.40
176 Barry Larkin	.25	.60
177 Tony Graffanino	.08	.25
178 Rich Garces	.08	.25
179 Juan Uribe	.08	.25
180 Tom Glavine	.25	.60
181 Eric Karros	.15	.40
182 Michael Cuddyer	.08	.25
183 Wade Miller	.08	.25
184 Matt Williams	.15	.40
185 Matt Morris	.15	.40
186 Rickey Henderson	.40	1.00
187 Trevor Hoffman	.15	.40
188 Wilson Betemit	.08	.25
189 Steve Karsay	.08	.25
190 Frank Catalanotto	.08	.25
191 Jason Schmidt	.15	.40
192 Roger Cedeno	.08	.25
193 Magglio Ordonez	.15	.40
194 Pat Hentgen	.08	.25
195 Mike Lieberthal	.15	.40
196 Andy Pettitte	.25	.60
197 Jay Gibbons	.08	.25
198 Rolando Arrojo	.08	.25
199 Joe Mays	.08	.25
200 Aubrey Huff	.15	.40
201 Nelson Figueroa	.08	.25
202 Paul Konerko	.15	.40
203 Ken Griffey Jr.	.60	1.50
204 Brandon Duckworth	.08	.25
205 Sammy Sosa	.40	1.00
206 Carl Everett	.15	.40
207 Scott Rolen	.25	.60
208 Orlando Hernandez	.15	.40
209 Todd Helton	.25	.60
210 Preston Wilson	.15	.40
211 Gil Meche	.08	.25
212 Bill Mueller	.15	.40
213 Craig Biggio	.25	.60
214 Dean Palmer	.15	.40
215 Randy Wolf	.08	.25
216 Jeff Suppan	.08	.25
217 Jimmy Rollins	.15	.40
218 Alexis Gomez	.08	.25
219 Ellis Burks	.15	.40
220 Ramon E. Martinez	.08	.25
221 Ramiro Mendoza	.08	.25
222 Einar Diaz	.08	.25
223 Brent Abernathy	.08	.25
224 Darin Erstad	.15	.40
225 Reggie Taylor	.08	.25
226 Jason Jennings	.08	.25
227 Ray Durham	.15	.40
228 John Parrish	.08	.25
229 Kevin Young	.08	.25
230 Xavier Nady	.08	.25
231 Juan Cruz	.08	.25
232 Greg Norton	.08	.25
233 Barry Bonds	1.00	2.50
234 Kip Wells	.08	.25
235 Paul LoDuca	.15	.40
236 Javy Lopez	.15	.40
237 Luis Castillo	.08	.25
238 Tom Gordon	.08	.25
239 Mike Mordecai	.08	.25
240 Damian Rolls	.08	.25
241 Julio Lugo	.08	.25
242 Ichiro Suzuki	.75	2.00
243 Tony Womack	.08	.25
244 Matt Anderson	.08	.25
245 Carlos Lee	.15	.40
246 Alex Rodriguez	.60	1.50
247 Bernie Williams	.25	.60
248 Scott Sullivan	.08	.25
249 Mike Hampton	.15	.40
250 Orlando Cabrera	.15	.40
251 Benito Santiago	.15	.40
252 Steve Finley	.15	.40
253 Dave Williams	.08	.25
254 Adam Kennedy	.08	.25
255 Omar Vizquel	.25	.60
256 Garrett Stephenson	.08	.25
257 Fernando Tatis	.08	.25
258 Mike Piazza	.60	1.50
259 Scott Spiezio	.08	.25
260 Jacque Jones	.15	.40
261 Russell Branyan	.08	.25
262 Mark McLemore	.08	.25
263 Mitch Meluskey	.08	.25
264 Marlon Byrd	.08	.25
265 Kyle Farnsworth	.08	.25
266 Billy Sylvester	.08	.25
267 C.C. Sabathia	.15	.40
268 Mark Buehrle	.15	.40
269 Geoff Blum	.08	.25
270 Bret Prinz	.08	.25
271 Placido Polanco	.08	.25
272 John Olerud	.15	.40
273 Pedro Martinez	.25	.60
274 Doug Mientkiewicz	.15	.40
275 Jason Bere	.08	.25
276 Bud Smith	.08	.25
277 Terrence Long	.08	.25
278 Troy Percival	.15	.40
279 Derek Jeter	1.00	2.50
280 Eric Owens	.08	.25
281 Jay Bell	.15	.40
282 Mike Cameron	.08	.25
283 Joe Randa	.15	.40
284 Brian Roberts	.15	.40
285 Ryan Klesko	.15	.40
286 Ryan Dempster	.08	.25
287 Cristian Guzman	.08	.25
288 Tim Salmon	.25	.60
289 Mark Johnson	.08	.25
290 Brian Giles	.15	.40
291 Jon Lieber	.08	.25
292 Fernando Vina	.08	.25
293 Mike Mussina	.25	.60
294 Juan Pierre	.15	.40
295 Carlos Beltran	.15	.40
296 Vladimir Guerrero	.40	1.00
297 Orlando Merced	.08	.25
298 Jose Hernandez	.08	.25
299 Mike Lamb	.08	.25
300 David Eckstein	.15	.40
301 Mark Loretta	.08	.25
302 Greg Vaughn	.08	.25
303 Jose Vidro	.08	.25
304 Jose Ortiz	.08	.25
305 Mark Grudzielanek	.08	.25
306 Rob Bell	.08	.25
307 Elmer Dessens	.08	.25
308 Tomas Perez	.08	.25
309 Jerry Hairston Jr.	.08	.25
310 Mike Stanton	.08	.25
311 Todd Walker	.08	.25
312 Jason Varitek	.40	1.00
313 Masato Yoshii	.08	.25
314 Ben Sheets	.15	.40
315 Roberto Hernandez	.08	.25
316 Eli Marrero	.08	.25
317 Josh Beckett	.15	.40
318 Robert Fick	.08	.25
319 Aramis Ramirez	.15	.40
320 Bartolo Colon	.15	.40
321 Kenny Kelly	.08	.25
322 Luis Gonzalez	.15	.40
323 John Smoltz	.25	.60
324 Homer Bush	.08	.25
325 Kevin Millwood	.15	.40
326 Manny Ramirez	.25	.60
327 Armando Benitez	.08	.25
328 Luis Alicea	.08	.25
329 Mark Kotsay	.15	.40
330 Felix Rodriguez	.08	.25
331 Eddie Taubensee	.08	.25
332 John Burkett	.08	.25
333 Ramon Ortiz	.08	.25
334 Daryle Ward	.08	.25
335 Jarrod Washburn	.08	.25
336 Benji Gil	.08	.25
337 Mike Lowell	.15	.40
338 Larry Walker	.15	.40
339 Andruw Jones	.25	.60
340 Scott Elarton	.08	.25
341 Tony McKnight	.08	.25
342 Frank Thomas	.40	1.00
343 Kevin Brown	.15	.40
344 Jermaine Dye	.15	.40
345 Luis Rivas	.08	.25
346 Jeff Conine	.15	.40
347 Bobby Kielty	.08	.25
348 Jeffrey Hammonds	.08	.25
349 Keith Foulke	.15	.40
350 Dave Martinez	.08	.25
351 Adam Eaton	.08	.25
352 Brandon Inge	.08	.25
353 Tyler Houston	.08	.25
354 Bobby Abreu	.15	.40
355 Ivan Rodriguez	.25	.60
356 Doug Glanville	.08	.25
357 Jorge Julio	.08	.25
358 Kerry Wood	.15	.40
359 Eric Munson	.08	.25
360 Joe Crede	.15	.40
361 Denny Neagle	.08	.25
362 Vance Wilson	.08	.25
363 Neifi Perez	.08	.25

364 Darryl Kile .15 .40
365 Jose Macias .08 .25
366 Michael Coleman .08 .25
367 Erubiel Durazo .08 .25
368 Darrin Fletcher .08 .25
369 Matt White .08 .25
370 Marvin Benard .08 .25
371 Brad Penny .08 .25
372 Chuck Finley .15 .40
373 Delino DeShields .08 .25
374 Adrian Brown .08 .25
375 Corey Koskie .08 .25
376 Kazuhiro Sasaki .15 .40
377 Brent Butler .08 .25
378 Paul Wilson .08 .25
379 Scott Williamson .08 .25
380 Mike Young .40 1.00
381 Toby Hall .08 .25
382 Shane Reynolds .08 .25
383 Tom Goodwin .08 .25
384 Seth Etherton .08 .25
385 Billy Wagner .15 .40
386 Josh Phelps .08 .25
387 Kyle Lohse .08 .25
388 Jeremy Fikac .08 .25
389 Jorge Posada .25 .60
390 Bret Boone .15 .40
391 Angel Berroa .08 .25
392 Matt Mantei .08 .25
393 Alex Gonzalez .08 .25
394 Scott Strickland .08 .25
395 Charles Johnson .15 .40
396 Ramon Hernandez .08 .25
397 Damian Jackson .08 .25
398 Albert Pujols .75 2.00
399 Gary Bennett .08 .25
400 Edgar Martinez .25 .60
401 Carl Pavano .15 .40
402 Chris Gomez .08 .25
403 Jaret Wright .08 .25
404 Lance Berkman .15 .40
405 Robert Person .08 .25
406 Brook Fordyce .08 .25
407 Adam Pettyjohn .08 .25
408 Chris Carpenter .15 .40
409 Rey Ordonez .08 .25
410 Eric Gagne .15 .40
411 Damion Easley .08 .25
412 A.J. Burnett .15 .40
413 Aaron Boone .15 .40
414 J.D. Drew .15 .40
415 Kelly Stinnett .08 .25
416 Mark Quinn .08 .25
417 Brad Radke .15 .40
418 Jose Cruz Jr. .08 .25
419 Greg Maddux .60 1.50
420 Steve Cox .08 .25
421 Torii Hunter .15 .40
422 Sandy Alomar Jr. .08 .25
423 Barry Zito .15 .40
424 Bill Hall .15 .40
425 Marquis Grissom .15 .40
426 Rich Aurilia .08 .25
427 Royce Clayton .08 .25
428 Travis Fryman .15 .40
429 Pablo Ozuna .08 .25
430 David Dellucci .08 .25
431 Vernon Wells .15 .40
432 Gregg Zaun CP .08 .25
433 Alex Gonzalez CP .08 .25
434 Hideo Nomo CP .40 1.00
435 Jeromy Burnitz CP .15 .40
436 Gary Sheffield CP .15 .40
437 Tino Martinez CP .25 .60
438 Tsuyoshi Shinjo CP .15 .40
439 Chan Ho Park CP .15 .40
440 Tony Clark CP .08 .25
441 Brad Fullmer CP .08 .25
442 Jason Giambi CP .08 .25
443 Billy Koch CP .08 .25
444 Mo Vaughn CP .15 .40
445 Alex Ochoa CP .08 .25
446 Darren Lewis CP .08 .25
447 John Rocker CP .15 .40
448 Scott Hatteberg CP .08 .25
449 Brady Anderson CP .15 .40
450 Chuck Knoblauch CP .15 .40
451 Pokey Reese CP .08 .25
452 Brian Jordan CP .15 .40
453 Albie Lopez CP .08 .25
454 David Bell CP .08 .25
455 Juan Gonzalez CP .15 .40
456 Terry Adams CP .08 .25
457 Kenny Lofton CP .15 .40
458 Shawn Estes CP .08 .25
459 Josh Fogg CP .08 .25
460 Dmitri Young CP .15 .40
461 Johnny Damon Sox CP .25 .60
462 Chris Singleton CP .08 .25
463 Ricky Ledee CP .08 .25
464 Dustin Hermanson CP .08 .25
465 Aaron Sele CP .08 .25
466 Chris Stynes CP .08 .25
467 Matt Stairs CP .08 .25
468 Kevin Appier CP .15 .40
469 Omar Daal CP .08 .25
470 Moises Alou CP .15 .40
471 Juan Encarnacion CP .08 .25
472 Robin Ventura CP .15 .40
473 Eric Hinske CP .08 .25
474 Rondell White CP .15 .40
475 Carlos Pena CP .08 .25
476 Craig Paquette CP .08 .25
477 Marty Cordova CP .08 .25
478 Brett Tomko CP .08 .25
479 Reggie Sanders CP .08 .25
480 Roberto Alomar CP .25 .60
481 Jeff Cirillo CP .08 .25
482 Todd Zeile CP .15 .40
483 John Vander Wal CP .08 .25
484 Rick Helling CP .08 .25
485 Jeff D'Amico CP .08 .25
486 David Justice CP .15 .40
487 Jason Isringhausen CP .15 .40
488 Shigetoshi Hasegawa CP .15 .40
489 Eric Young CP .08 .25
490 David Wells CP .15 .40
491 Ruben Sierra CP .08 .25
492 Aaron Cook FF RC .30 .75
493 Takahito Nomura FF RC .30 .75
494 Austin Kearns FF .20 .50
495 Kazuhisa Ishii FF RC .50 1.25
496 Mark Teixeira FF .75 2.00
497 Rene Reyes FF RC .30 .75
498 Tim Spooneybarger FF .20 .50
499 Ben Broussard FF .20 .50
500 Eric Cyr FF .20 .50
501 Anastacio Martinez FF RC .30 .75
502 Morgan Ensberg FF .30 .75
503 Steve Kent FF RC .30 .75
504 Franklin Nunez FF RC .30 .75
505 Adam Walker FF RC .30 .75
506 Anderson Machado FF RC .30 .75
507 Ryan Drese FF .20 .50
508 Luis Ugueto FF RC .30 .75
509 Jorge Nunez FF RC .30 .75
510 Colby Lewis FF .20 .50
511 Ron Calloway FF RC .30 .75
512 Hansel Izquierdo FF RC .30 .75
513 Jason Lane FF .30 .75
514 Rafael Soriano FF .20 .50
515 Jackson Melian FF .20 .50
516 Edwin Almonte FF RC .30 .75
517 Satoru Komiyama FF RC .30 .75
518 Corey Thurman FF RC .30 .75
519 Jorge De La Rosa FF RC .30 .75
520 Victor Martinez FF .75 2.00
521 Dewon Brazelton FF .20 .50
522 Marlon Byrd FF .20 .50
523 Jae Seo FF .20 .50
524 Orlando Hudson FF .20 .50
525 Sean Burroughs FF .20 .50
526 Ryan Langerhans FF .30 .75
527 David Kelton FF .20 .50
528 So Taguchi FF RC .50 1.25
529 Tyler Walker FF .20 .50
530 Hank Blalock FF .50 1.25
531 Mark Prior FF .50 1.25
532 Yankee Stadium CL .15 .40
533 Fenway Park CL .15 .40
534 Wrigley Field CL .15 .40
535 Dodger Stadium CL .15 .40
536 Camden Yards CL .15 .40
537 PacBell Park CL .08 .25
538 Jacobs Field CL .08 .25
539 SAFECO Field CL .08 .25
540 Miller Field CL .08 .25
P279 Derek Jeter Promo

2002 Fleer Gold Backs

Randomly inserted in packs, this is a parallel to the 2002 Fleer set. These cards can be differentiated from the regular cards by either the "gold" stats or text used on the back of the cards. It was announced that 15 percent of the print run featured these gold backs.

*GOLD BACK: .75X TO 2X BASIC
*GOLD BACK 492-531: .75X TO 2X BASIC

2002 Fleer Mini

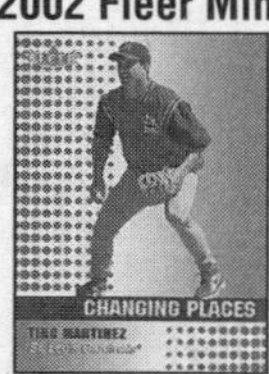

Randomly inserted in retail packs, these cards parallel the 2002 Fleer set. They are printed to a smaller size than the regular set and also were printed to a stated print run of 50 serial numbered sets.

*MINI: 10X TO 25X BASIC
*MINI 492-531: 5X TO 12X BASIC

2002 Fleer Tiffany

Randomly inserted in hobby packs, this is a parallel to the 2002 Fleer set and are printed to a stated print run of 200 serial numbered sets. These cards can be differentiated from the regular Fleer set by the glossy finish on the front.

*TIFFANY: 4X TO 10X BASIC
*TIFFANY 492-531: 2X TO 5X BASIC

2002 Fleer Barry Bonds Career Highlights

Issued at overall odds of one in 12 hobby packs and one in 36 retail packs, these 10 cards feature highlights from Barry Bonds career. These cards were issued in different rates depending on which card number it was.

COMPLETE SET (10) 15.00 40.00
COMMON CARD (1-3) 1.50 4.00
COMMON CARD (4-6) 2.00 5.00
COMMON CARD (7-9) 3.00 8.00
COMMON CARD (10) 2.00 5.00

1-3 ODDS 1:65 HOBBY, 1:225 RETAIL
4-6 ODDS 1:125 HOBBY, 1:400 RETAIL
7-9 ODDS 1:250 HOBBY, 1:500 RETAIL
10 ODDS 1:383 HOBBY, 1:800 RETAIL
OVERALL ODDS 1:12 HOBBY, 1:36 RETAIL

2002 Fleer Barry Bonds Career Highlights Autographs

Randomly inserted in packs, these 10 cards not only parallel the Bonds Career Highlight set but also include an autograph from Barry Bonds on the card. Each card was issued to a stated print run of 25 serial numbered sets and due to market scarcity no pricing is provided.

COMMON CARD (1-10) 125.00 200.00

2002 Fleer Classic Cuts Autographs

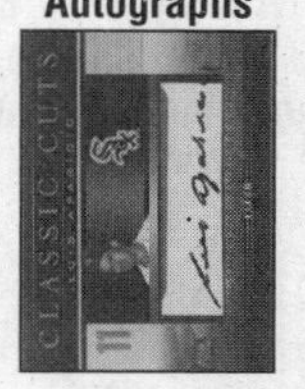

Inserted in packs at a stated rate of one in 432 hobby packs, these nine cards feature autographs from a retired legend. A few cards were issued to a smaller quantity and we have notated that information along with their stated print run next to their name in our checklist.

BRA Brooks Robinson SP/200 15.00 40.00
GPA Gaylord Perry SP/225 8.00 20.00
HKA Harmon Killebrew 20.00 50.00
JMA Juan Marichal 6.00 15.00
LAA Luis Aparicio 6.00 15.00
PRA Phil Rizzuto SP/125 30.00 60.00
RCA Ron Cey 6.00 15.00
RFA Rollie Fingers SP/35
TLA Tommy Lasorda SP/35

2002 Fleer Classic Cuts Game Used

Inserted at stated odds of one in 24, these 94 cards feature retired players along with an authentic game-used memorabilia piece of that player. Some cards were issued in shorter quantites and we have provided the stated print run next to the player's name in our checklist.

ADJ Andre Dawson Jsy 4.00 10.00
ATB Alan Trammell Bat 4.00 10.00
BBB Bobby Bonds Bat 4.00 10.00
BBJ Bobby Bonds Jsy 4.00 10.00
BDB Bill Dickey Bat/200 6.00 15.00
BJJ Bo Jackson Jsy 6.00 15.00
BMB Billy Martin Bat/65 10.00 25.00
BRB Brooks Robinson Bat/250 6.00 15.00
BTB Bill Terry Bat/85 20.00 50.00
CFB Carlton Fisk Bat 6.00 15.00
CFJ Carlton Fisk Jsy/150 6.00 15.00
CHJ Jim Hunter Jsy 6.00 15.00
CRBG Cal Ripken Btg Glv/100 40.00 80.00
CRFG Cal Ripken Fld Glv/60 40.00 80.00
CRJ Cal Ripken Jsy 15.00 40.00
CRP Cal Ripken Pants/200 15.00 40.00
DEB Dwight Evans Bat/250 6.00 15.00
DEJ Dwight Evans Jsy 6.00 15.00
DMB Don Mattingly Bat/200 10.00 25.00
DMJ Don Mattingly Jsy 10.00 25.00
DMP Don Mattingly Patch/50
DPB Dave Parker Bat 4.00 10.00
DRP Dave Righetti Patch
DWB Dave Winfield Bat 4.00 10.00
DWJ Dave Winfield Jsy/231 4.00 10.00
DWP Dave Winfield Pants 4.00 10.00
DWP Dave Winfield Patch/25
DZJ Don Zimmer Jsy/90 6.00 15.00
EMB Eddie Mathews Bat/200 6.00 15.00
EMB Eddie Murray Bat 6.00 15.00
EMJ Eddie Murray Jsy 6.00 15.00
EMP Eddie Murray Patch/45 15.00 40.00
EWJ Earl Weaver Jsy 4.00 10.00
FLB Fred Lynn Bat/25
GBB George Brett Bat/250 10.00 25.00
GBJ George Brett Jsy/250 10.00 25.00
GHB Gil Hodges Bat/200 6.00 15.00
GKB George Kell Bat/150 6.00 15.00
HBB Hank Bauer Bat 4.00 10.00
HGB Hank Greenberg Bat/13
HWB Hack Wilson Bat/8
HWP Hoyt Wilhelm Pants/150 4.00 10.00
JBB Johnny Bench Bat/100 10.00 25.00
JBJ Johnny Bench Jsy 6.00 15.00
JMB Joe Morgan Bat/250 4.00 10.00
JPJ Jim Palmer Jsy/273 4.00 10.00
JRB Jim Rice Bat/225 4.00 10.00
JRJ Jim Rice Jsy/90 6.00 15.00
JTJ Joe Torre Jsy/125 6.00 15.00
KGB Kirk Gibson Bat 4.00 10.00
KPB Kirby Puckett Bat/25
KPJ Kirby Puckett Jsy 6.00 15.00
LDB Larry Doby Bat/250 4.00 10.00
LPP Lou Piniella Pants 4.00 10.00
NFB Nellie Fox Bat/200 6.00 15.00
NRJ Nolan Ryan Jsy 15.00 40.00
NRP Nolan Ryan Pants/200 15.00 40.00
OCB Orlando Cepeda Bat/45 6.00 15.00
OCP Orlando Cepeda Pants 4.00 10.00
OSJ Ozzie Smith Jsy/250 10.00 25.00
PBB Paul Blair Bat 4.00 10.00
PMB Paul Molitor Bat/250 4.00 10.00
PMP Paul Molitor Patch/110 6.00 15.00
PRJ Preacher Roe Jsy/19
PWRJ Pee Wee Reese Jsy/20
RCB Roy Campanella Bat/7
RFJ Rollie Fingers Jsy 4.00 10.00
RJB Reggie Jackson Bat/50 10.00 25.00
RJP Reggie Jackson Pants 6.00 15.00
RKB Ralph Kiner Bat/47 6.00 15.00
RMP Roger Maris Pants/200 20.00 50.00
RSB Ryne Sandberg Bat 10.00 25.00
RYB Robin Yount Bat 6.00 15.00
SAP Sparky Anderson Pants 4.00 10.00
SCH Steve Carlton Hat/25
SCP Steve Carlton Pants 4.00 10.00
SGB Steve Garvey Bat 4.00 10.00
TJJ Tommy John Jsy/55 6.00 15.00
TJP Tommy John Patch/15
TKB Ted Kluszewski Bat/200 6.00 15.00
TKP Ted Kluszewski Pants 6.00 15.00
TLB Tony Lazzeri Bat/35
TMP Thurman Munson Pants/10
TPB Tony Perez Bat/250 4.00 10.00
TPJ Tony Perez Jsy 4.00 10.00
TWB Ted Williams Bat 40.00 80.00
TWP Ted Williams Pants 40.00 80.00
WBB Wade Boggs Bat/99 10.00 25.00
WBJ Wade Boggs Jsy 6.00 15.00
WBP Wade Boggs Patch/50 15.00 40.00
WMJ Willie McCovey Jsy/300 4.00 10.00
WRP Willie Randolph Patch/18
WSB Willie Stargell Bat/250 6.00 15.00
YBB Yogi Berra Bat/72 10.00 25.00

2002 Fleer Classic Cuts Game Used Autographs

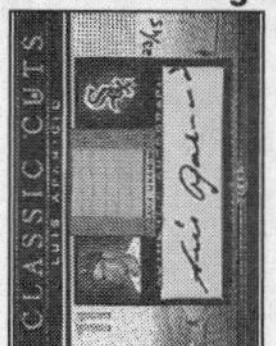

Randomly inserted in packs, these three cards feature not only a game-used piece from a retired player but also an authentic autograph. The stated print run for each player is listed next to their name in our checklist.

BRB Brooks Robinson Bat/45 30.00 60.00
LAB Luis Aparicio Bat/45 15.00 40.00
RFJ Rollie Fingers Bat/35 15.00 40.00

2002 Fleer Diamond Standouts

Randomly inserted in packs, these 10 cards have a stated print run of 1200 serial numbered sets. These cards feature players who most fans would consider the top 10 stars in Baseball.

COMPLETE SET (10) 30.00 80.00
1 Mike Piazza 3.00 8.00
2 Derek Jeter 5.00 12.00
3 Ken Griffey Jr. 3.00 8.00
4 Barry Bonds 5.00 12.00
5 Sammy Sosa 3.00 8.00
6 Alex Rodriguez 3.00 8.00
7 Ichiro Suzuki 4.00 10.00
8 Greg Maddux 3.00 8.00
9 Jason Giambi 3.00 8.00
10 Nomar Garciaparra 3.00 8.00

2002 Fleer Golden Memories

Issued in packs at a stated rate of one in 24 packs, these 15 cards feature players who have earned many honors during their playing career.

COMPLETE SET (15) 15.00 40.00
1 Frank Thomas 1.00 2.50
2 Derek Jeter 2.50 6.00
3 Albert Pujols 2.00 5.00

4 Barry Bonds 2.50 6.00
5 Alex Rodriguez 1.50 4.00
6 Randy Johnson 1.00 2.50
7 Jeff Bagwell .60 1.50
8 Greg Maddux 1.50 4.00
9 Ivan Rodriguez .60 1.50
10 Ichiro Suzuki 2.00 5.00
11 Mike Piazza 1.50 4.00
12 Pat Burrell .60 1.50
13 Rickey Henderson 1.00 2.50
14 Vladimir Guerrero 1.00 2.50
15 Sammy Sosa 1.00 2.50

2002 Fleer Headliners

Issued at a stated rate of one in eight hobby packs and one in 12 retail packs, these 20 cards feature players who achieved noteworthy feats during the 2001 season.

COMPLETE SET (20) 10.00 25.00
1 Randy Johnson .50 1.25
2 Alex Rodriguez .75 2.00
3 Todd Helton .40 1.00
4 Pedro Martinez .40 1.00
5 Ichiro Suzuki 1.00 2.50
6 Vladimir Guerrero .50 1.25
7 Derek Jeter 1.25 3.00
8 Adam Dunn .40 1.00
9 Luis Gonzalez .40 1.00
10 Kazuhiro Sasaki .40 1.00
11 Sammy Sosa .50 1.25
12 Jason Giambi .40 1.00
13 Ken Griffey Jr. .75 2.00
14 Roger Clemens 1.00 2.50
15 Brandon Duckworth .40 1.00
16 Nomar Garciaparra .75 2.00
17 Bud Smith .40 1.00
18 Juan Gonzalez .40 1.00
19 Chipper Jones .50 1.25
20 Barry Bonds 1.25 3.00

2002 Fleer Rookie Flashbacks

Issued at a stated rate of one in three retail packs, these 20 cards feature players who made their major league debut in 2001.

COMPLETE SET (20) 10.00 25.00
1 Bret Prinz .40 1.00
2 Albert Pujols 1.50 4.00
3 C.C. Sabathia .40 1.00
4 Ichiro Suzuki 1.50 4.00
5 Juan Cruz .40 1.00
6 Jay Gibbons .40 1.00
7 Bud Smith .40 1.00
8 Johnny Estrada .40 1.00
9 Roy Oswalt .40 1.00
10 Tsuyoshi Shinjo .40 1.00
11 Brandon Duckworth .40 1.00
12 Jackson Melian .40 1.00
13 Josh Beckett .40 1.00
14 Morgan Ensberg .40 1.00
15 Brian Lawrence .40 1.00
16 Eric Hinske .40 1.00
17 Juan Uribe .40 1.00
18 Matt White .40 1.00
19 Junior Spivey .40 1.00
20 Wilson Betemit .40 1.00

2002 Fleer Rookie Sensations

Randomly inserted in hobby packs and printed to a stated print run of 1500 serial numbered sets, these 20 cards feature players who made their major league debut in 2001.

COMPLETE SET (20) 20.00 50.00
1 Bret Prinz 2.00 5.00
2 Albert Pujols 6.00 15.00
3 C.C. Sabathia 2.00 5.00
4 Ichiro Suzuki 6.00 15.00
5 Juan Cruz 2.00 5.00
6 Jay Gibbons 2.00 5.00
7 Bud Smith 2.00 5.00
8 Johnny Estrada 2.00 5.00
9 Roy Oswalt 2.00 5.00
10 Tsuyoshi Shinjo 2.00 5.00
11 Brandon Duckworth 2.00 5.00
12 Jackson Melian 2.00 5.00
13 Josh Beckett 2.00 5.00
14 Morgan Ensberg 2.00 5.00
15 Brian Lawrence 2.00 5.00
16 Eric Hinske 2.00 5.00
17 Juan Uribe 2.00 5.00
18 Matt White 2.00 5.00
19 Junior Spivey 2.00 5.00
20 Wilson Betemit 2.00 5.00

2002 Fleer Then and Now

Randomly inserted in hobby packs, these 10 cards feature a player from the past who compares with one of today's stars. These cards are printed to a stated print run of 275 serial numbered sets.

COMPLETE SET (10) 60.00 150.00
1 Eddie Mathews 6.00 15.00
Chipper Jones
2 Willie McCovey 12.50 30.00
Barry Bonds
3 Johnny Bench 8.00 20.00
Mika Piazza
4 Ernie Banks 8.00 20.00
Alex Rodriguez
5 Rickey Henderson 10.00 25.00
Ichiro Suzuki
6 Tom Seaver 10.00 25.00
Roger Clemens
7 Juan Marichal 6.00 15.00
Pedro Martinez
8 Reggie Jackson 12.50 30.00
Derek Jeter
9 Nolan Ryan 20.00 50.00
Kerry Wood
10 Joe Morgan 8.00 20.00
Ken Griffey Jr.

2006 Fleer

COMP.FACT.SET (430) 20.00 50.00
COMPLETE SET (400) 15.00 40.00
COMMON CARD (1-400) .15 .40
COMMON ROOKIE .20 .50
COMMON ROOKIE (401-430) .25 .60
401-430 AVAIL. IN FLEER FACT.SET
1 Adam Kennedy .15 .40
2 Bartolo Colon .15 .40
3 Bengie Molina .15 .40
4 Chone Figgins .15 .40
5 Dallas McPherson .15 .40
6 Darin Erstad .15 .40
7 Francisco Rodriguez .15 .40
8 Garret Anderson .15 .40
9 Jarrod Washburn .15 .40
10 John Lackey .15 .40
11 Orlando Cabrera .15 .40
12 Ryan Theriot RC .20 .50
13 Steve Finley .15 .40
14 Vladimir Guerrero .40 1.00
15 Adam Everett .15 .40
16 Andy Pettitte .25 .60
17 Charlton Jimerson (RC) .20 .50
18 Brad Lidge .15 .40
19 Chris Burke .15 .40
20 Craig Biggio .25 .60
21 Jason Lane .15 .40
22 Jeff Bagwell .25 .60
23 Lance Berkman .15 .40
24 Morgan Ensberg .15 .40
25 Roger Clemens .75 2.00
26 Roy Oswalt .15 .40
27 Willy Taveras .15 .40
28 Barry Zito .15 .40
29 Bobby Crosby .15 .40
30 Bobby Kielty .15 .40
31 Dan Johnson .15 .40
32 Danny Haren .15 .40
33 Eric Chavez .15 .40
34 Huston Street .15 .40
35 Jason Kendall .15 .40
36 Jay Payton .15 .40
37 Joe Blanton .15 .40
38 Mark Kotsay .15 .40
39 Nick Swisher .15 .40
40 Rich Harden .15 .40
41 Ron Flores RC .20 .50
42 Alex Rios .15 .40
43 John-Ford Griffin (RC) .20 .50
44 Dave Bush .15 .40
45 Eric Hinske .15 .40
46 Frank Catalanotto .15 .40
47 Gustavo Chacin .15 .40
48 Josh Towers .15 .40
49 Miguel Batista .15 .40

50 Orlando Hudson .15 .40
51 Roy Halladay .15 .40
52 Shea Hillenbrand .15 .40
53 Shaun Marcum (RC) .20 .50
54 Vernon Wells .15 .40
55 Adam LaRoche .15 .40
56 Andruw Jones .25 .60
57 Chipper Jones .40 1.00
58 Anthony Lerew (RC) .20 .50
59 Jeff Francoeur .40 1.00
60 John Smoltz .25 .60
61 Johnny Estrada .15 .40
62 Julio Franco .15 .40
63 Joey Devine RC .20 .50
64 Marcus Giles .15 .40
65 Mike Hampton .15 .40
66 Rafael Furcal .15 .40
67 Chuck James (RC) .30 .75
68 Tim Hudson .15 .40
69 Ben Sheets .15 .40
70 Bill Hall .15 .40
71 Brady Clark .15 .40
72 Carlos Lee .15 .40
73 Chris Capuano .15 .40
74 Nelson Cruz (RC) .20 .50
75 Derrick Turnbow .15 .40
76 Doug Davis .15 .40
77 Geoff Jenkins .15 .40
78 J.J. Hardy .15 .40
79 Lyle Overbay .15 .40
80 Prince Fielder .60 1.50
81 Rickie Weeks .15 .40
82 Albert Pujols .75 2.00
83 Chris Carpenter .15 .40
84 David Eckstein .15 .40
85 Jason Isringhausen .15 .40
86 Tyler Johnson (RC) .20 .50
87 Adam Wainwright (RC) .20 .50
88 Jim Edmonds .25 .60
89 Chris Duncan (RC) .20 .50
90 Mark Grudzielanek .15 .40
91 Mark Mulder .15 .40
92 Matt Morris .15 .40
93 Reggie Sanders .15 .40
94 Scott Rolen .25 .60
95 Yadier Molina .15 .40
96 Aramis Ramirez .15 .40
97 Carlos Zambrano .15 .40
98 Corey Patterson .15 .40
99 Derrek Lee .15 .40
100 Glendon Rusch .15 .40
101 Greg Maddux .60 1.50
102 Jeromy Burnitz .15 .40
103 Kerry Wood .15 .40
104 Mark Prior .25 .60
105 Michael Barrett .15 .40
106 Geovany Soto (RC) .50 1.25
107 Nomar Garciaparra .40 1.00
108 Ryan Dempster .15 .40
109 Todd Walker .15 .40
110 Alex S. Gonzalez .15 .40
111 Aubrey Huff .15 .40
112 Victor Diaz .15 .40
113 Carl Crawford .15 .40
114 Danys Baez .15 .40
115 Joey Gathright .15 .40
116 Jonny Gomes .15 .40
117 Jorge Cantu .15 .40
118 Julio Lugo .15 .40
119 Rocco Baldelli .15 .40
120 Scott Kazmir .25 .60
121 Toby Hall .15 .40
122 Tim Corcoran RC .20 .50
123 Alex Cintron .15 .40
124 Brandon Webb .15 .40
125 Chad Tracy .15 .40
126 Dustin Nippert (RC) .20 .50
127 Claudio Vargas .15 .40
128 Craig Counsell .15 .40
129 Javier Vazquez .15 .40
130 Jose Valverde .15 .40
131 Luis Gonzalez .15 .40
132 Royce Clayton .15 .40
133 Russ Ortiz .15 .40
134 Shawn Green .15 .40
135 Tony Clark .15 .40
136 Troy Glaus .15 .40
137 Brad Penny .15 .40
138 Cesar Izturis .15 .40
139 Derek Lowe .15 .40
140 Eric Gagne .15 .40
141 Hee Seop Choi .15 .40
142 J.D. Drew .15 .40
143 Jason Phillips .15 .40
144 Jayson Werth .15 .40
145 Jeff Kent .15 .40
146 Jeff Weaver .15 .40
147 Milton Bradley .15 .40
148 Odalis Perez .15 .40
149 Hong-Chih Kuo (RC) .50 1.25
150 Brian Myrow RC .20 .50
151 Armando Benitez .15 .40
152 Edgardo Alfonzo .15 .40
153 J.T. Snow .15 .40
154 Jason Schmidt .15 .40
155 Lance Niekro .15 .40
156 Doug Clark (RC) .20 .50
157 Dan Ortmeier (RC) .20 .50
158 Moises Alou .15 .40
159 Noah Lowry .15 .40
160 Omar Vizquel .25 .60
161 Pedro Feliz .15 .40
162 Randy Winn .15 .40
163 Jeremy Accardo RC .20 .50
164 Aaron Boone .15 .40
165 Ryan Garko (RC) .20 .50
166 C.C. Sabathia .15 .40
167 Casey Blake .15 .40
168 Cliff Lee .15 .40
169 Coco Crisp .15 .40
170 Grady Sizemore .25 .60
171 Jake Westbrook .15 .40
172 Jhonny Peralta .15 .40
173 Kevin Millwood .15 .40
174 Scott Elarton .15 .40
175 Travis Hafner .15 .40
176 Victor Martinez .15 .40
177 Adrian Beltre .15 .40
178 Eddie Guardado .15 .40
179 Felix Hernandez .25 .60
180 Gil Meche .15 .40
181 Ichiro Suzuki .60 1.50
182 Jamie Moyer .15 .40
183 Jeremy Reed .15 .40
184 Jaime Bubela (RC) .15 .40
185 Raul Ibanez .15 .40
186 Richie Sexson .15 .40
187 Ryan Franklin .15 .40
188 Jeff Harris RC .15 .40
189 A.J. Burnett .15 .40
190 Josh Wilson (RC) .20 .50
191 Josh Johnson (RC) .30 .75
192 Carlos Delgado .15 .40
193 Dontrelle Willis .15 .40
194 Bernie Castro (RC) .20 .50
195 Josh Beckett .15 .40
196 Juan Encarnacion .15 .40
197 Juan Pierre .15 .40
198 Robert Andino RC .20 .50
199 Miguel Cabrera .25 .60
200 Ryan Jorgensen RC .20 .50
201 Paul Lo Duca .15 .40
202 Todd Jones .15 .40
203 Braden Looper .15 .40
204 Carlos Beltran .15 .40
205 Cliff Floyd .15 .40
206 David Wright .60 1.50
207 Doug Mientkiewicz .15 .40
208 Jae Seo .15 .40
209 Jose Reyes .40 1.00
210 Anderson Hernandez (RC) .20 .50
211 Miguel Cairo .15 .40
212 Mike Cameron .15 .40
213 Mike Piazza .40 1.00
214 Pedro Martinez .25 .60
215 Tom Glavine .25 .60
216 Tim Hamulack (RC) .15 .40
217 Brad Wilkerson .15 .40
218 Darrell Rasner (RC) .15 .40
219 Chad Cordero .15 .40
220 Cristian Guzman .15 .40
221 Jason Bergmann RC .20 .50
222 John Patterson .15 .40
223 Jose Guillen .15 .40
224 Jose Vidro .15 .40
225 Livan Hernandez .15 .40
226 Nick Johnson .15 .40
227 Preston Wilson .15 .40
228 Ryan Zimmerman (RC) 1.25 3.00
229 Vinny Castilla .15 .40
230 B.J. Ryan .15 .40
231 B.J. Surhoff .15 .40
232 Brian Roberts .15 .40
233 Walter Young (RC) .20 .50
234 Daniel Cabrera .15 .40
235 Erik Bedard .15 .40
236 Javy Lopez .15 .40
237 Jay Gibbons .15 .40
238 Luis Matos .15 .40
239 Melvin Mora .15 .40
240 Miguel Tejada .15 .40
241 Rafael Palmeiro .25 .60
242 Alejandro Freire RC .15 .40
243 Sammy Sosa .40 1.00
244 Adam Eaton .15 .40
245 Brian Giles .15 .40
246 Brian Lawrence .15 .40
247 Dave Roberts .15 .40
248 Jake Peavy .15 .40
249 Khalil Greene .25 .60
250 Mark Loretta .15 .40
251 Ramon Hernandez .15 .40
252 Ryan Klesko .15 .40
253 Trevor Hoffman .15 .40
254 Woody Williams .15 .40
255 Craig Breslow RC .20 .50
256 Billy Wagner .15 .40
257 Bobby Abreu .15 .40
258 Brett Myers .15 .40
259 Chase Utley .40 1.00
260 David Bell .15 .40
261 Jim Thome .25 .60
262 Jimmy Rollins .15 .40
263 Jon Lieber .15 .40
264 Danny Sandoval RC .20 .50
265 Mike Lieberthal .15 .40
266 Pat Burrell .15 .40
267 Randy Wolf .15 .40
268 Ryan Howard .60 1.50
269 J.J. Furmaniak (RC) .20 .50
270 Ronny Paulino (RC) .20 .50
271 Craig Wilson .15 .40
272 Bryan Bullington (RC) .20 .50
273 Jack Wilson .15 .40
274 Jason Bay .15 .40
275 Matt Capps (RC) .20 .50
276 Oliver Perez .15 .40
277 Rob Mackowiak .15 .40
278 Tom Gorzelanny (RC) .20 .50
279 Zach Duke .15 .40
280 Alfonso Soriano .15 .40
281 Chris R. Young .15 .40
282 David Dellucci .15 .40
283 Francisco Cordero .15 .40
284 Jason Botts (RC) UER .20 .50
Michael Young pictured
285 Hank Blalock .15 .40
286 Josh Rupe (RC) .20 .50
287 Kevin Mench .15 .40
288 Laynce Nix .15 .40
289 Mark Teixeira .25 .60
290 Michael Young .15 .40
291 Richard Hidalgo .15 .40
292 Scott Feldman RC .20 .50
293 Bill Mueller .15 .40
294 Hanley Ramirez (RC) .50 1.25
295 Curt Schilling .25 .60
296 David Ortiz .40 1.00
297 Alejandro Machado (RC) .20 .50
298 Edgar Renteria .15 .40
299 Jason Varitek .40 1.00
300 Johnny Damon .25 .60
301 Keith Foulke .15 .40
302 Manny Ramirez .25 .60
303 Matt Clement .15 .40
304 Craig Hansen RC .75 2.00
305 Tim Wakefield .15 .40
306 Trot Nixon .15 .40
307 Aaron Harang .15 .40
308 Adam Dunn .15 .40
309 Austin Kearns .15 .40
310 Brandon Claussen .15 .40
311 Chris Booker (RC) .20 .50
312 Edwin Encarnacion .15 .40
313 Chris Denorfia (RC) .20 .50
314 Felipe Lopez .15 .40
315 Miguel Perez (RC) .20 .50
316 Ken Griffey Jr. .60 1.50
317 Ryan Freel .15 .40
318 Sean Casey .15 .40
319 Wily Mo Pena .15 .40
320 Mike Esposito (RC) .20 .50
321 Aaron Miles .15 .40
322 Brad Hawpe .15 .40
323 Brian Fuentes .15 .40
324 Clint Barmes .15 .40
325 Cory Sullivan .15 .40
326 Garrett Atkins .15 .40
327 J.D. Closser .15 .40
328 Jeff Francis .15 .40
329 Luis Gonzalez .15 .40
330 Matt Holliday .40 1.00
331 Todd Helton .25 .60
332 Angel Berroa .15 .40
333 David DeJesus .15 .40
334 Emil Brown .15 .40
335 Jeremy Affeldt .15 .40
336 Chris Demaria RC .20 .50
337 Mark Teahen .15 .40
338 Matt Stairs .15 .40
339 Steve Stemle RC .20 .50
340 Mike Sweeney .15 .40
341 Runelvys Hernandez .15 .40
342 Jonah Bayliss RC .20 .50
343 Zack Greinke .15 .40
344 Brandon Inge .25 .60
345 Carlos Guillen .25 .60
346 Carlos Pena .15 .40
347 Chris Shelton .15 .40
348 Craig Monroe .15 .40
349 Dmitri Young .15 .40
350 Ivan Rodriguez .25 .60
351 Jeremy Bonderman .20 .50
352 Magglio Ordonez .15 .40
353 Mark Woodyard (RC) .20 .50
354 Omar Infante .15 .40
355 Placido Polanco .15 .40
356 Rondell White .15 .40
357 Brad Radke .15 .40
358 Carlos Silva .15 .40
359 Jacque Jones .15 .40
360 Joe Mauer .25 .60
361 Chris Heintz RC .20 .50
362 Joe Nathan .15 .40
363 Johan Santana .25 .60
364 Justin Morneau .15 .40
365 Francisco Liriano (RC) 1.00 2.50
366 Travis Bowyer (RC) .20 .50
367 Michael Cuddyer .15 .40
368 Scott Baker .15 .40
369 Shannon Stewart .15 .40
370 Torii Hunter .15 .40
371 A.J. Pierzynski .15 .40
372 Aaron Rowand .15 .40
373 Carl Everett .15 .40
374 Dustin Hermanson .15 .40
375 Frank Thomas .40 1.00
376 Freddy Garcia .15 .40
377 Jermaine Dye .15 .40
378 Joe Crede .15 .40
379 Jon Garland .15 .40
380 Jose Contreras .15 .40
381 Juan Uribe .15 .40
382 Mark Buehrle .15 .40
383 Orlando Hernandez .15 .40
384 Paul Konerko .15 .40
385 Scott Podsednik .15 .40
386 Tadahito Iguchi .15 .40
387 Alex Rodriguez .60 1.50
388 Bernie Williams .25 .60
389 Chien-Ming Wang .60 1.50
390 Derek Jeter 1.00 2.50
391 Gary Sheffield .15 .40
392 Hideki Matsui .60 1.50
393 Jason Giambi .15 .40
394 Jorge Posada .25 .60
395 Mike Vento (RC) .20 .50
396 Mariano Rivera .40 1.00
397 Mike Mussina .25 .60
398 Randy Johnson .40 1.00
399 Robinson Cano .25 .60
400 Tino Martinez .15 .40
401 Alay Soler RC .25 .60
402 Boof Bonser (RC) .40 1.00
403 Cole Hamels (RC) 1.00 2.50
404 Ian Kinsler (RC) .40 1.00
405 Jason Kubel (RC) .25 .60
406 Joel Zumaya (RC) .60 1.50
407 Jonathan Papelbon (RC) 1.25 3.00
408 Jered Weaver (RC) 1.25 3.00
409 Kendry Morales (RC) .60 1.50
410 Lastings Milledge (RC) .40 1.00
411 Matt Kemp (RC) .40 1.00
412 Taylor Buchholz (RC) .40 1.00
413 Andre Ethier (RC) .60 1.50
414 Dan Uggla (RC) .60 1.50
415 Jeremy Sowers (RC) .25 .60
416 Chad Billingsley (RC) .40 1.00
417 Josh Barfield (RC) .25 .60
418 Matt Cain (RC) .40 1.00
419 Fausto Carmona (RC) .25 .60
420 Josh Willingham (RC) .25 .60
421 Jeremy Hermida (RC) .25 .60
422 Conor Jackson (RC) .40 1.00
423 Dave Gassner (RC) .25 .60
424 Brian Bannister (RC) .25 .60
425 Fernando Nieve (RC) .25 .60
426 Justin Verlander (RC) 1.00 2.50
427 Scott Olsen (RC) .25 .60
428 Takashi Saito RC .25 .60
429 Willie Eyre (RC) .25 .60
430 Travis Ishikawa (RC) .25 .60

2006 Fleer Glossy Gold

STATED ODDS 1:144 HOBBY, 1:144 RETAIL
NO PRICING DUE TO SCARCITY

2006 Fleer Glossy Silver

*GLOSSY SILVER: 2X TO 5X BASIC
*GLOSSY SILVER: 1.5X TO 4X BASIC RC
STATED ODDS 1:12 HOBBY, 1:24 RETAIL

2006 Fleer Autographics

STATED ODDS 1:432 HOBBY, 1:432 RETAIL
SP PRINT RUNS PROVIDED BY UD
SP'S ARE NOT SERIAL-NUMBERED
NO SP PRICING ON QTY OF 25 OR LESS
AN Garret Anderson 6.00 15.00
CK Casey Kotchman SP/25 *
CS Chris Shelton 6.00 15.00
EC Eric Chavez 6.00 15.00
GA Garrett Atkins 6.00 15.00
GM Greg Maddux SP/15 *
JB Joe Blanton 6.00 15.00
JL Javy Lopez SP/25 *
JV Justin Verlander SP/25 *
KG Ken Griffey Jr.SP/150 * 40.00 80.00
KY Kevin Youkilis 10.00 25.00
MC Miguel Cabrera SP/25 *
MP Mark Prior SP/25 *
NS Nick Swisher 6.00 15.00
PM Pedro Martinez SP/15 *
TH Trevor Hoffman SP/25 *
TI Tadahito Iguchi 20.00 50.00

2006 Fleer Award Winners

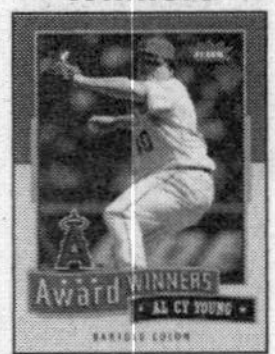

COMPLETE SET (6) 6.00 15.00
OVERALL INSERT ODDS ONE PER PACK
AW1 Albert Pujols 2.00 5.00
AW2 Alex Rodriguez 1.50 4.00
AW3 Chris Carpenter .40 1.00
AW4 Bartolo Colon .40 1.00
AW5 Ryan Howard 1.50 4.00
AW6 Huston Street .40 1.00

2006 Fleer Fabrics

STATED ODDS 1:36 HOBBY, 1:72 RETAIL
SP INFO PROVIDED BY UPPER DECK
AJ Andruw Jones Jsy 3.00 8.00
AP Albert Pujols Jsy 6.00 15.00
AR Aramis Ramirez Jsy 3.00 8.00
AS Alfonso Soriano Jsy 3.00 8.00
BA Bobby Abreu Jsy 3.00 8.00
CB Carlos Beltran Jsy 3.00 8.00
CJ Chipper Jones Jsy 4.00 10.00
CS Curt Schilling Jsy 3.00 8.00
DJ Derek Jeter Jsy 10.00 25.00
DL Derrek Lee Jsy 3.00 8.00
DO David Ortiz Pants 4.00 10.00
DW Dontrelle Willis Jsy SP 4.00 10.00
EC Eric Chavez Jsy 3.00 8.00
EG Eric Gagne Jsy 3.00 8.00
GM Greg Maddux Jsy 4.00 10.00
GR Khalil Greene Jsy 4.00 10.00
GS Gary Sheffield Jsy SP 4.00 10.00
IR Ivan Rodriguez Jsy 3.00 8.00
JE Jim Edmonds Jsy 3.00 8.00
JM Joe Mauer Jsy 4.00 10.00
JP Jake Peavy Jsy 3.00 8.00
JS Johan Santana Jsy 4.00 10.00
JT Jim Thome Jsy 4.00 10.00
KG Ken Griffey Jr. Jsy 6.00 15.00
LG Luis Gonzalez Jsy 3.00 8.00
MC Miguel Cabrera Jsy 4.00 10.00
MP Mark Prior Jsy 4.00 10.00
MR Manny Ramirez Jsy 4.00 10.00
MT Mark Teixeira Jsy 4.00 10.00
MY Michael Young Jsy 3.00 8.00
PM Pedro Martinez Jsy 4.00 10.00
RC Roger Clemens Jsy 6.00 15.00
RH Roy Halladay Jsy 3.00 8.00
RJ Randy Johnson Jsy 4.00 10.00
RW Rickie Weeks Jsy 3.00 8.00
SM John Smoltz Jsy 4.00 10.00
TE Miguel Tejada Jsy 3.00 8.00
TH Todd Helton Jsy 4.00 10.00
VG Vladimir Guerrero Jsy 4.00 10.00
WR David Wright Jsy 4.00 10.00

2006 Fleer Lumber Company

COMPLETE SET (25) 10.00 25.00
OVERALL INSERT ODDS ONE PER PACK
LC1 Adam Dunn .40 1.00
LC2 Albert Pujols 2.00 5.00
LC3 Alex Rodriguez 1.50 4.00
LC4 Alfonso Soriano .40 1.00
LC5 Andruw Jones .60 1.50
LC6 Aramis Ramirez .40 1.00
LC7 Bobby Abreu .40 1.00
LC8 Carlos Delgado .40 1.00
LC9 Carlos Lee .40 1.00
LC10 David Ortiz 1.00 2.50
LC11 David Wright 1.50 4.00
LC12 Derrek Lee .40 1.00
LC13 Eric Chavez .40 1.00
LC14 Gary Sheffield .40 1.00
LC15 Jeff Kent .40 1.00
LC16 Ken Griffey Jr. 1.50 4.00
LC17 Manny Ramirez .60 1.50
LC18 Mark Teixeira .60 1.50
LC19 Miguel Cabrera .60 1.50
LC20 Miguel Tejada .40 1.00
LC21 Paul Konerko .40 1.00
LC22 Richie Sexson .40 1.00
LC23 Todd Helton .60 1.50
LC24 Troy Glaus .40 1.00
LC25 Vladimir Guerrero 1.00 2.50

2006 Fleer Smoke 'n Heat

COMPLETE SET (15) 8.00 20.00
OVERALL INSERT ODDS ONE PER PACK
SH1 Carlos Zambrano .40 1.00
SH2 Chris Carpenter .40 1.00
SH3 Curt Schilling .60 1.50
SH4 Dontrelle Willis .40 1.00
SH5 Felix Hernandez .60 1.50
SH6 Jake Peavy .40 1.00
SH7 Johan Santana .60 1.50
SH8 John Smoltz .60 1.50
SH9 Mark Prior .60 1.50
SH10 Pedro Martinez .60 1.50
SH11 Randy Johnson 1.00 2.50
SH12 Roger Clemens 2.00 5.00
SH13 Roy Halladay .40 1.00
SH14 Roy Oswalt .40 1.00
SH15 Scott Kazmir .60 1.50

2006 Fleer Smooth Leather

COMPLETE SET (14) 10.00 25.00
OVERALL INSERT ODDS ONE PER PACK
SL1 Alex Rodriguez 1.50 4.00
SL2 Andruw Jones .60 1.50
SL3 Derek Jeter 2.50 6.00
SL4 Derrek Lee .40 1.00
SL5 Eric Chavez .40 1.00
SL6 Greg Maddux 1.50 4.00
SL7 Ichiro Suzuki 1.50 4.00
SL8 Ivan Rodriguez .60 1.50
SL9 Jim Edmonds .60 1.50
SL10 Mike Mussina .60 1.50
SL11 Omar Vizquel .60 1.50
SL12 Scott Rolen .60 1.50
SL13 Todd Helton .60 1.50
SL14 Torii Hunter .40 1.00

2006 Fleer Stars of Tomorrow

COMPLETE SET (10) 6.00 15.00
OVERALL INSERT ODDS ONE PER PACK
ST1 David Wright 1.50 4.00
ST2 Ryan Howard 1.50 4.00
ST3 Felix Hernandez .60 1.50
ST4 Jeff Francoeur 1.00 2.50
ST5 Joe Mauer .60 1.50
ST6 Mark Prior .60 1.50
ST7 Mark Teixeira .60 1.50
ST8 Miguel Cabrera .60 1.50
ST9 Prince Fielder 1.50 4.00
ST10 Rickie Weeks .40 1.00

2006 Fleer Team Fleer

OVERALL INSERT ODDS ONE PER PACK
TF1 Albert Pujols 15.00 40.00
TF2 Alex Rodriguez 15.00 40.00
TF3 Alfonso Soriano 6.00 15.00
TF4 Andruw Jones 10.00 25.00
TF5 Bobby Abreu 6.00 15.00
TF6 David Ortiz 10.00 25.00
TF7 David Wright 15.00 40.00
TF8 Eric Gagne 6.00 15.00
TF9 Ichiro Suzuki 15.00 40.00
TF10 Jason Varitek 10.00 25.00
TF11 Jeff Kent 6.00 15.00
TF12 Johan Santana 10.00 25.00
TF13 Jose Reyes 6.00 15.00
TF14 Manny Ramirez 10.00 25.00
TF15 Mariano Rivera 10.00 25.00
TF16 Miguel Cabrera 10.00 25.00
TF17 Miguel Tejada 6.00 15.00
TF18 Mike Piazza 10.00 25.00
TF19 Roger Clemens 15.00 40.00
TF20 Torii Hunter 6.00 15.00

2006 Fleer Team Leaders

COMPLETE SET (30) 15.00 40.00
OVERALL INSERT ODDS ONE PER PACK
TL1 Troy Glaus .40 1.00
Brandon Webb
TL2 Andruw Jones .60 1.50
John Smoltz
TL3 Miguel Tejada .40 1.00
Erik Bedard
TL4 David Ortiz 1.00 2.50
Curt Schilling
TL5 Derrek Lee .60 1.50
Mark Prior
TL6 Paul Konerko .40 1.00
Mark Buehrle
TL7 Ken Griffey Jr. 1.50 4.00
Aaron Harang
TL8 Travis Hafner .40 1.00
Cliff Lee
TL9 Todd Helton .60 1.50
Jeff Francis
TL10 Ivan Rodriguez .60 1.50
Jeremy Bonderman
TL11 Miguel Cabrera .60 1.50
Dontrelle Willis
TL12 Lance Berkman 2.00 5.00
Roger Clemens
TL13 Mike Sweeney .40 1.00
Zack Greinke
TL14 Jeff Kent .40 1.00
Derek Lowe
TL15 Carlos Lee .40 1.00
Ben Sheets
TL16 Torii Hunter .60 1.50
Johan Santana
TL17 David Wright 1.50 4.00
Pedro Martinez
TL18 Derek Jeter 2.50 6.00
Randy Johnson
TL19 Eric Chavez .40 1.00
Barry Zito
TL20 Bobby Abreu .40 1.00
Brett Myers
TL21 Jason Bay .40 1.00
Zach Duke
TL22 Brian Giles .40 1.00
Jake Peavy
TL23 Moises Alou .40 1.00
Jason Schmidt
TL24 Ichiro Suzuki 1.50 4.00
Felix Hernandez
TL25 Albert Pujols 2.00 5.00
Chris Carpenter
TL26 Carl Crawford .60 1.50
Scott Kazmir
TL27 Mark Teixeira .60 1.50
Kenny Rogers
TL28 Vernon Wells .40 1.00
Roy Halladay
TL29 Jose Guillen .40 1.00
Livan Hernandez
TL30 Vladimir Guerrero 1.00 2.50
Bartolo Colon

2006 Fleer Top 40

STATED ODDS 2:1 FAT PACKS
1 Ken Griffey Jr. 1.50 4.00
2 Derek Jeter 2.50 6.00
3 Albert Pujols 2.00 5.00
4 Alex Rodriguez 1.50 4.00

5 Vladimir Guerrero 1.00 2.50
6 Roger Clemens 2.00 5.00
7 Derrek Lee .40 1.00
8 David Ortiz 1.00 2.50
9 Miguel Cabrera .60 1.50
10 Bobby Abreu .40 1.00
11 Mark Teixeira .60 1.50
12 Johan Santana .60 1.50
13 Hideki Matsui 1.50 4.00
14 Ichiro Suzuki 1.50 4.00
15 Andruw Jones .60 1.50
16 Eric Chavez .40 1.00
17 Roy Oswalt .40 1.00
18 Curt Schilling .60 1.50
19 Randy Johnson 1.00 2.50
20 Ivan Rodriguez .60 1.50
21 Chipper Jones 1.00 2.50
22 Mark Prior .60 1.50
23 Jason Bay .40 1.00
24 Pedro Martinez .60 1.50
25 David Wright 1.50 4.00
26 Carlos Beltran .40 1.00
27 Jim Edmonds .60 1.50
28 Chris Carpenter .40 1.00
29 Roy Halladay .40 1.00
30 Jake Peavy .40 1.00
31 Paul Konerko .40 1.00
32 Travis Hafner .40 1.00
33 Barry Zito .40 1.00
34 Miguel Tejada .40 1.00
35 Josh Beckett .40 1.00
36 Todd Helton .60 1.50
37 Dontrelle Willis .40 1.00
38 Manny Ramirez .60 1.50
39 Mariano Rivera 1.00 2.50
40 Jeff Kent .40 1.00

2007 Fleer

COMPLETE SET (400) 30.00 60.00
COMP.FACT.SET (430) 30.00 60.00
COMMON CARD (1-430) .12 .30
COMMON RC .25 .60
401-430 ISSUED IN FACT.SET
OVERALL PRINTING PLATE ODDS 1:720
PLATE PRINT RUN 1 SET PER COLOR
BLACK-CYAN-MAGENTA-YELLOW ISSUED
NO PLATE PRICING DUE TO SCARCITY
1 Chad Cordero .12 .30
2 Alfonso Soriano .12 .30
3 Nick Johnson .12 .30
4 Austin Kearns .12 .30
5 Ramon Ortiz .12 .30
6 Brian Schneider .12 .30
7 Ryan Zimmerman .30 .75
8 Jose Vidro .12 .30
9 Felipe Lopez .12 .30
10 Cristian Guzman .12 .30
11 B.J. Ryan .12 .30
12 Alex Rios .12 .30
13 Vernon Wells .12 .30
14 Roy Halladay .12 .30
15 A.J. Burnett .12 .30
16 Lyle Overbay .12 .30
17 Troy Glaus .12 .30
18 Bengie Molina .12 .30
19 Gustavo Chacin .12 .30
20 Aaron Hill .12 .30
21 Vicente Padilla .12 .30
22 Kevin Millwood .12 .30
23 Akinori Otsuka .12 .30
24 Adam Eaton .12 .30
25 Hank Blalock .12 .30
26 Mark Teixeira .20 .50
27 Michael Young .12 .30
28 Mark DeRosa .12 .30
29 Gary Matthews .12 .30
30 Ian Kinsler .12 .30
31 Carlos Lee .12 .30
32 James Shields .12 .30
33 Scott Kazmir .20 .50
34 Carl Crawford .12 .30
35 Jonny Gomes .12 .30
36 Tim Corcoran .12 .30
37 B.J. Upton .12 .30
38 Rocco Baldelli .12 .30
39 Jae Seo .12 .30
40 Jorge Cantu .12 .30
41 Ty Wigginton .12 .30
42 Chris Carpenter .12 .30
43 Albert Pujols .60 1.50
44 Scott Rolen .20 .50
45 Jim Edmonds .20 .50
46 Jason Isringhausen .12 .30
47 Yadier Molina .12 .30
48 Adam Wainwright .12 .30
49 Mark Mulder .12 .30
50 Jason Marquis .12 .30
51 Juan Encarnacion .12 .30
52 Aaron Miles .12 .30
53 Ichiro Suzuki .50 1.25
54 Felix Hernandez .20 .50
55 Kenji Johjima .30 .75
56 Richie Sexson .12 .30
57 Yuniesky Betancourt .12 .30
58 J.J. Putz .12 .30
59 Jarrod Washburn .12 .30
60 Ben Broussard .12 .30
61 Adrian Beltre .12 .30
62 Raul Ibanez .12 .30
63 Jose Lopez .12 .30
64 Matt Cain .20 .50
65 Noah Lowry .12 .30
66 Jason Schmidt .12 .30
67 Pedro Feliz .12 .30
68 Matt Morris .12 .30
69 Ray Durham .12 .30
70 Steve Finley .12 .30
71 Randy Winn .12 .30
72 Moises Alou .12 .30
73 Eliezer Alfonzo .12 .30
74 Armando Benitez .12 .30
75 Omar Vizquel .20 .50
76 Chris R. Young .12 .30
77 Adrian Gonzalez .12 .30
78 Khalil Greene .20 .50
79 Mike Piazza .30 .75
80 Josh Barfield .12 .30
81 Brian Giles .12 .30
82 Jake Peavy .12 .30
83 Trevor Hoffman .12 .30
84 Mike Cameron .12 .30
85 Dave Roberts .12 .30
86 David Wells .12 .30
87 Zach Duke .12 .30
88 Ian Snell .12 .30
89 Jason Bay .12 .30
90 Freddy Sanchez .12 .30
91 Jack Wilson .12 .30
92 Tom Gorzelanny .12 .30
93 Chris Duffy .12 .30
94 Jose Castillo .12 .30
95 Matt Capps .12 .30
96 Mike Gonzalez .12 .30
97 Chase Utley .30 .75
98 Jimmy Rollins .12 .30
99 Aaron Rowand .12 .30
100 Ryan Howard .50 1.25
101 Cole Hamels .30 .75
102 Pat Burrell .12 .30
103 Shane Victorino .12 .30
104 Jamie Moyer .12 .30
105 Mike Lieberthal .12 .30
106 Tom Gordon .12 .30
107 Brett Myers .12 .30
108 Nick Swisher .12 .30
109 Barry Zito .12 .30
110 Jason Kendall .12 .30
111 Milton Bradley .12 .30
112 Bobby Crosby .12 .30
113 Huston Street .12 .30
114 Eric Chavez .12 .30
115 Frank Thomas .30 .75
116 Dan Haren .12 .30
117 Jay Payton .12 .30
118 Randy Johnson .30 .75
119 Mike Mussina .20 .50
120 Bobby Abreu .12 .30
121 Jason Giambi .12 .30
122 Derek Jeter .75 2.00
123 Alex Rodriguez .50 1.25
124 Jorge Posada .20 .50
125 Robinson Cano .20 .50
126 Mariano Rivera .30 .75
127 Chien-Ming Wang .50 1.25
128 Hideki Matsui .30 .75
129 Gary Sheffield .12 .30
130 Lastings Milledge .20 .50
131 Tom Glavine .20 .50
132 Billy Wagner .12 .30
133 Pedro Martinez .20 .50
134 Paul LoDuca .12 .30
135 Carlos Delgado .12 .30
136 Carlos Beltran .12 .30
137 David Wright .50 1.25
138 Jose Reyes .12 .30
139 Julio Franco .12 .30
140 Michael Cuddyer .12 .30
141 Justin Morneau .12 .30
142 Johan Santana .20 .50
143 Francisco Liriano .30 .75
144 Joe Mauer .20 .50
145 Torii Hunter .12 .30
146 Luis Castillo .12 .30
147 Joe Nathan .12 .30
148 Carlos Silva .12 .30
149 Boof Bonser .12 .30
150 Ben Sheets .12 .30
151 Prince Fielder .30 .75
152 Bill Hall .12 .30
153 Rickie Weeks .12 .30
154 Geoff Jenkins .12 .30
155 Kevin Mench .12 .30
156 Francisco Cordero .12 .30
157 Chris Capuano .12 .30
158 Brady Clark .12 .30
159 Tony Gwynn Jr. .12 .30
160 Chad Billingsley .12 .30
161 Russell Martin .12 .30
162 Wilson Betemit .12 .30
163 Nomar Garciaparra .30 .75
164 Kenny Lofton .12 .30
165 Rafael Furcal .12 .30
166 Julio Lugo .12 .30
167 Brad Penny .12 .30
168 Jeff Kent .12 .30
169 Greg Maddux .50 1.25
170 Derek Lowe .12 .30
171 Andre Ethier .20 .50
172 Chone Figgins .12 .30
173 Francisco Rodriguez .12 .30
174 Garret Anderson .12 .30
175 Orlando Cabrera .12 .30
176 Adam Kennedy .12 .30
177 John Lackey .12 .30
178 Vladimir Guerrero .30 .75
179 Bartolo Colon .12 .30
180 Jered Weaver .20 .50
181 Juan Rivera .12 .30
182 Howie Kendrick .12 .30
183 Ervin Santana .12 .30
184 Mark Redman .12 .30
185 David DeJesus .12 .30
186 Joey Gathright .12 .30
187 Mike Sweeney .12 .30
188 Mark Teahen .12 .30
189 Angel Berroa .12 .30
190 Ambiorix Burgos .12 .30
191 Luke Hudson .12 .30
192 Mark Grudzielanek .12 .30
193 Roger Clemens .50 1.25
194 Willy Taveras .12 .30
195 Craig Biggio .20 .50
196 Andy Pettitte .20 .50
197 Roy Oswalt .12 .30
198 Lance Berkman .12 .30
199 Morgan Ensberg .12 .30
200 Brad Lidge .12 .30
201 Chris Burke .12 .30
202 Miguel Cabrera .20 .50
203 Dontrelle Willis .12 .30
204 Josh Johnson .12 .30
205 Ricky Nolasco .12 .30
206 Dan Uggla .20 .50
207 Jeremy Hermida .12 .30
208 Scott Olsen .12 .30
209 Josh Willingham .12 .30
210 Joe Borowski .12 .30
211 Hanley Ramirez .20 .50
212 Mike Jacobs .12 .30
213 Kenny Rogers .12 .30
214 Justin Verlander .30 .75
215 Ivan Rodriguez .20 .50
216 Magglio Ordonez .12 .30
217 Todd Jones .12 .30
218 Joel Zumaya .20 .50
219 Jeremy Bonderman .12 .30
220 Nate Robertson .12 .30
221 Brandon Inge .12 .30
222 Craig Monroe .12 .30
223 Carlos Guillen .12 .30
224 Jeff Francis .12 .30
225 Brian Fuentes .12 .30
226 Todd Helton .20 .50
227 Matt Holliday .30 .75
228 Garrett Atkins .12 .30
229 Clint Barmes .12 .30
230 Jason Jennings .12 .30
231 Aaron Cook .12 .30
232 Brad Hawpe .12 .30
233 Cory Sullivan .12 .30
234 Aaron Boone .12 .30
235 C.C. Sabathia .12 .30
236 Grady Sizemore .20 .50
237 Travis Hafner .12 .30
238 Jhonny Peralta .12 .30
239 Jake Westbrook .12 .30
240 Jeremy Sowers .12 .30
241 Andy Marte .12 .30
242 Victor Martinez .12 .30
243 Jason Michaels .12 .30
244 Cliff Lee .12 .30
245 Bronson Arroyo .12 .30
246 Aaron Harang .12 .30
247 Ken Griffey Jr. .50 1.25
248 Adam Dunn .12 .30
249 Rich Aurilia .12 .30
250 Eric Milton .12 .30
251 David Ross .12 .30
252 Brandon Phillips .12 .30
253 Ryan Freel .12 .30
254 Eddie Guardado .12 .30
255 Jose Contreras .12 .30
256 Freddy Garcia .12 .30
257 Jon Garland .12 .30
258 Mark Buehrle .12 .30
259 Bobby Jenks .12 .30
260 Paul Konerko .12 .30
261 Jermaine Dye .12 .30
262 Joe Crede .12 .30
263 Jim Thome .20 .50
264 Javier Vazquez .12 .30
265 A.J. Pierzynski .12 .30
266 Tadahito Iguchi .12 .30
267 Carlos Zambrano .12 .30
268 Derrek Lee .12 .30
269 Aramis Ramirez .12 .30
270 Ryan Theriot .12 .30
271 Juan Pierre .12 .30
272 Rich Hill .12 .30
273 Ryan Dempster .12 .30
274 Jacque Jones .12 .30
275 Mark Prior .20 .50
276 Kerry Wood .12 .30
277 Josh Beckett .20 .50
278 David Ortiz .30 .75
279 Kevin Youkilis .12 .30
280 Jason Varitek .30 .75
281 Manny Ramirez .20 .50
282 Curt Schilling .20 .50
283 Jon Lester .12 .30
284 Jonathan Papelbon .30 .75
285 Alex Gonzalez .12 .30
286 Mike Lowell .12 .30
287 Kyle Snyder .12 .30
288 Miguel Tejada .12 .30
289 Erik Bedard .12 .30
290 Ramon Hernandez .12 .30
291 Melvin Mora .12 .30
292 Nick Markakis .20 .50
293 Brian Roberts .12 .30
294 Corey Patterson .12 .30
295 Kris Benson .12 .30
296 Jay Gibbons .12 .30
297 Rodrigo Lopez .12 .30
298 Chris Ray .12 .30
299 Andruw Jones .20 .50
300 Brian McCann .12 .30
301 Jeff Francoeur .30 .75
302 Chuck James .12 .30
303 John Smoltz .20 .50
304 Bob Wickman .12 .30
305 Edgar Renteria .12 .30
306 Adam LaRoche .12 .30
307 Marcus Giles .12 .30
308 Tim Hudson .12 .30
309 Chipper Jones .30 .75
310 Miguel Batista .12 .30
311 Claudio Vargas .12 .30
312 Brandon Webb .12 .30
313 Luis Gonzalez .12 .30
314 Livan Hernandez .12 .30
315 Stephen Drew .20 .50
316 Johnny Estrada .12 .30
317 Orlando Hudson .12 .30
318 Conor Jackson .12 .30
319 Chad Tracy .12 .30
320 Carlos Quentin .12 .30
321 Alvin Colina RC .60 1.50
322 Miguel Montero (RC) .25 .60
323 Jeff Fiorentino (RC) .25 .60
324 Jeff Baker (RC) .25 .60
325 Brian Burres (RC) .25 .60
326 David Murphy (RC) .25 .60
327 Francisco Cruceta (RC) .25 .60
328 Beltran Perez (RC) .25 .60
329 Scott Moore (RC) .25 .60
330 Sean Henn (RC) .25 .60
331 Ryan Sweeney (RC) .25 .60
332 Josh Fields (RC) .25 .60
333 Jerry Owens (RC) .25 .60
334 Vinny Rottino (RC) .25 .60
335 Kevin Kouzmanoff (RC) .25 .60
336 Alexi Casilla RC .40 1.00
337 Justin Hampson (RC) .25 .60
338 Troy Tulowitzki (RC) .60 1.50
339 Jose Garcia RC .25 .60
340 Andrew Miller RC 1.50 4.00
341 Glen Perkins (RC) .25 .60
342 Ubaldo Jimenez (RC) .25 .60
343 Doug Slaten RC .25 .60
344 Angel Sanchez RC .25 .60
345 Mitch Maier RC .25 .60
346 Ryan Braun RC .25 .60
347 Joselo Diaz (RC) .25 .60
348 Delwyn Young (RC) .25 .60
349 Kevin Hooper (RC) .25 .60
350 Dennis Sarfate (RC) .25 .60
351 Andy Cannizaro RC .25 .60
352 Devern Hansack RC .25 .60
353 Michael Bourn (RC) .25 .60
354 Carlos Maldonado (RC) .25 .60
355 Shane Youman RC .25 .60
356 Philip Humber (RC) .40 1.00
357 Hector Gimenez (RC) .25 .60
358 Fred Lewis (RC) .25 .60
359 Ryan Feierabend (RC) .25 .60
360 Juan Morillo (RC) .25 .60
361 Travis Chick (RC) .25 .60
362 Oswaldo Navarro RC .25 .60
363 Cesar Jimenez RC .25 .60
364 Brian Stokes (RC) .25 .60
365 Delmon Young (RC) .60 1.50
366 Juan Salas (RC) .25 .60
367 Shawn Riggans (RC) .25 .60
368 Adam Lind (RC) .25 .60
369 Joaquin Arias (RC) .25 .60
370 Eric Stults RC .25 .60
371 Brandon Webb CL .12 .30
372 John Smoltz CL .20 .50
373 Miguel Tejada CL .12 .30
374 David Ortiz CL .30 .75
375 Carlos Zambrano CL .12 .30
376 Jermaine Dye CL .12 .30
377 Ken Griffey Jr. CL .50 1.25
378 Victor Martinez CL .12 .30
379 Todd Helton CL .20 .50
380 Ivan Rodriguez CL .20 .50
381 Miguel Cabrera CL .20 .50
382 Lance Berkman CL .12 .30
383 Mike Sweeney CL .12 .30
384 Vladimir Guerrero CL .30 .75
385 Derek Lowe CL .12 .30
386 Bill Hall CL .12 .30
387 Johan Santana CL .20 .50
388 Carlos Beltran CL .12 .30
389 Derek Jeter CL .75 2.00
390 Nick Swisher CL .12 .30
391 Ryan Howard CL .50 1.25
392 Jason Bay CL .12 .30
393 Trevor Hoffman CL .12 .30
394 Omar Vizquel CL .20 .50
395 Ichiro Suzuki CL .50 1.25
396 Albert Pujols CL .60 1.50
397 Carl Crawford CL .12 .30
398 Mark Teixeira CL .20 .50
399 Roy Halladay CL .12 .30
400 Ryan Zimmerman CL .30 .75
401 Mark Reynolds RC 1.00 2.50
402 Micah Owings (RC) .25 .60
403 Jarrod Saltalamacchia (RC) .40 1.00
404 Daisuke Matsuzaka RC 2.50 6.00
405 Hideki Okajima RC 1.25 3.00
406 Felix Pie (RC) .25 .60
407 Mike Fontenot (RC) .25 .60
408 John Danks RC .25 .60
409 Josh Hamilton (RC) .60 1.50
410 Homey Bailey (RC) .40 1.00
411 Alejandro De Aza RC .40 1.00
412 Matt Lindstrom (RC) .25 .60
413 Hunter Pence (RC) 1.25 3.00
414 Alex Gordon RC 1.25 3.00
415 Billy Butler (RC) .40 1.00
416 Brandon Wood (RC) .25 .60
417 Andy LaRoche (RC) .25 .60
418 Ryan Bruan (RC) 1.50 4.00
419 Joe Smith RC .25 .60
420 Carlos Gomez RC .40 1.00
421 Tyler Clippard (RC) .40 1.00
422 Matt DeSalvo (RC) .25 .60
423 Phil Hughes (RC) 1.25 3.00
424 Kei Igawa RC .60 1.50
425 Chase Wright RC .60 1.50
426 Travis Buck (RC) .25 .60
427 Zack Segovia (RC) .25 .60
428 Tim Lincecum RC 2.00 5.00
429 Elijah Dukes RC .40 1.00
430 Akinori Iwamura RC .60 1.50

2007 Fleer Mini Die Cuts

*MINI: 1.25X TO 3X BASIC
*MINI RC: .6X TO 1.5X BASIC RC
STATED ODDS 1:2 HOBBY, 1:2 RETAIL

2007 Fleer Mini Die Cuts Gold

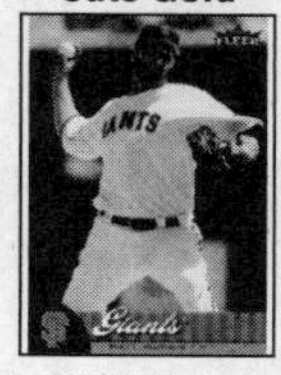

STATED ODDS 1:576 HOBBY, 1:576 RETAIL
NO PRICING DUE TO SCARCITY

2007 Fleer Autographics

STATED ODDS 1:720
NO PRICING ON MOST DUE TO SCARCITY
BH Bill Hall 20.00 50.00
BK Bobby Keppel
BU Alfonso Burke
CA Dustin Pedroia
CB Chris Booker 6.00 15.00
CI Cesar Izturis
CJ Conor Jackson
CK Casey Kotchman 6.00 15.00
DJ Dan Johnson 6.00 15.00
EJ Edwin Jackson
FG Franklyn German
FL Felipe Lopez SP
GC Gustavo Chacin
GO Jonny Gomes
HR Hanley Ramirez SP
JC Joe Crede SP
JD Joey Devine
JF Jeff Francis
JG Jon Garland SP
JJ Jorge Julio 6.00 15.00
JP Joel Peralta SP
KG Ken Griffey Jr. SP
KH Koyie Hill 6.00 15.00
LA Jason Lane
NS Nick Swisher 6.00 15.00
SF Scott Feldman

2007 Fleer Crowning Achievement

COMPLETE SET (20) 6.00 15.00
STATED ODDS 1:5
OVERALL PRINTING PLATE ODDS 1:720
PLATE PRINT RUN 1 SET PER COLOR
BLACK-CYAN-MAGENTA-YELLOW ISSUED
NO PLATE PRICING DUE TO SCARCITY
AP Albert Pujols 1.25 3.00
BZ Barry Zito .40 1.00
CD Carlos Delgado .40 1.00
CS Curt Schilling .60 1.50
DJ Derek Jeter 1.50 4.00
DO David Ortiz .60 1.50
FT Frank Thomas .60 1.50
GM Greg Maddux 1.00 2.50
IS Ichiro Suzuki 1.00 2.50
JS Johan Santana .60 1.50
JT Jim Thome .60 1.50
KG Ken Griffey Jr. 1.00 2.50
MC Miguel Cabrera .60 1.50
MP Mike Piazza .60 1.50
MR Manny Ramirez .60 1.50
PM Pedro Martinez .60 1.50
RC Roger Clemens 1.25 3.00
RH Ryan Howard 1.00 2.50
TG Tom Glavine .60 1.50
TH Trevor Hoffman .40 1.00

2007 Fleer Fresh Ink

STATED ODDS 1:720
NO PRICING ON MOST DUE TO SCARCITY
AC Aaron Cook
BB Brandon Backe SP
BW Brian Wilson
CB Clint Barmes SP
CC Craig Counsell 6.00 15.00
CR Coco Crisp SP
DB Denny Bautista SP
FG Franklyn German
GQ Guillermo Quiroz 6.00 15.00
GR Ken Griffey Jr. SP
JB Joe Blanton 6.00 15.00
JV John Van Benschoten
KG Khalil Greene 10.00 25.00
LN Leo Nunez 6.00 15.00
MM Matt Murton 15.00 40.00
MR Mike Rouse
RC Ryan Church
RE Chris Resop
RG Ryan Garko
RM Russell Martin
SC Sean Casey SP
SD Scott Dunn 6.00 15.00
SR Saul Rivera 6.00 15.00
YB Yuniesky Betancourt

2007 Fleer Genuine Coverage

STATED ODDS 1:720
MANY NOT PRICED DUE TO SCARCITY
AB Aaron Boone
AP Albert Pujols 8.00 20.00
AR Aramis Ramirez 4.00 10.00
AS Alfonso Soriano
BE Adrian Beltre 4.00 10.00
BR Brian Roberts 4.00 10.00
BS Ben Sheets 4.00 10.00
CB Carlos Beltran 6.00 15.00
CF Chone Figgins
CS C.C. Sabathia 4.00 10.00
DJ Derek Jeter 10.00 25.00
DW Dontrelle Willis 4.00 10.00
ES Johnny Estrada
FR Francisco Rodriguez
GJ Geoff Jenkins 4.00 10.00
HA Rich Harden 4.00 10.00
IR Ivan Rodriguez
IS Ian Snell 4.00 10.00
JB Josh Beckett
JE Jim Edmonds
JG Jason Giambi
JJ Josh Johnson
JM Justin Morneau 5.00 12.00
JN Joe Nathan
JP Jake Peavy 4.00 10.00
JS Johan Santana
JT Jim Thome
KG Ken Griffey Jr. 8.00 20.00
LB Lance Berkman
MR Manny Ramirez 6.00 15.00
PK Paul Konerko 4.00 10.00
PL Paul LoDuca
RB Rocco Baldelli
RC Robinson Cano
RF Rafael Furcal
RS Richie Sexson 4.00 10.00
SM John Smoltz
TH Torii Hunter 4.00 10.00
VG Vladimir Guerrero
VW Vernon Wells

2007 Fleer In the Zone

COMPLETE SET (10) 5.00 12.00
STATED ODDS 1:10 HOBBY, 1:10 RETAIL
OVERALL PRINTING PLATE ODDS 1:720
PLATE PRINT RUN 1 SET PER COLOR
BLACK-CYAN-MAGENTA-YELLOW ISSUED
NO PLATE PRICING DUE TO SCARCITY
AJ Andruw Jones .60 1.50
AP Albert Pujols 1.25 3.00
AR Alex Rodriguez 1.00 2.50
DO David Ortiz .60 1.50
DW David Wright 1.00 2.50
KG Ken Griffey Jr. 1.00 2.50
MC Miguel Cabrera .60 1.50
MT Mark Teixeira .60 1.50
RH Ryan Howard 1.00 2.50
VG Vladimir Guerrero .60 1.50

2007 Fleer Perfect 10

COMPLETE SET (20) 6.00 15.00
STATED ODDS 1:5
OVERALL PRINTING PLATE ODDS 1:720
PLATE PRINT RUN 1 SET PER COLOR
BLACK-CYAN-MAGENTA-YELLOW ISSUED
NO PLATE PRICING DUE TO SCARCITY
AP Albert Pujols 1.25 3.00
AS Alfonso Soriano .40 1.00
BH Bill Hall .40 1.00
CB Carlos Beltran .40 1.00

CC Carl Crawford .40 1.00
CJ Chipper Jones .60 1.50
CU Chase Utley .60 1.50
DJ Derek Jeter 1.50 4.00
DO David Ortiz .60 1.50
IR Ivan Rodriguez .60 1.50
JB Jason Bay .40 1.00
JD Jermaine Dye .40 1.00
JS Johan Santana .60 1.50
MC Miguel Cabrera .60 1.50
MM Mike Mussina .60 1.50
MY Michael Young .40 1.00
RC Roger Clemens 1.25 3.00
RH Roy Halladay .40 1.00
RH Ryan Howard 1.00 2.50
VG Vladimir Guerrero .60 1.50

2007 Fleer Rookie Sensations

COMPLETE SET (25) 6.00 15.00
STATED ODDS APPX 1:1 HOBBY, 1:1 RETAIL
OVERALL PRINTING PLATE ODDS 1:720
PLATE PRINT RUN 1 SET PER COLOR
BLACK-CYAN-MAGENTA-YELLOW ISSUED
NO PLATE PRICING DUE TO SCARCITY
BB Boof Bonser .40 1.00
CB Chad Billingsley .60 1.50
CH Cole Hamels .60 1.50
CJ Conor Jackson .60 1.50
DU Dan Uggla .60 1.50
FL Francisco Liriano 1.25 3.00
HR Hanley Ramirez .60 1.50
IK Ian Kinsler .40 1.00
JB Josh Barfield .40 1.00
JH Jeremy Hermida .60 1.50
JJ Josh Johnson .40 1.00
JL Jon Lester .60 1.50
JP Jonathan Papelbon .60 1.50
JS Jeremy Sowers .40 1.00
JV Justin Verlander .60 1.50
JW Jered Weaver .60 1.50
KJ Kenji Johjima .60 1.50
LO James Loney .60 1.50
MK Matt Kemp .60 1.50
NM Nick Markakis .60 1.50
PF Prince Fielder .60 1.50
RG Matt Garza .40 1.00
RN Ricky Nolasco .40 1.00
RZ Ryan Zimmerman .75 2.00
SO Scott Olsen .40 1.00

2007 Fleer Soaring Stars

STATED ODDS 1:2 FAT PACKS
OVERALL PRINTING PLATE ODDS 1:720
PLATE PRINT RUN 1 SET PER COLOR
BLACK-CYAN-MAGENTA-YELLOW ISSUED
NO PLATE PRICING DUE TO SCARCITY
AD Adam Dunn .40 1.00
AJ Andruw Jones .60 1.50
AL Alex Rodriguez 1.00 2.50
AP Albert Pujols 1.25 3.00
AR Alex Rios .40 1.00
AS Alfonso Soriano .40 1.00
BW Brandon Webb .40 1.00
BZ Barry Zito .40 1.00
CB Carlos Beltran .40 1.00
CJ Chipper Jones .60 1.50
CU Chase Utley .60 1.50
DA Johnny Damon .60 1.50
DJ Derek Jeter 1.50 4.00
DL Derrek Lee .40 1.00
DO David Ortiz .60 1.50
DW David Wright 1.00 2.50
HA Roy Halladay .40 1.00
IR Ivan Rodriguez .60 1.50
IS Ichiro Suzuki 1.00 2.50
JB Jason Bay .40 1.00
JD Jermaine Dye .40 1.00
JG Jon Garland .40 1.00
JM Joe Mauer .60 1.50
JS Johan Santana .60 1.50
JV Justin Verlander .60 1.50
KG Ken Griffey Jr. 1.00 2.50
LB Lance Berkman .40 1.00
MC Miguel Cabrera .60 1.50
MP Mike Piazza .60 1.50
MR Manny Ramirez .60 1.50
MT Mark Teixeira .60 1.50
NG Nomar Garciaparra .60 1.50
PF Prince Fielder .60 1.50
PM Pedro Martinez .60 1.50
RH Ryan Howard 1.00 2.50
RI Mariano Rivera .60 1.50
RO Roy Oswalt .40 1.00
TE Miguel Tejada .40 1.00
TG Tom Glavine .60 1.50
TH Travis Hafner .40 1.00
VG Vladimir Guerrero .60 1.50
WI Dontrelle Willis .40 1.00

2007 Fleer Year in Review

COMPLETE SET (20) 6.00 15.00
STATED ODDS 1:5
OVERALL PRINTING PLATE ODDS 1:720
PLATE PRINT RUN 1 SET PER COLOR
BLACK-CYAN-MAGENTA-YELLOW ISSUED
NO PLATE PRICING DUE TO SCARCITY
AP Albert Pujols 1.25 3.00
AR Alex Rodriguez 1.00 2.50
AS Alfonso Soriano .40 1.00
BA Bobby Abreu .40 1.00
CU Chase Utley .60 1.50

DJ Derek Jeter 1.50 4.00
DO David Ortiz .60 1.50
FL Francisco Liriano 1.25 3.00
FS Freddy Sanchez .40 1.00
HO Ryan Howard 1.00 2.50
JD Jermaine Dye .40 1.00
JM Joe Mauer .60 1.50
JR José Reyes .40 1.00
JV Justin Verlander .60 1.50
JW Jered Weaver .60 1.50
KG Ken Griffey Jr. 1.00 2.50
MD Mark DeRosa .40 1.00
MO Justin Morneau .40 1.00
RH Roy Halladay .40 1.00
TH Travis Hafner .40 1.00

2001 Fleer Genuine

The 2001 Fleer Genuine product was released in May, 2001 and featured a 130-card base set that was broken into tiers as follows: Base Veterans (1-100), and Rookies (100-130) featuring game-used materials and are serial numbered to 1500. Each pack contained five cards and carried a suggested retail price of $4.99. 500 exchange cards were seeded into packs for a Derek Jeter signed uncut sheet.

COMP.SET w/o SP's (90) 10.00 25.00
COMMON CARD (1-100) .20 .50
COMMON (101-130) 2.00 5.00
JETER AU SHEET AVAIL.VIA MAIL EXCH.
JETER SHEET EXCH. RANDOM IN PACKS
1 Derek Jeter 1.25 3.00
2 Nomar Garciaparra .75 2.00
3 Alex Rodriguez .75 2.00
4 Frank Thomas .50 1.25
5 Travis Fryman .20 .50
6 Gary Sheffield .20 .50
7 Jason Giambi .20 .50
8 Trevor Hoffman .20 .50
9 Todd Helton .30 .75
10 Ivan Rodriguez .30 .75
11 Roberto Alomar .30 .75
12 Barry Zito .30 .75
13 Kevin Brown .20 .50
14 Shawn Green .20 .50
15 Kenny Lofton .20 .50
16 Jeff Weaver .20 .50
17 Geoff Jenkins .20 .50
18 Carlos Delgado .20 .50
19 Mark Grace .30 .75
20 Ken Griffey Jr. .75 2.00
21 David Justice .20 .50
22 Brian Giles .20 .50
23 Scott Williamson .20 .50
24 Richie Sexson .20 .50
25 John Olerud .20 .50
26 Sammy Sosa .50 1.25
27 Bobby Higginson .20 .50
28 Matt Lawton .20 .50
29 Vinny Castilla .20 .50
30 Alex Gonzalez .20 .50
31 Manny Ramirez Sox .30 .75
32 Brad Radke .20 .50
33 Cal Ripken 1.50 4.00
34 Richard Hidalgo .20 .50
35 Al Leiter .20 .50
36 Freddy Garcia .20 .50
37 Juan Encarnacion .20 .50
38 Corey Koskie .20 .50
39 Greg Vaughn .20 .50
40 Rafael Palmeiro .30 .75
41 Vladimir Guerrero .50 1.25
42 Troy Glaus .20 .50
43 Mike Hampton .20 .50
44 Jose Vidro .20 .50
45 Ryan Rupe .20 .50
46 Troy O'Leary .20 .50
47 Ben Petrick .20 .50
48 Mike Lieberthal .20 .50
49 Mike Sweeney .20 .50
50 Scott Rolen .30 .75
51 Albert Belle .20 .50
52 Mark Quinn .20 .50
53 Mike Piazza .75 2.00
54 Mark McGwire 1.25 3.00
55 Brady Anderson .20 .50
56 Carlos Beltran .20 .50
57 Michael Barrett .20 .50
58 Jason Kendall .20 .50
59 Jim Edmonds .20 .50
60 Matt Williams .20 .50
61 Pokey Reese .20 .50
62 Bernie Williams .30 .75
63 Barry Bonds 1.25 3.00
64 David Wells .20 .50
65 Chipper Jones .50 1.25
66 Jim Parque .20 .50
67 Derrek Lee .30 .75
68 Darin Erstad .20 .50
69 Edgar Martinez .30 .75
70 Kerry Wood .20 .50
71 Omar Vizquel .30 .75
72 Jeromy Burnitz .20 .50
73 Warren Morris .20 .50
74 Rick Ankiel .20 .50
75 Andruw Jones .30 .75
76 Paul Konerko .20 .50
77 Mike Lowell .20 .50
78 Roger Clemens 1.00 2.50
79 Tim Hudson .20 .50
80 Rafael Furcal .20 .50
81 Craig Biggio .30 .75
82 Edgardo Alfonzo .20 .50
83 Pat Burrell .20 .50
84 Adrian Beltre .20 .50
85 Tony Gwynn .60 1.50
86 J.T. Snow .20 .50
87 Randy Johnson .50 1.25
88 Sean Casey .20 .50
89 Preston Wilson .20 .50
90 Mike Mussina .30 .75
91 Eric Chavez .20 .50
92 Tim Salmon .30 .75
93 Pedro Martinez .30 .75
94 Darryl Kile .20 .50
95 Greg Maddux .75 2.00
96 Magglio Ordonez .20 .50
97 Jeff Bagwell .30 .75
98 Timo Perez .20 .50
99 Jeff Kent .20 .50
100 Eric Owens .20 .50
101 Ichiro Suzuki GU RC 15.00 40.00
102 E. Guzman GU RC 2.00 5.00
103 T. Shinjo GU RC 2.50 6.00
104 Travis Hafner GU RC 6.00 15.00
105 Larry Barnes GU 2.00 5.00
106 J. Randolph GU RC 2.00 5.00
107 Paul Phillips GU RC 2.00 5.00
108 Erick Almonte GU RC 2.00 5.00
109 Nick Punto GU RC 2.00 5.00
110 Jack Wilson GU RC 2.50 6.00
111 Jeremy Owens GU RC 2.00 5.00
112 Esix Snead GU RC 2.00 5.00
113 Jay Gibbons GU RC 2.50 6.00
114 A. Hernandez GU RC 2.00 5.00
115 Matt White GU RC 2.00 5.00
116 Ryan Freel GU RC 2.00 5.00
117 Martin Vargas GU RC 2.00 5.00
118 Winston Abreu GU RC 2.00 5.00
119 Junior Spivey GU RC 2.50 6.00
120 Paxton Crawford GU 2.00 5.00
121 Randy Keisler GU 2.00 5.00
122 Juan Diaz GU RC 2.00 5.00
123 Aaron Rowand GU 2.00 5.00
124 Toby Hall GU 2.00 5.00
125 Brian Cole GU 2.00 5.00
126 Aubrey Huff GU 2.00 5.00
127 Corey Patterson GU 2.00 5.00
128 Sun Woo Kim GU 2.00 5.00
129 Jace Brewer GU 2.00 5.00
130 Cesar Izturis GU 2.00 5.00
NNO Derek Jeter 60.00 120.00
AU Sheet/500 EXCH

2002 Fleer Genuine

This 140 card was released in May, 2002. These cards were issued in five card packs with an SRP of $4.99 per pack and they were issued 24 packs to a box and six boxes per case. The first 100 card feature veteran players and the final forty player feature prospect cards. Cards number 101 through 140 have a stated print run of 2002 serial numbered sets.

COMP.SET w/o SP's (100) 10.00 25.00
COMMON CARD (1-100) .20 .50
COMMON CARD (101-140) 2.00 5.00
1 Alex Rodriguez .75 2.00
2 Manny Ramirez .30 .75
3 Jim Thome .30 .75
4 Eric Milton .20 .50
5 Todd Helton .30 .75
6 Mike Mussina .30 .75
7 Ichiro Suzuki 1.00 2.50
8 Randy Johnson .50 1.25
9 Mark Mulder .20 .50
10 Johnny Damon Sox .30 .75
11 Sean Casey .20 .50
12 Albert Pujols 1.00 2.50
13 Mark Grace .30 .75
14 Moises Alou .20 .50
15 Raul Mondesi .20 .50
16 Cliff Floyd .20 .50
17 Vladimir Guerrero .50 1.25
18 Pat Burrell .20 .50
19 Ryan Klesko .20 .50
20 Mike Hampton .20 .50
21 Shawn Green .20 .50
22 Rich Aurilia .20 .50
23 Matt Morris .20 .50
24 Curt Schilling .20 .50
25 Kevin Brown .20 .50
26 Adrian Beltre .20 .50
27 Joe Mays .20 .50
28 Luis Gonzalez .20 .50
29 Barry Larkin .30 .75
30 A.J. Burnett .20 .50
31 Eric Munson .20 .50
32 Juan Gonzalez .20 .50
33 Lance Berkman .20 .50
34 Fred McGriff .30 .75
35 Paul Konerko .20 .50
36 Pedro Martinez .30 .75
37 Adam Dunn .20 .50
38 Jeromy Burnitz .20 .50
39 Mike Sweeney .20 .50
40 Bret Boone .20 .50
41 Ken Griffey Jr. .75 2.00
42 Eric Chavez .20 .50
43 Mark Quinn .20 .50
44 Roberto Alomar .30 .75
45 Bobby Abreu .20 .50
46 Bartolo Colon .20 .50
47 Jimmy Rollins .20 .50
48 Chipper Jones .50 1.25
49 Ben Sheets .20 .50
50 Freddy Garcia .20 .50
51 Sammy Sosa .50 1.25
52 Rafael Palmeiro .30 .75
53 Preston Wilson .20 .50
54 Troy Glaus .20 .50
55 Josh Beckett .20 .50
56 C.C. Sabathia .20 .50
57 Magglio Ordonez .20 .50
58 Brian Giles .20 .50
59 Darin Erstad .20 .50
60 Gary Sheffield .20 .50
61 Paul LoDuca .20 .50
62 Derek Jeter 1.25 3.00
63 Greg Maddux .75 2.00
64 Kerry Wood .20 .50
65 Toby Hall .20 .50
66 Barry Bonds 1.25 3.00
67 Jeff Bagwell .30 .75
68 Jason Kendall .20 .50
69 Richard Hidalgo .20 .50
70 J.D. Drew .20 .50
71 Tom Glavine .30 .75
72 Javier Vazquez .20 .50
73 Doug Mientkiewicz .20 .50
74 Jason Giambi .20 .50
75 Carlos Delgado .20 .50
76 Aramis Ramirez .20 .50
77 Torii Hunter .20 .50
78 Ivan Rodriguez .30 .75
79 Charles Johnson .20 .50
80 Jeff Kent .20 .50
81 Jacque Jones .20 .50
82 Larry Walker .20 .50
83 Cristian Guzman .20 .50
84 Jermaine Dye .20 .50
85 Roger Clemens 1.00 2.50
86 Mike Piazza .75 2.00
87 Craig Biggio .30 .75
88 Phil Nevin .20 .50
89 Jeff Cirillo .20 .50
90 Barry Zito .20 .50
91 Ryan Dempster .20 .50
92 Mark Buehrle .20 .50
93 Nomar Garciaparra .75 2.00
94 Frank Thomas .50 1.25
95 Jim Edmonds .20 .50
96 Geoff Jenkins .20 .50
97 Scott Rolen .30 .75
98 Tim Hudson .20 .50
99 Shannon Stewart .20 .50
100 Richie Sexson .20 .50
101 Orlando Hudson UP 2.00 5.00
102 Doug Devore UP RC 2.00 5.00
103 Rene Reyes UP RC 2.00 5.00
104 Steve Bechler UP RC 2.00 5.00
105 Jorge Nunez UP RC 2.00 5.00
106 Mitch Wylie UP RC 2.00 5.00
107 Jaime Cerda UP RC 2.00 5.00
108 Brandon Puffer UP RC 2.00 5.00
109 Tyler Yates UP RC 2.00 5.00
110 Bill Hall UP 2.00 5.00
111 Pete Zamora UP RC 2.00 5.00
112 Jeff Deardorff UP 2.00 5.00
113 J.J. Putz UP RC 2.00 5.00
114 Scotty Layfield UP RC 2.00 5.00
115 Brandon Backe UP RC 3.00 8.00
116 Andy Pratt UP RC 2.00 5.00
117 Mark Prior UP 3.00 8.00
118 Franklyn German UP RC 2.00 5.00
119 Todd Donovan UP RC 2.00 5.00
120 Franklin Nunez UP RC 2.00 5.00
121 Adam Walker UP RC 2.00 5.00
122 Ron Calloway UP RC 2.00 5.00
123 Tim Kalita UP RC 2.00 5.00
124 Kazuhisa Ishii UP RC 3.00 8.00
125 Mark Teixeira UP 3.00 8.00
126 Nate Field UP RC 2.00 5.00
127 Nelson Castro UP RC 2.00 5.00
128 So Taguchi UP RC 3.00 8.00
129 Marlon Byrd UP 2.00 5.00
130 Drew Henson UP 2.00 5.00
131 Kenny Kelly UP 2.00 5.00
132 John Ennis UP RC 2.00 5.00
133 Anastacio Martinez UP RC 2.00 5.00
134 Matt Guerrier UP 2.00 5.00
135 Tom Wilson UP RC 2.00 5.00
136 Ben Howard UP RC 2.00 5.00
137 Chris Baker UP RC 2.00 5.00
138 Kevin Frederick UP RC 2.00 5.00
139 Wilson Valdez UP RC 2.00 5.00
140 Austin Kearns UP 2.00 5.00

2003 Fleer Genuine

This 145-card set was distributed in two separate series. The primary Genuine product - of which contained the first 130 cards from the basic set - was released in July, 2003. This set was issued in five card packs with an $5 SRP which came 24 packs to a box and 12 boxes to a case. Cards numbered 1 through 100 feature veterans while cards numbered 101 through 130 feature a mix of rookies and prospects and those cards were issued to a stated print run of 799 serial numbered sets. Cards 131-145 were randomly seeded within packs of Fleer Rookies and Greats of which was distributed in December, 2003. These fifteen update cards continued the Genuine Upside prospect subset established with cards 101-130 from the primary "low series" set. Each update card was serial numbered to 1000 copies.

COMP.LO SET w/o SP's (100) 10.00 25.00
COMMON CARD (1-100) .20 .50
COMMON CARD (101-145) 1.50 4.00
1 Derek Jeter 1.25 3.00
2 Mo Vaughn .20 .50
3 Adam Dunn .20 .50
4 Aubrey Huff .20 .50
5 Jacque Jones .20 .50
6 Kerry Wood .20 .50
7 Barry Bonds 1.25 3.00
8 Kevin Brown .20 .50
9 Sammy Sosa .50 1.25
10 Ray Durham .20 .50
11 Carlos Beltran .20 .50
12 Tony Batista .20 .50
13 Bobby Abreu .20 .50
14 Craig Biggio .30 .75
15 Gary Sheffield .20 .50
16 Jermaine Dye .20 .50
17 Carlos Pena .20 .50
18 Tim Salmon .30 .75
19 Mike Piazza .75 2.00
20 Moises Alou .20 .50
21 Edgardo Alfonzo .20 .50
22 Mike Sweeney .20 .50
23 Jay Gibbons .20 .50
24 Kevin Millwood .20 .50
25 A.J. Burnett .20 .50
26 Austin Kearns .20 .50
27 Rafael Palmeiro .30 .75
28 Vladimir Guerrero .50 1.25
29 Paul Konerko .20 .50
30 Scott Rolen .30 .75
31 Fred McGriff .30 .75
32 Frank Thomas .50 1.25
33 John Olerud .20 .50
34 Eric Gagne .20 .50
35 Nomar Garciaparra .75 2.00
36 Ryan Klesko .20 .50
37 Lance Berkman .20 .50
38 Andruw Jones .30 .75
39 Pat Burrell .20 .50
40 Juan Encarnacion .20 .50
41 Curt Schilling .20 .50
42 Jason Giambi .20 .50
43 Barry Larkin .30 .75
44 Alex Rodriguez .75 2.00
45 Kazuhisa Ishii .20 .50
46 Pedro Martinez .30 .75
47 Sean Burroughs .20 .50
48 Roy Oswalt .20 .50
49 Chipper Jones .50 1.25
50 Barry Zito .20 .50
51 Jeff Kent .20 .50
52 Rodrigo Lopez .20 .50
53 Jim Thome .30 .75
54 Ivan Rodriguez .30 .75
55 Luis Gonzalez .20 .50
56 Alfonso Soriano .20 .50
57 Josh Beckett .20 .50
58 Junior Spivey .20 .50
59 Bernie Williams .30 .75
60 Omar Vizquel .30 .75
61 Eric Hinske .20 .50
62 Jose Vidro .20 .50
63 Bartolo Colon .20 .50
64 Jim Edmonds .20 .50
65 Ben Sheets .20 .50
66 Mark Prior .30 .75
67 Edgar Martinez .30 .75
68 Raul Ibanez .20 .50
69 Darin Erstad .20 .50
70 Roger Clemens 1.00 2.50
71 C.C. Sabathia .20 .50
72 Carlos Delgado .20 .50
73 Tom Glavine .30 .75
74 Magglio Ordonez .20 .50
75 Ichiro Suzuki 1.00 2.50
76 Johnny Damon .30 .75
77 Brian Giles .20 .50
78 Jeff Bagwell .30 .75
79 Greg Maddux .75 2.00
80 Eric Chavez .20 .50
81 Larry Walker .20 .50
82 Randy Johnson .50 1.25
83 Miguel Tejada .20 .50
84 Todd Helton .30 .75
85 Jarrod Washburn .20 .50
86 Troy Glaus .20 .50
87 Ken Griffey Jr. .75 2.00
88 Albert Pujols 1.00 2.50
89 Torii Hunter .20 .50
90 Joe Crede .20 .50
91 Matt Morris .20 .50
92 Shawn Green .20 .50
93 Manny Ramirez .30 .75
94 Jason Kendall .20 .50
95 Preston Wilson .20 .50
96 Garret Anderson .20 .50
97 Cliff Floyd .20 .50
98 Sean Casey .20 .50
99 Juan Gonzalez .20 .50
100 Richie Sexson .20 .50
101 Joe Borchard GU 1.50 4.00
102 Josh Stewart GU RC 1.50 4.00
103 Francisco Rodriguez GU 1.50 4.00
104 Jeremy Bonderman GU RC 4.00 10.00
105 Walter Young GU 1.50 4.00
106 Brandon Webb GU RC 3.00 8.00
107 Lyle Overbay GU 1.50 4.00
108 Jose Contreras GU RC 2.00 5.00
109 Victor Martinez GU 2.00 5.00
110 Hideki Matsui GU RC 4.00 10.00
111 Brian Stokes GU RC 1.50 4.00
112 Daniel Cabrera GU RC 2.00 5.00
113 Josh Willingham GU RC 2.50 6.00
114 Mark Teixeira GU 2.00 5.00
115 Pete LaForest GU RC 1.50 4.00
116 Chris Waters GU RC 1.50 4.00
117 Chien-Ming Wang GU RC 12.50 30.00
118 Ian Ferguson GU RC 1.50 4.00
119 Rocco Baldelli GU 1.50 4.00
120 Termel Sledge GU RC 1.50 4.00
121 Hank Blalock GU 1.50 4.00
122 Alejandro Machado GU RC 1.50 4.00
123 Hee Seop Choi GU 1.50 4.00
124 Guillermo Quiroz GU RC 1.50 4.00
125 Chase Utley GU 2.00 5.00
126 Nook Logan GU RC 2.00 5.00
127 Josh Hall GU RC 1.50 4.00
128 Ryan Church GU 1.50 4.00
129 Lew Ford GU RC 2.00 5.00
130 Francisco Rosario GU RC 1.50 4.00
131 Dan Haren GU RC 2.00 5.00
132 Rickie Weeks GU RC 2.50 6.00
133 Prentice Redman GU RC 1.50 4.00
134 Craig Brazell GU RC 1.50 4.00
135 Jon Leicester GU RC 1.50 4.00
136 Ryan Wagner GU RC 1.50 4.00
137 Matt Kata GU RC 1.50 4.00
138 Edwin Jackson GU RC 2.00 5.00
139 Mike Ryan GU RC 1.50 4.00
140 Delmon Young GU RC 4.00 10.00
141 Bo Hart GU RC 1.50 4.00
142 Jeff Duncan GU RC 1.50 4.00
143 Robby Hammock GU RC 1.50 4.00
144 Michael Hessman GU RC 1.50 4.00
145 Clint Barmes GU RC 1.25 3.00

2004 Fleer Genuine Insider

This 130-card set was released in June, 2004. The set was issued in five-card packs with an $5 SRP which came 18 packs to a box and 12 boxes to a case. Cards numbered 1-90 feature veterans while cards numbered 91-100 and 121-130 feature rookies and cards 101-120 feature prospects. Cards numbered 91-120 were issued at a stated rate of one in 14 hobby and one in 72 retail. Cards numbered 91-100 were issued to a stated print run of 499 serial numbered sets while cards 101-120 were issued to a stated print run of 799 serial numbered sets. Cards numbered 121-130 are "mini-cards" and those cards were issued to a stated print run of 350 serial numbered sets and those cards are "inside" those cards from 91-100.

COMP.SET w/o SP's (90) 10.00 25.00
COMMON CARD (1-90) .20 .50
COMMON CARD (91-100) 1.50 4.00
91-100 PRINT RUN 499 SERIAL #'d SETS
COMMON CARD (101-120) 1.25 3.00
101-120 PRINT RUN 799 SERIAL #'d SETS
91-120 STATED ODDS 1:14 HOB, 1:72 RET
COMMON CARD (121-130) 2.00 5.00
121-130 SEEDED WITHIN RI 91-100 CARDS
121-130 PRINT RUN 350 SERIAL #'d SETS
121-130 ARE MINI-SIZED CARDS
1 Troy Glaus .20 .50
2 Eric Chavez .20 .50
3 Lance Berkman .20 .50
4 Pedro Martinez .30 .75
5 Jim Edmonds .20 .50
6 Tom Glavine .50 1.25
7 Ken Griffey Jr. .75 2.00
8 Vernon Wells .20 .50
9 Hideki Matsui .75 2.00
10 Jeff Bagwell .30 .75
11 Rafael Palmeiro .30 .75
12 Edgar Martinez .30 .75
13 Bernie Williams .30 .75
14 Josh Beckett .20 .50
15 Javy Lopez .20 .50
16 Ichiro Suzuki 1.00 2.50
17 Scott Podsednik .20 .50
18 Sammy Sosa .50 1.25
19 Mark Teixeira .30 .75
20 Jorge Posada .30 .75
21 Miguel Cabrera .50 1.25
22 Chipper Jones .50 1.25
23 Sean Burroughs .20 .50
24 Dmitri Young .20 .50
25 Brandon Webb .20 .50
26 Bobby Abreu .20 .50
27 Hideo Nomo .50 1.25
28 Frank Thomas .50 1.25
29 Alex Rodriguez .75 2.00
30 Derek Jeter 1.00 2.50
31 Todd Helton .30 .75
32 Andruw Jones .30 .75
33 Jason Kendall .20 .50
34 Eric Gagne .20 .50
35 Omar Vizquel .30 .75
36 Vladimir Guerrero .50 1.25
37 Jim Thome .30 .75
38 Mike Sweeney .20 .50
39 Manny Ramirez .30 .75
40 Scott Rolen .30 .75
41 Jose Vidro .20 .50
42 Adam Dunn .20 .50
43 Garret Anderson .20 .50
44 Mike Lieberthal .20 .50
45 Roy Oswalt .20 .50
46 Geoff Jenkins .20 .50
47 Magglio Ordonez .20 .50
48 Hank Blalock .20 .50
49 Barry Zito .20 .50
50 Dontrelle Willis .30 .75
51 Greg Maddux .75 2.00
52 Brian Giles .20 .50
53 Shawn Green .20 .50
54 Carlos Lee .20 .50
55 Carlos Delgado .20 .50
56 Alfonso Soriano .20 .50
57 Angel Berroa .20 .50
58 Kerry Wood .20 .50
59 Rocco Baldelli .20 .50
60 Gary Sheffield .20 .50
61 Ivan Rodriguez .30 .75
62 Richie Sexson .20 .50
63 Marlon Byrd .20 .50
64 Carlos Beltran .20 .50
65 Mark Prior .30 .75
66 Aubrey Huff .20 .50
67 Jason Giambi .20 .50
68 Curt Schilling .30 .75
69 Reggie Sanders .20 .50
70 Mike Piazza .75 2.00
71 Craig Monroe .20 .50
72 Randy Johnson .50 1.25
73 Pat Burrell .20 .50
74 Craig Biggio .30 .75
75 Nomar Garciaparra .75 2.00
76 Albert Pujols 1.00 2.50
77 Jose Reyes .20 .50
78 Preston Wilson .20 .50
79 Miguel Tejada .20 .50
80 Bret Boone .20 .50
81 Shannon Stewart .20 .50
82 Jody Gerut .20 .50
83 Tim Salmon .30 .75
84 Tim Hudson .20 .50
85 Juan Pierre .20 .50

86 Jay Gibbons .20 .50
87 Jason Schmidt .20 .50
88 Torii Hunter .20 .50
89 Austin Kearns .20 .50
90 Roy Halladay .20 .50
91 John Gall RI RC 2.00 5.00
92 Kaz Matsui RI RC 2.00 5.00
93 Merkin Valdez RI RC 2.00 5.00
94 William Bergolla RI RC 1.50 4.00
95 Angel Chavez RI RC 1.50 4.00
96 Hector Gimenez RI RC 1.50 4.00
97 Aarom Baldiris RI RC 2.00 5.00
98 Justin Leone RI RC 2.00 5.00
99 Onil Joseph RI RC 1.50 4.00
100 Freddy Guzman RI RC 1.50 4.00
101 Rickie Weeks UP 1.25 3.00
102 Chad Bentz UP RC 1.25 3.00
103 Bobby Crosby UP 1.25 3.00
104 Dallas McPherson UP 1.25 3.00
105 Brandon Watson UP 1.25 3.00
106 Garrett Atkins UP 1.25 3.00
107 Graham Koonce UP 1.25 3.00
108 Chien-Ming Wang UP 4.00 10.00
109 Jonny Gomes UP 1.25 3.00
110 Edwin Jackson UP 1.25 3.00
111 Alfredo Simon UP RC 1.25 3.00
112 Delmon Young UP 2.00 5.00
113 Angel Guzman UP 1.25 3.00
114 Ryan Howard UP 4.00 10.00
115 Scott Hairston UP 1.25 3.00
116 Edwin Encarnacion UP 1.25 3.00
117 Byron Gettis UP 1.25 3.00
118 Kevin Youkilis UP 1.25 3.00
119 Grady Sizemore UP 2.00 5.00
120 Corey Hart UP 1.25 3.00
121 Greg Dobbs MRI RC 2.00 5.00
122 Jerry Gil MRI RC 2.00 5.00
123 Shawn Hill MRI RC 2.00 5.00
124 John Labandeira MRI RC 2.00 5.00
125 Jason Bartlett MRI RC 2.00 5.00
126 Ronny Cedeno MRI RC 3.00 8.00
127 Don Kelly MRI RC 2.00 5.00
128 Ivan Ochoa MRI RC 2.00 5.00
129 Mariano Gomez MRI RC 2.00 5.00
130 Ruddy Yan MRI 2.00 5.00

2001 Fleer Legacy

The 2001 Fleer Legacy product was released in mid-July, 2001 and featured a 105-card base set that was broken into tiers as follows: Base Veterans (1-90) and Prospects (91-105) that are individually serial numbered to 799. Please note that the first 300 serial-numbered cards of Albert Pujols packed out as exchange cards for a copy actually signed by Pujols. Card number 98 does not exist. Each box contained 15 packs with five cards per pack.

COMP.SET w/o SP's (90) 15.00 40.00
COMMON CARD (1-90) .40 1.00
COMMON AUTO (91-100) 4.00 10.00
COMMON CARD (101-105) 3.00 8.00
1 Pedro Martinez .60 1.50
2 Andruw Jones .60 1.50
3 Mike Hampton .40 1.00
4 Gary Sheffield .40 1.00
5 Barry Zito .60 1.50
6 J.D. Drew .40 1.00
7 Charles Johnson .40 1.00
8 David Wells .40 1.00
9 Kazuhiro Sasaki .40 1.00
10 Vladimir Guerrero 1.00 2.50
11 Pat Burrell .40 1.00
12 Ruben Mateo .40 1.00
13 Greg Maddux 1.50 4.00
14 Sean Casey .40 1.00
15 Craig Biggio .60 1.50
16 Bernie Williams .60 1.50
17 Jeff Kent .40 1.00
18 Nomar Garciaparra 1.50 4.00
19 Cal Ripken 3.00 8.00
20 Larry Walker .40 1.00
21 Adrian Beltre .40 1.00
22 Johnny Damon .60 1.50
23 Rick Ankiel .40 1.00
24 Matt Williams .40 1.00
25 Magglio Ordonez .40 1.00
26 Richard Hidalgo .40 1.00
27 Robin Ventura .40 1.00
28 Jason Kendall .40 1.00
29 Tony Batista .40 1.00
30 Chipper Jones 1.00 2.50
31 Jim Thome .60 1.50
32 Kevin Brown .40 1.00
33 Mike Mussina .60 1.50
34 Mark McGwire 2.50 6.00
35 Darin Erstad .40 1.00
36 Manny Ramirez Sox .60 1.50
37 Bobby Higginson .40 1.00
38 Richie Sexson .40 1.00
39 Jason Giambi .40 1.00
40 Alex Rodriguez 1.50 4.00
41 Mark Grace .60 1.50
42 Ken Griffey Jr. 1.50 4.00
43 Moises Alou .40 1.00
44 Edgardo Alfonzo .40 1.00
45 Phil Nevin .40 1.00
46 Rafael Palmeiro .60 1.50
47 Javy Lopez .40 1.00
48 Juan Gonzalez .40 1.00
49 Jermaine Dye .40 1.00
50 Roger Clemens 2.00 5.00
51 Barry Bonds 2.50 6.00
52 Carl Everett .40 1.00
53 Ben Sheets .60 1.50
54 Juan Encarnacion .40 1.00
55 Jeromy Burnitz .40 1.00
56 Miguel Tejada .40 1.00
57 Ben Grieve .40 1.00
58 Randy Johnson 1.00 2.50
59 Frank Thomas 1.00 2.50
60 Preston Wilson .40 1.00
61 Mike Piazza 1.50 4.00
62 Brian Giles .40 1.00
63 Carlos Delgado .40 1.00
64 Tom Glavine .60 1.50
65 Roberto Alomar .60 1.50
66 Mike Sweeney .40 1.00
67 Orlando Hernandez .40 1.00
68 Edgar Martinez .60 1.50
69 Tim Salmon .60 1.50
70 Kerry Wood .40 1.00
71 Jack Wilson RC .60 1.50
72 Matt Lawton .40 1.00
73 Scott Rolen .60 1.50
74 Ivan Rodriguez .60 1.50
75 Steve Finley .40 1.00
76 Barry Larkin .60 1.50
77 Jeff Bagwell .60 1.50
78 Derek Jeter 2.50 6.00
79 Tony Gwynn 1.25 3.00
80 Raul Mondesi .40 1.00
81 Rafael Furcal .40 1.00
82 Todd Helton .60 1.50
83 Shawn Green .40 1.00
84 Tim Hudson .40 1.00
85 Jim Edmonds .40 1.00
86 Troy Glaus .40 1.00
87 Sammy Sosa 1.00 2.50
88 Cliff Floyd .40 1.00
89 Jose Vidro .40 1.00
90 Bob Abreu .40 1.00
91 Drew Henson AU RC 6.00 15.00
92 Andy Morales AU RC 4.00 10.00
93 Wilson Betemit AU RC 10.00 25.00
94 Elpidio Guzman AU RC 4.00 10.00
95 Esix Snead AU RC 4.00 10.00
96 Winston Abreu AU RC 4.00 10.00
97 Jeremy Owens AU RC 4.00 10.00
98 Does Not Exist
99 Junior Spivey AU RC 6.00 15.00
100 J. Randolph AU RC 4.00 10.00
101 Ichiro Suzuki RC 30.00 60.00
102 Albert Pujols/499 RC 100.00 200.00
102AU Albert Pujols AU/300 200.00 300.00
103 Tsuyoshi Shinjo RC 4.00 10.00
104 Jay Gibbons RC 4.00 10.00
105 Juan Uribe RC 4.00 10.00

2004 Fleer Legacy

This 75-card set was released in November, 2004. The set was issued in eight-card hobby packs which, although they had no SRP, were part of an $240 box which included a signed baseball. However, the autographed baseball, although it had a COA from Fleer had no stamping to indicate it was from the Legacy product. The retail packs had five cards with an $3 SRP and were issued 24 packs to a box and 20 boxes to a case. Cards numbered 1-60 feature veterans while cards 61-75 feature Rookie Cards which were issued to a stated print run of 599 serial numbered sets and were issued at a state rate of one per hobby pack and one in 96 retail packs.

COMP.SET w/o SP's (60) 50.00 100.00
COMMON CARD (1-60) .75 2.00
COMMON CARD (61-75) 2.00 5.00
61-75 ODDS 1:1 HOBBY, 1:96 RETAIL
61-75 PRINT RUN 599 SERIAL #'d SETS
1 Angel Berroa .75 2.00
2 Derek Jeter 2.50 6.00
3 Jody Gerut .75 2.00
4 Curt Schilling 1.25 3.00
5 Khalil Greene 1.25 3.00
6 Manny Ramirez 1.25 3.00
7 Rocco Baldelli .75 2.00
8 Sammy Sosa 1.25 3.00
9 Shawn Green .75 2.00
10 Austin Kearns .75 2.00
11 Frank Thomas 1.25 3.00
12 Alfonso Soriano 1.25 3.00
13 Alex Rodriguez 2.00 5.00
14 Carlos Delgado .75 2.00
15 Chipper Jones 1.25 3.00
16 Edgar Martinez 1.25 3.00
17 Ivan Rodriguez 1.25 3.00
18 Mark Prior 1.25 3.00
19 Mike Piazza 2.00 5.00
20 Orlando Cabrera .75 2.00
21 Adam Dunn .75 2.00
22 Andruw Jones 1.25 3.00
23 Eric Chavez .75 2.00
24 Mark Teixeira 1.25 3.00
25 Scott Podsednik .75 2.00
26 Torii Hunter .75 2.00
27 Miguel Cabrera 1.25 3.00
28 Hideki Matsui 2.00 5.00
29 Jose Reyes .75 2.00
30 Vladimir Guerrero 1.25 3.00
31 Albert Pujols 2.50 6.00
32 Greg Maddux 2.00 5.00
33 Jason Giambi .75 2.00
34 Randy Johnson 1.25 3.00
35 Roger Clemens 2.50 6.00
36 Casey Kotchman .75 2.00
37 Ken Griffey Jr. 2.00 5.00
38 Todd Helton 1.25 3.00
39 Javy Lopez .75 2.00
40 Jim Thome 1.25 3.00
41 Josh Beckett .75 2.00
42 Kerry Wood .75 2.00
43 Scott Rolen 1.25 3.00
44 Pat Burrell .75 2.00
45 Pedro Martinez 1.25 3.00
46 Barry Zito .75 2.00
47 Hank Blalock .75 2.00
48 Hideo Nomo 1.25 3.00
49 Jeff Bagwell 1.25 3.00
50 Magglio Ordonez .75 2.00
51 Ichiro Suzuki 2.50 6.00
52 Joe Mauer 1.25 3.00
53 Richie Sexson .75 2.00
54 Shannon Stewart .75 2.00
55 Craig Wilson .75 2.00
56 Miguel Tejada .75 2.00
57 Sean Casey .75 2.00
58 Tom Glavine 1.25 3.00
59 Jason Schmidt .75 2.00
60 Nomar Garciaparra 2.00 5.00
61 Kaz Matsui FL RC 3.00 8.00
62 Justin Leone FL RC 3.00 8.00
63 Merkin Valdez FL RC 3.00 8.00
64 Shingo Takatsu FL RC 3.00 8.00
65 Andres Blanco FL RC 2.00 5.00
66 Angel Chavez FL RC 2.00 5.00
67 Hector Gimenez FL RC 2.00 5.00
68 Akinori Otsuka FL RC 2.00 5.00
69 Jason Bartlett FL RC 3.00 8.00
70 Luis Gonzalez FL RC 2.00 5.00
71 Sean Henn FL RC 2.00 5.00
72 Mike Rouse FL RC 2.00 5.00
73 Chris Aguila FL RC 2.00 5.00
74 Aarom Baldiris FL RC 3.00 8.00
75 Jerry Gil FL RC 2.00 5.00

2001 Fleer Platinum

This 601-card set was distributed in two separate series. Series 1 was released in late May, 2001 with cards distributed in 10-card hobby packs with a suggested retail price of $2.99 and a 25-card jumbo pack for $9.99. Series 2 (entitled Platinum RC edition) was released in late December, 2001. The set features player photos printed in the original 1981 Fleer design. The first series contains 250 regular cards plus 31 dual short printed cards (251-280/301) and 20 All-Star cards (281-300) both with an insertion rate of 1:6 in the hobby packs and 1:2 in the jumbo packs. The second series set contains 300 cards composed of basic (302-401), Chart Toppers (402-431), Team Leaders (432-461), Franchise Futures (462-481), Postseason Glory (482-501) and Rookies (502-601), seeded at a rate of 1:3 packs). Notable Rookie Cards include Ichiro, Albert Pujols and Mark Tiexeira. According to representatives at Fleer, card 529 (Mark Prior RC) and card 402 (Freddy Garcia CT) were mistakenly switched with each other on the printing forms - thereby making card 402 a short-print (available at the same ratio as cards 502-601) and card 529 a basic card (available at the same rate as cards 302-501).

COMP. SERIES 1 (301) 100.00 200.00
COMP. SERIES 2 (300) 100.00 200.00
COMP.SER.1 w/o SP's (250) 15.00 40.00
COMP.SER.2 w/o SP's (200) 15.00 40.00
COMMON (1-250/302-501) .10 .30
COMMON (251-280) .75 2.00
COMMON AS (281-300) .75 2.00
COMMON (502-601) .75 2.00
1 Bobby Abreu .10 .30
2 Brad Radke .10 .30
3 Bill Mueller .10 .30
4 Adam Eaton .10 .30
5 Antonio Alfonseca .10 .30
6 Manny Ramirez Sox .20 .50
7 Adam Kennedy .10 .30
8 Jose Valentin .10 .30
9 Jaret Wright .10 .30
10 Aramis Ramirez .10 .30
11 Jeff Kent .10 .30
12 Juan Encarnacion .10 .30
13 Sandy Alomar Jr. .10 .30
14 Joe Randa .10 .30
15 Darryl Kile .10 .30
16 Darren Dreifort .10 .30
17 Matt Kinney .10 .30
18 Pokey Reese .10 .30
19 Ryan Klesko .10 .30
20 Shawn Estes .10 .30
21 Moises Alou .10 .30
22 Edgar Renteria .10 .30
23 Chuck Knoblauch .10 .30
24 Carl Everett .10 .30
25 Garret Anderson .10 .30
26 Shane Reynolds .10 .30
27 Billy Koch .10 .30
28 Carlos Febles .10 .30
29 Brian Anderson .10 .30
30 Armando Rios .10 .30
31 Ryan Kohlmeier .10 .30
32 Steve Finley .10 .30
33 Brady Anderson .10 .30
34 Cal Ripken 1.00 2.50
35 Paul Konerko .10 .30
36 Chuck Finley .10 .30
37 Rick Ankiel .10 .30
38 Mariano Rivera .30 .75
39 Corey Koskie .10 .30
40 Cliff Floyd .10 .30
41 Kevin Appier .10 .30
42 Henry Rodriguez .10 .30
43 Mark Kotsay .10 .30
44 Brook Fordyce .10 .30
45 Brad Ausmus .10 .30
46 Alfonso Soriano .20 .50
47 Ray Lankford .10 .30
48 Keith Foulke .10 .30
49 Rich Aurilia .10 .30
50 Alex Rodriguez .60 1.50
51 Eric Byrnes .10 .30
52 Travis Fryman .10 .30
53 Jeff Bagwell .20 .50
54 Scott Rolen .20 .50
55 Matt Lawton .10 .30
56 Brad Fullmer .10 .30
57 Tony Batista .10 .30
58 Nate Rolison .10 .30
59 Carlos Lee .10 .30
60 Rafael Furcal .10 .30
61 Jay Bell .10 .30
62 Jimmy Rollins .10 .30
63 Derrek Lee .20 .50
64 Andres Galarraga .10 .30
65 Derek Bell .10 .30
66 Tim Salmon .20 .50
67 Travis Lee .10 .30
68 Kevin Millwood .10 .30
69 Albert Belle .10 .30
70 Kazuhiro Sasaki .10 .30
71 Al Leiter .10 .30
72 Britt Reames .10 .30
73 Carlos Beltran .10 .30
74 Curt Schilling .10 .30
75 Curtis Leskanic .10 .30
76 Jeremy Giambi .10 .30
77 Adrian Beltre .10 .30
78 David Segui .10 .30
79 Mike Lieberthal .10 .30
80 Brian Giles .10 .30
81 Marvin Benard .10 .30
82 Aaron Sele .10 .30
83 Kenny Lofton .10 .30
84 Doug Glanville .10 .30
85 Kris Benson .10 .30
86 Richie Sexson .10 .30
87 Javy Lopez .10 .30
88 Doug Mientkiewicz .10 .30
89 Peter Bergeron .10 .30
90 Gary Sheffield .10 .30
91 Derek Lowe .10 .30
92 Tom Glavine .20 .50
93 Lance Berkman .10 .30
94 Chris Singleton .10 .30
95 Mike Lowell .10 .30
96 Luis Gonzalez .10 .30
97 Dante Bichette .10 .30
98 Mike Sirotka .10 .30
99 Julio Lugo .10 .30
100 Juan Gonzalez .10 .30
101 Craig Biggio .20 .50
102 Armando Benitez .10 .30
103 Greg Maddux .50 1.25
104 Mark Grace .20 .50
105 John Smoltz .20 .50
106 J.T. Snow .10 .30
107 Al Martin .10 .30
108 Danny Graves .10 .30
109 Barry Bonds .75 2.00
110 Lee Stevens .10 .30
111 Pedro Martinez .20 .50
112 Shawn Green .10 .30
113 Bret Boone .10 .30
114 Matt Stairs .10 .30
115 Tino Martinez .20 .50
116 Rusty Greer .10 .30
117 Mike Bordick .10 .30
118 Garrett Stephenson .10 .30
119 Edgar Martinez .20 .50
120 Ben Grieve .10 .30
121 Milton Bradley .10 .30
122 Aaron Boone .10 .30
123 Ruben Mateo .10 .30
124 Ken Griffey Jr. .50 1.25
125 Russell Branyan .10 .30
126 Shannon Stewart .10 .30
127 Fred McGriff .20 .50
128 Ben Petrick .10 .30
129 Kevin Brown .10 .30
130 B.J. Surhoff .10 .30
131 Mark McGwire .75 2.00
132 Carlos Guillen .10 .30
133 Adrian Brown .10 .30
134 Mike Sweeney .10 .30
135 Eric Milton .10 .30
136 Cristian Guzman .10 .30
137 Ellis Burks .10 .30
138 Fernando Tatis .10 .30
139 Bengie Molina .10 .30
140 Tony Gwynn .40 1.00
141 Jeromy Burnitz .10 .30
142 Miguel Tejada .10 .30
143 Raul Mondesi .10 .30
144 Jeffrey Hammonds .10 .30
145 Pat Burrell .10 .30
146 Frank Thomas .30 .75
147 Eric Munson .10 .30
148 Mike Hampton .10 .30
149 Mike Cameron .10 .30
150 Jim Thome .20 .50
151 Mike Mussina .20 .50
152 Rick Helling .10 .30
153 Ken Caminiti .10 .30
154 John VanderWal .10 .30
155 Denny Neagle .10 .30
156 Robb Nen .10 .30
157 Jose Canseco .20 .50
158 Mo Vaughn .10 .30
159 Phil Nevin .10 .30
160 Pat Hentgen .10 .30
161 Sean Casey .10 .30
162 Greg Vaughn .10 .30
163 Trot Nixon .10 .30
164 Roberto Hernandez .10 .30
165 Vinny Castilla .10 .30
166 Robin Ventura .10 .30
167 Alex Ochoa .10 .30
168 Orlando Hernandez .10 .30
169 Luis Castillo .10 .30
170 Quilvio Veras .10 .30
171 Troy O'Leary .10 .30
172 Livan Hernandez .10 .30
173 Roger Cedeno .10 .30
174 Jose Vidro .10 .30
175 John Olerud .10 .30
176 Richard Hidalgo .10 .30
177 Eric Chavez .10 .30
178 Fernando Vina .10 .30
179 Chris Stynes .10 .30
180 Bobby Higginson .10 .30
181 Bruce Chen .10 .30
182 Omar Vizquel .20 .50
183 Rey Ordonez .10 .30
184 Trevor Hoffman .10 .30
185 Jeff Cirillo .10 .30
186 Billy Wagner .10 .30
187 David Ortiz .30 .75
188 Tim Hudson .10 .30
189 Tony Clark .10 .30
190 Larry Walker .10 .30
191 Eric Owens .10 .30
192 Aubrey Huff .10 .30
193 Royce Clayton .10 .30
194 Todd Walker .10 .30
195 Rafael Palmeiro .20 .50
196 Todd Hundley .10 .30
197 Roger Clemens .60 1.50
198 Jeff Weaver .10 .30
199 Dean Palmer .10 .30
200 Geoff Jenkins .10 .30
201 Matt Clement .10 .30
202 David Wells .10 .30
203 Chan Ho Park .10 .30
204 Hideo Nomo .30 .75
205 Bartolo Colon .10 .30
206 John Wetteland .10 .30
207 Corey Patterson .10 .30
208 Freddy Garcia .10 .30
209 David Cone .10 .30
210 Rondell White .10 .30
211 Carl Pavano .10 .30
212 Charles Johnson .10 .30
213 Ron Coomer .10 .30
214 Matt Williams .10 .30
215 Jay Payton .10 .30
216 Nick Johnson .10 .30
217 Deivi Cruz .10 .30
218 Scott Elarton .10 .30
219 Neifi Perez .10 .30
220 Jason Isringhausen .10 .30
221 Jose Cruz Jr. .10 .30
222 Gerald Williams .10 .30
223 Timo Perez .10 .30
224 Damion Easley .10 .30
225 Jeff D'Amico .10 .30
226 Preston Wilson .10 .30
227 Robert Person .10 .30
228 Jacque Jones .10 .30
229 Johnny Damon .20 .50
230 Tony Womack .10 .30
231 Adam Piatt .10 .30
232 Brian Jordan .10 .30
233 Ben Davis .10 .30
234 Kerry Wood .10 .30
235 Mike Piazza .50 1.25
236 David Justice .10 .30
237 Dave Veres .10 .30
238 Eric Young .10 .30
239 Juan Pierre .10 .30
240 Gabe Kapler .10 .30
241 Ryan Dempster .10 .30
242 Dmitri Young .10 .30
243 Jorge Posada .20 .50
244 Eric Karros .10 .30
245 J.D. Drew .10 .30
246 Todd Zeile .10 .30
247 Mark Quinn .10 .30
248 Kenny Kelly UER .10 .30
Listed as a Mariner on the front
249 Jermaine Dye .10 .30
250 Barry Zito .20 .50
251 Jason Hart .75 2.00
Larry Barnes
252 Ichiro Suzuki RC 10.00 25.00
Elpidio Guzman RC
253 Tsuyoshi Shinjo RC 1.25 3.00
Brian Cole
254 John Barnes .75 2.00
Adrian Hernandez RC
255 Jason Tyner .75 2.00
Jace Brewer
256 Brian Buchanan .75 2.00
Luis Rivas
257 Brent Abernathy .75 2.00
Jose Ortiz
258 Marcus Giles .75 2.00
Keith Ginter
259 Tike Redman .75 2.00
Jaisen Randolph RC
260 Dane Sardinha .75 2.00
David Espinosa
261 Josh Beckett 1.25 3.00
Craig House
262 Jack Cust .75 2.00
Hiram Bocachica
263 Alex Escobar .75 2.00
Esix Snead RC
264 Chris Richard .75 2.00
Vernon Wells
265 Pedro Feliz .75 2.00
Xavier Nady
266 Brandon Inge 1.50 4.00
Joe Crede
267 Ben Sheets 1.50 4.00
Roy Oswalt
268 Drew Henson RC 1.25 3.00
Andy Morales RC
269 C.C. Sabathia .75 2.00
Justin Miller
270 David Eckstein .75 2.00
Jason Grabowski
271 Dee Brown .75 2.00
Chris Wakeland
272 Junior Spivey RC .75 2.00
Alex Cintron
273 Elvis Pena 1.25 3.00
Juan Uribe RC
274 Carlos Pena .75 2.00
Jason Romano
275 Winston Abreu 1.50 4.00
Wilson Betemit
276 Jose Mieses RC .75 2.00
Nick Neugebauer
277 Shea Hillenbrand .75 2.00
Dernell Stenson
278 Jared Sandberg .75 2.00
Toby Hall
279 Jay Gibbons RC 1.25 3.00
Ivanon Coffie
280 Pablo Ozuna .75 2.00
Santiago Perez
281 N.Garciaparra AS 3.00 8.00
282 Derek Jeter AS 5.00 12.00
283 Jason Giambi AS .75 2.00
284 Magglio Ordonez AS .75 2.00
285 Ivan Rodriguez AS 1.25 3.00
286 Troy Glaus AS .75 2.00
287 Carlos Delgado AS .75 2.00
288 Darin Erstad AS .75 2.00
289 Bernie Williams AS 1.25 3.00
290 Roberto Alomar AS 1.25 3.00
291 Barry Larkin AS 1.25 3.00
292 Chipper Jones AS 2.00 5.00
293 Vladimir Guerrero AS 2.00 5.00
294 Sammy Sosa AS 2.00 5.00
295 Todd Helton AS 1.25 3.00
296 Randy Johnson AS 2.00 5.00
297 Jason Kendall AS .75 2.00
298 Jim Edmonds AS .75 2.00
299 Andruw Jones AS 1.25 3.00
300 Edgardo Alfonzo AS .75 2.00
301 Albert Pujols RC 60.00 120.00
Donaldo Mendez RC/1500
302 Shawn Wooten .10 .30
303 Todd Walker .10 .30
304 Brian Buchanan .10 .30
305 Jim Edmonds .10 .30
306 Jarrod Washburn .10 .30
307 Jose Rijo .10 .30
308 Tim Raines .10 .30
309 Matt Morris .10 .30
310 Troy Glaus .10 .30
311 Barry Larkin .20 .50
312 Javier Vazquez .10 .30
313 Placido Polanco .10 .30
314 Darin Erstad .10 .30
315 Marty Cordova .10 .30
316 Vladimir Guerrero .30 .75
317 Kerry Robinson .10 .30
318 Byung-Hyun Kim .10 .30
319 C.C. Sabathia .10 .30
320 Edgardo Alfonzo .10 .30
321 Jason Tyner .10 .30
322 Reggie Sanders .10 .30
323 Roberto Alomar .20 .50
324 Matt Lawton .10 .30
325 Brent Abernathy .10 .30
326 Randy Johnson .30 .75
327 Todd Helton .20 .50
328 Andy Pettitte .20 .50
329 Josh Beckett .20 .50
330 Mark DeRosa .10 .30
331 Jose Ortiz .10 .30
332 Derek Jeter .75 2.00
333 Toby Hall .10 .30
334 Wes Helms .10 .30
335 Jose Macias .10 .30
336 Bernie Williams .20 .50
337 Ivan Rodriguez .20 .50
338 Chipper Jones .30 .75
339 Brandon Inge .10 .30
340 Jason Giambi .10 .30
341 Frank Catalanotto .10 .30
342 Andruw Jones .20 .50
343 Carlos Hernandez .10 .30
344 Jermaine Dye .10 .30
345 Mike Lamb .10 .30
346 Ken Caminiti .10 .30
347 A.J. Burnett .10 .30
348 Terrence Long .10 .30
349 Ruben Sierra .10 .30
350 Marcus Giles UER .10 .30
Listed as a pitcher on the back
351 Wade Miller .10 .30
352 Mark Mulder .10 .30
353 Carlos Delgado .10 .30
354 Chris Richard .10 .30
355 Daryle Ward .10 .30
356 Brad Penny .10 .30
357 Vernon Wells .10 .30
358 Jason Johnson .10 .30
359 Tim Redding .10 .30
360 Marlon Anderson .10 .30
361 Carlos Pena .10 .30
362 Nomar Garciaparra .50 1.25
363 Roy Oswalt .30 .75
364 Todd Ritchie .10 .30
365 Jose Mesa .10 .30
366 Shea Hillenbrand .10 .30
367 Dee Brown .10 .30
368 Jason Kendall .10 .30
369 Vinny Castilla .10 .30
370 Fred McGriff .20 .50
371 Neifi Perez .10 .30
372 Xavier Nady .10 .30
373 Abraham Nunez .10 .30
374 Jon Lieber .10 .30
375 Paul LoDuca .10 .30
376 Bubba Trammell .10 .30
377 Brady Clark .10 .30
378 Joel Pineiro .10 .30
379 Mark Grudzielanek .10 .30
380 D'Angelo Jimenez .10 .30
381 Junior Herndon .10 .30
382 Magglio Ordonez .10 .30
383 Ben Sheets .20 .50
384 John Vander Wal .10 .30
385 Pedro Astacio .10 .30
386 Jose Canseco .20 .50
387 Jose Hernandez .10 .30
388 Eric Davis .10 .30
389 Sammy Sosa .30 .75
390 Mark Buehrle .20 .50
391 Mark Loretta .10 .30
392 Andres Galarraga .10 .30
393 Scott Spiezio .10 .30
394 Joe Crede .30 .75
395 Luis Rivas .10 .30
396 David Bell .10 .30
397 Einar Diaz .10 .30
398 Adam Dunn .20 .50
399 A.J. Pierzynski .10 .30
400 Jamie Moyer .10 .30
401 Nick Johnson .10 .30
402 Freddy Garcia CT SP 4.00 10.00
403 Hideo Nomo CT .10 .30
404 Mark Mulder CT .10 .30
405 Steve Sparks CT .10 .30
406 Mariano Rivera CT .20 .50
407 Mark Buehrle .10 .30
Mike Mussina CT
408 Randy Johnson CT .20 .50
409 Randy Johnson CT .20 .50
410 Curt Schilling .10 .30
Matt Morris CT
411 Greg Maddux CT .30 .75
412 Robb Nen CT .10 .30
413 Randy Johnson CT .20 .50

414 Barry Bonds CT .40 1.00
415 Jason Giambi CT .10 .30
416 Ichiro Suzuki CT 2.00 5.00
417 Ichiro Suzuki CT 2.00 5.00
418 Alex Rodriguez CT .30 .75
419 Bret Boone CT .10 .30
420 Ichiro Suzuki CT 2.00 5.00
421 Alex Rodriguez CT .30 .75
422 Jason Giambi CT .10 .30
423 Alex Rodriguez CT .30 .75
424 Larry Walker CT .10 .30
425 Rich Aurilia CT .10 .30
426 Barry Bonds CT .40 1.00
427 Sammy Sosa CT .20 .50
428 Jimmy Rollins .10 .30
Juan Pierre CT
429 Sammy Sosa CT .20 .50
430 Lance Berkman CT .10 .30
431 Sammy Sosa CT .20 .50
432 Carlos Delgado TL .10 .30
433 Alex Rodriguez TL .30 .75
434 Greg Vaughn TL .10 .30
435 Albert Pujols TL 5.00 12.00
436 Ichiro Suzuki TL 2.00 5.00
437 Barry Bonds TL .40 1.00
438 Phil Nevin TL .10 .30
439 Brian Giles TL .10 .30
440 Bobby Abreu TL .10 .30
441 Jason Giambi TL .10 .30
442 Derek Jeter TL .40 1.00
443 Mike Piazza TL .30 .75
444 Vladimir Guerrero TL .20 .50
445 Corey Koskie TL .10 .30
446 Richie Sexson TL .10 .30
447 Shawn Green TL .10 .30
448 Mike Sweeney TL .10 .30
449 Jeff Bagwell TL .10 .30
450 Cliff Floyd TL .10 .30
451 Roger Cedeno TL .10 .30
452 Todd Helton TL .10 .30
453 Juan Gonzalez TL .10 .30
454 Sean Casey TL .10 .30
455 Magglio Ordonez TL .10 .30
456 Sammy Sosa TL .20 .50
457 Manny Ramirez Sox TL .20 .50
458 Jeff Conine TL .10 .30
459 Chipper Jones TL .20 .50
460 Luis Gonzalez TL .10 .30
461 Troy Glaus TL .10 .30
462 Ivan Rodriguez .10 .30
Jason Romano FF
463 Luis Gonzalez .10 .30
Jack Cust FF
464 Jim Thome .10 .30
C.C. Sabathia FF
465 Jason Giambi .10 .30
Jason Hart FF
466 Jeff Bagwell .30 .75
Roy Oswalt FF
467 Sammy Sosa .20 .50
Corey Patterson FF
468 Mike Piazza .30 .75
Alex Escobar FF
469 Ken Griffey Jr. .30 .75
Adam Dunn FF
470 Roger Clemens .30 .75
Nick Johnson FF
471 Cliff Floyd .10 .30
Josh Beckett FF
472 Cal Ripken Jr. .50 1.25
Jerry Hairston Jr. FF
473 Phil Nevin .10 .30
Xavier Nady FF
474 Scott Rolen .10 .30
Jimmy Rollins FF
475 Barry Larkin .10 .30
David Espinosa FF
476 Larry Walker .10 .30
Jose Ortiz FF
477 Chipper Jones .20 .50
Marcus Giles FF
478 Craig Biggio .10 .30
Keith Ginter FF
479 Maggio Ordonez .10 .30
Aaron Rowand FF
480 Alex Rodriguez .30 .75
Carlos Pena FF
481 Derek Jeter .40 1.00
Alfonso Soriano FF
482 Erubiel Durazo PG .10 .30
483 Bernie Williams PG .10 .30
484 Team Photo PG .10 .30
485 Team Photo PG .10 .30
486 Andy Pettitte PG .10 .30
487 Curt Schilling PG .10 .30
488 Randy Johnson PG .20 .50
489 Rudolph Guiliani PG .30 .75
Mayor of New York City
490 George W. Bush PG 2.00 5.00
President of United States
491 Roger Clemens PG .30 .75
492 Mariano Rivera PG .20 .50
493 Tino Martinez PG .10 .30
494 Derek Jeter PG .40 1.00
495 Scott Brosius PG .10 .30
496 Alfonso Soriano PG .10 .30
497 Matt Williams PG .10 .30
498 Tony Womack PG .10 .30
499 Luis Gonzalez PG .10 .30
500 Arizona Diamondbacks PG .30 .75
501 Randy Johnson .20 .50
Curt Schilling
Co-MVP's PG
502 Josh Fogg RC .75 2.00
503 Elpidio Guzman .75 2.00
504 Corky Miller RC .75 2.00
505 Cesar Crespo RC .75 2.00
506 Carlos Garcia RC .75 2.00
507 Carlos Valderrama RC .75 2.00
508 Joe Kennedy RC 1.25 3.00
509 Henry Mateo RC .75 2.00
510 B. Duckworth RC .75 2.00
511 Ichiro Suzuki 8.00 20.00
512 Zach Day RC .75 2.00
513 Ryan Freel RC 1.25 3.00
514 Brian Lawrence RC .75 2.00
515 Alexis Gomez RC .75 2.00
516 Will Ohman RC .75 2.00
517 Juan Diaz RC .75 2.00
518 Juan Moreno RC .75 2.00
519 Rob Mackowiak RC 1.25 3.00
520 Horacio Ramirez RC 1.25 3.00
521 Albert Pujols 20.00 50.00
522 Tsuyoshi Shinjo 1.25 3.00
523 Ryan Drese RC 1.25 3.00
524 Angel Berroa RC 1.25 3.00
525 Josh Towers RC 1.25 3.00
526 Junior Spivey 1.25 3.00
527 Greg Miller RC .75 2.00
528 Esix Snead .75 2.00
529 Mark Prior DP RC 3.00 8.00
530 Drew Henson 1.25 3.00
531 Brian Reith RC .75 2.00
532 Andres Torres RC .75 2.00
533 Casey Fossum RC .75 2.00
534 Wilmy Caceres RC .75 2.00
535 Matt White RC .75 2.00
536 Wilkin Ruan RC .75 2.00
537 Rick Bauer RC .75 2.00
538 Morgan Ensberg RC 1.50 4.00
539 Geronimo Gil RC .75 2.00
540 Dewon Brazelton RC .75 2.00
541 Johnny Estrada RC 1.25 3.00
542 Claudio Vargas RC .75 2.00
543 Donaldo Mendez .75 2.00
544 Kyle Lohse RC 1.25 3.00
545 Nate Frese RC .75 2.00
546 Christian Parker RC .75 2.00
547 Blaine Neal RC .75 2.00
548 Travis Hafner RC 4.00 10.00
549 Billy Sylvester RC .75 2.00
550 Adam Pettyjohn RC .75 2.00
551 Bill Ortega RC .75 2.00
552 Jose Acevedo RC .75 2.00
553 Steve Green RC .75 2.00
554 Jay Gibbons 1.25 3.00
555 Bert Snow RC .75 2.00
556 Erick Almonte RC .75 2.00
557 Jeremy Owens RC .75 2.00
558 Sean Douglass RC .75 2.00
559 Jason Smith RC .75 2.00
560 Ricardo Rodriguez RC .75 2.00
561 Mark Teixeira RC 5.00 12.00
562 Tyler Walker RC .75 2.00
563 Juan Uribe 1.25 3.00
564 Bud Smith RC .75 2.00
565 Angel Santos RC .75 2.00
566 Brandon Lyon RC .75 2.00
567 Eric Hinske RC UER 1.25 3.00
Front says he is a pitcher
568 Nick Punto RC .75 2.00
569 Winston Abreu .75 2.00
570 Jason Phillips RC .75 2.00
571 Rafael Soriano RC .75 2.00
572 Wilson Betemit 1.50 4.00
573 Endy Chavez RC .75 2.00
574 Juan Cruz RC .75 2.00
575 Cory Aldridge RC .75 2.00
576 Adrian Hernandez .75 2.00
577 Brandon Larson RC .75 2.00
578 Bret Prinz RC .75 2.00
579 Jackson Melian RC .75 2.00
580 Dave Maurer RC .75 2.00
581 Jason Michaels RC .75 2.00
582 Travis Phelps RC .75 2.00
583 Cody Ransom RC .75 2.00
584 Benito Baez RC .75 2.00
585 Brian Roberts RC 1.50 4.00
586 Nate Teut RC .75 2.00
587 Jack Wilson RC 1.25 3.00
588 Willie Harris RC .75 2.00
589 Martin Vargas RC .75 2.00
590 Steve Torrealba RC .75 2.00
591 Stubby Clapp RC .75 2.00
592 Dan Wright .75 2.00
593 Mike Rivera RC .75 2.00
594 Luis Pineda RC .75 2.00
595 Lance Davis RC .75 2.00
596 Ramon Vazquez RC .75 2.00
597 Dustan Mohr RC .75 2.00
598 Troy Mattes RC .75 2.00
599 Grant Balfour RC .75 2.00
600 Jared Fernandez RC .75 2.00
601 Jorge Julio RC .75 2.00

2001 Fleer Platinum Parallel

Randomly inserted in hobby packs, this 600-card set is a parallel version of the base set. Cards 1-250 and 302-501 are sequentially numbered to 201 and cards 251-300 and 502-601 to 21. Card number 300 was never produced as a Parallel.

*STARS 1-250/302-501: 2.5X TO 6X BASIC
*SUBSET RC'S 402-501: 2X TO 5X BASIC
435 Albert Pujols TL 50.00 80.00

2001 Fleer Platinum 20th Anniversary Reprints

Randomly inserted in hobby packs at the rate of one in eight and in jumbo packs at the rate of one in four, this 18-card set features reprints of Fleer's best rookie cards from the past 20 years of cards.

COMPLETE SET (18) 30.00 60.00
1 Cal Ripken 82F 5.00 12.00
2 Wade Boggs 83F 1.00 2.50
3 Ryne Sandberg 83F 2.50 6.00
4 Tony Gwynn 83F 2.00 5.00
5 Don Mattingly 84F 4.00 10.00
6 Roger Clemens 85F 3.00 8.00
7 Kirby Puckett 85F 1.50 4.00
8 Jose Canseco 86LL 1.00 2.50
9 Barry Bonds 87F 4.00 10.00
10 Ken Griffey Jr. 89F 2.50 6.00
11 Sammy Sosa 90F 1.50 4.00
12 Ivan Rodriguez 91UU 1.00 2.50
13 Jeff Bagwell 91UU 1.00 2.50
14 J.D. Drew 98UPD 1.00 2.50
15 Troy Glaus 98UPD 1.00 2.50
16 Rick Ankiel 99UPD 1.00 2.50
17 Xavier Nady 00GL 1.00 2.50
18 Jose Ortiz 00GL 1.00 2.50

2001 Fleer Platinum Classic Combinations

Randomly inserted in packs, this 40-card set features dual player cards which pair some of the greatest players in the game. Cards 1-10 are serially numbered to 250, 11-20 to 500, 21-30 to 1,000, and 31-40 to 2,000.

COMMON (CC1-CC10) 8.00 20.00
COMMON (CC11-CC20) 6.00 15.00
COMMON (CC21-CC30) 3.00 8.00
COMMON (CC31-CC40) 2.00 5.00
CC1 Derek Jeter 8.00 20.00
Alex Rodriguez
CC2 Willie Mays 10.00 25.00
Willie McCovey
CC3 Lou Gehrig 15.00 40.00
Babe Ruth
CC4 Mark McGwire 12.50 30.00
Ken Griffey Jr.
CC5 Johnny Bench 8.00 20.00
Roy Campanella
CC6 Ted Williams 10.00 25.00
Nomar Garciaparra
CC7 Yogi Berra 8.00 20.00
Mike Piazza
CC8 Ernie Banks 8.00 20.00
Sammy Sosa
CC9 Nolan Ryan 12.50 30.00
Randy Johnson
CC10 Roberto Clemente 10.00 25.00
Vladimir Guerrero
CC11 Stan Musial 12.50 30.00
Lou Gehrig
CC12 Bill Mazeroski 8.00 20.00
Roberto Clemente
CC13 Ernie Banks 6.00 15.00
Alex Rodriguez
CC14 Phil Rizzuto 10.00 25.00
Derek Jeter
CC15 Mike Piazza 6.00 15.00
Johnny Bench
CC16 Mark McGwire 10.00 25.00
Sammy Sosa
CC17 Ted Williams 8.00 20.00
Tony Gwynn
CC18 Eddie Mathews 8.00 20.00
Mike Schmidt
CC19 Barry Bonds 10.00 25.00
Willie Mays
CC20 Nolan Ryan 12.50 30.00
Pedro Martinez
CC21 Barry Bonds 8.00 20.00
Ken Griffey Jr.
CC22 Willie McCovey 2.00 5.00
Reggie Jackson
CC23 Roberto Clemente 6.00 15.00
Sammy Sosa
CC24 Willie Mays 6.00 15.00
Ernie Banks
CC25 Eddie Mathews 3.00 8.00
Chipper Jones
CC26 Mike Schmidt 6.00 15.00
Brooks Robinson
CC27 Stan Musial 8.00 20.00
Mark McGwire
CC28 Ted Williams 6.00 15.00
Roger Maris
CC29 Yogi Berra 2.00 5.00
Roy Campanella
CC30 Johnny Bench 3.00 8.00
Tony Perez
CC31 Bill Mazeroski 2.00 5.00
Joe Carter
CC32 Mike Piazza 3.00 8.00
Roy Campanella
CC33 Ernie Banks 2.00 5.00
Craig Biggio
CC34 Frank Robinson 2.00 5.00
Brooks Robinson
CC35 Mike Schmidt 4.00 10.00
Scott Rolen
CC36 Roger Maris 5.00 12.00
Mark McGwire
CC37 Stan Musial 3.00 8.00
Tony Gwynn
CC38 Ted Williams 4.00 10.00
Bill Terry
CC39 Derek Jeter 5.00 12.00
Reggie Jackson
CC40 Yogi Berra 2.00 5.00
Bill Dickey

2001 Fleer Platinum Classic Combinations Memorabilia

Randomly inserted in packs, this 11-card set features dual player cards which pair some of the greatest players in the game and contain pieces of game-used bats. Only 25 serially numbered sets were produced.

1 Yogi Berra Bat
Bill Dickey Bat
2 Yogi Berra Bat
Roy Campanella Bat
3 Roberto Clemente Bat
Vladimir Guerrero Bat
4 Eddie Mathews Bat
Chipper Jones Bat
5 Willie McCovey Bat
Reggie Jackson Bat
6 Phil Rizzuto Bat
Derek Jeter Bat
7 Frank Robinson Bat
Brooks Robinson Bat
8 Mike Schmidt Bat
Brooks Robinson Bat
9 Mike Schmidt Bat
Scott Rolen Bat
10 Ted Williams Bat
Bill Terry Bat
11 Ted Williams Bat
Tony Gwynn Bat

2001 Fleer Platinum Classic Combinations Retail

Randomly inserted into retail packs at the rate of one in 20, this 40-card set is a parallel version of the regular insert set.

COMPLETE SET (40) 150.00 300.00
CC1 Derek Jeter 5.00 12.00
Alex Rodriguez
CC2 Willie Mays 4.00 10.00
Willie McCovey
CC3 Lou Gehrig 6.00 15.00
Babe Ruth
CC4 Mark McGwire 5.00 12.00
Ken Griffey Jr.
CC5 Johnny Bench
Roy Campanella
CC6 Ted Williams 4.00 10.00
Nomar Garciaparra
CC7 Yogi Berra 3.00 8.00
Mike Piazza
CC8 Ernie Banks 2.00 5.00
Sammy Sosa
CC9 Nolan Ryan 5.00 12.00
Randy Johnson
CC10 Roberto Clemente 4.00 10.00
Vladimir Guerrero
CC11 Stan Musial 4.00 10.00
Lou Gehrig
CC12 Bill Mazeroski 4.00 10.00
Roberto Clemente
CC13 Ernie Banks 3.00 8.00
Alex Rodriguez
CC14 Phil Rizzuto 5.00 12.00
Derek Jeter
CC15 Mike Piazza 3.00 8.00
Johnny Bench
CC16 Mark McGwire 5.00 12.00
Sammy Sosa
CC17 Ted Williams 4.00 10.00
Tony Gwynn
CC18 Eddie Mathews 4.00 10.00
Mike Schmidt
CC19 Barry Bonds 5.00 12.00
Willie Mays
CC20 Nolan Ryan 5.00 12.00
Pedro Martinez
CC21 Barry Bonds 5.00 12.00
Ken Griffey Jr.
CC22 Willie McCovey 1.50 4.00
Reggie Jackson
CC23 Roberto Clemente 4.00 10.00
Sammy Sosa
CC24 Willie Mays 3.00 8.00
Ernie Banks
CC25 Eddie Mathews 2.00 5.00
Chipper Jones
CC26 Mike Schmidt 4.00 10.00
Brooks Robinson
CC27 Stan Musial 5.00 12.00
Mark McGwire
CC28 Ted Williams 4.00 10.00
Roger Maris
CC29 Yogi Berra 2.00 5.00
Roy Campanella
CC30 Johnny Bench 2.00 5.00
Tony Perez
CC31 Bill Mazeroski 1.50 4.00
Joe Carter
CC32 Mike Piazza 3.00 8.00
Roy Campanella
CC33 Ernie Banks 2.00 5.00
Craig Biggio
CC34 Frank Robinson 1.50 4.00
Brooks Robinson
CC35 Mike Schmidt 4.00 10.00
Scott Rolen
CC36 Roger Maris 5.00 12.00
Mark McGwire
CC37 Stan Musial 3.00 8.00
Tony Gwynn
CC38 Ted Williams 4.00 10.00
Bill Terry
CC39 Derek Jeter 5.00 12.00
Reggie Jackson
CC40 Yogi Berra 2.00 5.00
Bill Dickey

2001 Fleer Platinum Grandstand Greats

Randomly inserted in hobby packs at the rate of one in 12 and in jumbo packs at the rate of one in six, this 20-card set features color photos of the crowd-pleasers of the League.

COMPLETE SET (20) 40.00 80.00
GG1 Chipper Jones 1.25 3.00
GG2 Alex Rodriguez 2.00 5.00
GG3 Jeff Bagwell .75 2.00
GG4 Troy Glaus .75 2.00
GG5 Manny Ramirez Sox .75 2.00
GG6 Derek Jeter 3.00 8.00
GG7 Tony Gwynn 1.50 4.00
GG8 Greg Maddux 2.00 5.00
GG9 Nomar Garciaparra 2.00 5.00
GG10 Sammy Sosa 1.25 3.00
GG11 Mike Piazza 2.00 5.00
GG12 Barry Bonds 3.00 8.00
GG13 Mark McGwire 3.00 8.00
GG14 Vladimir Guerrero 1.25 3.00
GG15 Ivan Rodriguez .75 2.00
GG16 Ken Griffey Jr. 2.00 5.00
GG17 Todd Helton .75 2.00
GG18 Cal Ripken 4.00 10.00
GG19 Pedro Martinez .75 2.00
GG20 Frank Thomas 1.25 3.00

2001 Fleer Platinum Lumberjacks

This 27-card insert set features game-used bat chips from greats like Derek Jeter and Ivan Rodriguez. These cards were inserted at a stated rate of one per rack pack.

1 Roberto Alomar 6.00 15.00
2 Moises Alou 4.00 10.00
3 Adrian Beltre 4.00 10.00
4 Lance Berkman 4.00 10.00
5 Barry Bonds 10.00 25.00
6 Bret Boone 4.00 10.00
7 J.D. Drew
8 Adam Dunn 6.00 15.00
9 Darin Erstad 4.00 10.00
10 Cliff Floyd 4.00 10.00
11 Brian Giles 4.00 10.00
12 Luis Gonzalez 4.00 10.00
13 Vladimir Guerrero 6.00 15.00
14 Cristian Guzman 4.00 10.00
15 Tony Gwynn 6.00 15.00
16 Todd Helton 6.00 15.00
17 Drew Henson 6.00 15.00
18 Derek Jeter 10.00 25.00
19 Chipper Jones 6.00 15.00
20 Mike Piazza 6.00 15.00
21 Albert Pujols 60.00 100.00
22 Manny Ramirez Sox 6.00 15.00
23 Cal Ripken
24 Ivan Rodriguez 6.00 15.00
25 Gary Sheffield 4.00 10.00
26 Mike Sweeney 4.00 10.00
27 Larry Walker 4.00 10.00

2001 Fleer Platinum Lumberjacks Autographs

This eight-card set is a partial parallel to the 2001 Fleer Platinum Lumberjacks insert. Each card is autographed and signed on actual game-used lumber. Though they lack serial-numbering, the manufacturer announced production at 100 copies per card. Not all the cards were signed in time for inclusion in packs and those exchange cards could be redeemed until November 30, 2002. The following players were seeded into packs as exchange cards: Barry Bonds, Derek Jeter, Albert Pujols and Cal Ripken.

6 Barry Bonds 125.00 200.00
7 J.D. Drew
8 Adam Dunn 40.00 80.00
12 Luis Gonzalez 20.00 50.00
18 Derek Jeter 125.00 200.00
21 Albert Pujols 500.00 800.00
23 Cal Ripken 125.00 200.00
26 Mike Sweeney

2001 Fleer Platinum Nameplates

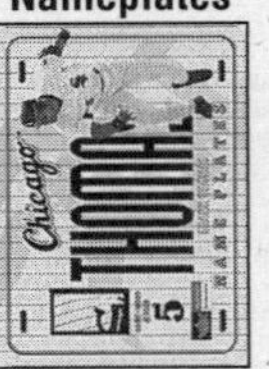

Randomly inserted in jumbo packs only at the rate of one in 12, this 42-card set features color images of top players on a license plate design background and pieces of actual name plates from players' uniforms embedded in the cards.

1 Carlos Beltran/90 10.00 25.00
2 Adrian Beltre/55 * 10.00 25.00
3 Sean Casey/21
4 J.D. Drew/170 10.00 25.00
5 Darin Erstad/39 10.00 25.00
6 Troy Glaus/85 10.00 25.00
7 Tom Glavine/125 15.00 40.00
8 Vladimir Guerrero/80 15.00 40.00
9 Vladimir Guerrero/90 15.00 40.00
10 Tony Gwynn/35 40.00 80.00
11 Tony Gwynn/65 20.00 50.00
12 Tony Gwynn/70 20.00 50.00
13 Jeffrey Hammonds/135 10.00 25.00
14 Randy Johnson/99 15.00 40.00
15 Chipper Jones/95 15.00 40.00
16 Javy Lopez/49 * 10.00 25.00
17 Greg Maddux/180 20.00 50.00
18 Edgar Martinez/87 15.00 40.00
19 Pedro Martinez/120 15.00 40.00
20 Kevin Millwood/130 10.00 25.00
21 Stan Musial/30 60.00 120.00
22 Mike Mussina/91 15.00 40.00
23 Manny Ramirez Sox/75 15.00 40.00
24 Manny Ramirez Sox/105 15.00 40.00
25 Cal Ripken/19
26 Cal Ripken/21
27 Cal Ripken/23
28 Cal Ripken/110 50.00 100.00
29 Ivan Rodriguez/177 15.00 40.00
30 Scott Rolen/65 15.00 40.00
31 Scott Rolen/125 15.00 40.00
32 Nolan Ryan/40 75.00 150.00
33 Nolan Ryan/55 75.00 150.00
34 Curt Schilling/110 * 10.00 25.00
35 Frank Thomas/35 15.00 40.00
36 Frank Thomas/75 15.00 40.00
37 Frank Thomas/80 15.00 40.00
38 Robin Ventura/99 10.00 25.00
39 Larry Walker/79 10.00 25.00
40 Larry Walker/85 10.00 25.00
41 Matt Williams/175 10.00 25.00
42 Dave Winfield/80 10.00 25.00

2001 Fleer Platinum National Patch Time

Randomly inserted in first and second series hobby packs at the rate of one in 24 and first and second series retail packs at the rate of one in 36, this set features color images of superstars of baseball with authentic game-worn jersey and pants swatches embedded in the cards. Jersey cards featuring the following players: Mo Vaughn, Kazuhiro Sasaki; Aaron Sele, Todd Walker, Jorge Posada, Vida Blue, Jim Palmer, Jim Rice, Mike Mussina, and Carl Yastrzemski were produced. However, due to MLB regulations these cards were pulled at the last minute from series one packs. Vaughn and Sasaki were eventually seeded into second series packs and a lone Mike Mussina copy was verified as coming from a second series pack, but no Mussina's or Yastrzemski's were intended for release. In late 2004 copies of the Yastrzemski card were reportedly sent out to collectors as exchange premiums for other issues Fleer could not fulfill.

1 Edgardo Alfonzo S1 4.00 10.00
2 B.Anderson Pants S1 4.00 10.00
3 Jeff Bagwell S2 6.00 15.00
4 Adrian Beltre S2 4.00 10.00
5 Wade Boggs S1 6.00 15.00
6 Barry Bonds S2 10.00 25.00
7 George Brett S1 10.00 25.00
8 Eric Chavez S2 4.00 10.00
9 Jeff Cirillo S1 4.00 10.00
10 R.Clemens Gray S1 10.00 25.00
11 R.Clemens White S2 10.00 25.00
12 Pedro Martinez S1 6.00 15.00
12 J.D. Drew S2 4.00 10.00
13 Darin Erstad S2 4.00 10.00
14 Carl Everett S1 4.00 10.00
15 Rollie Fingers Pants S1 4.00 10.00

Card	Low	High
16 Freddy Garcia White S1	4.00	10.00
17 Freddy Garcia White S2	4.00	10.00
18 Jason Giambi SP S2	4.00	10.00
19 Juan Gonzalez SP S2	4.00	10.00
20 Mark Grace S2	6.00	15.00
21 Shawn Green S2	4.00	10.00
22 Ben Grieve S2	4.00	10.00
23 Vladimir Guerrero S2	6.00	15.00
24 Tony Gwynn White S1	6.00	15.00
25 Tony Gwynn White S2	6.00	15.00
26 Todd Helton S2	6.00	15.00
27 Randy Johnson S2	6.00	15.00
28 Chipper Jones S2	6.00	15.00
29 David Justice S2	4.00	10.00
30 Jason Kendall S1	4.00	10.00
31 Jeff Kent S2	4.00	10.00
32 Paul LoDuca S2	4.00	10.00
33 Greg Maddux White S1	6.00	15.00
34 G.Maddux Gray-White S2	6.00	15.00
36 Fred McGriff S1	6.00	15.00
37 Eddie Murray S1	6.00	15.00
38 Mike Mussina S2 SP		
39 John Olerud S2	4.00	10.00
40 M.Ordonez Gray S1	4.00	10.00
41 M.Ordonez Gray SP S2	4.00	10.00
42 Adam Piatt S1	4.00	10.00
43 Jorge Posada S2	6.00	15.00
44 Manny Ramirez Sox S1	6.00	15.00
45 Cal Ripken Black S1	20.00	50.00
46 C.Ripken Gray-White S2	20.00	50.00
47 Mariano Rivera S2	6.00	15.00
48 Ivan Rodriguez Blue S1	6.00	15.00
49 I.Rodriguez Blue-WhiteS2	6.00	15.00
50 Scott Rolen S2	6.00	15.00
51 Nolan Ryan S1	15.00	40.00
52 Kazuhiro Sasaki S2	4.00	10.00
53 Mike Schmidt S1	10.00	25.00
54 Tom Seaver S1	6.00	15.00
55 Aaron Sele S2	4.00	10.00
56 Gary Sheffield S2	4.00	10.00
57 Ozzie Smith S1	6.00	15.00
58 John Smoltz S2	6.00	15.00
59 Frank Thomas S2	6.00	15.00
60 Mo Vaughn S2	4.00	10.00
61 Robin Ventura S2	4.00	10.00
62 Rondell White S1	4.00	10.00
63 Bernie Williams S2	6.00	15.00
64 Dave Winfield S1	4.00	10.00
65 Carl Yastrzemski Mail-In SP		

2001 Fleer Platinum Prime Numbers

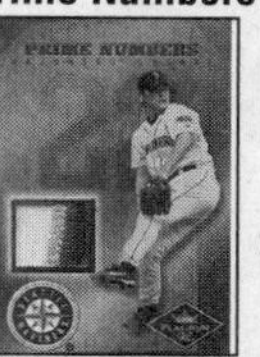

This 15-card insert set was issued in jumbo packs at 1:12, and features game-used jersey swatches from veteran players like Cal Ripken and Chipper Jones.

Card	Low	High
1 Jeff Bagwell	10.00	25.00
2 Cal Ripken	50.00	100.00
3 Barry Bonds	40.00	80.00
4 Todd Helton		
5 Derek Jeter	40.00	80.00
6 Tony Gwynn	15.00	40.00
7 Kazuhiro Sasaki	6.00	15.00
8 Chan Ho Park	6.00	15.00
9 Sean Casey		
10 Chipper Jones	10.00	25.00
11 Pedro Martinez	10.00	25.00
12 Mike Piazza	20.00	50.00
13 Carlos Delgado	6.00	15.00
14 Craig Biggio		
15 Roger Clemens	30.00	60.00

2001 Fleer Platinum Rack Pack Autographs

Randomly inserted in rack packs only, this 21-card set features actual autographed player cards and autographics cards from the last 20 years. These cards were almost all originally inserted in Fleer packs and were bought back for signing for this product.

Card	Low	High
1 H.Aaron 1997 SI/90	125.00	200.00
2 L.Brock 1998 SITN/15		
3 Roger Clemens 1998 SITN/125	50.00	100.00
4 Jose Cruz Jr. 1997 No Brand	2.00	5.00
5 J.Drew 1999 SI One's/10 *		
6 S.Garvey 1987 Fleer/15 *		
7 Bob Gibson 1998 SITN/300	10.00	25.00
8 B.Grieve No Brand/100 *	2.00	5.00
9 T.Gwynn 1998 SITN/125	20.00	50.00
10 Wes Helms 1997 No Brand	2.00	5.00
11 Harmon Killebrew 1998 SITN/300	15.00	40.00
12 Paul Konerko No Brand/135 *	10.00	25.00
13 W.Mays 1997 SI/115	75.00	150.00
14 Willie Mays 1998 SITN/120	75.00	150.00
15 K.Puckett 1997 SI/105	50.00	100.00
16 C.Ripken 1997 SI/5		
17 Brooks Robinson 1998 SITN/40	30.00	60.00
18 Frank Robinson 1997 SI/115	10.00	25.00
19 Scott Rolen 1998 SITN/150	10.00	25.00
20 Alex Rodriguez 1997 SI/94	75.00	150.00
21 Alex Rodriguez 1998 Promo/150	50.00	100.00

2001 Fleer Platinum Tickets Autographs

Randomly inserted in hobby boxes, this nine-card set is a partial parallel version of the regular insert set and is distinguished by the autographs on the tickets.

Card	Low	High
1 George Brett 3000th Hit 9/30/92		
2 Rod Carew 3000th Hit 8/4/85		
3 Steve Carlton 300th Win 9/23/83	15.00	30.00
4 Bob Gibson 1968 WS		
5 Stan Musial Last Game 9/29/63		
6 Cal Ripken 1991 AS MVP		
7 Cal Ripken 400th HR		
8 Mike Schmidt 500th HR 4/18/87		
9 Mike Schmidt Opening Day		

2001 Fleer Platinum Winning Combinations

This 40-card insert was issued in Series two hobby packs. The set pairs players that have similar abilities. Each card is serial numbered to either 2000, 1000, 500, or 250.

Card	Low	High
1 Derek Jeter Ozzie Smith/2000	5.00	12.00
2 Barry Bonds Mark McGwire/500	10.00	25.00
3 Ichiro Suzuki Albert Pujols/250	30.00	60.00
4 Ted Williams Manny Ramirez Sox/1000	6.00	15.00
5 Tony Gwynn Cal Ripken/250	15.00	40.00
6 Mike Piazza Derek Jeter/500	10.00	25.00
7 Dave Winfield Tony Gwynn/2000	2.50	6.00
8 Hideo Nomo Ichiro Suzuki/2000	8.00	20.00
9 Cal Ripken Ozzie Smith/1000	10.00	25.00
10 Mark McGwire Albert Pujols/2000	10.00	25.00
11 Jeff Bagwell Craig Biggio/1000	3.00	8.00
12 Bobby Bonds Barry Bonds/250	12.50	30.00
13 Ted Williams Stan Musial/250	10.00	25.00
14 Babe Ruth Reggie Jackson/500	12.50	30.00
15 Kazuhiro Sasaki Ichiro Suzuki/500	15.00	40.00
16 Nolan Ryan Roger Clemens/500	10.00	25.00
17 Roger Clemens Derek Jeter/250	12.50	30.00
18 Mike Piazza Ivan Rodriguez/1000	5.00	12.00
19 Vladimir Guerrero Sammy Sosa/2000	2.00	5.00
20 Barry Bonds Sammy Sosa/250	12.50	30.00
21 Roger Clemens Greg Maddux/1000	6.00	15.00
22 Juan Gonzalez Manny Ramirez Sox/2000	2.00	5.00
23 Todd Helton Jason Giambi/2000	2.00	5.00
24 Jeff Bagwell Lance Berkman/2000	2.00	5.00
25 Mike Sweeney George Brett/1000	5.00	12.00
26 Luis Gonzalez Babe Ruth/2000	6.00	15.00
27 Bill Skowron Don Mattingly/250	12.50	30.00
28 Yogi Berra Cal Ripken/2000	6.00	15.00
29 Pedro Martinez Nomar Garciaparra/500	6.00	15.00
30 Ted Kluszewski Frank Robinson/1000	3.00	8.00
31 Curt Schilling Randy Johnson/1000	3.00	8.00
32 Ken Griffey Jr. Cal Ripken/500	12.50	30.00
33 Mike Piazza Johnny Bench/1000	5.00	12.00
34 Stan Musial Albert Pujols	20.00	50.00
35 Jackie Robinson Nellie Fox/500	4.00	10.00
36 Lefty Grove Steve Carlton/250	6.00	15.00
37 Ty Cobb Tony Gwynn/250	8.00	20.00
38 Albert Pujols Frank Robinson/1000	12.50	30.00
39 Ryne Sandberg Sammy Sosa/500	10.00	25.00
40 Cal Ripken Lou Gehrig/250	15.00	40.00

2001 Fleer Platinum Winning Combinations Blue

This 40-card insert is a complete parallel of the 2001 Fleer Platinum Winning Combinations insert. Each blue bordered card can be found in jumbo packs at a rate of 1:12, rack packs at 1:6, and retail packs at 1:20.

Card	Low	High
1 Derek Jeter Ozzie Smith	5.00	12.00
2 Barry Bonds Mark McGwire	5.00	12.00
3 Ichiro Suzuki Albert Pujols	12.50	30.00
4 Ted Williams Manny Ramirez Sox	4.00	10.00
5 Tony Gwynn Cal Ripken	6.00	15.00
6 Mike Piazza Derek Jeter	5.00	12.00
7 Dave Winfield Tony Gwynn	2.50	6.00
8 Hideo Nomo Ichiro Suzuki	8.00	20.00
9 Cal Ripken Ozzie Smith	6.00	15.00
10 Mark McGwire Albert Pujols	8.00	20.00
11 Jeff Bagwell Craig Biggio	2.00	5.00
12 Bobby Bonds Barry Bonds	5.00	12.00
13 Ted Williams Stan Musial	4.00	10.00
14 Babe Ruth Reggie Jackson	6.00	15.00
15 Kazuhiro Sasaki Ichiro Suzuki	6.00	15.00
16 Nolan Ryan Roger Clemens	5.00	12.00
17 Roger Clemens Derek Jeter	5.00	12.00
18 Mike Piazza Ivan Rodriguez	3.00	8.00
19 Vladimir Guerrero Sammy Sosa	2.00	5.00
20 Barry Bonds Sammy Sosa	5.00	12.00
21 Roger Clemens Greg Maddux	4.00	10.00
22 Juan Gonzalez Manny Ramirez Sox	2.00	5.00
23 Todd Helton Jason Giambi	2.00	5.00
24 Jeff Bagwell Lance Berkman	2.00	5.00
25 Mike Sweeney George Brett	4.00	10.00
26 Luis Gonzalez Babe Ruth	6.00	15.00
27 Bill Skowron Don Mattingly	4.00	10.00
28 Yogi Berra Cal Ripken	6.00	15.00
29 Pedro Martinez Nomar Garciaparra	3.00	8.00
30 Ted Kluszewski Frank Robinson	2.00	5.00
31 Curt Schilling Randy Johnson	2.00	5.00
32 Ken Griffey Jr. Cal Ripken	6.00	15.00
33 Mike Piazza Johnny Bench	3.00	8.00
34 Stan Musial Albert Pujols	6.00	15.00
35 Jackie Robinson Nellie Fox	2.00	5.00
36 Lefty Grove Steve Carlton	2.00	5.00
37 Ty Cobb Tony Gwynn	3.00	8.00
38 Albert Pujols Frank Robinson	6.00	15.00
39 Ryne Sandberg Sammy Sosa	3.00	8.00
40 Cal Ripken Lou Gehrig	6.00	15.00

2001 Fleer Platinum Winning Combinations Memorabilia

This 25-card set is a partial parallel of the 2001 Fleer Platinum Winning Combinations insert, each card features game-used memorabilia. These cards were inserted into Series two hobby/jumbo packs, and are individually serial numbered to 25. Due to market scarcity, no pricing is provided.

1 Derek Jeter Ozzie Smith
3 Ichiro Suzuki Albert Pujols
4 Ted Williams Manny Ramirez Sox
5 Tony Gwynn Cal Ripken
6 Mike Piazza Derek Jeter
7 Dave Winfield Tony Gwynn
8 Hideo Nomo Ichiro Suzuki
9 Cal Ripken Ozzie Smith
11 Jeff Bagwell Craig Biggio
12 Bobby Bonds Barry Bonds
14 Babe Ruth Reggie Jackson
15 Kazuhiro Sasaki Ichiro Suzuki
16 Nolan Ryan Roger Clemens
17 Roger Clemens Derek Jeter
18 Mike Piazza Ivan Rodriguez
21 Roger Clemens Greg Maddux
22 Juan Gonzalez Manny Ramirez Sox
24 Jeff Bagwell Lance Berkman
25 Mike Sweeney George Brett
26 Luis Gonzalez Babe Ruth
27 Bill Skowron Don Mattingly
30 Ted Kluszewski Frank Robinson
33 Mike Piazza Johnny Bench
35 Jackie Robinson Nellie Fox
38 Albert Pujols Frank Robinson

2002 Fleer Platinum

This 301 card set was issued in early Spring, 2002. These cards were issued in three different ways: 10 card hobby and retail packs. These packs were issued 24 packs to a box and six boxes to a case and had an SRP of $3. This product was also issued in 25 card jumbo packs which were packaged 12 to a box and eight boxes to a case. These cards had an SRP of $6. In addition, these cards were also issued in 45-card rack packs which were issued six packs to a box and two boxes to a case. These packs had an SRP of $10 per pack. The first 250 cards were basic cards while cards 251 through 260 are a Decade of Dominance subset, cards 261-270 feature the 10 players considered among the best young prospect and then 271-300 feature dual players prospects. Cards numbered 301 and 302 feature Japanese imports for 2002, So Taguchi and Kazuhisa Ishii. Card number 280 was not issued upon release of this set but was scheduled for release later in the 2002 season. At season's end, it was decided by the manufacturer to NOT release this card. A few copies of this card (with a large square box cut out from Satoru Komiyama's image) erroneously made their way into packs. Due to scarcity, a value has not been established. In addition, 73 redemption cards were seeded into packs whereby the holder of the card could exchange it for an actual vintage 1986 Fleer Update Bonds XRC signed and certified by Barry himself and hand-numbered "X/73". The deadline to send this card in was April 30th, 2003.

Card	Low	High
COMPLETE SET (301)	100.00	200.00
COMP.SET w/o SP's (250)	10.00	25.00
COMMON CARD (1-250)	.10	.30
COMMON CARD (251-260)	1.25	3.00
COMMON CARD (261-270)	1.25	3.00
COMMON CARD (271-302)	1.25	3.00
1 Garret Anderson	.10	.30
2 Randy Johnson	.30	.75
3 Chipper Jones	.30	.75
4 David Cone	.10	.30
5 Corey Patterson	.10	.30
6 Carlos Lee	.10	.30
7 Barry Larkin	.20	.50
8 Jim Thome	.20	.50
9 Larry Walker	.10	.30
10 Randall Simon	.10	.30
11 Charles Johnson	.10	.30
12 Richard Hidalgo	.10	.30
13 Mark Quinn	.10	.30
14 Paul LoDuca	.10	.30
15 Cristian Guzman	.10	.30
16 Orlando Cabrera	.10	.30
17 Al Leiter	.10	.30
18 Nick Johnson	.10	.30
19 Eric Chavez	.10	.30
20 Miguel Tejada	.10	.30
21 Mike Lieberthal	.10	.30
22 Rob Mackowiak	.10	.30
23 Ryan Klesko	.10	.30
24 Jeff Kent	.10	.30
25 Edgar Martinez	.20	.50
26 Steve Kline	.10	.30
27 Toby Hall	.10	.30
28 Rusty Greer	.10	.30
29 Jose Cruz Jr.	.10	.30
30 Darin Erstad	.10	.30
31 Reggie Sanders	.10	.30
32 Javy Lopez	.10	.30
33 Carl Everett	.10	.30
34 Sammy Sosa	.30	.75
35 Magglio Ordonez	.10	.30
36 Todd Walker	.10	.30
37 Omar Vizquel	.20	.50
38 Matt Anderson	.10	.30
39 Jeff Weaver	.10	.30
40 Derrek Lee	.20	.50
41 Julio Lugo	.10	.30
42 Joe Randa	.10	.30
43 Chan Ho Park	.10	.30
44 Torii Hunter	.10	.30
45 Vladimir Guerrero	.30	.75
46 Rey Ordonez	.10	.30
47 Tino Martinez	.20	.50
48 Johnny Damon Sox	.20	.50
49 Barry Zito	.10	.30
50 Robert Person	.10	.30
51 Aramis Ramirez	.10	.30
52 Mark Kotsay	.10	.30
53 Jason Schmidt	.10	.30
54 Jamie Moyer	.10	.30
55 David Justice	.10	.30
56 Aubrey Huff	.10	.30
57 Rick Helling	.10	.30
58 Carlos Delgado	.10	.30
59 Troy Glaus	.10	.30
60 Curt Schilling	.10	.30
61 Greg Maddux	.50	1.25
62 Nomar Garciaparra	.50	1.25
63 Kerry Wood	.10	.30
64 Frank Thomas	.30	.75
65 Dmitri Young	.10	.30
66 Alex Ochoa	.10	.30
67 Jose Macias	.10	.30
68 Antonio Alfonseca	.10	.30
69 Mike Lowell	.10	.30
70 Wade Miller	.10	.30
71 Mike Sweeney	.10	.30
72 Gary Sheffield	.10	.30
73 Corey Koskie	.10	.30
74 Lee Stevens	.10	.30
75 Jay Payton	.10	.30
76 Mike Mussina	.20	.50
77 Jermaine Dye	.10	.30
78 Bobby Abreu	.10	.30
79 Scott Rolen	.20	.50
80 Todd Ritchie	.10	.30
81 D'Angelo Jimenez	.10	.30
82 Robb Nen	.10	.30
83 John Olerud	.10	.30
84 Matt Morris	.10	.30
85 Joe Kennedy	.10	.30
86 Gabe Kapler	.10	.30
87 Chris Carpenter	.10	.30
88 David Eckstein	.10	.30
89 Matt Williams	.10	.30
90 John Smoltz	.20	.50
91 Pedro Martinez	.20	.50
92 Eric Young	.10	.30
93 Jose Valentin	.10	.30
94 Erubiel Durazo	.10	.30
95 Jeff Cirillo	.10	.30
96 Brandon Inge	.10	.30
97 Josh Beckett	.10	.30
98 Preston Wilson	.10	.30
99 Damian Jackson	.10	.30
100 Adrian Beltre	.10	.30
101 Jeromy Burnitz	.10	.30
102 Joe Mays	.10	.30
103 Michael Barrett	.10	.30
104 Mike Piazza	.50	1.25
105 Brady Anderson	.10	.30
106 Jason Giambi Yankees	.10	.30
107 Marlon Anderson	.10	.30
108 Jimmy Rollins	.10	.30
109 Jack Wilson	.10	.30
110 Brian Lawrence	.10	.30
111 Russ Ortiz	.10	.30
112 Kazuhiro Sasaki	.10	.30
113 Placido Polanco	.10	.30
114 Damian Rolls	.10	.30
115 Rafael Palmeiro	.20	.50
116 Brad Fullmer	.10	.30
117 Tim Salmon	.20	.50
118 Tony Womack	.10	.30
119 Tony Batista	.10	.30
120 Trot Nixon	.10	.30
121 Mark Buehrle	.10	.30
122 Derek Jeter	.75	2.00
123 Ellis Burks	.10	.30
124 Mike Hampton	.10	.30
125 Roger Cedeno	.10	.30
126 A.J. Burnett	.10	.30
127 Moises Alou	.10	.30
128 Billy Wagner	.10	.30
129 Kevin Brown	.10	.30
130 Jose Hernandez	.10	.30
131 Doug Mientkiewicz	.10	.30
132 Javier Vazquez	.10	.30
133 Tsuyoshi Shinjo	.10	.30
134 Andy Pettitte	.20	.50
135 Tim Hudson	.10	.30
136 Pat Burrell	.10	.30
137 Brian Giles	.10	.30
138 Kevin Young	.10	.30
139 Xavier Nady	.10	.30
140 J.T. Snow	.10	.30
141 Aaron Sele	.10	.30
142 Albert Pujols	.60	1.50
143 Jason Tyner	.10	.30
144 Ivan Rodriguez	.20	.50
145 Raul Mondesi	.10	.30
146 Matt Lawton	.10	.30
147 Rafael Furcal	.10	.30
148 Jeff Conine	.10	.30
149 Hideo Nomo	.30	.75
150 Jose Canseco	.20	.50
151 Aaron Boone	.10	.30
152 Bartolo Colon	.10	.30
153 Todd Helton	.20	.50
154 Tony Clark	.10	.30
155 Pablo Ozuna	.10	.30
156 Jeff Bagwell	.20	.50
157 Carlos Beltran	.10	.30
158 Shawn Green	.10	.30
159 Geoff Jenkins	.10	.30
160 Eric Milton	.10	.30
161 Jose Vidro	.10	.30
162 Robin Ventura	.10	.30
163 Jorge Posada	.20	.50
164 Terrence Long	.10	.30
165 Brandon Duckworth	.10	.30
166 Chad Hermansen	.10	.30
167 Ben Davis	.10	.30
168 Phil Nevin	.10	.30
169 Bret Boone	.10	.30
170 J.D. Drew	.10	.30
171 Edgar Renteria	.10	.30
172 Randy Winn	.10	.30
173 Alex Rodriguez	.50	1.25
174 Shannon Stewart	.10	.30
175 Steve Finley	.10	.30
176 Marcus Giles	.10	.30
177 Jay Gibbons	.10	.30
178 Manny Ramirez	.20	.50
179 Ray Durham	.10	.30
180 Sean Casey	.10	.30
181 Travis Fryman	.10	.30
182 Denny Neagle	.10	.30
183 Deivi Cruz	.10	.30
184 Luis Castillo	.10	.30
185 Lance Berkman	.10	.30
186 Dee Brown	.10	.30
187 Jeff Shaw	.10	.30
188 Mark Loretta	.10	.30
189 David Ortiz	.30	.75
190 Edgardo Alfonzo	.10	.30
191 Roger Clemens	.60	1.50
192 Mariano Rivera	.30	.75
193 Jeremy Giambi	.10	.30
194 Johnny Estrada	.10	.30
195 Craig Wilson	.10	.30
196 Adam Eaton	.10	.30
197 Rich Aurilia	.10	.30
198 Mike Cameron	.10	.30
199 Jim Edmonds	.10	.30
200 Fernando Vina	.10	.30
201 Greg Vaughn	.10	.30
202 Mike Young	.30	.75
203 Vernon Wells	.10	.30
204 Luis Gonzalez	.10	.30
205 Tom Glavine	.20	.50
206 Chris Richard	.10	.30
207 Jon Lieber	.10	.30
208 Keith Foulke	.10	.30
209 Rondell White	.10	.30
210 Bernie Williams	.20	.50
211 Juan Pierre	.10	.30
212 Juan Encarnacion	.10	.30
213 Ryan Dempster	.10	.30
214 Tim Redding	.10	.30
215 Jeff Suppan	.10	.30
216 Mark Grudzielanek	.10	.30
217 Richie Sexson	.10	.30
218 Brad Radke	.10	.30
219 Armando Benitez	.10	.30
220 Orlando Hernandez	.10	.30
221 Alfonso Soriano	.10	.30
222 Mark Mulder	.10	.30
223 Travis Lee	.10	.30
224 Jason Kendall	.10	.30
225 Trevor Hoffman	.10	.30
226 Barry Bonds	.75	2.00
227 Freddy Garcia	.10	.30
228 Darryl Kile	.10	.30
229 Ben Grieve	.10	.30
230 Frank Catalanotto	.10	.30
231 Ruben Sierra	.10	.30
232 Homer Bush	.10	.30
233 Mark Grace	.20	.50
234 Andruw Jones	.20	.50
235 Brian Roberts	.10	.30
236 Fred McGriff	.20	.50
237 Paul Konerko	.10	.30
238 Ken Griffey Jr.	.50	1.25
239 John Burkett	.10	.30
240 Juan Uribe	.10	.30
241 Bobby Higginson	.10	.30
242 Cliff Floyd	.10	.30
243 Craig Biggio	.20	.50
244 Neifi Perez	.10	.30
245 Eric Karros	.10	.30
246 Ben Sheets	.10	.30
247 Tony Armas Jr.	.10	.30
248 Mo Vaughn	.10	.30
249 David Wells	.10	.30
250 Juan Gonzalez	.10	.30
251 Barry Bonds DD	3.00	8.00
252 Sammy Sosa DD	1.25	3.00
253 Ken Griffey Jr. DD	2.00	5.00
254 Roger Clemens DD	2.50	6.00
255 Greg Maddux DD	2.00	5.00
256 Chipper Jones DD	1.25	3.00
257 Alex Rodriguez Derek Jeter Nomar Garciaparra DD	2.50	6.00
258 Roberto Alomar DD	1.25	3.00
259 Jeff Bagwell DD	1.25	3.00
260 Mike Piazza DD	2.00	5.00
261 Mark Teixeira BB	1.50	4.00
262 Mark Prior BB	1.50	4.00
263 Alex Escobar BB	1.25	3.00
264 C.C. Sabathia BB	1.25	3.00
265 Drew Henson BB	1.25	3.00
266 Wilson Betemit BB	1.25	3.00
267 Roy Oswalt BB	1.25	3.00
268 Adam Dunn BB	1.25	3.00
269 Bud Smith BB	1.25	3.00
270 Dewon Brazelton BB	1.25	3.00
271 Brandon Backe RC	1.25	3.00

Jason Standridge
272 Wilfredo Rodriguez 1.25 3.00
Carlos Hernandez
273 Geronimo Gil 1.25 3.00
Luis Rivera
274 Carlos Pena 1.25 3.00
Jovanny Cedeno
275 Austin Kearns 1.25 3.00
Ben Broussard
276 Jorge De La RosaRC 1.25 3.00
Kenny Kelly
277 Ryan Drese 1.50 4.00
Victor Martinez
278 Joel Pinero 1.25 3.00
Nate Cornejo
279 David Kelton 1.25 3.00
Carlos Zambrano
280 Bill Ortega
Satoru Komiyama ERR
Not intended for public release
Card features large cut out square over Komiyama image
281 Donnie Bridges 1.25 3.00
Wilkin Ruan
282 Wily Mo Pena 1.25 3.00
Brandon Claussen
283 Jason Jennings 1.25 3.00
Rene Reyes RC
284 Steve Green 1.25 3.00
Alfredo Amezaga
285 Eric Hinske 1.25 3.00
Felipe Lopez
286 Anderson Machado RC 1.25 3.00
Brad Baisley
287 Carlos Garcia 1.25 3.00
Sean Douglass
288 Pat Strange 1.25 3.00
Jae Weong Seo
289 Marcus Thames 1.25 3.00
Alex Graman
290 Matt Childers RC 1.25 3.00
Hansel Izquierdo RC
291 Ron Calloway RC 1.25 3.00
Adam Walker RC
292 J.R. House 1.25 3.00
J.J. Davis
293 Ryan Anderson 1.25 3.00
Rafael Soriano
294 Mike Bynum 1.25 3.00
Dennis Tankersley
295 Kurt Ainsworth 1.25 3.00
Carlos Valderrama
296 Billy Hall 1.25 3.00
Cristian Guerrero
297 Miguel Olivo 1.25 3.00
Danny Wright
298 Marlon Byrd 1.25 3.00
Jorge Padilla RC
299 Juan Cruz 1.25 3.00
Ben Christensen
300 Adam Johnson 1.25 3.00
Michael Restovich
301 So Taguchi SP RC 1.25 3.00
302 Kazuhisa Ishii SP RC 1.25 3.00
NNO B.Bonds 1986 AU/73 250.00 400.00

2002 Fleer Platinum Parallel

Randomly inserted into packs, this is a parallel set version of the 2002 Fleer Platinum set. These cards have a stated print run of 202 cards for cards numbered 1 through 250 and 22 for cards numbered 251-302. Please note that no pricing is provided for cards numbered 251-302 due to market scarcity.

*PARALLEL 1-250: 2.5X TO 6X BASIC

2002 Fleer Platinum Clubhouse Memorabilia

Inserted into packs at stated odds of one in 32 hobby and one in 44 retail packs, these 39 cards feature game-used memorabilia pieces. Though not actually serial-numbered, Fleer announced the print runs for each of these cards upon release of the product and we have notated that information in our checklist.

1 Edgardo Alfonzo Jsy/1000 4.00 10.00
2 Rick Ankiel Jsy/500 4.00 10.00
3 Adrian Beltre Jsy/875 4.00 10.00
4 Craig Biggio Bat/600 6.00 15.00
5 Barry Bonds Jsy/1000 12.50 30.00
6 Sean Casey Jsy/800 4.00 10.00
7 Eric Chavez Jsy/1000 4.00 10.00
8 Roger Clemens Jsy/1000 10.00 25.00
9 J.Damon Sox Bat/700 6.00 15.00
10 Carlos Delgado Jsy/750 4.00 10.00
11 J.D. Drew Jsy/1000 4.00 10.00
12 Darin Erstad Jsy/850 4.00 10.00
13 N.Garciaparra Jsy/750 8.00 20.00
14 Juan Gonzalez Bat/1000 4.00 10.00
15 Todd Helton Jsy/925 6.00 15.00
16 Tim Hudson Jsy/825 4.00 10.00
17 D.Jeter Pants/1000 12.50 30.00
18 Randy Johnson Jsy/1000 6.00 15.00
19 A.Jones Jsy/1000 6.00 15.00
20 Jason Kendall Jsy/1000 4.00 10.00
21 Paul LoDuca Jsy/1000 4.00 10.00
22 Greg Maddux Jsy/875 6.00 15.00
23 Pedro Martinez Jsy/775 6.00 15.00
24 Raul Mondesi Bat/575 4.00 10.00
25 M.Ordonez Jsy/575 4.00 10.00
26 Mike Piazza Jsy/950 6.00 15.00
27 Mike Piazza Pants/1000 6.00 15.00
28 M.Ramirez Jsy/1000 6.00 15.00
29 Mariano Rivera Jsy/725 6.00 15.00
30 Alex Rodriguez Jsy/850 8.00 20.00
31 I.Rodriguez Jsy/1000 6.00 15.00
32 Scott Rolen Jsy/120 6.00 15.00
33 K.Sasaki Jsy/1000 4.00 10.00
34 Curt Schilling Jsy/1000 4.00 10.00
35 Gary Sheffield Jsy/775 4.00 10.00
36 Gary Sheffield Jsy/800 4.00 10.00
37 Frank Thomas Jsy/850 6.00 15.00
38 Jim Thome Bat/750 6.00 15.00
39 Omar Vizquel Jsy/1000 6.00 15.00

2002 Fleer Platinum Clubhouse Memorabilia Combos

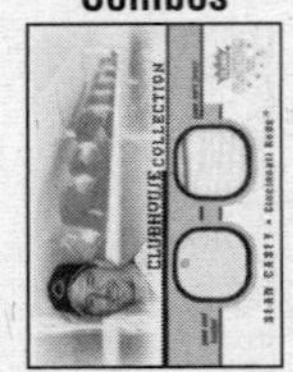

Inserted at a stated rate of one in 96 hobby packs and one in 192 retail packs, these 39 cards parallel the Clubhouse Memorabilia set. These cards can be differentiated by their having two distinct pieces of game-used memorabilia attached to the front. Since these cards have distinct press runs, we have notated that information in our checklist.

1 Edgardo Alfonzo Ball-Jsy/125 6.00 15.00
2 Rick Ankiel Bat-Jsy/200 6.00 15.00
3 Adrian Beltre Ball-Jsy/125 6.00 15.00
4 Craig Biggio Jsy-Bat/50
5 Barry Bonds Glove-Jsy/275 20.00 50.00
6 Sean Casey Ball-Jsy/125 6.00 15.00
7 Eric Chavez Base-Jsy/325 6.00 15.00
8 Roger Clemens Base-Jsy/325 15.00 40.00
9 J.Damon Sox Base-Bat/175 10.00 25.00
10 Carlos Delgado Bat-Jsy/325 6.00 15.00
11 J.D. Drew Ball-Jsy/125 6.00 15.00
12 Darin Erstad Bat-Jsy/125 6.00 15.00
13 N.Garciaparra Base-Jsy/275 15.00 40.00
14 Juan Gonzalez Jsy-Bat/75 6.00 15.00
15 Todd Helton Jsy-Bat/35
16 Tim Hudson Bat-Jsy/200 6.00 15.00
17 D.Jeter Btg Glv-Pants/200 20.00 50.00
18 Randy Johnson Bat-Jsy/125 10.00 25.00
19 And Jones Btg Glv-Jsy/100 10.00 25.00
20 Jason Kendall Ball-Jsy/50
21 Paul LoDuca Ball-Jsy/125 6.00 15.00
22 Greg Maddux Ball-Jsy/275 10.00 25.00
23 Pedro Martinez Base-Jsy/300 10.00 25.00
24 Raul Mondesi Bat-Btg Glv/75
25 M.Ordonez Bat-Jsy/325 6.00 15.00
26 Mike Piazza Ball-Jsy/125 15.00 40.00
27 Mike Piazza Ball-Pants/125 15.00 40.00
28 M.Ramirez Base-Jsy/350 10.00 25.00
29 Mariano Rivera Base-Jsy/175 10.00 25.00
30 Alex Rodriguez Base-Jsy/300 12.50 30.00
31 I.Rodriguez Btg Glv-Glv/100 10.00 25.00
32 Scott Rolen Ball-Jsy/125 10.00 25.00
33 K.Sasaki Base-Jsy/350 6.00 15.00
34 Curt Schilling Ball-Jsy/125 6.00 15.00
35 Gary Sheffield Ball-Bat/125 6.00 15.00
36 Gary Sheffield Ball-Jsy/125 6.00 15.00
37 Frank Thomas Base-Jsy/275 10.00 25.00
38 Jim Thome Base-Bat/275 10.00 25.00
39 Omar Vizquel Base-Jsy/300 10.00 25.00

2002 Fleer Platinum Cornerstones

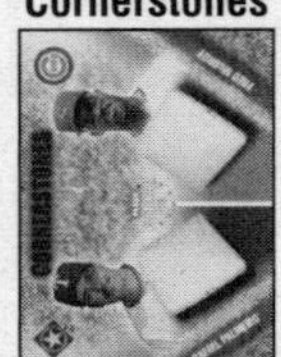

These cards were distributed in jumbo packs (1:12), rack packs (1:6) and retail packs (1:20). Each card features two prominent active and retired ballplayers paired up in a horizontal design with an image of a base floating in front of them. The cards are identical in design to the hobby-only Cornerstones Numbered except these cards lack serial-numbering, feature the word "Cornerstones" in brown lettering on front (the hobby-only versions are serial-numbered on back and feature white lettering for the "Cornerstones" moniker on front and oddly enough are entirely devoid of any checklist card number on back. The cards have been checklisted in our database using the same order as the hobby Cornerstones set.

COMPLETE SET (40) 100.00 200.00
1 Bill Terry 1.25 3.00
Johnny Mize
2 Cal Ripken 6.00 15.00
Eddie Murray
3 Eddie Mathews 2.00 5.00
Chipper Jones
4 Albert Pujols 4.00 10.00
George Sisler
5 Sean Casey 1.25 3.00
Tony Perez
6 Jimmie Foxx 2.00 5.00
Scott Rolen
7 Wade Boggs 4.00 10.00
George Brett
8 Rod Carew 1.25 3.00
Troy Glaus
9 Jeff Bagwell 1.25 3.00
Rafael Palmeiro
10 Willie Stargell 1.25 3.00
Pie Traynor
11 Cal Ripken 6.00 15.00
Brooks Robinson
12 Tony Perez 1.25 3.00
Ted Kluszewski
13 Jason Giambi 3.00 8.00
Don Mattingly
14 Hank Greenberg 2.00 5.00
Jimmie Foxx
15 Ernie Banks 2.00 5.00
Willie McCovey
16 Jim Thome 1.25 3.00
Travis Fryman
17 Ted Kluszewski 1.25 3.00
Sean Casey
18 Gil Hodges 2.00 5.00
Johnny Mize
19 Brooks Robinson 1.25 3.00
Boog Powell
20 Bill Terry 1.25 3.00
George Sisler
21 Wade Boggs 4.00 10.00
Don Mattingly
22 Jason Giambi Yankees 1.25 3.00
Carlos Delgado
23 Willie Stargell 1.25 3.00
Bill Madlock
24 Mark Grace 1.25 3.00
Matt Williams
25 Paul Molitor 4.00 10.00
George Brett
26 Carlos Delgado 1.25 3.00
Mo Vaughn
27 Bill Terry 1.25 3.00
Willie McCovey
28 Mike Sweeney 4.00 10.00
George Brett
29 Eddie Mathews 2.00 5.00
Ernie Banks
30 Eric Karros 2.00 5.00
Gil Hodges
31 Paul Molitor 4.00 10.00
Don Mattingly
32 Brooks Robinson 1.25 3.00
Rod Carew
33 Chipper Jones 4.00 10.00
Albert Pujols
34 Harry Heilmann 2.00 5.00
Hank Greenberg
35 Frank Thomas 2.00 5.00
Carlos Delgado
36 Jeff Bagwell 1.25 3.00
Todd Helton
37 Rafael Palmeiro 1.25 3.00
Fred McGriff
38 Cal Ripken 6.00 15.00
Wade Boggs
39 Orlando Cepeda 1.25 3.00
Willie McCovey
40 John Olerud 1.25 3.00
Mark Grace

2002 Fleer Platinum Cornerstones Memorabilia

Randomly inserted into packs, this 22-card set is a partial parallel of the Cornerstones Insert set. These cards have two pieces of memorabilia and all have stated print runs of 25 serial numbered sets. Due to market scarcity, no pricing is provided for this set.

1 Bill Terry Bat
Johnny Mize Bat
2 Cal Ripken Jsy
Eddie Murray Jsy
3 Eddie Mathews Bat
Chipper Jones Jsy
5 Sean Casey Jsy
Tony Perez Bat
6 Jimmie Foxx Bat
Scott Rolen Jsy
7 Wade Boggs Jsy
George Brett Jsy
9 Jeff Bagwell Bat
Rafael Palmeiro Jsy
11 Cal Ripken Jsy
Brooks Robinson Bat
12 Tony Perez Bat
Ted Kluszewski Jsy
14 Hank Greenberg Bat
Jimmie Foxx Bat
16 Jim Thome Bat
Travis Fryman Bat
17 Ted Kluszewski Jsy
Sean Casey Jsy
21 Wade Boggs Jsy
Don Mattingly Jsy
25 Paul Molitor Jsy
George Brett Jsy
27 Bill Terry Bat
Willie McCovey Jsy
28 Mike Sweeney Bat
George Brett Jsy
31 Paul Molitor Jsy
Don Mattingly Jsy
35 Frank Thomas Jsy
Carlos Delgado Jsy
36 Jeff Bagwell Bat
Todd Helton Jsy
38 Cal Ripken Jsy
Wade Boggs Jsy
39 Orlando Cepeda Jsy
Willie McCovey Jsy
40 John Olerud Jsy
Mark Grace Jsy

2002 Fleer Platinum Cornerstones Numbered

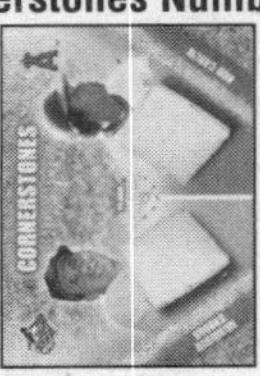

Randomly inserted into hobby packs, these 40 cards have different print runs depending on which group of cards they belong to. Cards numbered 1-10 were printed to a stated print run of 250 serial numbered sets while cards numbered 11-20 have a stated print run of 500 sets. Cards numbered 21-30 have a stated print run of 1000 sets and cards numbered 31-40 have a stated print run of 2000 sets. Other than Harry Heilmann, most of the players played a significant part of their career at either first or third base.

COMMON CARD (1-10) 6.00 15.00
COMMON CARD (11-20) 4.00 10.00
COMMON CARD (21-30) 3.00 8.00
COMMON CARD (31-40) 2.00 5.00
1 Bill Terry 6.00 15.00
Johnny Mize
2 Cal Ripken 15.00 40.00
Eddie Murray
3 Eddie Mathews 6.00 15.00
Chipper Jones
4 Albert Pujols 10.00 25.00
George Sisler
5 Sean Casey 6.00 15.00
Tony Perez
6 Jimmie Foxx 6.00 15.00
Scott Rolen
7 Wade Boggs 10.00 25.00
George Brett
8 Rod Carew 6.00 15.00
Troy Glaus
9 Jeff Bagwell 6.00 15.00
Rafael Palmeiro
10 Willie Stargell 6.00 15.00
Pie Traynor
11 Cal Ripken 12.50 30.00
Brooks Robinson
12 Tony Perez 4.00 10.00
Ted Kluszewski
13 Jason Giambi 10.00 25.00
Don Mattingly
14 Hank Greenberg 4.00 10.00
Jimmie Foxx
15 Ernie Banks 4.00 10.00
Willie McCovey
16 Jim Thome 4.00 10.00
Travis Fryman
17 Ted Kluszewski 4.00 10.00
Sean Casey
18 Gil Hodges 4.00 10.00
Johnny Mize
19 Brooks Robinson 4.00 10.00
Boog Powell
20 Bill Terry 4.00 10.00
George Sisler
21 Wade Boggs 6.00 15.00
Don Mattingly
22 Jason Giambi Yankees 3.00 8.00
Carlos Delgado
23 Willie Stargell 3.00 8.00
Bill Madlock
24 Mark Grace 3.00 8.00
Matt Williams
25 Paul Molitor 5.00 12.00
George Brett
26 Carlos Delgado 3.00 8.00
Mo Vaughn
27 Bill Terry 3.00 8.00
Willie McCovey
28 Mike Sweeney 5.00 12.00
George Brett
29 Eddie Mathews 3.00 8.00
Ernie Banks
30 Eric Karros 3.00 8.00
Gil Hodges
31 Paul Molitor 4.00 10.00
Don Mattingly
32 Brooks Robinson 2.00 5.00
Rod Carew
33 Chipper Jones 4.00 10.00
Albert Pujols
34 Harry Heilmann 2.00 5.00
Hank Greenberg
35 Frank Thomas 2.00 5.00
Carlos Delgado
36 Jeff Bagwell 2.00 5.00
Todd Helton
37 Rafael Palmeiro 2.00 5.00
Fred McGriff
38 Cal Ripken 6.00 15.00
Wade Boggs
39 Orlando Cepeda 2.00 5.00
Willie McCovey
40 John Olerud 2.00 5.00
Mark Grace

2002 Fleer Platinum Fence Busters

Randomly inserted into rack packs, these 22 cards feature some of the leading hitters in the game. We have provided the stated print runs for these cards in our checklist. The Jeff Bagwell card was not ready when Fleer went to press with this set and that card could be redeemed until April 30th, 2003.

1 Roberto Alomar/800 4.00 10.00
2 Moises Alou/800 3.00 8.00
3 Jeff Bagwell/400 4.00 10.00

4 Barry Bonds/700 10.00 25.00
5 J.D. Drew/800 3.00 8.00
6 Jim Edmonds/500 3.00 8.00
7 Brian Giles/700 3.00 8.00
8 Luis Gonzalez/625 3.00 8.00
9 Shawn Green/800 3.00 8.00
10 Todd Helton/675 4.00 10.00
11 Derek Jeter/400 10.00 25.00
12 Andruw Jones/800 4.00 10.00
13 Chipper Jones/800 4.00 10.00
14 Tino Martinez/800 4.00 10.00
15 Rafael Palmeiro/800 4.00 10.00
16 Mike Piazza/800 6.00 15.00
17 Manny Ramirez/800 4.00 10.00
18 Alex Rodriguez/675 6.00 15.00
19 Miguel Tejada/700 3.00 8.00
20 Frank Thomas/800 4.00 10.00
21 Jim Thome/800 4.00 10.00
22 Larry Walker/750 3.00 8.00

2002 Fleer Platinum Fence Busters Autographs

Randomly inserted into rack packs, these four cards feature signed copies of the Fence Busters insert set. These cards were all serial numbered to the selected player's 2001 home run total. All of these cards were issued as exchange cards and could be redeemed until April 30th, 2003.

1 Jeff Bagwell/39
2 Barry Bonds/73 125.00 200.00
3 Derek Jeter/21
4 Miguel Tejada/31

2002 Fleer Platinum National Patch Time

Inserted at stated odds at one in 12 jumbo packs, these 19 cards feature the selected player as well as game-worn jersey patch swatch of the featured player. The stated print runs for the players are listed next to their name in our checklist.

1 Barry Bonds/75 50.00 120.00
2 Pat Burrell/285 15.00 40.00
3 Jose Canseco/150 20.00 50.00
4 Carlos Delgado/70 20.00 50.00
5 J.D. Drew/210 15.00 40.00
6 Adam Dunn/75 20.00 50.00
7 Darin Erstad/315 15.00 40.00
8 Juan Gonzalez/50 25.00 60.00
9 Todd Helton/170 20.00 50.00
10 Derek Jeter/65 50.00 120.00
11 Greg Maddux/775 15.00 40.00
12 Pedro Martinez/45 25.00 60.00
13 Magglio Ordonez/85 20.00 50.00
14 Manny Ramirez/100 20.00 50.00
15 Cal Ripken/350 40.00 100.00
16 Alex Rodriguez/325 25.00 60.00
17 Ivan Rodriguez/225 15.00 40.00
18 Kazuhiro Sasaki/310 15.00 40.00
19 Miguel Tejada/55 20.00 50.00

2002 Fleer Platinum Wheelhouse

Inserted at stated odds of one in 12 hobby and one in 20 retail, these 20 cards feature some of the leading hitters in baseball.

COMPLETE SET (20) 40.00 80.00
1 Derek Jeter 3.00 8.00
2 Barry Bonds 3.00 8.00
3 Luis Gonzalez 1.25 3.00
4 Jason Giambi 1.25 3.00
5 Ivan Rodriguez 1.25 3.00
6 Mike Piazza 2.00 5.00
7 Troy Glaus 1.25 3.00
8 Nomar Garciaparra 2.00 5.00
9 Juan Gonzalez 1.25 3.00
10 Sammy Sosa 1.25 3.00
11 Albert Pujols 2.50 6.00
12 Ken Griffey Jr. 2.00 5.00
13 Scott Rolen 1.25 3.00
14 Jeff Bagwell 1.25 3.00
15 Ichiro Suzuki 2.50 6.00
16 Todd Helton 1.25 3.00
17 Chipper Jones 1.25 3.00
18 Alex Rodriguez 2.00 5.00
19 Vladimir Guerrero 1.25 3.00
20 Manny Ramirez 1.25 3.00

2003 Fleer Platinum

This 250 card set was release in February, 2003. These cards were issued in a variety of manners. Each box contained 14 wax packs as well as 4 jumbo packs and one rack pack. The wax packs had an SRP of $3, while the jumbos had an SRP of $5 amd the rack packs had an SRP of $10. There are several subsets in the product. Cards numbered 201 through 220 feature Unsung Heroes. Cards numbered 221 through 250 are prospects but those cards were issued in different ratios throughout the set.

COMP.SET w/o SP's (220) 10.00 25.00
COMMON CARD (1-220) .10 .30
COMMON CARD (221-235) .75 2.00
221-235 ODDS 1:4 WAX, 1:2 JUM, 1:1 RACK
COMMON CARD (236-240) .75 2.00
236-240 ODDS 1:12 WAX
COMMON CARD (241-245) 1.25 3.00
241-245 ODDS 1:6 JUMBO
COMMON CARD (246-250) 1.25 3.00
246-250 ODDS 1:2 RACK
1 Barry Bonds .75 2.00
2 Sean Casey .10 .30
3 Todd Walker .10 .30
4 Tony Batista .10 .30
5 Todd Zeile .10 .30
6 Ruben Sierra .10 .30
7 Jose Cruz Jr. .10 .30
8 Ben Grieve .10 .30
9 Rob Mackowiak .10 .30
10 Gary Sheffield .10 .30
11 Armando Benitez .10 .30
12 Tim Hudson .10 .30
13 Eric Milton .10 .30
14 Andy Pettitte .20 .50
15 Jeff Bagwell .20 .50
16 Jeff Kent .10 .30
17 Joe Randa .10 .30
18 Benito Santiago .10 .30
19 Russell Branyan .10 .30
20 Cliff Floyd .10 .30
21 Chris Richard .10 .30
22 Randy Winn .10 .30
23 Freddy Garcia .10 .30
24 Derek Lowe .10 .30
25 Ben Sheets .10 .30
26 Fred McGriff .20 .50
27 Bret Boone .10 .30
28 Jose Hernandez .10 .30
29 Phil Nevin .10 .30
30 Mike Piazza .50 1.25
31 Bobby Abreu .10 .30
32 Darin Erstad .10 .30
33 Andruw Jones .20 .50
34 Brad Wilkerson .10 .30
35 Brian Lawrence .10 .30
36 Vladimir Nunez .10 .30
37 Kazuhiro Sasaki .10 .30
38 Carlos Delgado .10 .30
39 Steve Cox .10 .30
40 Adrian Beltre .10 .30
41 Josh Bard .10 .30
42 Randall Simon .10 .30
43 Johnny Damon .20 .50
44 Ken Griffey Jr. .50 1.25
45 Sammy Sosa .30 .75
46 Kevin Brown .10 .30
47 Kazuhisa Ishii .10 .30
48 Matt Morris .10 .30
49 Mark Prior .20 .50
50 Kip Wells .10 .30
51 Hee Seop Choi .10 .30
52 Craig Biggio .20 .50
53 Derek Jeter .75 2.00
54 Albert Pujols .60 1.50
55 Joe Borchard .10 .30
56 Robert Fick .10 .30
57 Jacque Jones .10 .30
58 Juan Pierre .10 .30
59 Bernie Williams .20 .50
60 Elmer Dessens .10 .30
61 Al Leiter .10 .30
62 Curt Schilling .10 .30
63 Carlos Pena .10 .30
64 Tino Martinez .20 .50
65 Fernando Vina .10 .30
66 Aaron Boone .10 .30
67 Michael Barrett .10 .30
68 Frank Thomas .30 .75
69 J.D. Drew .10 .30
70 Vladimir Guerrero .30 .75
71 Shannon Stewart .10 .30
72 Mark Buehrle .10 .30
73 Jamie Moyer .10 .30
74 Brad Radke .10 .30
75 Mike Williams .10 .30
76 Ryan Klesko .10 .30
77 Roberto Alomar .20 .50
78 Edgardo Alfonzo .10 .30
79 Matt Williams .10 .30
80 Edgar Martinez .20 .50
81 Shawn Green .10 .30
82 Kenny Lofton .10 .30

83 Josh Beckett .10 .30
84 Trevor Hoffman .10 .30
85 Kevin Millwood .10 .30
86 Odalis Perez .10 .30
87 Jarrod Washburn .10 .30
88 Jason Giambi .10 .30
89 Eric Young .10 .30
90 Barry Larkin .20 .50
91 Aramis Ramirez .10 .30
92 Ivan Rodriguez .20 .50
93 Steve Finley .10 .30
94 Brian Jordan .10 .30
95 Manny Ramirez .20 .50
96 Preston Wilson .10 .30
97 Rodrigo Lopez .10 .30
98 Ramon Ortiz .10 .30
99 Jim Thome .20 .50
100 Luis Castillo .10 .30
101 Alex Rodriguez .50 1.25
102 Jared Sandberg .10 .30
103 Ellis Burks .10 .30
104 Pat Burrell .10 .30
105 Brian Giles .10 .30
106 Mark Kotsay .10 .30
107 Dave Roberts .10 .30
108 Roy Halladay .10 .30
109 Chan Ho Park .10 .30
110 Erubiel Durazo .10 .30
111 Bobby Hill .10 .30
112 Cristian Guzman .10 .30
113 Troy Glaus .10 .30
114 Lance Berkman .10 .30
115 Juan Encarnacion .10 .30
116 Chipper Jones .30 .75
117 Corey Patterson .10 .30
118 Vernon Wells .10 .30
119 Matt Clement .10 .30
120 Billy Koch .10 .30
121 Hideo Nomo .30 .75
122 Derrek Lee .20 .50
123 Todd Helton .20 .50
124 Sean Burroughs .10 .30
125 Jason Kendall .10 .30
126 Dmitri Young .10 .30
127 Adam Dunn .10 .30
128 Bobby Higginson .10 .30
129 Raul Mondesi .10 .30
130 Bubba Trammell .10 .30
131 A.J. Burnett .10 .30
132 Randy Johnson .30 .75
133 Mark Mulder .10 .30
134 Mariano Rivera .30 .75
135 Kerry Wood .10 .30
136 Mo Vaughn .10 .30
137 Jimmy Rollins .10 .30
138 Jose Valentin .10 .30
139 Brad Fullmer .10 .30
140 Mike Cameron .10 .30
141 Luis Gonzalez .10 .30
142 Kevin Appier .10 .30
143 Mike Hampton .10 .30
144 Pedro Martinez .20 .50
145 Javier Vazquez .10 .30
146 Doug Mientkiewicz .10 .30
147 Adam Kennedy .10 .30
148 Rafael Furcal .10 .30
149 Eric Chavez .10 .30
150 Mike Lieberthal .10 .30
151 Moises Alou .10 .30
152 Jermaine Dye .10 .30
153 Torii Hunter .10 .30
154 Trot Nixon .10 .30
155 Larry Walker .10 .30
156 Jorge Julio .10 .30
157 Mike Mussina .20 .50
158 Kirk Rueter .10 .30
159 Rafael Palmeiro .20 .50
160 Pokey Reese .10 .30
161 Miguel Tejada .10 .30
162 Robin Ventura .10 .30
163 Raul Ibanez .10 .30
164 Roger Cedeno .10 .30
165 Juan Gonzalez .10 .30
166 Carlos Lee .10 .30
167 Tim Salmon .20 .50
168 Orlando Hernandez .10 .30
169 Wade Miller .10 .30
170 Troy Percival .10 .30
171 Billy Wagner .10 .30
172 Jeff Conine .10 .30
173 Junior Spivey .10 .30
174 Edgar Renteria .10 .30
175 Scott Rolen .20 .50
176 Jason Varitek .30 .75
177 Ben Broussard .10 .30
178 Jeremy Giambi .10 .30
179 Gabe Kapler .10 .30
180 Armando Rios .10 .30
181 Ichiro Suzuki .60 1.50
182 Tom Glavine .20 .50
183 Greg Maddux .50 1.25
184 Roy Oswalt .10 .30
185 John Smoltz .20 .50
186 Eric Karros .10 .30
187 Alfonso Soriano .10 .30
188 Nomar Garciaparra .50 1.25
189 Joe Crede .10 .30
190 Javy Lopez .10 .30
191 Carlos Beltran .10 .30
192 Jim Edmonds .10 .30
193 Geoff Jenkins .10 .30
194 Magglio Ordonez .10 .30
195 Daryle Ward .10 .30
196 Roger Clemens .60 1.50
197 Byung-Hyun Kim .10 .30
198 Robb Nen .10 .30
199 C.C. Sabathia .10 .30
200 Barry Zito .10 .30
201 Mark Grace UH .10 .30
202 Paul Konerko UH .10 .30
203 Mike Sweeney UH .10 .30
204 John Olerud UH .10 .30
205 Jose Vidro UH .10 .30
206 Ray Durham UH .10 .30
207 Omar Vizquel UH .10 .30
208 Shea Hillenbrand UH .10 .30
209 Mike Lowell UH .10 .30
210 Aubrey Huff UH .10 .30
211 Eric Hinske UH .10 .30
212 Paul Lo Duca UH .10 .30
213 Jay Gibbons UH .10 .30
214 Austin Kearns UH .10 .30
215 Richie Sexson UH .10 .30
216 Garret Anderson UH .10 .30
217 Eric Gagne UH .10 .30
218 Jason Jennings UH .10 .30
219 Damian Moss UH .10 .30
220 David Eckstein UH .10 .30
221 Mark Teixeira PROS 1.25 3.00
222 Bill Hall PROS .75 2.00
223 Bobby Jenks PROS .75 2.00
224 Adam Morrissey PROS .75 2.00
225 Rodrigo Rosario PROS .75 2.00
226 Brett Myers PROS .75 2.00
227 Tony Alvarez PROS .75 2.00
228 Willie Bloomquist PROS .75 2.00
229 Ben Howard PROS .75 2.00
230 Nic Jackson PROS .75 2.00
231 Carl Crawford PROS .75 2.00
232 Omar Infante PROS .75 2.00
233 Francisco Rodriguez PROS .75 2.00
234 Andy Van Hekken PROS .75 2.00
235 Kirk Saarloos PROS .75 2.00
236 Dusty Wathan PROS RC .75 2.00
237 Jamey Carroll PROS .75 2.00
238 Jason Phillips PROS .75 2.00
239 Jose Castillo PROS .75 2.00
240 Arnaldo Munoz PROS RC .75 2.00
241 Orlando Hudson PROS 1.25 3.00
242 Drew Henson PROS 1.25 3.00
243 Jason Lane PROS 1.25 3.00
244 Vinny Chulk PROS 1.25 3.00
245 Prentice Redman PROS RC 1.25 3.00
246 Marlon Byrd PROS 1.25 3.00
247 Chin-Feng Chen PROS 1.25 3.00
248 Craig Brazell PROS RC 1.25 3.00
249 John Webb PROS 1.25 3.00
250 Adam LaRoche PROS 1.25 3.00

2003 Fleer Platinum Finish

Randomly inserted in packs, this is a parallel to the Fleer Platinum set. These cards with a "finished" type front were issued to a stated print run of 100 serial numbered sets.

*FINISH 1-220: 3X TO 8X BASIC
*FINISH 221-235: 1X TO 2.5X BASIC
*FINISH 236-240: 1X TO 2.5X BASIC
*FINISH 241-245: .6X TO 1.5X BASIC
*FINISH 2446-250: .6X TO 1.5X BASIC

2003 Fleer Platinum Barry Bonds Chasing History Game Used

Randomly inserted in packs, these five cards feature game used swatches from both Barry Bonds and various retired players whose records he was chasing. The cards with two game-worn swatches were issued to a stated print run of 250 serial numbered sets while the five player card was issued to a stated print run of 25 serial numbered sets.

BB Barry Bonds Jsy 15.00 40.00
Bobby Bonds Bat
BR Barry Bonds Jsy 125.00 200.00
Babe Ruth Bat
RM Barry Bonds Jsy 30.00 60.00
Roger Maris Pants
WM Barry Bonds Jsy 15.00 40.00
Willie McCovey Jsy
CH Barry BondsJsy
Bobby Bonds Bat
Roger Maris Pants
Willie McCovey Jsy
Babe Ruth Bat

2003 Fleer Platinum Guts and Glory

Inserted at a stated rate of one in four wax packs, one in two jumbo and one per rack pack, this 20 card set features some of the leading players in baseball.

COMPLETE SET (20) 10.00 25.00
1 Jason Giambi .40 1.00
2 Alfonso Soriano .40 1.00
3 Scott Rolen .40 1.00
4 Ivan Rodriguez .40 1.00
5 Barry Bonds 1.25 3.00
6 Jim Edmonds .40 1.00
7 Darin Erstad .40 1.00
8 Brian Giles .40 1.00
9 Luis Gonzalez .40 1.00
10 Adam Dunn .40 1.00
11 Torii Hunter .40 1.00
12 Andruw Jones .40 1.00
13 Sammy Sosa .50 1.25
14 Ichiro Suzuki 1.00 2.50
15 Miguel Tejada .40 1.00
16 Roger Clemens 1.00 2.50
17 Curt Schilling .40 1.00
18 Nomar Garciaparra .75 2.00
19 Derek Jeter 1.25 3.00
20 Alex Rodriguez .75 2.00

2003 Fleer Platinum Heart of the Order

Inserted in packs at a rate of one in 12 wax, one in six jumbo and one in three rack, these cards feature three players who are the key offensive weapons for their teams.

1 Jason Giambi 1.50 4.00
Derek Jeter
Alfonso Soriano
2 Todd Helton .75 2.00
Preston Wilson
Larry Walker
3 Rafael Palmeiro 1.25 3.00
Alex Rodriguez
Ivan Rodriguez
4 Adam Dunn 1.25 3.00
Ken Griffey Jr.
Austin Kearns
5 Jeff Bagwell .75 2.00
Craig Biggio
Lance Berkman
6 Eric Chavez .75 2.00
Miguel Tejada
Jermaine Dye
7 Troy Glaus .75 2.00
Garrett Anderson
Darin Erstad
8 Mike Piazza 1.25 3.00
Mo Vaughn
Roberto Alomar
9 Torii Hunter .75 2.00
Jacque Jones
Corey Koskie
10 Barry Bonds 2.00 5.00
Jeff Kent
Rich Aurilia
11 Pat Burrell .75 2.00
Bobby Abreu
Jimmy Rollins
12 Shawn Green .75 2.00
Adrian Beltre
Paul Lo Duca
13 Vladimir Guerrero .75 2.00
Brad Wilkerson
Jose Vidro
14 Chipper Jones .75 2.00
Andruw Jones
Gary Sheffield
15 Ichiro Suzuki 1.50 4.00
{Bret Boone
Edgar Martinez
16 Albert Pujols 1.50 4.00
Scott Rolen
J.D. Drew
17 Sammy Sosa .75 2.00
Fred McGriff
Moises Alou
18 Nomar Garciaparra 1.25 3.00
Shea Hillenbrand
Manny Ramirez
19 Frank Thomas .75 2.00
Magglio Ordonez
Paul Konerko
20 Jason Kendall .75 2.00
Brian Giles
Amaris Ramirez

2003 Fleer Platinum Heart of the Order Game Used

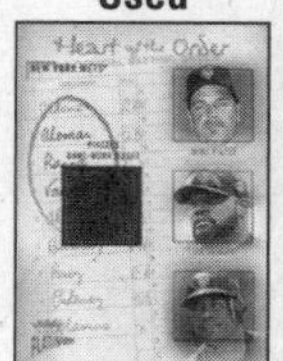

Inserted at a stated rate of one in two rack packs, this is a partial parallel to the Heart of the Order set. These cards feature a game-used memorabilia piece form one of the players on the card along with photos of the other two players. Each of these cards was issued to a stated print run of 400 serial numbered sets.

AB Adrian Beltre Jsy 3.00 8.00
Shawn Green
Paul Lo Duca
AK Austin Kearns Pants 3.00 8.00
Adam Dunn
Ken Griffey Jr.
AS Alfonso Soriano Bat 3.00 8.00
Jason Giambi
Derek Jeter
BB Bret Boone Jsy 3.00 8.00
Edgar Martinez
Ichiro Suzuki
BG Brian Giles Bat 3.00 8.00
Jason Kendall
Aramis Ramirez
CJ Chipper Jones Jsy 6.00 15.00
Andruw Jones
Gary Sheffield
DE Darin Erstad Jsy 3.00 8.00
Garret Anderson
Troy Glaus
FT Frank Thomas Jsy 6.00 15.00
Paul Konerko
Magglio Ordonez
JD J.D. Drew Jsy 3.00 8.00
Albert Pujols
Scott Rolen
JK Jeff Kent Jsy 3.00 8.00
Rich Aurilia
Barry Bonds
JR Jimmy Rollins Jsy 3.00 8.00
Bob Abreu
Pat Burrell
JV Jose Vidro Jsy 3.00 8.00
Vladimir Guerrero
Brad Wilkerson
LB Lance Berkman Bat 3.00 8.00
Jeff Bagwell
Craig Biggio
MP Mike Piazza Jsy 6.00 15.00
Roberto Alomar
Mo Vaughn
MR Manny Ramirez Jsy 4.00 10.00
Nomar Garciaparra
Shea Hillenbrand
RP Rafael Palmeiro Jsy 4.00 10.00
Alex Rodriguez
Ivan Rodriguez
SS Sammy Sosa Jsy 6.00 15.00
Moises Alou
Fred McGriff
TH Todd Helton Jsy 4.00 10.00
Larry Walker
Preston Wilson

2003 Fleer Platinum MLB Scouting Report

Randomly inserted in packs, this 32 card set features information about the noted player. Each card has some scouting type information to go with some hitting charts. These cards were issued to a stated print run of 400 serial numbered sets.

1 Jason Giambi 1.50 4.00
2 Paul Konerko 1.50 4.00
3 Jim Thome 1.50 4.00
4 Alfonso Soriano 1.50 4.00
5 Troy Glaus 1.50 4.00
6 Eric Hinske 1.50 4.00
7 Paul Lo Duca 1.50 4.00
8 Mike Piazza 2.50 6.00
9 Marlon Byrd 1.50 4.00
10 Garret Anderson 1.50 4.00
11 Barry Bonds 4.00 10.00
12 Pat Burrell 1.50 4.00
13 Joe Crede 1.50 4.00
14 J.D. Drew 1.50 4.00
15 Ken Griffey Jr. 2.50 6.00
16 Vladimir Guerrero 1.50 4.00
17 Torii Hunter 1.50 4.00
18 Chipper Jones 1.50 4.00
19 Austin Kearns 1.50 4.00
20 Albert Pujols 3.00 8.00
21 Manny Ramirez 1.50 4.00
22 Gary Sheffield 1.50 4.00
23 Sammy Sosa 1.50 4.00
24 Ichiro Suzuki 3.00 8.00
25 Bernie Williams 1.50 4.00
26 Randy Johnson 1.50 4.00
27 Greg Maddux 2.50 6.00
28 Hideo Nomo 1.50 4.00
29 Nomar Garciaparra 2.50 6.00
30 Derek Jeter 4.00 10.00
31 Alex Rodriguez 2.50 6.00
32 Miguel Tejada 1.50 4.00

2003 Fleer Platinum MLB Scouting Report Game Used

Randomly inserted in wax packs, this is a partial parallel to the Scouting Report insert set. These cards feature a game used piece to go with the scouting report information. These cards were issued to a stated print run of 250 serial numbered sets.

AK Austin Kearns Pants 4.00 10.00
AS Alfonso Soriano Bat 4.00 10.00
BB Barry Bonds Jsy 10.00 25.00
CJ Chipper Jones Jsy 6.00 15.00
DJ Derek Jeter Jsy 10.00 25.00
GM Greg Maddux Jsy 6.00 15.00
HN Hideo Nomo Jsy 12.50 30.00
JD J.D. Drew Jsy 4.00 10.00
JT Jim Thome Jsy 6.00 15.00
MP Mike Piazza Jsy 6.00 15.00
MR Manny Ramirez Jsy 6.00 15.00
RJ Randy Johnson Jsy 6.00 15.00
SS Sammy Sosa Jsy 6.00 15.00

2003 Fleer Platinum Nameplates

Inserted at a stated rate of one in eight jumbo packs, these 41 cards feature different amounts of the featured players. We have notated the print runs for the players in our checklist.

AD Adam Dunn/117 10.00 25.00
AJ Andruw Jones/170 10.00 25.00
AR Alex Rodriguez/248 20.00 50.00
BB Barry Bonds/251 30.00 60.00
BL Barry Larkin/97 15.00 40.00
BZ Barry Zito/248 10.00 25.00
CB Craig Biggio/152 10.00 25.00
CC Chin-Feng Chen/110 60.00 120.00
CJ Chipper Jones/251 12.50 30.00
CK Corey Koskie/130 10.00 25.00
EH Eric Hinske/173 10.00 25.00
EM Edgar Martinez/176 10.00 25.00
FT Frank Thomas/58 20.00 50.00
FT Frank Thomas/93 20.00 50.00
GM Greg Maddux/248 15.00 40.00
HN Hideo Nomo/150
IR Ivan Rodriguez/189 10.00 25.00
JB Jeff Bagwell/121 10.00 25.00
JD Johnny Damon/35 30.00 60.00
JO John Olerud/180 10.00 25.00
JR Jimmy Rollins/74 10.00 25.00
JT Jim Thome/158 10.00 25.00
KI Kazuhisa Ishii/35 20.00 50.00
KS Kazuhiro Sasaki/82 10.00 25.00
KW Kerry Wood/49 20.00 50.00
LB Lance Berkman/176 10.00 25.00
LW Larry Walker/161 10.00 25.00
MP Mike Piazza/200 15.00 40.00
MP2 Mark Prior/123 10.00 25.00
MR Manny Ramirez/94 15.00 40.00
MS Mike Sweeney/175 10.00 25.00
MT Miguel Tejada/225 10.00 25.00
NG Nomar Garciaparra/258 15.00 40.00
PB Pat Burrell/176 10.00 25.00
PM Pedro Martinez/244 10.00 25.00
PN Phil Nevin/134
RC Roger Clemens/141 30.00 60.00
RJ Randy Johnson/142
RO Roy Oswalt/155 10.00 25.00
RP Rafael Palmeiro/245 10.00 25.00
RS Richie Sexson/160 10.00 25.00
VG Vladimir Guerrero/102 20.00 50.00

2003 Fleer Platinum Portraits

Inserted at a stated rate of one in 20 wax packs, one in 10 jumbo packs and one in five rack packs, these 20 cards feature painting like cards of the featured player.

1 Josh Beckett 1.25 3.00
2 Roberto Alomar 1.25 3.00
3 Alfonso Soriano 1.25 3.00
4 Mike Piazza 2.00 5.00
5 Ivan Rodriguez 1.25 3.00
6 Edgar Martinez 1.25 3.00
7 Barry Bonds 3.00 8.00
8 Adam Dunn 1.25 3.00
9 Juan Gonzalez 1.25 3.00
10 Chipper Jones 1.25 3.00
11 Albert Pujols 2.50 6.00
12 Magglio Ordonez 1.25 3.00
13 Shea Hillenbrand 1.25 3.00
14 Larry Walker 1.25 3.00
15 Pedro Martinez 1.25 3.00
16 Kerry Wood 1.25 3.00
17 Barry Zito 1.25 3.00
18 Nomar Garciaparra 2.00 5.00
19 Derek Jeter 3.00 8.00
20 Alex Rodriguez 2.00 5.00

2003 Fleer Platinum Portraits Game Jersey

Inserted at a stated rate of one in 86 wax packs, this is a partial parallel to the Portraits insert set. These cards feature a game-worn jersey swatch on the front. The Derek Jeter card was issued in smaller quantity and we have notated that information in our data base.

AD Adam Dunn 3.00 8.00
BB Barry Bonds 8.00 20.00
BZ Barry Zito 3.00 8.00
CJ Chipper Jones 4.00 10.00
DJ Derek Jeter SP/150 12.50 30.00
IR Ivan Rodriguez 4.00 10.00
JB Josh Beckett 3.00 8.00
KW Kerry Wood 3.00 8.00
MP Mike Piazza 6.00 15.00
NG Nomar Garciaparra 6.00 15.00
PM Pedro Martinez 4.00 10.00

2003 Fleer Platinum Portraits Game Patch

Inserted at a stated rate of one in 86 wax packs, this is a partial parallel to the Portraits insert set. These cards feature a game-worn jersey swatch on the front. These cards were issued to a stated print run of 100 serial numbered sets.

AD Adam Dunn 15.00 40.00
BB Barry Bonds 30.00 60.00
BZ Barry Zito 15.00 40.00
CJ Chipper Jones 15.00 40.00
DJ Derek Jeter
IR Ivan Rodriguez 15.00 40.00
KW Kerry Wood 15.00 40.00
MP Mike Piazza 30.00 60.00
NG Nomar Garciaparra 30.00 60.00
PM Pedro Martinez 15.00 40.00

2004 Fleer Platinum

This 200-card set was released in February, 2004. The set was issued in seven-card packs with an $3 SRP which came 18 packs to a box and 16 boxes to a case. In addition, every hobby box had four jumbo packs included. Those jumbo packs had 20 cards in them. Plus rack packs were issued; those packs had 30 cards in each pack. Cards numbered 1-135 are major league veterans while cards numbered 136-143 were issued at a stated rate of one in three wax and one in 12 retail packs. Cards numbered 144-151 were issued at a stated rate of one per jumbo while cards 152 through 157 were issued exclusively in rack packs at a rate of one per and according to Fleer the stated print run of those cards was approximately 1000 cards. The set closes with the following subsets: UH (cards numbered 158 through 182 while cards numbered 183 through 200 feature multi-player prospect cards.

COMP.SET w/o SP's (178) 10.00 25.00
COMMON (1-135/158-182) .10 .30
COMMON CARD (183-200) .40 1.00
183-200 ARE NOT SHORT-PRINTS
COMMON CARD (136-143) .60 1.50
136-143 ODDS 1:3 WAX, 1:12 RETAIL
COMMON CARD (144-151) 1.00 2.50
144-151 ODDS ONE PER JUMBO
COMMON CARD (152-157) 3.00 8.00
152-157 ODDS ONE PER RACK PACK
152-157 STATED PRINT RUN APPX.1000 SETS
152-157 PRINT RUN PROVIDED BY FLEER
152-157 ARE NOT SERIAL-NUMBERED
1 Luis Castillo .10 .30
2 Preston Wilson .10 .30
3 Johan Santana .30 .75
4 Fred McGriff .20 .50
5 Albert Pujols .60 1.50
6 Reggie Sanders .10 .30
7 Ivan Rodriguez .20 .50
8 Roy Halladay .10 .30
9 Brian Giles .10 .30
10 Bernie Williams .20 .50
11 Barry Larkin .20 .50
12 Marlon Anderson .10 .30
13 Ramon Ortiz .10 .30
14 Luis Matos .10 .30
15 Esteban Loaiza .10 .30
16 Orlando Cabrera .10 .30
17 Jamie Moyer .10 .30
18 Tino Martinez .20 .50
19 Josh Beckett .10 .30
20 Derek Jeter .60 1.50
21 Derek Lowe .10 .30
22 Jack Wilson .10 .30
23 Bret Boone .10 .30
24 Matt Morris .10 .30
25 Javier Vazquez .10 .30
26 Joe Crede .10 .30
27 Jose Vidro .10 .30
28 Mike Piazza .50 1.25
29 Curt Schilling .20 .50
30 Alex Rodriguez .50 1.25
31 John Olerud .10 .30
32 Dontrelle Willis .20 .50
33 Larry Walker .10 .30
34 Joe Randa .10 .30
35 Paul Lo Duca .10 .30
36 Marlon Byrd .10 .30
37 Bo Hart .10 .30
38 Rafael Palmeiro .20 .50
39 Garret Anderson .10 .30
40 Tom Glavine .20 .50

41 Ichiro Suzuki .60 1.50
42 Derrek Lee .20 .50
43 Lance Berkman .10 .30
44 Nomar Garciaparra .50 1.25
45 Mike Sweeney .10 .30
46 A.J. Burnett .10 .30
47 Sean Casey .10 .30
48 Eric Gagne .10 .30
49 Joel Pineiro .10 .30
50 Russ Ortiz .10 .30
51 Placido Polanco .10 .30
52 Sammy Sosa .30 .75
53 Mark Teixeira .20 .50
54 Randy Wolf .10 .30
55 Vladimir Guerrero .30 .75
56 Tim Hudson .10 .30
57 Lew Ford .10 .30
58 Carlos Delgado .10 .30
59 Darin Erstad .10 .30
60 Mike Lieberthal .10 .30
61 Craig Biggio .20 .50
62 Ryan Klesko .10 .30
63 C.C. Sabathia .10 .30
64 Carlos Lee .10 .30
65 Al Leiter .10 .30
66 Brandon Webb .10 .30
67 Jacque Jones .10 .30
68 Kerry Wood .10 .30
69 Omar Vizquel .20 .50
70 Jeremy Bonderman .10 .30
71 Kevin Brown .10 .30
72 Richie Sexson .10 .30
73 Zach Day .10 .30
74 Mike Mussina .20 .50
75 Sidney Ponson .10 .30
76 Andruw Jones .20 .50
77 Woody Williams .10 .30
78 Kazuhiro Sasaki .10 .30
79 Matt Clement .10 .30
80 Shea Hillenbrand .10 .30
81 Bartolo Colon .10 .30
82 Ken Griffey Jr. .50 1.25
83 Todd Helton .20 .50
84 Dmitri Young .10 .30
85 Richard Hidalgo .10 .30
86 Carlos Beltran .10 .30
87 Brad Wilkerson .10 .30
88 Andy Pettitte .20 .50
89 Miguel Tejada .10 .30
90 Edgar Martinez .20 .50
91 Vernon Wells .10 .30
92 Magglio Ordonez .10 .30
93 Tony Batista .10 .30
94 Jose Reyes .10 .30
95 Matt Stairs .10 .30
96 Manny Ramirez .20 .50
97 Carlos Pena .10 .30
98 A.J. Pierzynski .10 .30
99 Jim Thome .20 .50
100 Aubrey Huff .10 .30
101 Roberto Alomar .20 .50
102 Luis Gonzalez .10 .30
103 Chipper Jones .30 .75
104 Jay Gibbons .10 .30
105 Adam Dunn .10 .30
106 Jay Payton .10 .30
107 Scott Podsednik .10 .30
108 Roy Oswalt .10 .30
109 Milton Bradley .10 .30
110 Shawn Green .10 .30
111 Ryan Wagner .10 .30
112 Eric Chavez .10 .30
113 Pat Burrell .10 .30
114 Frank Thomas .30 .75
115 Jason Kendall .10 .30
116 Jake Peavy .10 .30
117 Mike Cameron .10 .30
118 Jim Edmonds .10 .30
119 Hank Blalock .10 .30
120 Troy Glaus .10 .30
121 Jeff Kent .10 .30
122 Jason Schmidt .10 .30
123 Corey Patterson .10 .30
124 Austin Kearns .10 .30
125 Edwin Jackson .10 .30
126 Alfonso Soriano .10 .30
127 Bobby Abreu .10 .30
128 Scott Rolen .20 .50
129 Jeff Bagwell .20 .50
130 Shannon Stewart .10 .30
131 Rich Aurilia .10 .30
132 Ty Wigginton .10 .30
133 Randy Johnson .30 .75
134 Rocco Baldelli .10 .30
135 Hideo Nomo .30 .75
136 Greg Maddux WE 1.25 3.00
137 Johnny Damon WE .60 1.50
138 Mark Prior WE .60 1.50
139 Corey Koskie WE .60 1.50
140 Miguel Cabrera WE .60 1.50
141 Hideki Matsui WE 1.00 2.50
142 Jose Cruz Jr. WE .60 1.50
143 Barry Zito WE .60 1.50
144 Javy Lopez JE 1.00 2.50
145 Jason Varitek JE 1.25 3.00
146 Moises Alou JE 1.00 2.50
147 Torii Hunter JE 1.00 2.50
148 Juan Encarnacion JE 1.00 2.50
149 Jorge Posada JE 1.00 2.50
150 Marquis Grissom JE 1.00 2.50
151 Rich Harden JE 1.00 2.50
152 Gary Sheffield RE 3.00 8.00
153 Pedro Martinez RE 3.00 8.00
154 Brad Radke RE 3.00 8.00
155 Mike Lowell RE 3.00 8.00
156 Jason Giambi RE 3.00 8.00
157 Mark Mulder RE 3.00 8.00
158 Ben Weber UH .10 .30
159 Mark DeRosa UH .10 .30
160 Melvin Mora UH .10 .30
161 Bill Mueller UH .10 .30
162 Jon Garland UH .10 .30
163 Jody Gerut UH .10 .30
164 Javier Lopez UH .10 .30
165 Craig Monroe UH .10 .30
166 Juan Pierre UH .10 .30
167 Morgan Ensberg UH .10 .30
168 Angel Berroa UH .10 .30
169 Geoff Jenkins UH .10 .30
170 Matt LeCroy UH .10 .30
171 Livan Hernandez UH .10 .30
172 Jason Phillips UH .10 .30
173 Mariano Rivera UH .20 .50
174 Erubiel Durazo UH .10 .30
175 Jason Michaels UH .10 .30
176 Kip Wells UH .10 .30
177 Ray Durham UH .10 .30
178 Randy Winn UH .10 .30
179 Edgar Renteria UH .10 .30
180 Carl Crawford UH .10 .30
181 Laynce Nix UH .10 .30
182 Greg Myers UH .10 .30
183 Delmon Young .60 1.50
Chad Gaudin
184 Humberto Quintero .40 1.00
Bernie Castro
185 Craig Brazell .40 1.00
Danny Garcia
186 Ryan Wing RC .40 1.00
Francisco Cruceta
187 William Bergolla RC .40 1.00
Josh Hall
188 Clint Barmes .40 1.00
Garrett Atkins
189 Chris Bootcheck .40 1.00
Richard Fischer
190 Edgar Gonzalez .40 1.00
Matt Kata
191 Andrew Brown .40 1.00
Koyie Hill
192 John Gall RC .40 1.00
Dan Haren
193 Chad Bentz RC .40 1.00
Luis Ayala
194 Hector Gimenez RC .40 1.00
Eric Bruntlett
195 Boof Bonser .40 1.00
Rob Bowen
196 Chris Snelling .40 1.00
Rett Johnson
197 Rickie Weeks .40 1.00
Adam Morrissey
198 Noah Lowry .40 1.00
Todd Linden
199 Chris Waters .40 1.00
Brett Evert
200 Jorge De Paula 1.50 4.00
Chien-Ming Wang

2004 Fleer Platinum Finish

*FINISH 1-135/158-182: 3X TO 8X BASIC
*FINISH 183-200: 1X TO 2.5X BASIC
*FINISH 136-143: 1.25X TO 3X BASIC
*FINISH 144-151: .75X TO 2X BASIC
*FINISH 152-157: .25X TO .6X BASIC
STATED ODDS 1:15 WAX
STATED PRINT RUN 100 SERIAL #'d SETS

2004 Fleer Platinum Big Signs

ODDS 1:9 WAX, 1:2 JUMBO, 1:8 RETAIL
1 Albert Pujols 1.25 3.00
2 Derek Jeter 1.25 3.00
3 Mike Piazza 1.00 2.50
4 Jason Giambi .60 1.50
5 Ichiro Suzuki 1.25 3.00
6 Nomar Garciaparra 1.00 2.50
7 Mark Prior .60 1.50
8 Randy Johnson .60 1.50
9 Greg Maddux 1.00 2.50
10 Sammy Sosa .60 1.50
11 Ken Griffey Jr. 1.00 2.50
12 Dontrelle Willis .60 1.50
13 Alex Rodriguez 1.00 2.50
14 Chipper Jones .60 1.50
15 Hank Blalock .60 1.50

2004 Fleer Platinum Big Signs Autographs

Albert Pujols and Chipper Jones did not return their cards in time for pack out. Please note there is no expiration date to return these cards by.
RANDOM INSERTS IN WAX PACKS
STATED PRINT RUN 100 SERIAL #'d SETS
EXCHANGE DEADLINE INDEFINITE
AP Albert Pujols EXCH
CJ Chipper Jones EXCH
DW Dontrelle Willis 10.00 25.00
HB Hank Blalock 6.00 15.00

2004 Fleer Platinum Classic Combinations

STATED ODDS 1:108 WAX, 1:270 RETAIL
1 Ivan Rodriguez 5.00 12.00
Mike Piazza
2 Alex Rodriguez 5.00 12.00
Sammy Sosa
3 Dontrelle Willis 3.00 8.00
Angel Berroa
4 Nomar Garciaparra 6.00 15.00
Derek Jeter
5 Ichiro Suzuki 6.00 15.00
Hideo Nomo
6 Josh Beckett 3.00 8.00
Kerry Wood
7 Albert Pujols 6.00 15.00
Carlos Delgado
8 Alfonso Soriano 3.00 8.00
Joe Morgan
9 Jason Giambi 3.00 8.00
Reggie Jackson
10 Nolan Ryan 10.00 25.00
Tom Seaver

2004 Fleer Platinum Clubhouse Memorabilia

STATED ODDS 1:24 WAX, 1:96 RETAIL
SP INFO PROVIDED BY FLEER
*DUAL: 1X TO 2.5X BASIC
*DUAL: .75X TO 2X BASIC SP
DUAL RANDOM IN WAX AND RETAIL
DUAL PRINT RUN 50 SERIAL #'d SETS
DUAL FEATURE TWO JSY SWATCHES
AK Austin Kearns 3.00 8.00
AP Albert Pujols SP 8.00 20.00
AR Alex Rodriguez 4.00 10.00
AS Alfonso Soriano SP 3.00 8.00
CJ Chipper Jones SP 4.00 10.00
DJ Derek Jeter 8.00 20.00
DW Dontrelle Willis 4.00 10.00
GM Greg Maddux 4.00 10.00
HB Hank Blalock 3.00 8.00
HN Hideo Nomo 6.00 15.00
JB Josh Beckett 3.00 8.00
JG Jason Giambi 3.00 8.00
JT Jim Thome 4.00 10.00
MPI Mike Piazza 4.00 10.00
MPR Mark Prior SP 4.00 10.00
MT Miguel Tejada 3.00 8.00
NG Nomar Garciaparra 4.00 10.00
RB Rocco Baldelli 3.00 8.00
RS Richie Sexson 3.00 8.00
SS Sammy Sosa 4.00 10.00
THE Todd Helton 4.00 10.00
THU Torii Hunter 3.00 8.00
VG Vladimir Guerrero 4.00 10.00

2004 Fleer Platinum Inscribed

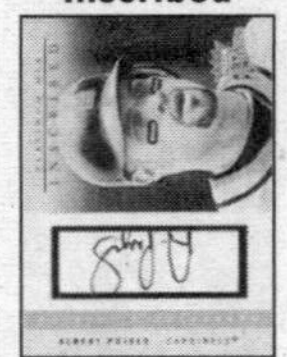

ONE PER RACK PACK
PRINT RUNS B/WN 20-315 COPIES PER
EXCH PRINT RUNS PROVIDED BY FLEER
EXCHANGE DEADLINE INDEFINITE
NO PRICING ON QTY OF 25 OR LESS
1CS Randy Johnson/100 EXCH
2AS Adam LaRoche/200 EXCH
AB Angel Berroa/210 4.00 10.00
AP Albert Pujols/100 125.00 200.00
BL Barry Larkin/75 EXCH
BWA Billy Wagner/300 EXCH
BWE Brandon Webb/150 6.00 15.00
CBE Chad Bentz/310 4.00 10.00
CBO Chris Bootcheck/210 4.00 10.00
CSN Chris Snelling/310 4.00 10.00
DH Dan Haren/200 4.00 10.00
DM Dallas McPherson/160 6.00 15.00
DW Dontrelle Willis/25
DY Delmon Young/210 10.00 25.00
EG Eric Gagne/130 15.00 40.00
EJ Edwin Jackson/200 4.00 10.00
JR1 Jose Reyes/20
JR2 Jose Reyes/150 EXCH
JV Javier Vazquez/160 6.00 15.00
KG Khalil Greene/310 10.00 25.00
KH Koyie Hill/300 4.00 10.00
LN Laynce Nix/200 4.00 10.00
MB Marlon Byrd/255 4.00 10.00
MC Miguel Cabrera/200 EXCH
MK Matt Kata/315 4.00 10.00
RB Rocco Baldelli/100 10.00 25.00
RHA Rich Harden/200 6.00 15.00
RHO Ryan Howard/160 30.00 60.00
RWA Ryan Wagner/300 EXCH
RWE Rickie Weeks/200 6.00 15.00
SP Scott Podsednik/180 10.00 25.00
SR Scott Rolen/55
VW Vernon Wells/200 6.00 15.00

2004 Fleer Platinum MLB Scouting Report

ODDS 1:45 WAX, 1:96 JUMBO, 1:190 RETAIL
STATED PRINT RUN 400 SERIAL #'d SETS
1 Josh Beckett 1.50 4.00
2 Todd Helton 1.50 4.00
3 Rocco Baldelli 1.50 4.00
4 Pedro Martinez 1.50 4.00
5 Jeff Bagwell 1.50 4.00
6 Mark Prior 1.50 4.00
7 Ichiro Suzuki 3.00 8.00
8 Barry Zito 1.50 4.00
9 Manny Ramirez 1.50 4.00
10 Miguel Cabrera 1.50 4.00
11 Richie Sexson 1.50 4.00
12 Hideki Matsui 2.50 6.00
13 Magglio Ordonez 1.50 4.00
14 Brandon Webb 1.50 4.00
15 Kerry Wood 1.50 4.00

2004 Fleer Platinum MLB Scouting Report Game Jersey

RANDOM IN WAX AND RETAIL PACKS
STATED PRINT RUN 250 SERIAL #'d SETS
BW Brandon Webb 4.00 10.00
JB Josh Beckett 4.00 10.00
JBAG Jeff Bagwell 6.00 15.00
KW Kerry Wood 4.00 10.00
MP Mark Prior 6.00 15.00
MR Manny Ramirez 6.00 15.00
PM Pedro Martinez 6.00 15.00
RB Rocco Baldelli 4.00 10.00
TH Todd Helton 6.00 15.00

2004 Fleer Platinum Nameplates Player

OVERALL NAMEPLATES ODDS 1:4 JUMBO
PRINT RUNS B/WN 25-320 COPIES PER
NO PRICING ON QTY OF 25 OR LESS
AK Austin Kearns/310 4.00 10.00
AP Albert Pujols/190 15.00 40.00
AR Alex Rodriguez/225 10.00 25.00
BZ Barry Zito/170 6.00 15.00
CJ Chipper Jones/150 10.00 25.00
CS Curt Schilling/260 8.00 20.00
GS Gary Sheffield/115 8.00 20.00
HB Hank Blalock/260 6.00 15.00
HN Hideo Nomo/85 20.00 50.00
HSC Hee Seop Choi/70 8.00 20.00
JB Josh Beckett/255 6.00 15.00
JP Juan Pierre/50 10.00 25.00
JR Jose Reyes/310 6.00 15.00
KB Kevin Brown/80 6.00 15.00
KW Kerry Wood/290 6.00 15.00
LC Luis Castillo/75 6.00 15.00
MB Marlon Byrd/75 6.00 15.00
MC Miguel Cabrera/75 10.00 25.00
MR Manny Ramirez/210 8.00 20.00
MT Mark Teixeira/250 8.00 20.00
NG Nomar Garciaparra/320 10.00 25.00
RJ Randy Johnson/200 8.00 20.00
RS Richie Sexson/165 6.00 15.00
SS Sammy Sosa/260 8.00 20.00
TG Tom Glavine/25

2004 Fleer Platinum Nameplates Team

OVERALL NAMEPLATES ODDS 1:4 JUMBO
PRINT RUNS B/WN 105-515 COPIES PER
AK Austin Kearns/515 4.00 10.00
AP Albert Pujols/470 12.50 30.00
AR Alex Rodriguez/510 8.00 20.00
BZ Barry Zito/515 4.00 10.00
CJ Chipper Jones/420 6.00 15.00
CS Curt Schilling/250 8.00 20.00
GS Gary Sheffield/500 4.00 10.00
HB Hank Blalock/515 4.00 10.00
HN Hideo Nomo/390 8.00 20.00

HSC Hee Seop Choi/220 6.00 15.00
JB Josh Beckett/390 4.00 10.00
JP Juan Pierre/110 8.00 20.00
JR Jose Reyes/510 4.00 10.00
KB Kevin Brown/220 4.00 10.00
KW Kerry Wood/510 4.00 10.00
LC Luis Castillo/225 4.00 10.00
MB Marlon Byrd/470 4.00 10.00
MC Miguel Cabrera/105 10.00 25.00
MR Manny Ramirez/480 6.00 15.00
MT Mark Teixeira/505 6.00 15.00
NG Nomar Garciaparra/250 10.00 25.00
RJ Randy Johnson/290 8.00 20.00
RS Richie Sexson/420 4.00 10.00
SS Sammy Sosa/490 6.00 15.00

2004 Fleer Platinum Portraits

ODDS 1:18 WAX, 1:4 JUMBO, 1:24 RETAIL
1 Jason Giambi 1.25 3.00
2 Nomar Garciaparra 2.00 5.00
3 Vladimir Guerrero 1.25 3.00
4 Mark Prior 1.25 3.00
5 Jim Thome 1.25 3.00
6 Derek Jeter 2.50 6.00
7 Sammy Sosa 1.25 3.00
8 Alex Rodriguez 2.00 5.00
9 Greg Maddux 2.00 5.00
10 Albert Pujols 2.50 6.00

2004 Fleer Platinum Portraits Game Jersey

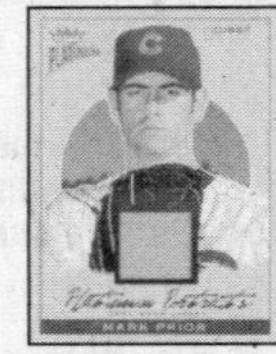

STATED ODDS 1:48 WAX, 1:120 RETAIL
SP INFO PROVIDED BY FLEER
*PATCH: .75X TO 2X BASIC
*PATCH: .6X TO 1.5X BASIC SP
PATCH RANDOM IN WAX AND RETAIL
PATCH PRINT RUN 100 SERIAL #'d SETS
AP Albert Pujols 6.00 15.00
AR Alex Rodriguez 4.00 10.00
DJ Derek Jeter 8.00 20.00
GM Greg Maddux SP 6.00 15.00
JG Jason Giambi 3.00 8.00
JT Jim Thome 4.00 10.00
MP Mark Prior SP 6.00 15.00
NG Nomar Garciaparra 4.00 10.00
SS Sammy Sosa 4.00 10.00
VG Vladimir Guerrero 4.00 10.00

2005 Fleer Platinum

This 125 card set was released in April, 2005. The set was released in either five-card hobby packs which came 18 packs to a box and 16 boxes to a case or in five-card retail packs which came 24 packs to a box and 20 boxes to a case. The first 100 cards of the set feature active veterans while the final 25 cards feature leading prospects. Those final cards were issued at a stated rate of one in 18 hobby and one in 60 retail packs and were issued to a stated print run of 1000 serial numbered sets.

COMP.SET w/o SP's (100) 10.00 25.00
COMMON CARD (1-100) .10 .30
COMMON CARD (101-125) 1.50 4.00
1 Nomar Garciaparra .30 .75
2 Matt Holliday .15 .40
3 Rickie Weeks .10 .30
4 Jim Thome .20 .50
5 Roy Halladay .10 .30
6 Paul Konerko .10 .30
7 Lance Berkman .10 .30
8 Ichiro Suzuki .60 1.50
9 Kerry Wood .10 .30
10 Lew Ford .10 .30
11 Omar Vizquel .20 .50
12 Manny Ramirez .20 .50
13 Carlos Beltran .10 .30
14 Lyle Overbay .10 .30
15 Billy Wagner .10 .30
16 Jose Vidro .10 .30
17 Vladimir Guerrero .30 .75
18 Miguel Tejada .10 .30
19 Alex Rodriguez .50 1.25
20 Rocco Baldelli .10 .30
21 David Ortiz .30 .75
22 Victor Martinez .10 .30
23 Shawn Green .10 .30
24 Jason Bay .10 .30
25 Pedro Martinez .20 .50
26 Travis Hafner .10 .30
27 Eric Gagne .10 .30
28 Jack Wilson .10 .30
29 Ivan Rodriguez .20 .50
30 Jody Gerut .10 .30
31 Adrian Beltre .10 .30
32 Craig Wilson .10 .30
33 J.D. Drew .10 .30
34 Craig Biggio .20 .50
35 Mark Mulder .10 .30
36 Mark Teixeira .20 .50
37 Melvin Mora .10 .30
38 Ken Griffey Jr. .50 1.25
39 Mike Sweeney .10 .30
40 Khalil Greene .20 .50
41 Rafael Palmeiro .20 .50
42 Austin Kearns .10 .30
43 Garret Anderson .10 .30
44 Trevor Hoffman .10 .30
45 Andruw Jones .20 .50
46 Adam Dunn .10 .30
47 Angel Berroa .10 .30
48 Ryan Klesko .10 .30
49 Sean Casey .10 .30
50 Kaz Matsui .10 .30
51 Jim Edmonds .10 .30
52 Magglio Ordonez .10 .30
53 Tom Glavine .20 .50
54 Larry Walker .20 .50
55 Johnny Estrada .10 .30
56 Brad Lidge .10 .30
57 Barry Zito .10 .30
58 Michael Young .10 .30
59 Chipper Jones .30 .75
60 Andy Pettitte .20 .50
61 Eric Chavez .10 .30
62 Carlos Delgado .10 .30
63 David Eckstein .10 .30
64 Dmitri Young .10 .30
65 Mike Piazza .30 .75
66 Albert Pujols .60 1.50
67 Luis Gonzalez .10 .30
68 Hideki Matsui .50 1.25
69 Gary Sheffield .10 .30
70 Carl Crawford .10 .30
71 Curt Schilling .20 .50
72 Todd Helton .20 .50
73 Ben Sheets .10 .30
74 Bobby Abreu .10 .30
75 Jose Guillen .10 .30
76 Richie Sexson .10 .30
77 Miguel Cabrera .20 .50
78 Bernie Williams .20 .50
79 Aubrey Huff .10 .30
80 John Smoltz .20 .50
81 Jeff Bagwell .20 .50
82 Tim Hudson .10 .30
83 Alfonso Soriano .10 .30
84 Freddy Garcia .10 .30
85 Johan Santana .30 .75
86 Bret Boone .10 .30
87 Troy Glaus .10 .30
88 Carlos Guillen .10 .30
89 Derek Jeter .60 1.50
90 Scott Rolen .20 .50
91 Sammy Sosa .30 .75
92 Jacque Jones .10 .30
93 Jason Schmidt .10 .30
94 Randy Johnson .30 .75
95 Dontrelle Willis .10 .30
96 Mariano Rivera .30 .75
97 Hank Blalock .10 .30
98 Mark Prior .20 .50
99 Torii Hunter .10 .30
100 Roger Clemens .50 1.25
101 David Wright ROO 3.00 8.00
102 Justin Morneau ROO 1.50 4.00
103 Scott Kazmir ROO 1.50 4.00
104 Gavin Floyd ROO 1.50 4.00
105 Justin Verlander ROO RC 3.00 8.00
106 Zack Greinke ROO 1.50 4.00
107 David Aardsma ROO 1.50 4.00
108 Ryan Raburn ROO 1.50 4.00
109 Joey Gathright ROO 1.50 4.00
110 J.D. Durbin ROO 1.50 4.00
111 Sean Burnett ROO 1.50 4.00
112 Jose Lopez ROO 1.50 4.00
113 Nick Swisher ROO 1.50 4.00
114 Bobby Jenks ROO 1.50 4.00
115 Kelly Johnson ROO 1.50 4.00
116 B.J. Upton ROO 1.50 4.00
117 Ronny Cedeno ROO 1.50 4.00
118 Edwin Encarnacion ROO 1.50 4.00
119 Jeff Baker ROO 1.50 4.00
120 Taylor Buchholz ROO 1.50 4.00
121 Luis Hernandez ROO RC 1.50 4.00
122 Dioner Navarro ROO 1.50 4.00
123 Victor Diaz ROO 1.50 4.00
124 Jon Knott ROO 1.50 4.00
125 Russ Adams ROO 1.50 4.00

2005 Fleer Platinum Extreme

OVERALL PARALLEL ODDS 1:9 H, 1:114 R
STATED PRINT RUN 20 SERIAL #'d SETS
NO PRICING DUE TO SCARCITY

2005 Fleer Platinum Finish

*FINISH 1-100: 2.5X TO 6X BASIC
*FINISH 101-125: .4X TO 1X BASIC
OVERALL PARALLEL ODDS 1:9 H, 1:114 R
STATED PRINT RUN 199 SERIAL #'d SETS

2005 Fleer Platinum Autograph Die Cuts

STATED ODDS 1:184 HOBBY
PRINT RUNS B/WN 10-99 COPIES PER
CARDS ARE NOT SERIAL-NUMBERED
PRINT RUN INFO PROVIDED BY FLEER
NO PRICING ON QTY OF 20 OR LESS

1 Lew Ford/99 *	4.00	10.00
3 Jason Bay/50 *	6.00	15.00
4 Travis Hafner/99 *	6.00	15.00
6 Brad Lidge/99 *	15.00	40.00
7 Michael Young/99 *	6.00	15.00
8 David Eckstein/99 *	12.50	30.00
9 Carl Crawford/50 *	6.00	15.00
10 Miguel Cabrera/50 *	10.00	25.00
11 David Wright ROO/50 *	20.00	50.00
12 Justin Morneau ROO/99 *		
13 Scott Kazmir ROO/99 *	8.00	20.00
14 Gavin Floyd ROO/99 *	4.00	10.00
15 Justin Verlander ROO/99 *	15.00	40.00
16 David Aardsma ROO/10 *		
18 Joey Gathright ROO/50 *	4.00	10.00
22 Russ Adams ROO/20 *		

2005 Fleer Platinum Decade of Excellence

STATED ODDS 1:99 HOBBY, 1:125 RETAIL

1 Albert Pujols	4.00	10.00
2 Derek Jeter	4.00	10.00
3 Randy Johnson	3.00	8.00
4 Ichiro Suzuki	4.00	10.00
5 Alex Rodriguez	3.00	8.00
6 Mike Piazza	3.00	8.00
7 Greg Maddux	3.00	8.00
8 Curt Schilling	3.00	8.00
9 Frank Thomas	3.00	8.00
10 Torii Hunter	2.00	5.00
11 Al Kaline	4.00	10.00
12 Travis Hafner	2.00	5.00
13 Ivan Rodriguez	3.00	8.00
14 Rafael Palmeiro	3.00	8.00
15 Mike Schmidt	6.00	15.00
16 Johnny Bench	4.00	10.00
17 Jim Edmonds	2.00	5.00
18 Pedro Martinez	3.00	8.00
19 Robin Yount	4.00	10.00
20 Sammy Sosa	3.00	8.00

2005 Fleer Platinum Decade of Excellence Autograph Jersey Platinum

OVERALL AU ODDS 1:144 H, AU-GU 1:48 R
STATED PRINT RUN 5 SERIAL #'d SETS
NO PRICING DUE TO SCARCITY
AK Al Kaline
JB Johnny Bench
MS Mike Schmidt
TH Travis Hafner
TH Torii Hunter

2005 Fleer Platinum Decade of Excellence Jersey Silver

STATED ODDS 1:54 HOBBY
*GOLD: .5X TO 1.2X BASIC

GOLD PRINT RUN 99 SERIAL #'d SETS
PATCH PLATINUM PRINT 10 #'d SETS
NO PATCH PLT.PRICING DUE TO SCARCITY
OVERALL GU ODDS 1:9 H, AU-GU 1:48 R

AK Al Kaline	6.00	15.00
AP Albert Pujols	6.00	15.00
CS Curt Schilling	4.00	10.00
FT Frank Thomas	4.00	10.00
GM Greg Maddux	4.00	10.00
IR Ivan Rodriguez	4.00	10.00
JB Johnny Bench	6.00	15.00
JE Jim Edmonds	3.00	8.00
MP Mike Piazza	4.00	10.00
MS Mike Schmidt	6.00	15.00
PM Pedro Martinez	4.00	10.00
RJ Randy Johnson	4.00	10.00
RP Rafael Palmeiro	4.00	10.00
RY Robin Yount	6.00	15.00
SS Sammy Sosa	4.00	10.00
TF Travis Hafner	3.00	8.00
TH Torii Hunter	3.00	8.00

2005 Fleer Platinum Diamond Dominators

*DOM: .4X TO 1X METAL DOM
STATED ODDS 1:12 RETAIL

13 Mariano Rivera	2.00	5.00
19 Scott Rolen	2.00	5.00

2005 Fleer Platinum Diamond Dominators Jersey Silver

STATED ODDS 1:45 HOBBY
*GOLD: .4X TO 1X BASIC
OVERALL GU ODDS 1:9H, AU-GU 1:48 R
GOLD PRINT RUN 199 SERIAL #'d SETS
*RED: .4X TO 1X BASIC
RED STATED ODDS 1:50 RETAIL

AB Adrian Beltre	3.00	8.00
AP Albert Pujols	6.00	15.00
AS Alfonso Soriano	3.00	8.00
CJ Chipper Jones	4.00	10.00
CS Curt Schilling	4.00	10.00
DO David Ortiz	4.00	10.00
EG Eric Gagne	3.00	8.00
IR Ivan Rodriguez	4.00	10.00
JG Jason Giambi	3.00	8.00
KG Khalil Greene	4.00	10.00
KM Kaz Matsui	3.00	8.00
MC Miguel Cabrera	4.00	10.00
MP Mike Piazza	4.00	10.00
RB Rocco Baldelli	3.00	8.00
RJ Randy Johnson	4.00	10.00
SR Scott Rolen	4.00	10.00
SS Sammy Sosa	4.00	10.00
TH Tim Hudson	3.00	8.00
VG Vladimir Guerrero	4.00	10.00

2005 Fleer Platinum Diamond Dominators Metal

STATED ODDS 1:18 HOBBY

1 Albert Pujols	3.00	8.00
2 Curt Schilling	2.00	5.00
3 Adrian Beltre	1.50	4.00
4 Randy Johnson	2.00	5.00
5 Ivan Rodriguez	2.00	5.00
6 Mike Piazza	2.00	5.00
7 Chipper Jones	2.00	5.00
8 Sammy Sosa	2.00	5.00
9 Tim Hudson	1.50	4.00
10 Rocco Baldelli	1.50	4.00
11 Alfonso Soriano	1.50	4.00
12 David Ortiz	2.00	5.00
13 Kaz Matsui	1.50	4.00
14 Khalil Greene	2.00	5.00
15 Eric Gagne	1.50	4.00
16 Vladimir Guerrero	2.00	5.00
17 Jason Giambi	1.50	4.00
18 Scott Rolen	2.00	5.00
19 Miguel Cabrera	2.00	5.00

2005 Fleer Platinum Diamond Dominators Metal Autograph

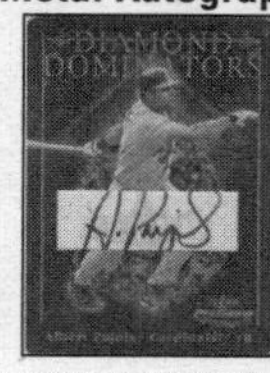

OVERALL AU ODDS 1:144 H, AU-GU 1:48 R
STATED PRINT RUN 10 SERIAL #'d SETS
NO PRICING DUE TO SCARCITY
AP Albert Pujols
CJ Chipper Jones
DO David Ortiz
EG Eric Gagne
HA Hank Aaron
KG Khalil Greene
MC Miguel Cabrera
MP Mike Piazza
RB Rocco Baldelli
RJ Randy Johnson
SR Scott Rolen

2005 Fleer Platinum Lumberjacks

STATED ODDS 1:6 HOBBY, 1:8 RETAIL

1 Albert Pujols	1.25	3.00
2 Jim Thome	.60	1.50
3 Andruw Jones	.60	1.50
4 Kaz Matsui	.40	1.00
5 Adam Dunn	.40	1.00
6 Bernie Williams	.60	1.50
7 Hank Blalock	.40	1.00
8 Bobby Abreu	.40	1.00
9 Rocco Baldelli	.40	1.00
10 Jacque Jones	.40	1.00
11 Mark Teixeira	.60	1.50
12 Ichiro Suzuki	1.25	3.00
13 Gary Sheffield	.40	1.00
14 Sean Casey	.40	1.00
15 Carl Crawford	.40	1.00

2005 Fleer Platinum Lumberjacks Autograph Platinum

OVERALL AU ODDS 1:144 H, AU-GU 1:48 R
STATED PRINT RUN 20 SERIAL #'d SETS
NO PRICING DUE TO SCARCITY
CC Carl Crawford
HB Hank Blalock
JT Jim Thome
MT Mark Teixeira
RB Rocco Baldelli

2005 Fleer Platinum Lumberjacks Bat Silver

OVERALL GU ODDS 1:9 HOBBY
*GOLD: .4X TO 1X BASIC
GOLD PRINT RUN 250 SERIAL #'d SETS
BAT-PATCH PLATINUM PRINT 20 #'d SETS
NO BAT-PATCH PLT.PRICING AVAILABLE

AD Adam Dunn	3.00	8.00
AJ Andruw Jones	4.00	10.00
AP Albert Pujols	6.00	15.00
BA Bobby Abreu	3.00	8.00
BW Bernie Williams	4.00	10.00
CC Carl Crawford	3.00	8.00
GS Gary Sheffield	3.00	8.00
HB Hank Blalock	3.00	8.00
JJ Jacque Jones	3.00	8.00
JT Jim Thome	4.00	10.00
KM Kaz Matsui	3.00	8.00
MT Mark Teixeira	4.00	10.00
RB Rocco Baldelli	3.00	8.00
SC Sean Casey	3.00	8.00

2005 Fleer Platinum Nameplates Patch Platinum

STATED PRINT RUN 25 SERIAL #'d SETS
MASTERPIECE PRINT RUN 1 #'d SET
OVERALL GU ODDS 1:9 H, AU-GU 1:48 R
NO PRICING DUE TO SCARCITY

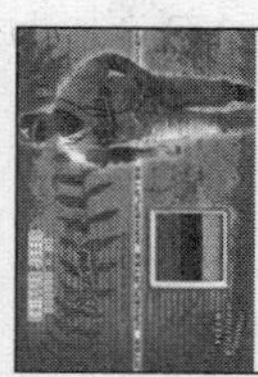

AD Adam Dunn
AP Albert Pujols
AS Alfonso Soriano
BR Brad Radke
CJ Chipper Jones
CS Curt Schilling
IR Ivan Rodriguez
JD Johnny Damon
JM Joe Mauer
JR Jose Reyes
JS Johan Santana
JT Jim Thome
KM Kaz Matsui
LB Lance Berkman
MB Marlon Byrd
MP Mike Piazza
MT Miguel Tejada
RJ Randy Johnson
SG Shawn Green
SK Scott Kazmir
SR Scott Rolen
SS Sammy Sosa
TG Troy Glaus
VG Vladimir Guerrero
VM Victor Martinez

2005 Fleer Platinum Nameplates Patch Autograph Platinum

OVERALL AU ODDS 1:144 H, AU-GU 1:48 R
STATED PRINT RUN 25 SERIAL #'d SETS
NO PRICING DUE TO SCARCITY
LB Lance Berkman
MB Marlon Byrd
SK Scott Kazmir
SR Scott Rolen

2005 Fleer Platinum Nameplates Dual Patch Platinum

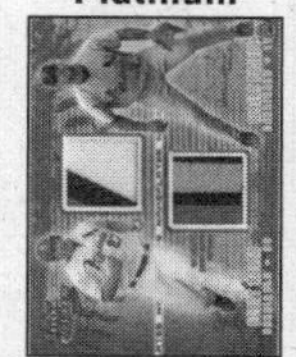

STATED PRINT RUN 25 SERIAL #'d SETS
MASTERPIECE PRINT RUN 1 #'d SET
OVERALL GU ODDS 1:9 H, AU-GU 1:48 R
NO PRICING DUE TO SCARCITY
ADSG Adam Dunn
Shawn Green
APJT Albert Pujols
Jim Thome
APSR Albert Pujols
Scott Rolen
JDCS Johnny Damon
Curt Schilling
JMBR Joe Mauer
Brad Radke
JSJM Johan Santana
Joe Mauer
KMJR Kaz Matsui
Jose Reyes
KMMT Kaz Matsui
Miguel Tejada
LBTG Lance Berkman
Troy Glaus
MBJT Marlon Byrd
Jim Thome
RJCS Randy Johnson
Curt Schilling
SKJS Scott Kazmir
Johan Santana
SSIR Sammy Sosa
Ivan Rodriguez
VGAS Vladimir Guerrero
Alfonso Soriano
VMMP Victor Martinez
Mike Piazza

2005 Fleer Platinum Nameplates Dual Patch Autograph Platinum

OVERALL AU ODDS 1:144 H, AU-GU 1:48 R
STATED PRINT RUN 1 SERIAL #'d SET
NO PRICING DUE TO SCARCITY
SKJR Scott Kazmir
Jose Reyes
SRMB Scott Rolen
Marlon Byrd

2001 Fleer Premium

The 2001 Fleer Premium product was released in early April, 2001 and features a 235-card base set that was broken into tiers as follows: Base Veterans (1-200), and Prospects (201-235) which were individually serial numbered to 1999. Please note that cards 231-235 all packed out as exchange cards and needed to have been exchanged to Fleer by 5/01/02. Each pack contained eight cards and carried a suggested retail price of $3.99.

COMP.SET w/o SP's (200)	12.50	30.00
COMMON CARD (1-200)	.15	.40
COMMON (201-230)	2.00	5.00
COMMON (231-235)	3.00	8.00
1 Cal Ripken	1.25	3.00
2 Derek Jeter	1.00	2.50
3 Edgardo Alfonzo	.15	.40
4 Luis Castillo	.15	.40
5 Mike Lieberthal	.15	.40
6 Kazuhiro Sasaki	.15	.40
7 Jeff Kent	.15	.40
8 Eric Karros	.15	.40
9 Tom Glavine	.25	.60
10 Jeromy Burnitz	.15	.40
11 Travis Fryman	.15	.40
12 Ron Coomer	.15	.40
13 Jeff D'Amico	.15	.40
14 Carlos Febles	.15	.40
15 Kevin Brown	.15	.40
16 Deivi Cruz	.15	.40
17 Tino Martinez	.25	.60
18 Bobby Abreu	.15	.40
19 Roger Clemens	.75	2.00
20 Jeffrey Hammonds	.15	.40
21 Peter Bergeron	.15	.40
22 Ray Lankford	.15	.40
23 Scott Rolen	.25	.60
24 Jermaine Dye	.15	.40
25 Rusty Greer	.15	.40
26 Frank Thomas	.40	1.00
27 Jeff Bagwell	.25	.60
28 Cliff Floyd	.15	.40
29 Chris Singleton	.15	.40
30 Steve Finley	.15	.40
31 Orlando Hernandez	.15	.40
32 Tom Goodwin	.15	.40
33 Larry Walker	.15	.40
34 Mike Sweeney	.15	.40
35 Tim Hudson	.15	.40
36 Kerry Wood	.15	.40
37 Mike Lowell	.15	.40
38 Andruw Jones	.30	.75
39 Alex Gonzalez	.15	.40
40 Juan Gonzalez	.30	.75
41 J.D. Drew	.15	.40
42 Mark McLemore	.15	.40
43 Royce Clayton	.15	.40
44 Paul O'Neill	.25	.60
45 Carlos Beltran	.15	.40
46 Phil Nevin	.15	.40
47 Rondell White	.15	.40
48 Gerald Williams	.15	.40
49 Geoff Jenkins	.15	.40
50 Marvin Benard	.15	.40
51 Alex Rodriguez	.60	1.50
52 Moises Alou	.15	.40
53 Mike Lansing	.15	.40
54 Omar Vizquel	.25	.60
55 Eric Chavez	.15	.40
56 Mark Quinn	.15	.40
57 Mike Lamb	.15	.40
58 Rick Ankiel	.15	.40
59 Lance Berkman	.15	.40
60 Jeff Conine	.15	.40
61 B.J. Surhoff	.15	.40
62 Todd Helton	.25	.60
63 J.T. Snow	.15	.40
64 John VanderWal	.15	.40
65 Johnny Damon	.25	.60
66 Bobby Higginson	.15	.40
67 Carlos Delgado	.30	.75
68 Shawn Green	.15	.40
69 Mike Redmond	.15	.40
70 Mike Piazza	.60	1.50
71 Adrian Beltre	.15	.40
72 Juan Encarnacion	.15	.40
73 Chipper Jones	.40	1.00
74 Garret Anderson	.15	.40
75 Paul Konerko	.15	.40
76 Barry Larkin	.25	.60
77 Tony Gwynn	.50	1.25
78 Rafael Palmeiro	.25	.60
79 Randy Johnson	.40	1.00
80 Mark Grace	.30	.75
81 Javy Lopez	.15	.40
82 Gabe Kapler	.15	.40
83 Henry Rodriguez	.15	.40
84 Raul Mondesi	.15	.40
85 Adam Piatt	.15	.40
86 Marquis Grissom	.15	.40
87 Charles Johnson	.15	.40
88 Sean Casey	.15	.40
89 Manny Ramirez	.25	.60
90 Curt Schilling	.15	.40
91 Fernando Tatis	.15	.40
92 Derek Bell	.15	.40
93 Tony Clark	.15	.40
94 Homer Bush	.15	.40
95 Nomar Garciaparra	.60	1.50
96 Vinny Castilla	.15	.40
97 Ben Davis	.15	.40
98 Carl Everett	.15	.40
99 Damion Easley	.15	.40
100 Craig Biggio	.25	.60
101 Todd Hollandsworth	.15	.40
102 Jay Payton	.15	.40
103 Gary Sheffield	.15	.40
104 Sandy Alomar Jr.	.15	.40
105 Doug Glanville	.15	.40
106 Barry Bonds	1.00	2.50
107 Tim Salmon	.25	.60
108 Terrence Long	.15	.40
109 Jorge Posada	.25	.60
110 Jose Offerman	.15	.40
111 Edgar Martinez	.25	.60
112 Jeremy Giambi	.15	.40
113 Dean Palmer	.15	.40
114 Roberto Alomar	.30	.75
115 Aaron Boone	.15	.40
116 Adam Kennedy	.15	.40
117 Joe Randa	.15	.40
118 Jose Vidro	.15	.40
119 Tony Batista	.15	.40
120 Kevin Young	.15	.40
121 Preston Wilson	.15	.40
122 Jason Kendall	.15	.40
123 Mark Kotsay	.15	.40
124 Timo Perez	.15	.40
125 Eric Young	.15	.40
126 Greg Maddux	.60	1.50
127 Richard Hidalgo	.15	.40
128 Brian Giles	.15	.40
129 Fred McGriff	.25	.60
130 Troy Glaus	.15	.40
131 Todd Walker	.15	.40
132 Brady Anderson	.15	.40
133 Jim Edmonds	.15	.40
134 Ben Grieve	.15	.40
135 Greg Vaughn	.15	.40
136 Robin Ventura	.15	.40
137 Sammy Sosa	.40	1.00
138 Rich Aurilia	.15	.40
139 Jose Valentin	.15	.40
140 Trot Nixon	.15	.40
141 Troy Percival	.15	.40
142 Bernie Williams	.25	.60
143 Warren Morris	.15	.40
144 Jacque Jones	.15	.40
145 Danny Bautista	.15	.40
146 A.J. Pierzynski	.15	.40
147 Mark McGwire	1.00	2.50
148 Rafael Furcal	.15	.40
149 Ray Durham	.15	.40
150 Mike Mussina	.30	.75
151 Jay Bell	.15	.40
152 David Wells	.15	.40
153 Ken Caminiti	.15	.40
154 Jim Thome	.25	.60
155 Ivan Rodriguez	.25	.60
156 Milton Bradley	.15	.40
157 Ken Griffey Jr.	.60	1.50
158 Al Leiter	.15	.40
159 Corey Koskie	.15	.40
160 Shannon Stewart	.15	.40
161 Mo Vaughn	.15	.40
162 Pedro Martinez	.25	.60
163 Todd Hundley	.15	.40
164 Darin Erstad	.30	.75
165 Ruben Rivera	.15	.40
166 Richie Sexson	.15	.40
167 Andres Galarraga	.15	.40
168 Darryl Kile	.15	.40
169 Jose Cruz Jr.	.15	.40
170 David Justice	.15	.40
171 Vladimir Guerrero	.40	1.00
172 Jeff Cirillo	.15	.40
173 John Olerud	.15	.40
174 Devon White	.15	.40
175 Ron Belliard	.15	.40
176 Pokey Reese	.15	.40
177 Mike Hampton	.15	.40
178 David Ortiz	.40	1.00
179 Magglio Ordonez	.15	.40
180 Ruben Mateo	.15	.40
181 Carlos Lee	.15	.40
182 Matt Williams	.15	.40
183 Miguel Tejada	.15	.40
184 Scott Elarton	.15	.40
185 Bret Boone	.15	.40
186 Pat Burrell	.15	.40
187 Brad Radke	.15	.40
188 Brian Jordan	.15	.40
189 Matt Lawton	.15	.40
190 Al Martin	.15	.40
191 Albert Belle	.15	.40
192 Tony Womack	.15	.40
193 Roger Cedeno	.15	.40
194 Travis Lee	.15	.40
195 Dmitri Young	.15	.40
196 Jay Buhner	.15	.40
197 Jason Giambi	.30	.75
198 Jason Tyner	.15	.40
199 Ben Petrick	.15	.40
200 Jose Canseco	.30	.75
201 Nick Johnson	2.00	5.00
202 Jace Brewer	2.00	5.00
203 Ryan Freel RC	2.00	5.00
204 Jaisen Randolph RC	2.00	5.00
205 Marcus Giles	2.00	5.00
206 Claudio Vargas RC	2.00	5.00
207 Brian Cole	2.00	5.00
208 Scott Hodges	2.00	5.00
209 Winston Abreu RC	2.00	5.00
210 Shea Hillenbrand	2.00	5.00
211 Larry Barnes	2.00	5.00
212 Paul Phillips RC	2.00	5.00
213 Pedro Santana RC	2.00	5.00
214 Ivanon Coffie	2.00	5.00
215 Junior Spivey RC	3.00	8.00
216 Donzell McDonald	2.00	5.00
217 Vernon Wells	2.00	5.00
218 Corey Patterson	2.00	5.00
219 Sang-Hoon Lee	2.00	5.00
220 Jack Cust	2.00	5.00
221 Jason Romano	2.00	5.00
222 Jack Wilson RC	3.00	8.00
223 Adam Everett	2.00	5.00
224 Esix Snead RC	2.00	5.00
225 Jason Hart	2.00	5.00
226 Joe Lawrence	2.00	5.00
227 Brandon Inge	2.00	5.00
228 Alex Escobar	2.00	5.00
229 Abraham Nunez	2.00	5.00
230 Jared Sandberg	2.00	5.00
231 Ichiro Suzuki RC	12.50	30.00
232 Tsuyoshi Shinjo RC	4.00	10.00
233 Albert Pujols RC	40.00	80.00
234 Wilson Betemit RC	4.00	10.00
235 Drew Henson RC	4.00	10.00
MM1 D.Jeter MM/1995	5.00	12.00
NNO Derek Jeter MM AU/95	60.00	120.00

2002 Fleer Premium

This 240 card set was released in early spring, 2002. This set was issued in 10 card packs which were issued 24 packs to a box. Cards numbered from 201 through 240 featured leading prospects entering the 2002 season and were seeded at stated odds of one in two packs. In late May, Fleer announced their "Player to be Named" program, whereby collectors could send in 10 copies of any of

the short-printed prospect cards (201-240) and in turn receive ten new prospect cards (241-250) each serial numbered to 2002. The "Player to be Named" cards were actually released in October, 2002.

COMP.MASTER SET (250) 50.00 120.00
COMPLETE SET (240) 30.00 80.00
COMP.SET w/o SP'S (200) 12.50 30.00
COMP.UPDATE SET (10) 15.00 40.00
COMMON CARD (1-200) .15 .40
COMMON CARD (201-240) .75 2.00
COMMON CARD (241-250) 1.50 4.00
1 Garret Anderson .15 .40
2 Derek Jeter 1.00 2.50
3 Ken Griffey Jr. .60 1.50
4 Luis Castillo .15 .40
5 Richie Sexson .15 .40
6 Mike Mussina .25 .60
7 Rickey Henderson .40 1.00
8 Bud Smith .15 .40
9 David Eckstein .15 .40
10 Nomar Garciaparra .60 1.50
11 Barry Larkin .25 .60
12 Cliff Floyd .15 .40
13 Ben Sheets .15 .40
14 Jorge Posada .25 .60
15 Phil Nevin .15 .40
16 Fernando Vina .15 .40
17 Darin Erstad .15 .40
18 Shea Hillenbrand .15 .40
19 Todd Walker .15 .40
20 Charles Johnson .15 .40
21 Cristian Guzman .15 .40
22 Mariano Rivera .40 1.00
23 Bubba Trammell .15 .40
24 Brent Abernathy .15 .40
25 Troy Glaus .15 .40
26 Pedro Martinez .25 .60
27 Dmitri Young .15 .40
28 Derrek Lee .25 .60
29 Torii Hunter .15 .40
30 Alfonso Soriano .15 .40
31 Rich Aurilia .15 .40
32 Ben Grieve .15 .40
33 Tim Salmon .25 .60
34 Trot Nixon .15 .40
35 Roberto Alomar .25 .60
36 Mike Lowell .15 .40
37 Jacque Jones .15 .40
38 Bernie Williams .25 .60
39 Barry Bonds 1.00 2.50
40 Toby Hall .15 .40
41 Mo Vaughn .15 .40
42 Hideo Nomo .40 1.00
43 Travis Fryman .15 .40
44 Preston Wilson .15 .40
45 Corey Koskie .15 .40
46 Eric Chavez .15 .40
47 Andres Galarraga .15 .40
48 Greg Vaughn .15 .40
49 Shawn Wooten .15 .40
50 Manny Ramirez .25 .60
51 Juan Gonzalez .15 .40
52 Moises Alou .15 .40
53 Joe Mays .15 .40
54 Johnny Damon .25 .60
55 Jeff Kent .15 .40
56 Frank Catalanotto .15 .40
57 Steve Finley .15 .40
58 Jason Varitek .40 1.00
59 Kenny Lofton .15 .40
60 Jeff Bagwell .25 .60
61 Doug Mientkiewicz .15 .40
62 Jermaine Dye .15 .40
63 John Vander Wal .15 .40
64 Gabe Kapler .15 .40
65 Luis Gonzalez .15 .40
66 Jon Lieber .15 .40
67 C.C. Sabathia .15 .40
68 Lance Berkman .15 .40
69 Eric Milton .15 .40
70 Jason Giambi Yankees .15 .40
71 Ichiro Suzuki .75 2.00
72 Rafael Palmeiro .25 .60
73 Mark Grace .25 .60
74 Fred McGriff .25 .60
75 Jim Thome .25 .60
76 Craig Biggio .25 .60
77 A.J. Pierzynski .15 .40
78 Ramon Hernandez .15 .40
79 Paul Abbott .15 .40
80 Alex Rodriguez .60 1.50
81 Randy Johnson .40 1.00
82 Corey Patterson .15 .40
83 Omar Vizquel .25 .60
84 Richard Hidalgo .15 .40
85 Luis Rivas .15 .40
86 Tim Hudson .15 .40
87 Bret Boone .15 .40
88 Ivan Rodriguez .25 .60
89 Junior Spivey .15 .40
90 Sammy Sosa .40 1.00
91 Jeff Cirillo .15 .40
92 Roy Oswalt .15 .40
93 Orlando Cabrera .15 .40
94 Terrence Long .15 .40
95 Mike Cameron .15 .40
96 Homer Bush .15 .40
97 Reggie Sanders .15 .40
98 Rondell White .15 .40
99 Mike Hampton .15 .40
100 Carlos Beltran .15 .40
101 Vladimir Guerrero .40 1.00
102 Miguel Tejada .15 .40
103 Freddy Garcia .15 .40
104 Jose Cruz Jr. .15 .40
105 Curt Schilling .15 .40
106 Kerry Wood .15 .40
107 Todd Helton .25 .60
108 Neifi Perez .15 .40
109 Javier Vazquez .15 .40
110 Barry Zito .15 .40
111 Edgar Martinez .25 .60
112 Carlos Delgado .15 .40
113 Matt Williams .15 .40
114 Eric Young .15 .40
115 Alex Ochoa .15 .40
116 Mark Quinn .15 .40
117 Jose Vidro .15 .40
118 Bobby Abreu .15 .40
119 David Bell .15 .40
120 Brad Fullmer .15 .40
121 Rafael Furcal .15 .40
122 Ray Durham .15 .40
123 Jose Ortiz .15 .40
124 Joe Randa .15 .40
125 Edgardo Alfonzo .15 .40
126 Marlon Anderson .15 .40
127 Jamie Moyer .15 .40
128 Alex Gonzalez .15 .40
129 Marcus Giles .15 .40
130 Keith Foulke .15 .40
131 Juan Pierre .15 .40
132 Mike Sweeney .15 .40
133 Matt Lawton .15 .40
134 Pat Burrell .15 .40
135 John Olerud .15 .40
136 Raul Mondesi .15 .40
137 Tom Glavine .25 .60
138 Paul Konerko .15 .40
139 Larry Walker .15 .40
140 Adrian Beltre .15 .40
141 Al Leiter .15 .40
142 Mike Lieberthal .15 .40
143 Kazuhiro Sasaki .15 .40
144 Shannon Stewart .15 .40
145 Andruw Jones .25 .60
146 Carlos Lee .15 .40
147 Roger Cedeno .15 .40
148 Kevin Brown .15 .40
149 Jay Payton .15 .40
150 Scott Rolen .25 .60
151 J.D. Drew .15 .40
152 Chipper Jones .40 1.00
153 Magglio Ordonez .15 .40
154 Tony Clark .15 .40
155 Shawn Green .15 .40
156 Mike Piazza .60 1.50
157 Jimmy Rollins .15 .40
158 Jim Edmonds .15 .40
159 Javy Lopez .15 .40
160 Chris Singleton .15 .40
161 Juan Encarnacion .15 .40
162 Eric Karros .15 .40
163 Tsuyoshi Shinjo .15 .40
164 Brian Giles .15 .40
165 Darryl Kile .15 .40
166 Greg Maddux .60 1.50
167 Frank Thomas .40 1.00
168 Shane Halter .15 .40
169 Paul LoDuca .15 .40
170 Robin Ventura .15 .40
171 Jason Kendall .15 .40
172 Jason Hart .15 .40
173 Brady Anderson .15 .40
174 Jose Valentin .15 .40
175 Bobby Higginson .15 .40
176 Gary Sheffield .15 .40
177 Roger Clemens .75 2.00
178 Aramis Ramirez .15 .40
179 Matt Morris .15 .40
180 Jeff Conine .15 .40
181 Aaron Boone .15 .40
182 Jose Macias .15 .40
183 Jeromy Burnitz .15 .40
184 Carl Everett .15 .40
185 Trevor Hoffman .15 .40
186 Placido Polanco .15 .40
187 Jay Gibbons .15 .40
188 Sean Casey .15 .40
189 Josh Beckett .15 .40
190 Jeffrey Hammonds .15 .40
191 Chuck Knoblauch .15 .40
192 Ryan Klesko .15 .40
193 Albert Pujols .75 2.00
194 Chris Richard .15 .40
195 Adam Dunn .15 .40
196 A.J. Burnett .15 .40
197 Geoff Jenkins .15 .40
198 Tino Martinez .25 .60
199 Ray Lankford .15 .40
200 Edgar Renteria .15 .40
201 Eric Cyr PROS .75 2.00
202 Travis Phelps PROS .75 2.00
203 Rick Bauer PROS .75 2.00
204 Mark Prior PROS 1.50 4.00
205 Wilson Betemit PROS .75 2.00
206 Dewon Brazelton PROS .75 2.00
207 Cody Ransom PROS .75 2.00
208 Donnie Bridges PROS .75 2.00
209 Justin Duchscherer PROS .75 2.00
210 Nate Cornejo PROS .75 2.00
211 Jason Romano PROS .75 2.00
212 Juan Cruz PROS .75 2.00
213 Pedro Santana PROS .75 2.00
214 Ryan Drese PROS .75 2.00
215 Bert Snow PROS .75 2.00
216 Nate Frese PROS .75 2.00
217 Rafael Soriano PROS .75 2.00
218 Franklin Nunez PROS RC .75 2.00
219 Tim Spooneybarger PROS .75 2.00
220 Willie Harris PROS .75 2.00
221 Billy Sylvester PROS .75 2.00
222 Carlos Hernandez PROS .75 2.00
223 Mark Teixeira PROS 1.50 4.00
224 Adrian Hernandez PROS .75 2.00
225 Andres Torres PROS .75 2.00
226 Marlon Byrd PROS .75 2.00
227 Juan Rivera PROS .75 2.00
228 Adam Johnson PROS .75 2.00
229 Justin Kaye PROS .75 2.00
230 Kyle Kessel PROS .75 2.00
231 Horacio Ramirez PROS .75 2.00
232 Brandon Larson PROS .75 2.00
233 Luis Lopez PROS .75 2.00
234 Rob Mackowiak PROS .75 2.00
235 Henry Mateo PROS .75 2.00
236 Corky Miller PROS .75 2.00
237 Greg Miller PROS .75 2.00
238 Dustan Mohr PROS .75 2.00
239 Bill Ortega PROS .75 2.00
240 Billy Hall PROS .75 2.00
241 Kazuhisa Ishii UPD RC 2.00 5.00
242 So Taguchi UPD RC 2.00 5.00
243 Takahito Nomura UPD RC 1.50 4.00
244 Satoru Komiyama UPD RC 1.50 4.00
245 Jorge Padilla UPD RC 1.50 4.00
246 Anastacio Martinez UPD RC 1.50 4.00
247 Rodrigo Rosario UPD RC 1.50 4.00
248 Ben Howard UPD RC 1.50 4.00
249 Reed Johnson UPD RC 2.00 5.00
250 Mike Crudale UPD RC 1.50 4.00
P2 Derek Jeter Promo 1.00 2.50

2000 Fleer Showcase

The 2000 Fleer Showcase product was released in October, 2000. The product featured a 140-card base set that was broken into tiers as follows: 100 Base Veterans (1-100), 40 Prospects (101-140). Please note that cards 101-115 were serial numbered to 1000, and cards 116-140 were serial numbered to 2000. Each pack contained five cards and carried a suggested retail price of $3.99.

COMP.SET w/o SP's (100) 10.00 25.00
COMMON CARD (1-100) .20 .50
COMMON (101-115) 3.00 8.00
COMMON (116-140) 2.00 5.00
1 Alex Rodriguez .75 2.00
2 Derek Jeter 1.25 3.00
3 Jeromy Burnitz .20 .50
4 John Olerud .20 .50
5 Paul Konerko .20 .50
6 Johnny Damon .30 .75
7 Curt Schilling .20 .50
8 Barry Larkin .30 .75
9 Adrian Beltre .20 .50
10 Scott Rolen .30 .75
11 Carlos Delgado .20 .50
12 Pedro Martinez .30 .75
13 Todd Helton .30 .75
14 Jacque Jones .20 .50
15 Jeff Kent .20 .50
16 Darin Erstad .20 .50
17 Juan Encarnacion .20 .50
18 Roger Clemens 1.00 2.50
19 Tony Gwynn .60 1.50
20 Nomar Garciaparra .75 2.00
21 Roberto Alomar .30 .75
22 Matt Lawton .20 .50
23 Rich Aurilia .20 .50
24 Charles Johnson .20 .50
25 Jim Thome .30 .75
26 Eric Milton .20 .50
27 Barry Bonds 1.25 3.00
28 Albert Belle .20 .50
29 Travis Fryman .20 .50
30 Ken Griffey Jr. .75 2.00
31 Phil Nevin .20 .50
32 Chipper Jones .50 1.25
33 Craig Biggio .30 .75
34 Mike Hampton .20 .50
35 Fred McGriff .30 .75
36 Cal Ripken 1.50 4.00
37 Manny Ramirez .30 .75
38 Jose Vidro .20 .50
39 Trevor Hoffman .20 .50
40 Tom Glavine .30 .75
41 Frank Thomas .50 1.25
42 Chris Widger .20 .50
43 J.D. Drew .20 .50
44 Andres Galarraga .20 .50
45 Pokey Reese .20 .50
46 Mike Piazza .75 2.00
47 Kevin Young .20 .50
48 Sean Casey .20 .50
49 Carlos Beltran .20 .50
50 Jason Kendall .20 .50
51 Vladimir Guerrero .50 1.25
52 Jermaine Dye .20 .50
53 Brian Giles .20 .50
54 Andruw Jones .30 .75
55 Richard Hidalgo .20 .50
56 Robin Ventura .20 .50
57 Ivan Rodriguez .30 .75
58 Greg Maddux .75 2.00
59 Billy Wagner .20 .50
60 Ruben Mateo .20 .50
61 Troy Glaus .20 .50
62 Dean Palmer .20 .50
63 Eric Chavez .20 .50
64 Edgar Martinez .30 .75
65 Randy Johnson .50 1.25
66 Preston Wilson .20 .50
67 Orlando Hernandez .20 .50
68 Jim Edmonds .20 .50
69 Carl Everett .20 .50
70 Larry Walker .20 .50
71 Ron Belliard .20 .50
72 Sammy Sosa .50 1.25
73 Matt Williams .20 .50
74 Cliff Floyd .20 .50
75 Bernie Williams .30 .75
76 Fernando Tatis .20 .50
77 Steve Finley .20 .50
78 Jeff Bagwell .30 .75
79 Edgardo Alfonzo .20 .50
80 Jose Canseco .30 .75
81 Magglio Ordonez .20 .50
82 Shawn Green .20 .50
83 Bobby Abreu .20 .50
84 Tony Batista .20 .50
85 Mo Vaughn .20 .50
86 Juan Gonzalez .20 .50
87 Paul O'Neill .30 .75
88 Mark McGwire 1.25 3.00
89 Mark Grace .30 .75
90 Kevin Brown .20 .50
91 Ben Grieve .20 .50
92 Shannon Stewart .20 .50
93 Erubiel Durazo .20 .50
94 Antonio Alfonseca .20 .50
95 Jeff Cirillo .20 .50
96 Greg Vaughn .20 .50
97 Kerry Wood .20 .50
98 Geoff Jenkins .20 .50
99 Jason Giambi .20 .50
100 Rafael Palmeiro .30 .75
101 Rafael Furcal PROS 3.00 8.00
102 Pablo Ozuna PROS 3.00 8.00
103 Brad Penny PROS 3.00 8.00
104 Mark Mulder PROS 3.00 8.00
105 Adam Piatt PROS 3.00 8.00
106 Mike Lamb PROS RC 4.00 10.00
107 K.Sasaki PROS RC 4.00 10.00
108 A.McNeal PROS RC 3.00 8.00
109 Pat Burrell PROS 3.00 8.00
110 Rick Ankiel PROS 3.00 8.00
111 Eric Munson PROS 3.00 8.00
112 Josh Beckett PROS 3.00 8.00
113 Adam Kennedy PROS 3.00 8.00
114 Alex Escobar PROS 3.00 8.00
115 C.Hermansen PROS 3.00 8.00
116 Kip Wells PROS 2.00 5.00
117 Matt LeCroy PROS 2.00 5.00
118 Julio Ramirez PROS 2.00 5.00
119 Ben Petrick PROS 2.00 5.00
120 Nick Johnson PROS 2.00 5.00
121 G.Dawkins PROS 2.00 5.00
122 Julio Zuleta PROS RC 2.00 5.00
123 A.Soriano PROS 3.00 8.00
124 K.McDonald RC 2.00 5.00
125 Kory DeHaan PROS 2.00 5.00
126 Vernon Wells PROS 2.00 5.00
127 D.Stenson PROS 2.00 5.00
128 David Eckstein PROS RC 2.00 5.00
129 Robert Fick PROS 2.00 5.00
130 Cole Liniak PROS 2.00 5.00
131 Mark Quinn PROS 2.00 5.00
132 Eric Gagne PROS 3.00 8.00
133 Wily Mo Pena PROS 2.00 5.00
134 A.Thompson RC 2.00 5.00
135 Steve Sisco PROS RC 2.00 5.00
136 P.Rigdon PROS RC 2.00 5.00
137 Rob Bell PROS 2.00 5.00
138 Carlos Guillen PROS 2.00 5.00
139 Jimmy Rollins PROS 2.00 5.00
140 Jason Conti PROS 2.00 5.00

2000 Fleer Showcase Legacy Collection

Randomly inserted into packs, this 140-card set is a complete parallel of the 2000 Fleer Showcase base set. Each card in the set is individually serial numbered to 20.

*STARS 1-100: 25X TO 60X BASIC

2000 Fleer Showcase Prospect Showcase First

Randomly inserted into packs, this 40-card set features MLB's top prospects. Each card is individually serial numbered to 500.

*PROSPECT 1-15: .4X TO 1X BASIC
*PROSPECT RC 1-15: .5X TO 1.2X BASIC
*PROSPECT 16-40: .6X TO 1.5X BASIC
*PROSPECT RC 16-40: .75X TO 2X BASIC

2000 Fleer Showcase Consummate Prose

Randomly inserted into packs at one in six, this 15-card die-cut set features players that perform at a higher level. Card backs carry a "CP" prefix.

COMPLETE SET (15) 12.50 30.00
CP1 Jeff Bagwell .40 1.00
CP2 Alex Rodriguez 1.00 2.50
CP3 Chipper Jones .60 1.50
CP4 Derek Jeter 1.50 4.00
CP5 Manny Ramirez .40 1.00
CP6 Tony Gwynn .75 2.00
CP7 Sammy Sosa .60 1.50
CP8 Ivan Rodriguez .40 1.00
CP9 Greg Maddux 1.00 2.50
CP10 Ken Griffey Jr. 1.00 2.50
CP11 Rick Ankiel .50 1.25
CP12 Cal Ripken 2.00 5.00
CP13 Pedro Martinez .40 1.00
CP14 Mike Piazza 1.00 2.50
CP15 Mark McGwire 1.50 4.00

2000 Fleer Showcase Feel the Game

Randomly inserted into packs at one in 72, this 10-card insert features game-used jersey cards of some of the biggest names in MLB. Card backs carry a "FG" prefix.

FG1 Barry Bonds 15.00 40.00
FG2 Gookie Dawkins 3.00 8.00
FG3 Darin Erstad 4.00 10.00
FG4 Troy Glaus 4.00 10.00
FG5 Scott Rolen 6.00 15.00
FG6 Alex Rodriguez 10.00 25.00
FG7 Andruw Jones 6.00 15.00
FG8 Robin Ventura 4.00 10.00
FG9 Sean Casey 4.00 10.00
FG10 Cal Ripken 20.00 50.00

2000 Fleer Showcase Final Answer

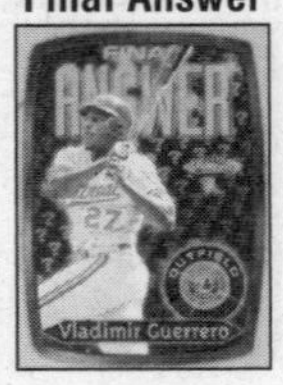

Randomly inserted into packs at one in 10, this 10-card set features hitters that get the job done in clutch situations. Card backs carry a "FA" prefix.

COMPLETE SET (10) 15.00 40.00
FA1 Alex Rodriguez 1.50 4.00
FA2 Vladimir Guerrero 1.00 2.50
FA3 Cal Ripken 3.00 8.00
FA4 Sammy Sosa 1.00 2.50
FA5 Barry Bonds 2.50 6.00
FA6 Derek Jeter 2.50 6.00
FA7 Ken Griffey Jr. 1.50 4.00
FA8 Mike Piazza 1.50 4.00
FA9 Nomar Garciaparra 1.50 4.00
FA10 Mark McGwire 2.50 6.00

2000 Fleer Showcase Fresh Ink

Randomly inserted into packs at one in 24, this 38-card insert set features autographs of many of MLB's top stars and prospects. Please note that Josh Beckett and Brad Penny packed out as exchange cards and must be submitted to Fleer by 07/01/01. These cards are not numbered and we have sequenced them in alphabetical order in our checklist.

1 Rick Ankiel 10.00 25.00
2 Josh Beckett 15.00 40.00
3 Barry Bonds 100.00 175.00
4 A.J. Burnett 6.00 15.00
5 Pat Burrell 6.00 15.00
6 Ken Caminiti 15.00 40.00
7 Sean Casey 6.00 15.00
8 Jose Cruz Jr. 4.00 10.00
9 Gookie Dawkins 4.00 10.00
10 Erubiel Durazo 4.00 10.00
11 Juan Encarnacion 6.00 15.00
12 Darin Erstad 6.00 15.00
13 Rafael Furcal 6.00 15.00
14 Nomar Garciaparra 50.00 100.00
15 Jason Giambi 10.00 25.00
16 Jeremy Giambi 4.00 10.00
17 Brian Giles 6.00 15.00
18 Troy Glaus 10.00 25.00
19 Vladimir Guerrero 15.00 40.00
20 Chad Hermansen 4.00 10.00
21 Randy Johnson 30.00 60.00
22 Andruw Jones 10.00 25.00
23 Jason Kendall 6.00 15.00
24 Paul Konerko 10.00 25.00
25 Mike Lowell 6.00 15.00
26 Aaron McNeal 4.00 10.00
27 Warren Morris 4.00 10.00
28 Paul O'Neill 10.00 25.00
29 Magglio Ordonez 6.00 15.00
30 Pablo Ozuna 4.00 10.00
31 Brad Penny 6.00 15.00
32 Ben Petrick 4.00 10.00
33 Pokey Reese 6.00 15.00
34 Cal Ripken 75.00 150.00
35 Alex Rodriguez 60.00 120.00
36 Scott Rolen 10.00 25.00
37 Jose Vidro 4.00 10.00
38 Kip Wells 4.00 10.00

2000 Fleer Showcase License to Skill

Randomly inserted into packs at one in 20, this 10-card set features highly skilled players. Card backs carry a "LS" prefix.

COMPLETE SET (10) 30.00 80.00
LS1 Vladimir Guerrero 2.00 5.00
LS2 Pedro Martinez 1.25 3.00
LS3 Nomar Garciaparra 3.00 8.00
LS4 Ivan Rodriguez 1.25 3.00
LS5 Mark McGwire 5.00 12.00
LS6 Derek Jeter 5.00 12.00
LS7 Ken Griffey Jr. 3.00 8.00
LS8 Randy Johnson 2.00 5.00
LS9 Sammy Sosa 2.00 5.00
LS10 Alex Rodriguez 3.00 8.00

2000 Fleer Showcase Long Gone

Randomly inserted into packs at one in 20, this 10-card set features hitters that are known for hitting the longball. Card backs carry a "LG" prefix.

COMPLETE SET (10) 10.00 25.00
LG1 Sammy Sosa .75 2.00
LG2 Derek Jeter 2.00 5.00
LG3 Nomar Garciaparra 1.25 3.00
LG4 Juan Gonzalez .30 .75
LG5 Vladimir Guerrero .75 2.00
LG6 Barry Bonds 2.00 5.00
LG7 Jeff Bagwell .50 1.25
LG8 Alex Rodriguez 1.25 3.00
LG9 Ken Griffey Jr. 1.25 3.00
LG10 Mark McGwire 2.00 5.00

2000 Fleer Showcase Noise of Summer

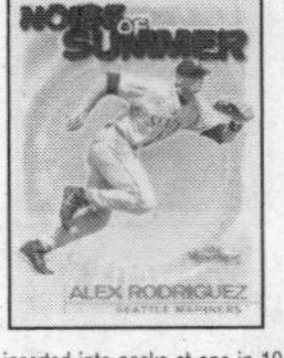

Randomly inserted into packs at one in 10, this 10-card set features players that make plenty of noise during the season. Card backs carry a "NS" prefix.

COMPLETE SET (10) 15.00 40.00
NS1 Chipper Jones 1.00 2.50
NS2 Jeff Bagwell .60 1.50
NS3 Manny Ramirez .60 1.50
NS4 Mark McGwire 2.50 6.00
NS5 Ken Griffey Jr. 1.50 4.00
NS6 Mike Piazza 1.50 4.00
NS7 Pedro Martinez .60 1.50
NS8 Alex Rodriguez 1.50 4.00
NS9 Derek Jeter 2.50 6.00
NS10 Randy Johnson 1.00 2.50

2000 Fleer Showcase Sweet Sigs

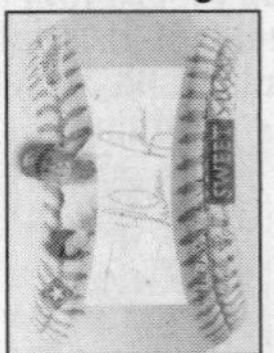

Randomly inserted into packs at one in 250, this 10-card set features autographs of MLB players like Alex Rodriguez and Nolan Ryan. Card backs carry a "SS" prefix. A month after the product went live, representatives at Fleer publicly released print run information on three short-printed cards (Clemens, Garciaparra and A.Rodriguez). Exact amounts are provided in our checklist.

SS1 N.Garciaparra SP/53 75.00 150.00
SS2 Alex Rodriguez SP/67 150.00 250.00
SS3 Tony Gwynn 20.00 50.00
SS4 Roger Clemens SP/79 100.00 200.00
SS5 Scott Rolen 15.00 40.00
SS6 Greg Maddux 50.00 100.00
SS7 Jose Cruz Jr. 6.00 15.00
SS8 Tony Womack 6.00 15.00
SS9 Jay Buhner 10.00 25.00
SS10 Nolan Ryan 75.00 150.00

2001 Fleer Showcase

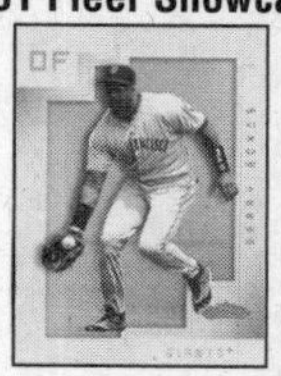

This 160-card set was distributed in five-card packs with a suggested retail price of $4.99. The set features color player images on Satin technology and contains the following subsets: Avant (101-115), Rookie Avant (116-125), and Rookie Showcase (126-160) with the first 20 sequentially numbered to 1,500 and the next 15 to 2,000)

COMP.SET w/o SP's (100) 12.50 30.00
COMMON CARD (1-100) .20 .50
COMMON (101-115) 2.00 5.00
COMMON (116-125) 3.00 8.00
COMMON (126-160) 2.00 5.00
1 Tony Gwynn .60 1.50
2 Barry Larkin .30 .75
3 Chan Ho Park .20 .50
4 Darin Erstad .20 .50
5 Rafael Furcal .20 .50
6 Roger Cedeno .20 .50
7 Timo Perez .20 .50
8 Rick Ankiel .20 .50
9 Pokey Reese .20 .50
10 Jeromy Burnitz .20 .50
11 Phil Nevin .20 .50
12 Matt Williams .20 .50
13 Mike Hampton .20 .50
14 Fernando Tatis .20 .50
15 Kazuhiro Sasaki .20 .50
16 Jim Thome .30 .75
17 Geoff Jenkins .20 .50
18 Jeff Kent .20 .50
19 Tom Glavine .30 .75
20 Dean Palmer .20 .50
21 Todd Zeile .20 .50
22 Edgar Renteria .20 .50
23 Andruw Jones .30 .75
24 Juan Encarnacion .20 .50
25 Robin Ventura .20 .50
26 J.D. Drew .20 .50
27 Ray Durham .20 .50
28 Richard Hidalgo .20 .50
29 Eric Chavez .20 .50
30 Rafael Palmeiro .30 .75
31 Steve Finley .20 .50
32 Jeff Weaver .20 .50
33 Al Leiter .20 .50
34 Jim Edmonds .20 .50
35 Garret Anderson .20 .50
36 Larry Walker .20 .50
37 Jose Vidro .20 .50
38 Mike Cameron .20 .50
39 Brady Anderson .20 .50
40 Mike Lowell .20 .50
41 Bernie Williams .30 .75
42 Gary Sheffield .20 .50
43 John Smoltz .30 .75
44 Mike Mussina .30 .75
45 Greg Vaughn .20 .50
46 Juan Gonzalez .20 .50
47 Matt Lawton .20 .50
48 Robb Nen .20 .50
49 Brad Radke .20 .50
50 Edgar Martinez .30 .75
51 Mike Bordick .20 .50
52 Shawn Green .20 .50
53 Carl Everett .20 .50
54 Adrian Beltre .20 .50
55 Kerry Wood .20 .50
56 Kevin Brown .20 .50
57 Brian Giles .20 .50
58 Greg Maddux .75 2.00
59 Preston Wilson .20 .50
60 Orlando Hernandez .20 .50
61 Ben Grieve .20 .50
62 Jermaine Dye .20 .50
63 Travis Lee .20 .50
64 Jose Cruz Jr. .20 .50
65 Rondell White .20 .50
66 Carlos Beltran .20 .50
67 Scott Rolen .30 .75
68 Brad Fullmer .20 .50
69 David Wells .20 .50
70 Mike Sweeney .20 .50
71 Barry Zito .30 .75
72 Tony Batista .20 .50
73 Curt Schilling .20 .50
74 Jeff Cirillo .20 .50
75 Edgardo Alfonzo .20 .50
76 John Olerud .20 .50
77 Carlos Lee .20 .50
78 Moises Alou .20 .50
79 Tim Hudson .20 .50
80 Andres Galarraga .20 .50
81 Roberto Alomar .30 .75
82 Richie Sexson .20 .50
83 Trevor Hoffman .20 .50
84 Omar Vizquel .30 .75
85 Jacque Jones .20 .50
86 J.T. Snow .20 .50
87 Sean Casey .20 .50
88 Craig Biggio .30 .75
89 Mariano Rivera .50 1.25
90 Rusty Greer .20 .50
91 Barry Bonds 1.25 3.00
92 Pedro Martinez .30 .75
93 Cal Ripken 1.50 4.00
94 Pat Burrell .20 .50
95 Chipper Jones .50 1.25
96 Magglio Ordonez .20 .50
97 Jeff Bagwell .30 .75
98 Randy Johnson .50 1.25
99 Frank Thomas .50 1.25
100 Jason Kendall .20 .50
101 N.Garciaparra AC 5.00 12.00
102 Mark McGwire AC 8.00 20.00
103 Troy Glaus AC 2.00 5.00
104 Ivan Rodriguez AC 2.00 5.00
105 Manny Ramirez Sox AC 2.00 5.00
106 Derek Jeter AC 8.00 20.00
107 Alex Rodriguez AC 5.00 12.00
108 Ken Griffey Jr. AC 5.00 12.00
109 Todd Helton AC 2.00 5.00
110 Sammy Sosa AC 3.00 8.00
111 Vladimir Guerrero AC 3.00 8.00
112 Mike Piazza AC 5.00 12.00
113 Roger Clemens AC 6.00 15.00
114 Jason Giambi AC 2.00 5.00
115 Carlos Delgado AC 2.00 5.00
116 Ichiro Suzuki AC RC 75.00 125.00
117 M.Ensberg AC RC 5.00 12.00
118 C. Valderrama AC RC 3.00 8.00
119 Erick Almonte AC RC 3.00 8.00
120 T.Shinjo AC RC 5.00 12.00
121 Albert Pujols AC RC 150.00 250.00
122 Wilson Betemit AC RC 5.00 12.00
123 A.Hernandez AC RC 3.00 8.00
124 J.Melian AC RC 3.00 8.00
125 Drew Henson AC RC 5.00 12.00
126 Paul Phillips RS RC 2.00 5.00
127 Esix Snead RS RC 2.00 5.00
128 Ryan Freel RS RC 2.00 5.00
129 Junior Spivey RS RC 3.00 8.00
130 E.Guzman RS RC 2.00 5.00
131 Juan Diaz RS RC 2.00 5.00
132 Andres Torres RS RC 2.00 5.00
133 Jay Gibbons RS RC 3.00 8.00
134 Bill Ortega RS RC 2.00 5.00
135 Alexis Gomez RS RC 2.00 5.00
136 Wilkin Ruan RS RC 2.00 5.00
137 Henry Mateo RS RC 2.00 5.00
138 Juan Uribe RS RC 3.00 8.00
139 J.Estrada RS RC 3.00 8.00
140 J.Randolph RS RC 2.00 5.00
141 Eric Hinske RS RC 3.00 8.00
142 Jack Wilson RS RC 3.00 8.00
143 Cody Ransom RS RC 2.00 5.00
144 Nate Frese RS RC 2.00 5.00
145 John Grabow RS RC 2.00 5.00
146 C.Parker RS RC 2.00 5.00
147 B.Lawrence RS RC 2.00 5.00
148 B. Duckworth RS RC 2.00 5.00
149 Winston Abreu RS RC 2.00 5.00
150 H.Ramirez RS RC 3.00 8.00
151 Nick Maness RS RC 2.00 5.00
152 Blaine Neal RS RC 2.00 5.00
153 Billy Sylvester RS RC 2.00 5.00
154 David Elder RS RC 2.00 5.00
155 Bert Snow RS RC 2.00 5.00
156 Claudio Vargas RS RC 2.00 5.00
157 Martin Vargas RS RC 2.00 5.00
158 Grant Balfour RS RC 2.00 5.00
159 Randy Keisler RS 2.00 5.00
160 Zach Day RS RC 2.00 5.00
P1 Tony Gwynn Promo .75 2.00
MM3 D.Jeter MM/2000 5.00 12.00
NNO D.Jeter MM AU/100 60.00 120.00

2001 Fleer Showcase Legacy

Randomly inserted in hobby packs only, this 160-card set is a parallel version of the base set. Only 50 serially numbered sets were produced.

*STARS 1-100: 8X TO 20X BASIC 1-100
*AVANT 101-115: 1.25X TO 3X BASIC 101-115
*AVANT 116-125: .75X TO 2X BASIC 116-125
*RS 126-145: 1.25X TO 3X BASIC 126-145
*RS 146-160: 1.5X TO 4X BASIC 146-160

2001 Fleer Showcase Awards Showcase

Randomly inserted in retail packs only at the rate of one in 20, this 20-card set features color photos of some of the big award winners from the 2000 season.

COMPLETE SET (20) 30.00 60.00
AS1 Derek Jeter 3.00 8.00
AS2 Derek Jeter 3.00 8.00
AS3 Jason Giambi .50 1.25
AS4 Jeff Kent .50 1.25
AS5 Pedro Martinez .75 2.00
AS6 Randy Johnson 1.25 3.00
AS7 Kazuhiro Sasaki .50 1.25
AS8 Rafael Furcal .50 1.25
AS9 Carlos Delgado .50 1.25
AS10 Todd Helton .75 2.00
AS11 Ivan Rodriguez .75 2.00
AS12 Darin Erstad .50 1.25
AS13 Bernie Williams .75 2.00
AS14 Greg Maddux 2.00 5.00
AS15 Jim Edmonds .50 1.25
AS16 Andruw Jones .75 2.00
AS17 Nomar Garciaparra 2.00 5.00
AS18 Todd Helton .75 2.00
AS19 Troy Glaus .50 1.25
AS20 Sammy Sosa 1.25 3.00

2001 Fleer Showcase Awards Showcase Memorabilia

Randomly inserted in hobby packs only, this 34-card set features color photos of players who were Cy Young and MVP winners with pieces of memorabilia embedded in the cards. Only 100 serially numbered sets were produced.

1 Johnny Bench Jsy 10.00 25.00
2 Yogi Berra Bat 10.00 25.00
3 George Brett Jsy 15.00 40.00
4 Lou Brock Bat 10.00 25.00
5 Roy Campanella Bat 15.00 40.00
6 Steve Carlton Jsy 6.00 15.00
7 Roger Clemens Jsy 15.00 40.00
9 Andre Dawson Jsy 6.00 15.00
10 Whitey Ford Jsy 10.00 25.00
12 Jimmie Foxx Bat 30.00 60.00
14 Kirk Gibson Bat 6.00 15.00
15 Tom Glavine Jsy 10.00 25.00
16 Juan Gonzalez Bat 6.00 15.00
17 Elston Howard Bat 10.00 25.00
18 Jim Hunter Jsy 10.00 25.00
19 Reggie Jackson Bat 10.00 25.00
20 Randy Johnson Jsy 10.00 25.00
21 Chipper Jones Bat 10.00 25.00
22 Harmon Killebrew Bat 10.00 25.00
23 Fred Lynn Bat 6.00 15.00
24 Greg Maddux Jsy 10.00 25.00
25 Don Mattingly Bat 15.00 40.00
27 Willie McCovey Jsy 6.00 15.00
28 Jim Palmer Jsy 6.00 15.00
29 Jim Rice Bat 6.00 15.00
30 Brooks Robinson Bat 10.00 25.00
31 Frank Robinson Bat 10.00 25.00
32 Jackie Robinson Pants 40.00 80.00
33 Ivan Rodriguez Jsy 10.00 25.00
34 Mike Schmidt Jsy 15.00 40.00
35 Tom Seaver Jsy 10.00 25.00
36 Willie Stargell Jsy 10.00 25.00
37 Ted Williams Jsy 50.00 100.00
38 Robin Yount Jsy 10.00 25.00

2001 Fleer Showcase Sticks

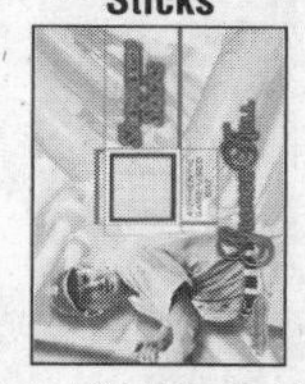

Randomly inserted into hobby packs at the rate of one in 24, this 36-card set color player photos with pieces of game-used bats embedded in the cards.

1 Roberto Alomar 6.00 15.00
2 Rick Ankiel 4.00 10.00
3 Adrian Beltre 4.00 10.00
4 Barry Bonds 10.00 25.00
5 Pat Burrell 4.00 10.00
6 Roger Cedeno 4.00 10.00
7 Tony Clark 4.00 10.00
8 Roger Clemens 6.00 15.00
9 Carlos Delgado 4.00 10.00
10 J.D. Drew 4.00 10.00
11 Steve Finley 4.00 10.00
12 Rafael Furcal 4.00 10.00
13 Alex Gonzalez 4.00 10.00
14 Juan Gonzalez 4.00 10.00
15 Shawn Green 4.00 10.00
16 Vladimir Guerrero 6.00 15.00
17 Richard Hidalgo 4.00 10.00
18 Reggie Jackson 6.00 15.00
19 Randy Johnson 6.00 15.00
20 Andruw Jones 6.00 15.00
21 Chipper Jones 6.00 15.00
22 Al Kaline 6.00 15.00
23 George Kell 4.00 10.00
24 Jason Kendall 4.00 10.00
25 Magglio Ordonez 4.00 10.00
26 Adam Piatt 4.00 10.00
27 Jorge Posada 6.00 15.00
28 Ivan Rodriguez 6.00 15.00
29 Scott Rolen 6.00 15.00
30 Tsuyoshi Shinjo 6.00 15.00
31 Shannon Stewart 4.00 10.00
32 Ichiro Suzuki 15.00 40.00
33 Frank Thomas 6.00 15.00
34 Jim Thome 6.00 15.00
35 Jose Vidro 4.00 10.00
36 Preston Wilson 4.00 10.00

2001 Fleer Showcase Sweet Sigs Leather

Randomly inserted in hobby packs at the rate of one in 24, this 23 card set features color player head shots with their autograph printed on a piece of simulated baseball leather. The following players cards were seeded into packs as exchange cards with a redemption deadline of 11/01/02: Bob Abreu, Wilson Betemit, Russell Branyan, Pat Burrell, Sean Casey, Eric Chavez, Rafael Furcal, Nomar Garciaparra, Juan Gonzalez, Elpidio Guzman, Brandon Inge, Willie Mays, Jackson Melian, Xavier Nady, Jose Ortiz, Ben Sheets and Mike Sweeney.

1 Bob Abreu SP/100 15.00 40.00
2 Wilson Betemit 10.00 25.00
3 Russell Branyan 6.00 15.00
4 Pat Burrell SP/75 15.00 40.00
5 Sean Casey SP/75 15.00 40.00
6 E.Chavez SP/100 EXCH 15.00 40.00
7 Rafael Furcal 6.00 15.00
8 Nomar Garciaparra SP/55 EXCH 50.00 100.00
9 Brian Giles SP/75 15.00 40.00
10 Juan Gonzalez SP/75 EXCH 15.00 40.00
11 Elpidio Guzman 6.00 15.00
12 Drew Henson SP/75 10.00 25.00
13 Brandon Inge 6.00 15.00
14 Derek Jeter SP/75 100.00 200.00
15 Andruw Jones SP/85 20.00 50.00
16 W.Mays SP/60 EXCH 125.00 200.00
17 Jackson Melian 6.00 15.00
18 Xavier Nady 6.00 15.00
19 Jose Ortiz 6.00 15.00
20 Albert Pujols SP/75 500.00 800.00
21 Ben Sheets 8.00 20.00
22 Mike Sweeney 6.00 15.00
23 Miguel Tejada SP/75 20.00 50.00

2001 Fleer Showcase Sweet Sigs Lumber

Randomly inserted in hobby packs at the rate of one in 24, this 23-card set features color player photos with their autograph printed on a piece of ash designed to look like a bat. The following players cards were seeded into packs as exchange cards with a redemption deadline of 11/01/02: Bob Abreu, Wilson Betemit, Russell Branyan, Sean Casey, Eric Chavez, Rafael Furcal, Nomar Garciaparra, Juan Gonzalez, Elpidio Guzman, Brandon Inge, Jackson Melian, Xavier Nady, Jose Ortiz, Ben Sheets and Mike Sweeney.

1 Bob Abreu 6.00 15.00
2 Wilson Betemit 10.00 25.00
3 Russell Branyan 6.00 15.00
4 Pat Burrell SP/300 10.00 25.00
5 Sean Casey SP/300 10.00 25.00
6 Eric Chavez 6.00 15.00
7 Rafael Furcal 6.00 15.00
8 Nomar Garciaparra SP/155 EXCH 50.00 100.00
9 Brian Giles SP/155 10.00 25.00
10 Juan Gonzalez SP/300 EXCH 10.00 25.00
11 Elpidio Guzman 6.00 15.00
12 Drew Henson SP/145 10.00 25.00
13 Brandon Inge 6.00 15.00
14 Derek Jeter SP/300 100.00 175.00
15 Andruw Jones SP/300 12.50 30.00
16 Willie Mays SP/155 75.00 150.00
17 Jackson Melian 6.00 15.00
18 Xavier Nady 6.00 15.00
19 Jose Ortiz 6.00 15.00
20 Albert Pujols SP/150 350.00 600.00
21 Ben Sheets 8.00 20.00
22 Mike Sweeney 6.00 15.00
23 Miguel Tejada SP/300 12.50 30.00

2001 Fleer Showcase Sweet Sigs Wall

Randomly inserted in hobby packs at the rate of one in 24, this 23-card set features color player photos with their autograph printed on an actual piece of game-used outfield wall. The following players cards were seeded into packs as exchange cards with a redemption deadline of 11/01/02: Bob Abreu, Wilson Betemit, Russell Branyan, Pat Burrell, Eric Chavez, Rafael Furcal, Nomar Garciaparra, Juan Gonzalez, Elpidio Guzman, Brandon Inge, Willie Mays, Jackson Melian, Xavier Nady, Jose Ortiz and Ben Sheets.

1 Bob Abreu 6.00 15.00
2 Wilson Betemit 10.00 25.00
3 Russell Branyan 6.00 15.00
4 Pat Burrell SP/93 12.50 30.00
5 Sean Casey SP/98 12.50 30.00
6 Eric Chavez 6.00 15.00
7 Rafael Furcal 6.00 15.00
8 Nomar Garciaparra SP/80 EXCH 50.00 100.00
9 Brian Giles SP/100 12.50 30.00
10 Juan Gonzalez SP/30 EXCH 15.00 40.00
11 Elpidio Guzman 6.00 15.00
12 Drew Henson SP/100 12.50 30.00
13 Brandon Inge 6.00 15.00
14 Derek Jeter SP/90 100.00 200.00
15 Andruw Jones SP/200 15.00 40.00
16 W.Mays SP/85 EXCH 125.00 200.00
17 Jackson Melian 6.00 15.00
18 Xavier Nady 6.00 15.00
19 Jose Ortiz 6.00 15.00
20 Albert Pujols SP/80 350.00 700.00
21 Ben Sheets 8.00 20.00
22 Mike Sweeney
23 Miguel Tejada SP/120 15.00 40.00

2002 Fleer Showcase

This 166 card standard-size set was released in June, 2002. It was issued in five card packs which came 24 packs to a box and four boxes to a case. Each pack had an SRP of $5. Cards numbered 1-125 featured standard cards of veterans while cards 126-135 featured special veteran "avant" cards (seeded at a rate of 1:12 packs) and cards numbered 136-166 feature rookies/prospects (randomly seeded into packs at an undisclosed rate). Those rookie/prospect cards were issued in the following way: cards 136-141 have a stated print run of 500 serial numbered sets, cards numbered 142-156 have a stated print run of 1000 serial numbered sets and cards numbered 157-166 have a stated print run of 1500 serial numbered sets.

COMP.SET w/o SP's (125) 12.50 30.00
COMMON CARD (1-125) .20 .50
COMMON CARD (126-135) 3.00 8.00
COMMON CARD (136-141) 4.00 10.00
COMMON CARD (142-166) 3.00 8.00
1 Albert Pujols 1.00 2.50
2 Pedro Martinez .30 .75
3 Frank Thomas .50 1.25
4 Gary Sheffield .20 .50
5 Roberto Alomar .30 .75
6 Luis Gonzalez .20 .50
7 Bobby Abreu .20 .50
8 Carlos Lee .20 .50
9 Preston Wilson .20 .50
10 Todd Helton .30 .75
11 Juan Gonzalez .20 .50
12 Chuck Knoblauch .20 .50
13 Jason Kendall .20 .50
14 Aaron Sele .20 .50
15 Greg Vaughn .20 .50
16 Fred McGriff .30 .75
17 Doug Mientkiewicz .20 .50
18 Richard Hidalgo .20 .50
19 Alfonso Soriano .20 .50
20 Matt Williams .20 .50
21 Bobby Higginson .20 .50
22 Mo Vaughn .20 .50
23 Andruw Jones .30 .75
24 Omar Vizquel .30 .75
25 Bret Boone .20 .50
26 Bernie Williams .30 .75
27 Rafael Furcal .20 .50
28 Jeff Bagwell .30 .75
29 Marty Cordova .20 .50
30 Lance Berkman .20 .50
31 Vernon Wells .20 .50
32 Garret Anderson .20 .50
33 Larry Bigbie .20 .50
34 Steve Finley .20 .50
35 Barry Bonds 1.25 3.00
36 Eric Chavez .20 .50
37 Tony Clark .20 .50
38 Roger Clemens 1.00 2.50
39 Adam Dunn .20 .50
40 Roger Cedeno .20 .50
41 Carlos Delgado .20 .50
42 Jermaine Dye .20 .50
43 Brian Jordan .20 .50
44 Darin Erstad .20 .50
45 Paul LoDuca .20 .50
46 Jim Edmonds .20 .50
47 Tom Glavine .30 .75
48 Cliff Floyd .20 .50
49 Jon Lieber .20 .50
50 Adrian Beltre .20 .50
51 Joel Pineiro .20 .50
52 Jim Thome .30 .75
53 Jimmy Rollins .20 .50
54 Pat Burrell .20 .50
55 Jeromy Burnitz .20 .50
56 Larry Walker .20 .50
57 Damon Minor .20 .50
58 John Olerud .20 .50
59 Carlos Beltran .20 .50
60 Vladimir Guerrero .50 1.25
61 David Justice .20 .50
62 Phil Nevin .20 .50
63 Tino Martinez .30 .75
64 Curt Schilling .20 .50
65 Corey Patterson .20 .50
66 Aubrey Huff .20 .50
67 Mark Grace .30 .75
68 Rafael Palmeiro .30 .75
69 Jorge Posada .30 .75
70 Craig Biggio .30 .75
71 Manny Ramirez .30 .75
72 Mark Quinn .20 .50
73 Raul Mondesi .20 .50
74 Shawn Green .20 .50
75 Brian Giles .20 .50
76 Paul Konerko .20 .50
77 Troy Glaus .20 .50
78 Mike Mussina .30 .75
79 Greg Maddux .75 2.00
80 Edgar Martinez .30 .75
81 Jose Vidro .20 .50
82 Scott Rolen .30 .75
83 Ben Grieve .20 .50
84 Jeff Kent .20 .50
85 Magglio Ordonez .20 .50
86 Freddy Garcia .20 .50
87 Ivan Rodriguez .30 .75
88 Pokey Reese .20 .50
89 Shannon Stewart .20 .50
90 Randy Johnson .50 1.25
91 Cristian Guzman .20 .50
92 Tsuyoshi Shinjo .20 .50
93 Steve Cox .20 .50
94 Mike Sweeney .20 .50
95 Robert Fick .20 .50
96 Sean Casey .20 .50
97 Tim Hudson .20 .50
98 Bud Smith .20 .50
99 Corey Koskie .20 .50
100 Richie Sexson .20 .50
101 Aramis Ramirez .20 .50
102 Barry Larkin .30 .75
103 Rich Aurilia .20 .50
104 Charles Johnson .20 .50
105 Ryan Klesko .20 .50
106 Ben Sheets .20 .50
107 J.D. Drew .20 .50
108 Jay Gibbons .20 .50
109 Kerry Wood .20 .50
110 C.C. Sabathia .20 .50
111 Eric Munson .20 .50
112 Josh Beckett .20 .50
113 Javier Vazquez .20 .50
114 Barry Zito .20 .50
115 Kazuhiro Sasaki .20 .50
116 Bubba Trammell .20 .50
117 Russell Branyan .20 .50
118 Todd Walker .20 .50
119 Mike Hampton .20 .50
120 Jeff Weaver .20 .50
121 Geoff Jenkins .20 .50
122 Edgardo Alfonzo .20 .50
123 Mike Lieberthal .20 .50
124 Mike Lowell .20 .50
125 Kevin Brown .20 .50
126 Derek Jeter AC 8.00 20.00
127 Ichiro Suzuki AC 6.00 15.00
128 Nomar Garciaparra AC 5.00 12.00
129 Ken Griffey Jr. AC 5.00 12.00
130 Jason Giambi AC 3.00 8.00
131 Alex Rodriguez AC 5.00 12.00
132 Chipper Jones AC 3.00 8.00
133 Mike Piazza AC 5.00 12.00
134 Sammy Sosa AC 3.00 8.00
135 Hideo Nomo AC 3.00 8.00
136 Kazuhisa Ishii AC RC 6.00 15.00
137 Satoru Komiyama AC RC 4.00 10.00
138 So Taguchi AC RC 6.00 15.00
139 Jorge Padilla AC RC 4.00 10.00
140 Rene Reyes AC RC 4.00 10.00
141 Jorge Nunez AC RC 4.00 10.00
142 Nelson Castro RS 3.00 8.00
143 Anderson Machado RS RC 3.00 8.00
144 Edwin Almonte RS RC 3.00 8.00
145 Luis Ugueto RS RC 3.00 8.00
146 Felix Escalona RS RC 3.00 8.00
147 Ron Calloway RS RC 3.00 8.00
148 Hansel Izquierdo RS RC 3.00 8.00
149 Mark Teixeira RS 4.00 10.00
150 Orlando Hudson RS 3.00 8.00
151 Aaron Cook RS RC 3.00 8.00
152 Aaron Taylor RS RC 3.00 8.00
153 Takahito Nomura RS RC 3.00 8.00
154 Matt Thornton RS RC 3.00 8.00
155 Mark Prior RS 4.00 10.00
156 Reed Johnson RS RC 4.00 10.00
157 Doug DeVore RS RC 3.00 8.00
158 Ben Howard RS RC 3.00 8.00
159 Francis Beltran RS RC 3.00 8.00
160 Brian Mallette RS RC 3.00 8.00
161 Sean Burroughs RS 3.00 8.00
162 Michael Restovich RS 3.00 8.00
163 Austin Kearns RS 3.00 8.00
164 Marlon Byrd RS 3.00 8.00
165 Hank Blalock RS 4.00 10.00
166 Mike Rivera RS 3.00 8.00

2002 Fleer Showcase Legacy

Issued at a stated rate of one per hobby box, this is a complete parallel of the Fleer Showcase set. Each of these cards have a stated print run of 175 serial numbered sets.

*LEGACY 1-125: 2.5X TO 6X BASIC
*LEGACY 126-135: .5X TO 1.2X BASIC
*LEGACY 136-141: .4X TO 1X BASIC
*LEGACY 142-166: .5X TO 1.2X BASIC

2002 Fleer Showcase Baseball's Best

Issued in hobby packs at a stated rate of one in eight and retail packs at a stated rate of one in 10, these 20 cards features the leading players in the game.

COMPLETE SET (20) 25.00 60.00
1 Derek Jeter 3.00 8.00

2 Barry Bonds 3.00 8.00
3 Mike Piazza 2.00 5.00
4 Alex Rodriguez 2.00 5.00
5 Pat Burrell .75 2.00
6 Rafael Palmeiro .75 2.00
7 Nomar Garciaparra 2.00 5.00
8 Todd Helton .75 2.00
9 Roger Clemens 2.50 6.00
10 Shawn Green .75 2.00
11 Chipper Jones 1.25 3.00
12 Pedro Martinez .75 2.00
13 Luis Gonzalez .75 2.00
14 Randy Johnson 1.25 3.00
15 Ichiro Suzuki 2.50 6.00
16 Ken Griffey Jr. 2.00 5.00
17 Vladimir Guerrero 1.25 3.00
18 Sammy Sosa 1.25 3.00
19 Jason Giambi .75 2.00
20 Albert Pujols 2.50 6.00

2002 Fleer Showcase Baseball's Best Memorabilia

Inserted in packs at stated odds of one in 12 hobby and one in 36 retail, these 19 cards are a partial parallel of the Baseball's Best insert set. Each of these cards have a memorabilia piece attached to them.

*MULTI-COLOR PATCH: 1X TO 2.5X BASIC
*GOLD: 1X TO 2.5X BASIC
GOLD RANDOM INSERTS IN PACKS
GOLD PRINT RUN 100 SERIAL #'d SETS

1 Derek Jeter Jsy 8.00 20.00
2 Barry Bonds Jsy 8.00 20.00
3 Mike Piazza Jsy 4.00 10.00
4 Alex Rodriguez Bat 6.00 15.00
6 Rafael Palmeiro Jsy 4.00 10.00
7 Nomar Garciaparra Jsy 6.00 15.00
8 Todd Helton Bat SP/350 4.00 10.00
9 Roger Clemens Jsy 6.00 15.00
10 Shawn Green Jsy 3.00 8.00
11 Chipper Jones Jsy 4.00 10.00
12 Pedro Martinez Jsy 4.00 10.00
13 Luis Gonzalez Jsy 3.00 8.00
14 Randy Johnson Jsy 4.00 10.00
15 Ichiro Suzuki Base 8.00 20.00
16 Ken Griffey Jr. Base 6.00 15.00
17 Vladimir Guerrero Base 3.00 8.00
18 Sammy Sosa Base 4.00 10.00
19 Jason Giambi Base 3.00 8.00
20 Albert Pujols Base 6.00 15.00

2002 Fleer Showcase Baseball's Best Memorabilia Autographs Silver

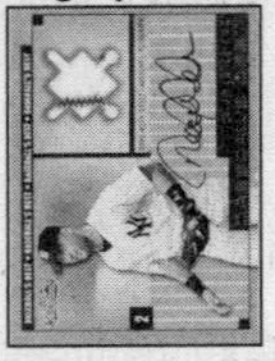

Randomly inserted in packs, these two cards are a parallel of the Baseball's Best Memorabilia insert set. Each of these cards have a stated print run of 400 serial numbered sets. Each of these cards feature not only the memorabilia swatch but also the player's autograph.

*GOLD: .6X TO 1.2X SILVER AU
GOLD PRINT RUN 100 SERIAL #'d SETS

1 Derek Jeter Jsy 75.00 150.00
2 Barry Bonds Jsy 100.00 175.00

2002 Fleer Showcase Derek Jeter Legacy Collection

Randomly inserted in packs, these 22 cards trace the entire career of Yankee superstar Derek Jeter who helped lead the Yankees to five pennants and four world championships in the first six years of his career.

COMPLETE SET (22) 40.00 100.00
COMMON CARD (1-22) 3.00 8.00

2002 Fleer Showcase Derek Jeter Legacy Collection Memorabilia

Randomly inserted in packs, these four cards feature various memorabilia which were part of Derek Jeter's career. Each card was printed to a different

stated print run and we have notated that information in our checklist.

1 D.Jeter YC Jsy/300 * 125.00 200.00
2 Derek Jeter Combo Jsy/175 * 150.00 250.00
Features white NY Yankees swatch and Blue Columbus Bombers swatch
3 D.Jeter WS Ball/50 * 125.00 200.00
4 D.Jeter Fldg Glv/425 * 50.00 100.00

2002 Fleer Showcase Sweet Sigs Leather

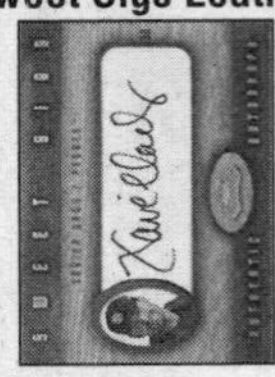

Randomly inserted in packs, these 13 cards feature player signatures on non game-used leather material. Since each player signed a different amount of cards we have put that stated information next to their name in our checklist. A few players signed less than 38 cards and those cards are not priced due to market scarcity.

1 Bobby Abreu/10
2 Russell Branyan/90 6.00 15.00
3 Pat Burrell/35
4 Sean Casey/35
5 Eric Chavez/20
6 Rafael Furcal/92 10.00 25.00
7 Nomar Garciaparra/5
8 Brandon Inge/122 5.00 12.00
9 Jackson Melian/37
10 Xavier Nady/301 6.00 15.00
11 Jose Ortiz/50 8.00 20.00
12 Ben Sheets/60 12.50 30.00
13 Mike Sweeney/103 8.00 20.00

2002 Fleer Showcase Sweet Sigs Lumber

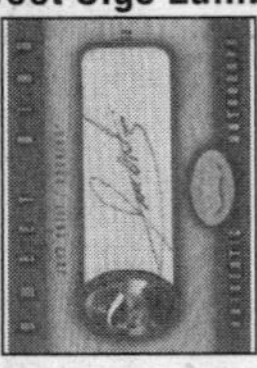

Randomly inserted in packs, these 13 cards feature player signatures on non game-used wood material. Since each player signed a different amount of cards we have put that stated information next to their name in our checklist.

1 Bobby Abreu/231 6.00 15.00
2 Russell Branyan/425 4.00 10.00
3 Pat Burrell/115 8.00 20.00
4 Sean Casey/64 12.50 30.00
5 Eric Chavez/256 6.00 15.00
6 Rafael Furcal/530 6.00 15.00
7 Nomar Garciaparra/25
8 Brandon Inge/528 4.00 10.00
9 Jackson Melian/636 4.00 10.00
10 Xavier Nady/589 4.00 10.00
11 Jose Ortiz/515 4.00 10.00
12 Ben Sheets/418 6.00 15.00
13 Mike Sweeney/495 6.00 15.00

2002 Fleer Showcase Sweet Sigs Wall

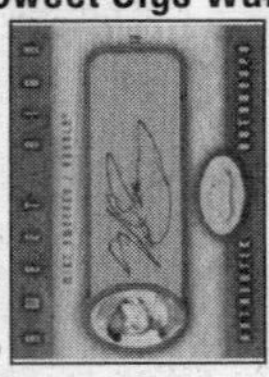

Randomly inserted in packs, these 13 cards feature player signatures on actual game-used wall pieces. Since each player signed a different amount of cards we have put that stated information next to their name in our checklist. Cards with a print run of 35 or fewer are not priced due to market scarcity.

1 Bobby Abreu/70 12.50 30.00
2 Russell Branyan/200 4.00 10.00
3 Pat Burrell/35
4 Sean Casey/35
5 Eric Chavez/108 8.00 20.00
6 Rafael Furcal/207 6.00 15.00
7 Nomar Garciaparra/25
8 Brandon Inge/187 5.00 12.00
9 Jackson Melian/146 5.00 12.00
10 Xavier Nady/286 4.00 10.00
11 Jose Ortiz/116 5.00 12.00
12 Ben Sheets/150 8.00 20.00
13 Mike Sweeney/371 6.00 15.00

2003 Fleer Showcase

This 145-card set was issued in two separtate series. The primary Showcase product was released in March, 2003. Cards 1-95 are active ballplayers and 96- 105 feature retired players. Cards 106 through 135 are a subset entitled Showcasing Talent of which features a selection of top prospects. Three pack types were produced for this product (Jersey, Leather and Lumber) eight of each were placed into the 24-ct sealed boxes. Each pack type contained a selection of commonly available cards plus other inserts and subsets of which were exclusive to the theme. Cards 136-145 were randomly seeded within Fleer Rookies and Greats packs of which was distributed in December, 2003. Each of these 10 update cards features a top prospect and is serial numbered to 750 copies.

COMP.LO SET w/o SP's (105) 10.00 25.00
COMMON CARD (1-95) .20 .50
COMMON CARD (96-105) .40 1.00
COMMON CARD (106-135) 1.25 3.00
106-135 ODDS 1:3 HOBBY, 1:12 RETAIL
106-115 DIST IN JERSEY AND RETAIL PACKS
116-125 DIST IN LEATHER AND RETAIL PACKS
126-135 DIST IN LUMBER AND RETAIL PACKS
COMMON CARD (136-145) 1.50 4.00

1 David Eckstein .20 .50
2 Curt Schilling .20 .50
3 Jay Gibbons .20 .50
4 Kerry Wood .20 .50
5 Jeff Bagwell .30 .75
6 Hideo Nomo .50 1.25
7 Tim Hudson .20 .50
8 J.D. Drew .20 .50
9 Josh Phelps .20 .50
10 Bartolo Colon .20 .50
11 Bobby Abreu .20 .50
12 Matt Morris .20 .50
13 Kazuhiro Sasaki .20 .50
14 Sean Burroughs .20 .50
15 Vicente Padilla .20 .50
16 Jorge Posada .30 .75
17 Torii Hunter .20 .50
18 Richie Sexson .20 .50
19 Lance Berkman .20 .50
20 Todd Helton .30 .75
21 Paul Konerko .20 .50
22 Pedro Martinez .30 .75
23 Rodrigo Lopez .20 .50
24 Gary Sheffield .20 .50
25 Darin Erstad .20 .50
26 Nomar Garciaparra .75 2.00
27 Adam Dunn .20 .50
28 Jason Giambi .20 .50
29 Miguel Tejada .20 .50
30 Chipper Jones .50 1.25
31 Alex Rodriguez .75 2.00
32 Barry Bonds 1.25 3.00
33 Roger Clemens 1.00 2.50
34 Sammy Sosa .50 1.25
35 Randy Johnson .50 1.25
36 Tim Salmon .30 .75
37 Shea Hillenbrand .20 .50
38 Larry Walker .20 .50
39 A.J. Burnett .20 .50
40 Shawn Green .20 .50
41 Cristian Guzman .20 .50
42 Bernie Williams .30 .75
43 Mark Mulder .20 .50
44 Brian Giles .20 .50
45 Bret Boone .20 .50
46 Juan Gonzalez .20 .50
47 Roy Halladay .20 .50
48 Wade Miller .20 .50
49 Jeff Kent .20 .50
50 Carlos Delgado .20 .50
51 Mike Lowell .20 .50
52 Jim Edmonds .20 .50
53 Ivan Rodriguez .30 .75
54 Aubrey Huff .20 .50
55 Ryan Klesko .20 .50
56 Paul Lo Duca .20 .50
57 Roy Oswalt .20 .50
58 Omar Vizquel .30 .75
59 Manny Ramirez .30 .75
60 Andruw Jones .30 .75
61 Troy Glaus .20 .50
62 Ichiro Suzuki 1.00 2.50
63 Albert Pujols 1.00 2.50
64 Derek Jeter 1.25 3.00
65 Mark Prior .30 .75
66 Ken Griffey Jr. .75 2.00
67 Vladimir Guerrero .50 1.25
68 Mike Piazza .75 2.00
69 Alfonso Soriano .20 .50
70 Greg Maddux .75 2.00
71 Adam Kennedy .20 .50
72 Junior Spivey .20 .50
73 Tom Glavine .30 .75
74 Derek Lowe .20 .50
75 Magglio Ordonez .20 .50
76 Jim Thome .30 .75
77 Robert Fick .20 .50
78 Josh Beckett .20 .50
79 Mike Sweeney .20 .50
80 Kazuhisa Ishii .20 .50
81 Roberto Alomar .30 .75
82 Barry Zito .20 .50
83 Pat Burrell .20 .50
84 Scott Rolen .30 .75
85 John Olerud .20 .50
86 Eric Hinske .20 .50
87 Rafael Palmeiro .30 .75
88 Edgar Martinez .30 .75
89 Eric Chavez .20 .50
90 Jose Vidro .20 .50
91 Craig Biggio .30 .75
92 Rich Aurilia .20 .50
93 Austin Kearns .20 .50
94 Luis Gonzalez .20 .50
95 Garret Anderson .20 .50
96 Yogi Berra .75 2.00
97 Al Kaline .75 2.00
98 Robin Yount .75 2.00
99 Reggie Jackson .60 1.50
100 Harmon Killebrew .75 2.00
101 Eddie Mathews .75 2.00
102 Willie McCovey .40 1.00
103 Nolan Ryan 1.50 4.00
104 Mike Schmidt 1.00 2.50
105 Tom Seaver .60 1.50
106 Francisco Rodriguez ST 1.25 3.00
107 Carl Crawford ST 1.25 3.00
108 Ben Howard ST 1.25 3.00
109 Hank Blalock ST 1.25 3.00
110 Hee Seop Choi ST 1.25 3.00
111 Kirk Saarloos ST 1.25 3.00
112 Lew Ford ST RC 2.00 5.00
113 Andy Van Hekken ST 1.25 3.00
114 Drew Henson ST 1.25 3.00
115 Marlon Byrd ST 1.25 3.00
116 Jayson Werth ST 1.25 3.00
117 Willie Bloomquist ST 1.25 3.00
118 Joe Borchard ST 1.25 3.00
119 Mark Teixeira ST 2.00 5.00
120 Bobby Hill ST 1.25 3.00
121 Jason Lane ST 1.25 3.00
122 Omar Infante ST 1.25 3.00
123 Victor Martinez ST 2.00 5.00
124 Jorge Padilla ST 1.25 3.00
125 John Lackey ST 1.25 3.00
126 Anderson Machado ST 1.25 3.00
127 Rodrigo Rosario ST 1.25 3.00
128 Freddy Sanchez ST 1.25 3.00
129 Tony Alvarez ST 1.25 3.00
130 Matt Thornton ST 1.25 3.00
131 Joe Thurston ST 1.25 3.00
132 Brett Myers ST 1.25 3.00
133 Nook Logan ST RC 2.00 5.00
134 Chris Snelling ST 1.25 3.00
135 Termel Sledge ST RC 1.25 3.00
136 Chien-Ming Wang ST RC 12.50 30.00
137 Rickie Weeks ST RC 3.00 8.00
138 Brandon Webb ST RC 2.50 6.00
139 Hideki Matsui ST RC 6.00 15.00
140 Michael Hessman ST RC 1.50 4.00
141 Ryan Wagner ST RC 1.50 4.00
142 Bo Hart ST RC 1.50 4.00
143 Edwin Jackson ST RC 2.00 5.00
144 Jose Contreras ST RC 2.00 5.00
145 Delmon Young ST RC 6.00 15.00

2003 Fleer Showcase Legacy

This 135 card set was distributed exclusively in three separate forms of hobby packs. Cards 1-35 and 126-135 were available exclusively in hobby Lumber packs (signified by an orange-bar wrapper), 36-70 and 116-125 in hobby Leather packs (signified by brown-bar wrapper) and 71-105 and 106-115 in hobby Jersey packs (signified by a gray-bar wrapper). Only 150 serial numbered sets were produced. Each card is serial numbered on back in gold foil.

*LEGACY 1-95: 2.5X TO 6X BASIC
*LEGACY 96-105: 3X TO 8X BASIC
*LEGACY 106-135: .6X TO 1.5X BASIC

2003 Fleer Showcase Baseball's Best

Issued at a stated rate of one in eight leather packs and one in 24 retail packs, this 15-card insert set features the best players in basbeball.

1 Curt Schilling 1.25 3.00
2 Barry Zito 1.25 3.00
3 Torii Hunter 1.25 3.00
4 Pedro Martinez 1.25 3.00
5 Bernie Williams 1.25 3.00
6 Magglio Ordonez 1.25 3.00
7 Alfonso Soriano 1.25 3.00
8 Hideo Nomo 1.25 3.00
9 Jason Giambi 1.25 3.00
10 Sammy Sosa 1.25 3.00
11 Vladimir Guerrero 1.25 3.00
12 Ken Griffey Jr. 2.00 5.00
13 Troy Glaus 1.25 3.00
14 Ichiro Suzuki 2.50 6.00
15 Albert Pujols 2.50 6.00

2003 Fleer Showcase Baseball's Best Game Jersey

These cards parallel the Baseball's Best insert set. Although the wrappper stated odds list these cards as 1:27 Leather hobby packs - our analysis of the case breakdown, coupled with reports from dealers in the field indicates the cards were actually seeded at a rate of 1:9 Leather hobby packs.

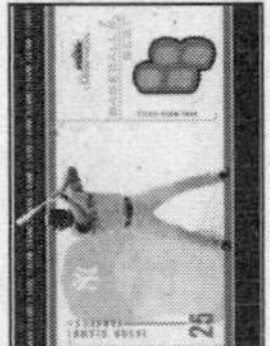

AS Alfonso Soriano 3.00 8.00
BW Bernie Williams 4.00 10.00
BZ Barry Zito 3.00 8.00
CS Curt Schilling 3.00 8.00
HN Hideo Nomo Sox 4.00 10.00
JG Jason Giambi 3.00 8.00
MO Magglio Ordonez 3.00 8.00
PM Pedro Martinez 4.00 10.00
SS Sammy Sosa 4.00 10.00
TH Torii Hunter 3.00 8.00

2003 Fleer Showcase Hot Gloves

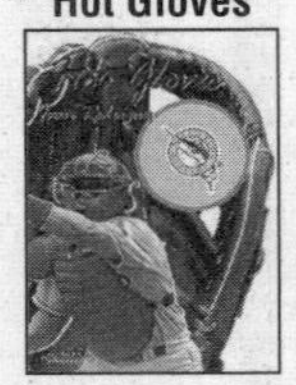

Inserted at a stated rate of one in 144 leather and one in 288 retail packs these 10 cards features some of the leading defensive players in baseball.

1 Greg Maddux 10.00 25.00
2 Ivan Rodriguez 6.00 15.00
3 Derek Jeter 15.00 40.00
4 Mike Piazza 10.00 25.00
5 Nomar Garciaparra 10.00 25.00
6 Andruw Jones 6.00 15.00
7 Scott Rolen 6.00 15.00
8 Barry Bonds 15.00 40.00
9 Roger Clemens 12.50 30.00
10 Alex Rodriguez 10.00 25.00

2003 Fleer Showcase Hot Gloves Game Jersey

Randomly inserted in lumber packs, this is a parallel to the Hot Gloves insert set. These cards have a game-worn jersey card as well as the player's photo pictured.

AJ Andruw Jones 6.00 15.00
AR Alex Rodriguez 8.00 20.00
BB Barry Bonds 12.50 30.00
DJ Derek Jeter 12.50 30.00
GM Greg Maddux 8.00 20.00
IR Ivan Rodriguez 6.00 15.00
MP Mike Piazza 8.00 20.00
NG Nomar Garciaparra 8.00 20.00
RC Roger Clemens 10.00 25.00
SR Scott Rolen 6.00 15.00

2003 Fleer Showcase Sweet Sigs

Randomly inserted in both leather and retail packs, these cards feature authentic signatures of either Barry Bonds or Derek Jeter. As these cards are issued to various print runs, we have notated that information in our checklist.

BB1 Barry Bonds 90 MVP/150 100.00 175.00
BB2 Barry Bonds 92 MVP/100 100.00 175.00
BB3 Barry Bonds 93 MVP/75 125.00 200.00
BB4 Barry Bonds 01 MVP/50 150.00 250.00
BB5 Barry Bonds 02 MVP/25
BB6 Barry Bonds 5X MVP/5
DJ2 Derek Jeter Blue Ink/250 75.00 150.00
DJ3 Derek Jeter Red Ink/50 150.00 250.00

2003 Fleer Showcase Sweet Stitches

Issued at a stated rate of one in eight jersey packs and one in 24 retail packs, these 10 cards feature information about what various stars do in their off-field activities.

1 Derek Jeter 3.00 8.00
2 Randy Johnson 1.25 3.00
3 Jeff Bagwell 1.25 3.00
4 Nomar Garciaparra 2.00 5.00
5 Roger Clemens 2.50 6.00
6 Todd Helton 1.25 3.00
7 Barry Bonds 3.00 8.00
8 Alfonso Soriano 1.25 3.00
9 Miguel Tejada 1.25 3.00
10 Mark Prior 1.25 3.00

2003 Fleer Showcase Sweet Stitches Game Jersey

Randomly inserted in jersey packs, this is a parallel to the Sweet Stitches insert set. These cards feature game-used jersey pieces and were issued to assorted print runs and we have notated that information next to the player's name in our checklist.

AR Alex Rodriguez/899 6.00 15.00
AS Alfonso Soriano/599 3.00 8.00
BB Barry Bonds/899 8.00 20.00
DJ Derek Jeter/599 10.00 25.00
JB Jeff Bagwell/899 4.00 10.00
JD J.D. Drew/899 3.00 8.00
MP Mike Piazza/899 6.00 15.00
MP Mark Prior/899 4.00 10.00
MT Miguel Tejada/899 3.00 8.00
NG Nomar Garciaparra/899 6.00 15.00
RC Roger Clemens/599 8.00 20.00
RJ Randy Johnson/899 4.00 10.00
SS Sammy Sosa/899 4.00 10.00
TH Todd Helton/899 4.00 10.00

2003 Fleer Showcase Sweet Stitches Patch

Randomly inserted in jersey packs, this is a parallel to the sweet stitches insert set. These cards feature game-used jersey patch pieces and were issued to assorted print runs and we have notated that information next to the player's name in our checklist.

1 Derek Jeter/50
2 Randy Johnson/150 15.00 40.00
3 Jeff Bagwell/150 15.00 40.00
4 Nomar Garciaparra/150 30.00 60.00
5 Roger Clemens/50
6 Todd Helton/75 20.00 50.00
7 Barry Bonds/150 40.00 80.00
8 Alfonso Soriano/50 10.00 25.00
9 Miguel Tejada/150 10.00 25.00
10 Mark Prior/150 15.00 40.00
11 Sammy Sosa/150 15.00 40.00
12 J.D. Drew/150 10.00 25.00
13 Alex Rodriguez/150 30.00 60.00
14 Mike Piazza/150 30.00 60.00

2003 Fleer Showcase Thunder Sticks

Inserted in packs at a stated rate of one in eight lumber and one in 24 retail, these 10 cards feature some of the leading power hitters in baseball.

1 Adam Dunn 1.25 3.00
2 Alex Rodriguez 2.00 5.00
3 Barry Bonds 3.00 8.00
4 Jim Thome 1.25 3.00
5 Chipper Jones 1.25 3.00
6 Manny Ramirez 1.25 3.00
7 Carlos Delgado 1.25 3.00
8 Mike Piazza 2.00 5.00
9 Shawn Green 1.25 3.00
10 Pat Burrell 1.25 3.00

2003 Fleer Showcase Thunder Sticks Game Bat

Randomly inserted in lumber packs, these cards parallel the Thunder Sticks insert set. These cards feature a game bat piece and were issued to a varying amount of cards. We have notated the print

run information next to the player's name in our checklist.

*GOLD: 1X TO 2.5X BASIC CARDS
GOLD PRINT RUN 99 SERIAL #'d SETS
AD Adam Dunn/799 3.00 8.00
AR Alex Rodriguez/799 6.00 15.00
BB Barry Bonds/899 8.00 20.00
CJ Chipper Jones/799 4.00 10.00
JT Jim Thome/799 4.00 10.00
MR Manny Ramirez/799 4.00 10.00
PB Pat Burrell/799 3.00 8.00
SG Shawn Green/799 3.00 8.00
TG Troy Glaus/799 3.00 8.00
VG Vladimir Guerrero/799 4.00 10.00

2004 Fleer Showcase

This 130-card set was released in March, 2004. The set was issued in five-card packs with an $5.50 SRP and came 24 packs to a box and 12 boxes to a case. Cards numbered 1-100 feature veterans while cards 101-130 feature veterans. Those final 30 cards were issued at a stated rate of one in six hobby and one in 12 retail packs.

COMP.SET w/o SP's (100) 10.00 25.00
COMMON CARD (1-100) .20 .50
COMMON CARD (101-130) .75 2.00
101-130 ODDS 1:6 HOBBY, 1:12 RETAIL
1 Corey Patterson .20 .50
2 Ken Griffey Jr. .75 2.00
3 Preston Wilson .20 .50
4 Juan Pierre .20 .50
5 Jose Reyes .20 .50
6 Jason Schmidt .20 .50
7 Rocco Baldelli .20 .50
8 Carlos Delgado .20 .50
9 Hideki Matsui .75 2.00
10 Nomar Garciaparra .75 2.00
11 Brian Giles .20 .50
12 Darin Erstad .20 .50
13 Larry Walker .20 .50
14 Bernie Williams .30 .75
15 Laynce Nix .20 .50
16 Manny Ramirez .30 .75
17 Magglio Ordonez .20 .50
18 Khalil Greene .30 .75
19 Jim Edmonds .20 .50
20 Troy Glaus .20 .50
21 Curt Schilling .20 .50
22 Chipper Jones .50 1.25
23 Sammy Sosa .50 1.25
24 Frank Thomas .50 1.25
25 Todd Helton .30 .75
26 Craig Biggio .30 .75
27 Shannon Stewart .20 .50
28 Mark Mulder .20 .50
29 Mike Lieberthal .20 .50
30 Reggie Sanders .20 .50
31 Edgar Martinez .30 .75
32 Bo Hart .20 .50
33 Mark Teixeira .30 .75
34 Jay Gibbons .20 .50
35 Roberto Alomar .30 .75
36 Kip Wells .20 .50
37 J.D. Drew .20 .50
38 Jason Varitek .50 1.25
39 Craig Monroe .20 .50
40 Roy Oswalt .20 .50
41 Edgardo Alfonzo .20 .50
42 Roy Halladay .20 .50
43 Gary Sheffield .20 .50
44 Lance Berkman .20 .50
45 Torii Hunter .20 .50
46 Vladimir Guerrero .50 1.25
47 Marlon Byrd .20 .50
48 Austin Kearns .20 .50
49 Angel Berroa .20 .50
50 Geoff Jenkins .20 .50
51 Aubrey Huff .20 .50
52 Dontrelle Willis .30 .75
53 Tony Batista .20 .50
54 Shawn Green .20 .50
55 Jason Kendall .20 .50
56 Garret Anderson .20 .50
57 Andruw Jones .30 .75
58 Dmitri Young .20 .50
59 Richie Sexson .20 .50
60 Jorge Posada .30 .75
61 Bobby Abreu .20 .50
62 Vernon Wells .20 .50
63 Javy Lopez .20 .50
64 Josh Beckett .20 .50
65 Eric Chavez .20 .50
66 Tim Salmon .30 .75
67 Brandon Webb .20 .50
68 Pedro Martinez .30 .75
69 Kerry Wood .20 .50
70 Jose Vidro .20 .50
71 Alfonso Soriano .20 .50
72 Barry Zito .20 .50
73 Sean Burroughs .20 .50
74 Jamie Moyer .20 .50
75 Luis Gonzalez .20 .50
76 Adam Dunn .20 .50
77 Mike Piazza .75 2.00
78 Pat Burrell .20 .50
79 Scott Rolen .30 .75
80 Milton Bradley .20 .50
81 Mike Sweeney .20 .50
82 Hank Blalock .20 .50
83 Esteban Loaiza .20 .50
84 Hideo Nomo .50 1.25
85 Derek Jeter 1.00 2.50
86 Albert Pujols 1.00 2.50
87 Greg Maddux .75 2.00
88 Mark Prior .30 .75
89 Mike Lowell .20 .50
90 Jeff Bagwell .30 .75
91 Scott Podsednik .20 .50
92 Tom Glavine .30 .75
93 Jason Giambi .20 .50
94 Jim Thome .30 .75
95 Ichiro Suzuki 1.00 2.50
96 Randy Johnson .50 1.25
97 Omar Vizquel .30 .75
98 Ivan Rodriguez .30 .75
99 Miguel Tejada .20 .50
100 Alex Rodriguez .75 2.00
101 Rickie Weeks ST .75 2.00
102 Chad Gaudin ST .75 2.00
103 Rich Harden ST .75 2.00
104 Edwin Jackson ST .75 2.00
105 Chien-Ming Wang ST 3.00 8.00
106 Matt Kata ST .75 2.00
107 Delmon Young ST 1.25 3.00
108 Ryan Wagner ST .75 2.00
109 Jeff Duncan ST .75 2.00
110 Prentice Redman ST .75 2.00
111 Clint Barmes ST .75 2.00
112 Jeremy Guthrie ST .75 2.00
113 Brian Stokes ST .75 2.00
114 David DeJesus ST .75 2.00
115 Felix Sanchez ST .75 2.00
116 Josh Stewart ST .75 2.00
117 Daniel Garcia ST .75 2.00
118 Jon Leicester ST .75 2.00
119 Francisco Cruceta ST .75 2.00
120 Oscar Villarreal ST .75 2.00
121 Michael Hessman ST .75 2.00
122 Michel Hernandez ST .75 2.00
123 Richard Fischer ST .75 2.00
124 Robby Hammock ST .75 2.00
125 Guillermo Quiroz ST .75 2.00
126 Craig Brazell ST .75 2.00
127 Wilfredo Ledezma ST .75 2.00
128 Josh Willingham ST .75 2.00
129 Ramon Nivar ST .75 2.00
130 Matt Diaz ST .75 2.00

2004 Fleer Showcase Legacy

*LEGACY 1-100: 6X TO 15X BASIC
*LEGACY 101-130: 1.5X TO 4X BASIC
OVERALL PARALLEL ODDS 1:24
STATED PRINT RUN 99 SERIAL #'d SETS

2004 Fleer Showcase Masterpiece

OVERALL PARALLEL ODDS 1:24
STATED PRINT RUN 1 SERIAL #'d SET
NO PRICING DUE TO SCARCITY

2004 Fleer Showcase Baseballs Best

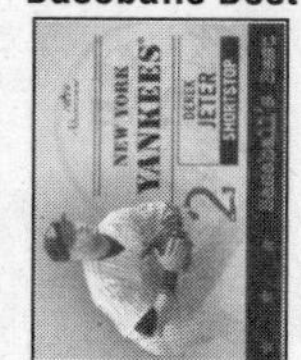

STATED ODDS 1:24 HOBBY, 1:12 RETAIL
1 Derek Jeter 2.50 6.00
2 Mark Prior 1.25 3.00
3 Mike Piazza 2.00 5.00
4 Jeff Bagwell 1.25 3.00
5 Kerry Wood 1.25 3.00
6 Ivan Rodriguez 1.25 3.00
7 Albert Pujols 2.50 6.00
8 Jim Thome 1.25 3.00
9 Sammy Sosa 1.25 3.00
10 Vladimir Guerrero 1.25 3.00
11 Eric Gagne 1.25 3.00
12 Randy Johnson 1.25 3.00
13 Todd Helton 1.25 3.00
14 Chipper Jones 1.25 3.00
15 Alex Rodriguez 2.00 5.00

2004 Fleer Showcase Baseballs Best Game Used

STATED ODDS 1:72 HOBBY, 1:48 RETAIL
*PATCH: 1.5X TO 4X BASIC
PATCH RANDOM INSERTS IN PACKS
PATCH PRINT RUN 50 SERIAL #'d SETS
*GOLD: .5X TO 1.2X BASIC
GOLD RANDOM INSERTS IN PACKS
GOLD PRINT RUN 150 SERIAL #'d SETS
*REWARD: 1X TO 2.5X BASIC
REWARD ISSUED ONLY IN DEALER PACKS
REWARD PRINTS B/WN 29-44 COPIES PER
AP Albert Pujols Jsy 6.00 15.00
AR Alex Rodriguez Jsy 4.00 10.00
CJ Chipper Jones Jsy 4.00 10.00
DJ Derek Jeter Bat 8.00 20.00
EG Eric Gagne Jsy 3.00 8.00
IR Ivan Rodriguez Jsy 4.00 10.00
JB Jeff Bagwell Jsy 4.00 10.00
JT Jim Thome Jsy 4.00 10.00
KW Kerry Wood Jsy 3.00 8.00
MPI Mike Piazza Jsy 4.00 10.00
MPR Mark Prior Jsy 4.00 10.00
RJ Randy Johnson Jsy 4.00 10.00
SS Sammy Sosa Jsy 4.00 10.00
TH Todd Helton Jsy 4.00 10.00
VG Vladimir Guerrero Jsy 4.00 10.00

2004 Fleer Showcase Grace

STATED ODDS 1:12 HOBBY/RETAIL
1 Kerry Wood 1.25 3.00
2 Derek Jeter 2.50 6.00
3 Nomar Garciaparra 2.00 5.00
4 Mike Piazza 2.00 5.00
5 Mark Prior 1.25 3.00
6 Jose Reyes 1.25 3.00
7 Dontrelle Willis 1.25 3.00
8 Pedro Martinez 1.25 3.00
9 Tim Hudson 1.25 3.00
10 Troy Glaus 1.25 3.00
11 Hank Blalock 1.25 3.00
12 Albert Pujols 2.50 6.00
13 Juan Pierre 1.25 3.00
14 Angel Berroa 1.25 3.00
15 Rocco Baldelli 1.25 3.00
16 Carlos Delgado 1.25 3.00
17 Manny Ramirez 1.25 3.00
18 Alex Rodriguez 2.00 5.00
19 Andruw Jones 1.25 3.00
20 Luis Gonzalez 1.25 3.00

2004 Fleer Showcase Grace Game Used

STATED ODDS 1:48 HOBBY/RETAIL
*PATCH: 1.5X TO 4X BASIC
PATCH RANDOM INSERTS IN PACKS
PATCH PRINT RUN 50 SERIAL #'d SETS
*GOLD: .5X TO 1.2X BASIC
GOLD RANDOM INSERTS IN PACKS
GOLD PRINT RUN 150 SERIAL #'d SETS
*REWARD p/r 44-55: 1X TO 2.5X BASIC
REWARD ISSUED ONLY IN DEALER PACKS
REWARD PRINTS B/WN 23-55 COPIES PER
NO REWARD PRICING ON QTY OF 23
AP Albert Pujols Jsy 6.00 15.00
AR Alex Rodriguez Jsy 4.00 10.00
DJ Derek Jeter Bat 8.00 20.00
DW Dontrelle Willis Jsy 4.00 10.00
MPI Mike Piazza Jsy 4.00 10.00
MPR Mark Prior Jsy 4.00 10.00
MR Manny Ramirez Jsy 4.00 10.00
NG Nomar Garciaparra Jsy 4.00 10.00
PM Pedro Martinez Jsy 4.00 10.00
RB Rocco Baldelli Jsy 3.00 8.00

2004 Fleer Showcase Hot Gloves

STATED ODDS 1:288 HOBBY, 1:576 RETAIL
NO MORE THAN 120 SETS PRODUCED
PRINT RUN INFO PROVIDED BY FLEER
CARDS ARE NOT SERIAL-NUMBERED
1 Derek Jeter 15.00 40.00
2 Nomar Garciaparra 12.50 30.00
3 Alex Rodriguez 12.50 30.00
4 Chipper Jones 10.00 25.00

5 Torii Hunter 10.00 25.00
6 Ichiro Suzuki 15.00 40.00
7 Mark Prior 10.00 25.00
8 Vladimir Guerrero 10.00 25.00
9 Albert Pujols 15.00 40.00
10 Ivan Rodriguez 10.00 25.00
11 Hideki Matsui 20.00 50.00
12 Sammy Sosa 10.00 25.00
13 Jim Thome 10.00 25.00
14 Rocco Baldelli 10.00 25.00
15 Jeff Bagwell 10.00 25.00

2004 Fleer Showcase Hot Gloves Game Used

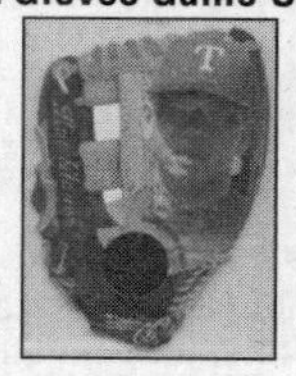

RANDOM INSERTS IN PACKS
STATED PRINT RUN 50 SERIAL #'d SETS
AP Albert Pujols Jsy 30.00 60.00
AR Alex Rodriguez Jsy 20.00 50.00
CJ Chipper Jones Jsy 12.50 30.00
DJ Derek Jeter Jsy 40.00 80.00
HM Hideki Matsui Base 50.00 100.00
IR Ivan Rodriguez Jsy 12.50 30.00
IS Ichiro Suzuki Base 60.00 120.00
JB Jeff Bagwell Jsy 12.50 30.00
JT Jim Thome Jsy 12.50 30.00
MP Mark Prior Jsy 12.50 30.00
NG Nomar Garciaparra Jsy 20.00 50.00
RB Rocco Baldelli Jsy 12.50 30.00
SS Sammy Sosa Jsy 12.50 30.00
TH Torii Hunter Jsy 12.50 30.00
VG Vladimir Guerrero Jsy 12.50 30.00

2004 Fleer Showcase Pujols Legacy Collection

COMMON CARD (1-10) 3.00 8.00
STATED ODDS 1:24
STATED PRINT RUN 1000 SERIAL #'d SETS

2004 Fleer Showcase Pujols Legacy Collection Autograph

OVERALL AUTOGRAPH ODDS 1:24
PRINT RUNS B/WN 1-10 COPIES PER
NO PRICING DUE TO SCARCITY
1 Albert Pujols Draft 99/1
2 Albert Pujols 01 ROY/2
3 Albert Pujols 01 Slugger/3
4 Albert Pujols 4 Pos/4
5 Albert Pujols NL Records/5
6 Albert Pujols 2X AS/6
7 Albert Pujols HR Record/7
8 Albert Pujols 300-100-100/8
9 Albert Pujols 03 Btg Champ/9
10 Albert Pujols 03 POY/10

2004 Fleer Showcase Pujols Legacy Collection Game Jersey

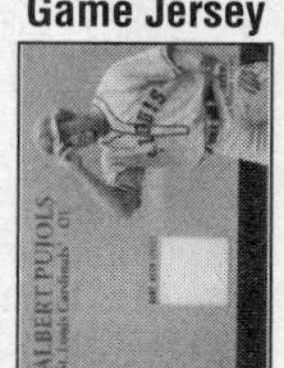

RANDOM INSERTS IN PACKS
PRINT RUNS B/WN 10-100 COPIES PER
NO PRICING ON QTY OF 40 OR LESS
1 Albert Pujols Draft 99/10
2 Albert Pujols 01 ROY/20
3 Albert Pujols 01 Slugger/30
4 Albert Pujols 4 Pos/40
5 Albert Pujols NL Records/50 12.50 30.00
6 Albert Pujols 2X AS/60 12.50 30.00
7 Albert Pujols HR Record/70 10.00 25.00
8 Albert Pujols 300-100-100/80 10.00 25.00
9 Albert Pujols 03 Btg Champ/90 10.00 25.00
10 Albert Pujols 03 POY/100 10.00 25.00

2004 Fleer Showcase Sweet Sigs

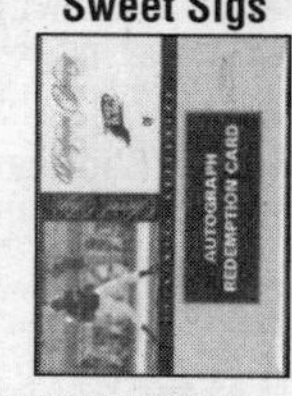

OVERALL AUTOGRAPH ODDS 1:24
PRINT RUNS B/WN 26-1000 COPIES PER
EXCH.PRINT RUNS PROVIDED BY FLEER
EXCHANGE DEADLINE INDEFINITE
AK Austin Kearns/224 4.00 10.00
AP1 Albert Pujols/199 EXCH 150.00 250.00
BH Bo Hart/667 4.00 10.00
BW Brandon Webb/1000 4.00 10.00
BZ Barry Zito/248 10.00 25.00
CPA Corey Patterson/176 6.00 15.00
CPE Carlos Pena/48 8.00 20.00
CW Chien Mien-Wang/35 125.00 200.00
DW Dontrelle Willis/26 30.00 60.00
DY Delmon Young/1000 EXCH
HB Hank Blalock/824 6.00 15.00
JG John Gall/900 EXCH
JR Jose Reyes/115 8.00 20.00
JW Josh Willingham/180 6.00 15.00
ML Mike Lowell/44 10.00 25.00
MR Michael Ryan/288 4.00 10.00
MT Miguel Tejada/52 15.00 40.00
RWA Ryan Wagner/700 EXCH
RWE Rickie Weeks/416 6.00 15.00
SR Scott Rolen/200 10.00 25.00
TB Taylor Buchholz/900 EXCH
TH Torii Hunter/294 6.00 15.00
WL Wilfredo Ledezma/376 4.00 10.00

2004 Fleer Showcase Sweet Sigs Game Jersey

OVERALL AUTOGRAPH ODDS 1:24
STATED PRINT RUN 5 SERIAL #'d CARDS
NO PRICING DUE TO SCARCITY
AP Albert Pujols/5

2005 Fleer Showcase

This 135-card set was released in January, 2005. The set was issued in either five card hobby or retail packs. These packs were issued 20 packs to a box and 12 boxes to a case for hobby accounts and 24 packs to a box and 20 boxes to a case for retail accounts. Cards numbered 1-100 feature veterans while cards 101-110 feature leading propsects and 111-135 feature retired greats. The cards 101-110 were issued at a stated rate of one in five hobby and one in 12 retail while cards 111-135 were issued at a stated rate of one in 20 hobby and one in 48 retail packs.

COMP.SET w/o SP's (100) 15.00 40.00
COMMON CARD (1-100) .30 .75
COMP.ST SUBSET (10) 10.00 25.00
COMMON CARD (101-110) .75 2.00
101-110 ODDS 1:5 HOBBY, 1:12 RETAIL
COMMON CARD (111-135) 1.25 3.00
111-135 ODDDS 1:20 HOBBY, 1:48 RETAIL
1 Albert Pujols 1.50 4.00
2 Rocco Baldelli .30 .75
3 Bernie Williams .50 1.25
4 Shawn Green .30 .75
5 Garret Anderson .30 .75
6 Paul Konerko .30 .75
7 Mike Sweeney .30 .75
8 Jim Thome .50 1.25
9 Mark Teixeira .50 1.25
10 Mark Prior .50 1.25
11 Angel Berroa .30 .75
12 Barry Zito .30 .75
13 Carlos Delgado .30 .75
14 Troy Glaus .30 .75
15 Travis Hafner .30 .75
16 Lyle Overbay .30 .75
17 David Ortiz .50 1.25
18 Ivan Rodriguez .50 1.25
19 Jack Wilson .30 .75
20 Jason Schmidt .30 .75
21 Mike Piazza .75 2.00
22 David Eckstein .30 .75
23 Ben Sheets .30 .75
24 Randy Johnson .75 2.00
25 Jacque Jones .30 .75
26 Jody Gerut .30 .75
27 Kris Benson .30 .75
28 Luis Gonzalez .30 .75
29 Victor Martinez .30 .75
30 Torii Hunter .30 .75
31 Gary Sheffield .30 .75
32 Miguel Tejada .30 .75
33 Dontrelle Willis .30 .75
34 Bret Boone .30 .75
35 Kaz Matsui .30 .75
36 Shea Hillenbrand .30 .75
37 Wily Mo Pena .30 .75
38 Johan Santana .75 2.00
39 Derek Jeter 1.50 4.00
40 Chipper Jones .75 2.00
41 Sean Casey .30 .75
42 Corey Koskie .30 .75
43 Alex Rodriguez 1.25 3.00
44 Andruw Jones .50 1.25
45 Austin Kearns .30 .75
46 Jose Vidro .30 .75
47 Adam Dunn .30 .75
48 Adrian Beltre .30 .75
49 Bobby Abreu .30 .75
50 Michael Young .30 .75
51 Freddy Garcia .30 .75
52 Eric Gagne .30 .75
53 Chase Utley .50 1.25
54 Alfonso Soriano .30 .75
55 Nick Johnson .30 .75
56 Johnny Estrada .30 .75
57 Jeff Bagwell .50 1.25
58 Randy Winn .30 .75
59 Roy Halladay .30 .75
60 J.D. Drew .30 .75
61 Craig Biggio .50 1.25
62 Scott Rolen .50 1.25
63 Nomar Garciaparra .75 2.00
64 Matt Holliday .40 1.00
65 Billy Wagner .30 .75
66 Carl Crawford .30 .75
67 Pedro Martinez .50 1.25
68 Jeremy Bonderman .30 .75
69 Jason Bay .30 .75
70 A.J. Pierzynski .30 .75
71 Vladimir Guerrero .75 2.00
72 Rickie Weeks .30 .75
73 Mark Loretta .30 .75
74 Todd Helton .50 1.25
75 Manny Ramirez .50 1.25
76 Carlos Guillen .30 .75
77 Khalil Greene .50 1.25
78 Javy Lopez .30 .75
79 Josh Beckett .30 .75
80 Ichiro Suzuki 1.50 4.00
81 Magglio Ordonez .30 .75
82 Ken Harvey .30 .75
83 Mark Mulder .30 .75
84 Hank Blalock .30 .75
85 Richard Hidalgo .30 .75
86 Curt Schilling .50 1.25
87 Jeromy Burnitz .30 .75
88 Craig Wilson .30 .75
89 Aubrey Huff .30 .75
90 Kerry Wood .30 .75
91 Andy Pettitte .50 1.25
92 Tim Hudson .30 .75
93 Jim Edmonds .30 .75
94 Melvin Mora .30 .75
95 Miguel Cabrera .30 .75
96 Trevor Hoffman .30 .75
97 J.T. Snow .30 .75
98 Sammy Sosa .75 2.00
99 Roger Clemens 1.25 3.00
100 Eric Chavez .30 .75
101 B.J. Upton ST 1.25 3.00
102 Gavin Floyd ST .75 2.00
103 Casey Kotchman ST .75 2.00
104 David Wright ST 4.00 10.00
105 Dioner Navarro ST .75 2.00
106 Scott Kazmir ST 2.00 5.00
107 Andres Blanco ST .75 2.00
108 Joey Gathright ST .75 2.00
109 Jon Knott ST .75 2.00
110 Charlton Jimerson ST .75 2.00
111 Larry Doby SH 1.25 3.00
112 Reggie Jackson SH 2.00 5.00
113 Enos Slaughter SH 1.25 3.00
114 Bill Skowron SH 1.25 3.00
115 Duke Snider SH 2.00 5.00
116 Harmon Killebrew SH 3.00 8.00
117 Willie McCovey SH 2.00 5.00
118 Rollie Fingers SH 1.25 3.00
119 Preacher Roe SH 1.25 3.00
120 Carlton Fisk SH 2.00 5.00
121 Andre Dawson SH 1.25 3.00
122 Orlando Cepeda SH 1.25 3.00
123 Bucky Dent SH 1.25 3.00
124 Cal Ripken SH 8.00 20.00
125 Nolan Ryan SH 6.00 15.00
126 Tony Perez SH 1.25 3.00
127 Mike Schmidt SH 5.00 12.00
128 Johnny Bench SH 3.00 8.00
129 Sparky Anderson SH 1.25 3.00
130 Ted Williams SH 5.00 12.00
131 Al Kaline SH 3.00 8.00
132 Carl Yastrzemski SH 4.00 10.00
133 Eddie Murray SH 3.00 8.00
134 Roberto Clemente SH 6.00 15.00
135 Yogi Berra SH 3.00 8.00

2005 Fleer Showcase Showdown

These cards parallel the basic 2005 Fleer Showcase, but the small action image in the foreground of the basic card has been pulled for the Showdown parallel, leaving only the larger posed image in the card's background.

BASIC PARALLEL ODDS 1:10 HOBBY
STATED PRINT RUN 15 SERIAL #'d SETS
NO PRICING DUE TO SCARCITY

2005 Fleer Showcase Showtime

These cards parallel the basic 2005 Fleer Showcase, but the posed player image in the background of the basic card has been pulled for the Showtime parallel, leaving only the smaller action image in the card's foreground.

*SHOWDOWN 1-100: 2.5X TO 6X BASIC
*SHOWDOWN 101-110: 1X TO 2.5X BASIC
*SHOWDOWN 111-135: .75X TO 2X BASIC

BASIC PARALLEL ODDS 1:10 HOBBY
STATED PRINT RUN 99 SERIAL #'d SETS

2005 Fleer Showcase Autographed Legacy

LEGACY PARALLEL ODDS 1:20 HOBBY
PRINT RUNS B/WN 7-460 COPIES PER
NO PRICING ON QTY OF 19 OR LESS
SKIP-NUMBERED 58-CARD SET
EXCHANGE DEADLINE 01/15/08
1 Albert Pujols/11
6 Paul Konerko/299 EXCH
8 Jim Thome/34 30.00 60.00
9 Mark Teixeira/102 EXCH
10 Mark Prior/43 15.00 40.00
12 Barry Zito/45 15.00 40.00
16 Lyle Overbay/450 EXCH
18 Ivan Rodriguez/217 20.00 50.00
19 Jack Wilson/298 6.00 15.00
20 Jason Schmidt/127 6.00 15.00
21 Mike Piazza/26 60.00 120.00
22 David Eckstein/40 20.00 50.00
23 Ben Sheets/427 6.00 15.00
26 Jody Gerut/299 EXCH
40 Chipper Jones/41 30.00 60.00
45 Austin Kearns/460 4.00 10.00
46 Jose Vidro/300 EXCH
47 Adam Dunn/52 15.00 40.00
48 Adrian Beltre/180 6.00 15.00
50 Michael Young/80 8.00 20.00
52 Eric Gagne/310 10.00 25.00
53 Chase Utley/450 EXCH 10.00 25.00
55 Nick Johnson/300 EXCH
59 Roy Halladay/99 8.00 20.00
60 J.D. Drew/14
65 Billy Wagner/12
66 Carl Crawford/290 EXCH
68 Jeremy Bonderman/97 8.00 20.00
72 Rickie Weeks/453 6.00 15.00
75 Manny Ramirez/31 40.00 80.00
77 Khalil Greene/299 10.00 25.00
81 Magglio Ordonez/300 EXCH
88 Craig Wilson/40 8.00 20.00
89 Aubrey Huff/453 6.00 15.00
90 Kerry Wood/28 15.00 40.00
92 Tim Hudson/183 10.00 25.00
95 Miguel Cabrera/32 15.00 40.00
99 Roger Clemens/64 60.00 120.00
100 Eric Chavez/204 10.00 25.00
101 B.J. Upton ST/299 EXCH
103 Casey Kotchman ST/454 6.00 15.00
104 David Wright ST/298 20.00 50.00
106 Scott Kazmir ST/458 UER 8.00 20.00
Seattle Mariners on front
107 Andres Blanco ST/23 8.00 20.00
109 Jon Knott ST/402 4.00 10.00
111 Larry Doby SH/25
112 Reggie Jackson SH/17
114 Bill Skowron SH/64 10.00 25.00
119 Preacher Roe SH/304 10.00 25.00
120 Carlton Fisk SH/86 12.50 30.00
122 Orlando Cepeda SH/19
123 Bucky Dent SH/99 8.00 20.00
124 Cal Ripken SH/53
125 Nolan Ryan SH/13
131 Al Kaline SH/7
132 Carl Yastrzemski SH/14
135 Yogi Berra SH/25 40.00 80.00

2005 Fleer Showcase Legacy

*LEGACY 1-100: 2.5X TO 6X BASIC
*LEGACY 101-110: 1X TO 2.5X BASIC
*LEGACY 111-135: .75X TO 2X BASIC
LEGACY PARALLEL ODDS 1:20 HOBBY
STATED PRINT RUN 99 SERIAL #'d SETS
SKIP-NUMBERED 50-CARD SET

2005 Fleer Showcase Masterpiece Legacy

M'PIECE PARALLEL ODDS 1:240 HOBBY
STATED PRINT RUN 1 SERIAL #'d SET
NO PRICING DUE TO SCARCITY

2005 Fleer Showcase Masterpiece Showdown

M'PIECE PARALLEL ODDS 1:240 HOBBY
STATED PRINT RUN 1 SERIAL #'d SET
NO PRICING DUE TO SCARCITY

2005 Fleer Showcase Masterpiece Showtime

M'PIECE PARALLEL ODDS 1:240 HOBBY
STATED PRINT RUN 1 SERIAL #'d SET
NO PRICING DUE TO SCARCITY

2005 Fleer Showcase Masterpiece Showpiece Patch

M'PIECE PARALLEL ODDS 1:240 HOBBY
STATED PRINT RUN 1 SERIAL #'d SET
NO PRICING DUE TO SCARCITY

2005 Fleer Showcase Masterpiece Showpiece Patch Showdown

M'PIECE PARALLEL ODDS 1:240 HOBBY
STATED PRINT RUN 1 SERIAL #'d SET
NO PRICING DUE TO SCARCITY

2005 Fleer Showcase Masterpiece Showpiece Patch Showtime

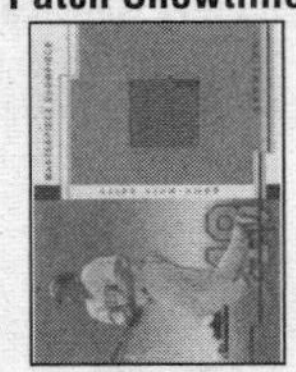

M'PIECE PARALLEL ODDS 1:240 HOBBY
STATED PRINT RUN 1 SERIAL #'d SET
NO PRICING DUE TO SCARCITY

2005 Fleer Showcase Masterpiece Showpiece Autograph Patch

M'PIECE PARALLEL ODDS 1:240 HOBBY
STATED PRINT RUN 1 SERIAL #'d SET
NO PRICING DUE TO SCARCITY

2005 Fleer Showcase Timepiece Extreme Autograph Barrel

OVERALL TIMEPIECE ODDS 1:510 HOBBY
OVERALL AU-GU ODDS 1:48 RETAIL
STATED PRINT RUN 1 SERIAL #'d SET
NO PRICING DUE TO SCARCITY
1 Albert Pujols
8 Jim Thome
9 Mark Teixeira
18 Ivan Rodriguez
47 Adam Dunn
66 Carl Crawford
72 Rickie Weeks
75 Manny Ramirez
84 Hank Blalock
95 Miguel Cabrera
112 Reggie Jackson
116 Harmon Killebrew
124 Cal Ripken
132 Carl Yastrzemski

2005 Fleer Showcase Timepiece Ink Autograph Bat Knob

OVERALL TIMEPIECE ODDS 1:510 HOBBY
OVERALL AU-GU ODDS 1:48 RETAIL
STATED PRINT RUN 10 SERIAL #'d SETS
NO PRICING DUE TO SCARCITY
1 Albert Pujols
8 Jim Thome
9 Mark Teixeira
18 Ivan Rodriguez
40 Chipper Jones

45 Austin Kearns
47 Adam Dunn
66 Carl Crawford
72 Rickie Weeks
75 Manny Ramirez
95 Miguel Cabrera
112 Reggie Jackson
132 Carl Yastrzemski

2005 Fleer Showcase Timepiece Teammates Autograph Dual

OVERALL TIMEPIECE ODDS 1:510 HOBBY
OVERALL AU-GU ODDS 1:48 RETAIL
STATED PRINT RUN 1 SERIAL #'d SET
NO PRICING DUE TO SCARCITY
PS Albert Pujols
Enos Slaughter
TB Mark Teixeira
Hank Blalock
YR Carl Yastrzemski
Manny Ramirez

2005 Fleer Showcase Timepiece Unique Autograph Bat-Patch

OVERALL TIMEPIECE ODDS 1:510 HOBBY
OVERALL AU-GU ODDS 1:48 RETAIL
STATED PRINT RUN 5 SERIAL #'d SETS
NO PRICING DUE TO SCARCITY
1 Albert Pujols
8 Jim Thome
9 Mark Teixeira
18 Ivan Rodriguez
21 Mike Piazza
40 Chipper Jones
47 Adam Dunn
75 Manny Ramirez
84 Hank Blalock
95 Miguel Cabrera
99 Roger Clemens
100 Eric Chavez
124 Cal Ripken

2005 Fleer Showcase Measure of Greatness

STATED ODDS 1:5 HOBBY, 1:5 RETAIL
1 Albert Pujols 2.50 6.00
2 Mike Piazza 1.25 3.00
3 Vladimir Guerrero 1.25 3.00
4 Jim Thome 1.25 3.00
5 Pedro Martinez 1.25 3.00
6 Rafael Palmeiro 1.25 3.00
7 Adrian Beltre .75 2.00
8 Sammy Sosa 1.25 3.00
9 Todd Helton 1.25 3.00
10 Randy Johnson 1.25 3.00
11 Jeff Bagwell 1.25 3.00
12 Jason Giambi .75 2.00
13 Scott Rolen 1.25 3.00
14 Greg Maddux 2.00 5.00
15 Alfonso Soriano .75 2.00
16 Mariano Rivera 1.25 3.00
17 Curt Schilling 1.25 3.00
18 Derek Jeter 2.50 6.00
19 Chipper Jones 1.25 3.00
20 Roger Clemens 2.00 5.00

2005 Fleer Showcase Measure of Greatness Jersey Red

STATED PRINT RUN 340 SERIAL #'d SETS
*GREEN: .6X TO 1.5X BASIC
GREEN ODDS 1:144 RETAIL
PATCH PRINT RUN 10 SERIAL #'d SETS
NO PATCH PRICING DUE TO SCARCITY
PATCH MP PRINT RUN 1 SERIAL #'d SET
NO PATCH MP PRICING DUE TO SCARCITY
OVERALL GAME-USED ODDS 1:10 HOBBY
AB Adrian Beltre 3.00 8.00
AP Albert Pujols 8.00 20.00
AS Alfonso Soriano 3.00 8.00
CJ Chipper Jones 4.00 10.00
JT Jim Thome 4.00 10.00
MP Mike Piazza 4.00 10.00
MR Mariano Rivera 4.00 10.00
PM Pedro Martinez 4.00 10.00
RC Roger Clemens 6.00 15.00
RJ Randy Johnson 4.00 10.00
RP Rafael Palmeiro 4.00 10.00
SR Scott Rolen 4.00 10.00
SS Sammy Sosa 4.00 10.00
TH Todd Helton 4.00 10.00
VG Vladimir Guerrero 4.00 10.00

2005 Fleer Showcase Swing Time

STATED ODDS 1:45 HOBBY, 1:96 RETAIL
1 Ivan Rodriguez 2.00 5.00
2 Gary Sheffield 2.00 5.00
3 Bernie Williams 2.00 5.00
4 Vladimir Guerrero 2.00 5.00
5 Jim Edmonds 2.00 5.00
6 Manny Ramirez 2.00 5.00
7 Todd Helton 2.00 5.00
8 Hank Blalock 2.00 5.00
9 Hideki Matsui 3.00 8.00
10 David Ortiz 2.00 5.00
11 Albert Pujols 4.00 10.00
12 Miguel Tejada 2.00 5.00
13 Miguel Cabrera 2.00 5.00
14 Alex Rodriguez 3.00 8.00
15 Ichiro Suzuki 4.00 10.00

2005 Fleer Showcase Swing Time Jersey Red

STATED PRINT RUN 610 SERIAL #'d SETS
*GREEN: .75X TO 2X BASIC
GREEN ODDS 1:444 RETAIL
*PATCH: 1.25X TO 3X BASIC
PATCH PRINT RUN 50 SERIAL #'d SETS
PATCH MP PRINT RUN 1 SERIAL #'d SET
NO PATCH MP PRICING DUE TO SCARCITY
OVERALL GAME-USED ODDS 1:10 HOBBY
AP Albert Pujols 6.00 15.00
BW Bernie Williams 3.00 8.00
DO David Ortiz 3.00 8.00
HB Hank Blalock 2.00 5.00
HM Hideki Matsui 8.00 20.00
IR Ivan Rodriguez 3.00 8.00
JE Jim Edmonds 2.00 5.00
MC Miguel Cabrera 3.00 8.00
MR Manny Ramirez 3.00 8.00
TH Todd Helton 3.00 8.00

2005 Fleer Showcase Wave of the Future

STATED ODDS 1:15 HOBBY, 1:15 RETAIL
1 Kaz Matsui 1.25 3.00
2 Johan Santana 2.00 5.00
3 Khalil Greene 2.00 5.00
4 Dontrelle Willis 1.25 3.00
5 Mark Teixeira 2.00 5.00
6 Travis Hafner 1.25 3.00
7 Jason Bay 1.25 3.00
8 Angel Berroa 1.25 3.00
9 Miguel Cabrera 2.00 5.00
10 Joe Mauer 2.00 5.00
11 Adam Dunn 1.25 3.00
12 B.J. Upton 2.00 5.00
13 Victor Martinez 1.25 3.00
14 Michael Young 1.25 3.00
15 David Wright 6.00 15.00

2005 Fleer Showcase Wave of the Future Jersey Red

STATED PRINT RUN 610 SERIAL #'d SETS
*GREEN: .4X TO 1X BASIC
GREEN ODDS 1:48 RETAIL
*PATCH: 1.25X TO 3X BASIC
PATCH PRINT RUN 50 SERIAL #'d SETS

PATCH MP PRINT RUN 1 SERIAL #'d SET
NO PATCH MP PRICING DUE TO SCARCITY
OVERALL GAME-USED ODDS 1:10 HOBBY
AB Angel Berroa 2.00 5.00
AD Adam Dunn 2.00 5.00
BU B.J. Upton 3.00 8.00
DW David Wright 8.00 20.00
DW Dontrelle Willis 2.00 5.00
JB Jason Bay 2.00 5.00
JM Joe Mauer 3.00 8.00
JS Johan Santana 3.00 8.00
KG Khalil Greene 3.00 8.00
KM Kaz Matsui 2.00 5.00
MC Miguel Cabrera 3.00 8.00
MT Mark Teixeira 3.00 8.00
MY Michael Young 2.00 5.00
TH Travis Hafner 2.00 5.00
VM Victor Martinez 2.00 5.00

1998 Fleer Tradition

The 600-card 1998 Fleer set was issued in two series. Series one consists of 350 cards and Series two consists of 250 cards. The packs for either series consisted of 12 cards and had a SRP of $1.49. Card fronts feature borderless color action player photos with UV-coating and foil stamping. The backs display player information and career statistics. The set contains the following topical subsets: Smoke 'N Heat (301-310), Golden Memories (311-320), Tale of the Tape (321-340) and Unforgettable Moments (576-600). The Golden Memories (1:6 packs), Tale of the Tape (1:4 packs) and Unforgettable Moments (1:4 packs) cards are shortprinted. An Alex Rodriguez Promo card was distributed to dealers along with their 1998 Fleer series one order forms. The card can be readily distinguished by the "Promotional Sample" text running diagonally across both the front and back of the card. 50 Fleer Flashback Exchange cards were hand-numbered and randomly inserted into packs. Each of these cards could be exchanged for a framed, uncut press sheet from one of Fleer's baseball sets dating anywhere from 1981 to 1993.

COMPLETE SET (600) 60.00 150.00
COMP. SERIES 1 (350) 35.00 90.00
COMP. SERIES 2 (250) 25.00 60.00
COMMON CARD (1-600) .10 .30
COMMON GM (311-320) .20 .50
COMMON TT (321-340) .25 .60
COMMON UM (576-600) .30 .75
1 Ken Griffey Jr. .50 1.25
2 Derek Jeter .75 2.00
3 Gerald Williams .10 .30
4 Carlos Delgado .10 .30
5 Nomar Garciaparra .50 1.25
6 Gary Sheffield .10 .30
7 Jeff King .10 .30
8 Cal Ripken 1.00 2.50
9 Matt Williams .10 .30
10 Chipper Jones .30 .75
11 Chuck Knoblauch .10 .30
12 Mark Grudzielanek .10 .30
13 Edgardo Alfonzo .10 .30
14 Andres Galarraga .10 .30
15 Tim Salmon .20 .50
16 Reggie Sanders .10 .30
17 Tony Clark .10 .30
18 Jason Kendall .10 .30
19 Juan Gonzalez .10 .30
20 Ben Grieve .10 .30
21 Roger Clemens .60 1.50
22 Raul Mondesi .10 .30
23 Robin Ventura .10 .30
24 Derrek Lee .20 .50
25 Mark McGwire .75 2.00
26 Luis Gonzalez .10 .30
27 Kevin Brown .20 .50
28 Kirk Rueter .10 .30
29 Bobby Estalella .10 .30
30 Shawn Green .10 .30
31 Greg Maddux .50 1.25
32 Jorge Velandia .10 .30
33 Larry Walker .10 .30
34 Joey Cora .10 .30
35 Frank Thomas .30 .75
36 Curtis King RC .10 .30
37 Aaron Boone .10 .30
38 Curt Schilling .10 .30
39 Bruce Aven .10 .30
40 Ben McDonald .10 .30
41 Andy Ashby .10 .30
42 Jason McDonald .10 .30
43 Eric Davis .10 .30
44 Mark Grace .20 .50
45 Pedro Martinez .20 .50
46 Lou Collier .10 .30
47 Chan Ho Park .10 .30
48 Shane Halter .10 .30
49 Brian Hunter .10 .30
50 Jeff Bagwell .20 .50
51 Bernie Williams .20 .50
52 J.T. Snow .10 .30
53 Todd Greene .10 .30
54 Shannon Stewart .10 .30
55 Darren Bragg .10 .30
56 Fernando Tatis .10 .30
57 Darryl Kile .10 .30
58 Chris Stynes .10 .30
59 Javier Valentin .10 .30
60 Brian McRae .10 .30
61 Tom Evans .10 .30
62 Randall Simon .10 .30
63 Darrin Fletcher .10 .30
64 Jaret Wright .10 .30
65 Luis Ordaz .10 .30
66 Jose Canseco .20 .50
67 Edgar Renteria .10 .30
68 Jay Buhner .10 .30
69 Paul Konerko .10 .30
70 Adrian Brown .10 .30
71 Chris Carpenter .10 .30
72 Mike Lieberthal .10 .30
73 Dean Palmer .10 .30
74 Jorge Fabregas .10 .30
75 Stan Javier .10 .30
76 Damion Easley .10 .30
77 David Cone .10 .30
78 Aaron Sele .10 .30
79 Antonio Alfonseca .10 .30
80 Bobby Jones .10 .30
81 David Justice .10 .30
82 Jeffrey Hammonds .10 .30
83 Doug Glanville .10 .30
84 Jason Dickson .10 .30
85 Brad Radke .10 .30
86 David Segui .10 .30
87 Greg Vaughn .10 .30
88 Mike Cather RC .10 .30
89 Alex Fernandez .10 .30
90 Billy Taylor .10 .30
91 Jason Schmidt .10 .30
92 Mike DeJean RC .15 .40
93 Domingo Cedeno .10 .30
94 Jeff Cirillo .10 .30
95 Manny Aybar RC .15 .40
96 Jaime Navarro .10 .30
97 Dennis Reyes .10 .30
98 Barry Larkin .20 .50
99 Troy O'Leary .10 .30
100 Alex Rodriguez .50 1.25
101 Pat Hentgen .10 .30
102 Bubba Trammell .10 .30
103 Glendon Rusch .10 .30
104 Kenny Lofton .10 .30
105 Craig Biggio .20 .50
106 Kelvim Escobar .10 .30
107 Mark Kotsay .10 .30
108 Rondell White .10 .30
109 Darren Oliver .10 .30
110 Jim Thome .20 .50
111 Rich Becker .10 .30
112 Chad Curtis .10 .30
113 Dave Hollins .10 .30
114 Bill Mueller .10 .30
115 Antone Williamson .10 .30
116 Tony Womack .10 .30
117 Randy Myers .10 .30
118 Rico Brogna .10 .30
119 Pat Watkins .10 .30
120 Eli Marrero .10 .30
121 Jay Bell .10 .30
122 Kevin Tapani .10 .30
123 Todd Erdos RC .10 .30
124 Neifi Perez .10 .30
125 Todd Hundley .10 .30
126 Jeff Abbott .10 .30
127 Todd Zeile .10 .30
128 Travis Fryman .10 .30
129 Sandy Alomar Jr. .10 .30
130 Fred McGriff .20 .50
131 Richard Hidalgo .10 .30
132 Scott Spiezio .10 .30
133 John Valentin .10 .30
134 Quilvio Veras .10 .30
135 Mike Lansing .10 .30
136 Paul Molitor .10 .30
137 Randy Johnson .30 .75
138 Harold Baines .10 .30
139 Doug Jones .10 .30
140 Abraham Nunez .10 .30
141 Alan Benes .10 .30
142 Matt Perisho .10 .30
143 Chris Clemons .10 .30
144 Andy Pettitte .20 .50
145 Jason Giambi .10 .30
146 Moises Alou .10 .30
147 Chad Fox RC .10 .30
148 Felix Martinez .10 .30
149 Carlos Mendoza RC .10 .30
150 Scott Rolen .20 .50
151 Jose Cabrera RC .10 .30
152 Justin Thompson .10 .30
153 Ellis Burks .10 .30
154 Pokey Reese .10 .30
155 Bartolo Colon .10 .30
156 Ray Durham .10 .30
157 Ugueth Urbina .10 .30
158 Tom Goodwin .10 .30
159 Dave Dellucci RC .25 .60
160 Rod Beck .10 .30
161 Ramon Martinez .10 .30
162 Joe Carter .10 .30
163 Kevin Orie .10 .30
164 Trevor Hoffman .10 .30
165 Emil Brown .10 .30
166 Robb Nen .10 .30
167 Paul O'Neill .20 .50
168 Ryan Long .10 .30
169 Ray Lankford .10 .30
170 Ivan Rodriguez .20 .50
171 Rick Aguilera .10 .30
172 Deivi Cruz .10 .30
173 Ricky Bottalico .10 .30
174 Garret Anderson .10 .30
175 Jose Vizcaino .10 .30
176 Omar Vizquel .20 .50
177 Jeff Blauser .10 .30
178 Orlando Cabrera .10 .30
179 Russ Johnson .10 .30
180 Matt Stairs .10 .30
181 Will Cunnane .10 .30
182 Adam Riggs .10 .30
183 Matt Morris .10 .30
184 Mario Valdez .10 .30
185 Larry Sutton .10 .30

186 Marc Pisciotta RC .10 .30
187 Dan Wilson .10 .30
188 John Franco .10 .30
189 Darren Daulton .10 .30
190 Todd Helton .20 .50
191 Brady Anderson .10 .30
192 Ricardo Rincon .10 .30
193 Kevin Stocker .10 .30
194 Jose Valentin .10 .30
195 Ed Sprague .10 .30
196 Ryan McGuire .10 .30
197 Scott Eyre .10 .30
198 Steve Finley .10 .30
199 T.J. Mathews .10 .30
200 Mike Piazza .50 1.25
201 Mark Wohlers .10 .30
202 Brian Giles .10 .30
203 Eduardo Perez .10 .30
204 Shigetoshi Hasegawa .10 .30
205 Mariano Rivera .30 .75
206 Jose Rosado .10 .30
207 Michael Coleman .10 .30
208 James Baldwin .10 .30
209 Russ Davis .10 .30
210 Billy Wagner .10 .30
211 Sammy Sosa .30 .75
212 Frank Catalanotto RC .25 .60
213 Delino DeShields .10 .30
214 John Olerud .10 .30
215 Heath Murray .10 .30
216 Jose Vidro .10 .30
217 Jim Edmonds .10 .30
218 Shawon Dunston .10 .30
219 Homer Bush .10 .30
220 Midre Cummings .10 .30
221 Tony Saunders .10 .30
222 Jeromy Burnitz .10 .30
223 Enrique Wilson .10 .30
224 Chili Davis .10 .30
225 Jerry DiPoto .10 .30
226 Dante Powell .10 .30
227 Javier Lopez .10 .30
228 Kevin Polcovich .10 .30
229 Deion Sanders .20 .50
230 Jimmy Key .10 .30
231 Rusty Greer .10 .30
232 Reggie Jefferson .10 .30
233 Ron Coomer .10 .30
234 Bobby Higginson .10 .30
235 Magglio Ordonez RC 1.00 2.50
236 Miguel Tejada .30 .75
237 Rick Gorecki .10 .30
238 Charles Johnson .10 .30
239 Lance Johnson .10 .30
240 Derek Bell .10 .30
241 Will Clark .20 .50
242 Brady Raggio .10 .30
243 Orel Hershiser .10 .30
244 Vladimir Guerrero .30 .75
245 John LeRoy .10 .30
246 Shawn Estes .10 .30
247 Brett Tomko .10 .30
248 Dave Nilsson .10 .30
249 Edgar Martinez .20 .50
250 Tony Gwynn .40 1.00
251 Mark Bellhorn .10 .30
252 Jed Hansen .10 .30
253 Butch Huskey .10 .30
254 Eric Young .10 .30
255 Vinny Castilla .10 .30
256 Hideki Irabu .10 .30
257 Mike Cameron .10 .30
258 Juan Encarnacion .10 .30
259 Brian Rose .10 .30
260 Brad Ausmus .10 .30
261 Dan Serafini .10 .30
262 Willie Greene .10 .30
263 Troy Percival .10 .30
264 Jeff Wallace .10 .30
265 Richie Sexson .10 .30
266 Rafael Palmeiro .20 .50
267 Brad Fullmer .10 .30
268 Jeremi Gonzalez .10 .30
269 Rob Stanifer RC .10 .30
270 Mickey Morandini .10 .30
271 Andruw Jones .20 .50
272 Royce Clayton .10 .30
273 T.Kashiwada RC .15 .40
274 Steve Woodard .10 .30
275 Jose Cruz Jr. .10 .30
276 Keith Foulke .10 .30
277 Brad Rigby .10 .30
278 Tino Martinez .20 .50
279 Todd Jones .10 .30
280 John Wetteland .10 .30
281 Alex Gonzalez .10 .30
282 Ken Cloude .10 .30
283 Jose Guillen .10 .30
284 Danny Clyburn .10 .30
285 David Ortiz .40 1.00
286 John Thomson .10 .30
287 Kevin Appier .10 .30
288 Ismael Valdes .10 .30
289 Gary DiSarcina .10 .30
290 Todd Dunwoody .10 .30
291 Wally Joyner .10 .30
292 Charles Nagy .10 .30
293 Jeff Shaw .10 .30
294 Kevin Millwood RC .40 1.00
295 Rigo Beltran RC .10 .30
296 Jeff Frye .10 .30
297 Oscar Henriquez .10 .30
298 Mike Thurman .10 .30
299 Garrett Stephenson .10 .30
300 Barry Bonds .75 2.00
301 Roger Clemens SH .30 .75
302 David Cone SH .10 .30
303 Hideki Irabu SH .10 .30
304 Randy Johnson SH .20 .50
305 Greg Maddux SH .30 .75
306 Pedro Martinez SH .20 .50
307 Mike Mussina SH .10 .30
308 Andy Pettitte SH .10 .30
309 Curt Schilling SH .10 .30
310 John Smoltz SH .10 .30
311 Roger Clemens GM 1.00 2.50
312 Jose Cruz JR. GM .20 .50
313 N.Garciaparra GM .75 2.00
314 Ken Griffey Jr. GM .75 2.00
315 Tony Gwynn GM .60 1.50
316 Hideki Irabu GM .20 .50
317 Randy Johnson GM .50 1.25
318 Mark McGwire GM 1.25 3.00
319 Curt Schilling GM .20 .50
320 Larry Walker GM .20 .50
321 Jeff Bagwell TT .40 1.00
322 Albert Belle TT .25 .60
323 Barry Bonds TT 1.50 4.00
324 Jay Buhner TT .25 .60
325 Tony Clark TT .25 .60
326 Jose Cruz Jr. TT .25 .60
327 Andres Galarraga TT .25 .60
328 Juan Gonzalez TT .25 .60
329 Ken Griffey Jr. TT 1.00 2.50
330 Andruw Jones TT .40 1.00
331 Tino Martinez TT .40 1.00
332 Mark McGwire TT 1.50 4.00
333 Rafael Palmeiro TT .40 1.00
334 Mike Piazza TT 1.00 2.50
335 Manny Ramirez TT .40 1.00
336 Alex Rodriguez TT 1.00 2.50
337 Frank Thomas TT .60 1.50
338 Jim Thome TT .40 1.00
339 Mo Vaughn TT .25 .60
340 Larry Walker TT .25 .60
341 Jose Cruz Jr. CL .10 .30
342 Ken Griffey Jr. CL .30 .75
343 Derek Jeter CL .40 1.00
344 Andruw Jones CL .10 .30
345 Chipper Jones CL .20 .50
346 Greg Maddux CL .30 .75
347 Mike Piazza CL .30 .75
348 Cal Ripken CL .50 1.25
349 Alex Rodriguez CL .30 .75
350 Frank Thomas CL .20 .50
351 Mo Vaughn .10 .30
352 Andres Galarraga .10 .30
353 Roberto Alomar .20 .50
354 Darin Erstad .10 .30
355 Albert Belle .10 .30
356 Matt Williams .10 .30
357 Darryl Kile .10 .30
358 Kenny Lofton .10 .30
359 Orel Hershiser .10 .30
360 Bob Abreu .10 .30
361 Chris Widger .10 .30
362 Glenallen Hill .10 .30
363 Chili Davis .10 .30
364 Kevin Brown .20 .50
365 Marquis Grissom .10 .30
366 Livan Hernandez .10 .30
367 Moises Alou .10 .30
368 Matt Lawton .10 .30
369 Rey Ordonez .10 .30
370 Kenny Rogers .10 .30
371 Lee Stevens .10 .30
372 Wade Boggs .20 .50
373 Luis Gonzalez .10 .30
374 Jeff Conine .10 .30
375 Esteban Loaiza .10 .30
376 Jose Canseco .20 .50
377 Henry Rodriguez .10 .30
378 Dave Burba .10 .30
379 Todd Hollandsworth .10 .30
380 Ron Gant .10 .30
381 Pedro Martinez .20 .50
382 Ryan Klesko .10 .30
383 Derrek Lee .20 .50
384 Doug Glanville .10 .30
385 David Wells .10 .30
386 Ken Caminiti .10 .30
387 Damon Hollins .10 .30
388 Manny Ramirez .20 .50
389 Mike Mussina .20 .50
390 Jay Bell .10 .30
391 Mike Piazza .50 1.25
392 Mike Lansing .10 .30
393 Mike Hampton .10 .30
394 Geoff Jenkins .10 .30
395 Jimmy Haynes .10 .30
396 Scott Servais .10 .30
397 Kent Mercker .10 .30
398 Jeff Kent .10 .30
399 Kevin Elster .10 .30
400 Masato Yoshii RC .15 .40
401 Jose Vizcaino .10 .30
402 Javier Martinez RC .10 .30
403 David Segui .10 .30
404 Tony Saunders .10 .30
405 Karim Garcia .10 .30
406 Armando Benitez .10 .30
407 Joe Randa .10 .30
408 Vic Darensbourg .10 .30
409 Sean Casey .10 .30
410 Eric Milton .10 .30
411 Trey Moore .10 .30
412 Mike Stanley .10 .30
413 Tom Gordon .10 .30
414 Hal Morris .10 .30
415 Braden Looper .10 .30
416 Mike Kelly .10 .30
417 John Smoltz .20 .50
418 Roger Cedeno .10 .30
419 Al Leiter .10 .30
420 Chuck Knoblauch .10 .30
421 Felix Rodriguez .10 .30
422 Bip Roberts .10 .30
423 Ken Hill .10 .30
424 Jermaine Allensworth .10 .30
425 Esteban Yan RC .15 .40
426 Scott Karl .10 .30
427 Sean Berry .10 .30
428 Rafael Medina .10 .30
429 Javier Vazquez .10 .30
430 Rickey Henderson .30 .75
431 Adam Butler .10 .30
432 Todd Stottlemyre .10 .30
433 Yamil Benitez .10 .30
434 Sterling Hitchcock .10 .30
435 Paul Sorrento .10 .30
436 Bobby Ayala .10 .30
437 Tim Raines .10 .30
438 Chris Hoiles .10 .30
439 Rod Beck .10 .30
440 Donnie Sadler .10 .30
441 Charles Johnson .10 .30
442 Russ Ortiz .10 .30
443 Pedro Astacio .10 .30
444 Wilson Alvarez .10 .30
445 Mike Blowers .10 .30
446 Todd Zeile .10 .30
447 Mel Rojas .10 .30
448 F.P. Santangelo .10 .30
449 Dmitri Young .10 .30
450 Brian Anderson .10 .30
451 Cecil Fielder .10 .30
452 Roberto Hernandez .10 .30
453 Todd Walker .10 .30
454 Tyler Green .10 .30
455 Jorge Posada .20 .50
456 Geronimo Berroa .10 .30
457 Jose Silva .10 .30
458 Bobby Bonilla .10 .30
459 Walt Weiss .10 .30
460 Darren Dreifort .10 .30
461 B.J. Surhoff .10 .30
462 Quinton McCracken .10 .30
463 Derek Lowe .10 .30
464 Jorge Fabregas .10 .30
465 Joey Hamilton .10 .30
466 Brian Jordan .10 .30
467 Allen Watson .10 .30
468 John Jaha .10 .30
469 Heathcliff Slocumb .10 .30
470 Gregg Jefferies .10 .30
471 Scott Brosius .10 .30
472 Chad Ogea .10 .30
473 A.J. Hinch .10 .30
474 Bobby Smith .10 .30
475 Brian Moehler .10 .30
476 DaRond Stovall .10 .30
477 Kevin Young .10 .30
478 Jeff Suppan .10 .30
479 Marty Cordova .10 .30
480 John Halama RC .15 .40
481 Bubba Trammell .10 .30
482 Mike Caruso .10 .30
483 Eric Karros .10 .30
484 Jamey Wright .10 .30
485 Mike Sweeney .10 .30
486 Aaron Sele .10 .30
487 Cliff Floyd .10 .30
488 Jeff Brantley .10 .30
489 Jim Leyritz .10 .30
490 Denny Neagle .10 .30
491 Travis Fryman .10 .30
492 Carlos Baerga .10 .30
493 Eddie Taubensee .10 .30
494 Darryl Strawberry .10 .30
495 Brian Johnson .10 .30
496 Randy Myers .10 .30
497 Jeff Blauser .10 .30
498 Jason Wood .10 .30
499 Rolando Arrojo RC .15 .40
500 Johnny Damon .20 .50
501 Jose Mercedes .10 .30
502 Tony Batista .10 .30
503 Mike Piazza Mets .50 1.25
504 Hideo Nomo .30 .75
505 Chris Gomez .10 .30
506 Jesus Sanchez RC .10 .30
507 Al Martin .10 .30
508 Brian Edmondson .10 .30
509 Joe Girardi .10 .30
510 Shayne Bennett .10 .30
511 Joe Carter .10 .30
512 Dave Mlicki .10 .30
513 Rich Butler RC .10 .30
514 Dennis Eckersley .10 .30
515 Travis Lee .10 .30
516 John Mabry .10 .30
517 Jose Mesa .10 .30
518 Phil Nevin .10 .30
519 Raul Casanova .10 .30
520 Mike Fetters .10 .30
521 Gary Sheffield .10 .30
522 Terry Steinbach .10 .30
523 Steve Trachsel .10 .30
524 Josh Booty .10 .30
525 Darryl Hamilton .10 .30
526 Mark McLemore .10 .30
527 Kevin Stocker .10 .30
528 Bret Boone .10 .30
529 Shane Andrews .10 .30
530 Robb Nen .10 .30
531 Carl Everett .10 .30
532 LaTroy Hawkins .10 .30
533 Fernando Vina .10 .30
534 Michael Tucker .10 .30
535 Mark Langston .10 .30
536 Mickey Mantle 2.00 5.00
537 Bernard Gilkey .10 .30
538 Francisco Cordova .10 .30
539 Mike Bordick .10 .30
540 Fred McGriff .20 .50
541 Cliff Politte .10 .30
542 Jason Varitek .30 .75
543 Shawon Dunston .10 .30
544 Brian Meadows .10 .30
545 Pat Meares .10 .30
546 Carlos Perez .10 .30
547 Desi Relaford .10 .30
548 Antonio Osuna .10 .30
549 Devon White .10 .30
550 Sean Runyan .10 .30
551 Mickey Morandini .10 .30
552 Dave Martinez .10 .30
553 Jeff Fassero .10 .30
554 Ryan Jackson RC .10 .30
555 Stan Javier .10 .30
556 Jaime Navarro .10 .30
557 Jose Offerman .10 .30
558 Mike Lowell RC .60 1.50
559 Darrin Fletcher .10 .30
560 Mark Lewis .10 .30
561 Dante Bichette .10 .30
562 Chuck Finley .10 .30
563 Kerry Wood .15 .40
564 Andy Benes .10 .30
565 Freddy Garcia .10 .30
566 Tom Glavine .20 .50
567 Jon Nunnally .10 .30
568 Miguel Cairo .10 .30
569 Shane Reynolds .10 .30
570 Roberto Kelly .10 .30
571 Jose Cruz Jr. CL .10 .30
572 Ken Griffey Jr. CL .30 .75
573 Mark McGwire CL .40 1.00
574 Cal Ripken CL .50 1.25
575 Frank Thomas CL .20 .50
576 Jeff Bagwell UM .50 1.25
577 Barry Bonds UM 2.00 5.00
578 Tony Clark UM .30 .75
579 Roger Clemens UM 1.50 4.00
580 Jose Cruz Jr. UM .30 .75
581 N.Garciaparra UM 1.25 3.00
582 Juan Gonzalez UM .30 .75
583 Ben Grieve UM .30 .75
584 Ken Griffey Jr. UM 1.25 3.00
585 Tony Gwynn UM 1.00 2.50
586 Derek Jeter UM 2.00 5.00
587 Randy Johnson UM .75 2.00
588 Chipper Jones UM .75 2.00
589 Greg Maddux UM 1.25 3.00
590 Mark McGwire UM 2.00 5.00
591 Andy Pettitte UM .50 1.25
592 Paul Molitor UM .30 .75
593 Cal Ripken UM 2.50 6.00
594 Alex Rodriguez UM 1.25 3.00
595 Scott Rolen UM .50 1.25
596 Curt Schilling UM .30 .75
597 Frank Thomas UM .75 2.00
598 Jim Thome UM .50 1.25
599 Larry Walker UM .30 .75
600 Bernie Williams UM .50 1.25
P100 A.Rodriguez Promo .60 1.50

1998 Fleer Tradition Vintage '63

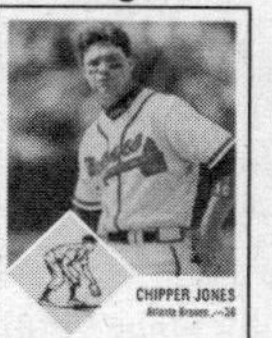

Randomly inserted one in every first and second series hobby pack, this 128-card set commemorates the 35th anniversary of the Fleer set and features color photos of top players printed in the 1963 Fleer Baseball card design.

*63 CLASSIC STARS: 30X TO 80X BASIC VINTAGE
63 CLASSIC RANDOM INS.IN HOBBY PACKS
63 CLASSIC PRINT RUN 63 SERIAL #'d SETS

1 Jason Dickson .15 .40
2 Tim Salmon .25 .60
3 Andruw Jones .25 .60
4 Chipper Jones .40 1.00
5 Kenny Lofton .15 .40
6 Greg Maddux .60 1.50
7 Rafael Palmeiro .25 .60
8 Cal Ripken 1.25 3.00
9 Nomar Garciaparra .60 1.50
10 Mark Grace .25 .60
11 Sammy Sosa .40 1.00
12 Frank Thomas .40 1.00
13 Deion Sanders .25 .60
14 Sandy Alomar Jr. .15 .40
15 David Justice .15 .40
16 Jim Thome .25 .60
17 Matt Williams .15 .40
18 Jaret Wright .15 .40
19 Vinny Castilla .15 .40
20 Andres Galarraga .15 .40
21 Todd Helton .25 .60
22 Larry Walker .15 .40
23 Tony Clark .15 .40
24 Moises Alou .15 .40
25 Kevin Brown .25 .60
26 Charles Johnson .15 .40
27 Edgar Renteria .15 .40
28 Gary Sheffield .15 .40
29 Jeff Bagwell .25 .60
30 Craig Biggio .25 .60
31 Raul Mondesi .15 .40
32 Mike Piazza .60 1.50
33 Chuck Knoblauch .15 .40
34 Paul Molitor .15 .40
35 Vladimir Guerrero .40 1.00
36 Pedro Martinez .25 .60
37 Todd Hundley .15 .40
38 Derek Jeter 1.00 2.50
39 Tino Martinez .25 .60
40 Paul O'Neill .25 .60
41 Andy Pettitte .25 .60
42 Mariano Rivera .40 1.00
43 Bernie Williams .25 .60
44 Ben Grieve .15 .40
45 Scott Rolen .25 .60
46 Curt Schilling .15 .40
47 Jason Kendall .15 .40
48 Tony Womack .15 .40
49 Ray Lankford .15 .40
50 Mark McGwire 1.00 2.50
51 Matt Morris .15 .40
52 Tony Gwynn .50 1.25
53 Barry Bonds 1.00 2.50
54 Jay Buhner .15 .40
55 Ken Griffey Jr. .60 1.50
56 Randy Johnson .40 1.00
57 Edgar Martinez .25 .60
58 Alex Rodriguez .60 1.50
59 Juan Gonzalez .15 .40
60 Rusty Greer .15 .40
61 Ivan Rodriguez .25 .60
62 Roger Clemens .75 2.00
63 Jose Cruz Jr. .15 .40
64 Darin Erstad .15 .40
65 Jay Bell .15 .40
66 Andy Benes .15 .40
67 Mickey Mantle 2.50 6.00
68 Karim Garcia .15 .40
69 Travis Lee .15 .40
70 Matt Williams .15 .40
71 Andres Galarraga .15 .40
72 Tom Glavine .25 .60
73 Ryan Klesko .15 .40
74 Denny Neagle .15 .40
75 John Smoltz .25 .60
76 Roberto Alomar .25 .60
77 Joe Carter .15 .40
78 Mike Mussina .25 .60
79 B.J. Surhoff .15 .40
80 Dennis Eckersley .15 .40
81 Pedro Martinez .25 .60
82 Mo Vaughn .15 .40
83 Henry Rodriguez .15 .40
84 Kerry Wood .20 .50
85 Albert Belle .15 .40
86 Sean Casey .15 .40
87 Travis Fryman .15 .40
88 Kenny Lofton .15 .40
89 Darryl Kile .15 .40
90 Mike Lansing .15 .40
91 Bobby Bonilla .15 .40
92 Cliff Floyd .15 .40
93 Livan Hernandez .15 .40
94 Derrek Lee .25 .60
95 Moises Alou .15 .40
96 Shane Reynolds .15 .40
97 Mike Piazza .60 1.50
98 Johnny Damon .25 .60
99 Eric Karros .15 .40
100 Hideo Nomo .40 1.00
101 Marquis Grissom .15 .40
102 Matt Lawton .15 .40
103 Todd Walker .15 .40
104 Gary Sheffield .15 .40
105 Bernard Gilkey .15 .40
106 Rey Ordonez .15 .40
107 Chili Davis .15 .40
108 Chuck Knoblauch .15 .40
109 Charles Johnson .15 .40
110 Rickey Henderson .40 1.00
111 Bob Abreu .15 .40
112 Doug Glanville .15 .40
113 Gregg Jefferies .15 .40
114 Al Martin .15 .40
115 Kevin Young .15 .40
116 Ron Gant .15 .40
117 Kevin Brown .25 .60
118 Ken Caminiti .15 .40
119 Joey Hamilton .15 .40
120 Jeff Kent .15 .40
121 Wade Boggs .25 .60
122 Quinton McCracken .15 .40
123 Fred McGriff .25 .60
124 Paul Sorrento .15 .40
125 Jose Canseco .25 .60
126 Randy Myers .15 .40
NNO Checklist 1 .15 .40
NNO Checklist 2 .15 .40

1998 Fleer Tradition Decade of Excellence

Randomly inserted in hobby packs only at the rate of one in 72, this 12-card set features 1988 season photos in Fleer's 1988 card design of current players who have been in playing major league baseball for ten years or more.

COMPLETE SET (12) 50.00 120.00
*RARE TRAD: 2X TO 5X BASIC DECADES
RARE TRAD. STATED ODDS 1:720 HOBBY

1 Roberto Alomar 1.50 4.00
2 Barry Bonds 6.00 15.00
3 Roger Clemens 5.00 12.00
4 David Cone 1.00 2.50
5 Andres Galarraga 1.00 2.50
6 Mark Grace 1.50 4.00
7 Tony Gwynn 3.00 8.00
8 Randy Johnson 2.50 6.00
9 Greg Maddux 4.00 10.00
10 Mark McGwire 6.00 15.00
11 Paul O'Neill 1.50 4.00
12 Cal Ripken 8.00 20.00

1998 Fleer Tradition Diamond Standouts

Randomly inserted in packs at the rate of one in 12, this 20-card set features color photos of great players on a diamond design silver foil background. The backs display detailed player information.

COMPLETE SET (20) 20.00 50.00
1 Jeff Bagwell .50 1.25
2 Barry Bonds 2.00 5.00
3 Roger Clemens 1.50 4.00
4 Jose Cruz Jr. .30 .75
5 Andres Galarraga .30 .75
6 Nomar Garciaparra 1.25 3.00
7 Juan Gonzalez .30 .75
8 Ken Griffey Jr. 1.25 3.00
9 Derek Jeter 2.00 5.00
10 Randy Johnson .75 2.00
11 Chipper Jones .75 2.00
12 Kenny Lofton .30 .75
13 Greg Maddux 1.25 3.00
14 Pedro Martinez .50 1.25
15 Mark McGwire 2.00 5.00
16 Mike Piazza 1.25 3.00
17 Alex Rodriguez 1.25 3.00
18 Curt Schilling .30 .75
19 Frank Thomas .75 2.00
20 Larry Walker .30 .75

1998 Fleer Tradition Diamond Tribute

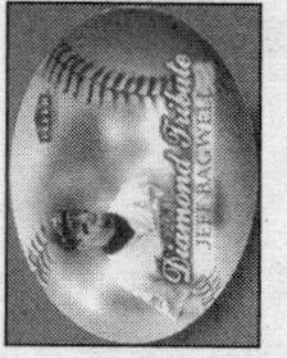

Randomly inserted in packs at a rate of one in 300, this 10-card insert set features color action photos printed on leatherette laminated stock with silver holofoil stamping.

COMPLETE SET (10) 75.00 200.00
DT1 Jeff Bagwell 4.00 10.00
DT2 Roger Clemens 12.50 30.00
DT3 Nomar Garciaparra 10.00 25.00
DT4 Juan Gonzalez 2.50 6.00
DT5 Ken Griffey Jr. 10.00 25.00
DT6 Mark McGwire 15.00 40.00
DT7 Mike Piazza 10.00 25.00
DT8 Cal Ripken 20.00 50.00
DT9 Alex Rodriguez 10.00 25.00
DT10 Frank Thomas 6.00 15.00

1998 Fleer Tradition In The Clutch

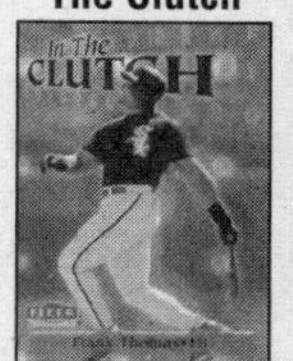

Randomly inserted in packs at a rate of one in 20, this 15-card insert offers color action photos on a green holofoil background.

COMPLETE SET (15) 30.00 80.00
IC1 Jeff Bagwell 1.00 2.50
IC2 Barry Bonds 4.00 10.00
IC3 Roger Clemens 3.00 8.00
IC4 Jose Cruz Jr. .60 1.50
IC5 Nomar Garciaparra 2.50 6.00
IC6 Juan Gonzalez .60 1.50
IC7 Ken Griffey Jr. 2.50 6.00
IC8 Tony Gwynn 2.00 5.00
IC9 Derek Jeter 4.00 10.00
IC10 Chipper Jones 1.50 4.00
IC11 Greg Maddux 2.50 6.00
IC12 Mark McGwire 4.00 10.00
IC13 Mike Piazza 2.50 6.00
IC14 Frank Thomas 1.50 4.00
IC15 Larry Walker .60 1.50

1998 Fleer Tradition Lumber Company

Randomly inserted in retail packs only at the rate of one in 36, this 15-card set features color photos of high-powered offensive players.

COMPLETE SET (15) 50.00 120.00
1 Jeff Bagwell 1.50 4.00
2 Barry Bonds 6.00 15.00
3 Jose Cruz Jr. 1.00 2.50
4 Nomar Garciaparra 4.00 10.00
5 Juan Gonzalez 1.00 2.50
6 Ken Griffey Jr. 4.00 10.00
7 Tony Gwynn 3.00 8.00
8 Chipper Jones 2.50 6.00
9 Tino Martinez 1.50 4.00
10 Mark McGwire 6.00 15.00
11 Mike Piazza 4.00 10.00
12 Cal Ripken 8.00 20.00
13 Alex Rodriguez 4.00 10.00
14 Frank Thomas 2.50 6.00
15 Larry Walker 1.00 2.50

1998 Fleer Tradition Mickey Mantle Monumental Moments

This 10 card set features highlights from Mickey Mantle's long and illustrious career with the New York Yankees. Mantle, who hit 536 Homers in his career and 18 more in the World Series is honored with these cards which were inserted one every 68 packs.

COMPLETE SET (10) 60.00 150.00
COMMON CARD (1-10) 10.00 25.00

*GOLD: 1.5X TO 4X BASIC MANTLE
GOLD: RANDOM INSERTS IN SER.2 PACKS
GOLD PRINT RUN 51 SERIAL #'d SETS

1998 Fleer Tradition Power Game

Randomly inserted in packs at the rate of one in 36, this 20-card set features color action player photos of great pitchers and hitters highlighted with purple metallic foil and glossy UV coating. The backs display player statistics.

COMPLETE SET (20) 50.00 120.00
1 Jeff Bagwell 1.50 4.00
2 Albert Belle 1.00 2.50
3 Barry Bonds 6.00 15.00
4 Tony Clark 1.00 2.50
5 Roger Clemens 5.00 12.00
6 Jose Cruz Jr. 1.00 2.50
7 Andres Galarraga 1.00 2.50
8 Nomar Garciaparra 4.00 10.00
9 Juan Gonzalez 1.00 2.50
10 Ken Griffey Jr. 4.00 10.00
11 Randy Johnson 2.50 6.00
12 Greg Maddux 4.00 10.00
13 Pedro Martinez 1.50 4.00
14 Tino Martinez 1.50 4.00
15 Mark McGwire 6.00 15.00
16 Mike Piazza 4.00 10.00
17 Curt Schilling 1.00 2.50
18 Frank Thomas 2.50 6.00
19 Jim Thome 1.50 4.00
20 Larry Walker 1.00 2.50

1998 Fleer Tradition Promising Forecast

Randomly inserted in packs at a rate of one in 12, this 20-card insert features color action photos on cards with flood aqueous coating, silver foil stamping and a white glow around the player's UV coated image.

COMPLETE SET (20) 6.00 15.00
PF1 Rolando Arrojo .50 1.25
PF2 Sean Casey .40 1.00
PF3 Brad Fullmer .40 1.00
PF4 Karim Garcia .40 1.00
PF5 Ben Grieve .40 1.00
PF6 Todd Helton .60 1.50
PF7 Richard Hidalgo .40 1.00
PF8 A.J. Hinch .40 1.00
PF9 Paul Konerko .40 1.00
PF10 Mark Kotsay .40 1.00
PF11 Derrek Lee .60 1.50
PF12 Travis Lee .40 1.00
PF13 Eric Milton .40 1.00
PF14 Magglio Ordonez 1.00 2.50
PF15 David Ortiz 1.25 3.00
PF16 Brian Rose .40 1.00
PF17 Miguel Tejada 1.00 2.50
PF18 Jason Varitek 1.00 2.50
PF19 Enrique Wilson .40 1.00
PF20 Kerry Wood .50 1.25

1998 Fleer Tradition Rookie Sensations

Randomly inserted in packs at the rate of one in 18, this 20-card set features gray-bordered action color images of the 1997 most promising players who were eligible for Rookie of the Year honors on multi-colored backgrounds.

COMPLETE SET (20) 15.00 40.00
1 Mike Cameron .60 1.50
2 Jose Cruz Jr. .60 1.50
3 Jason Dickson .60 1.50
4 Kelvim Escobar .60 1.50
5 Nomar Garciaparra 2.50 6.00
6 Ben Grieve .60 1.50
7 Vladimir Guerrero 1.50 4.00
8 Wilton Guerrero .60 1.50
9 Jose Guillen .60 1.50
10 Todd Helton 1.00 2.50
11 Livan Hernandez .60 1.50
12 Hideki Irabu .60 1.50
13 Andruw Jones 1.00 2.50
14 Matt Morris .60 1.50
15 Magglio Ordonez 3.00 8.00
16 Neifi Perez .60 1.50
17 Scott Rolen 1.00 2.50
18 Fernando Tatis .60 1.50
19 Brett Tomko .60 1.50
20 Jaret Wright .60 1.50

1998 Fleer Tradition Zone

Randomly inserted in packs at the rate of one in 288, this 15-card set features color photos of unstoppable players printed on cards with custom pattern rainbow foil and etching.

COMPLETE SET (15) 100.00 250.00
1 Jeff Bagwell 4.00 10.00
2 Barry Bonds 15.00 40.00
3 Roger Clemens 12.50 30.00
4 Jose Cruz Jr. 2.50 6.00
5 Nomar Garciaparra 10.00 25.00
6 Juan Gonzalez 2.50 6.00
7 Ken Griffey Jr. 10.00 25.00
8 Tony Gwynn 8.00 20.00
9 Chipper Jones 6.00 15.00
10 Greg Maddux 10.00 25.00
11 Mark McGwire 15.00 40.00
12 Mike Piazza 10.00 25.00
13 Alex Rodriguez 10.00 25.00
14 Frank Thomas 6.00 15.00
15 Larry Walker 2.50 6.00

1998 Fleer Tradition Update

The 1998 Fleer Update set was issued exclusively in factory set form. This set, issued in November, 1998, was created in large part to get the first J.D. Drew Rookie Card on the market. The set also took advantage of the "retro" themes that were popular in 1998 and represented the return of Fleer Update factory sets that had a rich history from 1984 through 1994. In addition to the aforementioned Drew, other notable RC's in this set include Troy Glaus, Orlando Hernandez and Gabe Kapler.

COMP.FACT.SET (100) 6.00 15.00
U1 Mark McGwire HL .50 1.25
U2 Sammy Sosa HL .10 .30
U3 Roger Clemens HL .40 1.00
U4 Barry Bonds HL .60 1.50
U5 Kerry Wood HL .08 .25
U6 Paul Molitor HL .07 .20
U7 Ken Griffey Jr. HL .30 .75
U8 Cal Ripken HL .60 1.50
U9 David Wells HL .07 .20
U10 Alex Rodriguez HL .30 .75
U11 Angel Pena RC .15 .40
U12 Bruce Chen .07 .20
U13 Craig Wilson .07 .20
U14 O.Hernandez RC .75 2.00
U15 Aramis Ramirez .07 .20
U16 Aaron Boone .07 .20
U17 Bob Henley .07 .20
U18 Juan Guzman .07 .20
U19 Darryl Hamilton .07 .20
U20 Jay Payton .07 .20
U21 Jeremy Powell .07 .20
U22 Ben Davis .07 .20
U23 Preston Wilson .07 .20
U24 Jim Parque RC .25 .60
U25 Odalis Perez RC .60 1.50
U26 Ronnie Belliard .07 .20
U27 Royce Clayton .07 .20
U28 George Lombard .07 .20
U29 Tony Phillips .07 .20
U30 F.Seguignol RC .15 .40
U31 Armando Rios RC .25 .60
U32 Jerry Hairston Jr. RC .25 .60
U33 Justin Baughman RC .15 .40
U34 Seth Greisinger .07 .20
U35 Alex Gonzalez .07 .20
U36 Michael Barrett .07 .20
U37 Carlos Beltran .40 1.00
U38 Ellis Burks .07 .20
U39 Jose Jimenez RC .40 1.00
U40 Carlos Guillen .07 .20
U41 Marlon Anderson .07 .20
U42 Scott Elarton .07 .20
U43 Glenallen Hill .07 .20
U44 Shane Monahan .07 .20
U45 Dennis Martinez .07 .20
U46 Carlos Febles RC .25 .60
U47 Carlos Perez .07 .20
U48 Wilton Guerrero .07 .20
U49 Randy Johnson .20 .50
U50 Brian Simmons RC .15 .40
U51 Carlton Loewer .07 .20
U52 Mark DeRosa RC .40 1.00
U53 Tim Young RC .15 .40
U54 Gary Gaetti .07 .20
U55 Eric Chavez .07 .20
U56 Carl Pavano .07 .20
U57 Mike Stanley .07 .20
U58 Todd Stottlemyre .07 .20
U59 Gabe Kapler RC .40 1.00
U60 Mike Jerzembeck RC .15 .40
U61 Mitch Meluskey RC .25 .60
U62 Bill Pulsipher .07 .20
U63 Derrick Gibson .07 .20
U64 John Rocker RC .40 1.00
U65 Calvin Pickering .07 .20
U66 Blake Stein .07 .20
U67 Fernando Tatis .07 .20
U68 Gabe Alvarez .07 .20
U69 Jeffrey Hammonds .07 .20
U70 Adrian Beltre .07 .20
U71 Ryan Bradley RC .15 .40
U72 Edgard Clemente .07 .20
U73 Rick Croushore RC .15 .40
U74 Matt Clement .07 .20
U75 Dermal Brown .07 .20
U76 Paul Bako .07 .20
U77 Placido Polanco RC .40 1.00
U78 Jay Tessmer .07 .20
U79 Jarrod Washburn .07 .20
U80 Kevin Witt .07 .20
U81 Mike Metcalfe .07 .20
U82 Daryle Ward .07 .20
U83 Benj Sampson RC .15 .40
U84 Mike Kinkade RC .15 .40
U85 Randy Winn .07 .20
U86 Jeff Shaw .07 .20
U87 Troy Glaus RC 1.25 3.00
U88 Hideo Nomo .20 .50
U89 Mark Grudzielanek .07 .20
U90 Mike Frank RC .15 .40
U91 Bobby Howry RC .15 .40
U92 Ryan Minor RC .15 .40
U93 Corey Koskie RC .40 1.00
U94 Matt Anderson RC .15 .40
U95 Joe Carter .07 .20
U96 Paul Konerko .07 .20
U97 Sidney Ponson .07 .20
U98 Jeremy Giambi RC .25 .60
U99 Jeff Kubenka RC .15 .40
U100 J.D. Drew RC 1.00 2.50

1999 Fleer Tradition

The 1999 Fleer set was issued in one series totalling 600 cards and was distributed in 10-card packs with a suggested retail price of $1.59. The fronts feature color action photos with gold foil player names. The backs carry another player photo with biographical information and career statistics. The set includes the following subsets: Franchise Futures (576-590) and Checklists (591-600).

COMPLETE SET (600) 30.00 60.00
1 Mark McGwire .75 2.00
2 Sammy Sosa .30 .75
3 Ken Griffey Jr. .50 1.25
4 Kerry Wood .10 .30
5 Derek Jeter .75 2.00
6 Stan Musial .60 1.50
7 J.D. Drew .10 .30
8 Cal Ripken 1.00 2.50
9 Alex Rodriguez .50 1.25
10 Travis Lee .07 .20
11 Andres Galarraga .10 .30
12 Nomar Garciaparra .50 1.25
13 Albert Belle .10 .30
14 Barry Larkin .20 .50
15 Dante Bichette .10 .30
16 Tony Clark .07 .20
17 Moises Alou .10 .30
18 Rafael Palmeiro .20 .50
19 Raul Mondesi .10 .30
20 Vladimir Guerrero .30 .75
21 John Olerud .10 .30
22 Bernie Williams .20 .50
23 Ben Grieve .07 .20
24 Scott Rolen .20 .50
25 Jeromy Burnitz .10 .30
26 Ken Caminiti .10 .30
27 Barry Bonds .75 2.00
28 Todd Helton .20 .50
29 Juan Gonzalez .10 .30
30 Roger Clemens .60 1.50
31 Andruw Jones .20 .50
32 Mo Vaughn .10 .30
33 Larry Walker .10 .30
34 Frank Thomas .30 .75
35 Manny Ramirez .20 .50
36 Randy Johnson .30 .75
37 Vinny Castilla .10 .30
38 Juan Encarnacion .07 .20
39 Jeff Bagwell .20 .50
40 Gary Sheffield .10 .30
41 Mike Piazza .50 1.25
42 Richie Sexson .10 .30
43 Tony Gwynn .40 1.00
44 Chipper Jones .30 .75
45 Jim Thome .20 .50
46 Craig Biggio .20 .50
47 Carlos Delgado .10 .30
48 Greg Vaughn .07 .20
49 Greg Maddux .50 1.25
50 Troy Glaus .20 .50
51 Roberto Alomar .20 .50
52 Dennis Eckersley .10 .30
53 Mike Caruso .07 .20
54 Bruce Chen .07 .20
55 Aaron Boone .10 .30
56 Bartolo Colon .10 .30
57 Derrick Gibson .07 .20
58 Brian Anderson .07 .20
59 Gabe Alvarez .07 .20
60 Todd Dunwoody .07 .20
61 Rod Beck .07 .20
62 Derek Bell .07 .20
63 Francisco Cordova .07 .20
64 Johnny Damon .20 .50
65 Adrian Beltre .10 .30
66 Garret Anderson .10 .30
67 Armando Benitez .07 .20
68 Edgardo Alfonzo .07 .20
69 Ryan Bradley .07 .20
70 Eric Chavez .10 .30
71 Bobby Abreu .10 .30
72 Andy Ashby .07 .20
73 Ellis Burks .10 .30
74 Jeff Cirillo .07 .20
75 Jay Buhner .10 .30
76 Ron Gant .10 .30
77 Rolando Arrojo .07 .20
78 Will Clark .20 .50
79 Chris Carpenter .10 .30
80 Jim Edmonds .10 .30
81 Tony Batista .07 .20
82 Shane Andrews .07 .20
83 Mark DeRosa .07 .20
84 Brady Anderson .10 .30
85 Tom Gordon .07 .20
86 Brant Brown .07 .20
87 Ray Durham .10 .30
88 Ron Coomer .07 .20
89 Bret Boone .10 .30
90 Travis Fryman .10 .30
91 Darryl Kile .10 .30
92 Paul Bako .07 .20
93 Cliff Floyd .10 .30
94 Scott Elarton .07 .20
95 Jeremy Giambi .07 .20
96 Darren Dreifort .07 .20
97 Marquis Grissom .10 .30
98 Marty Cordova .07 .20
99 Fernando Seguignol .07 .20
100 Orlando Hernandez .10 .30
101 Jose Cruz Jr. .07 .20
102 Jason Giambi .10 .30
103 Damion Easley .07 .20
104 Freddy Garcia .07 .20
105 Marlon Anderson .07 .20
106 Kevin Brown .20 .50
107 Joe Carter .10 .30
108 Russ Davis .07 .20
109 Brian Jordan .10 .30
110 Wade Boggs .20 .50
111 Tom Goodwin .07 .20
112 Scott Brosius .10 .30
113 Darin Erstad .10 .30
114 Jay Bell .10 .30
115 Tom Glavine .20 .50
116 Pedro Martinez .20 .50
117 Mark Grace .20 .50
118 Russ Ortiz .07 .20
119 Magglio Ordonez .10 .30
120 Sean Casey .10 .30
121 Rafael Roque RC .07 .20
122 Brian Giles .10 .30
123 Mike Lansing .07 .20
124 David Cone .10 .30
125 Alex Gonzalez .07 .20
126 Carl Everett .10 .30
127 Jeff King .07 .20
128 Charles Johnson .10 .30
129 Geoff Jenkins .07 .20
130 Corey Koskie .07 .20
131 Brad Fullmer .07 .20
132 Al Leiter .10 .30
133 Rickey Henderson .30 .75
134 Rico Brogna .07 .20
135 Jose Guillen .10 .30
136 Matt Clement .10 .30
137 Carlos Guillen .10 .30
138 Orel Hershiser .10 .30
139 Ray Lankford .10 .30
140 Miguel Cairo .07 .20
141 Chuck Finley .10 .30
142 Rusty Greer .10 .30
143 Kelvim Escobar .07 .20
144 Ryan Klesko .10 .30
145 Andy Benes .07 .20
146 Eric Davis .10 .30
147 David Wells .10 .30
148 Trot Nixon .10 .30
149 Jose Hernandez .07 .20
150 Mark Johnson .07 .20
151 Mike Frank .07 .20
152 Joey Hamilton .07 .20
153 David Justice .10 .30
154 Mike Mussina .20 .50
155 Neifi Perez .07 .20
156 Luis Gonzalez .10 .30
157 Livan Hernandez .10 .30
158 Dermal Brown .07 .20
159 Jose Lima .07 .20
160 Eric Karros .10 .30
161 Ronnie Belliard .07 .20
162 Matt Lawton .07 .20
163 Dustin Hermanson .07 .20
164 Brian McRae .07 .20
165 Mike Kinkade .07 .20
166 A.J. Hinch .07 .20
167 Doug Glanville .07 .20
168 Hideo Nomo .30 .75
169 Jason Kendall .10 .30
170 Steve Finley .10 .30
171 Jeff Kent .10 .30
172 Ben Davis .07 .20
173 Edgar Martinez .20 .50
174 Eli Marrero .07 .20
175 Quinton McCracken .07 .20
176 Rick Helling .07 .20
177 Tom Evans .07 .20
178 Carl Pavano .10 .30
179 Todd Greene .07 .20
180 Omar Daal .07 .20
181 George Lombard .07 .20
182 Ryan Minor .07 .20
183 Troy O'Leary .07 .20
184 Robb Nen .10 .30
185 Mickey Morandini .07 .20
186 Robin Ventura .10 .30
187 Pete Harnisch .07 .20
188 Kenny Lofton .10 .30
189 Eric Milton .07 .20
190 Bobby Higginson .10 .30
191 Jamie Moyer .10 .30
192 Mark Kotsay .10 .30
193 Shane Reynolds .07 .20
194 Carlos Febles .07 .20
195 Jeff Kubenka .07 .20
196 Chuck Knoblauch .10 .30
197 Kenny Rogers .10 .30
198 Bill Mueller .10 .30
199 Shane Monahan .07 .20
200 Matt Morris .10 .30
201 Fred McGriff .20 .50
202 Ivan Rodriguez .20 .50
203 Kevin Witt .07 .20
204 Troy Percival .10 .30
205 David Dellucci .07 .20
206 Kevin Millwood .10 .30
207 Jerry Hairston Jr. .07 .20
208 Mike Stanley .07 .20
209 Henry Rodriguez .07 .20
210 Trevor Hoffman .10 .30
211 Craig Wilson .07 .20
212 Reggie Sanders .10 .30
213 Carlton Loewer .07 .20
214 Omar Vizquel .20 .50
215 Gabe Kapler .10 .30
216 Derrek Lee .20 .50
217 Billy Wagner .10 .30
218 Dean Palmer .10 .30
219 Chan Ho Park .10 .30
220 Fernando Vina .07 .20
221 Roy Halladay .10 .30
222 Paul Molitor .10 .30
223 Ugueth Urbina .07 .20
224 Rey Ordonez .07 .20
225 Ricky Ledee .07 .20
226 Scott Spiezio .07 .20
227 Wendell Magee .07 .20
228 Aramis Ramirez .10 .30
229 Brian Simmons .07 .20
230 Fernando Tatis .07 .20
231 Bobby Smith .07 .20
232 Aaron Sele .07 .20
233 Shawn Green .10 .30
234 Mariano Rivera .30 .75
235 Tim Salmon .20 .50
236 Andy Fox .07 .20
237 Denny Neagle .07 .20
238 John Valentin .07 .20
239 Kevin Tapani .07 .20
240 Paul Konerko .10 .30
241 Robert Fick .07 .20
242 Edgar Renteria .10 .30
243 Brett Tomko .07 .20
244 Daryle Ward .07 .20
245 Carlos Beltran .20 .50
246 Angel Pena .07 .20
247 Steve Woodard .07 .20
248 David Ortiz .30 .75
249 Justin Thompson .07 .20
250 Rondell White .10 .30
251 Jaret Wright .07 .20
252 Ed Sprague .07 .20
253 Jay Payton .07 .20
254 Mike Lowell .10 .30
255 Orlando Cabrera .10 .30
256 Jason Schmidt .10 .30
257 David Segui .07 .20
258 Paul Sorrento .07 .20
259 John Wetteland .10 .30
260 Devon White .10 .30
261 Odalis Perez .07 .20
262 Calvin Pickering .07 .20
263 Tyler Green .07 .20
264 Preston Wilson .10 .30
265 Brad Radke .10 .30
266 Walt Weiss .07 .20
267 Tim Young .07 .20
268 Tino Martinez .20 .50
269 Matt Stairs .07 .20
270 Curt Schilling .10 .30
271 Tony Womack .07 .20
272 Ismael Valdes .07 .20
273 Wally Joyner .10 .30
274 Armando Rios .07 .20
275 Andy Pettitte .20 .50
276 Bubba Trammell .07 .20
277 Todd Zeile .10 .30
278 Shannon Stewart .10 .30
279 Matt Williams .10 .30
280 John Rocker .10 .30
281 B.J. Surhoff .10 .30
282 Eric Young .07 .20
283 Dmitri Young .10 .30
284 John Smoltz .20 .50
285 Todd Walker .07 .20
286 Paul O'Neill .20 .50
287 Blake Stein .07 .20
288 Kevin Young .10 .30
289 Quilvio Veras .07 .20
290 Kirk Rueter .07 .20
291 Randy Winn .07 .20
292 Miguel Tejada .10 .30
293 J.T. Snow .10 .30
294 Michael Tucker .07 .20
295 Jay Tessmer .07 .20
296 Scott Erickson .07 .20
297 Tim Wakefield .10 .30
298 Jeff Abbott .07 .20
299 Eddie Taubensee .07 .20
300 Darryl Hamilton .07 .20
301 Kevin Orie .07 .20
302 Jose Offerman .07 .20
303 Scott Karl .07 .20
304 Chris Widger .07 .20
305 Todd Hundley .07 .20
306 Desi Relaford .07 .20
307 Sterling Hitchcock .07 .20
308 Delino DeShields .07 .20
309 Alex Gonzalez .07 .20
310 Justin Baughman .07 .20
311 Jamey Wright .07 .20
312 Wes Helms .07 .20
313 Dante Powell .07 .20
314 Jim Abbott .20 .50
315 Manny Alexander .07 .20
316 Harold Baines .10 .30
317 Danny Graves .07 .20
318 Sandy Alomar Jr. .07 .20
319 Pedro Astacio .07 .20
320 Jermaine Allensworth .07 .20
321 Matt Anderson .07 .20
322 Chad Curtis .07 .20
323 Antonio Osuna .07 .20
324 Brad Ausmus .10 .30
325 Steve Trachsel .07 .20
326 Mike Blowers .07 .20
327 Brian Bohanon .07 .20
328 Chris Gomez .07 .20
329 Valerio De Los Santos .07 .20
330 Rich Aurilia .07 .20
331 Michael Barrett .07 .20
332 Rick Aguilera .07 .20
333 Adrian Brown .07 .20
334 Bill Spiers .07 .20
335 Matt Beech .07 .20
336 David Bell .07 .20
337 Juan Acevedo .07 .20
338 Jose Canseco .20 .50
339 Wilson Alvarez .07 .20
340 Luis Alicea .07 .20
341 Jason Dickson .07 .20
342 Mike Bordick .07 .20
343 Ben Ford .07 .20
344 Javy Lopez .10 .30
345 Jason Christiansen .07 .20
346 Darren Bragg .07 .20
347 Doug Brocail .07 .20
348 Jeff Blauser .07 .20
349 James Baldwin .07 .20
350 Jeffrey Hammonds .07 .20
351 Ricky Bottalico .07 .20
352 Russ Branyan .07 .20
353 Mark Brownson RC .07 .20
354 Dave Berg .07 .20
355 Sean Bergman .07 .20
356 Jeff Conine .10 .30
357 Shayne Bennett .07 .20
358 Bobby Bonilla .10 .30
359 Bob Wickman .07 .20
360 Carlos Baerga .07 .20
361 Chris Fussell .07 .20
362 Chili Davis .10 .30
363 Jerry Spradlin .07 .20
364 Carlos Hernandez .07 .20
365 Roberto Hernandez .07 .20
366 Marvin Benard .07 .20
367 Ken Cloude .07 .20
368 Tony Fernandez .07 .20
369 John Burkett .07 .20
370 Gary DiSarcina .07 .20
371 Alan Benes .07 .20
372 Karim Garcia .07 .20
373 Carlos Perez .07 .20
374 Damon Buford .07 .20
375 Mark Clark .07 .20
376 Edgard Clemente .07 .20
377 Chad Bradford RC .07 .20
378 Frank Catalanotto .07 .20
379 Vic Darensbourg .07 .20
380 Sean Berry .07 .20
381 Dave Burba .07 .20
382 Sal Fasano .07 .20
383 Steve Parris .07 .20
384 Roger Cedeno .07 .20
385 Chad Fox .07 .20
386 Wilton Guerrero .07 .20
387 Dennis Cook .07 .20
388 Joe Girardi .07 .20
389 LaTroy Hawkins .07 .20
390 Ryan Christenson .07 .20
391 Paul Byrd .07 .20
392 Lou Collier .07 .20
393 Jeff Fassero .07 .20
394 Jim Leyritz .07 .20
395 Shawn Estes .07 .20
396 Mike Kelly .07 .20
397 Rich Croushore .07 .20
398 Royce Clayton .07 .20
399 Rudy Seanez .07 .20
400 Darrin Fletcher .07 .20
401 Shigetoshi Hasegawa .10 .30
402 Bernard Gilkey .07 .20
403 Juan Guzman .07 .20
404 Jeff Frye .07 .20
405 Donovan Osborne .07 .20
406 Alex Fernandez .07 .20
407 Gary Gaetti .07 .20
408 Dan Miceli .07 .20
409 Mike Cameron .07 .20
410 Mike Remlinger .07 .20
411 Joey Cora .07 .20
412 Mark Gardner .07 .20
413 Aaron Ledesma .07 .20
414 Jerry Dipoto .07 .20
415 Ricky Gutierrez .07 .20
416 John Franco .10 .30
417 Mendy Lopez .07 .20
418 Hideki Irabu .07 .20
419 Mark Grudzielanek .07 .20
420 Bobby Hughes .07 .20
421 Pat Meares .07 .20
422 Jimmy Haynes .07 .20
423 Bob Henley .07 .20
424 Bobby Estalella .07 .20
425 Jon Lieber .07 .20
426 Giomar Guevara RC .07 .20
427 Jose Jimenez .07 .20
428 Deivi Cruz .07 .20
429 Jonathan Johnson .07 .20
430 Ken Hill .07 .20
431 Craig Grebeck .07 .20
432 Jose Rosado .07 .20
433 Danny Klassen .07 .20
434 Bobby Howry .07 .20
435 Gerald Williams .07 .20
436 Omar Olivares .07 .20
437 Chris Hoiles .07 .20
438 Seth Greisinger .07 .20
439 Scott Hatteberg .07 .20
440 Jeremi Gonzalez .07 .20
441 Wil Cordero .07 .20
442 Jeff Montgomery .07 .20
443 Chris Stynes .07 .20
444 Tony Saunders .07 .20
445 Einar Diaz .07 .20
446 Lariel Gonzalez .07 .20
447 Ryan Jackson .07 .20
448 Mike Hampton .10 .30
449 Todd Hollandsworth .07 .20
450 Gabe White .07 .20
451 John Jaha .07 .20
452 Bret Saberhagen .10 .30
453 Otis Nixon .07 .20
454 Steve Kline .07 .20
455 Butch Huskey .07 .20
456 Mike Jerzembeck .07 .20
457 Wayne Gomes .07 .20
458 Mike Macfarlane .07 .20
459 Jesus Sanchez .07 .20
460 Al Martin .07 .20
461 Dwight Gooden .10 .30
462 Ruben Rivera .07 .20

463 Pat Hentgen .07 .20
464 Jose Valentin .07 .20
465 Vladimir Nunez .07 .20
466 Charlie Hayes .07 .20
467 Jay Powell .07 .20
468 Raul Ibanez .07 .20
469 Kent Mercker .07 .20
470 John Mabry .07 .20
471 Woody Williams .07 .20
472 Roberto Kelly .07 .20
473 Jim Mecir .07 .20
474 Dave Hollins .07 .20
475 Rafael Medina .07 .20
476 Darren Lewis .07 .20
477 Felix Heredia .07 .20
478 Brian Hunter .07 .20
479 Matt Mantei .07 .20
480 Richard Hidalgo .07 .20
481 Bobby Jones .07 .20
482 Hal Morris .07 .20
483 Ramiro Mendoza .07 .20
484 Matt Luke .07 .20
485 Esteban Loaiza .07 .20
486 Mark Loretta .07 .20
487 A.J. Pierzynski .10 .30
488 Charles Nagy .07 .20
489 Kevin Sefcik .07 .20
490 Jason McDonald .07 .20
491 Jeremy Powell .07 .20
492 Scott Servais .07 .20
493 Abraham Nunez .07 .20
494 Stan Spencer .07 .20
495 Stan Javier .07 .20
496 Jose Paniagua .07 .20
497 Gregg Jefferies .07 .20
498 Gregg Olson .07 .20
499 Derek Lowe .10 .30
500 Willis Otanez .07 .20
501 Brian Moehler .07 .20
502 Glenallen Hill .07 .20
503 Bobby M. Jones .07 .20
504 Greg Norton .07 .20
505 Mike Jackson .07 .20
506 Kirt Manwaring .07 .20
507 Eric Weaver RC .07 .20
508 Mitch Meluskey .07 .20
509 Todd Jones .07 .20
510 Mike Matheny .07 .20
511 Benj Sampson .07 .20
512 Tony Phillips .07 .20
513 Mike Thurman .07 .20
514 Jorge Posada .20 .50
515 Bill Taylor .07 .20
516 Mike Sweeney .10 .30
517 Jose Silva .07 .20
518 Mark Lewis .07 .20
519 Chris Peters .07 .20
520 Brian Johnson .07 .20
521 Mike Timlin .07 .20
522 Mark McLemore .07 .20
523 Dan Plesac .07 .20
524 Kelly Stinnett .07 .20
525 Sidney Ponson .07 .20
526 Jim Parque .07 .20
527 Tyler Houston .07 .20
528 John Thomson .07 .20
529 Reggie Jefferson .07 .20
530 Robert Person .07 .20
531 Marc Newfield .07 .20
532 Javier Vazquez .10 .30
533 Terry Steinbach .07 .20
534 Turk Wendell .07 .20
535 Tim Raines .10 .30
536 Brian Meadows .07 .20
537 Mike Lieberthal .10 .30
538 Ricardo Rincon .07 .20
539 Dan Wilson .07 .20
540 John Johnstone .07 .20
541 Todd Stottlemyre .07 .20
542 Kevin Stocker .07 .20
543 Ramon Martinez .07 .20
544 Mike Simms .07 .20
545 Paul Quantrill .07 .20
546 Matt Walbeck .07 .20
547 Turner Ward .07 .20
548 Bill Pulsipher .07 .20
549 Donnie Sadler .07 .20
550 Lance Johnson .07 .20
551 Bill Simas .07 .20
552 Jeff Reed .07 .20
553 Jeff Shaw .07 .20
554 Joe Randa .10 .30
555 Paul Shuey .07 .20
556 Mike Redmond RC .07 .20
557 Sean Runyan .07 .20
558 Enrique Wilson .07 .20
559 Scott Radinsky .07 .20
560 Larry Sutton .07 .20
561 Masato Yoshii .07 .20
562 David Nilsson .07 .20
563 Mike Trombley .07 .20
564 Darryl Strawberry .10 .30
565 Dave Mlicki .07 .20
566 Placido Polanco .07 .20
567 Yorkis Perez .07 .20
568 Esteban Yan .07 .20
569 Lee Stevens .07 .20
570 Steve Sinclair .07 .20
571 Jarrod Washburn .07 .20
572 Lenny Webster .07 .20
573 Mike Sirotka .07 .20
574 Jason Varitek .30 .75
575 Terry Mulholland .07 .20
576 Adrian Beltre FF .07 .20
577 Eric Chavez FF .07 .20
578 J.D. Drew FF .07 .20
579 Juan Encarnacion FF .07 .20
580 Nomar Garciaparra FF .30 .75
581 Troy Glaus FF .10 .30
582 Ben Grieve FF .07 .20
583 Vladimir Guerrero FF .20 .50
584 Todd Helton FF .10 .30
585 Derek Jeter FF .40 1.00
586 Travis Lee FF .07 .20
587 Alex Rodriguez FF .30 .75
588 Scott Rolen FF .10 .30
589 Richie Sexson FF .07 .20
590 Kerry Wood FF .07 .20
591 Ken Griffey Jr. CL .30 .75
592 Chipper Jones CL .20 .50
593 Alex Rodriguez CL .30 .75
594 Sammy Sosa CL .20 .50
595 Mark McGwire CL .40 1.00
596 Cal Ripken CL .50 1.25
597 Nomar Garciaparra CL .30 .75
598 Derek Jeter CL .40 1.00
599 Kerry Wood CL .07 .20
600 J.D. Drew CL .07 .20
P7 J.D. Drew Promo .40 1.00

1999 Fleer Tradition Millenium

Fleer printed 5,000 Millenium factory sets, primarily intended for sale on Shop at Home at the end of the 1999 calendar year. Each set came shrink-wrapped in an attractive factory box, of which is sealed with a gold sticker serial numbered of 5,000. Each set contains 620 cards consisting of the 600-card basic issue set plus 20 cards from the Fleer Update set (rookies U1-U10 and highlights U141-U150). The cards hailing from the Update set have been renumbered. The Update rookies are numbered 601-610 and the Update highlights are numbered 611-620. All 620 cards contain a special gold foil "Year 2000" logo.

COMP.FACT.SET (620) 30.00 80.00
*STARS 1-600: 1X TO 2.5X BASIC CARDS
*ROOKIES 1-600: 1X TO 2.5X BASIC CARDS
601 Rick Ankiel 1.00 2.50
602 Peter Bergeron .30 .75
603 Pat Burrell 3.00 8.00
604 Eric Munson .60 1.50
605 Alfonso Soriano 6.00 15.00
606 Tim Hudson 3.00 8.00
607 Erubiel Durazo .60 1.50
608 Chad Hermansen .30 .75
609 Jeff Zimmerman .60 1.50
610 Jesus Pena .30 .75
611 Wade Boggs HL .50 1.25
612 Jose Canseco HL .50 1.25
613 Roger Clemens HL 1.50 4.00
614 David Cone HL .30 .75
615 Tony Gwynn HL 1.00 2.50
616 Mark McGwire HL 2.00 5.00
617 Cal Ripken HL 2.50 6.00
618 Alex Rodriguez HL 1.25 3.00
619 Fernando Tatis HL .20 .50
620 Robin Ventura HL .30 .75

1999 Fleer Tradition Warning Track

Cards from this parallel set were seeded at a rate of one per retail pack. Warning Track cards can be easily identified by the red foil "Warning Track Collection" logo at the base of the card front and the W suffix numbering on the card backs.

*STARS: 2.5X TO 6X BASIC CARDS

1999 Fleer Tradition Vintage '61

Inserted one in every hobby pack only, this 50-card set features the first 50 cards of the 1999 Fleer Tradition set in cards designed similar to the 1961 Fleer Baseball Greats set.

COMPLETE SET (50) 12.50 25.00
*SINGLES: .4X TO 1X BASE CARD HI

1999 Fleer Tradition Date With Destiny

These attractive bronze foil cards are designed to mimic the famous plaques on display at the Hall of Fame. Fleer selected ten of the games greatest active players, all of whom are well on their way to the Hall of Fame. Only 100 sets were printed (each card is serial numbered "X/100" on front) and the cards were randomly seeded into packs at an unannounced rate. Suffice to say, they're not easy to pull from packs.

1 Barry Bonds 25.00 60.00
2 Roger Clemens 20.00 50.00
3 Ken Griffey Jr. 15.00 40.00
4 Tony Gwynn 12.50 30.00
5 Greg Maddux 15.00 40.00
6 Mark McGwire 25.00 60.00
7 Mike Piazza 15.00 40.00
8 Cal Ripken 30.00 80.00
9 Alex Rodriguez 15.00 40.00
10 Frank Thomas 10.00 25.00

1999 Fleer Tradition Diamond Magic

Randomly inserted in packs at the rate of one in 96, this 15-card set features color action player images printed with a special die-cut treatment on a multi-layer card for a kaleidoscope effect behind the player image.

COMPLETE SET (15) 125.00 250.00
1 Barry Bonds 10.00 25.00
2 Roger Clemens 8.00 20.00
3 Nomar Garciaparra 6.00 15.00
4 Ken Griffey Jr. 6.00 15.00
5 Tony Gwynn 5.00 12.00
6 Orlando Hernandez 1.50 4.00
7 Derek Jeter 10.00 25.00
8 Randy Johnson 4.00 10.00
9 Chipper Jones 4.00 10.00
10 Greg Maddux 6.00 15.00
11 Mark McGwire 10.00 25.00
12 Alex Rodriguez 6.00 15.00
13 Sammy Sosa 4.00 10.00
14 Bernie Williams 2.50 6.00
15 Kerry Wood 1.50 4.00

1999 Fleer Tradition Going Yard

Randomly inserted in packs at the rate of one in 18, this 15-card set features color action photos of players who hit the longest home runs printed on extra wide cards to illustrate the greatness of their feats.

COMPLETE SET (15) 15.00 40.00
1 Moises Alou .40 1.00
2 Albert Belle .40 1.00
3 Jose Canseco .60 1.50
4 Vinny Castilla .40 1.00
5 Andres Galarraga .40 1.00
6 Juan Gonzalez .40 1.00
7 Ken Griffey Jr. 1.50 4.00
8 Chipper Jones 1.00 2.50
9 Mark McGwire 2.50 6.00
10 Rafael Palmeiro .60 1.50
11 Mike Piazza 1.50 4.00
12 Alex Rodriguez 1.50 4.00
13 Sammy Sosa 1.00 2.50
14 Greg Vaughn .25 .60
15 Mo Vaughn .40 1.00

1999 Fleer Tradition Golden Memories

Randomly inserted in packs at the rate of one in 54, this 15-card set features color action player photos with an embossed frame design.

COMPLETE SET (15) 75.00 150.00
1 Albert Belle 1.00 2.50
2 Barry Bonds 6.00 15.00
3 Roger Clemens 5.00 12.00
4 Nomar Garciaparra 4.00 10.00
5 Juan Gonzalez 1.00 2.50
6 Ken Griffey Jr. 4.00 10.00
7 Randy Johnson 2.50 6.00
8 Greg Maddux 4.00 10.00
9 Mark McGwire 6.00 15.00
10 Mike Piazza 4.00 10.00
11 Cal Ripken 8.00 20.00
12 Alex Rodriguez 4.00 10.00
13 Sammy Sosa 2.50 6.00
14 David Wells 1.00 2.50
15 Kerry Wood 1.00 2.50

1999 Fleer Tradition Stan Musial Monumental Moments

Randomly inserted in packs at the rate of one in 36, this 10-card set features photos of Stan Musial during his legendary career. As a bonus to collectors, Stan signed 50 of each of these cards in this set.

COMPLETE SET (10) 10.00 25.00
COMMON CARD (1-10) 1.00 2.50

1999 Fleer Tradition Stan Musial Monumental Moments Autographs

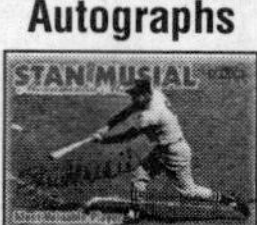

Fleer got legendary star Stan Musial to sign fifty of each Monumental Moments cards. Musial signed each card in bold blue ink on front. The cards are also serial numbered by hand in blue ink just beneath Musial's signature. Finally, each card was embossed with a circular Fleer logo to certify authenticity.

COMMON CARD (1-10) 30.00 60.00

1999 Fleer Tradition Rookie Flashback

Randomly inserted in packs at the rate of one in six, this 15-card set features color action photos of players who were rookies during the 1998 season printed on sculpture embossed cards.

COMPLETE SET (15) 4.00 10.00
1 Matt Anderson .20 .50
2 Rolando Arrojo .20 .50
3 Adrian Beltre .30 .75
4 Mike Caruso .20 .50
5 Eric Chavez .30 .75
6 J.D. Drew .30 .75
7 Juan Encarnacion .20 .50
8 Brad Fullmer .20 .50
9 Troy Glaus .50 1.25
10 Ben Grieve .20 .50
11 Todd Helton .50 1.25
12 Orlando Hernandez .30 .75
13 Travis Lee .20 .50
14 Richie Sexson .30 .75
15 Kerry Wood .30 .75

1999 Fleer Tradition Update

The 1999 Fleer Update set was issued in one series totalling 150 cards and distributed only as a factory boxed set. The fronts feature color action player photos. The backs carry player information. The set features the Season Highlights subset (Cards 141-150). Over 100 Rookie Cards are featured in this set. Among these Rookie Cards are Rick Ankiel, Josh Beckett, Pat Burrell, Tim Hudson, Eric Munson, Wily Mo Pena and Alfonso Soriano.

COMP.FACT.SET (150) 10.00 25.00
U1 Rick Ankiel RC 3.00 8.00
U2 Peter Bergeron RC .08 .25
U3 Pat Burrell RC .75 2.00
U4 Eric Munson RC .15 .40
U5 Alfonso Soriano RC 2.00 5.00
U6 Tim Hudson RC .75 2.00
U7 Erubiel Durazo RC .15 .40
U8 Chad Hermansen .07 .20
U9 Jeff Zimmerman RC .08 .25
U10 Jesus Pena RC .08 .25
U11 Ramon Hernandez .08 .25
U12 Trent Durrington RC .08 .25
U13 Tony Armas Jr. .07 .20
U14 Mike Fyhrie RC .08 .25
U15 Danny Kolb RC .30 .75
U16 Mike Porzio RC .08 .25
U17 Will Brunson RC .08 .25
U18 Mike Duvall RC .08 .25
U19 D.Mientkiewicz RC .30 .75
U20 Gabe Molina RC .08 .25
U21 Luis Vizcaino RC .08 .25
U22 Robinson Cancel RC .08 .25
U23 Brett Laxton RC .08 .25
U24 Joe McEwing RC .08 .25
U25 Justin Speier RC .08 .25
U26 Kip Wells RC .15 .40
U27 Armando Almanza RC .08 .25
U28 Joe Davenport RC .08 .25
U29 Yamid Haad RC .08 .25
U30 John Halama .07 .20
U31 Adam Kennedy .07 .20
U32 Micah Bowie RC .08 .25
U33 Gookie Dawkins RC .15 .40
U34 Ryan Rupe RC .08 .25
U35 B.J. Ryan RC .75 2.00
U36 Chance Sanford RC .08 .25
U37 A.Shumaker RC .08 .25
U38 Ryan Glynn RC .08 .25
U39 Roosevelt Brown RC .08 .25
U40 Ben Molina RC .30 .75
U41 Scott Williamson .07 .20
U42 Eric Gagne RC 1.50 4.00
U43 John McDonald RC .08 .25
U44 Scott Sauerbeck RC .08 .25
U45 Mike Venafro RC .08 .25
U46 Edwards Guzman RC .08 .25
U47 Richard Barker RC .08 .25
U48 Braden Looper .07 .20
U49 Chad Meyers RC .08 .25
U50 Scott Strickland RC .08 .25
U51 Billy Koch .07 .20
U52 David Newhan RC .15 .40
U53 David Riske RC .08 .25
U54 Jose Santiago RC .08 .25
U55 Miguel Del Toro RC .08 .25
U56 Orber Moreno RC .08 .25
U57 Dave Roberts RC .30 .75
U58 Tim Byrdak RC .08 .25
U59 David Lee RC .08 .25
U60 Guillermo Mota RC .08 .25
U61 Wilton Veras RC .08 .25
U62 Joe Mays RC .15 .40
U63 Jose Fernandez RC .08 .25
U64 Ray King RC .08 .25
U65 Chris Petersen RC .08 .25
U66 Vernon Wells .07 .20
U67 Ruben Mateo .07 .20
U68 Ben Petrick .07 .20
U69 Chris Tremie RC .08 .25
U70 Lance Berkman .07 .20
U71 Dan Smith RC .08 .25
U72 Carlos E. Hernandez RC .15 .40
U73 Chad Harville RC .08 .25
U74 Damaso Marte RC .08 .25
U75 Aaron Myette RC .08 .25
U76 Willis Roberts RC .08 .25
U77 Erik Sabel RC .08 .25
U78 Hector Almonte RC .08 .25
U79 Kris Benson .07 .20
U80 Pat Daneker RC .08 .25
U81 Freddy Garcia RC .40 1.00
U82 Byung-Hyun Kim RC .40 1.00
U83 Wily Pena RC 1.25 3.00
U84 Dan Wheeler RC .15 .40
U85 Tim Harikkala RC .08 .25
U86 Derrin Ebert RC .08 .25
U87 Horacio Estrada RC .08 .25
U88 Liu Rodriguez RC .08 .25
U89 J.Zimmerman RC .08 .25
U90 A.J. Burnett RC .40 1.00
U91 Doug Davis RC .40 1.00
U92 Rob Ramsay RC .08 .25
U93 Clay Bellinger RC .08 .25
U94 Charlie Greene RC .08 .25
U95 Bo Porter RC .08 .25
U96 Jorge Toca RC .15 .40
U97 Casey Blake RC .50 1.25
U98 Amaury Garcia RC .08 .25
U99 Jose Molina RC .15 .40
U100 Melvin Mora RC 1.00 2.50
U101 Joe Nathan RC .50 1.25
U102 Juan Pena RC .08 .25
U103 Dave Borkowski RC .08 .25
U104 Eddie Gaillard RC .08 .25
U105 Glen Barker RC .08 .25
U106 Brett Hinchliffe RC .08 .25
U107 Carlos Lee .07 .20
U108 Rob Ryan RC .08 .25
U109 Jeff Weaver RC .30 .75
U110 Ed Yarnall .07 .20
U111 Nelson Cruz RC .08 .25
U112 C.Davidson RC .08 .25
U113 Tim Kubinski RC .08 .25
U114 Sean Spencer RC .08 .25
U115 Joe Winkelsas RC .08 .25
U116 Mike Colangelo RC .08 .25
U117 Tom Davey RC .08 .25
U118 Warren Morris .07 .20
U119 Dan Murray RC .08 .25
U120 Jose Nieves RC .08 .25
U121 Mark Quinn RC .08 .25
U122 Josh Beckett RC 5.00 12.00
U123 Chad Allen RC .08 .25
U124 Mike Figga .08 .25
U125 Beiker Graterol RC .08 .25
U126 Aaron Scheffer RC .08 .25
U127 Wiki Gonzalez RC .15 .40
U128 Ramon E.Martinez RC .08 .25
U129 Matt Riley RC .15 .40
U130 Chris Woodward RC .08 .25
U131 Albert Belle .07 .20
U132 Roger Cedeno .07 .20
U133 Roger Clemens .40 1.00
U134 Brian Giles .07 .20
U135 Rickey Henderson .20 .50
U136 Randy Johnson .20 .50
U137 Brian Jordan .07 .20
U138 Paul Konerko .07 .20
U139 Hideo Nomo .20 .50
U140 Kenny Rogers .07 .20
U141 Wade Boggs HL .10 .30
U142 Jose Canseco HL .07 .20
U143 Roger Clemens HL .40 1.00
U144 David Cone HL .07 .20
U145 Tony Gwynn HL .25 .60
U146 Mark McGwire HL .50 1.25
U147 Cal Ripken HL .60 1.50
U148 Alex Rodriguez HL .30 .75
U149 Fernando Tatis HL .07 .20
U150 Robin Ventura HL .07 .20

2000 Fleer Tradition

This 450-card single series set was released in February, 2000. Ten-card hobby and retail packs carried an SRP of $1.59. The basic cards are somewhat reminiscent of the 1954 Topps baseball set featuring a large headshot set against a flat color background and a small, cut-out action shot. Subsets are as follows: League Leaders (1-10), Award Winners (435-440), Division Playoffs-World Series Highlights (441-450). Dual-player prospect cards, team cards and six checklist cards (featuring a floating head image of several of the game's top stars) are also sprinkled throughout the set. In addition, a Cal Ripken promotional card was distributed to dealers and hobby media several weeks prior to the product's release. The card is easy to identify by the "PROMOTIONAL SAMPLE" text running diagonally across the front and back.

COMPLETE SET (450) 20.00 50.00
1 Ken Griffey Jr / Rafael Palmeiro / Carlos Delgado LL .30 .75
2 Mark McGwire / Sammy Sosa / Chipper Jones LL .30 .75
3 Manny Ramirez / Rafael Palmeiro / Ken Griffey Jr. LL .10 .30
4 Mark McGwire / Matt Williams / Sammy Sosa LL .30 .75
5 Nomar Garciaparra / Derek Jeter / Bernie Williams LL .30 .75
6 Larry Walker / Luis Gonzalez / Bob Abreu LL .10 .30
7 Pedro Martinez / Bartolo Colon / Mike Mussina LL .10 .30
8 Mike Hampton / Jose Lima / Greg Maddux LL .10 .30
9 Pedro Martinez / David Cone / Mike Mussina LL .10 .30
10 Randy Johnson / Kevin Millwood / Mike Hampton LL .20 .50
11 Matt Mantei .10 .30
12 John Rocker .10 .30
13 Kyle Farnsworth .10 .30
14 Juan Guzman .10 .30
15 Manny Ramirez .20 .50
16 Matt Riley / Calvin Pickering .10 .30
17 Tony Clark .10 .30
18 Brian Meadows .10 .30
19 Orber Moreno .10 .30
20 Eric Karros .10 .30
21 Steve Woodard .10 .30
22 Scott Brosius .10 .30
23 Gary Bennett .10 .30
24 Jason Wood / Dave Borkowski .10 .30
25 Joe McEwing .10 .30
26 Juan Gonzalez .10 .30
27 Roy Halladay .10 .30
28 Trevor Hoffman .10 .30
29 Arizona Diamondbacks .10 .30
30 Domingo Guzman RC / Wiki Gonzalez .10 .30
31 Bret Boone .10 .30
32 Nomar Garciaparra .50 1.25
33 Bo Porter .10 .30
34 Eddie Taubensee .10 .30
35 Pedro Astacio .10 .30
36 Derek Bell .10 .30
37 Jacque Jones .10 .30
38 Ricky Ledee .10 .30
39 Jeff Kent .10 .30
40 Matt Williams .10 .30
41 Alfonso Soriano / D'Angelo Jimenez .30 .75
42 B.J. Surhoff .10 .30
43 Denny Neagle .10 .30
44 Omar Vizquel .20 .50
45 Jeff Bagwell .20 .50
46 Mark Grudzielanek .10 .30
47 LaTroy Hawkins .10 .30
48 Orlando Hernandez .10 .30
49 Ken Griffey Jr. CL .30 .75
50 Fernando Tatis .10 .30
51 Quilvio Veras .10 .30
52 Wayne Gomes .10 .30
53 Rick Helling .10 .30
54 Shannon Stewart .10 .30
55 Dermal Brown / Mark Quinn .10 .30
56 Randy Johnson .30 .75
57 Greg Maddux .50 1.25
58 Mike Cameron .10 .30
59 Matt Anderson .10 .30
60 Milwaukee Brewers .10 .30
61 Derrek Lee .20 .50
62 Mike Sweeney .10 .30
63 Fernando Vina .10 .30
64 Orlando Cabrera .10 .30
65 Doug Glanville .10 .30
66 Stan Spencer .10 .30
67 Ray Lankford .10 .30
68 Kelly Dransfeldt .10 .30
69 Alex Gonzalez .10 .30
70 Russ Branyan / Danny Peoples .10 .30
71 Jim Edmonds .10 .30
72 Brady Anderson .10 .30
73 Mike Stanley .10 .30
74 Travis Fryman .10 .30
75 Carlos Febles .10 .30
76 Bobby Higginson .10 .30
77 Carlos Perez .10 .30
78 Steve Cox / Alex Sanchez .10 .30
79 Dustin Hermanson .10 .30
80 Kenny Rogers .10 .30
81 Miguel Tejada .10 .30
82 Ben Davis .10 .30
83 Reggie Sanders .10 .30
84 Eric Davis .10 .30
85 J.D. Drew .10 .30

86 Ryan Rupe .10 .30
87 Bobby Smith .10 .30
88 Jose Cruz Jr. .10 .30
89 Carlos Delgado .10 .30
90 Toronto Blue Jays .10 .30
91 Denny Stark RC .10 .30
Gil Meche
92 Randy Velarde .10 .30
93 Aaron Boone .10 .30
94 Javy Lopez .10 .30
95 Johnny Damon .20 .50
96 Jon Lieber .10 .30
97 Montreal Expos .10 .30
98 Mark Kotsay .10 .30
99 Luis Gonzalez .10 .30
100 Larry Walker .10 .30
101 Adrian Beltre .10 .30
102 Alex Ochoa .10 .30
103 Michael Barrett .10 .30
104 Tampa Bay Devil Rays .10 .30
105 Rey Ordonez .10 .30
106 Derek Jeter .60 1.50
107 Mike Lieberthal .10 .30
108 Ellis Burks .10 .30
109 Steve Finley .10 .30
110 Ryan Klesko .10 .30
111 Steve Avery .10 .30
112 Dave Veres .10 .30
113 Cliff Floyd .10 .30
114 Shane Reynolds .10 .30
115 Kevin Brown .20 .50
116 Dave Nilsson .10 .30
117 Mike Trombley .10 .30
118 Todd Walker .10 .30
119 John Olerud .10 .30
120 Chuck Knoblauch .10 .30
121 Nomar Garciaparra CL .30 .75
122 Trot Nixon .10 .30
123 Erubiel Durazo .10 .30
124 Edwards Guzman .10 .30
125 Curt Schilling .10 .30
126 Brian Jordan .10 .30
127 Cleveland Indians .10 .30
128 Benito Santiago .10 .30
129 Frank Thomas .30 .75
130 Neifi Perez .10 .30
131 Alex Fernandez .10 .30
132 Jose Lima .10 .30
133 Jorge Toca .10 .30
Melvin Mora
134 Scott Karl .10 .30
135 Brad Radke .10 .30
136 Paul O'Neill .20 .50
137 Kris Benson .10 .30
138 Colorado Rockies .10 .30
139 Jason Phillips .10 .30
140 Robb Nen .10 .30
141 Ken Hill .10 .30
142 Charles Johnson .10 .30
143 Paul Konerko .10 .30
144 Dmitri Young .10 .30
145 Justin Thompson .10 .30
146 Mark Loretta .10 .30
147 Edgardo Alfonzo .10 .30
148 Armando Benitez .10 .30
149 Octavio Dotel .10 .30
150 Wade Boggs .20 .50
151 Ramon Hernandez .10 .30
152 Freddy Garcia .10 .30
153 Edgar Martinez .20 .50
154 Ivan Rodriguez .20 .50
155 Kansas City Royals .10 .30
156 Cleatus Davidson .10 .30
Cristian Guzman
157 Andy Benes .10 .30
158 Todd Dunwoody .10 .30
159 Pedro Martinez .20 .50
160 Mike Caruso .10 .30
161 Mike Sirotka .10 .30
162 Houston Astros .10 .30
163 Darryl Kile .10 .30
164 Chipper Jones .30 .75
165 Carl Everett .10 .30
166 Geoff Jenkins .10 .30
167 Dan Perkins .10 .30
168 Andy Pettitte .20 .50
169 Francisco Cordova .10 .30
170 Jay Buhner .10 .30
171 Jay Bell .10 .30
172 Andruw Jones .20 .50
173 Bobby Howry .10 .30
174 Chris Singleton .10 .30
175 Todd Helton .20 .50
176 A.J. Burnett .10 .30
177 Marquis Grissom .10 .30
178 Eric Milton .10 .30
179 Los Angeles Dodgers .10 .30
180 Kevin Appier .10 .30
181 Brian Giles .10 .30
182 Tom Davey .10 .30
183 Mo Vaughn .10 .30
184 Jose Hernandez .10 .30
185 Jim Parque .10 .30
186 Derrick Gibson .10 .30
187 Bruce Aven .10 .30
188 Jeff Cirillo .10 .30
189 Doug Mientkiewicz .10 .30
190 Eric Chavez .10 .30
191 Al Martin .10 .30
192 Tom Glavine .20 .50
193 Butch Huskey .10 .30
194 Ray Durham .10 .30
195 Greg Vaughn .10 .30
196 Vinny Castilla .10 .30
197 Ken Caminiti .10 .30
198 Joe Mays .10 .30
199 Chicago White Sox .10 .30
200 Mariano Rivera .30 .75
201 Mark McGwire CL .40 1.00
202 Pat Meares .10 .30
203 Andres Galarraga .10 .30
204 Tom Gordon .10 .30
205 Henry Rodriguez .10 .30
206 Brett Tomko .10 .30
207 Dante Bichette .10 .30
208 Craig Biggio .20 .50
209 Matt Lawton .10 .30
210 Tino Martinez .20 .50
211 Aaron Myette .10 .30
Josh Paul
212 Warren Morris .10 .30
213 San Diego Padres .10 .30
214 Ramon E. Martinez .10 .30
215 Troy Percival .10 .30
216 Jason Johnson .10 .30
217 Carlos Lee .10 .30
218 Scott Williamson .10 .30
219 Jeff Weaver .10 .30
220 Ronnie Belliard .10 .30
221 Jason Giambi .10 .30
222 Ken Griffey Jr. .50 1.25
223 John Halama .10 .30
224 Brett Hinchliffe .10 .30
225 Wilson Alvarez .10 .30
226 Rolando Arrojo .10 .30
227 Ruben Mateo .10 .30
228 Rafael Palmeiro .20 .50
229 David Wells .10 .30
230 Eric Gagne RC .30 .75
Jeff Williams RC
231 Tim Salmon .20 .50
232 Mike Mussina .20 .50
233 Magglio Ordonez .10 .30
234 Ron Villone .10 .30
235 Antonio Alfonseca .10 .30
236 Jeromy Burnitz .10 .30
237 Ben Grieve .10 .30
238 Giomar Guevara .10 .30
239 Garret Anderson .10 .30
240 John Smoltz .20 .50
241 Mark Grace .20 .50
242 Cole Liniak .10 .30
Jose Molina
243 Damion Easley .10 .30
244 Jeff Montgomery .10 .30
245 Kenny Lofton .10 .30
246 Masato Yoshii .10 .30
247 Philadelphia Phillies .10 .30
248 Raul Mondesi .10 .30
249 Marlon Anderson .10 .30
250 Shawn Green .10 .30
251 Sterling Hitchcock .10 .30
252 Randy Wolf .10 .30
Anthony Shumaker
253 Jeff Fassero .10 .30
254 Eli Marrero .10 .30
255 Cincinnati Reds .10 .30
256 Rick Ankiel .10 .30
Adam Kennedy
257 Darin Erstad .10 .30
258 Albert Belle .10 .30
259 Bartolo Colon .10 .30
260 Bret Saberhagen .10 .30
261 Carlos Beltran .10 .30
262 Glenallen Hill .10 .30
263 Gregg Jefferies .10 .30
264 Matt Clement .10 .30
265 Miguel Del Toro .10 .30
266 Robinson Cancel .10 .30
Kevin Barker
267 San Francisco Giants .10 .30
268 Kent Bottenfield .10 .30
269 Fred McGriff .20 .50
270 Chris Carpenter .10 .30
271 Atlanta Braves .10 .30
272 Wilton Veras .15 .40
Tomo Ohka RC
273 Will Clark .20 .50
274 Troy O'Leary .10 .30
275 Sammy Sosa CL .20 .50
276 Travis Lee .10 .30
277 Sean Casey .10 .30
278 Ron Gant .10 .30
279 Roger Clemens .60 1.50
280 Phil Nevin .10 .30
281 Mike Piazza .50 1.25
282 Mike Lowell .10 .30
283 Kevin Millwood .10 .30
284 Joe Randa .10 .30
285 Jeff Shaw .10 .30
286 Jason Varitek .30 .75
287 Harold Baines .10 .30
288 Gabe Kapler .10 .30
289 Chuck Finley .10 .30
290 Carl Pavano .10 .30
291 Brad Ausmus .10 .30
292 Brad Fullmer .10 .30
293 Boston Red Sox .10 .30
294 Bob Wickman .10 .30
295 Billy Wagner .10 .30
296 Shawn Estes .10 .30
297 Gary Sheffield .10 .30
298 Fernando Seguignol .10 .30
299 Omar Olivares .10 .30
300 Baltimore Orioles .10 .30
301 Matt Stairs .10 .30
302 Andy Ashby .10 .30
303 Todd Greene .10 .30
304 Jesse Garcia .10 .30
305 Kerry Wood .10 .30
306 Roberto Alomar .20 .50
307 New York Mets .10 .30
308 Dean Palmer .10 .30
309 Mike Hampton .10 .30
310 Devon White .10 .30
311 Chad Hermansen .10 .30
Mike Garcia RC
312 Tim Hudson .10 .30
313 John Franco .10 .30
314 Jason Schmidt .10 .30
315 J.T. Snow .10 .30
316 Ed Sprague .10 .30
317 Chris Widger .10 .30
318 Ben Petrick .10 .30
Luther Hackman RC
319 Jose Mesa .10 .30
320 Jose Canseco .20 .50
321 John Wetteland .10 .30
322 Minnesota Twins .10 .30
323 Jeff DaVanon RC .15 .40
Brian Cooper
324 Tony Womack .10 .30
325 Rod Beck .10 .30
326 Mickey Morandini .10 .30
327 Pokey Reese .10 .30
328 Jaret Wright .10 .30
329 Glen Barker .10 .30
330 Darren Dreifort .10 .30
331 Torii Hunter .10 .30
332 Tony Armas .10 .30
Peter Bergeron
333 Hideki Irabu .10 .30
334 Desi Relaford .10 .30
335 Barry Bonds .75 2.00
336 Gary DiSarcina .10 .30
337 Gerald Williams .10 .30
338 John Valentin .10 .30
339 David Justice .10 .30
340 Juan Encarnacion .10 .30
341 Jeremy Giambi .10 .30
342 Chan Ho Park .10 .30
343 Vladimir Guerrero .30 .75
344 Robin Ventura .20 .50
345 Bob Abreu .10 .30
346 Tony Gwynn .40 1.00
347 Jose Jimenez .10 .30
348 Royce Clayton .10 .30
349 Kelvim Escobar .10 .30
350 Chicago Cubs .10 .30
351 Travis Dawkins .10 .30
Jason LaRue
352 Barry Larkin .20 .50
353 Cal Ripken 1.00 2.50
354 Alex Rodriguez CL .30 .75
355 Todd Stottlemyre .10 .30
356 Terry Adams .10 .30
357 Pittsburgh Pirates .10 .30
358 Jim Thome .20 .50
359 Corey Lee .10 .30
Doug Davis
360 Moises Alou .10 .30
361 Todd Hollandsworth .10 .30
362 Marty Cordova .10 .30
363 David Cone .10 .30
364 Joe Nathan .10 .30
Wilson Delgado
365 Paul Byrd .10 .30
366 Edgar Renteria .10 .30
367 Rusty Greer .10 .30
368 David Segui .10 .30
369 New York Yankees .20 .50
370 Daryle Ward .10 .30
Carlos Hernandez
371 Troy Glaus .10 .30
372 Delino DeShields .10 .30
373 Jose Offerman .10 .30
374 Sammy Sosa .30 .75
375 Sandy Alomar Jr. .10 .30
376 Masao Kida .10 .30
377 Richard Hidalgo .10 .30
378 Ismael Valdes .10 .30
379 Ugueth Urbina .10 .30
380 Darryl Hamilton .10 .30
381 John Jaha .10 .30
382 St. Louis Cardinals .10 .30
383 Scott Sauerbeck .10 .30
384 Russ Ortiz .10 .30
385 Jamie Moyer .10 .30
386 Dave Martinez .10 .30
387 Todd Zeile .10 .30
388 Anaheim Angels .10 .30
389 Rob Ryan .10 .30
Nick Bierbrodt
390 Rickey Henderson .30 .75
391 Alex Rodriguez .50 1.25
392 Texas Rangers .10 .30
393 Roberto Hernandez .10 .30
394 Tony Batista .10 .30
395 Oakland Athletics .10 .30
396 Randall Simon .10 .30
Dave Cortes RC
397 Gregg Olson .10 .30
398 Sidney Ponson .10 .30
399 Micah Bowie .10 .30
400 Mark McGwire .75 2.00
401 Florida Marlins .10 .30
402 Chad Allen .10 .30
403 Casey Blake .10 .30
Vernon Wells
404 Pete Harnisch .10 .30
405 Preston Wilson .10 .30
406 Richie Sexson .10 .30
407 Rico Brogna .10 .30
408 Todd Hundley .10 .30
409 Wally Joyner .10 .30
410 Tom Goodwin .10 .30
411 Joey Hamilton .10 .30
412 Detroit Tigers .10 .30
413 Michael Tejera RC .10 .30
Ramon Castro
414 Alex Gonzalez .10 .30
415 Jermaine Dye .10 .30
416 Jose Rosado .10 .30
417 Wilton Guerrero .10 .30
418 Rondell White .10 .30
419 Al Leiter .10 .30
420 Bernie Williams .20 .50
421 A.J. Hinch .10 .30
422 Pat Burrell .10 .30
423 Scott Rolen .20 .50
424 Jason Kendall .10 .30
425 Kevin Young .10 .30
426 Eric Owens .10 .30
427 Derek Jeter CL .30 .75
428 Livan Hernandez .10 .30
429 Russ Davis .10 .30
430 Dan Wilson .10 .30
431 Quinton McCracken .10 .30
432 Homer Bush .10 .30
433 Seattle Mariners .10 .30
434 Chad Harville .10 .30
Luis Vizcaino
435 Carlos Beltran AW .10 .30
436 Scott Williamson AW .10 .30
437 Pedro Martinez AW .20 .50
438 Randy Johnson AW .20 .50
439 Ivan Rodriguez AW .10 .30
440 Chipper Jones AW .20 .50
441 Bernie Williams DIV .10 .30
442 Pedro Martinez DIV .20 .50
443 Derek Jeter DIV .40 1.00
444 Brian Jordan DIV .10 .30
445 Todd Pratt DIV .10 .30
446 Kevin Millwood DIV .10 .30
447 Orl.Hernandez WS .10 .30
448 Derek Jeter WS .40 1.00
449 Chad Curtis WS .10 .30
450 Roger Clemens WS .30 .75
P353 Cal Ripken Promo 1.25 3.00

2000 Fleer Tradition Glossy

The 2000 Fleer Glossy set was released in early December, 2000 and features a 500-card base set. Please note that you only receive 455 of the 500 total cards that make up this set per sealed factory set. Card 451-500 are short-printed and are inserted into sets at five per factory sealed set. Cards 451-500 are serial numbered to 1000. It's assumed a total of 10,000 sets were issued based upon the insertion rate of the serial #'d "high series" cards.

COMP.FACT.SET (455) 30.00 60.00
*STARS 1-450: .75X TO 2X BASIC
*ROOKIES 1-450: .75X TO 2X BASIC
451 Carlos Casimiro RC 4.00 10.00
452 Adam Melhuse RC 4.00 10.00
453 Adam Bernero RC 4.00 10.00
454 Dusty Allen RC 4.00 10.00
455 Chan Perry RC 4.00 10.00
456 Damian Rolls RC 4.00 10.00
457 Josh Phelps RC 4.00 10.00
458 Barry Zito 12.50 30.00
459 Hector Ortiz RC 4.00 10.00
460 Juan Pierre RC 6.00 15.00
461 Jose Ortiz RC 4.00 10.00
462 Chad Zerbe RC 6.00 15.00
463 Julio Zuleta RC 4.00 10.00
464 Eric Byrnes 4.00 10.00
465 Wilf. Rodriguez RC 4.00 10.00
466 Wascar Serrano RC 4.00 10.00
467 Aaron McNeal RC 4.00 10.00
468 Paul Rigdon RC 4.00 10.00
469 John Snyder RC 4.00 10.00
470 J.C. Romero RC 4.00 10.00
471 Talmadge Nunnari RC 4.00 10.00
472 Mike Lamb 6.00 15.00
473 Ryan Kohlmeier RC 4.00 10.00
474 Rodney Lindsey RC 4.00 10.00
475 Elvis Pena RC 4.00 10.00
476 Alex Cabrera 4.00 10.00
477 Chris Richard 4.00 10.00
478 Pedro Feliz RC 6.00 15.00
479 Ross Gload RC 4.00 10.00
480 Timo Perez RC 4.00 10.00
481 Jason Woolf RC 4.00 10.00
482 Kenny Kelly RC 4.00 10.00
483 Sang-Hoon Lee 4.00 10.00
484 John Riedling RC 4.00 10.00
485 Chris Wakeland RC 4.00 10.00
486 Britt Reames RC 4.00 10.00
487 Greg LaRocca RC 4.00 10.00
488 Randy Keisler RC 4.00 10.00
489 Xavier Nady RC 6.00 15.00
490 Keith Ginter RC 4.00 10.00
491 Joey Nation RC 4.00 10.00
492 Kazuhiro Sasaki 6.00 15.00
493 Lesli Brea RC 4.00 10.00
494 Jace Brewer 4.00 10.00
495 Yohanny Valera RC 4.00 10.00
496 Adam Piatt 4.00 10.00
497 Nate Rolison 4.00 10.00
498 Aubrey Huff 4.00 10.00
499 Jason Tyner 4.00 10.00
500 Corey Patterson 4.00 10.00

2000 Fleer Tradition Glossy Hawaii

This is a parallel set to the regular Fleer Glossy set. Each paying participant to the Hawaii Trade Show received one of these cards at the Meet the Industry Event at the CTA booth. All of the cards in this set are given a special Hawaii Trade show logo where it says the card is a "1 of 1". Since these cards are extremely limited, no pricing information is provided.

STATED PRINT RUN 1 SERIAL #'d SET

2000 Fleer Tradition Dividends

Inserted at a rate of one in six packs, these 15 cards feature some of the best players in the game.

COMPLETE SET (15) 7.50 15.00
D1 Alex Rodriguez .50 1.25
D2 Ben Grieve .10 .30
D3 Cal Ripken 1.00 2.50
D4 Chipper Jones .30 .75
D5 Derek Jeter .60 1.50
D6 Frank Thomas .30 .75
D7 Jeff Bagwell .20 .50
D8 Sammy Sosa .30 .75
D9 Tony Gwynn .40 1.00
D10 Scott Rolen .20 .50
D11 Nomar Garciaparra .50 1.25
D12 Mike Piazza .50 1.25
D13 Mark McGwire .75 2.00
D14 Ken Griffey Jr. .50 1.25
D15 Juan Gonzalez .10 .30

2000 Fleer Tradition Fresh Ink

Randomly inserted into packs at one in 144 packs, this insert set features autographed cards of players such as Rick Ankiel, Sean Casey and J.D. Drew.

1 Rick Ankiel 10.00 25.00
2 Carlos Beltran 6.00 15.00
3 Pat Burrell 4.00 10.00
4 Miguel Cairo 4.00 10.00
5 Sean Casey 6.00 15.00
6 Will Clark 10.00 25.00
7 Mike Darr 6.00 15.00
8 J.D. Drew 6.00 15.00
9 Erubiel Durazo 4.00 10.00
10 Carlos Febles 4.00 10.00
11 Freddy Garcia 4.00 10.00
12 Jason Grilli 4.00 10.00
13 Vladimir Guerrero 15.00 40.00
14 Tony Gwynn 20.00 50.00
15 Jerry Hairston Jr. 4.00 10.00
16 Tim Hudson 10.00 25.00
17 John Jaha 4.00 10.00
18 D'Angelo Jimenez 4.00 10.00
19 Andruw Jones 10.00 25.00
20 Gabe Kapler 6.00 15.00
21 Cesar King 4.00 10.00
22 Jason LaRue 4.00 10.00
23 Mike Lieberthal 6.00 15.00
24 Greg Maddux 60.00 120.00
25 Pedro Martinez 40.00 80.00
26 Gary Matthews Jr. 4.00 10.00
27 Orber Moreno 4.00 10.00
28 Eric Munson 4.00 10.00
29 Rafael Palmeiro 20.00 50.00
30 Jim Parque 4.00 10.00
31 Wily Pena 12.50 30.00
32 Cal Ripken 75.00 150.00
33 Alex Rodriguez 60.00 120.00
34 Tim Salmon 10.00 25.00
35 Chris Singleton 4.00 10.00
36 Alfonso Soriano 15.00 40.00
37 Ed Yarnall 4.00 10.00

2000 Fleer Tradition Grasskickers

Inserted at a rate of one in 30 packs, these 15 cards printed on rainbow holofoil feature players who put fear into their opponents.

COMPLETE SET (15) 25.00 60.00
GK1 Tony Gwynn 2.00 5.00
GK2 Scott Rolen 1.00 2.50
GK3 Nomar Garciaparra 2.50 6.00
GK4 Mike Piazza 2.50 6.00
GK5 Mark McGwire 4.00 10.00
GK6 Frank Thomas 1.50 4.00
GK7 Cal Ripken 5.00 12.00
GK8 Chipper Jones 1.50 4.00
GK9 Greg Maddux 2.50 6.00
GK10 Ken Griffey Jr. 2.50 6.00
GK11 Juan Gonzalez .60 1.50
GK12 Derek Jeter 3.00 8.00
GK13 Sammy Sosa 1.50 4.00
GK14 Roger Clemens 3.00 8.00
GK15 Alex Rodriguez 2.50 6.00

2000 Fleer Tradition Hall's Well

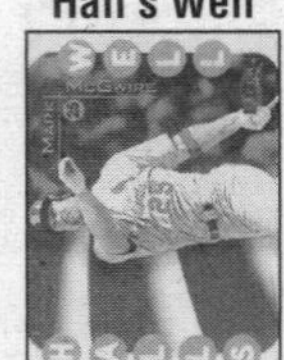

Inserted at a rate of one in 30 packs, these 15 cards feature players on their path to the Hall of Fame. The cards were printed on a combination of transparent plastic stock with overlays of silver foil stamping.

COMPLETE SET (15) 20.00 50.00
HW1 Mark McGwire 4.00 10.00
HW2 Alex Rodriguez 2.50 6.00
HW3 Cal Ripken 5.00 12.00
HW4 Chipper Jones 1.50 4.00
HW5 Derek Jeter 3.00 8.00
HW6 Frank Thomas 1.50 4.00
HW7 Greg Maddux 2.50 6.00
HW8 Juan Gonzalez .60 1.50
HW9 Ken Griffey Jr. 2.50 6.00
HW10 Mike Piazza 2.50 6.00
HW11 Nomar Garciaparra 2.50 6.00
HW12 Sammy Sosa 1.50 4.00
HW13 Roger Clemens 3.00 8.00
HW14 Ivan Rodriguez 1.00 2.50
HW15 Tony Gwynn 2.00 5.00

2000 Fleer Tradition Ripken Collection

Inserted at a rate of one in 30 packs, these 10 cards feature photos of Cal Ripken Jr. in the style of vintage Fleer cards. We have identified the style of the card and the sport next to Ripken's name.

COMMON CARD (1-10) 4.00 10.00

2000 Fleer Tradition Ten-4

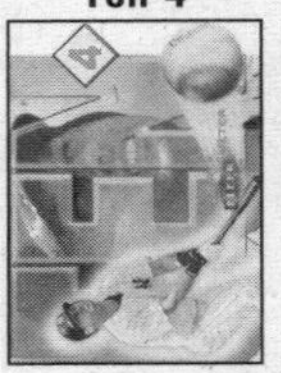

Issued at a rate of one in 18 packs, these 10 cards feature the best home run hitters highlighted on a die-cut card with silver foil stamping.

COMPLETE SET (10) 10.00 25.00
TF1 Sammy Sosa .75 2.00
TF2 Nomar Garciaparra 1.25 3.00
TF3 Mike Piazza 1.25 3.00
TF4 Mark McGwire 2.00 5.00
TF5 Ken Griffey Jr. 1.25 3.00
TF6 Juan Gonzalez .30 .75
TF7 Derek Jeter 1.50 4.00
TF8 Chipper Jones .75 2.00
TF9 Cal Ripken 2.50 6.00
TF10 Alex Rodriguez 1.25 3.00

2000 Fleer Tradition Who To Watch

Inserted at a rate of one in three, these 15 cards feature leading prospects against a nostalgic die-cut background.

COMPLETE SET (15) 2.00 5.00
WW1 Rick Ankiel .20 .50
WW2 Matt Riley .20 .50
WW3 Wilton Veras .20 .50
WW4 Ben Petrick .20 .50
WW5 Chad Hermansen .20 .50
WW6 Peter Bergeron .20 .50
WW7 Mark Quinn .20 .50
WW8 Russell Branyan .20 .50
WW9 Alfonso Soriano .40 1.00
WW10 Randy Wolf .20 .50
WW11 Ben Davis .20 .50
WW12 Jeff DaVanon .20 .50
WW13 D'Angelo Jimenez .20 .50
WW14 Vernon Wells .20 .50
WW15 Adam Kennedy .20 .50

2000 Fleer Tradition Glossy Lumberjacks

Inserted into Fleer Glossy sets at one per set, this 45-card insert set features game-used bat pieces from some of the top players in baseball. Print runs are listed below.

1 Edgardo Alfonzo/145 5.00 12.00
2 Roberto Alomar/627 6.00 15.00
3 Moises Alou/529 4.00 10.00
4 Carlos Beltran/489 4.00 10.00
5 Adrian Beltre/127 5.00 12.00
6 Wade Boggs/30
7 Barry Bonds/305 15.00 40.00
8 Jeromy Burnitz/34
9 Pat Burrell/45
10 Sean Casey/50
11 Eric Chavez/259 4.00 10.00

12 Tony Clark/70 6.00 15.00
13 Carlos Delgado/70 6.00 15.00
14 J.D. Drew/135 5.00 12.00
15 Erubiel Durazo/70 6.00 15.00
16 Ray Durham/35
17 Carlos Febles/120 5.00 12.00
18 Jason Giambi/220 4.00 10.00
19 Shawn Green/429 4.00 10.00
20 Vladimir Guerrero/809 6.00 15.00
21 Derek Jeter/180 25.00 60.00
22 Chipper Jones/725 6.00 15.00
23 Gabe Kapler/160 5.00 12.00
24 Jason Kendall/34
25 Paul Konerko/70 6.00 15.00
26 Ray Lankford/35
27 Mike Lieberthal/45
28 Edgar Martinez/211 6.00 15.00
29 Raul Mondesi/458 4.00 10.00
30 Warren Morris/35
31 Magglio Ordonez/190 5.00 12.00
32 Rafael Palmeiro/49
33 Pokey Reese/110 5.00 12.00
34 Cal Ripken/235 30.00 80.00
35 Alex Rodriguez/292 15.00 40.00
36 Ivan Rodriguez/602 6.00 15.00
37 Scott Rolen/502 6.00 15.00
38 Chris Singleton/68 6.00 15.00
39 Alfonso Soriano/285 6.00 15.00
40 Frank Thomas/489 6.00 15.00
41 Jim Thome/479 6.00 15.00
42 Robin Ventura/114 5.00 12.00
43 Jose Vidro/60 6.00 15.00
44 Bernie Williams/215 6.00 15.00
45 Matt Williams/152 5.00 12.00

2000 Fleer Tradition Update

The 2000 Fleer Tradition Update set was released in October, 2000 as a 150-card factory set. The set includes 10 Season Highlight cards (1-10), and 140 cards of players that were either traded during the season or who made their major league debut (cards 11-150). Each set originally carried a suggested retail price of $29.99. Please note that card number 50 does not exist. All cards have a "U" prefix. Notable Rookie Cards include Johan Santana, Kazuhiro Sasaki and Barry Zito. Finally, one in every 80 sets contained a Mickey Mantle game-worn jersey memorabilia card. According to representatives at Fleer, the Mickey Mantle MP1 card features a pair of grey, away, game-used pants.

COMP.FACT.SET (149) 10.00 25.00
1 Ken Griffey Jr. SH .30 .75
2 Cal Ripken SH .40 1.00
3 Randy Velarde SH .10 .30
4 Fred McGriff SH .10 .30
5 Derek Jeter SH .30 .75
6 Tom Glavine SH .10 .30
7 Brent Mayne SH .10 .30
8 Alex Ochoa SH .10 .30
9 Scott Sheldon SH .10 .30
10 Randy Johnson SH .20 .50
11 Daniel Garibay RC .10 .30
12 Brad Fullmer .10 .30
13 Kazuhiro Sasaki RC .25 .60
14 Andy Tracy RC .10 .30
15 Bret Boone .10 .30
16 Chad Durbin RC .15 .40
17 Mark Buehrle RC 1.00 2.50
18 Julio Zuleta RC .10 .30
19 Jeremy Giambi .10 .30
20 Gene Stechschulte RC .10 .30
21 Lou Pote .10 .30
Bengie Molina
22 Darrell Einertson RC .10 .30
23 Ken Griffey Jr. .50 1.25
24 Jeff Sparks RC .10 .30
Dan Wheeler
25 Aaron Fultz RC .10 .30
26 Derek Bell .10 .30
27 Rob Bell .10 .30
D.T. Cromer
28 Robert Fick .10 .30
29 Darryl Kile .10 .30
30 Clayton Andrews .10 .30
John Bale RC
31 Dave Veres .10 .30
32 Hector Mercado RC .10 .30
33 Willie Morales RC .10 .30
34 Kelly Wunsch .10 .30
Kip Wells
35 Hideki Irabu .10 .30
36 Sean DePaula RC .10 .30
37 DeWayne Wise .10 .30
Chris Woodward
38 Curt Schilling .10 .30
39 Mark Johnson .10 .30
40 Mike Cameron .10 .30
41 Scott Sheldon .10 .30
Tom Evans
42 Brett Tomko .10 .30
43 Johan Santana RC 5.00 12.00
44 Andy Benes .10 .30
45 Matt LeCroy .10 .30
Mark Redman
46 Ryan Klesko .10 .30
47 Andy Ashby .10 .30
48 Octavio Dotel .10 .30
49 Eric Byrnes RC .15 .40
50 Does Not Exist
51 Kenny Rogers .10 .30
52 Ben Weber RC .10 .30
53 Matt Blank .10 .30
Scott Strickland
54 Tom Goodwin .10 .30
55 Jim Edmonds Cards .10 .30
56 Derrick Turnbow RC .60 1.50
57 Mark Mulder .10 .30
58 Tarrick Brock .10 .30
Ruben Quevedo
59 Danny Young RC .10 .30
60 Fernando Vina .10 .30
61 Justin Brunette RC .10 .30
62 Jimmy Anderson .10 .30
63 Reggie Sanders .10 .30
64 Adam Kennedy .10 .30
65 Jesse Garcia .10 .30
B.J. Ryan
66 Al Martin .10 .30
67 Kevin Walker RC .10 .30
68 Brad Penny .10 .30
69 B.J. Surhoff .10 .30
70 Geoff Blum .10 .30
Trace Coquillette RC
71 Jose Jimenez .10 .30
72 Chuck Finley .10 .30
73 Valerio De Los Santos .10 .30
Everett Stull
74 Terry Adams .10 .30
75 Rafael Furcal .10 .30
76 John Roskos .10 .30
Mike Darr
77 Quilvio Veras .10 .30
78 Armando Almanza .10 .30
Nate Rolison
79 Greg Vaughn .10 .30
80 Keith McDonald RC .10 .30
81 Eric Cammack RC .10 .30
82 Horacio Estrada .10 .30
Ray King
83 Kory DeHaan .10 .30
84 Kevin Hodges RC .10 .30
85 Mike Lamb RC .25 .60
86 Shawn Green .10 .30
87 Dan Reichert .10 .30
Jason Rakers
88 Adam Piatt .10 .30
89 Mike Garcia .10 .30
90 Rodrigo Lopez RC .25 .60
91 John Olerud .10 .30
92 Barry Zito RC 1.50 4.00
Terrence Long
93 Jimmy Rollins .10 .30
94 Denny Neagle .10 .30
95 Rickey Henderson .30 .75
96 Adam Eaton .10 .30
Buddy Carlyle
97 Brian O'Connor RC .10 .30
98 Andy Thompson RC .10 .30
99 Jason Boyd RC .10 .30
100 Joel Pineiro RC .40 1.00
Carlos Guillen
101 Raul Gonzalez RC .10 .30
102 Brandon Kolb RC .10 .30
103 Jason Maxwell .10 .30
Mike Lincoln
104 Luis Matos RC .15 .40
105 Morgan Burkhart RC .10 .30
106 Ismael Villegas RC .10 .30
Steve Sisco RC
107 David Justice Yankees .10 .30
108 Pablo Ozuna .10 .30
109 Jose Canseco .20 .50
110 Alex Cora .10 .30
Shawn Gilbert
111 Will Clark Cardinals .20 .50
112 Keith Luuloa .10 .30
Eric Weaver
113 Bruce Chen .10 .30
114 Adam Hyzdu .10 .30
115 Scott Forster RC .10 .30
Yovanny Lara RC
116 Allen McDill RC .10 .30
Jose Macias
117 Kevin Nicholson .10 .30
118 Israel Alcantara .10 .30
Tim Young
119 Juan Alvarez RC .10 .30
120 Julio Lugo .10 .30
Mitch Meluskey
121 B.J. Waszgis RC .10 .30
122 Jeff M. D'Amico RC .10 .30
Brett Laxton
123 Ricky Ledee .10 .30
124 Mark DeRosa .10 .30
Jason Marquis
125 Alex Cabrera RC .15 .40
126 Augie Ojeda RC .10 .30
Gary Matthews Jr.
127 Richie Sexson .10 .30
128 Santiago Perez RC .10 .30
Hector Ramirez RC
129 Rondell White .10 .30
130 Craig House RC .10 .30
131 Kevin Beirne .10 .30
Jon Garland
132 Wayne Franklin RC .10 .30
133 Henry Rodriguez .10 .30
134 Jay Payton .10 .30
Jim Mann
135 Ron Gant .10 .30
136 Paxton Crawford RC .10 .30
Sang-Hoon Lee RC
137 Kent Bottenfield .10 .30
138 Rocky Biddle RC .10 .30
139 Travis Lee .10 .30
140 Ryan Vogelsong RC .10 .30
141 Jason Conti .10 .30
Geraldo Guzman RC
142 Tim Drew .10 .30
Mark Watson RC
143 John Parrish RC .10 .30
Chris Richard RC
144 Javier Cardona RC .10 .30
Brandon Villafuerte RC
145 Tike Redman RC .25 .60
Steve Sparks RC
146 Brian Schneider .10 .30
Matt Skrmetta RC
147 Pasqual Coco RC .10 .30
148 Lorenzo Barcelo RC .40 1.00
Joe Crede
149 Jace Brewer RC .10 .30
150 Milton Bradley .15 .40
Tomas De La Rosa RC
MP1 Mickey Mantle Pants 100.00 175.00

2001 Fleer Tradition

The 2001 Fleer Tradition product was released in early February, 2001 and initially featured a 450-card base set that was broken into tiers as follows: Base Veterans (1-350), Prospects (351-380), League Leaders (381-410), World Series Highlights (411-420), and Team Checklists (421-450). Each pack contained 10 cards and carried a suggested retail price of $1.99 per pack. In late October, 2001, a 485-card factory set carrying a $42.99 SRP was released. Each factory set contained the basic 450-card set plus 35 new cards (451-485) featuring a selection of rookies and prospects. Please note that there was also 100 exchange cards inserted into packs in which lucky collectors received an uncut sheet of 2001 Fleer.

COMP.FACT.SET (485) 50.00 100.00
COMPLETE SET (450) 20.00 50.00
COMMON CARD (1-450) .10 .30
COMMON (451-485) .20 .50
1 Andres Galarraga .10 .30
2 Armando Rios .10 .30
3 Julio Lugo .10 .30
4 Darryl Hamilton .10 .30
5 Dave Veres .10 .30
6 Edgardo Alfonzo .10 .30
7 Brook Fordyce .10 .30
8 Eric Karros .10 .30
9 Neifi Perez .10 .30
10 Jim Edmonds .10 .30
11 Barry Larkin .20 .50
12 Trot Nixon .10 .30
13 Andy Pettitte .20 .50
14 Jose Guillen .10 .30
15 David Wells .10 .30
16 Magglio Ordonez .10 .30
17 David Segui .10 .30
17A David Segui ERR .10 .30
Card has no number on the back
18 Juan Encarnacion .10 .30
19 Robert Person .10 .30
20 Quilvio Veras .10 .30
21 Mo Vaughn .10 .30
22 B.J. Surhoff .10 .30
23 Ken Caminiti .10 .30
24 Frank Catalanotto .10 .30
25 Luis Gonzalez .10 .30
26 Pete Harnisch .10 .30
27 Alex Gonzalez .10 .30
28 Mark Quinn .10 .30
29 Luis Castillo .10 .30
30 Rick Helling .10 .30
31 Barry Bonds .75 2.00
32 Warren Morris .10 .30
33 Aaron Boone .10 .30
34 Ricky Gutierrez .10 .30
35 Preston Wilson .10 .30
36 Erubiel Durazo .10 .30
37 Jermaine Dye .10 .30
38 John Rocker .10 .30
39 Mark Grudzielanek .10 .30
40 Pedro Martinez .20 .50
41 Phil Nevin .10 .30
42 Luis Matos .10 .30
43 Orlando Hernandez .10 .30
44 Steve Cox .10 .30
45 James Baldwin .10 .30
46 Rafael Furcal .10 .30
47 Todd Zeile .10 .30
48 Elmer Dessens .10 .30
49 Russell Branyan .10 .30
50 Juan Gonzalez .10 .30
51 Mac Suzuki .10 .30
52 Adam Kennedy .10 .30
53 Randy Velarde .10 .30
54 David Bell .10 .30
55 Royce Clayton .10 .30
56 Greg Colbrunn .10 .30
57 Rey Ordonez .10 .30
58 Kevin Millwood .10 .30
59 Fernando Vina .10 .30
60 Eddie Taubensee .10 .30
61 Enrique Wilson .10 .30
62 Jay Bell .10 .30
63 Brian Moehler .10 .30
64 Brad Fullmer .10 .30
65 Ben Petrick .10 .30
66 Orlando Cabrera .10 .30
67 Shane Reynolds .10 .30
68 Mitch Meluskey .10 .30
69 Jeff Shaw .10 .30
70 Chipper Jones .30 .75
71 Tomo Ohka .10 .30
72 Ruben Rivera .10 .30
73 Mike Sirotka .10 .30
74 Scott Rolen .20 .50
75 Glendon Rusch .10 .30
76 Miguel Tejada .10 .30
77 Brady Anderson .10 .30
78 Bartolo Colon .10 .30
79 Ron Coomer .10 .30
80 Gary DiSarcina .10 .30
81 Geoff Jenkins .10 .30
82 Billy Koch .10 .30
83 Mike Lamb .10 .30
84 Alex Rodriguez .50 1.25
85 Denny Neagle .10 .30
86 Michael Tucker .10 .30
87 Edgar Renteria .10 .30
88 Brian Anderson .10 .30
89 Glenallen Hill .10 .30
90 Aramis Ramirez .10 .30
91 Rondell White .10 .30
92 Tony Womack .10 .30
93 Jeffrey Hammonds .10 .30
94 Freddy Garcia .10 .30
95 Bill Mueller .10 .30
96 Mike Lieberthal .10 .30
97 Michael Barrett .10 .30
98 Derrek Lee .20 .50
99 Bill Spiers .10 .30
100 Derek Lowe .10 .30
101 Javy Lopez .10 .30
102 Adrian Beltre .10 .30
103 Jim Parque .10 .30
104 Marquis Grissom .10 .30
105 Eric Chavez .10 .30
106 Todd Jones .10 .30
107 Eric Owens .10 .30
108 Roger Clemens .60 1.50
109 Denny Hocking .10 .30
110 Roberto Hernandez .10 .30
111 Albert Belle .10 .30
112 Troy Glaus .10 .30
113 Ivan Rodriguez .20 .50
114 Carlos Guillen .10 .30
115 Chuck Finley .10 .30
116 Dmitri Young .10 .30
117 Paul Konerko .10 .30
118 Damon Buford .10 .30
119 Fernando Tatis .10 .30
120 Larry Walker .10 .30
121 Jason Kendall .10 .30
122 Matt Williams .10 .30
123 Henry Rodriguez .10 .30
124 Placido Polanco .10 .30
125 Bobby Estalella .10 .30
126 Pat Burrell .10 .30
127 Mark Loretta .10 .30
128 Moises Alou .10 .30
129 Tino Martinez .20 .50
130 Milton Bradley .10 .30
131 Todd Hundley .10 .30
132 Keith Foulke .10 .30
133 Robert Fick .10 .30
134 Cristian Guzman .10 .30
135 Rusty Greer .10 .30
136 John Olerud .10 .30
137 Mariano Rivera .30 .75
138 Jeromy Burnitz .10 .30
139 Dave Burba .10 .30
140 Ken Griffey Jr. .50 1.25
141 Tony Gwynn .40 1.00
142 Carlos Delgado .10 .30
143 Edgar Martinez .20 .50
144 Ramon Hernandez .10 .30
145 Pedro Astacio .10 .30
146 Ray Lankford .10 .30
147 Mike Mussina .20 .50
148 Ray Durham .10 .30
149 Lee Stevens .10 .30
150 Jay Canizaro .10 .30
151 Adrian Brown .10 .30
152 Mike Piazza .50 1.25
153 Cliff Floyd .10 .30
154 Jose Vidro .10 .30
155 Jason Giambi .10 .30
156 Andruw Jones .20 .50
157 Robin Ventura .10 .30
158 Gary Sheffield .10 .30
159 Jeff D'Amico .10 .30
160 Chuck Knoblauch .10 .30
161 Roger Cedeno .10 .30
162 Jim Thome .20 .50
163 Peter Bergeron .10 .30
164 Kerry Wood .10 .30
165 Gabe Kapler .10 .30
166 Corey Koskie .10 .30
167 Doug Glanville .10 .30
168 Brent Mayne .10 .30
169 Scott Spiezio .10 .30
170 Steve Karsay .10 .30
171 Al Martin .10 .30
172 Fred McGriff .20 .50
173 Gabe White .10 .30
174 Alex Gonzalez .10 .30
175 Mike Darr .10 .30
176 Bengie Molina .10 .30
177 Ben Grieve .10 .30
178 Marlon Anderson .10 .30
179 Brian Giles .10 .30
180 Jose Valentin .10 .30
181 Brian Jordan .10 .30
182 Randy Johnson .30 .75
183 Ricky Ledee .10 .30
184 Russ Ortiz .10 .30
185 Mike Lowell .10 .30
186 Curtis Leskanic .10 .30
187 Bob Abreu .10 .30
188 Derek Jeter .75 2.00
189 Lance Berkman .10 .30
190 Roberto Alomar .20 .50
191 Darin Erstad .10 .30
192 Richie Sexson .10 .30
193 Alex Ochoa .10 .30
194 Carlos Febles .10 .30
195 David Ortiz .30 .75
196 Shawn Green .10 .30
197 Mike Sweeney .10 .30
198 Vladimir Guerrero .30 .75
199 Jose Jimenez .10 .30
200 Travis Lee .10 .30
201 Rickey Henderson .30 .75
202 Bob Wickman .10 .30
203 Miguel Cairo .10 .30
204 Steve Finley .10 .30
205 Tony Batista .10 .30
206 Jamey Wright .10 .30
207 Terrence Long .10 .30
208 Trevor Hoffman .10 .30
209 John VanderWal .10 .30
210 Greg Maddux .50 1.25
211 Tim Salmon .20 .50
212 Herbert Perry .10 .30
213 Marvin Benard .10 .30
214 Jose Offerman .10 .30
215 Jay Payton .10 .30
216 Jon Lieber .10 .30
217 Mark Kotsay .10 .30
218 Scott Brosius .10 .30
219 Scott Williamson .10 .30
220 Omar Vizquel .20 .50
221 Mike Hampton .10 .30
222 Richard Hidalgo .10 .30
223 Rey Sanchez .10 .30
224 Matt Lawton .10 .30
225 Bruce Chen .10 .30
226 Ryan Klesko .10 .30
227 Garret Anderson .10 .30
228 Kevin Brown .10 .30
229 Mike Cameron .10 .30
230 Tony Clark .10 .30
231 Curt Schilling .10 .30
232 Vinny Castilla .10 .30
233 Carl Pavano .10 .30
234 Eric Davis .10 .30
235 Darrin Fletcher .10 .30
236 Matt Stairs .10 .30
237 Octavio Dotel .10 .30
238 Mark Grace .20 .50
239 John Smoltz .20 .50
240 Matt Clement .10 .30
241 Ellis Burks .10 .30
242 Charles Johnson .10 .30
243 Jeff Bagwell .20 .50
244 Derek Bell .10 .30
245 Nomar Garciaparra .50 1.25
246 Jorge Posada .20 .50
247 Ryan Dempster .10 .30
248 J.T. Snow .10 .30
249 Eric Young .10 .30
250 Daryle Ward .10 .30
251 Joe Randa .10 .30
252 Travis Fryman .10 .30
253 Mike Williams .10 .30
254 Jacque Jones .10 .30
255 Scott Elarton .10 .30
256 Mark McGwire .75 2.00
257 Jay Buhner .10 .30
258 Randy Wolf .10 .30
259 Sammy Sosa .30 .75
260 Chan Ho Park .10 .30
261 Damion Easley .10 .30
262 Rick Ankiel .10 .30
263 Frank Thomas .30 .75
264 Kris Benson .10 .30
265 Luis Alicea .10 .30
266 Jeromy Burnitz .10 .30
267 Geoff Blum .10 .30
268 Joe Girardi .10 .30
269 Livan Hernandez .10 .30
270 Jeff Conine .10 .30
271 Danny Graves .10 .30
272 Craig Biggio .20 .50
273 Jose Canseco .20 .50
274 Tom Glavine .20 .50
275 Ruben Mateo .10 .30
276 Jeff Kent .10 .30
277 Kevin Young .10 .30
278 A.J. Burnett .10 .30
279 Dante Bichette .10 .30
280 Sandy Alomar Jr. .10 .30
281 John Wetteland .10 .30
282 Torii Hunter .10 .30
283 Jarrod Washburn .10 .30
284 Rich Aurilia .10 .30
285 Jeff Cirillo .10 .30
286 Fernando Seguignol .10 .30
287 Darren Dreifort .10 .30
288 Deivi Cruz .10 .30
289 Pokey Reese .10 .30
290 Garrett Stephenson .10 .30
291 Bret Boone .10 .30
292 Tim Hudson .10 .30
293 John Flaherty .10 .30
294 Shannon Stewart .10 .30
295 Shawn Estes .10 .30
296 Wilton Guerrero .10 .30
297 Delino DeShields .10 .30
298 David Justice .10 .30
299 Harold Baines .10 .30
300 Al Leiter .10 .30
301 Wil Cordero .10 .30
302 Antonio Alfonseca .10 .30
303 Sean Casey .10 .30
304 Carlos Beltran .10 .30
305 Brad Radke .10 .30
306 Jason Varitek .30 .75
307 Shigetoshi Hasegawa .10 .30
308 Todd Stottlemyre .10 .30
309 Raul Mondesi .10 .30
310 Mike Bordick .10 .30
311 Darryl Kile .10 .30
312 Dean Palmer .10 .30
313 Johnny Damon .20 .50
314 Todd Helton .20 .50
315 Chad Hermansen .10 .30
316 Kevin Appier .10 .30
317 Greg Vaughn .10 .30
318 Robb Nen .10 .30
319 Jose Cruz Jr. .10 .30
320 Ron Belliard .10 .30
321 Bernie Williams .20 .50
322 Melvin Mora .10 .30
323 Kenny Lofton .10 .30
324 Armando Benitez .10 .30
325 Carlos Lee .10 .30
326 Damian Jackson .10 .30
327 Eric Milton .10 .30
328 J.D. Drew .10 .30
329 Byung-Hyun Kim .10 .30
330 Chris Stynes .10 .30
331 Kazuhiro Sasaki .10 .30
332 Troy O'Leary .10 .30
333 Pat Hentgen .10 .30
334 Brad Ausmus .10 .30
335 Todd Walker .10 .30
336 Jason Isringhausen .10 .30
337 Gerald Williams .10 .30
338 Aaron Sele .10 .30
339 Paul O'Neill .20 .50
340 Cal Ripken 1.00 2.50
341 Manny Ramirez .20 .50
342 Will Clark .20 .50
343 Mark Redman .10 .30
344 Bubba Trammell .10 .30
345 Troy Percival .10 .30
346 Chris Singleton .10 .30
347 Rafael Palmeiro .20 .50
348 Carl Everett .10 .30
349 Andy Benes .10 .30
350 Bobby Higginson .10 .30
351 Alex Cabrera .10 .30
352 Barry Zito .20 .50
353 Jace Brewer .10 .30
354 Paxton Crawford .10 .30
355 Oswaldo Mairena .10 .30
356 Joe Crede .30 .75
357 A.J. Pierzynski .10 .30
358 Daniel Garibay .10 .30
359 Jason Tyner .10 .30
360 Nate Rolison .10 .30
361 Scott Downs .10 .30
362 Keith Ginter .10 .30
363 Juan Pierre .10 .30
364 Adam Bernero .10 .30
365 Chris Richard .10 .30
366 Joey Nation .10 .30
367 Aubrey Huff .10 .30
368 Adam Eaton .10 .30
369 Jose Ortiz .10 .30
370 Eric Munson .10 .30
371 Matt Kinney .10 .30
372 Eric Byrnes .10 .30
373 Keith McDonald .10 .30
374 Matt Wise .10 .30
375 Timo Perez .10 .30
376 Julio Zuleta .10 .30
377 Jimmy Rollins .10 .30
378 Xavier Nady .10 .30
379 Ryan Kohlmeier .10 .30
380 Corey Patterson .10 .30
381 Todd Helton LL .10 .30
382 Moises Alou LL .10 .30
383 Vladimir Guerrero LL .20 .50
384 Luis Castillo LL .10 .30
385 Jeffrey Hammonds LL .10 .30
386 Nomar Garciaparra LL .30 .75
387 Carlos Delgado LL .10 .30
388 Darin Erstad LL .10 .30
389 Manny Ramirez LL .10 .30
390 Mike Sweeney LL .10 .30
391 Sammy Sosa LL .20 .50
392 Barry Bonds LL .40 1.00
393 Jeff Bagwell LL .10 .30
394 Richard Hidalgo LL .10 .30
395 Vladimir Guerrero LL .20 .50
396 Troy Glaus LL .10 .30
397 Frank Thomas LL .20 .50
398 Carlos Delgado LL .10 .30
399 David Justice LL .10 .30
400 Jason Giambi LL .10 .30
401 Randy Johnson LL .20 .50
402 Kevin Brown LL .10 .30
403 Greg Maddux LL .30 .75
404 Al Leiter LL .10 .30
405 Mike Hampton LL .10 .30
406 Pedro Martinez LL .20 .50
407 Roger Clemens LL .30 .75
408 Mike Sirotka LL .10 .30
409 Mike Mussina LL .10 .30
410 Bartolo Colon LL .10 .30
411 Subway Series WS .20 .50
412 Jose Vizcaino WS .20 .50
413 Jose Vizcaino WS .20 .50
414 Roger Clemens WS .30 .75
415 Armando Benitez .10 .30
Edgardo Alfonzo
Timo Perez WS
416 Al Leiter WS .20 .50
417 Luis Sojo WS .20 .50
418 Yankees 3-Peat WS .30 .75
419 Derek Jeter WS .40 1.00
420 Toast of the Town WS .20 .50
421 Rafael Furcal .10 .30
Chipper Jones
Greg Maddux
John Rocker
Tom Glavine CL
422 Armando Benitez .30 .75
Mike Piazza
Mike Hampton
Al Leiter CL
423 Ryan Dempster .10 .30
Luis Castillo
Antonio Alfonseca
Preston Wilson CL
424 Robert Person .10 .30
Scott Rolen
Randy Wolf
Bob Abreu
Doug Glanville CL
425 Vladimir Guerrero .10 .30
Peter Bergeron CL
426 Fernando Vina .10 .30
Dave Veres
Jim Edmonds
Rick Ankiel
Edgar Renteria
Darryl Kile CL
427 Danny Graves .10 .30
Ken Griffey Jr.
Sean Casey
Pokey Reese CL
428 Jon Lieber .20 .50
Sammy Sosa
Eric Young CL
429 Curtis Leskanic .10 .30
Geoff Jenkins
Jeff D'Amico
Jeromy Burnitz
Marquis Grissom CL
430 Scott Elarton .10 .30
Jeff Bagwell
Octavio Dotel
Moises Alou
Roger Cedeno CL
431 Mike Williams .20 .50
Jason Kendall
Kris Benson
Brian Giles CL
432 Livan Hernandez .10 .30
Jeff Kent
Robb Nen
Barry Bonds
Marvin Benard CL
433 Luis Gonzalez .10 .30
Steve Finley
Tony Womack
Randy Johnson CL
434 Jeff Shaw .10 .30
Gary Sheffield
Kevin Brown
Shawn Green
Chan Ho Park CL UER
B.Shaw should be J.Shaw
435 Jose Jimenez .10 .30
Todd Helton
Brian Bohanon
Tom Goodwin CL UER
C.Goodwin should be T.Goodwin
436 Trevor Hoffman .10 .30
Phil Nevin
Matt Clement
Eric Owens CL

437 Mariano Rivera .30 .75
Derek Jeter
Roger Clemens
Bernie Williams
Andy Pettitte CL
438 Pedro Martinez .20 .50
Nomar Garciaparra
Derek Lowe
Carl Everett CL
439 Ryan Kohlmeier .10 .30
Delino DeShields
Mike Mussina
Albert Belle CL
440 David Wells .10 .30
Carlos Delgado
Billy Koch
Raul Mondesi CL
441 Ramon Hernandez .10 .30
Fred McGriff
Miguel Cairo
Greg Vaughn CL
442 Mike Sirotka .20 .50
Frank Thomas
Keith Foulke
Ray Durham CL
443 Steve Karsay .10 .30
Manny Ramirez
Bartolo Colon
Roberto Alomar CL
444 Brian Moehler .10 .30
Deivi Cruz
Juan Encarnacion
Todd Jones
Bobby Higginson CL
445 Mac Suzuki .10 .30
Mike Sweeney
Johnny Damon
Jermaine Dye CL
446 Brad Radke .10 .30
Matt Lawton
Eric Milton
Jacque Jones
Cristian Guzman CL
447 Kazuhiro Sasaki .10 .30
Edgar Martinez
Aaron Sele
Rickey Henderson CL
448 Jason Isringhausen .10 .30
Jason Giambi
Tim Hudson
Randy Velarde CL
449 Shigetoshi Hasegawa .10 .30
Darin Erstad
Troy Percival
Troy Glaus CL
450 Rick Helling .10 .30
Rafael Palmeiro
John Wetteland
Luis Alicea CL
451 Albert Pujols RC 20.00 50.00
452 Ichiro Suzuki RC 6.00 15.00
453 Tsuyoshi Shinjo RC .30 .75
454 Johnny Estrada RC .30 .75
455 Elpidio Guzman RC .20 .50
456 Adrian Hernandez RC .20 .50
457 Rafael Soriano RC .20 .50
458 Drew Henson RC .30 .75
459 Juan Uribe RC .30 .75
460 Matt White RC .20 .50
461 Endy Chavez RC .20 .50
462 Bud Smith RC .20 .50
463 Morgan Ensberg RC 1.00 2.50
464 Jay Gibbons RC .30 .75
465 Jackson Melian RC .20 .50
466 Junior Spivey RC .30 .75
467 Juan Cruz RC .20 .50
468 Wilson Betemit RC 1.00 2.50
469 Alexis Gomez RC .20 .50
470 Mark Teixeira RC 4.00 10.00
471 Erick Almonte RC .20 .50
472 Travis Hafner RC 3.00 8.00
473 Carlos Valderrama RC .20 .50
474 Brandon Duckworth RC .20 .50
475 Ryan Freel RC .60 1.50
476 Wilkin Ruan RC .20 .50
477 Andres Torres RC .20 .50
478 Josh Towers RC .30 .75
479 Kyle Lohse RC .30 .75
480 Jason Michaels RC .20 .50
481 Alfonso Soriano .30 .75
482 C.C. Sabathia .20 .50
483 Roy Oswalt .50 1.25
484 Ben Sheets UER .30 .75
Wrong team logo on the front
485 Adam Dunn .30 .75
NNO Uncut Sheet EXCH/100

2001 Fleer Tradition Diamond Tributes

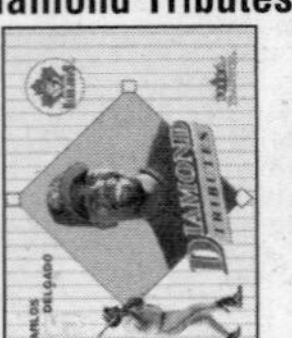

Randomly inserted into packs at one in seven, this 30-card insert is a tribute to some of the most classic players to ever step foot onto a playing field. Card backs carry a "DT" prefix.

COMPLETE SET (30) 30.00 60.00
DT1 Jackie Robinson .60 1.50
DT2 Mike Piazza 1.00 2.50
DT3 Alex Rodriguez 1.00 2.50
DT4 Barry Bonds 1.50 4.00
DT5 Nomar Garciaparra 1.00 2.50
DT6 Roger Clemens 1.25 3.00
DT7 Ivan Rodriguez .40 1.00
DT8 Cal Ripken 2.00 5.00
DT9 Manny Ramirez .40 1.00
DT10 Chipper Jones .60 1.50
DT11 Barry Larkin .40 1.00
DT12 Carlos Delgado .40 1.00
DT13 J.D. Drew .40 1.00
DT14 Carl Everett .40 1.00
DT15 Todd Helton .40 1.00
DT16 Greg Maddux 1.00 2.50
DT17 Scott Rolen .40 1.00
DT18 Troy Glaus .40 1.00
DT19 Brian Giles .40 1.00
DT20 Jeff Bagwell .40 1.00
DT21 Sammy Sosa .60 1.50
DT22 Randy Johnson .60 1.50
DT23 Andruw Jones .40 1.00
DT24 Ken Griffey Jr. 1.00 2.50
DT25 Mark McGwire 1.50 4.00
DT26 Derek Jeter 1.50 4.00
DT27 Vladimir Guerrero .60 1.50
DT28 Frank Thomas .60 1.50
DT29 Pedro Martinez .40 1.00
DT30 Bernie Williams .40 1.00

2001 Fleer Tradition Grass Roots

Inserted at a rate of one every 18 packs, this 15 card set describes some of the early moments of these star players careers.

COMPLETE SET (15) 30.00 60.00
GR1 Derek Jeter 2.50 6.00
GR2 Greg Maddux 1.50 4.00
GR3 Sammy Sosa 1.00 2.50
GR4 Alex Rodriguez 1.50 4.00
GR5 Vladimir Guerrero 1.00 2.50
GR6 Scott Rolen .60 1.50
GR7 Frank Thomas 1.00 2.50
GR8 Nomar Garciaparra 1.50 4.00
GR9 Cal Ripken 3.00 8.00
GR10 Mike Piazza 1.50 4.00
GR11 Ivan Rodriguez .60 1.50
GR12 Chipper Jones 1.00 2.50
GR13 Tony Gwynn 1.25 3.00
GR14 Ken Griffey Jr. 1.50 4.00
GR15 Mark McGwire 2.50 6.00

2001 Fleer Tradition Lumber Company

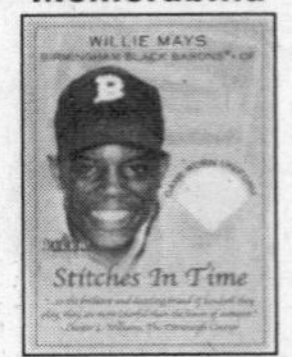

Randomly inserted into packs at one in 12, this 20-card insert set features players that are capable of breaking the game wide open with one swing of the bat. Card backs carry a "LC" prefix.

COMPLETE SET (20) 25.00 50.00
LC1 Vladimir Guerrero .75 2.00
LC2 Mo Vaughn .40 1.00
LC3 Ken Griffey Jr. 1.25 3.00
LC4 Juan Gonzalez .40 1.00
LC5 Tony Gwynn 1.00 2.50
LC6 Jim Edmonds .40 1.00
LC7 Jason Giambi .40 1.00
LC8 Alex Rodriguez 1.25 3.00
LC9 Derek Jeter 2.00 5.00
LC10 Darin Erstad .40 1.00
LC11 Andruw Jones .50 1.25
LC12 Cal Ripken 2.50 6.00
LC13 Magglio Ordonez .40 1.00
LC14 Nomar Garciaparra 1.25 3.00
LC15 Chipper Jones .75 2.00
LC16 Sean Casey .40 1.00
LC17 Shawn Green .40 1.00
LC18 Mike Piazza 1.25 3.00
LC19 Sammy Sosa .75 2.00
LC20 Barry Bonds 2.00 5.00

2001 Fleer Tradition Stitches in Time

Randomly inserted into packs at one in 18, this 24-card insert features Negro League greats like Josh Gibson and Satchel Paige. Card backs carry a "ST" prefix. It was originally believed that card ST3 did not exist. However, examples of the card have appeared on the secondary market. It is thought that the card possibly leaked to onto the secondary market after Fleer ceased operations. Please note that cards ST1 does not exist. The Henry Kimbro card is unnumbered.

COMPLETE SET (24) 50.00 100.00
ST1 Does Not Exist
ST2 Ernie Banks 2.00 5.00
ST3 Cool Papa Bell 2.00 5.00
ST4 Joe Black 1.25 3.00
ST5 Roy Campanella 2.50 6.00
ST6 Ray Dandridge 1.25 3.00
ST7 Leon Day 1.25 3.00
ST8 Larry Doby 1.25 3.00
ST9 Josh Gibson 2.00 5.00
ST10 Elston Howard 1.25 3.00
ST11 Monte Irvin 1.25 3.00
ST12 Buck Leonard 1.25 3.00
ST13 Max Manning 1.25 3.00
ST14 Willie Mays 4.00 10.00
ST15 Buck O'Neil 1.25 3.00
ST16 Satchel Paige 2.00 5.00
ST17 Ted Radcliffe 1.25 3.00
ST18 Jackie Robinson 2.00 5.00
ST19 Bill Perkins 1.25 3.00
ST20 Rube Foster 2.00 5.00
ST21 Judy Johnson 1.25 3.00
ST22 Oscar Charleston 1.25 3.00
ST23 Pop Lloyd 1.25 3.00
ST24 Artie Wilson 1.25 3.00
ST25 Sam Jethroe 1.25 3.00
NNO Henry Kimbro 1.25 3.00

2001 Fleer Tradition Stitches in Time Autographs

Randomly inserted at one in four boxes, this seven-card insert set features authentic autographs from players like Willie Mays and Ernie Banks. Please note that these cards are not numbered and are listed below in alphabetical order. Also note that Willie Mays and Artie Wilson packed out as exchange cards with a redemption deadline of 02/01/02.

1 Ernie Banks 40.00 80.00
2 Joe Black 15.00 40.00
3 Monte Irvin 20.00 50.00
4 Willie Mays 125.00 200.00
5 Buck O'Neil 30.00 60.00
6 Ted Radcliffe 30.00 60.00
7 Artie Wilson 10.00 25.00

2001 Fleer Tradition Stitches in Time Memorabilia

Randomly inserted at one in four boxes, this five-card insert set features actual swatches from game-used Bats or Pants from players like Willie Mays and Jackie Robinson. Please note that these cards are not numbered and are listed below in alphabetical order.

1 Roy Campanella Bat 40.00 80.00
2 Larry Doby Bat 15.00 40.00
3 Elston Howard Bat 20.00 50.00
4 Willie Mays Pants 75.00 150.00
5 Jackie Robinson Pants 75.00 150.00

2001 Fleer Tradition Turn Back the Clock Game Jersey

Randomly inserted at one in four boxes, this 21-card insert set features swatches from actual game-used jerseys from players like Cal Ripken and Chipper Jones. Card backs carry a "TBC" prefix.

TBC1 Tom Glavine 6.00 15.00
TBC2 Greg Maddux 15.00 40.00
TBC3 Sean Casey 4.00 10.00
TBC4 Pokey Reese 4.00 10.00
TBC5 Jason Giambi 4.00 10.00
TBC6 Tim Hudson 4.00 10.00
TBC7 Larry Walker 4.00 10.00
TBC8 Jeffrey Hammonds 4.00 10.00
TBC9 Scott Rolen 6.00 15.00
TBC10 Pat Burrell 4.00 10.00
TBC11 Chipper Jones 6.00 15.00
TBC12 Greg Maddux 15.00 40.00
TBC13 Troy Glaus 4.00 10.00
TBC14 Tony Gwynn 10.00 25.00
TBC15 Cal Ripken 25.00 60.00
TBC16 Tom Glavine 40.00 80.00
Greg Maddux
TBC17 Sean Casey 15.00 40.00
Pokey Reese
TBC18 Chipper Jones 50.00 100.00
Greg Maddux
TBC19 Larry Walker 15.00 40.00
Jeffrey Hammonds
TBC20 Scott Rolen 15.00 40.00
Pat Burrell
TBC21 Jason Giambi 15.00 40.00
Tim Hudson

2001 Fleer Tradition Warning Track

Randomly inserted into packs at one in 72, this 23-card insert takes a look at how today's power hitters stack up to yesterdays greats. Card backs carry a "WT" prefix. Please note, cards 2 and 5 (originally intended for Hank Aaron and Ernie Banks) were never produced, thus though numbered 1-25, the set is complete at 23 cards.

COMPLETE SET (23) 150.00 250.00
WT1 Josh Gibson 4.00 10.00
WT2 Does Not Exist
WT3 Willie Mays 6.00 15.00
WT4 Mark McGwire 8.00 20.00
WT5 Does Not Exist
WT6 Barry Bonds 8.00 20.00
WT7 Jose Canseco 2.00 5.00
WT8 Ken Griffey Jr. 5.00 12.00
WT9 Cal Ripken 10.00 25.00
WT10 Rafael Palmeiro 2.00 5.00
WT11 Sammy Sosa 3.00 8.00
WT12 Juan Gonzalez 2.00 5.00
WT13 Frank Thomas 3.00 8.00
WT14 Jeff Bagwell 2.00 5.00
WT15 Gary Sheffield 2.00 5.00
WT16 Larry Walker 2.00 5.00
WT17 Mike Piazza 5.00 12.00
WT18 Larry Doby 2.00 5.00
WT19 Roy Campanella 4.00 10.00
WT20 Manny Ramirez 2.00 5.00
WT21 Chipper Jones 3.00 8.00
WT22 Alex Rodriguez 5.00 12.00
WT23 Ivan Rodriguez 2.00 5.00
WT24 Vladimir Guerrero 3.00 8.00
WT25 Nomar Garciaparra 5.00 12.00

2002 Fleer Tradition

This 500 card set was issued early in 2002. This set was issued in 10 card packs and 36 packs to a box with a SRP of $1.49 per pack. The first 100 cards in this set were issued at an overall rate of one in two. In addition, cards numbered 436 through 470 featured leading prospects and cards numbered 471 through 500 featured players who had noteworthy seasons in 2001. These cards feature the 1934 Goudey-style design.

COMPLETE SET (500) 125.00 200.00
COMP.SET w/o SP's (400) 20.00 50.00
COMMON CARD (101-500) .10 .30
COMMON SP (1-100) 1.25 3.00
COMMON CARD (436-470) .20 .50
1 Barry Bonds SP 5.00 12.00
2 Cal Ripken SP 6.00 15.00
3 Tony Gwynn SP 2.50 6.00
4 Brad Radke SP 1.25 3.00
5 Jose Ortiz SP 1.25 3.00
6 Mark Mulder SP 1.25 3.00
7 Jon Lieber SP 1.25 3.00
8 John Olerud SP 1.25 3.00
9 Phil Nevin SP 1.25 3.00
10 Craig Biggio SP 1.25 3.00
11 Pedro Martinez SP 2.00 5.00
12 Fred McGriff SP 1.25 3.00
13 Vladimir Guerrero SP 2.00 5.00
14 Jason Giambi SP 1.25 3.00
15 Mark Kotsay SP 1.25 3.00
16 Bud Smith SP 1.25 3.00
17 Kevin Brown SP 1.25 3.00
18 Darin Erstad SP 1.25 3.00
19 Julio Franco SP 1.25 3.00
20 C.C. Sabathia SP 1.25 3.00
21 Larry Walker SP 1.25 3.00
22 Doug Mientkiewicz SP 1.25 3.00
23 Luis Gonzalez SP 1.25 3.00
24 Albert Pujols SP 4.00 10.00
25 Brian Lawrence SP 1.25 3.00
26 Al Leiter SP 1.25 3.00
27 Mike Sweeney SP 1.25 3.00
28 Jeff Weaver SP 1.25 3.00
29 Matt Morris SP 1.25 3.00
30 Hideo Nomo SP 2.00 5.00
31 Tom Glavine SP 1.25 3.00
32 Magglio Ordonez SP 1.25 3.00
33 Roberto Alomar SP 1.25 3.00
34 Roger Cedeno SP 1.25 3.00
35 Greg Vaughn SP 1.25 3.00
36 Chan Ho Park SP 1.25 3.00
37 Rich Aurilia SP 1.25 3.00
38 Tsuyoshi Shinjo SP 1.25 3.00
39 Eric Young SP 1.25 3.00
40 Bobby Higginson SP 1.25 3.00
41 Marlon Anderson SP 1.25 3.00
42 Mark Grace SP 1.25 3.00
43 Steve Cox SP 1.25 3.00
44 Cliff Floyd SP 1.25 3.00
45 Brian Roberts SP 1.25 3.00
46 Paul Konerko SP 1.25 3.00
47 Brandon Duckworth SP 1.25 3.00
48 Josh Beckett SP 1.25 3.00
49 David Ortiz SP 2.00 5.00
50 Geoff Jenkins SP 1.25 3.00
51 Ruben Sierra SP 1.25 3.00
52 John Franco SP 1.25 3.00
53 Einar Diaz SP 1.25 3.00
54 Luis Castillo SP 1.25 3.00
55 Mark Quinn SP 1.25 3.00
56 Shea Hillenbrand SP 1.25 3.00
57 Rafael Palmeiro SP 1.25 3.00
58 Paul O'Neill SP 1.25 3.00
59 Andruw Jones SP 1.25 3.00
60 Lance Berkman SP 1.25 3.00
61 Jimmy Rollins SP 1.25 3.00
62 Jose Hernandez SP 1.25 3.00
63 Rusty Greer SP 1.25 3.00
64 Wade Miller SP 1.25 3.00
65 David Eckstein SP 1.25 3.00
66 Jose Valentin SP 1.25 3.00
67 Javier Vazquez SP 1.25 3.00
68 Roger Clemens SP 4.00 10.00
69 Omar Vizquel SP 1.25 3.00
70 Roy Oswalt SP 1.25 3.00
71 Shannon Stewart SP 1.25 3.00
72 Byung-Hyun Kim SP 1.25 3.00
73 Jay Gibbons SP 1.25 3.00
74 Barry Larkin SP 1.25 3.00
75 Brian Giles SP 1.25 3.00
76 Andres Galarraga SP 1.25 3.00
77 Sammy Sosa SP 2.00 5.00
78 Manny Ramirez SP 1.25 3.00
79 Carlos Delgado SP 1.25 3.00
80 Jorge Posada SP 1.25 3.00
81 Todd Ritchie SP 1.25 3.00
82 Russ Ortiz SP 1.25 3.00
83 Brent Mayne SP 1.25 3.00
84 Mike Mussina SP 1.25 3.00
85 Raul Mondesi SP 1.25 3.00
86 Mark Loretta SP 1.25 3.00
87 Tim Raines SP 1.25 3.00
88 Ichiro Suzuki SP 4.00 10.00
89 Juan Pierre SP 1.25 3.00
90 Adam Dunn SP 1.25 3.00
91 Jason Tyner SP 1.25 3.00
92 Miguel Tejada SP 1.25 3.00
93 Elpidio Guzman SP 1.25 3.00
94 Freddy Garcia SP 1.25 3.00
95 Marcus Giles SP 1.25 3.00
96 Junior Spivey SP 1.25 3.00
97 Aramis Ramirez SP 1.25 3.00
98 Jose Rijo SP 1.25 3.00
99 Paul LoDuca SP 1.25 3.00
100 Mike Cameron SP 1.25 3.00
101 Alex Hernandez .10 .30
102 Benji Gil .10 .30
103 Benito Santiago .10 .30
104 Bobby Abreu .10 .30
105 Brad Penny .10 .30
106 Calvin Murray .10 .30
107 Chad Durbin .10 .30
108 Chris Singleton .10 .30
109 Chris Carpenter .10 .30
110 David Justice .10 .30
111 Eric Chavez .10 .30
112 Fernando Tatis .10 .30
113 Frank Castillo .10 .30
114 Jason LaRue .10 .30
115 Jim Edmonds .10 .30
116 Joe Kennedy .10 .30
117 Jose Jimenez .10 .30
118 Josh Towers .10 .30
119 Junior Herndon .10 .30
120 Luke Prokopec .10 .30
121 Mac Suzuki .10 .30
122 Mark DeRosa .10 .30
123 Marty Cordova .10 .30
124 Michael Tucker .10 .30
125 Michael Young .30 .75
126 Robin Ventura .10 .30
127 Shane Halter .10 .30
128 Shane Reynolds .10 .30
129 Tony Womack .10 .30
130 A.J. Pierzynski .10 .30
131 Aaron Rowand .10 .30
132 Antonio Alfonseca .10 .30
133 Arthur Rhodes .10 .30
134 Bob Wickman .10 .30
135 Brady Clark .10 .30
136 Chad Hermansen .10 .30
137 Marlon Byrd .10 .30
138 Dan Wilson .10 .30
139 David Cone .10 .30
140 Dean Palmer .10 .30
141 Denny Neagle .10 .30
142 Derek Jeter .75 2.00
143 Erubiel Durazo .10 .30
144 Felix Rodriguez .10 .30
145 Jason Hart .10 .30
146 Jay Bell .10 .30
147 Jeff Suppan .10 .30
148 Jeff Zimmerman .10 .30
149 Kerry Wood .10 .30
150 Kerry Robinson .10 .30
151 Kevin Appier .10 .30
152 Michael Barrett .10 .30
153 Mo Vaughn .10 .30
154 Rafael Furcal .10 .30
155 Sidney Ponson .10 .30
156 Terry Adams .10 .30
157 Tim Redding .10 .30
158 Toby Hall .10 .30
159 Aaron Sele .10 .30
160 Bartolo Colon .10 .30
161 Brad Ausmus .10 .30
162 Carlos Pena .10 .30
163 Jace Brewer .10 .30
164 David Wells .10 .30
165 David Segui .10 .30
166 Derek Lowe .10 .30
167 Derek Bell .10 .30
168 Jason Grabowski .10 .30
169 Johnny Damon .20 .50
170 Jose Mesa .10 .30
171 Juan Encarnacion .10 .30
172 Ken Caminiti .10 .30
173 Ken Griffey Jr. .50 1.25
174 Luis Rivas .10 .30
175 Mariano Rivera .30 .75
176 Mark Grudzielanek .10 .30
177 Mark McGwire .75 2.00
178 Mike Bordick .10 .30
179 Mike Hampton .10 .30
180 Nick Bierbrodt .10 .30
181 Paul Byrd .10 .30
182 Robb Nen .10 .30
183 Ryan Dempster .10 .30
184 Ryan Klesko .10 .30
185 Scott Spiezio .10 .30
186 Scott Strickland .10 .30
187 Todd Zeile .10 .30
188 Tom Gordon .10 .30
189 Troy Glaus .10 .30
190 Matt Williams .10 .30
191 Wes Helms .10 .30
192 Jerry Hairston Jr. .10 .30
193 Brook Fordyce .10 .30
194 Nomar Garciaparra .50 1.25
195 Kevin Tapani .10 .30
196 Mark Buehrle .10 .30
197 Dmitri Young .10 .30
198 John Rocker .10 .30
199 Juan Uribe .10 .30
200 Matt Anderson .10 .30
201 Alex Gonzalez .10 .30
202 Julio Lugo .10 .30
203 Roberto Hernandez .10 .30
204 Richie Sexson .10 .30
205 Corey Koskie .10 .30
206 Tony Armas Jr. .10 .30
207 Rey Ordonez .10 .30
208 Orlando Hernandez .10 .30
209 Pokey Reese .10 .30
210 Mike Lieberthal .10 .30
211 Kris Benson .10 .30
212 Jermaine Dye .10 .30
213 Livan Hernandez .10 .30
214 Bret Boone .10 .30
215 Dustin Hermanson .10 .30
216 Placido Polanco .10 .30
217 Jesus Colome .10 .30
218 Alex Gonzalez .10 .30
219 Adam Everett .10 .30
220 Adam Piatt .10 .30
221 Brad Fullmer .10 .30
222 Brian Buchanan .10 .30
223 Chipper Jones .30 .75
224 Chuck Finley .10 .30
225 David Bell .10 .30
226 Jack Wilson .10 .30
227 Jason Bere .10 .30
228 Jeff Conine .10 .30
229 Jeff Bagwell .20 .50
230 Joe McEwing .10 .30
231 Kip Wells .10 .30
232 Mike Lansing .10 .30
233 Neifi Perez .10 .30
234 Omar Daal .10 .30
235 Reggie Sanders .10 .30
236 Shawn Wooten .10 .30
237 Shawn Chacon .10 .30
238 Shawn Estes .10 .30
239 Steve Sparks .10 .30
240 Steve Kline .10 .30
241 Tino Martinez .20 .50
242 Tyler Houston .10 .30
243 Xavier Nady .10 .30
244 Bengie Molina .10 .30
245 Ben Davis .10 .30
246 Casey Fossum .10 .30
247 Chris Stynes .10 .30
248 Danny Graves .10 .30
249 Pedro Feliz .10 .30
250 Darren Oliver .10 .30
251 Dave Veres .10 .30
252 Deivi Cruz .10 .30
253 Desi Relaford .10 .30
254 Devon White .10 .30
255 Edgar Martinez .20 .50
256 Eric Munson .10 .30
257 Eric Karros .10 .30
258 Homer Bush .10 .30
259 Jason Kendall .10 .30
260 Javy Lopez .10 .30
261 Keith Foulke .10 .30
262 Keith Ginter .10 .30
263 Nick Johnson .10 .30
264 Pat Burrell .10 .30
265 Ricky Gutierrez .10 .30
266 Russ Johnson .10 .30
267 Steve Finley .10 .30
268 Terrence Long .10 .30
269 Tony Batista .10 .30
270 Torii Hunter .10 .30
271 Vinny Castilla .10 .30
272 A.J. Burnett .10 .30
273 Adrian Beltre .10 .30
274 Alex Rodriguez .50 1.25
275 Armando Benitez .10 .30
276 Billy Koch .10 .30
277 Brady Anderson .10 .30
278 Brian Jordan .10 .30
279 Carlos Febles .10 .30
280 Daryle Ward .10 .30
281 Eli Marrero .10 .30
282 Garret Anderson .10 .30
283 Jack Cust .10 .30
284 Jacque Jones .10 .30
285 Jamie Moyer .10 .30
286 Jeffrey Hammonds .10 .30
287 Jim Thome .20 .50
288 Jon Garland .10 .30
289 Jose Offerman .10 .30
290 Matt Stairs .10 .30
291 Orlando Cabrera .10 .30
292 Ramiro Mendoza .10 .30
293 Ray Durham .10 .30
294 Rickey Henderson .30 .75
295 Rob Mackowiak .10 .30
296 Scott Rolen .20 .50
297 Tim Hudson .10 .30
298 Todd Helton .20 .50
299 Tony Clark .10 .30
300 B.J. Surhoff .10 .30
301 Bernie Williams .20 .50
302 Bill Mueller .10 .30
303 Chris Richard .10 .30
304 Craig Paquette .10 .30
305 Curt Schilling .10 .30
306 Damian Jackson .10 .30
307 Derrek Lee .20 .50
308 Eric Milton .10 .30
309 Frank Catalanotto .10 .30
310 J.T. Snow .10 .30
311 Jared Sandberg .10 .30

312 Jason Varitek .30 .75
313 Jeff Cirillo .10 .30
314 Jeromy Burnitz .10 .30
315 Joe Crede .10 .30
316 Joel Pineiro .10 .30
317 Jose Cruz Jr. .10 .30
318 Kevin Young .10 .30
319 Marquis Grissom .10 .30
320 Moises Alou .10 .30
321 Randall Simon .10 .30
322 Royce Clayton .10 .30
323 Tim Salmon .20 .50
324 Travis Fryman .10 .30
325 Travis Lee .10 .30
326 Vance Wilson .10 .30
327 Jarrod Washburn .10 .30
328 Ben Petrick .10 .30
329 Ben Grieve .10 .30
330 Carl Everett .10 .30
331 Eric Byrnes .10 .30
332 Doug Glanville .10 .30
333 Edgardo Alfonzo .10 .30
334 Ellis Burks .10 .30
335 Gabe Kapler .10 .30
336 Gary Sheffield .10 .30
337 Greg Maddux .50 1.25
338 J.D. Drew .10 .30
339 Jamey Wright .10 .30
340 Jeff Kent .10 .30
341 Jeremy Giambi .10 .30
342 Joe Randa .10 .30
343 Joe Mays .10 .30
344 Jose Macias .10 .30
345 Kazuhiro Sasaki .10 .30
346 Mike Kinkade .10 .30
347 Mike Lowell .10 .30
348 Randy Johnson .30 .75
349 Randy Wolf .10 .30
350 Richard Hidalgo .10 .30
351 Ron Coomer .10 .30
352 Sandy Alomar Jr. .10 .30
353 Sean Casey .10 .30
354 Trevor Hoffman .10 .30
355 Adam Eaton .10 .30
356 Alfonso Soriano .10 .30
357 Barry Zito .10 .30
358 Billy Wagner .10 .30
359 Brent Abernathy .10 .30
360 Bret Prinz .10 .30
361 Carlos Beltran .10 .30
362 Carlos Guillen .10 .30
363 Charles Johnson .10 .30
364 Cristian Guzman .10 .30
365 Damion Easley .10 .30
366 Darryl Kile .10 .30
367 Delino DeShields .10 .30
368 Eric Davis .10 .30
369 Frank Thomas .30 .75
370 Ivan Rodriguez .20 .50
371 Jay Payton .10 .30
372 Jeff D'Amico .10 .30
373 John Burkett .10 .30
374 Melvin Mora .10 .30
375 Ramon Ortiz .10 .30
376 Robert Person .10 .30
377 Russell Branyan .10 .30
378 Shawn Green .10 .30
379 Todd Hollandsworth .10 .30
380 Tony McKnight .10 .30
381 Trot Nixon .10 .30
382 Vernon Wells .10 .30
383 Troy Percival .10 .30
384 Albie Lopez .10 .30
385 Alex Ochoa .10 .30
386 Andy Pettitte .20 .50
387 Brandon Inge .10 .30
388 Bubba Trammell .10 .30
389 Corey Patterson .10 .30
390 Damian Rolls .10 .30
391 Dee Brown .10 .30
392 Edgar Renteria .10 .30
393 Eric Gagne .10 .30
394 Jason Johnson .10 .30
395 Jeff Nelson .10 .30
396 John Vander Wal .10 .30
397 Johnny Estrada .10 .30
398 Jose Canseco .20 .50
399 Juan Gonzalez .10 .30
400 Kevin Millwood .10 .30
401 Lee Stevens .10 .30
402 Matt Lawton .10 .30
403 Mike Lamb .10 .30
404 Octavio Dotel .10 .30
405 Ramon Hernandez .10 .30
406 Ruben Quevedo .10 .30
407 Todd Walker .10 .30
408 Troy O'Leary .10 .30
409 Wascar Serrano .10 .30
410 Aaron Boone .10 .30
411 Aubrey Huff .10 .30
412 Ben Sheets .10 .30
413 Carlos Lee .10 .30
414 Chuck Knoblauch .10 .30
415 Steve Karsay .10 .30
416 Dante Bichette .10 .30
417 David Dellucci .10 .30
418 Esteban Loaiza .10 .30
419 Fernando Vina .10 .30
420 Ismael Valdes .10 .30
421 Jason Isringhausen .10 .30
422 Jeff Shaw .10 .30
423 John Smoltz .20 .50
424 Jose Vidro .10 .30
425 Kenny Lofton .10 .30
426 Mark Little .10 .30
427 Mark McLemore .10 .30
428 Marvin Benard .10 .30
429 Mike Piazza .50 1.25
430 Pat Hentgen .10 .30
431 Preston Wilson .10 .30
432 Rick Helling .10 .30
433 Robert Fick .10 .30
434 Rondell White .10 .30
435 Adam Kennedy .10 .30
436 David Espinosa PROS .20 .50
437 Dewon Brazelton PROS .20 .50
438 Drew Henson PROS .20 .50
439 Juan Cruz PROS .20 .50
440 Jason Jennings PROS .20 .50
441 Carlos Garcia PROS .20 .50
442 Carlos Hernandez PROS .20 .50
443 Wilkin Ruan PROS .20 .50
444 Wilson Betemit PROS .20 .50
445 Horacio Ramirez PROS .20 .50
446 Danys Baez PROS .20 .50
447 Abraham Nunez PROS .20 .50
448 Josh Hamilton PROS .40 1.00
449 Chris George PROS .20 .50
450 Rick Bauer PROS .20 .50
451 Donnie Bridges PROS .20 .50
452 Erick Almonte PROS .20 .50
453 Cory Aldridge PROS .20 .50
454 Ryan Drese PROS .20 .50
455 Jason Romano PROS .20 .50
456 Corky Miller PROS .20 .50
457 Rafael Soriano PROS .20 .50
458 Mark Prior PROS .50 1.25
459 Mark Teixeira PROS .50 1.25
460 Adrian Hernandez PROS .20 .50
461 Tim Spooneybarger PROS .20 .50
462 Bill Ortega PROS .20 .50
463 D'Angelo Jimenez PROS .20 .50
464 Andres Torres PROS .20 .50
465 Alexis Gomez PROS .20 .50
466 Angel Berroa PROS .20 .50
467 Henry Mateo PROS .20 .50
468 Endy Chavez PROS .20 .50
469 Billy Sylvester PROS .20 .50
470 Nate Frese PROS .20 .50
471 Luis Gonzalez BNR .10 .30
472 Barry Bonds BNR .75 2.00
473 Rich Aurilia BNR .10 .30
474 Albert Pujols BNR .60 1.50
475 Todd Helton BNR .20 .50
476 Moises Alou BNR .10 .30
477 Lance Berkman BNR .10 .30
478 Brian Giles BNR .10 .30
479 Cliff Floyd BNR .10 .30
480 Sammy Sosa BNR .30 .75
481 Shawn Green BNR .10 .30
482 Jon Lieber BNR .10 .30
483 Matt Morris BNR .10 .30
484 Curt Schilling BNR .10 .30
485 Randy Johnson BNR .20 .50
486 Manny Ramirez BNR .20 .50
487 Ichiro Suzuki BNR .60 1.50
488 Juan Gonzalez BNR .10 .30
489 Derek Jeter BNR .75 2.00
490 Alex Rodriguez BNR .50 1.25
491 Bret Boone BNR .10 .30
492 Roberto Alomar BNR .20 .50
493 Jason Giambi BNR .10 .30
494 Rafael Palmeiro BNR .20 .50
495 Doug Mientkiewicz BNR .10 .30
496 Jim Thome BNR .10 .30
497 Freddy Garcia BNR .10 .30
498 Mark Buehrle BNR .10 .30
499 Mark Mulder BNR .10 .30
500 Roger Clemens BNR .60 1.50

2002 Fleer Tradition Glossy

Randomly inserted into Fleer Tradition Update packs, this is a parallel of the basic Fleer Tradition set. These cards can be differentiated from the regular Fleer cards by their "glossy" sheen and have a stated print run of 200 serial numbered sets.

*GLOSSY 1-100: .5X TO 1.2X BASIC
*GLOSSY 101-435/471-500: 3X TO 8X BASIC
*GLOSSY 436-470: 2X TO 5X BASIC

2002 Fleer Tradition Diamond Tributes

Inserted into hobby packs at stated odds of one in six and retail packs at stated odds of one in 10, these 15 cards feature players who have performed on the field of play but have also had a positive impact on the community.

COMPLETE SET (15) 8.00 20.00
1 Cal Ripken 1.50 4.00
2 Tony Gwynn .60 1.50
3 Derek Jeter 1.25 3.00
4 Pedro Martinez .50 1.25
5 Mark McGwire 1.25 3.00
6 Sammy Sosa .50 1.25
7 Barry Bonds 1.25 3.00
8 Roger Clemens 1.00 2.50
9 Mike Piazza .75 2.00
10 Alex Rodriguez .75 2.00
11 Randy Johnson .50 1.25
12 Chipper Jones .50 1.25
13 Nomar Garciaparra .75 2.00
14 Ichiro Suzuki 1.00 2.50
15 Jason Giambi .50 1.25

2002 Fleer Tradition Grass Patch

This 10 card set is a parallel to the Grass Roots insert set. Each card in this set features not only the defensive whiz pictured but also a special game-worn jersey swatch. According to representatives at Fleer, each cards has a stated print run of 50 copies (though the cards lack any form of serial-numbering).

1 Jeff Bagwell 15.00 40.00
2 Barry Bonds 40.00 80.00
3 Derek Jeter
4 Greg Maddux 30.00 60.00
5 Cal Ripken 75.00 150.00
6 Alex Rodriguez 30.00 60.00
7 Ivan Rodriguez 15.00 40.00
8 Scott Rolen 15.00 40.00
9 Larry Walker 15.00 40.00
10 Bernie Williams 15.00 40.00

2002 Fleer Tradition Grass Roots

Inserted into hobby packs at stated odds of one in 18 and retail packs at stated odds of one in 20, these 10 cards feature leading defensive players.

COMPLETE SET (10) 12.50 30.00
1 Barry Bonds 2.50 6.00
2 Alex Rodriguez 1.50 4.00
3 Derek Jeter 2.50 6.00
4 Greg Maddux 1.50 4.00
5 Ivan Rodriguez .60 1.50
6 Cal Ripken 3.00 8.00
7 Bernie Williams .60 1.50
8 Jeff Bagwell .60 1.50
9 Scott Rolen .60 1.50
10 Larry Walker .60 1.50

2002 Fleer Tradition Heads Up

Inserted into hobby packs at stated odds of one in 36 and retail packs at stated odds of one in 40, these 10 cards feature leading players as they would look as bobbleheads.

COMPLETE SET (10) 30.00 80.00
1 Derek Jeter 4.00 10.00
2 Ichiro Suzuki 3.00 8.00
3 Sammy Sosa 2.50 6.00
4 Mike Piazza 2.50 6.00
5 Ken Griffey Jr. 2.50 6.00
6 Alex Rodriguez 2.50 6.00
7 Barry Bonds 4.00 10.00
8 Nomar Garciaparra 2.50 6.00
9 Mark McGwire 4.00 10.00
10 Cal Ripken 5.00 12.00

2002 Fleer Tradition Lumber Company

Inserted into packs at stated odds of one in 12 hobby and one in 20 retail, these 30 cards feature superstars who can hit the ball with above average skills.

COMPLETE SET (30) 25.00 60.00
1 Moises Alou .60 1.50
2 Luis Gonzalez .60 1.50
3 Todd Helton .60 1.50
4 Mike Piazza 1.50 4.00
5 J.D. Drew .60 1.50
6 Albert Pujols 2.00 5.00
7 Chipper Jones 1.00 2.50
8 Manny Ramirez .60 1.50
9 Miguel Tejada .60 1.50
10 Curt Schilling .60 1.50
11 Alex Rodriguez 1.50 4.00
12 Barry Larkin .60 1.50
13 Nomar Garciaparra 1.50 4.00
14 Cliff Floyd .60 1.50
15 Alfonso Soriano .60 1.50
16 Sean Casey .60 1.50
17 Scott Rolen .60 1.50
18 Jose Ortiz .60 1.50
19 Corey Patterson .60 1.50
20 Joe Crede .60 1.50
21 Jace Brewer .60 1.50
22 Derek Jeter 2.50 6.00
23 Jim Thome .60 1.50
24 Frank Thomas 1.00 2.50
25 Shawn Green .60 1.50
26 Drew Henson .60 1.50
27 Jimmy Rollins .60 1.50
28 David Justice .60 1.50
29 Roberto Alomar .60 1.50
30 Bernie Williams .60 1.50

2002 Fleer Tradition Lumber Company Game Bat

This parallel to the Lumber Company insert set was inserted in packs at a rate of one in 72 packs. These cards feature not only the player pictured but a bat piece swatch related to that player. Jace Brewer, Sean Casey, Joe Crede, Derek Jeter, Corey Patterson and Scott Rolen were all short-prints according to representatives at Fleer.

1 Roberto Alomar 6.00 15.00
2 Moises Alou 4.00 10.00
3 Jace Brewer SP/250 4.00 10.00
4 Sean Casey SP/250 4.00 10.00
5 Joe Crede SP/250 4.00 10.00
6 J.D. Drew 4.00 10.00
7 Cliff Floyd 4.00 10.00
8 Nomar Garciaparra 8.00 20.00
9 Luis Gonzalez 4.00 10.00
10 Shawn Green 4.00 10.00
11 Todd Helton 6.00 15.00
12 Drew Henson 4.00 10.00
13 Derek Jeter SP/250 15.00 40.00
14 Chipper Jones 6.00 15.00
15 David Justice 4.00 10.00
16 Barry Larkin 6.00 15.00
17 Jose Ortiz SP/250 4.00 10.00
18 Corey Patterson SP/250 4.00 10.00
19 Mike Piazza 6.00 15.00
20 Albert Pujols 10.00 25.00
21 Manny Ramirez 6.00 15.00
22 Alex Rodriguez 8.00 20.00
23 Scott Rolen SP/250 6.00 15.00
24 Jimmy Rollins 4.00 10.00
25 Curt Schilling 4.00 10.00
26 Alfonso Soriano 4.00 10.00
27 Miguel Tejada 4.00 10.00
28 Frank Thomas 6.00 15.00
29 Jim Thome 6.00 15.00
30 Bernie Williams 6.00 15.00

2002 Fleer Tradition This Day in History

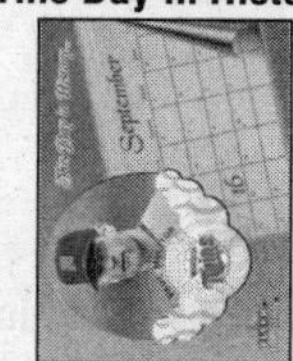

Inserted into hobby packs at stated odds of one in 18 and retail packs at stated odds of one in 24, these 29 cards feature highlights of some of the greatest days in baseball history. Please note that card number 24 (originally intended to feature Orel Hershiser) was pulled from production, thus the set is complete at 29 cards.

COMPLETE SET (29) 60.00 150.00
1 Cal Ripken 6.00 15.00
2 Barry Bonds 5.00 12.00
3 George Brett 4.00 10.00
4 Tony Gwynn 2.50 6.00
5 Nolan Ryan 5.00 12.00
6 Reggie Jackson 1.25 3.00
7 Paul Molitor 1.25 3.00
8 Ichiro Suzuki 4.00 10.00
9 Alex Rodriguez 3.00 8.00
10 Don Mattingly 4.00 10.00
11 Sammy Sosa 2.00 5.00
12 Mark McGwire 5.00 12.00
13 Derek Jeter 5.00 12.00
14 Roger Clemens 4.00 10.00
15 Jim Hunter 1.25 3.00
16 Greg Maddux 3.00 8.00
17 Ken Griffey Jr. 3.00 8.00
18 Gil Hodges 2.00 5.00
19 Edgar Martinez 1.25 3.00
20 Mike Piazza 3.00 8.00
21 Jimmie Foxx 2.00 5.00
22 Albert Pujols 4.00 10.00
23 Chipper Jones 2.00 5.00
24 Does Not Exist
25 Jeff Bagwell 1.25 3.00
26 Nomar Garciaparra 3.00 8.00
27 Randy Johnson 2.00 5.00
28 Todd Helton 1.25 3.00
29 Ted Kluszewski 1.25 3.00
30 Ivan Rodriguez 1.25 3.00

2002 Fleer Tradition This Day in History Autographs

Randomly inserted into packs, these eight cards feature autographs of the player notated. Most of the players did not sign their cards in time for inclusion in this product so they were available as exchange cards. Please note that Fleer provided print run information for these cards but they are not serial numbered. Exchange cards with a redemption deadline of 01/31/03 were seeded into packs for the following players: Gwynn, R.Jackson, R.Johnson, Mattingly, Molitor and Ripken.

1 Tony Gwynn/50
2 Reggie Jackson/50
3 Derek Jeter/100 60.00 120.00
4 Randy Johnson/75 40.00 80.00
5 Don Mattingly/50 50.00 100.00
6 Paul Molitor/50
7 Albert Pujols/50 150.00 250.00
8 Cal Ripken/50 75.00 150.00

2002 Fleer Tradition This Day in History Game Used

Randomly inserted into packs, these 22 cards feature memorabilia pieces from the noted player. As these cards are printed to different amounts, we have notated that information in our checklist.

1 Jeff Bagwell Bat/100 10.00 25.00
2 Barry Bonds Jsy/250 20.00 50.00
3 George Brett Jsy/50
4 Roger Clemens Jsy/150 15.00 40.00
5 Jimmie Foxx Bat/250 20.00 50.00
6 Todd Helton Bat/150 10.00 25.00
7 Gil Hodges Bat/50
8 Jim Hunter Jsy/250 10.00 25.00
10 Reggie Jackson Bat/50
11 Derek Jeter Jsy/250 25.00 60.00
12 Randy Johnson Jsy/50
13 Chipper Jones Bat/50
14 Ted Kluszewski Jsy/50
15 Greg Maddux Jsy/100 12.50 30.00
16 Don Mattingly Jsy/50
17 Paul Molitor Bat/50
18 Mike Piazza Bat/150 10.00 25.00
19 Albert Pujols Jsy/50
20 Cal Ripken Jsy/50
21 Alex Rodriguez Hat/250 15.00 40.00
22 Ivan Rodriguez Jsy/50
23 Nolan Ryan Pants/50

2002 Fleer Tradition Update

This 400 card set was released in October, 2003. This set was issued in 10 card packs which came 28 packs to a box and six boxes to a case with the packs having an SRP of $2. Cards numbered U1 through U100, which feature a mix of rookies and prospects, were issued at a stated rate of one per pack and are in shorter supply than the rest of the set. Other subsets include Diamond Standouts (U276-U297), All-Stars (U298-U360), Curtain Call (U361-U385) and Tale of the Tape (U386-U400).

COMPLETE SET (400) 60.00 120.00
COMP.SET w/o SP's (300) 15.00 40.00
COMMON CARD (U101-U400) .10 .30
COMMON CARD (U1-U100) .40 1.00
U1 P.J. Bevis SP RC .40 1.00
U2 Mike Crudale SP RC .40 1.00
U3 Ben Howard SP RC .40 1.00
U4 Travis Driskill SP RC .40 1.00
U5 Reed Johnson SP RC .60 1.50
U6 Kyle Kane SP RC .40 1.00
U7 Deivis Santos SP .40 1.00
U8 Tim Kalita SP RC .40 1.00
U9 Brandon Puffer SP RC .40 1.00
U10 Chris Snelling SP RC .60 1.50
U11 Juan Brito SP RC .40 1.00
U12 Tyler Yates SP RC .40 1.00
U13 Victor Alvarez SP RC .40 1.00
U14 Takahito Nomura SP RC .40 1.00
U15 Ron Calloway SP RC .40 1.00
U16 Satoru Komiyama SP RC .40 1.00
U17 Julius Matos SP RC .40 1.00
U18 Jorge Nunez SP RC .40 1.00
U19 Anderson Machado SP RC .40 1.00
U20 Scott Layfield SP RC .40 1.00
U21 Aaron Cook SP RC .40 1.00
U22 Alex Pelaez SP RC .40 1.00
U23 Corey Thurman SP RC .40 1.00
U24 Nelson Castro SP RC .40 1.00
U25 Jeff Austin SP RC .40 1.00
U26 Felix Escalona SP RC .40 1.00
U27 Luis Ugueto SP RC .40 1.00
U28 Jaime Cerda SP RC .40 1.00
U29 J.J. Trujillo SP RC .40 1.00
U30 Rodrigo Rosario SP RC .40 1.00
U31 Jorge Padilla SP RC .40 1.00
U32 Shawn Sedlacek SP RC .40 1.00
U33 Nate Field SP RC .40 1.00
U34 Earl Snyder SP RC .40 1.00
U35 Miguel Asencio SP RC .40 1.00
U36 Ken Huckaby SP RC .40 1.00
U37 Valentino Pascucci SP .40 1.00
U38 So Taguchi SP RC .50 1.25
U39 Brian Mallette SP RC .40 1.00
U40 Kazuhisa Ishii SP RC .50 1.25
U41 Matt Thornton SP RC .40 1.00
U42 Mark Corey SP RC .40 1.00
U43 Kirk Saarloos SP RC .40 1.00
U44 Josh Bard SP RC .40 1.00
U45 Hansel Izquierdo SP RC .40 1.00
U46 Rene Reyes SP RC .40 1.00
U47 Luis Garcia SP .40 1.00
U48 Jason Simontacchi SP RC .40 1.00
U49 John Ennis SP RC .40 1.00
U50 Franklyn German SP RC .40 1.00
U51 Aaron Guiel SP RC .40 1.00
U52 Howie Clark SP RC .40 1.00
U53 David Ross SP RC .50 1.25
U54 Jason Davis SP RC .40 1.00
U55 Francis Beltran SP RC .40 1.00
U56 Barry Wesson SP RC .40 1.00
U57 Run. Hernandez SP RC .40 1.00
U58 Oliver Perez SP RC .60 1.50
U59 Ryan Bukvich SP RC .40 1.00
U60 Steve Kent SP RC .40 1.00
U61 Julio Mateo SP RC .40 1.00
U62 Jason Jimenez SP RC .40 1.00
U63 Jayson Durocher SP RC .40 1.00
U64 Kevin Frederick SP RC .40 1.00
U65 Kevin Gryboski SP RC .40 1.00
U66 Edwin Almonte SP RC .40 1.00
U67 John Foster SP RC .40 1.00
U68 Doug Devore SP RC .40 1.00
U69 Tom Shearn SP RC .40 1.00
U70 Colin Young SP RC .40 1.00
U71 Jon Adkins SP RC .40 1.00
U72 Wilbert Nieves SP RC .40 1.00
U73 Matt Duff SP RC .40 1.00
U74 Carl Sadler SP RC .40 1.00
U75 Jason Kershner SP RC .40 1.00
U76 Brandon Backe SP RC .50 1.25
U77 Josh Hancock SP RC .50 1.25
U78 Chris Baker SP RC .40 1.00
U79 Travis Hughes SP RC .40 1.00
U80 Steve Bechler SP RC .40 1.00
U81 Allan Simpson SP RC .40 1.00
U82 Aaron Taylor SP RC .40 1.00
U83 Kevin Cash SP RC .40 1.00
U84 Chone Figgins SP RC .75 2.00
U85 Clay Condrey SP RC .40 1.00
U86 Shane Nance SP RC .40 1.00
U87 Freddy Sanchez SP RC 1.25 3.00
U88 Jim Rushford SP RC .40 1.00
U89 Jeriome Robertson SP RC .40 1.00
U90 Trey Lunsford SP RC .40 1.00
U91 Cody McKay SP RC .40 1.00
U92 Trey Hodges SP RC .40 1.00
U93 Hee Seop Choi SP .40 1.00
U94 Joe Borchard SP .40 1.00
U95 Orlando Hudson SP .40 1.00
U96 Carl Crawford SP .40 1.00
U97 Mark Prior SP .75 2.00
U98 Brett Myers SP .40 1.00
U99 Kenny Lofton SP .40 1.00
U100 Cliff Floyd SP .40 1.00
U101 Randy Winn .10 .30
U102 Ryan Dempster .10 .30
U103 Josh Phelps .10 .30
U104 Marcus Giles .10 .30
U105 Rickey Henderson .30 .75
U106 Jose Leon .10 .30
U107 Tino Martinez .20 .50
U108 Greg Norton .10 .30
U109 Odalis Perez .10 .30
U110 J.C. Romero .10 .30
U111 Gary Sheffield .10 .30
U112 Ismael Valdes .10 .30
U113 Juan Acevedo .10 .30
U114 Ben Broussard .10 .30
U115 Deivi Cruz .10 .30
U116 Geronimo Gil .10 .30
U117 Eric Hinske .10 .30
U118 Ted Lilly .10 .30
U119 Quinton McCracken .10 .30
U120 Antonio Alfonseca .10 .30
U121 Brent Abernathy .10 .30
U122 Johnny Damon Sox .20 .50
U123 Francisco Cordero .10 .30
U124 Sterling Hitchcock .10 .30
U125 Vladimir Nunez .10 .30
U126 Andres Galarraga .10 .30
U127 Timo Perez .10 .30
U128 Tsuyoshi Shinjo .10 .30
U129 Joe Girardi .10 .30
U130 Roberto Alomar .20 .50
U131 Ellis Burks .10 .30
U132 Mike DeJean .10 .30
U133 Alex Gonzalez .10 .30
U134 Johan Santana .50 1.25
U135 Kenny Lofton .10 .30
U136 Juan Encarnacion .10 .30
U137 Dewon Brazelton .10 .30
U138 Jeromy Burnitz .10 .30
U139 Elmer Dessens .10 .30
U140 Juan Gonzalez .10 .30
U141 Todd Hundley .10 .30
U142 Tomo Ohka .10 .30
U143 Robin Ventura .10 .30
U144 Rodrigo Lopez .10 .30
U145 Ruben Sierra .10 .30
U146 Jason Phillips .10 .30
U147 Ryan Rupe .10 .30

Card	Low	High
U148 Kevin Appier	.10	.30
U149 Sean Burroughs	.10	.30
U150 Masato Yoshii	.10	.30
U151 Juan Diaz	.10	.30
U152 Tony Graffanino	.10	.30
U153 Raul Ibanez	.10	.30
U154 Kevin Mench	.10	.30
U155 Pedro Astacio	.10	.30
U156 Brent Butler	.10	.30
U157 Kirk Rueter	.10	.30
U158 Eddie Guardado	.10	.30
U159 Hideki Irabu	.10	.30
U160 Wendell Magee	.10	.30
U161 Antonio Osuna	.10	.30
U162 Jose Vizcaino	.10	.30
U163 Danny Bautista	.10	.30
U164 Vinny Castilla	.10	.30
U165 Chris Singleton	.10	.30
U166 Mark Redman	.10	.30
U167 Olmedo Saenz	.10	.30
U168 Scott Erickson	.10	.30
U169 Ty Wigginton	.10	.30
U170 Jason Isringhausen	.10	.30
U171 Andy Van Hekken	.10	.30
U172 Chris Magruder	.10	.30
U173 Brandon Berger	.10	.30
U174 Roger Cedeno	.10	.30
U175 Kelvim Escobar	.10	.30
U176 Jose Guillen	.10	.30
U177 Damian Jackson	.10	.30
U178 Eric Owens	.10	.30
U179 Angel Berroa	.10	.30
U180 Alex Cintron	.10	.30
U181 Jeff Weaver	.10	.30
U182 Damon Minor	.10	.30
U183 Bobby Estalella	.10	.30
U184 David Justice	.10	.30
U185 Roy Halladay	.10	.30
U186 Brian Jordan	.10	.30
U187 Mike Maroth	.10	.30
U188 Pokey Reese	.10	.30
U189 Rey Sanchez	.10	.30
U190 Hank Blalock	.20	.50
U191 Jeff Cirillo	.10	.30
U192 Dmitri Young	.10	.30
U193 Carl Everett	.10	.30
U194 Joey Hamilton	.10	.30
U195 Jorge Julio	.10	.30
U196 Pablo Ozuna	.10	.30
U197 Jason Marquis	.10	.30
U198 Dustan Mohr	.10	.30
U199 Joe Borowski	.10	.30
U200 Tony Clark	.10	.30
U201 David Wells	.10	.30
U202 Josh Fogg	.10	.30
U203 Aaron Harang	.10	.30
U204 John McDonald	.10	.30
U205 John Stephens	.10	.30
U206 Chris Reitsma	.10	.30
U207 Alex Sanchez	.10	.30
U208 Milton Bradley	.10	.30
U209 Matt Clement	.10	.30
U210 Brad Fullmer	.10	.30
U211 Shigetoshi Hasegawa	.10	.30
U212 Austin Kearns	.10	.30
U213 Damaso Marte	.10	.30
U214 Vicente Padilla	.10	.30
U215 Raul Mondesi	.10	.30
U216 Russell Branyan	.10	.30
U217 Bartolo Colon	.10	.30
U218 Moises Alou	.10	.30
U219 Scott Hatteberg	.10	.30
U220 Bobby Kielty	.10	.30
U221 Kip Wells	.10	.30
U222 Scott Stewart	.10	.30
U223 Victor Martinez	.30	.75
U224 Marty Cordova	.10	.30
U225 Desi Relaford	.10	.30
U226 Reggie Sanders	.10	.30
U227 Jason Giambi	.10	.30
U228 Jimmy Haynes	.10	.30
U229 Billy Koch	.10	.30
U230 Damian Moss	.10	.30
U231 Chan Ho Park	.10	.30
U232 Cliff Floyd	.10	.30
U233 Todd Zeile	.10	.30
U234 Jeremy Giambi	.10	.30
U235 Rick Helling	.10	.30
U236 Matt Lawton	.10	.30
U237 Ramon Martinez	.10	.30
U238 Rondell White	.10	.30
U239 Scott Sullivan	.10	.30
U240 Hideo Nomo	.30	.75
U241 Todd Ritchie	.10	.30
U242 Ramon Santiago	.10	.30
U243 Jake Peavy	.20	.50
U244 Brad Wilkerson	.10	.30
U245 Reggie Taylor	.10	.30
U246 Carlos Pena	.10	.30
U247 Willis Roberts UER	.10	.30
No U in front of card number		
U248 Jason Schmidt	.10	.30
U249 Mike Williams	.10	.30
U250 Alan Zinter	.10	.30
U251 Michael Tejera	.10	.30
U252 Dave Roberts	.10	.30
U253 Scott Schoeneweis	.10	.30
U254 Woody Williams	.10	.30
U255 John Thomson	.10	.30
U256 Ricardo Rodriguez	.10	.30
U257 Aaron Sele	.10	.30
U258 Paul Wilson	.10	.30
U259 Brett Tomko	.10	.30
U260 Kenny Rogers	.10	.30
U261 Mo Vaughn	.10	.30
U262 John Burkett	.10	.30
U263 Dennis Stark	.10	.30
U264 Ray Durham	.10	.30
U265 Scott Rolen	.20	.50
U266 Gabe Kapler	.10	.30
U267 Todd Hollandsworth	.10	.30
U268 Bud Smith	.10	.30
U269 Jay Payton	.10	.30
U270 Tyler Houston	.10	.30
U271 Brian Moehler	.10	.30
U272 David Espinosa	.10	.30
U273 Placido Polanco	.10	.30
U274 John Patterson	.10	.30
U275 Adam Hyzdu	.10	.30
U276 Albert Pujols DS	.30	.75
U277 Larry Walker DS	.10	.30
U278 Magglio Ordonez DS	.10	.30
U279 Ryan Klesko DS	.10	.30
U280 Darin Erstad DS	.10	.30
U281 Jeff Kent DS	.10	.30
U282 Paul Lo Duca DS	.10	.30
U283 Jim Edmonds DS	.10	.30
U284 Chipper Jones DS	.20	.50
U285 Bernie Williams DS	.10	.30
U286 Pat Burrell DS	.10	.30
U287 Cliff Floyd DS	.10	.30
U288 Troy Glaus DS	.10	.30
U289 Brian Giles DS	.10	.30
U290 Jim Thome DS	.10	.30
U291 Greg Maddux DS	.30	.75
U292 Roberto Alomar DS	.10	.30
U293 Jeff Bagwell DS	.10	.30
U294 Rafael Furcal DS	.10	.30
U295 Josh Beckett DS	.10	.30
U296 Carlos Delgado DS	.10	.30
U297 Ken Griffey Jr. DS	.30	.75
U298 Jason Giambi AS	.10	.30
U299 Paul Konerko AS	.10	.30
U300 Mike Sweeney AS	.10	.30
U301 Alfonso Soriano AS	.10	.30
U302 Shea Hillenbrand AS	.10	.30
U303 Tony Batista AS	.10	.30
U304 Robin Ventura AS	.10	.30
U305 Alex Rodriguez AS	.30	.75
U306 Nomar Garciaparra AS	.30	.75
U307 Derek Jeter AS	.40	1.00
U308 Miguel Tejada AS	.10	.30
U309 Omar Vizquel AS	.10	.30
U310 Jorge Posada AS	.10	.30
U311 A.J. Pierzynski AS	.10	.30
U312 Ichiro Suzuki AS	.30	.75
U313 Manny Ramirez AS	.20	.50
U314 Torii Hunter AS	.10	.30
U315 Garret Anderson AS	.10	.30
U316 Robert Fick AS	.10	.30
U317 Randy Winn AS	.10	.30
U318 Mark Buehrle AS	.10	.30
U319 Freddy Garcia AS	.10	.30
U320 Eddie Guardado AS	.10	.30
U321 Roy Halladay AS	.10	.30
U322 Derek Lowe AS	.10	.30
U323 Pedro Martinez AS	.20	.50
U324 Mariano Rivera AS	.20	.50
U325 Kazuhiro Sasaki AS	.10	.30
U326 Barry Zito AS	.10	.30
U327 Johnny Damon Sox AS	.20	.50
U328 Ugueth Urbina AS	.10	.30
U329 Todd Helton AS	.10	.30
U330 Richie Sexson AS	.10	.30
U331 Jose Vidro AS	.10	.30
U332 Luis Castillo AS	.10	.30
U333 Junior Spivey AS	.10	.30
U334 Scott Rolen AS	.10	.30
U335 Mike Lowell AS	.10	.30
U336 Jimmy Rollins AS	.10	.30
U337 Jose Hernandez AS	.10	.30
U338 Mike Piazza AS	.30	.75
U339 Benito Santiago AS	.10	.30
U340 Sammy Sosa AS	.20	.50
U341 Barry Bonds AS	.40	1.00
U342 Vladimir Guerrero AS	.20	.50
U343 Lance Berkman AS	.10	.30
U344 Adam Dunn AS	.10	.30
U345 Shawn Green AS	.10	.30
U346 Luis Gonzalez AS	.10	.30
U347 Eric Gagne AS	.10	.30
U348 Tom Glavine AS	.10	.30
U349 Trevor Hoffman AS	.10	.30
U350 Randy Johnson AS	.20	.50
U351 Byung-Hyun Kim AS	.10	.30
U352 Matt Morris AS	.10	.30
U353 Odalis Perez AS	.10	.30
U354 Curt Schilling AS	.10	.30
U355 John Smoltz AS	.10	.30
U356 Mike Williams AS	.10	.30
U357 Andruw Jones AS	.10	.30
U358 Vicente Padilla AS	.10	.30
U359 Mike Remlinger AS	.10	.30
U360 Robb Nen AS	.10	.30
U361 Shawn Green CC	.10	.30
U362 Derek Jeter CC	.40	1.00
U363 Troy Glaus CC	.10	.30
U364 Ken Griffey Jr. CC	.30	.75
U365 Mike Piazza CC	.30	.75
U366 Jason Giambi CC	.10	.30
U367 Greg Maddux CC	.30	.75
U368 Albert Pujols CC	.30	.75
U369 Pedro Martinez CC	.20	.50
U370 Barry Zito CC	.10	.30
U371 Ichiro Suzuki CC	.30	.75
U372 Nomar Garciaparra CC	.30	.75
U373 Vladimir Guerrero CC	.20	.50
U374 Randy Johnson CC	.20	.50
U375 Barry Bonds CC	.40	1.00
U376 Sammy Sosa CC	.20	.50
U377 Hideo Nomo CC	.20	.50
U378 Jeff Bagwell CC	.10	.30
U379 Curt Schilling CC	.10	.30
U380 Jim Thome CC	.10	.30
U381 Todd Helton CC	.10	.30
U382 Roger Clemens CC	.30	.75
U383 Chipper Jones CC	.20	.50
U384 Alex Rodriguez CC	.30	.75
U385 Manny Ramirez CC	.20	.50
U386 Barry Bonds TT	.40	1.00
U387 Jim Thome TT	.10	.30
U388 Adam Dunn TT	.10	.30
U389 Alex Rodriguez TT	.30	.75
U390 Shawn Green TT	.10	.30
U391 Jason Giambi TT	.10	.30
U392 Lance Berkman TT	.10	.30
U393 Pat Burrell TT	.10	.30
U394 Eric Chavez TT	.10	.30
U395 Mike Piazza TT	.30	.75
U396 Vladimir Guerrero TT	.20	.50
U397 Paul Konerko TT	.10	.30
U398 Sammy Sosa TT	.20	.50
U399 Richie Sexson TT	.10	.30
U400 Torii Hunter TT	.10	.30

2002 Fleer Tradition Update Glossy

Randomly inserted into packs, this is a parallel to the basic Fleer Tradition Update set. These cards can be differentiated from the regular cards by their

"glossy" sheen on the front and each card has a stated print run of 200 serial numbered sets.

*GLOSSY 1-100: 1X TO 2.5X BASIC
*GLOSSY 101-275: 3X TO 8X BASIC
*GLOSSY 276-400: 6X TO 15X BASIC

2002 Fleer Tradition Update Diamond Debuts

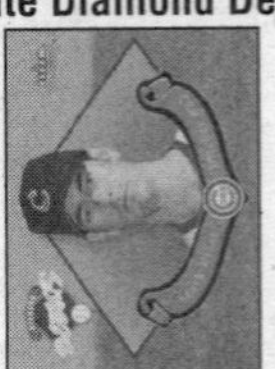

Inserted into packs at a stated rate of one in six, these 15 cards feature players who made their major league debut during the 2002 season.

Card	Low	High
COMPLETE SET (15)	6.00	15.00
U1 Mark Prior	.50	1.25
U2 Eric Hinske	.40	1.00
U3 Kazuhisa Ishii	.50	1.25
U4 Ben Broussard	.40	1.00
U5 Sean Burroughs	.40	1.00
U6 Austin Kearns	.40	1.00
U7 Hee Seop Choi	.40	1.00
U8 Kirk Saarloos	.40	1.00
U9 Orlando Hudson	.40	1.00
U10 So Taguchi	.50	1.25
U11 Kevin Mench	.40	1.00
U12 Carl Crawford	.40	1.00
U13 Marlon Byrd	.40	1.00
U14 Hank Blalock	.50	1.25
U15 Brett Myers	.40	1.00

2002 Fleer Tradition Update Grass Patch

Randomly inserted into packs, these seven cards feature some of the leading fielders in the game. Each card not only has a game-used memorabilia swatch on it but also has a stated print run of 50 serial numbered sets.

Card	Low	High
1 Roberto Alomar	15.00	40.00
2 Jim Edmonds	10.00	25.00
3 Nomar Garciaparra	40.00	80.00
4 Shawn Green	10.00	25.00
5 Torii Hunter	10.00	25.00
6 Andruw Jones	15.00	40.00
7 Alfonso Soriano	10.00	25.00

2002 Fleer Tradition Update Grass Roots

Inserted into packs at a stated rate of one in 18, this 10 card set honors some of the most exciting fielders in baseball.

Card	Low	High
COMPLETE SET (10)	6.00	15.00
U1 Alfonso Soriano	.75	2.00
U2 Torii Hunter	.75	2.00
U3 Andruw Jones	.75	2.00
U4 Jim Edmonds	.75	2.00
U5 Shawn Green	.75	2.00
U6 Todd Helton	.75	2.00
U7 Nomar Garciaparra	1.50	4.00
U8 Roberto Alomar	.75	2.00
U9 Vladimir Guerrero	1.00	2.50
U10 Ichiro Suzuki	2.00	5.00

2002 Fleer Tradition Update Heads Up

Inserted at a stated rate of one in 36, this 10 card set is designed in the style of the old Heads Up set of the 1930's.

Card	Low	High
U1 Roger Clemens	3.00	8.00
U2 Adam Dunn	1.25	3.00
U3 Kazuhisa Ishii	1.25	3.00
U4 Barry Zito	1.25	3.00
U5 Pedro Martinez	1.25	3.00
U6 Alfonso Soriano	1.25	3.00
U7 Mark Prior	1.50	4.00
U8 Chipper Jones	1.50	4.00
U9 Randy Johnson	1.50	4.00
U10 Lance Berkman	1.25	3.00

2002 Fleer Tradition Update Heads Up Game Used Caps

Randomly inserted in packs, these cards are designed in the style of the old Heads Up cards from the 1930's. However, they are different from the regular insert set as a piece of a game-used cap is also part of the card. Each card is also printed to a stated print run of 150.

Card	Low	High
1 Lance Berkman	8.00	20.00
2 Barry Bonds	25.00	60.00
3 Roger Clemens	20.00	50.00
4 Adam Dunn	8.00	20.00
5 Kazuhisa Ishii	6.00	15.00
6 Randy Johnson	10.00	25.00
7 Chipper Jones	10.00	25.00
8 Mike Piazza	12.50	30.00
9 Mark Prior	10.00	25.00
10 Alfonso Soriano	8.00	20.00
11 Barry Zito	8.00	20.00

2002 Fleer Tradition Update New York's Finest

Inserted into packs at stated odds of one in 83, these 15 cards honor some of the best players for either the New York Yankees or the New York Mets.

Card	Low	High
1 Edgardo Alfonzo	3.00	8.00
2 Roberto Alomar	3.00	8.00
3 Jeromy Burnitz	3.00	8.00
4 Satoru Komiyama	3.00	8.00
5 Rey Ordonez	3.00	8.00
6 Mike Piazza	5.00	12.00
7 Mo Vaughn	3.00	8.00
8 Roger Clemens	6.00	15.00
9 Jason Giambi	3.00	8.00
10 Derek Jeter	8.00	20.00
11 Mike Mussina	3.00	8.00
12 Jorge Posada	3.00	8.00
13 Alfonso Soriano	3.00	8.00
14 Robin Ventura	3.00	8.00
15 Bernie Williams	3.00	8.00

2002 Fleer Tradition Update New York's Finest Dual Swatch

Randomly inserted into packs, these six cards feature two leading players from New York along with a game-used memorabilia piece for both players.

Card	Low	High
1 Derek Jeter Jsy / Rey Ordonez Jsy	40.00	80.00
2 Alfonso Soriano Jsy / Roberto Alomar Jsy	15.00	40.00
3 Roger Clemens Jsy / Mike Piazza Jsy	60.00	120.00
4 Mike Mussina Jsy / Mo Vaughn Jsy	15.00	40.00
5 Bernie Williams Jsy / Jeromy Burnitz Jsy	15.00	40.00
6 Robin Ventura Jsy / Edgardo Alfonzo Jsy	10.00	25.00

2002 Fleer Tradition Update New York's Finest Single Swatch

Inserted into packs at stated odds of one in 112, these cards feature two star players from New York but only one memorabilia piece on each card. The player who has a memorabilia piece is listed first in

our checklist along with what type of memorabilia piece is used.

Card	Low	High
1 Derek Jeter Jsy / Rey Ordonez	12.50	30.00
2 Alfonso Soriano Jsy / Roberto Alomar	6.00	15.00
3 Roger Clemens Jsy / Mike Piazza	8.00	20.00
4 Mike Mussina Jsy / Mo Vaughn	6.00	15.00
5 Bernie Williams Jsy / Jeromy Burnitz	6.00	15.00
6 Derek Jeter Jsy / Satoru Komiyama	12.50	30.00
7 Robin Ventura Jsy / Edgardo Alfonzo	4.00	10.00
8 Jorge Posada Jsy / Mike Piazza	6.00	15.00
9 Jason Giambi Base SP / Mo Vaughn	4.00	10.00
10 Alfonso Soriano Jsy / Edgardo Alfonzo	4.00	10.00
11 Rey Ordonez Jsy / Derek Jeter	4.00	10.00
12 Roberto Alomar Jsy / Alfonso Soriano	6.00	15.00
13 Mike Piazza Jsy / Roger Clemens	6.00	15.00
14 Mo Vaughn Jsy / Mike Mussina	4.00	10.00
15 Jeromy Burnitz Jsy / Bernie Williams	4.00	10.00
16 Satoru Komiyama Bat / Derek Jeter	6.00	15.00
17 Edgardo Alfonzo Jsy / Robin Ventura	4.00	10.00
18 Mike Piazza Jsy / Jorge Posada	6.00	15.00
19 Mo Vaughn Jsy / Jason Giambi	4.00	10.00
20 Edgardo Alfonzo Jsy / Alfonso Soriano	4.00	10.00

2002 Fleer Tradition Update Plays of the Week

Inserted at stated odds of one in 12, these 30 cards feature some of the leading players of the 2002 season along with their highlight play of the season.

Card	Low	High
1 Troy Glaus	.60	1.50
2 Andruw Jones	.60	1.50
3 Curt Schilling	.60	1.50
4 Manny Ramirez	.60	1.50
5 Sammy Sosa	1.00	2.50
6 Magglio Ordonez	.60	1.50
7 Ken Griffey Jr.	1.50	4.00
8 Jim Thome	.60	1.50
9 Larry Walker	.60	1.50
10 Robert Fick	.60	1.50
11 Josh Beckett	.60	1.50
12 Roy Oswalt	.60	1.50
13 Mike Sweeney	.60	1.50
14 Shawn Green	.60	1.50
15 Torii Hunter	.60	1.50
16 Vladimir Guerrero	1.00	2.50
17 Mike Piazza	1.50	4.00
18 Jason Giambi	.60	1.50
19 Eric Chavez	.60	1.50
20 Pat Burrell	.60	1.50
21 Brian Giles	.60	1.50
22 Ryan Klesko	.60	1.50
23 Barry Bonds	2.50	6.00
24 Mike Cameron	.60	1.50
25 Albert Pujols	2.00	5.00
26 Alex Rodriguez	1.50	4.00
27 Carlos Delgado	.60	1.50
28 Richie Sexson	.60	1.50
29 Jay Gibbons	.60	1.50
30 Randy Winn	.60	1.50

2002 Fleer Tradition Update This Day In History

Inserted into packs at stated odds of one in 12, this 25 card set feature a mix of active and retired players along with an historical highlight that the player was involved with.

Card	Low	High
U1 Shawn Green	.60	1.50
U2 Ozzie Smith	1.25	3.00
U3 Derek Lowe	.60	1.50
U4 Ken Griffey Jr.	1.50	4.00
U5 Barry Bonds	2.50	6.00
U6 Juan Gonzalez	.60	1.50
U7 Wade Boggs	.75	2.00
U8 Mark Prior	1.00	2.50
U9 Thurman Munson	1.25	3.00
U10 Curt Schilling	.60	1.50
U11 Jason Giambi	.60	1.50
U12 Cal Ripken	4.00	10.00
U13 Craig Biggio	.60	1.50
U14 Drew Henson	.60	1.50
U15 Steve Carlton	.75	2.00
U16 Greg Maddux	1.50	4.00
U17 Adam Dunn	.60	1.50
U18 Vladimir Guerrero	1.00	2.50
U19 Alex Rodriguez	1.50	4.00
U20 Carlton Fisk	.75	2.00
U21 Ichiro Suzuki	2.00	5.00
U22 Johnny Bench	1.25	3.00
U23 Kazuhisa Ishii	.60	1.50
U24 Derek Jeter	2.50	6.00
U25 Jim Thome	.60	1.50

2002 Fleer Tradition Update This Day In History Autographs

Inserted into packs at a stated rate of one in 582, this is a partial parallel to the This Day in History insert set. A few players signed an amount of cards in much shorter supply than others. Fortunately, Fleer provided the specific quantities signed for the short prints and the information is detailed in full within our checklist. In addition, an exchange card with a redemption deadline of October 31st, 2003 was seeded into packs for the Greg Maddux card.

Card	Low	High
1 Barry Bonds SP/150	100.00	175.00
2 Mark Prior SP/64	10.00	25.00
3 Cal Ripken SP/35		
4 Drew Henson	8.00	20.00
5 Greg Maddux SP/99	125.00	200.00
6 Derek Jeter	60.00	120.00

2002 Fleer Tradition Update This Day In History Game Used

Inserted into packs at a stated rate of one in 28, these 20 cards form a partial parallel to the This Day in History insert set. These cards feature a game-used memorabilia piece of the featured player. A couple players are featured on more than one memorabilia card and we have notated that information in our checklist as well as the stated print run for the cards which were issued in notably shorter supply.

Card	Low	High
1 Craig Biggio Bat SP/80		
2 Craig Biggio Jsy	6.00	15.00
3 Wade Boggs Jsy	6.00	15.00
4 Wade Boggs Pants	6.00	15.00
5 Barry Bonds Bat	8.00	20.00
6 Barry Bonds Jsy	8.00	20.00
7 Adam Dunn Jsy	4.00	10.00
8 Carlton Fisk Bat	6.00	15.00
9 Juan Gonzalez Bat	4.00	10.00
10 Shawn Green Jsy	4.00	10.00
11 Kazuhisa Ishii Bat	4.00	10.00
12 Derek Jeter Pants	10.00	25.00
13 Greg Maddux Jsy	6.00	15.00
14 Thurman Munson Jsy SP/40		
15 Alex Rodriguez Bat	6.00	15.00
16 Alex Rodriguez Jsy	6.00	15.00
17 Curt Schilling Jsy	4.00	10.00
18 Ozzie Smith Jsy	8.00	20.00
19 Jim Thome Bat SP/120		
20 Jim Thome Jsy	6.00	15.00

2003 Fleer Tradition

This 485 card set, deisgned in the style of 1963 Fleer, was released in January, 2003. These cards were issued in 10 card packs which were packed 40 packs to a box and 20 boxes to a case with an SRP of $1.49 per pack. The following subsets are part of the set: Cards numbered 1 through 30 are Team Leader cards, cards number 67 through 85 are Missing Link (featuring players active but not on Fleer cards in 1963) cards, cards number 417 through 425 are Award Winner cards, cards number

426 through 460 are Prospect cards and cards numbered 461 through 485 are Banner Season cards. All cards numbered 1 through 100 were short printed and inserted at an rate of one per hobby pack and one per 12 retail pack. In addition, retail boxes had a special Barry Bonds pin as a box topper and a Derek Jeter promo card was issued a few weeks before this product became live so media and dealers could see what this set look like.

COMPLETE SET (485) 75.00 150.00
COMP.SET w/o SP's (385) 15.00 40.00
COMMON CARD (1-30) .40 1.00
COMM.SP (31-66/86-100) .40 1.00
COMMON ML (67-85) .60 1.50
COMMON CARD (.10 .30
COMMON PR (426-460) .10 .30
1 Jarrod Washburn .40 1.00
Troy Glaus
Garret Anderson
Ramon Ortiz TL SP
2 Luis Gonzalez .60 1.50
Randy Johnson TL SP
3 Andruw Jones .60 1.50
Chipper Jones
Tom Glavine
Kevin Millwood TL SP
4 Tony Batista .40 1.00
Rodrigo Lopez TL SP
5 Manny Ramirez .60 1.50
Nomar Garciaparra
Derek Lowe
Pedro Martinez TL SP
6 Sammy Sosa 1.00 2.50
Matt Clement
Kerry Wood TL SP
7 Matt Buehrle .40 1.00
Magglio Ordonez
Danny Wright TL SP
8 Adam Dunn .40 1.00
Aaron Boone
Jimmy Haynes TL SP
9 C.C. Sabathia .40 1.00
Jim Thome TL SP
10 Todd Helton .40 1.00
Jason Jennings TL SP
11 Randall Simon .40 1.00
Steve Sparks
Mark Redman TL SP
12 Derrek Lee .60 1.50
Mike Lowell
A.J. Burnett TL SP
13 Lance Berkman .40 1.00
Roy Oswalt TL SP
14 Paul Byrd .40 1.00
Carlos Beltran TL SP
15 Shawn Green .60 1.50
Hideo Nomo TL SP
16 Richie Sexson .40 1.00
Ben Sheets TL SP
17 Torii Hunter .60 1.50
Kyle Lohse
Johan Santana TL SP
18 Vladimir Guerrero .60 1.50
Tomo Ohka
Javier Vazquez TL SP
19 Mike Piazza 1.00 2.50
Al Leiter TL SP
20 Jason Giambi 1.00 2.50
David Wells
Roger Clemens TL SP
21 Eric Chavez .40 1.00
Miguel Tejada
Barry Zito TL SP
22 Pat Burrell .40 1.00
Vicente Padilla
Randy Wolf TL SP
23 Brian Giles .40 1.00
Josh Fogg
Kip Wells TL SP
24 Ryan Klesko .40 1.00
Brian Lawrence TL SP
25 Barry Bonds 1.00 2.50
Russ Ortiz
Jason Schmidt TL SP
26 Mike Cameron .40 1.00
Bret Boone
Freddy Garcia TL SP
27 Albert Pujols 1.00 2.50
Matt Morris TL SP
28 Aubry Huff .40 1.00
Randy Winn
Joe Kennedy
Tanyon Sturtze TL SP
29 Alex Rodriguez 1.00 2.50
Kenny Rogers
Chan Ho Park TL SP
30 Carlos Delgado .40 1.00
Roy Halladay TL SP
31 Greg Maddux SP 1.50 4.00
32 Nick Neugebauer SP .40 1.00
33 Larry Walker SP .40 1.00
34 Freddy Garcia SP .40 1.00
35 Rich Aurilia SP .40 1.00
36 Craig Wilson SP .40 1.00
37 Jeff Suppan SP .40 1.00
38 Joel Pineiro SP .40 1.00
39 Pedro Feliz SP .40 1.00
40 Bartolo Colon SP .40 1.00
41 Pete Walker SP .40 1.00
42 Mo Vaughn SP .40 1.00
43 Sidney Ponson SP .40 1.00
44 Jason Isringhausen SP .40 1.00
45 Hideki Irabu SP .40 1.00
46 Pedro Martinez SP .60 1.50
47 Tom Glavine SP .60 1.50
48 Matt Lawton SP .40 1.00
49 Kyle Lohse SP .40 1.00
50 Corey Patterson SP .40 1.00
51 Ichiro Suzuki SP UER 2.00 5.00
RBI total for 2002 incorrect
52 Wade Miller SP .40 1.00
53 Ben Diggins SP .40 1.00
54 Jayson Werth SP .40 1.00
55 Masato Yoshii SP .40 1.00
56 Mark Buehrle SP .40 1.00
57 Drew Henson SP .40 1.00
58 Dave Williams SP .40 1.00
59 Juan Rivera SP .40 1.00
60 Scott Schoeneweis SP .40 1.00
61 Josh Beckett SP .40 1.00
62 Vinny Castilla SP .40 1.00
63 Barry Zito SP .40 1.00
64 Jose Valentin SP .40 1.00
65 Jon Lieber SP .40 1.00
66 Jorge Padilla SP .40 1.00
67 Luis Aparicio ML SP .60 1.50
68 Boog Powell ML SP 1.00 2.50
69 Dick Radatz ML SP .60 1.50
70 Frank Malzone ML SP .60 1.50
71 Lou Brock ML SP 1.00 2.50
72 Billy Williams ML SP .60 1.50
73 Early Wynn ML SP .60 1.50
74 Jim Bunning ML SP 1.00 2.50
75 Al Kaline ML SP 1.50 4.00
76 Eddie Mathews ML SP 1.50 4.00
77 Harmon Killebrew ML SP 1.50 4.00
78 Gil Hodges ML SP 1.00 2.50
79 Duke Snider ML SP 1.00 2.50
80 Yogi Berra ML SP 1.50 4.00
81 Whitey Ford ML SP 1.00 2.50
82 Willie Stargell ML SP 1.00 2.50
83 Willie McCovey ML SP .60 1.50
84 Gaylord Perry ML SP .60 1.50
85 Red Schoendienst ML SP .60 1.50
86 Luis Castillo SP .40 1.00
87 Derek Jeter SP 2.50 6.00
88 Orlando Hudson SP .40 1.00
89 Bobby Higginson SP .40 1.00
90 Brent Butler SP .40 1.00
91 Brad Wilkerson SP .40 1.00
92 Craig Biggio SP .60 1.50
93 Marlon Anderson SP .40 1.00
94 Ty Wigginton SP .40 1.00
95 Hideo Nomo SP 1.00 2.50
96 Barry Larkin SP .60 1.50
97 Roberto Alomar SP .60 1.50
98 Omar Vizquel SP .60 1.50
99 Andres Galarraga SP .40 1.00
100 Shawn Green SP .40 1.00
101 Rafael Furcal .10 .30
102 Bill Selby .10 .30
103 Brent Abernathy .10 .30
104 Nomar Garciaparra .50 1.25
105 Michael Barrett .10 .30
106 Travis Hafner .10 .30
107 Carl Crawford .10 .30
108 Jeff Cirillo .10 .30
109 Mike Hampton .10 .30
110 Kip Wells .10 .30
111 Luis Alicea .10 .30
112 Ellis Burks .10 .30
113 Matt Anderson .10 .30
114 Carlos Beltran .10 .30
115 Paul Lo Duca .10 .30
116 Lance Berkman .10 .30
117 Moises Alou .10 .30
118 Roger Cedeno .10 .30
119 Brad Fullmer .10 .30
120 Sean Burroughs .10 .30
121 Eric Byrnes .10 .30
122 Milton Bradley .10 .30
123 Jason Giambi .10 .30
124 Brook Fordyce .10 .30
125 Kevin Appier .10 .30
126 Steve Cox .10 .30
127 Danny Bautista .10 .30
128 Edgardo Alfonzo .10 .30
129 Matt Clement .10 .30
130 Robb Nen .10 .30
131 Roy Halladay .10 .30
132 Brian Jordan .10 .30
133 A.J. Burnett .10 .30
134 Aaron Cook .10 .30
135 Paul Byrd .10 .30
136 Ramon Ortiz .10 .30
137 Adam Hyzdu .10 .30
138 Rafael Soriano .10 .30
139 Marty Cordova .10 .30
140 Nelson Cruz .10 .30
141 Jamie Moyer .10 .30
142 Raul Mondesi .10 .30
143 Josh Bard .10 .30
144 Elmer Dessens .10 .30
145 Rickey Henderson .30 .75
146 Joe McEwing .10 .30
147 Julio Rivas .10 .30
148 Armando Benitez .10 .30
149 Keith Foulke .10 .30
150 Zach Day .10 .30
151 Trey Lunsford .10 .30
152 Bobby Abreu .10 .30
153 Juan Cruz .10 .30
154 Ramon Hernandez .10 .30
155 Brandon Duckworth .10 .30
156 Matt Ginter .10 .30
157 Rob Mackowiak .10 .30
158 Josh Pearce .10 .30
159 Marlon Byrd .10 .30
160 Todd Walker .10 .30
161 Chad Hermansen .10 .30
162 Felix Escalona .10 .30
163 Ruben Mateo .10 .30
164 Mark Johnson .10 .30
165 Juan Pierre .10 .30
166 Gary Sheffield .10 .30
167 Edgar Martinez .20 .50
168 Randy Winn .10 .30
169 Pokey Reese .10 .30
170 Kevin Mench .10 .30
171 Albert Pujols .60 1.50
172 J.T. Snow .10 .30
173 Dean Palmer .10 .30
174 Jay Payton .10 .30
175 Abraham Nunez .10 .30
176 Richie Sexson .10 .30
177 Jose Vidro .10 .30
178 Geoff Jenkins .10 .30
179 Dan Wilson .10 .30
180 John Olerud .10 .30
181 Javy Lopez .10 .30
182 Carl Everett .10 .30
183 Vernon Wells .10 .30
184 Juan Gonzalez .10 .30
185 Jorge Posada .20 .50
186 Mike Sweeney .10 .30
187 Cesar Izturis .10 .30
188 Jason Schmidt .10 .30
189 Chris Richard .10 .30
190 Jason Phillips .10 .30
191 Fred McGriff .20 .50
192 Shea Hillenbrand .10 .30
193 Ivan Rodriguez .20 .50
194 Mike Lowell .10 .30
195 Neifi Perez .10 .30
196 Kenny Lofton .10 .30
197 A.J. Pierzynski .10 .30
198 Larry Bigbie .10 .30
199 Juan Uribe .10 .30
200 Jeff Bagwell .20 .50
201 Timo Perez .10 .30
202 Jeremy Giambi .10 .30
203 Deivi Cruz .10 .30
204 Marquis Grissom .10 .30
205 Chipper Jones .30 .75
206 Alex Gonzalez .10 .30
207 Steve Finley .10 .30
208 Ben Davis .10 .30
209 Mike Bordick .10 .30
210 Casey Fossum .10 .30
211 Aramis Ramirez .10 .30
212 Aaron Boone .10 .30
213 Orlando Cabrera .10 .30
214 Hee Seop Choi .10 .30
215 Jeromy Burnitz .10 .30
216 Todd Hollandsworth .10 .30
217 Rey Sanchez .10 .30
218 Jose Cruz .10 .30
219 Roosevelt Brown .10 .30
220 Odalis Perez .10 .30
221 Carlos Delgado .10 .30
222 Orlando Hernandez .10 .30
223 Adam Everett .10 .30
224 Adrian Beltre .10 .30
225 Ken Griffey Jr. .50 1.25
226 Brad Penny .10 .30
227 Carlos Lee .10 .30
228 J.C. Romero .10 .30
229 Ramon Martinez .10 .30
230 Matt Morris .10 .30
231 Ben Howard .10 .30
232 Damon Minor .10 .30
233 Jason Marquis .10 .30
234 Paul Wilson .10 .30
235 Ryan Dempster .10 .30
236 Jeffrey Hammonds .10 .30
237 Jaret Wright .10 .30
238 Carlos Pena .10 .30
239 Toby Hall .10 .30
240 Rick Helling .10 .30
241 Alex Escobar .10 .30
242 Trevor Hoffman .10 .30
243 Bernie Williams .20 .50
244 Jorge Julio .10 .30
245 Byung-Hyun Kim .10 .30
246 Mike Redmond .10 .30
247 Tony Armas .10 .30
248 Aaron Rowand .10 .30
249 Rusty Greer .10 .30
250 Aaron Harang .10 .30
251 Jeremy Fikac .10 .30
252 Jay Gibbons .10 .30
253 Brandon Puffer .10 .30
254 Dewayne Wise .10 .30
255 Chan Ho Park .10 .30
256 David Bell .10 .30
257 Kenny Rogers .10 .30
258 Mark Quinn .10 .30
259 Greg LaRocca .10 .30
260 Reggie Taylor .10 .30
261 Brett Tomko .10 .30
262 Jack Wilson .10 .30
263 Billy Wagner .10 .30
264 Greg Norton .10 .30
265 Tim Salmon .20 .50
266 Joe Randa .10 .30
267 Geronimo Gil .10 .30
268 Johnny Damon 1.00 2.50
269 Robin Ventura .10 .30
270 Frank Thomas .30 .75
271 Terrence Long .10 .30
272 Mark Redman .10 .30
273 Mark Kotsay .10 .30
274 Ben Sheets .10 .30
275 Reggie Sanders .10 .30
276 Mark Grace .20 .50
277 Eddie Guardado .10 .30
278 Julio Mateo .10 .30
279 Bengie Molina .10 .30
280 Bill Hall .10 .30
281 Eric Chavez .10 .30
282 Joe Kennedy .10 .30
283 John Valentin .10 .30
284 Ray Durham .10 .30
285 Trot Nixon .10 .30
286 Rondell White .10 .30
287 Alex Gonzalez .10 .30
288 Tomas Perez .10 .30
289 Jared Sandberg .10 .30
290 Jacque Jones .10 .30
291 Cliff Floyd .10 .30
292 Ryan Klesko .10 .30
293 Morgan Ensberg .10 .30
294 Jerry Hairston .10 .30
295 Doug Mientkiewicz .10 .30
296 Darin Erstad .10 .30
297 Jeff Conine .10 .30
298 Johnny Estrada .10 .30
299 Mark Mulder .10 .30
300 Jeff Kent .10 .30
301 Roger Clemens .60 1.50
302 Endy Chavez .10 .30
303 Joe Crede .10 .30
304 J.D. Drew .10 .30
305 David Dellucci .10 .30
306 Eli Marrero .10 .30
307 Josh Fogg .10 .30
308 Mike Crudale .10 .30
309 Bret Boone .10 .30
310 Mariano Rivera .30 .75
311 Mike Piazza .50 1.25
312 Jason Jennings .10 .30
313 Jason Varitek .30 .75
314 Vicente Padilla .10 .30
315 Kevin Millwood .10 .30
316 Nick Johnson .20 .50
317 Shane Reynolds .10 .30
318 Joe Thurston .10 .30
319 Mike Lamb .10 .30
320 Aaron Sele .10 .30
321 Fernando Tatis .10 .30
322 Randy Wolf .10 .30
323 David Justice .10 .30
324 Andy Pettitte .20 .50
325 Freddy Sanchez .10 .30
326 Scott Spiezio .10 .30
327 Randy Johnson .30 .75
328 Karim Garcia .10 .30
329 Eric Milton .10 .30
330 Jermaine Dye .10 .30
331 Kevin Brown .10 .30
332 Adam Pettyjohn .10 .30
333 Jason Lane .10 .30
334 Mark Prior .20 .50
335 Mike Lieberthal .10 .30
336 Matt White .10 .30
337 John Patterson .10 .30
338 Marcus Giles .10 .30
339 Kazuhisa Ishii .10 .30
340 Willie Harris .10 .30
341 Travis Phelps .10 .30
342 Randall Simon .10 .30
343 Manny Ramirez .20 .50
344 Kerry Wood .10 .30
345 Shannon Stewart .10 .30
346 Mike Mussina .20 .50
347 Joe Borchard .10 .30
348 Tyler Walker .10 .30
349 Preston Wilson .10 .30
350 Damian Moss .10 .30
351 Eric Karros .10 .30
352 Bobby Kielty .10 .30
353 Jason LaRue .10 .30
354 Phil Nevin .10 .30
355 Tony Graffanino .10 .30
356 Antonio Alfonseca .10 .30
357 Eddie Taubensee .10 .30
358 Luis Ugueto .10 .30
359 Greg Vaughn .10 .30
360 Corey Thurman .10 .30
361 Omar Infante .10 .30
362 Alex Cintron .10 .30
363 Esteban Loaiza .10 .30
364 Tino Martinez .20 .50
365 David Eckstein .10 .30
366 Dave Pember RC .10 .30
367 Damian Rolls .10 .30
368 Richard Hidalgo .10 .30
369 Brad Radke .10 .30
370 Alex Sanchez .10 .30
371 Ben Grieve .10 .30
372 Brandon Inge .10 .30
373 Adam Piatt .10 .30
374 Charles Johnson .10 .30
375 Rafael Palmeiro .20 .50
376 Joe Mays .10 .30
377 Derrek Lee .20 .50
378 Fernando Vina .10 .30
379 Andruw Jones .20 .50
380 Troy Glaus .10 .30
381 Bobby Hill .10 .30
382 C.C. Sabathia .10 .30
383 Jose Hernandez .10 .30
384 Al Leiter .10 .30
385 Jarrod Washburn .10 .30
386 Cody Ransom .10 .30
387 Matt Stairs .10 .30
388 Edgar Renteria .10 .30
389 Tsuyoshi Shinjo .10 .30
390 Matt Williams .10 .30
391 Bubba Trammell .10 .30
392 Jason Kendall .10 .30
393 Scott Rolen .20 .50
394 Chuck Knoblauch .10 .30
395 Jimmy Rollins .10 .30
396 Gary Bennett .10 .30
397 David Wells .10 .30
398 Ronnie Belliard .10 .30
399 Austin Kearns .10 .30
400 Tim Hudson .10 .30
401 Andy Van Hekken .10 .30
402 Ray Lankford .10 .30
403 Todd Helton .20 .50
404 Jeff Weaver .10 .30
405 Gabe Kapler .10 .30
406 Luis Gonzalez .10 .30
407 Sean Casey .10 .30
408 Kazuhiro Sasaki .10 .30
409 Mark Teixeira .20 .50
410 Brian Giles .10 .30
411 Robert Fick .10 .30
412 Wilkin Ruan .10 .30
413 Jose Rijo .10 .30
414 Ben Broussard .10 .30
415 Aubrey Huff .10 .30
416 Magglio Ordonez .10 .30
417 Barry Bonds AW .40 1.00
418 Miguel Tejada AW .10 .30
419 Randy Johnson AW .20 .50
420 Barry Zito AW .10 .30
421 Jason Jennings AW .10 .30
422 Eric Hinske AW .10 .30
423 Benito Santiago AW .10 .30
424 Adam Kennedy AW .10 .30
425 Troy Glaus AW .10 .30
426 Brandon Phillips PR .10 .30
427 Jake Peavy PR .10 .30
428 Jason Romano PR .10 .30
429 Jeriome Robertson PR .10 .30
430 Aaron Guiel PR .10 .30
431 Hank Blalock PR .10 .30
432 Brad Lidge PR .10 .30
433 Francisco Rodriguez PR .10 .30
434 Jaime Cerda PR .10 .30
435 Jung Bong PR .10 .30
436 Reed Johnson PR .10 .30
437 Rene Reyes PR .10 .30
438 Chris Snelling PR .10 .30
439 Miguel Olivo PR .10 .30
440 Brian Banks PR .10 .30
441 Eric Junge PR .10 .30
442 Kirk Saarloos PR .10 .30
443 Jamey Carroll PR .10 .30
444 Josh Hancock PR .10 .30
445 Michael Restovich PR .10 .30
446 Willie Bloomquist PR .10 .30
447 John Lackey PR .10 .30
448 Marcus Thames PR .10 .30
449 Victor Martinez PR .20 .50
450 Brett Myers PR .10 .30
451 Wes Obermueller PR .10 .30
452 Hansel Izquierdo PR .10 .30
453 Brian Tallet PR .10 .30
454 Craig Monroe PR .10 .30
455 Doug Devore PR .10 .30
456 John Buck PR .10 .30
457 Tony Alvarez PR .10 .30
458 Wily Mo Pena PR .30 .75
459 John Stephens PR .10 .30
460 Tony Torcato PR .10 .30
461 Adam Kennedy BNR .10 .30
462 Alex Rodriguez BNR .30 .75
463 Derek Lowe BNR .10 .30
464 Garret Anderson BNR .10 .30
465 Pat Burrell BNR .10 .30
466 Eric Gagne BNR .10 .30
467 Tomo Ohka BNR .10 .30
468 Josh Phelps BNR .10 .30
469 Sammy Sosa BNR .30 .75
470 Jim Thome BNR .10 .30
471 Vladimir Guerrero BNR .20 .50
472 Jason Simontacchi BNR .10 .30
473 Adam Dunn BNR .10 .30
474 Jim Edmonds BNR .20 .50
475 Barry Bonds BNR .40 1.00
476 Paul Konerko BNR .10 .30
477 Alfonso Soriano BNR .20 .50
478 Curt Schilling BNR .10 .30
479 John Smoltz BNR .10 .30
480 Torii Hunter BNR .10 .30
481 Rodrigo Lopez BNR .10 .30
482 Miguel Tejada BNR .10 .30
483 Eric Hinske BNR .10 .30
484 Roy Oswalt BNR .10 .30
485 Junior Spivey BNR .10 .30
P1 Barry Bonds Pin 3.00 8.00
P87 Derek Jeter Promo .75 2.00

2003 Fleer Tradition Glossy

*GLOSSY 1-100: 1.5X TO 4X BASIC
*GLOSSY 101-485: 5X TO 12X BASIC
RANDOM IN HOBBY UPDATE PACKS
STATED ODDS 1:24 RETAIL
STATED PRINT RUN 100 SERIAL #'d SETS

2003 Fleer Tradition Game Used

Inserted in packs at a stated rate of one in 35 hobby and one in 90 retail; these cards partially parallel the regular Fleer Tradition set. Some of these cards were issued to a shorter print run and we have notated that information next to the player's name in our checklist.

*GOLD: .75X TO 2X BASIC GU
*GOLD: .6X TO 1.5X GU p/r 150-200
*GOLD ML: .6X TO 1.5X GU p/r 150-200
*GOLD: .4X TO 1X GU p/r 50-60
GOLD RANDOM INSERTS IN PACKS
GOLD PRINT RUN 100 SERIAL #'d SETS
2 Adrian Beltre Jsy 3.00 8.00
7 Andruw Jones Bat SP/150 UER 6.00 15.00
Card has a piece of jersey
10 Barry Bonds AW Jsy SP/50 20.00 50.00
11 Barry Larkin Jsy SP/200 6.00 15.00
22 Barry Zito Jsy 3.00 8.00
31 Craig Biggio Bat 4.00 10.00
42 Chipper Jones Jsy 6.00 15.00
46 Darin Erstad Jsy 3.00 8.00
63 Derek Jeter Jsy SP/150 12.50 30.00
67 Edg Alfonzo Jsy SP/200 4.00 10.00
97 Eric Karros Jsy 3.00 8.00
104 Frank Thomas Jsy 6.00 15.00
128 Greg Maddux Jsy 6.00 15.00
180 Hideo Nomo Jsy SP/200 10.00 25.00
184 Ivan Rodriguez Jsy 4.00 10.00
185 Jeromy Burnitz Jsy SP/200 4.00 10.00
192 Jeff Bagwell Jsy SP/200 6.00 15.00
193 J.D. Drew Jsy 3.00 8.00
194 Juan Gonzalez Bat SP/200 4.00 10.00
200 Jason Jennings AW Pants 3.00 8.00
205 Jason Kendall Pants 3.00 8.00
215 John Olerud Jsy 3.00 8.00
224 Jorge Posada Bat 4.00 10.00
269 Jimmy Rollins Jsy 3.00 8.00
270 Kazuhisa Ishii Jsy 3.00 8.00
276 Kazuhiro Sasaki Jsy SP/200 4.00 10.00
296 Kerry Wood Jsy SP/200 4.00 10.00
301 Luis Aparicio ML Jsy SP/150 6.00 15.00
304 Mark Grace Jsy 4.00 10.00
311 Mike Lowell Bat 3.00 8.00
327 Mike Mussina Jsy 4.00 10.00
334 Mike Piazza Jsy SP/150 10.00 25.00
339 Mark Prior Jsy SP/200 6.00 15.00
343 Manny Ramirez Jsy SP/150 6.00 15.00
344 M.Tejada AW Bat SP/150 4.00 10.00
346 Mo Vaughn Jsy SP/60 6.00 15.00
351 N.Garciaparra Jsy SP/150 10.00 25.00
375 Pedro Martinez Jsy SP/200 6.00 15.00
379 Roger Clemens Jsy SP/150 10.00 25.00
392 Randy Johnson Jsy SP/150 6.00 15.00
395 Rafael Palmeiro Jsy 4.00 10.00
402 Robin Ventura Jsy 3.00 8.00
403 Shea Hillenbrand Bat 3.00 8.00
406 W.Stargell ML Pants SP/150 6.00 15.00

2003 Fleer Tradition Black-White Goudey

Inserted randomly into hobby packs, these cards were issued in the design of the 1936 Goudey Black and White set. To honor the 1936 set further each of these cards were issued to a stated print run of 1936 serial numbered sets.

*GOLD: 2.5X TO 6X BASIC B/W GOUDEY
GOLD RANDOM INSERTS IN HOBBY PACKS
GOLD PRINT RUN 36 SERIAL #'d SETS
*RED: X TO X BASIC B/W GOUDEY
RED RANDOM INSERTS IN RETAIL PACKS
RED PRINT RUN 500 SERIAL #'d SETS
1 Jim Thome 1.50 4.00
2 Derek Jeter 4.00 10.00
3 Alex Rodriguez 2.50 6.00
4 Mark Prior 1.50 4.00
5 Nomar Garciaparra 2.50 6.00
6 Curt Schilling 1.50 4.00
7 Pat Burrell 1.50 4.00
8 Frank Thomas 1.50 4.00
9 Roger Clemens 3.00 8.00
10 Chipper Jones 1.50 4.00
11 Barry Larkin 1.50 4.00
12 Hideo Nomo 1.50 4.00
13 Pedro Martinez 1.50 4.00
14 Jeff Bagwell 1.50 4.00
15 Greg Maddux 2.50 6.00
16 Vladimir Guerrero 1.50 4.00
17 Ichiro Suzuki 3.00 8.00
18 Mike Piazza 2.50 6.00
19 Drew Henson 1.50 4.00
20 Albert Pujols 3.00 8.00
21 Sammy Sosa 1.50 4.00
22 Jason Giambi 1.50 4.00
23 Randy Johnson 1.50 4.00
24 Ken Griffey Jr. 2.50 6.00
25 Barry Bonds 4.00 10.00

2003 Fleer Tradition Checklists

Inserted in packs at a stated rate of one in four, these 18 cards feature either Derek Jeter or Barry Bonds. These cards when matched together make up a puzzle of the featured players

COMP.JETER PUZZLE (9) 3.00 8.00
COMMON JETER .40 1.00
COMP.BONDS PUZZLE (9) 3.00 8.00
COMMON BONDS .40 1.00

2003 Fleer Tradition Hardball Preview

Inserted into packs at a stated rate of one in 400 hobby and one in 480 retail, this 10 card set was issued to preview what the new Hardball set that Fleer would be releasing slightly later in 2003.

1 Miguel Tejada 8.00 20.00
2 Derek Jeter 15.00 40.00
3 Mike Piazza 10.00 25.00
4 Barry Bonds 15.00 40.00
5 Mark Prior 8.00 20.00
6 Ichiro Suzuki 10.00 25.00
7 Alex Rodriguez 10.00 25.00
8 Nomar Garciaparra 10.00 25.00
9 Alfonso Soriano 8.00 20.00
10 Ken Griffey Jr. 10.00 25.00

2003 Fleer Tradition Lumber Company

Issued at a stated rate of one in 10 hobby and one in 12 retail, these 30 cards focus on players known for the prowess with the bat.

COMPLETE SET (30) 25.00 60.00
1 Mike Piazza 1.50 4.00

2 Derek Jeter 2.50 6.00
3 Alex Rodriguez 1.50 4.00
4 Miguel Tejada .60 1.50
5 Nomar Garciaparra 1.50 4.00
6 Andruw Jones .60 1.50
7 Pat Burrell .60 1.50
8 Albert Pujols 2.00 5.00
9 Jeff Bagwell .60 1.50
10 Chipper Jones 1.00 2.50
11 Ichiro Suzuki 2.00 5.00
12 Alfonso Soriano .60 1.50
13 Eric Chavez .60 1.50
14 Brian Giles .60 1.50
15 Shawn Green .60 1.50
16 Jim Thome .60 1.50
17 Lance Berkman .60 1.50
18 Bernie Williams .60 1.50
19 Manny Ramirez .60 1.50
20 Vladimir Guerrero 1.00 2.50
21 Carlos Delgado .60 1.50
22 Scott Rolen .60 1.50
23 Sammy Sosa 1.00 2.50
24 Ken Griffey Jr. 1.50 4.00
25 Barry Bonds 2.50 6.00
26 Todd Helton .60 1.50
27 Jason Giambi .60 1.50
28 Austin Kearns .60 1.50
29 Jeff Kent .60 1.50
30 Magglio Ordonez .60 1.50

2003 Fleer Tradition Lumber Company Game Used

Inserted at a stated rate of one in 108 hobby and one in 195 retail, this is a partial parallel to the Lumber Company insert set. A few cards were issued in shorter supply and we have notated the print run information in our checklist.

AJ Andruw Jones 4.00 10.00
AK Austin Kearns SP/75 6.00 15.00
AS Alfonso Soriano SP/200 4.00 10.00
BB Barry Bonds SP/150 12.50 30.00
BG Brian Giles SP/200 4.00 10.00
BW Bernie Williams 4.00 10.00
CD Carlos Delgado SP/200 4.00 10.00
CJ Chipper Jones 6.00 15.00
DJ Derek Jeter SP/96 15.00 40.00
EC Eric Chavez SP/125 4.00 10.00
JB Jeff Bagwell SP/200 6.00 15.00
JK Jeff Kent SP/200 4.00 10.00
JT Jim Thome SP/200 6.00 15.00
LB Lance Berkman SP/200 4.00 10.00
MO Magglio Ordonez 3.00 8.00
MP Mike Piazza SP/200 10.00 25.00
MR Manny Ramirez 4.00 10.00
MT Miguel Tejada 3.00 8.00
NG Nomar Garciaparra SP/200 8.00 20.00
PB Pat Burrell SP/75 6.00 15.00
RA Alex Rodriguez 6.00 15.00
SG Shawn Green SP/200 4.00 10.00
SR Scott Rolen SP/80 10.00 25.00
TH Todd Helton 4.00 10.00

2003 Fleer Tradition Lumber Company Game Used Gold

Randomly inserted in packs, this is a parallel to the Lumber Company Game Used insert set. These cards were printed to a stated print run matching the number of homers the featured player hit in 2002. If the card was issued to a stated print run of 25 or fewer, no pricing is provided due to market scarcity.

AJ Andruw Jones/35 15.00 40.00
AK Austin Kearns/13
AR Alex Rodriguez/57 20.00 50.00
AS Alfonso Soriano/39 10.00 25.00
BB Barry Bonds/46 30.00 80.00
BG Brian Giles/38 10.00 25.00
BW Bernie Williams/19
CD Carlos Delgado/33 10.00 25.00
CJ Chipper Jones/26 15.00 40.00
DJ Derek Jeter/18
EC Eric Chavez/34 10.00 25.00
JB Jeff Bagwell/31
JK Jeff Kent/37 10.00 25.00
JT Jim Thome/52 15.00 40.00
LB Lance Berkman/42 10.00 25.00
MO Magglio Ordonez/38 10.00 25.00
MP Mike Piazza/33 30.00 80.00
MR Manny Ramirez/33 15.00 40.00
MT Miguel Tejada/34 10.00 25.00
NG Nomar Garciaparra/24
PB Pat Burrell/37 10.00 25.00
SG Shawn Green/42 10.00 25.00
SR Scott Rolen/31 15.00 40.00
TH Todd Helton/30 15.00 40.00

2003 Fleer Tradition Milestones

Inserted in packs at a stated rate of one in five hobby and one in four retail, these 25 cards feature either milestones passed by active players in the 2002 season or by retired players in past seasons.

COMPLETE SET (25) 12.50 30.00
1 Eddie Mathews .75 2.00
2 Rickey Henderson .50 1.25
3 Harmon Killebrew .75 2.00
4 Al Kaline .75 2.00
5 Willie McCovey .75 2.00
6 Tom Seaver .75 2.00
7 Reggie Jackson .75 2.00
8 Mike Schmidt 1.25 3.00
9 Nolan Ryan 1.50 4.00
10 Mike Piazza .75 2.00
11 Randy Johnson .50 1.25
12 Bernie Williams .40 1.00
13 Rafael Palmeiro .40 1.00
14 Juan Gonzalez .40 1.00
15 Ken Griffey Jr. .75 2.00
16 Derek Jeter 1.25 3.00
17 Roger Clemens 1.00 2.50
18 Roberto Alomar .40 1.00
19 Manny Ramirez .40 1.00
20 Luis Gonzalez .40 1.00
21 Barry Bonds 1.25 3.00
22 Nomar Garciaparra .75 2.00
23 Fred McGriff .40 1.00
24 Greg Maddux .75 2.00
25 Barry Bonds 1.25 3.00

2003 Fleer Tradition Milestones Game Used

Inserted at a stated rate of one in 143 hobby and one in 270 retail these 14 cards feature memorabilia cards from the some of the featured players in the Milestone set. A few of these cards were issued to a smaller print run and we have notated that information along with the print run information provided in our checklist.

*GOLD: .75X TO 2X BASIC MILE
*GOLD: .6X TO 1.5X MILE SP/150-200
*GOLD: .5X TO 1.2X MILE SP/100
GOLD RANDOM INSERTS IN PACKS
GOLD PRINT RUN 100 SERIAL #'d SETS
BB1 B.Bonds 5 MVP Jsy SP/200 12.50 30.00
BB2 B.Bonds 600 HR Bat SP/100 15.00 40.00
BW Bernie Williams Jsy SP/200 6.00 15.00
DJ Derek Jeter Jsy SP/150 12.50 30.00
FM Fred McGriff Bat 4.00 10.00
GM Greg Maddux Jsy 6.00 15.00
JG Juan Gonzalez Bat SP/250 4.00 10.00
MP Mike Piazza Jsy SP/100 10.00 25.00
MR Manny Ramirez Jsy SP/150 6.00 15.00
NG N.Garciaparra Jsy SP/100 8.00 20.00
RA Roberto Alomar Bat SP/200 6.00 15.00
RC Roger Clemens Jsy SP/150 10.00 25.00
RJ Randy Johnson Jsy SP/100 6.00 15.00
RP Rafael Palmeiro Jsy SP/200 6.00 15.00

2003 Fleer Tradition Standouts

Inserted in packs at a stated rate of one in 40 hobby and one in 72 retail, these 15 cards become mini-standees when the player's photo is "popped-out" of the card.

1 Barry Bonds 4.00 10.00
2 Pat Burrell 2.00 5.00
3 Roger Clemens 3.00 8.00
4 Adam Dunn 2.00 5.00
5 Nomar Garciaparra 2.50 6.00
6 Ken Griffey Jr. 2.50 6.00
7 Vladimir Guerrero 2.00 5.00
8 Derek Jeter 4.00 10.00
9 Greg Maddux 2.50 6.00
10 Mike Piazza 2.50 6.00
11 Alex Rodriguez 2.50 6.00
12 Alfonso Soriano 2.00 5.00
13 Sammy Sosa 2.00 5.00
14 Ichiro Suzuki 3.00 8.00
15 Miguel Tejada 2.00 5.00

2003 Fleer Tradition Update

This 398 card set was released in October, 2003. The set was issued in 10-card packs with an $2 SRP which came 32 packs to a box and 20 boxes to a case. In addition, each sealed box contained a 25 card "mini-box". Cards numbered 1-200 featured veterans, cards numbered 201 through 259 featured all stars, cards 260 through 275 feature interleague match-up cards while cards numbered 276 through 285 is a Tale of the Tape subset. Cards numbered 286 through 299 feature 2003 rookies and those cards were inserted at a stated rate of one in four. Cards numbered 300 through 398 feature 2003 rookies and those cards were issued as part of the 25 card mini-boxes.

COMP.SET w/o SP's (285) 15.00 40.00
COMMON CARD (1-285) .10 .30
COMMON CARD (286-299) .40 1.00
COMMON RC (286-299) .40 1.00
286-299 STATED ODDS 1:4 HOB/RET
COMMON CARD (300-398) .40 1.00
COMMON RC (300-398) .40 1.00
300-398 ISSUED IN MINI-BOXES
ONE MINI-BOX PER UPDATE BOX
25 CARDS PER MINI-BOX
1 Aaron Boone .10 .30
2 Carl Everett .10 .30
3 Eduardo Perez .10 .30
4 Jason Michaels .10 .30
5 Karim Garcia .10 .30
6 Rainer Olmedo .10 .30
7 Scott Williamson .10 .30
8 Adam Kennedy .10 .30
9 Carl Pavano .10 .30
10 Eli Marrero .10 .30
11 Jason Simontacchi .10 .30
12 Keith Foulke .10 .30
13 Preston Wilson .10 .30
14 Scott Hatteberg .10 .30
15 Adam Dunn .10 .30
16 Carlos Baerga .10 .30
17 Elmer Dessens .10 .30
18 Javier Vazquez .10 .30
19 Kenny Rogers .10 .30
20 Quinton McCracken .10 .30
21 Shane Reynolds .10 .30
22 Adam Eaton .10 .30
23 Carlos Zambrano .10 .30
24 Enrique Wilson .10 .30
25 Jeff DaVanon .10 .30
26 Kenny Lofton .10 .30
27 Ramon Castro .10 .30
28 Shannon Stewart .10 .30
29 Al Martin .10 .30
30 Carlos Guillen .10 .30
31 Eric Karros .10 .30
32 Tim Worrell .10 .30
33 Kevin Millwood .10 .30
34 Randall Simon .10 .30
35 Shawn Chacon .10 .30
36 Alex Rodriguez .50 1.25
37 Casey Blake .10 .30
38 Eric Munson .10 .30
39 Jeff Kent .10 .30
40 Kris Benson .10 .30
41 Randy Winn .10 .30
42 Shea Hillenbrand .10 .30
43 Alfonso Soriano .10 .30
44 Chris George .10 .30
45 Eric Bruntlett .10 .30
46 Jeromy Burnitz .10 .30
47 Kyle Farnsworth .10 .30
48 Torii Hunter .10 .30
49 Sidney Ponson .10 .30
50 Andres Galarraga .10 .30
51 Chris Singleton .10 .30
52 Eric Gagne .10 .30
53 Jesse Foppert .10 .30
54 Lance Carter .10 .30
55 Ray Durham .10 .30
56 Tanyon Sturtze .10 .30
57 Andy Ashby .10 .30
58 Cliff Floyd .10 .30
59 Eric Young .10 .30
60 Jhonny Peralta .50 1.25
61 Livan Hernandez .10 .30
62 Reggie Sanders .10 .30
63 Tim Spooneybarger .10 .30
64 Angel Berroa .10 .30
65 Coco Crisp .20 .50
66 Eric Hinske .10 .30
67 Jim Edmonds .10 .30
68 Luis Matos .10 .30
69 Rickey Henderson .30 .75
70 Todd Walker .10 .30
71 Antonio Alfonseca .10 .30
72 Corey Koskie .10 .30
73 Erubiel Durazo .10 .30
74 Jim Thome .20 .50
75 Lyle Overbay .10 .30
76 Robert Fick .10 .30
77 Todd Hollandsworth .10 .30
78 Aramis Ramirez .10 .30
79 Cristian Guzman .10 .30
80 Esteban Loaiza .10 .30
81 Jody Gerut .10 .30
82 Mark Grudzielanek .10 .30
83 Roberto Alomar .20 .50
84 Todd Hundley .10 .30
85 Mike Hampton .10 .30
86 Curt Schilling .10 .30
87 Francisco Rodriguez .10 .30
88 John Lackey .10 .30
89 Mark Redman .10 .30
90 Robin Ventura .10 .30
91 Todd Zeile .10 .30
92 B.J. Surhoff .10 .30
93 Raul Mondesi .10 .30
94 Frank Catalanotto .10 .30
95 John Smoltz .20 .50
96 Mark Ellis .10 .30
97 Rocco Baldelli .10 .30
98 Todd Pratt .10 .30
99 Barry Bonds .75 2.00
100 Danny Graves .10 .30
101 Fred McGriff .20 .50
102 John Burkett .10 .30
103 Marquis Grissom .10 .30
104 Rocky Biddle .10 .30
105 Tom Glavine .20 .50
106 Bartolo Colon .10 .30
107 Darren Bragg .10 .30
108 Gabe Kapler .10 .30
109 John Franco .10 .30
110 Matt Mantei .10 .30
111 Rod Beck .10 .30
112 Tomo Ohka .10 .30
113 Ben Petrick .10 .30
114 Darren Dreifort .10 .30
115 Garret Anderson .10 .30
116 John Vander Wal .10 .30
117 Melvin Mora .10 .30
118 Rodrigo Lopez .10 .30
119 Raul Ibanez .10 .30
120 Benito Santiago .10 .30
121 David Ortiz Sox .30 .75
122 Gary Bennett .10 .30
123 Jon Garland .10 .30
124 Michael Young .20 .50
125 Rodrigo Rosario .10 .30
126 Travis Lee .10 .30
127 Bill Mueller .10 .30
128 Derek Lowe .10 .30
129 Gil Meche .10 .30
130 Jose Guillen .10 .30
131 Miguel Cabrera .30 .75
132 Ron Calloway .10 .30
133 Troy Percival .10 .30
134 Billy Koch .10 .30
135 Dmitri Young .10 .30
136 Glendon Rusch .10 .30
137 Jose Jimenez .10 .30
138 Miguel Tejada .10 .30
139 John Thomson .10 .30
140 Troy O'Leary .10 .30
141 Bobby Kielty .10 .30
142 Dontrelle Willis .30 .75
143 Greg Myers .10 .30
144 Jose Vizcaino .10 .30
145 Mike MacDougal .10 .30
146 Ronnie Belliard .10 .30
147 Tyler Houston .10 .30
148 Brady Clark .10 .30
149 Edgardo Alfonzo .10 .30
150 Guillermo Mota .10 .30
151 Jose Lima .10 .30
152 Mike Williams .10 .30
153 Roy Oswalt .10 .30
154 Scott Podsednik 2.00 5.00
155 Brandon Lyon .10 .30
156 Henry Mateo .10 .30
157 Jose Macias .10 .30
158 Mike Bordick .10 .30
159 Royce Clayton .10 .30
160 Vance Wilson .10 .30
161 Brent Abernathy .10 .30
162 Horacio Ramirez .10 .30
163 Jose Reyes .10 .30
164 Nick Punto .10 .30
165 Ruben Sierra .10 .30
166 Victor Zambrano .10 .30
167 Brett Tomko .10 .30
168 Ivan Rodriguez .20 .50
169 Jose Mesa .10 .30
170 Octavio Dotel .10 .30
171 Russ Ortiz .10 .30
172 Vladimir Guerrero .30 .75
173 Brian Lawrence .10 .30
174 Jae Weong Seo .10 .30
175 Jose Cruz Jr. .10 .30
176 Pat Burrell .10 .30
177 Russell Branyan .10 .30
178 Warren Morris .10 .30
179 Brian Boehringer .10 .30
180 Jason Johnson .10 .30
181 Josh Phelps .10 .30
182 Paul Konerko .10 .30
183 Ryan Franklin .10 .30
184 Wes Helms .10 .30
185 Brooks Kieschnick .10 .30
186 Jason Davis .10 .30
187 Juan Pierre .10 .30
188 Paul Wilson .10 .30
189 Sammy Sosa .30 .75
190 Wil Cordero .10 .30
191 Byung-Hyun Kim .10 .30
192 Juan Encarnacion .10 .30
193 Placido Polanco .10 .30
194 Sandy Alomar Jr. .10 .30
195 Julio Lugo .10 .30
196 Junior Spivey .10 .30
197 Woody Williams .10 .30
198 Xavier Nady .10 .30
199 Mark Loretta .10 .30
200 Deivi Cruz .10 .30
201 Jorge Posada AS .10 .30
202 Carlos Delgado AS .10 .30
203 Alfonso Soriano AS .10 .30
204 Alex Rodriguez AS .30 .75
205 Troy Glaus AS .10 .30
206 Garret Anderson AS .10 .30
207 Hideki Matsui AS .75 2.00
208 Ichiro Suzuki AS .30 .75
209 Esteban Loaiza AS .10 .30
210 Manny Ramirez AS .20 .50
211 Roger Clemens AS .30 .75
212 Roy Halladay AS .10 .30
213 Jason Giambi AS .10 .30
214 Edgar Martinez AS .10 .30
215 Bret Boone AS .10 .30
216 Hank Blalock AS .10 .30
217 Nomar Garciaparra AS .30 .75
218 Vernon Wells AS .10 .30
219 Melvin Mora AS .10 .30
220 Magglio Ordonez AS .10 .30
221 Mike Sweeney AS .10 .30
222 Barry Zito AS .10 .30
223 Carl Everett AS .10 .30
224 Shigetoshi Hasegawa AS .10 .30
225 Jamie Moyer AS .10 .30
226 Mark Mulder AS .10 .30
227 Eddie Guardado AS .10 .30
228 Ramon Hernandez AS .10 .30
229 Keith Foulke AS .10 .30
230 Javy Lopez AS .10 .30
231 Todd Helton AS .10 .30
232 Marcus Giles AS .10 .30
233 Edgar Renteria AS .10 .30
234 Scott Rolen AS .10 .30
235 Barry Bonds AS .40 1.00
236 Albert Pujols AS .30 .75
237 Gary Sheffield AS .10 .30
238 Jim Edmonds AS .10 .30
239 Jason Schmidt AS .10 .30
240 Mark Prior AS .10 .30
241 Dontrelle Willis AS .20 .50
242 Kerry Wood AS .10 .30
243 Kevin Brown AS .10 .30
244 Woody Williams AS .10 .30
245 Paul Lo Duca AS .10 .30
246 Richie Sexson AS .10 .30
247 Jose Vidro AS .10 .30
248 Luis Castillo AS .10 .30
249 Aaron Boone AS .10 .30
250 Mike Lowell AS .10 .30
251 Rafael Furcal AS .10 .30
252 Andruw Jones AS .10 .30
253 Preston Wilson AS .10 .30
254 John Smoltz AS .10 .30
255 Eric Gagne AS .10 .30
256 Randy Wolf AS .10 .30
257 Billy Wagner AS .10 .30
258 Luis Gonzalez AS .10 .30
259 Russ Ortiz AS .10 .30
260 Jim Thome .20 .50
Pedro Martinez IL
261 Alfonso Soriano .20 .50
Jeff Bagwell IL
262 Dontrelle Willis .20 .50
Rocco Baldelli IL
263 Carlos Delgado .20 .50
Vladimir Guerrero IL
264 Sammy Sosa .30 .75
Magglio Ordonez IL
265 Jason Giambi .10 .30
Adam Dunn IL
266 Mike Sweeney .30 .75
Albert Pujols IL
267 Barry Bonds .40 1.00
Torii Hunter IL
268 Ichiro Suzuki .30 .75
Andruw Jones IL
269 Chipper Jones .20 .50
Hank Blalock IL
270 Mark Prior .10 .30
Vernon Wells IL
271 Nomar Garciaparra .30 .75
Scott Rolen IL
272 Alex Rodriguez .30 .75
Lance Berkman IL
273 Roger Clemens .30 .75
Kerry Wood IL
274 Derek Jeter .40 1.00
Jose Reyes IL
275 Greg Maddux .30 .75
Barry Zito IL
276 Carlos Delgado TT .10 .30
277 J.D. Drew TT .10 .30
278 Barry Bonds TT .40 1.00
279 Albert Pujols TT .30 .75
280 Jim Thome TT .10 .30
281 Sammy Sosa TT .20 .50
282 Alfonso Soriano TT .10 .30
283 Hideki Matsui TT .75 2.00
284 Mike Piazza TT .30 .75
285 Vladimir Guerrero TT .20 .50
286 Rich Harden ROO .60 1.50
287 Chin-Hui Tsao ROO .40 1.00
288 Edwin Jackson ROO RC .60 1.50
289 Chien-Ming Wang ROO RC 4.00 10.00
290 Josh Willingham ROO RC 1.00 2.50
291 Matt Kata ROO RC .40 1.00
292 Jose Contreras ROO RC .75 2.00
293 Chris Bootcheck ROO .40 1.00
294 Javier A. Lopez ROO RC .40 1.00
295 Delmon Young ROO RC 3.00 8.00
296 Pedro Liriano ROO .40 1.00
297 Noah Lowry ROO .60 1.50
298 Khalil Greene ROO UER 1.00 2.50
First Name misspelled
299 Rob Bowen ROO .40 1.00
300 Bo Hart ROO RC .40 1.00
301 Beau Kemp ROO RC .40 1.00
302 Gerald Laird ROO .40 1.00
303 Miguel Ojeda ROO RC .40 1.00
304 Todd Wellemeyer ROO RC .40 1.00
305 Ryan Wagner ROO RC .40 1.00
306 Jeff Duncan ROO RC .40 1.00
307 Wilfredo Ledezma ROO RC .40 1.00
308 Wes Obermueller ROO .40 1.00
309 Bernie Castro ROO RC .40 1.00
310 Tim Olson ROO RC .40 1.00
311 Colin Porter ROO RC .40 1.00
312 Francisco Cruceta ROO RC .40 1.00
313 Guillermo Quiroz ROO RC .40 1.00
314 Brian Stokes ROO RC .40 1.00
315 Robby Hammock ROO RC .40 1.00
316 Lew Ford ROO RC .60 1.50
317 Todd Linden ROO .40 1.00
318 Mike Gallo ROO RC .40 1.00
319 Francisco Rosario ROO RC .40 1.00
320 Rosman Garcia ROO RC .40 1.00
321 Felix Sanchez ROO RC .40 1.00
322 Chad Gaudin ROO RC .40 1.00
323 Phil Seibel ROO RC .40 1.00
324 Jason Gilfillan ROO RC .40 1.00
325 Termel Sledge ROO RC .40 1.00
326 Alfredo Gonzalez ROO RC .40 1.00
327 Josh Stewart ROO RC .40 1.00
328 Jeremy Griffiths ROO RC .40 1.00
329 Cory Stewart ROO RC .40 1.00
330 Josh Hall ROO RC .40 1.00
331 Arnie Munoz ROO RC .40 1.00
332 Garrett Atkins ROO .40 1.00
333 Neal Cotts ROO .40 1.00
334 Dan Haren ROO RC .75 2.00
335 Shane Victorino ROO RC 1.00 2.50
336 David Sanders ROO RC .40 1.00
337 Oscar Villarreal ROO RC .40 1.00
338 Michael Hessman ROO RC .40 1.00
339 Andrew Brown ROO RC .60 1.50
340 Kevin Hooper ROO .40 1.00
341 Prentice Redman ROO RC .40 1.00
342 Brandon Webb ROO RC 2.00 5.00
343 Jimmy Gobble ROO .40 1.00
344 Pete LaForest ROO RC .40 1.00
345 Chris Waters ROO RC .40 1.00
346 Hideki Matsui ROO RC 3.00 8.00
347 Chris Capuano ROO RC .75 2.00
348 Jon Leicester ROO RC .40 1.00
349 Mike Nicolas ROO RC .40 1.00
350 Nook Logan ROO RC .60 1.50
351 Craig Brazell ROO RC .40 1.00
352 Aaron Looper ROO RC .40 1.00
353 D.J. Carrasco ROO RC .40 1.00
354 Clint Barmes ROO RC .75 2.00
355 Doug Waechter ROO RC .60 1.50
356 Julio Manon ROO RC .40 1.00
357 Jer. Bonderman ROO RC 2.50 6.00
358 D. Markwell ROO RC .40 1.00
359 Dave Matranga ROO RC .40 1.00
360 Luis Ayala ROO RC .40 1.00
361 Jason Stanford ROO .40 1.00
362 Roger Deago ROO RC .40 1.00
363 Geoff Geary ROO RC .40 1.00
364 Edgar Gonzalez ROO RC .40 1.00
365 Michel Hernandez ROO RC .40 1.00
366 Aquilino Lopez ROO RC .40 1.00
367 David Manning ROO .40 1.00
368 Carlos Mendez ROO RC .40 1.00
369 Matt Miller ROO RC .40 1.00
370 Mi. Nakamura ROO RC .40 1.00
371 Mike Neu ROO RC .40 1.00
372 Ramon Nivar ROO RC .40 1.00
373 Kevin Ohme ROO RC .40 1.00
374 Alex Prieto ROO RC .40 1.00
375 Stephen Randolph ROO RC .40 1.00
376 Brian Sweeney ROO RC .40 1.00
377 Matt Diaz ROO RC .75 2.00
378 Mike Gonzalez ROO .40 1.00
379 Daniel Cabrera ROO RC .75 2.00
380 Fernando Cabrera ROO RC .40 1.00
381 David DeJesus ROO RC .75 2.00
382 Mike Ryan ROO RC .40 1.00
383 Rick Roberts ROO RC .40 1.00
384 Seung Song ROO .40 1.00
385 Rickie Weeks ROO RC 2.00 5.00
386 Hum. Quintero ROO RC .40 1.00
387 Alexis Rios ROO .40 1.00
388 Aaron Miles ROO RC .60 1.50
389 Tom Gregorio ROO RC .40 1.00
390 Anthony Ferrari ROO RC .40 1.00
391 Kevin Correia ROO RC .40 1.00
392 Rafael Betancourt ROO RC .60 1.50
393 Rett Johnson ROO RC .40 1.00
394 Richard Fischer ROO RC .40 1.00
395 Greg Aquino ROO RC .40 1.00
396 Daniel Garcia ROO RC .40 1.00
397 Sergio Mitre ROO RC .60 1.50
398 Edwin Almonte ROO .40 1.00

2003 Fleer Tradition Update Glossy

*GLOSSY 1-285: 5X TO 12X BASIC
*GLOSSY 1-285: 3X TO 8X BASIC RC's
*GLOSSY MATSUI 207/283: 2.5X TO 6X BASIC
*GLOSSY 286-299: 1.5X TO 4X BASIC
*GLOSSY 286-299: 1.5X TO 4X BASIC RC's
*GLOSSY 300-398: 1.5X TO 4X BASIC
*GLOSSY 300-398: 1.5X TO 4X BASIC RC's
RANDOM INSERTS IN HOBBY PACKS
STATED ODDS 1:24 RETAIL
STATED PRINT RUN 100 SERIAL #'d SETS
289 Chien-Ming Wang ROO 30.00 60.00

2003 Fleer Tradition Update Diamond Debuts

STATED ODDS 1:10 HOBBY, 1:8 RETAIL
1 Dontrelle Willis 1.00 2.50
2 Bo Hart .40 1.00
3 Jose Reyes .40 1.00
4 Chin-Hui Tsao .40 1.00
5 Brandon Webb 1.50 4.00
6 Rich Harden .60 1.50
7 Jesse Foppert .40 1.00
8 Rocco Baldelli .40 1.00
9 Hideki Matsui 3.00 8.00
10 Ron Calloway .40 1.00
11 Jeremy Bonderman 2.00 5.00
12 Mark Teixeira .60 1.50
13 Ryan Wagner .40 1.00
14 Jose Contreras 1.00 2.50
15 Miguel Cabrera 1.00 2.50
16 Lew Ford .60 1.50
17 Jeff Duncan .40 1.00
18 Matt Kata .40 1.00
19 Jeremy Griffiths .40 1.00
20 Todd Wellemeyer .40 1.00
21 Robby Hammock .40 1.00
22 Dave Matranga .40 1.00

23 Laynce Nix .40 1.00
24 Jhonny Peralta 1.00 2.50
25 Oscar Villareal .40 1.00

2003 Fleer Tradition Update Long Gone!

RANDOM INSERTS IN HOBBY PACKS
STATED ODDS 1:72 RETAIL
1 Barry Bonds/475 5.00 12.00
2 Jason Giambi/440 2.00 5.00
3 Albert Pujols/452 4.00 10.00
4 Chipper Jones/420 2.00 5.00
5 Manny Ramirez/430 2.00 5.00
6 Sammy Sosa/536 2.00 5.00
7 Alfonso Soriano/440 2.00 5.00
8 Alex Rodriguez/430 3.00 8.00
9 Jim Thome/445 2.00 5.00
10 Vladimir Guerrero/502 2.00 5.00
11 Austin Kearns/430 2.00 5.00
12 Jeff Bagwell/420 2.00 5.00
13 Andruw Jones/430 2.00 5.00
14 Carlos Delgado/451 2.00 5.00
15 Nomar Garciaparra/440 3.00 8.00
16 Adam Dunn/464 2.00 5.00
17 Mike Piazza/450 3.00 8.00
18 Derek Jeter/410 5.00 12.00
19 Ken Griffey Jr./430 3.00 8.00
20 Hank Blalock/424 2.00 5.00

2003 Fleer Tradition Update Milestones

STATED ODDS 1:8 HOBBY, 1:6 RETAIL
1 Roger Clemens 1.50 4.00
2 Rafael Palmeiro .50 1.25
3 Jeff Bagwell .50 1.25
4 Barry Bonds 2.00 5.00
5 Sammy Sosa .75 2.00
6 Albert Pujols 1.50 4.00
7 Ichiro Suzuki 1.50 4.00
8 Alfonso Soriano .30 .75
9 Alex Rodriguez 1.25 3.00
10 Randy Johnson .75 2.00
11 Manny Ramirez .50 1.25
12 Chipper Jones .75 2.00
13 Todd Helton .50 1.25
14 Ken Griffey Jr. 1.25 3.00
15 Jim Thome .50 1.25
16 Frank Thomas .75 2.00
17 Pedro Martinez .50 1.25
18 Hideo Nomo .75 2.00
19 Jason Schmidt .30 .75
20 Carlos Delgado .30 .75

2003 Fleer Tradition Update Milestones Game Jersey

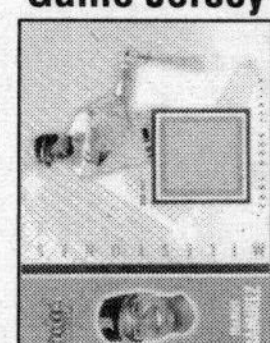

STATED ODDS 1:20 HOBBY, 1:96 RETAIL
*GOLD: .75X TO 2X BASIC
GOLD RANDOM IN HOB/RET PACKS
GOLD PRINT RUN 100 SERIAL #'d SETS
AR Alex Rodriguez 4.00 10.00
AS Alfonso Soriano 3.00 8.00
CD Carlos Delgado 3.00 8.00
CJ Chipper Jones 4.00 10.00
FT Frank Thomas 4.00 10.00
HN Hideo Nomo 4.00 10.00
JB Jeff Bagwell 4.00 10.00
JS Jason Schmidt 3.00 8.00
JT Jim Thome 4.00 10.00
MR Manny Ramirez 4.00 10.00
PM Pedro Martinez 4.00 10.00
RC Roger Clemens 6.00 15.00
RJ Randy Johnson 4.00 10.00
RP Rafael Palmeiro 4.00 10.00
SS Sammy Sosa 4.00 10.00
TH Todd Helton 4.00 10.00

2003 Fleer Tradition Update Throwback Threads

STATED ODDS 1:64 HOBBY, 1:288 RETAIL
*PATCH: 1X TO 2.5X BASIC
PATCH RANDOM INSERTS IN PACKS
PATCH PRINT RUN 100 SERIAL #'d SETS
AL Al Leiter 3.00 8.00
KM Kevin Millwood 3.00 8.00
MP Mike Piazza 6.00 15.00

TG Troy Glaus 3.00 8.00
VG Vladimir Guerrero 4.00 10.00

2003 Fleer Tradition Update Throwback Threads Dual

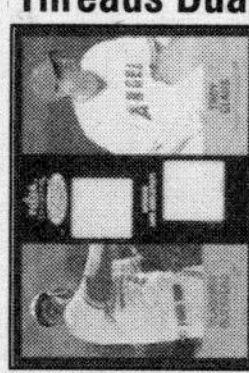

RANDOM INSERTS IN HOB/RET PACKS
STATED PRINT RUN 100 SERIAL #'d SETS
MPAL Mike Piazza 10.00 25.00
Al Leiter
VGTG Vladimir Guerrero 8.00 20.00
Troy Glaus

2003 Fleer Tradition Update Turn Back the Clock

STATED ODDS 1:160 HOBBY, 1:288 RETAIL
1 Yogi Berra 6.00 15.00
2 Mike Schmidt 8.00 20.00
3 Tom Seaver 4.00 10.00
4 Reggie Jackson 4.00 10.00
5 Pee Wee Reese 4.00 10.00
6 Phil Rizzuto 4.00 10.00
7 Jim Palmer 4.00 10.00
8 Robin Yount 6.00 15.00
9 Nolan Ryan 8.00 20.00
10 Al Kaline 6.00 15.00

2004 Fleer Tradition

This 500-card standard-size set was released in January, 2004. The set was issued in 10 card packs which came 36 packs to a box and six boxes to a case. Cards numbered 401 through 500 were printed in lesser quantity than the first 400 cards in this set. This set has these topical subsets: Cards 1 through 10 feature World Series highlights, Cards 11-40 feature Team Leaders. In the higher numbers cards 446 through 462 feature young players in an "Standout" subset which cards 462 through 471 feature players who won major awards in 2003. The set concludes with a 30-card three player prospect set which features leading prospects for each of the major league teams.

COMPLETE SET (500) 75.00 150.00
COMP.SET w/o SP's (400) 15.00 40.00
COMMON CARD (1-400) .10 .30
COMMON CARD (401-470) .40 1.00
COMMON CARD (471-500) .40 1.00
401-445 STATED ODDS 1:2
446-461 STATED ODDS 1:6
462-470 STATED ODDS 1:9
471-500 STATED ODDS 1:3
1 Juan Pierre WS .10 .30
2 Josh Beckett WS .10 .30
3 Ivan Rodriguez WS .20 .50
4 Miguel Cabrera WS .20 .50
5 Dontrelle Willis WS .20 .50
6 Derek Jeter WS .60 1.50
7 Jason Giambi-WS .10 .30
8 Bernie Williams WS .20 .50
9 Alfonso Soriano WS .10 .30
10 Hideki Matsui WS .50 1.25
11 Garret Anderson .10 .30
Garret Anderson
Ramon Ortiz
John Lackey TL
12 Luis Gonzalez .10 .30
Luis Gonzalez
Brandon Webb
Curt Schilling TL
13 Javy Lopez .10 .30
Gary Sheffield
Russ Ortiz
Russ Ortiz TL
14 Tony Batista .10 .30
Jay Gibbons
Sidney Ponson
Jason Johnson TL
15 Manny Ramirez .20 .50
Nomar Garciaparra
Derek Lowe
Pedro Martinez TL
16 Sammy Sosa .20 .50
Sammy Sosa
Mark Prior
Kerry Wood TL
17 Frank Thomas .20 .50
Carlos Lee
Esteban Loaiza
Esteban Loaiza TL
18 Adam Dunn .10 .30
Sean Casey
Chris Reitsma
Paul Wilson TL
19 Jody Gerut .10 .30
Jody Gerut
C.C. Sabathia
C.C. Sabathia TL
20 Preston Wilson .10 .30
Preston Wilson
Darren Oliver
Jason Jennings TL
21 Dmitri Young .10 .30
Dmitri Young
Mike Maroth
Jeremy Bonderman TL
22 Mike Lowell .20 .50
Mike Lowell
Dontrelle Willis
Josh Beckett TL
23 Jeff Bagwell .10 .30
Jeff Bagwell
Jeriome Robertson
Wade Miller TL
24 Carlos Beltran .10 .30
Carlos Beltran
Darrell May
Darrell May TL
25 Adrian Beltre .10 .30
Shawn Green
Hideo Nomo
Kevin Brown TL
26 Richie Sexson .10 .30
Richie Sexson
Ben Sheets
Ben Sheets TL
27 Torii Hunter .20 .50
Torii Hunter
Brad Radke
Johan Santana TL
28 Vladimir Guerrero .20 .50
Orlando Cabrera
Livan Hernandez
Javier Vazquez TL
29 Cliff Floyd .10 .30
Ty Wigginton
Steve Trachsel
Al Leiter TL
30 Jason Giambi .20 .50
Jason Giambi
Andy Pettitte
Mike Mussina TL
31 Eric Chavez .10 .30
Miguel Tejada
Tim Hudson
Tim Hudson TL
32 Jim Thome .10 .30
Jim Thome
Randy Wolf
Randy Wolf TL
33 Reggie Sanders .10 .30
Reggie Sanders
Josh Fogg
Kip Wells TL
34 Ryan Klesko .10 .30
Mark Loretta
Jake Peavy
Jake Peavy TL
35 Jose Cruz Jr. .10 .30
Edgardo Alfonzo
Jason Schmidt
Jason Schmidt TL
36 Bret Boone .10 .30
Bret Boone
Jamie Moyer
Joel Pineiro TL
37 Albert Pujols .30 .75
Albert Pujols
Woody Williams
Woody Williams TL
38 Aubrey Huff .10 .30
Aubrey Huff
Victor Zambrano
Victor Zambrano TL
39 Alex Rodriguez .30 .75
Alex Rodriguez
John Thomson
John Thomson TL
40 Carlos Delgado .10 .30
Carlos Delgado
Roy Halladay
Roy Halladay TL
41 Greg Maddux .50 1.25
42 Ben Grieve .10 .30
43 Darin Erstad .10 .30
44 Ruben Sierra .10 .30
45 Byung-Hyung Kim .10 .30
46 Freddy Garcia .10 .30
47 Richard Hidalgo .10 .30
48 Tike Redman .10 .30
49 Kevin Millwood .10 .30
50 Marquis Grissom .10 .30
51 Jae Weong Seo .10 .30
52 Wil Cordero .10 .30
53 LaTroy Hawkins .10 .30
54 Jolbert Cabrera .10 .30
55 Kevin Appier .10 .30
56 John Lackey .10 .30
57 Garret Anderson .10 .30
58 R.A. Dickey .10 .30
59 David Segui .10 .30
60 Erubiel Durazo .10 .30
61 Bobby Abreu .10 .30
62 Travis Hafner .10 .30
63 Victor Zambrano .10 .30
64 Randy Johnson .30 .75
65 Bernie Williams .20 .50
66 J.T. Snow .10 .30
67 Sammy Sosa .30 .75
68 Al Leiter .10 .30
69 Jason Jennings .10 .30
70 Matt Morris .10 .30
71 Mike Hampton .10 .30
72 Juan Encarnacion .10 .30
73 Alex Gonzalez .10 .30
74 Bartolo Colon .10 .30
75 Brett Myers .10 .30
76 Michael Young .10 .30
77 Ichiro Suzuki .60 1.50
78 Jason Johnson .10 .30
79 Brad Ausmus .10 .30
80 Ted Lilly .10 .30
81 Ken Griffey Jr. .50 1.25
82 Chone Figgins .10 .30
83 Edgar Martinez .20 .50
84 Adam Eaton .10 .30
85 Ken Harvey .10 .30
86 Francisco Rodriguez .10 .30
87 Bill Mueller .10 .30
88 Mike Maroth .10 .30
89 Charles Johnson .10 .30
90 Jhonny Peralta .10 .30
91 Kip Wells .10 .30
92 Cesar Izturis .10 .30
93 Matt Clement .10 .30
94 Lyle Overbay .10 .30
95 Kirk Rueter .10 .30
96 Cristian Guzman .10 .30
97 Garrett Stephenson .10 .30
98 Lance Berkman .10 .30
99 Brett Tomko .10 .30
100 Chris Stynes .10 .30
101 Nate Cornejo .10 .30
102 Aaron Rowand .10 .30
103 Javier Vazquez .10 .30
104 Jason Kendall .10 .30
105 Mark Redman .10 .30
106 Benito Santiago .10 .30
107 C.C. Sabathia .10 .30
108 David Wells .10 .30
109 Mark Ellis .10 .30
110 Casey Blake .10 .30
111 Sean Burroughs .10 .30
112 Carlos Beltran .10 .30
113 Ramon Hernandez .10 .30
114 Eric Hinske .10 .30
115 Luis Gonzalez .10 .30
116 Jarrod Washburn .10 .30
117 Ronnie Belliard .10 .30
118 Troy Percival .10 .30
119 Jose Valentin .10 .30
120 Chase Utley .20 .50
121 Odalis Perez .10 .30
122 Steve Finley .10 .30
123 Bret Boone .10 .30
124 Jeff Conine .10 .30
125 Josh Fogg .10 .30
126 Neifi Perez .10 .30
127 Ben Sheets .10 .30
128 Randy Winn .10 .30
129 Matt Stairs .10 .30
130 Carlos Delgado .10 .30
131 Morgan Ensberg .10 .30
132 Vinny Castilla .10 .30
133 Matt Mantei .10 .30
134 Alex Rodriguez .50 1.25
135 Matthew LeCroy .10 .30
136 Woody Williams .10 .30
137 Frank Catalanotto .10 .30
138 Rondell White .10 .30
139 Scott Rolen .20 .50
140 Cliff Floyd .10 .30
141 Chipper Jones .30 .75
142 Robin Ventura .10 .30
143 Mariano Rivera .30 .75
144 Brady Clark .10 .30
145 Ramon Ortiz .10 .30
146 Omar Infante .10 .30
147 Mike Matheny .10 .30
148 Pedro Martinez .20 .50
149 Carlos Baerga .10 .30
150 Shannon Stewart .10 .30
151 Travis Lee .10 .30
152 Eric Byrnes .10 .30
153 Rafael Furcal .10 .30
154 B.J. Surhoff .10 .30
155 Zach Day .10 .30
156 Marlon Anderson .10 .30
157 Mark Hendrickson .10 .30
158 Mike Mussina .20 .50
159 Randall Simon .10 .30
160 Jeff DaVanon .10 .30
161 Joel Pineiro .10 .30
162 Vernon Wells .10 .30
163 Adam Kennedy .10 .30
164 Trot Nixon .10 .30
165 Rodrigo Lopez .10 .30
166 Curt Schilling .10 .30
167 Horacio Ramirez .10 .30
168 Jason Marquis .10 .30
169 Magglio Ordonez .10 .30
170 Scott Schoeneweis .10 .30
171 Andruw Jones .20 .50
172 Tino Martinez .20 .50
173 Moises Alou .10 .30
174 Kelvim Escobar .10 .30
175 Xavier Nady .10 .30
176 Ramon Martinez .10 .30
177 Pat Hentgen .10 .30
178 Austin Kearns .10 .30
179 D'Angelo Jimenez .10 .30
180 Deivi Cruz .10 .30
181 John Smoltz .20 .50
182 Toby Hall .10 .30
183 Mark Buehrle .10 .30
184 Howie Clark .10 .30
185 David Ortiz .30 .75
186 Raul Mondesi .10 .30
187 Milton Bradley .10 .30
188 Jorge Julio .10 .30
189 Victor Martinez .10 .30
190 Gabe Kapler .10 .30
191 Julio Franco .10 .30
192 Ryan Freel .10 .30
193 Brad Fullmer .10 .30
194 Joe Borowski .10 .30
195 Darren Oliver .10 .30
196 Jason Varitek .30 .75
197 Greg Myers .10 .30
198 Eric Munson .10 .30
199 Tim Wakefield .10 .30
200 Kyle Farnsworth .10 .30
201 Johnny Vander Wal .10 .30
202 Alex Escobar .10 .30
203 Sean Casey .10 .30
204 John Thomson .10 .30
205 Carlos Zambrano .10 .30
206 Kenny Lofton .10 .30
207 Marcus Giles .10 .30
208 Wade Miller .10 .30
209 Geoff Blum .10 .30
210 Jason LaRue .10 .30
211 Omar Vizquel .20 .50
212 Carlos Pena .10 .30
213 Adam Dunn .10 .30
214 Oscar Villarreal .10 .30
215 Paul Konerko .10 .30
216 Hideo Nomo .30 .75
217 Mike Sweeney .10 .30
218 Coco Crisp .10 .30
219 Shawn Chacon .10 .30
220 Brandon Fordyce .10 .30
221 Josh Beckett .10 .30
222 Paul Wilson .10 .30
223 Josh Towers .10 .30
224 Geoff Jenkins .10 .30
225 Shawn Green .10 .30
226 Derrek Lee .20 .50
227 Karim Garcia .10 .30
228 Preston Wilson .10 .30
229 Dane Sardinha .10 .30
230 Aramis Ramirez .10 .30
231 Doug Mientkiewicz .10 .30
232 Jay Gibbons .10 .30
233 Adam Everett .10 .30
234 Brooks Kieschnick .10 .30
235 Dmitri Young .10 .30
236 Brad Penny .10 .30
237 Todd Zeile .10 .30
238 Eric Gagne .10 .30
239 Esteban Loaiza .10 .30
240 Billy Wagner .10 .30
241 Nomar Garciaparra .50 1.25
242 Desi Relaford .10 .30
243 Luis Rivas .10 .30
244 Andy Pettitte .20 .50
245 Ty Wigginton .10 .30
246 Edgar Gonzalez .10 .30
247 Brian Anderson .10 .30
248 Richie Sexson .10 .30
249 Russell Branyan .10 .30
250 Jose Guillen .10 .30
251 Chin-Hui Tsao .10 .30
252 Jose Hernandez .10 .30
253 Kevin Brown .10 .30
254 Pete LaForest .10 .30
255 Adrian Beltre .10 .30
256 Jacque Jones .10 .30
257 Jimmy Rollins .10 .30
258 Brandon Phillips .10 .30
259 Derek Jeter .60 1.50
260 Carl Everett .10 .30
261 Wes Helms .10 .30
262 Kyle Lohse .10 .30
263 Jason Phillips .10 .30
264 Jake Peavy .10 .30
265 Orlando Hernandez .10 .30
266 Keith Foulke .10 .30
267 Brad Wilkerson .10 .30
268 Corey Koskie .10 .30
269 Josh Hall .10 .30
270 Bobby Higginson .10 .30
271 Andres Galarraga .10 .30
272 Alfonso Soriano .10 .30
273 Carlos Rivera .10 .30
274 Steve Trachsel .10 .30
275 David Bell .10 .30
276 Endy Chavez .10 .30
277 Jay Payton .10 .30
278 Mark Mulder .10 .30
279 Terrence Long .10 .30
280 A.J. Burnett .10 .30
281 Pokey Reese .10 .30
282 Phil Nevin .10 .30
283 Jose Contreras .10 .30
284 Jim Thome .20 .50
285 Pat Burrell .10 .30
286 Luis Castillo .10 .30
287 Juan Uribe .10 .30
288 Raul Ibanez .10 .30
289 Sidney Ponson .10 .30
290 Scott Hatteberg .10 .30
291 Jack Wilson .10 .30
292 Reggie Sanders .10 .30
293 Brian Giles .10 .30
294 Craig Biggio .20 .50
295 Kazuhisa Ishii .10 .30
296 Jim Edmonds .10 .30
297 Trevor Hoffman .10 .30
298 Ray Durham .10 .30
299 Mike Lieberthal .10 .30
300 Tim Worrell .10 .30
301 Chris George .10 .30
302 Jamie Moyer .10 .30
303 Mike Cameron .10 .30
304 Matt Kinney .10 .30
305 Aubrey Huff .10 .30
306 Brian Lawrence .10 .30
307 Carlos Guillen .10 .30
308 J.D. Drew .10 .30
309 Paul Lo Duca .10 .30
310 Tim Salmon .20 .50
311 Jason Schmidt .10 .30
312 A.J. Pierzynski .10 .30
313 Lance Carter .10 .30
314 Julio Lugo .10 .30
315 Johan Santana .30 .75
316 Laynce Nix .10 .30
317 John Olerud .10 .30
318 Robb Quinlan .10 .30
319 Scott Spiezio .10 .30
320 Tony Clark .10 .30
321 Jose Vidro .10 .30
322 Shea Hillenbrand .10 .30
323 Doug Glanville .10 .30
324 Orlando Palmeiro .10 .30
325 Juan Gonzalez .10 .30
326 Jason Giambi .10 .30
327 Junior Spivey .10 .30
328 Tom Glavine .20 .50
329 Reed Johnson .10 .30
330 David Eckstein .10 .30
331 Damian Jackson .10 .30
332 Orlando Hudson .10 .30
333 Barry Zito .10 .30
334 Robert Fick .10 .30
335 Aaron Boone .10 .30
336 Rafael Palmeiro .20 .50
337 Bobby Kielty .10 .30
338 Tony Batista .10 .30
339 Ryan Dempster .10 .30
340 Derek Lowe .10 .30
341 Alex Cintron .10 .30
342 Jermaine Dye .10 .30
343 John Burkett .10 .30
344 Javy Lopez .10 .30
345 Eric Karros .10 .30
346 Corey Patterson .10 .30
347 John Phelps .10 .30
348 Ryan Klesko .10 .30
349 Craig Wilson .10 .30
350 Brian Roberts .10 .30
351 Roberto Alomar .20 .50
352 Frank Thomas .30 .75
353 Gary Sheffield .10 .30
354 Alex Gonzalez .10 .30
355 Jose Cruz Jr. .10 .30
356 Jerome Williams .10 .30
357 Mark Kotsay .10 .30
358 Chris Reitsma .10 .30
359 Carlos Lee .10 .30
360 Todd Helton .20 .50
361 Gil Meche .10 .30
362 Ryan Franklin .10 .30
363 Josh Bard .10 .30
364 Juan Pierre .10 .30
365 Barry Larkin .20 .50
366 Edgar Renteria .10 .30
367 Alex Sanchez .10 .30
368 Jeff Bagwell .20 .50
369 Ben Broussard .10 .30
370 Chan-Ho Park .10 .30
371 Darrell May .10 .30
372 Roy Oswalt .10 .30
373 Craig Monroe .10 .30
374 Fred McGriff .20 .50
375 Bengie Molina .10 .30
376 Aaron Guiel .10 .30
377 Jeriome Robertson .10 .30
378 Kenny Rogers .10 .30
379 Colby Lewis .10 .30
380 Jeromy Burnitz .10 .30
381 Orlando Cabrera .10 .30
382 Joe Randa .10 .30
383 Miguel Batista .10 .30
384 Brad Radke .10 .30
385 Jeremy Giambi .10 .30
386 Vladimir Guerrero .30 .75
387 Melvin Mora .10 .30
388 Royce Clayton .10 .30
389 Danny Garcia .10 .30
390 Manny Ramirez .20 .50
391 Dave McCarty .10 .30
392 Mark Grudzielanek .10 .30
393 Mike Piazza .50 1.25
394 Jorge Posada .20 .50
395 Tim Hudson .10 .30
396 Placido Polanco .10 .30
397 Mark Loretta .10 .30
398 Jesse Foppert .10 .30
399 Albert Pujols .60 1.50
400 Jeremi Gonzalez .10 .30
401 Paul Bako SP .40 1.00
402 Luis Matos SP .40 1.00
403 Johnny Damon SP .60 1.50
404 Kerry Wood SP .40 1.00
405 Joe Crede SP .40 1.00
406 Jason Davis SP .40 1.00
407 Larry Walker SP .40 1.00
408 Ivan Rodriguez SP .60 1.50
409 Nick Johnson SP .40 1.00
410 Jose Lima SP .40 1.00
411 Brian Jordan SP .40 1.00
412 Eddie Guardado SP .40 1.00
413 Ron Calloway SP .40 1.00
414 Aaron Heilman SP .40 1.00
415 Eric Chavez SP .40 1.00
416 Randy Wolf SP .40 1.00
417 Jason Bay SP .40 1.00
418 Edgardo Alfonzo SP .40 1.00
419 Kazuhiro Sasaki SP .40 1.00
420 Eduardo Perez SP .40 1.00
421 Carl Crawford SP .40 1.00
422 Troy Glaus SP .40 1.00
423 Joaquin Benoit SP .40 1.00
424 Russ Ortiz SP .40 1.00
425 Larry Bigbie SP .40 1.00
426 Todd Walker SP .40 1.00
427 Kris Benson SP .40 1.00
428 Sandy Alomar Jr. SP .40 1.00
429 Jody Gerut SP .40 1.00
430 Rene Reyes SP .40 1.00
431 Mike Lowell SP .40 1.00
432 Jeff Kent SP .40 1.00
433 Mike MacDougal SP .40 1.00
434 Dave Roberts SP .40 1.00
435 Torii Hunter SP .40 1.00
436 Tomo Ohka SP .40 1.00
437 Jeremy Griffiths SP .40 1.00
438 Miguel Tejada SP .40 1.00
439 Vicente Padilla SP .40 1.00
440 Bobby Hill SP .40 1.00
441 Rich Aurilia SP .40 1.00
442 Shigetoshi Hasegawa SP .40 1.00
443 So Taguchi SP .40 1.00
444 Damian Rolls SP .40 1.00
445 Roy Halladay SP .40 1.00
446 Rocco Baldelli SO SP .40 1.00
447 Dontrelle Willis SO SP .60 1.50
448 Mark Prior SO SP .60 1.50
449 Jason Lane SO SP .40 1.00
450 Angel Berroa SO SP .40 1.00
451 Jose Reyes SO SP .40 1.00
452 Ryan Wagner SO SP .40 1.00
453 Marlon Byrd SO SP .40 1.00
454 Hee Seop Choi SO SP .40 1.00
455 Brandon Webb SO SP .40 1.00
456 Bo Hart SO SP .40 1.00
457 Hank Blalock SO SP .40 1.00

458 Mark Teixeira SO SP .60 1.50
459 Hideki Matsui SO SP 1.50 4.00
460 Scott Podsednik SO SP .40 1.00
461 Miguel Cabrera SO SP .60 1.50
462 Josh Beckett AW SP .40 1.00
463 Mariano Rivera AW SP 1.00 2.50
464 Ivan Rodriguez AW SP .60 1.50
465 Alex Rodriguez AW SP 1.50 4.00
466 Albert Pujols AW SP 2.00 5.00
467 Roy Halladay AW SP .40 1.00
468 Eric Gagne AW SP .40 1.00
469 Angel Berroa AW SP .40 1.00
470 Dontrelle Willis AW SP .60 1.50
471 Chris Bootcheck .40 1.00
Tom Gregorio
Richard Fischer SP
472 Matt Kata .40 1.00
Tim Olson
Robby Hammock SP
473 Michael Hessman .40 1.00
Chris Waters
Greg Aquino SP
474 Carlos Mendez .40 1.00
Daniel Cabrera
Jeremy Guthrie SP
475 Edwin Almonte .40 1.00
Phil Seibel
Felix Sanchez SP
476 Todd Wellemeyer .40 1.00
Jon Leicester
Sergio Mitre SP
477 Josh Stewart .40 1.00
Neal Cotts
Aaron Miles SP
478 Terrmel Sledge .40 1.00
Josh Hall
Brandon Claussen SP
479 Francisco Cruceta .40 1.00
Jason Stanford
Rafael Betancourt SP
480 Javier A.Lopez .60 1.50
Garrett Atkins
Clint Barmes SP
481 Wilfredo Ledezma .60 1.50
Nook Logan
Jeremy Bonderman SP
482 Josh Willingham .40 1.00
Kevin Hooper
Rick Roberts SP
483 Colin Porter .40 1.00
Mike Gallo
Dave Matranga SP
484 David DeJesus .40 1.00
Jason Gilfillan
Jimmy Gobble SP
485 Koyie Hill .40 1.00
Alfredo Gonzalez
Andrew Brown SP
486 Rickie Weeks .60 1.50
Pedro Liriano
Wes Obermueller SP
487 Alex Prieto .40 1.00
Mike Ryan
Lew Ford SP
488 Julio Manon .40 1.00
Luis Ayala
Seung Song SP
489 Jeff Duncan .60 1.50
Prentice Redman
Craig Brazell SP
490 Chien-Ming Wang 2.00 5.00
Michel Hernandez
Mike Gonzalez SP
491 Rich Harden .60 1.50
Mike Neu
Geoff Geary SP
492 Diegomar Markwell .40 1.00
Chad Gaudin
David Sanders SP
493 Beau Kemp .40 1.00
Micheal Nakamura
D.J. Carrasco SP
494 Khalil Greene 1.00 2.50
Miguel Ojeda
Bernie Castro SP
495 Noah Lowry .60 1.50
Todd Linden
Kevin Correia SP
496 Aaron Looper .40 1.00
Brian Sweeney
Rett Johnson SP
497 John Gall RC 1.00 2.50
Dan Haren
Kevin Ohme SP
498 Delmon Young 1.00 2.50
Doug Waechter
Matt Diaz SP
499 Gerald Laird .40 1.00
Rosman Garcia
Ramon Nivar SP
500 Alexis Rios .60 1.50
Guillermo Quiroz
Francisco Rosario SP

2004 Fleer Tradition Career Tributes

PRINT RUNS B/WN 1956-1993 COPIES PER
*DIE CUT: 1.25X TO 3X BASIC
DIE CUT PRINTS B/WN 56-93 COPIES PER
OVERALL CAREER TRIBUTE ODDS 1:36
1 Mike Schmidt/1989 4.00 10.00
2 Nolan Ryan/1993 5.00 12.00
3 Tom Seaver/1986 2.00 5.00
4 Reggie Jackson/1987 2.00 5.00
5 Bob Gibson/1975 2.00 5.00
6 Harmon Killebrew/1975 3.00 8.00
7 Phil Rizzuto/1956 2.00 5.00
8 Lou Brock/1979 2.00 5.00
9 Eddie Mathews/1968 3.00 8.00
10 Al Kaline/1974 3.00 8.00

2004 Fleer Tradition Diamond Tributes

COMPLETE SET (20) 8.00 20.00
STATED ODDS 1:6
1 Derek Jeter 1.25 3.00
2 Chipper Jones .60 1.50
3 Vladimir Guerrero .60 1.50
4 Kerry Wood .40 1.00
5 Jim Thome .60 1.50
6 Nomar Garciaparra 1.00 2.50
7 Alex Rodriguez 1.00 2.50
8 Mike Piazza 1.00 2.50
9 Jason Giambi .40 1.00
10 Barry Zito .40 1.00
11 Dontrelle Willis .60 1.50
12 Albert Pujols 1.25 3.00
13 Todd Helton .60 1.50
14 Richie Sexson .40 1.00
15 Randy Johnson .60 1.50
16 Pedro Martinez .60 1.50
17 Josh Beckett .40 1.00
18 Manny Ramirez .60 1.50
19 Roy Halladay .40 1.00
20 Mark Prior .60 1.50

2004 Fleer Tradition Diamond Tributes Game Jersey

STATED ODDS 1:36
*PATCH: 1X TO 2.5X BASIC
PATCH RANDOM INSERTS IN PACKS
PATCH PRINT RUN 50 SERIAL #'d SETS
AP Albert Pujols 6.00 15.00
AR Alex Rodriguez 4.00 10.00
BZ Barry Zito 3.00 8.00
CJ Chipper Jones 4.00 10.00
DJ Derek Jeter 8.00 20.00
DW Dontrelle Willis 4.00 10.00
JB Josh Beckett 3.00 8.00
JG Jason Giambi 3.00 8.00
JT Jim Thome 4.00 10.00
KW Kerry Wood 3.00 8.00
MP Mike Piazza 4.00 10.00
MP2 Mark Prior 4.00 10.00
MR Manny Ramirez 4.00 10.00
NG Nomar Garciaparra 4.00 10.00
PM Pedro Martinez 4.00 10.00
RH Roy Halladay 3.00 8.00
RJ Randy Johnson 4.00 10.00
RS Richie Sexson 3.00 8.00
TH Todd Helton 4.00 10.00
VG Vladimir Guerrero 4.00 10.00

2004 Fleer Tradition Retrospection

STATED ODDS 1:360
1 Rickie Weeks 6.00 15.00
2 Delmon Young 8.00 20.00
3 Torii Hunter 6.00 15.00
4 Aubrey Huff 6.00 15.00
5 Rocco Baldelli 6.00 15.00
6 Mike Lowell 6.00 15.00
7 Dontrelle Willis 8.00 20.00
8 Albert Pujols 12.50 30.00
9 Bo Hart 6.00 15.00
10 Brandon Webb 6.00 15.00

2004 Fleer Tradition Retrospection Autographs

Please note that a few players did not return their autographs in time for inclusion in this product and no expiration date was set for redeeming those cards.

OVERALL AUTO ODDS 1:720
STATED PRINT RUN 60 SERIAL #'d SETS
AH Aubrey Huff 10.00 25.00
AK Austin Kearns 10.00 25.00
AP Albert Pujols EXCH
BO Bo Hart 10.00 25.00
BW Brandon Webb 10.00 25.00
CP Corey Patterson 10.00 25.00
DW Dontrelle Willis 15.00 40.00
DY Delmon Young EXCH
HB Hank Blalock 10.00 25.00
JR Jose Reyes 10.00 25.00
JW Josh Willingham 10.00 25.00
MR Mike Ryan 10.00 25.00
RW Ryan Wagner EXCH
RW Rickie Weeks 10.00 25.00
SR Scott Rolen 15.00 40.00
TH Torii Hunter 10.00 25.00

2004 Fleer Tradition Retrospection Autographs Dual

OVERALL AUTO ODDS 1:720
STATED PRINT RUN 19 SERIAL #'d SETS
NO PRICING DUE TO SCARCITY
EXCHANGE DEADLINE INDEFINITE
AHAK Aubrey Huff
Austin Kearns
APBH Albert Pujols
Bo Hart EXCH
BWRW Brandon Webb
Ryan Wagner EXCH
CPJR Corey Patterson
Jose Reyes
HBSR Hank Blalock
Scott Rolen
JWDW Josh Willingham
Dontrelle Willis
RWDY Rickie Weeks
Delmon Young EXCH
THMR Torii Hunter
Mike Ryan

2004 Fleer Tradition Stand Outs Game Used

STATED ODDS 1:41
GOLD RANDOM INSERTS IN PACKS
GOLD PRINTS B/WN 20-27 COPIES PER
NO GOLD PRICING DUE TO SCARCITY
AB Angel Berroa Pants 3.00 8.00
BH Bo Hart Jsy 3.00 8.00
BW Brandon Webb Pants 3.00 8.00
DW Dontrelle Willis Jsy 4.00 10.00
HB Hank Blalock Jsy 3.00 8.00
HC Hee Seop Choi Jsy 3.00 8.00
JR Jose Reyes Jsy 3.00 8.00
MB Marlon Byrd Jsy 3.00 8.00
MC Miguel Cabrera Jsy 4.00 10.00
MT Mark Teixeira Jsy 4.00 10.00
RB Rocco Baldelli Jsy 3.00 8.00

2004 Fleer Tradition This Day in History

STATED ODDS 1:18
1 Josh Beckett .60 1.50
2 Carlos Delgado .60 1.50
3 Javy Lopez .60 1.50
4 Greg Maddux 1.50 4.00
5 Rafael Palmeiro .60 1.50
6 Sammy Sosa 1.00 2.50
7 Jeff Bagwell .60 1.50
8 Frank Thomas 1.00 2.50
9 Kevin Millwood .60 1.50
10 Jose Reyes .60 1.50
11 Rafael Furcal .60 1.50
12 Alfonso Soriano .60 1.50
13 Eric Gagne .60 1.50
14 Hideki Matsui 1.50 4.00
15 Hank Blalock .60 1.50

2004 Fleer Tradition This Day in History Game Used

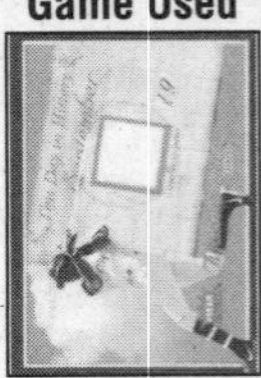

STATED ODDS 1:288
AS Alfonso Soriano Jsy 4.00 10.00
CD Carlos Delgado Jsy 4.00 10.00
FT Frank Thomas Jsy 6.00 15.00
GM Greg Maddux Jsy 6.00 15.00
JB Josh Beckett Jsy 4.00 10.00
JB Jeff Bagwell Jsy 6.00 15.00
JL Javy Lopez Jsy 4.00 10.00
JR Jose Reyes Jsy 4.00 10.00
RP Rafael Palmeiro Jsy 6.00 15.00
SS Sammy Sosa Bat 6.00 15.00

2004 Fleer Tradition This Day in History Game Used Dual

RANDOM INSERTS IN PACKS
STATED PRINT RUN 25 SERIAL #'d SETS
NO PRICING DUE TO SCARCITY
CDJR Carlos Delgado Jsy
Jose Reyes Jsy
FTJB Frank Thomas Jsy
Jeff Bagwell Jsy
JBGM Josh Beckett Jsy
Greg Maddux Jsy
JLAS Javy Lopez Jsy
Alfonso Soriano Jsy
RPSS Rafael Palmeiro Jsy
Sammy Sosa Bat

2005 Fleer Tradition

This 350-card set was released in February, 2005. The set was issued in 10-card hobby or retail packs. The hobby packs came 36 packs to a box and 20 boxes to a case while the retail packs came 24 packs to a box and 20 boxes to a case. The first 300 cards were all printed to the same quantity and there is a season leader subset in the first 12 cards. Cards 301-330 feature a grouping of prospects while 331-340 feature Award Winners and cards 341-350 feature Post-Season heroes. These cards were issued at an overall stated rate of one in two hobby packs and one in four retail packs. Many dealers believe that cards 301-330 were significantly tougher to pull than cards 331-350.

COMPLETE SET (350) 75.00 150.00
COMP.SET w/o SP's (300) 15.00 40.00
COMMON CARD (1-300) .10 .30
COMMON CARD (301-330) 2.00 5.00
COMMON CARD (331-350) .40 1.00
301-350 STATED ODDS 1:2 H, 1:4 R
1 Johan Santana .20 .50
Curt Schilling
Jake Westbrook SL
2 Ben Sheets .20 .50
Jake Peavy
Randy Johnson SL
3 Johan Santana .10 .30
Bartolo Colon
Curt Schilling SL
4 Carl Pavano .30 .75
Roy Oswalt
Roger Clemens SL
5 Johan Santana .10 .30
Pedro Martinez
Curt Schilling SL
6 Jason Schmidt .20 .50
Randy Johnson
Ben Sheets SL
7 Melvin Mora .30 .75
Vladimir Guerrero
Ichiro Suzuki SL
8 Adrian Beltre .10 .30
Todd Helton
Mark Loretta SL
9 Manny Ramirez .20 .50
Paul Konerko
David Ortiz SL
10 Albert Pujols .30 .75
Adrian Beltre
Adam Dunn SL
11 David Ortiz .20 .50
Manny Ramirez
Miguel Tejada SL
12 Albert Pujols .20 .50
Vinny Castilla
Scott Rolen SL
13 Jason Bay .10 .30
14 Greg Maddux .50 1.25
15 Melvin Mora .10 .30
16 Matt Stairs .10 .30
17 Scott Podsednik .10 .30
18 Bartolo Colon .10 .30
19 Roger Clemens .50 1.25
20 Eric Hinske .10 .30
21 Johnny Estrada .10 .30
22 Brett Tomko .10 .30
23 John Buck .10 .30
24 Nomar Garciaparra .30 .75
25 Milton Bradley .10 .30
26 Craig Biggio .20 .50
27 Kyle Denney .10 .30
28 Brad Penny .10 .30
29 Todd Helton .20 .50
30 Luis Gonzalez .10 .30
31 Bill Hall .10 .30
32 Ruben Sierra .10 .30
33 Zack Greinke .10 .30
34 Sandy Alomar Jr. .10 .30
35 Jason Giambi .10 .30
36 Ben Sheets .10 .30
37 Edgardo Alfonzo .10 .30
38 Kenny Rogers .10 .30
39 Coco Crisp .10 .30
40 Randy Choate .10 .30
41 Braden Looper .10 .30
42 Adam Dunn .10 .30
43 Adam Eaton .10 .30
44 Luis Castillo .10 .30
45 Casey Fossum .10 .30
46 Mike Piazza .30 .75
47 Juan Pierre .10 .30
48 Doug Davis .10 .30
49 Manny Ramirez .20 .50
50 Travis Hafner .10 .30
51 Jack Wilson .10 .30
52 Mike Maroth .10 .30
53 Ken Harvey .10 .30
54 Brooks Kieschnick .10 .30
55 Brad Fullmer .10 .30
56 Octavio Dotel .10 .30
57 Mike Matheny .10 .30
58 Andruw Jones .20 .50
59 Alfonso Soriano .10 .30
60 Royce Clayton .10 .30
61 Jon Garland .10 .30
62 John Mabry .10 .30
63 Rafael Palmeiro .20 .50
64 Garett Atkins .10 .30
65 Brian Meadows .10 .30
66 Tony Armas Jr. .10 .30
67 Toby Hall .10 .30
68 Carlos Baerga .10 .30
69 Barry Larkin .20 .50
70 Jody Gerut .10 .30
71 Brent Mayne .10 .30
72 Shigetoshi Hasegawa .10 .30
73 Jose Cruz Jr. .10 .30
74 Dan Wilson .10 .30
75 Sidney Ponson .10 .30
76 Jason Jennings .10 .30
77 A.J. Burnett .10 .30
78 Tony Batista .10 .30
79 Kris Benson .10 .30
80 Sean Burroughs .10 .30
81 Eric Young .10 .30
82 Casey Kotchman .10 .30
83 Derrek Lee .20 .50
84 Mariano Rivera .30 .75
85 Julio Franco .10 .30
86 Corey Patterson .10 .30
87 Carlos Beltran .10 .30
88 Trevor Hoffman .10 .30
89 Danny Garcia .10 .30
90 Marcos Scutaro .10 .30
91 Marquis Grissom .10 .30
92 Aubrey Huff .10 .30
93 Tony Womack .10 .30
94 Placido Polanco .10 .30
95 Bengie Molina .10 .30
96 Roger Cedeno .10 .30
97 Geoff Jenkins .10 .30
98 Kip Wells .10 .30
99 Derek Jeter .60 1.50
100 Omar Infante .10 .30
101 Phil Nevin .10 .30
102 Edgar Renteria .10 .30
103 B.J. Surhoff .10 .30
104 David DeJesus .10 .30
105 Raul Ibanez .10 .30
106 Hank Blalock .10 .30
107 Shawn Estes .10 .30
108 Wily Mo Pena .10 .30
109 Shawn Green .10 .30
110 David Wright .75 2.00
111 Kenny Lofton .10 .30
112 Matt Clement .10 .30
113 Cesar Izturis .10 .30
114 John Lackey .10 .30
115 Torii Hunter .10 .30
116 Charles Johnson .10 .30
117 Ray Durham .10 .30
118 Luke Hudson .10 .30
119 Jeremy Bonderman .10 .30
120 Sean Casey .10 .30
121 Johnny Damon .20 .50
122 Eric Milton .10 .30
123 Shea Hillenbrand .10 .30
124 Johan Santana .30 .75
125 Jim Edmonds .10 .30
126 Javier Vazquez .10 .30
127 Jon Adkins .10 .30
128 Mike Lowell .10 .30
129 Khalil Greene .20 .50
130 Quinton McCracken .10 .30
131 Edgar Martinez .20 .50
132 Matt Lawton .10 .30
133 Jeff Weaver .10 .30
134 Marlon Byrd .10 .30
135 John Smoltz .20 .50
136 Grady Sizemore .20 .50
137 Brian Roberts .10 .30
138 Dee Brown .10 .30
139 Joel Pineiro .10 .30
140 David Dellucci .10 .30
141 Bobby Higginson .10 .30
142 Ryan Madson .10 .30
143 Scott Hatteberg .10 .30
144 Greg Zaun .10 .30
145 Brian Jordan .10 .30
146 Jason Isringhausen .10 .30
147 Vinnie Chulk .10 .30
148 Al Leiter .10 .30
149 Pedro Martinez .20 .50
150 Carlos Guillen .10 .30
151 Randy Wolf .10 .30
152 Vernon Wells .10 .30
153 Barry Zito .10 .30
154 Pedro Feliz .10 .30
155 Omar Vizquel .20 .50
156 Chone Figgins .10 .30
157 David Ortiz .20 .50
158 Sunny Kim .10 .30
159 Adam Kennedy .10 .30
160 Carlos Lee .10 .30
161 Rick Ankiel .10 .30
162 Roy Oswalt .10 .30
163 Armando Benitez .10 .30
164 Erubiel Durazo .10 .30
165 Adam Hyzdu .10 .30
166 Esteban Yan .10 .30
167 Victor Santos .10 .30
168 Kevin Millwood .10 .30
169 Andy Pettitte .20 .50
170 Mike Cameron .10 .30
171 Scott Rolen .20 .50
172 Trot Nixon .10 .30
173 Eric Munson .10 .30
174 Roy Halladay .10 .30
175 Juan Encarnacion .10 .30
176 Eric Chavez .10 .30
177 Terrmel Sledge .10 .30
178 Jason Schmidt .10 .30
179 Endy Chavez .10 .30
180 Carlos Zambrano .10 .30
181 Carlos Delgado .10 .30
182 Dewon Brazelton .10 .30
183 J.D. Drew .10 .30
184 Orlando Cabrera .10 .30
185 Craig Wilson .10 .30
186 Chin-Hui Tsao .10 .30
187 Jolbert Cabrera .10 .30
188 Rod Barajas .10 .30
189 Craig Monroe .10 .30
190 Dave Berg .10 .30
191 Carlos Silva .10 .30
192 Eric Gagne .10 .30
193 Marcus Giles .10 .30
194 Nick Johnson .10 .30
195 Kelvim Escobar .10 .30
196 Wade Miller .10 .30
197 David Bell .10 .30
198 Rondell White .10 .30
199 Brian Giles .10 .30
200 Jeromy Burnitz .10 .30
201 Carl Pavano .10 .30
202 Alex Rios .10 .30
203 Ryan Freel .10 .30
204 R.A. Dickey .10 .30
205 Miguel Cairo .10 .30
206 Kerry Wood .10 .30
207 C.C. Sabathia .10 .30
208 Jaime Cerda .10 .30
209 Jerome Williams .10 .30
210 Ryan Wagner .10 .30
211 Javy Lopez .10 .30
212 Tike Redman .10 .30
213 Richie Sexson .10 .30
214 Shannon Stewart .10 .30
215 Ben Davis .10 .30
216 Jeff Bagwell .20 .50
217 David Wells .10 .30
218 Justin Leone .10 .30
219 Brad Radke .10 .30
220 Ramon Santiago .10 .30
221 Richard Hidalgo .10 .30
222 Aaron Miles .10 .30
223 Mark Loretta .10 .30
224 Aaron Boone .10 .30
225 Steve Trachsel .10 .30
226 Geoff Blum .10 .30
227 Shingo Takatsu .10 .30
228 Kevin Youkilis .10 .30
229 Laynce Nix .10 .30
230 Daniel Cabrera .10 .30
231 Kyle Lohse .10 .30
232 Todd Pratt .10 .30
233 Reed Johnson .10 .30
234 Lance Berkman .10 .30
235 Hideki Matsui .50 1.25
236 Randy Winn .10 .30
237 Joe Randa .10 .30
238 Bob Howry .10 .30
239 Jason LaRue .10 .30
240 Jose Valentin .10 .30
241 Livan Hernandez .10 .30
242 Jamie Moyer .10 .30
243 Garret Anderson .10 .30
244 Brad Ausmus .10 .30
245 Russell Branyan .10 .30
246 Paul Wilson .10 .30
247 Tim Wakefield .10 .30
248 Roberto Alomar .20 .50
249 Kazuhisa Ishii .10 .30
250 Tino Martinez .20 .50
251 Tomo Ohka .10 .30
252 Mark Redman .10 .30
253 Paul Byrd .10 .30
254 Greg Aquino .10 .30
255 Adrian Beltre .10 .30
256 Ricky Ledee .10 .30
257 Josh Fogg .10 .30
258 Derek Lowe .10 .30
259 Lew Ford .10 .30
260 Bobby Crosby .10 .30
261 Jim Thome .20 .50
262 Jaret Wright .10 .30
263 Chin-Feng Chen .10 .30
264 Troy Glaus .10 .30
265 Jorge Sosa .10 .30
266 Mike Lamb .10 .30
267 Russ Ortiz .10 .30
268 Reggie Sanders .10 .30
269 Orlando Hudson .10 .30
270 Rodrigo Lopez .10 .30
271 Jose Vidro .10 .30
272 Akinori Otsuka .10 .30
273 Victor Martinez .10 .30
274 Carl Crawford .10 .30
275 Roberto Novoa .10 .30
276 Brian Lawrence .10 .30
277 Angel Berroa .10 .30
278 Josh Beckett .10 .30
279 Lyle Overbay .10 .30
280 Dustin Hermanson .10 .30
281 Jeff Conine .10 .30
282 Mark Prior .20 .50
283 Kevin Brown .10 .30
284 Magglio Ordonez .10 .30
285 Dontrelle Willis .10 .30

286 Dallas McPherson .10 .30
287 Rafael Furcal .10 .30
288 Ty Wigginton .10 .30
289 Moises Alou .10 .30
290 A.J. Pierzynski .10 .30
291 Todd Walker .10 .30
292 Hideo Nomo .30 .75
293 Larry Walker .20 .50
294 Choo Freeman .10 .30
295 Eduardo Perez .10 .30
296 Miguel Tejada .10 .30
297 Corey Koskie .10 .30
298 Jermaine Dye .10 .30
299 John Riedling .10 .30
300 John Olerud .10 .30
301 Tim Bittner 2.00 5.00
Jake Woods
Bobby Jenks TP
302 Josh Kroeger 2.00 5.00
Casey Daigle
Brandon Medders TP
303 Kelly Johnson 2.00 5.00
Charles Thomas
Dan Meyer TP
304 Eddy Rodriguez 2.00 5.00
Ryan Hannaman
John Maine TP
305 Anastacio Martinez 2.00 5.00
Jerome Gamble
Lenny Dinardo TP
306 Ronny Cedeno 2.00 5.00
Carlos Vasquez
Renyel Pinto TP
307 Arnie Munoz 2.00 5.00
Ryan Wing
Felix Diaz TP
308 William Bergolla 2.00 5.00
Ray Olmedo
Edwin Encarnacion TP
309 Mariano Gomez 2.00 5.00
Ivan Ochoa
Kazuhito Tadano TP
310 Tony Miller 2.50 6.00
Jeff Baker
Matt Holliday TP
311 Preston Larrison 2.00 5.00
Curtis Granderson
Ryan Raburn TP
312 Josh Wilson 2.00 5.00
Logan Kensing
Kevin Cave TP
313 Hector Gimenez 2.00 5.00
Willy Taveras
Taylor Buchholz TP
314 Ruben Gotay 2.00 5.00
Brian Bass
Andres Blanco TP
315 Joel Hanrahan 2.00 5.00
Willy Aybar
Yhency Brazoban TP
316 Dave Krynzel 2.00 5.00
Ben Hendrickson
Corey Hart TP
317 Colby Miller 2.00 5.00
Jason Kubel
J.D. Durbin TP
318 Maicer Izturis 2.00 5.00
Chad Cordero
Brandon Watson TP
319 Victor Diaz 2.00 5.00
Aarom Baldiris
Wayne Lydon TP
320 Edwardo Sierra 2.00 5.00
Dioner Navarro
Sean Henn TP
321 Nick Swisher 2.00 5.00
Joe Blanton
Dan Johnson TP
322 Ryan Howard 2.00 5.00
Gavin Floyd
Keith Bucktrot TP
323 Ryan Doumit 2.00 5.00
Sean Burnett
Bobby Bradley TP
324 Justin Germano 2.00 5.00
Rusty Tucker
Freddy Guzman TP
325 David Aardsma 2.00 5.00
Justin Knoedler
Alfredo Simon TP
326 Jose Lopez 2.00 5.00
Rene Rivera
Cha Seung Baek TP
327 Yadier Molina 2.00 5.00
Evan Rust
Adam Wainwright TP
328 Jorge Cantu 2.00 5.00
Scott Kazmir
B.J. Upton TP
329 Adrian Gonzalez 2.00 5.00
Ramon Nivar
Jason Bourgeois TP
330 Russ Adams 2.00 5.00
Dustin McGowan
Gustavo Chacin TP
331 Alfonso Soriano AW .40 1.00
332 Albert Pujols AW 1.25 3.00
333 David Ortiz AW .60 1.50
334 Manny Ramirez AW .60 1.50
335 Jason Bay AW .40 1.00
336 Bobby Crosby AW .40 1.00
337 Roger Clemens AW 1.00 2.50
338 Johan Santana AW .60 1.50
339 Jim Thome AW .60 1.50
340 Vladimir Guerrero AW .60 1.50
341 David Ortiz PS .60 1.50
342 Alex Rodriguez PS 1.00 2.50
343 Albert Pujols PS 1.25 3.00
344 Carlos Beltran PS .40 1.00
345 Johnny Damon PS .60 1.50
346 Scott Rolen PS .60 1.50
347 Larry Walker PS .60 1.50
348 Curt Schilling PS .60 1.50
349 Pedro Martinez PS .60 1.50
350 David Ortiz PS .60 1.50

2005 Fleer Tradition Gray Backs

*GRAY BACK 1-300: 1.25X TO 3X BASIC
*GRAY BACK 301-330: .5X TO 1.2X BASIC
*GRAY BACK 331-350: .6X TO 1.5X BASIC
STATED ODDS 1:2 HOBBY, 1:2 RETAIL

2005 Fleer Tradition Gray Backs Gold Letter

*GOLD LTR: 6X TO 15X BASIC
STATED ODDS 1:96 HOBBY, 1:288 RETAIL
STATED APPROX. PRINT RUN 185 SETS
PRINT RUN INFO PROVIDED BY FLEER
CARDS ARE NOT SERIAL-NUMBERED

2005 Fleer Tradition Club 3000/500/300

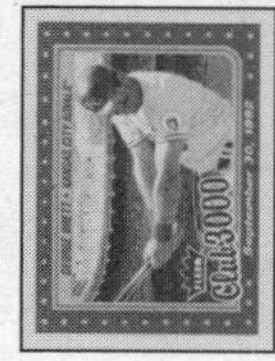

STATED ODDS 1:360 HOBBY, 1:480 RETAIL
STATED APPROX. PRINT RUN 175 SETS
PRINT RUN INFO PROVIDED BY FLEER
1 Ernie Banks 500 10.00 25.00
2 Stan Musial 3000 12.50 30.00
3 Steve Carlton 3000 6.00 15.00
4 Greg Maddux 300 10.00 25.00
5 Dave Winfield 3000 6.00 15.00
6 Rafael Palmeiro 500 8.00 20.00
7 Rickey Henderson 3000 10.00 25.00
8 Roger Clemens 3000 10.00 25.00
9 Don Sutton 300 6.00 15.00
10 George Brett 3000 12.50 30.00
11 Reggie Jackson 500 8.00 20.00
12 Wade Boggs 3000 8.00 20.00
13 Bob Gibson 3000 8.00 20.00
14 Eddie Murray 3000 10.00 25.00
15 Tom Seaver 3000 8.00 20.00
16 Willie McCovey 500 8.00 20.00
17 Rod Carew 3000 8.00 20.00
18 Fergie Jenkins 300 6.00 15.00
19 Phil Niekro 300 6.00 15.00
20 Frank Robinson 500 6.00 15.00

2005 Fleer Tradition Cooperstown Tribute

STATED ODDS 1:72 HOBBY
RANDOM INSERTS IN RETAIL PACKS
*GOLD: .4X TO 1X BASIC
GOLD ODDS 1:24 RETAIL
1 Mike Schmidt/1995 4.00 10.00
2 Al Kaline/1980 3.00 8.00
3 Yogi Berra/1972 3.00 8.00
4 Robin Yount/1999 3.00 8.00
5 Joe Morgan/1990 2.00 5.00
6 Willie Stargell/1988 2.00 5.00
7 Harmon Killebrew/1984 3.00 8.00
8 Nolan Ryan/1999 5.00 12.00
9 Carlton Fisk/2000 2.00 5.00
10 Johnny Bench/1989 3.00 8.00

2005 Fleer Tradition Cooperstown Tribute Jersey

STATED ODDS 1:200 H, 1:1250 R
STATED APPROX. PRINT RUN 400 SETS
STATED SP PRINT RUN 20 COPIES PER
PRINT RUN INFO PROVIDED BY FLEER
NO SP PRICING DUE TO SCARCITY
PATCH RANDOM IN HOB/RET PACKS
PATCH PRINT RUN 10 SERIAL #'d SETS
NO PATCH PRICING DUE TO SCARCITY
AK Al Kaline 10.00 25.00
CF Carlton Fisk 6.00 15.00
HK Harmon Killebrew 6.00 15.00
JB Johnny Bench 6.00 15.00
JM Joe Morgan SP/20 *
MS Mike Schmidt 8.00 20.00
NR Nolan Ryan 12.50 30.00
RY Robin Yount 6.00 15.00
WS Willie Stargell 6.00 15.00
YB Yogi Berra SP/20 *

2005 Fleer Tradition Diamond Tributes

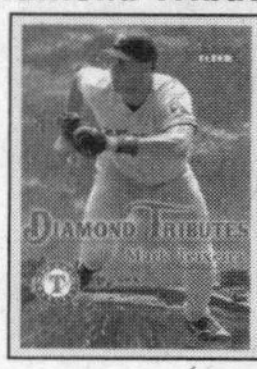

COMPLETE SET (25) 10.00 25.00
STATED ODDS 1:6 H, 1:8 R
1 Albert Pujols 1.25 3.00
2 Alex Rodriguez 1.00 2.50
3 Ken Griffey Jr. 1.00 2.50
4 Sammy Sosa .60 1.50
5 Chipper Jones .60 1.50
6 Johan Santana .60 1.50
7 Roger Clemens 1.00 2.50
8 Pedro Martinez .60 1.50
9 Jim Thome .60 1.50
10 Greg Maddux 1.00 2.50
11 Alfonso Soriano .40 1.00
12 Derek Jeter 1.25 3.00
13 Randy Johnson .60 1.50
14 Miguel Cabrera .40 1.00
15 Adrian Beltre .40 1.00
16 Ivan Rodriguez .60 1.50
17 Manny Ramirez .60 1.50
18 Mark Teixeira .60 1.50
19 Adam Dunn .40 1.00
20 Scott Rolen .60 1.50
21 Mike Piazza .60 1.50
22 J.D. Drew .40 1.00
23 Hideki Matsui 1.00 2.50
24 Nomar Garciaparra .60 1.50
25 Kaz Matsui .40 1.00

2005 Fleer Tradition Diamond Tributes Game Used

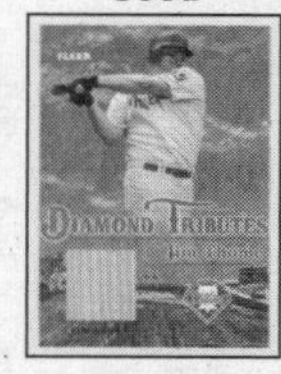

STATED ODDS 1:30 H, 1:625 R
SP PRINT RUNS PROVIDED BY FLEER
SP'S ARE NOT SERIAL-NUMBERED
NO SP PRICING DUE TO SCARCITY
AB Adrian Beltre Bat 3.00 8.00
AP Albert Pujols Bat 6.00 15.00
AS Alfonso Soriano Bat 3.00 8.00
CJ Chipper Jones Bat 4.00 10.00
GM Greg Maddux Jsy 4.00 10.00
HM Hideki Matsui Bat 6.00 15.00
JD J.D. Drew Bat 3.00 8.00
JS Johan Santana Jsy 4.00 10.00
JT Jim Thome Bat 4.00 10.00
KM Kaz Matsui Bat 3.00 8.00
MC Miguel Cabrera Bat SP/30 *
MP Mike Piazza Bat 4.00 10.00
MR Manny Ramirez Bat 4.00 10.00
MT Mark Teixeira Bat 4.00 10.00
NG Nomar Garciaparra Bat 4.00 10.00
PM Pedro Martinez Jsy 4.00 10.00
RC Roger Clemens Jsy 4.00 10.00
RJ Randy Johnson Jsy 4.00 10.00
SR Scott Rolen Bat SP/27 *
SS Sammy Sosa Bat 4.00 10.00

2005 Fleer Tradition Diamond Tributes Patch

*PATCH: 1X TO 2.5X BASIC DT JSY
RANDOM INSERTS IN HOB/RET PACKS
STATED PRINT RUN 50 SERIAL #'d SETS
IR Ivan Rodriguez 10.00 25.00
MC Miguel Cabrera 10.00 25.00
SR Scott Rolen 10.00 25.00

2005 Fleer Tradition Diamond Tributes Dual Patch

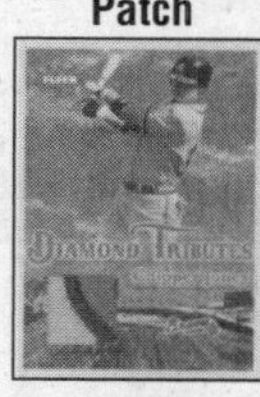

RANDOM INSERTS IN HOB/RET PACKS
STATED PRINT RUN 25 SERIAL #'d SETS
NO PRICING DUE TO SCARCITY
APSR Albert Pujols
Scott Rolen
ASMT Alfonso Soriano
Mark Teixeira
CJJD Chipper Jones
J.D. Drew
HMKM Hideki Matsui
Kaz Matsui
JTAB Jim Thome
Adrian Beltre
MPIR Mike Piazza
Ivan Rodriguez
PMMR Pedro Martinez
Manny Ramirez
RCJS Roger Clemens
Johan Santana
RJGM Randy Johnson
Greg Maddux
SSMC Miguel Cabrera
Sammy Sosa

2005 Fleer Tradition Standouts

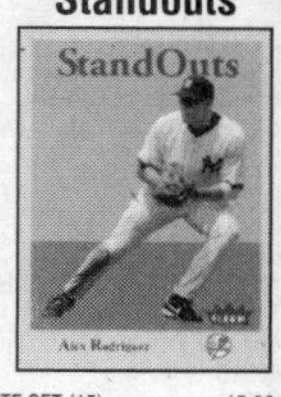

COMPLETE SET (15) 15.00 40.00
STATED ODDS 1:18 H, 1:24 R
1 Albert Pujols 2.00 5.00
2 Ichiro Suzuki 2.00 5.00
3 Derek Jeter 2.00 5.00
4 Randy Johnson 1.00 2.50
5 Greg Maddux 1.50 4.00
6 Hideki Matsui 1.50 4.00
7 Mike Piazza 1.00 2.50
8 Vladimir Guerrero 1.00 2.50
9 Sammy Sosa 1.00 2.50
10 Jim Thome 1.00 2.50
11 Chipper Jones 1.00 2.50
12 Alex Rodriguez 1.50 4.00
13 Roger Clemens 1.50 4.00
14 Nomar Garciaparra 1.00 2.50
15 Lance Berkman .60 1.50

2005 Fleer Tradition Standouts Jersey

STATED ODDS 1:65 H, 1:950 R
*PATCH: 1X TO 2.5X BASIC
PATCH RANDOM IN HOB/RET PACKS
PATCH PRINT RUN 50 SERIAL #'d SETS
AP Albert Pujols 6.00 15.00
CJ Chipper Jones 4.00 10.00
GM Greg Maddux 4.00 10.00
HM Hideki Matsui 8.00 20.00
JT Jim Thome 4.00 10.00
LB Lance Berkman 3.00 8.00
MP Mike Piazza 4.00 10.00
RC Roger Clemens 4.00 10.00
RJ Randy Johnson 4.00 10.00
SS Sammy Sosa 4.00 10.00
VG Vladimir Guerrero 4.00 10.00

2006 Fleer Tradition

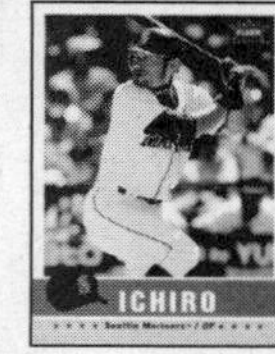

This 200-card set was released in August, 2006. The set was issued in 10-card hobby packs, with an $1.99 SRP which came 36 packs per box and 12 boxes per case. This product was also issued in a retail pack format. The major difference between the retail and hobby packs was that the hobby boxes had stated information that there was either a memorabilia or a printing plate card in every box.

COMPLETE SET (200) 12.50 30.00

2006 Fleer Tradition

COMMON CARD (1-200) .12 .30
COMMON RC (1-200) .20 .50
OVERALL PLATE ODDS 1:288 HOBBY
PLATE PRINT RUN 1 SET PER COLOR
BLACK-CYAN-MAGENTA-YELLOW ISSUED
NO PLATE PRICING DUE TO SCARCITY
EXQUISITE EXCH ODDS 1:864 HOBBY
EXQUISITE EXCH DEADLINE 07/27/07
1 Andruw Jones .20 .50
2 Chipper Jones .30 .75
3 John Smoltz .20 .50
4 Tim Hudson .12 .30
5 Joey Devine RC .20 .50
6 Chuck James (RC) .30 .75
7 Alay Soler RC .20 .50
8 Conor Jackson (RC) .30 .75
9 Luis Gonzalez .12 .30
10 Brandon Webb .12 .30
11 Chad Tracy .12 .30
12 Orlando Hudson .12 .30
13 Shawn Green .12 .30
14 Vladimir Guerrero .30 .75
15 Bartolo Colon .12 .30
16 Chone Figgins .12 .30
17 Garret Anderson .12 .30
18 Francisco Rodriguez .12 .30
19 Casey Kotchman .12 .30
20 Lance Berkman .12 .30
21 Craig Biggio .20 .50
22 Andy Pettitte .20 .50
23 Morgan Ensberg .12 .30
24 Brad Lidge .12 .30
25 Jered Weaver (RC) 1.00 2.50
26 Roy Oswalt .12 .30
27 Eric Chavez .12 .30
28 Rich Harden .12 .30
29 Cole Hamels (RC) .75 2.00
30 Huston Street .12 .30
31 Bobby Crosby .12 .30
32 Nick Swisher .12 .30
33 Vernon Wells .12 .30
34 Roy Halladay .12 .30
35 A.J. Burnett .12 .30
36 Troy Glaus .12 .30
37 B.J. Ryan .12 .30
38 Bengie Molina .12 .30
39 Alex Rios .12 .30
40 Prince Fielder (RC) .75 2.00
41 Jose Capellan (RC) .20 .50
42 Rickie Weeks .12 .30
43 Ben Sheets .12 .30
44 Carlos Lee .12 .30
45 J.J. Hardy .12 .30
46 Albert Pujols .60 1.50
47 Skip Schumaker (RC) .20 .50
48 Adam Wainwright (RC) .20 .50
49 Jim Edmonds .20 .50
50 Scott Rolen .20 .50
51 Chris Carpenter .20 .50
52 David Eckstein .12 .30
53 Derrek Lee .12 .30
54 Jon Lester RC 1.25 3.00
55 Mark Prior .20 .50
56 Aramis Ramirez .12 .30
57 Juan Pierre .12 .30
58 Greg Maddux .50 1.25
59 Michael Barrett .12 .30
60 Carl Crawford .12 .30
61 Scott Kazmir .20 .50
62 Jorge Cantu .12 .30
63 Jonny Gomes .12 .30
64 Julio Lugo .12 .30
65 Aubrey Huff .12 .30
66 Jeff Kent .12 .30
67 Nomar Garciaparra .30 .75
68 Rafael Furcal .12 .30
69 Tim Hamulack (RC) .20 .50
70 Chad Billingsley (RC) .30 .75
71 Hong-Chih Kuo (RC) .50 1.25
72 J.D. Drew .12 .30
73 Moises Alou .12 .30
74 Randy Winn .12 .30
75 Jason Schmidt .12 .30
76 Jeremy Accardo RC .20 .50
77 Matt Cain (RC) .30 .75
78 Joel Zumaya (RC) .50 1.25
79 Travis Hafner .12 .30
80 Victor Martinez .12 .30
81 Grady Sizemore .20 .50
82 C.C. Sabathia .12 .30
83 Jhonny Peralta .12 .30
84 Jason Michaels .12 .30
85 Jeremy Sowers (RC) .20 .50
86 Ichiro Suzuki .50 1.25
87 Richie Sexson .12 .30
88 Adrian Beltre .12 .30
89 Felix Hernandez .20 .50
90 Kenji Johjima RC 1.00 2.50
91 Jeff Harris RC .20 .50
92 Taylor Buchholz (RC) .30 .75
93 Miguel Cabrera .20 .50
94 Dontrelle Willis .12 .30
95 Jeremy Hermida (RC) .20 .50
96 Mike Jacobs (RC) .20 .50
97 Josh Johnson (RC) .30 .75
98 Hanley Ramirez (RC) .50 1.25
99 Josh Willingham (RC) .20 .50
100 Dan Uggla (RC) .50 1.25
101 David Wright .50 1.25
102 Jose Reyes .30 .75
103 Pedro Martinez .20 .50
104 Carlos Beltran .12 .30
105 Carlos Delgado .12 .30
106 Billy Wagner .12 .30
107 Lastings Milledge (RC) .30 .75
108 Alfonso Soriano .12 .30
109 Jose Vidro .12 .30
110 Livan Hernandez .12 .30
111 Matt Kemp (RC) .30 .75
112 Brandon Watson (RC) .20 .50
113 Ryan Zimmerman (RC) 1.25 3.00
114 Miguel Tejada .12 .30
115 Ramon Hernandez .12 .30
116 Brian Roberts .12 .30
117 Melvin Mora .12 .30
118 Erik Bedard .12 .30
119 Jay Gibbons .12 .30
120 Aaron Rakers (RC) .20 .50
121 Jake Peavy .12 .30
122 Brian Giles .12 .30
123 Khalil Greene .20 .50
124 Trevor Hoffman .12 .30
125 Josh Barfield (RC) .20 .50
126 Ben Johnson (RC) .20 .50
127 Ryan Howard .50 1.25
128 Bobby Abreu .12 .30
129 Chase Utley .30 .75
130 Pat Burrell .12 .30
131 Jimmy Rollins .12 .30
132 Brett Myers .12 .30
133 Mike Thompson RC .20 .50
134 Jason Bay .12 .30
135 Oliver Perez .12 .30
136 Matt Capps (RC) .20 .50
137 Paul Maholm (RC) .20 .50
138 Nate McLouth (RC) .20 .50
139 John Van Benschoten (RC) .20 .50
140 Mark Teixeira .20 .50
141 Michael Young .12 .30
142 Hank Blalock .12 .30
143 Kevin Millwood .12 .30
144 Laynce Nix .12 .30
145 Francisco Cordero .12 .30
146 Ian Kinsler (RC) .30 .75
147 David Ortiz .30 .75
148 Manny Ramirez .20 .50
149 Jason Varitek .30 .75
150 Curt Schilling .20 .50
151 Josh Beckett .12 .30
152 Coco Crisp .12 .30
153 Jonathan Papelbon (RC) 1.00 2.50
154 Ken Griffey Jr. .50 1.25
155 Adam Dunn .12 .30
156 Felipe Lopez .12 .30
157 Bronson Arroyo .12 .30
158 Ryan Freel .12 .30
159 Chris Denorfia (RC) .20 .50
160 Todd Helton .20 .50
161 Garrett Atkins .12 .30
162 Matt Holliday .30 .75
163 Clint Barmes .12 .30
164 Kendry Morales (RC) .50 1.25
165 Ryan Shealy (RC) .20 .50
166 Josh Wilson (RC) .20 .50
167 Reggie Sanders .12 .30
168 Angel Berroa .12 .30
169 Mike Sweeney .12 .30
170 Mark Grudzielanek .12 .30
171 Jeremy Affeldt .12 .30
172 Steve Stemle RC .20 .50
173 Justin Verlander (RC) .75 2.00
174 Ivan Rodriguez .20 .50
175 Chris Shelton .12 .30
176 Jeremy Bonderman .12 .30
177 Magglio Ordonez .12 .30
178 Carlos Guillen .12 .30
179 Placido Polanco .12 .30
180 Johan Santana .20 .50
181 Torii Hunter .12 .30
182 Joe Nathan .12 .30
183 Joe Mauer .20 .50
184 Dave Gassner (RC) .20 .50
185 Jason Kubel (RC) .20 .50
186 Francisco Liriano (RC) 1.00 2.50
187 Jim Thome .20 .50
188 Paul Konerko .12 .30
189 Scott Podsednik .12 .30
190 Tadahito Iguchi .12 .30
191 A.J. Pierzynski .12 .30
192 Jose Contreras .12 .30
193 Brian Anderson (RC) .20 .50
194 Hideki Matsui .30 .75
195 Wil Nieves (RC) .20 .50
196 Alex Rodriguez .50 1.25
197 Gary Sheffield .12 .30
198 Randy Johnson .30 .75
199 Johnny Damon .20 .50
200 Derek Jeter .75 2.00
NNO Exquisite Redemption

2006 Fleer Tradition Black and White

*B/W 1-200: 2.5X TO 6X BASIC
*B/W 1-200: 1.25X TO 3X BASIC RC
STATED ODDS 1:9 HOBBY, 1:36 RETAIL

2006 Fleer Tradition Sepia

*SEPIA 1-200: 1X TO 2.5X BASIC
*SEPIA 1-200: .5X TO 1.2X BASIC RC
STATED ODDS 1:3 HOBBY, 1:18 RETAIL

2006 Fleer Tradition 1934 Goudey Greats

STATED ODDS 1:36 HOBBY
OVERALL PLATE ODDS 1:288 HOBBY
PLATE PRINT RUN 1 SET PER COLOR
BLACK-CYAN-MAGENTA-YELLOW ISSUED
NO PLATE PRICING DUE TO SCARCITY

GG1 Andruw Jones	3.00	8.00
GG2 Chipper Jones	5.00	12.00
GG3 John Smoltz	3.00	8.00
GG4 Tim Hudson	2.00	5.00
GG5 Conor Jackson	3.00	8.00
GG6 Luis Gonzalez	2.00	5.00
GG7 Brandon Webb	2.00	5.00
GG8 Vladimir Guerrero	5.00	12.00
GG9 Bartolo Colon	2.00	5.00
GG10 Lance Berkman	2.00	5.00
GG11 Craig Biggio	3.00	8.00
GG12 Andy Pettitte	3.00	8.00
GG13 Morgan Ensberg	2.00	5.00
GG14 Roy Oswalt	2.00	5.00
GG15 Eric Chavez	2.00	5.00
GG16 Rich Harden	2.00	5.00
GG17 Huston Street	2.00	5.00
GG18 Vernon Wells	2.00	5.00
GG19 Roy Halladay	2.00	5.00
GG20 Troy Glaus	2.00	5.00
GG21 Prince Fielder	8.00	20.00
GG22 Rickie Weeks	2.00	5.00
GG23 Ben Sheets	2.00	5.00
GG24 Carlos Lee	2.00	5.00
GG25 Albert Pujols	10.00	25.00
GG26 Jim Edmonds	3.00	8.00
GG27 Scott Rolen	3.00	8.00
GG28 Chris Carpenter	2.00	5.00
GG29 Derrek Lee	2.00	5.00
GG30 Mark Prior	3.00	8.00
GG31 Greg Maddux	8.00	20.00
GG32 Carl Crawford	2.00	5.00
GG33 Scott Kazmir	3.00	8.00
GG34 Jorge Cantu	2.00	5.00
GG35 Jeff Kent	2.00	5.00
GG36 Nomar Garciaparra	5.00	12.00
GG37 J.D. Drew	2.00	5.00
GG38 Randy Winn	2.00	5.00
GG39 Jason Schmidt	2.00	5.00
GG40 Travis Hafner	2.00	5.00
GG41 Victor Martinez	2.00	5.00
GG42 Grady Sizemore	3.00	8.00
GG43 Jhonny Peralta	2.00	5.00
GG44 Ichiro Suzuki	8.00	20.00
GG45 Richie Sexson	2.00	5.00
GG46 Felix Hernandez	3.00	8.00
GG47 Kenji Johjima	10.00	25.00
GG48 Miguel Cabrera	3.00	8.00
GG49 Dontrelle Willis	2.00	5.00
GG50 Josh Willingham	2.00	5.00
GG51 David Wright	8.00	20.00
GG52 Jose Reyes	5.00	12.00
GG53 Pedro Martinez	3.00	8.00
GG54 Carlos Beltran	2.00	5.00
GG55 Alfonso Soriano	2.00	5.00
GG56 Ryan Zimmerman	12.00	30.00
GG57 Miguel Tejada	2.00	5.00
GG58 Brian Roberts	2.00	5.00
GG59 Jake Peavy	2.00	5.00
GG60 Brian Giles	2.00	5.00
GG61 Khalil Greene	3.00	8.00
GG62 Ryan Howard	8.00	20.00
GG63 Bobby Abreu	2.00	5.00
GG64 Chase Utley	5.00	12.00
GG65 Jimmy Rollins	2.00	5.00
GG66 Jason Bay	2.00	5.00
GG67 Mark Teixeira	3.00	8.00
GG68 Michael Young	2.00	5.00
GG69 Hank Blalock	2.00	5.00
GG70 David Ortiz	5.00	12.00
GG71 Manny Ramirez	3.00	8.00
GG72 Curt Schilling	3.00	8.00
GG73 Josh Beckett	2.00	5.00
GG74 Jonathan Papelbon	10.00	25.00
GG75 Ken Griffey Jr.	8.00	20.00
GG76 Adam Dunn	2.00	5.00
GG77 Todd Helton	3.00	8.00
GG78 Garrett Atkins	2.00	5.00
GG79 Matt Holliday	5.00	12.00
GG80 Reggie Sanders	2.00	5.00
GG81 Justin Verlander	8.00	20.00
GG82 Ivan Rodriguez	3.00	8.00
GG83 Chris Shelton	2.00	5.00
GG84 Jeremy Bonderman	2.00	5.00
GG85 Magglio Ordonez	2.00	5.00
GG86 Johan Santana	3.00	8.00
GG87 Torii Hunter	2.00	5.00
GG88 Joe Nathan	2.00	5.00
GG89 Joe Mauer	3.00	8.00
GG90 Francisco Liriano	5.00	12.00
GG91 Jim Thome	3.00	8.00
GG92 Paul Konerko	2.00	5.00
GG93 Scott Podsednik	2.00	5.00
GG94 Tadahito Iguchi	2.00	5.00
GG95 A.J. Pierzynski	2.00	5.00
GG96 Hideki Matsui	5.00	12.00
GG97 Alex Rodriguez	8.00	20.00
GG98 Gary Sheffield	2.00	5.00
GG99 Derek Jeter	12.00	30.00
GG100 Jason Giambi	2.00	5.00

2006 Fleer Tradition Blue Chip Prospects

COMPLETE SET (25) 12.50 30.00
STATED ODDS 1:6 HOBBY, 1:18 RETAIL

OVERALL PLATE ODDS 1:288 HOBBY
PLATE PRINT RUN 1 SET PER COLOR
BLACK-CYAN-MAGENTA-YELLOW ISSUED
NO PLATE PRICING DUE TO SCARCITY

BC1 Ryan Zimmerman	2.50	6.00
BC2 Conor Jackson	.60	1.50
BC3 Jonathan Papelbon	2.00	5.00
BC4 Justin Verlander	1.50	4.00
BC5 Jeremy Hermida	.40	1.00
BC6 Josh Willingham	.40	1.00
BC7 Hanley Ramirez	1.00	2.50
BC8 Prince Fielder	1.50	4.00
BC9 Francisco Liriano	1.00	2.50
BC10 Lastings Milledge	.60	1.50
BC11 Jon Lester	2.50	6.00
BC12 Matt Cain	.60	1.50
BC13 Adam Wainwright	.40	1.00
BC14 Chuck James	.60	1.50
BC15 Kenji Johjima	2.00	5.00
BC16 Josh Johnson	.60	1.50
BC17 Jason Kubel	.40	1.00
BC18 Brian Anderson	.40	1.00
BC19 Cole Hamels	1.50	4.00
BC20 Mike Jacobs	.40	1.00
BC21 Jered Weaver	2.00	5.00
BC22 Kendry Morales	1.00	2.50
BC23 Alay Soler	.40	1.00
BC24 Chris Denorfia	.40	1.00
BC25 Chad Billingsley	.60	1.50

2006 Fleer Tradition Diamond Tribute

COMPLETE SET (25) 12.50 30.00
STATED ODDS 1:9 HOBBY, 1:36 RETAIL
OVERALL PLATE ODDS 1:288 HOBBY
PLATE PRINT RUN 1 SET PER COLOR
BLACK-CYAN-MAGENTA-YELLOW ISSUED
NO PLATE PRICING DUE TO SCARCITY

DT1 Derek Jeter	2.50	6.00
DT2 Ken Griffey Jr.	1.50	4.00
DT3 Vladimir Guerrero	1.00	2.50
DT4 Albert Pujols	2.00	5.00
DT5 Derrek Lee	.40	1.00
DT6 David Ortiz	1.00	2.50
DT7 Miguel Tejada	.40	1.00
DT8 Jim Thome	.60	1.50
DT9 Travis Hafner	.40	1.00
DT10 Grady Sizemore	.60	1.50
DT11 Chris Shelton	.40	1.00
DT12 Dontrelle Willis	.40	1.00
DT13 Craig Biggio	.60	1.50
DT14 Roy Oswalt	.40	1.00
DT15 Prince Fielder	1.50	4.00
DT16 David Wright	1.50	4.00
DT17 Jose Reyes	1.00	2.50
DT18 Hideki Matsui	1.00	2.50
DT19 Rich Harden	.40	1.00
DT20 Bobby Abreu	.40	1.00
DT21 Jason Bay	.40	1.00
DT22 Jake Peavy	.40	1.00
DT23 Felix Hernandez	.60	1.50
DT24 Carl Crawford	.40	1.00
DT25 Vernon Wells	.40	1.00

2006 Fleer Tradition Grass Roots

COMPLETE SET (25) 12.50 30.00
STATED ODDS 1:6 HOBBY, 1:36 RETAIL
OVERALL PLATE ODDS 1:288 HOBBY
PLATE PRINT RUN 1 SET PER COLOR
BLACK-CYAN-MAGENTA-YELLOW ISSUED
NO PLATE PRICING DUE TO SCARCITY

GR1 Ken Griffey Jr.	1.50	4.00
GR2 Albert Pujols	2.00	5.00
GR3 Derek Jeter	2.50	6.00
GR4 Derrek Lee	.40	1.00
GR5 Vladimir Guerrero	1.00	2.50
GR6 Andruw Jones	.60	1.50
GR7 Manny Ramirez	.60	1.50
GR8 Johan Santana	.60	1.50
GR9 Victor Martinez	.40	1.00
GR10 Todd Helton	.60	1.50
GR11 Ivan Rodriguez	.60	1.50
GR12 Miguel Cabrera	.60	1.50
GR13 Lance Berkman	.40	1.00
GR14 Bartolo Colon	.40	1.00
GR15 Jeff Kent	.40	1.00
GR16 Carlos Lee	.40	1.00
GR17 Torii Hunter	.40	1.00
GR18 Carlos Beltran	.40	1.00
GR19 Alex Rodriguez	1.50	4.00
GR20 Randy Johnson	1.00	2.50
GR21 Eric Chavez	.40	1.00
GR22 Ryan Howard	1.50	4.00
GR23 Ichiro Suzuki	1.50	4.00
GR24 Chris Carpenter	.40	1.00
GR25 Mark Teixeira	.60	1.50

2006 Fleer Tradition Ken Griffey Jr. 1989 Autograph Buyback

RANDOM INSERT IN HOBBY PACKS
STATED PRINT RUN 99 CARDS
CARD IS NOT SERIAL-NUMBERED
PRINT RUN PROVIDED BY UPPER DECK
NO PRICING DUE TO SCARCITY
548 Ken Griffey Jr./99 *

2006 Fleer Tradition Signature Tradition

STATED ODDS 1:1269 HOBBY, 1:3456 RETAIL
SP INFO PROVIDED BY UPPER DECK
NO PRICING DUE TO SCARCITY
OVERALL PLATE ODDS: 1:288 HOBBY
PLATE PRINT RUN 1 SET PER COLOR
BLACK-CYAN-MAGENTA-YELLOW-ISSUED
PLATES DO NOT FEATURE AUTOS
NO PLATE PRICING DUE TO SCARCITY
AN Brian Anderson SP
CH Craig Hansen
CJ Conor Jackson
DE Joey Devine
GR Khalil Greene
HS Huston Street
IK Ian Kinsler
JH Jeremy Hermida
JM Joe Mauer SP
JW Josh Willingham
KG Ken Griffey Jr.
MC Miguel Cabrera SP
RH Ryan Howard
RZ Ryan Zimmerman
TH Travis Hafner SP
VM Victor Martinez
ZG Zack Greinke

2006 Fleer Tradition Traditional Threads

STATED ODDS 1:41 HOBBY, 1:108 RETAIL
SP INFO PROVIDED BY UPPER DECK
OVERALL PLATE ODDS: 1:288 HOBBY
PLATE PRINT RUN 1 SET PER COLOR
BLACK-CYAN-MAGENTA-YELLOW-ISSUED
PLATES DO NOT FEATURE MATERIAL
NO PLATE PRICING DUE TO SCARCITY

AP Albert Pujols Jsy	8.00	20.00
AR Aramis Ramirez Jsy	3.00	8.00
AS Alfonso Soriano Jsy	3.00	8.00
BA Jason Bay Jsy	3.00	8.00
BG Brian Giles Jsy	3.00	8.00
BR Brian Roberts Jsy	3.00	8.00
BS Ben Sheets Jsy	3.00	8.00
CF Chone Figgins Jsy	3.00	8.00
CK Casey Kotchman Jsy SP	4.00	10.00
CL Carlos Lee Jsy	3.00	8.00
CZ Carlos Zambrano Jsy SP	4.00	10.00
DJ Derek Jeter Pants	8.00	20.00
DL Derrek Lee Jsy	3.00	8.00
DO David Ortiz Jsy	4.00	10.00
EB Erik Bedard Jsy	3.00	8.00
FH Felix Hernandez Jsy	4.00	10.00
GJ Geoff Jenkins Jsy	3.00	8.00
GM Greg Maddux Jsy	4.00	10.00
GR Khalil Greene Jsy	4.00	10.00
HB Hank Blalock Jsy	3.00	8.00
JB Josh Barfield Jsy	3.00	8.00
JD Johnny Damon Jsy	4.00	10.00
JH Jeremy Hermida Jsy	4.00	10.00
JL Javy Lopez Jsy	3.00	8.00
JP Jake Peavy Jsy	3.00	8.00
JV Jose Vidro Jsy	3.00	8.00
KG Ken Griffey Jr. Jsy	6.00	15.00
LH Livan Hernandez Jsy	3.00	8.00
MG Marcus Giles Jsy	3.00	8.00
MM Melvin Mora Jsy	3.00	8.00
MT Miguel Tejada Pants	3.00	8.00
MY Michael Young Jsy	3.00	8.00
OV Omar Vizquel Jsy SP	4.00	10.00
PF Prince Fielder Jsy	4.00	10.00
RO Roy Oswalt Jsy	3.00	8.00
RW Rickie Weeks Jsy	3.00	8.00
RZ Ryan Zimmerman Jsy	6.00	15.00
SC Sean Casey Jsy	3.00	8.00
TE Mark Teixeira Jsy	4.00	10.00
VG Vladimir Guerrero Jsy	4.00	10.00
ZD Zach Duke Jsy	3.00	8.00

2006 Fleer Tradition Triple Crown Contenders

COMPLETE SET (15) 10.00 25.00
STATED ODDS 1:9 HOBBY, 1:36 RETAIL
OVERALL PLATE ODDS 1:288 HOBBY
PLATE PRINT RUN 1 SET PER COLOR
BLACK-CYAN-MAGENTA-YELLOW ISSUED
NO PLATE PRICING DUE TO SCARCITY

TC1 Albert Pujols	2.00	5.00
TC2 Derrek Lee	.40	1.00
TC3 Manny Ramirez	.60	1.50
TC4 David Ortiz	1.00	2.50
TC5 Mark Teixeira	.60	1.50
TC6 Alex Rodriguez	1.50	4.00
TC7 Andruw Jones	.60	1.50
TC8 Todd Helton	.60	1.50
TC9 Vladimir Guerrero	1.00	2.50
TC10 Miguel Cabrera	.60	1.50
TC11 Hideki Matsui	1.00	2.50
TC12 Travis Hafner	.40	1.00
TC13 David Wright	1.50	4.00
TC14 Ken Griffey Jr.	1.50	4.00
TC15 Jason Bay	.40	1.00

1933 Goudey

The cards in this 240-card set measure approximately 2 3/8" by 2 7/8". The 1933 Goudey set, was that company's first baseball issue. The four Babe Ruth and two Lou Gehrig cards in the set are extremely popular with collectors. Card number 106, Napoleon Lajoie, was not printed in 1933, and was circulated to a limited number of collectors in 1934 upon request (it was printed along with the 1934 Goudey cards). An album was offered to house the 1933 set. Several minor leaguers are depicted. Card number 1 (Bengough) is very rarely found in mint condition; in fact, as a general rule all the first series cards are more difficult to find in Mint condition. Players with more than one card are also sometimes differentiated below by their pose: BAT (Batting), FIELD (Fielding), PIT (Pitching), THROW (Throwing). One of the Babe Ruth cards was double printed (DP) apparently in place of the Lajoie and hence is easier to obtain than the others. Due to the scarcity of the Lajoie card, the set is considered complete at 239 cards and is priced as such below. One copy of card number 106 as Leo Durocher is known to exist. The card was apparently cut from a proof sheet and is the only known copy to exist. A large window display poster which measured 5 3/8" by 11 1/4" was sent to stores and used the same Babe Ruth photo as in the Goudey Premium set. The gum used was approximately the same dimension as the actual card. At the factory each piece was scored twice so it could be snapped into three pieces. The gum had a spearmint flavor and according to collectors who remember chewing said gum, the flavor did not last very long.

COMPLETE SET (239)	25000.00	40000.00
COMMON CARD (1-52)	45.00	75.00
COMMON (41/43/53-240)	35.00	60.00
WRAP.(1-CENT, BATTER)	75.00	100.00
WRAP.(1-CENT, AD FRONT)	150.00	175.00
1 Benny Bengough RC	900.00	1500.00
2 Dazzy Vance RC	125.00	200.00
3 Hugh Critz BAT RC	40.00	75.00
4 Heinie Schuble RC	45.00	75.00
5 Babe Herman RC	40.00	75.00
6 Jimmy Dykes RC	40.00	75.00
7 Ted Lyons RC	90.00	150.00
8 Roy Johnson RC	45.00	75.00
9 Dave Harris RC	45.00	75.00
10 Glenn Myatt RC	45.00	75.00
11 Billy Rogell RC	45.00	75.00
12 George Pipgras RC	45.00	75.00
13 Fresco Thompson RC	45.00	75.00
14 Henry Johnson RC	45.00	75.00
15 Victor Sorrell RC	45.00	75.00
16 George Blaeholder RC	45.00	75.00
17 Watson Clark RC	45.00	75.00
18 Muddy Ruel RC	45.00	75.00
19 Bill Dickey RC	200,00	350.00
20 Bill Terry THROW RC	150.00	250.00
21 Phil Collins RC	45.00	75.00
22 Pie Traynor RC	150.00	250.00
23 Kiki Cuyler RC	125.00	200.00
24 Horace Ford RC	45.00	75.00
25 Paul Waner RC	125.00	200.00
26 Bill Cissell RC	45.00	75.00
27 George Connally RC	45.00	75.00
28 Dick Bartell RC	40.00	75.00
29 Jimmie Foxx RC	350.00	600.00
30 Frank Hogan RC	45.00	75.00
31 Tony Lazzeri RC	250.00	400.00
32 Bud Clancy RC	40.00	75.00
33 Ralph Kress RC	45.00	75.00
34 Bob O'Farrell RC	45.00	75.00
35 Al Simmons RC	200.00	350.00
36 Tommy Thevenow RC	45.00	75.00
37 Jimmy Wilson RC	45.00	75.00
38 Fred Brickell RC	45.00	75.00
39 Mark Koenig RC	40.00	75.00
40 Taylor Douthit RC	45.00	75.00
41 Gus Mancuso CATCH	35.00	60.00
42 Eddie Collins RC	90.00	150.00
43 Lew Fonseca RC	35.00	60.00
44 Jim Bottomley RC	90.00	150.00
45 Larry Benton RC	45.00	75.00
46 Ethan Allen RC	40.00	75.00
47 Heinie Manush BAT RC	100.00	175.00
48 Marty McManus RC	45.00	75.00
49 Frankie Frisch RC	175.00	300.00
50 Ed Brandt RC	45.00	75.00
51 Charlie Grimm RC	40.00	75.00
52 Andy Cohen RC	45.00	75.00
53 Babe Ruth RC	5000.00	8000.00
54 Ray Kremer RC	35.00	60.00
55 Pat Malone RC	35.00	60.00
56 Red Ruffing RC	100.00	175.00
57 Earl Clark RC	35.00	60.00
58 Lefty O'Doul RC	75.00	125.00
59 Bing Miller RC	35.00	60.00
60 Waite Hoyt RC	75.00	125.00
61 Max Bishop RC	35.00	60.00
62 Pepper Martin RC	75.00	125.00
63 Joe Cronin BAT RC	90.00	150.00
64 Burleigh Grimes RC	150.00	250.00
65 Milt Gaston RC	35.00	60.00
66 George Grantham RC	35.00	60.00
67 Guy Bush RC	35.00	60.00
68 Horace Lisenbee RC	35.00	60.00
69 Randy Moore RC	35.00	60.00
70 Floyd (Pete) Scott RC	35.00	60.00
71 Robert J. Burke RC	35.00	60.00
72 Owen Carroll RC	35.00	60.00
73 Jesse Haines RC	75.00	125.00
74 Eppa Rixey RC	90.00	150.00
75 Willie Kamm RC	35.00	60.00
76 Mickey Cochrane RC	300.00	500.00
77 Adam Comorosky RC	35.00	60.00
78 Jack Quinn RC	35.00	60.00
79 Red Faber RC	75.00	125.00
80 Clyde Manion RC	35.00	60.00
81 Sam Jones RC	35.00	60.00
82 Dib Williams RC	35.00	60.00
83 Pete Jablonowski RC	35.00	60.00
84 Glenn Spencer RC	35.00	60.00
85 Heinie Sand RC	35.00	60.00
86 Phil Todt RC	35.00	60.00
87 Frank O'Rourke RC	35.00	60.00
88 Russell Rollings RC	35.00	60.00
89 Tris Speaker RET	175.00	300.00
90 Jess Petty RC	35.00	60.00
91 Tom Zachary RC	35.00	60.00
92 Lou Gehrig RC	1500.00	2500.00
93 John Welch RC	35.00	60.00
94 Bill Walker RC	35.00	60.00
95 Alvin Crowder RC	35.00	60.00
96 Willis Hudlin RC	35.00	60.00
97 Joe Morrissey RC	35.00	60.00
98 Wally Berger RC	45.00	75.00
99 Tony Cuccinello RC	45.00	75.00
100 George Uhle RC	35.00	60.00
101 Richard Coffman RC	35.00	60.00
102 Travis Jackson RC	90.00	150.00
103 Earle Combs RC	75.00	125.00
104 Fred Marberry RC	35.00	60.00
105 Bernie Friberg RC	35.00	60.00
106 Napoleon Lajoie SP (Not issued until 1934)	15000.00	25000.00
107 Heinie Manush RC	75.00	125.00
108 Joe Kuhel RC	35.00	60.00
109 Joe Cronin RC	175.00	300.00
110 Goose Goslin RC	150.00	250.00
111 Monte Weaver RC	35.00	60.00
112 Fred Schulte RC	35.00	60.00
113 Oswald Bluege POR RC	35.00	60.00
114 Luke Sewell FIELD RC	45.00	75.00
115 Cliff Heathcote RC	35.00	60.00
116 Eddie Morgan RC	35.00	60.00
117 Rabbit Maranville RC	75.00	125.00
118 Val Picinich RC	35.00	60.00
119 Rogers Hornsby Field RC	350.00	600.00
120 Carl Reynolds RC	35.00	60.00
121 Walter Stewart RC	35.00	60.00
122 Alvin Crowder RC	35.00	60.00
123 Jack Russell RC	35.00	60.00
124 Earl Whitehill RC	35.00	60.00
125 Bill Terry RC	150.00	250.00
126 Joe Moore BAT RC	35.00	60.00
127 Mel Ott RC	250.00	400.00
128 Chuck Klein RC	100.00	175.00
129 Hal Schumacher PIT RC	35.00	60.00
130 Fred Fitzsimmons POR RC	35.00	60.00
131 Fred Frankhouse RC	35.00	60.00
132 Jim Elliott RC	35.00	60.00
133 Fred Lindstrom RC	75.00	125.00
134 Sam Rice RC	125.00	200.00
135 Woody English RC	35.00	60.00
136 Flint Rhem RC	35.00	60.00
137 Red Lucas RC	35.00	60.00
138 Herb Pennock RC	100.00	175.00
139 Ben Cantwell RC	35.00	60.00
140 Bump Hadley RC	35.00	60.00
141 Ray Benge RC	35.00	60.00
142 Paul Richards RC	45.00	75.00
143 Glenn Wright RC	35.00	60.00
144 Babe Ruth Bat DP RC	2500.00	4000.00
145 Rube Walberg RC	35.00	60.00
146 Walter Stewart PIT RC	35.00	60.00
147 Leo Durocher RC	125.00	200.00
148 Eddie Farrell RC	35.00	60.00
149 Babe Ruth RC	3000.00	5000.00
150 Ray Kolp RC	35.00	60.00
151 Jake Flowers RC	35.00	60.00
152 Zack Taylor RC	35.00	60.00
153 Buddy Myer RC	35.00	60.00
154 Jimmie Foxx RC	350.00	600.00
155 Joe Judge RC	35.00	60.00
156 Danny MacFayden RC	35.00	60.00
157 Sam Byrd RC UER (Yankees on back is spelled Yankess)	35.00	60.00
158 Moe Berg RC	250.00	400.00
159 Oswald Bluege FIELD RC	35.00	60.00
160 Lou Gehrig RC	1800.00	3000.00
161 Al Spohrer RC	35.00	60.00
162 Leo Mangum RC	35.00	60.00
163 Luke Sewell POR RC	45.00	75.00
164 Lloyd Waner RC	150.00	250.00
165 Joe Sewell RC	75.00	125.00
166 Sam West RC	35.00	60.00
167 Jack Russell RC	35.00	60.00
168 Goose Goslin RC	125.00	200.00
169 Al Thomas RC	35.00	60.00
170 Harry McCurdy RC	35.00	60.00
171 Charlie Jamieson RC	35.00	60.00
172 Billy Hargrave RC	35.00	60.00
173 Roscoe Holm RC	35.00	60.00
174 Warren (Curly) Ogden RC	35.00	60.00
175 Dan Howley MG RC	35.00	60.00
176 John Ogden RC	35.00	60.00
177 Walter French RC	35.00	60.00
178 Jackie Warner RC	35.00	60.00
179 Fred Leach RC	35.00	60.00
180 Eddie Moore RC	35.00	60.00
181 Babe Ruth RC	3500.00	5000.00
182 Andy High RC	35.00	60.00
183 Rube Walberg RC	35.00	60.00
184 Charley Berry RC	35.00	60.00
185 Bob Smith RC	35.00	60.00
186 John Schulte RC	35.00	60.00
187 Heinie Manush RC	90.00	150.00
188 Rogers Hornsby RC	350.00	600.00
189 Joe Cronin RC	125.00	200.00
190 Fred Schulte RC	35.00	60.00
191 Ben Chapman RC	45.00	75.00
192 Walter Brown RC	35.00	60.00
193 Lynford Lary RC	35.00	60.00
194 Earl Averill RC	125.00	200.00
195 Evar Swanson RC	35.00	60.00
196 Leroy Mahaffey RC	35.00	60.00
197 Rick Ferrell RC	75.00	125.00
198 Jack Burns RC	35.00	60.00
199 Tom Bridges RC	35.00	60.00
200 Bill Hallahan RC	35.00	60.00
201 Ernie Orsatti RC	35.00	60.00
202 Gabby Hartnett RC	150.00	250.00
203 Lon Warneke RC	35.00	60.00
204 Riggs Stephenson RC	35.00	60.00
205 Heinie Meine RC	35.00	60.00
206 Gus Suhr RC	35.00	60.00
207 Mel Ott Bat RC	250.00	400.00
208 Bernie James RC	35.00	60.00
209 Adolfo Luque RC	45.00	75.00
210 Spud Davis RC	35.00	60.00
211 Hack Wilson RC	250.00	400.00
212 Billy Urbanski RC	35.00	60.00
213 Earl Adams RC	35.00	60.00
214 John Kerr RC	35.00	60.00
215 Russ Van Atta RC	35.00	60.00
216 Lefty Gomez RC	175.00	300.00
217 Frank Crosetti RC	90.00	150.00
218 Wes Ferrell RC	45.00	75.00
219 Mule Haas UER RC (Name spelled Hass on front)	35.00	60.00
220 Lefty Grove RC	300.00	500.00
221 Dale Alexander RC	35.00	60.00
222 Charley Gehringer RC	250.00	400.00
223 Dizzy Dean RC	500.00	800.00
224 Frank Demaree RC	35.00	60.00
225 Bill Jurges RC	35.00	60.00
226 Charley Root RC	35.00	60.00
227 Billy Herman RC	90.00	150.00
228 Tony Piet RC	35.00	60.00
229 Arky Vaughan RC	90.00	150.00
230 Carl Hubbell PIT RC	250.00	400.00
231 Joe Moore FIELD RC	35.00	60.00
232 Lefty O'Doul RC	75.00	125.00
233 Johnny Vergez RC	35.00	60.00
234 Carl Hubbell RC	250.00	400.00
235 Fred Fitzsimmons PIT RC	35.00	60.00
236 George Davis RC	35.00	60.00
237 Gus Mancuso FIELD RC	35.00	60.00
238 Hugh Critz FIELD RC	35.00	60.00
239 Leroy Parmelee RC	35.00	60.00
240 Hal Schumacher RC	75.00	125.00

1934 Goudey

The cards in this 96-card color set measure approximately 2 3/8" by 2 7/8". Cards 1-48 are considered to be the easiest to find (although card number 1, Foxx, is very scarce in mint condition) while 73-96 are much more difficult to find. Cards of this 1934 Goudey series are slightly less abundant than cards of the 1933 Goudey set. Of the 96 cards, 84 contain a "Lou Gehrig Says" line on the front in a blue design, while 12 of the high series (80-91) contain a "Chuck Klein Says" line in a red design. These Chuck Klein cards are indicated in the checklist below by CK and are in fact the 12 National Leaguers in the high series.

COMPLETE SET (96)	9000.00	16000.00
COMMON CARD (1-48)	30.00	50.00
COMMON CARD (49-72)	40.00	75.00
COMMON CARD (73-96)	100.00	175.00
WRAP.(1-CENT, WHITE)	75.00	100.00
WRAP.(1-CENT, CLEAR)	75.00	100.00
1 Jimmie Foxx	450.00	750.00
2 Mickey Cochrane	100.00	175.00
3 Charlie Grimm	35.00	60.00
4 Woody English	30.00	50.00
5 Ed Brandt	30.00	50.00
6 Dizzy Dean	400.00	700.00
7 Leo Durocher	100.00	175.00
8 Tony Piet	30.00	50.00
9 Ben Chapman	35.00	60.00
10 Chuck Klein	90.00	150.00
11 Paul Waner	90.00	150.00
12 Carl Hubbell	100.00	175.00
13 Frankie Frisch	100.00	175.00
14 Willie Kamm	30.00	50.00
15 Alvin Crowder	30.00	50.00

16 Joe Kuhel 30.00 50.00
17 Hugh Critz 30.00 50.00
18 Heinie Manush 75.00 125.00
19 Lefty Grove 175.00 300.00
20 Frank Hogan 30.00 50.00
21 Bill Terry 125.00 200.00
22 Arky Vaughan 75.00 125.00
23 Charley Gehringer 125.00 200.00
24 Ray Benge 30.00 50.00
25 Roger Cramer RC 35.00 60.00
26 Gerald Walker RC 30.00 50.00
27 Luke Appling RC 90.00 150.00
28 Ed Coleman RC 30.00 50.00
29 Larry French RC 30.00 50.00
30 Julius Solters RC 30.00 50.00
31 Buck Jordan RC 30.00 50.00
32 Blondy Ryan RC 30.00 50.00
33 Don Hurst RC 30.00 50.00
34 Chick Hafey RC 75.00 125.00
35 Ernie Lombardi RC 90.00 150.00
36 Walter Betts RC 30.00 50.00
37 Lou Gehrig 2000.00 3000.00
38 Oral Hildebrand RC 30.00 50.00
39 Fred Walker RC 30.00 50.00
40 John Stone 30.00 50.00
41 George Earnshaw RC 30.00 50.00
42 John Allen RC 30.00 50.00
43 Dick Porter RC 30.00 50.00
44 Tom Bridges 35.00 60.00
45 Oscar Melillo RC 30.00 50.00
46 Joe Stripp RC 30.00 50.00
47 John Frederick RC 30.00 50.00
48 Tex Carleton RC 30.00 50.00
49 Sam Leslie RC 40.00 75.00
50 Walter Beck RC 40.00 75.00
51 Rip Collins RC 40.00 75.00
52 Herman Bell RC 40.00 75.00
53 George Watkins RC 40.00 75.00
54 Wesley Schulmerich RC 40.00 75.00
55 Ed Holley RC 40.00 75.00
56 Mark Koenig 60.00 100.00
57 Bill Swift RC 40.00 75.00
58 Earl Grace RC 40.00 75.00
59 Joe Mowry RC 40.00 75.00
60 Lynn Nelson RC 40.00 75.00
61 Lou Gehrig 2000.00 3000.00
62 Hank Greenberg RC 400.00 700.00
63 Minter Hayes RC 40.00 75.00
64 Frank Grube RC 40.00 75.00
65 Cliff Bolton RC 40.00 75.00
66 Mel Harder RC 60.00 100.00
67 Bob Weiland RC 40.00 75.00
68 Bob Johnson RC 60.00 100.00
69 John Marcum RC 40.00 75.00
70 Pete Fox RC 40.00 75.00
71 Lyle Tinning RC 40.00 75.00
72 Arndt Jorgens RC 40.00 75.00
73 Ed Wells RC 100.00 175.00
74 Bob Boken RC 100.00 175.00
75 Bill Werber RC 100.00 175.00
76 Hal Trosky RC 125.00 200.00
77 Joe Vosmik RC 100.00 175.00
78 Pinky Higgins RC 125.00 200.00
79 Eddie Durham RC 100.00 175.00
80 Marty McManus CK 100.00 175.00
81 Bob Brown CK RC 100.00 175.00
82 Bill Hallahan CK 100.00 175.00
83 Jim Mooney CK RC 100.00 175.00
84 Paul Derringer CK RC 125.00 225.00
85 Adam Comorosky CK 100.00 175.00
86 Lloyd Johnson CK RC 100.00 175.00
87 George Darrow CK RC 100.00 175.00
88 Homer Peel CK RC 100.00 175.00
89 Linus Frey CK RC 100.00 175.00
90 KiKi Cuyler CK 200.00 350.00
91 Dolph Camilli CK RC 125.00 200.00
92 Steve Larkin RC 100.00 175.00
93 Fred Ostermueller RC 100.00 175.00
94 Red Rolfe RC 125.00 200.00
95 Myril Hoag RC 100.00 175.00
96 James DeShong RC 300.00 500.00

1935 Goudey 4-in-1

The cards in this confusing 36-card set (the number of different front pictures) measure approximately 2 3/8" by 2 7/8". The 1935 Goudey set is sometimes called the Goudey Puzzle set, or the Goudey 4-in-1 set. There are 36 different card fronts but 114 different front/back combinations. Our checklist details all 114 cards, grouped together by the 36 different card front combinations. The player combinations are listed alphabetically by reading the player names in clockwise order starting from the top left corner. The card backs can be arranged to form one of nine different puzzles picturing either a player or a team and each back specifically details both the puzzle (or "picture" as it states on the actual card backs) it belongs too using numbers 1-9 and the specific piece it is within the puzzle (using letters A-M). The following is the list of the puzzle back pictures: 1) Detroit Tigers; 2) Chuck Klein; 3) Frankie Frisch; 4) Mickey Cochrane; 5) Joe Cronin; 6) Jimmy Foxx; 7) Al Simmons; 8) Cleveland Indians; and 9) Washington Senators. The first seven puzzles were actually created in two separate combinations of card fronts; thus the Chuck Klein puzzle (catalogued as "Picture 2" on the card backs) is actually available in two different groups of six card fronts - one group of which has been verified as a short print. The SP cards have all been tagged in our checklist. Finally, a limited number of cards feature blue borders (rather than the standard red borders). Though they're not short-printed, we've tagged the cards for referential purposes.

COMPLETE SET (114) 8000.00 13500.00
COMMON CARDS (1-9) 30.00 50.00
COMMON CARDS (11-17) 45.00 80.00
WRAP (1-CENT, WHITE) 150.00 200.00
1-2 Charlie Berry 60.00 100.00
Bobby Burke
Red Kress
Dazzy Vance
2C SP (Chuck Klein Puzzle)
Blue Border
1-4 Charlie Berry 35.00 60.00
Bobby Burke
Red Kress
Dazzy Vance
4C (4A Mickey Cochrane Puzzle)
Blue Border
1-7 Charlie Berry 35.00 60.00
Bobby Burke
Red Kress
Dazzy Vance
7C (Al Simmons Puzzle)
Blue Border
2-8 Jack Burns 30.00 50.00
Rollie Hemsley
Frank Grube
Bob Weiland
8C (Cleveland Indians Puzzle)
2-9 Jack Burns 30.00 50.00
Rollie Hemsley
Frank Grube
Bob Weiland
9C (Washington Senators Puzzle)
3-8 Bruce Campbell 30.00 50.00
Billy Meyers
Ival Goodman
Alex Kampouris XRC
8D (Cleveland Indians Puzzle)
3-9 Bruce Campbell 30.00 50.00
Billy Meyers
Ival Goodman
Alex Kampouris XRC
9D (Washington Senators Puzzle)
4-1 Mickey Cochrane 60.00 120.00
Charlie Gehringer
Tommy Bridges
Billy Rogell#1D (Detroit Tigers Puzzle)
4-2 Mickey Cochrane 70.00 120.00
Charlie Gehringer
Tommy Bridges
Billy Rogell
2D (Chuck Klein Puzzle)
4-6 Mickey Cochrane 90.00 150.00
Charlie Gehringer
Tom Bridges
Billy Rogell#6D SP (Jimmie Foxx Puzzle)
4-7 Mickey Cochrane 90.00 150.00
Charlie Gehringer
Tom Bridges
Billy Rogell
7D SP (Al Simmons Puzzle)
5-2 Hugh Critz 90.00 150.00
Dick Bartell
Mel Ott
Gus Mancuso
2A SP (Chuck Klein Puzzle)
Blue Border
5-4 Hugh Critz 60.00 100.00
Dick Bartell
Mel Ott
Gus Mancuso
4A (Mickey Cochrane Puzzle)
Blue Border
5-7 Hugh Critz 60.00 100.00
Dick Bartell
Mel Ott
Gus Mancuso
7A (Al Simmons Puzzle)
Blue Border
6-1 Joe Cronin 60.00 100.00
Carl Reynolds
Max Bishop
Chalmer Cissell
1G SP (Detroit Tigers Puzzle)
6-3 Joe Cronin 60.00 100.00
Carl Reynolds
Max Bishop
Chalmer Cissell
3E SP (Frankie Frisch Puzzle)
6-5 Joe Cronin 60.00 100.00
Carl Reynolds
Max Bishop
Chalmer Cissell
5E SP (Joe Cronin Puzzle)
6-6 Joe Cronin 35.00 60.00
Carl Reynolds
Max Bishop
Chalmer Cissell
6E (Jimmie Foxx Puzzle)
7-8 Jimmy DeShong 30.00 50.00
Johnny Allen
Red Rolfe
Dixie Walker
8E (Cleveland Indians Puzzle)
7-9 Jimmy DeShong 30.00 50.00
Johnny Allen
Red Rolfe
Fred Walker
9E (Washington Senators Puzzle)
8-1 George Earnshaw 35.00 60.00
Jimmie Dykes
Luke Sewell
Luke Appling
1I (Detroit Tigers Puzzle)
8-2 George Earnshaw 35.00 60.00
Jimmie Dykes
Luke Sewell
Luke Appling
2F (Chuck Klein Puzzle)
8-6 George Earnshaw 60.00 100.00
Jimmie Dykes
Luke Sewell
Luke Appling
6F SP (Jimmie Foxx Puzzle)
8-7 George Earnshaw 60.00 100.00
Jimmie Dykes
Luke Sewell
Luke Appling
7F SP (Al Simmons Puzzle)
9-8 Pete Fox 60.00 100.00
Hank Greenberg
Gee Walker
Schoolboy Rowe
8F (Cleveland Indians Puzzle)
9-9 Pete Fox 60.00 100.00
Hank Greenberg
Gee Walker
Schoolboy Rowe
9F (Washington Senators Puzzle)
10-1 Frank Frisch 90.00 150.00
Dizzy Dean
Ernie Orsatti
Tex Carleton
1A (Detroit Tigers Puzzle)
10-2 Frank Frisch 90.00 150.00
Dizzy Dean
Ernie Orsatti
Tex Carleton
2A (Chuck Klein Puzzle)
10-6 Frank Frisch 150.00 250.00
Dizzy Dean
Ernie Orsatti
Tex Carleton
6A SP (Jimmie Foxx Puzzle)
10-7 Frank Frisch 150.00 250.00
Dizzy Dean
Ernie Orsatti
Tex Carleton
7A SP (Al Simmons Puzzle)
11-1 Burleigh Grimes 60.00 100.00
Chuck Klein
Kiki Cuyler
Woody English
1F (Detroit Tigers Puzzle)
11-3 Burleigh Grimes 60.00 100.00
Chuck Klein
Kiki Cuyler
Woody English
3D (Frankie Frisch Puzzle)
11-4 Burleigh Grimes 90.00 150.00
Chuck Klein
Kiki Cuyler
Woody English
4D SP (Mickey Cochrane Puzzle)
11-5 Burleigh Grimes 90.00 150.00
Chuck Klein
Kiki Cuyler
Woody English
5D SP (Joe Cronin Puzzle)
12-8 Minter Hayes 35.00 60.00
Ted Lyons
Mule Haas
Zeke Bonura
8B (Cleveland Indians Puzzle)
12-9 Minter Hayes 35.00 60.00
Ted Lyons
Mule Haas
Zeke Bonura
9B (Washington Senators Puzzle)
13-8 Babe Herman 35.00 60.00
Gus Suhr
Tom Padden XRC
Cy Blanton
8K (Cleveland Indians Puzzle)
13-9 Babe Herman 35.00 60.00
Gus Suhr
Tom Padden XRC
Cy Blanton
9K (Washington Senators Puzzle)
14-1 Willis Hudlin 60.00 100.00
George Myatt XRC
Adam Comorosky
Jim Bottomley
1K SP (Detroit Tigers Puzzle)
14-3 Willis Hudlin 60.00 100.00
George Myatt XRC
Adam Comorosky
Jim Bottomley
3B SP (Frankie Frisch Puzzle)
14-5 Willis Hudlin 35.00 60.00
George Myatt XRC
Adam Comorosky
Jim Bottomley
5B (Joe Cronin Puzzle)
14-6 Willis Hudlin 35.00 60.00
George Myatt XRC
Adam Comorosky
Jim Bottomley
6B (Jimmie Foxx Puzzle)
15-8 Bob Johnson 30.00 50.00
Ed Coleman
Johnny Marcum
Doc Cramer
8J (Cleveland Indians Puzzle)
15-9 Bob Johnson 30.00 50.00
Ed Coleman
Johnny Marcum
Doc Cramer
9J (Washington Senators Puzzle)
16-1 Willie Kamm 35.00 60.00
Oral Hildebrand
Earl Averill
Hal Trosky
1L (Detroit Tigers Puzzle)
16-2 Willie Kamm 35.00 60.00
Oral Hildebrand
Earl Averill
Hal Trosky
2E (Chuck Klein Puzzle)
16-6 Willie Kamm 60.00 100.00
Oral Hildebrand
Earl Averill
Hal Trosky
6E SP (Jimmie Foxx Puzzle)
16-7 Willie Kamm 60.00 100.00
Oral Hildebrand
Earl Averill
Hal Trosky
7E SP (Al Simmons Puzzle)
17-8 Mark Koenig 30.00 50.00
Fred Fitzsimmons
Ray Benge
Tom Zachary
8A (Cleveland Indians Puzzle)
17-8 Mark Koenig 30.00 50.00
Fred Fitzsimmons
Ray Benge
Tom Zachary
8M (Cleveland Indians Puzzle)
18-8 Joe Kuhel 30.00 50.00
Earl Whitehill
Buddy Myer
John Stone
8H (Cleveland Indians Puzzle)
18-9 Joe Kuhel 30.00 50.00
Earl Whitehill
Buddy Myer
John Stone
9H (Washington Senators Puzzle)
19-1 Sam Leslie 30.00 50.00
Lonnie Frey
Joe Stripp
Watson Clark
1G (Detroit Tigers Puzzle)
19-3 Sam Leslie 30.00 50.00
Lonnie Frey
Joe Stripp
Watson Clark
3E (Frankie Frisch Puzzle)
19-4 Sam Leslie 45.00 80.00
Lonnie Frey
Joe Stripp
Watson Clark
4E SP (Mickey Cochrane Puzzle)
19-5 Sam Leslie 30.00 50.00
Lonnie Frey
Joe Stripp
Watson Clark
5E (Joe Cronin Puzzle)
20-1 Roy Mahaffey 70.00 120.00
Jimmie Foxx
Dib Williams
Pinky Higgins
1B (Detroit Tigers Puzzle)
20-2 Roy Mahaffey 70.00 120.00
Jimmie Foxx
Dib Williams
Pinky Higgins
2B (Chuck Klein Puzzle)
20-6 Roy Mahaffey 90.00 150.00
Jimmie Foxx
Dib Williams
Pinky Higgins
6B SP (Jimmie Foxx Puzzle)
20-7 Roy Mahaffey 125.00 200.00
Jimmie Foxx
Dib Williams
Pinky Higgins
7B SP (Al Simmons Puzzle)
21-1 Heinie Manush 35.00 60.00
Lyn Lary
Monte Weaver
Bump Hadley
1C (Detroit Tigers Puzzle)
21-2 Heinie Manush 35.00 60.00
Lyn Lary
Monte Weaver
Bump Hadley
2C (Chuck Klein Puzzle)
21-6 Heinie Manush 60.00 100.00
Lyn Lary
Monte Weaver
Bump Hadley
6C SP (Jimmie Foxx Puzzle)
21-7 Heinie Manush 60.00 100.00
Lyn Lary
Monte Weaver
Bump Hadley
7C SP (Al Simmons Puzzle)
22-2 Pepper Martin BLUE 45.00 80.00
Bob O'Farrell
Sam Byrd
Danny MacFayden
2F SP (Chuck Klein Puzzle)
22-4 Pepper Martin BLUE 30.00 50.00
Bob O'Farrell
Sam Byrd
Danny MacFayden
4F (Mickey Cochrane Puzzle)
22-7 Pepper Martin BLUE 30.00 50.00
Bob O'Farrell
Sam Byrd
Danny MacFayden
7F (Al Simmons Puzzle)
23-2 Randy Moore BLUE 45.00 80.00
Shanty Hogan
Fred Frankhouse
Eddie Brandt
2E SP (Chuck Klein Puzzle)
23-4 Randy Moore BLUE 30.00 50.00
Shanty Hogan
Fred Frankhouse
Eddie Brandt
4E (Mickey Cochrane Puzzle)
23-7 Randy Moore BLUE 30.00 50.00
Shanty Hogan
Fred Frankhouse
Eddie Brandt
7E (Al Simmons Puzzle)
24-1 Tony Piet 35.00 60.00
Adam Comorosky
Jim Bottomley
Sparky Adams
1H (Detroit Tigers Puzzle)
24-3 Tony Piet 35.00 60.00
Adam Comorosky
Jim Bottomley
Sparky Adams
3F (Frankie Frisch Puzzle)
24-4 Tony Piet 60.00 100.00
Adam Comorosky
Jim Bottomley
Sparky Adams
4F SP (Mickey Cochrane Puzzle)
24-5 Tony Piet 60.00 100.00
Adam Comorosky
Jim Bottomley
Sparky Adams
5F SP (Joe Cronin Puzzle)
25-1 Muddy Ruel 90.00 150.00
Al Simmons
Willie Kamm
Mickey Cochrane
1J SP (Detroit Tigers Puzzle)
25-3 Muddy Ruel 90.00 150.00
Al Simmons
Willie Kamm
Mickey Cochrane
3A SP (Frankie Frisch Puzzle)
25-5 Muddy Ruel 60.00 100.00
Al Simmons
Willie Kamm
Mickey Cochrane
5A (Joe Cronin Puzzle)
25-6 Muddy Ruel 60.00 100.00
Al Simmons
Willie Kamm
Mickey Cochrane
6A (Jimmie Foxx Puzzle)
26-2 Red Ruffing 150.00 250.00
Pat Malone
Tony Lazzeri
Bill Dickey
2D SP (Chuck Klein Puzzle)
Blue Border
26-4 Red Ruffing 90.00 150.00
Pat Malone
Tony Lazzeri
Bill Dickey
4D (Mickey Cochrane Puzzle)
Blue Border
26-7 Red Ruffing 90.00 150.00
Pat Malone
Tony Lazzeri
Bill Dickey
7D (Al Simmons Puzzle)
Blue Border
27-1 Babe Ruth 600.00 1000.00
Marty McManus
Eddie Brandt
Rabbit Maranville
1J (Detroit Tigers Puzzle)
27-3 Babe Ruth 600.00 1000.00
Marty McManus
Eddie Brandt
Rabbit Maranville
3A (Frankie Frisch Puzzle)
27-4 Babe Ruth 1000.00 1500.00
Marty McManus
Eddie Brandt
Rabbit Maranville
4A SP (Mickey Cochrane Puzzle)
27-5 Babe Ruth 1000.00 1500.00
Marty McManus
Eddie Brandt
Rabbit Maranville
5A SP (Joe Cronin Puzzle)
28-1 Heine Schuble 60.00 100.00
Fred Marberry
Goose Goslin
General Crowder
1H SP (Detroit Tigers Puzzle)
28-3 Heine Schuble 60.00 100.00
Fred Marberry
Goose Goslin
General Crowder
3F SP (Frankie Frisch Puzzle)
28-5 Heine Schuble 35.00 60.00
Fred Marberry
Goose Goslin
General Crowder
5F (Joe Cronin Puzzle)
28-6 Heine Schuble 35.00 60.00
Fred Marberry
Goose Goslin
General Crowder
6F (Jimmie Foxx Puzzle)
29-8 Al Spohrer 30.00 50.00
Flint Rhem
Ben Cantwell
Larry Benton
8L (Cleveland Indians Puzzle)
29-9 Al Spohrer 30.00 50.00
Flint Rhem
Ben Cantwell
Larry Benton
9L (Washington Senators Puzzle)
30-1 Bill Terry 60.00 100.00
Hal Schumacher
Gus Mancuso
Travis Jackson
1K (Detroit Tigers Puzzle)
30-3 Bill Terry 60.00 100.00
Hal Schumacher
Gus Mancuso
Travis Jackson
3B (Frankie Frisch Puzzle)
30-4 Bill Terry 90.00 150.00
Hal Schumacher
Gus Mancuso
Travis Jackson
4B SP (Mickey Cochrane Puzzle)
30-5 Bill Terry 90.00 150.00
Hal Schumacher
Gus Mancuso
Travis Jackson
5B SP (Joe Cronin Puzzle)
31-2 Pie Traynor 60.00 100.00
Red Lucas
Tommy Thevenow
Glenn Wright
2B SP (Chuck Klein Puzzle)
Blue Border
31-4 Pie Traynor 35.00 60.00
Red Lucas
Tommy Thevenow
Glenn Wright
4B (Mickey Cochrane Puzzle)
Blue Border
31-7 Pie Traynor 35.00 60.00
Red Lucas
Tommy Thevenow
Glenn Wright
7B (Al Simmons Puzzle)
Blue Border
32-8 Joe Vosmik 30.00 50.00
Bill Knickerbocker
Mel Harder
Lefty Stewart
8I (Cleveland Indians Puzzle)
32-9 Joe Vosmik 30.00 50.00
Bill Knickerbocker
Mel Harder
Lefty Stewart
9I (Washington Senators Puzzle)
33-1 Paul Waner 60.00 100.00
Guy Bush
Waite Hoyt
Lloyd Waner
1E (Detroit Tigers Puzzle)
33-3 Paul Waner 60.00 100.00
Guy Bush
Waite Hoyt
Lloyd Waner
3C (Frankie Frisch Puzzle)
33-4 Paul Waner 90.00 150.00
Guy Bush
Waite Hoyt
Lloyd Waner
4C SP (Mickey Cochrane Puzzle)
33-5 Paul Waner 60.00 100.00
Guy Bush
Waite Hoyt
Lloyd Waner
5C (Joe Cronin Puzzle)
34-8 Billy Werber 35.00 60.00
Rick Ferrell
Wes Ferrell
Fritz Ostermueller
8G (Cleveland Indians Puzzle)
34-9 Billy Werber 35.00 60.00
Rick Ferrell
Wes Ferrell
Fritz Ostermueller
9G (Washington Senators Puzzle)
35-1 Sam West 45.00 80.00
Oscar Melillo
George Blaeholder
Dick Coffman
1F SP (Detroit Tigers Puzzle)
35-3 Sam West 45.00 80.00
Oscar Melillo
George Blaeholder
Dick Coffman
3D SP (Frankie Frisch Puzzle)
35-5 Sam West 30.00 50.00
Oscar Melillo
George Blaeholder
Dick Coffman
5D (Joe Cronin Puzzle)
35-6 Sam West 30.00 50.00
Oscar Melillo
George Blaeholder
Dick Coffman
6D (Jimmie Foxx Puzzle)
36-1 Jimmy Wilson 45.00 80.00
Ethan Allen
Bubba Jonnard XRC
Fred Brickell
1E SP (Detroit Tigers Puzzle)
36-3 Jimmy Wilson 45.00 80.00
Ethan Allen
Bubba Jonnard XRC
Fred Brickell
3C SP (Frankie Frisch Puzzle)
36-5 Jimmy Wilson 45.00 80.00
Ethan Allen
Bubba Jonnard XRC
Fred Brickell
5C SP (Joe Cronin Puzzle)
36-6 Jimmy Wilson 30.00 50.00
Ethan Allen
Bubba Jonnard XRC
Fred Brickell
6C (Jimmie Foxx Puzzle)

1936 Goudey Black and White

The cards in this 25-card black and white set measure approximately 2 3/8" by 2 7/8". In contrast to the color artwork of its previous sets, the 1936 Goudey set contained a simple black and white player photograph. A facsimile autograph appeared within the picture area. Each card was issued with a number of different "game situation" backs, and there may be as many as 200 different front/back combinations. This unnumbered set is checklisted and numbered below in alphabetical order for convenience. The cards were issued in penny packs which came 100 to a box.

COMPLETE SET (25) 1250.00 2500.00
WRAPPER (1-CENT) 150.00 200.00
1 Wally Berger 30.00 60.00
2 Zeke Bonura 40.00 80.00
3 Frenchy Bordagaray XRC 40.00 80.00
4 Bill Brubaker XRC 25.00 50.00
5 Dolph Camilli 30.00 60.00
6 Clyde Castleman XRC 25.00 50.00
7 Mickey Cochrane 125.00 250.00
8 Joe Coscarart XRC 25.00 50.00
9 Frank Crosetti 40.00 80.00
10 Kiki Cuyler 50.00 100.00
11 Paul Derringer 30.00 60.00
12 Jimmy Dykes 60.00 120.00
13 Rick Ferrell 50.00 100.00
14 Lefty Gomez 125.00 250.00
15 Hank Greenberg 150.00 300.00
16 Bucky Harris XRC 50.00 100.00
17 Rollie Hemsley 25.00 60.00
18 Pinky Higgins 30.00 60.00
19 Oral Hildebrand 25.00 50.00
20 Chuck Klein 75.00 150.00
21 Pepper Martin 40.00 80.00
22 Bobo Newsom XRC 30.00 60.00
23 Joe Vosmik 25.00 50.00
24 Paul Waner 75.00 150.00
25 Bill Werber 25.00 50.00

1938 Goudey Heads-Up

The cards in this 48-card set measure approximately 2 3/8" by 2 7/8". The 1938 Goudey set is commonly referred to as the Heads-Up set. These very popular but difficult to obtain cards came in two series of the same 24 players. The first series, numbers 241-264, is distinguished from the second series, numbers 265-288, in that the second contains etched cartoons and comments surrounding the player picture. Although the set starts with number 241, it is not a continuation of the 1933 Goudey set, but a separate set in its own right.

COMPLETE SET (48) 9000.00 15000.00
COMMON (241-264) 60.00 100.00
COMMON (265-288) 60.00 100.00
WRAP.(1-CENT, 6-FIGURE) 700.00 800.00

Card	Low	High
241 Charley Gehringer	175.00	300.00
242 Pete Fox	60.00	100.00
243 Joe Kuhel	60.00	100.00
244 Frank Demaree	60.00	100.00
245 Frank Pytlak XRC	60.00	100.00
246 Ernie Lombardi	100.00	175.00
247 Joe Vosmik	60.00	100.00
248 Dick Bartell	60.00	100.00
249 Jimmie Foxx	250.00	400.00
250 Joe DiMaggio XRC	2000.00	3500.00
251 Bump Hadley	60.00	100.00
252 Zeke Bonura	60.00	100.00
253 Hank Greenberg	250.00	400.00
254 Van Lingle Mungo	75.00	125.00
255 Moose Solters	60.00	100.00
256 Vernon Kennedy XRC	60.00	100.00
257 Al Lopez	125.00	200.00
258 Bobby Doerr XRC	150.00	250.00
259 Billy Werber	60.00	100.00
260 Rudy York XRC	75.00	125.00
261 Rip Radcliff XRC	60.00	100.00
262 Joe Medwick	150.00	250.00
263 Marvin Owen	60.00	100.00
264 Bob Feller XRC	350.00	600.00
265 Charley Gehringer	175.00	300.00
266 Pete Fox	60.00	100.00
267 Joe Kuhel	60.00	100.00
268 Frank Demaree	60.00	100.00
269 Frank Pytlak XRC	60.00	100.00
270 Ernie Lombardi	125.00	200.00
271 Joe Vosmik	60.00	100.00
272 Dick Bartell	60.00	100.00
273 Jimmie Foxx	250.00	400.00
274 Joe DiMaggio XRC	2000.00	3500.00
275 Bump Hadley	60.00	100.00
276 Zeke Bonura	60.00	100.00
277 Hank Greenberg	250.00	400.00
278 Van Lingle Mungo	75.00	125.00
279 Moose Solters	60.00	100.00
280 Vernon Kennedy XRC	60.00	100.00
281 Al Lopez	150.00	250.00
282 Bobby Doerr XRC	150.00	250.00
283 Billy Werber	60.00	100.00
284 Rudy York XRC	75.00	125.00
285 Rip Radcliff XRC	60.00	100.00
286 Joe Medwick	150.00	250.00
287 Marvin Owen	60.00	100.00
288 Bob Feller XRC	450.00	750.00

1941 Goudey

The cards in this 33-card set measure 2 3/8" by 2 7/8". The 1941 Series of blank backed baseball cards was the last baseball issue marketed by Goudey before the war closed the door on that company for good. Each black and white player photo comes with four color backgrounds (blue, green, red, or yellow). Cards without numbers are probably miscut. Cards 21-25 are especially scarce in relation to the rest of the set. In fact the eight hardest to find cards in the set are, in order, 22, 24, 23, 25, 21, 27, 29 and 32.

Card	Low	High
COMPLETE SET (33)	1200.00	2000.00
COMMON CARD (1-33)	15.00	30.00
COMMON SP		
WRAPPER (1-CENT)	150.00	200.00
1 Hugh Mulcahy	15.00	30.00
2 Harland Clift XRC	15.00	30.00
3 Louis Chiozza	15.00	30.00
4 Buddy Rosar XRC	15.00	30.00
5 George McQuinn	15.00	30.00
6 George Dickman	15.00	30.00
7 Wayne Ambler	15.00	30.00
8 Bob Muncrief XRC	15.00	30.00
9 Bill Dietrich XRC	15.00	30.00
10 Taft Wright	15.00	30.00
11 Don Heffner	15.00	30.00
12 Fritz Ostermueller	15.00	30.00
13 Frank Hayes	15.00	30.00
14 John Kramer XRC	15.00	30.00
15 Dario Lodigiani XRC	15.00	30.00
16 George Case	15.00	30.00
17 Vito Tamulis	15.00	30.00
18 Whitlow Wyatt	20.00	40.00
19 Bill Posedel	15.00	30.00
20 Carl Hubbell	50.00	80.00
21 Harold Warstler SP	60.00	120.00
22 Joe Sullivan SP XRC	175.00	300.00
23 Norman Young SP	100.00	200.00
24 Stanley Andrews SP XRC	125.00	250.00
25 Morris Arnovich SP	60.00	120.00
26 Elbert Fletcher	15.00	30.00
27 Bill Crouch XRC	40.00	60.00
28 Al Todd XRC	15.00	30.00
29 Debs Garms	30.00	50.00
30 Jim Tobin	15.00	30.00
31 Chester Ross XRC	15.00	30.00
32 George Coffman	20.00	40.00
33 Mel Ott	75.00	125.00

2000 Greats of the Game

The 2000 Fleer Greats of the Game set was released in late March, 2000 as a 107-card set that features some of the greatest players to ever play the game. There was only one series offered. Each pack contained six cards and carried a suggested retail price of 4.99. A promotional sample card featuring Nolan Ryan was distributed to dealers and hobby media several weeks before the product went live. Card fronts featured an attractive burgundy frame with (in most cases) a full color player image. Fueled by a great selection of autographs, the popular Yankee Clippings game-used jersey inserts and the aforementioned superior design of the base set, the product turned out to be one of the most popular releases of the 2000 calendar.

Card	Low	High
COMPLETE SET (107)	15.00	40.00
1 Mickey Mantle	4.00	10.00
2 Gil Hodges	.60	1.50
3 Monte Irvin	.40	1.00
4 Satchel Paige	.60	1.50
5 Roy Campanella	.60	1.50
6 Richie Ashburn	.40	1.00
7 Roger Maris	.60	1.50
8 Ozzie Smith	1.00	2.50
9 Reggie Jackson	.40	1.00
10 Eddie Mathews	.60	1.50
11 Dave Righetti	.25	.60
12 Dave Winfield	.25	.60
13 Lou Whitaker	.25	.60
14 Phil Garner	.25	.60
15 Ron Cey	.25	.60
16 Brooks Robinson	.40	1.00
17 Bruce Sutter	.25	.60
18 Dave Parker	.25	.60
19 Johnny Bench	.60	1.50
20 Fernando Valenzuela	.25	.60
21 George Brett	1.50	4.00
22 Paul Molitor	.25	.60
23 Hoyt Wilhelm	.25	.60
24 Luis Aparicio	.25	.60
25 Frank White	.25	.60
26 Herb Score	.25	.60
27 Kirk Gibson	.25	.60
28 Mike Schmidt	1.25	3.00
29 Don Baylor	.25	.60
30 Joe Pepitone	.25	.60
31 Hal McRae	.25	.60
32 Lee Smith	.25	.60
33 Nolan Ryan	1.50	4.00
34 Bill Mazeroski	.40	1.00
35 Bobby Doerr	.40	1.00
36 Duke Snider	.40	1.00
37 Dick Groat	.25	.60
38 Larry Doby	.25	.60
39 Kirby Puckett	.60	1.50
40 Steve Carlton	.25	.60
41 Dennis Eckersley	.25	.60
42 Jim Bunning	.40	1.00
43 Ron Guidry	.25	.60
44 Alan Trammell	.25	.60
45 Bob Feller	.25	.60
46 Dave Concepcion	.25	.60
47 Dwight Evans	.40	1.00
48 Enos Slaughter	.25	.60
49 Tom Seaver	.40	1.00
50 Tony Oliva	.25	.60
51 Mel Stottlemyre	.25	.60
52 Tommy John	.25	.60
53 Willie McCovey	.25	.60
54 Red Schoendienst	.25	.60
55 Gorman Thomas	.25	.60
56 Ralph Kiner	.25	.60
57 Robin Yount	1.00	2.50
58 Andre Dawson	.25	.60
59 Al Kaline	.60	1.50
60 Dom DiMaggio	.40	1.00
61 Juan Marichal	.25	.60
62 Jack Morris	.25	.60
63 Warren Spahn	.40	1.00
64 Preacher Roe	.25	.60
65 Darrell Evans	.25	.60
66 Jim Bouton	.25	.60
67 Rocky Colavito	.40	1.00
68 Bob Gibson	.40	1.00
69 Whitey Ford	.40	1.00
70 Moose Skowron	.25	.60
71 Boog Powell	.25	.60
72 Al Lopez	.40	1.00
73 Lou Brock	.40	1.00
74 Mickey Lolich	.25	.60
75 Rod Carew	.40	1.00
76 Bob Lemon	.40	1.00
77 Frank Howard	.25	.60
78 Phil Rizzuto	.60	1.50
79 Carl Yastrzemski	1.00	2.50
80 Rico Carty	.25	.60
81 Jim Kaat	.25	.60
82 Bert Blyleven	.25	.60
83 George Kell	.25	.60
84 Jim Palmer	.25	.60
85 Maury Wills	.25	.60
86 Jim Rice	.25	.60
87 Joe Carter	.25	.60
88 Clete Boyer	.25	.60
89 Yogi Berra	.60	1.50
90 Cecil Cooper	.25	.60
91 Davey Johnson	.25	.60
92 Lou Boudreau	.40	1.00
93 Orlando Cepeda	.25	.60
94 Tommy Henrich	.25	.60
95 Hank Bauer	.25	.60
96 Don Larsen	.25	.60
97 Vida Blue	.25	.60
98 Ben Oglivie	.25	.60
99 Don Mattingly	1.50	4.00
100 Dale Murphy	.40	1.00
101 Ferguson Jenkins	.25	.60
102 Bobby Bonds	.25	.60
103 Dick Allen	.25	.60
104 Stan Musial	1.00	2.50
105 Gaylord Perry	.25	.60
106 Willie Randolph	.25	.60
107 Willie Stargell	.40	1.00
P33 Nolan Ryan Promo	.60	1.50

2000 Greats of the Game Autographs

Randomly inserted in packs at one in six, this 90-card insert features autographed cards of some of the greatest players in major league history. The card design closely parallels the attractive basic issue cards, except of course for the player's

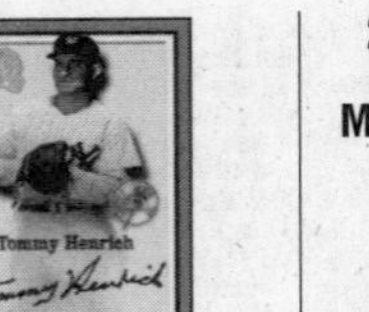

signature. Representatives at Fleer eventually released cryptic details on a few cards confirming widespread belief on suspected shortprints within the set. It's known that the scarcest cards are Johnny Bench and Mike Schmidt. Several other cards from this set experienced amazing surges iin value throughout the course of the year 2000 as collectors scrambled to complete their sets in the midst of heavy demand and rumours of additional short prints. Also, Herb Score mistakenly signed several of his basic autographs with an "ROY 55" notation. Score was supposed so sign only 55 purple-bordered Memorable Moments variations. Finally, a Derek Jeter card was released in early 2004. It's believed that the card was only made available as a redemption to collectors for autograph exchange cards of other players that they could not fulfill. Please note that these cards are unnumbered and we have sequenced them in alphabetical order.

JETER EXCH PRINT RUN 150 CARDS
JETER EXCH IS NOT SERIAL #'d
JETER PRINT RUN PROVIDED BY FLEER

Card	Low	High
1 Luis Aparicio	15.00	40.00
2 Hank Bauer	10.00	25.00
3 Don Baylor	10.00	25.00
4 Johnny Bench SP	150.00	250.00
5 Yogi Berra SP	125.00	200.00
6 Vida Blue	6.00	15.00
7 Bert Blyleven	10.00	25.00
8 Bobby Bonds	20.00	50.00
9 Lou Boudreau	90.00	150.00
10 Jim Bouton	10.00	25.00
11 Clete Boyer	10.00	25.00
12 George Brett SP	250.00	400.00
13 Lou Brock	15.00	40.00
14 Jim Bunning	15.00	40.00
15 Rod Carew	30.00	60.00
16 Steve Carlton	10.00	25.00
17 Joe Carter SP	90.00	150.00
18 Orlando Cepeda	10.00	25.00
19 Ron Cey	6.00	15.00
20 Rocky Colavito	40.00	80.00
21 Dave Concepcion	10.00	25.00
21A Dave Concepcion Signed in Red Ink	20.00	50.00
22 Cecil Cooper	6.00	15.00
23 Andre Dawson	10.00	25.00
24 Dom DiMaggio	50.00	100.00
25 Bobby Doerr	10.00	25.00
26 Darrell Evans	6.00	15.00
27 Bob Feller	15.00	40.00
28 Whitey Ford SP	100.00	175.00
29 Phil Garner	10.00	25.00
30 Bob Gibson	15.00	40.00
31 Kirk Gibson	15.00	40.00
32 Dick Groat	15.00	40.00
33 Ron Guidry	10.00	25.00
34 Tommy Henrich SP	150.00	250.00
35 Frank Howard	10.00	25.00
36 Reggie Jackson SP	125.00	200.00
37 Ferguson Jenkins	10.00	25.00
38 Derek Jeter Mail-In/150	300.00	450.00
39 Tommy John	10.00	25.00
40 Davey Johnson	6.00	15.00
41 Jim Kaat	10.00	25.00
42 Al Kaline	20.00	50.00
43 George Kell	10.00	25.00
44 Ralph Kiner	15.00	40.00
45 Don Larsen	10.00	25.00
46 Mickey Lolich	10.00	25.00
47 Juan Marichal	30.00	60.00
48 Eddie Mathews	125.00	200.00
49 Don Mattingly SP	300.00	450.00
50 Bill Mazeroski	30.00	60.00
51 Willie McCovey SP	125.00	200.00
52 Hal McRae	6.00	15.00
53 Paul Molitor	20.00	50.00
54 Jack Morris	6.00	15.00
55 Dale Murphy	15.00	40.00
56 Stan Musial SP	100.00	175.00
57 Ben Oglivie	10.00	25.00
58 Tony Oliva	10.00	25.00
59 Jim Palmer SP	100.00	175.00
60 Dave Parker	10.00	25.00
61 Joe Pepitone	10.00	25.00
62 Gaylord Perry	10.00	25.00
63 Boog Powell	10.00	25.00
64 Kirby Puckett SP	300.00	450.00
65 Willie Randolph	10.00	25.00
66 Jim Rice	15.00	40.00
67 Dave Righetti	10.00	25.00
68 Phil Rizzuto SP	150.00	250.00
69 Brooks Robinson	15.00	40.00
70 Preacher Roe	10.00	25.00
71 Nolan Ryan	125.00	200.00
72 Mike Schmidt SP	450.00	700.00
73 Red Schoendienst	10.00	25.00
74 Herb Score Card has no ROY 55 on signature	6.00	15.00
75 Herb Score ROY 55 in signature	30.00	60.00
76 Tom Seaver	60.00	120.00
77 Moose Skowron	10.00	25.00
78 Enos Slaughter	15.00	40.00
79 Lee Smith	10.00	25.00
80 Ozzie Smith SP	175.00	300.00
81 Duke Snider SP	150.00	250.00
82 Warren Spahn SP	200.00	350.00
83 Willie Stargell	60.00	120.00
84 Bruce Sutter	15.00	40.00
85 Gorman Thomas	6.00	15.00
86 Alan Trammell	10.00	25.00
87 Frank White	10.00	25.00
88 Hoyt Wilhelm	15.00	40.00
89 Maury Wills	10.00	25.00
90 Carl Yastrzemski	40.00	80.00
91 Robin Yount SP	200.00	350.00

2000 Greats of the Game Autographs Memorable Moments

Randomly inserted in packs, this insert features autographs of Ron Guidry, Nolan Ryan, Herb Score and Tom Seaver. Each card is autographed and contains a notion by the player related to a career achievement. Each card is serial-numbered to the year of that achievement. The fronts of these cards are purple-bordered instead of burgandy-bordered. Please note that Herb Score signed some of his regular burgandy-bordered autograph cards with the "HOF 55" notation. Please refer to the basic autograph set for price listings on that card.

Card	Low	High
1 Ron Guidry/CY 78	125.00	200.00
2 Nolan Ryan/HOF 99	350.00	500.00
3 Herb Score/ROY 55	125.00	200.00
4 Tom Seaver/CY 69	200.00	400.00

2000 Greats of the Game Retrospection

Randomly inserted in packs at one in six, this insert set pays tribute to 15 truly legendary players. Card backs carry a "R" prefix.

Card	Low	High
COMPLETE SET (15)	40.00	100.00
R1 Rod Carew	1.25	3.00
R2 Stan Musial	3.00	8.00
R3 Nolan Ryan	5.00	12.00
R4 Tom Seaver	1.25	3.00
R5 Brooks Robinson	1.25	3.00
R6 Al Kaline	2.00	5.00
R7 Mike Schmidt	4.00	10.00
R8 Thurman Munson	2.00	5.00
R9 Steve Carlton	.75	2.00
R10 Roger Maris	2.00	5.00
R11 Duke Snider	1.25	3.00
R12 Yogi Berra	2.00	5.00
R13 Carl Yastrzemski	3.00	8.00
R14 Reggie Jackson	1.25	3.00
R15 Johnny Bench	2.00	5.00

2000 Greats of the Game Yankees Clippings

Randomly inserted in packs at one in 48, this insert set features 15 cards that contain pieces of game-used jerseys of legendary New York Yankee players. Card backs carry a "YC" prefix. This set represents one of the earliest attempts by manufacturers to incorporate a theme into a memorabilia-based insert. According to representatives at Fleer, the Mantle card features a pair of home, pin-striped game-used pants.

Card	Low	High
YC1 Mickey Mantle Pants	100.00	200.00
YC2 Ron Guidry	8.00	20.00
YC3 Don Larsen	6.00	15.00
YC4 Elston Howard	8.00	20.00
YC5 Mel Stottlemyre	6.00	15.00
YC6 Don Mattingly	40.00	80.00
YC7 Reggie Jackson	8.00	20.00
YC8 Tommy John	6.00	15.00
YC9 Dave Winfield	6.00	15.00
YC10 Willie Randolph Uniform is home pinstripes	6.00	15.00
YC10A Willie Randolph Grey Uniform	6.00	15.00
YC11 Tommy Henrich	6.00	15.00
YC12 Billy Martin	30.00	60.00
YC13 Dave Righetti	6.00	15.00
YC14 Joe Pepitone	6.00	15.00
YC15 Thurman Munson	50.00	100.00

2001 Greats of the Game Promo Sheets

These six promo sheets were inserted into Sports Cards Magazine starting in February, 2001. Each uncut sheet features six Greats of the Game trading cards. Please note that Fleer released these one month at a time.

Card	Low	High
COMPLETE SET (6)	9.00	18.00
1 Rick Ankiel	1.50	3.00
Jeff Bagwell		
Barry Bonds		
Pat Burrell		
Roger Clemens		
Carlos Delgado		
2 J.D. Drew	1.50	3.00
Jim Edmonds		
Darin Erstad		
Andres Galarraga		
Nomar Garciaparra		
Jason Giambi		
3 Troy Glaus	1.50	3.00
Roberto Alomar		
Ken Griffey Jr.		
Vladimir Guerrero		
Tony Gwynn		
Todd Helton		
4 Derek Jeter	1.50	3.00
Randy Johnson		
Chipper Jones		
Andruw Jones		
Greg Maddux		
Pedro Martinez		
5 Mark McGwire	1.50	3.00
Magglio Ordonez		
Mike Piazza		
Manny Ramirez		
Cal Ripken		
Alex Rodriguez		
6 Ivan Rodriguez	1.50	3.00
Jeff Kent		
Gary Sheffield		
Sammy Sosa		
Frank Thomas		
Bernie Williams		

2001 Greats of the Game

The 2001 Fleer Greats of the Game product was released in March, 2001 and features a 137-card base set that includes many players that are in the Major League Hall of Fame. Each pack contains five cards and carried a suggested retail price of $4.99.

Card	Low	High
COMPLETE SET (137)	20.00	50.00
1 Roberto Clemente	2.50	6.00
2 George Anderson	.40	1.00
3 Babe Ruth	3.00	8.00
4 Paul Molitor	.40	1.00
5 Don Larsen	.40	1.00
6 Cy Young	1.00	2.50
7 Billy Martin	.60	1.50
8 Lou Brock	.60	1.50
9 Fred Lynn	.40	1.00
10 Johnny VanderMeer	.40	1.00
11 Harmon Killebrew	1.00	2.50
12 Dave Winfield	.40	1.00
13 Orlando Cepeda	.40	1.00
14 Johnny Mize	.60	1.50
15 Walter Johnson	1.00	2.50
16 Roy Campanella	1.00	2.50
17 Monte Irvin	.60	1.50
18 Mookie Wilson	.40	1.00
19 Elston Howard	.60	1.50
20 Walter Alston	.40	1.00
21 Rollie Fingers	.40	1.00
22 Brooks Robinson	.60	1.50
23 Hank Greenberg	1.00	2.50
24 Maury Wills	.40	1.00
25 Rich Gossage	.40	1.00
26 Leon Day	.40	1.00
27 Jimmie Foxx	1.00	2.50
28 Alan Trammell	.40	1.00
29 Dennis Martinez	.40	1.00
30 Don Drysdale	.60	1.50
31 Bob Feller	.40	1.00
32 Jackie Robinson	1.00	2.50
33 Whitey Ford	.60	1.50
34 Enos Slaughter	.40	1.00
35 Rod Carew	.60	1.50
36 Eddie Mathews	1.00	2.50
37 Ron Cey	.40	1.00
38 Thurman Munson	1.00	2.50
39 Henry Kimbro	.40	1.00
40 Ty Cobb	1.50	4.00
41 Rocky Colavito	1.00	2.50
42 Satchel Paige	1.00	2.50
43 Andre Dawson	.40	1.00
44 Phil Rizzuto	1.00	2.50
45 Roger Maris	1.00	2.50
46 Bobby Bonds	.40	1.00
47 Joe Carter	.40	1.00
48 Christy Mathewson	1.00	2.50
49 Tony Lazzeri	.40	1.00
50 Gil Hodges	1.00	2.50
51 Ray Dandridge	.40	1.00
52 Gaylord Perry	.40	1.00
53 Ernie Banks	1.00	2.50
54 Lou Gehrig	2.00	5.00
55 George Kell	.40	1.00
56 Wes Parker	.40	1.00
57 Sam Jethroe	.40	1.00
58 Joe Morgan	.40	1.00
59 Steve Garvey	.40	1.00
60 Joe Torre	.60	1.50
61 Roger Craig	.40	1.00
62 Warren Spahn	.60	1.50
63 Willie McCovey	.40	1.00
64 Cool Papa Bell	.40	1.00
65 Frank Robinson	.60	1.50
66 Richie Allen	.40	1.00
67 Bucky Dent	.40	1.00
68 George Foster	.40	1.00
69 Hoyt Wilhelm	.40	1.00
70 Phil Niekro	.40	1.00
71 Buck Leonard	.40	1.00
72 Preacher Roe	.40	1.00
73 Yogi Berra	1.00	2.50
74 Joe Black	.40	1.00
75 Nolan Ryan	2.50	6.00
76 Pop Lloyd	.40	1.00
77 Lester Lockett	.40	1.00
78 Paul Blair	.40	1.00
79 Ryne Sandberg	1.50	4.00
80 Bill Perkins	.40	1.00
81 Frank Howard	.40	1.00
82 Hack Wilson	.60	1.50
83 Robin Yount	1.00	2.50
84 Harry Heilmann	.40	1.00
85 Mike Schmidt	2.00	5.00
86 Vida Blue	.40	1.00
87 George Brett	2.00	5.00
88 Juan Marichal	.40	1.00
89 Tom Seaver	.60	1.50
90 Bill Skowron	.40	1.00
91 Don Mattingly	2.00	5.00
92 Jim Bunning	.60	1.50
93 Eddie Murray	1.00	2.50
94 Tommy Lasorda	.40	1.00
95 Pee Wee Reese	1.00	2.50
96 Bill Dickey	.60	1.50
97 Ozzie Smith	1.50	4.00
98 Dale Murphy	.60	1.50
99 Artie Wilson	.40	1.00
100 Bill Terry	.40	1.00
101 Jim Hunter	.60	1.50
102 Don Sutton	.40	1.00
103 Luis Aparicio	.40	1.00
104 Reggie Jackson	.60	1.50
105 Ted Radcliffe	.40	1.00
106 Carl Erskine	.40	1.00
107 Johnny Bench	1.00	2.50
108 Carl Furillo	.40	1.00
109 Stan Musial	1.50	4.00
110 Carlton Fisk	.60	1.50
111 Rube Foster	.40	1.00
112 Tony Oliva	.40	1.00
113 Hank Bauer	.40	1.00
114 Jim Rice	.40	1.00
115 Willie Mays	2.00	5.00
116 Ralph Kiner	.40	1.00
117 Al Kaline	1.00	2.50
118 Billy Williams	.40	1.00
119 Buck O'Neil	.40	1.00
120 Tony Perez	.40	1.00
121 Dave Parker	.40	1.00
122 Kirk Gibson	.40	1.00
123 Lou Piniella	.40	1.00
124 Ted Williams	2.00	5.00
125 Steve Carlton	.40	1.00
126 Dizzy Dean	1.00	2.50
127 Willie Stargell	.60	1.50
128 Joe Niekro	.40	1.00
129 Lloyd Waner	.60	1.50
130 Wade Boggs	.60	1.50
131 Wilmer Fields	.40	1.00
132 Bill Mazeroski	.60	1.50
133 Duke Snider	.60	1.50
134 Joe Williams	.40	1.00
135 Bob Gibson	.60	1.50
136 Jim Palmer	.40	1.00
137 Oscar Charleston	.40	1.00

2001 Greats of the Game Autographs

Randomly inserted into packs at one in eight Hobby, and one in 20 Retail, this 93-card insert set features authentic autographs from legendary players such as Nolan Ryan, Mike Schmidt, and recently inducted Hall of Famer Dave Winfield. Please note, the following players packed out as exchange cards with a redemption deadline of March 1st, 2002: Luis Aparicio, Sam Jethroe, Tommy Lasorda, Juan Marichal, Willie Mays, Phil Rizzuto and Willie Stargell. In addition, the following players had about 50 percent actual signed cards and 50 percent exchange cards seeded into packs: Jim Bunning, Ron Cey, Rollie Fingers, Carlton Fisk, Harmon Killebrew, Gaylord Perry and Brooks Robinson. Also, representatives at Fleer announced specific print runs for several short-printed cards within this set. Though the cards lack actual serial-numbering, the announced quantities for these SP's have been added to our checklist. Willie Stargell passed on before he could sign his card and Fleer used various redemption cards to send to those collectors who had pulled one of those cards from packs.

Card	Low	High
1 Richie Allen	6.00	15.00
2 Sparky Anderson	6.00	15.00
3 Luis Aparicio	6.00	15.00
4 Ernie Banks SP/250	75.00	150.00
5 Hank Bauer	6.00	15.00
6 Johnny Bench SP/400	50.00	100.00
7 Yogi Berra SP/500	40.00	80.00
8 Joe Black	6.00	15.00
9 Paul Blair	4.00	10.00
9A Paul Blair Double-Signed	6.00	15.00
10 Vida Blue	4.00	10.00
11 Wade Boggs	15.00	40.00
12 Bobby Bonds	15.00	40.00
13 George Brett SP/247	125.00	200.00
14 Lou Brock SP/500	30.00	60.00
15 Jim Bunning	15.00	40.00
16 Rod Carew	10.00	25.00
17 Steve Carlton	6.00	15.00
18 Joe Carter	6.00	15.00
19 Orlando Cepeda	6.00	15.00
20 Ron Cey	4.00	10.00
21 Rocky Colavito	30.00	60.00
22 Roger Craig	6.00	15.00
23 Andre Dawson	6.00	15.00
24 Bucky Dent	6.00	15.00
25 Carl Erskine	6.00	15.00
26 Bob Feller	6.00	15.00
27 Wilmer Fields	15.00	40.00
28 Rollie Fingers	6.00	15.00
29 Carlton Fisk	10.00	25.00
30 Whitey Ford	15.00	40.00
31 George Foster	4.00	10.00
32 Steve Garvey SP/400	15.00	40.00
33 Bob Gibson	10.00	25.00

1941 Goudey

34 Kirk Gibson 6.00 15.00
35 Rich Gossage 10.00 25.00
36 Frank Howard 6.00 15.00
37 Monte Irvin 6.00 15.00
38 Reg. Jackson SP/400 50.00 100.00
39 Sam Jethroe 20.00 50.00
40 Al Kaline 15.00 40.00
41 George Kell 6.00 15.00
42 H. Killebrew EXCH* 15.00 40.00
43 Ralph Kiner 15.00 40.00
44 Don Larsen 10.00 25.00
45 Tommy Lasorda SP/400 40.00 80.00
46 Lester Lockett 6.00 15.00
47 Fred Lynn 6.00 15.00
48 Juan Marichal 6.00 15.00
49 Dennis Martinez 4.00 10.00
50 Don Mattingly 40.00 80.00
51 Willie Mays SP/100 400.00 600.00
52 Bill Mazeroski UER 10.00 25.00
Baltimore Elite Giants logo on card back
53 Willie McCovey 10.00 25.00
54 Paul Molitor 6.00 15.00
55 Joe Morgan 6.00 15.00
56 Dale Murphy 10.00 25.00
57 Eddie Murray SP/140 200.00 350.00
58 Stan Musial SP/525 50.00 100.00
59 Joe Niekro 4.00 10.00
60 Phil Niekro 6.00 15.00
61 Tony Oliva 6.00 15.00
62 Buck O'Neil 30.00 60.00
63 Jim Palmer SP/600 15.00 40.00
64 Dave Parker 6.00 15.00
65 Tony Perez 10.00 25.00
66 Gaylord Perry 6.00 15.00
67 Lou Piniella 10.00 25.00
68 Ted Radcliffe 20.00 50.00
69 Jim Rice 6.00 15.00
70 Phil Rizzuto 30.00 60.00
EXCH SP/425
71 Brooks Robinson 10.00 25.00
72 Frank Robinson 10.00 25.00
73 Preacher Roe 8.00 20.00
74 Nolan Ryan SP/650 60.00 120.00
75 Ryne Sandberg 30.00 60.00
76 Mike Schmidt SP/213 125.00 200.00
77 Tom Seaver 30.00 60.00
78 Bill Skowron 6.00 15.00
79 Enos Slaughter 15.00 40.00
80 Ozzie Smith 20.00 50.00
81 Duke Snider SP/600 30.00 60.00
82 Warren Spahn 30.00 60.00
83 Willie Stargell NO AU 10.00 25.00
Stargell passed away before he had a chance to sign for this set
84 Don Sutton 4.00 10.00
85 Joe Torre SP/500 30.00 60.00
86 Alan Trammell 6.00 15.00
87 Hoyt Wilhelm 15.00 40.00
88 Billy Williams 6.00 15.00
89 Maury Wills 4.00 10.00
90 Artie Wilson 6.00 15.00
91 Mookie Wilson 6.00 15.00
92 Dave Winfield SP/370 15.00 40.00
93 Robin Yount SP/400 50.00 100.00

2001 Greats of the Game Dodger Blues

Randomly inserted into packs at one in 36 Hobby, this 15-card insert set features swatches from actual game-used Jerseys, Uniforms, and Bats from legendary Dodger players. The cards have been listed below in alphabetical order for convenience. Please note, according to representatives at Fleer less than 200 of each SP was produced.

1 Walter Alston Jsy 10.00 25.00
2 Walter Alston Uni 10.00 25.00
3 Roy Campanella Bat SP 100.00 200.00
4 Roger Craig Jsy 10.00 25.00
5 Don Drysdale Jsy 15.00 40.00
6 Carl Furillo Jsy 10.00 25.00
7 Steve Garvey Jsy 10.00 25.00
8 Gil Hodges Uni 15.00 40.00
9 Wes Parker Bat 10.00 25.00
10 Wes Parker Jsy 10.00 25.00
11 Pee Wee Reese Jsy 15.00 40.00
12 Jackie Robinson 125.00 250.00
Uni SP
13 Preacher Roe Jsy 10.00 25.00
14 Duke Snider Bat SP 75.00 150.00
15 Don Sutton Jsy 10.00 25.00

2001 Greats of the Game Feel the Game Classics

Randomly inserted into packs at one in 72 Hobby, and one in 400 Retail, this 24-card insert features swatches of actual game-used Bats or Jerseys from legendary players like Babe Ruth and Roger Maris. Please note that the cards are listed below in alphabetical order. Though the cards lack actual serial-numbering, specific print runs for several short-printed cards was publicly announced by representativces at Fleer. These figures are detailed in our checklist.

1 L. Aparicio Bat SP/200 10.00 25.00
2 George Brett Jsy SP/300 20.00 50.00
3 Lou Brock Jsy 6.00 15.00
4 O. Cepeda Bat SP/300 10.00 25.00
5 Whitey Ford Jsy 6.00 15.00
6 Hank Greenberg Bat SP/300 40.00 80.00
7 Elston Howard Bat SP/300 10.00 25.00
8 Jim Hunter Jsy 6.00 15.00
9 Harmon Killebrew Bat 6.00 15.00
10 Roger Maris Bat 20.00 50.00
11 Eddie Mathews Bat 6.00 15.00
12 Willie McCovey 10.00 25.00
Bat SP/200
13 Johnny Mize Bat 6.00 15.00
14 Paul Molitor Jsy 4.00 10.00
15 Jim Palmer Jsy 4.00 10.00
16 Tony Perez Bat 4.00 10.00
17 B.Robinson Bat SP/144 10.00 25.00
18 Babe Ruth Bat SP/250 125.00 200.00
19 Mike Schmidt Jsy 15.00 40.00
20 Tom Seaver Jsy 6.00 15.00
21 Enos Slaughter 10.00 25.00
Bat SP/200
22 Willie Stargell Jsy 6.00 15.00
23 Hack Wilson Bat 40.00 80.00
24 Harry Heilmann Bat 4.00 10.00

2001 Greats of the Game Retrospection

Randomly inserted into hobby and retail packs at one in six, this 10-card insert set takes a look at the careers of some of the best players to have ever played the game. Card backs carry a "RC" prefix.

COMPLETE SET (10) 15.00 30.00
RC1 Babe Ruth 6.00 15.00
RC2 Stan Musial 2.50 6.00
RC3 Jimmie Foxx 2.00 5.00
RC4 Roberto Clemente 5.00 12.00
RC5 Ted Williams 4.00 10.00
RC6 Mike Schmidt 3.00 8.00
RC7 Cy Young 2.00 5.00
RC8 Satchel Paige 2.00 5.00
RC9 Hank Greenberg 2.00 5.00
RC10 Jim Bunning 1.25 3.00

2002 Greats of the Game

This product was released in mid-December 2001, and featured a 100-card base set of Hall of Famers like Cy Young and Ted Williams. Each pack contained five-cards and carried a suggested retail price of $4.99.

COMPLETE SET (100) 20.00 50.00
1 Cal Ripken 3.00 8.00
2 Paul Molitor .40 1.00
3 Roberto Clemente 2.50 6.00
4 Cy Young 1.00 2.50
5 Tris Speaker 1.00 2.50
6 Lou Brock .60 1.50
7 Fred Lynn .40 1.00
8 Harmon Killebrew 1.00 2.50
9 Ted Williams 2.00 5.00
10 Dave Winfield .40 1.00
11 Orlando Cepeda .40 1.00
12 Johnny Mize .60 1.50
13 Walter Johnson 1.00 2.50
14 Roy Campanella 1.00 2.50
15 George Sisler .40 1.00
16 Bo Jackson 1.00 2.50
17 Rollie Fingers .40 1.00
18 Brooks Robinson .60 1.50
19 Billy Williams .40 1.00
20 Maury Wills .40 1.00
21 Jimmie Foxx 1.00 2.50
22 Alan Trammell .40 1.00
23 Rogers Hornsby 1.00 2.50
24 Don Drysdale .60 1.50
25 Bob Feller .40 1.00
26 Jackie Robinson 1.00 2.50
27 Whitey Ford .60 1.50
28 Enos Slaughter .40 1.00
29 Rod Carew .60 1.50
30 Eddie Mathews 1.00 2.50
31 Ron Cey .40 1.00
32 Thurman Munson 1.00 2.50
33 Ty Cobb 1.50 4.00
34 Rocky Colavito 1.00 2.50
35 Satchel Paige 1.00 2.50
36 Andre Dawson .40 1.00
37 Phil Rizzuto 1.00 2.50
38 Roger Maris 1.00 2.50
39 Earl Weaver .40 1.00
40 Joe Carter .40 1.00
41 Christy Mathewson 1.00 2.50
42 Tony Lazzeri .40 1.00
43 Gil Hodges 1.00 2.50
44 Gaylord Perry .40 1.00
45 Steve Carlton .40 1.00
46 George Kell .40 1.00
47 Mickey Cochrane .60 1.50
48 Joe Morgan .40 1.00
49 Steve Garvey .40 1.00
50 Bob Gibson .60 1.50
51 Lefty Grove .60 1.50
52 Warren Spahn .60 1.50
53 Willie McCovey .40 1.00
54 Frank Robinson .60 1.50
55 Rich Gossage .40 1.00
56 Hank Bauer .40 1.00
57 Hoyt Wilhelm .40 1.00
58 Mel Ott 1.00 2.50
59 Preacher Roe .40 1.00
60 Yogi Berra 1.00 2.50
61 Nolan Ryan 2.50 6.00
62 Dizzy Dean 1.00 2.50
63 Ryne Sandberg 1.50 4.00
64 Frank Howard .40 1.00
65 Hack Wilson .60 1.50
66 Robin Yount 1.00 2.50
67 Al Kaline 1.00 2.50
68 Mike Schmidt 2.00 5.00
69 Vida Blue .40 1.00
70 George Brett 2.00 5.00
71 Sparky Anderson .40 1.00
72 Tom Seaver .60 1.50
73 Bill Skowron .40 1.00
74 Don Mattingly 2.00 5.00
75 Carl Yastrzemski 1.50 4.00
76 Eddie Murray 1.00 2.50
77 Jim Palmer .40 1.00
78 Bill Dickey .60 1.50
79 Ozzie Smith 1.50 4.00
80 Dale Murphy .60 1.50
81 Nap Lajoie 1.00 2.50
82 Jim Hunter .60 1.50
83 Duke Snider .60 1.50
84 Luis Aparicio .40 1.00
85 Reggie Jackson .60 1.50
86 Honus Wagner 1.25 3.00
87 Johnny Bench 1.00 2.50
88 Stan Musial 1.50 4.00
89 Carlton Fisk .60 1.50
90 Tony Oliva .40 1.00
91 Wade Boggs .60 1.50
92 Jim Rice .40 1.00
93 Bill Mazeroski .60 1.50
94 Ralph Kiner .40 1.00
95 Tony Perez .40 1.00
96 Kirby Puckett 1.00 2.50
97 Bobby Bonds .40 1.00
98 Bill Terry .40 1.00
99 Juan Marichal .40 1.00
100 Hank Greenberg 1.00 2.50

2002 Greats of the Game Autographs

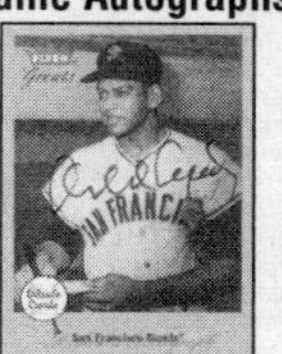

Randomly inserted into packs at one in 24, this insert set features authentic autographs from legendary players such as Nolan Ryan, Bob Gibson, and recently inducted Hall of Famer Ozzie Smith. Please note that a few of the players were short-printed and are listed below with an "SP" after their name. A number of exchange cards with a redemption deadline of 12/01/02 were seeded into packs. The following players were available via redemption: Al Kaline, Alan Trammell, Bobby Bonds, Bob Feller, Carlton Fisk, Rocky Colavito, Cal Ripken, Dave Winfield, Eddie Murray, Enos Slaughter, Harmon Killebrew, Juan Marichal, Kirby Puckett, Luis Aparicio, Lou Brock, Mike Schmidt, Dale Murphy, Maury Wills, Nolan Ryan, Ozzie Smith, Phil Rizzuto, Rod Carew, Rollie Fingers, Rich Gossage, Ralph Kiner, Robin Yount, Steve Garvey, Whitey Ford, Willie McCovey and Yogi Berra.

AD Andre Dawson 6.00 15.00
AK Al Kaline 15.00 40.00
AT Alan Trammell 6.00 15.00
BB Bobby Bonds 15.00 40.00
BF Bob Feller 6.00 15.00
BG Bob Gibson SP/200 12.50 30.00
BM Bill Mazeroski SP/200 12.50 30.00
BR Brooks Robinson 10.00 25.00
BS Bill Skowron 6.00 15.00
BW Billy Williams 6.00 15.00
CE Ron Cey 4.00 10.00
CF Carlton Fisk SP/100 40.00 80.00
CO Rocky Colavito 15.00 40.00
CR Cal Ripken SP/100 125.00 200.00
CY C.Yastrzemski SP/200 40.00 80.00
DM Don Mattingly SP/300 40.00 80.00
DP Dave Parker 6.00 15.00
DS Duke Snider 10.00 25.00
DW Dave Winfield SP/250 12.50 30.00
EM Eddie Murray SP/250 40.00 80.00
ES Enos Slaughter 10.00 25.00
FH Frank Howard 6.00 15.00
FL Fred Lynn 6.00 15.00
FR Frank Robinson SP/250 12.50 30.00
GB George Brett SP/150 75.00 150.00
GK George Kell 6.00 15.00
GP Gaylord Perry 6.00 15.00
HB Hank Bauer 6.00 15.00
HK Harmon Killebrew 12.50 30.00
HW Hoyt Wilhelm 10.00 25.00
JB Johnny Bench 30.00 60.00
JC Joe Carter 6.00 15.00
JM Juan Marichal 6.00 15.00
JM Joe Morgan 6.00 15.00
JP Jim Palmer 10.00 25.00
JR Jim Rice 6.00 15.00
KP Kirby Puckett SP/250 50.00 100.00
LA Luis Aparicio 6.00 15.00
LB Lou Brock SP/250 12.50 30.00
MS Mike Schmidt SP/150 60.00 120.00
MU Dale Murphy 10.00 25.00
MW Maury Wills 6.00 15.00
NR Nolan Ryan SP/150 60.00 120.00
OC Orlando Cepeda 6.00 15.00
OS Ozzie Smith SP/300 40.00 80.00
PB Paul Blair 4.00 10.00
PM Paul Molitor 6.00 15.00
PR Phil Rizzuto SP/300 30.00 60.00
PR Preacher Roe 6.00 15.00
RC Rod Carew SP/250 20.00 50.00
RF Rollie Fingers 6.00 15.00
RG Rich Gossage 6.00 15.00
RJ R.Jackson SP/150 40.00 80.00
RK Ralph Kiner SP/250 10.00 25.00
RS R.Sandberg SP/200 40.00 80.00
RY Robin Yount SP/250 40.00 80.00
SA Sparky Anderson 6.00 15.00
SC Steve Carlton 6.00 15.00
SG Steve Garvey 6.00 15.00
SM Stan Musial SP/200 40.00 80.00
TO Tony Oliva 6.00 15.00
TP Tony Perez 6.00 15.00
TS Tom Seaver SP/150 30.00 60.00
VB Vida Blue 6.00 15.00
WB Wade Boggs 10.00 25.00
WF Whitey Ford 15.00 40.00
WM Willie McCovey 10.00 25.00
WS Warren Spahn 15.00 40.00
YB Yogi Berra 20.00 50.00

2002 Greats of the Game Dueling Duos

This 29-card insert pairs contemporaries that competed against each other in their respective eras. These cards were inserted into packs at one in six.

1 Johnny Bench 1.50 4.00
Carlton Fisk
2 Roy Campanella 2.00 5.00
Yogi Berra
3 Stan Musial 2.50 6.00
Ted Williams
4 Carl Yastrzemski 2.00 5.00
Reggie Jackson
5 Babe Ruth 4.00 10.00
Jimmie Foxx
6 Kirby Puckett 2.50 6.00
Don Mattingly
7 Steve Carlton 3.00 8.00
Nolan Ryan
8 Wade Boggs 3.00 8.00
Don Mattingly
9 Brooks Robinson 1.50 4.00
Roger Maris
10 Paul Molitor 3.00 8.00
Don Mattingly
11 Sparky Anderson 1.25 3.00
Earl Weaver
12 Bob Gibson 1.25 3.00
Duke Snider
13 Yogi Berra 2.00 5.00
Gil Hodges
14 Joe Morgan 2.50 6.00
Ryne Sandberg
15 Tony Perez 2.00 5.00
Carl Yastrzemski
16 Jimmie Foxx 1.50 4.00
Bill Dickey
17 Ralph Kiner 1.25 3.00
Duke Snider
18 Nellie Fox 1.25 3.00
Rocky Colavito
19 Willie McCovey 1.50 4.00
Johnny Bench
20 Duke Snider 1.25 3.00
Eddie Mathews
21 Reggie Jackson 1.25 3.00
Jim Rice
22 Eddie Murray 1.50 4.00
Jim Rice
23 Paul Molitor 1.25 3.00
Dave Winfield
24 Robin Yount 1.50 4.00
Dave Winfield
25 Enos Slaughter 1.25 3.00
Ted Kluszewski
26 Wade Boggs 3.00 8.00
George Brett
27 George Brett 3.00 8.00
Mike Schmidt
28 George Brett 3.00 8.00
Eddie Murray
29 George Brett 5.00 12.00
Cal Ripken

2002 Greats of the Game Dueling Duos Autographs

This six-card insert set is a partial parallel of the 2002 Fleer Greats of the Game Dueling Duos insert, and features dual autographs from greats like Bench/Fisk. Each card has an announced print run of 25 copies. Due to market scarcity, no pricing is provided. The following cards were distributed in packs as exchange cards with a redemption deadline of 12/01/02: Bench/Fisk, Boggs/Mattingly, Brett/Schmidt and Puckett/Mattingly.

1 Johnny Bench
Carlton Fisk
2 Wade Boggs
Don Mattingly
3 George Brett
Mike Schmidt
4 Kirby Puckett
Don Mattingly
5 Duke Snider
Bob Gibson
6 Carl Yastrzemski
Reggie Jackson

2002 Greats of the Game Dueling Duos Game Used Double

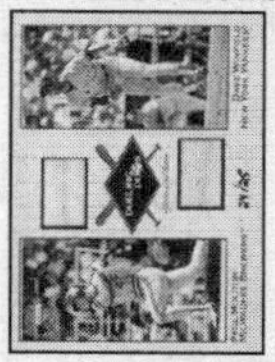

This 27-card insert is a partial parallel of the 2002 Fleer Greats of the Game Dueling Duos insert. Each card features dual jersey swatches from greats like Boggs/Brett, and is individually serial numbered to 25. Due to market scarcity, no pricing is provided.

1 Sparky Anderson Pants
Earl Weaver Pants
2 Johnny Bench Bat
Carlton Fisk Bat
3 Yogi Berra Bat
Gil Hodges Bat
4 Wade Boggs Bat
George Brett Bat
5 Wade Boggs Bat
Don Mattingly Bat
6 George Brett Bat
Eddie Murray Bat
7 George Brett Bat
Cal Ripken Bat
8 Roy Campanella Bat
Yogi Berra Bat
9 Steve Carlton Jsy
Nolan Ryan Jsy
10 Nellie Fox Bat
Rocky Colavito Bat
11 Jimmie Foxx Bat
Bill Dickey Bat
12 Bob Gibson Jsy
Duke Snider Bat
13 Reggie Jackson Bat
Jim Rice Bat
14 Ralph Kiner Bat
Duke Snider Bat
15 Willie McCovey Bat
Johnny Bench Bat
16 Paul Molitor Bat
Don Mattingly Bat
17 Paul Molitor Bat
Dave Winfield Bat
18 Joe Morgan Bat
Ryne Sandberg Bat
19 Eddie Murray Bat
Jim Rice Bat
20 Tony Perez Bat
Carl Yastrzemski Bat
21 Kirby Puckett Bat
Don Mattingly Bat
22 Brooks Robinson Bat
Roger Maris Pants
23 Babe Ruth Bat
Jimmie Foxx Bat
24 Enos Slaughter Bat
Ted Kluszewski Bat
25 Duke Snider Bat
Eddie Mathews Bat
26 Carl Yastrzemski Bat
Reggie Jackson Bat
27 Robin Yount Bat
Dave Winfield Bat

2002 Greats of the Game Dueling Duos Game Used Single

This 54-card insert features a single swatch of game-used jersey, and was inserted into packs at 1:24. Please note that a few of the players were short-printed and are notated as such in our checklist.

BD1 Jimmie Foxx 8.00 20.00
Bill Dickey Bat
BG1 Bob Gibson Jsy 8.00 20.00
Duke Snider SP/200
BR1 Brooks Robinson Bat 8.00 20.00
Roger Maris
BR1 Babe Ruth Bat
Jimmie Foxx SP/75
CF1 Johnny Bench 8.00 20.00
Carlton Fisk Bat
CR1 George Brett 15.00 40.00
Cal Ripken Bat
CY1 Carl Yastrzemski Bat 12.50 30.00
Reggie Jackson
CY2 Tony Perez 12.50 30.00
Carl Yastrzemski Bat
DM1 Kirby Puckett 8.00 20.00
Don Mattingly Bat
DM2 Wade Boggs 8.00 20.00
Don Mattingly Bat
DM3 Paul Molitor 8.00 20.00
Don Mattingly Bat
DS1 Bob Gibson 8.00 20.00
Duke Snider Bat SP/200
DS2 Ralph Kiner 8.00 20.00
Duke Snider Bat
DS3 Duke Snider Bat 8.00 20.00
Eddie Mathews
DW1 Paul Molitor 6.00 15.00
Dave Winfield Bat
DW2 Robin Yount 6.00 15.00
Dave Winfield Bat
EM1 Duke Snider 8.00 20.00
Eddie Mathews Bat
EM1 Eddie Murray Bat 8.00 20.00
Jim Rice
EM2 George Brett 8.00 20.00
Eddie Murray Bat
ES1 Enos Slaughter Bat 6.00 15.00
Ted Kluszewski
EW1 Sparky Anderson 6.00 15.00
Earl Weaver Pants SP/400
GB1 Wade Boggs 8.00 20.00
George Brett Bat
GB2 George Brett Bat 8.00 20.00
Eddie Murray
GB3 George Brett Bat 10.00 25.00
Cal Ripken
GH1 Yogi Berra 8.00 20.00
Gil Hodges Bat
JB1 Johnny Bench Bat 8.00 20.00
Carlton Fisk
JB2 Willie McCovey 8.00 20.00
Johnny Bench Bat
JF1 Babe Ruth
Jimmie Foxx Bat SP/75
JF2 Jimmie Foxx Bat 12.50 30.00
Bill Dickey SP/400
JM1 Joe Morgan Bat 6.00 15.00
Ryne Sandberg
JR1 Reggie Jackson 6.00 15.00
Jim Rice Bat
JR2 Eddie Murray 8.00 20.00
Jim Rice Bat
KP1 Kirby Puckett Bat 8.00 20.00
Don Mattingly
NF1 Nellie Fox Bat 8.00 20.00
Rocky Colavito
NR1 Steve Carlton
Nolan Ryan Jsy SP/100
PM1 Paul Molitor Bat 6.00 15.00
Don Mattingly
PM2 Paul Molitor Bat 6.00 15.00
Dave Winfield
RC1 Nellie Fox 8.00 20.00
Rocky Colavito Bat
RJ1 Carl Yastrzemski 8.00 20.00
Reggie Jackson Bat
RJ2 Reggie Jackson Bat 8.00 20.00
Jim Rice
RK1 Ralph Kiner Bat 8.00 20.00
Duke Snider
RM1 Brooks Robinson 20.00 50.00
Roger Maris Pants
RS1 Joe Morgan 10.00 25.00
Ryne Sandberg Bat
RY1 Robin Yount Bat 8.00 20.00
Dave Winfield
SA1 Sparky Anderson Pants SP/400 6.00 15.00
Earl Weaver
SC1 Steve Carlton Jersey
Nolan Ryan SP/100
TK1 Enos Slaughter 8.00 20.00
Ted Kluszewski Bat
TP1 Tony Perez Bat 6.00 15.00
Carl Yastrzemski
WB1 Wade Boggs Bat 8.00 20.00
Don Mattingly
WB2 Wade Boggs Bat 8.00 20.00
George Brett
WM1 Willie McCovey Bat 8.00 20.00
Johnny Bench
YB1 Roy Campanella 8.00 20.00
Yogi Berra Bat
YB2 Yogi Berra Bat 8.00 20.00
Gil Hodges
YB3 Roy Campanella 8.00 20.00
Yogi Berra Glove

2002 Greats of the Game Through the Years Level 1

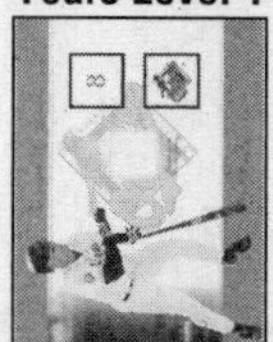

This 31-card insert features swatches of authentic game-used jersey on a silver-foil based card. These cards were inserted into packs at a rate of 1:24.

1 Johnny Bench Pants 8.00 20.00
2 Vida Blue 6.00 15.00
3 Wade Boggs 6.00 15.00
4 George Brett 10.00 25.00
5 Carlton Fisk Hitting 6.00 15.00
6 Carlton Fisk Fielding 6.00 15.00
7 Bo Jackson Royals 8.00 20.00
8 Bo Jackson White Sox 8.00 20.00
9 Reggie Jackson A's 6.00 15.00
10 Reggie Jackson Angels 6.00 15.00
11 Ted Kluszewski 6.00 15.00
12 Don Mattingly 10.00 25.00
13 Willie McCovey 6.00 15.00
14 Paul Molitor Blue Jays 6.00 15.00
15 Paul Molitor Brewers 6.00 15.00
16 Eddie Murray 8.00 20.00

17 Jim Palmer 6.00 15.00
18 Tony Perez 6.00 15.00
19 J.Rice Red Sox Home 6.00 15.00
20 Jim Rice Red Sox Road 6.00 15.00
21 C.Ripken Orioles Hitting 15.00 40.00
22 Cal Ripken Orioles Fielding 15.00 40.00
23 Brooks Robinson Bat 6.00 15.00
24 Frank Robinson 6.00 15.00
25 J.Robinson Pants SP/200 30.00 60.00
26 Nolan Ryan 15.00 40.00
27 Hoyt Wilhelm 6.00 15.00
28 Ted Williams SP/350 50.00 100.00
29 Dave Winfield 6.00 15.00
30 Carl Yastrzemski 10.00 25.00
31 Robin Yount 8.00 20.00

2002 Greats of the Game Through the Years Level 1 Patch

This 27-card insert features swatches of authentic jersey patch on a gold-foil based card. Each card is also individually serial numbered to 100.

1 Johnny Bench 20.00 50.00
2 Wade Boggs 15.00 40.00
3 George Brett 40.00 80.00
4 Carlton Fisk Hitting 15.00 40.00
5 Carlton Fisk Fielding 15.00 40.00
6 Bo Jackson Royals 20.00 50.00
7 Bo Jackson White Sox 20.00 50.00
8 Reggie Jackson A's 15.00 40.00
9 Reggie Jackson Angels 15.00 40.00
10 Ted Kluszewski 15.00 40.00
11 Don Mattingly 40.00 80.00
12 Willie McCovey 15.00 40.00
13 Paul Molitor Blue Jays 15.00 40.00
14 Paul Molitor Brewers 15.00 40.00
15 Eddie Murray 20.00 50.00
16 Jim Palmer 15.00 40.00
17 Tony Perez 15.00 40.00
18 Jim Rice Red Sox 15.00 40.00
19 Jim Rice Red Sox 15.00 40.00
20 Cal Ripken Hitting 50.00 100.00
21 Cal Ripken Fielding 50.00 100.00
22 Frank Robinson 15.00 40.00
23 Nolan Ryan 40.00 80.00
24 Ted Williams 60.00 120.00
25 Dave Winfield 15.00 40.00
26 Carl Yastrzemski 40.00 80.00
27 Robin Yount 20.00 50.00

2002 Greats of the Game Through the Years Level 2

This 22-card insert features swatches of authentic game-used jersey on a silver-foil based card. These cards were individually serial numbered to 100.

1 Johnny Bench 20.00 50.00
2 Wade Boggs 15.00 40.00
3 George Brett 40.00 80.00
4 Carlton Fisk White Sox 15.00 40.00
5 Bo Jackson Royals 20.00 50.00
6 Bo Jackson White Sox 20.00 50.00
7 Reggie Jackson A's 15.00 40.00
8 Ted Kluszewski 15.00 40.00
9 Don Mattingly 40.00 80.00
10 Willie McCovey 15.00 40.00
11 Paul Molitor Brewers 15.00 40.00
12 Eddie Murray 20.00 50.00
13 Jim Palmer 15.00 40.00
14 Jim Rice Home 15.00 40.00
15 Jim Rice Road 15.00 40.00
16 Cal Ripken Hitting 50.00 100.00
17 Cal Ripken Fielding 50.00 100.00
18 Nolan Ryan 40.00 80.00
19 Ted Williams 60.00 120.00
20 Dave Winfield 15.00 40.00
21 Carl Yastrzemski 40.00 80.00
22 Robin Yount 20.00 50.00

2002 Greats of the Game Through the Years Level 3

This 19-card insert features swatches of authentic game-used jersey on a silver-foil based card. These cards were individually serial numbered to 25. Due to market scarcity, no pricing is provided for these cards.

1 Johnny Bench
2 Wade Boggs
3 George Brett
4 Carlton Fisk White Sox
5 Reggie Jackson A's
6 Ted Kluszewski
7 Don Mattingly
8 Willie McCovey
9 Paul Molitor Brewers
10 Eddie Murray
11 Jim Rice Home
12 Jim Rice Road
13 Cal Ripken Hitting
14 Cal Ripken Batting
15 Nolan Ryan
16 Ted Williams
17 Dave Winfield
18 Carl Yastrzemski
19 Robin Yount

2004 Greats of the Game

This 80-card set was initially released in June, 2004. The set was issued in five card packs with an $10 SRP which came packed 15 packs to a box and 12 boxes to a case. An update entitled Cut Signature Edition was released in December, 2004 containing cards 81-145.

COMPLETE SERIES 1 (80) 15.00 40.00
COMPLETE SERIES 2 (65) 10.00 25.00
1 Lou Gehrig 1.25 3.00
2 Ty Cobb 1.00 2.50
3 Dizzy Dean .75 2.00
4 Jimmie Foxx .75 2.00
5 Hank Greenberg .75 2.00
6 Babe Ruth 2.00 5.00
7 Honus Wagner .75 2.00
8 Mickey Cochrane .30 .75
9 Pepper Martin .30 .75
10 Charlie Gehringer .30 .75
11 Carl Hubbell .50 1.25
12 Bill Terry .30 .75
13 Mel Ott .75 2.00
14 Bill Dickey .50 1.25
15 Ted Williams 1.50 4.00
16 Roger Maris Yanks .75 2.00
17 Thurman Munson .75 2.00
18 Phil Rizzuto .50 1.25
19 Stan Musial 1.25 3.00
20 Duke Snider Brooklyn .50 1.25
21 Reggie Jackson Yanks .50 1.25
22 Don Mattingly 1.50 4.00
23 Vida Blue .30 .75
24 Harmon Killebrew .75 2.00
25 Lou Brock .50 1.25
26 Al Kaline .75 2.00
27 Dave Parker .30 .75
28 Nolan Ryan Astros 2.00 5.00
29 Jim Rice .30 .75
30 Paul Molitor Brewers .30 .75
31 Dwight Evans .50 1.25
32 Brooks Robinson .50 1.25
33 Jose Canseco .50 1.25
34 Alan Trammell .30 .75
35 Johnny Bench .75 2.00
36 Carlton Fisk R.Sox .50 1.25
37 Jim Palmer .30 .75
38 George Brett 1.50 4.00
39 Mike Schmidt 1.50 4.00
40 Tony Perez .30 .75
41 Paul Blair .20 .50
42 Fred Lynn .30 .75
43 Carl Yastrzemski 1.25 3.00
44 Steve Carlton Phils .30 .75
45 Dennis Eckersley .50 1.25
46 Tom Seaver Mets .50 1.25
47 Juan Marichal .30 .75
48 Tony Gwynn 1.00 2.50
49 Moose Skowron .30 .75
50 Bob Gibson .50 1.25
51 Luis Tiant .30 .75
52 Eddie Murray O's .75 2.00
53 Frank Robinson Reds .30 .75
54 Rocky Colavito .50 1.25
55 Bobby Shantz .20 .50
56 Ernie Banks .75 2.00
57 Rod Carew Angels .50 1.25
58 Gorman Thomas .30 .75
59 Bernie Carbo .20 .50
60 Joe Rudi .20 .50
61 Graig Nettles .30 .75
62 Ron Guidry .30 .75
63 Whitey Ford .50 1.25
64 George Kell .30 .75
65 Cal Ripken 2.50 6.00
66 Willie McCovey .50 1.25
67 Bo Jackson .75 2.00
68 Kirby Puckett .75 2.00
69 Ted Kluszewski .50 1.25
70 Johnny Podres .30 .75
71 Davey Lopes .30 .75
72 Chris Short .20 .50
73 Jeff Torborg .20 .50
74 Bill Freehan .30 .75
75 Frank Tanana .30 .75
76 Jack Morris .30 .75
77 Rick Dempsey .20 .50
78 Yogi Berra .75 2.00
79 Tim McCarver .30 .75
80 Rusty Staub .30 .75
81 Tony Lazzeri .30 .75
82 Al Rosen .30 .75
83 Willie McGee .30 .75
84 Preacher Roe .30 .75
85 Dave Kingman .30 .75
86 Luis Aparicio .30 .75
87 John Kruk .50 1.25
88 Bing Miller .20 .50
89 Joe Charboneau .20 .50
90 Mark Fidrych .30 .75
91 Catfish Hunter .50 1.25
92 Nap Lajoie .50 1.25
93 Eddie Murray Indians .75 2.00
94 Johnny Pesky .20 .50
95 Tom Seaver Reds .50 1.25
96 Frank Robinson O's .30 .75
97 Enos Slaughter .30 .75
98 Cecil Travis .20 .50
99 Robin Yount .75 2.00
100 Don Zimmer .30 .75
101 Babe Herman .20 .50
102 Ron Santo .50 1.25
103 Willie Stargell .50 1.25
104 Paul Molitor Jays .30 .75
105 Jimmy Piersall .30 .75
106 Johnny Sain .30 .75
107 Joe Pepitone .30 .75
108 Ryne Sandberg 1.50 4.00
109 Jim Thorpe 1.25 3.00
110 Steve Garvey .30 .75
111 Ray Knight .20 .50
112 Fernando Valenzuela .30 .75
113 Will Clark .50 1.25
114 Tony Kubek .50 1.25
115 Jim Bouton .30 .75
116 Jerry Koosman .30 .75
117 Steve Carlton Cards .30 .75
118 Richie Ashburn .50 1.25
119 Roberto Clemente 2.00 5.00
120 Paul O'Neill .50 1.25
121 Reggie Jackson Angels .50 1.25
122 Andre Dawson .30 .75
123 Hoyt Wilhelm .30 .75
124 Dale Murphy .50 1.25
125 Dwight Gooden .30 .75
126 Roger Maris Cards .75 2.00
127 Bill Mazeroski .50 1.25
128 Don Newcombe .30 .75
129 Robin Roberts .30 .75
130 Duke Snider LA .50 1.25
131 Eddie Mathews .75 2.00
132 Wade Boggs .50 1.25
133 Rollie Fingers .30 .75
134 Frankie Frisch .30 .75
135 Billy Williams .30 .75
136 Rod Carew Twins .50 1.25
137 Dom DiMaggio .30 .75
138 Orel Hershiser .30 .75
139 Gary Carter .30 .75
140 Keith Hernandez .30 .75
141 Bob Lemon .30 .75
142 Nolan Ryan Angels 2.00 5.00
143 Ozzie Smith 1.25 3.00
144 Rick Sutcliffe .30 .75
145 Carlton Fisk W.Sox .50 1.25

2004 Greats of the Game Blue

*1-80 POST-WAR: 1.25X TO 3X
*1-80 PRE-WAR: 1X TO 2.5X
*81-145 POST-WAR p/r 81-96: 4X TO 10X
*81-145 POST-WAR p/r 51-80: 4X TO 10X
*81-145 POST-WAR p/r 36-50: 5X TO 12X
*81-145 PRE-WAR p/r 36-50: 4X TO 10X
*81-145 PRE-WAR p/r 26-35: 5X TO 12X
*81-145 PRE-WAR p/r 18-25: 6X TO 15X
1-80 SER.1 ODDS 1:7.5 H, 1:24 R
81-145 SER.2 ODDS 1:60 H, 1:110 R
1-80 PRINT RUN 500 SERIAL #'d SETS
81-145 PRINT RUN B/WN 1-96 COPIES PER
81-145 NO PRICING ON QTY OF 1

2004 Greats of the Game Autographs

OVERALL SER.1 AU ODDS 1:5 H, 1:960 R
OVERALL SER.2 AU ODDS 1:7.5 H, 1:960 R
GROUP A PRINT RUN 125-150 SETS
GROUP B PRINT RUN 175-250 SETS
GROUP C1 PRINT RUN 275-300 SETS
A-C CARDS ARE NOT SERIAL-NUMBERED
PRINT RUN INFO PROVIDED BY FLEER
EXCHANGE DEADLINE INDEFINITE
AD Andre Dawson C2 10.00 25.00
AK Al Kaline D1 15.00 40.00
AR Al Rosen E2 6.00 15.00
AT Alan Trammell F1 6.00 15.00
BC Bernie Carbo G1 6.00 15.00
BF Bill Freehan G1 6.00 15.00
BG Bob Gibson F1 10.00 25.00
BJ Bo Jackson C1 20.00 50.00
BM Bill Mazeroski C2 15.00 40.00
BR Brooks Robinson F1 10.00 25.00
BS Bobby Shantz G1 4.00 10.00
BW Billy Williams C2 10.00 25.00
CF1 Carlton Fisk R.Sox D1 15.00 40.00
CF2 Carlton Fisk W.Sox D2 15.00 40.00
CR Cal Ripken A1 75.00 150.00
CY Carl Yastrzemski D1 30.00 60.00
DC David Cone B2 EXCH
DD Dom DiMaggio B2 20.00 50.00
DE Dennis Eckersley B1 15.00 40.00
DEV Dwight Evans F1 10.00 25.00
DG Dwight Gooden B2 10.00 25.00
DK Dave Kingman E2 6.00 15.00
DL Davey Lopes G1 4.00 10.00
DM Don Mattingly A1 50.00 100.00
DMC Denny McLain G1 EXCH
DMU Dale Murphy C2 15.00 40.00
DN Don Newcombe C2 EXCH
DP Dave Parker G1 6.00 15.00
DS1 D.Snider Brooklyn D1 15.00 40.00
DS2 Duke Snider LA B2 15.00 40.00
DZ Don Zimmer C2 10.00 25.00
EB Ernie Banks A1 30.00 60.00
EM Eddie Murray B1 40.00 80.00
FL Fred Lynn F1 4.00 10.00
FR1 Frank Robinson Reds E1 10.00 25.00
FR2 Frank Robinson O's C2 15.00 40.00
FT Frank Tanana G1 6.00 15.00
GB George Brett A1 40.00 80.00
GC Gary Carter B2 EXCH
GK George Kell F1 6.00 15.00
GN Graig Nettles G1 6.00 15.00
GT Gorman Thomas G1 4.00 10.00
HK Harmon Killebrew F1 12.50 30.00
JB Johnny Bench D1 30.00 60.00
JBO Jim Bouton D2 6.00 15.00
JC Jose Canseco D1 10.00 25.00
JCH Joe Charboneau E2 6.00 15.00
JK Jerry Koosman E2 6.00 15.00
JKR John Kruk B2 10.00 25.00
JM Juan Marichal F1 6.00 15.00
JMO Jack Morris F1 6.00 15.00
JP Jim Palmer F1 6.00 15.00
JPI Jimmy Piersall D2 6.00 15.00
JPO Johnny Podres G1 4.00 10.00
JPP Joe Pepitone E2 6.00 15.00
JPS Johnny Pesky E2 15.00 40.00
JR Jim Rice F1 6.00 15.00
JRU Joe Rudi G1 4.00 10.00
JT Jeff Torborg G1 4.00 10.00
KH Keith Hernandez D2 6.00 15.00
KP Kirby Puckett A1 EXCH
LA Luis Aparicio E2 6.00 15.00
LB Lou Brock F1 10.00 25.00
LT Luis Tiant G1 4.00 10.00
MM Marty Marion G1 EXCH
MS Mike Schmidt B1 30.00 60.00
MSK Moose Skowron G1 6.00 15.00
NR1 Nolan Ryan Astros A1 60.00 120.00
NR2 Nolan Ryan Angels B2 60.00 120.00
OH Orel Hershiser A2 15.00 40.00
OS Ozzie Smith B2 20.00 50.00
PB Paul Blair G1 4.00 10.00
PM1 Paul Molitor Brewers B1 10.00 25.00
PM2 Paul Molitor Jays B2 EXCH
PO Paul O'Neill B2 15.00 40.00
PR Phil Rizzuto E1 EXCH
PRO Preacher Roe B2 10.00 25.00
RCO Rocky Colavito D1 40.00 80.00
RC1 Rod Carew Angels D1 10.00 25.00
RC2 Rod Carew Twins B2 EXCH
RD Rick Dempsey A1 10.00 25.00
RF Rollie Fingers D2 6.00 15.00
RG Ron Guidry G1 6.00 15.00
RJ1 R.Jackson Yanks A1 50.00 100.00
RJ2 R.Jackson Angels B2 15.00 40.00
RK Ray Knight E2 6.00 15.00
RR Robin Roberts E2 6.00 15.00
RS Ryne Sandberg B2 30.00 60.00
RST Rusty Staub G1 6.00 15.00
RST Ron Santo D2 10.00 25.00
RY Robin Yount B2 EXCH
SC1 Steve Carlton Phils D1 6.00 15.00
SC2 Steve Carlton Cards D2 6.00 15.00
SG Steve Garvey D2 6.00 15.00
SM Stan Musial A1 60.00 120.00
TG Tony Gwynn E1 15.00 40.00
TK Tony Kubek C2 15.00 40.00
TM Tim McCarver F1 6.00 15.00
TP Tony Perez F1 10.00 25.00
TS1 Tom Seaver Mets A1 40.00 80.00
TS2 Tom Seaver Reds A2 EXCH
VB Vida Blue G1 4.00 10.00
WB Wade Boggs A2 EXCH
WC Will Clark B2 EXCH
WF Whitey Ford D1 15.00 40.00
WM Willie McCovey E1 10.00 25.00
WMG Willie McGee D2 10.00 25.00
YB Yogi Berra B1 40.00 80.00

2004 Greats of the Game Announcing Greats

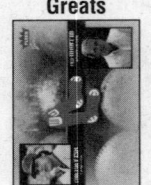

SER.2 STATED ODDS 1:12 RETAIL
1 Harry Kalas 4.00 10.00
Mike Schmidt
2 Vin Scully 3.00 8.00
Steve Garvey
3 Harry Caray 4.00 10.00
Ryne Sandberg
4 Ned Martin 3.00 8.00
Carlton Fisk
5 Ernie Harwell 2.00 5.00
Kirk Gibson
6 Ken Harrelson 3.00 8.00
Carl Yastrzemski
7 Phil Rizzuto 4.00 10.00
Don Mattingly
8 Mel Allen 3.00 8.00
Yogi Berra
9 Jon Miller 6.00 15.00
Cal Ripken
10 Marty Brennaman 3.00 8.00
Johnny Bench

2004 Greats of the Game Announcing Greats Autograph Dual

OVERALL SER.2 AU ODDS 1:7.5 HOBBY
OVERALL SER.2 AU-GU ODDS 1:24 RETAIL
PRINT RUNS B/WN 1-50 COPIES PER
NO PRICING ON QTY OF 8 OR LESS
EXCHANGE DEADLINE INDEFINITE
EHKG Ernie Harwell
Kirk Gibson/48 EXCH
HCRS Harry Caray
Ryne Sandberg/2
HKMS Harry Kalas 75.00 150.00
Mike Schmidt/25
JMCR Jon Miller
Cal Ripken/8 EXCH
KCCY Ken Harrelson
Carl Yastrzemski/50 EXCH
MAYB Mel Allen
Yogi Berra/1
MBJB Marty Brennaman
Johnny Bench/50 EXCH
PRDM Phil Rizzuto
Don Mattingly/26 EXCH

2004 Greats of the Game Battery Mates

RANDOM INSERTS IN SER.1 PACKS
PRINT RUNS B/WN 1934-1979 COPIES PER
1 Steve Carlton 1.50 4.00
Tim McCarver/1972
2 Don Drysdale 2.00 5.00
Roy Campanella/1957
3 Tom Seaver 2.00 5.00
Johnny Bench/1979
4 Whitey Ford 2.00 5.00
Yogi Berra/1956
5 Ron Guidry 2.00 5.00
Thurman Munson/1978
6 Nolan Ryan 4.00 10.00
Jeff Torborg/1973
7 Denny McLain 2.00 5.00
Bill Freehan/1968
8 Lefty Gomez 2.00 5.00
Bill Dickey/1934
9 Jim Palmer 1.50 4.00
Rick Dempsey/1977
10 Luis Tiant 2.00 5.00
Carlton Fisk/1973

2004 Greats of the Game Battery Mates Autograph

OVERALL SER.1 AU ODDS 1:5 H, 1:960 R
PRINT RUNS B/WN 56-79 COPIES PER
AUTO IS ONLY FOR 1ST PLAYER LISTED
DMBF Denny McLain w/Freehan/68
JPRD Jim Palmer w/Dempsey/77 8.00 20.00
NRJT Jeff Torborg w/Ryan/73 6.00 15.00
RGTM Ron Guidry w/Munson/78 10.00 25.00
SCTM Steve Carlton w/McCarver/72 8.00 20.00
TSJB Johnny Bench w/Seaver/79 20.00 50.00
WFYB Whitey Ford w/Berra/56 15.00 40.00

2004 Greats of the Game Battery Mates Autograph Dual

OVERALL SER.1 AU ODDS 1:5 H, 1:960 R
STATED PRINT RUN 10 SERIAL #'d SETS
NO PRICING DUE TO SCARCITY

2004 Greats of the Game Comparison Cuts

An innovative pairing of Wally Pipp and the guy who replaced him at 1st for the Yankees; Lou Gehrig, was a highlight of this set.

OVERALL SER.1 AU ODDS 1:5 H, 1:960 R
STATED PRINT RUN 1 SERIAL #'d SET
NO PRICING DUE TO SCARCITY
BRRM Babe Ruth
Roger Maris
JRLD Jackie Robinson
Larry Doby
LGCR Lou Gehrig
Cal Ripken
LGWP Lou Gehrig
Wally Pipp
LWPW Lloyd Waner
Paul Waner
TWCY Ted Williams
Carl Yastrzemski

2004 Greats of the Game Etched in Time Cuts

OVERALL SER.1 AU ODDS 1:5 H, 1:960 R
OVERALL SER.2 AU ODDS 1:7.5 HOBBY
OVERALL SER.2 AU-GU ODDS 1:24 RETAIL
PRINT RUNS B/WN 1-95 COPIES PER
NO PRICING ON QTY OF 10 OR LESS
BD Bill Dickey S1/1
BG Bob Grim S2/5
BGR Burleigh Grimes S2/5
BH Babe Herman S2/35 75.00 150.00
BL Bob Lemon S2/10
BT Bill Terry S1/3
BUD Buddy Myer S2/3
CAT Catfish Hunter S2/5
CG Charlie Gehringer S1/1
CH Carl Hubbell S1/3
CR Chico Ruiz S2/5
CS Chris Short S2/30 100.00 200.00
DC Dolph Camilli S2/40 100.00 200.00
DD Dizzy Dean S1/1
EA Ethan Allen S2/75 75.00 150.00
EAV Earl Averill S2/50 60.00 120.00
EC Earle Combs S2/1
ER Edd Roush S2/95 50.00 100.00
EW Early Wynn S2/5
FL Freddie Lindstrom S2/5
GB George H. Burns S2/4
GH Gabby Hartnett S2/5
GIL Gil Hodges S2/2
GK George Kelly S2/3
HG Hank Greenberg S1/1
HK Harvey Kuenn S2/32 60.00 120.00
HW Honus Wagner S1/1
HWI Hoyt Wilhelm S2/10
JC Joe Cronin S2/5
JF Jimmie Foxx S1/1
JM Joe Medwick S2/8
JT Jim Thorpe S2/1
LA Luke Appling S2/23 60.00 120.00
LOD Lefty O'Doul S2/3
MC Max Carey S2/1
MCO Mickey Cochrane S1/1
MO Mel Ott S1/1
NF Nellie Fox S2/2
NL Nap Lajoie S2/1
PR Pete Runnels S2/35 60.00 120.00
PT Pie Traynor S2/1
RA Richie Ashburn S2/2
RC Roy Campanella S1/1
RCL Roberto Clemente S1/1
RF Rick Ferrell S2/50 60.00 120.00
RR Red Ruffing S2/5
SM Sal Maglie S2/40 60.00 120.00
TC Ty Cobb S1/1
TCN Tony Conigliaro S2/1
TM Thurman Munson S1/1
TW1 Ted Williams S1/1
TW2 Ted Williams S2/1
WC Walker Cooper S2/20 60.00 120.00
WS Willie Stargell S2/16
ZW Zack Wheat S2/4

2004 Greats of the Game Forever

OVERALL SER.2 ODDS 1:5 HOB, 1:12 RET
PRINT RUNS B/WN 1909-1984 COPIES PER
1 Fernando Valenzuela/1980 2.00 5.00
2 Steve Garvey/1969 2.00 5.00
3 Zach Wheat/1909 2.00 5.00
4 Orel Hershiser/1983 2.00 5.00
5 Duke Snider/1947 2.50 6.00
6 Jim Rice/1974 2.00 5.00
7 Carlton Fisk/1969 2.50 6.00
8 Wade Boggs/1982 2.50 6.00
9 Ted Williams/1939 5.00 12.00
10 Carl Yastrzemski/1961 4.00 10.00
11 Dom DiMaggio/1940 2.50 6.00
12 Ron Santo/1960 2.50 6.00
13 Billy Williams/1959 2.00 5.00
14 Ryne Sandberg/1981 5.00 12.00
15 Ernie Banks/1953 2.50 6.00
16 Gabby Hartnett/1922 2.00 5.00
17 Hack Wilson/1923 2.50 6.00
18 Dwight Gooden/1984 2.00 5.00
19 Ray Knight/1974 2.00 5.00
20 Tom Seaver/1967 2.50 6.00
21 Nolan Ryan/1966 6.00 15.00
22 Keith Hernandez/1974 2.00 5.00
23 Darryl Strawberry/1983 2.00 5.00
24 Bob Gibson/1959 2.50 6.00
25 Pepper Martin/1928 2.00 5.00
26 Stan Musial/1941 4.00 10.00
27 Frankie Frisch/1919 2.00 5.00
28 Steve Carlton/1965 2.00 5.00
29 Ozzie Smith/1978 4.00 10.00

2004 Greats of the Game Forever Game Jersey

SER.2 STATED ODDS 1:24 RETAIL
SP INFO PROVIDED BY FLEER
NO SP PRICING DUE TO SCARCITY
EXCHANGE DEADLINE INDEFINITE
BG Bob Gibson 6.00 15.00
BW Billy Williams 4.00 10.00
CF Carlton Fisk 6.00 15.00
CY Carl Yastrzemski EXCH * 8.00 20.00
DD Dom DiMaggio 10.00 25.00
DG Dwight Gooden 4.00 10.00
DS Darryl Strawberry 4.00 10.00
JR Jim Rice EXCH 4.00 10.00
KH Keith Hernandez SP EXCH
NR Nolan Ryan EXCH 30.00 60.00
OH Orel Hershiser 4.00 10.00
OS Ozzie Smith 6.00 15.00
RK Ray Knight SP EXCH
RS Ryne Sandberg EXCH *
SC Steve Carlton 4.00 10.00
SG Steve Garvey SP EXCH
SM Stan Musial 10.00 25.00
TS Tom Seaver SP EXCH
TW Ted Williams 30.00 60.00
WB Wade Boggs 6.00 15.00

2004 Greats of the Game Forever Game Jersey Logo

STATED PRINT RUN 149 SERIAL #'d SETS
*JSY NBR: .5X TO 1.2X JSY LOGO
JSY NBR PRINT RUN 99 SERIAL #'d SETS
SER.2 GU ODDS 1:15 HOBBY
EXCHANGE DEADLINE INDEFINITE
BG Bob Gibson 6.00 15.00
BW Billy Williams 4.00 10.00
CF Carlton Fisk 6.00 15.00
CY Carl Yastrzemski 8.00 20.00
DD Dom DiMaggio 10.00 25.00
DG Dwight Gooden 4.00 10.00
DS Darryl Strawberry 4.00 10.00
EB Ernie Banks 10.00 25.00
FV Fernando Valenzuela EXCH
JR Jim Rice 4.00 10.00
KH Keith Hernandez EXCH
NR Nolan Ryan 30.00 60.00
OH Orel Hershiser 4.00 10.00
OS Ozzie Smith 6.00 15.00
RK Ray Knight 4.00 10.00
RS Ryne Sandberg 6.00 15.00
RST Ron Santo EXCH
SC Steve Carlton EXCH
SG Steve Garvey EXCH
SM Stan Musial 10.00 25.00
TS Tom Seaver EXCH
TW Ted Williams 30.00 60.00
WB Wade Boggs 6.00 15.00

2004 Greats of the Game Forever Game Patch Logo

STATED PRINT RUN 49 SERIAL #'d SETS
NUMBER PRINT RUN 25 SERIAL #'d SETS
NO NUMBER PRICING DUE TO SCARCITY
SER.2 GU ODDS 1:15 HOBBY
EXCHANGE DEADLINE INDEFINITE

BG Bob Gibson 10.00 25.00
BW Billy Williams
CF Carlton Fisk 10.00 25.00
CY Carl Yastrzemski 20.00 50.00
DD Dom DiMaggio
DG Dwight Gooden 6.00 15.00
DS Darryl Strawberry 6.00 15.00
EB Ernie Banks 40.00 80.00
FV Fernando Valenzuela EXCH
JR Jim Rice 10.00 25.00
KH Keith Hernandez EXCH
NR Nolan Ryan
OH Orel Hershiser
OS Ozzie Smith 20.00 50.00
RK Ray Knight
RS Ryne Sandberg 20.00 50.00
RST Ron Santo EXCH
SC Steve Carlton EXCH
SG Steve Garvey EXCH
SM Stan Musial
TS Tom Seaver EXCH
TW Ted Williams 60.00 120.00
WB Wade Boggs 10.00 25.00

2004 Greats of the Game Forever Game Patch Dual Logo

STATED PRINT RUN 19 SERIAL #'d SETS
DUAL NBR PRINT RUN 5 SERIAL #'d SETS
OVERALL SER.2 GU ODDS 1:15 HOBBY
EXCHANGE DEADLINE INDEFINITE
NO PRICING DUE TO SCARCITY
DGDS Dwight Gooden
Darryl Strawberry
FVSG Fernando Valenzuela
Steve Garvey EXCH
JRCF Jim Rice
Carlton Fisk
RKKH Ray Knight
Keith Hernandez EXCH
RSBW Ron Santo
Billy Williams EXCH
SMOS Stan Musial
Ozzie Smith
TSNR Tom Seaver
Nolan Ryan EXCH
TWCY Ted Williams
Carl Yastrzemski
TWDD Ted Williams
Dom DiMaggio
WBCY Wade Boggs
Carl Yastrzemski

2004 Greats of the Game Glory of Their Time

RANDOM INSERTS IN SER.1 PACKS
PRINT RUNS B/WN
1 Harmon Killebrew/1961 2.00 5.00
2 Johnny Bench/1974 2.00 5.00
3 George Brett/1980 3.00 8.00
4 Tony Gwynn/1987 2.00 5.00
5 Paul Molitor/1987 1.50 4.00
6 Don Mattingly/1986 3.00 8.00
7 Reggie Jackson/1980 2.00 5.00
8 Carlton Fisk/1985 2.00 5.00
9 Cal Ripken/1983 5.00 12.00
10 Brooks Robinson/1964 2.00 5.00
11 Eddie Murray/1980 2.00 5.00
12 Moose Skowron/1960 1.50 4.00
13 Lou Brock/1974 2.00 5.00
14 Don Drysdale/1962 2.00 5.00
15 Tony Gwynn/1997 2.00 5.00
16 Mike Schmidt/1980 3.00 8.00
17 Carl Yastrzemski/1967 2.50 6.00
18 Babe Ruth/1927 3.00 8.00
19 Nolan Ryan/1989 4.00 10.00
20 Yogi Berra/1950 2.00 5.00
21 Al Kaline/1955 2.00 5.00
22 Ty Cobb/1911 2.00 5.00
23 Duke Snider/1955 2.00 5.00
24 Stan Musial/1948 2.50 6.00
25 Jose Canseco/1988 2.00 5.00
26 Rocky Colavito/1958 2.00 5.00
27 Dave Winfield/1979 1.50 4.00
28 Nolan Ryan/1982 4.00 10.00
29 Thurman Munson/1977 2.00 5.00
30 Jackie Robinson/1949 2.00 5.00
31 Kirby Puckett/1988 2.00 5.00
32 Ted Kluszewski/1954 2.00 5.00
33 Warren Spahn/1953 2.00 5.00
34 Willie McCovey/1969 2.00 5.00
35 Phil Rizzuto/1950 2.00 5.00

2004 Greats of the Game Glory of Their Time Game Used

STATED PRINT RUN 250 SERIAL #'d SETS
*GOLD: .4X TO 1X BASIC
GOLD STATED ODDS 1:24 RETAIL
OVERALL SER.1 GU ODDS 1:30 H, 1:24 R
AK Al Kaline Pants 6.00 15.00
BR Brooks Robinson Jsy 6.00 15.00
CF1 Carlton Fisk Jsy 6.00 15.00
CF2 Carlton Fisk Bat 6.00 15.00
CR Cal Ripken Jsy 10.00 25.00
CY Carl Yastrzemski Jsy 8.00 20.00
DD Don Drysdale Jsy 6.00 15.00
DM Don Mattingly Pants 8.00 20.00
DW Dave Winfield Jsy 4.00 10.00
EM Eddie Murray Jsy 6.00 15.00
GB George Brett Jsy 8.00 20.00
HK Harmon Killebrew Bat 6.00 15.00
JB Johnny Bench Jsy 6.00 15.00
JC1 Jose Canseco Jsy 6.00 15.00
JC2 Jose Canseco Bat 6.00 15.00
KP Kirby Puckett Bat 6.00 15.00
LB Lou Brock Jsy 6.00 15.00
MS Mike Schmidt Jsy 8.00 20.00
MS Moose Skowron Pants 4.00 10.00
NR1 Nolan Ryan Jsy 10.00 25.00
NR2 Nolan Ryan Bat 10.00 25.00
PM Paul Molitor Jsy 4.00 10.00
PR Phil Rizzuto Pants 6.00 15.00
RC Rocky Colavito Bat 12.50 30.00
RJ Reggie Jackson Pants 6.00 15.00
TG1 Tony Gwynn White Jsy 6.00 15.00
TG2 Tony Gwynn Grey Jsy 6.00 15.00
TK Ted Kluszewski Pants 6.00 15.00
TM Thurman Munson Pants 10.00 25.00
WM Willie McCovey Pants 6.00 15.00
WS Warren Spahn Jsy 6.00 15.00
YB Yogi Berra Pants 6.00 15.00

2004 Greats of the Game Personality Cuts

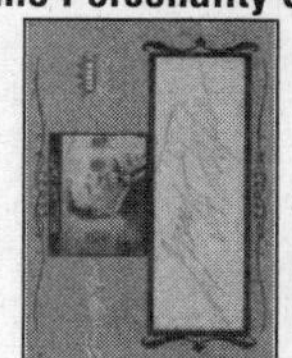

OVERALL SER.1 AU ODDS 1:5 H, 1:960 R
OVERALL SER.2 AU ODDS 1:7.5 HOBBY
OVERALL SER.2 AU-GU ODDS 1:24 RETAIL
PRINT RUNS B/WN 1-2 COPIES PER
NO PRICING DUE TO SCARCITY
AD Abner Doubleday S2/1
BC Bing Crosby S2/1
CF Charles O. Finley S2/2
CM Connie Mack S1/1
EG August Busch Jr. S2/1
HC Happy Chandler S1/1
RK Ray Kroc S2/1
RR Ronald Reagan S2/1
TY Tom Yawkey S2/1
WT William Taft S1/1

2004 Greats of the Game Yankees Clippings

SER.2 STATED ODDS 1:45 HOBBY
SP PRINT RUNS PROVIDED BY FLEER
SP'S ARE NOT SERIAL-NUMBERED
EXCHANGE DEADLINE INDEFINITE
BS Bill Skowron 20.00 50.00
DM Don Mattingly 40.00 80.00
LG R.Maris SP/150 * EXCH
PO Paul O'Neill 30.00 60.00
PR P.Rizzuto SP/150 * EXCH
RJ Reggie Jackson 30.00 60.00
WB Wade Boggs 20.00 50.00
YB Yogi Berra 40.00 80.00

2004 Greats of the Game Yankees Clippings Autograph

OVERALL SER.2 AU ODDS 1:7.5 HOBBY
PRINT RUNS B/WN 3-26 COPIES PER
NO PRICING DUE TO SCARCITY
EXCHANGE DEADLINE INDEFINITE

BS Bill Skowron/26
DM Don Mattingly/15 EXCH
LG Roger Maris/3 EXCH
PO Paul O'Neill/26
PR Phil Rizzuto/26 EXCH
RJ Reggie Jackson/15
WB Wade Boggs/26 EXCH
YB Yogi Berra/15

2006 Greats of the Game

This 100-card set, featuring all retired players, was released in April, 2006. The set was issued in 10-card hobby or retail packs which came 15 packs to a box and 12 boxes to a case. The set is sequenced in alphabetical order by the player's first name.

COMPLETE SET (100) 20.00 50.00
COMMON CARD (1-100) .30 .75
ONE PLATE PER FOIL PLATE PACK
PLATE PACKS ISSUED TO DEALERS
PLATE PRINT RUN 1 SET PER COLOR
BLACK-CYAN-MAGENTA-YELLOW ISSUED
NO PLATE PRICING DUE TO SCARCITY
1 Al Kaline .75 2.00
2 Alan Trammell .30 .75
3 Andre Dawson .30 .75
4 Barry Larkin .50 1.25
5 Bill Buckner .30 .75
6 Bill Freehan .30 .75
7 Bill Madlock .30 .75
8 Bill Mazeroski .50 1.25
9 Billy Williams .30 .75
10 Bo Jackson .75 2.00
11 Bob Feller .30 .75
12 Bob Gibson .50 1.25
13 Bobby Doerr .30 .75
14 Bobby Murcer .30 .75
15 Boog Powell .30 .75
16 Brooks Robinson .50 1.25
17 Bruce Sutter .30 .75
18 Bucky Dent .30 .75
19 Cal Ripken 3.00 8.00
20 Rico Petrocelli .30 .75
21 Carlton Fisk .50 1.25
22 Chris Chambliss .30 .75
23 Dave Concepcion .30 .75
24 Dave Parker .30 .75
25 Dave Winfield .30 .75
26 David Cone .30 .75
27 Denny McLain .30 .75
28 Don Mattingly 1.50 4.00
29 Don Newcombe .30 .75
30 Don Sutton .30 .75
31 Dusty Baker .30 .75
32 Dwight Evans .30 .75
33 Eric Davis .30 .75
34 Ernie Banks .75 2.00
35 Fergie Jenkins .30 .75
36 Frank Robinson .30 .75
37 Fred Lynn .30 .75
38 Fred McGriff .50 1.25
39 Andre Thornton .30 .75
40 Garry Maddox .30 .75
41 Gary Matthews .30 .75
42 Gaylord Perry .30 .75
43 George Foster .30 .75
44 George Kell .30 .75
45 Graig Nettles .30 .75
46 Greg Luzinski .30 .75
47 Harmon Killebrew .75 2.00
48 Jack Clark .30 .75
49 Jack Morris .30 .75
50 Jim Palmer .30 .75
51 Jim Rice .30 .75
52 Joe Morgan .30 .75
53 John Kruk .30 .75
54 Johnny Bench .75 2.00
55 Jose Canseco .50 1.25
56 Kirby Puckett .75 2.00
57 Kirk Gibson .30 .75
58 Lee Mazzilli .30 .75
59 Lou Brock .50 1.25
60 Lou Piniella .30 .75
61 Luis Aparicio .30 .75
62 Luis Tiant .30 .75
63 Mark Fidrych .30 .75
64 Mark Grace .50 1.25
65 Maury Wills .30 .75
66 Mike Schmidt 1.25 3.00
67 Nolan Ryan 2.00 5.00
68 Ozzie Smith 1.25 3.00
69 Paul Molitor .50 1.25
70 Paul O'Neill .50 1.25
71 Phil Niekro .30 .75
72 Ralph Kiner .50 1.25
73 Randy Hundley .30 .75
74 Red Schoendienst .30 .75
75 Reggie Jackson .50 1.25
76 Robin Yount .75 2.00
77 Rod Carew .50 1.25
78 Rollie Fingers .30 .75
79 Ron Cey .30 .75
80 Ron Guidry .30 .75
81 Ron Santo .50 1.25
82 Rusty Staub .30 .75
83 Ryne Sandberg 1.50 4.00
84 Sparky Lyle .30 .75
85 Stan Musial 1.25 3.00
86 Steve Carlton .30 .75
87 Steve Garvey .30 .75
88 Steve Sax .30 .75
89 Tommy Herr .30 .75
90 Tim McCarver .30 .75
91 Tim Raines .30 .75
92 Tom Seaver .50 1.25
93 Tony Gwynn .75 2.00
94 Tony Perez .30 .75
95 Wade Boggs .50 1.25
96 Whitey Ford .50 1.25
97 Will Clark .50 1.25
98 Willie Horton .30 .75
99 Willie McCovey .50 1.25
100 Yogi Berra .75 2.00

2006 Greats of the Game Copper

*COPPER: 1.5X TO 4X BASIC
STATED ODDS 1:15 H
STATED PRINT RUN 299 SERIAL #'d SETS

2006 Greats of the Game Pewter

*PEWTER: 1X TO 2.5X BASIC
STATED ODDS 1:5 H, 1:15 R

2006 Greats of the Game Autographs

Originally intended as a 99-card premium signed version of the basic 2006 Greats of the Game 100-card issue, this set actually contains 106 cards due to unintentional variations on several cards. The variations were the cause of problems with the dissemination of the clear stickers that each athlete signed. This set was intended to feature standard signatures, bereft of any inscriptions or nicknames. Due to problems at the production stage, however, several cards had signed stickers with inscribed nicknames (of which were earmarked for a separate signature insert for this product entitled Nickname Greats) placed on them. Our staff has researched the varying quantities seen on the secondary market for these variations and that information is detailed in our checklist within parentheses at the end of the card descriptions. The players with signature variations are as follows: Jack Clark (50% standard, 50% w/Jack the Ripper inscription), Will Clark (60% standard, 40% w/Will the Thrill inscription), Dwight Evans (90% standard, 10% w/Dewey inscription), Ron Guidry (50% standard, 50% with Gator inscription), Tommy Herr (100% w/T-Bird inscription), Bill Madlock (35% standard, 65% w/Maddog inscription), Gary Matthews (100% w/Sarge inscription), Tim Raines (50% standard, 50% w/Rock inscription), Rusty Staub (20% standard, 80% w/Le Grand Orange inscription), Andre Thornton (100% w/Thunder inscription). In addition, though all of these cards lack serial-numbering, representatives at Upper Deck provided print run information by breaking the set into four tiers of scarcity. Tier 4 cards (tagged with a "T4" notation in our checklist) have announced print runs between 301-600 copies per, Tier 3 between 151-300 per, Tier 2 between 100-150 per and Tier 1 between 50-90 per. Furthermore, specific quantities for each Tier 1 card were announced and that information is also provided in our checklist. These signed inserts were seeded at a rate of 1:15 hobby and retail packs.

Al Kaline T3
STATED ODDS 1:15 H, 1:15 R
TIER 1 QTY B/WN 50-90 COPIES PER
TIER 2 QTY B/WN 100-150 COPIES PER
TIER 3 QTY B/WN 151-300 COPIES PER
TIER 4 QTY B/WN 301-600 COPIES PER
CARDS ARE NOT SERIAL-NUMBERED
PRINT RUN INFO PROVIDED BY UD
SOME CARDS CARRY AU INSCRIPTIONS
AU INSCRIPTIONS NOT INTENDED FOR SET
AU INSCRIPTIONS DETAILED BELOW
PARENTHESES PERCENTAGE OF PRINT RUN
1 Al Kaline T3 8.00 20.00
2 Alan Trammell T3 4.00 10.00
3 Andre Dawson T3 8.00 20.00
4 Barry Larkin T3 10.00 25.00
5 Bill Buckner T3 6.00 15.00
6 Bill Freehan T4 4.00 10.00
7a Bill Madlock T4 (35) 4.00 10.00
7b Bill Madlock T4 (65) 5.00 12.00
Maddog
8 Bill Mazeroski T2 12.50 30.00
9 Billy Williams T3 6.00 15.00
10 Bo Jackson T2 30.00 60.00
11 Bob Feller T2 10.00 25.00
12 Bob Gibson T2 12.50 30.00
13 Bobby Doerr T3 6.00 15.00
14 Bobby Murcer T3 20.00 50.00
15 Boog Powell T4 4.00 10.00
16 Brooks Robinson T3 12.50 30.00
17 Bruce Sutter T3 10.00 25.00
18 Bucky Dent T3 5.00 12.00
19 Cal Ripken T1/50 * 40.00 80.00
20 Rico Petrocelli T4 4.00 10.00
21 Carlton Fisk T2 10.00 25.00
22 Chris Chambliss T3 4.00 10.00
23 Dave Concepcion T3 6.00 15.00
24 Dave Parker T2 6.00 15.00
25 Dave Winfield T2 12.50 30.00
26 David Cone T3 4.00 10.00
27 Denny McLain T3 6.00 15.00
28 Don Mattingly T2 40.00 80.00
29 Don Newcombe T4 6.00 15.00
30 Don Sutton T3 4.00 10.00
31 Dusty Baker T1/75 * 8.00 20.00
32a Dwight Evans T3 (90) 6.00 15.00
32b Dwight Evans T3 (10)
Dewey
33 Eric Davis T4 8.00 20.00
34 Ernie Banks T2 30.00 60.00
35 Fergie Jenkins T2 5.00 12.00
36 Frank Robinson T2 12.50 30.00
37 Fred Lynn T3 6.00 15.00
38 Fred McGriff T3 12.50 30.00
39 Andre Thornton T4 4.00 10.00
Thunder
40 Garry Maddox T2 6.00 15.00
41 Gary Matthews T4 4.00 10.00
Sarge
42 Gaylord Perry T3 5.00 12.00
43 George Foster T3 4.00 10.00
44 George Kell T3 6.00 15.00
45 Graig Nettles T3 6.00 15.00
46 Greg Luzinski T2 6.00 15.00
47 Harmon Killebrew T2 12.50 30.00
48a Jack Clark T4 (50) 8.00 20.00
48b Jack Clark T4 (50) 8.00 20.00
Jack the Ripper
49 Jack Morris T3 4.00 10.00
50 Jim Palmer T3 5.00 12.00
51 Jim Rice T3 6.00 15.00
52 Joe Morgan T2 10.00 25.00
53 John Kruk T3 6.00 15.00
54 Johnny Bench T2 15.00 40.00
56 Kirby Puckett T2 40.00 80.00
57 Kirk Gibson T2 8.00 20.00
58 Lee Mazzilli T3 4.00 10.00
59 Lou Brock T2 12.50 30.00
60 Lou Piniella T3 6.00 15.00
61 Luis Aparicio T3 6.00 15.00
62 Luis Tiant T3 4.00 10.00
63 Mark Fidrych T2 8.00 20.00
64 Mark Grace T3 10.00 25.00
65 Maury Wills T3 6.00 15.00
66 Mike Schmidt T2 12.50 30.00
67 Nolan Ryan T1/50 * 60.00 120.00
68 Ozzie Smith T2 15.00 40.00
69 Paul Molitor T3 8.00 20.00
70 Paul O'Neill T3 12.50 30.00
71 Phil Niekro T3 5.00 12.00
72 Ralph Kiner T2 12.50 30.00
73 Randy Hundley T4 4.00 10.00
74 Red Schoendienst T3 6.00 15.00
75 Reggie Jackson T2 15.00 40.00
76 Robin Yount T2 12.50 30.00
77 Rod Carew T3 10.00 25.00
78 Rollie Fingers T3 4.00 10.00
79 Ron Cey T3 4.00 10.00
80a Ron Guidry T3 (50) 12.50 30.00
80b Ron Guidry T3 (50) 15.00 40.00
Gator
81 Ron Santo T3 8.00 20.00
82a Rusty Staub T3 (20) 20.00 50.00
82b Rusty Staub T3 (80) 30.00 60.00
Le Grand Orange
83 Ryne Sandberg T1/90 * 20.00 50.00
84 Sparky Lyle T4 4.00 10.00
85 Stan Musial T2 20.00 50.00
86 Steve Carlton T3 6.00 15.00
87 Steve Garvey T2 5.00 12.00
88 Steve Sax T4 4.00 10.00
89 Tommy Herr T4 4.00 10.00
T-Bird
90 Tim McCarver T3 5.00 12.00
91a Tim Raines T3 (50) 10.00 25.00
91b Tim Raines T3 (50) 12.50 30.00
Rock
92 Tom Seaver T2 12.50 30.00
93 Tony Gwynn T2 12.50 30.00
94 Tony Perez T3 8.00 20.00
95 Wade Boggs T2 10.00 25.00
96 Whitey Ford T2 20.00 50.00
97a Will Clark T2 (60) 10.00 25.00
97b Will Clark T2 (40) 12.50 30.00
The Thrill
98 Willie Horton T4 5.00 12.00
99 Willie McCovey T1/75 * 12.50 30.00
100 Yogi Berra T2 15.00 40.00

2006 Greats of the Game Autographics

STATED ODDS 1:180 H, 1:960 R
PRINT RUNS B/WN 10-99 COPIES PER
CARDS ARE NOT SERIAL-NUMBERED
PRINT RUN INFO PROVIDED BY UD
NO PRICING ON QTY OF 25 OR LESS
ONE PLATE PER FOIL PLATE PACK
PLATE PACKS ISSUED TO DEALERS
PLATE PRINT RUN 1 SET PER COLOR
BLACK-CYAN-MAGENTA-YELLOW ISSUED
PLATES DO NOT FEATURE AUTOS
NO PLATE PRICING DUE TO SCARCITY

AD Andre Dawson/99 * 10.00 25.00
AK Al Kaline/50 * 30.00 60.00
BF Bob Feller/25 *
BG Bob Gibson/25 *
BI Bill Mazeroski/25 *
BJ Bo Jackson/25 *
BL Barry Larkin/50 * 15.00 40.00
BM Bobby Murcer/99 * 30.00 60.00
BR Brooks Robinson/50 * 15.00 40.00
BS Bruce Sutter/50 * 15.00 40.00
BW Billy Williams/50 * 15.00 40.00
CF Carlton Fisk/15 *
CR Cal Ripken/10 *
DB Dusty Baker/15 *
DN Don Newcombe/99 * 10.00 25.00
DP Dave Parker/99 * 15.00 40.00
DW Dave Winfield/15 *
EB Ernie Banks/10 *
FJ Fergie Jenkins/25 *
FM Fred McGriff/99 * 15.00 40.00
FR Frank Robinson/15 *
GF George Foster/50 * 10.00 25.00
The Destroyer
HK Harmon Killebrew/25 *
JB Johnny Bench/15 *
JM Joe Morgan/25 *
JP Jim Palmer/99 * 15.00 40.00
JR Jim Rice/99 * 10.00 25.00
KG Kirk Gibson/25 *
KP Kirby Puckett/10 *
LA Luis Aparicio/25 *
LB Lou Brock/25 *
MA Don Mattingly/10 *
MG Mark Grace/50 * 15.00 40.00
MS Mike Schmidt/15 *
MW Maury Wills/99 * 10.00 25.00
NR Nolan Ryan/10 *
OS Ozzie Smith/25 *
PM Paul Molitor/50 * 15.00 40.00
PN Phil Niekro/50 * 10.00 25.00
RC Rod Carew/25 *
RG Ron Guidry/99 * 15.00 40.00
RJ Reggie Jackson/10 *
RK Ralph Kiner/25 *
RP Rico Petrocelli/10 *
RS Ron Santo/99 * 15.00 40.00
RY Robin Yount/15 *
SA Ryne Sandberg/15 *
SC Steve Carlton/50 * 15.00 40.00
SG Steve Garvey/50 * 10.00 25.00
SM Stan Musial/10 *
SU Don Sutton/50 * 10.00 25.00
TG Tony Gwynn/15 *
TP Tony Perez/99 * 15.00 40.00
TS Tom Seaver/10 *
WB Wade Boggs/15 *
WC Will Clark/25 *
WF Whitey Ford/15 *
WM Willie McCovey/10 *
YB Yogi Berra/25 *

2006 Greats of the Game Bat Barrel Auto Greats

OVERALL AUTO ODDS 2:15 H, 2:15 R
PRINT RUNS B/WN 1-5 COPIES PER
NO PRICING DUE TO SCARCITY
ONE PLATE PER FOIL PLATE PACK
PLATE PACKS ISSUED TO DEALERS
PLATE PRINT RUN 1 SET PER COLOR
BLACK-CYAN-MAGENTA-YELLOW ISSUED
PLATES DO NOT FEATURE AUTOS OR GU
NO PLATE PRICING DUE TO SCARCITY

2006 Greats of the Game Cardinals Greats

OVERALL INSERTS ONE PER PACK
ONE PLATE PER FOIL PLATE PACK
PLATE PACKS ISSUED TO DEALERS
PLATE PRINT RUN 1 SET PER COLOR
BLACK-CYAN-MAGENTA-YELLOW ISSUED
NO PLATE PRICING DUE TO SCARCITY

BG Bob Gibson 1.25 3.00
DD Dizzy Dean 1.25 3.00
LB Lou Brock 1.25 3.00
OS Ozzie Smith 3.00 8.00
RH Rogers Hornsby 1.25 3.00
RS Red Schoendienst .75 2.00
SC Steve Carlton .75 2.00
SM Stan Musial 3.00 8.00
TH Tommy Herr .75 2.00
TM Tim McCarver .75 2.00

2006 Greats of the Game Cardinals Greats Memorabilia

OVERALL GAME-USED ODDS 2:15 H, 1:15 R
SP PRINT RUN INFO PROVIDED BY UD
SP's ARE NOT SERIAL-NUMBERED

BG Bob Gibson Pants 4.00 10.00
DD Dizzy Dean Jsy SP/99 * 20.00 50.00
LB Lou Brock Pants 4.00 10.00
OS Ozzie Smith Bat 6.00 15.00
RH Rogers Hornsby Bat 12.50 30.00
RS Red Schoendienst Bat 3.00 8.00
SC Steve Carlton Bat 3.00 8.00
SM Stan Musial Bat 6.00 15.00
TH Tommy Herr Bat 3.00 8.00
TM Tim McCarver Pants 3.00 8.00

2006 Greats of the Game Cardinals Greats Autograph

STATED PRINT RUN 30 SERIAL #'d SETS
*AUTO MEM: .4X TO 1X AUTO
AUTO MEM PRINT RUN 30 SERIAL #'d SETS
OVERALL AUTO ODDS 2:15 H, 2:15 R

BG Bob Gibson 20.00 50.00
LB Lou Brock 20.00 50.00
OS Ozzie Smith 30.00 60.00
RS Red Schoendienst 15.00 40.00
SC Steve Carlton 15.00 40.00
SM Stan Musial 50.00 100.00
TH Tommy Herr 10.00 25.00
TM Tim McCarver 10.00 25.00

2006 Greats of the Game Cubs Greats

OVERALL INSERTS ONE PER PACK
ONE PLATE PER FOIL PLATE PACK
PLATE PACKS ISSUED TO DEALERS
PLATE PRINT RUN 1 SET PER COLOR
BLACK-CYAN-MAGENTA-YELLOW ISSUED
NO PLATE PRICING DUE TO SCARCITY

AD Andre Dawson .75 2.00
BS Bruce Sutter .75 2.00
BW Billy Williams .75 2.00
EB Ernie Banks 2.00 5.00
FJ Fergie Jenkins .75 2.00
GM Gary Matthews .75 2.00
MG Mark Grace 1.25 3.00
RH Randy Hundley .75 2.00
RS Ron Santo 1.25 3.00
SA Ryne Sandberg 4.00 10.00

2006 Greats of the Game Cubs Greats Memorabilia

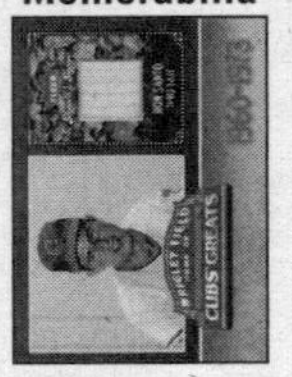

OVERALL GAME-USED ODDS 2:15 H, 1:15 R

AD Andre Dawson Bat 3.00 8.00
BS Bruce Sutter Pants 3.00 8.00
BW Billy Williams Jsy 3.00 8.00
EB Ernie Banks Pants 6.00 15.00
FJ Fergie Jenkins Jsy 3.00 8.00
GM Gary Matthews Bat 3.00 8.00
MG Mark Grace Bat 4.00 10.00
RS Ron Santo Bat 8.00 20.00
SA Ryne Sandberg Bat 6.00 15.00

2006 Greats of the Game Cubs Greats Autograph

STATED PRINT RUN 30 SERIAL #'d SETS
*AUTO MEM: .4X TO 1X AUTO
AUTO MEM PRINT RUN 30 SERIAL #'d SETS

OVERALL AUTO ODDS 2:15 H, 2:15 R

AD Andre Dawson 15.00 40.00
BS Bruce Sutter 15.00 40.00
BW Billy Williams 15.00 40.00
EB Ernie Banks 50.00 100.00
FJ Fergie Jenkins 10.00 25.00
GM Gary Matthews 10.00 25.00
MG Mark Grace 20.00 50.00
RS Ron Santo 30.00 60.00
SA Ryne Sandberg 30.00 60.00

2006 Greats of the Game Decade Greats

OVERALL INSERTS ONE PER PACK
ONE PLATE PER FOIL PLATE PACK
PLATE PACKS ISSUED TO DEALERS
PLATE PRINT RUN 1 SET PER COLOR
BLACK-CYAN-MAGENTA-YELLOW ISSUED
NO PLATE PRICING DUE TO SCARCITY

BF Bob Feller .75 2.00
BI Bill Madlock .75 2.00
BJ Bo Jackson 2.00 5.00
BM Bill Mazeroski 1.25 3.00
BR Brooks Robinson 1.25 3.00
CC Chris Chambliss .75 2.00
CR Cal Ripken 8.00 20.00
DP Dave Parker .75 2.00
EA Earl Averill .75 2.00
EM Eddie Mathews 2.00 5.00
JC Jack Clark .75 2.00
JK John Kruk .75 2.00
JM Johnny Mize .75 2.00
KP Kirby Puckett 2.00 5.00
MC Mickey Cochrane .75 2.00
MO Mel Ott .75 2.00
MS Mike Schmidt 3.00 8.00
NR Nolan Ryan 5.00 12.00
PM Paul Molitor .75 2.00
PT Pie Traynor .75 2.00
RC Roberto Clemente 6.00 15.00
RO Rod Carew 1.25 3.00
RY Robin Yount 2.00 5.00
SC Steve Carlton .75 2.00
TG Tony Gwynn 2.00 5.00
TR Tim Raines .75 2.00
TS Tom Seaver 1.25 3.00
WC Will Clark 1.25 3.00
WM Willie McCovey 1.25 3.00
WS Willie Stargell 1.25 3.00

2006 Greats of the Game Decade Greats Memorabilia

OVERALL GAME-USED ODDS 2:15 H, 1:15 R
SP PRINT RUNS B/WN 50-99 COPIES PER
SP PRINT RUN INFO PROVIDED BY UD
SP's ARE NOT SERIAL-NUMBERED

BF Bob Feller Pants 4.00 10.00
BI Bill Madlock Bat 3.00 8.00
BJ Bo Jackson Bat 6.00 15.00
BM Bill Mazeroski Bat 4.00 10.00
BR Brooks Robinson Bat 4.00 10.00
CC Chris Chambliss Bat 3.00 8.00
CR Cal Ripken Pants 8.00 20.00
DP Dave Parker Pants 3.00 8.00
EA Earl Averill Bat 8.00 20.00
EM Eddie Mathews Pants 6.00 15.00
JC Jack Clark Bat 3.00 8.00
JK John Kruk Bat 3.00 8.00
JM Johnny Mize Pants 4.00 10.00
KP Kirby Puckett Bat 6.00 15.00
MC M.Cochrane Bat SP/50 * 40.00 80.00
MO Mel Ott Bat SP/99 * 20.00 50.00
MS Mike Schmidt Bat 4.00 10.00
NR Nolan Ryan Jsy 6.00 15.00
PM Paul Molitor Bat 3.00 8.00
RC Roberto Clemente Jsy 20.00 50.00
RO Rod Carew Pants 4.00 10.00
RY Robin Yount Bat 4.00 10.00
SC Steve Carlton Bat 3.00 8.00
TG Tony Gwynn Pants 4.00 10.00
TR Tim Raines Jsy 3.00 8.00
TS Tom Seaver Jsy 4.00 10.00
WC Will Clark Jsy 4.00 10.00
WM Willie McCovey Bat 4.00 10.00
WS Willie Stargell Bat 4.00 10.00

2006 Greats of the Game Decade Greats Autograph

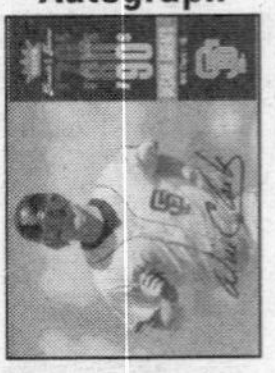

STATED PRINT RUN 30 SERIAL #'d SETS
*AUTO MEM: .4X TO 1X AUTO
AUTO MEM PRINT RUN 30 SERIAL #'d SETS
OVERALL AUTO ODDS 2:15 H, 2:15 R

BF Bob Feller 20.00 50.00
BI Bill Madlock 15.00 40.00
BJ Bo Jackson 40.00 80.00
BM Bill Mazeroski 30.00 60.00
BR Brooks Robinson 20.00 50.00
CC Chris Chambliss 10.00 25.00
CR Cal Ripken 90.00 150.00
DP Dave Parker 15.00 40.00
JC Jack Clark 10.00 25.00
JK John Kruk 15.00 40.00
KP Kirby Puckett 50.00 100.00
MS Mike Schmidt 40.00 80.00
NR Nolan Ryan 60.00 120.00
PM Paul Molitor 20.00 50.00
RO Rod Carew 20.00 50.00
RY Robin Yount 30.00 60.00
SC Steve Carlton 15.00 40.00
TG Tony Gwynn 30.00 60.00
TR Tim Raines 10.00 25.00
TS Tom Seaver 30.00 60.00
WC Will Clark 20.00 50.00
WM Willie McCovey 20.00 50.00

2006 Greats of the Game Dodger Greats

OVERALL INSERTS ONE PER PACK
ONE PLATE PER FOIL PLATE PACK
PLATE PACKS ISSUED TO DEALERS
PLATE PRINT RUN 1 SET PER COLOR
BLACK-CYAN-MAGENTA-YELLOW ISSUED
NO PLATE PRICING DUE TO SCARCITY

CA Roy Campanella 2.00 5.00
DB Dusty Baker .75 2.00
DD Don Drysdale 1.25 3.00
DS Don Sutton .75 2.00
JR Jackie Robinson 2.00 5.00
MW Maury Wills .75 2.00
PR Pee Wee Reese 1.25 3.00
RC Ron Cey .75 2.00
SG Steve Garvey .75 2.00
SS Steve Sax .75 2.00

2006 Greats of the Game Dodger Greats Memorabilia

OVERALL GAME-USED ODDS 2:15 H, 1:15 R
SP PRINT RUNS B/WN 25-199 COPIES PER
SP PRINT RUN INFO PROVIDED BY UD
SP's ARE NOT SERIAL-NUMBERED
NO PRICING ON QTY OF 30 OR LESS

CA Roy Campanella Jsy SP/25 *
DB Dusty Baker Jsy 3.00 8.00
DD Don Drysdale Jsy SP/69 * 8.00 20.00
DS Don Sutton Jsy SP/30 *
JR Jackie Robinson Bat SP/199 * 20.00 50.00
MW Maury Wills Bat 3.00 8.00
PR Pee Wee Reese Jsy 4.00 10.00
RC Ron Cey Jsy 3.00 8.00
SG Steve Garvey Jsy 3.00 8.00
SS Steve Sax Jsy 3.00 8.00

2006 Greats of the Game Dodger Greats Autograph

STATED PRINT RUN 30 SERIAL #'d SETS
*AUTO MEM: .4X TO 1X AUTO
AUTO MEM PRINT RUN 30 SERIAL #'d SETS
OVERALL AUTO ODDS 2:15 H, 2:15 R

DB Dusty Baker 20.00 50.00
DS Don Sutton 10.00 25.00
MW Maury Wills 10.00 25.00
RC Ron Cey 10.00 25.00
SG Steve Garvey 15.00 40.00
SS Steve Sax 10.00 25.00

2006 Greats of the Game Nickname Greats

OVERALL INSERTS ONE PER PACK
ONE PLATE PER FOIL PLATE PACK
PLATE PACKS ISSUED TO DEALERS
PLATE PRINT RUN 1 SET PER COLOR
BLACK-CYAN-MAGENTA-YELLOW ISSUED
NO PLATE PRICING DUE TO SCARCITY

AG Andres Galarraga 1.25 3.00
Big Cat
AH Al Hrabosky 1.25 3.00
The Mad Hungarian
AT Andre Thornton 1.25 3.00
Thunder
BE Steve Bedrosian 1.25 3.00
Bedrock
BF Bob Feller 1.25 3.00
Rapid Robert
BH Burt Hooton 1.25 3.00
Happy
BL Bill Lee 1.25 3.00
Spaceman
BM Bill Madlock 1.25 3.00
Mad Dog
CF Carlton Fisk 2.00 5.00
Pudge
CH Joe Charboneau 1.25 3.00
Super Joe
DB Don Baylor 1.25 3.00
Groove
DD Darren Daulton 1.25 3.00
Dutch
DE Dwight Evans 1.25 3.00
Dewey
DF Dan Ford 1.25 3.00
Disco Dan
DM Don Mattingly 6.00 15.00
Donny Baseball
DP Dave Parker 1.25 3.00
The Cobra
DR Dave Righetti 1.25 3.00
Rags
EV Ellis Valentine 1.25 3.00
Bubba
FR Frank Robinson 1.25 3.00
The Judge
FS Fred Stanley 1.25 3.00
Chicken
GF George Foster 1.25 3.00
The Destroyer
GH Glenn Hubbard 1.25 3.00
Bam Bam
GM Garry Maddox 1.25 3.00
The Secretary of Defense
GS George Scott 1.25 3.00
Boomer
HE Tommy Herr 1.25 3.00
T-Bird
HJ Howard Johnson 1.25 3.00
Hojo
JB Jim Bouton 1.25 3.00
Bulldog or Ball Four
JC Jack Clark 1.25 3.00
Jack the Ripper
JJ Jay Johnstone 1.25 3.00
Moon Man
JM John Montefusco 1.25 3.00
The Count
JP Joe Pepitone 1.25 3.00
Pepi
JS John Shelby 1.25 3.00
T-Bone
JW Jimmy Wynn 1.25 3.00
The Toy Cannon
KH Ken Harrelson 1.25 3.00
The Hawk
LA Luis Aparicio 1.25 3.00
Little Louie
LM Lee Mazzilli 1.25 3.00
The Italian Stallion
LP Lou Piniella 1.25 3.00
Sweet Lou
MA Gary Matthews 1.25 3.00
Sarge
MF Mark Fidrych 1.25 3.00
The Bird
MH Mike Hargrove 1.25 3.00
The Human Rain Delay
ML Mike Lavalliere 1.25 3.00
Spanky
MR Mickey Rivers 1.25 3.00
Mick the Quick
MW Mitch Williams 1.25 3.00
Wild Thing
MZ Dennis Martinez 1.25 3.00
El Presidente
RA Doug Rader 1.25 3.00
The Red Rooster
RB Rick Burleson 1.25 3.00
Rooster
RC Ron Cey 1.25 3.00
The Penguin
RG Ron Guidry 1.25 3.00
Louisiana Lightning (or Gator)
RR Rick Reuschel 1.25 3.00
Big Daddy
RS Rusty Staub 1.25 3.00
Le Grand Orange
SB Steve Balboni 1.25 3.00
Bye Bye
SF Sid Fernandez 1.25 3.00
El Sid
SL Sparky Lyle 1.25 3.00
The Count
SM Sam McDowell 1.25 3.00
Sudden Sam
ST Steve Trout 1.25 3.00
Rainbow
TB Tom Brunansky 1.25 3.00
Bruno
TH Tom Henke 1.25 3.00
The Terminator
TR Tim Raines 1.25 3.00
Rock
WC Will Clark 2.00 5.00
Will the Thrill
WM Willie McCovey 2.00 5.00
Stretch

2006 Greats of the Game Nickname Greats Autographs

Originally intended as a 54-card collection, this set actually contains 57 cards due to variations produced by unintentional mistakes at the production stage. It was the manufacturers intent for each of these Nickname Greats inserts to feature a signed sticker that would also include the featured athletes nickname. Unfortunately, some athletes didn't sign their stickers in the intended fashion and some nicknamed stickers were erroneously placed on other signed cards within the 2006 Greats of the Game product. Please note, our checklist has been carefully constructed to indicate which cards were correctly signed and which weren't. For cards that were correctly produced with nicknamed signature stickers the actual inscription will be listed after the player's name (for example, Al Hrabosky correctly signed all of his stickers as "Al 'The Mad Hungarian' Hrabosky" and all of those stickers were correctly placed on the cards - thus our description is listed as A.Hrabosky Hungarian). Other cards feature no cinknamed stickers whatsoever, such as Bill Madlock. Madlock did sign a good amount of his stickers as Bill "Maddog" Madlock, but those stickers were erroneously placed on other cards in this product and standard Madlock signed stickers were used for this set. Thus, Madlock's card in this set is simply listed as "Bill Madlock". Finally, variations for nicknamed and non-nicknamed stickers have been found for three cards as follows . . . George Foster (50% feature Destroyer inscription and 50% are standard), Andre Thornton (10% feature Thunder inscription and 90% are standard) and Steve Trout (80% feature Rainbow inscription and 20% are standard). Also, an exchange card with a redemption deadline of April 10th, 2009 was seeded into packs for the Dennis Martinez card. On average 1:15 hobby and retail packs contained a Nicknames Greats signed insert.

OVERALL AUTO ODDS 2:15 H, 2:15 R
TIER 1 QTY B/WN 29-50 COPIES PER
TIER 2 QTY 100 COPIES PER
TIER 3 QTY B/WN 175-250 COPIES PER
TIER 4 QTY B/WN 251-400 COPIES PER
TIER 5 QTY B/WN 401-650 COPIES PER
CARDS ARE NOT SERIAL-NUMBERED
PRINT RUN INFO PROVIDED BY UD
AU INSCRIPTIONS INTENDED FOR ALL CARDS
NOT ALL CARDS CARRY AU INSCRIPTIONS
AU INSCRIPTIONS ARE DETAILED BELOW
PARENTHESES PERCENTAGE OF PRINT RUN
NO MCCOVEY PRICING DUE TO SCARCITY
EXCHANGE DEADLINE 04/10/09

AH Al Hrabosky T5 6.00 15.00
The Mad Hungarian
AT1 Andre Thornton T5 (90) 4.00 10.00
AT2 Andre Thornton T5 (10) 6.00 15.00
Thunder
BE Steve Bedrosian T5 6.00 15.00
Bedrock
BF Bob Feller T2/100 * 20.00 50.00
Rapid Robert
BH Burt Hooton T5 4.00 10.00
Happy
BL Bill Lee T5 8.00 20.00
Spaceman
BM Bill Madlock T4 4.00 10.00
CF Carlton Fisk T1/50 * 20.00 50.00
CH Joe Charboneau T5 6.00 15.00
Super Joe
DD Darren Daulton T5 6.00 15.00
Dutch
DE Dwight Evans T2/100 * 10.00 25.00
DF Dan Ford T5 4.00 10.00
Disco Dan
DP Dave Parker T2/100 * 20.00 50.00
The Cobra
DR Dave Righetti T5 8.00 20.00
Rags
EV Ellis Valentine T5 4.00 10.00
Bubba
FR Frank Robinson T1/50 * 30.00 60.00
FS Fred Stanley T5 6.00 15.00
Chicken
GF1 George Foster T3 (50) 4.00 10.00
GF2 George Foster T3 (50) 6.00 15.00
The Destroyer
GH Glenn Hubbard T5 4.00 10.00
Bam Bam
GM Garry Maddox T5 6.00 15.00
The Secretary of Defense
GS George Scott T5 6.00 15.00
Boomer
HE Tommy Herr T5 4.00 10.00
HJ Howard Johnson T3 6.00 15.00
Hojo
JB Jim Bouton T3 6.00 15.00
Bulldog
JC Jack Clark T4 6.00 15.00
JJ Jay Johnstone T5 6.00 15.00
Moon Man
JM John Montefusco T5 6.00 15.00
The Count
JP Joe Pepitone T5 6.00 15.00
Pepi
JS John Shelby T5 4.00 10.00

T-Bone
JW Jimmy Wynn T5 6.00 15.00
The Toy Cannon
LM Lee Mazzilli T5 6.00 15.00
The Italian Stallion
LP Lou Piniella T2/100 * 20.00 50.00
Sweet Lou
MA Gary Matthews T5 4.00 10.00
Sarge
MF Mark Fidrych T4 12.50 30.00
The Bird
MF Mike Hargrove T5 8.00 20.00
The Human Rain Delay
ML Mike Lavalliere T5 4.00 10.00
Spanky
MR Mickey Rivers T3 8.00 20.00
Mick the Quick
MW Mitch Williams T5 6.00 15.00
Wild Thing
MZ Dennis Martinez T3 6.00 15.00
El Presidente EXCH
RA Doug Rader T5 6.00 15.00
The Red Rooster
RB Rick Burleson T5 4.00 10.00
Rooster
RG Ron Guidry T3 15.00 40.00
RR Rick Reuschel T5 8.00 20.00
Big Daddy
RS Rusty Staub T3 15.00 40.00
SB Steve Balboni T5 8.00 20.00
Bye Bye
SF Sid Fernandez T5 6.00 15.00
El Sid
SL Sparky Lyle T4 6.00 15.00
The Count
SM Sam McDowell T5 6.00 15.00
Sudden Sam
ST1 Steve Trout T5 (20) 6.00 15.00
ST2 Steve Trout T5 (80) 8.00 20.00
Rainbow
TB Tom Brunansky T5 4.00 10.00
Bruno
TH Tom Henke T5 6.00 15.00
The Terminator
TR Tim Raines T3 6.00 15.00
WC Will Clark T2/100 * 12.50 30.00
WM Willie McCovey T1/29 *

2006 Greats of the Game Red Sox Greats

OVERALL INSERTS ONE PER PACK
ONE PLATE PER FOIL PLATE PACK
PLATE PACKS ISSUED TO DEALERS
PLATE PRINT RUN 1 SET PER COLOR
BLACK-CYAN-MAGENTA-YELLOW ISSUED
NO PLATE PRICING DUE TO SCARCITY
BD Bobby Doerr .75 2.00
CF Carlton Fisk 1.25 3.00
DE Dwight Evans .75 2.00
FL Fred Lynn .75 2.00
JF Jimmie Foxx 2.00 5.00
JR Jim Rice .75 2.00
LT Luis Tiant .75 2.00
RP Rico Petrocelli .75 2.00
TW Ted Williams 5.00 12.00
WB Wade Boggs 1.25 3.00

2006 Greats of the Game Red Sox Greats Memorabilia

OVERALL GAME-USED ODDS 2:15 H, 1:15 R
SP PRINT RUNS B/WN 25-199 COPIES PER
SP PRINT RUN INFO PROVIDED BY UD
SP's ARE NOT SERIAL-NUMBERED
BD Bobby Doerr Bat 3.00 8.00
CF Carlton Fisk Pants 4.00 10.00
DE Dwight Evans Jsy 4.00 10.00
FL Fred Lynn Pants 3.00 8.00
JF Jimmie Foxx Bat SP/99 * 15.00 40.00
JR Jim Rice Bat 3.00 8.00
LT Luis Tiant Jsy 3.00 8.00
RP Rico Petrocelli Pants 3.00 8.00
TW Ted Williams Jsy SP/199 * 20.00 50.00
WB Wade Boggs Pants 4.00 10.00

2006 Greats of the Game Red Sox Greats Autograph

STATED PRINT RUN 30 SERIAL #'d SETS
*AUTO MEM: .4X TO 1X AUTO
AUTO MEM PRINT RUN 30 SERIAL #'d SETS
OVERALL AUTO ODDS 2:15 H, 2:15 R
BD Bobby Doerr 10.00 25.00
CF Carlton Fisk 20.00 50.00
DE Dwight Evans 30.00 60.00
FL Fred Lynn 10.00 25.00
JR Jim Rice 10.00 25.00
LT Luis Tiant 10.00 25.00
RP Rico Petrocelli 10.00 25.00
WB Wade Boggs 20.00 50.00

2006 Greats of the Game Reds Greats

OVERALL INSERTS ONE PER PACK
ONE PLATE PER FOIL PLATE PACK
PLATE PACKS ISSUED TO DEALERS
PLATE PRINT RUN 1 SET PER COLOR
BLACK-CYAN-MAGENTA-YELLOW ISSUED
NO PLATE PRICING DUE TO SCARCITY
BL Barry Larkin 1.25 3.00
DC Dave Concepcion .75 2.00
ED Eric Davis .75 2.00
FR Frank Robinson .75 2.00
GF George Foster .75 2.00
JB Johnny Bench 2.00 5.00
JM Joe Morgan .75 2.00
KG Ken Griffey Sr. .75 2.00
TP Tony Perez .75 2.00
TS Tom Seaver 1.25 3.00

2006 Greats of the Game Reds Greats Memorabilia

OVERALL GAME-USED ODDS 2:15 H, 1:15 R
BL Barry Larkin Pants 4.00 10.00
DC Dave Concepcion Bat 3.00 8.00
ED Eric Davis Jsy 3.00 8.00
FR Frank Robinson Bat 4.00 10.00
GF George Foster Bat 3.00 8.00
JB Johnny Bench Bat 6.00 15.00
JM Joe Morgan Bat 3.00 8.00
KG Ken Griffey Sr. Pants 3.00 8.00
TP Tony Perez Bat 3.00 8.00
TS Tom Seaver Bat 4.00 10.00

2006 Greats of the Game Reds Greats Autograph

STATED PRINT RUN 30 SERIAL #'d SETS
*AUTO MEM: .4X TO 1X AUTO
AUTO MEM PRINT RUN 30 SERIAL #'d SETS
OVERALL AUTO ODDS 2:15 H, 2:15 R
BL Barry Larkin 20.00 50.00
DC Dave Concepcion 15.00 40.00
ED Eric Davis 20.00 50.00
FR Frank Robinson 30.00 60.00
GF George Foster 15.00 40.00
The Destroyer
JB Johnny Bench 30.00 60.00
JM Joe Morgan 15.00 40.00
KG Ken Griffey Sr. 15.00 40.00
TP Tony Perez 15.00 40.00
TS Tom Seaver 30.00 60.00

2006 Greats of the Game Tigers Greats

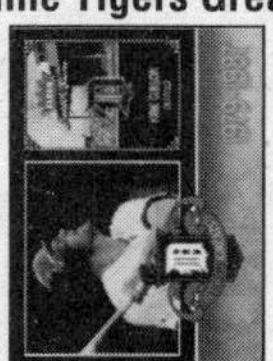

OVERALL INSERTS ONE PER PACK
ONE PLATE PER FOIL PLATE PACK
PLATE PACKS ISSUED TO DEALERS
PLATE PRINT RUN 1 SET PER COLOR
BLACK-CYAN-MAGENTA-YELLOW ISSUED
NO PLATE PRICING DUE TO SCARCITY
AK Al Kaline 2.00 5.00
AT Alan Trammell .75 2.00
BF Bill Freehan .75 2.00
DM Denny McLain .75 2.00
GK George Kell .75 2.00
JM Jack Morris .75 2.00
KG Kirk Gibson .75 2.00
MF Mark Fidrych .75 2.00
TC Ty Cobb 3.00 8.00
WH Willie Horton .75 2.00

2006 Greats of the Game Tigers Greats Memorabilia

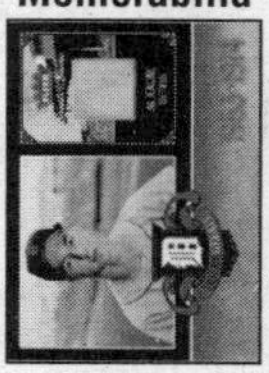

OVERALL GAME-USED ODDS 2:15 H, 1:15 R
SP PRINT RUNS 99 COPIES PER
SP PRINT RUN INFO PROVIDED BY UD
SP's ARE NOT SERIAL NUMBERED
AK Al Kaline Bat 4.00 10.00
AT Alan Trammell Bat 3.00 8.00
BF Bill Freehan Bat 3.00 8.00
GK George Kell Bat 4.00 10.00
JM Jack Morris Jsy 3.00 8.00
KG Kirk Gibson Jsy 4.00 10.00
MF Mark Fidrych Jsy 3.00 8.00
TC Ty Cobb Bat SP/99 * 60.00 120.00
WH Willie Horton Bat SP/99 * 4.00 10.00

2006 Greats of the Game Tigers Greats Autograph

STATED PRINT RUN 30 SERIAL #'d SETS
*AUTO MEM: .4X TO 1X AUTO
AUTO MEM PRINT RUN 30 SERIAL #'d SETS
OVERALL AUTO ODDS 2:15 H, 2:15 R
AK Al Kaline 30.00 60.00
AT Alan Trammell 15.00 40.00
BF Bill Freehan 15.00 40.00
DM Denny McLain 10.00 25.00
GK George Kell 20.00 50.00
JM Jack Morris 10.00 25.00
KG Kirk Gibson 15.00 40.00
MF Mark Fidrych 15.00 40.00
WH Willie Horton 10.00 25.00

2006 Greats of the Game Yankee Clippings

OVERALL INSERTS ONE PER PACK
ONE PLATE PER FOIL PLATE PACK
PLATE PACKS ISSUED TO DEALERS
PLATE PRINT RUN 1 SET PER COLOR
BLACK-CYAN-MAGENTA-YELLOW ISSUED
NO PLATE PRICING DUE TO SCARCITY
BM Bobby Murcer .75 2.00
BR Babe Ruth 5.00 12.00
DM Don Mattingly 4.00 10.00
GN Graig Nettles .75 2.00
JD Joe DiMaggio 4.00 10.00
RG Ron Guidry .75 2.00
RJ Reggie Jackson 1.25 3.00
TM Thurman Munson 2.00 5.00
WF Whitey Ford 1.25 3.00
YB Yogi Berra 2.00 5.00

2006 Greats of the Game Yankee Clippings Memorabilia

OVERALL GAME-USED ODDS 2:15 H, 1:15 R
SP PRINT RUNS B/WN 25-199 COPIES PER
SP PRINT RUN INFO PROVIDED BY UD
SP's ARE NOT SERIAL-NUMBERED
NO SP PRICING ON QTY OF 30 OR LESS
BM Bobby Murcer Bat 4.00 10.00
BR Babe Ruth Bat SP/25 *
DM Don Mattingly Bat 6.00 15.00
GN Graig Nettles Bat 3.00 8.00
JD Joe DiMaggio Pants SP/99 * 40.00 80.00
RG Ron Guidry Jsy 4.00 10.00
RJ Reggie Jackson Jsy 4.00 10.00
TM Thurman Munson Pants 8.00 20.00
WF Whitey Ford Pants 6.00 15.00
YB Yogi Berra Bat SP/199 * 8.00 20.00

2006 Greats of the Game Yankee Clippings Autograph

STATED PRINT RUN 30 SERIAL #'d SETS
*AUTO MEM: .4X TO 1X AUTO
AUTO MEM PRINT RUN 30 SERIAL #'d SETS
OVERALL AUTO ODDS 2:15 H, 2:15 R
BM Bobby Murcer 20.00 50.00
DM Don Mattingly 50.00 100.00
GN Graig Nettles 15.00 40.00
RG Ron Guidry 30.00 60.00
RJ Reggie Jackson 30.00 60.00
WF Whitey Ford 40.00 80.00
YB Yogi Berra 40.00 80.00

1912 Hassan Triple Folders T202

The cards in this 132-card set measure approximately 2 1/4" by 5 1/4". The 1912 T202 Hassan Triple Folder issue is perhaps the most ingenious baseball card ever issued. The two end cards of each panel are full color, T205-like individual cards whereas the black and white center panel pictures an action photo or portrait. The end cards can be folded across the center panel and stored in this manner. Seventy-six different center panels are known to exist; however, many of the center panels contain more than one combination of end cards. The center panel titles are listed below in alphabetical order while the different combinations of end cards are listed below each center panel as they appear left to right on the front of the card. A total of 132 different card fronts exist. The set price below includes all panel and player combinations listed in the checklist. Back color variations (red or black) also exist. The Birmingham's Home Run card is difficult to obtain as are other cards whose center panel exists with but one combination of end cards. The Devlin with Mathewson end panels on numbers 29A and 74C picture Devlin as a Giant. Devlin is pictured as a Rustler on 29B and 74D. Listed pricing references cards in raw "EX" condition.

COMPLETE SET (132) 20000.0035000.00
1 A Close Play at Home Plate 150.00 250.00
Bobby Wallace
Frank LaPorte
2 A Close Play at Home Plate 150.00 250.00
Bobby Wallace
Barney Pelty
3 A Desperate Slide for Third 900.00 1500.00
Charley O'Leary
Ty Cobb
4 A Great Batsman 125.00 200.00
Cy Barger
Bill Bergen
5 A Great Batsman 125.00 200.00
Nap Rucker
Bill Bergen
6 A Wide Throw Saves Crawford 125.00 200.00
George Mullin
Oscar Stanage
7 Ambrose McConnell at Bat 125.00 200.00
Walter Blair
Jack Quinn
8 Baker Gets His Man 250.00 400.00
Eddie Collins
Frank Baker
9 Birmingham Gets to Third 350.00 600.00
Walter Johnson
Gabby Street
10 Birmingham's Home Run 150.00 250.00
Doc Birmingham
Terry Turner
11 Bush Just Misses Austin 125.00 200.00
Pat Moran
Sherry Magee
12 Carrigan Blocks His Man 125.00 200.00
Harry Gaspar
Larry McLean
13 Carrigan Blocks His Man 125.00 200.00
Heinie Wagner
Bill Carrigan
14 Catching Him Napping 150.00 250.00
Rebel Oakes
Roger Bresnahan
15 Caught Asleep Off First 150.00 250.00
Roger Bresnahan
Robert Harmon
16 Chance Beats Out a Hit 150.00 250.00
Frank Chance
Bill Foxen
17 Chance Beats Out a Hit 125.00 200.00
Harry McIntire
Jimmy Archer
18 Chance Beats Out a Hit 125.00 200.00
Orval Overall
Jimmy Archer
19 Chance Beats Out a Hit 125.00 200.00
John Rowan
Jimmy Archer
20 Chance Beats Out a Hit 150.00 250.00
David Shean
Frank Chance
21 Chase Dives into Third 125.00 200.00
Hal Chase
Harry Wolter
22 Chase Dives into Third 150.00 250.00
George Gibson
Fred Clarke
23 Chase Dives into Third 125.00 200.00
Deacon Phillippe
George Gibson
24 Chase Gets Ball Too Late 125.00 200.00
Dick Egan
Mike Mitchell
25 Chase Gets Ball Too Late 125.00 200.00
Harry Wolter
Hal Chase
26 Chase Guarding First 125.00 200.00
Hal Chase
Harry Wolter
27 Chase Guarding First 125.00 200.00
George Gibson
Fred Clarke
28 Chase Guarding First 125.00 200.00
Lefty Leifield
George Gibson
29 Chase Ready for Squeeze Play 125.00 200.00
Dode Paskert
Sherry Magee
30 Chase Safe at Third 300.00 500.00
Jack Barry
Frank Baker
31 Chief Bender Waiting For a Good One 150.00 250.00
Chief Bender
Ira Thomas
32 Clarke Hikes for Home 125.00 200.00
Al Bridwell
Johnny Kling
33 Close at First 125.00 200.00
Neal Ball
George Stovall
34 Close at the Plate 125.00 200.00
Fred Payne
Doc White
35 Close at the Plate 150.00 250.00
Ed Walsh
Fred Payne
36 Close at Third 125.00 200.00
Bill Carrigan
Heinie Wagner
37 Close at Third 300.00 500.00
Joe Wood
Tris Speaker
38 Collins Easily Safe 150.00 250.00
Bobby Byrne
Fred Clarke
39 Collins Easily Safe 250.00 400.00
Eddie Collins
Frank Baker
40 Collins Easily Safe 150.00 250.00
Eddie Collins
Danny Murphy
41 Crawford About to Smash One 125.00 200.00
Oscar Stanage
Ed Summers
42 Cree Rolls Home 125.00 200.00
Jake Daubert
John Hummell
43 Davy Jones Great Slide 125.00 200.00
Jim Delahanty
Tom Jones
44 Devlin Gets His Man 500.00 800.00
Art Devlin (Giants)
Christy Mathewson
45 Devlin Gets His Man 500.00 800.00
Art Devlin (Rustlers)
Christy Mathewson
46 Devlin Gets His Man 350.00 600.00
Art Fletcher
Christy Mathewson
47 Devlin Gets His Man 300.00 500.00
Chief Meyers
Christy Mathewson
48 Donlin Out at First 125.00 200.00
Howie Camnitz
George Gibson
49 Donlin Out at First 125.00 200.00
Red Dooin
Sherry Magee
50 Donlin Out at First 125.00 200.00
Larry Doyle
Fred Merkle
51 Donlin Out at First 125.00 200.00
George Gibson
Deacon Phillippe
52 Donlin Out at First 125.00 200.00
Tommy Leach
Chief Wilson
53 Dooin Gets His Man 125.00 200.00
Red Dooin
Mickey Doolan
54 Dooin Gets His Man 125.00 200.00
Red Dooin
Hans Lobert
55 Dooin Gets His Man 125.00 200.00
Red Dooin
John Titus
56 Easy for Larry 125.00 200.00
Larry Doyle
Fred Merkle
57 Elberfeld Beats the Throw 125.00 200.00
Clyde Milan
Kid Elberfeld
58 Elberfeld Gets His Man 125.00 200.00
Clyde Milan
Kid Elberfeld
59 Engle in a Close Play 175.00 300.00
Tris Speaker
Hack Engle
60 Evers Makes a Safe Slide 150.00 250.00
Jimmy Archer
Johnny Evers
61 Evers Makes a Safe Slide 125.00 200.00
Jimmy Archer
Orval Overall
62 Evers Makes a Safe Slide 125.00 200.00
Jimmy Archer
Ed Reulbach
63 Evers Makes a Safe Slide 250.00 400.00
Frank Chance
Johnny Evers
64 Evers Makes a Safe Slide 500.00 800.00
Joe Tinker
Frank Chance
65 Fast Work at Third 900.00 1500.00
Charley O'Leary
Ty Cobb
66 Ford Putting Over a Spitter 125.00 200.00
Russ Ford
Jeff Sweeney
67 Ford Putting Over a Spitter 125.00 200.00
Russ Ford
Hippo Vaughn
68 Good Play at Third 900.00 1500.00
George Moriarty
Ty Cobb
69 Grant Gets His Man 125.00 200.00
Eddie Grant
Doc Hoblitzel
70 Hal Chase Too Late 125.00 200.00
Ambrose McConnell
Matty McIntyre
71 Hal Chase Too Late 125.00 200.00
Larry McLean
George Suggs
72 Harry Lord at Third: 150.00 250.00
Ed Lennox
Joe Tinker
73 Hartsel Strikes Out 125.00 200.00
Dolly Gray
Bob Groom
74 Hartzell Covering Third 125.00 200.00
Bill Dahlen
Doc Scanlon
75 Held at Third 125.00 200.00
Harry Lord
Jesse Tannehill
75 Jake Stahl Guarding First 125.00 200.00
Eddie Cicotte
Jake Stahl
77 Jim Delahanty at Bat 125.00 200.00
Jim Delahanty
Davy Jones
78 Just Before the Battle 125.00 200.00
Red Ames
Chief Meyers
79 Just Before the Battle 125.00 200.00
Josh Devore
Beals Becker
80 Just Before the Battle 250.00 400.00
Roger Bresnahan
John McGraw MG
81 Just Before the Battle 125.00 200.00
Doc Crandall
Chief Meyers
82 Just Before the Battle 350.00 600.00
Art Fletcher
Christy Mathewson
83 Just Before the Battle 150.00 250.00
Rube Marquard
Chief Meyers
84 Just Before the Battle 250.00 400.00
John McGraw MG
Hugh Jennings
85 Just Before the Battle 300.00 500.00
Chief Meyers
Christy Mathewson
86 Just Before the Battle 125.00 200.00
Chief Meyers
Hook Wiltse
87 Just Before the Battle 125.00 200.00
Fred Snodgrass
Red Murray
88 Knight Catches a Runner 350.00 600.00
Jack Knight
Walter Johnson
89 Lobert Almost Caught 125.00 200.00
Al Bridwell
Johnny Kling
90 Lobert Almost Caught 125.00 200.00
Johnny Kling
Harry Steinfeldt
91 Lobert Almost Caught 350.00 600.00
Johnny Kling
Cy Young
92 Lobert Almost Caught 125.00 200.00
Al Mattern
Johnny Kling
93 Lobert Gets Tenney 125.00 200.00
Red Dooin
Hans Lobert
94 Lord Catches His Man 125.00 200.00
Harry Lord
Lee Tannehill
95 McConnell Caught 125.00 200.00
Tom Needham
Lew Richie
96 McIntyre at Bat 125.00 200.00
Ambrose McConnell
Matty McIntrye
97 Moriarty Spiked 125.00 200.00
Oscar Stanage
Ed Willett
98 Nearly Caught 125.00 200.00
Johnny Bates
Bob Bescher
99 Oldring Almost Home 125.00 200.00
Harry Lord
Rube Oldring
100 Schaefer on First 125.00 200.00
George McBride
Clyde Milan
101 Schaefer Steals Second 125.00 200.00
George McBride
Clark Griffith
102 Scoring from Second 125.00 200.00
Harry Lord
Rube Oldring
103 Scrambling Back to First 125.00 200.00
Cy Barger
Bill Bergen
104 Scrambling Back to First 125.00 200.00
Harry Wolter
Hal Chase
105 Speaker Almost Caught 150.00 250.00
Dots Miller
Fred Clarke
106 Speaker Rounding Third 350.00 600.00
Joe Wood
Tris Speaker
107 Speaker Scores 300.00 500.00
Tris Speaker

Hack Engle
108 Stahl Safe 125.00 200.00
Jimmy Austin
George Stovall
109 Stone About to Swing 125.00 200.00
Wildfire Schulte
Jimmy Sheckard
110 Sullivan Puts Up a High One 150.00 250.00
Steve Evans
Miller Huggins
111 Sullivan Puts up a High One 125.00 200.00
Dolly Gray
Bob Groom
112 Sweeney Gets Stahl 125.00 200.00
Russ FordJeff Sweeney
113 Sweeney Gets Stahl 125.00 200.00
Russ Ford
Hippo Vaughn
114 Tenney Lands Safely 125.00 200.00
Arlie Latham
Bugs Raymond
115 The Athletic Infield 175.00 300.00
Jack Barry
Frank Baker
116 The Athletic Infield 150.00 250.00
Mordecai Brown
Peaches Graham
117 The Athletic Infield 125.00 200.00
Arnold Hauser
Ed Konetchy
118 The Athletic Infield 125.00 200.00
Harry Krause
Ira Thomas
119 The Pinch Hitter 125.00 200.00
Dick Egan
Doc Hoblitzel
120 The Scissors Slide 125.00 200.00
Doc Birmingham
Terry Turner
121 Tom Jones at Bat 125.00 200.00
Art Fromme
Larry McLean
122 Tom Jones at Bat 125.00 200.00
Harry Gaspar
Larry McLean
123 Too Late For Devlin 125.00 200.00
Red Ames
Chief Meyers
124 Too Late For Devlin 125.00 200.00
Doc Crandall
Chief Meyers
125 Too Late For Devlin 700.00 1200.00
Art Devlin (Giants)
Christy Mathewson
126 Too Late For Devlin 900.00 1500.00
Art Devlin (Rustlers)
Christy Mathewson
127 Too Late For Devlin 250.00 400.00
Rube Marquard
Chief Meyers
128 Too Late For Devlin 125.00 200.00
Chief Meyers
Hooks Wiltse
129 Ty Cobb Steals Third 1200.00 2000.00
Hughie Jennings
Ty Cobb
130 Ty Cobb Steals Third 1200.00 2000.00
George Moriarty
Ty Cobb
131 Ty Cobb Steals Third 600.00 1000.00
George Stovall
Jimmy Austin
132 Wheat Strikes Out 150.00 250.00
Bill Dahlen
Zach Wheat

2004 Hot Prospects Draft

This 120-card set was released in November, 2004. The set was issued in five-card hobby packs and though packs lacked an official SRP, estimates placed the average price at $8.50 per. Packs were issued 15 to a box and 12 boxes to a case. This set was also issued in six-card retail packs with an SRP of $3 per. Retail boxes featured 24 packs and retail cases contained 20 boxes. Cards numbered 1-60 feature veterans while cards 61-70 and 112-113 feature unsigned Rookie Cards issued to a stated print run of 1000 serial numbered copies per and seeded at a stated rate of one in 15 hobby packs and one in 120 retail packs. Cards numbered 71-111 and 114-120 are signed Rookie Cards featuring players from the 2004 MLB Draft. These cards were issued to a stated print run of 299 serial numbered copies per and seeded at a rate of one in nine hobby and one in 990 retail packs. Please note, the following cards packed out as exchange cards: 74, 84, 91, 112, 113, 114 and 118.

COMP.SET w/o RC's (60) 6.00 15.00
COMMON CARD (1-60) .20 .50
COMMON (61-70/112-113) 1.25 3.00
61-70/112-113 ODDS 1:15 H, 1:120 R
61-70/112-113 PRINT RUN 1000 #'d SETS
COMMON (71-110/114-120) 6.00 15.00
71-111/114-120 ODDS 1:9 H, 1:990 R
71-111/114-120 PRINT RUN 299 #'d SETS
EXCHANGE DEADLINE INDEFINITE
1 Miguel Tejada .20 .50
2 Jose Vidro .20 .50
3 Hideki Matsui .75 2.00
4 Roger Clemens 1.00 2.50
5 Craig Wilson .20 .50
6 Bobby Crosby .20 .50
7 Pat Burrell .20 .50
8 Mike Sweeney .20 .50
9 Craig Biggio .30 .75
10 Scott Rolen .30 .75
11 Roy Halladay .20 .50
12 Lyle Overbay .20 .50
13 Rocco Baldelli .20 .50
14 Mike Piazza .75 2.00
15 Rafael Palmeiro .30 .75
16 Hank Blalock .20 .50
17 Sammy Sosa .50 1.25
18 Dontrelle Willis .30 .75
19 Alfonso Soriano .20 .50
20 Gary Sheffield .20 .50
21 Jim Thome .30 .75
22 Ivan Rodriguez .30 .75
23 Adam Dunn .20 .50
24 Kerry Wood .20 .50
25 Khalil Greene .30 .75
26 Richie Sexson .20 .50
27 Nomar Garciaparra .75 2.00
28 Andruw Jones .30 .75
29 Tom Glavine .30 .75
30 Carlos Beltran .20 .50
31 Chipper Jones .50 1.25
32 Jeff Bagwell .30 .75
33 Tim Hudson .20 .50
34 Alex Rodriguez .75 2.00
35 Omar Vizquel .30 .75
36 Albert Pujols 1.00 2.50
37 Frank Thomas .50 1.25
38 Ben Sheets .20 .50
39 Jason Schmidt .20 .50
40 Miguel Cabrera .30 .75
41 Carlos Delgado .20 .50
42 Ichiro Suzuki 1.00 2.50
43 Curt Schilling .30 .75
44 Todd Helton .30 .75
45 Ken Griffey Jr. .75 2.00
46 Mark Prior .30 .75
47 Vladimir Guerrero .50 1.25
48 Pedro Martinez .30 .75
49 Manny Ramirez .30 .75
50 Joe Mauer .50 1.25
51 Jorge Posada .30 .75
52 Troy Glaus .20 .50
53 Randy Johnson .50 1.25
54 Adrian Beltre .20 .50
55 Eric Gagne .20 .50
56 Josh Beckett .20 .50
57 Jason Giambi .20 .50
58 Barry Zito .20 .50
59 Lance Berkman .20 .50
60 Derek Jeter 1.00 2.50
61 Kaz Matsui HP RC 2.00 5.00
62 Jason Bartlett HP RC 2.00 5.00
63 John Gall HP RC 2.00 5.00
64 Chris Saenz HP RC 1.25 3.00
65 Merkin Valdez HP RC 2.00 5.00
66 Akinori Otsuka HP RC 1.25 3.00
67 Joey Gathright HP RC 2.00 5.00
68 Brad Halsey HP RC 2.00 5.00
69 David Aardsma HP RC 2.00 5.00
70 Scott Kazmir HP RC 5.00 12.00
71 Matt Bush AU RC 20.00 40.00
72 John Bowker AU RC 12.50 30.00
73 Mike Ferris AU RC 6.00 15.00
74 Brian Bixler AU RC EXCH
75 Scott Elbert AU RC 15.00 40.00
76 Josh Fields AU RC 6.00 15.00
77 Bill Bray AU RC 6.00 15.00
78 Greg Golson AU RC 12.50 30.00
79 Neil Walker AU RC 20.00 40.00
80 Philip Hughes AU RC 30.00 60.00
81 Chris Nelson AU RC 20.00 40.00
82 Mark Rogers AU RC 10.00 25.00
83 Trevor Plouffe AU RC 10.00 25.00
84 Chris Garcia AU RC EXCH
85 Thomas Diamond AU RC 20.00 40.00
86 B.J. Szymanski AU RC 10.00 25.00
87 Richie Robnett AU RC 10.00 25.00
88 Seth Smith AU RC 10.00 25.00
89 Kyle Waldrop AU RC 10.00 25.00
90 Curtis Thigpen AU RC 6.00 15.00
91 J.P. Howell AU RC EXCH
92 Blake DeWitt AU RC 12.50 30.00
93 Taylor Tankersley AU RC 6.00 15.00
94 Zach Jackson AU RC 6.00 15.00
95 Justin Orenduff AU RC 6.00 15.00
96 Tyler Lumsden AU RC 6.00 15.00
97 Danny Putnam AU RC 6.00 15.00
98 Jon Poterson AU RC 6.00 15.00
99 Matt Fox AU RC 1.25 3.00
100 Gio Gonzalez AU RC 6.00 15.00
101 Huston Street AU RC 6.00 15.00
102 Jay Rainville AU RC 15.00 30.00
103 Matt Durkin AU RC 6.00 15.00
104 Brett Smith AU RC 10.00 25.00
105 Justin Hoyman AU RC 6.00 15.00
106 Erick San Pedro AU RC 6.00 15.00
107 Jeff Marquez AU RC 10.00 25.00
108 Hunter Pence AU RC 40.00 80.00
109 Dustin Pedroia AU RC 60.00 120.00
110 Kurt Suzuki AU RC 10.00 25.00
111 Billy Buckner AU RC 6.00 15.00
112 Yadier Molina HP RC EXCH
113 S.Takatsu HP RC EXCH
114 J.C. Holt AU RC EXCH
115 Homer Bailey AU RC 10.00 25.00
116 David Purcey AU RC 6.00 15.00
117 Jeremy Sowers AU RC 6.00 15.00
118 Chris Lambert AU RC EXCH
119 Eric Hurley AU RC 6.00 15.00
120 Grant Johnson AU RC 6.00 15.00

2004 Hot Prospects Draft Die Cuts

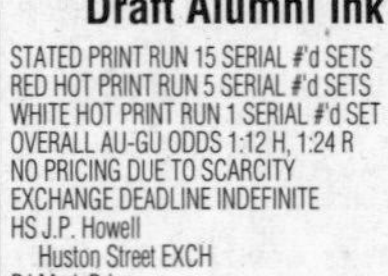

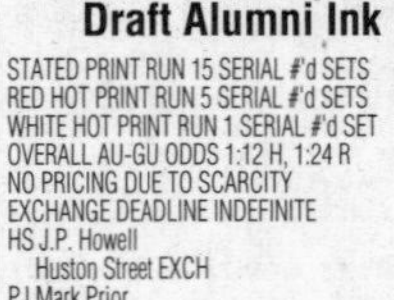

Forty-three of the 48 total Draft Pick autograph cards from the basic Hot Prospects product were featured in this Die Cut parallel. The cards were issued exclusively in 1-card red foil bonus packs. The red foil wrappers did not feature any print design indicating they contained Hot Prospect Draft autographs - they were simply blank red foil wrappers. Just shy of 2,000 red foil bonus packs were produced and sent in in early January, 2005 exclusively to Fleer's network of hobby distributors as an incentive to help move boxes of Hot Prospects Draft to their own network of hobby dealers and shop owners. Though the cards lack serial-numbering, representatives at Fleer publicly released print runs for all 43 cards to Beckett Media LP about eight weeks after the cards were issued. Print runs range from as few as 15 to as many as 92 copies of each card.

*DIE CUTp/r 47-64: .5X TO 1.2X BASIC
*DIE CUTp/r 92: .4X TO 1X BASIC
ONE PER RED FOIL BONUS PACK
RED PACKS ISSUED TO DISTRIBUTORS
PRINT RUNS B/WN 15-92 COPIES PER
NO PRICING ON QTY OFF 3 OR LESS
CARDS ARE NOT SERIAL-NUMBERED
PRINT RUN INFO PROVIDED BY FLEER
SEE BECKETT.COM FOR ALL PRINT RUNS
71 Matt Bush AU/59 * 20.00 50.00
72 John Bowker AU/26 *
73 Mike Ferris AU/28 *
75 Scott Elbert AU/51 * 20.00 50.00
76 Josh Fields AU/50 * 6.00 15.00
77 Bill Bray AU/29 *
78 Greg Golson AU/50 * 15.00 40.00
79 Neil Walker AU/15 *
80 Philip Hughes AU/47 * 200.00 300.00
81 Chris Nelson AU/62 * 20.00 50.00
82 Mark Rogers AU/59 * 15.00 40.00
83 Trevor Plouffe AU/58 * 12.50 30.00
85 Thomas Diamond AU/58 * 20.00 50.00
86 B.J. Szymanski AU/26 *
87 Richie Robnett AU/61 * 12.50 30.00
88 Seth Smith AU/25 *
89 Kyle Waldrop AU/62 * 12.50 30.00
90 Curtis Thigpen AU/29 *
92 Blake DeWitt AU/64 * 40.00 80.00
93 Taylor Tankersley AU/63 * 8.00 20.00
94 Zach Jackson AU/61 * 8.00 20.00
95 Justin Orenduff AU/26 *
96 Tyler Lumsden AU/59 * 8.00 20.00
97 Danny Putnam AU/61 * 8.00 20.00
98 Jon Poterson AU/58 * 8.00 20.00
99 Matt Fox AU/61 * 1.50 4.00
100 Gio Gonzalez AU/60 * 15.00 40.00
101 Huston Street AU/27 *
102 Jay Rainville AU/28 *
103 Matt Durkin AU/18 *
104 Brett Smith AU/30 *
105 Justin Hoyman AU/62 * 8.00 20.00
106 Erick San Pedro AU/33 *
107 Jeff Marquez AU/27 *
108 Hunter Pence AU/30 *
109 Dustin Pedroia AU/17 *
110 Kurt Suzuki AU/92 * 10.00 25.00
111 Billy Buckner AU/29 *
115 Homer Bailey AU/48 * 50.00 100.00
116 David Purcey AU/61 * 6.00 15.00
117 Jeremy Sowers AU/61 * 30.00 60.00
119 Eric Hurley AU/61 * 12.50 30.00
120 Grant Johnson AU/29 *

2004 Hot Prospects Draft Red Hot

*RED 1-60: 2.5X TO 6X BASIC
*RED 61-70: 1X TO 2.5X BASIC
1-70 PRINT RUN 150 SERIAL #'d SETS
71-120 PRINT RUN 25 SERIAL #'d SETS
71-120 NO PRICING DUE TO SCARCITY
OVERALL PARALLEL ODDS 1:15 H, 1:120 R
CARDS 112 AND 113 DO NOT EXIST
EXCHANGE DEADLINE INDEFINITE

2004 Hot Prospects Draft White Hot

OVERALL PARALLEL ODDS 1:15 H, 1:120 R
STATED PRINT RUN 1 SERIAL #'d SET
NO PRICING DUE TO SCARCITY
CARDS 112 AND 113 DO NOT EXIST
EXCHANGE DEADLINE INDEFINITE

2004 Hot Prospects Draft Alumni Ink

STATED PRINT RUN 15 SERIAL #'d SETS
RED HOT PRINT RUN 5 SERIAL #'d SETS
WHITE HOT PRINT RUN 1 SERIAL #'d SET
OVERALL AU-GU ODDS 1:12 H, 1:24 R
NO PRICING DUE TO SCARCITY
EXCHANGE DEADLINE INDEFINITE
HS J.P. Howell
Huston Street EXCH
PJ Mark Prior
Randy Johnson
TG Mark Teixeira
Nomar Garciaparra

2004 Hot Prospects Draft Double Team Jersey

STATED PRINT RUN 100 SERIAL #'d SETS
*RED HOT: .6X TO 1.5X BASIC
RED HOT PRINT RUN 25 SERIAL #'d SETS
WHITE HOT PRINT RUN 1 SERIAL #'d SET
NO WHITE HOT PRICING DUE TO SCARCITY
*PATCH: 1X TO 2.5X BASIC
PATCH PRINT RUN 50 SERIAL #'d SETS
PATCH RED HOT PRINT RUN 10 #'d SETS
NO PATCH RED HOT PRICING AVAILABLE
PATCH WHITE HOT PRINT RUN 1 #'d SET
NO PATCH WHITE HOT PRICING AVAILABLE
OVERALL AU-GU ODDS 1:12 H, 1:24 R
AS Alfonso Soriano Rgr-Yanks 4.00 10.00
CB Carlos Beltran Astros-Royals 4.00 10.00
EM Eddie Murray Mets-O's 10.00 25.00
GM Greg Maddux Braves-Cubs 8.00 20.00
HN Hideo Nomo Dgr-Sox 6.00 15.00
IR I.Rodriguez Marlins-Tigers 6.00 15.00
JG Jason Giambi A's-Yanks 4.00 10.00
MP Mike Piazza Dgr-Mets 8.00 20.00
MR Manny Ramirez Indians-Sox 6.00 15.00
MT Miguel Tejada A's-O's 4.00 10.00
NR Nolan Ryan Astros-Rgr 15.00 40.00
PM Pedro Martinez Expos-Sox 6.00 15.00
RCA Rod Carew Angels-Twins 10.00 25.00
RCL Roger Clemens Astros-Sox 8.00 20.00
RH R.Henderson A's-Padres 10.00 25.00
RJ Reggie Jackson A's-Yanks 10.00 25.00
SR Scott Rolen Cards-Phils 6.00 15.00
TG Tom Glavine Braves-Mets 6.00 15.00
VG Vlad Guerrero Angels-Expos 6.00 15.00

2004 Hot Prospects Draft Double Team Autograph Patch Red Hot

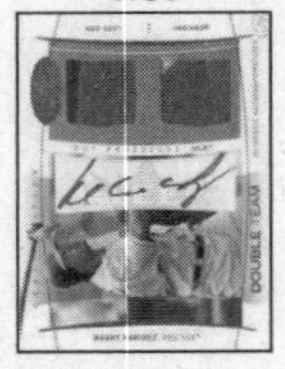

STATED PRINT RUN 22 SERIAL #'d SETS
WHITE HOT PRINT RUN 1 SERIAL #'d SET
NO WHITE HOT PRICING DUE TO SCARCITY
OVERALL AU-GU ODDS 1:12 H, 1:24 R
HN Hideo Nomo Dgr-Sox
IR I.Rodriguez Marlins-Tigers 50.00 100.00
MP Mike Piazza Dgr-Mets 100.00 200.00
MR Manny Ramirez Indians-Sox 60.00 120.00
RJ Reggie Jackson A's-Yanks 50.00 100.00
SR Scott Rolen Cards-Phils 40.00 80.00
VG Vlad Guerrero Angels-Expos 50.00 100.00

2004 Hot Prospects Draft MLB Hot Materials

STATED PRINT RUN 325 SERIAL #'d SETS
*RED HOT: .75X TO 2X BASIC
RED HOT PRINT RUN 50 SERIAL #'d SETS
WHITE HOT PRINT RUN 1 SERIAL #'d SET
NO WHITE HOT PRICING DUE TO SCARCITY
OVERALL AU-GU ODDS 1:12 H, 1:24 R
AD Adam Dunn Jsy 2.00 5.00
AJ Andruw Jones Jsy 3.00 8.00
APE Andy Pettitte Jsy 3.00 8.00
APU Albert Pujols Jsy 6.00 15.00
AS Alfonso Soriano Jsy 2.00 5.00
CD Carlos Delgado Jsy 2.00 5.00
CJ Chipper Jones Jsy 3.00 8.00
CS Curt Schilling Jsy 3.00 8.00
DW Dontrelle Willis Jsy 3.00 8.00
EG Eric Gagne Jsy 2.00 5.00
FT Frank Thomas Jsy 3.00 8.00
HB Hank Blalock Jsy 2.00 5.00
HM Hideki Matsui Jsy 8.00 20.00
HN Hideo Nomo Jsy 3.00 8.00
IR Ivan Rodriguez Jsy 3.00 8.00
JB Jeff Bagwell Jsy 3.00 8.00
JD J.D. Drew Jsy 2.00 5.00
JE Jim Edmonds Jsy 2.00 5.00
JM Joe Mauer Jsy 3.00 8.00
JP Jorge Posada Jsy 3.00 8.00
JS Jason Schmidt Jsy 2.00 5.00
JT Jim Thome Jsy 3.00 8.00
KM Kaz Matsui Jsy 3.00 8.00
KW Kerry Wood Jsy 2.00 5.00
LB Lance Berkman Jsy 2.00 5.00
LO Lyle Overbay Jsy 2.00 5.00
MC Miguel Cabrera Jsy 3.00 8.00
MM Mike Mussina Jsy 3.00 8.00
MPI Mike Piazza Jsy 4.00 10.00
MPR Mark Prior Jsy 3.00 8.00
MR Manny Ramirez Jsy 3.00 8.00
MTJ Miguel Tejada Jsy 2.00 5.00
MTX Mark Teixeira Jsy 3.00 8.00
RC Roger Clemens Jsy 4.00 10.00
RJ Randy Johnson Jsy 3.00 8.00
SS Sammy Sosa Jsy 3.00 8.00
THE Todd Helton Jsy 3.00 8.00
THN Torii Hunter Jsy 2.00 5.00
THU Tim Hudson Jsy 2.00 5.00
VG Vladimir Guerrero Jsy 3.00 8.00

2004 Hot Prospects Draft Past Present Future Autograph

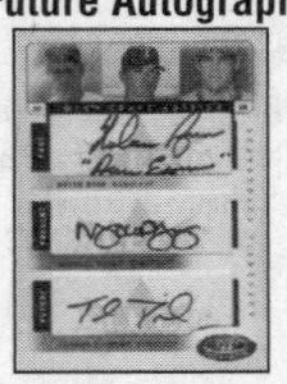

STATED PRINT RUN 33 SERIAL #'d SETS
RED HOT PRINT RUN 3 SERIAL #'d SETS
NO RED HOT PRICING DUE TO SCARCITY
WHITE HOT PRINT RUN 1 SERIAL #'d SET
NO WHITE HOT PRICING DUE TO SCARCITY
OVERALL AU-GU ODDS 1:12 H, 1:24 R
EXCHANGE DEADLINE INDEFINITE
BDB Johnny Bench 75.00 150.00
Adam Dunn
Homer Bailey
BMH Yogi Berra 125.00 200.00
Mike Mussina
Philip Hughes
BRP Bill Buckner 50.00 100.00
Manny Ramirez
Dustin Pedroia
CRP Joe Carter
Alexis Rios
David Purcey EXCH
CTG Steve Carlton 50.00 100.00
Jim Thome
Greg Golson
FMF Carlton Fisk 10.00 25.00
Ryan Meaux
Josh Fields
GGB Tony Gwynn
Khalil Greene
Matt Bush EXCH
GNE Kirk Gibson 200.00 350.00
Hideo Nomo
Scott Elbert
JCR Reggie Jackson
Eric Chavez
Richie Robnett EXCH
KBF Al Kaline
Jeremy Bonderman
Jeff Frazier EXCH
KFP Harmon Killebrew
Lew Ford
Trevor Plouffe EXCH
KWW Ralph Kiner 40.00 80.00
Jack Wilson
Neil Walker
MPL Stan Musial
Albert Pujols
Chris Lambert EXCH
RYD Nolan Ryan 125.00 200.00
Michael Young
Thomas Diamond
SCT Gary Sheffield
Miguel Cabrera
Taylor Tankersley
SPJ Ryne Sandberg
Mark Prior
Grant Johnson EXCH
WPD Mookie Wilson 75.00 150.00
Mike Piazza
Matt Durkin
YWR Robin Yount
Rickie Weeks
Mark Rogers EXCH

2004 Hot Prospects Draft Rewind

STATED ODDS 1:5
1 Joe Mauer 1.00 2.50
2 Derek Jeter 2.50 6.00
3 Chipper Jones 1.25 3.00
4 Greg Maddux 2.00 5.00
5 Alex Rodriguez 2.00 5.00
6 Nomar Garciaparra 2.00 5.00
7 Curt Schilling 1.25 3.00
8 Kerry Wood .75 2.00
9 Troy Glaus .75 2.00
10 Pat Burrell .75 2.00
11 Mark Mulder .75 2.00
12 Josh Beckett .75 2.00
13 Barry Zito .75 2.00
14 Mark Prior 1.25 3.00
15 Rickie Weeks .75 2.00
16 Khalil Greene 1.25 3.00
17 Ken Griffey Jr. 2.00 5.00
18 Gary Sheffield .75 2.00
19 Todd Helton 1.25 3.00
20 Barry Larkin 1.25 3.00
21 Kevin Brown .75 2.00
22 Frank Thomas 1.25 3.00
23 Manny Ramirez 1.25 3.00
24 Roger Clemens 2.50 6.00
25 Lance Berkman .75 2.00
26 Randy Johnson 1.25 3.00
27 Jason Giambi .75 2.00
28 Ben Sheets .75 2.00
29 Scott Rolen 1.25 3.00
30 Tom Glavine 1.25 3.00

2004 Hot Prospects Draft Rewind Jersey

PRINT RUNS B/WN 101-158 COPIES PER
RED HOT PRINT RUN 10 SERIAL #'d SETS
NO RED HOT PRICING DUE TO SCARCITY
WHITE HOT PRINT RUN 1 SERIAL #'d SET
NO WHITE HOT PRICING DUE TO SCARCITY
*PATCH p/r 68: .6X TO 1.5X BASIC
*PATCH p/r 41-57: .6X TO 1.5X BASIC
*PATCH p/r 20-29: .75X TO 2X BASIC
*PATCH p/r 16-19: 1X TO 2.5X BASIC
PATCH PRINT RUNS B/WN 10-68 PER
NO PATCH PRICING ON QTY OF 14 OR LESS
PATCH RED HOT PRINT RUN 5 #'d SETS
NO PATCH RED HOT PRICING AVAILABLE
PATCH WHITE HOT PRINT RUN 1 #'d SET
NO PATCH WHITE HOT PRICING AVAILABLE
OVERALL AU-GU ODDS 1:12 H, 1:24 R
BL Barry Larkin/104 4.00 10.00
BS Ben Sheets/110 3.00 8.00
BZ Barry Zito/109 3.00 8.00
CJ Chipper Jones/101 4.00 10.00
CK Casey Kotchman/113 6.00 15.00
CS Curt Schilling/139 4.00 10.00
EC Eric Chavez/110 3.00 8.00
FT Frank Thomas/107 4.00 10.00
GM Greg Maddux/131 6.00 15.00
GS Gary Sheffield/106 3.00 8.00
JB Josh Beckett/102 3.00 8.00
JG Jason Giambi/158 3.00 8.00
JM Joe Mauer/101 4.00 10.00
KB Kevin Brown/104 3.00 8.00
KG Khalil Greene/113 4.00 10.00
KW Kerry Wood/104 3.00 8.00
LB Lance Berkman/116 3.00 8.00
MM Mark Mulder/102 3.00 8.00
MP Mark Prior/102 4.00 10.00
MR Manny Ramirez/113 4.00 10.00
PB Pat Burrell/101 3.00 8.00
RB Rocco Baldelli/119 3.00 8.00
RC Roger Clemens/119 6.00 15.00
RJ Randy Johnson/136 4.00 10.00
RW Rickie Weeks/102 3.00 8.00
SR Scott Rolen/146 4.00 10.00
TG Troy Glaus/103 3.00 8.00
TG Tom Glavine/147 4.00 10.00
TH Todd Helton/108 4.00 10.00
ZG Zack Greinke/106 3.00 8.00

2004 Hot Prospects Draft Tandems

STATED ODDS 1:15 H/R
1 Mark Prior 2.00 5.00
Greg Maddux
2 Jim Thome 1.25 3.00
Pat Burrell
3 Ken Griffey Jr. 2.00 5.00
Adam Dunn
4 Mike Piazza 2.00 5.00
Tom Glavine
5 Alex Rodriguez 6.00 15.00
Derek Jeter
6 Roger Clemens 2.50 6.00
Andy Pettitte
7 Jason Giambi 2.00 5.00
Hideki Matsui
8 Alfonso Soriano .75 2.00
Hank Blalock
9 Manny Ramirez 1.25 3.00
David Ortiz
10 Miguel Cabrera 1.25 3.00
Dontrelle Willis
11 Hideki Matsui 3.00 8.00
Ichiro Suzuki
12 Albert Pujols 2.50 6.00
Scott Rolen
13 Pedro Martinez 1.25 3.00
Curt Schilling
14 Sammy Sosa 1.25 3.00
Nomar Garciaparra

15 Kaz Matsui Derek Jeter	2.50	6.00

1949 Leaf

TED WILLIAMS

The cards in this 98-card set measure 2 3/8" by 2 7/8". The 1949 Leaf set was the first post-war baseball series issued in color. This effort was not entirely successful due to a lack of refinement which resulted in many color variations and cards out of register. In addition, the set was skip numbered from 1-168, with 49 of the 98 cards printed in limited quantities (marked with SP in the checklist). Cards 102 and 136 have variations, and cards are sometimes found with overprinted, incorrect or blank backs. Some cards were produced with a 1948 copyright date but overwhelming evidence seemed to indicate that this set was not actually released until early in 1949. An album to hold these cards was available as a premium. The album could only be obtained by sending in five wrappers and 25 cents. Since so few albums appear on the secondary market, no value is attached to them. Notable Rookie Cards in this set include Stan Musial, Satchel Paige, and Jackie Robinson.

COMPLETE SET (98)	25000.00	40000.00
COMMON CARD (1-168)	15.00	25.00
COMMON SP's	200.00	300.00
WRAPPER (1-CENT)	120.00	160.00
1 Joe DiMaggio	1800.00	3000.00
3 Babe Ruth	1500.00	2500.00
4 Stan Musial	600.00	1000.00
5 Virgil Trucks SP RC	250.00	400.00
8 Satchel Paige SP RC	9000.00	15000.00
10 Dizzy Trout	25.00	40.00
11 Phil Rizzuto	200.00	350.00
13 Cass Michaels SP RC	200.00	300.00
14 Billy Johnson	25.00	40.00
17 Frank Overmire RC	15.00	25.00
19 Johnny Wyrostek SP	200.00	300.00
20 Hank Sauer SP	250.00	400.00
22 Al Evans RC	15.00	25.00
26 Sam Chapman	25.00	40.00
27 Mickey Harris RC	15.00	25.00
28 Jim Hegan RC	25.00	40.00
29 Elmer Valo RC	25.00	40.00
30 Billy Goodman SP RC	250.00	400.00
31 Lou Brissie RC	15.00	25.00
32 Warren Spahn	200.00	350.00
33 Peanuts Lowrey SP RC	200.00	300.00
36 Al Zarilla SP	200.00	300.00
38 Ted Kluszewski RC	125.00	200.00
39 Ewell Blackwell	35.00	60.00
42A Kent Peterson RC	15.00	25.00
42B Kent Peterson Red Cap		
43 Ed Stevens SP RC	200.00	300.00
45 Ken Keltner SP RC	200.00	300.00
46 Johnny Mize	60.00	100.00
47 George Vico RC	15.00	25.00
48 Johnny Schmitz SP RC	200.00	300.00
49 Del Ennis RC	35.00	60.00
50 Dick Wakefield RC	15.00	25.00
51 Al Dark SP RC	300.00	500.00
53 Johnny VanderMeer	60.00	100.00
54 Bobby Adams SP RC	200.00	300.00
55 Tommy Henrich SP	300.00	500.00
56 Larry Jansen	25.00	40.00
57 Bob McCall RC	15.00	25.00
59 Luke Appling	60.00	100.00
61 Jake Early RC	15.00	25.00
62 Eddie Joost SP	200.00	300.00
63 Barney McCosky SP	200.00	300.00
65 Bob Elliott UER	60.00	100.00
66 Orval Grove SP RC	200.00	300.00
68 Eddie Miller SP	200.00	300.00
70 Honus Wagner	200.00	350.00
72 Hank Edwards RC	15.00	25.00
73 Pat Seerey RC	15.00	25.00
75 Dom DiMaggio SP	350.00	600.00
76 Ted Williams	700.00	1200.00
77 Roy Smalley RC	15.00	25.00
78 Hoot Evers SP RC	200.00	300.00
79 Jackie Robinson RC	1200.00	2000.00
81 Whitey Kurowski SP RC	200.00	300.00
82 Johnny Lindell	25.00	40.00
83 Bobby Doerr	60.00	100.00
84 Sid Hudson	15.00	25.00
85 Dave Philley SP RC	250.00	400.00
86 Ralph Weigel RC	15.00	25.00
88 Frank Gustine SP RC	200.00	300.00
91 Ralph Kiner	125.00	200.00
93 Bob Feller SP	1400.00	2000.00
95 Snuffy Stirnweiss	25.00	40.00
97 Marty Marion	35.00	60.00
98 Hal Newhouser SP RC	350.00	600.00
102A G.Hermansk ERR	150.00	250.00
102B Gene Hermanski COR RC	25.00	40.00
104 Eddie Stewart SP RC	200.00	300.00
106 Lou Boudreau MG RC	60.00	100.00
108 Matt Batts SP RC	200.00	300.00
111 Jerry Priddy RC	15.00	25.00
113 Dutch Leonard SP	200.00	300.00
117 Joe Gordon RC	25.00	40.00
120 George Kell SP RC	350.00	600.00
121 Johnny Pesky SP RC	250.00	400.00
123 Cliff Fannin SP RC	200.00	300.00
125 Andy Pafko RC	15.00	25.00
127 Enos Slaughter SP	500.00	800.00
128 Buddy Rosar	15.00	25.00
129 Kirby Higbe SP	200.00	300.00
131 Sid Gordon SP	200.00	300.00
133 Tommy Holmes SP RC	300.00	500.00
136A Cliff Aberson Full sleeve) RC	15.00	25.00
136B Cliff Aberson Short Sleeve	150.00	250.00
137 Harry Walker SP RC	250.00	400.00
138 Larry Doby SP RC	400.00	700.00
139 Johnny Hopp RC	15.00	25.00
142 D.Murtaugh SP RC	250.00	400.00
143 Dick Sisler SP RC	200.00	300.00
144 Bob Dillinger SP RC	200.00	300.00
146 Pete Reiser SP	300.00	500.00
149 Hank Majeski SP RC	200.00	300.00
153 Floyd Baker SP RC	200.00	300.00
158 H.Brecheen SP RC	250.00	400.00
159 Mizell Platt RC	15.00	25.00
160 Bob Scheffing SP RC	200.00	300.00
161 V.Stephens SP RC	250.00	400.00
163 F.Hutchinson SP RC	250.00	400.00
165 Dale Mitchell SP RC	250.00	400.00
168 Phil Cavarretta SP RC	300.00	500.00
NNO Album		

1960 Leaf

The cards in this 144-card set measure the standard size. The 1960 Leaf set was issued in a regular gum package style but with a marble instead of gum. This set was issued in five card nickel packs which came 24 to a box. The series was a joint production by Sports Novelties, Inc., and Leaf, two Chicago-based companies. Cards 73-144 are more difficult to find than the lower numbers. Photo variations exist (probably proof cards) for the eight cards listed with an asterisk and there is a well-known error card, number 25 showing Brooks Lawrence (in a Reds uniform) with Jim Grant's name on front, and Grant's biography and record on back. The corrected version with Grant's photo is the more difficult variety. The only notable Rookie Card in this set is Dallas Green. The complete set price below includes both versions of Jim Grant.

COMPLETE SET (144)	1000.00	2000.00
COMMON CARD (1-72)	1.25	3.00
COMMON CARD (73-144)	12.50	30.00
WRAPPER	20.00	50.00
1 Luis Aparicio *	10.00	25.00
2 Woody Held	1.25	3.00
3 Frank Lary	1.50	4.00
4 Camilo Pascual	2.00	5.00
5 Pancho Herrera	1.25	3.00
6 Felipe Alou	3.00	8.00
7 Benjamin Daniels	1.25	3.00
8 Roger Craig	2.00	5.00
9 Eddie Kasko	1.25	3.00
10 Bob Grim	1.50	4.00
11 Jim Busby	1.50	4.00
12 Ken Boyer*	3.00	8.00
13 Bob Boyd	1.25	3.00
14 Sam Jones	1.50	4.00
15 Larry Jackson	1.50	4.00
16 Elroy Face	1.50	4.00
17 Walt Moryn *	1.25	3.00
18 Jim Gilliam	2.00	5.00
19 Don Newcombe	2.00	5.00
20 Glen Hobbie	1.25	3.00
21 Pedro Ramos	1.50	4.00
22 Ryne Duren	1.25	3.00
23 Joey Jay *	1.50	4.00
24 Lou Berberet	1.25	3.00
25A Jim Grant ERR (Photo actually Brooks Lawrence)	6.00	15.00
25B Jim Grant COR	10.00	25.00
26 Tom Borland RC	1.25	3.00
27 Brooks Robinson	15.00	40.00
28 Jerry Adair RC	1.25	3.00
29 Ron Jackson	1.25	3.00
30 George Strickland	1.25	3.00
31 Rocky Bridges	1.25	3.00
32 Bill Tuttle	1.50	4.00
33 Ken Hunt RC	1.25	3.00
34 Hal Griggs	1.25	3.00
35 Jim Coates *	1.25	3.00
36 Brooks Lawrence	1.25	3.00
37 Duke Snider	15.00	40.00
38 Al Spangler RC	1.25	3.00
39 Jim Owens	1.25	3.00
40 Bill Virdon	2.00	5.00
41 Ernie Broglio	1.25	3.00
42 Andre Rodgers	1.25	3.00
43 Julio Becquer	1.50	4.00
44 Tony Taylor	1.50	4.00
45 Jerry Lynch	1.50	4.00
46 Cletis Boyer	3.00	8.00
47 Jerry Lumpe	1.25	3.00
48 Charlie Maxwell	1.50	4.00
49 Jim Perry	1.50	4.00
50 Danny McDevitt	1.25	3.00
51 Juan Pizarro	1.25	3.00
52 Dallas Green RC	3.00	8.00
53 Bob Friend	1.50	4.00
54 Jack Sanford	1.50	4.00
55 Jim Rivera	1.25	3.00
56 Ted Wills RC	1.25	3.00
57 Milt Pappas	1.50	4.00
58 Hal Smith *	1.25	3.00
59 Bobby Avila	1.25	3.00
60 Clem Labine	2.00	5.00
61 Norman Rehm RC *	1.25	3.00
62 John Gabler RC	1.50	4.00
63 John Tsitouris RC	1.25	3.00
64 Dave Sisler	1.25	3.00
65 Vic Power	1.50	4.00
66 Earl Battey	1.25	3.00
67 Bob Purkey	1.25	3.00
68 Moe Drabowsky	1.50	4.00
69 Hoyt Wilhelm	6.00	15.00
70 Humberto Robinson	1.25	3.00
71 Whitey Herzog	3.00	8.00
72 Dick Donovan *	1.25	3.00
73 Gordon Jones	12.50	30.00
74 Joe Hicks RC	12.50	30.00
75 Ray Culp RC	15.00	40.00
76 Dick Drott	12.50	30.00
77 Bob Duliba RC	12.50	30.00
78 Art Ditmar	12.50	30.00
79 Steve Korcheck	12.50	30.00
80 Henry Mason RC	12.50	30.00
81 Harry Simpson	12.50	30.00
82 Gene Green	12.50	30.00
83 Bob Shaw	12.50	30.00
84 Howard Reed	12.50	30.00
85 Dick Stigman	12.50	30.00
86 Rip Repulski	12.50	30.00
87 Seth Morehead	12.50	30.00
88 Camilo Carreon RC	12.50	30.00
89 John Blanchard	15.00	40.00
90 Billy Hoeft	12.50	30.00
91 Fred Hopke RC	12.50	30.00
92 Joe Martin RC	12.50	30.00
93 Wally Shannon RC	12.50	30.00
94 Hal R. Smith Hal W. Smith	15.00	40.00
95 Al Schroll	12.50	30.00
96 John Kucks	12.50	30.00
97 Tom Morgan	12.50	30.00
98 Willie Jones	12.50	30.00
99 Marshall Renfroe RC	12.50	30.00
100 Willie Tasby	12.50	30.00
101 Irv Noren	12.50	30.00
102 Russ Snyder RC	12.50	30.00
103 Bob Turley	15.00	40.00
104 Jim Woods RC	12.50	30.00
105 Ronnie Kline	12.50	30.00
106 Steve Bilko	12.50	30.00
107 Elmer Valo	12.50	30.00
108 Tom McAvoy RC	12.50	30.00
109 Stan Williams	12.50	30.00
110 Earl Averill Jr.	12.50	30.00
111 Lee Walls	12.50	30.00
112 Paul Richards MG	12.50	30.00
113 Ed Sadowski	12.50	30.00
114 Stover McIlwain RC	12.50	30.00
115 Chuck Tanner UER (Photo actually Ken Kuhn)	15.00	40.00
116 Lou Klimchock RC	12.50	30.00
117 Neil Chrisley	12.50	30.00
118 John Callison	20.00	50.00
119 Hal Smith	12.50	30.00
120 Carl Sawatski	12.50	30.00
121 Frank Leja	12.50	30.00
122 Earl Torgeson	12.50	30.00
123 Art Schult	12.50	30.00
124 Jim Brosnan	12.50	30.00
125 Sparky Anderson	30.00	60.00
126 Joe Pignatano	12.50	30.00
127 Rocky Nelson	12.50	30.00
128 Orlando Cepeda	40.00	80.00
129 Daryl Spencer	12.50	30.00
130 Ralph Lumenti	12.50	30.00
131 Sam Taylor	12.50	30.00
132 Harry Brecheen CO	15.00	40.00
133 Johnny Groth	12.50	30.00
134 Wayne Terwilliger	12.50	30.00
135 Kent Hadley	12.50	30.00
136 Faye Throneberry	12.50	30.00
137 Jack Meyer	12.50	30.00
138 Chuck Cottier RC	12.50	30.00
139 Joe DeMaestri	12.50	30.00
140 Gene Freese	12.50	30.00
141 Curt Flood	20.00	50.00
142 Gino Cimoli	12.50	30.00
143 Clay Dalrymple RC	12.50	30.00
144 Jim Bunning	40.00	80.00

1990 Leaf

The 1990 Leaf set was the first premium set introduced by Donruss and represents one of the more significant products issued in the 1990's. The cards were issued in 15-card foil wrapped packs and were not available in factory sets. Each pack also contained one three-piece puzzle panel of a 63-piece Yogi Berra "Donruss Hall of Fame Diamond King" puzzle. This set, which was produced on high quality paper stock, was issued in two separate series of 264 standard-size cards each. The second series was issued approximately six weeks after the release of the first series. The cards feature full-color photos on both the front and back. Rookie Cards in the set include David Justice, John Olerud, Sammy Sosa, Frank Thomas and Larry Walker.

COMPLETE SET (528)	30.00	60.00
COMPLETE SERIES 1 (264)	20.00	40.00
COMPLETE SERIES 2 (264)	10.00	20.00
COMP. BERRA PUZZLE	.40	1.00
1 Introductory Card	.15	.40
2 Mike Henneman	.15	.40
3 Steve Bedrosian	.15	.40
4 Mike Scott	.15	.40
5 Allan Anderson	.15	.40
6 Rick Sutcliffe	.25	.60
7 Gregg Olson	.25	.60
8 Kevin Elster	.15	.40
9 Pete O'Brien	.15	.40
10 Carlton Fisk	.40	1.00
11 Joe Magrane	.15	.40
12 Roger Clemens	1.50	4.00
13 Tom Glavine	.40	1.00
14 Tom Gordon	.25	.60
15 Todd Benzinger	.15	.40
16 Hubie Brooks	.15	.40
17 Roberto Kelly	.15	.40
18 Barry Larkin	.40	1.00
19 Mike Boddicker	.15	.40
20 Roger McDowell	.15	.40
21 Nolan Ryan	2.00	5.00
22 John Farrell	.15	.40
23 Bruce Hurst	.15	.40
24 Wally Joyner	.25	.60
25 Greg Maddux	2.00	5.00
26 Chris Bosio	.15	.40
27 John Cerutti	.15	.40
28 Tim Burke	.15	.40
29 Dennis Eckersley	.25	.60
30 Glenn Davis	.15	.40
31 Jim Abbott	.40	1.00
32 Mike LaValliere	.15	.40
33 Andres Thomas	.15	.40
34 Lou Whitaker	.25	.60
35 Alvin Davis	.15	.40
36 Melido Perez	.15	.40
37 Craig Biggio	.60	1.50
38 Rick Aguilera	.25	.60
39 Pete Harnisch	.15	.40
40 David Cone	.25	.60
41 Scott Garrelts	.15	.40
42 Jay Howell	.15	.40
43 Eric King	.15	.40
44 Pedro Guerrero	.15	.40
45 Mike Bielecki	.15	.40
46 Bob Boone	.25	.60
47 Kevin Brown	.25	.60
48 Jerry Browne	.15	.40
49 Mike Scioscia	.15	.40
50 Chuck Cary	.15	.40
51 Wade Boggs	.40	1.00
52 Von Hayes	.15	.40
53 Tony Fernandez	.15	.40
54 Dennis Martinez	.25	.60
55 Tom Candiotti	.15	.40
56 Andy Benes	.25	.60
57 Rob Dibble	.25	.60
58 Chuck Crim	.15	.40
59 John Smoltz	.60	1.50
60 Mike Heath	.15	.40
61 Kevin Gross	.15	.40
62 Mark McGwire	1.50	4.00
63 Bert Blyleven	.25	.60
64 Bob Walk	.15	.40
65 Mickey Tettleton	.15	.40
66 Sid Fernandez	.15	.40
67 Terry Kennedy	.15	.40
68 Fernando Valenzuela	.25	.60
69 Don Mattingly	1.50	4.00
70 Paul O'Neill	.40	1.00
71 Robin Yount	1.00	2.50
72 Bret Saberhagen	.25	.60
73 Geno Petralli	.15	.40
74 Brook Jacoby	.15	.40
75 Roberto Alomar	.40	1.00
76 Devon White	.25	.60
77 Jose Lind	.15	.40
78 Pat Combs	.15	.40
79 Dave Stieb	.25	.60
80 Tim Wallach	.15	.40
81 Dave Stewart	.25	.60
82 Eric Anthony RC	.15	.40
83 Randy Bush	.15	.40
84 Rickey Henderson CL	.25	.60
85 Jaime Navarro	.15	.40
86 Tommy Gregg	.15	.40
87 Frank Tanana	.15	.40
88 Omar Vizquel	.60	1.50
89 Ivan Calderon	.15	.40
90 Vince Coleman	.15	.40
91 Barry Bonds	2.00	5.00
92 Randy Milligan	.15	.40
93 Frank Viola	.15	.40
94 Matt Williams	.25	.60
95 Alfredo Griffin	.15	.40
96 Steve Sax	.15	.40
97 Gary Gaetti	.25	.60
98 Ryne Sandberg	1.25	3.00
99 Danny Tartabull	.15	.40
100 Rafael Palmeiro	.40	1.00
101 Jesse Orosco	.15	.40
102 Garry Templeton	.15	.40
103 Frank DiPino	.15	.40
104 Tony Pena	.15	.40
105 Dickie Thon	.15	.40
106 Kelly Gruber	.15	.40
107 Marquis Grissom RC	.75	2.00
108 Jose Canseco	.40	1.00
109 Mike Blowers RC	.15	.40
110 Tom Browning	.15	.40
111 Greg Vaughn	.15	.40
112 Oddibe McDowell	.15	.40
113 Gary Ward	.15	.40
114 Jay Buhner	.25	.60
115 Eric Show	.15	.40
116 Bryan Harvey	.15	.40
117 Andy Van Slyke	.40	1.00
118 Jeff Ballard	.15	.40
119 Barry Lyons	.15	.40
120 Kevin Mitchell	.15	.40
121 Mike Gallego	.15	.40
122 Dave Smith	.15	.40
123 Kirby Puckett	.60	1.50
124 Jerome Walton	.15	.40
125 Bo Jackson	.60	1.50
126 Harold Baines	.25	.60
127 Scott Bankhead	.15	.40
128 Ozzie Guillen	.25	.60
129 Jose Oquendo UER (League misspelled as Legue)	.15	.40
130 John Dopson	.15	.40
131 Charlie Hayes	.15	.40
132 Fred McGriff	.60	1.50
133 Chet Lemon	.15	.40
134 Gary Carter	.25	.60
135 Rafael Ramirez	.15	.40
136 Shane Mack	.15	.40
137 Mark Grace UER (Card back has OB:L, should be B:L)	.40	1.00
138 Phil Bradley	.15	.40
139 Dwight Gooden	.25	.60
140 Harold Reynolds	.25	.60
141 Scott Fletcher	.15	.40
142 Ozzie Smith	1.00	2.50
143 Mike Greenwell	.15	.40
144 Pete Smith	.15	.40
145 Mark Gubicza	.15	.40
146 Chris Sabo	.15	.40
147 Ramon Martinez	.15	.40
148 Tim Leary	.15	.40
149 Randy Myers	.25	.60
150 Jody Reed	.15	.40
151 Bruce Ruffin	.15	.40
152 Jeff Russell	.15	.40
153 Doug Jones	.15	.40
154 Tony Gwynn	.75	2.00
155 Mark Langston	.15	.40
156 Mitch Williams	.15	.40
157 Gary Sheffield	.60	1.50
158 Tom Henke	.15	.40
159 Oil Can Boyd	.15	.40
160 Rickey Henderson	.60	1.50
161 Bill Doran	.15	.40
162 Chuck Finley	.25	.60
163 Jeff King	.15	.40
164 Nick Esasky	.15	.40
165 Cecil Fielder	.25	.60
166 Dave Valle	.15	.40
167 Robin Ventura	.60	1.50
168 Jim Deshaies	.15	.40
169 Juan Berenguer	.15	.40
170 Craig Worthington	.15	.40
171 Gregg Jefferies	.25	.60
172 Will Clark	.40	1.00
173 Kirk Gibson	.25	.60
174 Carlton Fisk CL	.25	.60
175 Bobby Thigpen	.15	.40
176 John Tudor	.15	.40
177 Andre Dawson	.25	.60
178 George Brett	1.50	4.00
179 Steve Buechele	.15	.40
180 Joey Belle	.60	1.50
181 Eddie Murray	.60	1.50
182 Bob Geren	.15	.40
183 Rob Murphy	.15	.40
184 Tom Herr	.15	.40
185 George Bell	.15	.40
186 Spike Owen	.15	.40
187 Cory Snyder	.15	.40
188 Fred Lynn	.15	.40
189 Eric Davis	.25	.60
190 Dave Parker	.25	.60
191 Jeff Blauser	.15	.40
192 Matt Nokes	.15	.40
193 Delino DeShields RC	.40	1.00
194 Scott Sanderson	.15	.40
195 Lance Parrish	.15	.40
196 Bobby Bonilla	.25	.60
197 Cal Ripken UER (Reisterstown, should be Reisterstown)	2.00	5.00
198 Kevin McReynolds	.15	.40
199 Robby Thompson	.15	.40
200 Tim Belcher	.15	.40
201 Jesse Barfield	.15	.40
202 Mariano Duncan	.15	.40
203 Bill Spiers	.15	.40
204 Frank White	.25	.60
205 Julio Franco	.25	.60
206 Greg Swindell	.15	.40
207 Benito Santiago	.25	.60
208 Johnny Ray	.15	.40
209 Gary Redus	.15	.40
210 Jeff Parrett	.15	.40
211 Jimmy Key	.25	.60
212 Tim Raines	.25	.60
213 Carney Lansford	.25	.60
214 Gerald Young	.15	.40
215 Gene Larkin	.15	.40
216 Dan Plesac	.15	.40
217 Lonnie Smith	.15	.40
218 Alan Trammell	.25	.60
219 Jeffrey Leonard	.15	.40
220 Sammy Sosa RC	5.00	12.00
221 Todd Zeile	.25	.60
222 Bill Landrum	.15	.40
223 Mike Devereaux	.15	.40
224 Mike Marshall	.15	.40
225 Jose Uribe	.15	.40
226 Juan Samuel	.15	.40
227 Mel Hall	.15	.40
228 Kent Hrbek	.25	.60
229 Shawon Dunston	.15	.40
230 Kevin Seitzer	.15	.40
231 Pete Incaviglia	.15	.40
232 Sandy Alomar Jr.	.25	.60
233 Bip Roberts	.15	.40
234 Scott Terry	.15	.40
235 Dwight Evans	.40	1.00
236 Ricky Jordan	.15	.40
237 John Olerud RC	1.25	3.00
238 Zane Smith	.15	.40
239 Walt Weiss	.15	.40
240 Alvaro Espinoza	.15	.40
241 Billy Hatcher	.15	.40
242 Paul Molitor	.25	.60
243 Dale Murphy	.40	1.00
244 Dave Bergman	.15	.40
245 Ken Griffey Jr.	2.00	5.00
246 Ed Whitson	.15	.40
247 Kirk McCaskill	.15	.40
248 Jay Bell	.25	.60
249 Ben McDonald RC	.40	1.00
250 Darryl Strawberry	.25	.60
251 Brett Butler	.25	.60
252 Terry Steinbach	.15	.40
253 Ken Caminiti	.25	.60
254 Dan Gladden	.15	.40
255 Dwight Smith	.15	.40
256 Kurt Stillwell	.15	.40
257 Ruben Sierra	.25	.60
258 Mike Schooler	.15	.40
259 Lance Johnson	.15	.40
260 Terry Pendleton	.25	.60
261 Ellis Burks	.40	1.00
262 Len Dykstra	.25	.60
263 Mookie Wilson	.25	.60
264 Nolan Ryan CL UER No TM after Ranger logo	.60	1.50
265 Nolan Ryan No Hit King	1.00	2.50
266 Brian DuBois RC	.15	.40
267 Don Robinson	.15	.40
268 Glenn Wilson	.15	.40
269 Kevin Tapani RC	.40	1.00
270 Marvell Wynne	.15	.40
271 Bill Ripken	.15	.40
272 Howard Johnson	.15	.40
273 Brian Holman	.15	.40
274 Dan Pasqua	.15	.40
275 Ken Dayley	.15	.40
276 Jeff Reardon	.25	.60
277 Jim Presley	.15	.40
278 Jim Eisenreich	.15	.40
279 Danny Jackson	.15	.40
280 Orel Hershiser	.25	.60
281 Andy Hawkins	.15	.40
282 Jose Rijo	.15	.40
283 Luis Rivera	.15	.40
284 John Kruk	.25	.60
285 Jeff Huson RC	.15	.40
286 Joel Skinner	.15	.40
287 Jack Clark	.25	.60
288 Chili Davis	.25	.60
289 Joe Girardi	.40	1.00
290 B.J. Surhoff	.25	.60
291 Luis Sojo RC	.15	.40
292 Tom Foley	.15	.40
293 Mike Moore	.15	.40
294 Ken Oberkfell	.15	.40
295 Luis Polonia	.15	.40
296 Doug Drabek	.15	.40
297 Dave Justice RC	1.25	3.00
298 Paul Gibson	.15	.40
299 Edgar Martinez	.40	1.00
300 F.Thomas UER RC No B in front of birthdate	5.00	12.00
301 Eric Yelding RC	.15	.40
302 Greg Gagne	.15	.40
303 Brad Komminsk	.15	.40
304 Ron Darling	.15	.40
305 Kevin Bass	.15	.40
306 Jeff Hamilton	.15	.40
307 Ron Karkovice	.15	.40
308 Milt Thompson UER (Ray Lankford pictured on card back)	.40	1.00
309 Mike Harkey	.15	.40
310 Mel Stottlemyre Jr.	.15	.40
311 Kenny Rogers	.25	.60
312 Mitch Webster	.15	.40
313 Kal Daniels	.15	.40
314 Matt Nokes	.15	.40
315 Dennis Lamp	.15	.40
316 Ken Howell	.15	.40
317 Glenallen Hill	.15	.40
318 Dave Martinez	.15	.40
319 Chris James	.15	.40
320 Mike Pagliarulo	.15	.40
321 Hal Morris	.15	.40
322 Rob Deer	.15	.40
323 Greg Olson (C) RC	.15	.40
324 Tony Phillips	.15	.40
325 Larry Walker RC	3.00	8.00
326 Ron Hassey	.15	.40
327 Jack Howell	.15	.40
328 John Smiley	.15	.40
329 Steve Finley	.25	.60
330 Dave Magadan	.15	.40
331 Greg Litton	.15	.40
332 Mickey Hatcher	.15	.40
333 Lee Guetterman	.15	.40
334 Norm Charlton	.15	.40
335 Edgar Diaz RC	.15	.40
336 Willie Wilson	.15	.40
337 Bobby Witt	.15	.40
338 Candy Maldonado	.15	.40
339 Craig Lefferts	.15	.40
340 Dante Bichette	.25	.60
341 Wally Backman	.15	.40
342 Dennis Cook	.15	.40
343 Pat Borders	.15	.40
344 Wallace Johnson	.15	.40
345 Willie Randolph	.25	.60
346 Danny Darwin	.15	.40
347 Al Newman	.15	.40
348 Mark Knudson	.15	.40
349 Joe Boever	.15	.40
350 Larry Sheets	.15	.40
351 Mike Jackson	.15	.40
352 Wayne Edwards RC	.15	.40
353 Bernard Gilkey RC	.40	1.00
354 Don Slaught	.15	.40
355 Joe Orsulak	.15	.40
356 John Franco	.25	.60
357 Jeff Brantley	.15	.40
358 Mike Morgan	.15	.40
359 Deion Sanders	.60	1.50
360 Terry Leach	.15	.40
361 Les Lancaster	.15	.40
362 Storm Davis	.15	.40
363 Scott Coolbaugh RC	.15	.40
364 Ozzie Smith CL	.40	1.00
365 Cecilio Guante	.15	.40
366 Joey Cora	.25	.60
367 Willie McGee	.25	.60
368 Jerry Reed	.15	.40
369 Darren Daulton	.25	.60
370 Manny Lee	.15	.40
371 Mark Gardner RC	.15	.40
372 Rick Honeycutt	.15	.40
373 Steve Balboni	.15	.40
374 Jack Armstrong	.15	.40
375 Charlie O'Brien	.15	.40
376 Ron Gant	.25	.60
377 Lloyd Moseby	.15	.40
378 Gene Harris	.15	.40
379 Joe Carter	.25	.60
380 Scott Bailes	.15	.40
381 R.J. Reynolds	.15	.40
382 Bob Melvin	.15	.40
383 Tim Teufel	.15	.40
384 John Burkett	.15	.40
385 Felix Jose	.15	.40
386 Larry Andersen	.15	.40
387 David West	.15	.40
388 Luis Salazar	.15	.40
389 Mike Macfarlane	.15	.40
390 Charlie Hough	.25	.60
391 Greg Briley	.15	.40
392 Donn Pall	.15	.40
393 Bryn Smith	.15	.40
394 Carlos Quintana	.15	.40
395 Steve Lake	.15	.40
396 Mark Whiten RC	.40	1.00
397 Edwin Nunez	.15	.40
398 Rick Parker RC	.15	.40
399 Mark Portugal	.15	.40
400 Roy Smith	.15	.40
401 Hector Villanueva RC	.15	.40
402 Bob Milacki	.15	.40
403 Alejandro Pena	.15	.40
404 Scott Bradley	.15	.40
405 Ron Kittle	.15	.40
406 Bob Tewksbury	.15	.40
407 Wes Gardner	.15	.40

408 Ernie Whitt .15 .40
409 Terry Shumpert RC .15 .40
410 Tim Layana RC .15 .40
411 Chris Gwynn .15 .40
412 Jeff D. Robinson .15 .40
413 Scott Scudder .15 .40
414 Kevin Romine .15 .40
415 Jose DeJesus .15 .40
416 Mike Jeffcoat .15 .40
417 Rudy Seanez RC .15 .40
418 Mike Dunne .15 .40
419 Dick Schofield .15 .40
420 Steve Wilson .15 .40
421 Bill Krueger .15 .40
422 Junior Felix .15 .40
423 Drew Hall .15 .40
424 Curt Young .15 .40
425 Franklin Stubbs .15 .40
426 Dave Winfield .25 .60
427 Rick Reed RC .40 1.00
428 Charlie Leibrandt .15 .40
429 Jeff M. Robinson .15 .40
430 Erik Hanson .15 .40
431 Barry Jones .15 .40
432 Alex Trevino .15 .40
433 John Moses .15 .40
434 Dave Wayne Johnson RC .15 .40
435 Mackey Sasser .15 .40
436 Rick Leach .15 .40
437 Lenny Harris .15 .40
438 Carlos Martinez .15 .40
439 Rex Hudler .15 .40
440 Domingo Ramos .15 .40
441 Gerald Perry .15 .40
442 Jeff Russell .15 .40
443 Carlos Baerga RC .40 1.00
444 Will Clark CL .25 .60
445 Stan Javier .15 .40
446 Kevin Maas RC .40 1.00
447 Tom Brunansky .15 .40
448 Carmelo Martinez .15 .40
449 Willie Blair RC .15 .40
450 Andres Galarraga .25 .60
451 Bud Black .15 .40
452 Greg W. Harris .15 .40
453 Joe Oliver .15 .40
454 Greg Brock .15 .40
455 Jeff Treadway .15 .40
456 Lance McCullers .15 .40
457 Dave Schmidt .15 .40
458 Todd Burns .15 .40
459 Max Venable .15 .40
460 Neal Heaton .15 .40
461 Mark Williamson .15 .40
462 Keith Miller .15 .40
463 Mike LaCoss .15 .40
464 Jose Offerman RC .40 1.00
465 Jim Leyritz RC .75 2.00
466 Glenn Braggs .15 .40
467 Ron Robinson .15 .40
468 Mark Davis .15 .40
469 Gary Pettis .15 .40
470 Keith Hernandez .25 .60
471 Dennis Rasmussen .15 .40
472 Mark Eichhorn .15 .40
473 Ted Power .15 .40
474 Terry Mulholland .15 .40
475 Todd Stottlemyre .25 .60
476 Jerry Goff RC .15 .40
477 Gene Nelson .15 .40
478 Rich Gedman .15 .40
479 Brian Harper .15 .40
480 Mike Felder .15 .40
481 Steve Avery .15 .40
482 Jack Morris .25 .60
483 Randy Johnson 1.25 3.00
484 Scott Radinsky RC .15 .40
485 Jose DeLeon .15 .40
486 Stan Belinda RC .15 .40
487 Brian Holton .15 .40
488 Mark Carreon .15 .40
489 Trevor Wilson .15 .40
490 Mike Sharperson .15 .40
491 Alan Mills RC .15 .40
492 John Candelaria .15 .40
493 Paul Assenmacher .15 .40
494 Steve Crawford .15 .40
495 Brad Arnsberg .15 .40
496 Sergio Valdez RC .15 .40
497 Mark Parent .15 .40
498 Tom Pagnozzi .15 .40
499 Greg A. Harris .15 .40
500 Randy Ready .15 .40
501 Duane Ward .15 .40
502 Nelson Santovenia .15 .40
503 Joe Klink RC .15 .40
504 Eric Plunk .15 .40
505 Jeff Reed .15 .40
506 Ted Higuera .15 .40
507 Joe Hesketh .15 .40
508 Dan Petry .15 .40
509 Matt Young .15 .40
510 Jerald Clark .15 .40
511 John Orton RC .15 .40
512 Scott Ruskin RC .15 .40
513 Chris Hoiles RC .40 1.00
514 Daryl Boston .15 .40
515 Francisco Oliveras .15 .40
516 Ozzie Canseco .15 .40
517 Xavier Hernandez RC .15 .40
518 Fred Manrique .15 .40
519 Shawn Boskie RC .15 .40
520 Jeff Montgomery .25 .60
521 Jack Daugherty RC .15 .40
522 Keith Comstock .15 .40
523 Greg Hibbard RC .15 .40
524 Lee Smith .25 .60
525 Dana Kiecker RC .15 .40
526 Darrel Akerfelds .15 .40
527 Greg Myers .15 .40
528 Ryne Sandberg CL .60 1.50

1991 Leaf

This 528-card standard size set was issued by Donruss in two separate series of 264 cards. Cards were exclusively issued in foil packs. The front design has color action player photos, with white and silver borders. A thicker stock was used for these (then) premium level cards. Production for the 1991 set was greatly increased due to the huge

demand for the benchmark 1990 Leaf set. However, the 1991 cards were met with modest enthusiasm due to a weak selection of Rookie Cards and superior competition from brands like 1991 Stadium Club.

COMPLETE SET (528) 6.00 15.00
COMP. SERIES 1 (264) 2.00 5.00
COMP. SERIES 2 (264) 4.00 10.00
COMP. KILLEBREW PUZZLE .50 1.00
1 The Leaf Card .02 .10
2 Kurt Stillwell .02 .10
3 Bobby Witt .02 .10
4 Tony Phillips .02 .10
5 Scott Garrelts .02 .10
6 Greg Swindell .02 .10
7 Billy Ripken .02 .10
8 Dave Martinez .02 .10
9 Kelly Gruber .02 .10
10 Juan Samuel .02 .10
11 Brian Holman .02 .10
12 Craig Biggio .10 .30
13 Lonnie Smith .02 .10
14 Ron Robinson .02 .10
15 Mike LaValliere .02 .10
16 Mark Davis .02 .10
17 Jack Daugherty .02 .10
18 Mike Henneman .02 .10
19 Mike Greenwell .02 .10
20 Dave Magadan .02 .10
21 Mark Williamson .02 .10
22 Marquis Grissom .07 .20
23 Pat Borders .02 .10
24 Mike Scioscia .02 .10
25 Shawon Dunston .02 .10
26 Randy Bush .02 .10
27 John Smoltz .10 .30
28 Chuck Crim .02 .10
29 Don Slaught .02 .10
30 Mike Macfarlane .02 .10
31 Wally Joyner .07 .20
32 Pat Combs .02 .10
33 Tony Pena .02 .10
34 Howard Johnson .02 .10
35 Leo Gomez .02 .10
36 Spike Owen .02 .10
37 Eric Davis .07 .20
38 Roberto Kelly .02 .10
39 Jerome Walton .02 .10
40 Shane Mack .02 .10
41 Kent Mercker .02 .10
42 B.J. Surhoff .07 .20
43 Jerry Browne .02 .10
44 Lee Smith .07 .20
45 Chuck Finley .07 .20
46 Terry Mulholland .02 .10
47 Tom Bolton .02 .10
48 Tom Herr .02 .10
49 Jim Deshaies .02 .10
50 Walt Weiss .02 .10
51 Hal Morris .02 .10
52 Lee Guetterman .02 .10
53 Paul Assenmacher .02 .10
54 Brian Harper .02 .10
55 Paul Gibson .02 .10
56 John Burkett .02 .10
57 Doug Jones .02 .10
58 Jose Oquendo .02 .10
59 Dick Schofield .02 .10
60 Dickie Thon .02 .10
61 Ramon Martinez .02 .10
62 Jay Buhner .07 .20
63 Mark Portugal .02 .10
64 Bob Welch .02 .10
65 Chris Sabo .02 .10
66 Chuck Cary .02 .10
67 Mark Langston .02 .10
68 Joe Boever .02 .10
69 Jody Reed .02 .10
70 Alejandro Pena .02 .10
71 Jeff King .02 .10
72 Tom Pagnozzi .02 .10
73 Joe Oliver .02 .10
74 Mike Witt .02 .10
75 Hector Villanueva .02 .10
76 Dan Gladden .02 .10
77 Dave Justice .07 .20
78 Mike Gallego .02 .10
79 Tom Candiotti .02 .10
80 Ozzie Smith .30 .75
81 Luis Polonia .02 .10
82 Randy Ready .02 .10
83 Greg A. Harris .02 .10
84 David Justice CL .02 .10
85 Kevin Mitchell .02 .10
86 Mark McLemore .02 .10
87 Terry Steinbach .02 .10
88 Tom Browning .02 .10
89 Matt Nokes .02 .10
90 Mike Harkey .02 .10
91 Omar Vizquel .10 .30
92 Dave Bergman .02 .10
93 Matt Williams .07 .20
94 Steve Olin .02 .10
95 Craig Wilson RC .02 .10
96 Dave Stieb .02 .10
97 Ruben Sierra .07 .20
98 Jay Howell .02 .10
99 Scott Bradley .02 .10
100 Eric Yelding .02 .10
101 Rickey Henderson .20 .50
102 Jeff Reed .02 .10
103 Jimmy Key .07 .20
104 Terry Shumpert .02 .10
105 Kenny Rogers .07 .20
106 Cecil Fielder .07 .20
107 Robby Thompson .02 .10
108 Alex Cole .02 .10
109 Randy Milligan .02 .10
110 Andres Galarraga .07 .20
111 Bill Spiers .02 .10
112 Kal Daniels .02 .10
113 Henry Cotto .02 .10
114 Casey Candaele .02 .10
115 Jeff Blauser .02 .10
116 Robin Yount .30 .75
117 Ben McDonald .02 .10
118 Bret Saberhagen .07 .20
119 Juan Gonzalez .20 .50
120 Lou Whitaker .07 .20
121 Ellis Burks .07 .20
122 Charlie O'Brien .02 .10
123 John Smiley .02 .10
124 Tim Burke .02 .10
125 John Olerud .07 .20
126 Eddie Murray .20 .50
127 Greg Maddux .30 .75
128 Kevin Tapani .02 .10
129 Ron Gant .07 .20
130 Jay Bell .07 .20
131 Chris Hoiles .02 .10
132 Tom Gordon .02 .10
133 Kevin Seitzer .02 .10
134 Jeff Huson .02 .10
135 Jerry Don Gleaton .02 .10
136 Jeff Brantley UER .02 .10
(Photo actually Rick Leach on back)
137 Felix Fermin .02 .10
138 Mike Devereaux .02 .10
139 Delino DeShields .07 .20
140 David Wells .07 .20
141 Tim Crews .02 .10
142 Erik Hanson .02 .10
143 Mark Davidson .02 .10
144 Tommy Gregg .02 .10
145 Jim Gantner .02 .10
146 Jose Lind .02 .10
147 Danny Tartabull .02 .10
148 Geno Petralli .02 .10
149 Travis Fryman .07 .20
150 Tim Naehring .02 .10
151 Kevin McReynolds .02 .10
152 Joe Orsulak .02 .10
153 Steve Frey .02 .10
154 Duane Ward .02 .10
155 Stan Javier .02 .10
156 Damon Berryhill .02 .10
157 Gene Larkin .02 .10
158 Greg Olson .02 .10
159 Mark Knudson .02 .10
160 Carmelo Martinez .02 .10
161 Storm Davis .02 .10
162 Jim Abbott .10 .30
163 Len Dykstra .07 .20
164 Tom Brunansky .02 .10
165 Dwight Gooden .07 .20
166 Jose Mesa .02 .10
167 Oil Can Boyd .02 .10
168 Barry Larkin .10 .30
169 Scott Sanderson .02 .10
170 Mark Grace .10 .30
171 Mark Guthrie .02 .10
172 Tom Glavine .10 .30
173 Gary Sheffield .07 .20
174 Roger Clemens CL .30 .75
175 Chris James .02 .10
176 Milt Thompson .02 .10
177 Donnie Hill .02 .10
178 Wes Chamberlain RC .02 .10
179 John Marzano .02 .10
180 Frank Viola .07 .20
181 Eric Anthony .02 .10
182 Jose Canseco .10 .30
183 Scott Scudder .02 .10
184 Dave Eiland .02 .10
185 Luis Salazar .02 .10
186 Pedro Munoz RC .02 .10
187 Steve Searcy .02 .10
188 Don Robinson .02 .10
189 Sandy Alomar Jr. .02 .10
190 Jose DeLeon .02 .10
191 John Orton .02 .10
192 Darren Daulton .07 .20
193 Mike Morgan .02 .10
194 Greg Briley .02 .10
195 Karl Rhodes .02 .10
196 Harold Baines .07 .20
197 Bill Doran .02 .10
198 Alvaro Espinoza .02 .10
199 Kirk McCaskill .02 .10
200 Jose DeJesus .02 .10
201 Jack Clark .07 .20
202 Daryl Boston .02 .10
203 Randy Tomlin RC .02 .10
204 Pedro Guerrero .07 .20
205 Billy Hatcher .02 .10
206 Tim Leary .02 .10
207 Ryne Sandberg .30 .75
208 Kirby Puckett .20 .50
209 Charlie Leibrandt .02 .10
210 Rick Honeycutt .02 .10
211 Joel Skinner .02 .10
212 Rex Hudler .02 .10
213 Bryan Harvey .02 .10
214 Charlie Hayes .02 .10
215 Matt Young .02 .10
216 Terry Kennedy .02 .10
217 Carl Nichols .02 .10
218 Mike Moore .02 .10
219 Paul O'Neill .10 .30
220 Steve Sax .02 .10
221 Shawn Boskie .02 .10
222 Rich DeLucia RC .02 .10
223 Lloyd Moseby .02 .10
224 Mike Kingery .02 .10
225 Carlos Baerga .02 .10
226 Bryn Smith .02 .10
227 Todd Stottlemyre .02 .10
228 Julio Franco .07 .20
229 Jim Gott .02 .10
230 Mike Schooler .02 .10
231 Steve Finley .07 .20
232 Dave Henderson .02 .10
233 Luis Quinones .02 .10
234 Mark Whiten .02 .10
235 Brian McRae RC .07 .20
236 Rich Gossage .07 .20
237 Rob Deer .02 .10
238 Will Clark .10 .30
239 Albert Belle .07 .20
240 Bob Melvin .02 .10
241 Larry Walker .20 .50
242 Dante Bichette .07 .20
243 Orel Hershiser .07 .20
244 Pete O'Brien .02 .10
245 Pete Harnisch .02 .10
246 Jeff Treadway .02 .10
247 Julio Machado .02 .10
248 Dave Johnson .02 .10
249 Kirk Gibson .07 .20
250 Kevin Brown .07 .20
251 Milt Cuyler .02 .10
252 Jeff Reardon .07 .20
253 David Cone .07 .20
254 Gary Redus .02 .10
255 Junior Noboa .02 .10
256 Greg Myers .02 .10
257 Dennis Cook .02 .10
258 Joe Girardi .02 .10
259 Allan Anderson .02 .10
260 Paul Marak RC .02 .10
261 Barry Bonds .60 1.50
262 Juan Bell .02 .10
263 Russ Morman .02 .10
264 George Brett CL .20 .50
265 Jerald Clark .02 .10
266 Dwight Evans .10 .30
267 Roberto Alomar .10 .30
268 Danny Jackson .02 .10
269 Brian Downing .02 .10
270 John Cerutti .02 .10
271 Robin Ventura .07 .20
272 Gerald Perry .02 .10
273 Wade Boggs .10 .30
274 Dennis Martinez .07 .20
275 Andy Benes .02 .10
276 Tony Fossas .02 .10
277 Franklin Stubbs .02 .10
278 John Kruk .07 .20
279 Kevin Gross .02 .10
280 Von Hayes .02 .10
281 Frank Thomas .20 .50
282 Rob Dibble .07 .20
283 Mel Hall .02 .10
284 Rick Mahler .02 .10
285 Dennis Eckersley .07 .20
286 Bernard Gilkey .02 .10
287 Dan Plesac .02 .10
288 Jason Grimsley .02 .10
289 Mark Lewis .02 .10
290 Tony Gwynn .25 .60
291 Jeff Russell .02 .10
292 Curt Schilling .20 .50
293 Pascual Perez .02 .10
294 Jack Morris .07 .20
295 Hubie Brooks .02 .10
296 Alex Fernandez .02 .10
297 Harold Reynolds .07 .20
298 Craig Worthington .02 .10
299 Willie Wilson .02 .10
300 Mike Maddux .02 .10
301 Dave Righetti .07 .20
302 Paul Molitor .07 .20
303 Gary Gaetti .07 .20
304 Terry Pendleton .07 .20
305 Kevin Elster .02 .10
306 Scott Fletcher .02 .10
307 Jeff Robinson .02 .10
308 Jesse Barfield .02 .10
309 Mike LaCoss .02 .10
310 Andy Van Slyke .10 .30
311 Glenallen Hill .02 .10
312 Bud Black .02 .10
313 Kent Hrbek .07 .20
314 Tim Teufel .02 .10
315 Tony Fernandez .02 .10
316 Beau Allred .02 .10
317 Curtis Wilkerson .02 .10
318 Bill Sampen .02 .10
319 Randy Johnson .25 .60
320 Mike Heath .02 .10
321 Sammy Sosa .20 .50
322 Mickey Tettleton .02 .10
323 Jose Vizcaino .02 .10
324 John Candelaria .02 .10
325 Dave Howard RC .02 .10
326 Jose Rijo .02 .10
327 Todd Zeile .02 .10
328 Gene Nelson .02 .10
329 Dwayne Henry .02 .10
330 Mike Boddicker .02 .10
331 Ozzie Guillen .07 .20
332 Sam Horn .02 .10
333 Wally Whitehurst .02 .10
334 Dave Parker .07 .20
335 George Brett .50 1.25
336 Bobby Thigpen .02 .10
337 Ed Whitson .02 .10
338 Ivan Calderon .02 .10
339 Mike Pagliarulo .02 .10
340 Jack McDowell .02 .10
341 Dana Kiecker .02 .10
342 Fred McGriff .10 .30
343 Mark Lee RC .02 .10
344 Alfredo Griffin .02 .10
345 Scott Bankhead .02 .10
346 Darrin Jackson .02 .10
347 Rafael Palmeiro .10 .30
348 Steve Farr .02 .10
349 Hensley Meulens .02 .10
350 Danny Cox .02 .10
351 Alan Trammell .07 .20
352 Edwin Nunez .02 .10
353 Joe Carter .07 .20
354 Eric Show .02 .10
355 Vance Law .02 .10
356 Jeff Gray RC .02 .10
357 Bobby Bonilla .07 .20
358 Ernest Riles .02 .10
359 Ron Hassey .02 .10
360 Willie McGee .07 .20
361 Mackey Sasser .02 .10
362 Glenn Braggs .02 .10
363 Mario Diaz .02 .10
364 Barry Bonds CL .40 1.00
365 Kevin Bass .02 .10
366 Pete Incaviglia .02 .10
367 Luis Sojo UER .02 .10
(1989 stats interspersed with 1990's)
368 Lance Parrish .07 .20
369 Mark Leonard RC .02 .10
370 Heath. Slocumb RC .07 .20
371 Jimmy Jones .02 .10
372 Ken Griffey Jr. .40 1.00
373 Chris Hammond .02 .10
374 Chili Davis .07 .20
375 Joey Cora .02 .10
376 Ken Hill .02 .10
377 Darryl Strawberry .07 .20
378 Ron Darling .02 .10
379 Sid Bream .02 .10
380 Bill Swift .02 .10
381 Shawn Abner .02 .10
382 Eric King .02 .10
383 Mickey Morandini .02 .10
384 Carlton Fisk .10 .30
385 Steve Lake .02 .10
386 Mike Jeffcoat .02 .10
387 Darren Holmes RC .07 .20
388 Tim Wallach .02 .10
389 George Bell .02 .10
390 Craig Lefferts .02 .10
391 Ernie Whitt .02 .10
392 Felix Jose .02 .10
393 Kevin Maas .02 .10
394 Devon White .07 .20
395 Otis Nixon .02 .10
396 Chuck Knoblauch .07 .20
397 Scott Coolbaugh .02 .10
398 Glenn Davis .02 .10
399 Manny Lee .02 .10
400 Andre Dawson .07 .20
401 Scott Chiamparino .02 .10
402 Bill Gullickson .02 .10
403 Lance Johnson .02 .10
404 Juan Agosto .02 .10
405 Danny Darwin .02 .10
406 Barry Jones .02 .10
407 Larry Andersen .02 .10
408 Luis Rivera .02 .10
409 Jaime Navarro .02 .10
410 Roger McDowell .02 .10
411 Brett Butler .07 .20
412 Dale Murphy .10 .30
413 Tim Raines UER .07 .20
(Listed as hitting .500 in 1980, should be .050)
414 Norm Charlton .02 .10
415 Greg Cadaret .02 .10
416 Chris Nabholz .02 .10
417 Dave Stewart .07 .20
418 Rich Gedman .02 .10
419 Willie Randolph .07 .20
420 Mitch Williams .02 .10
421 Brook Jacoby .02 .10
422 Greg W. Harris .02 .10
423 Nolan Ryan .75 2.00
424 Dave Rohde .02 .10
425 Don Mattingly .50 1.25
426 Greg Gagne .02 .10
427 Vince Coleman .02 .10
428 Dan Pasqua .02 .10
429 Alvin Davis .02 .10
430 Cal Ripken .60 1.50
431 Jamie Quirk .02 .10
432 Benito Santiago .07 .20
433 Jose Uribe .02 .10
434 Candy Maldonado .02 .10
435 Junior Felix .02 .10
436 Deion Sanders .10 .30
437 John Franco .07 .20
438 Greg Hibbard .02 .10
439 Floyd Bannister .02 .10
440 Steve Howe .02 .10
441 Steve Decker RC .02 .10
442 Vicente Palacios .02 .10
443 Pat Tabler .02 .10
444 Darryl Strawberry CL .02 .10
445 Mike Felder .02 .10
446 Al Newman .02 .10
447 Chris Donnels RC .02 .10
448 Rich Rodriguez RC .02 .10
449 Turner Ward RC .07 .20
450 Bob Walk .02 .10
451 Gilberto Reyes .02 .10
452 Mike Jackson .02 .10
453 Rafael Belliard .02 .10
454 Wayne Edwards .02 .10
455 Andy Allanson .02 .10
456 Dave Smith .02 .10
457 Gary Carter .07 .20
458 Warren Cromartie .02 .10
459 Jack Armstrong .02 .10
460 Bob Tewksbury .02 .10
461 Joe Klink .02 .10
462 Xavier Hernandez .02 .10
463 Scott Radinsky .02 .10
464 Jeff Robinson .02 .10
465 Gregg Jefferies .02 .10
466 Denny Neagle RC .20 .50
467 Carmelo Martinez .02 .10
468 Donn Pall .02 .10
469 Bruce Hurst .02 .10
470 Eric Bullock .02 .10
471 Rick Aguilera .07 .20
472 Charlie Hough .07 .20
473 Carlos Quintana .02 .10
474 Marty Barrett .02 .10
475 Kevin D. Brown .02 .10
476 Bobby Ojeda .02 .10
477 Edgar Martinez .10 .30
478 Bip Roberts .02 .10
479 Mike Flanagan .02 .10
480 John Habyan .02 .10
481 Larry Casian RC .02 .10
482 Wally Backman .02 .10
483 Doug Dascenzo .02 .10
484 Rick Dempsey .02 .10
485 Ed Sprague .02 .10
486 Steve Chitren RC .02 .10
487 Mark McGwire .60 1.50
488 Roger Clemens .60 1.50
489 Orlando Merced RC .02 .10
490 Rene Gonzales .02 .10
491 Mike Stanton .02 .10
492 Al Osuna RC .02 .10
493 Rick Cerone .02 .10
494 Mariano Duncan .02 .10
495 Zane Smith .02 .10
496 John Morris .02 .10
497 Frank Tanana .02 .10
498 Junior Ortiz .02 .10
499 Dave Winfield .07 .20
500 Gary Varsho .02 .10
501 Chico Walker .02 .10
502 Ken Caminiti .07 .20
503 Ken Griffey Sr. .07 .20
504 Randy Myers .02 .10
505 Steve Bedrosian .02 .10
506 Cory Snyder .02 .10
507 Cris Carpenter .02 .10
508 Tim Belcher .02 .10
509 Jeff Hamilton .02 .10
510 Steve Avery .02 .10
511 Dave Valle .02 .10
512 Tom Lampkin .02 .10
513 Shawn Hillegas .02 .10
514 Reggie Jefferson .02 .10
515 Ron Karkovice .02 .10
516 Doug Drabek .02 .10
517 Tom Henke .02 .10
518 Chris Bosio .02 .10
519 Gregg Olson .02 .10
520 Bob Scanlan RC .02 .10
521 Alonzo Powell RC .02 .10
522 Jeff Ballard .02 .10
523 Ray Lankford .07 .20
524 Tommy Greene .02 .10
525 Mike Timlin RC .07 .20
526 Juan Berenguer .02 .10
527 Scott Erickson .02 .10
528 Sandy Alomar Jr. CL .02 .10

1992 Leaf

The 1992 Leaf set consists of 528 cards, issued in two separate 264-card series. Cards were distributed in first and second series 15-card foil packs. Each pack contained a selection of basic cards and one black gold parallel card. The basic card fronts feature color action player photos on a silver card face. The player's name appears in a black bar edged at the bottom by a thin red stripe. The team logo overlaps the bar at the right corner. Rookie Cards in this set include Brian Jordan and Jeff Kent.

COMPLETE SET (528) 6.00 15.00
COMP. SERIES 1 (264) 2.00 5.00
COMP. SERIES 2 (264) 4.00 10.00
1 Jim Abbott .08 .25
2 Cal Eldred .01 .05
3 Bud Black .01 .05
4 Dave Howard .01 .05
5 Luis Sojo .01 .05
6 Gary Scott .01 .05
7 Joe Oliver .01 .05
8 Chris Gardner .01 .05
9 Sandy Alomar Jr. .01 .05
10 Greg W. Harris .01 .05
11 Doug Drabek .01 .05
12 Darryl Hamilton .01 .05
13 Mike Mussina .15 .40
14 Kevin Tapani .01 .05
15 Ron Gant .05 .15
16 Mark McGwire .40 1.00
17 Robin Ventura .05 .15
18 Pedro Guerrero .05 .15
19 Roger Clemens .30 .75
20 Steve Farr .01 .05
21 Frank Tanana .01 .05
22 Joe Hesketh .01 .05
23 Erik Hanson .01 .05
24 Greg Cadaret .01 .05
25 Rex Hudler .01 .05
26 Mark Grace .08 .25
27 Kelly Gruber .01 .05
28 Jeff Bagwell .15 .40
29 Darryl Strawberry .05 .15
30 Dave Smith .01 .05
31 Kevin Appier .05 .15
32 Steve Chitren .01 .05
33 Kevin Gross .01 .05
34 Rick Aguilera .05 .15
35 Juan Guzman .01 .05
36 Joe Orsulak .01 .05
37 Tim Raines .05 .15
38 Harold Reynolds .05 .15
39 Charlie Hough .05 .15
40 Tony Phillips .01 .05
41 Nolan Ryan .60 1.50
42 Vince Coleman .01 .05
43 Andy Van Slyke .08 .25
44 Tim Burke .01 .05
45 Luis Polonia .01 .05
46 Tom Browning .01 .05
47 Willie McGee .05 .15
48 Gary DiSarcina .01 .05
49 Mark Lewis .01 .05
50 Phil Plantier .01 .05
51 Doug Dascenzo .01 .05
52 Cal Ripken .50 1.25
53 Pedro Munoz .01 .05
54 Carlos Hernandez .01 .05
55 Jerald Clark .01 .05
56 Jeff Brantley .01 .05
57 Don Mattingly .40 1.00
58 Roger McDowell .01 .05
59 Steve Avery .01 .05
60 John Olerud .05 .15
61 Bill Gullickson .01 .05
62 Juan Gonzalez .08 .25
63 Felix Jose .01 .05
64 Robin Yount .25 .60
65 Greg Briley .01 .05
66 Steve Finley .05 .15
67 Frank Thomas CL .08 .25
68 Tom Gordon .01 .05
69 Rob Dibble .05 .15

70 Glenallen Hill .01 .05
71 Calvin Jones .01 .05
72 Joe Girardi .01 .05
73 Barry Larkin .08 .25
74 Andy Benes .01 .05
75 Milt Cuyler .01 .05
76 Kevin Bass .01 .05
77 Pete Harnisch .01 .05
78 Wilson Alvarez .01 .05
79 Mike Devereaux .01 .05
80 Doug Henry RC .02 .10
81 Orel Hershiser .05 .15
82 Shane Mack .01 .05
83 Mike Macfarlane .01 .05
84 Thomas Howard .01 .05
85 Alex Fernandez .01 .05
86 Reggie Jefferson .01 .05
87 Leo Gomez .01 .05
88 Mel Hall .01 .05
89 Mike Greenwell .01 .05
90 Jeff Russell .01 .05
91 Steve Buechele .01 .05
92 David Cone .05 .15
93 Kevin Reimer .01 .05
94 Mark Lemke .01 .05
95 Bob Tewksbury .01 .05
96 Zane Smith .01 .05
97 Mark Eichhorn .01 .05
98 Kirby Puckett .15 .40
99 Paul O'Neill .08 .25
100 Dennis Eckersley .05 .15
101 Duane Ward .01 .05
102 Matt Nokes .01 .05
103 Mo Vaughn .05 .15
104 Pat Kelly .01 .05
105 Ron Karkovice .01 .05
106 Bill Spiers .01 .05
107 Gary Gaetti .05 .15
108 Mackey Sasser .01 .05
109 Robby Thompson .01 .05
110 Marvin Freeman .01 .05
111 Jimmy Key .05 .15
112 Dwight Gooden .05 .15
113 Charlie Leibrandt .01 .05
114 Devon White .05 .15
115 Charles Nagy .01 .05
116 Rickey Henderson .15 .40
117 Paul Assenmacher .01 .05
118 Junior Felix .01 .05
119 Julio Franco .05 .15
120 Norm Charlton .01 .05
121 Scott Servais .01 .05
122 Gerald Perry .01 .05
123 Brian McRae .01 .05
124 Don Slaught .01 .05
125 Juan Samuel .01 .05
126 Harold Baines .05 .15
127 Scott Livingstone .01 .05
128 Jay Buhner .05 .15
129 Darrin Jackson .01 .05
130 Luis Mercedes .01 .05
131 Brian Harper .01 .05
132 Howard Johnson .01 .05
133 Nolan Ryan CL .15 .40
134 Dante Bichette .05 .15
135 Dave Righetti .05 .15
136 Jeff Montgomery .01 .05
137 Joe Grahe .01 .05
138 Delino DeShields .01 .05
139 Jose Rijo .01 .05
140 Ken Caminiti .05 .15
141 Steve Olin .01 .05
142 Kurt Stillwell .01 .05
143 Jay Bell .05 .15
144 Jaime Navarro .01 .05
145 Ben McDonald .01 .05
146 Greg Gagne .01 .05
147 Jeff Blauser .01 .05
148 Carney Lansford .05 .15
149 Ozzie Guillen .05 .15
150 Milt Thompson .01 .05
151 Jeff Reardon .05 .15
152 Scott Sanderson .01 .05
153 Cecil Fielder .05 .15
154 Greg A. Harris .01 .05
155 Rich DeLucia .01 .05
156 Roberto Kelly .01 .05
157 Bryn Smith .01 .05
158 Chuck McElroy .01 .05
159 Tom Henke .01 .05
160 Luis Gonzalez .05 .15
161 Steve Wilson .01 .05
162 Shawn Boskie .01 .05
163 Mark Davis .01 .05
164 Mike Moore .01 .05
165 Mike Scioscia .01 .05
166 Scott Erickson .01 .05
167 Todd Stottlemyre .01 .05
168 Alvin Davis .01 .05
169 Greg Hibbard .01 .05
170 David Valle .01 .05
171 Dave Winfield .05 .15
172 Alan Trammell .05 .15
173 Kenny Rogers .05 .15
174 John Franco .05 .15
175 Jose Lind .01 .05
176 Pete Schourek .01 .05
177 Von Hayes .01 .05
178 Chris Hammond .01 .05
179 John Burkett .01 .05
180 Dickie Thon .01 .05
181 Joel Skinner .01 .05
182 Scott Cooper .01 .05
183 Andre Dawson .05 .15
184 Billy Ripken .01 .05
185 Kevin Mitchell .01 .05
186 Brett Butler .05 .15
187 Tony Fernandez .01 .05
188 Cory Snyder .01 .05
189 John Habyan .01 .05
190 Dennis Martinez .05 .15
191 John Smoltz .08 .25
192 Greg Myers .01 .05
193 Rob Deer .01 .05
194 Ivan Rodriguez .15 .40
195 Ray Lankford .05 .15
196 Bill Wegman .01 .05
197 Edgar Martinez .08 .25
198 Darryl Kile .05 .15
199 Cal Ripken CL .15 .40
200 Brent Mayne .01 .05
201 Larry Walker .08 .25
202 Carlos Baerga .01 .05
203 Russ Swan .01 .05
204 Mike Morgan .01 .05
205 Hal Morris .01 .05
206 Tony Gwynn .20 .50
207 Mark Leiter .01 .05
208 Kirt Manwaring .01 .05
209 Al Osuna .01 .05
210 Bobby Thigpen .01 .05
211 Chris Hoiles .01 .05
212 B.J. Surhoff .05 .15
213 Lenny Harris .01 .05
214 Scott Leius .01 .05
215 Gregg Jefferies .01 .05
216 Bruce Hurst .01 .05
217 Steve Sax .01 .05
218 Dave Otto .01 .05
219 Sam Horn .01 .05
220 Charlie Hayes .01 .05
221 Frank Viola .05 .15
222 Jose Guzman .01 .05
223 Gary Redus .01 .05
224 Dave Gallagher .01 .05
225 Dean Palmer .05 .15
226 Greg Olson .01 .05
227 Jose DeLeon .01 .05
228 Mike LaValliere .01 .05
229 Mark Langston .01 .05
230 Chuck Knoblauch .05 .15
231 Bill Doran .01 .05
232 Dave Henderson .01 .05
233 Roberto Alomar .08 .25
234 Scott Fletcher .01 .05
235 Tim Naehring .01 .05
236 Mike Gallego .01 .05
237 Lance Johnson .01 .05
238 Paul Molitor .05 .15
239 Dan Gladden .01 .05
240 Willie Randolph .05 .15
241 Will Clark .08 .25
242 Sid Bream .01 .05
243 Derek Bell .05 .15
244 Bill Pecota .01 .05
245 Terry Pendleton .05 .15
246 Randy Ready .01 .05
247 Jack Armstrong .01 .05
248 Todd Van Poppel .01 .05
249 Shawon Dunston .01 .05
250 Bobby Rose .01 .05
251 Jeff Huson .01 .05
252 Bip Roberts .01 .05
253 Doug Jones .01 .05
254 Lee Smith .05 .15
255 George Brett .40 1.00
256 Randy Tomlin .01 .05
257 Todd Benzinger .01 .05
258 Dave Stewart .05 .15
259 Mark Carreon .01 .05
260 Pete O'Brien .01 .05
261 Tim Teufel .01 .05
262 Bob Milacki .01 .05
263 Mark Guthrie .01 .05
264 Darrin Fletcher .01 .05
265 Omar Vizquel .08 .25
266 Chris Bosio .01 .05
267 Jose Canseco .08 .25
268 Mike Boddicker .01 .05
269 Lance Parrish .05 .15
270 Jose Vizcaino .01 .05
271 Chris Sabo .01 .05
272 Royce Clayton .01 .05
273 Marquis Grissom .05 .15
274 Fred McGriff .08 .25
275 Barry Bonds .60 1.50
276 Greg Vaughn .01 .05
277 Gregg Olson .01 .05
278 Dave Hollins .01 .05
279 Tom Glavine .08 .25
280 Bryan Hickerson UER .01 .05
Name spelled Brian on front
281 Scott Radinsky .01 .05
282 Omar Olivares .01 .05
283 Ivan Calderon .01 .05
284 Kevin Maas .01 .05
285 Mickey Tettleton .01 .05
286 Wade Boggs .08 .25
287 Stan Belinda .01 .05
288 Bret Barberie .01 .05
289 Jose Oquendo .01 .05
290 Frank Castillo .01 .05
291 Dave Stieb .01 .05
292 Tommy Greene .01 .05
293 Eric Karros .05 .15
294 Greg Maddux .25 .60
295 Jim Eisenreich .01 .05
296 Rafael Palmeiro .08 .25
297 Ramon Martinez .01 .05
298 Tim Wallach .01 .05
299 Jim Thome .15 .40
300 Chito Martinez .01 .05
301 Mitch Williams .01 .05
302 Randy Johnson .15 .40
303 Carlton Fisk .08 .25
304 Travis Fryman .05 .15
305 Bobby Witt .01 .05
306 Dave Magadan .01 .05
307 Alex Cole .01 .05
308 Bobby Bonilla .05 .15
309 Bryan Harvey .01 .05
310 Rafael Belliard .01 .05
311 Mariano Duncan .01 .05
312 Chuck Crim .01 .05
313 John Kruk .05 .15
314 Ellis Burks .05 .15
315 Craig Biggio .08 .25
316 Glenn Davis .01 .05
317 Ryne Sandberg .25 .60
318 Mike Sharperson .01 .05
319 Rich Rodriguez .01 .05
320 Lee Guetterman .01 .05
321 Benito Santiago .05 .15
322 Jose Offerman .01 .05
323 Tony Pena .01 .05
324 Pat Borders .01 .05
325 Mike Henneman .01 .05
326 Kevin Brown .05 .15
327 Chris Nabholz .01 .05
328 Franklin Stubbs .01 .05
329 Tino Martinez .08 .25
330 Mickey Morandini .01 .05
331 Ryne Sandberg CL .15 .40
332 Mark Gubicza .01 .05
333 Bill Landrum .01 .05
334 Mark Whiten .01 .05
335 Darren Daulton .05 .15
336 Rick Wilkins .01 .05
337 Brian Jordan RC .20 .50
338 Kevin Ward .01 .05
339 Ruben Amaro .01 .05
340 Trevor Wilson .01 .05
341 Andujar Cedeno .01 .05
342 Michael Huff .01 .05
343 Brady Anderson .05 .15
344 Craig Grebeck .01 .05
345 Bob Ojeda .01 .05
346 Mike Pagliarulo .01 .05
347 Terry Shumpert .01 .05
348 Dann Bilardello .01 .05
349 Frank Thomas .15 .40
350 Albert Belle .05 .15
351 Jose Mesa .01 .05
352 Rich Monteleone .01 .05
353 Bob Walk .01 .05
354 Monty Fariss .01 .05
355 Luis Rivera .01 .05
356 Anthony Young .01 .05
357 Geno Petralli .01 .05
358 Otis Nixon .01 .05
359 Tom Pagnozzi .01 .05
360 Reggie Sanders .05 .15
361 Lee Stevens .01 .05
362 Kent Hrbek .05 .15
363 Orlando Merced .01 .05
364 Mike Bordick .01 .05
365 Dion James UER .01 .05
(Blue Jays logo
on card back)
366 Jack Clark .05 .15
367 Mike Stanley .01 .05
368 Randy Velarde .01 .05
369 Dan Pasqua .01 .05
370 Pat Listach RC .08 .25
371 Mike Fitzgerald .01 .05
372 Tom Foley .01 .05
373 Matt Williams .05 .15
374 Brian Hunter .01 .05
375 Joe Carter .05 .15
376 Bret Saberhagen .05 .15
377 Mike Stanton .01 .05
378 Hubie Brooks .01 .05
379 Eric Bell .01 .05
380 Walt Weiss .01 .05
381 Danny Jackson .01 .05
382 Manuel Lee .01 .05
383 Ruben Sierra .05 .15
384 Greg Swindell .01 .05
385 Ryan Bowen .01 .05
386 Kevin Ritz .01 .05
387 Curtis Wilkerson .01 .05
388 Gary Varsho .01 .05
389 Dave Hansen .01 .05
390 Bob Welch .01 .05
391 Lou Whitaker .05 .15
392 Ken Griffey Jr. .25 .60
393 Mike Maddux .01 .05
394 Arthur Rhodes .01 .05
395 Chili Davis .05 .15
396 Eddie Murray .15 .40
397 Robin Yount CL .08 .25
398 Dave Cochrane .01 .05
399 Kevin Seitzer .01 .05
400 Ozzie Smith .25 .60
401 Paul Sorrento .01 .05
402 Les Lancaster .01 .05
403 Junior Noboa .01 .05
404 David Justice .05 .15
405 Andy Ashby .01 .05
406 Danny Tartabull .01 .05
407 Bill Swift .01 .05
408 Craig Lefferts .01 .05
409 Tom Candiotti .01 .05
410 Lance Blankenship .01 .05
411 Jeff Tackett .01 .05
412 Sammy Sosa .15 .40
413 Jody Reed .01 .05
414 Bruce Ruffin .01 .05
415 Gene Larkin .01 .05
416 John Vander Wal RC .08 .25
417 Tim Belcher .01 .05
418 Steve Frey .01 .05
419 Dick Schofield .01 .05
420 Jeff King .01 .05
421 Kim Batiste .01 .05
422 Jack McDowell .01 .05
423 Damon Berryhill .01 .05
424 Gary Wayne .01 .05
425 Jack Morris .05 .15
426 Moises Alou .05 .15
427 Mark McLemore .01 .05
428 Juan Guerrero .01 .05
429 Scott Scudder .01 .05
430 Eric Davis .05 .15
431 Joe Slusarski .01 .05
432 Todd Zeile .01 .05
433 Dwayne Henry .01 .05
434 Cliff Brantley .01 .05
435 Butch Henry RC .02 .10
436 Todd Worrell .01 .05
437 Bob Scanlan .01 .05
438 Wally Joyner .05 .15
439 John Flaherty .01 .05
440 Brian Downing .01 .05
441 Darren Lewis .01 .05
442 Gary Carter .05 .15
443 Wally Ritchie .01 .05
444 Chris Jones .01 .05
445 Jeff Kent RC 1.00 2.50
446 Gary Sheffield .05 .15
447 Ron Darling .01 .05
448 Deion Sanders .08 .25
449 Andres Galarraga .05 .15
450 Chuck Finley .05 .15
451 Derek Lilliquist .01 .05
452 Carl Willis .01 .05
453 Wes Chamberlain .01 .05
454 Roger Mason .01 .05
455 Spike Owen .01 .05
456 Thomas Howard .01 .05
457 Dave Martinez .01 .05
458 Pete Incaviglia .01 .05
459 Keith A. Miller .01 .05
460 Mike Fetters .01 .05
461 Paul Gibson .01 .05
462 George Bell .01 .05
463 Bobby Bonilla CL .01 .05
464 Terry Mulholland .01 .05
465 Storm Davis .01 .05
466 Gary Pettis .01 .05
467 Randy Bush .01 .05
468 Ken Hill .01 .05
469 Rheal Cormier .01 .05
470 Andy Stankiewicz .01 .05
471 Dave Burba .01 .05
472 Henry Cotto .01 .05
473 Dale Sveum .01 .05
474 Rich Gossage .05 .15
475 William Suero .01 .05
476 Doug Strange .01 .05
477 Bill Krueger .01 .05
478 John Wetteland .05 .15
479 Melido Perez .01 .05
480 Lonnie Smith .01 .05
481 Mike Jackson .01 .05
482 Mike Gardiner .01 .05
483 David Wells .05 .15
484 Barry Jones .01 .05
485 Scott Bankhead .01 .05
486 Terry Leach .01 .05
487 Vince Horsman .01 .05
488 Dave Eiland .01 .05
489 Alejandro Pena .01 .05
490 Julio Valera .01 .05
491 Joe Boever .01 .05
492 Paul Miller RC .01 .05
493 Archi Cianfrocco RC .02 .10
494 Dave Fleming .01 .05
495 Kyle Abbott .01 .05
496 Chad Kreuter .01 .05
497 Chris James .01 .05
498 Donnie Hill .01 .05
499 Jacob Brumfield .01 .05
500 Ricky Bones .01 .05
501 Terry Steinbach .01 .05
502 Bernard Gilkey .01 .05
503 Dennis Cook .01 .05
504 Len Dykstra .05 .15
505 Mike Bielecki .01 .05
506 Bob Kipper .01 .05
507 Jose Melendez .01 .05
508 Rick Sutcliffe .05 .15
509 Ken Patterson .01 .05
510 Andy Allanson .01 .05
511 Al Newman .01 .05
512 Mark Gardner .01 .05
513 Jeff Schaefer .01 .05
514 Jim McNamara .01 .05
515 Peter Hoy .01 .05
516 Curt Schilling .08 .25
517 Kirk McCaskill .01 .05
518 Chris Gwynn .01 .05
519 Sid Fernandez .01 .05
520 Jeff Parrett .01 .05
521 Scott Ruskin .01 .05
522 Kevin McReynolds .01 .05
523 Rick Cerone .01 .05
524 Jesse Orosco .01 .05
525 Troy Afenir .01 .05
526 John Smiley .01 .05
527 Dale Murphy .08 .25
528 Leaf Set Card .01 .05

1993 Leaf

The 1993 Leaf baseball set consists of three series of 220, 220, and 110 standard-size cards, respectively. Cards were distributed in 14-card foil packs, jumbo packs and magazine packs. Rookie Cards in this set include J.T. Snow. White Sox slugger (and at that time, Leaf Representative) Frank Thomas signed 3,500 cards, which were randomly seeded into packs. In addition, a special card commemorating Dave Winfield's 3,000 hit was also seeded into packs. Both cards are listed at the end of our checklist but are not considered part of the 550-card basic set.

COMPLETE SET (550) 14.00 35.00
COMP. SERIES 1 (220) 6.00 15.00
COMP. SERIES 2 (220) 6.00 15.00
COMPLETE UPDATE (110) 2.00 5.00
COMMON RC .05 .15
1 Ben McDonald .05 .15
2 Sid Fernandez .05 .15
3 Juan Guzman .05 .15
4 Curt Schilling .10 .30
5 Ivan Rodriguez .20 .50
6 Don Slaught .05 .15
7 Terry Steinbach .05 .15
8 Todd Zeile .05 .15
9 Andy Stankiewicz .05 .15
10 Tim Teufel .05 .15
11 Marvin Freeman .05 .15
12 Jim Austin .05 .15
13 Bob Scanlan .05 .15
14 Rusty Meacham .05 .15
15 Casey Candaele .05 .15
16 Travis Fryman .10 .30
17 Jose Offerman .05 .15
18 Albert Belle .10 .30
19 John Vander Wal .05 .15
20 Dan Pasqua .05 .15
21 Frank Viola .10 .30
22 Terry Mulholland .05 .15
23 Gregg Olson .05 .15
24 Randy Tomlin .05 .15
25 Todd Stottlemyre .05 .15
26 Jose Oquendo .05 .15
27 Julio Franco .10 .30
28 Tony Gwynn .40 1.00
29 Ruben Sierra .10 .30
30 Robby Thompson .05 .15
31 Jim Bullinger .05 .15
32 Rick Aguilera .05 .15
33 Scott Servais .05 .15
34 Cal Eldred .05 .15
35 Mike Piazza 1.25 3.00
36 Brent Mayne .05 .15
37 Wil Cordero .05 .15
38 Milt Cuyler .05 .15
39 Howard Johnson .05 .15
40 Kenny Lofton .10 .30
41 Alex Fernandez .05 .15
42 Denny Neagle .10 .30
43 Tony Pena .05 .15
44 Bob Tewksbury .05 .15
45 Glenn Davis .05 .15
46 Fred McGriff .20 .50
47 John Olerud .10 .30
48 Steve Hosey .05 .15
49 Rafael Palmeiro .20 .50
50 David Justice .10 .30
51 Pete Harnisch .05 .15
52 Sam Militello .05 .15
53 Orel Hershiser .10 .30
54 Pat Mahomes .05 .15
55 Greg Colbrunn .05 .15
56 Greg Vaughn .05 .15
57 Vince Coleman .05 .15
58 Brian McRae .05 .15
59 Len Dykstra .10 .30
60 Dan Gladden .05 .15
61 Ted Power .05 .15
62 Donovan Osborne .05 .15
63 Ron Karkovice .05 .15
64 Frank Seminara .05 .15
65 Bob Zupcic .05 .15
66 Kirt Manwaring .05 .15
67 Mike Devereaux .05 .15
68 Mark Lemke .05 .15
69 Devon White .10 .30
70 Sammy Sosa .30 .75
71 Pedro Astacio .05 .15
72 Dennis Eckersley .10 .30
73 Chris Nabholz .05 .15
74 Melido Perez .05 .15
75 Todd Hundley .05 .15
76 Kent Hrbek .10 .30
77 Mickey Morandini .05 .15
78 Tim McIntosh .05 .15
79 Andy Van Slyke .20 .50
80 Kevin McReynolds .05 .15
81 Mike Henneman .05 .15
82 Greg W. Harris .05 .15
83 Sandy Alomar Jr. .05 .15
84 Mike Jackson .05 .15
85 Ozzie Guillen .10 .30
86 Jeff Blauser .10 .30
87 John Valentin .05 .15
88 Rey Sanchez .05 .15
89 Rick Sutcliffe .10 .30
90 Luis Gonzalez .10 .30
91 Jeff Fassero .05 .15
92 Kenny Rogers .10 .30
93 Bret Saberhagen .10 .30
94 Bob Welch .05 .15
95 Darren Daulton .10 .30
96 Mike Gallego .05 .15
97 Orlando Merced .05 .15
98 Chuck Knoblauch .10 .30
99 Bernard Gilkey .05 .15
100 Billy Ashley .05 .15
101 Kevin Appier .10 .30
102 Jeff Brantley .05 .15
103 Bill Gullickson .05 .15
104 John Smoltz .20 .50
105 Paul Sorrento .05 .15
106 Steve Buechele .05 .15
107 Steve Sax .05 .15
108 Andujar Cedeno .05 .15
109 Billy Hatcher .05 .15
110 Checklist .05 .15
111 Alan Mills .05 .15
112 John Franco .10 .30
113 Jack Morris .10 .30
114 Mitch Williams .05 .15
115 Nolan Ryan 1.25 3.00
116 Jay Bell .10 .30
117 Mike Bordick .05 .15
118 Geronimo Pena .05 .15
119 Danny Tartabull .05 .15
120 Checklist .05 .15
121 Steve Avery .05 .15
122 Ricky Bones .05 .15
123 Mike Morgan .05 .15
124 Jeff Montgomery .05 .15
125 Jeff Bagwell .20 .50
126 Tony Phillips .05 .15
127 Lenny Harris .05 .15
128 Glenallen Hill .05 .15
129 Marquis Grissom .10 .30
130 Gerald Williams UER .05 .15
(Bernie Williams
picture and stats)
131 Greg A. Harris .05 .15
132 Tommy Greene .05 .15
133 Chris Hoiles .05 .15
134 Bob Walk .05 .15
135 Duane Ward .05 .15
136 Tom Pagnozzi .05 .15
137 Jeff Huson .05 .15
138 Kurt Stillwell .05 .15
139 Dave Henderson .05 .15
140 Darrin Jackson .05 .15
141 Frank Castillo .05 .15
142 Scott Erickson .05 .15
143 Darryl Kile .10 .30
144 Bill Wegman .05 .15
145 Steve Wilson .05 .15
146 George Brett .75 2.00
147 Moises Alou .10 .30
148 Lou Whitaker .10 .30
149 Chico Walker .05 .15
150 Jerry Browne .05 .15
151 Kirk McCaskill .05 .15
152 Zane Smith .05 .15
153 Matt Young .05 .15
154 Lee Smith .10 .30
155 Leo Gomez .05 .15
156 Dan Walters .05 .15
157 Pat Borders .05 .15
158 Matt Williams .10 .30
159 Dean Palmer .10 .30
160 John Patterson .05 .15
161 Doug Jones .05 .15
162 John Habyan .05 .15
163 Pedro Martinez .60 1.50
164 Carl Willis .05 .15
165 Darrin Fletcher .05 .15
166 B.J. Surhoff .10 .30
167 Eddie Murray .30 .75
168 Keith Miller .05 .15
169 Ricky Jordan .05 .15
170 Juan Gonzalez .10 .30
171 Charles Nagy .05 .15
172 Mark Clark .05 .15
173 Bobby Thigpen .05 .15
174 Tim Scott .05 .15
175 Scott Cooper .05 .15
176 Royce Clayton .05 .15
177 Brady Anderson .10 .30
178 Sid Bream .05 .15
179 Derek Bell .05 .15
180 Otis Nixon .05 .15
181 Kevin Gross .05 .15
182 Ron Darling .05 .15
183 John Wetteland .10 .30
184 Mike Stanley .05 .15
185 Jeff Kent .30 .75
186 Brian Harper .05 .15
187 Mariano Duncan .05 .15
188 Robin Yount .50 1.25
189 Al Martin .05 .15
190 Eddie Zosky .05 .15
191 Mike Munoz .05 .15
192 Andy Benes .05 .15
193 Dennis Cook .05 .15
194 Bill Swift .05 .15
195 Frank Thomas .30 .75
195A Frank Thomas .50 1.25
Franklin visible on batting glove
196 Damon Berryhill .05 .15
197 Mike Greenwell .05 .15
198 Mark Grace .20 .50
199 Darryl Hamilton .05 .15
200 Derrick May .05 .15
201 Ken Hill .05 .15
202 Kevin Brown .10 .30
203 Dwight Gooden .10 .30
204 Bobby Witt .05 .15
205 Juan Bell .05 .15
206 Kevin Maas .05 .15
207 Jeff King .05 .15
208 Scott Leius .05 .15
209 Rheal Cormier .05 .15
210 Darryl Strawberry .10 .30
211 Tom Gordon .05 .15
212 Bud Black .05 .15
213 Mickey Tettleton .05 .15
214 Pete Smith .05 .15
215 Felix Fermin .05 .15
216 Rick Wilkins .05 .15
217 George Bell .05 .15
218 Eric Anthony .05 .15
219 Pedro Munoz .05 .15
220 Checklist .05 .15
221 Lance Blankenship .05 .15
222 Deion Sanders .20 .50
223 Craig Biggio .20 .50
224 Ryne Sandberg .50 1.25
225 Ron Gant .10 .30
226 Tom Brunansky .05 .15
227 Chad Curtis .05 .15
228 Joe Carter .10 .30
229 Brian Jordan .10 .30
230 Brett Butler .10 .30
231 Frank Bolick .05 .15
232 Rod Beck .05 .15
233 Carlos Baerga .05 .15
234 Eric Karros .10 .30
235 Jack Armstrong .05 .15
236 Bobby Bonilla .10 .30
237 Don Mattingly .75 2.00
238 Jeff Gardner .05 .15
239 Dave Hollins .05 .15
240 Steve Cooke .05 .15
241 Jose Canseco .20 .50
242 Ivan Calderon .05 .15
243 Tim Belcher .05 .15
244 Freddie Benavides .05 .15
245 Roberto Alomar .20 .50
246 Rob Deer .05 .15
247 Will Clark .20 .50
248 Mike Felder .05 .15
249 Harold Baines .10 .30
250 David Cone .10 .30
251 Mark Guthrie .05 .15
252 Ellis Burks .10 .30
253 Jim Abbott .20 .50
254 Chili Davis .10 .30
255 Chris Bosio .05 .15
256 Bret Barberie .05 .15
257 Hal Morris .05 .15
258 Dante Bichette .10 .30
259 Storm Davis .05 .15
260 Gary DiSarcina .05 .15
261 Ken Caminiti .10 .30
262 Paul Molitor .10 .30
263 Joe Oliver .05 .15
264 Pat Listach .05 .15
265 Gregg Jefferies .05 .15
266 Jose Guzman .05 .15
267 Eric Davis .10 .30
268 Delino DeShields .05 .15
269 Barry Bonds .75 2.00
270 Mike Bielecki .05 .15
271 Jay Buhner .10 .30
272 Scott Pose RC .05 .15
273 Tony Fernandez .05 .15
274 Chris Martinez .05 .15
275 Phil Plantier .05 .15
276 Pete Incaviglia .05 .15
277 Carlos Garcia .05 .15
278 Tom Henke .05 .15
279 Roger Clemens .60 1.50
280 Rob Dibble .10 .30
281 Daryl Boston .05 .15
282 Greg Gagne .05 .15
283 Cecil Fielder .10 .30
284 Carlton Fisk .20 .50
285 Wade Boggs .20 .50
286 Damion Easley .05 .15
287 Norm Charlton .05 .15

288 Jeff Conine .10 .30
289 Roberto Kelly .05 .15
290 Jerald Clark .05 .15
291 Rickey Henderson .30 .75
292 Chuck Finley .10 .30
293 Doug Drabek .05 .15
294 Dave Stewart .10 .30
295 Tom Glavine .20 .50
296 Jaime Navarro .05 .15
297 Ray Lankford .10 .30
298 Greg Hibbard .05 .15
299 Jody Reed .05 .15
300 Dennis Martinez .10 .30
301 Dave Martinez .05 .15
302 Reggie Jefferson .05 .15
303 John Cummings RC .05 .15
304 Orestes Destrade .05 .15
305 Mike Maddux .05 .15
306 David Segui .05 .15
307 Gary Sheffield .10 .30
308 Danny Jackson .05 .15
309 Craig Lefferts .05 .15
310 Andre Dawson .10 .30
311 Barry Larkin .20 .50
312 Alex Cole .05 .15
313 Mark Gardner .05 .15
314 Kirk Gibson .10 .30
315 Shane Mack .05 .15
316 Bo Jackson .30 .75
317 Jimmy Key .10 .30
318 Greg Myers .05 .15
319 Ken Griffey Jr. .50 1.25
320 Monty Fariss .05 .15
321 Kevin Mitchell .05 .15
322 Andres Galarraga .10 .30
323 Mark McGwire .75 2.00
324 Mark Langston .05 .15
325 Steve Finley .10 .30
326 Greg Maddux .50 1.25
327 Dave Nilsson .05 .15
328 Ozzie Smith .50 1.25
329 Candy Maldonado .05 .15
330 Checklist .05 .15
331 Tim Pugh RC .05 .15
332 Joe Girardi .05 .15
333 Junior Felix .05 .15
334 Greg Swindell .05 .15
335 Ramon Martinez .05 .15
336 Sean Berry .05 .15
337 Joe Orsulak .05 .15
338 Wes Chamberlain .05 .15
339 Stan Belinda .05 .15
340 Checklist UER .05 .15
(306 Luis Mercedes)
341 Bruce Hurst .05 .15
342 John Burkett .05 .15
343 Mike Mussina .20 .50
344 Scott Fletcher .05 .15
345 Rene Gonzales .05 .15
346 Roberto Hernandez .05 .15
347 Carlos Martinez .05 .15
348 Bill Krueger .05 .15
349 Felix Jose .05 .15
350 John Jaha .05 .15
351 Willie Banks .05 .15
352 Matt Nokes .05 .15
353 Kevin Seitzer .05 .15
354 Erik Hanson .05 .15
355 David Hulse RC .05 .15
356 Domingo Martinez RC .05 .15
357 Greg Olson .05 .15
358 Randy Myers .05 .15
359 Tom Browning .05 .15
360 Charlie Hayes .05 .15
361 Bryan Harvey .05 .15
362 Eddie Taubensee .05 .15
363 Tim Wallach .05 .15
364 Mel Rojas .05 .15
365 Frank Tanana .05 .15
366 John Kruk .10 .30
367 Tim Laker RC .05 .15
368 Rich Rodriguez .05 .15
369 Darren Lewis .05 .15
370 Harold Reynolds .10 .30
371 Jose Melendez .05 .15
372 Joe Grahe .05 .15
373 Lance Johnson .05 .15
374 Jose Mesa .05 .15
375 Scott Livingstone .05 .15
376 Wally Joyner .10 .30
377 Kevin Reimer .05 .15
378 Kirby Puckett .30 .75
379 Paul O'Neill .20 .50
380 Randy Johnson .30 .75
381 Manuel Lee .05 .15
382 Dick Schofield .05 .15
383 Darren Holmes .05 .15
384 Charlie Hough .10 .30
385 John Orton .05 .15
386 Edgar Martinez .20 .50
387 Terry Pendleton .10 .30
388 Dan Plesac .05 .15
389 Jeff Reardon .10 .30
390 David Nied .05 .15
391 Dave Magadan .05 .15
392 Larry Walker .10 .30
393 Ben Rivera .05 .15
394 Lonnie Smith .05 .15
395 Craig Shipley .05 .15
396 Willie McGee .10 .30
397 Arthur Rhodes .05 .15
398 Mike Stanton .05 .15
399 Luis Polonia .05 .15
400 Jack McDowell .05 .15
401 Mike Moore .05 .15
402 Jose Lind .05 .15
403 Bill Spiers .05 .15
404 Kevin Tapani .05 .15
405 Spike Owen .05 .15
406 Tino Martinez .20 .50
407 Charlie Leibrandt .05 .15
408 Ed Sprague .05 .15
409 Bryn Smith .05 .15
410 Benito Santiago .10 .30
411 Jose Rijo .05 .15
412 Pete O'Brien .05 .15
413 Willie Wilson .05 .15
414 Bip Roberts .05 .15
415 Eric Young .05 .15
416 Walt Weiss .05 .15
417 Milt Thompson .05 .15
418 Chris Sabo .05 .15
419 Scott Sanderson .05 .15
420 Tim Raines .10 .30
421 Alan Trammell .10 .30
422 Mike Macfarlane .05 .15
423 Dave Winfield .10 .30
424 Bob Wickman .05 .15
425 David Valle .05 .15
426 Gary Redus .05 .15
427 Turner Ward .05 .15
428 Reggie Sanders .10 .30
429 Todd Worrell .05 .15
430 Julio Valera .05 .15
431 Cal Ripken Jr. 1.00 2.50
432 Mo Vaughn .10 .30
433 John Smiley .05 .15
434 Omar Vizquel .20 .50
435 Billy Ripken .05 .15
436 Cory Snyder .05 .15
437 Carlos Quintana .05 .15
438 Omar Olivares .05 .15
439 Robin Ventura .10 .30
440 Checklist .05 .15
441 Kevin Higgins .05 .15
442 Carlos Hernandez .05 .15
443 Dan Peltier .05 .15
444 Derek Lilliquist .05 .15
445 Tim Salmon .20 .50
446 Sherman Obando RC .05 .15
447 Pat Kelly .05 .15
448 Todd Van Poppel .05 .15
449 Mark Whiten .05 .15
450 Checklist .05 .15
451 Pat Meares RC .15 .40
452 Tony Tarasco RC .05 .15
453 Chris Gwynn .05 .15
454 Armando Reynoso .05 .15
455 Danny Darwin .05 .15
456 Willie Greene .05 .15
457 Mike Blowers .05 .15
458 Kevin Roberson RC .05 .15
459 Graeme Lloyd RC .15 .40
460 David West .05 .15
461 Joey Cora .05 .15
462 Alex Arias .05 .15
463 Chad Kreuter .05 .15
464 Mike Lansing RC .15 .40
465 Mike Timlin .05 .15
466 Paul Wagner .05 .15
467 Mark Portugal .05 .15
468 Jim Leyritz .05 .15
469 Ryan Klesko .10 .30
470 Mario Diaz .05 .15
471 Guillermo Velasquez .05 .15
472 Fernando Valenzuela .10 .30
473 Raul Mondesi .10 .30
474 Mike Pagliarulo .05 .15
475 Chris Hammond .05 .15
476 Torey Lovullo .05 .15
477 Trevor Wilson .05 .15
478 Marcos Armas RC .05 .15
479 Dave Gallagher .05 .15
480 Jeff Treadway .05 .15
481 Jeff Branson .05 .15
482 Dickie Thon .05 .15
483 Eduardo Perez .05 .15
484 David Wells .10 .30
485 Brian Williams .05 .15
486 Domingo Cedeno RC .05 .15
487 Tom Candiotti .05 .15
488 Steve Frey .05 .15
489 Greg McMichael RC .05 .15
490 Marc Newfield .05 .15
491 Larry Andersen .05 .15
492 Damon Buford .05 .15
493 Ricky Gutierrez .05 .15
494 Jeff Russell .05 .15
495 Vinny Castilla .30 .75
496 Wilson Alvarez .05 .15
497 Scott Bullett .05 .15
498 Larry Casian .05 .15
499 Jose Vizcaino .05 .15
500 J.T. Snow RC .25 .60
501 Bryan Hickerson .05 .15
502 Jeremy Hernandez .05 .15
503 Jeromy Burnitz .10 .30
504 Steve Farr .05 .15
505 J. Owens RC .05 .15
506 Craig Paquette .05 .15
507 Jim Eisenreich .05 .15
508 Matt Whiteside RC .05 .15
509 Luis Aquino .05 .15
510 Mike LaValliere .05 .15
511 Jim Gott .05 .15
512 Mark McLemore .05 .15
513 Randy Milligan .05 .15
514 Gary Gaetti .10 .30
515 Lou Frazier RC .05 .15
516 Rich Amaral .05 .15
517 Gene Harris .05 .15
518 Aaron Sele .05 .15
519 Mark Wohlers .05 .15
520 Scott Kamieniecki .05 .15
521 Kent Mercker .05 .15
522 Jim Deshaies .05 .15
523 Kevin Stocker .05 .15
524 Jason Bere .05 .15
525 Tim Bogar RC .05 .15
526 Brad Pennington .05 .15
527 Curt Leskanic RC .15 .40
528 Wayne Kirby .05 .15
529 Tim Costo .05 .15
530 Doug Henry .05 .15
531 Trevor Hoffman .30 .75
532 Kelly Gruber .05 .15
533 Mike Harkey .05 .15
534 John Doherty .05 .15
535 Erik Pappas .05 .15
536 Brent Gates .05 .15
537 Roger McDowell .05 .15
538 Chris Haney .05 .15
539 Blas Minor .05 .15
540 Pat Hentgen .05 .15
541 Chuck Carr .05 .15
542 Doug Strange .05 .15
543 Xavier Hernandez .05 .15
544 Paul Quantrill .05 .15
545 Anthony Young .05 .15
546 Bret Boone .10 .30
547 Dwight Smith .05 .15
548 Bobby Munoz .05 .15
549 Russ Springer .05 .15
550 Roger Pavlik .05 .15
DW Dave Winfield .40 1.00
3000 Hits
FT Frank Thomas AU/3500 20.00 50.00

1994 Leaf

The 1994 Leaf baseball set consists of two series of 220 standard-size cards for a total of 440. Randomly seeded "Super Packs" contained complete insert sets. Cards featuring players from the Texas Rangers, Cleveland Indians, Milwaukee Brewers and Houston Astros were held out of the first series in order to have up-to-date photography in each team's new uniforms. A limited number of players from the San Francisco Giants are featured in the first series because of minor modifications to the team's uniforms. Randomly inserted in hobby packs at a rate of one in 36 was a stamped version of Frank Thomas' 1990 Leaf rookie card.

COMPLETE SET (440) 10.00 24.00
COMP. SERIES 1 (220) 5.00 12.00
COMP. SERIES 2 (220) 5.00 12.00
1 Cal Ripken Jr. 1.00 2.50
2 Tony Tarasco .05 .15
3 Joe Girardi .05 .15
4 Bernie Williams .20 .50
5 Chad Kreuter .05 .15
6 Troy Neel .05 .15
7 Tom Pagnozzi .05 .15
8 Kirk Rueter .05 .15
9 Chris Bosio .05 .15
10 Dwight Gooden .10 .30
11 Mariano Duncan .05 .15
12 Jay Bell .10 .30
13 Lance Johnson .05 .15
14 Richie Lewis .05 .15
15 Dave Martinez .05 .15
16 Orel Hershiser .10 .30
17 Rob Butler .05 .15
18 Glenallen Hill .05 .15
19 Chad Curtis .05 .15
20 Mike Stanton .05 .15
21 Tim Wallach .05 .15
22 Milt Thompson .05 .15
23 Kevin Young .05 .15
24 John Smiley .05 .15
25 Jeff Montgomery .05 .15
26 Robin Ventura .10 .30
27 Scott Lydy .05 .15
28 Todd Stottlemyre .05 .15
29 Mark Whiten .05 .15
30 Robby Thompson .05 .15
31 Bobby Bonilla .10 .30
32 Andy Ashby .05 .15
33 Greg Myers .05 .15
34 Billy Hatcher .05 .15
35 Brad Holman .05 .15
36 Mark McLemore .05 .15
37 Scott Sanders .05 .15
38 Jim Abbott .20 .50
39 David Wells .10 .30
40 Roberto Kelly .05 .15
41 Jeff Conine .10 .30
42 Sean Berry .05 .15
43 Mark Grace .20 .50
44 Eric Young .05 .15
45 Rick Aguilera .05 .15
46 Chipper Jones .30 .75
47 Mel Rojas .05 .15
48 Ryan Thompson .05 .15
49 Al Martin .05 .15
50 Cecil Fielder .10 .30
51 Pat Kelly .05 .15
52 Kevin Tapani .05 .15
53 Tim Costo .05 .15
54 Dave Hollins .05 .15
55 Kirt Manwaring .05 .15
56 Gregg Jefferies .05 .15
57 Ron Darling .05 .15
58 Bill Haselman .05 .15
59 Phil Plantier .05 .15
60 Frank Viola .10 .30
61 Todd Zeile .05 .15
62 Bret Barberie .05 .15
63 Roberto Mejia .05 .15
64 Chuck Knoblauch .10 .30
65 Jose Lind .05 .15
66 Brady Anderson .10 .30
67 Ruben Sierra .10 .30
68 Jose Vizcaino .05 .15
69 Joe Grahe .05 .15
70 Kevin Appier .10 .30
71 Wilson Alvarez .05 .15
72 Tom Candiotti .05 .15
73 John Burkett .05 .15
74 Anthony Young .05 .15
75 Scott Cooper .05 .15
76 Nigel Wilson .05 .15
77 John Valentin .05 .15
78 David McCarty .05 .15
79 Archi Cianfrocco .05 .15
80 Lou Whitaker .10 .30
81 Dante Bichette .10 .30
82 Mark Dewey .05 .15
83 Danny Jackson .05 .15
84 Harold Baines .10 .30
85 Todd Benzinger .05 .15
86 Damion Easley .05 .15
87 Danny Cox .05 .15
88 Jose Bautista .05 .15
89 Mike Lansing .05 .15
90 Phil Hiatt .05 .15
91 Tim Pugh .05 .15
92 Tino Martinez .20 .50
93 Raul Mondesi .10 .30
94 Greg Maddux .50 1.25
95 Al Leiter .10 .30
96 Benito Santiago .10 .30
97 Lenny Dykstra .10 .30
98 Sammy Sosa .30 .75
99 Tim Bogar .05 .15
100 Checklist .05 .15
101 Deion Sanders .20 .50
102 Bobby Witt .05 .15
103 Wil Cordero .05 .15
104 Rich Amaral .05 .15
105 Mike Mussina .20 .50
106 Reggie Sanders .10 .30
107 Ozzie Guillen .10 .30
108 Paul O'Neill .20 .50
109 Tim Salmon .20 .50
110 Rheal Cormier .05 .15
111 Billy Ashley .05 .15
112 Jeff Kent .20 .50
113 Derek Bell .05 .15
114 Danny Darwin .05 .15
115 Chip Hale .05 .15
116 Tim Raines .10 .30
117 Ed Sprague .05 .15
118 Darrin Fletcher .05 .15
119 Darren Holmes .05 .15
120 Alan Trammell .10 .30
121 Don Mattingly .75 2.00
122 Greg Gagne .05 .15
123 Jose Offerman .05 .15
124 Joe Orsulak .05 .15
125 Jack McDowell .05 .15
126 Barry Larkin .20 .50
127 Ben McDonald .05 .15
128 Mike Bordick .05 .15
129 Devon White .10 .30
130 Mike Perez .05 .15
131 Jay Buhner .10 .30
132 Phil Leftwich RC .05 .15
133 Tommy Greene .05 .15
134 Charlie Hayes .05 .15
135 Don Slaught .05 .15
136 Mike Gallego .05 .15
137 Dave Winfield .10 .30
138 Steve Avery .05 .15
139 Derrick May .05 .15
140 Bryan Harvey .05 .15
141 Wally Joyner .10 .30
142 Andre Dawson .10 .30
143 Andy Benes .05 .15
144 John Franco .10 .30
145 Jeff King .05 .15
146 Joe Oliver .05 .15
147 Bill Gullickson .05 .15
148 Armando Reynoso .05 .15
149 Dave Fleming .05 .15
150 Checklist .05 .15
151 Todd Van Poppel .05 .15
152 Bernard Gilkey .05 .15
153 Kevin Gross .05 .15
154 Mike Devereaux .05 .15
155 Tim Wakefield .20 .50
156 Andres Galarraga .10 .30
157 Pat Meares .05 .15
158 Jim Leyritz .05 .15
159 Mike Macfarlane .05 .15
160 Tony Phillips .05 .15
161 Brent Gates .05 .15
162 Mark Langston .05 .15
163 Allen Watson .05 .15
164 Randy Johnson .30 .75
165 Doug Brocail .05 .15
166 Rob Dibble .10 .30
167 Roberto Hernandez .05 .15
168 Felix Jose .05 .15
169 Steve Cooke .05 .15
170 Darren Daulton .10 .30
171 Eric Karros .10 .30
172 Geronimo Pena .05 .15
173 Gary DiSarcina .05 .15
174 Marquis Grissom .10 .30
175 Joey Cora .05 .15
176 Jim Eisenreich .05 .15
177 Brad Pennington .05 .15
178 Terry Steinbach .05 .15
179 Pat Borders .05 .15
180 Steve Buechele .05 .15
181 Jeff Fassero .05 .15
182 Mike Greenwell .05 .15
183 Mike Henneman .05 .15
184 Ron Karkovice .05 .15
185 Pat Hentgen .05 .15
186 Jose Guzman .05 .15
187 Brett Butler .10 .30
188 Charlie Hough .10 .30
189 Terry Pendleton .10 .30
190 Melido Perez .05 .15
191 Orestes Destrade .05 .15
192 Mike Morgan .05 .15
193 Joe Carter .10 .30
194 Jeff Blauser .05 .15
195 Chris Hoiles .05 .15
196 Ricky Gutierrez .05 .15
197 Mike Moore .05 .15
198 Carl Willis .05 .15
199 Aaron Sele .05 .15
200 Checklist .05 .15
201 Tim Naehring .05 .15
202 Scott Livingstone .05 .15
203 Luis Alicea .05 .15
204 Torey Lovullo .05 .15
205 Jim Gott .05 .15
206 Bob Wickman .05 .15
207 Greg McMichael .05 .15
208 Scott Brosius .10 .30
209 Chris Gwynn .05 .15
210 Steve Sax .05 .15
211 Dick Schofield .05 .15
212 Robb Nen .10 .30
213 Ben Rivera .05 .15
214 Vinny Castilla .10 .30
215 Jamie Moyer .10 .30
216 Wally Whitehurst .05 .15
217 Frank Castillo .05 .15
218 Mike Blowers .05 .15
219 Tim Scott .05 .15
220 Paul Wagner .05 .15
221 Jeff Bagwell .20 .50
222 Ricky Bones .05 .15
223 Sandy Alomar Jr. .05 .15
224 Rod Beck .05 .15
225 Roberto Alomar .20 .50
226 Jack Armstrong .05 .15
227 Scott Erickson .05 .15
228 Rene Arocha .05 .15
229 Eric Anthony .05 .15
230 Jeromy Burnitz .10 .30
231 Kevin Brown .10 .30
232 Tim Belcher .05 .15
233 Bret Boone .10 .30
234 Dennis Eckersley .10 .30
235 Tom Glavine .20 .50
236 Craig Biggio .20 .50
237 Pedro Astacio .05 .15
238 Ryan Bowen .05 .15
239 Brad Ausmus .20 .50
240 Vince Coleman .05 .15
241 Jason Bere .05 .15
242 Ellis Burks .10 .30
243 Wes Chamberlain .05 .15
244 Ken Caminiti .10 .30
245 Willie Banks .05 .15
246 Sid Fernandez .05 .15
247 Carlos Baerga .05 .15
248 Carlos Garcia .05 .15
249 Jose Canseco .20 .50
250 Alex Diaz .05 .15
251 Albert Belle .10 .30
252 Moises Alou .10 .30
253 Bobby Ayala .05 .15
254 Tony Gwynn .40 1.00
255 Roger Clemens .60 1.50
256 Eric Davis .10 .30
257 Wade Boggs .20 .50
258 Chili Davis .10 .30
259 Rickey Henderson .30 .75
260 Andujar Cedeno .05 .15
261 Cris Carpenter .05 .15
262 Juan Guzman .05 .15
263 David Justice .10 .30
264 Barry Bonds .75 2.00
265 Pete Incaviglia .05 .15
266 Tony Fernandez .05 .15
267 Cal Eldred .05 .15
268 Alex Fernandez .05 .15
269 Kent Hrbek .10 .30
270 Steve Farr .05 .15
271 Doug Drabek .05 .15
272 Brian Jordan .10 .30
273 Xavier Hernandez .05 .15
274 David Cone .10 .30
275 Brian Hunter .05 .15
276 Mike Harkey .05 .15
277 Delino DeShields .05 .15
278 David Hulse .05 .15
279 Mickey Tettleton .05 .15
280 Kevin McReynolds .05 .15
281 Darryl Hamilton .05 .15
282 Ken Hill .05 .15
283 Wayne Kirby .05 .15
284 Chris Hammond .05 .15
285 Mo Vaughn .10 .30
286 Ryan Klesko .10 .30
287 Rick Wilkins .05 .15
288 Bill Swift .05 .15
289 Rafael Palmeiro .20 .50
290 Brian Harper .05 .15
291 Chris Turner .05 .15
292 Luis Gonzalez .10 .30
293 Kenny Rogers .10 .30
294 Kirby Puckett .30 .75
295 Mike Stanley .05 .15
296 Carlos Reyes RC .05 .15
297 Charles Nagy .05 .15
298 Reggie Jefferson .05 .15
299 Bip Roberts .05 .15
300 Darrin Jackson .05 .15
301 Mike Jackson .05 .15
302 Dave Nilsson .05 .15
303 Ramon Martinez .05 .15
304 Bobby Jones .05 .15
305 Johnny Ruffin .05 .15
306 Brian McRae .05 .15
307 Bo Jackson .30 .75
308 Dave Stewart .10 .30
309 John Smoltz .20 .50
310 Dennis Martinez .10 .30
311 Dean Palmer .10 .30
312 David Nied .05 .15
313 Eddie Murray .30 .75
314 Darryl Kile .10 .30
315 Rick Sutcliffe .10 .30
316 Shawon Dunston .05 .15
317 John Jaha .05 .15
318 Salomon Torres .05 .15
319 Gary Sheffield .10 .30
320 Curt Schilling .10 .30
321 Greg Vaughn .05 .15
322 Jay Howell .05 .15
323 Todd Hundley .05 .15
324 Chris Sabo .05 .15
325 Stan Javier .05 .15
326 Willie Greene .05 .15
327 Hipolito Pichardo .05 .15
328 Doug Strange .05 .15
329 Dan Wilson .05 .15
330 Checklist .05 .15
331 Omar Vizquel .20 .50
332 Scott Servais .05 .15
333 Bob Tewksbury .05 .15
334 Matt Williams .10 .30
335 Tom Foley .05 .15
336 Jeff Russell .05 .15
337 Scott Leius .05 .15
338 Ivan Rodriguez .20 .50
339 Kevin Seitzer .05 .15
340 Jose Rijo .05 .15
341 Eduardo Perez .05 .15
342 Kirk Gibson .10 .30
343 Randy Milligan .05 .15
344 Edgar Martinez .20 .50
345 Fred McGriff .20 .50
346 Kurt Abbott RC .05 .15
347 John Kruk .10 .30
348 Mike Felder .05 .15
349 Dave Staton .05 .15
350 Kenny Lofton .10 .30
351 Graeme Lloyd .05 .15
352 David Segui .05 .15
353 Danny Tartabull .05 .15
354 Bob Welch .05 .15
355 Duane Ward .05 .15
356 Karl Rhodes .05 .15
357 Lee Smith .10 .30
358 Chris James .05 .15
359 Walt Weiss .05 .15
360 Pedro Munoz .05 .15
361 Paul Sorrento .05 .15
362 Todd Worrell .05 .15
363 Bob Hamelin .05 .15
364 Julio Franco .10 .30
365 Roberto Petagine .05 .15
366 Willie McGee .10 .30
367 Pedro Martinez .30 .75
368 Ken Griffey Jr. .50 1.25
369 B.J. Surhoff .10 .30
370 Kevin Mitchell .05 .15
371 John Doherty .05 .15
372 Manuel Lee .05 .15
373 Terry Mulholland .05 .15
374 Zane Smith .05 .15
375 Otis Nixon .05 .15
376 Jody Reed .05 .15
377 Doug Jones .05 .15
378 John Olerud .10 .30
379 Greg Swindell .05 .15
380 Checklist .05 .15
381 Royce Clayton .05 .15
382 Jim Thome .20 .50
383 Steve Finley .10 .30
384 Ray Lankford .10 .30
385 Henry Rodriguez .05 .15
386 Dave Magadan .05 .15
387 Gary Redus .05 .15
388 Orlando Merced .05 .15
389 Tom Gordon .05 .15
390 Luis Polonia .05 .15
391 Mark McGwire .75 2.00
392 Mark Lemke .05 .15
393 Doug Henry .05 .15
394 Chuck Finley .10 .30
395 Paul Molitor .10 .30
396 Randy Myers .05 .15
397 Larry Walker .10 .30
398 Pete Harnisch .05 .15
399 Darren Lewis .05 .15
400 Frank Thomas .30 .75
401 Jack Morris .10 .30
402 Greg Hibbard .05 .15
403 Jeffrey Hammonds .05 .15
404 Will Clark .20 .50
405 Travis Fryman .10 .30
406 Scott Sanderson .05 .15
407 Gene Harris .05 .15
408 Chuck Carr .05 .15
409 Ozzie Smith .50 1.25
410 Kent Mercker .05 .15
411 Andy Van Slyke .20 .50
412 Jimmy Key .10 .30
413 Pat Mahomes .05 .15
414 John Wetteland .10 .30
415 Todd Jones .05 .15
416 Greg Harris .05 .15
417 Kevin Stocker .05 .15
418 Juan Gonzalez .10 .30
419 Pete Smith .05 .15
420 Pat Listach .05 .15
421 Trevor Hoffman .20 .50
422 Scott Fletcher .05 .15
423 Mark Lewis .05 .15
424 Mickey Morandini .05 .15
425 Ryne Sandberg .50 1.25
426 Erik Hanson .05 .15
427 Gary Gaetti .10 .30
428 Harold Reynolds .10 .30
429 Mark Portugal .05 .15
430 David Valle .05 .15
431 Mitch Williams .05 .15
432 Howard Johnson .05 .15
433 Hal Morris .05 .15
434 Tom Henke .05 .15
435 Shane Mack .05 .15
436 Mike Piazza .60 1.50
437 Bret Saberhagen .10 .30
438 Jose Mesa .05 .15
439 Jaime Navarro .05 .15
440 Checklist .05 .15
A300 Frank Thomas .75 2.00
Leaf 5th Anniversary

1995 Leaf

The 1995 Leaf set was issued in two series of 200 standard-size cards for a total of 400. Full-bleed fronts contain diamond-shaped player hologram in the upper left. The team name is done in silver foil up the left side. Peculiar backs contain two photos, the card number within a stamp or seal like emblem in the upper right and '94 and career stats graph toward bottom left. Hideo Nomo is the only key Rookie Card in this set.

COMPLETE SET (400) 16.00 40.00
COMP. SERIES 1 (200) 6.00 15.00
COMP. SERIES 2 (200) 10.00 25.00
1 Frank Thomas .30 .75
2 Carlos Garcia .05 .15
3 Todd Hundley .05 .15
4 Damion Easley .05 .15
5 Roberto Mejia .05 .15
6 John Mabry .05 .15
7 Aaron Sele .05 .15
8 Kenny Lofton .10 .30
9 John Doherty .05 .15
10 Joe Carter .10 .30
11 Mike Lansing .05 .15
12 John Valentin .05 .15
13 Ismael Valdes .05 .15
14 Dave McCarty .05 .15
15 Melvin Nieves .05 .15
16 Bobby Jones .05 .15
17 Trevor Hoffman .10 .30

18 John Smoltz .20 .50
19 Leo Gomez .05 .15
20 Roger Pavlik .05 .15
21 Dean Palmer .10 .30
22 Rickey Henderson .30 .75
23 Eddie Taubensee .05 .15
24 Damon Buford .05 .15
25 Mark Wohlers .05 .15
26 Jim Edmonds .20 .50
27 Wilson Alvarez .05 .15
28 Matt Williams .10 .30
29 Jeff Montgomery .05 .15
30 Shawon Dunston .05 .15
31 Tom Pagnozzi .05 .15
32 Jose Lind .05 .15
33 Royce Clayton .05 .15
34 Cal Eldred .05 .15
35 Chris Gomez .05 .15
36 Henry Rodriguez .05 .15
37 Dave Fleming .05 .15
38 Jon Lieber .05 .15
39 Scott Servais .05 .15
40 Wade Boggs .20 .50
41 John Olerud .10 .30
42 Eddie Williams .05 .15
43 Paul Sorrento .05 .15
44 Ron Karkovice .05 .15
45 Kevin Foster .05 .15
46 Miguel Jimenez .05 .15
47 Reggie Sanders .10 .30
48 Rondell White .10 .30
49 Scott Leius .05 .15
50 Jose Valentin .05 .15
51 Wm. VanLandingham .05 .15
52 Denny Hocking .05 .15
53 Jeff Fassero .05 .15
54 Chris Hoiles .05 .15
55 Walt Weiss .05 .15
56 Geronimo Berroa .05 .15
57 Rich Rowland .05 .15
58 Dave Weathers .05 .15
59 Sterling Hitchcock .05 .15
60 Raul Mondesi .10 .30
61 Rusty Greer .10 .30
62 David Justice .10 .30
63 Cecil Fielder .10 .30
64 Brian Jordan .10 .30
65 Mike Lieberthal .10 .30
66 Rick Aguilera .05 .15
67 Chuck Finley .10 .30
68 Andy Ashby .05 .15
69 Alex Fernandez .05 .15
70 Ed Sprague .05 .15
71 Steve Buechele .05 .15
72 Willie Greene .05 .15
73 Dave Nilsson .05 .15
74 Bret Saberhagen .10 .30
75 Jimmy Key .10 .30
76 Darren Lewis .05 .15
77 Steve Cooke .05 .15
78 Kirk Gibson .10 .30
79 Ray Lankford .10 .30
80 Paul O'Neill .20 .50
81 Mike Bordick .05 .15
82 Wes Chamberlain .05 .15
83 Rico Brogna .05 .15
84 Kevin Appier .10 .30
85 Juan Guzman .05 .15
86 Kevin Seitzer .05 .15
87 Mickey Morandini .05 .15
88 Pedro Martinez .20 .50
89 Matt Mieske .05 .15
90 Tino Martinez .20 .50
91 Paul Shuey .05 .15
92 Bip Roberts .05 .15
93 Chili Davis .10 .30
94 Deion Sanders .20 .50
95 Darrell Whitmore .05 .15
96 Joe Orsulak .05 .15
97 Bret Boone .10 .30
98 Kent Mercker .05 .15
99 Scott Livingstone .05 .15
100 Brady Anderson .10 .30
101 James Mouton .05 .15
102 Jose Rijo .05 .15
103 Bobby Munoz .05 .15
104 Ramon Martinez .05 .15
105 Bernie Williams .20 .50
106 Troy Neel .05 .15
107 Ivan Rodriguez .20 .50
108 Salomon Torres .05 .15
109 Johnny Ruffin .05 .15
110 Darryl Kile .10 .30
111 Bobby Ayala .05 .15
112 Ron Darling .05 .15
113 Jose Lima .05 .15
114 Joey Hamilton .05 .15
115 Greg Maddux .50 1.25
116 Greg Colbrunn .05 .15
117 Ozzie Guillen .10 .30
118 Brian Anderson .05 .15
119 Jeff Bagwell .20 .50
120 Pat Listach .05 .15
121 Sandy Alomar Jr. .05 .15
122 Jose Vizcaino .05 .15
123 Rick Helling .05 .15
124 Allen Watson .05 .15
125 Pedro Munoz .05 .15
126 Craig Biggio .20 .50
127 Kevin Stocker .05 .15
128 Wil Cordero .05 .15
129 Rafael Palmeiro .20 .50
130 Gar Finnvold .05 .15
131 Darren Hall .05 .15
132 Heathcliff Slocumb .05 .15
133 Darrin Fletcher .05 .15
134 Cal Ripken 1.00 2.50
135 Dante Bichette .10 .30
136 Don Slaught .05 .15
137 Pedro Astacio .05 .15
138 Ryan Thompson .05 .15
139 Greg Gohr .05 .15
140 Javier Lopez .10 .30
141 Lenny Dykstra .10 .30
142 Pat Rapp .05 .15
143 Mark Kiefer .05 .15
144 Greg Gagne .05 .15
145 Eduardo Perez .05 .15
146 Felix Fermin .05 .15
147 Jeff Frye .05 .15
148 Terry Steinbach .05 .15
149 Jim Eisenreich .05 .15
150 Brad Ausmus .10 .30
151 Randy Myers .05 .15
152 Rick White .05 .15
153 Mark Portugal .05 .15
154 Delino DeShields .05 .15
155 Scott Cooper .05 .15
156 Pat Hentgen .05 .15
157 Mark Gubicza .05 .15
158 Carlos Baerga .05 .15
159 Joe Girardi .05 .15
160 Rey Sanchez .05 .15
161 Todd Jones .05 .15
162 Luis Polonia .05 .15
163 Steve Trachsel .05 .15
164 Roberto Hernandez .05 .15
165 John Patterson .05 .15
166 Rene Arocha .05 .15
167 Will Clark .20 .50
168 Jim Leyritz .05 .15
169 Todd Van Poppel .05 .15
170 Robb Nen .10 .30
171 Midre Cummings .05 .15
172 Jay Buhner .10 .30
173 Kevin Tapani .05 .15
174 Mark Lemke .05 .15
175 Marcus Moore .05 .15
176 Wayne Kirby .05 .15
177 Rich Amaral .05 .15
178 Lou Whitaker .10 .30
179 Jay Bell .10 .30
180 Rick Wilkins .05 .15
181 Paul Molitor .10 .30
182 Gary Sheffield .10 .30
183 Kirby Puckett .30 .75
184 Cliff Floyd .10 .30
185 Darren Oliver .05 .15
186 Tim Naehring .05 .15
187 John Hudek .05 .15
188 Eric Young .05 .15
189 Roger Salkeld .05 .15
190 Kirt Manwaring .05 .15
191 Kurt Abbott .05 .15
192 David Nied .05 .15
193 Todd Zeile .05 .15
194 Wally Joyner .10 .30
195 Dennis Martinez .10 .30
196 Billy Ashley .05 .15
197 Ben McDonald .05 .15
198 Bob Hamelin .05 .15
199 Chris Turner .05 .15
200 Lance Johnson .05 .15
201 Willie Banks .05 .15
202 Juan Gonzalez .10 .30
203 Scott Sanders .05 .15
204 Scott Brosius .10 .30
205 Curt Schilling .10 .30
206 Alex Gonzalez .05 .15
207 Travis Fryman .10 .30
208 Tim Raines .10 .30
209 Steve Avery .05 .15
210 Hal Morris .05 .15
211 Ken Griffey Jr. .50 1.25
212 Ozzie Smith .50 1.25
213 Chuck Carr .05 .15
214 Ryan Klesko .10 .30
215 Robin Ventura .10 .30
216 Luis Gonzalez .10 .30
217 Ken Ryan .05 .15
218 Mike Piazza .50 1.25
219 Matt Walbeck .05 .15
220 Jeff Kent .10 .30
221 Orlando Miller .05 .15
222 Kenny Rogers .10 .30
223 J.T. Snow .10 .30
224 Alan Trammell .10 .30
225 John Franco .10 .30
226 Gerald Williams .05 .15
227 Andy Benes .05 .15
228 Dan Wilson .05 .15
229 Dave Hollins .05 .15
230 Vinny Castilla .10 .30
231 Devon White .10 .30
232 Fred McGriff .20 .50
233 Quilvio Veras .05 .15
234 Tom Candiotti .05 .15
235 Jason Bere .05 .15
236 Mark Langston .05 .15
237 Mel Rojas .05 .15
238 Chuck Knoblauch .10 .30
239 Bernard Gilkey .05 .15
240 Mark McGwire .75 2.00
241 Kirk Rueter .05 .15
242 Pat Kelly .05 .15
243 Ruben Sierra .10 .30
244 Randy Johnson .30 .75
245 Shane Reynolds .05 .15
246 Danny Tartabull .05 .15
247 Darryl Hamilton .05 .15
248 Danny Bautista .05 .15
249 Tom Gordon .05 .15
250 Tom Glavine .20 .50
251 Orlando Merced .05 .15
252 Eric Karros .10 .30
253 Benji Gil .05 .15
254 Sean Bergman .05 .15
255 Roger Clemens .60 1.50
256 Roberto Alomar .20 .50
257 Benito Santiago .10 .30
258 Robby Thompson .05 .15
259 Marvin Freeman .05 .15
260 Jose Offerman .05 .15
261 Greg Vaughn .05 .15
262 David Segui .05 .15
263 Geronimo Pena .05 .15
264 Tim Salmon .20 .50
265 Eddie Murray .30 .75
266 Mariano Duncan .05 .15
267 Hideo Nomo RC .75 2.00
268 Derek Bell .05 .15
269 Mo Vaughn .10 .30
270 Jeff King .05 .15
271 Edgar Martinez .20 .50
272 Sammy Sosa .30 .75
273 Scott Ruffcorn .05 .15
274 Darren Daulton .10 .30
275 John Jaha .05 .15
276 Andres Galarraga .10 .30
277 Mark Grace .20 .50
278 Mike Moore .05 .15
279 Barry Bonds .75 2.00
280 Manny Ramirez .20 .50
281 Ellis Burks .10 .30
282 Greg Swindell .05 .15
283 Barry Larkin .20 .50
284 Albert Belle .10 .30
285 Shawn Green .10 .30
286 John Roper .05 .15
287 Scott Erickson .05 .15
288 Moises Alou .10 .30
289 Mike Blowers .05 .15
290 Brent Gates .05 .15
291 Sean Berry .05 .15
292 Mike Stanley .05 .15
293 Jeff Conine .10 .30
294 Tim Wallach .05 .15
295 Bobby Bonilla .10 .30
296 Bruce Ruffin .05 .15
297 Chad Curtis .05 .15
298 Mike Greenwell .05 .15
299 Tony Gwynn .40 1.00
300 Russ Davis .05 .15
301 Danny Jackson .05 .15
302 Pete Harnisch .05 .15
303 Don Mattingly .75 2.00
304 Rheal Cormier .05 .15
305 Larry Walker .10 .30
306 Hector Carrasco .05 .15
307 Jason Jacome .05 .15
308 Phil Plantier .05 .15
309 Harold Baines .10 .30
310 Mitch Williams .05 .15
311 Charles Nagy .05 .15
312 Ken Caminiti .10 .30
313 Alex Rodriguez .75 2.00
314 Chris Sabo .05 .15
315 Gary Gaetti .10 .30
316 Andre Dawson .10 .30
317 Mark Clark .05 .15
318 Vince Coleman .05 .15
319 Brad Clontz .05 .15
320 Steve Finley .10 .30
321 Doug Drabek .05 .15
322 Mark McLemore .05 .15
323 Stan Javier .05 .15
324 Ron Gant .10 .30
325 Charlie Hayes .05 .15
326 Carlos Delgado .10 .30
327 Ricky Bottalico .05 .15
328 Rod Beck .05 .15
329 Mark Acre .05 .15
330 Chris Bosio .05 .15
331 Tony Phillips .05 .15
332 Garret Anderson .10 .30
333 Pat Meares .05 .15
334 Todd Worrell .05 .15
335 Marquis Grissom .10 .30
336 Brent Mayne .05 .15
337 Lee Tinsley .05 .15
338 Terry Pendleton .10 .30
339 David Cone .10 .30
340 Tony Fernandez .05 .15
341 Jim Bullinger .05 .15
342 Armando Benitez .05 .15
343 John Smiley .05 .15
344 Dan Miceli .05 .15
345 Charles Johnson .10 .30
346 Lee Smith .10 .30
347 Brian McRae .05 .15
348 Jim Thome .20 .50
349 Jose Oliva .05 .15
350 Terry Mulholland .05 .15
351 Tom Henke .05 .15
352 Dennis Eckersley .10 .30
353 Sid Fernandez .05 .15
354 Paul Wagner .05 .15
355 John Dettmer .05 .15
356 John Wetteland .10 .30
357 John Burkett .05 .15
358 Marty Cordova .05 .15
359 Norm Charlton .05 .15
360 Mike Devereaux .05 .15
361 Alex Cole .05 .15
362 Brett Butler .10 .30
363 Mickey Tettleton .05 .15
364 Al Martin .05 .15
365 Tony Tarasco .05 .15
366 Pat Mahomes .05 .15
367 Gary DiSarcina .05 .15
368 Bill Swift .05 .15
369 Chipper Jones .30 .75
370 Orel Hershiser .10 .30
371 Kevin Gross .05 .15
372 Dave Winfield .10 .30
373 Andujar Cedeno .05 .15
374 Jim Abbott .20 .50
375 Glenallen Hill .05 .15
376 Otis Nixon .05 .15
377 Roberto Kelly .05 .15
378 Chris Hammond .05 .15
379 Mike Macfarlane .05 .15
380 J.R. Phillips .05 .15
381 Luis Alicea .05 .15
382 Bret Barberie .05 .15
383 Tom Goodwin .05 .15
384 Mark Whiten .05 .15
385 Jeffrey Hammonds .05 .15
386 Omar Vizquel .20 .50
387 Mike Mussina .20 .50
388 Ricky Bones .05 .15
389 Steve Ontiveros .05 .15
390 Jeff Blauser .05 .15
391 Jose Canseco .20 .50
392 Bob Tewksbury .05 .15
393 Jacob Brumfield .05 .15
394 Doug Jones .05 .15
395 Ken Hill .05 .15
396 Pat Borders .05 .15
397 Carl Everett .10 .30
398 Gregg Jefferies .05 .15
399 Jack McDowell .05 .15
400 Denny Neagle .10 .30
NNO Frank Thomas Jumbo/10,000
NNO Barry Bonds Jumbo/10,000

1995 Leaf 300 Club

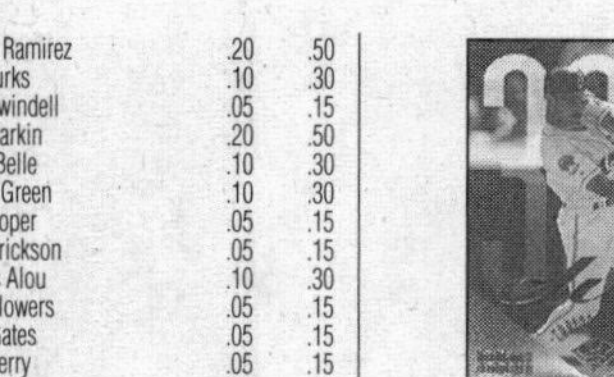

Randomly inserted in first and second series mini and retail packs at a rate of one every 12 packs, this set depicts all 18 players who had a career average of .300 or better entering the 1995 campaign. Full-bleed backs list the 18 players and their averages to that point.

COMPLETE SET (18) 40.00 100.00
COMPLETE SERIES 1 (9) 15.00 35.00
COMPLETE SERIES 2 (9) 25.00 65.00
1 Frank Thomas 2.50 6.00
2 Paul Molitor 1.00 2.50
3 Mike Piazza 4.00 10.00
4 Moises Alou 1.00 2.50
5 Mike Greenwell .50 1.25
6 Will Clark 1.50 4.00
7 Hal Morris .50 1.25
8 Edgar Martinez 1.50 4.00
9 Carlos Baerga .50 1.25
10 Ken Griffey Jr. 4.00 10.00
11 Wade Boggs 1.50 4.00
12 Jeff Bagwell 1.50 4.00
13 Tony Gwynn 3.00 8.00
14 John Kruk .50 1.25
15 Don Mattingly 6.00 15.00
16 Mark Grace 1.50 4.00
17 Kirby Puckett 2.50 6.00
18 Kenny Lofton 1.00 2.50

1995 Leaf Checklists

Four checklist cards were randomly inserted in either series for a total of eight standard-size cards. The set was composed of major award winners from the 1994 season.

COMPLETE SERIES 1 (4) .60 1.50
COMPLETE SERIES 2 (4) 1.25 3.00
1 Bob Hamelin UER .05 .15
(Name spelled Hamlin)
2 David Cone .10 .30
3 Frank Thomas .30 .75
4 Paul O'Neill .20 .50
5 Raul Mondesi .10 .30
6 Greg Maddux .50 1.25
7 Tony Gwynn .40 1.00
8 Jeff Bagwell .20 .50

1995 Leaf Cornerstones

Cards from this six-card standard-size set were randomly inserted in first series packs. Horizontally designed, leading first and thrid basemen from the same team are featured.

COMPLETE SET (6) 3.00 8.00
1 Frank Thomas / Robin Ventura .60 1.50
2 Cecil Fielder / Travis Fryman .25 .60
3 Don Mattingly / Wade Boggs 1.50 4.00
4 Jeff Bagwell / Ken Caminiti .40 1.00
5 Will Clark / Dean Palmer .40 1.00
6 J.R. Phillips / Matt Williams .25 .60

1995 Leaf Gold Rookies

Inserted in every other first series pack, this 16-card standard-size set showcases those that were expected to have an impact in 1995.

COMPLETE SET (16) 3.00 6.00
1 Alex Rodriguez 1.25 3.00
2 Garret Anderson .20 .50
3 Shawn Green .20 .50
4 Armando Benitez .08 .25
5 Darren Dreifort .08 .25
6 Orlando Miller .08 .25
7 Jose Oliva .08 .25
8 Ricky Bottalico .08 .25
9 Charles Johnson .20 .50
10 Brian L.Hunter .20 .50
11 Ray McDavid .08 .25
12 Chan Ho Park .08 .25
13 Mike Kelly .08 .25
14 Cory Bailey .08 .25
15 Alex Gonzalez .08 .25
16 Andrew Lorraine .08 .25

1995 Leaf Gold Stars

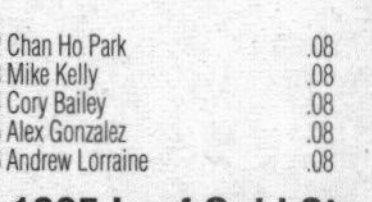

Randomly inserted in first and second series packs at a rate of one in 110, this 14-card standard-size set (eight first series, six second series) showcases some of the game's superstars.Individually numbered on back out of 10,000, the cards feature fronts that have a player photo superimposed metallic, refractive background..

COMPLETE SET (14) 60.00 160.00
COMPLETE SERIES 1 (8) 30.00 80.00
COMPLETE SERIES 2 (6) 30.00 80.00
1 Jeff Bagwell 2.50 6.00
2 Albert Belle 1.50 4.00
3 Tony Gwynn 5.00 12.00
4 Ken Griffey Jr. 6.00 15.00
5 Barry Bonds 10.00 25.00
6 Don Mattingly 10.00 25.00
7 Raul Mondesi 1.50 4.00
8 Joe Carter 1.50 4.00
9 Greg Maddux 6.00 15.00
10 Frank Thomas 4.00 10.00
11 Mike Piazza 6.00 15.00
12 Jose Canseco 2.50 6.00
13 Kirby Puckett 4.00 10.00
14 Matt Williams 1.50 4.00

1995 Leaf Great Gloves

This 16-card standard-size set was randomly inserted in series two packs at a rate of one every two packs. The cards are numbered "X" of 16 in the upper right.

COMPLETE SET (16) 4.00 10.00
1 Jeff Bagwell .20 .50
2 Roberto Alomar .20 .50
3 Barry Bonds .75 2.00
4 Wade Boggs .20 .50
5 Andres Galarraga .10 .30
6 Ken Griffey Jr. .50 1.25
7 Marquis Grissom .10 .30
8 Kenny Lofton .10 .30
9 Barry Larkin .20 .50
10 Don Mattingly .75 2.00
11 Greg Maddux .50 1.25
12 Kirby Puckett .30 .75
13 Ozzie Smith .50 1.25
14 Cal Ripken Jr. 1.00 2.50
15 Matt Williams .10 .30
16 Ivan Rodriguez .20 .50

1995 Leaf Heading for the Hall

This eight-card standard-size set was randomly inserted into series two hobby packs. The cards are individually numbered out of 5,000 as well.

COMPLETE SET (8) 60.00 150.00
1 Frank Thomas 5.00 12.00
2 Ken Griffey Jr. 8.00 20.00
3 Jeff Bagwell 3.00 8.00
4 Barry Bonds 12.50 30.00
5 Kirby Puckett 5.00 12.00
6 Cal Ripken 15.00 40.00
7 Tony Gwynn 6.00 15.00
8 Paul Molitor 2.00 5.00

1995 Leaf Opening Day

This eight-card standard-size set was available through a wrapper mail-in offer. Upon receipt of eight 1995 Leaf, Studio or Donruss wrappers, a collector received this set. Besides the wrappers, the set cost $2 in shipping and handling and the final deadline was Aug. 31, 1995. The fronts have the words "1995 Opening Day" on the left with the playerâ ™s picture and name on the right. The "Leaf 95" logo is in the upper right corner. All photos were taken on opening day including shots of Larry Walker as a Colorado Rockie and Jose Canseco in his Boston Red Sox debut. The cards are numbered "X" of 8 in the upper right corner.

COMPLETE SET (8) 7.00 10.00
1 Frank Thomas .25 .60
2 Jeff Bagwell .30 .75
3 Barry Bonds .60 1.50
4 Ken Griffey Jr. .75 2.00
5 Mike Piazza .75 2.00
6 Cal Ripken 1.25 3.00
7 Jose Canseco .25 .60
8 Larry Walker .15 .40

1995 Leaf Slideshow

This 16-card standard-size set was issued eight per series and randomly inserted at a rate of one per 30 hobby packs and one per 36 retail packs. The eight cards in the first series are numbered 1A-8A and repeated with different photos in the second series as 1B-8B. Both versions carry the same value.

COMPLETE SET (16) 30.00 80.00
COMPLETE SERIES 1 (8) 15.00 40.00
COMPLETE SERIES 2 (8) 15.00 40.00
1A Raul Mondesi .60 1.50
2A Frank Thomas 1.50 4.00
3A Fred McGriff 1.00 2.50
4A Cal Ripken 5.00 12.00
5A Jeff Bagwell 1.00 2.50
6A Will Clark 1.00 2.50
7A Matt Williams .60 1.50
8A Ken Griffey Jr. 2.50 6.00

1995 Leaf Statistical Standouts Promos

One of nine different Staistical Standouts Promo cards was inserted into 1995 Leaf dealer order forms and hobby media press releases. The cards parallel the standard Statistical Standouts inserts except for the clipped upper right corner and lack of serial numbering on back.

COMPLETE SET 12.00 25.00
1 Joe Carter .30 .75
2 Ken Griffey Jr. 2.00 5.00
3 Don Mattingly 1.50 4.00
4 Fred McGriff .40 1.00
5 Paul Molitor 1.00 2.50
6 Kirby Puckett 1.25 3.00
7 Cal Ripken 3.00 8.00
8 Frank Thomas .75 2.00
9 Matt Williams .50 1.25

1995 Leaf Statistical Standouts

Randomly inserted in first series hobby packs at a rate of one in 70, this set features nine players who stood out from the rest statistically.

COMPLETE SET (9) 60.00 150.00
1 Joe Carter 3.00 8.00
2 Ken Griffey Jr. 10.00 25.00
3 Don Mattingly 15.00 40.00
4 Fred McGriff 4.00 10.00
5 Paul Molitor 3.00 8.00
6 Kirby Puckett 6,00 15.00
7 Cal Ripken 20.00 50.00
8 Frank Thomas 6.00 15.00
9 Matt Williams 3.00 8.00

1995 Leaf Thomas

This six-card standard-size set was randomly inserted into series two packs at a rate of one in eighteen.

COMPLETE SET (6) 4.00 10.00
COMMON CARD (1-6) .75 2.00

1995 Leaf Thomas Akklaim

This one-card set features a borderless action photo of Frank Thomas with a small head photo in the upper left inside a baseball diamond frame. The front displays the words "Big Hurt" in big block silver foil lettering. The back shows player information and career statistics on a player picture background.

1 Frank Thomas 2.00 5.00

1996 Leaf

The 1996 Leaf set was issued in one series totalling 220 cards. The fronts feature color action player photos with silver foil printing and lines forming a border on the left and bottom. The backs display another player photo with 1995 season and career statistics. Card number 210 is a checklist for the insert sets and cards number 211-220 feature rookies. The fronts of these 10 cards are different in design from the first 200 with a color action player cut-out over a green-shadow background of the same picture and gold lettering.

COMPLETE SET (220) 8.00 20.00
1 John Smoltz .20 .50
2 Dennis Eckersley .10 .30
3 Delino DeShields .10 .30
4 Cliff Floyd .10 .30
5 Chuck Finley .10 .30
6 Cecil Fielder .10 .30
7 Tim Naehring .10 .30
8 Carlos Perez .10 .30
9 Brad Ausmus .10 .30
10 Matt Lawton RC .15 .40
11 Alan Trammell .10 .30
12 Steve Finley .10 .30
13 Paul O'Neill .20 .50
14 Gary Sheffield .10 .30
15 Mark McGwire .75 2.00
16 Bernie Williams .20 .50
17 Jeff Montgomery .10 .30
18 Chan Ho Park .10 .30
19 Greg Vaughn .10 .30
20 Jeff Kent .10 .30
21 Cal Ripken 1.00 2.50
22 Charles Johnson .10 .30
23 Eric Karros .10 .30
24 Alex Rodriguez .60 1.50
25 Chris Snopek .10 .30
26 Jason Isringhausen .10 .30
27 Chili Davis .10 .30
28 Chipper Jones .30 .75
29 Bret Saberhagen .10 .30
30 Tony Clark .10 .30
31 Marty Cordova .10 .30
32 Dwayne Hosey .10 .30
33 Fred McGriff .20 .50
34 Deion Sanders .20 .50
35 Orlando Merced .10 .30
36 Brady Anderson .10 .30
37 Ray Lankford .10 .30
38 Manny Ramirez .20 .50
39 Alex Fernandez .10 .30
40 Greg Colbrunn .10 .30
41 Ken Griffey Jr. .50 1.25
42 Mickey Morandini .10 .30
43 Chuck Knoblauch .10 .30
44 Quinton McCracken .10 .30
45 Tim Salmon .20 .50
46 Jose Mesa .10 .30
47 Marquis Grissom .10 .30
48 Greg Maddux .10 .30
Randy Johnson CL
49 Raul Mondesi .10 .30
50 Mark Grudzielanek .10 .30
51 Ray Durham .10 .30
52 Matt Williams .10 .30
53 Bob Hamelin .10 .30
54 Lenny Dykstra .10 .30
55 Jeff King .10 .30
56 LaTroy Hawkins .10 .30
57 Terry Pendleton .10 .30
58 Kevin Stocker .10 .30
59 Ozzie Timmons .10 .30
60 David Justice .10 .30
61 Ricky Bottalico .10 .30
62 Andy Ashby .10 .30
63 Larry Walker .10 .30
64 Jose Canseco .20 .50
65 Bret Boone .10 .30
66 Shawn Green .10 .30
67 Chad Curtis .10 .30
68 Travis Fryman .10 .30
69 Roger Clemens .60 1.50
70 David Bell .10 .30
71 Rusty Greer .10 .30
72 Bob Higginson .10 .30
73 Joey Hamilton .10 .30
74 Kevin Seitzer .10 .30
75 Julian Tavarez .10 .30
76 Troy Percival .10 .30
77 Kirby Puckett .30 .75
78 Barry Bonds .75 2.00
79 Michael Tucker .10 .30
80 Paul Molitor .10 .30
81 Carlos Garcia .10 .30
82 Johnny Damon .20 .50
83 Mike Hampton .10 .30
84 Ariel Prieto .10 .30
85 Tony Tarasco .10 .30
86 Pete Schourek .10 .30
87 Tom Glavine .20 .50
88 Rondell White .10 .30
89 Jim Edmonds .10 .30
90 Robby Thompson .10 .30
91 Wade Boggs .20 .50
92 Pedro Martinez .20 .50
93 Gregg Jefferies .10 .30
94 Albert Belle .10 .30
95 Benji Gil .10 .30
96 Denny Neagle .10 .30
97 Mark Langston .10 .30
98 Sandy Alomar Jr. .10 .30
99 Tony Gwynn .40 1.00
100 Todd Hundley .10 .30
101 Dante Bichette .10 .30
102 Eddie Murray .30 .75
103 Lyle Mouton .10 .30
104 John Jaha .10 .30
105 Barry Larkin .10 .30
Mo Vaughn CL
106 Jon Nunnally .10 .30
107 Juan Gonzalez .10 .30
108 Kevin Appier .10 .30
109 Brian McRae .10 .30
110 Lee Smith .10 .30
111 Tim Wakefield .10 .30
112 Sammy Sosa .30 .75
113 Jay Buhner .10 .30
114 Garret Anderson .10 .30
115 Edgar Martinez .20 .50
116 Edgardo Alfonzo .10 .30
117 Billy Ashley .10 .30
118 Joe Carter .10 .30
119 Javy Lopez .10 .30
120 Bobby Bonilla .10 .30
121 Ken Caminiti .10 .30
122 Barry Larkin .20 .50
123 Shannon Stewart .10 .30
124 Orel Hershiser .10 .30
125 Jeff Conine .10 .30
126 Mark Grace .20 .50
127 Kenny Lofton .10 .30
128 Luis Gonzalez .10 .30
129 Rico Brogna .10 .30
130 Mo Vaughn .10 .30
131 Brad Radke .10 .30
132 Jose Herrera .10 .30
133 Rick Aguilera .10 .30
134 Gary DiSarcina .10 .30
135 Andres Galarraga .10 .30
136 Carl Everett .10 .30
137 Steve Avery .10 .30
138 Vinny Castilla .10 .30
139 Dennis Martinez .10 .30
140 John Wetteland .10 .30
141 Alex Gonzalez .10 .30
142 Brian Jordan .10 .30
143 Todd Hollandsworth .10 .30
144 Terrell Wade .10 .30
145 Wilson Alvarez .10 .30
146 Reggie Sanders .10 .30
147 Will Clark .20 .50
148 Hideo Nomo .30 .75
149 J.T.Snow .10 .30
150 Frank Thomas .30 .75
151 Ivan Rodriguez .20 .50
152 Jay Bell .10 .30
153 Hideo Nomo CL .10 .30
Marty Cordova
154 David Cone .10 .30
155 Roberto Alomar .20 .50
156 Carlos Delgado .10 .30
157 Carlos Baerga .10 .30
158 Geronimo Berroa .10 .30
159 Joe Vitiello .10 .30
160 Terry Steinbach .10 .30
161 Doug Drabek .10 .30
162 David Segui .10 .30
163 Ozzie Smith .50 1.25
164 Kurt Abbott .10 .30
165 Randy Johnson .30 .75
166 John Valentin .10 .30
167 Mickey Tettleton .10 .30
168 Ruben Sierra .10 .30
169 Jim Thome .20 .50
170 Mike Greenwell .10 .30
171 Quilvio Veras .10 .30
172 Robin Ventura .10 .30
173 Bill Pulsipher .10 .30
174 Rafael Palmeiro .20 .50
175 Hal Morris .10 .30
176 Ryan Klesko .10 .30
177 Eric Young .10 .30
178 Shane Andrews .10 .30
179 Brian L.Hunter .10 .30
180 Brett Butler .10 .30
181 John Olerud .10 .30
182 Moises Alou .10 .30
183 Glenallen Hill .10 .30
184 Ismael Valdes .10 .30
185 Andy Pettitte .20 .50
186 Yamil Benitez .10 .30
187 Jason Bere .10 .30
188 Dean Palmer .10 .30
189 Jimmy Haynes .10 .30
190 Trevor Hoffman .10 .30
191 Mike Mussina .20 .50
192 Greg Maddux .50 1.25
193 Ozzie Guillen .10 .30
194 Pat Listach .10 .30
195 Derek Bell .10 .30
196 Darren Daulton .10 .30
197 John Mabry .10 .30
198 Ramon Martinez .10 .30
199 Jeff Bagwell .20 .50
200 Mike Piazza .50 1.25
201 Al Martin .10 .30
202 Aaron Sele .10 .30
203 Ed Sprague .10 .30
204 Rod Beck .10 .30
205 Tony Gwynn .10 .30
Edgar Martinez CL
206 Mike Lansing .10 .30
207 Craig Biggio .20 .50
208 Jeffrey Hammonds .10 .30
209 Dave Nilsson .10 .30
210 Dante Bichette .10 .30
Albert Belle CL
211 Derek Jeter .75 2.00
212 Alan Benes .10 .30
213 Jason Schmidt .20 .50
214 Alex Ochoa .10 .30
215 Ruben Rivera .10 .30
216 Roger Cedeno .10 .30
217 Jeff Suppan .10 .30
218 Billy Wagner .10 .30
219 Mark Loretta .10 .30
220 Karim Garcia .10 .30

1996 Leaf Bronze Press Proofs

This 220-card Bronze set is parallel to the regular Leaf set and between the three types of press proofs were inserted at a rate of one in 10 packs. Similar in design to the regular set, 2,000 non-serial numbered Bronze sets were produced and feature a special holographic foil.

*STARS: 4X TO 10X BASIC CARDS
*ROOKIES: 2.5X TO 6X BASIC CARDS

1996 Leaf Gold Press Proofs

This 220-card Gold set is parallel to the regular Leaf set. Only five hundred sets were produced and they were randomly inserted into packs. One in every ten packs contained either a Bronze, Gold or Silver Press Proof. Collectors need to be careful as the Bronze and the Gold press proofs look very similar. 500 non-serial numbered sets were produced.

*STARS: 12.5X TO 30X BASIC CARDS
*ROOKIES: 8X TO 20X BASIC CARDS

1996 Leaf Silver Press Proofs

This 220-card Silver set is also a parallel to the regular Leaf issue. One thousand sets were produced and the cards were randomly inserted into packs. One in every 10 packs contains either a bronze, gold or silver press proof. 1,000 non-serial numbered sets were produced.

*STARS: 8X TO 20X BASIC CARDS
*ROOKIES: 5X TO 12X BASIC CARDS

1996 Leaf All-Star Game MVP Contenders

This 20 card set features possible contenders for the MVP at the 1996 All-Star Game held in Philadelphia. The cards were randomly inserted into packs. If the player on the front of the card won the MVP Award (which turned out to be Mike Piazza), the holder could send it in for a special Gold MVP Contenders set of which only 5,000 were produced. The fronts display a color action player photo. The backs carry the instructions on how to redeem the card. The expiration date for the redemption was August 15th, 1996. The Piazza card when returned with the redemption set had a hole in it to indicate the set had been redeemed.

COMPLETE SET (20) 15.00 40.00
1 Frank Thomas .60 1.50
2 Mike Piazza W 1.50 4.00
3 Sammy Sosa .60 1.50
4 Cal Ripken 2.00 5.00
5 Jeff Bagwell .40 1.00
6 Reggie Sanders .25 .60
7 Mo Vaughn .25 .60
8 Tony Gwynn .75 2.00
9 Dante Bichette .25 .60
10 Tim Salmon .40 1.00
11 Chipper Jones .60 1.50
12 Kenny Lofton .25 .60
13 Manny Ramirez .40 1.00
14 Barry Bonds 1.50 4.00
15 Raul Mondesi .25 .60
16 Kirby Puckett .60 1.50
17 Albert Belle .25 .60
18 Ken Griffey Jr. 1.00 2.50
19 Greg Maddux 1.00 2.50
20 Bonus Card .25 .60

1996 Leaf Gold Stars

Randomly inserted in hobby and retail packs at a rate of one in 190, this 15-card set honors some of the games great players on 22 karat gold trim cards. Only 2,500 cards of each player were printed and are individually numbered.

COMPLETE SET (15) 125.00 300.00

1 Frank Thomas 8.00 20.00
2 Dante Bichette 3.00 8.00
3 Sammy Sosa 8.00 20.00
4 Ken Griffey Jr. 12.50 30.00
5 Mike Piazza 12.50 30.00
6 Tim Salmon 5.00 12.00
7 Hideo Nomo 8.00 20.00
8 Cal Ripken 25.00 60.00
9 Chipper Jones 8.00 20.00
10 Albert Belle 3.00 8.00
11 Tony Gwynn 10.00 25.00
12 Mo Vaughn 3.00 8.00
13 Barry Larkin 5.00 12.00
14 Manny Ramirez 5.00 12.00
15 Greg Maddux 12.50 30.00

1996 Leaf Hats Off

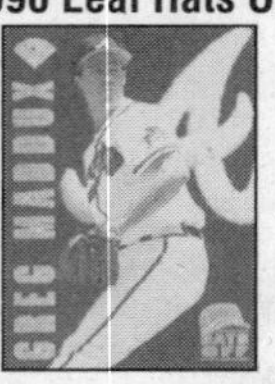

Randomly inserted in retail packs only at a rate of one in 72, this eight-card set was printed and embossed on a wool-like material with the feel of a Major League ball cap. Only 5,000 of each player was produced and is individually numbered.

COMPLETE SET (8) 40.00 100.00
1 Cal Ripken 12.50 30.00
2 Barry Larkin 2.50 6.00
3 Frank Thomas 4.00 10.00
4 Mo Vaughn 1.50 4.00
5 Ken Griffey Jr. 6.00 15.00
6 Hideo Nomo 4.00 10.00
7 Albert Belle 1.50 4.00
8 Greg Maddux 6.00 15.00

1996 Leaf Picture Perfect

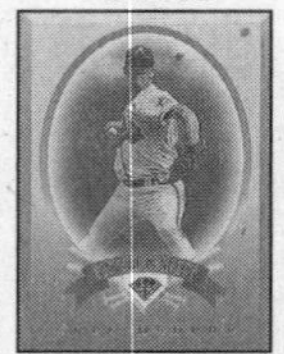

Randomly inserted in hobby (1-6) and retail (7-12) packs at a rate of one in 140, this 12-card set is printed on real wood with gold foil trim. The fronts feature a color player action framed photo. The backs carry another player photo with player information. Only 5,000 of each card were printed and each is individually numbered.

COMPLETE SET (12) 60.00 150.00
1 Frank Thomas 4.00 10.00
2 Cal Ripken 12.50 30.00
3 Greg Maddux 6.00 15.00
4 Manny Ramirez 2.50 6.00
5 Chipper Jones 4.00 10.00
6 Tony Gwynn 5.00 12.00
7 Ken Griffey Jr. 6.00 15.00
8 Albert Belle 1.50 4.00
9 Jeff Bagwell 2.50 6.00
10 Mike Piazza 6.00 15.00
11 Mo Vaughn 1.50 4.00
12 Barry Bonds 10.00 25.00

1996 Leaf Statistical Standouts

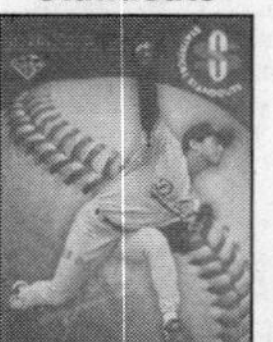

Randomly inserted in hobby packs only at a rate of one in 210, this eight-card set features players who stood out statistically. The cards were printed on a material with the feel of the leather that's between the seams or stitches of a baseball. Only 2,500 of each card was printed and each is numbered individually on the back.

COMPLETE SET (8) 60.00 150.00
1 Cal Ripken 20.00 50.00
2 Tony Gwynn 8.00 20.00
3 Frank Thomas 6.00 15.00
4 Ken Griffey Jr. 10.00 25.00
5 Hideo Nomo 6.00 15.00
6 Greg Maddux 10.00 25.00
7 Albert Belle 2.50 6.00
8 Chipper Jones 6.00 15.00

1996 Leaf Thomas Greatest Hits

Randomly inserted in hobby (1-4) and retail (5-7) packs at a rate of one in 210, this eight-card set was printed on die-cut plastic to simulate a compact disc. The cards feature the statistical highlights of Frank Thomas. The wrapper displays the details for the special mail-in offer to obtain card number 8. Five thousand sets were printed.

COMMON CARD (1-7) 5.00 12.00
COMMON EXCHANGE (8) 6.00 15.00

1996 Leaf Total Bases

Randomly inserted in hobby packs only at a rate of one in 72, this 12-card set is printed on canvas and features the top offensive stars. Only 5,000 of each card was printed and are individually numbered. The fronts carry a color action player cut-out over a base background. The backs display another player photo and 1995 stats.

COMPLETE SET (12) 40.00 100.00
1 Frank Thomas 3.00 8.00
2 Albert Belle 1.25 3.00
3 Rafael Palmeiro 2.00 5.00
4 Barry Bonds 8.00 20.00
5 Kirby Puckett 3.00 8.00
6 Joe Carter 1.25 3.00
7 Paul Molitor 1.25 3.00
8 Fred McGriff 2.00 5.00
9 Ken Griffey Jr. 5.00 12.00
10 Carlos Baerga 1.25 3.00
11 Juan Gonzalez 1.25 3.00
12 Cal Ripken 10.00 25.00

1997 Leaf

The 400-card Leaf set was issued in two separate 200-card series. 10-card packs carried a suggested retail of $2.99. Each card features color action player photos with foil enhancement. The backs carry another player photo and season and career statistics. The set contains the following subsets: Legacy (188-197/348-367), Checklists (198-200/398-400) and Gamers (368-397). Rookie Cards in this set include Jose Cruz Jr., Brian Giles and Hideki Irabu. In a tie in with the 50th anniversary of Jackie Robinson's major league debut, Donruss/Leaf also issued some collectible items. They made 42 all-leather jackets (issued to match Robinson's uniform number). There were also 311 leather jackets produced (to match Robinson's career batting average). 1,500 lithographs were also produced of which Rachel Robinson (Jackie's widow) signed 500 of them.

COMPLETE SET (400) 16.00 40.00
COMP. SERIES 1 (200) 8.00 20.00
COMP. SERIES 2 (200) 8.00 20.00
1 Wade Boggs .20 .50
2 Brian McRae .10 .30
3 Jeff D'Amico .10 .30
4 George Arias .10 .30
5 Billy Wagner .10 .30
6 Ray Lankford .10 .30
7 Will Clark .20 .50
8 Edgar Renteria .10 .30
9 Alex Ochoa .10 .30
10 Roberto Hernandez .10 .30
11 Joe Carter .10 .30
12 Gregg Jefferies .10 .30
13 Mark Grace .20 .50
14 Roberto Alomar .20 .50
15 Joe Randa .10 .30
16 Alex Rodriguez .50 1.25
17 Tony Gwynn .40 1.00
18 Steve Gibralter .10 .30
19 Scott Stahoviak .10 .30
20 Matt Williams .10 .30
21 Quinton McCracken .10 .30
22 Ugueth Urbina .10 .30
23 Jermaine Allensworth .10 .30
24 Paul Molitor .10 .30
25 Carlos Delgado .10 .30
26 Bob Abreu .20 .50
27 John Jaha .10 .30
28 Rusty Greer .10 .30
29 Kimera Bartee .10 .30
30 Ruben Rivera .10 .30
31 Jason Kendall .10 .30
32 Lance Johnson .10 .30
33 Robin Ventura .10 .30
34 Kevin Appier .10 .30
35 John Mabry .10 .30
36 Ricky Otero .10 .30
37 Mike Lansing .10 .30
38 Mark McGwire .75 2.00
39 Tim Naehring .10 .30
40 Tom Glavine .20 .50
41 Rey Ordonez .10 .30
42 Tony Clark .10 .30
43 Rafael Palmeiro .20 .50
44 Pedro Martinez .20 .50
45 Keith Lockhart .10 .30
46 Dan Wilson .10 .30
47 John Wetteland .10 .30
48 Chan Ho Park .10 .30
49 Gary Sheffield .10 .30
50 Shawn Estes .10 .30
51 Royce Clayton .10 .30
52 Jaime Navarro .10 .30
53 Raul Casanova .10 .30
54 Jeff Bagwell .20 .50
55 Barry Larkin .20 .50
56 Charles Nagy .10 .30
57 Ken Caminiti .10 .30
58 Todd Hollandsworth .10 .30
59 Pat Hentgen .10 .30
60 Jose Valentin .10 .30
61 Frank Rodriguez .10 .30
62 Mickey Tettleton .10 .30
63 Marty Cordova .10 .30
64 Cecil Fielder .10 .30
65 Barry Bonds .75 2.00
66 Scott Servais .10 .30
67 Ernie Young .10 .30
68 Wilson Alvarez .10 .30
69 Mike Grace .10 .30
70 Shane Reynolds .10 .30
71 Henry Rodriguez .10 .30
72 Eric Karros .10 .30
73 Mark Langston .10 .30
74 Scott Karl .10 .30
75 Trevor Hoffman .10 .30
76 Orel Hershiser .10 .30
77 John Smoltz .20 .50
78 Raul Mondesi .10 .30
79 Jeff Brantley .10 .30
80 Donne Wall .10 .30
81 Joey Cora .10 .30
82 Mel Rojas .10 .30
83 Chad Mottola .10 .30
84 Omar Vizquel .20 .50
85 Greg Maddux .50 1.25
86 Jamey Wright .10 .30
87 Chuck Finley .10 .30
88 Brady Anderson .10 .30
89 Alex Gonzalez .10 .30
90 Andy Benes .10 .30
91 Reggie Jefferson .10 .30
92 Paul O'Neill .20 .50
93 Javier Lopez .10 .30
94 Mark Grudzielanek .10 .30
95 Marc Newfield .10 .30
96 Kevin Ritz .10 .30
97 Fred McGriff .20 .50
98 Dwight Gooden .10 .30
99 Hideo Nomo .30 .75
100 Steve Finley .10 .30
101 Juan Gonzalez .10 .30
102 Jay Buhner .10 .30
103 Paul Wilson .10 .30
104 Alan Benes .10 .30
105 Manny Ramirez .20 .50
106 Kevin Elster .10 .30
107 Frank Thomas .30 .75
108 Orlando Miller .10 .30
109 Ramon Martinez .10 .30
110 Kenny Lofton .10 .30
111 Bernie Williams .20 .50
112 Robby Thompson .10 .30
113 Bernard Gilkey .10 .30
114 Ray Durham .10 .30
115 Jeff Cirillo .10 .30
116 Brian Jordan .10 .30
117 Rich Becker .10 .30
118 Al Leiter .10 .30
119 Mark Johnson .10 .30
120 Ellis Burks .10 .30
121 Sammy Sosa .30 .75
122 Willie Greene .10 .30
123 Michael Tucker .10 .30
124 Eddie Murray .30 .75
125 Joey Hamilton .10 .30
126 Antonio Osuna .10 .30
127 Bobby Higginson .10 .30
128 Tomas Perez .10 .30
129 Tim Salmon .20 .50
130 Mark Wohlers .10 .30
131 Charles Johnson .10 .30
132 Randy Johnson .30 .75
133 Brooks Kieschnick .10 .30
134 Al Martin .10 .30
135 Dante Bichette .10 .30
136 Andy Pettitte .20 .50
137 Jason Giambi .10 .30
138 James Baldwin .10 .30
139 Ben McDonald .10 .30
140 Shawn Green .10 .30
141 Geronimo Berroa .10 .30
142 Jose Offerman .10 .30
143 Curtis Pride .10 .30
144 Terrell Wade .10 .30
145 Ismael Valdes .10 .30
146 Mike Mussina .20 .50
147 Mariano Rivera .30 .75
148 Ken Hill .10 .30
149 Darin Erstad .10 .30
150 Jay Bell .10 .30
151 Mo Vaughn .10 .30
152 Ozzie Smith .50 1.25
153 Jose Mesa .10 .30
154 Osvaldo Fernandez .10 .30
155 Vinny Castilla .10 .30
156 Jason Isringhausen .10 .30
157 B.J. Surhoff .10 .30
158 Robert Perez .10 .30
159 Ron Coomer .10 .30
160 Darren Oliver .10 .30
161 Mike Mohler .10 .30
162 Russ Davis .10 .30
163 Bret Boone .10 .30
164 Ricky Bottalico .10 .30

Card	Low	High
165 Derek Jeter	.75	2.00
166 Orlando Merced	.10	.30
167 John Valentin	.10	.30
168 Andruw Jones	.20	.50
169 Angel Echevarria	.10	.30
170 Todd Walker	.10	.30
171 Desi Relaford	.10	.30
172 Trey Beamon	.10	.30
173 Brian Giles RC	.60	1.50
174 Scott Rolen	.20	.50
175 Shannon Stewart	.10	.30
176 Dmitri Young	.10	.30
177 Justin Thompson	.10	.30
178 Trot Nixon	.10	.30
179 Josh Booty	.10	.30
180 Robin Jennings	.10	.30
181 Marvin Benard	.10	.30
182 Luis Castillo	.10	.30
183 Wendell Magee	.10	.30
184 Vladimir Guerrero	.30	.75
185 Nomar Garciaparra	.50	1.25
186 Ryan Hancock	.10	.30
187 Mike Cameron	.10	.30
188 Cal Ripken LG	.50	1.25
189 Chipper Jones LG	.20	.50
190 Albert Belle LG	.10	.30
191 Mike Piazza LG	.30	.75
192 Chuck Knoblauch LG	.10	.30
193 Ken Griffey Jr. LG	.30	.75
194 Ivan Rodriguez LG	.10	.30
195 Jose Canseco LG	.10	.30
196 Ryne Sandberg LG	.30	.75
197 Jim Thome LG	.10	.30
198 Andy Pettitte CL	.10	.30
199 Andruw Jones CL	.10	.30
200 Derek Jeter CL	.40	1.00
201 Chipper Jones	.30	.75
202 Albert Belle	.10	.30
203 Mike Piazza	.50	1.25
204 Ken Griffey Jr.	.50	1.25
205 Ryne Sandberg	.50	1.25
206 Jose Canseco	.20	.50
207 Chili Davis	.10	.30
208 Roger Clemens	.60	1.50
209 Deion Sanders	.20	.50
210 Darryl Hamilton	.10	.30
211 Jermaine Dye	.10	.30
212 Matt Williams	.10	.30
213 Kevin Elster	.10	.30
214 John Wetteland	.10	.30
215 Garret Anderson	.10	.30
216 Kevin Brown	.10	.30
217 Matt Lawton	.10	.30
218 Cal Ripken	1.00	2.50
219 Moises Alou	.10	.30
220 Chuck Knoblauch	.10	.30
221 Ivan Rodriguez	.20	.50
222 Travis Fryman	.10	.30
223 Jim Thome	.20	.50
224 Eddie Murray	.30	.75
225 Eric Young	.10	.30
226 Ron Gant	.10	.30
227 Tony Phillips	.10	.30
228 Reggie Sanders	.10	.30
229 Johnny Damon	.20	.50
230 Bill Pulsipher	.10	.30
231 Jim Edmonds	.10	.30
232 Melvin Nieves	.10	.30
233 Ryan Klesko	.10	.30
234 David Cone	.10	.30
235 Derek Bell	.10	.30
236 Julio Franco	.10	.30
237 Juan Guzman	.10	.30
238 Larry Walker	.10	.30
239 Delino DeShields	.10	.30
240 Troy Percival	.10	.30
241 Andres Galarraga	.10	.30
242 Rondell White	.10	.30
243 John Burkett	.10	.30
244 J.T. Snow	.10	.30
245 Alex Fernandez	.10	.30
246 Edgar Martinez	.20	.50
247 Craig Biggio	.20	.50
248 Todd Hundley	.10	.30
249 Jimmy Key	.10	.30
250 Cliff Floyd	.10	.30
251 Jeff Conine	.10	.30
252 Curt Schilling	.10	.30
253 Jeff King	.10	.30
254 Tino Martinez	.20	.50
255 Carlos Baerga	.10	.30
256 Jeff Fassero	.10	.30
257 Dean Palmer	.10	.30
258 Robb Nen	.10	.30
259 Sandy Alomar Jr.	.10	.30
260 Carlos Perez	.10	.30
261 Rickey Henderson	.30	.75
262 Bobby Bonilla	.10	.30
263 Darren Daulton	.10	.30
264 Jim Leyritz	.10	.30
265 Dennis Martinez	.10	.30
266 Butch Huskey	.10	.30
267 Joe Vitiello	.10	.30
268 Steve Trachsel	.10	.30
269 Glenallen Hill	.10	.30
270 Terry Steinbach	.10	.30
271 Mark McLemore	.10	.30
272 Devon White	.10	.30
273 Jeff Kent	.10	.30
274 Tim Raines	.10	.30
275 Carlos Garcia	.10	.30
276 Hal Morris	.10	.30
277 Gary Gaetti	.10	.30
278 John Olerud	.10	.30
279 Wally Joyner	.10	.30
280 Brian Hunter	.10	.30
281 Steve Karsay	.10	.30
282 Denny Neagle	.10	.30
283 Jose Herrera	.10	.30
284 Todd Stottlemyre	.10	.30
285 Bip Roberts	.10	.30
286 Kevin Seitzer	.10	.30
287 Benji Gil	.10	.30
288 Dennis Eckersley	.10	.30
289 Brad Ausmus	.10	.30
290 Otis Nixon	.10	.30
291 Darryl Strawberry	.10	.30
292 Marquis Grissom	.10	.30
293 Darryl Kile	.10	.30
294 Quilvio Veras	.10	.30
295 Tom Goodwin	.10	.30
296 Benito Santiago	.10	.30
297 Mike Bordick	.10	.30
298 Roberto Kelly	.10	.30
299 David Justice	.10	.30
300 Carl Everett	.10	.30
301 Mark Whiten	.10	.30
302 Aaron Sele	.10	.30
303 Darren Dreifort	.10	.30
304 Bobby Jones	.10	.30
305 Fernando Vina	.10	.30
306 Ed Sprague	.10	.30
307 Andy Ashby	.10	.30
308 Tony Fernandez	.10	.30
309 Roger Pavlik	.10	.30
310 Mark Clark	.10	.30
311 Mariano Duncan	.10	.30
312 Tyler Houston	.10	.30
313 Eric Davis	.10	.30
314 Greg Vaughn	.10	.30
315 David Segui	.10	.30
316 Dave Nilsson	.10	.30
317 F.P. Santangelo	.10	.30
318 Wilton Guerrero	.10	.30
319 Jose Guillen	.10	.30
320 Kevin Orie	.10	.30
321 Derrek Lee	.20	.50
322 Bubba Trammell RC	.15	.40
323 Pokey Reese	.10	.30
324 Hideki Irabu RC	.15	.40
325 Scott Spiezio	.10	.30
326 Bartolo Colon	.10	.30
327 Damon Mashore	.10	.30
328 Ryan McGuire	.10	.30
329 Chris Carpenter	.10	.30
330 Jose Cruz Jr. RC	.15	.40
331 Todd Greene	.10	.30
332 Brian Moehler RC	.10	.30
333 Mike Sweeney	.10	.30
334 Neifi Perez	.10	.30
335 Matt Morris	.10	.30
336 Marvin Benard	.10	.30
337 Karim Garcia	.10	.30
338 Jason Dickson	.10	.30
339 Brant Brown	.10	.30
340 Jeff Suppan	.10	.30
341 Deivi Cruz RC	.15	.40
342 Antone Williamson	.10	.30
343 Curtis Goodwin	.10	.30
344 Brooks Kieschnick	.10	.30
345 Tony Womack RC	.15	.40
346 Rudy Pemberton	.10	.30
347 Todd Dunwoody	.10	.30
348 Frank Thomas LG	.20	.50
349 Andruw Jones LG	.10	.30
350 Alex Rodriguez LG	.30	.75
351 Greg Maddux LG	.30	.75
352 Jeff Bagwell LG	.10	.30
353 Juan Gonzalez LG	.10	.30
354 Barry Bonds LG	.40	1.00
355 Mark McGwire LG	.40	1.00
356 Tony Gwynn LG	.20	.50
357 Gary Sheffield LG	.10	.30
358 Derek Jeter LG	.40	1.00
359 Manny Ramirez LG	.10	.30
360 Hideo Nomo LG	.10	.30
361 Sammy Sosa LG	.20	.50
362 Paul Molitor LG	.10	.30
363 Kenny Lofton LG	.10	.30
364 Eddie Murray LG	.20	.50
365 Barry Larkin LG	.10	.30
366 Roger Clemens LG	.30	.75
367 John Smoltz LG	.10	.30
368 Alex Rodriguez GM	.30	.75
369 Frank Thomas GM	.20	.50
370 Cal Ripken GM	.50	1.25
371 Ken Griffey Jr. GM	.30	.75
372 Greg Maddux GM	.30	.75
373 Mike Piazza GM	.30	.75
374 Chipper Jones GM	.20	.50
375 Albert Belle GM	.10	.30
376 Chuck Knoblauch GM	.10	.30
377 Brady Anderson GM	.10	.30
378 David Justice GM	.10	.30
379 Randy Johnson GM	.20	.50
380 Wade Boggs GM	.10	.30
381 Kevin Brown GM	.10	.30
382 Tom Glavine GM	.10	.30
383 Raul Mondesi GM	.10	.30
384 Ivan Rodriguez GM	.10	.30
385 Larry Walker GM	.10	.30
386 Bernie Williams GM	.10	.30
387 Rusty Greer GM	.10	.30
388 Rafael Palmeiro GM	.10	.30
389 Matt Williams GM	.10	.30
390 Eric Young GM	.10	.30
391 Fred McGriff GM	.10	.30
392 Ken Caminiti GM	.10	.30
393 Roberto Alomar GM	.10	.30
394 Brian Jordan GM	.10	.30
395 Mark Grace GM	.10	.30
396 Jim Edmonds GM	.10	.30
397 Deion Sanders GM	.10	.30
398 Vladimir Guerrero CL	.20	.50
399 Darin Erstad CL	.10	.30
400 N. Garciaparra CL	.30	.75
NNO J.Robinson Reprint	10.00	25.00

1997 Leaf Fractal Matrix

Randomly inserted in packs, this 400-card set is parallel to the regular Leaf issue and features color player photos with either a bronze, silver or gold finish. Only 200 cards are bronze, 120 cards are silver, and 80 cards are gold. No card is available in more than one of the colors. In a convoluted effort, the fractal matrix parallel concept split the 400 card set into nine different tiered levels of parallels, each with print runs that varied from as many of several thousand of some cards (mostly the Bronze cards) to less than a few hundred of other cards (In the Gold X subset). Cards were split into colors (Bronze, Gold and Silver) and axis (X, Y and Z). Cards are listed in our checklist with color and axis designation. Unfortunately, the designers at Leaf failed to create any notable markings to differentiate the X, Y and Z axis for all the cards in this set. Leaf did issue an axis schematic on the back of the 1997 boxes and we've carefully incorporated that information into our checklist for accurate reference.

*BRONZE: 1.5X TO 4X BASIC CARDS
*SILVER: 2X TO 5X BASIC CARDS
*SILVER ROOKIES: .6X TO 1.5X BASIC
*GOLD Y/Z: 3X TO 8X BASIC CARDS
*GOLD X: 6X TO 15X BASIC CARDS
*GOLD X RC's: 2X TO 5X BASIC CARDS
RANDOM INSERTS IN PACKS
SEE WEBSITE FOR AXIS SCHEMATIC

1997 Leaf Fractal Matrix Die Cuts

This 400-card set is parallel to the regular set and features three different die-cut versions in three different finishes. 200 of the 400-card set are produced in the X-Axis cut with 150 of those bronze, 40 of those silver, and 10 of those gold. 120 of the 400-card set are available in type Y-Axis cut with 40 of those bronze, 60 silver, and 20 gold. Eighty of the 200-card set are produced in the Z-Axis cut with 10 of those bronze, 20 of those silver and 50 of those gold. No card was available in more than one color nor in more than one die-cut version. Unlike the non die-cut Fractal Matrix cards, these Die Cut parallels have distinguishable axis groupings based on the shape of the die cut edges.

*X-AXIS: 2X TO 5X BASIC CARDS
*X-AXIS ROOKIES: 1.25X TO 3X BASIC
*Y-AXIS: 3X TO 8X BASIC CARDS
*Y-AXIS ROOKIES: .75X TO 2X BASIC
*Z-AXIS: 2.5X TO 6X BASIC CARDS
RANDOM INSERTS IN PACKS
SEE WEBSITE FOR AXIS SCHEMATIC

1997 Leaf Banner Season

Randomly inserted in series one magazine packs, this 15-card set features color action player photos on die-cut cards and is printed on canvas card stock. Only 2500 of each card was produced and are sequentially numbered.

Card	Low	High
COMPLETE SET (15)	50.00	120.00
1 Jeff Bagwell	3.00	8.00
2 Ken Griffey Jr.	8.00	20.00
3 Juan Gonzalez	2.00	5.00
4 Frank Thomas	5.00	12.00
5 Alex Rodriguez	8.00	20.00
6 Kenny Lofton	2.00	5.00
7 Chuck Knoblauch	2.00	5.00
8 Mo Vaughn	2.00	5.00
9 Chipper Jones	5.00	12.00
10 Ken Caminiti	2.00	5.00
11 Craig Biggio	3.00	8.00
12 John Smoltz	3.00	8.00
13 Pat Hentgen	2.00	5.00
14 Derek Jeter	12.50	30.00
15 Todd Hollandsworth	2.00	5.00

1997 Leaf Dress for Success

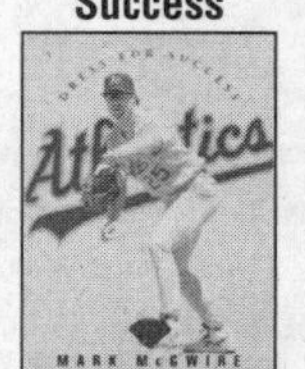

Randomly inserted in series one retail packs, this 18-card retail only set features color player photos prined on a jersey-simulated, nylon card stock and is accented with flocking on the team logo and gold-foil stamping. Only 3,500 of each card were produced and are sequentially numbered.

Card	Low	High
COMPLETE SET (18)	15.00	40.00
1 Greg Maddux	1.25	3.00
2 Cal Ripken	2.50	6.00
3 Albert Belle	.30	.75
4 Frank Thomas	.75	2.00
5 Dante Bichette	.30	.75
6 Gary Sheffield	.30	.75
7 Jeff Bagwell	.50	1.25
8 Mike Piazza	1.25	3.00
9 Mark McGwire	2.00	5.00
10 Ken Caminiti	.30	.75
11 Alex Rodriguez	1.25	3.00
12 Ken Griffey Jr.	1.25	3.00
13 Juan Gonzalez	.30	.75
14 Brian Jordan	.30	.75
15 Mo Vaughn	.30	.75
16 Ivan Rodriguez	.50	1.25
17 Andruw Jones	.50	1.25
18 Chipper Jones	.75	2.00

1997 Leaf Get-A-Grip

Randomly inserted in series one hobby packs, this 16-card double player insert set features color player photos of some of the current top pitchers matched against some of the league's current power hitters. The set is printed on full-silver, ploy-laminated card stock with gold-foil stamping. Only 3,500 of each card was produced and are sequentially numbered.

Card	Low	High
COMPLETE SET (16)	60.00	150.00
1 Ken Griffey Jr. / Greg Maddux	5.00	12.00
2 John Smoltz / Frank Thomas	3.00	8.00
3 Mike Piazza / Andy Pettitte	5.00	12.00
4 Randy Johnson / Chipper Jones	3.00	8.00
5 Tom Glavine / Alex Rodriguez	5.00	12.00
6 Pat Hentgen / Jeff Bagwell	2.00	5.00
7 Kevin Brown / Juan Gonzalez	1.25	3.00
8 Barry Bonds / Mike Mussina	8.00	20.00
9 Hideo Nomo / Albert Belle	3.00	8.00
10 Troy Percival / Andruw Jones	2.00	5.00
11 Roger Clemens / Brian Jordan	6.00	15.00
12 Paul Wilson / Ivan Rodriguez	2.00	5.00
13 Andy Benes / Mo Vaughn	1.25	3.00
14 Al Leiter / Derek Jeter	8.00	20.00
15 Bill Pulsipher / Cal Ripken	10.00	25.00
16 Mariano Rivera / Ken Caminiti	3.00	8.00

1997 Leaf Gold Stars

Randomly inserted in all series two packs, this 36-card set features color action images of some of Baseball's hottest names with actual 24kt. gold foil stamping. Only 2,500 of each card were produced and are sequentially numbered.

Card	Low	High
1 Frank Thomas	3.00	8.00
2 Alex Rodriguez	5.00	12.00
3 Ken Griffey Jr.	5.00	12.00
4 Andruw Jones	2.00	5.00
5 Chipper Jones	3.00	8.00
6 Jeff Bagwell	2.00	5.00
7 Derek Jeter	8.00	20.00
8 Deion Sanders	2.00	5.00
9 Ivan Rodriguez	2.00	5.00
10 Juan Gonzalez	1.25	3.00
11 Greg Maddux	5.00	12.00
12 Andy Pettitte	2.00	5.00
13 Roger Clemens	6.00	15.00
14 Hideo Nomo	3.00	8.00
15 Tony Gwynn	4.00	10.00
16 Barry Bonds	8.00	20.00
17 Kenny Lofton	2.00	5.00
18 Paul Molitor	1.25	3.00
19 Jim Thome	2.00	5.00
20 Albert Belle	1.25	3.00
21 Cal Ripken	10.00	25.00
22 Mark McGwire	8.00	20.00
23 Barry Larkin	2.00	5.00
24 Mike Piazza	5.00	12.00
25 Darin Erstad	1.25	3.00
26 Chuck Knoblauch	1.25	3.00
27 Vladimir Guerrero	3.00	8.00
28 Tony Clark	1.25	3.00
29 Scott Rolen	2.00	5.00
30 Nomar Garciaparra	5.00	12.00
31 Eric Young	1.25	3.00
32 Ryne Sandberg	5.00	12.00
33 Roberto Alomar	2.00	5.00
34 Eddie Murray	3.00	8.00
35 Rafael Palmeiro	2.00	5.00
36 Jose Guillen	1.25	3.00

1997 Leaf Knot-Hole Gang Samples

One of twelve different sample cards was distributed to dealers and hobby media prior to the release of 1997 Leaf to preview the set. The cards are marked "PROMO/5000" on back and are straight parallels to the basic Knot-Hole Gang insert cards.

Card	Low	High
COMPLETE SET (12)	16.00	40.00
1 Chuck Knoblauch	.40	1.00
2 Ken Griffey Jr.	1.50	4.00
3 Frank Thomas	.75	2.00
4 Tony Gwynn	1.50	4.00
5 Mike Piazza	2.50	6.00
6 Jeff Bagwell	.75	2.00
7 Rusty Greer	.40	1.00
8 Cal Ripken	3.00	8.00
9 Chipper Jones	1.50	4.00
10 Ryan Klesko	.30	.75
11 Barry Larkin	.60	1.50
12 Paul Molitor	1.00	2.50

1997 Leaf Knot-Hole Gang

This 12-card insert set, randomly seeded into first series hobby packs, features color action player photos printed on wooden card stock. The die-cut card resembles a wooden fence with the player being seen in action through a knot hole. Only 5,000 of this set was produced and is sequentially numbered.

Card	Low	High
COMPLETE SET (12)	20.00	50.00
1 Chuck Knoblauch	.60	1.50
2 Ken Griffey Jr.	2.50	6.00
3 Frank Thomas	1.50	4.00
4 Tony Gwynn	2.00	5.00
5 Mike Piazza	2.50	6.00
6 Jeff Bagwell	1.00	2.50
7 Rusty Greer	.60	1.50
8 Cal Ripken	5.00	12.00
9 Chipper Jones	1.50	4.00
10 Ryan Klesko	.60	1.50
11 Barry Larkin	1.00	2.50
12 Paul Molitor	.60	1.50

1997 Leaf Leagues of the Nation

Randomly inserted in all series two packs, this 15-card set celebrates the first season of interleague play with double-sided, die-cut cards that highlight some of the best interleague match-ups. Using flocking technology, the cards display color action player photos with the place and date of the game where the matchup between the pictured players took place. Only 2,500 of each card were produced and are sequentially numbered.

Card	Low	High
1 Juan Gonzalez / Barry Bonds	12.50	30.00
2 Cal Ripken / Chipper Jones	15.00	40.00
3 Mark McGwire / Ken Caminiti	12.50	30.00
4 Derek Jeter / Kenny Lofton	12.50	30.00
5 Ivan Rodriguez / Mike Piazza	8.00	20.00
6 Ken Griffey Jr. / Larry Walker	8.00	20.00
7 Frank Thomas / Sammy Sosa	5.00	12.00
8 Paul Molitor / Barry Larkin	2.00	5.00
9 Albert Belle / Deion Sanders	2.00	5.00
10 Matt Williams / Jeff Bagwell	3.00	8.00
11 Mo Vaughn / Gary Sheffield	2.00	5.00
12 Alex Rodriguez / Tony Gwynn	8.00	20.00
13 Tino Martinez / Scott Rolen	3.00	8.00
14 Darin Erstad / Wilton Guerrero	2.00	5.00
15 Tony Clark / Vladimir Guerrero	5.00	12.00

1997 Leaf Statistical Standouts

This 15-card insert set, randomly seeded into all first series packs, showcases some of the league's statistical leaders and is printed on full-leather, die-cut, foil-stamped card stock. The player's statistics are displayed beside a color player photo. Only 1,000 of this set were produced and are sequentially numbered.

Card	Low	High
1 Albert Belle	3.00	8.00
2 Juan Gonzalez	3.00	8.00
3 Ken Griffey Jr.	12.50	30.00
4 Alex Rodriguez	12.50	30.00
5 Frank Thomas	8.00	20.00
6 Chipper Jones	8.00	20.00
7 Greg Maddux	12.50	30.00
8 Mike Piazza	12.50	30.00
9 Cal Ripken	25.00	60.00
10 Mark McGwire	20.00	50.00
11 Barry Bonds	20.00	50.00
12 Derek Jeter	20.00	50.00
13 Ken Caminiti	3.00	8.00
14 John Smoltz	5.00	12.00
15 Paul Molitor	3.00	8.00

1997 Leaf Thomas Collection

Randomly inserted in all series two packs, this six-card set commemorates the multi-faceted talents of first baseman and at the time, Leaf Company spokesman, Frank Thomas with actual pieces of his game-used hats, jerseys (home and away), sweatbands, batting gloves or bats embedded in the cards. Only 100 of each card were produced and are sequentially numbered. This set, along with the 1997 Upper Deck Game Jersey inserts, represents one of the earliest forays by an mlb-licensed manufactuer into game-used memorabilia inserts.

Card	Low	High
1 Frank Thomas Game Hat/Blue Text	125.00	200.00
2 Frank Thomas Home Jersey/Orange Text	125.00	200.00
3 Frank Thomas Batting Glove/Yellow Text	125.00	200.00
4 Frank Thomas Bat/Green Text	125.00	200.00
5 Frank Thomas Sweatband/Purple Text	125.00	200.00
6 Frank Thomas Away Jersey/Red Text	125.00	200.00

1997 Leaf Warning Track

Randomly inserted in all series two packs, this 18-card set features color action photos of outstanding outfielders printed on embossed canvas card stock. Only 3,500 of each card were produced and are sequentially numbered.

Card	Low	High
COMPLETE SET (18)	40.00	100.00
1 Ken Griffey Jr.	5.00	12.00
2 Albert Belle	1.25	3.00
3 Barry Bonds	8.00	20.00
4 Andruw Jones	2.00	5.00
5 Kenny Lofton	1.25	3.00
6 Tony Gwynn	4.00	10.00
7 Manny Ramirez	2.00	5.00
8 Rusty Greer	1.25	3.00
9 Bernie Williams	2.00	5.00
10 Gary Sheffield	1.25	3.00
11 Juan Gonzalez	1.25	3.00
12 Raul Mondesi	1.25	3.00
13 Brady Anderson	1.25	3.00
14 Rondell White	1.25	3.00
15 Sammy Sosa	3.00	8.00
16 Deion Sanders	2.00	5.00
17 Dave Justice	1.25	3.00
18 Jim Edmonds	1.25	3.00

1998 Leaf

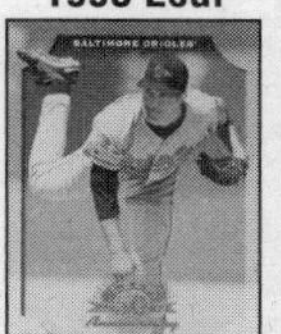

The 1998 Leaf set was issued in one series totalling 200 cards. The 10-card packs carried a suggested retail price of $2.99. The set contains the topical subsets: Curtain Calls (148-157), Gold Leaf Stars (158-177), and Gold Leaf Rookies (178-197). All three subsets are short-printed in relation to cards from 1-147 and 201. Those short prints represent one of the early efforts by a manufacturer to incorporate short-print subsets cards into a basic issue set. The product went live in mid-March, 1998. Card number 42 does not exist as Leaf retired the number in honor of Jackie Robinson.

COMPLETE SET (200) 25.00 60.00
COMP.SET w/o SP's (147) 6.00 15.00
COMMON CARD (1-201) .10 .30
COMMON SP (148-197) .60 1.50
1 Rusty Greer .10 .30
2 Tino Martinez .20 .50
3 Bobby Bonilla .10 .30
4 Jason Giambi .10 .30
5 Matt Morris .10 .30
6 Craig Counsell .10 .30
7 Reggie Jefferson .10 .30
8 Brian Rose .10 .30
9 Ruben Rivera .10 .30
10 Shawn Estes .10 .30
11 Tony Gwynn .40 1.00
12 Jeff Abbott .10 .30
13 Jose Cruz Jr. .10 .30
14 Francisco Cordova .10 .30
15 Ryan Klesko .10 .30
16 Tim Salmon .20 .50
17 Brett Tomko .10 .30
18 Matt Williams .10 .30
19 Joe Carter .10 .30
20 Harold Baines .10 .30
21 Gary Sheffield .10 .30
22 Charles Johnson .10 .30
23 Aaron Boone .10 .30
24 Eddie Murray .30 .75
25 Matt Stairs .10 .30
26 David Cone .10 .30
27 Jon Nunnally .10 .30
28 Chris Stynes .10 .30
29 Enrique Wilson .10 .30
30 Randy Johnson .30 .75
31 Garret Anderson .10 .30
32 Manny Ramirez .20 .50
33 Jeff Suppan .10 .30
34 Rickey Henderson .30 .75
35 Scott Spiezio .10 .30
36 Rondell White .10 .30
37 Todd Greene .10 .30
38 Delino DeShields .10 .30
39 Kevin Brown .20 .50
40 Chili Davis .10 .30
41 Jimmy Key .10 .30
43 Mike Mussina .20 .50
44 Joe Randa .10 .30
45 Chan Ho Park .10 .30
46 Brad Radke .10 .30
47 Geronimo Berroa .10 .30
48 Wade Boggs .20 .50
49 Kevin Appier .10 .30
50 Moises Alou .10 .30
51 David Justice .10 .30
52 Ivan Rodriguez .20 .50
53 J.T. Snow .10 .30
54 Brian Giles .10 .30
55 Will Clark .20 .50
56 Justin Thompson .10 .30
57 Javier Lopez .10 .30
58 Hideki Irabu .10 .30
59 Mark Grudzielanek .10 .30
60 Abraham Nunez .10 .30
61 Todd Hollandsworth .10 .30
62 Jay Bell .10 .30
63 Nomar Garciaparra .50 1.25
64 Vinny Castilla .10 .30
65 Lou Collier .10 .30
66 Kevin Orie .10 .30
67 John Valentin .10 .30
68 Robin Ventura .10 .30
69 Denny Neagle .10 .30
70 Tony Womack .10 .30
71 Dennis Reyes .10 .30
72 Wally Joyner .10 .30
73 Kevin Brown .20 .50
74 Ray Durham .10 .30
75 Mike Cameron .10 .30
76 Dante Bichette .10 .30
77 Jose Guillen .10 .30
78 Carlos Delgado .10 .30
79 Paul Molitor .10 .30
80 Jason Kendall .10 .30
81 Mark Bellhorn .10 .30
82 Damian Jackson .10 .30
83 Bill Mueller .10 .30
84 Kevin Young .10 .30
85 Curt Schilling .10 .30
86 Jeffrey Hammonds .10 .30
87 Sandy Alomar Jr. .10 .30
88 Bartolo Colon .10 .30
89 Wilton Guerrero .10 .30
90 Bernie Williams .20 .50
91 Deion Sanders .20 .50
92 Mike Piazza .50 1.25
93 Butch Huskey .10 .30
94 Edgardo Alfonzo .10 .30
95 Alan Benes .10 .30
96 Craig Biggio .20 .50
97 Mark Grace .20 .50
98 Shawn Green .10 .30
99 Derrek Lee .20 .50
100 Ken Griffey Jr. .50 1.25
101 Tim Raines .10 .30
102 Pokey Reese .10 .30
103 Lee Stevens .10 .30
104 Shannon Stewart .10 .30
105 John Smoltz .20 .50
106 Frank Thomas .30 .75
107 Jeff Fassero .10 .30
108 Jay Buhner .10 .30
109 Jose Canseco .20 .50
110 Omar Vizquel .20 .50
111 Travis Fryman .10 .30
112 Dave Nilsson .10 .30
113 John Olerud .10 .30
114 Larry Walker .10 .30
115 Jim Edmonds .10 .30
116 Bobby Higginson .10 .30
117 Todd Hundley .10 .30
118 Paul O'Neill .20 .50
119 Bip Roberts .10 .30
120 Ismael Valdes .10 .30
121 Pedro Martinez .20 .50
122 Jeff Cirillo .10 .30
123 Andy Benes .10 .30
124 Bobby Jones .10 .30
125 Brian Hunter .10 .30
126 Darryl Kile .10 .30
127 Pat Hentgen .10 .30
128 Marquis Grissom .10 .30
129 Eric Davis .10 .30
130 Chipper Jones .30 .75
131 Edgar Martinez .20 .50
132 Andy Pettitte .20 .50
133 Cal Ripken 1.00 2.50
134 Scott Rolen .20 .50
135 Ron Coomer .10 .30
136 Luis Castillo .10 .30
137 Fred McGriff .20 .50
138 Neifi Perez .10 .30
139 Eric Karros .10 .30
140 Alex Fernandez .10 .30
141 Jason Dickson .10 .30
142 Lance Johnson .10 .30
143 Ray Lankford .10 .30
144 Sammy Sosa .30 .75
145 Eric Young .10 .30
146 Bubba Trammell .10 .30
147 Todd Walker .10 .30
148 Mo Vaughn CC .60 1.50
149 Jeff Bagwell CC 1.00 2.50
150 Kenny Lofton CC .60 1.50
151 Raul Mondesi CC .60 1.50
152 Mike Piazza CC 2.50 6.00
153 Chipper Jones CC 1.50 4.00
154 Larry Walker CC .60 1.50
155 Greg Maddux CC 2.50 6.00
156 Ken Griffey Jr. CC 2.50 6.00
157 Frank Thomas CC 1.50 4.00
158 Darin Erstad GLS .60 1.50
159 Roberto Alomar GLS 1.00 2.50
160 Albert Belle GLS .60 1.50
161 Jim Thome GLS 1.00 2.50
162 Tony Clark GLS .60 1.50
163 Chuck Knoblauch GLS .60 1.50
164 Derek Jeter GLS 4.00 10.00
165 Alex Rodriguez GLS 2.50 6.00
166 Tony Gwynn GLS 2.00 5.00
167 Roger Clemens GLS 3.00 8.00
168 Barry Larkin GLS 1.00 2.50
169 Andres Galarraga GLS .60 1.50
170 Vlad. Guerrero GLS 1.50 4.00
171 Mark McGwire GLS 4.00 10.00
172 Barry Bonds GLS 4.00 10.00
173 Juan Gonzalez GLS .60 1.50
174 Andruw Jones GLS 1.00 2.50
175 Paul Molitor GLS .60 1.50
176 Hideo Nomo GLS 1.50 4.00
177 Cal Ripken GLS 5.00 12.00
178 Brad Fullmer GLR .60 1.50
179 Jaret Wright GLR .60 1.50
180 Bobby Estalella GLR .60 1.50
181 Ben Grieve GLR .60 1.50
182 Paul Konerko GLR .60 1.50
183 David Ortiz GLR 2.00 5.00
184 Todd Helton GLR 1.00 2.50
185 J.Encarnacion GLR .60 1.50
186 Miguel Tejada GLR 1.50 4.00
187 Jacob Cruz GLR .60 1.50
188 Mark Kotsay GLR .60 1.50
189 Fernando Tatis GLR .60 1.50
190 Ricky Ledee GLR .60 1.50
191 Richard Hidalgo GLR .60 1.50
192 Richie Sexson GLR .60 1.50
193 Luis Ordaz GLR .60 1.50
194 Eli Marrero GLR .60 1.50
195 Livan Hernandez GLR .60 1.50
196 Homer Bush GLR .60 1.50
197 Raul Ibanez GLR .60 1.50
198 Nomar Garciaparra CL .30 .75
199 Scott Rolen CL .10 .30
200 Jose Cruz Jr. CL .10 .30
201 Al Martin .10 .30

1998 Leaf Fractal Diamond Axis

Randomly inserted in packs, this 200-card set is parallel to the Leaf base set. Each card features die cut edges and blue foil fronts. Only 50 serially numbered sets were produced. Card number 42 does not exist.

*STARS 1-147/198-201: 15X TO 40X BASIC
*SP STARS 148-197: 3X TO 8X BASIC SP'S

1998 Leaf Fractal Matrix

Randomly inserted in packs, this 200-card set is parallel to the Leaf base set and features color player photos with either a bronze, silver or gold finish. Only 100 cards are bronze, 60 are silver, and 40 are gold. No card is available in more than one of the colors. The set is broken into nine tiers based on three colors (Bronze, Gold and Silver) and three axis (X, Y and Z). Unlike the previous year, the 1998 cards carry an axis-logo on the card front, allowing collectors to identify the specific tier. It's estimated that print runs range from as few as 50 to as many of 2000 of each card.

*BRONZE 1-147/198-201: 1.5X TO 4X BASIC
*BRONZE 148-197: .3X TO .8X BASIC
BRONZE X STATED PRINT RUN 1600 SETS
BRONZE Y STATED PRINT RUN 1800 SETS
BRONZE Z STATED PRINT RUN 1900 SETS
*SILVER 1-147/198-201: 3X TO 8X BASIC
*SILVER: 148-197: .6X TO 1.5X BASIC
SILVER X STATED PRINT RUN 600 SETS
SILVER Y STATED PRINT RUN 800 SETS
SILVER Z STATED PRINT RUN 900 SETS
*GOLD 1-147/198-201: 5X TO 12X BASIC
*GOLD: 148-197: 1X TO 2.5X BASIC
GOLD.X STATED PRINT RUN 100 SETS
GOLD Y STATED PRINT RUN 300 SETS
GOLD Z STATED PRINT RUN 400 SETS
RANDOM INSERTS IN PACKS
CARD NUMBER 42 DOES NOT EXIST

1998 Leaf Fractal Matrix Die Cuts

Randomly inserted in packs, this 200-card set is parallel to the regular set and features three different die-cut versions in three different finishes. Only 100 of the set are produced in the x-axis cut with 75 of those bronze, 20 silver, and five gold. Only 60 are available in the type y-axis cut with 20 of those bronze, 30 silver, and 10 gold. Only 40 are produced in the z-axis cut with five bronze, 10 silver and 25 gold. No card is available in more than one color nor in more than one die-cut version. Card number 42 does not exist.

*X-AXIS 1-147/198-201: 5X TO 12X BASIC
*X-AXIS 148-197: 1X TO 2.5X BASIC
X-AXIS STATED PRINT RUN 400 SETS
*Y-AXIS 1-147/198-201: 8X TO 20X BASIC
*Y-AXIS 148-197: 1.5X TO 4X BASIC
Y-AXIS STATED PRINT RUN 200 SETS
*Z-AXIS 1-147/198-201: 12.5X TO 30X BASIC
*Z-AXIS 148-197: 2.5X TO 6X BASIC
Z-AXIS STATED PRINT RUN 100 SETS
RANDOM INSERTS IN PACKS
CARD NUMBER 42 DOES NOT EXIST
SEE WEBSITE FOR AXIS SCHEMATIC

1998 Leaf Crusade Green

As part of the 1998 Donruss/Leaf Crusade insert program, 30 cards were exclusively issued in 1998 Leaf Packs. Please refer to 1998 Donruss Crusade for further information.

PLEASE SEE 1998 DONRUSS CRUSADE

1998 Leaf Heading for the Hall Samples

To preview the 1998 Leaf product, all dealer wholesale order forms contained one of these twenty different samples. The cards differ from the basic Heading for the Hall inserts in two ways: the large "SAMPLE" text printed diagonally across the card back and the lack of serial numbering on back.

COMPLETE SET (20) 32.00 80.00
1 Roberto Alomar .60 1.50
2 Jeff Bagwell .75 2.00
3 Albert Belle .30 .75
4 Wade Boggs 1.50 4.00
5 Barry Bonds 2.00 5.00
6 Roger Clemens 2.00 5.00
7 Juan Gonzalez .60 1.50
8 Ken Griffey Jr. 2.00 5.00
9 Tony Gwynn 2.00 5.00
10 Barry Larkin .60 1.50
11 Kenny Lofton .40 1.00
12 Greg Maddux 2.50 6.00
13 Mark McGwire 2.50 6.00
14 Paul Molitor 1.00 2.50
15 Eddie Murray .60 1.50
16 Mike Piazza 3.00 8.00
17 Cal Ripken 4.00 10.00
18 Ivan Rodriguez 1.25 3.00
19 Ryne Sandberg 1.50 4.00
20 Frank Thomas 1.00 2.50

1998 Leaf Heading for the Hall

This 20 card set was randomly inserted into 1998 Leaf packs. The fronts have a design similar to the Hall of Fame packs. The player's name and team is at top. The back has another photo along with a brief blurb. The cards are numbered "X of 3500" on the back as well.

COMPLETE SET (20) 40.00 100.00
1 Roberto Alomar 2.00 5.00
2 Jeff Bagwell 2.00 5.00
3 Albert Belle 1.25 3.00
4 Wade Boggs 2.00 5.00
5 Barry Bonds 8.00 20.00
6 Roger Clemens 6.00 15.00
7 Juan Gonzalez 1.25 3.00
8 Ken Griffey Jr. 5.00 12.00
9 Tony Gwynn 4.00 10.00
10 Barry Larkin 2.00 5.00
11 Kenny Lofton 1.25 3.00
12 Greg Maddux 5.00 12.00
13 Mark McGwire 8.00 20.00
14 Paul Molitor 1.25 3.00
15 Eddie Murray 3.00 8.00
16 Mike Piazza 5.00 12.00
17 Cal Ripken 10.00 25.00
18 Ivan Rodriguez 2.00 5.00
19 Ryne Sandberg 5.00 12.00
20 Frank Thomas 3.00 8.00

1998 Leaf State Representatives

This 30 card set was randomly inserted into packs. The fronts have the words 'State Representatives" on the top with the player's name and team on the bottom. The player's photo has a metallic sheen to it as he is pictured against a state outline. The back has a small player portrait along with some information about the player. The cards are serial numbered "X of 5,000" on the back.

COMPLETE SET (30) 60.00 150.00
1 Ken Griffey Jr. 4.00 10.00
2 Frank Thomas 2.50 6.00
3 Alex Rodriguez 4.00 10.00
4 Cal Ripken 8.00 20.00
5 Chipper Jones 2.50 6.00
6 Andruw Jones 1.50 4.00
7 Scott Rolen 1.50 4.00
8 Nomar Garciaparra 4.00 10.00
9 Tim Salmon 1.50 4.00
10 Manny Ramirez 1.50 4.00
11 Jose Cruz Jr. 1.00 2.50
12 Vladimir Guerrero 2.50 6.00
13 Tino Martinez 1.50 4.00
14 Larry Walker 1.00 2.50
15 Mo Vaughn 1.00 2.50
16 Jim Thome 1.50 4.00
17 Tony Clark 1.00 2.50
18 Derek Jeter 6.00 15.00
19 Juan Gonzalez 1.00 2.50
20 Jeff Bagwell 1.50 4.00
21 Ivan Rodriguez 1.50 4.00
22 Mark McGwire 6.00 15.00
23 David Justice 1.00 2.50
24 Chuck Knoblauch 1.00 2.50
25 Andy Pettitte 1.50 4.00
26 Raul Mondesi 1.00 2.50
27 Randy Johnson 2.50 6.00
28 Greg Maddux 4.00 10.00
29 Bernie Williams 1.50 4.00
30 Rusty Greer 1.00 2.50

1998 Leaf Statistical Standouts

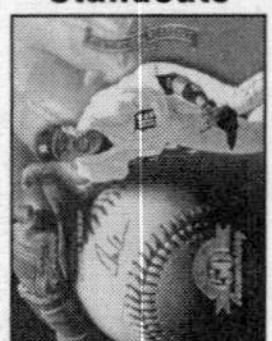

These 24 horizontal cards feature leading players. The front of the card has the players photo against a background of a glove and ball. The ball has been signed by that player. The card's front feels like leather and the words "Statistical Standouts" is printed on the side. The backs have year and career stats on the back along with another player photo. The cards are serial numbered "X of 2500" on the back, though only 2,250 of each card were produced due to the fact that the first 250 #'D sets were devoted to the Statistical Standouts Die Cut parallel..

COMPLETE SET (24) 100.00 250.00
*DIE CUTS: .75X TO 2X BASIC STAT.STAND.
DIE CUT PRINT RUN 250 SERIAL #'d SETS
RANDOM INSERTS IN PACKS
1 Frank Thomas 4.00 10.00
2 Ken Griffey Jr. 6.00 15.00
3 Alex Rodriguez 6.00 15.00
4 Mike Piazza 6.00 15.00
5 Greg Maddux 6.00 15.00
6 Cal Ripken 12.50 30.00
7 Chipper Jones 4.00 10.00
8 Juan Gonzalez 1.50 4.00
9 Jeff Bagwell 2.50 6.00
10 Mark McGwire 10.00 25.00
11 Tony Gwynn 5.00 12.00
12 Mo Vaughn 1.50 4.00
13 Nomar Garciaparra 6.00 15.00
14 Jose Cruz Jr. 1.50 4.00
15 Vladimir Guerrero 4.00 10.00
16 Scott Rolen 2.50 6.00
17 Andy Pettitte 2.50 6.00
18 Randy Johnson 4.00 10.00
19 Larry Walker 1.50 4.00
20 Kenny Lofton 1.50 4.00
21 Tony Clark 1.50 4.00
22 David Justice 1.50 4.00
23 Derek Jeter 10.00 25.00
24 Barry Bonds 10.00 25.00

2002 Leaf

This 200 card set was issued in late winter, 2002. This set was distributed in four card packs with an SRP of $3 which were sent in 24 packs to a box with 20 boxes to a case. Cards numbered from 151-200, which were inserted at a stated rate of one in six, featured 50 of the leading rookie prospects entering the 2002 season. Card number 42, which Leaf had previously retired in honor of Jackie Robinson, was originally intended to feature a short-print card honoring the sensational rookie season of Ichiro Suzuki. However, Leaf decided to continue honoring Robinson and never went through with printing card 42. Cards numbered 201 and 202 feature Japanese imports So Taguchi and Kazuhisa Ishii, both of which were short-printed in relation to the other prospect cards 151-200. The cards production runs were announced by the manufacturer as 250 copies for Ishii and 500 for Taguchi.

COMP.SET w/o SP's (149) 10.00 25.00
COMMON (1-41/43-150) .10 .30
COMMON CARD (151-200) 1.50 4.00
1 Tim Salmon .20 .50
2 Troy Glaus .10 .30
3 Curt Schilling .10 .30
4 Luis Gonzalez .10 .30
5 Mark Grace .20 .50
6 Matt Williams .10 .30
7 Randy Johnson .30 .75
8 Tom Glavine .20 .50
9 Brady Anderson .10 .30
10 Hideo Nomo .30 .75
11 Pedro Martinez .20 .50
12 Corey Patterson .10 .30
13 Paul Konerko .10 .30
14 Jon Lieber .10 .30
15 Carlos Lee .10 .30
16 Magglio Ordonez .10 .30
17 Adam Dunn .10 .30
18 Ken Griffey Jr. .50 1.25
19 C.C. Sabathia .10 .30
20 Jim Thome .20 .50
21 Juan Gonzalez .10 .30
22 Kenny Lofton .10 .30
23 Juan Encarnacion .10 .30
24 Tony Clark .10 .30
25 A.J. Burnett .10 .30
26 Josh Beckett .10 .30
27 Lance Berkman .10 .30
28 Eric Karros .10 .30
29 Shawn Green .10 .30
30 Brad Radke .10 .30
31 Joe Mays .10 .30
32 Javier Vazquez .10 .30
33 Alfonso Soriano .10 .30
34 Jorge Posada .20 .50
35 Eric Chavez .10 .30
36 Mark Mulder .10 .30
37 Miguel Tejada .10 .30
38 Tim Hudson .10 .30
39 Bob Abreu .10 .30
40 Pat Burrell .10 .30
41 Ryan Klesko .10 .30
43 John Olerud .10 .30
44 Ellis Burks .10 .30
45 Mike Cameron .10 .30
46 Jim Edmonds .10 .30
47 Ben Grieve .10 .30
48 Carlos Pena .10 .30
49 Alex Rodriguez .50 1.25
50 Raul Mondesi .10 .30
51 Billy Koch .10 .30
52 Manny Ramirez .20 .50
53 Darin Erstad .10 .30
54 Troy Percival .10 .30
55 Andruw Jones .10 .30
56 Chipper Jones .30 .75
57 David Segui .10 .30
58 Chris Stynes .10 .30
59 Trot Nixon .10 .30
60 Sammy Sosa .30 .75
61 Kerry Wood .10 .30
62 Frank Thomas .30 .75
63 Barry Larkin .20 .50
64 Bartolo Colon .10 .30
65 Kazuhiro Sasaki .10 .30
66 Roberto Alomar .20 .50
67 Mike Hampton .10 .30
68 Roger Cedeno .10 .30
69 Cliff Floyd .10 .30
70 Mike Lowell .10 .30
71 Billy Wagner .10 .30
72 Craig Biggio .20 .50
73 Jeff Bagwell .20 .50
74 Carlos Beltran .10 .30
75 Mark Quinn .10 .30
76 Mike Sweeney .10 .30
77 Gary Sheffield .10 .30
78 Kevin Brown .10 .30
79 Paul LoDuca .10 .30
80 Ben Sheets .10 .30
81 Jeromy Burnitz .10 .30
82 Richie Sexson .10 .30
83 Corey Koskie .10 .30
84 Eric Milton .10 .30
85 Jose Vidro .10 .30
86 Mike Piazza .50 1.25
87 Robin Ventura .10 .30
88 Andy Pettitte .20 .50
89 Mike Mussina .20 .50
90 Orlando Hernandez .10 .30
91 Roger Clemens .60 1.50
92 Barry Zito .10 .30
93 Jermaine Dye .10 .30
94 Jimmy Rollins .10 .30
95 Jason Kendall .10 .30
96 Rickey Henderson .30 .75
97 Andres Galarraga .10 .30
98 Bret Boone .10 .30
99 Freddy Garcia .10 .30
100 J.D. Drew .10 .30
101 Jose Cruz Jr. .10 .30
102 Greg Maddux .50 1.25
103 Javy Lopez .10 .30
104 Nomar Garciaparra .50 1.25
105 Fred McGriff .20 .50
106 Keith Foulke .10 .30
107 Ray Durham .10 .30
108 Sean Casey .10 .30
109 Todd Walker .10 .30
110 Omar Vizquel .20 .50
111 Travis Fryman .10 .30
112 Larry Walker .10 .30
113 Todd Helton .20 .50
114 Bobby Higginson .10 .30
115 Charles Johnson .10 .30
116 Moises Alou .10 .30
117 Richard Hidalgo .10 .30
118 Roy Oswalt .10 .30
119 Neifi Perez .10 .30
120 Adrian Beltre .10 .30
121 Chan Ho Park .10 .30
122 Geoff Jenkins .10 .30
123 Doug Mientkiewicz .10 .30
124 Torii Hunter .10 .30
125 Vladimir Guerrero .30 .75
126 Matt Lawton .10 .30
127 Tsuyoshi Shinjo .20 .50
128 Bernie Williams .20 .50
129 Derek Jeter .75 2.00
130 Mariano Rivera .30 .75
131 Tino Martinez .20 .50
132 Jason Giambi .10 .30
133 Scott Rolen .20 .50
134 Brian Giles .10 .30
135 Phil Nevin .10 .30
136 Trevor Hoffman .10 .30
137 Barry Bonds .75 2.00
138 Jeff Kent .10 .30
139 Shannon Stewart .10 .30
140 Shawn Estes .10 .30
141 Edgar Martinez .20 .50
142 Ichiro Suzuki .60 1.50
143 Albert Pujols .60 1.50
144 Bud Smith .10 .30
145 Matt Morris .10 .30
146 Frank Catalanotto .10 .30
147 Gabe Kapler .10 .30
148 Ivan Rodriguez .20 .50
149 Rafael Palmeiro .20 .50
150 Carlos Delgado .10 .30
151 Marlon Byrd ROO 1.50 4.00
152 Alex Herrera ROO 1.50 4.00
153 Brandon Backe ROO RC 2.00 5.00
154 Jorge De La Rosa ROO RC 1.50 4.00
155 Corky Miller ROO 1.50 4.00
156 Dennis Tankersley ROO 1.50 4.00
157 Kyle Kane ROO RC 1.50 4.00
158 Justin Duchscherer ROO 1.50 4.00
159 Brian Mallette ROO RC 1.50 4.00
160 Eric Hinske ROO 1.50 4.00
161 Jason Lane ROO 1.50 4.00
162 Hee Seop Choi ROO 1.50 4.00
163 Juan Cruz ROO 1.50 4.00
164 Rodrigo Rosario ROO RC 1.50 4.00
165 Matt Guerrier ROO 1.50 4.00
166 And. Machado ROO RC 1.50 4.00
167 Geronimo Gil ROO 1.50 4.00
168 Dewon Brazelton ROO 1.50 4.00
169 Mark Prior ROO 2.00 5.00
170 Bill Hall ROO 1.50 4.00
171 Jorge Padilla ROO RC 1.50 4.00
172 Josh Pearce ROO 1.50 4.00
173 Allan Simpson ROO RC 1.50 4.00
174 Doug Devore ROO RC 1.50 4.00
175 Luis Garcia ROO 1.50 4.00
176 Angel Berroa ROO 1.50 4.00
177 Steve Bechler ROO RC 1.50 4.00
178 Antonio Perez ROO 1.50 4.00
179 Mark Teixeira ROO 3.00 8.00
180 Mark Ellis ROO 1.50 4.00
181 Michael Cuddyer ROO 1.50 4.00
182 Michael Rivera ROO 1.50 4.00
183 Raul Chavez ROO RC 1.50 4.00
184 Juan Pena ROO 1.50 4.00
185 Austin Kearns ROO 1.50 4.00
186 Ryan Ludwick ROO 1.50 4.00
187 Ed Rogers ROO 1.50 4.00
188 Wilson Betemit ROO 1.50 4.00
189 Nick Neugebauer ROO 1.50 4.00
190 Tom Shearn ROO RC 1.50 4.00
191 Eric Cyr ROO 1.50 4.00
192 Victor Martinez ROO 3.00 8.00
193 Brandon Berger ROO 1.50 4.00
194 Erik Bedard ROO 1.50 4.00
195 Franklyn German ROO RC 1.50 4.00
196 Joe Thurston ROO 1.50 4.00
197 John Buck ROO 1.50 4.00
198 Jeff Deardorff ROO 1.50 4.00
199 Ryan Jamison ROO 1.50 4.00
200 Alfredo Amezaga ROO 1.50 4.00
201 So Taguchi ROO/500 RC * 6.00 15.00
202 Kazuhisa Ishii ROO/250 RC * 10.00 25.00

2002 Leaf Autographs

Taguchi signed 50 serial numbered cards and Ishii signed 25 serial numbered cards. The Taguchi autographs were distributed in packs but an exchange card with a deadline of October 1st, 2003 was seeded into packs for the Ishii autographs. Each card is a straight parallel of the basic RC's except for a signed silver foil sticker placed over the front and foil serial-numbering on back.

201 So Taguchi/50 20.00 50.00
202 Kazuhisa Ishii/25

2002 Leaf Lineage

Inserted in hobby packs at stated odds of one in 12, this is a mini-parallel of the 2002 Leaf set. Only the

first 150 cards from this set are featured and the set is split up into three sections: Cards numbered 1-50 feature 1999 replicas, while cards numbered from 51-100 feature 2000 replicas and cards numbered from 101-150 feature 2001 replicas.

*LINEAGE: 3X TO 8X BASIC CARDS

2002 Leaf Lineage Century

Randomly Iserted in hobby packs, this is a mini-parallel of the 2002 Leaf set. Only the first 150 cards from this set are featured and the set is split up into three sections: Cards numbered 1-50 feature 1999 replicas, while cards numbered from 51-100 feature 2000 replicas and cards numbered from 101-150 feature 2001 replicas. These cards are serial numbered to 100.

*CENTURY: 8X TO 20X BASIC CARDS

2002 Leaf Press Proofs Blue

Inserted at stated odds of one in 24 retail packs, this is a partial parallel of the 2002 Leaf set and featured the first 150 cards from that set.

*BLUE: 6X TO 15X BASIC CARDS

2002 Leaf Press Proofs Platinum

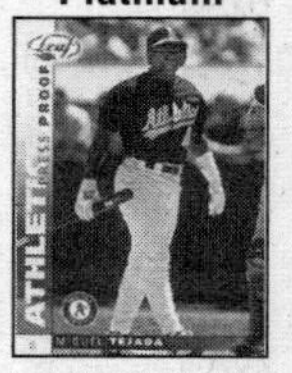

Randomly inserted in hobby packs, this is a mini-parallel of the 2002 Leaf set. Only the first 150 cards from the basic Leaf set and cards 201 and 202 are featured in this parallel. All cards except for card 202 are serial numbered to 25. Only ten serial-numbered copies of card number 202 (featuring Japanese pitcher Kazuhisa Ishii) were produced.

*PLATINUM: 30X TO 80X BASIC CARDS
201-202 NOT PRICED DUE TO SCARCITY

2002 Leaf Press Proofs Red

Issued at stated odds of one in 12 retail packs, this set parallels the first 150 cards of the 2002 Leaf set. In addition, the two cards of Japanese imports So Taguchi and Kazuhisa Ishii are printed to stated print runs of 500 and 250 respectively.

*RED 1-150: 3X TO 8X BASIC CARDS		
201 So Taguchi/500	6.00	15.00
202 Kazuhisa Ishii/250	10.00	25.00

2002 Leaf Burn and Turn

Issued at stated odds of one in 96 hobby and one in 120 retail packs, these 10 cards feature most of the leading double play duos in major league baseball.

COMPLETE SET (10)	40.00	100.00
1 Fernando Vina Edgar Renteria	3.00	8.00
2 Alex Rodriguez Mike Young	6.00	15.00
3 Derek Jeter Alfonso Soriano	10.00	25.00
4 Carlos Guillen Bret Boone	3.00	8.00
5 Jose Vidro Orlando Cabrera	3.00	8.00
6 Barry Larkin Todd Walker	3.00	8.00
7 Carlos Febles Neifi Perez	3.00	8.00
8 Jeff Kent Rich Aurilia	3.00	8.00
9 Craig Biggio Julio Lugo	3.00	8.00
10 Miguel Tejada Mark Ellis	3.00	8.00

2002 Leaf Clean Up Crew

Issued at stated odds of one in 192 hobby and one in 240 retail packs, these 15 cards feature leading sluggers of the game. The cards are set on conventional cardboard with silver foil stamping.

COMPLETE SET (15)	100.00	200.00
1 Barry Bonds	12.50	30.00
2 Sammy Sosa	5.00	12.00
3 Luis Gonzalez	4.00	10.00
4 Richie Sexson	4.00	10.00
5 Jim Thome	4.00	10.00
6 Chipper Jones	5.00	12.00
7 Alex Rodriguez	8.00	20.00
8 Troy Glaus	4.00	10.00
9 Rafael Palmeiro	4.00	10.00
10 Lance Berkman	4.00	10.00
11 Mike Piazza	8.00	20.00
12 Jason Giambi	4.00	10.00
13 Todd Helton	4.00	10.00
14 Shawn Green	4.00	10.00
15 Carlos Delgado	4.00	10.00

2002 Leaf Clubhouse Signatures Bronze

Randomly inserted in packs, these 33 cards feature a mix of signed cards of retired legends, superstar veterans and future stars. Each of these cards is serial numbered and we have listed the print run in our checklist. Cards with a print run of 100 or fewer are not priced due to market scarcity.

Card		
1 Adam Dunn/200	10.00	25.00
2 Alan Trammell/75	6.00	15.00
3 Alfonso Soriano/75		
4 Andre Dawson/100		
5 Aramis Ramirez/250	6.00	15.00
6 Austin Kearns/300	4.00	10.00
7 Barry Zito/100	12.50	30.00
8 Billy Williams/150	6.00	15.00
9 Bob Feller/250	6.00	15.00
10 Bud Smith/200	4.00	10.00
11 Don Mattingly/25		
12 Edgar Martinez/50		
13 J.D. Drew/25		
14 Jason Lane/250	6.00	15.00
15 Jermaine Dye/125	8.00	20.00
16 Joe Crede/200	6.00	15.00
17 Joe Mays/200	4.00	10.00
18 Johnny Estrada/250	4.00	10.00
19 Mark Ellis/300	4.00	10.00
20 Mark Mulder/50		
21 Marlon Byrd/200	4.00	10.00
22 Ozzie Smith/25		
23 Paul LoDuca/300	6.00	15.00
24 Phil Rizzuto/25		
25 Robert Fick/300	4.00	10.00
26 Ron Santo/300	10.00	25.00
27 Roy Oswalt/300	6.00	15.00
28 Ryne Sandberg/25		
29 Steve Garvey/200	6.00	15.00
30 Terrence Long/250	4.00	10.00
31 Tim Redding/300	4.00	10.00
32 Wilson Betemit/150	4.00	10.00
33 Xavier Nady/200	4.00	10.00

2002 Leaf Clubhouse Signatures Gold

Randomly inserted in packs, these 48 cards feature a mix of signed cards of retired legends, superstar veterans and future stars. Each of these cards is serial numbered to 25. An exchange card with a redemption deadline of October 1st, 2003 was seeded into packs for the Ozzie Smith card. Due to market scarcity, no pricing is provided for these cards.

1 Adam Dunn
2 Alan Trammell
3 Alfonso Soriano
4 Andre Dawson
5 Aramis Ramirez
6 Austin Kearns
7 Barry Zito
8 Billy Williams
9 Bob Feller
10 Bud Smith
11 Cal Ripken
12 Chan Ho Park
13 Don Mattingly
14 Edgar Martinez
15 Eric Chavez
16 J.D. Drew
17 Jason Lane
18 Javier Vazquez
19 Jermaine Dye
20 Joe Crede
21 Joe Mays
22 Johnny Estrada
23 Josh Beckett
24 Kirby Puckett
25 Luis Gonzalez
26 Mark Ellis
27 Mark Mulder
28 Marlon Byrd
29 Miguel Tejada
30 Mike Schmidt
31 Orel Hershiser
32 Ozzie Smith
33 Paul LoDuca
34 Phil Rizzuto
35 Rich Aurilia
36 Robert Fick
37 Roger Clemens
38 Ron Santo
39 Roy Oswalt
40 Ryne Sandberg
41 Sean Casey
42 Steve Garvey
43 Terrence Long
44 Tim Redding
45 Todd Helton
46 Vladimir Guerrero
47 Wilson Betemit
48 Xavier Nady

2002 Leaf Clubhouse Signatures Silver

Randomly inserted in packs, these 37 cards feature a mix of signed cards of retired legends, superstar veterans and future stars. Each of these cards is serial numbered and we have listed the print run in our checklist. Cards with a stated print run of 25 or fewer are not priced due to market scarcity.

Card		
1 Adam Dunn/75	12.50	30.00
2 Andre Dawson/100		
3 Aramis Ramirez/100	8.00	20.00
4 Austin Kearns/100	6.00	15.00
5 Barry Zito/100	12.50	30.00
6 Billy Williams/100	8.00	20.00
7 Bob Feller/100	8.00	20.00
8 Bud Smith/100	6.00	15.00
9 Cal Ripken/25		
10 Edgar Martinez/100	15.00	40.00
11 Eric Chavez/100	8.00	20.00
12 Jason Lane/100	8.00	20.00
13 Jermaine Dye/100	8.00	20.00
14 Joe Crede/50	8.00	20.00
15 Joe Mays/50	6.00	15.00
16 Johnny Estrada/100	6.00	15.00
17 Javier Vazquez/100	8.00	20.00
18 Mark Ellis/100	6.00	15.00
19 Mark Mulder/100	8.00	20.00
20 Marlon Byrd/100	6.00	15.00
21 Miguel Tejada/100	12.50	30.00
22 Mike Schmidt/75		
23 Paul LoDuca/100		
24 Phil Rizzuto/25		
25 Rich Aurilia/100	6.00	15.00
26 Robert Fick/100	6.00	15.00
27 Roger Clemens/25		
28 Ron Santo/100	12.50	30.00
29 Roy Oswalt/100	8.00	20.00
30 Sean Casey/50		
31 Steve Garvey/100	8.00	20.00
32 Terrence Long/100	6.00	15.00
33 Tim Redding/100	6.00	15.00
34 Todd Helton/25		
35 Vladimir Guerrero/25		
36 Wilson Betemit/100	6.00	15.00
37 Xavier Nady/100	6.00	15.00

2002 Leaf Cornerstones

Randomly inserted in packs, these 10 cards feature some of the elite performers with dual-player game-worn jersey swatches. These cards are serial numbered to 50. Due to market scarcity, no pricing is provided for these cards.

1 Andruw Jones
Chipper Jones
2 Craig Biggio
Jeff Bagwell
3 Ivan Rodriguez
Rafael Palmeiro
4 Curt Schilling
Randy Johnson
5 Gary Sheffield
Shawn Green
6 Larry Walker
Todd Helton
7 Carlos Delgado
Shannon Stewart
8 Omar Vizquel
Jim Thome
9 Vladimir Guerrero
Jose Vidro
10 Bernie Williams
Roger Clemens

2002 Leaf Future 500 Club

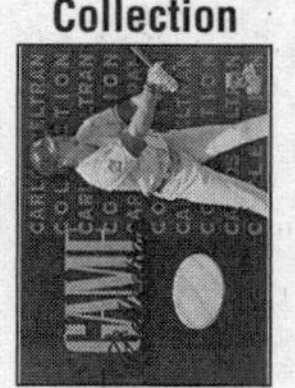

Inserted at stated odds of one in 64 hobby and one in 103 retail, these 10 cards honor players who appear to have good chances of reaching the 500 career homer mark. These cards have holo-foil stamping as well as the year that the player is projected to arrive at the 500 homer club.

COMPLETE SET (10)	40.00	80.00
1 Sammy Sosa	2.50	6.00
2 Mike Piazza	4.00	10.00
3 Alex Rodriguez	4.00	10.00
4 Chipper Jones	2.50	6.00
5 Jeff Bagwell	2.00	5.00
6 Carlos Delgado	2.00	5.00
7 Shawn Green	2.00	5.00
8 Ken Griffey Jr.	4.00	10.00
9 Rafael Palmeiro	2.00	5.00
10 Vladimir Guerrero	2.50	6.00

2002 Leaf Game Collection

Inserted into retail packs at stated odds of one in 62, these 46 cards feature game-used memorabilia from the featured player. Some cards were printed in shorter quantities and we have provided those stated print runs in our checklist. For cards with a stated print run of 25 or fewer, no pricing is provided due to market scarcity.

Card		
ABB Adrian Beltre Bat	4.00	10.00
ADBG Adam Dunn Btg Glv SP/25		
AGB Andres Galarraga Bat	4.00	10.00
AJB Andruw Jones Bat SP/300	10.00	25.00
BGB Brian Giles Bat	4.00	10.00
BHB Bobby Higginson Bat	4.00	10.00
BSH Ben Sheets Hat SP/25		
BWS Bernie Williams Shoes SP/25		
BZFG Barry Zito Fld Glv SP/25		
CBB Carlos Beltran Bat	4.00	10.00
CBIB Craig Biggio Bat	6.00	15.00
CFB Carlton Fisk Bat	6.00	15.00
CKB Chuck Knoblauch Bat	4.00	10.00
CPS Corey Patterson Shoes SP/25		
EMB Eddie Murray Bat SP/250	10.00	25.00
GJP Geoff Jenkins Pants	4.00	10.00
IRBG Ivan Rodriguez Btg Glv SP/25		
JBB Jeff Bagwell Bat SP/100		
JDH Johnny Damon Hat SP/25		
JEB Juan Encarnacion Bat	4.00	10.00
JGB Juan Gonzalez Bat	4.00	10.00
KLB Kenny Lofton Bat	4.00	10.00
KWS Kerry Wood Shoes SP/25		
LBBG Lance Berkman Btg Glv SP/25		
LWB Larry Walker Bat SP/50		
MBBG Marlon Byrd Btg Glv SP/25		
MGB Mark Grace Bat SP/200	10.00	25.00
MMFG Mike Mussina Fld Glv SP/25		
MOB Magglio Ordonez Bat SP/150	6.00	15.00
MPB Mike Piazza Bat SP/100		
PBB Pat Burrell Bat SP/100		
RAB Roberto Alomar Bat	6.00	15.00
RDB Ray Durham Bat	4.00	10.00
RGB Rusty Greer Bat	4.00	10.00
RJFG Randy Johnson Fld Glv SP/25		
RPB Rafael Palmeiro Bat	6.00	15.00
RPBG Rafael Palmeiro Btg Glv SP/25		
RVB Robin Ventura Bat	4.00	10.00
SCB Sean Casey Bat	4.00	10.00
SRB Scott Rolen Bat SP/250	10.00	25.00
SSH Shannon Stewart Hat SP/25		
TCB Tony Clark Bat	4.00	10.00
TGBG Tony Gwynn Btg Glv SP/25		
THB Todd Helton Bat	6.00	15.00
TNB Trot Nixon Bat	4.00	10.00
WBB Wade Boggs Bat	6.00	15.00

2002 Leaf Gold Rookies

Inserted at stated rate of one in 24 hobby or retail packs, these 10 cards feature the leading prospects entering the 2002 season. These cards are spotlighted on mirror board with gold foil.

COMPLETE SET (10)	25.00	50.00
1 Josh Beckett	1.50	4.00
2 Marlon Byrd	1.50	4.00
3 Dennis Tankersley	1.50	4.00
4 Jason Lane	1.50	4.00
5 Dewon Brazelton	1.50	4.00
6 Mark Prior	1.50	4.00
7 Bill Hall	1.50	4.00
8 Angel Berroa	1.50	4.00
9 Mark Teixeira	2.50	6.00
10 John Buck	1.50	4.00

2002 Leaf Heading for the Hall

Inserted at stated odds of one in 64 hobby and one in 240 retail, these 10 cards feature active or retired players who are virtually insured enshirement in the Baseball Hall of Fame.

COMPLETE SET (10)	40.00	80.00
1 Greg Maddux	4.00	10.00
2 Ozzie Smith	4.00	10.00
3 Andre Dawson	2.00	5.00
4 Dennis Eckersley	2.00	5.00
5 Roberto Alomar	2.00	5.00
6 Cal Ripken	8.00	20.00
7 Roger Clemens	5.00	12.00
8 Tony Gwynn	3.00	8.00
9 Alex Rodriguez	4.00	10.00
10 Jeff Bagwell	2.00	5.00

2002 Leaf Heading for the Hall Autographs

Randomly inserted in hobby packs, these cards parallel the Leaf Heading to the Hall insert set. Each player signed 50 cards for this product. These cards can also be differentiated from the regular cards as these cards are also die cut. No pricing is provided due to market scarcity.

1 Greg Maddux
2 Ozzie Smith
3 Andre Dawson
4 Dennis Eckersley
5 Roberto Alomar
6 Cal Ripken
7 Roger Clemens
8 Tony Gwynn
9 Alex Rodriguez
10 Jeff Bagwell

2002 Leaf League of Nations

Inserted at stated odds of one in 60, these 10 cards feature players from foreign countries. These cards are highlighted with holo-foil and color tint relating to their homeland colors.

Card		
1 Ichiro Suzuki	5.00	12.00
2 Tsuyoshi Shinjo	2.00	5.00
3 Chan Ho Park	2.00	5.00
4 Larry Walker	2.00	5.00
5 Andruw Jones	2.00	5.00
6 Hideo Nomo	5.00	12.00
7 Byung-Hyun Kim	2.00	5.00
8 Sun-Woo Kim	2.00	5.00
9 Orlando Hernandez	2.00	5.00
10 Luke Prokopec	2.00	5.00

2002 Leaf Retired Number Jerseys

Randomly inserted in packs, these five cards feature jersey swatches from players who have had their uniform numbers retired. This insert set is sequentially numbered to the player's jersey number. We have listed each print run in our checklist below. Please note that these cards are not priced due to market scarcity.

RN1 Mike Schmidt/20
RN2 Tom Seaver/41
RN3 Rod Carew/29
RN4 Ted Williams/9
RN5 Johnny Bench/5

2002 Leaf Rookie Reprints

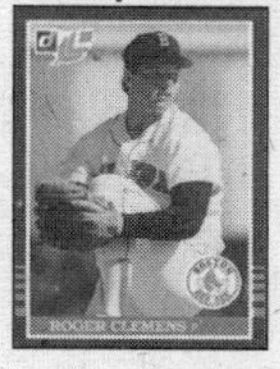

Randomly inserted in packs, these six cards feature reprints sequentially numbered to the card's original year of issue. We have listed those print runs in our checklist.

Card		
1 Roger Clemens/1985	6.00	15.00
2 Kirby Puckett/1985	3.00	8.00
3 Andres Galarraga/1986	2.00	5.00
4 Fred McGriff/1986	2.00	5.00
5 Sammy Sosa/1990	3.00	8.00
6 Frank Thomas/1990	3.00	8.00

2002 Leaf Shirt Off My Back

Inserted at stated odds of one in 29 hobby packs, these 60 cards feature a game-worn jersey swatch from either an active or retired star. Some cards were printed in shorter quantity than others, we have noted those cards with their stated print runs in our checklist. Cards with a stated print run of 50 or fewer are not priced due to market scarcity.

*MULTI-COLOR PATCH 1.25X TO 3X HI		
AB A.J. Burnett	4.00	10.00
AK Al Kaline SP/100	15.00	40.00
AP Andy Pettitte SP/50	20.00	50.00
AR Alex Rodriguez SP/150	15.00	40.00
BJA Bo Jackson SP/25		
BL Barry Larkin	6.00	15.00
BR Brad Radke	4.00	10.00
CB Carlos Beltran	4.00	10.00
CD Carlos Delgado	4.00	10.00
CF Cliff Floyd	4.00	10.00
CHP Chan Ho Park SP/100	10.00	25.00
CJ Chipper Jones SP/100	15.00	40.00
CL Carlos Lee	4.00	10.00
CR Cal Ripken SP/50	75.00	150.00
CS Curt Schilling SP/150	10.00	25.00
DE Darin Erstad SP/100	10.00	25.00
DM Don Mattingly SP/100	30.00	60.00
DW Dave Winfield SP/150	10.00	25.00
EK Eric Karros	4.00	10.00
EM Edgar Martinez SP/150	15.00	40.00
FG Freddy Garcia SP/100	10.00	25.00
GB George Brett SP/100	30.00	60.00
GM Greg Maddux SP/100	15.00	40.00
HN Hideo Nomo SP/100	15.00	40.00
JB Jeff Bagwell SP/100	15.00	40.00
JBU Jeromy Burnitz	4.00	10.00
JL Javy Lopez	4.00	10.00
JO John Olerud	4.00	10.00
JS John Smoltz	6.00	15.00
KB Kevin Brown SP/100	10.00	25.00
KM Kevin Millwood	4.00	10.00
KP Kirby Puckett SP/100	15.00	40.00
KS Kazuhiro Sasaki SP/100	10.00	25.00
LB Lance Berkman SP/300	10.00	25.00
LG Luis Gonzalez	4.00	10.00
LW Larry Walker SP/50	12.50	30.00
MB Michael Barrett	4.00	10.00
MBU Mark Buehrle	4.00	10.00
MH Mike Hampton	4.00	10.00
MO Magglio Ordonez	4.00	10.00
MP Mike Piazza SP/150	15.00	40.00
MR Manny Ramirez SP/100	15.00	40.00
MS Mike Sweeney	4.00	10.00
MT Miguel Tejada	4.00	10.00
MW Matt Williams	4.00	10.00
NG Nomar Garciaparra SP/25		
PM Pedro Martinez SP/100	15.00	40.00
RA Roberto Alomar SP/250	6.00	15.00
RD Ryan Dempster	4.00	10.00
RJ Randy Johnson SP/100	15.00	40.00
RP Rafael Palmeiro	6.00	15.00
RS Richie Sexson	4.00	10.00
SR Scott Rolen SP/250	15.00	40.00
TG Tony Gwynn SP/100	15.00	40.00
TG Tom Glavine	6.00	15.00
TGL Troy Glaus SP/275	10.00	25.00
TH Todd Helton	6.00	15.00
TH Tim Hudson	4.00	10.00
TP Troy Percival	4.00	10.00
TS Tsuyoshi Shinjo SP/100	10.00	25.00

2003 Leaf

This 329-card set was issued in two separate releases. The primary Leaf product - containing cards 1-320 from the basic set - was released in February, 2003. This product was issued in 10-card packs with an SRP of $3 per pack. These packs were issued in 24 pack boxes which came 20 boxes to a case. This set includes the following subsets: Passing the Torch (251 to 270) and a Rookies

subset (271-320). Jose Contreras, the cuban refugee signed to a large free-agent contract, had his very first card in this set. Cards 321-329 were issued within packs of DLP Rookies and Traded in December, 2003. There is no card number 42 as both Bobby Higginson and Carlos Pena share card number 41.

COMP.LO SET (320) 15.00 40.00
COMP.UPDATE SET (9) 3.00 8.00
COMMON CARD (1-270) .10 .30
COMMON CARD (271-320) .15 .40
COMMON CARD (321-329) .20 .50
1 Brad Fullmer .10 .30
2 Darin Erstad .10 .30
3 David Eckstein .10 .30
4 Garret Anderson .10 .30
5 Jarrod Washburn .10 .30
6 Kevin Appier .10 .30
7 Tim Salmon .20 .50
8 Troy Glaus .10 .30
9 Troy Percival .10 .30
10 Buddy Groom .10 .30
11 Jay Gibbons .10 .30
12 Jeff Conine .10 .30
13 Marty Cordova .10 .30
14 Melvin Mora .10 .30
15 Rodrigo Lopez .10 .30
16 Tony Batista .10 .30
17 Jorge Julio .10 .30
18 Cliff Floyd .10 .30
19 Derek Lowe .10 .30
20 Jason Varitek .30 .75
21 Johnny Damon .20 .50
22 Manny Ramirez .20 .50
23 Nomar Garciaparra .50 1.25
24 Pedro Martinez .20 .50
25 Rickey Henderson .30 .75
26 Shea Hillenbrand .10 .30
27 Trot Nixon .10 .30
28 Carlos Lee .10 .30
29 Frank Thomas .30 .75
30 Jose Valentin .10 .30
31 Magglio Ordonez .10 .30
32 Mark Buehrle .10 .30
33 Paul Konerko .10 .30
34 C.C. Sabathia .10 .30
35 Danys Baez .10 .30
36 Ellis Burks .10 .30
37 Jim Thome .20 .50
38 Omar Vizquel .20 .50
39 Ricky Gutierrez .10 .30
40 Travis Fryman .10 .30
41A Bobby Higginson .10 .30
41B Carlos Pena .10 .30
43 Juan Acevedo .10 .30
44 Mark Redman .10 .30
45 Randall Simon .10 .30
46 Robert Fick .10 .30
47 Steve Sparks .10 .30
48 Carlos Beltran .10 .30
49 Joe Randa .10 .30
50 Michael Tucker .10 .30
51 Mike Sweeney .10 .30
52 Paul Byrd .10 .30
53 Raul Ibanez .10 .30
54 Runelvys Hernandez .10 .30
55 A.J. Pierzynski .10 .30
56 Brad Radke .10 .30
57 Corey Koskie .10 .30
58 Cristian Guzman .10 .30
59 David Ortiz .30 .75
60 Doug Mientkiewicz .10 .30
61 Dustan Mohr .10 .30
62 Eddie Guardado .10 .30
63 Jacque Jones .10 .30
64 Torii Hunter .10 .30
65 Alfonso Soriano .10 .30
66 Andy Pettitte .20 .50
67 Bernie Williams .20 .50
68 David Wells .10 .30
69 Derek Jeter .75 2.00
70 Jason Giambi .10 .30
71 Jeff Weaver .10 .30
72 Jorge Posada .20 .50
73 Mike Mussina .20 .50
74 Nick Johnson .10 .30
75 Raul Mondesi .10 .30
76 Robin Ventura .10 .30
77 Roger Clemens .60 1.50
78 Barry Zito .10 .30
79 Billy Koch .10 .30
80 David Justice .10 .30
81 Eric Chavez .10 .30
82 Jermaine Dye .10 .30
83 Mark Mulder .10 .30
84 Miguel Tejada .10 .30
85 Ray Durham .10 .30
86 Scott Hatteberg .10 .30
87 Ted Lilly .10 .30
88 Tim Hudson .10 .30
89 Bret Boone .10 .30
90 Carlos Guillen .10 .30
91 Chris Snelling .10 .30
92 Dan Wilson .10 .30
93 Edgar Martinez .20 .50
94 Freddy Garcia .10 .30
95 Ichiro Suzuki .60 1.50
96 Jamie Moyer .10 .30
97 Joel Pineiro .10 .30
98 John Olerud .10 .30
99 Mark McLemore .10 .30
100 Mike Cameron .10 .30
101 Kazuhiro Sasaki .10 .30
102 Aubrey Huff .10 .30
103 Ben Grieve .10 .30
104 Joe Kennedy .10 .30
105 Paul Wilson .10 .30
106 Randy Winn .10 .30
107 Steve Cox .10 .30
108 Alex Rodriguez .50 1.25
109 Chan Ho Park .10 .30
110 Hank Blalock .10 .30
111 Herbert Perry .10 .30
112 Ivan Rodriguez .20 .50
113 Juan Gonzalez .10 .30
114 Kenny Rogers .10 .30
115 Kevin Mench .10 .30
116 Rafael Palmeiro .20 .50
117 Carlos Delgado .10 .30
118 Eric Hinske .10 .30
119 Jose Cruz .10 .30
120 Josh Phelps .10 .30
121 Roy Halladay .10 .30
122 Shannon Stewart .10 .30
123 Vernon Wells .10 .30
124 Curt Schilling .10 .30
125 Junior Spivey .10 .30
126 Luis Gonzalez .10 .30
127 Mark Grace .20 .50
128 Randy Johnson .30 .75
129 Steve Finley .10 .30
130 Tony Womack .10 .30
131 Andruw Jones .20 .50
132 Chipper Jones .30 .75
133 Gary Sheffield .10 .30
134 Greg Maddux .50 1.25
135 John Smoltz .20 .50
136 Kevin Millwood .10 .30
137 Rafael Furcal .10 .30
138 Tom Glavine .20 .50
139 Alex Gonzalez .10 .30
140 Corey Patterson .10 .30
141 Fred McGriff .20 .50
142 Jon Lieber .10 .30
143 Kerry Wood .10 .30
144 Mark Prior .20 .50
145 Matt Clement .10 .30
146 Moises Alou .10 .30
147 Sammy Sosa .30 .75
148 Aaron Boone .10 .30
149 Adam Dunn .10 .30
150 Austin Kearns .10 .30
151 Barry Larkin .20 .50
152 Danny Graves .10 .30
153 Elmer Dessens .10 .30
154 Ken Griffey Jr. .50 1.25
155 Sean Casey .10 .30
156 Todd Walker .10 .30
157 Gabe Kapler .10 .30
158 Jason Jennings .10 .30
159 Jay Payton .10 .30
160 Larry Walker .10 .30
161 Mike Hampton .10 .30
162 Todd Helton .20 .50
163 Todd Zeile .10 .30
164 A.J. Burnett .10 .30
165 Derrek Lee .20 .50
166 Josh Beckett .10 .30
167 Juan Encarnacion .10 .30
168 Luis Castillo .10 .30
169 Mike Lowell .10 .30
170 Preston Wilson .10 .30
171 Billy Wagner .10 .30
172 Craig Biggio .20 .50
173 Daryle Ward .10 .30
174 Jeff Bagwell .20 .50
175 Lance Berkman .10 .30
176 Octavio Dotel .10 .30
177 Richard Hidalgo .10 .30
178 Roy Oswalt .10 .30
179 Adrian Beltre .10 .30
180 Eric Gagne .10 .30
181 Eric Karros .10 .30
182 Hideo Nomo .30 .75
183 Kazuhisa Ishii .10 .30
184 Kevin Brown .10 .30
185 Mark Grudzielanek .10 .30
186 Odalis Perez .10 .30
187 Paul Lo Duca .10 .30
188 Shawn Green .10 .30
189 Alex Sanchez .10 .30
190 Ben Sheets .10 .30
191 Jeffrey Hammonds .10 .30
192 Jose Hernandez .10 .30
193 Takahito Nomura .10 .30
194 Richie Sexson .10 .30
195 Andres Galarraga .10 .30
196 Bartolo Colon .10 .30
197 Brad Wilkerson .10 .30
198 Javier Vazquez .10 .30
199 Jose Vidro .10 .30
200 Michael Barrett .10 .30
201 Tomo Ohka .10 .30
202 Vladimir Guerrero .30 .75
203 Al Leiter .10 .30
204 Armando Benitez .10 .30
205 Edgardo Alfonzo .10 .30
206 Mike Piazza .50 1.25
207 Mo Vaughn .10 .30
208 Pedro Astacio .10 .30
209 Roberto Alomar .20 .50
210 Roger Cedeno .10 .30
211 Timo Perez .10 .30
212 Bobby Abreu .10 .30
213 Jimmy Rollins .10 .30
214 Mike Lieberthal .10 .30
215 Pat Burrell .10 .30
216 Randy Wolf .10 .30
217 Travis Lee .10 .30
218 Vicente Padilla .10 .30
219 Aramis Ramirez .10 .30
220 Brian Giles .10 .30
221 Craig Wilson .10 .30
222 Jason Kendall .10 .30
223 Josh Fogg .10 .30
224 Kevin Young .10 .30
225 Kip Wells .10 .30
226 Mike Williams .10 .30
227 Brett Tomko .10 .30
228 Brian Lawrence .10 .30
229 Mark Kotsay .10 .30
230 Oliver Perez .10 .30
231 Phil Nevin .10 .30
232 Ryan Klesko .10 .30
233 Sean Burroughs .10 .30
234 Trevor Hoffman .10 .30
235 Barry Bonds .75 2.00
236 Benito Santiago .10 .30
237 Jeff Kent .10 .30
238 Kirk Rueter .10 .30
239 Livan Hernandez .10 .30
240 Kenny Lofton .10 .30
241 Rich Aurilia .10 .30
242 Russ Ortiz .10 .30
243 Albert Pujols .60 1.50
244 Edgar Renteria .10 .30
245 J.D. Drew .10 .30
246 Jason Isringhausen .10 .30
247 Jim Edmonds .10 .30
248 Matt Morris .10 .30
249 Tino Martinez .20 .50
250 Scott Rolen .20 .50
251 Curt Schilling PT .10 .30
252 Ivan Rodriguez PT .10 .30
253 Mike Piazza PT .30 .75
254 Sammy Sosa PT .20 .50
255 Matt Williams PT .10 .30
256 Frank Thomas PT .20 .50
257 Barry Bonds PT .40 1.00
258 Roger Clemens PT .30 .75
259 Rickey Henderson PT .30 .75
260 Ken Griffey Jr. PT .30 .75
261 Greg Maddux PT .30 .75
262 Randy Johnson PT .20 .50
263 Jeff Bagwell PT .10 .30
264 Roberto Alomar PT .10 .30
265 Tom Glavine PT .10 .30
266 Juan Gonzalez PT .10 .30
267 Mark Grace PT .10 .30
268 Mike Mussina PT .10 .30
269 Ryan Klesko PT .10 .30
270 Fred McGriff PT .10 .30
271 Joe Borchard ROO .15 .40
272 Chris Snelling ROO .15 .40
273 Brian Tallet ROO .15 .40
274 Cliff Lee ROO .15 .40
275 Freddy Sanchez ROO .15 .40
276 Chone Figgins ROO .15 .40
277 Kevin Cash ROO .15 .40
278 Josh Bard ROO .15 .40
279 Jeriome Robertson ROO .15 .40
280 Jeremy Hill ROO .15 .40
281 Shane Nance ROO .15 .40
282 Jeff Baker ROO .15 .40
283 Trey Hodges ROO .15 .40
284 Eric Eckenstahler ROO .15 .40
285 Jim Rushford ROO .15 .40
286 Carlos Rivera ROO .15 .40
287 Josh Bonifay ROO .15 .40
288 Garrett Atkins ROO .15 .40
289 Nic Jackson ROO .15 .40
290 Corwin Malone ROO .15 .40
291 Jimmy Gobble ROO .15 .40
292 Josh Wilson ROO .15 .40
293 Clint Barmes ROO RC .40 1.00
294 Jon Adkins ROO .15 .40
295 Tim Kalita ROO .15 .40
296 Nelson Castro ROO .15 .40
297 Colin Young ROO .15 .40
298 Adrian Burnside ROO .15 .40
299 Luis Martinez ROO .15 .40
300 Termel Sledge ROO RC .15 .40
301 Todd Donovan ROO .15 .40
302 Jeremy Ward ROO .15 .40
303 Wilson Valdez ROO .15 .40
304 Jose Contreras ROO RC .30 .75
305 Marshall McDougall ROO .15 .40
306 Mitch Wylie ROO .15 .40
307 Ron Calloway ROO .15 .40
308 Jose Valverde ROO .15 .40
309 Jason Davis ROO .15 .40
310 Scotty Layfield ROO .15 .40
311 Matt Thornton ROO .15 .40
312 Adam Walker ROO .15 .40
313 Gustavo Chacin ROO .15 .40
314 Ron Chiavacci ROO .15 .40
315 Wilbert Nieves ROO .15 .40
316 Cliff Bartosh ROO .15 .40
317 Mike Gonzalez ROO .15 .40
318 Jeremy Guthrie ROO .15 .40
319 Eric Junge ROO .15 .40
320 Ben Kozlowski ROO .15 .40
321 Hideki Matsui ROO RC .75 2.00
322 Ramon Nivar ROO RC .20 .50
323 Adam Loewen ROO RC .20 .50
324 Brandon Webb ROO RC 1.00 2.50
325 Chien-Ming Wang ROO RC 1.50 4.00
326 Delmon Young ROO RC 1.25 3.00
327 Ryan Wagner ROO RC .20 .50
328 Dan Haren ROO RC .20 .50
329 Rickie Weeks ROO RC .60 1.50

2003 Leaf Autographs

This nine card set was issued in two separate series. Card 304 features Yankees rookie Jose Contreras and was distributed within standard 2003 Leaf packs. The remaining eight cards from this set were randomly seeded into packs of 2003 DLP Rookies and Traded. Print runs range from 10-100 copies per and all cards are serial numbered.

304 Jose Contreras ROO/100 12.50 30.00
322 Ramon Nivar ROO/100 4.00 10.00
323 Adam Loewen ROO/100 6.00 15.00
324 Brandon Webb ROO/100 20.00 50.00
325 Chien-Ming Wang ROO/50 175.00 300.00
326 Delmon Young ROO/25
327 Ryan Wagner ROO/100 4.00 10.00
328 Dan Haren ROO/100 10.00 25.00
329 Rickie Weeks ROO/10

2003 Leaf Press Proofs Blue

Randomly inserted into packs, this is a parallel to the Leaf Set. Cards 321-329 were randomly seeded

into packs of DLP Rookies and Traded. These cards feature a blue foil logo and were issued to a stated print run of 50 serial numbered sets.

*BLUE 1-250: 6X TO 15X BASIC
*BLUE 251-270: 10X TO 25X BASIC
*BLUE 271-320: 4X TO 10X BASIC
*BLUE 271-320: 4X TO 10X BASIC RC's
*BLUE 321-329: 5X TO 12X BASIC
325 Chien-Ming Wang ROO 40.00 80.00

2003 Leaf Press Proofs Red

Inserted in packs at a stated rate of one in 12, this is a complete parallel to the Leaf Set. Cards 321-329 were randomly seeded into packs of DLP Rookies and Traded - and unlike the first 320 cards - are serial numbered to 100 copies per. These cards feature the words Press Proof printed in red foil on each card front.

*RED 1-250: 2.5X TO 6X BASIC
*RED 251-270: 4X TO 10X BASIC
*RED 271-320: 2.5X TO 6X BASIC
*RED 271-320: 2X TO 5X BASIC RC's
*RED 321-329: 3X TO 8X BASIC RC's
325 Chien-Ming Wang ROO 20.00 50.00

2003 Leaf 60

This 50 card insert set was issued at a stated rate of one in eight packs. These cards were designed in the style of the 1960 Leaf set and feature black and white photos.

*FOIL: 2X TO 5X BASIC CARDS
FOIL RANDOM INSERTS IN PACKS
FOIL PRINT RUN 60 SERIAL #'d SETS
1 Troy Glaus 1.25 3.00
2 Curt Schilling 1.25 3.00
3 Randy Johnson 1.50 4.00
4 Andruw Jones 1.25 3.00
5 Chipper Jones 1.50 4.00
6 Greg Maddux 2.50 6.00
7 Tom Glavine 1.25 3.00
8 Manny Ramirez 1.25 3.00
9 Nomar Garciaparra 2.50 6.00
10 Pedro Martinez 1.25 3.00
11 Rickey Henderson 1.50 4.00
12 Sammy Sosa 1.50 4.00
13 Frank Thomas 1.50 4.00
14 Magglio Ordonez 1.25 3.00
15 Mark Buehrle 1.25 3.00
16 Adam Dunn 1.25 3.00
17 Ken Griffey Jr. 2.50 6.00
18 Jim Thome 1.25 3.00
19 Omar Vizquel 1.25 3.00
20 Larry Walker 1.25 3.00
21 Todd Helton 1.25 3.00
22 Lance Berkman 1.25 3.00
23 Roy Oswalt 1.25 3.00
24 Mike Sweeney 1.25 3.00
25 Hideo Nomo 1.50 4.00
26 Kazuhisa Ishii 1.25 3.00
27 Shawn Green 1.25 3.00
28 Torii Hunter 1.25 3.00
29 Vladimir Guerrero 1.50 4.00
30 Mike Piazza 2.50 6.00
31 Alfonso Soriano 1.25 3.00
32 Bernie Williams 1.25 3.00
33 Derek Jeter 4.00 10.00
34 Jason Giambi 1.25 3.00
35 Roger Clemens 3.00 8.00
36 Barry Zito 1.25 3.00
37 Miguel Tejada 1.25 3.00
38 Pat Burrell 1.25 3.00
39 Ryan Klesko 1.25 3.00
40 Barry Bonds 4.00 10.00
41 Jeff Kent 1.25 3.00
42 Ichiro Suzuki 3.00 8.00
43 John Olerud 1.25 3.00
44 Albert Pujols 3.00 8.00
45 Jim Edmonds 1.25 3.00
46 Scott Rolen 1.25 3.00
47 Alex Rodriguez 2.50 6.00
48 Ivan Rodriguez 1.25 3.00
49 Rafael Palmeiro 1.25 3.00
50 Roy Halladay 1.25 3.00

2003 Leaf Certified Samples

Inserted in packs at a stated rate of one in 23, this 15-card insert set previews the upcoming Leaf

Certified set. These cards were printed on metalized film board.

*MIRROR RED: 1.5X TO 4X BASIC
MIRROR RED PRINT RUN 150 #'d SETS
*MIRROR BLUE: 1X TO 2.5X BASIC
MIRROR BLUE PRINT RUN 75 #'d SETS
MIRROR GOLD PRINT RUN 25 #'d SETS
MIRROR GOLD TOO SCARCE TO PRICE
MIRROR CARDS RANDOM INSERTS IN PACKS
1 Derek Jeter 4.00 10.00
2 Greg Maddux 2.50 6.00
3 Mike Piazza 2.50 6.00
4 Barry Bonds 4.00 10.00
5 Lance Berkman 1.25 3.00
6 Alex Rodriguez 2.50 6.00
7 Alfonso Soriano 1.25 3.00
8 Ichiro Suzuki 3.00 8.00
9 Sammy Sosa 1.50 4.00
10 Vladimir Guerrero 1.50 4.00
11 Albert Pujols 3.00 8.00
12 Pedro Martinez 1.25 3.00
13 Randy Johnson 1.50 4.00
14 Nomar Garciaparra 2.50 6.00
15 Barry Zito 1.25 3.00

2003 Leaf Clean Up Crew

Inserted in packs at a stated rate of one in 49, these ten cards feature the middle of the lineup for ten different major league teams.

1 Alex Rodriguez 2.50 6.00
Rafael Palmeiro
Ivan Rodriguez
2 Nomar Garciaparra 2.50 6.00
Manny Ramirez
Cliff Floyd
3 Jason Giambi 1.50 4.00
Bernie Williams
Jorge Posada
4 Rich Aurilia 4.00 10.00
Jeff Kent
Barry Bonds
5 Larry Walker 1.50 4.00
Todd Helton
Jay Payton
6 Lance Berkman 1.50 4.00
Jeff Bagwell
Darryl Ward
7 Scott Rolen 3.00 8.00
Albert Pujols
Jim Edmonds
8 Gary Sheffield 1.50 4.00
Chipper Jones
Andruw Jones
9 Miguel Tejada 1.50 4.00
Eric Chavez
Jermaine Dye
10 Sammy Sosa 1.50 4.00
Moises Alou
Fred McGriff

2003 Leaf Clean Up Crew Materials

Randomly inserted into packs, this is a parallel to the Clean Up Crew set. These cards feature a memorabilia piece from each of the three players featured and these cards were issued to a stated print run of 25 serial numbered sets.

1 Alex Rodriguez Jsy 15.00 40.00
Rafael Palmeiro Jsy
Ivan Rodriguez Jsy
2 Nomar Garciaparra Jsy 15.00 40.00
Manny Ramirez Jsy
Cliff Floyd Bat
3 Jason Giambi Ball 15.00 40.00
Bernie Williams Ball
Jorge Posada Ball
4 Rich Aurilia Ball 30.00 60.00
Jeff Kent Ball
Barry Bonds Ball
5 Larry Walker Jsy 15.00 40.00
Todd Helton Jsy
Jay Payton Jsy
6 Lance Berkman Jsy 15.00 40.00
Jeff Bagwell Jsy
Daryle Ward Bat
7 Scott Rolen Ball 30.00 60.00
Albert Pujols Ball
Jim Edmonds Base
8 Gary Sheffield Bat 15.00 40.00
Chipper Jones Jsy
Andruw Jones Jsy
9 Miguel Tejada Jsy 10.00 25.00
Eric Chavez Jsy
Jermaine Dye Bat
10 Sammy Sosa Ball 15.00 40.00
Moises Alou Ball
Fred McGriff Ball

2003 Leaf Clubhouse Signatures Bronze

Randomly inserted into packs, these 24 cards feature authentic signatures of the players. Some of these cards were issued to a smaller quantity and we have notated that information and the stated print run information next to the player's name in our checklist. Please note that for cards with a print run of 25 or fewer, no pricing is provided due to market scarcity.

1 Edwin Almonte 3.00 8.00
2 Franklin Nunez 3.00 8.00
3 Josh Bard 3.00 8.00
4 J.C. Romero 3.00 8.00
5 Omar Infante 3.00 8.00
6 Adam Dunn SP/10
7 Andre Dawson SP/50 10.00 25.00
8 Brian Tallet SP/100 4.00 10.00
9 Bobby Doerr SP/100 6.00 15.00
10 Chris Snelling SP/100 4.00 10.00
11 Corey Patterson SP/100 4.00 10.00
12 Doc Gooden SP/100 6.00 15.00
13 Eric Hinske 3.00 8.00
14 Jeff Baker SP/100 4.00 10.00
15 Jack Morris SP/100 6.00 15.00
16 Joe Crede SP/25
17 Torii Hunter SP/75 10.00 25.00
18 Kevin Mench 4.00 10.00
20 Alfonso Soriano SP/25
21 Angel Berroa SP/100 4.00 10.00
22 Brian Lawrence 3.00 8.00
23 Drew Henson SP/50 6.00 15.00
24 Jhonny Peralta 6.00 15.00
25 Magglio Ordonez SP/50 10.00 25.00

2003 Leaf Clubhouse Signatures Gold

This is a parallel to the Leaf Clubhouse Signatures set. These cards were issued to a stated print run of 25 serial numbered sets and no pricing is provided due to market scarcity.

1 Edwin Almonte
2 Franklin Nunez
3 Josh Bard
4 J.C. Romero
5 Omar Infante
6 Adam Dunn
7 Andre Dawson
8 Brian Tallet
9 Bobby Doerr
10 Chris Snelling
11 Corey Patterson
12 Doc Gooden
13 Eric Hinske
14 Jeff Baker
15 Jack Morris
16 Joe Crede
17 Torii Hunter
18 Kevin Mench
19 Vladimir Guerrero
20 Alfonso Soriano
21 Angel Berroa
22 Brian Lawrence
23 Drew Henson
24 Jhonny Peralta
25 Magglio Ordonez

2003 Leaf Clubhouse Signatures Silver

Randomly inserted into packs, this is a parallel to the Leaf Clubhouse Signatures set. These cards were issued to a stated print run of 100 serial numbered sets except for Andre Dawson who was issued to a stated print run of 25 serial numbered sets.

1 Edwin Almonte 3.00 8.00
2 Franklin Nunez 3.00 8.00
3 Josh Bard 3.00 8.00

4 J.C. Romero 3.00 8.00
5 Omar Infante 3.00 8.00
7 Andre Dawson SP/25
8 Brian Tallet 3.00 8.00
9 Bobby Doerr 6.00 15.00
10 Chris Snelling 3.00 8.00
12 Doc Gooden 6.00 15.00
13 Eric Hinske 3.00 8.00
14 Jeff Baker 3.00 8.00
15 Jack Morris 6.00 15.00
17 Torii Hunter 4.00 10.00
18 Kevin Mench 4.00 10.00
21 Angel Berroa 3.00 8.00
22 Brian Lawrence 3.00 8.00
23 Drew Henson 3.00 8.00
24 Jhonny Peralta 6.00 15.00
25 Magglio Ordonez 6.00 15.00

2003 Leaf Game Collection

Randomly inserted into packs, this set displays one swatch of game-used materials. These cards were issued to a stated print run of 150 serial numbered sets.

1 Miguel Tejada Hat 4.00 10.00
2 Shannon Stewart Hat 4.00 10.00
3 Mike Schmidt Jacket 20.00 50.00
4 Nolan Ryan Jacket 40.00 80.00
5 Rafael Palmeiro Fld Glv 10.00 25.00
6 Andruw Jones Shoe 6.00 15.00
7 Bernie Williams Shoe 6.00 15.00
8 Ivan Rodriguez Shoe 6.00 15.00
9 Lance Berkman Shoe 4.00 10.00
10 Magglio Ordonez Shoe 4.00 10.00
11 Roy Oswalt Fld Glv 6.00 15.00
12 Andy Pettitte Shoe 6.00 15.00
13 Vladimir Guerrero Fld Glv 15.00 40.00
14 Jason Jennings Fld Glv 6.00 15.00
15 Mike Sweeney Shoe 4.00 10.00
16 Joe Borchard Shoe 4.00 10.00
17 Mark Prior Shoe 6.00 15.00
18 Gary Carter Jacket 4.00 10.00
19 Austin Kearns Fld Glv 6.00 15.00
20 Ryan Klesko Fld Glv 6.00 15.00

2003 Leaf Gold Rookies

Issued at a stated rate of one in 24, this 10 card set features some of the leading candidates for Rookie of the Year. These cards were issued on a special foil board.

MIRROR GOLD RANDOM INSERTS IN PACKS
MIRROR GOLD PRINT RUN 25 #'d SETS
MIRROR GOLD TOO SCARCE TO PRICE
1 Joe Borchard 1.25 3.00
2 Chone Figgins 1.25 3.00
3 Alexis Gomez 1.25 3.00
4 Chris Snelling 1.25 3.00
5 Cliff Lee 1.25 3.00
6 Victor Martinez 2.00 5.00
7 Hee Seop Choi 1.25 3.00
8 Michael Restovich 1.25 3.00
9 Anderson Machado 1.25 3.00
10 Drew Henson 1.25 3.00

2003 Leaf Hard Hats

Issued at a stated rate of one in 13, these 12 cards feature the 1997 Studio design set against a rainbow board.

1 Alex Rodriguez 1.50 4.00
2 Bernie Williams .75 2.00
3 Ivan Rodriguez .75 2.00
4 Jeff Bagwell .75 2.00
5 Rafael Furcal .75 2.00
6 Rafael Palmeiro .75 2.00
7 Tony Gwynn 1.25 3.00
8 Vladimir Guerrero 1.00 2.50
9 Adrian Beltre .75 2.00
10 Shawn Green .75 2.00
11 Andruw Jones .75 2.00
12 George Brett 2.00 5.00

2003 Leaf Hard Hats Batting Helmets

Randomly inserted into packs, this is a parallel to the Hard Hats insert set. These cards feature a swatch of a game-worn batting helmet embedded on the card and these cards were issued to a stated print run of 100 serial numbered sets.

1 Alex Rodriguez 30.00 60.00
2 Bernie Williams 15.00 40.00
3 Ivan Rodriguez 15.00 40.00
4 Jeff Bagwell 15.00 40.00
5 Rafael Furcal 10.00 25.00
6 Rafael Palmeiro 15.00 40.00
7 Tony Gwynn 20.00 50.00
8 Vladimir Guerrero 15.00 40.00
9 Adrian Beltre 10.00 25.00
10 Shawn Green 10.00 25.00
11 Andruw Jones 15.00 40.00
12 George Brett 60.00 120.00

2003 Leaf Home/Away

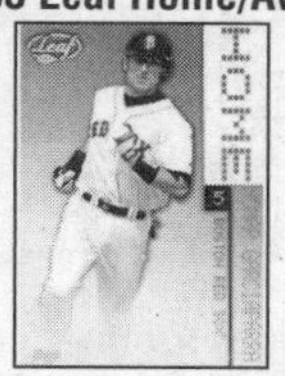

Issued at a stated rate of one in 34, these 20 cards feature either home or away stats for these 10 featured players. The last three year of stats are featured on the cards.

1A Andruw Jones A 1.50 4.00
1H Andruw Jones H 1.50 4.00
2A Cal Ripken A 6.00 15.00
2H Cal Ripken H 6.00 15.00
3A Edgar Martinez A 1.50 4.00
3H Edgar Martinez H 1.50 4.00
4A Jim Thome A 1.50 4.00
4H Jim Thome H 1.50 4.00
5A Larry Walker A 1.50 4.00
5H Larry Walker H 1.50 4.00
6A Nomar Garciaparra A 3.00 8.00
6H Nomar Garciaparra H 3.00 8.00
7A Mark Prior A 1.50 4.00
7H Mark Prior H 1.50 4.00
8A Mike Piazza A 3.00 8.00
8H Mike Piazza H 3.00 8.00
9A Vladimir Guerrero A 2.00 5.00
9H Vladimir Guerrero H 2.00 5.00
10A Chipper Jones A 2.00 5.00
10H Chipper Jones H 2.00 5.00

2003 Leaf Home/Away Materials

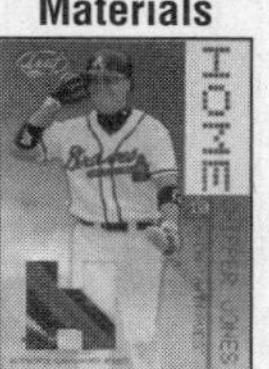

Randomly inserted into packs, this is a parallel to the Home/Away set. These cards feature jersey swatches displayed on the front and these cards were issued to a stated print run of 250 serial numbered sets.

1A Andruw Jones A 6.00 15.00
1H Andruw Jones H 6.00 15.00
2A Cal Ripken A 30.00 60.00
2H Cal Ripken H 30.00 60.00
3A Edgar Martinez A 6.00 15.00
3H Edgar Martinez H 6.00 15.00
4A Jim Thome A 6.00 15.00
4H Jim Thome H 6.00 15.00
5A Larry Walker A 4.00 10.00
5H Larry Walker H 4.00 10.00
6A Nomar Garciaparra A 8.00 20.00
6H Nomar Garciaparra H 8.00 20.00
7A Mark Prior A 6.00 15.00
7H Mark Prior H 6.00 15.00
8A Mike Piazza A 8.00 20.00
8H Mike Piazza H 8.00 20.00
9A Vladimir Guerrero A 6.00 15.00
9H Vladimir Guerrero H 6.00 15.00
10A Chipper Jones A 6.00 15.00
10H Chipper Jones H 6.00 15.00

2003 Leaf Maple and Ash

Randomly inserted into packs, these cards feature faux wood grain and also have a game-used bat piece. These cards were issued to a stated print run of 400 serial numbered sets.

1 Jorge Posada 6.00 15.00
2 Mike Piazza 8.00 20.00
3 Alex Rodriguez 8.00 20.00
4 Jeff Bagwell 6.00 15.00
5 Joe Borchard 4.00 10.00
6 Miguel Tejada 4.00 10.00
7 Adam Dunn 4.00 10.00
8 Jim Thome 6.00 15.00
9 Lance Berkman 4.00 10.00
10 Torii Hunter 4.00 10.00
11 Carlos Delgado 4.00 10.00
12 Reggie Jackson 6.00 15.00
13 Juan Gonzalez 4.00 10.00
14 Vladimir Guerrero 6.00 15.00
15 Richie Sexson 4.00 10.00

2003 Leaf Number Off My Back

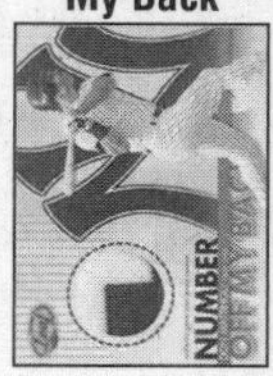

Randomly inserted in packs, these cards feature a swatch from a game-worn jersey number. These cards were issued to a stated print run of 50 serial numbered sets.

1 Carlos Delgado 10.00 25.00
2 Don Mattingly 60.00 120.00
3 Todd Helton 15.00 40.00
4 Vernon Wells 10.00 25.00
5 Bernie Williams 15.00 40.00
6 Luis Gonzalez 10.00 25.00
7 Kerry Wood 10.00 25.00
8 Eric Chavez 10.00 25.00
9 Shawn Green 10.00 25.00
10 Roy Oswalt 10.00 25.00
11 Nomar Garciaparra 30.00 60.00
12 Robin Yount 50.00 100.00
13 Troy Glaus 10.00 25.00
14 C.C. Sabathia 10.00 25.00
15 Alex Rodriguez 30.00 60.00
16 Mark Mulder 10.00 25.00
17 Will Clark 50.00 100.00
18 Alfonso Soriano 10.00 25.00
19 Andy Pettitte 15.00 40.00
20 Curt Schilling 10.00 25.00

2003 Leaf Shirt Off My Back

Randomly inserted into packs, this 20-card insert set features one swatch of game-worn jersey of the featured player. These cards were issued to a stated print run of 500 serial numbered sets.

1 Carlos Delgado 3.00 8.00
2 Don Mattingly 10.00 25.00
3 Todd Helton 4.00 10.00
4 Vernon Wells 3.00 8.00
5 Bernie Williams 4.00 10.00
6 Luis Gonzalez 3.00 8.00
7 Kerry Wood 3.00 8.00
8 Eric Chavez 3.00 8.00
9 Shawn Green 3.00 8.00
10 Roy Oswalt 3.00 8.00
11 Nomar Garciaparra 6.00 15.00
12 Robin Yount 6.00 15.00
13 Troy Glaus 3.00 8.00
14 C.C. Sabathia 3.00 8.00
15 Alex Rodriguez 4.00 10.00
16 Mark Mulder 3.00 8.00
17 Will Clark 6.00 15.00
18 Alfonso Soriano 3.00 8.00
19 Andy Pettitte 4.00 10.00
20 Curt Schilling 3.00 8.00

2003 Leaf Slick Leather

Issued at a stated rate of one in 21, this 15-card insert set features the most skilled fielders on cards featuring faux leather grain.

1 Omar Vizquel 1.25 3.00
2 Roberto Alomar 1.25 3.00
3 Ivan Rodriguez 1.25 3.00
4 Greg Maddux 2.50 6.00
5 Scott Rolen 1.25 3.00
6 Todd Helton 1.25 3.00
7 Andruw Jones 1.25 3.00
8 Jim Edmonds 1.25 3.00
9 Barry Bonds 4.00 10.00
10 Eric Chavez 1.25 3.00
11 Ichiro Suzuki 3.00 8.00
12 Mike Mussina 1.25 3.00
13 John Olerud 1.25 3.00
14 Torii Hunter 1.25 3.00
15 Larry Walker 1.25 3.00

2004 Leaf

This 301-card standard-size set was released in January, 2004. The set was issued in six-card packs with an $3 SRP which came 24 packs to a box and six boxes to a case. The first 200 cards were printed in higher quantities than the last 101 cards in this set. Cards numbered 201 through 251 feature 50 of the leading prospects. Cards numbered 252 through 271 feature 20 players in a Passing Through Time subset while the final 30 cards of the set feature team checklists. Card number 42 was not issued as this product does not use that number in honor of Jackie Robinson.

COMPLETE SET (301) 50.00 100.00
COMP.SETw/o SP's (200) 10.00 25.00
COMMON CARD (1-201) .10 .30
COMMON CARD (202-251) .40 1.00
COMMON CARD (252-301) .40 1.00
202-301 RANDOM INSERTS IN PACKS
CARD 42 DOES NOT EXIST
1 Darin Erstad .10 .30
2 Garret Anderson .10 .30
3 Jarrod Washburn .10 .30
4 Kevin Appier .10 .30
5 Tim Salmon .20 .50
6 Troy Glaus .10 .30
7 Troy Percival .10 .30
8 Jason Johnson .10 .30
9 Jay Gibbons .10 .30
10 Melvin Mora .10 .30
11 Sidney Ponson .10 .30
12 Tony Batista .10 .30
13 Derek Lowe .10 .30
14 Robert Person .10 .30
15 Manny Ramirez .20 .50
16 Nomar Garciaparra .50 1.25
17 Pedro Martinez .20 .50
18 Jorge De La Rosa .10 .30
19 Bartolo Colon .10 .30
20 Carlos Lee .10 .30
21 Esteban Loaiza .10 .30
22 Frank Thomas .30 .75
23 Joe Crede .10 .30
24 Magglio Ordonez .10 .30
25 Ryan Ludwick .10 .30
26 Luis Garcia .10 .30
27 Brandon Phillips .10 .30
28 C.C Sabathia .10 .30
29 Jhonny Peralta .10 .30
30 Josh Bard .10 .30
31 Omar Vizquel .20 .50
32 Fernando Rodney .10 .30
33 Mike Maroth .10 .30
34 Bobby Higginson .10 .30
35 Omar Infante .10 .30
36 Dmitri Young .10 .30
37 Eric Munson .10 .30
38 Jeremy Bonderman .10 .30
39 Carlos Beltran .10 .30
40 Jeremy Affeldt .10 .30
41 Dee Brown .10 .30
43 Mike Sweeney .10 .30
44 Brent Abernathy .10 .30
45 Runelvys Hernandez .10 .30
46 A.J. Pierzynski .10 .30
47 Corey Koskie .10 .30
48 Cristian Guzman .10 .30
49 Jacque Jones .10 .30
50 Kenny Rogers .10 .30
51 J.C. Romero .10 .30
52 Torii Hunter .10 .30
53 Alfonso Soriano .10 .30
54 Bernie Williams .20 .50
55 David Wells .10 .30
56 Derek Jeter .60 1.50
57 Hideki Matsui .50 1.25
58 Jason Giambi .10 .30
59 Jorge Posada .20 .50
60 Jose Contreras .10 .30
61 Mike Mussina .20 .50
62 Nick Johnson .10 .30
63 Roger Clemens .60 1.50
64 Barry Zito .10 .30
65 Justin Duchscherer .10 .30
66 Eric Chavez .10 .30
67 Erubial Durazo .10 .30
68 Miguel Tejada .10 .30
69 Mark Mulder .10 .30
70 Terrence Long .10 .30
71 Tim Hudson .10 .30
72 Bret Boone .10 .30
73 Dan Wilson .10 .30
74 Edgar Martinez .20 .50
75 Freddy Garcia .10 .30
76 Rafael Soriano .10 .30
77 Ichiro Suzuki .60 1.50
78 Jamie Moyer .10 .30
79 John Olerud .10 .30
80 Kazuhiro Sasaki .10 .30
81 Aubrey Huff .10 .30
82 Carl Crawford .10 .30
83 Joe Kennedy .10 .30
84 Rocco Baldelli .10 .30
85 Toby Hall .10 .30
86 Alex Rodriguez .50 1.25
87 Kevin Mench .10 .30
88 Hank Blalock .10 .30
89 Juan Gonzalez .10 .30
90 Mark Teixeira .20 .50
91 Rafael Palmeiro .20 .50
92 Carlos Delgado .10 .30
93 Eric Hinske .10 .30
94 Josh Phelps .10 .30
95 Brian Bowles .10 .30
96 Roy Halladay .10 .30
97 Shannon Stewart .10 .30
98 Vernon Wells .10 .30
99 Curt Schilling .10 .30
100 Junior Spivey .10 .30
101 Luis Gonzalez .10 .30
102 Lyle Overbay .10 .30
103 Mark Grace .20 .50
104 Randy Johnson .30 .75
105 Shea Hillenbrand .10 .30
106 Andruw Jones .20 .50
107 Chipper Jones .30 .75
108 Gary Sheffield .10 .30
109 Greg Maddux .50 1.25
110 Javy Lopez .10 .30
111 John Smoltz .20 .50
112 Marcus Giles .10 .30
113 Rafael Furcal .10 .30
114 Corey Patterson .10 .30
115 Juan Cruz .10 .30
116 Kerry Wood .10 .30
117 Mark Prior .20 .50
118 Moises Alou .10 .30
119 Sammy Sosa .30 .75
120 Aaron Boone .10 .30
121 Adam Dunn .10 .30
122 Austin Kearns .10 .30
123 Barry Larkin .20 .50
124 Ken Griffey Jr. .50 1.25
125 Brian Reith .10 .30
126 Wily Mo Pena .10 .30
127 Jason Jennings .10 .30
128 Jay Payton .10 .30
129 Larry Walker .10 .30
130 Preston Wilson .10 .30
131 Todd Helton .20 .50
132 Dontrelle Willis .20 .50
133 Ivan Rodriguez .20 .50
134 Josh Beckett .10 .30
135 Juan Encarnacion .10 .30
136 Mike Lowell .10 .30
137 Craig Biggio .20 .50
138 Jeff Bagwell .20 .50
139 Jeff Kent .10 .30
140 Lance Berkman .10 .30
141 Richard Hidalgo .10 .30
142 Roy Oswalt .10 .30
143 Eric Gagne .10 .30
144 Fred McGriff .20 .50
145 Hideo Nomo .30 .75
146 Kazuhisa Ishii .10 .30
147 Kevin Brown .10 .30
148 Paul Lo Duca .10 .30
149 Shawn Green .10 .30
150 Ben Sheets .10 .30
151 Geoff Jenkins .10 .30
152 Rey Sanchez .10 .30
153 Richie Sexson .10 .30
154 Wes Helms .10 .30
155 Shane Nance .10 .30
156 Fernando Tatis .10 .30
157 Javier Vazquez .10 .30
158 Jose Vidro .10 .30
159 Orlando Cabrera .10 .30
160 Henry Mateo .10 .30
161 Vladimir Guerrero .30 .75
162 Zach Day .10 .30
163 Edwin Almonte .10 .30
164 Al Leiter .10 .30
165 Cliff Floyd .10 .30
166 Jae Weong Seo .10 .30
167 Mike Piazza .50 1.25
168 Roberto Alomar .20 .50
169 Tom Glavine .20 .50
170 Bobby Abreu .10 .30
171 Brandon Duckworth .10 .30
172 Jim Thome .20 .50
173 Kevin Millwood .10 .30
174 Pat Burrell .10 .30
175 Aramis Ramirez .10 .30
176 Jack Wilson .10 .30
177 Brian Giles .10 .30
178 Jason Kendall .10 .30
179 Kenny Lofton .10 .30
180 Kip Wells .10 .30
181 Kris Benson .10 .30
182 Albert Pujols .60 1.50
183 J.D. Drew .10 .30
184 Jim Edmonds .10 .30
185 Matt Morris .10 .30
186 Scott Rolen .20 .50
187 Woody Williams .10 .30
188 Cliff Bartosh .10 .30
189 Brian Lawrence .10 .30
190 Ryan Klesko .10 .30
191 Sean Burroughs .10 .30
192 Xavier Nady .10 .30
193 Dennis Tankersley .10 .30
194 Donaldo Mendez .10 .30
195 Barry Bonds .75 2.00
196 Benito Santiago .10 .30
197 Edgardo Alfonzo .10 .30
198 Cody Ransom .10 .30
199 Jason Schmidt .10 .30
200 Rich Aurilia .10 .30
201 Ken Harvey .10 .30
202 Adam Loewen ROO .40 1.00
203 Alfredo Gonzalez ROO .40 1.00
204 Arnie Munoz ROO .40 1.00
205 Andrew Brown ROO .40 1.00
206 Josh Hall ROO .40 1.00
207 Josh Stewart PROS .40 1.00
208 Clint Barmes PROS .75 2.00
209 Brandon Webb PROS .40 1.00
210 Chien-Ming Wang PROS 2.00 5.00
211 Edgar Gonzalez PROS .40 1.00
212 Alejandro Machado PROS .40 1.00
213 Jeremy Griffiths PROS .40 1.00
214 Craig Brazell PROS .40 1.00
215 Daniel Cabrera PROS .40 1.00
216 Fernando Cabrera PROS .40 1.00
217 Terrmel Sledge PROS .40 1.00
218 Rob Hammock PROS .40 1.00
219 Francisco Rosario PROS .40 1.00
220 Francisco Cruceta PROS .40 1.00
221 Rett Johnson PROS .40 1.00
222 Guillermo Quiroz PROS .40 1.00
223 Hong-Chih Kuo PROS .75 2.00
224 Ian Ferguson PROS .40 1.00
225 Tim Olson PROS .40 1.00
226 Todd Wellemeyer PROS .40 1.00
227 Rich Fischer PROS .40 1.00
228 Phil Seibel PROS .40 1.00
229 Joe Valentine PROS .40 1.00
230 Matt Kata PROS .40 1.00
231 Michael Hessman PROS .40 1.00
232 Michel Hernandez PROS .40 1.00
233 Doug Waechter PROS .40 1.00
234 Prentice Redman PROS .40 1.00
235 Nook Logan PROS .40 1.00
236 Oscar Villarreal PROS .40 1.00
237 Pete LaForest PROS .40 1.00
238 Matt Bruback PROS .40 1.00
239 Josh Willingham PROS .40 1.00
240 Greg Aquino PROS .40 1.00
241 Lew Ford PROS .40 1.00
242 Jeff Duncan PROS .40 1.00
243 Chris Waters PROS .40 1.00
244 Miguel Ojeda PROS .40 1.00
245 Rosman Garcia PROS .40 1.00
246 Felix Sanchez PROS .40 1.00
247 Jon Leicester PROS .40 1.00
248 Roger Deago PROS .40 1.00
249 Mike Ryan PROS .40 1.00
250 Chris Capuano PROS .40 1.00
251 Matt White PROS .40 1.00
252 Bernie Williams PTT .40 1.00
253 Mark Grace PTT .40 1.00
254 Chipper Jones PTT .60 1.50
255 Greg Maddux PTT 1.00 2.50
256 Sammy Sosa PTT .60 1.50
257 Mike Mussina PTT .40 1.00
258 Tim Salmon PTT .40 1.00
259 Barry Larkin PTT .40 1.00
260 Randy Johnson PTT .60 1.50
261 Jeff Bagwell PTT .40 1.00
262 Roberto Alomar PTT .40 1.00
263 Tom Glavine PTT .40 1.00
264 Roger Clemens PTT 1.25 3.00
265 Barry Bonds PTT 1.50 4.00
266 Ivan Rodriguez PTT .40 1.00
267 Pedro Martinez PTT .40 1.00
268 Ken Griffey Jr. PTT 1.00 2.50
269 Jim Thome PTT .40 1.00
270 Frank Thomas PTT .60 1.50
271 Mike Piazza PTT 1.00 2.50
272 Troy Glaus TC .40 1.00
273 Melvin Mora TC .40 1.00
274 Nomar Garciaparra TC 1.00 2.50
275 Magglio Ordonez TC .40 1.00
276 Omar Vizquel TC .40 1.00
277 Dmitri Young TC .40 1.00
278 Mike Sweeney TC .40 1.00
279 Torii Hunter TC .40 1.00
280 Derek Jeter TC 1.25 3.00
281 Barry Zito TC .40 1.00
282 Ichiro Suzuki TC 1.25 3.00
283 Rocco Baldelli TC .40 1.00
284 Alex Rodriguez TC 1.00 2.50
285 Carlos Delgado TC .40 1.00
286 Randy Johnson TC .60 1.50
287 Greg Maddux TC 1.00 2.50
288 Sammy Sosa TC .60 1.50
289 Ken Griffey Jr. TC 1.00 2.50
290 Todd Helton TC .40 1.00
291 Ivan Rodriguez TC .40 1.00
292 Jeff Bagwell TC .40 1.00
293 Hideo Nomo TC .60 1.50
294 Richie Sexson TC .40 1.00
295 Vladimir Guerrero TC .60 1.50
296 Mike Piazza TC 1.00 2.50
297 Jim Thome TC .40 1.00
298 Jason Kendall TC .40 1.00
299 Albert Pujols TC 1.25 3.00
300 Ryan Klesko TC .40 1.00
301 Barry Bonds TC 1.50 4.00

2004 Leaf Second Edition

*2ND ED 1-201: .4X TO 1X BASIC
*2ND ED 202-301: .4X TO 1X BASIC
ISSUED IN SECOND EDITION PACKS

2004 Leaf Autographs

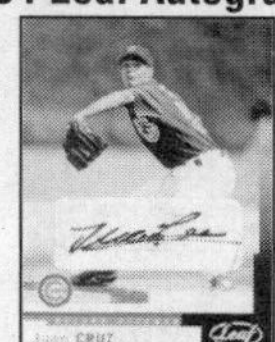

RANDOM INSERTS IN PACKS
SP INFO PROVIDED BY DONRUSS
SP'S ARE NOT SERIAL-NUMBERED
14 Robert Person 4.00 10.00
18 Jorge De La Rosa 4.00 10.00
25 Ryan Ludwick 12.50 30.00
26 Luis Garcia 4.00 10.00
29 Jhonny Peralta 6.00 15.00
30 Josh Bard 4.00 10.00
32 Fernando Rodney 4.00 10.00
33 Mike Maroth 4.00 10.00
35 Omar Infante 4.00 10.00
37 Eric Munson SP/9
41 Dee Brown 4.00 10.00
44 Brent Abernathy SP 6.00 15.00
51 J.C. Romero 4.00 10.00
65 Justin Duchscherer 6.00 15.00
70 Terrence Long SP 6.00 15.00
76 Rafael Soriano 4.00 10.00
85 Toby Hall SP 6.00 15.00
87 Kevin Mench 6.00 15.00
95 Brian Bowles 4.00 10.00
115 Juan Cruz 4.00 10.00
125 Brian Reith 4.00 10.00

126 Wily Mo Pena 6.00 15.00
127 Jason Jennings 4.00 10.00
150 Ben Sheets SP/17
155 Shane Nance 4.00 10.00
160 Henry Mateo SP 6.00 15.00
163 Edwin Almonte 4.00 10.00
171 Brandon Duckworth 4.00 10.00
176 Jack Wilson 6.00 15.00
180 Kip Wells 4.00 10.00
188 Cliff Bartosh 4.00 10.00
189 Brian Lawrence 4.00 10.00
193 Dennis Tankersley 4.00 10.00
194 Donaldo Mendez 4.00 10.00
198 Cody Ransom SP 6.00 15.00
247 Jon Leicester PROS SP 6.00 15.00

2004 Leaf Autographs Second Edition

*2ND ED: .4X TO 1X BASIC
*2ND ED: .4X TO 1X BASIC SP
RANDOM INSERTS IN PACKS
37 Eric Munson 4.00 10.00
150 Ben Sheets 10.00 25.00

2004 Leaf Press Proofs Blue

*BLUE 1-201: 4X TO 10X BASIC
*BLUE 202-251: 1.25X TO 3X BASIC
*BLUE 252-301: 2X TO 5X BASIC
RANDOM INSERTS IN PACKS
STATED PRINT RUN 100 SERIAL #'d SETS

2004 Leaf Press Proofs Gold

RANDOM INSERTS IN PACKS
STATED PRINT RUN 25 SERIAL #'d SETS
NO PRICING DUE TO SCARCITY

2004 Leaf Press Proofs Red

*RED 1-201: 2X TO 5X BASIC
*RED 202-251: .6X TO 1.5X BASIC
*RED 252-301: 1X TO 2.5X BASIC
STATED ODDS 1:8

2004 Leaf Press Proofs Silver

*SILVER 1-201: 6X TO 15X BASIC
*SILVER 202-251: 2X TO 5X BASIC
*SILVER 252-301: 3X TO 8X BASIC
RANDOM INSERTS IN PACKS
STATED PRINT RUN 50 SERIAL #'d SETS

2004 Leaf Clean Up Crew

STATED ODDS 1:49
*2ND ED: .4X TO 1X BASIC
2ND ED.ODDS 1:72 2ND ED.PACKS
1 Sammy Sosa 1.50 4.00
Moises Alou
Hee Seop Choi
2 Jason Giambi 3.00 8.00
Alfonso Soriano
Hideki Matsui
3 Vernon Wells 1.50 4.00
Carlos Delgado
Josh Phelps
4 Alex Rodriguez 2.50 6.00
Juan Gonzalez
Hank Blalock
5 Gary Sheffield 1.50 4.00
Chipper Jones
Andruw Jones
6 Ken Griffey Jr. 2.50 6.00
Austin Kearns
Aaron Boone
7 Albert Pujols 3.00 8.00
Jim Edmonds
Scott Rolen
8 Jeff Bagwell 1.50 4.00
Lance Berkman
Jeff Kent
9 Todd Helton 1.50 4.00
Preston Wilson
Larry Walker
10 Miguel Tejada 1.50 4.00
Erubial Durazo
Eric Chavez

2004 Leaf Clean Up Crew Materials

RANDOM INSERTS IN PACKS
STATED PRINT RUN 50 SERIAL #'d SETS
2ND ED.RANDOM IN 2ND ED.PACKS
2ND ED.PRINT RUNS 5 SERIAL #'d SETS
NO 2ND ED.PRICING DUE TO SCARCITY
1 Sammy Sosa Bat 15.00 40.00
Moises Alou Bat
Hee Seop Choi Jsy
2 Alfonso Soriano Base 30.00 60.00
Jason Giambi Base
Hideki Matsui Base
3 Vernon Wells Jsy 10.00 25.00
Carlos Delgado Jsy
Josh Phelps Jsy
4 Alex Rodriguez Bat 15.00 40.00
Juan Gonzalez Bat
Hank Blalock Bat
5 Gary Sheffield Jsy 15.00 40.00
Chipper Jones Jsy
Andruw Jones Bat
6 Ken Griffey Jr. Base 15.00 40.00
Austin Kearns Base
Aaron Boone Base
7 Albert Pujols Bat 20.00 50.00
Jim Edmonds Jsy
Scott Rolen Bat
8 Jeff Bagwell Bat 15.00 40.00
Lance Berkman Bat
Jeff Kent Jsy
9 Todd Helton Bat 15.00 40.00
Preston Wilson Bat
Larry Walker Jsy
10 Miguel Tejada Jsy 10.00 25.00
Erubial Durazo Bat
Eric Chavez Jsy

2004 Leaf Cornerstones

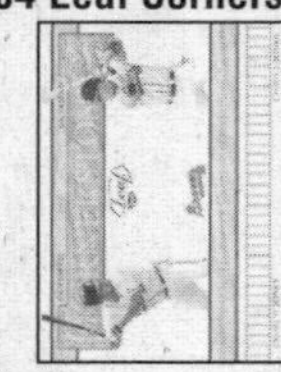

STATED ODDS 1:78
*2ND ED: .4X TO 1X BASIC
2ND ED.ODDS 1:90 2ND ED.PACKS
1 Alex Rodriguez 3.00 8.00
Hank Blalock
2 Kerry Wood 2.00 5.00
Mark Prior
3 Roger Clemens 4.00 10.00
Alfonso Soriano
4 Nomar Garicaparra 3.00 8.00
Manny Ramirez
5 Austin Kearns 2.00 5.00
Adam Dunn
6 Tom Glavine 3.00 8.00
Mike Piazza
7 Andruw Jones 2.00 5.00
Chipper Jones
8 Albert Pujols 4.00 10.00
Scott Rolen
9 Curt Schilling 2.00 5.00
Randy Johnson
10 Hideo Nomo 2.00 5.00
Kazuhisa Ishii

2004 Leaf Cornerstones Materials

RANDOM INSERTS IN PACKS
STATED PRINT RUN 50 SERIAL #'d SETS
2ND ED.RANDOM IN 2ND ED.PACKS
2ND ED.PRINT RUN 10 SERIAL #'d SETS
NO 2ND ED.PRICING DUE TO SCARCITY
1 Alex Rodriguez Bat 10.00 25.00
Hank Blalock Bat
2 Kerry Wood Jsy 6.00 15.00
Mark Prior Jsy

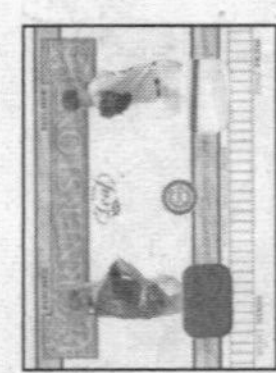

3 Roger Clemens Jsy 12.50 30.00
Alfonso Soriano Bat
4 Nomar Garicaparra Bat 10.00 25.00
Manny Ramirez Jsy
5 Austin Kearns Bat 6.00 15.00
Adam Dunn Jsy
6 Tom Glavine Jsy 10.00 25.00
Mike Piazza Bat
7 Andruw Jones Bat 10.00 25.00
Chipper Jones Jsy
8 Albert Pujols Bat 20.00 50.00
Scott Rolen Bat
9 Curt Schilling Jsy 10.00 25.00
Randy Johnson Jsy
10 Hideo Nomo Jsy 10.00 25.00
Kazuhisa Ishii Jsy

2004 Leaf Exhibits 1947-66 Made by Donruss-Playoff Print

This 51-card set features players in the design of the old exhibit company cards issued from 1921 through 1964. Please note that there were more than 40 varieties for each of these cards issued and we have notated what the multiplier is for each card.

STATED PRINT RUN 66 SERIAL #'d SETS
*1921 ACTIVE: .75X TO 2X
*1921 RETIRED: 1X TO 2.5X
1921 PRINT RUN 21 #'d SETS
*1921 AML ACTIVE: .75X TO 2X
*1921 AML RETIRED: 1X TO 2.5X
1921 AL P.RUN 21 #'d SETS
*1925 L ACTIVE: .75X TO 2X
*1925 L RETIRED: 1X TO 2.5X
1925 L PRINT RUN 25 #'d SETS
*1925 R ACTIVE: .75X TO 2X
*1925 R RETIRED: 1X TO 2.5X
1925 R PRINT RUN25 #'d SETS
*1926 B ACTIVE: .75X TO 2X
*1926 B RETIRED: 1X TO 2.5X
1926 B PRINT RUN 26 #'d SETS
*1926 BDP ACTIVE: .75X TO 2X
*1926 BDP RETIRED: 1X TO 2.5X
1926 BDP PRINT RUN 26 #'d SETS
*1926 U ACTIVE: .75X TO 2X
*1926 U RETIRED: 1X TO 2.5X
1926 U PRINT RUN 26 #'d SETS
*1926 UDP ACTIVE: .75X TO 2X
*1926 UDP RETIRED: 1X TO 2.5X
1926 UDP PRINT RUN 26 #'d SETS
*1927 ACTIVE: .75X TO 2X
*1927 RETIRED: 1X TO 2.5X
1927 PRINT RUN 27 #'d SETS
*1927 DP ACTIVE: .75X TO 2X
*1927 DP RETIRED: 1X TO 2.5X
1927 DP PRINT RUN 27 #'d SETS
*1939-46 BOLL: .5X TO 1.2X
1939-46 BOLL PRINT RUN 46 #'d SETS
*1939-46 BOLR: .5X TO 1.2X
1939-46 BOLR PRINT RUN 46 #'d SETS
*1939-46 BWL: .5X TO 1.2X
1939-46 BWL PRINT RUN 46 #'d SETS
*1939-46 BWR: .5X TO 1.2X
1939-46 BWR PRINT RUN 46 #'d SETS
*1939-46 CL: .5X TO 1.2X
1939-46 CL PRINT RUN 46 #'d SETS
*1939-46 CR: .5X TO 1.2X
1939-46 CR PRINT RUN 46 #'d SETS
*1939-46 CYL: .5X TO 1.2X
1939-46 CYL PRINT RUN 46 #'d SETS
*1939-46 CYR: .5X TO 1.2X
1939-46 CYR PRINT RUN 46 #'d SETS
*1939-46 SL: .5X TO 1.2X
1939-46 SL PRINT RUN 46 #'d SETS
*1939-46 SR: .5X TO 1.2X
1939-46 SR PRINT RUN 46 #'d SETS
*1939-46 SYL: .5X TO 1.2X
1939-46 SYL PRINT RUN 46 #'d SETS
*1939-46 SYR: .5X TO 1.2X
1939-46 SYR PRINT RUN 46 #'d SETS
*1939-46 TYL: .5X TO 1.2X
1939-46 TYL PRINT RUN 46 #'d SETS
*1939-46 TYR: .5X TO 1.2X
1939-46 TYR PRINT RUN 46 #'d SETS
*1939-46 VBWL: .5X TO 1.2X
1939-46 VBWL PRINT RUN 46 #'d SETS
*1939-46 VBWR: .5X TO 1.2X
1939-46 VBWR PRINT RUN 46 #'d SETS
*1939-46 VTYL: .5X TO 1.2X
1939-46 VTYL PRINT RUN 46 #'d SETS
*1939-46 VTYR: .5X TO 1.2X
1939-46 VTYR PRINT RUN 46 #'d SETS
*1939-46 YTL: .5X TO 1.2X
1939-46 YTL PRINT RUN 46 #'d SETS
*1939-46 YTR: .5X TO 1.2X
1939-46 YTR PRINT RUN 46 #'d SETS
*1947-66 DP SIG: .4X TO 1X
1947-66 DP SIG PRINT RUN 66 #'d SETS
*1947-66 MPRI: .4X TO 1X
1947-66 MPRI PRINT RUN 66 #'d SETS
*1947-66 MSIG: .4X TO 1X
1947-66 MSIG PRINT RUN 66 #'d SETS
*1947-66 PDPPRI: .4X TO 1X
1947-66 PDPPRI PRINT RUN 66 #'d SETS
*1947-66 PDPSIG: .4X TO 1X
1947-66 PDPSIG PRINT RUN 66 #'d SETS
*1947-66 PPRI: .4X TO 1X
1947-66 PPRI PRINT RUN 66 #'d SETS
*1947-66 PSIG: .4X TO 1X
1947-66 PSIG PRINT RUN 66 #'d SETS
*1962-63 NSNL: .4X TO 1X
1962-63 NSNL PRINT RUN 63 #'d SETS
*1962-63 NSNR: .4X TO 1X
1962-63 NSNR PRINT RUN 63 #'d SETS
*1962-63 SBNL: .4X TO 1X
1962-63 SBNL PRINT RUN 63 #'d SETS
*1962-63 SBNR: .4X TO 1X
1962-63 SBNR PRINT RUN 63 #'d SETS
*1962-63 SRNL: .4X TO 1X
1962-63 SRNL PRINT RUN 63 #'d SETS
*1962-63 SRNR: .4X TO 1X
1962-63 SRNR PRINT RUN 63 #'d SETS
RANDOM INSERTS IN PACKS
*ALL 2ND ED: .4X TO 1X
ALL 2ND ED.RANDOM IN 2ND ED.PACKS
SEE CARD BACKS FOR ABBREV.LEGEND
1 Adam Dunn 1.25 3.00
2 Albert Pujols 3.00 8.00
3 Alex Rodriguez 2.50 6.00
4 Alfonso Soriano 1.25 3.00
5 Andruw Jones 1.50 4.00
6 Barry Bonds 4.00 10.00
7 Barry Larkin 1.50 4.00
8 Barry Zito 1.25 3.00
9 Cal Ripken 6.00 15.00
10 Chipper Jones 1.50 4.00
11 Dale Murphy 1.50 4.00
12 Derek Jeter 3.00 8.00
13 Don Mattingly 3.00 8.00
14 Ernie Banks 1.50 4.00
15 Frank Thomas 1.50 4.00
16 George Brett 3.00 8.00
17 Greg Maddux 2.50 6.00
18 Hank Blalock 1.25 3.00
19 Hideo Nomo 1.50 4.00
20 Ichiro Suzuki 3.00 8.00
21 Jason Giambi 1.25 3.00
22 Jim Thome 1.50 4.00
23 Juan Gonzalez 1.25 3.00
24 Ken Griffey Jr. 2.50 6.00
25 Kirby Puckett 1.50 4.00
26 Mark Prior 1.50 4.00
27 Mike Mussina 1.50 4.00
28 Mike Piazza 1.50 4.00
29 Mike Schmidt 3.00 8.00
30 Nolan Ryan Angels 4.00 10.00
31 Nolan Ryan Astros 4.00 10.00
32 Nolan Ryan Rangers 4.00 10.00
33 Nomar Garciaparra 1.50 4.00
34 Ozzie Smith 2.50 6.00
35 Pedro Martinez 1.50 4.00
36 Randy Johnson 1.50 4.00
37 Reggie Jackson Yanks 1.50 4.00
38 Reggie Jackson A's 1.50 4.00
39 Rickey Henderson 1.50 4.00
40 Roberto Alomar 1.50 4.00
41 Roberto Clemente 4.00 10.00
42 Rod Carew 1.50 4.00
43 Roger Clemens 3.00 8.00
44 Sammy Sosa 1.50 4.00
45 Stan Musial 2.50 6.00
46 Tom Glavine 1.50 4.00
47 Tom Seaver 1.50 4.00
48 Tony Gwynn 2.00 5.00
49 Vladimir Guerrero 1.50 4.00
50 Yogi Berra 1.50 4.00

2004 Leaf Gamers

STATED ODDS 1:19
*QUANTUM: 1X TO 2.5X BASIC
QUANTUM RANDOM INSERTS IN PACKS
QUANTUM PRINT RUN 100 #'d SETS
*2ND ED: .4X TO 1X BASIC
2ND ED.ODDS 1:22 2ND ED.PACKS
2ND ED.QUAN.RANDOM IN 2ND ED.PACKS
2ND ED.QUANTUM PRINT RUN 10 #'d SETS
NO 2ND ED.QUAN.PRICE DUE TO SCARCITY
1 Albert Pujols 2.50 6.00
2 Alex Rodriguez 2.00 5.00
3 Alfonso Soriano .75 2.00
4 Barry Bonds 3.00 8.00
5 Barry Zito .75 2.00
6 Chipper Jones 1.25 3.00
7 Derek Jeter 2.50 6.00
8 Greg Maddux 2.50 6.00
9 Ichiro Suzuki 2.50 6.00
10 Jason Giambi .75 2.00
11 Jeff Bagwell 1.25 3.00
12 Ken Griffey Jr. 2.00 5.00
13 Manny Ramirez 1.25 3.00
14 Mark Prior 1.25 3.00
15 Mike Piazza 2.00 5.00
16 Nomar Garciaparra 2.00 5.00
17 Pedro Martinez 1.25 3.00
18 Randy Johnson 1.25 3.00
19 Roger Clemens 2.50 6.00
20 Sammy Sosa 1.25 3.00

2004 Leaf Gold Rookies

STATED ODDS 1:23
MIRROR RANDOM INSERTS IN PACKS
MIRROR PRINT RUN 25 SERIAL #'d SETS
NO MIRROR PRICING DUE TO SCARCITY
*2ND ED: .4X TO 1X BASIC
2ND ED.ODDS 1:24 2ND ED.PACKS
2ND ED.MIRR.RANDOM IN 2ND ED.PACKS
2ND ED.MIRROR PRINT RUN 5 #'d SETS
NO 2ND ED.MIRR.PRICE DUE TO SCARCITY
1 Adam Loewen 1.25 3.00
2 Rickie Weeks 1.25 3.00

3 Khalil Greene 2.00 5.00
4 Chad Tracy 1.25 3.00
5 Alexis Rios 1.25 3.00
6 Craig Brazell 1.25 3.00
7 Clint Barmes 1.00 2.50
8 Pete LaForest 1.25 3.00
9 Alfredo Gonzalez 1.25 3.00
10 Arnie Munoz 1.25 3.00

2004 Leaf Home/Away

STATED ODDS 1:35
*2ND ED: .4X TO 1X BASIC
2ND ED.ODDS 1:35 2ND ED.PACKS
1A Greg Maddux A 3.00 8.00
1H Greg Maddux H 3.00 8.00
2A Sammy Sosa A 2.00 5.00
2H Sammy Sosa H 2.00 5.00
3A Alex Rodriguez A 3.00 8.00
3H Alex Rodriguez H 3.00 8.00
4A Albert Pujols A 4.00 10.00
4H Albert Pujols H 4.00 10.00
5A Jason Giambi A 1.50 4.00
5H Jason Giambi H 1.50 4.00
6A Chipper Jones A 2.00 5.00
6H Chipper Jones H 2.00 5.00
7A Vladimir Guerrero A 2.00 5.00
7H Vladimir Guerrero H 2.00 5.00
8A Mike Piazza A 3.00 8.00
8H Mike Piazza H 3.00 8.00
9A Nomar Garciaparra A 3.00 8.00
9H Nomar Garciaparra H 3.00 8.00
10A Austin Kearns A 1.50 4.00
10H Austin Kearns H 1.50 4.00

2004 Leaf Home/Away Jerseys

STATED ODDS 1:119
*PRIME: 1.25X TO 3X BASIC
PRIME RANDOM INSERTS IN PACKS
PRIME PRINT RUN 50 #'d SETS
*2ND ED: .4X TO 1X BASIC
2ND ED.RANDOM IN 2ND.ED PACKS
2ND ED.PRIME RANDOM IN 2ND ED.PACKS
2ND ED.PRIME PRINT RUN 5 #'d SETS
NO 2ND ED.PRIME PRICE DUE SCARCITY
1A Greg Maddux A 4.00 10.00
1H Greg Maddux H 4.00 10.00
2A Sammy Sosa A 3.00 8.00
2H Sammy Sosa H 3.00 8.00
3A Alex Rodriguez A 4.00 10.00
3H Alex Rodriguez H 4.00 10.00
4A Albert Pujols A 6.00 15.00
4H Albert Pujols H 6.00 15.00
5A Jason Giambi A 2.00 5.00
5H Jason Giambi H 2.00 5.00
6A Chipper Jones A 3.00 8.00
6H Chipper Jones H 3.00 8.00
7A Vladimir Guerrero A 3.00 8.00
7H Vladimir Guerrero H 3.00 8.00
8A Mike Piazza A 4.00 10.00
8H Mike Piazza H 4.00 10.00
9A Nomar Garciaparra A 4.00 10.00
9H Nomar Garciaparra H 4.00 10.00
10A Austin Kearns A 2.00 5.00
10H Austin Kearns H 2.00 5.00

2004 Leaf Limited Previews

*GOLD: 1.25X TO 3X BASIC
GOLD PRINT RUN 50 SERIAL #'d SETS
*SILVER: .75X TO 2X BASIC
SILVER PRINT RUN 100 SERIAL #'d SETS
RANDOM INSERTS IN PACKS
1 Derek Jeter 3.00 8.00
2 Barry Zito 1.50 4.00
3 Ichiro Suzuki 3.00 8.00
4 Pedro Martinez 1.50 4.00
5 Alfonso Soriano 1.50 4.00
6 Alex Rodriguez 2.50 6.00
7 Greg Maddux 2.50 6.00
Back of card talks about Tom Glavine
8 Mike Piazza 2.50 6.00
9 Mark Prior 1.50 4.00
10 Albert Pujols 3.00 8.00
11 Sammy Sosa 1.50 4.00
12 Ken Griffey Jr. 2.50 6.00
13 Nomar Garciaparra 2.50 6.00
14 Randy Johnson 1.50 4.00
15 Jason Giambi 1.50 4.00
16 Barry Bonds 4.00 10.00
17 Manny Ramirez 1.50 4.00
18 Chipper Jones 1.50 4.00
19 Jeff Bagwell 1.50 4.00
20 Roger Clemens 3.00 8.00

2004 Leaf MVP Winners

STATED ODDS 1:11
*GOLD: .6X TO 1.5X BASIC
GOLD RANDOM INSERTS IN PACKS
GOLD PRINT RUN 500 SERIAL #'d SETS
*2ND ED: .4X TO 1X BASIC
2ND ED.ODDS 1:12 2ND ED.PACKS
2ND ED.GOLD RANDOM IN 2ND ED.PACKS
2ND ED.GOLD PRINT RUN 25 #'d SETS
NO 2ND ED.GOLD PRICE DUE TO SCARCITY
1 Stan Musial 1.50 4.00
2 Ernie Banks 1.25 3.00
3 Roberto Clemente 2.00 5.00
4 George Brett 2.00 5.00
5 Mike Schmidt 2.00 5.00
6 Cal Ripken 83 3.00 8.00
7 Dale Murphy 1.25 3.00
8 Ryne Sandberg 2.00 5.00
9 Don Mattingly 2.00 5.00
10 Roger Clemens 2.00 5.00
11 Rickey Henderson 1.25 3.00
12 Cal Ripken 91 3.00 8.00
13 Barry Bonds 92 2.50 6.00
14 Barry Bonds 93 2.50 6.00
15 Frank Thomas 1.25 3.00
16 Ken Griffey Jr. 1.50 4.00
17 Sammy Sosa 1.25 3.00
18 Chipper Jones 1.25 3.00
19 Jason Giambi 1.25 3.00
20 Ichiro Suzuki 2.00 5.00

2004 Leaf Picture Perfect

STATED ODDS 1:37
*2ND ED: .4X TO 1X BASIC
2ND ED.ODDS 1:45 2ND ED.PACKS
1 Albert Pujols 4.00 10.00
2 Alex Rodriguez 3.00 8.00
3 Alfonso Soriano 1.25 3.00
4 Austin Kearns 1.25 3.00
5 Carlos Delgado 1.25 3.00
6 Chipper Jones 2.00 5.00
7 Hank Blalock 1.25 3.00
8 Jason Giambi 1.25 3.00
9 Jeff Bagwell 2.00 5.00
10 Jim Thome 2.00 5.00
11 Manny Ramirez 2.00 5.00
12 Mike Piazza 3.00 8.00
13 Nomar Garciaparra 3.00 8.00
14 Sammy Sosa 2.00 5.00
15 Todd Helton 2.00 5.00

2004 Leaf Picture Perfect Bats

STATED ODDS 1:437
*2ND ED: .4X TO 1X BASIC
2ND ED.RANDOM IN 2ND ED.PACKS
1 Albert Pujols 6.00 15.00
2 Alex Rodriguez 4.00 10.00
3 Alfonso Soriano 2.00 5.00
4 Austin Kearns 2.00 5.00
5 Carlos Delgado 2.00 5.00
6 Chipper Jones 3.00 8.00
7 Hank Blalock 2.00 5.00
8 Jason Giambi 2.00 5.00
9 Jeff Bagwell 3.00 8.00
10 Jim Thome 3.00 8.00
11 Manny Ramirez 3.00 8.00
12 Mike Piazza 4.00 10.00
13 Nomar Garciaparra 4.00 10.00
14 Sammy Sosa 3.00 8.00
15 Todd Helton 3.00 8.00

2004 Leaf Players Collection Jersey Green

*LEAF GREEN: .4X TO 1X PRESTIGE
*LEAF PLAT: 1X TO 2.5X PRESTIGE
PLATINUM PRINT RUN 25 SERIAL #'d SETS
RANDOM INSERTS IN PACKS

2004 Leaf Recollection Autographs

RANDOM INSERTS IN PACKS
PRINT RUNS B/WN 1-31 COPIES PER
NO PRICING ON QTY OF 25 OR LESS
ALL CARDS ARE 1990 LEAF BUYBACKS
3 Jesse Barfield 90/29 12.50 30.00
15 Charlie Hough 90/31 8.00 20.00

2004 Leaf Shirt Off My Back

STATED ODDS 1:47
*2ND ED: .4X TO 1X BASIC
2ND ED.RANDOM IN 2ND ED.PACKS
1 Shawn Green 2.00 5.00
2 Andruw Jones 3.00 8.00
3 Ivan Rodriguez 3.00 8.00
4 Hideo Nomo 3.00 8.00
5 Don Mattingly 6.00 15.00
6 Mark Prior 3.00 8.00
7 Alfonso Soriano 2.00 5.00
8 Richie Sexson 2.00 5.00
9 Vernon Wells 2.00 5.00
10 Nomar Garciaparra 4.00 10.00
11 Jason Giambi 2.00 5.00
12 Austin Kearns 2.00 5.00
13 Chipper Jones 3.00 8.00
14 Rickey Henderson 3.00 8.00
15 Alex Rodriguez 4.00 10.00
16 Garret Anderson 2.00 5.00
17 Vladimir Guerrero 3.00 8.00
18 Sammy Sosa 3.00 8.00
19 Mike Piazza 4.00 10.00
20 David Wells 2.00 5.00
21 Scott Rolen 3.00 8.00
22 Adam Dunn 2.00 5.00
23 Carlos Delgado 2.00 5.00
24 Greg Maddux 4.00 10.00
25 Hank Blalock 2.00 5.00

2004 Leaf Shirt Off My Back Autographs Second Edition

RANDOM INSERTS IN PACKS
STATED PRINT RUN 1 SERIAL #'d SET
NO PRICING DUE TO SCARCITY

2004 Leaf Shirt Off My Back Jersey Number Patch

RANDOM INSERTS IN PACKS
STATED PRINT RUN 50 SERIAL #'d SETS
BLALOCK PRINT RUN 32 SERIAL #'d CARDS
SOSA PRINT RUN 42 SERIAL #'d CARDS
2ND ED.RANDOM IN 2ND.ED PACKS
2ND ED.PRINT RUN SERIAL 5 #'d SETS
NO 2ND ED.PRICING DUE TO SCARCITY
1 Shawn Green 6.00 15.00
2 Andruw Jones 10.00 25.00
3 Ivan Rodriguez 10.00 25.00
4 Hideo Nomo 10.00 25.00
5 Don Mattingly 15.00 40.00
6 Mark Prior 10.00 25.00
7 Alfonso Soriano 6.00 15.00
8 Richie Sexson 6.00 15.00
9 Vernon Wells 6.00 15.00
10 Nomar Garciaparra 12.50 30.00
11 Jason Giambi 6.00 15.00
12 Austin Kearns 6.00 15.00
13 Chipper Jones 10.00 25.00
14 Rickey Henderson 10.00 25.00
15 Alex Rodriguez 12.50 30.00
16 Garret Anderson 6.00 15.00
17 Vladimir Guerrero 10.00 25.00
18 Sammy Sosa/42 10.00 25.00
19 Mike Piazza 12.50 30.00
20 David Wells 6.00 15.00
21 Scott Rolen 10.00 25.00
22 Adam Dunn 6.00 15.00
23 Carlos Delgado 6.00 15.00
24 Greg Maddux 12.50 30.00
25 Hank Blalock/32 6.00 15.00

2004 Leaf Shirt Off My Back Jersey Number Patch Autographs

RANDOM INSERTS IN PACKS
STATED PRINT RUN 5 SERIAL #'d SETS
2ND ED.RANDOM IN 2ND.ED PACKS
2ND ED.PRINT RUN 5 SERIAL #'d SETS
NO PRICING DUE TO SCARCITY

2004 Leaf Shirt Off My Back Team Logo Patch

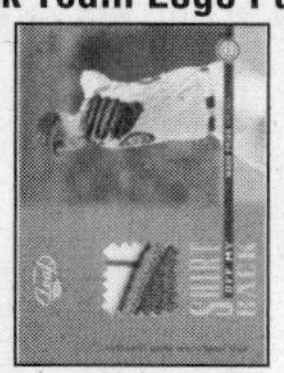

RANDOM INSERTS IN PACKS
PRINT RUNS B/WN 7-75 COPIES PER
NO PRICING ON QTY OF 25 OR LESS
2ND ED.RANDOM IN 2ND ED.PACKS
2ND ED.PRINT RUN 5 SERIAL #'d SETS
NO 2ND ED.PRICING DUE TO SCARCITY
1 Shawn Green/41 6.00 15.00
2 Andruw Jones/75 10.00 25.00
3 Ivan Rodriguez/75 10.00 25.00
4 Hideo Nomo/74 12.50 30.00
5 Don Mattingly/7
6 Mark Prior/46 10.00 25.00
7 Alfonso Soriano/28 8.00 20.00
8 Richie Sexson/38 6.00 15.00
9 Vernon Wells/74 6.00 15.00
10 Nomar Garciaparra/75 12.50 30.00
11 Jason Giambi/26 8.00 20.00
12 Austin Kearns/32 8.00 20.00
13 Chipper Jones/75 10.00 25.00
14 Rickey Henderson/40 10.00 25.00
15 Alex Rodriguez/75 12.50 30.00
16 Garret Anderson/71 6.00 15.00
17 Vladimir Guerrero/55 10.00 25.00
18 Sammy Sosa/39 10.00 25.00
19 Mike Piazza/75 12.50 30.00
20 David Wells/74 6.00 15.00
21 Scott Rolen/29 12.50 30.00
22 Adam Dunn/32 8.00 20.00
23 Carlos Delgado/56 6.00 15.00
24 Greg Maddux/75 12.50 30.00
25 Hank Blalock/62 6.00 15.00

2004 Leaf Shirt Off My Back Team Logo Patch Autographs

RANDOM INSERTS IN PACKS
STATED PRINT RUN 5 SERIAL #'d SETS
2ND ED.RANDOM IN 2ND ED.PACKS
2ND ED.PRINT RUN 5 SERIAL #'d SETS
NO PRICING DUE TO SCARCITY

2004 Leaf Sunday Dress

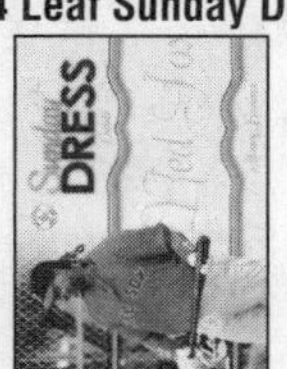

STATED ODDS 1:17
*2ND ED: .4X TO 1X BASIC
2ND ED.ODDS 1:20 2ND ED.PACKS
1 Frank Thomas 1.00 2.50
2 Barry Zito .75 2.00
3 Mike Piazza 1.50 4.00
4 Mark Prior .75 2.00
5 Jeff Bagwell .75 2.00
6 Roy Oswalt .75 2.00
7 Todd Helton .75 2.00
8 Magglio Ordonez .75 2.00
9 Alex Rodriguez 1.50 4.00
10 Manny Ramirez .75 2.00

2004 Leaf Sunday Dress Jerseys

STATED ODDS 1:119
*PRIME: .75X TO 2X BASIC
PRIME RANDOM INSERTS IN PACKS
PRIME PRINT RUN 100 SERIAL #'d SETS
*2ND ED: .4X TO 1X BASIC
2ND ED.RANDOM IN 2ND ED.PACKS
2ND ED.PRIME RANDOM IN 2ND ED.PACKS
2ND ED.PRIME PRINT RUN 15 #'d SETS
NO 2ND ED.PRIME PRICE DUE SCARCITY
1 Frank Thomas 3.00 8.00
2 Barry Zito 2.00 5.00
3 Mike Piazza 4.00 10.00
4 Mark Prior 3.00 8.00
5 Jeff Bagwell 3.00 8.00
6 Roy Oswalt 2.00 5.00
7 Todd Helton 3.00 8.00
8 Magglio Ordonez 2.00 5.00
9 Alex Rodriguez 4.00 10.00
10 Manny Ramirez 3.00 8.00

2005 Leaf

This 300-card set was released in January, 2005. The set was issued in eight-card packs with an $3 SRP which came 24 packs to a box and 12 boxes to a case. Cards numbered 1-200 feature veterans while cards 201 through 250 feature players who were prospects during the 2004 season. Cards 251 through 270 feature the traditional passing through time subset while cards 271 through 300 are team checklist cards. All cards numbered above 200 were inserted at rates between one in three and one in six.

COMPLETE SET (300) 75.00 150.00
COMP.SETw/o SP's (200) 10.00 25.00
COMMON CARD (1-200) .10 .30
COMMON CARD (201-250) .75 2.00
201-250 STATED ODDS 1:3
COMMON CARD (251-300) .60 1.50
251-270 STATED ODDS 1:6
271-300 STATED ODDS 1:4
1 Bartolo Colon .10 .30
2 Casey Kotchman .10 .30
3 Chone Figgins .10 .30
4 Darin Erstad .10 .30
5 Francisco Rodriguez .10 .30
6 Garret Anderson .10 .30
7 Jarrod Washburn .10 .30
8 Troy Glaus .10 .30
9 Vladimir Guerrero .30 .75
10 Brandon Webb .10 .30
11 Casey Fossum .10 .30
12 Luis Gonzalez .10 .30
13 Randy Johnson .30 .75
14 Richie Sexson .10 .30
15 Andruw Jones .20 .50
16 Chipper Jones .30 .75
17 J.D. Drew .10 .30
18 John Smoltz .20 .50
19 Johnny Estrada .10 .30
20 Marcus Giles .10 .30
21 Rafael Furcal .10 .30
22 Russ Ortiz .10 .30
23 Javy Lopez .10 .30
24 Jay Gibbons .10 .30
25 Melvin Mora .10 .30
26 Miguel Tejada .10 .30
27 Rafael Palmeiro .20 .50
28 Sidney Ponson .10 .30
29 Bill Mueller .10 .30
30 Curt Schilling .20 .50
31 David Ortiz .40 1.00
32 Doug Mientkiewicz .10 .30
33 Jason Varitek .30 .75
34 Johnny Damon .20 .50
35 Manny Ramirez .20 .50
36 Pedro Martinez .20 .50
37 Trot Nixon .10 .30
38 Aramis Ramirez .10 .30
39 Corey Patterson .10 .30
40 Derrek Lee .20 .50
41 Greg Maddux .50 1.25
42 Kerry Wood .10 .30
43 Mark Prior .20 .50
44 Moises Alou .10 .30
45 Nomar Garciaparra .30 .75
46 Sammy Sosa .30 .75
47 Carlos Lee .10 .30
48 Kip Wells .10 .30
49 Magglio Ordonez .10 .30
50 Mark Buehrle .10 .30
51 Paul Konerko .10 .30
52 Roberto Alomar .20 .50
53 Adam Dunn .10 .30
54 Austin Kearns .10 .30
55 Barry Larkin .20 .50
56 Danny Graves .10 .30
57 Ken Griffey Jr. .50 1.25
58 Sean Casey .10 .30
59 C.C. Sabathia .10 .30
60 Cliff Lee .10 .30
61 Jody Gerut .10 .30
62 Omar Vizquel .10 .30
63 Travis Hafner .10 .30
64 Victor Martinez .10 .30
65 Charles Johnson .10 .30
66 Jason Jennings .10 .30
67 Jeromy Burnitz .10 .30
68 Preston Wilson .10 .30
69 Todd Helton .20 .50
70 Bobby Higginson .10 .30
71 Dmitri Young .10 .30
72 Eric Munson .10 .30
73 Ivan Rodriguez .20 .50
74 Jeremy Bonderman .10 .30
75 Rondell White .10 .30
76 A.J. Burnett .10 .30
77 Carl Pavano .10 .30
78 Dontrelle Willis .10 .30
79 Hee Seop Choi .10 .30
80 Josh Beckett .10 .30
81 Juan Pierre .10 .30
82 Miguel Cabrera .20 .50
83 Mike Lowell .10 .30
84 Paul Lo Duca .10 .30
85 Andy Pettitte .20 .50
86 Carlos Beltran .10 .30
87 Craig Biggio .20 .50
88 Jeff Bagwell .20 .50
89 Jeff Kent .10 .30
90 Lance Berkman .10 .30
91 Roger Clemens .50 1.25
92 Roy Oswalt .10 .30
93 Andres Blanco .10 .30
94 Jeremy Affeldt .10 .30
95 Juan Gonzalez .10 .30
96 Ken Harvey .10 .30
97 Mike Sweeney .10 .30
98 Zack Greinke .10 .30
99 Adrian Beltre .10 .30
100 Brad Penny .10 .30
101 Eric Gagne .10 .30
102 Kazuhisa Ishii .10 .30
103 Milton Bradley .10 .30
104 Shawn Green .10 .30
105 Steve Finley .10 .30
106 Ben Sheets .10 .30
107 Bill Hall .10 .30
108 Danny Kolb .10 .30
109 Geoff Jenkins .10 .30
110 Junior Spivey .10 .30
111 Lyle Overbay .10 .30
112 Scott Podsednik .10 .30
113 A.J. Pierzynski .10 .30
114 Brad Radke .10 .30
115 Corey Koskie .10 .30
116 Jacque Jones .10 .30
117 Joe Mauer .30 .75
118 Joe Nathan .10 .30
119 Shannon Stewart .10 .30
120 Torii Hunter .10 .30
121 Brad Wilkerson .10 .30
122 Jeff Fassero .10 .30
123 Jose Vidro .10 .30
124 Livan Hernandez .10 .30
125 Nick Johnson .10 .30
126 Al Leiter .10 .30
127 Jose Reyes .10 .30
128 Kazuo Matsui .10 .30
129 Mike Cameron .10 .30
130 Mike Piazza .30 .75
131 Richard Hidalgo .10 .30
132 Tom Glavine .20 .50
133 Alex Rodriguez .50 1.25
134 Bernie Williams .20 .50
135 Derek Jeter .60 1.50
136 Gary Sheffield .10 .30
137 Jason Giambi .10 .30
138 Javier Vazquez .10 .30
139 Jorge Posada .20 .50
140 Kevin Brown .10 .30
141 Mariano Rivera .30 .75
142 Mike Mussina .20 .50
143 Barry Zito .10 .30
144 Bobby Crosby .10 .30
145 Eric Chavez .10 .30
146 Erubiel Durazo .10 .30
147 Jermaine Dye .10 .30
148 Mark Mulder .10 .30
149 Tim Hudson .10 .30
150 Bobby Abreu .10 .30
151 Eric Milton .10 .30
152 Jim Thome .20 .50
153 Kevin Millwood .10 .30
154 Mike Lieberthal .10 .30
155 Pat Burrell .10 .30
156 Randy Wolf .10 .30
157 Craig Wilson .10 .30
158 Jack Wilson .10 .30
159 Jason Bay .10 .30
160 Jason Kendall .10 .30
161 Kris Benson .10 .30
162 Brian Giles .10 .30
163 Jake Peavy .10 .30
164 Jay Payton .10 .30
165 Khalil Greene .20 .50
166 Mark Loretta .10 .30
167 Ryan Klesko .10 .30
168 Sean Burroughs .10 .30
169 David Aardsma .10 .30
170 Edgardo Alfonzo .10 .30
171 Jason Schmidt .10 .30
172 Merkin Valdez .10 .30
173 Ray Durham .10 .30
174 Bret Boone .10 .30
175 Dan Wilson .10 .30
176 Ichiro Suzuki .60 1.50
177 Jamie Moyer .10 .30
178 Rich Aurilia .10 .30
179 Albert Pujols .60 1.50
180 Edgar Renteria .10 .30
181 Jason Isringhausen .10 .30
182 Jeff Suppan .10 .30
183 Jim Edmonds .10 .30
184 Scott Rolen .20 .50
185 Woody Williams .10 .30
186 Aubrey Huff .10 .30
187 Carl Crawford .10 .30
188 Dewon Brazelton .10 .30
189 Jose Cruz Jr. .10 .30
190 Rocco Baldelli .10 .30
191 Alfonso Soriano .10 .30
192 Hank Blalock .10 .30
193 Kenny Rogers .10 .30
194 Laynce Nix .10 .30
195 Mark Teixeira .20 .50
196 Michael Young .10 .30
197 Alexis Rios .10 .30
198 Carlos Delgado .10 .30
199 Roy Halladay .10 .30
200 Vernon Wells .10 .30
201 Josh Kroeger PROS .75 2.00
202 Angel Guzman PROS .75 2.00
203 Brad Halsey PROS .75 2.00
204 Bucky Jacobsen PROS .75 2.00
205 Carlos Hines PROS .75 2.00
206 Carlos Vasquez PROS .75 2.00
207 Billy Traber PROS .75 2.00
208 Bubba Crosby PROS .75 2.00
209 Chris Oxspring PROS .75 2.00
210 Chris Shelton PROS 1.25 3.00
211 Colby Miller PROS .75 2.00
212 Dave Crouthers PROS .75 2.00
213 Dennis Sarfate PROS .75 2.00
214 Don Kelly PROS .75 2.00
215 Edwardo Sierra PROS .75 2.00
216 Edwin Moreno PROS .75 2.00
217 Fernando Nieve PROS .75 2.00
218 Freddy Guzman PROS .75 2.00
219 Greg Dobbs PROS .75 2.00
220 Hector Gimenez PROS .75 2.00
221 Andy Green PROS .75 2.00
222 Jason Bartlett PROS .75 2.00
223 Jerry Gil PROS .75 2.00
224 Jesse Crain PROS 1.25 3.00
225 Joey Gathright PROS .75 2.00
226 John Gall PROS .75 2.00
227 Jorge Sequea PROS .75 2.00
228 Jorge Vasquez PROS .75 2.00
229 Josh Labandeira PROS .75 2.00
230 Justin Leone PROS .75 2.00
231 Lance Cormier PROS .75 2.00
232 Lincoln Holdzkom PROS .75 2.00
233 Miguel Olivo PROS .75 2.00
234 Mike Rouse PROS .75 2.00
235 Onil Joseph PROS .75 2.00
236 Phil Stockman PROS .75 2.00
237 Ramon Ramirez PROS .75 2.00
238 Robb Quinlan PROS .75 2.00
239 Roberto Novoa PROS .75 2.00
240 Ronald Belisario PROS .75 2.00
241 Ronny Cedeno PROS 1.25 3.00
242 Ruddy Yan PROS .75 2.00
243 Ryan Meaux PROS .75 2.00
244 Ryan Wing PROS .75 2.00
245 Scott Proctor PROS .75 2.00
246 Sean Henn PROS .75 2.00
247 Tim Bausher PROS .75 2.00
248 Tim Bittner PROS .75 2.00
249 William Bergolla PROS .75 2.00
250 Yadier Molina PROS 1.25 3.00
251 Bernie Williams PTT .75 2.00
252 Craig Biggio PTT .75 2.00
253 Chipper Jones PTT .75 2.00
254 Greg Maddux PTT 1.25 3.00
255 Sammy Sosa PTT .75 2.00
256 Mike Mussina PTT .75 2,00
257 Tim Salmon PTT .75 2.00
258 Barry Larkin PTT .75 2.00
259 Randy Johnson PTT .75 2.00
260 Jeff Bagwell PTT .75 2.00
261 Roberto Alomar PTT .75 2.00
262 Tom Glavine PTT .75 2.00
263 Roger Clemens PTT 1.25 3.00
264 Alex Rodriguez PTT 1.25 3.00
265 Ivan Rodriguez PTT .75 2.00
266 Pedro Martinez PTT .75 2.00
267 Ken Griffey Jr. PTT 1.25 3.00
268 Jim Thome PTT .75 2.00
269 Frank Thomas PTT .75 2.00
270 Mike Piazza PTT .75 2.00
271 Garret Anderson TC .60 1.50
272 Luis Gonzalez TC .60 1.50
273 John Smoltz TC .75 2.00
274 Rafael Palmeiro TC .75 2.00
275 Curt Schilling TC .75 2.00
276 Mark Prior TC .75 2.00
277 Magglio Ordonez TC .60 1.50
278 Adam Dunn TC .60 1.50
279 Travis Hafner TC .60 1.50
280 Jeromy Burnitz TC .60 1.50
281 Carlos Guillen TC .60 1.50
282 Dontrelle Willis TC .60 1.50
283 Carlos Beltran TC .60 1.50
284 Zack Greinke TC .60 1.50
285 Adrian Beltre TC .60 1.50
286 Ben Sheets TC .60 1.50
287 Johan Santana TC .75 2.00
288 Livan Hernandez TC .60 1.50
289 Kazuo Matsui TC .60 1.50
290 Derek Jeter TC 1.50 4.00
291 Tim Hudson TC .60 1.50
292 Eric Milton TC .60 1.50
293 Jason Kendall TC .60 1.50
294 Jake Peavy TC .60 1.50
295 Ray Durham TC .60 1.50
296 Ichiro Suzuki TC 1.50 4.00
297 Scott Rolen TC .75 2.00
298 Carl Crawford TC .60 1.50
299 Hank Blalock TC .60 1.50
300 Roy Halladay TC .60 1.50

2005 Leaf Black

*BLACK 1-200: 1X TO 2.5X BASIC
*BLACK 201-250: .4X TO 1X BASIC
*BLACK 251-300: .5X TO 1.2X BASIC
ONE PER RETAIL PACK

2005 Leaf Green

*GREEN 1-200: 1.5X TO 4X BASIC
*GREEN 201-250: .4X TO 1X BASIC
*GREEN 251-300: .6X TO 1.5X BASIC
ONE PER RETAIL BLASTER PACK

2005 Leaf Orange

*ORANGE 1-200: 1.5X TO 4X BASIC
*ORANGE 201-250: .4X TO 1X BASIC
*ORANGE 251-300: .6X TO 1.5X BASIC
ONE PER RETAIL BLISTER PACK

2005 Leaf Press Proofs Blue

*BLUE 1-200: 5X TO 12X BASIC
*BLUE 201-250: .75X TO 2X BASIC
*BLUE 251-300: 2X TO 5X BASIC
RANDOM INSERTS IN PACKS
STATED PRINT RUN 75 SERIAL #'d SETS

2005 Leaf Press Proofs Gold

*GOLD 1-200: 5X TO 12X BASIC
*GOLD 201-250: 1.5X TO 4X BASIC
*GOLD 251-300: 4X TO 10X BASIC
RANDOM INSERTS IN PACKS
STATED PRINT RUN 25 SERIAL #'d SETS

2005 Leaf Press Proofs Red

*RED 1-200: 2X TO 5X BASIC
*RED 201-250: .4X TO 1X BASIC
*RED 251-300: .75X TO 2X BASIC
STATED ODDS 1:8

2005 Leaf Autographs

RANDOM INSERTS IN PACKS
SP INFO BASED ON BECKETT RESEARCH
201 Josh Kroeger PROS 4.00 10.00
202 Angel Guzman PROS 4.00 10.00
203 Brad Halsey PROS 4.00 10.00
204 Bucky Jacobsen PROS 4.00 10.00
205 Carlos Hines PROS 4.00 10.00
207 Billy Traber PROS 4.00 10.00
208 Bubba Crosby PROS 4.00 10.00
210 Chris Shelton PROS 6.00 15.00
211 Colby Miller PROS 4.00 10.00
212 Dave Crouthers PROS 4.00 10.00
216 Edwin Moreno PROS SP
217 Fernando Nieve PROS 4.00 10.00
220 Hector Gimenez PROS 4.00 10.00
221 Andy Green PROS 4.00 10.00
222 Jason Bartlett PROS 4.00 10.00
223 Jerry Gil PROS SP
225 Joey Gathright PROS SP
226 John Gall PROS SP
227 Jorge Sequea PROS SP
228 Jorge Vasquez PROS 4.00 10.00
232 Lincoln Holdzkom PROS 4.00 10.00
233 Miguel Olivo PROS 4.00 10.00
234 Mike Rouse PROS 4.00 10.00
235 Onil Joseph PROS SP
236 Phil Stockman PROS 4.00 10.00
237 Ramon Ramirez PROS 4.00 10.00
242 Ruddy Yan PROS 4.00 10.00
245 Scott Proctor PROS 4.00 10.00
246 Sean Henn PROS SP
247 Tim Bausher PROS 4.00 10.00
248 Tim Bittner PROS SP
249 William Bergolla PROS 4.00 10.00

2005 Leaf Autographs Red

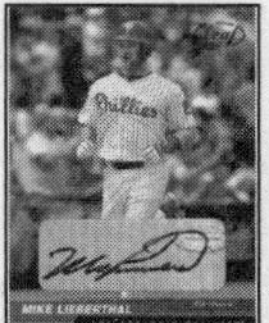

PRINT RUNS B/WN 50-100 COPIES PER
BLUE PRINT RUNS B/WN 15-25 PER
NO BLUE PRICING DUE TO SCARCITY
GOLD PRINT RUNS B/WN 9-10 PER
NO GOLD PRICING DUE TO SCARCITY
RANDOM INSERTS IN PACKS
3 Chone Figgins/100 4.00 10.00
19 Johnny Estrada/100 4.00 10.00
24 Jay Gibbons/100 4.00 10.00
47 Carlos Lee/100 6.00 15.00
56 Danny Graves/100 4.00 10.00
60 Cliff Lee/100 4.00 10.00
63 Travis Hafner/50 8.00 20.00
74 Jeremy Bonderman/100 6.00 15.00
94 Jeremy Affeldt/100 4.00 10.00
96 Ken Harvey/100 4.00 10.00
103 Milton Bradley/100 6.00 15.00
111 Lyle Overbay/50 5.00 12.00
118 Joe Nathan/100 10.00 25.00
144 Bobby Crosby/100 6.00 15.00
154 Mike Lieberthal/50 8.00 20.00
157 Craig Wilson/50 5.00 12.00
158 Jack Wilson/100 6.00 15.00
163 Jake Peavy/50 12.50 30.00
172 Merkin Valdez/100 4.00 10.00
182 Jeff Suppan/100 6.00 15.00
187 Carl Crawford/50 8.00 20.00
188 Dewon Brazelton/50 5.00 12.00
194 Laynce Nix/100 4.00 10.00
201 Josh Kroeger PROS/100 4.00 10.00
202 Angel Guzman PROS/100 4.00 10.00
203 Brad Halsey PROS/100 4.00 10.00
204 Bucky Jacobsen PROS/100 4.00 10.00
205 Carlos Hines PROS/100 4.00 10.00
207 Billy Traber PROS/100 4.00 10.00
208 Bubba Crosby PROS/100 4.00 10.00
210 Chris Shelton PROS/100 10.00 25.00
211 Colby Miller PROS/100 4.00 10.00
212 Dave Crouthers PROS/100 4.00 10.00
217 Fernando Nieve PROS/100 4.00 10.00
218 Freddy Guzman PROS/100 4.00 10.00
220 Hector Gimenez PROS/100 4.00 10.00
221 Andy Green PROS/100 4.00 10.00
222 Jason Bartlett PROS/100 4.00 10.00
224 Jesse Crain PROS/100 6.00 15.00
227 Jorge Sequea PROS/84 4.00 10.00
228 Jorge Vasquez PROS/100 4.00 10.00
233 Miguel Olivo PROS/100 4.00 10.00
234 Mike Rouse PROS/100 4.00 10.00
236 Phil Stockman PROS/100 4.00 10.00
237 Ramon Ramirez PROS/100 4.00 10.00
238 Robb Quinlan PROS/100 4.00 10.00
241 Ronny Cedeno PROS/65 10.00 25.00
242 Ruddy Yan PROS/100 4.00 10.00
243 Ryan Meaux PROS/93 4.00 10.00
247 Tim Bausher PROS/100 4.00 10.00
249 William Bergolla PROS/100 4.00 10.00
250 Yadier Molina PROS/100 6.00 15.00

2005 Leaf 4 Star Staffs

STATED ODDS 1:48
*DIE CUT: .6X TO 1.5X BASIC
DIE CUT RANDOM INSERTS IN PACKS
DIE CUT PRINT RUN 250 SERIAL #'d SETS
1 Tom Glavine 2.50 6.00
Greg Maddux
John Smoltz
Kevin Millwood
2 Josh Beckett 1.00 2.50
A.J. Burnett
Dontrelle Willis
Carl Pavano
3 Roger Clemens 2.50 6.00
Mike Mussina
David Wells
Andy Pettitte
4 Mark Prior 2.50 6.00
Greg Maddux
Kerry Wood
Carlos Zambrano
5 Roger Clemens 2.50 6.00
Andy Pettitte
Mike Mussina
Mariano Rivera
6 Pedro Martinez 1.50 4.00
Curt Schilling
Derek Lowe
Tim Wakefield
7 Mark Mulder 1.00 2.50
Barry Zito
Tim Hudson
Rich Harden
8 Randy Johnson 1.50 4.00
Curt Schilling
Brandon Webb
Byung-Hyun Kim
9 Nolan Ryan 4.00 10.00
Kevin Brown
Jamie Moyer
Kenny Rogers
10 Woody Williams 2.50 6.00
Roger Clemens
Roy Halladay
Kelvim Escobar
11 Roger Clemens 2.50 6.00
Andy Pettitte
Roy Oswalt
Wade Miller
12 Barry Zito 1.00 2.50
Mark Mulder
Tim Hudson
Billy Koch
13 Hideo Nomo 1.50 4.00
Kevin Brown
Kazuhisa Ishii
Eric Gagne
14 Tom Glavine 2.50 6.00
John Smoltz
Greg Maddux
Jason Schmidt
15 Hideo Nomo 1.50 4.00
Pedro Martinez
Derek Lowe
Tim Wakefield

2005 Leaf Alternate Threads

STATED ODDS 1:18
*HOLO: .75X TO 2X BASIC
HOLO RANDOM INSERTS IN PACKS
HOLO PRINT RUN 150 SERIAL #'d SETS
*HOLO DC: 1.5X TO 4X BASIC
HOLO DC RANDOM INSERTS IN PACKS
HOLO DC PRINT RUN 50 SERIAL #'d SETS
1 Adam Dunn .75 2.00
2 C.C. Sabathia .75 2.00
3 Curt Schilling 1.25 3.00
4 Dontrelle Willis .75 2.00
5 Greg Maddux 2.00 5.00
6 Hank Blalock .75 2.00
7 Ichiro Suzuki 2.50 6.00
8 Jeff Bagwell 1.25 3.00
9 Ken Griffey Jr. 2.00 5.00
10 Ken Harvey .75 2.00
11 Magglio Ordonez .75 2.00
12 Mark Mulder .75 2.00
13 Mark Teixeira 1.25 3.00
14 Michael Young .75 2.00
15 Miguel Tejada .75 2.00
16 Mike Piazza 1.25 3.00
17 Pedro Martinez 1.25 3.00
18 Randy Johnson 1.25 3.00
19 Roger Clemens 2.00 5.00
20 Sammy Sosa 1.25 3.00
21 Tim Hudson .75 2.00
22 Todd Helton 1.25 3.00
23 Torii Hunter .75 2.00
24 Travis Hafner .75 2.00
25 Vernon Wells .75 2.00

2005 Leaf Certified Materials Preview

STATED ODDS 1:21
*BLUE: 1.25X TO 3X BASIC
BLUE RANDOM INSERTS IN PACKS
BLUE PRINT RUN 100 SERIAL #'d SETS
*GOLD: 3X TO 8X BASIC
GOLD RANDOM INSERTS IN PACKS
GOLD PRINT RUN 25 SERIAL #'d SETS
*RED: 1X TO 2.5X BASIC
RED RANDOM INSERTS IN PACKS
RED PRINT RUN 200 SERIAL #'d SETS
1 Albert Pujols 2.00 5.00
2 Alex Rodriguez 1.50 4.00
3 Alfonso Soriano .60 1.50
4 Curt Schilling 1.00 2.50
5 Derek Jeter 2.00 5.00
6 Greg Maddux 1.50 4.00
7 Ichiro Suzuki 2.00 5.00
8 Jim Thome 1.00 2.50
9 Ken Griffey Jr. 1.50 4.00
10 Manny Ramirez 1.00 2.50
11 Mark Prior 1.00 2.50
12 Randy Johnson 1.00 2.50
13 Roger Clemens 1.50 4.00
14 Sammy Sosa 1.00 2.50
15 Vladimir Guerrero 1.00 2.50

2005 Leaf Clean Up Crew

STATED ODDS 1:49
*DIE CUT: .6X TO 1.5X BASIC
DIE CUT RANDOM INSERTS IN PACKS
DIE CUT PRINT RUN 250 SERIAL #'d SETS
1 Albert Pujols 3.00 8.00
Jim Edmonds
Scott Rolen
2 Melvin Mora 1.50 4.00
Miguel Tejada
Rafael Palmeiro
3 Alfonso Soriano 1.00 2.50
Michael Young
Hank Blalock
4 Gary Sheffield 3.00 8.00
Alex Rodriguez
Hideki Matsui
5 Moises Alou 1.50 4.00
Sammy Sosa
Nomar Garciaparra
6 Paul Lo Duca 1.50 4.00
Mike Lowell
Miguel Cabrera
7 Carlos Beltran 1.50 4.00
Lance Berkman
Jeff Bagwell
8 Paul Konerko 1.50 4.00
Magglio Ordonez
Frank Thomas
9 Sean Casey 2.50 6.00
Ken Griffey Jr.
Adam Dunn
10 Vladimir Guerrero 1.50 4.00
Garret Anderson
Troy Glaus
11 Joe Morgan 1.50 4.00
Johnny Bench
Tony Perez
12 Keith Hernandez 1.00 2.50
Darryl Strawberry
Gary Carter
13 Jim Rice 2.50 6.00
Carl Yastrzemski
Dwight Evans
14 Ryne Sandberg 3.00 8.00
Andre Dawson
Mark Grace
15 Cal Ripken 5.00 12.00
Eddie Murray
Rafael Palmeiro

2005 Leaf Cornerstones

STATED ODDS 1:37
1 Albert Pujols 3.00 8.00
Scott Rolen
2 Hideki Matsui 2.50 6.00
Jorge Posada
3 Sammy Sosa 1.50 4.00
Nomar Garciaparra
4 Manny Ramirez 1.50 4.00
David Ortiz
5 Miguel Cabrera 1.50 4.00
Mike Lowell
6 Hank Blalock 1.50 4.00
Mark Teixeira
7 Chipper Jones 1.50 4.00
J.D. Drew
8 Craig Biggio 1.50 4.00
Jeff Bagwell
9 Mike Piazza 1.50 4.00
Kazuo Matsui
10 Shawn Green 1.00 2.50
Adrian Beltre
11 Jim Thome 1.50 4.00
Bobby Abreu
12 Mike Schmidt 3.00 8.00
Steve Carlton
13 Cal Ripken 5.00 12.00
Eddie Murray
14 Carl Yastrzemski 2.50 6.00
Dwight Evans
15 Johnny Bench 1.50 4.00
Joe Morgan
16 Dale Murphy 1.50 4.00
Phil Niekro
17 Alan Trammell 1.00 2.50
Kirk Gibson
18 Jose Canseco 1.50 4.00
Rickey Henderson
19 Paul Molitor 1.50 4.00
Robin Yount
20 George Brett 3.00 8.00
Bo Jackson

2005 Leaf Cornerstones Bats

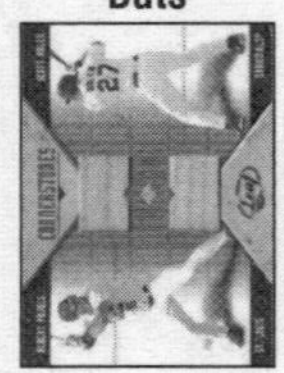

RANDOM INSERTS IN PACKS
1 Albert Pujols 10.00 25.00
Scott Rolen
2 Hideki Matsui 15.00 40.00
Jorge Posada
3 Sammy Sosa 6.00 15.00
Nomar Garciaparra
4 Manny Ramirez 10.00 25.00
David Ortiz
5 Miguel Cabrera 6.00 15.00
Mike Lowell
6 Hank Blalock 6.00 15.00
Mark Teixeira
7 Chipper Jones 6.00 15.00
J.D. Drew
8 Craig Biggio 6.00 15.00
Jeff Bagwell
9 Mike Piazza 6.00 15.00
Kazuo Matsui
10 Shawn Green 4.00 10.00
Adrian Beltre

2005 Leaf Cornerstones Jerseys

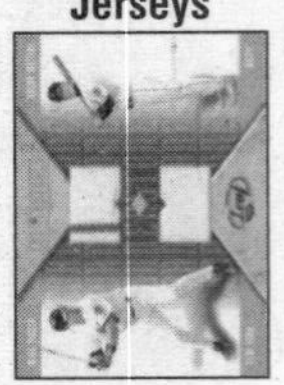

STATED PRINT RUN 250 SERIAL #'d SETS
*PRIME p/r 50: 1X TO 2.5X BASIC
*PRIME p/r 25: 1.2X TO 3X BASIC
PRIME PRINT RUN B/WN 25-50 PER
RANDOM INSERTS IN PACKS
1 Albert Pujols 10.00 25.00
Scott Rolen
2 Hideki Matsui 15.00 40.00
Jorge Posada
4 Manny Ramirez 10.00 25.00
David Ortiz
5 Miguel Cabrera 6.00 15.00
Mike Lowell
6 Hank Blalock 6.00 15.00
Mark Teixeira
8 Craig Biggio 6.00 15.00
Jeff Bagwell
9 Mike Piazza 6.00 15.00
Kazuo Matsui
10 Shawn Green 4.00 10.00
Adrian Beltre

2005 Leaf Cy Young Winners

STATED ODDS 1:31
*GOLD: .6X TO 1.5X BASIC
GOLD RANDOM INSERTS IN PACKS
GOLD PRINT RUN 350 SERIAL #'d SETS
*GOLD DC: 1X TO 2.5X BASIC
GOLD DC RANDOM INSERTS IN PACKS
GOLD DC PRINT RUN 100 SERIAL #'d SETS
1 Warren Spahn 1.25 3.00
2 Whitey Ford 1.25 3.00
3 Bob Gibson 1.25 3.00
4 Tom Seaver 1.25 3.00
5 Steve Carlton .75 2.00
6 Jim Palmer .75 2.00
7 Rollie Fingers .75 2.00
8 Dwight Gooden .75 2.00
9 Roger Clemens 2.00 5.00
10 Orel Hershiser .75 2.00
11 Greg Maddux 2.00 5.00
12 Dennis Eckersley .75 2.00
13 Randy Johnson 1.25 3.00
14 Pedro Martinez 1.25 3.00
15 Eric Gagne .75 2.00

2005 Leaf Fans of the Game

STATED ODDS 1:24
1 Sean Astin .75 2.00
2 Tony Danza .75 2.00
3 Taye Diggs .75 2.00

2005 Leaf Fans of the Game Autographs

RANDOM INSERTS IN PACKS
SP PRINT RUNS PROVIDED BY DONRUSS
SP'S ARE NOT SERIAL-NUMBERED
1 Sean Astin 12.50 30.00
2 Tony Danza SP/50 150.00 250.00
3 Taye Diggs 10.00 25.00

2005 Leaf Game Collection

STATED ODDS 1:118
SP INFO BASED ON BECKETT RESEARCH
1 Cal Ripken Bat 15.00 40.00
2 Carl Crawford Jsy 3.00 8.00
3 Dale Murphy Bat SP 8.00 20.00
4 Don Mattingly Bat SP 10.00 25.00
5 George Brett Jsy SP 10.00 25.00
6 Victor Martinez Bat SP 4.00 10.00
7 Sean Casey Bat 3.00 8.00
8 Torii Hunter Bat 3.00 8.00
9 Magglio Ordonez Bat 3.00 8.00
10 Lance Berkman Bat 3.00 8.00
11 Mike Schmidt Bat SP 10.00 25.00
12 Nolan Ryan Jkt SP 15.00 40.00
13 Paul Lo Duca Bat 3.00 8.00
14 Preston Wilson Bat 3.00 8.00
15 Rod Carew Jkt SP 8.00 20.00
16 Reggie Jackson Bat SP 8.00 20.00
17 Ivan Rodriguez Bat 4.00 10.00
18 L.Walker Cards Bat 4.00 10.00
19 Miguel Tejada Bat SP 4.00 10.00
20 Vladimir Guerrero Bat SP 6.00 15.00

2005 Leaf Game Collection Autograph

RANDOM INSERTS IN PACKS
PRINT RUNS B/WN 5-200 COPIES PER
NO PRICING ON QTY OF 25 OR LESS
1 Cal Ripken Jkt/5
2 Carl Crawford Jsy/200 10.00 25.00
3 Dale Murphy Bat/25
4 Don Mattingly Bat/5
5 George Brett Jsy/5
6 Victor Martinez Bat/200 10.00 25.00
7 Sean Casey Bat/200 10.00 25.00
8 Torii Hunter Bat/50 12.50 30.00
9 Magglio Ordonez Bat/25
10 Lance Berkman Bat/5
11 Mike Schmidt Bat/5
12 Nolan Ryan Jkt/10
13 Paul Lo Duca Bat/100 10.00 25.00
15 Rod Carew Jkt/5

2005 Leaf Gamers

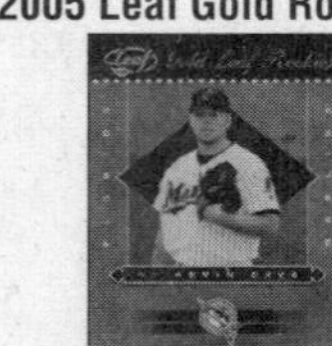

STATED ODDS 1:13
*QUANTUM: 1.25X TO 3X BASIC
QUANTUM RANDOM INSERTS IN PACKS
QUANTUM PRINT RUN 175 SER.#'d SETS
*QUANTUM DC: 2.5X TO 6X BASIC
QUANTUM DC RANDOM INSERTS IN PACKS
QUANTUM DC PRINT RUN 50 SER.#'d SETS
1 Albert Pujols 1.50 4.00
2 Alex Rodriguez 1.25 3.00
3 Alfonso Soriano .50 1.25
4 Chipper Jones .75 2.00
5 Derek Jeter 1.50 4.00
6 Greg Maddux 1.25 3.00
7 Ichiro Suzuki 1.50 4.00
8 Jim Thome .75 2.00
9 Ken Griffey Jr. 1.25 3.00
10 Lance Berkman .50 1.25
11 Miguel Tejada .50 1.25
12 Mike Piazza .75 2.00
13 Roger Clemens 1.25 3.00
14 Scott Rolen .75 2.00
15 Vladimir Guerrero .75 2.00

2005 Leaf Gold Rookies

STATED ODDS 1:24
*MIRROR: 2X TO 5X BASIC
MIRROR RANDOM INSERTS IN PACKS
MIRROR PRINT RUN 25 SERIAL #'d SETS
1 Dennis Sarfate 1.25 3.00
2 Don Kelly 1.25 3.00
3 Eddy Rodriguez 1.25 3.00
4 Edwin Moreno 1.25 3.00
5 Greg Dobbs 1.25 3.00
6 Josh Labandeira 1.25 3.00
7 Kevin Cave 1.25 3.00
8 Mariano Gomez 1.25 3.00
9 Ronald Belisario 1.25 3.00
10 Ruddy Yan 1.25 3.00

2005 Leaf Gold Rookies Autograph

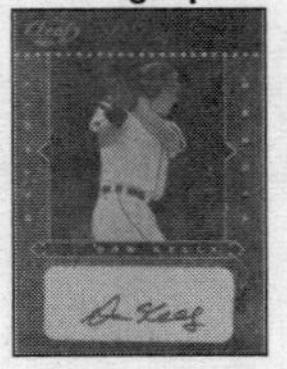

SP INFO BASED ON BECKETT RESEARCH
MIRROR PRINT RUN 25 SERIAL #'d SETS
NO MIRROR PRICING DUE TO SCARCITY
RANDOM INSERTS IN PACKS
1 Dennis Sarfate SP
2 Don Kelly 4.00 10.00
3 Eddy Rodriguez SP
4 Edwin Moreno SP
5 Greg Dobbs 4.00 10.00
6 Josh Labandeira SP
7 Kevin Cave SP
8 Mariano Gomez SP
9 Ronald Belisario 4.00 10.00
10 Ruddy Yan 4.00 10.00

2005 Leaf Gold Stars

STATED ODDS 1:27
*MIRROR: 2.5X TO 6X BASIC
MIRROR RANDOM INSERTS IN PACKS
MIRROR PRINT RUN 25 SERIAL #'d SETS
1 Albert Pujols 2.50 6.00
2 Ichiro Suzuki 2.50 6.00
3 Derek Jeter 2.50 6.00
4 Alex Rodriguez 2.00 5.00
5 Scott Rolen 1.25 3.00
6 Randy Johnson 1.25 3.00
7 Roger Clemens 2.00 5.00
8 Greg Maddux 2.00 5.00
9 Alfonso Soriano .75 2.00
10 Mark Mulder .75 2.00
11 Sammy Sosa 1.25 3.00
12 Mike Piazza 1.25 3.00
13 Rafael Palmeiro 1.25 3.00
14 Ivan Rodriguez 1.25 3.00
15 Miguel Cabrera 1.25 3.00
16 Stan Musial 2.00 5.00
17 Nolan Ryan 3.00 8.00
18 Don Mattingly 2.50 6.00
19 George Brett 2.50 6.00
20 Cal Ripken 4.00 10.00

2005 Leaf Home/Road

STATED ODDS 1:22
HOME AND ROAD VALUED EQUALLY
1H Albert Pujols H 2.50 6.00
1R Albert Pujols R 2.50 6.00
2H Alfonso Soriano H .75 2.00
2R Alfonso Soriano R .75 2.00
3H Carlos Beltran H .75 2.00
3R Carlos Beltran R .75 2.00
4H Chipper Jones H 1.25 3.00
4R Chipper Jones R 1.25 3.00
5H Frank Thomas H 1.25 3.00
5R Frank Thomas R 1.25 3.00
6H Hank Blalock H .75 2.00
6R Hank Blalock R .75 2.00
7H Ivan Rodriguez H 1.25 3.00
7R Ivan Rodriguez R 1.25 3.00
8H Manny Ramirez H 1.25 3.00
8R Manny Ramirez R 1.25 3.00
9H Mark Prior H 1.25 3.00
9R Mark Prior R 1.25 3.00
10H Miguel Cabrera H 1.25 3.00
10R Miguel Cabrera R 1.25 3.00
11H Miguel Tejada H .75 2.00
11R Miguel Tejada R .75 2.00
12H Mike Piazza H 1.25 3.00
12R Mike Piazza R 1.25 3.00
13H Roger Clemens H 2.00 5.00
13R Roger Clemens R 2.00 5.00
14H Todd Helton H 1.25 3.00
14R Todd Helton R 1.25 3.00
15H Vladimir Guerrero H 1.25 3.00
15R Vladimir Guerrero R 1.25 3.00

2005 Leaf Home/Road Jersey

RANDOM INSERTS IN PACKS
SP INFO BASED ON BECKETT RESEARCH
1H Albert Pujols H 8.00 20.00
1R Albert Pujols R 8.00 20.00
2H Alfonso Soriano H 3.00 8.00
3H Carlos Beltran H 3.00 8.00
3R Carlos Beltran R 3.00 8.00
4R Chipper Jones R 4.00 10.00
5H Frank Thomas H 4.00 10.00
5R Frank Thomas R 4.00 10.00

6H Hank Blalock H 3.00 8.00
7H Ivan Rodriguez H 4.00 10.00
7R Ivan Rodriguez R 4.00 10.00
8R Manny Ramirez R 4.00 10.00
9H Mark Prior H 4.00 10.00
10H Miguel Cabrera H SP
10R Miguel Cabrera R SP
11H Miguel Tejada H 3.00 8.00
11R Miguel Tejada R 3.00 8.00
12H Mike Piazza H 4.00 10.00
13H Roger Clemens H 6.00 15.00
13R Roger Clemens R 6.00 15.00
14H Todd Helton H 4.00 10.00
14R Todd Helton R 4.00 10.00
15H Vladimir Guerrero H 4.00 10.00

2005 Leaf Home/Road Jersey Prime

*PRIME: 1X TO 2.5X BASIC
RANDOM INSERTS IN PACKS
STATED PRINT RUN 50 SERIAL #'d SETS
4H Chipper Jones H 10.00 25.00
6R Hank Blalock R 8.00 20.00
8H Manny Ramirez H 10.00 25.00
9R Mark Prior R 10.00 25.00
10H Miguel Cabrera H 10.00 25.00
10R Miguel Cabrera R 10.00 25.00
12R Mike Piazza R 10.00 25.00
15R Vladimir Guerrero R 10.00 25.00

2005 Leaf Patch Off My Back

*PATCH: 1X TO 2.5X SHIRT OFF BACK
*PATCH: .6X TO 1.5X SHIRT OFF BACK SP
RANDOM INSERTS IN PACKS
STATED PRINT RUN 50 SERIAL #'d SETS
2 Aubrey Huff 6.00 15.00
3 Austin Kearns 6.00 15.00
24 Mariano Rivera 10.00 25.00

2005 Leaf Patch Off My Back Autograph

RANDOM INSERTS IN PACKS
PRINT RUNS B/WN 10-75 COPIES PER
NO PRICING ON QTY OF 25 OR LESS
1 Adam Dunn/10
2 Aubrey Huff/50 15.00 40.00
4 Bobby Crosby/75 15.00 40.00
5 C.C. Sabathia/75 15.00 40.00
7 David Ortiz/50 40.00 80.00
8 Dewon Brazelton/75 10.00 25.00
11 Garret Anderson/25
14 Jack Wilson/75 15.00 40.00
16 Jay Gibbons/50 10.00 25.00
18 Jody Gerut/75 10.00 25.00
20 Johan Santana/50 30.00 60.00
22 Jose Vidro/75 10.00 25.00
25 Mark Teixeira/10
26 Michael Young/75 15.00 40.00
29 Omar Vizquel/10
33 Sean Burroughs/25
34 Sean Casey/10
36 Torii Hunter/10
39 Vernon Wells/10
40 Victor Martinez/75

2005 Leaf Picture Perfect

STATED ODDS 1:20
*DIE CUT: 1.25X TO 3X BASIC
DIE CUT RANDOM INSERTS IN PACKS
DIE CUT PRINT RUN 100 SERIAL #'d SETS
1 Albert Pujols 2.00 5.00
2 Alex Rodriguez 1.50 4.00
3 Alfonso Soriano .60 1.50

4 Derek Jeter 2.00 5.00
5 Greg Maddux 1.50 4.00
6 Hideki Matsui 1.50 4.00
7 Ichiro Suzuki 2.00 5.00
8 Ivan Rodriguez 1.00 2.50
9 Jim Thome 1.00 2.50
10 Mark Mulder .60 1.50
11 Mark Prior 1.00 2.50
12 Miguel Tejada .60 1.50
13 Mike Mussina 1.00 2.50
14 Mike Piazza 1.00 2.50
15 Nomar Garciaparra 1.00 2.50
16 Randy Johnson 1.00 2.50
17 Roger Clemens 1.50 4.00
18 Sammy Sosa 1.00 2.50
19 Scott Rolen 1.00 2.50
20 Vladimir Guerrero 1.00 2.50

2005 Leaf Recollection Autographs

RANDOM INSERTS IN PACKS
PRINT RUNS B/WN 1-29 COPIES PER
NO PRICING DUE TO SCARCITY
1 Harold Baines 90/1
2 Craig Biggio 90/1
3 George Brett 90/1
4 Jose Canseco 90/2
5 Gary Carter 90/7
6 Will Clark 90 Black/1
7 Will Clark 90 Blue/1
8 Will Clark 90 CL/1
9 David Cone 90/3
10 Eric Davis 90/7
11 Dwight Evans 90/6
12 Kirk Gibson 90/10
13 Doc Gooden 90/4
14 Mark Grace 90/7
15 Tony Gwynn 90/2
16 Bo Jackson 90/1
17 Randy Johnson 90/1
18 Edgar Martinez 90/2
19 Don Mattingly 90/3
20 Paul Molitor 90/6
21 Jack Morris 90/2
22 Dale Murphy 90/10
23 Dave Parker 90/5
24 Tony Pena 90/5
25 Terry Pendleton 90/29
26 Billy Ripken 90/7
27 Nolan Ryan 90/2
28 Nolan Ryan 90 CL/1
29 Nolan Ryan 90 No-Hit/1
30 Ryne Sandberg 90/1
31 Ryne Sandberg 90 CL/1
32 Deion Sanders 90/1
33 Sammy Sosa 90/1
34 Terry Steinbach 90/13
35 Dave Stewart 90/7
36 Dave Stieb 90/7
37 Alan Trammell 90/1
38 Omar Vizquel 90/8
39 Dave Winfield 90/6
40 Robin Yount 90/1

2005 Leaf Shirt Off My Back

STATED ODDS 1:48
SP INFO BASED ON BECKETT RESEARCH
1 Adam Dunn SP 4.00 10.00
4 Bobby Crosby SP 4.00 10.00
5 C.C. Sabathia SP 4.00 10.00
7 David Ortiz SP 6.00 15.00
8 Dewon Brazelton 3.00 8.00
9 Edgar Martinez 4.00 10.00
10 Frankie Francisco 3.00 8.00
11 Garret Anderson 3.00 8.00
12 Hideki Matsui SP 10.00 25.00
13 Hideo Nomo 4.00 10.00
14 Jack Wilson 3.00 8.00
15 Javy Lopez SP 4.00 10.00
16 Jay Gibbons SP 4.00 10.00
17 Jim Edmonds SP
18 Jody Gerut SP 4.00 10.00
19 Joey Gathright 3.00 8.00
20 Johan Santana 4.00 10.00
21 Jose Reyes 3.00 8.00
22 Jose Vidro 3.00 8.00
23 Lance Berkman SP 4.00 10.00
25 Mark Teixeira 4.00 10.00
26 Michael Young SP 4.00 10.00
27 Mike Cameron 3.00 8.00
28 Mike Sweeney 3.00 8.00
29 Omar Vizquel SP 6.00 15.00
30 Preston Wilson SP 4.00 10.00
31 Rocco Baldelli SP 4.00 10.00
32 Scott Rolen SP 6.00 15.00
33 Sean Burroughs SP 4.00 10.00
34 Sean Casey 3.00 8.00
35 Tim Hudson 3.00 8.00
36 Torii Hunter 3.00 8.00
37 Trevor Hoffman 3.00 8.00
38 Troy Glaus 3.00 8.00
39 Vernon Wells 3.00 8.00
40 Victor Martinez SP 4.00 10.00

2005 Leaf Sportscasters 70 Green Batting-Ball

STATED PRINT RUN 70 SERIAL #'d SETS
*PARALLEL #'d OF 50-65: .4X TO 1X
*PARALLEL #'d OF 40-45: .5X TO 1.2X
*PARALLEL #'d OF 30-35: .6X TO 1.5X
*PARALLEL #'d OF 20-25: .75X TO 2X
*PARALLEL #'d OF 15: 1X TO 2.5X
PARALLELS #'d FROM 5-65 COPIES PER
NO PRICING ON QTY OF 10 OR LESS
OVERALL SPORTSCASTER ODDS 1:4
1 Adam Dunn 1.25 3.00
2 Al Kaline 1.50 4.00
3 Albert Pujols 3.00 8.00
4 Alex Rodriguez 2.50 6.00
5 Alfonso Soriano 1.25 3.00
6 Bob Gibson 1.50 4.00
7 Cal Ripken 6.00 15.00
8 Carl Yastrzemski 2.50 6.00
9 Dale Murphy 1.50 4.00
10 Derek Jeter 3.00 8.00
11 Don Mattingly 3.00 8.00
12 Duke Snider 1.50 4.00
13 Eric Gagne 1.25 3.00
14 Ernie Banks 1.50 4.00
15 Frank Robinson 1.25 3.00
16 George Brett 3.00 8.00
17 Greg Maddux 2.50 6.00
18 Harmon Killebrew 1.50 4.00
19 Ichiro Suzuki 3.00 8.00
20 Ivan Rodriguez 1.50 4.00
21 Jim Edmonds 1.25 3.00
22 Jim Palmer 1.25 3.00
23 Jim Thome 1.50 4.00
24 Johnny Bench 1.50 4.00
25 Ken Griffey Jr. 2.50 6.00
26 Larry Walker 1.50 4.00
27 Mark Mulder 1.25 3.00
28 Mark Prior 1.50 4.00
29 Miguel Tejada 1.25 3.00
30 Mike Mussina 1.50 4.00
31 Mike Piazza 1.50 4.00
32 Mike Schmidt 3.00 8.00
33 Nolan Ryan 4.00 10.00
34 Nomar Garciaparra 1.50 4.00
35 Pedro Martinez 1.50 4.00
36 Rafael Palmeiro 1.50 4.00
37 Randy Johnson 1.50 4.00
38 Reggie Jackson 1.50 4.00
39 Rickey Henderson 1.50 4.00
40 Roberto Clemente 4.00 10.00
41 Rod Carew 1.50 4.00
42 Roger Clemens 3.00 8.00
43 Ryne Sandberg 3.00 8.00
44 Sammy Sosa 1.50 4.00
45 Stan Musial 2.50 6.00
46 Steve Carlton 1.25 3.00
47 Tony Gwynn UER 2.00 5.00
Name spelled as Green in text on back
48 Vladimir Guerrero 1.50 4.00
49 Warren Spahn 1.50 4.00
50 Willie McCovey 1.50 4.00

2004 Leaf Certified Cuts

This 300-card set was released in September, 2004. The first 200 cards in this set consist of veteran players. Cards 201-221 consists of players who switched teams in the off-season while cards 221-250 are retired legends of baseball and cards 251-300 all feature Rookie Cards. Cards numbered 201 through 250 were randomly inserted into packs and were issued to a stated print run of 599 serial numbered sets. Most cards from 251 through 300 were issued to a stated print run of 499 serial numbered sets and those cards are all autographed by the featured player except fo Kazuo Matsui.

COMP.SET w/o SP's (200) 20.00 50.00
COMMON CARD (1-200) .30 .75
COMMON CARD (201-221) 1.25 3.00
COMMON CARD (222-250) 1.25 3.00
201-250 RANDOM INSERTS IN PACKS
201-250 PRINT RUN 599 SERIAL #'d SETS
COMMON CARD (251-300) 2.00 5.00
251-300 RANDOM INSERTS IN PACKS
251-300 PRINT RUN 499 SERIAL #'d SETS
OVERALL AU ODDS THREE PER BOX
AUTO PRINT RUNS B/WN 99-499 #'d PER
*OTSUKA JAPANESE SIG: .75X TO 2X HI
1 Vladimir Guerrero .75 2.00
2 Garret Anderson .30 .75
3 John Lackey .30 .75
4 Bartolo Colon .30 .75
5 Troy Glaus .30 .75
6 Tim Salmon .50 1.25
7 Shea Hillenbrand .30 .75
8 Brandon Webb .30 .75
9 Roberto Alomar .50 1.25
10 Randy Johnson .75 2.00
11 Alex Cintron .30 .75
12 Richie Sexson .30 .75
13 Luis Gonzalez .30 .75
14 Adam LaRoche .30 .75
15 Rafael Furcal .30 .75
16 Chipper Jones .75 2.00
17 Marcus Giles .30 .75
18 Andruw Jones .50 1.25
19 Russ Ortiz .30 .75
20 Rafael Palmeiro .50 1.25
21 Melvin Mora .30 .75
22 Luis Matos .30 .75
23 Jay Gibbons .30 .75
24 Adam Loewen .30 .75
25 Larry Bigbie .30 .75
26 Rodrigo Lopez .30 .75
27 Javy Lopez .30 .75
28 Miguel Tejada .30 .75
29 Trot Nixon .30 .75
30 Curt Schilling .50 1.25
31 Jason Varitek .75 2.00
32 Manny Ramirez .50 1.25
33 Keith Foulke Sox .30 .75
34 Derek Lowe .30 .75
35 Pedro Martinez .50 1.25
36 Nomar Garciaparra 1.25 3.00
37 Bill Mueller .30 .75
38 Johnny Damon .50 1.25
39 David Ortiz .75 2.00
40 Mark Prior .50 1.25
41 Kerry Wood .30 .75
42 Sammy Sosa .75 2.00
43 Derrek Lee .50 1.25
44 Greg Maddux 1.25 3.00
45 Aramis Ramirez .30 .75
46 Matt Clement .30 .75
47 Carlos Zambrano .30 .75
48 Todd Walker .30 .75
49 Moises Alou .30 .75
50 Corey Patterson .30 .75
51 Frank Thomas .75 2.00
52 Magglio Ordonez .30 .75
53 Carlos Lee .30 .75
54 Mark Buehrle .30 .75
55 Esteban Loaiza .30 .75
56 Joe Crede .30 .75
57 Paul Konerko .30 .75
58 Adam Dunn .30 .75
59 Austin Kearns .30 .75
60 Barry Larkin .50 1.25
61 Ryan Wagner .30 .75
62 Danny Graves .30 .75
63 Sean Casey .30 .75
64 Ken Griffey Jr. 1.25 3.00
65 Jody Gerut .30 .75
66 Cliff Lee .30 .75
67 Victor Martinez .30 .75
68 C.C. Sabathia .30 .75
69 Omar Vizquel .50 1.25
70 Travis Hafner .30 .75
71 Todd Helton .50 1.25
72 Preston Wilson .30 .75
73 Jeromy Burnitz .30 .75
74 Larry Walker .30 .75
75 Ivan Rodriguez .50 1.25
76 Rondell White .30 .75
77 Miguel Cabrera .50 1.25
78 Luis Castillo .30 .75
79 Josh Beckett .30 .75
80 Mike Lowell .30 .75
81 Dontrelle Willis .50 1.25
82 Brad Penny .30 .75
83 Hee Seop Choi .30 .75
84 Juan Pierre .30 .75
85 Andy Pettitte .50 1.25
86 Jeff Bagwell .50 1.25
87 Roy Oswalt .30 .75
88 Lance Berkman .30 .75
89 Morgan Ensberg .30 .75
90 Craig Biggio .50 1.25
91 Octavio Dotel .30 .75
92 Wade Miller .30 .75
93 Jeff Kent .30 .75
94 Richard Hidalgo .30 .75
95 Roger Clemens 1.50 4.00
96 Carlos Beltran .30 .75
97 Angel Berroa .30 .75
98 Jeremy Affeldt .30 .75
99 Juan Gonzalez .30 .75
100 Mike Sweeney .30 .75
101 Kazuhisa Ishii .30 .75
102 Shawn Green .30 .75
103 Milton Bradley .30 .75
104 Paul Lo Duca .30 .75
105 Hideo Nomo .75 2.00
106 Eric Gagne .30 .75
107 Adrian Beltre .30 .75
108 Scott Podsednik .30 .75
109 Rickie Weeks .30 .75
110 Ben Sheets .30 .75
111 Geoff Jenkins .30 .75
112 Jacque Jones .30 .75
113 Johan Santana .50 1.25
114 Shannon Stewart .30 .75
115 Corey Koskie .30 .75
116 Lew Ford .30 .75
117 Torii Hunter .30 .75
118 Chad Cordero .30 .75
119 Orlando Cabrera .30 .75
120 Jose Vidro .30 .75
121 Nick Johnson .30 .75
122 Brad Wilkerson .30 .75
123 Mike Piazza 1.25 3.00
124 Jae Weong Seo .30 .75
125 Jose Reyes .30 .75
126 Tom Glavine .50 1.25
127 Jorge Posada .50 1.25
128 Gary Sheffield .30 .75
129 Bernie Williams .50 1.25
130 Mike Mussina .50 1.25
131 Mariano Rivera .75 2.00
132 Bubba Crosby .30 .75
133 Kevin Brown .30 .75
134 Javier Vazquez .30 .75
135 Jason Giambi .30 .75
136 Derek Jeter 1.50 4.00
137 Alex Rodriguez 1.25 3.00
138 Hideki Matsui 1.25 3.00
139 Mark Mulder .30 .75
140 Jermaine Dye .30 .75
141 Tim Hudson .30 .75
142 Barry Zito .30 .75
143 Eric Chavez .30 .75
144 Bobby Crosby .30 .75
145 Eric Byrnes .30 .75
146 Marlon Byrd .30 .75
147 Billy Wagner .30 .75
148 Mike Lieberthal .30 .75
149 Jimmy Rollins .30 .75
150 Jim Thome .50 1.25
151 Bobby Abreu .30 .75
152 Pat Burrell .30 .75
153 Jose Castillo .30 .75
154 Craig Wilson .30 .75
155 Jason Bay .30 .75
156 Jason Kendall .30 .75
157 Raul Mondesi .30 .75
158 Jay Payton .30 .75
159 Trevor Hoffman .30 .75
160 Jake Peavy .30 .75
161 Sean Burroughs .30 .75
162 Phil Nevin .30 .75
163 Brian Giles .30 .75
164 Ryan Klesko .30 .75
165 Todd Linden .30 .75
166 Jerome Williams .30 .75
167 Jason Schmidt .30 .75
168 Ray Durham .30 .75
169 Marquis Grissom .30 .75
170 Shigetoshi Hasegawa .30 .75
171 Edgar Martinez .50 1.25
172 Freddy Garcia .30 .75
173 Bret Boone .30 .75
174 Raul Ibanez .30 .75
175 Ichiro Suzuki 1.50 4.00
176 Randy Winn .30 .75
177 Scott Rolen .50 1.25
178 Jim Edmonds .30 .75
179 Albert Pujols 1.50 4.00
180 Matt Morris .30 .75
181 Edgar Renteria .30 .75
182 Aubrey Huff .30 .75
183 Delmon Young .50 1.25
184 Dewon Brazelton .30 .75
185 Rocco Baldelli .30 .75
186 Carl Crawford .30 .75
187 Mark Teixeira .50 1.25
188 Hank Blalock .30 .75
189 Michael Young .30 .75
190 Laynce Nix .30 .75
191 Alfonso Soriano .30 .75
192 Kevin Mench .30 .75
193 Adrian Gonzalez .30 .75
194 Alexis Rios .30 .75
195 Roy Halladay .30 .75
196 Vernon Wells .30 .75
197 Carlos Delgado .30 .75
198 Bill Hall .30 .75
199 Jose Guillen .30 .75
200 Jeremy Bonderman .30 .75
201 Roger Clemens Yanks SP 3.00 8.00
202 Alex Rodriguez Rgr SP 3.00 8.00
203 Greg Maddux Braves SP 3.00 8.00
204 Miguel Tejada A's SP 1.25 3.00
205 Alfonso Soriano Yanks SP 1.25 3.00
206 Andy Pettitte Yanks SP 2.00 5.00
207 Curt Schilling D'backs SP 1.25 3.00
208 Gary Sheffield Braves SP 2.00 5.00
209 Ivan Rodriguez Marlins SP 2.00 5.00
210 Jim Thome Indians SP 2.00 5.00
211 Mike Mussina O's SP 2.00 5.00
212 Mike Piazza Dodgers SP 3.00 8.00
213 Randy Johnson M's SP 2.00 5.00
214 Roger Clemens Sox SP 3.00 8.00
215 Sammy Sosa Sox SP 2.00 5.00
216 Alex Rodriguez M's SP 3.00 8.00
217 Randy Johnson Astros SP 2.00 5.00
218 Vladimir Guerrero Expos SP 2.00 5.00
219 Rafael Palmeiro Rgr SP 2.00 5.00
220 Manny Ramirez Indians SP 2.00 5.00
221 Mike Piazza Marlins SP 3.00 8.00
222 Cal Ripken LGD 6.00 15.00
223 Ted Williams LGD 4.00 10.00
224 Duke Snider LGD 2.00 5.00
225 Ernie Banks LGD 2.00 5.00
226 Ryne Sandberg LGD 4.00 10.00
227 Mark Grace LGD 2.00 5.00
228 Andre Dawson LGD 1.25 3.00
229 Bob Feller LGD 2.00 5.00
230 Ty Cobb LGD 3.00 8.00
231 George Brett LGD 4.00 10.00
232 Bo Jackson LGD 2.00 5.00
233 Robin Yount LGD 2.00 5.00
234 Harmon Killebrew LGD 2.00 5.00
235 Gary Carter LGD 1.25 3.00
236 Don Mattingly LGD 4.00 10.00
237 Phil Rizzuto LGD 2.00 5.00
238 Babe Ruth LGD 4.00 10.00
239 Lou Gehrig LGD 3.00 8.00
240 Reggie Jackson LGD 2.00 5.00
241 Rickey Henderson LGD 2.00 5.00
242 Mike Schmidt LGD 4.00 10.00
243 Roberto Clemente LGD 4.00 10.00
244 Tony Gwynn LGD 3.00 8.00
245 Will Clark LGD 2.00 5.00
246 Lou Brock LGD 2.00 5.00
247 Bob Gibson LGD 2.00 5.00
248 Stan Musial LGD 3.00 8.00
249 Nolan Ryan LGD 5.00 12.00
250 Dale Murphy LGD 2.00 5.00
251 A.Baldiris ROO AU/499 RC 3.00 8.00
252 A.Otsuka ROO AU/99 RC 12.50 30.00
253 A.Blanco ROO AU/499 RC 3.00 8.00
254 A.Chavez ROO AU/499 RC 3.00 8.00
255 C.Hines ROO AU/199 RC 4.00 10.00
256 C.Vasquez ROO AU/499 RC 4.00 10.00
257 Casey Daigle ROO/499 RC 2.00 5.00
258 C.Oxspring ROO AU/499 RC 3.00 8.00
259 C.Miller ROO AU/499 RC 3.00 8.00
260 D.Crouthers ROO AU/199 RC 4.00 10.00
261 D.Kelly ROO AU/499 RC 3.00 8.00
262 E.Rodriguez ROO AU/499 RC 4.00 10.00
263 E.Sierra ROO AU/299 RC 4.00 10.00
264 E.Moreno ROO AU/499 RC 4.00 10.00
265 F.Nieve ROO AU/499 RC 3.00 8.00
266 F.Guzman ROO AU/499 RC 3.00 8.00
267 G.Dobbs ROO AU/499 RC 3.00 8.00
268 B.Halsey ROO AU/499 RC 4.00 10.00
269 H.Gimenez ROO AU/499 RC 3.00 8.00
270 I.Ochoa ROO AU/499 RC 3.00 8.00
271 J.Woods ROO AU/499 RC 3.00 8.00
272 J.Brown ROO AU/499 RC 3.00 8.00
273 J.Bartlett ROO AU/499 RC 4.00 10.00
274 J.Szuminski ROO AU/499 RC 3.00 8.00
275 John Gall ROO/499 RC 3.00 8.00
276 J.Vasquez ROO AU/499 RC 3.00 8.00
277 J.Labandeira ROO AU/499 RC 3.00 8.00
278 J.Hampson ROO AU/499 RC 3.00 8.00
279 Kazuo Matsui ROO/499 RC 2.00 5.00
280 K.Cave ROO AU/499 RC 3.00 8.00
281 L.Cormier ROO AU/499 RC 3.00 8.00
282 L.Holdzkom ROO AU/199 RC 4.00 10.00
283 M.Valdez ROO AU/199 RC 4.00 10.00
284 M.Wuertz ROO AU/499 RC 4.00 10.00
285 M.Johnston ROO AU/499 RC 3.00 8.00
286 M.Rouse ROO AU/329 RC 3.00 8.00
287 O.Joseph ROO AU/499 RC 3.00 8.00
288 P.Stockman ROO AU/499 RC 3.00 8.00
289 R.Novoa ROO AU/499 RC 3.00 8.00
290 R.Belisario ROO AU/499 RC 3.00 8.00
291 R.Cedeno ROO AU/499 RC 6.00 15.00
292 R.Meaux ROO AU/499 RC 3.00 8.00
293 Scott Proctor ROO/499 RC 3.00 8.00
294 S.Henn ROO AU/199 RC 4.00 10.00
295 S.Camp ROO AU/499 RC 3.00 8.00
296 S.Hill ROO AU/499 RC 3.00 8.00
297 S.Takatsu ROO AU/99 RC 10.00 25.00
298 T.Bittner ROO AU/199 RC 4.00 10.00
299 William Bergolla ROO/499 RC 2.00 5.00
300 Y.Molina ROO AU/499 RC 10.00 25.00

2004 Leaf Certified Cuts Marble Black

RANDOM INSERTS IN PACKS
STATED PRINT RUN 1 SERIAL #'d SET
NO PRICING DUE TO SCARCITY

2004 Leaf Certified Cuts Marble Blue

*BLUE 1-200: 2.5X TO 6X BASIC
*BLUE 201-221: 1.25X TO 3X BASIC
*BLUE 222-250: 1.25X TO 3X BASIC
*BLUE 251-300: .6X TO 1.5X BASIC
*BLUE 251-300: .3X TO .8X AU p/r 299-499
*BLUE 251-300: .25X TO .6X AU p/r 199
*BLUE 251-300: .15X TO .4X AU p/r 99
RANDOM INSERTS IN PACKS
STATED PRINT RUN 50 SERIAL #'d SETS

2004 Leaf Certified Cuts Marble Emerald

RANDOM INSERTS IN PACKS
STATED PRINT RUN 5 SERIAL #'d SETS
NO PRICING DUE TO SCARCITY

2004 Leaf Certified Cuts Marble Gold

*GOLD 1-200: 4X TO 10X BASIC
*GOLD 201-221: 2X TO 5X BASIC
*GOLD 222-250: 2X TO 5X BASIC
RANDOM INSERTS IN PACKS
STATED PRINT RUN 25 SERIAL #'d SETS
251-300 NO PRICING DUE TO SCARCITY

2004 Leaf Certified Cuts Marble Red

*RED 1-200: 1.5X TO 4X BASIC
*RED 201-221: .75X TO 2X BASIC
*RED 222-250: .75X TO 2X BASIC
*RED 251-300: .4X TO 1X BASIC
*RED 251-300: .2X TO .5X AU p/r 299-499
*RED 251-300: .15X TO .4X AU p/r 199
*RED 251-300: .1X TO .25X AU p/r 99
RANDOM INSERTS IN PACKS
STATED PRINT RUN 100 SERIAL #'d SETS

2004 Leaf Certified Cuts Marble Material Black Number

OVERALL GU ODDS ONE PER BOX
STATED PRINT RUN 1 SERIAL #'d SET
NO PRICING DUE TO SCARCITY

2004 Leaf Certified Cuts Marble Material Black Position

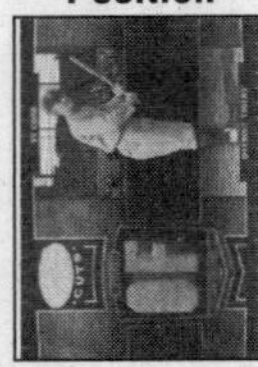

OVERALL GU ODDS ONE PER BOX
STATED PRINT RUN 1 SERIAL #'d SET
NO PRICING DUE TO SCARCITY

2004 Leaf Certified Cuts Marble Material Black Prime

OVERALL GU ODDS ONE PER BOX
STATED PRINT RUN 1 SERIAL #'d SET
NO PRICING DUE TO SCARCITY

2004 Leaf Certified Cuts Marble Material Blue Number

*BLUE p/r 66-100: .4X TO 1X RED p/r 66-100
*BLUE p/r 36-65: .6X TO 1.5X RED p/r 66-100
*BLUE p/r 36-65: .25X TO .6X RED p/r 20-35
*BLUE p/r 36-65: .2X TO .5X RED p/r 15-19
*BLUE p/r 20-35: 1X TO 2.5X RED p/r 66-100
*BLUE p/r 20-35: .6X TO 1.5X RED p/r 36-65
*BLUE p/r 20-35: .4X TO 1X RED p/r 20-35
*BLUE p/r 20-35: .3X TO .8X RED p/r 15-19
*BLUE p/r 15-19: 1.25X TO 3X RED p/r 66-100
*BLUE p/r 15-19: .75X TO 2X RED p/r 36-65
*BLUE p/r 15-19: .5X TO 1.2X RED p/r 20-35
*BLUE p/r 15-19: .4X TO 1X RED p/r 15-19
OVERALL GU ODDS ONE PER BOX
PRINT RUNS B/WN 1-75 COPIES PER
NO PRICING ON QTY OF 14 OR LESS

2004 Leaf Certified Cuts Marble Material Emerald Prime

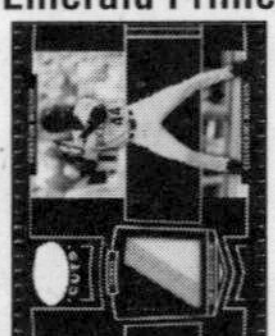

OVERALL GU ODDS ONE PER BOX
STATED PRINT RUN 5 SERIAL #'d SETS
NO PRICING DUE TO SCARCITY

2004 Leaf Certified Cuts Marble Material Red Position

OVERALL GU ODDS ONE PER BOX
PRINT RUNS B/WN 1-100 COPIES PER
NO PRICING ON QTY OF 10 OR LESS
1 Vladimir Guerrero Jsy/100 4.00 10.00
2 Garret Anderson Jsy/100 2.00 5.00
5 Troy Glaus Jsy/75 2.00 5.00
6 Tim Salmon Jsy/75 3.00 8.00
8 Brandon Webb Jsy/10
10 Randy Johnson Jsy/100 4.00 10.00
12 Richie Sexson Jsy/10
13 Luis Gonzalez Jsy/100 2.00 5.00
15 Rafael Furcal Jsy/100 2.00 5.00
16 Chipper Jones Jsy/100 4.00 10.00
17 Marcus Giles Jsy/100 2.00 5.00
18 Andruw Jones Jsy/100 3.00 8.00
20 Rafael Palmeiro Jsy/100 3.00 8.00
21 Melvin Mora Jsy/50 3.00 8.00
22 Luis Matos Jsy/50 3.00 8.00
23 Jay Gibbons Jsy/100 2.00 5.00
25 Larry Bigbie Jsy/50 3.00 8.00
26 Rodrigo Lopez Jsy/50 3.00 8.00
27 Javy Lopez Jsy/25 5.00 12.00
28 Miguel Tejada Jsy/100 2.00 5.00
30 Curt Schilling Jsy/50 5.00 12.00
31 Jason Varitek Jsy/100 4.00 10.00
32 Manny Ramirez Jsy/100 3.00 8.00
35 Pedro Martinez Jsy/100 3.00 8.00
37 Nomar Garciaparra Jsy/100 4.00 10.00
40 Mark Prior Jsy/100 3.00 8.00
41 Kerry Wood Pants/100 2.00 5.00
42 Sammy Sosa Jsy/100 4.00 10.00
44 Greg Maddux Jsy/50 8.00 20.00
45 Aramis Ramirez Jsy/100 2.00 5.00
49 Moises Alou Jsy/10
51 Frank Thomas Jsy/100 4.00 10.00
52 Magglio Ordonez Jsy/100 2.00 5.00
53 Carlos Lee Jsy/100 2.00 5.00
54 Mark Buehrle Jsy/100 2.00 5.00
57 Paul Konerko Jsy/50 3.00 8.00
58 Adam Dunn Jsy/100 2.00 5.00
59 Austin Kearns Jsy/100 2.00 5.00
60 Barry Larkin Jsy/100 2.00 5.00
63 Sean Casey Jsy/10
65 Jody Gerut Jsy/100 2.00 5.00
66 Cliff Lee Jsy/100 2.00 5.00
67 Victor Martinez Jsy/100 2.00 5.00
68 C.C. Sabathia Jsy/100 2.00 5.00
69 Omar Vizquel Jsy/100 3.00 8.00
70 Travis Hafner Jsy/100 2.00 5.00
71 Todd Helton Jsy/100 3.00 8.00
72 Preston Wilson Jsy/100 2.00 5.00
73 Jeromy Burnitz Jsy/10
74 Larry Walker Jsy/10
75 Ivan Rodriguez Jsy/50 5.00 12.00
77 Miguel Cabrera Jsy/100 3.00 8.00
79 Josh Beckett Jsy/100 2.00 5.00
81 Dontrelle Willis Jsy/100 3.00 8.00
82 Brad Penny Jsy/100 2.00 5.00
85 Andy Pettitte Jsy/10
86 Jeff Bagwell Jsy/100 3.00 8.00
87 Roy Oswalt Jsy/100 2.00 5.00
88 Lance Berkman Jsy/100 2.00 5.00
89 Morgan Ensberg Jsy/100 2.00 5.00
90 Craig Biggio Jsy/100 3.00 8.00
93 Jeff Kent Jsy/100 2.00 5.00
94 Richard Hidalgo Pants/100 2.00 5.00
95 Roger Clemens Jsy/25 12.50 30.00
96 Carlos Beltran Jsy/100 2.00 5.00
97 Angel Berroa Pants/100 2.00 5.00
100 Mike Sweeney Jsy/100 2.00 5.00
101 Kazuhisa Ishii Jsy/100 2.00 5.00
102 Shawn Green Jsy/100 2.00 5.00
104 Paul Lo Duca Jsy/100 2.00 5.00
105 Hideo Nomo Jsy/100 4.00 10.00
107 Adrian Beltre Jsy/100 2.00 5.00
110 Ben Sheets Jsy/100 2.00 5.00
111 Geoff Jenkins Jsy/100 2.00 5.00
112 Jacque Jones Jsy/100 2.00 5.00
113 Johan Santana Jsy/100 3.00 8.00
114 Shannon Stewart Jsy/100 2.00 5.00
117 Torii Hunter Jsy/75 2.00 5.00
119 Orlando Cabrera Jsy/10
120 Jose Vidro Jsy/10
123 Mike Piazza Jsy/100 5.00 12.00
124 Jae Weong Seo Jsy/10
125 Jose Reyes Jsy/75 2.00 5.00
126 Tom Glavine Jsy/75 3.00 8.00
127 Jorge Posada Jsy/100 3.00 8.00
129 Bernie Williams Jsy/100 3.00 8.00
130 Mike Mussina Jsy/25 8.00 20.00
131 Mariano Rivera Jsy/100 4.00 10.00
135 Jason Giambi Jsy/10
138 Hideki Matsui Jsy/100 12.50 30.00
139 Mark Mulder Jsy/100 2.00 5.00
141 Tim Hudson Jsy/10
142 Barry Zito Jsy/100 2.00 5.00
143 Eric Chavez Jsy/100 2.00 5.00
146 Marlon Byrd Jsy/100 2.00 5.00
150 Jim Thome Jsy/100 3.00 8.00
151 Bobby Abreu Jsy/100 2.00 5.00
152 Pat Burrell Jsy/100 2.00 5.00
154 Craig Wilson Jsy/100 2.00 5.00
156 Jason Kendall Jsy/100 2.00 5.00
161 Sean Burroughs Jsy/100 2.00 5.00
163 Brian Giles Jsy/10
164 Ryan Klesko Jsy/100 2.00 5.00
166 Jerome Williams Jsy/25 5.00 12.00
171 Edgar Martinez Jsy/100 3.00 8.00
172 Freddy Garcia Jsy/100 2.00 5.00
177 Scott Rolen Jsy/100 3.00 8.00
178 Jim Edmonds Jsy/100 2.00 5.00
179 Albert Pujols Jsy/100 10.00 25.00
180 Matt Morris Jsy/75 2.00 5.00
181 Edgar Renteria Jsy/25 5.00 12.00
182 Aubrey Huff Jsy/100 2.00 5.00
184 Dewon Brazelton Jsy/100 2.00 5.00
185 Rocco Baldelli Jsy/100 2.00 5.00
186 Carl Crawford Jsy/100 2.00 5.00
187 Mark Teixeira Jsy/25 8.00 20.00
188 Hank Blalock Jsy/100 2.00 5.00
191 Alfonso Soriano Jsy/100 2.00 5.00
192 Kevin Mench Jsy/100 2.00 5.00
195 Roy Halladay Jsy/100 2.00 5.00
196 Vernon Wells Jsy/100 2.00 5.00
197 Carlos Delgado Jsy/100 2.00 5.00
200 Jeremy Bonderman Jsy/100 2.00 5.00
201 R.Clemens Yanks Jsy/100 5.00 12.00
202 Alex Rodriguez Rgr Jsy/100 5.00 12.00
203 G.Maddux Braves Jsy/100 5.00 12.00
204 Miguel Tejada A's Jsy/100 2.00 5.00
205 Alf Soriano Yanks Jsy/100 2.00 5.00
206 A.Pettitte Yanks Jsy/100 3.00 8.00
207 C.Schilling D'backs Jsy/100 2.00 5.00
208 G.Sheffield Braves Jsy/50 3.00 8.00
209 I.Rodriguez Marlins Jsy/100 3.00 8.00
210 Jim Thome Indians Jsy/25 8.00 20.00
211 Mike Mussina O's Jsy/50 5.00 12.00
212 M.Piazza Dodgers Jsy/100 5.00 12.00
213 R.Johnson M's Jsy/100 4.00 10.00
214 R.Clemens Sox Jsy/100 5.00 12.00
215 Sammy Sosa Sox Jsy/50 6.00 15.00
216 A.Rodriguez M's Jsy/100 5.00 12.00
217 R.Johnson Astros Jsy/100 4.00 10.00
218 V.Guerrero Expos Jsy/100 4.00 10.00
219 R.Palmeiro Rgr Jsy/100 3.00 8.00
221 M.Piazza Marlins Jsy/100 5.00 12.00
222 Cal Ripken LGD Jsy/50 30.00 60.00
223 Ted Williams LGD Jsy/25 60.00 120.00
225 Ernie Banks LGD Jsy/50 8.00 20.00
226 R.Sandberg LGD Jsy/100 8.00 20.00
227 Mark Grace LGD Jsy/25 10.00 25.00
228 Andre Dawson LGD Jsy/100 3.00 8.00
229 Bob Feller LGD Jsy/25 10.00 25.00
230 Ty Cobb LGD Pants/1
231 George Brett LGD Jsy/100 8.00 20.00
232 Bo Jackson LGD Jsy/100 6.00 15.00
233 Robin Yount LGD Jsy/100 6.00 15.00
234 H.Killebrew LGD Jsy/25 12.50 30.00
235 Gary Carter LGD Jkt/100 3.00 8.00
236 Don Mattingly LGD Jsy/50 12.50 30.00
237 Phil Rizzuto LGD Pants/25 10.00 25.00
238 Babe Ruth LGD Pants/50 125.00 200.00
239 Lou Gehrig LGD Pants/50 75.00 150.00
240 R.Jackson LGD Jsy/100 5.00 12.00
241 R.Henderson LGD Jsy/100 6.00 15.00
242 Mike Schmidt LGD Jsy/50 12.50 30.00
243 R.Clemente LGD Jsy/50 50.00 100.00
244 Tony Gwynn LGD Jsy/100 6.00 15.00
245 Will Clark LGD Jsy/100 5.00 12.00
246 Lou Brock LGD Jsy/25 10.00 25.00
247 Bob Gibson LGD Jsy/25 10.00 25.00
248 Stan Musial LGD Jsy/25 20.00 50.00
249 Nolan Ryan LGD Jsy/50 15.00 40.00
250 Dale Murphy LGD Jsy/100 5.00 12.00

2004 Leaf Certified Cuts Marble Signature Black

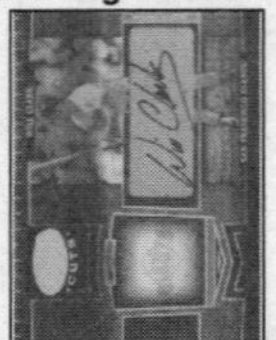

OVERALL AU ODDS THREE PER BOX
STATED PRINT RUN 1 SERIAL #'d SET
NO PRICING DUE TO SCARCITY

2004 Leaf Certified Cuts Marble Signature Blue

*1-250 p/r 75: .4X TO 1X RED p/r 66-100
*1-250 p/r 50: .5X TO 1.2X RED p/r 66-100
*1-250 p/r 50: .4X TO 1X RED p/r 36-65
*1-250 p/r 50: .3X TO .8X RED p/r 20-35
*1-250 p/r 50: .25X TO .6X RED p/r 15-19
*1-250 p/r 25: .6X TO 1.5X RED p/r 66-100
*1-250 p/r 25: .5X TO 1.2X RED p/r 36-65
*1-250 p/r 25: .4X TO 1X RED p/r 20-35
*251-300 p/r 65-75: .4X TO 1X RED p/r 66-100
OVERALL AU ODDS THREE PER BOX
PRINT RUNS B/WN 1-75 COPIES PER
1-250 NO PRICING ON QTY OF 10 OR LESS
251-300 NO PRICING ON QTY 25 OR LESS
265 Fernando Nieve ROO/75 5.00 12.00

2004 Leaf Certified Cuts Marble Signature Emerald

OVERALL AU ODDS THREE PER BOX
PRINT RUNS B/WN 1-5 COPIES PER
NO PRICING DUE TO SCARCITY

2004 Leaf Certified Cuts Marble Signature Gold

*1-250 p/r 25: .6X TO 1.5X RED p/r 66-100
*1-250 p/r 25: .5X TO 1.2X RED p/r 36-65
*1-250 p/r 25: .4X TO 1X RED p/r 20-35
*1-250 p/r 25: .3X TO .8X RED p/r 15-19
OVERALL AU ODDS THREE PER BOX
PRINT RUNS B/WN 1-25 COPIES PER
1-250 NO PRICING ON QTY OF 10 OR LESS
251-300 NO PRICING DUE TO SCARCITY
33 Keith Foulke Sox/25 15.00 40.00

2004 Leaf Certified Cuts Marble Signature Red

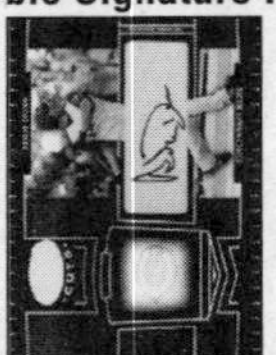

OVERALL AU ODDS THREE PER BOX
PRINT RUNS B/WN 1-100 COPIES PER
1-250 NO PRICING ON QTY OF 10 OR LESS
251-300 NO PRICING ON QTY 25 OR LESS
2 Garret Anderson/50 8.00 20.00
3 John Lackey/100 6.00 15.00
7 Shea Hillenbrand/100 6.00 15.00
8 Brandon Webb/100 8.00 20.00
9 Roberto Alomar/1
11 Alex Cintron/100 4.00 10.00
14 Adam LaRoche/100 4.00 10.00
15 Rafael Furcal/50 8.00 20.00
16 Chipper Jones/1
17 Marcus Giles/50 8.00 20.00
18 Andruw Jones/1
19 Russ Ortiz/100 4.00 10.00
20 Rafael Palmeiro/1
21 Melvin Mora/100 6.00 15.00
22 Luis Matos/100 4.00 10.00
23 Jay Gibbons/100 4.00 10.00
24 Adam Loewen/17 8.00 20.00
25 Larry Bigbie/100 6.00 15.00
26 Rodrigo Lopez/100 4.00 10.00
29 Trot Nixon/50 8.00 20.00
32 Manny Ramirez/1
33 Keith Foulke Sox/100 10.00 25.00
39 David Ortiz/50 20.00 50.00
40 Mark Prior/25 12.50 30.00
41 Kerry Wood/10
42 Sammy Sosa/10
43 Derrek Lee/50 12.50 30.00
44 Greg Maddux/1
45 Aramis Ramirez/100 6.00 15.00
46 Matt Clement/25 10.00 25.00
47 Carlos Zambrano/100 10.00 25.00
48 Todd Walker/100 4.00 10.00
51 Frank Thomas/5
53 Carlos Lee/100 6.00 15.00
54 Mark Buehrle/50 12.50 30.00
55 Esteban Loaiza/100 4.00 10.00
58 Adam Dunn/25 15.00 40.00
59 Austin Kearns/25 6.00 15.00
60 Barry Larkin/5
63 Sean Casey/25 10.00 25.00
65 Jody Gerut/100 4.00 10.00
66 Cliff Lee/100 6.00 15.00
67 Victor Martinez/100 6.00 15.00
68 C.C. Sabathia/100 6.00 15.00
70 Travis Hafner/100 6.00 15.00
71 Todd Helton/1
72 Preston Wilson/100 6.00 15.00
77 Miguel Cabrera/50 12.50 30.00
80 Mike Lowell/25 10.00 25.00
81 Dontrelle Willis/5
82 Brad Penny/100 4.00 10.00
85 Andy Pettitte/1
86 Jeff Bagwell/10
88 Lance Berkman/5
89 Morgan Ensberg/100 6.00 15.00
90 Craig Biggio/25 15.00 40.00
91 Octavio Dotel/100 4.00 10.00
92 Wade Miller/100 4.00 10.00
95 Roger Clemens/1
96 Carlos Beltran/50 8.00 20.00
97 Angel Berroa/50 5.00 12.00
98 Jeremy Affeldt/100 4.00 10.00
99 Juan Gonzalez/5
101 Kazuhisa Ishii/1
102 Shawn Green/1
103 Milton Bradley/100 6.00 15.00
104 Paul Lo Duca/50 8.00 20.00
105 Hideo Nomo/1
108 Scott Podsednik/100 10.00 25.00
109 Rickie Weeks/25 10.00 25.00
112 Jacque Jones/100 6.00 15.00
113 Johan Santana/50 12.50 30.00
114 Shannon Stewart/50 8.00 20.00
116 Lew Ford/100 4.00 10.00
117 Torii Hunter/25 10.00 25.00
118 Chad Cordero/100 6.00 15.00
119 Orlando Cabrera/100 6.00 15.00
120 Jose Vidro/50 5.00 12.00
123 Mike Piazza/5
124 Jae Weong Seo/5
127 Jorge Posada/5
128 Gary Sheffield/10
129 Bernie Williams/1
130 Mike Mussina/5
131 Mariano Rivera/1
132 Bubba Crosby/100 4.00 10.00
139 Mark Mulder/25 10.00 25.00
140 Jermaine Dye/100 6.00 15.00
141 Tim Hudson/1
142 Barry Zito/1
144 Bobby Crosby/100 6.00 15.00
145 Eric Byrnes/100 4.00 10.00
146 Marlon Byrd/100 4.00 10.00
148 Mike Lieberthal/100 6.00 15.00
153 Jose Castillo/100 4.00 10.00
154 Craig Wilson/100 4.00 10.00
155 Jason Bay/100 6.00 15.00
158 Jay Payton/100 4.00 10.00
161 Sean Burroughs/25 6.00 15.00
165 Todd Linden/100 4.00 10.00
170 Shigetoshi Hasegawa/50 20.00 50.00
171 Edgar Martinez/25 20.00 50.00
174 Raul Ibanez/100 4.00 10.00
177 Scott Rolen/50 12.50 30.00
178 Jim Edmonds/5
179 Albert Pujols/10
182 Aubrey Huff/100 6.00 15.00
183 Delmon Young/25 15.00 40.00
184 Dewon Brazelton/100 4.00 10.00
186 Carl Crawford/100 6.00 15.00
187 Mark Teixeira/25 15.00 40.00
188 Hank Blalock/50 8.00 20.00
189 Michael Young/100 6.00 15.00
190 Laynce Nix/100 4.00 10.00
191 Alfonso Soriano/25 15.00 40.00
193 Adrian Gonzalez/100 4.00 10.00
194 Alexis Rios/100 6.00 15.00
195 Roy Halladay/5
196 Vernon Wells/50 8.00 20.00
198 Bill Hall/100 4.00 10.00
199 Jose Guillen/100 6.00 15.00
200 Jeremy Bonderman/100 6.00 15.00
201 Roger Clemens Yanks/1
203 Greg Maddux Braves/1
205 Alfonso Soriano Yanks/25 15.00 40.00
206 Andy Pettitte Yanks/1
208 Gary Sheffield Braves/10
211 Mike Mussina O's/1
212 Mike Piazza Dodgers/5
215 Sammy Sosa Sox/5
220 Manny Ramirez Indians/1
221 Mike Piazza Marlins/5
222 Cal Ripken LGD/25 100.00 200.00
224 Duke Snider LGD/25 15.00 40.00
226 Ryne Sandberg LGD/5
227 Mark Grace LGD/5
228 Andre Dawson LGD/100 6.00 15.00
229 Bob Feller LGD/100 10.00 25.00
231 George Brett LGD/10
232 Bo Jackson LGD/5
234 Harmon Killebrew LGD/10
235 Gary Carter LGD/25 10.00 25.00
236 Don Mattingly LGD/5
237 Phil Rizzuto LGD/25 15.00 40.00
240 Reggie Jackson LGD/10
241 Rickey Henderson LGD/1
242 Mike Schmidt LGD/1
244 Tony Gwynn LGD/5
245 Will Clark LGD/25 12.50 30.00
246 Lou Brock LGD/10
247 Bob Gibson LGD/25 15.00 40.00
248 Stan Musial LGD/25 40.00 80.00
249 Nolan Ryan LGD/25 75.00 150.00
250 Dale Murphy LGD/50 12.50 30.00
251 Aarom Baldiris ROO/100 4.00 10.00
252 Akinori Otsuka ROO/25
253 Andres Blanco ROO/100 3.00 8.00
254 Angel Chavez ROO/100 3.00 8.00
255 Carlos Hines ROO/100 3.00 8.00
256 Carlos Vasquez ROO/100 5.00 12.00
258 Chris Oxspring ROO/100 3.00 8.00
259 Colby Miller ROO/100 3.00 8.00
260 Dave Crouthers ROO/50 4.00 10.00
261 Don Kelly ROO/100 3.00 8.00
262 Eddy Rodriguez ROO/100 5.00 12.00
263 Edwardo Sierra ROO/100 5.00 12.00
264 Edwin Moreno ROO/100 5.00 12.00
266 Freddy Guzman ROO/100 3.00 8.00
267 Greg Dobbs ROO/100 3.00 8.00
268 Brad Halsey ROO/100 5.00 12.00
269 Hector Gimenez ROO/100 3.00 8.00
270 Ivan Ochoa ROO/100 3.00 8.00
271 Jake Woods ROO/100 3.00 8.00
272 Jamie Brown ROO/100 3.00 8.00
273 Jason Bartlett ROO/100 5.00 12.00
274 Jason Szuminski ROO/100 3.00 8.00
275 John Gall ROO/100 5.00 12.00
276 Jorge Vasquez ROO/100 3.00 8.00
277 Josh Labandeira ROO/100 3.00 8.00
280 Kevin Cave ROO/100 3.00 8.00
281 Lance Cormier ROO/100 3.00 8.00
283 Merkin Valdez ROO/100 5.00 12.00
284 Michael Wuertz ROO/100 5.00 12.00
285 Mike Johnston ROO/100 3.00 8.00
287 Onil Joseph ROO/100 3.00 8.00
288 Phil Stockman ROO/100 3.00 8.00
289 Roberto Novoa ROO/100 4.00 10.00
291 Ronny Cedeno ROO/100 8.00 20.00
292 Ryan Meaux ROO/100 3.00 8.00
293 Scott Proctor ROO/100 5.00 12.00
295 Shawn Camp ROO/100 3.00 8.00
297 Shingo Takatsu ROO/25
299 William Bergolla ROO/100 3.00 8.00
300 Yadier Molina ROO/100 12.50 30.00

2004 Leaf Certified Cuts Marble Signature Material Black Number

OVERALL AU ODDS THREE PER BOX
STATED PRINT RUN 1 SERIAL #'d SET
NO PRICING DUE TO SCARCITY

2004 Leaf Certified Cuts Marble Signature Material Black Position

OVERALL AU ODDS THREE PER BOX
STATED PRINT RUN 1 SERIAL #'d SET
NO PRICING DUE TO SCARCITY

2004 Leaf Certified Cuts Marble Signature Material Black Prime

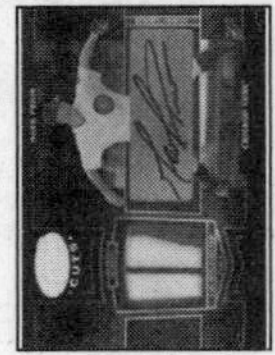

OVERALL AU ODDS THREE PER BOX
STATED PRINT RUN 1 SERIAL #'d SET
NO PRICING DUE TO SCARCITY

2004 Leaf Certified Cuts Marble Signature Material Emerald Prime

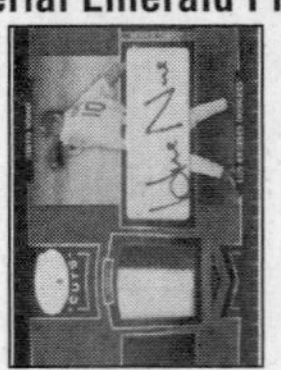

OVERALL AU ODDS THREE PER BOX
STATED PRINT RUN 5 SERIAL #'d SETS
CARD 233 PRINT RUN 2 #'d CARDS
NO PRICING DUE TO SCARCITY

2004 Leaf Certified Cuts Marble Signature Material Gold Number

*1-221 p/r 35-65: .6X TO 1.5X RED p/r 66-100
*1-221 p/r 35-65: .5X TO 1.2X RED p/r 36-65
*1-221 p/r 35-65: .4X TO 1X RED p/r 20-35
*1-221 p/r 20-35: .75X TO 2X RED p/r 66-100
*1-221 p/r 20-35: .6X TO 1.5X RED p/r 36-65
*1-221 p/r 20-35: .5X TO 1.2X RED p/r 20-35
*1-221 p/r 15-19: 1X TO 2.5X RED p/r 66-100
*1-221 p/r 15-19: .75X TO 2X RED p/r 36-65
*222-250 p/r 36-65: .4X TO 1X RED p/r 66-100
*222-250p/r20-35: .5X TO 1.2X REDp/r20-35
*222-250p/r15-19: 1X TO 2.5X REDp/r66-100
OVERALL AU ODDS THREE PER BOX
PRINT RUNS B/WN 1-57 COPIES PER
NO PRICING ON QTY OF 13 OR LESS
18 Andruw Jones Jsy/25 20.00 50.00
32 Manny Ramirez Jsy/24 40.00 80.00
41 Kerry Wood Pants/34 20.00 50.00
42 Sammy Sosa Jsy/21 50.00 100.00
44 Greg Maddux Jsy/31 60.00 120.00
51 Frank Thomas Jsy/35 30.00 60.00
52 Magglio Ordonez Jsy/30 12.50 30.00
71 Todd Helton Jsy/17 30.00 60.00
81 Dontrelle Willis Jsy/35 20.00 50.00
85 Andy Pettitte Jsy/21 30.00 60.00
88 Lance Berkman Jsy/17 30.00 60.00
101 Kazuhisa Ishii Jsy/17 15.00 40.00
102 Shawn Green Jsy/15 30.00 60.00
123 Mike Piazza Jsy/31 75.00 150.00
124 Jae Weong Seo Jsy/26 12.50 30.00
127 Jorge Posada Jsy/20 30.00 60.00
130 Mike Mussina Jsy/35 20.00 50.00
141 Tim Hudson Jsy/15 30.00 60.00
178 Jim Edmonds Jsy/15 30.00 60.00
195 Roy Halladay Jsy/32 12.50 30.00
227 Mark Grace LGD Jsy/17 30.00 60.00
232 Bo Jackson LGD Jsy/16 75.00 150.00
236 D.Mattingly LGD Jsy/23 50.00 100.00
240 R.Jackson LGD Jsy/44 30.00 60.00
241 R.Henderson LGD Jsy/35 40.00 80.00
242 M.Schmidt LGD Pants/20 50.00 100.00
244 Tony Gwynn LGD Jsy/19 50.00 100.00
246 Lou Brock LGD Jsy/20 20.00 50.00

2004 Leaf Certified Cuts Marble Signature Material Gold Position

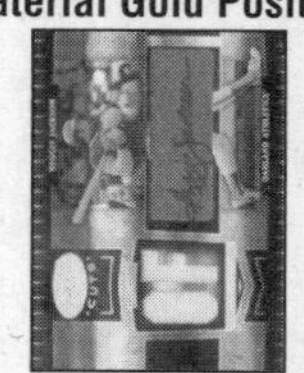

*1-221 p/r 50: .6X TO 1.5X RED p/r 66-100
*1-221 p/r 50: .5X TO 1.2X RED p/r 36-65
*1-221 p/r 50: .4X TO 1X RED p/r 20-35
*1-221 p/r 25: .6X TO 1.5X RED p/r 36-65
*1-221 p/r 25: .5X TO 1.2X RED p/r 20-35
*222-250 p/r 50: .6X TO 1.5X RED p/r 66-100
*222-250 p/r 25: .6X TO 1.5X RED p/r 36-65
OVERALL AU ODDS THREE PER BOX
PRINT RUNS B/WN 1-50 COPIES PER
NO PRICING ON QTY OF 10 OR LESS
234 H.Killebrew LGD Jsy/25 40.00 80.00

2004 Leaf Certified Cuts Check Signature Blue

OVERALL AU ODDS THREE PER BOX
PRINT RUNS B/WN 2-60 COPIES PER
NO PRICING ON QTY OF 10 OR LESS
ALL CARDS FEATURE BLUE CHECKS
1 Al Kaline/22 40.00 80.00
2 Andre Dawson/22 12.50 30.00
4 Bob Gibson/10
5 Bobby Doerr/10
6 Brooks Robinson/10
7 Cal Ripken/5
8 Cal Ripken/5
9 Cal Ripken/5
10 Cal Ripken/5
11 Carl Yastrzemski/3
12 Carl Yastrzemski/3
13 Carlton Fisk W.Sox/10
14 Carlton Fisk R.Sox/10
16 Dale Murphy/10
17 Dale Murphy/10
18 Don Mattingly/5
19 Don Mattingly/5
20 Don Mattingly/5
21 Don Mattingly/5
22 Duke Snider/20 20.00 50.00
23 Ozzie Smith Padres/4
24 Ozzie Smith Cards/4
25 Ozzie Smith Cards/4
26 Frank Robinson/10
27 George Brett/10
28 George Brett/10
29 George Brett/10
31 George Kell/60 10.00 25.00
33 Harmon Killebrew/10
34 Harmon Killebrew/10
35 Honus Wagner/2
38 Kirby Puckett/5
39 Kirby Puckett/5
41 Lou Brock/10
43 Luis Aparicio/10
44 Mark Grace/10
46 Mike Schmidt/5
47 Mike Schmidt/5
48 Mike Schmidt/5
49 Mike Schmidt/5
50 Nolan Ryan Astros/10
51 Nolan Ryan Rgr/10
52 Nolan Ryan Angels/10
53 Paul Molitor/10
57 Red Schoendienst/10
63 Ron Santo/5
65 Ryne Sandberg/10
67 Stan Musial/8
68 Stan Musial/8
69 Stan Musial/8
70 Steve Carlton Phils/5
71 Steve Carlton W.Sox/5
73 Tony Gwynn/10
74 Tony Gwynn/10
77 Whitey Ford/16 30.00 60.00
78 Will Clark/10
79 Will Clark/10

2004 Leaf Certified Cuts Check Signature Green

*GREEN p/r 15-18: .6X TO 1.5X BLUE p/r 60
*GREEN p/r 15-18: .4X TO 1X BLUE p/r 16
OVERALL AU ODDS THREE PER BOX
PRINT RUNS B/WN 1-18 COPIES PER
NO PRICING ON QTY OF 5 OR LESS
ALL BUT RYAN FEATURE GREEN CHECKS
RYAN IS BLUE CHECK W/GREEN HOF LOGO

2004 Leaf Certified Cuts Check Signature Red

*RED p/r 36: .4X TO 1X BLUE p/r 60
*RED p/r 16-17: .5X TO 1.2X BLUE p/r 20
*RED p/r 16-17: .4X TO 1X BLUE p/r 16
OVERALL AU ODDS THREE PER BOX
PRINT RUNS B/WN 3-36 COPIES PER
NO PRICING ON QTY OF 11 OR LESS
ALL BUT RYAN FEATURE RED CHECKS
RYAN IS BLUE CHECK W/RED 34 LOGO

2004 Leaf Certified Cuts Check Signature Material Blue

OVERALL AU ODDS THREE PER BOX
PRINT RUNS B/WN 1-100 COPIES PER
NO PRICING ON QTY OF 6 OR LESS
1 Al Kaline Bat/50 30.00 60.00
2 Andre Dawson Jsy/50 10.00 25.00
3 Babe Ruth Jsy/2
4 Bob Gibson Hat/50 15.00 40.00
5 Bobby Doerr Jsy/50 10.00 25.00
6 Brooks Robinson Bat/50 15.00 40.00
7 Cal Ripken White Jsy/25 125.00 250.00
8 Cal Ripken Orange Jsy/25 125.00 250.00
9 Cal Ripken Bat/25 125.00 250.00
10 Cal Ripken Jkt/25 125.00 250.00
11 Carl Yastrzemski Jsy/6
12 Carl Yastrzemski Bat/6
13 Carlton Fisk Jkt/35 20.00 50.00
14 Carlton Fisk Jsy/35 20.00 50.00
15 Catfish Hunter Jsy/2
16 Dale Murphy White Jsy/50 15.00 40.00
17 Dale Murphy Gray Jsy/50 15.00 40.00
18 Don Mattingly White Jsy/25 50.00 100.00
19 Don Mattingly Gray Jsy/25 50.00 100.00
20 Don Mattingly Bat/25 50.00 100.00
21 Don Mattingly Jkt/25 50.00 100.00
22 Duke Snider Pants/100 15.00 40.00
23 Ozzie Smith Padres Jsy/40 40.00 80.00
24 Ozzie Smith Cards Jsy/40 40.00 80.00
25 Ozzie Smith Bat/40 40.00 80.00
26 Frank Robinson Bat/50 15.00 40.00
27 George Brett White Jsy/30 50.00 100.00
28 George Brett Blue Jsy/30 50.00 100.00
29 George Brett Bat/30 50.00 100.00
30 Hack Wilson Bat/2
32 Hal Newhouser Jsy/15 20.00 50.00
33 Harmon Killebrew Shoe/35 40.00 80.00
34 Harmon Killebrew Bat/35 40.00 80.00
36 Jackie Robinson Jkt/1
37 Jimmie Foxx Bat/3
38 Kirby Puckett Fld Glv/25 50.00 100.00
39 Kirby Puckett Bat/25 50.00 100.00
40 Lou Boudreau Jsy/15 60.00 120.00
41 Lou Brock Jsy/50 15.00 40.00
42 Lou Gehrig Pants/2
43 Luis Aparicio Pants/50 10.00 25.00
44 Mark Grace Fld Glv/50 15.00 40.00
45 Mel Ott Bat/1
46 Mike Schmidt Fld Glv/25 50.00 100.00
47 Mike Schmidt Jsy/25 50.00 100.00
48 Mike Schmidt Jkt/25 50.00 100.00
49 Mike Schmidt Bat/25 50.00 100.00
50 Nolan Ryan Astros Jkt/30 75.00 150.00
51 Nolan Ryan Rgr Pants/30 75.00 150.00
52 Nolan Ryan Angels Jkt/30 75.00 150.00
53 Paul Molitor Bat/50 10.00 25.00
54 Pee Wee Reese Bat/5
57 Red Schoendienst Bat/50 10.00 25.00
58 Roberto Clemente Bat/2
61 Roger Maris Pants/1
62 Rogers Hornsby Bat/2
63 Ron Santo Bat/25 20.00 50.00
64 Roy Campanella Pants/1
65 Ryne Sandberg Jsy/50 40.00 80.00
66 Satchel Paige CO Jsy/1
67 Stan Musial White Jsy/30 50.00 100.00
68 Stan Musial Gray Jsy/30 50.00 100.00
69 Stan Musial Bat/30 50.00 100.00
70 Steve Carlton Pants/25 12.50 30.00
71 Steve Carlton Jsy/25 12.50 30.00
72 Ted Williams Jsy/2
73 Tony Gwynn White Jsy/50 30.00 60.00
74 Tony Gwynn Navy Jsy/50 30.00 60.00
75 Ty Cobb Pants/2
77 Whitey Ford Pants/50 15.00 40.00
78 Will Clark Jsy/50 15.00 40.00
79 Will Clark Bat/50 15.00 40.00
80 Willie Stargell Jsy/2

2004 Leaf Certified Cuts Check Signature Material Green

*GREEN p/r 25-33: .6X TO 1.5X BLUE p/r 100
*GREEN p/r 25-33: .5X TO 1.2X BLUE p/r 50
*GREEN p/r 15: .6X TO 1.5X BLUE p/r 50
OVERALL AU ODDS THREE PER BOX
PRINT RUNS B/WN 5-33 COPIES PER
NO PRICING ON QTY OF 10 OR LESS

2004 Leaf Certified Cuts Check Signature Material Red

*RED p/r 50: .5X TO 1.2X BLUE p/r 100
*RED p/r 25: .5X TO 1.2X BLUE p/r 36-65
*RED p/r 25: .4X TO 1X BLUE p/r 20-35
*RED p/r 15: .5X TO 1.2X BLUE p/r 20-35
OVERALL AU ODDS THREE PER BOX
PRINT RUNS B/WN 6-50 COPIES PER
NO PRICING ON QTY OF 14 OR LESS

2004 Leaf Certified Cuts Hall of Fame Souvenirs

RANDOM INSERTS IN PACKS
PRINT RUNS B/WN 75-100 COPIES PER
1 Ernie Banks/84 4.00 10.00
2 Stan Musial/93 6.00 15.00
3 Nolan Ryan/99 10.00 25.00
4 Duke Snider/87 3.00 8.00
5 Bob Feller/94 3.00 8.00
6 George Brett/98 8.00 20.00
7 Robin Yount/78 4.00 10.00
8 Harmon Killebrew/83 4.00 10.00
9 Gary Carter/78 2.00 5.00
10 Phil Rizzuto/75 3.00 8.00
11 Reggie Jackson/94 3.00 8.00
12 Mike Schmidt/97 8.00 20.00
13 Lou Brock/80 3.00 8.00
14 Bob Gibson/84 3.00 8.00
15 Bobby Doerr/75 2.00 5.00
16 Tony Perez/77 2.00 5.00
17 Whitey Ford/78 3.00 8.00
18 Juan Marichal/84 2.00 5.00
19 Monte Irvin/75 2.00 5.00
20 Fergie Jenkins/75 2.00 5.00
21 Ralph Kiner/75 3.00 8.00
22 Eddie Murray/85 4.00 10.00
23 George Kell/75 2.00 5.00
24 Hoyt Wilhelm/84 2.00 5.00
25 Carlton Fisk/80 3.00 8.00
26 Rod Carew/91 3.00 8.00
27 Frank Robinson/89 2.00 5.00
28 Gaylord Perry/77 2.00 5.00
29 Red Schoendienst/75 2.00 5.00
30 Brooks Robinson/92 3.00 8.00
31 Al Kaline/88 4.00 10.00
32 Orlando Cepeda/75 2.00 5.00
33 Steve Carlton/96 2.00 5.00
34 Luis Aparicio/85 2.00 5.00
35 Warren Spahn/83 3.00 8.00
36 Kirby Puckett/82 4.00 10.00
37 Phil Niekro/80 2.00 5.00
38 Jim Bunning/75 2.00 5.00
39 Tom Seaver/99 3.00 8.00
40 Paul Molitor/85 2.00 5.00
41 Johnny Bench/96 4.00 10.00
42 Don Sutton/82 2.00 5.00
43 Robin Roberts/87 2.00 5.00
44 Jim Palmer/93 2.00 5.00
45 Joe Morgan/82 2.00 5.00
46 Roberto Clemente/93 10.00 25.00
47 Lou Gehrig/100 5.00 12.00
48 Babe Ruth/95 8.00 20.00
49 Ty Cobb/98 4.00 10.00
50 Ted Williams/94 10.00 25.00

2004 Leaf Certified Cuts Hall of Fame Souvenirs Material

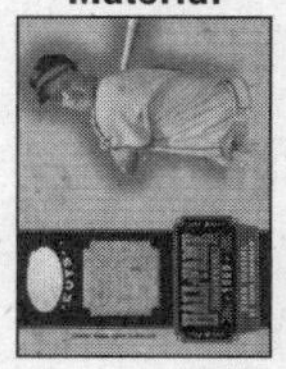

OVERALL GU ODDS ONE PER BOX
STATED PRINT RUN 25 SERIAL #'d SETS
1 Ernie Banks Jsy 12.50 30.00
2 Stan Musial Jsy 20.00 50.00
3 Nolan Ryan Jsy 30.00 60.00
4 Duke Snider Pants 10.00 25.00
5 Bob Feller Jsy 10.00 25.00
6 George Brett Jsy 20.00 50.00
7 Robin Yount Jsy 12.50 30.00
8 Harmon Killebrew Jsy 12.50 30.00
9 Gary Carter Jkt 6.00 15.00
10 Phil Rizzuto Pants 10.00 25.00
11 Reggie Jackson Jsy 10.00 25.00
12 Mike Schmidt Jsy 20.00 50.00
13 Lou Brock Jsy 10.00 25.00
14 Bob Gibson Jsy 10.00 25.00
15 Bobby Doerr Jsy 6.00 15.00
16 Tony Perez Bat 6.00 15.00
17 Whitey Ford Pants 10.00 25.00
18 Juan Marichal Jsy 6.00 15.00
20 Fergie Jenkins Pants 6.00 15.00
21 Ralph Kiner Bat 10.00 25.00
22 Eddie Murray Jsy 12.50 30.00
24 Hoyt Wilhelm Jsy 6.00 15.00
25 Carlton Fisk Jsy 10.00 25.00
26 Rod Carew Jsy 10.00 25.00
27 Frank Robinson Jsy 6.00 15.00
29 Red Schoendienst Jsy 6.00 15.00
30 Brooks Robinson Bat 10.00 25.00
31 Al Kaline Pants 12.50 30.00
32 Orlando Cepeda Bat 6.00 15.00
33 Steve Carlton Pants 6.00 15.00
34 Luis Aparicio Pants 6.00 15.00
35 Warren Spahn Pants 12.50 30.00
36 Kirby Puckett Jsy 12.50 30.00
37 Phil Niekro Jsy 6.00 15.00
39 Tom Seaver Jsy 10.00 25.00
40 Paul Molitor Bat 6.00 15.00
41 Johnny Bench Jsy 12.50 30.00
42 Don Sutton Jsy 6.00 15.00
43 Robin Roberts Hat 6.00 15.00
44 Jim Palmer Jsy 6.00 15.00
45 Joe Morgan Jsy 6.00 15.00
46 Roberto Clemente Jsy 50.00 100.00
47 Lou Gehrig Pants 75.00 150.00
48 Babe Ruth Pants 150.00 250.00
49 Ty Cobb Pants 60.00 120.00
50 Ted Williams Jsy 60.00 120.00

2004 Leaf Certified Cuts Hall of Fame Souvenirs Signature

OVERALL AU ODDS THREE PER BOX
PRINT RUNS B/WN 5-50 COPIES PER
NO PRICING ON QTY OF 10 OR LESS
2 Stan Musial/10
3 Nolan Ryan/34 75.00 150.00
4 Duke Snider/50 12.50 30.00
5 Bob Feller/50 12.50 30.00
6 George Brett/5
8 Harmon Killebrew/25 30.00 60.00
9 Gary Carter/50 8.00 20.00
10 Phil Rizzuto/50 12.50 30.00
11 Reggie Jackson/9
12 Mike Schmidt/20 40.00 80.00
13 Lou Brock/50 12.50 30.00
14 Bob Gibson/45 12.50 30.00
15 Bobby Doerr/50 8.00 20.00
16 Tony Perez/50 8.00 20.00
17 Whitey Ford/16 20.00 50.00
18 Juan Marichal/50 8.00 20.00
19 Monte Irvin/50 12.50 30.00
20 Fergie Jenkins/50 8.00 20.00
21 Ralph Kiner/50 12.50 30.00
22 Eddie Murray/33 40.00 80.00
23 George Kell/50 8.00 20.00
24 Hoyt Wilhelm/49 12.50 30.00
25 Carlton Fisk/27 15.00 40.00
26 Rod Carew/29 15.00 40.00
28 Gaylord Perry/50 8.00 20.00
29 Red Schoendienst/50 8.00 20.00
30 Brooks Robinson/50 12.50 30.00
31 Al Kaline/50 20.00 50.00
32 Orlando Cepeda/50 8.00 20.00
33 Steve Carlton/50 8.00 20.00
34 Luis Aparicio/50 8.00 20.00
35 Warren Spahn/21 30.00 60.00
36 Kirby Puckett/34 50.00 100.00
37 Phil Niekro/50 8.00 20.00
38 Jim Bunning/50 8.00 20.00
40 Paul Molitor/25 10.00 25.00
41 Johnny Bench/5
42 Don Sutton/50 8.00 20.00
43 Robin Roberts/50 8.00 20.00
44 Jim Palmer/22 10.00 25.00
45 Joe Morgan/25 10.00 25.00

2004 Leaf Certified Cuts Hall of Fame Souvenirs Signature Material

*MTL AU p/r 36-45: .5X TO 1.2X AU p/r 36-50
*MTL AU p/r 20-35: .6X TO 1.5X AU p/r 36-50
*MTL AU p/r 20-35: .5X TO 1.2X AU p/r 20-35
*MTL AU p/r 16-19: .75X TO 2X AU p/r 36-50
*MTL AU p/r 16-19: .6X TO 1.5X AU p/r 20-35
*MTL AU p/r 16-19: .5X TO 1.2X AU p/r 15-19
OVERALL AU ODDS THREE PER BOX
PRINT RUNS B/WN 1-45 COPIES PER
NO PRICING ON QTY OF 11 OR LESS

2004 Leaf Certified Cuts K-Force

1-44 PRINT RUNS B/WN 17-500 #'d PER
45-50 PRINT RUNS B/WN 20-500 #'d PER
RANDOM INSERTS IN PACKS
1 Nolan Ryan Rgr/500 4.00 10.00
2 Steve Carlton/500 1.25 3.00
3 Roger Clemens Astros/500 3.00 8.00
4 Randy Johnson D'backs/500 1.25 3.00
5 Bert Blyleven/500 1.25 3.00
6 Tom Seaver Reds/500 1.50 4.00
7 Don Sutton/500 1.25 3.00
8 Gaylord Perry/500 1.25 3.00
9 Phil Niekro/500 1.25 3.00
10 Fergie Jenkins/500 1.25 3.00
11 Bob Gibson/500 1.50 4.00
12 Nolan Ryan Angels/383 4.00 10.00
13 Randy Johnson M's/308 1.25 3.00
14 Bob Feller/348 1.50 4.00
15 Curt Schilling Phils/319 1.25 3.00
16 Pedro Martinez Sox/313 1.25 3.00
17 Dwight Gooden/276 1.25 3.00
18 John Smoltz/276 1.25 3.00
19 Curt Schilling D'backs/316 1.25 3.00
20 Randy Johnson Astros/329 1.25 3.00
21 Pedro Martinez Expos/305 1.25 3.00
22 Roger Clemens Sox/291 3.00 8.00
23 Roger Clemens Jays/292 3.00 8.00
24 Tom Seaver Mets/289 1.50 4.00
25 Hal Newhouser/275 1.25 3.00
26 Jim Bunning/201 1.50 4.00
27 Robin Roberts/198 1.50 4.00
28 Warren Spahn/191 2.00 5.00
29 Jack Morris/232 1.50 4.00
30 Nolan Ryan Astros/270 4.00 10.00
31 Hideo Nomo/236 1.50 4.00
32 Barry Zito/205 1.50 4.00
33 Mike Mussina/214 1.50 4.00
34 Roy Oswalt/208 1.50 4.00
35 Mark Prior/245 1.50 4.00
36 Kerry Wood/266 1.25 3.00
37 Roy Halladay/204 1.50 4.00
38 Esteban Loaiza/207 1.50 4.00
39 Whitey Ford/94 3.00 8.00
40 Bob Gibson/17 6.00 15.00
41 Ben Sheets/18 4.00 10.00
42 Hoyt Wilhelm/139 1.50 4.00
43 Satchel Paige/91 4.00 10.00
44 Burleigh Grimes/136 1.50 4.00
45 Mark Prior
Kerry Wood/500 1.50 4.00
46 Nolan Ryan
Roger Clemens/500 4.00 10.00
47 Steve Carlton
Randy Johnson/500 1.50 4.00
48 Nolan Ryan
Roger Clemens/500 4.00 10.00
49 Nolan Ryan
Steve Carlton/500 4.00 10.00
50 Kerry Wood
Roger Clemens/20 15.00 40.00

2004 Leaf Certified Cuts K-Force Material

1-44 PRINT RUNS B/WN 2-100 #'d PER
1-44 NO PRICING ON QTY OF 5 OR LESS
45-50 PRINT RUN 50 SERIAL #'d SETS
OVERALL GU ODDS ONE PER BOX
1 Nolan Ryan Rgr Jsy/100 10.00 25.00
2 Steve Carlton Jsy/32 6.00 15.00
3 R.Clemens Astros Jsy/25 12.50 30.00
4 R.Johnson D'backs Jsy/51 6.00 15.00
5 Bert Blyleven Jsy/28 6.00 15.00
6 Tom Seaver Reds Jsy/25 10.00 25.00
7 Don Sutton Jsy/2
8 Gaylord Perry Jsy/36 4.00 10.00
9 Phil Niekro Jsy/35 6.00 15.00
10 Fergie Jenkins Pants/31 6.00 15.00
11 Bob Gibson Jsy/45 6.00 15.00
12 Nolan Ryan Angels Jkt/100 10.00 25.00
13 Randy Johnson M's Jsy/51 6.00 15.00
14 Bob Feller Jsy/25 10.00 25.00
15 Curt Schilling Phils Jsy/25 5.00 12.00
16 Pedro Martinez Sox Jsy/45 5.00 12.00
17 Dwight Gooden Jsy/25 6.00 15.00
18 John Smoltz Jsy/25 8.00 20.00
19 C.Schilling D'backs Jsy/25 5.00 12.00
20 R.Johnson Astros Jsy/51 6.00 15.00
21 P.Martinez Expos Jsy/45 5.00 12.00
22 R.Clemens Sox Jsy/100 5.00 12.00
25 Hal Newhouser Jsy/25 10.00 25.00
28 Warren Spahn Jsy/50 8.00 20.00
29 Jack Morris Jsy/47 4.00 10.00
30 N.Ryan Astros Jkt/100 10.00 25.00
31 Hideo Nomo Jsy/25 10.00 25.00
32 Barry Zito Jsy/25 5.00 12.00
33 Mike Mussina Jsy/25 8.00 20.00
34 Roy Oswalt Jsy/44 3.00 8.00
35 Mark Prior Jsy/50 5.00 12.00
36 Kerry Wood Jsy/34 5.00 12.00
37 Roy Halladay Jsy/5
39 Whitey Ford Jsy/50 6.00 15.00
40 Bob Gibson Jsy/50 6.00 15.00
41 Ben Sheets Jsy/25 5.00 12.00
43 Satchel Paige CO Jsy/100 30.00 60.00
44 Burleigh Grimes Pants/100 20.00 50.00
45 Mark Prior Jsy 10.00 25.00
Kerry Wood Pants/50
46 Nolan Ryan Jsy 20.00 50.00
Roger Clemens Astros Jsy/50
47 Steve Carlton Jsy 10.00 25.00
Randy Johnson Jsy/50
48 Nolan Ryan Pants 20.00 50.00
Roger Clemens Yanks Jsy/50
49 Nolan Ryan Jsy 15.00 40.00
Steve Carlton Pants/50
50 Kerry Wood Jsy 10.00 25.00
Roger Clemens Jsy/50

2004 Leaf Certified Cuts K-Force Signature

OVERALL AU ODDS THREE PER BOX
PRINT RUNS B/WN 1-50 COPIES PER
NO PRICING ON QTY OF 10 OR LESS
1 Nolan Ryan Rgr/10
2 Steve Carlton/50 8.00 20.00
3 Roger Clemens Astros/1
5 Bert Blyleven/50 8.00 20.00
6 Tom Seaver Reds/5
7 Don Sutton/50 8.00 20.00
8 Gaylord Perry/50 8.00 20.00
9 Phil Niekro/50 12.50 30.00
10 Fergie Jenkins/50 8.00 20.00
11 Bob Gibson/10
12 Nolan Ryan Angels/10
14 Bob Feller/50 12.50 30.00
15 Curt Schilling Phils/1
16 Pedro Martinez Sox/1
17 Dwight Gooden/50 8.00 20.00
19 Curt Schilling D'backs/1
21 Pedro Martinez Expos/1
22 Roger Clemens Sox/1
23 Roger Clemens Jays/1
24 Tom Seaver Mets/5
26 Jim Bunning/50 12.50 30.00
27 Robin Roberts/50 8.00 20.00
28 Warren Spahn/10
29 Jack Morris/50 8.00 20.00
30 Nolan Ryan Astros/10
31 Hideo Nomo/1
32 Barry Zito/1
33 Mike Mussina/1
34 Roy Oswalt/50 8.00 20.00
35 Mark Prior/10
36 Kerry Wood/5
37 Roy Halladay/10
38 Esteban Loaiza/50 5.00 12.00
39 Whitey Ford/5
40 Bob Gibson/10
45 Mark Prior
Kerry Wood/10
46 Nolan Ryan
Roger Clemens Astros/1
48 Nolan Ryan
Roger Clemens Yanks/1
49 Nolan Ryan
Steve Carlton/5
50 Kerry Wood
Roger Clemens/1

2004 Leaf Certified Cuts K-Force Signature Material

*A.MTL AU p/r 36-50: .5X TO 1.2X AU p/r 50
*R.MTL AU p/r 36-50: .5X TO 1.2X AU p/r 50
*R.MTL AU p/r 20-35: .6X TO 1.5X AU p/r 50
*R.MTL AU p/r 15-19: .75X TO 2X AU p/r 50
PRINT RUNS B/WN 1-47 COPIES PER
NO PRICING ON QTY OF 5 OR LESS
PRIME PRINT RUN 1 SERIAL #'d SET
NO PRIME PRICING DUE TO SCARCITY
OVERALL AU ODDS THREE PER BOX
1 Nolan Ryan Rgr Jsy/34 75.00 150.00
11 Bob Gibson Jsy/45 15.00 40.00
12 Nolan Ryan Angels Jkt/34 75.00 150.00
28 Warren Spahn Jsy/21 40.00 80.00
30 Nolan Ryan Astros Jkt/34 75.00 150.00
36 Kerry Wood Jsy/45 20.00 50.00
37 Roy Halladay Jsy/32 12.50 30.00
39 Whitey Ford Jsy/16 30.00 60.00
40 Bob Gibson Jsy/45 15.00 40.00

2004 Leaf Certified Cuts Stars

RANDOM INSERTS IN PACKS
STATED PRINT RUN 599 SERIAL #'d SETS
1 Ryne Sandberg 3.00 8.00
2 Mark Prior 1.25 3.00
3 Andre Dawson 1.25 3.00
4 Don Mattingly 3.00 8.00
5 Vladimir Guerrero 1.25 3.00

6 Garret Anderson 1.25 3.00
7 Dale Murphy 1.50 4.00
8 Cal Ripken 6.00 15.00
9 Mark Grace 1.50 4.00
10 Kerry Wood 1.25 3.00
11 Frank Thomas 1.25 3.00
12 Magglio Ordonez 1.25 3.00
13 Adam Dunn 1.25 3.00
14 Preston Wilson 1.25 3.00
15 Bo Jackson 1.50 4.00
16 Carlos Beltran 1.25 3.00
17 Tony Gwynn 2.50 6.00
18 Will Clark 1.50 4.00
19 Edgar Martinez 1.25 3.00
20 Scott Rolen 1.25 3.00
21 Alfonso Soriano 1.25 3.00
22 Randy Johnson 1.25 3.00
23 Chipper Jones 1.25 3.00
24 Andruw Jones 1.25 3.00
25 Javy Lopez 1.25 3.00
26 Curt Schilling 1.25 3.00
27 Manny Ramirez 1.25 3.00
28 Sammy Sosa 1.25 3.00
29 Greg Maddux 2.00 5.00
30 Todd Helton 1.25 3.00
31 Jeff Bagwell 1.25 3.00
32 Shawn Green 1.25 3.00
33 Mike Piazza 2.00 5.00
34 Jorge Posada 1.25 3.00
35 Gary Sheffield 1.25 3.00
36 Mike Mussina 1.25 3.00
37 Miguel Cabrera 1.25 3.00
38 Rickey Henderson 1.50 4.00
39 Albert Pujols 2.50 6.00
40 Vernon Wells 1.25 3.00
41 Fred Lynn 1.25 3.00
42 Alan Trammell 1.25 3.00
43 Lenny Dykstra 1.25 3.00
44 Dwight Gooden 1.25 3.00
45 Keith Hernandez 1.25 3.00
46 Luis Tiant 1.25 3.00
47 Orel Hershiser 1.25 3.00
48 George Foster 1.25 3.00
49 Darryl Strawberry 1.25 3.00
50 Marty Marion 1.25 3.00

2004 Leaf Certified Cuts Stars Signature

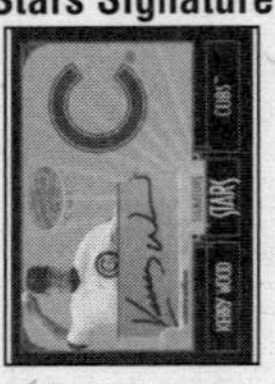

OVERALL AU ODDS THREE PER BOX
PRINT RUNS B/WN 1-50 COPIES PER
NO PRICING ON QTY OF 10 OR LESS
1 Ryne Sandberg/5
2 Mark Prior/5
3 Andre Dawson/50 8.00 20.00
4 Don Mattingly/25 40.00 80.00
5 Vladimir Guerrero/5
6 Garret Anderson/50 8.00 20.00
7 Dale Murphy/50 12.50 30.00
8 Cal Ripken/5
9 Mark Grace/5
10 Kerry Wood/5
11 Frank Thomas/10
12 Magglio Ordonez/25 10.00 25.00
13 Adam Dunn/25 15.00 40.00
14 Preston Wilson/50 8.00 20.00
15 Bo Jackson/5
16 Carlos Beltran/50 8.00 20.00
17 Tony Gwynn/5
18 Will Clark/25 15.00 40.00
19 Edgar Martinez/25 20.00 50.00
20 Scott Rolen/25 15.00 40.00
21 Alfonso Soriano/5
23 Chipper Jones/5
24 Andruw Jones/5
26 Curt Schilling/5
27 Manny Ramirez/5
28 Sammy Sosa/5
29 Greg Maddux/5
30 Todd Helton/5
31 Jeff Bagwell/5
32 Shawn Green/5
33 Mike Piazza/5
34 Jorge Posada/10
35 Gary Sheffield/10
36 Mike Mussina/5
37 Miguel Cabrera/50 12.50 30.00
38 Rickey Henderson/5
39 Albert Pujols/5
40 Vernon Wells/25 10.00 25.00
41 Fred Lynn/50 5.00 12.00
42 Alan Trammell/50 8.00 20.00
43 Lenny Dykstra/50 8.00 20.00
44 Dwight Gooden/50 8.00 20.00
45 Keith Hernandez/50 8.00 20.00
46 Luis Tiant/50 8.00 20.00
47 Orel Hershiser/50 12.50 30.00
48 George Foster/50 5.00 12.00
49 Darryl Strawberry/50 8.00 20.00

2004 Leaf Certified Cuts Stars Signature Jersey

*JSY AU p/r 36-50: .5X TO 1.2X AU p/r 36-50
*JSY AU p/r 36-50: .6X TO 1.5X AU p/r 36-50

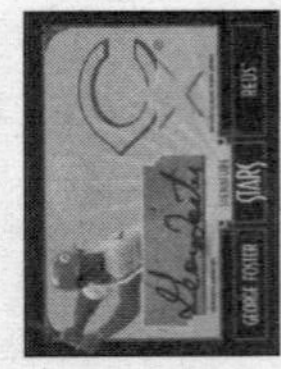

*JSY AU p/r 20-35: .6X TO 1.5X AU p/r 36-50
*JSY AU p/r 20-35: .5X TO 1.2X AU p/r 20-35
*JSY AU p/r 15-19: .75X TO 2X AU p/r 36-50
PRINT RUNS B/WN 1-44 COPIES PER
NO PRICING ON QTY OF 12 OR LESS
PRIME PRINT RUN 1 SERIAL #'d SET
NO PRIME PRICING DUE TO SCARCITY
OVERALL AU ODDS THREE PER BOX
1 Ryne Sandberg/23 50.00 100.00
2 Mark Prior/22 15.00 40.00
5 Vladimir Guerrero/27 30.00 60.00
9 Mark Grace/17 30.00 60.00
10 Kerry Wood/34 20.00 50.00
11 Frank Thomas/35 30.00 60.00
15 Bo Jackson/16 75.00 150.00
17 Tony Gwynn/19 50.00 100.00
24 Andruw Jones/25 20.00 50.00
28 Sammy Sosa/21 50.00 100.00
29 Greg Maddux/31 60.00 120.00
30 Todd Helton/17 30.00 60.00
32 Shawn Green/15 30.00 60.00
34 Jorge Posada/20 30.00 60.00
50 Marty Marion/25 12.50 30.00

2001 Leaf Certified Materials

This 160 card set was issued in five card packs. Cards numbered 111-160 feature young players along with a piece of game-used memorabilia. These cards are serial numbered to 200.

COMP.SET w/o SP's (110) 15.00 40.00
COMMON CARD (1-110) .40 1.00
COMMON (111-160) 4.00 10.00
1 Alex Rodriguez 1.50 4.00
2 Barry Bonds 2.50 6.00
3 Cal Ripken 3.00 8.00
4 Chipper Jones 1.00 2.50
5 Derek Jeter 2.50 6.00
6 Troy Glaus .40 1.00
7 Frank Thomas 1.00 2.50
8 Greg Maddux 1.50 4.00
9 Ivan Rodriguez .60 1.50
10 Jeff Bagwell .60 1.50
11 Eric Karros .40 1.00
12 Todd Helton .60 1.50
13 Ken Griffey Jr. 1.50 4.00
14 Manny Ramirez Sox .60 1.50
15 Mark McGwire 2.50 6.00
16 Mike Piazza 1.50 4.00
17 Nomar Garciaparra 1.50 4.00
18 Pedro Martinez .60 1.50
19 Randy Johnson 1.00 2.50
20 Rick Ankiel .40 1.00
21 Rickey Henderson 1.00 2.50
22 Roger Clemens 2.00 5.00
23 Sammy Sosa 1.00 2.50
24 Tony Gwynn 1.25 3.00
25 Vladimir Guerrero 1.00 2.50
26 Kazuhiro Sasaki .40 1.00
27 Roberto Alomar .60 1.50
28 Barry Zito .60 1.50
29 Pat Burrell .40 1.00
30 Harold Baines .40 1.00
31 Carlos Delgado .40 1.00
32 J.D. Drew .40 1.00
33 Jim Edmonds .40 1.00
34 Darin Erstad .40 1.00
35 Jason Giambi .40 1.00
36 Tom Glavine .60 1.50
37 Juan Gonzalez .40 1.00
38 Mark Grace .60 1.50
39 Shawn Green .40 1.00
40 Tim Hudson .40 1.00
41 Andruw Jones .60 1.50
42 Jeff Kent .40 1.00
43 Barry Larkin .60 1.50
44 Rafael Furcal .40 1.00
45 Mike Mussina .60 1.50
46 Hideo Nomo 1.00 2.50
47 Rafael Palmeiro .60 1.50
48 Scott Rolen .60 1.50
49 Gary Sheffield .40 1.00
50 Bernie Williams .60 1.50
51 Bob Abreu .40 1.00
52 Edgardo Alfonzo .40 1.00
53 Edgar Martinez .60 1.50
54 Magglio Ordonez .40 1.00
55 Kerry Wood .40 1.00
56 Adrian Beltre .40 1.00
57 Lance Berkman .40 1.00
58 Kevin Brown .40 1.00
59 Sean Casey .40 1.00
60 Eric Chavez .40 1.00
61 Bartolo Colon .40 1.00
62 Johnny Damon .60 1.50
63 Jermaine Dye .40 1.00
64 Juan Encarnacion UER .40 1.00
Card has him playing for Detroit Lions
65 Carl Everett .40 1.00
66 Brian Giles .40 1.00
67 Mike Hampton .40 1.00
68 Richard Hidalgo .40 1.00
69 Geoff Jenkins .40 1.00
70 Jacque Jones .40 1.00
71 Jason Kendall .40 1.00
72 Ryan Klesko .40 1.00
73 Chan Ho Park .40 1.00
74 Richie Sexson .40 1.00
75 Mike Sweeney .40 1.00
76 Fernando Tatis .40 1.00
77 Miguel Tejada .40 1.00
78 Jose Vidro .40 1.00
79 Larry Walker .40 1.00
80 Preston Wilson .40 1.00
81 Craig Biggio .60 1.50
82 Fred McGriff .60 1.50
83 Jim Thome .60 1.50
84 Garret Anderson .40 1.00
85 Russell Branyan .40 1.00
86 Tony Batista .40 1.00
87 Terrence Long .40 1.00
88 Deion Sanders .60 1.50
89 Rusty Greer .40 1.00
90 Orlando Hernandez .40 1.00
91 Gabe Kapler .40 1.00
92 Paul Konerko .40 1.00
93 Carlos Lee .40 1.00
94 Kenny Lofton .40 1.00
95 Raul Mondesi .40 1.00
96 Jorge Posada .60 1.50
97 Tim Salmon .60 1.50
98 Greg Vaughn .40 1.00
99 Mo Vaughn .40 1.00
100 Omar Vizquel .60 1.50
101 Ray Durham .40 1.00
102 Jeff Cirillo .40 1.00
103 Dean Palmer .40 1.00
104 Ryan Dempster .40 1.00
105 Carlos Beltran .40 1.00
106 Timo Perez .40 1.00
107 Robin Ventura .40 1.00
108 Andy Pettitte .60 1.50
109 Aramis Ramirez .40 1.00
110 Phil Nevin .40 1.00
111 Alex Escobar FF Fld Glv 4.00 10.00
112 Johnny Estrada FF Fld Glv RC 6.00 15.00
113 Pedro Feliz FF Fld Glv 4.00 10.00
114 Nate Frese FF Fld Glv RC 4.00 10.00
115 Joe Kennedy FF Fld Glv RC 6.00 15.00
116 Brandon Larson FF Fld Glv RC 4.00 10.00
117 Alexis Gomez FF Fld Glv RC 4.00 10.00
118 Jason Hart FF 4.00 10.00
119 Jason Michaels FF Fld Glv RC 4.00 10.00
120 Marcus Giles FF Fld Glv 4.00 10.00
121 Christian Parker FF RC 4.00 10.00
122 Jackson Melian FF RC 4.00 10.00
123 Donaldo Mendez FF Spikes RC 4.00 10.00
124 Adrian Hernandez FF RC 4.00 10.00
125 Bud Smith FF RC 4.00 10.00
126 Jose Mieses FF Fld Glv RC 4.00 10.00
127 Roy Oswalt FF Spikes 10.00 25.00
128 Eric Munson FF 4.00 10.00
129 Xavier Nady FF Fld Glv 4.00 10.00
130 Horacio Ramirez FF Fld Glv RC 6.00 15.00
131 Abraham Nunez FF Spikes 4.00 10.00
132 Jose Ortiz FF 4.00 10.00
133 Jeremy Owens FF RC 4.00 10.00
134 Claudio Vargas FF RC 4.00 10.00
135 R.Rodriguez FF Fld Glv RC 4.00 10.00
136 Aubrey Huff FF Jsy 4.00 10.00
137 Ben Sheets FF 6.00 15.00
138 Adam Dunn FF Fld Glv 6.00 15.00
139 Andres Torres FF Fld Glv RC 4.00 10.00
140 Elpidio Guzman FF Fld Glv RC 4.00 10.00
141 Jay Gibbons FF Fld Glv RC 6.00 15.00
142 Wilkin Ruan FF RC 4.00 10.00
143 Tsuyoshi Shinjo FF Base RC 6.00 15.00
144 Alfonso Soriano FF 6.00 15.00
145 Josh Towers FF Fld Glv RC 6.00 15.00
146 Ichiro Suzuki FF Base RC 90.00 150.00
147 Juan Uribe FF RC 6.00 15.00
148 Joe Crede FF Fld Glv 10.00 25.00
149 Carlos Valderrama FF RC 4.00 10.00
150 Matt White FF Fld Glv RC 4.00 10.00
151 Dee Brown FF Jsy 4.00 10.00
152 Juan Cruz FF Spikes RC 4.00 10.00
153 Cory Aldridge FF RC 4.00 10.00
154 Wilmy Caceres FF RC 4.00 10.00
155 Josh Beckett FF 6.00 15.00
156 Wilson Betemit FF Spikes RC 8.00 20.00
157 Corey Patterson FF Pants 4.00 10.00
158 Albert Pujols FF Hat RC 200.00 350.00
159 Rafael Soriano FF Fld Glv RC 4.00 10.00
160 Jack Wilson FF RC 6.00 15.00

2001 Leaf Certified Materials Mirror Gold

Randomly inserted into packs, these 160 cards parallel the basic Leaf Certified Material set. Each card is serial numbered to 25.

*STARS 1-110: 10X TO 25X BASIC CARDS

2001 Leaf Certified Materials Mirror Red

Randomly inserted into packs, these 160 cards parallel the basic Leaf Certified Material set. Each card is serial numbered to 75. An exchange card with a redemption deadline of November 1st, 2003 was seeded into packs for card 125 Bud Smith.

*STARS 1-110: 4X TO 10X BASIC CARDS
111 Alex Escobar FF Fld Glv AU 6.00 15.00
112 Johnny Estrada FF Fld Glv AU 10.00 25.00
113 Pedro Feliz FF Fld Glv AU 6.00 15.00
114 Nate Frese FF Fld Glv AU 6.00 15.00
115 Joe Kennedy FF Fld Glv 6.00 15.00
116 Brandon Larson FF Fld Glv AU 4.00 10.00
117 Alexis Gomez FF Fld Glv AU 4.00 10.00
118 Jason Hart FF AU 6.00 15.00
119 Jason Michaels FF Fld Glv AU 6.00 15.00
120 Marcus Giles FF Fld Glv AU 10.00 25.00
121 Christian Parker FF AU 4.00 10.00
122 Jackson Melian FF 4.00 10.00
123 Donaldo Mendez FF Spikes AU 4.00 10.00
124 Adrian Hernandez FF AU 4.00 10.00
125 Bud Smith FF AU 4.00 10.00
126 Jose Mieses FF Fld Glv AU 6.00 15.00
127 Roy Oswalt FF Spikes AU 20.00 50.00
128 Eric Munson FF 4.00 10.00
129 Xavier Nady FF Fld Glv AU 10.00 25.00
130 Horacio Ramirez FF Fld Glv AU 10.00 25.00
131 Abraham Nunez FF Spikes AU 6.00 15.00
132 Jose Ortiz FF AU 6.00 15.00
133 Jeremy Owens FF AU 6.00 15.00
134 Claudio Vargas FF AU 4.00 10.00
135 Ricardo Rodriguez FF Fld Glv AU 6.00 15.00
136 Aubrey Huff FF Jsy AU 10.00 25.00
137 Ben Sheets FF AU 15.00 40.00
138 Adam Dunn FF Fld Glv AU 15.00 40.00
139 Andres Torres FF Fld Glv AU 4.00 10.00
140 Elpidio Guzman FF Fld Glv AU 4.00 10.00
141 Jay Gibbons FF Fld Glv AU 10.00 25.00
142 Wilkin Ruan FF AU 6.00 15.00
143 Tsuyoshi Shinjo FF Base 6.00 15.00
144 Alfonso Soriano FF AU 15.00 40.00
145 Josh Towers FF Fld Glv AU 10.00 25.00
146 Ichiro Suzuki FF Base 150.00 250.00
147 Juan Uribe FF AU 10.00 25.00
148 Joe Crede FF Fld Glv AU 15.00 40.00
149 Carlos Valderrama FF AU 4.00 10.00
150 Matt White FF Fld Glv AU 6.00 15.00
151 Dee Brown FF Jsy AU 6.00 15.00
152 Juan Cruz FF Spikes AU 6.00 15.00
153 Cory Aldridge FF AU 4.00 10.00
154 Wilmy Caceres FF AU 6.00 15.00
155 Josh Beckett FF AU 15.00 40.00
156 Wilson Betemit FF Spikes AU 12.50 30.00
157 Corey Patterson FF Pants AU 6.00 15.00
158 Albert Pujols FF Hat AU 500.00 800.00
159 Rafael Soriano FF Fld Glv AU 6.00 15.00
160 Jack Wilson FF AU 10.00 25.00

2001 Leaf Certified Materials Fabric of the Game

Randomly inserted into packs, 118 players are featured in this set. Each player has a base card as well as cards serial numbered to a key career stat, jersey number, a key seasonal stat or a Century card. All the Century cards are serial numbered to 21. Certain players had less basic cards issued, these cards are notated with an SP and according to the manufacturer less than 100 of these cards were produced. In addition, exchange cards with a redemption deadline of November 1st, 2003 were seeded into packs for the following: Jeff Bagwell CE AU, Ernie Banks JN AU, Roger Clemens JN AU, Vladimir Guerrero JN AU, Tony Gwynn CE AU, Don Mattingly CE AU, Kirby Puckett JN AU, Nolan Ryan CE AU, Ryne Sandberg CE AU and Mike Schmidt JN AU. Card 32 was originally intended to feature Jackie Robinson but was pulled from production. We've since verified a basic (non-serial-numbered) copy of the Robinson card in circulation in the secondary market but it's likely less than a handful of copies exist given only one copy has been seen since the product was released in 2001.

1BA Lou Gehrig SP
1CE Lou Gehrig/21
1CR Lou Gehrig/23
1JN Lou Gehrig/4
1SN Lou Gehrig/184 150.00 250.00
2BA Babe Ruth SP
2CE Babe Ruth/21
2CR Babe Ruth/136 175.00 300.00
2JN Babe Ruth/3
2SN Babe Ruth/60 250.00 400.00
3BA Stan Musial SP 40.00 80.00
3CE Stan Musial/21
3CR Stan Musial/177 20.00 50.00
3JN Stan Musial/6
3SN Stan Musial/39 50.00 100.00
4BA Nolan Ryan 20.00 50.00
4CE Nolan Ryan AU/21
4CR Nolan Ryan/61 50.00 100.00
4JN Nolan Ryan/34 60.00 120.00
4SN Nolan Ryan/22
5BA Roberto Clemente SP
5CE Roberto Clemente/21
5CR R. Clemente/166 60.00 120.00
5JN Roberto Clemente/21
5SN Roberto Clemente/29 150.00 250.00
6BA Al Kaline SP 15.00 40.00
6CE Al Kaline/21
6CR Al Kaline/137 15.00 40.00
6JN Al Kaline/6
6SN Al Kaline/29 40.00 80.00
7BA Brooks Robinson 10.00 25.00
7CE Brooks Robinson/21
7CR Brooks Robinson/68 15.00 40.00
7JN Brooks Robinson/5
7SN Brooks Robinson/28 40.00 80.00
8BA Mel Ott 20.00 50.00
8CE Mel Ott/21
8CR Mel Ott/72 30.00 60.00
8JN Mel Ott/4
8SN Mel Ott/42 40.00 80.00
9BA Dave Winfield SP 10.00 25.00
9CE Dave Winfield/21
9CR Dave Winfield/88 10.00 25.00
9JN Dave Winfield/31 15.00 40.00
9SN Dave Winfield/37 15.00 40.00
10BA Eddie Mathews SP 15.00 40.00
10CE Eddie Mathews/21
10CR Eddie Mathews/72 15.00 40.00
10JN Eddie Mathews/41 25.00 60.00
10SN Eddie Mathews/47 25.00 60.00
11BA Ernie Banks 10.00 25.00
11CE Ernie Banks/21
11CR Ernie Banks/50 15.00 40.00
11JN Ernie Banks AU/14
11SN Ernie Banks/47 25.00 60.00
12BA Frank Robinson SP 15.00 40.00
12CE Frank Robinson/21
12CR Frank Robinson/72 15.00 40.00
12JN Frank Robinson/20
12SN Frank Robinson/49 25.00 60.00
13BA George Brett SP 20.00 50.00
13CE George Brett/21
13CR George Brett/137 20.00 50.00
13JN George Brett/5
13SN George Brett/30 50.00 100.00
14BA Hank Aaron SP 60.00 120.00
14CE Hank Aaron/21
14CR Hank Aaron/98 40.00 80.00
14JN Hank Aaron/44 125.00 200.00
14SN Hank Aaron/47 75.00 150.00
15BA Harmon Killebrew 10.00 25.00
15CE Harmon Killebrew/21
15CR Harmon Killebrew/24
15JN Harmon Killebrew/3
15SN H. Killebrew/49 25.00 60.00
16BA Joe Morgan SP 10.00 25.00
16CE Joe Morgan/21
16CR Joe Morgan/96 10.00 25.00
16JN Joe Morgan/8
16SN Joe Morgan/27 20.00 50.00
17BA Johnny Bench 10.00 25.00
17CE Johnny Bench/21
17CR Johnny Bench/68 15.00 40.00
17JN Johnny Bench/5
17SN Johnny Bench/45 25.00 60.00
18BA Kirby Puckett SP 15.00 40.00
18CE Kirby Puckett/21
18CR Kirby Puckett/134 15.00 40.00
18JN Kirby Puckett AU/34 125.00 200.00
18SN Kirby Puckett/31 40.00 80.00
19BA Mike Schmidt SP 20.00 50.00
19CE Mike Schmidt/21
19CR Mike Schmidt/59 30.00 60.00
19JN Mike Schmidt AU/20
19SN Mike Schmidt/48 40.00 80.00
20BA Phil Rizzuto SP 15.00 40.00
20CE Phil Rizzuto/21
20CR Phil Rizzuto/149 15.00 40.00
20JN Phil Rizzuto/10
20SN Phil Rizzuto/7
21BA Reggie Jackson SP 15.00 40.00
21CE Reggie Jackson/21
21CR Reggie Jackson/49 25.00 60.00
21JN Reggie Jackson/44 25.00 60.00
21SN Reggie Jackson/47 25.00 60.00
22BA Jim Hunter 10.00 25.00
22CE Jim Hunter/21
22CR Jim Hunter/42 25.00 60.00
22JN Jim Hunter/27 40.00 80.00
22SN Jim Hunter/25
23BA Rod Carew SP 15.00 40.00
23CE Rod Carew/21
23CR Rod Carew/92 15.00 40.00
23JN Rod Carew/29 40.00 80.00
23SN Rod Carew/100 15.00 40.00
24BA Bob Feller 6.00 15.00
24CE Bob Feller/21
24CR Bob Feller/44 15.00 40.00
24JN Bob Feller/19
24SN Bob Feller/36 15.00 40.00
25BA Lou Brock SP 15.00 40.00
25CE Lou Brock/21
25CR Lou Brock/141 15.00 40.00
25JN Lou Brock/20
25SN Lou Brock/21
26BA Tom Seaver SP 15.00 40.00
26CE Tom Seaver/21
26CR Tom Seaver/61 15.00 40.00
26JN Tom Seaver/41 25.00 60.00
26SN Tom Seaver/25
27BA Paul Molitor SP 10.00 25.00
27CE Paul Molitor/21
27CR Paul Molitor/114 10.00 25.00
27JN Paul Molitor/4
27SN Paul Molitor/41 15.00 40.00
28BA Willie McCovey SP 10.00 25.00
28CE Willie McCovey/21
28CR Willie McCovey/18
28JN Willie McCovey/44 15.00 40.00
28SN Willie McCovey/126 10.00 25.00
29BA Yogi Berra 10.00 25.00
29CE Yogi Berra/21
29CR Yogi Berra/49 25.00 60.00
29JN Yogi Berra/35 40.00 80.00
29SN Yogi Berra/30 40.00 80.00
30BA Don Drysdale SP 15.00 40.00
30CE Don Drysdale/21
30CR Don Drysdale/49 25.00 60.00
30JN Don Drysdale/53 15.00 40.00
30SN Don Drysdale/25
31BA Duke Snider SP 15.00 40.00
31CE Duke Snider/21
31CR Duke Snider/99 15.00 40.00
31JN Duke Snider/4
31SN Duke Snider/43 25.00 60.00
32BA Jackie Robinson SP *
33BA Orlando Cepeda 6.00 15.00
33CE Orlando Cepeda/21
33CR Orlando Cepeda/27 20.00 50.00
33JN Orlando Cepeda/30 20.00 50.00
33SN Orlando Cepeda/46 15.00 40.00
34BA Casey Stengel SP 15.00 40.00
34CE Casey Stengel/21
34CR Casey Stengel/10
34JN Casey Stengel/37 25.00 60.00
34SN Casey Stengel/103 15.00 40.00
35BA Robin Yount SP 15.00 40.00
35CE Robin Yount/21
35CR Robin Yount/126 15.00 40.00
35JN Robin Yount/19
35SN Robin Yount/29 40.00 80.00
36BA Eddie Murray 10.00 25.00
36CE Eddie Murray/21
36CR Eddie Murray/35 40.00 80.00
36JN Eddie Murray/22
36SN Eddie Murray/33 40.00 80.00
37BA Jim Palmer 6.00 15.00
37CE Jim Palmer/21
37CR Jim Palmer/53 10.00 25.00
37JN Jim Palmer/22
37SN Jim Palmer/23
38BA Juan Marichal 6.00 15.00
38CE Juan Marichal/21
38CR Juan Marichal/52 10.00 25.00
38JN Juan Marichal/27 20.00 50.00
38SN Juan Marichal/26 20.00 50.00
39BA Willie Stargell 10.00 25.00
39CE Willie Stargell/21
39CR Willie Stargell/55 15.00 40.00
39JN Willie Stargell/8
39SN Willie Stargell/48 25.00 60.00
40BA Ted Williams SP 50.00 100.00
40CE Ted Williams/21
40CR Ted Williams/71 50.00 100.00
40JN Ted Williams/9
40SN Ted Williams/43 75.00 150.00
41BA Cal Ripken 15.00 40.00
41CE Cal Ripken/21
41CR Cal Ripken/277 20.00 50.00
41JN Cal Ripken/8
41SN Cal Ripken/114 50.00 100.00
42BA V. Guerrero SP 10.00 25.00
42CE Vladimir Guerrero/21
42CR V. Guerrero/322 6.00 15.00
42JN Vladimir Guerrero AU/27
42SN V. Guerrero/44 20.00 50.00
43BA Greg Maddux 10.00 25.00
43CE Greg Maddux/21
43CR Greg Maddux/240 10.00 25.00
43JN Greg Maddux/31 40.00 80.00
43SN Greg Maddux/20
44BA Barry Bonds 12.50 30.00
44CE Barry Bonds/21
44CR Barry Bonds/289 15.00 40.00
44JN Barry Bonds/25
44SN Barry Bonds/49 50.00 100.00
45BA Pedro Martinez 6.00 15.00
45CE Pedro Martinez/21
45CR Pedro Martinez/268 6.00 15.00
45JN Pedro Martinez/45 20.00 50.00
45SN Pedro Martinez/23
46BA Ivan Rodriguez 6.00 15.00
46CE Ivan Rodriguez/21
46CR Ivan Rodriguez/304 6.00 15.00
46JN Ivan Rodriguez/7
46SN Ivan Rodriguez/35 25.00 60.00
47BA Roger Maris 20.00 50.00
47CE Roger Maris/21
47CR Roger Maris/275 20.00 50.00
47JN Roger Maris/3
47SN Roger Maris/61 50.00 100.00
48BA Randy Johnson 6.00 15.00
48CE Randy Johnson/21
48CR Randy Johnson/179 6.00 15.00
48JN Randy Johnson/51 15.00 40.00
48SN Randy Johnson/20
49BA Roger Clemens 10.00 25.00
49CE Roger Clemens/21
49CR Roger Clemens/260 12.50 30.00
49JN Roger Clemens AU/22
49SN Roger Clemens/24
50BA Todd Helton 6.00 15.00
50CE Todd Helton/21
50CR Todd Helton/334 6.00 15.00
50JN Todd Helton/17
50SN Todd Helton/42 20.00 50.00
51BA Tony Gwynn 6.00 15.00
51CE Tony Gwynn AU/21
51CR Tony Gwynn/134 15.00 40.00
51JN Tony Gwynn/19
51SN Tony Gwynn/119 15.00 40.00
52BA Troy Glaus 4.00 10.00
52CE Troy Glaus/21
52CR Troy Glaus/256 4.00 10.00
52JN Troy Glaus/25
52SN Troy Glaus/47 12.50 30.00
53BA Phil Niekro 6.00 15.00
53CE Phil Niekro/21
53CR Phil Niekro/245 6.00 15.00
53JN Phil Niekro/35 20.00 50.00
53SN Phil Niekro/23
54BA Don Sutton 6.00 15.00
54CE Don Sutton/21
54CR Don Sutton/178 6.00 15.00
54JN Don Sutton/20
54SN Don Sutton/21
55BA Frank Thomas 6.00 15.00
55CE Frank Thomas/21
55CR Frank Thomas/321 6.00 15.00
55JN Frank Thomas/35 25.00 60.00
55SN Frank Thomas/43 20.00 50.00
56BA Jeff Bagwell 6.00 15.00
56CE Jeff Bagwell AU/21
56CR Jeff Bagwell/305 6.00 15.00
56JN Jeff Bagwell/5
56SN Jeff Bagwell/135 10.00 25.00
57BA Rickey Henderson 6.00 15.00
57CE Rickey Henderson/21
57CR R. Henderson/282 6.00 15.00
57JN R. Henderson/35 25.00 60.00
57SN R. Henderson/28 25.00 60.00
58BA Darin Erstad SP 6.00 15.00
58CE Darin Erstad/21
58CR Darin Erstad/301 4.00 10.00
58JN Darin Erstad/17
58SN Darin Erstad/100 6.00 15.00
59BA Andruw Jones 6.00 15.00
59CE Andruw Jones/21
59CR Andruw Jones/272 6.00 15.00
59JN Andruw Jones/25
59SN Andruw Jones/36 20.00 50.00
60BA Roberto Alomar 6.00 15.00
60CE Roberto Alomar/21
60CR Roberto Alomar/170 6.00 15.00
60JN Roberto Alomar/12
60SN Roberto Alomar/120 10.00 25.00
61BA Mike Piazza SP 15.00 40.00
61CE Mike Piazza/21

Card	Low	High
61CR Mike Piazza/328	10.00	25.00
61JN Mike Piazza/31	40.00	80.00
61SN Mike Piazza/40	40.00	80.00
62BA Chipper Jones	6.00	15.00
62CE Chipper Jones/21		
62CR Chipper Jones/189	6.00	15.00
62JN Chipper Jones/10		
62SN Chipper Jones/45	20.00	50.00
63BA Shawn Green	4.00	10.00
63CE Shawn Green/21		
63CR Shawn Green/143	6.00	15.00
63JN Shawn Green/15		
63SN Shawn Green/123	6.00	15.00
64BA Don Mattingly SP	20.00	50.00
64CE Don Mattingly AU/21		
64CR Don Mattingly/222	15.00	40.00
64JN Don Mattingly/23		
64SN Don Mattingly/145	20.00	50.00
65BA Rafael Palmeiro	6.00	15.00
65CE Rafael Palmeiro/21		
65CR Rafael Palmeiro/296	6.00	15.00
65JN Rafael Palmeiro/25		
65SN Rafael Palmeiro/47	20.00	50.00
66BA Wade Boggs	10.00	25.00
66CE Wade Boggs/21		
66CR Wade Boggs/116	15.00	40.00
66JN Wade Boggs/26	40.00	80.00
66SN Wade Boggs/89	15.00	40.00
67BA Hoyt Wilhelm	6.00	15.00
67CE Hoyt Wilhelm/21		
67CR Hoyt Wilhelm/143	10.00	25.00
67JN Hoyt Wilhelm/31	20.00	50.00
67SN Hoyt Wilhelm/27	20.00	50.00
68BA Andre Dawson	6.00	15.00
68CE Andre Dawson/21		
68CR Andre Dawson/314	6.00	15.00
68JN Andre Dawson/8		
68SN Andre Dawson/49	15.00	40.00
69BA Ryne Sandberg	15.00	40.00
69CE Ryne Sandberg AU/21		
69CR Ryne Sandberg/282	10.00	25.00
69JN Ryne Sandberg/23		
69SN Ryne Sandberg/40	40.00	80.00
70BA N.Garciaparra SP	15.00	40.00
70CE Nomar Garciaparra/21		
70CR N.Garciaparra/333	10.00	25.00
70JN Nomar Garciaparra/5		
70SN N.Garciaparra/35	50.00	100.00
71BA Tom Glavine	6.00	15.00
71CE Tom Glavine/21		
71CR Tom Glavine/208	6.00	15.00
71JN Tom Glavine/47	20.00	50.00
71SN Tom Glavine/247	6.00	15.00
72BA Magglio Ordonez	4.00	10.00
72CE Magglio Ordonez/21		
72CR M.Ordonez/301	4.00	10.00
72JN Magglio Ordonez/30	15.00	40.00
72SN Magglio Ordonez/126	6.00	15.00
73BA Bernie Williams	6.00	15.00
73CE Bernie Williams/21		
73CR Bernie Williams/304	6.00	15.00
73JN Bernie Williams/51	15.00	40.00
73SN Bernie Williams/30	25.00	60.00
74BA Jim Edmonds	4.00	10.00
74CE Jim Edmonds/21		
74CR Jim Edmonds/291	6.00	15.00
74JN Jim Edmonds/15		
74SN Jim Edmonds/108	6.00	15.00
75BA Hideo Nomo	20.00	50.00
75CE Hideo Nomo/21		
75CR Hideo Nomo/69	50.00	100.00
75JN Hideo Nomo/11		
75SN Hideo Nomo/16		
76BA Barry Larkin	6.00	15.00
76CE Barry Larkin/21		
76CR Barry Larkin/300	6.00	15.00
76JN Barry Larkin/11		
76SN Barry Larkin/33	25.00	60.00
77BA Scott Rolen	6.00	15.00
77CE Scott Rolen/21		
77CR Scott Rolen/284	6.00	15.00
77JN Scott Rolen/17		
77SN Scott Rolen/31	25.00	60.00
78BA Miguel Tejada	4.00	10.00
78CE Miguel Tejada/21		
78CR Miguel Tejada/253	4.00	10.00
78JN Miguel Tejada/4		
78SN Miguel Tejada/30	15.00	40.00
79BA Freddy Garcia	4.00	10.00
79CE Freddy Garcia/21		
79CR Freddy Garcia/249	4.00	10.00
79JN Freddy Garcia/34	15.00	40.00
79SN Freddy Garcia/170	4.00	10.00
80BA Edgar Martinez	6.00	15.00
80CE Edgar Martinez/21		
80CR Edgar Martinez/320	6.00	15.00
80JN Edgar Martinez/11		
80SN Edgar Martinez/37	20.00	50.00
81BA Edgardo Alfonzo	4.00	10.00
81CE Edgardo Alfonzo/21		
81CR E. Alfonzo/296	4.00	10.00
81JN Edgardo Alfonzo/13		
81SN E. Alfonzo/108	6.00	15.00
82BA Steve Garvey	6.00	15.00
82CE Steve Garvey/21		
82CR Steve Garvey/272	6.00	15.00
82JN Steve Garvey/6		
82SN Steve Garvey/33	20.00	50.00
83BA Larry Walker	4.00	10.00
83CE Larry Walker/21		
83CR Larry Walker/311	4.00	10.00
83JN Larry Walker/12		
83SN Larry Walker/49	12.50	30.00
84BA A.J. Burnett	4.00	10.00
84CE A.J. Burnett/21		
84CR A.J. Burnett/90	6.00	15.00
84JN A.J. Burnett/43	12.50	30.00
84SN A.J. Burnett/57	10.00	25.00
85BA Richie Sexson	4.00	10.00
85CE Richie Sexson/21		
85CR Richie Sexson/242	4.00	10.00
85JN Richie Sexson/11		
85SN Richie Sexson/116	6.00	15.00
86BA Mark Mulder	4.00	10.00
86CE Mark Mulder/21		
86CR Mark Mulder/88	6.00	15.00
86JN Mark Mulder/20		
86SN Mark Mulder/9		
87BA Kerry Wood	4.00	10.00
87CE Kerry Wood/21		
87CR Kerry Wood/21		
87JN Kerry Wood/34	15.00	40.00
87SN Kerry Wood/233	4.00	10.00
88BA Sean Casey	4.00	10.00
88CE Sean Casey/21		
88CR Sean Casey/312	4.00	10.00
88JN Sean Casey/21		
88SN Sean Casey/25		
89BA Jermaine Dye SP	6.00	15.00
89CE Jermaine Dye/21		
89CR Jermaine Dye/286	4.00	10.00
89JN Jermaine Dye/24		
89SN Jermaine Dye/118	6.00	15.00
90BA Kevin Brown SP	6.00	15.00
90CE Kevin Brown/21		
90CR Kevin Brown/170	4.00	10.00
90JN Kevin Brown/27	15.00	40.00
90SN Kevin Brown/257	4.00	10.00
91BA Craig Biggio	6.00	15.00
91CE Craig Biggio/21		
91CR Craig Biggio/291	6.00	15.00
91JN Craig Biggio/7		
91SN Craig Biggio/88	10.00	25.00
92BA Mike Sweeney SP	6.00	15.00
92CE Mike Sweeney/21		
92CR Mike Sweeney/302	4.00	10.00
92JN Mike Sweeney/29	15.00	40.00
92SN Mike Sweeney/144	6.00	15.00
93BA Jim Thome	6.00	15.00
93CE Jim Thome/21		
93CR Jim Thome/233	6.00	15.00
93JN Jim Thome/25		
93SN Jim Thome/40	20.00	50.00
94BA Al Leiter	4.00	10.00
94CE Al Leiter/21		
94CR Al Leiter/106	6.00	15.00
94JN Al Leiter/22		
94SN Al Leiter/247	4.00	10.00
95BA Barry Zito	6.00	15.00
95CE Barry Zito/21		
95CR Barry Zito/272	6.00	15.00
95JN Barry Zito/75	10.00	25.00
95SN Barry Zito/78	10.00	25.00
96BA Rafael Furcal	4.00	10.00
96CE Rafael Furcal/21		
96CR Rafael Furcal/295	4.00	10.00
96JN Rafael Furcal/1		
96SN Rafael Furcal/37	12.50	30.00
97BA J.D. Drew	4.00	10.00
97CE J.D. Drew/21		
97CR J.D. Drew/276	4.00	10.00
97JN J.D. Drew/7		
97SN J.D. Drew/18		
98BA Andres Galarraga	4.00	10.00
98CE Andres Galarraga/21		
98CR A. Galarraga/291	4.00	10.00
98JN Andres Galarraga/14		
98SN A. Galarraga/150	4.00	10.00
99BA Kazuhiro Sasaki	4.00	10.00
99CE Kazuhiro Sasaki/21		
99CR Kazuhiro Sasaki/266	4.00	10.00
99JN Kazuhiro Sasaki/22		
99SN Kazuhiro Sasaki/45	12.50	30.00
100BA Chan Ho Park	4.00	10.00
100CE Chan Ho Park/21		
100CR Chan Ho Park/65	10.00	25.00
100JN Chan Ho Park/61	10.00	25.00
100SN Chan Ho Park/217	4.00	10.00
101BA Eric Milton	4.00	10.00
101CE Eric Milton/21		
101CR Eric Milton/28	15.00	40.00
101JN Eric Milton/21		
101SN Eric Milton/163	4.00	10.00
102BA Carlos Lee	4.00	10.00
102CE Carlos Lee/21		
102CR Carlos Lee/297	4.00	10.00
102JN Carlos Lee/45	12.50	30.00
102SN Carlos Lee/24		
103BA Preston Wilson	4.00	10.00
103CE Preston Wilson/21		
103CR P. Wilson/266	4.00	10.00
103JN Preston Wilson/44	12.50	30.00
103SN Preston Wilson/31	15.00	40.00
104BA Adrian Beltre	4.00	10.00
104CE Adrian Beltre/21		
104CR Adrian Beltre/272	4.00	10.00
104JN Adrian Beltre/29	15.00	40.00
104SN Adrian Beltre/85	6.00	15.00
105BA Luis Gonzalez	4.00	10.00
105CE Luis Gonzalez/21		
105CR Luis Gonzalez/281	4.00	10.00
105JN Luis Gonzalez/20		
105SN Luis Gonzalez/114	6.00	15.00
106BA Kenny Lofton	4.00	10.00
106CE Kenny Lofton/21		
106CR Kenny Lofton/306	4.00	10.00
106JN Kenny Lofton/7		
106SN Kenny Lofton/15		
107BA Shannon Stewart	4.00	10.00
107CE Shannon Stewart/21		
107CR S. Stewart/297	4.00	10.00
107JN Shannon Stewart/24		
107SN Shannon Stewart/21		
108BA Javy Lopez	4.00	10.00
108CE Javy Lopez/21		
108CR Javy Lopez/290	4.00	10.00
108JN Javy Lopez/8		
108SN Javy Lopez/106	6.00	15.00
109BA Raul Mondesi	4.00	10.00
109CE Raul Mondesi/21		
109CR Raul Mondesi/286	4.00	10.00
109JN Raul Mondesi/43	12.50	30.00
109SN Raul Mondesi/33	15.00	40.00
110BA Mark Grace	6.00	15.00
110CE Mark Grace/21		
110CR Mark Grace/308	6.00	15.00
110JN Mark Grace/17		
110SN Mark Grace/51	15.00	40.00
111BA Curt Schilling	4.00	10.00
111CE Curt Schilling/21		
111CR Curt Schilling/110	6.00	15.00
111JN Curt Schilling/38	12.50	30.00
111SN Curt Schilling/235	4.00	10.00
112BA Cliff Floyd	4.00	10.00
112CE Cliff Floyd/21		
112CR Cliff Floyd/275	4.00	10.00
112JN Cliff Floyd/30	15.00	40.00
112SN Cliff Floyd/22		
113BA Moises Alou	4.00	10.00
113CE Moises Alou/21		
113CR Moises Alou/303	4.00	10.00
113JN Moises Alou/18		
113SN Moises Alou/124	6.00	15.00
114BA Aaron Sele	4.00	10.00
114CE Aaron Sele/21		
114CR Aaron Sele/92	6.00	15.00
114JN Aaron Sele/30	15.00	40.00
114SN Aaron Sele/19		
115BA Jose Cruz Jr.	4.00	10.00
115CE Jose Cruz Jr./21		
115CR Jose Cruz Jr./245	4.00	10.00
115JN Jose Cruz Jr./23		
115SN Jose Cruz Jr./31	15.00	40.00
116BA John Olerud	4.00	10.00
116CE John Olerud/21		
116CR John Olerud/186	4.00	10.00
116JN John Olerud/5		
116SN John Olerud/107	6.00	15.00
117BA Jose Vidro	4.00	10.00
117CE Jose Vidro/21		
117CR Jose Vidro/296	4.00	10.00
117JN Jose Vidro/3		
117SN Jose Vidro/24		
118BA John Smoltz	6.00	15.00
118CE John Smoltz/21		
118CR John Smoltz/335	6.00	15.00
118JN John Smoltz/29	25.00	60.00
118SN John Smoltz/24		

2002 Leaf Certified

This 200-card set was released in early September, 2002. It was issued in five card packs which came 12 packs to a box and six boxes to a case. The first 150 card featured veteran stars while the final 50 cards features rookies and prospects along with a game-used memorabilia piece for each of them. Those final fifty cards have a stated print run of 500 serial numbered sets.

Card	Low	High
COMP.SET w/o SP's (150)	30.00	80.00
COMMON CARD (1-150)	.40	1.00
COMMON CARD (151-200)	3.00	8.00
1 Alex Rodriguez	1.50	4.00
2 Luis Gonzalez	.40	1.00
3 Javier Vazquez	.40	1.00
4 Juan Uribe	.40	1.00
5 Ben Sheets	.40	1.00
6 George Brett	2.00	5.00
7 Magglio Ordonez	.40	1.00
8 Randy Johnson	1.00	2.50
9 Joe Kennedy	.40	1.00
10 Richie Sexson	.40	1.00
11 Larry Walker	.40	1.00
12 Lance Berkman	.40	1.00
13 Jose Cruz Jr.	.40	1.00
14 Doug Davis	.40	1.00
15 Cliff Floyd	.40	1.00
16 Ryan Klesko	.40	1.00
17 Troy Glaus	.40	1.00
18 Robert Person	.40	1.00
19 Bartolo Colon	.40	1.00
20 Adam Dunn	.40	1.00
21 Kevin Brown	.40	1.00
22 John Smoltz	.60	1.50
23 Edgar Martinez	.60	1.50
24 Eric Karros	.40	1.00
25 Tony Gwynn	1.25	3.00
26 Mark Mulder	.40	1.00
27 Don Mattingly	2.00	5.00
28 Brandon Duckworth	.40	1.00
29 C.C. Sabathia	.40	1.00
30 Nomar Garciaparra	1.50	4.00
31 Adam Johnson	.40	1.00
32 Miguel Tejada	.40	1.00
33 Ryne Sandberg	2.00	5.00
34 Roger Clemens	2.00	5.00
35 Edgardo Alfonzo	.40	1.00
36 Jason Jennings	.40	1.00
37 Todd Helton	.60	1.50
38 Nolan Ryan	2.50	6.00
39 Paul LoDuca	.40	1.00
40 Cal Ripken	3.00	8.00
41 Terrence Long	.40	1.00
42 Mike Sweeney	.40	1.00
43 Carlos Lee	.40	1.00
44 Ben Grieve	.40	1.00
45 Tony Armas Jr.	.40	1.00
46 Joe Mays	.40	1.00
47 Jeff Kent	.40	1.00
48 Andy Pettitte	.60	1.50
49 Kirby Puckett	1.00	2.50
50 Aramis Ramirez	.40	1.00
51 Tim Redding	.40	1.00
52 Freddy Garcia	.40	1.00
53 Javy Lopez	.40	1.00
54 Mike Schmidt	2.00	5.00
55 Wade Miller	.40	1.00
56 Ramon Ortiz	.40	1.00
57 Ray Durham	.40	1.00
58 J.D. Drew	.40	1.00
59 Bret Boone	.40	1.00
60 Mark Buehrle	.40	1.00
61 Geoff Jenkins	.40	1.00
62 Greg Maddux	1.50	4.00
63 Mark Grace	.60	1.50
64 Toby Hall	.40	1.00
65 A.J. Burnett	.40	1.00
66 Bernie Williams	.60	1.50
67 Roy Oswalt	.40	1.00
68 Shannon Stewart	.40	1.00
69 Barry Zito	.40	1.00
70 Juan Pierre	.40	1.00
71 Preston Wilson	.40	1.00
72 Rafael Furcal	.40	1.00
73 Sean Casey	.40	1.00
74 John Olerud	.40	1.00
75 Paul Konerko	.40	1.00
76 Vernon Wells	.40	1.00
77 Juan Gonzalez	.40	1.00
78 Ellis Burks	.40	1.00
79 Jim Edmonds	.40	1.00
80 Robert Fick	.40	1.00
81 Michael Cuddyer	.40	1.00
82 Tim Hudson	.40	1.00
83 Phil Nevin	.40	1.00
84 Curt Schilling	.40	1.00
85 Juan Cruz	.40	1.00
86 Jeff Bagwell	.60	1.50
87 Raul Mondesi	.40	1.00
88 Bud Smith	.40	1.00
89 Omar Vizquel	.60	1.50
90 Vladimir Guerrero	1.00	2.50
91 Garret Anderson	.40	1.00
92 Mike Piazza	1.50	4.00
93 Josh Beckett	.40	1.00
94 Carlos Delgado	.40	1.00
95 Kazuhiro Sasaki	.40	1.00
96 Chipper Jones	1.00	2.50
97 Jacque Jones	.40	1.00
98 Pedro Martinez	.60	1.50
99 Marcus Giles	.40	1.00
100 Craig Biggio	.60	1.50
101 Orlando Cabrera	.40	1.00
102 Al Leiter	.40	1.00
103 Michael Barrett	.40	1.00
104 Hideo Nomo	1.00	2.50
105 Mike Mussina	.60	1.50
106 Jeremy Giambi	.40	1.00
107 Cristian Guzman	.40	1.00
108 Frank Thomas	1.00	2.50
109 Carlos Beltran	.40	1.00
110 Jorge Posada	.60	1.50
111 Roberto Alomar	.60	1.50
112 Bob Abreu	.40	1.00
113 Robin Ventura	.40	1.00
114 Pat Burrell	.40	1.00
115 Kenny Lofton	.40	1.00
116 Adrian Beltre	.40	1.00
117 Gary Sheffield	.40	1.00
118 Jermaine Dye	.40	1.00
119 Manny Ramirez	.60	1.50
120 Brian Giles	.40	1.00
121 Tsuyoshi Shinjo	.40	1.00
122 Rafael Palmeiro	.60	1.50
123 Mo Vaughn UER Yankee Logo on back	.40	1.00
124 Kerry Wood	.40	1.00
125 Moises Alou	.40	1.00
126 Rickey Henderson	1.00	2.50
127 Corey Patterson	.40	1.00
128 Jim Thome	.60	1.50
129 Richard Hidalgo	.40	1.00
130 Darin Erstad	.40	1.00
131 Johnny Damon Sox	.60	1.50
132 Juan Encarnacion	.40	1.00
133 Scott Rolen	.60	1.50
134 Tom Glavine	.60	1.50
135 Ivan Rodriguez	.60	1.50
136 Jay Gibbons	.40	1.00
137 Trot Nixon	.40	1.00
138 Nick Neugebauer	.40	1.00
139 Barry Larkin	.60	1.50
140 Andruw Jones	.60	1.50
141 Shawn Green	.40	1.00
142 Jose Vidro	.40	1.00
143 Derek Jeter	2.50	6.00
144 Ichiro Suzuki	2.00	5.00
145 Ken Griffey Jr.	1.50	4.00
146 Barry Bonds	2.50	6.00
147 Albert Pujols	2.00	5.00
148 Sammy Sosa	1.00	2.50
149 Jason Giambi	.40	1.00
150 Alfonso Soriano	.40	1.00
151 Drew Henson NG Bat	3.00	8.00
152 Luis Garcia NG Bat	3.00	8.00
153 Geronimo Gil NG Jsy	3.00	8.00
154 Corky Miller NG Jsy	3.00	8.00
155 Mike Rivera NG Bat	3.00	8.00
156 Mark Ellis NG Jsy	3.00	8.00
157 Josh Pearce NG Bat	3.00	8.00
158 Ryan Ludwick NG Bat	3.00	8.00
159 So Taguchi NG Bat RC	4.00	10.00
160 Cody Ransom NG Jsy	3.00	8.00
161 Jeff Deardorff NG Bat	3.00	8.00
162 Fr. German NG Bat RC	3.00	8.00
163 Ed Rogers NG Jsy	3.00	8.00
164 Eric Cyr NG Jsy	3.00	8.00
165 Victor Alvarez NG Jsy RC	3.00	8.00
166 Victor Martinez NG Jsy	4.00	10.00
167 Brandon Berger NG Jsy	3.00	8.00
168 Juan Diaz NG Jsy	3.00	8.00
169 Kevin Frederick NG Jsy RC	3.00	8.00
170 Earl Snyder NG Bat RC	3.00	8.00
171 Morgan Ensberg NG Bat	3.00	8.00
172 Ryan Jamison NG Jsy	3.00	8.00
173 Rod. Rosario NG Jsy RC	3.00	8.00
174 Willie Harris NG Bat	3.00	8.00
175 Ramon Vazquez NG Bat	3.00	8.00
176 Kazuhisa Ishii NG Bat RC	4.00	10.00
177 Hank Blalock NG Jsy	4.00	10.00
178 Mark Prior NG Bat	4.00	10.00
179 Dewon Brazelton NG Jsy	3.00	8.00
180 Doug Devore NG Jsy RC	3.00	8.00
181 Jorge Padilla NG Bat RC	3.00	8.00
182 Mark Teixeira NG Jsy	4.00	10.00
183 Orlando Hudson NG Bat	3.00	8.00
184 John Buck NG Jsy	3.00	8.00
185 Erik Bedard NG Jsy	3.00	8.00
186 Allan Simpson NG Jsy RC	3.00	8.00
187 Travis Hafner NG Jsy	3.00	8.00
188 Jason Lane NG Jsy	3.00	8.00
189 Marlon Byrd NG Jsy	3.00	8.00
190 Joe Thurston NG Jsy	3.00	8.00
191 Brandon Backe NG Jsy RC	4.00	10.00
192 Josh Phelps NG Jsy	3.00	8.00
193 Bill Hall NG Bat	3.00	8.00
194 Chris Snelling NG Bat RC	3.00	8.00
195 Austin Kearns NG Jsy	3.00	8.00
196 Antonio Perez NG Bat	3.00	8.00
197 Angel Berroa NG Bat	3.00	8.00
198 Andy Machado NG Jsy RC	3.00	8.00
199 Alfredo Amezaga NG Jsy	3.00	8.00
200 Eric Hinske NG Bat	3.00	8.00

2002 Leaf Certified Mirror Blue

Randomly inserted in packs, this is a parallel to the Leaf Certified set. These cards used blue tint and foil

and are printed to a stated print run of 75 serial numbered set.

*MIRROR BLUE 1-150: .6X TO 1.5X MIR.RED
*MIRROR BLUE 151-200: .6X TO 1.5X MIR.RED

2002 Leaf Certified Mirror Red

Randomly inserted in packs, this is a parallel to the Leaf Certified set. These cards used red tint and foil and are printed to a stated print run of 150 serial numbered sets.

Card	Low	High
1 Alex Rodriguez Jsy	10.00	25.00
2 Luis Gonzalez Jsy	4.00	10.00
3 Javier Vazquez Jsy	4.00	10.00
4 Juan Uribe Jsy	4.00	10.00
5 Ben Sheets Jsy	4.00	10.00
6 George Brett Jsy	20.00	50.00
7 Magglio Ordonez Jsy	4.00	10.00
8 Randy Johnson Jsy	8.00	20.00
9 Joe Kennedy Jsy	4.00	10.00
10 Richie Sexson Jsy	4.00	10.00
11 Larry Walker Jsy	4.00	10.00
12 Lance Berkman Jsy	4.00	10.00
13 Jose Cruz Jr. Jsy	4.00	10.00
14 Doug Davis Jsy	4.00	10.00
15 Cliff Floyd Jsy	4.00	10.00
16 Ryan Klesko Bat SP/100	4.00	10.00
17 Troy Glaus Jsy	4.00	10.00
18 Robert Person Jsy	4.00	10.00
19 Bartolo Colon Jsy	4.00	10.00
20 Adam Dunn Jsy	4.00	10.00
21 Kevin Brown Jsy	4.00	10.00
22 John Smoltz Jsy	6.00	15.00
23 Edgar Martinez Jsy	6.00	15.00
24 Eric Karros Jsy	4.00	10.00
25 Tony Gwynn Jsy	10.00	25.00
26 Mark Mulder Jsy	4.00	10.00
27 Don Mattingly Jsy	20.00	50.00
28 Brandon Duckworth Jsy	4.00	10.00
29 C.C. Sabathia Jsy	4.00	10.00
30 Nomar Garciaparra Jsy	10.00	25.00
31 Adam Johnson Jsy	4.00	10.00
32 Miguel Tejada Jsy	4.00	10.00
33 Ryne Sandberg Jsy	20.00	50.00
34 Roger Clemens Jsy	15.00	40.00
35 Edgardo Alfonzo Jsy	4.00	10.00
36 Jason Jennings Jsy	4.00	10.00
37 Todd Helton Jsy	6.00	15.00
38 Nolan Ryan Jsy	40.00	80.00
39 Paul LoDuca Jsy	4.00	10.00
40 Cal Ripken Jsy	40.00	80.00
41 Terrence Long Jsy	4.00	10.00
42 Mike Sweeney Jsy	4.00	10.00
43 Carlos Lee Jsy	4.00	10.00
44 Ben Grieve Jsy	4.00	10.00
45 Tony Armas Jr. Jsy	4.00	10.00
46 Joe Mays Jsy	4.00	10.00
47 Jeff Kent Jsy	4.00	10.00
48 Andy Pettitte Jsy	6.00	15.00
49 Kirby Puckett Jsy	8.00	20.00
50 Aramis Ramirez Jsy	4.00	10.00
51 Tim Redding Jsy	4.00	10.00
52 Freddy Garcia Jsy	4.00	10.00
53 Javy Lopez Jsy	4.00	10.00
54 Mike Schmidt Jsy	20.00	50.00
55 Wade Miller Jsy	4.00	10.00
56 Ramon Ortiz Jsy	4.00	10.00
57 Ray Durham Jsy	4.00	10.00
58 J.D. Drew Jsy	4.00	10.00
59 Bret Boone Jsy	4.00	10.00
60 Mark Buehrle Jsy	4.00	10.00
61 Geoff Jenkins Jsy	4.00	10.00
62 Greg Maddux Jsy	10.00	25.00
63 Mark Grace Jsy	6.00	15.00
64 Toby Hall Jsy	4.00	10.00
65 A.J. Burnett Jsy	4.00	10.00
66 Bernie Williams Jsy	6.00	15.00
67 Roy Oswalt Jsy	4.00	10.00
68 Shannon Stewart Jsy	4.00	10.00
69 Barry Zito Jsy	4.00	10.00
70 Juan Pierre Jsy	4.00	10.00
71 Preston Wilson Jsy	4.00	10.00
72 Rafael Furcal Jsy	4.00	10.00
73 Sean Casey Jsy	4.00	10.00
74 John Olerud Jsy	4.00	10.00
75 Paul Konerko Jsy	4.00	10.00
76 Vernon Wells Jsy	4.00	10.00
77 Juan Gonzalez Jsy	4.00	10.00
78 Ellis Burks Jsy	4.00	10.00
79 Jim Edmonds Jsy	4.00	10.00
80 Robert Fick Jsy	4.00	10.00
81 Michael Cuddyer Jsy	4.00	10.00
82 Tim Hudson Jsy	4.00	10.00
83 Phil Nevin Jsy	4.00	10.00
84 Curt Schilling Jsy	4.00	10.00
85 Juan Cruz Jsy	4.00	10.00
86 Jeff Bagwell Jsy	6.00	15.00
87 Raul Mondesi Jsy	4.00	10.00
88 Bud Smith Jsy	4.00	10.00
89 Omar Vizquel Jsy	6.00	15.00
90 Vladimir Guerrero Jsy	8.00	20.00
91 Garret Anderson Jsy	4.00	10.00
92 Mike Piazza Jsy	10.00	25.00
93 Josh Beckett Jsy	4.00	10.00
94 Carlos Delgado Jsy	4.00	10.00
95 Kazuhiro Sasaki Jsy	4.00	10.00
96 Chipper Jones Jsy	8.00	20.00
97 Jacque Jones Jsy	4.00	10.00
98 Pedro Martinez Jsy	6.00	15.00
99 Marcus Giles Jsy	4.00	10.00
100 Craig Biggio Jsy	6.00	15.00
101 Orlando Cabrera Jsy	4.00	10.00
102 Al Leiter Jsy	4.00	10.00
103 Michael Barrett Jsy	4.00	10.00
104 Hideo Nomo Jsy	8.00	20.00
105 Mike Mussina Jsy	6.00	15.00
106 Jeremy Giambi Jsy	4.00	10.00
107 Cristian Guzman Jsy	4.00	10.00
108 Frank Thomas Jsy	8.00	20.00
109 Carlos Beltran Bat	4.00	10.00
110 Jorge Posada Bat	6.00	15.00
111 Roberto Alomar Bat	6.00	15.00
112 Bob Abreu Bat	4.00	10.00
113 Robin Ventura Bat	4.00	10.00
114 Pat Burrell Bat	4.00	10.00
115 Kenny Lofton Bat	4.00	10.00
116 Adrian Beltre Bat	4.00	10.00
117 Gary Sheffield Bat	4.00	10.00
118 Jermaine Dye Bat	4.00	10.00
119 Manny Ramirez Bat	6.00	15.00
120 Brian Giles Bat	4.00	10.00
121 Tsuyoshi Shinjo Bat	4.00	10.00
122 Rafael Palmeiro Bat	6.00	15.00
123 Mo Vaughn Bat	4.00	10.00
124 Kerry Wood Bat	4.00	10.00
125 Moises Alou Bat	4.00	10.00
126 Rickey Henderson Bat	8.00	20.00
127 Corey Patterson Bat	4.00	10.00
128 Jim Thome Bat	6.00	15.00
129 Richard Hidalgo Bat	4.00	10.00
130 Darin Erstad Bat	4.00	10.00
131 Johnny Damon Sox Bat	6.00	15.00
132 Juan Encarnacion Bat	4.00	10.00
133 Scott Rolen Bat	6.00	15.00
134 Tom Glavine Bat	6.00	15.00
135 Ivan Rodriguez Bat	6.00	15.00
136 Jay Gibbons Bat	4.00	10.00
137 Trot Nixon Bat	4.00	10.00
138 Nick Neugebauer Bat	4.00	10.00
139 Barry Larkin Bat	6.00	15.00
140 Andruw Jones Bat	6.00	15.00
141 Shawn Green Bat	4.00	10.00
142 Jose Vidro Jsy	4.00	10.00
143 Derek Jeter Base	12.50	30.00
144 Ichiro Suzuki Base	10.00	25.00
145 Ken Griffey Jr. Base	8.00	20.00
146 Barry Bonds Base	12.50	30.00
147 Albert Pujols Base	8.00	20.00
148 Sammy Sosa Base	8.00	20.00
149 Jason Giambi Base	4.00	10.00
150 Alfonso Soriano Jsy	4.00	10.00
151 Drew Henson NG Bat	3.00	8.00
152 Luis Garcia NG Bat	3.00	8.00
153 Geronimo Gil NG Jsy	3.00	8.00
154 Corky Miller NG Jsy	3.00	8.00
155 Mike Rivera NG Bat	3.00	8.00
156 Mark Ellis NG Jsy	3.00	8.00
157 Josh Pearce NG Bat	3.00	8.00
158 Ryan Ludwick NG Bat	3.00	8.00
159 So Taguchi NG Bat	4.00	10.00
160 Cody Ransom NG Jsy	3.00	8.00
161 Jeff Deardorff NG Bat	3.00	8.00
162 Franklyn German NG Bat	3.00	8.00
163 Ed Rogers NG Jsy	3.00	8.00
164 Eric Cyr NG Jsy	3.00	8.00
165 Victor Alvarez NG Jsy	3.00	8.00
166 Victor Martinez NG Jsy	4.00	10.00
167 Brandon Berger NG Jsy	3.00	8.00
168 Juan Diaz NG Jsy	3.00	8.00
169 Kevin Frederick NG Jsy	3.00	8.00
170 Earl Snyder NG Bat	3.00	8.00
171 Morgan Ensberg NG Bat	3.00	8.00
172 Ryan Jamison NG Jsy	3.00	8.00
173 Rodrigo Rosario NG Jsy	3.00	8.00
174 Willie Harris NG Bat	3.00	8.00
175 Ramon Vazquez NG Bat	3.00	8.00
176 Kazuhisa Ishii NG Bat	4.00	10.00
177 Hank Blalock NG Jsy	4.00	10.00
178 Mark Prior NG Bat	4.00	10.00
179 Dewon Brazelton NG Jsy	3.00	8.00
180 Doug Devore NG Jsy	3.00	8.00
181 Jorge Padilla NG Bat	3.00	8.00
182 Mark Teixeira NG Jsy	4.00	10.00
183 Orlando Hudson NG Bat	3.00	8.00
184 John Buck NG Jsy	3.00	8.00
185 Erik Bedard NG Jsy	3.00	8.00
186 Allan Simpson NG Jsy	3.00	8.00
187 Travis Hafner NG Jsy	3.00	8.00
188 Jason Lane NG Jsy	3.00	8.00
189 Marlon Byrd NG Jsy	3.00	8.00
190 Joe Thurston NG Jsy	3.00	8.00
191 Brandon Backe NG Jsy	4.00	10.00
192 Josh Phelps NG Jsy	3.00	8.00
193 Bill Hall NG Bat	3.00	8.00
194 Chris Snelling NG Bat	3.00	8.00
195 Austin Kearns NG Jsy	3.00	8.00
196 Antonio Perez NG Bat	3.00	8.00
197 Angel Berroa NG Bat	3.00	8.00
198 Anderson Machado NG Jsy	3.00	8.00
199 Alfredo Amezaga NG Jsy	3.00	8.00
200 Eric Hinske NG Bat	3.00	8.00

2002 Leaf Certified All-Certified Team

Inserted at stated odds of one in 17, these 25 card feature major stars using mirror board and gold foil stamping.

Card	Low	High
COMPLETE SET (25)	40.00	100.00
*BLUE: 2X TO 5X BASIC ALL-CERT.TEAM		

BLUE: RANDOM INSERTS IN PACKS
BLUE PRINT RUN 50 SERIAL #'d SETS
GOLD: RANDOM INSERTS IN PACKS
GOLD PRINT RUN 25 SERIAL #'d SETS
NO GOLD PRICING DUE TO SCARCITY
*RED: 1.25X TO 3X BASIC ALL-CERT.TEAM
RED: RANDOM INSERTS IN PACKS
RED PRINT RUN 75 SERIAL #'d SETS
1 Ichiro Suzuki 3.00 8.00
2 Alex Rodriguez 2.50 6.00
3 Sammy Sosa 1.50 4.00
4 Jeff Bagwell 1.25 3.00
5 Greg Maddux 2.50 6.00
6 Todd Helton 1.25 3.00
7 Nomar Garciaparra 2.50 6.00
8 Ken Griffey Jr. 2.50 6.00
9 Roger Clemens 3.00 8.00
10 Adam Dunn 1.25 3.00
11 Chipper Jones 1.50 4.00
12 Hideo Nomo 1.50 4.00
13 Lance Berkman 1.25 3.00
14 Barry Bonds 4.00 10.00
15 Manny Ramirez 1.25 3.00
16 Jason Giambi 1.25 3.00
17 Rickey Henderson 1.50 4.00
18 Randy Johnson 1.50 4.00
19 Derek Jeter 4.00 10.00
20 Kazuhisa Ishii 1.25 3.00
21 Frank Thomas 1.50 4.00
22 Mike Piazza 2.50 6.00
23 Albert Pujols 3.00 8.00
24 Pedro Martinez 1.25 3.00
25 Vladimir Guerrero 1.50 4.00

2002 Leaf Certified Fabric of the Game

Randomly inserted in packs, these 703 cards feature a game-used swatch and are broken up into the following categories. There is a base card which has a stated print run of anywhere from five to 100 copies and cut into a design of a base. There is also pattern which have a stated print run of five to 50 copies with the swatch cut into the shape of the player's position. There is also a jersey subset which is cut into the shape of the player's uniform number. These cards range anywhere from a stated print run to anywhere from one to 75 serial numbered cards. There is also the debut year subset which has a stated print run of anywhere from 14 to 101 serial numbered cards. In addition, an unannounced subset featured either information about the player's induction into the Hall of Fame or their nickname. These cards mostly have stated print runs of 25 or less and therefore are not priced due to market scarcity.

1BA Bobby Doerr/10
1DY Bobby Doerr/37 12.50 30.00
1IN Bobby Doerr HOF 86/4
1JN Bobby Doerr/1
1PS Bobby Doerr/25
1INA Bobby Doerr HOF 86 AU/1
2BA Ozzie Smith/15
2DY Ozzie Smith/78 15.00 40.00
2JN Ozzie Smith/1
2PS Ozzie Smith/15
2INA Ozzie Smith HOF 02 AU/5
3BA Pee Wee Reese/5
3DY Pee Wee Reese/40 20.00 50.00
3IN Pee Wee Reese HOF 84/5
3JN Pee Wee Reese/1
3PS Pee Wee Reese/10
4BA Tommy Lasorda/80 6.00 15.00
4DY Tommy Lasorda/54 10.00 25.00
4IN Tommy Lasorda HOF 97/20
4JN Tommy Lasorda/2
4PS Tommy Lasorda/50 10.00 25.00
5BA Red Schoendienst/5
5DY Red Schoendienst/45 12.50 30.00
5IN Red Schoendienst HOF 89/5
5JN Red Schoendienst/2
5PS Red Schoendienst/10
6BA Lou Gehrig/5
6DY Lou Gehrig/23
6IN Lou Gehrig HOF 39/5
6JN Lou Gehrig/4
6PS Lou Gehrig/10
7BA Harmon Killebrew/10
7DY Harmon Killebrew/54 15.00 40.00
7JN Harmon Killebrew/3
7PS Harmon Killebrew/20
7INA Harmon Killebrew HOF 84 AU/5
8BA Roger Maris A's/10
8DY Roger Maris A's/57 60.00 120.00
8JN Roger Maris A's/3
8PS Roger Maris A's/10
9BA Babe Ruth/5
9DY Babe Ruth/14
9IN Babe Ruth HOF 36/5
9JN Babe Ruth/3
9PS Babe Ruth/10
10BA Mel Ott/5
10DY Mel Ott/26 50.00 100.00
10IN Mel Ott HOF 51/5
10JN Mel Ott/4
10PS Mel Ott/10
11BA Paul Molitor/100 6.00 15.00
11DY Paul Molitor/78 6.00 15.00
11JN Paul Molitor/4
11PS Paul Molitor/50 10.00 25.00
12BA Duke Snider/5
12DY Duke Snider/47 20.00 50.00
12JN Duke Snider/4
12PS Duke Snider/10
12INA Duke Snider HOF 80 AU/5
13BA Brooks Robinson/5
13DY Brooks Robinson/55 15.00 40.00
13JN Brooks Robinson/5
13PS Brooks Robinson/10
13INA Brooks Robinson HOF 83 AU/5
14BA George Brett/40 40.00 80.00
14DY George Brett/73 30.00 60.00
14IN George Brett HOF 99/5
14JN George Brett/5
14PS George Brett/25
14INA George Brett HOF 99 AU/5
15BA Johnny Bench/80 10.00 25.00
15DY Johnny Bench/67 15.00 40.00
15IN Johnny Bench HOF 89/15
15JN Johnny Bench/5
15PS Johnny Bench/50 15.00 40.00
15INA Johnny Bench HOF 89 AU/5
16BA Lou Boudreau/5
16DY Lou Boudreau/38 12.50 30.00
16IN Lou Boudreau HOF 70/5
16JN Lou Boudreau/5
16PS Lou Boudreau/10
17BA Stan Musial/5
17DY Stan Musial/41 40.00 80.00
17JN Stan Musial/6
17PS Stan Musial/10
17INA Stan Musial HOF 69 AU/5
18BA Al Kaline/5
18DY Al Kaline/53 15.00 40.00
18JN Al Kaline/6
18PS Al Kaline/10
18INA Al Kaline HOF 80 AU/5
19BA Steve Garvey/100 6.00 15.00
19DY Steve Garvey/69 10.00 25.00
19JN Steve Garvey/6
19PS Steve Garvey/45 12.50 30.00
20BA Nomar Garciaparra/100 12.50 30.00
20DY Nomar Garciaparra/96 12.50 30.00
20PS Nomar Garciaparra/50 15.00 40.00
20JNA Nomar Garciaparra AU /5
21BA Joe Morgan/80 6.00 15.00
21DY Joe Morgan/63 10.00 25.00
21IN Joe Morgan HOF 90/15
21JN Joe Morgan/8
21PS Joe Morgan/50 10.00 25.00
21INA Joe Morgan HOF 90 AU/5
22BA Willie Stargell/5
22DY Willie Stargell/62 15.00 40.00
22IN Willie Stargell HOF 88/5
22JN Willie Stargell/8
22PS Willie Stargell/10
23BA Andre Dawson/80 6.00 15.00
23DY Andre Dawson/76 6.00 15.00
23IN Andre Dawson Hawk/15
23JN Andre Dawson/8
23PS Andre Dawson/50 10.00 25.00
23INA Andre Dawson Hawk AU/5
24BA Gary Carter/100 6.00 15.00
24DY Gary Carter/74 10.00 25.00
24JN Gary Carter/8
24PS Gary Carter/50 10.00 25.00
25BA Reggie Jackson A's/10
25DY Reggie Jackson A's/67 15.00 40.00
25JN Reggie Jackson A's/9
25PS Reggie Jackson A's/25
25INA Reggie Jackson A's HOF 93 AU/5
26BA Ted Williams/5
26DY Ted Williams/39
26IN Ted Williams HOF 66/5
26JN Ted Williams/9
26PS Ted Williams/10
27BA Phil Rizzuto/5
27DY Phil Rizzuto/41 20.00 50.00
27JN Phil Rizzuto/10
27PS Phil Rizzuto/10
27INA Phil Rizzuto HOF 94 AU/5
28BA Luis Aparicio/5
28DY Luis Aparicio/56 10.00 25.00
28JN Luis Aparicio/11
28PS Luis Aparicio/10
28INA Luis Aparicio HOF 84 AU/5
29BA Robin Yount/80 10.00 25.00
29DY Robin Yount/74 15.00 40.00
29IN Robin Yount HOF 99/15
29JN Robin Yount/19
29PS Robin Yount/50 15.00 40.00
29INA Robin Yount HOF 99 AU/5
30BA Tony Gwynn/100 10.00 25.00
30DY Tony Gwynn/82 10.00 25.00
30JN Tony Gwynn/14
30PS Tony Gwynn/50 15.00 40.00
30JNA Tony Gwynn AU/5
31BA Ernie Banks/5
31DY Ernie Banks/53 15.00 40.00
31JN Ernie Banks/14
31PS Ernie Banks/10
31INA Ernie Banks HOF 77 AU/5
32BA Joe Torre/50 15.00 40.00
32DY Joe Torre/60 15.00 40.00
32JN Joe Torre/15
32PS Joe Torre/25
33BA Bo Jackson/100 10.00 25.00
33DY Bo Jackson/86 10.00 25.00
33JN Bo Jackson/16
33PS Bo Jackson/35 30.00 60.00
34BA Alfonso Soriano/80 6.00 15.00
34DY Alfonso Soriano/99 6.00 15.00
34JN Alfonso Soriano/12
34PS Alfonso Soriano/50 10.00 25.00
35BA Cal Ripken/80 40.00 80.00
35DY Cal Ripken/81 40.00 80.00
35IN Cal Ripken Iron Man/15
35JN Cal Ripken/8
35PS Cal Ripken/50 50.00 100.00
35INA Cal Ripken Iron Man AU/5
36BA Miguel Tejada/100 6.00 15.00
36DY Miguel Tejada/97 6.00 15.00
36JN Miguel Tejada/4
36PS Miguel Tejada/50 10.00 25.00
37BA Alex Rodriguez M's/100 10.00 25.00
37DY Alex Rodriguez M's/94 10.00 25.00
37JN Alex Rodriguez M's/3
37PS Alex Rodriguez M's/50 15.00 40.00
38BA Mike Schmidt/80 20.00 50.00
38DY Mike Schmidt/72 20.00 50.00
38IN Mike Schmidt HOF 95/15
38JN Mike Schmidt/20
38PS Mike Schmidt/50 30.00 60.00
38INA Mike Schmidt HOF 95 AU/5
39BA Lou Brock/5
39DY Lou Brock/61 15.00 40.00
39JN Lou Brock/20
39PS Lou Brock/10
39INA Lou Brock HOF 85 AU/5
40BA Don Sutton/80 6.00 15.00
40DY Don Sutton/66 10.00 25.00
40IN Don Sutton HOF 98/15
40JN Don Sutton/20
40PS Don Sutton/50 10.00 25.00
40INA Don Sutton HOF 98 AU/5
41BA Roberto Clemente/5
41DY Roberto Clemente/55 75.00 150.00
41IN Roberto Clemente HOF 73/5
41JN Roberto Clemente/21
41PS Roberto Clemente/10
42BA Jim Palmer/20
42DY Jim Palmer/65 10.00 25.00
42JN Jim Palmer/22
42PS Jim Palmer/15
42INA Jim Palmer HOF 90 AU/5
43BA Don Mattingly/40 40.00 80.00
43DY Don Mattingly/82 20.00 50.00
43IN Don Mattingly Donnie BB/5
43JN Don Mattingly/23
43PS Don Mattingly/25
43INA Don Mattingly Donnie BB AU/5
44BA Ryne Sandberg 40 40.00 80.00
44DY Ryne Sandberg/81 30.00 60.00
44IN Ryne Sandberg Ryno/5
44JN Ryne Sandberg/23
44PS Ryne Sandberg/25
44INA Ryne Sandberg Ryno AU/5
45BA Early Wynn/5
45DY Early Wynn/39 12.50 30.00
45IN Early Wynn HOF 72/5
45JN Early Wynn/24
45PS Early Wynn/10
46BA Mike Piazza Dodgers/100 10.00 25.00
46DY Mike Piazza Dodgers/92 10.00 25.00
46JN Mike Piazza Dodgers/31 20.00 50.00
46PS Mike Piazza Dodgers/50 12.50 30.00
47BA Wade Boggs/100 10.00 25.00
47DY Wade Boggs/82 10.00 25.00
47JN Wade Boggs/26 30.00 60.00
47PS Wade Boggs/45 20.00 50.00
48BA Catfish Hunter/10
48DY Catfish Hunter/65 15.00 40.00
48IN Catfish Hunter HOF 87/5
48JN Catfish Hunter/27 30.00 60.00
48PS Catfish Hunter/25
49BA Juan Marichal/20
49DY Juan Marichal/60 10.00 25.00
49JN Juan Marichal/27 15.00 40.00
49PS Juan Marichal/15
49INA Juan Marichal HOF 83 AU/5
50BA Carlton Fisk Red Sox/80 10.00 25.00
50DY Carlton Fisk Red Sox/69 15.00 40.00
50IN Carlton Fisk Red Sox HOF 00/15
50JN Carlton Fisk Red Sox/27 30.00 60.00
50PS Carlton Fisk Red Sox/50 15.00 40.00
50INA Carlton Fisk Red Sox HOF 00 AU/5
51BA Curt Schilling/100 6.00 15.00
51DY Curt Schilling/88 6.00 15.00
51JN Curt Schilling/38 12.50 30.00
51PS Curt Schilling/50 10.00 25.00
52BA Rod Carew Angels/80 10.00 25.00
52DY Rod Carew Angels/67 15.00 40.00
52IN Rod Carew Angels HOF 91/15
52JN Rod Carew Angels/29
52PS Rod Carew Angels/50 15.00 40.00
52INA Rod Carew Angels HOF 91 AU/5
53BA Rod Carew Twins/10
53DY Rod Carew Twins/67 15.00 40.00
53JN Rod Carew Twins/29
53PS Rod Carew Twins/25
53INA Rod Carew Twins HOF 91 AU/5
54BA Joe Carter/100 6.00 15.00
54DY Joe Carter/83 6.00 15.00
54JN Joe Carter/29 15.00 40.00
54PS Joe Carter/50 10.00 25.00
55BA Nolan Ryan Angels/5
55DY Nolan Ryan Angels/66 40.00 80.00
55IN Nolan Ryan Angels HOF 99/5
55JN Nolan Ryan Angels/30
55PS Nolan Ryan Angels/10
55INA Nolan Ryan Angels HOF 99 AU/5
56BA Orlando Cepeda/80 6.00 15.00
56DY Orlando Cepeda/58 10.00 25.00
56IN Orlando Cepeda HOF 99/15
56JN Orlando Cepeda/30 15.00 40.00
56PS Orlando Cepeda/50 10.00 25.00
56INA Orlando Cepeda HOF 99 AU/5
57BA Dave Winfield/80 6.00 15.00
57DY Dave Winfield/73 10.00 25.00
57IN Dave Winfield HOF 01/15
57JN Dave Winfield/31 15.00 40.00
57PS Dave Winfield/50 10.00 25.00
57INA Dave Winfield HOF 01 AU/5
58BA Hoyt Wilhelm/80 6.00 15.00
58DY Hoyt Wilhelm/52 10.00 25.00
58IN Hoyt Wilhelm HOF 85/15
58JN Hoyt Wilhelm/31 15.00 40.00
58PS Hoyt Wilhelm/50 10.00 25.00
58INA Hoyt Wilhelm HOF 85 AU/5
59BA Steve Carlton/80 6.00 15.00
59DY Steve Carlton/65 10.00 25.00
59IN Steve Carlton HOF 94/15
59JN Steve Carlton/32 15.00 40.00
59PS Steve Carlton/50 10.00 25.00
59INA Steve Carlton HOF 94 AU/5
60BA Eddie Murray/100 10.00 25.00
60DY Eddie Murray/77 10.00 25.00
60JN Eddie Murray/33 30.00 60.00
60PS Eddie Murray/50 15.00 40.00
61BA Nolan Ryan Rangers/40 50.00 100.00
61DY Nolan Ryan Rangers/66 40.00 80.00
61IN Nolan Ryan Rangers HOF 99/5
61JN Nolan Ryan Rangers/34 50.00 100.00
61PS Nolan Ryan Rangers/25
61INA Nolan Ryan Rangers HOF 99 AU/5
62BA Nolan Ryan Astros/40 50.00 100.00
62DY Nolan Ryan Astros/66 40.00 80.00
62IN Nolan Ryan Astros HOF 99/5
62JN Nolan Ryan Astros/34 50.00 100.00
62PS Nolan Ryan Astros/25
62INA Nolan Ryan Astros HOF 99 AU/5
63BA Kirby Puckett/40 20.00 50.00
63DY Kirby Puckett/84 10.00 25.00
63IN Kirby Puckett HOF 01/5
63JN Kirby Puckett/34 30.00 60.00
63PS Kirby Puckett/25
63INA Kirby Puckett HOF 01 AU/5
64BA Yogi Berra/5
64DY Yogi Berra/46 20.00 50.00
64JN Yogi Berra/35 30.00 60.00
64PS Yogi Berra/10
64INA Yogi Berra HOF 72 AU/5
65BA Phil Niekro/80 6.00 15.00
65DY Phil Niekro/64 10.00 25.00
65IN Phil Niekro HOF 97/15
65JN Phil Niekro/35 15.00 40.00
65PS Phil Niekro/50 10.00 25.00
65INA Phil Niekro HOF 97 AU/5
66BA Gaylord Perry/80 6.00 15.00
66DY Gaylord Perry/62 10.00 25.00
66IN Gaylord Perry HOF 91/20
66JN Gaylord Perry/36 12.50 30.00
66PS Gaylord Perry/50 10.00 25.00
67BA Pedro Martinez Expos/100 10.00 25.00
67DY Pedro Martinez Expos/92 10.00 25.00
67JN Pedro Martinez Expos/45 20.00 50.00
67PS Pedro Martinez Expos/50 15.00 40.00
68BA Alex Rodriguez Rgr/100 10.00 25.00
68DY Alex Rodriguez Rgr/94 10.00 25.00
68PS Alex Rodriguez Rgr/50 15.00 40.00
68JNA Alex Rodriguez Rgr AU/3
69BA Dave Parker/100 6.00 15.00
69DY Dave Parker/73 10.00 25.00
69JN Dave Parker/39 12.50 30.00
69PS Dave Parker/50 10.00 25.00
70BA Darin Erstad/100 6.00 15.00
70DY Darin Erstad/96 6.00 15.00
70JN Darin Erstad 17
70PS Darin Erstad/50 10.00 25.00
71BA Eddie Mathews/5
71DY Eddie Mathews/52 15.00 40.00
71IN Eddie Mathews HOF 78/5
71JN Eddie Mathews/41 20.00 50.00
71PS Eddie Mathews/10
72BA Tom Seaver Mets/5
72DY Tom Seaver Mets/67 15.00 40.00
72JN Tom Seaver Mets/41 20.00 50.00
72PS Tom Seaver Mets/10
72INA Tom Seaver Mets HOF 92 AU/5
73BA Tom Seaver Reds/10
73DY Tom Seaver Reds/67 15.00 40.00
73JN Tom Seaver Reds/41 20.00 50.00
73PS Tom Seaver Reds/25
73INA Tom Seaver Reds HOF 92 AU/5
74BA Jackie Robinson/5
74DY Jackie Robinson/47 50.00 100.00
74IN Jackie Robinson HOF 62/5
74JN Jackie Robinson/42 50.00 100.00
74PS Jackie Robinson/10
75BA Randy Johnson M's/80 10.00 25.00
75DY Randy Johnson M's/88 10.00 25.00
75IN Randy Johnson M's Big Unit/20
75JN Randy Johnson M's/51 15.00 40.00
75PS Randy Johnson M's/50 15.00 40.00
76BA Reggie Jackson Yanks/10
76DY Reggie Jackson Yanks/67 15.00 40.00
76JN Reggie Jackson Yanks/44 20.00 50.00
76PS Reggie Jackson Yanks/25
76INA Reggie Jackson Yanks HOF 93 AU/5
77BA Reggie Jackson Angels/80 10.00 25.00
77DY Reggie Jackson Angels/67 15.00 40.00
77IN Reggie Jackson Angels HOF 93/15
77JN Reggie Jackson Angels/44 20.00 50.00
77PS Reggie Jackson Angels/50 15.00 40.00
77INA Reggie Jackson Angels HOF 93 AU/5
78BA Willie McCovey/80 6.00 15.00
78DY Willie McCovey/59 10.00 25.00
78IN Willie McCovey HOF 86/15
78JN Willie McCovey/44 12.50 30.00
78PS Willie McCovey/50 10.00 25.00
78INA Willie McCovey HOF 86 AU/5
79BA Eric Davis/100 6.00 15.00
79DY Eric Davis/84 6.00 15.00
79JN Eric Davis/34 15.00 40.00
79PS Eric Davis/50 10.00 25.00
79JNA Eric Davis AU/10
80BA Carlos Delgado/95 6.00 15.00
80DY Carlos Delgado/93 6.00 15.00
80JN Carlos Delgado/25
80PS Carlos Delgado/25
81BA Dale Murphy/100 10.00 25.00
81DY Dale Murphy/76 10.00 25.00
81PS Dale Murphy/50 15.00 40.00
81JNA Dale Murphy AU/3
82BA Brian Giles/100 6.00 15.00
82DY Brian Giles/95 6.00 15.00
82JN Brian Giles/24
82PS Brian Giles/50 10.00 25.00
83BA Kazuhiro Sasaki/100 6.00 15.00
83DY Kazuhiro Sasaki/100 6.00 15.00
83JN Kazuhiro Sasaki/22
83PS Kazuhiro Sasaki 50 10.00 25.00
84BA Phil Nevin/100 6.00 15.00
84DY Phil Nevin/95 6.00 15.00
84JN Phil Nevin/23
84PS Phil Nevin/50 10.00 25.00
85BA Frank Thomas/100 10.00 25.00
85DY Frank Thomas/90 10.00 25.00
85IN Frank Thomas Big Hurt/15
85JN Frank Thomas/35 30.00 60.00
85PS Frank Thomas/50 15.00 40.00
85INA Frank Thomas Big Hurt AU/5
86BA Raul Mondesi/100 6.00 15.00
86DY Raul Mondesi/93 6.00 15.00
86JN Raul Mondesi/43 12.50 30.00
86PS Raul Mondesi/50 10.00 25.00
87BA Don Drysdale/5
87DY Don Drysdale/56 15.00 40.00
87IN Don Drysdale HOF 84/5
87JN Don Drysdale/53 15.00 40.00
87PS Don Drysdale/10
88BA Gary Sheffield/100 6.00 15.00
88DY Gary Sheffield/88 6.00 15.00
88JN Gary Sheffield/10
88PS Gary Sheffield/50 10.00 25.00
89BA Andy Pettitte/100 10.00 25.00
89DY Andy Pettitte/95 10.00 25.00
89JN Andy Pettitte/46 20.00 50.00
89PS Andy Pettitte/50 15.00 40.00
90BA Lance Berkman/45 12.50 30.00
90DY Lance Berkman/99 6.00 15.00
90JN Lance Berkman/17
90PS Lance Berkman/25
90JNA Lance Berkman AU/5
91BA Paul Lo Duca/100 6.00 15.00
91DY Paul Lo Duca/98 6.00 15.00
91JN Paul Lo Duca/16
91PS Paul Lo Duca/50 10.00 25.00
92BA Kevin Brown/25
92DY Kevin Brown/86 6.00 15.00
92JN Kevin Brown/27 15.00 40.00
92PS Kevin Brown/25
93BA Jim Thome/100 10.00 25.00
93DY Jim Thome/91 10.00 25.00
93JN Jim Thome/20
93PS Jim Thome/50 15.00 40.00
93JNA Jim Thome AU/5
94BA Mike Sweeney/100 6.00 15.00
94DY Mike Sweeney/95 6.00 15.00
94JN Mike Sweeney/29 15.00 40.00
94PS Mike Sweeney/50 10.00 25.00
95BA Pedro Martinez Red Sox/100 10.00 25.00
95DY Pedro Martinez Red Sox/92 10.00 25.00
95JN Pedro Martinez Red Sox/45 20.00 50.00
95PS Pedro Martinez Red Sox/45 20.00 50.00
96BA Cliff Floyd/100 6.00 15.00
96DY Cliff Floyd/93 6.00 15.00
96JN Cliff Floyd/30 15.00 40.00
96PS Cliff Floyd/50 10.00 25.00
97BA Larry Walker/100 6.00 15.00
97DY Larry Walker/89 6.00 15.00
97JN Larry Walker/33 15.00 40.00
97PS Larry Walker/50 10.00 25.00
98BA Ivan Rodriguez/80 10.00 25.00
98DY Ivan Rodriguez/91 10.00 25.00
98IN Ivan Rodriguez Pudge/15
98JN Ivan Rodriguez/7
98PS Ivan Rodriguez/50 15.00 40.00
98INA Ivan Rodriguez Pudge AU/5
99BA Aramis Ramirez/100 6.00 15.00
99DY Aramis Ramirez/98 6.00 15.00
99JN Aramis Ramirez/16
99PS Aramis Ramirez/50 10.00 25.00
100BA Roberto Alomar/100 10.00 25.00
100DY Roberto Alomar/88 10.00 25.00
100JN Roberto Alomar/12
100PS Roberto Alomar/50 15.00 40.00
101BA Ben Sheets/100 6.00 15.00
101DY Ben Sheets/101 6.00 15.00
101JN Ben Sheets/15
101PS Ben Sheets/50 10.00 25.00
102BA Adam Dunn/5
102DY Adam Dunn/101 6.00 15.00
102JN Adam Dunn/39 12.50 30.00
102PS Adam Dunn/5
102JNA Adam Dunn AU/5
103BA Hideo Nomo/15
103DY Hideo Nomo/95 15.00 40.00
103JN Hideo Nomo/11
103PS Hideo Nomo/20
104BA C.C. Sabathia/50 10.00 25.00
104DY C.C. Sabathia/101 6.00 15.00
104JN C.C. Sabathia/52 10.00 25.00
104PS C.C. Sabathia/50 10.00 25.00
105BA R.Henderson A's/100 10.00 25.00
105DY Rickey Henderson A's/79 10.00 25.00
105JN R.Henderson A's/30 30.00 60.00
105PS Rickey Henderson A's/50 15.00 40.00
105JNA Rickey Henderson A's AU/5
106BA Carlton Fisk W.Sox/80 10.00 25.00
106DY Carlton Fisk W.Sox/69 15.00 40.00
106IN Carlton Fisk W.Sox HOF 00/15
106JN Carlton Fisk W.Sox/72 15.00 40.00
106PS Carlton Fisk W.Sox/50 15.00 40.00
106INA Carlton Fisk W.Sox HOF 00 AU/5
107BA Chan Ho Park/100 6.00 15.00
107DY Chan Ho Park/94 6.00 15.00
107JN Chan Ho Park/61 10.00 25.00
107PS Chan Ho Park/50 10.00 25.00
108BA Mike Mussina/100 10.00 25.00
108DY Mike Mussina/91 10.00 25.00
108JN Mike Mussina 35 30.00 60.00
108PS Mike Mussina/50 15.00 40.00
109BA Mark Mulder/100 6.00 15.00
109DY Mark Mulder/100 6.00 15.00
109JN Mark Mulder/20
109PS Mark Mulder/35 15.00 40.00
110BA Tsuyoshi Shinjo/100 6.00 15.00
110DY Tsuyoshi Shinjo/101 6.00 15.00
110JN Tsuyoshi Shinjo/5
110PS Tsuyoshi Shinjo/30 15.00 40.00
111BA Pat Burrell/100 6.00 15.00
111DY Pat Burrell/100 6.00 15.00
111JN Pat Burrell/5
111PS Pat Burrell/50 10.00 25.00
112BA Edgar Martinez/100 10.00 25.00
112DY Edgar Martinez/87 10.00 25.00
112JN Edgar Martinez/11
112PS Edgar Martinez/50 15.00 40.00
113BA Barry Larkin/100 10.00 25.00
113DY Barry Larkin/86 10.00 25.00
113JN Barry Larkin/11
113PS Barry Larkin/50 15.00 40.00
114BA Jeff Kent/100 6.00 15.00
114DY Jeff Kent/92 6.00 15.00
114JN Jeff Kent/21
114PS Jeff Kent/50 10.00 25.00
115BA Chipper Jones/100 10.00 25.00
115DY Chipper Jones/93 10.00 25.00
115JN Chipper Jones/10
115PS Chipper Jones/50 15.00 40.00
116BA Magglio Ordonez/100 6.00 15.00
116DY Magglio Ordonez/97 6.00 15.00
116JN Magglio Ordonez/30 15.00 40.00
116PS Magglio Ordonez/50 10.00 25.00
117BA Jim Edmonds/100 6.00 15.00
117DY Jim Edmonds/93 6.00 15.00
117JN Jim Edmonds/15
117PS Jim Edmonds/50 10.00 25.00
118BA Andruw Jones/100 10.00 25.00
118DY Andruw Jones/96 10.00 25.00
118JN Andruw Jones/25
118PS Andruw Jones/45 20.00 50.00
119BA Jose Canseco/100 10.00 25.00
119DY Jose Canseco/85 10.00 25.00
119JN Jose Canseco/23
119PS Jose Canseco/50 15.00 40.00
119JNA Jose Canseco AU/10
120BA Manny Ramirez/100 10.00 25.00
120DY Manny Ramirez/93 10.00 25.00
120JN Manny Ramirez/24
120PS Manny Ramirez/50 15.00 40.00
121BA Sean Casey/100 6.00 15.00
121DY Sean Casey/97 6.00 15.00
121JN Sean Casey/21
121PS Sean Casey/50 10.00 25.00
122BA Bret Boone/100 6.00 15.00
122DY Bret Boone/92 6.00 15.00
122JN Bret Boone/29 15.00 40.00
122PS Bret Boone/50 10.00 25.00
123BA Tim Hudson/100 6.00 15.00
123DY Tim Hudson/99 6.00 15.00
123JN Tim Hudson/15
123PS Tim Hudson/50 10.00 25.00
124BA Craig Biggio/100 10.00 25.00
124DY Craig Biggio/88 10.00 25.00
124JN Craig Biggio/7
124PS Craig Biggio/50 15.00 40.00
125BA Mike Piazza Mets/100 10.00 25.00
125DY Mike Piazza Mets/92 10.00 25.00
125JN Mike Piazza Mets/31 20.00 50.00
125PS Mike Piazza Mets/50 12.50 30.00
126BA Jack Morris/100 6.00 15.00
126DY Jack Morris/77 6.00 15.00
126JN Jack Morris/47 12.50 30.00
126PS Jack Morris/25
127BA Roy Oswalt/100 6.00 15.00
127DY Roy Oswalt/101 6.00 15.00
127JN Roy Oswalt/39 12.50 30.00
127PS Roy Oswalt/50 10.00 25.00
127JNA Roy Oswalt AU/5
128BA Shawn Green/100 6.00 15.00
128DY Shawn Green/93 6.00 15.00
128JN Shawn Green/15
128PS Shawn Green/50 10.00 25.00
129BA Carlos Beltran/100 6.00 15.00
129DY Carlos Beltran/98 6.00 15.00
129JN Carlos Beltran/15
129PS Carlos Beltran/50 10.00 25.00
130BA Todd Helton/100 10.00 25.00
130DY Todd Helton/97 10.00 25.00
130JN Todd Helton/17
130PS Todd Helton/50 15.00 40.00
131BA Barry Zito/75 6.00 15.00
131DY Barry Zito/100 6.00 15.00
131JN Barry Zito/75 6.00 15.00
131PS Barry Zito/30 15.00 40.00
132BA J.D. Drew/100 6.00 15.00
132DY J.D. Drew/98 6.00 15.00
132JN J.D. Drew/7
132PS J.D. Drew/50 10.00 25.00
133BA Mark Grace/100 10.00 25.00
133DY Mark Grace 88 10.00 25.00
133JN Mark Grace/17
133PS Mark Grace/50 15.00 40.00
134BA R.Henderson Mets/100 10.00 25.00
134DY R.Henderson Mets/79 10.00 25.00
134JN Rickey Henderson Mets/24
134PS R.Henderson Mets/50 15.00 40.00
135BA Greg Maddux/100 10.00 25.00
135DY Greg Maddux/86 10.00 25.00
135JN Greg Maddux/31
135PS Greg Maddux/50 12.50 30.00
136BA Garret Anderson/100 6.00 15.00
136DY Garret Anderson/94 6.00 15.00
136JN Garret Anderson/16
136PS Garret Anderson/50 10.00 25.00
137BA Rafael Palmeiro/100 10.00 25.00
137DY Rafael Palmeiro/86 10.00 25.00
137JN Rafael Palmeiro/20
137PS Rafael Palmeiro/50 15.00 40.00
137JNA Rafael Palmeiro AU/5
138BA Luis Gonzalez/50 10.00 25.00
138DY Luis Gonzalez/90 6.00 15.00
138JN Luis Gonzalez/20
138PS Luis Gonzalez/45 12.50 30.00
139BA Nick Johnson/100 6.00 15.00
139DY Nick Johnson/101 6.00 15.00
139JN Nick Johnson/26 15.00 40.00
139PS Nick Johnson/50 10.00 25.00
139JNA Nick Johnson AU/10
140BA Vladimir Guerrero/80 10.00 25.00
140DY Vladimir Guerrero/96 10.00 25.00
140JN Vladimir Guerrero/22
140PS Vladimir Guerrero/50 15.00 40.00
140JNA Vladimir Guerrero AU/5
141BA Mark Buehrle/20
141DY Mark Buehrle/100 6.00 15.00
141JN Mark Buehrle/56 10.00 25.00
141PS Mark Buehrle/20
142BA Troy Glaus/100 6.00 15.00
142DY Troy Glaus/98 6.00 15.00
142JN Troy Glaus/25
142PS Troy Glaus/50 10.00 25.00
143BA Juan Gonzalez/100 6.00 15.00
143DY Juan Gonzalez/89 6.00 15.00
143JN Juan Gonzalez/22
143PS Juan Gonzalez/50 10.00 25.00
144BA Kerry Wood/100 6.00 15.00
144DY Kerry Wood/98 6.00 15.00
144JN Kerry Wood/34 15.00 40.00
144PS Kerry Wood/50 10.00 25.00
145BA Roger Clemens/80 15.00 40.00
145DY Roger Clemens/84 15.00 40.00
145IN Roger Clemens Rocket/16
145JN Roger Clemens/20
145PS Roger Clemens/50 30.00 60.00
145INA Roger Clemens Rocket AU/5
146BA Bob Abreu/100 6.00 15.00
146DY Bob Abreu/96 6.00 15.00
146JN Bob Abreu/53 10.00 25.00
146PS Bob Abreu/50 10.00 25.00
147BA Bernie Williams/95 10.00 25.00
147DY Bernie Williams/91 10.00 25.00
147JN Bernie Williams/51 15.00 40.00
147PS Bernie Williams/25
148BA Tom Glavine/100 10.00 25.00
148DY Tom Glavine/87 10.00 25.00
148JN Tom Glavine/47 20.00 50.00
148PS Tom Glavine/50 15.00 40.00
149BA Jorge Posada/100 10.00 25.00
149DY Jorge Posada/95 10.00 25.00
149JN Jorge Posada/20
149PS Jorge Posada/50 15.00 40.00
150BA R.Johnson D'Backs/80 10.00 25.00
150DY R.Johnson D'Backs/88 10.00 25.00
150IN Randy Johnson D'Backs Big Unit/20
150JN R.Johnson D'Backs/51 15.00 40.00
150PS R.Johnson D'Backs/50 15.00 40.00

2002 Leaf Certified Skills

Inserted at stated odds of one in 17, these 20 cards feature players who have have already established excellent stats be it for a game, season or career. These cards are produced on mirror board with silver foil stamping.

COMPLETE SET (20) 50.00 120.00
*BLUE: 1.25X TO 3X BASIC SKILLS
BLUE: RANDOM INSERTS IN PACKS

BLUE PRINT RUN 75 SERIAL #'d SETS
GOLD: RANDOM INSERTS IN PACKS
GOLD PRINT RUN 25 SERIAL #'d SETS
NO GOLD PRICING DUE TO SCARCITY
*RED: .75X TO 2X BASIC SKILLS
RED: RANDOM INSERTS IN PACKS
RED PRINT RUN 150 SERIAL #'d SETS

1 Barry Bonds 4.00 10.00
2 Greg Maddux 2.50 6.00
3 Rickey Henderson 1.50 4.00
4 Ichiro Suzuki 3.00 8.00
5 Pedro Martinez 1.25 3.00
6 Kazuhisa Ishii 1.25 3.00
7 Alex Rodriguez 2.50 6.00
8 Mike Piazza 2.50 6.00
9 Sammy Sosa 1.50 4.00
10 Derek Jeter 4.00 10.00
11 Albert Pujols 3.00 8.00
12 Roger Clemens 3.00 8.00
13 Mark Prior 1.00 2.50
14 Chipper Jones 1.50 4.00
15 Ken Griffey Jr. 2.50 6.00
16 Frank Thomas 1.50 4.00
17 Randy Johnson 1.50 4.00
18 Vladimir Guerrero 1.50 4.00
19 Nomar Garciaparra 2.50 6.00
20 Jeff Bagwell 1.25 3.00

2003 Leaf Certified Materials

This 259-card set was issued in two separate series. The primary Leaf Certified Materials brand - containing cards 1-250 from the basic set - was released in August, 2003. The set was issued in seven card packs with an $10 SRP which were packaged 10 to a box and 20 boxes to a case. Cards numbered 1 through 200 feature veterans. Cards numbered 201 through 205 featured some baseball legends while cards numbered 206 through 250 are entitled New Generation and feature top prospects and rookies. Those cards, with the exception of card 220 were issued to a stated print run of 400 serial numbered sets. Card 220, featuring Jose Contreras, was issued to a stated print run of 100 serial numbered sets. Cards 251-259 were randomly seeded into packs of DLP Rookies and Traded of which was distributed in December, 2003. The nine update cards carry on the New Generation subset featuring top prospects, and like the earlier cards feature certified autographs. Serial numbered print runs for these update cards range from 100-250 copies per.

COMP.LO SET w/o SP's (200) 20.00 50.00
COMMON CARD (1-200) .40 1.00
COMMON CARD (201-205) 4.00 10.00
COM (201-219/221-250) 4.00 10.00
201-219/221-250 RANDOM IN LCM PACKS
COMMON (251-259) p/r 250 4.00 10.00

1 Troy Glaus .40 1.00
2 Alfredo Amezaga .40 1.00
3 Garret Anderson .40 1.00
4 Nolan Ryan Angels 2.50 6.00
5 Darin Erstad .40 1.00
6 Junior Spivey .40 1.00
7 Randy Johnson 1.00 2.50
8 Curt Schilling .40 1.00
9 Luis Gonzalez .40 1.00
10 Steve Finley .40 1.00
11 Matt Williams .40 1.00
12 Greg Maddux 1.50 4.00
13 Chipper Jones 1.00 2.50
14 Gary Sheffield .40 1.00
15 Adam LaRoche .40 1.00
16 Andruw Jones .60 1.50
17 Robert Fick .40 1.00
18 John Smoltz .60 1.50
19 Javy Lopez .40 1.00
20 Jay Gibbons .40 1.00
21 Geronimo Gil .40 1.00
22 Cal Ripken 3.00 8.00
23 Nomar Garciaparra 1.50 4.00
24 Pedro Martinez .60 1.50
25 Freddy Sanchez .40 1.00
26 Rickey Henderson 1.00 2.50
27 Manny Ramirez .60 1.50
28 Casey Fossum .40 1.00
29 Sammy Sosa 1.00 2.50
30 Kerry Wood .40 1.00
31 Corey Patterson .40 1.00
32 Nic Jackson .40 1.00
33 Mark Prior .60 1.50
34 Juan Cruz .40 1.00
35 Steve Smyth .40 1.00
36 Magglio Ordonez .40 1.00
37 Joe Borchard .40 1.00
38 Frank Thomas 1.00 2.50
39 Mark Buehrle .40 1.00
40 Joe Crede .40 1.00
41 Carlos Lee .40 1.00
42 Paul Konerko .40 1.00
43 Adam Dunn .40 1.00
44 Corky Miller .40 1.00
45 Brandon Larson .40 1.00
46 Ken Griffey Jr. 1.50 4.00
47 Barry Larkin .60 1.50
48 Sean Casey .40 1.00
49 Wily Mo Pena .40 1.00
50 Austin Kearns .40 1.00
51 Victor Martinez .60 1.50
52 Brian Tallet .40 1.00
53 Cliff Lee .40 1.00
54 Jeremy Guthrie .40 1.00
55 C.C. Sabathia .40 1.00
56 Ricardo Rodriguez .40 1.00
57 Omar Vizquel .60 1.50
58 Travis Hafner .40 1.00
59 Todd Helton .60 1.50
60 Jason Jennings .40 1.00
61 Jeff Baker .40 1.00
62 Larry Walker .40 1.00
63 Travis Chapman .40 1.00
64 Mike Maroth .40 1.00
65 Josh Beckett .40 1.00
66 Ivan Rodriguez .60 1.50
67 Brad Penny .40 1.00
68 A.J. Burnett .40 1.00
69 Craig Biggio .60 1.50
70 Roy Oswalt .40 1.00
71 Jason Lane .40 1.00
72 Nolan Ryan Astros 2.50 6.00
73 Wade Miller .40 1.00
74 Richard Hidalgo .40 1.00
75 Jeff Bagwell .60 1.50
76 Lance Berkman .40 1.00
77 Rodrigo Rosario .40 1.00
78 Jeff Kent .40 1.00
79 John Buck .40 1.00
80 Angel Berroa .40 1.00
81 Mike Sweeney .40 1.00
82 Mac Suzuki .40 1.00
83 Alexis Gomez .40 1.00
84 Carlos Beltran .40 1.00
85 Runelvys Hernandez .40 1.00
86 Hideo Nomo 1.00 2.50
87 Paul Lo Duca .40 1.00
88 Cesar Izturis .40 1.00
89 Kazuhisa Ishii .40 1.00
90 Shawn Green .40 1.00
91 Joe Thurston .40 1.00
92 Adrian Beltre .40 1.00
93 Kevin Brown .40 1.00
94 Richie Sexson .40 1.00
95 Ben Sheets .40 1.00
96 Takahito Nomura .40 1.00
97 Geoff Jenkins .40 1.00
98 Bill Hall .40 1.00
99 Torii Hunter .40 1.00
100 A.J. Pierzynski .40 1.00
101 Michael Cuddyer .40 1.00
102 Jose Morban .40 1.00
103 Brad Radke .40 1.00
104 Jacque Jones .40 1.00
105 Eric Milton .40 1.00
106 Joe Mays .40 1.00
107 Adam Johnson .40 1.00
108 Javier Vazquez .40 1.00
109 Vladimir Guerrero 1.00 2.50
110 Jose Vidro .40 1.00
111 Michael Barrett .40 1.00
112 Orlando Cabrera .40 1.00
113 Tom Glavine .60 1.50
114 Roberto Alomar .60 1.50
115 Tsuyoshi Shinjo .40 1.00
116 Cliff Floyd .40 1.00
117 Mike Piazza 1.50 4.00
118 Al Leiter .40 1.00
119 Don Mattingly 2.00 5.00
120 Roger Clemens 2.00 5.00
121 Derek Jeter 2.50 6.00
122 Alfonso Soriano .40 1.00
123 Drew Henson .40 1.00
124 Brandon Claussen .40 1.00
125 Christian Parker .40 1.00
126 Jason Giambi .40 1.00
127 Mike Mussina .60 1.50
128 Bernie Williams .60 1.50
129 Jason Anderson .40 1.00
130 Nick Johnson .40 1.00
131 Jorge Posada .60 1.50
132 Andy Pettitte .60 1.50
133 Barry Zito .40 1.00
134 Miguel Tejada .40 1.00
135 Eric Chavez .40 1.00
136 Tim Hudson .40 1.00
137 Mark Mulder .40 1.00
138 Terrence Long .40 1.00
139 Mark Ellis .40 1.00
140 Jim Thome .60 1.50
141 Pat Burrell .40 1.00
142 Marlon Byrd .40 1.00
143 Bobby Abreu .40 1.00
144 Brandon Duckworth .40 1.00
145 Robert Person .40 1.00
146 Anderson Machado .40 1.00
147 Aramis Ramirez .40 1.00
148 Jack Wilson .40 1.00
149 Carlos Rivera .40 1.00
150 Jose Castillo .40 1.00
151 Walter Young .40 1.00
152 Brian Giles .40 1.00
153 Jason Kendall .40 1.00
154 Ryan Klesko .40 1.00
155 Mike Rivera .40 1.00
156 Sean Burroughs .40 1.00
157 Brian Lawrence .40 1.00
158 Xavier Nady .40 1.00
159 Dennis Tankersley .40 1.00
160 Phil Nevin .40 1.00
161 Barry Bonds 2.50 6.00
162 Kenny Lofton .40 1.00
163 Rich Aurilia .40 1.00
164 Ichiro Suzuki 2.00 5.00
165 Edgar Martinez .60 1.50
166 Chris Snelling .40 1.00
167 Rafael Soriano .40 1.00
168 John Olerud .40 1.00
169 Bret Boone .40 1.00
170 Freddy Garcia .40 1.00
171 Aaron Sele .40 1.00
172 Kazuhiro Sasaki .40 1.00
173 Albert Pujols 2.00 5.00
174 Scott Rolen .60 1.50
175 So Taguchi .40 1.00
176 Jim Edmonds .40 1.00
177 Edgar Renteria .40 1.00
178 J.D. Drew .40 1.00
179 Antonio Perez .40 1.00
180 Dewon Brazelton .40 1.00
181 Aubrey Huff .40 1.00
182 Toby Hall .40 1.00
183 Ben Grieve .40 1.00
184 Joe Kennedy .40 1.00
185 Alex Rodriguez 1.50 4.00
186 Rafael Palmeiro .60 1.50
187 Hank Blalock .40 1.00
188 Mark Teixeira .60 1.50
189 Juan Gonzalez .40 1.00
190 Kevin Mench .40 1.00
191 Nolan Ryan Rgr 2.50 6.00
192 Doug Davis .40 1.00
193 Eric Hinske .40 1.00
194 Vinny Chulk .40 1.00
195 Alexis Rios .40 1.00
196 Carlos Delgado .40 1.00
197 Shannon Stewart .40 1.00
198 Josh Phelps .40 1.00
199 Vernon Wells .40 1.00
200 Roy Halladay .40 1.00
201 Babe Ruth RET 8.00 20.00
202 Lou Gehrig RET 5.00 12.00
203 Jackie Robinson RET 4.00 10.00
204 Ty Cobb RET 6.00 15.00
205 Thurman Munson RET 4.00 10.00
206 Pr. Redman NG AU RC 4.00 10.00
207 Craig Brazell NG AU RC 4.00 10.00
208 Nook Logan NG AU RC 6.00 15.00
209 Hong-Chih Kuo NG AU RC 60.00 120.00
210 Matt Kata NG AU RC 4.00 10.00
211 C.Wang NG AU RC 125.00 200.00
212 Alej Machado NG AU RC 4.00 10.00
213 Mike Hessman NG AU RC 4.00 10.00
214 Franc Rosario NG AU RC 4.00 10.00
215 Pedro Liriano NG AU 4.00 10.00
216 J.Bonderman NG AU RC 15.00 40.00
217 Oscar Villarreal NG AU RC 4.00 10.00
218 Arnie Munoz NG AU RC 4.00 10.00
219 Tim Olson NG AU RC 4.00 10.00
220 J.Contreras NG AU/100 RC 15.00 40.00
221 Franc Cruceta NG AU RC 4.00 10.00
222 John Webb NG AU 4.00 10.00
223 Phil Seibel NG AU RC 4.00 10.00
224 Aaron Looper NG AU RC 4.00 10.00
225 Brian Stokes NG AU RC 4.00 10.00
226 G.Quiroz NG AU RC 4.00 10.00
227 Fern Cabrera NG AU RC 4.00 10.00
228 Josh Hall NG AU RC 4.00 10.00
229 Diego Markwell NG AU RC 4.00 10.00
230 Andrew Brown NG AU RC 6.00 15.00
231 Doug Waechter NG AU RC 6.00 15.00
232 Felix Sanchez NG AU RC 4.00 10.00
233 Gerardo Garcia NG AU 4.00 10.00
234 Matt Bruback NG AU RC 4.00 10.00
235 Mi. Hernandez NG AU RC 4.00 10.00
236 Rett Johnson NG AU RC 4.00 10.00
237 Ryan Cameron NG AU RC 4.00 10.00
238 Rob Hammock NG AU RC 4.00 10.00
239 Clint Barmes NG AU RC 6.00 15.00
240 Brandon Webb NG AU RC 20.00 50.00
241 Jon Leicester NG AU RC 4.00 10.00
242 Shane Bazzell NG AU RC 4.00 10.00
243 Joe Valentine NG AU RC 4.00 10.00
244 Josh Stewart NG AU RC 4.00 10.00
245 Pete LaForest NG AU RC 4.00 10.00
246 Shane Victorino NG AU RC 12.50 30.00
247 Termel Sledge NG AU RC 4.00 10.00
248 Lew Ford NG AU RC 6.00 15.00
249 T.Wellemeyer NG AU RC 4.00 10.00
250 Hideki Matsui NG RC 6.00 15.00
251 A.Loewen NG AU/250 RC 6.00 15.00
252 Dan Haren NG AU/250 RC 8.00 20.00
253 D.Willis NG AU/150 10.00 25.00
254 Ramon Nivar NG AU/250 RC 4.00 10.00
255 Chad Gaudin NG AU/250 RC 4.00 10.00
256 Kevin Correia NG AU/150 RC 4.00 10.00
257 R.Weeks NG AU/100 RC 40.00 80.00
258 R.Wagner NG AU/250 RC 4.00 10.00
259 Del.Young NG AU/100 RC 125.00 175.00

2003 Leaf Certified Materials Mirror Black

1-250 RANDOM INSERTS IN PACKS
251-259 RANDOM IN DLP R/T PACKS
STATED PRINT RUN 1 SERIAL #'d SET
NO PRICING DUE TO SCARCITY

2003 Leaf Certified Materials Mirror Black Autographs

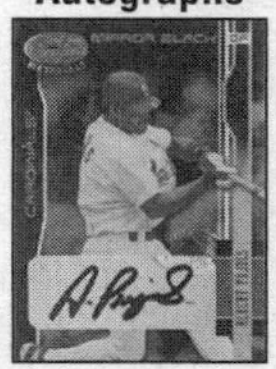

1-250 RANDOM INSERTS IN PACKS
251-259 RANDOM IN DLP R/T PACKS
STATED PRINT RUN 1 SERIAL #'d SET
NO PRICING DUE TO SCARCITY

2003 Leaf Certified Materials Mirror Black Materials

RANDOM INSERTS IN PACKS
STATED PRINT RUN 1 SERIAL #'d SET
NO PRICING DUE TO SCARCITY

2003 Leaf Certified Materials Mirror Blue

*BLUE 1-200: 3X TO 8X BASIC
*BLUE 201-205: 1X TO 2.5X BASIC
*BLUE 206-219/221-249: .3X TO .8X BASIC
*BLUE 220: .2X TO .5X BASIC 220
*BLUE 250: .75X TO 2X BASIC 250
*BLUE 251-259: .3X TO .8X BASIC p/r 250
*BLUE 251-259: .2X TO .5X BASIC p/r 100-150
1-250 RANDOM INSERTS IN PACKS
251-259 RANDOM IN DLP R/T PACKS
STATED PRINT RUN 50 SERIAL #'d SETS
209 Hong-Chih Kuo NG 30.00 60.00
211 Chien-Ming Wang NG 50.00 100.00

2003 Leaf Certified Materials Mirror Blue Autographs

1-250 RANDOM INSERTS IN PACKS
251-259 RANDOM IN DLP R/T PACKS
PRINT RUNS B/WN 5-50 COPIES PER
NO PRICING ON QTY OF 25 OR LESS

2 Alfredo Amezaga/50 6.00 15.00
3 Garret Anderson/10
4 Nolan Ryan Angels/5
6 Junior Spivey/50 6.00 15.00
15 Adam LaRoche/50 6.00 15.00
17 Robert Fick/10
20 Jay Gibbons/50 6.00 15.00
21 Geronimo Gil/50 6.00 15.00
22 Cal Ripken/5
25 Freddy Sanchez/17
28 Casey Fossum/50 6.00 15.00
31 Corey Patterson/5
32 Nic Jackson/50 6.00 15.00
33 Mark Prior/50 12.50 30.00
34 Juan Cruz/50 6.00 15.00
35 Steve Smyth/50 6.00 15.00
37 Joe Borchard/50 6.00 15.00
39 Mark Buehrle/50 15.00 40.00
40 Joe Crede/30 10.00 25.00
41 Carlos Lee/5
45 Brandon Larson/50 6.00 15.00
49 Wily Mo Pena/50 10.00 25.00
51 Victor Martinez/50 15.00 40.00
52 Brian Tallet/50 6.00 15.00
53 Cliff Lee/50 6.00 15.00
54 Jeremy Guthrie/50 6.00 15.00
55 C.C. Sabathia/4
56 Ricardo Rodriguez/50 6.00 15.00
60 Jason Jennings/50 6.00 15.00
61 Jeff Baker/50 6.00 15.00
63 Travis Chapman/50 6.00 15.00
64 Mike Maroth/50 6.00 15.00
70 Roy Oswalt/50 10.00 25.00
71 Jason Lane/50 10.00 25.00
72 Nolan Ryan Astros/10
73 Wade Miller/50 6.00 15.00
74 Richard Hidalgo/5
77 Rodrigo Rosario/50 6.00 15.00
79 John Buck/10
80 Angel Berroa/50 6.00 15.00
81 Mike Sweeney/5
82 Mac Suzuki/50 10.00 25.00
83 Alexis Gomez/10
85 Runelvys Hernandez/50 6.00 15.00
86 Hideo Nomo/15
87 Paul Lo Duca/10
88 Cesar Izturis/50 6.00 15.00
89 Kazuhisa Ishii/5
91 Joe Thurston/50 6.00 15.00
94 Richie Sexson/5
95 Ben Sheets/5
96 Takahito Nomura/10
98 Bill Hall/30 6.00 15.00
100 A.J. Pierzynski/5
102 Jose Morban/50 6.00 15.00
107 Adam Johnson/50 6.00 15.00
108 Javier Vazquez/10
110 Jose Vidro/10
116 Cliff Floyd/5
117 Mike Piazza/15
119 Don Mattingly/5
122 Alfonso Soriano/10
123 Drew Henson/5
124 Brandon Claussen/50 6.00 15.00
125 Christian Parker/50 6.00 15.00
129 Jason Anderson/50 6.00 15.00
130 Nick Johnson/10
133 Barry Zito/5
134 Miguel Tejada/5
135 Eric Chavez/5
136 Tim Hudson/5
138 Terrence Long/50 6.00 15.00
142 Marlon Byrd/50 6.00 15.00
143 Bobby Abreu/5
144 Brandon Duckworth/50 6.00 15.00
145 Robert Person/50 6.00 15.00
146 Anderson Machado/50 6.00 15.00
147 Aramis Ramirez/8
148 Jack Wilson/50 10.00 25.00
149 Carlos Rivera/50 6.00 15.00
150 Jose Castillo/50 6.00 15.00
151 Walter Young/50 6.00 15.00
154 Ryan Klesko/5
155 Mike Rivera/50 6.00 15.00
157 Brian Lawrence/50 6.00 15.00
158 Xavier Nady/50 6.00 15.00
159 Dennis Tankersley/50 6.00 15.00
165 Edgar Martinez/5
166 Chris Snelling/50 6.00 15.00
167 Rafael Soriano/50 6.00 15.00
170 Freddy Garcia/5
173 Albert Pujols/5
176 Jim Edmonds/10
179 Antonio Perez/50 6.00 15.00
180 Dewon Brazelton/50 6.00 15.00
181 Aubrey Huff/50 10.00 25.00
182 Toby Hall/50 6.00 15.00
184 Joe Kennedy/50 6.00 15.00
187 Hank Blalock/50 10.00 25.00
188 Mark Teixeira/50 15.00 40.00
189 Juan Gonzalez/10
190 Kevin Mench/50 10.00 25.00
191 Nolan Ryan Rgr/5
193 Eric Hinske/50 6.00 15.00
194 Vinny Chulk/50 6.00 15.00
195 Alexis Rios/50 10.00 25.00
197 Shannon Stewart/10
206 Prentice Redman NG/50 6.00 15.00
207 Craig Brazell NG/50 6.00 15.00
208 Nook Logan NG/50 10.00 25.00
209 Hong-Chih Kuo NG/40 75.00 150.00
210 Matt Kata NG/50 6.00 15.00
211 Chien-Ming Wang NG/40 175.00 300.00
212 Alejandro Machado NG/50 6.00 15.00
213 Michael Hessman NG/50 6.00 15.00
214 Francisco Rosario NG/50 6.00 15.00
215 Pedro Liriano NG/50 6.00 15.00
216 Jeremy Bonderman NG/50 30.00 60.00
217 Oscar Villarreal NG/50 6.00 15.00
218 Arnie Munoz NG/50 6.00 15.00
219 Tim Olson NG/50 6.00 15.00
220 Jose Contreras NG/15
221 Francisco Cruceta NG/50 6.00 15.00
222 John Webb NG/50 6.00 15.00
223 Phil Seibel NG/50 6.00 15.00
224 Aaron Looper NG/50 6.00 15.00
225 Brian Stokes NG/50 6.00 15.00
226 Guillermo Quiroz NG/50 6.00 15.00
227 Fernando Cabrera NG/50 6.00 15.00
228 Josh Hall NG/50 6.00 15.00
229 Diegomar Markwell NG/50 6.00 15.00
230 Andrew Brown NG/50 10.00 25.00
231 Doug Waechter NG/50 10.00 25.00
232 Felix Sanchez NG/50 6.00 15.00
233 Gerardo Garcia NG/50 6.00 15.00
234 Matt Bruback NG/50 6.00 15.00
235 Michel Hernandez NG/50 6.00 15.00
236 Rett Johnson NG/50 6.00 15.00
237 Ryan Cameron NG/50 6.00 15.00
238 Rob Hammock NG/50 6.00 15.00
239 Clint Barmes NG/50 12.50 30.00
240 Brandon Webb NG/50 50.00 100.00
241 Jon Leicester NG/50 6.00 15.00
242 Shane Bazzell NG/50 6.00 15.00
243 Joe Valentine NG/50 6.00 15.00
244 Josh Stewart NG/50 6.00 15.00
245 Pete LaForest NG/50 6.00 15.00
246 Shane Victorino NG/50 20.00 50.00
247 Termel Sledge NG/50 6.00 15.00
248 Lew Ford NG/50 10.00 25.00
249 Todd Wellemeyer NG/50 6.00 15.00
251 Adam Loewen NG/50 15.00 40.00
252 Dan Haren NG/50 15.00 40.00
253 Dontrelle Willis NG/25
254 Ramon Nivar NG/50 6.00 15.00
255 Chad Gaudin NG/50 6.00 15.00
256 Kevin Correia NG/25
257 Rickie Weeks NG/15
258 Ryan Wagner NG/50 6.00 15.00
259 Delmon Young NG/25

2003 Leaf Certified Materials Mirror Blue Materials

RANDOM INSERTS IN PACKS
PRINT RUNS B/WN 10-100 COPIES PER
NO PRICING ON QTY OF 25 OR FEWER

1 Troy Glaus Jsy/100 4.00 10.00
2 Alfredo Amezaga Jsy/100 4.00 10.00
3 Garret Anderson Bat/100 4.00 10.00
4 Nolan Ryan Angels Jsy/15
5 Darin Erstad Bat/100 4.00 10.00
6 Junior Spivey Bat/100 4.00 10.00
7 Randy Johnson Jsy/100 6.00 15.00
8 Curt Schilling Jsy/100 4.00 10.00
9 Luis Gonzalez Jsy/100 4.00 10.00
10 Steve Finley Jsy/100 4.00 10.00
11 Matt Williams Jsy/100 4.00 10.00
12 Greg Maddux Jsy/100 10.00 25.00
13 Chipper Jones Jsy/50 10.00 25.00
14 Gary Sheffield Bat/100 4.00 10.00
15 Adam LaRoche Bat/100 4.00 10.00
16 Andruw Jones Jsy/100 6.00 15.00
17 Robert Fick Bat/100 4.00 10.00
18 John Smoltz Jsy/100 6.00 15.00
19 Javy Lopez Jsy/100 4.00 10.00
20 Jay Gibbons Jsy/100 4.00 10.00
21 Geronimo Gil Jsy/100 4.00 10.00
22 Cal Ripken Jsy/15
23 Nomar Garciaparra Jsy/100 12.50 30.00
24 Pedro Martinez Jsy/100 6.00 15.00
25 Freddy Sanchez Bat/100 4.00 10.00
26 Rickey Henderson Bat/100 6.00 15.00
27 Manny Ramirez Jsy/100 6.00 15.00
28 Casey Fossum Jsy/100 4.00 10.00
29 Sammy Sosa Jsy/100 6.00 15.00
30 Kerry Wood Jsy/100 4.00 10.00
31 Corey Patterson Bat/100 4.00 10.00
32 Nic Jackson Bat/100 4.00 10.00
33 Mark Prior Jsy/100 6.00 15.00
34 Juan Cruz Jsy/100 4.00 10.00
35 Steve Smyth Jsy/100 4.00 10.00
36 Magglio Ordonez Jsy/100 4.00 10.00
37 Joe Borchard Jsy/100 4.00 10.00
38 Frank Thomas Jsy/100 6.00 15.00
39 Mark Buehrle Jsy/100 4.00 10.00
40 Joe Crede Hat/100 4.00 10.00
41 Carlos Lee Jsy/100 4.00 10.00
42 Paul Konerko Jsy/100 4.00 10.00
43 Adam Dunn Jsy/100 4.00 10.00
45 Brandon Larson Spikes/40 6.00 15.00
46 Ken Griffey Jr. Base/100 10.00 25.00
47 Barry Larkin Jsy/100 6.00 15.00
48 Sean Casey Bat/100 4.00 10.00
49 Wily Mo Pena Bat/100 4.00 10.00
50 Austin Kearns Jsy/100 4.00 10.00
51 Victor Martinez Jsy/100 6.00 15.00
55 C.C. Sabathia Jsy/100 4.00 10.00
56 Ricardo Rodriguez Bat/100 4.00 10.00
57 Omar Vizquel Jsy/100 6.00 15.00
58 Travis Hafner Bat/100 4.00 10.00
59 Todd Helton Jsy/100 6.00 15.00
60 Jason Jennings Jsy/100 4.00 10.00
62 Larry Walker Jsy/100 4.00 10.00
63 Travis Chapman Bat/100 4.00 10.00
64 Mike Maroth Jsy/100 4.00 10.00
65 Josh Beckett Jsy/100 4.00 10.00
66 Ivan Rodriguez Bat/100 6.00 15.00
67 Brad Penny Jsy/100 4.00 10.00
68 A.J. Burnett Jsy/100 4.00 10.00
69 Craig Biggio Jsy/100 6.00 15.00
70 Roy Oswalt Jsy/100 4.00 10.00
71 Jason Lane Jsy/100 4.00 10.00
72 Nolan Ryan Astros Jsy/15
73 Wade Miller Jsy/100 4.00 10.00
74 Richard Hidalgo Pants/100 4.00 10.00
75 Jeff Bagwell Jsy/100 6.00 15.00
76 Lance Berkman Jsy/100 4.00 10.00
77 Rodrigo Rosario Jsy/100 4.00 10.00
78 Jeff Kent Bat/100 4.00 10.00
79 John Buck Jsy/100 4.00 10.00
80 Angel Berroa Bat/100 4.00 10.00
81 Mike Sweeney Jsy/100 4.00 10.00
84 Carlos Beltran Jsy/100 4.00 10.00
86 Hideo Nomo Jsy/100 15.00 40.00
87 Paul Lo Duca Jsy/100 4.00 10.00
88 Cesar Izturis Pants/100 4.00 10.00
89 Kazuhisa Ishii Jsy/100 4.00 10.00
90 Shawn Green Jsy/100 4.00 10.00
91 Joe Thurston Jsy/100 4.00 10.00
92 Adrian Beltre Bat/100 4.00 10.00
93 Kevin Brown Jsy/100 4.00 10.00
94 Richie Sexson Jsy/100 4.00 10.00
95 Ben Sheets Jsy/100 4.00 10.00
97 Geoff Jenkins Jsy/100 4.00 10.00
98 Bill Hall Bat/100 4.00 10.00
99 Torii Hunter Jsy/100 4.00 10.00
101 Michael Cuddyer Jsy/100 4.00 10.00
102 Jose Morban Bat/100 4.00 10.00
103 Brad Radke Jsy/100 4.00 10.00
104 Jacque Jones Jsy/100 4.00 10.00
105 Eric Milton Jsy/100 4.00 10.00
106 Joe Mays Jsy/100 4.00 10.00
107 Adam Johnson Jsy/100 4.00 10.00
108 Javier Vazquez Jsy/100 4.00 10.00
109 Vladimir Guerrero Jsy/100 6.00 15.00
110 Jose Vidro Jsy/100 4.00 10.00
111 Michael Barrett Jsy/40 6.00 15.00
112 Orlando Cabrera Jsy/100 4.00 10.00
113 Tom Glavine Bat/100 6.00 15.00
114 Roberto Alomar Bat/100 6.00 15.00
115 Tsuyoshi Shinjo Jsy/100 4.00 10.00
116 Cliff Floyd Bat/100 4.00 10.00
117 Mike Piazza Jsy/100 10.00 25.00
118 Al Leiter Jsy/100 4.00 10.00
119 Don Mattingly Jsy/15
120 Roger Clemens Jsy/100 12.50 30.00
121 Derek Jeter Base/100 12.50 30.00
122 Alfonso Soriano Jsy/100 4.00 10.00
123 Drew Henson Bat/100 4.00 10.00
124 Brandon Claussen Hat/40 6.00 15.00
125 Christian Parker Pants/100 4.00 10.00
126 Jason Giambi Jsy/100 4.00 10.00
127 Mike Mussina Jsy/40 10.00 25.00
128 Bernie Williams Jsy/100 6.00 15.00
130 Nick Johnson Jsy/100 4.00 10.00
131 Jorge Posada Jsy/100 6.00 15.00
132 Andy Pettitte Jsy/100 6.00 15.00
133 Barry Zito Jsy/100 4.00 10.00
134 Miguel Tejada Jsy/100 4.00 10.00
135 Eric Chavez Jsy/100 4.00 10.00
136 Tim Hudson Jsy/100 4.00 10.00
137 Mark Mulder Jsy/100 4.00 10.00
138 Terrence Long Jsy/100 4.00 10.00
139 Mark Ellis Jsy/100 4.00 10.00
140 Jim Thome Bat/100 6.00 15.00
141 Pat Burrell Bat/100 4.00 10.00
142 Marlon Byrd Jsy/100 4.00 10.00
143 Bobby Abreu Jsy/100 4.00 10.00
144 Brandon Duckworth Jsy/100 4.00 10.00
145 Robert Person Jsy/100 4.00 10.00
146 Anderson Machado Jsy/100 4.00 10.00
147 Aramis Ramirez Jsy/100 4.00 10.00
148 Jack Wilson Bat/100 4.00 10.00
150 Jose Castillo Bat/100 4.00 10.00
151 Walter Young Bat/100 4.00 10.00

152 Brian Giles Bat/100 4.00 10.00
153 Jason Kendall Jsy/100 4.00 10.00
154 Ryan Klesko Jsy/50 6.00 15.00
155 Mike Rivera Bat/100 4.00 10.00
157 Brian Lawrence Bat/100 4.00 10.00
158 Xavier Nady Hat/40 6.00 15.00
159 Dennis Tankersley Jsy/100 4.00 10.00
160 Phil Nevin Jsy/100 4.00 10.00
161 Barry Bonds Base/100 12.50 30.00
162 Kenny Lofton Bat/100 4.00 10.00
163 Rich Aurilia Jsy/100 4.00 10.00
164 Ichiro Suzuki Base/100 15.00 40.00
165 Edgar Martinez Jsy/100 6.00 15.00
166 Chris Snelling Bat/100 4.00 10.00
167 Rafael Soriano Jsy/100 4.00 10.00
168 John Olerud Jsy/100 4.00 10.00
169 Bret Boone Jsy/100 4.00 10.00
170 Freddy Garcia Jsy/100 4.00 10.00
171 Aaron Sele Jsy/100 4.00 10.00
172 Kazuhiro Sasaki Jsy/100 4.00 10.00
173 Albert Pujols Jsy/100 15.00 40.00
174 Scott Rolen Bat/100 6.00 15.00
175 So Taguchi Jsy/100 4.00 10.00
176 Jim Edmonds Jsy/100 4.00 10.00
177 Edgar Renteria Jsy/100 4.00 10.00
178 J.D. Drew Jsy/100 4.00 10.00
179 Antonio Perez Bat/100 4.00 10.00
180 Dewon Brazelton Jsy/100 4.00 10.00
181 Aubrey Huff Jsy/50 6.00 15.00
182 Toby Hall Jsy/100 4.00 10.00
183 Ben Grieve Jsy/100 4.00 10.00
184 Joe Kennedy Jsy/100 4.00 10.00
185 Alex Rodriguez Jsy/100 12.50 30.00
186 Rafael Palmeiro Jsy/100 6.00 15.00
187 Hank Blalock Jsy/100 4.00 10.00
188 Mark Teixeira Jsy/100 6.00 15.00
189 Juan Gonzalez Bat/100 4.00 10.00
190 Kevin Mench Jsy/100 4.00 10.00
191 Nolan Ryan Rgr Jsy/15
192 Doug Davis Jsy/100 4.00 10.00
193 Eric Hinske Jsy/100 4.00 10.00
196 Carlos Delgado Jsy/100 4.00 10.00
197 Shannon Stewart Jsy/100 4.00 10.00
198 Josh Phelps Jsy/100 4.00 10.00
199 Vernon Wells Jsy/100 4.00 10.00
200 Roy Halladay Jsy/100 4.00 10.00
201 Babe Ruth RET Pants/10
202 Lou Gehrig RET Pants/10
203 Jackie Robinson RET Jsy/10
204 Ty Cobb RET Pants/10
205 Thurman Munson RET Jsy/10

2003 Leaf Certified Materials Mirror Emerald

1-250 RANDOM INSERTS IN PACKS
251-259 RANDOM IN DLP R/T PACKS
STATED PRINT RUN 5 SERIAL #'d SETS
NO PRICING DUE TO SCARCITY

2003 Leaf Certified Materials Mirror Emerald Autographs

1-250 RANDOM INSERTS IN PACKS
251-259 RANDOM IN DLP R/T PACKS
STATED PRINT RUN 5 SERIAL #'d SETS
NO PRICING DUE TO SCARCITY

2003 Leaf Certified Materials Mirror Emerald Materials

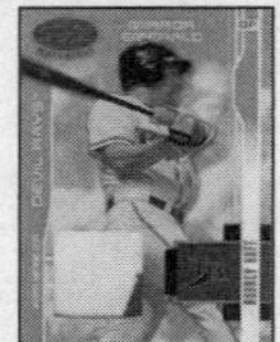

RANDOM INSERTS IN PACKS
STATED PRINT RUN 5 SERIAL #'d SETS
NO PRICING DUE TO SCARCITY

2003 Leaf Certified Materials Mirror Gold

1-250 RANDOM INSERTS IN PACKS
251-259 RANDOM IN DLP R/T PACKS
STATED PRINT RUN 25 SERIAL #'d SETS
NO PRICING DUE TO SCARCITY

2003 Leaf Certified Materials Mirror Gold Autographs

1-250 RANDOM INSERTS IN PACKS
251-259 RANDOM IN DLP R/T PACKS
PRINT RUNS B/WN 5-25 COPIES PER
NO PRICING DUE TO SCARCITY

2003 Leaf Certified Materials Mirror Gold Materials

RANDOM INSERTS IN PACKS
PRINT RUNS B/WN 5-25 COPIES PER
NO PRICING DUE TO SCARCITY

2003 Leaf Certified Materials Mirror Red

*ACTIVE RED 1-200: 2X TO 5X BASIC
*RETIRED RED 1-200: 2.5X TO 6X BASIC
*RED 201-205: .75X TO 2X BASIC
*RED 206-219/221-250: .2X TO .5X BASIC
*RED 220: .12X TO .3X BASIC 220
*RED 250: .5X TO 1.2X BASIC 250
*RED 251-259: .2X TO .5X BASIC p/r 250
*RED 251-259: .15X TO .4X BASIC p/r 100-150
1-250 RANDOM INSERTS IN PACKS
251-259 RANDOM IN DLP R/T PACKS
STATED PRINT RUN 100 SERIAL #'d SETS
209 Hong-Chih Kuo NG 20.00 50.00
211 Chien-Ming Wang NG 30.00 60.00

2003 Leaf Certified Materials Mirror Red Autographs

1-250 RANDOM INSERTS IN PACKS
251-259 RANDOM IN DLP R/T PACKS
PRINT RUNS B/WN 5-100 COPIES PER
NO PRICING ON QTY OF 25 OR LESS
2 Alfredo Amezaga/100 6.00 15.00
3 Garret Anderson/10
4 Nolan Ryan Angels/5
6 Junior Spivey/15
15 Adam LaRoche/100 6.00 15.00
17 Robert Fick/15
20 Jay Gibbons/100 6.00 15.00
21 Geronimo Gil/15
22 Cal Ripken/5
25 Freddy Sanchez/100 6.00 15.00
28 Casey Fossum/50 6.00 15.00
31 Corey Patterson/6
32 Nic Jackson/100 6.00 15.00
33 Mark Prior/15
34 Juan Cruz/15
35 Steve Smyth/94 6.00 15.00
37 Joe Borchard/15
39 Mark Buehrle/15
40 Joe Crede/15
45 Brandon Larson/100 6.00 15.00
49 Wily Mo Pena/100 10.00 25.00
51 Victor Martinez/15
52 Brian Tallet/15
53 Cliff Lee/15
54 Jeremy Guthrie/15
56 Ricardo Rodriguez/100 6.00 15.00
60 Jason Jennings/15
61 Jeff Baker/15
63 Travis Chapman/100 6.00 15.00
64 Mike Maroth/100 6.00 15.00
70 Roy Oswalt/15
71 Jason Lane/100 10.00 25.00
72 Nolan Ryan Astros/5
73 Wade Miller/15
74 Richard Hidalgo/10
77 Rodrigo Rosario/100 6.00 15.00
79 John Buck/15
80 Angel Berroa/15
81 Mike Sweeney/10
82 Mac Suzuki/15
83 Alexis Gomez/15
85 Runelvys Hernandez/100 6.00 15.00
86 Hideo Nomo/16
87 Paul Lo Duca/15
88 Cesar Izturis/100 6.00 15.00
89 Kazuhisa Ishii/5
91 Joe Thurston/100 6.00 15.00
94 Richie Sexson/10
95 Ben Sheets/10
96 Takahito Nomura/15
98 Bill Hall/100 6.00 15.00
100 A.J. Pierzynski/10
102 Jose Morban/100 6.00 15.00
106 Joe Mays/9
107 Adam Johnson/15
108 Javier Vazquez/15
110 Jose Vidro/15
116 Cliff Floyd/10
117 Mike Piazza/20
119 Don Mattingly/5
122 Alfonso Soriano/15
123 Drew Henson/10
124 Brandon Claussen/60 6.00 15.00
125 Christian Parker/15
129 Jason Anderson/100 6.00 15.00
130 Nick Johnson/15
133 Barry Zito/10
134 Miguel Tejada/10
135 Eric Chavez/10
136 Tim Hudson/10
138 Terrence Long/15
141 Pat Burrell/6
142 Marlon Byrd/100 6.00 15.00
143 Bobby Abreu/10
144 Brandon Duckworth/15
145 Robert Person/15
146 Anderson Machado/100 6.00 15.00
148 Jack Wilson/15
149 Carlos Rivera/100 6.00 15.00
150 Jose Castillo/100 6.00 15.00
151 Walter Young/100 6.00 15.00
152 Brian Giles/15
154 Ryan Klesko/10
155 Mike Rivera/100 6.00 15.00
157 Brian Lawrence/100 6.00 15.00
158 Xavier Nady Hat/15
159 Dennis Tankersley/15
165 Edgar Martinez/10
166 Chris Snelling/100 6.00 15.00
167 Rafael Soriano/15
170 Freddy Garcia/15
173 Albert Pujols/10
176 Jim Edmonds/10
179 Antonio Perez/15
180 Dewon Brazelton/15
181 Aubrey Huff/15
182 Toby Hall/15
184 Joe Kennedy/15
187 Hank Blalock/15
188 Mark Teixeira/15
189 Juan Gonzalez/10
190 Kevin Mench/100 10.00 25.00
191 Nolan Ryan Rgr/5
193 Eric Hinske/100 6.00 15.00
194 Vinny Chulk/100 6.00 15.00
195 Alexis Rios/100 8.00 20.00
197 Shannon Stewart/15
206 Prentice Redman NG/100 4.00 10.00
207 Craig Brazell NG/100 4.00 10.00
208 Nook Logan NG/100 6.00 15.00
209 Hong-Chih Kuo NG/50 60.00 120.00
210 Matt Kata NG/100 4.00 10.00
211 Chien-Ming Wang NG/50 175.00 300.00
212 Alejandro Machado NG/100 4.00 10.00
213 Michael Hessman NG/100 4.00 10.00
214 Francisco Rosario NG/100 4.00 10.00
215 Pedro Liriano NG/100 4.00 10.00
216 Jeremy Bonderman NG/100 20.00 50.00
217 Oscar Villarreal NG/100 4.00 10.00
218 Arnie Munoz NG/100 4.00 10.00
219 Tim Olson NG/100 4.00 10.00
220 Jose Contreras NG/5
221 Francisco Cruceta NG/100 4.00 10.00
222 John Webb NG/100 4.00 10.00
223 Phil Seibel NG/100 4.00 10.00
224 Aaron Looper NG/100 4.00 10.00
225 Brian Stokes NG/100 4.00 10.00
226 Guillermo Quiroz NG/100 4.00 10.00
227 Fernando Cabrera NG/100 4.00 10.00
228 Josh Hall NG/100 4.00 10.00
229 Diegomar Markwell NG/100 4.00 10.00
230 Andrew Brown NG/100 6.00 15.00
231 Doug Waechter NG/100 6.00 15.00
232 Felix Sanchez NG/100 4.00 10.00
233 Gerardo Garcia NG/100 4.00 10.00
234 Matt Bruback NG/100 4.00 10.00
235 Michel Hernandez NG/100 4.00 10.00
236 Rett Johnson NG/100 4.00 10.00
237 Ryan Cameron NG/100 4.00 10.00
238 Rob Hammock NG/100 4.00 10.00
239 Clint Barmes NG/100 10.00 25.00
240 Brandon Webb NG/100 20.00 50.00
241 Jon Leicester NG/100 4.00 10.00
242 Shane Bazzell NG/100 4.00 10.00
243 Joe Valentine NG/100 4.00 10.00
244 Josh Stewart NG/100 4.00 10.00
245 Pete LaForest NG/100 4.00 10.00
246 Shane Victorino NG/100 15.00 40.00
247 Termel Sledge NG/100 4.00 10.00
248 Lew Ford NG/100 6.00 15.00
249 Todd Wellemeyer NG/100 4.00 10.00
251 Adam Loewen NG/100 10.00 25.00
252 Dan Haren NG/100 10.00 25.00
253 Dontrelle Willis NG/50 15.00 40.00
254 Ramon Nivar NG/100 4.00 10.00
255 Chad Gaudin NG/100 4.00 10.00
256 Kevin Correia NG/100 4.00 10.00
257 Rickie Weeks NG/25
258 Ryan Wagner NG/100 4.00 10.00
259 Delmon Young NG/50 150.00 250.00

2003 Leaf Certified Materials Mirror Red Materials

RANDOM INSERTS IN PACKS
PRINT RUNS B/WN 15-250 COPIES PER
NO PRICING ON QTY OF 25 OR LESS
1 Troy Glaus Jsy/250 3.00 8.00
2 Alfredo Amezaga Jsy/100 4.00 10.00
3 Garret Anderson Bat/250 3.00 8.00
4 Nolan Ryan Angels Jsy/35 40.00 80.00
5 Darin Erstad Bat/250 3.00 8.00
6 Junior Spivey Bat/250 3.00 8.00
7 Randy Johnson Jsy/250 4.00 10.00
8 Curt Schilling Jsy/250 3.00 8.00
9 Luis Gonzalez Jsy/250 3.00 8.00
10 Steve Finley Jsy/250 3.00 8.00
11 Matt Williams Jsy/100 4.00 10.00
12 Greg Maddux Jsy/250 8.00 20.00
13 Chipper Jones Jsy/250 4.00 10.00
14 Gary Sheffield Bat/125 4.00 10.00
15 Adam LaRoche Bat/250 3.00 8.00
16 Andruw Jones Jsy/250 4.00 10.00
17 Robert Fick Bat/250 3.00 8.00
18 John Smoltz Jsy/250 4.00 10.00
19 Javy Lopez Jsy/250 3.00 8.00
20 Jay Gibbons Jsy/250 3.00 8.00
21 Geronimo Gil Jsy/250 3.00 8.00
22 Cal Ripken Jsy/35 60.00 120.00
23 Nomar Garciaparra Jsy/250 10.00 25.00
24 Pedro Martinez Jsy/250 4.00 10.00
25 Freddy Sanchez Bat/250 3.00 8.00
26 Rickey Henderson Bat/250 4.00 10.00
27 Manny Ramirez Jsy/250 4.00 10.00
28 Casey Fossum Jsy/250 3.00 8.00
29 Sammy Sosa Jsy/250 4.00 10.00
30 Kerry Wood Jsy/250 3.00 8.00
31 Corey Patterson Bat/250 3.00 8.00
32 Nic Jackson Bat/250 3.00 8.00
33 Mark Prior Jsy/250 4.00 10.00
34 Juan Cruz Jsy/250 3.00 8.00
35 Steve Smyth Jsy/250 3.00 8.00
36 Magglio Ordonez Jsy/250 3.00 8.00
37 Joe Borchard Jsy/250 3.00 8.00
38 Frank Thomas Jsy/250 4.00 10.00
39 Mark Buehrle Jsy/250 3.00 8.00
40 Joe Crede Hat/100 4.00 10.00
41 Carlos Lee Jsy/250 3.00 8.00
42 Paul Konerko Jsy/250 3.00 8.00
43 Adam Dunn Jsy/250 3.00 8.00
45 Brandon Larson Spikes/150 3.00 8.00
46 Ken Griffey Jr. Base/250 8.00 20.00
47 Barry Larkin Jsy/250 4.00 10.00
48 Sean Casey Bat/250 3.00 8.00
49 Wily Mo Pena Bat/250 3.00 8.00
50 Austin Kearns Jsy/250 3.00 8.00
51 Victor Martinez Jsy/100 6.00 15.00
55 C.C. Sabathia Jsy/250 3.00 8.00
56 Ricardo Rodriguez Bat/250 3.00 8.00
57 Omar Vizquel Jsy/250 4.00 10.00
58 Travis Hafner Bat/250 3.00 8.00
59 Todd Helton Jsy/250 4.00 10.00
60 Jason Jennings Jsy/250 3.00 8.00
62 Larry Walker Jsy/250 3.00 8.00
63 Travis Chapman Bat/250 3.00 8.00
64 Mike Maroth Jsy/250 3.00 8.00
65 Josh Beckett Jsy/250 3.00 8.00
66 Ivan Rodriguez Bat/250 4.00 10.00
67 Brad Penny Jsy/250 3.00 8.00
68 A.J. Burnett Jsy/250 3.00 8.00
69 Craig Biggio Jsy/250 4.00 10.00
70 Roy Oswalt Jsy/250 3.00 8.00
71 Jason Lane Jsy/250 3.00 8.00
72 Nolan Ryan Astros Jsy/35 40.00 80.00
73 Wade Miller Jsy/250 3.00 8.00
74 Richard Hidalgo Pants/250 3.00 8.00
75 Jeff Bagwell Jsy/250 4.00 10.00
76 Lance Berkman Jsy/250 3.00 8.00
77 Rodrigo Rosario Jsy/250 3.00 8.00
78 Jeff Kent Bat/250 3.00 8.00
79 John Buck Jsy/250 3.00 8.00
80 Angel Berroa Bat/250 4.00 10.00
81 Mike Sweeney Jsy/250 3.00 8.00
84 Carlos Beltran Jsy/250 3.00 8.00
86 Hideo Nomo Jsy/250 12.50 30.00
87 Paul Lo Duca Jsy/250 3.00 8.00
88 Cesar Izturis Pants/250 3.00 8.00
89 Kazuhisa Ishii Jsy/250 3.00 8.00
90 Shawn Green Jsy/250 3.00 8.00
91 Joe Thurston Jsy/250 3.00 8.00
92 Adrian Beltre Bat/250 3.00 8.00
93 Kevin Brown Jsy/250 3.00 8.00
94 Richie Sexson Jsy/250 3.00 8.00
95 Ben Sheets Jsy/250 3.00 8.00
97 Geoff Jenkins Jsy/250 3.00 8.00
98 Bill Hall Bat/250 3.00 8.00
99 Torii Hunter Jsy/250 3.00 8.00
101 Michael Cuddyer Jsy/250 3.00 8.00
102 Jose Morban Bat/250 3.00 8.00
103 Brad Radke Jsy/250 3.00 8.00
104 Jacque Jones Jsy/250 3.00 8.00
105 Eric Milton Jsy/250 3.00 8.00
106 Joe Mays Jsy/250 3.00 8.00
107 Adam Johnson Jsy/250 3.00 8.00
108 Javier Vazquez Jsy/250 3.00 8.00
109 Vladimir Guerrero Jsy/250 4.00 10.00
110 Jose Vidro Jsy/250 3.00 8.00
111 Michael Barrett Jsy/50 6.00 15.00
112 Orlando Cabrera Jsy/250 3.00 8.00
113 Tom Glavine Bat/250 4.00 10.00
114 Roberto Alomar Bat/250 4.00 10.00
115 Tsuyoshi Shinjo Jsy/250 3.00 8.00
116 Cliff Floyd Bat/250 3.00 8.00
117 Mike Piazza Jsy/250 8.00 20.00
118 Al Leiter Jsy/250 3.00 8.00
119 Don Mattingly Jsy/35 40.00 80.00
120 Roger Clemens Jsy/250 10.00 25.00
121 Derek Jeter Base/250 10.00 25.00
122 Alfonso Soriano Jsy/250 3.00 8.00
123 Drew Henson Bat/250 3.00 8.00
124 Brandon Claussen Hat/50 6.00 15.00
125 Christian Parker Pants/250 3.00 8.00
126 Jason Giambi Jsy/250 3.00 8.00
127 Mike Mussina Jsy/250 4.00 10.00
128 Bernie Williams Jsy/250 4.00 10.00
130 Nick Johnson Jsy/250 3.00 8.00
131 Jorge Posada Jsy/250 4.00 10.00
132 Andy Pettitte Jsy/250 4.00 10.00
133 Barry Zito Jsy/250 3.00 8.00
134 Miguel Tejada Jsy/250 3.00 8.00
135 Eric Chavez Jsy/250 3.00 8.00
136 Tim Hudson Jsy/250 3.00 8.00
137 Mark Mulder Jsy/250 3.00 8.00
138 Terrence Long Jsy/250 3.00 8.00
139 Mark Ellis Jsy/250 3.00 8.00
140 Jim Thome Bat/250 4.00 10.00
141 Pat Burrell Bat/250 3.00 8.00
142 Marlon Byrd Jsy/250 3.00 8.00
143 Bobby Abreu Jsy/250 3.00 8.00
144 Brandon Duckworth Jsy/250 3.00 8.00
145 Robert Person Jsy/250 3.00 8.00
146 Anderson Machado Jsy/250 3.00 8.00
147 Aramis Ramirez Jsy/250 3.00 8.00
148 Jack Wilson Bat/250 3.00 8.00
150 Jose Castillo Bat/250 3.00 8.00
151 Walter Young Bat/250 3.00 8.00
152 Brian Giles Bat/250 3.00 8.00
153 Jason Kendall Jsy/250 3.00 8.00
154 Ryan Klesko Jsy/25
155 Mike Rivera Bat/250 3.00 8.00
157 Brian Lawrence Bat/250 3.00 8.00
158 Xavier Nady Hat/60 6.00 15.00
159 Dennis Tankersley Jsy/250 3.00 8.00
160 Phil Nevin Jsy/250 3.00 8.00
161 Barry Bonds Base/250 10.00 25.00
162 Kenny Lofton Bat/250 3.00 8.00
163 Rich Aurilia Jsy/250 3.00 8.00
164 Ichiro Suzuki Base/250 12.50 30.00
165 Edgar Martinez Jsy/100 6.00 15.00
166 Chris Snelling Bat/250 3.00 8.00
167 Rafael Soriano Jsy/250 3.00 8.00
168 John Olerud Jsy/250 3.00 8.00
169 Bret Boone Jsy/250 3.00 8.00
170 Freddy Garcia Jsy/250 3.00 8.00
171 Aaron Sele Jsy/250 3.00 8.00
172 Kazuhiro Sasaki Jsy/250 3.00 8.00
173 Albert Pujols Jsy/250 12.50 30.00
174 Scott Rolen Bat/250 4.00 10.00
175 So Taguchi Jsy/250 3.00 8.00
176 Jim Edmonds Jsy/250 3.00 8.00
177 Edgar Renteria Jsy/250 3.00 8.00
178 J.D. Drew Jsy/250 3.00 8.00
179 Antonio Perez Bat/250 3.00 8.00
180 Dewon Brazelton Jsy/250 3.00 8.00
181 Aubrey Huff Jsy/50 6.00 15.00
182 Toby Hall Jsy/250 3.00 8.00
183 Ben Grieve Jsy/100 4.00 10.00
184 Joe Kennedy Jsy/250 3.00 8.00
185 Alex Rodriguez Jsy/250 10.00 25.00
186 Rafael Palmeiro Jsy/250 4.00 10.00
187 Hank Blalock Jsy/250 3.00 8.00
188 Mark Teixeira Jsy/250 4.00 10.00
189 Juan Gonzalez Bat/250 3.00 8.00
190 Kevin Mench Jsy/250 3.00 8.00
191 Nolan Ryan Rgr Jsy/35 40.00 80.00
192 Doug Davis Jsy/250 3.00 8.00
193 Eric Hinske Jsy/250 3.00 8.00
196 Carlos Delgado Jsy/250 3.00 8.00
197 Shannon Stewart Jsy/250 3.00 8.00
198 Josh Phelps Jsy/250 3.00 8.00
199 Vernon Wells Jsy/250 3.00 8.00
200 Roy Halladay Jsy/250 3.00 8.00
201 Babe Ruth RET Pants/15
202 Lou Gehrig RET Pants/15
203 Jackie Robinson RET Jsy/15
204 Ty Cobb RET Pants/15
205 Thurman Munson RET Jsy/15

2003 Leaf Certified Materials Fabric of the Game

Randomly inserted into packs, these 900 cards feature six versions of 150 different cards. The set is broken down into BA (designed like a Base); DY (indicating the year the team was 1st known by their current nomenclature); IN (inscription; JN (Jersey Number); JY (Jersey Year that this jersey was used in) and PS (Position). We have put the stated print run next to the player's name in our checklist.

PRINT RUNS BETWEEN 1-102 COPIES PER
NO PRICING ON QTY OF 25 OR LESS
1BA Bobby Doerr BA/50 4.00 10.00
1DY Bobby Doerr DY/7
1IN Bobby Doerr IN/25
1JN Bobby Doerr JN/1
1JY Bobby Doerr JY/39 6.00 15.00
1PS Bobby Doerr PS/50 4.00 10.00
2BA Ozzie Smith BA/100 10.00 25.00
2DY Ozzie Smith DY/1
2IN Ozzie Smith IN/50 12.50 30.00
2JN Ozzie Smith JN/1
2JY Ozzie Smith JY/88 10.00 25.00
2PS Ozzie Smith PS/50 12.50 30.00
3BA Pee Wee Reese BA/20
3DY Pee Wee Reese DY/32 12.50 30.00
3IN Pee Wee Reese IN/15
3JN Pee Wee Reese JN/1
3JY Pee Wee Reese JY/58 6.00 15.00
3PS Pee Wee Reese PS/20
4BA Jeff Bagwell Pants BA/100 4.00 10.00
4DY Jeff Bagwell Pants DY/65 6.00 15.00
4IN Jeff Bagwell Pants IN/50 6.00 15.00
4JN Jeff Bagwell Pants JN/5
4JY Jeff Bagwell Pants JY/98 4.00 10.00
4PS Jeff Bagwell Pants PS/50 6.00 15.00
5BA Tommy Lasorda BA/100 4.00 10.00
5DY Tommy Lasorda DY/58 4.00 10.00
5IN Tommy Lasorda IN/25
5JN Tommy Lasorda JN/2
5JY Tommy Lasorda JY/84 4.00 10.00
5PS Tommy Lasorda PS/50 4.00 10.00
6BA Red Schoendienst BA/25
6DY Red Schoendienst DY/1
6IN Red Schoendienst IN/15
6JN Red Schoendienst JN/2
6JY Red Schoendienst JY/55 4.00 10.00
6PS Red Schoendienst PS/50 4.00 10.00
7BA Harmon Killebrew BA/50 6.00 15.00
7DY Harmon Killebrew DY/61 6.00 15.00
7IN Harmon Killebrew IN/50 6.00 15.00
7JN Harmon Killebrew JN/3
7JY Harmon Killebrew JY/71 6.00 15.00
7PS Harmon Killebrew PS/50 6.00 15.00
8BA Roger Maris BA/25
8DY Roger Maris DY/55 15.00 40.00
8IN Roger Maris IN/20
8JN Roger Maris JN/3
8JY Roger Maris JY/58 15.00 40.00
8PS Roger Maris PS/50 15.00 40.00
9BA Alex Rodriguez M's BA/100 6.00 15.00
9DY Alex Rodriguez M's DY/77 6.00 15.00
9IN Alex Rodriguez M's IN/50 10.00 25.00
9JN Alex Rodriguez M's JN/3
9JY Alex Rodriguez M's JY/99 6.00 15.00
9PS Alex Rodriguez M's PS/50 10.00 25.00
10BA Alex Rodriguez Rgr BA/100 6.00 15.00
10DY Alex Rodriguez Rgr DY/72 10.00 25.00
10IN Alex Rodriguez Rgr IN/50 10.00 25.00
10JN Alex Rodriguez Rgr JN/3
10JY Alex Rodriguez Rgr JY/101 6.00 15.00
10PS Alex Rodriguez Rgr PS/50 10.00 25.00
11BA Dale Murphy BA/50 6.00 15.00
11DY Dale Murphy DY/66 6.00 15.00
11IN Dale Murphy IN/50 6.00 15.00
11JN Dale Murphy JN/3
11JY Dale Murphy JY/85 6.00 15.00
11PS Dale Murphy PS/50 6.00 15.00
12BA Alan Trammell BA/100 4.00 10.00
12DY Alan Trammell DY/1
12IN Alan Trammell IN/50 4.00 10.00
12JN Alan Trammell JN/3
12JY Alan Trammell JY/90 4.00 10.00
12PS Alan Trammell PS/50 4.00 10.00
13BA Babe Ruth Pants BA/10
13DY Babe Ruth Pants DY/13
13IN Babe Ruth Pants IN/10
13JN Babe Ruth Pants JN/3
13JY Babe Ruth Pants JY/30 200.00 350.00
13PS Babe Ruth Pants PS/10
14BA Lou Gehrig BA/10
14DY Lou Gehrig DY/13
14IN Lou Gehrig IN/10
14JN Lou Gehrig JN/4
14JY Lou Gehrig JY/38 175.00 300.00
14PS Lou Gehrig PS/10
15BA Babe Ruth BA/10
15DY Babe Ruth DY/13
15IN Babe Ruth IN/10
15JN Babe Ruth JN/3
15JY Babe Ruth JY/30 250.00 400.00
15PS Babe Ruth PS/10
16BA Mel Ott BA/10
16DY Mel Ott DY/1
16IN Mel Ott IN/10
16JN Mel Ott JN/4
16JY Mel Ott JY/46 15.00 40.00
16PS Mel Ott PS/10
17BA Paul Molitor BA/100 4.00 10.00
17DY Paul Molitor DY/70 4.00 10.00
17IN Paul Molitor IN/50 4.00 10.00
17JN Paul Molitor JN/4
17JY Paul Molitor JY/84 4.00 10.00
17PS Paul Molitor PS/50 4.00 10.00
18BA Duke Snider BA/15
18DY Duke Snider DY/58 6.00 15.00
18IN Duke Snider IN/15
18JN Duke Snider JN/4
18JY Duke Snider JY/62 6.00 15.00
18PS Duke Snider PS/15
19BA Miguel Tejada BA/50 4.00 10.00
19DY Miguel Tejada DY/68 4.00 10.00
19IN Miguel Tejada IN/50 4.00 10.00
19JN Miguel Tejada JN/4
19JY Miguel Tejada JY/99 3.00 8.00
19PS Miguel Tejada PS/50 4.00 10.00
20BA Lou Gehrig Pants BA/10
20DY Lou Gehrig Pants DY/13
20IN Lou Gehrig Pants IN/10
20JN Lou Gehrig Pants JN/4
20JY Lou Gehrig Pants JY/38 150.00 250.00
20PS Lou Gehrig Pants PS/10
21BA Brooks Robinson BA/15
21DY Brooks Robinson DY/54 6.00 15.00
21IN Brooks Robinson IN/15
21JN Brooks Robinson JN/5
21JY Brooks Robinson JY/66 6.00 15.00
21PS Brooks Robinson PS/15
22BA George Brett BA/50 15.00 40.00
22DY George Brett DY/69 15.00 40.00
22IN George Brett IN/50 15.00 40.00
22JN George Brett JN/5
22JY George Brett JY/91 12.50 30.00
22PS George Brett PS/50 15.00 40.00
23BA Johnny Bench BA/50 6.00 15.00
23DY Johnny Bench DY/59 6.00 15.00
23IN Johnny Bench IN/50 6.00 15.00
23JN Johnny Bench JN/5
23JY Johnny Bench JY/81 6.00 15.00
23PS Johnny Bench PS/50 6.00 15.00
24BA Lou Boudreau BA/15
24DY Lou Boudreau DY/15
24IN Lou Boudreau IN/15
24JN Lou Boudreau JN/5
24JY Lou Boudreau JY/48 6.00 15.00
24PS Lou Boudreau PS/15
25BA Nomar Garciaparra BA/100 10.00 25.00

25DY Nomar Garciaparra DY/7
25IN Nomar Garciaparra IN/50 10.00 25.00
25JN Nomar Garciaparra JN/5
25JY Nomar Garciaparra JY/100 10.00 25.00
25PS Nomar Garciaparra PS/50 10.00 25.00
26BA Tsuyoshi Shinjo BA/50 4.00 10.00
26DY Tsuyoshi Shinjo DY/62 4.00 10.00
26IN Tsuyoshi Shinjo IN/25
26JN Tsuyoshi Shinjo JN/5
26JY Tsuyoshi Shinjo JY/101 3.00 8.00
26PS Tsuyoshi Shinjo PS/25
27BA Pat Burrell BA/100 3.00 8.00
27DY Pat Burrell DY/46 5.00 12.00
27IN Pat Burrell IN/25
27JN Pat Burrell JN/5
27JY Pat Burrell JY/101 3.00 8.00
27PS Pat Burrell PS/25
28BA Albert Pujols BA/100 10.00 25.00
28DY Albert Pujols DY/1
28IN Albert Pujols IN/50 12.50 30.00
28JN Albert Pujols JN/5
28JY Albert Pujols JY/101 10.00 25.00
28PS Albert Pujols PS/50 12.50 30.00
29BA Stan Musial BA/10
29DY Stan Musial DY/1
29IN Stan Musial IN/10
29JN Stan Musial JN/6
29JY Stan Musial JY/43 15.00 40.00
29PS Stan Musial PS/10
30BA Al Kaline BA/20
30DY Al Kaline DY/1
30IN Al Kaline IN/15
30JN Al Kaline JN/6
30JY Al Kaline JY/64 6.00 15.00
30PS Al Kaline PS/15
31BA Ivan Rodriguez BA/100 4.00 10.00
31DY Ivan Rodriguez DY/72 6.00 15.00
31IN Ivan Rodriguez IN/50 6.00 15.00
31JN Ivan Rodriguez JN/7
31JY Ivan Rodriguez JY/101 4.00 10.00
31PS Ivan Rodriguez PS/50 6.00 15.00
32BA Craig Biggio BA/100 4.00 10.00
32DY Craig Biggio DY/65 6.00 15.00
32IN Craig Biggio IN/25
32JN Craig Biggio JN/7
32JY Craig Biggio JY/101 4.00 10.00
32PS Craig Biggio PS/50 6.00 15.00
33BA Joe Morgan BA/10
33DY Joe Morgan DY/59 4.00 10.00
33IN Joe Morgan IN/10
33JN Joe Morgan JN/8
33JY Joe Morgan JY/74 4.00 10.00
33PS Joe Morgan PS/10
34BA Willie Stargell BA/50 6.00 15.00
34DY Willie Stargell DY/1
34IN Willie Stargell IN/15
34JN Willie Stargell JN/8
34JY Willie Stargell JY/68 6.00 15.00
34PS Willie Stargell PS/50 6.00 15.00
35BA Andre Dawson BA/100 4.00 10.00
35DY Andre Dawson DY/7
35IN Andre Dawson IN/50 4.00 10.00
35JN Andre Dawson JN/8
35JY Andre Dawson JY/87 4.00 10.00
35PS Andre Dawson PS/50 4.00 10.00
36BA Gary Carter BA/100 4.00 10.00
36DY Gary Carter DY/62 4.00 10.00
36IN Gary Carter IN/50 4.00 10.00
36JN Gary Carter JN/8
36JY Gary Carter JY/85 4.00 10.00
36PS Gary Carter PS/50 4.00 10.00
37BA Cal Ripken BA/50 30.00 60.00
37DY Cal Ripken DY/54 30.00 60.00
37IN Cal Ripken IN/50 30.00 60.00
37JN Cal Ripken JN/8
37JY Cal Ripken JY/101 20.00 50.00
37PS Cal Ripken PS/50 30.00 60.00
38BA Enos Slaughter BA/15
38DY Enos Slaughter DY/1
38IN Enos Slaughter IN/15
38JN Enos Slaughter JN/9
38JY Enos Slaughter JY/53 6.00 15.00
38PS Enos Slaughter PS/25
39BA Reggie Jackson A's BA/50 6.00 15.00
39DY Reggie Jackson A's DY/68 6.00 15.00
39IN Reggie Jackson A's IN/25
39JN Reggie Jackson A's JN/9
39JY Reggie Jackson A's JY/75 6.00 15.00
39PS Reggie Jackson A's PS/50 6.00 15.00
40BA Phil Rizzuto BA/20
40DY Phil Rizzuto DY/13
40IN Phil Rizzuto IN/15
40JN Phil Rizzuto JN/10
40JY Phil Rizzuto JY/47 10.00 25.00
40PS Phil Rizzuto PS/15
41BA Chipper Jones BA/100 4.00 10.00
41DY Chipper Jones DY/66 6.00 15.00
41IN Chipper Jones IN/50 6.00 15.00
41JN Chipper Jones JN/10
41JY Chipper Jones JY/101 4.00 10.00
41PS Chipper Jones PS/50 6.00 15.00
42BA H.Nomo Dodgers BA/100 4.00 10.00
42DY H.Nomo Dodgers DY/58 6.00 15.00
42IN H.Nomo Dodgers IN/50 6.00 15.00
42JN H.Nomo Dodgers JN/16
42JY H.Nomo Dodgers JY/95 4.00 10.00
42PS H.Nomo Dodgers PS/50 6.00 15.00
43BA Luis Aparicio BA/25
43DY Luis Aparicio DY/4
43IN Luis Aparicio IN/15
43JN Luis Aparicio JN/11
43JY Luis Aparicio JY/69 4.00 10.00
43PS Luis Aparicio PS/20
44BA H.Nomo R.Sox BA/100 4.00 10.00
44DY H.Nomo R.Sox DY/7
44IN H.Nomo R.Sox IN/50 6.00 15.00
44JN H.Nomo R.Sox JN/11
44JY H.Nomo R.Sox JY/101 4.00 10.00
44PS H.Nomo R.Sox PS/50 6.00 15.00
45BA Edgar Martinez BA/100 4.00 10.00
45DY Edgar Martinez DY/77 4.00 10.00
45IN Edgar Martinez IN/25
45JN Edgar Martinez JN/11
45JY Edgar Martinez JY/100 4.00 10.00
45PS Edgar Martinez PS/50 6.00 15.00
46BA Barry Larkin BA/100 4.00 10.00
46DY Barry Larkin DY/59 6.00 15.00
46IN Barry Larkin IN/25
46JN Barry Larkin JN/11
46JY Barry Larkin JY/100 4.00 10.00
46PS Barry Larkin PS/50 6.00 15.00
47BA Alfonso Soriano BA/100 3.00 8.00
47DY Alfonso Soriano DY/13
47IN Alfonso Soriano IN/50 4.00 10.00
47JN Alfonso Soriano JN/12
47JY Alfonso Soriano JY/102 3.00 8.00
47PS Alfonso Soriano PS/50 4.00 10.00
48BA Wade Boggs Rays BA/100 6.00 15.00
48DY Wade Boggs Rays DY/98 6.00 15.00
48IN Wade Boggs Rays IN/50 6.00 15.00
48JN Wade Boggs Rays JN/12
48JY Wade Boggs Rays JY/99 6.00 15.00
48PS Wade Boggs Rays PS/50 6.00 15.00
49BA Wade Boggs Yanks BA/50 6.00 15.00
49DY Wade Boggs Yanks DY/13
49IN Wade Boggs Yanks IN/50 6.00 15.00
49JN Wade Boggs Yanks JN/12
49JY Wade Boggs Yanks JY/94 6.00 15.00
49PS Wade Boggs Yanks PS/50 6.00 15.00
50BA Ernie Banks BA/15
50DY Ernie Banks DY/7
50IN Ernie Banks IN/15
50JN Ernie Banks JN/14
50JY Ernie Banks JY/68 6.00 15.00
50PS Ernie Banks PS/15
51BA Joe Torre BA/50 4.00 10.00
51DY Joe Torre DY/66 4.00 10.00
51IN Joe Torre IN/50 4.00 10.00
51JN Joe Torre JN/15
51JY Joe Torre JY/66 4.00 10.00
51PS Joe Torre PS/50 4.00 10.00
52BA Tim Hudson BA/100 3.00 8.00
52DY Tim Hudson DY/68 4.00 10.00
52IN Tim Hudson IN/25
52JN Tim Hudson JN/15
52JY Tim Hudson JY/101 3.00 8.00
52PS Tim Hudson PS/50 4.00 10.00
53BA Shawn Green BA/100 3.00 8.00
53DY Shawn Green DY/58 4.00 10.00
53IN Shawn Green IN/25
53JN Shawn Green JN/15
53JY Shawn Green JY/102 3.00 8.00
53PS Shawn Green PS/50 4.00 10.00
54BA Carlos Beltran BA/100 3.00 8.00
54DY Carlos Beltran DY/69 4.00 10.00
54IN Carlos Beltran IN/25
54JN Carlos Beltran JN/15
54JY Carlos Beltran JY/101 3.00 8.00
54PS Carlos Beltran PS/50 4.00 10.00
55BA Bo Jackson BA/50 6.00 15.00
55DY Bo Jackson DY/69 6.00 15.00
55IN Bo Jackson IN/25
55JN Bo Jackson JN/16
55JY Bo Jackson JY/90 6.00 15.00
55PS Bo Jackson PS/50 6.00 15.00
56BA Hal Newhouser BA/50 4.00 10.00
56DY Hal Newhouser DY/15
56IN Hal Newhouser IN/25
56JN Hal Newhouser JN/16
56JY Hal Newhouser JY/55 4.00 10.00
56PS Hal Newhouser PS/50 4.00 10.00
57BA Jason Giambi A's BA/100 3.00 8.00
57DY Jason Giambi A's DY/68 4.00 10.00
57IN Jason Giambi A's IN/50 4.00 10.00
57JN Jason Giambi A's JN/16
57JY Jason Giambi A's JY/101 3.00 8.00
57PS Jason Giambi A's PS/50 4.00 10.00
58BA Lance Berkman BA/100 3.00 8.00
58DY Lance Berkman DY/65 4.00 10.00
58IN Lance Berkman IN/50 4.00 10.00
58JN Lance Berkman JN/17
58JY Lance Berkman JY/102 3.00 8.00
58PS Lance Berkman PS/50 4.00 10.00
59BA Todd Helton BA/100 4.00 10.00
59DY Todd Helton DY/93 4.00 10.00
59IN Todd Helton IN/25
59JN Todd Helton JN/17
59JY Todd Helton JY/100 4.00 10.00
59PS Todd Helton PS/50 6.00 15.00
60BA Mark Grace BA/100 4.00 10.00
60DY Mark Grace DY/7
60IN Mark Grace IN/25
60JN Mark Grace JN/17
60JY Mark Grace JY/95 4.00 10.00
60PS Mark Grace PS/50 6.00 15.00
61BA Fred Lynn BA/100 4.00 10.00
61DY Fred Lynn DY/7
61IN Fred Lynn IN/25
61JN Fred Lynn JN/19
61JY Fred Lynn JY/75 4.00 10.00
61PS Fred Lynn PS/50 4.00 10.00
62BA Bob Feller BA/10
62DY Bob Feller DY/15
62IN Bob Feller IN/10
62JN Bob Feller JN/19
62JY Bob Feller JY/52 6.00 15.00
62PS Bob Feller PS/10
63BA Robin Yount BA/100 6.00 15.00
63DY Robin Yount DY/70 6.00 15.00
63IN Robin Yount IN/50 6.00 15.00
63JN Robin Yount JN/19
63JY Robin Yount JY/88 6.00 15.00
63PS Robin Yount PS/50 6.00 15.00
64BA Tony Gwynn BA/100 8.00 20.00
64DY Tony Gwynn DY/69 10.00 25.00
64IN Tony Gwynn IN/50 10.00 25.00
64JN Tony Gwynn JN/19
64JY Tony Gwynn JY/99 10.00 25.00
64PS Tony Gwynn PS/50 8.00 20.00
65BA Tony Gwynn Pants BA/100 8.00 20.00
65DY Tony Gwynn Pants DY/69 10.00 25.00
65IN Tony Gwynn Pants IN/50 10.00 25.00
65JN Tony Gwynn Pants JN/19
65JY Tony Gwynn Pants JY/99 8.00 20.00
65PS Tony Gwynn Pants PS/50 10.00 25.00
66BA Frank Robinson BA/10
66DY Frank Robinson DY/54 6.00 15.00
66IN Frank Robinson IN/10
66JN Frank Robinson JN/20
66JY Frank Robinson JY/70 6.00 15.00
66PS Frank Robinson PS/10
67BA Mike Schmidt BA/50 15.00 40.00
67DY Mike Schmidt DY/46 15.00 40.00
67IN Mike Schmidt IN/50 15.00 40.00
67JN Mike Schmidt JN/20
67JY Mike Schmidt JY/81 12.50 30.00
67PS Mike Schmidt PS/50 15.00 40.00
68BA Lou Brock BA/20
68DY Lou Brock DY/1
68IN Lou Brock IN/15
68JN Lou Brock JN/20
68JY Lou Brock JY/66 6.00 15.00
68PS Lou Brock PS/15
69BA Don Sutton BA/50 4.00 10.00
69DY Don Sutton DY/58 4.00 10.00
69IN Don Sutton IN/25
69JN Don Sutton JN/20
69JY Don Sutton JY/72 4.00 10.00
69PS Don Sutton PS/25
70BA Mark Mulder BA/100 3.00 8.00
70DY Mark Mulder DY/68 4.00 10.00
70IN Mark Mulder IN/25
70JN Mark Mulder JN/20
70JY Mark Mulder JY/101 3.00 8.00
70PS Mark Mulder PS/50 4.00 10.00
71BA Luis Gonzalez BA/100 3.00 8.00
71DY Luis Gonzalez DY/98 3.00 8.00
71IN Luis Gonzalez IN/25
71JN Luis Gonzalez JN/20
71JY Luis Gonzalez JY/101 3.00 8.00
71PS Luis Gonzalez PS/50 4.00 10.00
72BA Jorge Posada BA/100 4.00 10.00
72DY Jorge Posada DY/13
72IN Jorge Posada IN/25
72JN Jorge Posada JN/20
72JY Jorge Posada JY/101 4.00 10.00
72PS Jorge Posada PS/50 6.00 15.00
73BA Sammy Sosa BA/100 4.00 10.00
73DY Sammy Sosa DY/7
73IN Sammy Sosa IN/50 6.00 15.00
73JN Sammy Sosa JN/21
73JY Sammy Sosa JY/101 4.00 10.00
73PS Sammy Sosa PS/50 6.00 15.00
74BA Roberto Alomar BA/100 4.00 10.00
74DY Roberto Alomar DY/62 6.00 15.00
74IN Roberto Alomar IN/25
74JN Roberto Alomar JN/12
74JY Roberto Alomar JY/102 4.00 10.00
74PS Roberto Alomar PS/50 6.00 15.00
75BA Roberto Clemente BA/10
75DY Roberto Clemente DY/1
75IN Roberto Clemente IN/10
75JN Roberto Clemente JN/21
75JY Roberto Clemente JY/69 60.00 120.00
75PS Roberto Clemente PS/10
76BA Jeff Kent BA/100 3.00 8.00
76DY Jeff Kent DY/58 4.00 10.00
76IN Jeff Kent IN/25
76JN Jeff Kent JN/21
76JY Jeff Kent JY/101 3.00 8.00
76PS Jeff Kent PS/50 4.00 10.00
77BA Sean Casey BA/20
77DY Sean Casey DY/59 4.00 10.00
77IN Sean Casey IN/25
77JN Sean Casey JN/21
77JY Sean Casey JY/100 3.00 8.00
77PS Sean Casey PS/25
78BA R.Clemens R.Sox BA/50 10.00 25.00
78DY R.Clemens R.Sox DY/7
78IN R.Clemens R.Sox IN/50 10.00 25.00
78JN R.Clemens R.Sox JN/21
78JY R.Clemens R.Sox JY/95 10.00 25.00
78PS R.Clemens R.Sox PS/50 10.00 25.00
79BA Warren Spahn BA/20
79DY Warren Spahn DY/53 6.00 15.00
79IN Warren Spahn IN/15
79JN Warren Spahn JN/21
79JY Warren Spahn JY/58 6.00 15.00
79PS Warren Spahn PS/15
80BA R.Clemens Yanks BA/100 10.00 25.00
80DY R.Clemens Yanks DY/13
80IN R.Clemens Yanks IN/50 10.00 25.00
80JN R.Clemens Yanks JN/22
80JY R.Clemens Yanks JY/102 10.00 25.00
80PS R.Clemens Yanks PS/50 10.00 25.00
81BA Jim Palmer BA/50 6.00 15.00
81DY Jim Palmer DY/54 6.00 15.00
81IN Jim Palmer IN/25
81JN Jim Palmer JN/22
81JY Jim Palmer JY/69 6.00 15.00
81PS Jim Palmer PS/50 6.00 15.00
82BA Juan Gonzalez BA/50 4.00 10.00
82DY Juan Gonzalez DY/15
82IN Juan Gonzalez IN/25
82JN Juan Gonzalez JN/22
82JY Juan Gonzalez JY/101 3.00 8.00
82PS Juan Gonzalez PS/50 4.00 10.00
83BA Will Clark BA/100 6.00 15.00
83DY Will Clark DY/58 6.00 15.00
83IN Will Clark IN/25
83JN Will Clark JN/22
83JY Will Clark JY/88 6.00 15.00
83PS Will Clark PS/50 6.00 15.00
84BA Don Mattingly BA/50 12.50 30.00
84DY Don Mattingly DY/13
84IN Don Mattingly IN/50 12.50 30.00
84JN Don Mattingly JN/23
84JY Don Mattingly JY/93 12.50 30.00
84PS Don Mattingly PS/50 12.50 30.00
85BA Ryne Sandberg BA/40 15.00 40.00
85DY Ryne Sandberg DY/7
85IN Ryne Sandberg IN/50 15.00 40.00
85JN Ryne Sandberg JN/23
85JY Ryne Sandberg JY/85 12.50 30.00
85PS Ryne Sandberg PS/50 15.00 40.00
86BA Early Wynn BA/20
86DY Early Wynn DY/15
86IN Early Wynn IN/15
86JN Early Wynn JN/24
86JY Early Wynn JY/55 4.00 10.00
86PS Early Wynn PS/15
87BA Manny Ramirez BA/50 6.00 15.00
87DY Manny Ramirez DY/7
87IN Manny Ramirez IN/25
87JN Manny Ramirez JN/24
87JY Manny Ramirez JY/102 4.00 10.00
87PS Manny Ramirez PS/50 6.00 15.00
88BA R.Henderson Mets BA/100 4.00 10.00
88DY R.Henderson Mets DY/62 6.00 15.00
88IN R.Henderson Mets IN/50 6.00 15.00
88JN R.Henderson Mets JN/24
88JY R.Henderson Mets JY/99 4.00 10.00
88PS R.Henderson Mets PS/50 6.00 15.00
89BA R.Henderson Padres BA/100 4.00 10.00
89DY R.Henderson Padres DY/69 6.00 15.00
89IN R.Henderson Padres IN/25
89JN R.Henderson Padres JN/24
89JY R.Henderson Padres JY/102 4.00 10.00
89PS R.Henderson Padres PS/50 6.00 15.00
90BA Jason Giambi Yanks BA/100 3.00 8.00
90DY Jason Giambi Yanks DY/13
90IN Jason Giambi Yanks IN/50 4.00 10.00
90JN Jason Giambi Yanks JN/25
90JY Jason Giambi Yanks JY/102 3.00 8.00
90PS Jason Giambi Yanks PS/50 4.00 10.00
91BA Carlos Delgado BA/100 3.00 8.00
91DY Carlos Delgado DY/77 3.00 8.00
91IN Carlos Delgado IN/25
91JN Carlos Delgado JN/25
91JY Carlos Delgado JY/100 3.00 8.00
91PS Carlos Delgado PS/50 4.00 10.00
92BA Jim Thome BA/100 4.00 10.00
92DY Jim Thome DY/15
92IN Jim Thome IN/25
92JN Jim Thome JN/25
92JY Jim Thome JY/102 4.00 10.00
92PS Jim Thome PS/50 6.00 15.00
93BA Andruw Jones BA/100 4.00 10.00
93DY Andruw Jones DY/66 6.00 15.00
93IN Andruw Jones IN/25
93JN Andruw Jones JN/25
93JY Andruw Jones JY/101 4.00 10.00
93PS Andruw Jones PS/50 6.00 15.00
94BA Rafael Palmeiro BA/100 4.00 10.00
94DY Rafael Palmeiro DY/72 6.00 15.00
94IN Rafael Palmeiro IN/25
94JN Rafael Palmeiro JN/25
94JY Rafael Palmeiro JY/102 4.00 10.00
94PS Rafael Palmeiro PS/50 6.00 15.00
95BA Troy Glaus BA/100 3.00 8.00
95DY Troy Glaus DY/97 3.00 8.00
95IN Troy Glaus IN/50 4.00 10.00
95JN Troy Glaus JN/25
95JY Troy Glaus JY/100 3.00 8.00
95PS Troy Glaus PS/50 4.00 10.00
96BA Wade Boggs R.Sox BA/100 6.00 15.00
96DY Wade Boggs R.Sox DY/7
96IN Wade Boggs R.Sox IN/50 6.00 15.00
96JN Wade Boggs R.Sox JN/26 12.50 30.00
96JY Wade Boggs R.Sox JY/86 6.00 15.00
96PS Wade Boggs R.Sox PS/50 6.00 15.00
97BA Catfish Hunter BA/50 6.00 15.00
97DY Catfish Hunter DY/68 6.00 15.00
97IN Catfish Hunter IN/25
97JN Catfish Hunter JN/27 12.50 30.00
97JY Catfish Hunter JY/68 6.00 15.00
97PS Catfish Hunter PS/50 6.00 15.00
98BA Juan Marichal BA/50 4.00 10.00
98DY Juan Marichal DY/58 4.00 10.00
98IN Juan Marichal IN/25
98JN Juan Marichal JN/27 8.00 20.00
98JY Juan Marichal JY/67 4.00 10.00
98PS Juan Marichal PS/50 4.00 10.00
99BA Carlton Fisk R.Sox BA/50 6.00 15.00
99DY Carlton Fisk R.Sox DY/7
99IN Carlton Fisk R.Sox IN/25
99JN Carlton Fisk R.Sox JN/27 12.50 30.00
99JY Carlton Fisk R.Sox JY/80 6.00 15.00
99PS Carlton Fisk R.Sox PS/50 6.00 15.00
100BA Vladimir Guerrero BA/100 4.00 10.00
100DY Vladimir Guerrero DY/69 6.00 15.00
100IN Vladimir Guerrero IN/25
100JN Vladimir Guerrero JN/27 10.00 25.00
100JY Vladimir Guerrero JY/101 4.00 10.00
100PS Vladimir Guerrero PS/50 6.00 15.00
101BA Rod Carew Angels BA/50 6.00 15.00
101DY Rod Carew Angels DY/65 6.00 15.00
101IN Rod Carew Angels IN/25
101JN Rod Carew Angels JN/29 12.50 30.00
101JY Rod Carew Angels JY/85 6.00 15.00
101PS Rod Carew Angels PS/50 6.00 15.00
102BA Rod Carew Twins BA/50 6.00 15.00
102DY Rod Carew Twins DY/61 6.00 15.00
102IN Rod Carew Twins IN/25
102JN Rod Carew Twins JN/29 12.50 30.00
102JY Rod Carew Twins JY/71 6.00 15.00
102PS Rod Carew Twins PS/50 6.00 15.00
103BA Joe Carter BA/50 4.00 10.00
103DY Joe Carter DY/77 4.00 10.00
103IN Joe Carter IN/25
103JN Joe Carter JN/29 8.00 20.00
103JY Joe Carter JY/94 4.00 10.00
103PS Joe Carter PS/25
104BA Mike Sweeney BA/100 3.00 8.00
104DY Mike Sweeney DY/69 4.00 10.00
104IN Mike Sweeney IN/25
104JN Mike Sweeney JN/29 6.00 15.00
104JY Mike Sweeney JY/101 3.00 8.00
104PS Mike Sweeney PS/50 4.00 10.00
105BA Nolan Ryan Angels BA/25
105DY Nolan Ryan Angels DY/65 15.00 40.00
105IN Nolan Ryan Angels IN/25
105JN Nolan Ryan Angels JN/30 20.00 50.00
105JY N.Ryan Angels JY/70 UER 15.00 40.00
Jersey year is credited to 1970; Ryan did not arrive in California till 1972
105PS Nolan Ryan Angels PS/50 15.00 40.00
106BA Orlando Cepeda BA/50 4.00 10.00
106DY Orlando Cepeda DY/58 4.00 10.00
106IN Orlando Cepeda IN/50 4.00 10.00
106JN Orlando Cepeda JN/30 8.00 20.00
106JY Orlando Cepeda JY/65 4.00 10.00
106PS Orlando Cepeda PS/50 4.00 10.00
107BA Magglio Ordonez BA/100 3.00 8.00
107DY Magglio Ordonez DY/4
107IN Magglio Ordonez IN/25
107JN Magglio Ordonez JN/30 6.00 15.00
107JY Magglio Ordonez JY/102 3.00 8.00
107PS Magglio Ordonez PS/50 4.00 10.00
108BA Hoyt Wilhelm BA/50 4.00 10.00
108DY Hoyt Wilhelm DY/4
108IN Hoyt Wilhelm IN/25
108JN Hoyt Wilhelm JN/31 8.00 20.00
108JY Hoyt Wilhelm JY/68 4.00 10.00
108PS Hoyt Wilhelm PS/50 4.00 10.00
109BA Mike Piazza BA/100 6.00 15.00
109DY Mike Piazza DY/62 10.00 25.00
109IN Mike Piazza IN/50 10.00 25.00
109JN Mike Piazza JN/31 15.00 40.00
109JY Mike Piazza JY/100 6.00 15.00
109PS Mike Piazza PS/50 10.00 25.00
110BA Greg Maddux BA/100 6.00 15.00
110DY Greg Maddux DY/66 10.00 25.00
110IN Greg Maddux IN/50 10.00 25.00
110JN Greg Maddux JN/31 15.00 40.00
110JY Greg Maddux JY/102 6.00 15.00
110PS Greg Maddux PS/50 10.00 25.00
111BA Mark Prior BA/100 4.00 10.00
111DY Mark Prior DY/7
111IN Mark Prior IN/50 6.00 15.00
111JN Mark Prior JN/22
111JY Mark Prior JY/102 4.00 10.00
111PS Mark Prior PS/50 6.00 15.00
112BA Torii Hunter BA/100 3.00 8.00
112DY Torii Hunter DY/61 4.00 10.00
112IN Torii Hunter IN/50 4.00 10.00
112JN Torii Hunter JN/48 5.00 12.00
112JY Torii Hunter JY/101 3.00 8.00
112PS Torii Hunter PS/50 4.00 10.00
113BA Steve Carlton BA/100 4.00 10.00
113DY Steve Carlton DY/46 6.00 15.00
113IN Steve Carlton IN/50 4.00 10.00
113JN Steve Carlton JN/32 8.00 20.00
113JY Steve Carlton JY/81 4.00 10.00
113PS Steve Carlton PS/50 4.00 10.00
114BA Jose Canseco BA/100 6.00 15.00
114DY Jose Canseco DY/68 6.00 15.00
114IN Jose Canseco IN/50 6.00 15.00
114JN Jose Canseco JN/33 6.00 15.00
114JY Jose Canseco JY/89 6.00 15.00
114PS Jose Canseco PS/50 6.00 15.00
115BA Nolan Ryan Rgr BA/50 15.00 40.00
115DY Nolan Ryan Rgr DY/72 15.00 40.00
115IN Nolan Ryan Rgr IN/50 15.00 40.00
115JN Nolan Ryan Rgr JN/34 20.00 50.00
115JY Nolan Ryan Rgr JY/90 15.00 40.00
115PS Nolan Ryan Rgr PS/50 15.00 40.00
116BA Nolan Ryan Astros BA/50 15.00 40.00
116DY Nolan Ryan Astros DY/65 15.00 40.00
116IN Nolan Ryan Astros IN/25
116JN Nolan Ryan Astros JN/34 20.00 50.00
116JY Nolan Ryan Astros JY/84 15.00 40.00
116PS Nolan Ryan Astros PS/50 15.00 40.00
117BA Ty Cobb Pants BA/25
117DY Ty Cobb Pants DY/1
117IN Ty Cobb Pants IN/25
117JN Ty Cobb Pants JN/1
117JY Ty Cobb Pants JY/27 75.00 150.00
117PS Ty Cobb Pants PS/10
118BA Kerry Wood BA/100 3.00 8.00
118DY Kerry Wood DY/7
118IN Kerry Wood IN/25
118JN Kerry Wood JN/34 6.00 15.00
118JY Kerry Wood JY/101 3.00 8.00
118PS Kerry Wood PS/50 4.00 10.00
119BA M.Mussina Yanks BA/50 6.00 15.00
119DY M.Mussina Yanks DY/13
119IN M.Mussina Yanks IN/25
119JN M.Mussina Yanks JN/35 10.00 25.00
119JY M.Mussina Yanks JY/101 4.00 10.00
119PS M.Mussina Yanks PS/50 6.00 15.00
120BA Yogi Berra BA/10
120DY Yogi Berra DY/13
120IN Yogi Berra IN/10
120JN Yogi Berra JN/35 12.50 30.00
120JY Yogi Berra JY/47 10.00 25.00
120PS Yogi Berra PS/10
121BA Thurman Munson BA/25
121DY Thurman Munson DY/13
121IN Thurman Munson IN/25
121JN Thurman Munson JN/15
121JY Thurman Munson JY/79 15.00 40.00
121PS Thurman Munson PS/5
122BA Frank Thomas BA/100 4.00 10.00
122DY Frank Thomas DY/4
122IN Frank Thomas IN/25
122JN Frank Thomas JN/35 10.00 25.00
122JY Frank Thomas JY/94 4.00 10.00
122PS Frank Thomas PS/50 6.00 15.00
123BA R.Henderson A's BA/50 6.00 15.00
123DY R.Henderson A's DY/68 6.00 15.00
123IN R.Henderson A's IN/25
123JN R.Henderson A's JN/35 10.00 25.00
123JY R.Henderson A's JY/80 4.00 10.00
123PS R.Henderson A's PS/50 6.00 15.00
124BA M.Muss O's Pants BA/100 4.00 10.00
124DY M.Muss O's Pants DY/54 6.00 15.00
124IN M.Muss O's Pants IN/25
124JN M.Muss O's Pants JN/35 10.00 25.00
124JY M.Muss O's Pants JY/97 4.00 10.00
124PS M.Muss O's Pants PS/50 6.00 15.00
125BA Gaylord Perry BA/100 4.00 10.00
125DY Gaylord Perry DY/77 4.00 10.00
125IN Gaylord Perry IN/25
125JN Gaylord Perry JN/36 6.00 15.00
125JY Gaylord Perry JY/82 4.00 10.00
125PS Gaylord Perry PS/50 4.00 10.00
126BA Nick Johnson BA/100 3.00 8.00
126DY Nick Johnson DY/13
126IN Nick Johnson IN/25
126JN Nick Johnson JN/36 5.00 12.00
126JY Nick Johnson JY/102 3.00 8.00
126PS Nick Johnson PS/50 4.00 10.00
127BA Curt Schilling BA/100 3.00 8.00
127DY Curt Schilling DY/98 3.00 8.00
127IN Curt Schilling IN/25
127JN Curt Schilling JN/38 5.00 12.00
127JY Curt Schilling JY/102 3.00 8.00
127PS Curt Schilling PS/50 4.00 10.00
128BA Dave Parker BA/100 4.00 10.00
128DY Dave Parker DY/1
128IN Dave Parker IN/25
128JN Dave Parker JN/39 6.00 15.00
128JY Dave Parker JY/80 4.00 10.00
128PS Dave Parker PS/50 4.00 10.00
129BA Eddie Mathews BA/15
129DY Eddie Mathews DY/53 6.00 15.00
129IN Eddie Mathews IN/15
129JN Eddie Mathews JN/41 10.00 25.00
129JY Eddie Mathews JY/59 6.00 15.00
129PS Eddie Mathews PS/15
130BA Tom Seaver Mets BA/10
130DY Tom Seaver Mets DY/62 6.00 15.00
130IN Tom Seaver Mets IN/10
130JN Tom Seaver Mets JN/41 10.00 25.00
130JY Tom Seaver Mets JY/69 6.00 15.00
130PS Tom Seaver Mets PS/10
131BA Tom Seaver Reds BA/10
131DY Tom Seaver Reds DY/59 6.00 15.00
131IN Tom Seaver Reds IN/10
131JN Tom Seaver Reds JN/41 10.00 25.00
131JY Tom Seaver Reds JY/78 6.00 15.00
131PS Tom Seaver Reds PS/22
132BA Jackie Robinson BA/10
132DY Jackie Robinson DY/32
132IN Jackie Robinson IN/10
132JN Jackie Robinson JN/42 40.00 80.00
132JY Jackie Robinson JY/52 40.00 80.00
132PS Jackie Robinson PS/10
133BA R.Jackson Angels BA/100 6.00 15.00
133DY R.Jackson Angels DY/65 6.00 15.00
133IN R.Jackson Angels IN/50 6.00 15.00
133JN R.Jackson Angels JN/44 10.00 25.00
133JY R.Jackson Angels JY/80 6.00 15.00
133PS R.Jackson Angels PS/50 6.00 15.00
134BA Willie McCovey BA/100 4.00 10.00
134DY Willie McCovey DY/58 4.00 10.00
134IN Willie McCovey IN/25
134JN Willie McCovey JN/44 6.00 15.00
134JY Willie McCovey JY/77 4.00 10.00
134PS Willie McCovey PS/50 4.00 10.00
135BA Eric Davis BA/100 4.00 10.00
135DY Eric Davis DY/59 4.00 10.00
135IN Eric Davis IN/25
135JN Eric Davis JN/44 6.00 15.00
135JY Eric Davis JY/89 4.00 10.00
135PS Eric Davis PS/50 4.00 10.00
136BA Adam Dunn BA/100 3.00 8.00
136DY Adam Dunn DY/59 4.00 10.00
136IN Adam Dunn IN/25
136JN Adam Dunn JN/44 5.00 12.00
136JY Adam Dunn JY/102 3.00 8.00
136PS Adam Dunn PS/50 4.00 10.00
137BA Roy Oswalt BA/100 3.00 8.00
137DY Roy Oswalt DY/65 4.00 10.00
137IN Roy Oswalt IN/50 4.00 10.00
137JN Roy Oswalt JN/44 5.00 12.00
137JY Roy Oswalt JY/102 3.00 8.00
137PS Roy Oswalt PS/50 4.00 10.00
138BA P.Martinez Expos BA/50 6.00 15.00
138DY P.Martinez Expos DY/69 6.00 15.00
138IN P.Martinez Expos IN/25
138JN P.Martinez Expos JN/45 8.00 20.00
138JY P.Martinez Expos JY/95 4.00 10.00
138PS P.Martinez Expos PS/50 6.00 15.00
139BA P.Martinez R.Sox BA/100 4.00 10.00
139DY P.Martinez R.Sox DY/7
139IN P.Martinez R.Sox IN/50 6.00 15.00
139JN P.Martinez R.Sox JN/45 8.00 20.00
139JY P.Martinez R.Sox JY/102 4.00 10.00
139PS P.Martinez R.Sox PS/50 6.00 15.00
140BA Andy Pettitte BA/100 4.00 10.00
140DY Andy Pettitte DY/13
140IN Andy Pettitte IN/25
140JN Andy Pettitte JN/46 8.00 20.00
140JY Andy Pettitte JY/97 4.00 10.00
140PS Andy Pettitte PS/50 6.00 15.00
141BA Jack Morris BA/100 4.00 10.00
141DY Jack Morris DY/1
141IN Jack Morris IN/50 4.00 10.00
141JN Jack Morris JN/47 6.00 15.00
141JY Jack Morris JY/85 4.00 10.00
141PS Jack Morris PS/50 4.00 10.00
142BA Tom Glavine BA/100 4.00 10.00
142DY Tom Glavine DY/66 6.00 15.00
142IN Tom Glavine IN/25
142JN Tom Glavine JN/47 8.00 20.00
142JY Tom Glavine JY/100 4.00 10.00
142PS Tom Glavine PS/50 6.00 15.00
143BA R.Johnson M's BA/100 4.00 10.00
143DY R.Johnson M's DY/77 4.00 10.00
143IN R.Johnson M's IN/50 6.00 15.00
143JN R.Johnson M's JN/51 6.00 15.00
143JY R.Johnson M's JY/98 4.00 10.00
143PS R.Johnson M's PS/50 6.00 15.00
144BA Bernie Williams BA/100 4.00 10.00
144DY Bernie Williams DY/13
144IN Bernie Williams IN/50 6.00 15.00
144JN Bernie Williams JN/51 6.00 15.00
144JY Bernie Williams JY/100 4.00 10.00
144PS Bernie Williams PS/50 6.00 15.00
145BA R.Johnson D'backs BA/50 6.00 15.00
145DY R.Johnson D'backs DY/98 4.00 10.00
145IN R.Johnson D'backs IN/50 6.00 15.00
145JN R.Johnson D'backs JN/51 6.00 15.00
145JY R.Johnson D'backs JY/102 4.00 10.00
145PS R.Johnson D'backs PS/50 6.00 15.00
146BA Don Drysdale BA/15
146DY Don Drysdale DY/58 6.00 15.00
146IN Don Drysdale IN/25
146JN Don Drysdale JN/53 6.00 15.00
146JY Don Drysdale JY/64 6.00 15.00
146PS Don Drysdale PS/25
147BA Mark Buehrle BA/100 3.00 8.00
147DY Mark Buehrle DY/4
147IN Mark Buehrle IN/25
147JN Mark Buehrle JN/56 4.00 10.00
147JY Mark Buehrle JY/101 3.00 8.00
147PS Mark Buehrle PS/50 4.00 10.00
148BA Chan Ho Park BA/100 4.00 10.00
148DY Chan Ho Park DY/58 6.00 15.00
148IN Chan Ho Park IN/25
148JN Chan Ho Park JN/61 6.00 15.00
148JY Chan Ho Park JY/101 4.00 10.00
148PS Chan Ho Park PS/50 6.00 15.00
149BA Carlton Fisk W.Sox BA/100 6.00 15.00
149DY Carlton Fisk W.Sox DY/4
149IN Carlton Fisk W.Sox IN/50 6.00 15.00
149JN Carlton Fisk W.Sox JN/72 6.00 15.00
149JY Carlton Fisk W.Sox JY/92 6.00 15.00
149PS Carlton Fisk W.Sox PS/50 6.00 15.00
150BA Barry Zito BA/100 3.00 8.00
150DY Barry Zito DY/68 4.00 10.00
150IN Barry Zito IN/25
150JN Barry Zito JN/75 4.00 10.00
150JY Barry Zito JY/101 3.00 8.00
150PS Barry Zito PS/50 4.00 10.00

2003 Leaf Certified Materials Fabric of the Game Autographs

This is a partial parallel to the Fabric of the Game insert set. Each of these cards were signed, using Donruss/Playoff "band-aid" autographs to a stated print run of five or fewer cards. We have put the announced print run next to the player's name in our checklist and please note there is no pricing due to market scarcity. In addition, because of the use of stickered autographs, please note that autographs of deceased players such as Enos Slaughter and Hoyt Wilhelm are included in this set.

RANDOM INSERTS IN PACKS
CARDS DISPLAY CUMULATIVE PRINT RUNS
ACTUAL PRINT RUNS B/WN 1-5 COPIES PER
SKIP-NUMBERED 302-CARD SET
NO PRICING DUE TO SCARCITY

2004 Leaf Certified Materials

This 300-card set was released in July, 2004. The set was issued in five-card packs with an $10 SRP which were issued 10 packs per box and 24 boxes per case. The first 200 cards featured active players while cards numbered 201-211 feature players who moved teams in the off-season in their old uniform. Cards numbered 201-211 were inserted at a stated rate of one in 120. Cards 212 through 240 featured retired legends while cards 241-300 featured signed Rookie Cards (except for Kaz Matsui). Cards 212-240 were issued to a stated print run of 500 serial numbered sets and cards numbered 241-300 were issued to a stated print run of 1000 serial numbered sets unless noted in our checklist.

COMP.SET w/o SP's (200) 15.00 40.00
COMMON CARD (1-200) .25 .60
COMMON CARD (201-211) 1.00 2.50
201-211 STATED ODDS 1:120
COMMON CARD (212 1.00 2.50
212-240 PRINT RUN 500 SERIAL #'d SETS
COMMON NO AU (241-300) .75 2.00
241-300 NO AU PRINT RUN 500 #'d PER
OVERALL AU ODDS 1:10
AU PRINT RUNS B/WN 100-1000 PER
AU PRINT RUN 500 #'d PER UNLESS NOTED
1 A.J. Burnett .25 .60
2 Adam Dunn .25 .60
3 Adam LaRoche .25 .60
4 Adam Loewen .25 .60
5 Adrian Beltre .25 .60
6 Al Leiter .25 .60
7 Albert Pujols 1.25 3.00
8 Alex Rodriguez Yanks 1.00 2.50
9 Alexis Rios .25 .60
10 Alfonso Soriano Rgr .25 .60
11 Andruw Jones .40 1.00
12 Andy Pettitte .40 1.00
13 Angel Berroa .25 .60
14 Aramis Ramirez .25 .60
15 Aubrey Huff .25 .60
16 Austin Kearns .25 .60
17 Barry Larkin .40 1.00
18 Barry Zito .25 .60
19 Ben Sheets .25 .60
20 Bernie Williams .40 1.00
21 Bobby Abreu .25 .60
22 Brad Penny .25 .60
23 Brad Wilkerson .25 .60
24 Brandon Webb .25 .60
25 Brendan Harris .25 .60
26 Bret Boone .25 .60
27 Brett Myers .25 .60
28 Bubba Crosby .25 .60
29 Brian Giles .25 .60
30 Chad Cordero .25 .60
31 Bubba Nelson .25 .60
32 Byron Gettis .25 .60
33 C.C. Sabathia .25 .60
34 Carl Crawford .25 .60
35 Carl Everett .25 .60
36 Carlos Beltran .25 .60
37 Carlos Delgado .25 .60
38 Carlos Lee .25 .60
39 Chad Gaudin .25 .60
40 Cliff Lee .25 .60
41 Chipper Jones .60 1.50
42 Cliff Floyd .25 .60
43 Clint Barmes .25 .60
44 Corey Patterson .25 .60
45 Craig Biggio .40 1.00
46 Curt Schilling Sox .40 1.00
47 Dan Haren .25 .60
48 Darin Erstad .25 .60
49 David Ortiz .60 1.50
50 Delmon Young .40 1.00
51 Derek Jeter 1.25 3.00
52 Dewon Brazelton .25 .60
53 Dontrelle Willis .40 1.00
54 Edgar Martinez .40 1.00
55 Edgar Renteria .25 .60
56 Edwin Almonte .25 .60
57 Edwin Jackson .25 .60
58 Eric Chavez .25 .60
59 Eric Hinske .25 .60
60 Eric Munson .25 .60
61 Erubiel Durazo .25 .60
62 Frank Thomas .60 1.50
63 Fred McGriff .40 1.00
64 Freddy Garcia .25 .60
65 Garret Anderson .25 .60
66 Garrett Atkins .25 .60
67 Gary Sheffield .25 .60
68 Geoff Jenkins .25 .60
69 Greg Maddux Cubs 1.00 2.50
70 Hank Blalock .25 .60
71 Hee Seop Choi .25 .60
72 Hideki Matsui 1.00 2.50
73 Hideo Nomo .60 1.50
74 Craig Wilson .25 .60
75 Ichiro Suzuki 1.25 3.00
76 Ivan Rodriguez Tigers .40 1.00
77 J.D. Drew .25 .60
78 John Lackey .25 .60
79 Jacque Jones .25 .60
80 Jae Weong Seo .25 .60
81 Jamie Moyer .25 .60
82 Jason Giambi Yanks .25 .60
83 Jason Jennings .25 .60
84 Jason Kendall .25 .60
85 Melvin Mora .25 .60
86 Jason Varitek .60 1.50
87 Javier Vazquez .25 .60
88 Javy Lopez .25 .60
89 Jay Gibbons .25 .60
90 Jay Payton .25 .60
91 Jeff Bagwell .40 1.00
92 Jeff Baker .25 .60
93 Jeff Kent .25 .60
94 Jeremy Bonderman .25 .60
95 Milton Bradley .25 .60
96 Jerome Williams .25 .60
97 Jim Edmonds .25 .60
98 Jim Thome .40 1.00
99 Jody Gerut .25 .60
100 Joe Borchard .25 .60
101 Joe Crede .25 .60
102 Johan Santana .60 1.50
103 John Olerud .25 .60
104 John Smoltz .40 1.00
105 Johnny Damon .40 1.00
106 Jorge Posada .40 1.00
107 Jose Castillo .25 .60
108 Jose Reyes .25 .60
109 Jose Vidro .25 .60
110 Josh Beckett .25 .60
111 Josh Phelps .25 .60
112 Juan Encarnacion .25 .60
113 Juan Gonzalez .25 .60
114 Junior Spivey .25 .60
115 Kazuhisa Ishii .25 .60
116 Kenny Lofton .25 .60
117 Kerry Wood .25 .60
118 Kevin Millwood .25 .60
119 Kevin Youkilis .25 .60
120 Lance Berkman .25 .60
121 Larry Bigbie .25 .60
122 Larry Walker .25 .60
123 Luis Castillo .25 .60
124 Luis Gonzalez .25 .60
125 Luis Matos .25 .60
126 Lyle Overbay .25 .60
127 Magglio Ordonez .25 .60
128 Manny Ramirez .40 1.00
129 Marcus Giles .25 .60
130 Mariano Rivera .60 1.50
131 Mark Buehrle .25 .60
132 Mark Mulder .25 .60
133 Mark Prior .40 1.00
134 Mark Teixeira .40 1.00
135 Marlon Byrd .25 .60
136 Matt Morris .25 .60
137 Miguel Cabrera .40 1.00
138 Mike Lowell .25 .60
139 Mike Mussina .40 1.00
140 Mike Piazza 1.00 2.50
141 Mike Sweeney .25 .60
142 Morgan Ensberg .25 .60
143 Nick Johnson .25 .60
144 Nomar Garciaparra 1.00 2.50
145 Omar Vizquel .40 1.00
146 Orlando Cabrera .25 .60
147 Orlando Hudson .25 .60
148 Pat Burrell .25 .60
149 Paul Konerko .25 .60
150 Paul Lo Duca .25 .60
151 Pedro Martinez .40 1.00
152 Jermaine Dye .25 .60
153 Preston Wilson .25 .60
154 Rafael Furcal .25 .60
155 Rafael Palmeiro O's .40 1.00
156 Randy Johnson .60 1.50
157 Rich Aurilia .25 .60
158 Rich Harden .25 .60
159 Richard Hidalgo .25 .60
160 Richie Sexson .25 .60
161 Rickie Weeks .25 .60
162 Roberto Alomar .40 1.00
163 Rocco Baldelli .25 .60
164 Roger Clemens Astros 1.25 3.00
165 Roy Halladay .25 .60
166 Roy Oswalt .25 .60
167 Ryan Howard 3.00 8.00
168 Ryan Klesko .25 .60
169 Rodrigo Lopez .25 .60
170 Sammy Sosa .60 1.50
171 Scott Podsednik .25 .60
172 Scott Rolen .40 1.00
173 Sean Burroughs .25 .60
174 Sean Casey .25 .60
175 Shannon Stewart .25 .60
176 Shawn Green .25 .60
177 Shea Hillenbrand .25 .60
178 Shigetoshi Hasegawa .25 .60
179 Steve Finley .25 .60
180 Tim Hudson .25 .60
181 Todd Helton .40 1.00
182 Tom Glavine .40 1.00
183 Torii Hunter .25 .60
184 Trot Nixon .25 .60
185 Troy Glaus .25 .60
186 Vernon Wells .25 .60
187 Victor Martinez .25 .60
188 Vladimir Guerrero Angels .60 1.50
189 Wade Miller .25 .60
190 Brandon Larson .25 .60
191 Travis Hafner .25 .60
192 Tim Salmon .40 1.00
193 Tim Redding .25 .60
194 Runelvys Hernandez .25 .60
195 Ramon Nivar .25 .60
196 Moises Alou .25 .60
197 Michael Young .25 .60
198 Laynce Nix .25 .60
199 Tino Martinez .40 1.00
200 Randall Simon .25 .60
201 Roger Clemens Yanks SP 2.50 6.00
202 Greg Maddux Braves SP 2.50 6.00
203 Vladimir Guerrero Expos SP 1.50 4.00
204 Miguel Tejada SP 1.00 2.50
205 Kevin Brown SP 1.00 2.50
206 Jason Giambi A's SP 1.00 2.50
207 Curt Schilling D'backs SP 1.00 2.50
208 Alex Rodriguez Rgr SP 2.50 6.00
209 Alfonso Soriano Yanks SP 1.00 2.50
210 Ivan Rodriguez Marlins SP 1.50 4.00
211 Rafael Palmeiro Rgr SP 1.50 4.00
212 Gary Carter LGD 1.00 2.50
213 Duke Snider LGD 1.50 4.00
214 Whitey Ford LGD 1.50 4.00
215 Bob Feller LGD 1.00 2.50
216 Reggie Jackson LGD 1.50 4.00
217 Ryne Sandberg LGD 3.00 8.00
218 Dale Murphy LGD 1.50 4.00
219 Tony Gwynn LGD 2.50 6.00
220 Don Mattingly LGD 3.00 8.00
221 Mike Schmidt LGD 3.00 8.00
222 Rickey Henderson LGD 1.50 4.00
223 Cal Ripken LGD 5.00 12.00
224 Nolan Ryan LGD 4.00 10.00
225 George Brett LGD 3.00 8.00
226 Bob Gibson LGD 1.50 4.00
227 Lou Brock LGD 1.50 4.00
228 Andre Dawson LGD 1.00 2.50
229 Rod Carew LGD 1.50 4.00
230 Wade Boggs LGD 1.50 4.00
231 Roberto Clemente LGD 4.00 10.00
232 Roy Campanella LGD 1.50 4.00
233 Babe Ruth LGD 4.00 10.00
234 Lou Gehrig LGD 3.00 8.00
235 Ty Cobb LGD 2.50 6.00
236 Roger Maris LGD 1.50 4.00
237 Satchel Paige LGD 1.50 4.00
238 Ernie Banks LGD 1.50 4.00
239 Ted Williams LGD 3.00 8.00
240 Stan Musial LGD 2.50 6.00
241 Hector Gimenez NG AU RC 3.00 8.00
242 Justin Germano NG AU RC 4.00 10.00
243 Ian Snell NG AU RC 6.00 15.00
244 Graham Koonce NG AU 3.00 8.00
245 Jose Capellan NG AU RC 3.00 8.00
246 Onil Joseph NG AU RC 3.00 8.00
247 S.Takatsu NG AU/200 RC 6.00 15.00
248 Carlos Hines NG AU RC 3.00 8.00
249 Linc Holdzkom NG AU RC 3.00 8.00
250 Mike Gosling NG AU RC 3.00 8.00
251 Eduardo Sierra NG AU RC 4.00 10.00
252 Renyel Pinto NG AU RC 3.00 8.00
253 Merkin Valdez NG AU RC 3.00 8.00
254 Angel Chavez NG AU RC 3.00 8.00
255 I.Ochoa NG AU/1000 RC 3.00 8.00
256 G.Dobbs NG AU/300 RC 3.00 8.00
257 William Bergolla NG AU RC 3.00 8.00
258 Aarom Baldiris NG AU RC 3.00 8.00
259 Kazuo Matsui NG RC 1.25 3.00
260 Carlos Vasquez NG AU RC 4.00 10.00
261 Freddy Guzman NG AU RC 3.00 8.00
262 Aki Otsuka NG AU/200 RC 12.50 30.00
263 M.Gomez NG AU/200 RC 4.00 10.00
264 Nick Regilio NG AU RC 3.00 8.00
265 Jamie Brown NG AU RC 3.00 8.00
266 Shawn Hill NG AU RC 3.00 8.00
267 Roberto Novoa NG AU RC 3.00 8.00
268 Sean Henn NG AU RC 3.00 8.00
269 Ramon Ramirez NG AU RC 3.00 8.00
270 R.Cedeno NG AU/1000 RC 6.00 15.00
271 Ryan Wing NG AU/400 RC 3.00 8.00
272 Ruddy Yan NG AU 3.00 8.00
273 Fernando Nieve NG AU RC 3.00 8.00
274 Rusty Tucker NG AU RC 4.00 10.00
275 Jason Bartlett NG AU RC 4.00 10.00
276 Mike Rouse NG AU RC 3.00 8.00
277 Dennis Sarfate NG AU RC 3.00 8.00
278 Cory Sullivan NG AU RC 3.00 8.00
279 C.Daigle NG AU/250 RC 4.00 10.00
280 C.Shelton NG AU/400 RC 10.00 25.00
281 J.Harper NG AU/400 RC 3.00 8.00
282 Michael Wuertz NG AU RC 4.00 10.00
283 T.Bausher NG AU/400 RC 3.00 8.00
284 Jorge Sequea NG AU RC 3.00 8.00
285 J.Labandeira NG AU/100 RC 5.00 12.00
286 Justin Leone NG AU RC 4.00 10.00
287 Tim Bittner NG AU RC 3.00 8.00
288 Andres Blanco NG AU RC 3.00 8.00
289 K.Cave NG AU/1000 RC 3.00 8.00
290 M.Johnston NG AU/1000 RC 3.00 8.00
291 J.Szuminski NG AU RC 3.00 8.00
292 Shawn Camp NG RC .75 2.00
293 Colby Miller NG AU RC 3.00 8.00
294 Jake Woods NG AU RC 3.00 8.00
295 Ryan Meaux NG AU RC 3.00 8.00
296 Don Kelly NG AU RC 3.00 8.00
297 Edwin Moreno NG AU RC 3.00 8.00
298 Phil Stockman NG AU RC 3.00 8.00
299 Jorge Vasquez NG RC 1.25 3.00
300 Kaz Tadano NG AU RC 6.00 15.00

2004 Leaf Certified Materials Mirror Black

RANDOM INSERTS IN PACKS
STATED PRINT RUN 1 SERIAL #'d SET
NO PRICING DUE TO SCARCITY

2004 Leaf Certified Materials Mirror Blue

*1-200: 2.5X TO 6X BASIC
*BLUE 201-211: 1.25X TO 3X BASIC
*BLUE 212-240: 1.25X TO 3X BASIC
*241-300: .6X TO 1.5X BASIC NO AU
*241-300: .3X TO .8X BASIC AU/1000
*241-300: .3X TO .8X BASIC AU/300-500
*241-300: .25X TO .6X BASIC AU/200-250
*BLUE 241-300: .15X TO .4X BASIC AU/100
RANDOM INSERTS IN PACKS
STATED PRINT RUN 50 SERIAL #'d SETS

2004 Leaf Certified Materials Mirror Emerald

RANDOM INSERTS IN PACKS
STATED PRINT RUN 5 SERIAL #'d SETS
NO PRICING DUE TO SCARCITY

2004 Leaf Certified Materials Mirror Gold

*GOLD 1-200: 4X TO 10X BASIC
*GOLD 201-211: 2X TO 5X BASIC
*GOLD 212-240: 2X TO 5X BASIC
RANDOM INSERTS IN PACKS
STATED PRINT RUN 25 SERIAL #'d SETS
241-300 NO PRICING DUE TO SCARCITY

2004 Leaf Certified Materials Mirror Red

*RED 1-200: 1.5X TO 4X BASIC
*RED 201-211: .75X TO 2X BASIC
*RED 212-240: .75X TO 2X BASIC
*RED 241-300: .4X TO 1X BASIC NO AU
*RED 241-300: .2X TO .5X BASIC AU/1000
*RED 241-300: .2X TO .5X BASIC AU/300-500
*RED 241-300: .15X TO .4X BASIC AU/200-250
*RED 241-300: .1X TO .25X BASIC AU/100
RANDOM INSERTS IN PACKS
STATED PRINT RUN 100 SERIAL #'d SETS

2004 Leaf Certified Materials Mirror White

*WHITE 1-200: 1.5X TO 4X BASIC
*WHITE 201-211: .75X TO 2X BASIC
*WHITE 212-240: .75X TO 2X BASIC
*WHITE 241-300: .4X TO 1X BASIC NO AU
*WHITE 241-300: .2X TO .5X AU/1000
*WHITE 241-300: .2X TO .5X AU/400-500
*WHITE 241-300: .15X TO .4X AU/200-300
*WHITE 241-300: .12X TO .3X AU/100
RANDOM INSERTS IN PACKS
PRINT RUN 100 SERIAL #'d SETS

2004 Leaf Certified Materials Mirror Autograph Black

OVERALL AU ODDS 1:10
STATED PRINT RUN 1 SERIAL #'d SET
NO PRICING DUE TO SCARCITY

2004 Leaf Certified Materials Mirror Autograph Blue

*1-240 p/r 100: .5X TO 1.2X RED p/r 200-250
*1-240 p/r 100: .4X TO 1X RED p/r 100
*1-240 p/r 50: .6X TO 1.5X RED p/r 200-250
*1-240 p/r 50: .5X TO 1.2X RED p/r 100

*1-240 p/r 50: .4X TO 1X RED p/r 50
*1-240 p/r 25: 1X TO 2.5X RED p/r 250
*1-240 p/r 25: .6X TO 1.5X RED p/r 50
*1-240 p/r 25: .4X TO 1X RED p/r 25
*241-300 p/r 100: .5X TO 1.2X REDp/r200-250
*241-300 p/r 100: .4X TO 1X RED p/r 100
*241-300 p/r 50: .4X TO 1X RED p/r 50
OVERALL AU ODDS 1:10
PRINT RUNS B/WN 1-100 COPIES PER
NO PRICING ON QTY OF 10 OR LESS
2 Adam Dunn/47 12.50 30.00
167 Ryan Howard/100 40.00 80.00

2004 Leaf Certified Materials Mirror Autograph Emerald

OVERALL AU ODDS 1:10
PRINT RUNS B/WN 1-5 COPIES PER
NO PRICING DUE TO SCARCITY

2004 Leaf Certified Materials Mirror Autograph Gold

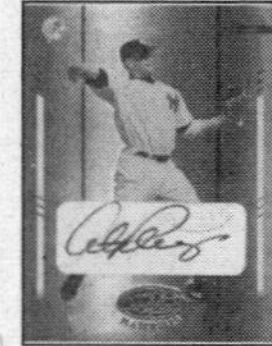

*1-240 p/r 25: 1X TO 2.5X RED p/r 200-250
*1-240 p/r 25: .75X TO 2X RED p/r 100
*1-240 p/r 25: .6X TO 1.5X RED p/r 50
*1-240 p/r 25: .4X TO 1X RED p/r 25
OVERALL AU ODDS 1:10
PRINT RUNS B/WN 1-25 COPIES PER
1-240 NO PRICING ON QTY OF 10 OR LESS
241-300 NO PRICING ON QTY OF 25 OR LESS
167 Ryan Howard/25 75.00 150.00

2004 Leaf Certified Materials Mirror Autograph Red

OVERALL AU ODDS 1:10
PRINT RUNS B/WN 1-250 COPIES PER
NO PRICING ON QTY OF 10 OR LESS
3 Adam LaRoche/250 3.00 8.00
4 Adam Loewen/250 3.00 8.00
7 Albert Pujols/25 150.00 250.00
8 Alex Rodriguez Yanks/1
9 Alexis Rios/250 5.00 12.00
10 Alfonso Soriano Rgr/25 20.00 50.00
11 Andruw Jones/25 20.00 50.00
12 Andy Pettitte/25 20.00 50.00
13 Angel Berroa/100 4.00 10.00
14 Aramis Ramirez/100 6.00 15.00
15 Aubrey Huff/250 5.00 12.00
16 Austin Kearns/200 3.00 8.00
17 Barry Larkin/25 20.00 50.00
18 Barry Zito/10
20 Bernie Williams/5
22 Brad Penny/25 8.00 20.00
24 Brandon Webb/250 3.00 8.00
25 Brendan Harris/50 5.00 12.00
27 Brett Myers/100 6.00 15.00
28 Bubba Crosby/250 3.00 8.00
30 Chad Cordero/250 5.00 12.00
31 Bubba Nelson/250 3.00 8.00
32 Byron Gettis/250 3.00 8.00
36 Carlos Beltran/100 6.00 15.00
38 Carlos Lee/250 5.00 12.00
39 Chad Gaudin/100 4.00 10.00
40 Cliff Lee/250 3.00 8.00
41 Chipper Jones/5
43 Clint Barmes/100 6.00 15.00
45 Craig Biggio/1
46 Curt Schilling Sox/5
47 Dan Haren/250 3.00 8.00
49 David Ortiz/250 15.00 40.00
50 Delmon Young/50 12.50 30.00
52 Dewon Brazelton/250 3.00 8.00
53 Dontrelle Willis/100 10.00 25.00
56 Edwin Almonte/250 3.00 8.00
57 Edwin Jackson/250 3.00 8.00
58 Eric Chavez/25 12.50 30.00
59 Eric Hinske/5
62 Frank Thomas/50 20.00 50.00
63 Fred McGriff/10
65 Garret Anderson/250 5.00 12.00
67 Gary Sheffield/50 12.50 30.00
70 Hank Blalock/100 6.00 15.00
73 Hideo Nomo/1
74 Craig Wilson/250 3.00 8.00
77 J.D. Drew/1
78 John Lackey/250 5.00 12.00
79 Jacque Jones/250 5.00 12.00
80 Jae Weong Seo/100 6.00 15.00
85 Melvin Mora/250 5.00 12.00
86 Jason Varitek/100 15.00 40.00
87 Javier Vazquez/5
89 Jay Gibbons/250 3.00 8.00
90 Jay Payton/250 3.00 8.00
91 Jeff Bagwell/50 20.00 50.00
92 Jeff Baker/25 8.00 20.00
96 Jerome Williams/100 4.00 10.00
97 Jim Edmonds/25 20.00 50.00
99 Jody Gerut/250 3.00 8.00
100 Joe Borchard/250 3.00 8.00
101 Joe Crede/50 8.00 20.00
102 Johan Santana/250 10.00 25.00
106 Jorge Posada/25 20.00 50.00
107 Jose Castillo/250 3.00 8.00
108 Jose Reyes/10
109 Jose Vidro/250 3.00 8.00
110 Josh Beckett/25 20.00 50.00
111 Josh Phelps/10
113 Juan Gonzalez/25 12.50 30.00
114 Junior Spivey/25 8.00 20.00
115 Kazuhisa Ishii/10
117 Kerry Wood/50 12.50 30.00
119 Kevin Youkilis/250 3.00 8.00
120 Lance Berkman/25 12.50 30.00
121 Larry Bigbie/250 5.00 12.00
123 Luis Castillo/25 8.00 20.00
125 Luis Matos/250 3.00 8.00
127 Magglio Ordonez/250 5.00 12.00
128 Manny Ramirez/1
129 Marcus Giles/250 5.00 12.00
130 Mariano Rivera/1
131 Mark Buehrle/250 8.00 20.00
132 Mark Mulder/250 5.00 12.00
133 Mark Prior/100 10.00 25.00
134 Mark Teixeira/100 10.00 25.00
135 Marlon Byrd/250 3.00 8.00
137 Miguel Cabrera/250 8.00 20.00
138 Mike Lowell/5
139 Mike Mussina/1
140 Mike Piazza/25 75.00 150.00
142 Morgan Ensberg/250 5.00 12.00
143 Nick Johnson/1
146 Orlando Cabrera/25 12.50 30.00
147 Orlando Hudson/10
150 Paul Lo Duca/25 12.50 30.00
151 Pedro Martinez/1
152 Jermaine Dye/250 5.00 12.00
153 Preston Wilson/250 5.00 12.00
154 Rafael Furcal/100 6.00 15.00
155 Rafael Palmeiro O's/5
156 Randy Johnson/5
157 Rich Aurilia/25 8.00 20.00
158 Rich Harden/203 5.00 12.00
160 Richie Sexson/1
161 Rickie Weeks/4
162 Roberto Alomar/10
163 Rocco Baldelli/5
165 Roy Halladay/50 8.00 20.00
166 Roy Oswalt/50 8.00 20.00
167 Ryan Howard/100 40.00 80.00
169 Rodrigo Lopez/250 3.00 8.00
170 Sammy Sosa/50 50.00 100.00
171 Scott Podsednik/250 8.00 20.00
172 Scott Rolen/100 10.00 25.00
175 Shannon Stewart/100 6.00 15.00
176 Shawn Green/25 20.00 50.00
177 Shea Hillenbrand/250 5.00 12.00
178 Shigetoshi Hasegawa/250 15.00 40.00
179 Steve Finley/100 6.00 15.00
180 Tim Hudson/10
181 Todd Helton/10
182 Tom Glavine/5
183 Torii Hunter/250 5.00 12.00
184 Trot Nixon/250 5.00 12.00
185 Troy Glaus/1
186 Vernon Wells/5
187 Victor Martinez/250 5.00 12.00
188 Vlad Guerrero Angels/50 20.00 50.00
189 Wade Miller/5
190 Brandon Larson/200 3.00 8.00
191 Travis Hafner/250 5.00 12.00
195 Ramon Nivar/10
197 Michael Young/250 8.00 20.00
203 Vladimir Guerrero Expos/5
204 Miguel Tejada/1
207 Curt Schilling D'backs/1
208 Alex Rodriguez Rgr/1
209 Alfonso Soriano Yanks/5
211 Rafael Palmeiro Rgr/1
212 Gary Carter LGD/250 5.00 12.00
213 Duke Snider LGD/250 8.00 20.00
214 Whitey Ford LGD/50 20.00 50.00
215 Bob Feller LGD/250 8.00 20.00
216 Reggie Jackson LGD/50 20.00 50.00
217 Ryne Sandberg LGD/50 40.00 80.00
218 Dale Murphy LGD/50 12.50 30.00
219 Tony Gwynn LGD/50 30.00 60.00
220 Don Mattingly LGD/50 40.00 80.00
221 Mike Schmidt LGD/50 40.00 80.00
222 Rickey Henderson LGD/50 40.00 80.00
223 Cal Ripken LGD/50 125.00 200.00
224 Nolan Ryan LGD/50 60.00 120.00
225 George Brett LGD/50 40.00 80.00
226 Bob Gibson LGD/100 10.00 25.00
227 Lou Brock LGD/100 10.00 25.00
228 Andre Dawson LGD/250 5.00 12.00
229 Rod Carew LGD/50 12.50 30.00
230 Wade Boggs LGD/50 12.50 30.00
238 Ernie Banks LGD/50 30.00 60.00
240 Stan Musial LGD/100 20.00 50.00
241 Hector Gimenez NG/200 3.00 8.00
242 Justin Germano NG/100 5.00 12.00
243 Ian Snell NG/100 6.00 15.00
244 Graham Koonce NG/200 3.00 8.00
245 Jose Capellan NG/100 4.00 10.00

246 Onil Joseph NG/200 3.00 8.00
247 Shingo Takatsu NG/50 10.00 25.00
248 Carlos Hines NG/200 3.00 8.00
249 Lincoln Holdzkom NG/100 4.00 10.00
250 Mike Gosling NG/100 4.00 10.00
251 Eduardo Sierra NG/200 4.00 10.00
252 Renyel Pinto NG/100 4.00 10.00
253 Merkin Valdez NG/200 3.00 8.00
254 Angel Chavez NG/200 3.00 8.00
255 Ivan Ochoa NG/200 3.00 8.00
257 William Bergolla NG/200 3.00 8.00
258 Aarom Baldiris NG/100 4.00 10.00
260 Carlos Vasquez NG/200 4.00 10.00
261 Freddy Guzman NG/200 3.00 8.00
262 Akinori Otsuka NG/50 15.00 40.00
264 Nick Regilio NG/200 3.00 8.00
266 Shawn Hill NG/200 3.00 8.00
268 Sean Henn NG/200 3.00 8.00
269 Ramon Ramirez NG/200 3.00 8.00
270 Ronny Cedeno NG/100 6.00 15.00
273 Fernando Nieve NG/200 3.00 8.00
274 Rusty Tucker NG/200 4.00 10.00
275 Jason Bartlett NG/200 4.00 10.00
276 Mike Rouse NG/200 3.00 8.00
277 Dennis Sarfate NG/200 3.00 8.00
278 Cory Sullivan NG/200 3.00 8.00
282 Michael Wuertz NG/200 4.00 10.00
284 Jorge Sequea NG/100 4.00 10.00
287 Tim Bittner NG/250 3.00 8.00
288 Andres Blanco NG/100 4.00 10.00
289 Kevin Cave NG/100 4.00 10.00
290 Mike Johnston NG/100 4.00 10.00
293 Colby Miller NG/100 4.00 10.00
294 Jake Woods NG/100 4.00 10.00
295 Ryan Meaux NG/200 3.00 8.00
296 Don Kelly NG/100 4.00 10.00
297 Edwin Moreno NG/100 4.00 10.00
298 Phil Stockman NG/100 4.00 10.00

2004 Leaf Certified Materials Mirror Autograph White

*1-240 p/r 100: .5X TO 1.2X RED p/r 250
*1-240 p/r 100: .4X TO 1X RED p/r 100
*1-240 p/r 50: .6X TO 1.5X RED p/r 200-250
*1-240 p/r 50: .5X TO 1.2X RED p/r 100
*1-240 p/r 50: .4X TO 1X RED p/r 50
*1-240 p/r 25: 1X TO 2.5X RED p/r 203
*1-240 p/r 25: .75X TO 2X RED p/r 100
*1-240 p/r 25: .6X TO 1.5X RED p/r 50
*1-240 p/r 25: .4X TO 1X RED p/r 25
*241-300 p/r 100: .5X TO 1.2X RED p/r 200
*241-300 p/r 100: .4X TO 1X RED p/r 100
*241-300 p/r 50: .6X TO 1.5X RED p/r 200-250
*241-300 p/r 50: .5X TO 1.2X RED p/r 100
OVERALL AU ODDS 1:10
PRINT RUNS B/WN 1-100 COPIES PER
NO PRICING ON QTY OF 10 OR LESS
2 Adam Dunn/24 20.00 50.00
167 Ryan Howard/25 75.00 150.00

2004 Leaf Certified Materials Mirror Bat Blue

*BLUE p/r 100: .5X TO 1.2X RED p/r 175-250
*BLUE p/r 50: .75X TO 2X RED p/r 150-250
*BLUE p/r 25: 1X TO 2.5X RED p/r 100
RANDOM INSERTS IN PACKS
PRINT RUNS B/WN 25-100 COPIES PER
23 Brad Wilkerson/100 2.00 5.00
58 Eric Chavez/50 3.00 8.00
142 Morgan Ensberg/50 3.00 8.00
151 Pedro Martinez/50 5.00 12.00
156 Randy Johnson/50 6.00 15.00
166 Roy Oswalt/50 3.00 8.00
172 Scott Rolen/50 5.00 12.00
180 Tim Hudson/50 3.00 8.00
182 Tom Glavine/50 5.00 12.00
207 Curt Schilling D'backs/50 3.00 8.00
217 Ryne Sandberg LGD/50 12.50 30.00
218 Dale Murphy LGD/50 6.00 15.00
219 Tony Gwynn LGD/50 10.00 25.00
221 Mike Schmidt LGD/50 12.50 30.00
223 Cal Ripken LGD/50 25.00 60.00
224 Nolan Ryan LGD/50 15.00 40.00
225 George Brett LGD/50 12.50 30.00

2004 Leaf Certified Materials Mirror Bat Gold

*GOLD p/r 25: 1.25X TO 3X RED p/r 150-250
*GOLD p/r 25: 1X TO 2.5X RED p/r 100
RANDOM INSERTS IN PACKS
207 SCHILLING PRINT RUN 20 COPIES
18 Barry Zito 5.00 12.00
19 Ben Sheets 5.00 12.00
22 Brad Penny 5.00 12.00
23 Brad Wilkerson 5.00 12.00
46 Curt Schilling Sox 8.00 20.00
58 Eric Chavez 5.00 12.00
69 Greg Maddux Cubs 12.50 30.00
142 Morgan Ensberg 5.00 12.00
151 Pedro Martinez 8.00 20.00
156 Randy Johnson 10.00 25.00
166 Roy Oswalt 5.00 12.00
172 Scott Rolen 8.00 20.00
180 Tim Hudson 5.00 12.00
182 Tom Glavine 8.00 20.00
207 Curt Schilling D'backs/20 5.00 12.00
213 Duke Snider LGD 10.00 25.00
217 Ryne Sandberg LGD 20.00 50.00
218 Dale Murphy LGD 10.00 25.00
219 Tony Gwynn LGD 15.00 40.00
221 Mike Schmidt LGD 20.00 50.00
223 Cal Ripken LGD 40.00 100.00
224 Nolan Ryan LGD 25.00 60.00
225 George Brett LGD 20.00 50.00
231 Roberto Clemente LGD 40.00 100.00
232 Roy Campanella LGD 12.50 30.00
233 Babe Ruth LGD 150.00 250.00
234 Lou Gehrig LGD 75.00 150.00
235 Ty Cobb LGD 60.00 120.00
236 Roger Maris LGD 20.00 50.00
238 Ernie Banks LGD 12.50 30.00
239 Ted Williams LGD 40.00 100.00

2004 Leaf Certified Materials Mirror Bat Red

PRINT RUNS B/WN 100-250 COPIES PER
BLACK PRINT RUN 1 SERIAL #'d SET
NO BLACK PRICING DUE TO SCARCITY
EMERALD PRINT RUN 5 SERIAL #'d SETS
NO EMERALD PRICING DUE TO SCARCITY
RANDOM INSERTS IN PACKS
2 Adam Dunn/150 2.00 5.00
3 Adam LaRoche/250 2.00 5.00
5 Adrian Beltre/150 2.00 5.00
7 Albert Pujols/150 6.00 15.00
8 Alex Rodriguez Yanks/250 4.00 10.00
9 Alexis Rios/250 2.00 5.00
10 Alfonso Soriano Rgr/150 2.00 5.00
11 Andruw Jones/150 3.00 8.00
12 Andy Pettitte/250 3.00 8.00
13 Angel Berroa/150 2.00 5.00
15 Aubrey Huff/150 2.00 5.00
16 Austin Kearns/150 2.00 5.00
17 Barry Larkin/150 3.00 8.00
20 Bernie Williams/150 3.00 8.00
21 Bobby Abreu/150 2.00 5.00
24 Brandon Webb/150 2.00 5.00
25 Brendan Harris/250 2.00 5.00
26 Bret Boone/150 2.00 5.00
29 Brian Giles/250 2.00 5.00
35 Carl Everett/250 2.00 5.00
36 Carlos Beltran/150 2.00 5.00
37 Carlos Delgado/150 2.00 5.00
38 Carlos Lee/150 2.00 5.00
41 Chipper Jones/150 3.00 8.00
42 Cliff Floyd/250 2.00 5.00
43 Clint Barmes/250 2.00 5.00
44 Corey Patterson/250 2.00 5.00
45 Craig Biggio/150 3.00 8.00
47 Dan Haren/150 2.00 5.00
48 Darin Erstad/150 2.00 5.00
49 David Ortiz/250 3.00 8.00
50 Delmon Young/250 3.00 8.00
51 Derek Jeter/150 8.00 20.00
54 Edgar Martinez/150 3.00 8.00
55 Edgar Renteria/150 2.00 5.00
59 Eric Hinske/150 2.00 5.00
60 Eric Munson/250 2.00 5.00
61 Erubial Durazo/250 2.00 5.00
62 Frank Thomas/150 3.00 8.00
63 Fred McGriff/150 3.00 8.00
65 Garret Anderson/150 2.00 5.00
67 Gary Sheffield/250 2.00 5.00
68 Geoff Jenkins/150 2.00 5.00
70 Hank Blalock/150 2.00 5.00
71 Hee Seop Choi/250 2.00 5.00
73 Hideo Nomo/150 3.00 8.00
76 Ivan Rodriguez Tigers/250 3.00 8.00
77 J.D. Drew/250 2.00 5.00
79 Jacque Jones/150 2.00 5.00
82 Jason Giambi Yanks/150 2.00 5.00
83 Jason Jennings/150 2.00 5.00
86 Jason Varitek/150 3.00 8.00
88 Javy Lopez/250 2.00 5.00
89 Jay Gibbons/150 2.00 5.00
91 Jeff Bagwell/150 3.00 8.00
92 Jeff Baker/250 2.00 5.00
93 Jeff Kent/150 2.00 5.00
97 Jim Edmonds/150 2.00 5.00
98 Jim Thome/150 3.00 8.00
100 Joe Borchard/150 2.00 5.00
101 Joe Crede/250 2.00 5.00
103 John Olerud/150 2.00 5.00
105 Johnny Damon/250 3.00 8.00
106 Jorge Posada/150 3.00 8.00
107 Jose Castillo/250 2.00 5.00
108 Jose Reyes/150 2.00 5.00
109 Jose Vidro/150 2.00 5.00
110 Josh Beckett/150 2.00 5.00
111 Josh Phelps/150 2.00 5.00
112 Juan Encarnacion/250 2.00 5.00
113 Juan Gonzalez/250 2.00 5.00
114 Junior Spivey/250 2.00 5.00
115 Kazuhisa Ishii/150 2.00 5.00
116 Kenny Lofton/250 2.00 5.00
117 Kerry Wood/150 2.00 5.00
119 Kevin Youkilis/250 2.00 5.00
120 Lance Berkman/150 2.00 5.00
122 Larry Walker/150 2.00 5.00
123 Luis Castillo/150 2.00 5.00
124 Luis Gonzalez/150 2.00 5.00
126 Lyle Overbay/250 2.00 5.00
127 Magglio Ordonez/150 2.00 5.00
128 Manny Ramirez/150 3.00 8.00
129 Marcus Giles/250 2.00 5.00
131 Mark Buehrle/150 2.00 5.00
132 Mark Mulder/150 2.00 5.00
133 Mark Prior/150 3.00 8.00
134 Mark Teixeira/150 3.00 8.00
135 Marlon Byrd/150 2.00 5.00
137 Miguel Cabrera/250 3.00 8.00
138 Mike Lowell/150 2.00 5.00
140 Mike Piazza/150 4.00 10.00
141 Mike Sweeney/150 2.00 5.00
143 Nick Johnson/250 2.00 5.00
144 Nomar Garciaparra/150 5.00 12.00
145 Omar Vizquel/150 3.00 8.00
146 Orlando Cabrera/250 2.00 5.00
147 Orlando Hudson/150 2.00 5.00
148 Pat Burrell/150 2.00 5.00
149 Paul Konerko/150 2.00 5.00
150 Paul Lo Duca/150 2.00 5.00
152 Jermaine Dye/250 2.00 5.00
153 Preston Wilson/150 2.00 5.00
154 Rafael Furcal/150 2.00 5.00
155 Rafael Palmeiro O's/150 3.00 8.00
157 Rich Aurilia/250 2.00 5.00
159 Richard Hidalgo/150 2.00 5.00
160 Richie Sexson/250 2.00 5.00
161 Rickie Weeks/250 2.00 5.00
162 Roberto Alomar/250 3.00 8.00
163 Rocco Baldelli/150 2.00 5.00
164 Roger Clemens Astros/250 4.00 10.00
168 Ryan Klesko/150 2.00 5.00
170 Sammy Sosa/150 3.00 8.00
174 Sean Casey/250 2.00 5.00
175 Shannon Stewart/150 2.00 5.00
176 Shawn Green/150 2.00 5.00
181 Todd Helton/150 3.00 8.00
183 Torii Hunter/150 2.00 5.00
184 Trot Nixon/150 2.00 5.00
185 Troy Glaus/150 2.00 5.00
186 Vernon Wells/150 2.00 5.00
187 Victor Martinez/250 2.00 5.00
188 Vladimir Guerrero Angels/250 3.00 8.00
189 Wade Miller/250 2.00 5.00
190 Brandon Larson/175 2.00 5.00
191 Travis Hafner/150 2.00 5.00
192 Tim Salmon/150 3.00 8.00
195 Ramon Nivar/150 2.00 5.00
196 Moises Alou/250 2.00 5.00
197 Michael Young/250 2.00 5.00
198 Laynce Nix/150 2.00 5.00
199 Tino Martinez/250 3.00 8.00
200 Randall Simon/250 2.00 5.00
201 Roger Clemens Yanks/150 4.00 10.00
203 Vladimir Guerrero Expos/150 3.00 8.00
204 Miguel Tejada/150 2.00 5.00
206 Jason Giambi A's/150 2.00 5.00
208 Alex Rodriguez Rgr/150 4.00 10.00
209 Alfonso Soriano Yanks/150 2.00 5.00
210 Ivan Rodriguez Marlins/150 3.00 8.00
211 Rafael Palmeiro Rgr/150 3.00 8.00
212 Gary Carter LGD/150 3.00 8.00
216 Reggie Jackson LGD/150 4.00 10.00
220 Don Mattingly LGD/150 6.00 15.00
222 Rickey Henderson LGD/150 4.00 10.00
227 Lou Brock LGD/150 4.00 10.00
228 Andre Dawson LGD/150 3.00 8.00
229 Rod Carew LGD/150 4.00 10.00
230 Wade Boggs LGD/150 4.00 10.00
240 Stan Musial LGD/100 10.00 25.00

2004 Leaf Certified Materials Mirror Bat White

*WHITE p/r 200: .4X TO 1X RED p/r 250
*WHITE p/r 100: .5X TO 1.2X RED p/r 150
*WHITE p/r 50: .6X TO 1.5X RED p/r 100
RANDOM INSERTS IN PACKS
PRINT RUNS B/WN 25-200 COPIES PER
14 Aramis Ramirez/100 2.00 5.00
23 Brad Wilkerson/200 2.00 5.00
156 Randy Johnson/100 4.00 10.00
166 Roy Oswalt/100 2.00 5.00
180 Tim Hudson/100 2.00 5.00
182 Tom Glavine/100 3.00 8.00
205 Kevin Brown/100 2.00 5.00
218 Dale Murphy LGD/100 5.00 12.00
219 Tony Gwynn LGD/100 6.00 15.00
221 Mike Schmidt LGD/100 8.00 20.00
223 Cal Ripken LGD/100 15.00 40.00
224 Nolan Ryan LGD/100 10.00 25.00
225 George Brett LGD/100 8.00 20.00
231 Roberto Clemente LGD/50 30.00 80.00
232 Roy Campanella LGD/50 8.00 20.00
233 Babe Ruth LGD/25 150.00 250.00
234 Lou Gehrig LGD/25 75.00 150.00
235 Ty Cobb LGD/25 60.00 120.00
236 Roger Maris LGD/25 20.00 50.00
238 Ernie Banks LGD/25 8.00 20.00
239 Ted Williams LGD/25 40.00 100.00

2004 Leaf Certified Materials Mirror Combo Red

2-211 PRINT RUN 250 SERIAL #'d SETS
212-239 PRINT RUNS B/WN 50-250 PER
BLACK PRIME PRINT RUN 1 SERIAL #'d SET
NO BLACK PRIME PRICING AVAILABLE
RANDOM INSERTS IN PACKS
2 Adam Dunn Bat-Jsy 3.00 8.00
5 Adrian Beltre Bat-Jsy 3.00 8.00
7 Albert Pujols Bat-Jsy 10.00 25.00
11 Andruw Jones Bat-Jsy 5.00 12.00
13 Angel Berroa Bat-Pants 3.00 8.00
15 Aubrey Huff Bat-Jsy 3.00 8.00
16 Austin Kearns Bat-Jsy 3.00 8.00
17 Barry Larkin Bat-Jsy 5.00 12.00
18 Barry Zito Bat-Jsy 3.00 8.00
19 Ben Sheets Bat-Jsy 3.00 8.00
20 Bernie Williams Bat-Jsy 5.00 12.00
21 Bobby Abreu Bat-Jsy 3.00 8.00
22 Brad Penny Bat-Jsy 3.00 8.00
24 Brandon Webb Bat-Jsy 3.00 8.00
26 Bret Boone Bat-Jsy 3.00 8.00
36 Carlos Beltran Bat-Jsy 3.00 8.00
37 Carlos Delgado Bat-Jsy 3.00 8.00
38 Carlos Lee Bat-Jsy 3.00 8.00
41 Chipper Jones Bat-Jsy 5.00 12.00
45 Craig Biggio Bat-Pants 5.00 12.00
47 Dan Haren Bat-Jsy 3.00 8.00
51 Derek Jeter Bat-Jsy 12.50 30.00
52 Dewon Brazelton Fld Glv-Jsy 3.00 8.00
54 Edgar Martinez Bat-Jsy 5.00 12.00
55 Edgar Renteria Bat-Jsy 3.00 8.00
58 Eric Chavez Bat-Jsy 3.00 8.00
59 Eric Hinske Bat-Jsy 3.00 8.00
62 Frank Thomas Bat-Jsy 5.00 12.00
63 Fred McGriff Bat-Jsy 5.00 12.00
65 Garret Anderson Bat-Jsy 3.00 8.00
68 Geoff Jenkins Bat-Jsy 3.00 8.00
70 Hank Blalock Bat-Jsy 3.00 8.00
73 Hideo Nomo Bat-Jsy 5.00 12.00
79 Jacque Jones Bat-Jsy 3.00 8.00
82 Jason Giambi Yanks Bat-Jsy 3.00 8.00
83 Jason Jennings Bat-Jsy 3.00 8.00
86 Jason Varitek Bat-Jsy 5.00 12.00
89 Jay Gibbons Bat-Jsy 3.00 8.00
91 Jeff Bagwell Bat-Jsy 5.00 12.00
93 Jeff Kent Bat-Jsy 3.00 8.00
97 Jim Edmonds Bat-Jsy 3.00 8.00
98 Jim Thome Bat-Jsy 5.00 12.00
100 Joe Borchard Bat-Jsy 3.00 8.00
103 John Olerud Bat-Jsy 3.00 8.00
106 Jorge Posada Bat-Jsy 5.00 12.00
108 Jose Reyes Bat-Jsy 3.00 8.00
109 Jose Vidro Bat-Jsy 3.00 8.00
110 Josh Beckett Bat-Jsy 3.00 8.00
111 Josh Phelps Bat-Jsy 3.00 8.00
115 Kazuhisa Ishii Bat-Jsy 3.00 8.00
117 Kerry Wood Bat-Jsy 3.00 8.00
120 Lance Berkman Bat-Jsy 3.00 8.00
122 Larry Walker Bat-Jsy 3.00 8.00
123 Luis Castillo Bat-Jsy 3.00 8.00
124 Luis Gonzalez Bat-Jsy 3.00 8.00
127 Magglio Ordonez Bat-Jsy 3.00 8.00
128 Manny Ramirez Bat-Jsy 5.00 12.00
131 Mark Buehrle Bat-Jsy 3.00 8.00
132 Mark Mulder Bat-Jsy 3.00 8.00
133 Mark Prior Bat-Jsy 5.00 12.00
134 Mark Teixeira Bat-Jsy 5.00 12.00
135 Marlon Byrd Bat-Jsy 3.00 8.00
138 Mike Lowell Bat-Jsy 3.00 8.00
140 Mike Piazza Bat-Jsy 6.00 15.00
141 Mike Sweeney Bat-Jsy 3.00 8.00
142 Morgan Ensberg Bat-Jsy 3.00 8.00
144 Nomar Garciaparra Bat-Jsy 6.00 15.00
145 Omar Vizquel Bat-Jsy 5.00 12.00
147 Orlando Hudson Bat-Jsy 3.00 8.00
148 Pat Burrell Bat-Jsy 3.00 8.00
149 Paul Konerko Bat-Jsy 3.00 8.00
150 Paul Lo Duca Bat-Jsy 3.00 8.00
151 Pedro Martinez Bat-Jsy 5.00 12.00
153 Preston Wilson Bat-Jsy 3.00 8.00
154 Rafael Furcal Bat-Jsy 3.00 8.00
155 Rafael Palmeiro O's Bat-Jsy 5.00 12.00
156 Randy Johnson Bat-Jsy 5.00 12.00
159 Richard Hidalgo Bat-Pants 3.00 8.00
163 Rocco Baldelli Bat-Jsy 3.00 8.00
166 Roy Oswalt Bat-Jsy 3.00 8.00
168 Ryan Klesko Bat-Jsy 3.00 8.00
170 Sammy Sosa Bat-Jsy 5.00 12.00
172 Scott Rolen Bat-Jsy 5.00 12.00
175 Shannon Stewart Bat-Jsy 3.00 8.00
176 Shawn Green Bat-Jsy 3.00 8.00
180 Tim Hudson Bat-Jsy 3.00 8.00
181 Todd Helton Bat-Jsy 5.00 12.00
182 Tom Glavine Bat-Jsy 5.00 12.00
183 Torii Hunter Bat-Jsy 3.00 8.00
184 Trot Nixon Bat-Jsy 3.00 8.00
185 Troy Glaus Bat-Jsy 3.00 8.00
186 Vernon Wells Bat-Jsy 3.00 8.00
191 Travis Hafner Bat-Jsy 3.00 8.00
192 Tim Salmon Bat-Jsy 3.00 8.00
195 Ramon Nivar Bat-Jsy 3.00 8.00
201 R.Clemens Yanks Bat-Jsy 6.00 15.00
203 Vlad Guerrero Expos Bat-Jsy 5.00 12.00
204 Miguel Tejada Bat-Jsy 3.00 8.00
206 Jason Giambi A's Bat-Jsy 3.00 8.00
207 Curt Schilling D'backs Bat-Jsy 3.00 8.00
208 Alex Rodriguez Rgr Bat-Jsy 6.00 15.00
209 Alf Soriano Yanks Bat-Jsy 3.00 8.00
210 Ivan Rod Marlins Bat-Jsy 5.00 12.00
211 Rafael Palmeiro Rgr Bat-Jsy 5.00 12.00
212 G.Carter LGD Bat-Pants/250 4.00 10.00
216 R.Jackson LGD Bat-Jsy/250 6.00 15.00
217 R.Sandberg LGD Bat-Jsy/250 10.00 25.00
218 D.Murphy LGD Bat-Jsy/250 6.00 15.00
219 T.Gwynn LGD Bat-Jsy/250 6.00 15.00
220 D.Mattingly LGD Bat-Jsy/250 10.00 25.00
221 M.Schm LGD Bat-Pants/250 10.00 25.00
222 R.Hend LGD Bat-Jsy/250 6.00 15.00
223 C.Ripken LGD Bat-Jsy/250 15.00 40.00
224 N.Ryan LGD Bat-Jsy/250 15.00 40.00
225 G.Brett LGD Bat-Jsy/250 10.00 25.00
227 L.Brock LGD Bat-Jsy/250 6.00 15.00
228 A.Dawson LGD Bat-Jsy/250 4.00 10.00
229 R.Carew LGD Bat-Jkt/250 6.00 15.00
230 W.Boggs LGD Bat-Jsy/250 6.00 15.00
231 R.Clemente LGD Bat-Jsy/100 60.00 120.00
232 R.Campy LGD Bat-Pants/100 8.00 20.00
233 B.Ruth LGD Bat-Pants/50 200.00 350.00
234 L.Gehrig LGD Bat-Pants/50 100.00 200.00
235 T.Cobb LGD Bat-Pants/50 100.00 200.00
236 R.Maris LGD Bat-Pants/100 20.00 50.00
238 E.Banks LGD Bat-Pants/100 8.00 20.00
239 T.Williams LGD Bat-Jkt/100 50.00 100.00

2004 Leaf Certified Materials Mirror Fabric Blue Position

*1-211 p/r 100: .5X TO 1.2X RED p/r 150-250
1-211 PRINT RUN 100 SERIAL #'d SETS
*212-239 p/r 100: .5X TO 1.2X REDp/r150-250
*212-239 p/r 25: 1X TO 2.5X RED p/r 100
212-239 PRINT RUNS 25-100 #'d COPIES PER
RANDOM INSERTS IN PACKS
24 Brandon Webb Jsy 2.00 5.00
26 Bret Boone Jsy 2.00 5.00
37 Carlos Delgado Jsy 2.00 5.00
52 Dewon Brazelton Jsy 2.00 5.00
65 Garret Anderson Jsy 2.00 5.00
80 Jae Weong Seo Jsy 2.00 5.00
100 Joe Borchard Jsy 2.00 5.00
106 Jorge Posada Jsy 3.00 8.00
127 Magglio Ordonez Jsy 2.00 5.00
128 Manny Ramirez Jsy 3.00 8.00
132 Mark Mulder Jsy 2.00 5.00
134 Mark Teixeira Jsy 3.00 8.00
138 Mike Lowell Jsy 2.00 5.00
149 Paul Konerko Jsy 2.00 5.00
150 Paul Lo Duca Jsy 2.00 5.00
155 Rafael Palmeiro O's Jsy 3.00 8.00
166 Roy Oswalt Jsy 2.00 5.00
183 Torii Hunter Jsy 2.00 5.00
184 Trot Nixon Jsy 2.00 5.00
211 Rafael Palmeiro Rgr Jsy 3.00 8.00
214 W.Ford LGD Jsy/100 5.00 12.00
216 R.Jackson LGD Jsy/100 5.00 12.00
217 R.Sandberg LGD Jsy/100 8.00 20.00
218 D.Murphy LGD Jsy/100 5.00 12.00
219 T.Gwynn LGD Jsy/100 6.00 15.00
220 Don Mattingly LGD Jsy/100 8.00 20.00
221 M.Schmidt LGD Pants/100 8.00 20.00
222 R.Henderson LGD Jsy/100 6.00 15.00
223 Cal Ripken LGD Jsy/100 15.00 40.00
224 Nolan Ryan LGD Jsy/100 10.00 25.00
225 George Brett LGD Jsy/100 8.00 20.00
227 L.Brock LGD Jsy/100 5.00 12.00
228 A.Dawson LGD Jsy/100 3.00 8.00
229 R.Carew LGD Jkt/100 5.00 12.00
230 W.Boggs LGD Jsy/100 5.00 12.00
231 R.Clemente LGD Jsy/25 40.00 100.00
232 R.Campy LGD Pants/25 12.50 30.00
233 Babe Ruth LGD Pants/25 150.00 250.00
234 Lou Gehrig LGD Pants/25 75.00 150.00
235 Ty Cobb LGD Pants/25 60.00 120.00
236 Roger Maris LGD Pants/25 20.00 50.00
238 E.Banks LGD Pants/25 12.50 30.00
239 Ted Williams LGD Jkt/25 40.00 100.00

2004 Leaf Certified Materials Mirror Fabric Gold Number

*1-211 p/r 25: 1.25X TO 3X RED p/r 150-250
1-211 PRINT RUN 25 SERIAL #'d SETS
*212-239 p/r 25: 1.25X TO 3X RED p/r 150-250
212-239 PRINT RUNS B/WN 10-25 #'d PER
212-239 NO PRICING ON QTY OF 10 OR LESS
RANDOM INSERTS IN PACKS
24 Brandon Webb Jsy 5.00 12.00
26 Bret Boone Jsy 5.00 12.00
37 Carlos Delgado Jsy 5.00 12.00
52 Dewon Brazelton Jsy 5.00 12.00
63 Fred McGriff Jsy 8.00 20.00
65 Garret Anderson Jsy 5.00 12.00
80 Jae Weong Seo Jsy 5.00 12.00
100 Joe Borchard Jsy 5.00 12.00
106 Jorge Posada Jsy 8.00 20.00
127 Magglio Ordonez Jsy 5.00 12.00
128 Manny Ramirez Jsy 8.00 20.00
132 Mark Mulder Jsy 5.00 12.00
134 Mark Teixeira Jsy 8.00 20.00
138 Mike Lowell Jsy 5.00 12.00
149 Paul Konerko Jsy 5.00 12.00
150 Paul Lo Duca Jsy 5.00 12.00
155 Rafael Palmeiro O's Jsy 8.00 20.00
166 Roy Oswalt Jsy 5.00 12.00
183 Torii Hunter Jsy 5.00 12.00
184 Trot Nixon Jsy 5.00 12.00
211 Rafael Palmeiro Rgr Jsy 8.00 20.00
214 Whitey Ford LGD Jsy/25 10.00 25.00
215 B.Feller LGD Jsy/25 6.00 15.00
216 R.Jackson LGD Jsy/25 10.00 25.00
217 Ryne Sandberg LGD Jsy/25 20.00 50.00
218 D.Murphy LGD Jsy/25 10.00 25.00
219 Tony Gwynn LGD Jsy/25 15.00 40.00
220 Don Mattingly LGD Jsy/25 20.00 50.00
221 Mike Schmidt LGD Pants/25 20.00 50.00
222 R.Henderson LGD Jsy/25 12.50 30.00
223 Cal Ripken LGD Jsy/25 40.00 100.00
224 Nolan Ryan LGD Jsy/25 25.00 60.00
225 George Brett LGD Jsy/25 20.00 50.00
227 L.Brock LGD Jsy/25 10.00 25.00
228 A.Dawson LGD Jsy/25 6.00 15.00
229 R.Carew LGD Jkt/25 10.00 25.00
230 W.Boggs LGD Jsy/25 10.00 25.00
231 R.Clemente LGD Jsy/10
232 R.Campy LGD Pants/10
233 B.Ruth LGD Pants/10
234 L.Gehrig LGD Pants/10
235 T.Cobb LGD Pants/10
236 R.Maris LGD Pants/10
238 E.Banks LGD Pants/10
239 Ted Williams LGD Jkt/10

2004 Leaf Certified Materials Mirror Fabric Red

PRINT RUNS B/WN 100-250 COPIES PER
BLACK AL/NL PRINT RUN 1 SERIAL #'d SET
NO BLACK AL/NL PRICING DUE TO SCARCITY
BLACK NUMBER PRINT RUN 1 #'d SET
NO BLACK NBR.PRICING DUE TO SCARCITY
BLACK POSITION PRINT RUN 1 #'d SET
NO BLACK POS.PRICING DUE TO SCARCITY
BLACK PRIME PRINT RUN 1 SERIAL #'d SET
NO BLK PRIME PRICING DUE TO SCARCITY
EMERALD PRINT RUN 1-5 COPIES PER
NO EMERALD PRICING DUE TO SCARCITY
RANDOM INSERTS IN PACKS
1 A.J. Burnett Jsy/250 2.00 5.00
2 Adam Dunn Jsy/150 2.00 5.00
5 Adrian Beltre Jsy/150 2.00 5.00
6 Al Leiter Jsy/250 2.00 5.00
7 Albert Pujols Jsy/150 6.00 15.00
11 Andruw Jones Jsy/150 3.00 8.00
13 Angel Berroa Pants/150 2.00 5.00
15 Aubrey Huff Jsy/150 2.00 5.00
16 Austin Kearns Jsy/150 2.00 5.00
17 Barry Larkin Jsy/150 3.00 8.00
18 Barry Zito Jsy/150 2.00 5.00
19 Ben Sheets Jsy/150 2.00 5.00
20 Bernie Williams Jsy/150 3.00 8.00
21 Bobby Abreu Jsy/150 2.00 5.00
22 Brad Penny Jsy/150 2.00 5.00
27 Brett Myers Jsy/250 2.00 5.00
33 C.C. Sabathia Jsy/250 2.00 5.00
34 Carl Crawford Jsy/250 2.00 5.00
36 Carlos Beltran Jsy/150 2.00 5.00
38 Carlos Lee Jsy/150 2.00 5.00
39 Chad Gaudin Jsy/250 2.00 5.00
41 Chipper Jones Jsy/150 3.00 8.00
45 Craig Biggio Pants/150 3.00 8.00
47 Dan Haren Jsy/150 2.00 5.00
48 Darin Erstad Jsy/250 2.00 5.00
51 Derek Jeter Jsy/150 8.00 20.00
53 Dontrelle Willis Jsy/250 3.00 8.00
54 Edgar Martinez Jsy/150 3.00 8.00
55 Edgar Renteria Jsy/150 2.00 5.00
58 Eric Chavez Jsy/150 2.00 5.00
59 Eric Hinske Jsy/150 2.00 5.00
62 Frank Thomas Jsy/150 3.00 8.00
64 Freddy Garcia Jsy/250 2.00 5.00
66 Garrett Atkins Jsy/250 2.00 5.00
68 Geoff Jenkins Jsy/150 2.00 5.00
70 Hank Blalock Jsy/150 2.00 5.00
72 Hideki Matsui Base/250 6.00 15.00
73 Hideo Nomo Jsy/150 3.00 8.00
75 Ichiro Suzuki Base/250 6.00 15.00
79 Jacque Jones Jsy/150 2.00 5.00
81 Jamie Moyer Jsy/250 2.00 5.00
82 Jason Giambi Yanks Jsy/150 2.00 5.00
83 Jason Jennings Jsy/150 2.00 5.00
84 Jason Kendall Jsy/250 2.00 5.00
86 Jason Varitek Jsy/150 3.00 8.00
89 Jay Gibbons Jsy/150 2.00 5.00
91 Jeff Bagwell Jsy/150 3.00 8.00
93 Jeff Kent Jsy/150 2.00 5.00
96 Jerome Williams Jsy/250 2.00 5.00
97 Jim Edmonds Jsy/150 2.00 5.00
98 Jim Thome Jsy/150 3.00 8.00
102 Johan Santana Jsy/250 3.00 8.00
103 John Olerud Jsy/150 2.00 5.00
104 John Smoltz Jsy/250 3.00 8.00
108 Jose Reyes Jsy/150 2.00 5.00
109 Jose Vidro Jsy/150 2.00 5.00
110 Josh Beckett Jsy/150 2.00 5.00
111 Josh Phelps Jsy/150 2.00 5.00
115 Kazuhisa Ishii Jsy/150 2.00 5.00
117 Kerry Wood Jsy/150 2.00 5.00
118 Kevin Millwood Jsy/250 2.00 5.00
120 Lance Berkman Jsy/150 2.00 5.00
121 Larry Bigbie Jsy/250 2.00 5.00
122 Larry Walker Jsy/150 2.00 5.00
123 Luis Castillo Jsy/150 2.00 5.00
124 Luis Gonzalez Jsy/150 2.00 5.00
130 Mariano Rivera Jsy/250 3.00 8.00
131 Mark Buehrle Jsy/150 2.00 5.00
133 Mark Prior Jsy/150 3.00 8.00
135 Marlon Byrd Jsy/150 2.00 5.00
136 Matt Morris Jsy/250 2.00 5.00
139 Mike Mussina Jsy/250 3.00 8.00
140 Mike Piazza Jsy/150 4.00 10.00
141 Mike Sweeney Jsy/150 2.00 5.00
142 Morgan Ensberg Jsy/150 2.00 5.00

144 Nomar Garciaparra Jsy/150 5.00 12.00
145 Omar Vizquel Jsy/150 3.00 8.00
147 Orlando Hudson Jsy/150 2.00 5.00
148 Pat Burrell Jsy/150 2.00 5.00
151 Pedro Martinez Jsy/150 3.00 8.00
153 Preston Wilson Jsy/150 2.00 5.00
154 Rafael Furcal Jsy/150 2.00 5.00
156 Randy Johnson Jsy/150 3.00 8.00
158 Rich Harden Jsy/250 2.00 5.00
159 Richard Hidalgo Pants/150 2.00 5.00
163 Rocco Baldelli Jsy/150 2.00 5.00
165 Roy Halladay Jsy/250 2.00 5.00
168 Ryan Klesko Jsy/150 2.00 5.00
170 Sammy Sosa Jsy/150 3.00 8.00
172 Scott Rolen Jsy/150 3.00 8.00
173 Sean Burroughs Jsy/250 2.00 5.00
175 Shannon Stewart Jsy/150 2.00 5.00
176 Shawn Green Jsy/150 2.00 5.00
179 Steve Finley Jsy/250 2.00 5.00
180 Tim Hudson Jsy/150 2.00 5.00
181 Todd Helton Jsy/150 3.00 8.00
182 Tom Glavine Jsy/150 3.00 8.00
185 Troy Glaus Jsy/150 2.00 5.00
186 Vernon Wells Jsy/150 2.00 5.00
191 Travis Hafner Jsy/150 2.00 5.00
192 Tim Salmon Jsy/150 3.00 8.00
193 Tim Redding Jsy/250 2.00 5.00
194 Runelvys Hernandez Jsy/250 2.00 5.00
195 Ramon Nivar Jsy/150 2.00 5.00
201 R.Clemens Yanks Jsy/150 4.00 10.00
202 G.Maddux Braves Jsy/250 5.00 12.00
203 V.Guerrero Expos Jsy/150 3.00 8.00
204 Miguel Tejada Jsy/150 2.00 5.00
205 Kevin Brown Jsy/250 2.00 5.00
206 Jason Giambi A's Jsy/150 2.00 5.00
207 C.Schilling D'backs Jsy/150 2.00 5.00
208 Alex Rodriguez Rgr Jsy/150 4.00 10.00
209 Alf Soriano Yanks Jsy/150 2.00 5.00
210 Ivan Rod Marlins Jsy/150 3.00 8.00
212 Gary Carter LGD Pants/150 3.00 8.00
226 Bob Gibson LGD Jsy/250 4.00 10.00
237 S.Paige LGD CO Jsy/100 25.00 60.00

2004 Leaf Certified Materials Mirror Fabric White

*1-211 p/r 200-215: .4X TO 1X REDp/r150-250
*1-211 p/r 100: .5X TO 1.2X RED p/r 150-250
*1-211 p/r 50: .75X TO 2X RED p/r 250
*212-239 p/r 200: .4X TO 1X RED p/r 150
*212-239 p/r 50: 1.25X TO 3X RED p/r 250
*212-239 p/r 25: 1X TO 2.5X RED p/r 100
212-239 PRINT RUNS B/WN 25-200 #'d PER
RANDOM INSERTS IN PACKS
24 Brandon Webb Pants/200 2.00 5.00
37 Carlos Delgado Jsy/200 2.00 5.00
52 Dewon Brazelton Jsy/200 2.00 5.00
65 Garret Anderson Jsy/200 2.00 5.00
106 Jorge Posada Jsy/200 3.00 8.00
127 Magglio Ordonez Jsy/200 2.00 5.00
128 Manny Ramirez Jsy/200 3.00 8.00
132 Mark Mulder Jsy/200 2.00 5.00
134 Mark Teixeira Jsy/200 3.00 8.00
138 Mike Lowell Jsy/75 2.00 5.00
149 Paul Konerko Jsy/100 2.00 5.00
150 Paul Lo Duca Jsy/200 2.00 5.00
155 Rafael Palmeiro O's Jsy/50 5.00 12.00
166 Roy Oswalt Jsy/100 2.00 5.00
183 Torii Hunter Jsy/200 2.00 5.00
184 Trot Nixon Jsy/50 3.00 8.00
211 Rafael Palmeiro Rgr Jsy/200 3.00 8.00
216 Reggie Jackson LGD Jsy/25 10.00 25.00
217 Ryne Sandberg LGD Jsy/25 20.00 50.00
219 Tony Gwynn LGD Jsy/25 15.00 40.00
220 Don Mattingly LGD Jsy/25 20.00 50.00
221 Mike Schmidt LGD Pants/25 20.00 50.00
222 R.Henderson LGD Jsy/25 12.50 30.00
223 Cal Ripken LGD Jsy/25 40.00 100.00
224 Nolan Ryan LGD Jsy/25 25.00 60.00
225 George Brett LGD Jsy/25 20.00 50.00
227 Lou Brock LGD Jsy/25 10.00 25.00
228 Andre Dawson LGD Jsy/25 6.00 15.00
229 Rod Carew LGD Jkt/25 10.00 25.00
230 Wade Boggs LGD Jsy/25 10.00 25.00
231 R.Clemente LGD Jsy/25 40.00 100.00
232 R.Campy LGD Pants/25 12.50 30.00
233 Babe Ruth LGD Pants/25 150.00 250.00
234 Lou Gehrig LGD Pants/25 75.00 150.00
235 Ty Cobb LGD Pants/25 60.00 120.00
236 Roger Maris LGD Pants/25 20.00 50.00
238 Ernie Banks LGD Pants/25 12.50 30.00
239 Ted Williams LGD Jkt/25 40.00 100.00

2004 Leaf Certified Materials Fabric of the Game

This set was highlighted by the debut of swatches cut from a 1968 Atlanta Braves jersey of Negro League legend Satchel Paige who was serving as a coach for the Braves at that time so he could qualify for a baseball pension.

RANDOM INSERTS IN PACKS
PRINT RUNS B/WN 1-100 COPIES PER
NO PRICING ON QTY OF 10 OR LESS
1 Ozzie Smith Padres Jsy/100 6.00 15.00
2 Al Kaline Pants/100 6.00 15.00
3 Alan Trammell Jsy/100 3.00 8.00
4 Albert Pujols Grey Jsy/100 10.00 25.00
5 Alex Rodriguez M's Jsy/100 5.00 12.00
6 Alex Rodriguez Rgr Jsy/100 5.00 12.00
7 A.Dawson Cubs Jsy/100 3.00 8.00
8 A.Dawson Cubs Pants/100 3.00 8.00
9 Babe Ruth Jsy/10
10 Babe Ruth Pants/10
11 Billy Williams Jsy/100 3.00 8.00
12 Bo Jackson Royals Jsy/100 6.00 15.00
13 Bob Feller Jsy/50 6.00 15.00
14 Bob Gibson Jsy/50 6.00 15.00
15 Bobby Doerr Jsy/100 3.00 8.00
16 Brooks Robinson Jsy/25 10.00 25.00
17 Cal Ripken Jsy/100 15.00 40.00
18 Carl Yastrzemski Jsy/100 8.00 20.00
19 Carlton Fisk R.Sox Jsy/100 5.00 12.00
20 Dale Murphy Jsy/100 5.00 12.00
21 D.Strawberry Mets Pants/100 3.00 8.00
22 D.Strawberry Dgr Jsy/100 3.00 8.00
23 Dave Parker Reds Jsy/100 3.00 8.00
24 Dave Parker Pirates Jsy/100 3.00 8.00
25 D.Winfield Yanks Jsy/50 4.00 10.00
26 D.Winfield Padres Jsy/100 3.00 8.00
27 Deion Sanders Jsy/25 10.00 25.00
28 Derek Jeter Jsy/100 10.00 25.00
29 Don Drysdale Jsy/100 6.00 15.00
30 Don Mattingly Jsy/100 8.00 20.00
31 Don Mattingly Jkt/100 8.00 20.00
32 Don Sutton Jsy/100 3.00 8.00
33 Duke Snider Jsy/100 5.00 12.00
34 Dwight Gooden Jsy/100 3.00 8.00
35 Early Wynn Jsy/100 3.00 8.00
36 Eddie Mathews Jsy/50 8.00 20.00
37 Eddie Murray Dgr Jsy/100 5.00 12.00
38 Eddie Murray O's Jsy/100 5.00 12.00
39 Enos Slaughter Jsy/100 6.00 15.00
40 Eric Davis Jsy/50 4.00 10.00
41 Ernie Banks Jsy/100 6.00 15.00
42 Fergie Jenkins Pants/100 3.00 8.00
43 Frank Robinson Jsy/100 3.00 8.00
44 Fred Lynn Jsy/10
45 Gary Carter Jsy/100 3.00 8.00
46 Gaylord Perry Jsy/25 6.00 15.00
47 George Brett White Jsy/100 8.00 20.00
48 George Foster Jsy/100 3.00 8.00
49 Hal Newhouser Jsy/100 3.00 8.00
50 Harmon Killebrew Jsy/25 12.50 30.00
51 Harmon Killebrew Pants/25 12.50 30.00
52 Harold Baines Jsy/100 3.00 8.00
53 Hoyt Wilhelm Jsy/50 4.00 10.00
54 Jack Morris Jsy/100 3.00 8.00
55 Jackie Robinson Jsy/10
56 Catfish Hunter Jsy/100 5.00 12.00
57 Jim Palmer Jsy/100 4.00 10.00
58 Jim Rice Jsy/100 3.00 8.00
59 Joe Carter Jsy/100 3.00 8.00
60 Joe Morgan Reds Jsy/100 3.00 8.00
61 Tommy Lasorda Jsy/100 3.00 8.00
62 Johnny Mize Pants/100 5.00 12.00
63 Johnny Bench Jsy/100 6.00 15.00
64 Jose Canseco Grey Jsy/100 5.00 12.00
65 Juan Marichal Jsy/100 3.00 8.00
66 Kirby Puckett Jsy/100 6.00 15.00
67 Lou Boudreau Jsy/100 3.00 8.00
68 Lou Brock Jsy/100 5.00 12.00
69 Lou Gehrig Jsy/10
70 Lou Gehrig Pants/10
71 Luis Aparicio Jsy/100 3.00 8.00
72 Luis Aparicio Pants/100 3.00 8.00
73 Mariano Rivera Jsy/100 4.00 10.00
74 Mark Grace Cubs Jsy/100 5.00 12.00
75 Mark Prior Jsy/100 3.00 8.00
76 Mel Ott Jsy/25 20.00 50.00
77 Mel Ott Pants/25 20.00 50.00
78 Mike Schmidt Jsy/100 8.00 20.00
79 Mike Schmidt Pants/100 8.00 20.00
80 Mike Schmidt Jkt/100 8.00 20.00
81 Nolan Ryan Angels Jsy/100 10.00 25.00
82 Nolan Ryan Angels Jkt/100 10.00 25.00
83 Nolan Ryan Astros Jsy/100 10.00 25.00
84 Nolan Ryan Astros Jkt/100 10.00 25.00
85 Nolan Ryan Rgr Jsy/100 10.00 25.00
86 Nolan Ryan Rgr Pants/100 10.00 25.00
87 Ty Cobb Pants/10
88 Ozzie Smith Cards Jsy/100 6.00 15.00
89 Paul Molitor Jsy/100 3.00 8.00
90 Pee Wee Reese Jsy/100 5.00 12.00
91 Phil Niekro Jsy/100 3.00 8.00
92 Phil Rizzuto Jsy/100 5.00 12.00
93 Phil Rizzuto Pants/100 5.00 12.00
94 Red Schoendienst Jsy/100 3.00 8.00
95 R.Jackson A's Jkt/100 5.00 12.00
96 R.Jackson Angels Jsy/100 5.00 12.00
97 Richie Ashburn Jsy/100 10.00 25.00
98 R.Henderson Yanks Jsy/50 6.00 15.00
99 Roberto Clemente Jsy/50 30.00 80.00
100 Robin Yount Jsy/100 6.00 15.00
101 R.Carew Angels Jsy/100 5.00 12.00
102 R.Carew Angels Pants/100 5.00 12.00
103 R.Carew Angels Jkt/100 5.00 12.00
104 R.Carew Twins Jsy/100 5.00 12.00
105 R.Clemens Sox Jsy/100 5.00 12.00
106 R.Clemens Yanks Jsy/100 5.00 12.00
107 Roger Maris A's Jsy/100 15.00 40.00
108 Roger Maris A's Pants/100 12.50 30.00
109 Roger Maris Yanks Jsy/100 15.00 40.00
110 Roy Campanella Pants/100 6.00 15.00
111 Ryne Sandberg Jsy/100 8.00 20.00
112 Stan Musial White Jsy/50 12.50 30.00
113 Steve Carlton Phils Jsy/100 3.00 8.00
114 Ted Williams Jsy/100 30.00 80.00
115 Ted Williams Jkt/100 25.00 60.00
116 Thurman Munson Jsy/100 10.00 25.00
117 T.Munson Pants/100 10.00 25.00
118 Tony Gwynn Jsy/100 6.00 15.00
119 Wade Boggs Yanks Jsy/100 5.00 12.00
120 Wade Boggs Sox Jsy/100 5.00 12.00
121 Warren Spahn Jsy/100 6.00 15.00
122 Warren Spahn Pants/100 6.00 15.00
123 Whitey Ford Jsy/100 5.00 12.00
124 Whitey Ford Pants/100 5.00 12.00
125 Will Clark Jsy/100 5.00 12.00
126 Willie McCovey Jsy/100 5.00 12.00
127 W.Stargell Black Jsy/100 5.00 12.00
128 Yogi Berra Jsy/25 12.50 30.00
129 Frankie Frisch Jkt/100 8.00 20.00
130 Marty Marion Jsy/100 3.00 8.00
131 Tommy John Pants/100 3.00 8.00
132 Chipper Jones Jsy/100 4.00 10.00
133 S.Sosa White Jsy/100 4.00 10.00
134 R.Henderson Dgr Jsy/100 4.00 10.00
135 Mike Piazza Dgr Jsy/100 5.00 12.00
136 Mike Piazza Mets Jsy/100 5.00 12.00
137 N.Garciaparra Grey Jsy/100 5.00 12.00
138 Hideo Nomo Dgr Jsy/100 4.00 10.00
139 Hideo Nomo Mets Jsy/50 6.00 15.00
140 R.Johnson M's Jsy/100 4.00 10.00
141 R.Johnson D'backs Jsy/100 4.00 10.00
142 R.Johnson Astros Jsy/100 4.00 10.00
143 J.Giambi Yanks Jsy/100 2.00 5.00
144 Jason Giambi A's Jsy/100 2.00 5.00
145 C.Schilling Phils Jsy/100 2.00 5.00
146 Dennis Eckersley Jsy/100 5.00 12.00
147 Carlton Fisk W.Sox Jkt/100 5.00 12.00
148 Tom Seaver Mets Jsy/25 10.00 25.00
149 Joe Torre Jsy/100 5.00 12.00
150 P.Martinez Sox Jsy/100 3.00 8.00
151 A.Pujols White Jsy/100 10.00 25.00
152 Andre Dawson Sox Jsy/50 4.00 10.00
153 Bert Blyleven Jsy/100 3.00 8.00
154 Bo Jackson Sox Jsy/100 6.00 15.00
155 Cal Ripken Pants/100 15.00 40.00
156 C.Fisk W.Sox Jsy/100 5.00 12.00
157 C.Schill D'backs Jsy/100 2.00 5.00
158 D.Strawberry Yanks Jsy/100 3.00 8.00
159 Dave Concepcion Jsy/100 3.00 8.00
160 Dwight Evans Jsy/100 5.00 12.00
161 Ernie Banks Pants/100 6.00 15.00
162 Fred McGriff Jsy/1
163 Gary Carter Pants/100 3.00 8.00
164 Gary Sheffield Jsy/100 2.00 5.00
165 George Brett Blue Jsy/100 8.00 20.00
166 Greg Maddux Jsy/100 5.00 12.00
167 Ivan Rodriguez Jsy/100 3.00 8.00
168 Joe Morgan Giants Jsy/100 3.00 8.00
169 J.Canseco White Jsy/100 5.00 12.00
170 J.Gonzalez Rgr Jsy/100 2.00 5.00
171 J.Gonzalez Indians Jsy/100 2.00 5.00
172 Keith Hernandez Jsy/100 3.00 8.00
173 Ken Boyer Jsy/100 8.00 20.00
174 Kerry Wood Jsy/100 2.00 5.00
175 Lee Smith Jsy/100 3.00 8.00
176 Luis Tiant Jsy/100 3.00 8.00
177 Manny Ramirez Jsy/100 3.00 8.00
178 M.Grace D'backs Jsy/100 5.00 12.00
179 Matt Williams Jsy/100 3.00 8.00
180 Miguel Tejada Jsy/100 2.00 5.00
181 Mike Mussina Jsy/100 3.00 8.00
182 M.Piazza Marlins Jsy/100 5.00 12.00
183 N.Garc White Jsy/100 5.00 12.00
184 P.Martinez Dgr Jsy/100 3.00 8.00
185 Rafael Palmeiro Jsy/100 3.00 8.00
186 R.Jackson Yanks Pants/100 5.00 12.00
187 R.Henderson M's Jsy/100 4.00 10.00
188 R.Hend Mets Pants/100 4.00 10.00
189 R.Henderson A's Jsy/100 4.00 10.00
190 Sammy Sosa Blue Jsy/100 4.00 10.00
191 Satchel Paige CO Jsy/100 25.00 60.00
192 Shawn Green Jsy/100 2.00 5.00
193 Stan Musial Grey Jsy/50 12.50 30.00
194 Steve Carlton Sox Jsy/100 3.00 8.00
195 Steve Garvey Jsy/100 3.00 8.00
196 Tom Seaver Reds Jsy/100 5.00 12.00
197 Tony Gwynn Pants/100 6.00 15.00
198 Vladimir Guerrero Jsy/100 4.00 10.00
199 Wade Boggs Rays Jsy/100 5.00 12.00
200 W.Stargell Grey Jsy/100 5.00 12.00

2004 Leaf Certified Materials Fabric of the Game AL/NL

*AL/NL p/r 100: 4X TO 1X FOTG p/r 100
*AL/NL p/r 50: .6X TO 1.5X FOTG p/r 100
*AL/NL p/r 50: .4X TO 1X FOTG p/r 50
*AL/NL p/r 25: 1X TO 2.5X FOTG p/r 100
*AL/NL p/r 25: .6X TO 1.5X FOTG p/r 50
*AL/NL p/r 25: .4X TO 1X FOTG p/r 25
RANDOM INSERTS IN PACKS
PRINT RUNS B/WN 1-100 #'d COPIES PER
NO PRICING ON QTY OF 10 OR LESS

2004 Leaf Certified Materials Fabric of the Game Jersey Number

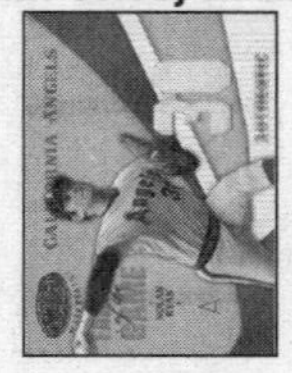

*JSY # p/r 72: .4X TO 1X FOTG p/r 100
*JSY # p/r 36-53: .6X TO 1.5X FOTG p/r 100
*JSY # p/r 36-53: .4X TO 1X FOTG p/r 50
*JSY # p/r 36-53: .25X TO .6X FOTG p/r 25
*JSY # p/r 20-35: 1X TO 2.5X FOTG p/r 100
*JSY # p/r 20-35: .6X TO 1.5X FOTG p/r 50
*JSY # p/r 20-35: .4X TO 1X FOTG p/r 25
*JSY # p/r 15-19: 1.25X TO 3X FOTG p/r 100
*JSY # p/r 15-19: .75X TO 2X FOTG p/r 50
RANDOM INSERTS IN PACKS
PRINT RUNS B/WN 1-72 #'d COPIES PER
NO PRICING ON QTY OF 14 OR LESS
44 Fred Lynn Jsy/19 8.00 20.00
55 Jackie Robinson Jsy/42 25.00 60.00

2004 Leaf Certified Materials Fabric of the Game Jersey Year

*JSY YR p/r 66-99: .4X TO 1X FOTG p/r 100
*JSY YR p/r 66-99: .25X TO .6X FOTG p/r 50
*JSY YR p/r 66-99: .15X TO .4X FOTG p/r 25
*JSY YR p/r 38-65: .6X TO 1.5X FOTG p/r 100
*JSY YR p/r 38-65: .4X TO 1X FOTG p/r 50
*JSY YR p/r 38-65: .25X TO .6X FOTG p/r 25
*JSY YR p/r 20-34: 1X TO 2.5X FOTG p/r 100
*JSY YR p/r 19: 1.25X TO 3X FOTG p/r 100
*JSY YR p/r 19: .75X TO 2X FOTG p/r 50
*JSY YR p/r 19: .5X TO 1.2X FOTG p/r 25
RANDOM INSERTS IN PACKS
PRINT RUNS B/WN 1-99 COPIES PER
NO PRICING ON QTY OF 1 CARD
9 Babe Ruth Jsy/25 300.00 500.00
10 Babe Ruth Pants/30 150.00 250.00
44 Fred Lynn Jsy/19 8.00 20.00
55 Jackie Robinson Jsy/19 40.00 100.00
69 Lou Gehrig Jsy/19 175.00 300.00
70 Lou Gehrig Pants/38 100.00 200.00
87 Ty Cobb Pants/25 60.00 120.00

2004 Leaf Certified Materials Fabric of the Game Position

*POS p/r 100: .4X TO 1X FOTG p/r 100
*POS p/r 50: .6X TO 1.5X FOTG p/r 100
*POS p/r 50: .4X TO 1X FOTG p/r 50
*POS p/r 25: 1X TO 2.5X FOTG p/r 100
*POS p/r 25: .6X TO 1.5X FOTG p/r 50
*POS p/r 25: .4X TO 1X FOTG p/r 25
RANDOM INSERTS IN PACKS
PRINT RUNS B/WN 1-100 COPIES PER
NO PRICING ON QTY OF 10 OR LESS

2004 Leaf Certified Materials Fabric of the Game Prime

RANDOM INSERTS IN PACKS
STATED PRINT RUN 1 SERIAL #'d SET
NO PRICING DUE TO SCARCITY

2004 Leaf Certified Materials Fabric of the Game Reward

*RWD p/r 50: .6X TO 1.5X FOTG p/r 100
*RWD p/r 50: .4X TO 1X FOTG p/r 50
*RWD p/r 25: 1X TO 2.5X FOTG p/r 100
*RWD p/r 25: .6X TO 1.5X FOTG p/r 50
*RWD p/r 25: .4X TO 1X FOTG p/r 25
RANDOM INSERTS IN PACKS
PRINT RUNS B/WN 1-50 #'d COPIES PER
NO PRICING ON QTY OF 10 OR LESS
87 Ty Cobb Pants/50 50.00 100.00

2004 Leaf Certified Materials Fabric of the Game Stats

*STAT p/r 66: .4X TO 1X FOTG p/r 100
*STAT p/r 36-57: .6X TO 1.5X FOTG p/r 100
*STAT p/r 36-57: .4X TO 1X FOTG p/r 50
*STAT p/r 36-57: .25X TO .6X FOTG p/r 25
*STAT p/r 20-35: 1X TO 2.5X FOTG p/r 100
*STAT p/r 20-35: .6X TO 1.5X FOTG p/r 50
*STAT p/r 20-35: .4X TO 1X FOTG p/r 25
*STAT p/r 15-19: 1.25X TO 3X FOTG p/r 100
*STAT p/r 15-19: .75X TO 2X FOTG p/r 50
RANDOM INSERTS IN PACKS
PRINT RUNS B/WN 1-66 #'d COPIES PER

NO PRICING ON QTY OF 14 OR LESS
55 Jackie Robinson Jsy/19 40.00 100.00

2004 Leaf Certified Materials Fabric of the Game Autograph

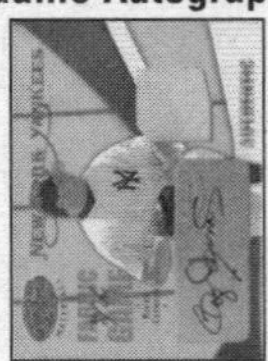

RANDOM INSERTS IN PACKS
PRINT RUNS B/WN 1-10 COPIES PER
NO PRICING DUE TO SCARCITY

2004 Leaf Certified Materials Fabric of the Game Autograph AL/NL

RANDOM INSERTS IN PACKS
PRINT RUNS B/WN 1-25 COPIES PER
NO PRICING ON QTY OF 10 OR LESS
15 Bobby Doerr Jsy/25 15.00 40.00

2004 Leaf Certified Materials Fabric of the Game Autograph Jersey Number

RANDOM INSERTS IN PACKS
PRINT RUNS B/WN 1-8 COPIES PER
NO PRICING DUE TO SCARCITY

2004 Leaf Certified Materials Fabric of the Game Autograph Jersey Year

RANDOM INSERTS IN PACKS
PRINT RUNS B/WN 1-8 COPIES PER
NO PRICING DUE TO SCARCITY

2004 Leaf Certified Materials Fabric of the Game Autograph Position

RANDOM INSERTS IN PACKS
PRINT RUNS B/WN 1-8 COPIES PER
NO PRICING DUE TO SCARCITY

2004 Leaf Certified Materials Fabric of the Game Autograph Reward

RANDOM INSERTS IN PACKS
PRINT RUNS B/WN 1-8 COPIES PER
NO PRICING DUE TO SCARCITY

2004 Leaf Certified Materials Fabric of the Game Autograph Stats

RANDOM INSERTS IN PACKS
PRINT RUNS B/WN 1-8 COPIES PER
NO PRICING DUE TO SCARCITY

2005 Leaf Certified Materials

This 250-card set was released in July, 2005. The set was issued in five-card packs with an $10 SRP which came 10 packs to a box and 24 boxes to a case. Cards numbered 1-190 feature active veterans while cards 191-200 feature retired legends and cards 201-250 feature rookies. Cards 201-243 and 249-250 were all signed by the player. Most of the cards 201-250 had a stated print run of 499 serial numbered sets except for those cards noted as T2 which had a print run of 299 serial numbered sets and card number 211 was printed to a stated print run of 115 sets. All cards 201-250 were randomly inserted into packs.

COMP.SET w/o SP's (200) 15.00 40.00
COMMON CARD (1-190) .25 .60
COMMON CARD (191-200) .25 .60
COMMON (201-250) p/r 499 1.25 3.00
COMMON AU (201-250) p/r 499 3.00 8.00
COMMON AU (201-250) p/r 299 4.00 10.00
COMMON AU (211) p/r 115 6.00 15.00
1 A.J. Burnett .25 .60
2 Adam Dunn .25 .60
3 Adrian Beltre .25 .60
4 Bret Boone .25 .60
5 Albert Pujols 1.25 3.00
6 Alex Rodriguez 1.00 2.50
7 Alfonso Soriano .25 .60
8 Andruw Jones .40 1.00
9 Andy Pettitte .40 1.00
10 Aramis Ramirez .25 .60
11 Aubrey Huff .25 .60
12 Austin Kearns .25 .60
13 B.J. Upton .25 .60
14 Brandon Webb .25 .60
15 Barry Zito .25 .60
16 Tim Salmon .40 1.00
17 Bobby Abreu .25 .60
18 Bobby Crosby .25 .60
19 Brad Penny .25 .60
20 Preston Wilson .25 .60
21 C.C. Sabathia .25 .60
22 Carl Crawford .25 .60
23 Keith Foulke .25 .60
24 Carlos Beltran .25 .60
25 Casey Kotchman .25 .60
26 Chipper Jones .60 1.50
27 Chone Figgins .25 .60
28 Craig Biggio .40 1.00
29 Craig Wilson .25 .60
30 Curt Schilling Sox .40 1.00
31 Danny Kolb .25 .60
32 David Ortiz Sox .60 1.50
33 Orlando Hudson .25 .60
34 David Wright 1.00 2.50
35 Derek Jeter 1.25 3.00
36 Jake Peavy .25 .60
37 Derrek Lee .40 1.00
38 Dontrelle Willis .25 .60
39 Edgar Renteria .25 .60
40 Angel Berroa .25 .60
41 Eric Chavez .25 .60
42 Akinori Otsuka .25 .60
43 Francisco Rodriguez .25 .60
44 Garret Anderson .25 .60
45 Gary Sheffield .25 .60
46 Greg Maddux Cubs 1.00 2.50
47 Hideki Matsui 1.00 2.50
48 Hideo Nomo .60 1.50
49 Ichiro Suzuki 1.25 3.00
50 Ivan Rodriguez Tigers .40 1.00

51 J.D. Drew .25 .60
52 J.T. Snow .25 .60
53 Jack Wilson .25 .60
54 Jamie Moyer .25 .60
55 Jason Bay .25 .60
56 Jason Giambi .25 .60
57 Trot Nixon .25 .60
58 Jason Schmidt .25 .60
59 Jason Varitek .25 .60
60 Roy Oswalt .25 .60
61 Javy Lopez .25 .60
62 Eric Byrnes .25 .60
63 Jeff Bagwell .40 1.00
64 Jeff Kent Dgr .25 .60
65 Jeff Suppan .25 .60
66 Jeremy Bonderman .25 .60
67 Jermaine Dye .25 .60
68 Kazuhito Tadano .25 .60
69 Jim Edmonds .25 .60
70 Jim Thome .40 1.00
71 Johan Santana .60 1.50
72 John Smoltz .40 1.00
73 Johnny Damon .40 1.00
74 Johnny Estrada .25 .60
75 Brett Myers .25 .60
76 Jose Guillen .25 .60
77 Jose Vidro .25 .60
78 Josh Beckett .25 .60
79 Edwin Jackson .25 .60
80 Raul Ibanez .25 .60
81 Rich Harden .25 .60
82 Justin Morneau .25 .60
83 Kazuhisa Ishii .25 .60
84 Kazuo Matsui .25 .60
85 Ken Griffey Jr. 1.00 2.50
86 Ken Harvey .25 .60
87 Frank Thomas .60 1.50
88 Kerry Wood .25 .60
89 Wade Miller .25 .60
90 Kevin Millwood .25 .60
91 Jeremy Affeldt .25 .60
92 Francisco Cordero .25 .60
93 Lance Berkman .25 .60
94 Larry Walker Cards .40 1.00
95 Laynce Nix .25 .60
96 Luis Gonzalez .25 .60
97 Lyle Overbay .25 .60
98 Carlos Zambrano .25 .60
99 Manny Ramirez .40 1.00
100 Marcus Giles .25 .60
101 Mark Buehrle .25 .60
102 Mark Loretta .25 .60
103 Mark Mulder .25 .60
104 Mark Prior .40 1.00
105 Mark Teixeira .40 1.00
106 Marlon Byrd .25 .60
107 Rafael Furcal .25 .60
108 Melvin Mora .25 .60
109 Michael Young .25 .60
110 Miguel Cabrera .40 1.00
111 Miguel Tejada O's .25 .60
112 Mike Lowell .25 .60
113 Mike Mussina .40 1.00
114 Mike Piazza .60 1.50
115 Moises Alou .25 .60
116 Livan Hernandez .25 .60
117 Nomar Garciaparra .60 1.50
118 Omar Vizquel .40 1.00
119 Orlando Cabrera .25 .60
120 Pat Burrell .25 .60
121 Paul Konerko .25 .60
122 Paul Lo Duca .25 .60
123 Pedro Martinez Mets .40 1.00
124 Rafael Palmeiro O's .40 1.00
125 Randy Johnson .60 1.50
126 Richard Hidalgo .25 .60
127 Richie Sexson .25 .60
128 Magglio Ordonez .25 .60
129 Roger Clemens Astros 1.00 2.50
130 Russ Ortiz .25 .60
131 Sammy Sosa Cubs .60 1.50
132 Scott Podsednik .25 .60
133 Scott Rolen .40 1.00
134 Sean Burroughs .25 .60
135 Sean Casey .25 .60
136 Shawn Green D'backs .25 .60
137 Jorge Posada .40 1.00
138 Roy Halladay .25 .60
139 Steve Finley .25 .60
140 Tim Hudson Braves .25 .60
141 Todd Helton .40 1.00
142 Tom Glavine Mets .40 1.00
143 Torii Hunter .25 .60
144 Travis Hafner .25 .60
145 Trevor Hoffman .25 .60
146 Troy Glaus D'backs .25 .60
147 Vernon Wells .25 .60
148 Victor Martinez .25 .60
149 Vladimir Guerrero Angels .60 1.50
150 Sammy Sosa O's .60 1.50
151 Hank Blalock .25 .60
152 Danny Graves .25 .60
153 Rocco Baldelli .25 .60
154 Carlos Delgado Marlins .25 .60
155 Bubba Nelson .25 .60
156 Kevin Youkilis .25 .60
157 Jacque Jones .25 .60
158 Mike Lieberthal .25 .60
159 Ben Sheets .25 .60
160 Lew Ford .25 .60
161 Ervin Santana .25 .60
162 Jody Gerut .25 .60
163 Nick Johnson .25 .60
164 Brian Roberts .25 .60
165 Joe Nathan .25 .60
166 Mike Sweeney .25 .60
167 Ryan Wagner .25 .60
168 David Dellucci .25 .60
169 Jae Weong Seo .25 .60
170 Tom Gordon .25 .60
171 Carlos Lee .25 .60
172 Octavio Dotel .25 .60
173 Jose Castillo .25 .60
174 Troy Percival .25 .60
175 Carlos Delgado Jays .25 .60
176 Curt Schilling D'backs .25 .60
177 David Ortiz Twins .60 1.50
178 Greg Maddux Braves 1.00 2.50
179 Ivan Rodriguez Rgr .40 1.00
180 Jeff Kent Giants .25 .60
181 Larry Walker Rockies .25 .60
182 Miguel Tejada A's .25 .60
183 Pedro Martinez Sox .40 1.00
184 Rafael Palmeiro Rgr .40 1.00
185 Roger Clemens Yanks 1.00 2.50
186 Shawn Green Dgr .25 .60
187 Tim Hudson A's .25 .60
188 Tom Glavine Braves .40 1.00
189 Troy Glaus Angels .25 .60
190 Vladimir Guerrero Expos .60 1.50
191 Cal Ripken LGD 2.00 5.00
192 Don Mattingly LGD 1.25 3.00
193 George Brett LGD 1.25 3.00
194 Harmon Killebrew LGD .60 1.50
195 Mike Schmidt LGD 1.25 3.00
196 Nolan Ryan LGD 1.50 4.00
197 Stan Musial LGD 1.00 2.50
198 Tony Gwynn LGD .75 2.00
199 Wade Boggs LGD .40 1.00
200 Willie Mays LGD 1.25 3.00
201 A.Concepcion NG AU RC 3.00 8.00
202 Agustin Montero NG AU RC 3.00 8.00
203 Carlos Ruiz NG AU RC 4.00 10.00
204 C.Rogowski NG AU RC 4.00 10.00
205 Chris Resop NG AU RC 4.00 10.00
206 Chris Roberson NG AU RC 3.00 8.00
207 Colter Bean NG RC 1.25 3.00
208 Danny Rueckel NG AU RC 3.00 8.00
209 Dave Gassner NG AU RC 3.00 8.00
210 Devon Lowery NG AU RC 3.00 8.00
211 N.Nakamura NG AU T3 RC 15.00 40.00
212 E.Threets NG AU T2 RC 4.00 10.00
213 Garrett Jones NG AU T2 RC 4.00 10.00
214 Geovany Soto NG AU RC 20.00 50.00
215 J.Gothreaux NG AU RC 4.00 10.00
216 J.Hammel NG AU T2 RC 4.00 10.00
217 Jeff Miller NG AU T2 RC 4.00 10.00
218 Jeff Niemann NG AU T2 RC 6.00 15.00
219 Huston Street NG 1.50 4.00
220 John Hattig NG AU RC 3.00 8.00
221 J.Verlander NG AU T2 RC 20.00 40.00
222 Justin Wechsler NG AU RC 3.00 8.00
223 Luke Scott NG AU RC 10.00 25.00
224 Mark McLemore NG AU RC 3.00 8.00
225 M.Woodyard NG AU T2 RC 4.00 10.00
226 M.Lindstrom NG AU T2 RC 4.00 10.00
227 Miguel Negron NG AU RC 4.00 10.00
228 Mike Morse NG AU RC 4.00 10.00
229 Nate McLouth NG AU RC 6.00 15.00
230 P.Reynoso NG AU T2 RC 4.00 10.00
231 Phil Humber NG AU T2 RC 8.00 20.00
232 Tony Pena NG AU RC 3.00 8.00
233 R.Messenger NG AU RC 3.00 8.00
234 Raul Tablado NG AU RC 3.00 8.00
235 Russ Rohlicek NG AU RC 3.00 8.00
236 Ryan Speier NG AU RC 3.00 8.00
237 Scott Munter NG AU RC 3.00 8.00
238 Sean Thompson NG AU RC 3.00 8.00
239 Sean Tracey NG AU T2 RC 4.00 10.00
240 Marcos Carvajal NG RC 1.25 3.00
241 Travis Bowyer NG AU RC 3.00 8.00
242 Ubaldo Jimenez NG AU RC 8.00 20.00
243 W.Balentien NG AU RC 4.00 10.00
244 Eude Brito NG RC 1.25 3.00
245 Ambiorix Burgos NG RC 1.25 3.00
246 Tadahito Iguchi NG RC 3.00 8.00
247 Dae-Sung Koo NG RC 1.25 3.00
248 Chris Seddon NG RC 1.25 3.00
249 Keiichi Yabu NG RC 6.00 15.00
250 Y.Betancourt NG AU RC 12.50 30.00

2005 Leaf Certified Materials Mirror Black

RANDOM INSERTS IN PACKS
STATED PRINT RUN 1 SERIAL #'d SET
NO PRICING DUE TO SCARCITY

2005 Leaf Certified Materials Mirror Blue

*1-190: 2.5X TO 6X BASIC
*BLUE 212-240: 1.25X TO 3X BASIC
*201-250: .75X TO 2X BASIC NO AU
*201-250: .3X TO .8X BASIC AU/299-499
*BLUE 241-300: .15X TO .4X BASIC AU/100
RANDOM INSERTS IN PACKS
STATED PRINT RUN 50 SERIAL #'d SETS
249 Keiichi Yabu NG 2.50 6.00

2005 Leaf Certified Materials Mirror Emerald

RANDOM INSERTS IN PACKS
STATED PRINT RUN 5 SERIAL #'d SETS
NO PRICING DUE TO SCARCITY

2005 Leaf Certified Materials Mirror Gold

*GOLD 1-190: 4X TO 10X BASIC
*GOLD 191-200: 4X TO 10X BASIC
RANDOM INSERTS IN PACKS
STATED PRINT RUN 25 SERIAL #'d SETS
201-250 NO PRICING DUE TO SCARCITY

2005 Leaf Certified Materials Mirror Red

*1-190: 1.5X TO 4X BASIC
*191-200: 1.5X TO 4X BASIC
*201-250: .5X TO 1.2X BASIC NO AU
*201-250: .2X TO .5X BASIC AU/299-499
RANDOM INSERTS IN PACKS
STATED PRINT RUN 100 SERIAL #'d SETS
249 Keiichi Yabu NG 1.50 4.00

2005 Leaf Certified Materials Mirror White

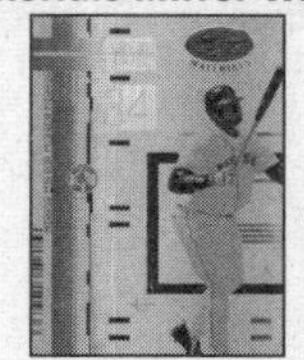

*1-190: 1.5X TO 4X BASIC
*191-200: 1.5X TO 4X BASIC
*201-250: .5X TO 1.2X BASIC NO AU
*201-250: .2X TO .5X BASIC AU/299-499
RANDOM INSERTS IN PACKS
249 Keiichi Yabu NG 1.50 4.00

2005 Leaf Certified Materials Mirror Autograph Black

OVERALL AU-GU ODDS 4 PER BOX
STATED PRINT RUN 1 SERIAL #'d SET
NO PRICING DUE TO SCARCITY

2005 Leaf Certified Materials Mirror Autograph Blue

*1-190 p/r 100: .5X TO 1.2X RED p/r 250
*1-190 p/r 50: .5X TO 1.2X RED p/r 100
*1-190 p/r 25: .5X TO 1.2X RED p/r 50
*1-190 p/r 25: .4X TO 1X RED p/r 25
*201-250 p/r 49: .5X TO 1.2X RED p/r 99
OVERALL AU-GU ODDS 4 PER BOX
PRINT RUNS B/WN 1-100 COPIES PER
1-200 NO PRICING ON 10 OR LESS
201-250 NO PRICING ON 25 OR LESS

2005 Leaf Certified Materials Mirror Autograph Emerald

OVERALL AU-GU ODDS 4 PER BOX
PRINT RUNS B/WN 1-5 COPIES PER
NO PRICING DUE TO SCARCITY

2005 Leaf Certified Materials Mirror Autograph Gold

*1-190 p/r 25: .75X TO 2X RED p/r 250
*1-190 p/r 25: .6X TO 1.5X RED p/r 100
*1-190 p/r 25: .5X TO 1.2X RED p/r 50
*1-190 p/r 25: .4X TO 1X RED p/r 25
OVERALL AU-GU ODDS 4 PER BOX
PRINT RUNS B/WN 1-25 COPIES PER
1-200 NO PRICING ON QTY OF 5 OR LESS
201-250 NO PRICING DUE TO SCARCITY
2 Adam Dunn/25 15.00 40.00
11 Aubrey Huff/25 10.00 25.00
12 Austin Kearns/25 6.00 15.00
13 B.J. Upton/25 10.00 25.00
14 Brandon Webb/25 6.00 15.00
19 Brad Penny/25 6.00 15.00
21 C.C. Sabathia/25 10.00 25.00
23 Keith Foulke/25 15.00 40.00
27 Chone Figgins/25 6.00 15.00
29 Craig Wilson/25 6.00 15.00
31 Danny Kolb/25 6.00 15.00
34 David Wright/25 30.00 60.00
36 Jake Peavy/25 15.00 40.00
37 Derrek Lee/25 20.00 50.00
39 Edgar Renteria/25 10.00 25.00
40 Angel Berroa/25 6.00 15.00
41 Eric Chavez/25 10.00 25.00
42 Akinori Otsuka/25 10.00 25.00
43 Francisco Rodriguez/25 15.00 40.00
44 Garret Anderson/25 10.00 25.00
54 Jamie Moyer/25 10.00 25.00
55 Jason Bay/25 10.00 25.00
57 Trot Nixon/25 10.00 25.00
60 Roy Oswalt/25 10.00 25.00
63 Jeff Bagwell/25 30.00 60.00
65 Jeff Suppan/25 10.00 25.00
75 Brett Myers/25 10.00 25.00
76 Jose Guillen/25 10.00 25.00
77 Jose Vidro/25 10.00 25.00
81 Rich Harden/25 10.00 25.00
97 Lyle Overbay/25 10.00 25.00
98 Carlos Zambrano/25 15.00 40.00
101 Mark Buehrle/25 15.00 40.00
102 Mark Loretta/25 6.00 15.00
107 Rafael Furcal/25 10.00 25.00
109 Michael Young/25 10.00 25.00
110 Miguel Cabrera/25 15.00 40.00
116 Livan Hernandez/25 10.00 25.00
118 Omar Vizquel/25 15.00 40.00
119 Orlando Cabrera/25 10.00 25.00
121 Paul Konerko/25 15.00 40.00
128 Magglio Ordonez/25 10.00 25.00
130 Russ Ortiz/25 6.00 15.00
134 Sean Burroughs/25 6.00 15.00
135 Sean Casey/25 10.00 25.00
139 Steve Finley/25 10.00 25.00
143 Torii Hunter/25 10.00 25.00
144 Travis Hafner/25 10.00 25.00
147 Vernon Wells/25 10.00 25.00
152 Danny Graves/25 6.00 15.00
157 Jacque Jones/25 10.00 25.00
158 Mike Lieberthal/25 10.00 25.00
163 Nick Johnson/25 10.00 25.00
170 Tom Gordon/25 6.00 15.00
171 Carlos Lee/25 10.00 25.00
172 Octavio Dotel/25 6.00 15.00
174 Troy Percival/25 10.00 25.00
194 Harmon Killebrew LGD/25 20.00 50.00

2005 Leaf Certified Materials Mirror Autograph Red

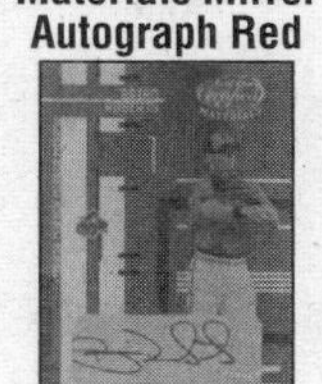

OVERALL AU-GU ODDS 4 PER BOX
PRINT RUNS B/WN 1-250 COPIES PER
1-200 NO PRICING ON QTY OF 10 OR LESS
201-250 NO PRICING ON QTY OF 19 OR LESS
16 Tim Salmon/25 15.00 40.00
18 Bobby Crosby/50 8.00 20.00
25 Casey Kotchman/50 8.00 20.00
33 Orlando Hudson/250 3.00 8.00
53 Jack Wilson/50 8.00 20.00
62 Eric Byrnes/50 5.00 12.00
66 Jeremy Bonderman/50 8.00 20.00
67 Jermaine Dye/50 8.00 20.00
68 Kazuhito Tadano/100 6.00 15.00
79 Edwin Jackson/250 3.00 8.00
80 Raul Ibanez/50 5.00 12.00
86 Ken Harvey/250 3.00 8.00
89 Wade Miller/250 3.00 8.00
91 Jeremy Affeldt/250 3.00 8.00
92 Francisco Cordero/25 10.00 25.00
95 Laynce Nix/100 4.00 10.00
106 Marlon Byrd/250 3.00 8.00
155 Bubba Nelson/250 3.00 8.00
156 Kevin Youkilis/50 5.00 12.00
160 Lew Ford/50 5.00 12.00
161 Ervin Santana/250 3.00 8.00
162 Jody Gerut/50 5.00 12.00
164 Brian Roberts/25 10.00 25.00
165 Joe Nathan/50 8.00 20.00
167 Ryan Wagner/50 5.00 12.00
168 David Dellucci/50 12.50 30.00
169 Jae Weong Seo/25 6.00 15.00
173 Jose Castillo/250 3.00 8.00
202 Agustin Montero NG/99 3.00 8.00
211 Norihiro Nakamura NG/99 20.00 50.00
218 Jeff Niemann NG/49 10.00 25.00
221 Justin Verlander NG/49 30.00 60.00
223 Luke Scott NG/99 12.50 30.00
229 Nate McLouth NG/99 8.00 20.00
230 Paulino Reynoso NG/49 4.00 10.00
231 Phil Humber NG/49 12.50 30.00
234 Raul Tablado NG/99 3.00 8.00
239 Sean Tracey NG/49 4.00 10.00
243 Wladimir Balentien NG/99 8.00 20.00

2005 Leaf Certified Materials Mirror Autograph White

*1-190 p/r 50: .6X TO 1.5X RED p/r 250
*1-190 p/r 50: .5X TO 1.2X RED p/r 100
*1-190 p/r 25: .75X TO 2X RED p/r 250
*1-190 p/r 25: .5X TO 1.2X RED p/r 50
*201-250 p/r 49: .5X TO 1.2X RED p/r 99
*201-250 p/r 49: .4X TO 1X RED p/r 49
OVERALL AU-GU ODDS 4 PER BOX
PRINT RUNS B/WN 1-50 COPIES PER
1-200 NO PRICING ON QTY OF 10 OR LESS
201-250 NO PRICING ON QTY OF 15 OR LESS
19 Brad Penny/25 6.00 15.00
81 Rich Harden/25 8.00 20.00
211 Norihiro Nakamura NG/49 30.00 60.00

2005 Leaf Certified Materials Mirror Bat Black

OVERALL AU-GU ODDS 4 PER BOX
STATED PRINT RUN 1 SERIAL #'d SET
NO PRICING DUE TO SCARCITY

2005 Leaf Certified Materials Mirror Bat Blue

*BLUEp/r75-100: .5X TO 1.2X REDp/r200-250
*BLUE p/r 75-100: .4X TO 1X RED p/r 100
OVERALL AU-GU ODDS 4 PER BOX
PRINT RUNS B/WN 75-100 COPIES PER
32 David Ortiz Sox/100 3.00 8.00
37 Derrek Lee/100 3.00 8.00
117 Nomar Garciaparra/100 4.00 10.00
144 Travis Hafner/100 2.50 6.00

2005 Leaf Certified Materials Mirror Bat Emerald

OVERALL AU-GU ODDS 4 PER BOX
STATED PRINT RUN 5 SERIAL #'d SETS
NO PRICING DUE TO SCARCITY

2005 Leaf Certified Materials Mirror Bat Gold

*GOLD: .75X TO 2X RED p/r 200-250
*GOLD: .6X TO 1.5X RED p/r 100
*GOLD: .5X TO 1.2X RED p/r 50
OVERALL AU-GU ODDS 4 PER BOX
STATED PRINT RUN 25 SERIAL #'d SETS
7 Alfonso Soriano 4.00 10.00
24 Carlos Beltran 4.00 10.00
30 Curt Schilling Sox 5.00 12.00
32 David Ortiz Sox 5.00 12.00
37 Derrek Lee 5.00 12.00
39 Edgar Renteria 4.00 10.00
78 Josh Beckett 4.00 10.00
84 Kazuo Matsui 4.00 10.00
88 Kerry Wood 4.00 10.00
97 Lyle Overbay 4.00 10.00
117 Nomar Garciaparra 6.00 15.00
140 Tim Hudson Braves 4.00 10.00
144 Travis Hafner 4.00 10.00

2005 Leaf Certified Materials Mirror Bat Red

OVERALL AU-GU ODDS 4 PER BOX
PRINT RUNS B/WN 50-250 COPIES PER
2 Adam Dunn/250 2.00 5.00
5 Albert Pujols/250 6.00 15.00
8 Andruw Jones/250 2.50 6.00
11 Aubrey Huff/250 2.00 5.00
13 B.J. Upton/250 2.00 5.00
14 Brandon Webb/100 2.50 6.00
16 Tim Salmon/250 2.50 6.00
25 Casey Kotchman/250 2.00 5.00
26 Chipper Jones/250 3.00 8.00
28 Craig Biggio/50 4.00 10.00
29 Craig Wilson/250 2.00 5.00
34 David Wright/250 4.00 10.00
38 Dontrelle Willis/250 2.00 5.00
44 Garret Anderson/250 2.00 5.00
45 Gary Sheffield/250 2.00 5.00
59 Jason Varitek/250 3.00 8.00
61 Javy Lopez/250 2.00 5.00
63 Jeff Bagwell/250 2.50 6.00
77 Jose Vidro/250 2.00 5.00
93 Lance Berkman/250 2.00 5.00
99 Manny Ramirez/250 2.50 6.00
105 Mark Teixeira/250 2.50 6.00
109 Michael Young/250 2.00 5.00
110 Miguel Cabrera/250 2.50 6.00
111 Miguel Tejada O's/250 2.00 5.00
121 Paul Konerko/250 2.00 5.00
124 Rafael Palmeiro O's/250 2.50 6.00
128 Magglio Ordonez/250 2.00 5.00
136 Shawn Green D'backs/250 2.00 5.00
141 Todd Helton/250 2.50 6.00
142 Tom Glavine Mets/250 2.50 6.00
143 Torii Hunter/200 2.00 5.00
148 Victor Martinez/250 2.00 5.00
149 Vladimir Guerrero Angels/250 3.00 8.00
150 Sammy Sosa O's/250 3.00 8.00
153 Rocco Baldelli/250 2.00 5.00
160 Lew Ford/250 2.00 5.00
166 Mike Sweeney/100 2.50 6.00
184 Rafael Palmeiro Rgr/100 3.00 8.00
188 Tom Glavine Braves/250 2.50 6.00
190 Vladimir Guerrero Expos/250 3.00 8.00

2005 Leaf Certified Materials Mirror Bat White

*WHITE p/r 250: .4X TO 1X RED p/r 200-250
*WHITE p/r 250: .3X TO .8X RED p/r 100
*WHITEp/r75-100: .5XTO1.2X REDp/r200-250
*WHITE p/r 75-100: .3X TO .8X RED p/r 50
*WHITE p/r 50: .5X TO 1.2X RED p/r 100
OVERALL AU-GU ODDS 4 PER BOX
PRINT RUNS B/WN 50-250 COPIES PER

2005 Leaf Certified Materials Mirror Fabric Black HR

OVERALL AU-GU ODDS 4 PER BOX
STATED PRINT RUN 1 SERIAL #'d SET
NO PRICING DUE TO SCARCITY

2005 Leaf Certified Materials Mirror Fabric Black MLB Logo

OVERALL AU-GU ODDS 4 PER BOX
STATED PRINT RUN 1 SERIAL #'d SET
NO PRICING DUE TO SCARCITY

2005 Leaf Certified Materials Mirror Fabric Black Number

OVERALL AU-GU ODDS 4 PER BOX
STATED PRINT RUN 1 SERIAL #'d SET
NO PRICING DUE TO SCARCITY

2005 Leaf Certified Materials Mirror Fabric Black Position

OVERALL AU-GU ODDS 4 PER BOX
STATED PRINT RUN 1 SERIAL #'d SET
NO PRICING DUE TO SCARCITY

2005 Leaf Certified Materials Mirror Fabric Black Prime

OVERALL AU-GU ODDS 4 PER BOX
STATED PRINT RUN 1 SERIAL #'d SET
NO PRICING DUE TO SCARCITY

2005 Leaf Certified Materials Mirror Fabric Blue

*BLUE p/r 100: .5X TO 1.2X RED p/r 225-250
*BLUE p/r 100: .4X TO 1X RED p/r 100
*BLUE p/r 50: .6X TO 1.5X RED p/r 225-250
OVERALL AU-GU ODDS 4 PER BOX
PRINT RUNS B/WN 50-100 COPIES PER
18 Bobby Crosby Jsy/50 3.00 8.00
73 Johnny Damon Jsy/100 3.00 8.00
78 Josh Beckett Jsy/100 2.50 6.00
113 Mike Mussina Jsy/50 4.00 10.00
151 Hank Blalock Jsy/100 2.50 6.00

2005 Leaf Certified Materials Mirror Fabric Emerald

OVERALL AU-GU ODDS 4 PER BOX
STATED PRINT RUN 5 SERIAL #'d SETS
NO PRICING DUE TO SCARCITY

2005 Leaf Certified Materials Mirror Fabric Gold

*GOLD: .75X TO 2X RED p/r 225-250
*GOLD: .6X TO 1.5X RED p/r 100
OVERALL AU-GU ODDS 4 PER BOX
STATED PRINT RUN 25 SERIAL #'d SETS
18 Bobby Crosby Jsy 4.00 10.00
55 Jason Bay Jsy 4.00 10.00
77 Jose Vidro Jsy 4.00 10.00
78 Josh Beckett Jsy 4.00 10.00
105 Mark Teixeira Jsy 5.00 12.00
108 Melvin Mora Jsy 4.00 10.00
151 Hank Blalock Jsy 4.00 10.00

2005 Leaf Certified Materials Mirror Fabric Red

OVERALL AU-GU ODDS 4 PER BOX
PRINT RUNS B/WN 100-250 COPIES PER
2 Adam Dunn Jsy/250 2.00 5.00
5 Albert Pujols Jsy/250 6.00 15.00
7 Alfonso Soriano Jsy/250 2.00 5.00
8 Andruw Jones Jsy/250 2.50 6.00
10 Aramis Ramirez Jsy/250 2.00 5.00
11 Aubrey Huff Jsy/250 2.00 5.00
13 B.J. Upton Jsy/250 2.00 5.00
14 Brandon Webb Pants/100 2.50 6.00
15 Barry Zito Jsy/250 2.00 5.00
17 Bobby Abreu Jsy/250 2.00 5.00
20 Preston Wilson Jsy/250 2.00 5.00
25 Casey Kotchman Jsy/250 2.00 5.00
26 Chipper Jones Jsy/250 3.00 8.00
28 Craig Biggio Jsy/250 2.50 6.00
30 Curt Schilling Sox Jsy/250 2.50 6.00
32 David Ortiz Sox Jsy/250 3.00 8.00
37 Derrek Lee Jsy/250 2.50 6.00
38 Dontrelle Willis Jsy/225 2.00 5.00
41 Eric Chavez Jsy/250 2.00 5.00
43 Francisco Rodriguez Jsy/250 2.00 5.00
44 Garret Anderson Jsy/250 2.00 5.00
45 Gary Sheffield Jsy/250 2.00 5.00
46 Greg Maddux Cubs Jsy/250 4.00 10.00
47 Hideki Matsui Jsy/250 6.00 15.00
48 Hideo Nomo Jsy/250 3.00 8.00
50 Ivan Rodriguez Tigers Jsy/250 2.50 6.00
57 Trot Nixon Jsy/250 2.00 5.00
60 Roy Oswalt Jsy/250 2.00 5.00
61 Javy Lopez Jsy/250 2.00 5.00
63 Jeff Bagwell Jsy/250 2.50 6.00
69 Jim Edmonds Jsy/250 2.00 5.00
70 Jim Thome Jsy/250 2.50 6.00
71 Johan Santana Jsy/250 3.00 8.00
82 Justin Morneau Jsy/250 2.00 5.00
84 Kazuo Matsui Jsy/250 2.00 5.00
87 Frank Thomas Jsy/250 3.00 8.00
88 Kerry Wood Jsy/250 2.00 5.00
92 Francisco Cordero Jsy/250 2.00 5.00
93 Lance Berkman Jsy/250 2.00 5.00
94 Larry Walker Cards Jsy/250 2.50 6.00
96 Luis Gonzalez Jsy/250 2.00 5.00
97 Lyle Overbay Jsy/250 2.00 5.00
98 Carlos Zambrano Jsy/250 2.00 5.00
99 Manny Ramirez Jsy/250 2.50 6.00
104 Mark Prior Jsy/250 2.50 6.00
109 Michael Young Jsy/250 2.00 5.00
110 Miguel Cabrera Jsy/250 2.50 6.00
111 Miguel Tejada O's Jsy/250 2.00 5.00
114 Mike Piazza Jsy/250 3.00 8.00
121 Paul Konerko Jsy/250 2.00 5.00
124 Rafael Palmeiro O's Jsy/250 2.50 6.00
129 Roger Clemens Astros Jsy/250 4.00 10.00
131 Sammy Sosa Cubs Jsy/250 3.00 8.00
133 Scott Rolen Jsy/250 2.50 6.00
135 Sean Casey Jsy/250 2.00 5.00
138 Roy Halladay Jsy/250 2.00 5.00
141 Todd Helton Jsy/250 2.50 6.00
144 Travis Hafner Jsy/250 2.00 5.00
147 Vernon Wells Jsy/250 2.00 5.00
148 Victor Martinez Jsy/250 2.00 5.00
149 Vladimir Guerrero Angels Jsy/250 3.00 8.00
153 Rocco Baldelli Jsy/250 2.00 5.00
159 Ben Sheets Jsy/250 2.00 5.00
160 Lew Ford Jsy/250 2.00 5.00
166 Mike Sweeney Jsy/250 2.00 5.00
178 G.Maddux Braves Jsy/250 10.00 25.00
179 I.Rodriguez Rgr Jsy/250 2.50 6.00
183 P.Martinez Sox Jsy/250 2.50 6.00
184 Rafael Palmeiro Rgr Jsy/250 2.50 6.00
185 Roger Clemens Yanks Jsy/250 4.00 10.00
188 T.Glav Braves Jsy/250 2.50 6.00
190 V.Guer Expos Jsy/100 4.00 10.00

2005 Leaf Certified Materials Mirror Fabric White

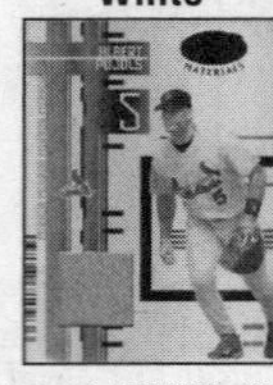

*WHITEp/r150-250: .4XTO1X REDp/r225-250
*WHITEp/r100: .5X TO 1.2X REDp/r225-250
*WHITE p/r 50: .6X TO 1.5X RED p/r 225-250
*WHITE p/r 25: .75X TO 2X RED p/r 225-250
OVERALL AU-GU ODDS 4 PER BOX
PRINT RUNS B/WN 25-250 COPIES PER
34 David Wright Jsy/100 5.00 12.00
78 Josh Beckett Jsy/250 2.00 5.00
95 Laynce Nix Jsy/100 2.50 6.00
113 Mike Mussina Jsy/100 3.00 8.00
151 Hank Blalock Jsy/100 2.50 6.00

2005 Leaf Certified Materials Cuts Blue

OVERALL AU-GU ODDS 4 PER BOX
PRINT RUNS B/WN 1-80 COPIES PER
NO PRICING ON QTY OF 10 OR LESS
3 Willie Mays/26 90.00 150.00
7 Jim Palmer/50 8.00 20.00
12 Steve Carlton/50 8.00 20.00
15 Maury Wills/80 6.00 15.00
20 Dale Murphy/50 12.50 30.00

2005 Leaf Certified Materials Cuts Green

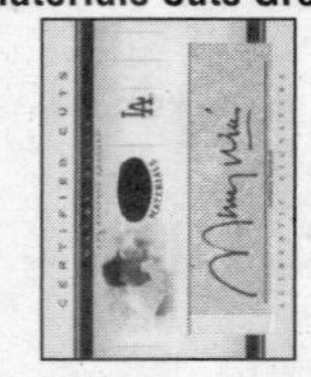

*GREEN p/r 80: .4X TO 1X BLUE p/r 80
*GREEN p/r 50: .4X TO 1X BLUE p/r 50
OVERALL AU-GU ODDS 4 PER BOX
PRINT RUNS B/WN 3-80 COPIES PER
NO PRICING ON QTY OF 11 OR LESS

2005 Leaf Certified Materials Cuts Red

*RED p/r 60: .5X TO 1.2X BLUE p/r 80
*RED p/r 50: .4X TO 1X BLUE p/r 50
OVERALL AU-GU ODDS 4 PER BOX
PRINT RUNS B/WN 1-60 COPIES PER
NO PRICING ON QTY OF 10 OR LESS

2005 Leaf Certified Materials Cuts Material Blue

OVERALL AU-GU ODDS 4 PER BOX
PRINT RUNS B/WN 4-43 COPIES PER
NO PRICING ON QTY OF 8 OR LESS
2 Hank Aaron Bat/43 200.00 300.00
3 Willie Mays Pants/24 125.00 200.00
4 Sandy Koufax Jsy/32 175.00 300.00
5 Cal Ripken Pants/8
6 Nolan Ryan Jsy/34 60.00 120.00
7 Jim Palmer Hat/22 15.00 40.00
8 Tony Gwynn Pants/19 30.00 60.00
9 Rod Carew Jsy/29 15.00 40.00
10 Ryne Sandberg Jsy/23 60.00 120.00
12 Steve Carlton Pants/32 10.00 25.00
14 Mike Schmidt Jsy/20 40.00 80.00
16 Harmon Killebrew Jsy/5
18 Duke Snider Pants/4
19 Don Mattingly Jsy/23 50.00 100.00
20 Dale Murphy Jsy/7

2005 Leaf Certified Materials Cuts Material Green

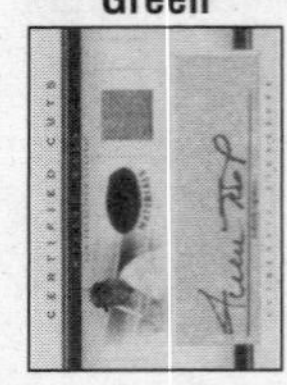

*GRN p/r 20-32: .4X TO 1X BLUE p/r 20-34
*GRN p/r 19: .4X TO 1X BLUE p/r 19
OVERALL AU-GU ODDS 4 PER BOX
PRINT RUNS B/WN 4-32 COPIES PER
NO PRICING ON QTY OF 10 OR LESS
3 Willie Mays Pants/24 125.00 200.00

2005 Leaf Certified Materials Cuts Material Red

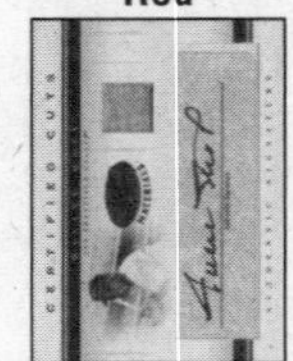

*RED p/r 20-32: .4X TO 1X BLUE p/r 20-34
*RED p/r 19: .4X TO 1X BLUE p/r 19
OVERALL AU-GU ODDS 4 PER BOX
PRINT RUNS B/WN 4-32 COPIES PER
NO PRICING ON QTY OF 10 OR LESS
3 Willie Mays Pants/24 125.00 200.00

2005 Leaf Certified Materials Fabric of the Game

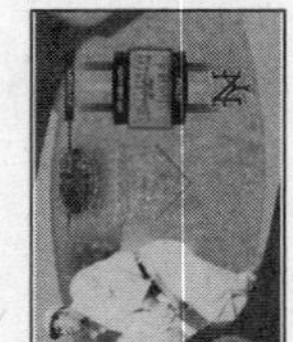

1-160 PRINT RUNS B/WN 5-100 COPIES PER
161-180 PRINTS B/WN 10-100 COPIES PER
OVERALL AU-GU ODDS 4 PER BOX
NO PRICING ON QTY OF 10 OR LESS
1 Al Oliver Jsy/50 4.00 10.00
2 Alan Trammell Jsy/100 3.00 8.00
3 Andres Galarraga Braves Jsy/100 3.00 8.00
4 Andres Galarraga Giants Jsy/100 3.00 8.00
5 Babe Ruth Jsy/10
6 Babe Ruth Pants/25 175.00 300.00
7 Billy Martin Pants/100 4.00 10.00
8 Billy Williams Jsy/50 4.00 10.00
9 Bo Jackson Sox Jsy/100 5.00 12.00
10 B.Jackson Royals Jsy/100 5.00 12.00
11 Bob Feller Pants/5
12 Bob Gibson Jsy/25 6.00 15.00
13 Bobby Doerr Pants/50 4.00 10.00
14 Burleigh Grimes Pants/25 30.00 60.00
15 Cal Ripken Jsy/50 15.00 40.00
16 Cal Ripken Jsy/50 15.00 40.00
17 Carl Yastrzemski Pants/50 6.00 15.00
18 Carlton Fisk Jkt/50 5.00 12.00
19 Catfish Hunter Pants/50 4.00 10.00
20 Darryl Strawberry Yanks Jsy/25 5.00 12.00
21 Darryl Strawberry Dgr Jsy/100 3.00 8.00
22 Dave Concepcion Jsy/50 4.00 10.00
23 Dave Righetti Jsy/50 4.00 10.00
24 Dave Winfield Pants/100 3.00 8.00
25 David Cone Jsy/100 3.00 8.00
26 David Justice Jsy/100 4.00 10.00
27 D.Sanders Yanks Jsy/50 5.00 12.00
28 D.Sanders Reds Jsy/50 5.00 12.00
29 Dennis Eckersley Cards Jsy/50 4.00 10.00
30 Dennis Eckersley A's Pants/50 4.00 10.00
31 Don Mattingly Jsy/100 6.00 15.00
32 Don Sutton Astros Jsy/25 5.00 12.00
33 Don Sutton Dgr Jsy/50 4.00 10.00
34 Duke Snider Dgr Jsy/10
35 Duke Snider Mets Jsy/10
36 Dwight Evans Jsy/5
37 Dwight Gooden Jsy/100 3.00 8.00
38 Eddie Murray Dgr Jsy/25 8.00 20.00
39 Eddie Murray O's Pants/50 6.00 15.00
40 Edgar Martinez Jsy/100 3.00 8.00
41 Ernie Banks Jsy/25 8.00 20.00
42 Fergie Jenkins Jsy/50 4.00 10.00
43 Frankie Frisch Jkt/50 6.00 15.00
44 Fred Lynn Jsy/50 4.00 10.00
45 Fred McGriff Jsy/100 4.00 10.00
46 Gary Carter Mets Jsy/50 4.00 10.00
47 Gary Carter Expos Jsy/50 4.00 10.00
48 Gaylord Perry M's Jsy/50 4.00 10.00
49 Gaylord Perry Giants Jsy/50 4.00 10.00
50 George Brett Jsy/25 10.00 25.00
51 Hal Newhouser Jsy/50 5.00 12.00
52 Hank Aaron Atl Jsy/5
53 Hank Aaron Mil Jsy/5
54 Harmon Killebrew Twins Jsy/25 8.00 20.00
55 Harmon Killebrew Senators Jsy/50 6.00 15.00
56 Harold Baines Jsy/50 4.00 10.00
57 Hoyt Wilhelm Jsy/100 3.00 8.00
58 Jack Morris Jsy/100 3.00 8.00
59 Jim Thorpe Jsy/25 125.00 200.00
60 Jose Cruz Jsy/100 3.00 8.00
61 Jim Rice Jsy/50 4.00 10.00
62 Joe Cronin Jsy/50 6.00 15.00
63 Joe Cronin Pants/100 5.00 12.00
64 Joe Morgan Jsy/50 4.00 10.00
65 Joe Torre Jsy/50 5.00 12.00
66 John Kruk Jsy/100 4.00 10.00
67 Johnny Bench Jsy/50 6.00 15.00
68 Juan Marichal Pants/100 3.00 8.00
69 Keith Hernandez Jsy/10
70 Kirby Puckett Jsy/10
71 Kirk Gibson Jsy/100 3.00 8.00
72 Lee Smith Jsy/100 3.00 8.00
73 Lenny Dykstra Jsy/100 3.00 8.00
74 Lou Boudreau Jsy/25 6.00 15.00
75 Luis Aparicio Jsy/50 4.00 10.00
76 Luis Tiant Pants/100 3.00 8.00
77 Mark Grace Jsy/50 5.00 12.00
78 Hoyt Wilhelm Jsy/100 3.00 8.00
79 Matt Williams Giants Jsy/100 4.00 10.00
80 Matt Williams D'acks Jsy/50 5.00 12.00
81 Mike Schmidt Jkt/5
82 Nolan Ryan Astros Jsy/50 10.00 25.00
83 Nolan Ryan Rgr Jsy/15 15.00 40.00
84 Nolan Ryan Mets Jsy/25 12.50 30.00
85 Nolan Ryan Angels Jsy/25 12.50 30.00
86 Orlando Cepeda Pants/50 4.00 10.00
87 Ozzie Smith Pants/25 8.00 20.00
88 Paul Molitor Brewers Jsy/50 4.00 10.00
89 Paul Molitor Twins Jsy/50 4.00 10.00
90 Paul Molitor Brewers Pants/50 4.00 10.00
91 Phil Niekro Jsy/50 4.00 10.00
92 Reggie Jack Yanks Pants/100 4.00 10.00
93 R.Jackson A's Jkt/100 4.00 10.00
94 Reggie Jackson Angels Jsy/50 5.00 12.00
95 Reggie Jackson A's Jsy/50 5.00 12.00
96 Rickey Henderson Mets Jkt/100 5.00 12.00
97 Rickey Henderson Dgr Jsy/50 6.00 15.00
98 Rickey Henderson A's Jsy/50 6.00 15.00
99 Rickey Henderson M's Jsy/50 6.00 15.00
100 Rickey Henderson Yanks Jsy/50 6.00 15.00
101 Rickey Henderson Padres Pants/50 6.00 15.00
102 Robin Ventura Yanks Jsy/100 3.00 8.00
103 R.Ventura Mets Jsy/100 3.00 8.00
104 Robin Yount Jsy/50 6.00 15.00
105 Rod Carew Angels Jsy/100 4.00 10.00
106 Rod Carew Twins Jsy/100 4.00 10.00
107 Roger Maris Pants/50 12.50 30.00
108 Ron Cey Jsy/50 4.00 10.00
109 Ron Guidry Pants/100 3.00 8.00
110 Ryne Sandberg Jsy/50 15.00 40.00
111 Sandy Koufax Jsy/25 75.00 150.00
112 Stan Musial Jsy/25 10.00 25.00
113 Stan Musial Pants/25 10.00 25.00
114 Steve Garvey Jsy/100 3.00 8.00
115 Ted Williams Jkt/50 20.00 50.00
116 Ted Williams Jsy/25 30.00 60.00
117 Tom Seaver Jsy/50 5.00 12.00
118 Tom Seaver Pants/50 5.00 12.00
119 Tommy John Jsy/100 3.00 8.00
120 Tommy John Pants/100 3.00 8.00
121 Tommy Lasorda Jsy/100 4.00 10.00
122 Tony Gwynn Jsy/100 5.00 12.00
123 Tony Gwynn Pants/100 5.00 12.00
124 Tony Perez Jsy/50 4.00 10.00
125 Wade Boggs Jsy/100 4.00 10.00
126 Warren Spahn Jsy/25 6.00 15.00
127 Whitey Ford Jsy/25 6.00 15.00
128 Will Clark Jsy/50 5.00 12.00
129 Willie Mays Pants/50 15.00 40.00
130 Willie McCovey Pants/100 4.00 10.00
131 Roger Clemens Astros Jsy/50 6.00 15.00
132 R.Clemens Yanks Jsy/50 6.00 15.00
133 Roger Clemens Sox Jsy/50 6.00 15.00
134 Randy Johnson M's Jsy/50 5.00 12.00
135 R.Johnson Expos Jsy/50 5.00 12.00
136 Cal Ripken Jsy/50 15.00 40.00
137 Don Mattingly Jsy/100 6.00 15.00
138 George Brett Jsy/25 10.00 25.00
139 Harmon Killebrew Twins Jsy/25 8.00 20.00
140 Mike Schmidt Jsy/50 8.00 20.00
141 Nolan Ryan Angels Jkt/25 12.50 30.00
142 Stan Musial Jsy/5
143 Tony Gwynn Jsy/100 5.00 12.00
144 Wade Boggs Jsy/50 5.00 12.00
145 Willie Mays Jsy/25 20.00 50.00
146 Hideo Nomo Jsy/100 4.00 10.00
147 D.Murphy Braves Jsy/100 4.00 10.00
148 D.Murphy Phils Jsy/100 4.00 10.00
149 Bo Jackson Royals Jsy/50 6.00 15.00
150 Darryl Strawberry Dgr Jsy/50 4.00 10.00
151 D.Sanders Yanks Jsy/50 5.00 12.00
152 Deion Sanders Yanks Pants/50 5.00 12.00
153 Dennis Eckersley A's Jsy/50 4.00 10.00
154 Dwight Gooden Jsy/100 3.00 8.00
155 Edgar Martinez Jsy/100 4.00 10.00
156 Lou Brock Jsy/50 5.00 12.00
157 Steve Carlton Pants/50 4.00 10.00
158 Albert Pujols Jsy/50 10.00 25.00
159 Tom Glavine Jsy/100 4.00 10.00
160 Hideki Matsui Pants/50 10.00 25.00
161 Babe Ruth Pants / Jim Thorpe Jsy/25 300.00 500.00
162 Ted Will Jkt / Stan Musial Jsy/50 30.00 60.00
163 Willie Mays Jsy / Bob Gibson Jsy/10
164 Whitey Ford Jsy / Sandy Koufax Jsy/25 75.00 150.00
165 Roger Maris Pants / Don Matt Jsy/25 40.00 80.00
166 Nolan Ryan Jsy / Tom Seaver Jsy/50 15.00 40.00
167 Cal Ripken Jsy / George Brett Jsy/100 20.00 50.00
168 Ryne Sandberg Jsy / Mike Schmidt Jsy/50 15.00 40.00
169 Tony Gwynn Jsy / Wade Boggs Jsy/50 8.00 20.00
170 Carlton Fisk Jsy / Johnny Bench Pants/50 8.00 20.00
171 Duke Snider Pants / Harmon Killebrew Jsy/10
172 Reggie Jackson Pants / Darryl Strawberry Jsy/50 6.00 15.00
173 Robin Yount Jsy / Paul Molitor Jsy/50 8.00 20.00
174 Warren Spahn Pants / Juan Marichal Jsy/50 6.00 15.00
175 Bo Jackson Jsy / Deion Sanders Pants/100 6.00 15.00
176 Tony Gwynn Jsy / Rickey Henderson Jsy/100 10.00 25.00
177 Hideki Matsui Jsy / Jim Edmonds Jsy/100 10.00 25.00
178 Rickey Henderson Pants / Lou Brock Jsy/100 6.00 15.00
179 Roger Clemens Jsy / Albert Pujols Jsy/100 10.00 25.00
180 Hideo Nomo Jsy / Kazuhisa Ishii Jsy/100 6.00 15.00

2005 Leaf Certified Materials Fabric of the Game Jersey Number

*1-160 p/r 72: .3X TO .8X FOTG p/r 50
*1-160 p/r 36-55: .5X TO 1.2X FOTG p/r 100
*1-160 p/r 36-55: .4X TO 1X FOTG p/r 50
*1-160 p/r 36-55: .3X TO .8X FOTG p/r 25
*1-160 p/r 20-35: .6X TO 1.5X FOTG p/r 100
*1-160 p/r 20-35: .5X TO 1.2X FOTG p/r 50
*1-160 p/r 20-35: .4X TO 1X FOTG p/r 25
*1-160 p/r 20-35: .3X TO .8X FOTG p/r 15
*1-160 p/r 15-19: .75X TO 2X FOTG p/r 100
*1-160 p/r 15-19: .6X TO 1.5X FOTG p/r 50
*1-160 p/r 15-19: .5X TO 1.2X FOTG p/r 25
1-160 PRINT RUNS B/WN 1-72 COPIES PER
*161-180 p/r 50: .5X TO 1.2X FOTG p/r 100
*161-180 p/r 50: .4X TO 1X FOTG p/r 50
*161-180 p/r 25: .6X TO 1.5X FOTG p/r 100
*161-180 p/r 25: .5X TO 1.2X FOTG p/r 50
161-180 PRINTS B/WN 3-50 COPIES PER
OVERALL AU-GU ODDS 4 PER BOX
NO PRICING ON QTY OF 14 OR LESS
36 Dwight Evans Jsy/24 6.00 15.00
52 Hank Aaron Atl Jsy/44 20.00 50.00
53 Hank Aaron Mil Jsy/44 20.00 50.00
111 Sandy Koufax Jsy/32 75.00 150.00

2005 Leaf Certified Materials Fabric of the Game Position

*1-160 p/r 100: .4X TO 1X FOTG p/r 100
*1-160 p/r 100: .3X TO .8X FOTG p/r 50
*1-160 p/r 50: .5X TO 1.2X FOTG p/r 100
*1-160 p/r 50: .4X TO 1X FOTG p/r 50
*1-160 p/r 25: .6X TO 1.5X FOTG p/r 100
*1-160 p/r 25: .5X TO 1.2X FOTG p/r 50
*1-160 p/r 25: .4X TO 1X FOTG p/r 25
1-160 PRINT RUNS B/WN 3-100 COPIES PER
*161-180 p/r 100: .4X TO 1X FOTG p/r 100
*161-180 p/r 100: .3X TO .8X FOTG p/r 50
*161-180 p/r 50: .5X TO 1.2X FOTG p/r 100
*161-180 p/r 50: .4X TO 1X FOTG p/r 50
*161-180 p/r 25: .5X TO 1.2X FOTG p/r 50
*161-180 p/r 25: .4X TO 1X FOTG p/r 25
161-180 PRINTS B/WN 5-100 COPIES PER
OVERALL AU-GU ODDS 4 PER BOX
NO PRICING ON QTY OF 10 OR LESS
111 Sandy Koufax Jsy/25 75.00 150.00
161 Babe Ruth Pants / Jim Thorpe Jsy/25 300.00 500.00
164 Whitey Ford Jsy / Sandy Koufax Jsy/25 75.00 150.00

2005 Leaf Certified Materials Fabric of the Game Reward

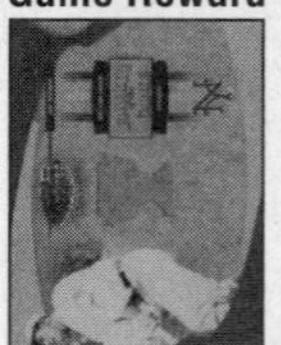

*1-160 p/r 50: .5X TO 1.2X FOTG p/r 100
*1-160 p/r 50: .4X TO 1X FOTG p/r 50
*1-160 p/r 50: .3X TO .8X FOTG p/r 25
*1-160 p/r 25: .6X TO 1.5X FOTG p/r 100
*1-160 p/r 25: .5X TO 1.2X FOTG p/r 50
*1-160 p/r 25: .4X TO 1X FOTG p/r 25
1-160 PRINT RUNS B/WN 3-100 COPIES PER
*161-180 p/r 50: .5X TO 1.2X FOTG p/r 100
*161-180 p/r 50: .4X TO 1X FOTG p/r 50
*161-180 p/r 25: .5X TO 1.2X FOTG p/r 50
*161-180 p/r 25: .4X TO 1X FOTG p/r 25
161-180 PRINTS B/WN 10-50 COPIES PER
OVERALL AU-GU ODDS 4 PER BOX
NO PRICING ON QTY OF 10 OR LESS
111 Sandy Koufax Jsy/25 75.00 150.00

161 Babe Ruth Pants 300.00 500.00
Jim Thorpe Jsy/25
163 Willie Mays Pants 20.00 50.00
Bob Gibson Jsy/25
164 Whitey Ford Jsy 75.00 150.00
Sandy Koufax Jsy/25

2005 Leaf Certified Materials Fabric of the Game Stats

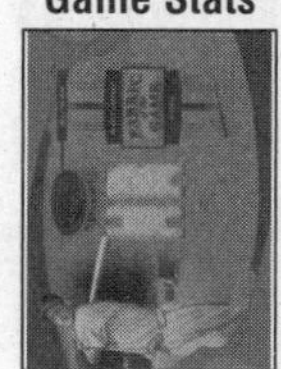

*1-160 p/r 75: .4X TO 1X FOTG p/r 100
*1-160 p/r 75: .3X TO .8X FOTG p/r 50
*1-160 p/r 75: .25X TO .6X FOTG p/r 25
*1-160 p/r 50: .5X TO 1.2X FOTG p/r 100
*1-160 p/r 50: .4X TO 1X FOTG p/r 50
*1-160 p/r 25: .6X TO 1.5X FOTG p/r 100
*1-160 p/r 25: .5X TO 1.2X FOTG p/r 50
*1-160 p/r 25: .4X TO 1X FOTG p/r 25
1-160 PRINT RUNS B/WN 3-75 COPIES PER
*161-180 p/r 50: .5X TO 1.2X FOTG p/r 100
*161-180 p/r 50: .4X TO 1X FOTG p/r 50
*161-180 p/r 25: .5X TO 1.2X FOTG p/r 50
*161-180 p/r 25: .4X TO 1X FOTG p/r 25
161-180 PRINTS B/WN 10-50 COPIES PER
OVERALL AU-GU ODDS 4 PER BOX
NO PRICING ON QTY OF 10 OR LESS
111 Sandy Koufax Jsy/25 75.00 150.00
142 Stan Musial Jsy/25 10.00 25.00
161 Babe Ruth Pants 300.00 500.00
Jim Thorpe Jsy/25
163 Willie Mays Pants 20.00 50.00
Bob Gibson Jsy/25
164 Whitey Ford Jsy 75.00 150.00
Sandy Koufax Jsy/25

2005 Leaf Certified Materials Fabric of the Game Prime

*1-160 p/r 25: 1X TO 2.5X FOTG p/r 100
*1-160 p/r 25: .75X TO 2X FOTG p/r 50
*1-160 p/r 25: .6X TO 1.5X FOTG p/r 25
*1-160 p/r 25: .5X TO 1.2X FOTG p/r 15
*1-160 p/r 17-18: .75X TO 2X FOTG p/r 50
*1-160 p/r 17-18: .6X TO 1.5X FOTG p/r 25
1-160 PRINT RUNS B/WN 5-25 COPIES PER
161-180 PRINTS B/WN 3-5 COPIES PER
OVERALL AU-GU ODDS 4 PER BOX
NO PRICING ON QTY OF 13 OR LESS
36 Dwight Evans Jsy/25 10.00 25.00
69 Keith Hernandez Jsy/25 8.00 20.00
81 Mike Schmidt Jsy/25

2005 Leaf Certified Materials Fabric of the Game Autograph

OVERALL AU-GU ODDS 4 PER BOX
STATED PRINT RUN 1 SERIAL #'d SET
NO PRICING DUE TO SCARCITY

2005 Leaf Certified Materials Fabric of the Game Autograph Jersey Number

OVERALL AU-GU ODDS 4 PER BOX
STATED PRINT RUN 1 SERIAL #'d SET
NO PRICING DUE TO SCARCITY

2005 Leaf Certified Materials Fabric of the Game Autograph Position

OVERALL AU-GU ODDS 4 PER BOX
STATED PRINT RUN 1 SERIAL #'d SET
NO PRICING DUE TO SCARCITY

2005 Leaf Certified Materials Fabric of the Game Autograph Reward

OVERALL AU-GU ODDS 4 PER BOX
STATED PRINT RUN 1 SERIAL #'d SET
NO PRICING DUE TO SCARCITY

2005 Leaf Certified Materials Fabric of the Game Autograph Stats

OVERALL AU-GU ODDS 4 PER BOX
STATED PRINT RUN 1 SERIAL #'d SET
NO PRICING DUE TO SCARCITY

2005 Leaf Certified Materials Fabric of the Game Autograph Prime

OVERALL AU-GU ODDS 4 PER BOX
STATED PRINT RUN 1 SERIAL #'d SET
NO PRICING DUE TO SCARCITY

2005 Leaf Certified Materials Gold Team

STATED ODDS 1:7
*MIRROR: 1.25X TO 3X BASIC
MIRROR RANDOM INSERTS IN PACKS
1 Albert Pujols 2.00 5.00
2 Alex Rodriguez 1.50 4.00
3 Carlos Beltran Astros .75 2.00
4 Chipper Jones 1.25 3.00
5 Curt Schilling 1.25 3.00
6 Derek Jeter 2.00 5.00
7 Greg Maddux 1.50 4.00
8 Hank Blalock .75 2.00
9 Ichiro Suzuki 2.00 5.00
10 Ivan Rodriguez 1.25 3.00
11 Jim Thome 1.25 3.00
12 Ken Griffey Jr. 1.50 4.00
13 Lyle Overbay .75 2.00
14 Manny Ramirez 1.25 3.00
15 Mark Mulder A's .75 2.00
16 Mark Prior 1.25 3.00
17 Michael Young .75 2.00
18 Miguel Cabrera 1.25 3.00
19 Mike Piazza 1.25 3.00
20 Pedro Martinez 1.25 3.00
21 Randy Johnson M's 1.25 3.00
22 Roger Clemens 1.50 4.00
23 Sammy Sosa Cubs 1.25 3.00
24 Tim Hudson A's .75 2.00
25 Todd Helton 1.25 3.00

2005 Leaf Certified Materials Gold Team Autograph

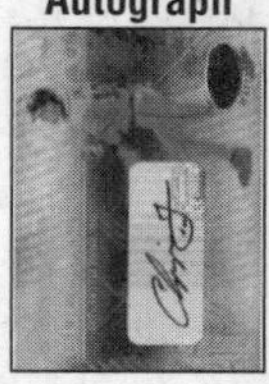

OVERALL AU-GU ODDS 4 PER BOX
PRINT RUNS B/WN 5-10 COPIES PER
NO PRICING DUE TO SCARCITY

2005 Leaf Certified Materials Gold Team Jersey Number

OVERALL AU-GU ODDS 4 PER BOX
PRINT RUNS B/WN 100-250 COPIES PER
1 Albert Pujols/100 8.00 20.00
3 Carlos Beltran Astros/200 2.00 5.00
4 Chipper Jones/100 4.00 10.00
5 Curt Schilling/250 2.50 6.00
7 Greg Maddux/100 5.00 12.00
8 Hank Blalock/250 2.00 5.00
10 Ivan Rodriguez/120 3.00 8.00
11 Jim Thome/250 2.50 6.00
13 Lyle Overbay/250 2.00 5.00
14 Manny Ramirez/250 2.50 6.00
15 Mark Mulder A's/250 2.00 5.00
16 Mark Prior/100 3.00 8.00
17 Michael Young/250 2.00 5.00
18 Miguel Cabrera/100 3.00 8.00
19 Mike Piazza/250 3.00 8.00
20 Pedro Martinez/100 3.00 8.00
21 Randy Johnson M's/250 3.00 8.00
22 Roger Clemens/250 4.00 10.00
23 Sammy Sosa Cubs/250 3.00 8.00
24 Tim Hudson A's/100 2.50 6.00
25 Todd Helton/100 3.00 8.00

2005 Leaf Certified Materials Gold Team Jersey Number Prime

*PRIME p/r 25: 1.25X TO 3X JSY p/r 200-250
*PRIME p/r 25: 1X TO 2.5X JSY p/r 100-120
OVERALL AU-GU ODDS 4 PER BOX
PRINT RUNS B/WN 5-25 COPIES PER
NO PRICING ON QTY OF 10 OR LESS

2005 Leaf Certified Materials Skills

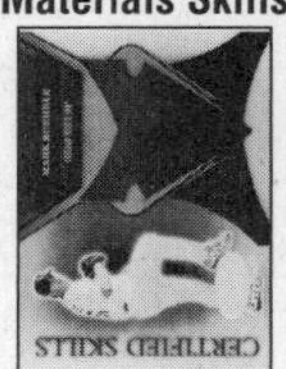

STATED ODDS 1:7
*MIRROR: 1.25X TO 3X BASIC
MIRROR RANDOM INSERTS IN PACKS
1 Andy Pettitte 1.25 3.00
2 Barry Zito .75 2.00
3 Bobby Crosby .75 2.00
4 Brandon Webb .75 2.00
5 Craig Biggio 1.25 3.00
6 David Ortiz 1.25 3.00
7 Dontrelle Willis .75 2.00
8 Francisco Rodriguez .75 2.00
9 Gary Sheffield .75 2.00
10 Jack Wilson .75 2.00
11 Jason Bay .75 2.00
12 Jeff Bagwell 1.25 3.00
13 Jim Edmonds .75 2.00
14 Josh Beckett .75 2.00
15 Kerry Wood .75 2.00
16 Lance Berkman .75 2.00
17 Mark Buehrle .75 2.00
18 Mark Teixeira 1.25 3.00
19 Miguel Tejada .75 2.00
20 Paul Konerko .75 2.00
21 Scott Rolen 1.25 3.00
22 Sean Burroughs .75 2.00
23 Vernon Wells .75 2.00
24 Victor Martinez .75 2.00
25 Vladimir Guerrero 1.25 3.00

2005 Leaf Certified Materials Skills Autograph

OVERALL AU-GU ODDS 4 PER BOX
PRINT RUNS B/WN 5-25 COPIES PER
NO PRICING ON QTY OF 10 OR LESS
3 Bobby Crosby/25 10.00 25.00
11 Jason Bay/25 10.00 25.00

2005 Leaf Certified Materials Skills Jersey Position

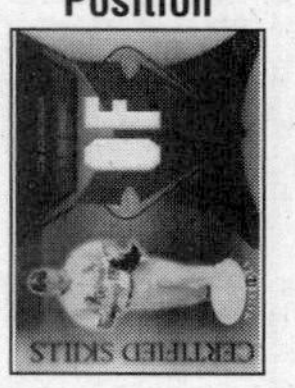

OVERALL AU-GU ODDS 4 PER BOX
PRINT RUNS B/WN 100-250 COPIES PER
1 Andy Pettitte/250 2.50 6.00
2 Barry Zito/250 2.00 5.00
3 Bobby Crosby/100 2.50 6.00
4 Brandon Webb Pants/100 2.50 6.00
5 Craig Biggio/250 2.50 6.00
6 David Ortiz/250 2.50 6.00
7 Dontrelle Willis/100 2.50 6.00
8 Francisco Rodriguez/250 2.00 5.00
9 Gary Sheffield/50 3.00 8.00
10 Jack Wilson/50 3.00 8.00
11 Jason Bay/100 2.50 6.00
12 Jeff Bagwell/250 2.50 6.00
13 Jim Edmonds/250 2.00 5.00
14 Josh Beckett/250 2.00 5.00
15 Kerry Wood/50 3.00 8.00
16 Lance Berkman/250 2.00 5.00
17 Mark Buehrle/150 2.00 5.00
19 Miguel Tejada/250 2.00 5.00
20 Paul Konerko/100 2.50 6.00
21 Scott Rolen/100 3.00 8.00
22 Sean Burroughs/100 2.50 6.00
23 Vernon Wells/250 2.00 5.00
24 Victor Martinez/250 2.00 5.00
25 Vladimir Guerrero/250 3.00 8.00

2005 Leaf Certified Materials Skills Jersey Position Prime

*PRIME p/r 25: 1.25X TO 3X JSY p/r 150-250
*PRIME p/r 25: 1X TO 2.5X JSY p/r 100
*PRIME p/r 25: .75X TO 2X JSY p/r 50
OVERALL AU-GU ODDS 4 PER BOX
PRINT RUNS B/WN 5-25 COPIES PER
NO PRICING ON QTY OF 5
18 Mark Teixeira/25 8.00 20.00

1994 Leaf Limited

This 160-card standard-size set was issued exclusively to hobby dealers. The set is organized alphabetically within teams with AL preceding NL.

COMPLETE SET (160) 30.00 80.00
1 Jeffrey Hammonds .20 .50
2 Ben McDonald .20 .50
3 Mike Mussina .60 1.50
4 Rafael Palmeiro .60 1.50
5 Cal Ripken Jr. 3.00 8.00
6 Lee Smith .40 1.00
7 Roger Clemens 2.00 5.00
8 Scott Cooper .20 .50
9 Andre Dawson .40 1.00
10 Mike Greenwell .20 .50
11 Aaron Sele .20 .50
12 Mo Vaughn .40 1.00
13 Brian Anderson RC .40 1.00
14 Chad Curtis .20 .50
15 Chili Davis .40 1.00
16 Gary DiSarcina .20 .50
17 Mark Langston .20 .50
18 Tim Salmon .60 1.50
19 Wilson Alvarez .20 .50
20 Jason Bere .20 .50
21 Julio Franco .40 1.00
22 Jack McDowell .20 .50
23 Tim Raines .40 1.00
24 Frank Thomas 1.00 2.50
25 Robin Ventura .40 1.00
26 Carlos Baerga .20 .50
27 Albert Belle .40 1.00
28 Kenny Lofton .40 1.00
29 Eddie Murray 1.00 2.50
30 Manny Ramirez 1.00 2.50
31 Cecil Fielder .40 1.00
32 Travis Fryman .40 1.00
33 Mickey Tettleton .20 .50
34 Alan Trammell .40 1.00
35 Lou Whitaker .40 1.00
36 David Cone .40 1.00
37 Gary Gaetti .40 1.00
38 Greg Gagne .20 .50
39 Bob Hamelin .20 .50
40 Wally Joyner .40 1.00
41 Brian McRae .20 .50
42 Ricky Bones .20 .50
43 Brian Harper .20 .50
44 John Jaha .20 .50
45 Pat Listach .20 .50
46 Dave Nilsson .20 .50
47 Greg Vaughn .20 .50
48 Kent Hrbek .40 1.00
49 Chuck Knoblauch .40 1.00
50 Shane Mack .20 .50
51 Kirby Puckett 1.00 2.50
52 Dave Winfield .40 1.00
53 Jim Abbott .60 1.50
54 Wade Boggs .60 1.50
55 Jimmy Key .40 1.00
56 Don Mattingly 2.50 6.00
57 Paul O'Neill .60 1.50
58 Danny Tartabull .20 .50
59 Dennis Eckersley .40 1.00
60 Rickey Henderson 1.00 2.50
61 Mark McGwire 2.50 6.00
62 Troy Neel .20 .50
63 Ruben Sierra .40 1.00
64 Eric Anthony .20 .50
65 Jay Buhner .40 1.00
66 Ken Griffey Jr. 1.50 4.00
67 Randy Johnson 1.00 2.50
68 Edgar Martinez .60 1.50
69 Tino Martinez .60 1.50
70 Jose Canseco .60 1.50
71 Will Clark .60 1.50
72 Juan Gonzalez .40 1.00
73 Dean Palmer .40 1.00
74 Ivan Rodriguez .60 1.50
75 Roberto Alomar .60 1.50
76 Joe Carter .40 1.00
77 Carlos Delgado .60 1.50
78 Paul Molitor .40 1.00
79 John Olerud .40 1.00
80 Devon White .40 1.00
81 Steve Avery .20 .50
82 Tom Glavine .60 1.50
83 David Justice .40 1.00
84 Roberto Kelly .20 .50
85 Ryan Klesko .40 1.00
86 Javier Lopez .40 1.00
87 Greg Maddux 1.50 4.00
88 Fred McGriff .60 1.50
89 Shawon Dunston .20 .50
90 Mark Grace .60 1.50
91 Derrick May .20 .50
92 Sammy Sosa 1.00 2.50
93 Rick Wilkins .20 .50
94 Bret Boone .40 1.00
95 Barry Larkin .60 1.50
96 Kevin Mitchell .20 .50
97 Hal Morris .20 .50
98 Deion Sanders .60 1.50
99 Reggie Sanders .40 1.00
100 Dante Bichette .40 1.00
101 Ellis Burks .40 1.00
102 Andres Galarraga .40 1.00
103 Joe Girardi .20 .50
104 Charlie Hayes .20 .50
105 Chuck Carr .20 .50
106 Jeff Conine .40 1.00
107 Bryan Harvey .20 .50
108 Benito Santiago .40 1.00
109 Gary Sheffield .40 1.00
110 Jeff Bagwell .60 1.50
111 Craig Biggio .60 1.50
112 Ken Caminiti .40 1.00
113 Andujar Cedeno .20 .50
114 Doug Drabek .20 .50
115 Luis Gonzalez .40 1.00
116 Brett Butler .40 1.00
117 Delino DeShields .20 .50
118 Eric Karros .40 1.00
119 Raul Mondesi .40 1.00
120 Mike Piazza 2.00 5.00
121 Henry Rodriguez .20 .50
122 Tim Wallach .20 .50
123 Moises Alou .40 1.00
124 Cliff Floyd .40 1.00
125 Marquis Grissom .40 1.00
126 Ken Hill .20 .50
127 Larry Walker .40 1.00
128 John Wetteland .40 1.00
129 Bobby Bonilla .40 1.00
130 John Franco .40 1.00
131 Jeff Kent .60 1.50
132 Bret Saberhagen .40 1.00
133 Ryan Thompson .20 .50
134 Darren Daulton .40 1.00
135 Mariano Duncan .20 .50
136 Lenny Dykstra .40 1.00
137 Danny Jackson .20 .50
138 John Kruk .40 1.00
139 Jay Bell .40 1.00
140 Jeff King .20 .50
141 Al Martin .20 .50
142 Orlando Merced .20 .50
143 Andy Van Slyke .60 1.50
144 Bernard Gilkey .20 .50
145 Gregg Jefferies .20 .50
146 Ray Lankford .40 1.00
147 Ozzie Smith 1.50 4.00
148 Mark Whiten .20 .50
149 Todd Zeile .20 .50
150 Derek Bell .20 .50
151 Andy Benes .20 .50
152 Tony Gwynn 1.25 3.00
153 Phil Plantier .20 .50
154 Bip Roberts .20 .50
155 Rod Beck .20 .50
156 Barry Bonds 2.50 6.00
157 John Burkett .20 .50
158 Royce Clayton .20 .50
159 Bill Swift .20 .50
160 Matt Williams .40 1.00

1994 Leaf Limited Gold All-Stars

Randomly inserted in packs at a rate of one in seven, this 18-card standard-size set features the starting players at each position in both the National and American leagues for the 1994 All-Star Game. They are identical in design to the basic Limited product except for being gold and individually numbered out of 10,000.

COMPLETE SET (18) 15.00 40.00
1 Frank Thomas .75 2.00
2 Gregg Jefferies .15 .40
3 Roberto Alomar .50 1.25
4 Mariano Duncan .15 .40
5 Wade Boggs .50 1.25
6 Matt Williams .30 .75
7 Cal Ripken Jr. 2.50 6.00
8 Ozzie Smith 1.25 3.00
9 Kirby Puckett .75 2.00
10 Barry Bonds 2.00 5.00
11 Ken Griffey Jr. 1.25 3.00
12 Tony Gwynn 1.00 2.50
13 Joe Carter .30 .75
14 David Justice .30 .75
15 Ivan Rodriguez .50 1.25
16 Mike Piazza 1.50 4.00
17 Jimmy Key .30 .75
18 Greg Maddux 1.25 3.00

1994 Leaf Limited Rookies

This 80-card standard-size premium set was issued by Donruss exclusively to hobby dealers. The set showcases top rookies and prospects of 1994. Rookie Cards in this set include Armando Benitez, Rusty Greer and Chan Ho Park.

COMPLETE SET (80) 10.00 25.00
1 Charles Johnson .30 .75
2 Rico Brogna .15 .40
3 Melvin Nieves .15 .40
4 Rich Becker .15 .40
5 Russ Davis .15 .40
6 Matt Mieske .15 .40
7 Paul Shuey .15 .40
8 Hector Carrasco .15 .40
9 J.R. Phillips .15 .40
10 Scott Ruffcorn .15 .40
11 Kurt Abbott RC .15 .40
12 Danny Bautista .15 .40
13 Rick White .15 .40
14 Steve Dunn .15 .40
15 Joe Ausanio .15 .40
16 Salomon Torres .15 .40
17 Ricky Bottalico RC .15 .40
18 Johnny Ruffin .15 .40
19 Kevin Foster RC .15 .40
20 W.VanLandingham RC .15 .40
21 Troy O'Leary .15 .40
22 Mark Acre RC .15 .40
23 Norberto Martin .15 .40
24 Jason Jacome RC .15 .40
25 Steve Trachsel .15 .40
26 Denny Hocking .15 .40
27 Mike Lieberthal .30 .75
28 Gerald Williams .15 .40
29 John Mabry RC .30 .75
30 Greg Blosser .15 .40
31 Carl Everett .30 .75
32 Steve Karsay .15 .40
33 Jose Valentin .15 .40
34 Jon Lieber .30 .75
35 Chris Gomez .15 .40
36 Jesus Tavarez RC .15 .40
37 Tony Longmire .15 .40
38 Luis Lopez .15 .40
39 Matt Walbeck .15 .40
40 Rikkert Faneyte RC .15 .40
41 Shane Reynolds .15 .40
42 Joey Hamilton .15 .40
43 Ismael Valdes RC .30 .75
44 Danny Miceli .15 .40
45 Darren Bragg RC .15 .40
46 Alex Gonzalez .15 .40
47 Rick Helling .15 .40
48 Jose Oliva .15 .40
49 Jim Edmonds .75 2.00
50 Miguel Jimenez .15 .40
51 Tony Eusebio .15 .40

52 Shawn Green .75 2.00
53 Billy Ashley .15 .40
54 Rondell White .30 .75
55 Cory Bailey RC .15 .40
56 Tim Davis .15 .40
57 John Hudek RC .15 .40
58 Darren Hall .15 .40
59 Darren Dreifort .15 .40
60 Mike Kelly .15 .40
61 Marcus Moore .15 .40
62 Garret Anderson .75 2.00
63 Brian L. Hunter .15 .40
64 Mark Smith .15 .40
65 Garey Ingram RC .15 .40
66 Rusty Greer RC .50 1.25
67 Marc Newfield .15 .40
68 Gar Finnvold .15 .40
69 Paul Spoljaric .15 .40
70 Ray McDavid .15 .40
71 Orlando Miller .15 .40
72 Jorge Fabregas .15 .40
73 Ray Holbert .15 .40
74 Armando Benitez RC .30 .75
75 Ernie Young RC .30 .75
76 James Mouton .15 .40
77 Robert Perez RC .15 .40
78 Chan Ho Park RC .50 1.25
79 Roger Salkeld .15 .40
80 Tony Tarasco .15 .40

1994 Leaf Limited Rookies Phenoms

This 10-card standard-size set was randomly inserted in Leaf Limited Rookies packs at a rate of approximately of one in twelve. This set showcases top 1994 rookies especially Alex Rodriguez. The fronts are designed much like the Limited Rookies basic set cards except the card is comprised of gold foil instead of silver on the front. Gold backs are also virtually identical to the Limited Rookies in terms of content and layout. The cards are individually numbered on back out of 5,000. The Rodriguez card, primarily because of it's status as one of A-Rod's earliest serial-numbered MLB-liscensed issues (coupled with high-end production qualities and a known print run) has become one of the more desirable cards issued in the 1990's. Collectors should take caution of trimmed copies when purchasing this card in "raw" form.

1 Raul Mondesi 3.00 8.00
2 Bob Hamelin 2.00 5.00
3 Midre Cummings 2.00 5.00
4 Carlos Delgado 4.00 10.00
5 Cliff Floyd 3.00 8.00
6 Jeffrey Hammonds 2.00 5.00
7 Ryan Klesko 3.00 8.00
8 Javier Lopez 3.00 8.00
9 Manny Ramirez 8.00 20.00
10 Alex Rodriguez 300.00 600.00

1995 Leaf Limited

This 192 standard-size card set was issued in two series. Each series contained 96 cards. These cards were issued in six-box cases with 20 packs per box and five cards per pack. Forty-five thousand boxes of each series was produced. Rookie Cards in this set include Bob Higginson and Hideo Nomo.

COMPLETE SET (192) 15.00 40.00
COMPLETE SERIES 1 (96) 8.00 20.00
COMPLETE SERIES 2 (96) 8.00 20.00
1 Frank Thomas .50 1.25
2 Geronimo Berroa .08 .25
3 Tony Phillips .08 .25
4 Roberto Alomar .30 .75
5 Steve Avery .08 .25
6 Darryl Hamilton .08 .25
7 Scott Cooper .08 .25
8 Mark Grace .30 .75
9 Billy Ashley .08 .25
10 Wil Cordero .08 .25
11 Barry Bonds 1.25 3.00
12 Kenny Lofton .20 .50
13 Jay Buhner .20 .50
14 Alex Rodriguez 1.25 3.00
15 Bobby Bonilla .20 .50
16 Brady Anderson .20 .50
17 Ken Caminiti .20 .50
18 Charlie Hayes .08 .25
19 Jay Bell .20 .50
20 Will Clark .30 .75
21 Jose Canseco .30 .75
22 Bret Boone .20 .50
23 Dante Bichette .20 .50
24 Kevin Appier .20 .50
25 Chad Curtis .08 .25
26 Marty Cordova .08 .25
27 Jason Bere .08 .25
28 Jimmy Key .20 .50
29 Rickey Henderson .50 1.25
30 Tim Salmon .30 .75
31 Joe Carter .20 .50
32 Tom Glavine .30 .75
33 Pat Listach .08 .25
34 Brian Jordan .20 .50
35 Brian McRae .08 .25
36 Eric Karros .20 .50
37 Pedro Martinez .30 .75
38 Royce Clayton .08 .25
39 Eddie Murray .50 1.25
40 Randy Johnson .50 1.25
41 Jeff Conine .20 .50
42 Brett Butler .20 .50
43 Jeffrey Hammonds .08 .25
44 Andujar Cedeno .08 .25
45 Dave Hollins .08 .25
46 Jeff King .08 .25
47 Benji Gil .08 .25
48 Roger Clemens 1.00 2.50
49 Barry Larkin .30 .75
50 Joe Girardi .08 .25
51 Bob Hamelin .08 .25
52 Travis Fryman .20 .50
53 Chuck Knoblauch .20 .50
54 Ray Durham .20 .50
55 Don Mattingly 1.25 3.00
56 Ruben Sierra .20 .50
57 J.T. Snow .20 .50
58 Derek Bell .08 .25
59 David Cone .20 .50
60 Marquis Grissom .20 .50
61 Kevin Seitzer .08 .25
62 Ozzie Smith .75 2.00
63 Rick Wilkins .08 .25
64 Hideo Nomo RC 1.25 3.00
65 Tony Tarasco .08 .25
66 Manny Ramirez .30 .75
67 Charles Johnson .20 .50
68 Craig Biggio .30 .75
69 Bobby Jones .08 .25
70 Mike Mussina .30 .75
71 Alex Gonzalez .08 .25
72 Gregg Jefferies .08 .25
73 Rusty Greer .20 .50
74 Mike Greenwell .08 .25
75 Hal Morris .08 .25
76 Paul O'Neill .30 .75
77 Luis Gonzalez .20 .50
78 Chipper Jones .50 1.25
79 Mike Piazza .75 2.00
80 Rondell White .20 .50
81 Glenallen Hill .08 .25
82 Shawn Green .20 .50
83 Bernie Williams .30 .75
84 Jim Thome .30 .75
85 Terry Pendleton .20 .50
86 Rafael Palmeiro .30 .75
87 Tony Gwynn .60 1.50
88 Mickey Tettleton .08 .25
89 John Valentin .08 .25
90 Deion Sanders .30 .75
91 Larry Walker .20 .50
92 Michael Tucker .08 .25
93 Alan Trammell .20 .50
94 Tim Raines .20 .50
95 David Justice .20 .50
96 Tino Martinez .30 .75
97 Cal Ripken Jr. 1.50 4.00
98 Deion Sanders .30 .75
99 Darren Daulton .20 .50
100 Paul Molitor .20 .50
101 Randy Myers .08 .25
102 Wally Joyner .20 .50
103 Carlos Perez RC .20 .50
104 Brian Hunter .08 .25
105 Wade Boggs .30 .75
106 Bob Higginson RC .30 .75
107 Jeff Kent .20 .50
108 Jose Offerman .08 .25
109 Dennis Eckersley .20 .50
110 Dave Nilsson .08 .25
111 Chuck Finley .20 .50
112 Devon White .20 .50
113 Bip Roberts .08 .25
114 Ramon Martinez .08 .25
115 Greg Maddux .75 2.00
116 Curtis Goodwin .08 .25
117 John Jaha .08 .25
118 Ken Griffey Jr. .75 2.00
119 Geronimo Pena .08 .25
120 Shawon Dunston .08 .25
121 Ariel Prieto RC .08 .25
122 Kirby Puckett .50 1.25
123 Carlos Baerga .08 .25
124 Todd Hundley .08 .25
125 Tim Naehring .08 .25
126 Gary Sheffield .20 .50
127 Dean Palmer .20 .50
128 Rondell White .20 .50
129 Greg Gagne .08 .25
130 Jose Rijo .08 .25
131 Ivan Rodriguez .30 .75
132 Jeff Bagwell .30 .75
133 Greg Vaughn .08 .25
134 Chili Davis .20 .50
135 Al Martin .08 .25
136 Kenny Rogers .20 .50
137 Aaron Sele .08 .25
138 Raul Mondesi .20 .50
139 Cecil Fielder .20 .50
140 Tim Wallach .08 .25
141 Andres Galarraga .20 .50
142 Lou Whitaker .20 .50
143 Jack McDowell .08 .25
144 Matt Williams .20 .50
145 Ryan Klesko .20 .50
146 Carlos Garcia .08 .25
147 Albert Belle .20 .50
148 Ryan Thompson .08 .25
149 Roberto Kelly .08 .25
150 Edgar Martinez .30 .75
151 Robby Thompson .08 .25
152 Mo Vaughn .20 .50
153 Todd Zeile .08 .25
154 Harold Baines .20 .50
155 Phil Plantier .08 .25
156 Mike Stanley .08 .25
157 Ed Sprague .08 .25
158 Moises Alou .20 .50
159 Quilvio Veras .08 .25
160 Reggie Sanders .20 .50
161 Delino DeShields .08 .25
162 Rico Brogna .08 .25
163 Greg Colbrunn .08 .25
164 Steve Finley .20 .50
165 Orlando Merced .08 .25
166 Mark McGwire 1.25 3.00
167 Garret Anderson .20 .50
168 Paul Sorrento .08 .25
169 Mark Langston .08 .25
170 Danny Tartabull .08 .25
171 Vinny Castilla .20 .50
172 Javier Lopez .20 .50
173 Bret Saberhagen .20 .50
174 Eddie Williams .08 .25
175 Scott Leius .08 .25
176 Juan Gonzalez .20 .50
177 Gary Gaetti .20 .50
178 Jim Edmonds .30 .75
179 John Olerud .20 .50
180 Lenny Dykstra .20 .50
181 Ray Lankford .20 .50
182 Ron Gant .20 .50
183 Doug Drabek .08 .25
184 Fred McGriff .30 .75
185 Andy Benes .08 .25
186 Kurt Abbott .08 .25
187 Bernard Gilkey .08 .25
188 Sammy Sosa .50 1.25
189 Lee Smith .20 .50
190 Dennis Martinez .20 .50
191 Ozzie Guillen .20 .50
192 Robin Ventura .20 .50

1995 Leaf Limited Gold

These 24 standard-size quasi-parallel cards were inserted one per series one pack. Players from both series were included in this set. While using the same design as the regular issue, they are distinguished by different photos, different numbers and gold holographic foil.

1 Frank Thomas .50 1.25
2 Jeff Bagwell .30 .75
3 Raul Mondesi .20 .50
4 Barry Bonds 1.25 3.00
5 Albert Belle .20 .50
6 Ken Griffey Jr. .75 2.00
7 Cal Ripken UER 1.50 4.00
Name spelled Ripkin on card
8 Will Clark .30 .75
9 Jose Canseco .30 .75
10 Larry Walker .20 .50
11 Kirby Puckett .50 1.25
12 Don Mattingly 1.25 3.00
13 Tim Salmon .30 .75
14 Roberto Alomar .30 .75
15 Greg Maddux .75 2.00
16 Mike Piazza .75 2.00
17 Matt Williams .20 .50
18 Kenny Lofton .20 .50
19 Alex Rodriguez UER 1.25 3.00
Name spelled Rodriquez on card
20 Tony Gwynn .60 1.50
21 Mo Vaughn .20 .50
22 Chipper Jones .50 1.25
23 Manny Ramirez .30 .75
24 Deion Sanders .30 .75

1995 Leaf Limited Bat Patrol

These 24 standard-size cards were inserted one per series two pack. The cards are numbered in the upper right corner as "X" of 24.

COMPLETE SET (24) 10.00 25.00
1 Frank Thomas .50 1.25
2 Tony Gwynn .60 1.50
3 Wade Boggs .30 .75
4 Larry Walker .20 .50
5 Ken Griffey, Jr. .75 2.00
6 Jeff Bagwell .30 .75
7 Manny Ramirez .30 .75
8 Mark Grace .30 .75
9 Kenny Lofton .20 .50
10 Mike Piazza .75 2.00
11 Will Clark .30 .75
12 Mo Vaughn .20 .50
13 Carlos Baerga .08 .25
14 Rafael Palmeiro .30 .75
15 Barry Bonds 1.25 3.00
16 Kirby Puckett .50 1.25
17 Roberto Alomar .30 .75
18 Barry Larkin .30 .75
19 Eddie Murray .50 1.25
20 Tim Salmon .30 .75
21 Don Mattingly 1.25 3.00
22 Fred McGriff .30 .75
23 Albert Belle .20 .50
24 Dante Bichette .20 .50

1995 Leaf Limited Lumberjacks

These eight standard-size cards were randomly inserted into second series packs. The cards are individually numbered out of 5,000. The fronts feature a player photo surrounded by his name, the word "Lumberjacks" and "Handcrafted" in a semi-circular pattern on a simulated wood grain stock.

Please note, these cards do not feature elements of game-used material.

COMPLETE SET (16) 80.00 200.00
COMPLETE SERIES 1 (8) 40.00 100.00
COMPLETE SERIES 2 (8) 40.00 100.00
1 Albert Belle 1.50 4.00
2 Barry Bonds 10.00 25.00
3 Juan Gonzalez 1.50 4.00
4 Ken Griffey Jr. 6.00 15.00
5 Fred McGriff 2.50 6.00
6 Mike Piazza 6.00 15.00
7 Kirby Puckett 4.00 10.00
8 Mo Vaughn 1.50 4.00
9 Frank Thomas 4.00 10.00
10 Jeff Bagwell 2.50 6.00
11 Matt Williams 1.50 4.00
12 Jose Canseco 2.50 6.00
13 Raul Mondesi 1.50 4.00
14 Manny Ramirez 2.50 6.00
15 Cecil Fielder 1.50 4.00
16 Cal Ripken 12.50 30.00

1996 Leaf Limited

The 1996 Leaf Limited set was issued exclusively to hobby outlets with a maximum production run of 45,000 boxes. Each box contained two smaller mini-boxes, enabling the dealer to use his imagination in the marketing of this product. The five-card packs carried a suggested retail price of $3.24. Each Master Box was sequentially numbered via a box topper. If this number matched the 1996 year-ending stats, the collector and the dealer both had a chance to win prizes such as a Frank Thomas game-used bat, autographed batting glove, or a "Two Biggest Weapons" poster. The collector would return the winning box number to the hobby shop, and the dealer would mail it to Donruss with both receiving the same prize. The card fronts displayed color player photos with another photo and player information on the backs.

COMPLETE SET (90) 20.00 50.00
1 Ivan Rodriguez .40 1.00
2 Roger Clemens 1.25 3.00
3 Gary Sheffield .25 .60
4 Tino Martinez .40 1.00
5 Sammy Sosa .60 1.50
6 Reggie Sanders .25 .60
7 Ray Lankford .25 .60
8 Manny Ramirez .40 1.00
9 Jeff Bagwell .40 1.00
10 Greg Maddux 1.00 2.50
11 Ken Griffey Jr. 1.00 2.50
12 Rondell White .25 .60
13 Mike Piazza 1.00 2.50
14 Marc Newfield .25 .60
15 Cal Ripken 2.00 5.00
16 Carlos Delgado .25 .60
17 Tim Salmon .40 1.00
18 Andres Galarraga .25 .60
19 Chuck Knoblauch .25 .60
20 Matt Williams .25 .60
21 Mark McGwire 1.50 4.00
22 Ben McDonald .25 .60
23 Frank Thomas .60 1.50
24 Johnny Damon .40 1.00
25 Gregg Jefferies .25 .60
26 Travis Fryman .25 .60
27 Chipper Jones .60 1.50
28 David Cone .25 .60
29 Kenny Lofton .25 .60
30 Mike Mussina .40 1.00
31 Alex Rodriguez 1.25 3.00
32 Carlos Baerga .25 .60
33 Brian Hunter .25 .60
34 Juan Gonzalez .25 .60
35 Bernie Williams .40 1.00
36 Wally Joyner .25 .60
37 Fred McGriff .40 1.00
38 Randy Johnson .60 1.50
39 Marty Cordova .25 .60
40 Garret Anderson .25 .60
41 Albert Belle .25 .60
42 Edgar Martinez .40 1.00
43 Barry Larkin .40 1.00
44 Paul O'Neill .40 1.00
45 Cecil Fielder .25 .60
46 Rusty Greer .25 .60
47 Mo Vaughn .25 .60
48 Dante Bichette .25 .60
49 Ryan Klesko .25 .60
50 Roberto Alomar .40 1.00
51 Raul Mondesi .25 .60
52 Robin Ventura .25 .60
53 Tony Gwynn .75 2.00
54 Mark Grace .40 1.00
55 Jim Thome .40 1.00
56 Jason Giambi .25 .60
57 Tom Glavine .40 1.00
58 Jim Edmonds .25 .60
59 Pedro Martinez .40 1.00
60 Charles Johnson .25 .60
61 Wade Boggs .40 1.00
62 Orlando Merced .25 .60
63 Craig Biggio .40 1.00
64 Brady Anderson .25 .60
65 Hideo Nomo .60 1.50
66 Ozzie Smith 1.00 2.50
67 Eddie Murray .60 1.50
68 Will Clark .40 1.00
69 Jay Buhner .25 .60
70 Kirby Puckett .60 1.50
71 Barry Bonds 1.50 4.00
72 Ray Durham .25 .60
73 Sterling Hitchcock .25 .60
74 John Smoltz .40 1.00
75 Andre Dawson .25 .60
76 Joe Carter .25 .60
77 Ryne Sandberg 1.00 2.50
78 Rickey Henderson .60 1.50
79 Brian Jordan .25 .60
80 Greg Vaughn .25 .60
81 Andy Pettitte .40 1.00
82 Dean Palmer .25 .60
83 Paul Molitor .25 .60
84 Rafael Palmeiro .40 1.00
85 Henry Rodriguez .25 .60
86 Larry Walker .25 .60
87 Ismael Valdes .25 .60
88 Derek Bell .25 .60
89 J.T. Snow .25 .60
90 Jack McDowell .25 .60

1996 Leaf Limited Gold

Randomly inserted into one in every 11 packs, cards from this 90-card insert set parallel the regular Leaf Limited issue. Similar in design, it differs from the regular set with its gold holographic foil treatment.

*STARS: 2.5X TO 6X BASIC CARDS

1996 Leaf Limited Lumberjacks Samples

One of ten different Leaf Limited Lumberjacks Samples cards was inserted into 1996 Leaf Limited dealer order forms and hobby media press releases. The cards parallel the standard Lumberjacks inserts except for the text "sample card" running diagonally across the front and back of the card and "PROMO/5000" text on back.

COMPLETE SET (10) 32.00 80.00
1 Ken Griffey Jr. 3.00 8.00
2 Sammy Sosa 2.00 5.00
3 Cal Ripken 6.00 15.00
4 Frank Thomas 1.25 3.00
5 Alex Rodriguez 4.00 10.00
6 Mo Vaughn .60 1.50
7 Chipper Jones 3.00 8.00
8 Mike Piazza 4.00 10.00
9 Jeff Bagwell 1.50 4.00
10 Mark McGwire 4.00 10.00

1996 Leaf Limited Lumberjacks

Printed with maple stock that puts wood grains on both sides (but does not incorporate game-used bat chips), this 10-card insert set features the league's top sluggers. The fronts carry color player photos with player information and statistics on the backs. Only 5,000 sets were produced and each card is individually numbered.

COMPLETE SET (10) 50.00 120.00
*BLACK: 1.5X TO 4X BASIC LUMBERJACK
BLACK PRINT RUN 500 SERIAL #'d SETS
1 Ken Griffey Jr. 5.00 12.00
2 Sammy Sosa 3.00 8.00
3 Cal Ripken 10.00 25.00
4 Frank Thomas 3.00 8.00
5 Alex Rodriguez 6.00 15.00
6 Mo Vaughn 1.25 3.00
7 Chipper Jones 3.00 8.00
8 Mike Piazza 5.00 12.00
9 Jeff Bagwell 2.00 5.00
10 Mark McGwire 8.00 20.00

1996 Leaf Limited Pennant Craze Promos

Issued to promote the Leaf Limited Pennant Craze insert set, these cards are differentiated from the regular Leaf Limited insert cards as they are numbered 0000/2500 on the back.

COMPLETE SET (10) 16.00 40.00
1 Juan Gonzalez .75 2.00
2 Cal Ripken 4.00 10.00
3 Frank Thomas .75 2.00
4 Ken Griffey Jr. 2.00 5.00
5 Albert Belle .30 .75
6 Greg Maddux 2.50 6.00
7 Paul Molitor 1.00 2.50
8 Alex Rodriguez 2.00 5.00
9 Barry Bonds 2.00 5.00
10 Chipper Jones 2.00 5.00

1996 Leaf Limited Pennant Craze

This 10-card insert set features 10 superstars who have a thirst for the pennant. A special flocking technique puts the felt feel of a pennant on a die cut card. Only 2,500 sets were produced and are individually numbered.

COMPLETE SET (10) 80.00 200.00
1 Juan Gonzalez 2.50 6.00
2 Cal Ripken 20.00 50.00
3 Frank Thomas 6.00 15.00
4 Ken Griffey Jr. 10.00 25.00
5 Albert Belle 2.50 6.00
6 Greg Maddux 10.00 25.00
7 Paul Molitor 2.50 6.00
8 Alex Rodriguez 12.50 30.00
9 Barry Bonds 15.00 40.00
10 Chipper Jones 6.00 15.00

1996 Leaf Limited Rookies

Randomly inserted in packs at a rate of one in seven, this 10-card set printed in silver holographic foil features some of the hottest rookies of the year. A first year card of Darin Erstad is in this set.

COMPLETE SET (10) 20.00 40.00
*GOLD: 1X TO 2.5X BASIC ROOKIES
GOLD: RANDOM INSERTS IN PACKS
1 Alex Ochoa .40 1.00
2 Darin Erstad 1.50 4.00
3 Ruben Rivera .40 1.00
4 Derek Jeter 6.00 15.00
5 Jermaine Dye .75 2.00
6 Jason Kendall .75 2.00
7 Mike Grace .40 1.00
8 Andruw Jones 1.25 3.00
9 Rey Ordonez .40 1.00
10 George Arias .40 1.00

2001 Leaf Limited

This hobby-exclusive product was released in mid-December 2001, and featured a 375-card base set that was broken into tiers as follows: 150 Base Veterans, 50 Lumberjacks (numbered to either 500, 250, or 100), 100 Rookies (numbered to either 1500 or 1000), 25 Autographed Rookies (numbered to 1000, 750, or 500), and 50 Memorabilia Rookies (see print runs below). Each pack contained three cards, and carried a $6.99 S.R.P..

COMP.SET w/o SP'S (150) 40.00 100.00
COMMON CARD (1-150) .40 1.00
COMMON HAT (326-375) 10.00 25.00
COMMON LUM/500 (151-200) 3.00 8.00
COMMON LUM/250 (151-200) 4.00 10.00
COMMON LUM/100 (151-200) 6.00 15.00
COMMON (201-250) 2.00 5.00
COMMON (251-300) 2.00 5.00
COMMON (301-325) 4.00 10.00
COMMON BASE (326-375) 6.00 15.00
COMMON BAT (326-375) 3.00 8.00
COMMON JSY (326-375) 3.00 8.00
COMMON PANTS (326-375) 3.00 8.00
COMMON SPIKES (326-375) 10.00 25.00
1 Curt Schilling .40 1.00
2 Craig Biggio .60 1.50
3 Brian Giles .40 1.00
4 Scott Brosius .40 1.00
5 Barry Larkin .60 1.50
6 Bartolo Colon .40 1.00
7 John Olerud .40 1.00
8 Cal Ripken 3.00 8.00
9 Moises Alou .40 1.00
10 Barry Zito .60 1.50
11 Ken Griffey Jr. 1.50 4.00
12 Garret Anderson .40 1.00
13 Andy Pettitte .60 1.50
14 Jim Edmonds .40 1.00
15 Tom Glavine .60 1.50
16 Jose Canseco .60 1.50
17 Fred McGriff .60 1.50
18 Robin Ventura .40 1.00
19 Tony Gwynn 1.25 3.00
20 Jeff Cirillo .40 1.00
21 Brad Radke .40 1.00
22 Ellis Burks .40 1.00
23 Scott Rolen .60 1.50
24 Rickey Henderson 1.00 2.50
25 Edgar Martinez .60 1.50
26 Kerry Wood .40 1.00

27 Al Leiter .40 1.00
28 Jose Cruz Jr. .40 1.00
29 Sean Casey .40 1.00
30 Eric Chavez .40 1.00
31 Jarrod Washburn .40 1.00
32 Gary Sheffield .40 1.00
33 Jermaine Dye .40 1.00
34 Bernie Williams .60 1.50
35 Tony Armas Jr. .40 1.00
36 Carlos Beltran .40 1.00
37 Geoff Jenkins .40 1.00
38 Shawn Green .40 1.00
39 Ryan Klesko .40 1.00
40 Richie Sexson .40 1.00
41 Pat Burrell .40 1.00
42 J.D. Drew .40 1.00
43 Larry Walker .40 1.00
44 Andres Galarraga .40 1.00
45 Tino Martinez .60 1.50
46 Rafael Furcal .40 1.00
47 Cristian Guzman .40 1.00
48 Omar Vizquel .60 1.50
49 Bret Boone .40 1.00
50 Wade Miller .40 1.00
51 Eric Milton .40 1.00
52 Gabe Kapler .40 1.00
53 Johnny Damon .60 1.50
54 Shannon Stewart .40 1.00
55 Kenny Lofton .40 1.00
56 Raul Mondesi .40 1.00
57 Jorge Posada .60 1.50
58 Mark Grace .60 1.50
59 Robert Fick .40 1.00
60 Phil Nevin .40 1.00
61 Mike Mussina .60 1.50
62 Joe Mays .40 1.00
63 Todd Helton .60 1.50
64 Tim Hudson .40 1.00
65 Manny Ramirez Sox .60 1.50
66 Sammy Sosa 1.00 2.50
67 Darin Erstad .40 1.00
68 Roberto Alomar .60 1.50
69 Jeff Bagwell .60 1.50
70 Mark McGwire 2.50 6.00
71 Jason Giambi .40 1.00
72 Cliff Floyd .40 1.00
73 Barry Bonds 2.50 6.00
74 Juan Gonzalez .40 1.00
75 Jeremy Giambi .40 1.00
76 Carlos Lee .40 1.00
77 Randy Johnson 1.00 2.50
78 Frank Thomas 1.00 2.50
79 Carlos Delgado .40 1.00
80 Pedro Martinez .60 1.50
81 Rusty Greer .40 1.00
82 Brian Jordan .40 1.00
83 Vladimir Guerrero 1.00 2.50
84 Mike Sweeney .40 1.00
85 Jose Vidro .40 1.00
86 Paul LoDuca .40 1.00
87 Matt Morris .40 1.00
88 Adrian Beltre .40 1.00
89 Aramis Ramirez .40 1.00
90 Derek Jeter 2.50 6.00
91 Rich Aurilia .40 1.00
92 Freddy Garcia .40 1.00
93 Preston Wilson .40 1.00
94 Greg Maddux 1.50 4.00
95 Miguel Tejada .40 1.00
96 Luis Gonzalez .40 1.00
97 Torii Hunter .40 1.00
98 Nomar Garciaparra 1.50 4.00
99 Jamie Moyer .40 1.00
100 Javier Vazquez .40 1.00
101 Ben Grieve .40 1.00
102 Mike Piazza 1.50 4.00
103 Paul O'Neill .60 1.50
104 Terrence Long .40 1.00
105 Charles Johnson .40 1.00
106 Rafael Palmeiro .60 1.50
107 David Cone .40 1.00
108 Alex Rodriguez 1.50 4.00
109 John Burkett .40 1.00
110 Chipper Jones 1.00 2.50
111 Ryan Dempster .40 1.00
112 Bobby Abreu .40 1.00
113 Brad Fullmer .40 1.00
114 Kazuhiro Sasaki .40 1.00
115 Mariano Rivera 1.00 2.50
116 Edgardo Alfonzo .40 1.00
117 Ray Durham .40 1.00
118 Richard Hidalgo .40 1.00
119 Jeff Weaver .40 1.00
120 Paul Konerko .40 1.00
121 Jon Lieber .40 1.00
122 Mike Hampton .40 1.00
123 Mike Cameron .40 1.00
124 Kevin Brown .40 1.00
125 Doug Mientkiewicz .40 1.00
126 Jim Thome .60 1.50
127 Corey Koskie .40 1.00
128 Trot Nixon .40 1.00
129 Darryl Kile .40 1.00
130 Ivan Rodriguez .60 1.50
131 Carl Everett .40 1.00
132 Jeff Kent .40 1.00
133 Rondell White .40 1.00
134 Chan Ho Park .40 1.00
135 Robert Person .40 1.00
136 Troy Glaus .40 1.00
137 Aaron Sele .40 1.00
138 Roger Clemens 2.00 5.00
139 Tony Clark .40 1.00
140 Mark Buehrle .60 1.50
141 David Justice .40 1.00
142 Magglio Ordonez .40 1.00
143 Bobby Higginson .40 1.00
144 Hideo Nomo 1.00 2.50
145 Tim Salmon .60 1.50
146 Mark Mulder .40 1.00
147 Troy Percival .40 1.00
148 Lance Berkman .40 1.00
149 Russ Ortiz .40 1.00
150 Andruw Jones .60 1.50
151 Mike Piazza LUM/500 6.00 15.00
152 M.Ramirez Sox LUM/500 4.00 10.00
153 B.Williams LUM/500 4.00 10.00
154 N.Garciaparra LUM/500 6.00 15.00
155 A.Galarraga LUM/500 3.00 8.00
156 K.Lofton LUM/500 3.00 8.00
157 Scott Rolen LUM/250 6.00 15.00
158 Jim Thome LUM/500 4.00 10.00
159 Darin Erstad LUM/500 3.00 8.00
160 G.Anderson LUM/500 3.00 8.00
161 A.Jones LUM/500 4.00 10.00
162 J.Gonzalez LUM/500 3.00 8.00
163 R.Palmeiro LUM/500 4.00 10.00
164 M.Ordonez LUM/500 3.00 8.00
165 Jeff Bagwell LUM/250 6.00 15.00
166 Eric Chavez LUM/500 3.00 8.00
167 Brian Giles LUM/500 3.00 8.00
168 A.Beltre LUM/500 3.00 8.00
169 T.Gwynn LUM/500 6.00 15.00
170 S.Green LUM/500 3.00 8.00
171 Todd Helton LUM/500 4.00 10.00
172 Troy Glaus LUM/100 6.00 15.00
173 L.Berkman LUM/500 3.00 8.00
174 I.Rodriguez LUM/500 4.00 10.00
175 Sean Casey LUM/500 3.00 8.00
176 A.Ramirez LUM/100 6.00 15.00
177 J.D. Drew LUM/500 3.00 8.00
178 Barry Bonds LUM/250 12.50 30.00
179 Barry Larkin LUM/500 4.00 10.00
180 Cal Ripken LUM/500 15.00 40.00
181 F.Thomas LUM/500 4.00 10.00
182 Craig Biggio LUM/250 6.00 15.00
183 Carlos Lee LUM/500 3.00 8.00
184 C. Jones LUM/500 4.00 10.00
185 Miguel Tejada LUM/250 4.00 10.00
186 Jose Vidro LUM/500 3.00 8.00
187 T.Long LUM/500 3.00 8.00
188 Moises Alou LUM/500 3.00 8.00
189 Trot Nixon LUM/500 3.00 8.00
190 S.Stewart LUM/500 3.00 8.00
191 Ryan Klesko LUM/500 3.00 8.00
192 C.Beltran LUM/500 3.00 8.00
193 V.Guerrero LUM/500 4.00 10.00
194 E.Martinez LUM/500 4.00 10.00
195 L.Gonzalez LUM/500 3.00 8.00
196 R.Hidalgo LUM/500 3.00 8.00
197 R.Alomar LUM/500 4.00 10.00
198 M.Sweeney LUM/100 6.00 15.00
199 B.Abreu LUM/250 4.00 10.00
200 Cliff Floyd LUM/500 3.00 8.00
201 Jackson Melian RC 2.00 5.00
202 Jason Jennings 2.00 5.00
203 Toby Hall 2.00 5.00
204 Jason Karnuth RC 2.00 5.00
205 Jason Smith RC 2.00 5.00
206 Mike Maroth RC 3.00 8.00
207 Sean Douglass RC 2.00 5.00
208 Adam Johnson 2.00 5.00
209 Luke Hudson RC 2.00 5.00
210 Nick Maness RC 2.00 5.00
211 Les Walrond RC 2.00 5.00
212 Travis Phelps RC 2.00 5.00
213 Carlos Garcia RC 2.00 5.00
214 Bill Ortega RC 2.00 5.00
215 Gene Altman RC 2.00 5.00
216 Nate Frese RC 2.00 5.00
217 Bob File RC 2.00 5.00
218 Steve Green RC 2.00 5.00
219 Kris Keller RC 2.00 5.00
220 Matt White RC 2.00 5.00
221 Nate Teut RC 2.00 5.00
222 Nick Johnson 2.00 5.00
223 Jeremy Fikac RC 2.00 5.00
224 Abraham Nunez 2.00 5.00
225 Mike Penney RC 2.00 5.00
226 Roy Smith RC 2.00 5.00
227 Tim Christman RC 2.00 5.00
228 Carlos Pena 2.00 5.00
229 Joe Beimel RC 2.00 5.00
230 Mike Koplove RC 2.00 5.00
231 Scott MacRae RC 2.00 5.00
232 Kyle Lohse RC 3.00 8.00
233 Jerrod Riggan RC 2.00 5.00
234 Scott Podsednik RC 6.00 15.00
235 Winston Abreu RC 2.00 5.00
236 Ryan Freel RC 3.00 8.00
237 Ken Vining RC 2.00 5.00
238 Bret Prinz RC 2.00 5.00
239 Paul Phillips RC 2.00 5.00
240 Josh Fogg RC 2.00 5.00
241 Saul Rivera RC 2.00 5.00
242 Esix Snead RC 2.00 5.00
243 John Grabow RC 2.00 5.00
244 Tony Cogan RC 2.00 5.00
245 Pedro Santana RC 2.00 5.00
246 Jack Cust 2.00 5.00
247 Joe Crede 3.00 8.00
248 Juan Moreno RC 2.00 5.00
249 Kevin Joseph RC 2.00 5.00
250 Scott Stewart RC 2.00 5.00
251 Rob Mackowiak RC 3.00 8.00
252 Luis Pineda RC 2.00 5.00
253 Bert Snow RC 2.00 5.00
254 Dustan Mohr RC 2.00 5.00
255 Justin Kaye RC 2.00 5.00
256 Chad Paronto RC 2.00 5.00
257 Nick Punto RC 2.00 5.00
258 Brian Roberts RC 3.00 8.00
259 Eric Hinske RC 3.00 8.00
260 Victor Zambrano RC 3.00 8.00
261 Juan Pena RC 2.00 5.00
262 Rick Bauer RC 2.00 5.00
263 Jorge Julio RC 2.00 5.00
264 Craig Monroe RC 3.00 8.00
265 Stubby Clapp RC 2.00 5.00
266 Martin Vargas RC 2.00 5.00
267 Josue Perez RC 2.00 5.00
268 Cody Ransom RC 2.00 5.00
269 Will Ohman RC 2.00 5.00
270 Juan Diaz RC 2.00 5.00
271 Ramon Vazquez RC 2.00 5.00
272 Grant Balfour RC 2.00 5.00
273 Ryan Jensen RC 2.00 5.00
274 Benito Baez RC 2.00 5.00
275 Angel Santos RC 2.00 5.00
276 Brian Reith RC 2.00 5.00
277 Brandon Lyon RC 2.00 5.00
278 Erik Hiljus RC 2.00 5.00
279 Brandon Knight RC 2.00 5.00
280 Jose Acevedo RC 2.00 5.00
281 Cesar Crespo RC 2.00 5.00
282 Kevin Olsen RC 2.00 5.00
283 Duaner Sanchez RC 2.00 5.00
284 Endy Chavez RC 2.00 5.00
285 Blaine Neal RC 2.00 5.00
286 Brett Jodie RC 2.00 5.00
287 Brad Voyles RC 2.00 5.00
288 Doug Nickle RC 2.00 5.00
289 Junior Spivey RC 3.00 8.00
290 Henry Mateo RC 2.00 5.00
291 Xavier Nady 2.00 5.00
292 Lance Davis RC 2.00 5.00
293 Willie Harris RC 2.00 5.00
294 Mark Lukasiewicz RC 2.00 5.00
295 Ryan Drese RC 3.00 8.00
296 Morgan Ensberg RC 3.00 8.00
297 Jose Mieses RC 2.00 5.00
298 Jason Michaels RC 2.00 5.00
299 Kris Foster RC 2.00 5.00
300 J.Duchscherer RC 2.00 5.00
301 Elpidio Guzman AU RC 4.00 10.00
302 Cory Aldridge AU RC 4.00 10.00
303 A.Berroa AU/500 RC 6.00 15.00
304 Travis Hafner AU RC 40.00 80.00
305 H.Ramirez AU RC 6.00 15.00
306 Juan Uribe AU RC 6.00 15.00
307 M.Prior AU/500 RC 30.00 60.00
308 B.Larson AU RC 4.00 10.00
309 N.Neugebauer AU/750 4.00 10.00
310 Zach Day AU/750 RC 4.00 10.00
311 Jeremy Owens AU RC 4.00 10.00
312 D.Brazelton AU/500 RC 4.00 10.00
313 B.Duckworth AU/750 RC 4.00 10.00
314 A.Hernandez AU RC 4.00 10.00
315 M.Teixeira AU/500 RC 30.00 60.00
316 Brian Rogers AU RC 4.00 10.00
317 D.Brous AU/750 RC 4.00 10.00
318 Geronimo Gil AU RC 4.00 10.00
319 Erick Almonte AU RC 4.00 10.00
320 Claudio Vargas AU RC 4.00 10.00
321 Wilkin Ruan AU RC 4.00 10.00
322 David Williams AU RC 4.00 10.00
323 Alexis Gomez AU RC 4.00 10.00
324 Mike Rivera AU RC 4.00 10.00
325 B.Berger AU RC 4.00 10.00
326 Keith Ginter Bat/125 10.00 25.00
327 Brandon Inge Bat/700 3.00 8.00
328 B.Abernathy Bat/700 3.00 8.00
329 B.Sylvester Bat/700 RC 3.00 8.00
330 B.Miadich Jsy/500 RC 3.00 8.00
331 T.Shinjo Jsy/500 RC 4.00 10.00
332 E.Valent Spikes/125 10.00 25.00
333 Dee Brown Jsy/500 3.00 8.00
334 A.Torres Spikes/125 RC 10.00 25.00
335 Timo Perez Bat/700 3.00 8.00
336 C.Izturis Pants/650 3.00 8.00
337 P.Feliz Spikes/125 10.00 25.00
338 Jason Hart Bat/200 4.00 10.00
339 G.Miller Bat/700 RC 3.00 8.00
340 Eric Munson Bat/700 3.00 8.00
341 Aubrey Huff Jsy/450 3.00 8.00
342 W.Caceres Bat/700 RC 3.00 8.00
343 A.Escobar Pants/650 3.00 8.00
344 B.Lawrence Bat/700 RC 3.00 8.00
345 Adam Pettyjohn Pants/650 RC 3.00 8.00
346 D.Mendez Bat/700 RC 3.00 8.00
347 Carlos Valderrama Jsy/250 RC 4.00 10.00
348 C.Parker Pants/650 RC 3.00 8.00
349 C.Miller Jsy/500 RC 3.00 8.00
350 M.Cuddyer Jsy/500 3.00 8.00
351 Adam Dunn Bat/500 4.00 10.00
352 J.Beckett Pants/650 4.00 10.00
353 Juan Cruz Jsy/500 RC 3.00 8.00
354 Ben Sheets Jsy/400 4.00 10.00
355 Roy Oswalt Bat/100 15.00 40.00
356 R.Soriano Pants/650 RC 3.00 8.00
357 R.Rodriguez Pants/650 RC 3.00 8.00
358 J.Rollins Base/300 6.00 15.00
359 C.C. Sabathia Jsy/500 3.00 8.00
360 B.Smith Jsy/500 RC 3.00 8.00
361 Jose Ortiz Hat/100 10.00 25.00
362 Marcus Giles Jsy/400 3.00 8.00
363 J.Wilson Hat/100 RC 10.00 25.00
364 W.Betemit Hat/100 RC 10.00 25.00
365 C.Patterson Pants/650 3.00 8.00
366 J.Gibbons Spikes/125 RC 15.00 40.00
367 A.Pujols Jsy/250 RC 150.00 300.00
368 J.Kennedy Hat/100 RC 10.00 25.00
369 A.Soriano Hat/100 15.00 40.00
370 D.James Pants/650 RC 3.00 8.00
371 J.Towers Pants/650 RC 4.00 10.00
372 J.Affeldt Pants/650 RC 3.00 8.00
373 Tim Redding Jsy/500 3.00 8.00
374 I.Suzuki Base/100 RC 400.00 600.00
375 J.Estrada Bat/100 RC 10.00 25.00

2003 Leaf Limited

This 204 card set was issued in two separate series. The primary Leaf Limited product - containing cards 1-200 from the basic set - was released in September, 2003. The set was issued in four card packs with an $70 SRP which came four packs to a box and 10 boxes to a case. The first 150 cards feature active veteran players and were issued to a stated print run of 999 serial numbered sets. Cards numbered 151 through 170 feature retired greats and were randomly inserted into packs and issued to a stated print run of 399 serial numbered sets. Cards numbered 171 through 200 are entitled Phenoms and feature rookie players, most of whom signed their cards and most of those cards were issued to a stated print run of 99 serial numbered sets. Cards number 174 and 199 are not autographed and those cards just feature game-used pieces of memorabilia. Cards 201-204 were randomly seeded within packs of DLP Rookies and Traded released in December, 2003. Each of these Update cards was signed by the featured athltete, serial-numbered to 99 copies and continued the Phenoms subset established in cards 171-200.

COMMON CARD (1-151) 1.25 3.00
1-151 PRINT RUN 999 SERIAL #'d SETS
COMMON CARD (151-170) 1.50 4.00
151-170 RANDOM INSERTS IN PACKS
151-170 PRINT RUN 399 SERIAL #'d SETS
COMMON AU GU (171-200) 6.00 15.00
AU GU 171-200 PRINT 99 SERIAL #'d SETS
GU 174/199 PRINT RUN 99 SERIAL #'d SETS
COMMON AU (171-204) p/r 99 6.00 15.00
AU 171-204 PRINT B/WN 49-99 COPIES PER
171-200 RANDOM INSERTS IN PACKS
201-204 RANDOM IN DLP R/T PACKS
A EQUALS AWAY UNIFORM IMAGE
H EQUALS HOME UNIFORM IMAGE

1 Derek Jeter Btg 3.00 8.00
2 Eric Chavez 1.25 3.00
3 Alex Rodriguez Rgr A 2.50 6.00
4 Miguel Tejada Fldg 1.25 3.00
5 Nomar Garciaparra H 1.50 4.00
6 Jeff Bagwell H 1.25 3.00
7 Jim Thome Phils A 1.25 3.00
8 Pat Burrell w/Bat 1.25 3.00
9 Albert Pujols H 3.00 8.00
10 Juan Gonzalez Rgr Btg 1.25 3.00
11 Shawn Green Jays 1.25 3.00
12 Craig Biggio H 1.25 3.00
13 Chipper Jones H 1.50 4.00
14 H.Nomo Dodgers 1.50 4.00
15 Vernon Wells 1.25 3.00
16 Gary Sheffield 1.25 3.00
17 Barry Larkin 1.25 3.00
18 Josh Beckett White 1.25 3.00
19 Edgar Martinez A 1.25 3.00
20 I.Rodriguez Marlins 1.25 3.00
21 Jeff Kent Astros 1.25 3.00
22 Roberto Alomar Mets A 1.25 3.00
23 Alfonso Soriano A 1.25 3.00
24 Jim Thome Indians H 1.25 3.00
25 J.Gonzalez Indians Btg 1.25 3.00
26 Carlos Beltran 1.25 3.00
27 S.Green Dodgers H 1.25 3.00
28 Tim Hudson H 1.25 3.00
29 Deion Sanders 1.25 3.00
30 Rafael Palmeiro O's 1.25 3.00
31 Todd Helton H 1.25 3.00
32 L.Berkman No Socks 1.25 3.00
33 M.Mussina Yanks H 1.25 3.00
34 Kazuhisa Ishii H 1.25 3.00
35 Pat Burrell Run 1.25 3.00
36 Miguel Tejada Btg 1.25 3.00
37 J.Gonzalez Rgr Stand 1.25 3.00
38 Roberto Alomar Mets H 1.25 3.00
39 R.Alom Indians Bunt 1.25 3.00
40 Luis Gonzalez 1.25 3.00
41 Jorge Posada 1.25 3.00
42 Mark Mulder Leg 1.25 3.00
43 Sammy Sosa H 1.50 4.00
44 Mark Prior H 1.25 3.00
45 R.Clemens Yanks H 3.00 8.00
46 Tom Glavine Mets H 1.25 3.00
47 Mark Teixeira A 1.25 3.00
48 Manny Ramirez H 1.25 3.00
49 Frank Thomas Swing 1.50 4.00
50 Troy Glaus White 1.25 3.00
51 Andruw Jones H 1.25 3.00
52 J.Giambi Yanks H 1.25 3.00
53 Jim Thome Phils H 1.25 3.00
54 Barry Bonds H 4.00 10.00
55 R.Palmeiro Rgr A 1.25 3.00
56 Edgar Martinez H 1.25 3.00
57 Vladimir Guerrero H 1.50 4.00
58 Roberto Alomar O's 1.25 3.00
59 Mike Sweeney 1.25 3.00
60 Magglio Ordonez A 1.25 3.00
61 Ken Griffey Jr. Btg 2.50 6.00
62 Craig Biggio A 1.25 3.00
63 Greg Maddux H 2.50 6.00
64 Mike Piazza Mets H 2.50 6.00
65 T.Glavine Braves A 1.25 3.00
66 Kerry Wood H 1.25 3.00
67 Frank Thomas Arms 1.50 4.00
68 M.Mussina Yanks A 1.25 3.00
69 Nick Johnson H 1.25 3.00
70 Bernie Williams H 1.25 3.00
71 Scott Rolen 1.25 3.00
72 C.Schill D'backs Leg 1.25 3.00
73 Adam Dunn A 1.25 3.00
74 Roy Oswalt A 1.25 3.00
75 P.Martinez Sox H 1.25 3.00
76 Tom Glavine Mets A 1.25 3.00
77 Torii Hunter Swing 1.25 3.00
78 Austin Kearns 1.25 3.00
79 R.Johnson D'backs A 1.50 4.00
80 Bernie Williams A 1.25 3.00
81 Ichiro Suzuki Btg 3.00 8.00
82 Kerry Wood A 1.25 3.00
83 Kazuhisa Ishii A 1.25 3.00
84 R.Johnson Astros 1.50 4.00
85 Nick Johnson A 1.25 3.00
86 J.Beckett Pinstripe 1.25 3.00
87 Curt Schilling Phils 1.25 3.00
88 Mike Mussina O's 1.25 3.00
89 P.Martinez Dodgers 1.25 3.00
90 Barry Zito A 1.25 3.00
91 Jim Edmonds 1.25 3.00
92 R.Henderson Sox 1.50 4.00
93 R.Henderson Padres 1.50 4.00
94 R.Henderson M's 1.50 4.00
95 R.Henderson Mets 1.50 4.00
96 R.Henderson Jays 1.50 4.00
97 R.Johnson M's Arm Up 1.50 4.00
98 Mark Grace 1.25 3.00
99 P.Martinez Expos 1.25 3.00
100 Hee Seop Choi 1.25 3.00
101 Ivan Rodriguez Rgr 1.25 3.00
102 Jeff Kent Giants 1.25 3.00
103 Hideo Nomo Sox 1.50 4.00
104 Hideo Nomo Mets 1.50 4.00
105 Mike Piazza Dodgers 2.50 6.00
106 T.Glavine Braves H 1.25 3.00
107 R.Alom Indians Swing 1.25 3.00
108 Roger Clemens Sox 3.00 8.00
109 Jason Giambi A's H 1.25 3.00
110 Jim Thome Indians A 1.25 3.00
111 Alex Rodriguez M's H 2.50 6.00
112 J.Gonz Indians Hands 1.25 3.00
113 Torii Hunter Crouch 1.25 3.00
114 Roy Oswalt H 1.25 3.00
115 C.Schill D'backs Throw 1.25 3.00
116 Magglio Ordonez H 1.25 3.00
117 R.Palmeiro Rgr H 1.25 3.00
118 Andruw Jones A 1.25 3.00
119 Manny Ramirez A 1.25 3.00
120 Mark Teixeira H 1.25 3.00
121 Mark Mulder Stance 1.25 3.00
122 Garret Anderson 1.25 3.00
123 Tim Hudson A 1.25 3.00
124 Todd Helton A 1.25 3.00
125 Troy Glaus Pinstripe 1.25 3.00
126 Derek Jeter Run 3.00 8.00
127 Barry Bonds A 4.00 10.00
128 Greg Maddux A 2.50 6.00
129 R.Clemens Yanks A 3.00 8.00
130 Nomar Garciaparra A 1.50 4.00
131 Mike Piazza Mets A 2.50 6.00
132 Alex Rodriguez Rgr H 2.50 6.00
133 Ichiro Suzuki Run 3.00 8.00
134 R.Johnson D'backs H 1.50 4.00
135 Sammy Sosa A 1.50 4.00
136 Ken Griffey Jr. Fldg 2.50 6.00
137 Alfonso Soriano H 1.25 3.00
138 J.Giambi Yanks A 1.25 3.00
139 Albert Pujols A 3.00 8.00
140 Chipper Jones A 1.50 4.00
141 Adam Dunn H 1.25 3.00
142 P.Martinez Sox A 1.25 3.00
143 Vladimir Guerrero A 1.50 4.00
144 Mark Prior A 1.25 3.00
145 Barry Zito H 1.25 3.00
146 Jeff Bagwell A 1.25 3.00
147 Lance Berkman Socks 1.25 3.00
148 S.Green Dodgers A 1.25 3.00
149 Jason Giambi A's A 1.25 3.00
150 R.Johnson M's Arm Out 1.50 4.00
151 Alex Rodriguez M's A 2.50 6.00
152 Babe Ruth 4.00 10.00
153 Ty Cobb 2.50 6.00
154 Jackie Robinson 2.00 5.00
155 Lou Gehrig 3.00 8.00
156 Thurman Munson 2.00 5.00
157 Roberto Clemente 4.00 10.00
158 Nolan Ryan Rgr 4.00 10.00
159 Nolan Ryan Angels 4.00 10.00
160 Nolan Ryan Astros 4.00 10.00
161 Cal Ripken 6.00 15.00
162 Don Mattingly 3.00 8.00
163 Stan Musial 3.00 8.00
164 Tony Gwynn 3.00 8.00
165 Yogi Berra 2.00 5.00
166 Johnny Bench 2.00 5.00
167 Mike Schmidt 3.00 8.00
168 George Brett 3.00 8.00
169 Ryne Sandberg 3.00 8.00
170 Ernie Banks 2.00 5.00
171 J.Bonder A PH AU Jsy RC 30.00 60.00
172 J.Contreras A PH AU RC 15.00 40.00
173 C.Wang PH AU RC 250.00 400.00
174 H.Matsui H PH Base RC 10.00 25.00
175 H.Kuo PH AU Bat RC 100.00 175.00
176 B.Webb A PH AU Bat RC 30.00 60.00
177 Rich Fischer PH AU RC 6.00 15.00
178 R.Hammock PH AU Bat RC 6.00 15.00
179 T.Welle Stance PH AU/49 RC 10.00 25.00
180 P.Redman PH AU Bat RC 6.00 15.00
181 Nook Logan PH AU RC 10.00 25.00
182 Craig Brazell PH AU RC 6.00 15.00
183 Tim Olson PH AU Bat RC 6.00 15.00
184 Matt Kata PH AU Bat RC 6.00 15.00
185 Alej Machado PH AU RC 6.00 15.00
186 Mike Hessman PH AU RC 6.00 15.00
187 Oscar Villarreal PH AU RC 6.00 15.00
188 G.Quiroz PH AU Bat RC 6.00 15.00
189 M.Hernandez PH AU RC 6.00 15.00
190 C.Barmes H PH AU Bat RC 10.00 25.00
191 P.LaForest PH AU Bat RC 6.00 15.00
192 Adam Loewen PH AU RC 15.00 40.00
193 T.Sledge PH AU Bat RC 6.00 15.00
194 Lew Ford PH AU Bat RC 10.00 25.00
195 T.Welle Throw PH AU/49 RC 10.00 25.00
196 C.Barmes A PH AU Bat RC 10.00 25.00
197 J.Bonder H PH AU Jsy RC 30.00 60.00
198 B.Webb H PH AU Jsy RC 30.00 60.00
199 H.Matsui A PH Base RC 10.00 25.00
200 J.Contreras H PH AU RC 15.00 40.00
201 Delmon Young PH AU RC 150.00 250.00
202 Rickie Weeks PH AU RC 50.00 100.00
203 Edwin Jackson PH AU RC 20.00 50.00
204 Dan Haren PH AU RC 15.00 40.00
NNO Roger Clemens
Jeremy Bonderman
Jumbo/900

2003 Leaf Limited Gold Spotlight

*GOLD 1-151: 1.25X TO 3X BASIC
*GOLD 152-170: 1.25X TO 3X BASIC
1-170 PRINT RUN 50 SERIAL #'d SETS
171-204 PRINT RUN 25 SERIAL #'d SETS
179/195/202 PRINT RUN 10 SERIAL #'d PER
171-204 NO PRICING DUE TO SCARCITY
1-200 RANDOM INSERTS IN PACKS
201-204 RANDOM IN DLP R/T PACKS

2003 Leaf Limited Silver Spotlight

*SILVER 1-151: .75X TO 2X BASIC
*SILVER 152-170: .75X TO 2X BASIC
1-170 PRINT RUN 100 SERIAL #'d SETS
*SILVER AU GU 171-200: .5X TO 1.2X
*SILVER GU 174/199: .6X TO 1.5X
*SILVER AU 171-204 p/r 50: .5X TO 1.2X
171-204 PRINT RUN 50 SERIAL #'d SETS
179/195 PRINT 29 SERIAL #'d COPIES PER
CARD 202 PRINT RUN 25 SERIAL #'d COPIES
NO PRICING ON QTY OF 29 OR LESS
1-200 RANDOM INSERTS IN PACKS
201-204 RANDOM IN DLP R/T PACKS
171 J.Bonderman A PH AU Jsy 40.00 80.00
173 Chien-Ming Wang PH AU 300.00 500.00
174 Hideki Matsui H PH Base 15.00 40.00
175 Hong-Chih Kuo PH AU Bat 200.00 400.00
190 C.Barmes A PH AU Bat 20.00 40.00
196 C.Barmes A PH AU Bat 20.00 40.00
197 J.Bonderman H PH AU Jsy 40.00 80.00
199 Hideki Matsui A PH Base 15.00 40.00
201 Delmon Young PH AU 175.00 300.00

2003 Leaf Limited Moniker

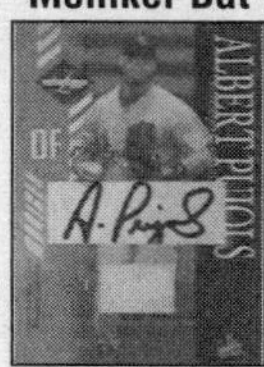

RANDOM INSERTS IN PACKS
PRINT RUNS B/WN 1-10 COPIES PER
NO PRICING DUE TO SCARCITY

2003 Leaf Limited Moniker Bat

RANDOM INSERTS IN PACKS
PRINT RUNS B/WN 1-25 COPIES PER
NO PRICING ON QTY OF 10 OR LESS

2003 Leaf Limited Moniker Jersey

RANDOM INSERTS IN PACKS
PRINT RUNS B/WN 1-25 COPIES PER
NO PRICING ON QTY OF 10 OR LESS

2003 Leaf Limited Moniker Jersey Number

RANDOM INSERTS IN PACKS
PRINT RUNS B/WN 1-25 COPIES PER
NO PRICING ON QTY OF 10 OR LESS

2003 Leaf Limited Moniker Jersey Position

RANDOM INSERTS IN PACKS
PRINT RUNS B/WN 1-25 COPIES PER
NO PRICING ON QTY OF 10 OR LESS

2003 Leaf Limited Threads

RANDOM INSERTS IN PACKS
PRINT RUNS B/WN 5-100 COPIES PER
NO PRICING ON QTY OF 10 OR LESS
1 Derek Jeter Btg Base/50 15.00 40.00
2 Eric Chavez/25 6.00 15.00
3 Alex Rodriguez Rgr A/100 6.00 15.00
4 Miguel Tejada Fldg/50 4.00 10.00
5 Nomar Garciaparra H/100 6.00 15.00
6 Jeff Bagwell H/50 6.00 15.00

7 Jim Thome Phils A/50 6.00 15.00
8 Pat Burrell w/Bat/25 6.00 15.00
9 Albert Pujols H/100 10.00 25.00
10 Juan Gonzalez Rgr Btg/25 6.00 15.00
11 Shawn Green Jays/25 6.00 15.00
12 Craig Biggio H/25 10.00 25.00
13 Chipper Jones H/50 6.00 15.00
14 H.Nomo Dodgers/100 8.00 20.00
15 Vernon Wells/25 6.00 15.00
16 Gary Sheffield/25 6.00 15.00
17 Barry Larkin/25 10.00 25.00
18 Josh Beckett White/25 6.00 15.00
19 Edgar Martinez A/25 10.00 25.00
20 I.Rodriguez Marlins/25 10.00 25.00
21 Jeff Kent Astros/25 6.00 15.00
22 Roberto Alomar Mets A/25 10.00 25.00
23 Alfonso Soriano A/100 3.00 8.00
24 Jim Thome Indians H/25 10.00 25.00
25 J.Gonzalez Indians Btg/25 6.00 15.00
26 Carlos Beltran/25 6.00 15.00
27 S.Green Dodgers H/50 4.00 10.00
28 Tim Hudson H/25 6.00 15.00
29 Deion Sanders/25 10.00 25.00
30 Rafael Palmeiro O's/25 10.00 25.00
31 Todd Helton H/50 6.00 15.00
32 L.Berkman No Socks/25 6.00 15.00
33 M.Mussina Yanks H/50 6.00 15.00
34 Kazuhisa Ishii H/50 4.00 10.00
35 Pat Burrell Run/25 6.00 15.00
36 Miguel Tejada Btg/50 4.00 10.00
37 J.Gonzalez Rgr Stand/25 6.00 15.00
38 Roberto Alomar Mets H/25 10.00 25.00
39 R.Alom Indians Bunt/25 10.00 25.00
40 Luis Gonzalez/25 6.00 15.00
41 Jorge Posada/50 6.00 15.00
42 Mark Mulder Leg/25 6.00 15.00
43 Sammy Sosa H/100 4.00 10.00
44 Mark Prior H/50 6.00 15.00
45 R.Clemens Yanks H/100 6.00 15.00
46 Tom Glavine Mets H/25 10.00 25.00
47 Mark Teixeira A/25 10.00 25.00
48 Manny Ramirez H/50 6.00 15.00
49 Frank Thomas Swing/25 10.00 25.00
50 Troy Glaus White/50 4.00 10.00
51 Andruw Jones H/50 6.00 15.00
52 J.Giambi Yanks H/100 3.00 8.00
53 Jim Thome Phils H/50 6.00 15.00
54 Barry Bonds H Base/50 15.00 40.00
55 R.Palmeiro Rgr H/25 10.00 25.00
56 Edgar Martinez H/25 10.00 25.00
57 Vladimir Guerrero H/50 6.00 15.00
58 Roberto Alomar O's/25 10.00 25.00
59 Mike Sweeney/25 6.00 15.00
60 Magglio Ordonez A/25 6.00 15.00
62 Craig Biggio A/25 10.00 25.00
63 Greg Maddux H/100 6.00 15.00
64 Mike Piazza Mets H/100 6.00 15.00
65 T.Glavine Braves A/25 10.00 25.00
66 Kerry Wood H/25 6.00 15.00
67 Frank Thomas Arms/25 10.00 25.00
68 M.Mussina Yanks A/50 6.00 15.00
69 Nick Johnson H/25 6.00 15.00
70 Bernie Williams H/50 6.00 15.00
71 Scott Rolen/25 10.00 25.00
72 C.Schill D'backs Leg/25 6.00 15.00
73 Adam Dunn A/50 4.00 10.00
74 Roy Oswalt A/25 6.00 15.00
75 P.Martinez Sox H/50 6.00 15.00
76 Tom Glavine Mets A/25 10.00 25.00
77 Torii Hunter Swing/25 6.00 15.00
78 Austin Kearns/25 6.00 15.00
79 R.Johnson D'backs A/100 4.00 10.00
80 Bernie Williams A/50 6.00 15.00
81 Ichiro Suzuki Btg Base/50 15.00 40.00
82 Kerry Wood A/25 6.00 15.00
83 Kazuhisa Ishii A/50 4.00 10.00
84 R.Johnson Astros/50 6.00 15.00
85 Nick Johnson A/25 6.00 15.00
86 J.Beckett Pinstripe/25 6.00 15.00
87 Curt Schilling Phils/25 6.00 15.00
88 Mike Mussina O's/50 6.00 15.00
89 P.Martinez Dodgers/25 10.00 25.00
90 Barry Zito A/50 4.00 10.00
91 Jim Edmonds/100 3.00 8.00
92 R.Henderson Sox/100 4.00 10.00
93 R.Henderson Padres/50 6.00 15.00
94 R.Henderson M's/50 6.00 15.00
95 R.Henderson Mets/50 6.00 15.00
96 R.Henderson Jays/50 6.00 15.00
97 R.Johnson M's Arm Up/50 6.00 15.00
98 Mark Grace/50 6.00 15.00
99 P.Martinez Expos/25 10.00 25.00
100 Hee Seop Choi/25 6.00 15.00
101 Ivan Rodriguez Rgr/25 10.00 25.00
102 Jeff Kent Giants/25 6.00 15.00
103 Hideo Nomo Sox/5
104 Hideo Nomo Mets/50 8.00 20.00
105 Mike Piazza Dodgers/100 6.00 15.00
106 T.Glavine Braves H/25 10.00 25.00
107 R.Alom Indians Swing/25 10.00 25.00
108 Roger Clemens Sox/100 6.00 15.00
109 Jason Giambi A's H/25 6.00 15.00
110 Jim Thome Indians A/25 10.00 25.00
111 Alex Rodriguez M's H/100 6.00 15.00
112 J.Gonz Indians Hands/25 6.00 15.00
113 Torii Hunter Crouch/25 6.00 15.00
114 Roy Oswalt H/25 6.00 15.00
115 C.Schill D'backs Throw/25 6.00 15.00
116 Magglio Ordonez H/50 6.00 15.00
117 R.Palmeiro Rgr H/25 10.00 25.00
118 Andruw Jones A/50 6.00 15.00
119 Manny Ramirez A/50 6.00 15.00
120 Mark Teixeira H/25 10.00 25.00
121 Mark Mulder Stance/25 6.00 15.00
123 Tim Hudson A/25 6.00 15.00
124 Todd Helton A/50 6.00 15.00
125 Troy Glaus Pinstripe/50 4.00 10.00
126 Derek Jeter Run Base/50 15.00 40.00
127 Barry Bonds A Base/50 15.00 40.00
128 Greg Maddux A/100 6.00 15.00
129 R.Clemens Yanks A/100 6.00 15.00
130 Nomar Garciaparra A/100 6.00 15.00
131 Mike Piazza Mets A/100 6.00 15.00
132 Alex Rodriguez Rgr H/100 6.00 15.00
133 Ichiro Suzuki Run Base/50 15.00 40.00
134 R.Johnson D'backs H/100 4.00 10.00
135 Sammy Sosa A/100 4.00 10.00
137 Alfonso Soriano H/100 3.00 8.00
138 J.Giambi Yanks A/100 3.00 8.00
139 Albert Pujols A/100 10.00 25.00
140 Chipper Jones A/25 10.00 25.00
141 Adam Dunn H/50 4.00 10.00
142 P.Martinez Sox A/50 6.00 15.00
143 Vladimir Guerrero A/50 6.00 15.00
144 Mark Prior A/50 6.00 15.00
145 Barry Zito H/50 4.00 10.00
146 Jeff Bagwell A/50 6.00 15.00
147 Lance Berkman Socks/25 6.00 15.00
148 S.Green Dodgers A/25 6.00 15.00
149 Jason Giambi A's A/25 6.00 15.00
150 R.Johnson M's Arm Out/25 10.00 25.00
151 Alex Rodriguez M's A/100 6.00 15.00
152 Babe Ruth/5
153 Ty Cobb Pants/100 100.00 200.00
154 Jackie Robinson/50 30.00 60.00
155 Lou Gehrig/5
156 Thurman Munson/100 10.00 25.00
157 Roberto Clemente/10
158 Nolan Ryan Rgr/100 20.00 50.00
159 Nolan Ryan Angels/100 20.00 50.00
160 Nolan Ryan Astros/100 20.00 50.00
161 Cal Ripken/100 25.00 60.00
162 Don Mattingly/100 15.00 40.00
163 Stan Musial/100 15.00 40.00
164 Tony Gwynn/100 8.00 20.00
165 Yogi Berra/100 8.00 20.00
166 Johnny Bench/100 8.00 20.00
167 Mike Schmidt/100 15.00 40.00
168 George Brett/100 15.00 40.00
169 Ryne Sandberg/100 15.00 40.00
170 Ernie Banks/50 20.00 50.00

2003 Leaf Limited Threads Button

RANDOM INSERTS IN PACKS
STATED PRINT RUN 6 SERIAL #'d SETS
CARD 74 OSWALT PRINT RUN 2 CARDS
CARD 100 CHOI PRINT RUN 5 CARDS
NO PRICING DUE TO SCARCITY

2003 Leaf Limited Threads Double

RANDOM INSERTS IN PACKS
PRINT RUNS B/WN 5-25 COPIES PER
NO PRICING ON QTY 15 OR LESS

3 A.Rod Rgr A Hat-Jsy/25 25.00 60.00
4 M.Tejada Fldg Hat-Jsy/25 10.00 25.00
9 Albert Pujols H Hat-Jsy/15
10 J.Gonz Rgr Btg Hat-Jsy/25 10.00 25.00
12 Craig Biggio H Hat-Jsy/25 15.00 40.00
14 H.Nomo Dgr Jsy-Pants/25 30.00 80.00
15 Vernon Wells Hat-Jsy/25 10.00 25.00
26 Carlos Beltran Hat-Jsy/25 10.00 25.00
28 Tim Hudson H Hat-Jsy/25 10.00 25.00
31 Todd Helton H Hat-Jsy/25 15.00 40.00
32 L.Berk No Socks Hat-Jsy/25 10.00 25.00
34 Kazuhisa Ishii H Hat-Jsy/25 10.00 25.00
37 J.Gonz Rgr Stand Hat-Jsy/25 10.00 25.00
43 Sammy Sosa H Hat-Jsy/25 15.00 40.00
44 Mark Prior H Hat-Jsy/25 15.00 40.00
47 Mark Teixeira A Hat-Jsy/25 15.00 40.00
51 Andruw Jones H Hat-Jsy/25 15.00 40.00
54 Barry Bonds H Ball-Base/25 30.00 80.00
55 R.Palmeiro Rgr A Hat-Jsy/25 15.00 40.00
60 M.Ordonez A Hat-Jsy/25 10.00 25.00
66 Kerry Wood H Hat-Jsy/5
73 Adam Dunn A Hat-Jsy/25 10.00 25.00
75 P.Martinez Sox H Hat-Jsy/25 15.00 40.00
78 Austin Kearns Hat-Jsy/25 10.00 25.00
81 I.Suzuki Btg Ball-Base/25 30.00 80.00
90 Barry Zito A Hat-Jsy/25 10.00 25.00
94 R.Hend M's Hat-Jsy/25 15.00 40.00
101 I.Rodriguez Rgr Hat-Jsy/25 15.00 40.00
109 J.Giambi A's H Hat-Jsy/25 10.00 25.00
116 M.Ordonez H Hat-Jsy/25 10.00 25.00
117 R.Palmeiro Rgr H Hat-Jsy/25 15.00 40.00
118 Andruw Jones A Hat-Jsy/25 15.00 40.00
120 Mark Teixeira H Hat-Jsy/25 15.00 40.00
123 Tim Hudson A Hat-Jsy/25 10.00 25.00
124 Todd Helton A Hat-Jsy/25 15.00 40.00
127 Barry Bonds A Ball-Base/25 30.00 80.00
132 A.Rod Rgr H Hat-Jsy/25 25.00 60.00
133 I.Suzuki Run Ball-Base/25 30.00 80.00
135 Sammy Sosa A Hat-Jsy/25 15.00 40.00
141 Adam Dunn H Hat-Jsy/25 10.00 25.00
142 P.Martinez Sox A Hat-Jsy/25 15.00 40.00
144 Mark Prior A Hat-Jsy/25 15.00 40.00
145 Barry Zito H Hat-Jsy/25 10.00 25.00
146 Jeff Bagwell A Jsy-Pants/25 15.00 40.00
147 L.Berkman Socks Hat-Jsy/25 10.00 25.00
149 J.Giambi A's A Hat-Jsy/25 10.00 25.00
152 Babe Ruth Jsy-Pants/5
155 Lou Gehrig Jsy-Pants/5
157 Roberto Clemente Hat-Jsy/5
158 N.Ryan Rgr Jsy-Pants/25 50.00 120.00
162 D.Mattingly Btg Glv-Jsy/25 40.00 100.00
164 Tony Gwynn Btg Glv-Jsy/25 25.00 60.00
167 Mike Schmidt Hat-Jsy/25 40.00 100.00
168 George Brett Hat-Jsy/25 40.00 100.00
169 Ryne Sandberg Hat-Jsy/25 50.00 120.00

2003 Leaf Limited Threads Double Prime

RANDOM INSERTS IN PACKS
PRINT RUNS B/WN 1-10 COPIES PER
NO PRICING DUE TO SCARCITY

2003 Leaf Limited Threads Number

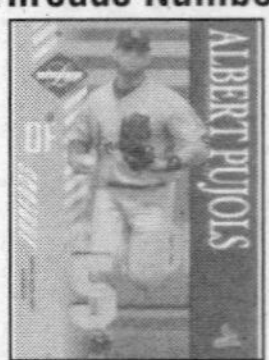

RANDOM INSERTS IN PACKS
PRINT RUNS B/WN 1-75 COPIES PER
NO PRICING ON QTY OF 19 OR LESS

7 Jim Thome Phils A/25 10.00 25.00
18 Josh Beckett White/61 4.00 10.00
24 Jim Thome Indians H/25 10.00 25.00
25 J.Gonzalez Indians Btg/22 10.00 25.00
29 Deion Sanders/21 15.00 40.00
30 Rafael Palmeiro O's/25 10.00 25.00
33 M.Mussina Yanks H/35 10.00 25.00
40 Luis Gonzalez/20 10.00 25.00
41 Jorge Posada/20 15.00 40.00
42 Mark Mulder Leg/20 10.00 25.00
43 Sammy Sosa/21 15.00 40.00
44 Mark Prior H/22 15.00 40.00
45 R.Clemens Yanks H/22 25.00 60.00
46 Tom Glavine Mets H/47 6.00 15.00
47 Mark Teixeira A/23 15.00 40.00
48 Manny Ramirez H/24 15.00 40.00
49 Frank Thomas Swing/35 10.00 25.00
50 Troy Glaus White/25 6.00 15.00
51 Andruw Jones H/25 10.00 25.00
52 J.Giambi Yanks H/25 6.00 15.00
53 Jim Thome Phils H/25 10.00 25.00
55 R.Palmeiro Rgr A/25 10.00 25.00
57 Vladimir Guerrero H/27 10.00 25.00
59 Mike Sweeney/29 6.00 15.00
60 Magglio Ordonez A/30 6.00 15.00
63 Greg Maddux H/31 15.00 40.00
64 Mike Piazza Mets H/31 15.00 40.00
65 T.Glavine Braves A/47 6.00 15.00
66 Kerry Wood H/52 4.00 10.00
67 Frank Thomas Arms/35 10.00 25.00
68 M.Mussina Yanks A/35 10.00 25.00
69 Nick Johnson H/36 4.00 10.00
70 Bernie Williams H/51 6.00 15.00
71 Scott Rolen/27 10.00 25.00
72 C.Schill D'backs Leg/38 4.00 10.00
73 Adam Dunn A/44 4.00 10.00
74 Roy Oswalt A/44 4.00 10.00
75 P.Martinez Sox H/45 6.00 15.00
76 Tom Glavine Mets A/47 6.00 15.00
77 Torii Hunter Swing/48 4.00 10.00
78 Austin Kearns/28 6.00 15.00
79 R.Johnson D'backs A/51 6.00 15.00
80 Bernie Williams A/51 6.00 15.00
82 Kerry Wood A/34 6.00 15.00
84 R.Johnson Astros/51 6.00 15.00
85 Nick Johnson A/36 4.00 10.00
86 J.Beckett Pinstripe/61 4.00 10.00
87 Curt Schilling Phils/38 4.00 10.00
88 Mike Mussina O's/35 10.00 25.00
89 P.Martinez Dodgers/45 6.00 15.00
90 Barry Zito A/75 4.00 10.00
92 R.Henderson Sox/35 10.00 25.00
93 R.Henderson Padres/24 15.00 40.00
94 R.Henderson M's/35 10.00 25.00
95 R.Henderson Mets/24 15.00 40.00
96 R.Henderson Jays/24 15.00 40.00
97 R.Johnson M's Arm Up/51 6.00 15.00
99 P.Martinez Expos/45 6.00 15.00
102 Jeff Kent Giants/21 10.00 25.00
105 Mike Piazza Dodgers/31 15.00 40.00
106 T.Glavine Braves H/47 6.00 15.00
108 Roger Clemens Sox/21 25.00 60.00
110 Jim Thome Indians A/25 10.00 25.00
112 J.Gonz Indians Hands/22 10.00 25.00
113 Torii Hunter Crouch/48 4.00 10.00
114 Roy Oswalt H/44 4.00 10.00
115 C.Schill D'backs Throw/38 4.00 10.00
116 Magglio Ordonez H/30 6.00 15.00
117 R.Palmeiro Rgr H/25 10.00 25.00
118 Andruw Jones A/25 10.00 25.00
119 Manny Ramirez A/24 15.00 40.00
120 Mark Teixeira H/23 15.00 40.00
121 Mark Mulder Stance/20 10.00 25.00
125 Troy Glaus Pinstripe/25 6.00 15.00
128 Greg Maddux A/31 15.00 40.00
129 R.Clemens Yanks A/22 25.00 60.00
131 Mike Piazza Mets A/31 15.00 40.00
134 R.Johnson D'backs H/51 6.00 15.00
135 Sammy Sosa A/21 15.00 40.00
138 J.Giambi Yanks A/25 6.00 15.00
141 Adam Dunn H/44 4.00 10.00
142 P.Martinez Sox A/45 6.00 15.00
143 Vladimir Guerrero A/27 10.00 25.00
145 Barry Zito H/75 4.00 10.00
150 R.Johnson M's Arm Out/51 6.00 15.00
154 Jackie Robinson/42 30.00 60.00
157 Roberto Clemente/21 60.00 120.00
158 Nolan Ryan Rgr/34 30.00 80.00
159 Nolan Ryan Angels/30 30.00 80.00
160 Nolan Ryan Astros/34 30.00 80.00
162 Don Mattingly/23 25.00 60.00
165 Yogi Berra/42 10.00 25.00
167 Mike Schmidt/20 25.00 60.00
169 Ryne Sandberg/23 30.00 80.00

2003 Leaf Limited Threads Position

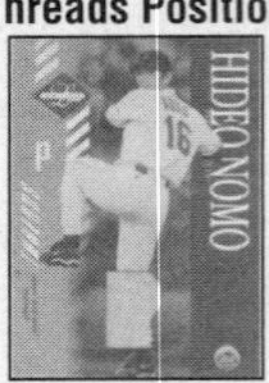

RANDOM INSERTS IN PACKS
2-151 PRINT RUNS 25 SERIAL #'d SETS
152-170 PRINTS B/WN 5-25 COPIES PER
NO PRICING ON QTY OF 10 OR LESS

2 Eric Chavez 6.00 15.00
3 Alex Rodriguez Rgr A 15.00 40.00
4 Miguel Tejada Fldg 6.00 15.00
5 Nomar Garciaparra H 15.00 40.00
6 Jeff Bagwell H 10.00 25.00
7 Jim Thome Phils A 10.00 25.00
8 Pat Burrell w/Bat 6.00 15.00
9 Albert Pujols H 25.00 60.00
10 Juan Gonzalez Rgr Btg 6.00 15.00
11 Shawn Green Jays 6.00 15.00
12 Craig Biggio H 10.00 25.00
13 Chipper Jones H 10.00 25.00
14 Hideo Nomo Dodgers 20.00 50.00
15 Vernon Wells 6.00 15.00
16 Gary Sheffield 6.00 15.00
17 Barry Larkin 10.00 25.00
18 Josh Beckett White 6.00 15.00
19 Edgar Martinez A 10.00 25.00
20 Ivan Rodriguez Marlins 10.00 25.00
21 Jeff Kent Astros 6.00 15.00
22 Roberto Alomar Mets A 10.00 25.00
23 Alfonso Soriano A 6.00 15.00
24 Jim Thome Indians H 10.00 25.00
25 J.Gonzalez Indians Btg 6.00 15.00
26 Carlos Beltran 6.00 15.00
27 S.Green Dodgers H 6.00 15.00
28 Tim Hudson H 6.00 15.00
29 Deion Sanders 10.00 25.00
30 Rafael Palmeiro O's 10.00 25.00
31 Todd Helton H 10.00 25.00
32 L.Berkman No Socks 6.00 15.00
33 Mike Mussina Yanks H 10.00 25.00
34 Kazuhisa Ishii H 6.00 15.00
35 Pat Burrell Run 6.00 15.00
36 Miguel Tejada Btg 6.00 15.00
37 J.Gonzalez Rgr Stand 6.00 15.00
38 Roberto Alomar Mets H 10.00 25.00
39 R.Alomar Indians Bunt 10.00 25.00
40 Luis Gonzalez 6.00 15.00
41 Jorge Posada 10.00 25.00
42 Mark Mulder Leg 6.00 15.00
43 Sammy Sosa H 10.00 25.00
44 Mark Prior H 10.00 25.00
45 R.Clemens Yanks H 15.00 40.00
46 Tom Glavine Mets H 10.00 25.00
47 Mark Teixeira A 10.00 25.00
48 Manny Ramirez H 10.00 25.00
49 Frank Thomas Swing 10.00 25.00
50 Troy Glaus White 6.00 15.00
51 Andruw Jones H 10.00 25.00
52 Jason Giambi Yanks H 10.00 25.00
53 Jim Thome Phils H 10.00 25.00
55 Rafael Palmeiro Rgr A 10.00 25.00
56 Edgar Martinez H 10.00 25.00
57 Vladimir Guerrero H 10.00 25.00
58 Roberto Alomar O's 10.00 25.00
59 Mike Sweeney 6.00 15.00
60 Magglio Ordonez A 6.00 15.00
62 Craig Biggio A 10.00 25.00
63 Greg Maddux H 15.00 40.00
64 Mike Piazza Mets H 15.00 40.00
65 T.Glavine Braves A 10.00 25.00
66 Kerry Wood H 6.00 15.00
67 Frank Thomas Arms 10.00 25.00
68 Mike Mussina Yanks A 10.00 25.00
69 Nick Johnson H 6.00 15.00
70 Bernie Williams H 10.00 25.00
71 Scott Rolen 10.00 25.00
72 C.Schilling D'backs Leg 6.00 15.00
73 Adam Dunn A 6.00 15.00
74 Roy Oswalt A 6.00 15.00
75 Pedro Martinez Sox H 10.00 25.00
76 Tom Glavine Mets A 10.00 25.00
77 Torii Hunter Swing 6.00 15.00
78 Austin Kearns 6.00 15.00
79 R.Johnson D'backs A 10.00 25.00
80 Bernie Williams A 10.00 25.00
82 Kerry Wood A 6.00 15.00
83 Kazuhisa Ishii A 6.00 15.00
84 Randy Johnson Astros 10.00 25.00
85 Nick Johnson A 6.00 15.00
86 J.Beckett Pinstripe 6.00 15.00
87 Curt Schilling Phils 6.00 15.00
88 Mike Mussina O's 10.00 25.00
89 P.Martinez Dodgers 10.00 25.00
90 Barry Zito A 6.00 15.00
91 Jim Edmonds 6.00 15.00
92 R.Henderson Sox 10.00 25.00
93 R.Henderson Padres 10.00 25.00
94 R.Henderson M's 10.00 25.00
95 R.Henderson Mets 10.00 25.00
96 R.Henderson Jays 10.00 25.00
97 R.Johnson M's Arm Up 10.00 25.00
98 Mark Grace 10.00 25.00
99 Pedro Martinez Expos 10.00 25.00
100 Hee Seop Choi 6.00 15.00
101 Ivan Rodriguez Rgr 10.00 25.00
102 Jeff Kent Giants 6.00 15.00
103 Hideo Nomo Sox 20.00 50.00
104 Hideo Nomo Mets 20.00 50.00
105 Mike Piazza Dodgers 15.00 40.00
106 Tom Glavine Braves H 10.00 25.00
107 R.Alomar Indians Swing 10.00 25.00
108 Roger Clemens Sox 15.00 40.00
109 Jason Giambi A's H 6.00 15.00
110 Jim Thome Indians A 10.00 25.00
111 Alex Rodriguez M's H 15.00 40.00
112 J.Gonz Indians Hands 6.00 15.00
113 Torii Hunter Crouch 6.00 15.00
114 Roy Oswalt H 6.00 15.00
115 C.Schilling D'backs Throw 6.00 15.00
116 Magglio Ordonez H 6.00 15.00
117 Rafael Palmeiro Rgr H 10.00 25.00
118 Andruw Jones A 10.00 25.00
119 Manny Ramirez A 10.00 25.00
120 Mark Teixeira H 10.00 25.00
121 Mark Mulder Stance 6.00 15.00
123 Tim Hudson A 6.00 15.00
124 Todd Helton A 10.00 25.00
125 Troy Glaus Pinstripe 6.00 15.00
128 Greg Maddux A 15.00 40.00
129 Roger Clemens Yanks A 15.00 40.00
130 Nomar Garciaparra A 15.00 40.00
131 Mike Piazza Mets A 15.00 40.00
132 Alex Rodriguez Rgr H 15.00 40.00
134 R.Johnson D'backs H 10.00 25.00
135 Sammy Sosa A 10.00 25.00
137 Alfonso Soriano H 6.00 15.00
138 J.Giambi Yanks A 10.00 25.00
139 Albert Pujols A 25.00 60.00
140 Chipper Jones A 10.00 25.00
141 Adam Dunn H 6.00 15.00
142 Pedro Martinez Sox A 10.00 25.00
143 Vladimir Guerrero A 10.00 25.00
144 Mark Prior A 10.00 25.00
145 Barry Zito H 6.00 15.00
146 Jeff Bagwell A 10.00 25.00
147 Lance Berkman Socks 6.00 15.00
148 S.Green Dodgers A 6.00 15.00
149 Jason Giambi A's A 6.00 15.00
150 R.Johnson M's Arm Out 10.00 25.00
151 Alex Rodriguez M's A 15.00 40.00
152 Babe Ruth/5
153 Ty Cobb Pants 75.00 150.00
154 Jackie Robinson/10
155 Lou Gehrig/5
156 Thurman Munson 20.00 50.00
157 Roberto Clemente/5
158 Nolan Ryan Rgr 30.00 80.00
159 Nolan Ryan Angels 30.00 80.00
160 Nolan Ryan Astros 30.00 80.00
161 Cal Ripken 50.00 120.00
162 Don Mattingly 25.00 60.00
163 Stan Musial 30.00 80.00
164 Tony Gwynn 15.00 40.00
165 Yogi Berra 12.50 30.00
166 Johnny Bench 12.50 30.00
167 Mike Schmidt 25.00 60.00
168 George Brett 25.00 60.00
169 Ryne Sandberg 30.00 80.00
170 Ernie Banks/5

2003 Leaf Limited Threads Prime

RANDOM INSERTS IN PACKS
2-151 PRINTS 25 #'d PER UNLESS NOTED
152-170 PRINTS B/WN 3-25 COPIES PER
NO PRICING ON QTY OF 10 OR LESS

2 Eric Chavez 10.00 25.00
3 Alex Rodriguez Rgr A 25.00 60.00
4 Miguel Tejada Fldg 10.00 25.00
5 Nomar Garciaparra H 25.00 60.00
6 Jeff Bagwell H 15.00 40.00
7 Jim Thome Phils A/20 20.00 50.00
8 Pat Burrell w/Bat 10.00 25.00
9 Albert Pujols H 40.00 100.00
10 Juan Gonzalez Rgr Btg 10.00 25.00
11 Shawn Green Jays 10.00 25.00
12 Craig Biggio H 15.00 40.00
13 Chipper Jones H 15.00 40.00
14 Hideo Nomo Dodgers 30.00 80.00
15 Vernon Wells 10.00 25.00
16 Gary Sheffield 10.00 25.00
17 Barry Larkin 15.00 40.00
18 Josh Beckett White 10.00 25.00
19 Edgar Martinez A 15.00 40.00
20 Ivan Rodriguez Marlins 15.00 40.00
21 Jeff Kent Astros 10.00 25.00
22 Roberto Alomar Mets A 15.00 40.00
23 Alfonso Soriano A 10.00 25.00
24 Jim Thome Indians H 15.00 40.00
25 J.Gonzalez Indians Btg 10.00 25.00
26 Carlos Beltran 10.00 25.00
27 S.Green Dodgers H 10.00 25.00
28 Tim Hudson H 10.00 25.00
29 Deion Sanders 15.00 40.00
30 Rafael Palmeiro O's 15.00 40.00
31 Todd Helton H 15.00 40.00
32 L.Berkman No Socks 10.00 25.00
33 Mike Mussina Yanks H 15.00 40.00
34 Kazuhisa Ishii H 10.00 25.00
35 Pat Burrell Run 10.00 25.00
36 Miguel Tejada Btg 10.00 25.00
37 J.Gonzalez Rgr Stand 10.00 25.00
38 Roberto Alomar Mets H 15.00 40.00
39 R.Alomar Indians Bunt 15.00 40.00
40 Luis Gonzalez 10.00 25.00
41 Jorge Posada 15.00 40.00
42 Mark Mulder Leg 10.00 25.00
43 Sammy Sosa H 15.00 40.00
44 Mark Prior H 15.00 40.00
45 Roger Clemens Yanks H 25.00 60.00
46 Tom Glavine Mets H 15.00 40.00
47 Mark Teixeira A 15.00 40.00
48 Manny Ramirez H 15.00 40.00
49 Frank Thomas Swing 15.00 40.00
50 Troy Glaus White 10.00 25.00
51 Andruw Jones H 15.00 40.00
52 Jason Giambi Yanks H 10.00 25.00
53 Jim Thome Phils H 15.00 40.00
55 Rafael Palmeiro Rgr A 15.00 40.00
56 Edgar Martinez H 15.00 40.00
57 Vladimir Guerrero H 15.00 40.00
58 Roberto Alomar O's 15.00 40.00
59 Mike Sweeney 10.00 25.00
60 Magglio Ordonez A 10.00 25.00
62 Craig Biggio A 15.00 40.00
63 Greg Maddux H 25.00 60.00
64 Mike Piazza Mets H 25.00 60.00
65 Tom Glavine Braves A 15.00 40.00
66 Kerry Wood H 10.00 25.00
67 Frank Thomas Arms 15.00 40.00
68 Mike Mussina Yanks A 15.00 40.00
69 Nick Johnson H 10.00 25.00
70 Bernie Williams H 15.00 40.00
71 Scott Rolen 15.00 40.00
72 C.Schilling D'backs Leg 10.00 25.00
73 Adam Dunn A 10.00 25.00
74 Roy Oswalt A 10.00 25.00
75 Pedro Martinez Sox H 15.00 40.00
76 Tom Glavine Mets A 15.00 40.00
77 Torii Hunter Swing 10.00 25.00
78 Austin Kearns 10.00 25.00
79 R.Johnson D'backs A 15.00 40.00
80 Bernie Williams A 15.00 40.00
82 Kerry Wood A 10.00 25.00
83 Kazuhisa Ishii A 10.00 25.00
84 Randy Johnson Astros 15.00 40.00
85 Nick Johnson A 10.00 25.00
86 J.Beckett Pinstripe 10.00 25.00
87 Curt Schilling Phils 10.00 25.00
88 Mike Mussina O's 15.00 40.00
89 P.Martinez Dodgers 15.00 40.00
90 Barry Zito A 10.00 25.00
91 Jim Edmonds 10.00 25.00
92 R.Henderson Sox 15.00 40.00
93 R.Henderson Padres 15.00 40.00
94 R.Henderson M's 15.00 40.00
95 R.Henderson Mets 15.00 40.00
96 R.Henderson Jays 15.00 40.00
97 R.Johnson M's Arm Up 15.00 40.00
98 Mark Grace 15.00 40.00
99 Pedro Martinez Expos 15.00 40.00
100 Hee Seop Choi 10.00 25.00
101 Ivan Rodriguez Rgr 15.00 40.00
102 Jeff Kent Giants 10.00 25.00
104 Hideo Nomo Mets 30.00 80.00
105 Mike Piazza Dodgers 25.00 60.00
106 Tom Glavine Braves H 15.00 40.00
107 R.Alomar Indians Swing 15.00 40.00
108 Roger Clemens Sox 25.00 60.00
109 Jason Giambi A's H 10.00 25.00
110 Jim Thome Indians A 15.00 40.00
111 Alex Rodriguez M's H 25.00 60.00
112 J.Gonz Indians Hands 10.00 25.00
113 Torii Hunter Crouch 10.00 25.00
114 Roy Oswalt H 10.00 25.00
115 C.Schilling D'backs Throw 10.00 25.00
116 Magglio Ordonez H 10.00 25.00
117 Rafael Palmeiro Rgr H 15.00 40.00
118 Andruw Jones A 15.00 40.00
119 Manny Ramirez A 15.00 40.00
120 Mark Teixeira H 15.00 40.00
121 Mark Mulder Stance 10.00 25.00
123 Tim Hudson A 10.00 25.00
124 Todd Helton A 15.00 40.00
125 Troy Glaus Pinstripe 10.00 25.00
128 Greg Maddux A 25.00 60.00
129 Roger Clemens Yanks A 25.00 60.00
130 Nomar Garciaparra A 25.00 60.00
131 Mike Piazza Mets A 25.00 60.00
132 Alex Rodriguez Rgr H 25.00 60.00
134 R.Johnson D'backs H 15.00 40.00
135 Sammy Sosa A 15.00 40.00
137 Alfonso Soriano H 10.00 25.00
138 J.Giambi Yanks A 15.00 40.00
139 Albert Pujols A 40.00 100.00
140 Chipper Jones A 15.00 40.00
141 Adam Dunn H 10.00 25.00
142 P.Martinez Sox A 15.00 40.00
143 Vladimir Guerrero A 15.00 40.00
144 Mark Prior A 15.00 40.00
145 Barry Zito H 10.00 25.00
146 Jeff Bagwell A 15.00 40.00
147 Lance Berkman Socks 10.00 25.00
148 S.Green Dodgers A 10.00 25.00
149 Jason Giambi A's A 10.00 25.00
150 R.Johnson M's Arm Out 15.00 40.00
151 Alex Rodriguez M's A 25.00 60.00
152 Babe Ruth/3
153 Ty Cobb Pants 100.00 200.00
154 Jackie Robinson/10
155 Lou Gehrig/5
156 Thurman Munson 30.00 80.00
157 Roberto Clemente/5
158 Nolan Ryan Rgr 50.00 120.00
159 Nolan Ryan Angels 50.00 120.00
160 Nolan Ryan Astros 50.00 120.00
161 Cal Ripken 60.00 150.00
162 Don Mattingly 40.00 100.00
163 Stan Musial 60.00 150.00
164 Tony Gwynn 25.00 60.00
165 Yogi Berra 20.00 50.00
166 Johnny Bench 20.00 50.00
167 Mike Schmidt 40.00 100.00
168 George Brett 40.00 100.00
169 Ryne Sandberg 50.00 120.00
170 Ernie Banks/10

2003 Leaf Limited Timber

RANDOM INSERTS IN PACKS
STATED PRINT RUN 25 SERIAL #'d SETS
CARD 170 PRINT RUN 1 SERIAL #'d CARD
NO 170 PRICING DUE TO SCARCITY
2 Eric Chavez 6.00 15.00
3 Alex Rodriguez Rgr A 15.00 40.00
4 Miguel Tejada Fldg 6.00 15.00
5 Nomar Garciaparra H 15.00 40.00
6 Jeff Bagwell H 10.00 25.00
7 Jim Thome Phils A 10.00 25.00
8 Pat Burrell w/Bat 6.00 15.00
9 Albert Pujols H 25.00 60.00
10 Juan Gonzalez Rgr Btg 6.00 15.00
11 Shawn Green Jays 6.00 15.00
12 Craig Biggio H 10.00 25.00
13 Chipper Jones H 10.00 25.00
14 Hideo Nomo Dodgers 20.00 50.00
15 Vernon Wells 6.00 15.00
16 Gary Sheffield 6.00 15.00
17 Barry Larkin 10.00 25.00
18 Josh Beckett White 6.00 15.00
19 Edgar Martinez A 10.00 25.00
20 Ivan Rodriguez Marlins 10.00 25.00
21 Jeff Kent Astros 6.00 15.00
22 Roberto Alomar Mets A 10.00 25.00
23 Alfonso Soriano A 6.00 15.00
24 Jim Thome Indians H 10.00 25.00
25 J.Gonzalez Indians Btg 6.00 15.00
26 Carlos Beltran 6.00 15.00
27 S.Green Dodgers H 6.00 15.00
28 Tim Hudson H 6.00 15.00
30 Rafael Palmeiro O's 10.00 25.00
31 Todd Helton H 10.00 25.00
32 L.Berkman No Socks 6.00 15.00
33 Mike Mussina Yanks H 10.00 25.00
34 Kazuhisa Ishii H 6.00 15.00
35 Pat Burrell Run 6.00 15.00
36 Miguel Tejada Btg 6.00 15.00
37 J.Gonzalez Rgr Stand 6.00 15.00
38 Roberto Alomar Mets H 10.00 25.00
39 R.Alomar Indians Bunt 10.00 25.00
40 Luis Gonzalez 6.00 15.00
41 Jorge Posada 10.00 25.00
42 Mark Mulder Leg 6.00 15.00
43 Sammy Sosa H 10.00 25.00
44 Mark Prior H 10.00 25.00
45 R.Clemens Yanks H 15.00 40.00
46 Tom Glavine Mets H 10.00 25.00
47 Mark Teixeira A 10.00 25.00
48 Manny Ramirez H 10.00 25.00
49 Frank Thomas Swing 10.00 25.00
50 Troy Glaus White 6.00 15.00
51 Andruw Jones H 10.00 25.00
52 Jason Giambi Yanks H 6.00 15.00
53 Jim Thome Phils H 10.00 25.00
55 Rafael Palmeiro Rgr A 10.00 25.00
56 Edgar Martinez H 10.00 25.00
57 Vladimir Guerrero H 10.00 25.00
58 Roberto Alomar O's 10.00 25.00
59 Mike Sweeney 6.00 15.00
60 Magglio Ordonez A 6.00 15.00
62 Craig Biggio A 10.00 25.00
63 Greg Maddux H 15.00 40.00
64 Mike Piazza Mets H 15.00 40.00
65 T.Glavine Braves A 10.00 25.00
66 Kerry Wood H 6.00 15.00
67 Frank Thomas Arms 10.00 25.00
68 Mike Mussina Yanks A 10.00 25.00
69 Nick Johnson H 6.00 15.00
70 Bernie Williams H 10.00 25.00
71 Scott Rolen 10.00 25.00
72 C.Schilling D'backs Leg 6.00 15.00
73 Adam Dunn A 6.00 15.00
74 Roy Oswalt A 6.00 15.00
75 Pedro Martinez Sox H 10.00 25.00
76 Tom Glavine Mets A 10.00 25.00
77 Torii Hunter Swing 6.00 15.00
78 Austin Kearns 6.00 15.00
79 R.Johnson D'backs A 10.00 25.00
80 Bernie Williams A 10.00 25.00
82 Kerry Wood A 6.00 15.00
83 Kazuhisa Ishii A 6.00 15.00
84 Randy Johnson Astros 10.00 25.00
85 Nick Johnson A 6.00 15.00
86 J.Beckett Pinstripe 6.00 15.00
87 Curt Schilling Phils 6.00 15.00
88 Mike Mussina O's 10.00 25.00
89 P.Martinez Dodgers 10.00 25.00
90 Barry Zito A 6.00 15.00
91 Jim Edmonds 6.00 15.00
92 R.Henderson Sox 10.00 25.00
93 R.Henderson Padres 10.00 25.00
94 R.Henderson M's 10.00 25.00
95 R.Henderson Mets 10.00 25.00
96 R.Henderson Jays 10.00 25.00
97 R.Johnson M's Arm Up 10.00 25.00
98 Mark Grace 10.00 25.00
99 Pedro Martinez Expos 10.00 25.00
101 Ivan Rodriguez Rgr 10.00 25.00
102 Jeff Kent Giants 6.00 15.00
103 Hideo Nomo Sox 20.00 50.00
104 Hideo Nomo Mets 20.00 50.00
105 Mike Piazza Dodgers 15.00 40.00
106 Tom Glavine Braves H 10.00 25.00
107 R.Alomar Indians Swing 10.00 25.00
108 Roger Clemens Sox 15.00 40.00
109 Jason Giambi A's H 6.00 15.00
110 Jim Thome Indians A 10.00 25.00
111 Alex Rodriguez M's H 15.00 40.00
112 J.Gonz Indians Hands 6.00 15.00
113 Torii Hunter Crouch 6.00 15.00
114 Roy Oswalt H 6.00 15.00
115 C.Schilling D'backs Throw 6.00 15.00
116 Magglio Ordonez H 6.00 15.00
117 Rafael Palmeiro Rgr H 10.00 25.00
118 Andruw Jones A 10.00 25.00
119 Manny Ramirez A 10.00 25.00
120 Mark Teixeira H 10.00 25.00
121 Mark Mulder Stance 6.00 15.00
122 Garret Anderson 6.00 15.00
123 Tim Hudson A 6.00 15.00
124 Todd Helton A 10.00 25.00
125 Troy Glaus Pinstripe 6.00 15.00
128 Greg Maddux A 15.00 40.00
129 Roger Clemens Yanks A 15.00 40.00
130 Nomar Garciaparra A 15.00 40.00
131 Mike Piazza Mets A 15.00 40.00
132 Alex Rodriguez Rgr H 15.00 40.00
134 R.Johnson D'backs H 10.00 25.00
135 Sammy Sosa A 10.00 25.00
137 Alfonso Soriano H 6.00 15.00
138 J.Giambi Yanks A 6.00 15.00
139 Albert Pujols A 25.00 60.00
140 Chipper Jones A 10.00 25.00
141 Adam Dunn H 6.00 15.00
142 Pedro Martinez Sox A 10.00 25.00
143 Vladimir Guerrero A 10.00 25.00
144 Mark Prior A 10.00 25.00
145 Barry Zito H 6.00 15.00
146 Jeff Bagwell A 10.00 25.00
147 Lance Berkman Socks 6.00 15.00
148 S.Green Dodgers A 6.00 15.00
149 Jason Giambi A's A 6.00 15.00
150 R.Johnson M's Arm Out 10.00 25.00
151 Alex Rodriguez M's A 15.00 40.00
152 Babe Ruth 125.00 250.00
153 Ty Cobb 60.00 120.00
155 Lou Gehrig 75.00 150.00
156 Thurman Munson 20.00 50.00
157 Roberto Clemente 60.00 120.00
158 Nolan Ryan Rgr 30.00 80.00
159 Nolan Ryan Angels 30.00 80.00
160 Nolan Ryan Astros 30.00 80.00
161 Cal Ripken 50.00 120.00
162 Don Mattingly 25.00 60.00
163 Stan Musial 25.00 60.00
164 Tony Gwynn 15.00 40.00
165 Yogi Berra 12.50 30.00
166 Johnny Bench 12.50 30.00
167 Mike Schmidt 25.00 60.00
168 George Brett 25.00 60.00
169 Ryne Sandberg 30.00 80.00
170 Ernie Banks/1

2003 Leaf Limited TNT

RANDOM INSERTS IN PACKS
PRINT RUNS B/WN 1-25 COPIES PER
NO PRICING ON QTY OF 10 OR LESS
2 Eric Chavez Bat-Jsy 10.00 25.00
3 A.Rod Rgr A Bat-Jsy 20.00 50.00
4 M.Tejada Fldg Bat-Jsy/10
5 N.Garciaparra H Bat-Jsy 20.00 50.00
6 Jeff Bagwell H Bat-Jsy 15.00 40.00
7 J.Thome Phils A Bat-Jsy 15.00 40.00
8 P.Burrell w/Bat Bat-Jsy 10.00 25.00
9 Albert Pujols H Bat-Jsy 25.00 60.00
10 J.Gonz Rgr Btg Bat-Jsy 10.00 25.00
11 S.Green Jays Bat-Jsy 10.00 25.00
12 Craig Biggio H Bat-Jsy 15.00 40.00
13 C.Jones H Bat-Jsy 15.00 40.00
14 H.Nomo Dodgers Bat-Jsy 20.00 50.00
15 Vernon Wells Bat-Jsy 10.00 25.00
16 G.Sheffield Bat-Jsy 10.00 25.00
17 Barry Larkin Bat-Jsy 15.00 40.00
18 J.Beckett White Bat-Jsy 10.00 25.00
19 E.Martinez A Bat-Jsy 15.00 40.00
20 I.Rodriguez Marlins Bat-Jsy 15.00 40.00
21 Jeff Kent Astros Bat-Jsy 10.00 25.00
22 R.Alomar Mets A Bat-Jsy 15.00 40.00
23 A.Soriano A Bat-Jsy 10.00 25.00
24 J.Thome Indians H Bat-Jsy 15.00 40.00
25 J.Gonz Indians Btg Bat-Jsy 10.00 25.00
26 Carlos Beltran Bat-Jsy 10.00 25.00
27 S.Green Dodgers H Bat-Jsy 10.00 25.00
28 Tim Hudson H Bat-Jsy 10.00 25.00
30 R.Palmeiro O's Bat-Jsy 15.00 40.00
31 Todd Helton H Bat-Jsy 15.00 40.00
32 L.Berk No Socks Bat-Jsy 10.00 25.00
33 M.Mussina Yanks H Bat-Jsy 15.00 40.00
34 Kazuhisa Ishii H Bat-Jsy 10.00 25.00
35 Pat Burrell Run Bat-Jsy 10.00 25.00
36 M.Tejada Btg Bat-Jsy/10
37 J.Gonz Rgr Stand Bat-Jsy 10.00 25.00
38 R.Alomar Mets H Bat-Jsy 15.00 40.00
39 R.Alom Indians Bunt Bat-Jsy 15.00 40.00
40 Luis Gonzalez Bat-Jsy 10.00 25.00
41 Jorge Posada Bat-Jsy 15.00 40.00
42 M.Mulder Leg Bat-Jsy 10.00 25.00
43 Sammy Sosa H Bat-Jsy 15.00 40.00
44 Mark Prior H Bat-Jsy 15.00 40.00
45 R.Clemens Yanks H Bat-Jsy 20.00 50.00
46 T.Glavine Mets H Bat-Jsy 15.00 40.00
47 Mark Teixeira A Bat-Jsy 15.00 40.00
48 Manny Ramirez H Bat-Jsy 15.00 40.00
49 F.Thomas Swing Bat-Jsy 15.00 40.00
50 Troy Glaus White Bat-Jsy 10.00 25.00
51 Andruw Jones H Bat-Jsy 15.00 40.00
52 J.Giambi Yanks H Bat-Jsy 10.00 25.00
53 J.Thome Phils H Bat-Jsy 15.00 40.00
55 R.Palmeiro Rgr A Bat-Jsy 15.00 40.00
56 E.Martinez H Bat-Jsy 15.00 40.00
57 V.Guerrero H Bat-Jsy 15.00 40.00
59 Mike Sweeney Bat-Jsy 10.00 25.00
60 M.Ordonez A Bat-Jsy 10.00 25.00
62 Craig Biggio A Bat-Jsy 15.00 40.00
63 Greg Maddux H Bat-Jsy 20.00 50.00
64 M.Piazza Mets H Bat-Jsy 20.00 50.00
65 T.Glavine Braves A Bat-Jsy 15.00 40.00
66 Kerry Wood H Bat-Jsy 10.00 25.00
67 F.Thomas Arms Bat-Jsy 15.00 40.00
68 M.Mussina Yanks A Bat-Jsy 15.00 40.00
69 Nick Johnson H Bat-Jsy 10.00 25.00
70 Bernie Williams H Bat-Jsy 15.00 40.00
71 Scott Rolen Bat-Jsy 15.00 40.00
72 C.Schill D'backs Leg Bat-Jsy 10.00 25.00
73 Adam Dunn A Bat-Jsy 10.00 25.00
74 Roy Oswalt A Bat-Jsy 10.00 25.00
75 P.Martinez Sox H Bat-Jsy 15.00 40.00
76 T.Glavine Mets A Bat-Jsy 15.00 40.00
77 T.Hunter Swing Bat-Jsy 10.00 25.00
78 Austin Kearns Bat-Jsy 10.00 25.00
79 R.John D'backs A Bat-Jsy 15.00 40.00
80 Bernie Williams A Bat-Jsy 15.00 40.00
82 Kerry Wood A Bat-Jsy 10.00 25.00
83 Kazuhisa Ishii A Bat-Jsy 10.00 25.00
84 R.Johnson Astros Bat-Jsy 15.00 40.00
85 Nick Johnson A Bat-Jsy 10.00 25.00
86 J.Beckett Pinstripe Bat-Jsy 10.00 25.00
87 C.Schilling Phils Bat-Jsy 10.00 25.00
88 Mike Mussina O's Bat-Jsy 15.00 40.00
89 P.Martinez Dgr Bat-Jsy 15.00 40.00
90 Barry Zito A Bat-Jsy 10.00 25.00
91 Jim Edmonds Bat-Jsy 10.00 25.00
92 R.Henderson Sox Bat-Jsy 15.00 40.00
93 R.Hend Padres Bat-Jsy 15.00 40.00
94 R.Henderson M's Bat-Jsy 15.00 40.00
95 R.Hend Mets Bat-Jsy 15.00 40.00
96 R.Hend Jays Bat-Jsy 15.00 40.00
97 R.John M's Arm Up Bat-Jsy 15.00 40.00
98 Mark Grace Bat-Jsy 15.00 40.00
99 P.Martinez Expos Bat-Jsy 15.00 40.00
101 I.Rodriguez Rgr Bat-Jsy 15.00 40.00
102 Jeff Kent Giants Bat-Jsy 10.00 25.00
103 Hideo Nomo Sox Bat-Jsy 20.00 50.00
104 Hideo Nomo Mets Bat-Jsy 20.00 50.00
105 M.Piazza Dodgers Bat-Jsy 20.00 50.00
106 T.Glav Braves H Bat-Jsy 15.00 40.00
107 R.Alom Ind Swing Bat-Jsy 15.00 40.00
108 R.Clemens Sox Bat-Jsy 20.00 50.00
109 J.Giambi A's H Bat-Jsy 10.00 25.00
110 J.Thome Indians A Bat-Jsy 15.00 40.00
111 A.Rod M's H Bat-Jsy 20.00 50.00
112 J.Gonz Ind Hands Bat-Jsy 10.00 25.00
113 T.Hunter Crouch Bat-Jsy 10.00 25.00
114 Roy Oswalt H Bat-Jsy 10.00 25.00
115 C.Schill D'b Throw Bat-Jsy 10.00 25.00
116 M.Ordonez H Bat-Jsy 10.00 25.00
117 R.Palmeiro Rgr H Bat-Jsy 15.00 40.00
118 Andruw Jones A Bat-Jsy 15.00 40.00
119 Manny Ramirez A Bat-Jsy 15.00 40.00
120 Mark Teixeira H Bat-Jsy 15.00 40.00
121 M.Mulder Stance Bat-Jsy 10.00 25.00
123 Tim Hudson A Bat-Jsy 10.00 25.00
124 Todd Helton A Bat-Jsy 15.00 40.00
125 T.Glaus Pinstripe Bat-Jsy 10.00 25.00
128 Greg Maddux A Bat-Jsy 20.00 50.00
129 R.Clemens Yanks A Bat-Jsy 20.00 50.00
130 N.Garciaparra A Bat-Jsy 20.00 50.00
131 M.Piazza Mets A Bat-Jsy 20.00 50.00
132 A.Rod Rgr H Bat-Jsy 20.00 50.00
134 R.John D'backs H Bat-Jsy 15.00 40.00
135 Sammy Sosa A Bat-Jsy 15.00 40.00
137 A.Soriano H Bat-Jsy 10.00 25.00
138 J.Giambi Yanks A Bat-Jsy 10.00 25.00
139 Albert Pujols A Bat-Jsy 25.00 60.00
140 Chipper Jones A Bat-Jsy 15.00 40.00
141 Adam Dunn H Bat-Jsy 10.00 25.00
142 P.Martinez Sox A Bat-Jsy 15.00 40.00
143 V.Guerrero A Bat-Jsy 15.00 40.00
144 Mark Prior A Bat-Jsy 15.00 40.00
145 Barry Zito H Bat-Jsy 10.00 25.00
146 Jeff Bagwell A Bat-Jsy 15.00 40.00
147 L.Berkman Socks Bat-Jsy 10.00 25.00
148 S.Green Dgr A Bat-Jsy 10.00 25.00
149 J.Giambi A's A Bat-Jsy 10.00 25.00
150 R.John M's Arm Out Bat-Jsy 15.00 40.00
151 A.Rod M's A Bat-Jsy 20.00 50.00
152 Babe Ruth Bat-Jsy/5
153 Ty Cobb Bat-Pants/10
155 Lou Gehrig Bat-Jsy/5
156 Thurman Munson Bat-Jsy 30.00 80.00
157 Roberto Clemente Bat-Jsy/5
158 Nolan Ryan Rgr Bat-Jsy 40.00 100.00
159 N.Ryan Angels Bat-Jsy 40.00 100.00
160 N.Ryan Astros Bat-Jsy 40.00 100.00
161 Cal Ripken Bat-Jsy 50.00 120.00
162 Don Mattingly Bat-Jsy 30.00 80.00
163 Stan Musial Bat-Jsy 40.00 100.00
164 Tony Gwynn Bat-Jsy 20.00 50.00
165 Yogi Berra Bat-Jsy 25.00 60.00
166 Johnny Bench Bat-Jsy 25.00 60.00
167 Mike Schmidt Bat-Jsy 30.00 80.00
168 George Brett Bat-Jsy 30.00 80.00
169 Ryne Sandberg Bat-Jsy 40.00 100.00
170 Ernie Banks Bat-Jsy/1

2003 Leaf Limited TNT Prime

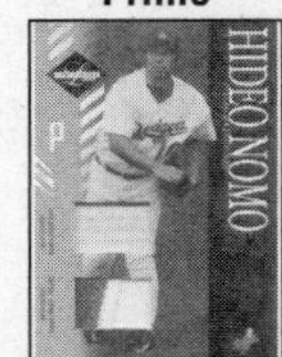

*TNT PRIME: .5X TO 1.2X BASIC TNT
RANDOM INSERTS PACKS
PRINT RUNS B/WN 1-25 COPIES PER
NO PRICING ON QTY OF 10 OR LESS

2003 Leaf Limited 7th Inning Stretch Jersey

RANDOM INSERTS IN PACKS
PRINT RUNS B/WN 40-50 COPIES PER
1 Alex Rodriguez 10.00 25.00
3 Sammy Sosa 6.00 15.00
4 Juan Gonzalez 6.00 15.00
5 Albert Pujols 15.00 40.00
6 Chipper Jones 6.00 15.00
7 Alfonso Soriano/40 6.00 15.00
8 Jim Thome 6.00 15.00
9 Mike Piazza 10.00 25.00
10 Rafael Palmeiro 6.00 15.00

2003 Leaf Limited Jersey Numbers

1-54 PRINT RUNS B/WN 5-100 COPIES PER
55-100 PRINT RUNS B/WN 5-25 COPIES PER
NO PRICING ON QTY OF 10 OR LESS
RANDOM INSERTS IN PACKS
1 Rod Carew Angels/50 10.00 25.00
2 Nolan Ryan Angels/50 25.00 60.00
3 Reggie Jackson Angels/50 10.00 25.00
4 Brooks Robinson/50 10.00 25.00
5 Frank Robinson/25 10.00 25.00
6 Cal Ripken/100 25.00 60.00
7 Carlton Fisk W.Sox/50 10.00 25.00
8 Roger Clemens/100 8.00 20.00
9 Carlton Fisk R.Sox/5
10 Lou Boudreau/50 6.00 15.00
11 Bob Feller/25 10.00 25.00
12 Al Kaline/10
13 Alan Trammell/50 6.00 15.00
14 Harmon Killebrew/50 15.00 40.00
15 Rod Carew Twins/50 10.00 25.00
16 Kirby Puckett/50 15.00 40.00
17 Babe Ruth/5
18 Lou Gehrig/5
19 Yogi Berra/50 15.00 40.00
20 Thurman Munson/50 15.00 40.00
21 Don Mattingly/100 15.00 40.00
22 Roger Maris Pants/10
23 Rickey Henderson/5
24 Reggie Jackson A's/5
25 Alex Rodriguez/100 8.00 20.00
26 Randy Johnson M's/50 6.00 15.00
27 Nolan Ryan Rgr/100 20.00 50.00
28 Dale Murphy/50 10.00 25.00
29 Warren Spahn/50 15.00 40.00
30 Eddie Mathews/50 15.00 40.00
31 Ernie Banks/5
32 Ryne Sandberg/100 15.00 40.00
33 Johnny Bench/50 15.00 40.00
34 Joe Morgan/50 6.00 15.00
35 Randy Johnson Astros/50 6.00 15.00
36 Nolan Ryan Astros/100 20.00 50.00
37 Pee Wee Reese/50 10.00 25.00
38 Duke Snider/50 10.00 25.00
39 Jackie Robinson/25 40.00 100.00
40 Robin Yount/50 15.00 40.00
41 Paul Molitor/50 6.00 15.00
42 Pedro Martinez/50 6.00 15.00
43 Randy Johnson Expos/50 6.00 15.00
44 Tom Seaver/25 15.00 40.00
45 Gary Carter/50 6.00 15.00
46 Mike Schmidt/50 20.00 50.00
47 Steve Carlton/50 6.00 15.00
48 Willie Stargell/50 10.00 25.00
49 Roberto Clemente/5
50 Ozzie Smith/50 20.00 50.00
51 Stan Musial/100 15.00 40.00
52 Enos Slaughter/50 15.00 40.00
53 Orlando Cepeda/50 6.00 15.00
54 Willie McCovey/50 6.00 15.00
55 Brooks Robinson
Frank Robinson/10
56 Lou Boudreau
Bob Feller/14
57 Harmon Killebrew 40.00 100.00
Rod Carew/25
58 Harmon Killebrew 40.00 100.00
Kirby Puckett/25
59 Babe Ruth
Lou Gehrig/5
60 Babe Ruth
Yogi Berra/5
61 Babe Ruth
Thurman Munson/5
62 Babe Ruth
Don Mattingly/5
63 Babe Ruth
Roger Maris Pants/5
64 Lou Gehrig
Yogi Berra/5
65 Lou Gehrig
Thurman Munson/5
66 Lou Gehrig
Don Mattingly/5
67 Lou Gehrig
Roger Maris Pants/5
68 Yogi Berra 30.00 80.00
Thurman Munson/25
69 Yogi Berra 40.00 100.00
Don Mattingly/25
70 Yogi Berra
Roger Maris/5
71 Dale Murphy 30.00 80.00
Warren Spahn/25
72 Dale Murphy 30.00 80.00
Eddie Mathews/25
73 Warren Spahn 30.00 80.00
Eddie Mathews/25
74 Johnny Bench 25.00 60.00
Joe Morgan/25
75 Pee Wee Reese 25.00 60.00
Duke Snider/25
76 Pee Wee Reese
Jackie Robinson/10
77 Duke Snider
Jackie Robinson/10
78 Robin Yount 30.00 80.00
Paul Molitor/25
79 Mike Schmidt
Steve Carlton/25
80 Willie Stargell
Roberto Clemente/5
81 Ozzie Smith 40.00 100.00
Stan Musial/25
82 Stan Musial 40.00 100.00
Enos Slaughter/25
83 Orlando Cepeda 25.00 60.00
Willie McCovey/25
84 Nolan Ryan 40.00 100.00
Reggie Jackson/25
85 Brooks Robinson
Cal Ripken/25
86 Frank Robinson
Cal Ripken/10
87 Carlton Fisk
Roger Clemens/5
88 Al Kaline
Alan Trammell/10
89 Rickey Henderson
Reggie Jackson/5
90 Alex Rodriguez 20.00 50.00
Randy Johnson/25
91 Pedro Martinez 20.00 50.00
Randy Johnson/25
92 Tom Seaver
Gary Carter/10
93 Ernie Banks
Ryne Sandberg/10
94 Reggie Jackson A's 25.00 60.00
Reggie Jackson Angels/25
95 Nolan Ryan Angels 40.00 100.00
Nolan Ryan Rgr/25
96 Nolan Ryan Rgr 40.00 100.00
Nolan Ryan Astros/25
97 Nolan Ryan Astros 40.00 100.00
Nolan Ryan Angels/25
98 Nolan Ryan 40.00 100.00
Randy Johnson/25
99 Cal Ripken 60.00 120.00
Rafael Palmeiro/25
100 Dale Murphy 30.00 80.00
Deion Sanders/25

2003 Leaf Limited Jersey Numbers Retired

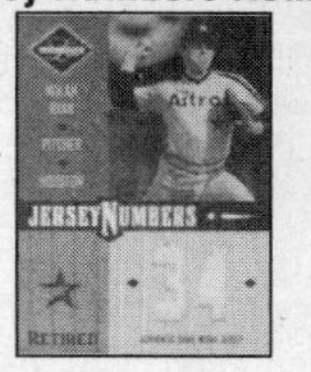

RANDOM INSERTS IN PACKS
PRINT RUNS B/WN 1-72 COPIES PER
NO PRICING ON QTY OF 19 OR LESS
1 Rod Carew Angels/29 15.00 40.00
2 Nolan Ryan Angels/30 30.00 80.00
4 Brooks Robinson/5
5 Frank Robinson/20 12.50 30.00
7 Carlton Fisk R.Sox/27 15.00 40.00
9 Carlton Fisk W.Sox/72 10.00 25.00
10 Lou Boudreau/5
11 Bob Feller/19
12 Al Kaline/6
14 Harmon Killebrew/3
15 Rod Carew Twins/29 15.00 40.00
16 Kirby Puckett/34 20.00 50.00
17 Babe Ruth/3
18 Lou Gehrig/4
19 Yogi Berra/8
20 Thurman Munson/15
21 Don Mattingly/23 25.00 60.00
22 R.Maris Pants/9
27 Nolan Ryan Rgr/34 30.00 80.00
28 Dale Murphy/3
29 Warren Spahn/21 25.00 60.00
30 Eddie Mathews/41 10.00 25.00
31 Ernie Banks/14
33 Johnny Bench/5
34 Joe Morgan/8
36 Nolan Ryan Astros/34 30.00 80.00
37 Pee Wee Reese/1
38 Duke Snider/4
39 Jackie Robinson/42 30.00 80.00
40 Robin Yount/19
41 Paul Molitor/4
44 Tom Seaver/41 10.00 25.00
46 Mike Schmidt/20 25.00 60.00
47 Steve Carlton/32 10.00 25.00
48 Willie Stargell/8
49 Roberto Clemente/21 60.00 120.00
50 Ozzie Smith/1
51 Stan Musial/6
52 Enos Slaughter/9
53 Orlando Cepeda/30 10.00 25.00
54 Willie McCovey/44 6.00 15.00

2003 Leaf Limited Leather

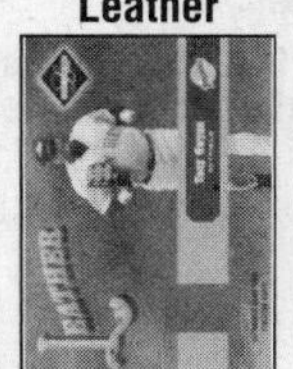

RANDOM INSERTS IN PACKS
PRINT RUNS B/WN 10-25 COPIES PER
NO PRICNG ON QTY OF 10 OR LESS
1 Alex Rodriguez/25 25.00 60.00
2 Chipper Jones/25 15.00 40.00
3 Jimmie Foxx/25 50.00 100.00
4 Kirby Puckett/25 15.00 40.00
5 Mike Schmidt/25 40.00 100.00
6 Roger Clemens/25 25.00 60.00
7 Steve Carlton/25 15.00 40.00
8 Tony Gywnn/25 25.00 60.00
9 Nolan Ryan/10
10 Vladimir Guerrero/25 15.00 40.00
11 Adam Dunn/25 15.00 40.00
12 Andruw Jones/25 15.00 40.00
13 Curt Schilling/25 15.00 40.00
14 Randy Johnson/25 15.00 40.00
15 Mark Prior/25 15.00 40.00

2003 Leaf Limited Leather Gold

RANDOM INSERTS IN PACKS
STATED PRINT RUN 10 SERIAL #'d SETS
RYAN PRINT RUN 5 SERIAL #'d CARDS
NO PRICING DUE TO SCARCITY

2003 Leaf Limited Leather and Lace

RANDOM INSERTS IN PACKS
STATED PRINT RUN 10 SERIAL #'d SETS
N.RYAN PRINT RUN 5 SERIAL #'d CARDS
NO PRICING DUE TO SCARCITY

2003 Leaf Limited Leather and Lace Gold

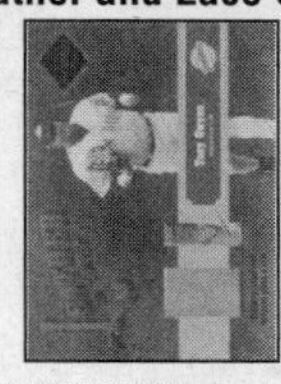

RANDOM INSERTS IN PACKS
STATED PRINT RUN 5 SERIAL #'d SETS
NO PRICING DUE TO SCARCITY

2003 Leaf Limited Lineups Bat

RANDOM INSERTS IN PACKS
PRINT RUNS B/WN 25-50 COPIES PER
ALL ARE DUAL BAT CARDS UNLESS NOTED
CARD NUMBER 3 DOES NOT EXIST
1 Paul Molitor 15.00 40.00
Robin Yount/50
2 Don Mattingly 20.00 50.00
Bernie Williams/50
4 Hideki Matsui Ball 30.00 80.00
Derek Jeter Ball/25
5 Ryne Sandberg 20.00 50.00
Andre Dawson/50
6 George Brett 30.00 80.00
Bo Jackson/50
7 Reggie Jackson 15.00 40.00
Jose Canseco/50
8 Mark Grace 20.00 50.00
Ryne Sandberg/50
9 Rickey Henderson 15.00 40.00
Jose Canseco/50
10 Mike Piazza 15.00 40.00
Hideo Nomo/50

2003 Leaf Limited Lineups Button

RANDOM INSERTS IN PACKS
STATED PRINT RUN 1 SERIAL #'d SET
NO PRICING DUE TO SCARCITY
2 Don Mattingly
Bernie Williams
3 Sammy Sosa
Hee Seop Choi
6 George Brett
Bo Jackson
10 Mike Piazza
Hideo Nomo

2003 Leaf Limited Lineups Jersey

RANDOM INSERTS IN PACKS
PRINT RUNS B/WN 25
NO PRICING ON QTY OF 5 OR LESS
ALL ARE DUAL JSY CARDS UNLESS NOTED
1 Paul Molitor 15.00 40.00
Robin Yount/50
2 Don Mattingly 20.00 50.00
Bernie Williams/50
3 Sammy Sosa 15.00 40.00
Hee Seop Choi/50
4 Hideki Matsui Base 15.00 40.00
Derek Jeter Base/50
5 Ryne Sandberg 20.00 50.00
Andre Dawson/50
6 George Brett 30.00 80.00
Bo Jackson/50
7 Reggie Jackson
Jose Canseco/5
8 Mark Grace 20.00 50.00
Ryne Sandberg/50
9 Rickey Henderson
Jose Canseco/5
10 Mike Piazza 15.00 40.00
Hideo Nomo/50

2003 Leaf Limited Lineups Jersey Tag

RANDOM INSERTS IN PACKS
PRINT RUNS B/WN 4-5 COPIES PER
NO PRICING DUE TO SCARCITY
1 Paul Molitor
Robin Yount/5
2 Don Mattingly
Bernie Williams/5
3 Sammy Sosa
Hee Seop Choi/5
6 George Brett
Bo Jackson/5
7 Reggie Jackson
Jose Canseco/4
8 Mark Grace
Ryne Sandberg/5
9 Rickey Henderson
Jose Canseco/4
10 Mike Piazza
Hideo Nomo/5

2003 Leaf Limited Lumberjacks Barrel

RANDOM INSERTS IN PACKS
PRINT RUNS B/WN 1-2 COPIES PER
NO PRICING DUE TO SCARCITY
1 Babe Ruth/2
2 Lou Gehrig/1
3 Roberto Clemente/1
4 Stan Musial/1
5 Rogers Hornsby/1
6 Don Mattingly/1
7 Rickey Henderson/2
8 Cal Ripken/1
9 Yogi Berra/1
10 Reggie Jackson/1
11 George Brett/1
12 Mel Ott/1
13 Roger Maris/1
14 Ryne Sandberg/1
15 Eddie Mathews/1
16 Richie Ashburn/1
17 Mike Schmidt/1
18 Tony Gwynn/1
19 Ty Cobb/1
20 Thurman Munson/2
21 Jimmie Foxx/1
22 Duke Snider/1
23 Ernie Banks/2
24 Alex Rodriguez/1
25 Nomar Garciaparra/2
29 Mike Piazza/1
30 Alfonso Soriano/2
31 Al Kaline/1
32 Harmon Killebrew/2
33 Dale Murphy/1
34 Orlando Cepeda/1
35 Willie McCovey/1
36 Willie Stargell/1
37 Brooks Robinson/1

2003 Leaf Limited Lumberjacks Bat

1-37 PRINT RUNS B/WN 1-25 COPIES PER
38-45 PRINT RUNS B/WN 1-25 COPIES PER
NO PRICING ON QTY OF 15 OR LESS
RANDOM INSERTS IN PACKS
1 Babe Ruth/25 125.00 250.00
2 Lou Gehrig/25 75.00 150.00
3 Roberto Clemente/25 60.00 120.00
4 Stan Musial/25 25.00 60.00
5 Rogers Hornsby/25 30.00 80.00
6 Don Mattingly/25 25.00 60.00
7 Rickey Henderson/25 10.00 25.00
8 Cal Ripken/25 50.00 120.00
9 Yogi Berra/25 20.00 50.00
10 Reggie Jackson/25 15.00 40.00
11 George Brett/25 25.00 60.00
12 Mel Ott/25 25.00 60.00
13 Roger Maris/25 40.00 100.00
14 Ryne Sandberg/25 30.00 80.00
15 Eddie Mathews/15
16 Richie Ashburn/25 15.00 40.00
17 Mike Schmidt/25 25.00 60.00
18 Tony Gwynn/25 15.00 40.00
19 Ty Cobb/25 60.00 120.00
20 Thurman Munson/25 20.00 50.00
21 Jimmie Foxx/25 30.00 80.00
22 Duke Snider/25 15.00 40.00
23 Ernie Banks/1
24 Alex Rodriguez/25 15.00 40.00
25 Nomar Garciaparra/25 15.00 40.00
26 Hideki Matsui Base/25 30.00 80.00
27 Ichiro Suzuki Base/25 25.00 60.00
28 Barry Bonds Base/25 25.00 60.00
29 Mike Piazza/25 15.00 40.00
30 Alfonso Soriano/25 10.00 25.00
31 Al Kaline/25 20.00 50.00
32 Harmon Killebrew/5
33 Dale Murphy/25 15.00 40.00
34 Orlando Cepeda/5
35 Willie McCovey/25 10.00 25.00
36 Willie Stargell/5
37 Brooks Robinson/25 15.00 40.00
38 Hideki Matsui Base 60.00 120.00
Ichiro Suzuki Base/25
39 Ryne Sandberg
Ernie Banks/1
40 Don Mattingly 100.00 200.00
Lou Gehrig/25
41 Yogi Berra 30.00 80.00
Thurman Munson/25
42 Mike Schmidt 40.00 100.00
Richie Ashburn/25
43 Stan Musial 50.00 100.00
Rogers Hornsby/25
44 Don Mattingly 60.00 120.00
Roger Maris/25
45 Babe Ruth
Lou Gehrig/15

2003 Leaf Limited Lumberjacks Bat Black

RANDOM INSERTS IN PACKS
PRINT RUNS B/WN 1-5 COPIES PER
NO PRICING DUE TO SCARCITY

2003 Leaf Limited Lumberjacks Bat Silver

RANDOM INSERTS IN PACKS
PRINT RUNS B/WN 1-10 COPIES PER
NO PRICING DUE TO SCARCITY

2003 Leaf Limited Lumberjacks Bat-Jersey

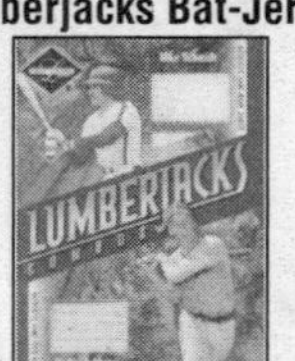

1-37 PRINT RUNS B/WN 1-25 COPIES PER
38-45 PRINT RUNS B/WN 1-25 COPIES PER
NO PRICING ON QTY OF 15 OR LESS
RANDOM INSERTS IN PACKS
ALL ARE BAT-JSY COMBOS UNLESS NOTED
1 Babe Ruth/5
2 Lou Gehrig/10
3 Roberto Clemente/10
4 Stan Musial/25 40.00 100.00
6 Don Mattingly/25 40.00 100.00
7 Rickey Henderson/5
8 Cal Ripken/25 60.00 150.00
9 Yogi Berra/25 25.00 60.00
10 Reggie Jackson/5
11 George Brett/25 40.00 100.00
12 Mel Ott/15
13 Roger Maris Bat-Pants/25 60.00 120.00
14 Ryne Sandberg/25 50.00 120.00
15 Eddie Mathews/25 25.00 60.00
17 Mike Schmidt/25 40.00 100.00
18 Tony Gwynn/25 25.00 60.00
19 Ty Cobb Bat-Pants/15
20 Thurman Munson/25 30.00 80.00
22 Duke Snider/15
23 Ernie Banks/1
24 Alex Rodriguez/25 25.00 60.00
25 Nomar Garciaparra/25 25.00 60.00
26 Hideki Matsui Base-Ball/25 50.00 100.00
27 Ichiro Suzuki Base-Ball/25 30.00 80.00
28 Barry Bonds Base-Ball/25 30.00 80.00
29 Mike Piazza/25 25.00 60.00
30 Alfonso Soriano/25 15.00 40.00
31 Al Kaline/10
32 Harmon Killebrew/10
33 Dale Murphy/25 20.00 50.00
34 Orlando Cepeda/5
35 Willie McCovey/25 12.50 30.00
36 Willie Stargell/25 20.00 50.00
37 Brooks Robinson/25 20.00 50.00
38A Hideki Matsui Base 60.00 120.00
Ichiro Suzuki Ball/25
38B Hideki Matsui Ball 60.00 120.00
Ichiro Suzuki Base/25
39A Ryne Sandberg Bat
Ernie Banks Jsy/5
39B Ryne Sandberg Jsy
Ernie Banks Bat/1
40A Don Mattingly Jsy
Lou Gehrig Bat/10
40B Don Mattingly Bat
Lou Gehrig Jsy/5
41A Yogi Berra Jsy 30.00 80.00
Thurman Munson Bat/25
41B Yogi Berra Bat 30.00 80.00
Thurman Munson Jsy/25
42 Mike Schmidt Jsy 40.00 100.00
Richie Ashburn Bat/25
43 Stan Musial Jsy 50.00 100.00
Rogers Hornsby Bat/25
44 Don Mattingly Bat
Roger Maris Pants/5
45A Babe Ruth Jsy
Lou Gehrig Bat/5
45B Babe Ruth Bat
Lou Gehrig Jsy/5

2003 Leaf Limited Lumberjacks Bat-Jersey Black

RANDOM INSERTS IN PACKS
PRINT RUNS B/WN 1-5 COPIES PER
NO PRICING DUE TO SCARCITY

2003 Leaf Limited Lumberjacks Bat-Jersey Silver

RANDOM INSERTS IN PACKS
PRINT RUNS B/WN 1-10 COPIES PER
NO PRICING DUE TO SCARCITY

2003 Leaf Limited Lumberjacks Jersey

1-37 PRINT RUNS B/WN 1-25 COPIES PER
38-45 PRINT RUNS B/WN 1-25 COPIES PER
NO PRICING ON QTY OF 15 OR LESS
RANDOM INSERTS IN PACKS
1 Babe Ruth/5
2 Lou Gehrig/10
3 Roberto Clemente/10
4 Stan Musial/25 25.00 60.00
6 Don Mattingly/25 25.00 60.00
7 Rickey Henderson/10
8 Cal Ripken/25 50.00 120.00
9 Yogi Berra/25 15.00 40.00
10 Reggie Jackson/10
11 George Brett/25 25.00 60.00
12 Mel Ott/25 25.00 60.00
13 Roger Maris Pants/10
14 Ryne Sandberg/25 30.00 80.00
15 Eddie Mathews/25 15.00 40.00
17 Mike Schmidt/25 25.00 60.00
18 Tony Gwynn/25 15.00 40.00
19 Ty Cobb Pants/5
20 Thurman Munson/25 20.00 50.00
22 Duke Snider/25 12.50 30.00
23 Ernie Banks/5
24 Alex Rodriguez/25 15.00 40.00
25 Nomar Garciaparra/25 15.00 40.00
26 Hideki Matsui Ball/25 30.00 80.00
27 Ichiro Suzuki Ball/25 25.00 60.00
28 Barry Bonds Ball/25 25.00 60.00
29 Mike Piazza/25 15.00 40.00
30 Alfonso Soriano/25 10.00 25.00
31 Al Kaline/10
32 Harmon Killebrew/25 15.00 40.00
33 Dale Murphy/25 12.50 30.00
34 Orlando Cepeda/25 8.00 20.00
35 Willie McCovey/25 8.00 20.00
36 Willie Stargell/25 12.50 30.00
37 Brooks Robinson/25 12.50 30.00
38 Hideki Matsui Ball 60.00 120.00
Ichiro Suzuki Ball/25
39 Ryne Sandberg
Ernie Banks/5
40 Don Mattingly
Lou Gehrig/15
41 Yogi Berra 30.00 80.00
Thurman Munson/25
44 Don Mattingly
Roger Maris Pants/5
45 Babe Ruth
Lou Gehrig/5

2003 Leaf Limited Lumberjacks Jersey Black

RANDOM INSERTS IN PACKS
PRINT RUNS B/WN 1-5 COPIES PER
NO PRICING DUE TO SCARCITY

2003 Leaf Limited Lumberjacks Jersey Silver

RANDOM INSERTS IN PACKS
PRINT RUNS B/WN 3-10 COPIES PER
NO PRICING DUE TO SCARCITY

2003 Leaf Limited Player Threads

RANDOM INSERTS IN PACKS
PRINT RUNS B/WN 5-50 COPIES PER
NO PRICING ON QTY OF 5 OR LESS
1 Roger Clemens/50 10.00 25.00
2 Alex Rodriguez/50 10.00 25.00
3 Pedro Martinez/50 6.00 15.00
4 Randy Johnson/50 6.00 15.00
5 Curt Schilling/50 4.00 10.00
6 Reggie Jackson/5
7 Nolan Ryan/50 25.00 60.00
8 Hideo Nomo/50 15.00 40.00
9 Mike Piazza/50 10.00 25.00
10 Rickey Henderson Padres/5
11 Rickey Henderson Mets/50 6.00 15.00
12 Ivan Rodriguez/50 6.00 15.00
13 Gary Sheffield/50 4.00 10.00
14 Jeff Kent/50 4.00 10.00
15 Roberto Alomar/50 6.00 15.00
16 Rafael Palmeiro/50 6.00 15.00
17 Juan Gonzalez/50 4.00 10.00
18 Shawn Green/50 4.00 10.00
19 Jason Giambi/50 4.00 10.00
20 Jim Thome/50 6.00 15.00
21 Scott Rolen/50 6.00 15.00
22 Mike Mussina/50 6.00 15.00
23 Tom Glavine/50 6.00 15.00
24 Sammy Sosa/50 6.00 15.00

2003 Leaf Limited Player Threads Prime

RANDOM INSERTS IN PACKS
PRINT RUNS B/WN 5-10 COPIES PER
NO PRICING DUE TO SCARCITY

2003 Leaf Limited Player Threads Double

RANDOM INSERTS IN PACKS
STATED PRINT RUN 50 SERIAL #'d SETS
CARD 6/10 PRINT RUN 5 SERIAL #'d SETS
1 R.Clemens Yanks-Sox 15.00 40.00
2 Alex Rodriguez Rgr-M's 15.00 40.00
3 P.Martinez Sox-Dodgers 10.00 25.00
4 Randy Johnson D'backs-Astros 10.00 25.00
5 C.Schilling D'backs-Phils 6.00 15.00
6 R.Jackson A's-Angels/5
7 Nolan Ryan Rgr-Astros 30.00 80.00
8 H.Nomo Dodgers-Sox 25.00 60.00
9 M.Piazza Mets-Dodgers 15.00 40.00
10 R.Henderson Padres-Sox/5
11 R.Henderson Mets-M's 10.00 25.00
12 I.Rodriguez Marlins-Rgr 10.00 25.00
13 G.Sheffield Braves-Dodgers 6.00 15.00
14 Jeff Kent Astros-Giants 6.00 15.00
15 R.Alomar Mets-Indians 10.00 25.00
16 Rafael Palmeiro Rgr-O's 10.00 25.00
17 J.Gonzalez Rgr-Indians 6.00 15.00
18 S.Green Dodgers-Jays 6.00 15.00
19 Jason Giambi Yanks-A's 6.00 15.00
20 Jim Thome Phils-Indians 10.00 25.00
21 Scott Rolen Cards-Phils 10.00 25.00
22 Mike Mussina Yanks-O's 10.00 25.00
23 Tom Glavine Mets-Braves 10.00 25.00
24 Sammy Sosa Cubs-Sox 10.00 25.00

2003 Leaf Limited Player Threads Double Prime

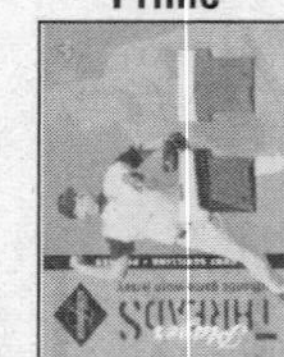

RANDOM INSERTS IN PACKS
PRINT RUNS B/WN 5-10 COPIES PER
NO PRICING DUE TO SCARCITY

2003 Leaf Limited Player Threads Triple

RANDOM INSERTS IN PACKS
STATED PRINT RUN 50 SERIAL #'d SETS
HENDERSON PADRES-SOX-A'S 5 #'d CARDS
NO HENDERSON PADRES-SOX-A'S PRICING
4 R.John D'backs-Astros-M's 15.00 40.00
7 N.Ryan Rgr-Astros-Angels 40.00 100.00
8 H.Nomo Dodgers-Sox-Mets 40.00 100.00
10 R.Henderson Padres-Sox-A's/5
11 R.Henderson Mets-M's-Jays 15.00 40.00
13 G.Sheffield Braves-Dgr-Brew 10.00 25.00
14 J.Kent Astros-Giants-Jays 10.00 25.00
15 R.Alomar Mets-Indians-O's 15.00 40.00

2003 Leaf Limited Player Threads Triple Prime

RANDOM INSERTS IN PACKS
PRINT RUNS B/WN 5-10 COPIES PER
NO PRICING DUE TO SCARCITY

2003 Leaf Limited Team Threads

RANDOM INSERTS IN PACKS
PRINT RUNS B/WN 10-50 COPIES PER
NO PRICING ON QTY OF 10 OR LESS
25 Jackie Robinson
Duke Snider/10
26 Alex Rodriguez 30.00 80.00
Nolan Ryan/50
27 Mike Piazza 15.00 40.00
Hideo Nomo/50
28 Cal Ripken 40.00 100.00
Mike Mussina/50
29 Hideo Nomo 15.00 40.00
Kazuhisa Ishii/50
30 Nolan Ryan 20.00 50.00
Randy Johnson/50

2003 Leaf Limited Team Threads Prime

RANDOM INSERTS IN PACKS
PRINT RUNS B/WN 5-10 COPIES PER
NO PRICING DUE TO SCARCITY

2003 Leaf Limited Team Trademarks Autographs

RANDOM INSERTS IN PACKS
PRINT RUNS B/WN 5-25 COPIES PER
NO PRICING ON QTY OF 10 OR LESS
1 Alan Trammell/25 20.00 50.00
2 Joe Morgan/5
3 Jim Palmer/25 20.00 50.00
4 Bob Feller/5
5 Gary Carter/25 20.00 50.00
6 Andre Dawson/25 20.00 50.00
7 Duke Snider/5
8 Dale Murphy/25 30.00 60.00
9 Bo Jackson/5
10 Bobby Doerr/25 15.00 40.00
11 Brooks Robinson/25 30.00 60.00
12 Eric Davis/25 20.00 50.00
13 Fred Lynn/25 15.00 40.00
14 Harmon Killebrew/10
15 Jack Morris/25 15.00 40.00
16 Al Kaline/25 40.00 80.00
17 Deion Sanders/25 60.00 120.00
18 Luis Aparicio/25 15.00 40.00
19 Orlando Cepeda/5
20 Phil Rizzuto/25 30.00 60.00
21 Reggie Jackson/5
22 Robin Yount/5
23 Rod Carew Twins/5
24 Will Clark/25 60.00 120.00
25 Willie McCovey/5
26 Tony Gwynn/5
27 Nolan Ryan Astros/5
28 Cal Ripken/5
29 Stan Musial/5
30 Mike Schmidt/5
31 Rod Carew Angels/5
32 Nolan Ryan Rgr/5
33 George Brett/5
34 Nolan Ryan Angels/5
35 Alex Rodriguez/5
36 Roger Clemens/5
37 Greg Maddux/5
38 Albert Pujols/5
39 Alfonso Soriano/5
40 Mark Grace/5

2003 Leaf Limited Team Trademarks Autographs Jersey

RANDOM INSERTS IN PACKS
PRINT RUNS B/WN 1-47 COPIES PER
NO PRICING ON QTY OF 24 OR LESS
1 Alan Trammell/3
2 Joe Morgan/8
3 Jim Palmer/22
4 Bob Feller/19
5 Gary Carter/8
6 Andre Dawson/8
7 Duke Snider/4
8 Dale Murphy/3
9 Bo Jackson/16
10 Bobby Doerr/1
11 Brooks Robinson/5
12 Eric Davis/44 20.00 50.00
13 Fred Lynn/19
14 Harmon Killebrew/3
15 Jack Morris/47 15.00 40.00
16 Al Kaline/6
17 Deion Sanders/24
18 Luis Aparicio/11
19 Orlando Cepeda/30 20.00 50.00
20 Phil Rizzuto/10
21 Reggie Jackson/9
22 Robin Yount/19
23 Rod Carew Twins/29 40.00 80.00
24 Will Clark/22
25 Willie McCovey/44 30.00 60.00
26 Tony Gwynn/19
27 Nolan Ryan Astros/34 75.00 150.00
28 Cal Ripken/8
29 Stan Musial/6
30 Mike Schmidt/20
31 Rod Carew Angels/29 40.00 80.00
32 Nolan Ryan Rgr/34 75.00 150.00
33 George Brett/5
34 Nolan Ryan Angels/30 75.00 150.00
35 Alex Rodriguez/3
36 Roger Clemens/22
37 Greg Maddux/31 100.00 200.00
38 Albert Pujols/5
39 Alfonso Soriano/12
40 Mark Grace/17

2003 Leaf Limited Team Trademarks Threads Number

RANDOM INSERTS IN PACKS
PRINT RUNS B/WN 1-47 COPIES PER
NO PRICING ON QTY OF 19 OR LESS
1 Alan Trammell/3
2 Joe Morgan/8
3 Jim Palmer/22 12.50 30.00
4 Bob Feller/19
5 Gary Carter/8
6 Andre Dawson/8
7 Duke Snider/4
8 Dale Murphy/3
9 Bo Jackson/16
10 Bobby Doerr/1
11 Brooks Robinson/5
12 Eric Davis/44 6.00 15.00
13 Fred Lynn/19
14 Harmon Killebrew/3
15 Jack Morris/47 6.00 15.00
16 Al Kaline/6
17 Deion Sanders/24 20.00 50.00
18 Luis Aparicio/11
19 Orlando Cepeda/30 10.00 25.00
20 Phil Rizzuto/10
21 Reggie Jackson/9
22 Robin Yount/19
23 Rod Carew Twins/29 15.00 40.00
24 Will Clark/22 40.00 100.00
25 Willie McCovey/44 6.00 15.00
26 Tony Gwynn/19
27 Nolan Ryan Astros/34 30.00 80.00
28 Cal Ripken/8
29 Stan Musial/6
30 Mike Schmidt/20 25.00 60.00
31 Rod Carew Angels/29 15.00 40.00
32 Nolan Ryan Rgr/34 30.00 80.00
33 George Brett/5
34 Nolan Ryan Angels/30 30.00 80.00
35 Alex Rodriguez/3
36 Roger Clemens/22 25.00 60.00
37 Greg Maddux/31 15.00 40.00
38 Albert Pujols/5
39 Alfonso Soriano/12
40 Mark Grace/17

2003 Leaf Limited Team Trademarks Threads Prime

RANDOM INSERTS IN PACKS
PRINT RUNS B/WN 5-25 COPIES PER
NO PRICING ON QTY OF 10 OR LESS
1 Alan Trammell/25 15.00 40.00
2 Joe Morgan/25 15.00 40.00
3 Jim Palmer/25 15.00 40.00

4 Bob Feller/10
5 Gary Carter/25 15.00 40.00
6 Andre Dawson/25 15.00 40.00
7 Duke Snider/25 25.00 60.00
8 Dale Murphy/25 25.00 60.00
9 Bo Jackson/25 25.00 60.00
10 Bobby Doerr/20 20.00 50.00
11 Brooks Robinson/25 25.00 60.00
12 Eric Davis/25 15.00 40.00
13 Fred Lynn/25 10.00 25.00
14 Harmon Killebrew/25 30.00 80.00
15 Jack Morris/25 10.00 25.00
16 Al Kaline/5
17 Deion Sanders/25 25.00 60.00
18 Luis Aparicio/25 15.00 40.00
19 Orlando Cepeda/25 15.00 40.00
20 Phil Rizzuto/10
21 Reggie Jackson/5
22 Robin Yount/25 25.00 60.00
23 Rod Carew Twins/25 25.00 60.00
24 Will Clark/25 50.00 100.00
25 Willie McCovey/25 15.00 40.00
26 Tony Gwynn/25 25.00 60.00
27 Nolan Ryan Astros/25 50.00 100.00
28 Cal Ripken/25 60.00 120.00
29 Stan Musial/25 60.00 120.00
30 Mike Schmidt/25 40.00 100.00
31 Rod Carew Angels/25 25.00 60.00
32 Nolan Ryan Rgr/25 50.00 100.00
33 George Brett/25 40.00 100.00
34 Nolan Ryan Angels/25 50.00 100.00
35 Alex Rodriguez/25 25.00 60.00
36 Roger Clemens/20 30.00 80.00
37 Greg Maddux/25 25.00 60.00
38 Albert Pujols/25 40.00 100.00
39 Alfonso Soriano/25 15.00 40.00
40 Mark Grace/25 25.00 60.00

2004 Leaf Limited

This 275-card set was relased in October, 2004. The set was issued in four-card packs with an $70 SRP which came four packs to a box and 10 boxes to a case. The first 200 cards in this set and cards numbered 230 through 250 comprise the basic set. Cards numbered 201 through 229 feature retired greats that were issued to a stated print run of 499 serial numbered sets and cards numbered 251 through 275 are autographed rookie cards which were issued to a stated print run of 99 serial numbered sets.

COMMON CARD (1-200/230-250) 1.25 3.00
COMMON CARD (201-229) 1.50 4.00
201-229 PRINT RUN 499 SERIAL #'d SETS
COMMON AUTO (251-275) 6.00 15.00
251-275: OVERALL AU-GU ONE PER PACK
251-275 AUTO PRINT RUN 99 #'d SETS
1 Adam Dunn A 1.25 3.00
2 Adrian Beltre 1.25 3.00
3 Albert Pujols H 3.00 8.00
4 Alex Rodriguez Yanks 2.50 6.00
5 Alfonso Soriano Rgr 1.25 3.00
6 Andruw Jones 1.25 3.00
7 Andy Pettitte Astros 1.25 3.00
8 Angel Berroa 1.25 3.00
9 Aramis Ramirez 1.25 3.00
10 Aubrey Huff 1.25 3.00
11 Austin Kearns 1.25 3.00
12 Barry Larkin 1.25 3.00
13 Barry Zito H 1.25 3.00
14 Bartolo Colon 1.25 3.00
15 Ben Sheets 1.25 3.00
16 Bernie Williams 1.25 3.00
17 Bobby Abreu 1.25 3.00
18 Brandon Webb 1.25 3.00
19 Brian Giles 1.25 3.00
20 C.C. Sabathia 1.25 3.00
21 Carlos Beltran Royals A 1.25 3.00
22 Carlos Delgado 1.25 3.00
23 Chipper Jones H 1.50 4.00
24 Craig Biggio 1.25 3.00
25 Curt Schilling Sox 1.25 3.00
26 Darin Erstad 1.25 3.00
27 Delmon Young 1.25 3.00
28 Derek Jeter 3.00 8.00
29 Derrek Lee 1.25 3.00
30 Dontrelle Willis 1.25 3.00
31 Edgar Renteria 1.25 3.00
32 Eric Chavez 1.25 3.00
33 Esteban Loaiza 1.25 3.00
34 Frank Thomas 1.50 4.00
35 Fred McGriff 1.25 3.00
36 Garret Anderson H 1.25 3.00
37 Gary Sheffield Yanks 1.25 3.00
38 Geoff Jenkins 1.25 3.00
39 Greg Maddux Cubs 2.50 6.00
40 Hank Blalock H 1.25 3.00
41 Hideki Matsui 2.50 6.00
42 Hideo Nomo Dodgers 1.50 4.00
43 Ichiro Suzuki 3.00 8.00
44 Ivan Rodriguez Tigers 1.25 3.00
45 J.D. Drew 1.25 3.00
46 Jacque Jones 1.25 3.00
47 Jae Weong Seo 1.25 3.00
48 Jake Peavy 1.25 3.00
49 Jamie Moyer 1.25 3.00
50 Jason Giambi Yanks 1.25 3.00
51 Jason Kendall 1.25 3.00
52 Jason Schmidt 1.25 3.00
53 Jason Varitek 1.50 4.00
54 Javier Vazquez 1.25 3.00
55 Javy Lopez 1.25 3.00
56 Jay Gibbons 1.25 3.00
57 Jay Payton 1.25 3.00
58 Jeff Bagwell H 1.25 3.00
59 Jeff Kent 1.25 3.00
60 Jeremy Bonderman 1.25 3.00
61 Jermaine Dye 1.25 3.00
62 Jeromy Burnitz 1.25 3.00
63 Jim Edmonds 1.25 3.00
64 Jim Thome Phils 1.25 3.00
65 Jimmy Rollins 1.25 3.00
66 Jody Gerut 1.25 3.00
67 Johan Santana 1.50 4.00
68 John Olerud 1.25 3.00
69 John Smoltz 1.25 3.00
70 Johnny Damon 1.25 3.00
71 Jorge Posada 1.25 3.00
72 Jose Contreras 1.25 3.00
73 Jose Reyes 1.25 3.00
74 Jose Vidro 1.25 3.00
75 Josh Beckett H 1.25 3.00
76 Juan Gonzalez Royals 1.25 3.00
77 Juan Pierre 1.25 3.00
78 Junior Spivey 1.25 3.00
79 Kazuhisa Ishii 1.25 3.00
80 Keith Foulke Sox 1.25 3.00
81 Ken Griffey Jr. Reds 2.50 6.00
82 Ken Harvey 1.25 3.00
83 Kenny Rogers 1.25 3.00
84 Kerry Wood 1.25 3.00
85 Kevin Brown Yanks 1.25 3.00
86 Kevin Millwood 1.25 3.00
87 Kip Wells 1.25 3.00
88 Lance Berkman 1.25 3.00
89 Larry Bigbie 1.25 3.00
90 Larry Walker 1.25 3.00
91 Laynce Nix 1.25 3.00
92 Luis Castillo 1.25 3.00
93 Luis Gonzalez 1.25 3.00
94 Luis Matos 1.25 3.00
95 Lyle Overbay 1.25 3.00
96 Magglio Ordonez H 1.25 3.00
97 Manny Ramirez Sox 1.25 3.00
98 Marcus Giles 1.25 3.00
99 Mark Buehrle 1.25 3.00
100 Mark Mulder 1.25 3.00
101 Mark Prior H 1.25 3.00
102 Mark Teixeira 1.25 3.00
103 Marlon Byrd 1.25 3.00
104 Matt Morris 1.25 3.00
105 Melvin Mora 1.25 3.00
106 Michael Young 1.25 3.00
107 Miguel Cabrera Batting 1.25 3.00
108 Miguel Tejada O's 1.25 3.00
109 Mike Lowell 1.25 3.00
110 Mike Mussina Yanks 1.25 3.00
111 Mike Piazza Mets 2.50 6.00
112 Mike Sweeney 1.25 3.00
113 Milton Bradley 1.25 3.00
114 Moises Alou 1.25 3.00
115 Morgan Ensberg 1.25 3.00
116 Nick Johnson 1.25 3.00
117 Nomar Garciaparra 2.50 6.00
118 Omar Vizquel 1.25 3.00
119 Orlando Cabrera 1.25 3.00
120 Pat Burrell 1.25 3.00
121 Paul Konerko 1.25 3.00
122 Paul Lo Duca 1.25 3.00
123 Pedro Martinez Sox 1.25 3.00
124 Preston Wilson H 1.25 3.00
125 Rafael Furcal 1.25 3.00
126 Rafael Palmeiro O's 1.25 3.00
127 Randy Johnson D'backs 1.50 4.00
128 Rich Harden 1.25 3.00
129 Richard Hidalgo 1.25 3.00
130 Richie Sexson 1.25 3.00
131 Rickie Weeks 1.25 3.00
132 Roberto Alomar 1.25 3.00
133 Robin Ventura 1.25 3.00
134 Rocco Baldelli 1.25 3.00
135 Roger Clemens Astros 3.00 8.00
136 Roy Halladay 1.25 3.00
137 Roy Oswalt A 1.25 3.00
138 Russ Ortiz 1.25 3.00
139 Ryan Klesko 1.25 3.00
140 Sammy Sosa H 1.50 4.00
141 Scott Podsednik 1.25 3.00
142 Scott Rolen Cards A 1.25 3.00
143 Sean Burroughs 1.25 3.00
144 Sean Casey 1.25 3.00
145 Shannon Stewart 1.25 3.00
146 Shawn Green Dodgers 1.25 3.00
147 Shigetoshi Hasegawa 1.25 3.00
148 Sidney Ponson 1.25 3.00
149 Steve Finley 1.25 3.00
150 Tim Hudson 1.25 3.00
151 Tim Salmon 1.25 3.00
152 Tino Martinez 1.25 3.00
153 Todd Helton H 1.25 3.00
154 Tom Glavine Mets 1.25 3.00
155 Torii Hunter 1.25 3.00
156 Trot Nixon 1.25 3.00
157 Troy Glaus 1.25 3.00
158 Vernon Wells H 1.25 3.00
159 Victor Martinez A 1.25 3.00
160 Vinny Castilla 1.25 3.00
161 Vladimir Guerrero Angels 1.50 4.00
162 Alex Rodriguez Rgr 2.50 6.00
163 Alfonso Soriano Yanks 1.25 3.00
164 Andy Pettitte Yanks 1.25 3.00
165 Curt Schilling D'backs 1.25 3.00
166 Gary Sheffield Braves 1.25 3.00
167 Greg Maddux Braves 2.50 6.00
168 Hideo Nomo Sox 1.50 4.00
169 Ivan Rodriguez Marlins 1.25 3.00
170 Jason Giambi A's 1.25 3.00
171 Jim Thome Indians 1.25 3.00
172 Juan Gonzalez Rgr 1.25 3.00
173 Ken Griffey Jr. M's 2.50 6.00
174 Kevin Brown Dodgers 1.25 3.00
175 Manny Ramirez Indians 1.25 3.00
176 Miguel Tejada A's 1.25 3.00
177 Mike Mussina O's 1.25 3.00
178 Mike Piazza Dodgers 2.50 6.00
179 Pedro Martinez Expos 1.25 3.00
180 Rafael Palmeiro Rgr 1.25 3.00
181 Randy Johnson Astros 1.50 4.00
182 Roger Clemens Sox 3.00 8.00
183 Scott Rolen Phils 1.25 3.00
184 Shawn Green Jays 1.25 3.00
185 Tom Glavine Braves 1.25 3.00
186 Vladimir Guerrero Expos 1.50 4.00
187 Alex Rodriguez M's 2.50 6.00
188 Mike Piazza Marlins 2.50 6.00
189 Randy Johnson M's 1.50 4.00
190 Roger Clemens Yanks 3.00 8.00
191 Albert Pujols A 3.00 8.00
192 Barry Zito A 1.25 3.00
193 Chipper Jones A 1.50 4.00
194 Garret Anderson A 1.25 3.00
195 Jeff Bagwell A 1.25 3.00
196 Josh Beckett A 1.25 3.00
197 Magglio Ordonez A 1.25 3.00
198 Mark Prior A 1.25 3.00
199 Sammy Sosa A 1.50 4.00
200 Todd Helton A 1.25 3.00
201 Andre Dawson RET 1.50 4.00
202 Babe Ruth RET 4.00 10.00
203 Bob Feller RET 2.00 5.00
204 Bob Gibson RET 2.00 5.00
205 Bobby Doerr RET 1.50 4.00
206 Cal Ripken RET 8.00 20.00
207 Dale Murphy RET 2.00 5.00
208 Don Mattingly RET 4.00 10.00
209 Gary Carter RET 1.50 4.00
210 George Brett RET 4.00 10.00
211 Jackie Robinson RET 2.00 5.00
212 Lou Brock RET 2.00 5.00
213 Lou Gehrig RET 3.00 8.00
214 Mark Grace RET 2.00 5.00
215 Maury Wills RET 1.50 4.00
216 Mike Schmidt RET 4.00 10.00
217 Nolan Ryan RET 4.00 10.00
218 Orel Hershiser RET 1.50 4.00
219 Paul Molitor RET 1.50 4.00
220 Roberto Clemente RET 5.00 12.00
221 Rod Carew RET 2.00 5.00
222 Roy Campanella RET 2.00 5.00
223 Ryne Sandberg RET 4.00 10.00
224 Stan Musial RET 3.00 8.00
225 Ted Williams RET 4.00 10.00
226 Tony Gwynn RET 3.00 8.00
227 Ty Cobb RET 2.50 6.00
228 Whitey Ford RET 2.00 5.00
229 Yogi Berra RET 2.00 5.00
230 Carlos Beltran Astros H 1.25 3.00
231 David Ortiz H 1.50 4.00
232 David Ortiz A 1.50 4.00
233 Carlos Zambrano 1.25 3.00
234 Carlos Lee 1.25 3.00
235 Travis Hafner 1.25 3.00
236 Brad Penny 1.25 3.00
237 Wade Miller 1.25 3.00
238 Edgar Martinez 1.25 3.00
239 Carl Crawford 1.25 3.00
240 Roy Oswalt H 1.25 3.00
241 Kazuo Matsui RC 2.00 5.00
242 Carlos Beltran Astros A 1.25 3.00
243 Carlos Beltran Royals H 1.25 3.00
244 Miguel Cabrera Fielding 1.25 3.00
245 Scott Rolen Cards H 1.25 3.00
246 Hank Blalock A 1.25 3.00
247 Vernon Wells A 1.25 3.00
248 Adam Dunn H 1.25 3.00
249 Preston Wilson A 1.25 3.00
250 Victor Martinez H 1.25 3.00
251 Aarom Baldiris PH AU RC 6.00 15.00
252 Akinori Otsuka PH AU RC 10.00 25.00
253 Andres Blanco PH AU RC 6.00 15.00
254 Brad Halsey PH AU RC 6.00 15.00
255 Joey Gathright PH AU RC 6.00 15.00
256 Colby Miller PH AU RC 6.00 15.00
257 Fernando Nieve PH AU RC 6.00 15.00
258 Freddy Guzman PH AU RC 6.00 15.00
259 Hector Gimenez PH AU RC 6.00 15.00
260 Jake Woods PH AU RC 6.00 15.00
261 Jason Bartlett PH AU RC 6.00 15.00
262 John Gall PH AU RC 6.00 15.00
263 Jose Capellan PH AU RC 6.00 15.00
264 Josh Labandeira PH AU RC 6.00 15.00
265 Justin Germano PH AU RC 6.00 15.00
266 Kazuhito Tadano PH AU RC 12.50 30.00
267 Lance Cormier PH AU RC 6.00 15.00
268 Merkin Valdez PH AU RC 4.00 10.00
269 Mike Gosling PH AU RC 6.00 15.00
270 Ramon Ramirez PH AU RC 6.00 15.00
271 Rusty Tucker PH AU RC 6.00 15.00
272 Shawn Hill PH AU RC 6.00 15.00
273 Shingo Takatsu PH AU RC 10.00 25.00
274 William Bergolla PH AU RC 6.00 15.00
275 Yadier Molina PH AU RC 25.00 50.00

2004 Leaf Limited Bronze Spotlight

*BRONZE 1-200/230-250: .75X TO 2X
*BRONZE 201-229: .75X TO 2X
*BRONZE RC'S 1-200/230-250: .6X TO 1.5X
RANDOM INSERTS IN PACKS
STATED PRINT RUN 100 SERIAL #'d SETS

2004 Leaf Limited Gold Spotlight

*GOLD 1-200/230-250: 2X TO 5X
*GOLD 201-229: 2X TO 5X
RANDOM INSERTS IN PACKS
STATED PRINT RUN 25 SERIAL #'d SETS
NO RC YR PRICING DUE TO SCARCITY

2004 Leaf Limited Platinum Spotlight

RANDOM INSERTS IN PACKS
STATED PRINT RUN 1 SERIAL #'d SET
NO PRICING DUE TO SCARCITY

2004 Leaf Limited Silver Spotlight

*SILVER 1-200/230-250: 1.25X TO 3X
*SILVER 201-229: 1.25X TO 3X
*SILVER RC'S 1-200/230-250: 1X TO 2.5X
RANDOM INSERTS IN PACKS
STATED PRINT RUN 50 SERIAL #'d SETS

2004 Leaf Limited Barrels

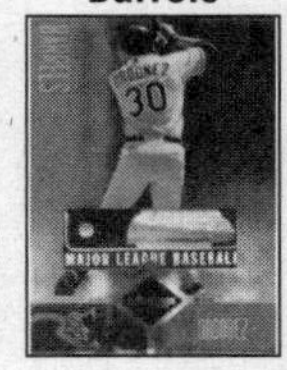

OVERALL AU-GU ODDS ONE PER PACK
PRINT RUNS B/WN 1-5 COPIES PER
NO PRICING DUE TO SCARCITY

2004 Leaf Limited Moniker Bronze

OVERALL AU-GU ODDS ONE PER PACK
PRINT RUNS B/WN 1-100 COPIES PER
NO PRICING ON QTY OF 10 OR LESS
1 Adam Dunn A/50 12.50 30.00
3 Albert Pujols H/25 150.00 250.00
5 Alfonso Soriano Rgr/100 10.00 25.00
6 Andruw Jones/50 12.50 30.00
7 Andy Pettitte Astros/10
8 Angel Berroa/25 6.00 15.00
9 Aramis Ramirez/10
10 Aubrey Huff/10
11 Austin Kearns/50 5.00 12.00
12 Barry Larkin/1
13 Barry Zito H/10
15 Ben Sheets/10
16 Bernie Williams/10
17 Bobby Abreu/9
18 Brandon Webb/21 6.00 15.00
20 C.C. Sabathia/10
21 Carlos Beltran Royals A/50 8.00 20.00
23 Chipper Jones H/25 30.00 60.00
24 Craig Biggio/25 15.00 40.00
27 Delmon Young/10
29 Derrek Lee/10
30 Dontrelle Willis/25 15.00 40.00
31 Edgar Renteria/25 10.00 25.00
32 Eric Chavez/10
33 Esteban Loaiza/10
34 Frank Thomas/50 20.00 50.00
35 Fred McGriff/10
36 Garret Anderson H/50 8.00 20.00
37 Gary Sheffield Yanks/50 12.50 30.00
39 Greg Maddux Cubs/25 50.00 100.00
40 Hank Blalock H/50 8.00 20.00
42 Hideo Nomo Dodgers/1
46 Jacque Jones/25 10.00 25.00
48 Jake Peavy/10
53 Jason Varitek/3
54 Javier Vazquez/10
56 Jay Gibbons/10
57 Jay Payton/10
58 Jeff Bagwell H/25 40.00 80.00
60 Jeremy Bonderman/10
61 Jermaine Dye/10
66 Jody Gerut/10
67 Johan Santana/10
71 Jorge Posada/25 20.00 50.00
72 Jose Contreras/10
73 Jose Reyes/10
74 Jose Vidro/10
76 Juan Gonzalez Royals/25 10.00 25.00
79 Kazuhisa Ishii/25 10.00 25.00
80 Keith Foulke Sox/10
82 Ken Harvey/10
84 Kerry Wood/25 15.00 40.00
88 Lance Berkman/50 12.50 30.00
89 Larry Bigbie/10
91 Laynce Nix/10
94 Luis Matos/10
95 Lyle Overbay/10
97 Manny Ramirez Sox/10
98 Marcus Giles/25 10.00 25.00
99 Mark Buehrle/10
100 Mark Mulder/100 6.00 15.00
101 Mark Prior H/50 10.00 25.00
102 Mark Teixeira/50 12.50 30.00
105 Melvin Mora/10
106 Michael Young/50 8.00 20.00
107 Miguel Cabrera Batting/50 12.50 30.00
109 Mike Lowell/25 10.00 25.00
110 Mike Mussina Yanks/10
111 Mike Piazza Mets/1
113 Milton Bradley/10
115 Morgan Ensberg/10
122 Paul Lo Duca/25 10.00 25.00
123 Pedro Martinez Sox/5
125 Rafael Furcal/10
127 Randy Johnson D'backs/10
128 Rich Harden/10
131 Rickie Weeks/25 10.00 25.00
132 Roberto Alomar/10
133 Robin Ventura/10
135 Roger Clemens Astros/5
136 Roy Halladay/10
137 Roy Oswalt A/50 8.00 20.00
140 Sammy Sosa H/25 50.00 100.00
141 Scott Podsednik/10
142 Scott Rolen Cards A/25 15.00 40.00
143 Sean Burroughs/10
144 Sean Casey/25 10.00 25.00
145 Shannon Stewart/25 10.00 25.00
146 Shawn Green Dodgers/10
149 Steve Finley/5
153 Todd Helton H/25 15.00 40.00
154 Tom Glavine Mets/10
155 Torii Hunter/50 8.00 20.00
156 Trot Nixon/25 10.00 25.00
158 Vernon Wells H/25 10.00 25.00
159 Victor Martinez A/10
163 Alfonso Soriano Yanks/100 10.00 25.00
164 Andy Pettitte Yanks/10
166 Gary Sheffield Braves/50 12.50 30.00
167 Greg Maddux Braves/25 50.00 100.00
168 Hideo Nomo Sox/1
172 Juan Gonzalez Rgr/25 10.00 25.00
175 Manny Ramirez Indians/10
177 Mike Mussina O's/10
178 Mike Piazza Dodgers/1
179 Pedro Martinez Expos/10
181 Randy Johnson Astros/10
182 Roger Clemens Sox/5
183 Scott Rolen Phils/25 15.00 40.00
184 Shawn Green Jays/10
185 Tom Glavine Braves/10
188 Mike Piazza Marlins/1
189 Randy Johnson M's/10
190 Roger Clemens Yanks/5
191 Albert Pujols A/25 150.00 250.00
192 Barry Zito A/10
193 Chipper Jones A/25 30.00 60.00
194 Garret Anderson A/50 8.00 20.00
195 Jeff Bagwell A/25 40.00 80.00
198 Mark Prior A/50 10.00 25.00
199 Sammy Sosa A/25 50.00 100.00
200 Todd Helton A/25 15.00 40.00
201 Andre Dawson RET/100 6.00 15.00
203 Bob Feller RET/100 10.00 25.00
204 Bob Gibson RET/100 10.00 25.00
205 Bobby Doerr RET/100 6.00 15.00
206 Cal Ripken RET/25 125.00 200.00
207 Dale Murphy RET/100 10.00 25.00
208 Don Mattingly RET/100 30.00 60.00
209 Gary Carter RET/100 6.00 15.00
210 George Brett RET/25 40.00 80.00
212 Lou Brock RET/100 10.00 25.00
214 Mark Grace RET/100 10.00 25.00
215 Maury Wills RET/100 6.00 15.00
216 Mike Schmidt RET/100 30.00 60.00
217 Nolan Ryan RET/100 50.00 100.00
218 Orel Hershiser RET/25 15.00 40.00
219 Paul Molitor RET/100 6.00 15.00
221 Rod Carew RET/100 10.00 25.00
223 Ryne Sandberg RET/100 20.00 50.00
224 Stan Musial RET/100 30.00 60.00
226 Tony Gwynn RET/100 15.00 40.00
228 Whitey Ford RET/10
229 Yogi Berra RET/10
230 Carlos Beltran Astros H/50 8.00 20.00
231 David Ortiz H/50 20.00 50.00
232 David Ortiz A/50 20.00 50.00
233 Carlos Zambrano/25 15.00 40.00
234 Carlos Lee/25 10.00 25.00
235 Travis Hafner/10
236 Brad Penny/10
237 Wade Miller/10
238 Edgar Martinez/25 20.00 50.00
239 Carl Crawford/10
240 Roy Oswalt H/50 8.00 20.00
242 Carlos Beltran Astros A/50 8.00 20.00
243 Carlos Beltran Royals H/50 8.00 20.00
244 Miguel Cabrera Fielding/50 12.50 30.00
245 Scott Rolen Cards H/25 15.00 40.00
246 Hank Blalock A/50 8.00 20.00
247 Vernon Wells A/25 10.00 25.00
248 Adam Dunn H/50 12.50 30.00
250 Victor Martinez H/10

2004 Leaf Limited Moniker Gold

*1-220/230-250 p/r 25: .6X TO 1.5X p/r 100
*1-220/230-250 p/r 25: .5X TO 1.2X p/r 50
*201-229 p/r 25: .6X TO 1.5X p/r 100
OVERALL AU-GU ODDS ONE PER PACK
PRINT RUNS B/WN 1-25 COPIES PER
NO PRICING ON QTY OF 10 OR LESS

2004 Leaf Limited Moniker Platinum

OVERALL AU-GU ODDS ONE PER PACK
STATED PRINT RUN 1 SERIAL #'d SET
NO PRICING DUE TO SCARCITY

2004 Leaf Limited Moniker Silver

*1-200/230-250 p/r 50: .5X TO 1.2X p/r 100
*1-200/230-250 p/r 25: .5X TO 1.2X p/r 50
*201-229 p/r 50: .5X TO 1.2X p/r 50
OVERALL AU-GU ODDS ONE PER PACK
PRINT RUNS B/WN 1-50 COPIES PER
NO PRICING ON QTY OF 10 OR LESS

2004 Leaf Limited Moniker Bat

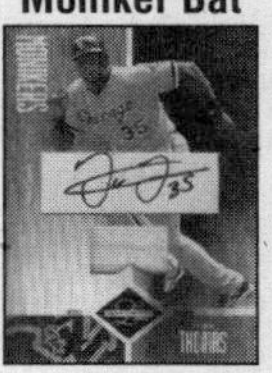

*1-200/230-250 p/r 40-50: .5X TO 1.2X Jsy/75
*1-200/230-250p/r40-50: .4X TO 1X Jsy/38-50
*1-200/230-250 p/r 40-50: .3X TO .8X Jsy/25
*1-200/230-250 p/r 25: .5X TO 1.2X Jsy/50
*1-200/230-250 p/r 25: .4X TO 1X Jsy/25
*1-200/230-250 p/r 15: .6X TO 1.5X Jsy/50
*1-200/230-250 p/r 15: .5X TO 1.2X Jsy/25
*201-229 p/r 100: .4X TO 1X Jsy/100
*201-229 p/r 50: .5X TO 1.2X Jsy/100
*201-229 p/r 50: .4X TO 1X Jsy/50
*201-229 p/r 50: .3X TO .8X Jsy/25
*201-229 p/r 25: .5X TO 1.2X Jsy/50
*201-229 p/r 25: .4X TO 1X Jsy/25
OVERALL AU-GU ODDS ONE PER PACK
PRINT RUNS B/WN 1-100 COPIES PER
NO PRICING ON QTY OF 10 OR LESS
27 Delmon Young/50 15.00 40.00
31 Edgar Renteria/25 12.50 30.00
37 Gary Sheffield Yanks/25 20.00 50.00
61 Jermaine Dye/25 12.50 30.00
106 Michael Young/50 10.00 25.00
131 Rickie Weeks/25 12.50 30.00
212 Lou Brock RET/50 15.00 40.00
214 Mark Grace RET/25 20.00 50.00
250 Victor Martinez H/25 12.50 30.00

2004 Leaf Limited Moniker Jersey

OVERALL AU-GU ODDS ONE PER PACK
PRINT RUNS B/WN 1-100 COPIES PER
NO PRICING ON QTY OF 10 OR LESS
1 Adam Dunn A/50 15.00 40.00
3 Albert Pujols H/10
5 Alfonso Soriano Rgr/50 15.00 40.00
6 Andruw Jones/25 20.00 50.00
7 Andy Pettitte Astros/10
8 Angel Berroa Pants/25 8.00 20.00
9 Aramis Ramirez/25 12.50 30.00
10 Aubrey Huff/25 12.50 30.00
11 Austin Kearns/25 8.00 20.00
12 Barry Larkin/1
13 Barry Zito H/10
15 Ben Sheets/25 12.50 30.00
16 Bernie Williams/10
17 Bobby Abreu/5
18 Brandon Webb/25 8.00 20.00
20 C.C. Sabathia/25 12.50 30.00
21 Carlos Beltran Royals A/50 10.00 25.00
23 Chipper Jones H/25 40.00 80.00
24 Craig Biggio/25 20.00 50.00
30 Dontrelle Willis/25 20.00 50.00

31 Edgar Renteria/10
32 Eric Chavez/50 10.00 25.00
34 Frank Thomas/25 40.00 80.00
35 Fred McGriff/25 20.00 50.00
36 Garret Anderson H/50 10.00 25.00
39 Greg Maddux Cubs/10
40 Hank Blalock H/50 10.00 25.00
42 Hideo Nomo Dodgers/1
46 Jacque Jones/25 12.50 30.00
53 Jason Varitek/1
56 Jay Gibbons/5
58 Jeff Bagwell H/10
60 Jeremy Bonderman/5
63 Jim Edmonds/25 20.00 50.00
66 Jody Gerut/25 8.00 20.00
67 Johan Santana/25 20.00 50.00
71 Jorge Posada/25 30.00 60.00
73 Jose Reyes/5
74 Jose Vidro/25 8.00 20.00
76 Juan Gonzalez Royals/10
78 Junior Spivey/1
79 Kazuhisa Ishii/10
84 Kerry Wood/25 20.00 50.00
88 Lance Berkman/25 20.00 50.00
89 Larry Bigbie/25 12.50 30.00
94 Luis Matos/10
97 Manny Ramirez Sox/10
98 Marcus Giles/25 12.50 30.00
99 Mark Buehrle/25 20.00 50.00
100 Mark Mulder/75 8.00 20.00
101 Mark Prior H/50 12.50 30.00
102 Mark Teixeira/25 20.00 50.00
103 Marlon Byrd/1
105 Melvin Mora/25 12.50 30.00
107 Miguel Cabrera Batting/38 15.00 40.00
109 Mike Lowell/25 12.50 30.00
110 Mike Mussina Yanks/5
111 Mike Piazza Mets/5
115 Morgan Ensberg/25 8.00 20.00
122 Paul Lo Duca/25 12.50 30.00
123 Pedro Martinez Sox/10
124 Preston Wilson H/25 12.50 30.00
125 Rafael Furcal/10
127 Randy Johnson D'backs/10
128 Rich Harden/1
135 Roger Clemens Astros/10
137 Roy Oswalt A/25 12.50 30.00
140 Sammy Sosa H/10
142 Scott Rolen Cards A/50 15.00 40.00
143 Sean Burroughs/25 8.00 20.00
144 Sean Casey/25 12.50 30.00
145 Shannon Stewart/25 12.50 30.00
146 Shawn Green Dodgers/10
149 Steve Finley/25 12.50 30.00
153 Todd Helton H/25 20.00 50.00
154 Tom Glavine Mets/25 20.00 50.00
155 Torii Hunter/25 12.50 30.00
156 Trot Nixon/25 12.50 30.00
158 Vernon Wells H/50 10.00 25.00
159 Victor Martinez A/50 10.00 25.00
162 Alex Rodriguez Rgr/1
163 Alfonso Soriano Yanks/50 15.00 40.00
164 Andy Pettitte Yanks/10
166 Gary Sheffield Braves/25 20.00 50.00
167 Greg Maddux Braves/10
168 Hideo Nomo Sox/1
172 Juan Gonzalez Rgr/25 12.50 30.00
177 Mike Mussina O's/5
178 Mike Piazza Dodgers/5
179 Pedro Martinez Expos/10
181 Randy Johnson Astros/10
182 Roger Clemens Sox/10
183 Scott Rolen Phils/50 15.00 40.00
184 Shawn Green Jays/10
185 Tom Glavine Braves/25 20.00 50.00
187 Alex Rodriguez M's/1
188 Mike Piazza Marlins/5
189 Randy Johnson M's/10
190 Roger Clemens Yanks/10
191 Albert Pujols A/10
192 Barry Zito A/10
193 Chipper Jones A/25 40.00 80.00
194 Garret Anderson A/50 10.00 25.00
195 Jeff Bagwell A/10
198 Mark Prior A/50 12.50 30.00
199 Sammy Sosa A/10
200 Todd Helton A/25 20.00 50.00
201 Andre Dawson RET/50 10.00 25.00
203 Bob Feller RET Pants/5
204 Bob Gibson RET/50 15.00 40.00
205 Bobby Doerr RET/50 10.00 25.00
206 Cal Ripken RET/10
207 Dale Murphy RET/100 12.50 30.00
208 Don Mattingly RET/50 40.00 80.00
209 Gary Carter RET/100 8.00 20.00
210 George Brett RET/10
212 Lou Brock RET/5
214 Mark Grace RET/10
216 Mike Schmidt RET/50 40.00 80.00
217 Nolan Ryan RET/100 60.00 120.00
218 Orel Hershiser RET/50 15.00 40.00
219 Paul Molitor RET/50 10.00 25.00
221 Rod Carew RET/50 15.00 40.00
223 Ryne Sandberg RET/25 50.00 100.00
224 Stan Musial RET/25 50.00 100.00
226 Tony Gwynn RET/100 20.00 50.00
228 Whitey Ford RET Pants/25 20.00 50.00
229 Yogi Berra RET/25 40.00 80.00
230 Carlos Beltran Astros H/50 10.00 25.00
231 David Ortiz H/50 30.00 60.00
232 David Ortiz A/50 30.00 60.00
234 Carlos Lee/50 10.00 25.00
235 Travis Hafner/25 12.50 30.00
236 Brad Penny/25 8.00 20.00
237 Wade Miller/25 8.00 20.00
238 Edgar Martinez/50 20.00 50.00
239 Carl Crawford/25 12.50 30.00
240 Roy Oswalt H/25 12.50 30.00
242 Carlos Beltran Astros A/50 10.00 25.00
243 Carlos Beltran Royals H/50 10.00 25.00
244 Miguel Cabrera Fielding/50 15.00 40.00
245 Scott Rolen Cards H/50 15.00 40.00
246 Hank Blalock A/50 10.00 25.00
247 Vernon Wells A/50 10.00 25.00
248 Adam Dunn H/50 15.00 40.00
249 Preston Wilson A/25 12.50 30.00

2004 Leaf Limited Moniker Jersey Prime

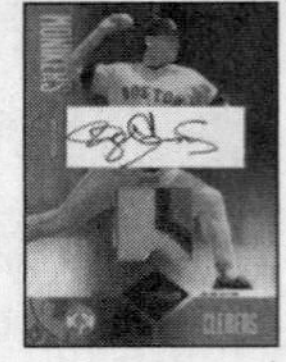

OVERALL AU-GU ODDS ONE PER PACK
STATED PRINT RUN 1 SERIAL #'d SET
NO PRICING DUE TO SCARCITY

2004 Leaf Limited Moniker Jersey Number

*1-200/230-250 p/r 75: .4X TO 1X Jsy/75
*1-200/230-250 p/r 50: .4X TO 1X Jsy/38-50
*1-200/230-250 p/r 25: .5X TO 1.2X Jsy/50
*1-200/230-250 p/r 25: .4X TO 1X Jsy/25
*201-229 p/r 100: .4X TO 1X Jsy/100
*201-229 p/r 50: .4X TO 1X Jsy/50
*201-229 p/r 25: .5X TO 1.2X Jsy/50
*201-229 p/r 25: .4X TO 1X Jsy/25
OVERALL AU-GU ODDS ONE PER PACK
PRINT RUNS B/WN 1-100 COPIES PER
NO PRICING ON QTY OF 10 OR LESS
140 Sammy Sosa H/25 50.00 100.00
199 Sammy Sosa A/25 50.00 100.00

2004 Leaf Limited Moniker Jersey Number Prime

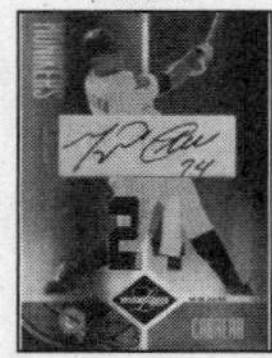

OVERALL AU-GU ODDS ONE PER PACK
STATED PRINT RUN 1 SERIAL #'d SET
NO PRICING DUE TO SCARCITY

2004 Leaf Limited Threads Button

OVERALL AU-GU ODDS ONE PER PACK
PRINT RUNS B/WN 1-6 COPIES PER
NO PRICING DUE TO SCARCITY

2004 Leaf Limited Threads Jersey

OVERALL AU-GU ODDS ONE PER PACK
PRINT RUNS B/WN 1-100 COPIES PER
NO PRICING ON QTY OF 10 OR LESS
NO RC YR PRICING DUE TO SCARCITY
1 Adam Dunn A/25 5.00 12.00
2 Adrian Beltre/5
3 Albert Pujols H/50 10.00 25.00
5 Alfonso Soriano Rgr/25 5.00 12.00
6 Andruw Jones/25 8.00 20.00
7 Andy Pettitte Astros/5
8 Angel Berroa Pants/5
9 Aramis Ramirez/5
10 Aubrey Huff/5
11 Austin Kearns/25 5.00 12.00
12 Barry Larkin/25 8.00 20.00
13 Barry Zito H/25 5.00 12.00
15 Ben Sheets/5
16 Bernie Williams/50 5.00 12.00
17 Bobby Abreu/5
18 Brandon Webb/5
19 Brian Giles/5
20 C.C. Sabathia/5
21 Carlos Beltran Royals A/25 5.00 12.00
22 Carlos Delgado/25 5.00 12.00
23 Chipper Jones H/50 6.00 15.00
24 Craig Biggio/25 8.00 20.00
25 Curt Schilling Sox/25 8.00 20.00
26 Darin Erstad/10
30 Dontrelle Willis/25 8.00 20.00
31 Edgar Renteria/25 5.00 12.00
32 Eric Chavez/25 5.00 12.00
34 Frank Thomas/25 10.00 25.00
35 Fred McGriff/10
36 Garret Anderson H/25 5.00 12.00
38 Geoff Jenkins/5
39 Greg Maddux Cubs/50 8.00 20.00
40 Hank Blalock H/25 5.00 12.00
41 Hideki Matsui/50 20.00 50.00
42 Hideo Nomo Dodgers/50 6.00 15.00
44 Ivan Rodriguez Tigers/25 8.00 20.00
46 Jacque Jones/10
47 Jae Weong Seo/5
49 Jamie Moyer/5
50 Jason Giambi Yanks/50 3.00 8.00
51 Jason Kendall/5
53 Jason Varitek/5
55 Javy Lopez/25 5.00 12.00
56 Jay Gibbons/5
58 Jeff Bagwell H/50 5.00 12.00
59 Jeff Kent/50 3.00 8.00
60 Jeremy Bonderman/5
62 Jeromy Burnitz/1
63 Jim Edmonds/25 5.00 12.00
64 Jim Thome Phils/50 5.00 12.00
65 Jimmy Rollins/5
66 Jody Gerut/5
67 Johan Santana/5
68 John Olerud/10
69 John Smoltz/25 8.00 20.00
71 Jorge Posada/25 8.00 20.00
73 Jose Reyes/5
74 Jose Vidro/5
75 Josh Beckett H/25 5.00 12.00
76 Juan Gonzalez Royals/25 5.00 12.00
78 Junior Spivey/1
79 Kazuhisa Ishii/10
84 Kerry Wood/50 3.00 8.00
86 Kevin Millwood/10
88 Lance Berkman/50 3.00 8.00
89 Larry Bigbie/5
90 Larry Walker/25 5.00 12.00
92 Luis Castillo/5
93 Luis Gonzalez/25 5.00 12.00
94 Luis Matos/5
96 Magglio Ordonez H/25 5.00 12.00
97 Manny Ramirez Sox/50 5.00 12.00
98 Marcus Giles/5
99 Mark Buehrle/10
100 Mark Mulder/25 5.00 12.00
101 Mark Prior H/50 5.00 12.00
102 Mark Teixeira/10
103 Marlon Byrd/5
104 Matt Morris/10
105 Melvin Mora/5
107 Miguel Cabrera Batting/25 8.00 20.00
108 Miguel Tejada O's/25 5.00 12.00
109 Mike Lowell/1
110 Mike Mussina Yanks/50 5.00 12.00
111 Mike Piazza Mets/50 8.00 20.00
112 Mike Sweeney/25 5.00 12.00
115 Morgan Ensberg/5
118 Omar Vizquel/5
119 Orlando Cabrera/5
120 Pat Burrell/5
121 Paul Konerko/10
122 Paul Lo Duca/10
123 Pedro Martinez Sox/50 5.00 12.00
124 Preston Wilson H/5
125 Rafael Furcal/5
126 Rafael Palmeiro O's/25 8.00 20.00
127 Randy Johnson D'backs/25 10.00 25.00
128 Rich Harden/1
129 Richard Hidalgo Pants/5
130 Richie Sexson/10
134 Rocco Baldelli/10
135 Roger Clemens Astros/5
136 Roy Halladay/1
137 Roy Oswalt A/25 5.00 12.00
139 Ryan Klesko/5
140 Sammy Sosa H/50 6.00 15.00
142 Scott Rolen Cards A/25 8.00 20.00
143 Sean Burroughs/5
144 Sean Casey/5
145 Shannon Stewart/10
146 Shawn Green Dodgers/25 5.00 12.00
149 Steve Finley/5
150 Tim Hudson/25 5.00 12.00
151 Tim Salmon/5
152 Tino Martinez/5
153 Todd Helton H/50 5.00 12.00
154 Tom Glavine Mets/25 8.00 20.00
155 Torii Hunter/25 5.00 12.00
156 Trot Nixon/1
157 Troy Glaus/25 5.00 12.00
158 Vernon Wells H/25 5.00 12.00
159 Victor Martinez A/5
160 Vinny Castilla/5
161 Vladimir Guerrero Angels/25 10.00 25.00
162 Alex Rodriguez Rgr/100 5.00 12.00
163 Alfonso Soriano Yanks/50 3.00 8.00
164 Andy Pettitte Yanks/25 8.00 20.00
165 Curt Schilling D'backs/25 5.00 12.00
166 Gary Sheffield Braves/25 5.00 12.00
167 Greg Maddux Braves/50 8.00 20.00
168 Hideo Nomo Sox/25 10.00 25.00
169 Ivan Rodriguez Marlins/50 5.00 12.00
170 Jason Giambi A's/25 5.00 12.00
171 Jim Thome Indians/10
172 Juan Gonzalez Rgr/25 5.00 12.00
174 Kevin Brown Dodgers/25 5.00 12.00
176 Miguel Tejada A's/25 5.00 12.00
177 Mike Mussina O's/50 5.00 12.00
178 Mike Piazza Dodgers/25 12.50 30.00
179 Pedro Martinez Expos/25 8.00 20.00
180 Rafael Palmeiro Rgr/25 8.00 20.00
181 Randy Johnson Astros/50 6.00 15.00
182 Roger Clemens Sox/100 5.00 12.00
183 Scott Rolen Phils/25 8.00 20.00
184 Shawn Green Jays/25 5.00 12.00
185 Tom Glavine Braves/25 8.00 20.00
186 Vladimir Guerrero Expos/25 10.00 25.00
187 Alex Rodriguez M's/100 5.00 12.00
188 Mike Piazza Marlins/10
189 Randy Johnson M's/50 6.00 15.00
190 Roger Clemens Yanks/100 5.00 12.00
191 Albert Pujols A/50 10.00 25.00
192 Barry Zito A/25 5.00 12.00
193 Chipper Jones A/25 6.00 15.00
194 Garret Anderson A/25 5.00 12.00
195 Jeff Bagwell A/50 5.00 12.00
196 Josh Beckett A/25 5.00 12.00
197 Magglio Ordonez A/25 5.00 12.00
198 Mark Prior A/50 5.00 12.00
199 Sammy Sosa A/50 6.00 15.00
200 Todd Helton A/50 5.00 12.00
201 Andre Dawson RET/50 4.00 10.00
202 Babe Ruth RET/25 250.00 400.00
203 Bob Feller RET Pants/25 10.00 25.00
204 Bob Gibson RET/1
205 Bobby Doerr RET/50 4.00 10.00
206 Cal Ripken RET/100 20.00 50.00
207 Dale Murphy RET/100 5.00 12.00
208 Don Mattingly RET/50 12.50 30.00
209 Gary Carter RET/50 4.00 10.00
210 George Brett RET/100 8.00 20.00
211 J.Robinson RET Jkt/50 20.00 50.00
212 Lou Brock RET/25 10.00 25.00
213 Lou Gehrig RET/25 100.00 175.00
214 Mark Grace RET/25 10.00 25.00
215 Maury Wills RET/50 4.00 10.00
216 Mike Schmidt RET/100 8.00 20.00
217 Nolan Ryan RET/100 10.00 25.00
218 Orel Hershiser RET/25 10.00 25.00
219 Paul Molitor RET/50 4.00 10.00
220 Roberto Clemente RET/25 50.00 100.00
221 Rod Carew RET/100 5.00 12.00
222 R.Campanella RET Pants/50 8.00 20.00
223 Ryne Sandberg RET/50 12.50 30.00
224 Stan Musial RET/25 20.00 50.00
225 Ted Williams RET/50 30.00 80.00
226 Tony Gwynn RET/100 6.00 15.00
227 Ty Cobb RET Pants/100 40.00 80.00
228 Whitey Ford RET Pants/25 10.00 25.00
229 Yogi Berra RET/25 12.50 30.00
230 Carlos Beltran Astros H/25 5.00 12.00
231 David Ortiz H/25 10.00 25.00
232 David Ortiz A/25 10.00 25.00
234 Carlos Lee/10
235 Travis Hafner/5
236 Brad Penny/5
237 Wade Miller/5
238 Edgar Martinez/25 8.00 20.00
239 Carl Crawford/5
240 Roy Oswalt H/25 5.00 12.00
241 Kazuo Matsui/25
242 Carlos Beltran Astros A/25 5.00 12.00
243 Carlos Beltran Royals H/25 5.00 12.00
244 Miguel Cabrera Fielding/25 8.00 20.00
245 Scott Rolen Cards H/25 8.00 20.00
246 Hank Blalock A/25 5.00 12.00
247 Vernon Wells A/25 5.00 12.00
248 Adam Dunn H/25 5.00 12.00
249 Preston Wilson A/5

2004 Leaf Limited Threads Jersey Prime

OVERALL AU-GU ODDS ONE PER PACK
STATED PRINT RUN 1 SERIAL #'d SET
NO PRICING DUE TO SCARCITY

2004 Leaf Limited Threads Jersey Number

*1-200/230-250 p/r 100: .4X TO 1X Thrd/100
*1-200/230-250 p/r 50: .4X TO 1X Thrd/50
*1-200/230-250 p/r 25: .6X TO 1.5X Thrd/50
*1-200/230-250 p/r 25: .4X TO 1X Thrd/25
*201-229 p/r 100: .4X TO 1X Thrd/100
*201-229 p/r 100: .3X TO .8X Thrd/50
*201-229 p/r 50: .4X TO 1X Thrd/50
*201-229 p/r 25: .4X TO 1X Thrd/25
OVERALL AU-GU ODDS ONE PER PACK
PRINT RUNS B/WN 1-100 COPIES PER
NO PRICING ON QTY OF 10 OR LESS

2004 Leaf Limited Threads Jersey Number Prime

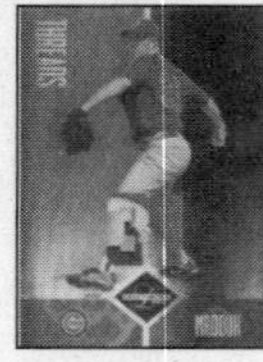

OVERALL AU-GU ODDS ONE PER PACK
STATED PRINT RUN 1 SERIAL #'d SET
NO PRICING DUE TO SCARCITY

2004 Leaf Limited Threads MLB Logo

OVERALL AU-GU ODDS ONE PER PACK
STATED PRINT RUN 1 SERIAL #'d SET
NO PRICING DUE TO SCARCITY

2004 Leaf Limited Timber

*1-200/230-250 p/r 100: .4X TO 1X Thrd/100
*1-200/230-250 p/r 50: .4X TO 1X Thrd/50
*1-200/230-250 p/r 25: 1X TO 2.5X Thrd/100
*1-200/230-250 p/r 25: .6X TO 1.5X Thrd/50
*1-200/230-250 p/r 25: .4X TO 1X Thrd/25
*201-229 p/r 100: .4X TO 1X Thrd/100
*201-229 p/r 100: .25X TO .6X Thrd/50
*201-229 p/r 100: .15X TO .4X Thrd/25
*201-229 p/r 50: .6X TO 1.5X Thrd/100
*201-229 p/r 50: .4X TO 1X Thrd/50
*201-229 p/r 25: 1X TO 2.5X Thrd/100
*201-229 p/r 25: .6X TO 1.5X Thrd/50
*201-229 p/r 25: .4X TO 1X Thrd/25
OVERALL AU-GU ODDS ONE PER PACK
PRINT RUNS B/WN 1-100 COPIES PER
NO PRICING ON QTY OF 10 OR LESS
4 Alex Rodriguez Yanks/100 5.00 12.00
7 Andy Pettitte Astros/25 8.00 20.00
35 Fred McGriff/25 8.00 20.00
37 Gary Sheffield Yanks/25 5.00 12.00
85 Kevin Brown Yanks/25 5.00 12.00
102 Mark Teixeira/25 8.00 20.00
106 Michael Young/25 5.00 12.00
109 Mike Lowell/25 5.00 12.00
116 Nick Johnson/25 5.00 12.00
117 Nomar Garciaparra/25 12.50 30.00
122 Paul Lo Duca/25 5.00 12.00
130 Richie Sexson/25 5.00 12.00
134 Rocco Baldelli/25 5.00 12.00
135 Roger Clemens Astros/25 12.50 30.00
156 Trot Nixon/25 5.00 12.00
171 Jim Thome Indians/25 8.00 20.00
175 Manny Ramirez Indians/25 8.00 20.00
188 Mike Piazza Marlins/25 12.50 30.00
202 Babe Ruth RET/100 75.00 150.00
213 Lou Gehrig RET/100 60.00 120.00
220 Roberto Clemente RET/100 40.00 80.00
225 Ted Williams RET/100 25.00 60.00

2004 Leaf Limited TNT

*1-200/230-250 p/r 100: .5X TO 1.2X Thrd/100
*1-200/230-250 p/r 100: .3X TO .8X Thrd/50
*1-200/230-250 p/r 50: .5X TO 1.2X Thrd/50
*1-200/230-250 p/r 50: .3X TO .8X Thrd/25
*1-200/230-250 p/r 25: .75X TO 2X Thrd/50
*1-200/230-250 p/r 25: .5X TO 1.2X Thrd/25
*201-229 p/r 100: .5X TO 1.2X Thrd/100
*201-229 p/r 100: .3X TO .8X Thrd/50
*201-229 p/r 50: .75X TO 2X Thrd/100
*201-229 p/r 50: .5X TO 1.2X Thrd/50
*201-229 p/r 25: .75X TO 2X Thrd/50
*201-229 p/r 25: .5X TO 1.2X Thrd/25
OVERALL AU-GU ODDS ONE PER PACK
PRINT RUNS B/WN 5-100 COPIES PER
NO PRICING ON QTY OF 10 OR LESS
102 Mark Teixeira Bat-Jsy/25 10.00 25.00
109 Mike Lowell Bat-Jsy/25 6.00 15.00

2004 Leaf Limited TNT Prime

OVERALL AU-GU ODDS ONE PER PACK
STATED PRINT RUN 1 SERIAL #'d SET
NO PRICING DUE TO SCARCITY

2004 Leaf Limited Cuts

OVERALL AU-GU ODDS ONE PER PACK
PRINT RUNS B/WN 50-100 COPIES PER

CUTS FABRIC IS NOT GAME-USED
1 Nolan Ryan/100 75.00 150.00
2 Bob Gibson/50 20.00 50.00
3 Harmon Killebrew/100 20.00 50.00
4 Duke Snider/100 15.00 40.00
5 George Brett/100 40.00 80.00
6 Stan Musial/100 50.00 100.00
7 Alan Trammell/100 10.00 25.00
8 Cal Ripken/100 100.00 200.00
9 Steve Carlton/50 12.50 30.00
10 Phil Rizzuto/100 15.00 40.00
11 Mark Prior/50 20.00 50.00
12 Will Clark/100 15.00 40.00
13 Lou Brock/100 15.00 40.00
14 Ozzie Smith/100 30.00 60.00
15 Bob Feller/100 15.00 40.00
16 Gary Carter/50 12.50 30.00
17 Al Kaline/100 20.00 50.00
18 Brooks Robinson/100 15.00 40.00
19 Tony Gwynn/100 30.00 60.00
20 Mike Schmidt/100 40.00 80.00
21 Ralph Kiner/50 20.00 50.00
22 Jim Palmer/50 20.00 50.00
23 Don Mattingly/100 40.00 80.00
24 Paul Molitor/50 12.50 30.00
25 Dale Murphy/100 15.00 40.00

2004 Leaf Limited Cuts Gold

*GOLD p/r 45: .4X TO 1X BASIC p/r 50
*GOLD p/r 20-35: .6X TO 1.5X BASIC p/r 100
*GOLD p/r 20-35: .5X TO 1.2X BASIC p/r 50
*GOLD p/r 19: .75X TO 2X BASIC p/r 100
OVERALL AU-GU ODDS ONE PER PACK
PRINT RUNS B/WN 1-45 COPIES PER
NO PRICING ON QTY OF 10 OR LESS
CUTS FABRIC IS NOT GAME-USED

2004 Leaf Limited Legends Material Number

PRINT RUNS B/WN 5-100 COPIES PER
*POSITION: .4X TO 1X NUMBER
POSITION PRINT RUNS B/WN 5-100 PER
OVERALL AU-GU ODDS ONE PER PACK
NO PRICING ON QTY OF 5 OR LESS
1 Al Kaline Pants/50 8.00 20.00
2 Babe Ruth Pants/50 125.00 200.00
3 Bob Feller Jsy/50 6.00 15.00
4 Bob Gibson Jsy/50 6.00 15.00
5 Brooks Robinson Jsy/5
6 Burleigh Grimes Pants/100 20.00 50.00
7 Carl Yastrzemski Jsy/100 8.00 20.00
8 Harmon Killebrew Jsy/25 12.50 30.00
9 Hoyt Wilhelm Jsy/100 3.00 8.00
10 Johnny Mize Pants/100 5.00 12.00
11 Ernie Banks Pants/50 8.00 20.00
12 Lou Brock Jsy/50 6.00 15.00
13 Luis Aparicio Pants/100 3.00 8.00
14 Pee Wee Reese Jsy/50 6.00 15.00
15 Reggie Jackson Jsy/100 5.00 12.00
16 Red Schoendienst Jsy/50 4.00 10.00
17 Roberto Clemente Jsy/25 50.00 100.00
18 Roger Maris Pants/100 12.50 30.00
19 Stan Musial Jsy/100 10.00 25.00
20 Ted Williams Jsy/50 30.00 80.00
21 Ty Cobb Pants/50 50.00 100.00
22 Warren Spahn Jsy/100 6.00 15.00
23 Whitey Ford Pants/100 5.00 12.00
24 Yogi Berra Jsy/50 8.00 20.00
25 Satchel Paige CO Jsy/100 30.00 60.00

2004 Leaf Limited Legends Material Autographs Number

PRINT RUNS B/WN 5-50 COPIES PER
*POSITION: .4X TO 1X NUMBER
POSITION PRINT RUNS B/WN 5-100 PER
OVERALL AU-GU ODDS ONE PER PACK
NO PRICING ON QTY OF 10 OR LESS
1 Al Kaline Pants/50 30.00 60.00
3 Bob Feller Jsy/50 15.00 40.00
4 Bob Gibson Jsy/50 15.00 40.00
5 Brooks Robinson Jsy/5
7 Carl Yastrzemski Jsy/25 50.00 100.00
8 Harmon Killebrew Jsy/25 40.00 80.00
9 Hoyt Wilhelm Jsy/25 20.00 50.00
12 Lou Brock Jsy/50 15.00 40.00
13 Luis Aparicio Pants/50 10.00 25.00
15 Reggie Jackson Jsy/50 30.00 60.00
16 Red Schoendienst Jsy/50 15.00 40.00
19 Stan Musial Jsy/50 40.00 80.00
22 Warren Spahn Jsy/10
23 Whitey Ford Pants/25 20.00 50.00
24 Yogi Berra Jsy/25 40.00 80.00

2004 Leaf Limited Lumberjacks

1-40 PRINT RUNS B/WN 16-714 PER
41-50 PRINT RUN 500 #'d SETS
RANDOM INSERTS IN PACKS
1 Al Kaline/399 2.00 5.00
2 Albert Pujols/114 6.00 15.00
3 Andre Dawson/438 1.25 3.00
4 Babe Ruth/714 3.00 8.00
5 Bo Jackson/141 2.50 6.00
6 Bobby Doerr/223 1.50 4.00
7 Brooks Robinson/268 1.50 4.00
8 Cal Ripken/431 6.00 15.00
9 Carlton Fisk/376 1.50 4.00
10 Dale Murphy/398 1.50 4.00
11 Darryl Strawberry/335 1.25 3.00
12 Don Mattingly/222 4.00 10.00
13 Duke Snider/407 1.50 4.00
14 Eddie Mathews/512 2.00 5.00
15 Eddie Murray/504 2.00 5.00
16 Frank Robinson/586 1.25 3.00
17 Frank Thomas/418 2.00 5.00
18 Gary Carter/324 1.25 3.00
19 George Brett/317 3.00 8.00
20 Harmon Killebrew/573 2.00 5.00
21 Hideki Matsui/16 20.00 50.00
22 Lou Gehrig/493 2.50 6.00
23 Mark Grace/173 2.00 5.00
24 Mike Piazza/358 2.00 5.00
25 Mike Schmidt/548 3.00 8.00
26 Orlando Cepeda/379 1.25 3.00
27 Rafael Palmeiro/528 1.25 3.00
28 Ralph Kiner/369 1.25 3.00
29 Reggie Jackson/563 1.50 4.00
30 Rickey Henderson/297 2.00 5.00
31 Roger Maris/275 2.00 5.00
32 Ryne Sandberg/282 3.00 8.00
33 Sammy Sosa/539 2.00 5.00
34 Scott Rolen/192 1.50 4.00
35 Stan Musial/475 2.50 6.00
36 Ted Williams/521 3.00 8.00
37 Thurman Munson/113 3.00 8.00
38 Vladimir Guerrero/234 2.50 6.00
39 Willie McCovey/521 1.50 4.00
40 Willie Stargell/475 1.50 4.00
41 Roberto Clemente 3.00 8.00
Stan Musial
42 Cal Ripken 6.00 15.00
Ernie Banks
43 Babe Ruth 3.00 8.00
Lou Gehrig
44 George Brett 3.00 8.00
Mike Schmidt
45 Frank Robinson 2.00 5.00
Jackie Robinson
46 Don Mattingly 3.00 8.00
Roger Maris
47 Nomar Garciaparra 3.00 8.00
Ted Williams
48 Johnny Bench 2.00 5.00
Mike Piazza
49 Reggie Jackson 2.00 5.00
Sammy Sosa
50 Mel Ott 2.00 5.00
Willie McCovey

2004 Leaf Limited Lumberjacks Black

*1-40 p/r 66: 1.5X TO 4X LJ p/r 251+
*1-40 p/r 37-61: 1.5X TO 4X LJ p/r 251+
*1-40 p/r 37-61: .75X TO 2X LJ p/r 126-250
*1-40 p/r 37-61: .6X TO 1.5X LJ p/r 66-125
*1-40 p/r 20-35: 2X TO 5X LJ p/r 251+
*1-40 p/r 20-35: 1.5X TO 4X LJ p/r 126-250
*1-40 p/r 20-35: 1.25X TO 3X LJ p/r 66-125
*1-40 p/r 16-17: 2X TO 5X LJ p/r 126-250
*1-40 p/r 16-17: .4X TO 1X LJ p/r 16
1-40 PRINT RUNS B/WN 16-66 COPIES PER
*BLACK 41-50: 1X TO 2.5X LJ 41-50
41-50 PRINT RUN 100 SERIAL #'d SETS
RANDOM INSERTS IN PACKS

2004 Leaf Limited Lumberjacks Autographs

OVERALL AU-GU ODDS ONE PER PACK
PRINT RUNS B/WN 1-100 COPIES PER
NO PRICING ON QTY OF 10 OR LESS
1 Al Kaline/100 15.00 40.00
2 Albert Pujols/10
3 Andre Dawson/100 6.00 15.00
5 Bo Jackson/25 30.00 60.00
6 Bobby Doerr/100 6.00 15.00
7 Brooks Robinson/100 10.00 25.00
8 Cal Ripken/25 125.00 200.00
9 Carlton Fisk/25 15.00 40.00
10 Dale Murphy/100 10.00 25.00
11 Darryl Strawberry/100 6.00 15.00
12 Don Mattingly/25 40.00 80.00
13 Duke Snider/100 10.00 25.00
15 Eddie Murray/10
16 Frank Robinson/100 10.00 25.00
17 Frank Thomas/50 20.00 50.00
18 Gary Carter/100 6.00 15.00
19 George Brett/25 40.00 80.00
20 Harmon Killebrew/100 15.00 40.00
23 Mark Grace/25 15.00 40.00
24 Mike Piazza/10
25 Mike Schmidt/50 30.00 60.00
26 Orlando Cepeda/1
27 Rafael Palmeiro/1
28 Ralph Kiner/100 10.00 25.00
29 Reggie Jackson/25 30.00 60.00
30 Rickey Henderson/25 30.00 60.00
32 Ryne Sandberg/25 40.00 80.00
33 Sammy Sosa/10
34 Scott Rolen/25 15.00 40.00
35 Stan Musial/50 30.00 60.00
39 Willie McCovey/25 15.00 40.00

2004 Leaf Limited Lumberjacks Autographs Bat

*BAT p/r 100: .5X TO1.2X AU p/r 100
*BAT p/r 50: .6X TO1.5X AU p/r 100
*BAT p/r 50: .5X TO1.2X AU p/r 50
*BAT p/r 25: .75X TO2X AU p/r 100
*BAT p/r 25: .6X TO1.5X AU p/r 50
*BAT p/r 25: .5X TO1.2X AU p/r 25
*BAT p/r 17: .6X TO1.5X AU p/r 25
OVERALL AU-GU ODDS ONE PER PACK
PRINT RUNS B/WN 1-100 COPIES PER
NO PRICING ON QTY OF 10 OR LESS

2004 Leaf Limited Lumberjacks Autographs Jersey

*JSY p/r 100: .5X TO 1.2X AU p/r 100
*JSY p/r 50: .6X TO 1.5X AU p/r 100
*JSY p/r 50: .5X TO 1.2X AU p/r 50
*JSY p/r 50: .4X TO 1X AU p/r 25
*JSY p/r 25: .75X TO 2X AU p/r 100
*JSY p/r 25: .6X TO 1.5X AU p/r 50
*JSY p/r 25: .5X TO 1.2X AU p/r 25
*JSY p/r 17: .6X TO 1.5X AU p/r 25
OVERALL AU-GU ODDS ONE PER PACK
PRINT RUNS B/WN 5-100 COPIES PER
NO PRICING ON QTY OF 10 OR LESS
15 Eddie Murray/25 40.00 80.00
26 Orlando Cepeda Pants/50 10.00 25.00

2004 Leaf Limited Lumberjacks Barrel

OVERALL AU-GU ODDS ONE PER PACK
PRINT RUNS B/WN 1-5 COPIES PER
NO PRICING DUE TO SCARCITY

2004 Leaf Limited Lumberjacks Bat

OVERALL AU-GU ODDS ONE PER PACK
PRINT RUNS B/WN 25-100 COPIES PER
1 Al Kaline/100 6.00 15.00
2 Albert Pujols/100 6.00 15.00
3 Andre Dawson/25 6.00 15.00
4 Babe Ruth/100 100.00 175.00
5 Bo Jackson/50 8.00 20.00
6 Bobby Doerr/25 6.00 15.00
7 Brooks Robinson/100 5.00 12.00
8 Cal Ripken/100 20.00 50.00
9 Carlton Fisk/100 5.00 12.00
10 Dale Murphy/50 6.00 15.00
11 Darryl Strawberry/25 6.00 15.00
12 Don Mattingly/100 8.00 20.00
14 Eddie Mathews/100 6.00 15.00
15 Eddie Murray/100 6.00 15.00
16 Frank Robinson/100 3.00 8.00
17 Frank Thomas/25 10.00 25.00
18 Gary Carter/50 4.00 10.00
19 George Brett/100 8.00 20.00
20 Harmon Killebrew/100 6.00 15.00
21 Hideki Matsui/100 12.50 30.00
22 Lou Gehrig/100 60.00 120.00
23 Mark Grace/25 10.00 25.00
24 Mike Piazza/50 8.00 20.00
25 Mike Schmidt/100 8.00 20.00
26 Orlando Cepeda/50 4.00 10.00
27 Rafael Palmeiro/50 5.00 12.00
28 Ralph Kiner/100 3.00 8.00
29 Reggie Jackson/100 5.00 12.00
30 Rickey Henderson/100 6.00 15.00
31 Roger Maris/100 12.50 30.00
32 Ryne Sandberg/100 8.00 20.00
33 Sammy Sosa/100 4.00 10.00
34 Scott Rolen/25 8.00 20.00
35 Stan Musial/100 10.00 25.00
36 Ted Williams/100 25.00 60.00
37 Thurman Munson/100 10.00 25.00
38 Vladimir Guerrero/25 10.00 25.00
39 Willie McCovey/100 5.00 12.00
40 Willie Stargell/50 6.00 15.00
41 Roberto Clemente 50.00 100.00
Stan Musial /100
42 Cal Ripken 50.00 100.00
Ernie Banks /50
43 Babe Ruth 175.00 300.00
Lou Gehrig /25
44 George Brett 20.00 50.00
Mike Schmidt /50
46 Don Mattingly 20.00 50.00
Roger Maris /50
47 Nomar Garciaparra 30.00 80.00
Ted Williams /100
48 Johnny Bench 15.00 40.00
Mike Piazza /25
49 Reggie Jackson 10.00 25.00
Sammy Sosa /50
50 Mel Ott 15.00 40.00
Willie McCovey /100

2004 Leaf Limited Lumberjacks Jersey

*1-40 p/r 100: .4X TO 1X BAT p/r 100
*1-40 p/r 100: .25X TO .6X BAT p/r 50
*1-40 p/r 100: .15X TO .4X BAT p/r 25
*1-40 p/r 50: .6X TO 1.5X BAT p/r 100
*1-40 p/r 50: .4X TO 1X BAT p/r 50
*1-40 p/r 50: .25X TO .6X BAT p/r 25
*1-40 p/r 25: 1X TO 2.5X BAT p/r 100
*1-40 p/r 25: .4X TO 1X BAT p/r 25
*41-50 p/r 100: .25X TO .6X BAT p/r 50
*41-50 p/r 100: .15X TO .4X BAT p/r 25
*41-50 p/r 50: .6X TO 1.5X BAT p/r 100
*41-50 p/r 25: 1X TO 2.5X BAT p/r 100
*41-50 p/r 25: .4X TO 1X BAT p/r 25
OVERALL AU-GU ODDS ONE PER PACK
PRINT RUNS B/WN 4-100 COPIES PER
NO PRICING ON QTY OF 4 OR LESS

2004 Leaf Limited Lumberjacks Combos

*COMBO p/r 100: .5X TO 1.2X BAT p/r 100
*COMBO p/r 100: .3X TO .8X BAT p/r 50
*COMBO p/r 50: .75X TO 2X BAT p/r 100
*COMBO p/r 50: .5X TO 1.2X BAT p/r 50
*COMBO p/r 50: .3X TO .8X BAT p/r 25
*COMBO p/r 25: 1.25X TO 3X BAT p/r 100
*COMBO p/r 25: .5X TO 1.2X BAT p/r 25
*COMBO p/r 17: .6X TO 1.5X BAT p/r 25
OVERALL AU-GU ODDS ONE PER PACK
PRINT RUNS B/WN 17-100 COPIES PER

2004 Leaf Limited Matching Numbers

PRINT RUN B/WN 25-100 COPIES PER
PRIME PRINT RUN 1 SERIAL #'d SET
NO PRIME PRICING DUE TO SCARCITY
OVERALL AU-GU ODDS ONE PER PACK
1 Bobby Doerr Jsy 6.00 15.00
Pee Wee Reese Jsy/100
2 Lou Gehrig Pants 125.00 200.00
Mel Ott Jsy/50
3 Albert Pujols Jsy 15.00 40.00
George Brett Jsy/100
4 Cal Ripken Jsy 30.00 60.00
Carl Yastrzemski Jsy/100
5 Dwight Gooden Jsy 8.00 20.00
Whitey Ford Pants/50
6 Mark Grace Jsy 12.50 30.00
Todd Helton Jsy/25
7 Robin Yount Jsy 20.00 50.00
Tony Gwynn Jsy/50
8 Frank Robinson Jsy 12.50 30.00
Mike Schmidt Jsy/100
9 Roberto Clemente Jsy 40.00 80.00
Sammy Sosa Jsy/100
10 Roger Clemens Jsy 12.50 30.00
Warren Spahn Pants/100
11 Mark Prior Jsy 12.50 30.00
Roger Clemens Jsy/50
12 Don Mattingly Jkt 15.00 40.00
Ryne Sandberg Jsy/100
13 Billy Williams Jsy 6.00 15.00
Wade Boggs Jsy/100
14 Catfish Hunter Jsy 6.00 15.00
Juan Marichal Jsy/50
15 Fergie Jenkins Pants 10.00 25.00
Greg Maddux Jsy/50
16 Kerry Wood Pants 15.00 40.00
Nolan Ryan Jsy/100
17 Rickey Henderson Jsy 15.00 40.00
Roger Maris Pants/100
18 Dontrelle Willis Jsy 8.00 20.00
Mike Mussina Jsy/50
19 Reggie Jackson Jsy 6.00 15.00
Willie McCovey Jsy/100
20 Bob Gibson Jsy 8.00 20.00
Pedro Martinez Jsy/50
21 Duke Snider Jsy 6.00 15.00
Paul Molitor Jsy/100
22 Johnny Bench Jsy 8.00 20.00
Lou Boudreau Jsy/100
23 Andre Dawson Jsy 8.00 20.00
Chipper Jones Jsy/100
24 Ernie Banks Jsy 8.00 20.00
Ken Boyer Jsy/100
25 Manny Ramirez Jsy 8.00 20.00
Rickey Henderson Jsy/100
26 Carlton Fisk Jsy 6.00 15.00
Scott Rolen Jsy/100
27 Nolan Ryan Jsy 12.50 30.00
Orlando Cepeda Pants/100
28 Roy Halladay Jsy 4.00 10.00
Steve Carlton Jsy/100
29 Eddie Mathews Jsy 8.00 20.00
Tom Seaver Jsy/100
30 Brandon Webb Jsy 6.00 15.00
Orel Hershiser Jsy/100

2004 Leaf Limited Player Threads Jersey Number

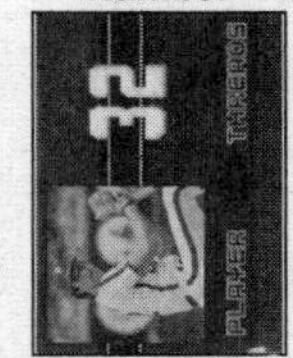

PRINT RUNS B/WN 10-100 COPIES PER
NO PRICING ON QTY OF 10 OR LESS
PRIME PRINT RUN 1 SERIAL #'d SET
NO PRIME PRICING DUE TO SCARCITY
OVERALL AU-GU ODDS ONE PER PACK
1 Mike Piazza/100 5.00 12.00
2 Roger Clemens/10
3 Nolan Ryan Jkt/100 10.00 25.00
4 Reggie Jackson/100 5.00 12.00
5 Wade Boggs/50 6.00 15.00
6 Steve Carlton Pants/100 3.00 8.00
7 Ivan Rodriguez/25 8.00 20.00
8 Pedro Martinez/50 5.00 12.00
9 R.Henderson Yanks/10
10 R.Hend Mets Pants/100 6.00 15.00
11 Randy Johnson/50 6.00 15.00
12 Curt Schilling/25 8.00 20.00
13 Roger Maris/50 20.00 50.00
14 Sammy Sosa/100 4.00 10.00
15 Gary Carter Pants/50 4.00 10.00
16 Gary Sheffield/25 5.00 12.00
17 Eddie Murray/50 8.00 20.00
18 Hideo Nomo/50 6.00 15.00
19 Rafael Palmeiro/50 5.00 12.00
20 Andre Dawson/50 4.00 10.00

2004 Leaf Limited Player Threads Double

*DBL p/r 100: .6X TO 1.5X PT p/r 100
*DBL p/r 100: .4X TO 1X PT p/r 50
*DBL p/r 100: .25X TO .6X PT p/r 25
*DBL p/r 50: .6X TO 1.5X PT p/r 50
*DBL p/r 50: .4X TO 1X PT p/r 25
OVERALL AU-GU ODDS ONE PER PACK
PRINT RUNS B/WN 50-100 COPIES PER
2 R.Clemens Sox-Yanks/100 10.00 25.00
9 R.Henderson A's-Jays/50 12.50 30.00

2004 Leaf Limited Player Threads Triple

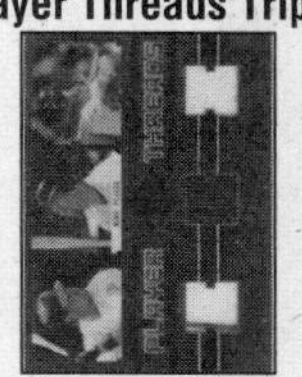

*TRIPLE p/r 50: 1.25X TO 3X PT p/r 100
*TRIPLE p/r 50: .75X TO 2X PT p/r 50
*TRIPLE p/r 25: 1.5X TO 4X PT p/r 100
*TRIPLE p/r 25: 1X TO 2.5X PT p/r 50
*TRIPLE p/r 25: .6X TO 1.5X PT p/r 25
OVERALL AU-GU ODDS ONE PER PACK
PRINT RUNS B/WN 10-50 COPIES PER
NO PRICING ON QTY OF 10 OR LESS
2 R.Clem Astros-Sox-Yanks/25 25.00 60.00
13 Roger Maris 75.00 150.00
A's Pants-Cards Bat-Yanks Jsy/25

2004 Leaf Limited Team Threads Jersey Number

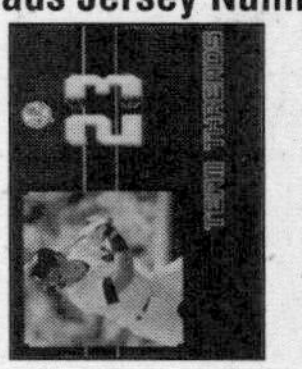

STATED PRINT RUN 100 SERIAL #'d SETS
PRIME PRINT RUN 1 SERIAL #'d SET
NO PRIME PRICING DUE TO SCARCITY
OVERALL AU-GU ODDS ONE PER PACK
ALL ARE DUAL JSY CARDS UNLESS NOTED
1 Stan Musial 20.00 50.00
Albert Pujols
2 Cal Ripken Jkt 20.00 50.00
Mike Mussina
3 Carlton Fisk 12.50 30.00
Roger Clemens
4 Dale Murphy 8.00 20.00
Chipper Jones
5 Tony Gwynn 12.50 30.00
Dave Winfield
6 Don Mattingly 30.00 60.00
Hideki Matsui
7 Lou Boudreau 8.00 20.00
Early Wynn
8 Ernie Banks 15.00 40.00
Sammy Sosa
9 Nolan Ryan Jkt 30.00 60.00
Jeff Bagwell
10 Mike Schmidt 12.50 30.00
Jim Thome

2004 Leaf Limited Team Trademarks

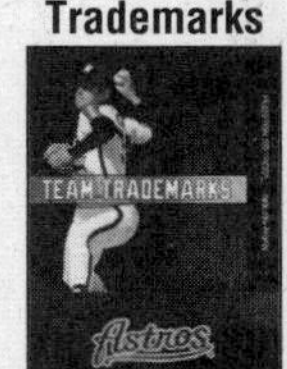

STATED PRINT RUN 100 SERIAL #'d SETS
GOLD PRINT RUN 10 SERIAL #'d SETS
NO GOLD PRICING DUE TO SCARCITY
RANDOM INSERTS IN PACKS
1 Bob Gibson 4.00 10.00
2 Cal Ripken 15.00 40.00
3 Carl Yastrzemski 6.00 15.00
4 Dale Murphy 4.00 10.00
5 Gary Carter 3.00 8.00
6 George Brett 8.00 20.00
7 Tom Seaver 4.00 10.00
8 Kerry Wood 2.00 5.00
9 Lou Brock 4.00 10.00
10 Luis Aparicio 3.00 8.00
11 Mike Piazza 5.00 12.00
12 Nolan Ryan Astros 8.00 20.00
13 Nolan Ryan Rgr 8.00 20.00
14 Randy Johnson 3.00 8.00
15 Reggie Jackson 4.00 10.00
16 Rickey Henderson 4.00 10.00
17 Robin Yount 4.00 10.00
18 Rod Carew 4.00 10.00
19 Ryne Sandberg 8.00 20.00
20 Steve Carlton 3.00 8.00
21 Steve Garvey 3.00 8.00
22 Johnny Bench 4.00 10.00
23 Tony Gwynn 6.00 15.00
24 Whitey Ford 4.00 10.00
25 Will Clark 4.00 10.00

2004 Leaf Limited Team Trademarks Autographs

OVERALL AU-GU ODDS ONE PER PACK
PRINT RUNS B/WN 5-100 COPIES PER
NO PRICING ON QTY OF 10 OR LESS
1 Bob Gibson/100 10.00 25.00
2 Cal Ripken/25 125.00 200.00
3 Carl Yastrzemski/25 40.00 80.00
4 Dale Murphy/100 10.00 25.00
5 Gary Carter/100 6.00 15.00
6 George Brett/25 40.00 80.00
7 Tom Seaver/25 30.00 60.00
8 Kerry Wood/25 15.00 40.00
9 Lou Brock/100 10.00 25.00
10 Luis Aparicio/100 6.00 15.00
11 Mike Piazza/5
12 Nolan Ryan Astros/25 60.00 120.00
13 Nolan Ryan Rgr/25 60.00 120.00
14 Randy Johnson/5
15 Reggie Jackson/25 30.00 60.00
16 Rickey Henderson/10
17 Robin Yount/50 30.00 60.00
18 Rod Carew/50 12.50 30.00
19 Ryne Sandberg/25 40.00 80.00
20 Steve Carlton/100 6.00 15.00
21 Steve Garvey/50 8.00 20.00
22 Johnny Bench/25 30.00 60.00
23 Tony Gwynn/100 15.00 40.00
24 Whitey Ford/25 15.00 40.00
25 Will Clark/34 15.00 40.00

2004 Leaf Limited Team Trademarks Autographs Jersey Number

*JSY NBR p/r 84-100: .5X TO 1.2X AU p/r 100
*JSY NBR p/r 84-100: .3X TO .8X AU p/r 25-34
*JSY NBR p/r 50: .6X TO 1.5X AU p/r 100
*JSY NBR p/r 50: .5X TO 1.2X AU p/r 50
*JSY NBR p/r 50: .4X TO 1X AU p/r 25-34
*JSY NBR p/r 25: .75X TO 2X AU p/r 100
*JSY NBR p/r 25: .5X TO 1.2X AU p/r 25-34
PRINT RUNS B/WN 5-100 COPIES PER
NO PRICING ON QTY OF 10 OR LESS
PRIME PRINT RUN 1 SERIAL #'d SET
NO PRIME PRICING DUE TO SCARCITY
OVERALL AU-GU ODDS ONE PER PACK

2004 Leaf Limited Team Trademarks Jersey Number

PRINT RUNS B/WN 6-100 COPIES PER
NO PRICING ON QTY OF 6 OR LESS
PRIME PRINT RUN 1 SERIAL #'d SET
NO PRIME PRICING DUE TO SCARCITY
OVERALL AU-GU ODDS ONE PER PACK
1 Bob Gibson/100 5.00 12.00
2 Cal Ripken Pants/100 20.00 50.00
3 Carl Yastrzemski/100 8.00 20.00
4 Dale Murphy/100 5.00 12.00
5 Gary Carter/100 3.00 8.00
6 George Brett/100 8.00 20.00
7 Tom Seaver/100 5.00 12.00
8 Kerry Wood Pants/50 3.00 8.00
9 Lou Brock/100 5.00 12.00
10 Luis Aparicio Pants/100 3.00 8.00
11 Mike Piazza/50 8.00 20.00
12 Nolan Ryan Astros/100 10.00 25.00
13 Nolan Ryan Rgr/100 10.00 25.00
14 Randy Johnson/50 6.00 15.00
15 Reggie Jackson Pants/100 5.00 12.00
16 Rickey Henderson/100 6.00 15.00
17 Robin Yount/100 6.00 15.00
18 Rod Carew Jkt/100 5.00 12.00
19 Ryne Sandberg/100 8.00 20.00
20 Steve Carlton/50 4.00 10.00
21 Steve Garvey/6
22 Johnny Bench/100 6.00 15.00

23 Tony Gwynn/100 6.00 15.00
24 Whitey Ford/100 5.00 12.00
25 Will Clark/50 6.00 15.00

2005 Leaf Limited

This 204-card set was released in August, 2005. The set was issued in four-card tins with an $70 SRP which were issued one pack per box and 10 boxes per case. The first 150 cards in the set feature active veterans with the 1st 20 cards featuring players in home and away uniforms. Each of those cards were issued to a stated print run of 699 serial numbered sets. Cards numbered 151 through 168 feature retired greats, while cards 169-175 feature active players in uniforms they wore during key parts of their career. The set concludes with cards number 176 through 204 which feature signed Rookie Cards (with the excepption of Tadahito Iguchi). All cards numbered 151 through 205 were issued to a stated print run of 99 serial numbered sets except for a couple exceptions which we have notated in our checklist. Cards numbered 176 through 205 were issued at a stated rate of one in two. Card number 204 was not issued.

COMMON CARD (1-150) 1.25 3.00
COMMON CARD (151-168) 2.00 5.00
COMMON CARD (169-175) 2.00 5.00
201-205 CUTS FABRIC IS NOT GAME-USED
1 Roger Clemens H 2.50 6.00
2 Roger Clemens A 2.50 6.00
3 Ichiro Suzuki H 3.00 8.00
4 Ichiro Suzuki A 3.00 8.00
5 Todd Helton H 1.50 4.00
6 Todd Helton A 1.50 4.00
7 Vladimir Guerrero H 2.00 5.00
8 Vladimir Guerrero A 1.50 4.00
9 Miguel Cabrera H 1.50 4.00
10 Miguel Cabrera A 1.50 4.00
11 Albert Pujols H 3.00 8.00
12 Albert Pujols A 3.00 8.00
13 Mark Prior H 1.50 4.00
14 Mark Prior A 1.50 4.00
15 Chipper Jones H 1.50 4.00
16 Chipper Jones A 1.50 4.00
17 Jeff Bagwell H 1.50 4.00
18 Jeff Bagwell A 1.50 4.00
19 Kerry Wood H 1.25 3.00
20 Kerry Wood A 1.25 3.00
21 Gary Sheffield 1.25 3.00
22 Carl Crawford 1.25 3.00
23 Mariano Rivera 1.50 4.00
24 Curt Schilling 1.50 4.00
25 Ben Sheets 1.25 3.00
26 Jimmy Rollins 1.25 3.00
27 Melvin Mora 1.25 3.00
28 Corey Patterson 1.25 3.00
29 Rafael Furcal 1.25 3.00
30 Jim Thome 1.50 4.00
31 Derek Jeter 3.00 8.00
32 Jake Peavy 1.25 3.00
33 Francisco Cordero 1.25 3.00
34 Aramis Ramirez 1.25 3.00
35 Javy Lopez 1.25 3.00
36 Aaron Rowand 1.25 3.00
37 Jason Bay 1.25 3.00
38 Michael Young 1.25 3.00
39 Ivan Rodriguez 1.50 4.00
40 Joe Nathan 1.25 3.00
41 Oliver Perez 1.25 3.00
42 Adam Dunn 1.25 3.00
43 Eric Chavez 1.25 3.00
44 Pedro Martinez 1.50 4.00
45 Roy Oswalt 1.25 3.00
46 Carlos Delgado 1.25 3.00
47 Jeff Kent 1.25 3.00
48 Johnny Damon 1.50 4.00
49 Edgar Renteria 1.25 3.00
50 Mark Buehrle 1.25 3.00
51 Carl Pavano 1.25 3.00
52 J.D. Drew 1.25 3.00
53 Hank Blalock 1.25 3.00
54 Moises Alou 1.25 3.00
55 Brad Radke 1.25 3.00
56 Brad Wilkerson 1.25 3.00
57 Sean Casey 1.25 3.00
58 Mike Lowell 1.25 3.00
59 Octavio Dotel 1.25 3.00
60 Francisco Rodriguez 1.25 3.00
61 Jose Guillen 1.25 3.00
62 Greg Maddux 2.50 6.00
63 A.J. Burnett 1.25 3.00
64 Chris Carpenter 1.25 3.00
65 Jose Reyes 1.25 3.00
66 Travis Hafner 1.25 3.00
67 Rich Harden 1.25 3.00
68 Bret Boone 1.25 3.00
69 Scott Podsednik 1.25 3.00
70 Andruw Jones 1.50 4.00
71 Milton Bradley 1.25 3.00
72 Zack Greinke 1.25 3.00
73 Torii Hunter 1.25 3.00
74 Paul Konerko 1.25 3.00
75 David Wells 1.25 3.00
76 Tim Hudson 1.25 3.00
77 Sammy Sosa 1.50 4.00
78 Jason Varitek 1.50 4.00
79 Lance Berkman 1.25 3.00
80 Justin Morneau 1.25 3.00
81 Troy Glaus 1.25 3.00
82 José Vidro 1.25 3.00
83 Joe Mauer 2.00 5.00
84 Josh Beckett 1.25 3.00
85 Craig Biggio 1.50 4.00
86 Luis Gonzalez 1.25 3.00
87 Larry Walker 1.50 4.00
88 Barry Zito 1.25 3.00
89 Jacque Jones 1.25 3.00
90 Lyle Overbay 1.25 3.00
91 Roy Halladay 1.25 3.00
92 Orlando Cabrera 1.25 3.00
93 Magglio Ordonez 1.25 3.00
94 Mike Sweeney 1.25 3.00
95 Rafael Palmeiro 1.50 4.00
96 Brandon Webb 1.25 3.00
97 Preston Wilson 1.25 3.00
98 Shannon Stewart 1.25 3.00
99 Trot Nixon 1.25 3.00
100 Mike Piazza 1.50 4.00
101 Dontrelle Willis 1.25 3.00
102 Ken Griffey Jr. 2.50 6.00
103 Andy Pettitte 1.50 4.00
104 Kazuo Matsui 1.25 3.00
105 Bobby Crosby 1.25 3.00
106 Shawn Green 1.25 3.00
107 Alfonso Soriano 1.25 3.00
108 Carlos Zambrano 1.25 3.00
109 Keith Foulke 1.25 3.00
110 Aubrey Huff 1.25 3.00
111 Adrian Beltre 1.25 3.00
112 Mark Teixeira 1.50 4.00
113 Randy Johnson 1.50 4.00
114 Miguel Tejada 1.25 3.00
115 Alex Rodriguez 2.50 6.00
116 Carlos Beltran 1.25 3.00
117 Bobby Abreu 1.25 3.00
118 Johan Santana 2.00 5.00
119 Manny Ramirez 1.50 4.00
120 Juan Pierre 1.25 3.00
121 Scott Rolen 1.50 4.00
122 Livan Hernandez 1.25 3.00
123 Carlos Lee 1.25 3.00
124 Derrek Lee 1.50 4.00
125 Brian Giles 1.25 3.00
126 Nomar Garciaparra 1.50 4.00
127 John Smoltz 1.50 4.00
128 Jim Edmonds 1.25 3.00
129 Bartolo Colon 1.25 3.00
130 Garret Anderson 1.25 3.00
131 Austin Kearns 1.25 3.00
132 Shingo Takatsu 1.25 3.00
133 Omar Vizquel 1.50 4.00
134 Tom Glavine 1.25 3.00
135 Mark Mulder 1.25 3.00
136 Bernie Williams 1.50 4.00
137 Richie Sexson 1.25 3.00
138 Mike Mussina 1.50 4.00
139 Mark Loretta 1.25 3.00
140 Vernon Wells 1.25 3.00
141 David Wright 2.50 6.00
142 Marcus Giles 1.25 3.00
143 David Ortiz 1.50 4.00
144 Victor Martinez 1.25 3.00
145 Hideki Matsui 2.50 6.00
146 C.C. Sabathia 1.25 3.00
147 Angel Berroa 1.25 3.00
148 Troy Percival 1.25 3.00
149 Paul Lo Duca 1.25 3.00
150 Jorge Posada 1.50 4.00
151 Willie Mays LGD 4.00 10.00
152 Ryne Sandberg LGD 5.00 12.00
153 Rickey Henderson LGD 3.00 8.00
154 Ted Williams LGD 5.00 12.00
155 Roberto Clemente LGD 6.00 15.00
156 George Brett LGD 5.00 12.00
157 Whitey Ford LGD 2.50 6.00
158 Duke Snider LGD 2.50 6.00
159 Don Mattingly LGD 5.00 12.00
160 Bob Gibson LGD 2.50 6.00
161 Hank Aaron LGD 4.00 10.00
162 Al Kaline LGD 3.00 8.00
163 Nolan Ryan LGD 5.00 12.00
164 Stan Musial LGD 3.00 8.00
165 George Kell LGD 2.00 5.00
166 Harmon Killebrew LGD 3.00 8.00
167 Cal Ripken LGD 8.00 20.00
168 Babe Ruth LGD 5.00 12.00
169 Roger Clemens Sox SP 4.00 10.00
170 Curt Schilling D'backs SP 2.00 5.00
171 Rafael Palmeiro Rgr SP 2.50 6.00
172 Randy Johnson M's SP 3.00 8.00
173 Mike Piazza Dgr SP 3.00 8.00
174 Greg Maddux Braves SP 4.00 10.00
175 Sammy Sosa Cubs SP 3.00 8.00
176 Hayden Penn PH AU RC 10.00 25.00
177 A.Concepcion PH AU RC 6.00 15.00
178 Casey Rogowski PH AU RC 8.00 20.00
179 Prince Fielder PH AU RC 50.00 100.00
180 Geovany Soto PH AU RC 60.00 120.00
181 W.Balentien PH AU RC 10.00 25.00
182 Jason Hammel PH AU RC 6.00 15.00
183 Keiichi Yabu PH AU RC 10.00 25.00
184 B.McCarthy PH AU RC 20.00 50.00
185 Ubaldo Jimenez PH AU RC 12.50 30.00
186 Keiichi Yabu PH AU RC 10.00 25.00
187 Miguel Negron PH AU RC 8.00 20.00
188 Mike Morse PH AU RC 6.00 15.00
189 Nate McLouth PH AU RC 10.00 25.00
190 N.Nakamura PH AU RC 15.00 40.00
191 B.McCarthy PH AU RC 20.00 50.00
192 Tony Pena PH AU RC 6.00 15.00
193 A.Concepcion PH AU RC 6.00 15.00
194 Raul Tablado PH AU RC 6.00 15.00
195 Hayden Penn PH AU RC 10.00 25.00
196 Sean Thompson PH AU RC 6.00 15.00
197 Tadahito Iguchi PH RC 6.00 15.00
198 Ubaldo Jimenez PH AU RC 12.50 30.00
199 W.Balentien PH AU RC 10.00 25.00
200 Prince Fielder PH AU RC 90.00 150.00
201 P.Humber PHC AU/99 RC 20.00 50.00
202 J.Niemann PHC AU/95 RC 20.00 50.00
203 J.Verlander PHC AU/70 RC 60.00 120.00
205 Y.Betan PHC AU/99 RC 50.00 80.00

2005 Leaf Limited Bronze Spotlight

*BRZ 1-150: .6X TO 1.5X BASIC
*BRZ 151-168: .4X TO 1X BASIC
*BRZ 169-175: .4X TO 1X BASIC
*BRZ 176-196/298-200: .12X TO .3X BASIC AU
*BRZ 197: .3X TO .8X BASIC
OVERALL INSERT ODDS ONE PER PACK
STATED PRINT RUN 99 SERIAL #'d SETS
180 Geovany Soto PH 15.00 40.00
183 Keiichi Yabu PH 2.00 5.00
186 Keiichi Yabu PH 2.00 5.00

2005 Leaf Limited Gold Spotlight

*GOLD 1-150: 1.5X TO 4X BASIC
*GOLD 151-168: 1X TO 2.5X BASIC
*GOLD 169-175: 1X TO 2.5X BASIC
OVERALL INSERT ODDS ONE PER PACK
1-200 PRINT RUN 25 SERIAL #'d SETS
201-205 AU PRINTS B/WN 5-25 COPIES PER
176-205 NO PRICING DUE TO SCARCITY
201-205 CUTS FABRIC IS NOT GAME-USED
CARD 204 DOES NOT EXIST

2005 Leaf Limited Platinum Spotlight

OVERALL INSERT ODDS ONE PER PACK
STATED PRINT RUN 1 SERIAL #'d SET
NO PRICING DUE TO SCARCITY
201-205 CUTS FABRIC IS NOT GAME-USED
CARD 204 DOES NOT EXIST

2005 Leaf Limited Silver Spotlight

*SILV 1-150: .75X TO 2X BASIC
*SILV 151-168: .5X TO 1.2X BASIC
*SILV 169-175: .5X TO 1.2X BASIC
*SILV 176-196/298-200: .15X TO .4X BASE AU
*SILV 197: .4X TO 1X BASIC
OVERALL INSERT ODDS ONE PER PACK
STATED PRINT RUN 50 SERIAL #'d SETS
180 Geovany Soto PH 20.00 50.00
183 Keiichi Yabu PH 2.50 6.00
186 Keiichi Yabu PH 2.50 6.00

2005 Leaf Limited Monikers Bronze

OVERALL AU-GU ODDS ONE PER PACK
PRINT RUNS B/WN 1-100 COPIES PER
1-175 NO PRICING ON QTY OF 12 OR LESS
176-200 NO PRICING ON QTY 20 OR LESS
1 Roger Clemens H/1
2 Roger Clemens A/1
5 Todd Helton H/1
6 Todd Helton A/1
9 Miguel Cabrera H/100 10.00 25.00
10 Miguel Cabrera A/100 10.00 25.00
11 Albert Pujols H/1
12 Albert Pujols A/1
13 Mark Prior H/50 10.00 25.00
14 Mark Prior A/50 10.00 25.00
15 Chipper Jones H/10
16 Chipper Jones A/10
17 Jeff Bagwell H/1
18 Jeff Bagwell A/1
21 Gary Sheffield/1
22 Carl Crawford/4
24 Curt Schilling/1
25 Ben Sheets/100 6.00 15.00
27 Melvin Mora/50 8.00 20.00
29 Rafael Furcal/25 10.00 25.00
32 Jake Peavy/50 12.50 30.00
33 Francisco Cordero/25 10.00 25.00
37 Jason Bay/10
38 Michael Young/25 10.00 25.00
40 Joe Nathan/25 10.00 25.00
43 Eric Chavez/25 10.00 25.00
44 Pedro Martinez/1
45 Roy Oswalt/50 8.00 20.00
49 Edgar Renteria/25 10.00 25.00
50 Mark Buehrle/25 15.00 40.00
57 Sean Casey/50 8.00 20.00
59 Octavio Dotel/25 6.00 15.00
60 Francisco Rodriguez/25 15.00 40.00
61 Jose Guillen/25 10.00 25.00
62 Greg Maddux/1
66 Travis Hafner/50 8.00 20.00
67 Rich Harden/50 8.00 20.00
71 Milton Bradley/25 10.00 25.00
73 Torii Hunter/25 10.00 25.00
74 Paul Konerko/50 12.50 30.00
76 Tim Hudson/25 15.00 40.00
80 Justin Morneau/100 6.00 15.00
82 Jose Vidro/25 10.00 25.00
84 Josh Beckett/25 15.00 40.00
85 Craig Biggio/25 15.00 40.00
88 Barry Zito/1
89 Jacque Jones/50 8.00 20.00
91 Roy Halladay/25 10.00 25.00
92 Orlando Cabrera/10
93 Magglio Ordonez/100 6.00 15.00
95 Rafael Palmeiro/1
96 Brandon Webb/50 5.00 12.00
97 Preston Wilson/50 8.00 20.00
98 Shannon Stewart/50 8.00 20.00
99 Trot Nixon/50 12.50 30.00
100 Mike Piazza/1
101 Dontrelle Willis/10
105 Bebby Crosby/40 8.00 20.00
106 Shawn Green/1
107 Alfonso Soriano/25 10.00 25.00
108 Carlos Zambrano/50 15.00 40.00
109 Keith Foulke/25 15.00 40.00
110 Aubrey Huff/50 8.00 20.00
111 Adrian Beltre/10
112 Mark Teixeira/100 10.00 25.00
116 Carlos Beltran/25 10.00 25.00
118 Johan Santana/100 12.50 30.00
119 Manny Ramirez/1
121 Scott Rolen/25 15.00 40.00
122 Livan Hernandez/5
123 Carlos Lee/50 8.00 20.00
124 Derrek Lee/50 12.50 30.00
128 Jim Edmonds/1
130 Garret Anderson/100 6.00 15.00
131 Austin Kearns/100 4.00 10.00
132 Shingo Takatsu/5
133 Omar Vizquel/50 12.50 30.00
135 Mark Mulder/50 8.00 20.00
139 Mark Loretta/25 6.00 15.00
140 Vernon Wells/12
141 David Wright/50 20.00 50.00
144 Victor Martinez/25 10.00 25.00
147 Angel Berroa/5
148 Troy Percival/5
149 Paul Lo Duca/5
151 Willie Mays LGD/25 100.00 175.00
152 Ryne Sandberg LGD/25 30.00 60.00
153 Rickey Henderson LGD/1
156 George Brett LGD/1
157 Whitey Ford LGD/5
158 Duke Snider LGD/50 12.50 30.00
159 Don Mattingly LGD/25 30.00 60.00
160 Bob Gibson LGD/50 12.50 30.00
161 Hank Aaron LGD/1
162 Al Kaline LGD/50 15.00 40.00
163 Nolan Ryan LGD/25 50.00 100.00
164 Stan Musial LGD/25 30.00 60.00
165 George Kelt LGD/50 8.00 20.00
166 Harmon Killebrew LGD/50 15.00 40.00
167 Cal Ripken LGD/25 60.00 120.00
169 Roger Clemens Sox/1
170 Curt Schilling D'backs/1
171 Rafael Palmeiro Rgr/1
173 Mike Piazza Dgr/1
174 Greg Maddux Braves/1
176 Hayden Penn PH/50 12.50 30.00
177 Ambiorix Concepcion PH/50 6.00 15.00
178 Casey Rogowski PH/20
179 Prince Fielder PH/50 125.00 250.00
180 Geovany Soto PH/10
181 Wladimir Balentien PH/50 12.50 30.00
182 Jason Hammel PH/50 6.00 15.00
183 Keiichi Yabu PH/50 15.00 40.00
184 Brandon McCarthy PH/50 30.00 60.00
185 Ubaldo Jimenez PH/50 15.00 40.00
186 Keiichi Yabu PH/50 15.00 40.00
187 Miguel Negron PH/50 10.00 25.00
188 Mike Morse PH/50 8.00 20.00
189 Nate McLouth PH/50 15.00 40.00
190 Norihiro Nakamura PH/50 20.00 50.00
191 Brandon McCarthy PH/50 30.00 60.00
192 Tony Pena PH/50 6.00 15.00
193 Ambiorix Concepcion PH/50 6.00 15.00
194 Raul Tablado PH/50 6.00 15.00
195 Hayden Penn PH/50 12.50 30.00
196 Sean Thompson PH/50 6.00 15.00
198 Ubaldo Jimenez PH/50 15.00 40.00
199 Wladimir Balentien PH/50 12.50 30.00
200 Prince Fielder PH/50 125.00 250.00

2005 Leaf Limited Monikers Gold

*1-175 p/r 25: .6X TO 1.5X BRZ p/r 100
*1-175 p/r 25: .5X TO 1.2X BRZ p/r 40-50
*1-175 p/r 25: .4X TO 1X BRZ p/r 25
OVERALL AU-GU ODDS ONE PER PACK
PRINT RUNS B/WN 1-25 COPIES PER
1-175 NO PRICING ON QTY OF 10 OR LESS
176-200 NO PRICING DUE TO SCARCITY
21 Gary Sheffield/25 15.00 40.00
37 Jason Bay/25 10.00 25.00
88 Barry Zito/25 10.00 25.00
90 Lyle Overbay/25 6.00 15.00
151 Willie Mays LGD/25 100.00 175.00
163 Nolan Ryan LGD/25 50.00 100.00
167 Cal Ripken LGD/25 60.00 120.00

2005 Leaf Limited Monikers Platinum

OVERALL AU-GU ODDS ONE PER PACK
STATED PRINT RUN 1 SERIAL #'d SET
NO PRICING DUE TO SCARCITY

2005 Leaf Limited Monikers Silver

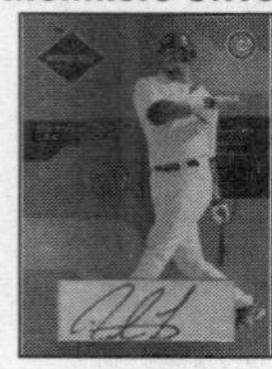

*1-175 p/r 50: .5X TO 1.2X BRZ p/r 100
*1-175 p/r 50: .4X TO 1X BRZ p/r 40-50
*1-175 p/r 25: .5X TO 1.2X BRZ p/r 40-50
*1-175 p/r 25: .4X TO 1X BRZ p/r 25
OVERALL AU-GU ODDS ONE PER PACK
PRINT RUNS B/WN 1-50 COPIES PER
1-175 NO PRICING ON QTY OF 10 OR LESS
176-200 NO PRICING DUE TO SCARCITY
151 Willie Mays LGD/25 100.00 175.00
163 Nolan Ryan LGD/25 50.00 100.00
167 Cal Ripken LGD/25 60.00 120.00

2005 Leaf Limited Monikers Material Bat Bronze

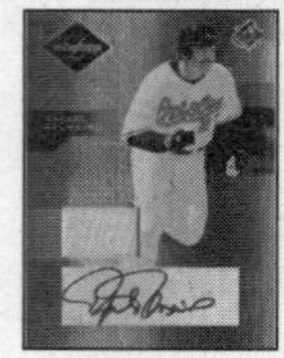

*1-175 p/r 100: .5X TO 1.2X BRZ p/r 100
*1-175 p/r 100: .4X TO 1X BRZ p/r 40-50
*1-175 p/r 100: .3X TO .8X BRZ p/r 25
*1-175 p/r 50: .6X TO 1.5X BRZ p/r 100
*1-175 p/r 50: .5X TO 1.2X BRZ p/r 40-50
*1-175 p/r 50: .4X TO 1X BRZ p/r 25
*1-175 p/r 25: .6X TO 1.5X BRZ p/r 40-50
*1-175 p/r 25: .5X TO 1.2X BRZ p/r 25
OVERALL AU-GU ODDS ONE PER PACK
PRINT RUNS B/WN 1-100 COPIES PER
NO PRICING ON QTY OF 10 OR LESS
34 Aramis Ramirez/100 8.00 20.00
37 Jason Bay/100 8.00 20.00
111 Adrian Beltre/25 12.50 30.00
140 Vernon Wells/50 10.00 25.00
143 David Ortiz/50 20.00 50.00
147 Angel Berroa/100 5.00 12.00

2005 Leaf Limited Monikers Material Bat Platinum

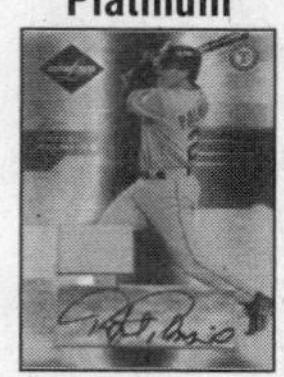

OVERALL AU-GU ODDS ONE PER PACK
STATED PRINT RUN 1 SERIAL #'d SET
NO PRICING DUE TO SCARCITY

2005 Leaf Limited Monikers Material Button Gold

PRINT RUNS B/WN 1-5 COPIES PER
PLATINUM PRINT RUN 1 SERIAL #'d SET
OVERALL AU-GU ODDS ONE PER PACK
NO PRICING DUE TO SCARCITY

2005 Leaf Limited Monikers Material Jersey Prime Gold

*1-175 p/r 100: .5X TO 1.2X BRZ p/r 40-50
*1-175 p/r 100: .4X TO 1X BRZ p/r 25
*1-175 p/r 50: .75X TO 2X BRZ p/r 100
*1-175 p/r 50: .6X TO 1.5X BRZ p/r 40-50
*1-175 p/r 50: .5X TO 1.2X BRZ p/r 25
*1-175 p/r 20-30: 1X TO 2.5X BRZ p/r 100
*1-175 p/r 20-30: .75X TO 2X BRZ p/r 40-50
*1-175 p/r 20-30: .6X TO 1.5X BRZ p/r 25
PRINT RUNS B/WN 1-100 COPIES PER
NO PRICING ON QTY OF 10 OR LESS
PLATINUM PRINT RUN 1 SERIAL #'d SET
NO PLATINUM PRICING DUE TO SCARCITY
OVERALL AU-GU ODDS ONE PER PACK
34 Aramis Ramirez/100 10.00 25.00
70 Andruw Jones/50 15.00 40.00
88 Barry Zito/25 15.00 40.00
103 Andy Pettitte/20 30.00 60.00
117 Bobby Abreu/100 10.00 25.00
128 Jim Edmonds/25 30.00 60.00
140 Vernon Wells/50 12.50 30.00
163 Nolan Ryan LGD/25 60.00 120.00
167 Cal Ripken LGD/25 125.00 200.00

2005 Leaf Limited Monikers Material Jersey Number Silver

*1-175 p/r 75: .5X TO 1.2X BRZ p/r 100
*1-175 p/r 75: .4X TO 1X BRZ p/r 40-50
*1-175 p/r 75: .3X TO .8X BRZ p/r 25
*1-175 p/r 50: .6X TO 1.5X BRZ p/r 100
*1-175 p/r 50: .5X TO 1.2X BRZ p/r 40-50
*1-175 p/r 50: .4X TO 1X BRZ p/r 25
*1-175 p/r 24-25: .6X TO 1.5X BRZ p/r 40-50
*1-175 p/r 24-25: .5X TO 1.2X BRZ p/r 25
*1-175 p/r 15: 1X TO 2.5X BRZ p/r 100
PRINT RUNS B/WN 1-75 COPIES PER
NO PRICING ON QTY OF 10 OR LESS
PRIME PLATINUM PRINT RUN 1 #'d SET
NO PRIME PLAT.PRICING DUE TO SCARCITY
OVERALL AU-GU ODDS ONE PER PACK
34 Aramis Ramirez/75 8.00 20.00
70 Andruw Jones/25 20.00 50.00
90 Lyle Overbay/75 5.00 12.00
101 Dontrelle Willis/24 12.50 30.00
117 Bobby Abreu/75 8.00 20.00
128 Jim Edmonds/25 20.00 50.00
140 Vernon Wells/50 10.00 25.00
143 David Ortiz/75 15.00 40.00
163 Nolan Ryan LGD/25 50.00 100.00
167 Cal Ripken LGD/25 75.00 150.00

2005 Leaf Limited Threads Button

OVERALL AU-GU ODDS ONE PER PACK
PRINT RUNS B/WN 1-7 COPIES PER
NO PRICING DUE TO SCARCITY

2005 Leaf Limited Threads Jersey Prime

OVERALL AU-GU ODDS ONE PER PACK
PRINT RUNS B/WN 5-100 COPIES PER
NO PRICING ON QTY OF 5
PRICES ARE FOR 2 COLOR PATCHES
REDUCE 20% FOR 1-COLOR PATCH
ADD 20% FOR 3-4 COLOR PATCH
ADD 50% FOR 5-COLOR+ PATCH
1 Roger Clemens H/25 12.50 30.00
5 Todd Helton H/100 5.00 12.00

6 Todd Helton A/100 5.00 12.00
7 Vladimir Guerrero H/100 6.00 15.00
8 Vladimir Guerrero A Jkt/30 10.00 25.00
9 Miguel Cabrera H/100 5.00 12.00
10 Miguel Cabrera A/100 5.00 12.00
12 Albert Pujols A/50 15.00 40.00
13 Mark Prior H/100 5.00 12.00
14 Mark Prior A/25 8.00 20.00
15 Chipper Jones H/100 6.00 15.00
16 Chipper Jones A/100 6.00 15.00
17 Jeff Bagwell H/100 5.00 12.00
18 Jeff Bagwell A/100 5.00 12.00
19 Kerry Wood H/100 3.00 8.00
22 Carl Crawford/100 3.00 8.00
23 Mariano Rivera/60 8.00 20.00
25 Ben Sheets/100 3.00 8.00
27 Melvin Mora/25 5.00 12.00
28 Corey Patterson/100 3.00 8.00
29 Rafael Furcal/100 3.00 8.00
30 Jim Thome/100 5.00 12.00
34 Aramis Ramirez/50 4.00 10.00
35 Javy Lopez/100 3.00 8.00
38 Michael Young/100 3.00 8.00
39 Ivan Rodriguez/100 5.00 12.00
42 Adam Dunn/100 3.00 8.00
43 Eric Chavez/100 3.00 8.00
45 Roy Oswalt/100 3.00 8.00
48 Johnny Damon/50 6.00 15.00
50 Mark Buehrle/50 4.00 10.00
53 Hank Blalock/100 3.00 8.00
55 Brad Radke/50 4.00 10.00
57 Sean Casey/50 4.00 10.00
58 Mike Lowell/100 3.00 8.00
60 Francisco Rodriguez/100 3.00 8.00
62 Greg Maddux/25 12.50 30.00
63 A.J. Burnett/75 3.00 8.00
66 Travis Hafner/100 3.00 8.00
68 Bret Boone/100 3.00 8.00
70 Andruw Jones/100 5.00 12.00
73 Torii Hunter/100 3.00 8.00
74 Paul Konerko/100 3.00 8.00
79 Lance Berkman/100 3.00 8.00
80 Justin Morneau/100 3.00 8.00
82 Jose Vidro/100 3.00 8.00
84 Josh Beckett/100 3.00 8.00
86 Luis Gonzalez/100 3.00 8.00
88 Barry Zito/100 3.00 8.00
91 Roy Halladay/100 3.00 8.00
94 Mike Sweeney/100 3.00 8.00
95 Rafael Palmeiro/100 5.00 12.00
97 Preston Wilson/100 3.00 8.00
98 Shannon Stewart/50 4.00 10.00
99 Trot Nixon/25 5.00 12.00
100 Mike Piazza/100 6.00 15.00
101 Dontrelle Willis/100 3.00 8.00
103 Andy Pettitte/50 6.00 15.00
104 Kazuo Matsui/100 3.00 8.00
107 Alfonso Soriano/100 3.00 8.00
110 Aubrey Huff/100 3.00 8.00
111 Adrian Beltre/50 4.00 10.00
112 Mark Teixeira/60 6.00 15.00
114 Miguel Tejada/100 3.00 8.00
117 Bobby Abreu/100 3.00 8.00
119 Manny Ramirez/60 6.00 15.00
121 Scott Rolen/100 5.00 12.00
124 Derrek Lee/50 6.00 15.00
127 John Smoltz/100 5.00 12.00
128 Jim Edmonds/100 3.00 8.00
130 Garret Anderson/60 4.00 10.00
131 Austin Kearns/100 3.00 8.00
138 Mike Mussina/50 6.00 15.00
140 Vernon Wells/100 3.00 8.00
141 David Wright/100 12.50 30.00
142 Marcus Giles/100 3.00 8.00
144 Victor Martinez/75 3.00 8.00
145 Hideki Matsui/100 20.00 50.00
146 C.C. Sabathia/100 3.00 8.00
150 Jorge Posada/75 5.00 12.00
152 Ryne Sandberg LGD/50 12.50 30.00
153 Rickey Henderson LGD/25 12.50 30.00
154 Ted Williams LGD/5
156 George Brett LGD/50 12.50 30.00
159 Don Mattingly LGD/50 12.50 30.00
160 Bob Gibson LGD/25 10.00 25.00
161 Hank Aaron LGD/25 40.00 80.00
163 Nolan Ryan LGD/100 12.50 30.00
167 Cal Ripken LGD/100 15.00 40.00
169 Roger Clemens Sox/50 10.00 25.00
170 Curt Schilling D'backs/100 3.00 8.00
171 Rafael Palmeiro Rgr/100 3.00 8.00
173 Mike Piazza Dgr/100 6.00 15.00
174 Greg Maddux Braves/100 8.00 20.00
175 Sammy Sosa Cubs/100 6.00 15.00

2005 Leaf Limited Threads Jersey Number

*151-168 p/r 50: .3X TO .8X JPR p/r 100
*151-168 p/r 50: .25X TO .6X JPR p/r 50
OVERALL AU-GU ODDS ONE PER PACK
PRINT RUNS B/WN 1-100 COPIES PER
NO PRICING ON QTY OF 10 OR LESS
154 Ted Williams LGD/25 30.00 60.00
157 Whitey Ford LGD/50 5.00 12.00
158 Duke Snider LGD/25 6.00 15.00
164 Stan Musial LGD/25 12.50 30.00
166 Harmon Killebrew LGD/50 6.00 15.00
168 Babe Ruth LGD/25 175.00 300.00

2005 Leaf Limited Threads MLB Logo

OVERALL AU-GU ODDS ONE PER PACK
STATED PRINT RUN 1 SERIAL #'d SET
NO PRICING DUE TO SCARCITY

2005 Leaf Limited Timber Barrel

OVERALL AU-GU ODDS ONE PER PACK
PRINT RUNS B/WN 1-3 COPIES PER
NO PRICING DUE TO SCARCITY

2005 Leaf Limited TNT

*1-150/169-175p/r50: .4XTO1X JPRp/r75-100
*1-150/169-175p/r50: .3XTO.8X JPRp/r50-60
*1-150/169-175p/r50: .25X TO.6XJPRp/r25-30
*1-150 p/r 25-30: .5X TO 1.2X JPR p/r 75-100
*1-150 p/r 25-30: .3X TO .8X JPR p/r 25-30
*151-168 p/r 50: .4X TO 1X JPR p/r 100
*151-168 p/r 50: .3X TO .8X JPR p/r 50
*151-168 p/r 25: .25X TO .6X JPR p/r 25
*151-168 p/r 25: .3X TO .8X JPR p/r 25
OVERALL AU-GU ODDS ONE PER PACK
PRINT RUNS B/WN 1-50 COPIES PER
NO PRICING ON QTY OF 10 OR LESS
11 Albert Pujols H Bat-Jsy/50 12.50 30.00
143 David Ortiz Bat-Jsy/50 5.00 12.00
151 Willie Mays LGD Bat-Jsy/25 30.00 60.00
154 T.Williams LGD Bat-Jsy/25 50.00 100.00
164 S.Musial LGD Bat-Jsy/25 15.00 40.00
166 H.Killebrew LGD Bat-Jsy/25 10.00 25.00
172 R.Johnson M's Bat-Jsy/25 8.00 20.00

2005 Leaf Limited TNT Prime

*1-150/169-75pr75-100: .4XTO1XJPRpr 75-100
*1-150 p/r 75-100: .3X TO .8X JPR p/r 50-60
*1-150/169-175pr40-60: .5XTO1.2XpR75-100
*1-150/169-175p/r40-60: .4XTO1XJPRpr50-60
*1-150 p/r 40-60: .3X TO .8X JPR p/r25-30
*1-150 p/r 25: .6X TO 1.5X JPR p/r 75-100
*1-150 p/r 25: .5X TO 1.2X JPR p/r 50-60
*1-150 p/r 25: .4X TO 1X JPR p/r 25-30
*1-150 p/r 15: .6X TO 1.5X JPR p/r 50-60
*151-168 p/r 100: .4X TO 1X JPR p/r 100
*151-168 p/r 50: .5X TO 1.2X JPR p/r 100
*151-168 p/r 50: .4X TO 1X JPR p/r 50
*151-168 p/r 25: .4X TO 1X JPR p/r 25
OVERALL AU-GU ODDS ONE PER PACK
PRINT RUNS B/WN 5-100 COPIES PER
NO PRICING ON QTY OF 10 OR LESS
PRICES ARE FOR 2-COLOR PATCHES
REDUCE 20% FOR 1-COLOR PATCH
ADD 20% FOR 3-4 COLOR PATCH
ADD 50% FOR 5-COLOR+ PATCH

2005 Leaf Limited Cuts Gold

*GOLD p/r 22-30: .6X TO 1.5X SILVER p/r 99
*GOLD p/r 22-30: .4X TO 1X SILVER p/r 20-34
OVERALL AU-GU ODDS ONE PER PACK
PRINT RUNS B/WN 3-30 COPIES PER
NO PRICING ON QTY OF 12 OR LESS
CUTS FABRIC IS NOT GAME-USED
4 Sandy Koufax/30 250.00 400.00
20 Craig Biggio/25 20.00 50.00

2005 Leaf Limited Cuts Silver

PRINT RUNS B/WN 7-99 COPIES PER
NO PRICING ON QTY OF 7
PLATINUM PRINT RUN 1 SERIAL #'d SET
NO PLATINUM PRICING DUE TO SCARCITY
OVERALL AU-GU ODDS ONE PER PACK
CUTS FABRIC IS NOT GAME-USED
1 Orlando Cepeda/30 15.00 40.00
2 Hank Aaron/44 175.00 300.00
3 Willie Mays/24 125.00 200.00
4 Sandy Koufax/32 250.00 400.00
5 Cal Ripken/25 100.00 175.00
6 Nolan Ryan/34 60.00 120.00
7 Jim Palmer/22 15.00 40.00
8 Tony Gwynn/19 30.00 60.00
9 Rod Carew/29 20.00 50.00
10 Ryne Sandberg/23 40.00 80.00
11 Stan Musial/28 40.00 80.00
12 Steve Carlton/32 15.00 40.00
14 Mike Schmidt/20 40.00 80.00
15 Harmon Killebrew/25 30.00 60.00
17 Duke Snider/53 20.00 50.00
18 Don Mattingly/25 40.00 80.00
19 Dale Murphy/25 20.00 50.00
20 Craig Biggio/7
21 Juan Marichal/99 10.00 25.00
22 Greg Maddux/36 100.00 175.00
23 Lou Brock/20 20.00 50.00
24 Paul Molitor/25 15.00 40.00
25 Wade Boggs/26 20.00 50.00
26 Mark Prior/27 15.00 40.00
28 Al Kaline/28 30.00 60.00
29 Minnie Minoso/25 20.00 50.00

2005 Leaf Limited Legends

STATED PRINT RUN 50 SERIAL #'d SETS
FOIL PRINT RUN 10 SERIAL #'d SETS
NO FOIL PRICING DUE TO SCARCITY
OVERALL INSERT ODDS ONE PER PACK
1 Billy Martin 3.00 8.00
2 Bobby Doerr 2.50 6.00
3 Carlton Fisk 3.00 8.00
4 Harmon Killebrew 4.00 10.00
5 Duke Snider 3.00 8.00
6 George Brett 6.00 15.00
7 Johnny Bench 4.00 10.00
8 Lou Boudreau 2.50 6.00
9 Brooks Robinson 3.00 8.00
10 Al Kaline 4.00 10.00
11 Stan Musial 4.00 10.00
12 Burleigh Grimes 2.50 6.00
13 Cal Ripken 10.00 25.00
14 Carl Yastrzemski 5.00 12.00
15 Willie Stargell 3.00 8.00
16 Yogi Berra 4.00 10.00
17 Enos Slaughter 2.50 6.00
18 Phil Rizzuto 3.00 8.00
19 Luis Aparicio 2.50 6.00
20 Ernie Banks 4.00 10.00
21 Hal Newhouser 2.50 6.00
22 Whitey Ford 3.00 8.00
23 Tony Gwynn 4.00 10.00
24 Bob Feller 2.50 6.00
25 Don Sutton 2.50 6.00
26 Lou Brock 3.00 8.00
27 Jim Palmer 2.50 6.00
28 Billy Williams 2.50 6.00
29 Juan Marichal 2.50 6.00
30 Rod Carew 3.00 8.00
31 Catfish Hunter 2.50 6.00
32 Maury Wills 2.50 6.00
33 Joe Cronin 2.50 6.00
34 Fergie Jenkins 2.50 6.00
35 Sandy Koufax 40.00 80.00
36 Steve Carlton 2.50 6.00
37 Eddie Murray 4.00 10.00
38 Roger Maris 4.00 10.00
39 Gaylord Perry 2.50 6.00
40 Bob Gibson 3.00 8.00
41 Tom Seaver 3.00 8.00
42 Dennis Eckersley 2.50 6.00
43 Reggie Jackson 3.00 8.00
44 Willie McCovey 3.00 8.00
45 Willie Mays NY 5.00 12.00
46 Willie Mays SF 5.00 12.00
47 Rickey Henderson M's 4.00 10.00
48 Rickey Henderson Mets 4.00 10.00
49 Nolan Ryan Angels 6.00 15.00
50 Nolan Ryan Mets 6.00 15.00

2005 Leaf Limited Legends Jersey Number

OVERALL AU-GU ODDS ONE PER PACK
PRINT RUNS B/WN 1-50 COPIES PER
NO PRICING ON QTY OF 14 OR LESS
1 Billy Martin/1
2 Bobby Doerr Pants/1
3 Carlton Fisk/50 5.00 12.00
4 Harmon Killebrew/3
5 Duke Snider/4

6 George Brett/5
7 Johnny Bench Pants/5
8 Lou Boudreau/5
9 Brooks Robinson/5
10 Al Kaline Pants/6
11 Stan Musial/6
12 Burleigh Grimes Pants/25 40.00 80.00
13 Cal Ripken/1
14 Carl Yastrzemski/8
15 Willie Stargell/8
16 Yogi Berra Pants/8
17 Enos Slaughter/9
18 Phil Rizzuto Pants/10
19 Luis Aparicio/11
20 Ernie Banks/14
21 Hal Newhouser/16 5.00 12.00
22 Whitey Ford/16 8.00 20.00
23 Tony Gwynn/1
24 Bob Feller Pants/19 8.00 20.00
25 Don Sutton/20 4.00 10.00
26 Lou Brock/20 6.00 15.00
27 Jim Palmer/22 4.00 10.00
28 Billy Williams/26 4.00 10.00
29 Juan Marichal/27 4.00 10.00
30 Rod Carew/29 6.00 15.00
31 Catfish Hunter Pants/29 4.00 10.00
32 Maury Wills/1
33 Joe Cronin/4
34 Fergie Jenkins/31 4.00 10.00
35 Sandy Koufax/32 75.00 150.00
36 Steve Carlton/32 4.00 10.00
37 Eddie Murray/33 8.00 20.00
38 Roger Maris Pants/1
39 Gaylord Perry/36 3.00 8.00
40 Bob Gibson/45 5.00 12.00
41 Tom Seaver/41 5.00 12.00
42 Dennis Eckersley/45 3.00 8.00
43 Reggie Jackson Pants/44 5.00 12.00
44 Willie McCovey/44 5.00 12.00
45 Willie Mays NY/24 15.00 40.00
46 Willie Mays SF/24 15.00 40.00
47 Rickey Henderson M's/1
48 Rickey Henderson Mets/1
49 Nolan Ryan Angels/30 12.50 30.00
50 Nolan Ryan Mets/30 12.50 30.00

2005 Leaf Limited Legends Jersey Number Prime

*PRIME p/r 25: .75X TO 2X NBR p/r 36-50
*PRIME p/r 25: .6X TO 1.5X NBR p/r 20-33
*PRIME p/r 15: .75X TO 2X NBR p/r 20-33
OVERALL AU-GU ODDS ONE PER PACK
PRINT RUNS B/WN 1-25 COPIES PER
NO PRICING ON QTY OF 10 OR LESS
PRICES ARE FOR 2 COLOR PATCHES
REDUCE 20% FOR 1-COLOR PATCH
ADD 20% FOR 3-4 COLOR PATCH
ADD 50% FOR 5-COLOR+ PATCH
6 George Brett/25 15.00 40.00
7 Johnny Bench/15 15.00 40.00
11 Stan Musial/25 20.00 50.00
13 Cal Ripken/25 30.00 60.00
14 Carl Yastrzemski/25 12.50 30.00
15 Willie Stargell/25 10.00 25.00
20 Ernie Banks/25 15.00 40.00
23 Tony Gwynn/25 12.50 30.00
47 Rickey Henderson M's/25 12.50 30.00
48 Rickey Henderson Mets/25 12.50 30.00

2005 Leaf Limited Legends Signature

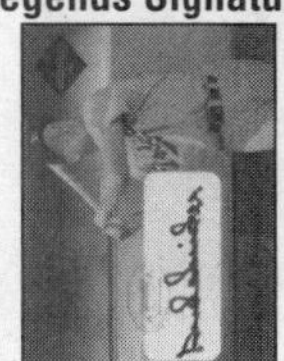

OVERALL AU-GU ODDS ONE PER PACK
PRINT RUNS B/WN 2-50 COPIES PER
NO PRICING ON QTY OF 10 OR LESS
2 Bobby Doerr/50 8.00 20.00
3 Carlton Fisk/10
4 Harmon Killebrew/50 15.00 40.00
5 Duke Snider/25 15.00 40.00
6 George Brett/5
7 Johnny Bench/10
9 Brooks Robinson/50 12.50 30.00
10 Al Kaline/50 15.00 40.00
11 Stan Musial/10
13 Cal Ripken/8
18 Phil Rizzuto/50 12.50 30.00
19 Luis Aparicio/50 8.00 20.00
20 Ernie Banks/4
22 Whitey Ford/5
23 Tony Gwynn/10
24 Bob Feller/50 8.00 20.00
25 Don Sutton/50 8.00 20.00
26 Lou Brock/50 12.50 30.00
27 Jim Palmer/50 8.00 20.00
28 Billy Williams/25 10.00 25.00
29 Juan Marichal/50 8.00 20.00
30 Rod Carew/25 15.00 40.00
32 Maury Wills/50 8.00 20.00
34 Fergie Jenkins/50 8.00 20.00
35 Sandy Koufax/5
36 Steve Carlton/50 8.00 20.00
39 Gaylord Perry/50 8.00 20.00
40 Bob Gibson/25 15.00 40.00
41 Tom Seaver/10
42 Dennis Eckersley/50 8.00 20.00
43 Reggie Jackson/5
44 Willie McCovey/10
45 Willie Mays NY/5
46 Willie Mays SF/5
47 Rickey Henderson M's/5
48 Rickey Henderson Mets/2
49 Nolan Ryan Angels/5
50 Nolan Ryan Mets/5

2005 Leaf Limited Legends Signature Jersey Number

*NBR p/r 20-30: .6X TO 1.5X SIG p/r 50
*NBR p/r 20-30: .5X TO 1.2X SIG p/r 25
*NBR p/r 15-16: .6X TO 1.5X SIG p/r 25
OVERALL AU-GU ODDS ONE PER PACK
PRINT RUNS B/WN 5-30 COPIES PER
NO PRICING ON QTY OF 14 OR LESS
11 Stan Musial/25 40.00 80.00
13 Cal Ripken/25 75.00 150.00
22 Whitey Ford/16 30.00 60.00
23 Tony Gwynn/25 20.00 50.00
44 Willie McCovey/25 20.00 50.00
45 Willie Mays NY/24 125.00 200.00
46 Willie Mays SF/24 125.00 200.00
49 Nolan Ryan Angels/30 50.00 100.00
50 Nolan Ryan Mets/30 50.00 100.00

2005 Leaf Limited Legends Signature Jersey Number Prime

*PRIME p/r 20-25: .75X TO 2X SIG p/r 50
*PRIME p/r 20-25: .6X TO 1.5X SIG p/r 25
*PRIME p/r 15: 1X TO 2.5X SIG p/r 50
OVERALL AU-GU ODDS ONE PER PACK
PRINT RUNS B/WN 1-25 COPIES PER
NO PRICING ON QTY OF 14 OR LESS
3 Carlton Fisk/15 40.00 80.00
11 Stan Musial/25 60.00 120.00
13 Cal Ripken/25 125.00 200.00
23 Tony Gwynn/25 30.00 60.00
44 Willie McCovey/20 30.00 60.00

2005 Leaf Limited Lettermen

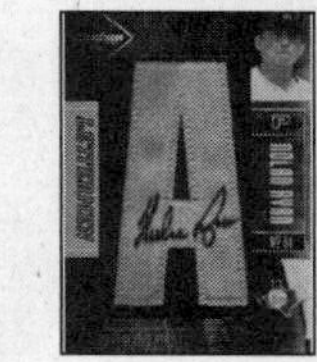

A.BELTRE p/r 20 60.00 120.00
A.BELTRE p/r 10 75.00 150.00
C.BIGGIO p/r 10 150.00 250.00
C.BIGGIO p/r 5 175.00 300.00
C.JONES p/r 5 175.00 300.00
C.RIPKEN p/r 8 300.00 450.00
D.MATTINGLY p/r 10 150.00 250.00
D.MATTINGLY p/r 5 175.00 300.00
D.SNIDER p/r 11 125.00 200.00
D.MURPHY p/r 20 75.00 150.00
M.CABRERA p/r 20 125.00 200.00
M.CABRERA p/r 10 150.00 250.00
M.SCHMIDT p/r 4-5 150.00 250.00
N.RYAN p/r 21 150.00 250.00
P.MOLITOR p/r 10 75.00 150.00
P.MOLITOR p/r 5 125.00 200.00
R.SANDBERG p/r 11 150.00 250.00
S.MUSIAL p/r 6 150.00 250.00
T.GWYNN p/r 21 125.00 200.00
T.GWYNN p/r 10-11 175.00 300.00
OVERALL AU-GU ODDS ONE PER PACK
PRINT RUNS B/WN 4-21 COPIES PER
LETTERMEN FABRIC IS NOT GAME-USED

2005 Leaf Limited Lumberjacks

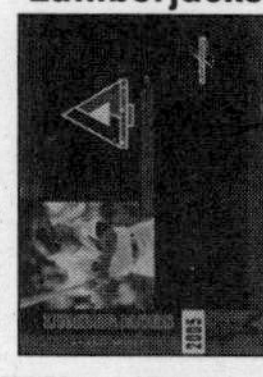

STATED PRINT RUN 50 SERIAL #'d SETS
FOIL PRINT RUN 10 SERIAL #'d SETS
NO FOIL PRICING DUE TO SCARCITY
OVERALL INSERT ODDS ONE PER PACK
1 Al Kaline 4.00 10.00
2 Albert Pujols 6.00 15.00
3 Andre Dawson 2.50 6.00
4 Babe Ruth 6.00 15.00
5 Cal Ripken 10.00 25.00
6 Chipper Jones 4.00 10.00
7 Dale Murphy 3.00 8.00
8 Dave Winfield 2.50 6.00
9 Don Mattingly 6.00 15.00
10 Duke Snider 3.00 8.00
11 Eddie Murray 4.00 10.00
12 Frank Robinson 2.50 6.00
13 Frank Thomas 4.00 10.00
14 Gary Carter 2.50 6.00
15 Hack Wilson 3.00 8.00
16 Hank Aaron 5.00 12.00
17 Harmon Killebrew 4.00 10.00
18 Joe Morgan 2.50 6.00
19 Johnny Bench 4.00 10.00
20 Kirby Puckett 4.00 10.00
21 Kirk Gibson 2.50 6.00
22 Manny Ramirez 3.00 8.00
23 Mark Grace 3.00 8.00
24 Mike Piazza 4.00 10.00
25 Mike Schmidt 6.00 15.00
26 Orlando Cepeda 2.50 6.00
27 Paul Molitor 2.50 6.00
28 Rafael Palmeiro 3.00 8.00
29 Ralph Kiner 2.50 6.00
30 Reggie Jackson 3.00 8.00
31 Richie Ashburn 3.00 8.00
32 Rickey Henderson 4.00 10.00
33 Robin Yount 4.00 10.00
34 Rod Carew 3.00 8.00
35 Ryne Sandberg 6.00 15.00
36 Stan Musial 4.00 10.00
37 Ted Williams 6.00 15.00
38 Tony Gwynn 4.00 10.00
39 Vladimir Guerrero 4.00 10.00
40 Willie Mays 5.00 12.00
41 Ernie Banks 4.00 10.00
Billy Williams
42 Ted Williams 6.00 15.00
Joe Cronin
43 George Brett 6.00 15.00
Bo Jackson
44 John Kruk 3.00 8.00
Jim Thome
45 Willie Mays 5.00 12.00
Jim Thorpe
46 Wade Boggs 3.00 8.00
Johnny Damon
47 Matt Williams 3.00 8.00
Will Clark
48 Willie Stargell 3.00 8.00
Dave Parker
49 Ichiro Suzuki 6.00 15.00
Edgar Martinez
50 Carl Yastrzemski 5.00 12.00
Carlton Fisk

2005 Leaf Limited Lumberjacks Barrel

OVERALL AU-GU ODDS ONE PER PACK
PRINT RUNS B/WN 1-5 COPIES PER
NO PRICING DUE TO SCARCITY

2005 Leaf Limited Lumberjacks Bat

1-40 PRINT RUNS B/WN 1-50 COPIES PER
41-50 PRINT RUNS B/WN 5-50 COPIES PER
OVERALL AU-GU ODDS ONE PER PACK
NO PRICING ON QTY OF 5 OR LESS
1 Al Kaline/50 6.00 15.00
2 Albert Pujols/1
3 Andre Dawson Pants/1
4 Babe Ruth/25 125.00 200.00
6 Chipper Jones/1
7 Dale Murphy/1
8 Dave Winfield/50 3.00 8.00
9 Don Mattingly/1
11 Eddie Murray/25 10.00 25.00
12 Frank Robinson/50 3.00 8.00

13 Frank Thomas/1
14 Gary Carter/25 5.00 12.00
15 Hack Wilson/50 20.00 50.00
16 Hank Aaron/50 15.00 40.00
17 Harmon Killebrew/3
18 Joe Morgan/25 5.00 12.00
19 Johnny Bench/50 6.00 15.00
20 Kirby Puckett/50 6.00 15.00
21 Kirk Gibson/1
22 Manny Ramirez/1
23 Mark Grace/1
24 Mike Piazza/1
25 Mike Schmidt/50 8.00 20.00
26 Orlando Cepeda/25 5.00 12.00
27 Paul Molitor/50 3.00 8.00
28 Rafael Palmeiro/1
29 Ralph Kiner/25 8.00 20.00
30 Reggie Jackson/1
31 Richie Ashburn/25 8.00 20.00
32 Rickey Henderson/1
33 Robin Yount/25 10.00 25.00
34 Rod Carew/1
35 Ryne Sandberg/25 10.00 25.00
36 Stan Musial/50 10.00 25.00
37 Ted Williams/50 20.00 50.00
38 Tony Gwynn/1
39 Vladimir Guerrero/1
40 Willie Mays/50 12.50 30.00
43 George Brett 10.00 25.00
Bo Jackson/50
46 Wade Boggs
Johnny Damon/5
47 Matt Williams 8.00 20.00
Will Clark/50
48 Willie Stargell 8.00 20.00
Dave Parker/50
50 Carl Yastrzemski 10.00 25.00
Carlton Fisk/50

2005 Leaf Limited Lumberjacks Combos

*COMBO p/r 50: .5X TO 1.2X BAT p/r 50
*COMBO p/r 50: .4X TO 1X BAT p/r 25
*COMBO p/r 25: .6X TO 1.5X BAT p/r 50
*COMBO p/r 25: .5X TO 1.2X BAT p/r 25
OVERALL AU-GU ODDS ONE PER PACK
PRINT RUNS B/WN 1-50 COPIES PER
NO PRICING ON QTY OF 10 OR LESS
2 Albert Pujols Bat-Jsy/50 12.50 30.00
4 Babe Ruth Bat-Jsy/25 300.00 500.00
5 Cal Ripken Bat-Jsy/50 15.00 40.00
6 Chipper Jones Bat-Jsy/25 10.00 25.00
7 Dale Murphy Bat-Jsy/50 6.00 15.00
13 Frank Thomas Bat-Jsy/25 10.00 25.00
21 Kirk Gibson Bat-Jsy/50 4.00 10.00
22 Manny Ramirez Bat-Jsy/50 6.00 15.00
23 Mark Grace Bat-Jsy/50 6.00 15.00
24 Mike Piazza Bat-Jsy/50 8.00 20.00

2005 Leaf Limited Lumberjacks Combos Prime

*PRIME p/r 50: .6X TO 1.5X BAT p/r 50
*PRIME p/r 50: .5X TO 1.2X BAT p/r 25
*PRIME p/r 25: .6X TO 1.5X BAT p/r 25
OVERALL AU-GU ODDS ONE PER PACK
PRINT RUNS B/WN 1-50 COPIES PER
NO PRICING ON QTY OF 10 OR LESS
PRICES ARE FOR 2-COLOR PATCHES
REDUCE 20% FOR 1-COLOR PATCH
ADD 20% FOR 3-4 COLOR PATCH
ADD 50% FOR 5-COLOR+ PATCH
2 Albert Pujols Bat-Jsy/50 15.00 40.00
3 Andre Dawson Bat-Jsy/50 4.00 10.00
5 Cal Ripken Bat-Jsy/25 30.00 60.00
6 Chipper Jones Bat-Jsy/50 8.00 20.00
13 Frank Thomas Bat-Jsy/50 8.00 20.00
21 Kirk Gibson Bat-Jsy/50 4.00 10.00
22 Manny Ramirez Bat-Jsy/25 8.00 20.00
24 Mike Piazza Bat-Jsy/50 8.00 20.00
28 Rafael Palmeiro Bat-Jsy/50 6.00 15.00
32 R.Henderson Bat-Jsy/25 10.00 25.00
34 Rod Carew Bat-Jsy/50 6.00 15.00
39 V.Guerrero Bat-Jsy/50 8.00 20.00

2005 Leaf Limited Lumberjacks Jersey

*JSY 1-40 p/r 50: .4X TO 1X BAT p/r 50
*JSY 1-40 p/r 50: .3X TO .8X BAT p/r 25
*JSY 1-40 p/r 25: .5X TO 1.2X BAT p/r 50
*JSY 1-40 p/r 25: .4X TO 1X BAT p/r 25
1-40 PRINT RUNS B/WN 1-50 COPIES PER
*JSY 41-50 p/r 50: .4X TO 1X BAT p/r 50
*JSY 41-50 p/r 25: .5X TO 1.2X BAT p/r 50
41-50 PRINT RUNS B/WN 5-50 COPIES PER
OVERALL AU-GU ODDS ONE PER PACK
NO PRICING ON QTY OF 5 OR LESS
4 Babe Ruth/25 175.00 300.00
10 Duke Snider Pants/50 5.00 12.00
30 Reggie Jackson/50 5.00 12.00
41 Ernie Banks 15.00 40.00
Billy Williams/25
42 Ted Williams 30.00 60.00
Joe Cronin/25
44 John Kruk 10.00 25.00
Jim Thome/25
45 Willie Mays 125.00 200.00
Jim Thorpe/25
46 Wade Boggs 8.00 20.00
Johnny Damon/50

2005 Leaf Limited Lumberjacks Jersey Prime

*PRIME 1-40 p/r 50: .5X TO 1.2X BAT p/r 25
*PRIME 1-40 p/r 25: .75X TO 2X BAT p/r 50
*PRIME 1-40 p/r 25: .6X TO 1.5X BAT p/r 25
1-40 PRINT RUNS B/WN 1-50 COPIES PER
41-50 PRINT RUNS B/WN 1-5 COPIES PER
OVERALL AU-GU ODDS ONE PER PACK
NO PRICING ON QTY OF 10 OR LESS
PRICES ARE FOR 2 COLOR PATCHES
REDUCE 20% FOR 1-COLOR PATCH
ADD 20% FOR 3-4 COLOR PATCH
ADD 50% FOR 5-COLOR+ PATCH
2 Albert Pujols/25 20.00 50.00
3 Andre Dawson/50 5.00 12.00
5 Cal Ripken/25 30.00 60.00
6 Chipper Jones/50 10.00 25.00
13 Frank Thomas/50 10.00 25.00
21 Kirk Gibson/50 5.00 12.00
24 Mike Piazza/50 10.00 25.00
28 Rafael Palmeiro/50 8.00 20.00
32 Rickey Henderson/25 12.50 30.00
34 Rod Carew/50 8.00 20.00
38 Tony Gwynn/50 10.00 25.00
39 Vladimir Guerrero/25 10.00 25.00

2005 Leaf Limited Lumberjacks Signature

OVERALL AU-GU ODDS ONE PER PACK
PRINT RUNS B/WN 1-50 COPIES PER
NO PRICING ON QTY OF 10 OR LESS
1 Al Kaline/50 15.00 40.00
2 Albert Pujols/1
3 Andre Dawson/25 10.00 25.00
5 Cal Ripken/21 60.00 120.00
6 Chipper Jones/10
7 Dale Murphy/50 12.50 30.00
8 Dave Winfield/1
9 Don Mattingly/50 20.00 50.00
10 Duke Snider/50 12.50 30.00
11 Eddie Murray/10
12 Frank Robinson/50 8.00 20.00
13 Frank Thomas/25 20.00 50.00
14 Gary Carter/50 8.00 20.00
16 Hank Aaron/10
17 Harmon Killebrew/50 15.00 40.00
18 Joe Morgan/25 10.00 25.00
19 Johnny Bench/50 15.00 40.00
20 Kirby Puckett/25 50.00 100.00
21 Kirk Gibson/10
22 Manny Ramirez/1
23 Mark Grace/25 15.00 40.00
25 Mike Schmidt/50 20.00 50.00
26 Orlando Cepeda/1
27 Paul Molitor/50 8.00 20.00
29 Ralph Kiner/50 12.50 30.00
30 Reggie Jackson/1
32 Rickey Henderson/10
33 Robin Yount/10
34 Rod Carew/50 12.50 30.00
35 Ryne Sandberg/50 20.00 50.00
36 Stan Musial/50 20.00 50.00
38 Tony Gwynn/50 15.00 40.00
40 Willie Mays/25 100.00 175.00

2005 Leaf Limited Lumberjacks Signature Bat

*BAT p/r 100: .4X TO 1X SIG p/r 50
*BAT p/r 100: .3X TO .8X SIG p/r 21-25
*BAT p/r 50: .5X TO 1.2X SIG p/r 50
*BAT p/r 50: .4X TO 1X SIG p/r 21-25
*BAT p/r 25: .6X TO 1.5X SIG p/r 50
*BAT p/r 25: .5X TO 1.2X SIG p/r 21-25
OVERALL AU-GU ODDS ONE PER PACK
PRINT RUNS B/WN 1-100 COPIES PER
NO PRICING ON QTY OF 10 OR LESS
21 Kirk Gibson/25 12.50 30.00
26 Orlando Cepeda/100 8.00 20.00
33 Robin Yount/25 30.00 60.00

2005 Leaf Limited Lumberjacks Signature Combos

*COMBO p/r 100: .4X TO 1X SIG p/r 50
*COMBO p/r 100: .3X TO .8X SIG p/r 21-25
*COMBO p/r 50: .5X TO 1.2X SIG p/r 50
*COMBO p/r 25: .6X TO 1.5X SIG p/r 50
*COMBO p/r 25: .5X TO 1.2X SIG p/r 21-25
OVERALL AU-GU ODDS ONE PER PACK
PRINT RUNS B/WN 1-100 COPIES PER
NO PRICING ON QTY OF 10 OR LESS

2005 Leaf Limited Lumberjacks Signature Combos Prime

*PRIME p/r 25: .75X TO 2X SIG p/r 50
*PRIME p/r 25: .6X TO 1.5X SIG p/r 21-25
OVERALL AU-GU ODDS ONE PER PACK
PRINT RUNS B/WN 1-25 COPIES PER
NO PRICING ON QTY OF 10 OR LESS
5 Cal Ripken Bat-Jsy/25 125.00 200.00

2005 Leaf Limited Lumberjacks Signature Jersey

*JSY p/r 100: .4X TO 1X SIG p/r 50
*JSY p/r 100: .3X TO .8X SIG p/r 21-25
*JSY p/r 50: .5X TO 1.2X SIG p/r 50
*JSY p/r 25: .6X TO 1.5X SIG p/r 50
*JSY p/r 25: .5X TO 1.2X SIG p/r 21-25
OVERALL AU-GU ODDS ONE PER PACK
PRINT RUNS B/WN 1-100 COPIES PER
NO PRICING ON QTY OF 10 OR LESS
30 Reggie Jackson/25 30.00 60.00
33 Robin Yount/25 30.00 60.00

2005 Leaf Limited Lumberjacks Signature Jersey Prime

*PRIME p/r 25: .75X TO 2X SIG p/r 50
*PRIME p/r 25: .6X TO 1.5X SIG p/r 21-25
OVERALL AU-GU ODDS ONE PER PACK
PRINT RUNS B/WN 1-25 COPIES PER
NO PRICING ON QTY OF 10 OR LESS
5 Cal Ripken/25 125.00 200.00
33 Robin Yount/25 40.00 80.00

2005 Leaf Limited Matching Numbers

PRINT RUNS B/WN 5-50 COPIES PER
NO PRICING ON QTY OF 5
PRIME PRINT RUNS 1-5 COPIES PER
NO PRIME PRICING DUE TO SCARCITY
OVERALL AU-GU ODDS ONE PER PACK
1 Ted Williams Jsy 100.00 200.00
Roger Maris Jsy/25
2 Nolan Ryan Jsy 15.00 40.00
Kerry Wood Jsy/50

3 Cal Ripken Jsy 20.00 50.00
Gary Carter Jsy/50
4 Willie Mays Pants 40.00 80.00
Rickey Henderson Jsy/25
5 Johnny Bench Pants 15.00 40.00
Albert Pujols Jsy/50
6 Roger Clemens Jsy 15.00 40.00
Will Clark Jsy/50
7 Willie McCovey Jsy 10.00 25.00
Reggie Jackson Jsy/25
8 Ryne Sandberg Jsy 15.00 40.00
Don Mattingly Jsy/50
9 Duke Snider Pants 12.50 30.00
Joe Cronin Pants/25
10 Roberto Clemente Jsy
Roger Clemens Jsy/5

2005 Leaf Limited Team Trademarks

STATED PRINT RUN 50 SERIAL #'d SETS
FOIL PRINT RUN 10 SERIAL #'d SETS
NO FOIL PRICING DUE TO SCARCITY
OVERALL INSERT ODDS ONE PER PACK
1 Ryne Sandberg 6.00 15.00
2 George Brett 6.00 15.00
3 Steve Carlton 2.50 6.00
4 Reggie Jackson 3.00 8.00
5 Edgar Martinez 3.00 8.00
6 Barry Larkin 3.00 8.00
7 Ozzie Smith 5.00 12.00
8 Carlton Fisk 3.00 8.00
9 Wade Boggs 3.00 8.00
10 Will Clark 3.00 8.00
11 Nolan Ryan 6.00 15.00
12 Gary Carter 2.50 6.00
13 Don Mattingly 6.00 15.00
14 Willie Stargell 3.00 8.00
15 Don Sutton 2.50 6.00
16 Kirk Gibson 2.50 6.00
17 Kirby Puckett 4.00 10.00
18 Dale Murphy 3.00 8.00
19 Rickey Henderson 4.00 10.00
20 Willie Mays 5.00 12.00
21 Cal Ripken 10.00 25.00
22 Paul Molitor 2.50 6.00
23 Tony Gwynn 4.00 10.00
24 Andre Dawson 2.50 6.00
25 Bob Feller 2.50 6.00
26 Alan Trammell 2.50 6.00
27 Dave Parker 2.50 6.00
28 Dave Righetti 2.50 6.00
29 Dwight Gooden 2.50 6.00
30 Harold Baines 2.50 6.00
31 Jack Morris 2.50 6.00
32 John Kruk 3.00 8.00
33 Lee Smith 2.50 6.00
34 Lenny Dykstra 2.50 6.00
35 Luis Tiant 2.50 6.00
36 Matt Williams 3.00 8.00
37 Ron Guidry 2.50 6.00
38 Tony Oliva 2.50 6.00

2005 Leaf Limited Team Trademarks Jersey Number

*NBR p/r 44-50: .25X TO .6X PRIME p/r 40-50
*NBR p/r 20-32: .3X TO .8X PRIME p/r 40-50
*NBR p/r 20-32: .25X TO .6X PRIME p/r 25-26
OVERALL AU-GU ODDS ONE PER PACK
PRINT RUNS B/WN 1-50 COPIES PER
NO PRICING ON QTY OF 8 OR LESS
20 Willie Mays/24 15.00 40.00
25 Bob Feller/19 8.00 20.00

2005 Leaf Limited Team Trademarks Jersey Number Prime

OVERALL AU-GU ODDS ONE PER PACK
PRINT RUNS B/WN 1-50 COPIES PER
NO PRICING ON QTY OF 1
PRICES ARE FOR 2 COLOR PATCHES
REDUCE 20% FOR 1-COLOR PATCH
ADD 20% FOR 3-4 COLOR PATCH
ADD 50% FOR 5-COLOR+ PATCH
1 Ryne Sandberg/50 12.50 30.00
2 George Brett/50 12.50 30.00
3 Steve Carlton/50 5.00 12.00
4 Reggie Jackson/50 8.00 20.00

5 Edgar Martinez/50 8.00 20.00
6 Barry Larkin/50 8.00 20.00
7 Ozzie Smith/50 10.00 25.00
8 Carlton Fisk/50 8.00 20.00
9 Wade Boggs/50 8.00 20.00
10 Will Clark/50 8.00 20.00
11 Nolan Ryan/50 12.50 30.00
12 Gary Carter/50 5.00 12.00
13 Don Mattingly/40 12.50 30.00
14 Willie Stargell/50 8.00 20.00
15 Don Sutton/25 6.00 15.00
16 Kirk Gibson/50 5.00 12.00
17 Kirby Puckett/1
18 Dale Murphy/50 8.00 20.00
19 Rickey Henderson/50 10.00 25.00
21 Cal Ripken/25 30.00 60.00
23 Tony Gwynn/50 10.00 25.00
24 Andre Dawson/25 6.00 15.00
26 Alan Trammell/25 6.00 15.00
27 Dave Parker/50 5.00 12.00
29 Dwight Gooden/50 5.00 12.00
30 Harold Baines/25 6.00 15.00
31 Jack Morris/47 5.00 12.00
32 John Kruk/25 10.00 25.00
33 Lee Smith/47 5.00 12.00
34 Lenny Dykstra/25 6.00 15.00
38 Tony Oliva/26 6.00 15.00

2005 Leaf Limited Team Trademarks Signature

OVERALL AU-GU ODDS ONE PER PACK
PRINT RUNS B/WN 5-100 COPIES PER
NO PRICING ON QTY OF 5
1 Ryne Sandberg/25 30.00 60.00
2 George Brett/5
3 Steve Carlton/25 10.00 25.00
4 Reggie Jackson/25 20.00 50.00
5 Edgar Martinez/50 12.50 30.00
6 Barry Larkin/50 12.50 30.00
7 Ozzie Smith/50 15.00 40.00
8 Carlton Fisk/50 12.50 30.00
9 Wade Boggs/25 15.00 40.00
10 Will Clark/50 12.50 30.00
11 Nolan Ryan/50 40.00 80.00
12 Gary Carter/50 8.00 20.00
13 Don Mattingly/25 30.00 60.00
15 Don Sutton/100 6.00 15.00
16 Kirk Gibson/50 8.00 20.00
17 Kirby Puckett/25 50.00 100.00
18 Dale Murphy/100 10.00 25.00
19 Rickey Henderson/5
20 Willie Mays/25 100.00 175.00
21 Cal Ripken/50 50.00 100.00
22 Paul Molitor/25 10.00 25.00
23 Tony Gwynn/25 20.00 50.00
24 Andre Dawson/100 6.00 15.00
25 Bob Feller/50 8.00 20.00
26 Alan Trammell/25 10.00 25.00
27 Dave Parker/50 8.00 20.00
28 Dave Righetti/25 10.00 25.00
29 Dwight Gooden/50 8.00 20.00
30 Harold Baines/50 8.00 20.00
31 Jack Morris/50 8.00 20.00
32 John Kruk/25 15.00 40.00
33 Lee Smith/50 8.00 20.00
34 Lenny Dykstra/25 10.00 25.00
35 Luis Tiant/50 8.00 20.00
36 Matt Williams/50 12.50 30.00
37 Ron Guidry/25 10.00 25.00
38 Tony Oliva/50 8.00 20.00

2005 Leaf Limited Team Trademarks Signature Jersey Number

*NBR p/r 72: .4X TO 1X SIG p/r 50
*NBR p/r 39-49: .5X TO 1.2X SIG p/r 50
*NBR p/r 39-49: .4X TO 1X SIG p/r 25
*NBR p/r 20-34: .75X TO 2X SIG p/r 100
*NBR p/r 20-34: .6X TO 1.5X SIG p/r 50
*NBR p/r 20-34: .5X TO 1.2X SIG p/r 25
*NBR p/r 16-19: .75X TO 2X SIG p/r 50
*NBR p/r 16-19: .6X TO 1.5X SIG p/r 25
OVERALL AU-GU ODDS ONE PER PACK
PRINT RUNS B/WN 1-72 COPIES PER
NO PRICING ON QTY OF 11 OR LESS
11 Nolan Ryan Pants/34 50.00 100.00
19 Rickey Henderson/24 30.00 60.00
20 Willie Mays/24 125.00 200.00

2005 Leaf Limited Team Trademarks Signature Jersey Number Prime

*PRIME p/r 39-47: .6X TO 1.5X SIG p/r 50
*PRIME p/r 25-29: 1X TO 2.5X SIG p/r 100
*PRIME p/r 25-29: .75X TO 2X SIG p/r 50
*PRIME p/r 25-29: .6X TO 1.5X SIG p/r 25
*PRIME p/r 16: 1X TO 2.5X SIG p/r 50
OVERALL AU-GU ODDS ONE PER PACK
PRINT RUNS B/WN 1-47 COPIES PER
NO PRICING ON QTY OF 10 OR LESS

1998 Leaf Rookies and Stars

The 1998 Leaf Rookies and Stars set was issued in one series totalling 339 cards. The nine-card packs retailed for $2.99 each. The product was released very late in the year going live in December, 1998. This late release allowed for the inclusion of several rookies added to the 40 man roster at the end of the 1998 season. The set contains the topical subsets: Power Tools (131-160), Team Line-Up (161-190), and Rookies (191-300). Cards 131-230 were shortprinted, being seeded at a rate of 1:2 packs. In addition, 39 cards were tacked on to the end of the set (301-339) just prior to release. These cards were seeded at noticeably shorter rates (approximately 1:8 packs) than other subsets. Several key Rookie Cards, including J.D. Drew, Troy Glaus, Gabe Kapler and Ruben Mateo appear within this run of "high series" cards. Though not confirmed by the manufacturer, it is believed that card number 317 Ryan Minor was printed in a lesser amount than the other cards in the high series. All card fronts feature full-bleed color action photos. The featured player's name lines the bottom of the card with his jersey number in the lower left corner. This product was originally created by Pinnacle in their final days as a card manufacturer. After Playoff went out of business, Playoff paid for the right to distribute this product and release it late in 1998 as much of the product had already been created. Because of the especially strong selection of Rookie Cards and an large number of shortprints, this set endured to become one of the more popular and notable base brand issues of the late 1990's.

COMPLETE SET (339) 125.00 250.00
COMP.SET w/o SP's (200) 10.00 25.00
COMMON (1-130/231-300) .10 .30
COMMON (131-190) .40 1.00
COMMON (191-230) .75 2.00
COMMON RC (191-230) .75 2.00
COMMON (301-339) 1.00 2.50
COMMON RC (301-339) 1.00 2.50
1 Andy Pettitte .20 .50
2 Roberto Alomar .20 .50
3 Randy Johnson .30 .75
4 Manny Ramirez .20 .50
5 Paul Molitor .10 .30
6 Mike Mussina .20 .50
7 Jim Thome .20 .50
8 Tino Martinez .20 .50
9 Gary Sheffield .10 .30
10 Chuck Knoblauch .10 .30
11 Bernie Williams .20 .50
12 Tim Salmon .20 .50
13 Sammy Sosa .30 .75
14 Wade Boggs .20 .50
15 Andres Galarraga .10 .30
16 Pedro Martinez .20 .50
17 David Justice .10 .30
18 Chan Ho Park .10 .30
19 Jay Buhner .10 .30
20 Ryan Klesko .10 .30
21 Barry Larkin .20 .50
22 Will Clark .20 .50
23 Raul Mondesi .10 .30
24 Rickey Henderson .30 .75
25 Jim Edmonds .10 .30
26 Ken Griffey Jr. .50 1.25
27 Frank Thomas .30 .75
28 Cal Ripken 1.00 2.50
29 Alex Rodriguez .50 1.25
30 Mike Piazza .50 1.25
31 Greg Maddux .50 1.25
32 Chipper Jones .30 .75
33 Tony Gwynn .40 1.00
34 Derek Jeter .75 2.00
35 Jeff Bagwell .20 .50
36 Juan Gonzalez .10 .30
37 Nomar Garciaparra .50 1.25
38 Andruw Jones .20 .50
39 Hideo Nomo .30 .75
40 Roger Clemens .60 1.50
41 Mark McGwire .75 2.00
42 Scott Rolen .20 .50
43 Vladimir Guerrero .30 .75
44 Barry Bonds .75 2.00
45 Darin Erstad .10 .30
46 Albert Belle .10 .30
47 Kenny Lofton .10 .30
48 Mo Vaughn .10 .30

Card	Low	High
49 Ivan Rodriguez	.20	.50
50 Jose Cruz Jr.	.10	.30
51 Tony Clark	.10	.30
52 Larry Walker	.10	.30
53 Mark Grace	.20	.50
54 Edgar Martinez	.20	.50
55 Fred McGriff	.20	.50
56 Rafael Palmeiro	.20	.50
57 Matt Williams	.10	.30
58 Craig Biggio	.20	.50
59 Ken Caminiti	.10	.30
60 Jose Canseco	.20	.50
61 Brady Anderson	.10	.30
62 Moises Alou	.10	.30
63 Justin Thompson	.10	.30
64 John Smoltz	.20	.50
65 Carlos Delgado	.10	.30
66 J.T. Snow	.10	.30
67 Jason Giambi	.10	.30
68 Garret Anderson	.10	.30
69 Rondell White	.10	.30
70 Eric Karros	.10	.30
71 Javier Lopez	.10	.30
72 Pat Hentgen	.10	.30
73 Dante Bichette	.10	.30
74 Charles Johnson	.10	.30
75 Tom Glavine	.20	.50
76 Rusty Greer	.10	.30
77 Travis Fryman	.10	.30
78 Todd Hundley	.10	.30
79 Ray Lankford	.10	.30
80 Denny Neagle	.10	.30
81 Henry Rodriguez	.10	.30
82 Sandy Alomar Jr.	.10	.30
83 Robin Ventura	.10	.30
84 John Olerud	.10	.30
85 Omar Vizquel	.20	.50
86 Darren Dreifort	.10	.30
87 Kevin Brown	.10	.30
88 Curt Schilling	.10	.30
89 Francisco Cordova	.10	.30
90 Brad Radke	.10	.30
91 David Cone	.10	.30
92 Paul O'Neill	.20	.50
93 Vinny Castilla	.10	.30
94 Marquis Grissom	.10	.30
95 Brian L.Hunter	.10	.30
96 Kevin Appier	.10	.30
97 Bobby Bonilla	.10	.30
98 Eric Young	.10	.30
99 Jason Kendall	.10	.30
100 Shawn Green	.10	.30
101 Edgardo Alfonzo	.10	.30
102 Alan Benes	.10	.30
103 Bobby Higginson	.10	.30
104 Todd Greene	.10	.30
105 Jose Guillen	.10	.30
106 Neifi Perez	.10	.30
107 Edgar Renteria	.10	.30
108 Chris Stynes	.10	.30
109 Todd Walker	.10	.30
110 Brian Jordan	.10	.30
111 Joe Carter	.10	.30
112 Ellis Burks	.10	.30
113 Brett Tomko	.10	.30
114 Mike Cameron	.10	.30
115 Shannon Stewart	.10	.30
116 Kevin Orie	.10	.30
117 Brian Giles	.10	.30
118 Hideki Irabu	.10	.30
119 Delino DeShields	.10	.30
120 David Segui	.10	.30
121 Dustin Hermanson	.10	.30
122 Kevin Young	.10	.30
123 Jay Bell	.10	.30
124 Doug Glanville	.10	.30
125 John Roskos RC	.10	.30
126 Damon Hollins	.10	.30
127 Matt Stairs	.10	.30
128 Cliff Floyd	.10	.30
129 Derek Bell	.10	.30
130 Darryl Strawberry	.10	.30
131 Ken Griffey Jr. PT SP	1.50	4.00
132 Tim Salmon PT SP	.60	1.50
133 M.Ramirez PT SP	.60	1.50
134 Paul Konerko PT SP	.40	1.00
135 Frank Thomas PT SP	1.00	2.50
136 Todd Helton PT SP	.60	1.50
137 Larry Walker PT SP	.40	1.00
138 Mo Vaughn PT SP	.40	1.00
139 Travis Lee PT SP	.40	1.00
140 Ivan Rodriguez PT SP	.60	1.50
141 Ben Grieve PT SP	.40	1.00
142 Brad Fullmer PT SP	.40	1.00
143 Alex Rodriguez PT SP	1.50	4.00
144 Mike Piazza PT SP	1.50	4.00
145 Greg Maddux PT SP	1.50	4.00
146 Chipper Jones PT SP	1.00	2.50
147 Kenny Lofton PT SP	.40	1.00
148 Albert Belle PT SP	.40	1.00
149 Barry Bonds PT SP	2.50	6.00
150 V.Guerrero PT SP	1.00	2.50
151 Tony Gwynn PT SP	1.25	3.00
152 Derek Jeter PT SP	2.50	6.00
153 Jeff Bagwell PT SP	.60	1.50
154 Juan Gonzalez PT SP	.40	1.00
155 N.Garciaparra PT SP	1.50	4.00
156 Andruw Jones PT SP	.60	1.50
157 Hideo Nomo PT SP	1.00	2.50
158 Roger Clemens PT SP	2.00	5.00
159 Mark McGwire PT SP	2.50	6.00
160 Scott Rolen PT SP	.60	1.50
161 Travis Lee TLU SP	.40	1.00
162 Ben Grieve TLU SP	.40	1.00
163 Jose Guillen TLU SP	.40	1.00
164 Mike Piazza TLU SP	1.50	4.00
165 Kevin Appier TLU SP	.40	1.00
166 M.Grissom TLU SP	.40	1.00
167 Rusty Greer TLU SP	.40	1.00
168 Ken Caminiti TLU SP	.40	1.00
169 Craig Biggio TLU SP	.60	1.50
170 K.Griffey Jr. TLU SP	1.50	4.00
171 Larry Walker TLU SP	.40	1.00
172 Barry Larkin TLU SP	.60	1.50
173 A.Galarraga TLU SP	.40	1.00
174 Wade Boggs TLU SP	.60	1.50
175 Sammy Sosa TLU SP	1.00	2.50
176 T.Dunwoody TLU SP	.40	1.00
177 Jim Thome TLU SP	.60	1.50
178 Paul Molitor TLU SP	.40	1.00
179 Tony Clark TLU SP	.40	1.00
180 Jose Cruz Jr. TLU SP	.40	1.00
181 Darin Erstad TLU SP	.40	1.00
182 Barry Bonds TLU SP	2.50	6.00
183 Vlad.Guerrero TLU SP	1.00	2.50
184 Scott Rolen TLU SP	.60	1.50
185 M.McGwire TLU SP	2.50	6.00
186 N.Garciaparra TLU SP	1.50	4.00
187 Gary Sheffield TLU SP	.40	1.00
188 Cal Ripken TLU SP	3.00	8.00
189 F.Thomas TLU SP	1.00	2.50
190 Andy Pettitte TLU SP	.60	1.50
191 Paul Konerko SP	.75	2.00
192 Todd Helton SP	1.25	3.00
193 Mark Kotsay SP	.75	2.00
194 Brad Fullmer SP	.75	2.00
195 K.Millwood SP RC	3.00	8.00
196 David Ortiz SP	5.00	12.00
197 Kerry Wood SP	1.00	2.50
198 Miguel Tejada SP	2.00	5.00
199 Fernando Tatis SP	.75	2.00
200 Jaret Wright SP	.75	2.00
201 Ben Grieve SP	.75	2.00
202 Travis Lee SP	.75	2.00
203 Wes Helms SP	.75	2.00
204 Geoff Jenkins SP	4.00	10.00
205 Russell Branyan SP	.75	2.00
206 Esteban Yan SP RC	1.25	3.00
207 Ben Ford SP RC	.75	2.00
208 Rich Butler SP RC	.75	2.00
209 Ryan Jackson SP RC	.75	2.00
210 A.J. Hinch SP	.75	2.00
211 Magglio Ordonez RC	10.00	25.00
212 Dave Dellucci SP RC	2.00	5.00
213 Billy McMillon SP	.75	2.00
214 Mike Lowell SP RC	4.00	10.00
215 Todd Erdos SP RC	.75	2.00
216 C.Mendoza SP RC	.75	2.00
217 F.Catalanotto SP RC	2.00	5.00
218 Julio Ramirez SP RC	1.25	3.00
219 John Halama SP RC	1.25	3.00
220 Wilson Delgado SP	.75	2.00
221 Mike Judd SP RC	1.25	3.00
222 Rolando Arrojo SP RC	1.25	3.00
223 Jason LaRue SP RC	1.25	3.00
224 Manny Aybar SP RC	1.25	3.00
225 Jorge Velandia SP	.75	2.00
226 Mike Kinkade SP RC	1.25	3.00
227 Carlos Lee SP RC	6.00	15.00
228 Bobby Hughes SP	.75	2.00
229 R.Christenson SP RC	.75	2.00
230 Masato Yoshii SP RC	1.25	3.00
231 Richard Hidalgo	.10	.30
232 Rafael Medina	.10	.30
233 Damian Jackson	.10	.30
234 Derek Lowe	.10	.30
235 Mario Valdez	.10	.30
236 Eli Marrero	.10	.30
237 Juan Encarnacion	.10	.30
238 Livan Hernandez	.10	.30
239 Bruce Chen	.10	.30
240 Eric Milton	.10	.30
241 Jason Varitek	.30	.75
242 Scott Elarton	.10	.30
243 Manuel Barrios RC	.10	.30
244 Mike Caruso	.10	.30
245 Tom Evans	.10	.30
246 Pat Cline	.10	.30
247 Matt Clement	.10	.30
248 Karim Garcia	.10	.30
249 Richie Sexson	.10	.30
250 Sidney Ponson	.10	.30
251 Randall Simon	.10	.30
252 Tony Saunders	.10	.30
253 Javier Valentin	.10	.30
254 Danny Clyburn	.10	.30
255 Michael Coleman	.10	.30
256 Hanley Frias RC	.10	.30
257 Miguel Cairo	.10	.30
258 Rob Stanifer RC	.10	.30
259 Lou Collier	.10	.30
260 Abraham Nunez	.10	.30
261 Ricky Ledee	.10	.30
262 Carl Pavano	.10	.30
263 Derrek Lee	.20	.50
264 Jeff Abbott	.10	.30
265 Bob Abreu	.10	.30
266 Bartolo Colon	.10	.30
267 Mike Drumright	.10	.30
268 Daryle Ward	.10	.30
269 Gabe Alvarez	.10	.30
270 Josh Booty	.10	.30
271 Damian Moss	.10	.30
272 Brian Rose	.10	.30
273 Jarrod Washburn	.10	.30
274 Bobby Estalella	.10	.30
275 Enrique Wilson	.10	.30
276 Derrick Gibson	.10	.30
277 Ken Cloude	.10	.30
278 Kevin Witt	.10	.30
279 Donnie Sadler	.10	.30
280 Sean Casey	.10	.30
281 Jacob Cruz	.10	.30
282 Ron Wright	.10	.30
283 Jeremi Gonzalez	.10	.30
284 Desi Relaford	.10	.30
285 Bobby Smith	.10	.30
286 Javier Vazquez	.10	.30
287 Steve Woodard	.10	.30
288 Greg Norton	.10	.30
289 Cliff Politte	.10	.30
290 Felix Heredia	.10	.30
291 Braden Looper	.10	.30
292 Felix Martinez	.10	.30
293 Brian Meadows	.10	.30
294 Edwin Diaz	.10	.30
295 Pat Watkins	.10	.30
296 Marc Pisciotta RC	.10	.30
297 Rick Gorecki	.10	.30
298 DaRond Stovall	.10	.30
299 Andy Larkin	.10	.30
300 Felix Rodriguez	.10	.30
301 Blake Stein SP	1.00	2.50
302 John Rocker SP RC	2.50	6.00
303 J.Baughman SP RC	1.00	2.50
304 Jesus Sanchez SP RC	1.50	4.00
305 Randy Winn SP	1.00	2.50
306 Lou Merloni SP	1.00	2.50
307 Jim Parque SP RC	1.50	4.00
308 Dennis Reyes SP	1.00	2.50
309 O.Hernandez SP RC	4.00	10.00
310 Jason Johnson SP	1.00	2.50
311 Torii Hunter SP	1.00	2.50
312 M.Piazza Marlins SP	4.00	10.00
313 Mike Frank SP RC	1.00	2.50
314 Troy Glaus SP RC	30.00	60.00
315 Jin Ho Cho SP RC	1.50	4.00
316 Ruben Mateo SP RC	1.00	2.50
317 Ryan Minor SP RC	1.50	4.00
318 Aramis Ramirez SP	1.00	2.50
319 Adrian Beltre SP	1.00	2.50
320 Matt Anderson SP RC	1.00	2.50
321 Gabe Kapler SP RC	2.50	6.00
322 Jeremy Giambi SP RC	1.50	4.00
323 Carlos Beltran SP	3.00	8.00
324 Dermal Brown SP	1.00	2.50
325 Ben Davis SP	1.00	2.50
326 Eric Chavez SP	1.00	2.50
327 Bobby Howry SP RC	1.00	2.50
328 Roy Halladay SP	1.00	2.50
329 George Lombard SP	1.00	2.50
330 Michael Barrett SP	1.00	2.50
331 F. Seguignol SP RC	1.00	2.50
332 J.D. Drew SP RC	5.00	12.00
333 Odalis Perez SP RC	4.00	10.00
334 Alex Cora SP RC	1.50	4.00
335 P.Polanco SP RC	2.00	5.00
336 Armando Rios SP RC	1.50	4.00
337 Sammy Sosa HR SP	2.50	6.00
338 Mark McGwire HR SP	6.00	15.00
339 Sammy Sosa Mark McGwire CL SP	4.00	10.00

1998 Leaf Rookies and Stars Longevity

Randomly inserted in packs, this 339-card set is a parallel to the Leaf Rookies and Stars base set. The set is serially numbered to 50 (although only 49 sets were actually produced because the first set - cards numbered "1/50" were given a holographic foil coating) and printed on foil board with foil stamping.

*STARS 1-130/231-300: 15X TO 40X BASIC
*RC's 1-130/231-300: 25X TO 50X BASIC
*STARS 131-190: 3X TO 8X BASIC
*STARS 191-230: 3X TO 8X BASIC
*RC's 191-230: 2X TO 4X BASIC
*STARS 301-339: 2.5X TO 6X BASIC
*RC's 301-339: 1.5X TO 3X BASIC

Card	Low	High
314 Troy Glaus	125.00	200.00

1998 Leaf Rookies and Stars True Blue

Randomly inserted in packs, this 339-card set is a parallel to the Leaf Rookies and Stars base set. Only 500 sets were printed (though the cards are not serial numbered - instead, they say "1 of 500" on back) and each card features blue foil stamping accents.

*STARS 1-130/231-300: 6X TO 15X BASIC
*ROOKIES 1-130/231-300: 3X TO 8X BASIC CARDS
*LO SP STARS 131-190: 1X TO 2.5X BASIC
*LO SP STARS 191-230: 2X TO 5X BASIC
*ROOKIES 191-230: .5X TO 1.2X BASIC
*STARS 301-339: .75X TO 2X BASIC
*ROOKIES 301-339: .4X TO 1X BASIC

1998 Leaf Rookies and Stars Crosstraining

Randomly inserted in packs, this 10-card set is an insert to the Leaf Rookies and Stars brand. The set is sequentially numbered to 1000. The cards are printed on foil board. Each card front highlights a color action player photo surrounded by a crosstraining shoe sole design. The same player is highlighted on the back with information on his different skills.

Card	Low	High
COMPLETE SET (10)	50.00	120.00
1 Kenny Lofton	1.50	4.00
2 Ken Griffey Jr.	6.00	15.00
3 Alex Rodriguez	6.00	15.00
4 Greg Maddux	6.00	15.00
5 Barry Bonds	10.00	25.00
6 Ivan Rodriguez	2.50	6.00
7 Chipper Jones	4.00	10.00
8 Jeff Bagwell	2.50	6.00
9 Nomar Garciaparra	6.00	15.00
10 Derek Jeter	10.00	25.00

1998 Leaf Rookies and Stars Crusade Update Green

Randomly inserted in packs, this 30-card set is an insert to the Leaf Rookies and Stars brand and was intended as an update to the 100 Crusade insert cards seeded in 1998 Donruss Update, 1998 Leaf and 1998 Donruss packs (thus the numbering 101-130). The set is sequentially numbered to 250. The fronts feature color action photos placed on a background of a Crusade shield design. The set features three parallel versions printed with a "Spectra-tech" holographic technology. First year serial-numbered cards of Kevin Millwood and Magglio Ordonez are featured in this set.

Card	Low	High
COMPLETE SET (30)	125.00	300.00
101 Richard Hidalgo	4.00	10.00
102 Paul Konerko	6.00	15.00
103 Miguel Tejada	10.00	25.00
104 Fernando Tatis	4.00	10.00
105 Travis Lee	4.00	10.00
106 Wes Helms	4.00	10.00
107 Rich Butler	4.00	10.00
108 Mark Kotsay	6.00	15.00
109 Eli Marrero	4.00	10.00
110 David Ortiz	12.50	30.00
111 Juan Encarnacion	4.00	10.00
112 Jaret Wright	4.00	10.00
113 Livan Hernandez	6.00	15.00
114 Ron Wright	4.00	10.00
115 Ryan Christenson	4.00	10.00
116 Eric Milton	4.00	10.00
117 Brad Fullmer	4.00	10.00
118 Karim Garcia	4.00	10.00
119 Abraham Nunez	4.00	10.00
120 Ricky Ledee	4.00	10.00
121 Carl Pavano	6.00	15.00
122 Derrek Lee	8.00	20.00
123 A.J. Hinch	4.00	10.00
124 Brian Rose	4.00	10.00
125 Bobby Estalella	4.00	10.00
126 Kevin Millwood	10.00	25.00
127 Kerry Wood	6.00	15.00
128 Sean Casey	6.00	15.00
129 Russell Branyan	4.00	10.00
130 Magglio Ordonez	15.00	40.00

1998 Leaf Rookies and Stars Crusade Update Purple

Randomly inserted in packs, this 30-card set is a parallel insert to the Leaf Rookies and Stars Crusade Update set. The set is sequentially numbered to 100.

*PURPLE: .75X TO 2X GREEN
*PURPLE: .75X TO 2X GREEN RC'S

1998 Leaf Rookies and Stars Extreme Measures

Randomly inserted in packs, this 10-card set is an insert to the Leaf Rookies and Stars brand. The cards are printed on foil board and sequentially numbered to 1000. However, a parallel version was created wherby a specific amount of each card was die cut to a featured statistic. The result, was varying print runs of the non-die cut cards. Specific print runs for each card are provided in our checklist after the player's name. Card fronts feature color action photos and highlights the featured player's extreme statistics.

Card	Low	High
COMPLETE SET (10)	50.00	120.00
1 Ken Griffey Jr./944	6.00	15.00
2 Frank Thomas/653	4.00	10.00
3 Tony Gwynn/628	5.00	12.00
4 Mark McGwire/942	10.00	25.00
5 Larry Walker/280	2.50	6.00
6 Mike Piazza/960	6.00	15.00
7 Roger Clemens/708	8.00	20.00
8 Greg Maddux/980	6.00	15.00
9 Jeff Bagwell/873	2.50	6.00
10 Nomar Garciaparra/989	6.00	15.00

1998 Leaf Rookies and Stars Extreme Measures Die Cuts

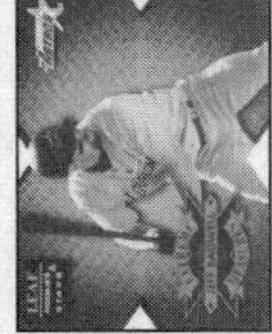

Randomly inserted in packs, this 10-card set is a parallel insert to the Leaf Rookies and Stars Extreme Measures set. The set is sequentially numbered to 1000. The low serial numbered cards are die-cut to showcase a specific statistic for each player. For example, Ken Griffey hit 56 home runs last year, so the 1st 56 of his cards are die-cut and cards serial numbered from 57 through 1000 are not.

Card	Low	High
NO PRICING ON 11 OR LESS		
1 Ken Griffey Jr./56	20.00	50.00
2 Frank Thomas/347	6.00	15.00
3 Tony Gwynn/372	6.00	15.00
4 Mark McGwire/58	40.00	80.00
5 Larry Walker/720	4.00	10.00
6 Mike Piazza/40	20.00	50.00
7 Roger Clemens/292	10.00	25.00
8 Greg Maddux/20		
9 Jeff Bagwell/127	8.00	20.00
10 Nomar Garciaparra/11		

1998 Leaf Rookies and Stars Freshman Orientation Samples

To preview the late-released 1998 Leaf Rookies and Stars product, all dealer wholesale order forms contained one sample card from four different insert sets (Freshman Orientation, Great American Heroes, Major League Hard Drives and Standing Ovations). The samples each feature the large "SAMPLE" text printed diagonally across the card back and a blank area intended for serial numbering on back. Apparently, MLB disallowed Donruss/Leaf the rights to use the word "chase" in a product name, fearing it insinuated aspects of gambling. However, the name was officially changed after Playoff took over Pinnacle's bankruptcy assets.

Card	Low	High
COMPLETE SET (20)	16.00	40.00
1 Todd Helton	2.00	5.00
2 Ben Grieve	.40	1.00
3 Travis Lee	.40	1.00
4 Paul Konerko	1.50	4.00
5 Jaret Wright	.40	1.00
6 Livan Hernandez	.75	2.00
7 Brad Fullmer	.40	1.00
8 Carl Pavano	.40	1.00
9 Richard Hidalgo	.40	1.00
10 Miguel Tejada	1.50	4.00
11 Mark Kotsay	.40	1.00
12 David Ortiz	1.50	4.00
13 Juan Encarnacion	.60	1.50
14 Fernando Tatis	.60	1.50
15 Kevin Millwood	2.00	5.00
16 Kerry Wood	1.25	3.00
17 Magglio Ordonez	4.00	10.00
18 Derrek Lee	1.50	4.00
19 Jose Cruz Jr.	.60	1.50
20 A.J. Hinch	.40	1.00

1998 Leaf Rookies and Stars Freshman Orientation

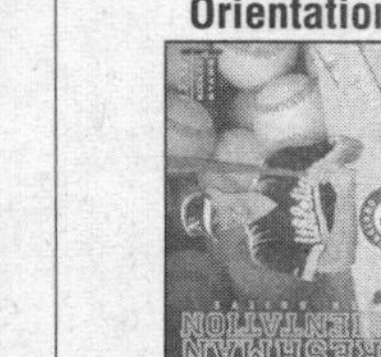

Randomly inserted in packs, this 20-card set is an insert to the Leaf Rookies and Stars brand. The set is sequentially numbered to 5000 and printed with holographic foil. The fronts feature color photos of the top up and coming stars in the game today surrounded by a background of banners and baseballs. The backs highlight the date of the featured player's Major League debut.

Card	Low	High
COMPLETE SET (20)	10.00	25.00
1 Todd Helton	.75	2.00
2 Ben Grieve	.40	1.00
3 Travis Lee	.40	1.00
4 Paul Konerko	.60	1.50
5 Jaret Wright	.40	1.00
6 Livan Hernandez	.60	1.50
7 Brad Fullmer	.40	1.00
8 Carl Pavano	.60	1.50
9 Richard Hidalgo	.40	1.00
10 Miguel Tejada	1.25	3.00
11 Mark Kotsay	.60	1.50
12 David Ortiz	1.50	4.00
13 Juan Encarnacion	.40	1.00
14 Fernando Tatis	.40	1.00
15 Kevin Millwood	1.25	3.00
16 Kerry Wood	.60	1.50
17 Magglio Ordonez	1.50	4.00
18 Derrek Lee	.75	2.00
19 Jose Cruz Jr.	.40	1.00
20 A.J. Hinch	.40	1.00

1998 Leaf Rookies and Stars Great American Heroes Samples

To preview the late-released 1998 Leaf Rookies and Stars product, all dealer wholesale order forms contained one sample card from four different insert sets (Freshman Orientation, Great American Heroes, Major League Hard Drives and Standing Ovations). The samples each feature the large "SAMPLE" text printed diagonally across the card back and a blank area intended for serial numbering on back. Apparently, MLB disallowed Donruss/Leaf the rights to use the word "chase" in a product name, fearing it insinuated aspects of gambling. However, the name was officially changed after Playoff took over Pinnacle's bankruptcy assets.

Card	Low	High
COMPLETE SET (20)	32.00	80.00
1 Frank Thomas	1.00	2.50
2 Cal Ripken	4.00	10.00
3 Ken Griffey Jr.	2.00	5.00
4 Alex Rodriguez	2.50	6.00
5 Greg Maddux	2.00	5.00
6 Mike Piazza	2.50	6.00
7 Chipper Jones	2.00	5.00
8 Tony Gwynn	1.50	4.00
9 Jeff Bagwell	1.00	2.50
10 Juan Gonzalez	.75	2.00
11 Hideo Nomo	2.00	5.00
12 Roger Clemens	2.00	5.00
13 Mark McGwire	2.50	6.00
14 Barry Bonds	2.00	5.00
15 Kenny Lofton	.40	1.00
16 Larry Walker	.30	.75
17 Paul Molitor	1.00	2.50
18 Wade Boggs	1.00	2.50
19 Barry Larkin	.60	1.50
20 Andres Galarraga	.40	1.00

1998 Leaf Rookies and Stars Great American Heroes

Randomly inserted in packs, this 20-card set is an insert to the Leaf Rookies and Stars brand. The set is sequentially numbered to 2500 and stamped with holographic foil. The fronts feature color player photos placed in an open star with "Great American Heroes" written in the upper right corner. In remembrance of his turbulent 1998 season, Mike Piazza is featured on three different versions (pictured separately as a Dodger, Marlin and Met).

Card	Low	High
COMPLETE SET (20)	60.00	150.00
1 Frank Thomas	2.50	6.00
2 Cal Ripken	8.00	20.00
3 Ken Griffey Jr.	4.00	10.00
4 Alex Rodriguez	4.00	10.00
5 Greg Maddux	4.00	10.00
6A Mike Piazza Dodgers	4.00	10.00
6B Mike Piazza Marlins	4.00	10.00
6C Mike Piazza Mets	4.00	10.00
7 Chipper Jones	2.50	6.00
8 Tony Gwynn	3.00	8.00
9 Jeff Bagwell	1.50	4.00
10 Juan Gonzalez	1.00	2.50
11 Hideo Nomo	2.50	6.00
12 Roger Clemens	5.00	12.00
13 Mark McGwire	6.00	15.00
14 Barry Bonds	6.00	15.00
15 Kenny Lofton	1.00	2.50
16 Larry Walker	1.00	2.50
17 Paul Molitor	1.00	2.50
18 Wade Boggs	1.50	4.00
19 Barry Larkin	1.50	4.00
20 Andres Galarraga	1.00	2.50

1998 Leaf Rookies and Stars Greatest Hits

Randomly inserted in packs, this 20-card set features color photos of the season's great rookies as well as stars of the game. The backs carry player information. Only 2500 serially numbered sets were produced.

Card	Low	High
COMPLETE SET (20)	50.00	120.00
1 Ken Griffey Jr.	4.00	10.00
2 Frank Thomas	2.50	6.00
3 Cal Ripken	8.00	20.00
4 Alex Rodriguez	4.00	10.00
5 Ben Grieve	2.50	6.00
6 Mike Piazza	4.00	10.00
7 Chipper Jones	2.50	6.00
8 Tony Gwynn	3.00	8.00
9 Derek Jeter	6.00	15.00
10 Jeff Bagwell	1.50	4.00
11 Tino Martinez	1.50	4.00
12 Juan Gonzalez	1.00	2.50
13 Nomar Garciaparra	4.00	10.00
14 Mark McGwire	6.00	15.00
15 Scott Rolen	1.50	4.00
16 David Justice	1.00	2.50
17 Darin Erstad	1.00	2.50
18 Mo Vaughn	1.00	2.50
19 Ivan Rodriguez	1.50	4.00
20 Travis Lee	1.50	4.00

1998 Leaf Rookies and Stars Home Run Derby

Randomly inserted in packs, this 20-card set is an insert to the Leaf Rookies and Stars brand. The set is sequentially numbered to 2500 and printed on foil

board. The card fronts feature color player photos of today's top homerun hitters surrounded by a nostalgic bordered background that takes a look at the TV show from the 50's with the same name.

COMPLETE SET (20) 40.00 100.00
1 Tino Martinez 1.50 4.00
2 Jim Thome 1.50 4.00
3 Larry Walker 1.00 2.50
4 Tony Clark 1.00 2.50
5 Jose Cruz Jr. 1.00 2.50
6 Barry Bonds 6.00 15.00
7 Scott Rolen 1.50 4.00
8 Paul Konerko 1.00 2.50
9 Travis Lee 1.00 2.50
10 Todd Helton 2.50 6.00
11 Mark McGwire 6.00 15.00
12 Andruw Jones 1.50 4.00
13 Nomar Garciaparra 4.00 10.00
14 Juan Gonzalez 1.00 2.50
15 Jeff Bagwell 1.50 4.00
16 Chipper Jones 2.50 6.00
17 Mike Piazza 4.00 10.00
18 Frank Thomas 2.50 6.00
19 Ken Griffey Jr. 4.00 10.00
20 Albert Belle 1.00 2.50

1998 Leaf Rookies and Stars Leaf MVP's

Randomly inserted in packs, this 20-card set is an insert to the Leaf Rookies and Stars brand. Each card is printed on foil board, with a red background and sequentially numbered to 5000 - although the first 500 of each card was die cut for a parallel set. Thus, only cards serial numbered from 501 through 5000 are featured in this set. The fronts feature color action photos on top of an "MVP" logo in the background.

COMPLETE SET (20) 30.00 80.00
*PENNANT ED: 1.5X TO 4X BASIC LEAF MVP
PENNANT ED.1ST 500 SERIAL #'d SETS 1.504.00
RANDOM INSERTS IN PACKS
1 Frank Thomas 1.50 4.00
2 Chuck Knoblauch .60 1.50
3 Cal Ripken 5.00 12.00
4 Alex Rodriguez 2.50 6.00
5 Ivan Rodriguez 1.00 2.50
6 Albert Belle .60 1.50
7 Ken Griffey Jr. 2.50 6.00
8 Juan Gonzalez .60 1.50
9 Roger Clemens 3.00 8.00
10 Mo Vaughn .60 1.50
11 Jeff Bagwell 1.00 2.50
12 Craig Biggio 1.00 2.50
13 Chipper Jones 1.50 4.00
14 Barry Larkin 1.00 2.50
15 Mike Piazza 2.50 6.00
16 Barry Bonds 4.00 10.00
17 Andruw Jones 1.00 2.50
18 Tony Gwynn 2.00 5.00
19 Greg Maddux 2.50 6.00
20 Mark McGwire 4.00 10.00

1998 Leaf Rookies and Stars Major League Hard Drives Samples

To preview the late-released 1998 Leaf Rookies and Stars product, all dealer wholesale order forms contained one sample card from four different insert sets (Freshman Orientation, Great American Heroes, Major League Hard Drives and Standing Ovations). The samples each feature the large "SAMPLE" text printed diagonally across the card back and a blank area intended for serial numbering on back. Apparently, MLB disallowed Donruss/Leaf the rights to use the word "chase" in a product name, fearing it insinuated aspects of gambling. However, the name was officially changed after Playoff took over Pinnacle's bankruptcy assets.

COMPLETE SET (20) 24.00 60.00
1 Jeff Bagwell 1.00 2.50
2 Juan Gonzalez .75 2.00
3 Nomar Garciaparra 2.50 6.00
4 Ken Griffey Jr. 2.00 5.00
5 Frank Thomas 1.00 2.50
6 Cal Ripken 4.00 10.00
7 Alex Rodriguez 2.50 6.00
8 Mike Piazza 2.50 6.00
9 Chipper Jones 2.00 5.00
10 Tony Gwynn 1.50 4.00
11 Derek Jeter 4.00 10.00
12 Mo Vaughn .30 .75
13 Ben Grieve .20 .50
14 Manny Ramirez 1.00 2.50
15 Vladimir Guerrero 1.25 3.00
16 Scott Rolen .60 1.50
17 Darin Erstad .60 1.50
18 Kenny Lofton .40 1.00
19 Brad Fullmer .20 .50
20 David Justice .40 1.00

1998 Leaf Rookies and Stars Major League Hard Drives

Randomly inserted in packs, this 20-card set is an insert to the Leaf Rookies and Stars brand. The set is printed with holographic foil stamping and sequentially numbered to 2500. The fronts feature color action photos of some of today's hottest hitting machines placed in a baseball diamond background. In remembrance of his turbulent 1998 season, Mike Piazza is featured on three different versions (pictured separately as a Dodger, Marlin and Met). All three versions of the Piazza card had 2500 cards printed.

COMPLETE SET (20) 60.00 150.00
1 Jeff Bagwell 1.50 4.00
2 Juan Gonzalez 1.00 2.50
3 Nomar Garciaparra 4.00 10.00
4 Ken Griffey Jr. 4.00 10.00
5 Frank Thomas 2.50 6.00
6 Cal Ripken 8.00 20.00
7 Alex Rodriguez 4.00 10.00
8 Mike Piazza Dodgers 4.00 10.00
8B Mike Piazza Marlins 4.00 10.00
8C Mike Piazza Mets 4.00 10.00
9 Chipper Jones 2.50 6.00
10 Tony Gwynn 3.00 8.00
11 Derek Jeter 6.00 15.00
12 Mo Vaughn 1.00 2.50
13 Ben Grieve 2.50 6.00
14 Manny Ramirez 1.50 4.00
15 Vladimir Guerrero 2.50 6.00
16 Scott Rolen 1.50 4.00
17 Darin Erstad 1.00 2.50
18 Kenny Lofton 1.00 2.50
19 Brad Fullmer 1.00 2.50
20 David Justice 1.00 2.50

1998 Leaf Rookies and Stars Standing Ovations Samples

To preview the late-released 1998 Leaf Rookies and Stars product, all dealer wholesale order forms contained one sample card from four different insert sets (Freshman Orientation, Great American Heroes, Major League Hard Drives and Standing Ovations). The samples each feature the large "SAMPLE" text printed diagonally across the card back and a blank area intended for serial numbering on back. Apparently, MLB disallowed Donruss/Leaf the rights to use the word "chase" in a product name, fearing it insinuated aspects of gambling. However, the name was officially changed after Playoff took over Pinnacle's bankruptcy assets.

COMPLETE SET (10) 20.00 50.00
1 Barry Bonds 2.00 5.00
2 Mark McGwire 2.50 6.00
3 Ken Griffey Jr. 2.00 5.00
4 Frank Thomas 1.00 2.50
5 Tony Gwynn 1.50 4.00
6 Cal Ripken 4.00 10.00
7 Greg Maddux 2.50 6.00
8 Roger Clemens 2.00 5.00
9 Paul Molitor 1.00 2.50
10 Ivan Rodriguez 1.00 2.50

1998 Leaf Rookies and Stars Standing Ovations

Randomly inserted in packs, this 10-card set is an insert to the Leaf Rookies and Stars brand set. The set is sequentially numbered to 5000 and printed with holographic foil stamping. The fronts feature full-bleed color photos. The featured player's ovation deserved accomplishments are found lining the bottom of the card along with his name and team.

COMPLETE SET (10) 20.00 50.00
1 Barry Bonds 4.00 10.00
2 Mark McGwire 4.00 10.00
3 Ken Griffey Jr. 2.50 6.00
4 Frank Thomas 1.50 4.00
5 Tony Gwynn 2.00 5.00
6 Cal Ripken 5.00 12.00
7 Greg Maddux 2.50 6.00
8 Roger Clemens 3.00 8.00
9 Paul Molitor .60 1.50
10 Ivan Rodriguez 1.00 2.50

1998 Leaf Rookies and Stars Ticket Masters

Randomly inserted in packs, this 20-card set is an insert to the Leaf Rookies and Stars base set. The set is sequentially numbered to 2500, but the first 250 cards were die cut for a parallel set. This double-sided set is printed on foil board and features color photos of players from the same team.

COMPLETE SET (20) 60.00 150.00
*DIE CUTS: 1.25X TO 3X BASIC TICKET
DIE CUTS 1ST 250 SERIAL #'d SETS
RANDOM INSERTS IN PACKS
1 Ken Griffey Jr. 5.00 12.00
Alex Rodriguez
2 Frank Thomas 3.00 8.00
Albert Belle
3 Cal Ripken 10.00 25.00
Roberto Alomar
4 Greg Maddux 5.00 12.00
Chipper Jones
5 Tony Gwynn 4.00 10.00
Ken Caminiti
6 Derek Jeter 8.00 20.00
Andy Pettitte
7 Jeff Bagwell 2.00 5.00
Craig Biggio
8 Juan Gonzalez 2.00 5.00
Ivan Rodriguez
9 Nomar Garciaparra 5.00 12.00
Mo Vaughn
10 Vladimir Guerrero 3.00 8.00
Brad Fullmer
11 Andruw Jones 2.00 5.00
Andres Galarraga
12 Tino Martinez 2.00 5.00
Chuck Knoblauch
13 Raul Mondesi 1.25 3.00
Paul Konerko
14 Roger Clemens 6.00 15.00
Jose Cruz Jr.
15 Mark McGwire 8.00 20.00
Brian Jordan
16 Kenny Lofton 2.00 5.00
Manny Ramirez
17 Larry Walker 1.25 3.00
Todd Helton
18 Darin Erstad 1.25 3.00
Tim Salmon
19 Travis Lee 1.25 3.00
Matt Williams
20 Ben Grieve 1.25 3.00
Jason Giambi

2001 Leaf Rookies and Stars Samples

Inserted one per sealed Beckett Baseball Card Monthly issue number 202, these 100 cards feature veterans from the Leaf Rookies and Stars set. Each card has the word Sample stamped on the back.

*SINGLES: 1.5X TO 4X BASIC CARDS

2001 Leaf Rookies and Stars

This 300 card set was issued in five card packs. All cards numbered over 100 were shortprinted. Cards numbered 101-200 were inserted at a rate of one in four while cards numbered 201-300 were inserted at a rate of one in 24.

COMP.SET w/o SP'S (100) 8.00 20.00
COMMON CARD (1-100) .10 .30
COMMON (101-200) 1.25 3.00
COMMON (201-300) 2.00 5.00
1 Alex Rodriguez .50 1.25
2 Derek Jeter .75 2.00
3 Aramis Ramirez .10 .30
4 Cliff Floyd .10 .30
5 Nomar Garciaparra .50 1.25
6 Craig Biggio .20 .50
7 Ivan Rodriguez .20 .50
8 Cal Ripken 1.00 2.50
9 Fred McGriff .20 .50
10 Chipper Jones .30 .75
11 Roberto Alomar .20 .50
12 Moises Alou .10 .30
13 Freddy Garcia .10 .30
14 Bobby Abreu .10 .30
15 Shawn Green .10 .30
16 Jason Giambi .10 .30
17 Todd Helton .20 .50
18 Robert Fick .10 .30
19 Tony Gwynn .40 1.00
20 Luis Gonzalez .10 .30
21 Sean Casey .10 .30
22 Roger Clemens .60 1.50
23 Brian Giles .10 .30
24 Manny Ramirez Sox .20 .50
25 Barry Bonds .75 2.00
26 Richard Hidalgo .10 .30
27 Vladimir Guerrero .30 .75
28 Kevin Brown UER .10 .30
Batting headers for stats
29 Mike Sweeney .10 .30
30 Ken Griffey Jr. .50 1.25
31 Mike Piazza .50 1.25
32 Richie Sexson .10 .30
33 Matt Morris .10 .30
34 Jorge Posada .20 .50
35 Eric Chavez .10 .30
36 Mark Buehrle .20 .50
37 Jeff Bagwell .20 .50
38 Curt Schilling .10 .30
39 Bartolo Colon .10 .30
40 Mark Quinn .10 .30
41 Tony Clark .10 .30
42 Brad Radke .10 .30
43 Gary Sheffield .10 .30
44 Doug Mientkiewicz .10 .30
45 Pedro Martinez .20 .50
46 Carlos Lee .10 .30
47 Troy Glaus .10 .30
48 Preston Wilson .10 .30
49 Phil Nevin .10 .30
50 Chan Ho Park .10 .30
51 Randy Johnson .30 .75
52 Jermaine Dye .10 .30
53 Terrence Long .10 .30
54 Joe Mays .10 .30
55 Scott Rolen .20 .50
56 Miguel Tejada .10 .30
57 Jim Thome .20 .50
58 Jose Vidro .10 .30
59 Gabe Kapler .10 .30
60 Darin Erstad .10 .30
61 Jim Edmonds .10 .30
62 Jarrod Washburn .10 .30
63 Tom Glavine .20 .50
64 Adrian Beltre .10 .30
65 Sammy Sosa .30 .75
66 Juan Gonzalez .10 .30
67 Rafael Furcal .10 .30
68 Mike Mussina .20 .50
69 Mark McGwire .75 2.00
70 Ryan Klesko .10 .30
71 Raul Mondesi .10 .30
72 Trot Nixon .10 .30
73 Barry Larkin .20 .50
74 Rafael Palmeiro .20 .50
75 Mark Mulder .10 .30
76 Carlos Delgado .10 .30
77 Mike Hampton .10 .30
78 Carl Everett .10 .30
79 Paul Konerko .10 .30
80 Larry Walker .10 .30
81 Kerry Wood .10 .30
82 Frank Thomas .30 .75
83 Andruw Jones .20 .50
84 Eric Milton .10 .30
85 Ben Grieve .10 .30
86 Carlos Beltran .10 .30
87 Tim Hudson .10 .30
88 Hideo Nomo .30 .75
89 Greg Maddux .50 1.25
90 Edgar Martinez .20 .50
91 Lance Berkman .10 .30
92 Pat Burrell .10 .30
93 Jeff Kent .10 .30
94 Magglio Ordonez .10 .30
95 Cristian Guzman .10 .30
96 Jose Canseco .20 .50
97 J.D. Drew .10 .30
98 Bernie Williams .20 .50
99 Kazuhiro Sasaki .10 .30
100 Rickey Henderson .30 .75
101 Wilson Guzman RC 1.25 3.00
102 Nick Neugebauer 1.25 3.00
103 Lance Davis RC 1.25 3.00
104 Felipe Lopez 1.25 3.00
105 Toby Hall 1.25 3.00
106 Jack Cust 1.25 3.00
107 Jason Karnuth RC 1.25 3.00
108 Bart Miadich RC 1.25 3.00
109 Brian Roberts RC 3.00 8.00
110 Brandon Larson RC 1.25 3.00
111 Sean Douglass RC 1.25 3.00
112 Joe Crede 2.00 5.00
113 Tim Redding 1.25 3.00
114 Adam Johnson 1.25 3.00
115 Marcus Giles 1.25 3.00
116 Jose Ortiz 1.25 3.00
117 Jose Mieses RC 1.25 3.00
118 Nick Maness RC 1.25 3.00
119 Les Walrond RC 1.25 3.00
120 Travis Phelps RC 1.25 3.00
121 Troy Mattes RC 1.25 3.00
122 Carlos Garcia RC 1.25 3.00
123 Bill Ortega RC 1.25 3.00
124 Gene Altman RC 1.25 3.00
125 Nate Frese RC 1.25 3.00
126 Alfonso Soriano 2.00 5.00
127 Jose Nunez RC 1.25 3.00
128 Bob File RC 1.25 3.00
129 Dan Wright 1.25 3.00
130 Nick Johnson 1.25 3.00
131 Brent Abernathy 1.25 3.00
132 Steve Green RC 1.25 3.00
133 Billy Sylvester RC 1.25 3.00
134 Scott MacRae RC 1.25 3.00
135 Kris Keller RC 1.25 3.00
136 Scott Stewart RC 1.25 3.00
137 Henry Mateo RC 1.25 3.00
138 Timo Perez 1.25 3.00
139 Nate Teut RC 1.25 3.00
140 Jason Michaels RC 1.25 3.00
141 Junior Spivey RC 2.00 5.00
142 Carlos Pena 1.25 3.00
143 Wilmy Caceres RC 1.25 3.00
144 David Lundquist 1.25 3.00
145 Jack Wilson RC 2.00 5.00
146 Jeremy Fikac RC 1.25 3.00
147 Alex Escobar 1.25 3.00
148 Abraham Nunez 1.25 3.00
149 Xavier Nady 1.25 3.00
150 Michael Cuddyer 1.25 3.00
151 Greg Miller RC 1.25 3.00
152 Eric Munson 1.25 3.00
153 Aubrey Huff 1.25 3.00
154 Tim Christman RC 1.25 3.00
155 Erick Almonte RC 1.25 3.00
156 Mike Penney RC 1.25 3.00
157 Delvin James RC 1.25 3.00
158 Ben Sheets 2.00 5.00
159 Jason Hart 1.25 3.00
160 Jose Acevedo RC 1.25 3.00
161 Will Ohman RC 1.25 3.00
162 Erik Hiljus RC 1.25 3.00
163 Juan Moreno RC 1.25 3.00
164 Mike Koplove RC 1.25 3.00
165 Pedro Santana RC 1.25 3.00
166 Jimmy Rollins 1.25 3.00
167 Matt White RC 1.25 3.00
168 Cesar Crespo RC 1.25 3.00
169 Carlos Hernandez 1.25 3.00
170 Chris George 1.25 3.00
171 Brad Voyles RC 1.25 3.00
172 Luis Pineda RC 1.25 3.00
173 Carlos Zambrano RC 2.00 5.00
174 Nate Cornejo 1.25 3.00
175 Jason Smith RC 1.25 3.00
176 Craig Monroe RC 3.00 8.00
177 Cody Ransom RC 1.25 3.00
178 John Grabow RC 1.25 3.00
179 Pedro Feliz 1.25 3.00
180 Jeremy Owens RC 1.25 3.00
181 Kurt Ainsworth 1.25 3.00
182 Luis Lopez 1.25 3.00
183 Stubby Clapp RC 1.25 3.00
184 Ryan Freel RC 3.00 8.00
185 Duaner Sanchez RC 1.25 3.00
186 Jason Jennings 1.25 3.00
187 Kyle Lohse RC 2.00 5.00
188 Jerrod Riggan RC 1.25 3.00
189 Joe Beimel RC 1.25 3.00
190 Nick Punto RC 1.25 3.00
191 Willie Harris RC 1.25 3.00
192 Ryan Jensen RC 1.25 3.00
193 Adam Pettyjohn RC 1.25 3.00
194 Donaldo Mendez RC 1.25 3.00
195 Bret Prinz RC 1.25 3.00
196 Paul Phillips RC 1.25 3.00
197 Brian Lawrence RC 1.25 3.00
198 Cesar Izturis 1.25 3.00
199 Blaine Neal RC 1.25 3.00
200 Josh Fogg RC 2.00 5.00
201 Josh Towers RC 3.00 8.00
202 T.Spooneybarger RC 2.00 5.00
203 Michael Rivera RC 2.00 5.00
204 Juan Cruz RC 2.00 5.00
205 Albert Pujols RC 60.00 120.00
206 Josh Beckett 3.00 8.00
207 Roy Oswalt 3.00 8.00
208 Elpidio Guzman RC 2.00 5.00
209 Horacio Ramirez RC 3.00 8.00
210 Corey Patterson 2.00 5.00
211 Geronimo Gil RC 2.00 5.00
212 Jay Gibbons RC 3.00 8.00
213 O.Woodards RC 2.00 5.00
214 David Espinosa 2.00 5.00
215 Angel Berroa RC 3.00 8.00
216 B.Duckworth RC 2.00 5.00
217 Brian Reith RC 2.00 5.00
218 David Brous RC 2.00 5.00
219 Bud Smith RC 2.00 5.00
220 Ramon Vazquez RC 2.00 5.00
221 Mark Teixeira RC 12.50 30.00
222 Justin Atchley RC 2.00 5.00
223 Tony Cogan RC 2.00 5.00
224 Grant Balfour RC 2.00 5.00
225 Ricardo Rodriguez RC 2.00 5.00
226 Brian Rogers RC 2.00 5.00
227 Adam Dunn 3.00 8.00
228 Wilson Betemit RC 3.00 8.00
229 Juan Diaz RC 2.00 5.00
230 Jackson Melian RC 2.00 5.00
231 Claudio Vargas RC 2.00 5.00
232 Wilkin Ruan RC 2.00 5.00
233 J.Duchscherer RC 2.00 5.00
234 Kevin Olsen RC 2.00 5.00
235 Tony Fiore RC 2.00 5.00
236 Jeremy Affeldt RC 2.00 5.00
237 Mike Maroth RC 2.00 5.00
238 C.C. Sabathia 2.00 5.00
239 Cory Aldridge RC 2.00 5.00
240 Zach Day RC 2.00 5.00
241 Brett Jodie RC 2.00 5.00
242 Winston Abreu RC 2.00 5.00
243 Travis Hafner RC 10.00 25.00
244 Joe Kennedy RC 3.00 8.00
245 Rick Bauer RC 2.00 5.00
246 Mike Young 3.00 8.00
247 Ken Vining RC 2.00 5.00
248 Doug Nickle RC 2.00 5.00
249 Pablo Ozuna 2.00 5.00
250 Dustan Mohr RC 2.00 5.00
251 Ichiro Suzuki RC 20.00 50.00
252 Ryan Drese RC 3.00 8.00
253 Morgan Ensberg RC 3.00 8.00
254 George Perez RC 2.00 5.00
255 Roy Smith RC 2.00 5.00
256 Juan Uribe RC 3.00 8.00
257 Dewon Brazelton RC 2.00 5.00
258 Endy Chavez RC 2.00 5.00
259 Kris Foster 2.00 5.00
260 Eric Knott RC 2.00 5.00
261 Corky Miller RC 2.00 5.00
262 Larry Bigbie 2.00 5.00
263 Andres Torres RC 2.00 5.00
264 Adrian Hernandez RC 2.00 5.00
265 Johnny Estrada RC 3.00 8.00
266 David Williams RC 2.00 5.00
267 Steve Lomasney 2.00 5.00
268 Victor Zambrano RC 3.00 8.00
269 Keith Ginter 2.00 5.00
270 Casey Fossum RC 2.00 5.00
271 Josue Perez RC 2.00 5.00
272 Josh Phelps 2.00 5.00
273 Mark Prior RC 10.00 25.00
274 Brandon Berger RC 2.00 5.00
275 Scott Podsednik RC 5.00 12.00
276 Jorge Julio RC 2.00 5.00
277 Esix Snead RC 2.00 5.00
278 Brandon Knight RC 2.00 5.00
279 Saul Rivera RC 2.00 5.00
280 Benito Baez RC 2.00 5.00
281 Rob MacKowiak RC 3.00 8.00
282 Eric Hinske RC 3.00 8.00
283 Juan Rivera 2.00 5.00
284 Kevin Joseph RC 2.00 5.00
285 Juan A. Pena RC 2.00 5.00
286 Brandon Lyon RC 2.00 5.00
287 Adam Everett 2.00 5.00
288 Eric Valent 2.00 5.00
289 Ken Harvey 2.00 5.00
290 Bert Snow RC 2.00 5.00
291 Wily Mo Pena 2.00 5.00
292 Rafael Soriano RC 2.00 5.00
293 Carlos Valderrama RC 2.00 5.00
294 Christian Parker RC 2.00 5.00
295 Tsuyoshi Shinjo RC 3.00 8.00
296 Martin Vargas RC 2.00 5.00
297 Luke Hudson RC 2.00 5.00
298 Dee Brown 2.00 5.00
299 Alexis Gomez RC 2.00 5.00
300 Angel Santos RC 2.00 5.00

2001 Leaf Rookies and Stars Autographs

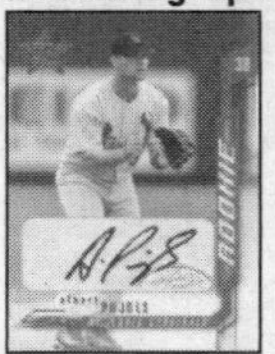

Randomly inserted in packs, these 76 cards feature signed cards of some of the prospects and rookies included in the Leaf Rookie and Stars set. According to Donruss/Playoff most players signed 250 cards for inclusion in this product. A few signed 100 cards so we have included that information in our checklist next to the player's name.

107 Jason Karnuth/250 * 4.00 10.00
110 Brandon Larson/100 * 6.00 15.00
117 Jose Mieses/250 * 4.00 10.00
118 Nick Maness/250 * 4.00 10.00
119 Les Walrond/250 * 4.00 10.00
122 Carlos Garcia/250 * 4.00 10.00
123 Bill Ortega/250 * 4.00 10.00
124 Gene Altman/250 * 4.00 10.00
125 Nate Frese/250 * 4.00 10.00
130 Nick Johnson/100 * 10.00 25.00
133 Billy Sylvester/250 * 4.00 10.00
135 Kris Keller/250 * 4.00 10.00
139 Nate Teut/250 * 4.00 10.00
140 Jason Michaels/250 * 4.00 10.00
143 Wilmy Caceres/250 * 4.00 10.00
145 Jack Wilson/100 * 10.00 25.00
151 Greg Miller/250 * 4.00 10.00
155 Erick Almonte/250 * 4.00 10.00
156 Mike Penney/250 * 4.00 10.00
157 Delvin James/250 * 4.00 10.00
161 Will Ohman/250 * 4.00 10.00
167 Matt White/250 * 4.00 10.00
180 Jeremy Owens/250 * 4.00 10.00
184 Ryan Freel/250 * 10.00 25.00
185 Duaner Sanchez/250 * 4.00 10.00
193 Adam Pettyjohn/100 * 6.00 15.00
194 Donaldo Mendez/100 * 6.00 15.00
196 Paul Phillips/250 * 4.00 10.00
197 Brian Lawrence/100 * 6.00 15.00
199 Blaine Neal/250 * 4.00 10.00
201 Josh Towers/100 * 6.00 15.00
203 Michael Rivera/250 * 4.00 10.00
204 Juan Cruz/100 * 6.00 15.00
205 Albert Pujols/50 *
207 Roy Oswalt/50 * 30.00 60.00
208 Elpidio Guzman/100 * 6.00 15.00
209 Horacio Ramirez/250 * 6.00 15.00
210 Corey Patterson/50 * 10.00 25.00
211 Geronimo Gil/250 * 4.00 10.00
212 Jay Gibbons/100 * 10.00 25.00
213 Orlando Woodards/250 * 4.00 10.00
215 Angel Berroa/100 * 10.00 25.00
216 Brandon Duckworth/100 * 6.00 15.00
218 David Brous/250 * 4.00 10.00
219 Bud Smith/50 * 10.00 25.00
221 Mark Teixeira/100 * 150.00 250.00
223 Tony Cogan/250 * 4.00 10.00
225 Ricardo Rodriguez/250 * 4.00 10.00
226 Brian Rogers/250 * 4.00 10.00
227 Adam Dunn/50 * 20.00 50.00
228 Wilson Betemit/100 * 15.00 40.00
231 Claudio Vargas/250 * 4.00 10.00
232 Wilkin Ruan/250 * 4.00 10.00
234 Kevin Olsen/250 * 4.00 10.00
236 Jeremy Affeldt/250 * 4.00 10.00
237 Mike Maroth/250 * 6.00 15.00
238 C.C. Sabathia/50 * 10.00 25.00
239 Cory Aldridge/250 * 4.00 10.00
240 Zach Day/250 * 4.00 10.00
243 Travis Hafner/250 * 60.00 120.00
244 Joe Kennedy/100 * 6.00 15.00
254 George Perez/250 * 4.00 10.00
256 Juan Uribe/250 * 6.00 15.00
257 Dewon Brazelton/100 * 6.00 15.00
261 Corky Miller/100 * 6.00 15.00
263 Andres Torres/100 * 6.00 15.00
265 Johnny Estrada/100 * 6.00 15.00
266 David Williams/250 * 4.00 10.00
270 Casey Fossum/250 * 4.00 10.00
273 Mark Prior/100 * 125.00 200.00
274 Brandon Berger/250 * 4.00 10.00
277 Esix Snead/250 * 4.00 10.00
282 Eric Hinske/250 * 6.00 15.00
292 Rafael Soriano/250 * 4.00 10.00
293 Carlos Valderrama/250 * 4.00 10.00
299 Alexis Gomez/250 * 4.00 10.00

2001 Leaf Rookies and Stars Longevity

Randomly inserted into packs, these cards parallel the Leaf Rookie and Stars set. Cards numbered 1-100 are serial numbered to 50 while cards

numbered 101-300 are serial numbered to 25.
*LONGEVITY: 1-100: 12.5X TO 30X BASIC CARDS

2001 Leaf Rookies and Stars Dress for Success

Inserted one per 96 packs, these 25 cards feature two swatches of game-used memorabilia on each card.

DFS1 Cal Ripken 20.00 50.00
DFS2 Mike Piazza 10.00 25.00
DFS3 Barry Bonds 20.00 50.00
DFS4 Frank Thomas 8.00 20.00
DFS5 Nomar Garciaparra 12.50 30.00
DFS6 Richie Sexson 6.00 15.00
DFS7 Brian Giles 6.00 15.00
DFS8 Todd Helton 8.00 20.00
DFS9 Ivan Rodriguez 8.00 20.00
DFS10 Andruw Jones 8.00 20.00
DFS11 Juan Gonzalez 6.00 15.00
DFS12 Vladimir Guerrero 8.00 20.00
DFS13 Greg Maddux 10.00 25.00
DFS14 Tony Gwynn 10.00 25.00
DFS15 Randy Johnson 8.00 20.00
DFS16 Jeff Bagwell 8.00 20.00
DFS17 Kerry Wood SP
DFS18 Roberto Alomar 8.00 20.00
DFS19 Chipper Jones 8.00 20.00
DFS20 Pedro Martinez 8.00 20.00
DFS21 Shawn Green 6.00 15.00
DFS22 Magglio Ordonez 6.00 15.00
DFS23 Darin Erstad SP
DFS24 Rafael Palmeiro SP
DFS25 Edgar Martinez 8.00 20.00

2001 Leaf Rookies and Stars Dress for Success Prime Cuts

Randomly inserted into packs, these cards parallel the Dress for Success insert set. Each card had a stated print run of 50 serial numbered sets.

*PRIME CUTS: 1.25X TO 3X BASIC DRESS
DFS17 Kerry Wood 15.00 40.00
DFS23 Darin Erstad 15.00 40.00
DFS24 Rafael Palmeiro 20.00 50.00

2001 Leaf Rookies and Stars Freshman Orientation

Inserted into packs at odds of one in 96, these 25 cards feature leading prospects along with a piece of game-used memorabilia. The Dunn, Pujols and Gibbons cards are shortprinted compared to the rest of the set.

FO1 Adam Dunn Bat SP
FO2 Josh Towers Pants 6.00 15.00
FO3 Vernon Wells Jsy 4.00 10.00
FO4 Corey Patterson Pants 4.00 10.00
FO5 Albert Pujols Bat SP
FO6 Ben Sheets Jsy 6.00 15.00
FO7 Pedro Feliz Bat 4.00 10.00
FO8 Keith Ginter Bat 4.00 10.00
FO9 Luis Rivas Bat 4.00 10.00
FO10 Andres Torres Bat 4.00 10.00
FO11 Carlos Valderrama Jsy 4.00 10.00
FO12 Brandon Inge Jsy 4.00 10.00
FO13 Jay Gibbons Cap SP
FO14 Cesar Izturis Bat 4.00 10.00
FO15 Marcus Giles Jsy 4.00 10.00
FO16 Tsuyoshi Shinjo Jsy 6.00 15.00
FO17 Eric Valent Bat 4.00 10.00
FO18 David Espinosa Bat 4.00 10.00
FO19 Aubrey Huff Jsy 4.00 10.00
FO20 Wilmy Caceres Jsy 4.00 10.00
FO21 Bud Smith Jsy 4.00 10.00
FO22 Ricardo Rodriguez Pants 4.00 10.00
FO23 Wes Helms Jsy 4.00 10.00
FO24 Jason Hart Bat 4.00 10.00
FO25 Dee Brown Jsy 4.00 10.00

2001 Leaf Rookies and Stars Freshman Orientation Autographs

Randomly inserted into packs, these 21 cards parallel the Freshman Orientation insert set. Each of these players signed 100 cards or less for this product. If the player signed less than 100 cards we have notated that with an SP in our checklist.

FO1 Adam Dunn Bat SP
FO2 Josh Towers Pants SP
FO4 Corey Patterson Pants SP
FO5 Albert Pujols Bat SP
FO6 Ben Sheets Jsy SP
FO7 Pedro Feliz Bat 8.00 20.00
FO8 Keith Ginter Bat 8.00 20.00
FO9 Luis Rivas Bat 8.00 20.00
FO10 Andres Torres Bat 8.00 20.00
FO11 Carlos Valderrama Jsy 8.00 20.00
FO13 Jay Gibbons Cap 10.00 25.00
FO14 Cesar Izturis Bat 8.00 20.00
FO15 Marcus Giles Jsy 8.00 20.00
FO17 Eric Valent Bat 8.00 20.00
FO18 David Espinosa Bat 8.00 20.00
FO19 Aubrey Huff Jsy 8.00 20.00
FO20 Wilmy Caceres Jsy 8.00 20.00
FO21 Bud Smith Jsy SP
FO22 Ricardo Rodriguez Pants 8.00 20.00
FO24 Jason Hart Bat 8.00 20.00
FO25 Dee Brown Jsy 8.00 20.00

2001 Leaf Rookies and Stars Freshman Orientation Class Officers

Randomly inserted into packs, these cards parallel the Freshman Orientation insert set. Each card had a stated print run of 50 serial numbered sets.

*CLASS OFFICER: .75X TO 2X BASIC FRESH
FO1 Adam Dunn Bat 8.00 20.00
FO5 Albert Pujols Bat 150.00 250.00
FO13 Jay Gibbons Cap 8.00 20.00

2001 Leaf Rookies and Stars Great American Treasures

Inserted at a rate of one in 1,120 packs, these 20 cards feature pieces of memorabilia from key moments in a players career.

PRINT RUN INFO PROVIDED BY DONRUSS
CARDS ARE NOT SERIAL-NUMBERED
NO PRICING ON QTY OF 25 DUE TO SCARCITY
GT1 B.Bonds 517 HR Jsy/50 * 125.00 200.00
GT2 M.Ordonez HR Bat/200 * 15.00 40.00
GT3 D.Jeter 1st Game Ball/25 *
GT4 N.Ryan 7th No-Hit Ball/25 *
GT5 S.Sosa June HR Ball/25 *
GT6 T.Glavine 96 WS Jsy/100 * 30.00 60.00
GT7 I.Rod 99 MVP Bat/200 * 20.00 50.00
GT8 P.Martinez 300 K Ball/25 *
GT9 M.McGwire 60 HR Ball/25 *
GT10 T.Williams 517 HR Ball/25 *
GT11 R.Sandberg 91 AS Bat/200 * 40.00 80.00
GT12 B.Bonds 500 HR Ball/25 *
GT13 H.Nomo No-Hit Ball/25 *
GT14 R.Maris 61 HR Ball/25 *
GT15 T.Cobb 09 WS Ball/25 *
GT16 H.Killebrew 570 HR Bat/50 * 40.00 80.00
GT17 M.Ordonez 00 AS Cap/100 * 20.00 50.00
GT18 W.Boggs WS Bat/200 * 20.00 50.00
GT19 H.Aaron 755 HR Cap/25 *
GT20 D.Cone Perfect Game Ball/25 *

2001 Leaf Rookies and Stars Great American Treasures Autograph

This four card parallel to the Great American Treasure set features signed cards by these players on cards relating to a key event in their career. Due

to scarcity, no pricing information is provided.

GT6 Tom Glavine 96 WS Jsy
GT11 Ryne Sandberg 91 AS Bat
GT16 Harmon Killebrew 570 HR Bat
GT18 Wade Boggs WS Bat

2001 Leaf Rookies and Stars Players Collection

Randomly inserted into packs, these 15 cards feature four different types of memorabilia from three key superstars. Each player also had a quad card with one piece each of the four types of memorabilia featured. Each card is serial numbered to 100 except for the quad cards which are serial numbered to 25.

PC1 Tony Gwynn Bat SP 10.00 25.00
PC2 Tony Gwynn Jsy 10.00 25.00
PC3 Tony Gwynn Pants 10.00 25.00
PC4 Tony Gwynn Shoe 10.00 25.00
PC5 Tony Gwynn Quad/25
PC6 Cal Ripken White Jsy SP 30.00 60.00
PC7 Cal Ripken Bat SP 30.00 60.00
PC8 Cal Ripken Glove 30.00 60.00
PC9 Cal Ripken Gray Jsy 30.00 60.00
PC10 Cal Ripken Quad
PC11 Barry Bonds Jsy 20.00 50.00
PC12 Barry Bonds Shoe 20.00 50.00
PC13 Barry Bonds Pants 20.00 50.00
PC14 Barry Bonds Bat 20.00 50.00
PC15 Barry Bonds Quad/25

2001 Leaf Rookies and Stars Players Collection Autographs

Randomly inserted into packs, these three cards feature signed cards of the players along with a memorabilia piece. Due to market scarcity, no pricing is provided.

PC1 Tony Gwynn Bat
PC6 Cal Ripken Jsy
PC7 Cal Ripken Bat

2001 Leaf Rookies and Stars Slideshow

Randomly inserted into packs, each card features a jersey swatch along with a snapshot of major league action. Most players have 100 serial numbered cards but a few have less and we have notated those players with an SP.

VIEW MASTER PRINT RUN 25 #'d SETS
NO V'MASTER PRICING DUE TO SCARCITY
S1 Cal Ripken 20.00 50.00
S2 Chipper Jones SP 10.00 25.00
S3 Jeff Bagwell 10.00 25.00
S4 Larry Walker 6.00 15.00
S5 Greg Maddux SP 10.00 25.00
S6 Ivan Rodriguez 10.00 25.00
S7 Andruw Jones SP 10.00 25.00
S8 Lance Berkman SP 6.00 15.00
S9 Luis Gonzalez SP 6.00 15.00
S10 Tony Gwynn 10.00 25.00
S11 Troy Glaus SP 6.00 15.00
S12 Todd Helton 10.00 25.00
S13 Roberto Alomar 10.00 25.00
S14 Barry Bonds 20.00 50.00
S15 Vladimir Guerrero SP 10.00 25.00
S16 Sean Casey SP 6.00 15.00
S17 Curt Schilling SP 6.00 15.00
S18 Frank Thomas 10.00 25.00
S19 Pedro Martinez 10.00 25.00
S20 Juan Gonzalez 6.00 15.00
S21 Randy Johnson 10.00 25.00
S22 Kerry Wood SP 6.00 15.00
S23 Mike Sweeney 6.00 15.00
S24 Magglio Ordonez 6.00 15.00
S25 Kazuhiro Sasaki 6.00 15.00
S26 Manny Ramirez Sox 10.00 25.00
S27 Roger Clemens 15.00 40.00
S28 Albert Pujols SP 90.00 150.00
S29 Hideo Nomo 10.00 25.00
S30 Miguel Tejada SP 6.00 15.00

2001 Leaf Rookies and Stars Statistical Standouts

Inserted at packs at a rate of one in 96, these 25 cards feature star players along with a swatch of game-used materials. A few of these cards were printed in shorter quantites than the others and we have notated those with an SP.

*SUPER: 1X TO 2.5X BASIC STAT. STANDOUT
SUPER STATED PRINT RUN 50 SERIAL #'D SETS
RANDOM INSERTS IN PACKS
SS1 Ichiro Suzuki 15.00 40.00
SS2 Barry Bonds SP
SS3 Ivan Rodriguez 6.00 15.00
SS4 Jeff Bagwell 6.00 15.00
SS5 Vladimir Guerrero SP
SS6 Mike Sweeney 4.00 10.00
SS7 Miguel Tejada 4.00 10.00
SS8 Mike Piazza SP
SS9 Darin Erstad 4.00 10.00
SS10 Alex Rodriguez 10.00 25.00
SS11 Jason Giambi 4.00 10.00
SS12 Cal Ripken 15.00 40.00
SS13 Albert Pujols 30.00 60.00
SS14 Carlos Delgado 4.00 10.00
SS15 Rafael Palmeiro 6.00 15.00
SS16 Lance Berkman 4.00 10.00
SS17 Luis Gonzalez SP
SS18 Sammy Sosa SP
SS19 Andruw Jones SP
SS20 Derek Jeter 15.00 40.00
SS21 Edgar Martinez 6.00 15.00
SS22 Troy Glaus 4.00 10.00
SS23 Magglio Ordonez 4.00 10.00
SS24 Mark McGwire 15.00 40.00
SS25 Manny Ramirez Sox 6.00 15.00

2001 Leaf Rookies and Stars Statistical Standouts Super

This parallel to the Statistical Standout set was randomly inserted into packs. Each of these cards are serial numbered to 50.

*SUPER: 1X TO 2.5X BASIC STAT.STAND

2001 Leaf Rookies and Stars Triple Threads

Randomly inserted into packs, each of these cards feature three swatches of game-worn jerseys from players of the same franchise. Each of these cards are serial numbered to 100.

TT1 Pedro Martinez 50.00 100.00
Manny Ramirez Sox
Nomar Garciaparra
TT2 Frank Robinson 75.00 150.00
Cal Ripken
Brooks Robinson
TT3 Babe Ruth 350.00 500.00
Lou Gehrig
Yogi Berra
TT4 Andre Dawson 75.00 150.00
Ryne Sandberg
Ernie Banks
TT5 Warren Spahn 75.00 150.00
Hank Aaron
Eddie Mathews
TT6 Greg Maddux 50.00 100.00
Chipper Jones
Andruw Jones
TT7 Nolan Ryan 75.00 150.00
Ivan Rodriguez
Juan Gonzalez
TT8 Lance Berkman 40.00 80.00
Jeff Bagwell
Craig Biggio
TT9 Rod Carew 75.00 150.00
Harmon Killebrew
Kirby Puckett
TT10 Luis Gonzalez 40.00 80.00
Curt Schilling
Randy Johnson

2002 Leaf Rookies and Stars Samples

45 Chuck Knoblauch
96 Brent Abernathy
97 Chan Ho Park
98 Alex Rodriguez
99 Juan Gonzalez
100 Rafael Palmeiro

2002 Leaf Rookies and Stars

This 502 card set was issued in November, 2002. This set was issued in six card packs which came 24 packs to a box and 20 boxes to a case with an SRP of $3 per pack. Originally designed as a 400 card set, this set mushroomed to 501 when 101 variations of some of the basic cards were discovered upon release. These cards feature some of the players who have been on more than one team with cards from their time with that earlier team. Those variation cards were inserted at stated odds of one in four. In addition, cards numbered 301 through 400, which featured a mix of rookies and prospects, were issued at stated odds of one in two. Another subset, which was not printed in shorter supply, was an award winner group from cards numbered 251 through 300.

COMP.SET w/o SP's (300) 15.00 40.00
COMMON CARD (1-300) .10 .30
COMMON SP (1-300) .75 2.00
COMMON CARD (301-400) .40 1.00
1 Darin Erstad .10 .30
2 Garret Anderson .10 .30
3 Troy Glaus .10 .30
4 David Eckstein .10 .30
5 Adam Kennedy .10 .30
6 Kevin Appier Angels .10 .30
6A Kevin Appier Mets SP .75 2.00
6B Kevin Appier Royals SP .75 2.00
7 Jarrod Washburn .10 .30
8 David Segui .10 .30
9 Jay Gibbons .10 .30
10 Tony Batista .10 .30
11 Scott Erickson .10 .30
12 Jeff Conine .10 .30
13 Melvin Mora .10 .30
14 Shea Hillenbrand .10 .30
15 Manny Ramirez Red Sox .20 .50
15A Manny Ramirez Indians SP 1.00 2.50
16 Pedro Martinez Red Sox .20 .50
16A Ped. Martinez Dodgers SP 1.00 2.50
16B Pedro Martinez Expos SP 1.00 2.50
17 Nomar Garciaparra .50 1.25
18 Rickey Henderson Red Sox .30 .75
18A Ri. Henderson Angels SP 1.50 4.00
18B Rickey Henderson A's SP 1.50 4.00
18C Ri. Henderson Bl.Jays SP 1.50 4.00
18D Rickey Henderson M's SP 1.50 4.00
18E Rickey Henderson Mets SP 1.50 4.00
18F Ri. Henderson Padres SP 1.50 4.00
18G Ri. Henderson Yanks SP 1.50 4.00
19 Johnny Damon Red Sox .20 .50
19A Johnny Damon A's SP 1.00 2.50
19B Johnny Damon Royals SP 1.00 2.50
20 Trot Nixon .10 .30
21 Derek Lowe .10 .30
22 Jason Varitek .30 .75
23 Tim Wakefield .10 .30
24 Frank Thomas .30 .75
25 Kenny Lofton White Sox .10 .30
25A Kenny Lofton Indians SP .75 2.00
25B Kenny Lofton Giants SP .75 2.00
26 Magglio Ordonez .10 .30
27 Ray Durham .10 .30
28 Mark Buehrle .10 .30
29 Paul Konerko White Sox .10 .30
29A Paul Konerko Dodgers SP .75 2.00
29B Paul Konerko Reds SP .75 2.00
30 Jose Valentin .10 .30
31 C.C. Sabathia .10 .30
32 Ellis Burks Indians .10 .30
32A Ellis Burks Giants SP .75 2.00
32B Ellis Burks Red Sox SP .75 2.00
32C Ellis Burks Rockies SP .75 2.00
33 Omar Vizquel Indians .20 .50
33A Omar Vizquel Mariners SP 1.00 2.50
34 Jim Thome .20 .50
35 Matt Lawton .10 .30
36 Travis Fryman Indians .10 .30
36A Travis Fryman Tigers SP .75 2.00
37 Robert Fick .10 .30
38 Bobby Higginson .10 .30
39 Steve Sparks .10 .30
40 Mike Rivera .10 .30
41 Wendell Magee .10 .30
42 Randall Simon .10 .30
43 Carlos Pena Yankees .10 .30
43A Carlos Pena A's SP .75 2.00
43B Carlos Pena Rangers SP .75 2.00
44 Mike Sweeney .10 .30
45 Chuck Knoblauch .10 .30
46 Carlos Beltran .10 .30
47 Joe Randa .10 .30
48 Paul Byrd .10 .30
49 Mac Suzuki .10 .30
50 Torii Hunter .10 .30
51 Jacque Jones .10 .30
52 David Ortiz .30 .75
53 Corey Koskie .10 .30
54 Brad Radke .10 .30
55 Doug Mientkiewicz .10 .30
56 A.J. Pierzynski .10 .30
57 Dustan Mohr .10 .30
58 Derek Jeter .75 2.00
59 Bernie Williams .20 .50
60 Roger Clemens Yankees .60 1.50
60A R.Clemens Blue Jays SP 3.00 8.00
60B R.Clemens Red Sox SP 3.00 8.00
61 Mike Mussina Yankees .20 .50
61A Mike Mussina Orioles SP 1.00 2.50
62 Jorge Posada .20 .50
63 Alfonso Soriano .10 .30
64 Jason Giambi Yankees .10 .30
64A Jason Giambi A's SP .75 2.00
65 Robin Ventura Yankees .10 .30
65A Robin Ventura Mets SP .75 2.00
65B Robin Ventura White Sox SP .75 2.00
66 Andy Pettitte .20 .50
67 David Wells Yankees .10 .30
67A David Wells Blue Jays SP .75 2.00
67B David Wells Tigers SP .75 2.00
68 Nick Johnson .10 .30
69 Jeff Weaver Yankees .10 .30
69A Jeff Weaver Tigers SP .75 2.00
70 Raul Mondesi Yankees .10 .30
70A R.Mondesi Blue Jays SP .75 2.00
70B Raul Mondesi Dodgers SP .75 2.00
71 Tim Hudson .10 .30
72 Barry Zito .10 .30
73 Mark Mulder .10 .30
74 Miguel Tejada .10 .30
75 Eric Chavez .10 .30
76 Billy Koch A's .10 .30
76A Billy Koch Blue Jays SP .75 2.00
77 Jermaine Dye A's .10 .30
77A Jermaine Dye Royals SP .75 2.00
78 Scott Hatteberg .10 .30
79 Ichiro Suzuki .60 1.50
80 Edgar Martinez .20 .50
81 Mike Cameron Mariners .10 .30
81A M.Cameron White Sox SP .75 2.00
82 John Olerud Mariners .10 .30
82A John Olerud Blue Jays SP .75 2.00
82B John Olerud Mets SP .75 2.00
83 Bret Boone .10 .30
84 Dan Wilson .10 .30
85 Freddy Garcia .10 .30
86 Jamie Moyer .10 .30
87 Carlos Guillen .10 .30
88 Ruben Sierra .10 .30
89 Kazuhiro Sasaki .10 .30
90 Mark McLemore .10 .30
91 Ben Grieve .10 .30
92 Aubrey Huff .10 .30
93 Steve Cox .10 .30
94 Toby Hall .10 .30
95 Randy Winn .10 .30
96 Brent Abernathy .10 .30
97 Chan Ho Park Rangers .10 .30
97A Chan Ho Park Dodgers SP .75 2.00
98 Alex Rodriguez Rangers .50 1.25
98A A.Rodriguez Mariners SP 2.50 6.00
99 Juan Gonzalez Rangers .10 .30
99A Juan Gonzalez Indians SP .75 2.00
99B Juan Gonzalez Tigers SP .75 2.00
100 Rafael Palmeiro Rangers .20 .50
100A Rafael Palmeiro Cubs SP 1.00 2.50
100B Raf. Palmeiro Orioles SP 1.00 2.50
101 Ivan Rodriguez .20 .50
102 Rusty Greer .10 .30
103 Kenny Rogers Rangers .10 .30
103A Kenny Rogers A's SP .75 2.00
103B Ken. Rogers Yankees SP .75 2.00
104 Hank Blalock .20 .50
105 Mark Teixeira .30 .75
106 Carlos,Delgado .10 .30
107 Shannon Stewart .10 .30
108 Eric Hinske .10 .30
109 Roy Halladay .10 .30
110 Felipe Lopez .10 .30
111 Vernon Wells .10 .30
112 Curt Schilling D'backs .10 .30
112A Curt Schilling Phillies SP .75 2.00
113 Randy Johnson D'backs .30 .75
113A Randy Johnson Astros SP 1.50 4.00
113B Randy Johnson Expos SP 1.50 4.00
113C R.Johnson Mariners SP 1.50 4.00
114 Luis Gonzalez D'backs .10 .30
114A Luis Gonzalez Astros SP .75 2.00
114B Luis Gonzalez Cubs SP .75 2.00
115 Mark Grace D'backs .20 .50
115A Mark Grace Cubs SP 1.00 2.50
116 Junior Spivey .10 .30
117 Tony Womack .10 .30
118 Matt Williams D'backs .10 .30
118A Matt Williams Giants SP .75 2.00
118B Matt Williams Indians SP .75 2.00
119 Danny Bautista .10 .30
120 Byung-Hyun Kim .10 .30
121 Craig Counsell .10 .30
122 Greg Maddux Braves .50 1.25
122A Greg Maddux Cubs SP 2.50 6.00
123 Tom Glavine .20 .50
124 John Smoltz Braves .20 .50
124A John Smoltz Tigers SP 1.00 2.50
125 Chipper Jones .30 .75
126 Gary Sheffield .10 .30
127 Andruw Jones .20 .50
128 Vinny Castilla .10 .30
129 Damian Moss .10 .30
130 Rafael Furcal .10 .30
131 Kerry Wood .10 .30
132 Fred McGriff Cubs .20 .50
132A F.McGriff Blue Jays SP 1.00 2.50
132B Fred McGriff Braves SP 1.00 2.50
132C F.McGriff Devil Rays SP 1.00 2.50
132D Fred McGriff Padres SP 1.00 2.50
133 Sammy Sosa Cubs .30 .75
133A Sammy Sosa Rangers SP 1.50 4.00
133B S.Sosa White Sox SP 1.50 4.00
134 Alex Gonzalez .10 .30
135 Corey Patterson .10 .30
136 Moises Alou .10 .30
137 Mark Prior 2.00 5.00
138 Jon Lieber .10 .30
139 Matt Clement .10 .30
140 Ken Griffey Jr. Reds .50 1.25
140A K.Griffey Jr. Mariners SP 2.50 6.00
141 Barry Larkin .20 .50
142 Adam Dunn .10 .30
143 Sean Casey Reds .10 .30
143A Sean Casey Indians SP .75 2.00
144 Jose Rijo .10 .30

145 Elmer Dessens .10 .30
146 Austin Kearns .10 .30
147 Corky Miller .10 .30
148 Todd Walker Reds .10 .30
148A Todd Walker Rockies SP .75 2.00
149 Chris Reitsma .10 .30
150 Ryan Dempster .10 .30
151 Larry Walker Rockies .10 .30
151A Larry Walker Expos SP .75 2.00
152 Todd Helton .20 .50
153 Juan Uribe .10 .30
154 Juan Pierre .10 .30
155 Mike Hampton .10 .30
156 Todd Zeile .10 .30
157 Josh Beckett .10 .30
158 Mike Lowell Marlins .10 .30
158A Mike Lowell Yankees SP .75 2.00
159 Derrek Lee .20 .50
160 A.J. Burnett .10 .30
161 Luis Castillo .10 .30
162 Tim Raines .10 .30
163 Preston Wilson .10 .30
164 Juan Encarnacion .10 .30
165 Jeff Bagwell .20 .50
166 Craig Biggio .20 .50
167 Lance Berkman .10 .30
168 Wade Miller .10 .30
169 Roy Oswalt .10 .30
170 Richard Hidalgo .10 .30
171 Carlos Hernandez .10 .30
172 Daryle Ward .10 .30
173 Shawn Green Dodgers .10 .30
173A S.Green Blue Jays SP .75 2.00
174 Adrian Beltre .10 .30
175 Paul Lo Duca .10 .30
176 Eric Karros .10 .30
177 Kevin Brown .10 .30
178 Hideo Nomo Dodgers .30 .75
178A Hideo Nomo Brewers SP 1.50 4.00
178B Hideo Nomo Mets SP 1.50 4.00
178C Hideo Nomo Red Sox SP 1.50 4.00
178D Hideo Nomo Tigers SP 1.50 4.00
179 Odalis Perez .10 .30
180 Eric Gagne .10 .30
181 Brian Jordan .10 .30
182 Cesar Izturis .10 .30
183 Geoff Jenkins .10 .30
184 Richie Sexson Brewers .10 .30
184A Richie Sexson Indians SP .75 2.00
185 Jose Hernandez .10 .30
186 Ben Sheets .10 .30
187 Ruben Quevedo .10 .30
188 Jeffrey Hammonds .10 .30
189 Alex Sanchez .10 .30
190 Vladimir Guerrero .30 .75
191 Jose Vidro .10 .30
192 Orlando Cabrera .10 .30
193 Michael Barrett .10 .30
194 Javier Vazquez .10 .30
195 Tony Armas Jr. .10 .30
196 Andres Galarraga .10 .30
197 Tomo Ohka .10 .30
198 Bartolo Colon Expos .10 .30
198A Bartolo Colon Indians SP .75 2.00
199 Cliff Floyd Expos .10 .30
199A Cliff Floyd Marlins SP .75 2.00
199B Cliff Floyd Red Sox SP .75 2.00
200 Mike Piazza Mets .50 1.25
200A Mike Piazza Dodgers SP 2.50 6.00
200B Mike Piazza Marlins SP 2.50 6.00
201 Jeromy Burnitz .10 .30
202 Roberto Alomar Mets .20 .50
202A Rob. Alomar Bl.Jays SP 1.00 2.50
202B Ro. Alomar Indians SP 1.00 2.50
202C Ro. Alomar Orioles SP 1.00 2.50
202D Ro. Alomar Padres SP 1.00 2.50
203 Mo Vaughn Mets .10 .30
203A Mo Vaughn Angels SP .75 2.00
203B Mo Vaughn Red Sox SP .75 2.00
204 Al Leiter Mets .10 .30
204A Al Leiter Blue Jays SP .75 2.00
205 Pedro Astacio .10 .30
206 Edgardo Alfonzo .10 .30
207 Armando Benitez .10 .30
208 Scott Rolen .20 .50
209 Pat Burrell .10 .30
210 Bobby Abreu Phillies .10 .30
210A Bobby Abreu Astros SP .75 2.00
211 Mike Lieberthal .10 .30
212 Brandon Duckworth .10 .30
213 Jimmy Rollins .10 .30
214 Jeremy Giambi .10 .30
215 Vicente Padilla .10 .30
216 Travis Lee .10 .30
217 Jason Kendall .10 .30
218 Brian Giles Pirates .10 .30
218A Brian Giles Indians SP .75 2.00
219 Aramis Ramirez .10 .30
220 Pokey Reese .10 .30
221 Kip Wells .10 .30
222 Josh Fogg Pirates .10 .30
222A Josh Fogg White Sox SP .75 2.00
223 Mike Williams .10 .30
224 Ryan Klesko Padres .10 .30
224A Ryan Klesko Braves SP .75 2.00
225 Phil Nevin Padres .10 .30
225A Phil Nevin Tigers SP .75 2.00
226 Brian Lawrence .10 .30
227 Mark Kotsay .10 .30
228 Brett Tomko .10 .30
229 Trevor Hoffman Padres .10 .30
229A Tr. Hoffman Marlins SP .75 2.00
230 Barry Bonds Giants .75 2.00
230A Barry Bonds Pirates SP 4.00 10.00
231 Jeff Kent Giants .10 .30
231A Jeff Kent Blue Jays SP .75 2.00
232 Rich Aurilia .10 .30
233 Tsuyoshi Shinjo Giants .10 .30
233A Tsuyoshi Shinjo Mets SP .75 2.00
234 Benito Santiago Giants .10 .30
234A Ben. Santiago Padres SP .75 2.00
235 Kirk Rueter .10 .30
236 Kurt Ainsworth .10 .30
237 Livan Hernandez .10 .30
238 Russ Ortiz .10 .30
239 David Bell .10 .30
240 Jason Schmidt .10 .30
241 Reggie Sanders .10 .30
242 Jim Edmonds Cardinals .10 .30
242A Jim Edmonds Angels SP .75 2.00
243 J.D. Drew .10 .30
244 Albert Pujols .60 1.50
245 Fernando Vina .10 .30
246 Tino Martinez Cardinals .20 .50
246A T.Martinez Mariners SP 1.00 2.50
246B T.Martinez Yankees SP 1.00 2.50
247 Edgar Renteria .10 .30
248 Matt Morris .10 .30
249 Woody Williams .10 .30
250 Jason Isringhausen Cards .10 .30
250A J.Isringhausen A's SP .75 2.00
251 Cal Ripken 82 ROY 1.00 2.50
252 Cal Ripken 83 MVP 1.00 2.50
253 Cal Ripken 91 MVP 1.00 2.50
254 Cal Ripken 91 AS 1.00 2.50
255 Ryne Sandberg 84 MVP .60 1.50
256 Don Mattingly 85 MVP .60 1.50
257 Don Mattingly 85-94 GLV .60 1.50
258 Roger Clemens 01 CY .60 1.50
259 Roger Clemens 87 CY .60 1.50
260 Roger Clemens 91 CY .60 1.50
261 Roger Clemens 97 CY .60 1.50
262 Roger Clemens 98 CY .60 1.50
263 Roger Clemens 86 CY .60 1.50
264 Roger Clemens 86 MVP .60 1.50
265 Rickey Henderson 90 MVP .30 .75
266 Rickey Henderson 81 GLV .30 .75
267 Jose Canseco 88 MVP .20 .50
268 Barry Bonds 01 MVP .75 2.00
269 Barry Bonds 90 MVP .75 2.00
270 Barry Bonds 92 MVP .75 2.00
271 Barry Bonds 93 MVP .75 2.00
272 Jeff Bagwell 94 MVP .10 .30
273 Kirby Puckett 91 ALCS .30 .75
274 Kirby Puckett 93 AS .30 .75
275 Greg Maddux 95 CY .50 1.25
276 Greg Maddux 92 CY .50 1.25
277 Greg Maddux 93 CY .50 1.25
278 Greg Maddux 94 CY .50 1.25
279 Ken Griffey Jr. 97 MVP .50 1.25
280 Mike Piazza 93 ROY .50 1.25
281 Kirby Puckett 86-89 GLV .30 .75
282 Mike Piazza 96 AS .50 1.25
283 Frank Thomas 93 MVP .20 .50
284 Hideo Nomo 95 ROY .20 .50
285 Randy Johnson 01 CY .20 .50
286 Juan Gonzalez 96 MVP .10 .30
287 Derek Jeter 96 ROY .75 2.00
288 Derek Jeter 00 WS .75 2.00
289 Derek Jeter 00 AS .75 2.00
290 Nomar Garciaparra 97 ROY .50 1.25
291 Pedro Martinez 00 CY .20 .50
292 Kerry Wood 98 ROY .10 .30
293 Sammy Sosa 98 MVP .20 .50
294 Chipper Jones 99 MVP .20 .50
295 Ivan Rodriguez 99 MVP .10 .30
296 Ivan Rodriguez 92-01 GLV .10 .30
297 Albert Pujols 01 ROY .60 1.50
298 Ichiro Suzuki 01 ROY .60 1.50
299 Ichiro Suzuki 01 MVP .60 1.50
300 Ichiro Suzuki 01 GLV .60 1.50
301 So Taguchi RS RC .50 1.25
302 Kazuhisa Ishii RS RC .50 1.25
303 Jeremy Lambert RS RC .40 1.00
304 Sean Burroughs RS .40 1.00
305 P.J. Bevis RS RC .40 1.00
306 Jon Rauch RS .40 1.00
307 Scotty Layfield RS RC .40 1.00
308 Miguel Asencio RS RC .40 1.00
309 Franklyn German RS RC .40 1.00
310 Luis Ugueto RS RC .40 1.00
311 Jorge Sosa RS RC .50 1.25
312 Felix Escalona RS RC .40 1.00
313 Jose Valverde RS RC .40 1.00
314 Jeremy Ward RS RC .40 1.00
315 Kevin Gryboski RS RC .40 1.00
316 Francis Beltran RS RC .40 1.00
317 Joe Thurston RS .40 1.00
318 Cliff Lee RS RC .75 2.00
319 Takahito Nomura RS RC .40 1.00
320 Bill Hall RS .40 1.00
321 Marlon Byrd RS .40 1.00
322 Andy Shibilo RS RC .40 1.00
323 Edwin Almonte RS RC .40 1.00
324 Brandon Backe RS RC .50 1.25
325 Chone Figgins RS RC .75 2.00
326 Brian Mallette RS RC .40 1.00
327 Rodrigo Rosario RS RC .40 1.00
328 Anderson Machado RS RC .40 1.00
329 Jorge Padilla RS RC .40 1.00
330 Allan Simpson RS RC .40 1.00
331 Doug Devore RS RC .40 1.00
332 Drew Henson RS .40 1.00
333 Raul Chavez RS RC .40 1.00
334 Tom Shearn RS RC .40 1.00
335 Ben Howard RS RC .40 1.00
336 Chris Baker RS RC .40 1.00
337 Travis Hughes RS RC .40 1.00
338 Kevin Mench RS .40 1.00
339 Brian Tallet RS RC .40 1.00
340 Mike Moriarty RS RC .40 1.00
341 Corey Thurman RS RC .40 1.00
342 Terry Pearson RS RC .40 1.00
343 Steve Kent RS RC .40 1.00
344 Satoru Komiyama RS RC .40 1.00
345 Jason Lane RS .40 1.00
346 Freddy Sanchez RS RC 1.25 3.00
347 Brandon Puffer RS RC .40 1.00
348 Clay Condrey RS RC .40 1.00
349 Rene Reyes RS RC .40 1.00
350 Hee Seop Choi RS .40 1.00
351 Rodrigo Lopez RS .40 1.00
352 Colin Young RS RC .40 1.00
353 Jason Simontacchi RS RC .40 1.00
354 Oliver Perez RS RC .75 2.00
355 Kirk Saarloos RS RC .40 1.00
356 Marcus Thames RS .40 1.00
357 Jeff Austin RS RC .40 1.00
358 Justin Kaye RS .40 1.00
359 Julio Mateo RS RC .40 1.00
360 Mike A. Smith RS RC .40 1.00
361 Chris Snelling RS RC .60 1.50
362 Dennis Tankersley RS .40 1.00
363 Runelvys Hernandez RS RC .40 1.00
364 Aaron Cook RS RC .40 1.00
365 Joe Borchard RS .40 1.00
366 Earl Snyder RS RC .40 1.00
367 Shane Nance RS RC .40 1.00
368 Aaron Guiel RS RC .40 1.00
369 Steve Bechler RS RC .40 1.00
370 Tim Kalita RS RC .40 1.00
371 Shawn Sedlacek RS RC .40 1.00
372 Eric Good RS RC .40 1.00
373 Eric Junge RS RC .40 1.00
374 Matt Thornton RS RC .40 1.00
375 Travis Driskill RS RC .40 1.00
376 Mitch Wylie RS RC .40 1.00
377 John Ennis RS RC .40 1.00
378 Reed Johnson RS RC .75 2.00
379 Juan Brito RS RC .40 1.00
380 Ron Calloway RS RC .40 1.00
381 Adrian Burnside RS RC .40 1.00
382 Josh Bard RS RC .40 1.00
383 Matt Childers RS RC .40 1.00
384 Gustavo Chacin RS RC .75 2.00
385 Luis Martinez RS RC .40 1.00
386 Trey Hodges RS RC .40 1.00
387 Hansel Izquierdo RS RC .40 1.00
388 Jeriome Robertson RS RC .40 1.00
389 Victor Alvarez RS RC .40 1.00
390 David Ross RS RC .50 1.25
391 Ron Chiavacci RS .40 1.00
392 Adam Walker RS RC .40 1.00
393 Mike Gonzalez RS RC .40 1.00
394 John Foster RS RC .40 1.00
395 Kyle Kane RS RC .40 1.00
396 Cam Esslinger RS RC .40 1.00
397 Kevin Frederick RS RC .40 1.00
398 Franklin Nunez RS RC .40 1.00
399 Todd Donovan RS RC .40 1.00
400 Kevin Cash RS RC .40 1.00

2002 Leaf Rookies and Stars Great American Signings

Randomly inserted into packs, this is a partial parallel to the basic Leaf Rookies and Stars set. These cards feature the basic card along with the attached "sticker" autograph. Since cards were issued to different stated print runs, we have notated that information next to the player's name in our checklist. If a card has a stated print run of 25 or fewer it is not printed due to market scarcity.

9 Jay Gibbons/150 4.00 10.00
18 Rickey Henderson/20
40 Mike Rivera/175 4.00 10.00
49 Mac Suzuki/100 15.00 40.00
59 Bernie Williams/15
60 Roger Clemens/10
63 Alfonso Soriano/25
68 Nick Johnson/175 6.00 15.00
92 Aubrey Huff/175 6.00 15.00
96 Brent Abernathy/175 4.00 10.00
108 Eric Hinske/175 4.00 10.00
131 Kerry Wood/25
141 Barry Larkin/25
142 Adam Dunn/25
146 Austin Kearns/75 6.00 15.00
169 Roy Oswalt/100 6.00 15.00
182 Cesar Izturis/175 4.00 10.00
190 Vladimir Guerrero/15
210 Bobby Abreu/25
221 Kip Wells/175 4.00 10.00
226 Brian Lawrence/175 4.00 10.00
244 Albert Pujols/25
256 Don Mattingly/25
301 So Taguchi/50 15.00 40.00
302 Kazuhisa Ishii/25
309 Franklyn German/175 4.00 10.00
310 Luis Ugueto/175 4.00 10.00
312 Felix Escalona/100 6.00 15.00
316 Francis Beltran/175 4.00 10.00
320 Bill Hall/175 6.00 15.00
324 Brandon Backe/175 6.00 15.00
327 Rodrigo Rosario/175 4.00 10.00
328 Anderson Machado/175 4.00 10.00
329 Jorge Padilla/175 4.00 10.00
331 Doug Devore/175 4.00 10.00
332 Drew Henson/50 6.00 15.00
333 Raul Chavez/175 4.00 10.00
334 Tom Shearn/175 4.00 10.00
335 Ben Howard/175 4.00 10.00
336 Chris Baker/175 4.00 10.00
337 Travis Hughes/175 4.00 10.00
341 Corey Thurman/175 4.00 10.00
344 Satoru Komiyama/75 10.00 25.00
345 Jason Lane/150 6.00 15.00
349 Rene Reyes/175 4.00 10.00
354 Oliver Perez/175 15.00 40.00
361 Chris Snelling/175 8.00 20.00
362 Dennis Tankersley/175 4.00 10.00

2002 Leaf Rookies and Stars Longevity

Randomly inserted into packs, this is a parallel to the basic Leaf Rookie and Stars set. Cards numbered between 1-300 (and including all of the variations) were printed to a stated print run of 100 serial numbered sets while cards 301 through 400 were printed to a stated print run of 25 serial numbered sets.

*LONGEVITY 1-300: 6X TO 15X BASIC
*LONGEVITY 1-300: 1.25X TO 3X BASIC SP'S
*RETIRED STARS 251-300: 12.5X TO 30X

2002 Leaf Rookies and Stars BLC Homers

Randomly inserted into packs, these 30 cards feature pieces of baseball's used during the Big League Challenge held in Las Vegas before the 2002 season began. Each card has a stated print run of 25 serial numbered sets.

LUIS GONZALEZ (1-3) 10.00 25.00
TODD HELTON (4-11) 15.00 40.00
JIM THOME (12-14) 15.00 40.00
RAFAEL PALMEIRO (15-19) 15.00 40.00
TROY GLAUS (20-22) 10.00 25.00
GARY SHEFFIELD (23-25) 10.00 25.00
MIKE PIAZZA (26-30) 20.00 50.00

2002 Leaf Rookies and Stars Dress for Success

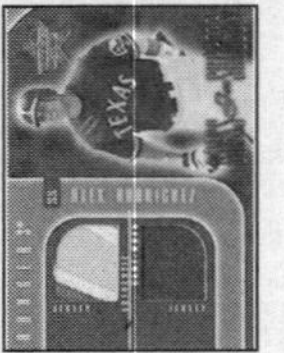

Randomly inserted into packs, these 15 cards feature two game-used memorabilia pieces from the featured players. Each card was also issued to a stated print run of 250 serial numbered sets.

1 Mike Piazza Jsy-Jsy 10.00 25.00
2 Cal Ripken Jsy-Jsy 30.00 60.00
3 Carlos Delgado Jsy-Jsy 8.00 20.00
4 Chipper Jones Jsy-Jsy 10.00 25.00
5 Bernie Williams Jsy-Shoe 10.00 25.00
6 Carlos Beltran Jsy-Shoe 8.00 20.00
7 Curt Schilling Jsy-Jsy 8.00 20.00
8 Greg Maddux Jsy-Jsy 10.00 25.00
9 Ivan Rodriguez Jsy-Jsy 10.00 25.00
10 Alex Rodriguez Jsy-Jsy 15.00 40.00
11 Roger Clemens Jsy-Jsy 15.00 40.00
12 Todd Helton Jsy-Jsy 10.00 25.00
13 Jim Edmonds Shoe-Jsy 8.00 20.00
14 Manny Ramirez Jsy-Fld Glv 10.00 25.00
15 Mark Buehrle Jsy-Shoe 8.00 20.00

2002 Leaf Rookies and Stars Freshman Orientation

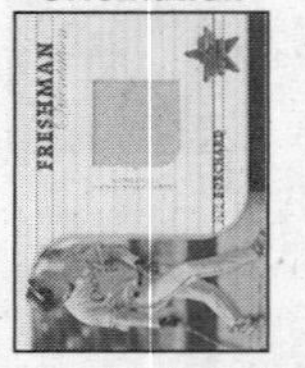

Inserted in packs at a stated rate of one in 142, these 20 cards feature not only players who debuted during the 2002 season but also a game-used memorabilia piece from that player.

*CLASS OFFICERS: .6X TO 1.5X BASIC
CLASS OFFICERS RANDOM IN PACKS
CLASS OFFICERS PRINT RUN 50 #'d SETS

1 Andres Torres Bat 4.00 10.00
2 Mark Ellis Jsy 4.00 10.00
3 Erik Bedard Bat 4.00 10.00
4 Delvin James Jsy 4.00 10.00
5 Austin Kearns Bat 4.00 10.00
6 Josh Pearce Bat 4.00 10.00
7 Rafael Soriano Jsy 4.00 10.00
8 Jason Lane Bat 4.00 10.00
9 Mark Prior Jsy 4.00 10.00
10 Alfredo Amezaga Bat 4.00 10.00
11 Ryan Ludwick Bat 4.00 10.00
12 So Taguchi Bat 6.00 15.00
13 Duaner Sanchez Bat 4.00 10.00
14 Kazuhisa Ishii Jsy 6.00 15.00
15 Zach Day Pants 4.00 10.00
16 Eric Cyr Bat 4.00 10.00
17 Francis Beltran Jsy 4.00 10.00
18 Joe Borchard Jsy 4.00 10.00
19 Jeremy Affeldt Shoe 4.00 10.00
20 Alexis Gomez Shoe 4.00 10.00

2002 Leaf Rookies and Stars Statistical Standouts

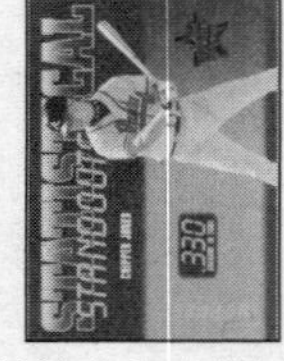

Issued at stated odds of one in 12, these 50 cards feature some of the leading players in baseball.

1 Adam Dunn 1.00 2.50
2 Alex Rodriguez 4.00 10.00
3 Andruw Jones 1.50 4.00
4 Brian Giles 1.00 2.50
5 Chipper Jones 2.50 6.00
6 Cliff Floyd 1.00 2.50
7 Craig Biggio 1.50 4.00
8 Frank Thomas 2.50 6.00
9 Fred McGriff 1.50 4.00
10 Garret Anderson 1.00 2.50
11 Greg Maddux 4.00 10.00
12 Luis Gonzalez 1.00 2.50
13 Magglio Ordonez 1.00 2.50
14 Ivan Rodriguez 1.50 4.00
15 Ken Griffey Jr. 4.00 10.00
16 Ichiro Suzuki 5.00 12.00
17 Jason Giambi 1.00 2.50
18 Derek Jeter 6.00 15.00
19 Sammy Sosa 2.50 6.00
20 Albert Pujols 5.00 12.00
21 J.D. Drew 1.00 2.50
22 Jeff Bagwell 1.50 4.00
23 Jim Edmonds 1.00 2.50
24 Jose Vidro 1.00 2.50
25 Juan Encarnacion 1.00 2.50
26 Kerry Wood 1.00 2.50
27 Al Leiter 1.00 2.50
28 Curt Schilling 1.00 2.50
29 Manny Ramirez 1.50 4.00
30 Lance Berkman 1.00 2.50
31 Miguel Tejada 1.00 2.50
32 Mike Piazza 4.00 10.00
33 Nomar Garciaparra 4.00 10.00
34 Omar Vizquel 1.50 4.00
35 Pat Burrell 1.00 2.50
36 Paul Konerko 1.00 2.50
37 Rafael Palmeiro 1.50 4.00
38 Randy Johnson 2.50 6.00
39 Richie Sexson 1.00 2.50
40 Roger Clemens 5.00 12.00
41 Shawn Green 1.00 2.50
42 Todd Helton 1.50 4.00
43 Tom Glavine 1.50 4.00
44 Troy Glaus 1.00 2.50
45 Vladimir Guerrero 2.50 6.00
46 Mike Sweeney 1.00 2.50
47 Alfonso Soriano 1.00 2.50
48 Barry Zito 1.00 2.50
49 John Smoltz 1.50 4.00
50 Ellis Burks 1.00 2.50

2002 Leaf Rookies and Stars Statistical Standouts Materials

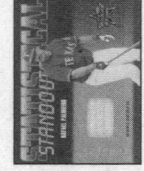

Randomly inserted into packs, this is a parallel to the basic Statistical Standouts insert set. These cards feature a game-used memorabilia piece from each player. Please note that some cards were issued in shorter supply and we have notated that information along with the stated print run information next to the player's name in our checklist.

SUPER: RANDOM INSERTS IN PACKS
SUPER PRINT RUN 25 SERIAL #'d SETS
SUPER: NO PRICING DUE TO SCARCITY

1 Adam Dunn Bat/200 4.00 10.00
2 Alex Rodriguez Bat/200 8.00 20.00
3 Andruw Jones Bat/200 6.00 15.00
4 Brian Giles Bat 4.00 10.00
5 Chipper Jones Bat/200 6.00 15.00
6 Cliff Floyd Jsy 4.00 10.00
7 Craig Biggio Pants 6.00 15.00
8 Frank Thomas Jsy/125 6.00 15.00
9 Fred McGriff Bat 6.00 15.00
10 Garret Anderson Bat
11 Greg Maddux Jsy/200 8.00 20.00
12 Luis Gonzalez Jsy 4.00 10.00
13 Magglio Ordonez Bat/150 4.00 10.00
14 Ivan Rodriguez Jsy/100
15 Ken Griffey Jr. Base/100 10.00 25.00
16 Ichiro Suzuki Base/100
17 Jason Giambi Base 4.00 10.00
18 Derek Jeter Base/100
19 Sammy Sosa Base/100 6.00 15.00
20 Albert Pujols Base/100
21 J.D. Drew Bat/150 4.00 10.00
22 Jeff Bagwell Pants/150
23 Jim Edmonds Bat 4.00 10.00
24 Jose Vidro Bat 4.00 10.00
25 Juan Encarnacion Bat 4.00 10.00
26 Kerry Wood Jsy/200 4.00 10.00
27 Al Leiter Jsy 4.00 10.00
28 Curt Schilling Jsy/225
29 Manny Ramirez Bat/100 6.00 15.00
30 Lance Berkman Bat/150
31 Miguel Tejada Jsy 4.00 10.00
32 Mike Piazza Bat/200 8.00 20.00
33 Nomar Garciaparra Bat/200 10.00 25.00
34 Omar Vizquel Jsy 6.00 15.00
35 Pat Burrell Bat 4.00 10.00
36 Paul Konerko Jsy 4.00 10.00
37 Rafael Palmeiro Bat 6.00 15.00
38 Randy Johnson Jsy/200 6.00 15.00
39 Richie Sexson Jsy 4.00 10.00
40 Roger Clemens Jsy/200 12.50 30.00
41 Shawn Green Jsy 4.00 10.00
42 Todd Helton Jsy/175 6.00 15.00
43 Tom Glavine Jsy/125 6.00 15.00
44 Troy Glaus Jsy 4.00 10.00
45 Vladimir Guerrero Jsy 6.00 15.00
46 Mike Sweeney Bat 4.00 10.00
47 Alfonso Soriano Jsy/200 4.00 10.00
48 Barry Zito Jsy/100 4.00 10.00
49 John Smoltz Jsy
50 Ellis Burks Jsy/50 4.00 10.00

2002 Leaf Rookies and Stars Triple Threads

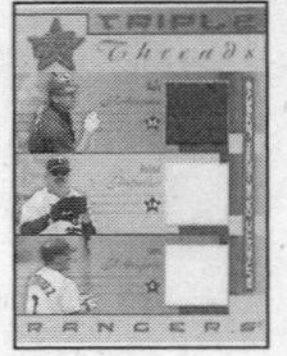

Randomly inserted into packs, this 10 card set featured three players who have something in common along with a memorabilia piece of each player featured on the card. Each card was also issued to a stated print run of 100 serial numbered sets.

1 Reggie Jackson 50.00 100.00
Alfonso Soriano
Don Mattingly
2 Alex Rodriguez 30.00 60.00
Rafael Palmeiro
Ivan Rodriguez
3 Mike Piazza 30.00 60.00
Gary Carter
Rickey Henderson
4 Dale Murphy 20.00 50.00
Andruw Jones
Chipper Jones
5 Mike Schmidt 50.00 100.00
Steve Carlton
Scott Rolen
6 Rickey Henderson 20.00 50.00
Rickey Henderson
Rickey Henderson
7 Johnny Bench 50.00 100.00
Joe Morgan
Tom Seaver
8 Randy Johnson 20.00 50.00
Pedro Martinez
Vladimir Guerrero
9 Nolan Ryan 50.00 100.00
Rod Carew
Troy Glaus
10 Lou Brock 50.00 100.00
J.D. Drew
Stan Musial

2002 Leaf Rookies and Stars View Masters

Randomly inserted into packs, these 20 cards feature some of the leading players in the game in a style reminiscent of the old "View Masters" which became popular in the 1950's. Each of these cards were printed to a stated print run of 100 serial numbered sets and have a game used-memorabilia piece attached to them.

SLIDESHOW: RANDOM INSERTS IN PACKS
SLIDESHOW PRINT 25 SERIAL #'d SETS
SLIDESHOW: NO PRICE DUE TO SCARCITY

1 Carlos Delgado 6.00 15.00
2 Todd Helton 10.00 25.00
3 Tony Gwynn 15.00 40.00
4 Bernie Williams 10.00 25.00
5 Luis Gonzalez 6.00 15.00
6 Larry Walker 6.00 15.00
7 Troy Glaus 6.00 15.00
8 Alfonso Soriano 6.00 15.00
9 Curt Schilling 6.00 15.00
10 Chipper Jones 10.00 25.00
11 Vladimir Guerrero 10.00 25.00
12 Adam Dunn 6.00 15.00
13 Rickey Henderson 10.00 25.00
14 Miguel Tejada 6.00 15.00
15 Kazuhisa Ishii 10.00 25.00
16 Greg Maddux 15.00 40.00
17 Pedro Martinez 10.00 25.00
18 Nomar Garciaparra 20.00 50.00
19 Mike Piazza 15.00 40.00
20 Lance Berkman 6.00 15.00

1996 Leaf Signature

The 1996 Leaf Signature Set was issued by Donruss in two series totalling 150 cards. The four-card packs carried a suggested retail price of $9.99 each. It's interesting to note that the Extended Series was the last of the 1996 releases. In fact, it was released in January, 1997 - so late in the year that it's categorization as a 1996 issue was a bit of a stretch at that time. Production for the Extended Series was only 40 percent that of the regular issue. Extended Series packs actually contained a mix of both series cards, thus the Extended Series cards are somewhat scarcer. Card fronts feature borderless color action player photos with the card name printed in a silver foil emblem. The backs carry player information. Rookie Cards include Darin Erstad. This product was a benchmark release in hobby history due to it's inclusion of one or more autograph cards per pack (explaining it's high suggested retail pack price). The product was highly successful upon release and opened the doors for wide incorporation of autograph cards into a wide array of brands from that point forward.

COMPLETE SET (150)	40.00	100.00
COMP. SERIES 1 (100)	25.00	60.00
COMPLETE SERIES 2 (50)	15.00	40.00
COMMON CARD (1-100)	.20	.50
COMMON (101-150)	.10	.30
1 Mike Piazza	.75	2.00
2 Juan Gonzalez	.20	.50
3 Greg Maddux	.75	2.00
4 Marc Newfield	.20	.50
5 Wade Boggs	.30	.75
6 Ray Lankford	.20	.50
7 Frank Thomas	.50	1.25
8 Rico Brogna	.20	.50
9 Tim Salmon	.30	.75
10 Ken Griffey Jr.	.75	2.00
11 Manny Ramirez	.30	.75
12 Cecil Fielder	.20	.50
13 Gregg Jefferies	.20	.50
14 Rondell White	.20	.50
15 Cal Ripken	1.50	4.00
16 Alex Rodriguez	1.00	2.50
17 Bernie Williams	.30	.75
18 Andres Galarraga	.20	.50
19 Mike Mussina	.30	.75
20 Chuck Knoblauch	.20	.50
21 Joe Carter	.20	.50
22 Jeff Bagwell	.30	.75
23 Mark McGwire	1.25	3.00
24 Sammy Sosa	.50	1.25
25 Reggie Sanders	.20	.50
26 Chipper Jones	.50	1.25
27 Jeff Cirillo	.20	.50
28 Roger Clemens	1.00	2.50
29 Craig Biggio	.30	.75
30 Gary Sheffield	.30	.75
31 Paul O'Neill	.30	.75
32 Johnny Damon	.30	.75
33 Jason Isringhausen	.20	.50
34 Jay Bell	.20	.50
35 Henry Rodriguez	.20	.50
36 Matt Williams	.20	.50
37 Randy Johnson	.50	1.25
38 Fred McGriff	.30	.75
39 Jason Giambi	.20	.50
40 Ivan Rodriguez	.30	.75
41 Raul Mondesi	.20	.50
42 Barry Larkin	.30	.75
43 Ryan Klesko	.20	.50
44 Joey Hamilton	.20	.50
45 Todd Hundley	.20	.50
46 Jim Edmonds	.20	.50
47 Dante Bichette	.20	.50
48 Roberto Alomar	.30	.75
49 Mark Grace	.30	.75
50 Brady Anderson	.20	.50
51 Hideo Nomo	.50	1.25
52 Ozzie Smith	.75	2.00
53 Robin Ventura	.20	.50
54 Andy Pettitte	.30	.75
55 Kenny Lofton	.20	.50
56 John Mabry	.20	.50
57 Paul Molitor	.20	.50
58 Rey Ordonez	.20	.50
59 Albert Belle	.20	.50
60 Charles Johnson	.20	.50
61 Edgar Martinez	.30	.75
62 Derek Bell	.20	.50
63 Carlos Delgado	.20	.50
64 Raul Casanova	.20	.50
65 Ismael Valdes	.20	.50
66 J.T. Snow	.20	.50
67 Derek Jeter	1.25	3.00
68 Jason Kendall	.20	.50
69 John Smoltz	.30	.75
70 Chad Mottola	.20	.50
71 Jim Thome	.30	.75
72 Will Clark	.30	.75
73 Mo Vaughn	.20	.50
74 John Wasdin	.20	.50
75 Rafael Palmeiro	.30	.75
76 Mark Grudzielanek	.20	.50
77 Larry Walker	.20	.50
78 Alan Benes	.20	.50
79 Michael Tucker	.20	.50
80 Billy Wagner	.20	.50
81 Paul Wilson	.20	.50
82 Greg Vaughn	.20	.50
83 Dean Palmer	.20	.50
84 Ryne Sandberg	.75	2.00
85 Eric Young	.20	.50
86 Jay Buhner	.20	.50
87 Tony Clark	.20	.50
88 Jermaine Dye	.20	.50
89 Barry Bonds	1.25	3.00
90 Ugueth Urbina	.20	.50
91 Charles Nagy	.20	.50
92 Ruben Rivera	.20	.50
93 Todd Hollandsworth	.20	.50
94 Darin Erstad RC	1.50	4.00
95 Brooks Kieschnick	.20	.50
96 Edgar Renteria	.20	.50
97 Lenny Dykstra	.20	.50
98 Tony Gwynn	.60	1.50
99 Kirby Puckett	.50	1.25
100 Checklist	.20	.50
101 Andruw Jones	1.00	2.50
102 Alex Ochoa	.10	.30
103 David Cone	.20	.50
104 Rusty Greer	.20	.50
105 Jose Canseco	.30	.75
106 Ken Caminiti	.20	.50
107 Mariano Rivera	.50	1.25
108 Ron Gant	.20	.50
109 Darryl Strawberry	.20	.50
110 Vladimir Guerrero	1.25	3.00
111 George Arias	.10	.30
112 Jeff Conine	.20	.50
113 Bobby Higginson	.20	.50
114 Eric Karros	.20	.50
115 Brian Hunter	.10	.30
116 Eddie Murray	.50	1.25
117 Todd Walker	.10	.30
118 Chan Ho Park	.20	.50
119 John Jaha	.10	.30
120 Dave Justice	.20	.50
121 Makoto Suzuki	.10	.30
122 Scott Rolen	.50	1.25
123 Tino Martinez	.30	.75
124 Kimera Bartee	.10	.30
125 Garret Anderson	.20	.50
126 Brian Jordan	.20	.50
127 Andre Dawson	.20	.50
128 Javier Lopez	.20	.50
129 Bill Pulsipher	.10	.30
130 Dwight Gooden	.20	.50
131 Al Martin	.10	.30
132 Terrell Wade	.10	.30
133 Steve Gibralter	.10	.30
134 Tom Glavine	.30	.75
135 Kevin Appier	.20	.50
136 Tim Raines	.20	.50
137 Curtis Pride	.10	.30
138 Todd Greene	.10	.30
139 Bobby Bonilla	.20	.50
140 Trey Beamon	.10	.30
141 Marty Cordova	.10	.30
142 Rickey Henderson	.50	1.25
143 Ellis Burks	.20	.50
144 Dennis Eckersley	.20	.50
145 Kevin Brown	.20	.50
146 Carlos Baerga	.10	.30
147 Brett Butler	.20	.50
148 Marquis Grissom	.20	.50
149 Karim Garcia	.10	.30
150 Frank Thomas CL	.30	.75

1996 Leaf Signature Gold Press Proofs

Randomly inserted in first series packs at an approximate rate of one in 12 and second series packs at an approximate rate of one in 8, this 150-card set is parallel to the regular version. The design is similar to the regular card with the exception of the card name being printed in a gold foil emblem and the words "Press Proof" printed in gold foil vertically down the side.

*SER.1 STARS: 4X TO 10X BASIC CARDS
*SER.1 ROOKIES: 1.25X TO 3X BASIC CARDS
*SER.2 STARS: 3X TO 8X BASIC CARDS

1996 Leaf Signature Platinum Press Proofs

Randomly inserted exclusively into Extended Series packs at the rate of one in 24, this 150-card set is parallel to the regular Leaf Signature Set. Only 150 sets were produced. Unlike the multi-series base set and Gold Press Proofs, these scarce Platinum cards were issued in one comprehensive series. The cards are similar in design to the regular set with the exception of holographic platinum foil stamping.

*SER.1 STARS: 10X TO 25X BASIC CARDS
*SER. 1 ROOKIES: 2.5X TO 6X BASIC CARDS
*SER.2 STARS: 8X TO 20X BASIC CARDS

1996 Leaf Signature Autographs

Inserted into 1996 Leaf Signature Series first series packs, these unnumbered cards were one of the first major autograph issues featured in an MLB-licensed trading card set. First series packs contained at least one autograph, with the chance of getting more. Donruss/Leaf reports that all but 10 players in the Leaf Signature Series signed close to 5,000 total autographs (3,500 bronze, 1,000 silver, 500 gold). The 10 players who signed 1,000 (700 bronze, 200 silver, 100 gold) are: Roberto Alomar, Wade Boggs, Derek Jeter, Kenny Lofton, Paul Molitor, Raul Mondesi, Manny Ramirez, Alex Rodriguez, Frank Thomas and Mo Vaughn. It's also important to note that six additional players did not submit their cards in time to be included in first series packs. Thus, their cards were thrown into Extended series packs. Those six players are as follows: Brian L.Hunter, Carlos Delgado, Phil Plantier, Jim Thome, Terrell Wade and Ernie Young. Thome signed only silver and gold foil cards, thus the Bronze set is considered complete at 251 cards. Prices below refer exclusively to Bronze versions. Blue and black ink variations have been found for Carlos Delgado, Alex Rodriguez and Michael Tucker. No consistent premiums for these variations has been tracked. Finally, an autographed jumbo silver foil version of the Frank Thomas card was distributed to dealers in March, 1997. Dealers received either this first series or the Extended Series jumbo Thomas for every Extended Series case ordered. Each Thomas jumbo is individually serial numbered to 1,500. A standard-size promo card of Frank Thomas with a facsimile signature was also created and released several weeks before this set's release. An Otis Nixon card surfaced in the secondary market in 2005. Nixon's cards were never seeded into packs, but it's believed that the cards were printed and sent to Nixon, of whom signed them but failed to return them to the manufacturer.

1 Kurt Abbott	2.00	5.00
2 Juan Acevedo	2.00	5.00
3 Terry Adams	2.00	5.00
4 Manny Alexander	2.00	5.00
5 Roberto Alomar SP	20.00	50.00
6 Moises Alou	4.00	10.00
7 Wilson Alvarez	2.00	5.00
8 Garret Anderson	6.00	15.00
9 Shane Andrews	2.00	5.00
10 Andy Ashby	2.00	5.00
11 Pedro Astacio	2.00	5.00
12 Brad Ausmus	6.00	15.00
13 Bobby Ayala	2.00	5.00
14 Carlos Baerga	4.00	10.00
15 Harold Baines	4.00	10.00
16 Jason Bates	2.00	5.00
17 Allen Battle	2.00	5.00
18 Rich Becker	2.00	5.00
19 David Bell	2.00	5.00
20 Rafael Belliard	4.00	10.00
21 Andy Benes	2.00	5.00
22 Armando Benitez	2.00	5.00
23 Jason Bere	2.00	5.00
24 Geronimo Berroa	2.00	5.00
25 Willie Blair	2.00	5.00
26 Mike Blowers	2.00	5.00
27 Wade Boggs SP	30.00	60.00
28 Ricky Bones	2.00	5.00
29 Mike Bordick	4.00	10.00
30 Toby Borland	2.00	5.00
31 Ricky Bottalico	2.00	5.00
32 Darren Bragg	2.00	5.00
33 Jeff Branson	2.00	5.00
34 Tilson Brito	2.00	5.00
35 Rico Brogna	2.00	5.00
36 Scott Brosius	4.00	10.00
37 Damon Buford	2.00	5.00
38 Mike Busby	2.00	5.00
39 Tom Candiotti	2.00	5.00
40 Frank Castillo	2.00	5.00
41 Andujar Cedeno	2.00	5.00
42 Domingo Cedeno	2.00	5.00
43 Roger Cedeno	2.00	5.00
44 Norm Charlton	2.00	5.00
45 Jeff Cirillo	4.00	10.00
46 Will Clark	6.00	15.00
47 Jeff Conine	4.00	10.00
48 Steve Cooke	2.00	5.00
49 Joey Cora	2.00	5.00
50 Marty Cordova	2.00	5.00
51 Rheal Cormier	2.00	5.00
52 Felipe Crespo	2.00	5.00
53 Chad Curtis	2.00	5.00
54 Johnny Damon	10.00	25.00
55 Russ Davis	2.00	5.00
56 Andre Dawson	6.00	15.00
57 Carlos Delgado	6.00	15.00
58 Doug Drabek	2.00	5.00
59 Darren Dreifort	2.00	5.00
60 Shawon Dunston	2.00	5.00
61 Ray Durham	4.00	10.00
62 Jim Edmonds	10.00	25.00
63 Joey Eischen	2.00	5.00
64 Jim Eisenreich	2.00	5.00
65 Sal Fasano	2.00	5.00
66 Jeff Fassero	2.00	5.00
67 Alex Fernandez	2.00	5.00
68 Darrin Fletcher	2.00	5.00
69 Chad Fonville	2.00	5.00
70 Kevin Foster	2.00	5.00
71 John Franco	4.00	10.00
72 Julio Franco	4.00	10.00
73 Marvin Freeman	2.00	5.00
74 Travis Fryman	4.00	10.00
75 Gary Gaetti	4.00	10.00
76 Carlos Garcia	2.00	5.00
77 Jason Giambi	6.00	15.00
78 Benji Gil	2.00	5.00
79 Greg Gohr	2.00	5.00
80 Chris Gomez	2.00	5.00
81 Leo Gomez	2.00	5.00
82 Tom Goodwin	2.00	5.00
83 Mike Grace	2.00	5.00
84 Mike Greenwell	6.00	15.00
85 Rusty Greer	4.00	10.00
86 Mark Grudzielanek	2.00	5.00
87 Mark Gubicza	2.00	5.00
88 Juan Guzman	2.00	5.00
89 Darryl Hamilton	2.00	5.00
90 Joey Hamilton	2.00	5.00
91 Chris Hammond	2.00	5.00
92 Mike Hampton	4.00	10.00
93 Chris Haney	2.00	5.00
94 Todd Haney	2.00	5.00
95 Erik Hanson	2.00	5.00
96 Pete Harnisch	2.00	5.00
97 LaTroy Hawkins	2.00	5.00
98 Charlie Hayes	2.00	5.00
99 Jimmy Haynes	2.00	5.00
100 Roberto Hernandez	2.00	5.00
101 Bobby Higginson	4.00	10.00
102 Glenallen Hill	2.00	5.00
103 Ken Hill	2.00	5.00
104 Sterling Hitchcock	2.00	5.00
105 Trevor Hoffman	6.00	15.00
106 Dave Hollins	2.00	5.00
107 Dwayne Hosey	2.00	5.00
108 Thomas Howard	2.00	5.00
109 Steve Howe	2.00	5.00
110 John Hudek	2.00	5.00
111 Rex Hudler	2.00	5.00
112 Brian L.Hunter	2.00	5.00
113 Butch Huskey	2.00	5.00
114 Mark Hutton	2.00	5.00
115 Jason Jacome	2.00	5.00
116 John Jaha	2.00	5.00
117 Reggie Jefferson	2.00	5.00
118 Derek Jeter SP	125.00	200.00
119 Bobby Jones	2.00	5.00
120 Todd Jones	4.00	10.00
121 Brian Jordan	4.00	10.00
122 Kevin Jordan	2.00	5.00
123 Jeff Juden	2.00	5.00
124 Ron Karkovice	2.00	5.00
125 Roberto Kelly	2.00	5.00
126 Mark Kiefer	2.00	5.00
127 Brooks Kieschnick	2.00	5.00
128 Jeff King	2.00	5.00
129 Mike Lansing	2.00	5.00
130 Matt Lawton	2.00	5.00
131 Al Leiter	4.00	10.00
132 Mark Leiter	2.00	5.00
133 Curtis Leskanic	4.00	10.00
134 Darren Lewis	2.00	5.00
135 Mark Lewis	2.00	5.00
136 Felipe Lira	2.00	5.00
137 Pat Listach	2.00	5.00
138 Keith Lockhart	2.00	5.00
139 Kenny Lofton SP	15.00	40.00
140 John Mabry	4.00	10.00
141 Mike Macfarlane	2.00	5.00
142 Kirt Manwaring	2.00	5.00
143 Al Martin	2.00	5.00
144 Norberto Martin	2.00	5.00
145 Dennis Martinez	4.00	10.00
146 Pedro Martinez	20.00	50.00
147 Sandy Martinez	2.00	5.00
148 Mike Matheny	2.00	5.00
149 T.J. Mathews	2.00	5.00
150 David McCarty	2.00	5.00
151 Ben McDonald	2.00	5.00
152 Pat Meares	2.00	5.00
153 Orlando Merced	2.00	5.00
154 Jose Mesa	2.00	5.00
155 Matt Mieske	2.00	5.00
156 Orlando Miller	2.00	5.00
157 Mike Mimbs	2.00	5.00
158 Paul Molitor SP	20.00	50.00
159 Raul Mondesi SP	15.00	40.00
160 Jeff Montgomery	2.00	5.00
161 Mickey Morandini	2.00	5.00
162 Lyle Mouton	2.00	5.00
163 James Mouton	2.00	5.00
164 Jamie Moyer	4.00	10.00
165 Rodney Myers	2.00	5.00
166 Denny Neagle	2.00	5.00
167 Robb Nen	4.00	10.00
168 Marc Newfield	2.00	5.00
169 Dave Nilsson	2.00	5.00
170 Otis Nixon *	50.00	100.00
171 Jon Nunnally	2.00	5.00
172 Chad Ogea	2.00	5.00
173 Troy O'Leary	2.00	5.00
174 Rey Ordonez	4.00	10.00
175 Jayhawk Owens	2.00	5.00
176 Tom Pagnozzi	2.00	5.00
177 Dean Palmer	2.00	5.00
178 Roger Pavlik	2.00	5.00
179 Troy Percival	6.00	15.00
180 Carlos Perez	2.00	5.00
181 Robert Perez	2.00	5.00
182 Andy Pettitte	10.00	25.00
183 Phil Plantier	2.00	5.00
184 Mike Potts	2.00	5.00
185 Curtis Pride	2.00	5.00
186 Ariel Prieto	2.00	5.00
187 Bill Pulsipher	2.00	5.00
188 Brad Radke	4.00	10.00
189 Manny Ramirez SP	20.00	50.00
190 Joe Randa	4.00	10.00
191 Pat Rapp	2.00	5.00
192 Bryan Rekar	2.00	5.00
193 Shane Reynolds	2.00	5.00
194 Arthur Rhodes	2.00	5.00
195 Mariano Rivera	50.00	100.00
196 Alex Rodriguez SP	60.00	120.00
197 Frank Rodriguez	2.00	5.00
198 Mel Rojas	2.00	5.00
199 Ken Ryan	2.00	5.00
200 Bret Saberhagen	4.00	10.00
201 Tim Salmon	6.00	15.00
202 Rey Sanchez	2.00	5.00
203 Scott Sanders	2.00	5.00
204 Steve Scarsone	2.00	5.00
205 Curt Schilling	10.00	25.00
206 Jason Schmidt	6.00	15.00
207 David Segui	4.00	10.00
208 Kevin Seitzer	2.00	5.00
209 Scott Servais	2.00	5.00
210 Don Slaught	2.00	5.00
211 Zane Smith	2.00	5.00
212 Paul Sorrento	2.00	5.00
213 Scott Stahoviak	2.00	5.00
214 Mike Stanley	2.00	5.00
215 Terry Steinbach	2.00	5.00
216 Kevin Stocker	2.00	5.00
217 Jeff Suppan	4.00	10.00
218 Bill Swift	2.00	5.00
219 Greg Swindell	2.00	5.00
220 Kevin Tapani	2.00	5.00
221 Danny Tartabull	2.00	5.00
222 Julian Tavarez	2.00	5.00
223 Frank Thomas SP	30.00	60.00
224 Ozzie Timmons	2.00	5.00
225 Michael Tucker	2.00	5.00
226 Ismael Valdes	2.00	5.00
227 Jose Valentin	2.00	5.00
228 Todd Van Poppel	2.00	5.00
229 Mo Vaughn SP	15.00	40.00
230 Quilvio Veras	2.00	5.00
231 Fernando Vina	2.00	5.00
232 Joe Vitiello	2.00	5.00
233 Jose Vizcaino	2.00	5.00
234 Omar Vizquel	6.00	15.00
235 Terrell Wade	2.00	5.00
236 Paul Wagner	2.00	5.00
237 Matt Walbeck	2.00	5.00
238 Jerome Walton	2.00	5.00
239 Turner Ward	2.00	5.00
240 Allen Watson	2.00	5.00
241 David Weathers	2.00	5.00
242 Walt Weiss	2.00	5.00
243 Turk Wendell	2.00	5.00
244 Rondell White	4.00	10.00
245 Brian Williams	2.00	5.00
246 George Williams	2.00	5.00
247 Paul Wilson	2.00	5.00
248 Bobby Witt	2.00	5.00
249 Bob Wolcott	2.00	5.00
250 Eric Young	2.00	5.00
251 Ernie Young	2.00	5.00
252 Greg Zaun	2.00	5.00
NNO F.Thomas Jumbo AU/1500	20.00	50.00
NNO Frank Thomas Sample Fascimile Auto	.75	2.00

1996 Leaf Signature Autographs Gold

Randomly inserted primarily in first series packs, this 252-card set is parallel to the regular set and is similar in design with the exception of the gold foil printing on each card front. Each player signed 500 cards, except for the SP's of which only 100 of each are signed. Jim Thome erroneously signed 514 Gold cards.

*GOLD: .6X TO 1.5X BRONZE CARDS

223 Jim Thome SP/514	15.00	40.00

1996 Leaf Signature Autographs Silver

Randomly inserted primarily in first series packs, this 252-card set is parallel to the regular set and is similar in design with the exception of the silver foil printing on each card front. Each player signed 1000 silver cards, except for the SP's of which only 200 are signed. Jim Thome erroneously signed 410 Silver cards.

*SILVER: .4X TO 1X BRONZE CARDS

223 Jim Thome SP/410	15.00	40.00

1996 Leaf Signature Extended Autographs

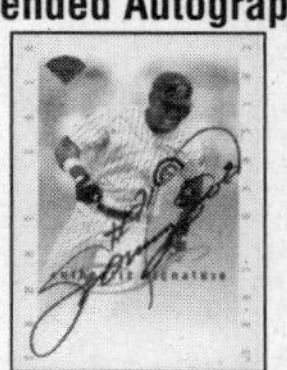

At least two autographed cards from this 217-card set were inserted in every Extended Series pack. Super Packs with four autographed cards were seeded one in every 12 packs. Most players signed 5000 cards, but short prints (500-2500 of each) do exist. On average, one in every nine packs contains a short print. All short print cards are individually noted in our checklist. By mistake, Andruw Jones, Ryan Klesko, Andy Pettitte, Kirby Puckett and Frank Thomas signed a few hundred of each of their cards in blue ink instead of black. No difference in price has been noted. Also, the Juan Gonzalez, Andruw Jones and Alex Rodriguez cards available in packs were not signed. All three cards had information on the back on how to mail them into Donruss/Leaf for an actual signed version. The deadline to exchange these cards was December 31st, 1998. In addition, middle relievers Doug Creek and Steve Parris failed to sign all 5000 of their cards. Creek submitted 1,950 cards and Parris submitted 1,800. Finally, an autographed jumbo version of the Extended Series Frank Thomas card was distributed to dealers in March, 1997. Dealers received either this card or the first series jumbo Thomas for every Extended Series case ordered. Each Extended Thomas jumbo is individually serial numbered to 1,500. A very popular Sammy Sosa card, one of his only certified autographs, is the key card in the set.

1 Scott Aldred	2.00	5.00
2 Mike Aldrete	2.00	5.00
3 Rich Amaral	2.00	5.00
4 Alex Arias	2.00	5.00
5 Paul Assenmacher	2.00	5.00
6 Roger Bailey	2.00	5.00
7 Erik Bennett	2.00	5.00
8 Sean Bergman	2.00	5.00
9 Doug Bochtler	2.00	5.00
10 Tim Bogar	2.00	5.00
11 Pat Borders	2.00	5.00
12 Pedro Borbon	2.00	5.00
13 Shawn Boskie	2.00	5.00
14 Rafael Bournigal	2.00	5.00
15 Mark Brandenburg	2.00	5.00
16 John Briscoe	2.00	5.00
17 Jorge Brito	2.00	5.00
18 Doug Brocail	2.00	5.00
19 Jay Buhner SP/1000	15.00	40.00
20 Scott Bullett	2.00	5.00
21 Dave Burba	2.00	5.00
22 Ken Caminiti SP/1000	40.00	80.00
23 John Cangelosi	2.00	5.00
24 Cris Carpenter	2.00	5.00
25 Chuck Carr	2.00	5.00
26 Larry Casian	2.00	5.00
27 Tony Castillo	2.00	5.00
28 Jason Christiansen	2.00	5.00
29 Archi Cianfrocco	2.00	5.00
30 Mark Clark	2.00	5.00
31 Terry Clark	2.00	5.00
32 R. Clemens SP1000	100.00	175.00
33 Jim Converse	2.00	5.00
34 Dennis Cook	2.00	5.00
35 Francisco Cordova	2.00	5.00
36 Jim Corsi	2.00	5.00
37 Tim Crabtree	2.00	5.00
38 Doug Creek SP/1950	6.00	15.00
39 John Cummings	2.00	5.00
40 Omar Daal	2.00	5.00
41 Rich DeLucia	2.00	5.00
42 Mark Dewey	2.00	5.00
43 Alex Diaz	2.00	5.00
44 Jermaine Dye SP/2500	10.00	25.00
45 Ken Edenfield	2.00	5.00
46 Mark Eichhorn	2.00	5.00
47 John Ericks	2.00	5.00
48 Darin Erstad	6.00	15.00
49 Alvaro Espinoza	2.00	5.00
50 Jorge Fabregas	2.00	5.00
51 Mike Fetters	2.00	5.00
52 John Flaherty	2.00	5.00
53 Bryce Florie	2.00	5.00
54 Tony Fossas	2.00	5.00
55 Lou Frazier	2.00	5.00
56 Mike Gallego	2.00	5.00
57 Karim Garcia SP/2500	6.00	15.00
58 Jason Giambi	6.00	15.00
59 Ed Giovanola	2.00	5.00
60 Tom Glavine SP/1250	20.00	50.00
61 Juan Gonzalez SP/1000	20.00	50.00
62 Craig Grebeck	2.00	5.00
63 Buddy Groom	2.00	5.00
64 Kevin Gross	2.00	5.00
65 Eddie Guardado	4.00	10.00
66 Mark Guthrie	2.00	5.00
67 Tony Gwynn SP/1000	40.00	80.00
68 Chip Hale	2.00	5.00
69 Darren Hall	2.00	5.00
70 Lee Hancock	2.00	5.00
71 Dave Hansen	2.00	5.00
72 Bryan Harvey	2.00	5.00
73 Bill Haselman	2.00	5.00
74 Mike Henneman	2.00	5.00
75 Doug Henry	2.00	5.00
76 Gil Heredia	2.00	5.00
77 Carlos Hernandez	2.00	5.00
78 Jose Hernandez	2.00	5.00
79 Darren Holmes	2.00	5.00
80 Mark Holzemer	2.00	5.00
81 Rick Honeycutt	2.00	5.00
82 Chris Hook	2.00	5.00
83 Chris Howard	2.00	5.00
84 Jack Howell	2.00	5.00
85 David Hulse	2.00	5.00
86 Edwin Hurtado	2.00	5.00
87 Jeff Huson	2.00	5.00
88 Mike James	2.00	5.00
89 Derek Jeter SP/1000	90.00	150.00
90 Brian Johnson	2.00	5.00
91 R. Johnson SP1000	60.00	120.00
92 Mark Johnson	2.00	5.00
93 Andruw Jones SP/2000	10.00	25.00
94 Chris Jones	2.00	5.00
95 Ricky Jordan	2.00	5.00
96 Matt Karchner	2.00	5.00
97 Scott Karl	2.00	5.00
98 Jason Kendall SP/2500	10.00	25.00
99 Brian Keyser	2.00	5.00
100 Mike Kingery	2.00	5.00
101 Wayne Kirby	2.00	5.00
102 Ryan Klesko SP/1000	20.00	50.00
103 C. Knoblauch SP1000	15.00	40.00
104 Chad Kreuter	2.00	5.00
105 Tom Lampkin	2.00	5.00
106 Scott Leius	2.00	5.00
107 Jon Lieber	4.00	10.00
108 Nelson Liriano	2.00	5.00
109 Scott Livingstone	2.00	5.00
110 Graeme Lloyd	2.00	5.00
111 Kenny Lofton SP/1000	15.00	40.00
112 Luis Lopez	2.00	5.00
113 Torey Lovullo	2.00	5.00
114 Greg Maddux SP/500	150.00	300.00
115 Mike Maddux	2.00	5.00
116 Dave Magadan	2.00	5.00
117 Mike Magnante	2.00	5.00
118 Joe Magrane	2.00	5.00
119 Pat Mahomes	2.00	5.00
120 Matt Mantei	2.00	5.00
121 John Marzano	2.00	5.00
122 Terry Mathews	2.00	5.00
123 Chuck McElroy	2.00	5.00
124 Fred McGriff SP/1000	40.00	80.00
125 Mark McLemore	2.00	5.00
126 Greg McMichael	2.00	5.00
127 Blas Minor	2.00	5.00
128 Dave Mlicki	2.00	5.00
129 Mike Mohler	2.00	5.00
130 Paul Molitor SP/1000	30.00	60.00
131 Steve Montgomery	2.00	5.00
132 Mike Mordecai	2.00	5.00
133 Mike Morgan	2.00	5.00
134 Mike Munoz	2.00	5.00
135 Greg Myers	2.00	5.00
136 Jimmy Myers	2.00	5.00
137 Mike Myers	2.00	5.00
138 Bob Natal	2.00	5.00
139 Dan Naulty	2.00	5.00
140 Jeff Nelson	4.00	10.00
141 Warren Newson	2.00	5.00
142 Chris Nichting	2.00	5.00
143 Melvin Nieves	2.00	5.00
144 Charlie O'Brien	2.00	5.00
145 Alex Ochoa	2.00	5.00
146 Omar Olivares	2.00	5.00
147 Joe Oliver	2.00	5.00
148 Lance Painter	2.00	5.00
149 R. Palmeiro SP2000	20.00	50.00
150 Mark Parent	2.00	5.00
151 Steve Parris SP/1800	6.00	15.00
152 Bob Patterson	2.00	5.00
153 Tony Pena	2.00	5.00
154 Eddie Perez	2.00	5.00
155 Yorkis Perez	2.00	5.00
156 Robert Person	2.00	5.00
157 Mark Petkovsek	2.00	5.00
158 Andy Pettitte SP/1000	20.00	50.00
159 J.R. Phillips	2.00	5.00
160 Hipolito Pichardo	2.00	5.00
161 Eric Plunk	2.00	5.00
162 Jimmy Poole	2.00	5.00
163 K. Puckett SP/1000	60.00	120.00
164 Paul Quantrill	2.00	5.00
165 Tom Quinlan	2.00	5.00
166 Jeff Reboulet	2.00	5.00
167 Jeff Reed	2.00	5.00
168 Steve Reed	2.00	5.00
169 Carlos Reyes	2.00	5.00
170 Bill Risley	2.00	5.00

171 Kevin Ritz 2.00 5.00
172 Kevin Roberson 2.00 5.00
173 Rich Robertson 2.00 5.00
174 A. Rodriguez SP/500 125.00 250.00
175 I. Rodriguez SP1250 30.00 60.00
176 Bruce Ruffin 2.00 5.00
177 Juan Samuel 2.00 5.00
178 Tim Scott 2.00 5.00
179 Kevin Sefcik 2.00 5.00
180 Jeff Shaw 2.00 5.00
181 Danny Sheaffer 2.00 5.00
182 Craig Shipley 2.00 5.00
183 Dave Silvestri 2.00 5.00
184 Aaron Small 4.00 10.00
185 John Smoltz SP/1000 30.00 60.00
186 Luis Sojo 2.00 5.00
187 S. Sosa SP/1000 100.00 200.00
188 Steve Sparks 2.00 5.00
189 Tim Spehr 2.00 5.00
190 Russ Springer 2.00 5.00
191 Matt Stairs 2.00 5.00
192 Andy Stankiewicz 2.00 5.00
193 Mike Stanton 2.00 5.00
194 Kelly Stinnett 2.00 5.00
195 Doug Strange 2.00 5.00
196 Mark Sweeney 2.00 5.00
197 Jeff Tabaka 2.00 5.00
198 Jesus Tavarez 2.00 5.00
199 F. Thomas SP1000 30.00 60.00
200 Larry Thomas 2.00 5.00
201 Mark Thompson 2.00 5.00
202 Mike Timlin 6.00 15.00
203 Steve Trachsel 2.00 5.00
204 Tom Urbani 2.00 5.00
205 Julio Valera 2.00 5.00
206 Dave Valle 2.00 5.00
207 Wm. VanLandingham 2.00 5.00
208 Mo Vaughn SP/1000 15.00 40.00
209 Dave Veres 2.00 5.00
210 Ed Vosberg 2.00 5.00
211 Don Wengert 2.00 5.00
212 Matt Whiteside 2.00 5.00
213 Bob Wickman 4.00 10.00
214 M.Williams SP/1250 15.00 40.00
215 Mike Williams 2.00 5.00
216 Woody Williams 4.00 10.00
217 Craig Worthington 2.00 5.00
NNO F.Thomas Jumbo AU 15.00 40.00

1996 Leaf Signature Extended Autographs Century Marks

Randomly inserted exclusively into Extended Series packs, cards from this 31-card parallel set feature a selection of star and rising young prospect players taken from the more comprehensive 217-card Extended Autograph set. The cards differ by a special blue holographic foil treatment. Only 100 of each card exists. In addition, Juan Gonzalez, Derek Jeter, Andruw Jones, Rafael Palmeiro and Alex Rodriguez did not sign the cards distributed in packs. All of these players cards had information on the back on how to mail them into Leaf/Donruss to receive a signed version.

1 Jay Buhner 30.00 60.00
2 Ken Caminiti 60.00 120.00
3 Roger Clemens 250.00 400.00
4 Jermaine Dye 30.00 60.00
5 Darin Erstad 20.00 50.00
6 Karim Garcia 10.00 25.00
7 Jason Giambi 30.00 60.00
8 Tom Glavine 75.00 150.00
9 Juan Gonzalez 30.00 60.00
10 Tony Gwynn 75.00 150.00
11 Derek Jeter 300.00 450.00
12 Randy Johnson 75.00 150.00
13 Andruw Jones 60.00 120.00
14 Jason Kendall 30.00 60.00
15 Ryan Klesko 30.00 60.00
16 Chuck Knoblauch 30.00 60.00
17 Kenny Lofton 30.00 60.00
18 Greg Maddux 250.00 400.00
19 Fred McGriff 60.00 120.00
20 Paul Molitor 50.00 100.00
21 Alex Ochoa 10.00 25.00
22 Rafael Palmeiro 75.00 150.00
23 Andy Pettitte 75.00 150.00
24 Kirby Puckett 250.00 350.00
25 Alex Rodriguez 250.00 400.00
26 Ivan Rodriguez 75.00 150.00
27 John Smoltz 75.00 150.00
28 Sammy Sosa 250.00 400.00
29 Frank Thomas 75.00 150.00
30 Mo Vaughn 30.00 60.00
31 Matt Williams 30.00 60.00

1911 Mecca Double Folders T201

The cards in this 50-card set measure approximately 2 1/4" by 4 11/16". The 1911 Mecca Double Folder issue contains unnumbered cards. This issue was one of the first to list statistics of players portrayed on the cards. Each card portrays two players, one when the card is folded, another when the card is unfolded. The card of Dougherty and Lord is considered scarce.

COMPLETE SET (50) 4000.00 6000.00
1 Bill Abstein 90.00 150.00
Johnny Butler
2 Harry Baker 90.00 150.00
Thomas Downie
UER No Player named Baker played for K.C. in 1910
UER (Sic Downey)
3 Jimmy Barrett 90.00 150.00
Ulysses McGlyn
4 Chief Bender 125.00 200.00
Rube Oldring
5 Mordecai Brown 125.00 200.00
Solly Hofman
6 Hal Chase 125.00 200.00
Ed Sweeney
7 Eddie Cicotte 125.00 200.00
Johny Thoney
8 Fred Clarke 125.00 200.00
Bobby Byrne
9 Eddie Collins 175.00 300.00
Frank Baker
10 Sam Crawford 1200.00 2000.00
Ty Cobb
11 Bill Donovan 90.00 150.00
Ralph Stroud
12 Red Downs 90.00 150.00
Fred Odwell
13 Larry Doyle 90.00 150.00
Chief Meyers
14 Johnny Evers 250.00 400.00
Frank Chance
15 Russ Ford 90.00 150.00
Otis Johnson
16 Edward Foster 90.00 150.00
Joseph Ward
17 Harry Gasper 90.00 150.00
Tommy Clarke
18 Eddie Grant 90.00 150.00
Larry McLean
19 Roy Hartzell 90.00 150.00
Walter Blair
20 Charles Hickman 90.00 150.00
Harry Hinchman
21 Miller Huggins 175.00 300.00
Roger Bresnahan
22 Walter Johnson 400.00 700.00
Gabby Street
23 E.H. Killian 90.00 150.00
Edward Fitzpatrick
24 Johnny Kling 90.00 150.00
Leonard Cole
25 Nap Lajoie 250.00 400.00
Cy Falkenberg
26 Joe Lake 125.00 200.00
Bobby Wallace
27 Frank LaPorte 90.00 150.00
James Stephens
28 Jack Lapp 90.00 150.00
Jack Barry
29 Tommy Leach 90.00 150.00
George Gibson
30 Lefty Leifield 90.00 150.00
Michael Simon
31 Hans Lobert 90.00 150.00
Earl Moore
32 Harry Lord 150.00 250.00
Patsy Dougherty
33 Johnny Lush 90.00 150.00
Arnold Hauser
34 Al Mattern 90.00 150.00
Peaches Graham
35 Christy Matthewson 400.00 700.00
Al Bridwell
UER (Sic Mathewson)
36 George McBride 90.00 150.00
Kid Elberfeld
37 James McCabe 90.00 150.00
Charles Starr
38 Joe McGinnity 125.00 200.00
Tom McCarty
39 Dots Miller 90.00 150.00
Buck Herzog
40 Nap Rucker 90.00 150.00
Jake Daubert
41 Cy Seymour 90.00 150.00
Jimmy Dygert
42 Tris Speaker 250.00 400.00
Larry Gardner
43 Ed Summers 125.00 200.00
Hugh Jennings
44 Ira Thomas 90.00 150.00
Jack Coombs
45 John Titus 90.00 150.00
Red Dooin
46 Terry Turner 90.00 150.00
George Stovall
47 Ed Walsh 125.00 200.00
Fred Payne
48 Zach Wheat 125.00 200.00
Bill Bergen
49 Hooks Wiltse 90.00 150.00
Fred Merkle
50 Sam Woodruff 90.00 150.00
Otto Williams

1887-90 Old Judge N172

The Goodwin Company's baseball series depicts hundreds of ballplayers from more than 40 major and minor league teams as well as boxers and wrestlers. The cards (approximately 1 1/2" by 2 1/2") are actually photographs from the Hall studio in New York which were pasted onto thick cardboard. The pictures are sepia in color with either a white or pink cast, and the cards are blank backed. They are found either numbered or unnumbered, with or without a copyright date, and with hand printed or machine printed names. All known cards have the name "Goodwin Co., New York" at the base. The cards were marketed during the period 1887-1890 in packs of "Old Judge" and "Gypsy Queen" cigarettes (cards marked with the latter brand are worth double the values listed below). They have been listed alphabetically and assigned numbers in the checklist below for simplicity's sake; the various poses known for some players also have not been listed for the same reason. Some of the players are pictured in horizontal (HOR) poses. In all, more than 2300 different Goodwin cards are known to collectors, with more being discovered every year. Cards from the "Spotted Tie" sub-series are denoted in the checklist below by SPOT. The Lee Gibson and Egyptian Healey cards are currently considered unique and are not priced due to market scarcity. The Stephen Behel card is drawing extra interest as there is debate as to whether or not he is the first Jewish player depicted on a card.

COMP.SET 500000.00 1000000.00
COMMON CARD 150.00 300.00
COMMON (DOUBLE) 200.00 400.00
COM.BROWNS CHAMP 250.00 500.00
COMMON CARD (PCL) 20000.0050000.00
COMMON SPOTTED TIE 500.00 1000.00
1 Gus Albert 300.00 500.00
2 Charles Alcott 300.00 500.00
3 Alexander 300.00 500.00
4 Myron Allen 300.00 500.00
5 Bob Allen 300.00 500.00
6 Uncle Bill Alvord 300.00 500.00
7 Varney Anderson 300.00 500.00
8 Ed Andrews: Phila. 300.00 500.00
9 Ed Andrews and Buster Hoover 350.00 600.00
10 Wally Andrews 300.00 500.00
11 Bill Annis 300.00 500.00
12A Cap Anson: Chicago (In uniform)
12B Cap Anson: Chicago (Not in uniform) 5000.00 8000.00
13 Old Hoss Ardner 300.00 500.00
14 Tug Arundel: Indianapolis-Whites 300.00 500.00
15 Jersey Bakley: Cleve. 300.00 500.00
16 Clarence Baldwin: Cincinnati 300.00 500.00
17 Mark(Fido) Baldwin: Chicago-Columbus 300.00 500.00
18 Lady Baldwin: Detroit 350.00 600.00
19 James Banning: Wash. 300.00 500.00
20 Samuel Barkley: Pittsburgh-K.C. 300.00 500.00
21 Bald Billy Barnie: Mgr. Baltimore 350.00 600.00
22 Charles Bassett: Indianapolis-N.Y. 300.00 500.00
23 Charles Bastian: Phila.-Chicago 300.00 500.00
24 Charles Bastian and Schriver: Philadelphia 350.00 600.00
25 Ebenezer Beatin: Cleve. 300.00 500.00
26 Jake Beckley: Eagle Eye Whites-Pittsburgh 2500.00 4000.00
27 Stephen Behel SPOT 6000.0010000.00
28 Charles Bennett: Detroit-Boston 300.00 500.00
29 Louis Bierbauer: A's 300.00 500.00
30 Louis Bierbauer and Robert Gamble: Athletics 350.00 600.00
31 Bill Bishop: Pittsburgh-Syracuse 300.00 500.00
32 William Blair: A's-Hamiltons 300.00 500.00
33 Ned Bligh: Columbus 300.00 500.00
34 Bogart: Indianapolis 300.00 500.00
35 Boyce: Washington 300.00 500.00
36 Jake Boyd: Maroons 350.00 600.00
37 Honest John Boyle: St. Louis-Chicago 300.00 500.00
38 Handsome Henry Boyle Indianapolis-N.Y. 300.00 500.00
39 Nick Bradley: K.C.- Worchester 300.00 500.00
40 George(Grin) Bradley Sioux City 300.00 500.00
41 Stephen Brady SPOT 900.00 1500.00
42 E.L. Breckinridge: Sacramento PCL
43 Timothy Brosnan: Minneapolis 300.00 500.00
44 Timothy Brosnan Sioux City 300.00 500.00
45 Cal Broughton: St. Paul 300.00 500.00
46 Big Dan Brouthers: Detroit-Boston 1500.00 2500.00
47 Thomas Brown: Pittsburgh-Boston 300.00 500.00
48 California Brown: New York 300.00 500.00
49 Pete Browning: Gladiator Louisville 3000.00 5000.00
50 Charles Brynan: Chicago-Des Moines 300.00 500.00
51 Al Buckenberger MG: Columbus 300.00 500.00
52 Dick Buckley: Indianapolis-N.Y. 300.00 500.00
53 Charles Buffington: Philadelphia 300.00 500.00
54 Ernest Burch: Brooklyn-Whites 300.00 500.00
55 Bill Burdick: Omaha-Indianapolis 300.00 500.00
56 Black Jack Burdock: Boston-Brooklyn 300.00 500.00
57 Robert Burks: Sioux City 300.00 500.00
58 George Burnham Watch Mgr. Indianapolis 350.00 600.00
59 Burns: Omaha 300.00 500.00
60 Jimmy Burns: K.C. 300.00 500.00
61 Tommy(Oyster) Burns Baltimore-Brooklyn 350.00 600.00
62 Thomas E. Burns: Chicago 300.00 500.00
63 Doc Bushong: Brook. 300.00 500.00
64 Doc Bushong: Browns Champs 500.00 800.00
65 Patsy Cahill: Ind. 300.00 500.00
66 Count Campau: Kansas City-Detroit 300.00 500.00
67 Jimmy Canavan: Omaha 300.00 500.00
68 Bart Cantz: Whites-Baltimore 300.00 500.00
69 Handsome Jack Carney Washington 300.00 500.00
70 Hick Carpenter Cincinnati 300.00 500.00
71 Cliff Carroll: Wash. 300.00 500.00
72 Scrappy Carroll: St.Paul-Chicago 300.00 500.00
73 Frederick Carroll: Pitts. 300.00 500.00
74 Jumbo Cartwright: Kansas City-St. Joe 300.00 500.00
75 Bob Caruthers: Parisian Brooklyn 500.00 800.00
76 Bob Caruthers: Parisian Browns Champs 500.00 800.00
77 Daniel Casey: Phila. 300.00 500.00
78 Icebox Chamberlain: St. Louis 300.00 500.00
79 Cupid Childs: Phila.-Syracuse 300.00 500.00
80 Bob Clark: Washington 300.00 500.00
81 Owen Clark: Washington 300.00 500.00
82 William H. Clarke and Mickey Hughes: Brooklyn HOR 350.00 600.00
83 William(Dad) Clarke: Chicago-Omaha 300.00 500.00
84 Pete Connell: Des Moines 300.00 500.00
85 John Clarkson: Chicago-Boston 1200.00 2000.00
86 Jack Clements: Philadelphia 300.00 500.00
87 Elmer Cleveland: Omaha-New York 300.00 500.00
88 Monk Cline: K.C.-Sioux City 300.00 500.00
89 Mike Cody: Des Moines 300.00 500.00
90 John Coleman: Pittsburgh - A's 300.00 500.00
91 Bill Collins: New York-Newark 300.00 500.00
92 Hub Collins: Louisville-Brooklyn 300.00 500.00
93 Charles Comiskey: Browns Champs 2500.00 4000.00
94 Commy Comiskey: St. Louis-Chicago 1800.00 3000.00
95 Roger Connor: Script 2500.00 4000.00
96 Roger Connor: New York 2500.00 4000.00
97 Richard Conway: Boston-Worchester 300.00 500.00
98 Peter Conway: Det.-Pitts.-Ind. 300.00 500.00
99 James Conway: K.C. 300.00 500.00
100 Paul Cook: Louisville 300.00 500.00
101 Jimmy Cooney: Omaha-Chicago 300.00 500.00
102 Larry Corcoran: Indianapolis-London 500.00 800.00
103 Pop Corkhill: Cincinnati-Brooklyn 300.00 500.00
104 Cannon Ball Crane: New York 300.00 500.00
105 Samuel Crane: Wash. 300.00 500.00
106 Jack Crogan Maroons 350.00 600.00
107 John Crooks: Whites-Omaha 300.00 500.00
108 Lave Cross: Louisville-A's-Phila. 300.00 500.00
109 Bill Crossley: Milw. 300.00 500.00
110 Joe Crotty SPOT 900.00 1500.00
111 Joe Crotty: Sioux City 300.00 500.00
112 Billy Crowell: Cleveland-St. Joe 300.00 500.00
113 Jim Cudworth: St. Louis-Worchester 300.00 500.00
114 Bert Cunningham: Baltimore-Phila. 300.00 500.00
115 Tacks Curtis: St. Joe 300.00 500.00
116 Ed Cushman SPOT 900.00 1500.00
117 Ed Cushman: Toledo 300.00 500.00
118 Tony Cusick: Mil. 300.00 500.00
119 Vincent Dailey Oakland PCL
120 Edward Dailey: Phil.-Wash.-Columbus 300.00 500.00
121 Edward Dailey: Columbus 500.00 800.00
122 Bill Daley: Boston 300.00 500.00
123 Con Daley: Boston-Indianapolis 300.00 500.00
124 Abner Dalrymple: Pittsburgh-Denver 300.00 500.00
125 Tom Daly: Chicago-Wash.-Cleve. 350.00 600.00
126 James Daly: Minn. 300.00 500.00
127 Law Daniels: K.C. 300.00 500.00
128 Dell Darling: Chicago 300.00 500.00
129 Wm. Darnbrough: Denver 300.00 500.00
130 D. Davin: Milwaukee 300.00 1500.00
131 Jumbo Davis: K.C. 300.00 500.00
132 Pat Dealey: Wash 300.00 500.00
133 Thomas Deasley: New York-Washington Throwing 300.00 500.00
134 Thomas Deasley Fielding 300.00 500.00
135 Edward Decker: Phil. 300.00 500.00
136 Big Ed Delahanty: Philadelphia 5000.00 8000.00
137 Jeremiah Denny: Indianapolis-New York 300.00 500.00
138 James Devlin: St.L. 300.00 500.00
139 Thomas Dolan: Whites-St. Louis-Denver 300.00 500.00
140 Jack Donahue: San Francisco PCL
141 James Donahue SPOT 900.00 1500.00
142 James Donahue: K.C. 300.00 500.00
143 James Donnelly: Washington 300.00 500.00
144 Charles Dooley Oakland PCL
145 J. Doran: Omaha 500.00 800.00
146 Michael Dorgan: N.Y. 300.00 500.00
147 Cornelius Doyle San Fran. PCL
148 Homerun Duffe: St.L. 300.00 500.00
149 Hugh Duffy: Chicago 1500.00 2500.00
150 Dan Dugdale: Maroons-Minneapolis 350.00 600.00
151 Duck Duke: Minn. 300.00 500.00
152 Sure Shot Dunlap: Pittsburgh 300.00 500.00
153 J. Dunn: Maroons 350.00 600.00
154 Jesse(Cyclone)Duryea St. Paul-Cinc. 300.00 500.00
155 John Dwyer: Chicago-Maroons 350.00 600.00
156 Billy Earle: Cincinnati-St.Paul 300.00 500.00
157 Buck Ebright: Wash. 300.00 500.00
158 Red Ehret: Louisville 300.00 500.00
159 R. Emmerke: Des Moines 300.00 500.00
160 Dude Esterbrook: Louisville-Ind.-New York-All Star 300.00 500.00
161 Henry Esterday: K.C.-Columbus 300.00 500.00
162 Long John Ewing: Louisville-N.Y. 300.00 500.00
163 Buck Ewing New York 1500.00 2500.00
164 Buck Ewing and Mascot: New York 1500.00 2500.00
165 Jay Faatz: Cleveland 300.00 500.00
166 Clinkgers Fagan: Kansas City-Denver 300.00 500.00
167 William Farmer: Pittsburgh-St. Paul 300.00 500.00
168 Sidney Farrar: Philadelphia 350.00 600.00
169 John(Moose) Farrell: Wash.-Baltimore 300.00 500.00
170 Charles(Duke)Farrell Chicago 300.00 500.00
171 Frank Fennelly: Cincinnati-A's 300.00 500.00
172 Chas. Ferguson: Phila. 300.00 500.00
173 Colonel Ferson: Washington 300.00 500.00
174 Wallace Fessenden: Umpire National 350.00 600.00
175 Jocko Fields: Pitts. 300.00 500.00
176 Fischer: Maroons 350.00 600.00
177 Thomas Flanigan: Cleve.-Sioux City 300.00 500.00
178 Silver Flint: Chicago 300.00 500.00
179 Thomas Flood: St. Joe 300.00 500.00
180 Flynn: Omaha 1500.00
181 James Fogarty: Philadelphia 300.00 500.00
182 Frank(Monkey)Foreman Baltimore-Cinc. 300.00 500.00
183 Thomas Forster: Milwaukee-Hartford 300.00 500.00
184 Elmer E. Foster SPOT 900.00 1500.00
185 Elmer Foster: New York-Chicago 300.00 500.00
186 F.W. Foster SPOT T.W. Forster (Sic) 900.00 1500.00
187 Scissors Foutz: Browns Champ 500.00 800.00
188 Scissors Foutz: Brooklyn 300.00 500.00
189 Julie Freeman: St.L.-Milwaukee 300.00 500.00
190 Will Fry: St. Joe 300.00 500.00
191 Fred Fudger Oakland PCL
192 William Fuller: Milwaukee 300.00 500.00
193 Shorty Fuller: St.Louis 300.00 500.00
194 Christopher Fullmer: Baltimore 300.00 500.00
195 Christopher Fullmer and Tom Tucker: Baltimore HOR 350.00 600.00
196 Honest John Gaffney: Mgr. Washington 500.00 800.00
197 Pud Galvin: Pitts.. 1800.00 3000.00
198 Robert Gamble: A's 300.00 500.00
199 Charles Ganzel: Detroit-Boston 300.00 500.00
200 Frank(Gid) Gardner: Phila.-Washington 300.00 500.00
201 Gid Gardner and Miah Murray: Washington HOR 350.00 600.00
202 Hank Gastreich: Columbus 300.00 500.00
203 Emil Geiss: Chicago 300.00 500.00
204 Frenchy Genins: Sioux City 300.00 500.00
205 William George: N.Y. 300.00 500.00
206 Move Up Joe Gerhardt All Star-Jersey City 300.00 500.00
207 Pretzels Getzein: Detroit-Ind. 300.00 500.00
208 Lee Gibson: A's 300.00 500.00
209 Robert Gilks: Cleve. 300.00 500.00
210 Pete Gillespie: N.Y. 300.00 500.00
211 Barney Gilligan Washington-Detroit 300.00 500.00
212 Frank Gilmore: Wash. 300.00 500.00
213 Pebbly Jack Glasscock Indianapolis-N.Y. 500.00 800.00
214 Kid Gleason: Phila. 500.00 800.00
215 Brother Bill Gleason A's-Louisville 300.00 500.00
216 William Bill Gleason Browns Champs 500.00 800.00
217 Mouse Glenn: Sioux City 300.00 500.00
218 Michael Goodfellow: Cleveland-Detroit 300.00 500.00
219 George Gore (Pianolegs) New York 300.00 500.00
220 Frank Graves: Minn. 300.00 500.00
221 William Greenwood: Baltimore-Columbus 300.00 500.00
222 Michael Greer: Cleveland-Brooklyn 300.00 500.00
223 Mike Griffin: Baltimore-Phila NL 300.00 500.00
224 Clark Griffith: Milwaukee 1800.00 3000.00
225 Henry Gruber: Cleve. 300.00 500.00
226 Addison Gumbert: Chicago-Boston 300.00 500.00
227 Thomas Gunning: Philadelphia-A's 300.00 500.00
228 Joseph Gunson: K.C. 300.00 500.00
229 George Haddock: Washington 300.00 500.00
230 William Hafner: K.C. 300.00 500.00
231 Willie Hahm: Chicago Mascot 300.00 500.00
232 William Hallman: Philadelphia 300.00 500.00
233 Billy Hamilton: Kansas City-Phila. 1200.00 2000.00
234 Willie Hamm and Ned Williamson: Chicago 500.00 800.00
235 Frank Hankinson: SPOT 900.00 1500.00
236 Frank Hankinson: Kansas City 300.00 500.00
237 Ned Hanlon: Det.-Boston-Pitts. 1200.00 2000.00
238 William Hanrahan: Maroons-Minn. 350.00 600.00
239 A.G. Hapeman: Sacramento PCL
240 Pa Harkins: Brooklyn-Baltimore 300.00 500.00
241 William Hart: Cinc.-Des Moines 300.00 500.00
242 Wm. Hasamdear: K.C. 300.00 500.00
243 Colonel Hatfield: New York 300.00 500.00
244 Egyptian Healey: Wash.-Indianapolis 300.00 500.00
245 Egyptian Healey Washington 300.00 500.00
246 J.C. Healy: Omaha-Denver 300.00 500.00
247 Guy Hecker: Louisville 300.00 500.00
248 Tony Hellman: Sioux City 300.00 500.00
249 Hardie Henderson: Brook.-Pitts.-Balt. 300.00 500.00
250 Hardie Henderson and Michael Greer: Brooklyn 350.00 600.00
251 Moxie Hengle: Maroons-Minneapolis 350.00 600.00
252 John Henry: Phila. 300.00 500.00
253 Edward Herr: Whites-Milwaukee 300.00 500.00
254 Hunkey Hines: Whites 300.00 500.00
255 Paul Hines: Wash.-Indianapolis 300.00 500.00
256 Texas Wonder Hoffman: Denver 300.00 500.00
257 Eddie Hogan: Cleve. 300.00 500.00
258 William Holbert SPOT 900.00 1500.00
259 William Holbert: Brooklyn-Mets-Jersey City 300.00 500.00
260 James(Bugs) Holliday: Des Moines-Cinc. 300.00 500.00
261 Charles Hoover: Maroons-Chi.-K.C. 350.00 600.00
262 Buster Hoover: Phila.-Toronto 300.00 500.00
263 Jack Horner: Milwaukee-New Haven 300.00 500.00
264 Jack Horner and E.H. Warner: Milwaukee 350.00 600.00
265 Michael Horning: Boston-Balt.-N.Y. 300.00 500.00
266 Pete Hotaling: Cleveland 300.00 500.00
267 William Howes: Minn..-St. Paul 300.00 500.00
268 Dummy Hoy: Washington 1800.00 3000.00
269 Nat Hudson: Browns Champ 500.00 800.00
270 Nat Hudson: St. Louis 300.00 500.00

271 Mickey Hughes: Brk. 300.00 500.00
272 Hungler: Sioux City 300.00 500.00
273 Wild Bill Hutchinson: Chicago 300.00 500.00
274 John Irwin: Wash.-Wilkes Barre 300.00 500.00
275 Cutrate Irwin: Phila.-Boston-Wash. 300.00 500.00
276 A.C. Jantzen: Minn. 300.00 500.00
277 Frederick Jevne: Minn.-St. Paul 300.00 500.00
278 John Johnson: K.C.-Columbus 300.00 500.00
279 Richard Johnston: Boston 300.00 500.00
280 Jordan Minneapolis 300.00 500.00
281 Heinie Kappell: Columbus-Cincinnati 300.00 500.00
282 Sir Timothy Keefe: New York 1200.00 2000.00
283 Tim Keefe and Danny Richardson: Stealing 2nd Base New York HOR 700.00 1200.00
284 George Keefe: Wash. 300.00 500.00
285 James Keenan: Cinc. 300.00 500.00
286 Mike King Kelly 10,000 Chic-Boston 3000.00 5000.00
287 Honest John Kelly: Mgr. Louisville 500.00 800.00
288 Kelly: (Umpire) Western Association 350.00 600.00
289 Charles Kelly: Philadelphia 600.00 1000.00
290 Kelly and Powell: Umpire and Manager Sioux City 350.00 600.00
291 Rudolph Kemmler: Browns Champ 500.00 800.00
292 Rudolph Kemmler: St. Paul 300.00 500.00
293 Theodore Kennedy: Des Moines-Omaha 350.00 600.00
294 J.J. Kenyon: Whites-Des Moines 300.00 500.00
295 John Kerins: Louisville 300.00 500.00
296 Matthew Kilroy: Baltimore-Boston 300.00 500.00
297 Charles King: St.L.-Chi. 300.00 500.00
298 Aug. Kloff: Minn.-St.Joe 300.00 500.00
299 William Klusman: Milwaukee-Denver 300.00 500.00
300 Phillip Knell: St. Joe-Phila. 300.00 500.00
301 Fred Knouf: St. Louis 300.00 500.00
302 Charles Kremmeyer: Sacramento PCL
303 William Krieg: Wash.-St. Joe-Minn. 300.00 500.00
304 William Krieg and Aug. Kloff: Minneapolis 350.00 600.00
305 Gus Krock: Chicago 300.00 500.00
306 Willie Kuehne: Pittsburgh 300.00 500.00
307 Frederick Lange: Maroons 350.00 600.00
308 Ted Larkin: A's 300.00 500.00
309 Arlie Latham: Browns Champ 600.00 1000.00
310 Arlie Latham: St. Louis-Chicago 500.00 800.00
311 John Lauer: Pittsburgh 300.00 500.00
312 John Leighton Omaha 300.00 500.00
313 Rube Levy San Fran. PCL
314 Tom Loftus MG: Whites-Cleveland 300.00 500.00
315 Herman(Germany)Long Maroons-K.C. 500.00 800.00
316 Danny Long Oak. PCL
317 Tom Lovett: Omaha-Brooklyn 300.00 500.00
318 Bobby(Link) Lowe: Milwaukee 500.00 800.00
319 Jack Lynch SPOT 900.00 1500.00
320 John Lynch: All Stars 300.00 500.00
321 Dennis Lyons: A's 300.00 500.00
322 Harry Lyons: St. L. 300.00 500.00
323 Connie Mack: Wash. 3500.00 6000.00
324 Joe(Reddie) Mack: Louisville 300.00 500.00
325 James(Little Mack) Macullar: Des Moines-Milwaukee 300.00 500.00
326 Kid Madden: Boston 300.00 500.00
327 Daniel Mahoney: St. Joe 300.00 500.00
328 Willard(Grasshopper) Maines: St. Paul 300.00 500.00
329 Fred Mann: St.Louis-Hartford 300.00 500.00
330 Jimmy Manning: K.C. 300.00 500.00
331 Charles(Lefty) Marr: Col.-Cinc. 300.00 500.00
332 Mascot(Willie Breslin): New York 350.00 600.00
333 Samuel Maskery: Milwaukee-Des Moines 300.00 500.00
334 Bobby Mathews: A's 300.00 500.00
335 Michael Mattimore: New York-A's 300.00 500.00
336 Albert Maul: Pitts. 300.00 500.00
337 Albert Mays SPOT 900.00 1500.00
338 Albert Mays: Columbus 300.00 500.00
339 James McAleer: Cleveland 300.00 500.00
340 Thomas McCarthy: Phila.-St. Louis 1500.00 2500.00
341 John McCarthy: K.C. 300.00 500.00
342 James McCauley: Maroons-Phila. 350.00 600.00
343 William McClellan: Brooklyn-Denver 300.00 500.00
344 John McCormack: Whites 300.00 500.00
345 Big Jim McCormick: Chicago-Pittsburgh 300.00 500.00
346 McCreachery: Mgr. Indianapolis
347 James(Chippy)McGarr: St. Louis-K.C. 300.00 500.00
348 Jack McGeachy: Ind. 300.00 500.00
349 John McGlone: Cleveland-Detroit 300.00 500.00
350 James(Deacon)McGuire Phila.-Toronto 300.00 500.00
351 Bill McGunnigle: Mgr. Brooklyn 500.00 800.00
352 Ed McKean: Cleveland 300.00 500.00
353 Alex McKinnon: Pittsburgh 300.00 500.00
354 Thomas McLaughlin SPOT 900.00 1500.00
355 John(Bid) McPhee: Cincinnati 3000.00 5000.00
356 James McQuaid: Denver 300.00 500.00
357 John McQuaid: Umpire Amer. Assoc. 350.00 600.00
358 Jame McTamany: Brook.-Col.-K.C. 300.00 500.00
359 George McVey: Mil.-Denver-St. Joe 300.00 500.00
360 Peter Meegan San Fran. PCL
361 John Messitt: Omaha 300.00 500.00
362 George(Doggie)Miller Pittsburgh 300.00 500.00
363 Joseph Miller: Omaha-Minneapolis 300.00 500.00
364 Jocko Milligan: St. Louis-Phila. 300.00 500.00
365 E.L. Mills: Milwaukee 300.00 500.00
366 Daniel (Minahan) Minnehan: Minneapolis 300.00 500.00
367 Samuel Moffet: Ind. 300.00 500.00
368 Honest Morrell: Boston-Washington 300.00 500.00
369 Ed Morris (Cannonball): Pittsburgh 300.00 500.00
370 Morrisey: St. Paul 300.00 500.00
371 Tony(Count) Mullane: Cincinnati 500.00 800.00
372 Joseph Mulvey: Philadelphia 300.00 500.00
373 P.L. Murphy: St. Paul 300.00 500.00
374 Pat J. Murphy: New York 300.00 500.00
375 Miah Murray: Wash. 300.00 500.00
376 James(Truthful) Mutrie: Mgr. N.Y. 350.00 600.00
377 George Myers: Indianapolis-Phila. 300.00 500.00
378 Al(Cod) Myers: Washington 300.00 500.00
379 Thomas Nagle: Omaha-Chi. 300.00 500.00
380 Billy Nash: Boston 300.00 500.00
381 Jack(Candy) Nelson: SPOT 900.00 1500.00
382 Kid Nichols: Omaha 2500.00 4000.00
383 Samuel Nichols: Pittsburgh 300.00 500.00
384 J.W. Nicholson Maroons-Minn. 350.00 600.00
385 Tom Nicholson (Parson) Whites-Cleveland 300.00 500.00
386 Nicholls Nicol Browns Champ 500.00 800.00
387 Hugh Nicol: Cinc. 300.00 500.00
388 Hugh Nicol and Long John Reilly: Cincinnati 350.00 600.00
389 Frederick Nyce Whites-Burlington 300.00 500.00
390 Doc Oberlander Cleveland-Syracuse 300.00 500.00
391 Jack O'Brien Brooklyn-Baltimore 300.00 500.00
392 William O'Brien: Washington 300.00 500.00
393 William O'Brien and John Irwin: Washington 350.00 600.00
394 Darby O'Brien: Brooklyn 300.00 500.00
395 John O'Brien: Cleve. 300.00 500.00
396 P.J. O'Connell: Omaha-Des Moines 300.00 500.00
397 John O'Connor: Cincinnati-Columbus 300.00 500.00
398 Hank O'Day: Washington-New York 500.00 800.00
399 O'Day Sacramento 300.00 500.00
400 James O'Neil: St. Louis-Chicago 300.00 500.00
401 James O'Neil: Browns Champs 500.00 800.00
402 Norris Tip O'Neill Oakland PCL
403 Jim O'Rourke: New York 1800.00 3000.00
404 Thomas O'Rourke: Boston-Jersey City 300.00 500.00
405 David Orr SPOT 900.00 1500.00
406 David Orr: All Star-Brooklyn-Columbus 300.00 500.00
407 Parsons: Minneapolis 300.00 500.00
408 Owen Patton: Minn.-Des Moines 300.00 500.00
409 James Peeples: Brooklyn-Columbus 300.00 500.00
410 James Peeples and Hardie Henderson: Brooklyn 350.00 600.00
411 Hip Perrier: San Francisco PCL
412 Patrick Pettee: Milwaukee-London 300.00 500.00
413 Patrick Pettee and Bobby Lowe: Milwaukee 350.00 600.00
414 Dandelion Pfeffer: Chi. 300.00 500.00
415 Dick Phelan: Des Moines 300.00 500.00
416 William Phillips: Brooklyn-Kansas City 300.00 500.00
417 John Pickett: St. Paul-K.C.-Phila. 300.00 500.00
418 George Pinkney: Brooklyn 300.00 500.00
419 Thomas Poorman: A's-Milwaukee 300.00 500.00
420 Henry Porter: Brooklyn-Kansas City 300.00 500.00
421 James Powell: Sioux City 300.00 500.00
422 Tom Powers: San Francisco PCL
423 Bill Purcell: (Blondie) Baltimore-A's 300.00 500.00
424 Thomas Quinn: Baltimore 300.00 500.00
425 Joseph Quinn: Des Moines-Boston 300.00 500.00
426 Old Hoss Radbourne: Boston (Portrait) 2500.00 4000.00
427 Old Hoss Radbourne: Boston (Non-portrait) 2500.00 4000.00
428 Shorty Radford: Brooklyn-Cleveland 300.00 500.00
429 Tom Ramsey: Louisville 300.00 500.00
430 Rehse: Minneapolis 300.00 500.00
431 Long John Reilly: Cincinnati 300.00 500.00
432 Charles Reilly: (Princeton) St.Paul 300.00 500.00
433 Charles Reynolds: Kansas City 300.00 500.00
434 Hardie Richardson Detroit-Boston 300.00 500.00
435 Danny Richardson: New York 300.00 500.00
436 Charles Ripslager SPOT 900.00 1500.00
437 John Roach New York 300.00 500.00
438 Wilbert Robinson Uncle Robbie: A's 1500.00 2500.00
439 M.C. Robinson: Minn. 300.00 500.00
440 Yank Robinson: St. Louis 300.00 500.00
441 Wm.(Yank) Robinson: Browns Champs 500.00 800.00
442 George Rooks: Maroons-Detroit 350.00 600.00
443 James(Chief) Roseman SPOT 900.00 1500.00
444 Davis Rowe: Mgr. K.C.-Denver 300.00 500.00
445 Jack Rowe: Detroit-Pittsburgh 300.00 500.00
446 Amos (Hoosier Thunderbolt) Rusie: Indianapolis 3500.00 6000.00
447 Amos Rusie New York 3500.00 6000.00
448 James Ryan: Chicago 500.00 800.00
449 Henry Sage: Des Moines-Toledo 300.00 500.00
450 Henry Sage and William Van Dyke: Des Moines-Toledo 350.00 600.00
451 Sanders: Omaha 300.00 500.00
452 Al(Ben) Sanders: Philadelphia 300.00 500.00
453 Frank Scheibeck: Detroit 300.00 500.00
454 Albert Schellhase: St. Joseph 300.00 500.00
455 William Schenkle: Milwaukee 300.00 500.00
456 Bill Schildknecht: Des Moines-Milwaukee 300.00 500.00
457 Gus(Pink Whiskers) Schmelz Mgr. Cincinnati 300.00 500.00
458 Lewis Schoeneck (Jumbo): Maroons-Indianapolis 350.00 600.00
459 Pop Schriver: Phila. 300.00 500.00
460 John Seery: Ind. 300.00 500.00
461 William Serad Cincinnnati-Toronto 300.00 500.00
462 Edward Seward: A's 300.00 500.00
463 George(Orator)Shafer Des Moines 300.00 500.00
464 Frank Shafer: St. Paul 300.00 500.00
465 Daniel Shannon: Omaha-L'ville-Phila. 300.00 500.00
466 William Sharsig: Mgr. Athletics 350.00 600.00
467 Samuel Shaw: Baltimore-Newark 300.00 500.00
468 John Shaw: Minneapolis 300.00 500.00
469 William Shindle: Baltimore-Phila. 300.00 500.00
470 George Shock: Wash. 300.00 500.00
471 Otto Shomberg: Ind. 300.00 500.00
472 Lev Shreve: Ind. 300.00 500.00
473 Ed(Baldy) Silch: Brooklyn-Denver 300.00 500.00
474 Michael Slattery: New York 300.00 500.00
475 Sam(Skyrocket)Smith: Louisville 300.00 500.00
476 John(Phenomenal) Smith (Portrait) 1500.00 2500.00
477 John(Phenomenal) Smith: Balt.-A's (Non-portrait) 300.00 500.00
478 Elmer Smith: Cincinnati 300.00 500.00
479 Fred(Sam) Smith: Des Moines 300.00 500.00
480 George Smith (Germany) Brooklyn 300.00 500.00
481 Pop Smith: Pitt.-Bos.-Phila. 300.00 500.00
482 Nick Smith: St. Joe 300.00 500.00
483 P.T. Somers: St. Louis 300.00 500.00
484 Joe Sommer: Balt. 300.00 500.00
485 Pete Sommers: Chicago-New York 300.00 500.00
486 William Sowders: Boston-Pittsburgh 300.00 500.00
487 John Sowders: St. Paul-Kansas City 300.00 500.00
488 Charles Sprague: Maroons-Chi.-Cleve. 350.00 600.00
489 Edward Sproat: Whites 300.00 500.00
490 Harry Staley: Whites-Pittsburgh 300.00 500.00
491 Daniel Stearns: Des Moines-K.C. 300.00 500.00
492 Billy(Cannonball) Stemmyer: Boston-Cleveland 300.00 500.00
493 B.F. Stephens: Milw. 300.00 500.00
494 John C. Sterling: Minneapolis 300.00 500.00
495 Leonard Stockwell S.F. PCL
496 Harry Stovey: A's-Boston 600.00 1000.00
497 C. Scott Stratton: Louisville 300.00 500.00
498 Joseph Straus: Omaha-Milwaukee 300.00 500.00
499 John(Cub) Stricker: Cleveland 300.00 500.00
500 Marty Sullivan: Chicago-Ind. 300.00 500.00
501 Michael Sullivan: A's 300.00 500.00
502 Billy Sunday: Chicago-Pittsburgh 900.00 1500.00
503 Sy Sutcliffe: Cleve. 300.00 500.00
504 Ezra Sutton: Boston-Milwaukee 300.00 500.00
505 Ed Cyrus Swartwood: Brook.-D.Moines-Ham. 300.00 500.00
506 Parke Swartzel: K.C. 300.00 500.00
507 Peter Sweeney: Wash. 300.00 500.00
508 Louis Sylvester Sacramento PCL
509 Ed(Dimples) Tate: Boston-Baltimore 300.00 500.00
510 Patsy Tebeau: Chi.-Cleve.-Minn. 500.00 800.00
511 John Tener: Chicago 350.00 600.00
512 Bill(Adonis) Terry: Brooklyn 300.00 500.00
513 Big Sam Thompson: Detroit-Philadelphia 1500.00 2500.00
514 Silent Mike Tiernan: New York 350.00 600.00
515 Ledell Titcomb: N.Y. 300.00 500.00
516 Phillip Tomney: Louisville 300.00 500.00
517 Stephen Toole: Brooklyn-K.C.-Rochester 300.00 500.00
518 George Townsend A's 300.00 500.00
519 William Traffley: Des Moines 300.00 500.00
520 George Treadway: St. Paul-Denver 300.00 500.00
521 Samuel Trott: Baltimore-Newark 300.00 500.00
522 Sam Trott and Tommy(Oyster) Burns: Baltimore HOR 350.00 600.00
523 Tom(Foghorn) Tucker: Baltimore 300.00 500.00
524 William Tuckerman: St. Paul 300.00 500.00
525 Turner: Minneapolis 300.00 500.00
526 Lawrence Twitchell: Detroit-Cleveland 300.00 500.00
527 James Tyng: Phila. 300.00 500.00
528 William Van Dyke: Des Moines-Toledo 300.00 500.00
529 George(Rip) VanHaltren Chicago 300.00 500.00
530 Harry Vaughn: (Farmer) Louisville-New York 300.00 500.00
531 Peek-a-Boo Veach: St. Paul 500.00 800.00
532 Veach: Sacra. PCL
533 Leon Viau: Cincinnati 300.00 500.00
534 William Vinton: Minneapolis 300.00 500.00
535 Joseph Visner: Brooklyn 300.00 500.00
536 Christian Von Der Ahe Owner Browns Champs 500.00 800.00
537 Joseph Walsh Omaha 300.00 500.00
538 John (Monte) Ward: New York 1800.00 3000.00
539 E.H. Warner: Milwaukee 500.00 800.00
540 William Watkins: Mgr. Detroit-Kansas City 350.00 600.00
541 Bill Weaver: (Farmer) Louisville 300.00 500.00
542 Charles Weber: Sioux City 300.00 500.00
543 George Weidman (Stump): Detroit-New York 300.00 500.00
544 William Weidner: Columbus 300.00 500.00
545 Curtis Welch: Browns Champ 500.00 800.00
546 Curtis Welch: A's 350.00 600.00
547 Curtis Welch and Bill Gleason: Athletics 500.00 800.00
548 Smilin' Mickey Welch: All Star-New York 1800.00 3000.00
549 Jake Wells: K.C. 300.00 500.00
550 Frank Wells: Des Moines-Mil. 350.00 600.00
551 Joseph Werrick: Louisville-St. Paul 300.00 500.00
552 Milton(Buck) West: Minneapolis 300.00 500.00
553 Gus(Cannonball) Weyhing: A's 300.00 500.00
554 John Weyhing: Athletics-Columbus 300.00 500.00
555 Bobby Wheelock: Boston-Detroit 300.00 500.00
556 Whitacre: A's 300.00 500.00
557 Pat Whitaker: Balt. 300.00 500.00
558 Deacon White: Detroit-Pittsburgh 500.00 800.00
559 William White: Louisville 300.00 500.00
560 Jim(Grasshopper) Whitney: Wash.-Indianapolis 300.00 500.00
561 Arthur Whitney: Pittsburgh-New York 300.00 500.00
562 G. Whitney: St. Joseph 300.00 500.00
563 James Williams: Mgr. Cleveland 350.00 600.00
564 Ned Williamson: Chi. 500.00 800.00
565 Williamson and Mascot 350.00 600.00
566 C.H. Willis: Omaha 300.00 500.00
567 Walt Wilmot: Washington-Chicago 300.00 500.00
568 George Winkleman: Minneapolis-Hartford Issued only in 1889 600.00 1000.00
569 Samuel Wise: Boston-Washington 300.00 500.00
570 William Wolf (Chicken) Louisville 300.00 500.00
571 George(Dandy) Wood: Philadelphia 300.00 500.00
572 Peter Wood: Phila. 300.00 500.00
573 Harry Wright: Mgr. Philadelphia 5000.00 8000.00
574 Charles Zimmer (Chief) Cleveland 300.00 500.00
575 Frank Zinn: Athletics 300.00 500.00

1994 Pacific

The 660 standard-size cards comprising this set feature color player action shots on their fronts that are borderless, except at the bottom, where a team color-coded marbleized border set off by a gold-foil line carries the team color-coded player's name. The cards are grouped alphabetically within teams. The set closes with an Award Winners subset (655-660). There are no key Rookie Cards in this set.

COMPLETE SET (660) 20.00 50.00
1 Steve Avery .02 .10
2 Steve Bedrosian .02 .10
3 Damon Berryhill .02 .10
4 Jeff Blauser .02 .10
5 Sid Bream .02 .10
6 Francisco Cabrera .02 .10
7 Ramon Caraballo .02 .10
8 Ron Gant .07 .20
9 Tom Glavine .10 .30
10 Chipper Jones .20 .50
11 Dave Justice .07 .20
12 Ryan Klesko .07 .20
13 Mark Lemke .02 .10
14 Javier Lopez .07 .20
15 Greg Maddux .30 .75
16 Fred McGriff .10 .30
17 Greg McMichael .02 .10
18 Kent Mercker .02 .10
19 Otis Nixon .02 .10
20 Terry Pendleton .07 .20
21 Deion Sanders .10 .30
22 John Smoltz .10 .30
23 Tony Tarasco .02 .10
24 Manny Alexander .02 .10
25 Brady Anderson .07 .20
26 Harold Baines .07 .20
27 Damon Buford .02 .10
28 Paul Carey .02 .10
29 Mike Devereaux .02 .10
30 Todd Frohwirth .02 .10
31 Leo Gomez .02 .10
32 Jeffrey Hammonds .02 .10
33 Chris Hoiles .02 .10
34 Tim Hulett .02 .10
35 Ben McDonald .02 .10
36 Mark McLemore .02 .10
37 Alan Mills .02 .10
38 Mike Mussina .10 .30
39 Sherman Obando .02 .10
40 Gregg Olson .02 .10
41 Mike Pagliarulo .02 .10
42 Jim Poole .02 .10
43 Harold Reynolds .07 .20
44 Cal Ripken .60 1.50
45 David Segui .02 .10
46 Fernando Valenzuela .07 .20
47 Jack Voigt .02 .10
48 Scott Bankhead .02 .10
49 Roger Clemens .40 1.00
50 Scott Cooper .02 .10
51 Danny Darwin .02 .10
52 Andre Dawson .07 .20
53 John Dopson .02 .10
54 Scott Fletcher .02 .10
55 Tony Fossas .02 .10
56 Mike Greenwell .02 .10
57 Billy Hatcher .02 .10
58 Jeff McNeely .02 .10
59 Jose Melendez .02 .10
60 Tim Naehring .02 .10
61 Tony Pena .02 .10
62 Paul Quantrill .02 .10
63 Carlos Quintana .02 .10
64 Luis Rivera .02 .10
65 Jeff Russell .02 .10
66 Aaron Sele .02 .10
67 John Valentin .02 .10
68 Mo Vaughn .07 .20
69 Frank Viola .07 .20
70 Bob Zupcic .02 .10
71 Mike Butcher .02 .10
72 Rod Correia .02 .10
73 Chad Curtis .02 .10
74 Chili Davis .07 .20
75 Gary DiSarcina .02 .10
76 Damion Easley .02 .10
77 John Farrell .02 .10
78 Chuck Finley .07 .20
79 Joe Grahe .02 .10
80 Stan Javier .02 .10
81 Mark Langston .02 .10
82 Phil Leftwich RC .02 .10
83 Torey Lovullo .02 .10
84 Joe Magrane .02 .10
85 Greg Myers .02 .10
86 Eduardo Perez .02 .10
87 Luis Polonia .02 .10
88 Tim Salmon .10 .30
89 J.T. Snow .07 .20
90 Kurt Stillwell .02 .10
91 Ron Tingley .02 .10
92 Chris Turner .02 .10
93 Julio Valera .02 .10
94 Jose Bautista .02 .10
95 Shawn Boskie .02 .10
96 Steve Buechele .02 .10
97 Frank Castillo .02 .10
98 Mark Grace UER (stats have 98 home runs in 1993; should be 14) .10 .30
99 Jose Guzman .02 .10
100 Mike Harkey .02 .10
101 Greg Hibbard .02 .10
102 Doug Jennings .02 .10
103 Derrick May .02 .10
104 Mike Morgan .02 .10
105 Randy Myers .02 .10
106 Karl Rhodes .02 .10
107 Kevin Roberson .02 .10
108 Rey Sanchez .02 .10
109 Ryne Sandberg .30 .75
110 Tommy Shields .02 .10
111 Dwight Smith .02 .10
112 Sammy Sosa .20 .50
113 Jose Vizcaino .02 .10
114 Turk Wendell .02 .10
115 Rick Wilkins .02 .10
116 Willie Wilson .02 .10
117 Ed. Zambrano RC .02 .10
118 Wilson Alvarez .02 .10
119 Tim Belcher .02 .10
120 Jason Bere .02 .10
121 Rodney Bolton .02 .10
122 Ellis Burks .07 .20
123 Joey Cora .02 .10
124 Alex Fernandez .02 .10
125 Ozzie Guillen .07 .20
126 Craig Grebeck .02 .10
127 Roberto Hernandez .02 .10
128 Bo Jackson .20 .50
129 Lance Johnson .02 .10
130 Ron Karkovice .02 .10
131 Mike LaValliere .02 .10
132 Norberto Martin .02 .10
133 Kirk McCaskill .02 .10
134 Jack McDowell .02 .10
135 Scott Radinsky .02 .10
136 Tim Raines .07 .20
137 Steve Sax .02 .10
138 Frank Thomas .20 .50
139 Dan Pasqua .02 .10
140 Robin Ventura .07 .20
141 Jeff Branson .02 .10
142 Tom Browning .02 .10
143 Jacob Brumfield .02 .10
144 Tim Costo .02 .10
145 Rob Dibble .07 .20
146 Brian Dorsett .02 .10
147 Steve Foster .02 .10
148 Cesar Hernandez .02 .10
149 Roberto Kelly .02 .10
150 Barry Larkin .10 .30
151 Larry Luebbers .02 .10
152 Kevin Mitchell .02 .10
153 Joe Oliver .02 .10
154 Tim Pugh .02 .10
155 Jeff Reardon .07 .20
156 Jose Rijo .02 .10
157 Bip Roberts .02 .10
158 Chris Sabo .02 .10
159 Juan Samuel .02 .10
160 Reggie Sanders .07 .20
161 John Smiley .02 .10
162 Jerry Spradlin .02 .10
163 Gary Varsho .02 .10
164 Sandy Alomar Jr. .02 .10
165 Albert Belle .07 .20
166 Carlos Baerga .02 .10
167 Mark Clark .02 .10
168 Alvaro Espinoza .02 .10
169 Felix Fermin .02 .10
170 Reggie Jefferson .02 .10

171 Wayne Kirby .02 .10
172 Tom Kramer .02 .10
173 Kenny Lofton .07 .20
174 Jesse Levis .02 .10
175 Candy Maldonado .02 .10
176 Carlos Martinez .02 .10
177 Jose Mesa .02 .10
178 Jeff Mutis .02 .10
179 Charles Nagy .02 .10
180 Bob Ojeda .02 .10
181 Junior Ortiz .02 .10
182 Eric Plunk .02 .10
183 Manny Ramirez .20 .50
184 Jeff Treadway .02 .10
185 Bill Wertz .02 .10
186 Paul Sorrento .02 .10
187 Freddie Benavides .02 .10
188 Dante Bichette .07 .20
189 Willie Blair .02 .10
190 Daryl Boston .02 .10
191 Pedro Castellano .02 .10
192 Vinny Castilla .07 .20
193 Jerald Clark .02 .10
194 Alex Cole .02 .10
195 Andres Galarraga .07 .20
196 Joe Girardi .02 .10
197 Charlie Hayes .02 .10
198 Darren Holmes .02 .10
199 Chris Jones .02 .10
200 Curt Leskanic .02 .10
201 Roberto Mejia .02 .10
202 David Nied .02 .10
203 Jayhawk Owens .02 .10
204 Steve Reed .02 .10
205 Armando Reynoso .02 .10
206 Bruce Ruffin .02 .10
207 Keith Shepherd .02 .10
208 Jim Tatum .02 .10
209 Eric Young .02 .10
210 Skeeter Barnes .02 .10
211 Danny Bautista .02 .10
212 Tom Bolton .02 .10
213 Eric Davis .07 .20
214 Storm Davis .02 .10
215 Cecil Fielder .07 .20
216 Travis Fryman .07 .20
217 Kirk Gibson .07 .20
218 Dan Gladden .02 .10
219 John Doherty .02 .10
220 Chris Gomez .02 .10
221 David Haas .02 .10
222 Bill Krueger .02 .10
223 Chad Kreuter .02 .10
224 Mark Leiter .02 .10
225 Bob MacDonald .02 .10
226 Mike Moore .02 .10
227 Tony Phillips .02 .10
228 Rich Rowland .02 .10
229 Mickey Tettleton .02 .10
230 Alan Trammell .07 .20
231 Lou Whitaker .07 .20
232 David Wells .07 .20
233 Luis Aquino .02 .10
234 Alex Arias .02 .10
235 Jack Armstrong .02 .10
236 Ryan Bowen .02 .10
237 Chuck Carr .02 .10
238 Matias Carrillo .02 .10
239 Jeff Conine .07 .20
240 Henry Cotto .02 .10
241 Orestes Destrade .02 .10
242 Chris Hammond .02 .10
243 Bryan Harvey .02 .10
244 Charlie Hough .07 .20
245 Richie Lewis .02 .10
246 Mitch Lyden .02 .10
247 Dave Magadan .02 .10
248 Bob Natal .02 .10
249 Benito Santiago .07 .20
250 Gary Sheffield .07 .20
251 Matt Turner .02 .10
252 David Weathers .02 .10
253 Walt Weiss .02 .10
254 Darrell Whitmore .02 .10
255 Nigel Wilson .02 .10
256 Eric Anthony .02 .10
257 Jeff Bagwell .10 .30
258 Kevin Bass .02 .10
259 Craig Biggio .10 .30
260 Ken Caminiti .07 .20
261 Andujar Cedeno .02 .10
262 Chris Donnels .02 .10
263 Doug Drabek .02 .10
264 Tom Edens .02 .10
265 Steve Finley .07 .20
266 Luis Gonzalez .07 .20
267 Pete Harnisch .02 .10
268 Xavier Hernandez .02 .10
269 Todd Jones .02 .10
270 Darryl Kile .07 .20
271 Al Osuna .02 .10
272 Rick Parker .02 .10
273 Mark Portugal .02 .10
274 Scott Servais .02 .10
275 Greg Swindell .02 .10
276 Eddie Taubensee .02 .10
277 Jose Uribe .02 .10
278 Brian Williams .02 .10
279 Kevin Appier .07 .20
280 Billy Brewer .02 .10
281 David Cone .07 .20
282 Greg Gagne .02 .10
283 Tom Gordon .02 .10
284 Chris Gwynn .02 .10
285 John Habyan .02 .10
286 Chris Haney .02 .10
287 Phil Hiatt .02 .10
288 David Howard .02 .10
289 Felix Jose .02 .10
290 Wally Joyner .07 .20
291 Kevin Koslofski .02 .10
292 Jose Lind .02 .10
293 Brent Mayne .02 .10
294 Mike Macfarlane .02 .10
295 Brian McRae .02 .10
296 Kevin McReynolds .02 .10
297 Keith Miller .02 .10
298 Jeff Montgomery .02 .10
299 Hipolito Pichardo .02 .10
300 Rico Rossy .02 .10
301 Curtis Wilkerson .02 .10
302 Pedro Astacio .02 .10
303 Rafael Bournigal .02 .10
304 Brett Butler .07 .20
305 Tom Candiotti .02 .10
306 Omar Daal .02 .10
307 Jim Gott .02 .10
308 Kevin Gross .02 .10
309 Dave Hansen .02 .10
310 Carlos Hernandez .02 .10
311 Orel Hershiser .07 .20
312 Eric Karros .07 .20
313 Pedro Martinez .20 .50
314 Ramon Martinez .02 .10
315 Roger McDowell .02 .10
316 Raul Mondesi .07 .20
317 Jose Offerman .02 .10
318 Mike Piazza .40 1.00
319 Jody Reed .02 .10
320 Henry Rodriguez .02 .10
321 Cory Snyder .02 .10
322 Darryl Strawberry .07 .20
323 Tim Wallach .02 .10
324 Steve Wilson .02 .10
325 Juan Bell .02 .10
326 Ricky Bones .02 .10
327 Alex Diaz RC .02 .10
328 Cal Eldred .02 .10
329 Darryl Hamilton .02 .10
330 Doug Henry .02 .10
331 John Jaha .02 .10
332 Pat Listach .02 .10
333 Graeme Lloyd .02 .10
334 Carlos Maldonado .02 .10
335 Angel Miranda .02 .10
336 Jaime Navarro .02 .10
337 Dave Nilsson .02 .10
338 Rafael Novoa .02 .10
339 Troy O'Leary .02 .10
340 Jesse Orosco .02 .10
341 Kevin Seitzer .02 .10
342 Bill Spiers .02 .10
343 William Suero .02 .10
344 B.J. Surhoff .07 .20
345 Dickie Thon .02 .10
346 Jose Valentin .02 .10
347 Greg Vaughn .02 .10
348 Robin Yount .30 .75
349 Willie Banks .02 .10
350 Bernardo Brito .02 .10
351 Scott Erickson .02 .10
352 Mark Guthrie .02 .10
353 Chip Hale .02 .10
354 Brian Harper .02 .10
355 Kent Hrbek .07 .20
356 Terry Jorgensen .02 .10
357 Chuck Knoblauch .07 .20
358 Gene Larkin .02 .10
359 Scott Leius .02 .10
360 Shane Mack .02 .10
361 David McCarty .02 .10
362 Pat Meares .02 .10
363 Pedro Munoz .02 .10
364 Derek Parks .02 .10
365 Kirby Puckett .20 .50
366 Jeff Reboulet .02 .10
367 Kevin Tapani .02 .10
368 Mike Trombley .02 .10
369 George Tsamis .02 .10
370 Carl Willis .02 .10
371 Dave Winfield .07 .20
372 Moises Alou .07 .20
373 Brian Barnes .02 .10
374 Sean Berry .02 .10
375 Frank Bolick .02 .10
376 Wil Cordero .02 .10
377 Delino DeShields .02 .10
378 Jeff Fassero .02 .10
379 Darrin Fletcher .02 .10
380 Cliff Floyd .07 .20
381 Lou Frazier .02 .10
382 Marquis Grissom .07 .20
383 Gil Heredia .02 .10
384 Mike Lansing .02 .10
385 Oreste Marrero RC .02 .10
386 Dennis Martinez .07 .20
387 Curtis Pride RC .07 .20
388 Mel Rojas .02 .10
389 Kirk Rueter .02 .10
390 Joe Siddall .02 .10
391 John Vander Wal .02 .10
392 Larry Walker .07 .20
393 John Wetteland .07 .20
394 Rondell White .07 .20
395 Tim Bogar .02 .10
396 Bobby Bonilla .07 .20
397 Jeromy Burnitz .07 .20
398 Mike Draper .02 .10
399 Sid Fernandez .02 .10
400 John Franco .07 .20
401 Dave Gallagher .02 .10
402 Dwight Gooden .07 .20
403 Eric Hillman .02 .10
404 Todd Hundley .02 .10
405 Butch Huskey .02 .10
406 Jeff Innis .02 .10
407 Howard Johnson .02 .10
408 Jeff Kent .10 .30
409 Ced Landrum .02 .10
410 Mike Maddux .02 .10
411 Josias Manzanillo .02 .10
412 Jeff McKnight .02 .10
413 Eddie Murray .20 .50
414 Tito Navarro .02 .10
415 Joe Orsulak .02 .10
416 Bret Saberhagen .07 .20
417 Dave Telgheder .02 .10
418 Ryan Thompson .02 .10
419 Chico Walker .02 .10
420 Jim Abbott .10 .30
421 Wade Boggs .10 .30
422 Mike Gallego .02 .10
423 Mark Hutton .02 .10
424 Dion James .02 .10
425 Domingo Jean .02 .10
426 Pat Kelly .02 .10
427 Jimmy Key .07 .20
428 Jim Leyritz .02 .10
429 Kevin Maas .02 .10
430 Don Mattingly .50 1.25
431 Bobby Munoz .02 .10
432 Matt Nokes .02 .10
433 Paul O'Neill .10 .30
434 Spike Owen .02 .10
435 Melido Perez .02 .10
436 Lee Smith .07 .20
437 Andy Stankiewicz .02 .10
438 Mike Stanley .02 .10
439 Danny Tartabull .02 .10
440 Randy Velarde .02 .10
441 Bernie Williams .10 .30
442 Gerald Williams .02 .10
443 Mike Witt .02 .10
444 Marcos Armas .02 .10
445 Lance Blankenship .02 .10
446 Mike Bordick .02 .10
447 Ron Darling UER .02 .10
Reversed negative on front
448 Dennis Eckersley .07 .20
449 Brent Gates .02 .10
450 Rich Gossage .07 .20
451 Scott Hemond .02 .10
452 Dave Henderson .02 .10
453 Shawn Hillegas .02 .10
454 Rick Honeycutt .02 .10
455 Scott Lydy .02 .10
456 Mark McGwire .50 1.25
457 Henry Mercedes .02 .10
458 Mike Mohler .02 .10
459 Troy Neel .02 .10
460 Edwin Nunez .02 .10
461 Craig Paquette .02 .10
462 Ruben Sierra .07 .20
463 Terry Steinbach .02 .10
464 Todd Van Poppel .02 .10
465 Bob Welch .02 .10
466 Bobby Witt .02 .10
467 Ruben Amaro .02 .10
468 Larry Andersen .02 .10
469 Kim Batiste .02 .10
470 Wes Chamberlain .02 .10
471 Darren Daulton .07 .20
472 Mariano Duncan .02 .10
473 Len Dykstra .07 .20
474 Jim Eisenreich .02 .10
475 Tommy Greene .02 .10
476 Dave Hollins .02 .10
477 Pete Incaviglia .02 .10
478 Danny Jackson .02 .10
479 John Kruk .07 .20
480 Tony Longmire .02 .10
481 Jeff Manto .02 .10
482 Mickey Morandini .02 .10
483 Terry Mulholland .02 .10
484 Todd Pratt .02 .10
485 Ben Rivera .02 .10
486 Curt Schilling .07 .20
487 Kevin Stocker .02 .10
488 Milt Thompson .02 .10
489 David West .02 .10
490 Mitch Williams .02 .10
491 Jeff Ballard .02 .10
492 Jay Bell .07 .20
493 Scott Bullett .02 .10
494 Dave Clark .02 .10
495 Steve Cooke .02 .10
496 Midre Cummings .02 .10
497 Mark Dewey .02 .10
498 Carlos Garcia .02 .10
499 Jeff King .02 .10
500 Al Martin .02 .10
501 Lloyd McClendon .02 .10
502 Orlando Merced .02 .10
503 Blas Minor .02 .10
504 Denny Neagle .07 .20
505 Tom Prince .02 .10
506 Don Slaught .02 .10
507 Zane Smith .02 .10
508 Randy Tomlin .02 .10
509 Andy Van Slyke .10 .30
510 Paul Wagner .02 .10
511 Tim Wakefield .10 .30
512 Bob Walk .02 .10
513 John Wehner .02 .10
514 Kevin Young .02 .10
515 Billy Bean .02 .10
516 Andy Benes .02 .10
517 Derek Bell .02 .10
518 Doug Brocail .02 .10
519 Jarvis Brown .02 .10
520 Phil Clark .02 .10
521 Mark Davis .02 .10
522 Jeff Gardner .02 .10
523 Pat Gomez .02 .10
524 Ricky Gutierrez .02 .10
525 Tony Gwynn .25 .60
526 Gene Harris .02 .10
527 Kevin Higgins .02 .10
528 Trevor Hoffman .10 .30
529 Luis Lopez .02 .10
530 Pedro A.Martinez RC .02 .10
531 Melvin Nieves .02 .10
532 Phil Plantier .02 .10
533 Frank Seminara .02 .10
534 Craig Shipley .02 .10
535 Tim Teufel .02 .10
536 Guillermo Velasquez .02 .10
537 Wally Whitehurst .02 .10
538 Rod Beck .02 .10
539 Todd Benzinger .02 .10
540 Barry Bonds .60 1.50
541 Jeff Brantley .02 .10
542 Dave Burba .02 .10
543 John Burkett .02 .10
544 Will Clark .10 .30
545 Royce Clayton .02 .10
546 Bryan Hickerson .02 .10
547 Mike Jackson .02 .10
548 Darren Lewis .02 .10
549 Kirt Manwaring .02 .10
550 Dave Martinez .02 .10
551 Willie McGee .07 .20
552 Jeff Reed .02 .10
553 Dave Righetti .07 .20
554 Kevin Rogers .02 .10
555 Steve Scarsone .02 .10
556 Bill Swift .02 .10
557 Robby Thompson .02 .10
558 Salomon Torres .02 .10
559 Matt Williams .07 .20
560 Trevor Wilson .02 .10
561 Rich Amaral .02 .10
562 Mike Blowers .02 .10
563 Chris Bosio .02 .10
564 Jay Buhner .07 .20
565 Norm Charlton .02 .10
566 Jim Converse .02 .10
567 Rich DeLucia .02 .10
568 Mike Felder .02 .10
569 Dave Fleming .02 .10
570 Ken Griffey Jr. .30 .75
571 Bill Haselman .02 .10
572 Dwayne Henry .02 .10
573 Brad Holman .02 .10
574 Randy Johnson .20 .50
575 Greg Litton .02 .10
576 Edgar Martinez .10 .30
577 Tino Martinez .10 .30
578 Jeff Nelson .02 .10
579 Marc Newfield .02 .10
580 Roger Salkeld .02 .10
581 Mackey Sasser .02 .10
582 Brian Turang RC .02 .10
583 Omar Vizquel .10 .30
584 Dave Valle .02 .10
585 Luis Alicea .02 .10
586 Rene Arocha .02 .10
587 Rheal Cormier .02 .10
588 Tripp Cromer .02 .10
589 Bernard Gilkey .02 .10
590 Lee Guetterman .02 .10
591 Gregg Jefferies .02 .10
592 Tim Jones .02 .10
593 Paul Kilgus .02 .10
594 Les Lancaster .02 .10
595 Omar Olivares .02 .10
596 Jose Oquendo .02 .10
597 Donovan Osborne .02 .10
598 Tom Pagnozzi .02 .10
599 Erik Pappas .02 .10
600 Geronimo Pena .02 .10
601 Mike Perez .02 .10
602 Gerald Perry .02 .10
603 Stan Royer .02 .10
604 Ozzie Smith .30 .75
605 Bob Tewksbury .02 .10
606 Allen Watson .02 .10
607 Mark Whiten .02 .10
608 Todd Zeile .02 .10
609 Jeff Bronkey .02 .10
610 Kevin Brown .07 .20
611 Jose Canseco .10 .30
612 Doug Dascenzo .02 .10
613 Butch Davis .02 .10
614 Mario Diaz .02 .10
615 Julio Franco .07 .20
616 Benji Gil .02 .10
617 Juan Gonzalez .07 .20
618 Tom Henke .02 .10
619 Jeff Huson .02 .10
620 David Hulse .02 .10
621 Craig Lefferts .02 .10
622 Rafael Palmeiro .10 .30
623 Dean Palmer .07 .20
624 Bob Patterson .02 .10
625 Roger Pavlik .02 .10
626 Gary Redus .02 .10
627 Ivan Rodriguez .10 .30
628 Kenny Rogers .07 .20
629 Jon Shave .02 .10
630 Doug Strange .02 .10
631 Matt Whiteside .02 .10
632 Roberto Alomar .10 .30
633 Pat Borders .02 .10
634 Scott Brow .02 .10
635 Rob Butler .02 .10
636 Joe Carter .07 .20
637 Tony Castillo .02 .10
638 Mark Eichhorn .02 .10
639 Tony Fernandez .02 .10
640 Huck Flener RC .02 .10
641 Alfredo Griffin .02 .10
642 Juan Guzman .02 .10
643 Rickey Henderson .20 .50
644 Pat Hentgen .02 .10
645 Randy Knorr .02 .10
646 Al Leiter .07 .20
647 Domingo Martinez .02 .10
648 Paul Molitor .07 .20
649 Jack Morris .07 .20
650 John Olerud .07 .20
651 Ed Sprague .02 .10
652 Dave Stewart .07 .20
653 Devon White .07 .20
654 Woody Williams .07 .20
655 Barry Bonds MVP .30 .75
656 Greg Maddux CY .20 .50
657 Jack McDowell CY .02 .10
658 Mike Piazza ROY .20 .50
659 Tim Salmon ROY .07 .20
660 Frank Thomas MVP .10 .30

1995 Pacific

This 450-card standard-size set was issued in one series. The full-bleed fronts have action photos; the "Pacific Collection" logo is on the upper left and the player's name is at the bottom. The horizontal backs have a player photo on the left with 1994 stats and some career highlights on the right. The career highlights are in both English and Spanish. The cards are numbered in the lower right corner. The cards are grouped alphabetically within teams and checklisted below alphabetically according to teams for each league. There are no key Rookie Cards in this set.

COMPLETE SET (450) 20.00 50.00
1 Steve Avery .02 .10
2 Rafael Belliard .02 .10
3 Jeff Blauser .02 .10
4 Tom Glavine .10 .30
5 David Justice .07 .20
6 Mike Kelly .02 .10
7 Roberto Kelly .02 .10
8 Ryan Klesko .07 .20
9 Mark Lemke .02 .10
10 Javier Lopez .07 .20
11 Greg Maddux .30 .75
12 Fred McGriff .10 .30
13 Greg McMichael .02 .10
14 Jose Oliva .02 .10
15 John Smoltz .10 .30
16 Tony Tarasco .02 .10
17 Brady Anderson .07 .20
18 Harold Baines .07 .20
19 Armando Benitez .02 .10
20 Mike Devereaux .02 .10
21 Leo Gomez .02 .10
22 Jeffrey Hammonds .02 .10
23 Chris Hoiles .02 .10
24 Ben McDonald .02 .10
25 Mark McLemore .02 .10
26 Jamie Moyer .07 .20
27 Mike Mussina .10 .30
28 Rafael Palmeiro .10 .30
29 Jim Poole .02 .10
30 Cal Ripken Jr. .60 1.50
31 Lee Smith .07 .20
32 Mark Smith .02 .10
33 Jose Canseco .10 .30
34 Roger Clemens .40 1.00
35 Scott Cooper .02 .10
36 Andre Dawson .07 .20
37 Tony Fossas .02 .10
38 Mike Greenwell .02 .10
39 Chris Howard .02 .10
40 Jose Melendez .02 .10
41 Nate Minchey .02 .10
42 Tim Naehring .02 .10
43 Otis Nixon .02 .10
44 Carlos Rodriguez .02 .10
45 Aaron Sele .02 .10
46 Lee Tinsley .02 .10
47 Sergio Valdez .02 .10
48 John Valentin .02 .10
49 Mo Vaughn .07 .20
50 Brian Anderson .02 .10
51 Garret Anderson .07 .20
52 Rod Correia .02 .10
53 Chad Curtis .02 .10
54 Mark Dalesandro .02 .10
55 Chili Davis .07 .20
56 Gary DiSarcina .02 .10
57 Damion Easley .02 .10
58 Jim Edmonds .10 .30
59 Jorge Fabregas .02 .10
60 Chuck Finley .07 .20
61 Bo Jackson .20 .50
62 Mark Langston .02 .10
63 Eduardo Perez .02 .10
64 Tim Salmon .10 .30
65 J.T. Snow .07 .20
66 Willie Banks .02 .10
67 Jose Bautista .02 .10
68 Shawon Dunston .02 .10
69 Kevin Foster .02 .10
70 Mark Grace .10 .30
71 Jose Guzman .02 .10
72 Jose Hernandez .02 .10
73 Blaise Ilsley .02 .10
74 Derrick May .02 .10
75 Randy Myers .02 .10
76 Karl Rhodes .02 .10
77 Kevin Roberson .02 .10
78 Rey Sanchez .02 .10
79 Sammy Sosa .20 .50
80 Steve Trachsel .02 .10
81 Eddie Zambrano .02 .10
82 Wilson Alvarez .02 .10
83 Jason Bere .02 .10
84 Joey Cora .02 .10
85 Jose DeLeon .02 .10
86 Alex Fernandez .02 .10
87 Julio Franco .07 .20
88 Ozzie Guillen .07 .20
89 Joe Hall .02 .10
90 Roberto Hernandez .02 .10
91 Darrin Jackson .02 .10
92 Lance Johnson .02 .10
93 Norberto Martin .02 .10
94 Jack McDowell .02 .10
95 Tim Raines .07 .20
96 Olmedo Saenz .02 .10
97 Frank Thomas .20 .50
98 Robin Ventura .07 .20
99 Bret Boone .07 .20
100 Jeff Brantley .02 .10
101 Jacob Brumfield .02 .10
102 Hector Carrasco .02 .10
103 Brian Dorsett .02 .10
104 Tony Fernandez .02 .10
105 Willie Greene .02 .10
106 Erik Hanson .02 .10
107 Kevin Jarvis .02 .10
108 Barry Larkin .10 .30
109 Kevin Mitchell .02 .10
110 Hal Morris .02 .10
111 Jose Rijo .02 .10
112 Johnny Ruffin .02 .10
113 Deion Sanders .10 .30
114 Reggie Sanders .07 .20
115 Sandy Alomar Jr. .02 .10
116 Ruben Amaro .02 .10
117 Carlos Baerga .02 .10
118 Albert Belle .07 .20
119 Alvaro Espinoza .02 .10
120 Rene Gonzales .02 .10
121 Wayne Kirby .02 .10
122 Kenny Lofton .07 .20
123 Candy Maldonado .02 .10
124 Dennis Martinez .07 .20
125 Eddie Murray .20 .50
126 Charles Nagy .02 .10
127 Tony Pena .02 .10
128 Manny Ramirez .10 .30
129 Paul Sorrento .02 .10
130 Jim Thome .10 .30
131 Omar Vizquel .10 .30
132 Dante Bichette .07 .20
133 Ellis Burks .07 .20
134 Vinny Castilla .07 .20
135 Marvin Freeman .02 .10
136 Andres Galarraga .07 .20
137 Joe Girardi .02 .10
138 Charlie Hayes .02 .10
139 Mike Kingery .02 .10
140 Nelson Liriano .02 .10
141 Roberto Mejia .02 .10
142 David Nied .02 .10
143 Steve Reed .02 .10
144 Armando Reynoso .02 .10
145 Bruce Ruffin .02 .10
146 John Vander Wal .02 .10
147 Walt Weiss .02 .10
148 Skeeter Barnes .02 .10
149 Tim Belcher .02 .10
150 Junior Felix .02 .10
151 Cecil Fielder .07 .20
152 Travis Fryman .07 .20
153 Kirk Gibson .07 .20
154 Chris Gomez .02 .10
155 Buddy Groom .02 .10
156 Chad Kreuter .02 .10
157 Mike Moore .02 .10
158 Tony Phillips .02 .10
159 Juan Samuel .02 .10
160 Mickey Tettleton .02 .10
161 Alan Trammell .07 .20
162 David Wells .07 .20
163 Lou Whitaker .07 .20
164 Kurt Abbott .02 .10
165 Luis Aquino .02 .10
166 Alex Arias .02 .10
167 Bret Barberie .02 .10
168 Jerry Browne .02 .10
169 Chuck Carr .02 .10
170 Matias Carrillo .02 .10
171 Greg Colbrunn .02 .10
172 Jeff Conine .07 .20
173 Carl Everett .07 .20
174 Robb Nen .07 .20
175 Yorkis Perez .02 .10
176 Pat Rapp .02 .10
177 Benito Santiago .07 .20
178 Gary Sheffield .07 .20
179 Darrell Whitmore .02 .10
180 Jeff Bagwell .10 .30
181 Kevin Bass .02 .10
182 Craig Biggio .10 .30
183 Andujar Cedeno .02 .10
184 Doug Drabek .02 .10
185 Tony Eusebio .02 .10
186 Steve Finley .07 .20
187 Luis Gonzalez .07 .20
188 Pete Harnisch .02 .10
189 John Hudek .02 .10
190 Orlando Miller .02 .10
191 James Mouton .02 .10
192 Roberto Petagine .02 .10
193 Shane Reynolds .02 .10
194 Greg Swindell .02 .10
195 Dave Veres .02 .10
196 Kevin Appier .07 .20
197 Stan Belinda .02 .10
198 Vince Coleman .02 .10
199 David Cone .07 .20
200 Gary Gaetti .07 .20
201 Greg Gagne .02 .10
202 Mark Gubicza .02 .10
203 Bob Hamelin .02 .10
204 Dave Henderson .02 .10
205 Felix Jose .02 .10
206 Wally Joyner .07 .20
207 Jose Lind .02 .10
208 Mike Macfarlane .02 .10
209 Brian McRae .02 .10
210 Jeff Montgomery .02 .10
211 Hipolito Pichardo .02 .10
212 Pedro Astacio .02 .10
213 Brett Butler .07 .20
214 Omar Daal .02 .10
215 Delino DeShields .02 .10
216 Darren Dreifort .02 .10
217 Carlos Hernandez .02 .10
218 Orel Hershiser .07 .20
219 Garey Ingram .02 .10
220 Eric Karros .07 .20
221 Ramon Martinez .02 .10
222 Raul Mondesi .07 .20
223 Jose Offerman .02 .10
224 Mike Piazza .30 .75
225 Henry Rodriguez .02 .10
226 Ismael Valdes .07 .20
227 Tim Wallach .02 .10
228 Jeff Cirillo .02 .10
229 Alex Diaz .02 .10
230 Cal Eldred .02 .10
231 Mike Fetters .02 .10
232 Brian Harper .02 .10
233 Ted Higuera .02 .10
234 John Jaha .02 .10
235 Graeme Lloyd .02 .10
236 Jose Mercedes .02 .10
237 Jaime Navarro .02 .10
238 Dave Nilsson .02 .10
239 Jesse Orosco .02 .10
240 Jody Reed .02 .10
241 Jose Valentin .02 .10
242 Greg Vaughn .02 .10
243 Turner Ward .02 .10
244 Rick Aguilera .02 .10
245 Rich Becker .02 .10
246 Jim Deshaies .02 .10
247 Steve Dunn .02 .10
248 Scott Erickson .02 .10
249 Kent Hrbek .07 .20
250 Chuck Knoblauch .07 .20
251 Scott Leius .02 .10
252 David McCarty .02 .10
253 Pat Meares .02 .10
254 Pedro Munoz .02 .10
255 Kirby Puckett .20 .50
256 Carlos Pulido .02 .10
257 Kevin Tapani .02 .10
258 Matt Walbeck .02 .10
259 Dave Winfield .07 .20
260 Moises Alou .07 .20
261 Juan Bell .02 .10
262 Freddie Benavides .02 .10
263 Sean Berry .02 .10
264 Wil Cordero .02 .10
265 Jeff Fassero .02 .10
266 Darrin Fletcher .02 .10

267 Cliff Floyd .07 .20
268 Marquis Grissom .07 .20
269 Gil Heredia .02 .10
270 Ken Hill .02 .10
271 Pedro Martinez .10 .30
272 Mel Rojas .02 .10
273 Larry Walker .07 .20
274 John Wetteland .07 .20
275 Rondell White .07 .20
276 Tim Bogar .02 .10
277 Bobby Bonilla .07 .20
278 Rico Brogna .02 .10
279 Jeromy Burnitz .07 .20
280 John Franco .07 .20
281 Eric Hillman .02 .10
282 Todd Hundley .02 .10
283 Jeff Kent .07 .20
284 Mike Maddux .02 .10
285 Joe Orsulak .02 .10
286 Luis Rivera .02 .10
287 Bret Saberhagen .07 .20
288 David Segui .02 .10
289 Ryan Thompson .02 .10
290 Fernando Vina .02 .10
291 Jose Vizcaino .02 .10
292 Jim Abbott .10 .30
293 Wade Boggs .10 .30
294 Russ Davis .02 .10
295 Mike Gallego .02 .10
296 Xavier Hernandez .02 .10
297 Steve Howe .02 .10
298 Jimmy Key .07 .20
299 Don Mattingly .50 1.25
300 Terry Mulholland .02 .10
301 Paul O'Neill .10 .30
302 Luis Polonia .02 .10
303 Mike Stanley .02 .10
304 Danny Tartabull .02 .10
305 Randy Velarde .02 .10
306 Bob Wickman .02 .10
307 Bernie Williams .10 .30
308 Mark Acre .02 .10
309 Geronimo Berroa .02 .10
310 Mike Bordick .02 .10
311 Dennis Eckersley .07 .20
312 Rickey Henderson .20 .50
313 Stan Javier .02 .10
314 Miguel Jimenez .02 .10
315 Francisco Matos RC .02 .10
316 Mark McGwire .50 1.25
317 Troy Neel .02 .10
318 Steve Ontiveros .02 .10
319 Carlos Reyes .02 .10
320 Ruben Sierra .07 .20
321 Terry Steinbach .02 .10
322 Bob Welch .02 .10
323 Bobby Witt .02 .10
324 Larry Andersen .02 .10
325 Kim Batiste .02 .10
326 Darren Daulton .07 .20
327 Mariano Duncan .02 .10
328 Lenny Dykstra .07 .20
329 Jim Eisenreich .02 .10
330 Danny Jackson .02 .10
331 John Kruk .07 .20
332 Tony Longmire .02 .10
333 Tom Marsh .02 .10
334 Mickey Morandini .02 .10
335 Bobby Munoz .02 .10
336 Todd Pratt .02 .10
337 Tom Quinlan .02 .10
338 Kevin Stocker .02 .10
339 Fernando Valenzuela .07 .20
340 Jay Bell .07 .20
341 Dave Clark .02 .10
342 Steve Cooke .02 .10
343 Carlos Garcia .02 .10
344 Jeff King .02 .10
345 Jon Lieber .02 .10
346 Ravelo Manzanillo .02 .10
347 Al Martin .02 .10
348 Orlando Merced .02 .10
349 Denny Neagle .07 .20
350 Alejandro Pena .02 .10
351 Don Slaught .02 .10
352 Zane Smith .02 .10
353 Andy Van Slyke .10 .30
354 Rick White .02 .10
355 Kevin Young .02 .10
356 Andy Ashby .02 .10
357 Derek Bell .02 .10
358 Andy Benes .02 .10
359 Phil Clark .02 .10
360 Donnie Elliott .02 .10
361 Ricky Gutierrez .02 .10
362 Tony Gwynn .25 .60
363 Trevor Hoffman .07 .20
364 Tim Hyers .02 .10
365 Luis Lopez .02 .10
366 Jose Martinez .02 .10
367 Pedro A. Martinez .02 .10
368 Phil Plantier .02 .10
369 Bip Roberts .02 .10
370 A.J. Sager .02 .10
371 Jeff Tabaka .02 .10
372 Todd Benzinger .02 .10
373 Barry Bonds .40 1.00
374 John Burkett .02 .10
375 Mark Carreon .02 .10
376 Royce Clayton .02 .10
377 Pat Gomez .02 .10
378 Erik Johnson .02 .10
379 Darren Lewis .02 .10
380 Kirt Manwaring .02 .10
381 Dave Martinez .02 .10
382 John Patterson .02 .10
383 Mark Portugal .02 .10
384 Darryl Strawberry .07 .20
385 Salomon Torres .02 .10
386 W. VanLandingham .02 .10
387 Matt Williams .07 .20
388 Rich Amaral .02 .10
389 Bobby Ayala .02 .10
390 Mike Blowers .02 .10
391 Chris Bosio .02 .10
392 Jay Buhner .07 .20
393 Jim Converse .02 .10
394 Tim Davis .02 .10
395 Felix Fermin .02 .10
396 Dave Fleming .02 .10
397 Goose Gossage .07 .20
398 Ken Griffey Jr. .30 .75
399 Randy Johnson .20 .50
400 Edgar Martinez .10 .30
401 Tino Martinez .10 .30
402 Alex Rodriguez .50 1.25
403 Dan Wilson .02 .10
404 Luis Alicea .02 .10
405 Rene Arocha .02 .10
406 Bernard Gilkey .02 .10
407 Gregg Jefferies .02 .10
408 Ray Lankford .07 .20
409 Terry McGriff .02 .10
410 Omar Olivares .02 .10
411 Jose Oquendo .02 .10
412 Vicente Palacios .02 .10
413 Geronimo Pena .02 .10
414 Mike Perez .02 .10
415 Gerald Perry .02 .10
416 Ozzie Smith .30 .75
417 Bob Tewksbury .02 .10
418 Mark Whiten .02 .10
419 Todd Zeile .02 .10
420 Esteban Beltre .02 .10
421 Kevin Brown .07 .20
422 Cris Carpenter .02 .10
423 Will Clark .10 .30
424 Hector Fajardo .02 .10
425 Jeff Frye .02 .10
426 Juan Gonzalez .07 .20
427 Rusty Greer .07 .20
428 Rick Honeycutt .02 .10
429 David Hulse .02 .10
430 Manny Lee .02 .10
431 Junior Ortiz .02 .10
432 Dean Palmer .07 .20
433 Ivan Rodriguez .10 .30
434 Dan Smith .02 .10
435 Roberto Alomar .10 .30
436 Pat Borders .02 .10
437 Scott Brow .02 .10
438 Rob Butler .02 .10
439 Joe Carter .07 .20
440 Tony Castillo .02 .10
441 Domingo Cedeno .02 .10
442 Brad Cornett .02 .10
443 Carlos Delgado .07 .20
444 Alex Gonzalez .02 .10
445 Juan Guzman .02 .10
446 Darren Hall .02 .10
447 Paul Molitor .07 .20
448 John Olerud .07 .20
449 Robert Perez .02 .10
450 Devon White .07 .20

1996 Pacific

This 450-card set was issued in 12-card packs. The fronts feature borderless color action player photos with double-etched gold foil printing. The horizontal backs carry a color player portrait with player information in both English and Spanish and 1995 season player statistics.

COMPLETE SET (450) 20.00 40.00
1 Steve Avery .07 .20
2 Ryan Klesko .07 .20
3 Pedro Borbon .07 .20
4 Chipper Jones .20 .50
5 Kent Mercker .07 .20
6 Greg Maddux .30 .75
7 Greg McMichael .07 .20
8 Mark Wohlers .07 .20
9 Fred McGriff .10 .30
10 John Smoltz .10 .30
11 Rafael Belliard .07 .20
12 Mark Lemke .07 .20
13 Tom Glavine .10 .30
14 Javier Lopez .07 .20
15 Jeff Blauser .07 .20
16 David Justice .07 .20
17 Marquis Grissom .07 .20
18 Greg Maddux CY .20 .50
19 Randy Myers .07 .20
20 Scott Servais .07 .20
21 Sammy Sosa .20 .50
22 Kevin Foster .07 .20
23 Jose Hernandez .07 .20
24 Jim Bullinger .07 .20
25 Mike Perez .07 .20
26 Shawon Dunston .07 .20
27 Rey Sanchez .07 .20
28 Frank Castillo .07 .20
29 Jaime Navarro .07 .20
30 Brian McRae .07 .20
31 Mark Grace .10 .30
32 Roberto Rivera .07 .20
33 Luis Gonzalez .07 .20
34 Hector Carrasco .07 .20
35 Bret Boone .07 .20
36 Thomas Howard .07 .20
37 Hal Morris .07 .20
38 John Smiley .07 .20
39 Jeff Brantley .07 .20
40 Barry Larkin .10 .30
41 Mariano Duncan .07 .20
42 Xavier Hernandez .07 .20
43 Pete Schourek .07 .20
44 Reggie Sanders .07 .20
45 Dave Burba .07 .20
46 Jeff Branson .07 .20
47 Mark Portugal .07 .20
48 Ron Gant .07 .20
49 Benito Santiago .07 .20
50 Barry Larkin MVP .07 .20
51 Steve Reed .07 .20
52 Kevin Ritz .07 .20
53 Dante Bichette .07 .20
54 Darren Holmes .07 .20
55 Ellis Burks .07 .20
56 Walt Weiss .07 .20
57 Armando Reynoso .07 .20
58 Vinny Castilla .07 .20
59 Jason Bates .07 .20
60 Mike Kingery .07 .20
61 Bryan Rekar .07 .20
62 Curtis Leskanic .07 .20
63 Bret Saberhagen .07 .20
64 Andres Galarraga .07 .20
65 Larry Walker .07 .20
66 Joe Girardi .07 .20
67 Quilvio Veras .07 .20
68 Robb Nen .07 .20
69 Mario Diaz .07 .20
70 Chuck Carr .07 .20
71 Alex Arias .07 .20
72 Pat Rapp .07 .20
73 Rich Garces .07 .20
74 Kurt Abbott .07 .20
75 Andre Dawson .07 .20
76 Greg Colbrunn .07 .20
77 John Burkett .07 .20
78 Terry Pendleton .07 .20
79 Jesus Tavarez .07 .20
80 Charles Johnson .07 .20
81 Yorkis Perez .07 .20
82 Jeff Conine .07 .20
83 Gary Sheffield .07 .20
84 Brian L. Hunter .07 .20
85 Derrick May .07 .20
86 Greg Swindell .07 .20
87 Derek Bell .07 .20
88 Dave Veres .07 .20
89 Jeff Bagwell .10 .30
90 Todd Jones .07 .20
91 Orlando Miller .07 .20
92 Pedro A. Martinez .07 .20
93 Tony Eusebio .07 .20
94 Craig Biggio .10 .30
95 Shane Reynolds .07 .20
96 James Mouton .07 .20
97 Doug Drabek .07 .20
98 Dave Magadan .07 .20
99 Ricky Gutierrez .07 .20
100 Hideo Nomo .20 .50
101 Delino DeShields .07 .20
102 Tom Candiotti .07 .20
103 Mike Piazza .30 .75
104 Ramon Martinez .07 .20
105 Pedro Astacio .07 .20
106 Chad Fonville .07 .20
107 Raul Mondesi .07 .20
108 Ismael Valdes .07 .20
109 Jose Offerman .07 .20
110 Todd Worrell .07 .20
111 Eric Karros .07 .20
112 Brett Butler .07 .20
113 Juan Castro .07 .20
114 Roberto Kelly .07 .20
115 Omar Daal .07 .20
116 Antonio Osuna .07 .20
117 Hideo Nomo ROY .10 .30
118 Mike Lansing .07 .20
119 Mel Rojas .07 .20
120 Sean Berry .07 .20
121 David Segui .07 .20
122 Tavo Alvarez .07 .20
123 Pedro J.Martinez .10 .30
124 F.P. Santangelo .07 .20
125 Rondell White .07 .20
126 Cliff Floyd .07 .20
127 Henry Rodriguez .07 .20
128 Tony Tarasco .07 .20
129 Yamil Benitez .07 .20
130 Carlos Perez .07 .20
131 Wil Cordero .07 .20
132 Jeff Fassero .07 .20
133 Moises Alou .07 .20
134 John Franco .07 .20
135 Rico Brogna .07 .20
136 Dave Mlicki .07 .20
137 Bill Pulsipher .07 .20
138 Jose Vizcaino .07 .20
139 Carl Everett .07 .20
140 Edgardo Alfonzo .07 .20
141 Bobby Jones .07 .20
142 Alberto Castillo .07 .20
143 Joe Orsulak .07 .20
144 Jeff Kent .07 .20
145 Ryan Thompson .07 .20
146 Jason Isringhausen .07 .20
147 Todd Hundley .07 .20
148 Alex Ochoa .07 .20
149 Charlie Hayes .07 .20
150 Michael Mimbs .07 .20
151 Darren Daulton .07 .20
152 Toby Borland .07 .20
153 Andy Van Slyke .10 .30
154 Mickey Morandini .07 .20
155 Sid Fernandez .07 .20
156 Tom Marsh .07 .20
157 Kevin Stocker .07 .20
158 Paul Quantrill .07 .20
159 Gregg Jefferies .07 .20
160 Ricky Bottalico .07 .20
161 Lenny Dykstra .07 .20
162 Mark Whiten .07 .20
163 Tyler Green .07 .20
164 Jim Eisenreich .07 .20
165 Heathcliff Slocumb .07 .20
166 Esteban Loaiza .07 .20
167 Rich Aude .07 .20
168 Jason Christiansen .07 .20
169 Ramon Morel .07 .20
170 Orlando Merced .07 .20
171 Paul Wagner .07 .20
172 Jeff King .07 .20
173 Jay Bell .07 .20
174 Jacob Brumfield .07 .20
175 Nelson Liriano .07 .20
176 Dan Miceli .07 .20
177 Carlos Garcia .07 .20
178 Denny Neagle .07 .20
179 Angelo Encarnacion .07 .20
180 Al Martin .07 .20
181 Midre Cummings .07 .20
182 Eddie Williams .07 .20
183 Roberto Petagine .07 .20
184 Tony Gwynn .25 .60
185 Andy Ashby .07 .20
186 Melvin Nieves .07 .20
187 Phil Clark .07 .20
188 Brad Ausmus .07 .20
189 Bip Roberts .07 .20
190 Fernando Valenzuela .07 .20
191 Marc Newfield .07 .20
192 Steve Finley .07 .20
193 Trevor Hoffman .07 .20
194 Andujar Cedeno .07 .20
195 Jody Reed .07 .20
196 Ken Caminiti .07 .20
197 Joey Hamilton .07 .20
198 Tony Gwynn BAC .10 .30
199 Shawn Barton .07 .20
200 Deion Sanders .10 .30
201 Rikkert Faneyte .07 .20
202 Barry Bonds .60 1.50
203 Matt Williams .07 .20
204 Jose Bautista .07 .20
205 Mark Leiter .07 .20
206 Mark Carreon .07 .20
207 Robby Thompson .07 .20
208 Terry Mulholland .07 .20
209 Rod Beck .07 .20
210 Royce Clayton .07 .20
211 J.R. Phillips .07 .20
212 Kirt Manwaring .07 .20
213 Glenallen Hill .07 .20
214 W.VanLandingham .07 .20
215 Scott Cooper .07 .20
216 Bernard Gilkey .07 .20
217 Allen Watson .07 .20
218 Donovan Osborne .07 .20
219 Ray Lankford .07 .20
220 Tony Fossas .07 .20
221 Tom Pagnozzi .07 .20
222 John Mabry .07 .20
223 Tripp Cromer .07 .20
224 Mark Petkovsek .07 .20
225 Mike Morgan .07 .20
226 Ozzie Smith .30 .75
227 Tom Henke .07 .20
228 Jose Oquendo .07 .20
229 Brian Jordan .07 .20
230 Cal Ripken .60 1.50
231 Scott Erickson .07 .20
232 Harold Baines .07 .20
233 Jeff Manto .07 .20
234 Jesse Orosco .07 .20
235 Jeffrey Hammonds .07 .20
236 Brady Anderson .07 .20
237 Manny Alexander .07 .20
238 Chris Hoiles .07 .20
239 Rafael Palmeiro .10 .30
240 Ben McDonald .07 .20
241 Curtis Goodwin .07 .20
242 Bobby Bonilla .07 .20
243 Mike Mussina .10 .30
244 Kevin Brown .07 .20
245 Armando Benitez .07 .20
246 Jose Canseco .10 .30
247 Erik Hanson .07 .20
248 Mo Vaughn .07 .20
249 Tim Naehring .07 .20
250 Vaughn Eshelman .07 .20
251 Mike Greenwell .07 .20
252 Troy O'Leary .07 .20
253 Tim Wakefield .07 .20
254 Dwayne Hosey .07 .20
255 John Valentin .07 .20
256 Rick Aguilera .07 .20
257 Mike Macfarlane .07 .20
258 Roger Clemens .40 1.00
259 Luis Alicea .07 .20
260 Mo Vaughn MVP .07 .20
261 Mark Langston .07 .20
262 Jim Edmonds .07 .20
263 Rod Correia .07 .20
264 Tim Salmon .10 .30
265 J.T. Snow .07 .20
266 Orlando Palmeiro .07 .20
267 Jorge Fabregas .07 .20
268 Jim Abbott .10 .30
269 Eduardo Perez .07 .20
270 Lee Smith .07 .20
271 Gary DiSarcina .07 .20
272 Damion Easley .07 .20
273 Tony Phillips .07 .20
274 Garret Anderson .07 .20
275 Chuck Finley .07 .20
276 Chili Davis .07 .20
277 Lance Johnson .07 .20
278 Alex Fernandez .07 .20
279 Robin Ventura .07 .20
280 Chris Snopek .07 .20
281 Brian Keyser .07 .20
282 Lyle Mouton .07 .20
283 Luis Andujar .07 .20
284 Tim Raines .07 .20
285 Larry Thomas .07 .20
286 Ozzie Guillen .07 .20
287 Frank Thomas .20 .50
288 Roberto Hernandez .07 .20
289 Dave Martinez .07 .20
290 Ray Durham .07 .20
291 Ron Karkovice .07 .20
292 Wilson Alvarez .07 .20
293 Omar Vizquel .10 .30
294 Eddie Murray .20 .50
295 Sandy Alomar Jr. .07 .20
296 Orel Hershiser .07 .20
297 Jose Mesa .07 .20
298 Julian Tavarez .07 .20
299 Dennis Martinez .07 .20
300 Carlos Baerga .07 .20
301 Manny Ramirez .10 .30
302 Jim Thome .10 .30
303 Kenny Lofton .07 .20
304 Tony Pena .07 .20
305 Alvaro Espinoza .07 .20
306 Paul Sorrento .07 .20
307 Albert Belle .07 .20
308 Danny Bautista .07 .20
309 Chris Gomez .07 .20
310 Jose Lima .07 .20
311 Phil Nevin .07 .20
312 Alan Trammell .07 .20
313 Chad Curtis .07 .20
314 John Flaherty .07 .20
315 Travis Fryman .07 .20
316 Todd Steverson .07 .20
317 Brian Bohanon .07 .20
318 Lou Whitaker .07 .20
319 Bobby Higginson .07 .20
320 Steve Rodriguez .07 .20
321 Cecil Fielder .07 .20
322 Felipe Lira .07 .20
323 Juan Samuel .07 .20
324 Bob Hamelin .07 .20
325 Tom Goodwin .07 .20
326 Johnny Damon .10 .30
327 Hipolito Pichardo .07 .20
328 Dilson Torres .07 .20
329 Kevin Appier .07 .20
330 Mark Gubicza .07 .20
331 Jon Nunnally .07 .20
332 Gary Gaetti .07 .20
333 Brent Mayne .07 .20
334 Brent Cookson .07 .20
335 Tom Gordon .07 .20
336 Wally Joyner .07 .20
337 Greg Gagne .07 .20
338 Fernando Vina .07 .20
339 Joe Oliver .07 .20
340 John Jaha .07 .20
341 Jeff Cirillo .07 .20
342 Pat Listach .07 .20
343 Dave Nilsson .07 .20
344 Steve Sparks .07 .20
345 Ricky Bones .07 .20
346 David Hulse .07 .20
347 Scott Karl .07 .20
348 Darryl Hamilton .07 .20
349 B.J. Surhoff .07 .20
350 Angel Miranda .07 .20
351 Sid Roberson .07 .20
352 Matt Mieske .07 .20
353 Jose Valentin .07 .20
354 Matt Lawton RC .15 .40
355 Eddie Guardado .07 .20
356 Brad Radke .07 .20
357 Pedro Munoz .07 .20
358 Scott Stahoviak .07 .20
359 Erik Schullstrom .07 .20
360 Pat Meares .07 .20
361 Marty Cordova .07 .20
362 Scott Leius .07 .20
363 Matt Walbeck .07 .20
364 Rich Becker .07 .20
365 Kirby Puckett .20 .50
366 Oscar Munoz .07 .20
367 Chuck Knoblauch .07 .20
368 Marty Cordova ROY .07 .20
369 Bernie Williams .10 .30
370 Mike Stanley .07 .20
371 Andy Pettitte .10 .30
372 Jack McDowell .07 .20
373 Sterling Hitchcock .07 .20
374 David Cone .07 .20
375 Randy Velarde .07 .20
376 Don Mattingly .50 1.25
377 Melido Perez .07 .20
378 Wade Boggs .10 .30
379 Ruben Sierra .07 .20
380 Tony Fernandez .07 .20
381 John Wetteland .07 .20
382 Mariano Rivera .20 .50
383 Derek Jeter .50 1.25
384 Paul O'Neill .10 .30
385 Mark McGwire .50 1.25
386 Scott Brosius .07 .20
387 Don Wengert .07 .20
388 Terry Steinbach .07 .20
389 Brent Gates .07 .20
390 Craig Paquette .07 .20
391 Mike Bordick .07 .20
392 Ariel Prieto .07 .20
393 Dennis Eckersley .07 .20
394 Carlos Reyes .07 .20
395 Todd Stottlemyre .07 .20
396 Rickey Henderson .20 .50
397 Geronimo Berroa .07 .20
398 Steve Ontiveros .07 .20
399 Mike Gallego .07 .20
400 Stan Javier .07 .20
401 Randy Johnson .20 .50
402 Norm Charlton .07 .20
403 Mike Blowers .07 .20
404 Tino Martinez .10 .30
405 Dan Wilson .07 .20
406 Andy Benes .07 .20
407 Alex Diaz .07 .20
408 Edgar Martinez .10 .30
409 Chris Bosio .07 .20
410 Ken Griffey Jr. .30 .75
411 Luis Sojo .07 .20
412 Bob Wolcott .07 .20
413 Vince Coleman .07 .20
414 Rich Amaral .07 .20
415 Jay Buhner .07 .20
416 Alex Rodriguez .40 1.00
417 Joey Cora .07 .20
418 Randy Johnson CY .10 .30
419 Edgar Martinez BAC .07 .20
420 Ivan Rodriguez .10 .30
421 Mark McLemore .07 .20
422 Mickey Tettleton .07 .20
423 Juan Gonzalez .07 .20
424 Will Clark .10 .30
425 Kevin Gross .07 .20
426 Dean Palmer .07 .20
427 Kenny Rogers .07 .20
428 Bob Tewksbury .07 .20
429 Benji Gil .07 .20
430 Jeff Russell .07 .20
431 Rusty Greer .07 .20
432 Roger Pavlik .07 .20
433 Esteban Beltre .07 .20
434 Otis Nixon .07 .20
435 Paul Molitor .07 .20
436 Carlos Delgado .07 .20
437 Ed Sprague .07 .20
438 Juan Guzman .07 .20
439 Domingo Cedeno .07 .20
440 Pat Hentgen .07 .20
441 Tomas Perez .07 .20
442 John Olerud .07 .20
443 Shawn Green .07 .20
444 Al Leiter .07 .20
445 Joe Carter .07 .20
446 Robert Perez .07 .20
447 Devon White .07 .20
448 Tony Castillo .07 .20
449 Alex Gonzalez .07 .20
450 Roberto Alomar .10 .30

1997 Pacific

This 450-card set was issued in one series and distributed in 12-card packs. The fronts feature color action player photos foiled in gold. The backs carry player information in both English and Spanish with player statistics. No subsets are featured as the manufacturer focused on providing collectors with the most comprehensive selection of major league players as possible. Rookie Cards include Brian Giles.

COMPLETE SET (450) 20.00 50.00
1 Garret Anderson .10 .30
2 George Arias .10 .30
3 Chili Davis .10 .30
4 Gary DiSarcina .10 .30
5 Jim Edmonds .10 .30
6 Darin Erstad .10 .30
7 Jorge Fabregas .10 .30
8 Chuck Finley .10 .30
9 Rex Hudler .10 .30
10 Mark Langston .10 .30
11 Orlando Palmeiro .10 .30
12 Troy Percival .10 .30
13 Tim Salmon .20 .50
14 J.T. Snow .10 .30
15 Randy Velarde .10 .30
16 Manny Alexander .10 .30
17 Roberto Alomar .20 .50
18 Brady Anderson .10 .30
19 Armando Benitez .10 .30
20 Bobby Bonilla .10 .30
21 Rocky Coppinger .10 .30
22 Scott Erickson .10 .30
23 Jeffrey Hammonds .10 .30
24 Chris Hoiles .10 .30
25 Eddie Murray .30 .75
26 Mike Mussina .20 .50
27 Randy Myers .10 .30
28 Rafael Palmeiro .20 .50
29 Cal Ripken 1.00 2.50
30 B.J. Surhoff .10 .30
31 Tony Tarasco .10 .30
32 Esteban Beltre .10 .30
33 Darren Bragg .10 .30
34 Jose Canseco .20 .50
35 Roger Clemens .60 1.50
36 Wil Cordero .10 .30
37 Alex Delgado .10 .30
38 Jeff Frye .10 .30
39 Nomar Garciaparra .50 1.25
40 Tom Gordon .10 .30
41 Mike Greenwell .10 .30
42 Reggie Jefferson .10 .30
43 Tim Naehring .10 .30
44 Troy O'Leary .10 .30
45 Heathcliff Slocumb .10 .30
46 Lee Tinsley .10 .30
47 John Valentin .10 .30
48 Mo Vaughn .10 .30
49 Wilson Alvarez .10 .30
50 Harold Baines .10 .30
51 Ray Durham .10 .30
52 Alex Fernandez .10 .30
53 Ozzie Guillen .10 .30
54 Roberto Hernandez .10 .30
55 Ron Karkovice .10 .30
56 Darren Lewis .10 .30
57 Norberto Martin .10 .30
58 Dave Martinez .10 .30
59 Lyle Mouton .10 .30
60 Jose Munoz .10 .30
61 Tony Phillips .10 .30
62 Kevin Tapani .10 .30
63 Danny Tartabull .10 .30
64 Frank Thomas .30 .75
65 Robin Ventura .10 .30
66 Sandy Alomar Jr. .10 .30
67 Albert Belle .10 .30
68 Julio Franco .10 .30
69 Brian Giles RC .60 1.50
70 Danny Graves .10 .30
71 Orel Hershiser .10 .30
72 Jeff Kent .10 .30
73 Kenny Lofton .10 .30
74 Dennis Martinez .10 .30
75 Jack McDowell .10 .30
76 Jose Mesa .10 .30
77 Charles Nagy .10 .30
78 Manny Ramirez .20 .50
79 Julian Tavarez .10 .30
80 Jim Thome .20 .50
81 Jose Vizcaino .10 .30
82 Omar Vizquel .20 .50
83 Brad Ausmus .10 .30
84 Kimera Bartee .10 .30
85 Raul Casanova .10 .30
86 Tony Clark .10 .30
87 Travis Fryman .10 .30
88 Bobby Higginson .10 .30
89 Mark Lewis .10 .30
90 Jose Lima .10 .30
91 Felipe Lira .10 .30
92 Phil Nevin .10 .30
93 Melvin Nieves .10 .30
94 Curtis Pride .10 .30
95 Ruben Sierra .10 .30
96 Alan Trammell .10 .30
97 Kevin Appier .10 .30
98 Tim Belcher .10 .30
99 Johnny Damon .20 .50
100 Tom Goodwin .10 .30
101 Bob Hamelin .10 .30
102 David Howard .10 .30
103 Jason Jacome .10 .30

104 Keith Lockhart .10 .30
105 Mike Macfarlane .10 .30
106 Jeff Montgomery .10 .30
107 Jose Offerman .10 .30
108 Hipolito Pichardo .10 .30
109 Joe Randa .10 .30
110 Bip Roberts .10 .30
111 Chris Stynes .10 .30
112 Mike Sweeney .10 .30
113 Joe Vitiello .10 .30
114 Jeromy Burnitz .10 .30
115 Chuck Carr .10 .30
116 Jeff Cirillo .10 .30
117 Mike Fetters .10 .30
118 David Hulse .10 .30
119 John Jaha .10 .30
120 Scott Karl .10 .30
121 Jesse Levis .10 .30
122 Mark Loretta .10 .30
123 Mike Matheny .10 .30
124 Ben McDonald .10 .30
125 Matt Mieske .10 .30
126 Angel Miranda .10 .30
127 Dave Nilsson .10 .30
128 Jose Valentin .10 .30
129 Fernando Vina .10 .30
130 Ron Villone .10 .30
131 Gerald Williams .10 .30
132 Rick Aguilera .10 .30
133 Rich Becker .10 .30
134 Ron Coomer .10 .30
135 Marty Cordova .10 .30
136 Eddie Guardado .10 .30
137 Denny Hocking .10 .30
138 Roberto Kelly .10 .30
139 Chuck Knoblauch .10 .30
140 Matt Lawton .10 .30
141 Pat Meares .10 .30
142 Paul Molitor .10 .30
143 Greg Myers .10 .30
144 Jeff Reboulet .10 .30
145 Scott Stahoviak .10 .30
146 Todd Walker .10 .30
147 Wade Boggs .20 .50
148 David Cone .10 .30
149 Mariano Duncan .10 .30
150 Cecil Fielder .10 .30
151 Dwight Gooden .10 .30
152 Derek Jeter .75 2.00
153 Jim Leyritz .10 .30
154 Tino Martinez .20 .50
155 Paul O'Neill .20 .50
156 Andy Pettitte .20 .50
157 Tim Raines .10 .30
158 Mariano Rivera .30 .75
159 Ruben Rivera .10 .30
160 Kenny Rogers .10 .30
161 Darryl Strawberry .10 .30
162 John Wetteland .10 .30
163 Bernie Williams .20 .50
164 Tony Batista .10 .30
165 Geronimo Berroa .10 .30
166 Mike Bordick .10 .30
167 Scott Brosius .10 .30
168 Brent Gates .10 .30
169 Jason Giambi .10 .30
170 Jose Herrera .10 .30
171 Brian Lesher RC .10 .30
172 Damon Mashore .10 .30
173 Mark McGwire .75 2.00
174 Ariel Prieto .10 .30
175 Carlos Reyes .10 .30
176 Matt Stairs .10 .30
177 Terry Steinbach .10 .30
178 John Wasdin .10 .30
179 Ernie Young .10 .30
180 Rich Amaral .10 .30
181 Bobby Ayala .10 .30
182 Jay Buhner .10 .30
183 Rafael Carmona .10 .30
184 Norm Charlton .10 .30
185 Joey Cora .10 .30
186 Ken Griffey Jr. .50 1.25
187 Sterling Hitchcock .10 .30
188 Dave Hollins .10 .30
189 Randy Johnson .30 .75
190 Edgar Martinez .20 .50
191 Jamie Moyer .10 .30
192 Alex Rodriguez .50 1.25
193 Paul Sorrento .10 .30
194 Salomon Torres .10 .30
195 Bob Wells .10 .30
196 Dan Wilson .10 .30
197 Will Clark .20 .50
198 Kevin Elster .10 .30
199 Rene Gonzales .10 .30
200 Juan Gonzalez .10 .30
201 Rusty Greer .10 .30
202 Darryl Hamilton .10 .30
203 Mike Henneman .10 .30
204 Ken Hill .10 .30
205 Mark McLemore .10 .30
206 Darren Oliver .10 .30
207 Dean Palmer .10 .30
208 Roger Pavlik .10 .30
209 Ivan Rodriguez .20 .50
210 Kurt Stillwell .10 .30
211 Mickey Tettleton .10 .30
212 Bobby Witt .10 .30
213 Tilson Brito .10 .30
214 Jacob Brumfield .10 .30
215 Miguel Cairo .10 .30
216 Joe Carter .10 .30
217 Felipe Crespo .10 .30
218 Carlos Delgado .10 .30
219 Alex Gonzalez .10 .30
220 Shawn Green .10 .30
221 Juan Guzman .10 .30
222 Pat Hentgen .10 .30
223 Charlie O'Brien .10 .30
224 John Olerud .10 .30
225 Robert Perez .10 .30
226 Tomas Perez .10 .30
227 Juan Samuel .10 .30
228 Ed Sprague .10 .30
229 Mike Timlin .10 .30
230 Rafael Belliard .10 .30
231 Jermaine Dye .10 .30
232 Tom Glavine .20 .50
233 Marquis Grissom .10 .30
234 Andruw Jones .20 .50
235 Chipper Jones .30 .75
236 David Justice .10 .30
237 Ryan Klesko .10 .30
238 Mark Lemke .10 .30
239 Javier Lopez .10 .30
240 Greg Maddux .50 1.25
241 Fred McGriff .20 .50
242 Denny Neagle .10 .30
243 Eddie Perez .10 .30
244 John Smoltz .20 .50
245 Mark Wohlers .10 .30
246 Brant Brown .10 .30
247 Scott Bullett .10 .30
248 Leo Gomez .10 .30
249 Luis Gonzalez .10 .30
250 Mark Grace .20 .50
251 Jose Hernandez .10 .30
252 Brooks Kieschnick .10 .30
253 Brian McRae .10 .30
254 Jaime Navarro .10 .30
255 Mike Perez .10 .30
256 Rey Sanchez .10 .30
257 Ryne Sandberg .50 1.25
258 Scott Servais .10 .30
259 Sammy Sosa .30 .75
260 Pedro Valdes .10 .30
261 Turk Wendell .10 .30
262 Bret Boone .10 .30
263 Jeff Branson .10 .30
264 Jeff Brantley .10 .30
265 Dave Burba .10 .30
266 Hector Carrasco .10 .30
267 Eric Davis .10 .30
268 Willie Greene .10 .30
269 Lenny Harris .10 .30
270 Thomas Howard .10 .30
271 Barry Larkin .20 .50
272 Hal Morris .10 .30
273 Joe Oliver .10 .30
274 Eric Owens .10 .30
275 Jose Rijo .10 .30
276 Reggie Sanders .10 .30
277 Eddie Taubensee .10 .30
278 Jason Bates .10 .30
279 Dante Bichette .10 .30
280 Ellis Burks .10 .30
281 Vinny Castilla .10 .30
282 Andres Galarraga .10 .30
283 Quinton McCracken .10 .30
284 Jayhawk Owens .10 .30
285 Jeff Reed .10 .30
286 Bryan Rekar .10 .30
287 Armando Reynoso .10 .30
288 Kevin Ritz .10 .30
289 Bruce Ruffin .10 .30
290 John Vander Wal .10 .30
291 Larry Walker .10 .30
292 Walt Weiss .10 .30
293 Eric Young .10 .30
294 Kurt Abbott .10 .30
295 Alex Arias .10 .30
296 Miguel Batista .10 .30
297 Kevin Brown .10 .30
298 Luis Castillo .10 .30
299 Greg Colbrunn .10 .30
300 Jeff Conine .10 .30
301 Charles Johnson .10 .30
302 Al Leiter .10 .30
303 Robb Nen .10 .30
304 Joe Orsulak .10 .30
305 Yorkis Perez .10 .30
306 Edgar Renteria .10 .30
307 Gary Sheffield .10 .30
308 Jesus Tavarez .10 .30
309 Quilvio Veras .10 .30
310 Devon White .10 .30
311 Jeff Bagwell .20 .50
312 Derek Bell .10 .30
313 Sean Berry .10 .30
314 Craig Biggio .20 .50
315 Doug Drabek .10 .30
316 Tony Eusebio .10 .30
317 Ricky Gutierrez .10 .30
318 Xavier Hernandez .10 .30
319 Brian L. Hunter .10 .30
320 Darryl Kile .10 .30
321 Derrick May .10 .30
322 Orlando Miller .10 .30
323 James Mouton .10 .30
324 Bill Spiers .10 .30
325 Pedro Astacio .10 .30
326 Brett Butler .10 .30
327 Juan Castro .10 .30
328 Roger Cedeno .10 .30
329 Delino DeShields .10 .30
330 Karim Garcia .10 .30
331 Todd Hollandsworth .10 .30
332 Eric Karros .10 .30
333 Oreste Marrero .10 .30
334 Ramon Martinez .10 .30
335 Raul Mondesi .10 .30
336 Hideo Nomo .30 .75
337 Antonio Osuna .10 .30
338 Chan Ho Park .10 .30
339 Mike Piazza .50 1.25
340 Ismael Valdes .10 .30
341 Moises Alou .10 .30
342 Omar Daal .10 .30
343 Jeff Fassero .10 .30
344 Cliff Floyd .10 .30
345 Mark Grudzielanek .10 .30
346 Mike Lansing .10 .30
347 Pedro Martinez .20 .50
348 Sherman Obando .10 .30
349 Jose Paniagua .10 .30
350 Henry Rodriguez .10 .30
351 Mel Rojas .10 .30
352 F.P. Santangelo .10 .30
353 David Segui .10 .30
354 Dave Silvestri .10 .30
355 Ugueth Urbina .10 .30
356 Rondell White .10 .30
357 Edgardo Alfonzo .10 .30
358 Carlos Baerga .10 .30
359 Tim Bogar .10 .30
360 Rico Brogna .10 .30
361 Alvaro Espinoza .10 .30
362 Carl Everett .10 .30
363 John Franco .10 .30
364 Bernard Gilkey .10 .30
365 Todd Hundley .10 .30
366 Butch Huskey .10 .30
367 Jason Isringhausen .10 .30
368 Bobby Jones .10 .30
369 Lance Johnson .10 .30
370 Brent Mayne .10 .30
371 Alex Ochoa .10 .30
372 Rey Ordonez .10 .30
373 Ron Blazier .10 .30
374 Ricky Bottalico .10 .30
375 David Doster .10 .30
376 Lenny Dykstra .10 .30
377 Jim Eisenreich .10 .30
378 Bobby Estalella .10 .30
379 Gregg Jefferies .10 .30
380 Kevin Jordan .10 .30
381 Ricardo Jordan .10 .30
382 Mickey Morandini .10 .30
383 Ricky Otero .10 .30
384 Benito Santiago .10 .30
385 Gene Schall .10 .30
386 Curt Schilling .10 .30
387 Kevin Sefcik .10 .30
388 Kevin Stocker .10 .30
389 Jermaine Allensworth .10 .30
390 Jay Bell .10 .30
391 Jason Christiansen .10 .30
392 Francisco Cordova .10 .30
393 Mark Johnson .10 .30
394 Jason Kendall .10 .30
395 Jeff King .10 .30
396 Jon Lieber .10 .30
397 Nelson Liriano .10 .30
398 Esteban Loaiza .10 .30
399 Al Martin .10 .30
400 Orlando Merced .10 .30
401 Ramon Morel .10 .30
402 Luis Alicea .10 .30
403 Alan Benes .10 .30
404 Andy Benes .10 .30
405 Terry Bradshaw .10 .30
406 Royce Clayton .10 .30
407 Dennis Eckersley .10 .30
408 Gary Gaetti .10 .30
409 Mike Gallego .10 .30
410 Ron Gant .10 .30
411 Brian Jordan .10 .30
412 Ray Lankford .10 .30
413 John Mabry .10 .30
414 Willie McGee .10 .30
415 Tom Pagnozzi .10 .30
416 Ozzie Smith .50 1.25
417 Todd Stottlemyre .10 .30
418 Mark Sweeney .10 .30
419 Andy Ashby .10 .30
420 Ken Caminiti .10 .30
421 Archi Cianfrocco .10 .30
422 Steve Finley .10 .30
423 Chris Gomez .10 .30
424 Tony Gwynn .40 1.00
425 Joey Hamilton .10 .30
426 Rickey Henderson .30 .75
427 Trevor Hoffman .10 .30
428 Brian Johnson .10 .30
429 Wally Joyner .10 .30
430 Scott Livingstone .10 .30
431 Jody Reed .10 .30
432 Craig Shipley .10 .30
433 Fernando Valenzuela .10 .30
434 Greg Vaughn .10 .30
435 Rich Aurilia .10 .30
436 Kim Batiste .10 .30
437 Jose Bautista .10 .30
438 Rod Beck .10 .30
439 Marvin Benard .10 .30
440 Barry Bonds .75 2.00
441 Shawon Dunston .10 .30
442 Shawn Estes .10 .30
443 Osvaldo Fernandez .10 .30
444 Stan Javier .10 .30
445 David McCarty .10 .30
446 Bill Mueller RC .50 1.25
447 Steve Scarsone .10 .30
448 Robby Thompson .10 .30
449 Rick Wilkins .10 .30
450 Matt Williams .10 .30

1998 Pacific

The 1998 Pacific set was issued in one series totalling 450 cards and distributed in 12-card packs with a suggested retail price of $2.49. The fronts features borderless color player photos with gold foil highlights. The backs carry player information in both Spanish and English. As is standard with base-brand Pacific, the entire set is devoid of subset cards, instead focusing on a comprehensive selection of major league players.

COMPLETE SET (450) 30.00 60.00
1 Luis Alicea .10 .30
2 Garret Anderson .10 .30
3 Jason Dickson .10 .30
4 Gary DiSarcina .10 .30
5 Jim Edmonds .10 .30
6 Darin Erstad .10 .30
7 Chuck Finley .10 .30
8 Shigetoshi Hasegawa .10 .30
9 Rickey Henderson .30 .75
10 Dave Hollins .10 .30
11 Mark Langston .10 .30
12 Orlando Palmeiro .10 .30
13 Troy Percival .10 .30
14 Tony Phillips .10 .30
15 Tim Salmon .20 .50
16 Allen Watson .10 .30
17 Roberto Alomar .20 .50
18 Brady Anderson .10 .30
19 Harold Baines .10 .30
20 Armando Benitez .10 .30
21 Geronimo Berroa .10 .30
22 Mike Bordick .10 .30
23 Eric Davis .10 .30
24 Scott Erickson .10 .30
25 Chris Hoiles .10 .30
26 Jimmy Key .10 .30
27 Aaron Ledesma .10 .30
28 Mike Mussina .20 .50
29 Randy Myers .10 .30
30 Jesse Orosco .10 .30
31 Rafael Palmeiro .20 .50
32 Jeff Reboulet .10 .30
33 Cal Ripken 1.00 2.50
34 B.J. Surhoff .10 .30
35 Steve Avery .10 .30
36 Darren Bragg .10 .30
37 Wil Cordero .10 .30
38 Jeff Frye .10 .30
39 Nomar Garciaparra .50 1.25
40 Tom Gordon .10 .30
41 Bill Haselman .10 .30
42 Scott Hatteberg .10 .30
43 Butch Henry .10 .30
44 Reggie Jefferson .10 .30
45 Tim Naehring .10 .30
46 Troy O'Leary .10 .30
47 Jeff Suppan .10 .30
48 John Valentin .10 .30
49 Mo Vaughn .10 .30
50 Tim Wakefield .10 .30
51 James Baldwin .10 .30
52 Albert Belle .10 .30
53 Tony Castillo .10 .30
54 Doug Drabek .10 .30
55 Ray Durham .10 .30
56 Jorge Fabregas .10 .30
57 Ozzie Guillen .10 .30
58 Matt Karchner .10 .30
59 Norberto Martin .10 .30
60 Dave Martinez .10 .30
61 Lyle Mouton .10 .30
62 Jaime Navarro .10 .30
63 Frank Thomas .30 .75
64 Mario Valdez .10 .30
65 Robin Ventura .10 .30
66 Sandy Alomar Jr. .10 .30
67 Paul Assenmacher .10 .30
68 Tony Fernandez .10 .30
69 Brian Giles .10 .30
70 Marquis Grissom .10 .30
71 Orel Hershiser .10 .30
72 Mike Jackson .10 .30
73 David Justice .10 .30
74 Albie Lopez .10 .30
75 Jose Mesa .10 .30
76 Charles Nagy .10 .30
77 Chad Ogea .10 .30
78 Manny Ramirez .20 .50
79 Jim Thome .20 .50
80 Omar Vizquel .20 .50
81 Matt Williams .10 .30
82 Jaret Wright .10 .30
83 Willie Blair .10 .30
84 Raul Casanova .10 .30
85 Tony Clark .10 .30
86 Deivi Cruz .10 .30
87 Damion Easley .10 .30
88 Travis Fryman .10 .30
89 Bobby Higginson .10 .30
90 Brian L. Hunter .10 .30
91 Todd Jones .10 .30
92 Dan Miceli .10 .30
93 Brian Moehler .10 .30
94 Mel Nieves .10 .30
95 Jody Reed .10 .30
96 Justin Thompson .10 .30
97 Bubba Trammell .10 .30
98 Kevin Appier .10 .30
99 Jay Bell .10 .30
100 Yamil Benitez .10 .30
101 Johnny Damon .20 .50
102 Chili Davis .10 .30
103 Jermaine Dye .10 .30
104 Jed Hansen .10 .30
105 Jeff King .10 .30
106 Mike Macfarlane .10 .30
107 Felix Martinez .10 .30
108 Jeff Montgomery .10 .30
109 Jose Offerman .10 .30
110 Dean Palmer .10 .30
111 Hipolito Pichardo .10 .30
112 Jose Rosado .10 .30
113 Jeromy Burnitz .10 .30
114 Jeff Cirillo .10 .30
115 Cal Eldred .10 .30
116 John Jaha .10 .30
117 Doug Jones .10 .30
118 Scott Karl .10 .30
119 Jesse Levis .10 .30
120 Mark Loretta .10 .30
121 Ben McDonald .10 .30
122 Jose Mercedes .10 .30
123 Matt Mieske .10 .30
124 Dave Nilsson .10 .30
125 Jose Valentin .10 .30
126 Fernando Vina .10 .30
127 Gerald Williams .10 .30
128 Rick Aguilera .10 .30
129 Rich Becker .10 .30
130 Ron Coomer .10 .30
131 Marty Cordova .10 .30
132 Eddie Guardado .10 .30
133 LaTroy Hawkins .10 .30
134 Denny Hocking .10 .30
135 Chuck Knoblauch .10 .30
136 Matt Lawton .10 .30
137 Pat Meares .10 .30
138 Paul Molitor .10 .30
139 David Ortiz .40 1.00
140 Brad Radke .10 .30
141 Terry Steinbach .10 .30
142 Bob Tewksbury .10 .30
143 Javier Valentin .10 .30
144 Wade Boggs .20 .50
145 David Cone .10 .30
146 Chad Curtis .10 .30
147 Cecil Fielder .10 .30
148 Joe Girardi .10 .30
149 Dwight Gooden .10 .30
150 Hideki Irabu .10 .30
151 Derek Jeter .75 2.00
152 Tino Martinez .20 .50
153 Ramiro Mendoza .10 .30
154 Paul O'Neill .20 .50
155 Andy Pettitte .20 .50
156 Jorge Posada .20 .50
157 Mariano Rivera .30 .75
158 Rey Sanchez .10 .30
159 Luis Sojo .10 .30
160 David Wells .10 .30
161 Bernie Williams .20 .50
162 Rafael Bournigal .10 .30
163 Scott Brosius .10 .30
164 Jose Canseco .20 .50
165 Jason Giambi .10 .30
166 Ben Grieve .10 .30
167 Dave Magadan .10 .30
168 Brent Mayne .10 .30
169 Jason McDonald .10 .30
170 Izzy Molina .10 .30
171 Ariel Prieto .10 .30
172 Carlos Reyes .10 .30
173 Scott Spiezio .10 .30
174 Matt Stairs .10 .30
175 Bill Taylor .10 .30
176 Dave Telgheder .10 .30
177 Steve Wojciechowski .10 .30
178 Rich Amaral .10 .30
179 Bobby Ayala .10 .30
180 Jay Buhner .10 .30
181 Rafael Carmona .10 .30
182 Ken Cloude .10 .30
183 Joey Cora .10 .30
184 Russ Davis .10 .30
185 Jeff Fassero .10 .30
186 Ken Griffey Jr. .50 1.25
187 Raul Ibanez .10 .30
188 Randy Johnson .30 .75
189 Roberto Kelly .10 .30
190 Edgar Martinez .20 .50
191 Jamie Moyer .10 .30
192 Omar Olivares .10 .30
193 Alex Rodriguez .50 1.25
194 Heathcliff Slocumb .10 .30
195 Paul Sorrento .10 .30
196 Dan Wilson .10 .30
197 Scott Bailes .10 .30
198 John Burkett .10 .30
199 Domingo Cedeno .10 .30
200 Will Clark .20 .50
201 Hanley Frias RC .10 .30
202 Juan Gonzalez .10 .30
203 Tom Goodwin .10 .30
204 Rusty Greer .10 .30
205 Wilson Heredia .10 .30
206 Darren Oliver .10 .30
207 Bill Ripken .10 .30
208 Ivan Rodriguez .20 .50
209 Lee Stevens .10 .30
210 Fernando Tatis .10 .30
211 John Wetteland .10 .30
212 Bobby Witt .10 .30
213 Jacob Brumfield .10 .30
214 Joe Carter .10 .30
215 Roger Clemens .60 1.50
216 Felipe Crespo .10 .30
217 Jose Cruz Jr. .10 .30
218 Carlos Delgado .10 .30
219 Mariano Duncan .10 .30
220 Carlos Garcia .10 .30
221 Alex Gonzalez .10 .30
222 Juan Guzman .10 .30
223 Pat Hentgen .10 .30
224 Orlando Merced .10 .30
225 Tomas Perez .10 .30
226 Paul Quantrill .10 .30
227 Benito Santiago .10 .30
228 Woody Williams .10 .30
229 Rafael Belliard .10 .30
230 Jeff Blauser .10 .30
231 Pedro Borbon .10 .30
232 Tom Glavine .20 .50
233 Tony Graffanino .10 .30
234 Andruw Jones .20 .50
235 Chipper Jones .30 .75
236 Ryan Klesko .10 .30
237 Mark Lemke .10 .30
238 Kenny Lofton .10 .30
239 Javier Lopez .10 .30
240 Fred McGriff .20 .50
241 Greg Maddux .50 1.25
242 Denny Neagle .10 .30
243 John Smoltz .20 .50
244 Michael Tucker .10 .30
245 Mark Wohlers .10 .30
246 Manny Alexander .10 .30
247 Miguel Batista .10 .30
248 Mark Clark .10 .30
249 Doug Glanville .10 .30
250 Jeremi Gonzalez .10 .30
251 Mark Grace .20 .50
252 Jose Hernandez .10 .30
253 Lance Johnson .10 .30
254 Brooks Kieschnick .10 .30
255 Kevin Orie .10 .30
256 Ryne Sandberg .50 1.25
257 Scott Servais .10 .30
258 Sammy Sosa .30 .75
259 Kevin Tapani .10 .30
260 Ramon Tatis .10 .30
261 Bret Boone .10 .30
262 Dave Burba .10 .30
263 Brook Fordyce .10 .30
264 Willie Greene .10 .30
265 Barry Larkin .20 .50
266 Pedro A. Martinez .10 .30
267 Hal Morris .10 .30
268 Joe Oliver .10 .30
269 Eduardo Perez .10 .30
270 Pokey Reese .10 .30
271 Felix Rodriguez .10 .30
272 Deion Sanders .20 .50
273 Reggie Sanders .10 .30
274 Jeff Shaw .10 .30
275 Scott Sullivan .10 .30
276 Brett Tomko .10 .30
277 Roger Bailey .10 .30
278 Dante Bichette .10 .30
279 Ellis Burks .10 .30
280 Vinny Castilla .10 .30
281 Frank Castillo .10 .30
282 Mike DeJean RC .10 .30
283 Andres Galarraga .10 .30
284 Darren Holmes .10 .30
285 Kirt Manwaring .10 .30
286 Quinton McCracken .10 .30
287 Neifi Perez .10 .30
288 Steve Reed .10 .30
289 John Thomson .10 .30
290 Larry Walker .10 .30
291 Walt Weiss .10 .30
292 Kurt Abbott .10 .30
293 Antonio Alfonseca .10 .30
294 Moises Alou .10 .30
295 Alex Arias .10 .30
296 Bobby Bonilla .10 .30
297 Kevin Brown .20 .50
298 Craig Counsell .10 .30
299 Darren Daulton .10 .30
300 Jim Eisenreich .10 .30
301 Alex Fernandez .10 .30
302 Felix Heredia .10 .30
303 Livan Hernandez .10 .30
304 Charles Johnson .10 .30
305 Al Leiter .10 .30
306 Robb Nen .10 .30
307 Edgar Renteria .10 .30
308 Gary Sheffield .10 .30
309 Devon White .10 .30
310 Bob Abreu .10 .30
311 Brad Ausmus .10 .30
312 Jeff Bagwell .20 .50
313 Derek Bell .10 .30
314 Sean Berry .10 .30
315 Craig Biggio .20 .50
316 Ramon Garcia .10 .30
317 Luis Gonzalez .10 .30
318 Ricky Gutierrez .10 .30
319 Mike Hampton .10 .30
320 Richard Hidalgo .10 .30
321 Thomas Howard .10 .30
322 Darryl Kile .10 .30
323 Jose Lima .10 .30
324 Shane Reynolds .10 .30
325 Bill Spiers .10 .30
326 Tom Candiotti .10 .30
327 Roger Cedeno .10 .30
328 Greg Gagne .10 .30
329 Karim Garcia .10 .30
330 Wilton Guerrero .10 .30
331 Todd Hollandsworth .10 .30
332 Eric Karros .10 .30
333 Ramon Martinez .10 .30
334 Raul Mondesi .10 .30
335 Otis Nixon .10 .30
336 Hideo Nomo .30 .75
337 Antonio Osuna .10 .30
338 Chan Ho Park .10 .30
339 Mike Piazza .50 1.25
340 Dennis Reyes .10 .30
341 Ismael Valdes .10 .30
342 Todd Worrell .10 .30
343 Todd Zeile .10 .30
344 Darrin Fletcher .10 .30
345 Mark Grudzielanek .10 .30
346 Vladimir Guerrero .30 .75
347 Dustin Hermanson .10 .30
348 Mike Lansing .10 .30
349 Pedro Martinez .20 .50
350 Ryan McGuire .10 .30
351 Jose Paniagua .10 .30
352 Carlos Perez .10 .30
353 Henry Rodriguez .10 .30
354 F.P. Santangelo .10 .30
355 David Segui .10 .30
356 Ugueth Urbina .10 .30
357 Marc Valdes .10 .30
358 Jose Vidro .10 .30
359 Rondell White .10 .30
360 Juan Acevedo .10 .30
361 Edgardo Alfonzo .10 .30
362 Carlos Baerga .10 .30
363 Carl Everett .10 .30
364 John Franco .10 .30
365 Bernard Gilkey .10 .30
366 Todd Hundley .10 .30
367 Butch Huskey .10 .30
368 Bobby Jones .10 .30
369 T.Kashiwada RC .10 .30
370 Greg McMichael .10 .30
371 Brian McRae .10 .30
372 Alex Ochoa .10 .30
373 John Olerud .10 .30
374 Rey Ordonez .10 .30
375 Turk Wendell .10 .30
376 Ricky Bottalico .10 .30
377 Rico Brogna .10 .30
378 Len Dykstra .10 .30
379 Bobby Estalella .10 .30
380 Wayne Gomes .10 .30
381 Tyler Green .10 .30
382 Gregg Jefferies .10 .30
383 Mark Leiter .10 .30
384 Mike Lieberthal .10 .30
385 Mickey Morandini .10 .30
386 Scott Rolen .20 .50
387 Curt Schilling .10 .30
388 Kevin Stocker .10 .30
389 Danny Tartabull .10 .30
390 Jermaine Allensworth .10 .30
391 Adrian Brown .10 .30
392 Jason Christiansen .10 .30
393 Steve Cooke .10 .30
394 Francisco Cordova .10 .30
395 Jose Guillen .10 .30
396 Jason Kendall .10 .30
397 Jon Lieber .10 .30
398 Esteban Loaiza .10 .30
399 Al Martin .10 .30
400 Kevin Polcovich .10 .30
401 Joe Randa .10 .30
402 Ricardo Rincon .10 .30
403 Tony Womack .10 .30
404 Kevin Young .10 .30
405 Andy Benes .10 .30
406 Royce Clayton .10 .30
407 Delino DeShields .10 .30
408 Mike Difelice RC .10 .30
409 Dennis Eckersley .10 .30
410 John Frascatore .10 .30
411 Gary Gaetti .10 .30
412 Ron Gant .10 .30
413 Brian Jordan .10 .30

414 Ray Lankford .10 .30
415 Willie McGee .10 .30
416 Mark McGwire .75 2.00
417 Matt Morris .10 .30
418 Luis Ordaz .10 .30
419 Todd Stottlemyre .10 .30
420 Andy Ashby .10 .30
421 Jim Bruske .10 .30
422 Ken Caminiti .10 .30
423 Will Cunnane .10 .30
424 Steve Finley .10 .30
425 John Flaherty .10 .30
426 Chris Gomez .10 .30
427 Tony Gwynn .40 1.00
428 Joey Hamilton .10 .30
429 Carlos Hernandez .10 .30
430 Sterling Hitchcock .10 .30
431 Trevor Hoffman .10 .30
432 Wally Joyner .10 .30
433 Greg Vaughn .10 .30
434 Quilvio Veras .10 .30
435 Wilson Alvarez .10 .30
436 Rod Beck .10 .30
437 Barry Bonds .75 2.00
438 Jacob Cruz .10 .30
439 Shawn Estes .10 .30
440 Darryl Hamilton .10 .30
441 Roberto Hernandez .10 .30
442 Glenallen Hill .10 .30
443 Stan Javier .10 .30
444 Brian Johnson .10 .30
445 Jeff Kent .10 .30
446 Bill Mueller .10 .30
447 Kirk Rueter .10 .30
448 J.T. Snow .10 .30
449 Julian Tavarez .10 .30
450 Jose Vizcaino .10 .30

1999 Pacific

This 500 card standard-size set was issued in 10 card packs that had a SRP of $2.19 per pack. Each Box containted 36 packs and each case had 20 boxes. Continuing the trend begun in 1998 with Pacific On-Line, Pacific issued two versions of 50 of the star or leading prospect players in the set with both an action version as well as a head shot. Thus the cards are actually numbered from 1 through 450, but the 50 additional headshot cards (carrying identical numbering to the action cards) bring the total number of cards in the set to 500. The complete set includes both versions of each player. The head shots were inserted one per pack. An unnumbered Tony Gwynn sample card was distributed to dealers and hobby media prior to the product's release. The card is easy to recognize by the bold, diagonal "SAMPLE" text running across the back.

COMPLETE SET (500) 40.00 80.00
1 Garret Anderson .10 .30
2 Jason Dickson .10 .30
3 Gary DiSarcina .10 .30
4 Jim Edmonds .10 .30
5 Darin Erstad .10 .30
6 Chuck Finley .10 .30
7 Shigetoshi Hasegawa .10 .30
8 Ken Hill .10 .30
9 Dave Hollins .10 .30
10 Phil Nevin .10 .30
11 Troy Percival .10 .30
12 Tim Salmon * .20 .50
12A Tim Salmon Headshot .20 .50
13 Brian Anderson .10 .30
14 Tony Batista .10 .30
15 Jay Bell .10 .30
16 Andy Benes .10 .30
17 Yamil Benitez .10 .30
18 Omar Daal .10 .30
19 David Dellucci .10 .30
20 Karim Garcia .10 .30
21 Bernard Gilkey .10 .30
22 Travis Lee * .10 .30
22A Travis Lee Headshot .10 .30
23 Aaron Small .10 .30
24 Kelly Stinnett .10 .30
25 Devon White .10 .30
26 Matt Williams .10 .30
27 Bruce Chen * .10 .30
27A Bruce Chen Headshot .10 .30
28 Andres Galarraga * .10 .30
28A A.Galarraga Headshot .10 .30
29 Tom Glavine .20 .50
30 Ozzie Guillen .10 .30
31 Andruw Jones .20 .50
32 Chipper Jones * .30 .75
32A C.Jones Headshot .30 .75
33 Ryan Klesko .10 .30
34 George Lombard .10 .30
35 Javy Lopez .10 .30
36 Greg Maddux * .50 1.25
36A G.Maddux Headshot .50 1.25
37 Marty Malloy * .10 .30
37A M.Malloy Headshot .10 .30
38 Dennis Martinez .10 .30
39 Kevin Millwood .10 .30
40 Alex Rodriguez * .50 1.25
40A Alex Rodriguez Headshot .50 1.25
41 Denny Neagle .10 .30
42 John Smoltz .20 .50
43 Michael Tucker .10 .30
44 Walt Weiss .10 .30
45 Roberto Alomar * .20 .50
45A R.Alomar Headshot .20 .50
46 Brady Anderson .10 .30
47 Harold Baines .10 .30
48 Mike Bordick .10 .30
49 Danny Clyburn * .10 .30
49A D.Clyburn Headshot .10 .30
50 Eric Davis .10 .30
51 Scott Erickson .10 .30
52 Chris Hoiles .10 .30
53 Jimmy Key .10 .30
54 Ryan Minor * .10 .30
54A Ryan Minor Headshot .10 .30
55 Mike Mussina .20 .50
56 Jesse Orosco .10 .30
57 Rafael Palmeiro * .20 .50
57A R.Palmeiro Headshot .20 .50
58 Sidney Ponson .10 .30
59 Arthur Rhodes .10 .30
60 Cal Ripken * 1.00 2.50
60A Cal Ripken Headshot 1.00 2.50
61 B.J. Surhoff .10 .30
62 Steve Avery .10 .30
63 Darren Bragg .10 .30
64 Dennis Eckersley .10 .30
65 Nomar Garciaparra * .50 1.25
65A Nomar Garciaparra Headshot .50 1.25
66 Sammy Sosa * .30 .75
66A S.Sosa Headshot .30 .75
67 Tom Gordon .10 .30
68 Reggie Jefferson .10 .30
69 Darren Lewis .10 .30
70 Mark McGwire * .75 2.00
70A M.McGwire Headshot .75 2.00
71 Pedro Martinez .20 .50
72 Troy O'Leary .10 .30
73 Bret Saberhagen .10 .30
74 Mike Stanley .10 .30
75 John Valentin .10 .30
76 Jason Varitek .30 .75
77 Mo Vaughn .10 .30
78 Tim Wakefield .10 .30
79 Manny Alexander .10 .30
80 Rod Beck .10 .30
81 Brant Brown .10 .30
82 Mark Clark .10 .30
83 Gary Gaetti .10 .30
84 Mark Grace .20 .50
85 Jose Hernandez .10 .30
86 Lance Johnson .10 .30
87 Jason Maxwell * .10 .30
87A J.Maxwell Headshot .10 .30
88 Mickey Morandini .10 .30
89 Terry Mulholland .10 .30
90 Henry Rodriguez .10 .30
91 Scott Servais .10 .30
92 Kevin Tapani .10 .30
93 Pedro Valdes .10 .30
94 Kerry Wood .10 .30
95 Jeff Abbott .10 .30
96 James Baldwin .10 .30
97 Albert Belle .10 .30
98 Mike Cameron .10 .30
99 Mike Caruso .10 .30
100 Wil Cordero .10 .30
101 Ray Durham .10 .30
102 Jaime Navarro .10 .30
103 Greg Norton .10 .30
104 Magglio Ordonez .10 .30
105 Mike Sirotka .10 .30
106 Frank Thomas * .30 .75
106A F.Thomas Headshot .30 .75
107 Robin Ventura .10 .30
108 Craig Wilson .10 .30
109 Aaron Boone .10 .30
110 Bret Boone .10 .30
111 Sean Casey .10 .30
112 Pete Harnisch .10 .30
113 John Hudek .10 .30
114 Barry Larkin .20 .50
115 Eduardo Perez .10 .30
116 Mike Remlinger .10 .30
117 Reggie Sanders .10 .30
118 Chris Stynes .10 .30
119 Eddie Taubensee .10 .30
120 Brett Tomko .10 .30
121 Pat Watkins .10 .30
122 Dmitri Young .10 .30
123 Sandy Alomar Jr. .10 .30
124 Dave Burba .10 .30
125 Bartolo Colon .10 .30
126 Joey Cora .10 .30
127 Brian Giles .10 .30
128 Dwight Gooden .10 .30
129 Mike Jackson .10 .30
130 David Justice .10 .30
131 Kenny Lofton .10 .30
132 Charles Nagy .10 .30
133 Chad Ogea .10 .30
134 Manny Ramirez * .20 .50
134A M.Ramirez Headshot .20 .50
135 Richie Sexson .10 .30
136 Jim Thome * .20 .50
136A J.Thome Headshot .20 .50
137 Omar Vizquel .20 .50
138 Jaret Wright .10 .30
139 Pedro Astacio .10 .30
140 Jason Bates .10 .30
141 Dante Bichette * .10 .30
141A Dante Bichette Headshot .10 .30
142 Vinny Castilla * .10 .30
142A V.Castilla Headshot .10 .30
143 Edgard Clemente * .10 .30
143A Edgard Clemente Headshot .10 .30
144 Derrick Gibson * .10 .30
144A D. Gibson Headshot .10 .30
145 Curtis Goodwin .10 .30
146 Todd Helton * .20 .50
146A T.Helton Headshot .20 .50
147 Bobby Jones .10 .30
148 Darryl Kile .10 .30
149 Mike Lansing .10 .30
150 Chuck McElroy .10 .30
151 Neifi Perez .10 .30
152 Jeff Reed .10 .30
153 John Thomson .10 .30
154 Larry Walker * .10 .30
154A L.Walker Headshot .10 .30
155 Jamey Wright .10 .30
156 Kimera Bartee .10 .30
157 Geronimo Berroa .10 .30
158 Raul Casanova .10 .30
159 Frank Catalanotto .10 .30
160 Tony Clark .10 .30
161 Deivi Cruz .10 .30
162 Damion Easley .10 .30
163 Juan Encarnacion .10 .30
164 Luis Gonzalez .10 .30
165 Seth Greisinger .10 .30
166 Bob Higginson .10 .30
167 Brian L.Hunter .10 .30
168 Todd Jones .10 .30
169 Justin Thompson .10 .30
170 Antonio Alfonseca .10 .30
171 Dave Berg .10 .30
172 John Cangelosi .10 .30
173 Craig Counsell .10 .30
174 Todd Dunwoody .10 .30
175 Cliff Floyd .10 .30
176 Alex Gonzalez .10 .30
177 Livan Hernandez .10 .30
178 Ryan Jackson .10 .30
179 Mark Kotsay .10 .30
180 Derrek Lee .20 .50
181 Matt Mantei .10 .30
182 Brian Meadows .10 .30
183 Edgar Renteria .10 .30
184 Moises Alou * .10 .30
184A M.Alou Headshot .10 .30
185 Brad Ausmus .10 .30
186 Jeff Bagwell * .20 .50
186A J.Bagwell Headshot .20 .50
187 Derek Bell .10 .30
188 Sean Berry .10 .30
189 Craig Biggio .20 .50
190 Carl Everett .10 .30
191 Ricky Gutierrez .10 .30
192 Mike Hampton .10 .30
193 Doug Henry .10 .30
194 Richard Hidalgo .10 .30
195 Randy Johnson .30 .75
196 Russ Johnson * .10 .30
196A R.Johnson Headshot .10 .30
197 Shane Reynolds .10 .30
198 Bill Spiers .10 .30
199 Kevin Appier .10 .30
200 Tim Belcher .10 .30
201 Jeff Conine .10 .30
202 Johnny Damon .20 .50
203 Jermaine Dye .10 .30
204 Jeremy Giambi * .10 .30
204A Je. Giambi Headshot .10 .30
205 Jeff King .10 .30
206 Shane Mack .10 .30
207 Jeff Montgomery .10 .30
208 Hal Morris .10 .30
209 Jose Offerman .10 .30
210 Dean Palmer .10 .30
211 Jose Rosado .10 .30
212 Glendon Rusch .10 .30
213 Larry Sutton .10 .30
214 Mike Sweeney .10 .30
215 Bobby Bonilla .10 .30
216 Alex Cora .10 .30
217 Darren Dreifort .10 .30
218 Mark Grudzielanek .10 .30
219 Todd Hollandsworth .10 .30
220 Trenidad Hubbard .10 .30
221 Charles Johnson .10 .30
222 Eric Karros .10 .30
223 Matt Luke .10 .30
224 Ramon Martinez .10 .30
225 Raul Mondesi .10 .30
226 Chan Ho Park .10 .30
227 Jeff Shaw .10 .30
228 Gary Sheffield .10 .30
229 Eric Young .10 .30
230 Jeromy Burnitz .10 .30
231 Jeff Cirillo .10 .30
232 Marquis Grissom .10 .30
233 Bobby Hughes .10 .30
234 John Jaha .10 .30
235 Geoff Jenkins .10 .30
236 Scott Karl .10 .30
237 Mark Loretta .10 .30
238 Mike Matheny .10 .30
239 Mike Myers .10 .30
240 Dave Nilsson .10 .30
241 Bob Wickman .10 .30
242 Jose Valentin .10 .30
243 Fernando Vina .10 .30
244 Rick Aguilera .10 .30
245 Ron Coomer .10 .30
246 Marty Cordova .10 .30
247 Denny Hocking .10 .30
248 Matt Lawton .10 .30
249 Pat Meares .10 .30
250 Paul Molitor * .20 .50
250A P.Molitor Headshot .20 .50
251 Otis Nixon .10 .30
252 Alex Ochoa .10 .30
253 David Ortiz .30 .75
254 A.J. Pierzynski .10 .30
255 Brad Radke .10 .30
256 Terry Steinbach .10 .30
257 Bob Tewksbury .10 .30
258 Todd Walker .10 .30
259 Shane Andrews .10 .30
260 Shayne Bennett .10 .30
261 Orlando Cabrera .10 .30
262 Brad Fullmer .10 .30
263 Vladimir Guerrero .30 .75
264 Wilton Guerrero .10 .30
265 Dustin Hermanson .10 .30
266 Terry Jones RC .10 .30
267 Steve Kline .10 .30
268 Carl Pavano .10 .30
269 F.P. Santangelo .10 .30
270 Fernando Seguignol * .10 .30
270A Fernando Seguignol Headshot .10 .30
271 Ugueth Urbina .10 .30
272 Jose Vidro .10 .30
273 Chris Widger .10 .30
274 Edgardo Alfonzo .10 .30
275 Carlos Baerga .10 .30
276 John Franco .10 .30
277 Todd Hundley .10 .30
278 Butch Huskey .10 .30
279 Bobby Jones .10 .30
280 Al Leiter .10 .30
281 Greg McMichael .10 .30
282 Brian McRae .10 .30
283 Hideo Nomo .30 .75
284 John Olerud .10 .30
285 Rey Ordonez .10 .30
286 Mike Piazza * .50 1.25
286A M.Piazza Headshot .50 1.25
287 Turk Wendell .10 .30
288 Masato Yoshii .10 .30
289 David Cone .10 .30
290 Chad Curtis .10 .30
291 Joe Girardi .10 .30
292 Orlando Hernandez .10 .30
293 Hideki Irabu * .10 .30
293A H.Irabu Headshot .10 .30
294 Derek Jeter * .75 2.00
294A D.Jeter Headshot .75 2.00
295 Chuck Knoblauch .10 .30
296 Mike Lowell * .10 .30
296A M.Lowell Headshot .10 .30
297 Tino Martinez .20 .50
298 Ramiro Mendoza .10 .30
299 Paul O'Neill .20 .50
300 Andy Pettitte .20 .50
301 Jorge Posada .20 .50
302 Tim Raines .10 .30
303 Mariano Rivera .30 .75
304 David Wells .10 .30
305 Bernie Williams * .20 .50
305A Bernie Williams Headshot .20 .50
306 Mike Blowers .10 .30
307 Tom Candiotti .10 .30
308 Eric Chavez * .10 .30
308A E.Chavez Headshot .10 .30
309 Ryan Christenson .10 .30
310 Jason Giambi .10 .30
311 Ben Grieve * .10 .30
311A Ben Grieve Headshot .10 .30
312 Rickey Henderson .30 .75
313 A.J. Hinch .10 .30
314 Jason McDonald .10 .30
315 Bip Roberts .10 .30
316 Kenny Rogers .10 .30
317 Scott Spiezio .10 .30
318 Matt Stairs .10 .30
319 Miguel Tejada .10 .30
320 Bob Abreu .10 .30
321 Alex Arias .10 .30
322 Gary Bennett RC .10 .30
322A Gary Bennett RC Headshot .10 .30
323 Ricky Bottalico .10 .30
324 Rico Brogna .10 .30
325 Bobby Estalella .10 .30
326 Doug Glanville .10 .30
327 Kevin Jordan .10 .30
328 Mark Leiter .10 .30
329 Wendell Magee .10 .30
330 Mark Portugal .10 .30
331 Desi Relaford .10 .30
332 Scott Rolen .20 .50
333 Curt Schilling .10 .30
334 Kevin Sefcik .10 .30
335 Adrian Brown .10 .30
336 Emil Brown .10 .30
337 Lou Collier .10 .30
338 Francisco Cordova .10 .30
339 Freddy Garcia .10 .30
340 Jose Guillen .10 .30
341 Jason Kendall .10 .30
342 Al Martin .10 .30
343 Abraham Nunez .10 .30
344 Aramis Ramirez .10 .30
345 Ricardo Rincon .10 .30
346 Jason Schmidt .10 .30
347 Turner Ward .10 .30
348 Tony Womack .10 .30
349 Kevin Young .10 .30
350 Juan Acevedo .10 .30
351 Delino DeShields .10 .30
352 J.D. Drew * .10 .30
352A J.D. Drew Headshot .10 .30
353 Ron Gant .10 .30
354 Brian Jordan .10 .30
355 Ray Lankford .10 .30
356 Eli Marrero .10 .30
357 Kent Mercker .10 .30
358 Matt Morris .10 .30
359 Luis Ordaz .10 .30
360 Donovan Osborne .10 .30
361 Placido Polanco .10 .30
362 Fernando Tatis .10 .30
363 Andy Ashby .10 .30
364 Kevin Brown .20 .50
365 Ken Caminiti .10 .30
366 Steve Finley .10 .30
367 Chris Gomez .10 .30
368 Tony Gwynn * .40 1.00
368A T.Gwynn Headshot .40 1.00
369 Joey Hamilton .10 .30
370 Carlos Hernandez .10 .30
371 Trevor Hoffman .10 .30
372 Wally Joyner .10 .30
373 Jim Leyritz .10 .30
374 Ruben Rivera .10 .30
375 Greg Vaughn .10 .30
376 Quilvio Veras .10 .30
377 Rich Aurilia .10 .30
378 Barry Bonds * .75 2.00
378A B.Bonds Headshot .60 1.50
379 Ellis Burks .10 .30
380 Joe Carter .10 .30
381 Stan Javier .10 .30
382 Brian Johnson .10 .30
383 Jeff Kent .10 .30
384 Jose Mesa .10 .30
385 Bill Mueller .10 .30
386 Robb Nen .10 .30
387 Armando Rios * .10 .30
387A A.Rios Headshot .10 .30
388 Kirk Rueter .10 .30
389 Rey Sanchez .10 .30
390 J.T. Snow .10 .30
391 David Bell .10 .30
392 Jay Buhner .10 .30
393 Ken Cloude .10 .30
394 Russ Davis .10 .30
395 Jeff Fassero .10 .30
396 Ken Griffey Jr. * .50 1.25
396A Ken Griffey Jr. Headshot .50 1.25
397 Giomar Guevara RC .10 .30
398 Carlos Guillen .10 .30
399 Edgar Martinez .20 .50
400 Shane Monahan .10 .30
401 Jamie Moyer .10 .30
402 David Segui .10 .30
403 Makoto Suzuki .10 .30
404 Mike Timlin .10 .30
405 Dan Wilson .10 .30
406 Wilson Alvarez .10 .30
407 Rolando Arrojo .10 .30
408 Wade Boggs .20 .50
409 Miguel Cairo .10 .30
410 Roberto Hernandez .10 .30
411 Mike Kelly .10 .30
412 Aaron Ledesma .10 .30
413 Albie Lopez .10 .30
414 Dave Martinez .10 .30
415 Quinton McCracken .10 .30
416 Fred McGriff .20 .50
417 Bryan Rekar .10 .30
418 Paul Sorrento .10 .30
419 Randy Winn .10 .30
420 John Burkett .10 .30
421 Will Clark .20 .50
422 Royce Clayton .10 .30
423 Juan Gonzalez * .10 .30
423A Juan Gonzalez Headshot .10 .30
424 Tom Goodwin .10 .30
425 Rusty Greer .10 .30
426 Rick Helling .10 .30
427 Roberto Kelly .10 .30
428 Mark McLemore .10 .30
429 Ivan Rodriguez * .20 .50
429A Ivan Rodriguez Headshot .20 .50
430 Aaron Sele .10 .30
431 Lee Stevens .10 .30
432 Todd Stottlemyre .10 .30
433 John Wetteland .10 .30
434 Todd Zeile .10 .30
435 Jose Canseco * .20 .50
435A J.Canseco Headshot .20 .50
436 Roger Clemens * .60 1.50
436A R.Clemens Headshot .60 1.50
437 Felipe Crespo .10 .30
438 Jose Cruz Jr. .10 .30
439 Carlos Delgado .10 .30
440 Tom Evans * .10 .30
440A T.Evans Headshot .10 .30
441 Tony Fernandez .10 .30
442 Darrin Fletcher .10 .30
443 Alex Gonzalez .10 .30
444 Shawn Green .10 .30
445 Roy Halladay .10 .30
446 Pat Hentgen .10 .30
447 Juan Samuel .10 .30
448 Benito Santiago .10 .30
449 Shannon Stewart .10 .30
450 Woody Williams .10 .30
NNO Tony Gwynn Sample .40 1.00

2000 Pacific

Though numbered 1-450, fifty supertsars were featured in both action and portrait variations on the card front photos. Therefore the set is considered complete at 500 cards. The product was issued in 12 card packs with 24 packs in each box and 20 boxes per case. The packs carried a suggested retail price of $2.49 each. Special Jewel Collection packs were issued for the 7/11 convenience store chain and they contained 12 cards with an SRP of $2.99. A Tony Gwynn Sample card was distributed to dealers and hobby media several weeks prior to the release of the product. The Gwynn card is readily identifiable by the bold "SAMPLE" text running diagonally across the card back.

COMPLETE SET (500) 20.00 50.00
1 Garret Anderson .10 .30
2 Tim Belcher .10 .30
3 Gary DiSarcina .10 .30
4 Trent Durrington .10 .30
5 Jim Edmonds .10 .30
6 Darin Erstad ACTION .10 .30
6A Darin Erstad POR .10 .30
7 Chuck Finley .10 .30
8 Troy Glaus .10 .30
9 Todd Greene .10 .30
10 Bret Hemphill .10 .30
11 Ken Hill .10 .30
12 Ramon Ortiz .10 .30
13 Troy Percival .10 .30
14 Mark Petkovsek .10 .30
15 Tim Salmon .20 .50
16 Mo Vaughn ACTION .10 .30
16A Mo Vaughn POR .10 .30
17 Jay Bell .10 .30
18 Omar Daal .10 .30
19 Erubiel Durazo .10 .30
20 Steve Finley .10 .30
21 Bernard Gilkey .10 .30
22 Luis Gonzalez .10 .30
23 Randy Johnson .30 .75
24 Byung-Hyun Kim .10 .30
25 Travis Lee .10 .30
26 Matt Mantei .10 .30
27 Armando Reynoso .10 .30
28 Rob Ryan .10 .30
29 Kelly Stinnett .10 .30
30 Todd Stottlemyre .10 .30
31 Matt Williams ACTION .10 .30
31A Matt Williams POR .10 .30
32 Tony Womack .10 .30
33 Bret Boone .10 .30
34 Andres Galarraga .10 .30
35 Tom Glavine .20 .50
36 Ozzie Guillen .10 .30
37 Andruw Jones ACTION .20 .50
37A Andruw Jones POR .20 .50
38 Chipper Jones ACTION .30 .75
38A Chipper Jones POR .30 .75
39 Brian Jordan .10 .30
40 Ryan Klesko .10 .30
41 Javy Lopez .10 .30
42 Greg Maddux ACTION .50 1.25
42A Greg Maddux POR .50 1.25
43 Kevin Millwood .10 .30
44 John Rocker .10 .30
45 Randall Simon .10 .30
46 John Smoltz .20 .50
47 Gerald Williams .10 .30
48 Brady Anderson .10 .30
49 Albert Belle ACTION .10 .30
49A Albert Belle POR .10 .30
50 Mike Bordick .10 .30
51 Will Clark .20 .50
52 Jeff Conine .10 .30
53 Delino DeShields .10 .30
54 Jerry Hairston Jr. .10 .30
55 Charles Johnson .10 .30
56 Eugene Kingsale .10 .30
57 Ryan Minor .10 .30
58 Mike Mussina .20 .50
59 Sidney Ponson .10 .30
60 Cal Ripken ACTION 1.00 2.50
60A Cal Ripken POR 1.00 2.50
61 B.J. Surhoff .10 .30
62 Mike Timlin .10 .30
63 Rod Beck .10 .30
64 N.Garciaparra ACTION .50 1.25
64A N.Garciaparra POR .50 1.25
65 Tom Gordon .10 .30
66 Butch Huskey .10 .30
67 Derek Lowe .10 .30
68 P.Martinez ACTION .20 .50
68A Pedro Martinez POR .20 .50
69 Trot Nixon .10 .30
70 Jose Offerman .10 .30
71 Troy O'Leary .10 .30
72 Pat Rapp .10 .30
73 Donnie Sadler .10 .30
74 Mike Stanley .10 .30
75 John Valentin .10 .30
76 Jason Varitek .30 .75
77 Wilton Veras .10 .30
78 Tim Wakefield .10 .30
79 Rick Aguilera .10 .30
80 Manny Alexander .10 .30
81 Roosevelt Brown .10 .30
82 Mark Grace .20 .50
83 Glenallen Hill .10 .30
84 Lance Johnson .10 .30
85 Jon Lieber .10 .30
86 Cole Liniak .10 .30
87 Chad Meyers .10 .30
88 Mickey Morandini .10 .30
89 Jose Nieves .10 .30
90 Henry Rodriguez .10 .30
91 Sammy Sosa ACTION .30 .75
91A Sammy Sosa POR .30 .75
92 Kevin Tapani .10 .30
93 Kerry Wood .10 .30
94 Mike Caruso .10 .30
95 Ray Durham .10 .30
96 Brook Fordyce .10 .30
97 Bobby Howry .10 .30
98 Paul Konerko .10 .30
99 Carlos Lee .10 .30
100 Aaron Myette .10 .30
101 Greg Norton .10 .30
102 Magglio Ordonez .10 .30
103 Jim Parque .10 .30
104 Liu Rodriguez .10 .30
105 Chris Singleton .10 .30
106 Mike Sirotka .10 .30
107 F.Thomas ACTION .30 .75
107A Frank Thomas POR .30 .75
108 Kip Wells .10 .30
109 Aaron Boone .10 .30
110 Mike Cameron .10 .30
111 Sean Casey ACTION .10 .30
111A Sean Casey POR .10 .30
112 Jeffrey Hammonds .10 .30
113 Pete Harnisch .10 .30
114 Barry Larkin ACTION .20 .50
114A Barry Larkin POR .20 .50
115 Jason LaRue .10 .30
116 Denny Neagle .10 .30
117 Pokey Reese .10 .30
118 Scott Sullivan .10 .30
119 Eddie Taubensee .10 .30
120 Greg Vaughn .10 .30
121 Scott Williamson .10 .30
122 Dmitri Young .10 .30
123 R.Alomar ACTION .20 .50
123A R.Alomar POR .20 .50
124 Sandy Alomar Jr. .10 .30
125 Harold Baines .10 .30
126 Russell Branyan .10 .30
127 Dave Burba .10 .30
128 Bartolo Colon .10 .30
129 Travis Fryman .10 .30
130 Mike Jackson .10 .30
131 David Justice .10 .30
132 Kenny Lofton ACTION .10 .30
132A Kenny Lofton POR .10 .30
133 Charles Nagy .10 .30
134 M.Ramirez ACTION .20 .50
134A Manny Ramirez POR .20 .50
135 Dave Roberts .10 .30
136 Richie Sexson .10 .30
137 Jim Thome .20 .50
138 Omar Vizquel .20 .50
139 Jaret Wright .10 .30
140 Pedro Astacio .10 .30
141 Dante Bichette .10 .30
142 Brian Bohanon .10 .30
143 Vinny Castilla ACTION .10 .30
143A Vinny Castilla POR .10 .30
144 Edgard Clemente .10 .30
145 Derrick Gibson .10 .30
146 Todd Helton .20 .50
147 Darryl Kile .10 .30
148 Mike Lansing .10 .30
149 Kirt Manwaring .10 .30
150 Neifi Perez .10 .30
151 Ben Petrick .10 .30
152 Juan Sosa RC .10 .30
153 Dave Veres .10 .30
154 Larry Walker ACTION .10 .30
154A Larry Walker POR .10 .30

155 Brad Ausmus .10 .30
156 Dave Borkowski .10 .30
157 Tony Clark .10 .30
158 Francisco Cordero .10 .30
159 Deivi Cruz .10 .30
160 Damion Easley .10 .30
161 Juan Encarnacion .10 .30
162 Robert Fick .10 .30
163 Bobby Higginson .10 .30
164 Gabe Kapler .10 .30
165 Brian Moehler .10 .30
166 Dean Palmer .10 .30
167 Luis Polonia .10 .30
168 Justin Thompson .10 .30
169 Jeff Weaver .10 .30
170 Antonio Alfonseca .10 .30
171 Bruce Aven .10 .30
172 A.J. Burnett .10 .30
173 Luis Castillo .10 .30
174 Ramon Castro .10 .30
175 Ryan Dempster .10 .30
176 Alex Fernandez .10 .30
177 Cliff Floyd .10 .30
178 Amaury Garcia .10 .30
179 Alex Gonzalez .10 .30
180 Mark Kotsay .10 .30
181 Mike Lowell .10 .30
182 Brian Meadows .10 .30
183 Kevin Orie .10 .30
184 Julio Ramirez .10 .30
185 Preston Wilson .10 .30
186 Moises Alou .10 .30
187 Jeff Bagwell ACTION .20 .50
187A Jeff Bagwell POR .20 .50
188 Glen Barker .10 .30
189 Derek Bell .10 .30
190 Craig Biggio ACTION .20 .50
190A Craig Biggio POR .20 .50
191 Ken Caminiti .10 .30
192 Scott Elarton .10 .30
193 Carl Everett .10 .30
194 Mike Hampton .10 .30
195 Carlos E. Hernandez .10 .30
196 Richard Hidalgo .10 .30
197 Jose Lima .10 .30
198 Shane Reynolds .10 .30
199 Bill Spiers .10 .30
200 Billy Wagner .10 .30
201 C. Beltran ACTION .10 .30
201A Carlos Beltran POR .10 .30
202 Dermal Brown .10 .30
203 Johnny Damon .20 .50
204 Jermaine Dye .10 .30
205 Carlos Febles .10 .30
206 Jeremy Giambi .10 .30
207 Mark Quinn .10 .30
208 Joe Randa .10 .30
209 Dan Reichert .10 .30
210 Jose Rosado .10 .30
211 Rey Sanchez .10 .30
212 Jeff Suppan .10 .30
213 Mike Sweeney .10 .30
214 Kevin Brown ACTION .10 .30
214A Kevin Brown POR .10 .30
215 Darren Dreifort .10 .30
216 Eric Gagne .30 .75
217 Mark Grudzielanek .10 .30
218 Todd Hollandsworth .10 .30
219 Todd Hundley .10 .30
220 Eric Karros .10 .30
221 Raul Mondesi .10 .30
222 Chan Ho Park .10 .30
223 Jeff Shaw .10 .30
224 G.Sheffield ACTION .10 .30
224A Gary Sheffield POR .10 .30
225 Ismael Valdes .10 .30
226 Devon White .10 .30
227 Eric Young .10 .30
228 Kevin Barker .10 .30
229 Ron Belliard .10 .30
230 J.Burnitz ACTION .10 .30
230A Jeromy Burnitz POR .10 .30
231 Jeff Cirillo .10 .30
232 Marquis Grissom .10 .30
233 Geoff Jenkins .10 .30
234 Mark Loretta .10 .30
235 David Nilsson .10 .30
236 Hideo Nomo .30 .75
237 Alex Ochoa .10 .30
238 Kyle Peterson .10 .30
239 Fernando Vina .10 .30
240 Bob Wickman .10 .30
241 Steve Woodard .10 .30
242 Chad Allen .10 .30
243 Ron Coomer .10 .30
244 Marty Cordova .10 .30
245 Cristian Guzman .10 .30
246 Denny Hocking .10 .30
247 Jacque Jones .10 .30
248 Corey Koskie .10 .30
249 Matt Lawton .10 .30
250 Joe Mays .10 .30
251 Eric Milton .10 .30
252 Brad Radke .10 .30
253 Mark Redman .10 .30
254 Terry Steinbach .10 .30
255 Todd Walker .10 .30
256 Tony Armas Jr. .10 .30
257 Michael Barrett .10 .30
258 Peter Bergeron .10 .30
259 Geoff Blum .10 .30
260 Orlando Cabrera .10 .30
261 Trace Coquillette RC .10 .30
262 Brad Fullmer .10 .30
263 V.Guerrero ACTION .30 .75
263A V.Guerrero POR .30 .75
264 Wilton Guerrero .10 .30
265 Dustin Hermanson .10 .30
266 Manny Martinez RC .10 .30
267 Ryan McGuire .10 .30
268 Ugueth Urbina .10 .30
269 Jose Vidro .10 .30
270 Rondell White .10 .30
271 Chris Widger .10 .30
272 Edgardo Alfonzo .10 .30
273 Armando Benitez .10 .30
274 Roger Cedeno .10 .30
275 Dennis Cook .10 .30
276 Octavio Dotel .10 .30
277 John Franco .10 .30
278 Darryl Hamilton .10 .30
279 Rickey Henderson .30 .75
280 Orel Hershiser .10 .30
281 Al Leiter .10 .30
282 John Olerud ACTION .10 .30
282A John Olerud POR .10 .30
283 Rey Ordonez .10 .30
284 Mike Piazza ACTION .50 1.25
284A Mike Piazza POR .50 1.25
285 Kenny Rogers .10 .30
286 Jorge Toca .10 .30
287 Robin Ventura .20 .50
288 Scott Brosius .10 .30
289 R.Clemens ACTION .60 1.50
289A Roger Clemens POR .60 1.50
290 David Cone .10 .30
291 Chili Davis .10 .30
292 Orlando Hernandez .10 .30
293 Hideki Irabu .10 .30
294 Derek Jeter ACTION .75 2.00
294A Derek Jeter POR .75 2.00
295 Chuck Knoblauch .10 .30
296 Ricky Ledee .10 .30
297 Jim Leyritz .10 .30
298 Tino Martinez .20 .50
299 Paul O'Neill .20 .50
300 Andy Pettitte .20 .50
301 Jorge Posada .20 .50
302 Mariano Rivera .30 .75
303 Alfonso Soriano .30 .75
304 B.Williams ACTION .20 .50
304A Bernie Williams POR .20 .50
305 Ed Yarnall .10 .30
306 Kevin Appier .10 .30
307 Rich Becker .10 .30
308 Eric Chavez .10 .30
309 Jason Giambi .10 .30
310 Ben Grieve .10 .30
311 Ramon Hernandez .10 .30
312 Tim Hudson .10 .30
313 John Jaha .10 .30
314 Doug Jones .10 .30
315 Omar Olivares .10 .30
316 Mike Oquist .10 .30
317 Matt Stairs .10 .30
318 Miguel Tejada .10 .30
319 Randy Velarde .10 .30
320 Bob Abreu .10 .30
321 Marlon Anderson .10 .30
322 Alex Arias .10 .30
323 Rico Brogna .10 .30
324 Paul Byrd .10 .30
325 Ron Gant .10 .30
326 Doug Glanville .10 .30
327 Wayne Gomes .10 .30
328 Mike Lieberthal .10 .30
329 Robert Person .10 .30
330 Desi Relaford .10 .30
331 Scott Rolen ACTION .20 .50
331A Scott Rolen POR .20 .50
332 Curt Schilling ACTION .10 .30
332A Curt Schilling POR .10 .30
333 Kris Benson .10 .30
334 Adrian Brown .10 .30
335 Brant Brown .10 .30
336 Brian Giles .10 .30
337 Chad Hermansen .10 .30
338 Jason Kendall .10 .30
339 Al Martin .10 .30
340 Pat Meares .10 .30
341 W.Morris ACTION .10 .30
341A Warren Morris POR .10 .30
342 Todd Ritchie .10 .30
343 Jason Schmidt .10 .30
344 Ed Sprague .10 .30
345 Mike Williams .10 .30
346 Kevin Young .10 .30
347 Rick Ankiel .10 .30
348 Ricky Bottalico .10 .30
349 Kent Bottenfield .10 .30
350 Darren Bragg .10 .30
351 Eric Davis .10 .30
352 J.D. Drew ACTION .10 .30
352A J.D. Drew POR .10 .30
353 Adam Kennedy .10 .30
354 Ray Lankford .10 .30
355 Joe McEwing .10 .30
356 M.McGwire ACTION .75 2.00
356A Mark McGwire POR .75 2.00
357 Matt Morris .10 .30
358 Darren Oliver .10 .30
359 Edgar Renteria .10 .30
360 Fernando Tatis .10 .30
361 Andy Ashby .10 .30
362 Ben Davis .10 .30
363 Tony Gwynn ACTION .40 1.00
363A Tony Gwynn POR .40 1.00
364 Sterling Hitchcock .10 .30
365 Trevor Hoffman .10 .30
366 Damian Jackson .10 .30
367 Wally Joyner .10 .30
368 Dave Magadan .10 .30
369 Gary Matthews Jr. .10 .30
370 Phil Nevin .10 .30
371 Eric Owens .10 .30
372 Ruben Rivera .10 .30
373 R.Sanders ACTION .10 .30
373A Reggie Sanders POR .10 .30
374 Quilvio Veras .10 .30
375 Rich Aurilia .10 .30
376 Marvin Benard .10 .30
377 Barry Bonds ACTION .75 2.00
377A Barry Bonds POR .75 2.00
378 Ellis Burks .10 .30
379 Shawn Estes .10 .30
380 Livan Hernandez .10 .30
381 Jeff Kent ACTION .10 .30
381A Jeff Kent POR .10 .30
382 Brent Mayne .10 .30
383 Bill Mueller .10 .30
384 Calvin Murray .10 .30
385 Robb Nen .10 .30
386 Russ Ortiz .10 .30
387 Kirk Rueter .10 .30
388 J.T. Snow .10 .30
389 David Bell .10 .30
390 Jay Buhner .10 .30
391 Russ Davis .10 .30
392 Freddy Garcia ACTION .10 .30
392A Freddy Garcia POR .10 .30
393 K.Griffey Jr. ACTION .50 1.25
393A Ken Griffey Jr. POR .50 1.25
394 Carlos Guillen .10 .30
395 John Halama .10 .30
396 Brian L.Hunter .10 .30
397 Ryan Jackson .10 .30
398 Edgar Martinez .20 .50
399 Gil Meche .10 .30
400 Jose Mesa .10 .30
401 Jamie Moyer .10 .30
402 A.Rodriguez ACTION .50 1.25
402A Alex Rodriguez POR .50 1.25
403 Dan Wilson .10 .30
404 Wilson Alvarez .10 .30
405 Rolando Arrojo .10 .30
406 Wade Boggs ACTION .20 .50
406A Wade Boggs POR .20 .50
407 Miguel Cairo .10 .30
408 Jose Canseco ACTION .20 .50
408A Jose Canseco POR .20 .50
409 John Flaherty .10 .30
410 Jose Guillen .10 .30
411 Roberto Hernandez .10 .30
412 Terrell Lowery .10 .30
413 Dave Martinez .10 .30
414 Quinton McCracken .10 .30
415 Fred McGriff ACTION .20 .50
415A Fred McGriff POR .20 .50
416 Ryan Rupe .10 .30
417 Kevin Stocker .10 .30
418 Bubba Trammell .10 .30
419 Royce Clayton .10 .30
420 J.Gonzalez ACTION .10 .30
420A Juan Gonzalez POR .10 .30
421 Tom Goodwin .10 .30
422 Rusty Greer .10 .30
423 Rick Helling .10 .30
424 Roberto Kelly .10 .30
425 Ruben Mateo .10 .30
426 Mark McLemore .10 .30
427 Mike Morgan .10 .30
428 Rafael Palmeiro .20 .50
429 I.Rodriguez ACTION .20 .50
429A Ivan Rodriguez POR .20 .50
430 Aaron Sele .10 .30
431 Lee Stevens .10 .30
432 John Wetteland .10 .30
433 Todd Zeile .10 .30
434 Jeff Zimmerman .10 .30
435 Tony Batista .10 .30
436 Casey Blake .10 .30
437 Homer Bush .10 .30
438 Chris Carpenter .10 .30
439 Jose Cruz Jr. .10 .30
440 C.Delgado ACTION .10 .30
440A Carlos Delgado POR .10 .30
441 Tony Fernandez .10 .30
442 Darrin Fletcher .10 .30
443 Alex Gonzalez .10 .30
444 Shawn Green ACTION .10 .30
444A Shawn Green POR .10 .30
445 Roy Halladay .10 .30
446 Billy Koch .10 .30
447 David Segui .10 .30
448 Shannon Stewart .10 .30
449 David Wells .10 .30
450 Vernon Wells .10 .30
SAMP T.Gwynn Sample .40 1.00

2001 Pacific

The 2001 Pacific product was released in December, 2000 and features a 500-card base set. Each pack contained 12 cards, and carried a suggested retail price of 2.99.

COMPLETE SET (500) 50.00 100.00
1 Garret Anderson .10 .30
2 Gary DiSarcina .10 .30
3 Darin Erstad .10 .30
4 Seth Etherton .10 .30
5 Ron Gant .10 .30
6 Troy Glaus .10 .30
7 Shigetoshi Hasegawa .10 .30
8 Adam Kennedy .10 .30
9 Ben Molina .10 .30
10 Ramon Ortiz .10 .30
11 Troy Percival .10 .30
12 Tim Salmon .20 .50
13 Scott Schoeneweis .10 .30
14 Mo Vaughn .10 .30
15 Jarrod Washburn .10 .30
16 Brian Anderson .10 .30
17 Danny Bautista .10 .30
18 Jay Bell .10 .30
19 Greg Colbrunn .10 .30
20 Erubiel Durazo .10 .30
21 Steve Finley .10 .30
22 Luis Gonzalez .10 .30
23 Randy Johnson .30 .75
24 Byung-Hyun Kim .10 .30
25 Matt Mantei .10 .30
26 Armando Reynoso .10 .30
27 Todd Stottlemyre .10 .30
28 Matt Williams .10 .30
29 Tony Womack .10 .30
30 Andy Ashby .10 .30
31 Bobby Bonilla .10 .30
32 Rafael Furcal .10 .30
33 Andres Galarraga .10 .30
34 Tom Glavine .20 .50
35 Andruw Jones .20 .50
36 Chipper Jones .30 .75
37 Brian Jordan .10 .30
38 Wally Joyner .10 .30
39 Keith Lockhart .10 .30
40 Javy Lopez .10 .30
41 Greg Maddux .50 1.25
42 Kevin Millwood .10 .30
43 John Rocker .10 .30
44 Reggie Sanders .10 .30
45 John Smoltz .20 .50
46 B.J. Surhoff .10 .30
47 Quilvio Veras .10 .30
48 Walt Weiss .10 .30
49 Brady Anderson .10 .30
50 Albert Belle .10 .30
51 Jeff Conine .10 .30
52 Delino DeShields .10 .30
53 Brook Fordyce .10 .30
54 Jerry Hairston Jr. .10 .30
55 Mark Lewis .10 .30
56 Luis Matos .10 .30
57 Melvin Mora .10 .30
58 Mike Mussina .20 .50
59 Chris Richard .10 .30
60 Cal Ripken 1.00 2.50
61 Manny Alexander .10 .30
62 Rolando Arrojo .10 .30
63 Midre Cummings .10 .30
64 Carl Everett .10 .30
65 Nomar Garciaparra .50 1.25
66 Mike Lansing .10 .30
67 Darren Lewis .10 .30
68 Derek Lowe .10 .30
69 Pedro Martinez .20 .50
70 Ramon Martinez .10 .30
71 Trot Nixon .10 .30
72 Troy O'Leary .10 .30
73 Jose Offerman .10 .30
74 Tomo Ohka .10 .30
75 Jason Varitek .30 .75
76 Rick Aguilera .10 .30
77 Shane Andrews .10 .30
78 Brant Brown .10 .30
79 Damon Buford .10 .30
80 Joe Girardi .10 .30
81 Mark Grace .20 .50
82 Willie Greene .10 .30
83 Ricky Gutierrez .10 .30
84 Jon Lieber .10 .30
85 Sammy Sosa .30 .75
86 Kevin Tapani .10 .30
87 Rondell White .10 .30
88 Kerry Wood .10 .30
89 Eric Young .10 .30
90 Harold Baines .10 .30
91 James Baldwin .10 .30
92 Ray Durham .10 .30
93 Cal Eldred .10 .30
94 Keith Foulke .10 .30
95 Charles Johnson .10 .30
96 Paul Konerko .10 .30
97 Carlos Lee .10 .30
98 Magglio Ordonez .10 .30
99 Jim Parque .10 .30
100 Herbert Perry .10 .30
101 Chris Singleton .10 .30
102 Mike Sirotka .10 .30
103 Frank Thomas .30 .75
104 Jose Valentin .10 .30
105 Rob Bell .10 .30
106 Aaron Boone .10 .30
107 Sean Casey .10 .30
108 Danny Graves .10 .30
109 Ken Griffey Jr. .50 1.25
110 Pete Harnisch .10 .30
111 Brian Hunter .10 .30
112 Barry Larkin .20 .50
113 Pokey Reese .10 .30
114 Benito Santiago .10 .30
115 Chris Stynes .10 .30
116 Michael Tucker .10 .30
117 Ron Villone .10 .30
118 Scott Williamson .10 .30
119 Dmitri Young .10 .30
120 Roberto Alomar .20 .50
121 Sandy Alomar Jr. .10 .30
122 Russell Branyan .10 .30
123 Dave Burba .10 .30
124 Bartolo Colon .10 .30
125 Wil Cordero .10 .30
126 Einar Diaz .10 .30
127 Chuck Finley .10 .30
128 Travis Fryman .10 .30
129 Kenny Lofton .10 .30
130 Charles Nagy .10 .30
131 Manny Ramirez .20 .50
132 David Segui .10 .30
133 Jim Thome .20 .50
134 Omar Vizquel .20 .50
135 Brian Bohanon .10 .30
136 Jeff Cirillo .10 .30
137 Jeff Frye .10 .30
138 Jeffrey Hammonds .10 .30
139 Todd Helton .20 .50
140 Todd Hollandsworth .10 .30
141 Jose Jimenez .10 .30
142 Brent Mayne .10 .30
143 Neifi Perez .10 .30
144 Ben Petrick .10 .30
145 Juan Pierre .10 .30
146 Larry Walker .10 .30
147 Todd Walker .10 .30
148 Masato Yoshii .10 .30
149 Brad Ausmus .10 .30
150 Rich Becker .10 .30
151 Tony Clark .10 .30
152 Deivi Cruz .10 .30
153 Damion Easley .10 .30
154 Juan Encarnacion .10 .30
155 Robert Fick .10 .30
156 Juan Gonzalez .10 .30
157 Bobby Higginson .10 .30
158 Todd Jones .10 .30
159 Wendell Magee Jr. .10 .30
160 Brian Moehler .10 .30
161 Hideo Nomo .30 .75
162 Dean Palmer .10 .30
163 Jeff Weaver .10 .30
164 Antonio Alfonseca .10 .30
165 Dave Berg .10 .30
166 A.J. Burnett .10 .30
167 Luis Castillo .10 .30
168 Ryan Dempster .10 .30
169 Cliff Floyd .10 .30
170 Alex Gonzalez .10 .30
171 Mark Kotsay .10 .30
172 Derrek Lee .20 .50
173 Mike Lowell .10 .30
174 Mike Redmond .10 .30
175 Henry Rodriguez .10 .30
176 Jesus Sanchez .10 .30
177 Preston Wilson .10 .30
178 Moises Alou .10 .30
179 Jeff Bagwell .20 .50
180 Glen Barker .10 .30
181 Lance Berkman .10 .30
182 Craig Biggio .20 .50
183 Tim Bogar .10 .30
184 Ken Caminiti .10 .30
185 Roger Cedeno .10 .30
186 Scott Elarton .10 .30
187 Tony Eusebio .10 .30
188 Richard Hidalgo .10 .30
189 Jose Lima .10 .30
190 Mitch Meluskey .10 .30
191 Shane Reynolds .10 .30
192 Bill Spiers .10 .30
193 Billy Wagner .10 .30
194 Daryle Ward .10 .30
195 Carlos Beltran .10 .30
196 Ricky Bottalico .10 .30
197 Johnny Damon .20 .50
198 Jermaine Dye .10 .30
199 Jorge Fabregas .10 .30
200 David McCarty .10 .30
201 Mark Quinn .10 .30
202 Joe Randa .10 .30
203 Jeff Reboulet .10 .30
204 Rey Sanchez .10 .30
205 Blake Stein .10 .30
206 Jeff Suppan .10 .30
207 Mac Suzuki .10 .30
208 Mike Sweeney .10 .30
209 Greg Zaun .10 .30
210 Adrian Beltre .10 .30
211 Kevin Brown .10 .30
212 Alex Cora .10 .30
213 Darren Dreifort .10 .30
214 Tom Goodwin .10 .30
215 Shawn Green .10 .30
216 Mark Grudzielanek .10 .30
217 Todd Hundley .10 .30
218 Eric Karros .10 .30
219 Chad Kreuter .10 .30
220 Jim Leyritz .10 .30
221 Chan Ho Park .10 .30
222 Jeff Shaw .10 .30
223 Gary Sheffield .10 .30
224 Devon White .10 .30
225 Ron Belliard .10 .30
226 Henry Blanco .10 .30
227 Jeromy Burnitz .10 .30
228 Jeff D'Amico .10 .30
229 Marquis Grissom .10 .30
230 Charlie Hayes .10 .30
231 Jimmy Haynes .10 .30
232 Tyler Houston .10 .30
233 Geoff Jenkins .10 .30
234 Mark Loretta .10 .30
235 James Mouton .10 .30
236 Richie Sexson .10 .30
237 Jamey Wright .10 .30
238 Jay Canizaro .10 .30
239 Ron Coomer .10 .30
240 Cristian Guzman .10 .30
241 Denny Hocking .10 .30
242 Torii Hunter .10 .30
243 Jacque Jones .10 .30
244 Corey Koskie .10 .30
245 Matt Lawton .10 .30
246 Matt LeCroy .10 .30
247 Eric Milton .10 .30
248 David Ortiz .30 .75
249 Brad Radke .10 .30
250 Mark Redman .10 .30
251 Michael Barrett .10 .30
252 Peter Bergeron .10 .30
253 Milton Bradley .10 .30
254 Orlando Cabrera .10 .30
255 Vladimir Guerrero .30 .75
256 Wilton Guerrero .10 .30
257 Dustin Hermanson .10 .30
258 Hideki Irabu .10 .30
259 Fernando Seguignol .10 .30
260 Lee Stevens .10 .30
261 Andy Tracy .10 .30
262 Javier Vazquez .10 .30
263 Jose Vidro .10 .30
264 Edgardo Alfonzo .10 .30
265 Derek Bell .10 .30
266 Armando Benitez .10 .30
267 Mike Bordick .10 .30
268 John Franco .10 .30
269 Darryl Hamilton .10 .30
270 Mike Hampton .10 .30
271 Lenny Harris .10 .30
272 Al Leiter .10 .30
273 Joe McEwing .10 .30
274 Rey Ordonez .10 .30
275 Jay Payton .10 .30
276 Mike Piazza .50 1.25
277 Glendon Rusch .10 .30
278 Bubba Trammell .10 .30
279 Robin Ventura .10 .30
280 Todd Zeile .10 .30
281 Scott Brosius .10 .30
282 Jose Canseco .20 .50
283 Roger Clemens .60 1.50
284 David Cone .10 .30
285 Dwight Gooden .10 .30
286 Orlando Hernandez .10 .30
287 Glenallen Hill .10 .30
288 Derek Jeter .75 2.00
289 David Justice .10 .30
290 Chuck Knoblauch .10 .30
291 Tino Martinez .20 .50
292 Denny Neagle .10 .30
293 Paul O'Neill .20 .50
294 Andy Pettitte .20 .50
295 Jorge Posada .20 .50
296 Mariano Rivera .30 .75
297 Luis Sojo .10 .30
298 Jose Vizcaino .10 .30
299 Bernie Williams .20 .50
300 Kevin Appier .10 .30
301 Eric Chavez .10 .30
302 Ryan Christenson .10 .30
303 Jason Giambi .10 .30
304 Jeremy Giambi .10 .30
305 Ben Grieve .10 .30
306 Gil Heredia .10 .30
307 Ramon Hernandez .10 .30
308 Tim Hudson .10 .30
309 Jason Isringhausen .10 .30
310 Terrence Long .10 .30
311 Mark Mulder .10 .30
312 Adam Piatt .10 .30
313 Matt Stairs .10 .30
314 Miguel Tejada .10 .30
315 Randy Velarde .10 .30
316 Alex Arias .10 .30
317 Pat Burrell .10 .30
318 Omar Daal .10 .30
319 Travis Lee .10 .30
320 Mike Lieberthal .10 .30
321 Randy Wolf .10 .30
322 Bobby Abreu .10 .30
323 Jeff Brantley .10 .30
324 Bruce Chen .10 .30
325 Doug Glanville .10 .30
326 Kevin Jordan .10 .30
327 Robert Person .10 .30
328 Scott Rolen .20 .50
329 Jimmy Anderson .10 .30
330 Mike Benjamin .10 .30
331 Kris Benson .10 .30
332 Adrian Brown .10 .30
333 Brian Giles .10 .30
334 Jason Kendall .10 .30
335 Pat Meares .10 .30
336 Warren Morris .10 .30
337 Aramis Ramirez .10 .30
338 Todd Ritchie .10 .30
339 Jason Schmidt .10 .30
340 John VanderWal .10 .30
341 Mike Williams .10 .30
342 Enrique Wilson .10 .30
343 Kevin Young .10 .30
344 Rick Ankiel .10 .30
345 Andy Benes .10 .30
346 Will Clark .20 .50
347 Eric Davis .10 .30
348 J.D. Drew .10 .30
349 Shawon Dunston .10 .30
350 Jim Edmonds .10 .30
351 Pat Hentgen .10 .30
352 Darryl Kile .10 .30
353 Ray Lankford .10 .30
354 Mike Matheny .10 .30
355 Mark McGwire .75 2.00
356 Craig Paquette .10 .30
357 Edgar Renteria .10 .30
358 Garrett Stephenson .10 .30
359 Fernando Tatis .10 .30
360 Dave Veres .10 .30
361 Fernando Vina .10 .30
362 Bret Boone .10 .30
363 Matt Clement .10 .30
364 Ben Davis .10 .30
365 Adam Eaton .10 .30
366 Wiki Gonzalez .10 .30
367 Tony Gwynn .40 1.00
368 Damian Jackson .10 .30
369 Ryan Klesko .10 .30
370 John Mabry .10 .30
371 Dave Magadan .10 .30
372 Phil Nevin .10 .30
373 Eric Owens .10 .30
374 Desi Relaford .10 .30
375 Ruben Rivera .10 .30
376 Woody Williams .10 .30
377 Rich Aurilia .10 .30
378 Marvin Benard .10 .30
379 Barry Bonds .75 2.00
380 Ellis Burks .10 .30
381 Bobby Estalella .10 .30
382 Shawn Estes .10 .30
383 Mark Gardner .10 .30
384 Livan Hernandez .10 .30
385 Jeff Kent .10 .30
386 Bill Mueller .10 .30
387 Robb Nen .10 .30
388 Russ Ortiz .10 .30
389 Armando Rios .10 .30
390 Kirk Rueter .10 .30
391 J.T. Snow .10 .30
392 David Bell .10 .30
393 Jay Buhner .10 .30
394 Mike Cameron .10 .30
395 Freddy Garcia .10 .30
396 Carlos Guillen .10 .30
397 John Halama .10 .30
398 Rickey Henderson .30 .75
399 Al Martin .10 .30
400 Edgar Martinez .20 .50
401 Mark McLemore .10 .30
402 Jamie Moyer .10 .30
403 John Olerud .10 .30
404 Joe Oliver .10 .30
405 Alex Rodriguez .50 1.25
406 Kazuhiro Sasaki .10 .30
407 Aaron Sele .10 .30
408 Dan Wilson .10 .30
409 Miguel Cairo .10 .30
410 Vinny Castilla .10 .30
411 Steve Cox .10 .30
412 John Flaherty .10 .30
413 Jose Guillen .10 .30
414 Roberto Hernandez .10 .30
415 Russ Johnson .10 .30
416 Felix Martinez .10 .30
417 Fred McGriff .20 .50
418 Greg Vaughn .10 .30
419 Gerald Williams .10 .30
420 Luis Alicea .10 .30
421 Frank Catalanotto .10 .30
422 Royce Clayton .10 .30
423 Chad Curtis .10 .30
424 Rusty Greer .10 .30
425 Bill Haselman .10 .30
426 Rick Helling .10 .30
427 Gabe Kapler .10 .30
428 Mike Lamb .10 .30
429 Ricky Ledee .10 .30
430 Ruben Mateo .10 .30
431 Rafael Palmeiro .20 .50
432 Ivan Rodriguez .20 .50
433 Kenny Rogers .10 .30
434 John Wetteland .10 .30
435 Jeff Zimmerman .10 .30
436 Tony Batista .10 .30
437 Homer Bush .10 .30

438 Chris Carpenter .10 .30
439 Marty Cordova .10 .30
440 Jose Cruz Jr. .10 .30
441 Carlos Delgado .10 .30
442 Darrin Fletcher .10 .30
443 Brad Fullmer .10 .30
444 Alex Gonzalez .10 .30
445 Billy Koch .10 .30
446 Raul Mondesi .10 .30
447 Mickey Morandini .10 .30
448 Shannon Stewart .10 .30
449 Steve Trachsel .10 .30
450 David Wells .10 .30
451 Juan Alvarez .10 .30
452 Shawn Wooten .10 .30
453 Ismael Villegas .10 .30
454 Carlos Casimiro .10 .30
455 Morgan Burkhart .10 .30
456 Paxton Crawford .10 .30
457 Dernell Stenson .10 .30
458 Ross Gload .10 .30
459 Raul Gonzalez .10 .30
460 Corey Patterson .10 .30
461 Julio Zuleta .10 .30
462 Rocky Biddle .10 .30
463 Joe Crede .30 .75
464 Matt Ginter .10 .30
465 Aaron Myette .10 .30
466 Mike Bell .10 .30
467 Travis Dawkins .10 .30
468 Mark Watson .10 .30
469 Elvis Pena .10 .30
470 Eric Munson .10 .30
471 Pablo Ozuna .10 .30
472 Frank Charles .10 .30
473 Mike Judd .10 .30
474 Hector Ramirez .10 .30
475 Jack Cressend .10 .30
476 Talmadge Nunnari .10 .30
477 Jorge Toca .10 .30
478 Alfonso Soriano .20 .50
479 Jay Tessmer .10 .30
480 Jake Westbrook .10 .30
481 Eric Byrnes .10 .30
482 Jose Ortiz .10 .30
483 Tike Redman .10 .30
484 Domingo Guzman .10 .30
485 Rodrigo Lopez .10 .30
486 Xavier Nady .10 .30
487 Pedro Feliz .10 .30
488 Damon Minor .10 .30
489 Ryan Vogelsong .10 .30
490 Joel Pineiro .10 .30
491 Justin Brunette .10 .30
492 Keith McDonald .10 .30
493 Aubrey Huff .10 .30
494 Kenny Kelly .10 .30
495 Damian Rolls .10 .30
496 John Bale UER .10 .30
1999 ERA is in save column
497 Pasqual Coco .10 .30
498 Matt DeWitt .10 .30
499 Leo Estrella .10 .30
500 Josh Phelps .10 .30

1992 Pinnacle

The 1992 Pinnacle set (issued by Score) consists of two series each with 310 standard-size cards. Cards were distributed in first and second series 16-card foil packs and 27-card cello packs. An anti-counterfeit device appears in the bottom border of each card back. A special ribbed plastic lenticular detector card was made available that allowed the user to view the anti-counterfeit device and unscramble the coding with the word "Pinnacle" appearing. Special subsets featured include '92 Rookie Prospects (52, 55, 168, 247-261, 263-280), Idols (281-286/584-591), Sidelines (287-294/592-596), Draft Picks (295-304), Shades (305-310/601-605), Grips (606-612), and Technicians (614-620). Rookie Cards in the set include Brian Jordan, Jeff Kent and Manny Ramirez.

COMPLETE SET (620) 15.00 40.00
COMP. SERIES 1 (310) 10.00 25.00
COMP. SERIES 2 (310) 6.00 15.00
1 Frank Thomas .20 .50
2 Benito Santiago .07 .20
3 Carlos Baerga .02 .10
4 Cecil Fielder .07 .20
5 Barry Larkin .10 .30
6 Ozzie Smith .30 .75
7 Willie McGee .07 .20
8 Paul Molitor .07 .20
9 Andy Van Slyke .10 .30
10 Ryne Sandberg .30 .75
11 Kevin Seitzer .02 .10
12 Len Dykstra .07 .20
13 Edgar Martinez .10 .30
14 Ruben Sierra .07 .20
15 Howard Johnson .02 .10
16 Dave Henderson .02 .10
17 Devon White .07 .20
18 Terry Pendleton .07 .20
19 Steve Finley .07 .20
20 Kirby Puckett .20 .50
21 Orel Hershiser .07 .20
22 Hal Morris .02 .10
23 Don Mattingly .50 1.25
24 Delino DeShields .02 .10
25 Dennis Eckersley .07 .20
26 Ellis Burks .07 .20
27 Jay Buhner .07 .20
28 Matt Williams .07 .20
29 Lou Whitaker .07 .20
30 Alex Fernandez .02 .10
31 Albert Belle .07 .20
32 Todd Zeile .02 .10
33 Tony Pena .02 .10
34 Jay Bell .07 .20
35 Rafael Palmeiro .10 .30
36 Wes Chamberlain .02 .10
37 George Bell .02 .10
38 Robin Yount .30 .75
39 Vince Coleman .02 .10
40 Bruce Hurst .02 .10
41 Harold Baines .07 .20
42 Chuck Finley .07 .20
43 Ken Caminiti .07 .20
44 Ben McDonald .02 .10
45 Roberto Alomar .10 .30
46 Chili Davis .07 .20
47 Bill Doran .02 .10
48 Jerald Clark .02 .10
49 Jose Lind .02 .10
50 Nolan Ryan .75 2.00
51 Phil Plantier .02 .10
52 Gary DiSarcina .02 .10
53 Kevin Bass .02 .10
54 Pat Kelly .02 .10
55 Mark Wohlers .02 .10
56 Walt Weiss .02 .10
57 Lenny Harris .02 .10
58 Ivan Calderon .02 .10
59 Harold Reynolds .07 .20
60 George Brett .50 1.25
61 Gregg Olson .02 .10
62 Orlando Merced .02 .10
63 Steve Decker .02 .10
64 John Franco .07 .20
65 Greg Maddux .30 .75
66 Alex Cole .02 .10
67 Dave Hollins .02 .10
68 Kent Hrbek .07 .20
69 Tom Pagnozzi .02 .10
70 Jeff Bagwell .20 .50
71 Jim Gantner .02 .10
72 Matt Nokes .02 .10
73 Brian Harper .02 .10
74 Andy Benes .02 .10
75 Tom Glavine .10 .30
76 Terry Steinbach .07 .20
77 Dennis Martinez .07 .20
78 John Olerud .07 .20
79 Ozzie Guillen .07 .20
80 Darryl Strawberry .07 .20
81 Gary Gaetti .07 .20
82 Dave Righetti .07 .20
83 Chris Hoiles .02 .10
84 Andujar Cedeno .02 .10
85 Jack Clark .07 .20
86 David Howard .02 .10
87 Bill Gullickson .02 .10
88 Bernard Gilkey .02 .10
89 Kevin Elster .02 .10
90 Kevin Maas .02 .10
91 Mark Lewis .02 .10
92 Greg Vaughn .02 .10
93 Bret Barberie .02 .10
94 Dave Smith .02 .10
95 Roger Clemens .40 1.00
96 Doug Drabek .02 .10
97 Omar Vizquel .10 .30
98 Jose Guzman .02 .10
99 Juan Samuel .02 .10
100 Dave Justice .07 .20
101 Tom Browning .02 .10
102 Mark Gubicza .02 .10
103 Mickey Morandini .02 .10
104 Ed Whitson .02 .10
105 Lance Parrish .07 .20
106 Scott Erickson .02 .10
107 Jack McDowell .02 .10
108 Dave Stieb .02 .10
109 Mike Moore .02 .10
110 Travis Fryman .07 .20
111 Dwight Gooden .07 .20
112 Fred McGriff .10 .30
113 Alan Trammell .07 .20
114 Roberto Kelly .02 .10
115 Andre Dawson .07 .20
116 Bill Landrum .02 .10
117 Brian McRae .02 .10
118 B.J. Surhoff .07 .20
119 Chuck Knoblauch .07 .20
120 Steve Olin .02 .10
121 Robin Ventura .07 .20
122 Will Clark .10 .30
123 Tino Martinez .10 .30
124 Dale Murphy .10 .30
125 Pete O'Brien .02 .10
126 Ray Lankford .07 .20
127 Juan Gonzalez .10 .30
128 Ron Gant .07 .20
129 Marquis Grissom .07 .20
130 Jose Canseco .10 .30
131 Mike Greenwell .02 .10
132 Mark Langston .02 .10
133 Brett Butler .07 .20
134 Kelly Gruber .02 .10
135 Chris Sabo .02 .10
136 Mark Grace .10 .30
137 Tony Fernandez .02 .10
138 Glenn Davis .02 .10
139 Pedro Munoz .02 .10
140 Craig Biggio .10 .30
141 Pete Schourek .02 .10
142 Mike Boddicker .02 .10
143 Robby Thompson .02 .10
144 Mel Hall .02 .10
145 Bryan Harvey .02 .10
146 Mike LaValliere .02 .10
147 John Kruk .07 .20
148 Joe Carter .07 .20
149 Greg Olson .02 .10
150 Julio Franco .07 .20
151 Darryl Hamilton .02 .10
152 Felix Fermin .02 .10
153 Jose Offerman .02 .10
154 Paul O'Neill .10 .30
155 Tommy Greene .02 .10
156 Ivan Rodriguez .20 .50
157 Dave Stewart .07 .20
158 Jeff Reardon .07 .20
159 Felix Jose .02 .10
160 Doug Dascenzo .02 .10
161 Tim Wallach .02 .10
162 Dan Plesac .02 .10
163 Luis Gonzalez .07 .20
164 Mike Henneman .02 .10
165 Mike Devereaux .02 .10
166 Luis Polonia .02 .10
167 Mike Sharperson .02 .10
168 Chris Donnels .02 .10
169 Greg W. Harris .02 .10
170 Deion Sanders .10 .30
171 Mike Schooler .02 .10
172 Jose DeJesus .02 .10
173 Jeff Montgomery .02 .10
174 Milt Cuyler .02 .10
175 Wade Boggs .10 .30
176 Kevin Tapani .02 .10
177 Bill Spiers .02 .10
178 Tim Raines .07 .20
179 Randy Milligan .02 .10
180 Rob Dibble .07 .20
181 Kirt Manwaring .02 .10
182 Pascual Perez .02 .10
183 Juan Guzman .02 .10
184 John Smiley .02 .10
185 David Segui .02 .10
186 Omar Olivares .02 .10
187 Joe Slusarski .02 .10
188 Erik Hanson .02 .10
189 Mark Portugal .02 .10
190 Walt Terrell .02 .10
191 John Smoltz .10 .30
192 Wilson Alvarez .02 .10
193 Jimmy Key .07 .20
194 Larry Walker .10 .30
195 Lee Smith .07 .20
196 Pete Harnisch .02 .10
197 Mike Harkey .02 .10
198 Frank Tanana .02 .10
199 Terry Mulholland .02 .10
200 Cal Ripken .60 1.50
201 Dave Magadan .02 .10
202 Bud Black .02 .10
203 Terry Shumpert .02 .10
204 Mike Mussina .20 .50
205 Mo Vaughn .07 .20
206 Steve Farr .02 .10
207 Darrin Jackson .02 .10
208 Jerry Browne .02 .10
209 Jeff Russell .02 .10
210 Mike Scioscia .02 .10
211 Rick Aguilera .07 .20
212 Jaime Navarro .02 .10
213 Randy Tomlin .02 .10
214 Bobby Thigpen .02 .10
215 Mark Gardner .02 .10
216 Norm Charlton .02 .10
217 Mark McGwire .50 1.25
218 Skeeter Barnes .02 .10
219 Bob Tewksbury .02 .10
220 Junior Felix .02 .10
221 Sam Horn .02 .10
222 Jody Reed .02 .10
223 Luis Sojo .02 .10
224 Jerome Walton .02 .10
225 Darryl Kile .07 .20
226 Mickey Tettleton .02 .10
227 Dan Pasqua .02 .10
228 Jim Gott .02 .10
229 Bernie Williams .10 .30
230 Shane Mack .02 .10
231 Steve Avery .02 .10
232 Dave Valle .02 .10
233 Mark Leonard .02 .10
234 Spike Owen .02 .10
235 Gary Sheffield .07 .20
236 Steve Chitren .02 .10
237 Zane Smith .02 .10
238 Tom Gordon .02 .10
239 Jose Oquendo .02 .10
240 Todd Stottlemyre .02 .10
241 Darren Daulton .07 .20
242 Tim Naehring .02 .10
243 Tony Phillips .02 .10
244 Shawon Dunston .02 .10
245 Manuel Lee .02 .10
246 Mike Pagliarulo .02 .10
247 Jim Thome .20 .50
248 Luis Mercedes .02 .10
249 Cal Eldred .02 .10
250 Derek Bell .07 .20
251 Arthur Rhodes .02 .10
252 Scott Cooper .02 .10
253 Roberto Hernandez .02 .10
254 Mo Sanford .02 .10
255 Scott Servais .02 .10
256 Eric Karros .07 .20
257 Andy Mota .02 .10
258 Keith Mitchell .02 .10
259 Joel Johnston .02 .10
260 John Wehner .02 .10
261 Gino Minutelli .02 .10
262 Greg Gagne .02 .10
263 Stan Royer .02 .10
264 Carlos Garcia .02 .10
265 Andy Ashby .02 .10
266 Kim Batiste .02 .10
267 Julio Valera .02 .10
268 Royce Clayton .02 .10
269 Gary Scott .02 .10
270 Kirk Dressendorfer .02 .10
271 Sean Berry .02 .10
272 Lance Dickson .02 .10
273 Rob Maurer .02 .10
274 Scott Brosius RC .30 .75
275 Dave Fleming .02 .10
276 Lenny Webster .02 .10
277 Mike Humphreys .02 .10
278 Freddie Benavides .02 .10
279 Harvey Pulliam .02 .10
280 Jeff Carter .02 .10
281 Jim Abbott I .20 .50
Nolan Ryan
282 Wade Boggs I .20 .50
George Brett
283 Ken Griffey Jr. I .20 .50
Rickey Henderson
284 Wally Joyner .10 .30
Dale Murphy
285 Chuck Knoblauch I .10 .30
Ozzie Smith
286 Robin Ventura I .20 .50
Lou Gehrig
287 Robin Yount SIDE .20 .50
288 Bob Tewksbury SIDE .02 .10
289 Kirby Puckett SIDE .10 .30
290 Kenny Lofton SIDE .07 .20
291 Jack McDowell SIDE .02 .10
292 John Burkett SIDE .02 .10
293 Dwight Smith SIDE .02 .10
294 Nolan Ryan SIDE .40 1.00
295 Manny Ramirez RC 1.50 4.00
296 Cliff Floyd UER RC .40 1.00
(Throws right, not left as indicated on back)
297 Al Shirley RC .05 .15
298 Brian Barber RC .05 .15
299 Jon Farrell RC .05 .15
300 Scott Ruffcorn RC .05 .15
301 Tyrone Hill RC .05 .15
302 Benji Gil RC .15 .40
303 Tyler Green RC .05 .15
304 Allen Watson RC .05 .15
305 Jay Buhner SH .02 .10
306 Roberto Alomar SH .07 .20
307 Chuck Knoblauch SH .02 .10
308 Darryl Strawberry SH .02 .10
309 Danny Tartabull SH .02 .10
310 Bobby Bonilla SH .02 .10
311 Mike Felder .02 .10
312 Storm Davis .02 .10
313 Tim Teufel .02 .10
314 Tom Brunansky .02 .10
315 Rex Hudler .02 .10
316 Dave Otto .02 .10
317 Jeff King .02 .10
318 Dan Gladden .02 .10
319 Bill Pecota .02 .10
320 Franklin Stubbs .02 .10
321 Gary Carter .07 .20
322 Melido Perez .02 .10
323 Eric Davis .07 .20
324 Greg Myers .02 .10
325 Pete Incaviglia .02 .10
326 Von Hayes .02 .10
327 Greg Swindell .02 .10
328 Steve Sax .02 .10
329 Chuck McElroy .02 .10
330 Gregg Jefferies .02 .10
331 Joe Oliver .02 .10
332 Paul Faries .02 .10
333 David West .02 .10
334 Craig Grebeck .02 .10
335 Chris Hammond .02 .10
336 Billy Ripken .02 .10
337 Scott Sanderson .02 .10
338 Dick Schofield .02 .10
339 Bob Milacki .02 .10
340 Kevin Reimer .02 .10
341 Jose DeLeon .02 .10
342 Henry Cotto .02 .10
343 Daryl Boston .02 .10
344 Kevin Gross .02 .10
345 Milt Thompson .02 .10
346 Luis Rivera .02 .10
347 Al Osuna .02 .10
348 Rob Deer .02 .10
349 Tim Leary .02 .10
350 Mike Stanton .02 .10
351 Dean Palmer .07 .20
352 Trevor Wilson .02 .10
353 Mark Eichhorn .02 .10
354 Scott Aldred .02 .10
355 Mark Whiten .02 .10
356 Leo Gomez .02 .10
357 Rafael Belliard .02 .10
358 Carlos Quintana .02 .10
359 Mark Davis .02 .10
360 Chris Nabholz .02 .10
361 Carlton Fisk .10 .30
362 Joe Orsulak .02 .10
363 Eric Anthony .02 .10
364 Greg Hibbard .02 .10
365 Scott Leius .02 .10
366 Hensley Meulens .02 .10
367 Chris Bosio .02 .10
368 Brian Downing .02 .10
369 Sammy Sosa .20 .50
370 Stan Belinda .02 .10
371 Joe Grahe .02 .10
372 Luis Salazar .02 .10
373 Lance Johnson .02 .10
374 Kal Daniels .02 .10
375 Dave Winfield .07 .20
376 Brook Jacoby .02 .10
377 Mariano Duncan .02 .10
378 Ron Darling .02 .10
379 Randy Johnson .20 .50
380 Chito Martinez .02 .10
381 Andres Galarraga .07 .20
382 Willie Randolph .07 .20
383 Charles Nagy .02 .10
384 Tim Belcher .02 .10
385 Duane Ward .02 .10
386 Vicente Palacios .02 .10
387 Mike Gallego .02 .10
388 Rich DeLucia .02 .10
389 Scott Radinsky .02 .10
390 Damon Berryhill .02 .10
391 Kirk McCaskill .02 .10
392 Pedro Guerrero .07 .20
393 Kevin Mitchell .02 .10
394 Dickie Thon .02 .10
395 Bobby Bonilla .07 .20
396 Bill Wegman .02 .10
397 Dave Martinez .07 .20
398 Rick Sutcliffe .07 .20
399 Larry Andersen .02 .10
400 Tony Gwynn .25 .60
401 Rickey Henderson .20 .50
402 Greg Cadaret .02 .10
403 Keith Miller .02 .10
404 Bip Roberts .02 .10
405 Kevin Brown .07 .20
406 Mitch Williams .02 .10
407 Frank Viola .07 .20
408 Darren Lewis .02 .10
409 Bob Welch .02 .10
410 Bob Walk .02 .10
411 Todd Frohwirth .02 .10
412 Brian Hunter .02 .10
413 Ron Karkovice .02 .10
414 Mike Morgan .02 .10
415 Joe Hesketh .02 .10
416 Don Slaught .02 .10
417 Tom Henke .02 .10
418 Kurt Stillwell .02 .10
419 Hector Villanueva .02 .10
420 Glenallen Hill .02 .10
421 Pat Borders .02 .10
422 Charlie Hough .07 .20
423 Charlie Leibrandt .02 .10
424 Eddie Murray .20 .50
425 Jesse Barfield .02 .10
426 Mark Lemke .02 .10
427 Kevin McReynolds .02 .10
428 Gilberto Reyes .02 .10
429 Ramon Martinez .02 .10
430 Steve Buechele .02 .10
431 David Wells .07 .20
432 Kyle Abbott .02 .10
433 John Habyan .02 .10
434 Kevin Appier .07 .20
435 Gene Larkin .02 .10
436 Sandy Alomar Jr. .02 .10
437 Mike Jackson .02 .10
438 Todd Benzinger .02 .10
439 Teddy Higuera .02 .10
440 Reggie Sanders .07 .20
441 Mark Carreon .02 .10
442 Bret Saberhagen .07 .20
443 Gene Nelson .02 .10
444 Jay Howell .02 .10
445 Roger McDowell .02 .10
446 Sid Bream .02 .10
447 Mackey Sasser .02 .10
448 Bill Swift .02 .10
449 Hubie Brooks .02 .10
450 David Cone .07 .20
451 Bobby Witt .02 .10
452 Brady Anderson .07 .20
453 Lee Stevens .02 .10
454 Luis Aquino .02 .10
455 Carney Lansford .07 .20
456 Carlos Hernandez .02 .10
457 Danny Jackson .02 .10
458 Gerald Young .02 .10
459 Tom Candiotti .02 .10
460 Billy Hatcher .02 .10
461 John Wetteland .07 .20
462 Mike Bordick .02 .10
463 Don Robinson .02 .10
464 Jeff Johnson .02 .10
465 Lonnie Smith .02 .10
466 Paul Assenmacher .02 .10
467 Alvin Davis .02 .10
468 Jim Eisenreich .02 .10
469 Brent Mayne .02 .10
470 Jeff Brantley .02 .10
471 Tim Burke .02 .10
472 Pat Mahomes RC .15 .40
473 Ryan Bowen .02 .10
474 Bryn Smith .02 .10
475 Mike Flanagan .02 .10
476 Reggie Jefferson .02 .10
477 Jeff Blauser .02 .10
478 Craig Lefferts .02 .10
479 Todd Worrell .02 .10
480 Scott Scudder .02 .10
481 Kirk Gibson .07 .20
482 Kenny Rogers .07 .20
483 Jack Morris .07 .20
484 Russ Swan .02 .10
485 Mike Huff .02 .10
486 Ken Hill .02 .10
487 Geronimo Pena .02 .10
488 Charlie O'Brien .02 .10
489 Mike Maddux .02 .10
490 Scott Livingstone .02 .10
491 Carl Willis .02 .10
492 Kelly Downs .02 .10
493 Dennis Cook .02 .10
494 Joe Magrane .02 .10
495 Bob Kipper .02 .10
496 Jose Mesa .02 .10
497 Charlie Hayes .02 .10
498 Joe Girardi .02 .10
499 Doug Jones .02 .10
500 Barry Bonds .60 1.50
501 Bill Krueger .02 .10
502 Glenn Braggs .02 .10
503 Eric King .02 .10
504 Frank Castillo .02 .10
505 Mike Gardiner .02 .10
506 Cory Snyder .02 .10
507 Steve Howe .02 .10
508 Jose Rijo .02 .10
509 Sid Fernandez .02 .10
510 Archi Cianfrocco RC .05 .15
511 Mark Guthrie .02 .10
512 Bob Ojeda .02 .10
513 John Doherty RC .05 .15
514 Dante Bichette .07 .20
515 Juan Berenguer .02 .10
516 Jeff M. Robinson .02 .10
517 Mike Macfarlane .02 .10
518 Matt Young .02 .10
519 Otis Nixon .02 .10
520 Brian Holman .02 .10
521 Chris Haney .02 .10
522 Jeff Kent RC 1.00 2.50
523 Chad Curtis RC .15 .40
524 Vince Horsman .02 .10
525 Rod Nichols .02 .10
526 Peter Hoy .02 .10
527 Shawn Boskie .02 .10
528 Alejandro Pena .02 .10
529 Dave Burba .02 .10
530 Ricky Jordan .02 .10
531 Dave Silvestri .02 .10
532 John Patterson UER RC .02 .10
(Listed as being born in 1960; should be 1967)
533 Jeff Branson .02 .10
534 Derrick May .07 .20
535 Esteban Beltre .02 .10
536 Jose Melendez .02 .10
537 Wally Joyner .07 .20
538 Eddie Taubensee RC .15 .40
539 Jim Abbott .10 .30
540 Brian Williams RC .05 .15
541 Donovan Osborne .02 .10
542 Patrick Lennon .02 .10
543 Mike Groppuso RC .05 .15
544 Jarvis Brown .02 .10
545 Shawn Livsey RC .05 .15
546 Jeff Ware .02 .10
547 Danny Tartabull .02 .10
548 Bobby Jones RC .15 .40
549 Ken Griffey Jr. .30 .75
550 Rey Sanchez RC .15 .40
551 Pedro Astacio RC .15 .40
552 Juan Guerrero .02 .10
553 Jacob Brumfield .02 .10
554 Ben Rivera .02 .10
555 Brian Jordan RC .30 .75
556 Denny Neagle .07 .20
557 Cliff Brantley .02 .10
558 Anthony Young .02 .10
559 John Vander Wal .02 .10
560 Monty Fariss .02 .10
561 Russ Springer RC .05 .15
562 Pat Listach RC .15 .40
563 Pat Hentgen .02 .10
564 Andy Stankiewicz .02 .10
565 Mike Perez .02 .10
566 Mike Bielecki .02 .10
567 Butch Henry RC .05 .15
568 Dave Nilsson .02 .10
569 Scott Hatteberg RC .15 .40
570 Ruben Amaro .02 .10
571 Todd Hundley .02 .10
572 Moises Alou .07 .20
573 Hector Fajardo RC .05 .15
574 Todd Van Poppel .02 .10
575 Willie Banks .02 .10
576 Bob Zupcic RC .05 .15
577 J.J. Johnson RC .05 .15
578 John Burkett .02 .10
579 Trever Miller RC .05 .15
580 Scott Bankhead .02 .10
581 Rich Amaral .02 .10
582 Kenny Lofton .10 .30
583 Matt Stairs RC .15 .40
584 Don Mattingly .20 .50
Rod Carew IDOLS
585 Steve Avery .02 .10
Jack Morris IDOLS
586 Roberto Alomar .07 .20
Sandy Alomar SR. IDOLS
587 Scott Sanderson .07 .20
Catfish Hunter IDOLS
588 Dave Justice .07 .20
Willie Stargell IDOLS
589 Rex Hudler .20 .50
Roger Staubach IDOLS
590 David Cone .07 .20
Jackie Gleason IDOLS
591 Tony Gwynn .10 .30
Willie Davis IDOLS
592 Orel Hershiser SIDE .02 .10
593 John Wetteland SIDE .02 .10
594 Tom Glavine SIDE .07 .20
595 Randy Johnson SIDE .10 .30
596 Jim Gott SIDE .02 .10
597 Donald Harris .02 .10
598 Shawn Hare RC .05 .15
599 Chris Gardner .02 .10
600 Rusty Meacham .02 .10
601 Benito Santiago .07 .20
602 Eric Davis SHADE .02 .10
603 Jose Lind SHADE .02 .10
604 Dave Justice SHADE .02 .10
605 Tim Raines SHADE .02 .10
606 Randy Tomlin GRIP .02 .10
607 Jack McDowell GRIP .02 .10
608 Greg Maddux GRIP .20 .50
609 Charles Nagy GRIP .02 .10
610 Tom Candiotti GRIP .02 .10
611 David Cone GRIP .02 .10
612 Steve Avery GRIP .02 .10
613 Rod Beck GRIP .15 .40
614 R. Henderson TECH .10 .30
615 Benito Santiago TECH .02 .10
616 Ruben Sierra TECH .02 .10
617 Ryne Sandberg TECH .20 .50
618 Nolan Ryan TECH .40 1.00
619 Brett Butler TECH .02 .10
620 Dave Justice TECH .02 .10

1993 Pinnacle

The 1993 Pinnacle set (by Score) contains 620 standard-size cards issued in two series of 310 cards each. Cards were distributed in hobby and retail foil packs and 27-card jumbo superpacks. The set includes the following topical subsets: Rookies (238-288, 575-620), Now and Then (289-296, 470-476), Idols (297-303, 477-483), Hometown Heroes (304-310, 484-490), and Draft Picks (455-469). Rookie Cards in this set include Derek Jeter, Jason Kendall and Shannon Stewart.

COMPLETE SET (620) 15.00 40.00
COMP. SERIES 1 (310) 6.00 15.00
COMP. SERIES 2 (310) 10.00 25.00
1 Gary Sheffield .10 .30
2 Cal Eldred .05 .15
3 Larry Walker .10 .30
4 Deion Sanders .20 .50
5 Dave Fleming .05 .15
6 Carlos Baerga .05 .15
7 Bernie Williams .20 .50
8 John Kruk .10 .30
9 Jimmy Key .10 .30
10 Jeff Bagwell .20 .50
11 Jim Abbott .20 .50
12 Terry Steinbach .05 .15
13 Bob Tewksbury .05 .15
14 Eric Karros .10 .30
15 Ryne Sandberg .50 1.25
16 Will Clark .20 .50
17 Edgar Martinez .20 .50
18 Eddie Murray .30 .75
19 Andy Van Slyke .20 .50
20 Cal Ripken Jr. 1.00 2.50

21 Ivan Rodriguez .20 .50
22 Barry Larkin .20 .50
23 Don Mattingly .75 2.00
24 Gregg Jefferies .05 .15
25 Roger Clemens .60 1.50
26 Cecil Fielder .10 .30
27 Kent Hrbek .10 .30
28 Robin Ventura .10 .30
29 Rickey Henderson .30 .75
30 Roberto Alomar .20 .50
31 Luis Polonia .05 .15
32 Andujar Cedeno .05 .15
33 Pat Listach .05 .15
34 Mark Grace .20 .50
35 Otis Nixon .05 .15
36 Felix Jose .05 .15
37 Mike Sharperson .05 .15
38 Dennis Martinez .10 .30
39 Willie McGee .10 .30
40 Kenny Lofton .10 .30
41 Randy Johnson .30 .75
42 Andy Benes .05 .15
43 Bobby Bonilla .10 .30
44 Mike Mussina .20 .50
45 Len Dykstra .10 .30
46 Ellis Burks .10 .30
47 Chris Sabo .05 .15
48 Jay Bell .10 .30
49 Jose Canseco .20 .50
50 Craig Biggio .20 .50
51 Wally Joyner .10 .30
52 Mickey Tettleton .05 .15
53 Tim Raines .10 .30
54 Brian Harper .05 .15
55 Rene Gonzales .05 .15
56 Mark Langston .05 .15
57 Jack Morris .10 .30
58 Mark McGwire .75 2.00
59 Ken Caminiti .10 .30
60 Terry Pendleton .10 .30
61 Dave Nilsson .05 .15
62 Tom Pagnozzi .05 .15
63 Mike Morgan .05 .15
64 Darryl Strawberry .10 .30
65 Charles Nagy .05 .15
66 Ken Hill .05 .15
67 Matt Williams .10 .30
68 Jay Buhner .10 .30
69 Vince Coleman .05 .15
70 Brady Anderson .10 .30
71 Fred McGriff .20 .50
72 Ben McDonald .05 .15
73 Terry Mulholland .05 .15
74 Randy Tomlin .05 .15
75 Nolan Ryan 1.25 3.00
76 Frank Viola UER .10 .30
(Card incorrectly states
he has a surgically
repaired elbow)
77 Jose Rijo .05 .15
78 Shane Mack .05 .15
79 Travis Fryman .10 .30
80 Jack McDowell .05 .15
81 Mark Gubicza .05 .15
82 Matt Nokes .05 .15
83 Bert Blyleven .10 .30
84 Eric Anthony .05 .15
85 Mike Bordick .05 .15
86 John Olerud .10 .30
87 B.J. Surhoff .10 .30
88 Bernard Gilkey .05 .15
89 Shawon Dunston .05 .15
90 Tom Glavine .20 .50
91 Brett Butler .10 .30
92 Moises Alou .10 .30
93 Albert Belle .10 .30
94 Darren Lewis .05 .15
95 Omar Vizquel .20 .50
96 Dwight Gooden .10 .30
97 Gregg Olson .05 .15
98 Tony Gwynn .40 1.00
99 Darren Daulton .10 .30
100 Dennis Eckersley .10 .30
101 Rob Dibble .10 .30
102 Mike Greenwell .05 .15
103 Jose Lind .05 .15
104 Julio Franco .10 .30
105 Tom Gordon .05 .15
106 Scott Livingstone .05 .15
107 Chuck Knoblauch .10 .30
108 Frank Thomas .30 .75
109 Melido Perez .05 .15
110 Ken Griffey Jr. .50 1.25
111 Harold Baines .10 .30
112 Gary Gaetti .10 .30
113 Pete Harnisch .05 .15
114 David Wells .10 .30
115 Charlie Leibrandt .05 .15
116 Ray Lankford .10 .30
117 Kevin Seitzer .05 .15
118 Robin Yount .50 1.25
119 Lenny Harris .05 .15
120 Chris James .05 .15
121 Delino DeShields .05 .15
122 Kirt Manwaring .05 .15
123 Glenallen Hill .05 .15
124 Hensley Meulens .05 .15
125 Darrin Jackson .05 .15
126 Todd Hundley .05 .15
127 Dave Hollins .05 .15
128 Sam Horn .05 .15
129 Roberto Hernandez .05 .15
130 Vicente Palacios .05 .15
131 George Brett .75 2.00
132 Dave Martinez .05 .15
133 Kevin Appier .10 .30
134 Pat Kelly .05 .15
135 Pedro Munoz .05 .15
136 Mark Carreon .05 .15
137 Lance Johnson .05 .15
138 Devon White .10 .30
139 Julio Valera .05 .15
140 Eddie Taubensee .05 .15
141 Willie Wilson .05 .15
142 Stan Belinda .05 .15
143 John Smoltz .20 .50
144 Darryl Hamilton .05 .15
145 Sammy Sosa .30 .75
146 Carlos Hernandez .05 .15
147 Tom Candiotti .05 .15
148 Mike Felder .05 .15
149 Rusty Meacham .05 .15
150 Ivan Calderon .05 .15
151 Pete O'Brien .05 .15
152 Erik Hanson .05 .15
153 Billy Ripken .05 .15
154 Kurt Stillwell .05 .15
155 Jeff Kent .30 .75
156 Mickey Morandini .05 .15
157 Randy Milligan .05 .15
158 Reggie Sanders .10 .30
159 Luis Rivera .05 .15
160 Orlando Merced .05 .15
161 Dean Palmer .10 .30
162 Mike Perez .05 .15
163 Scott Erickson .05 .15
164 Kevin McReynolds .05 .15
165 Kevin Maas .05 .15
166 Ozzie Guillen .10 .30
167 Rob Deer .05 .15
168 Danny Tartabull .05 .15
169 Lee Stevens .05 .15
170 Dave Henderson .05 .15
171 Derek Bell .05 .15
172 Steve Finley .10 .30
173 Greg Olson .05 .15
174 Geronimo Pena .05 .15
175 Paul Quantrill .05 .15
176 Steve Buechele .05 .15
177 Kevin Gross .05 .15
178 Tim Wallach .05 .15
179 Dave Valle .05 .15
180 Dave Silvestri .05 .15
181 Bud Black .05 .15
182 Henry Rodriguez .05 .15
183 Tim Teufel .05 .15
184 Mark McLemore .05 .15
185 Bret Saberhagen .10 .30
186 Chris Hoiles .05 .15
187 Ricky Jordan .05 .15
188 Don Slaught .05 .15
189 Mo Vaughn .10 .30
190 Joe Oliver .05 .15
191 Juan Gonzalez .10 .30
192 Scott Leius .05 .15
193 Milt Cuyler .05 .15
194 Chris Haney .05 .15
195 Ron Karkovice .05 .15
196 Steve Farr .05 .15
197 John Orton .05 .15
198 Kelly Gruber .05 .15
199 Ron Darling .05 .15
200 Ruben Sierra .10 .30
201 Chuck Finley .10 .30
202 Mike Moore .05 .15
203 Pat Borders .05 .15
204 Sid Bream .05 .15
205 Todd Zeile .05 .15
206 Rick Wilkins .05 .15
207 Jim Gantner .05 .15
208 Frank Castillo .05 .15
209 Dave Hansen .05 .15
210 Trevor Wilson .05 .15
211 Sandy Alomar Jr. .05 .15
212 Sean Berry .05 .15
213 Tino Martinez .20 .50
214 Chito Martinez .05 .15
215 Dan Walters .05 .15
216 John Franco .10 .30
217 Glenn Davis .05 .15
218 Mariano Duncan .05 .15
219 Mike LaValliere .05 .15
220 Rafael Palmeiro .20 .50
221 Jack Clark .10 .30
222 Hal Morris .05 .15
223 Ed Sprague .05 .15
224 John Valentin .05 .15
225 Sam Militello .05 .15
226 Bob Wickman .05 .15
227 Damion Easley .05 .15
228 John Jaha .05 .15
229 Bob Ayrault .05 .15
230 Mo Sanford .05 .15
231 Walt Weiss .05 .15
232 Dante Bichette .10 .30
233 Steve Decker .05 .15
234 Jerald Clark .05 .15
235 Bryan Harvey .05 .15
236 Joe Girardi .05 .15
237 Dave Magadan .05 .15
238 David Nied .05 .15
239 Eric Wedge RC .15 .40
240 Rico Brogna .05 .15
241 J.T. Bruett .05 .15
242 Jonathan Hurst .05 .15
243 Bret Boone .10 .30
244 Manny Alexander .05 .15
245 Scooter Tucker .05 .15
246 Troy Neel .05 .15
247 Eddie Zosky .05 .15
248 Melvin Nieves .05 .15
249 Ryan Thompson .05 .15
250 Shawn Barton RC .05 .15
251 Ryan Klesko .10 .30
252 Mike Piazza 1.25 3.00
253 Steve Hosey .05 .15
254 Shane Reynolds .05 .15
255 Dan Wilson .10 .30
256 Tom Marsh .05 .15
257 Barry Manuel .05 .15
258 Paul Miller .05 .15
259 Pedro Martinez .60 1.50
260 Steve Cooke .05 .15
261 Johnny Guzman .05 .15
262 Mike Butcher .05 .15
263 Bien Figueroa .05 .15
264 Rich Rowland .05 .15
265 Shawn Jeter .05 .15
266 Gerald Williams .05 .15
267 Derek Parks .05 .15
268 Henry Mercedes .05 .15
269 David Hulse RC .05 .15
270 Tim Pugh RC .05 .15
271 William Suero .05 .15
272 Ozzie Canseco .05 .15
273 Fernando Ramsey RC .05 .15
274 Bernardo Brito .05 .15
275 Dave Mlicki .05 .15
276 Tim Salmon .20 .50
277 Mike Raczka .05 .15
278 Ken Ryan RC .15 .40
279 Rafael Bournigal .05 .15
280 Wil Cordero .05 .15
281 Billy Ashley .05 .15
282 Paul Wagner .05 .15
283 Blas Minor .05 .15
284 Rick Trlicek .05 .15
285 Willie Greene .05 .15
286 Ted Wood .05 .15
287 Phil Clark .05 .15
288 Jesse Levis .05 .15
289 Tony Gwynn NT .20 .50
290 Nolan Ryan NT .60 1.50
291 Dennis Martinez NT .05 .15
292 Eddie Murray NT .10 .30
293 Robin Yount NT .30 .75
294 George Brett NT .40 1.00
295 Dave Winfield NT .05 .15
296 Bert Blyleven NT .05 .15
297 Jeff Bagwell .30 .75
Carl Yastrzemski
298 John Smoltz .10 .30
Jack Morris
299 Larry Walker .10 .30
Mike Bossy
300 Gary Sheffield .10 .30
Barry Larkin
301 Ivan Rodriguez .10 .30
Carlton Fisk
302 Delino DeShields .30 .75
Malcolm X
303 Tim Salmon .20 .50
Dwight Evans
304 Bernard Gilkey HH .05 .15
305 Cal Ripken Jr. HH .50 1.25
306 Barry Larkin HH .10 .30
307 Kent Hrbek HH .05 .15
308 Rickey Henderson HH .20 .50
309 Darryl Strawberry HH .05 .15
310 John Franco HH .05 .15
311 Todd Stottlemyre .05 .15
312 Luis Gonzalez .10 .30
313 Tommy Greene .05 .15
314 Randy Velarde .05 .15
315 Steve Avery .05 .15
316 Jose Oquendo .05 .15
317 Rey Sanchez .05 .15
318 Greg Vaughn .05 .15
319 Orel Hershiser .10 .30
320 Paul Sorrento .05 .15
321 Royce Clayton .05 .15
322 John Vander Wal .05 .15
323 Henry Cotto .05 .15
324 Pete Schourek .05 .15
325 David Segui .05 .15
326 Arthur Rhodes .05 .15
327 Bruce Hurst .05 .15
328 Wes Chamberlain .05 .15
329 Ozzie Smith .50 1.25
330 Scott Cooper .05 .15
331 Felix Fermin .05 .15
332 Mike Macfarlane .05 .15
333 Dan Gladden .05 .15
334 Kevin Tapani .05 .15
335 Steve Sax .05 .15
336 Jeff Montgomery .05 .15
337 Gary DiSarcina .05 .15
338 Lance Blankenship .05 .15
339 Brian Williams .05 .15
340 Duane Ward .05 .15
341 Chuck McElroy .05 .15
342 Joe Magrane .05 .15
343 Jaime Navarro .05 .15
344 Dave Justice .10 .30
345 Jose Offerman .05 .15
346 Marquis Grissom .10 .30
347 Bill Swift .05 .15
348 Jim Thome .20 .50
349 Archi Cianfrocco .05 .15
350 Anthony Young .05 .15
351 Leo Gomez .05 .15
352 Bill Gullickson .05 .15
353 Alan Trammell .10 .30
354 Dan Pasqua .05 .15
355 Jeff King .05 .15
356 Kevin Brown .10 .30
357 Tim Belcher .05 .15
358 Bip Roberts .05 .15
359 Brent Mayne .05 .15
360 Rheal Cormier .05 .15
361 Mark Guthrie .05 .15
362 Craig Grebeck .05 .15
363 Andy Stankiewicz .05 .15
364 Juan Guzman .05 .15
365 Bobby Witt .05 .15
366 Mark Portugal .05 .15
367 Brian McRae .05 .15
368 Mark Lemke .05 .15
369 Bill Wegman .05 .15
370 Donovan Osborne .05 .15
371 Derrick May .05 .15
372 Carl Willis .05 .15
373 Chris Nabholz .05 .15
374 Mark Lewis .05 .15
375 John Burkett .05 .15
376 Luis Mercedes .05 .15
377 Ramon Martinez .05 .15
378 Kyle Abbott .05 .15
379 Mark Wohlers .05 .15
380 Bob Walk .05 .15
381 Kenny Rogers .10 .30
382 Tim Naehring .05 .15
383 Alex Fernandez .05 .15
384 Keith Miller .05 .15
385 Mike Henneman .05 .15
386 Rick Aguilera .05 .15
387 George Bell .05 .15
388 Mike Gallego .05 .15
389 Howard Johnson .05 .15
390 Kim Batiste .05 .15
391 Jerry Browne .05 .15
392 Damon Berryhill .05 .15
393 Ricky Bones .05 .15
394 Omar Olivares .05 .15
395 Mike Harkey .05 .15
396 Pedro Astacio .05 .15
397 John Wetteland .10 .30
398 Rod Beck .05 .15
399 Thomas Howard .05 .15
400 Mike Devereaux .05 .15
401 Tim Wakefield .30 .75
402 Curt Schilling .10 .30
403 Zane Smith .05 .15
404 Bob Zupcic .05 .15
405 Tom Browning .05 .15
406 Tony Phillips .05 .15
407 John Doherty .05 .15
408 Pat Mahomes .05 .15
409 John Habyan .05 .15
410 Steve Olin .05 .15
411 Chad Curtis .05 .15
412 Joe Grahe .05 .15
413 John Patterson .05 .15
414 Brian Hunter .05 .15
415 Doug Henry .05 .15
416 Lee Smith .10 .30
417 Bob Scanlan .05 .15
418 Kent Mercker .05 .15
419 Mel Rojas .05 .15
420 Mark Whiten .05 .15
421 Carlton Fisk .20 .50
422 Candy Maldonado .05 .15
423 Doug Drabek .05 .15
424 Wade Boggs .20 .50
425 Mark Davis .05 .15
426 Kirby Puckett .30 .75
427 Joe Carter .10 .30
428 Paul Molitor .10 .30
429 Eric Davis .10 .30
430 Darryl Kile .10 .30
431 Jeff Parrett .05 .15
432 Jeff Blauser .05 .15
433 Dan Plesac .05 .15
434 Andres Galarraga .10 .30
435 Jim Gott .05 .15
436 Jose Mesa .05 .15
437 Ben Rivera .05 .15
438 Dave Winfield .10 .30
439 Norm Charlton .05 .15
440 Chris Bosio .05 .15
441 Wilson Alvarez .05 .15
442 Dave Stewart .10 .30
443 Doug Jones .05 .15
444 Jeff Russell .05 .15
445 Ron Gant .10 .30
446 Paul O'Neill .20 .50
447 Charlie Hayes .05 .15
448 Joe Hesketh .05 .15
449 Chris Hammond .05 .15
450 Hipolito Pichardo .05 .15
451 Scott Radinsky .05 .15
452 Bobby Thigpen .05 .15
453 Xavier Hernandez .05 .15
454 Lonnie Smith .05 .15
455 Jamie Arnold DP RC .05 .15
456 B.J. Wallace DP .05 .15
457 Derek Jeter DP RC 8.00 20.00
458 Jason Kendall DP RC .50 1.25
459 Rick Helling DP .05 .15
460 Derek Wallace DP RC .05 .15
461 Sean Lowe DP RC .05 .15
462 S. Stewart DP RC .40 1.00
463 Benji Grigsby DP RC .05 .15
464 T. Steverson DP RC .05 .15
465 Dan Serafini DP RC .05 .15
466 Michael Tucker DP .05 .15
467 Chris Roberts DP .05 .15
468 Pete Janicki DP RC .05 .15
469 Jeff Schmidt DP RC .05 .15
470 Don Mattingly NT .40 1.00
471 Cal Ripken Jr. NT .50 1.25
472 Jack Morris NT .05 .15
473 Terry Pendleton NT .05 .15
474 Dennis Eckersley NT .10 .30
475 Carlton Fisk NT .10 .30
476 Wade Boggs NT .10 .30
477 Len Dykstra .10 .30
Ken Stabler
478 Danny Tartabull .05 .15
Jose Tartabull
479 Jeff Conine .20 .50
Dale Murphy
480 Gregg Jefferies .05 .15
Ron Cey
481 Paul Molitor .10 .30
Harmon Killebrew
482 John Valentin .05 .15
Dave Concepcion
483 Alex Arias .05 .15
Dave Winfield
484 Barry Bonds HH .40 1.00
485 Doug Drabek HH .05 .15
486 Dave Winfield HH .05 .15
487 Brett Butler HH .05 .15
488 Harold Baines HH .05 .15
489 David Cone HH .05 .15
490 Willie McGee HH .05 .15
491 Robby Thompson .05 .15
492 Pete Incaviglia .05 .15
493 Manuel Lee .05 .15
494 Rafael Belliard .05 .15
495 Scott Fletcher .05 .15
496 Jeff Frye .05 .15
497 Andre Dawson .10 .30
498 Mike Scioscia .05 .15
499 Spike Owen .05 .15
500 Sid Fernandez .05 .15
501 Joe Orsulak .05 .15
502 Benito Santiago .10 .30
503 Dale Murphy .20 .50
504 Barry Bonds .75 2.00
505 Jose Guzman .05 .15
506 Tony Pena .05 .15
507 Greg Swindell .05 .15
508 Mike Pagliarulo .05 .15
509 Lou Whitaker .10 .30
510 Greg Gagne .05 .15
511 Butch Henry .05 .15
512 Jeff Brantley .05 .15
513 Jack Armstrong .05 .15
514 Danny Jackson .05 .15
515 Junior Felix .05 .15
516 Milt Thompson .05 .15
517 Greg Maddux .50 1.25
518 Eric Young .05 .15
519 Jody Reed .05 .15
520 Roberto Kelly .05 .15
521 Darren Holmes .05 .15
522 Craig Lefferts .05 .15
523 Charlie Hough .10 .30
524 Bo Jackson .30 .75
525 Bill Spiers .05 .15
526 Orestes Destrade .05 .15
527 Greg Hibbard .05 .15
528 Roger McDowell .05 .15
529 Cory Snyder .05 .15
530 Harold Reynolds .10 .30
531 Kevin Reimer .05 .15
532 Rick Sutcliffe .10 .30
533 Tony Fernandez .05 .15
534 Tom Brunansky .05 .15
535 Jeff Reardon .10 .30
536 Chili Davis .10 .30
537 Bob Ojeda .05 .15
538 Greg Colbrunn .05 .15
539 Phil Plantier .05 .15
540 Brian Jordan .10 .30
541 Pete Smith .05 .15
542 Frank Tanana .05 .15
543 John Smiley .05 .15
544 David Cone .10 .30
545 Daryl Boston .05 .15
546 Tom Henke .05 .15
547 Bill Krueger .05 .15
548 Freddie Benavides .05 .15
549 Randy Myers .05 .15
550 Reggie Jefferson .05 .15
551 Kevin Mitchell .05 .15
552 Dave Stieb .05 .15
553 Bret Barberie .05 .15
554 Tim Crews .05 .15
555 Doug Dascenzo .05 .15
556 Alex Cole .05 .15
557 Jeff Innis .05 .15
558 Carlos Garcia .05 .15
559 Steve Howe .05 .15
560 Kirk McCaskill .05 .15
561 Frank Seminara .05 .15
562 Cris Carpenter .05 .15
563 Mike Stanley .05 .15
564 Carlos Quintana .05 .15
565 Mitch Williams .05 .15
566 Juan Bell .05 .15
567 Eric Fox .05 .15
568 Al Leiter .10 .30
569 Mike Stanton .05 .15
570 Scott Kamieniecki .05 .15
571 Ryan Bowen .05 .15
572 Andy Ashby .05 .15
573 Bob Welch .05 .15
574 Scott Sanderson .05 .15
575 Joe Kmak .05 .15
576 Scott Pose RC .05 .15
577 Ricky Gutierrez .05 .15
578 Mike Trombley .05 .15
579 Sterling Hitchcock RC .15 .40
580 Rodney Bolton .05 .15
581 Tyler Green .05 .15
582 Tim Costo .05 .15
583 Tim Laker RC .05 .15
584 Steve Reed RC .05 .15
585 Tom Kramer RC .05 .15
586 Robb Nen .10 .30
587 Jim Tatum RC .05 .15
588 Frank Bolick .05 .15
589 Kevin Young .10 .30
590 Matt Whiteside RC .05 .15
591 Cesar Hernandez .05 .15
592 Mike Mohler RC .15 .40
593 Alan Embree .05 .15
594 Terry Jorgensen .05 .15
595 John Cummings RC .05 .15
596 Domingo Martinez RC .05 .15
597 Benji Gil .05 .15
598 Todd Pratt RC .15 .40
599 Rene Arocha RC .15 .40
600 Dennis Moeller .05 .15
601 Jeff Conine .10 .30
602 Trevor Hoffman .30 .75
603 Daniel Smith .05 .15
604 Lee Tinsley .05 .15
605 Dan Peltier .05 .15
606 Billy Brewer .05 .15
607 Matt Walbeck RC .15 .40
608 Richie Lewis RC .05 .15
609 J.T. Snow RC .25 .60
610 Pat Gomez RC .05 .15
611 Phil Hiatt .05 .15
612 Alex Arias .05 .15
613 Kevin Rogers .05 .15
614 Al Martin .05 .15
615 Greg Gohr .05 .15
616 Graeme Lloyd RC .15 .40
617 Kent Bottenfield .05 .15
618 Chuck Carr .05 .15
619 Darrell Sherman RC .05 .15
620 Mike Lansing RC .15 .40

1994 Pinnacle

The 540-card 1994 Pinnacle standard-size set was issued in two series of 270. Cards were issued in hobby and retail foil-wrapped packs. The card fronts feature full-bleed color action player photos with a small foil logo and players name at the base. Subsets include Rookie Prospects (224-261) and Draft Picks (262-270/430-438). Notable Rookie Cards include Trot Nixon, Chan Ho Park and Billy Wagner. A Carlos Delgado Super Rookie one shot insert was put into packs at a rate of one in 360. It is labeled SR1 and is listed at the end of the set.

COMPLETE SET (540) 8.00 20.00
COMP. SERIES 1 (270) 4.00 10.00
COMP. SERIES 2 (270) 4.00 10.00
1 Frank Thomas .20 .50
2 Carlos Baerga .02 .10
3 Sammy Sosa .20 .50
4 Tony Gwynn .25 .60
5 John Olerud .07 .20
6 Ryne Sandberg .30 .75
7 Moises Alou .07 .20
8 Steve Avery .02 .10
9 Tim Salmon .10 .30
10 Cecil Fielder .07 .20
11 Greg Maddux .30 .75
12 Barry Larkin .10 .30
13 Mike Devereaux .02 .10
14 Charlie Hayes .02 .10
15 Albert Belle .07 .20
16 Andy Van Slyke .10 .30
17 Mo Vaughn .07 .20
18 Brian McRae .02 .10
19 Cal Eldred .02 .10
20 Craig Biggio .10 .30
21 Kirby Puckett .20 .50
22 Derek Bell .02 .10
23 Don Mattingly .50 1.25
24 John Burkett .02 .10
25 Roger Clemens .40 1.00
26 Barry Bonds .60 1.50
27 Paul Molitor .07 .20
28 Mike Piazza .40 1.00
29 Robin Ventura .07 .20
30 Jeff Conine .07 .20
31 Wade Boggs .10 .30
32 Dennis Eckersley .07 .20
33 Bobby Bonilla .07 .20
34 Lenny Dykstra .07 .20
35 Manny Alexander .02 .10
36 Ray Lankford .07 .20
37 Greg Vaughn .02 .10
38 Chuck Finley .07 .20
39 Todd Benzinger .02 .10
40 Dave Justice .07 .20
41 Rob Dibble .07 .20
42 Tom Henke .02 .10
43 David Nied .02 .10
44 Sandy Alomar Jr. .02 .10
45 Pete Harnisch .02 .10
46 Jeff Russell .02 .10
47 Terry Mulholland .02 .10
48 Kevin Appier .07 .20
49 Randy Tomlin .02 .10
50 Cal Ripken Jr. .60 1.50
51 Andy Benes .02 .10
52 Jimmy Key .07 .20
53 Kirt Manwaring .02 .10
54 Kevin Tapani .02 .10
55 Jose Guzman .02 .10
56 Todd Stottlemyre .02 .10
57 Jack McDowell .02 .10
58 Orel Hershiser .07 .20
59 Chris Hammond .02 .10
60 Chris Nabholz .02 .10
61 Ruben Sierra .07 .20
62 Dwight Gooden .07 .20
63 John Kruk .07 .20
64 Omar Vizquel .10 .30
65 Tim Naehring .02 .10
66 Dwight Smith .02 .10
67 Mickey Tettleton .02 .10
68 J.T. Snow .07 .20
69 Greg McMichael .02 .10
70 Kevin Mitchell .02 .10
71 Kevin Brown .07 .20
72 Scott Cooper .02 .10
73 Jim Thome .10 .30
74 Joe Girardi .02 .10
75 Eric Anthony .02 .10
76 Orlando Merced .02 .10
77 Felix Jose .02 .10
78 Tommy Greene .02 .10
79 Bernard Gilkey .02 .10
80 Phil Plantier .02 .10
81 Danny Tartabull .02 .10
82 Trevor Wilson .02 .10
83 Chuck Knoblauch .07 .20
84 Rick Wilkins .02 .10
85 Devon White .07 .20
86 Lance Johnson .02 .10
87 Eric Karros .07 .20
88 Gary Sheffield .07 .20
89 Wil Cordero .02 .10
90 Ron Darling .02 .10
91 Darren Daulton .07 .20
92 Joe Orsulak .02 .10
93 Steve Cooke .02 .10
94 Darryl Hamilton .02 .10
95 Aaron Sele .02 .10
96 John Doherty .02 .10
97 Gary DiSarcina .02 .10
98 Jeff Blauser .02 .10
99 John Smiley .02 .10
100 Ken Griffey Jr. .30 .75
101 Dean Palmer .07 .20
102 Felix Fermin .02 .10
103 Jerald Clark .02 .10
104 Doug Drabek .02 .10
105 Curt Schilling .07 .20
106 Jeff Montgomery .02 .10
107 Rene Arocha .02 .10
108 Carlos Garcia .02 .10
109 Wally Whitehurst .02 .10
110 Jim Abbott .10 .30
111 Royce Clayton .02 .10
112 Chris Hoiles .02 .10
113 Mike Morgan .02 .10
114 Joe Magrane .02 .10
115 Tom Candiotti .02 .10
116 Ron Karkovice .02 .10
117 Ryan Bowen .02 .10
118 Rod Beck .02 .10
119 John Wetteland .07 .20
120 Terry Steinbach .02 .10
121 Dave Hollins .02 .10
122 Jeff Kent .10 .30
123 Ricky Bones .02 .10
124 Brian Jordan .07 .20
125 Chad Kreuter .02 .10
126 John Valentin .02 .10
127 Hilly Hathaway .02 .10
128 Wilson Alvarez .02 .10
129 Tino Martinez .10 .30
130 Rodney Bolton .02 .10
131 David Segui .02 .10
132 Wayne Kirby .02 .10
133 Eric Young .02 .10
134 Scott Servais .02 .10
135 Scott Radinsky .02 .10
136 Bret Barberie .02 .10
137 John Roper .02 .10
138 Ricky Gutierrez .02 .10
139 Bernie Williams .10 .30

140 Bud Black .02 .10
141 Jose Vizcaino .02 .10
142 Gerald Williams .02 .10
143 Duane Ward .02 .10
144 Danny Jackson .02 .10
145 Allen Watson .02 .10
146 Scott Fletcher .02 .10
147 Delino DeShields .02 .10
148 Shane Mack .02 .10
149 Jim Eisenreich .02 .10
150 Troy Neel .02 .10
151 Jay Bell .07 .20
152 B.J. Surhoff .07 .20
153 Mark Whiten .02 .10
154 Mike Henneman .02 .10
155 Todd Hundley .02 .10
156 Greg Myers .02 .10
157 Ryan Klesko .07 .20
158 Dave Fleming .02 .10
159 Mickey Morandini .02 .10
160 Blas Minor .02 .10
161 Reggie Jefferson .02 .10
162 David Hulse .02 .10
163 Greg Swindell .02 .10
164 Roberto Hernandez .02 .10
165 Brady Anderson .07 .20
166 Jack Armstrong .02 .10
167 Phil Clark .02 .10
168 Melido Perez .02 .10
169 Darren Lewis .02 .10
170 Sam Horn .02 .10
171 Mike Harkey .02 .10
172 Juan Guzman .02 .10
173 Bob Natal .02 .10
174 Deion Sanders .10 .30
175 Carlos Quintana .02 .10
176 Mel Rojas .02 .10
177 Willie Banks .02 .10
178 Ben Rivera .02 .10
179 Kenny Lofton .07 .20
180 Leo Gomez .02 .10
181 Roberto Mejia .02 .10
182 Mike Perez .02 .10
183 Travis Fryman .07 .20
184 Ben McDonald .02 .10
185 Steve Frey .02 .10
186 Kevin Young .02 .10
187 Dave Magadan .02 .10
188 Bobby Munoz .02 .10
189 Pat Rapp .02 .10
190 Jose Offerman .02 .10
191 Vinny Castilla .07 .20
192 Ivan Calderon .02 .10
193 Ken Caminiti .07 .20
194 Benji Gil .02 .10
195 Chuck Carr .02 .10
196 Derrick May .02 .10
197 Pat Kelly .02 .10
198 Jeff Brantley .02 .10
199 Jose Lind .02 .10
200 Steve Buechele .02 .10
201 Wes Chamberlain .02 .10
202 Eduardo Perez .02 .10
203 Bret Saberhagen .07 .20
204 Gregg Jefferies .02 .10
205 Darrin Fletcher .02 .10
206 Kent Hrbek .07 .20
207 Kim Batiste .02 .10
208 Jeff King .02 .10
209 Donovan Osborne .02 .10
210 Dave Nilsson .02 .10
211 Al Martin .02 .10
212 Mike Moore .02 .10
213 Sterling Hitchcock .02 .10
214 Geronimo Pena .02 .10
215 Kevin Higgins .02 .10
216 Norm Charlton .02 .10
217 Don Slaught .02 .10
218 Mitch Williams .02 .10
219 Derek Lilliquist .02 .10
220 Armando Reynoso .02 .10
221 Kenny Rogers .07 .20
222 Doug Jones .02 .10
223 Luis Aquino .02 .10
224 Mike Oquist .02 .10
225 Darryl Scott .02 .10
226 Kurt Abbott RC .02 .10
227 Andy Tomberlin .02 .10
228 Norberto Martin .02 .10
229 Pedro Castellano .02 .10
230 Curtis Pride RC .15 .40
231 Jeff McNeely .02 .10
232 Scott Lydy .02 .10
233 Darren Oliver RC .15 .40
234 Danny Bautista .02 .10
235 Butch Huskey .02 .10
236 Chipper Jones .20 .50
237 Eddie Zambrano RC .02 .10
238 Domingo Jean .02 .10
239 Javier Lopez .07 .20
240 Nigel Wilson .02 .10
241 Drew Denson .02 .10
242 Raul Mondesi .07 .20
243 Luis Ortiz .02 .10
244 Manny Ramirez .20 .50
245 Greg Blosser .02 .10
246 Rondell White .07 .20
247 Steve Karsay .02 .10
248 Scott Stahoviak .02 .10
249 Jose Valentin .02 .10
250 Marc Newfield .02 .10
251 Keith Kessinger .02 .10
252 Carl Everett .07 .20
253 John O'Donoghue .02 .10
254 Turk Wendell .02 .10
255 Scott Ruffcorn .02 .10
256 Tony Tarasco .02 .10
257 Andy Cook .02 .10
258 Matt Mieske .02 .10
259 Luis Lopez .02 .10
260 Ramon Caraballo .02 .10
261 Salomon Torres .02 .10
262 Brooks Kieschnick RC .02 .10
263 Daron Kirkreit .02 .10
264 Bill Wagner RC .75 2.00
265 Matt Drews RC .02 .10
266 Scott Christman RC .02 .10
267 Torii Hunter RC .60 1.50
268 Jamey Wright RC .02 .10
269 Jeff Granger .02 .10
270 Trot Nixon RC .50 1.25
271 Randy Myers .02 .10
272 Trevor Hoffman .10 .30
273 Bob Wickman .02 .10
274 Willie McGee .07 .20
275 Hipolito Pichardo .02 .10
276 Bobby Witt .02 .10
277 Gregg Olson .02 .10
278 Randy Johnson .20 .50
279 Robb Nen .07 .20
280 Paul O'Neill .10 .30
281 Lou Whitaker .07 .20
282 Chad Curtis .02 .10
283 Doug Henry .02 .10
284 Tom Glavine .10 .30
285 Mike Greenwell .02 .10
286 Roberto Kelly .02 .10
287 Roberto Alomar .10 .30
288 Charlie Hough .07 .20
289 Alex Fernandez .02 .10
290 Jeff Bagwell .10 .30
291 Wally Joyner .07 .20
292 Andujar Cedeno .02 .10
293 Rick Aguilera .02 .10
294 Darryl Strawberry .07 .20
295 Mike Mussina .10 .30
296 Jeff Gardner .02 .10
297 Chris Gwynn .02 .10
298 Matt Williams .07 .20
299 Brent Gates .02 .10
300 Mark McGwire .50 1.25
301 Jim Deshaies .02 .10
302 Edgar Martinez .10 .30
303 Danny Darwin .02 .10
304 Pat Meares .02 .10
305 Benito Santiago .07 .20
306 Jose Canseco .10 .30
307 Jim Gott .02 .10
308 Paul Sorrento .02 .10
309 Scott Kamieniecki .02 .10
310 Larry Walker .07 .20
311 Mark Langston .02 .10
312 John Jaha .02 .10
313 Stan Javier .02 .10
314 Hal Morris .02 .10
315 Robby Thompson .02 .10
316 Pat Hentgen .02 .10
317 Tom Gordon .02 .10
318 Joey Cora .02 .10
319 Luis Alicea .02 .10
320 Andre Dawson .07 .20
321 Darryl Kile .07 .20
322 Jose Rijo .02 .10
323 Luis Gonzalez .07 .20
324 Billy Ashley .02 .10
325 David Cone .07 .20
326 Bill Swift .02 .10
327 Phil Hiatt .02 .10
328 Craig Paquette .02 .10
329 Bob Welch .02 .10
330 Tony Phillips .02 .10
331 Archi Cianfrocco .02 .10
332 Dave Winfield .07 .20
333 David McCarty .02 .10
334 Al Leiter .07 .20
335 Tom Browning .02 .10
336 Mark Grace .10 .30
337 Jose Mesa .02 .10
338 Mike Stanley .02 .10
339 Roger McDowell .02 .10
340 Damion Easley .02 .10
341 Angel Miranda .02 .10
342 John Smoltz .10 .30
343 Jay Buhner .07 .20
344 Bryan Harvey .02 .10
345 Joe Carter .07 .20
346 Dante Bichette .07 .20
347 Jason Bere .02 .10
348 Frank Viola .07 .20
349 Ivan Rodriguez .10 .30
350 Juan Gonzalez .07 .20
351 Steve Finley .07 .20
352 Mike Felder .02 .10
353 Ramon Martinez .02 .10
354 Greg Gagne .02 .10
355 Ken Hill .02 .10
356 Pedro Munoz .02 .10
357 Todd Van Poppel .02 .10
358 Marquis Grissom .07 .20
359 Milt Cuyler .02 .10
360 Reggie Sanders .07 .20
361 Scott Erickson .02 .10
362 Billy Hatcher .02 .10
363 Gene Harris .02 .10
364 Rene Gonzales .02 .10
365 Kevin Rogers .02 .10
366 Eric Plunk .02 .10
367 Todd Zeile .02 .10
368 John Franco .07 .20
369 Brett Butler .07 .20
370 Bill Spiers .02 .10
371 Terry Pendleton .07 .20
372 Chris Bosio .02 .10
373 Orestes Destrade .02 .10
374 Dave Stewart .07 .20
375 Darren Holmes .02 .10
376 Doug Strange .02 .10
377 Brian Turang .02 .10
378 Carl Willis .02 .10
379 Mark McLemore .02 .10
380 Bobby Jones .02 .10
381 Scott Sanders .02 .10
382 Kirk Rueter .02 .10
383 Randy Velarde .02 .10
384 Fred McGriff .10 .30
385 Charles Nagy .02 .10
386 Rich Amaral .02 .10
387 Geronimo Berroa .02 .10
388 Eric Davis .07 .20
389 Ozzie Smith .30 .75
390 Alex Arias .02 .10
391 Brad Ausmus .10 .30
392 Cliff Floyd .07 .20
393 Roger Salkeld .02 .10
394 Jim Edmonds .20 .50
395 Jeromy Burnitz .07 .20
396 Dave Staton .02 .10
397 Rob Butler .02 .10
398 Marcos Armas .02 .10
399 Darrell Whitmore .02 .10
400 Ryan Thompson .02 .10
401 Ross Powell RC .02 .10
402 Joe Oliver .02 .10
403 Paul Carey .02 .10
404 Bob Hamelin .02 .10
405 Chris Turner .02 .10
406 Nate Minchey .02 .10
407 Lonnie Maclin RC .02 .10
408 Harold Baines .07 .20
409 Brian Williams .02 .10
410 Johnny Ruffin .02 .10
411 Julian Tavarez RC .02 .10
412 Mark Hutton .02 .10
413 Carlos Delgado .10 .30
414 Chris Gomez .02 .10
415 Mike Hampton .07 .20
416 Alex Diaz RC .02 .10
417 Jeffrey Hammonds .02 .10
418 Jayhawk Owens .02 .10
419 J.R. Phillips .02 .10
420 Cory Bailey RC .02 .10
421 Denny Hocking .02 .10
422 Jon Shave .02 .10
423 Damon Buford .02 .10
424 Troy O'Leary .02 .10
425 Tripp Cromer .02 .10
426 Albie Lopez .02 .10
427 Tony Fernandez .02 .10
428 Ozzie Guillen .07 .20
429 Alan Trammell .07 .20
430 John Wasdin RC .02 .10
431 Marc Valdes .02 .10
432 Brian Anderson RC .15 .40
433 Matt Brunson RC .02 .10
434 Wayne Gomes RC .02 .10
435 Jay Powell RC .02 .10
436 Kirk Presley RC .02 .10
437 Jon Ratliff RC .02 .10
438 Derrek Lee RC 1.25 3.00
439 Tom Pagnozzi .02 .10
440 Kent Mercker .02 .10
441 Phil Leftwich RC .02 .10
442 Jamie Moyer .07 .20
443 John Flaherty .02 .10
444 Mark Wohlers .02 .10
445 Jose Bautista .02 .10
446 Andres Galarraga .07 .20
447 Mark Lemke .02 .10
448 Tim Wakefield .10 .30
449 Pat Listach .02 .10
450 Rickey Henderson .20 .50
451 Mike Gallego .02 .10
452 Bob Tewksbury .02 .10
453 Kirk Gibson .07 .20
454 Pedro Astacio .02 .10
455 Mike Lansing .02 .10
456 Sean Berry .02 .10
457 Bob Walk .02 .10
458 Chili Davis .07 .20
459 Ed Sprague .02 .10
460 Kevin Stocker .02 .10
461 Mike Stanton .02 .10
462 Tim Raines .07 .20
463 Mike Bordick .02 .10
464 David Wells .07 .20
465 Tim Laker .02 .10
466 Cory Snyder .02 .10
467 Alex Cole .02 .10
468 Pete Incaviglia .02 .10
469 Roger Pavlik .02 .10
470 Greg W. Harris .02 .10
471 Xavier Hernandez .02 .10
472 Erik Hanson .02 .10
473 Jesse Orosco .02 .10
474 Greg Colbrunn .02 .10
475 Harold Reynolds .07 .20
476 Greg A. Harris .02 .10
477 Pat Borders .02 .10
478 Melvin Nieves .02 .10
479 Mariano Duncan .02 .10
480 Greg Hibbard .02 .10
481 Tim Pugh .02 .10
482 Bobby Ayala .02 .10
483 Sid Fernandez .02 .10
484 Tim Wallach .02 .10
485 Randy Milligan .02 .10
486 Walt Weiss .02 .10
487 Matt Walbeck .02 .10
488 Mike Macfarlane .02 .10
489 Jerry Browne .02 .10
490 Chris Sabo .02 .10
491 Tim Belcher .02 .10
492 Spike Owen .02 .10
493 Rafael Palmeiro .10 .30
494 Brian Harper .02 .10
495 Eddie Murray .20 .50
496 Ellis Burks .07 .20
497 Karl Rhodes .02 .10
498 Otis Nixon .02 .10
499 Lee Smith .07 .20
500 Bip Roberts .02 .10
501 Pedro Martinez .20 .50
502 Brian Hunter .02 .10
503 Tyler Green .02 .10
504 Bruce Hurst .02 .10
505 Alex Gonzalez .02 .10
506 Mark Portugal .02 .10
507 Bob Ojeda .02 .10
508 Dave Henderson .02 .10
509 Bo Jackson .20 .50
510 Bret Boone .07 .20
511 Mark Eichhorn .02 .10
512 Luis Polonia .02 .10
513 Will Clark .10 .30
514 Dave Valle .02 .10
515 Dan Wilson .02 .10
516 Dennis Martinez .07 .20
517 Jim Leyritz .02 .10
518 Howard Johnson .02 .10
519 Jody Reed .02 .10
520 Julio Franco .07 .20
521 Jeff Reardon .07 .20
522 Willie Greene .02 .10
523 Shawon Dunston .02 .10
524 Keith Mitchell .02 .10
525 Rick Helling .02 .10
526 Mark Kiefer .02 .10
527 Chan Ho Park RC .30 .75
528 Tony Longmire .02 .10
529 Rich Becker .02 .10
530 Tim Hyers RC .02 .10
531 Darrin Jackson .02 .10
532 Jack Morris .07 .20
533 Rick White .02 .10
534 Mike Kelly .02 .10
535 James Mouton .02 .10
536 Steve Trachsel .02 .10
537 Tony Eusebio .02 .10
538 Kelly Stinnett RC .15 .40
539 Paul Spoljaric .02 .10
540 Darren Dreifort .02 .10
SR1 Carlos Delgado Super Rookie 2.00 5.00

1995 Pinnacle

This 450-card standard-size set was issued in two series of 225 cards. They were released in 12-card packs, 24 packs to a box and 18 boxes in a case. The full-bleed fronts feature action photos. The player's last name is printed in black ink against a dramatic gold foil background at the base of the card. There are no notable Rookie Cards in this set.

COMPLETE SET (450) 12.00 30.00
COMP. SERIES 1 (225) 6.00 15.00
COMP. SERIES 2 (225) 6.00 15.00
1 Jeff Bagwell .10 .30
2 Roger Clemens .40 1.00
3 Mark Whiten .02 .10
4 Shawon Dunston .02 .10
5 Bobby Bonilla .07 .20
6 Kevin Tapani .02 .10
7 Eric Karros .07 .20
8 Cliff Floyd .07 .20
9 Pat Kelly .02 .10
10 Jeffrey Hammonds .02 .10
11 Jeff Conine .07 .20
12 Fred McGriff .10 .30
13 Chris Bosio .02 .10
14 Mike Mussina .10 .30
15 Danny Bautista .02 .10
16 Mickey Morandini .02 .10
17 Chuck Finley .07 .20
18 Jim Thome .10 .30
19 Luis Ortiz .02 .10
20 Walt Weiss .02 .10
21 Don Mattingly .50 1.25
22 Bob Hamelin .02 .10
23 Melido Perez .02 .10
24 Keith Mitchell .02 .10
25 John Smoltz .10 .30
26 Hector Carrasco .02 .10
27 Pat Hentgen .02 .10
28 Derrick May .02 .10
29 Mike Kingery .02 .10
30 Chuck Carr .02 .10
31 Billy Ashley .02 .10
32 Todd Hundley .02 .10
33 Luis Gonzalez .07 .20
34 Marquis Grissom .07 .20
35 Jeff King .02 .10
36 Eddie Williams .02 .10
37 Tom Pagnozzi .02 .10
38 Chris Hoiles .02 .10
39 Sandy Alomar Jr. .02 .10
40 Mike Greenwell .02 .10
41 Lance Johnson .02 .10
42 Junior Felix .02 .10
43 Felix Jose .02 .10
44 Scott Leius .02 .10
45 Ruben Sierra .07 .20
46 Kevin Seitzer .02 .10
47 Wade Boggs .10 .30
48 Reggie Jefferson .02 .10
49 Jose Canseco .10 .30
50 David Justice .07 .20
51 John Smiley .02 .10
52 Joe Carter .07 .20
53 Rick Wilkins .02 .10
54 Ellis Burks .07 .20
55 Dave Weathers .02 .10
56 Pedro Astacio .02 .10
57 Ryan Thompson .02 .10
58 James Mouton .02 .10
59 Mel Rojas .02 .10
60 Orlando Merced .02 .10
61 Matt Williams .07 .20
62 Bernard Gilkey .02 .10
63 J.R. Phillips .02 .10
64 Lee Smith .07 .20
65 Jim Edmonds .10 .30
66 Darrin Jackson .02 .10
67 Scott Cooper .02 .10
68 Ron Karkovice .02 .10
69 Chris Gomez .02 .10
70 Kevin Appier .07 .20
71 Bobby Jones .02 .10
72 Doug Drabek .02 .10
73 Matt Mieske .02 .10
74 Sterling Hitchcock .02 .10
75 John Valentin .02 .10
76 Reggie Sanders .07 .20
77 Wally Joyner .07 .20
78 Turk Wendell .02 .10
79 Charlie Hayes .02 .10
80 Bret Barberie .02 .10
81 Troy Neel .02 .10
82 Ken Caminiti .07 .20
83 Milt Thompson .02 .10
84 Paul Sorrento .02 .10
85 Trevor Hoffman .07 .20
86 Jay Bell .07 .20
87 Mark Portugal .02 .10
88 Sid Fernandez .02 .10
89 Charles Nagy .02 .10
90 Jeff Montgomery .02 .10
91 Chuck Knoblauch .07 .20
92 Jeff Frye .02 .10
93 Tony Gwynn .25 .60
94 John Olerud .07 .20
95 David Nied .02 .10
96 Chris Hammond .02 .10
97 Edgar Martinez .10 .30
98 Kevin Stocker .02 .10
99 Jeff Fassero .02 .10
100 Curt Schilling .07 .20
101 Dave Clark .02 .10
102 Delino DeShields .02 .10
103 Leo Gomez .02 .10
104 Dave Hollins .02 .10
105 Tim Naehring .02 .10
106 Otis Nixon .02 .10
107 Ozzie Guillen .07 .20
108 Jose Lind .02 .10
109 Stan Javier .02 .10
110 Greg Vaughn .02 .10
111 Chipper Jones .20 .50
112 Ed Sprague .02 .10
113 Mike Macfarlane .02 .10
114 Steve Finley .07 .20
115 Ken Hill .02 .10
116 Carlos Garcia .02 .10
117 Lou Whitaker .07 .20
118 Todd Zeile .02 .10
119 Gary Sheffield .07 .20
120 Ben McDonald .02 .10
121 Pete Harnisch .02 .10
122 Ivan Rodriguez .10 .30
123 Wilson Alvarez .02 .10
124 Travis Fryman .07 .20
125 Pedro Munoz .02 .10
126 Mark Lemke .02 .10
127 Jose Valentin .02 .10
128 Ken Griffey Jr. .30 .75
129 Omar Vizquel .10 .30
130 Milt Cuyler .04 .10
131 Steve Trachsel .02 .10
132 Alex Rodriguez .50 1.25
133 Garret Anderson .07 .20
134 Armando Benitez .02 .10
135 Shawn Green .07 .20
136 Jorge Fabregas .02 .10
137 Orlando Miller .02 .10
138 Rikkert Faneyte .02 .10
139 Ismael Valdes .02 .10
140 Jose Oliva .02 .10
141 Aaron Small .02 .10
142 Tim Davis .02 .10
143 Ricky Bottalico .02 .10
144 Mike Matheny .02 .10
145 Roberto Petagine .02 .10
146 Fausto Cruz .02 .10
147 Bryce Florie .02 .10
148 Jose Lima .02 .10
149 John Hudek .02 .10
150 Duane Singleton .02 .10
151 John Mabry .02 .10
152 Robert Eenhoorn .02 .10
153 Jon Lieber .02 .10
154 Garey Ingram .02 .10
155 Paul Shuey .02 .10
156 Mike Lieberthal .07 .20
157 Steve Dunn .02 .10
158 Charles Johnson .07 .20
159 Ernie Young .02 .10
160 Jose Martinez .02 .10
161 Kurt Miller .02 .10
162 Joey Eischen .02 .10
163 Dave Stevens .02 .10
164 Brian L.Hunter .02 .10
165 Jeff Cirillo .02 .10
166 Mark Smith .02 .10
167 M. Christensen RC .02 .10
168 C.J. Nitkowski .02 .10
169 A. Williamson RC .02 .10
170 Paul Konerko .40 1.00
171 Scott Elarton RC .08 .25
172 Jacob Shumate .02 .10
173 Terrence Long .02 .10
174 Mark Johnson RC .08 .25
175 Ben Grieve .02 .10
176 Jayson Peterson RC .02 .10
177 Checklist .02 .10
178 Checklist .02 .10
179 Checklist .02 .10
180 Checklist .02 .10
181 Brian Anderson .02 .10
182 Steve Buechele .02 .10
183 Mark Clark .02 .10
184 Cecil Fielder .07 .20
185 Steve Avery .02 .10
186 Devon White .07 .20
187 Craig Shipley .02 .10
188 Brady Anderson .07 .20
189 Kenny Lofton .07 .20
190 Alex Cole .02 .10
191 Brent Gates .02 .10
192 Dean Palmer .07 .20
193 Alex Gonzalez .02 .10
194 Steve Cooke .02 .10
195 Ray Lankford .07 .20
196 Mark McGwire .50 1.25
197 Marc Newfield .02 .10
198 Pat Rapp .02 .10
199 Darren Lewis .02 .10
200 Carlos Baerga .02 .10
201 Rickey Henderson .20 .50
202 Kurt Abbott .02 .10
203 Kirt Manwaring .02 .10
204 Cal Ripken .60 1.50
205 Darren Daulton .07 .20
206 Greg Colbrunn .02 .10
207 Darryl Hamilton .02 .10
208 Bo Jackson .20 .50
209 Tony Phillips .02 .10
210 Geronimo Berroa .02 .10
211 Rich Becker .02 .10
212 Tony Tarasco .02 .10
213 Karl Rhodes .02 .10
214 Phil Plantier .02 .10
215 J.T. Snow .07 .20
216 Mo Vaughn .07 .20
217 Greg Gagne .02 .10
218 Ricky Bones .02 .10
219 Mike Bordick .02 .10
220 Chad Curtis .02 .10
221 Royce Clayton .02 .10
222 Roberto Alomar .10 .30
223 Jose Rijo .02 .10
224 Ryan Klesko .07 .20
225 Mark Langston .02 .10
226 Frank Thomas .20 .50
227 Juan Gonzalez .07 .20
228 Ron Gant .07 .20
229 Javier Lopez .07 .20
230 Sammy Sosa .20 .50
231 Kevin Brown .07 .20
232 Gary DiSarcina .02 .10
233 Albert Belle .07 .20
234 Jay Buhner .07 .20
235 Pedro Martinez .10 .30
236 Bob Tewksbury .02 .10
237 Mike Piazza .30 .75
238 Darryl Kile .07 .20
239 Bryan Harvey .02 .10
240 Andres Galarraga .07 .20
241 Jeff Blauser .07 .20
242 Jeff Kent .07 .20
243 Bobby Munoz .02 .10
244 Greg Maddux .30 .75
245 Paul O'Neill .10 .30
246 Lenny Dykstra .07 .20
247 Todd Van Poppel .02 .10
248 Bernie Williams .10 .30
249 Glenallen Hill .02 .10
250 Duane Ward .02 .10
251 Dennis Eckersley .07 .20
252 Pat Mahomes .02 .10
253 Rusty Greer .07 .20
254 Roberto Kelly .02 .10
255 Randy Myers .02 .10
256 Scott Ruffcorn .02 .10
257 Robin Ventura .07 .20
258 Eduardo Perez .02 .10
259 Aaron Sele .02 .10
260 Paul Molitor .07 .20
261 Juan Guzman .02 .10
262 Darren Oliver .02 .10
263 Mike Stanley .02 .10
264 Tom Glavine .10 .30
265 Rico Brogna .02 .10
266 Craig Biggio .10 .30
267 Darrell Whitmore .02 .10
268 Jimmy Key .07 .20
269 Will Clark .10 .30
270 David Cone .07 .20
271 Brian Jordan .07 .20
272 Barry Bonds .60 1.50
273 Danny Tartabull .02 .10
274 Ramon J.Martinez .02 .10
275 Al Martin .02 .10
276 Fred McGriff SM .07 .20
277 Carlos Delgado SM .02 .10
278 Juan Gonzalez SM .02 .10
279 Shawn Green SM .02 .10
280 Carlos Baerga SM .02 .10
281 Cliff Floyd SM .02 .10
282 Ozzie Smith SM .20 .50
283 Alex Rodriguez SM .20 .50
284 Kenny Lofton SM .02 .10
285 Dave Justice SM .02 .10
286 Tim Salmon SM .07 .20
287 Manny Ramirez SM .07 .20
288 Will Clark SM .07 .20
289 Garret Anderson SM .02 .10
290 Billy Ashley SM .02 .10
291 Tony Gwynn SM .10 .30
292 Raul Mondesi SM .02 .10
293 Rafael Palmeiro SM .07 .20
294 Matt Williams SM .02 .10
295 Don Mattingly SM .25 .60
296 Kirby Puckett SM .10 .30
297 Paul Molitor SM .02 .10
298 Albert Belle SM .02 .10
299 Barry Bonds SM .30 .75
300 Mike Piazza SM .20 .50
301 Jeff Bagwell SM .07 .20
302 Frank Thomas SM .10 .30
303 Chipper Jones SM .10 .30
304 Ken Griffey Jr. SM .20 .50
305 Cal Ripken Jr. SM .30 .75
306 Eric Anthony .02 .10
307 Todd Benzinger .02 .10
308 Jacob Brumfield .02 .10
309 Wes Chamberlain .02 .10
310 Tino Martinez .10 .30
311 Roberto Mejia .02 .10
312 Jose Offerman .02 .10
313 David Segui .02 .10
314 Eric Young .02 .10
315 Rey Sanchez .02 .10
316 Raul Mondesi .07 .20
317 Bret Boone .07 .20
318 Andre Dawson .07 .20
319 Brian McRae .02 .10
320 Dave Nilsson .02 .10
321 Moises Alou .07 .20
322 Don Slaught .02 .10
323 Dave McCarty .02 .10
324 Mike Huff .02 .10
325 Rick Aguilera .02 .10
326 Rod Beck .02 .10
327 Kenny Rogers .07 .20
328 Andy Benes .02 .10
329 Allen Watson .02 .10
330 Randy Johnson .20 .50
331 Willie Greene .02 .10
332 Hal Morris .02 .10
333 Ozzie Smith .30 .75
334 Jason Bere .02 .10
335 Scott Erickson .02 .10
336 Dante Bichette .07 .20
337 Willie Banks .02 .10
338 Eric Davis .07 .20
339 Rondell White .07 .20
340 Kirby Puckett .20 .50
341 Deion Sanders .10 .30
342 Eddie Murray .20 .50
343 Mike Harkey .02 .10
344 Joey Hamilton .02 .10
345 Roger Salkeld .02 .10
346 Wil Cordero .02 .10
347 John Wetteland .07 .20
348 Geronimo Pena .02 .10
349 Kirk Gibson .07 .20
350 Manny Ramirez .10 .30
351 Wm.VanLandingham .02 .10
352 B.J. Surhoff .07 .20
353 Ken Ryan .02 .10
354 Terry Steinbach .02 .10
355 Bret Saberhagen .07 .20
356 John Jaha .02 .10
357 Joe Girardi .02 .10

358 Steve Karsay .02 .10
359 Alex Fernandez .02 .10
360 Salomon Torres .02 .10
361 John Burkett .02 .10
362 Derek Bell .02 .10
363 Tom Henke .02 .10
364 Gregg Jefferies .02 .10
365 Jack McDowell .02 .10
366 Andujar Cedeno .02 .10
367 Dave Winfield .07 .20
368 Carl Everett .07 .20
369 Danny Jackson .02 .10
370 Jeromy Burnitz .07 .20
371 Mark Grace .10 .30
372 Larry Walker .07 .20
373 Bill Swift .02 .10
374 Dennis Martinez .07 .20
375 Mickey Tettleton .02 .10
376 Mel Nieves .02 .10
377 Cal Eldred .02 .10
378 Orel Hershiser .07 .20
379 David Wells .07 .20
380 Gary Gaetti .07 .20
381 Tim Raines .07 .20
382 Barry Larkin .10 .30
383 Jason Jacome .02 .10
384 Tim Wallach .02 .10
385 Robby Thompson .02 .10
386 Frank Viola .07 .20
387 Dave Stewart .07 .20
388 Bip Roberts .02 .10
389 Ron Darling .02 .10
390 Carlos Delgado .07 .20
391 Tim Salmon .10 .30
392 Alan Trammell .07 .20
393 Kevin Foster .02 .10
394 Jim Abbott .10 .30
395 John Kruk .07 .20
396 Andy Van Slyke .10 .30
397 Dave Magadan .02 .10
398 Rafael Palmeiro .10 .30
399 Mike Devereaux .02 .10
400 Benito Santiago .07 .20
401 Brett Butler .07 .20
402 John Franco .07 .20
403 Matt Walbeck .02 .10
404 Terry Pendleton .07 .20
405 Chris Sabo .02 .10
406 Andrew Lorraine .02 .10
407 Dan Wilson .02 .10
408 Mike Lansing .02 .10
409 Ray McDavid .02 .10
410 Shane Andrews .02 .10
411 Tom Gordon .02 .10
412 Chad Ogea .02 .10
413 James Baldwin .02 .10
414 Russ Davis .02 .10
415 Ray Holbert .02 .10
416 Ray Durham .07 .20
417 Matt Nokes .02 .10
418 Rod Henderson .02 .10
419 Gabe White .02 .10
420 Todd Hollandsworth .02 .10
421 Midre Cummings .02 .10
422 Harold Baines .07 .20
423 Troy Percival .07 .20
424 Joe Vitiello .02 .10
425 Andy Ashby .02 .10
426 Michael Tucker .02 .10
427 Mark Gubicza .02 .10
428 Jim Bullinger .02 .10
429 Jose Malave .02 .10
430 Pete Schourek .02 .10
431 Bobby Ayala .02 .10
432 Marvin Freeman .02 .10
433 Pat Listach .02 .10
434 Eddie Taubensee .02 .10
435 Steve Howe .02 .10
436 Kent Mercker .02 .10
437 Hector Fajardo .02 .10
438 Scott Kamieniecki .02 .10
439 Robb Nen .07 .20
440 Mike Kelly .02 .10
441 Tom Candiotti .02 .10
442 Albie Lopez .02 .10
443 Jeff Granger .02 .10
444 Rich Aude .02 .10
445 Luis Polonia .02 .10
446 Frank Thomas CL .10 .30
447 Ken Griffey Jr. CL .20 .50
448 Mike Piazza CL .20 .50
449 Jeff Bagwell CL .07 .20
450 Jeff Bagwell CL .20 .50
Frank Thomas
Ken Griffey Jr.
Mike Piazza

1996 Pinnacle

The 1996 Pinnacle set was issued in two separate series of 200 cards each. The 10-card packs retailed for $2.49. On 20-point card stock, the fronts feature full-bleed color action photos, bordered at the bottom by a gold foil triangle. The Series I set features the following topical subsets: The Naturals (134-163), '95 Rookies (164-193) and Checklists (194-200). Series II set features these subsets: Hardball Heroes (30 cards), 300 Series (17 cards), Rookies (25 cards), and Checklists (7 cards). Numbering for the 300 Series subset was based on player's career batting average. At that time, both Paul Molitor and Jeff Bagwell had identical career batting averages of .305, thus Pinnacle numbered both of their 300 Series subset cards as 305. Due to this quirky numbering, the set only runs through card 399, but actually contains 400 cards. A special Cal Ripken Jr. Tribute card was inserted in first series packs at the rate of one in 150.

COMPLETE SET (400) 12.00 30.00
COMP. SERIES 1 (200) 6.00 15.00
COMP. SERIES 2 (200) 6.00 15.00
1 Greg Maddux .30 .75
2 Bill Pulsipher .07 .20
3 Dante Bichette .07 .20
4 Mike Piazza .30 .75
5 Garret Anderson .07 .20
6 Steve Finley .07 .20
7 Andy Benes .07 .20
8 Chuck Knoblauch .07 .20
9 Tom Gordon .07 .20
10 Jeff Bagwell .10 .30
11 Wil Cordero .07 .20
12 John Mabry .07 .20
13 Jeff Frye .07 .20
14 Travis Fryman .07 .20
15 John Wetteland .07 .20
16 Jason Bates .07 .20
17 Danny Tartabull .07 .20
18 Charles Nagy .07 .20
19 Robin Ventura .07 .20
20 Reggie Sanders .07 .20
21 Dave Clark .07 .20
22 Jaime Navarro .07 .20
23 Joey Hamilton .07 .20
24 Al Leiter .07 .20
25 Deion Sanders .10 .30
26 Tim Salmon .10 .30
27 Tino Martinez .10 .30
28 Mike Greenwell .07 .20
29 Phil Plantier .07 .20
30 Bobby Bonilla .07 .20
31 Kenny Rogers .07 .20
32 Chili Davis .07 .20
33 Joe Carter .07 .20
34 Mike Mussina .10 .30
35 Matt Williams .07 .20
36 Jose Canseco .10 .30
37 Brad Radke .07 .20
38 Juan Gonzalez .07 .20
39 David Segui .07 .20
40 Alex Fernandez .07 .20
41 Jeff Kent .07 .20
42 Todd Zeile .07 .20
43 Darryl Strawberry .07 .20
44 Jose Rijo .07 .20
45 Ramon Martinez .07 .20
46 Manny Ramirez .10 .30
47 Gregg Jefferies .07 .20
48 Bryan Rekar .07 .20
49 Jeff King .07 .20
50 John Olerud .07 .20
51 Marc Newfield .07 .20
52 Charles Johnson .07 .20
53 Robby Thompson .07 .20
54 Brian L. Hunter .07 .20
55 Mike Blowers .07 .20
56 Keith Lockhart .07 .20
57 Ray Lankford .07 .20
58 Tim Wallach .07 .20
59 Ivan Rodriguez .10 .30
60 Ed Sprague .07 .20
61 Paul Molitor .07 .20
62 Eric Karros .07 .20
63 Glenallen Hill .07 .20
64 Jay Bell .07 .20
65 Tom Pagnozzi .07 .20
66 Greg Colbrunn .07 .20
67 Edgar Martinez .10 .30
68 Paul Sorrento .07 .20
69 Kirt Manwaring .07 .20
70 Pete Schourek .07 .20
71 Orlando Merced .07 .20
72 Shawon Dunston .07 .20
73 Ricky Bottalico .07 .20
74 Brady Anderson .07 .20
75 Steve Ontiveros .07 .20
76 Jim Abbott .10 .30
77 Carl Everett .07 .20
78 Mo Vaughn .07 .20
79 Pedro Martinez .10 .30
80 Harold Baines .07 .20
81 Alan Trammell .07 .20
82 Steve Avery .07 .20
83 Jeff Cirillo .07 .20
84 John Valentin .07 .20
85 Bernie Williams .10 .30
86 Andre Dawson .07 .20
87 Dave Winfield .07 .20
88 B.J. Surhoff .07 .20
89 Jeff Blauser .07 .20
90 Barry Larkin .10 .30
91 Cliff Floyd .07 .20
92 Sammy Sosa .20 .50
93 Andres Galarraga .07 .20
94 Dave Nilsson .07 .20
95 James Mouton .07 .20
96 Marquis Grissom .07 .20
97 Matt Williams .07 .20
98 John Jaha .07 .20
99 Don Mattingly .50 1.25
100 Tim Naehring .07 .20
101 Kevin Appier .07 .20
102 Bobby Higginson .07 .20
103 Andy Pettitte .10 .30
104 Ozzie Smith .30 .75
105 Kenny Lofton .07 .20
106 Ken Caminiti .07 .20
107 Walt Weiss .07 .20
108 Jack McDowell .07 .20
109 Brian McRae .07 .20
110 Gary Gaetti .07 .20
111 Curtis Goodwin .07 .20
112 Dennis Martinez .07 .20
113 Omar Vizquel .10 .30
114 Chipper Jones .20 .50
115 Mark Gubicza .07 .20
116 Ruben Sierra .07 .20
117 Eddie Murray .20 .50
118 Chad Curtis .07 .20
119 Hal Morris .07 .20
120 Ben McDonald .07 .20
121 Marty Cordova .07 .20
122 Ken Griffey Jr. UER .30 .75
Card says Ken homered from both sides
He is only a left hitter
123 Gary Sheffield .07 .20
124 Charlie Hayes .07 .20
125 Shawn Green UER .07 .20
Picture on back is Ed Sprague
126 Jason Giambi .07 .20
127 Mark Langston .07 .20
128 Mark Whiten .07 .20
129 Greg Vaughn .07 .20
130 Mark McGwire .50 1.25
131 Hideo Nomo .20 .50
132 Eric Karros .20 .50
Mike Piazza
Raul Mondesi
Hideo Nomo
133 Jason Bere .07 .20
134 Ken Griffey Jr. NAT .20 .50
135 Frank Thomas NAT .10 .30
136 Cal Ripken NAT .30 .75
137 Albert Belle NAT .07 .20
138 Mike Piazza NAT .20 .50
139 Dante Bichette NAT .07 .20
140 Sammy Sosa NAT .10 .30
141 Mo Vaughn NAT .07 .20
142 Tim Salmon NAT .07 .20
143 Reggie Sanders NAT .07 .20
144 Cecil Fielder NAT .07 .20
145 Jim Edmonds NAT .07 .20
146 Rafael Palmeiro NAT .07 .20
147 Edgar Martinez NAT .07 .20
148 Barry Bonds NAT .30 .75
149 Manny Ramirez NAT .07 .20
150 Larry Walker NAT .07 .20
151 Jeff Bagwell NAT .07 .20
152 Ron Gant NAT .07 .20
153 Andres Galarraga NAT .07 .20
154 Eddie Murray NAT .10 .30
155 Kirby Puckett NAT .10 .30
156 Will Clark NAT .07 .20
157 Don Mattingly NAT .25 .60
158 Mark McGwire NAT .25 .60
159 Dean Palmer NAT .07 .20
160 Matt Williams NAT .07 .20
161 Fred McGriff NAT .07 .20
162 Joe Carter NAT .07 .20
163 Juan Gonzalez NAT .07 .20
164 Alex Ochoa .07 .20
165 Ruben Rivera .07 .20
166 Tony Clark .07 .20
167 Brian Barber .07 .20
168 Matt Lawton RC .15 .40
169 Terrell Wade .07 .20
170 Johnny Damon .10 .30
171 Derek Jeter .50 1.25
172 Phil Nevin .07 .20
173 Robert Perez .07 .20
174 C.J. Nitkowski .07 .20
175 Joe Vitiello .07 .20
176 Roger Cedeno .07 .20
177 Ron Coomer .07 .20
178 Chris Widger .07 .20
179 Jimmy Haynes .07 .20
180 Mike Sweeney RC .40 1.00
181 Howard Battle .07 .20
182 John Wasdin .07 .20
183 Jim Pittsley .07 .20
184 Bob Wolcott .07 .20
185 LaTroy Hawkins .07 .20
186 Nigel Wilson .07 .20
187 Dustin Hermanson .07 .20
188 Chris Snopek .07 .20
189 Mariano Rivera .20 .50
190 Jose Herrera .07 .20
191 Chris Stynes .07 .20
192 Larry Thomas .07 .20
193 David Bell .07 .20
194 Frank Thomas CL .10 .30
195 Ken Griffey Jr. CL .20 .50
196 Cal Ripken CL .30 .75
197 Jeff Bagwell CL .07 .20
198 Mike Piazza CL .20 .50
199 Barry Bonds CL .30 .75
200 Garret Anderson CL .10 .30
Chipper Jones
201 Frank Thomas .20 .50
202 Michael Tucker .07 .20
203 Kirby Puckett .20 .50
204 Alex Gonzalez .07 .20
205 Tony Gwynn .25 .60
206 Moises Alou .07 .20
207 Albert Belle .07 .20
208 Barry Bonds .60 1.50
209 Fred McGriff .10 .30
210 Dennis Eckersley .07 .20
211 Craig Biggio .10 .30
212 David Cone .07 .20
213 Will Clark .10 .30
214 Cal Ripken .60 1.50
215 Wade Boggs .10 .30
216 Pete Schourek .07 .20
217 Darren Daulton .07 .20
218 Carlos Baerga .07 .20
219 Larry Walker .07 .20
220 Denny Neagle .07 .20
221 Jim Edmonds .07 .20
222 Lee Smith .07 .20
223 Jason Isringhausen .07 .20
224 Jay Buhner .07 .20
225 John Olerud .07 .20
226 Jeff Conine .07 .20
227 Dean Palmer .07 .20
228 Jim Abbott .10 .30
229 Raul Mondesi .07 .20
230 Tom Glavine .10 .30
231 Kevin Seitzer .07 .20
232 Lenny Dykstra .07 .20
233 Brian Jordan .07 .20
234 Rondell White .07 .20
235 Bret Boone .07 .20
236 Randy Johnson .20 .50
237 Paul O'Neill .10 .30
238 Jim Thome .10 .30
239 Edgardo Alfonzo .07 .20
240 Terry Pendleton .07 .20
241 Harold Baines .07 .20
242 Roberto Alomar .10 .30
243 Mark Grace .10 .30
244 Derek Bell .07 .20
245 Vinny Castilla .07 .20
246 Cecil Fielder .07 .20
247 Roger Clemens .40 1.00
248 Orel Hershiser .07 .20
249 J.T. Snow .07 .20
250 Rafael Palmeiro .10 .30
251 Bret Saberhagen .07 .20
252 Todd Hollandsworth .07 .20
253 Ryan Klesko .07 .20
254 Greg Maddux HH .20 .50
255 Ken Griffey Jr. HH .20 .50
256 Hideo Nomo HH .10 .30
257 Frank Thomas HH .10 .30
258 Cal Ripken HH .30 .75
259 Jeff Bagwell HH .07 .20
260 Barry Bonds HH .30 .75
261 Mo Vaughn HH .07 .20
262 Albert Belle HH .07 .20
263 Sammy Sosa HH .10 .30
264 Reggie Sanders HH .07 .20
265 Mike Piazza HH .20 .50
266 Chipper Jones HH .10 .30
267 Tony Gwynn HH .10 .30
268 Kirby Puckett HH .10 .30
269 Wade Boggs HH .07 .20
270 Will Clark HH .07 .20
271 Gary Sheffield HH .07 .20
272 Dante Bichette HH .07 .20
273 Randy Johnson HH .10 .30
274 Matt Williams HH .07 .20
275 Alex Rodriguez HH .40 1.00
276 Tim Salmon HH .07 .20
277 Johnny Damon HH .07 .20
278 Manny Ramirez HH .07 .20
279 Derek Jeter HH .25 .60
280 Eddie Murray HH .10 .30
281 Ozzie Smith HH .20 .50
282 Garret Anderson HH .07 .20
283 Raul Mondesi HH .07 .20
284 Terry Steinbach .07 .20
285 Carlos Garcia .07 .20
286 Dave Justice .07 .20
287 Eric Anthony .07 .20
288 Benji Gil .07 .20
289 Bob Hamelin .07 .20
290 Dwayne Hosey .07 .20
291 Andy Pettitte HH .07 .20
292 Rod Beck .07 .20
293 Shane Andrews .07 .20
294 Julian Tavarez .07 .20
295 Willie Greene .07 .20
296 Ismael Valdes .07 .20
297 Glenallen Hill .07 .20
298 Troy Percival .07 .20
299 Ray Durham .07 .20
300 Jeff Conine 300 .07 .20
301 Ken Griffey Jr. 300 .20 .50
302 Will Clark 300 .07 .20
303 Mike Greenwell 300 .07 .20
304 Carlos Baerga 300 .07 .20
305A Paul Molitor 300 .07 .20
305B Jeff Bagwell 300 .07 .20
306 Mark Grace 300 .07 .20
307 Don Mattingly 300 .25 .60
308 Hal Morris 300 .07 .20
309 Butch Huskey .07 .20
310 Ozzie Guillen .07 .20
311 Erik Hanson .07 .20
312 Kenny Lofton 300 .07 .20
313 Edgar Martinez 300 .07 .20
314 Kurt Abbott .07 .20
315 John Smoltz .10 .30
316 Ariel Prieto .07 .20
317 Mark Carreon .07 .20
318 Kirby Puckett 300 .10 .30
319 Carlos Perez .07 .20
320 Gary DiSarcina .07 .20
321 Trevor Hoffman .07 .20
322 Mike Piazza 300 .20 .50
323 Frank Thomas 300 .10 .30
324 Juan Acevedo .07 .20
325 Bip Roberts .07 .20
326 Javier Lopez .07 .20
327 Benito Santiago .07 .20
328 Mark Lewis .07 .20
329 Royce Clayton .07 .20
330 Tom Gordon .07 .20
331 Ben McDonald .07 .20
332 Dan Wilson .07 .20
333 Ron Gant .07 .20
334 Wade Boggs 300 .07 .20
335 Paul Molitor .07 .20
336 Tony Gwynn 300 .10 .30
337 Sean Berry .07 .20
338 Rickey Henderson .20 .50
339 Wil Cordero .07 .20
340 Kent Mercker .07 .20
341 Kenny Rogers .07 .20
342 Ryne Sandberg .30 .75
343 Charlie Hayes .07 .20
344 Andy Benes .07 .20
345 Sterling Hitchcock .07 .20
346 Bernard Gilkey .07 .20
347 Julio Franco .07 .20
348 Ken Hill .07 .20
349 Russ Davis .07 .20
350 Mike Blowers .07 .20
351 B.J. Surhoff .07 .20
352 Lance Johnson .07 .20
353 Darryl Hamilton .07 .20
354 Shawon Dunston .07 .20
355 Rick Aguilera .07 .20
356 Danny Tartabull .07 .20
357 Todd Stottlemyre .07 .20
358 Mike Bordick .07 .20
359 Jack McDowell .07 .20
360 Todd Zeile .07 .20
361 Tino Martinez .10 .30
362 Greg Gagne .07 .20
363 Mike Kelly .07 .20
364 Tim Raines .07 .20
365 Ernie Young .07 .20
366 Mike Stanley .07 .20
367 Wally Joyner .07 .20
368 Karim Garcia .07 .20
369 Paul Wilson .07 .20
370 Sal Fasano .07 .20
371 Jason Schmidt .07 .20
372 Livan Hernandez RC .40 1.00
373 George Arias .07 .20
374 Steve Gibralter .07 .20
375 Jermaine Dye .07 .20
376 Jason Kendall .07 .20
377 Brooks Kieschnick .07 .20
378 Jeff Ware .07 .20
379 Alan Benes .07 .20
380 Rey Ordonez .07 .20
381 Jay Powell .07 .20
382 O. Fernandez RC .08 .25
383 Wilton Guerrero RC .08 .25
384 Eric Owens .07 .20
385 George Williams RC .08 .25
386 Chan Ho Park .07 .20
387 Jeff Suppan .07 .20
388 F.P. Santangelo RC .15 .40
389 Terry Adams .07 .20
390 Bob Abreu .20 .50
391 Quinton McCracken .07 .20
392 Mike Busby RC .08 .25
393 Cal Ripken CL .30 .75
394 Ken Griffey Jr. CL .20 .50
395 Frank Thomas CL .10 .30
396 Chipper Jones CL .10 .30
397 Greg Maddux CL .20 .50
398 Mike Piazza CL .20 .50
399 Ken Griffey Jr CL .20 .50
Cal Ripken Jr.
Chipper Jones
Frank Thomas
Greg Maddux
Mike Piazza
CR1 Cal Ripken Tribute 6.00 15.00

1997 Pinnacle

The 1997 Pinnacle set was issued as one series of 200 cards. Cards were distributed in 10-card hobby and retail packs (SRP $2.49) and seven-card magazine packs. This set was released in February, 1997. The set contains the following subsets: Rookies (156-185), Clout (186-197) and Checklists (198-200).

COMPLETE SET (200) 8.00 20.00
1 Cecil Fielder .10 .30
2 Garret Anderson .10 .30
3 Charles Nagy .10 .30
4 Darryl Hamilton .10 .30
5 Greg Myers .10 .30
6 Eric Davis .10 .30
7 Jeff Frye .10 .30
8 Marquis Grissom .10 .30
9 Curt Schilling .10 .30
10 Jeff Fassero .10 .30
11 Alan Benes .10 .30
12 Orlando Miller .10 .30
13 Alex Fernandez .10 .30
14 Andy Pettitte .20 .50
15 Andre Dawson .10 .30
16 Mark Grudzielanek .10 .30
17 Joe Vitiello .10 .30
18 Juan Gonzalez .10 .30
19 Mark Whiten .10 .30
20 Lance Johnson .10 .30
21 Trevor Hoffman .10 .30
22 Marc Newfield .10 .30
23 Jim Eisenreich .10 .30
24 Joe Carter .10 .30
25 Jose Canseco .20 .50
26 Bill Swift .10 .30
27 Ellis Burks .10 .30
28 Ben McDonald .10 .30
29 Edgar Martinez .20 .50
30 Jamie Moyer .10 .30
31 Chan Ho Park .10 .30
32 Carlos Delgado .10 .30
33 Kevin Mitchell .10 .30
34 Carlos Garcia .10 .30
35 Darryl Strawberry .10 .30
36 Jim Thome .20 .50
37 Jose Offerman .10 .30
38 Ryan Klesko .10 .30
39 Ruben Sierra .10 .30
40 Devon White .10 .30
41 Brian Jordan .10 .30
42 Tony Gwynn .40 1.00
43 Rafael Palmeiro .20 .50
44 Dante Bichette .10 .30
45 Scott Stahoviak .10 .30
46 Roger Cedeno .10 .30
47 Ivan Rodriguez .20 .50
48 Bob Abreu .20 .50
49 Darryl Kile .10 .30
50 Darren Dreifort .10 .30
51 Shawon Dunston .10 .30
52 Mark McGwire .75 2.00
53 Tim Salmon .20 .50
54 Gene Schall .10 .30
55 Roger Clemens .60 1.50
56 Rondell White .10 .30
57 Ed Sprague .10 .30
58 Craig Paquette .10 .30
59 David Segui .10 .30
60 Jaime Navarro .10 .30
61 Tom Glavine .20 .50
62 Jeff Brantley .10 .30
63 Kimera Bartee .10 .30
64 Fernando Vina .10 .30
65 Eddie Murray .30 .75
66 Lenny Dykstra .10 .30
67 Kevin Elster .10 .30
68 Vinny Castilla .10 .30
69 Mike Fetters .10 .30
70 Brett Butler .10 .30
71 Robby Thompson .10 .30
72 Reggie Jefferson .10 .30
73 Todd Hundley .10 .30
74 Jeff King .10 .30
75 Ernie Young .10 .30
76 Jeff Bagwell .20 .50
77 Dan Wilson .10 .30
78 Paul Molitor .10 .30
79 Kevin Seitzer .10 .30
80 Kevin Brown .10 .30
81 Ron Gant .10 .30
82 Dwight Gooden .10 .30
83 Todd Stottlemyre .10 .30
84 Ken Caminiti .10 .30
85 James Baldwin .10 .30
86 Jermaine Dye .10 .30
87 Harold Baines .10 .30
88 Pat Hentgen .10 .30
89 Frank Rodriguez .10 .30
90 Mark Johnson .10 .30
91 Jason Kendall .10 .30
92 Alex Rodriguez .50 1.25
93 Alan Trammell .10 .30
94 Scott Brosius .10 .30
95 Delino DeShields .10 .30
96 Chipper Jones .30 .75
97 Barry Bonds .75 2.00
98 Brady Anderson .10 .30
99 Ryne Sandberg .50 1.25
100 Albert Belle .10 .30
101 Jeff Cirillo .10 .30
102 Frank Thomas .30 .75
103 Mike Piazza .50 1.25
104 Rickey Henderson .30 .75
105 Rey Ordonez .10 .30
106 Mark Grace .20 .50
107 Terry Steinbach .10 .30
108 Ray Durham .10 .30
109 Barry Larkin .20 .50
110 Tony Clark .10 .30
111 Bernie Williams .20 .50
112 John Smoltz .20 .50
113 Moises Alou .10 .30
114 Alex Gonzalez .10 .30
115 Rico Brogna .10 .30
116 Eric Karros .10 .30
117 Jeff Conine .10 .30
118 Todd Hollandsworth .10 .30
119 Troy Percival .10 .30
120 Paul Wilson .10 .30
121 Orel Hershiser .10 .30
122 Ozzie Smith .50 1.25
123 Dave Hollins .10 .30
124 Ken Hill .10 .30
125 Rick Wilkins .10 .30
126 Scott Servais .10 .30
127 Fernando Valenzuela .10 .30
128 Mariano Rivera .30 .75
129 Mark Loretta .10 .30
130 Shane Reynolds .10 .30
131 Darren Oliver .10 .30
132 Steve Trachsel .10 .30
133 Darren Bragg .10 .30
134 Jason Dickson .10 .30
135 Darrin Fletcher .10 .30
136 Gary Gaetti .10 .30
137 Joey Cora .10 .30
138 Terry Pendleton .10 .30
139 Derek Jeter .75 2.00
140 Danny Tartabull .10 .30
141 John Flaherty .10 .30
142 B.J. Surhoff .10 .30
143 Mike Sweeney .10 .30
144 Chad Mottola .10 .30
145 Andujar Cedeno .10 .30
146 Tim Belcher .10 .30
147 Mark Thompson .10 .30
148 Rafael Bournigal .10 .30
149 Marty Cordova .10 .30
150 Osvaldo Fernandez .10 .30
151 Mike Stanley .10 .30
152 Ricky Bottalico .10 .30
153 Donne Wall .10 .30
154 Omar Vizquel .20 .50
155 Mike Mussina .20 .50
156 Brant Brown .10 .30
157 F.P. Santangelo .10 .30
158 Ryan Hancock .10 .30
159 Jeff D'Amico .10 .30
160 Luis Castillo .10 .30
161 Darin Erstad .10 .30
162 Ugueth Urbina .10 .30
163 Andruw Jones .20 .50
164 Steve Gibralter .10 .30
165 Robin Jennings .10 .30
166 Mike Cameron .10 .30
167 George Arias .10 .30
168 Chris Stynes .10 .30
169 Justin Thompson .10 .30
170 Jamey Wright .10 .30
171 Todd Walker .10 .30
172 Nomar Garciaparra .50 1.25
173 Jose Paniagua .10 .30
174 Marvin Benard .10 .30
175 Rocky Coppinger .10 .30
176 Quinton McCracken .10 .30
177 Amaury Telemaco .10 .30
178 Neifi Perez .10 .30
179 Todd Greene .10 .30
180 Jason Thompson .10 .30
181 Wilton Guerrero .10 .30
182 Edgar Renteria .10 .30
183 Billy Wagner .10 .30
184 Alex Ochoa .10 .30
185 Dmitri Young .10 .30
186 Kenny Lofton CT .10 .30
187 Andres Galarraga CT .10 .30
188 Chuck Knoblauch CT .10 .30
189 Greg Maddux CT .50 1.25
190 Mo Vaughn CT .10 .30
191 Cal Ripken CT 1.00 2.50
192 Hideo Nomo CT .30 .75
193 Ken Griffey Jr. CT .50 1.25
194 Sammy Sosa CT .20 .50
195 Jay Buhner CT .10 .30
196 Manny Ramirez CT .10 .30
197 Matt Williams CT .10 .30
198 Andruw Jones CL .10 .30
199 Darin Erstad CL .10 .30
200 Trey Beamon CL .10 .30

1998 Pinnacle

The 1998 Pinnacle set was issued in one series totalling 200 cards and was distributed in 10-card packs with a suggested retail price of $2.99. The fronts feature borderless color player photos with player information on the backs. The set contains the following subsets: Rookies (158-181), Field of Vision (182-187), Goin' Jake (188-197) and Checklists (198-200). Three variations of each card 1-157 were issued. The cards have home, away or seasonal stats on the back and were all produced in equal quantities. This concept of variations on the statistics was met with utter lack of interest and all three versions trade for equal values. In fact, complete sets typically carry a mix of all three stat variations.

COMPLETE SET (200)	10.00	25.00
1 Tony Gwynn	.40	1.00
2 Pedro Martinez	.20	.50
3 Kenny Lofton	.10	.30
4 Curt Schilling	.10	.30
5 Shawn Estes	.10	.30
6 Tom Glavine	.20	.50
7 Mike Piazza	.50	1.25
8 Ray Lankford	.10	.30
9 Barry Larkin	.20	.50
10 Tony Womack	.10	.30
11 Jeff Blauser	.10	.30
12 Rod Beck	.10	.30
13 Larry Walker	.10	.30
14 Greg Maddux	.50	1.25
15 Mark Grace	.20	.50
16 Ken Caminiti	.10	.30
17 Bobby Jones	.10	.30
18 Chipper Jones	.30	.75
19 Javier Lopez	.10	.30
20 Moises Alou	.10	.30
21 Royce Clayton	.10	.30
22 Darryl Kile	.10	.30
23 Barry Bonds	.75	2.00
24 Steve Finley	.10	.30
25 Andres Galarraga	.10	.30
26 Denny Neagle	.10	.30
27 Todd Hundley	.10	.30
28 Jeff Bagwell	.20	.50
29 Andy Pettitte	.20	.50
30 Darin Erstad	.10	.30
31 Carlos Delgado	.10	.30
32 Matt Williams	.10	.30
33 Will Clark	.20	.50
34 Vinny Castilla	.10	.30
35 Brad Radke	.10	.30
36 John Olerud	.10	.30
37 Andruw Jones	.20	.50
38 Jason Giambi	.10	.30
39 Scott Rolen	.20	.50
40 Gary Sheffield	.10	.30
41 Jimmy Key	.10	.30
42 Kevin Appier	.10	.30
43 Wade Boggs	.20	.50
44 Hideo Nomo	.30	.75
45 Manny Ramirez	.20	.50
46 Wilton Guerrero	.10	.30
47 Travis Fryman	.10	.30
48 Chili Davis	.10	.30
49 Jeromy Burnitz	.10	.30
50 Craig Biggio	.20	.50
51 Tim Salmon	.20	.50
52 Jose Cruz Jr.	.10	.30
53 Sammy Sosa	.30	.75
54 Hideki Irabu	.10	.30
55 Chan Ho Park	.10	.30
56 Robin Ventura	.10	.30
57 Jose Guillen	.10	.30
58 Deion Sanders	.20	.50
59 Jose Canseco	.20	.50
60 Jay Buhner	.10	.30
61 Rafael Palmeiro	.20	.50
62 Vladimir Guerrero	.30	.75
63 Mark McGwire	.75	2.00
64 Derek Jeter	.75	2.00
65 Bobby Bonilla	.10	.30
66 Raul Mondesi	.10	.30
67 Paul Molitor	.10	.30
68 Joe Carter	.10	.30
69 Marquis Grissom	.10	.30
70 Juan Gonzalez	.10	.30
71 Kevin Orie	.10	.30
72 Rusty Greer	.10	.30
73 Henry Rodriguez	.10	.30
74 Fernando Tatis	.10	.30
75 John Valentin	.10	.30
76 Matt Morris	.10	.30
77 Ray Durham	.10	.30
78 Geronimo Berroa	.10	.30
79 Scott Brosius	.10	.30
80 Willie Greene	.10	.30
81 Rondell White	.10	.30
82 Doug Drabek	.10	.30
83 Derek Bell	.10	.30
84 Butch Huskey	.10	.30
85 Doug Jones	.10	.30
86 Jeff Kent	.10	.30
87 Jim Edmonds	.10	.30
88 Mark McLemore	.10	.30
89 Todd Zeile	.10	.30
90 Edgardo Alfonzo	.10	.30
91 Carlos Baerga	.10	.30
92 Jorge Fabregas	.10	.30
93 Alan Benes	.10	.30
94 Troy Percival	.10	.30
95 Edgar Renteria	.10	.30
96 Jeff Fassero	.10	.30
97 Reggie Sanders	.10	.30
98 Dean Palmer	.10	.30
99 J.T. Snow	.10	.30
100 Dave Nilsson	.10	.30
101 Dan Wilson	.10	.30
102 Robb Nen	.10	.30
103 Damion Easley	.10	.30
104 Kevin Foster	.10	.30
105 Jose Offerman	.10	.30
106 Steve Cooke	.10	.30
107 Matt Stairs	.10	.30
108 Darryl Hamilton	.10	.30
109 Steve Karsay	.10	.30
110 Gary DiSarcina	.10	.30
111 Dante Bichette	.10	.30
112 Billy Wagner	.10	.30
113 David Segui	.10	.30
114 Bobby Higginson	.10	.30
115 Jeffrey Hammonds	.10	.30
116 Kevin Brown	.10	.30
117 Paul Sorrento	.10	.30
118 Mark Leiter	.10	.30
119 Charles Nagy	.10	.30
120 Danny Patterson	.10	.30
121 Brian McRae	.10	.30
122 Jay Bell	.10	.30
123 Jamie Moyer	.10	.30
124 Carl Everett	.10	.30
125 Greg Colbrunn	.10	.30
126 Jason Kendall	.10	.30
127 Luis Sojo	.10	.30
128 Mike Lieberthal	.10	.30
129 Reggie Jefferson	.10	.30
130 Cal Eldred	.10	.30
131 Orel Hershiser	.10	.30
132 Doug Glanville	.10	.30
133 Willie Blair	.10	.30
134 Neifi Perez	.10	.30
135 Sean Berry	.10	.30
136 Chuck Finley	.10	.30
137 Alex Gonzalez	.10	.30
138 Dennis Eckersley	.10	.30
139 Kenny Rogers	.10	.30
140 Troy O'Leary	.10	.30
141 Roger Bailey	.10	.30
142 Yamil Benitez	.10	.30
143 Wally Joyner	.10	.30
144 Bobby Witt	.10	.30
145 Pete Schourek	.10	.30
146 Terry Steinbach	.10	.30
147 B.J. Surhoff	.10	.30
148 Esteban Loaiza	.10	.30
149 Heathcliff Slocumb	.10	.30
150 Ed Sprague	.10	.30
151 Gregg Jefferies	.10	.30
152 Scott Erickson	.10	.30
153 Jaime Navarro	.10	.30
154 David Wells	.10	.30
155 Alex Fernandez	.10	.30
156 Tim Belcher	.10	.30
157 Mark Grudzielanek	.10	.30
158 Scott Hatteberg	.10	.30
159 Paul Konerko	.10	.30
160 Ben Grieve	.10	.30
161 Abraham Nunez	.10	.30
162 Shannon Stewart	.10	.30
163 Jaret Wright	.10	.30
164 Derrek Lee	.20	.50
165 Todd Dunwoody	.10	.30
166 Steve Woodard	.10	.30
167 Ryan McGuire	.10	.30
168 Jeremi Gonzalez	.10	.30
169 Mark Kotsay	.10	.30
170 Brett Tomko	.10	.30
171 Bobby Estalella	.10	.30
172 Livan Hernandez	.10	.30
173 Todd Helton	.20	.50
174 Garrett Stephenson	.10	.30
175 Pokey Reese	.10	.30
176 Tony Saunders	.10	.30
177 Antone Williamson	.10	.30
178 Bartolo Colon	.10	.30
179 Karim Garcia	.10	.30
180 Juan Encarnacion	.10	.30
181 Jacob Cruz	.10	.30
182 Alex Rodriguez FV	.50	1.25
183 Cal Ripken FV Roberto Alomar	.75	2.00
184 Roger Clemens FV	.60	1.50
185 Derek Jeter FV	.75	2.00
186 Frank Thomas FV	.30	.75
187 Ken Griffey Jr. FV	.50	1.25
188 Mark McGwire GJ	.75	2.00
189 Tino Martinez GJ	.20	.50
190 Larry Walker GJ	.10	.30
191 Brady Anderson GJ	.10	.30
192 Jeff Bagwell GJ	.20	.50
193 Ken Griffey Jr. GJ	.50	1.25
194 Chipper Jones GJ	.20	.50
195 Ray Lankford GJ	.10	.30
196 Jim Thome GJ	.20	.50
197 Nomar Garciaparra GJ	.50	1.25
198 Brady Anderson Jeff Bagwell Nomar Garciaparra Ken Griffey Jr. Chipper Jones Ray Lankford Tino Martinez Mark McGwire Jim Thome Larry Walker	.20	.50
199 Tino Martinez CL	.20	.50
200 Jacobs Field CL	.10	.30

1939 Play Ball

The cards in this 161-card set measure approximately 2 1/2" by 3 1/8". Gum Incorporated introduced a brief (war-shortened) but innovative era of baseball card production with its set of 1939. The combination of actual player photos (black and white), large card size, and extensive biography proved extremely popular. Player names are found either entirely capitalized or with initial caps only, and a "sample card" overprint is not uncommon. The "sample card" overprint variations are valued at double the prices below. Card number 126 was never issued, and cards 116-162 were produced in lesser quantities than cards 1-115. A card of Ted Williams in his rookie season as well as an early card of Joe DiMaggio are the key cards in the set.

COMPLETE SET (161)	6000.00	10000.00
COMMON CARD (1-115)	12.00	20.00
COMMON (116-162)	40.00	75.00
WRAPPER (1-CENT)	150.00	200.00
1 Jake Powell RC	30.00	60.00
2 Lee Grissom RC	12.00	20.00
3 Red Ruffing	40.00	75.00
4 Eldon Auker RC	12.00	20.00
5 Luke Sewell	15.00	25.00
6 Leo Durocher	60.00	100.00
7 Bobby Doerr RC	40.00	75.00
8 Henry Pippen RC	12.00	20.00
9 James Tobin RC	12.00	20.00
10 James DeShong	12.00	20.00
11 Johnny Rizzo RC	12.00	20.00
12 Hershel Martin RC	12.00	20.00
13 Luke Hamlin RC	12.00	20.00
14 Jim Tabor RC	12.00	20.00
15 Paul Derringer	18.00	30.00
16 John Peacock RC	12.00	20.00
17 Emerson Dickman RC	12.00	20.00
18 Harry Danning RC	12.00	20.00
19 Paul Dean RC	25.00	40.00
20 Joe Heving RC	12.00	20.00
21 Dutch Leonard RC	18.00	30.00
22 Bucky Walters RC	18.00	30.00
23 Burgess Whitehead RC	12.00	20.00
24 Richard Coffman	12.00	20.00
25 George Selkirk RC	25.00	40.00
26 Joe DiMaggio RC	900.00	1400.00
27 Fred Ostermueller	12.00	20.00
28 Sylvester Johnson RC	12.00	20.00
29 John(Jack) Wilson RC	12.00	20.00
30 Bill Dickey	75.00	125.00
31 Sam West	12.00	20.00
32 Bob Seeds RC	12.00	20.00
33 Del Young RC	12.00	20.00
34 Frank Demaree	12.00	20.00
35 Bill Jurges	12.00	20.00
36 Frank McCormick RC	12.00	20.00
37 Virgil Davis	12.00	20.00
38 Billy Myers RC	12.00	20.00
39 Rick Ferrell	40.00	75.00
40 James Bagby Jr. RC	12.00	20.00
41 Lon Warneke	15.00	25.00
42 Arndt Jorgens	12.00	20.00
43 Melo Almada RC	15.00	25.00
44 Don Heffner RC	12.00	20.00
45 Merrill May RC	12.00	20.00
46 Morris Arnovich RC	12.00	20.00
47 Buddy Lewis RC	12.00	20.00
48 Lefty Gomez	75.00	125.00
49 Eddie Miller RC	12.00	20.00
50 Charley Gehringer	75.00	125.00
51 Mel Ott	75.00	125.00
52 Tommy Henrich RC	25.00	40.00
53 Carl Hubbell	75.00	125.00
54 Harry Gumpert RC	12.00	20.00
55 Arky Vaughan	40.00	75.00
56 Hank Greenberg	125.00	200.00
57 Buddy Hassett RC	12.00	20.00
58 Lou Chiozza RC	12.00	20.00
59 Ken Chase RC	12.00	20.00
60 Schoolboy Rowe RC	25.00	40.00
61 Tony Cuccinello	15.00	25.00
62 Tom Carey RC	12.00	20.00
63 Emmett Mueller RC	12.00	20.00
64 Wally Moses RC	15.00	25.00
65 Harry Craft RC	15.00	25.00
66 Jimmy Ripple RC	12.00	20.00
67 Ed Joost RC	15.00	25.00
68 Fred Sington RC	12.00	20.00
69 Elbie Fletcher RC	12.00	20.00
70 Fred Frankhouse	12.00	20.00
71 Monte Pearson RC	18.00	30.00
72 Debs Garms RC	12.00	20.00
73 Hal Schumacher	15.00	25.00
74 Cookie Lavagetto RC	15.00	25.00
75 Stan Bordagaray RC	12.00	20.00
76 Goody Rosen RC	12.00	20.00
77 Lew Riggs RC	12.00	20.00
78 Julius Solters	12.00	20.00
79 Jo Jo Moore	12.00	20.00
80 Pete Fox	12.00	20.00
81 Babe Dahlgren RC	18.00	30.00
82 Chuck Klein	60.00	100.00
83 Gus Suhr	12.00	20.00
84 Skeeter Newsom RC	12.00	20.00
85 Johnny Cooney RC	12.00	20.00
86 Dolph Camilli	15.00	25.00
87 Milburn Shoffner RC	12.00	20.00
88 Charlie Keller RC	25.00	40.00
89 Lloyd Waner	40.00	75.00
90 Robert Klinger RC	12.00	20.00
91 John Knott RC	12.00	20.00
92 Ted Williams RC	1000.00	1800.00
93 Charles Gelbert RC	12.00	20.00
94 Heinie Manush	40.00	75.00
95 Whit Wyatt RC	15.00	25.00
96 Babe Phelps RC	12.00	20.00
97 Bob Johnson	18.00	30.00
98 Pinky Whitney RC	12.00	20.00
99 Wally Berger	18.00	30.00
100 Buddy Myer	15.00	25.00
101 Roger Cramer	15.00	25.00
102 Lem (Pep) Young RC	12.00	20.00
103 Moe Berg	75.00	125.00
104 Tom Bridges	15.00	25.00
105 Rabbit McNair RC	12.00	20.00
106 Dolly Stark UMP	18.00	30.00
107 Joe Vosmik	12.00	20.00
108 Frank Hayes RC	12.00	20.00
109 Myril Hoag	12.00	20.00
110 Fred Fitzsimmons	15.00	25.00
111 Van Lingle Mungo RC	18.00	30.00
112 Paul Waner	60.00	100.00
113 Al Schacht	18.00	30.00
114 Cecil Travis RC	15.00	25.00
115 Ralph Kress	12.00	20.00
116 Gene Desautels RC	40.00	75.00
117 Wayne Ambler RC	40.00	75.00
118 Lynn Nelson	40.00	75.00
119 Will Hershberger RC	50.00	100.00
120 Rabbit Warstler RC	40.00	75.00
121 Bill Posedel RC	40.00	75.00
122 George McQuinn RC	40.00	75.00
123 Ray T. Davis RC	40.00	75.00
124 Walter Brown	40.00	75.00
125 Cliff Melton RC	40.00	75.00
126 Not issued		
127 Gil Brack RC	40.00	75.00
128 Joe Bowman RC	40.00	75.00
129 Bill Swift	40.00	75.00
130 Bill Brubaker RC	40.00	75.00
131 Mort Cooper RC	50.00	100.00
132 Jim Brown RC	40.00	75.00
133 Lynn Myers RC	40.00	75.00
134 Tot Presnell RC	40.00	75.00
135 Mickey Owen RC	50.00	100.00
136 Roy Bell RC	40.00	75.00
137 Pete Appleton	40.00	75.00
138 George Case RC	50.00	100.00
139 Vito Tamulis RC	40.00	75.00
140 Ray Hayworth RC	40.00	75.00
141 Pete Coscarart RC	40.00	75.00
142 Ira Hutchinson RC	40.00	75.00
143 Earl Averill	100.00	175.00
144 Zeke Bonura RC	50.00	100.00
145 Hugh Mulcahy RC	40.00	75.00
146 Tom Sunkel RC	40.00	75.00
147 George Coffman RC	40.00	75.00
148 Bill Trotter RC	40.00	75.00
149 Max West RC	40.00	75.00
150 James Walkup RC	40.00	75.00
151 Hugh Casey RC	50.00	100.00
152 Roy Weatherly RC	40.00	75.00
153 Dizzy Trout RC	50.00	100.00
154 Johnny Hudson RC	40.00	75.00
155 Jimmy Outlaw RC	40.00	75.00
156 Ray Berres RC	40.00	75.00
157 Don Padgett RC	40.00	75.00
158 Bud Thomas RC	40.00	75.00
159 Red Evans RC	40.00	75.00
160 Gene Moore RC	40.00	75.00
161 Lonnie Frey	40.00	75.00
162 Whitey Moore RC	50.00	100.00

1940 Play Ball

The cards in this 240-card series measure approximately 2 1/2" by 3 1/8". Gum Inc. improved upon its 1939 design by enclosing the 1940 black and white player photo with a frame line and printing the player's name in a panel below the picture (often using a nickname). The set included many Hall of Famers and Old Timers. Cards 1-114 are numbered in team groupings. Cards 181-240 are scarcer than cards 1-180. The backs contain an extensive biography and a dated copyright line. The key cards in the set are the cards of Joe DiMaggio, Shoeless Joe Jackson, and Ted Williams.

COMPLETE SET (240)	10000.00	15000.00
COMMON CARD (1-120)	12.00	20.00
COMMON (121-180)	12.00	20.00
COMMON (181-240)	35.00	70.00
WRAP.(1-CENT, DIFF. COLORS)	700.00	800.00
1 Joe DiMaggio	1500.00	2500.00
2 Art Jorgens	15.00	25.00
3 Babe Dahlgren	15.00	25.00
4 Tommy Henrich	25.00	50.00
5 Monte Pearson	15.00	25.00
6 Lefty Gomez	90.00	150.00
7 Bill Dickey	100.00	175.00
8 George Selkirk	15.00	25.00
9 Charlie Keller	25.00	50.00
10 Red Ruffing	50.00	90.00
11 Jake Powell	15.00	25.00
12 Johnny Schulte	12.00	20.00
13 Jack Knott	12.00	20.00
14 Rabbit McNair	12.00	20.00
15 George Case	15.00	25.00
16 Cecil Travis	15.00	25.00
17 Buddy Myer	15.00	25.00
18 Charlie Gelbert	12.00	20.00
19 Ken Chase	12.00	20.00
20 Buddy Lewis	12.00	20.00
21 Rick Ferrell	45.00	80.00
22 Sammy West	12.00	20.00
23 Dutch Leonard	15.00	25.00
24 Frank Hayes	12.00	20.00
25 Bob Johnson	15.00	25.00
26 Wally Moses	15.00	25.00
27 Ted Williams	800.00	1200.00
28 Gene Desautels	12.00	20.00
29 Doc Cramer	15.00	25.00
30 Moe Berg	90.00	150.00
31 Jack Wilson	12.00	20.00
32 Jim Bagby	12.00	20.00
33 Fritz Ostermueller	12.00	20.00
34 John Peacock	12.00	20.00
35 Joe Heving	12.00	20.00
36 Jim Tabor	12.00	20.00
37 Emerson Dickman	12.00	20.00
38 Bobby Doerr	50.00	90.00
39 Tom Carey	12.00	20.00
40 Hank Greenberg	100.00	200.00
41 Charley Gehringer	90.00	150.00
42 Bud Thomas	12.00	20.00
43 Pete Fox	12.00	20.00
44 Dizzy Trout	15.00	25.00
45 Red Kress	12.00	20.00
46 Earl Averill	50.00	90.00
47 Oscar Vitt RC	12.00	20.00
48 Luke Sewell	15.00	25.00
49 Stormy Weatherly	12.00	20.00
50 Hal Trosky	15.00	25.00
51 Don Heffner	12.00	20.00
52 Myril Hoag	12.00	20.00
53 George McQuinn	15.00	25.00
54 Bill Trotter	12.00	20.00
55 Slick Coffman	12.00	20.00
56 Eddie Miller RC	15.00	25.00
57 Max West	12.00	20.00
58 Bill Posedel	12.00	20.00
59 Rabbit Warstler	12.00	20.00
60 John Cooney	12.00	20.00
61 Tony Cuccinello	15.00	25.00
62 Buddy Hassett	12.00	20.00
63 Pete Coscarart	12.00	20.00
64 Van Lingle Mungo	15.00	25.00
65 Fred Fitzsimmons	15.00	25.00
66 Babe Phelps	12.00	20.00
67 Whit Wyatt	15.00	25.00
68 Dolph Camilli	15.00	25.00
69 Cookie Lavagetto	15.00	25.00
70 Luke Hamlin (Hot Potato)	12.00	20.00
71 Mel Almada	12.00	20.00
72 Chuck Dressen RC	15.00	25.00
73 Bucky Walters	15.00	25.00
74 Paul(Duke) Derringer	15.00	25.00
75 Frank (Buck) McCormick	15.00	25.00
76 Lonny Frey	12.00	20.00
77 Willard Hershberger	15.00	25.00
78 Lew Riggs	12.00	20.00
79 Harry Craft	15.00	25.00
80 Billy Myers	12.00	20.00
81 Wally Berger	15.00	25.00
82 Hank Gowdy CO	15.00	25.00
83 Cliff Melton	12.00	20.00
84 Jo Jo Moore	12.00	20.00
85 Hal Schumacher	15.00	25.00
86 Harry Gumbert	12.00	20.00
87 Carl Hubbell	75.00	125.00
88 Mel Ott	100.00	175.00
89 Bill Jurges	12.00	20.00
90 Frank Demaree	12.00	20.00
91 Bob Seeds	12.00	20.00
92 Whitey Whitehead	12.00	20.00
93 Harry Danning	12.00	20.00
94 Gus Suhr	12.00	20.00
95 Hugh Mulcahy	12.00	20.00
96 Heinie Mueller	12.00	20.00
97 Morry Arnovich	12.00	20.00
98 Pinky May	12.00	20.00
99 Syl Johnson	12.00	20.00
100 Hersh Martin	12.00	20.00
101 Del Young	12.00	20.00
102 Chuck Klein	60.00	100.00
103 Elbie Fletcher	12.00	20.00
104 Paul Waner	50.00	90.00
105 Lloyd Waner	45.00	80.00
106 Pep Young	12.00	20.00
107 Arky Vaughan	45.00	80.00
108 Johnny Rizzo	12.00	20.00
109 Don Padgett	12.00	20.00
110 Tom Sunkel	12.00	20.00
111 Mickey Owen	15.00	25.00
112 Jimmy Brown	12.00	20.00
113 Mort Cooper	15.00	25.00
114 Lon Warneke	15.00	25.00
115 Mike Gonzalez CO	15.00	25.00
116 Al Schacht	15.00	25.00
117 Dolly Stark UMP	15.00	25.00
118 Waite Hoyt	50.00	90.00
119 Grover C. Alexander	100.00	175.00
120 Walter Johnson	100.00	200.00
121 Atley Donald RC	15.00	25.00
122 Sandy Sundra RC	15.00	25.00
123 Hildy Hildebrand	15.00	25.00
124 Earle Combs	60.00	100.00
125 Art Fletcher RC	15.00	25.00
126 Jake Solters	12.00	20.00
127 Muddy Ruel	12.00	20.00
128 Pete Appleton	12.00	20.00
129 Bucky Harris MG RC	45.00	80.00
130 Clyde Milan RC	15.00	25.00
131 Zeke Bonura	15.00	25.00
132 Connie Mack MG RC	75.00	150.00
133 Jimmie Foxx	100.00	200.00
134 Joe Cronin	60.00	100.00
135 Line Drive Nelson	12.00	20.00
136 Cotton Pippen	12.00	20.00
137 Bing Miller	12.00	20.00
138 Beau Bell	12.00	20.00
139 Elden Auker	12.00	20.00
140 Dick Coffman	12.00	20.00
141 Casey Stengel MG RC	100.00	175.00
142 George Kelly RC	50.00	90.00
143 Gene Moore	12.00	20.00
144 Joe Vosmik	12.00	20.00
145 Vito Tamulis	12.00	20.00
146 Tot Pressnell	12.00	20.00
147 Johnny Hudson	12.00	20.00
148 Hugh Casey	15.00	25.00
149 Pinky Shoffner	12.00	20.00
150 Whitey Moore	12.00	20.00
151 Edwin Joost	15.00	25.00
152 Jimmy Wilson	12.00	20.00
153 Bill McKechnie MG RC	45.00	80.00
154 Jumbo Brown	12.00	20.00
155 Ray Hayworth	12.00	20.00
156 Daffy Dean	25.00	50.00
157 Lou Chiozza	12.00	20.00
158 Travis Jackson	50.00	90.00
159 Pancho Snyder RC	12.00	20.00
160 Hans Lobert CO	12.00	20.00
161 Debs Garms	12.00	20.00
162 Joe Bowman	12.00	20.00
163 Spud Davis	12.00	20.00
164 Ray Berres	12.00	20.00
165 Bob Klinger	12.00	20.00
166 Bill Brubaker	12.00	20.00
167 Frankie Frisch MG	50.00	90.00
168 Honus Wagner CO	100.00	200.00
169 Gabby Street	12.00	20.00
170 Tris Speaker	100.00	175.00
171 Harry Heilmann	45.00	80.00
172 Chief Bender	45.00	80.00
173 Napoleon Lajoie	100.00	175.00
174 Johnny Evers	50.00	90.00
175 Christy Mathewson	150.00	250.00
176 Heinie Manush	50.00	90.00
177 Frank Baker	60.00	100.00
178 Max Carey	50.00	90.00
179 George Sisler	75.00	125.00
180 Mickey Cochrane	90.00	150.00
181 Spud Chandler RC	45.00	80.00
182 Knick Knickerbocker RC	35.00	70.00
183 Marvin Breuer RC	35.00	70.00
184 Mule Haas	35.00	70.00
185 Joe Kuhel	35.00	70.00
186 Taft Wright RC	35.00	70.00
187 Jimmy Dykes MG	45.00	80.00
188 Joe Krakauskas RC	35.00	70.00
189 Jim Bloodworth RC	35.00	70.00
190 Charley Berry	35.00	70.00
191 John Babich RC	35.00	70.00
192 Dick Siebert RC	35.00	70.00
193 Chubby Dean RC	35.00	70.00
194 Sam Chapman RC	35.00	70.00
195 Dee Miles RC	35.00	70.00
196 Red (Nonny) Nonnenkamp RC	35.00	70.00
197 Lou Finney RC	35.00	70.00
198 Denny Galehouse RC	35.00	70.00
199 Pinky Higgins	35.00	70.00
200 Soup Campbell RC	35.00	70.00
201 Barney McCosky RC	35.00	70.00
202 Al Milnar RC	35.00	70.00
203 Bad News Hale RC	35.00	70.00
204 Harry Eisenstat RC	35.00	70.00
205 Rollie Hemsley RC	35.00	70.00
206 Chet Laabs RC	35.00	70.00
207 Gus Mancuso	35.00	70.00
208 Lee Gamble RC	35.00	70.00
209 Hy Vandenberg RC	35.00	70.00
210 Bill Lohrman RC	35.00	70.00
211 Pop Joiner RC	35.00	70.00
212 Babe Young RC	35.00	70.00
213 John Rucker RC	35.00	70.00
214 Ken O'Dea RC	35.00	70.00
215 Johnnie McCarthy RC	35.00	70.00
216 Joe Marty RC	35.00	70.00
217 Walter Beck	35.00	70.00
218 Wally Millies RC	35.00	70.00
219 Russ Bauers RC	35.00	70.00
220 Mace Brown RC	35.00	70.00
221 Lee Handley RC	35.00	70.00
222 Max Butcher RC	35.00	70.00
223 Hughie Jennings	90.00	150.00
224 Pie Traynor	100.00	175.00
225 Joe Jackson	1500.00	2500.00
226 Harry Hooper	90.00	150.00
227 Jesse Haines	90.00	150.00
228 Charlie Grimm	45.00	80.00
229 Buck Herzog	35.00	70.00
230 Red Faber	100.00	175.00
231 Dolf Luque	60.00	100.00
232 Goose Goslin	90.00	150.00
233 George Earnshaw	45.00	80.00
234 Frank Chance	90.00	150.00
235 John McGraw	100.00	175.00
236 Jim Bottomley	90.00	150.00
237 Willie Keeler	100.00	175.00
238 Tony Lazzeri	100.00	175.00
239 George Uhle	35.00	70.00
240 Bill Atwood RC	60.00	100.00

1941 Play Ball

The cards in this 72-card set measure approximately 2 1/2" by 3 1/8". Many of the cards in the 1941 Play Ball series are simply color versions of pictures appearing in the 1940 set. This was the only color baseball card set produced by Gum, Inc.. Card numbers 49-72 are slightly more difficult to obtain as they were not issued until 1942. In 1942, numbers 1-48 were also reissued but without the copyright date. The cards were also printed on paper without a cardboard backing; these are generally encountered in sheets or strips. The set features a card of Pee Wee Reese in his rookie year.

COMPLETE SET (72)	6000.00	10000.00
COMMON CARD (1-48)	20.00	40.00
COMMON CARD (49-72)	30.00	60.00
WRAPPER (1-CENT)	700.00	800.00
1 Eddie Miller	75.00	125.00
2 Max West	20.00	40.00
3 Bucky Walters	25.00	45.00
4 Paul Derringer	30.00	50.00
5 Frank (Buck) McCormick	25.00	45.00
6 Carl Hubbell	100.00	175.00
7 Harry Danning	20.00	40.00
8 Mel Ott	125.00	225.00
9 Pinky May	20.00	40.00
10 Arky Vaughan	60.00	100.00
11 Debs Garms	20.00	40.00
12 Jimmy Brown	20.00	40.00
13 Jimmie Foxx	175.00	300.00
14 Ted Williams	900.00	1500.00
15 Joe Cronin	75.00	125.00
16 Hal Trosky	25.00	45.00
17 Roy Weatherly	20.00	40.00
18 Hank Greenberg	175.00	300.00
19 Charley Gehringer	125.00	200.00
20 Red Ruffing	75.00	125.00
21 Charlie Keller	35.00	60.00
22 Bob Johnson	30.00	50.00
23 George McQuinn	20.00	40.00
24 Dutch Leonard	25.00	45.00
25 Gene Moore	20.00	40.00
26 Harry Gumpert	20.00	40.00
27 Babe Young	20.00	40.00
28 Joe Marty	20.00	40.00
29 Jack Wilson	20.00	40.00
30 Lou Finney	20.00	40.00
31 Joe Kuhel	20.00	40.00
32 Taft Wright	20.00	40.00
33 Al Milnar	20.00	40.00
34 Rollie Hemsley	20.00	40.00
35 Pinky Higgins	25.00	45.00
36 Barney McCosky	20.00	40.00
37 Bruce Campbell RC	20.00	40.00
38 Atley Donald	30.00	50.00
39 Tommy Henrich	35.00	60.00
40 John Babich	20.00	40.00
41 Frank (Blimp) Hayes	20.00	40.00
42 Wally Moses	25.00	45.00
43 Al Brancato RC	20.00	40.00
44 Sam Chapman	20.00	40.00
45 Eldon Auker	20.00	40.00
46 Sid Hudson RC	20.00	40.00
47 Buddy Lewis	20.00	40.00
48 Cecil Travis	25.00	45.00
49 Babe Dahlgren	35.00	65.00
50 Johnny Cooney	30.00	60.00
51 Dolph Camilli	35.00	65.00
52 Kirby Higbe RC	30.00	60.00
53 Luke Hamlin	30.00	60.00
54 Pee Wee Reese RC	350.00	600.00
55 Whit Wyatt	35.00	65.00
56 Johnny VanderMeer RC	60.00	100.00

57 Moe Arnovich 30.00 60.00
58 Frank Demaree 30.00 60.00
59 Bill Jurges 30.00 60.00
60 Chuck Klein 90.00 150.00
61 Vince DiMaggio RC 125.00 225.00
62 Elbie Fletcher 30.00 60.00
63 Dom DiMaggio RC 150.00 250.00
64 Bobby Doerr 100.00 175.00
65 Tommy Bridges 35.00 65.00
66 Harland Clift RC 30.00 60.00
67 Walt Judnich RC 30.00 60.00
68 John Knott 30.00 60.00
69 George Case 35.00 65.00
70 Bill Dickey 250.00 400.00
71 Joe DiMaggio 1500.00 2500.00
72 Lefty Gomez 275.00 475.00

2004 Prime Cuts

This 50-card set was released in November, 2003. Each four-card pack retailed for $150 and contained four cards per pack along with an encased (but not Graded) BGS card. Each case continued fifteen of these one-pack boxes. Please note a Babe Ruth "Santa" card was randomly inserted into packs and is not considered part of the basic set.

COMPLETE SET (50) 125.00 225.00
STATED PRINT RUN 949 SERIAL #'d SETS
B.RUTH SANTA STATED ODDS 1:15
1 Roger Clemens Yanks 4.00 10.00
2 Nomar Garciaparra 3.00 8.00
3 Albert Pujols 4.00 10.00
4 Sammy Sosa 2.00 5.00
5 Greg Maddux Braves 3.00 8.00
6 Jason Giambi 1.50 4.00
7 Hideo Nomo Dodgers 2.00 5.00
8 Mike Piazza Mets 3.00 8.00
9 Ichiro Suzuki 4.00 10.00
10 Jeff Bagwell 2.00 5.00
11 Derek Jeter 4.00 10.00
12 Manny Ramirez 2.00 5.00
13 R.Henderson Dodgers 2.00 5.00
14 Alex Rodriguez Rgr 3.00 8.00
15 Troy Glaus 1.50 4.00
16 Mike Mussina 2.00 5.00
17 Kerry Wood 1.50 4.00
18 Kazuhisa Ishii 1.50 4.00
19 Hideki Matsui 3.00 8.00
20 Frank Thomas 2.00 5.00
21 Barry Bonds Giants 5.00 12.00
22 Adam Dunn 1.50 4.00
23 Randy Johnson D'backs 2.00 5.00
24 Alfonso Soriano 1.50 4.00
25 Pedro Martinez Sox 2.00 5.00
26 Andruw Jones 2.00 5.00
27 Mark Prior 2.00 5.00
28 Vladimir Guerrero 2.00 5.00
29 Chipper Jones 2.00 5.00
30 Todd Helton 2.00 5.00
31 Rafael Palmeiro 2.00 5.00
32 Mark Grace 2.00 5.00
33 Pedro Martinez Dodgers 2.00 5.00
34 Randy Johnson M's 2.00 5.00
35 Randy Johnson Astros 2.00 5.00
36 Roger Clemens Sox 4.00 10.00
37 Roger Clemens Jays 4.00 10.00
38 Alex Rodriguez M's 3.00 8.00
39 Greg Maddux Cubs 3.00 8.00
40 Mike Piazza Dodgers 3.00 8.00
41 Mike Piazza Marlins 3.00 8.00
42 Hideo Nomo Mets 2.00 5.00
43 R.Henderson Yanks 2.00 5.00
44 Rickey Henderson A's 2.00 5.00
45 Barry Bonds Pirates 5.00 12.00
46 Ivan Rodriguez 2.00 5.00
47 George Brett 4.00 10.00
48 Cal Ripken 8.00 20.00
49 Nolan Ryan 5.00 12.00
50 Don Mattingly 4.00 10.00
BRS1 Babe Ruth Santa 6.00 15.00

2004 Prime Cuts Century

*CENTURY 1-45: .75X TO 2X BASIC
*CENTURY MATSUI: 1X TO 2.5X BASIC
*CENTURY 47-50: 1.25X TO 3X BASIC
RANDOM INSERTS IN PACKS
STATED PRINT RUN 100 SERIAL #'d SETS

2004 Prime Cuts Century Gold

RANDOM INSERTS IN PACKS
STATED PRINT RUN 10 SERIAL #'d SETS
NO PRICING DUE TO SCARCITY

2004 Prime Cuts Century Proofs

RANDOM INSERTS IN PACKS
STATED PRINT RUN 1 SERIAL #'d SET
NO PRICING DUE TO SCARCITY

2004 Prime Cuts Material

RANDOM INSERTS IN PACKS
PRINT RUNS B/WN 10-50 COPIES PER
NO PRICING ON QTY OF 10 OR LESS
ALL CARDS FEATURE PRIME SWATCHES
1 Roger Clemens Yanks Jsy/50 15.00 40.00
2 Nomar Garciaparra Jsy/50 15.00 40.00
3 Albert Pujols Jsy/50 20.00 50.00
4 Sammy Sosa Jsy/50 10.00 25.00
5 Greg Maddux Jsy/50 15.00 40.00
6 Jason Giambi Jsy/25 10.00 25.00
7 H.Nomo Dodgers Jsy/50 15.00 40.00
8 Mike Piazza Mets Jsy/50 15.00 40.00
9 Ichiro Suzuki Base/25 40.00 80.00
10 Jeff Bagwell Jsy/25 15.00 40.00
11 Derek Jeter Base/25 40.00 80.00
12 Manny Ramirez Jsy/25 10.00 25.00
13 R.Henderson Dodgers Jsy/50 10.00 25.00
14 Alex Rodriguez Rgr Jsy/25 20.00 50.00
15 Troy Glaus Jsy/25 10.00 25.00
16 Mike Mussina Jsy/10
17 Kerry Wood Jsy/25 10.00 25.00
18 Kazuhisa Ishii Jsy/25 10.00 25.00
19 Hideki Matsui Base/25 40.00 80.00
20 Frank Thomas Jsy/25 15.00 40.00
21 Barry Bonds Base/25 40.00 80.00
22 Adam Dunn Jsy/25 10.00 25.00
23 R.Johnson D'backs Jsy/25 15.00 40.00
24 Alfonso Soriano Jsy/35 6.00 15.00
25 Pedro Martinez Sox Jsy/25 15.00 40.00
26 Andruw Jones Jsy/25 15.00 40.00
27 Mark Prior Jsy/50 10.00 25.00
28 Vladimir Guerrero Jsy/25 15.00 40.00
29 Chipper Jones Jsy/25 15.00 40.00
30 Todd Helton Jsy/25 15.00 40.00
31 Rafael Palmeiro Jsy/25 15.00 40.00
32 Mark Grace Jsy/25 15.00 40.00
33 P.Martinez Dodgers Jsy/25 15.00 40.00
34 Randy Johnson M's Jsy/25 15.00 40.00
35 R.Johnson Astros Jsy/25 15.00 40.00
36 Roger Clemens Sox Jsy/50 15.00 40.00
38 Alex Rodriguez M's Jsy/25 30.00 60.00
40 Mike Piazza Dodgers Jsy/50 15.00 40.00
41 Mike Piazza Marlins Jsy/50 15.00 40.00
42 Hideo Nomo Mets Jsy/50 15.00 40.00
43 R.Henderson Yanks Jsy/50 10.00 25.00
44 R.Henderson A's Jsy/50 10.00 25.00
46 Ivan Rodriguez Jsy/25 15.00 40.00
47 George Brett Jsy/50 20.00 50.00
48 Cal Ripken Jsy/50 30.00 60.00
49 Nolan Ryan Jsy/50 20.00 50.00
50 Don Mattingly Jsy/50 20.00 50.00

2004 Prime Cuts Material Combos

RANDOM INSERTS IN PACKS
STATED PRINT RUN 25 SERIAL #'d SETS
ALL CARDS FEATURE PRIME SWATCHES
1 R.Clemens Yanks Bat-Jsy 30.00 60.00
2 Nomar Garciaparra Bat-Jsy 30.00 60.00
3 Albert Pujols Bat-Jsy 50.00 100.00
4 Sammy Sosa Bat-Jsy 20.00 50.00
5 Greg Maddux Bat-Jsy 30.00 60.00
6 Jason Giambi Bat-Jsy 15.00 40.00
7 H.Nomo Dodgers Bat-Jsy 30.00 60.00
8 Mike Piazza Mets Bat-Jsy 30.00 60.00
9 Ichiro Suzuki Ball-Base 40.00 80.00
10 Jeff Bagwell Bat-Jsy 20.00 50.00
11 Derek Jeter Ball-Base 40.00 80.00
12 Manny Ramirez Bat-Jsy 20.00 50.00
13 R.Henderson Dodgers Bat-Jsy 20.00 50.00
14 Alex Rodriguez Rgr Bat-Jsy 30.00 60.00
15 Troy Glaus Bat-Jsy 15.00 40.00
16 Mike Mussina Bat-Jsy 20.00 50.00
17 Kerry Wood Bat-Jsy 15.00 40.00
18 Kazuhisa Ishii Bat-Jsy 15.00 40.00
19 Hideki Matsui Ball-Base 50.00 100.00
20 Frank Thomas Bat-Jsy 20.00 50.00
21 Barry Bonds Ball-Base 50.00 100.00
22 Adam Dunn Bat-Jsy 15.00 40.00
23 R.Johnson D'backs Bat-Jsy 20.00 50.00
24 Alfonso Soriano Bat-Jsy 15.00 40.00
25 Pedro Martinez Sox Bat-Jsy 20.00 50.00
26 Andruw Jones Bat-Jsy 20.00 50.00
27 Mark Prior Bat-Jsy 20.00 50.00
28 Vladimir Guerrero Bat-Jsy 20.00 50.00
29 Chipper Jones Bat-Jsy 20.00 50.00
30 Todd Helton Bat-Jsy 20.00 50.00
31 Rafael Palmeiro Bat-Jsy 20.00 50.00
32 Mark Grace Bat-Jsy 20.00 50.00
33 P.Martinez Dodgers Bat-Jsy 20.00 50.00
34 Randy Johnson M's Bat-Jsy 20.00 50.00
35 R.Johnson Astros Bat-Jsy 20.00 50.00
36 Roger Clemens Sox Bat-Jsy 30.00 60.00
38 Alex Rodriguez M's Bat-Jsy 30.00 60.00
40 M.Piazza Dodgers Bat-Jsy 30.00 60.00
42 Hideo Nomo Mets Bat-Jsy 30.00 60.00
43 R.Henderson Yanks Bat-Jsy 20.00 50.00
44 R.Henderson A's Bat-Jsy 20.00 50.00
46 Ivan Rodriguez Bat-Jsy 20.00 50.00
47 George Brett Bat-Jsy 50.00 100.00
48 Cal Ripken Bat-Jsy 60.00 120.00
49 Nolan Ryan Bat-Jsy 50.00 100.00
50 Don Mattingly Bat-Jsy 50.00 100.00

2004 Prime Cuts Material Signature

RANDOM INSERTS IN PACKS
PRINT RUNS B/WN 5-50 COPIES PER
NO PRICING ON QTY OF 10 OR LESS
ALL CARDS FEATURE PRIME SWATCHES
1 R.Clemens Yanks Jsy/25 150.00 250.00
3 Albert Pujols Jsy/25 175.00 250.00
5 Greg Maddux Jsy/25 75.00 150.00
7 H.Nomo Dodgers Jsy/10
8 Mike Piazza Mets Jsy/10
10 Jeff Bagwell Jsy/25 50.00 100.00
12 Manny Ramirez Jsy/25 50.00 100.00
13 R.Hend Dodgers Jsy/25 50.00 100.00
14 Alex Rodriguez Rgr Jsy/25 150.00 250.00
15 Troy Glaus Jsy/50 30.00 60.00
16 Mike Mussina Jsy/25 40.00 80.00
17 Kerry Wood Jsy/25 40.00 80.00
18 Kazuhisa Ishii Jsy/50 15.00 40.00
20 Frank Thomas Jsy/25 50.00 100.00
22 Adam Dunn Jsy/50 30.00 60.00
23 R.Johnson D'backs Jsy/10
24 Alfonso Soriano Jsy/25 40.00 80.00
25 Pedro Martinez Sox Jsy/10
26 Andruw Jones Jsy/25 40.00 80.00
27 Mark Prior Jsy/50 20.00 50.00
28 Vladimir Guerrero Jsy/50 40.00 80.00
29 Chipper Jones Jsy/50 40.00 80.00
30 Todd Helton Jsy/50 30.00 60.00
31 Rafael Palmeiro Jsy/25 50.00 100.00
32 Mark Grace Jsy/50 40.00 80.00
33 P.Martinez Dodgers Jsy/10
34 Randy Johnson M's Jsy/10
35 R.Johnson Astros Jsy/10
36 Roger Clemens Sox Jsy/25 150.00 250.00
38 Alex Rodriguez M's Jsy/25 150.00 250.00
40 Mike Piazza Dodgers Jsy/10
42 Hideo Nomo Mets Jsy/5
43 R.Henderson Yanks Jsy/5
44 R.Henderson A's Jsy/25 50.00 100.00
46 Ivan Rodriguez Jsy/25 50.00 100.00
47 George Brett Jsy/50 75.00 150.00
48 Cal Ripken Jsy/50 150.00 250.00
49 Nolan Ryan Jsy/50 125.00 200.00
50 Don Mattingly Jsy/50 75.00 150.00

2004 Prime Cuts MLB Icons Material

RANDOM INSERTS IN PACKS
PRINT RUNS B/WN 9-50 COPIES PER
NO PRICING ON QTY OF 9 OR LESS
1 Ty Cobb Pants/9
2 Babe Ruth Pants/9
3 Lou Gehrig Pants/9
4 Johnny Bench Jsy/50 20.00 50.00
5 Lefty Grove A's Hat/25 75.00 150.00
6 Carlton Fisk Jsy/50 15.00 40.00
7 Mel Ott Jsy/25 50.00 100.00
8 Bob Feller Jsy/25 15.00 40.00
9 Jackie Robinson Jsy/25 60.00 120.00
10 Ted Williams Jsy/50 60.00 120.00
11 Roy Campanella Pants/50 30.00 60.00
12 Stan Musial Jsy/50 30.00 60.00
13 Yogi Berra Jsy/50 20.00 50.00
14 Babe Ruth Jsy/25 800.00 1200.00
15 Roberto Clemente Jsy/50 75.00 150.00
16 Warren Spahn Jsy/50 20.00 50.00
17 Ernie Banks Jsy/50 20.00 50.00
18 Eddie Mathews Jsy/50 20.00 50.00
19 Ryne Sandberg Jsy/50 30.00 60.00
20 Rod Carew Angels Jsy/50 15.00 40.00
21 Duke Snider Jsy/50 15.00 40.00
22 Jim Palmer Jsy/50 10.00 25.00
24 Frank Robinson Jsy/50 10.00 25.00
25 Brooks Robinson Jsy/50 15.00 40.00
26 Harmon Killebrew Jsy/50 20.00 50.00
27 Carl Yastrzemski Jsy/50 30.00 60.00
28 Reggie Jackson A's Jsy/50 15.00 40.00
29 Mike Schmidt Jsy/50 20.00 50.00
30 Robin Yount Jsy/50 20.00 50.00
31 George Brett Jsy/50 20.00 50.00
32 Nolan Ryan Rgr Jsy/50 30.00 60.00
33 Kirby Puckett Jsy/50 20.00 50.00
34 Cal Ripken Jsy/50 40.00 80.00
35 Don Mattingly Jsy/50 20.00 50.00
36 Tony Gwynn Jsy/19 40.00 80.00
37 Deion Sanders Jsy/19 20.00 50.00
38 Dave Winfield Yanks Jsy/19 15.00 40.00
39 Eddie Murray Jsy/19 30.00 60.00
40 Tom Seaver Jsy/19 20.00 50.00
41 Willie Stargell Jsy/19 20.00 50.00
42 Wade Boggs Yanks Jsy/19 20.00 50.00
43 Ozzie Smith Jsy/19 30.00 60.00
44 Willie McCovey Jsy/19 15.00 40.00
45 R.Jackson Angels Jsy/19 20.00 50.00
46 Whitey Ford Jsy/19 20.00 50.00
47 Lou Brock Jsy/19 20.00 50.00
48 Lou Boudreau Jsy/19 15.00 40.00
49 Steve Carlton Jsy/19 15.00 40.00
50 Rod Carew Twins Jsy/19 20.00 50.00
51 Bob Gibson Jsy/19 20.00 50.00
52 Thurman Munson Jsy/19 30.00 60.00
53 Roger Maris Jsy/19 60.00 120.00
54 Nolan Ryan Astros Jsy/50 30.00 60.00
55 Nolan Ryan Angels Jsy/50 30.00 60.00
56 Bo Jackson Jsy/19 30.00 60.00
57 Joe Morgan Jsy/19 15.00 40.00
58 Phil Rizzuto Jsy/19 20.00 50.00
59 Gary Carter Jsy/19 15.00 40.00
60 Paul Molitor Jsy/19 15.00 40.00
61 Don Drysdale Jsy/19 30.00 60.00
62 Catfish Hunter Jsy/19 20.00 50.00
63 Fergie Jenkins Pants/19 15.00 40.00
64 Pee Wee Reese Jsy/19 20.00 50.00
65 Dave Winfield Padres Jsy/19 15.00 40.00
66 Wade Boggs Sox Jsy/19 20.00 50.00
67 Lefty Grove Sox Hat/19 75.00 150.00
68 Rickey Henderson Jsy/19 30.00 60.00
69 Roger Clemens Sox Jsy/19 30.00 60.00
70 R.Clemens Yanks Jsy/19 30.00 60.00

2004 Prime Cuts MLB Icons Material Combos Prime

RANDOM INSERTS IN PACKS
PRINT RUNS B/WN 1-25 COPIES PER
NO PRICING ON QTY OF 15 OR LESS
1 Ty Cobb Bat-Pants/9
2 Babe Ruth Bat-Pants/9
3 Lou Gehrig Bat-Pants/9
4 Johnny Bench Bat-Jsy/5
6 Carlton Fisk Bat-Jsy/25 40.00 80.00
7 Mel Ott Bat-Jsy/25
10 Ted Williams Bat-Jsy/9
11 R.Campanella Bat-Pants/25 50.00 100.00
12 Stan Musial Bat-Jsy/1
13 Yogi Berra Bat-Jsy/1
15 R.Clemente Bat-Jsy/25 100.00 200.00
17 Ernie Banks Bat-Jsy/25 50.00 100.00
18 Eddie Mathews Bat-Jsy/25 50.00 100.00
19 Ryne Sandberg Bat-Jsy/25 60.00 120.00
20 R.Carew Angels Bat-Jsy/25 40.00 80.00
21 Duke Snider Bat-Jsy/15
24 Frank Robinson Bat-Jsy/25 30.00 60.00
25 Brooks Robinson Bat-Jsy/25 40.00 80.00
26 Harmon Killebrew Bat-Jsy/5
27 Carl Yastrzemski Bat-Jsy/25 75.00 150.00
28 R.Jackson A's Bat-Jsy/25 40.00 80.00
29 Mike Schmidt Bat-Jsy/25 50.00 100.00
30 Robin Yount Bat-Jsy/25 50.00 100.00
31 George Brett Bat-Jsy/25 50.00 100.00
32 Nolan Ryan Rgr Bat-Jsy/25 60.00 120.00
33 Kirby Puckett Bat-Jsy/25 60.00 120.00
34 Cal Ripken Bat-Jsy/25 75.00 150.00
35 Don Mattingly Bat-Jsy/25 50.00 100.00
36 Tony Gwynn Bat-Jsy/19 60.00 120.00
37 Deion Sanders Bat-Jsy/19 40.00 80.00
38 D.Winfield Yanks Bat-Jsy/19 30.00 60.00
39 Eddie Murray Bat-Jsy/19 60.00 120.00
41 Willie Stargell Bat-Jsy/19 40.00 80.00
42 W.Boggs Yanks Bat-Jsy/19 40.00 80.00
43 Ozzie Smith Bat-Jsy/19 75.00 150.00
44 Willie McCovey Bat-Jsy/19 30.00 60.00
45 R.Jackson Angels Bat-Jsy/19 40.00 80.00
46 Whitey Ford Jsy-Pants/19 40.00 80.00
47 Lou Brock Bat-Jsy/19 50.00 100.00
48 Lou Boudreau Bat-Jsy/19 30.00 60.00
49 Steve Carlton Bat-Jsy/19 30.00 60.00
50 Rod Carew Twins Bat-Jsy/19 40.00 80.00
52 T.Munson Bat-Jsy/19 60.00 120.00
53 Roger Maris Bat-Jsy/19 100.00 200.00
54 N.Ryan Astros Bat-Jsy/19 75.00 150.00
55 N.Ryan Angels Bat-Jsy/19 75.00 150.00
56 Bo Jackson Bat-Jsy/19 50.00 100.00
57 Joe Morgan Bat-Jsy/19 30.00 60.00
58 Phil Rizzuto Bat-Pants/19 40.00 80.00
59 Gary Carter Bat-Jsy/19 30.00 60.00
60 Paul Molitor Bat-Jsy/19 30.00 60.00
63 F.Jenkins Fld Glv-Pants/19 30.00 60.00
64 P.Reese Bat-Jsy/19 50.00 100.00
65 D.Winfield Padres Bat-Jsy/19 30.00 60.00
66 W.Boggs Sox Bat-Jsy/19 40.00 80.00
68 R.Henderson Bat-Jsy/19 40.00 80.00
69 R.Clemens Sox Bat-Jsy/19 30.00 60.00
70 R.Clemens Yanks Bat-Jsy/19 50.00 100.00

2004 Prime Cuts MLB Icons Material Prime

RANDOM INSERTS IN PACKS
PRINT RUNS B/WN 1-25 COPIES PER
NO PRICING ON QTY OF 9 OR LESS
1 Ty Cobb Pants/9

2 Babe Ruth Pants/9
3 Lou Gehrig Pants/9
4 Johnny Bench Jsy/1
5 Lefty Grove A's Hat/9
6 Carlton Fisk Jsy/25 30.00 60.00
7 Mel Ott Jsy/25 100.00 200.00
8 Bob Feller Jsy/5
9 Jackie Robinson Jsy/9
10 Ted Williams Jsy/9
11 Roy Campanella Pants/25 40.00 80.00
12 Stan Musial Jsy/1
13 Yogi Berra Jsy/1
15 Roberto Clemente Jsy/25 100.00 200.00
16 Warren Spahn Jsy/25 60.00 120.00
17 Ernie Banks Jsy/25 40.00 80.00
18 Eddie Mathews Jsy/25 40.00 80.00
19 Ryne Sandberg Jsy/25 50.00 100.00
20 Rod Carew Angels Jsy/25 30.00 60.00
21 Duke Snider Jsy/9
22 Jim Palmer Jsy/25 20.00 50.00
24 Frank Robinson Jsy/25 20.00 50.00
25 Brooks Robinson Jsy/25 30.00 60.00
26 Harmon Killebrew Jsy/8
27 Carl Yastrzemski Jsy/25 50.00 100.00
28 Reggie Jackson A's Jsy/25 30.00 60.00
29 Mike Schmidt Jsy/25 40.00 80.00
30 Robin Yount Jsy/25 40.00 80.00
31 George Brett Jsy/25 40.00 80.00
32 Nolan Ryan Rgr Jsy/25 50.00 100.00
33 Kirby Puckett Jsy/25 40.00 80.00
34 Cal Ripken Jsy/25 60.00 120.00
35 Don Mattingly Jsy/25 40.00 80.00
36 Tony Gwynn Jsy/19 50.00 100.00
37 Deion Sanders Jsy/19 30.00 60.00
38 Dave Winfield Yanks Jsy/19 20.00 50.00
39 Eddie Murray Jsy/19 50.00 100.00
40 Tom Seaver Jsy/19 30.00 60.00
41 Willie Stargell Jsy/19 30.00 60.00
42 Wade Boggs Yanks Jsy/19 30.00 60.00
43 Ozzie Smith Jsy/19 40.00 80.00
44 Willie McCovey Jsy/19 20.00 50.00
45 R.Jackson Angels Jsy/19 30.00 60.00
46 Whitey Ford Jsy/19 30.00 60.00
47 Lou Brock Jsy/19 40.00 80.00
48 Lou Boudreau Jsy/19 20.00 50.00
49 Steve Carlton Jsy/19 20.00 50.00
50 Rod Carew Twins Jsy/19 30.00 60.00
51 Bob Gibson Jsy/19 40.00 80.00
52 Thurman Munson Jsy/19 50.00 100.00
53 Roger Maris Jsy/19 75.00 150.00
54 Nolan Ryan Astros Jsy/19 50.00 100.00
55 Nolan Ryan Angels Jsy/19 50.00 100.00
56 Bo Jackson Jsy/19 40.00 80.00
57 Joe Morgan Jsy/19 20.00 50.00
58 Phil Rizzuto Jsy/5
59 Gary Carter Jsy/19 20.00 50.00
60 Paul Molitor Jsy/19 20.00 50.00
61 Don Drysdale Jsy/19 50.00 100.00
62 Catfish Hunter Jsy/19 30.00 60.00
63 Fergie Jenkins Pants/19 20.00 50.00
64 Pee Wee Reese Jsy/19 30.00 60.00
65 Dave Winfield Padres Jsy/19 20.00 50.00
66 Wade Boggs Sox Jsy/19 30.00 60.00
67 Lefty Grove Sox Hat/19 90.00 180.00
68 Rickey Henderson Jsy/19 40.00 80.00
69 Roger Clemens Sox Jsy/19 40.00 80.00
70 R.Clemens Yanks Jsy/19 40.00 80.00

2004 Prime Cuts MLB Icons Material Signature

RANDOM INSERTS IN PACKS
PRINT RUNS B/WN 16-45 COPIES PER
4 Johnny Bench Jsy/18 75.00 150.00
8 Bob Feller Jsy/45 40.00 80.00
12 Stan Musial Jsy/30 75.00 150.00
13 Yogi Berra Jsy/42 60.00 120.00
21 Duke Snider Jsy/35 50.00 100.00
26 Harmon Killebrew Jsy/30 60.00 120.00
33 Kirby Puckett Jsy/16 75.00 150.00
69 Roger Clemens Sox Jsy/25 125.00 200.00

2004 Prime Cuts MLB Icons Material Signature Prime

RANDOM INSERTS IN PACKS
PRINT RUNS B/WN 1-50 COPIES PER
NO PRICING ON QTY OF 15 OR LESS
1 Ty Cobb Pants/1
2 Babe Ruth Pants/1
3 Lou Gehrig Pants/1
4 Johnny Bench Jsy/5
5 Lefty Grove A's Hat/1
6 Carlton Fisk Jsy/50 40.00 80.00
7 Mel Ott Jsy/1
8 Bob Feller Jsy/5
9 Jackie Robinson Jsy/1
10 Ted Williams Jsy/1
11 Roy Campanella Pants/1
12 Stan Musial Jsy/20 125.00 200.00
13 Yogi Berra Jsy/8
16 Warren Spahn Jsy/25 125.00 200.00
17 Ernie Banks Jsy/50 60.00 120.00
18 Eddie Mathews Jsy/1
19 Ryne Sandberg Jsy/50 75.00 150.00
20 Rod Carew Angels Jsy/50 40.00 80.00
21 Duke Snider Jsy/15
22 Jim Palmer Jsy/50 30.00 60.00
24 Frank Robinson Jsy/50 30.00 60.00
25 Brooks Robinson Jsy/50 40.00 80.00
26 Harmon Killebrew Jsy/20 75.00 150.00
27 Carl Yastrzemski Jsy/50 75.00 150.00
28 Reggie Jackson A's Jsy/50 50.00 100.00
29 Mike Schmidt Jsy/20 125.00 200.00
30 Robin Yount Jsy/50 60.00 120.00
31 George Brett Jsy/50 75.00 150.00
32 Nolan Ryan Rgr Jsy/50 125.00 200.00
33 Kirby Puckett Jsy/34 50.00 100.00
34 Cal Ripken Jsy/50 150.00 250.00
35 Don Mattingly Jsy/50 75.00 150.00
36 Tony Gwynn Jsy/50 50.00 100.00
37 Deion Sanders Jsy/50 60.00 120.00
38 Dave Winfield Yanks Jsy/50 40.00 80.00
39 Eddie Murray Jsy/50 60.00 120.00
40 Tom Seaver Jsy/10
41 Willie Stargell Jsy/1
42 Wade Boggs Yanks Jsy/50 50.00 100.00
43 Ozzie Smith Jsy/50 75.00 150.00
44 Willie McCovey Jsy/50 40.00 80.00
45 R.Jackson Angels Jsy/50 50.00 100.00
46 Whitey Ford Jsy/50 50.00 100.00
47 Lou Brock Jsy/25 75.00 150.00
48 Lou Boudreau Jsy/50 75.00 150.00
49 Steve Carlton Jsy/50 30.00 60.00
50 Rod Carew Twins Jsy/50 40.00 80.00
51 Bob Gibson Jsy/50 60.00 120.00
52 Thurman Munson Jsy/1
53 Roger Maris Jsy/1
54 Nolan Ryan Astros Jsy/50 125.00 200.00
55 Nolan Ryan Angels Jsy/50 125.00 200.00
56 Bo Jackson Jsy/50 60.00 120.00
57 Joe Morgan Jsy/50 30.00 60.00
58 Phil Rizzuto Pants/50 40.00 80.00
59 Gary Carter Jsy/50 30.00 60.00
60 Paul Molitor Jsy/50 30.00 60.00
61 Don Drysdale Jsy/1
62 Catfish Hunter Jsy/1
63 Fergie Jenkins Pants/50 30.00 60.00
64 Pee Wee Reese Jsy/1
65 D.Winfield Padres Jsy/50 40.00 80.00
66 Wade Boggs Sox Jsy/50 50.00 100.00
67 Lefty Grove Sox Hat/1
68 Rickey Henderson Jsy/50 75.00 150.00
69 Roger Clemens Sox Jsy/25 150.00 250.00
70 R.Clemens Yanks Jsy/50 125.00 200.00

2004 Prime Cuts MLB Icons Signature

RANDOM INSERTS IN PACKS
PRINT RUNS B/WN 1-50 COPIES PER
NO PRICING ON QTY OF 12 OR LESS
4 Johnny Bench/50 40.00 80.00
6 Carlton Fisk/50 30.00 60.00
8 Bob Feller/50 20.00 50.00
12 Stan Musial/50 50.00 100.00
13 Yogi Berra/50 40.00 80.00
16 Warren Spahn/25 75.00 150.00
17 Ernie Banks/50 50.00 100.00
18 Eddie Mathews/12
19 Ryne Sandberg/50 60.00 120.00
20 Rod Carew Angels/5
21 Duke Snider/25 40.00 80.00
22 Jim Palmer/25 30.00 60.00
24 Frank Robinson/50 20.00 50.00
25 Brooks Robinson/50 30.00 60.00
26 Harmon Killebrew/25 60.00 120.00
27 Carl Yastrzemski/50 50.00 100.00
28 Reggie Jackson A's/50 40.00 80.00
29 Mike Schmidt/20 60.00 120.00
30 Robin Yount/25 60.00 120.00
31 George Brett/25 60.00 120.00
32 Nolan Ryan Rgr/50 75.00 150.00
33 Kirby Puckett/25 50.00 100.00
34 Cal Ripken/25 150.00 250.00
35 Don Mattingly/50 50.00 100.00
36 Tony Gwynn/25 50.00 100.00
37 Deion Sanders/10
38 Dave Winfield Yanks/25 40.00 80.00
39 Eddie Murray/25 60.00 120.00
40 Tom Seaver/25
42 Wade Boggs Yanks/25 50.00 100.00
43 Ozzie Smith/25 75.00 150.00
44 Willie McCovey/25 40.00 80.00
45 Reggie Jackson Angels/25 50.00 100.00
46 Whitey Ford/10
47 Lou Brock/25 40.00 80.00
48 Lou Boudreau/25 75.00 150.00
49 Steve Carlton/10
50 Rod Carew Twins/5
51 Bob Gibson/25 40.00 80.00
53 Roger Maris/1
54 Nolan Ryan Astros/10
55 Nolan Ryan Angels/10
56 Bo Jackson/25 60.00 120.00
57 Joe Morgan/25 30.00 60.00
58 Phil Rizzuto/10
59 Gary Carter/25 30.00 60.00

60 Paul Molitor/25 30.00 60.00
61 Don Drysdale/1
62 Catfish Hunter/1
63 Fergie Jenkins/10
64 Pee Wee Reese/1
65 Dave Winfield Padres/25 40.00 80.00
66 Wade Boggs Sox/25 50.00 100.00
67 Lefty Grove/1
68 Rickey Henderson A's/10
69 Roger Clemens Sox/10
70 Roger Clemens Yanks/10

2004 Prime Cuts MLB Icons Signature Proofs

RANDOM INSERTS IN PACKS
STATED PRINT RUN 1 SERIAL #'d SET
NO PRICING DUE TO SCARCITY

2004 Prime Cuts Signature

RANDOM INSERTS IN PACKS
PRINT RUNS B/WN 5-25 COPIES PER
NO PRICING ON QTY OF 14 OR LESS
1 Roger Clemens Yanks/25 75.00 150.00
3 Albert Pujols/25 150.00 250.00
5 Greg Maddux Braves/10
7 Hideo Nomo Dodgers/10
8 Mike Piazza Mets/10
10 Jeff Bagwell/25 40.00 80.00
12 Manny Ramirez/14
13 R.Henderson Dodgers/25 40.00 80.00
14 Alex Rodriguez Rgr/25 75.00 150.00
15 Troy Glaus/25 30.00 60.00
16 Mike Mussina/25 30.00 60.00
17 Kerry Wood/25 30.00 60.00
18 Kazuhisa Ishii/25 15.00 40.00
20 Frank Thomas/25 40.00 80.00
22 Adam Dunn/25 15.00 40.00
23 Randy Johnson D'backs/10
24 Alfonso Soriano/25 30.00 60.00
25 Pedro Martinez Sox/10
26 Andruw Jones/25 30.00 60.00
27 Mark Prior/25 20.00 50.00
28 Vladimir Guerrero/25 40.00 80.00
29 Chipper Jones/25 40.00 80.00
30 Todd Helton/17 30.00 60.00
31 Rafael Palmeiro/25 40.00 80.00
32 Mark Grace/25 40.00 80.00
33 Pedro Martinez Dodgers/10
34 Randy Johnson M's/10
35 Randy Johnson Astros/10
36 Roger Clemens Sox/25 75.00 150.00
37 Roger Clemens Jays/25 75.00 150.00
38 Alex Rodriguez M's/25 75.00 150.00
39 Greg Maddux Cubs/10
40 Mike Piazza Dodgers/10
41 Mike Piazza Marlins/5
42 Hideo Nomo Mets/5
43 Rickey Henderson Yanks/25 40.00 80.00
44 Rickey Henderson A's/25 40.00 80.00
46 Ivan Rodriguez/25 40.00 80.00
47 George Brett/25 75.00 150.00
48 Cal Ripken/25 100.00 200.00
49 Nolan Ryan/25 75.00 150.00
50 Don Mattingly/25 60.00 120.00

2004 Prime Cuts Signature Proofs

RANDOM INSERTS IN PACKS
STATED PRINT RUN 1 SERIAL #'d SET
NO PRICING DUE TO SCARCITY

2004 Prime Cuts Timeline Dual Achievements Material

RANDOM INSERTS IN PACKS
PRINT RUNS B/WN 9-19 COPIES PER
NO PRICING ON QTY OF 9 OR LESS
1 Roy Campanella Pants
Yogi Berra Jsy/9
2 Jackie Robinson Jsy
Ted Williams Jsy/9
3 Stan Musial Jsy 125.00 200.00
Ted Williams Jsy/19
4 Mike Schmidt Jsy 60.00 120.00
George Brett Jsy/19
5 Dale Murphy Jsy 60.00 120.00
Cal Ripken Jsy/19
6 Roger Clemens Jsy 50.00 100.00
Mike Schmidt Jsy/19
7 Ty Cobb Pants
Babe Ruth Pants/9
8 Roy Campanella Pants
Stan Musial Jsy/9
10 George Brett Jsy 60.00 120.00
Nolan Ryan Jsy/19
11 Jackie Robinson Jsy
Roy Campanella Pants/9
12 Al Kaline Pants 40.00 80.00
Duke Snider Jsy/19

2004 Prime Cuts Timeline Dual Achievements Material Combos

RANDOM INSERTS IN PACKS
PRINT RUNS B/WN 1-19 COPIES PER
NO PRICING ON QTY OF 15 OR LESS
1 Roy Campanella Bat-Pants
Yogi Berra Bat-Jsy/1
3 Stan Musial Bat-Jsy
Ted Williams Bat-Jsy/1
4 Mike Schmidt Bat-Jsy 150.00 250.00
George Brett Bat-Jsy/19
5 Dale Murphy Bat-Jsy 100.00 200.00
Cal Ripken Bat-Jsy/19
6 Roger Clemens Bat-Jsy 75.00 150.00
Mike Schmidt Bat-Jsy/19
7 Ty Cobb Bat-Pants
Babe Ruth Bat-Pants/9
8 Roy Campanella Bat-Pants
Stan Musial Bat-Jsy/2
10 George Brett Bat-Jsy 150.00 250.00
Nolan Ryan Bat-Jsy/19
12 Al Kaline Bat-Pants
Duke Snider Bat-Jsy/15

2004 Prime Cuts Timeline Dual Achievements Material Prime

RANDOM INSERTS IN PACKS
PRINT RUNS B/WN 1-19 COPIES PER
NO PRICING ON QTY OF 15 OR LESS
1 Roy Campanella Pants
Yogi Berra Jsy/1
2 Jackie Robinson Jsy
Ted Williams Jsy/9
3 Stan Musial Jsy
Ted Williams Jsy/2
4 Mike Schmidt Jsy 100.00 200.00
George Brett Jsy/19
5 Dale Murphy Jsy 100.00 200.00
Cal Ripken Jsy/19
6 Roger Clemens Jsy 75.00 150.00
Mike Schmidt Jsy/19
7 Ty Cobb Pants
Babe Ruth Pants/9
8 Roy Campanella Pants
Stan Musial Jsy/2
10 George Brett Jsy 100.00 200.00
Nolan Ryan Jsy/19
11 Jackie Robinson Jsy
Roy Campanella Pants/9
12 Al Kaline Pants
Duke Snider Jsy/15

2004 Prime Cuts Timeline Dual Achievements Material Signature

RANDOM INSERTS IN PACKS
PRINT RUNS B/WN 1-25 COPIES PER
NO PRICING ON QTY OF 15 OR LESS
2 Jackie Robinson Jsy
Ted Williams Jsy/1
3 Stan Musial Jsy
Ted Williams Jsy/1
4 Mike Schmidt Jsy 175.00 300.00
George Brett Jsy/24
5 Dale Murphy Jsy 175.00 300.00
Cal Ripken Jsy/25
6 Roger Clemens Jsy 175.00 300.00
Mike Schmidt Jsy/24
7 Ty Cobb Pants
Babe Ruth Pants/1
10 George Brett Jsy 200.00 350.00
Nolan Ryan Jsy/25
12 Al Kaline Pants
Duke Snider Jsy/15

2004 Prime Cuts Timeline Dual Achievements Signature

RANDOM INSERTS IN PACKS
PRINT RUNS B/WN 24-25 COPIES PER
4 Mike Schmidt 150.00 250.00
George Brett/24
5 Dale Murphy 150.00 250.00
Cal Ripken/25
6 Roger Clemens 150.00 250.00
Mike Schmidt/24
10 George Brett 175.00 300.00
Nolan Ryan/25
12 Al Kaline 75.00 150.00
Duke Snider/25

2004 Prime Cuts Timeline Dual Achievements Signature Proofs

RANDOM INSERTS IN PACKS
STATED PRINT RUN 1 SERIAL #'d SET
NO PRICING DUE TO SCARCITY

2004 Prime Cuts Timeline Dual League Leaders Material

RANDOM INSERTS IN PACKS
PRINT RUNS B/WN 9-19 COPIES PER
NO PRICING ON QTY OF 9 OR LESS
1 Mel Ott Jsy
Lou Gehrig Pants/9
2 Mel Ott Jsy
Ted Williams Jsy/9
4 Steve Carlton Jsy 30.00 60.00
Jim Palmer Jsy/19
6 Roberto Clemente Jsy
Carl Yastrzemski Jsy/9
7 Steve Carlton Jsy 50.00 100.00
Nolan Ryan Jsy/19
8 Don Mattingly Jsy 50.00 100.00
Tony Gwynn Jsy/19
9 Roger Clemens Jsy 60.00 120.00
Nolan Ryan Jsy/19
10 Babe Ruth Pants
Lou Gehrig Pants/9

2004 Prime Cuts Timeline Dual League Leaders Material Combos

RANDOM INSERTS IN PACKS
PRINT RUNS B/WN 9-19 COPIES PER
NO PRICING ON QTY OF 9 OR LESS
1 Mel Ott Bat-Jsy
Lou Gehrig Bat-Pants/9
2 Mel Ott Bat-Jsy
Ted Williams Bat-Jsy/9
6 Roberto Clemente Bat-Jsy
Carl Yastrzemski Bat-Jsy/9
7 Steve Carlton Bat-Jsy 75.00 150.00
Nolan Ryan Bat-Jsy/19
8 Don Mattingly Bat-Jsy 75.00 150.00
Tony Gwynn Bat-Jsy/19
9 Roger Clemens Bat-Jsy 100.00 200.00
Nolan Ryan Bat-Jsy/19
10 Babe Ruth Bat-Pants
Lou Gehrig Bat-Pants/9

2004 Prime Cuts Timeline Dual League Leaders Material Prime

RANDOM INSERTS IN PACKS
PRINT RUNS B/WN 9-19 COPIES PER
NO PRICING DUE TO SCARCITY
1 Mel Ott Jsy
Lou Gehrig Pants/9
2 Mel Ott Jsy
Ted Williams Jsy/9
4 Steve Carlton Jsy 50.00 100.00
Jim Palmer Jsy/19
6 Roberto Clemente Jsy
Carl Yastrzemski Jsy/9
7 Steve Carlton Jsy 75.00 150.00
Nolan Ryan Jsy/19
8 Don Mattingly Jsy 75.00 150.00
Tony Gwynn Jsy/19
9 Roger Clemens Jsy 100.00 200.00
Nolan Ryan Jsy/19
10 Babe Ruth Pants
Lou Gehrig Pants/9

2004 Prime Cuts Timeline Dual League Leaders Material Signature

RANDOM INSERTS IN PACKS
PRINT RUNS B/WN 1-50 COPIES PER
NO PRICING ON QTY OF 1
1 Mel Ott Jsy
Lou Gehrig Pants/1
2 Mel Ott Jsy
Ted Williams Jsy/1
4 Steve Carlton Jsy 60.00 120.00
Jim Palmer Jsy/50
6 Roberto Clemente Jsy
Carl Yastrzemski Jsy/1
7 Steve Carlton Jsy 150.00 250.00
Nolan Ryan Jsy/25
8 Don Mattingly Jsy 150.00 250.00
Tony Gwynn Jsy/25
9 Roger Clemens Jsy 300.00 500.00
Nolan Ryan Jsy/25
10 Babe Ruth Pants
Lou Gehrig Pants/1

2004 Prime Cuts Timeline Dual League Leaders Signature

RANDOM INSERTS IN PACKS
PRINT RUNS B/WN 25-50 COPIES PER
4 Steve Carlton 50.00 100.00
Jim Palmer/50
7 Steve Carlton 125.00 200.00
Nolan Ryan/25
8 Don Mattingly 125.00 200.00
Tony Gwynn/25
9 Roger Clemens 250.00 400.00
Nolan Ryan/25

2004 Prime Cuts Timeline Dual League Leaders Signature Proofs

RANDOM INSERTS IN PACKS
STATED PRINT RUN 1 SERIAL #'d SET
NO PRICING DUE TO SCARCITY

2004 Prime Cuts Timeline Material

RANDOM INSERTS IN PACKS
NO PRICING ON QTY OF 9 OR LESS
1 Ty Cobb Pants/9
2 Babe Ruth Pants/9
3 Lou Gehrig Pants/9
4 Ted Williams TC Jsy/50 60.00 120.00
5 Roy Campanella Pants/50 30.00 60.00
6 Stan Musial MVP Jsy/50 30.00 60.00
7 Yogi Berra 51M Jsy/50 20.00 50.00
9 R.Clemente MVP Jsy/50 75.00 150.00
10 Will Clark Jsy/25 20.00 50.00
12 Carl Yastrzemski Jsy/50 30.00 60.00
13 Mike Schmidt Jsy/50 20.00 50.00
14 George Brett MVP Jsy/50 20.00 50.00
15 Nolan Ryan WIN Jsy/50 30.00 60.00
16 Stan Musial BA Jsy/50 30.00 60.00
17 Ted Williams BA Jsy/50 60.00 120.00
18 R.Clemente BTG Jsy/50 75.00 150.00
19 Greg Maddux Jsy/50 20.00 50.00
21 Robin Yount Jsy/50 20.00 50.00
22 Nolan Ryan HOF Jsy/50 30.00 60.00
23 Ted Williams RET Jsy/50 60.00 120.00
24 George Brett RET Jsy/50 20.00 50.00
25 Yogi Berra 55M Jsy/50 20.00 50.00
26 Rod Carew Jsy/50 15.00 40.00
27 Dale Murphy Jsy/25 20.00 50.00

2004 Prime Cuts Timeline Material Combos

RANDOM INSERTS IN PACKS
PRINT RUNS B/WN 1-19 COPIES PER
NO PRICING ON QTY OF 9 OR LESS
1 Ty Cobb Bat-Pants/9
2 Babe Ruth Bat-Pants/9
3 Lou Gehrig Bat-Pants/9
4 Ted Williams TC Bat-Jsy/9
5 Roy Campanella Bat-Pants/9
6 Stan Musial MVP Bat-Jsy/1
7 Yogi Berra 51M Bat-Jsy/2
9 R.Clemente MVP Bat-Jsy/9
10 Will Clark Bat-Jsy/19 75.00 150.00
12 Carl Yastrzemski Bat-Jsy/19 75.00 150.00
13 Mike Schmidt Bat-Jsy/19 60.00 120.00
14 G.Brett MVP Bat-Jsy/19 60.00 120.00
15 N.Ryan WIN Bat-Jsy/19 75.00 150.00
16 Stan Musial BA Bat-Jsy/1
17 Ted Williams BA Bat-Jsy/9
18 R.Clemente BTG Bat-Jsy/9
19 Greg Maddux Bat-Jsy/19 50.00 100.00
21 Robin Yount Bat-Jsy/19 50.00 100.00
22 N.Ryan HOF Bat-Jsy/19 75.00 150.00
23 Ted Williams RET Bat-Jsy/9
24 G.Brett RET Bat-Jsy/19 60.00 120.00
25 Yogi Berra 55M Bat-Jsy/2
26 Rod Carew Bat-Jsy/19 40.00 80.00
27 Dale Murphy Bat-Jsy/19 40.00 80.00

2004 Prime Cuts Timeline Material Prime

RANDOM INSERTS IN PACKS
PRINT RUNS B/WN 1-25 COPIES PER
NO PRICING ON QTY OF 9 OR LESS
1 Ty Cobb Pants/9
2 Babe Ruth Pants/9
3 Lou Gehrig Pants/9
4 Ted Williams TC Jsy/9
5 Roy Campanella Pants/25 40.00 80.00
6 Stan Musial MVP Jsy/2
7 Yogi Berra 51M Jsy/1
9 R.Clemente MVP Jsy/25 75.00 150.00
10 Will Clark Jsy/25 40.00 80.00
12 Carl Yastrzemski Jsy/25 60.00 120.00
13 Mike Schmidt Jsy/25 50.00 100.00
14 George Brett MVP Jsy/25 50.00 100.00
15 Nolan Ryan WIN Jsy/25 50.00 100.00
16 Stan Musial BA Jsy/2
17 Ted Williams BA Jsy/9
18 R.Clemente BTG Jsy/25 75.00 150.00
19 Greg Maddux Jsy/25 40.00 80.00
21 Robin Yount Jsy/25 40.00 80.00
22 Nolan Ryan HOF Jsy/25 50.00 100.00
23 Ted Williams RET Jsy/9
24 George Brett RET Jsy/25 50.00 100.00
25 Yogi Berra 55M Jsy/1
26 Rod Carew Jsy/25 40.00 80.00
27 Dale Murphy Jsy/25 40.00 80.00

2004 Prime Cuts Timeline Material Signature

RANDOM INSERTS IN PACKS
PRINT RUNS B/WN 33-42 COPIES PER
6 Stan Musial MVP Jsy/33 75.00 150.00
7 Yogi Berra 51M Jsy/42 60.00 120.00
16 Stan Musial BA Jsy/38 75.00 150.00
25 Yogi Berra 55M Jsy/42 60.00 120.00

2004 Prime Cuts Timeline Material Signature Prime

RANDOM INSERTS IN PACKS
PRINT RUNS B/WN 1-50 COPIES PER
NO PRICING ON QTY OF 10 OR LESS
1 Ty Cobb Pants/1
2 Babe Ruth Pants/1
3 Lou Gehrig Pants/1
6 Stan Musial MVP Jsy/10
7 Yogi Berra 51M Jsy/8
9 Roberto Clemente Jsy/1
10 Will Clark Jsy/50 60.00 120.00
12 Carl Yastrzemski Jsy/50 75.00 150.00
13 Mike Schmidt Jsy/20 125.00 200.00
14 George Brett MVP Jsy/25 125.00 200.00
15 Nolan Ryan WIN Jsy/50 125.00 200.00
16 Stan Musial BA Jsy/10
19 Greg Maddux Jsy/50 125.00 200.00
21 Robin Yount Jsy/50 60.00 120.00
22 Nolan Ryan HOF Jsy/50 125.00 200.00
24 George Brett RET Jsy/25 125.00 200.00
25 Yogi Berra 55M Jsy/8
26 Rod Carew Jsy/50 40.00 80.00
27 Dale Murphy Jsy/50 40.00 80.00

2004 Prime Cuts Timeline Signature

RANDOM INSERTS IN PACKS
PRINT RUNS B/WN 10-50 COPIES PER
NO PRICING ON QTY OF 20 OR LESS
6 Stan Musial MVP/50 50.00 100.00
7 Yogi Berra 51M/50 40.00 80.00
10 Will Clark/25 75.00 150.00
12 Carl Yastrzemski/50 50.00 100.00
13 Mike Schmidt/20 60.00 120.00
14 George Brett MVP/25 60.00 120.00
15 Nolan Ryan WIN/50 75.00 150.00
16 Stan Musial BA/50 50.00 100.00
19 Greg Maddux/31 75.00 150.00
21 Robin Yount/25 60.00 120.00
22 Nolan Ryan HOF/50 75.00 150.00
24 George Brett RET/25 60.00 120.00
25 Yogi Berra 55M/50 40.00 80.00
26 Rod Carew/10
27 Dale Murphy/25 40.00 80.00

2004 Prime Cuts Timeline Signature Proofs

RANDOM INSERTS IN PACKS
STATED PRINT RUN 1 SERIAL #'d SET
NO PRICING DUE TO SCARCITY

2004 Prime Cuts II

This 100-card set was released in November, 2004. The set was issued in four-card packs with an $150 SRP which were packed 1 to a box and 15 box-packs to a case. Each pack included a card which were put into special holders. The first 91 cards of the basic set feature active veterans while cards numbered 92-100 feature retired greats and all of

these cards have a stated print run of 699 serial numbered sets.

COMMON CARD (1-91)	1.50	4.00
COMMON CARD (92-100)	1.50	4.00
1 Mark Prior	2.00	5.00
2 Derek Jeter	4.00	10.00
3 Eric Chavez	1.50	4.00
4 Carlos Delgado	1.50	4.00
5 Albert Pujols	4.00	10.00
6 Miguel Cabrera	2.00	5.00
7 Ivan Rodriguez	2.00	5.00
8 Javy Lopez	1.50	4.00
9 Hank Blalock	1.50	4.00
10 Chipper Jones	2.00	5.00
11 Gary Sheffield	1.50	4.00
12 Alfonso Soriano	1.50	4.00
13 Alex Rodriguez Yanks	3.00	8.00
14 Edgar Renteria	1.50	4.00
15 Jim Edmonds	1.50	4.00
16 Garret Anderson	1.50	4.00
17 Lance Berkman	1.50	4.00
18 Brandon Webb	1.50	4.00
19 Mike Lowell	1.50	4.00
20 Mark Mulder	1.50	4.00
21 Sammy Sosa	2.00	5.00
22 Roger Clemens Astros	3.00	8.00
23 Mark Teixeira	2.00	5.00
24 Manny Ramirez	2.00	5.00
25 Rafael Palmeiro	2.00	5.00
26 Ichiro Suzuki	4.00	10.00
27 Vladimir Guerrero	2.00	5.00
28 Austin Kearns	1.50	4.00
29 Troy Glaus	1.50	4.00
30 Ken Griffey Jr.	3.00	8.00
31 Greg Maddux	3.00	8.00
32 Roy Halladay	1.50	4.00
33 Roy Oswalt	1.50	4.00
34 Kerry Wood	1.50	4.00
35 Mike Mussina Yanks	2.00	5.00
36 Michael Young	1.50	4.00
37 Juan Gonzalez	1.50	4.00
38 Curt Schilling	2.00	5.00
39 Shannon Stewart	1.50	4.00
40 Todd Helton	2.00	5.00
41 Larry Walker Cards	2.00	5.00
42 Mariano Rivera	2.00	5.00
43 Nomar Garciaparra	3.00	8.00
44 Adam Dunn	1.50	4.00
45 Pedro Martinez Sox	2.00	5.00
46 Bernie Williams	2.00	5.00
47 Tom Glavine	2.00	5.00
48 Torii Hunter	1.50	4.00
49 David Ortiz	2.00	5.00
50 Frank Thomas	2.00	5.00
51 Randy Johnson D'backs	2.00	5.00
52 Jason Giambi	1.50	4.00
53 Carlos Lee	1.50	4.00
54 Mike Sweeney	1.50	4.00
55 Hideki Matsui	3.00	8.00
56 Dontrelle Willis	2.00	5.00
57 Tim Hudson	1.50	4.00
58 Jose Vidro	1.50	4.00
59 Jeff Bagwell	2.00	5.00
60 Rocco Baldelli	1.50	4.00
61 Craig Biggio	2.00	5.00
62 Mike Piazza Mets	3.00	8.00
63 Magglio Ordonez	1.50	4.00
64 Hideo Nomo	2.00	5.00
65 Miguel Tejada	1.50	4.00
66 Vernon Wells	1.50	4.00
67 Barry Larkin	2.00	5.00
68 Jacque Jones	1.50	4.00
69 Scott Rolen	2.00	5.00
70 Jeff Kent	1.50	4.00
71 Steve Finley	1.50	4.00
72 Kazuo Matsui RC	2.00	5.00
73 Carlos Beltran	1.50	4.00
74 Shawn Green	1.50	4.00
75 Barry Zito	1.50	4.00
76 Aramis Ramirez	1.50	4.00
77 Paul Lo Duca	1.50	4.00
78 Kazuhisa Ishii	1.50	4.00
79 Aubrey Huff	1.50	4.00
80 Jim Thome	2.00	5.00
81 Andy Pettitte Astros	2.00	5.00
82 Andruw Jones	2.00	5.00
83 Josh Beckett	1.50	4.00
84 Sean Casey	1.50	4.00
85 Alex Rodriguez M's	3.00	8.00
86 Roger Clemens Yanks	3.00	8.00
87 Mike Mussina O's	2.00	5.00
88 Pedro Martinez Dgr	2.00	5.00
89 Randy Johnson Astros	2.00	5.00
90 Mike Piazza Dgr	3.00	8.00
91 Andy Pettitte Yanks	2.00	5.00
92 Cal Ripken	6.00	15.00
93 Dale Murphy	2.00	5.00
94 Don Mattingly	3.00	8.00
95 Gary Carter	1.50	4.00
96 George Brett	3.00	8.00
97 Nolan Ryan	4.00	10.00
98 Ozzie Smith	3.00	8.00
99 Steve Carlton	1.50	4.00
100 Tony Gwynn	3.00	8.00

2004 Prime Cuts II Century Gold

*GOLD 1-91: 1X TO 2.5X BASIC
*GOLD 92-100: 1X TO 2.5X BASIC
RANDOM INSERTS IN PACKS
STATED PRINT RUN 25 SERIAL #'d SETS
NO RC YR PRICING DUE TO SCARCITY

2004 Prime Cuts II Century Platinum

RANDOM INSERTS IN PACKS
STATED PRINT RUN 1 SERIAL #'d SET
NO PRICING DUE TO SCARCITY

2004 Prime Cuts II Century Silver

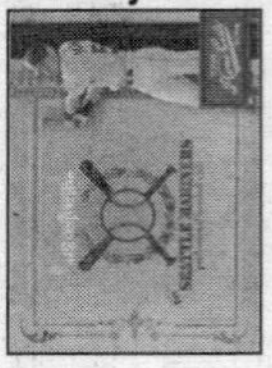

*SILVER 1-91: .6X TO 1.5X BASIC
*SILVER 92-100: .6X TO 1.5X BASIC
RANDOM INSERTS IN PACKS
STATED PRINT RUN 50 SERIAL #'d SETS

2004 Prime Cuts II Material Number

*1-91 p/r 25: .3X TO .8X COMBO p/r 22
*92-100 p/r 25: .3X TO .8X COMBO p/r 25
OVERALL AU-GU ODDS 1:1
PRINT RUNS B/WN 1-25 COPIES PER
NO PRICING ON QTY OF 10 OR LESS

2004 Prime Cuts II Material Prime

OVERALL AU-GU ODDS 1:1
PRINT RUNS B/WN 1-10 COPIES PER
NO PRICING DUE TO SCARCITY

2004 Prime Cuts II Material Combo

OVERALL AU-GU ODDS 1:1
PRINT RUNS B/WN 1-35 COPIES PER
NO PRICING ON QTY OF 10 OR LESS

1 Mark Prior Hat-Jsy/22	10.00	25.00
3 Eric Chavez Bat-Jsy/3		
4 Carlos Delgado Bat-Jsy/1		
5 Albert Pujols Bat-Jsy/5		
6 Miguel Cabrera Bat-Jsy/5		
7 Ivan Rodriguez Bat-Jsy/7		
8 Javy Lopez Bat-Jsy/5		
9 Hank Blalock Bat-Jsy/1		
10 Chipper Jones Bat-Jsy/10		
12 Alfonso Soriano Bat-Jsy/25	6.00	15.00
14 Edgar Renteria Bat-Jsy/1		
15 Jim Edmonds Bat-Jsy/15	8.00	20.00
16 Garret Anderson Bat-Jsy/16	8.00	20.00
17 Lance Berkman Hat-Jsy/17	8.00	20.00
19 Mike Lowell Bat-Jsy/1		
20 Mark Mulder Bat-Jsy/1		
21 Sammy Sosa Bat-Jsy/21	12.50	30.00
22 R.Clem Astros Bat-Jsy/22	20.00	50.00
23 Mark Teixeira Fld Glv-Jsy/1		
24 Manny Ramirez Bat-Jsy/24	10.00	25.00
25 Rafael Palmeiro Bat-Jsy/25	10.00	25.00
27 Vlad Guerrero Bat-Jsy/27	12.50	30.00
29 Troy Glaus Bat-Jsy/1		
31 Greg Maddux Bat-Jsy/31	20.00	50.00
32 Roy Halladay Jsy-Jsy/1		
33 Roy Oswalt Fld Glv-Jsy/1		
34 Kerry Wood Jsy-Pants/10		
35 M.Muss Yanks Bat-Jsy/35	10.00	25.00
36 Michael Young Bat-Jsy/1		
37 Juan Gonzalez Bat-Jsy/1		
38 Curt Schilling Bat-Jsy/1		
40 Todd Helton Bat-Jsy/17	12.50	30.00
44 Adam Dunn Bat-Jsy/1		
45 P.Martinez Sox Jsy-Pants/1		
46 Bernie Williams Jsy-Jsy/1		
47 Tom Glavine Bat-Jsy/1		
48 Torii Hunter Bat-Jsy/1		
49 David Ortiz Bat-Jsy/1		
50 Frank Thomas Jsy-Pants/1		
51 R.John D'backs Bat-Jsy/10		
52 Jason Giambi Bat-Jsy/1		
55 Hideki Matsui Bat-Jsy/5		
56 Dontrelle Willis Jsy-Jsy/1		
57 Tim Hudson Hat-Jsy/1		
59 Jeff Bagwell Bat-Jsy/5		
60 Rocco Baldelli Bat-Jsy/1		
61 Craig Biggio Bat-Jsy/1		
62 Mike Piazza Mets Jsy-Jsy/10		
63 Magglio Ordonez Bat-Jsy/1		
64 Hideo Nomo Jsy-Pants/10		
65 Miguel Tejada Bat-Jsy/1		
66 Vernon Wells Bat-Jsy/1		
67 Barry Larkin Bat-Jsy/1		
69 Scott Rolen Bat-Jsy/5		
72 Kazuo Matsui Bat-Jsy/5		
73 Carlos Beltran Bat-Jsy/1		
74 Shawn Green Bat-Jsy/1		
75 Barry Zito Bat-Jsy/1		
78 Kazuhisa Ishii Bat-Jsy/1		
80 Jim Thome Bat-Jsy/1		
81 A.Pettitte Astros Bat-Jsy/1		
82 Andruw Jones Bat-Jsy/1		
83 Josh Beckett Bat-Jsy/1		
84 Sean Casey Bat-Jsy/1		
86 R.Clem Ynk Fld Glv-Jsy/22	20.00	50.00
87 M.Muss O's Jsy-Pants/1		
88 P.Martinez Dgr Bat-Jsy/1		
89 R.John Astros Bat-Jsy/10		
90 Mike Piazza Dgr Bat-Jsy/10		
91 A.Pettitte Yanks Jsy-Jsy/1		
92 Cal Ripken Bat-Jsy/25	50.00	100.00
93 Dale Murphy Bat-Jsy/25	12.50	30.00
94 Don Mattingly Bat-Jsy/25	30.00	60.00
95 Gary Carter Jkt-Jsy/10		
96 George Brett Bat-Jsy/25	30.00	60.00
97 Nolan Ryan Bat-Jkt/25	30.00	60.00
98 Ozzie Smith Bat-Jsy/25	20.00	50.00
99 Steve Carlton Bat-Jsy/10		
100 Tony Gwynn Bat-Jsy/10		

2004 Prime Cuts II Material Combo Prime

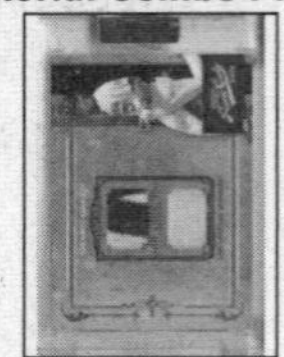

OVERALL AU-GU ODDS 1:1
PRINT RUNS B/WN 1-9 COPIES PER
NO PRICING DUE TO SCARCITY

2004 Prime Cuts II Signature Century Gold

*1-91 p/r 15-19: .5X TO 1.2X SILV p/r 25
*92-100 p/r 15-19: .5X TO 1.2X SILV p/r 25
OVERALL AU-GU ODDS 1:1
PRINT RUNS B/WN 1-19 COPIES PER
NO PRICING ON QTY OF 11 OR LESS

2004 Prime Cuts II Signature Century Platinum

OVERALL AU-GU ODDS 1:1
STATED PRINT RUN 1 SERIAL #'d SET
NO PRICING DUE TO SCARCITY

2004 Prime Cuts II Signature Century Silver

OVERALL AU-GU ODDS 1:1
PRINT RUNS B/WN 1- COPIES PER
NO PRICING ON QTY OF OR LESS

1 Mark Prior/22	12.50	30.00
3 Eric Chavez/10		
5 Albert Pujols/10		
6 Miguel Cabrera/24	15.00	40.00
9 Hank Blalock/25	10.00	25.00
10 Chipper Jones/1		
11 Gary Sheffield/25	15.00	40.00
14 Edgar Renteria/10		
15 Jim Edmonds/25	15.00	40.00
16 Garret Anderson/25	10.00	25.00
17 Lance Berkman/25	15.00	40.00
19 Mike Lowell/19	12.50	30.00
20 Mark Mulder/20	10.00	25.00
21 Sammy Sosa/21	50.00	100.00
22 Roger Clemens Astros/10		
23 Mark Teixeira/23	15.00	40.00
24 Manny Ramirez/24	40.00	80.00
25 Rafael Palmeiro/25	30.00	60.00
27 Vladimir Guerrero/5		
31 Greg Maddux/31	60.00	120.00
34 Kerry Wood/34	15.00	40.00
35 Mike Mussina Yanks/35	15.00	40.00
37 Juan Gonzalez/22	10.00	25.00
38 Curt Schilling/10		
40 Todd Helton/17	20.00	50.00
44 Adam Dunn/44	12.50	30.00
45 Pedro Martinez Sox/10		
46 Bernie Williams/10		
48 Torii Hunter/10		
49 David Ortiz/34	20.00	50.00
50 Frank Thomas/35	20.00	50.00
51 Randy Johnson D'backs/10		
56 Dontrelle Willis/10		
57 Tim Hudson/15	20.00	50.00
59 Jeff Bagwell/10		
61 Craig Biggio/25	15.00	40.00
62 Mike Piazza Mets/10		
63 Magglio Ordonez/30	10.00	25.00
64 Hideo Nomo/1		
66 Vernon Wells/25	10.00	25.00
67 Barry Larkin/11		
69 Scott Rolen/27	15.00	40.00
73 Carlos Beltran/15	12.50	30.00
74 Shawn Green/15	20.00	50.00
75 Barry Zito/10		
78 Kazuhisa Ishii/17	12.50	30.00
81 Andy Pettitte Astros/10		
82 Andruw Jones/25	15.00	40.00
83 Josh Beckett/21	15.00	40.00
84 Sean Casey/10		
86 Roger Clemens Yanks/10		
87 Mike Mussina O's/35	15.00	40.00
88 Pedro Martinez Dgr/10		
89 Randy Johnson Astros/10		
90 Mike Piazza Dgr/10		
91 Andy Pettitte Yanks/10		
92 Cal Ripken/25	100.00	200.00
93 Dale Murphy/25	15.00	40.00
94 Don Mattingly/23	40.00	80.00
95 Gary Carter/25	10.00	25.00
96 George Brett/10		
97 Nolan Ryan/34	60.00	120.00
98 Ozzie Smith/10		
99 Steve Carlton/32	10.00	25.00
100 Tony Gwynn/25	30.00	60.00

2004 Prime Cuts II Signature Material Number

*1-91 p/r 20-35: .5X TO 1.2X SILV p/r 20-35
*1-91 p/r 15-19: .6X TO 1.5X SILV p/r 20-25
*1-91 p/r 15-19: .5X TO 1.2X SILV p/r 15-19
*92-100 p/r 20-35: .5X TO 1.2X SILV p/r 20-35
*92-100 p/r 15-19: .6X TO 1.5X SILV p/r 20-25
OVERALL AU-GU ODDS 1:1
PRINT RUNS B/WN 1- COPIES PER
NO PRICING ON QTY OF OR LESS

2004 Prime Cuts II Signature Material Prime

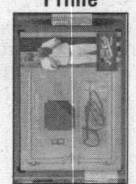

OVERALL AU-GU ODDS 1:1
PRINT RUNS B/WN 1-9 COPIES PER
NO PRICING DUE TO SCARCITY

2004 Prime Cuts II Signature Material Combo

*1-91 p/r 20-35: .6X TO 1.5X SILV p/r 20-35
*1-91 p/r 15-19: .75X TO 2X SILV p/r 20-35
*1-91 p/r 15-19: .6X TO 1.5X SILV p/r 15-19
*92-100 p/r 20-35: .6X TO 1.5X SILV p/r 20-35
OVERALL AU-GU ODDS 1:1
PRINT RUNS B/WN 1-25 COPIES PER
NO PRICING ON QTY OF 10 OR LESS

2004 Prime Cuts II Signature Material Combo Prime

OVERALL AU-GU ODDS 1:1
PRINT RUNS B/WN 1-9 COPIES PER
NO PRICING DUE TO SCARCITY

2004 Prime Cuts II MLB Icons

RANDOM INSERTS IN PACKS
STATED PRINT RUN 50 SERIAL #'d SETS

1 Dale Murphy	3.00	8.00
2 Eddie Mathews	4.00	10.00
3 Brooks Robinson	3.00	8.00
4 Cal Ripken Right	15.00	40.00
5 Cal Ripken Left	15.00	40.00
6 Eddie Murray	4.00	10.00
7 Frank Robinson	2.00	5.00
8 Jim Palmer	2.00	5.00
9 Bobby Doerr	2.00	5.00
10 Carl Yastrzemski	6.00	15.00
11 Carlton Fisk R.Sox	3.00	8.00
12 Dennis Eckersley	3.00	8.00
13 Luis Aparicio	2.00	5.00
14 Luis Tiant	2.00	5.00
15 Ted Williams	6.00	15.00
16 Wade Boggs Sox	3.00	8.00
17 Duke Snider Dgr	3.00	8.00
18 Jackie Robinson	3.00	8.00
19 Pee Wee Reese	3.00	8.00
20 Burleigh Grimes	2.00	5.00
21 Nolan Ryan Angels	10.00	25.00
22 Reggie Jackson Angels	3.00	8.00
23 Rod Carew White	3.00	8.00
24 Rod Carew Navy	3.00	8.00
25 Billy Williams	2.00	5.00
26 Ernie Banks	4.00	10.00
27 Mark Grace	3.00	8.00
28 Ron Santo	3.00	8.00
29 Paul Molitor Brew	2.00	5.00
30 Bo Jackson Sox	4.00	10.00
31 Carlton Fisk W.Sox	3.00	8.00
32 Johnny Bench	4.00	10.00
33 Tom Seaver Reds	3.00	8.00
34 Tony Perez	2.00	5.00
35 Bob Feller	2.00	5.00
36 Lou Boudreau	2.00	5.00
37 Al Kaline	4.00	10.00
38 Alan Trammell	2.00	5.00
39 Ty Cobb	4.00	10.00
40 Don Sutton	2.00	5.00
41 Nolan Ryan Astros	10.00	25.00
42 Roger Maris A's	4.00	10.00
43 Bo Jackson Royals	4.00	10.00
44 George Brett Gray	8.00	20.00
45 George Brett White	8.00	20.00
46 Maury Wills	2.00	5.00
47 Warren Spahn	3.00	8.00
48 Robin Yount	4.00	10.00
49 Harmon Killebrew Twins	4.00	10.00
50 Kirby Puckett	6.00	15.00
51 Paul Molitor Twins	2.00	5.00
52 Andre Dawson	2.00	5.00
53 Mel Ott Pinstripe	3.00	8.00
54 Mel Ott White	3.00	8.00
55 Duke Snider Mets	3.00	8.00
56 Rickey Henderson Mets	4.00	10.00
57 Tom Seaver Mets	3.00	8.00
58 Babe Ruth w/Bats	6.00	15.00
59 Babe Ruth Gray	6.00	15.00
60 Catfish Hunter	3.00	8.00
61 Dave Righetti	2.00	5.00
62 Dave Winfield Yanks	2.00	5.00
63 Don Mattingly White	8.00	20.00
64 Don Mattingly Navy	8.00	20.00
65 Lou Gehrig w/o Cap	4.00	10.00
66 Lou Gehrig w/Cap	4.00	10.00
67 Phil Niekro	2.00	5.00
68 Phil Rizzuto	3.00	8.00
69 Reggie Jackson Yanks	3.00	8.00
70 Rickey Henderson Yanks	4.00	10.00
71 Roger Maris Yanks	4.00	10.00
72 Thurman Munson w/Bat	4.00	10.00
73 Thurman Munson w/o Bat	4.00	10.00
74 Wade Boggs Yanks	3.00	8.00
75 Whitey Ford	3.00	8.00
76 Yogi Berra	4.00	10.00
77 Lefty Grove	2.00	5.00
78 Mike Schmidt w/Bat	8.00	20.00
79 Mike Schmidt w/o Bat	8.00	20.00
80 Steve Carlton Phils	2.00	5.00
81 Ralph Kiner	2.00	5.00
82 Roberto Clemente w/Bat	10.00	25.00
83 Roberto Clemente w/o Bat	10.00	25.00
84 Dave Winfield Padres	2.00	5.00
85 Rickey Henderson Padres	4.00	10.00
86 Steve Garvey	2.00	5.00
87 Tony Gwynn Gray	6.00	15.00
88 Tony Gwynn White	6.00	15.00
89 Gaylord Perry	2.00	5.00
90 Joe Morgan	2.00	5.00
91 Juan Marichal	2.00	5.00
92 Steve Carlton Giants	2.00	5.00
93 Will Clark	3.00	8.00
94 Willie McCovey	3.00	8.00
95 Bob Gibson	3.00	8.00
96 Lou Brock	3.00	8.00
97 Stan Musial	6.00	15.00
98 Fergie Jenkins	2.00	5.00
99 Nolan Ryan Rgr	10.00	25.00
100 Harmon Killebrew Senators	4.00	10.00

2004 Prime Cuts II MLB Icons Century Gold

RANDOM INSERTS IN PACKS
STATED PRINT RUN 10 SERIAL #'d SETS
NO PRICING DUE TO SCARCITY

2004 Prime Cuts II MLB Icons Century Platinum

RANDOM INSERTS IN PACKS
STATED PRINT RUN 1 SERIAL #'d SET
NO PRICING DUE TO SCARCITY

2004 Prime Cuts II MLB Icons Century Silver

*SILVER: .6X TO 1.5X BASIC
RANDOM INSERTS IN PACKS
STATED PRINT RUN 25 SERIAL #'d SETS

2004 Prime Cuts II MLB Icons Material Number

*RUTH SWATCH W/P'STRIPE: ADD 25%
OVERALL AU-GU ODDS 1:1
PRINT RUNS B/WN 1- COPIES PER
NO PRICING ON QTY OF OR LESS

1 Dale Murphy Jsy/25	10.00	25.00
2 Eddie Mathews Jsy/5		
3 Brooks Robinson Jsy/25	10.00	25.00
4 Cal Ripken Jsy/25	40.00	80.00
5 Cal Ripken Jkt/25	40.00	80.00
6 Eddie Murray Jsy/25	15.00	40.00
7 Frank Robinson Jsy/25	6.00	15.00
8 Jim Palmer Jsy/25	6.00	15.00
9 Bobby Doerr Jsy/25	6.00	15.00
10 Carl Yastrzemski Jsy/25	20.00	50.00
11 Carlton Fisk R.Sox Jsy/25	10.00	25.00
12 Dennis Eckersley Jsy/10		
13 Luis Aparicio Jsy/10		
14 Luis Tiant Jsy/1		
15 Ted Williams Jsy/50	50.00	100.00
16 Wade Boggs Sox Jsy/10		
17 Duke Snider Dgr Jsy/25	10.00	25.00
18 Jackie Robinson Jkt/50	40.00	80.00
19 Pee Wee Reese Jsy/25	10.00	25.00
20 Burleigh Grimes Pants/25	30.00	60.00
21 Nolan Ryan Angels Jsy/25	20.00	50.00
22 R.Jackson Angels Jsy/25	10.00	25.00
23 Rod Carew Jsy/25	10.00	25.00
24 Rod Carew Jkt/25	10.00	25.00
25 Billy Williams Jsy/25	6.00	15.00
26 Ernie Banks Jsy/25	12.50	30.00
27 Mark Grace Jsy/1		
28 Ron Santo Bat/10		
29 Paul Molitor Brew Pants/25	6.00	15.00
30 Bo Jackson Sox Jsy/1		
31 Carlton Fisk W.Sox Jsy/25	10.00	25.00
32 Johnny Bench Jsy/25	12.50	30.00
33 Tom Seaver Reds Jsy/25	10.00	25.00
35 Bob Feller Jsy/25	6.00	15.00
36 Lou Boudreau Jsy/25	12.50	30.00

37 Al Kaline Pants/6
38 Alan Trammell Jsy/3
39 Ty Cobb Pants/50 60.00 120.00
40 Don Sutton Jsy/5
41 Nolan Ryan Astros Jsy/25 20.00 50.00
42 Roger Maris A's Jsy/25 30.00 60.00
43 Bo Jackson Royals Jsy/10
44 George Brett Jsy/25 20.00 50.00
45 George Brett Jsy/25 20.00 50.00
46 Maury Wills Jsy/1
47 Warren Spahn Jsy/25 12.50 30.00
48 Robin Yount Jsy/25 12.50 30.00
49 H.Killebrew Twins Jsy/25 15.00 40.00
50 Kirby Puckett Jsy/25 12.50 30.00
51 Paul Molitor Twins Jsy/25 6.00 15.00
52 Andre Dawson Jsy/1
53 Mel Ott Jsy/25 20.00 50.00
54 Mel Ott Pants/25 20.00 50.00
55 Duke Snider Mets Jsy/25 10.00 25.00
56 R.Henderson Mets Jsy/1
57 Tom Seaver Mets Jsy/5
58 Babe Ruth Jsy/25 200.00 350.00
59 Babe Ruth Pants/50 150.00 250.00
60 Catfish Hunter Jsy/25 10.00 25.00
61 Dave Righetti Jsy/1
62 D.Winfield Yanks Pants/10
63 Don Mattingly Jsy/25 20.00 50.00
64 Don Mattingly Jkt/25 20.00 50.00
65 Lou Gehrig Jsy/25 100.00 200.00
66 Lou Gehrig Pants/50 75.00 150.00
67 Phil Niekro Jsy/5
68 Phil Rizzuto Pants/25 10.00 25.00
69 R.Jackson Yanks Jsy/25 10.00 25.00
70 R.Henderson Yanks Jsy/1
71 R.Maris Yanks Pants/25 20.00 50.00
72 Thurman Munson Jsy/50 15.00 40.00
73 Thurman Munson Pants/50 15.00 40.00
74 Wade Boggs Yanks Jsy/10
75 Whitey Ford Pants/16 15.00 40.00
76 Yogi Berra Jsy/8
77 Lefty Grove Hat/25 75.00 150.00
78 Mike Schmidt Jsy/20 20.00 50.00
79 Mike Schmidt Jkt/20 20.00 50.00
80 S.Carlton Phils Pants/10
81 Ralph Kiner Bat/10
82 Roberto Clemente Jsy/21 75.00 150.00
83 Roberto Clemente Hat/21 75.00 150.00
84 Dave Winfield Padres Jsy/10
85 R.Henderson Padres Jsy/1
86 Steve Garvey Jsy/6
87 Tony Gwynn White Jsy/10
88 Tony Gwynn Navy Jsy/10
89 Gaylord Perry Jsy/10
90 Joe Morgan Jsy/8
91 Juan Marichal Jsy/25 6.00 15.00
92 Steve Carlton Giants Jsy/10
93 Will Clark Jsy/22 10.00 25.00
94 Willie McCovey Jsy/25 10.00 25.00
95 Bob Gibson Jsy/25 10.00 25.00
96 Lou Brock Jkt/20 10.00 25.00
97 Stan Musial Jsy/6
98 Fergie Jenkins Hat/10
99 Nolan Ryan Rgr Pants/25 20.00 50.00
100 H.Killebrew Senators Jsy/25 15.00 40.00

2004 Prime Cuts II MLB Icons Material Prime

OVERALL AU-GU ODDS 1:1
PRINT RUNS B/WN 1-10 COPIES PER
NO PRICING DUE TO SCARCITY

2004 Prime Cuts II MLB Icons Material Combo

*p/r 20-25: .6X TO 1.5X NBR p/r 50
*p/r 20-25: .5X TO 1.2X NBR p/r 25
*p/r 16-19: .6X TO 1.5X NBR p/r 25
*p/r 16-19: .5X TO 1.2X NBR p/r 16
OVERALL AU-GU ODDS 1:1
PRINT RUNS B/WN 1-25 COPIES PER
NO PRICING ON QTY OF 14 OR LESS
39 Ty Cobb Bat-Pants/25 125.00 200.00
58 Babe Ruth Bat-Jsy/25 250.00 400.00
59 Babe Ruth Bat-Pants/25 200.00 350.00
65 Lou Gehrig Bat-Jsy/25 175.00 300.00
66 Lou Gehrig Bat-Pants/25 150.00 250.00

2004 Prime Cuts II MLB Icons Material Combo Prime

OVERALL AU-GU ODDS 1:1
PRINT RUNS B/WN 1-10 COPIES PER
NO PRICING DUE TO SCARCITY

2004 Prime Cuts II MLB Icons Signature Century Gold

*p/r 20-25: .5X TO 1.2X SILV p/r 36-50
*p/r 20-25: .4X TO 1X SILV p/r 20-35
*p/r 16-19: .6X TO 1.5X SILV p/r 36-50
*p/r 16-19: .5X TO 1.2X SILV p/r 20-35
OVERALL AU-GU ODDS 1:1
PRINT RUNS B/WN 1-25 COPIES PER
NO PRICING ON QTY OF 11 OR LESS

2004 Prime Cuts II MLB Icons Signature Century Platinum

OVERALL AU-GU ODDS 1:1
STATED PRINT RUN 1 SERIAL #'d SET
NO PRICING DUE TO SCARCITY

2004 Prime Cuts II MLB Icons Signature Century Silver

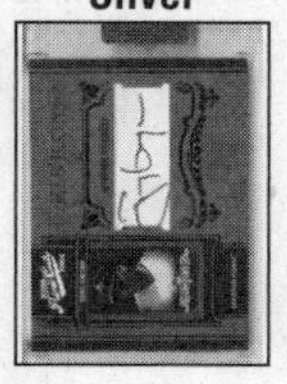

OVERALL AU-GU ODDS 1:1
PRINT RUNS B/WN 1-50 COPIES PER
NO PRICING ON QTY OF 12 OR LESS
1 Dale Murphy/25 15.00 40.00
3 Brooks Robinson/50 12.50 30.00
4 Cal Ripken Right/25 100.00 200.00
5 Cal Ripken Left/25 100.00 200.00
6 Eddie Murray/25 30.00 60.00
7 Frank Robinson/50 12.50 30.00
8 Jim Palmer/50 12.50 30.00
9 Bobby Doerr/25 10.00 25.00
10 Carl Yastrzemski/25 40.00 80.00
11 Carlton Fisk R.Sox/27 15.00 40.00
12 Dennis Eckersley/43 12.50 30.00
13 Luis Aparicio/25 10.00 25.00
14 Luis Tiant/1
16 Wade Boggs Sox/26 15.00 40.00
17 Duke Snider Dgr/50 12.50 30.00
21 Nolan Ryan Angels/30 60.00 120.00
22 Reggie Jackson Angels/25 30.00 60.00
23 Rod Carew White/29 15.00 40.00
24 Rod Carew Navy/29 15.00 40.00
25 Billy Williams/26 10.00 25.00
27 Mark Grace/1
28 Ron Santo/1
29 Paul Molitor Brew/25 10.00 25.00
30 Bo Jackson Sox/25 30.00 60.00
31 Carlton Fisk W.Sox/25 15.00 40.00
32 Johnny Bench/50 20.00 50.00
33 Tom Seaver Reds/25 15.00 40.00
34 Tony Perez/25 15.00 40.00
35 Bob Feller/25 10.00 25.00
37 Al Kaline/50 20.00 50.00
38 Alan Trammell/1
40 Don Sutton/20 10.00 25.00
41 Nolan Ryan Astros/34 60.00 120.00
43 Bo Jackson Royals/25 30.00 60.00
44 George Brett Gray/25 50.00 100.00
45 George Brett White/25 50.00 100.00
46 Maury Wills/1
47 Warren Spahn/1
48 Robin Yount/19 40.00 80.00
49 H.Killebrew Twins/50 20.00 50.00
50 Kirby Puckett/10
51 Paul Molitor Twins/50 8.00 20.00
52 Andre Dawson/1
55 Duke Snider Mets/50 12.50 30.00
56 Rickey Henderson Mets/24 30.00 60.00
57 Tom Seaver Mets/25 15.00 40.00
62 Dave Winfield Yanks/31 15.00 40.00
63 Don Mattingly White/50 30.00 60.00
64 Don Mattingly Navy/50 30.00 60.00
67 Phil Niekro/35 10.00 25.00
68 Phil Rizzuto/25 15.00 40.00
69 Reggie Jackson Yanks/25 30.00 60.00
70 Rickey Henderson Yanks/24 30.00 60.00
74 Wade Boggs Yanks/12
75 Whitey Ford/25 30.00 60.00
76 Yogi Berra/25 30.00 60.00
78 Mike Schmidt w/Bat/20 40.00 80.00
79 Mike Schmidt w/o Bat/20 40.00 80.00
80 Steve Carlton Phils/32 10.00 25.00
81 Ralph Kiner/25 15.00 40.00
84 Dave Winfield Padres/31 15.00 40.00
85 R.Henderson Padres/24 30.00 60.00
86 Steve Garvey/1
87 Tony Gwynn Gray/50 20.00 50.00
88 Tony Gwynn White/50 20.00 50.00
89 Gaylord Perry/36 8.00 20.00
90 Joe Morgan/24 10.00 25.00
91 Juan Marichal/27 10.00 25.00
92 Steve Carlton Giants/32 10.00 25.00
93 Will Clark/22 15.00 40.00
94 Willie McCovey/25 15.00 40.00
95 Bob Gibson/45 12.50 30.00
96 Lou Brock/50 12.50 30.00
97 Stan Musial/50 40.00 80.00
98 Fergie Jenkins/31 10.00 25.00
99 Nolan Ryan Rgr/34 60.00 120.00
100 H.Killebrew Senators/50 20.00 50.00

2004 Prime Cuts II MLB Icons Signature Material Number

*p/r 36-50: .5X TO 1.2X SILV p/r 36-50
*p/r 36-50: .4X TO 1X SILV p/r 20-35
*p/r 20-35: .6X TO 1.5X SILV p/r 36-50
*p/r 20-35: .5X TO 1.2X SILV p/r 20-35
*p/r 20-35: .4X TO 1X SILV p/r 15-19
*p/r 15-19: .75X TO 2X SILV p/r 36-50
*p/r 15-19: .6X TO 1.5X SILV p/r 20-35
OVERALL AU-GU ODDS 1:1
PRINT RUNS B/WN 1-45 COPIES PER
NO PRICING ON QTY OF 12 OR LESS
27 Mark Grace Jsy/17 30.00 60.00

2004 Prime Cuts II MLB Icons Signature Material Prime

OVERALL AU-GU ODDS 1:1
PRINT RUNS B/WN 1-10 COPIES PER
NO PRICING DUE TO SCARCITY

2004 Prime Cuts II MLB Icons Signature Material Combo

*p/r 20-35: .75X TO 2X SILV p/r 36-50
*p/r 20-35: .6X TO 1.5X SILV p/r 20-35
*p/r 15-19: 1X TO 2.5X SILV p/r 36-50
*p/r 15-19: .75X TO 2X SILV p/r 20-35
*p/r 15-19: .6X TO 1.5X SILV p/r 15-19
OVERALL AU-GU ODDS 1:1
PRINT RUNS B/WN 1-32 COPIES PER
NO PRICING ON QTY OF 11 OR LESS

2004 Prime Cuts II MLB Icons Signature Material Combo Prime

OVERALL AU-GU ODDS 1:1
PRINT RUNS B/WN 1-10 COPIES PER
NO PRICING DUE TO SCARCITY

2004 Prime Cuts II Timeline

RANDOM INSERTS IN PACKS
STATED PRINT RUN 50 SERIAL #'d SETS
1 Al Kaline 4.00 10.00
2 Alex Rodriguez 6.00 15.00
3 Andre Dawson 2.00 5.00
4 Babe Ruth 6.00 15.00
5 Barry Zito 2.00 5.00
6 Bob Feller 2.00 5.00
7 Bob Gibson 3.00 8.00
8 Bobby Doerr 2.00 5.00
9 Brooks Robinson 3.00 8.00
10 Cal Ripken 15.00 40.00
11 Carl Hubbell 2.00 5.00
12 Carl Yastrzemski 6.00 15.00
13 Carlton Fisk 3.00 8.00
14 Catfish Hunter 3.00 8.00
15 Chipper Jones 4.00 10.00
16 Cy Young 3.00 8.00
17 Dale Murphy 3.00 8.00
18 Dave Parker 2.00 5.00
19 Dennis Eckersley 3.00 8.00
20 Don Drysdale 3.00 8.00
21 Don Mattingly 8.00 20.00
22 Duke Snider 3.00 8.00
23 Dwight Gooden 2.00 5.00
24 Early Wynn 2.00 5.00
25 Eddie Mathews 4.00 10.00
26 Eddie Murray 4.00 10.00
27 Enos Slaughter 2.00 5.00
28 Ernie Banks 4.00 10.00
29 Fergie Jenkins 2.00 5.00
30 Frank Robinson 2.00 5.00
31 Frank Thomas 4.00 10.00
32 Frankie Frisch 2.00 5.00
33 Fred Lynn 2.00 5.00
34 Gary Carter 2.00 5.00
35 Gaylord Perry 2.00 5.00
36 George Brett 8.00 20.00
37 Greg Maddux 6.00 15.00
38 Hal Newhouser 2.00 5.00
39 Harmon Killebrew 4.00 10.00
40 Honus Wagner 3.00 8.00
41 Hoyt Wilhelm 2.00 5.00
42 Ivan Rodriguez 3.00 8.00
43 Jackie Robinson 3.00 8.00
44 Jason Giambi 2.00 5.00
45 Jeff Bagwell 3.00 8.00
46 Jim Palmer 2.00 5.00
47 Jimmie Foxx 3.00 8.00
48 Joe Morgan 2.00 5.00
49 Johnny Bench 4.00 10.00
50 Johnny Mize 2.00 5.00
51 Jose Canseco 3.00 8.00
52 Juan Gonzalez 2.00 5.00
53 Juan Marichal 2.00 5.00
54 Keith Hernandez 2.00 5.00
55 Kirby Puckett 6.00 15.00
56 Lefty Grove 2.00 5.00
57 Lou Boudreau 2.00 5.00
58 Lou Brock 3.00 8.00
59 Lou Gehrig 4.00 10.00
60 Luis Aparicio 2.00 5.00
61 Marty Marion 2.00 5.00
62 Mel Ott 3.00 8.00
63 Miguel Tejada 2.00 5.00
64 Mike Schmidt 8.00 20.00
65 Nellie Fox 3.00 8.00
66 Nolan Ryan 10.00 25.00
67 Orel Hershiser 2.00 5.00
68 Orlando Cepeda 2.00 5.00
69 Paul Molitor 2.00 5.00
70 Pedro Martinez 3.00 8.00
71 Pee Wee Reese 3.00 8.00
72 Phil Niekro 2.00 5.00
73 Phil Rizzuto 3.00 8.00
74 Ralph Kiner 2.00 5.00
75 Randy Johnson 4.00 10.00
76 Red Schoendienst 2.00 5.00
77 Reggie Jackson 3.00 8.00
78 Rickey Henderson 4.00 10.00
79 Roberto Clemente 10.00 25.00
80 Robin Yount 4.00 10.00
81 Rod Carew 3.00 8.00
82 Roger Clemens 6.00 15.00
83 Roger Maris 4.00 10.00
84 Rogers Hornsby 3.00 8.00
85 Roy Campanella 4.00 10.00
86 Ozzie Smith 6.00 15.00
87 Sammy Sosa 4.00 10.00
88 Satchel Paige 3.00 8.00
89 Stan Musial 6.00 15.00
90 Steve Carlton 2.00 5.00
91 Ted Williams 6.00 15.00
92 Thurman Munson 4.00 10.00
93 Tom Seaver 3.00 8.00
94 Ty Cobb 4.00 10.00
95 Walter Johnson 3.00 8.00
96 Warren Spahn 3.00 8.00
97 Whitey Ford 3.00 8.00
98 Willie McCovey 3.00 8.00
99 Willie Stargell 3.00 8.00
100 Yogi Berra 4.00 10.00

2004 Prime Cuts II Timeline Century Gold

RANDOM INSERTS IN PACKS
STATED PRINT RUN 10 SERIAL #'d SETS
NO PRICING DUE TO SCARCITY

2004 Prime Cuts II Timeline Century Platinum

RANDOM INSERTS IN PACKS
STATED PRINT RUN 1 SERIAL #'d SET
NO PRICING DUE TO SCARCITY

2004 Prime Cuts II Timeline Century Silver

*SILVER: .6X TO 1.5X BASIC
RANDOM INSERTS IN PACKS
STATED PRINT RUN 25 SERIAL #'d SETS

2004 Prime Cuts II Timeline Material Number

*RUTH SWATCH W/P'STRIPE: ADD 25%
OVERALL AU-GU ODDS 1:1
PRINT RUNS B/WN 1-42 COPIES PER
NO PRICING ON QTY OF 11 OR LESS
1 Al Kaline Pants/6
4 Babe Ruth Jsy/25 250.00 400.00
6 Bob Feller Pants/19 8.00 20.00
7 Bob Gibson Jsy/25 10.00 25.00
8 Bobby Doerr Jsy/5
9 Brooks Robinson Jsy/5
10 Cal Ripken Jsy/25 40.00 80.00
12 Carl Yastrzemski Jsy/25 20.00 50.00
13 Carlton Fisk Jsy/27 10.00 25.00
14 Catfish Hunter Jsy/27 10.00 25.00
17 Dale Murphy Jsy/10
20 Don Drysdale Jsy/25 20.00 50.00
21 Don Mattingly Pants/10
22 Duke Snider Pants/25 10.00 25.00
24 Early Wynn Jsy/24 6.00 15.00
25 Eddie Mathews Jsy/25 15.00 40.00
26 Eddie Murray Jsy/25 15.00 40.00
27 Enos Slaughter Jsy/9
28 Ernie Banks Jsy/25 12.50 30.00
29 Fergie Jenkins Pants/1
30 Frank Robinson Jsy/5
32 Frankie Frisch Jkt/25 15.00 40.00
34 Gary Carter Jsy/8
36 George Brett Jsy/25 20.00 50.00
38 Hal Newhouser Jsy/16 15.00 40.00
39 Harmon Killebrew Jsy/25 15.00 40.00
41 Hoyt Wilhelm Jsy/5
43 Jackie Robinson Jkt/42 40.00 80.00
46 Jim Palmer Jsy/22 6.00 15.00
47 Jimmie Foxx Fld Glv/25 50.00 100.00
48 Joe Morgan Jsy/8
49 Johnny Bench Jsy/25 12.50 30.00
50 Johnny Mize Pants/10
53 Juan Marichal Jsy/25 6.00 15.00
55 Kirby Puckett Jsy/25 12.50 30.00
56 Lefty Grove Hat/10
57 Lou Boudreau Jsy/5
58 Lou Brock Jsy/20 10.00 25.00
59 Lou Gehrig Jsy/25 100.00 200.00
60 Luis Aparicio Jsy/11
61 Marty Marion Jsy/4
62 Mel Ott Pants/25 20.00 50.00
64 Mike Schmidt Jsy/20 20.00 50.00
65 Nellie Fox Bat/2
66 Nolan Ryan Jsy/25 20.00 50.00
67 Orel Hershiser Jsy/5
68 Orlando Cepeda Pants/25 6.00 15.00
69 Paul Molitor Jsy/4
71 Pee Wee Reese Jsy/25 10.00 25.00
72 Phil Niekro Jsy/5
73 Phil Rizzuto Pants/10
74 Ralph Kiner Bat/25 6.00 15.00
76 Red Schoendienst Jsy/2
77 Reggie Jackson Jsy/25 10.00 25.00
78 Rickey Henderson Jsy/5
79 Roberto Clemente Jsy/5
80 Robin Yount Jsy/19 15.00 40.00
81 Rod Carew Jsy/25 10.00 25.00
82 Roger Clemens Jsy/21 12.50 30.00
83 Roger Maris Jsy/25 30.00 60.00
84 Rogers Hornsby Bat/25 40.00 80.00
85 Roy Campanella Pants/25 12.50 30.00
86 Ozzie Smith Jsy/25 15.00 40.00
87 Sammy Sosa Jsy/21 10.00 25.00
88 Satchel Paige CO Jsy/25 40.00 80.00
89 Stan Musial Jsy/6
90 Steve Carlton Jsy/25 6.00 15.00
91 Ted Williams Jsy/25 60.00 120.00
92 Thurman Munson Jsy/25 20.00 50.00
93 Tom Seaver Pants/25 10.00 25.00
94 Ty Cobb Pants/25 75.00 150.00
96 Warren Spahn Jsy/21 12.50 30.00
97 Whitey Ford Jsy/16 15.00 40.00
98 Willie McCovey Jsy/25 10.00 25.00
99 Willie Stargell Jsy/8
100 Yogi Berra Jsy/8

2004 Prime Cuts II Timeline Material Position

*RET p/r 36-50: .4X TO 1X NBR p/r 36-50
*ACT p/r 20-35: .4X TO 1X NBR p/r 20-35
*RET p/r 20-35: .4X TO 1X NBR p/r 20-35
*RET p/r 15-19: .5X TO 1.2X NBR p/r 20-35
*RET p/r 15-19: .4X TO 1X NBR p/r 15-19
OVERALL AU-GU ODDS 1:1
PRINT RUNS B/WN 1-42 COPIES PER
NO PRICING ON QTY OF 11 OR LESS
4 Babe Ruth Jsy/25 250.00 400.00
59 Lou Gehrig Jsy/25 100.00 200.00

2004 Prime Cuts II Timeline Material Prime

OVERALL AU-GU ODDS 1:1
PRINT RUNS B/WN 1-10 COPIES PER
NO PRICING DUE TO SCARCITY

2004 Prime Cuts II Timeline Material Combo

*RET p/r 36-50: .5X TO 1.2X NBR p/r 36-50
*RET p/r 36-50: .4X TO 1X NBR p/r 20-35
*ACT p/r 20-35: .5X TO 1.2X NBR p/r 20-35
*RET p/r 20-35: .5X TO 1.2X NBR p/r 20-35
*RET p/r 15-19: .6X TO 1.5X NBR p/r 20-35
*RET p/r 15-19: .5X TO 1.2X NBR p/r 15-19
OVERALL AU-GU ODDS 1:1
PRINT RUNS B/WN 1-42 COPIES PER
NO PRICING ON QTY OF 14 OR LESS
4 Babe Ruth Jsy-Jsy/25 300.00 500.00
17 Dale Murphy Bat-Jsy/25 12.50 30.00
21 D.Matt Btg Glv-Pants/25 30.00 60.00
59 Lou Gehrig Jsy-Pants/25 175.00 300.00
79 R.Clemente Hat-Jsy/21 100.00 200.00

2004 Prime Cuts II Timeline Material Combo CY

*ACT p/r 20-35: .5X TO 1.2X NBR p/r 20-35
*RET p/r 20-35: .5X TO 1.2X NBR p/r 20-35
*RET p/r 15-19: .5X TO 1.2X NBR p/r 15-19
OVERALL AU-GU ODDS 1:1
PRINT RUNS B/WN 1-32 COPIES PER
NO PRICING ON QTY OF 10 OR LESS
70 Pedro Martinez Bat-Jsy/25 30.00 60.00

2004 Prime Cuts II Timeline Material Trio

*ACT p/r 20-35: .6X TO 1.5X NBR p/r 20-35
*RET p/r 20-35: .6X TO 1.5X NBR p/r 20-35
*RET p/r 15-19: .75X TO 2X NBR p/r 20-35
*RET p/r 15-19: .6X TO 1.5X NBR p/r 15-19
OVERALL AU-GU ODDS 1:1
PRINT RUNS B/WN 1-25 COPIES PER
NO PRICING ON QTY OF 10 OR LESS
17 Dale Murphy Bat-Jsy-Jsy/25 15.00 40.00
21 D.Matt Bat-Jkt-Pants/25 40.00 80.00
26 E.Murray Bat-Jsy-Shoe/25 60.00 120.00

2004 Prime Cuts II Timeline Material Trio HOF

OVERALL AU-GU ODDS 1:1
PRINT RUNS B/WN 1-9 COPIES PER
NO PRICING DUE TO SCARCITY

2004 Prime Cuts II Timeline Material Trio HOF Presidential Edition

94 Ty Cobb Bat-Pants-Pants/1

2004 Prime Cuts II Timeline Material Trio MVP

*RET p/r 15-19: .75X TO 2X NBR p/r 20-35
OVERALL AU-GU ODDS 1:1
PRINT RUNS B/WN 1-15 COPIES PER
NO PRICING ON QTY OF 10 OR LESS

2004 Prime Cuts II Timeline Material Trio Stats

*RET p/r 15-19: .75X TO 2X NBR p/r 20-35
OVERALL AU-GU ODDS 1:1
PRINT RUNS B/WN 1-15 COPIES PER
NO PRICING ON QTY OF 10 OR LESS

2004 Prime Cuts II Timeline Material Quad

OVERALL AU-GU ODDS 1:1
PRINT RUNS B/WN 1-25 COPIES PER
NO PRICING ON QTY OF 10 OR LESS
B ='s Bat, BG ='s Btg Glv, FG ='s Fld Glv
H ='s Hat, J ='s Jsy, JK ='s Jkt, P ='s Pants
4 Babe Ruth B-J-J-P/25 600.00 1000.00
91 Ted Williams B-JK-J-J/25 175.00 300.00

2004 Prime Cuts II Timeline Signature Century Gold

OVERALL AU-GU ODDS 1:1
PRINT RUNS B/WN 1-5 COPIES PER
NO PRICING DUE TO SCARCITY

2004 Prime Cuts II Timeline Signature Century Platinum

OVERALL AU-GU ODDS 1:1
STATED PRINT RUN 1 SERIAL #'d SET
NO PRICING DUE TO SCARCITY

2004 Prime Cuts II Timeline Signature Century Silver

OVERALL AU-GU ODDS 1:1
PRINT RUNS B/WN 1-10 COPIES PER
NO PRICING DUE TO SCARCITY

2004 Prime Cuts II Timeline Signature Material Number

OVERALL AU-GU ODDS 1:1
PRINT RUNS B/WN 1-34 COPIES PER
NO PRICING ON QTY OF 11 OR LESS
1 Al Kaline Pants/6
3 Andre Dawson Jsy/8
4 Babe Ruth Jsy/1
5 Barry Zito Jsy/5
6 Bob Feller Pants/19 15.00 40.00
7 Bob Gibson Jsy/25 20.00 50.00
8 Bobby Doerr Jsy/25 12.50 30.00
9 Brooks Robinson Jsy/5
10 Cal Ripken Jsy/1
12 Carl Yastrzemski Jsy/8
13 Carlton Fisk Jsy/5
15 Chipper Jones Jsy/10
17 Dale Murphy Jsy/3
18 Dave Parker Jsy/1
20 Don Drysdale Jsy/1
21 Don Mattingly Pants/23 50.00 100.00
22 Duke Snider Pants/4
23 Dwight Gooden Jsy/5
26 Eddie Murray Jsy/1
27 Enos Slaughter Jsy/1
29 Fergie Jenkins Pants/1
30 Frank Robinson Jsy/5
31 Frank Thomas Jsy/5
32 Frankie Frisch Jkt/1
33 Fred Lynn Jsy/1
34 Gary Carter Jsy/8
35 Gaylord Perry Jsy/10
36 George Brett Jsy/5
37 Greg Maddux Jsy/5
38 Hal Newhouser Jsy/1
39 Harmon Killebrew Jsy/3
41 Hoyt Wilhelm Jsy/5
45 Jeff Bagwell Jsy/5
46 Jim Palmer Jsy/22 20.00 50.00
47 Jimmie Foxx Fld Glv/1
48 Joe Morgan Jsy/8
49 Johnny Bench Jsy/5
50 Johnny Mize Pants/1
51 Jose Canseco Jsy/5
52 Juan Gonzalez Jsy/5
53 Juan Marichal Jsy/27 12.50 30.00
54 Keith Hernandez Jsy/5
54 Keith Hernandez Jsy/5
55 Kirby Puckett Jsy/1
56 Lefty Grove Hat/1
57 Lou Boudreau Jsy/1
58 Lou Brock Jsy/20 20.00 50.00
60 Luis Aparicio Jsy/11
61 Marty Marion Jsy/1
64 Mike Schmidt Jsy/5
66 Nolan Ryan Jsy/34 75.00 150.00
67 Orel Hershiser Jsy/5
68 Orlando Cepeda Pants/1
69 Paul Molitor Jsy/4
70 Pedro Martinez Jsy/1
71 Pee Wee Reese Jsy/1
72 Phil Niekro Jsy/5
73 Phil Rizzuto Pants/10
74 Ralph Kiner Bat/4
75 Randy Johnson Jsy/1
76 Red Schoendienst Jsy/2
77 Reggie Jackson Jsy/9
78 Rickey Henderson Jsy/1
79 Roberto Clemente Jsy/1
80 Robin Yount Jsy/5
81 Rod Carew Jsy/5
82 Roger Clemens Jsy/1
84 Rogers Hornsby Bat/1
86 Ozzie Smith Jsy/1
87 Sammy Sosa Jsy/1
88 Satchel Paige CO Jsy/1
89 Stan Musial Jsy/6
90 Steve Carlton Jsy/32 12.50 30.00
91 Ted Williams Jsy/1
93 Tom Seaver Pants/5
94 Ty Cobb Pants/1
96 Warren Spahn Jsy/1
97 Whitey Ford Jsy/5
98 Willie McCovey Jsy/4
100 Yogi Berra Jsy/8

2004 Prime Cuts II Timeline Signature Material Position

*RET p/r 20-35: .4X TO 1X NBR p/r 20-35
*RET p/r 15-19: .4X TO 1X NBR p/r 15-19
OVERALL AU-GU ODDS 1:1
PRINT RUNS B/WN 1-34 COPIES PER
NO PRICING ON QTY OF 11 OR LESS

2004 Prime Cuts II Timeline Signature Material Prime

OVERALL AU-GU ODDS 1:1
PRINT RUNS B/WN 1-9 COPIES PER
NO PRICING DUE TO SCARCITY

2004 Prime Cuts II Timeline Signature Material Combo

*RET p/r 20-35: .5X TO 1.2X NBR p/r 20-35
OVERALL AU-GU ODDS 1:1
PRINT RUNS B/WN 1-25 COPIES PER
NO PRICING ON QTY OF 11 OR LESS

2004 Prime Cuts II Timeline Signature Material Combo CY

*RET p/r 20-35: .5X TO 1.2X NBR p/r 20-35
OVERALL AU-GU ODDS 1:1
PRINT RUNS B/WN 1-25 COPIES PER
NO PRICING ON QTY OF 5 OR LESS

2004 Prime Cuts II Timeline Signature Material Trio

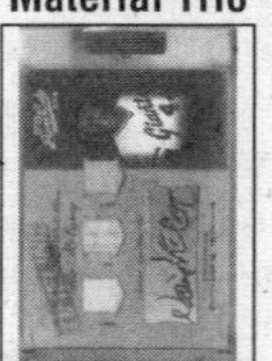

OVERALL AU-GU ODDS 1:1
PRINT RUNS B/WN 1-9 COPIES PER
NO PRICING DUE TO SCARCITY

2004 Prime Cuts II Timeline Signature Material Trio HOF

OVERALL AU-GU ODDS 1:1
PRINT RUNS B/WN 1-9 COPIES PER
NO PRICING DUE TO SCARCITY

2004 Prime Cuts II Timeline Signature Material Trio MVP

OVERALL AU-GU ODDS 1:1
PRINT RUNS B/WN 1-8 COPIES PER
NO PRICING DUE TO SCARCITY

2004 Prime Cuts II Timeline Signature Material Trio Stats

OVERALL AU-GU ODDS 1:1
PRINT RUNS B/WN 1-9 COPIES PER
NO PRICING DUE TO SCARCITY

2004 Prime Cuts II Timeline Signature Material Quad

OVERALL AU-GU ODDS 1:1
PRINT RUNS B/WN 1-25 COPIES PER
NO PRICING ON QTY OF OR LESS
B ='s Bat, BG ='s Btg Glv, FG ='s Fld Glv
H ='s Hat, J ='s Jsy, JK ='s Jkt, P ='s Pants
17 Dale Murphy B-J-J-J/25 60.00 120.00

2005 Prime Cuts

This 100-card set was released in October, 2005. The set was issued in six-card packs which came one pack to a box and 15 boxes to a case. Cards numbered 1-91 feature active players while cards numbered 92 through 100 feature retired players. All cards in this set were issued to stated print runs of 399, 449 or 499 cards issued. We have placed next to the player's name what print run that card is.

COMMON CARD (1-91) 1.50 4.00
COMMON CARD (92-100) 1.50 4.00
PRINT RUNS B/WN 399-499 COPIES PER
1 Vladimir Guerrero Angels/499 2.00 5.00
2 Roger Clemens Astros/499 3.00 8.00
3 Carlos Beltran/499 1.50 4.00
4 Johan Santana/499 2.00 5.00
5 Alfonso Soriano/499 1.50 4.00
6 Derek Jeter/499 4.00 10.00
7 Chipper Jones/499 2.00 5.00
8 David Ortiz/499 2.00 5.00
9 Josh Beckett/499 1.50 4.00
10 Mike Piazza Mets/499 2.00 5.00
11 Alex Rodriguez/449 3.00 8.00
12 Albert Pujols/449 4.00 10.00
13 Mike Sweeney/449 1.50 4.00
14 Miguel Tejada/449 1.50 4.00
15 Barry Zito/449 1.50 4.00
16 Mark Mulder/449 1.50 4.00
17 Tim Hudson/449 1.50 4.00
18 Troy Glaus/449 1.50 4.00
19 Ichiro Suzuki/449 4.00 10.00
20 Ken Griffey Jr./449 3.00 8.00
21 Miguel Cabrera/449 2.00 5.00
22 Jeff Bagwell/449 2.00 5.00
23 Todd Helton/449 2.00 5.00
24 Mark Buehrle/449 1.50 4.00
25 Greg Maddux Cubs/449 3.00 8.00
26 Ivan Rodriguez/449 2.00 5.00
27 Carlos Lee/449 1.50 4.00
28 Nick Johnson/449 1.50 4.00
29 Mike Mussina/449 2.00 5.00
30 Mark Teixeira/499 2.00 5.00
31 Adrian Beltre/499 1.50 4.00
32 Torii Hunter/499 1.50 4.00
33 Jim Edmonds/499 1.50 4.00
34 Manny Ramirez/499 2.00 5.00
35 Pedro Martinez/499 2.00 5.00
36 Jim Thome/499 2.00 5.00
37 Craig Biggio/499 2.00 5.00
38 Garret Anderson/499 1.50 4.00
39 Paul Konerko/499 1.50 4.00
40 Adam Dunn/499 1.50 4.00
41 Brian Roberts/449 1.50 4.00
42 Derrek Lee/449 2.00 5.00
43 Hank Blalock/449 1.50 4.00
44 Justin Morneau/449 1.50 4.00
45 David Wright/449 3.00 8.00
46 Richie Sexson/449 1.50 4.00
47 Ben Sheets/449 1.50 4.00
48 Gary Sheffield/449 1.50 4.00
49 Pat Burrell/449 1.50 4.00
50 Larry Walker/449 2.00 5.00
51 Johnny Damon/449 2.00 5.00
52 Jeff Kent/449 1.50 4.00
53 Aubrey Huff/449 1.50 4.00
54 Shawn Green/449 1.50 4.00
55 Milton Bradley/449 1.50 4.00
56 Magglio Ordonez/449 1.50 4.00
57 J.T. Snow/449 1.50 4.00
58 Scott Rolen/449 2.00 5.00
59 Michael Young/449 1.50 4.00
60 Roy Oswalt/449 1.50 4.00
61 Carlos Zambrano/499 1.50 4.00
62 Dontrelle Willis/499 1.50 4.00
63 Curt Schilling/499 2.00 5.00
64 Roy Halladay/499 1.50 4.00
65 Eric Chavez/499 1.50 4.00
66 Randy Johnson Yanks/499 2.00 5.00
67 Mark Prior/499 2.00 5.00
68 Victor Martinez/399 1.50 4.00
69 Sammy Sosa O's/399 2.00 5.00
70 Lance Berkman/399 1.50 4.00
71 Jeremy Bonderman/399 1.50 4.00
72 Frank Thomas/399 2.00 5.00
73 Jake Peavy/399 1.50 4.00
74 Jason Schmidt/399 1.50 4.00
75 Carlos Delgado/399 1.50 4.00
76 Andruw Jones/399 2.00 5.00
77 Vernon Wells/399 1.50 4.00
78 Sean Casey/399 1.50 4.00
79 Jason Bay/399 1.50 4.00
80 Hideki Matsui/399 3.00 8.00
81 Jason Varitek/399 2.00 5.00
82 Kerry Wood/399 1.50 4.00
83 Moises Alou/399 1.50 4.00
84 Joe Mauer/399 2.00 5.00
85 Rafael Palmeiro/399 2.00 5.00
86 Mike Piazza Dgr/399 2.00 5.00
87 Sammy Sosa Cubs/399 2.00 5.00
88 Randy Johnson Astros/399 2.00 5.00
89 Vladimir Guerrero Expos/399 2.00 5.00
90 Greg Maddux Braves/399 3.00 8.00
91 Roger Clemens Yanks/399 3.00 8.00
92 Nolan Ryan/399 3.00 8.00
93 Cal Ripken/399 5.00 12.00
94 Tony Gwynn/399 2.50 6.00
95 Wade Boggs/449 2.00 5.00
96 Ryne Sandberg/449 3.00 8.00
97 Dale Murphy/449 2.00 5.00
98 Mike Schmidt/449 3.00 8.00
99 Don Mattingly/449 3.00 8.00
100 Willie Mays/449 2.50 6.00

2005 Prime Cuts Century Gold

*GOLD 1-91: 1X TO 2.5X BASIC
*GOLD 92-100: 1X TO 2.5X BASIC
RANDOM INSERTS IN PACKS
STATED PRINT RUN 25 SERIAL #'d SETS

2005 Prime Cuts Century Platinum

RANDOM INSERTS IN PACKS
STATED PRINT RUN 1 SERIAL #'d SET
NO PRICING DUE TO SCARCITY

2005 Prime Cuts Century Silver

*SILVER 1-91: .6X TO 1.5X BASIC
*SILVER 92-100: .6X TO 1.5X BASIC
RANDOM INSERTS IN PACKS
STATED PRINT RUN 50 SERIAL #'d SETS

2005 Prime Cuts Material Bat

*1-91 p/r 48-50: .4X TO 1X JSY p/r 50
*92-100 p/r 50: .4X TO 1X JSY p/r 50
OVERALL AU-GU ODDS ONE PER PACK
PRINT RUNS B/WN 1-50 COPIES PER
NO PRICING ON QTY OF 7 OR LESS
1 Vladimir Guerrero Angels/50 5.00 12.00
3 Carlos Beltran/50 3.00 8.00
16 Mark Mulder/50 3.00 8.00
17 Tim Hudson/30 4.00 10.00
18 Troy Glaus/50 3.00 8.00

24 Mark Buehrle/50 3.00 8.00
26 Ivan Rodriguez/50 4.00 10.00
27 Carlos Lee/50 3.00 8.00
28 Nick Johnson/50 3.00 8.00
29 Mike Mussina/48 4.00 10.00
35 Pedro Martinez/50 4.00 10.00
40 Adam Dunn/50 3.00 8.00
46 Richie Sexson/50 3.00 8.00
50 Larry Walker/18 6.00 15.00
52 Jeff Kent/50 3.00 8.00
54 Shawn Green/50 3.00 8.00
56 Magglio Ordonez/50 3.00 8.00
66 Randy Johnson Yanks/50 5.00 12.00
69 Sammy Sosa O's/50 5.00 12.00
81 Jason Varitek/50 5.00 12.00
83 Moises Alou/50 3.00 8.00
95 Wade Boggs/50 5.00 12.00

2005 Prime Cuts Material Jersey

OVERALL AU-GU ODDS ONE PER PACK
PRINT RUNS B/WN 11-50 COPIES PER
NO PRICING ON QTY OF 13 OR LESS
2 Roger Clemens Astros/50 6.00 15.00
4 Johan Santana/50 5.00 12.00
5 Alfonso Soriano/50 3.00 8.00
7 Chipper Jones/50 5.00 12.00
8 David Ortiz/50 4.00 10.00
9 Josh Beckett/50 3.00 8.00
10 Mike Piazza Mets/50 5.00 12.00
12 Albert Pujols/50 8.00 20.00
13 Mike Sweeney/50 3.00 8.00
14 Miguel Tejada/50 3.00 8.00
15 Barry Zito/50 3.00 8.00
21 Miguel Cabrera/50 4.00 10.00
22 Jeff Bagwell/50 4.00 10.00
23 Todd Helton/50 4.00 10.00
24 Mark Buehrle/13
25 Greg Maddux Cubs/50 6.00 15.00
26 Ivan Rodriguez/27 5.00 12.00
29 Mike Mussina/50 4.00 10.00
30 Mark Teixeira/50 4.00 10.00
31 Adrian Beltre/50 3.00 8.00
32 Torii Hunter/50 3.00 8.00
33 Jim Edmonds/50 3.00 8.00
34 Manny Ramirez/50 4.00 10.00
36 Jim Thome/50 4.00 10.00
37 Craig Biggio/50 4.00 10.00
38 Garret Anderson/50 3.00 8.00
39 Paul Konerko/50 3.00 8.00
40 Adam Dunn/11
41 Brian Roberts/50 3.00 8.00
42 Derrek Lee/50 4.00 10.00
43 Hank Blalock/50 3.00 8.00
44 Justin Morneau/50 3.00 8.00
45 David Wright/50 6.00 15.00
47 Ben Sheets/50 3.00 8.00
48 Gary Sheffield/50 3.00 8.00
49 Pat Burrell/50 3.00 8.00
50 Larry Walker/50 4.00 10.00
53 Aubrey Huff/50 3.00 8.00
57 J.T. Snow/50 3.00 8.00
58 Scott Rolen/50 4.00 10.00
59 Michael Young/50 3.00 8.00
60 Roy Oswalt/50 3.00 8.00
61 Carlos Zambrano/50 3.00 8.00
62 Dontrelle Willis/50 3.00 8.00
63 Curt Schilling/50 4.00 10.00
64 Roy Halladay/22 4.00 10.00
65 Eric Chavez/50 3.00 8.00
67 Mark Prior/50 4.00 10.00
68 Victor Martinez/50 3.00 8.00
70 Lance Berkman/50 3.00 8.00
72 Frank Thomas/50 5.00 12.00
75 Carlos Delgado/50 3.00 8.00
76 Andruw Jones/50 4.00 10.00
77 Vernon Wells/50 3.00 8.00
78 Sean Casey/50 3.00 8.00
79 Jason Bay/50 3.00 8.00
80 Hideki Matsui/50 12.50 30.00
82 Kerry Wood/50 3.00 8.00
85 Rafael Palmeiro/50 4.00 10.00
86 Mike Piazza Dgr/50 5.00 12.00
87 Sammy Sosa Cubs/50 5.00 12.00
88 Randy Johnson Astros/50 5.00 12.00
89 Vladimir Guerrero Expos/50 5.00 12.00
90 Greg Maddux Braves/50 6.00 15.00
91 Roger Clemens Yanks/50 6.00 15.00
92 Nolan Ryan/38 10.00 25.00
93 Cal Ripken/50 10.00 25.00
94 Tony Gwynn/50 6.00 15.00
96 Ryne Sandberg/50 8.00 20.00
97 Dale Murphy/50 5.00 12.00
98 Mike Schmidt/50 6.00 15.00
99 Don Mattingly/50 6.00 15.00
100 Willie Mays/50 10.00 25.00

2005 Prime Cuts Material Jersey Number

*1-91 p/r 50: .4X TO 1X JSY p/r 50
*1-91 p/r 50: .3X TO .8X JSY p/r 27
*92-100 p/r 50: .4X TO 1X JSY p/r 50
STATED PRINT RUN 50 SERIAL #'d SETS

PRIME PRINT RUN B/WN 5-10 COPIES PER
NO PRIME PRICING DUE TO SCARCITY
OVERALL AU-GU ODDS ONE PER PACK
1 Vladimir Guerrero Angels 5.00 12.00
24 Mark Buehrle 3.00 8.00
40 Adam Dunn 3.00 8.00

2005 Prime Cuts Material Jersey Position

*1-91 p/r 50: .4X TO 1X JSY p/r 50
*1-91 p/r 50: .3X TO .8X JSY p/r 22-27
*1-91 p/r 25: .5X TO 1.2X JSY p/r 50
*92-100 p/r 50: .4X TO 1X JSY p/r 38-50
OVERALL AU-GU ODDS ONE PER PACK
PRINT RUNS B/WN 25-50 COPIES PER
1 Vladimir Guerrero Angels/50 5.00 12.00
24 Mark Buehrle/50 3.00 8.00
40 Adam Dunn/50 3.00 8.00
71 Jeremy Bonderman/50 3.00 8.00

2005 Prime Cuts Material Combo

*1-91 p/r 50: .5X TO 1.2X JSY p/r 50
*1-91 p/r 25: .6X TO 1.5X JSY p/r 50
*1-91 p/r 25: .5X TO 1.2X JSY p/r 22-27
*92-100 p/r 50: .5X TO 1.2X JSY p/r 50
PRINT RUNS B/WN 1-50 COPIES PER
NO PRICING ON QTY OF 10 OR LESS
PRIME PRINT RUN B/WN 1-10 COPIES PER
NO PRIME PRICING DUE TO SCARCITY
OVERALL AU-GU ODDS ONE PER PACK
24 Mark Buehrle Bat-Jsy/50 4.00 10.00
40 Adam Dunn Bat-Jsy/18 6.00 15.00
51 Johnny Damon Bat-Jsy/15 8.00 20.00

2005 Prime Cuts Signature Century Gold

*GOLD p/r 25: .4X TO 1X SILVER p/r 25
OVERALL AU-GU ODDS ONE PER PACK
PRINT RUNS B/WN 1-25 COPIES PER
NO PRICING ON QTY OF 10 OR LESS

2005 Prime Cuts Signature Century Platinum

OVERALL AU-GU ODDS ONE PER PACK
STATED PRINT RUN 1 SERIAL #'d SET
NO PRICING DUE TO SCARCITY

2005 Prime Cuts Signature Century Silver

OVERALL AU-GU ODDS ONE PER PACK
PRINT RUNS B/WN 1-25 COPIES PER
NO PRICING ON QTY OF 10 OR LESS
2 Roger Clemens Astros/10
3 Carlos Beltran/25 10.00 25.00
4 Johan Santana/25 15.00 40.00
5 Alfonso Soriano/25 10.00 25.00
7 Chipper Jones/10
8 David Ortiz/5
9 Josh Beckett/5

12 Albert Pujols/5
15 Barry Zito/5
16 Mark Mulder/10
17 Tim Hudson/10
21 Miguel Cabrera/25 15.00 40.00
22 Jeff Bagwell/10
23 Todd Helton/10
24 Mark Buehrle/5
25 Greg Maddux Cubs/10
27 Carlos Lee/5
28 Nick Johnson/5
30 Mark Teixeira/10
31 Adrian Beltre/5
32 Torii Hunter/5
33 Jim Edmonds/5
34 Manny Ramirez/10
35 Pedro Martinez/10
37 Craig Biggio/5
38 Garret Anderson/5
39 Paul Konerko/5
42 Derrek Lee/5
44 Justin Morneau/5
45 David Wright/5
47 Ben Sheets/5
48 Gary Sheffield/5
53 Aubrey Huff/5
54 Shawn Green/5
55 Milton Bradley/5
56 Magglio Ordonez/5
58 Scott Rolen/5
59 Michael Young/5
60 Roy Oswalt/5
63 Curt Schilling/5
64 Roy Halladay/5
65 Eric Chavez/5
66 Randy Johnson Yanks/5
67 Mark Prior/5
68 Victor Martinez/5
69 Sammy Sosa O's/1
71 Jeremy Bonderman/5
72 Frank Thomas/5
73 Jake Peavy/5
78 Sean Casey/5
79 Jason Bay/5
87 Sammy Sosa Cubs/1
88 Randy Johnson Astros/5
90 Greg Maddux Braves/5
91 Roger Clemens Yanks/5
92 Nolan Ryan/10
93 Cal Ripken/1
94 Tony Gwynn/10
95 Wade Boggs/10
96 Ryne Sandberg/10
97 Dale Murphy/10
98 Mike Schmidt/10
99 Don Mattingly/10
100 Willie Mays/5

2005 Prime Cuts Signature Material Jersey Number

PRINT RUNS B/WN 1-10 COPIES PER
PRIME PRINT RUN B/WN 1-10 COPIES PER
OVERALL AU-GU ODDS ONE PER PACK
NO PRICING DUE TO SCARCITY

2005 Prime Cuts Signature Material Combo

PRINT RUNS B/WN 1-10 COPIES PER
PRIME PRINT RUN B/WN 1-10 COPIES PER
OVERALL AU-GU ODDS ONE PER PACK
NO PRICING DUE TO SCARCITY

2005 Prime Cuts MLB Icons

STATED PRINT RUN 100 SERIAL #'d SETS
*GOLD: .75X TO 2X BASIC
GOLD PRINT RUN 25 SERIAL #'d SETS
PLATINUM PRINT RUN 1 SERIAL #'d SET
NO PLATINUM PRICING DUE TO SCARCITY
*SILVER: .5X TO 1.2X BASIC
SILVER PRINT RUN 50 SERIAL #'d SETS
RANDOM INSERTS IN PACKS
1 Andre Dawson 2.00 5.00
2 Babe Ruth 4.00 10.00
3 Billy Williams 2.00 5.00
4 Bob Feller 2.00 5.00
5 Bob Gibson 2.50 6.00
6 Bobby Doerr 2.00 5.00
7 Brooks Robinson 2.50 6.00
8 Burleigh Grimes 2.00 5.00
9 Cal Ripken 6.00 15.00
10 Carlton Fisk 2.50 6.00
11 Dale Murphy 2.50 6.00
12 Don Mattingly 4.00 10.00
13 Don Sutton 2.00 5.00
14 Ted Williams 4.00 10.00
15 Ernie Banks 2.50 6.00
16 Frank Robinson 2.00 5.00
17 Gary Carter 2.00 5.00
18 Gaylord Perry 2.00 5.00
19 Hank Aaron 3.00 8.00
20 Harmon Killebrew 2.50 6.00
21 Jim Palmer 2.00 5.00
22 Jim Thorpe 2.50 6.00
23 Babe Ruth 4.00 10.00
24 Johnny Bench 2.50 6.00
25 Juan Marichal 2.00 5.00
26 Kirby Puckett 2.50 6.00
27 Lou Brock 2.50 6.00
28 Luis Aparicio 2.00 5.00
29 Marty Marion 2.00 5.00
30 Mike Schmidt 4.00 10.00
31 Nolan Ryan 4.00 10.00
32 Red Schoendienst 2.00 5.00
33 Rickey Henderson 2.50 6.00
34 Roberto Clemente 6.00 15.00
35 Rod Carew 2.50 6.00
36 Sandy Koufax 10.00 25.00
37 Stan Musial 3.00 8.00
38 Steve Carlton 2.00 5.00
39 Steve Garvey 2.00 5.00
40 Ted Williams 4.00 10.00
41 Tom Seaver 2.50 6.00
42 Tony Gwynn 3.00 8.00
43 Whitey Ford 2.50 6.00
44 Willie Mays 3.00 8.00
45 Willie McCovey 2.50 6.00

2005 Prime Cuts MLB Icons Material Bat

*BAT p/r 50: .4X TO 1X JSY p/r 50
*BAT p/r 50: .3X TO .8X JSY p/r 24-35
OVERALL AU-GU ODDS ONE PER PACK
PRINT RUNS B/WN 13-50 COPIES PER
NO PRICING ON QTY OF 13
2 Babe Ruth/50 100.00 175.00
7 Brooks Robinson/50 5.00 12.00
23 Babe Ruth/50 100.00 175.00
26 Kirby Puckett/50 6.00 15.00
27 Lou Brock/50 5.00 12.00
28 Luis Aparicio/50 4.00 10.00
32 Red Schoendienst/50 4.00 10.00
34 Roberto Clemente/50 30.00 60.00

2005 Prime Cuts MLB Icons Material Jersey

OVERALL AU-GU ODDS ONE PER PACK
PRINT RUNS B/WN 1-50 COPIES PER
NO PRICING ON QTY OF 12 OR LESS
1 Andre Dawson/50 4.00 10.00
2 Babe Ruth/25 200.00 300.00
3 Billy Williams/50 4.00 10.00
4 Bob Feller/8
5 Bob Gibson/25 6.00 15.00
6 Bobby Doerr Pants/50 4.00 10.00
7 Brooks Robinson/11
8 Burleigh Grimes Pants/50 30.00 60.00
9 Cal Ripken/50 10.00 25.00
10 Carlton Fisk/50 5.00 12.00
11 Dale Murphy/50 5.00 12.00
12 Don Mattingly/50 6.00 15.00
13 Don Sutton/24 5.00 12.00
14 Ted Williams/25 30.00 60.00
15 Ernie Banks/25 8.00 20.00
16 Frank Robinson/25 5.00 12.00
17 Gary Carter/50 4.00 10.00
18 Gaylord Perry/50 4.00 10.00
19 Hank Aaron/25 20.00 50.00
20 Harmon Killebrew/50 6.00 15.00
22 Jim Thorpe/50 100.00 175.00
23 Babe Ruth/25 200.00 300.00
24 Johnny Bench/50 6.00 15.00
25 Juan Marichal/50 4.00 10.00
26 Kirby Puckett/12
28 Luis Aparicio/1
30 Mike Schmidt/35 8.00 20.00
31 Nolan Ryan Pants/50 10.00 25.00
32 Red Schoendienst/10
33 Rickey Henderson/50 6.00 15.00
34 Roberto Clemente/5
35 Rod Carew/50 5.00 12.00
36 Sandy Koufax/5
37 Stan Musial/50 8.00 20.00
38 Steve Carlton/30 5.00 12.00
39 Steve Garvey/50 4.00 10.00
40 Ted Williams/25 30.00 60.00
41 Tom Seaver/50 5.00 12.00
42 Tony Gwynn/50 6.00 15.00
43 Whitey Ford/50 5.00 12.00
44 Willie Mays/50 10.00 25.00
45 Willie McCovey/50 5.00 12.00

2005 Prime Cuts MLB Icons Material Jersey Number

*NBR p/r 25: .5X TO 1.2X JSY p/r 50
*NBR p/r 25: .4X TO 1X JSY p/r 25
OVERALL AU-GU ODDS ONE PER PACK
PRINT RUNS B/WN 5-25 COPIES PER
NO PRICING ON QTY OF 10 OR LESS
23 Babe Ruth/25 200.00 300.00
36 Sandy Koufax/25 75.00 150.00

2005 Prime Cuts MLB Icons Material Jersey Number Prime

*PRIME p/r 20-25: .75X TO 2X JSY p/r 50
*PRIME p/r 20-25: .6X TO 1.5X JSY p/r 24-35
*PRIME p/r 15: 1X TO 2.5X JSY p/r 50
OVERALL AU-GU ODDS ONE PER PACK
PRINT RUNS B/WN 1-25 COPIES PER
NO PRICING ON QTY OF 10 OR LESS

2005 Prime Cuts MLB Icons Material Jersey Position

*POS p/r 50: .4X TO 1X JSY p/r 50
*POS p/r 50: .3X TO .8X JSY p/r 24-35
OVERALL AU-GU ODDS ONE PER PACK
PRINT RUNS B/WN 25-50 COPIES PER
2 Babe Ruth/50 175.00 300.00
4 Bob Feller Pants/50 4.00 10.00
22 Jim Thorpe/50 100.00 175.00
23 Babe Ruth/50 175.00 300.00
28 Luis Aparicio/25 5.00 12.00
29 Marty Marion/50 4.00 10.00
34 Roberto Clemente/25 40.00 80.00

2005 Prime Cuts MLB Icons Material Combo

*COMBO p/r 25: .6X TO 1.5X JSY p/r 50
*COMBO p/r 25: .5X TO 1.2X JSY p/r 25
PRINT RUNS B/WN 1-25 COPIES PER
NO PRICING ON QTY OF 10 OR LESS
PRIME PRINT RUN B/WN 1-10 COPIES PER
NO PRIME PRICING DUE TO SCARCITY
OVERALL AU-GU ODDS ONE PER PACK

2005 Prime Cuts MLB Icons Material Trio MLB

PRINT RUNS B/WN 1-25 COPIES PER
NO PRICING ON QTY OF 10 OR LESS
PRIME PRINT RUN B/WN 1-10 COPIES PER
NO PRIME PRICING DUE TO SCARCITY
OVERALL AU-GU ODDS ONE PER PACK
B=Bat; BG=Btg Glv; H=Hat; J=Jsy; JK=Jkt
P=Pants; S=Shoe
22 Jim Thorpe J-J-J/25 200.00 300.00
34 Roberto Clemente B-B-H/25 75.00 150.00

2005 Prime Cuts MLB Icons Signature Century Gold

OVERALL AU-GU ODDS ONE PER PACK
PRINT RUNS B/WN 1-15 COPIES PER
NO PRICING ON QTY OF 10 OR LESS
36 Sandy Koufax/15 300.00 400.00

2005 Prime Cuts MLB Icons Signature Century Platinum

OVERALL AU-GU ODDS ONE PER PACK
STATED PRINT RUN 1 SERIAL #'d SET
NO PRICING DUE TO SCARCITY

2005 Prime Cuts MLB Icons Signature Century Silver

OVERALL AU-GU ODDS ONE PER BOX
PRINT RUNS B/WN 1-32 COPIES PER
NO PRICING ON QTY OF 10 OR LESS
1 Andre Dawson/10
3 Billy Williams/25 10.00 25.00
4 Bob Feller/25 10.00 25.00
5 Bob Gibson/25 15.00 40.00
6 Bobby Doerr/25 10.00 25.00
7 Brooks Robinson/25 15.00 40.00
9 Cal Ripken/1
10 Carlton Fisk/25 15.00 40.00
11 Dale Murphy/10
12 Don Mattingly/20 30.00 60.00
13 Don Sutton/25 10.00 25.00
15 Ernie Banks/20 20.00 50.00
16 Frank Robinson/25 10.00 25.00
17 Gary Carter/25 10.00 25.00
18 Gaylord Perry/25 10.00 25.00
19 Hank Aaron/15 125.00 200.00
20 Harmon Killebrew/25 20.00 50.00
21 Jim Palmer/25 10.00 25.00
24 Johnny Bench/25 20.00 50.00
25 Juan Marichal/25 10.00 25.00
26 Kirby Puckett/25 50.00 100.00
27 Lou Brock/25 15.00 40.00
28 Luis Aparicio/25 10.00 25.00
29 Marty Marion/25 10.00 25.00
30 Mike Schmidt/25 30.00 60.00
31 Nolan Ryan/25 50.00 100.00
32 Red Schoendienst/25 10.00 25.00
33 Rickey Henderson/10
35 Rod Carew/25 15.00 40.00
36 Sandy Koufax/32 225.00 300.00
37 Stan Musial/25 30.00 60.00
38 Steve Carlton/25 10.00 25.00
39 Steve Garvey/10
41 Tom Seaver/25 20.00 50.00
42 Tony Gwynn/25 20.00 50.00
43 Whitey Ford/25 15.00 40.00
44 Willie Mays/10
45 Willie McCovey/25 15.00 40.00

2005 Prime Cuts MLB Icons Signature Material Jersey Number

OVERALL AU-GU ODDS ONE PER BOX
PRINT RUNS B/WN 1-25 COPIES PER
NO PRICING ON QTY OF 10 OR LESS
9 Cal Ripken/25 75.00 150.00

2005 Prime Cuts MLB Icons Signature Material Jersey Number Prime

*PRIME p/r 20: .6X TO 1.5X SILV p/r 20-32
*PRIME p/r 15: .75X TO 2X SILV p/r 20-32
OVERALL AU-GU ODDS ONE PER PACK
PRINT RUNS B/WN 1-25 COPIES PER
NO PRICING ON QTY OF 10 OR LESS
9 Cal Ripken/25 75.00 150.00

2005 Prime Cuts MLB Icons Signature Material Combo

*COMBO p/r 25: .5X TO 1.2X SILV p/r 20-32
PRINT RUNS B/WN 1-25 COPIES PER
NO PRICING ON QTY OF 10 OR LESS
PRIME PRINT RUN B/WN 1-10 COPIES PER
NO PRIME PRICING DUE TO SCARCITY
OVERALL AU-GU ODDS ONE PER PACK
11 Dale Murphy Bat-Jsy/25 20.00 50.00

2005 Prime Cuts MLB Icons Signature Material Trio MLB

PRINT RUNS B/WN 1-10 COPIES PER
NO PRICING DUE TO SCARCITY
PRIME PRINT RUN B/WN 1-10 COPIES PER
NO PRIME PRICING DUE TO SCARCITY
OVERALL AU-GU ODDS ONE PER PACK

2005 Prime Cuts Souvenir Cuts

OVERALL AU-GU ODDS ONE PER PACK
PRINT RUNS B/WN 1-50 COPIES PER
NO PRICING ON QTY OF 12 OR LESS
1 Tony Lazzeri/2
2 Al Barlick/7
3 Al Lopez/50 60.00 120.00
4 Bill Terry/50 100.00 175.00
5 Billy Herman/4
6 Buck Leonard/50 100.00 175.00
7 Bucky Harris/3
8 Cal Hubbard/26 75.00 150.00
9 Carl Hubbell/50 75.00 150.00
10 Charlie Gehringer/50 75.00 150.00
11 Connie Mack/3
12 Cool Papa Bell/5
13 David Bancroft/2
14 Earl Averill/47 60.00 120.00
15 Earle Combs/3
16 Edd Roush/48 60.00 120.00
17 Eddie Collins/1
18 Sam Rice/27 125.00 200.00
19 Ernie Lombardi/50 75.00 150.00
20 Ford Frick/50 100.00 175.00
21 Gabby Hartnett/50 150.00 250.00
22 George Kelly/50 75.00 150.00
23 Grover C. Alexander/1
24 Harry Caray/1
25 Heinie Manush/33 125.00 200.00
26 Hugh Duffy/1
27 Joe McCarthy/44 125.00 200.00
28 Joe Medwick/50 125.00 200.00
29 Joe Sewell/4
31 Kenesaw Landis/1
32 Lefty Gomez/32 100.00 175.00
33 Leo Durocher/1
34 Leon Day/1
35 Luke Appling/35 75.00 150.00
36 Max Carey/2
37 Mel Allen/1
38 Paul Waner/1
39 Pie Traynor/1

40 Ray Schalk/2
41 Sam Crawford/1
42 Ted Lyons/2
43 Waite Hoyt/50 75.00 150.00
44 Walter Alston/22 125.00 200.00
45 William Harridge/1
46 Jocko Conlan/35 75.00 150.00
47 Lloyd Waner/50 100.00 175.00
48 Rube Marquard/50 75.00 150.00
49 Hank Greenberg/43 200.00 350.00
50 Travis Jackson/50 75.00 150.00
51 Joe Cronin/50 75.00 150.00
52 Bill Dickey/26 125.00 200.00
53 Red Ruffing/26 175.00 300.00
54 Jesse Haines/50 150.00 250.00
55 Chick Hafey/50 125.00 200.00
56 Fred Lindstrom/3
57 Happy Chandler /1
58 Stanley Coveleski/4
60 Larry Doby/1
62 Red Faber/1
63 Rick Ferrell/1
64 Frankie Frisch/12
65 Warren Giles /1
66 Goose Goslin/1
67 Harry Hooper/3
68 Judy Johnson/2
69 Bob Lemon/2
73 Branch Rickey/1
74 Eppa Rixey/1
75 Warren Spahn/1
76 Bill Veeck/1
77 Ed Walsh/1
79 Zack Wheat/1
81 Harvey Haddix/1
82 Johnny Vander Meer/1
83 Ted Kluszewski/1
86 Joe Wood/2
87 Joe Dugan/1
88 Bob Meusel/1
89 Stan Hack/1
90 Joe Gordon/1
91 Charlie Keller/1
92 Allie Reynolds/1
93 Carl Furillo/1
94 Elston Howard/1
95 Burleigh Grimes/2
96 Catfish Hunter/2
97 Early Wynn/2
98 Sal Maglie/1
99 Victor Wertz/1
100 Elmer Flick/2
101 Enos Slaughter/3
102 Hal Newhouser/24 75.00 150.00
103 Hoyt Wilhelm/9
104 Lou Boudreau/48 60.00 120.00
105 Pee Wee Reese/28 150.00 250.00
106 Richie Ashburn/2
107 Roberto Clemente/2
108 Ted Williams/9
109 Willie Stargell/23 75.00 150.00
110 Roger Maris/3
111 Buck Leonard/50 100.00 175.00
112 Carl Hubbell/50 75.00 150.00
113 Charlie Gehringer/40 75.00 150.00
114 Gabby Hartnett/12
115 Joe Medwick/32 125.00 200.00
116 Lloyd Waner/10
117 Rube Marquard/37 75.00 150.00
118 Travis Jackson/7
119 Joe Cronin/3
120 Jesse Haines/27 150.00 250.00
121 Chick Hafey/25 125.00 200.00

2005 Prime Cuts Timeline

STATED PRINT RUN 100 SERIAL #'d SETS
*GOLD: .75X TO 2X BASIC
GOLD PRINT RUN 25 SERIAL #'d SETS
PLATINUM PRINT RUN 1 SERIAL #'d SET
NO PLATINUM PRICING DUE TO SCARCITY
*SILVER: .5X TO 1.2X BASIC
SILVER PRINT RUN 50 SERIAL #'d SETS
RANDOM INSERTS IN PACKS
1 Dale Murphy 2.50 6.00
2 Dennis Eckersley 2.00 5.00
3 Fergie Jenkins 2.00 5.00
4 Greg Maddux 4.00 10.00
5 Orel Hershiser 2.00 5.00
6 Stan Musial 3.00 8.00
7 Don Mattingly 4.00 10.00
8 Willie Mays NY Giants 3.00 8.00
9 Ozzie Smith 3.00 8.00
10 Roger Clemens Yanks 4.00 10.00
11 Cal Ripken 6.00 15.00
12 Duke Snider 2.50 6.00
13 Hank Aaron 3.00 8.00
14 Lou Brock 2.50 6.00
15 Paul Molitor 2.00 5.00
16 Ted Williams 4.00 10.00
17 Dwight Gooden 2.00 5.00
18 Frankie Frisch 2.00 5.00
19 Pedro Martinez 2.50 6.00
20 Robin Yount 2.50 6.00
21 Babe Ruth 4.00 10.00
22 Carl Yastrzemski 3.00 8.00
23 Rod Carew 2.50 6.00
24 Willie Mays SF Giants 3.00 8.00
25 Eddie Murray 2.50 6.00
26 Ivan Rodriguez 2.50 6.00
27 Roger Clemens Sox 4.00 10.00
28 Willie McCovey 2.50 6.00
29 Bob Feller 2.00 5.00
30 Catfish Hunter 2.50 6.00
31 Gaylord Perry 2.00 5.00
32 Wade Boggs 2.50 6.00
33 Phil Rizzuto 2.50 6.00
34 Roger Maris 2.50 6.00
35 Bob Gibson 2.50 6.00
36 Chipper Jones 2.50 6.00
37 Ernie Banks 2.50 6.00
38 George Brett 4.00 10.00
39 Keith Hernandez 2.00 5.00
40 Ryne Sandberg 4.00 10.00
41 Reggie Jackson 2.50 6.00
42 Sandy Koufax 10.00 25.00
43 Warren Spahn 2.50 6.00
44 Nolan Ryan Mets 4.00 10.00
45 Yogi Berra 2.50 6.00
46 Cal Ripken 6.00 15.00
47 Willie Mays NY Mets 3.00 8.00
48 Nolan Ryan Angels 4.00 10.00
49 Stan Musial 3.00 8.00
50 Roberto Clemente 6.00 15.00

2005 Prime Cuts Timeline Material Bat

*BAT p/r 50: .4X TO 1X JSY p/r 49-50
*BAT p/r 50: .3X TO .8X JSY p/r 24-35
*BAT p/r 22: .4X TO 1X JSY p/r 24-35
*BAT p/r 15: .6X TO 1.5X JSY p/r 49-50
OVERALL AU-GU ODDS ONE PER PACK
PRINT RUNS B/WN 3-50 COPIES PER
NO PRICING ON QTY OF 3
8 Willie Mays NY Giants/50 10.00 25.00
14 Lou Brock/50 5.00 12.00
21 Babe Ruth/50 100.00 175.00
50 Roberto Clemente/50 30.00 60.00

2005 Prime Cuts Timeline Material Jersey

OVERALL AU-GU ODDS ONE PER PACK
PRINT RUNS B/WN 5-50 COPIES PER
NO PRICING ON QTY OF 5
1 Dale Murphy/50 5.00 12.00
2 Dennis Eckersley/50 4.00 10.00
3 Fergie Jenkins/50 4.00 10.00
4 Greg Maddux/50 6.00 15.00
5 Orel Hershiser/50 4.00 10.00
6 Stan Musial/50 8.00 20.00
7 Don Mattingly/49 6.00 15.00
9 Ozzie Smith/17 12.50 30.00
10 Roger Clemens Yanks/50 6.00 15.00
11 Cal Ripken/50 10.00 25.00
12 Duke Snider/24 6.00 15.00
13 Hank Aaron/50 15.00 40.00
15 Paul Molitor/50 4.00 10.00
16 Ted Williams/50 20.00 50.00
17 Dwight Gooden/50 4.00 10.00
19 Pedro Martinez/50 5.00 12.00
20 Robin Yount/50 6.00 15.00
21 Babe Ruth/25 250.00 350.00
22 Carl Yastrzemski/50 8.00 20.00
23 Rod Carew/50 5.00 12.00
24 Willie Mays SF Giants/50 10.00 25.00
25 Eddie Murray/50 6.00 15.00
26 Ivan Rodriguez/50 5.00 12.00
27 Roger Clemens Sox/50 6.00 15.00
28 Willie McCovey/50 5.00 12.00
32 Wade Boggs/50 5.00 12.00
33 Phil Rizzuto/50 5.00 12.00
34 Roger Maris/50 15.00 40.00
35 Bob Gibson/50 5.00 12.00
36 Chipper Jones/50 6.00 15.00
37 Ernie Banks/50 6.00 15.00
38 George Brett/50 6.00 15.00
39 Keith Hernandez/5
40 Ryne Sandberg/50 8.00 20.00
41 Reggie Jackson/35 6.00 15.00
42 Sandy Koufax/5
43 Warren Spahn/50 5.00 12.00
44 Nolan Ryan Mets/50 10.00 25.00
45 Yogi Berra/50 6.00 15.00
46 Cal Ripken/50 10.00 25.00
47 Willie Mays NY Mets/50 10.00 25.00
48 Nolan Ryan Angels/50 10.00 25.00
49 Stan Musial/25 10.00 25.00

2005 Prime Cuts Timeline Material Jersey Number Prime

*PRIME p/r 25: .75X TO 2X JSY p/r 49-50
*PRIME p/r 15: .6X TO 1.5X JSY p/r 17
PRINT RUNS B/WN 1-25 COPIES PER
NO PRICING ON QTY OF 10 OR LESS
NBR PRINT RUN B/WN 1-10 COPIES PER
NO NUMBER PRICING DUE TO SCARCITY
OVERALL AU-GU ODDS ONE PER PACK
39 Keith Hernandez/25 8.00 20.00

2005 Prime Cuts Timeline Material Jersey Position

*POS p/r 23-25: .5X TO 1.2X JSY p/r 49-50
*POS p/r 23-25: .4X TO 1X JSY p/r 24-35
OVERALL AU-GU ODDS ONE PER PACK
PRINT RUNS B/WN 10-25 COPIES PER
NO PRICING ON QTY OF 12 OR LESS
14 Lou Brock Jkt/25 6.00 15.00
18 Frankie Frisch Jkt/23 8.00 20.00
21 Babe Ruth/25 200.00 300.00
30 Catfish Hunter/18 6.00 15.00
39 Keith Hernandez/25 5.00 12.00

2005 Prime Cuts Timeline Material Combo

*COMBO p/r 25: .6X TO 1.5X JSY p/r 49-50
*COMBO p/r 25: .5X TO 1.2X JSY p/r 24-35
OVERALL AU-GU ODDS ONE PER PACK
PRINT RUNS B/WN 1-25 COPIES PER
NO PRICING ON QTY OF 10 OR LESS
21 Babe Ruth Bat-Jsy/25 350.00 450.00

2005 Prime Cuts Timeline Material Combo Prime

*PRIME p/r 25: .75X TO 2X JSY p/r 49-50
OVERALL AU-GU ODDS ONE PER PACK
PRINT RUNS B/WN 1-25 COPIES PER
NO PRICING ON QTY OF 10 OR LESS
14 Lou Brock Bat-Jsy/25 12.50 30.00
39 Keith Hernandez Bat-Jsy/15 12.50 30.00

2005 Prime Cuts Timeline Material Combo CY HR

*CY HR p/r 25: .6X TO 1.5X JSY p/r 49-50
*CY HR p/r 25: .5X TO 1.2X JSY p/r 24-35
*CY HR p/r 25: .4X TO 1X JSY p/r 17
OVERALL AU-GU ODDS ONE PER PACK
PRINT RUNS B/WN 1-25 COPIES PER
NO PRICING ON QTY OF 10 OR LESS
8 W.Mays NYG Bat-Jsy/25 15.00 40.00
14 Lou Brock Bat-Jkt/25 8.00 20.00
18 Frankie Frisch Jkt-Jkt/25 10.00 25.00
21 Babe Ruth Bat-Pants/25 250.00 400.00
42 Sandy Koufax Jsy-Jsy/25 75.00 150.00

2005 Prime Cuts Timeline Material Combo CY HR Prime

*PRIME p/r 25: .75X TO 2X JSY p/r 49-50
OVERALL AU-GU ODDS ONE PER PACK
PRINT RUNS B/WN 1-25 COPIES PER
NO PRICING ON QTY OF 10 OR LESS

2005 Prime Cuts Timeline Material Trio

PRINT RUNS B/WN 1-10 COPIES PER
PRIME PRINT RUN B/WN 1-10 COPIES PER
OVERALL AU-GU ODDS ONE PER PACK
NO PRICING DUE TO SCARCITY

2005 Prime Cuts Timeline Material Trio HOF

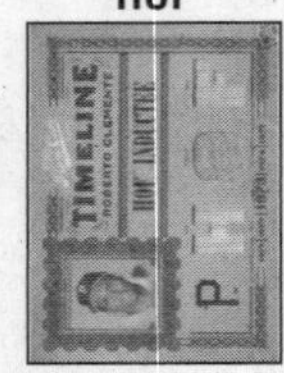

PRINT RUNS B/WN 1-10 COPIES PER
PRIME PRINT RUN B/WN 1-10 COPIES PER
OVERALL AU-GU ODDS ONE PER PACK
NO PRICING DUE TO SCARCITY

2005 Prime Cuts Timeline Material Trio MVP

*MVP p/r 50: .6X TO 1.5X JSY p/r 49-50
*MVP p/r 50: .5X TO 1.2X JSY p/r 24-35
*MVP p/r 25: .75X TO 2X JSY p/r 49-50
PRINT RUNS B/WN 1-50 COPIES PER
NO PRICING ON QTY OF 10 OR LESS
PRIME PRINT RUN B/WN 1-10 COPIES PER
NO PRIME PRICING DUE TO SCARCITY
OVERALL AU-GU ODDS ONE PER PACK
21 Babe Ruth B-J-P/50 400.00 550.00
50 Roberto Clemente B-B-B/50 50.00 100.00

2005 Prime Cuts Timeline Material Trio Stats

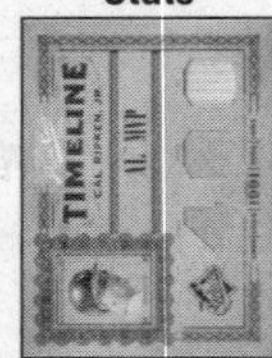

PRINT RUNS B/WN 1-5 COPIES PER
PRIME PRINT RUN B/WN 1-5 COPIES PER
OVERALL AU-GU ODDS ONE PER PACK
NO PRICING DUE TO SCARCITY

2005 Prime Cuts Timeline Material Quad

PRINT RUNS B/WN 1-5 COPIES PER
PRIME PRINT RUN B/WN 1-5 COPIES PER
OVERALL AU-GU ODDS ONE PER PACK
NO PRICING DUE TO SCARCITY

2005 Prime Cuts Timeline Material Custom Names

*NAME 3P p/r 50: .2X TO .5X NBR 4P p/r 25
*NAME 4P p/r 50: .5X TO 1.2X NBR 3P p/r 50
*NAME 4P p/r 50: .4X TO 1X NBR 4P p/r 50
*NAME 4P p/r 25: .6X TO 1.5X NBR 4P p/r 50
*NAME 4P p/r 15: .5X TO 1.2X NBR 4P p/r 25
PRINT RUNS B/WN 1-50 COPIES PER

NO PRICING ON QTY OF 1
PRIME PRINT RUN B/WN 1-5 COPIES PER
NO PRIME PRICING DUE TO SCARCITY
OVERALL AU-GU ODDS ONE PER PACK
16 Ted Williams B-J-J-J/50 125.00 200.00
21 Babe Ruth B-B-J-P/50 500.00 800.00
34 Roger Maris B-B-J-P/50 50.00 100.00

2005 Prime Cuts Timeline Material Custom Nicknames

*NICK 3P p/r 50: .4X TO 1X NBR 3P p/r 50
*NICK 4P p/r 50: .4X TO 1X NBR 4P p/r 50
PRINT RUNS B/WN 5-50 COPIES PER
NO PRICING ON QTY OF 10 OR LESS
PRIME PRINT RUN B/WN 1-5 COPIES PER
NO PRIME PRICING DUE TO SCARCITY
OVERALL AU-GU ODDS ONE PER PACK
6 S.Musial B-B-J-J-P/50 60.00 120.00
21 Babe Ruth B-J-J-P/50 600.00 900.00
24 W.Mays SF B-B-B-J-J/50 75.00 150.00
37 E.Banks B-B-H-J-J/50 50.00 100.00
47 W.Mays NY B-B-B-J-J/50 75.00 150.00

2005 Prime Cuts Timeline Material Custom Numbers

PRINT RUNS B/WN 1-50 COPIES PER
NO PRICING ON QTY OF 10 OR LESS
PRIME PRINT RUN B/WN 1-10 COPIES PER
NO PRIME PRICING DUE TO SCARCITY
OVERALL AU-GU ODDS ONE PER PACK
1 D.Murphy B-B-J-J/50 10.00 25.00
2 D.Eckersley J-P-P/50 6.00 15.00
3 Fergie Jenkins Fld Glv-Fld Glv-Jsy-Jsy/5
4 G.Maddux B-J-J/50 20.00 50.00
5 O.Hershiser J-J-P/50 6.00 15.00
6 Stan Musial B-B-J-P/50 30.00 60.00
7 D.Mattingly B/BG-H-JK-J/25 40.00 80.00
8 Willie Mays NY Giants Bat-Bat-Jsy-Jsy/1
9 Ozzie Smith Bat-Bat-Pants-Pants/5
10 R.Clem Yanks B-B-J-J/50 20.00 50.00
11 C.Ripken B-H-J-P/50 40.00 80.00
12 Duke Snider J-J-P-P/50 15.00 40.00
13 Hank Aaron B-B-J-J/50 40.00 80.00
14 Lou Brock B-B-J-J/25 15.00 40.00
15 P.Molitor B-J-P-S/50 8.00 20.00
16 T.Williams B-JK-J-J/50 60.00 120.00
17 D.Gooden B-FG-H-J/50 8.00 20.00
18 F.Frisch JK-JK-JK-JK/50 20.00 50.00
19 P.Martinez B-B-J-P/50 10.00 25.00
20 Robin Yount Bat-Bat-Jsy-Jsy/10
21 Babe Ruth B-B-J-P/50 500.00 800.00
22 C.Yaz B-H-J-P/50 30.00 60.00
23 R.Carew B-J-J-S/25 15.00 40.00
24 W.Mays SFG B-B-J-J/50 30.00 60.00
25 E.Murray B-J-P-S/50 15.00 40.00
26 I.Rod B-FG-J-S/50 10.00 25.00
27 R.Clem Sox B-B-J-J/50 20.00 50.00
28 W.McCovey J-J-P-P/50 10.00 25.00
29 Bob Feller Jsy-Jsy-Jsy-Jsy/1
30 Catfish Hunter Jsy-Jsy-Jsy-Jsy/1
32 Wade Boggs B-H-J-J/50 10.00 25.00
33 Phil Rizzuto Jsy-Jsy-Pants-Pants/5
34 Roger Maris B-B-J-P/50 50.00 100.00
35 Bob Gibson Hat-Jsy-Jsy-Jsy/1
36 C.Jones B-FG-J-J/50 20.00 50.00
37 Ernie Banks B-B-H-J/50 20.00 50.00
38 G.Brett B-H-J-J/50 30.00 60.00
39 Keith Hernandez Bat-Bat-Jsy-Jsy/1
40 R.Sandberg B-FG-H-J/50 40.00 80.00
41 Reggie Jackson Jkt-Jsy-Jsy-Jsy/5
42 Sandy Koufax Jsy-Jsy-Jsy-Jsy/5
43 W.Spahn J-J-P-P/50 20.00 50.00
44 N.Ryan Mets B-B-J-J/50 40.00 80.00
45 Yogi Berra B-J-P-P/50 30.00 60.00
46 C.Ripken B-H-J-P/50 40.00 80.00
47 W.Mays NYM B-B-J-J/50 30.00 60.00
50 R.Clemente B-B-H-J/25 150.00 250.00

2005 Prime Cuts Timeline Signature Century Gold

OVERALL AU-GU ODDS ONE PER PACK
PRINT RUNS B/WN 1-8 COPIES PER
NO PRICING DUE TO SCARCITY

2005 Prime Cuts Timeline Signature Century Platinum

OVERALL AU-GU ODDS ONE PER PACK
STATED PRINT RUN 1 SERIAL #'d SET
NO PRICING DUE TO SCARCITY

2005 Prime Cuts Timeline Signature Century Silver

OVERALL AU-GU ODDS ONE PER PACK
PRINT RUNS B/WN 1-32 COPIES PER
NO PRICING ON QTY OF 10 OR LESS
1 Dale Murphy/10
2 Dennis Eckersley/25 10.00 25.00
3 Fergie Jenkins/25 10.00 25.00
4 Greg Maddux/10
5 Orel Hershiser/10
6 Stan Musial/25 30.00 60.00
7 Don Mattingly/10
8 Willie Mays NY Giants/5
9 Ozzie Smith/25 20.00 50.00
10 Roger Clemens Yanks/10
11 Cal Ripken/1
12 Duke Snider/25 15.00 40.00
13 Hank Aaron/15 125.00 200.00
14 Lou Brock/25 15.00 40.00
15 Paul Molitor/25 10.00 25.00
17 Dwight Gooden/10
19 Pedro Martinez/5
20 Robin Yount/5
23 Rod Carew/25 15.00 40.00
24 Willie Mays SF Giants/5
27 Roger Clemens Sox/10
28 Willie McCovey/25 15.00 40.00
29 Bob Feller/25 10.00 25.00
31 Gaylord Perry/25 10.00 25.00
32 Wade Boggs/25 15.00 40.00
33 Phil Rizzuto/25 15.00 40.00
35 Bob Gibson/25 15.00 40.00
36 Chipper Jones/25 20.00 50.00
37 Ernie Banks/5
38 George Brett/25 40.00 80.00
39 Keith Hernandez/10
40 Ryne Sandberg/25 40.00 80.00
42 Sandy Koufax/32 225.00 300.00
44 Nolan Ryan Mets/25 50.00 100.00
46 Cal Ripken/1
47 Willie Mays NY Mets/5
48 Nolan Ryan Angels/25 50.00 100.00
49 Stan Musial/25 30.00 60.00

2005 Prime Cuts Timeline Signature Material Jersey Number

PRINT RUNS B/WN 1-10 COPIES PER
PRIME PRINT RUN B/WN 1-10 COPIES PER
OVERALL AU-GU ODDS ONE PER PACK
NO PRICING DUE TO SCARCITY

2005 Prime Cuts Timeline Signature Material Combo

PRINT RUNS B/WN 1-10 COPIES PER
PRIME PRINT RUN B/WN 1-10 COPIES PER
OVERALL AU-GU ODDS ONE PER PACK
NO PRICING DUE TO SCARCITY

2005 Prime Cuts Timeline Signature Material Combo CY HR

*CY HR: .5X TO 1.2X SILVER
OVERALL AU-GU ODDS ONE PER PACK
PRINT RUNS B/WN 5-25 COPIES PER
NO PRICING ON QTY OF 10 OR LESS

1 Dale Murphy Bat-Jsy/25	20.00	50.00
7 Don Mattingly Jsy-Jsy/25	40.00	80.00
11 Cal Ripken Bat-Jsy/25	75.00	150.00
13 Hank Aaron Bat-Jsy/25	125.00	200.00
17 D.Gooden Jsy-Jsy/25	12.50	30.00
24 W.Mays SFG Bat-Jsy/25	100.00	175.00
46 Cal Ripken Jsy-Pants/25	75.00	150.00
47 W.Mays NYM Bat-Jsy/25	100.00	175.00

2005 Prime Cuts Timeline Signature Material Combo CY HR Prime

*PRIME p/r 25: .75X TO 2X SILVER p/r 25
OVERALL AU-GU ODDS ONE PER PACK
PRINT RUNS B/WN 1-25 COPIES PER
NO PRICING ON QTY OF 10 OR LESS

24 W.Mays SFG Bat-Jsy/25	150.00	250.00
47 W.Mays NYM Bat-Jsy/25	150.00	250.00

2005 Prime Cuts Timeline Signature Material Trio

PRINT RUNS B/WN 1-10 COPIES PER
PRIME PRINT RUN B/WN 1-5 COPIES PER
OVERALL AU-GU ODDS ONE PER PACK
NO PRICING DUE TO SCARCITY

2005 Prime Cuts Timeline Signature Material Trio HOF

PRINT RUNS B/WN 1-10 COPIES PER
PRIME PRINT RUN B/WN 1-10 COPIES PER
OVERALL AU-GU ODDS ONE PER PACK
NO PRICING DUE TO SCARCITY

2005 Prime Cuts Timeline Signature Material Trio MVP

PRINT RUNS B/WN 1-10 COPIES PER
PRIME PRINT RUN B/WN 1-10 COPIES PER
OVERALL AU-GU ODDS ONE PER PACK
NO PRICING DUE TO SCARCITY

2005 Prime Cuts Timeline Signature Material Trio Stats

PRINT RUNS B/WN 1-5 COPIES PER
PRIME PRINT RUN B/WN 1-5 COPIES PER
OVERALL AU-GU ODDS ONE PER PACK
NO PRICING DUE TO SCARCITY

2005 Prime Cuts Timeline Signature Material Quad

PRINT RUNS B/WN 1-5 COPIES PER
PRIME PRINT RUN B/WN 1-5 COPIES PER
OVERALL AU-GU ODDS ONE PER PACK
NO PRICING DUE TO SCARCITY

2005 Prime Cuts Timeline Signature Material Custom Names

PRINT RUNS B/WN 1-50 COPIES PER
NO PRICING ON QTY OF 5 OR LESS
PRIME PRINT RUN B/WN 1-5 COPIES PER
NO PRIME PRICING DUE TO SCARCITY
OVERALL AU-GU ODDS ONE PER PACK

11 Cal Ripken B-H-J-P/50	125.00	200.00
24 Willie Mays SFG B-B-J-J/50	125.00	200.00

2005 Prime Cuts Timeline Signature Material Custom Numbers

PRINT RUNS B/WN 1-50 COPIES PER
NO PRICING ON QTY OF 10 OR LESS
PRIME PRINT RUN B/WN 1-10 COPIES PER
NO PRIME PRICING DUE TO SCARCITY
OVERALL AU-GU ODDS ONE PER PACK

24 Willie Mays SFG B-B-J-J/50	125.00	200.00
46 Cal Ripken B-H-J-P/50	150.00	250.00
47 Willie Mays NYM B-B-J-J/50	125.00	200.00

2004 Reflections

This 390-card set was released in May, 2004. The set was issued in four card packs with an $15 SRP which came eight packs to a box and 14 boxes to a case. Cards numbered 1 through 100 feature veterans while cards to 130 feature rookies. Those cards numbered 101 through 130 were inserted at a stated rate of one in eight and were issued to a stated print run of 1250 serial numbered sets. Cards numbered 131 through 298 feature jersey swatches and were inserted at an overall stated rate of one in two packs. Cards numbered 299 through 340 feature autographed cards with a stated print run of 35 serial numbered sets which were inserted at a stated rate of one in 16 packs. Cards numbered 341 through 390 were issued as "random insert sets" in Upper Deck series 2 boxes. An Ichiro Suzuki promo card for this set was released during the Hawaii trade show. That card is printed to a stated serial number print run of 500 sets.

COMP.SET w/o SP's (100)	15.00	40.00
COMP.UPDATE SET (50)	12.50	30.00
COMMON CARD (1-100)	.30	.75
COMMON CARD (101-130)	1.50	4.00
COMMON CARD (131-214)	2.50	6.00
SP CL: 132/142/144/146/153/156/159		
SP CL: 161-162/164/178/184/186/188		
SP CL: 190-191/197-198/201/207/214		
SP INFO PROVIDED BY UPPER DECK		
COMMON CARD (215-298)	3.00	8.00
COMMON CARD (299-340)	10.00	25.00
COMMON CARD (341-390)	.25	.60
1 Adam Dunn	.30	.75
2 Albert Pujols	1.50	4.00
3 Alex Rodriguez Yanks	1.25	3.00
4 Alfonso Soriano	.30	.75
5 Andruw Jones	.50	1.25
6 Austin Kearns	.30	.75
7 Rafael Furcal	.30	.75
8 Barry Zito	.30	.75
9 Bartolo Colon	.30	.75
10 Ben Sheets	.30	.75
11 Bernie Williams	.50	1.25
12 Bobby Abreu	.30	.75
13 Brandon Webb	.30	.75
14 Bret Boone	.30	.75
15 Brian Giles	.30	.75
16 Carlos Beltran	.30	.75
17 Carlos Delgado	.30	.75
18 Carlos Lee	.30	.75
19 Chipper Jones	.75	2.00
20 Corey Patterson	.30	.75
21 Curt Schilling	.50	1.25
22 Delmon Young	.50	1.25
23 Derek Jeter	1.50	4.00
24 Dmitri Young	.30	.75
25 Dontrelle Willis	.50	1.25
26 Edgar Martinez	.50	1.25
27 Edgar Renteria	.30	.75
28 Eric Chavez	.30	.75
29 Eric Gagne	.30	.75
30 Frank Thomas	.75	2.00
31 Garrett Anderson	.30	.75
32 Gary Sheffield	.30	.75
33 Geoff Jenkins	.30	.75
34 Greg Maddux	1.25	3.00
35 Hank Blalock	.30	.75
36 Hideki Matsui	1.25	3.00
37 Hideo Nomo	.75	2.00
38 Ichiro Suzuki	1.50	4.00
39 Ivan Rodriguez	.50	1.25
40 Jacque Jones	.30	.75
41 Jason Giambi	.30	.75
42 Jason Schmidt	.30	.75
43 Javy Lopez	.30	.75
44 Jay Gibbons	.30	.75
45 Jeff Bagwell	.50	1.25
46 Jeff Kent	.30	.75
47 Jeremy Bonderman	.30	.75
48 Jim Edmonds	.30	.75
49 Jim Thome	.50	1.25
50 Johnny Damon	.50	1.25
51 Jorge Posada	.50	1.25
52 Jose Contreras	.30	.75
53 Jose Reyes	.30	.75
54 Jose Vidro	.30	.75
55 Josh Beckett	.30	.75
56 Juan Gonzalez	.30	.75
57 Ken Griffey Jr.	1.25	3.00
58 Kerry Wood	.30	.75
59 Kevin Brown	.30	.75
60 Kevin Millwood	.30	.75
61 Lance Berkman	.30	.75
62 Larry Walker	.30	.75
63 Luis Gonzalez	.30	.75
64 Magglio Ordonez	.30	.75
65 Manny Ramirez	.50	1.25
66 Mark Mulder	.30	.75
67 Mark Prior	.50	1.25
68 Mark Teixeira	.50	1.25
69 Miguel Cabrera	.50	1.25
70 Miguel Tejada	.30	.75
71 Mike Lowell	.30	.75
72 Mike Mussina	.50	1.25
73 Mike Piazza	1.25	3.00
74 Mike Sweeney	.30	.75
75 Milton Bradley	.30	.75
76 Nomar Garciaparra	1.25	3.00
77 Orlando Cabrera	.30	.75
78 Pedro Martinez	.50	1.25
79 Phil Nevin	.30	.75
80 Preston Wilson	.30	.75
81 Rafael Palmeiro	.50	1.25
82 Randy Johnson	.75	2.00
83 Rich Harden	.30	.75
84 Richie Sexson	.30	.75
85 Rickie Weeks	.30	.75
86 Rocco Baldelli	.30	.75
87 Roy Halladay	.30	.75
88 Roy Oswalt	.30	.75
89 Ryan Klesko	.30	.75
90 Sammy Sosa	.75	2.00
91 Scott Rolen	.50	1.25
92 Shannon Stewart	.30	.75
93 Shawn Green	.30	.75
94 Tim Hudson	.30	.75
95 Todd Helton	.50	1.25
96 Torii Hunter	.30	.75
97 Trot Nixon	.30	.75
98 Troy Glaus	.30	.75
99 Vernon Wells	.30	.75
100 Vladimir Guerrero	.75	2.00
101 Brandon Medders RC	1.50	4.00
102 Colby Miller RC	1.50	4.00
103 Dave Crouthers RC	1.50	4.00
104 Dennis Sarfate RC	1.50	4.00
105 Donnie Kelly RC	1.50	4.00
106 Alec Zumwalt RC	1.50	4.00
107 Chris Aguila RC	1.50	4.00
108 Greg Dobbs RC	1.50	4.00
109 Ian Snell RC	2.00	5.00
110 Jake Woods RC	1.50	4.00
111 Jamie Brown RC	1.50	4.00
112 Jason Frasor RC	1.50	4.00
113 Jerome Gamble RC	1.50	4.00
114 Jesse Harper RC	1.50	4.00
115 Josh Labandeira RC	1.50	4.00
116 Justin Hampson RC	1.50	4.00
117 Justin Huisman RC	1.50	4.00
118 Justin Leone RC	2.00	5.00
119 Kazuo Matsui RC	2.00	5.00
120 Lincoln Holdzkom RC	1.50	4.00
121 Mike Bumatay RC	1.50	4.00
122 Mike Gosling RC	1.50	4.00
123 Mike Johnston RC	1.50	4.00
124 Mike Rouse RC	1.50	4.00
125 Nick Regilio RC	1.50	4.00
126 Ryan Meaux RC	1.50	4.00
127 Scott Dohmann RC	1.50	4.00
128 Sean Henn RC	1.50	4.00
129 Tim Bausher RC	1.50	4.00
130 Tim Bittner RC	1.50	4.00
131 Adam Dunn Jsy L1	2.50	6.00
132 Andruw Jones Jsy L1 SP	5.00	12.00
133 Austin Kearns Jsy L1	2.50	6.00
134 Bartolo Colon Jsy L1	2.50	6.00
135 Ben Sheets Jsy L1	2.50	6.00
136 Bernie Williams Jsy L1	4.00	10.00
137 Bobby Abreu Jsy L1	2.50	6.00
138 Brian Giles Jsy L1	2.50	6.00
139 Carlos Lee Jsy L1	2.50	6.00
140 Chipper Jones Jsy L1	4.00	10.00
141 Corey Patterson Jsy L1	2.50	6.00
142 Darin Erstad Jsy L1 SP	3.00	8.00
143 Edgar Martinez Jsy L1	4.00	10.00
144 Vladimir Guerrero Jsy L1 SP	5.00	12.00
145 Eric Gagne Jsy L1	2.50	6.00
146 Frank Thomas Jsy L1 SP	5.00	12.00
147 Garret Anderson Jsy L1	2.50	6.00
148 Roger Clemens Jsy L1	6.00	15.00
149 Greg Maddux Jsy L1	4.00	10.00
150 Jacque Jones Jsy L1	2.50	6.00
151 Randy Johnson Jsy L1	4.00	10.00
152 Javy Lopez Jsy L1	2.50	6.00
153 Mike Piazza Jsy L1 SP	6.00	15.00
154 Albert Pujols Jsy L1	6.00	15.00
155 Jim Edmonds Jsy L1	2.50	6.00
156 Eric Milton Jsy L1 SP	3.00	8.00
157 Jorge Posada Jsy L1	4.00	10.00
158 J.D. Drew Jsy L1	2.50	6.00
159 Jose Vidro Jsy L1 SP	3.00	8.00
160 Kevin Millwood Jsy L1	2.50	6.00
161 Larry Walker Jsy L1 SP	3.00	8.00
162 Luis Gonzalez Jsy L1 SP	3.00	8.00
163 Mike Sweeney Jsy L1	2.50	6.00
164 Kerry Wood Jsy L1 SP	3.00	8.00
165 Mike Cameron Jsy L1	2.50	6.00
166 Phil Nevin Jsy L1	2.50	6.00
167 Rocco Baldelli Jsy L1	2.50	6.00
168 Ryan Klesko Jsy L1	2.50	6.00
169 Shannon Stewart Jsy L1	2.50	6.00
170 Torii Hunter Jsy L1	2.50	6.00
171 Trot Nixon Jsy L1	2.50	6.00
172 Vernon Wells Jsy L1	2.50	6.00
173 Alfonso Soriano Jsy L2	2.50	6.00
174 Andruw Jones Jsy L2	4.00	10.00
175 Barry Zito Jsy L2	2.50	6.00
176 Brandon Webb Jsy L2	2.50	6.00
177 Bret Boone Jsy L2	2.50	6.00
178 Scott Rolen Jsy L2 SP	5.00	12.00
179 Carlos Delgado Jsy L2	2.50	6.00
180 Curt Schilling Jsy L2	4.00	10.00
181 Dontrelle Willis Jsy L2	4.00	10.00
182 Eric Chavez Jsy L2	2.50	6.00
183 Frank Thomas Jsy L2	4.00	10.00
184 Gary Sheffield Jsy L2 SP	3.00	8.00
185 Greg Maddux Jsy L2	4.00	10.00
186 Hank Blalock Jsy L2 SP	3.00	8.00
187 Hideki Matsui Jsy L2	10.00	25.00
188 Hideo Nomo Jsy L2 SP	5.00	12.00
189 Ichiro Suzuki Jsy L2	6.00	15.00
190 Ivan Rodriguez Jsy L2 SP	5.00	12.00
191 Jason Giambi Jsy L2 SP	3.00	8.00
192 Rafael Furcal Jsy L2	2.50	6.00
193 Jeff Bagwell Jsy L2	4.00	10.00
194 Jeff Kent Jsy L2	2.50	6.00
195 Jim Thome Jsy L2	4.00	10.00
196 Jose Reyes Jsy L2	2.50	6.00
197 Josh Beckett Jsy L2 SP	3.00	8.00
198 Juan Gonzalez Jsy L2 SP	3.00	8.00
199 Ken Griffey Jr. Jsy L2	6.00	15.00
200 Kevin Brown Jsy L2	2.50	6.00
201 Lance Berkman Jsy L2 SP	3.00	8.00
202 Magglio Ordonez Jsy L2	2.50	6.00
203 Mark Mulder Jsy L2	2.50	6.00
204 Mark Teixeira Jsy L2	4.00	10.00
205 Miguel Tejada Jsy L2	2.50	6.00
206 Mike Mussina Jsy L2	4.00	10.00
207 Preston Wilson Jsy L2 SP	3.00	8.00
208 Rafael Palmeiro Jsy L2	4.00	10.00
209 Alex Rodriguez Jsy L2	6.00	15.00
210 Richie Sexson Jsy L2	2.50	6.00
211 Roy Halladay Jsy L2	2.50	6.00
212 Roy Oswalt Jsy L2	2.50	6.00
213 Tim Hudson Jsy L2	2.50	6.00
214 Troy Glaus Jsy L2 SP	3.00	8.00
215 Adam Dunn Jsy L3	3.00	8.00
216 Austin Kearns Jsy L3	3.00	8.00
217 Bartolo Colon Jsy L3	3.00	8.00
218 Ben Sheets Jsy L3	3.00	8.00
219 Bernie Williams Jsy L3	5.00	12.00
220 Bobby Abreu Jsy L3	3.00	8.00
221 Bret Boone Jsy L3	3.00	8.00
222 Todd Helton Jsy L3	5.00	12.00
223 Chipper Jones Jsy L3	5.00	12.00
224 Corey Patterson Jsy L3	3.00	8.00
225 Darin Erstad Jsy L3	3.00	8.00
226 Dontrelle Willis Jsy L3	5.00	12.00
227 Edgar Martinez Jsy L3	5.00	12.00
228 Eric Gagne Jsy L3	3.00	8.00
229 Garret Anderson Jsy L3	3.00	8.00
230 Roger Clemens Jsy L3	8.00	20.00
231 Hank Blalock Jsy L3	3.00	8.00
232 Jacque Jones Jsy L3	3.00	8.00
233 Jeff Bagwell Jsy L3	5.00	12.00
234 Jeff Kent Jsy L3	3.00	8.00
235 Jeremy Bonderman Jsy L3	3.00	8.00
236 Jim Edmonds Jsy L3	3.00	8.00
237 Jorge Posada Jsy L3	5.00	12.00
238 J.D. Drew Jsy L3	3.00	8.00
239 Jose Reyes Jsy L3	3.00	8.00
240 Jose Vidro Jsy L3	3.00	8.00
241 Kevin Millwood Jsy L3	3.00	8.00
242 Luis Gonzalez Jsy L3	3.00	8.00
243 Mike Sweeney Jsy L3	3.00	8.00
244 Jason Giambi Jsy L3	3.00	8.00
245 Manny Ramirez Jsy L3	5.00	12.00
246 Phil Nevin Jsy L3	3.00	8.00
247 Preston Wilson Jsy L3	3.00	8.00
248 Alex Rodriguez Jsy L3	8.00	20.00
249 Richie Sexson Jsy L3	3.00	8.00
250 Rocco Baldelli Jsy L3	3.00	8.00
251 Ryan Klesko Jsy L3	3.00	8.00
252 Sammy Sosa Jsy L3	5.00	12.00
253 Torii Hunter Jsy L3	3.00	8.00
254 Mike Lowell Jsy L3	3.00	8.00
255 Troy Glaus Jsy L3	3.00	8.00
256 Vernon Wells Jsy L3	3.00	8.00
257 Albert Pujols Jsy L4	10.00	25.00
258 Alex Rodriguez Jsy L4	8.00	20.00
259 Alfonso Soriano Jsy L4	3.00	8.00
260 Roger Clemens Jsy L4	8.00	20.00
261 Barry Zito Jsy L4	3.00	8.00
262 Brandon Webb Jsy L4	3.00	8.00
263 Carlos Delgado Jsy L4	3.00	8.00
264 Curt Schilling Jsy L4	5.00	12.00
265 Derek Jeter Jsy L4	12.50	30.00
266 Eric Chavez Jsy L4	3.00	8.00
267 Gary Sheffield Jsy L4	3.00	8.00
268 Hideki Matsui Jsy L4	12.50	30.00
269 Hideo Nomo Jsy L4	5.00	12.00
270 Ichiro Suzuki Jsy L4	10.00	25.00
271 Ivan Rodriguez Jsy L4	5.00	12.00
272 Jason Giambi Jsy L4	3.00	8.00
273 Jim Thome Jsy L4	5.00	12.00
274 Josh Beckett Jsy L4	3.00	8.00
275 Juan Gonzalez Jsy L4	3.00	8.00
276 Ken Griffey Jr. Jsy L4	8.00	20.00
277 Kerry Wood Jsy L4	3.00	8.00
278 Kevin Brown Jsy L4	3.00	8.00
279 Lance Berkman Jsy L4	3.00	8.00
280 Magglio Ordonez Jsy L4	3.00	8.00
281 Manny Ramirez Jsy L4	5.00	12.00
282 Mark Mulder Jsy L4	3.00	8.00
283 Mark Prior Jsy L4	5.00	12.00
284 Mark Teixeira Jsy L4	5.00	12.00
285 Miguel Tejada Jsy L4	3.00	8.00
286 Mike Mussina Jsy L4	5.00	12.00
287 Mike Piazza Jsy L4	8.00	20.00
288 Pedro Martinez Jsy L4	5.00	12.00
289 Rafael Palmeiro Jsy L4	5.00	12.00
290 Randy Johnson Jsy L4	5.00	12.00
291 Roy Halladay Jsy L4	3.00	8.00
292 Roy Oswalt Jsy L4	3.00	8.00
293 Sammy Sosa Jsy L4	5.00	12.00
294 Scott Rolen Jsy L4	5.00	12.00
295 Shawn Green Jsy L4	3.00	8.00
296 Tim Hudson Jsy L4	3.00	8.00
297 Todd Helton Jsy L4	5.00	12.00
298 Vladimir Guerrero Jsy L4	5.00	12.00
299 Bret Boone AU	15.00	40.00
300 Alex Rodriguez AU	125.00	200.00
301 Dontrelle Willis AU	20.00	50.00
302 Barry Larkin AU	20.00	50.00
303 Barry Zito AU	20.00	50.00
304 Eric Chavez AU	15.00	40.00
305 Bernie Williams AU	60.00	120.00
306 Brandon Webb AU	10.00	25.00
307 Cal Ripken AU	125.00	200.00
308 Carl Yastrzemski AU	40.00	80.00
309 Carlos Delgado AU	15.00	40.00
310 Shawn Green AU	20.00	50.00
311 Eric Gagne AU	5.00	12.00
312 Frank Thomas AU	30.00	60.00
313 Carlos Lee AU	10.00	25.00
314 Garret Anderson AU	15.00	40.00
315 Hideki Matsui AU	200.00	350.00
316 Jim Edmonds AU	20.00	50.00
317 Jeff Bagwell AU	20.00	50.00
318 Luis Gonzalez AU	15.00	40.00
319 Mike Mussina AU	20.00	50.00
320 John Smoltz AU	50.00	100.00
321 Jose Reyes AU	15.00	40.00
322 Josh Beckett AU	20.00	50.00
323 Juan Gonzalez AU	15.00	40.00
324 Ken Griffey Jr. AU	75.00	150.00
325 Rich Harden AU	10.00	25.00
326 Pat Burrell AU	15.00	40.00
327 Mark Teixeira AU	20.00	50.00
328 Roy Oswalt AU	15.00	40.00
329 Miguel Tejada AU	20.00	50.00
330 Mike Hampton AU	15.00	40.00
331 Mike Piazza AU	125.00	200.00
332 Nolan Ryan AU	75.00	150.00
333 Orlando Hernandez AU	15.00	40.00
334 Paul Lo Duca AU	15.00	40.00
335 Roberto Alomar AU	20.00	50.00
336 Rocco Baldelli AU	15.00	40.00
337 Trevor Hoffman AU	20.00	50.00
338 Tom Glavine AU	20.00	50.00
339 Tom Seaver AU	30.00	60.00
340 Mark Prior AU	15.00	40.00
341 Shingo Takatsu RC	.60	1.50
342 Franklyn Gracesqui RC	.25	.60
343 Angel Chavez RC	.40	1.00
344 Jorge Sequea RC	.40	1.00
345 David Aardsma RC	.60	1.50
346 Ramon Ramirez RC	.40	1.00
347 Lino Urdaneta RC	.40	1.00
348 Orlando Rodriguez RC	.40	1.00
349 Jason Szuminski RC	.25	.60
350 Luis A. Gonzalez RC	.60	1.50
351 John Gall RC	.60	1.50
352 Kevin Cave RC	.40	1.00
353 Chris Oxspring RC	.40	1.00
354 Freddy Guzman RC	.40	1.00
355 Jeff Bennett RC	.40	1.00
356 Jorge Vasquez RC	.40	1.00
357 Merkin Valdez RC	.60	1.50
358 Tim Hamulack RC	.25	.60
359 Hector Gimenez RC	.25	.60
360 Jerry Gil RC	.40	1.00
361 Ryan Wing RC	.40	1.00
362 Shawn Hill RC	.40	1.00
363 Jason Bartlett RC	.60	1.50
364 Renyel Pinto RC	.60	1.50
365 Carlos Vasquez RC	.60	1.50
366 Mike Vento RC	.60	1.50
367 Casey Daigle RC	.40	1.00
368 Chad Bentz RC	.40	1.00
369 Chris Saenz RC	.40	1.00
370 Shawn Camp RC	.25	.60
371 Carlos Hines RC	.40	1.00
372 Edwin Moreno RC	.40	1.00
373 Michael Wuertz RC	.60	1.50
374 Aarom Baldiris RC	.60	1.50
375 Ronny Cedeno RC	1.00	2.50
376 Akinori Otsuka RC	1.50	4.00
377 Jose Capellan RC	.60	1.50
378 Justin Germano RC	.40	1.00
379 Justin Knoedler RC	.40	1.00
380 Mariano Gomez RC	.40	1.00
381 Fernando Nieve RC	1.00	2.50
382 Scott Proctor RC	2.00	5.00
383 Roman Colon RC	.25	.60
384 Onil Joseph RC	.40	1.00
385 Eddy Rodriguez RC	.60	1.50
386 Enemencio Pacheco RC	.40	1.00
387 William Bergolla RC	.40	1.00
388 Ivan Ochoa RC	.40	1.00
389 Rusty Tucker RC	.60	1.50
390 Roberto Novoa RC	.60	1.50
S38 Ichiro Suzuki Promo		

2004 Reflections Black

1-100 OVERALL PARALLEL ODDS 1:4
101-130/299-340 OVERALL AU ODDS 1:16
173-214/257-298 OVERALL GU ODDS 1:2
1-100/173-340 PRINT RUN 1 SERIAL #'d SET
101-130 PRINT RUN 5 SERIAL #'d SETS
NO PRICING DUE TO SCARCITY

2004 Reflections Blue

*BLUE 1-100: 1.25X TO 3X BASIC
1-100 OVERALL PARALLEL ODDS 1:4
1-100 PRINT RUN 250 SERIAL #'d SETS
*BLUE JSY 215-256: 1.25X TO 3X BASIC
215-256 OVERALL GU ODDS 1:2
215-256 PRINT RUN 15 SERIAL #'d SETS

2004 Reflections Gold

*GOLD 1-100: 5X TO 12X BASIC
1-100 PRINT RUN 15 SERIAL #'d SETS
101-130 PRINT RUN 250 SERIAL #'d SETS
*GOLD JSY 131-172: 1.5X TO 4X BASIC
*GOLD JSY 131-172: 1.25X TO 3X BASIC SP
131-172 PRINT RUN 15 SERIAL #'d SETS
257-298 PRINT RUN 5 SERIAL #'d SETS
257-398 NO PRICING DUE TO SCARCITY
*GOLD AU JSY 299-340: .6X TO 1.2X BASIC
299-340 PRINT RUN 15 SERIAL #'d SETS
1-100 OVERALL PARALLEL ODDS 1:4
101-130/299-340 OVERALL AU ODDS 1:16
131-172/257-298 OVERALL GU ODDS 1:2

101 Brandon Medders AU	4.00	10.00
102 Colby Miller AU	4.00	10.00
103 Dave Crouthers AU	4.00	10.00
104 Dennis Sarfate AU	4.00	10.00
105 Donnie Kelly AU	4.00	10.00
106 Alec Zumwalt AU	4.00	10.00
107 Chris Aguila AU	4.00	10.00
108 Greg Dobbs AU	4.00	10.00
109 Ian Snell AU	8.00	20.00
110 Jake Woods AU	4.00	10.00
111 Jamie Brown AU	4.00	10.00
112 Jason Frasor AU	4.00	10.00
113 Jerome Gamble AU	4.00	10.00
114 Jesse Harper AU	4.00	10.00
115 Josh Labandeira AU	4.00	10.00
116 Justin Hampson AU	4.00	10.00
117 Justin Huisman AU	4.00	10.00
118 Justin Leone AU	6.00	15.00
120 Lincoln Holdzkom AU	4.00	10.00
121 Mike Bumatay AU	4.00	10.00
122 Mike Gosling AU	4.00	10.00
123 Mike Johnston AU	4.00	10.00
124 Mike Rouse AU	4.00	10.00
125 Nick Regilio AU	4.00	10.00
126 Ryan Meaux AU	4.00	10.00
127 Scott Dohmann AU	4.00	10.00
128 Sean Henn AU	4.00	10.00
129 Tim Bausher AU	4.00	10.00
130 Tim Bittner AU	4.00	10.00

2004 Reflections Gold Rookie Autograph 125

*GOLD AU 125: .4X TO 1X GOLD AU 250
OVERALL AU ODDS 1:16
STATED PRINT RUN 125 SERIAL #'d SETS

2004 Reflections Red

*RED 1-100: 2X TO 5X BASIC
1-100 OVERALL PARALLEL ODDS 1:4
*RED JSY 131-214: .6X TO 1.5X BASIC
*RED JSY 131-214: .5X TO 1.2X BASIC SP
*RED JSY 215-256: .5X TO 1.2X BASIC
131-256 OVERALL GU ODDS 1:2
STATED PRINT RUN 50 SERIAL #'d SETS

2005 Reflections

This product was released in June, 2005. The product was issued in four-card packs with a $10 SRP of which came 12 packs to a box and 18 boxes per case. Cards 1-200 were issued in standard packs and cards 201-286 were issued in packs of '05 Upper Deck Update in February, 2006. Cards numbered 1 through 100 feature active veterans while cards numbered 101 through 150 feature leading young players and cards numbered 151 through 200 feature retired greats. Cards numbered 101 through 200 were issued at a stated rate of one every two packs. Cards 201-286 were seeded at a stated rate of one per '05 Upper Deck Update pack.

COMP.SET w/o SP's (100) 15.00 40.00
COMP.UPDATE SET (86)
COMMON CARD (1-100) .30 .75
COMMON CARD (101-150) 1.25 3.00
COMMON CARD (151-200) 1.25 3.00
COMMON CARD (201-286) .40 1.00
201-286 ONE PER '05 UD UPDATE PACK
1 Corey Patterson .30 .75
2 Curt Schilling .50 1.25
3 Todd Helton .50 1.25
4 Johnny Damon .50 1.25
5 Alex Rodriguez 1.25 3.00
6 Vladimir Guerrero .75 2.00
7 John Smoltz .50 1.25
8 Ivan Rodriguez .50 1.25
9 Roy Halladay .30 .75
10 Carlos Beltran .30 .75
11 Ichiro Suzuki 1.50 4.00
12 Jim Edmonds .30 .75
13 Andruw Jones .50 1.25
14 Scott Podsednik .30 .75
15 Troy Glaus .30 .75
16 Miguel Cabrera .50 1.25
17 Adrian Beltre .30 .75
18 Ben Sheets .30 .75
19 Alfonso Soriano .30 .75
20 Brian Giles .30 .75
21 Carl Crawford .30 .75
22 Frank Thomas .75 2.00
23 Jeff Kent .30 .75
24 Eric Gagne .30 .75
25 Shawn Green .30 .75
26 Sammy Sosa .75 2.00
27 Carlos Lee .30 .75
28 Ken Griffey Jr. 1.25 3.00
29 Mike Lowell .30 .75
30 Magglio Ordonez .30 .75
31 Aubrey Huff .30 .75
32 Travis Hafner .30 .75
33 Albert Pujols 1.50 4.00
34 Vernon Wells .30 .75
35 Roy Oswalt .30 .75
36 Jose Guillen .30 .75
37 Jim Thome .50 1.25
38 Bobby Abreu .30 .75
39 Bret Boone .30 .75
40 Mark Teixeira .50 1.25
41 Garret Anderson .30 .75
42 Jose Reyes .30 .75
43 Bernie Williams .50 1.25
44 Greg Maddux 1.25 3.00
45 Gary Sheffield .30 .75
46 Josh Beckett .30 .75
47 Chipper Jones .75 2.00
48 Hank Blalock .30 .75
49 C.C. Sabathia .30 .75
50 Manny Ramirez .50 1.25
51 Pedro Martinez .50 1.25
52 Michael Young .30 .75
53 Jacque Jones .30 .75
54 Marcus Giles .30 .75
55 Steve Finley .30 .75
56 Miguel Tejada .30 .75
57 Mike Sweeney .30 .75
58 Lance Berkman .30 .75
59 J.D. Drew .30 .75
60 Jeromy Burnitz .30 .75
61 Johan Santana .75 2.00
62 Victor Martinez .30 .75
63 Carl Pavano .30 .75
64 Roger Clemens 1.25 3.00
65 Richie Sexson .30 .75
66 Tim Hudson .30 .75
67 Melvin Mora .30 .75
68 Angel Berroa .30 .75
69 Rafael Palmeiro .50 1.25
70 Randy Johnson .75 2.00
71 Torii Hunter .30 .75
72 Luis Gonzalez .30 .75
73 Kazuo Matsui .30 .75
74 Hideki Matsui 1.25 3.00
75 Mark Prior .50 1.25
76 Jeff Bagwell .50 1.25
77 Eric Chavez .30 .75
78 Mark Loretta .30 .75
79 Adam Dunn .30 .75
80 Kerry Wood .30 .75
81 Jose Vidro .30 .75
82 Jason Schmidt .30 .75
83 Carlos Delgado .30 .75
84 Scott Rolen .50 1.25
85 David Ortiz .75 2.00
86 Edgar Renteria .30 .75
87 Nomar Garciaparra .75 2.00
88 Mike Piazza .75 2.00
89 Mark Mulder .30 .75
90 Tom Glavine .50 1.25
91 Paul Konerko .30 .75
92 Larry Walker .50 1.25
93 Derek Jeter 1.50 4.00
94 Jake Peavy .30 .75
95 Carlos Zambrano .30 .75
96 Russ Ortiz .30 .75
97 Barry Zito .30 .75
98 Austin Kearns .30 .75
99 Pedro Feliz .30 .75
100 Rich Harden .30 .75
101 Adam LaRoche FUT 1.25 3.00
102 Brandon Claussen FUT 1.25 3.00
103 Gavin Floyd FUT 1.25 3.00
104 Daniel Cabrera FUT 1.25 3.00
105 Joe Mauer FUT 1.50 4.00
106 Khalil Greene FUT 1.50 4.00
107 David Wright FUT 2.00 5.00
108 Rickie Weeks FUT 1.25 3.00
109 Robb Quinlan FUT 1.25 3.00
110 Bucky Jacobsen FUT 1.25 3.00
111 Ryan Howard FUT 2.00 5.00
112 Jeff Francis FUT 1.25 3.00
113 Jason Lane FUT 1.25 3.00
114 Alexis Rios FUT 1.25 3.00
115 Bobby Madritsch FUT 1.25 3.00
116 Jesse Crain FUT 1.25 3.00
117 Oliver Perez FUT 1.25 3.00
118 Garrett Atkins FUT 1.25 3.00
119 Casey Kotchman FUT 1.25 3.00
120 B.J. Upton FUT 1.25 3.00
121 Laynce Nix FUT 1.25 3.00
122 Adrian Gonzalez FUT 1.25 3.00
123 Joe Blanton FUT 1.25 3.00
124 Gabe Gross FUT 1.25 3.00
125 Scott Kazmir FUT 1.25 3.00
126 Zack Greinke FUT 1.25 3.00
127 Edwin Jackson FUT 1.25 3.00
128 Jason Bay FUT 1.25 3.00
129 J.D. Closser FUT 1.25 3.00
130 Jason DuBois FUT 1.25 3.00
131 Dallas McPherson FUT 1.25 3.00
132 Chad Cordero FUT 1.25 3.00
133 Angel Guzman FUT 1.25 3.00
134 Jayson Werth FUT 1.25 3.00
135 Ryan Wagner FUT 1.25 3.00
136 Guillermo Quiroz FUT 1.25 3.00
137 Scott Proctor FUT 1.25 3.00
138 Chris Burke FUT 1.25 3.00
139 Nick Swisher FUT 1.25 3.00
140 David DeJesus FUT 1.25 3.00
141 Yhency Brazoban FUT 1.25 3.00
142 Bobby Crosby FUT 1.25 3.00
143 Chase Utley FUT 1.50 4.00
144 Wily Mo Pena FUT 1.25 3.00
145 Roman Colon FUT 1.25 3.00
146 Eddy Rodriguez FUT 1.25 3.00
147 Gerald Laird FUT 1.25 3.00
148 Jose Capellan FUT 1.25 3.00
149 Aaron Rowand FUT 1.25 3.00
150 Kevin Youkilis FUT 1.25 3.00
151 Bob Feller LGD 1.50 4.00
152 Robin Yount LGD 1.50 4.00
153 Willie Stargell LGD 1.50 4.00
154 Cal Ripken LGD 4.00 10.00
155 Monte Irvin LGD 1.25 3.00
156 Nolan Ryan LGD 3.00 8.00
157 Bob Lemon LGD 1.25 3.00
158 Richie Ashburn LGD 1.50 4.00
159 Billy Williams LGD 1.25 3.00
160 Luis Aparicio LGD 1.25 3.00
161 Phil Niekro LGD 1.25 3.00
162 Bobby Doerr LGD 1.25 3.00
163 Mike Schmidt LGD 2.50 6.00
164 Stan Musial LGD 2.00 5.00
165 George Kell LGD 1.25 3.00
166 Joe Morgan LGD 1.25 3.00
167 Whitey Ford LGD 1.50 4.00
168 Rick Ferrell LGD 1.25 3.00
169 Catfish Hunter LGD 1.50 4.00
170 Red Schoendienst LGD 1.25 3.00
171 Tom Seaver LGD 1.50 4.00
172 Pee Wee Reese LGD 1.50 4.00
173 Lou Boudreau LGD 1.25 3.00
174 Hal Newhouser LGD 1.25 3.00
175 Harmon Killebrew LGD 1.50 4.00
176 Jim Bunning LGD 1.25 3.00
177 Willie McCovey LGD 1.50 4.00
178 Bob Gibson LGD 1.50 4.00
179 Juan Marichal LGD 1.25 3.00
180 Robin Roberts LGD 1.25 3.00
181 Gaylord Perry LGD 1.25 3.00
182 Brooks Robinson LGD 1.50 4.00
183 Al Lopez LGD 1.25 3.00
184 Joe DiMaggio LGD 2.50 6.00
185 Al Kaline LGD 1.50 4.00
186 Rollie Fingers LGD 1.25 3.00
187 Mickey Mantle LGD 8.00 20.00
188 Enos Slaughter LGD 1.25 3.00
189 Ernie Banks LGD 1.50 4.00
190 Eddie Mathews LGD 1.50 4.00
191 Tommy Lasorda LGD 1.25 3.00
192 Fergie Jenkins LGD 1.25 3.00
193 Lou Brock LGD 1.50 4.00
194 Larry Doby LGD 1.25 3.00
195 Phil Rizzuto LGD 1.50 4.00
196 Warren Spahn LGD 1.50 4.00
197 Ralph Kiner LGD 1.50 4.00
198 Hoyt Wilhelm LGD 1.25 3.00
199 Early Wynn LGD 1.25 3.00
200 Yogi Berra LGD 1.50 4.00
201 Adam Shabala FR RC .40 1.00
202 Ambiorix Burgos FR RC .40 1.00
203 Ambiorix Concepcion FR RC .40 1.00
204 Anibal Sanchez FR RC 1.25 3.00
205 Bill McCarthy FR RC .40 1.00
206 Brandon McCarthy FR RC .60 1.50
207 Brian Burres FR RC .40 1.00
208 Carlos Ruiz FR RC .40 1.00
209 Casey Rogowski FR RC .50 1.25
210 Chad Orvella FR RC .40 1.00
211 Chris Resop FR RC .40 1.00
212 Chris Roberson FR RC .40 1.00
213 Chris Seddon FR RC .40 1.00
214 Colter Bean FR RC .40 1.00
215 Dae-Sung Koo FR RC .40 1.00
216 Yuniesky Betancourt FR RC .75 2.00
217 Dave Gassner FR RC .40 1.00
218 Brian Anderson FR RC .60 1.50
219 D.J. Houlton FR RC .40 1.00
220 Derek Wathan FR RC .40 1.00
221 Devon Lowery FR RC .40 1.00
222 Enrique Gonzalez FR RC .40 1.00
223 Ryan Zimmerman FR RC 3.00 8.00
224 Eude Brito FR RC .40 1.00
225 Francisco Butto FR RC .40 1.00
226 Franquelis Osoria FR RC .40 1.00
227 Garrett Jones FR RC .40 1.00
228 Geovany Soto FR RC 1.50 4.00
229 Hayden Penn FR RC .50 1.25
230 Ismael Ramirez FR RC .40 1.00
231 Jared Gothreaux FR RC .40 1.00
232 Jason Hammel FR RC .40 1.00
233 Chris Denorfia FR RC .50 1.25
234 Jeff Miller FR RC .40 1.00
235 Jeff Niemann FR RC .50 1.25
236 Dana Eveland FR RC .40 1.00
237 Joel Peralta FR RC .40 1.00
238 John Hattig FR RC .40 1.00
239 Jorge Campillo FR RC .40 1.00
240 Juan Morillo FR RC .40 1.00
241 Justin Verlander FR RC 1.50 4.00
242 Ryan Garko FR RC .75 2.00
243 Keiichi Yabu FR RC .40 1.00
244 Kendry Morales FR RC 1.00 2.50
245 Luis Hernandez FR RC .40 1.00
246 Jermaine Van Buren FR .40 1.00
247 Luis Pena FR RC .40 1.00
248 Luis O.Rodriguez FR RC .40 1.00
249 Luke Scott FR RC .75 2.00
250 Marcos Carvajal FR RC .40 1.00
251 Mark Woodyard FR RC .40 1.00
252 Matt A.Smith FR RC .40 1.00
253 Matthew Lindstrom FR RC .40 1.00
254 Miguel Negron FR RC .50 1.25
255 Mike Morse FR RC .40 1.00
256 Nate McLouth FR RC .50 1.25
257 Nelson Cruz FR RC .75 2.00
258 Nick Masset FR RC .40 1.00
259 Mark McLemore FR RC .40 1.00
260 Oscar Robles FR RC .40 1.00
261 Paulino Reynoso FR RC .40 1.00
262 Pedro Lopez FR RC .40 1.00
263 Pete Orr FR RC .40 1.00
264 Philip Humber FR RC .50 1.25
265 Prince Fielder FR RC 1.50 4.00
266 Randy Messenger FR RC .40 1.00
267 Randy Williams FR RC .40 1.00
268 Raul Tablado FR RC .40 1.00
269 Ronny Paulino FR RC .50 1.25
270 Russ Rohlicek FR RC .40 1.00
271 Russell Martin FR RC .75 2.00
272 Scott Baker FR RC .50 1.25
273 Scott Munter FR RC .40 1.00
274 Sean Thompson FR RC .40 1.00
275 Sean Tracey FR RC .40 1.00
276 Shane Costa FR RC .40 1.00
277 Stephen Drew FR RC 2.00 5.00
278 Steve Schmoll FR RC .40 1.00
279 Ryan Spilborghs FR RC .50 1.25
280 Tadahito Iguchi FR RC .75 2.00
281 Tony Giarratano FR RC .40 1.00
282 Tony Pena FR RC .40 1.00
283 Travis Bowyer FR RC .40 1.00
284 Ubaldo Jimenez FR RC .75 2.00
285 Wladimir Balentien FR RC .50 1.25
286 Yorman Bazardo FR RC .40 1.00

2005 Reflections Blue

*BLUE 1-100: 1.5X TO 4X BASIC
*BLUE 101-150: 1X TO 2.5X BASIC
*BLUE 151-200: 1X TO 2.5X BASIC
1-200 OVERALL PARALLEL ODDS 1:6
*BLUE 201-286: 2X TO 5X BASIC
201-286 ISSUED IN '05 UD UPDATE PACKS
201-286 ONE #'d CARD OR AU PER PACK
STATED PRINT RUN 75 SERIAL #'d SETS
1 Corey Patterson 1.25 3.00
187 Mickey Mantle LGD 25.00 60.00

2005 Reflections Emerald

*EMERALD 1-100: 3X TO 8X BASIC
*EMERALD 101-150: 2X TO 5X BASIC
*EMERALD 151-200: 2X TO 5X BASIC
1-200 OVERALL PARALLEL ODDS 1:6
201-286 ISSUED IN '05 UD UPDATE PACKS
201-286 ONE #'d CARD OR AU PER PACK
STATED PRINT RUN 25 SERIAL #'d SETS
201-286 NO PRICING DUE TO SCARCITY
1 Corey Patterson 2.50 6.00
187 Mickey Mantle LGD 40.00 100.00

2005 Reflections Platinum

1-200 OVERALL PARALLEL ODDS 1:6
201-286 ISSUED IN '05 UD UPDATE PACKS
201-286 ONE #'d CARD OR AU PER PACK
STATED PRINT RUN 1 SERIAL #'d SET
NO PRICING DUE TO SCARCITY
1 Corey Patterson

2005 Reflections Purple

*PURPLE 1-100: 1.5X TO 4X BASIC
*PURPLE 101-150: 1X TO 2.5X BASIC
*PURPLE 151-200: 1X TO 2.5X BASIC
1-200 OVERALL PARALLEL ODDS 1:6
*PURPLE 201-286: 1.5X TO 4X BASIC
201-286 ISSUED IN '05 UD UPDATE PACKS
201-286 ONE #'d CARD OR AU PER PACK
STATED PRINT RUN 99 SERIAL #'d SETS
1 Corey Patterson 1.25 3.00
187 Mickey Mantle LGD 25.00 60.00

2005 Reflections Red

*RED 1-100: 1.5X TO 4X BASIC
*RED 101-150: 1X TO 2.5X BASIC
*RED 151-200: 1X TO 2.5X BASIC
1-200 OVERALL PARALLEL ODDS 1:6
*RED 201-286: 1.5X TO 4X BASIC
201-286 ISSUED IN '05 UD UPDATE PACKS
201-286 ONE #'d CARD OR AU PER PACK
STATED PRINT RUN 99 SERIAL #'d SETS
1 Corey Patterson 1.25 3.00
187 Mickey Mantle LGD 25.00 60.00

2005 Reflections Turquoise

*TURQUOISE 1-100: 2X TO 5X BASIC
*TURQUOISE 101-150: 1.25X TO 3X BASIC
*TURQUOISE 151-200: 1.25X TO 3X BASIC
1-200 OVERALL PARALLEL ODDS 1:6
*TURQUOISE 201-286: 2.5X TO 6X BASIC
201-286 ISSUED IN '05 UD UPDATE PACKS
201-286 ONE #'d CARD OR AU PER PACK
STATED PRINT RUN 50 SERIAL #'d SETS
1 Corey Patterson 1.50 4.00
187 Mickey Mantle LGD 30.00 80.00

2005 Reflections Cut From the Same Cloth Dual Jersey

STATED PRINT RUN 225 SERIAL #'d SETS
*BLUE: .6X TO 1.5X BASIC
BLUE PRINT RUN 50 SERIAL #'d SETS
PLATINUM PRINT RUN 1 SERIAL #'d SET
NO PLATINUM PRICING DUE TO SCARCITY
*RED: .5X TO 1.2X BASIC
RED PRINT RUN 99 SERIAL #'d SETS
OVERALL DUAL GU ODDS 1:12
AA Adrian Beltre 6.00 15.00
Albert Pujols
AB Bobby Abreu 4.00 10.00
Carlos Beltran
AG Garret Anderson 5.00 12.00
Vladimir Guerrero
AH Alfonso Soriano 4.00 10.00
Hank Blalock
AJ Albert Pujols 6.00 15.00
Jim Thome
AM Adrian Beltre 4.00 10.00
Miguel Cabrera
AT Bobby Abreu 4.00 10.00
Jim Thome
AW Albert Pujols 6.00 15.00
Will Clark
BB Craig Biggio 5.00 12.00
Jeff Bagwell
BD1 Carlos Beltran Mets 4.00 10.00
Johnny Damon Sox
BD2 Carlos Beltran Royals 4.00 10.00
Johnny Damon Royals
BG Carlos Beltran 6.00 15.00
Ken Griffey Jr.
BM George Brett 6.00 15.00
Paul Molitor
BO Josh Beckett 4.00 10.00
Roy Oswalt
BP Johnny Bench Pants 6.00 15.00
Mike Piazza
BR Adrian Beltre 4.00 10.00
Scott Rolen
BS George Brett 10.00 25.00
Mike Schmidt
BT Hank Blalock 4.00 10.00
Mark Teixeira
BW David Wright 6.00 15.00
Hank Blalock
CB Bobby Crosby 4.00 10.00
Jason Bay
CC Bobby Crosby 4.00 10.00
Eric Chavez
CG Bobby Crosby 4.00 10.00
Khalil Greene
CL Miguel Cabrera 4.00 10.00
Mike Lowell
CP Carl Crawford 4.00 10.00
Scott Podsednik
CR Eric Chavez 4.00 10.00
Scott Rolen
CT Bobby Crosby 4.00 10.00
Miguel Tejada
DM Dale Murphy Pants 10.00 25.00
Mike Schmidt
DR Johnny Damon 4.00 10.00
Manny Ramirez
GG1 Ken Griffey Jr. Reds 8.00 20.00
Ken Griffey Sr. Reds
GG2 Ken Griffey Jr. M's 8.00 20.00
Ken Griffey Sr. M's
GI Brian Giles 4.00 10.00
Marcus Giles
GS Ken Griffey Jr. 6.00 15.00
Sammy Sosa
GV Jose Guillen 4.00 10.00
Jose Vidro
HH Rich Harden 4.00 10.00
Tim Hudson
HK Harmon Killebrew 10.00 25.00
Kent Hrbek
JD Chipper Jones 5.00 12.00
J.D. Drew
JH Jacque Jones 4.00 10.00
Torii Hunter
JJ Andruw Jones 5.00 12.00
Chipper Jones
JM Derek Jeter 15.00 40.00
Don Mattingly
JR Nolan Ryan 10.00 25.00
Randy Johnson
JS Johan Santana 4.00 10.00
Steve Carlton
JT Derek Jeter 8.00 20.00
Miguel Tejada
KH Jason Kendall 4.00 10.00
Tim Hudson
KM Casey Kotchman 4.00 10.00
Dallas McPherson
MB Don Mattingly 10.00 25.00
Wade Boggs Pants
MC Don Mattingly 10.00 25.00
Will Clark
MH Mark Mulder 4.00 10.00
Tim Hudson
MJ Chipper Jones 8.00 20.00
Dale Murphy Pants
MK Harmon Killebrew 8.00 20.00
Justin Morneau
MM Hideki Matsui 15.00 40.00
Kazuo Matsui
MS Joe Mauer 4.00 10.00
Johan Santana
MW Dallas McPherson 6.00 15.00
David Wright
MY Paul Molitor 10.00 25.00
Robin Yount
OD David Ortiz 4.00 10.00
Johnny Damon
OT Akinori Otsuka 4.00 10.00
Shingo Takatsu
PB Jim Bunning 4.00 10.00
Jim Palmer
PC Albert Pujols 6.00 15.00
Miguel Cabrera
PG Albert Pujols 6.00 15.00
Vladimir Guerrero
PP Jorge Posada 5.00 12.00
Mike Piazza
PR Albert Pujols 6.00 15.00
Scott Rolen
PS Mark Prior 4.00 10.00
Tom Seaver
PT Albert Pujols 6.00 15.00
Mark Teixeira
RJ Cal Ripken 15.00 40.00
Derek Jeter
RM Ivan Rodriguez 4.00 10.00
Victor Martinez
RO David Ortiz 6.00 15.00
Manny Ramirez
RP Ivan Rodriguez 5.00 12.00
Mike Piazza
RR Brooks Robinson 15.00 40.00
Cal Ripken
RT Cal Ripken 12.50 30.00
Miguel Tejada
RW David Wright 6.00 15.00
Scott Rolen
SB Ryne Sandberg 12.50 30.00
Wade Boggs
SM Curt Schilling 4.00 10.00
Pedro Martinez
SO Curt Schilling 4.00 10.00
David Ortiz
SP Ben Sheets 4.00 10.00
Mark Prior
SR Mike Schmidt 6.00 15.00
Scott Rolen
ST Alfonso Soriano 4.00 10.00
Mark Teixeira
TC Mark Teixeira 4.00 10.00
Miguel Cabrera
TH Jim Thome 4.00 10.00
Todd Helton
TP Miguel Tejada 4.00 10.00
Rafael Palmeiro
TR Jim Thome 4.00 10.00
Manny Ramirez
TS Jim Thome 8.00 20.00
Mike Schmidt
UJ B.J. Upton 8.00 20.00
Derek Jeter
UK B.J. Upton 4.00 10.00
Scott Kazmir
UW B.J. Upton 4.00 10.00
David Wright
VJ Jose Vidro 4.00 10.00
Nick Johnson
WB Bernie Williams 4.00 10.00
Carlos Beltran
WJ Bernie Williams 12.50 30.00
Derek Jeter
WM Bernie Williams 12.50 30.00
Hideki Matsui
WP Kerry Wood 6.00 15.00
Mark Prior
WR Kerry Wood 10.00 25.00
Nolan Ryan
YR Carl Yastrzemski 10.00 25.00
Manny Ramirez
ZM Barry Zito 4.00 10.00
Mark Mulder

2005 Reflections Cut From the Same Cloth Dual Patch

*PATCH: 1X TO 2.5X BASIC
OVERALL PREMIUM AU-GU ODDS 1:24
STATED PRINT RUN 99 SERIAL #'d SETS
BS George Brett 20.00 50.00
Mike Schmidt
CP Gary Carter 12.50 30.00
Mike Piazza
DG Adam Dunn 20.00 50.00
Ken Griffey Jr.
GC Ken Griffey Jr. 20.00 50.00
Miguel Cabrera
JM Derek Jeter 40.00 80.00
Don Mattingly
JR Cal Ripken 40.00 80.00
Derek Jeter
MP Joe Mauer 12.50 30.00
Mike Piazza
MY Paul Molitor 20.00 50.00
Robin Yount
OB David Ortiz 10.00 25.00
Wade Boggs
RJ Nolan Ryan 20.00 50.00
Randy Johnson
RR Brooks Robinson 30.00 60.00
Cal Ripken
RW Kerry Wood 20.00 50.00
Nolan Ryan
SB Ryne Sandberg 40.00 80.00
Wade Boggs
TO Mark Teixeira 10.00 25.00
David Ortiz
YO Carl Yastrzemski 20.00 50.00
David Ortiz

2005 Reflections Cut From the Same Cloth Dual Patch Autograph

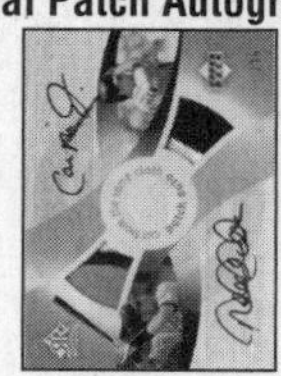

OVERALL PREMIUM AU-GU ODDS 1:24
STATED PRINT RUN 25 SERIAL #'d SETS
NO PRICING DUE TO SCARCITY
AM Adrian Beltre
Miguel Cabrera
BR Adrian Beltre
Scott Rolen
BT Hank Blalock
Mark Teixeira
CB Bobby Crosby
Jason Bay
CG Bobby Crosby
Khalil Greene
CP Gary Carter
Mike Piazza
CR Eric Chavez
Scott Rolen
DG Adam Dunn
Ken Griffey Jr.
GC Ken Griffey Jr.
Miguel Cabrera
GG1 Ken Griffey Jr. Reds
Ken Griffey Sr. Reds
GG2 Ken Griffey Jr. M's
Ken Griffey Sr. M's
GI Brian Giles
Marcus Giles
JC Randy Johnson
Roger Clemens
JM Derek Jeter
Don Mattingly
JR Cal Ripken
Derek Jeter
KM Casey Kotchman
Dallas McPherson
MJ Chipper Jones
Dale Murphy Pants
MP Joe Mauer
Mike Piazza
MW Dallas McPherson
David Wright
MY Paul Molitor
Robin Yount
OB David Ortiz
Wade Boggs
OT Akinori Otsuka
Shingo Takatsu
PB Adrian Beltre
Albert Pujols
PC Albert Pujols
Miguel Cabrera
PR Albert Pujols
Scott Rolen
RC Nolan Ryan
Roger Clemens
RJ Nolan Ryan
Randy Johnson
RP Ivan Rodriguez
Mike Piazza
RR Brooks Robinson
Cal Ripken
RW Kerry Wood
Nolan Ryan
SB Ryne Sandberg
Wade Boggs
SC Johan Santana
Roger Clemens
SP Ben Sheets
Mark Prior
TC Mark Teixeira
Miguel Cabrera
TO Mark Teixeira
David Ortiz
UJ B.J. Upton
Derek Jeter
UW B.J. Upton
David Wright
WB David Wright
Hank Blalock
WP Kerry Wood
Mark Prior
WR David Wright
Scott Rolen
YO Carl Yastrzemski
David Ortiz

2005 Reflections Dual Signatures

TIER 3 PRINT RUNS 275 OR MORE PER
TIER 2 PRINT RUNS B/WN 125-199 PER
TIER 1 PRINT RUNS 75 OR LESS PER
CARDS ARE NOT SERIAL-NUMBERED
PRINT RUN INFO PROVIDED BY UD
PLATINUM PRINT RUN 1 SERIAL #'d SET
NO PLATINUM PRICING DUE TO SCARCITY
OVERALL DUAL AUTO ODDS 1:12
EXCHANGE DEADLINE 06/07/08
ABAR Adrian Beltre
Al Rosen T1
ABDM Adrian Beltre 10.00 25.00
Dallas McPherson T1 EXCH
ABDW Adrian Beltre 30.00 60.00
David Wright T1
ABEC Adrian Beltre 12.50 30.00
Eric Chavez T1
ABJL Adrian Beltre 10.00 25.00
Justin Leone T1
ABSR Adrian Beltre
Scott Rolen T1 EXCH
AHBU Aubrey Huff 12.50 30.00
B.J. Upton T1
AHCC Aubrey Huff 10.00 25.00
Carl Crawford T1 EXCH
AKDM Al Kaline
Dale Murphy T1
AOST Akinori Otsuka 15.00 40.00
Shingo Takatsu T3
ARCC Alexis Rios 8.00 20.00
Carl Crawford T3 EXCH
ARKG Alexis Rios 40.00 80.00
Ken Griffey Jr. T1
ARTH Al Rosen 10.00 25.00
Travis Hafner T2
BAKY Bronson Arroyo 20.00 50.00
Kevin Youkilis T1
BCCR Bobby Crosby
Cal Ripken T1 EXCH
BCDJ Bobby Crosby 75.00 150.00
Derek Jeter T1 EXCH
BCEC Bobby Crosby 10.00 25.00
Eric Chavez T1 EXCH
BCJB Bobby Crosby 10.00 25.00
Jason Bay T1 EXCH
BCKG Bobby Crosby
Khalil Greene T1 EXCH
BDWB Bobby Doerr
Wade Boggs T1
BGMG Brian Giles 10.00 25.00
Marcus Giles T1 EXCH
BPFH Boog Powell 12.50 30.00
Frank Howard T1
BRRS Brooks Robinson 20.00 50.00
Ron Santo T1
BSJC Ben Sheets 8.00 20.00
Jose Capellan T2
BSRW Ben Sheets 10.00 25.00
Rickie Weeks T1
BSSK Ben Sheets 10.00 25.00
Scott Kazmir T1
BUCC B.J. Upton
Carl Crawford T1 EXCH
BUDJ B.J. Upton 75.00 150.00
Derek Jeter T1
BURW B.J. Upton 10.00 25.00
Rickie Weeks T1
BUSK B.J. Upton 10.00 25.00
Scott Kazmir T2
BWKG Billy Williams 50.00 100.00
Ken Griffey Jr. T1
CCNJ Chad Cordero 8.00 20.00
Nick Johnson T2
CKDM Casey Kotchman 8.00 20.00
Dallas McPherson T3 EXCH
CKKH Casey Kotchman 8.00 20.00
Keith Hernandez T3
CKMT Casey Kotchman 12.50 30.00
Mark Teixeira T1
CTDM Charles Thomas 12.50 30.00
Dale Murphy T1
CTJC Charles Thomas 6.00 15.00
Jose Capellan T3
CTRH Charles Thomas 20.00 50.00
Ryan Howard T3
CZJS Carlos Zambrano 30.00 60.00
Johan Santana T1 EXCH
CZLT Carlos Zambrano
Luis Tiant T1
DGDB Dwight Gooden 6.00 15.00
Dewon Brazelton T3
DGJB Dwight Gooden 8.00 20.00
Jim Bouton T3
DGJS Dwight Gooden 12.50 30.00
Johan Santana T1 EXCH
DJDM Derek Jeter 150.00 250.00
Don Mattingly T1
DJKG Derek Jeter 75.00 150.00
Khalil Greene T1 EXCH
DKFH Dave Kingman 15.00 40.00
Frank Howard T3
DMDW Dallas McPherson 30.00 60.00
David Wright T2 EXCH
DMJB Dale Murphy 20.00 50.00
Jason Bay T1
DMJL Dallas McPherson 6.00 15.00
Justin Leone T3EXCH
DMKY Dallas McPherson 6.00 15.00
Kevin Youkilis T3 EXCH
DMMS Dallas McPherson 50.00 100.00
Mike Schmidt T1 EXCH
DMRH Dallas McPherson 20.00 50.00
Ryan Howard T3 EXCH
DMSR Dallas McPherson
Scott Rolen T1 EXCH
DMWC Don Mattingly
Will Clark T1
DOKY David Ortiz 30.00 60.00
Kevin Youkilis T1
DWJL David Wright 20.00 50.00
Justin Leone T3
DWKH David Wright 20.00 50.00
Keith Hernandez T1
DWKY David Wright 30.00 60.00
Kevin Youkilis T3
DWMS David Wright 50.00 100.00
Mike Schmidt T1
DWSR David Wright 30.00 60.00
Scott Rolen T1 EXCH
ECSR Eric Chavez
Scott Rolen T1 EXCH
FHMT Frank Howard 12.50 30.00
Mark Teixeira T1
FHNJ Frank Howard 8.00 20.00
Nick Johnson T3
GPJP Gaylord Perry 10.00 25.00
Jake Peavy T1
ISJC Ian Snell 6.00 15.00
Jose Capellan T3
ISMV Ian Snell 6.00 15.00
Merkin Valdez T3
ISSK Ian Snell 10.00 25.00
Scott Kazmir T3
JBIS Joe Blanton 6.00 15.00
Ian Snell T3
JBJP Jim Bunning 12.50 30.00
Jim Palmer T1
JBMV Joe Blanton 6.00 15.00
Merkin Valdez T3
JBRH Joe Blanton 8.00 20.00
Rich Harden T3
JBSK Joe Blanton 10.00 25.00
Scott Kazmir T3
JCMV Jose Capellan 6.00 15.00
Merkin Valdez T3
JLRH Justin Leone 20.00 50.00
Ryan Howard T3
JPJB Joe Blanton 10.00 25.00
Jake Peavy T2
JPKG Jake Peavy 20.00 50.00
Khalil Greene T1
JPRH Jake Peavy 10.00 25.00
Rich Harden T2
JPSK Jake Peavy 10.00 25.00
Scott Kazmir T1
JRDW Jose Reyes 40.00 80.00
David Wright T1
JSMP Johan Santana 40.00 80.00
Mark Prior T1 EXCH
JSSC Johan Santana 30.00 60.00
Steve Carlton T1 EXCH
JSSK Johan Santana 20.00 50.00
Scott Kazmir T1 EXCH
JVMG Jose Vidro 10.00 25.00
Marcus Giles T1 EXCH
KGKG Ken Griffey Sr. 60.00 120.00
Ken Griffey Jr. T2
KGMC Ken Griffey Jr. 50.00 100.00
Miguel Cabrera T1
KYWB Kevin Youkilis 20.00 50.00
Wade Boggs T1
MCRH Miguel Cabrera 30.00 60.00
Ryan Howard T1
MGRW Marcus Giles 10.00 25.00
Rickie Weeks T1 EXCH
MTHB Mark Teixeira 12.50 30.00
Hank Blalock T1
MTMC Mark Teixeira 20.00 50.00
Miguel Cabrera T1
MTRH Mark Teixeira 20.00 50.00
Ryan Howard T1
MVRH Merkin Valdez 8.00 20.00
Rich Harden T3
PBKG Pat Burrell 40.00 80.00
Ken Griffey Jr. T1 EXCH
PBMC Pat Burrell 12.50 30.00
Miguel Cabrera T1 EXCH
RHDO Ryan Howard 60.00 120.00
David Ortiz T1
RHRO Rich Harden 10.00 25.00
Roy Oswalt T1
RHSK Rich Harden 10.00 25.00
Scott Kazmir T3
THVM Travis Hafner 12.50 30.00
Victor Martinez T1
TOKH Tony Oliva 10.00 25.00
Kent Hrbek T3
VMYM Victor Martinez 8.00 20.00
Yadier Molina T3

2005 Reflections Dual Signatures Blue

*BLUE: .6X TO 1.5X BASIC T3
*BLUE: .6X TO 1.5X BASIC T2
*BLUE: .5X TO 1.2X BASIC T1
OVERALL AUTO ODDS 1:12
STATED PRINT RUN 35 SERIAL #'d SETS
EXCHANGE DEADLINE 06/07/08
ABAR Adrian Beltre 12.50 30.00
Al Rosen
ABSR Adrian Beltre 15.00 40.00
Scott Rolen EXCH
AKDM Al Kaline 40.00 80.00
Dale Murphy
ARKG Alexis Rios 50.00 100.00
Ken Griffey Jr.
BAKY Bronson Arroyo 30.00 60.00
Kevin Youkilis
BCCR Bobby Crosby 125.00 200.00
Cal Ripken EXCH
BCDJ Bobby Crosby 125.00 200.00
Derek Jeter EXCH
BCKG Bobby Crosby 15.00 40.00
Khalil Greene EXCH
BDWB Bobby Doerr 30.00 60.00
Wade Boggs
BSSK Ben Sheets 12.50 30.00
Scott Kazmir
BUCC B.J. Upton
Carl Crawford EXCH
BUDJ B.J. Upton 125.00 200.00
Derek Jeter
BWKG Billy Williams 60.00 120.00
Ken Griffey Jr.
CZLT Carlos Zambrano 15.00 40.00
Luis Tiant
DJDM Derek Jeter 175.00 300.00
Don Mattingly
DJKG Derek Jeter 125.00 200.00
Khalil Greene
DMMS Dallas McPherson 60.00 120.00
Mike Schmidt EXCH
DMSR Dallas McPherson 15.00 40.00
Scott Rolen EXCH
DMWC Don Mattingly 40.00 80.00
Will Clark
DWKH David Wright 30.00 60.00
Keith Hernandez
DWMS David Wright 75.00 150.00
Mike Schmidt
DWSR David Wright
Scott Rolen EXCH
ECSR Eric Chavez
Scott Rolen EXCH
KGKG Ken Griffey Sr. 125.00 200.00
Ken Griffey Jr.
KGMC Ken Griffey Jr. 60.00 120.00
Miguel Cabrera
MTHB Mark Teixeira 15.00 40.00
Hank Blalock
PBKG Pat Burrell 50.00 100.00
Ken Griffey Jr. EXCH
THVM Travis Hafner 15.00 40.00
Victor Martinez

2005 Reflections Dual Signatures Red

*RED: .5X TO 1.2X BASIC T3
*RED: .5X TO 1.2X BASIC T2
*RED: .4X TO 1X BASIC T1
OVERALL AUTO ODDS 1:12
STATED PRINT RUN 99 SERIAL #'d SETS
EXCHANGE DEADLINE 06/07/08
ABAR Adrian Beltre 10.00 25.00
Al Rosen
ABSR Adrian Beltre 12.50 30.00
Scott Rolen EXCH
AKDM Al Kaline 30.00 60.00
Dale Murphy
BAKY Bronson Arroyo 20.00 50.00
Kevin Youkilis
BCCR Bobby Crosby 75.00 150.00
Cal Ripken EXCH
BCDJ Bobby Crosby 75.00 150.00
Derek Jeter EXCH
BCKG Bobby Crosby
Khalil Greene EXCH
BDWB Bobby Doerr 20.00 50.00
Wade Boggs
BSSK Ben Sheets 10.00 25.00
Scott Kazmir
BUCC B.J. Upton 12.50 30.00
Carl Crawford EXCH
BUDJ B.J. Upton 75.00 150.00
Derek Jeter
BWKG Billy Williams 50.00 100.00
Ken Griffey Jr.
CZLT Carlos Zambrano 12.50 30.00
Luis Tiant
DJDM Derek Jeter 150.00 250.00
Don Mattingly
DJKG Derek Jeter 75.00 150.00
Khalil Greene
DMMS Dallas McPherson 50.00 100.00
Mike Schmidt EXCH
DMSR Dallas McPherson
Scott Rolen EXCH
DMWC Don Mattingly 50.00 100.00
Will Clark
DWKH David Wright 20.00 50.00
Keith Hernandez
DWMS David Wright 60.00 120.00
Mike Schmidt
DWSR David Wright 30.00 60.00
Scott Rolen EXCH
ECSR Eric Chavez 12.50 30.00
Scott Rolen EXCH
KGKG Ken Griffey Sr. 75.00 150.00
Ken Griffey Jr.
KGMC Ken Griffey Jr. 50.00 100.00
Miguel Cabrera
MTHB Mark Teixeira 12.50 30.00
Hank Blalock
RHDO Ryan Howard 50.00 100.00
David Ortiz
THVM Travis Hafner 10.00 25.00
Victor Martinez

2005 Reflections Fabric Jersey

STATED ODDS 1:12
SP INFO PROVIDED BY UPPER DECK
AB Adrian Beltre 3.00 8.00
AP Albert Pujols 6.00 15.00
AS Alfonso Soriano 3.00 8.00
BW Bernie Williams 3.00 8.00
CB Carlos Beltran 3.00 8.00
CJ Chipper Jones 4.00 10.00
CR Cal Ripken SP 15.00 40.00
CS Curt Schilling 3.00 8.00
CY Carl Yastrzemski SP 10.00 25.00
DJ Derek Jeter SP 10.00 25.00
DM Don Mattingly SP 10.00 25.00
DO David Ortiz 3.00 8.00
DW David Wright 4.00 10.00
EC Eric Chavez 3.00 8.00
GB George Brett SP 10.00 25.00
GM Greg Maddux 4.00 10.00
HB Hank Blalock 3.00 8.00
HM Hideki Matsui 8.00 20.00
IR Ivan Rodriguez 3.00 8.00
JD Johnny Damon 3.00 8.00
JS Johan Santana 4.00 10.00
JT Jim Thome 3.00 8.00
KG Ken Griffey Jr. 6.00 15.00
KW Kerry Wood 3.00 8.00
MC Miguel Cabrera 3.00 8.00
MP Mark Prior 3.00 8.00
MR Manny Ramirez 3.00 8.00
MS Mike Schmidt SP 10.00 25.00
MT Mark Teixeira 3.00 8.00
NR Nolan Ryan SP 12.50 30.00
PI Mike Piazza 4.00 10.00
PM Paul Molitor SP 4.00 10.00
RJ Randy Johnson 4.00 10.00
RY Robin Yount SP 8.00 20.00
SR Scott Rolen 3.00 8.00
TE Miguel Tejada 3.00 8.00
TH Todd Helton 3.00 8.00
VG Vladimir Guerrero 4.00 10.00
WB Wade Boggs SP 6.00 15.00
WC Will Clark SP 6.00 15.00

2005 Reflections Fabric Patch

*PATCH ACTIVE: .75X TO 2X BASIC
*PATCH ACTIVE: .6X TO 1.5X BASIC SP
*PATCH RETIRED: .6X TO 1.5X BASIC SP
OVERALL PREMIUM AU-GU ODDS 1:24
STATED PRINT RUN 99 SERIAL #'d SETS
AJ Andruw Jones 6.00 15.00
BC Bobby Crosby 6.00 15.00
BS Ben Sheets 6.00 15.00
BU B.J. Upton 6.00 15.00
CZ Carlos Zambrano 6.00 15.00
DG Dwight Gooden 6.00 15.00
DJ Derek Jeter 20.00 50.00
DM Dale Murphy 6.00 15.00
GP Gaylord Perry 6.00 15.00
GR Khalil Greene 6.00 15.00
JB Jason Bay 6.00 15.00
JP Jake Peavy 6.00 15.00
KG Ken Griffey Jr. 15.00 40.00
MC Dallas McPherson 6.00 15.00
MG Marcus Giles 6.00 15.00
PB Pat Burrell 6.00 15.00
PI Mike Piazza 8.00 20.00
RH Rich Harden 6.00 15.00
RO Roy Oswalt 6.00 15.00
SK Scott Kazmir 6.00 15.00
ST Shingo Takatsu 6.00 15.00

2005 Reflections Fabric Patch Autograph

OVERALL PREMIUM AU-GU ODDS 1:24
STATED PRINT RUN 50 SERIAL #'d SETS
EXHANGE DEADLINE 06/07/08
AB Adrian Beltre 15.00 40.00
AJ Andruw Jones 40.00 80.00
AP Albert Pujols 175.00 300.00
BC Bobby Crosby EXCH 15.00 40.00
BS Ben Sheets 15.00 40.00
BU B.J. Upton 15.00 40.00
CA Miguel Cabrera 20.00 50.00
CR Cal Ripken 150.00 250.00
CZ Carlos Zambrano 15.00 40.00
DG Dwight Gooden 15.00 40.00
DJ Derek Jeter 175.00 300.00
DM Dale Murphy 20.00 50.00
DO David Ortiz 40.00 80.00
DW David Wright 60.00 120.00
EC Eric Chavez 15.00 40.00
GP Gaylord Perry 15.00 40.00
GR Khalil Greene 20.00 50.00
HB Hank Blalock 15.00 40.00
JB Jason Bay 20.00 50.00
JP Jake Peavy 20.00 50.00
JS Johan Santana EXCH 20.00 50.00
KG Ken Griffey Jr. 75.00 150.00
MA Don Mattingly 60.00 120.00
MC Dallas McPherson EXCH 15.00 40.00
MG Marcus Giles EXCH
MP Mark Prior 20.00 50.00
MS Mike Schmidt 60.00 120.00
MT Mark Teixeira 20.00 50.00
NR Nolan Ryan 75.00 150.00
PB Pat Burrell EXCH 15.00 40.00
PI Mike Piazza EXCH 60.00 120.00
PM Paul Molitor 15.00 40.00
RH Rich Harden 15.00 40.00
RJ Randy Johnson 60.00 120.00
RO Roy Oswalt 15.00 40.00
RY Robin Yount 40.00 80.00
SK Scott Kazmir 15.00 40.00
SR Scott Rolen EXCH 20.00 50.00
ST Shingo Takatsu 15.00 40.00
WB Wade Boggs 20.00 50.00

2005 Reflections Super Swatch

STATED PRINT RUN 50 SERIAL #'d SETS
BLUE PRINT RUN 10 SERIAL #'d SETS
NO BLUE PRICING DUE TO SCARCITY
RED PRINT RUN 25 SERIAL #'d SETS

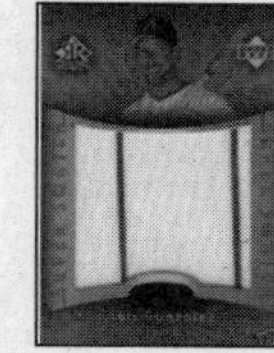

NO RED PRICING DUE TO SCARCITY
OVERALL PREMIUM AU-GU ODDS 1:24
AB Adrian Beltre 6.00 15.00
AD Adam Dunn 6.00 15.00
AH Aubrey Huff 6.00 15.00
AJ Andruw Jones 6.00 15.00
AO Akinori Otsuka 10.00 25.00
AP Albert Pujols 15.00 40.00
AS Alfonso Soriano 6.00 15.00
BA Jeff Bagwell 6.00 15.00
BB Bret Boone 10.00 25.00
BC Bobby Crosby 6.00 15.00
BE Josh Beckett 6.00 15.00
BG Brian Giles 6.00 15.00
BI Craig Biggio 6.00 15.00
BO Bobby Abreu 6.00 15.00
BS Ben Sheets 6.00 15.00
BW Bernie Williams 6.00 15.00
BZ Barry Zito 6.00 15.00
CB Carlos Beltran 6.00 15.00
CC Carl Crawford 6.00 15.00
CD Carlos Delgado 6.00 15.00
CJ Chipper Jones 15.00 40.00
CP Corey Patterson 6.00 15.00
CS C.C. Sabathia 6.00 15.00
DA Johnny Damon 6.00 15.00
DJ Derek Jeter 20.00 50.00
DM Dallas McPherson 6.00 15.00
DO David Ortiz 6.00 15.00
DW David Wright 10.00 25.00
EC Eric Chavez 6.00 15.00
EG Eric Gagne 6.00 15.00
ER Edgar Renteria 6.00 15.00
GA Garret Anderson 6.00 15.00
GM Greg Maddux 15.00 40.00
GR Khalil Greene 6.00 15.00
GS Gary Sheffield 6.00 15.00
HA Roy Halladay 6.00 15.00
HB Hank Blalock 6.00 15.00
HE Todd Helton 6.00 15.00
HM Hideki Matsui 15.00 40.00
HN Hideo Nomo 15.00 40.00
HO Trevor Hoffman 6.00 15.00
HU Torii Hunter 6.00 15.00
IR Ivan Rodriguez 6.00 15.00
JB Jason Bay 6.00 15.00
JD J.D. Drew 6.00 15.00
JE Jim Edmonds 6.00 15.00
JG Jason Giambi 6.00 15.00
JJ Jacque Jones 6.00 15.00
JK Jason Kendall 6.00 15.00
JM Justin Morneau 6.00 15.00
JP Jorge Posada 6.00 15.00
JR Jose Reyes 6.00 15.00
JS Jason Schmidt 6.00 15.00
JT Jim Thome 6.00 15.00
JV Jose Vidro 6.00 15.00
KB Kevin Brown 6.00 15.00
KF Keith Foulke 6.00 15.00
KG Ken Griffey Jr. 15.00 40.00
KM Kazuo Matsui 6.00 15.00
KW Kerry Wood 6.00 15.00
LB Lance Berkman 6.00 15.00
LG Luis Gonzalez 6.00 15.00
MA Moises Alou 6.00 15.00
MC Miguel Cabrera 6.00 15.00
MG Marcus Giles 6.00 15.00
ML Mike Lowell 6.00 15.00
MM Mark Mulder 6.00 15.00
MO Magglio Ordonez 6.00 15.00
MP Mark Prior 6.00 15.00
MR Manny Ramirez 6.00 15.00
MS Mike Sweeney 6.00 15.00
MT Mark Teixeira 6.00 15.00
MU Mike Mussina 6.00 15.00
PI Mike Piazza 8.00 20.00
PM Pedro Martinez 6.00 15.00
RA Roberto Alomar 6.00 15.00
RB Rocco Baldelli 6.00 15.00
RH Rich Harden 6.00 15.00
RJ Randy Johnson 8.00 20.00
RO Roy Oswalt 6.00 15.00
RP Rafael Palmeiro 6.00 15.00
RS Richie Sexson 6.00 15.00
SA Johan Santana 8.00 20.00
SC Curt Schilling 6.00 15.00
SG Shawn Green 6.00 15.00
SK Scott Kazmir 6.00 15.00
SP Scott Podsednik 6.00 15.00
SR Scott Rolen 6.00 15.00
SS Sammy Sosa 8.00 20.00
ST Shingo Takatsu 6.00 15.00
TE Miguel Tejada 6.00 15.00
TG Tom Glavine 10.00 25.00
TH Tim Hudson 6.00 15.00
VG Vladimir Guerrero 8.00 20.00
VM Victor Martinez 6.00 15.00
VW Vernon Wells 6.00 15.00
WA Billy Wagner 6.00 15.00

1988 Score

This set consists of 660 standard-size cards. The set was distributed by Major League Marketing and features six distinctive border colors on the front.

Subsets include Reggie Jackson Tribute (500-504), Highlights (652-660) and Rookie Prospects (623-647). Card number 501, showing Reggie as a member of the Baltimore Orioles, is one of the few opportunities collectors have to visually remember Reggie's one-year stay with the Orioles. The set is distinguished by the fact that each card back shows a full-color picture of the player. Rookie Cards in this set include Ellis Burks, Ken Caminiti, Tom Glavine and Matt Williams.

COMPLETE SET (660) 5.00 10.00
COMP.FACT.SET (660) 7.50 15.00
1 Don Mattingly .25 .60
2 Wade Boggs .05 .15
3 Tim Raines .02 .10
4 Andre Dawson .02 .10
5 Mark McGwire .60 1.50
6 Kevin Seitzer .01 .05
7 Wally Joyner .02 .10
8 Jesse Barfield .02 .10
9 Pedro Guerrero .02 .10
10 Eric Davis .02 .10
11 George Brett .20 .50
12 Ozzie Smith .10 .30
13 Rickey Henderson .07 .20
14 Jim Rice .02 .10
15 Matt Nokes RC .08 .25
16 Mike Schmidt .20 .50
17 Dave Parker .02 .10
18 Eddie Murray .07 .20
19 Andres Galarraga .02 .10
20 Tony Fernandez .01 .05
21 Kevin McReynolds .01 .05
22 B.J. Surhoff .02 .10
23 Pat Tabler .01 .05
24 Kirby Puckett .07 .20
25 Benny Santiago .02 .10
26 Ryne Sandberg .15 .40
27 Kelly Downs .01 .05
28 Jose Cruz .02 .10
29 Pete O'Brien .01 .05
30 Mark Langston .01 .05
31 Lee Smith .02 .10
32 Juan Samuel .01 .05
33 Kevin Bass .01 .05
34 R.J. Reynolds .01 .05
35 Steve Sax .01 .05
36 John Kruk .02 .10
37 Alan Trammell .02 .10
38 Chris Bosio .01 .05
39 Brook Jacoby .01 .05
40 Willie McGee UER .02 .10
(Excited misspelled
as excitd)
41 Dave Magadan .01 .05
42 Fred Lynn .02 .10
43 Kent Hrbek .02 .10
44 Brian Downing .02 .10
45 Jose Canseco .20 .50
46 Jim Presley .01 .05
47 Mike Stanley .01 .05
48 Tony Pena .01 .05
49 David Cone .02 .10
50 Rick Sutcliffe .02 .10
51 Doug Drabek .01 .05
52 Bill Doran .01 .05
53 Mike Scioscia .02 .10
54 Candy Maldonado .01 .05
55 Dave Winfield .02 .10
56 Lou Whitaker .02 .10
57 Tom Henke .01 .05
58 Ken Gerhart .01 .05
59 Glenn Braggs .01 .05
60 Julio Franco .02 .10
61 Charlie Leibrandt .01 .05
62 Gary Gaetti .02 .10
63 Bob Boone .02 .10
64 Luis Polonia RC .08 .25
65 Dwight Evans .05 .15
66 Phil Bradley .01 .05
67 Mike Boddicker .01 .05
68 Vince Coleman .01 .05
69 Howard Johnson .02 .10
70 Tim Wallach .01 .05
71 Keith Moreland .01 .05
72 Barry Larkin .05 .15
73 Alan Ashby .01 .05
74 Rick Rhoden .01 .05
75 Darrell Evans .02 .10
76 Dave Stieb .02 .10
77 Dan Plesac .01 .05
78 Will Clark UER .07 .20
(Born 3/17/64,
should be 3/13/64)
79 Frank White .02 .10
80 Joe Carter .02 .10
81 Mike Witt .01 .05
82 Terry Steinbach .02 .10
83 Alvin Davis .01 .05
84 Tommy Herr .02 .10
85 Vance Law .01 .05
86 Kal Daniels .01 .05
87 Rick Honeycutt UER .01 .05
(Wrong years for
stats on back)
88 Alfredo Griffin .01 .05
89 Bret Saberhagen .02 .10
90 Bert Blyleven .02 .10
91 Jeff Reardon .02 .10
92 Cory Snyder .01 .05
93A Greg Walker ERR .75 2.00
(93 of 66)
93B Greg Walker COR .01 .05
(93 of 660)
94 Joe Magrane RC .08 .25
95 Rob Deer .01 .05
96 Ray Knight .02 .10
97 Casey Candaele .01 .05
98 John Cerutti .01 .05
99 Buddy Bell .02 .10
100 Jack Clark .02 .10
101 Eric Bell .01 .05
102 Willie Wilson .02 .10
103 Dave Schmidt .01 .05
104 Dennis Eckersley UER .05 .15
(Complete games stats
are wrong)
105 Don Sutton .02 .10
106 Danny Tartabull .01 .05
107 Fred McGriff .07 .20
108 Les Straker .01 .05
109 Lloyd Moseby .01 .05
110 Roger Clemens .40 1.00
111 Glenn Hubbard .01 .05
112 Ken Williams RC .01 .05
113 Ruben Sierra .02 .10
114 Stan Jefferson .01 .05
115 Milt Thompson .01 .05
116 Bobby Bonilla .02 .10
117 Wayne Tolleson .01 .05
118 Matt Williams RC .30 .75
119 Chet Lemon .02 .10
120 Dale Sveum .01 .05
121 Dennis Boyd .01 .05
122 Brett Butler .02 .10
123 Terry Kennedy .01 .05
124 Jack Howell .01 .05
125 Curt Young .01 .05
126A Dave Valle ERR .02 .10
(Misspelled Dale
on card front)
126B Dave Valle COR .01 .05
127 Curt Wilkerson .01 .05
128 Tim Teufel .01 .05
129 Ozzie Virgil .01 .05
130 Brian Fisher .01 .05
131 Lance Parrish .02 .10
132 Tom Browning .01 .05
133A Larry Andersen ERR .02 .10
(Misspelled Anderson
on card front)
133B Larry Andersen COR .01 .05
134A Bob Brenly ERR .02 .10
(Misspelled Brenley
on card front)
134B Bob Brenly COR .01 .05
135 Mike Marshall .01 .05
136 Gerald Perry .01 .05
137 Bobby Meacham .01 .05
138 Larry Herndon .01 .05
139 Fred Manrique .01 .05
140 Charlie Hough .02 .10
141 Ron Darling .02 .10
142 Herm Winningham .01 .05
143 Mike Diaz .01 .05
144 Mike Jackson RC .08 .25
145 Denny Walling .01 .05
146 Robby Thompson .01 .05
147 Franklin Stubbs .01 .05
148 Albert Hall .01 .05
149 Bobby Witt .01 .05
150 Lance McCullers .01 .05
151 Scott Bradley .01 .05
152 Mark McLemore .01 .05
153 Tim Laudner .01 .05
154 Greg Swindell .01 .05
155 Marty Barrett .01 .05
156 Mike Heath .01 .05
157 Gary Ward .01 .05
158A Lee Mazzilli ERR .02 .10
(Misspelled Mazilli
on card front)
158B Lee Mazzilli COR .02 .10
159 Tom Foley .01 .05
160 Robin Yount .10 .30
161 Steve Bedrosian .01 .05
162 Bob Walk .01 .05
163 Nick Esasky .01 .05
164 Ken Caminiti RC .75 2.00
165 Jose Uribe .01 .05
166 Dave Anderson .01 .05
167 Ed Whitson .01 .05
168 Ernie Whitt .01 .05
169 Cecil Cooper .02 .10
170 Mike Pagliarulo .01 .05
171 Pat Sheridan .01 .05
172 Chris Bando .01 .05
173 Lee Lacy .01 .05
174 Steve Lombardozzi .01 .05
175 Mike Greenwell .01 .05
176 Greg Minton .01 .05
177 Moose Haas .01 .05
178 Mike Kingery .01 .05
179 Greg A. Harris .01 .05
180 Bo Jackson .07 .20
181 Carmelo Martinez .01 .05
182 Alex Trevino .01 .05
183 Ron Oester .01 .05
184 Danny Darwin .01 .05
185 Mike Krukow .01 .05
186 Rafael Palmeiro .15 .40
187 Tim Burke .01 .05
188 Roger McDowell .01 .05
189 Garry Templeton .02 .10
190 Terry Pendleton .02 .10
191 Larry Parrish .01 .05
192 Rey Quinones .01 .05
193 Joaquin Andujar .02 .10
194 Tom Brunansky .01 .05
195 Donnie Moore .01 .05
196 Dan Pasqua .01 .05
197 Jim Gantner .01 .05
198 Mark Eichhorn .01 .05
199 John Grubb .01 .05
200 Bill Ripken RC .08 .25
201 Sam Horn RC .02 .10
202 Todd Worrell .01 .05
203 Terry Leach .01 .05
204 Garth Iorg .01 .05
205 Brian Dayett .01 .05
206 Bo Diaz .01 .05
207 Craig Reynolds .01 .05
208 Brian Holton .01 .05
209 Marvell Wynne UER .01 .05
(Misspelled Marvelle
on card front)
210 Dave Concepcion .02 .10
211 Mike Davis .01 .05
212 Devon White .02 .10
213 Mickey Brantley .01 .05
214 Greg Gagne .01 .05
215 Oddibe McDowell .01 .05
216 Jimmy Key .02 .10
217 Dave Bergman .01 .05
218 Calvin Schiraldi .01 .05
219 Larry Sheets .01 .05
220 Mike Easler .01 .05
221 Kurt Stillwell .01 .05
222 Chuck Jackson .01 .05
223 Dave Martinez .01 .05
224 Tim Leary .01 .05
225 Steve Garvey .02 .10
226 Greg Mathews .01 .05
227 Doug Sisk .01 .05
228 Dave Henderson .01 .05
(Wearing Red Sox uniform;
Red Sox logo on back)
229 Jimmy Dwyer .01 .05
230 Larry Owen .01 .05
231 Andre Thornton .01 .05
232 Mark Salas .01 .05
233 Tom Brookens .01 .05
234 Greg Brock .01 .05
235 Rance Mulliniks .01 .05
236 Bob Brower .01 .05
237 Joe Niekro .01 .05
238 Scott Bankhead .01 .05
239 Doug DeCinces .01 .05
240 Tommy John .02 .10
241 Rich Gedman .01 .05
242 Ted Power .01 .05
243 Dave Meads .01 .05
244 Jim Sundberg .02 .10
245 Ken Oberkfell .01 .05
246 Jimmy Jones .01 .05
247 Ken Landreaux .01 .05
248 Jose Oquendo .01 .05
249 John Mitchell RC .02 .10
250 Don Baylor .02 .10
251 Scott Fletcher .01 .05
252 Al Newman .01 .05
253 Carney Lansford .02 .10
254 Johnny Ray .01 .05
255 Gary Pettis .01 .05
256 Ken Phelps .01 .05
257 Rick Leach .01 .05
258 Tim Stoddard .01 .05
259 Ed Romero .01 .05
260 Sid Bream .01 .05
261A T.Niedenfuer ERR .02 .10
Misspelled Neidenfuer
on card front
261B T.Niedenfuer COR .01 .05
262 Rick Dempsey .01 .05
263 Lonnie Smith .01 .05
264 Bob Forsch .01 .05
265 Barry Bonds .75 2.00
266 Willie Randolph .02 .10
267 Mike Ramsey .01 .05
268 Don Slaught .01 .05
269 Mickey Tettleton .01 .05
270 Jerry Reuss .01 .05
271 Marc Sullivan .01 .05
272 Jim Morrison .01 .05
273 Steve Balboni .01 .05
274 Dick Schofield .01 .05
275 John Tudor .02 .10
276 Gene Larkin RC .08 .25
277 Harold Reynolds .02 .10
278 Jerry Browne .01 .05
279 Willie Upshaw .01 .05
280 Ted Higuera .01 .05
281 Terry McGriff .01 .05
282 Terry Puhl .01 .05
283 Mark Wasinger .01 .05
284 Luis Salazar .01 .05
285 Ted Simmons .02 .10
286 John Shelby .01 .05
287 John Smiley RC .08 .25
288 Curt Ford .01 .05
289 Steve Crawford .01 .05
290 Dan Quisenberry .01 .05
291 Alan Wiggins .01 .05
292 Randy Bush .01 .05
293 John Candelaria .01 .05
294 Tony Phillips .01 .05
295 Mike Morgan .01 .05
296 Bill Wegman .01 .05
297A Terry Francona ERR .02 .10
(Misspelled Franconia
on card front)
297B Terry Francona COR .02 .10
298 Mickey Hatcher .01 .05
299 Andres Thomas .01 .05
300 Bob Stanley .01 .05
301 Al Pedrique .01 .05
302 Jim Lindeman .01 .05
303 Wally Backman .01 .05
304 Paul O'Neill .05 .15
305 Hubie Brooks .01 .05
306 Steve Buechele .01 .05
307 Bobby Thigpen .01 .05
308 George Hendrick .02 .10
309 John Moses .01 .05
310 Ron Guidry .02 .10
311 Bill Schroeder .01 .05
312 Jose Nunez .01 .05
313 Bud Black .01 .05
314 Joe Sambito .01 .05
315 Scott McGregor .01 .05
316 Rafael Santana .01 .05
317 Frank Williams .01 .05
318 Mike Fitzgerald .01 .05
319 Rick Mahler .01 .05
320 Jim Gott .01 .05
321 Mariano Duncan .01 .05
322 Jose Guzman .01 .05
323 Lee Guetterman .01 .05
324 Dan Gladden .01 .05
325 Gary Carter .02 .10
326 Tracy Jones .01 .05
327 Floyd Youmans .01 .05
328 Bill Dawley .01 .05
329 Paul Noce .01 .05
330 Angel Salazar .01 .05
331 Goose Gossage .02 .10
332 George Frazier .01 .05
333 Ruppert Jones .01 .05
334 Billy Joe Robidoux .01 .05
335 Mike Scott .02 .10
336 Randy Myers .02 .10
337 Bob Sebra .01 .05
338 Eric Show .01 .05
339 Mitch Williams .01 .05
340 Paul Molitor .02 .10
341 Gus Polidor .01 .05
342 Steve Trout .01 .05
343 Jerry Don Gleaton .01 .05
344 Bob Knepper .01 .05
345 Mitch Webster .01 .05
346 John Morris .01 .05
347 Andy Hawkins .01 .05
348 Dave Leiper .01 .05
349 Ernest Riles .01 .05
350 Dwight Gooden .02 .10
351 Dave Righetti .02 .10
352 Pat Dodson .01 .05
353 John Habyan .01 .05
354 Jim Deshaies .01 .05
355 Butch Wynegar .01 .05
356 Bryn Smith .01 .05
357 Matt Young .01 .05
358 Tom Pagnozzi RC .02 .10
359 Floyd Rayford .01 .05
360 Darryl Strawberry .02 .10
361 Sal Butera .01 .05
362 Domingo Ramos .01 .05
363 Chris Brown .01 .05
364 Jose Gonzalez .01 .05
365 Dave Smith .01 .05
366 Andy McGaffigan .01 .05
367 Stan Javier .01 .05
368 Henry Cotto .01 .05
369 Mike Birkbeck .01 .05
370 Len Dykstra .02 .10
371 Dave Collins .01 .05
372 Spike Owen .01 .05
373 Geno Petralli .01 .05
374 Ron Karkovice .01 .05
375 Shane Rawley .01 .05
376 DeWayne Buice .01 .05
377 Bill Pecota RC .02 .10
378 Leon Durham .01 .05
379 Ed Olwine .01 .05
380 Bruce Hurst .01 .05
381 Bob McClure .01 .05
382 Mark Thurmond .01 .05
383 Buddy Biancalana .01 .05
384 Tim Conroy .01 .05
385 Tony Gwynn .10 .30
386 Greg Gross .01 .05
387 Barry Lyons .01 .05
388 Mike Felder .01 .05
389 Pat Clements .01 .05
390 Ken Griffey .02 .10
391 Mark Davis .01 .05
392 Jose Rijo .02 .10
393 Mike Young .01 .05
394 Willie Fraser .01 .05
395 Dion James .01 .05
396 Steve Shields .01 .05
397 Randy St.Claire .01 .05
398 Danny Jackson .01 .05
399 Cecil Fielder .02 .10
400 Keith Hernandez .02 .10
401 Don Carman .01 .05
402 Chuck Crim .01 .05
403 Rob Woodward .01 .05
404 Junior Ortiz .01 .05
405 Glenn Wilson .01 .05
406 Ken Howell .01 .05
407 Jeff Kunkel .01 .05
408 Jeff Reed .01 .05
409 Chris James .01 .05
410 Zane Smith .01 .05
411 Ken Dixon .01 .05
412 Ricky Horton .01 .05
413 Frank DiPino .01 .05
414 Shane Mack .01 .05
415 Danny Cox .01 .05
416 Andy Van Slyke .05 .15
417 Danny Heep .01 .05
418 John Cangelosi .01 .05
419A J.Christensen ERR .02 .10
Christiansen
on card front
419B J.Christensen COR .01 .05
420 Joey Cora RC .08 .25
421 Mike LaValliere .01 .05
422 Kelly Gruber .01 .05
423 Bruce Benedict .01 .05
424 Len Matuszek .01 .05
425 Kent Tekulve .01 .05
426 Rafael Ramirez .01 .05
427 Mike Flanagan .01 .05
428 Mike Gallego .01 .05
429 Juan Castillo .01 .05
430 Neal Heaton .01 .05
431 Phil Garner .02 .10
432 Mike Dunne .01 .05
433 Wallace Johnson .01 .05
434 Jack O'Connor .01 .05
435 Steve Jeltz .01 .05
436 Donell Nixon .01 .05
437 Jack Lazorko .01 .05
438 Keith Comstock .01 .05
439 Jeff D. Robinson .01 .05
440 Graig Nettles .02 .10
441 Mel Hall .01 .05
442 Gerald Young .01 .05
443 Gary Redus .01 .05
444 Charlie Moore .01 .05
445 Bill Madlock .02 .10
446 Mark Clear .01 .05
447 Greg Booker .01 .05
448 Rick Schu .01 .05
449 Ron Kittle .01 .05
450 Dale Murphy .05 .15
451 Bob Dernier .01 .05
452 Dale Mohorcic .01 .05
453 Rafael Belliard .01 .05
454 Charlie Puleo .01 .05
455 Dwayne Murphy .01 .05
456 Jim Eisenreich .01 .05
457 David Palmer .01 .05
458 Dave Stewart .02 .10
459 Pascual Perez .01 .05
460 Glenn Davis .01 .05
461 Dan Petry .01 .05
462 Jim Winn .01 .05
463 Darrell Miller .01 .05
464 Mike Moore .01 .05
465 Mike LaCoss .01 .05
466 Steve Farr .01 .05
467 Jerry Mumphrey .01 .05
468 Kevin Gross .01 .05
469 Bruce Bochy .01 .05
470 Orel Hershiser .02 .10
471 Eric King .01 .05
472 Ellis Burks RC .15 .40
473 Darren Daulton .02 .10
474 Mookie Wilson .02 .10
475 Frank Viola .02 .10
476 Ron Robinson .01 .05
477 Bob Melvin .01 .05
478 Jeff Musselman .01 .05
479 Charlie Kerfeld .01 .05
480 Richard Dotson .01 .05
481 Kevin Mitchell .02 .10
482 Gary Roenicke .01 .05
483 Tim Flannery .01 .05
484 Rich Yett .01 .05
485 Pete Incaviglia .01 .05
486 Rick Cerone .01 .05
487 Tony Armas .02 .10
488 Jerry Reed .01 .05
489 Dave Lopes .02 .10
490 Frank Tanana .02 .10
491 Mike Loynd .01 .05
492 Bruce Ruffin .01 .05
493 Chris Speier .01 .05
494 Tom Hume .01 .05
495 Jesse Orosco .01 .05
496 Robbie Wine UER .01 .05
(Misspelled Robby
on card front)
497 Jeff Montgomery RC .08 .25
498 Jeff Dedmon .01 .05
499 Luis Aguayo .01 .05
500 Reggie Jackson A's .05 .15
501 Reggie Jackson O's .05 .15
502 Reggie Jackson Yanks .05 .15
503 Reggie Jackson Angels .05 .15
504 Reggie Jackson A's .05 .15
505 Billy Hatcher .01 .05
506 Ed Lynch .01 .05
507 Willie Hernandez .01 .05
508 Jose DeLeon .01 .05
509 Joel Youngblood .01 .05
510 Bob Welch .02 .10
511 Steve Ontiveros .01 .05
512 Randy Ready .01 .05
513 Juan Nieves .01 .05
514 Jeff Russell .01 .05
515 Von Hayes .01 .05
516 Mark Gubicza .01 .05
517 Ken Dayley .01 .05
518 Don Aase .01 .05
519 Rick Reuschel .02 .10
520 Mike Henneman RC .08 .25
521 Rick Aguilera .01 .05
522 Jay Howell .01 .05
523 Ed Correa .01 .05
524 Manny Trillo .01 .05
525 Kirk Gibson .07 .20
526 Wally Ritchie .01 .05
527 Al Nipper .01 .05
528 Atlee Hammaker .01 .05
529 Shawon Dunston .01 .05
530 Jim Clancy .01 .05
531 Tom Paciorek .01 .05
532 Joel Skinner .01 .05
533 Scott Garrelts .01 .05
534 Tom O'Malley .01 .05
535 John Franco .02 .10
536 Paul Kilgus .01 .05
537 Darrell Porter .01 .05
538 Walt Terrell .01 .05
539 Bill Long .01 .05
540 George Bell .02 .10
541 Jeff Sellers .01 .05
542 Joe Boever .01 .05
543 Steve Howe .01 .05
544 Scott Sanderson .01 .05
545 Jack Morris .02 .10
546 Todd Benzinger RC .08 .25
547 Steve Henderson .01 .05
548 Eddie Milner .01 .05
549 Jeff M. Robinson .01 .05
550 Cal Ripken .30 .75
551 Jody Davis .01 .05
552 Kirk McCaskill .01 .05
553 Craig Lefferts .01 .05
554 Darnell Coles .01 .05
555 Phil Niekro .02 .10
556 Mike Aldrete .01 .05
557 Pat Perry .01 .05
558 Juan Agosto .01 .05
559 Rob Murphy .01 .05
560 Dennis Rasmussen .01 .05
561 Manny Lee .01 .05
562 Jeff Blauser RC .08 .25
563 Bob Ojeda .01 .05
564 Dave Dravecky .01 .05
565 Gene Garber .01 .05
566 Ron Roenicke .01 .05
567 Tommy Hinzo .01 .05
568 Eric Nolte .01 .05
569 Ed Hearn .01 .05
570 Mark Davidson .01 .05
571 Jim Walewander .01 .05
572 Donnie Hill UER .01 .05
(84 Stolen Base
total listed as 7)
573 Jamie Moyer .02 .10
574 Ken Schrom .01 .05
575 Nolan Ryan .40 1.00
576 Jim Acker .01 .05
577 Jamie Quirk .01 .05
578 Jay Aldrich .01 .05
579 Claudell Washington .01 .05
580 Jeff Leonard .01 .05
581 Carmen Castillo .01 .05
582 Daryl Boston .01 .05
583 Jeff DeWillis .01 .05
584 John Marzano .01 .05
585 Bill Gullickson .01 .05
586 Andy Allanson .01 .05
587 Lee Tunnell UER .01 .05
(1987 stat line
reads .4.84 ERA)
588 Gene Nelson .01 .05
589 Dave LaPoint .01 .05
590 Harold Baines .02 .10
591 Bill Buckner .02 .10
592 Carlton Fisk .05 .15
593 Rick Manning .01 .05
594 Doug Jones RC .08 .25
595 Tom Candiotti .01 .05
596 Steve Lake .01 .05
597 Jose Lind RC .08 .25
598 Ross Jones .01 .05
599 Gary Matthews .02 .10
600 Fernando Valenzuela .02 .10
601 Dennis Martinez .02 .10
602 Les Lancaster .01 .05
603 Ozzie Guillen .02 .10
604 Tony Bernazard .01 .05
605 Chili Davis .02 .10
606 Roy Smalley .01 .05
607 Ivan Calderon .01 .05
608 Jay Tibbs .01 .05
609 Guy Hoffman .01 .05
610 Doyle Alexander .01 .05
611 Mike Bielecki .01 .05
612 Shawn Hillegas .01 .05
613 Keith Atherton .01 .05
614 Eric Plunk .01 .05
615 Sid Fernandez .01 .05
616 Dennis Lamp .01 .05
617 Dave Engle .01 .05
618 Harry Spilman .01 .05
619 Don Robinson .01 .05
620 John Farrell RC .02 .10
621 Nelson Liriano .01 .05
622 Floyd Bannister .01 .05
623 Randy Milligan RC .02 .10
624 Kevin Elster .01 .05
625 Jody Reed RC .08 .25
626 Shawn Abner .01 .05
627 Kirt Manwaring RC .08 .25
628 Pete Stanicek .01 .05
629 Rob Ducey .01 .05
630 Steve Kiefer .01 .05
631 Gary Thurman .01 .05
632 Darrel Akerfelds .01 .05
633 Dave Clark .01 .05
634 Roberto Kelly RC .08 .25
635 Keith Hughes .01 .05
636 John Davis .01 .05
637 Mike Devereaux RC .08 .25
638 Tom Glavine RC 1.00 2.50
639 Keith A. Miller RC .08 .25
640 Chris Gwynn UER RC .08 .25
(Wrong batting and
throwing on back)
641 Tim Crews RC .08 .25
642 Mackey Sasser RC .08 .25
643 Vicente Palacios .01 .05
644 Kevin Romine .01 .05
645 Gregg Jefferies RC .08 .25
646 Jeff Treadway RC .08 .25
647 Ron Gant RC .15 .40
648 Mark McGwire .30 .75
Matt Nokes
649 Eric Davis .02 .10
Tim Raines
650 Don Mattingly .10 .30
Jack Clark
651 Tony Fernandez .08 .25
Alan Trammell
Cal Ripken
652 Vince Coleman HL .01 .05
653 Kirby Puckett HL .05 .15
654 Benito Santiago HL .01 .05
655 Juan Nieves HL .01 .05
656 Steve Bedrosian HL .01 .05
657 Mike Schmidt HL .07 .20
658 Don Mattingly HL .10 .30
659 Mark McGwire HL .30 .75
660 Paul Molitor HL .01 .05

1988 Score Glossy

This 660 card set is a parallel to the regular 1988 Score set. According to the manufacturer, 5,000 of these sets were produced. These sets are considered glossy as "UV Coating" was added to the fronts of the card. These sets were issued in factory set versions only and released solely through Major League Marketing's hobby accounts.

COMP.FACT.SET (660) 60.00 120.00
*STARS: 5X TO 12X BASIC CARDS
*ROOKIES: 5X TO 12X BASIC CARDS

1988 Score Box Cards

There are six different wax box bottom panels each featuring three players and a trivia (related to a particular stadium for a given year) question. The players and trivia question cards are individually numbered. The trivia are numbered below with the prefix T in order to avoid confusion. The trivia cards are very unpopular with collectors since they do not picture any players. When panels of four are cut into individuals, the cards are standard size. The card backs of the players feature the respective League logos most prominently.

COMPLETE SET (24) 4.00 10.00
1 Terry Kennedy .02 .10
2 Don Mattingly .60 1.50
3 Willie Randolph .07 .20
4 Wade Boggs .50 1.00
5 Cal Ripken 1.25 3.00
6 George Bell .02 .10
7 Rickey Henderson .50 1.25
8 Dave Winfield .30 .75
9 Bret Saberhagen .07 .20
10 Gary Carter .30 .75
11 Jack Clark .07 .20
12 Ryne Sandberg .60 1.50
13 Mike Schmidt .30 .75
14 Ozzie Smith .60 1.50
15 Eric Davis .07 .20
16 Andre Dawson .20 .50
17 Darryl Strawberry .07 .20
18 Mike Scott .02 .10
T1 Ted Williams .75 2.00
Fenway Park '60
T2 Fred Lynn .07 .20
Comiskey Park '83
T3 Mark McGwire .75 2.00

Anaheim Stadium '87
T4 Gabby Hartnett .07 .20
Wrigley Field '38
T5 Red Schoendienst .07 .20
Comiskey Park '50
T6 John Farrell .20 .50
Paul Molitor
County Stadium '87

1988 Score Rookie/Traded

This 110-card standard-size set issued exclusively in a boxes factory-set form features traded players (1-65) and rookies (66-110) for the 1988 season. The cards are distinguishable from the regular Score set by the orange borders and by the fact that the numbering on the back has a T suffix. Apparently Score's first attempt at a Rookie/Traded set was produced very conservatively, resulting in a set which is now recognized as being much tougher to find than the other Rookie/Traded sets from the other major companies of that year. Extended Rookie Cards in this set include Roberto Alomar, Brady Anderson, Craig Biggio, Jay Buhner and Mark Grace.

COMP.FACT.SET (110) 15.00 40.00
1T Jack Clark .30 .75
2T Danny Jackson .08 .25
3T Brett Butler .30 .75
4T Kurt Stillwell .08 .25
5T Tom Brunansky .08 .25
6T Dennis Lamp .08 .25
7T Jose DeLeon .08 .25
8T Tom Herr .08 .25
9T Keith Moreland .08 .25
10T Kirk Gibson .75 2.00
11T Bud Black .08 .25
12T Rafael Ramirez .08 .25
13T Luis Salazar .08 .25
14T Goose Gossage .30 .75
15T Bob Welch .30 .75
16T Vance Law .08 .25
17T Ray Knight .30 .75
18T Dan Quisenberry .08 .25
19T Don Slaught .08 .25
20T Lee Smith .30 .75
21T Rick Cerone .08 .25
22T Pat Tabler .08 .25
23T Larry McWilliams .08 .25
24T Ricky Horton .08 .25
25T Graig Nettles .30 .75
26T Dan Petry .08 .25
27T Jose Rijo .30 .75
28T Chili Davis .30 .75
29T Dickie Thon .08 .25
30T Mackey Sasser .08 .25
31T Mickey Tettleton .08 .25
32T Rick Dempsey .08 .25
33T Ron Hassey .08 .25
34T Phil Bradley .08 .25
35T Jay Howell .08 .25
36T Bill Buckner .30 .75
37T Alfredo Griffin .08 .25
38T Gary Pettis .08 .25
39T Calvin Schiraldi .08 .25
40T John Candelaria .08 .25
41T Joe Orsulak .08 .25
42T Willie Upshaw .08 .25
43T Herm Winningham .08 .25
44T Ron Kittle .08 .25
45T Bob Dernier .08 .25
46T Steve Balboni .08 .25
47T Steve Shields .08 .25
48T Henry Cotto .08 .25
49T Dave Henderson .08 .25
50T Dave Parker .30 .75
51T Mike Young .08 .25
52T Mark Salas .08 .25
53T Mike Davis .08 .25
54T Rafael Santana .08 .25
55T Don Baylor .30 .75
56T Dan Pasqua .08 .25
57T Ernest Riles .08 .25
58T Glenn Hubbard .08 .25
59T Mike Smithson .08 .25
60T Richard Dotson .08 .25
61T Jerry Reuss .08 .25
62T Mike Jackson .30 .75
63T Floyd Bannister .08 .25
64T Jesse Orosco .08 .25
65T Larry Parrish .08 .25
66T Jeff Bittiger .08 .25
67T Ray Hayward .08 .25
68T Ricky Jordan XRC .30 .75
69T Tommy Gregg .08 .25
70T Brady Anderson XRC .50 1.25
71T Jeff Montgomery .30 .75
72T Darryl Hamilton XRC .30 .75
73T Cecil Espy XRC .08 .25
74T Greg Briley XRC .08 .25
75T Joey Meyer .08 .25
76T Mike Macfarlane XRC .30 .75
77T Oswald Peraza .08 .25
78T Jack Armstrong XRC .08 .25
79T Don Heinkel .08 .25
80T Mark Grace XRC 3.00 8.00
81T Steve Curry .08 .25
82T Damon Berryhill XRC .30 .75
83T Steve Ellsworth .08 .25
84T Pete Smith XRC .08 .25
85T Jack McDowell XRC .50 1.25
86T Rob Dibble XRC .50 1.25
87T Bryan Harvey XRC .30 .75
UER Games Pitched 47, Innings 5) XRC
88T John Dopson .08 .25
89T Dave Gallagher .08 .25
90T Todd Stottlemyre XRC .30 .75
91T Mike Schooler .08 .25
92T Don Gordon .08 .25
93T Sil Campusano .08 .25
94T Jeff Pico .08 .25
95T Jay Buhner XRC .75 2.00
96T Nelson Santovenia .08 .25
97T Al Leiter XRC 1.25 3.00
98T Luis Alicea XRC .30 .75
99T Pat Borders XRC .30 .75
100T Chris Sabo XRC .50 1.25
101T Tim Belcher .08 .25
102T Walt Weiss XRC .50 1.25
103T Craig Biggio XRC 5.00 12.00
104T Don August .08 .25
105T Roberto Alomar XRC 4.00 10.00
106T Todd Burns .08 .25
107T John Costello .08 .25
108T Melido Perez XRC .30 .75
109T Darrin Jackson XRC .08 .25
110T O.Destrade XRC .08 .25

1988 Score Rookie/Traded Glossy

This 110-card standard-size set was issued as a parallel vesion to the regular Score Rookie/Traded set. This set was issued only in boxed factory-set form. According to published reports, only 3,000 of these sets were created. The sets were sold solely through Score's dealer's accounts of the time.

COMP.FACT.SET (110) 75.00 150.00
*STARS: 1X TO 2.5X BASIC CARDS
*ROOKIES: 1X TO 2.5X BASIC CARDS

1988 Score Young Superstars I

This attractive high-gloss 40-card standard-size set of "Young Superstars" was distributed in a small blue box which had the checklist of the set on a side panel of the box. The cards were also distributed as an insert, one per rack pack. These attractive cards are in full color on the front and also have a full-color small portrait on the card back. The cards in this series are distinguishable from the cards in Series II by the fact that this series has a blue and green border on the card front instead of the (Series II) blue and pink border.

COMPLETE SET (40) 3.00 8.00
1 Mark McGwire 1.00 2.50
2 Benito Santiago .02 .10
3 Sam Horn .01 .05
4 Chris Bosio .01 .05
5 Matt Nokes .01 .05
6 Ken Williams .05 .15
7 Dion James .01 .05
8 B.J. Surhoff .05 .15
9 Joe Magrane .01 .05
10 Kevin Seitzer .01 .05
11 Stanley Jefferson .01 .05
12 Devon White .02 .10
13 Nelson Liriano .01 .05
14 Chris James .01 .05
15 Mike Henneman .02 .10
16 Terry Steinbach .01 .05
17 John Kruk .02 .10
18 Matt Williams .40 1.00
19 Kelly Downs .01 .05
20 Bill Ripken .01 .05
21 Ozzie Guillen .05 .15
22 Luis Polonia .01 .05
23 Dave Magadan .01 .05
24 Mike Greenwell .01 .05
25 Will Clark .40 1.00
26 Mike Dunne .01 .05
27 Wally Joyner .02 .10
28 Robby Thompson .01 .05
29 Ken Caminiti .30 .75
30 Jose Canseco .40 1.00
31 Todd Benzinger .01 .05
32 Pete Incaviglia .01 .05
33 John Farrell .01 .05
34 Casey Candaele .01 .05
35 Mike Aldrete .01 .05
36 Ruben Sierra .05 .15
37 Ellis Burks .07 .20
38 Tracy Jones .01 .05
39 Kal Daniels .01 .05
40 Cory Snyder .01 .05

1988 Score Young Superstars II

This attractive high-gloss 40-card standard-size set of "Young Superstars" was distributed in a small purple box which had the checklist of the set on a side panel of the box. The cards were not distributed as an insert with rak paks as the first series was, but were only available as a complete set from hobby dealers or through a mail-in offer direct from the company. These attractive cards are in full color on the front and also have a full-color small portrait on

the card back. The cards in this series are distinguishable from the cards in Series I by the fact that this series has a blue and pink border on the card front instead of the (Series I) blue and green border.

COMP.FACT.SET (40) 2.00 5.00
1 Don Mattingly .40 1.00
2 Glenn Braggs .01 .05
3 Dwight Gooden .02 .10
4 Jose Lind .01 .05
5 Danny Tartabull .01 .05
6 Tony Fernandez .02 .10
7 Julio Franco .02 .10
8 Andres Galarraga .07 .20
9 Bobby Bonilla .02 .10
10 Eric Davis .02 .10
11 Gerald Young .01 .05
12 Barry Bonds .30 .75
13 Jerry Browne .01 .05
14 Jeff Blauser .02 .10
15 Mickey Brantley .01 .05
16 Floyd Youmans .01 .05
17 Bret Saberhagen .02 .10
18 Shawon Dunston .01 .05
19 Len Dykstra .02 .10
20 Darryl Strawberry .02 .10
21 Rick Aguilera .02 .10
22 Ivan Calderon .01 .05
23 Roger Clemens .40 1.00
24 Vince Coleman .01 .05
25 Gary Thurman .01 .05
26 Jeff Treadway .01 .05
27 Oddibe McDowell .01 .05
28 Fred McGriff .07 .20
29 Mark McLemore .01 .05
30 Jeff Musselman .01 .05
31 Mitch Williams .01 .05
32 Dan Plesac .01 .05
33 Juan Nieves .01 .05
34 Barry Larkin .07 .20
35 Greg Mathews .01 .05
36 Shane Mack .01 .05
37 Scott Bankhead .01 .05
38 Eric Bell .01 .05
39 Greg Swindell .01 .05
40 Kevin Elster .01 .05

1989 Score

This 660-card standard-size set was distributed by Major League Marketing. Cards were issued primarily in fin-wrapped plastic packs and factory sets. Cards feature six distinctive inner border (inside a white outer border) colors on the front. Subsets include Highlights (652-660) and Rookie Prospects (621-651). Rookie Cards in this set include Brady Anderson, Craig Biggio, Randy Johnson, Gary Sheffield, and John Smoltz.

COMPLETE SET (660) 6.00 15.00
COMP.FACT.SET (660) 6.00 15.00
1 Jose Canseco .08 .25
2 Andre Dawson .02 .10
3 Mark McGwire UER .40 1.00
4 Benito Santiago .02 .10
5 Rick Reuschel .02 .10
6 Fred McGriff .05 .15
7 Kal Daniels .01 .05
8 Gary Gaetti .02 .10
9 Ellis Burks .02 .10
10 Darryl Strawberry .02 .10
11 Julio Franco .02 .10
12 Lloyd Moseby .01 .05
13 Jeff Pico .01 .05
14 Johnny Ray .01 .05
15 Cal Ripken .30 .75
16 Dick Schofield .01 .05
17 Mel Hall .01 .05
18 Bill Ripken .01 .05
19 Brook Jacoby .01 .05
20 Kirby Puckett .08 .25
21 Bill Doran .01 .05
22 Pete O'Brien .01 .05
23 Matt Nokes .01 .05
24 Brian Fisher .01 .05
25 Jack Clark .02 .10
26 Gary Pettis .01 .05
27 Dave Valle .01 .05
28 Willie Wilson .02 .10
29 Curt Young .01 .05
30 Dale Murphy .05 .15
31 Barry Larkin .05 .15
32 Dave Stewart .02 .10
33 Mike LaValliere .01 .05
34 Glenn Hubbard .01 .05
35 Ryne Sandberg .15 .40
36 Tony Pena .01 .05
37 Greg Walker .01 .05
38 Von Hayes .01 .05
39 Kevin Mitchell .02 .10
40 Tim Raines .02 .10
41 Keith Hernandez .02 .10
42 Keith Moreland .01 .05
43 Ruben Sierra .02 .10
44 Chet Lemon .02 .10
45 Willie Randolph .02 .10
46 Andy Allanson .01 .05
47 Candy Maldonado .01 .05
48 Sid Bream .01 .05
49 Denny Walling .01 .05
50 Dave Winfield .02 .10
51 Alvin Davis .01 .05
52 Cory Snyder .01 .05
53 Hubie Brooks .01 .05
54 Chili Davis .02 .10
55 Kevin Seitzer .01 .05
56 Jose Uribe .01 .05
57 Tony Fernandez .01 .05
58 Tim Teufel .01 .05
59 Oddibe McDowell .01 .05
60 Les Lancaster .01 .05
61 Billy Hatcher .01 .05
62 Dan Gladden .01 .05
63 Marty Barrett .01 .05
64 Nick Esasky .01 .05
65 Wally Joyner .02 .10
66 Mike Greenwell .01 .05
67 Ken Williams .01 .05
68 Bob Horner .02 .10
69 Steve Sax .01 .05
70 Rickey Henderson .08 .25
71 Mitch Webster .01 .05
72 Rob Deer .01 .05
73 Jim Presley .01 .05
74 Albert Hall .01 .05
75 George Brett COR .25 .60
(At age 35)
75A George Brett ERR .40 1.00
(At age 33)
76 Brian Downing .02 .10
77 Dave Martinez .01 .05
78 Scott Fletcher .01 .05
79 Phil Bradley .01 .05
80 Ozzie Smith .15 .40
81 Larry Sheets .01 .05
82 Mike Aldrete .01 .05
83 Darnell Coles .01 .05
84 Len Dykstra .02 .10
85 Jim Rice .02 .10
86 Jeff Treadway .01 .05
87 Jose Lind .01 .05
88 Willie McGee .02 .10
89 Mickey Brantley .01 .05
90 Tony Gwynn .10 .30
91 R.J. Reynolds .01 .05
92 Milt Thompson .01 .05
93 Kevin McReynolds .01 .05
94 Eddie Murray UER .08 .25
('86 batting .205, should be .305)
95 Lance Parrish .02 .10
96 Ron Kittle .01 .05
97 Gerald Young .01 .05
98 Ernie Whitt .01 .05
99 Jeff Reed .01 .05
100 Don Mattingly .25 .60
101 Gerald Perry .01 .05
102 Vance Law .01 .05
103 John Shelby .01 .05
104 Chris Sabo RC .15 .40
105 Danny Tartabull .01 .05
106 Glenn Wilson .01 .05
107 Mark Davidson .01 .05
108 Dave Parker .02 .10
109 Eric Davis .02 .10
110 Alan Trammell .02 .10
111 Ozzie Virgil .01 .05
112 Frank Tanana .02 .10
113 Rafael Ramirez .01 .05
114 Dennis Martinez .02 .10
115 Jose DeLeon .01 .05
116 Bob Ojeda .01 .05
117 Doug Drabek .01 .05
118 Andy Hawkins .01 .05
119 Greg Maddux .20 .50
120 Cecil Fielder UER .02 .10
Reversed Photo on back
121 Mike Scioscia .02 .10
122 Dan Petry .01 .05
123 Terry Kennedy .01 .05
124 Kelly Downs .01 .05
125 Greg Gross UER .01 .05
(Gregg on back)
126 Fred Lynn .02 .10
127 Barry Bonds .60 1.50
128 Harold Baines .02 .10
129 Doyle Alexander .01 .05
130 Kevin Elster .01 .05
131 Mike Heath .01 .05
132 Teddy Higuera .01 .05
133 Charlie Leibrandt .01 .05
134 Tim Laudner .01 .05
135A Ray Knight ERR .02 .10
(Reverse negative)
135B Ray Knight COR .02 .10
136 Howard Johnson .02 .10
137 Terry Pendleton .02 .10
138 Andy McGaffigan .01 .05
139 Ken Oberkfell .01 .05
140 Butch Wynegar .01 .05
141 Rob Murphy .01 .05
142 Rich Renteria .01 .05
143 Jose Guzman .01 .05
144 Andres Galarraga .02 .10
145 Ricky Horton .01 .05
146 Frank DiPino .01 .05
147 Glenn Braggs .01 .05
148 John Kruk .02 .10
149 Mike Schmidt .20 .50
150 Lee Smith .02 .10
151 Robin Yount .15 .40
152 Mark Eichhorn .01 .05
153 DeWayne Buice .01 .05
154 B.J. Surhoff .02 .10
155 Vince Coleman .01 .05
156 Tony Phillips .01 .05
157 Willie Fraser .01 .05
158 Lance McCullers .01 .05
159 Greg Gagne .01 .05
160 Jesse Barfield .02 .10
161 Mark Langston .01 .05
162 Kurt Stillwell .01 .05
163 Dion James .01 .05
164 Glenn Davis .01 .05
165 Walt Weiss .01 .05
166 Dave Concepcion .02 .10
167 Alfredo Griffin .01 .05
168 Don Heinkel .01 .05
169 Luis Rivera .01 .05
170 Shane Rawley .01 .05
171 Darrell Evans .02 .10
172 Robby Thompson .01 .05
173 Jody Davis .01 .05
174 Andy Van Slyke .05 .15
175 Wade Boggs UER .05 .15
(Bio says .364, should be .356)
176 Garry Templeton .02 .10
('85 stats off-centered)
177 Gary Redus .01 .05
178 Craig Lefferts .01 .05
179 Carney Lansford .02 .10
180 Ron Darling .02 .10
181 Kirk McCaskill .01 .05
182 Tony Armas .02 .10
183 Steve Farr .01 .05
184 Tom Brunansky .01 .05
185 B.Harvey RC UER .08 .25
'87 games 47, should be 3
186 Mike Marshall .01 .05
187 Bo Diaz .01 .05
188 Willie Upshaw .01 .05
189 Mike Pagliarulo .01 .05
190 Mike Krukow .01 .05
191 Tommy Herr .01 .05
192 Jim Pankovits .01 .05
193 Dwight Evans .05 .15
194 Kelly Gruber .01 .05
195 Bobby Bonilla .02 .10
196 Wallace Johnson .01 .05
197 Dave Stieb .02 .10
198 Pat Borders RC .08 .25
199 Rafael Palmeiro .08 .25
200 Dwight Gooden .02 .10
201 Pete Incaviglia .01 .05
202 Chris James .01 .05
203 Marvell Wynne .01 .05
204 Pat Sheridan .01 .05
205 Don Baylor .02 .10
206 Paul O'Neill .05 .15
207 Pete Smith .01 .05
208 Mark McLemore .01 .05
209 Henry Cotto .01 .05
210 Kirk Gibson .02 .10
211 Claudell Washington .01 .05
212 Randy Bush .01 .05
213 Joe Carter .02 .10
214 Bill Buckner .02 .10
215 Bert Blyleven UER .02 .10
(Wrong birth year)
216 Brett Butler .02 .10
217 Lee Mazzilli .02 .10
218 Spike Owen .01 .05
219 Bill Swift .01 .05
220 Tim Wallach .01 .05
221 David Cone .02 .10
222 Don Carman .01 .05
223 Rich Gossage .02 .10
224 Bob Walk .01 .05
225 Dave Righetti .02 .10
226 Kevin Bass .01 .05
227 Kevin Gross .01 .05
228 Tim Burke .01 .05
229 Rick Mahler .01 .05
230 Lou Whitaker UER .02 .10
(252 games in '85, should be 152)
231 Luis Alicea RC .08 .25
232 Roberto Alomar .08 .25
233 Bob Boone .02 .10
234 Dickie Thon .01 .05
235 Shawon Dunston .01 .05
236 Pete Stanicek .01 .05
237 Craig Biggio RC 1.50 4.00
(Inconsistent design, portrait on front)
238 Dennis Boyd .01 .05
239 Tom Candiotti .01 .05
240 Gary Carter .02 .10
241 Mike Stanley .01 .05
242 Ken Phelps .01 .05
243 Chris Bosio .01 .05
244 Les Straker .01 .05
245 Dave Smith .01 .05
246 John Candelaria .01 .05
247 Joe Orsulak .01 .05
248 Storm Davis .01 .05
249 Floyd Bannister UER .01 .05
(ML Batting Record)
250 Jack Morris .02 .10
251 Bret Saberhagen .02 .10
252 Tom Niedenfuer .01 .05
253 Neal Heaton .01 .05
254 Eric Show .01 .05
255 Juan Samuel .01 .05
256 Dale Sveum .01 .05
257 Jim Gott .01 .05
258 Scott Garrelts .01 .05
259 Larry McWilliams .01 .05
260 Steve Bedrosian .01 .05
261 Jack Howell .01 .05
262 Jay Tibbs .01 .05
263 Jamie Moyer .02 .10
264 Doug Sisk .01 .05
265 Todd Worrell .01 .05
266 John Farrell .01 .05
267 Dave Collins .01 .05
268 Sid Fernandez .01 .05
269 Tom Brookens .01 .05
270 Shane Mack .01 .05
271 Paul Kilgus .01 .05
272 Chuck Crim .01 .05
273 Bob Knepper .01 .05
274 Mike Moore .01 .05
275 Guillermo Hernandez .01 .05
276 Dennis Eckersley .05 .15
277 Graig Nettles .02 .10
278 Rich Dotson .01 .05
279 Larry Herndon .01 .05
280 Gene Larkin .01 .05
281 Roger McDowell .01 .05
282 Greg Swindell .01 .05
283 Juan Agosto .01 .05
284 Jeff M. Robinson .01 .05
285 Mike Dunne .01 .05
286 Greg Mathews .01 .05
287 Kent Tekulve .01 .05
288 Jerry Mumphrey .01 .05
289 Jack McDowell .02 .10
290 Frank Viola .02 .10
291 Mark Gubicza .01 .05
292 Dave Schmidt .01 .05
293 Mike Henneman .01 .05
294 Jimmy Jones .01 .05
295 Charlie Hough .02 .10
296 Rafael Santana .01 .05
297 Chris Speier .01 .05
298 Mike Witt .01 .05
299 Pascual Perez .01 .05
300 Nolan Ryan .40 1.00
301 Mitch Williams .01 .05
302 Mookie Wilson .02 .10
303 Mackey Sasser .01 .05
304 John Cerutti .01 .05
305 Jeff Reardon .02 .10
306 Randy Myers UER .02 .10
(6 hits in '87, should be 61)
307 Greg Brock .01 .05
308 Bob Welch .02 .10
309 Jeff D. Robinson .01 .05
310 Harold Reynolds .02 .10
311 Jim Walewander .01 .05
312 Dave Magadan .01 .05
313 Jim Gantner .01 .05
314 Walt Terrell .01 .05
315 Wally Backman .01 .05
316 Luis Salazar .01 .05
317 Rick Rhoden .01 .05
318 Tom Henke .01 .05
319 Mike Macfarlane RC .08 .25
320 Dan Plesac .01 .05
321 Calvin Schiraldi .01 .05
322 Stan Javier .01 .05
323 Devon White .02 .10
324 Scott Bradley .01 .05
325 Bruce Hurst .01 .05
326 Manny Lee .01 .05
327 Rick Aguilera .02 .10
328 Bruce Ruffin .01 .05
329 Ed Whitson .01 .05
330 Bo Jackson .08 .25
331 Ivan Calderon .01 .05
332 Mickey Hatcher .01 .05
333 Barry Jones .01 .05
334 Ron Hassey .01 .05
335 Bill Wegman .01 .05
336 Damon Berryhill .01 .05
337 Steve Ontiveros .01 .05
338 Dan Pasqua .01 .05
339 Bill Pecota .01 .05
340 Greg Cadaret .01 .05
341 Scott Bankhead .01 .05
342 Ron Guidry .02 .10
343 Danny Heep .01 .05
344 Bob Brower .01 .05
345 Rich Gedman .01 .05
346 Nelson Santovenia .01 .05
347 George Bell .02 .10
348 Ted Power .01 .05
349 Mark Grant .01 .05
350 Roger Clemens COR .40 1.00
(78 career wins)
350A Roger Clemens ERR .75 2.00
(778 career wins)
351 Bill Long .01 .05
352 Jay Bell .02 .10
353 Steve Balboni .01 .05
354 Bob Kipper .01 .05
355 Steve Jeltz .01 .05
356 Jesse Orosco .01 .05
357 Bob Dernier .01 .05
358 Mickey Tettleton .01 .05
359 Duane Ward .01 .05
360 Darrin Jackson .02 .10
361 Rey Quinones .01 .05
362 Mark Grace .08 .25
363 Steve Lake .01 .05
364 Pat Perry .01 .05
365 Terry Steinbach .02 .10
366 Alan Ashby .01 .05
367 Jeff Montgomery .01 .05
368 Steve Buechele .01 .05
369 Chris Brown .01 .05
370 Orel Hershiser .02 .10
371 Todd Benzinger .01 .05
372 Ron Gant .02 .10
373 Paul Assenmacher .01 .05
374 Joey Meyer .01 .05
375 Neil Allen .01 .05
376 Mike Davis .01 .05
377 Jeff Parrett .01 .05
378 Jay Howell .01 .05
379 Rafael Belliard .01 .05
380 Luis Polonia UER .01 .05
(2 triples in '87, should be 10)
381 Keith Atherton .01 .05
382 Kent Hrbek .02 .10
383 Bob Stanley .01 .05
384 Dave LaPoint .01 .05
385 Rance Mulliniks .01 .05
386 Melido Perez .01 .05
387 Doug Jones .01 .05
388 Steve Lyons .01 .05
389 Alejandro Pena .01 .05
390 Frank White .02 .10
391 Pat Tabler .01 .05
392 Eric Plunk .01 .05
393 Mike Maddux .01 .05
394 Allan Anderson .01 .05
395 Bob Brenly .01 .05
396 Rick Cerone .01 .05
397 Scott Terry .01 .05
398 Mike Jackson .01 .05
399 Bobby Thigpen UER .01 .05
Bio says 37 saves in '88, should be 34
400 Don Sutton .02 .10
401 Cecil Espy .01 .05
402 Junior Ortiz .01 .05
403 Mike Smithson .01 .05
404 Bud Black .01 .05
405 Tom Foley .01 .05
406 Andres Thomas .01 .05
407 Rick Sutcliffe .02 .10
408 Brian Harper .01 .05

409 John Smiley .01 .05
410 Juan Nieves .01 .05
411 Shawn Abner .01 .05
412 Wes Gardner .01 .05
413 Darren Daulton .02 .10
414 Juan Berenguer .01 .05
415 Charles Hudson .01 .05
416 Rick Honeycutt .01 .05
417 Greg Booker .01 .05
418 Tim Belcher .01 .05
419 Don August .01 .05
420 Dale Mohorcic .01 .05
421 Steve Lombardozzi .01 .05
422 Atlee Hammaker .01 .05
423 Jerry Don Gleaton .01 .05
424 Scott Bailes .01 .05
425 Bruce Sutter .02 .10
426 Randy Ready .01 .05
427 Jerry Reed .01 .05
428 Bryn Smith .01 .05
429 Tim Leary .01 .05
430 Mark Clear .01 .05
431 Terry Leach .01 .05
432 John Moses .01 .05
433 Ozzie Guillen .02 .10
434 Gene Nelson .01 .05
435 Gary Ward .01 .05
436 Luis Aguayo .01 .05
437 Fernando Valenzuela .02 .10
438 Jeff Russell UER .01 .05
(Saves total does
not add up correctly)
439 Cecilio Guante .01 .05
440 Don Robinson .01 .05
441 Rick Anderson .01 .05
442 Tom Glavine .08 .25
443 Daryl Boston .01 .05
444 Joe Price .01 .05
445 Stu Cliburn .01 .05
446 Manny Trillo .01 .05
447 Joel Skinner .01 .05
448 Charlie Puleo .01 .05
449 Carlton Fisk .05 .15
450 Will Clark .05 .15
451 Otis Nixon .01 .05
452 Rick Schu .01 .05
453 Todd Stottlemyre UER .01 .05
(ML Batting Record)
454 Tim Birtsas .01 .05
455 Dave Gallagher .01 .05
456 Barry Lyons .01 .05
457 Fred Manrique .01 .05
458 Ernest Riles .01 .05
459 Doug Jennings .01 .05
460 Joe Magrane .01 .05
461 Jamie Quirk .01 .05
462 Jack Armstrong RC .08 .25
463 Bobby Witt .01 .05
464 Keith A. Miller .01 .05
465 Todd Burns .01 .05
466 John Dopson .01 .05
467 Rich Yett .01 .05
468 Craig Reynolds .01 .05
469 Dave Bergman .01 .05
470 Rex Hudler .01 .05
471 Eric King .01 .05
472 Joaquin Andujar .02 .10
473 Sil Campusano .01 .05
474 Terry Mulholland .01 .05
475 Mike Flanagan .01 .05
476 Greg A. Harris .01 .05
477 Tommy John .02 .10
478 Dave Anderson .01 .05
479 Fred Toliver .01 .05
480 Jimmy Key .02 .10
481 Donell Nixon .01 .05
482 Mark Portugal .01 .05
483 Tom Pagnozzi .01 .05
484 Jeff Kunkel .01 .05
485 Frank Williams .01 .05
486 Jody Reed .01 .05
487 Roberto Kelly .01 .05
488 Shawn Hillegas UER .01 .05
(165 innings in '87,
should be 165.2)
489 Jerry Reuss .01 .05
490 Mark Davis .01 .05
491 Jeff Sellers .01 .05
492 Zane Smith .01 .05
493 Al Newman .01 .05
494 Mike Young .01 .05
495 Larry Parrish .01 .05
496 Herm Winningham .01 .05
497 Carmen Castillo .01 .05
498 Joe Hesketh .01 .05
499 Darrell Miller .01 .05
500 Mike LaCoss .01 .05
501 Charlie Lea .01 .05
502 Bruce Benedict .01 .05
503 Chuck Finley .02 .10
504 Brad Wellman .01 .05
505 Tim Crews .01 .05
506 Ken Gerhart .01 .05
507A Brian Holton ERR .01 .05
(Born 1/25/65 Denver,
should be 11/29/59
in McKeesport)
507B Brian Holton COR .75 2.00
508 Dennis Lamp .01 .05
509 Bobby Meacham UER .01 .05
('84 games 099)
510 Tracy Jones .01 .05
511 Mike R. Fitzgerald .01 .05
512 Jeff Bittiger .01 .05
513 Tim Flannery .01 .05
514 Ray Hayward .01 .05
515 Dave Leiper .01 .05
516 Rod Scurry .01 .05
517 Carmelo Martinez .01 .05
518 Curtis Wilkerson .01 .05
519 Stan Jefferson .01 .05
520 Dan Quisenberry .01 .05
521 Lloyd McClendon .01 .05
522 Steve Trout .01 .05
523 Larry Andersen .01 .05
524 Don Aase .01 .05
525 Bob Forsch .01 .05
526 Geno Petralli .01 .05
527 Angel Salazar .01 .05
528 Mike Schooler .01 .05
529 Jose Oquendo .01 .05
530 Jay Buhner UER .02 .10
(Wearing 43 on front,
listed as 34 on back)
531 Tom Bolton .01 .05
532 Al Nipper .01 .05
533 Dave Henderson .01 .05
534 John Costello .01 .05
535 Donnie Moore .01 .05
536 Mike Laga .01 .05
537 Mike Gallego .01 .05
538 Jim Clancy .01 .05
539 Joel Youngblood .01 .05
540 Rick Leach .01 .05
541 Kevin Romine .01 .05
542 Mark Salas .01 .05
543 Greg Minton .01 .05
544 Dave Palmer .01 .05
545 Dwayne Murphy UER .01 .05
(Game-sinning)
546 Jim Deshaies .01 .05
547 Don Gordon .01 .05
548 Ricky Jordan RC .08 .25
549 Mike Boddicker .01 .05
550 Mike Scott .02 .10
551 Jeff Ballard .01 .05
552A Jose Rijo ERR .02 .10
(Uniform listed as
27 on back)
552B Jose Rijo COR .02 .10
(Uniform listed as
24 on back)
553 Danny Darwin .01 .05
554 Tom Browning .01 .05
555 Danny Jackson .01 .05
556 Rick Dempsey .01 .05
557 Jeffrey Leonard .01 .05
558 Jeff Musselman .01 .05
559 Ron Robinson .01 .05
560 John Tudor .02 .10
561 Don Slaught UER .01 .05
(237 games in 1987)
562 Dennis Rasmussen .01 .05
563 Brady Anderson RC .15 .40
564 Pedro Guerrero .02 .10
565 Paul Molitor .02 .10
566 Terry Clark .01 .05
567 Terry Puhl .01 .05
568 Mike Campbell .01 .05
569 Paul Mirabella .01 .05
570 Jeff Hamilton .01 .05
571 Oswald Peraza .01 .05
572 Bob McClure .01 .05
573 Jose Bautista RC .02 .10
574 Alex Trevino .01 .05
575 John Franco .02 .10
576 Mark Parent .01 .05
577 Nelson Liriano .01 .05
578 Steve Shields .01 .05
579 Odell Jones .01 .05
580 Al Leiter .08 .25
581 Dave Stapleton .01 .05
582 Orel Hershiser .08 .25
Jose Canseco
Kirk Gibson
Dave Stewart WS
583 Donnie Hill .01 .05
584 Chuck Jackson .01 .05
585 Rene Gonzales .01 .05
586 Tracy Woodson .01 .05
587 Jim Adduci .01 .05
588 Mario Soto .02 .10
589 Jeff Blauser .01 .05
590 Jim Traber .01 .05
591 Jon Perlman .01 .05
592 Mark Williamson .01 .05
593 Dave Meads .01 .05
594 Jim Eisenreich .01 .05
595A Paul Gibson P1 .40 1.00
595B Paul Gibson P2 .01 .05
(Airbrushed leg on
player in background)
596 Mike Birkbeck .01 .05
597 Terry Francona .02 .10
598 Paul Zuvella .01 .05
599 Franklin Stubbs .02 .10
600 Gregg Jefferies .01 .05
601 John Cangelosi .01 .05
602 Mike Sharperson .01 .05
603 Mike Diaz .01 .05
604 Gary Varsho .01 .05
605 Terry Blocker .01 .05
606 Charlie O'Brien .01 .05
607 Jim Eppard .01 .05
608 John Davis .01 .05
609 Ken Griffey Sr. .02 .10
610 Buddy Bell .02 .10
611 Ted Simmons UER .02 .10
('78 stats Cardinal)
612 Matt Williams .08 .25
613 Danny Cox .01 .05
614 Al Pedrique .01 .05
615 Ron Oester .01 .05
616 John Smoltz RC .60 1.50
617 Bob Melvin .01 .05
618 Rob Dibble RC .15 .40
619 Kirt Manwaring .01 .05
620 Felix Fermin .01 .05
621 Doug Dascenzo .01 .05
622 Bill Brennan .01 .05
623 Carlos Quintana RC .02 .10
624 Mike Harkey RC UER .02 .10
(13 and 31 walks in '88,
should be 35 and 33
625 Gary Sheffield RC .60 1.50
626 Tom Prince .01 .05
627 Steve Searcy .01 .05
628 Charlie Hayes RC .08 .25
(Listed as outfielder)
629 Felix Jose RC UER .02 .10
(Modesto misspelled
as Modesta)
630 Sandy Alomar Jr. RC .15 .40
(Inconsistent design,
portrait on front)
631 Derek Lilliquist RC .02 .10
632 Geronimo Berroa .01 .05
633 Luis Medina .01 .05
634 Tom Gordon RC UER .20 .50
Height 6'0"
635 Ramon Martinez RC .08 .25
636 Craig Worthington .01 .05
637 Edgar Martinez .08 .25
638 Chad Kreuter RC .08 .25
639 Ron Jones .02 .10
640 Van Snider RC .02 .10
641 Lance Blankenship RC .02 .10
642 Dwight Smith RC UER .08 .25
10 HR's in '87, should be 18
643 Cameron Drew .01 .05
644 Jerald Clark RC .02 .10
645 Randy Johnson RC 1.00 2.50
646 Norm Charlton RC .08 .25
647 Todd Frohwirth UER .01 .05
(Southpaw on back)
648 Luis De Los Santos .01 .05
649 Tim Jones .01 .05
650 Dave West RC UER .02 .10
ML hits 3
should be 6
651 Bob Milacki .01 .05
652 Wrigley Field HL .02 .10
653 Orel Hershiser HL .01 .05
654A W.Boggs HL ERR .05 .15
('seasaon' on back
654B W.Boggs HL COR .02 .10
655 Jose Canseco HL .08 .25
656 Doug Jones HL .01 .05
657 Rickey Henderson HL .05 .15
658 Tom Browning HL .01 .05
659 Mike Greenwell HL .01 .05
660 Boston Red Sox HL .01 .05

1989 Score Rookie/Traded

The 1989 Score Rookie and Traded set contains 110 standard-size cards. The set was issued exclusively in factory set form through hobby dealers. The set was distributed in a blue box with 10 Magic Motion trivia cards. The fronts have coral green borders with pink diamonds at the bottom. Cards 1-80 feature traded players; cards 81-110 feature 1989 rookies. Rookie Cards in this set include Jim Abbott, Joey (Albert) Belle, Ken Griffey Jr. and John Wetteland.

COMP.FACT.SET (110) 6.00 15.00
1T Rafael Palmeiro .08 .25
2T Nolan Ryan .60 1.50
3T Jack Clark .02 .10
4T Dave LaPoint .01 .05
5T Mike Moore .01 .05
6T Pete O'Brien .01 .05
7T Jeffrey Leonard .01 .05
8T Rob Murphy .01 .05
9T Tom Herr .01 .05
10T Claudell Washington .01 .05
11T Mike Pagliarulo .01 .05
12T Steve Lake .01 .05
13T Spike Owen .01 .05
14T Andy Hawkins .01 .05
15T Todd Benzinger .01 .05
16T Mookie Wilson .02 .10
17T Bert Blyleven .02 .10
18T Jeff Treadway .01 .05
19T Bruce Hurst .01 .05
20T Steve Sax .01 .05
21T Juan Samuel .01 .05
22T Jesse Barfield .02 .10
23T Carmen Castillo .01 .05
24T Terry Leach .01 .05
25T Mark Langston .01 .05
26T Eric King .01 .05
27T Steve Balboni .01 .05
28T Len Dykstra .02 .10
29T Keith Moreland .01 .05
30T Terry Kennedy .01 .05
31T Eddie Murray .08 .25
32T Mitch Williams .01 .05
33T Jeff Parrett .01 .05
34T Wally Backman .01 .05
35T Julio Franco .02 .10
36T Lance Parrish .02 .10
37T Nick Esasky .01 .05
38T Luis Polonia .01 .05
39T Kevin Gross .01 .05
40T John Dopson .01 .05
41T Willie Randolph .02 .10
42T Jim Clancy .01 .05
43T Tracy Jones .01 .05
44T Phil Bradley .01 .05
45T Milt Thompson .01 .05
46T Chris James .01 .05
47T Scott Fletcher .01 .05
48T Kal Daniels .01 .05
49T Steve Bedrosian .01 .05
50T Rickey Henderson .08 .25
51T Dion James .01 .05
52T Tim Leary .01 .05
53T Roger McDowell .01 .05
54T Mel Hall .01 .05
55T Dickie Thon .01 .05
56T Zane Smith .01 .05
57T Danny Heep .01 .05
58T Bob McClure .01 .05
59T Brian Holton .01 .05
60T Randy Ready .01 .05
61T Bob Melvin .01 .05
62T Harold Baines .02 .10
63T Lance McCullers .01 .05
64T Jody Davis .01 .05
65T Darrell Evans .02 .10
66T Joel Youngblood .01 .05
67T Frank Viola .02 .10
68T Mike Aldrete .01 .05
69T Greg Cadaret .01 .05
70T John Kruk .02 .10
71T Pat Sheridan .01 .05
72T Oddibe McDowell .01 .05
73T Tom Brookens .01 .05
74T Bob Boone .02 .10
75T Walt Terrell .01 .05
76T Joel Skinner .01 .05
77T Randy Johnson .60 1.50
78T Felix Fermin .01 .05
79T Rick Mahler .01 .05
80T Richard Dotson .01 .05
81T Cris Carpenter RC .02 .10
82T Bill Spiers RC .08 .25
83T Junior Felix RC .02 .10
84T Joe Girardi RC .15 .40
85T Jerome Walton RC .08 .25
86T Greg Litton .01 .05
87T Greg W.Harris RC .02 .10
88T Jim Abbott RC .40 1.00
89T Kevin Brown .08 .25
90T John Wetteland RC .15 .40
91T Gary Wayne .01 .05
92T Rich Monteleone .01 .05
93T Bob Geren RC .01 .05
94T Clay Parker .01 .05
95T Steve Finley RC .30 .75
96T Gregg Olson RC .08 .25
97T Ken Patterson .01 .05
98T Ken Hill RC .08 .25
99T Scott Scudder RC .02 .10
100T Ken Griffey Jr. RC 2.50 6.00
101T Jeff Brantley RC .08 .25
102T Donn Pall .01 .05
103T Carlos Martinez RC .02 .10
104T Joe Oliver RC .08 .25
105T Omar Vizquel RC .40 1.00
106T Joey Belle RC .40 1.00
107T Kenny Rogers RC .75 2.00
108T Mark Carreon .01 .05
109T Rolando Roomes .01 .05
110T Pete Harnisch RC .08 .25

1989 Score Young Superstars I

The 1989 Score Young Superstars I set contains 42 standard-size cards. The fronts are pink, white and blue. The vertically oriented backs have color facial shots, 1988 and career stats, and biographical information. One card was included in each 1989 Score rack pack, and the cards were also distributed as a boxed set with five Magic Motion trivia cards.

COMPLETE SET (42) 3.00 8.00
1 Gregg Jefferies .15 .40
2 Jody Reed .08 .25
3 Mark Grace .40 1.00
4 Dave Gallagher .08 .25
5 Bo Jackson .40 1.00
6 Jay Buhner .15 .40
7 Melido Perez .08 .25
8 Bobby Witt .08 .25
9 David Cone .15 .40
10 Chris Sabo .08 .25
11 Pat Borders .08 .25
12 Mark Grant .08 .25
13 Mike Macfarlane .08 .25
14 Mike Jackson .08 .25
15 Ricky Jordan .08 .25
16 Ron Gant .15 .40
17 Al Leiter .40 1.00
18 Jeff Parrett .08 .25
19 Pete Smith .08 .25
20 Walt Weiss .15 .40
21 Doug Drabek .08 .25
22 Kirt Manwaring .08 .25
23 Keith A. Miller .08 .25
24 Damon Berryhill .08 .25
25 Gary Sheffield 2.00 5.00
26 Brady Anderson .25 .60
27 Mitch Williams .08 .25
28 Roberto Alomar .40 1.00
29 Bobby Thigpen .08 .25
30 Bryan Harvey UER .08 .25
(47 games in '87)
31 Jose Rijo .08 .25
32 Dave West .08 .25
33 Joey Meyer .08 .25
34 Allan Anderson .08 .25
35 Rafael Palmeiro .40 1.00
36 Tim Belcher .08 .25
37 John Smiley .08 .25
38 Mackey Sasser .08 .25
39 Greg Maddux .75 2.00
40 Ramon Martinez .15 .40
41 Randy Myers .15 .40
42 Scott Bankhead .08 .25

1989 Score Young Superstars II

The 1989 Score Young Superstars II set contains 42 standard-size cards. The fronts are orange, white and purple. The vertically oriented backs have color facial shots, 1988 and career stats, and biographical information. The cards were distributed as a boxed set with five Magic Motion trivia cards. A first year card of Ken Griffey Jr. highlights the set.

COMP.FACT.SET (42) 10.00 25.00
1 Sandy Alomar Jr. .25 .60
2 Tom Gordon .25 .60
3 Ron Jones .08 .25
4 Todd Burns .08 .25
5 Paul O'Neill .25 .60
6 Gene Larkin .08 .25
7 Eric King .08 .25
8 Jeff M. Robinson .08 .25
9 Bill Wegman .08 .25
10 Cecil Espy .08 .25
11 Jose Guzman .08 .25
12 Kelly Gruber .08 .25
13 Duane Ward .08 .25
14 Mark Gubicza .08 .25
15 Norm Charlton .15 .40
16 Jose Oquendo .08 .25
17 Geronimo Berroa .08 .25
18 Ken Griffey Jr. 6.00 15.00
19 Lance McCullers .08 .25
20 Todd Stottlemyre .25 .60
21 Craig Worthington .08 .25
22 Mike Devereaux .08 .25
23 Tom Glavine .40 1.00
24 Dale Sveum .08 .25
25 Roberto Kelly .15 .40
26 Luis Medina .08 .25
27 Steve Searcy .08 .25
28 Don August .08 .25
29 Shawn Hillegas .08 .25
30 Mike Campbell .08 .25
31 Mike Harkey .08 .25
32 Randy Johnson 3.00 8.00
33 Craig Biggio 2.00 5.00
34 Mike Schooler .08 .25
35 Andres Thomas .08 .25
36 Jerome Walton .15 .40
37 Cris Carpenter .08 .25
38 Kevin Mitchell .15 .40
39 Eddie Williams .08 .25
40 Chad Kreuter .08 .25
41 Danny Jackson .08 .25
42 Kurt Stillwell .08 .25

1990 Score

The 1990 Score set contains 704 standard-size cards. Cards were distributed in plastic-wrap packs and factory sets. The front borders are red, blue, green or white. The vertically oriented backs are white with borders that match the fronts, and feature color mugshots. Subsets include Draft Picks (661-682) and Dream Team (683-695). A special black and white horizontal-designed card of Bo Jackson in football pads holding a bat above his shoulders was a big hit in 1990. That card traded for as much as $10 but has since cooled off. Nevertheless, it remains one of the most noteworthy cards issued in the early 1990's. Rookie Cards of note include Juan Gonzalez, Dave Justice, Chuck Knoblauch, Dean Palmer, Sammy Sosa, Frank Thomas, Mo Vaughn, Larry Walker and Bernie Williams. A ten-card set of Dream Team Rookies was inserted into each hobby factory set, but was not included in retail factory sets.

COMPLETE SET (704) 6.00 15.00
COMP.RETAIL SET (704) 6.00 15.00
COMP.HOBBY SET (714) 6.00 15.00
1 Don Mattingly .25 .60
2 Cal Ripken .30 .75
3 Dwight Evans .05 .15
4 Barry Bonds .40 1.00
5 Kevin McReynolds .01 .05
6 Ozzie Guillen .02 .10
7 Terry Kennedy .01 .05
8 Bryan Harvey .01 .05
9 Alan Trammell .02 .10
10 Cory Snyder .01 .05
11 Jody Reed .01 .05
12 Roberto Alomar .05 .15
13 Pedro Guerrero .01 .05
14 Gary Redus .01 .05
15 Marty Barrett .01 .05
16 Ricky Jordan .01 .05
17 Joe Magrane .01 .05
18 Sid Fernandez .01 .05
19 Richard Dotson .01 .05
20 Jack Clark .02 .10
21 Bob Walk .01 .05
22 Ron Karkovice .01 .05
23 Lenny Harris .01 .05
24 Phil Bradley .01 .05
25 Andres Galarraga .02 .10
26 Brian Downing .01 .05
27 Dave Martinez .01 .05
28 Eric King .01 .05
29 Barry Lyons .01 .05
30 Dave Schmidt .01 .05
31 Mike Boddicker .01 .05
32 Tom Foley .01 .05
33 Brady Anderson .02 .10
34 Jim Presley .01 .05
35 Lance Parrish .01 .05
36 Von Hayes .01 .05
37 Lee Smith .02 .10
38 Herm Winningham .01 .05
39 Alejandro Pena .01 .05
40 Mike Scott .01 .05
41 Joe Orsulak .01 .05
42 Rafael Ramirez .01 .05
43 Gerald Young .01 .05
44 Dick Schofield .01 .05
45 Dave Smith .01 .05
46 Dave Magadan .01 .05
47 Dennis Martinez .02 .10
48 Greg Minton .01 .05
49 Milt Thompson .01 .05
50 Orel Hershiser .02 .10
51 Bip Roberts .01 .05
52 Jerry Browne .01 .05
53 Bob Ojeda .01 .05
54 Fernando Valenzuela .02 .10
55 Matt Nokes .01 .05
56 Brook Jacoby .01 .05
57 Frank Tanana .01 .05
58 Scott Fletcher .01 .05
59 Ron Oester .01 .05
60 Bob Boone .02 .10
61 Dan Gladden .01 .05
62 Darnell Coles .01 .05
63 Gregg Olson .02 .10
64 Todd Burns .01 .05
65 Todd Benzinger .01 .05
66 Dale Murphy .05 .15
67 Mike Flanagan .01 .05
68 Jose Oquendo .01 .05
69 Cecil Espy .01 .05
70 Chris Sabo .01 .05
71 Shane Rawley .01 .05
72 Tom Brunansky .01 .05
73 Vance Law .01 .05
74 B.J. Surhoff .02 .10
75 Lou Whitaker .02 .10
76 Ken Caminiti UER .02 .10
Euclid and Ohio should be
Hanford and California
77 Nelson Liriano .01 .05
78 Tommy Gregg .01 .05
79 Don Slaught .01 .05
80 Eddie Murray .08 .25
81 Joe Boever .01 .05
82 Charlie Leibrandt .01 .05
83 Jose Lind .01 .05
84 Tony Phillips .01 .05
85 Mitch Webster .01 .05
86 Dan Plesac .01 .05
87 Rick Mahler .01 .05
88 Steve Lyons .01 .05
89 Tony Fernandez .01 .05
90 Ryne Sandberg .15 .40
91 Nick Esasky .01 .05
92 Luis Salazar .01 .05
93 Pete Incaviglia .01 .05
94 Ivan Calderon .01 .05
95 Jeff Treadway .01 .05
96 Kurt Stillwell .01 .05
97 Gary Sheffield .08 .25
98 Jeffrey Leonard .01 .05
99 Andres Thomas .01 .05
100 Roberto Kelly .01 .05
101 Alvaro Espinoza .01 .05
102 Greg Gagne .01 .05
103 John Farrell .01 .05
104 Willie Wilson .01 .05
105 Glenn Braggs .01 .05
106 Chet Lemon .01 .05
107A Jamie Moyer ERR .02 .10
(Scintilating)
107B Jamie Moyer COR .20 .50
(Scintillating)
108 Chuck Crim .01 .05
109 Dave Valle .01 .05
110 Walt Weiss .01 .05
111 Larry Sheets .01 .05
112 Don Robinson .01 .05
113 Danny Heep .01 .05
114 Carmelo Martinez .01 .05
115 Dave Gallagher .01 .05
116 Mike LaValliere .01 .05
117 Bob McClure .01 .05
118 Rene Gonzales .01 .05
119 Mark Parent .01 .05
120 Wally Joyner .02 .10
121 Mark Gubicza .01 .05
122 Tony Pena .01 .05
123 Carmelo Castillo .01 .05
124 Howard Johnson .01 .05
125 Steve Sax .01 .05
126 Tim Belcher .01 .05
127 Tim Burke .01 .05
128 Al Newman .01 .05
129 Dennis Rasmussen .01 .05
130 Doug Jones .01 .05
131 Fred Lynn .01 .05
132 Jeff Hamilton .01 .05
133 German Gonzalez .01 .05
134 John Morris .01 .05
135 Dave Parker .02 .10
136 Gary Pettis .01 .05
137 Dennis Boyd .01 .05
138 Candy Maldonado .01 .05
139 Rick Cerone .01 .05
140 George Brett .25 .60
141 Dave Clark .01 .05
142 Dickie Thon .01 .05
143 Junior Ortiz .01 .05
144 Don August .01 .05
145 Gary Gaetti .02 .10
146 Kirt Manwaring .01 .05
147 Jeff Reed .01 .05
148 Jose Alvarez .01 .05
149 Mike Schooler .01 .05
150 Mark Grace .05 .15
151 Geronimo Berroa .01 .05
152 Barry Jones .01 .05
153 Geno Petralli .01 .05
154 Jim Deshaies .01 .05
155 Barry Larkin .05 .15
156 Alfredo Griffin .01 .05
157 Tom Henke .01 .05
158 Mike Jeffcoat .01 .05
159 Bob Welch .01 .05
160 Julio Franco .02 .10
161 Henry Cotto .01 .05
162 Terry Steinbach .01 .05
163 Damon Berryhill .01 .05
164 Tim Crews .01 .05
165 Tom Browning .01 .05
166 Fred Manrique .01 .05
167 Harold Reynolds .02 .10
168A Ron Hassey ERR .01 .05
(27 on back)
168B Ron Hassey COR .20 .50
(24 on back)
169 Shawon Dunston .01 .05
170 Bobby Bonilla .02 .10
171 Tommy Herr .01 .05
172 Mike Heath .01 .05
173 Rich Gedman .01 .05
174 Bill Ripken .01 .05

175 Pete O'Brien .01 .05
176A L.McClendon ERR .01 .05
Uniform number on
back listed as 1
176B L.McClendon COR .20 .50
Uniform number on
back listed as 10
177 Brian Holton .01 .05
178 Jeff Blauser .01 .05
179 Jim Eisenreich .01 .05
180 Bert Blyleven .02 .10
181 Rob Murphy .01 .05
182 Bill Doran .01 .05
183 Curt Ford .01 .05
184 Mike Henneman .01 .05
185 Eric Davis .02 .10
186 Lance McCullers .01 .05
187 Steve Davis RC .01 .05
188 Bill Wegman .01 .05
189 Brian Harper .01 .05
190 Mike Moore .01 .05
191 Dale Mohorcic .01 .05
192 Tim Wallach .01 .05
193 Keith Hernandez .02 .10
194 Dave Righetti .01 .05
195A B.Saberhagen ERR .02 .10
Joke
195B B.Saberhagen COR .20 .50
Joker
196 Paul Kilgus .01 .05
197 Bud Black .01 .05
198 Juan Samuel .01 .05
199 Kevin Seitzer .01 .05
200 Darryl Strawberry .02 .10
201 Dave Stieb .02 .10
202 Charlie Hough .02 .10
203 Jack Morris .02 .10
204 Rance Mulliniks .01 .05
205 Alvin Davis .01 .05
206 Jack Howell .01 .05
207 Ken Patterson .01 .05
208 Terry Pendleton .02 .10
209 Craig Lefferts .01 .05
210 Kevin Brown UER .02 .10
(First mention of '89
Rangers should be '88)
211 Dan Petry .01 .05
212 Dave Leiper .01 .05
213 Daryl Boston .01 .05
214 Kevin Hickey .01 .05
215 Mike Krukow .01 .05
216 Terry Francona .02 .10
217 Kirk McCaskill .01 .05
218 Scott Bailes .01 .05
219 Bob Forsch .01 .05
220A Mike Aldrete ERR .01 .05
(25 on back)
220B Mike Aldrete COR .20 .50
(24 on back)
221 Steve Buechele .01 .05
222 Jesse Barfield .01 .05
223 Juan Berenguer .01 .05
224 Andy McGaffigan .01 .05
225 Pete Smith .01 .05
226 Mike Witt .01 .05
227 Jay Howell .01 .05
228 Scott Bradley .01 .05
229 Jerome Walton .01 .05
230 Greg Swindell .01 .05
231 Atlee Hammaker .01 .05
232A Mike Devereaux ERR .01 .05
(RF on front)
232B M.Devereaux COR .20 .50
CF on front
233 Ken Hill .02 .10
234 Craig Worthington .01 .05
235 Scott Terry .01 .05
236 Brett Butler .02 .10
237 Doyle Alexander .01 .05
238 Dave Anderson .01 .05
239 Bob Milacki .01 .05
240 Dwight Smith .01 .05
241 Otis Nixon .01 .05
242 Pat Tabler .01 .05
243 Derek Lilliquist .01 .05
244 Danny Tartabull .01 .05
245 Wade Boggs .05 .15
246 Scott Garrelts .01 .05
(Should say Relief
Pitcher on front)
247 Spike Owen .01 .05
248 Norm Charlton .01 .05
249 Gerald Perry .01 .05
250 Nolan Ryan .40 1.00
251 Kevin Gross .01 .05
252 Randy Milligan .01 .05
253 Mike LaCoss .01 .05
254 Dave Bergman .01 .05
255 Tony Gwynn .10 .30
256 Felix Fermin .01 .05
257 Greg W. Harris .01 .05
258 Junior Felix .01 .05
259 Mark Davis .01 .05
260 Vince Coleman .01 .05
261 Paul Gibson .01 .05
262 Mitch Williams .01 .05
263 Jeff Russell .01 .05
264 Omar Vizquel .08 .25
265 Andre Dawson .02 .10
266 Storm Davis .01 .05
267 Guillermo Hernandez .01 .05
268 Mike Felder .01 .05
269 Tom Candiotti .01 .05
270 Bruce Hurst .01 .05
271 Fred McGriff .08 .25
272 Glenn Davis .01 .05
273 John Franco .02 .10
274 Rich Yett .01 .05
275 Craig Biggio .08 .25
276 Gene Larkin .01 .05
277 Rob Dibble .02 .10
278 Randy Bush .01 .05
279 Kevin Bass .01 .05
280A Bo Jackson ERR .08 .25
(Watham)
280B Bo Jackson COR .30 .75
(Wathan)
281 Wally Backman .01 .05
282 Larry Andersen .01 .05
283 Chris Bosio .01 .05
284 Juan Agosto .01 .05
285 Ozzie Smith .15 .40
286 George Bell .01 .05
287 Rex Hudler .01 .05
288 Pat Borders .01 .05
289 Danny Jackson .01 .05
290 Carlton Fisk .05 .15
291 Tracy Jones .01 .05
292 Allan Anderson .01 .05
293 Johnny Ray .01 .05
294 Lee Guetterman .01 .05
295 Paul O'Neill .05 .15
296 Carney Lansford .02 .10
297 Tom Brookens .01 .05
298 Claudell Washington .01 .05
299 Hubie Brooks .01 .05
300 Will Clark .05 .15
301 Kenny Rogers .02 .10
302 Darrell Evans .02 .10
303 Greg Briley .01 .05
304 Donn Pall .01 .05
305 Teddy Higuera .01 .05
306 Dan Pasqua .01 .05
307 Dave Winfield .02 .10
308 Dennis Powell .01 .05
309 Jose DeLeon .01 .05
310 Roger Clemens UER .40 1.00
(Dominate, should
say dominant)
311 Melido Perez .01 .05
312 Devon White .02 .10
313 Dwight Gooden .02 .10
314 Carlos Martinez .01 .05
315 Dennis Eckersley .02 .10
316 Clay Parker UER .01 .05
(Height 6'11-inch)
317 Rick Honeycutt .01 .05
318 Tim Laudner .01 .05
319 Joe Carter .02 .10
320 Robin Yount .15 .40
321 Felix Jose .01 .05
322 Mickey Tettleton .01 .05
323 Mike Gallego .01 .05
324 Edgar Martinez .05 .15
325 Dave Henderson .01 .05
326 Chili Davis .02 .10
327 Steve Balboni .01 .05
328 Jody Davis .01 .05
329 Shawn Hillegas .01 .05
330 Jim Abbott .05 .15
331 John Dopson .01 .05
332 Mark Williamson .01 .05
333 Jeff D. Robinson .01 .05
334 John Smiley .01 .05
335 Bobby Thigpen .01 .05
336 Garry Templeton .01 .05
337 Marvell Wynne .01 .05
338A Ken Griffey Sr. ERR .02 .10
(Uniform number on
back listed as 25)
338B Ken Griffey Sr. COR .20 .50
(Uniform number on
back listed as 30)
339 Steve Finley .02 .10
340 Ellis Burks .05 .15
341 Frank Williams .01 .05
342 Mike Morgan .01 .05
343 Kevin Mitchell .01 .05
344 Joel Youngblood .01 .05
345 Mike Greenwell .01 .05
346 Glenn Wilson .01 .05
347 John Costello .01 .05
348 Wes Gardner .01 .05
349 Jeff Ballard .01 .05
350 Mark Thurmond UER .01 .05
(ERA is 192,
should be 1.92)
351 Randy Myers .02 .10
352 Shawn Abner .01 .05
353 Jesse Orosco .01 .05
354 Greg Walker .01 .05
355 Pete Harnisch .01 .05
356 Steve Farr .01 .05
357 Dave LaPoint .01 .05
358 Willie Fraser .01 .05
359 Mickey Hatcher .01 .05
360 Rickey Henderson .08 .25
361 Mike Fitzgerald .01 .05
362 Bill Schroeder .01 .05
363 Mark Carreon .01 .05
364 Ron Jones .01 .05
365 Jeff Montgomery .02 .10
366 Bill Krueger .01 .05
367 John Cangelosi .01 .05
368 Jose Gonzalez .01 .05
369 Greg Hibbard RC .02 .10
370 John Smoltz .08 .25
371 Jeff Brantley .01 .05
372 Frank White .02 .10
373 Ed Whitson .01 .05
374 Willie McGee .02 .10
375 Jose Canseco .05 .15
376 Randy Ready .01 .05
377 Don Aase .01 .05
378 Tony Armas .01 .05
379 Steve Bedrosian .01 .05
380 Chuck Finley .02 .10
381 Kent Hrbek .02 .10
382 Jim Gantner .01 .05
383 Mel Hall .01 .05
384 Mike Marshall .01 .05
385 Mark McGwire .40 1.00
386 Wayne Tolleson .01 .05
387 Brian Holman .01 .05
388 John Wetteland .08 .25
389 Darren Daulton .02 .10
390 Rob Deer .01 .05
391 John Moses .01 .05
392 Todd Worrell .01 .05
393 Chuck Cary .01 .05
394 Stan Javier .01 .05
395 Willie Randolph .02 .10
396 Bill Buckner .02 .10
397 Robby Thompson .01 .05
398 Mike Scioscia .01 .05
399 Lonnie Smith .01 .05
400 Kirby Puckett .08 .25
401 Mark Langston .01 .05
402 Danny Darwin .01 .05
403 Greg Maddux .15 .40
404 Lloyd Moseby .01 .05
405 Rafael Palmeiro .05 .15
406 Chad Kreuter .01 .05
407 Jimmy Key .02 .10
408 Tim Birtsas .01 .05
409 Tim Raines .02 .10
410 Dave Stewart .02 .10
411 Eric Yelding RC .01 .05
412 Kent Anderson .01 .05
413 Les Lancaster .01 .05
414 Rick Dempsey .01 .05
415 Randy Johnson .20 .50
416 Gary Carter .02 .10
417 Rolando Roomes .01 .05
418 Dan Schatzeder .01 .05
419 Bryn Smith .01 .05
420 Ruben Sierra .02 .10
421 Steve Jeltz .01 .05
422 Ken Oberkfell .01 .05
423 Sid Bream .01 .05
424 Jim Clancy .01 .05
425 Kelly Gruber .01 .05
426 Rick Leach .01 .05
427 Len Dykstra .02 .10
428 Jeff Pico .01 .05
429 John Cerutti .01 .05
430 David Cone .02 .10
431 Jeff Kunkel .01 .05
432 Luis Aquino .01 .05
433 Ernie Whitt .01 .05
434 Bo Diaz .01 .05
435 Steve Lake .01 .05
436 Pat Perry .01 .05
437 Mike Davis .01 .05
438 Cecilio Guante .01 .05
439 Duane Ward .01 .05
440 Andy Van Slyke .05 .15
441 Gene Nelson .01 .05
442 Luis Polonia .01 .05
443 Kevin Elster .01 .05
444 Keith Moreland .01 .05
445 Roger McDowell .01 .05
446 Ron Darling .01 .05
447 Ernest Riles .01 .05
448 Mookie Wilson .02 .10
449A Billy Spiers ERR .01 .05
(No birth year)
449B Billy Spiers COR .20 .50
(Born in 1966)
450 Rick Sutcliffe .02 .10
451 Nelson Santovenia .01 .05
452 Andy Allanson .01 .05
453 Bob Melvin .01 .05
454 Benito Santiago .02 .10
455 Jose Uribe .01 .05
456 Bill Landrum .01 .05
457 Bobby Witt .01 .05
458 Kevin Romine .01 .05
459 Lee Mazzilli .01 .05
460 Paul Molitor .02 .10
461 Ramon Martinez .01 .05
462 Frank DiPino .01 .05
463 Walt Terrell .01 .05
464 Bob Geren .01 .05
465 Rick Reuschel .01 .05
466 Mark Grant .01 .05
467 John Kruk .02 .10
468 Gregg Jefferies .02 .10
469 R.J. Reynolds .01 .05
470 Harold Baines .02 .10
471 Dennis Lamp .01 .05
472 Tom Gordon .02 .10
473 Terry Puhl .01 .05
474 Curt Wilkerson .01 .05
475 Dan Quisenberry .01 .05
476 Oddibe McDowell .01 .05
477A Zane Smith ERR .01 .05
(Career ERA .393)
477B Zane Smith COR .20 .50
(career ERA 3.93)
478 Franklin Stubbs .01 .05
479 Wallace Johnson .01 .05
480 Jay Tibbs .01 .05
481 Tom Glavine .05 .15
482 Manny Lee .01 .05
483 Joe Hesketh UER .01 .05
Says Rookiess on back,
should say Rookies
484 Mike Bielecki .01 .05
485 Greg Brock .01 .05
486 Pascual Perez .01 .05
487 Kirk Gibson .02 .10
488 Scott Sanderson .01 .05
489 Domingo Ramos .01 .05
490 Kal Daniels .01 .05
491A David Wells ERR .02 .10
(Reverse negative
photo on card back)
491B David Wells COR .20 .50
492 Jerry Reed .01 .05
493 Eric Show .01 .05
494 Mike Pagliarulo .01 .05
495 Ron Robinson .01 .05
496 Brad Komminsk .01 .05
497 Greg Litton .01 .05
498 Chris James .01 .05
499 Luis Quinones .01 .05
500 Frank Viola .01 .05
501 Tim Teufel UER .01 .05
(Twins '85, the s is
lower case, should
be upper case)
502 Terry Leach .01 .05
503 Matt Williams UER .02 .10
(Wearing 10 on front,
listed as 9 on back)
504 Tim Leary .01 .05
505 Doug Drabek .01 .05
506 Mariano Duncan .01 .05
507 Charlie Hayes .01 .05
508 Joey Belle .08 .25
509 Pat Sheridan .01 .05
510 Mackey Sasser .01 .05
511 Jose Rijo .01 .05
512 Mike Smithson .01 .05
513 Gary Ward .01 .05
514 Dion James .01 .05
515 Jim Gott .01 .05
516 Drew Hall .01 .05
517 Doug Bair .01 .05
518 Scott Scudder .01 .05
519 Rick Aguilera .02 .10
520 Rafael Belliard .01 .05
521 Jay Buhner .02 .10
522 Jeff Reardon .02 .10
523 Steve Rosenberg .01 .05
524 Randy Velarde .01 .05
525 Jeff Musselman .01 .05
526 Bill Long .01 .05
527 Gary Wayne .01 .05
528 Dave Wayne Johnson RC .01 .05
529 Ron Kittle .01 .05
530 Erik Hanson UER .01 .05
(5th line on back
says seson, should
say season)
531 Steve Wilson .01 .05
532 Joey Meyer .01 .05
533 Curt Young .01 .05
534 Kelly Downs .01 .05
535 Joe Girardi .05 .15
536 Lance Blankenship .01 .05
537 Greg Mathews .01 .05
538 Donell Nixon .01 .05
539 Mark Knudson .01 .05
540 Jeff Wetherby RC .01 .05
541 Darrin Jackson .01 .05
542 Terry Mulholland .01 .05
543 Eric Hetzel .01 .05
544 Rick Reed RC .08 .25
545 Dennis Cook .01 .05
546 Mike Jackson .01 .05
547 Brian Fisher .01 .05
548 Gene Harris .01 .05
549 Jeff King .01 .05
550 Dave Dravecky .08 .25
551 Randy Kutcher .01 .05
552 Mark Portugal .01 .05
553 Jim Corsi .01 .05
554 Todd Stottlemyre .02 .10
555 Scott Bankhead .01 .05
556 Ken Dayley .01 .05
557 Rick Wrona .01 .05
558 Sammy Sosa RC 1.00 2.50
559 Keith Miller .01 .05
560 Ken Griffey Jr. .30 .75
561A R.Sandberg HL ERR 3.00 8.00
Position on front
listed as 3B
561B R.Sandberg HL COR .08 .25
562 Billy Hatcher .01 .05
563 Jay Bell .02 .10
564 Jack Daugherty RC .01 .05
565 Rich Monteleone .01 .05
566 Bo Jackson AS-MVP .02 .10
567 Tony Fossas RC .01 .05
568 Roy Smith .01 .05
569 Jaime Navarro .01 .05
570 Lance Johnson .01 .05
571 Mike Dyer RC .01 .05
572 Kevin Ritz RC .01 .05
573 Dave West .01 .05
574 Gary Mielke RC .01 .05
575 Scott Lusader .01 .05
576 Joe Oliver .01 .05
577 Sandy Alomar Jr. .02 .10
578 Andy Benes UER .02 .10
(Extra comma between
day and year)
579 Tim Jones .01 .05
580 Randy McCament RC .01 .05
581 Curt Schilling .40 1.00
582 John Orton RC .02 .10
583A Milt Cuyler ERR RC .02 .10
(998 games)
583B Milt Cuyler COR .20 .50
(98 games; the extra 9
was ghosted out and
may still be visible)
584 Eric Anthony RC .02 .10
585 Greg Vaughn .01 .05
586 Deion Sanders .08 .25
587 Jose DeJesus .01 .05
588 Chip Hale RC .01 .05
589 John Olerud RC .20 .50
590 Steve Olin RC .08 .25
591 Marquis Grissom RC .15 .40
592 Moises Alou RC .30 .75
593 Mark Lemke .01 .05
594 Dean Palmer RC .08 .25
595 Robin Ventura .08 .25
596 Tino Martinez .20 .50
597 Mike Huff RC .01 .05
598 Scott Hemond RC .02 .10
599 Wally Whitehurst .01 .05
600 Todd Zeile .01 .05
601 Glenallen Hill .01 .05
602 Hal Morris .01 .05
603 Juan Bell .01 .05
604 Bobby Rose .01 .05
605 Matt Merullo .01 .05
606 Kevin Maas RC .08 .25
607 Randy Nosek RC .01 .05
608A Billy Bates RC .01 .05
(Text mentions 12
triples in tenth line)
608B Billy Bates .01 .05
(Text has no mention
of triples)
609 Mike Stanton RC .08 .25
610 Mauro Gozzo RC .01 .05
611 Charles Nagy .01 .05
612 Scott Coolbaugh RC .01 .05
613 Jose Vizcaino RC .08 .25
614 Greg Smith RC .01 .05
615 Jeff Huson RC .02 .10
616 Mickey Weston RC .01 .05
617 John Pawlowski .01 .05
618A Joe Skalski ERR .01 .05
(27 on back)
618B Joe Skalski COR .20 .50
(67 on back)
619 Bernie Williams RC .60 1.50
620 Shawn Holman RC .01 .05
621 Gary Eave RC .01 .05
622 Darrin Fletcher UER .02 .10
Elmherst, should be Elmhurst
623 Pat Combs .01 .05
624 Mike Blowers RC .02 .10
625 Kevin Appier .02 .10
626 Pat Austin .01 .05
627 Kelly Mann RC .01 .05
628 Matt Kinzer RC .01 .05
629 Chris Hammond RC .02 .10
630 Dean Wilkins RC .01 .05
631 Larry Walker UER RC .40 1.00
Uniform number 55 on front
and 33 on back;
Home is Maple Ridge,
not Maple River
632 Blaine Beatty RC .01 .05
633A Tommy Barrett ERR .01 .05
(29 on back)
633B Tommy Barrett COR .20 .50
(14 on back)
634 Stan Belinda RC .02 .10
635 Mike (Texas) Smith RC .01 .05
636 Hensley Meulens .01 .05
637 J.Gonzalez UER RC .40 1.00
Sarasots on back,
should be Sarasota
638 Lenny Webster RC .02 .10
639 Mark Gardner RC .02 .10
640 Tommy Greene RC .02 .10
641 Mike Hartley RC .01 .05
642 Phil Stephenson .01 .05
643 Kevin Mmahat RC .01 .05
644 Ed Whited RC .01 .05
645 Delino DeShields RC .08 .25
646 Kevin Blankenship .01 .05
647 Paul Sorrento RC .08 .25
648 Mike Roesler RC .01 .05
649 Jason Grimsley RC .02 .10
650 Dave Justice RC .20 .50
651 Scott Cooper RC .02 .10
652 Dave Eiland .01 .05
653 Mike Munoz RC .01 .05
654 Jeff Fischer RC .01 .05
655 Terry Jorgensen RC .01 .05
656 George Canale RC .01 .05
657 Brian DuBois UER RC .01 .05
(Misspelled Dubois
on card)
658 Carlos Quintana .01 .05
659 Luis de los Santos .01 .05
660 Jerald Clark .01 .05
661 Donald Harris RC .01 .05
662 Paul Coleman RC .02 .10
663 Frank Thomas RC .75 2.00
664 Brent Mayne DC RC .08 .25
665 Eddie Zosky RC .02 .10
666 Steve Hosey RC .02 .10
667 Scott Bryant RC .02 .10
668 Tom Goodwin RC .08 .25
669 Cal Eldred RC .08 .25
670 Earl Cunningham RC .02 .10
671 Alan Zinter DC RC .02 .10
672 Chuck Knoblauch RC .15 .40
673 Kyle Abbott RC .02 .10
674 Roger Salkeld RC .02 .10
675 Mo Vaughn RC .20 .50
676 Keith (Kiki) Jones RC .01 .05
677 Tyler Houston RC .08 .25
678 Jeff Jackson RC .02 .10
679 Greg Gohr RC .02 .10
680 Ben McDonald DC RC .08 .25
681 Greg Blosser RC .02 .10
682 Willie Greene UER RC .08 .25
Name spelled as Green
683A W.Boggs DT ERR .02 .10
Text says 215 hits in
'89, should be 205
683B W.Boggs DT COR .20 .50
Text says 205 hits in '89
684 Will Clark DT .02 .10
685 Tony Gwynn DT UER .05 .15
(Text reads battling
instead of batting)
686 Rickey Henderson DT .05 .15
687 Bo Jackson DT .02 .10
688 Mark Langston DT .01 .05
689 Barry Larkin DT .02 .10
690 Kirby Puckett DT .05 .15
691 Ryne Sandberg DT .08 .25
692 Mike Scott DT .01 .05
693A Terry Steinbach DT .01 .05
ERR (cathers)
693B Terry Steinbach DT .01 .05
COR (catchers)
694 Bobby Thigpen DT .01 .05
695 Mitch Williams DT .01 .05
696 Nolan Ryan HL .15 .40
697 Bo Jackson FB/BB .20 .50
698 Rickey Henderson .05 .15
ALCS-MVP
699 Will Clark .02 .10
NLCS-MVP
700 Dave Stewart .02 .10
Mike Moore WS
701 Lights Out .08 .25
702 Carney Lansford .05 .15
Rickey Henderson
Jose Canseco
Dave Henderson WS
703 WS Game 4/Wrap-up .01 .05
704 Wade Boggs HL .02 .10

1990 Score Rookie Dream Team

A ten-card set of Dream Team Rookies was inserted only into hobby factory sets.These standard size cards carry a B prefix on the card number and include a player at each position plus a commemorative card honoring the late Baseball Commissioner A. Bartlett Giamatti.

COMPLETE SET (10) 2.00 4.00
B1 A.Bartlett Giamatti .40 1.00
COMM MEM
B2 Pat Combs .07 .20
B3 Todd Zeile .15 .40
B4 Luis de los Santos .07 .20
B5 Mark Lemke .07 .20
B6 Robin Ventura .40 1.00
B7 Jeff Huson .15 .40
B8 Greg Vaughn .07 .20
B9 Marquis Grissom .60 1.50
B10 Eric Anthony .15 .40

1990 Score Rookie/Traded

The standard-size 110-card 1990 Score Rookie and Traded set marked the third consecutive year Score had issued an end of the year set to note trades and give rookies early cards. The set was issued through hobby accounts and only in factory set form. The first 66 cards are traded players while the last 44 cards are rookie cards. Hockey star Eric Lindros is included in this set. Rookie Cards in the set include Derek Bell, Todd Hundley and Ray Lankford.

COMP.FACT.SET (110) 1.25 3.00
1T Dave Winfield .02 .10
2T Kevin Bass .01 .05
3T Nick Esasky .01 .05
4T Mitch Webster .01 .05
5T Pascual Perez .01 .05
6T Gary Pettis .01 .05
7T Tony Pena .01 .05
8T Candy Maldonado .01 .05
9T Cecil Fielder .02 .10
10T Carmelo Martinez .01 .05
11T Mark Langston .01 .05
12T Dave Parker .02 .10
13T Don Slaught .01 .05
14T Tony Phillips .01 .05
15T John Franco .02 .10
16T Randy Myers .02 .10
17T Jeff Reardon .02 .10
18T Sandy Alomar Jr. .02 .10
19T Joe Carter .02 .10
20T Fred Lynn .01 .05
21T Storm Davis .01 .05
22T Craig Lefferts .01 .05
23T Pete O'Brien .01 .05
24T Dennis Boyd .01 .05
25T Lloyd Moseby .01 .05
26T Mark Davis .01 .05
27T Tim Leary .01 .05
28T Gerald Perry .01 .05
29T Don Aase .01 .05
30T Ernie Whitt .01 .05
31T Dale Murphy .05 .15
32T Alejandro Pena .01 .05
33T Juan Samuel .01 .05
34T Hubie Brooks .01 .05
35T Gary Carter .02 .10
36T Jim Presley .01 .05
37T Wally Backman .01 .05
38T Matt Nokes .01 .05
39T Dan Petry .01 .05
40T Franklin Stubbs .01 .05
41T Jeff Huson .01 .05
42T Billy Hatcher .01 .05
43T Terry Leach .01 .05
44T Phil Bradley .01 .05
45T Claudell Washington .01 .05
46T Luis Polonia .01 .05
47T Daryl Boston .01 .05
48T Lee Smith .02 .10
49T Tom Brunansky .01 .05
50T Mike Witt .01 .05
51T Willie Randolph .02 .10
52T Stan Javier .01 .05
53T Brad Komminsk .01 .05
54T John Candelaria .01 .05
55T Bryn Smith .01 .05
56T Glenn Braggs .01 .05
57T Keith Hernandez .02 .10
58T Ken Oberkfell .01 .05
59T Steve Jeltz .01 .05
60T Chris James .01 .05
61T Scott Sanderson .01 .05
62T Bill Long .01 .05
63T Rick Cerone .01 .05
64T Scott Bailes .01 .05
65T Larry Sheets .01 .05
66T Junior Ortiz .01 .05
67T Francisco Cabrera .01 .05
68T Gary DiSarcina RC .08 .25
69T Greg Olson (C) RC .01 .05
70T Beau Allred RC .01 .05
71T Oscar Azocar RC .01 .05
72T Kent Mercker RC .08 .25
73T John Burkett .01 .05
74T Carlos Baerga RC .08 .25
75T Dave Hollins RC .08 .25
76T Todd Hundley RC .08 .25
77T Rick Parker RC .01 .05
78T Steve Cummings RC .01 .05
79T Bill Sampen RC .01 .05
80T Jerry Kutzler RC .01 .05
81T Derek Bell RC .08 .25
82T Kevin Tapani RC .08 .25
83T Jim Leyritz RC .08 .25
84T Ray Lankford RC .15 .40
85T Wayne Edwards RC .01 .05
86T Frank Thomas .75 2.00
87T Tim Naehring RC .02 .10
88T Willie Blair RC .02 .10
89T Alan Mills RC .02 .10
90T Scott Radinsky RC .02 .10
91T Howard Farmer RC .01 .05
92T Julio Machado RC .01 .05
93T Rafael Valdez RC .01 .05
94T Shawn Boskie RC .02 .10
95T David Segui RC .15 .40
96T Chris Hoiles RC .08 .25

Card	Low	High
97T D.J. Dozier RC	.02	.10
98T Hector Villanueva RC	.01	.05
99T Eric Gunderson RC	.01	.05
100T Eric Lindros	.40	1.00
101T Dave Otto	.01	.05
102T Dana Kiecker RC	.01	.05
103T Tim Drummond RC	.01	.05
104T Mickey Pina RC	.01	.05
105T Craig Grebeck RC	.02	.10
106T Bernard Gilkey RC	.08	.25
107T Tim Layana RC	.01	.05
108T Scott Chiamparino RC	.01	.05
109T Steve Avery	.01	.05
110T Terry Shumpert RC	.01	.05

1990 Score Rising Stars

The 1990 Score Rising Stars set contains 100 standard size cards. The fronts are green, blue and white. The vertically oriented backs feature a large color facial shot and career highlights. The cards were distributed as a set in a blister pack, which also included a full color booklet with more information about each player.

Card	Low	High
COMP.FACT.SET (100)	6.00	15.00
1 Tom Gordon	.08	.25
2 Jerome Walton	.02	.10
3 Ken Griffey Jr.	.75	2.00
4 Dwight Smith	.02	.10
5 Jim Abbott	.15	.40
6 Todd Zeile	.08	.25
7 Donn Pall	.02	.10
8 Rick Reed	.25	.60
9 Joey Belle	.25	.60
10 Gregg Jefferies	.08	.25
11 Kevin Ritz	.02	.10
12 Charlie Hayes	.02	.10
13 Kevin Appier	.08	.25
14 Jeff Huson	.02	.10
15 Gary Wayne	.02	.10
16 Eric Yelding	.02	.10
17 Clay Parker	.02	.10
18 Junior Felix	.02	.10
19 Derek Lilliquist	.02	.10
20 Gary Sheffield	.25	.60
21 Craig Worthington	.02	.10
22 Jeff Brantley	.02	.10
23 Eric Hetzel	.02	.10
24 Greg W.Harris	.02	.10
25 John Wetteland	.25	.60
26 Joe Oliver	.02	.10
27 Kevin Maas	.08	.25
28 Kevin Brown	.08	.25
29 Mike Stanton	.02	.10
30 Greg Vaughn	.02	.10
31 Ron Jones	.02	.10
32 Gregg Olson	.08	.25
33 Joe Girardi	.15	.40
34 Ken Hill	.08	.25
35 Sammy Sosa	1.25	3.00
36 Geronimo Berroa	.02	.10
37 Omar Vizquel	.25	.60
38 Dean Palmer	.25	.60
39 John Olerud	.40	1.00
40 Deion Sanders	.25	.60
41 Randy Kramer	.02	.10
42 Scott Lusader	.02	.10
43 Dave Wayne Johnson	.02	.10
44 Jeff Wetherby	.02	.10
45 Eric Anthony	.02	.10
46 Kenny Rogers	.08	.25
47 Matt Winters	.02	.10
48 Mauro Gozzo	.02	.10
49 Carlos Quintana	.02	.10
50 Bob Geren	.02	.10
51 Chad Kreuter	.02	.10
52 Randy Johnson	.60	1.50
53 Hensley Meulens	.02	.10
54 Gene Harris	.02	.10
55 Bill Spiers	.02	.10
56 Kelly Mann	.02	.10
57 Tom McCarthy	.02	.10
58 Steve Finley	.08	.25
59 Ramon Martinez	.02	.10
60 Greg Briley	.02	.10
61 Jack Daugherty	.02	.10
62 Tim Jones	.02	.10
63 Doug Strange	.02	.10
64 John Orton	.02	.10
65 Scott Scudder	.02	.10
66 Mark Gardner	.02	.10
67 Mark Carreon	.02	.10
68 Bob Milacki	.02	.10
69 Andy Benes	.08	.25
70 Carlos Martinez	.02	.10
71 Jeff King	.02	.10
72 Brad Arnsberg	.02	.10
73 Rick Wrona	.02	.10
74 Cris Carpenter	.02	.10
75 Dennis Cook	.02	.10
76 Pete Harnisch	.02	.10
77 Greg Hibbard	.02	.10
78 Ed Whited	.02	.10
79 Scott Coolbaugh	.02	.10
80 Billy Bates	.02	.10
81 German Gonzalez	.02	.10
82 Lance Blankenship	.02	.10
83 Lenny Harris	.02	.10
84 Milt Cuyler	.02	.10
85 Erik Hanson	.02	.10
86 Kent Anderson	.02	.10
87 Hal Morris	.02	.10
88 Mike Brumley	.02	.10
89 Ken Patterson	.02	.10
90 Mike Devereaux	.02	.10
91 Greg Litton	.02	.10
92 Rolando Roomes	.02	.10
93 Ben McDonald	.02	.10
94 Curt Schilling	.75	2.00
95 Jose DeJesus	.02	.10
96 Robin Ventura	.25	.60
97 Steve Searcy	.02	.10
98 Chip Hale	.02	.10
99 Marquis Grissom	.25	.60
100 Luis de los Santos	.02	.10

1990 Score Young Superstars I

1990 Score Young Superstars I are glossy full color cards featuring 42 standard-size cards of popular young players. The first series was issued with 1990 Score baseball rack packs while the second series was available only via a mailaway from the company.

Card	Low	High
COMPLETE SET (42)	4.00	10.00
1 Bo Jackson	.50	1.25
2 Dwight Smith	.08	.25
3 Albert Belle	.50	1.25
4 Gregg Olson	.20	.50
5 Jim Abbott	.30	.75
6 Felix Fermin	.08	.25
7 Brian Holman	.08	.25
8 Clay Parker	.08	.25
9 Junior Felix	.08	.25
10 Joe Oliver	.08	.25
11 Steve Finley	.20	.50
12 Greg Briley	.08	.25
13 Greg Vaughn	.08	.25
14 Bill Spiers	.08	.25
15 Eric Yelding	.08	.25
16 Jose Gonzalez	.08	.25
17 Mark Carreon	.08	.25
18 Greg W. Harris	.08	.25
19 Felix Jose	.08	.25
20 Bob Milacki	.08	.25
21 Kenny Rogers	.20	.50
22 Rolando Roomes	.08	.25
23 Bip Roberts	.08	.25
24 Jeff Brantley	.08	.25
25 Jeff Ballard	.08	.25
26 John Dopson	.08	.25
27 Ken Patterson	.08	.25
28 Omar Vizquel	.50	1.25
29 Kevin Brown	.20	.50
30 Derek Lilliquist	.08	.25
31 David Wells	.20	.50
32 Ken Hill	.20	.50
33 Greg Litton	.08	.25
34 Rob Ducey	.08	.25
35 Carlos Martinez	.08	.25
36 John Smoltz	.50	1.25
37 Lenny Harris	.08	.25
38 Charlie Hayes	.08	.25
39 Tommy Gregg	.08	.25
40 John Wetteland	.50	1.25
41 Jeff Huson	.08	.25
42 Eric Anthony	.08	.25

1990 Score Young Superstars II

1990 Score Young Superstars II are glossy full color cards featuring 42 standard-size cards of popular young players. Whereas the first series was issued with 1990 Score baseball rack packs, this second series was available only via a mailaway from the company.

Card	Low	High
COMP.FACT.SET (42)	10.00	25.00
1 Todd Zeile	.20	.50
2 Ben McDonald	.08	.25
3 Delino DeShields	.60	1.50
4 Pat Combs	.08	.25
5 John Olerud	1.25	3.00
6 Marquis Grissom	.60	1.50
7 Mike Stanton	.08	.25
8 Robin Ventura	.60	1.50
9 Larry Walker	1.50	4.00
10 Dante Bichette	.20	.50
11 Jack Armstrong	.08	.25
12 Jay Bell	.20	.50
13 Andy Benes	.20	.50
14 Joey Cora	.20	.50
15 Rob Dibble	.20	.50
16 Jeff King	.08	.25
17 Jeff Hamilton	.08	.25
18 Erik Hanson	.08	.25
19 Pete Harnisch	.08	.25
20 Greg Hibbard	.08	.25
21 Stan Javier	.08	.25
22 Mark Lemke	.08	.25
23 Steve Olin	.20	.50
24 Tommy Greene	.08	.25
25 Sammy Sosa	2.50	6.00
26 Gary Wayne	.08	.25
27 Deion Sanders	.60	1.50
28 Steve Wilson	.08	.25
29 Joe Girardi	.20	.50
30 John Orton	.08	.25
31 Kevin Tapani	.60	1.50
32 Carlos Baerga	.20	.50
33 Glenallen Hill	.08	.25
34 Mike Blowers	.20	.50
35 Dave Hollins	.20	.50
36 Lance Blankenship	.08	.25
37 Hal Morris	.08	.25
38 Lance Johnson	.08	.25
39 Chris Gwynn	.08	.25
40 Doug Dascenzo	.08	.25
41 Jerald Clark	.08	.25
42 Carlos Quintana	.08	.25

1991 Score

The 1991 Score set contains 893 standard-size cards issued in two separate series of 441 and 452 cards each. This set marks the fourth consecutive year that Score issued a major set but the first time Score issued the set in two series. Cards were distributed in plastic-wrap packs, blister packs and factory sets. The card fronts feature one of four different solid color borders (black, blue, teal and white) framing the full-color photo of the cards. Subsets include Rookie Prospects (331-379), First Draft Picks (380-391, 671-682), AL All-Stars (392-401), Master Blasters (402-406, 689-693), K-Men (407-411, 684-688), Rifleman (412-416, 694-698), NL All-Stars (661-670), No-Hitters (699-707), Franchise (849-874), Award Winners (875-881) and Dream Team (882-893). An American Flag card (737) was issued to honor the American soldiers involved in Desert Storm. Rookie Cards in the set include Carl Everett, Jeff Conine, Chipper Jones, Mike Mussina and Rondell White. There are a number of pitchers whose card backs show Innings Pitched totals which do not equal the added year-by-year total; the following card numbers were affected, 4, 24, 29, 30, 51, 81, 109, 111, 118, 141, 150, 156, 177, 204, 218, 232, 235, 255, 287, 289, 311, and 328.

Card	Low	High
COMPLETE SET (893)	8.00	20.00
COMP.FACT.SET (900)	10.00	25.00
1 Jose Canseco	.05	.15
2 Ken Griffey Jr.	.20	.50
3 Ryne Sandberg	.15	.40
4 Nolan Ryan	.40	1.00
5 Bo Jackson	.08	.25
6 Bret Saberhagen UER	.01	.05
(In bio, missed		
misspelled as mised)		
7 Will Clark	.05	.15
8 Ellis Burks	.02	.10
9 Joe Carter	.02	.10
10 Rickey Henderson	.08	.25
11 Ozzie Guillen	.02	.10
12 Wade Boggs	.05	.15
13 Jerome Walton	.01	.05
14 John Franco	.02	.10
15 Ricky Jordan UER	.01	.05
(League misspelled		
as legue)		
16 Wally Backman	.01	.05
17 Rob Dibble	.02	.10
18 Glenn Braggs	.01	.05
19 Cory Snyder	.01	.05
20 Kal Daniels	.01	.05
21 Mark Langston	.01	.05
22 Kevin Gross	.01	.05
23 Don Mattingly UER	.25	.60
First line, ' is missing from Yankee		
24 Dave Righetti	.02	.10
25 Roberto Alomar	.05	.15
26 Robby Thompson	.01	.05
27 Jack McDowell	.01	.05
28 Bip Roberts UER	.01	.05
(Bio reads playd)		
29 Jay Howell	.01	.05
30 Dave Stieb UER	.01	.05
(17 wins in bio,		
18 in stats)		
31 Johnny Ray	.01	.05
32 Steve Sax	.01	.05
33 Terry Mulholland	.01	.05
34 Lee Guetterman	.01	.05
35 Tim Raines	.02	.10
36 Scott Fletcher	.01	.05
37 Lance Parrish	.02	.10
38 Tony Phillips UER	.01	.05
(Born 4/15		
should be 4/25)		
39 Todd Stottlemyre	.01	.05
40 Alan Trammell	.02	.10
41 Todd Burns	.01	.05
42 Mookie Wilson	.02	.10
43 Chris Bosio	.01	.05
44 Jeffrey Leonard	.01	.05
45 Doug Jones	.01	.05
46 Mike Scott UER	.01	.05
(In first line,		
dominate should		
read dominating)		
47 Andy Hawkins	.01	.05
48 Harold Reynolds	.02	.10
49 Paul Molitor	.02	.10
50 John Farrell	.01	.05
51 Danny Darwin	.01	.05
52 Jeff Blauser	.01	.05
53 John Tudor UER	.01	.05
(41 wins in '81)		
54 Milt Thompson	.01	.05
55 Dave Justice	.02	.10
56 Greg Olson	.01	.05
57 Willie Blair	.01	.05
58 Rick Parker	.01	.05
59 Shawn Boskie	.01	.05
60 Kevin Tapani	.01	.05
61 Dave Hollins	.01	.05
62 Scott Radinsky	.01	.05
63 Francisco Cabrera	.01	.05
64 Tim Layana	.01	.05
65 Jim Leyritz	.01	.05
66 Wayne Edwards	.01	.05
67 Lee Stevens	.01	.05
68 Bill Sampen UER	.01	.05
Fourth line, long is spelled along		
69 Craig Grebeck UER	.01	.05
Born in Cerritos, not Johnstown		
70 John Burkett	.01	.05
71 Hector Villanueva	.01	.05
72 Oscar Azocar	.01	.05
73 Alan Mills	.01	.05
74 Carlos Baerga	.01	.05
75 Charles Nagy	.01	.05
76 Tim Drummond	.01	.05
77 Dana Kiecker	.01	.05
78 Tom Edens RC	.01	.05
79 Kent Mercker	.01	.05
80 Steve Avery	.01	.05
81 Lee Smith	.02	.10
82 Dave Martinez	.01	.05
83 Dave Winfield	.02	.10
84 Bill Spiers	.01	.05
85 Dan Pasqua	.01	.05
86 Randy Milligan	.01	.05
87 Tracy Jones	.01	.05
88 Greg Myers	.01	.05
89 Keith Hernandez	.02	.10
90 Todd Benzinger	.01	.05
91 Mike Jackson	.01	.05
92 Mike Stanley	.01	.05
93 Candy Maldonado	.01	.05
94 John Kruk UER	.02	.10
(No decimal point		
before 1990 BA)		
95 Cal Ripken UER	.30	.75
(Genius spelled genuis)		
96 Willie Fraser	.01	.05
97 Mike Felder	.01	.05
98 Bill Landrum	.01	.05
99 Chuck Crim	.01	.05
100 Chuck Finley	.02	.10
101 Kirt Manwaring	.01	.05
102 Jaime Navarro	.01	.05
103 Dickie Thon	.01	.05
104 Brian Downing	.01	.05
105 Jim Abbott	.05	.15
106 Tom Brookens	.01	.05
107 Darryl Hamilton UER	.01	.05
(Bio info is for		
Jeff Hamilton)		
108 Bryan Harvey	.01	.05
109 Greg A. Harris UER	.01	.05
Shown pitching lefty, bio says righty		
110 Greg Swindell	.01	.05
111 Juan Berenguer	.01	.05
112 Mike Heath	.01	.05
113 Scott Bradley	.01	.05
114 Jack Morris	.02	.10
115 Barry Jones	.01	.05
116 Kevin Romine	.01	.05
117 Garry Templeton	.01	.05
118 Scott Sanderson	.01	.05
119 Roberto Kelly	.01	.05
120 George Brett	.25	.60
121 Oddibe McDowell	.01	.05
122 Jim Acker	.01	.05
123 Bill Swift UER	.01	.05
(Born 12/27/61,		
should be 10/27)		
124 Eric King	.01	.05
125 Jay Buhner	.02	.10
126 Matt Young	.01	.05
127 Alvaro Espinoza	.01	.05
128 Greg Hibbard	.01	.05
129 Jeff M. Robinson	.01	.05
130 Mike Greenwell	.01	.05
131 Dion James	.01	.05
132 Donn Pall UER	.01	.05
(1988 ERA in stats 0.00)		
133 Lloyd Moseby	.01	.05
134 Randy Velarde	.01	.05
135 Allan Anderson	.01	.05
136 Mark Davis	.01	.05
137 Eric Davis	.02	.10
138 Phil Stephenson	.01	.05
139 Felix Fermin	.01	.05
140 Pedro Guerrero	.02	.10
141 Charlie Hough	.02	.10
142 Mike Henneman	.01	.05
143 Jeff Montgomery	.01	.05
144 Lenny Harris	.01	.05
145 Bruce Hurst	.01	.05
146 Eric Anthony	.01	.05
147 Paul Assenmacher	.01	.05
148 Jesse Barfield	.01	.05
149 Carlos Quintana	.01	.05
150 Dave Stewart	.02	.10
151 Roy Smith	.01	.05
152 Paul Gibson	.01	.05
153 Mickey Hatcher	.01	.05
154 Jim Eisenreich	.01	.05
155 Kenny Rogers	.02	.10
156 Dave Schmidt	.01	.05
157 Lance Johnson	.01	.05
158 Dave West	.01	.05
159 Steve Balboni	.01	.05
160 Jeff Brantley	.01	.05
161 Craig Biggio	.05	.15
162 Brook Jacoby	.01	.05
163 Dan Gladden	.01	.05
164 Jeff Reardon UER	.02	.10
(Total IP shown as		
943.2, should be 943.1)		
165 Mark Carreon	.01	.05
166 Mel Hall	.01	.05
167 Gary Mielke	.01	.05
168 Cecil Fielder	.02	.10
169 Darrin Jackson	.01	.05
170 Rick Aguilera	.02	.10
171 Walt Weiss	.01	.05
172 Steve Farr	.01	.05
173 Jody Reed	.01	.05
174 Mike Jeffcoat	.01	.05
175 Mark Grace	.05	.15
176 Larry Sheets	.01	.05
177 Bill Gullickson	.01	.05
178 Chris Gwynn	.01	.05
179 Melido Perez	.01	.05
180 Sid Fernandez UER	.01	.05
(779 runs in 1990)		
181 Tim Burke	.01	.05
182 Gary Pettis	.01	.05
183 Rob Murphy	.01	.05
184 Craig Lefferts	.01	.05
185 Howard Johnson	.01	.05
186 Ken Caminiti	.02	.10
187 Tim Belcher	.01	.05
188 Greg Cadaret	.01	.05
189 Matt Williams	.02	.10
190 Dave Magadan	.01	.05
191 Geno Petralli	.01	.05
192 Jeff D. Robinson	.01	.05
193 Jim Deshaies	.01	.05
194 Willie Randolph	.02	.10
195 George Bell	.01	.05
196 Hubie Brooks	.01	.05
197 Tom Gordon	.01	.05
198 Mike Fitzgerald	.01	.05
199 Mike Pagliarulo	.01	.05
200 Kirby Puckett	.08	.25
201 Shawon Dunston	.01	.05
202 Dennis Boyd	.01	.05
203 Junior Felix UER	.01	.05
(Text has him in NL)		
204 Alejandro Pena	.01	.05
205 Pete Smith	.01	.05
206 Tom Glavine UER	.05	.15
(Lefty spelled leftie)		
207 Luis Salazar	.01	.05
208 John Smoltz	.05	.15
209 Doug Dascenzo	.01	.05
210 Tim Wallach	.01	.05
211 Greg Gagne	.01	.05
212 Mark Gubicza	.01	.05
213 Mark Parent	.01	.05
214 Ken Oberkfell	.01	.05
215 Gary Carter	.02	.10
216 Rafael Palmeiro	.05	.15
217 Tom Niedenfuer	.01	.05
218 Dave LaPoint	.01	.05
219 Jeff Treadway	.01	.05
220 Mitch Williams UER	.01	.05
('89 ERA shown as 2.76,		
should be 2.64)		
221 Jose DeLeon	.01	.05
222 Mike LaValliere	.01	.05
223 Darrel Akerfelds	.01	.05
224A Kent Anderson ERR	.02	.10
(First line& flachy		
should read flashy)		
224B Kent Anderson COR	.02	.10
(Corrected in		
factory sets)		
225 Dwight Evans	.05	.15
226 Gary Redus	.01	.05
227 Paul O'Neill	.05	.15
228 Marty Barrett	.01	.05
229 Tom Browning	.01	.05
230 Terry Pendleton	.02	.10
231 Jack Armstrong	.01	.05
232 Mike Boddicker	.01	.05
233 Neal Heaton	.01	.05
234 Marquis Grissom	.02	.10
235 Bert Blyleven	.02	.10
236 Curt Young	.01	.05
237 Don Carman	.01	.05
238 Charlie Hayes	.01	.05
239 Mark Knudson	.01	.05
240 Todd Zeile	.01	.05
241 Larry Walker UER	.08	.25
(Maple River, should		
be Maple Ridge)		
242 Jerald Clark	.01	.05
243 Jeff Ballard	.01	.05
244 Jeff King	.01	.05
245 Tom Brunansky	.01	.05
246 Darren Daulton	.02	.10
247 Scott Terry	.01	.05
248 Rob Deer	.01	.05
249 Brady Anderson UER	.02	.10
(1990 Hagerstown 1 hit,		
should say 13 hits)		
250 Len Dykstra	.02	.10
251 Greg W. Harris	.01	.05
252 Mike Hartley	.01	.05
253 Joey Cora	.01	.05
254 Ivan Calderon	.01	.05
255 Ted Power	.01	.05
256 Sammy Sosa	.08	.25
257 Steve Buechele	.01	.05
258 Mike Devereaux UER	.01	.05
(No comma between		
city and state)		
259 Brad Komminsk UER	.01	.05
(Last text line,		
Ba should be BA)		
260 Ted Higuera	.01	.05
261 Shawn Abner	.01	.05
262 Dave Valle	.01	.05
263 Jeff Huson	.01	.05
264 Edgar Martinez	.05	.15
265 Carlton Fisk	.05	.15
266 Steve Finley	.02	.10
267 John Wetteland	.02	.10
268 Kevin Appier	.02	.10
269 Steve Lyons	.01	.05
270 Mickey Tettleton	.01	.05
271 Luis Rivera	.01	.05
272 Steve Jeltz	.01	.05
273 R.J. Reynolds	.01	.05
274 Carlos Martinez	.01	.05
275 Dan Plesac	.01	.05
276 Mike Morgan UER	.01	.05
Total IP shown as		
1149.1, should be 1149		
277 Jeff Russell	.01	.05
278 Pete Incaviglia	.01	.05
279 Kevin Seitzer UER	.01	.05
Bio has 200 hits twice		
and .300 four times,		
should be once and		
three times		
280 Bobby Thigpen	.01	.05
281 Stan Javier UER	.01	.05
(Born 1/9,		
should say 9/1)		
282 Henry Cotto	.01	.05
283 Gary Wayne	.01	.05
284 Shane Mack	.01	.05
285 Brian Holman	.01	.05
286 Gerald Perry	.01	.05
287 Steve Crawford	.01	.05
288 Nelson Liriano	.01	.05
289 Don Aase	.01	.05
290 Randy Johnson	.10	.30
291 Harold Baines	.02	.10
292 Kent Hrbek	.02	.10
293A Les Lancaster ERR	.01	.05
(No comma between		
Dallas and Texas)		
293B Les Lancaster COR	.01	.05
(Corrected in		
factory sets)		
294 Jeff Musselman	.01	.05
295 Kurt Stillwell	.01	.05
296 Stan Belinda	.01	.05
297 Lou Whitaker	.02	.10
298 Glenn Wilson	.01	.05
299 Omar Vizquel UER	.05	.15
Born 5/15, should be		
4/24, there is a decimal		
before GP total for '90		
300 Ramon Martinez	.01	.05
301 Dwight Smith	.01	.05
302 Tim Crews	.01	.05
303 Lance Blankenship	.01	.05
304 Sid Bream	.01	.05
305 Rafael Ramirez	.01	.05
306 Steve Wilson	.01	.05
307 Mackey Sasser	.01	.05
308 Franklin Stubbs	.01	.05
309 Jack Daugherty UER	.01	.05
(Born 6/3/60,		
should say July)		
310 Eddie Murray	.08	.25
311 Bob Welch	.01	.05
312 Brian Harper	.01	.05
313 Lance McCullers	.01	.05
314 Dave Smith	.01	.05
315 Bobby Bonilla	.02	.10
316 Jerry Don Gleaton	.01	.05
317 Greg Maddux	.15	.40
318 Keith Miller	.01	.05
319 Mark Portugal	.01	.05
320 Robin Ventura	.02	.10
321 Bob Ojeda	.01	.05
322 Mike Harkey	.01	.05
323 Jay Bell	.02	.10
324 Mark McGwire	.30	.75
325 Gary Gaetti	.02	.10
326 Jeff Pico	.01	.05
327 Kevin McReynolds	.01	.05
328 Frank Tanana	.01	.05
329 Eric Yelding UER	.01	.05
(Listed as 6'3		
should be 5'11		
330 Barry Bonds	.40	1.00
331 Brian McRae UER RC	.08	.25
(No comma between		
city and state)		
332 Pedro Munoz RC	.02	.10
333 Daryl Irvine RC	.01	.05
334 Chris Hoiles	.01	.05
335 Thomas Howard	.01	.05
336 Jeff Schulz RC	.01	.05
337 Jeff Manto	.01	.05
338 Beau Allred	.01	.05
339 Mike Bordick RC	.15	.40
340 Todd Hundley	.01	.05
341 Jim Vatcher UER RC (Height 6'9 should be 5'9)		
.01	.05	
342 Luis Sojo	.01	.05
343 Jose Offerman UER	.01	.05
(Born 1969, should		
say 1968)		
344 Pete Coachman RC	.01	.05
345 Mike Benjamin	.01	.05
346 Ozzie Canseco	.01	.05
347 Tim McIntosh	.01	.05
348 Phil Plantier RC	.02	.10
349 Terry Shumpert	.01	.05
350 Darren Lewis	.01	.05
351 David Walsh RC	.01	.05
352A Scott Chiamparino	.02	.10
ERR		
Bats left, should be right		
352B Scott Chiamparino	.02	.10
COR		
corrected in factory sets		
353 Julio Valera	.01	.05
UER (Progressed mis-		
spelled as progessed)		
354 Anthony Telford RC	.01	.05
355 Kevin Wickander	.01	.05
356 Tim Naehring	.01	.05
357 Jim Poole	.01	.05
358 Mark Whiten UER	.01	.05
Shown hitting lefty, bio says righty		
359 Terry Wells RC	.01	.05
360 Rafael Valdez	.01	.05
361 Mel Stottlemyre Jr.	.01	.05
362 David Segui	.01	.05
363 Paul Abbott RC	.01	.05
364 Steve Howard	.01	.05
365 Karl Rhodes	.01	.05
366 Rafael Novoa RC	.01	.05
367 Joe Grahe RC	.01	.05
368 Darren Reed	.01	.05
369 Jeff McKnight	.01	.05
370 Scott Leius	.01	.05
371 Mark Dewey RC	.01	.05
372 Mark Lee UER RC	.02	.10
(Shown hitting left,		
bio says righty,		
born in Dakota,		
should say North Dakota)		
373 Rosario Rodriguez UER RC	.01	.05
Shown hitting lefty, bio says righty)		
374 Chuck McElroy	.01	.05
375 Mike Bell RC	.01	.05
376 Mickey Morandini	.01	.05
377 Bill Haselman RC	.01	.05
378 Dave Pavlas RC	.01	.05
379 Derrick May	.01	.05
380 Jeromy Burnitz RC	.15	.40
381 Donald Peters RC	.01	.05
382 Alex Fernandez FDP	.01	.05
383 Mike Mussina RC	.75	2.00
384 Dan Smith RC	.02	.10
385 Lance Dickson RC	.02	.10
386 Carl Everett RC	.20	.50
387 Tom Nevers RC	.02	.10
388 Adam Hyzdu RC	.08	.25
389 Todd Van Poppel RC	.08	.25
390 Rondell White RC	.15	.40
391 Marc Newfield RC	.02	.10
392 Julio Franco AS	.01	.05
393 Wade Boggs AS	.02	.10
394 Ozzie Guillen AS	.01	.05
395 Cecil Fielder AS	.01	.05
396 Ken Griffey Jr. AS	.08	.25
397 Rickey Henderson AS	.05	.15
398 Jose Canseco AS	.02	.10

399 Roger Clemens AS .15 .40
400 Sandy Alomar Jr. AS .01 .05
401 Bobby Thigpen AS .01 .05
402 Bobby Bonilla MB .01 .05
403 Eric Davis MB .01 .05
404 Fred McGriff MB .02 .10
405 Glenn Davis MB .01 .05
406 Kevin Mitchell MB .01 .05
407 Rob Dibble KM .01 .05
408 Ramon Martinez KM .01 .05
409 David Cone KM .01 .05
410 Bobby Witt KM .01 .05
411 Mark Langston KM .01 .05
412 Bo Jackson RIF .02 .10
413 Shawon Dunston RIF UER .01 .05
In the baseball, should say in baseball
414 Jesse Barfield RIF .01 .05
415 Ken Caminiti RIF .01 .05
416 Benito Santiago RIF .01 .05
417 Nolan Ryan HL .20 .50
418 B.Thigpen HL UER .01 .05
Back refers to Hal McRae Jr., should say Brian McRae
419 Ramon Martinez HL .01 .05
420 Bo Jackson HL .02 .10
421 Carlton Fisk HL .02 .10
422 Jimmy Key .02 .10
423 Junior Noboa .01 .05
424 Al Newman .01 .05
425 Pat Borders .01 .05
426 Von Hayes .01 .05
427 Tim Teufel .01 .05
428 Eric Plunk UER .01 .05
Text says Eric's had, no apostrophe needed
429 John Moses .01 .05
430 Mike Witt .01 .05
431 Otis Nixon .01 .05
432 Tony Fernandez .01 .05
433 Rance Mulliniks .01 .05
434 Dan Petry .01 .05
435 Bob Geren .01 .05
436 Steve Frey .01 .05
437 Jamie Moyer .02 .10
438 Junior Ortiz .01 .05
439 Tom O'Malley .01 .05
440 Pat Combs .01 .05
441 Jose Canseco DT .05 .15
442 Alfredo Griffin .01 .05
443 Andres Galarraga .02 .10
444 Bryn Smith .01 .05
445 Andre Dawson .02 .10
446 Juan Samuel .01 .05
447 Mike Aldrete .01 .05
448 Ron Gant .02 .10
449 Fernando Valenzuela .02 .10
450 Vince Coleman UER .01 .05
Should say topped majors in steals four times, not three times
451 Kevin Mitchell .01 .05
452 Spike Owen .01 .05
453 Mike Bielecki .01 .05
454 Dennis Martinez .02 .10
455 Brett Butler .02 .10
456 Ron Darling .01 .05
457 Dennis Rasmussen .01 .05
458 Ken Howell .01 .05
459 Steve Bedrosian .01 .05
460 Frank Viola .02 .10
461 Jose Lind .01 .05
462 Chris Sabo .01 .05
463 Dante Bichette .02 .10
464 Rick Mahler .01 .05
465 John Smiley .01 .05
466 Devon White .02 .10
467 John Orton .01 .05
468 Mike Stanton .01 .05
469 Billy Hatcher .01 .05
470 Wally Joyner .02 .10
471 Gene Larkin .01 .05
472 Doug Drabek .01 .05
473 Gary Sheffield .02 .10
474 David Wells .02 .10
475 Andy Van Slyke .05 .15
476 Mike Gallego .01 .05
477 B.J. Surhoff .02 .10
478 Gene Nelson .01 .05
479 Mariano Duncan .01 .05
480 Fred McGriff .05 .15
481 Jerry Browne .01 .05
482 Alvin Davis .01 .05
483 Bill Wegman .01 .05
484 Dave Parker .02 .10
485 Dennis Eckersley .02 .10
486 Erik Hanson UER .01 .05
(Basketball misspelled as basketball)
487 Bill Ripken .01 .05
488 Tom Candiotti .01 .05
489 Mike Schooler .01 .05
490 Gregg Olson .01 .05
491 Chris James .01 .05
492 Pete Harnisch .01 .05
493 Julio Franco .02 .10
494 Greg Briley .01 .05
495 Ruben Sierra .02 .10
496 Steve Olin .01 .05
497 Mike Fetters .01 .05
498 Mark Williamson .01 .05
499 Bob Tewksbury .01 .05
500 Tony Gwynn .10 .30
501 Randy Myers .01 .05
502 Keith Comstock .01 .05
503 C.Worthington UER .01 .05
DeCinces misspelled DiCinces on back
504 Mark Eichhorn UER .01 .05
Stats incomplete, doesn't have '89 Braves stint
505 Barry Larkin .05 .15
506 Dave Johnson .01 .05
507 Bobby Witt .01 .05
508 Joe Orsulak .01 .05
509 Pete O'Brien .01 .05
510 Brad Arnsberg .01 .05
511 Storm Davis .01 .05
512 Bob Milacki .01 .05
513 Bill Pecota .01 .05
514 Glenallen Hill .01 .05
515 Danny Tartabull .01 .05
516 Mike Moore .01 .05
517 Ron Robinson UER .01 .05
(577 K's in 1990)
518 Mark Gardner .01 .05
519 Rick Wrona .01 .05
520 Mike Scioscia .01 .05
521 Frank Wills .01 .05
522 Greg Brock .01 .05
523 Jack Clark .02 .10
524 Bruce Ruffin .01 .05
525 Robin Yount .15 .40
526 Tom Foley .01 .05
527 Pat Perry .01 .05
528 Greg Vaughn .01 .05
529 Wally Whitehurst .01 .05
530 Norm Charlton .01 .05
531 Marvell Wynne .01 .05
532 Jim Gantner .01 .05
533 Greg Litton .01 .05
534 Manny Lee .01 .05
535 Scott Bailes .01 .05
536 Charlie Leibrandt .01 .05
537 Roger McDowell .01 .05
538 Andy Benes .01 .05
539 Rick Honeycutt .01 .05
540 Dwight Gooden .02 .10
541 Scott Garrelts .01 .05
542 Dave Clark .01 .05
543 Lonnie Smith .01 .05
544 Rick Reuschel .01 .05
545 Delino DeShields UER .02 .10
(Rockford misspelled as Rock Ford in '88)
546 Mike Sharperson .01 .05
547 Mike Kingery .01 .05
548 Terry Kennedy .01 .05
549 David Cone .02 .10
550 Orel Hershiser .02 .10
551 Matt Nokes .01 .05
552 Eddie Williams .01 .05
553 Frank DiPino .01 .05
554 Fred Lynn .01 .05
555 Alex Cole .01 .05
556 Terry Leach .01 .05
557 Chet Lemon .01 .05
558 Paul Mirabella .01 .05
559 Bill Long .01 .05
560 Phil Bradley .01 .05
561 Duane Ward .01 .05
562 Dave Bergman .01 .05
563 Eric Show .01 .05
564 Xavier Hernandez .01 .05
565 Jeff Parrett .01 .05
566 Chuck Cary .01 .05
567 Ken Hill .02 .10
568 Bob Welch Hand .01 .05
(Complement should be compliment) UER
569 John Mitchell .01 .05
570 Travis Fryman .02 .10
571 Derek Lilliquist .01 .05
572 Steve Lake .01 .05
573 John Barfield .01 .05
574 Randy Bush .01 .05
575 Joe Magrane .01 .05
576 Eddie Diaz .01 .05
577 Casey Candaele .01 .05
578 Jesse Orosco .01 .05
579 Tom Henke .01 .05
580 Rick Cerone UER .01 .05
(Actually his third go-round with Yankees)
581 Drew Hall .01 .05
582 Tony Castillo .01 .05
583 Jimmy Jones .01 .05
584 Rick Reed .01 .05
585 Joe Girardi .01 .05
586 Jeff Gray RC .01 .05
587 Luis Polonia .01 .05
588 Joe Klink .01 .05
589 Rex Hudler .01 .05
590 Kirk McCaskill .01 .05
591 Juan Agosto .01 .05
592 Wes Gardner .01 .05
593 Rich Rodriguez RC .01 .05
594 Mitch Webster .01 .05
595 Kelly Gruber .01 .05
596 Dale Mohorcic .01 .05
597 Willie McGee .02 .10
598 Bill Krueger .01 .05
599 Bob Walk UER .01 .05
Cards says he's 33, but actually he's 34
600 Kevin Maas .01 .05
601 Danny Jackson .01 .05
602 Craig McMurtry UER .01 .05
(Anonymously misspelled anonimously)
603 Curtis Wilkerson .01 .05
604 Adam Peterson .01 .05
605 Sam Horn .01 .05
606 Tommy Gregg .01 .05
607 Ken Dayley .01 .05
608 Carmelo Castillo .01 .05
609 John Shelby .01 .05
610 Don Slaught .01 .05
611 Calvin Schiraldi .01 .05
612 Dennis Lamp .01 .05
613 Andres Thomas .01 .05
614 Jose Gonzalez .01 .05
615 Randy Ready .01 .05
616 Kevin Bass .01 .05
617 Mike Marshall .01 .05
618 Daryl Boston .01 .05
619 Andy McGaffigan .01 .05
620 Joe Oliver .01 .05
621 Jim Gott .01 .05
622 Jose Oquendo .01 .05
623 Jose DeJesus .01 .05
624 Mike Brumley .01 .05
625 John Olerud .02 .10
626 Ernest Riles .01 .05
627 Gene Harris .01 .05
628 Jose Uribe .01 .05
629 Darnell Coles .01 .05
630 Carney Lansford .02 .10
631 Tim Leary .01 .05
632 Tim Hulett .01 .05
633 Kevin Elster .01 .05
634 Tony Fossas .01 .05
635 Francisco Oliveras .01 .05
636 Bob Patterson .01 .05
637 Gary Ward .01 .05
638 Rene Gonzales .01 .05
639 Don Robinson .01 .05
640 Darryl Strawberry .02 .10
641 Dave Anderson .01 .05
642 Scott Scudder .01 .05
643 Reggie Harris UER .01 .05
(Hepatitis misspelled as hepititis)
644 Dave Henderson .01 .05
645 Ben McDonald .01 .05
646 Bob Kipper .01 .05
647 Hal Morris UER .01 .05
(It's should be its)
648 Tim Birtsas .01 .05
649 Steve Searcy .01 .05
650 Dale Murphy .05 .15
651 Ron Oester .01 .05
652 Mike LaCoss .01 .05
653 Ron Jones .01 .05
654 Kelly Downs .01 .05
655 Roger Clemens .30 .75
656 Herm Winningham .01 .05
657 Trevor Wilson .01 .05
658 Jose Rijo .01 .05
659 Dann Bilardello UER .01 .05
Bio has 13 games, 1 hit, and 32 AB, stats show 19, 2, and 37
660 Gregg Jefferies .01 .05
661 Doug Drabek AS UER .01 .05
(Through is mis-spelled though)
662 Randy Myers AS .01 .05
663 Benny Santiago AS .01 .05
664 Will Clark AS .02 .10
665 Ryne Sandberg AS .08 .25
666 Barry Larkin AS UER .02 .10
Line 13, coolly misspelled cooly
667 Matt Williams AS .01 .05
668 Barry Bonds AS .20 .50
669 Eric Davis AS .01 .05
670 Bobby Bonilla AS .01 .05
671 Chipper Jones RC 1.50 4.00
672 Eric Christopherson RC .02 .10
673 Robbie Beckett RC .02 .10
674 Shane Andrews RC .08 .25
675 Steve Karsay RC .08 .25
676 Aaron Holbert RC .02 .10
677 Donovan Osborne RC .02 .10
678 Todd Ritchie RC .08 .25
679 Ronnie Walden RC .02 .10
680 Tim Costo RC .02 .10
681 Dan Wilson RC .08 .25
682 Kurt Miller RC .02 .10
683 Mike Lieberthal RC .15 .40
684 Roger Clemens KM .15 .40
685 Dwight Gooden KM .01 .05
686 Nolan Ryan KM .20 .50
687 Frank Viola KM .01 .05
688 Erik Hanson KM .01 .05
689 Matt Williams MB .01 .05
690 J.Canseco MB UER .02 .10
Mammoth misspelled as monmouth
691 Darryl Strawberry MB .01 .05
692 Bo Jackson MB .02 .10
693 Cecil Fielder MB .01 .05
694 Sandy Alomar Jr. RF .01 .05
695 Cory Snyder RF .01 .05
696 Eric Davis RF .01 .05
697 Ken Griffey Jr. RF .08 .25
698 A.Van Slyke RF UER .02 .10
Line 2, outfielders does not need
699 Mark Langston NH .01 .05
Mike Witt
700 Randy Johnson NH .05 .15
701 Nolan Ryan NH .20 .50
702 Dave Stewart NH .01 .05
703 F.Valenzuela NH .01 .05
704 Andy Hawkins NH .01 .05
705 Melido Perez NH .01 .05
706 Terry Mulholland NH .01 .05
707 Dave Stieb NH .01 .05
708 Brian Barnes RC .01 .05
709 Bernard Gilkey .01 .05
710 Steve Decker RC .01 .05
711 Paul Faries RC .01 .05
712 Paul Marak RC .01 .05
713 Wes Chamberlain RC .02 .10
714 Kevin Belcher RC .01 .05
715 Dan Boone UER .01 .05
(IP adds up to 101, but card has 101.2)
716 Steve Adkins RC .01 .05
717 Geronimo Pena .01 .05
718 Howard Farmer .01 .05
719 Mark Leonard RC .01 .05
720 Tom Lampkin .01 .05
721 Mike Gardiner RC .01 .05
722 Jeff Conine RC .15 .40
723 Efrain Valdez RC .01 .05
724 Chuck Malone .01 .05
725 Leo Gomez .01 .05
726 Paul McClellan RC .01 .05
727 Mark Leiter RC .02 .10
728 Rich DeLucia UER .01 .05
(Line 2, all told is written alltold)
729 Mel Rojas .01 .05
730 Hector Wagner RC .01 .05
731 Ray Lankford .02 .10
732 Turner Ward RC .02 .10
733 Gerald Alexander RC .01 .05
734 Scott Anderson RC .01 .05
735 Tony Perezchica .01 .05
736 Jimmy Kremers .01 .05
737 American Flag .08 .25
(Pray for Peace)
738 Mike York RC .01 .05
739 Mike Rochford .01 .05
740 Scott Aldred .01 .05
741 Rico Brogna .01 .05
742 Dave Burba RC .08 .25
743 Ray Stephens RC .01 .05
744 Eric Gunderson .01 .05
745 Troy Afenir RC .01 .05
746 Jeff Shaw .01 .05
747 Orlando Merced RC .02 .10
748 O.Olivares UER RC .02 .10
Line 9, league is misspelled legaue
749 Jerry Kutzler .01 .05
750 Mo Vaughn UER .02 .10
(44 SB's in 1990)
751 Matt Stark RC .01 .05
752 Randy Hennis RC .01 .05
753 Andujar Cedeno .01 .05
754 Kelvin Torve .01 .05
755 Joe Kraemer .01 .05
756 Phil Clark RC .02 .10
757 Ed Vosberg RC .01 .05
758 Mike Perez RC .02 .10
759 Scott Lewis RC .01 .05
760 Steve Chitren RC .01 .05
761 Ray Young RC .01 .05
762 Andres Santana .01 .05
763 Rodney McCray RC .01 .05
764 Sean Berry UER RC .02 .10
(Name misspelled Barry on card front)
765 Brent Mayne .01 .05
766 Mike Simms RC .01 .05
767 Glenn Sutko RC .01 .05
768 Gary DiSarcina .01 .05
769 George Brett HL .08 .25
770 Cecil Fielder HL .01 .05
771 Jim Presley .01 .05
772 John Dopson .01 .05
773 Bo Jackson Breaker .02 .10
774 Brent Knackert UER .01 .05
Born in 1954, shown throwing righty, but bio says lefty
775 Bill Doran UER .01 .05
(Reds in NL East)
776 Dick Schofield .01 .05
777 Nelson Santovenia .01 .05
778 Mark Guthrie .01 .05
779 Mark Lemke .01 .05
780 Terry Steinbach .01 .05
781 Tom Bolton .01 .05
782 Randy Tomlin RC .02 .10
783 Jeff Kunkel .01 .05
784 Felix Jose .01 .05
785 Rick Sutcliffe .02 .10
786 John Cerutti .01 .05
787 Jose Vizcaino UER .01 .05
(Offerman, not Opperman)
788 Curt Schilling .08 .25
789 Ed Whitson .01 .05
790 Tony Pena .01 .05
791 John Candelaria .01 .05
792 Carmelo Martinez .01 .05
793 Sandy Alomar Jr. UER .01 .05
(Indian's should say Indians')
794 Jim Neidlinger RC .01 .05
795 Barry Larkin WS .02 .10
and Chris Sabo
796 Paul Sorrento .01 .05
797 Tom Pagnozzi .01 .05
798 Tino Martinez .08 .25
799 Scott Ruskin UER .01 .05
(Text says first three seasons but lists averages for four)
800 Kirk Gibson .02 .10
801 Walt Terrell .01 .05
802 John Russell .01 .05
803 Chili Davis .02 .10
804 Chris Nabholz .01 .05
805 Juan Gonzalez .08 .25
806 Ron Hassey .01 .05
807 Todd Worrell .01 .05
808 Tommy Greene .01 .05
809 Joel Skinner UER .01 .05
Joel, not Bob, was drafted in 1979
810 Benito Santiago .02 .10
811 Pat Tabler UER .01 .05
Line 3, always misspelled always
812 Scott Erickson UER RC .01 .05
813 Moises Alou .02 .10
814 Dale Sveum .01 .05
815 R.Sandberg MANYR .08 .25
816 Rick Dempsey .01 .05
817 Scott Bankhead .01 .05
818 Jason Grimsley .01 .05
819 Doug Jennings .01 .05
820 Tom Herr .01 .05
821 Rob Ducey .01 .05
822 Luis Quinones .01 .05
823 Greg Minton .01 .05
824 Mark Grant .01 .05
825 Ozzie Smith UER .15 .40
(Shortstop misspelled shortsop)
826 Dave Eiland .01 .05
827 Danny Heep .01 .05
828 Hensley Meulens .01 .05
829 Charlie O'Brien .01 .05
830 Glenn Davis .01 .05
831 John Marzano UER .01 .05
(International mis-spelled Internaional)
832 Steve Ontiveros .01 .05
833 Ron Karkovice .01 .05
834 Jerry Goff .01 .05
835 Ken Griffey Sr. .02 .10
836 Kevin Reimer .01 .05
837 Randy Kutcher UER .01 .05
(Infectious mis-spelled infectous)
838 Mike Blowers .01 .05
839 Mike Macfarlane .01 .05
840 Frank Thomas UER .08 .25
1989 Sarasota stats, 15 games but 188 AB
841 Ken Griffey Jr. .15 .40
Ken Griffey Sr.
842 Jack Howell .01 .05
843 Goose Gozzo .01 .05
844 Gerald Young .01 .05
845 Zane Smith .01 .05
846 Kevin Brown .02 .10
847 Sil Campusano .01 .05
848 Larry Andersen .01 .05
849 Cal Ripken FRAN .15 .40
850 Roger Clemens FRAN .15 .40
851 S.Alomar Jr. FRAN .01 .05
852 Alan Trammell FRAN .02 .10
853 George Brett FRAN .08 .25
854 Robin Yount FRAN .08 .25
855 Kirby Puckett FRAN .05 .15
856 Don Mattingly FRAN .10 .30
857 R.Henderson FRAN .05 .15
858 Ken Griffey Jr. FRAN .08 .25
859 Ruben Sierra FRAN .01 .05
860 John Olerud FRAN .01 .05
861 Dave Justice FRAN .01 .05
862 Ryne Sandberg FRAN .08 .25
863 Eric Davis FRAN .01 .05
864 D.Strawberry FRAN .01 .05
865 Tim Wallach FRAN .01 .05
866 Dwight Gooden FRAN .01 .05
867 Len Dykstra FRAN .01 .05
868 Barry Bonds FRAN .20 .50
869 Todd Zeile FRAN UER .01 .05
(Powerful misspelled as poweful)
870 Benito Santiago FRAN .01 .05
871 Will Clark FRAN .02 .10
872 Craig Biggio FRAN .02 .10
873 Wally Joyner FRAN .01 .05
874 Frank Thomas FRAN .05 .15
875 R.Henderson MVP .05 .15
876 Barry Bonds MVP .20 .50
877 Bob Welch CY .01 .05
878 Doug Drabek CY .01 .05
879 S.Alomar Jr. ROY .01 .05
880 Dave Justice ROY .01 .05
881 Damon Berryhill .01 .05
882 Frank Viola DT .01 .05
883 Dave Stewart DT .01 .05
884 Doug Jones DT .01 .05
885 Randy Myers DT .01 .05
886 Will Clark DT .02 .10
887 Roberto Alomar DT .02 .10
888 Barry Larkin DT .02 .10
889 Wade Boggs DT .05 .15
890 Rickey Henderson DT .08 .25
891 Kirby Puckett DT .05 .15
892 Ken Griffey Jr DT .20 .50
893 Benny Santiago DT .02 .10

1991 Score Cooperstown

This seven-card standard-size set was available only in complete set form as an insert with 1991 Score factory sets. The card design is not like the regular 1991 Score cards. The card front features a portrait of the player in an oval on a white background. The words "Cooperstown Card" are prominently displayed on the front. The cards are numbered on the back with a B prefix.

COMPLETE SET (7) 2.50 6.00
B1 Wade Boggs .25 .60
B2 Barry Larkin .25 .60
B3 Ken Griffey Jr. .75 2.00
B4 Rickey Henderson .40 1.00
B5 George Brett 1.00 2.50
B6 Will Clark .25 .60
B7 Nolan Ryan 1.50 4.00

1991 Score Hot Rookies

This ten-card standard-size set was inserted in the one per 1991 Score 100-card blister pack. The front features a color action player photo, with white borders and the words "Hot Rookie" in yellow above the picture. The card background shades from orange to yellow to orange as one moves down the card face. In a horizontal format, the left half of the back has a color head shot, while the right half has career summary.

COMPLETE SET (10) 3.00 8.00
1 Dave Justice .40 1.00
2 Kevin Maas .20 .50
3 Hal Morris .20 .50
4 Frank Thomas .75 2.00
5 Jeff Conine .40 1.00
6 Sandy Alomar Jr. .20 .50
7 Ray Lankford .40 1.00
8 Steve Decker .20 .50
9 Juan Gonzalez .75 2.00
10 Jose Offerman .20 .50

1991 Score Mantle

This seven-card standard-size set features Mickey Mantle at various points in his career. The fronts are full-color glossy shots of Mantle while the backs are in a horizontal format with a full-color photo and some narrative information. The cards were randomly inserted in second series packs. 2,500 serial numbered cards were actually signed by Mantle and stamped with certification press. A similar version of this set was also released to dealers and media members on Score's mailing list and was individually to 5,000 numbered on the back. The cards were sent in seven-card packs. The card number and the set serial number appear on the back.

COMPLETE SET (7) 50.00 100.00
COMMON MANTLE (1-7) 6.00 15.00
AU Mickey Mantle AU/2500 350.00 600.00

1991 Score Rookie/Traded

The 1991 Score Rookie and Traded contains 110 standard-size player cards and was issued exclusively in factory set form along with 10 "World Series II" magic motion trivia cards through hobby dealers. The front design is identical to the regular issue 1991 Score set except for the distinctive mauve borders and T-suffixed numbering. Cards 1T-80T feature traded players, while cards 81T-110T focus on rookies. Rookie Cards in the set include Jeff Bagwell and Ivan Rodriguez.

COMP.FACT.SET (110) 2.00 5.00
1T Bo Jackson .20 .50
2T Mike Flanagan .02 .10
3T Pete Incaviglia .02 .10
4T Jack Clark .08 .25
5T Hubie Brooks .02 .10
6T Ivan Calderon .02 .10
7T Glenn Davis .02 .10
8T Wally Backman .02 .10
9T Dave Smith .02 .10
10T Tim Raines .08 .25
11T Joe Carter .08 .25
12T Sid Bream .02 .10
13T George Bell .02 .10
14T Steve Bedrosian .02 .10
15T Willie Wilson .02 .10
16T Darryl Strawberry .08 .25
17T Danny Jackson .02 .10
18T Kirk Gibson .08 .25
19T Willie McGee .08 .25
20T Junior Felix .02 .10
21T Steve Farr .02 .10
22T Pat Tabler .02 .10
23T Brett Butler .08 .25
24T Danny Darwin .02 .10
25T Mickey Tettleton .02 .10
26T Gary Carter .08 .25
27T Mitch Williams .02 .10
28T Candy Maldonado .02 .10
29T Otis Nixon .02 .10
30T Brian Downing .02 .10
31T Tom Candiotti .02 .10
32T John Candelaria .02 .10
33T Rob Murphy .02 .10
34T Deion Sanders .15 .40
35T Willie Randolph .08 .25
36T Pete Harnisch .02 .10
37T Dante Bichette .08 .25
38T Garry Templeton .02 .10
39T Gary Gaetti .08 .25
40T John Cerutti .02 .10
41T Rick Cerone .02 .10
42T Mike Pagliarulo .02 .10
43T Ron Hassey .02 .10
44T Roberto Alomar .15 .40
45T Mike Boddicker .02 .10
46T Bud Black .02 .10
47T Rob Deer .02 .10
48T Devon White .08 .25
49T Luis Sojo .02 .10
50T Terry Pendleton .08 .25
51T Kevin Gross .02 .10
52T Mike Huff .02 .10
53T Dave Righetti .08 .25
54T Matt Young .02 .10
55T Earnest Riles .02 .10
56T Bill Gullickson .02 .10
57T Vince Coleman .02 .10
58T Fred McGriff .15 .40
59T Franklin Stubbs .02 .10
60T Eric King .02 .10
61T Cory Snyder .02 .10
62T Dwight Evans .15 .40
63T Gerald Perry .02 .10
64T Eric Show .02 .10
65T Shawn Hillegas .02 .10
66T Tony Fernandez .02 .10
67T Tim Teufel .02 .10
68T Mitch Webster .02 .10
69T Mike Heath .02 .10
70T Chili Davis .08 .25
71T Larry Andersen .02 .10
72T Gary Varsho .02 .10
73T Juan Berenguer .02 .10
74T Jack Morris .08 .25
75T Barry Jones .02 .10
76T Rafael Belliard .02 .10
77T Steve Buechele .02 .10
78T Scott Sanderson .02 .10
79T Bob Ojeda .02 .10
80T Curt Schilling .20 .50
81T Brian Drahman RC .02 .10
82T Ivan Rodriguez RC .75 2.00
83T David Howard RC .02 .10
84T H.Slocumb RC .08 .25
85T Mike Timlin RC .08 .25
86T Darryl Kile .08 .25
87T Pete Schourek RC .02 .10
88T Bruce Walton RC .02 .10
89T Al Osuna RC .02 .10
90T Gary Scott RC .02 .10
91T Doug Simons RC .02 .10
92T Chris Jones RC .02 .10
93T Chuck Knoblauch .08 .25
94T Dana Allison RC .02 .10
95T Erik Pappas RC .02 .10
96T Jeff Bagwell RC .60 1.50
97T K.Dressendorfer RC .02 .10
98T Freddie Benavides RC .02 .10
99T Luis Gonzalez RC .20 .50
100T Wade Taylor RC .02 .10

101T Ed Sprague .02 .10
102T Bob Scanlan RC .02 .10
103T Rick Wilkins RC .02 .10
104T Chris Donnels RC .02 .10
105T Joe Slusarski RC .02 .10
106T Mark Lewis .02 .10
107T Pat Kelly RC .02 .10
108T John Briscoe RC .02 .10
109T Luis Lopez RC .02 .10
110T Jeff Johnson RC .02 .10

1991 Score Rookies

This 40-card standard-sized set was distributed with five magic motion trivia cards. The fronts feature high glossy color action player photos, on a blue card face with meandering green lines.

COMP.FACT.SET (40) 1.50 4.00
1 Mel Rojas .01 .05
2 Ray Lankford .10 .30
3 Scott Aldred .01 .05
4 Turner Ward .01 .05
5 Omar Olivares .01 .05
6 Mo Vaughn .60 1.50
7 Phil Clark .01 .05
8 Brent Mayne .01 .05
9 Scott Lewis .01 .05
10 Brian Barnes .01 .05
11 Bernard Gilkey .01 .05
12 Steve Decker .01 .05
13 Paul Marak .01 .05
14 Wes Chamberlain .01 .05
15 Kevin Belcher .01 .05
16 Steve Adkins .01 .05
17 Geronimo Pena .01 .05
18 Mark Leonard .01 .05
19 Jeff Conine .02 .10
20 Leo Gomez .01 .05
21 Chuck Malone .01 .05
22 Beau Allred .01 .05
23 Todd Hundley .10 .30
24 Lance Dickson .01 .05
25 Mike Benjamin .01 .05
26 Jose Offerman .01 .05
27 Terry Shumpert .01 .05
28 Darren Lewis .01 .05
29 Scott Chiamparino .01 .05
30 Tim Naehring .01 .05
31 David Segui .02 .10
32 Karl Rhodes .01 .05
33 Mickey Morandini .01 .05
34 Chuck McElroy .01 .05
35 Tim McIntosh .01 .05
36 Derrick May .01 .05
37 Rich DeLucia .01 .05
38 Tino Martinez .40 1.00
39 Hensley Meulens .01 .05
40 Andujar Cedeno .01 .05

1992 Score

The 1992 Score set marked the second year that Score released their set in two different series. The first series contains 442 cards while the second series contains 451 cards. Cards were distributed in plastic wrapped packs, blister packs, jumbo packs and factory sets. Each pack included a special "World Series II" trivia card. Topical subsets include Rookie Prospects (395-424/736-772/814-877), No-Hit Club (425-428/784-787), Highlights (429-430), AL All-Stars (431-440; with color montages displaying Chris Greco's player caricatures), Dream Team (441-442/883-893), NL All-Stars (773-782), Highlights (783, 795-797), Draft Picks (799-810), and Memorabilia (878-882). The memorabilia cards all feature items from the famed Barry Halper collecion. Halper was a part-owner of Score at the time. All of the Rookie Prospects (736-772) can be found with or without the Rookie Prospect stripe. Rookie Cards in the set include Vinny Castilla and Manny Ramirez. Chuck Knoblauch, 1991 American League Rookie of the Year, autographed 3,000 of his own 1990 Score Draft Pick cards (card number 672) in gold ink, 2,989 were randomly inserted in Series two poly packs, while the other 11 were given away in a sweepstakes. The backs of these Knoblauch autograph cards have special holograms to differentiate them.

COMPLETE SET (893) 6.00 15.00
COMP.FACT.SET (910) 8.00 20.00
COMP. SERIES 1 (442) 3.00 8.00
COMP. SERIES 2 (451) 3.00 8.00
1 Ken Griffey Jr. .15 .40
2 Nolan Ryan .40 1.00
3 Will Clark .05 .15
4 Dave Justice .05 .15
5 Dave Henderson .01 .05
6 Bret Saberhagen .02 .10
7 Fred McGriff .05 .15
8 Erik Hanson .01 .05
9 Darryl Strawberry .02 .10
10 Dwight Gooden .02 .10
11 Juan Gonzalez .05 .15
12 Mark Langston .01 .05
13 Lonnie Smith .01 .05
14 Jeff Montgomery .01 .05
15 Roberto Alomar .05 .15
16 Delino DeShields .02 .10
17 Steve Bedrosian .01 .05
18 Terry Pendleton .02 .10
19 Mark Carreon .01 .05
20 Mark McGwire .25 .60
21 Roger Clemens .20 .50
22 Chuck Crim .01 .05
23 Don Mattingly .25 .60
24 Dickie Thon .01 .05
25 Ron Gant .02 .10
26 Milt Cuyler .01 .05
27 Mike Macfarlane .01 .05
28 Dan Gladden .01 .05
29 Melido Perez .01 .05
30 Willie Randolph .02 .10
31 Albert Belle .02 .10
32 Dave Winfield .02 .10
33 Jimmy Jones .01 .05
34 Kevin Gross .01 .05
35 Andres Galarraga .02 .10
36 Mike Devereaux .01 .05
37 Chris Bosio .01 .05
38 Mike LaValliere .01 .05
39 Gary Gaetti .02 .10
40 Felix Jose .01 .05
41 Alvaro Espinoza .01 .05
42 Rick Aguilera .02 .10
43 Mike Gallego .01 .05
44 Eric Davis .02 .10
45 George Bell .01 .05
46 Tom Brunansky .01 .05
47 Steve Farr .01 .05
48 Duane Ward .01 .05
49 David Wells .02 .10
50 Cecil Fielder .02 .10
51 Walt Weiss .01 .05
52 Todd Zeile .01 .05
53 Doug Jones .01 .05
54 Bob Walk .01 .05
55 Rafael Palmeiro .05 .15
56 Rob Deer .01 .05
57 Paul O'Neill .05 .15
58 Jeff Reardon .02 .10
59 Randy Ready .01 .05
60 Scott Erickson .01 .05
61 Paul Molitor .02 .10
62 Jack McDowell .01 .05
63 Jim Acker .01 .05
64 Jay Buhner .02 .10
65 Travis Fryman .02 .10
66 Marquis Grissom .02 .10
67 Mike Harkey .01 .05
68 Luis Polonia .01 .05
69 Ken Caminiti .02 .10
70 Chris Sabo .01 .05
71 Gregg Olson .01 .05
72 Carlton Fisk .05 .15
73 Juan Samuel .01 .05
74 Todd Stottlemyre .01 .05
75 Andre Dawson .02 .10
76 Alvin Davis .01 .05
77 Bill Doran .01 .05
78 B.J. Surhoff .02 .10
79 Kirk McCaskill .01 .05
80 Dale Murphy .05 .15
81 Jose DeLeon .01 .05
82 Alex Fernandez .01 .05
83 Ivan Calderon .01 .05
84 Brent Mayne .01 .05
85 Jody Reed .01 .05
86 Randy Tomlin .01 .05
87 Randy Milligan .01 .05
88 Pascual Perez .01 .05
89 Hensley Meulens .01 .05
90 Joe Carter .02 .10
91 Mike Moore .01 .05
92 Ozzie Guillen .02 .10
93 Shawn Hillegas .01 .05
94 Chili Davis .02 .10
95 Vince Coleman .01 .05
96 Jimmy Key .02 .10
97 Billy Ripken .01 .05
98 Dave Smith .01 .05
99 Tom Bolton .01 .05
100 Barry Larkin .05 .15
101 Kenny Rogers .02 .10
102 Mike Boddicker .01 .05
103 Kevin Elster .01 .05
104 Ken Hill .01 .05
105 Charlie Leibrandt .01 .05
106 Pat Combs .01 .05
107 Hubie Brooks .01 .05
108 Julio Franco .02 .10
109 Vicente Palacios .01 .05
110 Kal Daniels .01 .05
111 Bruce Hurst .01 .05
112 Willie McGee .02 .10
113 Ted Power .01 .05
114 Milt Thompson .01 .05
115 Doug Drabek .01 .05
116 Rafael Belliard .01 .05
117 Scott Garrelts .01 .05
118 Terry Mulholland .01 .05
119 Jay Howell .01 .05
120 Danny Jackson .01 .05
121 Scott Ruskin .01 .05
122 Robin Ventura .02 .10
123 Bip Roberts .01 .05
124 Jeff Russell .01 .05
125 Hal Morris .01 .05
126 Teddy Higuera .01 .05
127 Luis Sojo .01 .05
128 Carlos Baerga .01 .05
129 Jeff Ballard .01 .05
130 Tom Gordon .01 .05
131 Sid Bream .01 .05
132 Rance Mulliniks .01 .05
133 Andy Benes .01 .05
134 Mickey Tettleton .01 .05
135 Rich DeLucia .01 .05
136 Tom Pagnozzi .01 .05
137 Harold Baines .02 .10
138 Danny Darwin .01 .05
139 Kevin Bass .01 .05
140 Chris Nabholz .01 .05
141 Pete O'Brien .01 .05
142 Jeff Treadway .01 .05
143 Mickey Morandini .01 .05
144 Eric King .01 .05
145 Danny Tartabull .01 .05
146 Lance Johnson .01 .05
147 Casey Candaele .01 .05
148 Felix Fermin .01 .05
149 Rich Rodriguez .01 .05
150 Dwight Evans .05 .15
151 Joe Klink .01 .05
152 Kevin Reimer .01 .05
153 Orlando Merced .01 .05
154 Mel Hall .01 .05
155 Randy Myers .01 .05
156 Greg A. Harris .01 .05
157 Jeff Brantley .01 .05
158 Jim Eisenreich .01 .05
159 Luis Rivera .01 .05
160 Cris Carpenter .01 .05
161 Bruce Ruffin .01 .05
162 Omar Vizquel .05 .15
163 Gerald Alexander .01 .05
164 Mark Guthrie .01 .05
165 Scott Lewis .01 .05
166 Bill Sampen .01 .05
167 Dave Anderson .01 .05
168 Kevin McReynolds .01 .05
169 Jose Vizcaino .01 .05
170 Bob Geren .01 .05
171 Mike Morgan .01 .05
172 Jim Gott .01 .05
173 Mike Pagliarulo .01 .05
174 Mike Jeffcoat .01 .05
175 Craig Lefferts .01 .05
176 Steve Finley .02 .10
177 Wally Backman .01 .05
178 Kent Mercker .01 .05
179 John Cerutti .01 .05
180 Jay Bell .02 .10
181 Dale Sveum .01 .05
182 Greg Gagne .01 .05
183 Donnie Hill .01 .05
184 Rex Hudler .01 .05
185 Pat Kelly .01 .05
186 Jeff D. Robinson .01 .05
187 Jeff Gray .01 .05
188 Jerry Willard .01 .05
189 Carlos Quintana .01 .05
190 Dennis Eckersley .02 .10
191 Kelly Downs .01 .05
192 Gregg Jefferies .01 .05
193 Darrin Fletcher .01 .05
194 Mike Jackson .01 .05
195 Eddie Murray .08 .25
196 Bill Landrum .01 .05
197 Eric Yelding .01 .05
198 Devon White .02 .10
199 Larry Walker .05 .15
200 Ryne Sandberg .15 .40
201 Dave Magadan .01 .05
202 Steve Chitren .01 .05
203 Scott Fletcher .01 .05
204 Dwayne Henry .01 .05
205 Scott Coolbaugh .01 .05
206 Tracy Jones .01 .05
207 Von Hayes .01 .05
208 Bob Melvin .01 .05
209 Scott Scudder .01 .05
210 Luis Gonzalez .02 .10
211 Scott Sanderson .01 .05
212 Chris Donnels .01 .05
213 Heathcliff Slocumb .01 .05
214 Mike Timlin .01 .05
215 Brian Harper .01 .05
216 Juan Berenguer UER .01 .05
(Decimal point missing in IP total)
217 Mike Henneman .01 .05
218 Bill Spiers .01 .05
219 Scott Terry .01 .05
220 Frank Viola .02 .10
221 Mark Eichhorn .01 .05
222 Ernest Riles .01 .05
223 Ray Lankford .02 .10
224 Pete Harnisch .01 .05
225 Bobby Bonilla .02 .10
226 Mike Scioscia .01 .05
227 Joel Skinner .01 .05
228 Brian Holman .01 .05
229 Gilberto Reyes .01 .05
230 Matt Williams .02 .10
231 Jaime Navarro .01 .05
232 Jose Rijo .01 .05
233 Atlee Hammaker .01 .05
234 Tim Teufel .01 .05
235 John Kruk .02 .10
236 Kurt Stillwell .01 .05
237 Dan Pasqua .01 .05
238 Tim Crews .01 .05
239 Dave Gallagher .01 .05
240 Leo Gomez .01 .05
241 Steve Avery .01 .05
242 Bill Gullickson .01 .05
243 Mark Portugal .01 .05
244 Lee Guetterman .01 .05
245 Benito Santiago .02 .10
246 Jim Gantner .01 .05
247 Robby Thompson .01 .05
248 Terry Shumpert .01 .05
249 Mike Bell .01 .05
250 Harold Reynolds .02 .10
251 Mike Felder .01 .05
252 Bill Pecota .01 .05
253 Bill Krueger .01 .05
254 Alfredo Griffin .01 .05
255 Lou Whitaker .02 .10
256 Roy Smith .01 .05
257 Jerald Clark .01 .05
258 Sammy Sosa .08 .25
259 Tim Naehring .01 .05
260 Dave Righetti .02 .10
261 Paul Gibson .01 .05
262 Chris James .01 .05
263 Larry Andersen .01 .05
264 Storm Davis .01 .05
265 Jose Lind .01 .05
266 Greg Hibbard .01 .05
267 Norm Charlton .01 .05
268 Paul Kilgus .01 .05
269 Greg Maddux .15 .40
270 Ellis Burks .02 .10
271 Frank Tanana .01 .05
272 Gene Larkin .01 .05
273 Ron Hassey .01 .05
274 Jeff M. Robinson .01 .05
275 Steve Howe .01 .05
276 Daryl Boston .01 .05
277 Mark Lee .01 .05
278 Jose Segura .01 .05
279 Lance Blankenship .01 .05
280 Don Slaught .01 .05
281 Russ Swan .01 .05
282 Bob Tewksbury .01 .05
283 Geno Petralli .01 .05
284 Shane Mack .01 .05
285 Bob Scanlan .01 .05
286 Tim Leary .01 .05
287 John Smoltz .05 .15
288 Pat Borders .01 .05
289 Mark Davidson .01 .05
290 Sam Horn .01 .05
291 Lenny Harris .01 .05
292 Franklin Stubbs .01 .05
293 Thomas Howard .01 .05
294 Steve Lyons .01 .05
295 Francisco Oliveras .01 .05
296 Terry Leach .01 .05
297 Barry Jones .01 .05
298 Lance Parrish .02 .10
299 Wally Whitehurst .01 .05
300 Bob Welch .01 .05
301 Charlie Hayes .01 .05
302 Charlie Hough .02 .10
303 Gary Redus .01 .05
304 Scott Bradley .01 .05
305 Jose Oquendo .01 .05
306 Pete Incaviglia .01 .05
307 Marvin Freeman .01 .05
308 Gary Pettis .01 .05
309 Joe Slusarski .01 .05
310 Kevin Seitzer .01 .05
311 Jeff Reed .01 .05
312 Pat Tabler .01 .05
313 Mike Maddux .01 .05
314 Bob Milacki .01 .05
315 Eric Anthony .01 .05
316 Dante Bichette .02 .10
317 Steve Decker .01 .05
318 Jack Clark .02 .10
319 Doug Dascenzo .01 .05
320 Scott Leius .01 .05
321 Jim Lindeman .01 .05
322 Bryan Harvey .01 .05
323 Spike Owen .01 .05
324 Roberto Kelly .01 .05
325 Stan Belinda .01 .05
326 Joey Cora .01 .05
327 Jeff Innis .01 .05
328 Willie Wilson .01 .05
329 Juan Agosto .01 .05
330 Charles Nagy .01 .05
331 Scott Bailes .01 .05
332 Pete Schourek .01 .05
333 Mike Flanagan .01 .05
334 Omar Olivares .01 .05
335 Dennis Lamp .01 .05
336 Tommy Greene .01 .05
337 Randy Velarde .01 .05
338 Tom Lampkin .01 .05
339 John Russell .01 .05
340 Bob Kipper .01 .05
341 Todd Burns .01 .05
342 Ron Jones .01 .05
343 Dave Valle .01 .05
344 Mike Heath .01 .05
345 John Olerud .02 .10
346 Gerald Young .01 .05
347 Ken Patterson .01 .05
348 Les Lancaster .01 .05
349 Steve Crawford .01 .05
350 John Candelaria .01 .05
351 Mike Aldrete .01 .05
352 Mariano Duncan .01 .05
353 Julio Machado .01 .05
354 Ken Williams .01 .05
355 Walt Terrell .01 .05
356 Mitch Williams .01 .05
357 Al Newman .01 .05
358 Bud Black .01 .05
359 Joe Hesketh .01 .05
360 Paul Assenmacher .01 .05
361 Bo Jackson .08 .25
362 Jeff Blauser .01 .05
363 Mike Brumley .01 .05
364 Jim Deshaies .01 .05
365 Brady Anderson .02 .10
366 Chuck McElroy .01 .05
367 Matt Merullo .01 .05
368 Tim Belcher .01 .05
369 Luis Aquino .01 .05
370 Joe Oliver .01 .05
371 Greg Swindell .01 .05
372 Lee Stevens .01 .05
373 Mark Knudson .01 .05
374 Bill Wegman .01 .05
375 Jerry Don Gleaton .01 .05
376 Pedro Guerrero .02 .10
377 Randy Bush .01 .05
378 Greg W. Harris .01 .05
379 Eric Plunk .01 .05
380 Jose DeJesus .01 .05
381 Bobby Witt .01 .05
382 Curtis Wilkerson .01 .05
383 Gene Nelson .01 .05
384 Wes Chamberlain .01 .05
385 Tom Henke .01 .05
386 Mark Lemke .01 .05
387 Greg Briley .01 .05
388 Rafael Ramirez .01 .05
389 Tony Fossas .01 .05
390 Henry Cotto .01 .05
391 Tim Hulett .01 .05
392 Dean Palmer .02 .10
393 Glenn Braggs .01 .05
394 Mark Salas .01 .05
395 Rusty Meacham .01 .05
396 Andy Ashby .01 .05
397 Jose Melendez .01 .05
398 Warren Newson .01 .05
399 Frank Castillo .01 .05
400 Chito Martinez .01 .05
401 Bernie Williams .05 .15
402 Derek Bell .02 .10
403 Javier Ortiz .01 .05
404 Tim Sherrill .01 .05
405 Rob MacDonald .01 .05
406 Phil Plantier .01 .05
407 Troy Afenir .01 .05
408 Gino Minutelli .01 .05
409 Reggie Jefferson .01 .05
410 Mike Remlinger .01 .05
411 Carlos Rodriguez .01 .05
412 Joe Redfield .01 .05
413 Alonzo Powell .01 .05
414 S.Livingstone UER .01 .05
(Travis Fryman, not Woodie, should be referenced on back)
415 Scott Kamieniecki .01 .05
416 Tim Spehr .01 .05
417 Brian Hunter .01 .05
418 Ced Landrum .01 .05
419 Bret Barberie .01 .05
420 Kevin Morton .01 .05
421 Doug Henry RC .02 .10
422 Doug Piatt .01 .05
423 Pat Rice .01 .05
424 Juan Guzman .01 .05
425 Nolan Ryan NH .20 .50
426 Tommy Greene NH .01 .05
427 Bob Milacki and .01 .05
Mike Flanagan NH
(Mark Williamson and Gregg Olson)
428 Wilson Alvarez NH .01 .05
429 Otis Nixon HL .01 .05
430 Rickey Henderson HL .05 .15
431 Cecil Fielder AS .01 .05
432 Julio Franco AS .01 .05
433 Cal Ripken AS .15 .40
434 Wade Boggs AS .02 .10
435 Joe Carter AS .01 .05
436 Ken Griffey Jr. AS .08 .25
437 Ruben Sierra AS .01 .05
438 Scott Erickson AS .01 .05
439 Tom Henke AS .01 .05
440 Terry Steinbach AS .01 .05
441 Rickey Henderson DT .08 .25
442 Ryne Sandberg DT .15 .40
443 Otis Nixon .01 .05
444 Scott Radinsky UER .01 .05
Photo on front is Tom Drees
445 Mark Grace .05 .15
446 Tony Pena .01 .05
447 Billy Hatcher .01 .05
448 Glenallen Hill .01 .05
449 Chris Gwynn .01 .05
450 Tom Glavine .05 .15
451 John Habyan .01 .05
452 Al Osuna .01 .05
453 Tony Phillips .01 .05
454 Greg Cadaret .01 .05
455 Rob Dibble .02 .10
456 Rick Honeycutt .01 .05
457 Jerome Walton .01 .05
458 Mookie Wilson .02 .10
459 Mark Gubicza .01 .05
460 Craig Biggio .05 .15
461 Dave Cochrane .01 .05
462 Keith Miller .01 .05
463 Alex Cole .01 .05
464 Pete Smith .01 .05
465 Brett Butler .02 .10
466 Jeff Huson .01 .05
467 Steve Lake .01 .05
468 Lloyd Moseby .01 .05
469 Tim McIntosh .01 .05
470 Dennis Martinez .02 .10
471 Greg Myers .01 .05
472 Mackey Sasser .01 .05
473 Junior Ortiz .01 .05
474 Greg Olson .01 .05
475 Steve Sax .01 .05
476 Ricky Jordan .01 .05
477 Max Venable .01 .05
478 Brian McRae .01 .05
479 Doug Simons .01 .05
480 Rickey Henderson .08 .25
481 Gary Varsho .01 .05
482 Carl Willis .01 .05
483 Rick Wilkins .01 .05
484 Donn Pall .01 .05
485 Edgar Martinez .05 .15
486 Tom Foley .01 .05
487 Mark Williamson .01 .05
488 Jack Armstrong .01 .05
489 Gary Carter .02 .10
490 Ruben Sierra .02 .10
491 Gerald Perry .01 .05
492 Rob Murphy .01 .05
493 Zane Smith .01 .05
494 Darryl Kile .02 .10
495 Kelly Gruber .01 .05
496 Jerry Browne .01 .05
497 Darryl Hamilton .01 .05
498 Mike Stanton .01 .05
499 Mark Leonard .01 .05
500 Jose Canseco .05 .15
501 Dave Martinez .01 .05
502 Jose Guzman .01 .05
503 Terry Kennedy .01 .05
504 Ed Sprague .01 .05
505 Frank Thomas UER .08 .25
(His Gulf Coast League stats are wrong)
506 Darren Daulton .02 .10
507 Kevin Tapani .01 .05
508 Luis Salazar .01 .05
509 Paul Faries .01 .05
510 Sandy Alomar Jr. .01 .05
511 Jeff King .01 .05
512 Gary Thurman .01 .05
513 Chris Hammond .01 .05
514 Pedro Munoz .01 .05
515 Alan Trammell .02 .10
516 Geronimo Pena .01 .05
517 Rodney McCray UER .01 .05
Stole 6 bases in 1990, not 5; career totals are correct at 7
518 Manny Lee .01 .05
519 Junior Felix .01 .05
520 Kirk Gibson .02 .10
521 Darrin Jackson .01 .05
522 John Burkett .01 .05
523 Jeff Hershiser .01 .05
524 Jim Corsi .01 .05
525 Robin Yount .15 .40
526 Jamie Quirk .01 .05
527 Bob Ojeda .01 .05
528 Mark Lewis .01 .05
529 Bryn Smith .01 .05
530 Kent Hrbek .02 .10
531 Dennis Boyd .01 .05
532 Ron Karkovice .01 .05
533 Don August .01 .05
534 Todd Frohwirth .01 .05
535 Wally Joyner .02 .10
536 Dennis Rasmussen .01 .05
537 Andy Allanson .01 .05
538 Rich Gossage .02 .10
539 John Marzano .01 .05
540 Cal Ripken .30 .75
541 Bill Swift UER .01 .05
(Brewers logo on front)
542 Kevin Appier .02 .10
543 Dave Bergman .01 .05
544 Bernard Gilkey .01 .05
545 Mike Greenwell .01 .05
546 Jose Uribe .01 .05
547 Jesse Orosco .01 .05
548 Bob Patterson .01 .05
549 Mike Stanley .01 .05
550 Howard Johnson .01 .05
551 Joe Orsulak .01 .05
552 Dick Schofield .01 .05
553 Dave Hollins .01 .05
554 David Segui .01 .05
555 Barry Bonds .40 1.00
556 Mo Vaughn .02 .10
557 Craig Wilson .01 .05
558 Bobby Rose .01 .05
559 Rod Nichols .01 .05
560 Len Dykstra .02 .10
561 Craig Grebeck .01 .05
562 Darren Lewis .01 .05
563 Todd Benzinger .01 .05
564 Ed Whitson .01 .05
565 Jesse Barfield .01 .05
566 Lloyd McClendon .01 .05
567 Dan Plesac .01 .05
568 Danny Cox .01 .05
569 Skeeter Barnes .01 .05
570 Bobby Thigpen .01 .05
571 Deion Sanders .05 .15
572 Chuck Knoblauch .02 .10
573 Matt Nokes .01 .05
574 Herm Winningham .01 .05
575 Tom Candiotti .01 .05
576 Jeff Bagwell .08 .25
577 Brook Jacoby .01 .05
578 Chico Walker .01 .05
579 Brian Downing .01 .05
580 Dave Stewart .02 .10
581 Francisco Cabrera .01 .05
582 Rene Gonzales .01 .05
583 Stan Javier .01 .05
584 Randy Johnson .08 .25
585 Chuck Finley .02 .10
586 Mark Gardner .01 .05
587 Mark Whiten .01 .05
588 Garry Templeton .01 .05
589 Gary Sheffield .02 .10
590 Ozzie Smith .15 .40
591 Candy Maldonado .01 .05
592 Mike Sharperson .01 .05
593 Carlos Martinez .01 .05
594 Scott Bankhead .01 .05
595 Tim Wallach .01 .05
596 Tino Martinez .05 .15
597 Roger McDowell .01 .05
598 Cory Snyder .01 .05
599 Andujar Cedeno .01 .05
600 Kirby Puckett .08 .25
601 Rick Parker .01 .05
602 Todd Hundley .01 .05
603 Greg Litton .01 .05
604 Dave Johnson .01 .05
605 John Franco .02 .10
606 Mike Fetters .01 .05
607 Luis Alicea .01 .05
608 Trevor Wilson .01 .05
609 Rob Ducey .01 .05
610 Ramon Martinez .01 .05
611 Dave Burba .01 .05
612 Dwight Smith .01 .05
613 Kevin Maas .01 .05
614 John Costello .01 .05
615 Glenn Davis .01 .05
616 Shawn Abner .01 .05
617 Scott Hemond .01 .05
618 Tom Prince .01 .05
619 Wally Ritchie .01 .05
620 Jim Abbott .05 .15
621 Charlie O'Brien .01 .05
622 Jack Daugherty .01 .05
623 Tommy Gregg .01 .05
624 Jeff Shaw .01 .05
625 Tony Gwynn .10 .30
626 Mark Leiter .01 .05
627 Jim Clancy .01 .05
628 Tim Layana .01 .05
629 Jeff Schaefer .01 .05
630 Lee Smith .02 .10
631 Wade Taylor .01 .05
632 Mike Simms .01 .05
633 Terry Steinbach .01 .05
634 Shawon Dunston .01 .05
635 Tim Raines .02 .10
636 Kirt Manwaring .01 .05
637 Warren Cromartie .01 .05
638 Luis Quinones .01 .05
639 Greg Vaughn .01 .05
640 Kevin Mitchell .01 .05
641 Chris Hoiles .01 .05
642 Tom Browning .01 .05
643 Mitch Webster .01 .05
644 Steve Olin .01 .05
645 Tony Fernandez .01 .05
646 Juan Bell .01 .05
647 Joe Boever .01 .05
648 Carney Lansford .02 .10
649 Mike Benjamin .01 .05
650 George Brett .25 .60
651 Tim Burke .01 .05
652 Jack Morris .02 .10
653 Orel Hershiser .02 .10
654 Mike Schooler .01 .05

655 Andy Van Slyke .05 .15
656 Dave Stieb .01 .05
657 Dave Clark .01 .05
658 Ben McDonald .01 .05
659 John Smiley .01 .05
660 Wade Boggs .05 .15
661 Eric Bullock .01 .05
662 Eric Show .01 .05
663 Lenny Webster .01 .05
664 Mike Huff .01 .05
665 Rick Sutcliffe .02 .10
666 Jeff Manto .01 .05
667 Mike Fitzgerald .01 .05
668 Matt Young .01 .05
669 Dave West .01 .05
670 Mike Hartley .01 .05
671 Curt Schilling .05 .15
672 Brian Bohanon .01 .05
673 Cecil Espy .01 .05
674 Joe Grahe .01 .05
675 Sid Fernandez .01 .05
676 Edwin Nunez .01 .05
677 Hector Villanueva .01 .05
678 Sean Berry .01 .05
679 Dave Eiland .01 .05
680 David Cone .02 .10
681 Mike Bordick .01 .05
682 Tony Castillo .01 .05
683 John Barfield .01 .05
684 Jeff Hamilton .01 .05
685 Ken Dayley .01 .05
686 Carmelo Martinez .01 .05
687 Mike Capel .01 .05
688 Scott Chiamparino .01 .05
689 Rich Gedman .01 .05
690 Rich Monteleone .01 .05
691 Alejandro Pena .01 .05
692 Oscar Azocar .01 .05
693 Jim Poole .01 .05
694 Mike Gardiner .01 .05
695 Steve Buechele .01 .05
696 Rudy Seanez .01 .05
697 Paul Abbott .01 .05
698 Steve Searcy .01 .05
699 Jose Offerman .01 .05
700 Ivan Rodriguez .08 .25
701 Joe Girardi .01 .05
702 Tony Perezchica .01 .05
703 Paul McClellan .01 .05
704 David Howard .01 .05
705 Dan Petry .01 .05
706 Jack Howell .01 .05
707 Jose Mesa .01 .05
708 Randy St. Claire .01 .05
709 Kevin Brown .02 .10
710 Ron Darling .01 .05
711 Jason Grimsley .01 .05
712 John Orton .01 .05
713 Shawn Boskie .01 .05
714 Pat Clements .01 .05
715 Brian Barnes .01 .05
716 Luis Lopez .01 .05
717 Bob McClure .01 .05
718 Mark Davis .01 .05
719 Dann Bilardello .01 .05
720 Tom Edens .01 .05
721 Willie Fraser .01 .05
722 Curt Young .01 .05
723 Neal Heaton .01 .05
724 Craig Worthington .02 .10
725 Mel Rojas .01 .05
726 Daryl Irvine .01 .05
727 Roger Mason .01 .05
728 Kirk Dressendorfer .01 .05
729 Scott Aldred .01 .05
730 Willie Blair .01 .05
731 Allan Anderson .01 .05
732 Dana Kiecker .01 .05
733 Jose Gonzalez .01 .05
734 Brian Drahman .01 .05
735 Brad Komminsk .01 .05
736 Arthur Rhodes .01 .05
737 Terry Mathews .01 .05
738 Jeff Fassero .01 .05
739 Mike Magnante RC .02 .10
740 Kip Gross .01 .05
741 Jim Hunter .01 .05
742 Jose Mota .01 .05
743 Joe Bitker .01 .05
744 Tim Mauser .01 .05
745 Ramon Garcia .01 .05
746 Rod Beck RC .08 .25
747 Jim Austin RC .01 .05
748 Keith Mitchell .01 .05
749 Wayne Rosenthal .01 .05
750 Bryan Hickerson RC .02 .10
751 Bruce Egloff .01 .05
752 John Wehner .01 .05
753 Darren Holmes .01 .05
754 Dave Hansen .01 .05
755 Mike Mussina .08 .25
756 Anthony Young .01 .05
757 Ron Tingley .01 .05
758 Ricky Bones .01 .05
759 Mark Wohlers .01 .05
760 Wilson Alvarez .01 .05
761 Harvey Pulliam .01 .05
762 Ryan Bowen .01 .05
763 Terry Bross .01 .05
764 Joel Johnston .01 .05
765 Terry McDaniel .01 .05
766 Esteban Beltre .01 .05
767 Rob Maurer .01 .05
768 Ted Wood .01 .05
769 Mo Sanford .01 .05
770 Jeff Carter .01 .05
771 Gil Heredia RC .08 .25
772 Monty Fariss .01 .05
773 Will Clark AS .02 .10
774 Ryne Sandberg AS .08 .25
775 Barry Larkin AS .02 .10
776 Howard Johnson AS .01 .05
777 Barry Bonds AS .20 .50
778 Brett Butler AS .01 .05
779 Tony Gwynn AS .05 .15
780 Ramon Martinez AS .01 .05
781 Lee Smith AS .01 .05
782 Mike Scioscia AS .01 .05
783 D.Martinez HL UER .01 .05
Card has both 13th and 15th perfect game in Major League history
784 Dennis Martinez NH .01 .05
785 Mark Gardner NH .01 .05
786 Bret Saberhagen NH .01 .05
787 Kent Mercker NH .01 .05
Mark Wohlers
Alejandro Pena
788 Cal Ripken MVP .15 .40
789 Terry Pendleton MVP .01 .05
790 Roger Clemens CY .08 .25
791 Tom Glavine CY .02 .10
792 C.Knoblauch ROY .01 .05
793 Jeff Bagwell ROY .05 .15
794 Cal Ripken MANYR .15 .40
795 David Cone HL .01 .05
796 Kirby Puckett HL .05 .15
797 Steve Avery HL .01 .05
798 Jack Morris HL .01 .05
799 Allen Watson RC .02 .10
800 Manny Ramirez RC 1.50 4.00
801 Cliff Floyd RC .30 .75
802 Al Shirley RC .02 .10
803 Brian Barber RC .02 .10
804 Jon Farrell RC .02 .10
805 Brent Gates RC .02 .10
806 Scott Ruffcorn RC .02 .10
807 Tyrone Hill RC .02 .10
808 Benji Gil RC .08 .25
809 Aaron Sele RC .08 .25
810 Tyler Green RC .02 .10
811 Chris Jones .01 .05
812 Steve Wilson .01 .05
813 Freddie Benavides .01 .05
814 Don Wakamatsu .01 .05
815 Mike Humphreys .01 .05
816 Scott Servais .01 .05
817 Rico Rossy .01 .05
818 John Ramos .01 .05
819 Rob Mallicoat .01 .05
820 Milt Hill .01 .05
821 Carlos Garcia .01 .05
822 Stan Royer .01 .05
823 Jeff Plympton .01 .05
824 Braulio Castillo .01 .05
825 David Haas .01 .05
826 Luis Mercedes .01 .05
827 Eric Karros .02 .10
828 Shawn Hare RC .02 .10
829 Reggie Sanders .02 .10
830 Tom Goodwin .01 .05
831 Dan Gakeler .01 .05
832 Stacy Jones .01 .05
833 Kim Batiste .01 .05
834 Cal Eldred .01 .05
835 Chris George .01 .05
836 Wayne Housie .01 .05
837 Mike Ignasiak .01 .05
838 Josias Manzanillo RC .02 .10
839 Jim Olander .01 .05
840 Gary Cooper .01 .05
841 Royce Clayton .01 .05
842 Hector Fajardo RC .02 .10
843 Blaine Beatty .01 .05
844 Jorge Pedre .01 .05
845 Kenny Lofton .05 .15
846 Scott Brosius RC .20 .50
847 Chris Cron .01 .05
848 Denis Boucher .01 .05
849 Kyle Abbott .01 .05
850 Bob Zupcic RC .02 .10
851 Rheal Cormier .01 .05
852 Jimmy Lewis RC .01 .05
853 Anthony Telford .01 .05
854 Cliff Brantley .01 .05
855 Kevin Campbell .01 .05
856 Craig Shipley .01 .05
857 Chuck Carr .01 .05
858 Tony Eusebio .02 .10
859 Jim Thome .08 .25
860 Vinny Castilla RC .40 1.00
861 Dann Howitt .01 .05
862 Kevin Ward .01 .05
863 Steve Wapnick .01 .05
864 Rod Brewer RC .02 .10
865 Todd Van Poppel .01 .05
866 Jose Hernandez RC .08 .25
867 Amalio Carreno .01 .05
868 Calvin Jones .01 .05
869 Jeff Gardner .01 .05
870 Jarvis Brown .01 .05
871 Eddie Taubensee RC .08 .25
872 Andy Mota .01 .05
873 Chris Haney .01 .05
874 Roberto Hernandez .01 .05
875 Laddie Renfroe .01 .05
876 Scott Cooper .01 .05
877 Armando Reynoso RC .08 .25
878 Ty Cobb MEMO .08 .25
879 Babe Ruth MEMO .20 .50
880 Honus Wagner MEMO .08 .25
881 Lou Gehrig MEMO .15 .40
882 Satchel Paige MEMO .08 .25
883 Will Clark DT .02 .10
884 Cal Ripken DT .75 2.00
885 Wade Boggs DT .02 .10
886 Kirby Puckett DT .05 .15
887 Tony Gwynn DT .05 .15
888 Craig Biggio DT .02 .10
889 Scott Erickson DT .01 .05
890 Tom Glavine DT .02 .10
891 Rob Dibble DT .01 .05
892 Mitch Williams DT .01 .05
893 Frank Thomas DT .05 .15
X672 Chuck Knoblauch 10.00 25.00
1990 Score AU/3000

1992 Score DiMaggio

This five-card standard-size insert set was issued in honor of one of baseball's all-time greats, Joe DiMaggio. These cards were randomly inserted in first series packs. According to sources at Score, 30,000 of each card were produced. On a white card face, the fronts have vintage photos that have been colorized and accented by red, white, and blue border stripes. DiMaggio autographed 2,500 cards for this promotion. 2,495 of these cards were inserted in packs while the other five were used as prizes in a mail-in sweepstakes. The autographed cards are individually numbered out of 2,500.

COMPLETE SET (5) 30.00 60.00
COMMON CARD (1-5) 6.00 15.00
AU Joe DiMaggio AU/2500 300.00 500.00

1992 Score Factory Inserts

This 17-card insert standard-size set was distributed only in 1992 Score factory sets and consists of four topical subsets. Cards B1-B7 capture a moment from each game of the 1991 World Series. Cards B8-B11 are Cooperstown cards, honoring future Hall of Famers. Cards B12-B14 form a "Joe D" subset paying tribute to Joe DiMaggio. Cards B15-B17, subtitled "Yaz", conclude the set by commemorating Carl Yastrzemski's heroic feats twenty-five years ago in winning the Triple Crown and lifting the Red Sox to their first American League pennant in 21 years. Each subset displayed a different front design. The World Series cards carry full-bleed color action photos except for a blue stripe at the bottom, while the Cooperstown cards have a color portrait on a white card face. Both the DiMaggio and Yastrzemski subsets have action photos with silver borders; they differ in that the DiMaggio photos are black and white, the Yastrzemski photos color. The DiMaggio and Yastrzemski subsets are numbered on the back within each subset (e.g., "1 of 3") and as a part of the 17-card insert set (e.g., "B1"). In the DiMaggio and Yastrzemski subsets, Score varied the insert set slightly in retail versus hobby factory sets. In the hobby set, the DiMaggio cards display different black-and-white photos that are bordered beneath by a dark blue stripe (the stripe is green in the retail factory insert). On the backs, these hobby inserts have a red stripe at the bottom; the same stripe is dark blue on the retail inserts. The Yastrzemski cards in the hobby set have different color photos on their fronts than the retail inserts.

COMPLETE SET (17) 3.00 6.00
B1 Greg Gagne WS .15 .40
B2 Scott Leius WS .15 .40
B3 Mark Lemke WS .15 .40
David Justice
B4 Lonnie Smith WS .15 .40
Brian Harper
B5 David Justice WS .30 .75
B6 Kirby Puckett WS .75 2.00
B7 Gene Larkin WS .15 .40
B8 Carlton Fisk .50 1.25
B9 Ozzie Smith 1.25 3.00
B10 Dave Winfield .30 .75
B11 Robin Yount 1.25 3.00
B12 Joe DiMaggio .40 1.00
The Hard Hitter
B13 Joe DiMaggio .40 1.00
The Stylish Fielder
B14 Joe DiMaggio .40 1.00
The Championship Player
B15 Carl Yastrzemski .20 .50
The Impossible Dream
B16 Carl Yastrzemski .20 .50
The Triple Crown
B17 Carl Yastrzemski .20 .50
The World Series

1992 Score Franchise

This four-card standard-size set features three all-time greats, Stan Musial, Mickey Mantle, and Carl Yastrzemski. Score produced 150,000 of each Franchise cardof which were randomly inserted in 1992 Score Series II poly packs, blister packs, and cello packs.

COMPLETE SET (4) 15.00 30.00
1 Stan Musial 2.00 5.00
2 Mickey Mantle 4.00 10.00
3 Carl Yastrzemski 2.00 5.00
4 The Franchise Players 4.00 10.00
Stan Musial
Mickey Mantle
Carl Yastrzemski

1992 Score Franchise Autographs

Randomly seeded into packs at an unspecified rate, this four card set is composed of legends Mickey Mantle, Stan Musial and Carl Yastrzemski (including a fourth card that combines all three players). The individually signed cards (each serial-numbered to 2,000 copies on back) are signed in blue ink of which is prone to fading. The triple-signed card (limited to only 500 serial-numbered copies) was signed in gold paint pen bvy each player and is recognized as one of the touchstone cards in the development of certified autograph trading cards within the modern era:

AU1 Stan Musial 30.00 60.00
AU2 Mickey Mantle 300.00 500.00
AU3 Carl Yastrzemski 40.00 80.00
AU4 Stan Musial 400.00 800.00
Mickey Mantle
Carl Yastrzemski
AU/500

1992 Score Hot Rookies

This ten-card standard-size set features color action player photos on a white face. These cards were inserted at a stated rate of one per blister pack.

COMPLETE SET (10) 4.00 8.00
1 Cal Eldred .20 .50
2 Royce Clayton .20 .50
3 Kenny Lofton .75 2.00
4 Todd Van Poppel .20 .50
5 Scott Cooper .20 .50
6 Todd Hundley .20 .50
7 Tino Martinez .75 2.00
8 Anthony Telford .20 .50
9 Derek Bell .20 .50
10 Reggie Jefferson .20 .50

1992 Score Impact Players

The 1992 Score Impact Players insert set was issued in two series each with 45 standard-size cards with the respective series of the 1992 regular issue Score cards. Five of these cards were inserted in each 1992 Score jumbo pack.

COMPLETE SERIES 1 (45) 5.00 12.00
COMPLETE SERIES 2 (45) 2.50 6.00
1 Chuck Knoblauch .10 .30
2 Jeff Bagwell .30 .75
3 Juan Guzman .05 .15
4 Milt Cuyler .05 .15
5 Ivan Rodriguez .30 .75
6 Rich DeLucia .05 .15
7 Orlando Merced .05 .15
8 Ray Lankford .10 .30
9 Brian Hunter .05 .15
10 Roberto Alomar .20 .50
11 Wes Chamberlain .05 .15
12 Steve Avery .05 .15
13 Scott Erickson .05 .15
14 Jim Abbott .20 .50
15 Mark Whiten .05 .15
16 Leo Gomez .05 .15
17 Doug Henry .10 .30
18 Brent Mayne .05 .15
19 Charles Nagy .05 .15
20 Phil Plantier .05 .15
21 Mo Vaughn .10 .30
22 Craig Biggio .20 .50
23 Derek Bell .10 .30
24 Royce Clayton .05 .15
25 Gary Cooper .05 .15
26 Scott Cooper .05 .15
27 Juan Gonzalez .20 .50
28 Ken Griffey Jr. .50 1.25
29 Larry Walker .20 .50
30 John Smoltz .20 .50
31 Todd Hundley .05 .15
32 Kenny Lofton .20 .50
33 Andy Mota .05 .15
34 Todd Zeile .05 .15
35 Arthur Rhodes .05 .15
36 Jim Thome .30 .75
37 Todd Van Poppel .05 .15
38 Mark Wohlers .05 .15
39 Anthony Young .05 .15
40 Sandy Alomar Jr. .05 .15
41 John Olerud .10 .30
42 Robin Ventura .10 .30
43 Frank Thomas .30 .75
44 Dave Justice .10 .30
45 Hal Morris .05 .15
46 Ruben Sierra .10 .30
47 Travis Fryman .10 .30
48 Mike Mussina .30 .75
49 Tom Glavine .20 .50
50 Barry Larkin .20 .50
51 Will Clark UER .20 .50
Career Totals spelled To als
52 Jose Canseco .20 .50
53 Bo Jackson .30 .75
54 Dwight Gooden .10 .30
55 Barry Bonds 1.25 3.00
56 Fred McGriff .20 .50
57 Roger Clemens .60 1.50
58 Benito Santiago .10 .30
59 Darryl Strawberry .10 .30
60 Cecil Fielder .10 .30
61 John Franco .10 .30
62 Matt Williams .10 .30
63 Marquis Grissom .10 .30
64 Danny Tartabull .05 .15
65 Ron Gant .10 .30
66 Paul O'Neill .20 .50
67 Devon White .10 .30
68 Rafael Palmeiro .20 .50
69 Tom Gordon .05 .15
70 Shawon Dunston .05 .15
71 Rob Dibble .10 .30
72 Eddie Zosky .05 .15
73 Jack McDowell .05 .15
74 Len Dykstra .10 .30
75 Ramon Martinez .05 .15
76 Reggie Sanders .10 .30
77 Greg Maddux .50 1.25
78 Ellis Burks .10 .30
79 John Smiley .05 .15
80 Roberto Kelly .05 .15
81 Ben McDonald .05 .15
82 Mark Lewis .05 .15
83 Jose Rijo .05 .15
84 Ozzie Guillen .10 .30
85 Lance Dickson .05 .15
86 Kim Batiste .05 .15
87 Gregg Olson .05 .15
88 Andy Benes .05 .15
89 Cal Eldred .05 .15
90 David Cone .10 .30

1992 Score Rookie/Traded

The 1992 Score Rookie and Traded set contains 110 standard-size cards featuring traded veterans and rookies. This set was issued in complete set form and was released through hobby dealers. The set is arranged numerically such that cards 1T-79T are traded players and cards 80T-110T feature rookies. Notable Rookie Cards in this set include Brian Jordan and Jeff Kent.

COMP.FACT.SET (110) 3.00 8.00
1T Gary Sheffield .10 .30
2T Kevin Seitzer .07 .20
3T Danny Tartabull .07 .20
4T Steve Sax .07 .20
5T Bobby Bonilla .10 .30
6T Frank Viola .10 .30
7T Dave Winfield .10 .30
8T Rick Sutcliffe .10 .30
9T Jose Canseco .20 .50
10T Greg Swindell .07 .20
11T Eddie Murray .30 .75
12T Randy Myers .07 .20
13T Wally Joyner .10 .30
14T Kenny Lofton .20 .50
15T Jack Morris .10 .30
16T Charlie Hayes .07 .20
17T Pete Incaviglia .07 .20
18T Kevin Mitchell .07 .20
19T Kurt Stillwell .07 .20
20T Bret Saberhagen .10 .30
21T Steve Buechele .07 .20
22T John Smiley .07 .20
23T Sammy Sosa .30 .75
24T George Bell .07 .20
25T Curt Schilling .20 .50
26T Dick Schofield .07 .20
27T David Cone .10 .30
28T Dan Gladden .07 .20
29T Kirk McCaskill .07 .20
30T Mike Gallego .07 .20
31T Kevin McReynolds .07 .20
32T Bill Swift .07 .20
33T Dave Martinez .07 .20
34T Storm Davis .07 .20
35T Willie Randolph .10 .30
36T Melido Perez .07 .20
37T Mark Carreon .07 .20
38T Doug Jones .07 .20
39T Gregg Jefferies .07 .20
40T Mike Jackson .07 .20
41T Dickie Thon .07 .20
42T Eric King .07 .20
43T Herm Winningham .07 .20
44T Derek Lilliquist .07 .20
45T Dave Anderson .07 .20
46T Jeff Reardon .10 .30
47T Scott Bankhead .07 .20
48T Cory Snyder .07 .20
49T Al Newman .07 .20
50T Keith Miller .07 .20
51T Dave Burba .07 .20
52T Bill Pecota .07 .20
53T Chuck Crim .07 .20
54T Mariano Duncan .07 .20
55T Dave Gallagher .07 .20
56T Chris Gwynn .07 .20
57T Scott Ruskin .07 .20
58T Jack Armstrong .07 .20
59T Gary Carter .10 .30
60T Andres Galarraga .10 .30
61T Ken Hill .07 .20
62T Eric Davis .10 .30
63T Ruben Sierra .10 .30
64T Darrin Fletcher .07 .20
65T Tim Belcher .07 .20
66T Mike Morgan .07 .20
67T Scott Scudder .07 .20
68T Tom Candiotti .07 .20
69T Hubie Brooks .07 .20
70T Kal Daniels .07 .20
71T Bruce Ruffin .07 .20
72T Billy Hatcher .07 .20
73T Bob Melvin .07 .20
74T Lee Guetterman .07 .20
75T Rene Gonzales .07 .20
76T Kevin Bass .07 .20
77T Tom Bolton .07 .20
78T John Wetteland .10 .30
79T Bip Roberts .07 .20
80T Pat Listach RC .15 .40
81T John Doherty RC .07 .20
82T Sam Militello .07 .20
83T Brian Jordan RC .25 .60
84T Jeff Kent RC 1.25 3.00
85T Dave Fleming .07 .20
86T Jeff Tackett .07 .20
87T Chad Curtis RC .15 .40
88T Eric Fox RC .07 .20
89T Denny Neagle .10 .30
90T Donovan Osborne .07 .20
91T Carlos Hernandez .07 .20
92T Tim Wakefield RC 1.25 3.00
93T Tim Salmon .20 .50
94T Dave Nilsson .07 .20
95T Mike Perez .07 .20
96T Pat Hentgen .07 .20
97T Frank Seminara RC .07 .20
98T Ruben Amaro .07 .20
99T Archi Cianfrocco RC .07 .20
100T Andy Stankiewicz .07 .20
101T Jim Bullinger .07 .20
102T Pat Mahomes RC .15 .40
103T Hipolito Pichardo RC .07 .20
104T Bret Boone .20 .50
105T John Vander Wal .07 .20
106T Vince Horsman .07 .20
107T Jim Austin .07 .20
108T Brian Williams RC .07 .20
109T Dan Walters .07 .20
110T Wil Cordero .07 .20

1992 Score Rookies

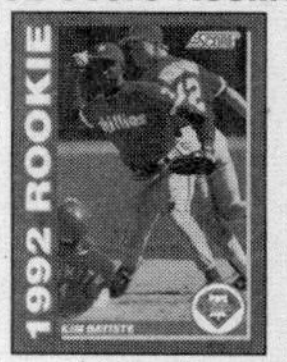

This 40-card boxed set measures the standard size and features glossy color action player photos on a kelly green face with meandering purple stripes.

COMP.FACT SET (40) 1.60 4.00
1 Todd Van Poppel .01 .05
2 Kyle Abbott .01 .05
3 Derek Bell .01 .05
4 Jim Thome .60 1.50
5 Mark Wohlers .01 .05
6 Todd Hundley .08 .25
7 Arthur Lee Rhodes .01 .05
8 John Ramos .01 .05
9 Chris George .01 .05
10 Kenny Lofton .40 1.00
11 Ted Wood .01 .05
12 Royce Clayton .01 .05
13 Scott Cooper .01 .05
14 Anthony Young .01 .05
15 Joel Johnston .01 .05
16 Andy Mota .01 .05
17 Lenny Webster .01 .05
18 Andy Ashby .01 .05
19 Jose Mota .01 .05
20 Tim McIntosh .01 .05
21 Terry Bross .01 .05
22 Harvey Pulliam .01 .05
23 Hector Fajardo .01 .05
24 Esteban Beltre .01 .05
25 Gary DiSarcina .01 .05
26 Mike Humphreys .01 .05
27 Jarvis Brown .01 .05
28 Gary Cooper .01 .05
29 Chris Donnels .01 .05
30 Monty Fariss .01 .05
31 Eric Karros .30 .75
32 Braulio Castillo .01 .05
33 Cal Eldred .01 .05
34 Tom Goodwin .01 .05
35 Reggie Sanders .20 .50
36 Scott Servais .01 .05
37 Kim Batiste .01 .05
38 Eric Wedge .08 .25
39 Willie Banks .01 .05
40 Mo Sanford .01 .05

1993 Score

The 1993 Score baseball set consists of 660 standard-size cards issued in one single series. The cards were distributed in 16-card poly packs and 35-card jumbo superpacks. Topical subsets featured are Award Winners (481-486), Draft Picks (487-501), All-Star Caricature (502-512 [AL], 522-531 [NL]), Highlights (513-519), World Series Highlights (520-521), Dream Team (532-542) and Rookies (sprinkled throughout the set). Rookie Cards in this set include Derek Jeter, Jason Kendall and Shannon Stewart.

COMPLETE SET (660) 15.00 40.00
1 Ken Griffey Jr. .30 .75
2 Gary Sheffield .07 .20
3 Frank Thomas .20 .50
4 Ryne Sandberg .30 .75
5 Larry Walker .07 .20
6 Cal Ripken Jr. .60 1.50
7 Roger Clemens .40 1.00
8 Bobby Bonilla .07 .20

9 Carlos Baerga .02 .10
10 Darren Daulton .07 .20
11 Travis Fryman .07 .20
12 Andy Van Slyke .10 .30
13 Jose Canseco .10 .30
14 Roberto Alomar .10 .30
15 Tom Glavine .10 .30
16 Barry Larkin .10 .30
17 Gregg Jefferies .02 .10
18 Craig Biggio .10 .30
19 Shane Mack .02 .10
20 Brett Butler .07 .20
21 Dennis Eckersley .07 .20
22 Will Clark .10 .30
23 Don Mattingly .50 1.25
24 Tony Gwynn .25 .60
25 Ivan Rodriguez .10 .30
26 Shawon Dunston .02 .10
27 Mike Mussina .10 .30
28 Marquis Grissom .07 .20
29 Charles Nagy .02 .10
30 Len Dykstra .07 .20
31 Cecil Fielder .07 .20
32 Jay Bell .07 .20
33 B.J. Surhoff .07 .20
34 Bob Tewksbury .02 .10
35 Danny Tartabull .02 .10
36 Terry Pendleton .07 .20
37 Jack Morris .07 .20
38 Hal Morris .02 .10
39 Luis Polonia .02 .10
40 Ken Caminiti .07 .20
41 Robin Ventura .07 .20
42 Darryl Strawberry .07 .20
43 Wally Joyner .07 .20
44 Fred McGriff .10 .30
45 Kevin Tapani .02 .10
46 Matt Williams .07 .20
47 Robin Yount .30 .75
48 Ken Hill .02 .10
49 Edgar Martinez .10 .30
50 Mark Grace .10 .30
51 Juan Gonzalez .07 .20
52 Curt Schilling .07 .20
53 Dwight Gooden .07 .20
54 Chris Hoiles .02 .10
55 Frank Viola .07 .20
56 Ray Lankford .07 .20
57 George Brett .50 1.25
58 Kenny Lofton .07 .20
59 Nolan Ryan .75 2.00
60 Mickey Tettleton .02 .10
61 John Smoltz .10 .30
62 Howard Johnson .02 .10
63 Eric Karros .07 .20
64 Rick Aguilera .02 .10
65 Steve Finley .07 .20
66 Mark Langston .02 .10
67 Bill Swift .02 .10
68 John Olerud .07 .20
69 Kevin McReynolds .02 .10
70 Jack McDowell .02 .10
71 Rickey Henderson .20 .50
72 Brian Harper .02 .10
73 Mike Morgan .02 .10
74 Rafael Palmeiro .10 .30
75 Dennis Martinez .07 .20
76 Tino Martinez .10 .30
77 Eddie Murray .20 .50
78 Ellis Burks .07 .20
79 John Kruk .07 .20
80 Gregg Olson .02 .10
81 Bernard Gilkey .02 .10
82 Milt Cuyler .02 .10
83 Mike LaValliere .02 .10
84 Albert Belle .07 .20
85 Bip Roberts .02 .10
86 Melido Perez .02 .10
87 Otis Nixon .02 .10
88 Bill Spiers .02 .10
89 Jeff Bagwell .10 .30
90 Orel Hershiser .07 .20
91 Andy Benes .02 .10
92 Devon White .07 .20
93 Willie McGee .07 .20
94 Ozzie Guillen .07 .20
95 Ivan Calderon .02 .10
96 Keith Miller .02 .10
97 Steve Buechele .02 .10
98 Kent Hrbek .07 .20
99 Dave Hollins .02 .10
100 Mike Bordick .02 .10
101 Randy Tomlin .02 .10
102 Omar Vizquel .10 .30
103 Lee Smith .07 .20
104 Leo Gomez .02 .10
105 Jose Rijo .02 .10
106 Mark Whiten .02 .10
107 Dave Justice .07 .20
108 Eddie Taubensee .02 .10
109 Lance Johnson .02 .10
110 Felix Jose .02 .10
111 Mike Harkey .02 .10
112 Randy Milligan .02 .10
113 Anthony Young .02 .10
114 Rico Brogna .02 .10
115 Bret Saberhagen .07 .20
116 Sandy Alomar Jr. .02 .10
117 Terry Mulholland .02 .10
118 Darryl Hamilton .02 .10
119 Todd Zeile .02 .10
120 Bernie Williams .10 .30
121 Zane Smith .02 .10
122 Derek Bell .02 .10
123 Deion Sanders .10 .30
124 Luis Sojo .02 .10
125 Joe Oliver .02 .10
126 Craig Grebeck .02 .10
127 Andujar Cedeno .02 .10
128 Brian McRae .02 .10
129 Jose Offerman .02 .10
130 Pedro Munoz .02 .10
131 Bud Black .02 .10
132 Mo Vaughn .07 .20
133 Bruce Hurst .02 .10
134 Dave Henderson .02 .10
135 Tom Pagnozzi .02 .10
136 Erik Hanson .02 .10
137 Orlando Merced .02 .10
138 Dean Palmer .07 .20
139 John Franco .07 .20
140 Brady Anderson .07 .20
141 Ricky Jordan .02 .10
142 Jeff Blauser .02 .10
143 Sammy Sosa .20 .50
144 Bob Walk .02 .10
145 Delino DeShields .02 .10
146 Kevin Brown .07 .20
147 Mark Lemke .02 .10
148 Chuck Knoblauch .07 .20
149 Chris Sabo .02 .10
150 Bobby Witt .02 .10
151 Luis Gonzalez .07 .20
152 Ron Karkovice .02 .10
153 Jeff Brantley .02 .10
154 Kevin Appier .07 .20
155 Darrin Jackson .02 .10
156 Kelly Gruber .02 .10
157 Royce Clayton .02 .10
158 Chuck Finley .07 .20
159 Jeff King .02 .10
160 Greg Vaughn .02 .10
161 Geronimo Pena .02 .10
162 Steve Farr .02 .10
163 Jose Oquendo .02 .10
164 Mark Lewis .02 .10
165 John Wetteland .07 .20
166 Mike Henneman .02 .10
167 Todd Hundley .02 .10
168 Wes Chamberlain .02 .10
169 Steve Avery .02 .10
170 Mike Devereaux .02 .10
171 Reggie Sanders .07 .20
172 Jay Buhner .07 .20
173 Eric Anthony .02 .10
174 John Burkett .02 .10
175 Tom Candiotti .02 .10
176 Phil Plantier .02 .10
177 Doug Henry .02 .10
178 Scott Leius .02 .10
179 Kirt Manwaring .02 .10
180 Jeff Parrett .02 .10
181 Don Slaught .02 .10
182 Scott Radinsky .02 .10
183 Luis Alicea .02 .10
184 Tom Gordon .02 .10
185 Rick Wilkins .02 .10
186 Todd Stottlemyre .02 .10
187 Moises Alou .07 .20
188 Joe Grahe .02 .10
189 Jeff Kent .20 .50
190 Bill Wegman .02 .10
191 Kim Batiste .02 .10
192 Matt Nokes .02 .10
193 Mark Wohlers .02 .10
194 Paul Sorrento .02 .10
195 Chris Hammond .02 .10
196 Scott Livingstone .02 .10
197 Doug Jones .02 .10
198 Scott Cooper .02 .10
199 Ramon Martinez .02 .10
200 Dave Valle .02 .10
201 Mariano Duncan .02 .10
202 Ben McDonald .02 .10
203 Darren Lewis .02 .10
204 Kenny Rogers .07 .20
205 Manuel Lee .02 .10
206 Scott Erickson .02 .10
207 Dan Gladden .02 .10
208 Bob Welch .02 .10
209 Greg Olson .02 .10
210 Dan Pasqua .02 .10
211 Tim Wallach .02 .10
212 Jeff Montgomery .02 .10
213 Derrick May .02 .10
214 Ed Sprague .02 .10
215 David Haas .02 .10
216 Darrin Fletcher .02 .10
217 Brian Jordan .07 .20
218 Jaime Navarro .02 .10
219 Randy Velarde .02 .10
220 Ron Gant .07 .20
221 Paul Quantrill .02 .10
222 Damion Easley .02 .10
223 Charlie Hough .07 .20
224 Brad Brink .02 .10
225 Barry Manuel .02 .10
226 Kevin Koslofski .02 .10
227 Ryan Thompson .02 .10
228 Mike Munoz .02 .10
229 Dan Wilson .07 .20
230 Peter Hoy .02 .10
231 Pedro Astacio .02 .10
232 Matt Stairs .02 .10
233 Jeff Reboulet .02 .10
234 Manny Alexander .02 .10
235 Willie Banks .02 .10
236 John Jaha .02 .10
237 Scooter Tucker .02 .10
238 Russ Springer .02 .10
239 Paul Miller .02 .10
240 Dan Peltier .02 .10
241 Ozzie Canseco .02 .10
242 Ben Rivera .02 .10
243 John Valentin .02 .10
244 Henry Rodriguez .02 .10
245 Derek Parks .02 .10
246 Carlos Garcia .02 .10
247 Tim Pugh RC .02 .10
248 Melvin Nieves .02 .10
249 Rich Amaral .02 .10
250 Willie Greene .02 .10
251 Tim Scott .02 .10
252 Dave Silvestri .02 .10
253 Rob Mallicoat .02 .10
254 Donald Harris .02 .10
255 Craig Colbert .02 .10
256 Jose Guzman .02 .10
257 Domingo Martinez RC .02 .10
258 William Suero .02 .10
259 Juan Guerrero .02 .10
260 J.T. Snow RC .20 .50
261 Tony Pena .02 .10
262 Tim Fortugno .02 .10
263 Tom Marsh .02 .10
264 Kurt Knudsen .02 .10
265 Tim Costo .02 .10
266 Steve Shifflett .02 .10
267 Billy Ashley .02 .10
268 Jerry Nielsen .02 .10
269 Pete Young .02 .10
270 Johnny Guzman .02 .10
271 Greg Colbrunn .02 .10
272 Jeff Nelson .02 .10
273 Kevin Young .07 .20
274 Jeff Frye .02 .10
275 J.T. Bruett .02 .10
276 Todd Pratt RC .08 .25
277 Mike Butcher .02 .10
278 John Flaherty .02 .10
279 John Patterson .02 .10
280 Eric Hillman .02 .10
281 Bien Figueroa .02 .10
282 Shane Reynolds .07 .20
283 Rich Rowland .02 .10
284 Steve Foster .02 .10
285 Dave Milicki .02 .10
286 Mike Piazza 1.25 3.00
287 Mike Trombley .02 .10
288 Jim Pena .02 .10
289 Bob Ayrault .02 .10
290 Henry Mercedes .02 .10
291 Bob Wickman .02 .10
292 Jacob Brumfield .02 .10
293 David Hulse RC .02 .10
294 Ryan Klesko .07 .20
295 Doug Linton .02 .10
296 Steve Cooke .02 .10
297 Eddie Zosky .02 .10
298 Gerald Williams .02 .10
299 Jonathan Hurst .02 .10
300 Larry Carter RC .02 .10
301 William Pennyfeather .02 .10
302 Cesar Hernandez .02 .10
303 Steve Hosey .02 .10
304 Blas Minor .02 .10
305 Jeff Grotewald .02 .10
306 Bernardo Brito .02 .10
307 Rafael Bournigal .02 .10
308 Jeff Branson .02 .10
309 Tom Quinlan RC .02 .10
310 Pat Gomez RC .02 .10
311 Sterling Hitchcock RC .08 .25
312 Kent Bottenfield .02 .10
313 Alan Trammell .07 .20
314 Cris Colon .02 .10
315 Paul Wagner .02 .10
316 Matt Maysey .02 .10
317 Mike Stanton .02 .10
318 Rick Trlicek .02 .10
319 Kevin Rogers .02 .10
320 Mark Clark .02 .10
321 Pedro Martinez .40 1.00
322 Al Martin .02 .10
323 Mike Macfarlane .02 .10
324 Rey Sanchez .02 .10
325 Roger Pavlik .02 .10
326 Troy Neel .02 .10
327 Kerry Woodson .02 .10
328 Wayne Kirby .02 .10
329 Ken Ryan RC .08 .25
330 Jesse Levis .02 .10
331 Jim Austin .02 .10
332 Dan Walters .02 .10
333 Brian Williams .02 .10
334 Wil Cordero .02 .10
335 Bret Boone .07 .20
336 Hipolito Pichardo .02 .10
337 Pat Mahomes .02 .10
338 Andy Stankiewicz .02 .10
339 Jim Bullinger .02 .10
340 Archi Cianfrocco .02 .10
341 Ruben Amaro .02 .10
342 Frank Seminara .02 .10
343 Pat Hentgen .02 .10
344 Dave Nilsson .02 .10
345 Mike Perez .02 .10
346 Tim Salmon .10 .30
347 Tim Wakefield .20 .50
348 Carlos Hernandez .02 .10
349 Donovan Osborne .02 .10
350 Denny Neagle .07 .20
351 Sam Militello .02 .10
352 Eric Fox .02 .10
353 John Doherty .02 .10
354 Chad Curtis .02 .10
355 Jeff Tackett .02 .10
356 Dave Fleming .02 .10
357 Pat Listach .02 .10
358 Kevin Wickander .02 .10
359 John Vander Wal .02 .10
360 Arthur Rhodes .02 .10
361 Bob Scanlan .02 .10
362 Bob Zupcic .02 .10
363 Mel Rojas .02 .10
364 Jim Thome .10 .30
365 Bill Pecota .02 .10
366 Mark Carreon .02 .10
367 Mitch Williams .02 .10
368 Cal Eldred .02 .10
369 Stan Belinda .02 .10
370 Pat Kelly .02 .10
371 Rheal Cormier .02 .10
372 Juan Guzman .02 .10
373 Damon Berryhill .02 .10
374 Gary DiSarcina .02 .10
375 Norm Charlton .02 .10
376 Roberto Hernandez .02 .10
377 Scott Kamieniecki .02 .10
378 Rusty Meacham .02 .10
379 Kurt Stillwell .02 .10
380 Lloyd McClendon .02 .10
381 Mark Leonard .02 .10
382 Jerry Browne .02 .10
383 Glenn Davis .02 .10
384 Randy Johnson .20 .50
385 Mike Greenwell .02 .10
386 Scott Chiamparino .02 .10
387 George Bell .02 .10
388 Steve Olin .02 .10
389 Chuck McElroy .02 .10
390 Mark Gardner .02 .10
391 Rod Beck .02 .10
392 Dennis Rasmussen .02 .10
393 Charlie Leibrandt .02 .10
394 Julio Franco .07 .20
395 Pete Harnisch .02 .10
396 Sid Bream .02 .10
397 Milt Thompson .02 .10
398 Glenallen Hill .02 .10
399 Chico Walker .02 .10
400 Alex Cole .02 .10
401 Trevor Wilson .02 .10
402 Jeff Conine .07 .20
403 Kyle Abbott .02 .10
404 Tom Browning .02 .10
405 Jerald Clark .02 .10
406 Vince Horsman .02 .10
407 Kevin Mitchell .02 .10
408 Pete Smith .02 .10
409 Jeff Innis .02 .10
410 Mike Timlin .02 .10
411 Charlie Hayes .02 .10
412 Alex Fernandez .02 .10
413 Jeff Russell .02 .10
414 Jody Reed .02 .10
415 Mickey Morandini .02 .10
416 Darnell Coles .02 .10
417 Xavier Hernandez .02 .10
418 Steve Sax .02 .10
419 Joe Girardi .02 .10
420 Mike Fetters .02 .10
421 Danny Jackson .02 .10
422 Jim Gott .02 .10
423 Tim Belcher .02 .10
424 Jose Mesa .02 .10
425 Junior Felix .02 .10
426 Thomas Howard .02 .10
427 Julio Valera .02 .10
428 Dante Bichette .07 .20
429 Mike Sharperson .02 .10
430 Darryl Kile .07 .20
431 Lonnie Smith .02 .10
432 Monty Fariss .02 .10
433 Reggie Jefferson .02 .10
434 Bob McClure .02 .10
435 Craig Lefferts .02 .10
436 Duane Ward .02 .10
437 Shawn Abner .02 .10
438 Roberto Kelly .02 .10
439 Paul O'Neill .10 .30
440 Alan Mills .02 .10
441 Roger Mason .02 .10
442 Gary Pettis .02 .10
443 Steve Lake .02 .10
444 Gene Larkin .02 .10
445 Larry Andersen .02 .10
446 Doug Dascenzo .02 .10
447 Daryl Boston .02 .10
448 John Candelaria .02 .10
449 Storm Davis .02 .10
450 Tom Edens .02 .10
451 Mike Maddux .02 .10
452 Tim Naehring .02 .10
453 John Orton .02 .10
454 Joey Cora .02 .10
455 Chuck Crim .02 .10
456 Dan Plesac .02 .10
457 Mike Bielecki .02 .10
458 Terry Jorgensen .02 .10
459 John Habyan .02 .10
460 Pete O'Brien .02 .10
461 Jeff Treadway .02 .10
462 Frank Castillo .02 .10
463 Jimmy Jones .02 .10
464 Tommy Greene .02 .10
465 Tracy Woodson .02 .10
466 Rich Rodriguez .02 .10
467 Joe Hesketh .02 .10
468 Greg Myers .02 .10
469 Kirk McCaskill .02 .10
470 Ricky Bones .02 .10
471 Lenny Webster .02 .10
472 Francisco Cabrera .02 .10
473 Turner Ward .02 .10
474 Dwayne Henry .02 .10
475 Al Osuna .02 .10
476 Craig Wilson .02 .10
477 Chris Nabholz .02 .10
478 Rafael Belliard .02 .10
479 Terry Leach .02 .10
480 Tim Teufel .02 .10
481 Dennis Eckersley AW .07 .20
482 Barry Bonds AW .30 .75
483 Dennis Eckersley AW .07 .20
484 Greg Maddux AW .20 .50
485 Pat Listach AW .02 .10
486 Eric Karros AW .02 .10
487 Jamie Arnold DP RC .02 .10
488 B.J. Wallace DP .02 .10
489 Derek Jeter DP RC 5.00 12.00
490 Jason Kendall DP RC .40 1.00
491 Rick Helling DP .02 .10
492 Derek Wallace DP RC .02 .10
493 Sean Lowe DP RC .02 .10
494 S.Stewart DP RC .30 .75
495 Benji Grigsby DP RC .02 .10
496 T.Steverson DP RC .02 .10
497 Dan Serafini DP RC .02 .10
498 Michael Tucker DP .02 .10
499 Chris Roberts DP .02 .10
500 Pete Janicki DP RC .02 .10
501 Jeff Schmidt DP RC .02 .10
502 Edgar Martinez AS .07 .20
503 Omar Vizquel AS .07 .20
504 Ken Griffey Jr. AS .20 .50
505 Kirby Puckett AS .10 .30
506 Joe Carter AS .02 .10
507 Ivan Rodriguez AS .07 .20
508 Jack Morris AS .02 .10
509 Dennis Eckersley AS .07 .20
510 Frank Thomas AS .10 .30
511 Roberto Alomar AS .07 .20
512 Mickey Morandini AS .02 .10
513 Dennis Eckersley HL .07 .20
514 Jeff Reardon HL .02 .10
515 Danny Tartabull HL .02 .10
516 Bip Roberts HL .02 .10
517 George Brett HL .25 .60
518 Robin Yount HL .20 .50
519 Kevin Gross HL .02 .10
520 Ed Sprague WS .02 .10
521 Dave Winfield WS .02 .10
522 Ozzie Smith AS .20 .50
523 Barry Bonds AS .30 .75
524 Andy Van Slyke AS .07 .20
525 Tony Gwynn AS .10 .30
526 Darren Daulton AS .02 .10
527 Greg Maddux AS .20 .50
528 Fred McGriff AS .10 .30
529 Lee Smith AS .02 .10
530 Ryne Sandberg AS .20 .50
531 Gary Sheffield AS .02 .10
532 Ozzie Smith DT .20 .50
533 Kirby Puckett DT .10 .30
534 Gary Sheffield DT .02 .10
535 Andy Van Slyke DT .07 .20
536 Ken Griffey Jr. DT .20 .50
537 Ivan Rodriguez DT .07 .20
538 Charles Nagy DT .02 .10
539 Tom Glavine DT .07 .20
540 Dennis Eckersley DT .07 .20
541 Frank Thomas DT .10 .30
542 Roberto Alomar DT .07 .20
543 Sean Berry .02 .10
544 Mike Schooler .02 .10
545 Chuck Carr .02 .10
546 Lenny Harris .02 .10
547 Gary Scott .02 .10
548 Derek Lilliquist .02 .10
549 Brian Hunter .02 .10
550 Kirby Puckett MOY .10 .30
551 Jim Eisenreich .02 .10
552 Andre Dawson .07 .20
553 David Nied .02 .10
554 Spike Owen .02 .10
555 Greg Gagne .02 .10
556 Sid Fernandez .02 .10
557 Mark McGwire .50 1.25
558 Bryan Harvey .02 .10
559 Harold Reynolds .07 .20
560 Barry Bonds .60 1.50
561 Eric Wedge RC .08 .25
562 Ozzie Smith .30 .75
563 Rick Sutcliffe .07 .20
564 Jeff Reardon .07 .20
565 Alex Arias .02 .10
566 Greg Swindell .02 .10
567 Brook Jacoby .02 .10
568 Pete Incaviglia .02 .10
569 Butch Henry .02 .10
570 Eric Davis .07 .20
571 Kevin Seitzer .02 .10
572 Tony Fernandez .02 .10
573 Steve Reed RC .02 .10
574 Cory Snyder .02 .10
575 Joe Carter .07 .20
576 Greg Maddux .30 .75
577 Bert Blyleven UER .07 .20
(Should say 3701
career strikeouts)
578 Kevin Bass .02 .10
579 Carlton Fisk .10 .30
580 Doug Drabek .02 .10
581 Mark Gubicza .02 .10
582 Bobby Thigpen .02 .10
583 Chili Davis .07 .20
584 Scott Bankhead .02 .10
585 Harold Baines .07 .20
586 Eric Young .02 .10
587 Lance Parrish .07 .20
588 Juan Bell .02 .10
589 Bob Ojeda .02 .10
590 Joe Orsulak .02 .10
591 Benito Santiago .07 .20
592 Wade Boggs .10 .30
593 Robby Thompson .02 .10
594 Eric Plunk .02 .10
595 Hensley Meulens .02 .10
596 Lou Whitaker .07 .20
597 Dale Murphy .10 .30
598 Paul Molitor .07 .20
599 Greg W. Harris .02 .10
600 Darren Holmes .02 .10
601 Dave Martinez .02 .10
602 Tom Henke .02 .10
603 Mike Benjamin .02 .10
604 Rene Gonzales .02 .10
605 Roger McDowell .02 .10
606 Kirby Puckett .20 .50
607 Randy Myers .02 .10
608 Ruben Sierra .07 .20
609 Wilson Alvarez .02 .10
610 David Segui .02 .10
611 Juan Samuel .02 .10
612 Tom Brunansky .02 .10
613 Willie Randolph .07 .20
614 Tony Phillips .02 .10
615 Candy Maldonado .02 .10
616 Chris Bosio .02 .10
617 Bret Barberie .02 .10
618 Scott Sanderson .02 .10
619 Ron Darling .02 .10
620 Dave Winfield .07 .20
621 Mike Felder .02 .10
622 Greg Hibbard .02 .10
623 Mike Scioscia .02 .10
624 John Smiley .02 .10
625 Alejandro Pena .02 .10
626 Terry Steinbach .02 .10
627 Freddie Benavides .02 .10
628 Kevin Reimer .02 .10
629 Braulio Castillo .02 .10
630 Dave Stieb .02 .10
631 Dave Magadan .02 .10
632 Scott Fletcher .02 .10
633 Cris Carpenter .02 .10
634 Kevin Maas .02 .10
635 Todd Worrell .02 .10
636 Rob Deer .02 .10
637 Dwight Smith .02 .10
638 Chito Martinez .02 .10
639 Jimmy Key .07 .20
640 Greg A. Harris .02 .10
641 Mike Moore .02 .10
642 Pat Borders .02 .10
643 Bill Gullickson .02 .10
644 Gary Gaetti .07 .20
645 David Howard .02 .10
646 Jim Abbott .10 .30
647 Willie Wilson .02 .10
648 David Wells .07 .20
649 Andres Galarraga .07 .20
650 Vince Coleman .02 .10
651 Rob Dibble .07 .20
652 Frank Tanana .02 .10
653 Steve Decker .02 .10
654 David Cone .07 .20
655 Jack Armstrong .02 .10
656 Dave Stewart .07 .20
657 Billy Hatcher .02 .10
658 Tim Raines .07 .20
659 Walt Weiss .02 .10
660 Jose Lind .02 .10

1993 Score Boys of Summer

Randomly inserted exclusively into one in every four 1993 Score 35-card super packs, cards from this standard-size set feature 30 rookies expected to be the best in their class. Early cards of Pedro Martinez and Mike Piazza highlight this set.

COMPLETE SET (30) 25.00 50.00
1 Billy Ashley .60 1.50
2 Tim Salmon 1.25 3.00
3 Pedro Martinez 4.00 10.00
4 Luis Mercedes .60 1.50
5 Mike Piazza 4.00 10.00
6 Troy Neel .60 1.50
7 Melvin Nieves .60 1.50
8 Ryan Klesko .75 2.00
9 Ryan Thompson .60 1.50
10 Kevin Young .75 2.00
11 Gerald Williams .60 1.50
12 Willie Greene .60 1.50
13 John Patterson .60 1.50
14 Carlos Garcia .60 1.50
15 Ed Zosky .60 1.50
16 Sean Berry .60 1.50
17 Rico Brogna .60 1.50
18 Larry Carter .60 1.50
19 Bobby Ayala .60 1.50
20 Alan Embree .60 1.50
21 Donald Harris .60 1.50
22 Sterling Hitchcock .75 2.00
23 David Nied .60 1.50
24 Henry Mercedes .60 1.50
25 Ozzie Canseco .60 1.50
26 David Hulse .60 1.50
27 Al Martin .60 1.50
28 Dan Wilson .60 1.50
29 Paul Miller .60 1.50
30 Rich Rowland .60 1.50

1993 Score Franchise

This 28-card set honors the top player on each of the major league teams. These cards were randomly inserted into one in every 24 16-card packs. The set is arranged in alphabetical team order by league, with the exception of cards 29 and 30 which honor a player from the 1993 expansion teams.

COMPLETE SET (28) 50.00 120.00
1 Cal Ripken 10.00 25.00
2 Roger Clemens 6.00 15.00
3 Mark Langston .60 1.50
4 Frank Thomas 3.00 8.00
5 Carlos Baerga .60 1.50
6 Cecil Fielder 1.25 3.00
7 Gregg Jefferies .60 1.50
8 Robin Yount 5.00 12.00
9 Kirby Puckett 3.00 8.00
10 Don Mattingly 8.00 20.00
11 Dennis Eckersley 1.25 3.00
12 Ken Griffey Jr. 5.00 12.00
13 Juan Gonzalez 1.25 3.00
14 Roberto Alomar 2.00 5.00
15 Terry Pendleton 1.25 3.00
16 Ryne Sandberg 5.00 12.00
17 Barry Larkin 2.00 5.00
18 Jeff Bagwell 2.00 5.00
19 Brett Butler 1.25 3.00
20 Larry Walker 1.25 3.00
21 Bobby Bonilla 1.25 3.00
22 Darren Daulton 1.25 3.00
23 Andy Van Slyke 2.00 5.00
24 Ray Lankford 1.25 3.00
25 Gary Sheffield 1.25 3.00
26 Will Clark 2.00 5.00
27 Bryan Harvey .60 1.50
28 David Nied .60 1.50

1993 Score Gold Dream Team

Cards from this 12-card standard-size set feature Score's selection of the best players in baseball at each position. The cards were available only through a mail-in offer. Each card front features sepia tone photos of the players out of uniform, with the exception of Griffey's card (of whom is pictured in his Mariners togs). The photo edges are rounded with an airbrush effect.

COMPLETE SET (12) 2.00 5.00
1 Ozzie Smith .30 .75

2 Kirby Puckett .20 .50
3 Gary Sheffield .07 .20
4 Andy Van Slyke .10 .30
5 Ken Griffey Jr. .30 .75
6 Ivan Rodriguez .10 .30
7 Charles Nagy .02 .10
8 Tom Glavine .10 .30
9 Dennis Eckersley .07 .20
10 Frank Thomas .20 .50
11 Roberto Alomar .10 .30
NNO Header Card .02 .10

1994 Score

The 1994 Score set of 660 standard-size cards was issued in two series of 330. Cards were distributed in 14-card hobby and retail packs. Each pack contained 13 basic cards plus one Gold Rush parallel card. Cards were also distributed in retail Jumbo packs. 4,875 cases of 1994 Score baseball were printed for the hobby. This figure does not take into account additional product printed for retail outlets. Among the subsets are American League stadiums (317-330) and National League stadiums (647-660). Rookie Cards include Trot Nixon and Billy Wagner.

COMPLETE SET (660) 10.00 24.00
COMP.SERIES 1 (330) 5.00 12.00
COMP.SERIES 2 (330) 5.00 12.00
1 Barry Bonds .60 1.50
2 John Olerud .07 .20
3 Ken Griffey Jr. .30 .75
4 Jeff Bagwell .10 .30
5 John Burkett .02 .10
6 Jack McDowell .02 .10
7 Albert Belle .07 .20
8 Andres Galarraga .07 .20
9 Mike Mussina .10 .30
10 Will Clark .10 .30
11 Travis Fryman .07 .20
12 Tony Gwynn .25 .60
13 Robin Yount .30 .75
14 Dave Magadan .02 .10
15 Paul O'Neill .10 .30
16 Ray Lankford .07 .20
17 Damion Easley .02 .10
18 Andy Van Slyke .10 .30
19 Brian McRae .02 .10
20 Ryne Sandberg .30 .75
21 Kirby Puckett .20 .50
22 Dwight Gooden .07 .20
23 Don Mattingly .50 1.25
24 Kevin Mitchell .02 .10
25 Roger Clemens .40 1.00
26 Eric Karros .07 .20
27 Juan Gonzalez .07 .20
28 John Kruk .07 .20
29 Gregg Jefferies .02 .10
30 Tom Glavine .10 .30
31 Ivan Rodriguez .10 .30
32 Jay Bell .07 .20
33 Randy Johnson .20 .50
34 Darren Daulton .07 .20
35 Rickey Henderson .20 .50
36 Eddie Murray .20 .50
37 Brian Harper .02 .10
38 Delino DeShields .02 .10
39 Jose Lind .02 .10
40 Benito Santiago .07 .20
41 Frank Thomas .20 .50
42 Mark Grace .10 .30
43 Roberto Alomar .10 .30
44 Andy Benes .02 .10
45 Luis Polonia .02 .10
46 Brett Butler .07 .20
47 Terry Steinbach .02 .10
48 Craig Biggio .10 .30
49 Greg Vaughn .02 .10
50 Charlie Hayes .02 .10
51 Mickey Tettleton .02 .10
52 Jose Rijo .02 .10
53 Carlos Baerga .02 .10
54 Jeff Blauser .02 .10
55 Leo Gomez .02 .10
56 Bob Tewksbury .02 .10
57 Mo Vaughn .07 .20
58 Orlando Merced .02 .10
59 Tino Martinez .10 .30
60 Lenny Dykstra .07 .20
61 Jose Canseco .10 .30
62 Tony Fernandez .02 .10
63 Donovan Osborne .02 .10
64 Ken Hill .02 .10
65 Kent Hrbek .07 .20
66 Bryan Harvey .02 .10
67 Wally Joyner .07 .20
68 Derrick May .02 .10
69 Lance Johnson .02 .10
70 Willie McGee .07 .20
71 Mark Langston .02 .10
72 Terry Pendleton .07 .20
73 Joe Carter .07 .20
74 Barry Larkin .10 .30
75 Jimmy Key .07 .20
76 Joe Girardi .02 .10
77 B.J. Surhoff .07 .20
78 Pete Harnisch .02 .10
79 Lou Whitaker UER .07 .20
(Milt Cuyler pictured on front)
80 Cory Snyder .02 .10
81 Kenny Lofton .07 .20
82 Fred McGriff .10 .30
83 Mike Greenwell .02 .10
84 Mike Perez .02 .10
85 Cal Ripken .60 1.50
86 Don Slaught .02 .10
87 Omar Vizquel .10 .30
88 Curt Schilling .07 .20
89 Chuck Knoblauch .07 .20
90 Moises Alou .07 .20
91 Greg Gagne .02 .10
92 Bret Saberhagen .07 .20
93 Ozzie Guillen .07 .20
94 Matt Williams .07 .20
95 Chad Curtis .02 .10
96 Mike Harkey .02 .10
97 Devon White .07 .20
98 Walt Weiss .02 .10
99 Kevin Brown .07 .20
100 Gary Sheffield .07 .20
101 Wade Boggs .10 .30
102 Orel Hershiser .07 .20
103 Tony Phillips .02 .10
104 Andujar Cedeno .02 .10
105 Bill Spiers .02 .10
106 Otis Nixon .02 .10
107 Felix Fermin .02 .10
108 Bip Roberts .02 .10
109 Dennis Eckersley .07 .20
110 Dante Bichette .07 .20
111 Ben McDonald .02 .10
112 Jim Poole .02 .10
113 John Dopson .02 .10
114 Rob Dibble .07 .20
115 Jeff Treadway .02 .10
116 Ricky Jordan .02 .10
117 Mike Henneman .02 .10
118 Willie Blair .02 .10
119 Doug Henry .02 .10
120 Gerald Perry .02 .10
121 Greg Myers .02 .10
122 John Franco .07 .20
123 Roger Mason .02 .10
124 Chris Hammond .02 .10
125 Hubie Brooks .02 .10
126 Kent Mercker .02 .10
127 Jim Abbott .10 .30
128 Kevin Bass .02 .10
129 Rick Aguilera .02 .10
130 Mitch Webster .02 .10
131 Eric Plunk .02 .10
132 Mark Carreon .02 .10
133 Dave Stewart .07 .20
134 Willie Wilson .02 .10
135 Dave Fleming .02 .10
136 Jeff Tackett .02 .10
137 Geno Petralli .02 .10
138 Gene Harris .02 .10
139 Scott Bankhead .02 .10
140 Trevor Wilson .02 .10
141 Alvaro Espinoza .02 .10
142 Ryan Bowen .02 .10
143 Mike Moore .02 .10
144 Bill Pecota .02 .10
145 Jaime Navarro .02 .10
146 Jack Daugherty .02 .10
147 Bob Wickman .02 .10
148 Chris Jones .02 .10
149 Todd Stottlemyre .02 .10
150 Brian Williams .02 .10
151 Chuck Finley .07 .20
152 Lenny Harris .02 .10
153 Alex Fernandez .02 .10
154 Candy Maldonado .02 .10
155 Jeff Montgomery .02 .10
156 David West .02 .10
157 Mark Williamson .02 .10
158 Milt Thompson .02 .10
159 Ron Darling .02 .10
160 Stan Belinda .02 .10
161 Henry Cotto .02 .10
162 Mel Rojas .02 .10
163 Doug Strange .02 .10
164 Rene Arocha .02 .10
165 Tim Hulett .02 .10
166 Steve Avery .02 .10
167 Jim Thome .10 .30
168 Tom Browning .02 .10
169 Mario Diaz .02 .10
170 Steve Reed .02 .10
171 Scott Livingstone .02 .10
172 Chris Donnels .02 .10
173 John Jaha .02 .10
174 Carlos Hernandez .02 .10
175 Dion James .02 .10
176 Bud Black .02 .10
177 Tony Castillo .02 .10
178 Jose Guzman .02 .10
179 Torey Lovullo .02 .10
180 John Vander Wal .02 .10
181 Mike LaValliere .02 .10
182 Sid Fernandez .02 .10
183 Brent Mayne .02 .10
184 Terry Mulholland .02 .10
185 Willie Banks .02 .10
186 Steve Cooke .02 .10
187 Brent Gates .02 .10
188 Erik Pappas .02 .10
189 Bill Haselman .02 .10
190 Fernando Valenzuela .07 .20
191 Gary Redus .02 .10
192 Danny Darwin .02 .10
193 Mark Portugal .02 .10
194 Derek Lilliquist .02 .10
195 Charlie O'Brien .02 .10
196 Matt Nokes .02 .10
197 Danny Sheaffer .02 .10
198 Bill Gullickson .02 .10
199 Alex Arias .02 .10
200 Mike Fetters .02 .10
201 Brian Jordan .07 .20
202 Joe Grahe .02 .10
203 Tom Candiotti .02 .10
204 Jeremy Hernandez .02 .10
205 Mike Stanton .02 .10
206 David Howard .02 .10
207 Darren Holmes .02 .10
208 Rick Honeycutt .02 .10
209 Danny Jackson .02 .10
210 Rich Amaral .02 .10
211 Blas Minor .02 .10
212 Kenny Rogers .07 .20
213 Jim Leyritz .02 .10
214 Mike Morgan .02 .10
215 Dan Gladden .02 .10
216 Randy Velarde .02 .10
217 Mitch Williams .02 .10
218 Hipolito Pichardo .02 .10
219 Dave Burba .02 .10
220 Wilson Alvarez .02 .10
221 Bob Zupcic .02 .10
222 Francisco Cabrera .02 .10
223 Julio Valera .02 .10
224 Paul Assenmacher .02 .10
225 Jeff Branson .02 .10
226 Todd Frohwirth .02 .10
227 Armando Reynoso .02 .10
228 Rich Rowland .02 .10
229 Freddie Benavides .02 .10
230 Wayne Kirby .02 .10
231 Darryl Kile .07 .20
232 Skeeter Barnes .02 .10
233 Ramon Martinez .02 .10
234 Tom Gordon .02 .10
235 Dave Gallagher .02 .10
236 Ricky Bones .02 .10
237 Larry Andersen .02 .10
238 Pat Meares .02 .10
239 Zane Smith .02 .10
240 Tim Leary .02 .10
241 Phil Clark .02 .10
242 Danny Cox .02 .10
243 Mike Jackson .02 .10
244 Mike Gallego .02 .10
245 Lee Smith .07 .20
246 Todd Jones .02 .10
247 Steve Bedrosian .02 .10
248 Troy Neel .02 .10
249 Jose Bautista .02 .10
250 Steve Frey .02 .10
251 Jeff Reardon .07 .20
252 Stan Javier .02 .10
253 Mo Sanford .02 .10
254 Steve Sax .02 .10
255 Luis Aquino .02 .10
256 Domingo Jean .02 .10
257 Scott Servais .02 .10
258 Brad Pennington .02 .10
259 Dave Hansen .02 .10
260 Rich Gossage .07 .20
261 Jeff Fassero .02 .10
262 Junior Ortiz .02 .10
263 Anthony Young .02 .10
264 Chris Bosio .02 .10
265 Ruben Amaro .02 .10
266 Mark Eichhorn .02 .10
267 Dave Clark .02 .10
268 Gary Thurman .02 .10
269 Les Lancaster .02 .10
270 Jamie Moyer .07 .20
271 Ricky Gutierrez .02 .10
272 Greg A. Harris .02 .10
273 Mike Benjamin .02 .10
274 Gene Nelson .02 .10
275 Damon Berryhill .02 .10
276 Scott Radinsky .02 .10
277 Mike Aldrete .02 .10
278 Jerry DiPoto .02 .10
279 Chris Haney .02 .10
280 Richie Lewis .02 .10
281 Jarvis Brown .02 .10
282 Juan Bell .02 .10
283 Joe Klink .02 .10
284 Graeme Lloyd .02 .10
285 Casey Candaele .02 .10
286 Bob MacDonald .02 .10
287 Mike Sharperson .02 .10
288 Gene Larkin .02 .10
289 Brian Barnes .02 .10
290 David McCarty .02 .10
291 Jeff Innis .02 .10
292 Bob Patterson .02 .10
293 Ben Rivera .02 .10
294 John Habyan .02 .10
295 Rich Rodriguez .02 .10
296 Edwin Nunez .02 .10
297 Rod Brewer .02 .10
298 Mike Timlin .02 .10
299 Jesse Orosco .02 .10
300 Gary Gaetti .07 .20
301 Todd Benzinger .02 .10
302 Jeff Nelson .02 .10
303 Rafael Belliard .02 .10
304 Matt Whiteside .02 .10
305 Vinny Castilla .07 .20
306 Matt Turner .02 .10
307 Eduardo Perez .02 .10
308 Joel Johnston .02 .10
309 Chris Gomez .02 .10
310 Pat Rapp .02 .10
311 Jim Tatum .02 .10
312 Kirk Rueter .02 .10
313 John Flaherty .02 .10
314 Tom Kramer .02 .10
315 Mark Whiten .02 .10
316 Chris Bosio .02 .10
317 Baltimore Orioles CL .02 .10
318 Bos.Red Sox CL UER .02 .10
Viola listed as 316; should be 331
319 California Angels CL .02 .10
320 Chicago White Sox CL .02 .10
321 Cleveland Indians CL .02 .10
322 Detroit Tigers CL .02 .10
323 KC Royals CL .02 .10
324 Milw. Brewers CL .02 .10
325 Minnesota Twins CL .02 .10
326 New York Yankees CL .02 .10
327 Oakland Athletics CL .02 .10
328 Seattle Mariners CL .02 .10
329 Texas Rangers CL .02 .10
330 Toronto Blue Jays CL .02 .10
331 Frank Viola .07 .20
332 Ron Gant .07 .20
333 Charles Nagy .02 .10
334 Roberto Kelly .02 .10
335 Brady Anderson .07 .20
336 Alex Cole .02 .10
337 Alan Trammell .07 .20
338 Derek Bell .02 .10
339 Bernie Williams .10 .30
340 Jose Offerman .02 .10
341 Bill Wegman .02 .10
342 Ken Caminiti .07 .20
343 Pat Borders .02 .10
344 Kirt Manwaring .02 .10
345 Chili Davis .07 .20
346 Steve Buechele .02 .10
347 Robin Ventura .07 .20
348 Teddy Higuera .02 .10
349 Jerry Browne .02 .10
350 Scott Kamieniecki .02 .10
351 Kevin Tapani .02 .10
352 Marquis Grissom .07 .20
353 Jay Buhner .07 .20
354 Dave Hollins .02 .10
355 Dan Wilson .02 .10
356 Bob Walk .02 .10
357 Chris Hoiles .02 .10
358 Todd Zeile .02 .10
359 Kevin Appier .07 .20
360 Chris Sabo .02 .10
361 David Segui .02 .10
362 Jerald Clark .02 .10
363 Tony Pena .02 .10
364 Steve Finley .07 .20
365 Roger Pavlik .02 .10
366 John Smoltz .10 .30
367 Scott Fletcher .02 .10
368 Jody Reed .02 .10
369 David Wells .07 .20
370 Jose Vizcaino .02 .10
371 Pat Listach .02 .10
372 Orestes Destrade .02 .10
373 Danny Tartabull .02 .10
374 Greg W. Harris .02 .10
375 Juan Guzman .02 .10
376 Larry Walker .07 .20
377 Gary DiSarcina .02 .10
378 Bobby Bonilla .07 .20
379 Tim Raines .07 .20
380 Tommy Greene .02 .10
381 Chris Gwynn .02 .10
382 Jeff King .02 .10
383 Shane Mack .02 .10
384 Ozzie Smith .30 .75
385 Eddie Zambrano RC .02 .10
386 Mike Devereaux .02 .10
387 Erik Hanson .02 .10
388 Scott Cooper .02 .10
389 Dean Palmer .07 .20
390 John Wetteland .07 .20
391 Reggie Jefferson .02 .10
392 Mark Lemke .02 .10
393 Cecil Fielder .07 .20
394 Reggie Sanders .07 .20
395 Darryl Hamilton .02 .10
396 Daryl Boston .02 .10
397 Pat Kelly .02 .10
398 Joe Orsulak .02 .10
399 Ed Sprague .02 .10
400 Eric Anthony .02 .10
401 Scott Sanderson .02 .10
402 Jim Gott .02 .10
403 Ron Karkovice .02 .10
404 Phil Plantier .02 .10
405 David Cone .07 .20
406 Robby Thompson .02 .10
407 Dave Winfield .07 .20
408 Dwight Smith .02 .10
409 Ruben Sierra .07 .20
410 Jack Armstrong .02 .10
411 Mike Felder .02 .10
412 Wil Cordero .02 .10
413 Julio Franco .07 .20
414 Howard Johnson .02 .10
415 Mark McLemore .02 .10
416 Pete Incaviglia .02 .10
417 John Valentin .02 .10
418 Tim Wakefield .10 .30
419 Jose Mesa .02 .10
420 Bernard Gilkey .02 .10
421 Kirk Gibson .07 .20
422 Dave Justice .07 .20
423 Tom Brunansky .02 .10
424 John Smiley .02 .10
425 Kevin Maas .02 .10
426 Doug Drabek .02 .10
427 Paul Molitor .07 .20
428 Darryl Strawberry .07 .20
429 Tim Naehring .02 .10
430 Bill Swift .02 .10
431 Ellis Burks .07 .20
432 Greg Hibbard .02 .10
433 Felix Jose .02 .10
434 Bret Barberie .02 .10
435 Pedro Munoz .02 .10
436 Darrin Fletcher .02 .10
437 Bobby Witt .02 .10
438 Wes Chamberlain .02 .10
439 Mackey Sasser .02 .10
440 Mark Whiten .02 .10
441 Harold Reynolds .07 .20
442 Greg Olson .02 .10
443 Billy Hatcher .02 .10
444 Joe Oliver .02 .10
445 Sandy Alomar Jr. .02 .10
446 Tim Wallach .02 .10
447 Karl Rhodes .02 .10
448 Royce Clayton .02 .10
449 Cal Eldred .02 .10
450 Rick Wilkins .02 .10
451 Mike Stanley .02 .10
452 Charlie Hough .07 .20
453 Jack Morris .07 .20
454 Jon Ratliff RC .02 .10
455 Rene Gonzales .02 .10
456 Eddie Taubensee .02 .10
457 Roberto Hernandez .02 .10
458 Todd Hundley .02 .10
459 Mike Macfarlane .02 .10
460 Mickey Morandini .02 .10
461 Scott Erickson .02 .10
462 Lonnie Smith .02 .10
463 Dave Henderson .02 .10
464 Ryan Klesko .07 .20
465 Edgar Martinez .10 .30
466 Tom Pagnozzi .02 .10
467 Charlie Leibrandt .02 .10
468 Brian Anderson RC .08 .25
469 Harold Baines .07 .20
470 Tim Belcher .02 .10
471 Andre Dawson .07 .20
472 Eric Young .02 .10
473 Paul Sorrento .02 .10
474 Luis Gonzalez .07 .20
475 Rob Deer .02 .10
476 Mike Piazza .40 1.00
477 Kevin Reimer .02 .10
478 Jeff Gardner .02 .10
479 Melido Perez .02 .10
480 Darren Lewis .02 .10
481 Duane Ward .02 .10
482 Rey Sanchez .02 .10
483 Mark Lewis .02 .10
484 Jeff Conine .07 .20
485 Joey Cora .02 .10
486 Trot Nixon RC .40 1.00
487 Kevin McReynolds .02 .10
488 Mike Lansing .02 .10
489 Mike Pagliarulo .02 .10
490 Mariano Duncan .02 .10
491 Mike Bordick .02 .10
492 Kevin Young .02 .10
493 Dave Valle .02 .10
494 Wayne Gomes RC .02 .10
495 Rafael Palmeiro .10 .30
496 Deion Sanders .10 .30
497 Rick Sutcliffe .07 .20
498 Randy Milligan .02 .10
499 Carlos Quintana .02 .10
500 Chris Turner .02 .10
501 Thomas Howard .02 .10
502 Greg Swindell .02 .10
503 Chad Kreuter .02 .10
504 Eric Davis .07 .20
505 Dickie Thon .02 .10
506 Matt Drews RC .02 .10
507 Spike Owen .02 .10
508 Rod Beck .02 .10
509 Pat Hentgen .02 .10
510 Sammy Sosa .20 .50
511 J.T. Snow .07 .20
512 Chuck Carr .02 .10
513 Bo Jackson .20 .50
514 Dennis Martinez .07 .20
515 Phil Hiatt .02 .10
516 Jeff Kent .10 .30
517 Brooks Kieschnick RC .02 .10
518 Kirk Presley RC .02 .10
519 Kevin Seitzer .02 .10
520 Carlos Garcia .02 .10
521 Mike Blowers .02 .10
522 Luis Alicea .02 .10
523 David Hulse .02 .10
524 Greg Maddux UER .30 .75
(career strikeout totals listed as 113; should be 1134)
525 Gregg Olson .02 .10
526 Hal Morris .02 .10
527 Daron Kirkreit .02 .10
528 David Nied .02 .10
529 Jeff Russell .02 .10
530 Kevin Gross .02 .10
531 John Doherty .02 .10
532 Matt Brunson RC .02 .10
533 Dave Nilsson .02 .10
534 Randy Myers .02 .10
535 Steve Farr .02 .10
536 Billy Wagner RC .50 1.25
537 Darnell Coles .02 .10
538 Frank Tanana .02 .10
539 Tim Salmon .10 .30
540 Kim Batiste .02 .10
541 George Bell .02 .10
542 Tom Henke .02 .10
543 Sam Horn .02 .10
544 Doug Jones .02 .10
545 Scott Leius .02 .10
546 Al Martin .02 .10
547 Bob Welch .02 .10
548 Scott Christman RC .02 .10
549 Norm Charlton .02 .10
550 Mark McGwire .50 1.25
551 Greg McMichael .02 .10
552 Tim Costo .02 .10
553 Rodney Bolton .02 .10
554 Pedro Martinez .20 .50
555 Marc Valdes .02 .10
556 Darrell Whitmore .02 .10
557 Tim Bogar .02 .10
558 Steve Karsay .02 .10
559 Danny Bautista .02 .10
560 Jeffrey Hammonds .02 .10
561 Aaron Sele .02 .10
562 Russ Springer .02 .10
563 Jason Bere .02 .10
564 Billy Brewer .02 .10
565 Sterling Hitchcock .02 .10
566 Bobby Munoz .02 .10
567 Craig Paquette .02 .10
568 Bret Boone .07 .20
569 Dan Peltier .02 .10
570 Jeromy Burnitz .07 .20
571 John Wasdin RC .02 .10
572 Chipper Jones .20 .50
573 Jamey Wright RC .02 .10
574 Jeff Granger .02 .10
575 Jay Powell RC .02 .10
576 Ryan Thompson .02 .10
577 Lou Frazier .02 .10
578 Paul Wagner .02 .10
579 Brad Ausmus .10 .30
580 Jack Voigt .02 .10
581 Kevin Rogers .02 .10
582 Damon Buford .02 .10
583 Paul Quantrill .02 .10
584 Marc Newfield .02 .10
585 Derrek Lee RC .60 1.50
586 Shane Reynolds .02 .10
587 Cliff Floyd .07 .20
588 Jeff Schwarz .02 .10
589 Ross Powell RC .02 .10
590 Gerald Williams .02 .10
591 Mike Trombley .02 .10
592 Ken Ryan .02 .10
593 John O'Donoghue .02 .10
594 Rod Correia .02 .10
595 Darrell Sherman .02 .10
596 Steve Scarsone .02 .10
597 Sherman Obando .02 .10
598 Kurt Abbott RC .07 .20
599 Dave Telgheder .02 .10
600 Rick Trlicek .02 .10
601 Carl Everett .07 .20
602 Luis Ortiz .02 .10
603 Larry Luebbers .02 .10
604 Kevin Roberson .02 .10
605 Butch Huskey .02 .10
606 Benji Gil .02 .10
607 Todd Van Poppel .02 .10
608 Mark Hutton .02 .10
609 Chip Hale .02 .10
610 Matt Maysey .02 .10
611 Scott Ruffcorn .02 .10
612 Hilly Hathaway .02 .10
613 Allen Watson .02 .10
614 Carlos Delgado .10 .30
615 Roberto Mejia .02 .10
616 Turk Wendell .02 .10
617 Tony Tarasco .02 .10
618 Raul Mondesi .07 .20
619 Kevin Stocker .02 .10
620 Javier Lopez .07 .20
621 Keith Kessinger .02 .10
622 Bob Hamelin .02 .10
623 John Roper .02 .10
624 Lenny Dykstra WS .02 .10
625 Joe Carter WS .02 .10
626 Jim Abbott HL .07 .20
627 Lee Smith HL .02 .10
628 Ken Griffey Jr. HL .20 .50
629 Dave Winfield HL .02 .10
630 Darryl Kile HL .02 .10
631 F.Thomas AL MVP .10 .30
632 Barry Bonds NL MVP .30 .75
633 Jack McDowell AL CY .02 .10
634 Greg Maddux NL CY .20 .50
635 Tim Salmon AL ROY .07 .20
636 Mike Piazza NL ROY .20 .50
637 Brian Turang RC .02 .10
638 Rondell White .07 .20
639 Nigel Wilson .02 .10
640 Torii Hunter RC .40 1.00
641 Salomon Torres .02 .10
642 Kevin Higgins .02 .10
643 Eric Wedge .02 .10
644 Roger Salkeld .02 .10
645 Manny Ramirez .20 .50
646 Jeff McNeely .02 .10
647 Atlanta Braves CL .02 .10
648 Chicago Cubs CL .02 .10
649 Cincinnati Reds CL .02 .10
650 Colorado Rockies CL .02 .10
651 Florida Marlins CL .02 .10
652 Houston Astros CL .02 .10
653 L.A. Dodgers CL .02 .10
654 Montreal Expos CL .02 .10
655 New York Mets CL .02 .10
656 Phi. Phillies CL .02 .10
657 Pittsburgh Pirates CL .02 .10
658 St. Louis Cardinals CL .02 .10
659 San Diego Padres CL .02 .10
660 S.F. Giants CL .02 .10

1994 Score Gold Rush

This 660-card standard-size set is parallel to the basic Score issue. This set features metallicized and gold-bordered fronts. Gold Rush cards came one per 14-card pack or super pack. They were also issued two per jumbo. These cards were inserted into both hobby and retail packs.

COMPLETE SET (660) 60.00 120.00
COMP. SERIES 1 (330) 30.00 60.00
COMP. SERIES 2 (330) 30.00 60.00
*STARS: 1.5X to 4X BASIC CARDS
*ROOKIES: 1.25X TO 3X BASIC

1994 Score Boys of Summer

Randomly inserted in super packs at a rate of one in four, this 60-card set features top young stars and hopefuls. The set was issued in two series of 30 cards.

COMPLETE SET (60) 25.00 60.00
COMPLETE SERIES 1 (30) 10.00 25.00
COMPLETE SERIES 2 (30) 15.00 35.00
1 Jeff Conine .75 2.00
2 Aaron Sele .40 1.00
3 Kevin Stocker .40 1.00
4 Pat Meares .40 1.00
5 Jeromy Burnitz .75 2.00
6 Mike Piazza 3.00 8.00
7 Allen Watson .40 1.00
8 Jeffrey Hammonds .40 1.00
9 Kevin Roberson .40 1.00
10 Hilly Hathaway .40 1.00
11 Kirk Rueter .40 1.00
12 Eduardo Perez .40 1.00
13 Ricky Gutierrez .40 1.00
14 Domingo Jean .40 1.00
15 David Nied .40 1.00
16 Wayne Kirby .40 1.00
17 Mike Lansing .40 1.00
18 Jason Bere .40 1.00
19 Brent Gates .40 1.00
20 Javier Lopez .75 2.00
21 Greg McMichael .40 1.00
22 David Hulse .40 1.00
23 Roberto Mejia .40 1.00
24 Tim Salmon 1.25 3.00
25 Rene Arocha .40 1.00
26 Bret Boone .75 2.00
27 David McCarty .40 1.00

28 Todd Van Poppel .40 1.00
29 Lance Painter .40 1.00
30 Erik Pappas .40 1.00
31 Chuck Carr .40 1.00
32 Mark Hutton .40 1.00
33 Jeff McNeely .40 1.00
34 Willie Greene .40 1.00
35 Nigel Wilson .40 1.00
36 Rondell White .75 2.00
37 Brian Turang .40 1.00
38 Manny Ramirez 2.00 5.00
39 Salomon Torres .40 1.00
40 Melvin Nieves .40 1.00
41 Ryan Klesko .75 2.00
42 Keith Kessinger .40 1.00
43 Brad Ausmus 1.25 3.00
44 Bob Hamelin .40 1.00
45 Carlos Delgado 1.25 3.00
46 Marc Newfield .40 1.00
47 Raul Mondesi .75 2.00
48 Tim Costo .40 1.00
49 Pedro Martinez 2.00 5.00
50 Steve Karsay .40 1.00
51 Danny Bautista .40 1.00
52 Butch Huskey .40 1.00
53 Kurt Abbott .40 1.00
54 Darrell Sherman .40 1.00
55 Damon Buford .40 1.00
56 Ross Powell .40 1.00
57 Darrell Whitmore .40 1.00
58 Chipper Jones 2.00 5.00
59 Jeff Granger .40 1.00
60 Cliff Floyd .75 2.00

1994 Score Cycle

This 20-card set was randomly inserted in second series foil at a rate of one in 72 and jumbo packs at a rate of one in 36. The set is arranged according to players with the most singles (1-5), doubles (6-10), triples (11-15) and home runs (16-20). The cards are number with a "TC" prefix.

COMPLETE SET (20) 60.00 150.00
TC1 Brett Butler 2.00 5.00
TC2 Kenny Lofton 2.00 5.00
TC3 Paul Molitor 2.00 5.00
TC4 Carlos Baerga 1.00 2.50
TC5 Gregg Jefferies 1.00 2.50
Tony Phillips
TC6 John Olerud 2.00 5.00
TC7 Charlie Hayes 1.00 2.50
TC8 Lenny Dykstra 2.00 5.00
TC9 Dante Bichette 2.00 5.00
TC10 Devon White 2.00 5.00
TC11 Lance Johnson 1.00 2.50
TC12 Joey Cora 2.00 5.00
Steve Finley
TC13 Tony Fernandez 1.00 2.50
TC14 David Hulse 2.00 5.00
Brett Butler
TC15 Jay Bell 2.00 5.00
Brian McRae
Mickey Morandini
TC16 Juan Gonzalez 15.00 40.00
Barry Bonds
TC17 Ken Griffey Jr. 8.00 20.00
TC18 Frank Thomas 5.00 12.00
TC19 Dave Justice 2.00 5.00
TC20 Matt Williams 2.00 5.00
Albert Belle

1994 Score Dream Team

Randomly inserted in first series foil and jumbo packs at a rate of one in 72, this ten-card set feature's baseball's Dream Team as selected by Pinnacle Brands. Banded by forest green stripes above and below, the player photos on the fronts feature ten of baseball's best players sporting historical team uniforms from the 1930's. A Barry Larkin promo card was distributed to dealers and hobby media to preview the set.

COMPLETE SET (10) 25.00 60.00
1 Mike Mussina 3.00 8.00
2 Tom Glavine 3.00 8.00
3 Don Mattingly 12.50 30.00
4 Carlos Baerga 1.00 2.50
5 Barry Larkin 3.00 8.00
6 Matt Williams 2.00 5.00
7 Juan Gonzalez 2.00 5.00
8 Andy Van Slyke 3.00 8.00
9 Larry Walker 2.00 5.00
10 Mike Stanley 1.00 2.50
S5 Barry Larkin Sample .40 1.00

1994 Score Gold Stars

Randomly inserted at a rate of one in every 18 hobby packs, this 60-card set features National and American stars. Split into two series of 30 cards, the first series (1-30) comprises of National League players and the second series (31-60) American Leaguers.

COMPLETE SET (60) 100.00 250.00

COMPLETE NL (30) 40.00 100.00
COMPLETE AL (30) 60.00 150.00
1 Barry Bonds 10.00 25.00
2 Orlando Merced .60 1.50
3 Mark Grace 2.00 5.00
4 Darren Daulton 1.25 3.00
5 Jeff Blauser .60 1.50
6 Deion Sanders 2.00 5.00
7 John Kruk 1.25 3.00
8 Jeff Bagwell 2.00 5.00
9 Gregg Jefferies .60 1.50
10 Matt Williams 1.25 3.00
11 Andres Galarraga 1.25 3.00
12 Jay Bell 1.25 3.00
13 Mike Piazza 6.00 15.00
14 Ron Gant 1.25 3.00
15 Barry Larkin 2.00 5.00
16 Tom Glavine 2.00 5.00
17 Lenny Dykstra 1.25 3.00
18 Fred McGriff 2.00 5.00
19 Andy Van Slyke 2.00 5.00
20 Gary Sheffield 1.25 3.00
21 John Burkett .60 1.50
22 Dante Bichette 1.25 3.00
23 Tony Gwynn 4.00 10.00
24 Dave Justice 1.25 3.00
25 Marquis Grissom 1.25 3.00
26 Bobby Bonilla 1.25 3.00
27 Larry Walker 1.25 3.00
28 Brett Butler 1.25 3.00
29 Robby Thompson .60 1.50
30 Jeff Conine 1.25 3.00
31 Joe Carter 1.25 3.00
32 Ken Griffey Jr. 5.00 12.00
33 Juan Gonzalez 1.25 3.00
34 Rickey Henderson 3.00 8.00
35 Bo Jackson 3.00 8.00
36 Cal Ripken 10.00 25.00
37 John Olerud 1.25 3.00
38 Carlos Baerga .60 1.50
39 Jack McDowell .60 1.50
40 Cecil Fielder 1.25 3.00
41 Kenny Lofton 1.25 3.00
42 Roberto Alomar 2.00 5.00
43 Randy Johnson 3.00 8.00
44 Tim Salmon 2.00 5.00
45 Frank Thomas 3.00 8.00
46 Albert Belle 1.25 3.00
47 Greg Vaughn .60 1.50
48 Travis Fryman 1.25 3.00
49 Don Mattingly 8.00 20.00
50 Wade Boggs 2.00 5.00
51 Mo Vaughn 1.25 3.00
52 Kirby Puckett 3.00 8.00
53 Devon White 1.25 3.00
54 Tony Phillips .60 1.50
55 Brian Harper .60 1.50
56 Chad Curtis .60 1.50
57 Paul Molitor 1.25 3.00
58 Ivan Rodriguez 2.00 5.00
59 Rafael Palmeiro 2.00 5.00
60 Brian McRae .60 1.50

1994 Score Rookie/Traded Samples

Issued to preview the designs of Score's 1994 Rookie/Traded set and its inserts, these 11 standard-size cards feature color player action shots on their fronts. The Jackson card is from the one-per-pack Gold Rush insert set. The Palmeiro card represents the randomly inserted Changing Places insert set, and the Ramirez card is an example of the randomly inserted Super Rookies set. Except for the title card, all the cards carry the word "Sample" in diagonal white lettering on their fronts and backs. The cards are numbered on the back with prefixes as shown below.

COMPLETE SET (11) 4.80 12.00
CP2 Rafael Palmeiro 1.00 2.50
RT1 Will Clark .75 2.00
RT2 Lee Smith .30 .75
RT3 Bo Jackson .75 2.00
RT4 Ellis Burks .30 .75
RT5 Eddie Murray 1.00 2.50
RT6 Delino DeShields .20 .50
RT102 Carlos Delgado 1.00 2.50
SU2 Manny Ramirez 1.00 2.50
NNO Title Card .20 .50
NNO September Call-Up .20 .50
Redemption Sample

1994 Score Rookie/Traded

The 1994 Score Rookie and Traded set consists of 165 standard-size cards featuring rookie standouts, traded players, and new young prospects. The set is delineated by traded players (RT1-RT70) and rookies/young prospects (RT71-RT163). The set closes with checklists (RT164-RT165). Each foil pack contained one Gold Rush card. The cards are numbered on the back with an "RT" prefix. Several leading dealers are under the belief that Jose Lima's

card (number RT158) was short-printed. Conversely, extra cards of John Mabry are typically found in place of the short Lima's. A special unnumbered September Call-Up Redemption card could be exchanged for an Alex Rodriguez card. The expiration date was January 31st, 1995. Odds of finding a redemption card were approximately one in 240 retail and hobby packs. Rookie Cards include Jose Lima and Chan Ho Park.

COMPLETE SET (165) 6.00 15.00
ACTUAL CARD REDEEMED IN 1995
RT1 Will Clark .20 .50
RT2 Lee Smith .10 .30
RT3 Bo Jackson .30 .75
RT4 Ellis Burks .10 .30
RT5 Eddie Murray .30 .75
RT6 Delino DeShields .05 .15
RT7 Erik Hanson .05 .15
RT8 Rafael Palmeiro .20 .50
RT9 Luis Polonia .05 .15
RT10 Omar Vizquel .20 .50
RT11 Kurt Abbott .05 .15
RT12 Vince Coleman .05 .15
RT13 Rickey Henderson .30 .75
RT14 Terry Mulholland .05 .15
RT15 Greg Hibbard .05 .15
RT16 Walt Weiss .05 .15
RT17 Chris Sabo .05 .15
RT18 Dave Henderson .05 .15
RT19 Rick Sutcliffe .10 .30
RT20 Harold Reynolds .10 .30
RT21 Jack Morris .10 .30
RT22 Dan Wilson .05 .15
RT23 Dave Magadan .05 .15
RT24 Dennis Martinez .10 .30
RT25 Wes Chamberlain .05 .15
RT26 Otis Nixon .05 .15
RT27 Eric Anthony .05 .15
RT28 Randy Milligan .05 .15
RT29 Julio Franco .10 .30
RT30 Kevin McReynolds .05 .15
RT31 Anthony Young .05 .15
RT32 Brian Harper .05 .15
RT33 Gene Harris .05 .15
RT34 Eddie Taubensee .05 .15
RT35 David Segui .05 .15
RT36 Stan Javier .05 .15
RT37 Felix Fermin .05 .15
RT38 Darrin Jackson .05 .15
RT39 Tony Fernandez .05 .15
RT40 Jose Vizcaino .05 .15
RT41 Willie Banks .05 .15
RT42 Brian Hunter .05 .15
RT43 Reggie Jefferson .05 .15
RT44 Junior Felix .05 .15
RT45 Jack Armstrong .05 .15
RT46 Bip Roberts .05 .15
RT47 Jerry Browne .05 .15
RT48 Marvin Freeman .05 .15
RT49 Jody Reed .05 .15
RT50 Alex Cole .05 .15
RT51 Sid Fernandez .05 .15
RT52 Pete Smith .05 .15
RT53 Xavier Hernandez .05 .15
RT54 Scott Sanderson .05 .15
RT55 Turner Ward .05 .15
RT56 Rex Hudler .05 .15
RT57 Deion Sanders .20 .50
RT58 Sid Bream .05 .15
RT59 Tony Pena .05 .15
RT60 Bret Boone .10 .30
RT61 Bobby Ayala .05 .15
RT62 Pedro Martinez .30 .75
RT63 Howard Johnson .05 .15
RT64 Mark Portugal .05 .15
RT65 Roberto Kelly .05 .15
RT66 Spike Owen .05 .15
RT67 Jeff Treadway .05 .15
RT68 Mike Harkey .05 .15
RT69 Doug Jones .05 .15
RT70 Steve Farr .05 .15
RT71 Billy Taylor RC .05 .15
RT72 Manny Ramirez .30 .75
RT73 Bob Hamelin .05 .15
RT74 Steve Karsay .05 .15
RT75 Ryan Klesko .10 .30
RT76 Cliff Floyd .10 .30
RT77 Jeffrey Hammonds .05 .15
RT78 Javier Lopez .10 .30
RT79 Roger Salkeld .05 .15
RT80 Hector Carrasco .05 .15
RT81 Gerald Williams .05 .15
RT82 Raul Mondesi .10 .30
RT83 Sterling Hitchcock .05 .15
RT84 Danny Bautista .05 .15
RT85 Chris Turner .05 .15
RT86 Shane Reynolds .05 .15
RT87 Rondell White .10 .30
RT88 Salomon Torres .05 .15
RT89 Turk Wendell .05 .15
RT90 Tony Tarasco .05 .15
RT91 Shawn Green .30 .75
RT92 Greg Colbrunn .05 .15
RT93 Eddie Zambrano .05 .15
RT94 Rich Becker .05 .15
RT95 Chris Gomez .05 .15
RT96 John Patterson .05 .15
RT97 Derek Parks .05 .15
RT98 Rich Rowland .05 .15
RT99 James Mouton .05 .15
RT100 Tim Hyers RC .05 .15
RT101 Jose Valentin .05 .15
RT102 Carlos Delgado .20 .50
RT103 Robert Eenhoorn .05 .15
RT104 John Hudek RC .05 .15
RT105 Domingo Cedeno .05 .15
RT106 Denny Hocking .05 .15
RT107 Greg Pirkl .05 .15
RT108 Mark Smith .05 .15
RT109 Paul Shuey .05 .15
RT110 Jorge Fabregas .05 .15
RT111 Rikkert Faneyte RC .05 .15
RT112 Rob Butler .05 .15
RT113 Darren Oliver RC .10 .30
RT114 Troy O'Leary .05 .15
RT115 Scott Brow .05 .15
RT116 Tony Eusebio .05 .15
RT117 Carlos Reyes .05 .15
RT118 J.R. Phillips .05 .15
RT119 Alex Diaz .05 .15
RT120 Charles Johnson .10 .30
RT121 Nate Minchey .05 .15
RT122 Scott Sanders .05 .15
RT123 Daryl Boston .05 .15
RT124 Joey Hamilton .05 .15
RT125 Brian Anderson .10 .30
RT126 Dan Miceli .05 .15
RT127 Tom Brunansky .05 .15
RT128 Dave Staton .05 .15
RT129 Mike Oquist .05 .15
RT130 John Mabry RC .10 .30
RT131 Norberto Martin .05 .15
RT132 Hector Fajardo .05 .15
RT133 Mark Hutton .05 .15
RT134 Fernando Vina .05 .15
RT135 Lee Tinsley .05 .15
RT136 Chan Ho Park RC .20 .50
RT137 Paul Spoljaric .05 .15
RT138 Matias Carrillo .05 .15
RT139 Mark Kiefer .05 .15
RT140 Stan Royer .05 .15
RT141 Bryan Eversgerd .05 .15
RT142 Brian L. Hunter .05 .15
RT143 Joe Hall .05 .15
RT144 Johnny Ruffin .05 .15
RT145 Alex Gonzalez .05 .15
RT146 Keith Lockhart RC .10 .30
RT147 Tom Marsh .05 .15
RT148 Tony Longmire .05 .15
RT149 Keith Mitchell .05 .15
RT150 Melvin Nieves .05 .15
RT151 Kelly Stinnett RC .05 .15
RT152 Miguel Jimenez .05 .15
RT153 Jeff Juden .05 .15
RT154 Matt Walbeck .05 .15
RT155 Marc Newfield .05 .15
RT156 Matt Mieske .05 .15
RT157 Marcus Moore .05 .15
RT158 Jose Lima SP RC 2.00 5.00
RT159 Mike Kelly .05 .15
RT160 Jim Edmonds .30 .75
RT161 Steve Trachsel .05 .15
RT162 Greg Blosser .05 .15
RT163 Marc Acre RC .05 .15
RT164 AL Checklist .05 .15
RT165 NL Checklist .05 .15
HC1 Alex Rodriguez 400.00 700.00
Call-Up Redemption
NNO Sept. Call-Up Trade EXP .75 2.00

1994 Score Rookie/Traded Gold Rush

Issued one per pack, these cards are a gold foil version of the 165-card Rookie/Traded set. The differences between the basic card and Gold Rush version are the gold foil borders that surround a metallicized player photo. The only difference on the back is a Gold Rush logo.

COMPLETE SET (165) 20.00 50.00
*STARS: 1X TO 2.5X BASIC CARDS
*ROOKIES: 1X TO 2.5X BASIC CARDS

1994 Score Rookie/Traded Changing Places

Randomly inserted in both retail and hobby packs at a rate of one in 36 Rookie/Traded packs, this 10-card standard-size set focuses on ten veteran superstar players who were traded prior to or during the 1994 season. Cards fronts feature a color photo with a slanted design. The backs have a short write-up and a distorted photo.

COMPLETE SET (10) 15.00 30.00
CP1 Will Clark 2.50 6.00
CP2 Rafael Palmeiro 2.50 6.00
CP3 Roberto Kelly .75 2.00
CP4 Bo Jackson 4.00 10.00
CP5 Otis Nixon .75 2.00
CP6 Rickey Henderson 4.00 10.00
CP7 Ellis Burks 1.50 4.00
CP8 Lee Smith 1.50 4.00
CP9 Delino DeShields .75 2.00
CP10 Deion Sanders 2.50 6.00

1994 Score Rookie/Traded Super Rookies

Randomly inserted in hobby packs at a rate of one in 36, this 18-card standard-size set focuses on top rookies of 1994. Odds of finding one of these cards is approximately one in 36 hobby packs. Designed much like the Gold Rush, the cards have an all-foil design. The fronts have a player photo and the backs have a photo that serves as background to the Super Rookies logo and text.

COMPLETE SET (18) 40.00 80.00
SU1 Carlos Delgado 3.00 8.00
SU2 Manny Ramirez 4.00 10.00
SU3 Ryan Klesko 2.00 5.00
SU4 Raul Mondesi 2.00 5.00
SU5 Bob Hamelin 1.50 4.00
SU6 Steve Karsay 1.50 4.00
SU7 Jeffrey Hammonds 1.50 4.00
SU8 Cliff Floyd 2.00 5.00
SU9 Kurt Abbott 1.50 4.00
SU10 Marc Newfield 1.50 4.00
SU11 Javier Lopez 2.00 5.00
SU12 Rich Becker 1.50 4.00
SU13 Greg Pirkl 1.50 4.00
SU14 Rondell White 2.00 5.00
SU15 James Mouton 1.50 4.00
SU16 Tony Tarasco 1.50 4.00
SU17 Brian Anderson 2.00 5.00
SU18 Jim Edmonds 4.00 10.00

1995 Score

The 1995 Score set consists of 605 standard-size cards issued in hobby, retail and jumbo packs. Hobby packs featured a special signed Ryan Klesko (RG1)card. Retail packs also had a Klesko card (SG1) but these were not signed.

COMPLETE SET (605) 10.00 24.00
COMP. SERIES 1 (330) 5.00 12.00
COMP. SERIES 2 (275) 5.00 12.00
1 Frank Thomas .20 .50
2 Roberto Alomar .10 .30
3 Cal Ripken .60 1.50
4 Jose Canseco .10 .30
5 Matt Williams .07 .20
6 Esteban Beltre .02 .10
7 Domingo Cedeno .02 .10
8 John Valentin .02 .10
9 Glenallen Hill .02 .10
10 Rafael Belliard .02 .10
11 Randy Myers .02 .10
12 Mo Vaughn .07 .20
13 Hector Carrasco .02 .10
14 Chili Davis .07 .20
15 Dante Bichette .07 .20
16 Darrin Jackson .02 .10
17 Mike Piazza .30 .75
18 Junior Felix .02 .10
19 Moises Alou .07 .20
20 Mark Gubicza .02 .10
21 Bret Saberhagen .07 .20
22 Lenny Dykstra .07 .20
23 Steve Howe .02 .10
24 Mark Dewey .02 .10
25 Brian Harper .02 .10
26 Ozzie Smith .30 .75
27 Scott Erickson .02 .10
28 Tony Gwynn .25 .60
29 Bob Welch .02 .10
30 Barry Bonds .60 1.50
31 Leo Gomez .02 .10
32 Greg Maddux .30 .75
33 Mike Greenwell .02 .10
34 Sammy Sosa .20 .50
35 Darnell Coles .02 .10
36 Tommy Greene .02 .10
37 Will Clark .10 .30
38 Steve Ontiveros .02 .10
39 Stan Javier .02 .10
40 Bip Roberts .02 .10
41 Paul O'Neill .10 .30
42 Bill Haselman .02 .10
43 Shane Mack .02 .10
44 Orlando Merced .02 .10
45 Kevin Seitzer .02 .10
46 Trevor Hoffman .07 .20
47 Greg Gagne .02 .10
48 Jeff Kent .07 .20
49 Tony Phillips .02 .10
50 Ken Hill .02 .10
51 Carlos Baerga .02 .10
52 Henry Rodriguez .02 .10
53 Scott Sanderson .02 .10
54 Jeff Conine .07 .20
55 Chris Turner .02 .10
56 Ken Caminiti .07 .20
57 Harold Baines .07 .20
58 Charlie Hayes .02 .10
59 Roberto Kelly .02 .10
60 John Olerud .07 .20
61 Tim Davis .02 .10
62 Rich Rowland .02 .10
63 Rey Sanchez .02 .10
64 Junior Ortiz .02 .10
65 Ricky Gutierrez .02 .10
66 Rex Hudler .02 .10
67 Johnny Ruffin .02 .10
68 Jay Buhner .07 .20
69 Tom Pagnozzi .02 .10
70 Julio Franco .07 .20
71 Eric Young .02 .10
72 Mike Bordick .02 .10
73 Don Slaught .02 .10
74 Goose Gossage .07 .20
75 Lonnie Smith .02 .10
76 Jimmy Key .07 .20
77 Dave Hollins .02 .10
78 Mickey Tettleton .02 .10
79 Luis Gonzalez .07 .20
80 Dave Winfield .07 .20
81 Ryan Thompson .02 .10
82 Felix Jose .02 .10
83 Rusty Meacham .02 .10
84 Darryl Hamilton .02 .10
85 John Wetteland .07 .20
86 Tom Brunansky .02 .10
87 Mark Lemke .02 .10
88 Spike Owen .02 .10
89 Shawon Dunston .02 .10
90 Wilson Alvarez .02 .10
91 Lee Smith .07 .20
92 Scott Kamieniecki .02 .10
93 Jacob Brumfield .02 .10
94 Kirk Gibson .07 .20
95 Joe Girardi .02 .10
96 Mike Macfarlane .02 .10
97 Greg Colbrunn .02 .10
98 Ricky Bones .02 .10
99 Delino DeShields .02 .10
100 Pat Meares .02 .10
101 Jeff Fassero .02 .10
102 Jim Leyritz .02 .10
103 Gary Redus .02 .10
104 Terry Steinbach .02 .10
105 Kevin McReynolds .02 .10
106 Felix Fermin .02 .10
107 Danny Jackson .02 .10
108 Chris James .02 .10
109 Jeff King .02 .10
110 Pat Hentgen .02 .10
111 Gerald Perry .02 .10
112 Tim Raines .07 .20
113 Eddie Williams .02 .10
114 Jamie Moyer .07 .20
115 Bud Black .02 .10
116 Chris Gomez .02 .10
117 Luis Lopez .02 .10
118 Roger Clemens .40 1.00
119 Javier Lopez .07 .20
120 Dave Nilsson .02 .10
121 Karl Rhodes .02 .10
122 Rick Aguilera .02 .10
123 Tony Fernandez .02 .10
124 Bernie Williams .10 .30
125 James Mouton .02 .10
126 Mark Langston .02 .10
127 Mike Lansing .02 .10
128 Tino Martinez .10 .30
129 Joe Orsulak .02 .10
130 David Hulse .02 .10
131 Pete Incaviglia .02 .10
132 Mark Clark .02 .10
133 Tony Eusebio .02 .10
134 Chuck Finley .07 .20
135 Lou Frazier .02 .10
136 Craig Grebeck .02 .10
137 Kelly Stinnett .02 .10
138 Paul Shuey .02 .10
139 David Nied .02 .10
140 Billy Brewer .02 .10
141 Dave Weathers .02 .10
142 Scott Leius .02 .10
143 Brian Jordan .07 .20
144 Melido Perez .02 .10
145 Tony Tarasco .02 .10
146 Dan Wilson .02 .10
147 Rondell White .07 .20
148 Mike Henneman .02 .10
149 Brian Johnson .02 .10
150 Tom Henke .02 .10
151 John Patterson .02 .10
152 Bobby Witt .02 .10
153 Eddie Taubensee .02 .10
154 Pat Borders .02 .10
155 Ramon Martinez .02 .10
156 Mike Kingery .02 .10
157 Zane Smith .02 .10
158 Benito Santiago .07 .20
159 Matias Carrillo .02 .10
160 Scott Brosius .07 .20
161 Dave Clark .02 .10
162 Mark McLemore .02 .10
163 Curt Schilling .07 .20
164 J.T. Snow .07 .20
165 Rod Beck .02 .10
166 Scott Fletcher .02 .10
167 Bob Tewksbury .02 .10
168 Mike LaValliere .02 .10
169 Dave Hansen .02 .10
170 Pedro Martinez .10 .30
171 Kirk Rueter .02 .10
172 Jose Lind .02 .10
173 Luis Alicea .02 .10
174 Mike Moore .02 .10
175 Andy Ashby .02 .10
176 Jody Reed .02 .10
177 Darryl Kile .07 .20
178 Carl Willis .02 .10
179 Jeromy Burnitz .07 .20
180 Mike Gallego .02 .10
181 Bill VanLandingham .02 .10
182 Sid Fernandez .02 .10
183 Kim Batiste .02 .10
184 Greg Myers .02 .10
185 Steve Avery .02 .10
186 Steve Farr .02 .10
187 Robb Nen .07 .20
188 Dan Pasqua .02 .10
189 Bruce Ruffin .02 .10
190 Jose Valentin .02 .10
191 Willie Banks .02 .10
192 Mike Aldrete .02 .10
193 Randy Milligan .02 .10

194 Steve Karsay .02 .10
195 Mike Stanley .02 .10
196 Jose Mesa .02 .10
197 Tom Browning .02 .10
198 John Vander Wal .02 .10
199 Kevin Brown .07 .20
200 Mike Oquist .02 .10
201 Greg Swindell .02 .10
202 Eddie Zambrano .02 .10
203 Joe Boever .02 .10
204 Gary Varsho .02 .10
205 Chris Gwynn .02 .10
206 David Howard .02 .10
207 Jerome Walton .02 .10
208 Danny Darwin .02 .10
209 Darryl Strawberry .07 .20
210 Todd Van Poppel .02 .10
211 Scott Livingstone .02 .10
212 Dave Fleming .02 .10
213 Todd Worrell .02 .10
214 Carlos Delgado .07 .20
215 Bill Pecota .02 .10
216 Jim Lindeman .02 .10
217 Rick White .02 .10
218 Jose Oquendo .02 .10
219 Tony Castillo .02 .10
220 Fernando Vina .02 .10
221 Jeff Bagwell .10 .30
222 Randy Johnson .20 .50
223 Albert Belle .07 .20
224 Chuck Carr .02 .10
225 Mark Leiter .02 .10
226 Hal Morris .02 .10
227 Robin Ventura .07 .20
228 Mike Munoz .02 .10
229 Jim Thome .10 .30
230 Mario Diaz .02 .10
231 John Doherty .02 .10
232 Bobby Jones .02 .10
233 Raul Mondesi .07 .20
234 Ricky Jordan .02 .10
235 John Jaha .02 .10
236 Carlos Garcia .02 .10
237 Kirby Puckett .20 .50
238 Orel Hershiser .07 .20
239 Don Mattingly .50 1.25
240 Sid Bream .02 .10
241 Brent Gates .02 .10
242 Tony Longmire .02 .10
243 Robby Thompson .02 .10
244 Rick Sutcliffe .07 .20
245 Dean Palmer .07 .20
246 Marquis Grissom .07 .20
247 Paul Molitor .07 .20
248 Mark Carreon .02 .10
249 Jack Voigt .02 .10
250 Greg McMichael UER .02 .10
(photo on front is Mike Stanton)
251 Damon Berryhill .02 .10
252 Brian Dorsett .02 .10
253 Jim Edmonds .10 .30
254 Barry Larkin .10 .30
255 Jack McDowell .02 .10
256 Wally Joyner .07 .20
257 Eddie Murray .20 .50
258 Lenny Webster .02 .10
259 Milt Cuyler .02 .10
260 Todd Benzinger .02 .10
261 Vince Coleman .02 .10
262 Todd Stottlemyre .02 .10
263 Turner Ward .02 .10
264 Ray Lankford .07 .20
265 Matt Walbeck .02 .10
266 Deion Sanders .10 .30
267 Gerald Williams .02 .10
268 Jim Gott .02 .10
269 Jeff Frye .02 .10
270 Jose Rijo .02 .10
271 Dave Justice .07 .20
272 Ismael Valdes .02 .10
273 Ben McDonald .02 .10
274 Darren Lewis .02 .10
275 Graeme Lloyd .02 .10
276 Luis Ortiz .02 .10
277 Julian Tavarez .02 .10
278 Mark Dalesandro .02 .10
279 Brett Merriman .02 .10
280 Ricky Bottalico .02 .10
281 Robert Eenhoorn .02 .10
282 Rikkert Faneyte .02 .10
283 Mike Kelly .02 .10
284 Mark Smith .02 .10
285 Turk Wendell .02 .10
286 Greg Blosser .02 .10
287 Garey Ingram .02 .10
288 Jorge Fabregas .02 .10
289 Blaise Ilsley .02 .10
290 Joe Hall .02 .10
291 Orlando Miller .02 .10
292 Jose Lima .02 .10
293 Greg O'Halloran RC .02 .10
294 Mark Kiefer .02 .10
295 Jose Oliva .02 .10
296 Rich Becker .02 .10
297 Brian L. Hunter .02 .10
298 Dave Silvestri .02 .10
299 Armando Benitez .02 .10
300 Darren Dreifort .02 .10
301 John Mabry .02 .10
302 Greg Pirkl .02 .10
303 J.R. Phillips .02 .10
304 Shawn Green .07 .20
305 Roberto Petagine .02 .10
306 Keith Lockhart .02 .10
307 Jonathan Hurst .02 .10
308 Paul Spoljaric .02 .10
309 Mike Lieberthal .07 .20
310 Garret Anderson .07 .20
311 John Johnstone .02 .10
312 Alex Rodriguez .50 1.25
313 Kent Mercker HL .02 .10
314 John Valentin HL .02 .10
315 Kenny Rogers HL .07 .20
316 Fred McGriff HL .07 .20
317 Team Checklists .02 .10
318 Team Checklists .02 .10
319 Team Checklists .02 .10
320 Team Checklists .02 .10
321 Team Checklists .02 .10
322 Team Checklists .02 .10
323 Team Checklists .02 .10
324 Team Checklists .02 .10
325 Team Checklists .02 .10
326 Team Checklists .02 .10
327 Team Checklists .02 .10
328 Team Checklists .02 .10
329 Team Checklists .02 .10
330 Team Checklists .02 .10
331 Pedro Munoz .02 .10
332 Ryan Klesko .07 .20
333 Andre Dawson .07 .20
334 Derrick May .02 .10
335 Aaron Sele .02 .10
336 Kevin Mitchell .02 .10
337 Steve Trachsel .02 .10
338 Andres Galarraga .07 .20
339 Terry Pendleton .07 .20
340 Gary Sheffield .07 .20
341 Travis Fryman .07 .20
342 Bo Jackson .20 .50
343 Gary Gaetti .07 .20
344 Brett Butler .07 .20
345 B.J. Surhoff .07 .20
346 Larry Walker .07 .20
347 Kevin Tapani .02 .10
348 Rick Wilkins .02 .10
349 Wade Boggs .10 .30
350 Mariano Duncan .02 .10
351 Ruben Sierra .07 .20
352 Andy Van Slyke .10 .30
353 Reggie Jefferson .02 .10
354 Gregg Jefferies .02 .10
355 Tim Naehring .02 .10
356 John Roper .02 .10
357 Joe Carter .07 .20
358 Kurt Abbott .02 .10
359 Lenny Harris .02 .10
360 Lance Johnson .02 .10
361 Brian Anderson .02 .10
362 Jim Eisenreich .02 .10
363 Jerry Browne .02 .10
364 Mark Grace .10 .30
365 Devon White .07 .20
366 Reggie Sanders .07 .20
367 Ivan Rodriguez .10 .30
368 Kirt Manwaring .02 .10
369 Pat Kelly .02 .10
370 Ellis Burks .07 .20
371 Charles Nagy .02 .10
372 Kevin Bass .02 .10
373 Lou Whitaker .07 .20
374 Rene Arocha .02 .10
375 Derek Parks .02 .10
376 Mark Whiten .02 .10
377 Mark McGwire .50 1.25
378 Doug Drabek .02 .10
379 Greg Vaughn .02 .10
380 Al Martin .02 .10
381 Ron Darling .02 .10
382 Tim Wallach .02 .10
383 Alan Trammell .07 .20
384 Randy Velarde .02 .10
385 Chris Sabo .02 .10
386 Wil Cordero .02 .10
387 Darrin Fletcher .02 .10
388 David Segui .02 .10
389 Steve Buechele .02 .10
390 Dave Gallagher .02 .10
391 Thomas Howard .02 .10
392 Chad Curtis .02 .10
393 Cal Eldred .02 .10
394 Jason Bere .02 .10
395 Bret Barberie .02 .10
396 Paul Sorrento .02 .10
397 Steve Finley .07 .20
398 Cecil Fielder .07 .20
399 Eric Karros .07 .20
400 Jeff Montgomery .02 .10
401 Cliff Floyd .07 .20
402 Matt Mieske .02 .10
403 Brian Hunter .02 .10
404 Alex Cole .02 .10
405 Kevin Stocker .02 .10
406 Eric Davis .07 .20
407 Marvin Freeman .02 .10
408 Dennis Eckersley .07 .20
409 Todd Zeile .02 .10
410 Keith Mitchell .02 .10
411 Andy Benes .02 .10
412 Juan Bell .02 .10
413 Royce Clayton .02 .10
414 Ed Sprague .02 .10
415 Mike Mussina .10 .30
416 Todd Hundley .02 .10
417 Pat Listach .02 .10
418 Joe Oliver .02 .10
419 Rafael Palmeiro .10 .30
420 Tim Salmon .10 .30
421 Brady Anderson .07 .20
422 Kenny Lofton .07 .20
423 Craig Biggio .10 .30
424 Bobby Bonilla .07 .20
425 Kenny Rogers .07 .20
426 Derek Bell .02 .10
427 Scott Cooper .02 .10
428 Ozzie Guillen .07 .20
429 Omar Vizquel .10 .30
430 Phil Plantier .02 .10
431 Chuck Knoblauch .07 .20
432 Darren Daulton .07 .20
433 Bob Hamelin .02 .10
434 Tom Glavine .10 .30
435 Walt Weiss .02 .10
436 Jose Vizcaino .02 .10
437 Ken Griffey Jr. .30 .75
438 Jay Bell .07 .20
439 Juan Gonzalez .07 .20
440 Jeff Blauser .07 .20
441 Rickey Henderson .20 .50
442 Bobby Ayala .02 .10
443 David Cone .07 .20
444 Pedro Martinez .10 .30
445 Manny Ramirez .10 .30
446 Mark Portugal .02 .10
447 Damion Easley .02 .10
448 Gary DiSarcina .02 .10
449 Roberto Hernandez .02 .10
450 Jeffrey Hammonds .02 .10
451 Jeff Treadway .02 .10
452 Jim Abbott .10 .30
453 Carlos Rodriguez .02 .10
454 Joey Cora .02 .10
455 Bret Boone .07 .20
456 Danny Tartabull .02 .10
457 John Franco .07 .20
458 Roger Salkeld .02 .10
459 Fred McGriff .10 .30
460 Pedro Astacio .02 .10
461 Jon Lieber .02 .10
462 Luis Polonia .02 .10
463 Geronimo Pena .02 .10
464 Tom Gordon .02 .10
465 Brad Ausmus .07 .20
466 Willie McGee .07 .20
467 Doug Jones .02 .10
468 John Smoltz .10 .30
469 Troy Neel .02 .10
470 Luis Sojo .02 .10
471 John Smiley .02 .10
472 Rafael Bournigal .02 .10
473 Bill Taylor .02 .10
474 Juan Guzman .02 .10
475 Dave Magadan .02 .10
476 Mike Devereaux .02 .10
477 Andujar Cedeno .02 .10
478 Edgar Martinez .10 .30
479 Milt Thompson .02 .10
480 Allen Watson .02 .10
481 Ron Karkovice .02 .10
482 Joey Hamilton .02 .10
483 Vinny Castilla .07 .20
484 Tim Belcher .02 .10
485 Bernard Gilkey .02 .10
486 Scott Servais .02 .10
487 Cory Snyder .02 .10
488 Mel Rojas .02 .10
489 Carlos Reyes .02 .10
490 Chip Hale .02 .10
491 Bill Swift .02 .10
492 Pat Rapp .02 .10
493 Brian McRae .02 .10
494 Mickey Morandini .02 .10
495 Tony Pena .02 .10
496 Danny Bautista .02 .10
497 Armando Reynoso .02 .10
498 Ken Ryan .02 .10
499 Billy Ripken .02 .10
500 Pat Mahomes .02 .10
501 Mark Acre .02 .10
502 Geronimo Berroa .02 .10
503 Norberto Martin .02 .10
504 Chad Kreuter .02 .10
505 Howard Johnson .02 .10
506 Eric Anthony .02 .10
507 Mark Wohlers .02 .10
508 Scott Sanders .02 .10
509 Pete Harnisch .02 .10
510 Wes Chamberlain .02 .10
511 Tom Candiotti .02 .10
512 Albie Lopez .02 .10
513 Denny Neagle .07 .20
514 Sean Berry .02 .10
515 Billy Hatcher .02 .10
516 Todd Jones .02 .10
517 Wayne Kirby .02 .10
518 Butch Henry .02 .10
519 Sandy Alomar Jr. .02 .10
520 Kevin Appier .07 .20
521 Roberto Mejia .02 .10
522 Steve Cooke .02 .10
523 Terry Shumpert .02 .10
524 Mike Jackson .02 .10
525 Kent Mercker .02 .10
526 David Wells .07 .20
527 Juan Samuel .02 .10
528 Salomon Torres .02 .10
529 Duane Ward .02 .10
530 Rob Dibble .07 .20
531 Mike Blowers .02 .10
532 Mark Eichhorn .02 .10
533 Alex Diaz .02 .10
534 Dan Miceli .02 .10
535 Jeff Branson .02 .10
536 Dave Stevens .02 .10
537 Charlie O'Brien .02 .10
538 Shane Reynolds .02 .10
539 Rich Amaral .02 .10
540 Rusty Greer .07 .20
541 Alex Arias .02 .10
542 Eric Plunk .02 .10
543 John Hudek .02 .10
544 Kirk McCaskill .02 .10
545 Jeff Reboulet .02 .10
546 Sterling Hitchcock .02 .10
547 Warren Newson .02 .10
548 Bryan Harvey .02 .10
549 Mike Huff .02 .10
550 Lance Parrish .07 .20
551 Ken Griffey Jr. HIT .20 .50
552 Matt Williams HIT .07 .20
553 R.Alomar HIT UER .07 .20
Card says he's a NL All-Star
He plays in the AL
554 Jeff Bagwell HIT .07 .20
555 Dave Justice HIT .07 .20
556 Cal Ripken Jr. HIT .30 .75
557 Albert Belle HIT .07 .20
558 Mike Piazza HIT .15 .40
559 Kirby Puckett HIT .10 .30
560 Wade Boggs HIT .07 .20
561 Tony Gwynn HIT UER .10 .30
card has him winning AL batting titles
he's played whole career in the NL
562 Barry Bonds HIT .30 .75
563 Mo Vaughn HIT .02 .10
564 Don Mattingly HIT .25 .60
565 Carlos Baerga HIT .02 .10
566 Paul Molitor HIT .02 .10
567 Raul Mondesi HIT .02 .10
568 Manny Ramirez HIT .07 .20
569 Alex Rodriguez HIT .20 .50
570 Will Clark HIT .07 .20
571 Frank Thomas HIT .10 .30
572 Moises Alou HIT .02 .10
573 Jeff Conine HIT .02 .10
574 Joe Ausanio .02 .10
575 Charles Johnson .07 .20
576 Ernie Young .02 .10
577 Jeff Granger .02 .10
578 Robert Perez .02 .10
579 Melvin Nieves .02 .10
580 Gar Finnvold .02 .10
581 Duane Singleton .02 .10
582 Chan Ho Park .07 .20
583 Fausto Cruz .02 .10
584 Dave Staton .02 .10
585 Denny Hocking .02 .10
586 Nate Minchey .02 .10
587 Marc Newfield .02 .10
588 Jayhawk Owens UER .02 .10
Front Photo is Jim Tatum
589 Darren Bragg .02 .10
590 Kevin King .02 .10
591 Kurt Miller .02 .10
592 Aaron Small .02 .10
593 Troy O'Leary .02 .10
594 Phil Stidham .02 .10
595 Steve Dunn .02 .10
596 Cory Bailey .02 .10
597 Alex Gonzalez .02 .10
598 Jim Bowie RC .02 .10
599 Jeff Cirillo .02 .10
600 Mark Hutton .02 .10
601 Russ Davis .02 .10
602 Checklist .02 .10
603 Checklist .02 .10
604 Checklist .02 .10
605 Checklist .02 .10
RG1 R.Klesko Rook.Great. .40 1.00
SG1 Ryan Klesko AU/6100 4.00 10.00

1995 Score Gold Rush

Parallel to the basic Score issue, these cards were inserted one per foil pack and two per jumbo pack. The fronts were printed in gold foil and the backs contain the Gold Rush logo. As part of the Gold Rush program, one Platinum Team Redemption card was randomly inserted in Score packs at a rate of one in 36. This redemption card and up to four Gold Rush team sets (and $2) could be redeemed for platinum versions of the team set(s). The Gold Rush sets that were sent in would be returned with a stamp indicating they were already used for redemption purposes. The Platinum Upgrade offer was good through 7/13/95 for series 1, 10/1/95 for series 2.

COMPLETE SET (605) 40.00 100.00
COMP. SERIES 1 (330) 20.00 50.00
COMP. SERIES 2 (275) 20.00 50.00
*STARS: 2X TO 5X BASIC CARDS

1995 Score Platinum Team Sets

After completing a Score Gold Rush team set in either series, a collector could mail in those cards along with a platinum redemption card. In return, the collector would receive a complete Platinum Team Set. The cards are similar to the gold cards except they have sparkling platinum-foil fronts and come in a small card case. The top card is the certificate for the team set. Only 4,950 of each platinum team set was produced.

*STARS: 5X TO 12X BASIC CARDS

1995 Score You Trade Em

This skip-numbered 11-card set was available only by redeeming the randomly inserted Score You Trade Em redemption card. The set features a selection of veteran players that were traded to new teams at the beginning of the 1995 season. The numbering and card design parallel the corresponding cards within the regular issue 1995 Score set, but these Trade cards feature the players in their new uniforms.

COMPLETE SET (11) .60 1.50
333T Andre Dawson UER .15 .40
position listed as DH
339T Terry Pendleton .15 .40
344T Brett Butler .15 .40
346T Larry Walker .15 .40
352T Andy Van Slyke .25 .60
392T Chad Curtis .07 .20
427T Scott Cooper .07 .20
443T David Cone .15 .40
452T Jim Abbott .25 .60
493T Brian McRae .07 .20
530T Rob Dibble .15 .40
NNO Expired Trade Card .20 .50

1995 Score Airmail

This 18-card set was randomly inserted in series two jumbo packs at a rate of one in 24.

COMPLETE SET (18) 25.00 50.00
AM1 Bob Hamelin .60 1.50
AM2 John Mabry .60 1.50
AM3 Marc Newfield .60 1.50
AM4 Jose Oliva .60 1.50
AM5 Charles Johnson 1.00 2.50
AM6 Russ Davis .60 1.50
AM7 Ernie Young .60 1.50
AM8 Billy Ashley .60 1.50
AM9 Ryan Klesko 1.00 2.50
AM10 J.R. Phillips .60 1.50
AM11 Cliff Floyd 1.00 2.50
AM12 Carlos Delgado 1.00 2.50
AM13 Melvin Nieves .60 1.50
AM14 Raul Mondesi 1.00 2.50
AM15 Manny Ramirez 1.50 4.00
AM16 Mike Kelly .60 1.50
AM17 Alex Rodriguez 6.00 15.00
AM18 Rusty Greer 1.00 2.50

1995 Score Contest Redemption

These cards were mailed to collectors who correctly identified intentional errors in two Pinnacle print ads depicting baseball scenes. The Alex Rodriguez card was the prize for the first ad, the Ivan Rodriguez card for the second ad.

COMPLETE SET (2) 3.20 8.00
AD1 Alex Rodriguez 2.50 6.00
AD2 Ivan Rodriguez 1.25 3.00

1995 Score Double Gold Champs

This 12-card set was randomly inserted in second series hobby packs at a rate of one in 36.

COMPLETE SET (12) 30.00 80.00
GC1 Frank Thomas 2.00 5.00
GC2 Ken Griffey Jr. 3.00 8.00
GC3 Barry Bonds 6.00 15.00
GC4 Tony Gwynn 2.50 6.00
GC5 Don Mattingly 5.00 12.00
GC6 Greg Maddux 3.00 8.00
GC7 Roger Clemens 4.00 10.00
GC8 Kenny Lofton .75 2.00
GC9 Jeff Bagwell 1.25 3.00
GC10 Matt Williams .75 2.00
GC11 Kirby Puckett 2.00 5.00
GC12 Cal Ripken 6.00 15.00

1995 Score Draft Picks

Randomly inserted in first series hobby packs at a rate of one in 36, this 18-card set takes a look at top picks selected in June of 1994. The cards are numbered with a "DP" prefix.

COMPLETE SET (18) 10.00 25.00
DP1 McKay Christensen .40 1.00
DP2 Bret Wagner .40 1.00
DP3 Paul Wilson .40 1.00
DP4 C.J. Nitkowski .40 1.00
DP5 Josh Booty .40 1.00
DP6 Antone Williamson .40 1.00
DP7 Paul Konerko 2.00 5.00
DP8 Scott Elarton .60 1.50
DP9 Jacob Shumate .40 1.00
DP10 Terrence Long .40 1.00
DP11 Mark Johnson .60 1.50
DP12 Ben Grieve .40 1.00
DP13 Doug Million .40 1.00
DP14 Jayson Peterson .40 1.00
DP15 Dustin Hermanson .40 1.00
DP16 Matt Smith .40 1.00
DP17 Kevin Witt .40 1.00
DP18 Brian Buchanan .40 1.00

1995 Score Dream Team

Randomly inserted in first series hobby and retail packs at a rate of one in 72 packs, this 12-card hologram set showcases top performers from the 1994 season. The cards are numbered with a "DG" prefix.

COMPLETE SET (12) 40.00 100.00
DG1 Frank Thomas 3.00 8.00
DG2 Roberto Alomar 2.00 5.00
DG3 Cal Ripken 10.00 25.00
DG4 Matt Williams 1.25 3.00
DG5 Mike Piazza 5.00 12.00
DG6 Albert Belle 1.25 3.00
DG7 Ken Griffey Jr. 5.00 12.00
DG8 Tony Gwynn 4.00 10.00
DG9 Paul Molitor 1.25 3.00
DG10 Jimmy Key 1.25 3.00
DG11 Greg Maddux 5.00 12.00
DG12 Lee Smith 1.25 3.00

1995 Score Hall of Gold

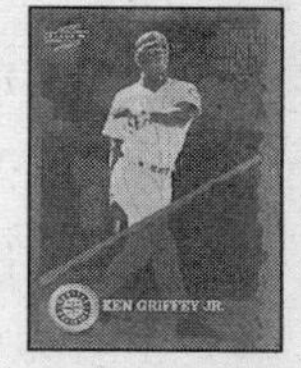

Randomly inserted in packs at a rate one in six, this 110-card multi-series set is a collection of top stars and young hopefuls. Cards numbered one through 55 were seeded in first series packs and cards 56-100 were seeded in second series packs.

COMP. SERIES 1 (55) 20.00 50.00
COMP.SERIES 2 (55) 12.50 30.00
*YTE CARDS: .4X TO 1X BASIC HALL
ONE YTE SET VIA MAIL PER YTE TRADE CARD
HG1 Ken Griffey Jr. 2.00 5.00
HG2 Matt Williams .50 1.25
HG3 Roberto Alomar .75 2.00
HG4 Jeff Bagwell .75 2.00
HG5 Dave Justice .50 1.25
HG6 Cal Ripken 4.00 10.00
HG7 Randy Johnson 1.25 3.00
HG8 Barry Larkin .75 2.00
HG9 Albert Belle .50 1.25
HG10 Mike Piazza 2.00 5.00
HG11 Kirby Puckett 1.25 3.00
HG12 Moises Alou .50 1.25
HG13 Jose Canseco .75 2.00
HG14 Tony Gwynn 1.50 4.00
HG15 Roger Clemens 2.50 6.00
HG16 Barry Bonds 4.00 10.00
HG17 Mo Vaughn .50 1.25
HG18 Greg Maddux 2.00 5.00
HG19 Dante Bichette .50 1.25
HG20 Will Clark .75 2.00
HG21 Lenny Dykstra .50 1.25
HG22 Don Mattingly 3.00 8.00
HG23 Carlos Baerga .25 .60
HG24 Ozzie Smith 2.00 5.00
HG25 Paul Molitor .50 1.25
HG26 Paul O'Neill .75 2.00
HG27 Deion Sanders .75 2.00
HG28 Jeff Conine .50 1.25
HG29 John Olerud .50 1.25
HG30 Jose Rijo .25 .60
HG31 Sammy Sosa 1.25 3.00
HG32 Robin Ventura .50 1.25
HG33 Raul Mondesi .50 1.25
HG34 Eddie Murray 1.25 3.00
HG35 Marquis Grissom .50 1.25
HG36 Darryl Strawberry .50 1.25
HG37 Dave Nilsson .25 .60
HG38 Manny Ramirez .75 2.00
HG39 Delino DeShields .25 .60
HG40 Lee Smith .50 1.25
HG41 Alex Rodriguez 3.00 8.00
HG42 Julio Franco .50 1.25
HG43 Bret Saberhagen .50 1.25
HG44 Ken Hill .25 .60
HG45 Roberto Kelly .25 .60
HG46 Hal Morris .25 .60
HG47 Jimmy Key .50 1.25
HG48 Terry Steinbach .25 .60
HG49 Mickey Tettleton .25 .60
HG50 Tony Phillips .25 .60
HG51 Carlos Garcia .25 .60
HG52 Jim Edmonds .75 2.00
HG53 Rod Beck .25 .60
HG54 Shane Mack .25 .60
HG55 Ken Caminiti .50 1.25
HG56 Frank Thomas 1.25 3.00
HG57 Kenny Lofton .50 1.25
HG58 Juan Gonzalez .50 1.25
HG59 Jason Bere .25 .60
HG60 Joe Carter .50 1.25
HG61 Gary Sheffield .50 1.25
HG62 Andres Galarraga .50 1.25
HG63 Ellis Burks .50 1.25
HG64 Bobby Bonilla .50 1.25
HG65 Tom Glavine .75 2.00
HG66 John Smoltz .75 2.00
HG67 Fred McGriff .75 2.00
HG68 Craig Biggio .75 2.00
HG69 Reggie Sanders .50 1.25
HG70 Kevin Mitchell .25 .60
HG71 Larry Walker .50 1.25
HG72 Carlos Delgado .50 1.25

HG73 Alex Gonzalez .25 .60
HG74 Ivan Rodriguez .75 2.00
HG75 Ryan Klesko .50 1.25
HG76 John Kruk .25 .60
HG77 Brian McRae .25 .60
HG78 Tim Salmon .75 2.00
HG79 Travis Fryman .50 1.25
HG80 Chuck Knoblauch .50 1.25
HG81 Jay Bell .50 1.25
HG82 Cecil Fielder .50 1.25
HG83 Cliff Floyd .50 1.25
HG84 Ruben Sierra .50 1.25
HG85 Mike Mussina .75 2.00
HG86 Mark Grace .75 2.00
HG87 Dennis Eckersley .50 1.25
HG88 Dennis Martinez .25 .60
HG89 Rafael Palmeiro .75 2.00
HG90 Ben McDonald .25 .60
HG91 Dave Hollins .25 .60
HG92 Steve Avery .25 .60
HG93 David Cone .50 1.25
HG94 Darren Daulton .50 1.25
HG95 Bret Boone .50 1.25
HG96 Wade Boggs .75 2.00
HG97 Doug Drabek .25 .60
HG98 Andy Benes .25 .60
HG99 Jim Thome .75 2.00
HG100 Chili Davis .50 1.25
HG101 J.Hammonds .25 .60
HG102 R.Henderson 1.25 3.00
HG103 Brett Butler .50 1.25
HG104 Tim Wallach .25 .60
HG105 Wil Cordero .25 .60
HG106 Mark Whiten .25 .60
HG107 Bob Hamelin .25 .60
HG108 Rondell White .50 1.25
HG109 Devon White .50 1.25
HG110 Tony Tarasco .25 .60

1995 Score Hall of Gold You Trade Em

This skip-numbered five-card set was available only by redeeming the randomly inserted Hall of Gold Trade card inserted in second series packs of 1995 Score. The set features a selection of veterans that joined new teams prior to the 1995 season. The design and numbering of the cards parallel the regular Hall of Gold inserts.

HG71T Larry Walker .50 1.25
HG76T John Kruk .25 .60
HG77T Brian McRae .25 .60
HG93T David Cone .50 1.25
HG110T Tony Tarasco .25 .60
NNO Exp. Hall of Gold Trade Card .20 .50

1995 Score Rookie Dream Team

This 12-card set was randomly inserted in second series retail and hobby packs at a rate of one in 12. The cards are numbered with a "RDT" prefix.

COMPLETE SET (12) 30.00 60.00
RDT1 J.R. Phillips 1.00 2.50
RDT2 Alex Gonzalez 1.00 2.50
RDT3 Alex Rodriguez 8.00 20.00
RDT4 Jose Oliva 1.00 2.50
RDT5 Charles Johnson 2.00 5.00
RDT6 Shawn Green 2.00 5.00
RDT7 Brian Hunter 1.00 2.50
RDT8 Garret Anderson 2.00 5.00
RDT9 Julian Tavarez 1.00 2.50
RDT10 Jose Lima 1.00 2.50
RDT11 Armando Benitez 1.00 2.50
RDT12 Ricky Bottalico 1.00 2.50

1995 Score Rules

Randomly inserted in first series jumbo packs, this 30-card standard-size set features top big league players. The cards are numbered with an "SR" prefix.

COMPLETE SET (30) 50.00 120.00
*JUMBO'S: .5X TO 1.2X
JUMBOS ISSUED ONE PER COLLECTOR KIT
SR1 Ken Griffey Jr. 3.00 8.00
SR2 Frank Thomas 2.00 5.00
SR3 Mike Piazza 3.00 8.00
SR4 Jeff Bagwell 1.25 3.00
SR5 Alex Rodriguez 5.00 12.00
SR6 Albert Belle .75 2.00
SR7 Matt Williams .75 2.00
SR8 Roberto Alomar 1.25 3.00
SR9 Barry Bonds 6.00 15.00
SR10 Raul Mondesi .75 2.00
SR11 Jose Canseco 1.25 3.00
SR12 Kirby Puckett 2.00 5.00
SR13 Fred McGriff 1.25 3.00
SR14 Kenny Lofton .75 2.00
SR15 Greg Maddux 3.00 8.00
SR16 Juan Gonzalez .75 2.00
SR17 Cliff Floyd .75 2.00
SR18 Cal Ripken Jr. 6.00 15.00
SR19 Will Clark 1.25 3.00
SR20 Tim Salmon 1.25 3.00
SR21 Paul O'Neill 1.25 3.00
SR22 Jason Bere .40 1.00
SR23 Tony Gwynn 2.50 6.00
SR24 Manny Ramirez 1.25 3.00
SR25 Don Mattingly 5.00 12.00
SR26 Dave Justice .75 2.00
SR27 Javier Lopez .75 2.00
SR28 Ryan Klesko .75 2.00
SR29 Carlos Delgado .75 2.00
SR30 Mike Mussina 1.25 3.00

1996 Score

This set consists of 517 standard-size cards. These cards were issued in packs of 10 that retailed for 99 cents per pack. The fronts feature an action photo surrounded by white borders. The "Score 96" logo is in the upper left, while the player is identified on the bottom. The backs have season and career stats as well as a player photo and some text. A Cal Ripken tribute card was issued at a rate of 1 every 300 packs.

COMPLETE SET (517) 10.00 24.00
COMP. SERIES 1 (275) 5.00 12.00
COMP. SERIES 2 (242) 5.00 12.00
1 Will Clark .10 .30
2 Rich Becker .07 .20
3 Ryan Klesko .07 .20
4 Jim Edmonds .07 .20
5 Barry Larkin .10 .30
6 Jim Thome .10 .30
7 Raul Mondesi .07 .20
8 Don Mattingly .50 1.25
9 Jeff Conine .07 .20
10 Rickey Henderson .20 .50
11 Chad Curtis .07 .20
12 Darren Daulton .07 .20
13 Larry Walker .07 .20
14 Carlos Garcia .07 .20
15 Carlos Baerga .07 .20
16 Tony Gwynn .25 .60
17 Jon Nunnally .07 .20
18 Deion Sanders .10 .30
19 Mark Grace .10 .30
20 Alex Rodriguez .40 1.00
21 Frank Thomas .20 .50
22 Brian Jordan .07 .20
23 J.T. Snow .07 .20
24 Shawn Green .07 .20
25 Tim Wakefield .07 .20
26 Curtis Goodwin .07 .20
27 John Smoltz .10 .30
28 Devon White .07 .20
29 Brian L. Hunter .07 .20
30 Tim Salmon .10 .30
31 Rafael Palmeiro .10 .30
32 Bernard Gilkey .07 .20
33 John Valentin .07 .20
34 Randy Johnson .20 .50
35 Garret Anderson .07 .20
36 Rikkert Faneyte .07 .20
37 Ray Durham .07 .20
38 Bip Roberts .07 .20
39 Jaime Navarro .07 .20
40 Mark Johnson .07 .20
41 Darren Lewis .07 .20
42 Tyler Green .07 .20
43 Bill Pulsipher .07 .20
44 Jason Giambi .07 .20
45 Kevin Ritz .07 .20
46 Jack McDowell .07 .20
47 Felipe Lira .07 .20
48 Rico Brogna .07 .20
49 Terry Pendleton .07 .20
50 Rondell White .07 .20
51 Andre Dawson .07 .20
52 Kirby Puckett .20 .50
53 Wally Joyner .07 .20
54 B.J. Surhoff .07 .20
55 Randy Velarde .07 .20
56 Greg Vaughn .07 .20
57 Roberto Alomar .10 .30
58 David Justice .07 .20
59 Kevin Seitzer .07 .20
60 Cal Ripken .60 1.50
61 Ozzie Smith .30 .75
62 Mo Vaughn .07 .20
63 Ricky Bones .07 .20
64 Gary DiSarcina .07 .20
65 Matt Williams .07 .20
66 Wilson Alvarez .07 .20
67 Lenny Dykstra .07 .20
68 Brian McRae .07 .20
69 Todd Stottlemyre .07 .20
70 Bret Boone .07 .20
71 Sterling Hitchcock .07 .20
72 Albert Belle .07 .20
73 Todd Hundley .07 .20
74 Vinny Castilla .07 .20
75 Moises Alou .07 .20
76 Cecil Fielder .07 .20
77 Brad Radke .07 .20
78 Quilvio Veras .07 .20
79 Eddie Murray .20 .50
80 James Mouton .07 .20
81 Pat Listach .07 .20
82 Mark Gubicza .07 .20
83 Dave Winfield .07 .20
84 Fred McGriff .10 .30
85 Darryl Hamilton .07 .20
86 Jeffrey Hammonds .07 .20
87 Pedro Munoz .07 .20
88 Craig Biggio .10 .30
89 Cliff Floyd .07 .20
90 Tim Naehring .07 .20
91 Brett Butler .07 .20
92 Kevin Foster .07 .20
93 Pat Kelly .07 .20
94 John Smiley .07 .20
95 Terry Steinbach .07 .20
96 Orel Hershiser .07 .20
97 Darrin Fletcher .07 .20
98 Walt Weiss .07 .20
99 John Wetteland .07 .20
100 Alan Trammell .07 .20
101 Steve Avery .07 .20
102 Tony Eusebio .07 .20
103 Sandy Alomar Jr. .07 .20
104 Joe Girardi .07 .20
105 Rick Aguilera .07 .20
106 Tony Tarasco .07 .20
107 Chris Hammond .07 .20
108 Mike Macfarlane .07 .20
109 Doug Drabek .07 .20
110 Derek Bell .07 .20
111 Ed Sprague .07 .20
112 Todd Hollandsworth .07 .20
113 Otis Nixon .07 .20
114 Keith Lockhart .07 .20
115 Donovan Osborne .07 .20
116 Dave Magadan .07 .20
117 Edgar Martinez .10 .30
118 Chuck Carr .07 .20
119 J.R. Phillips .07 .20
120 Sean Bergman .07 .20
121 Andujar Cedeno .07 .20
122 Eric Young .07 .20
123 Al Martin .07 .20
124 Mark Lemke .07 .20
125 Jim Eisenreich .07 .20
126 Benito Santiago .07 .20
127 Ariel Prieto .07 .20
128 Jim Bullinger .07 .20
129 Russ Davis .07 .20
130 Jim Abbott .10 .30
131 Jason Isringhausen .07 .20
132 Carlos Perez .07 .20
133 David Segui .07 .20
134 Troy O'Leary .07 .20
135 Pat Meares .07 .20
136 Chris Hoiles .07 .20
137 Ismael Valdes .07 .20
138 Jose Oliva .07 .20
139 Carlos Delgado .07 .20
140 Tom Goodwin .07 .20
141 Bob Tewksbury .07 .20
142 Chris Gomez .07 .20
143 Jose Oquendo .07 .20
144 Mark Lewis .07 .20
145 Salomon Torres .07 .20
146 Luis Gonzalez .07 .20
147 Mark Carreon .07 .20
148 Lance Johnson .07 .20
149 Melvin Nieves .07 .20
150 Lee Smith .07 .20
151 Jacob Brumfield .07 .20
152 Armando Benitez .07 .20
153 Curt Schilling .07 .20
154 Javier Lopez .07 .20
155 Frank Rodriguez .07 .20
156 Alex Gonzalez .07 .20
157 Todd Worrell .07 .20
158 Benji Gil .07 .20
159 Greg Gagne .07 .20
160 Tom Henke .07 .20
161 Randy Myers .07 .20
162 Joey Cora .07 .20
163 Scott Ruffcorn .07 .20
164 W. VanLandingham .07 .20
165 Tony Phillips .07 .20
166 Eddie Williams .07 .20
167 Bobby Bonilla .07 .20
168 Denny Neagle .07 .20
169 Troy Percival .07 .20
170 Billy Ashley .07 .20
171 Andy Van Slyke .10 .30
172 Jose Offerman .07 .20
173 Mark Parent .07 .20
174 Edgardo Alfonzo .07 .20
175 Trevor Hoffman .07 .20
176 David Cone .07 .20
177 Dan Wilson .07 .20
178 Steve Ontiveros .07 .20
179 Dean Palmer .07 .20
180 Mike Kelly .07 .20
181 Jim Leyritz .07 .20
182 Ron Karkovice .07 .20
183 Kevin Brown .07 .20
184 Jose Valentin .07 .20
185 Jorge Fabregas .07 .20
186 Jose Mesa .07 .20
187 Brent Mayne .07 .20
188 Carl Everett .07 .20
189 Paul Sorrento .07 .20
190 Pete Schourek .07 .20
191 Scott Kamieniecki .07 .20
192 Roberto Hernandez .07 .20
193 Randy Johnson RR .10 .30
194 Greg Maddux RR .20 .50
195 Hideo Nomo RR .10 .30
196 David Cone RR .07 .20
197 Mike Mussina RR .07 .20
198 Andy Benes RR .07 .20
199 Kevin Appier RR .07 .20
200 John Smoltz RR .07 .20
201 John Wetteland RR .07 .20
202 Mark Wohlers RR .07 .20
203 Stan Belinda .07 .20
204 Brian Anderson .07 .20
205 Mike Devereaux .07 .20
206 Mark Wohlers .07 .20
207 Omar Vizquel .10 .30
208 Jose Rijo .07 .20
209 Willie Blair .07 .20
210 Jamie Moyer .07 .20
211 Craig Shipley .07 .20
212 Shane Reynolds .07 .20
213 Chad Fonville .07 .20
214 Jose Vizcaino .07 .20
215 Sid Fernandez .07 .20
216 Andy Ashby .07 .20
217 Frank Castillo .07 .20
218 Kevin Tapani .07 .20
219 Kent Mercker .07 .20
220 Karim Garcia .07 .20
221 Antonio Osuna .07 .20
222 Tim Unroe .07 .20
223 Johnny Damon .10 .30
224 LaTroy Hawkins .07 .20
225 Mariano Rivera .20 .50
226 Jose Alberro .07 .20
227 Angel Martinez .07 .20
228 Jason Schmidt .10 .30
229 Tony Clark .07 .20
230 Kevin Jordan UER .07 .20
Ricky Jordan pictured on both sides
231 Mark Thompson .07 .20
232 Jim Dougherty .07 .20
233 Roger Cedeno .07 .20
234 Ugueth Urbina .07 .20
235 Ricky Otero .07 .20
236 Mark Smith .07 .20
237 Brian Barber .07 .20
238 Kevin Flora .07 .20
239 Joe Rosselli .07 .20
240 Derek Jeter .50 1.25
241 Michael Tucker .07 .20
242 Ben Blomdahl .07 .20
243 Joe Vitiello .07 .20
244 Todd Steverson .07 .20
245 James Baldwin .07 .20
246 Alan Embree .07 .20
247 Shannon Penn .07 .20
248 Chris Stynes .07 .20
249 Oscar Munoz .07 .20
250 Jose Herrera .07 .20
251 Scott Sullivan .07 .20
252 Reggie Williams .07 .20
253 Mark Grudzielanek .07 .20
254 Steve Rodriguez .07 .20
255 Terry Bradshaw .07 .20
256 F.P. Santangelo .07 .20
257 Lyle Mouton .07 .20
258 George Williams .07 .20
259 Larry Thomas .07 .20
260 Rudy Pemberton .07 .20
261 Jim Pittsley .07 .20
262 Les Norman .07 .20
263 Ruben Rivera .07 .20
264 Cesar Devarez .07 .20
265 Greg Zaun .07 .20
266 Dustin Hermanson .07 .20
267 John Frascatore .07 .20
268 Joe Randa .07 .20
269 Jeff Bagwell CL .07 .20
270 Mike Piazza CL .20 .50
271 Dante Bichette CL .07 .20
272 Frank Thomas CL .10 .30
273 Ken Griffey Jr. CL .20 .50
274 Cal Ripken CL .30 .75
275 Greg Maddux CL .07 .20
Albert Belle
276 Greg Maddux .30 .75
277 Pedro Martinez .10 .30
278 Bobby Higginson .07 .20
279 Ray Lankford .07 .20
280 Shawon Dunston .07 .20
281 Gary Sheffield .07 .20
282 Ken Griffey Jr. .30 .75
283 Paul Molitor .07 .20
284 Kevin Appier .07 .20
285 Chuck Knoblauch .07 .20
286 Alex Fernandez .07 .20
287 Steve Finley .07 .20
288 Jeff Blauser .07 .20
289 Charles Johnson .07 .20
290 John Franco .07 .20
291 Mark Langston .07 .20
292 Bret Saberhagen .07 .20
293 John Mabry .07 .20
294 Ramon Martinez .07 .20
295 Mike Blowers .07 .20
296 Paul O'Neill .10 .30
297 Dave Nilsson .07 .20
298 Dante Bichette .07 .20
299 Marty Cordova .07 .20
300 Jay Bell .07 .20
301 Mike Mussina .10 .30
302 Ivan Rodriguez .10 .30
303 Jose Canseco .10 .30
304 Jeff Bagwell .10 .30
305 Manny Ramirez .10 .30
306 Dennis Martinez .07 .20
307 Charlie Hayes .07 .20
308 Joe Carter .07 .20
309 Travis Fryman .07 .20
310 Mark McGwire .50 1.25
311 Reggie Sanders UER .07 .20
Photo on front is John Roper
312 Julian Tavarez .07 .20
313 Jeff Montgomery .07 .20
314 Andy Benes .07 .20
315 John Jaha .07 .20
316 Jeff Kent .07 .20
317 Mike Piazza .30 .75
318 Erik Hanson .07 .20
319 Kenny Rogers .07 .20
320 Hideo Nomo .20 .50
321 Gregg Jefferies .07 .20
322 Chipper Jones .20 .50
323 Jay Buhner .07 .20
324 Dennis Eckersley .07 .20
325 Kenny Lofton .07 .20
326 Robin Ventura .07 .20
327 Tom Glavine .10 .30
328 Tim Salmon .10 .30
329 Andres Galarraga .07 .20
330 Hal Morris .07 .20
331 Brady Anderson .07 .20
332 Chili Davis .07 .20
333 Roger Clemens .40 1.00
334 Marquis Grissom .07 .20
335 Mike Greenwell UER .07 .20
Name spelled Jeff on Front
336 Sammy Sosa .20 .50
337 Ron Gant .07 .20
338 Ken Caminiti .07 .20
339 Danny Tartabull .07 .20
340 Barry Bonds .60 1.50
341 Ben McDonald .07 .20
342 Ruben Sierra .07 .20
343 Bernie Williams .10 .30
344 Wil Cordero .07 .20
345 Wade Boggs .10 .30
346 Gary Gaetti .07 .20
347 Greg Colbrunn .07 .20
348 Juan Gonzalez .07 .20
349 Marc Newfield .07 .20
350 Charles Nagy .07 .20
351 Robby Thompson .07 .20
352 Roberto Petagine .07 .20
353 Darryl Strawberry .07 .20
354 Tino Martinez .10 .30
355 Eric Karros .07 .20
356 Cal Ripken SS .30 .75
357 Cecil Fielder SS .07 .20
358 Kirby Puckett SS .10 .30
359 Jim Edmonds SS .07 .20
360 Matt Williams SS .07 .20
361 Alex Rodriguez SS .20 .50
362 Barry Larkin SS .07 .20
363 Rafael Palmeiro SS .07 .20
364 David Cone SS .07 .20
365 Roberto Alomar SS .07 .20
366 Eddie Murray SS .10 .30
367 Randy Johnson SS .10 .30
368 Ryan Klesko SS .07 .20
369 Raul Mondesi SS .07 .20
370 Mo Vaughn SS .07 .20
371 Will Clark SS .07 .20
372 Carlos Baerga SS .07 .20
373 Frank Thomas SS .10 .30
374 Larry Walker SS .07 .20
375 Garret Anderson SS .07 .20
376 Edgar Martinez SS .07 .20
377 Don Mattingly SS .25 .60
378 Tony Gwynn SS .10 .30
379 Albert Belle SS .07 .20
380 J.Isringhausen SS .07 .20
381 Ruben Rivera SS .07 .20
382 Johnny Damon SS .07 .20
383 Karim Garcia SS .07 .20
384 Derek Jeter SS .25 .60
385 David Justice SS .07 .20
386 Royce Clayton .07 .20
387 Mark Whiten .07 .20
388 Mickey Tettleton .07 .20
389 Steve Trachsel .07 .20
390 Danny Bautista .07 .20
391 Midre Cummings .07 .20
392 Scott Leius .07 .20
393 Manny Alexander .07 .20
394 Brent Gates .07 .20
395 Rey Sanchez .07 .20
396 Andy Pettitte .10 .30
397 Jeff Cirillo .07 .20
398 Kurt Abbott .07 .20
399 Lee Tinsley .07 .20
400 Paul Assenmacher .07 .20
401 Scott Erickson .07 .20
402 Todd Zeile .07 .20
403 Tom Pagnozzi .07 .20
404 Ozzie Guillen .07 .20
405 Jeff Frye .07 .20
406 Kirt Manwaring .07 .20
407 Chad Ogea .07 .20
408 Harold Baines .07 .20
409 Jason Bere .07 .20
410 Chuck Finley .07 .20
411 Jeff Fassero .07 .20
412 Joey Hamilton .07 .20
413 John Olerud .07 .20
414 Kevin Stocker .07 .20
415 Eric Anthony .07 .20
416 Aaron Sele .07 .20
417 Chris Bosio .07 .20
418 Michael Mimbs .07 .20
419 Orlando Miller .07 .20
420 Stan Javier .07 .20
421 Matt Mieske .07 .20
422 Jason Bates .07 .20
423 Orlando Merced .07 .20
424 John Flaherty .07 .20
425 Reggie Jefferson .07 .20
426 Scott Stahoviak .07 .20
427 John Burkett .07 .20
428 Rod Beck .07 .20
429 Bill Swift .07 .20
430 Scott Cooper .07 .20
431 Mel Rojas .07 .20
432 Todd Van Poppel .07 .20
433 Bobby Jones .07 .20
434 Mike Harkey .07 .20
435 Sean Berry .07 .20
436 Glenallen Hill .07 .20
437 Ryan Thompson .07 .20
438 Luis Alicea .07 .20
439 Esteban Loaiza .07 .20
440 Jeff Reboulet .07 .20
441 Vince Coleman .07 .20
442 Ellis Burks .07 .20
443 Allen Battle .07 .20
444 Jimmy Key .07 .20
445 Ricky Bottalico .07 .20
446 Delino DeShields .07 .20
447 Albie Lopez .07 .20
448 Mark Petkovsek .07 .20
449 Tim Raines .07 .20
450 Bryan Harvey .07 .20
451 Pat Hentgen .07 .20
452 Tim Laker .07 .20
453 Tom Gordon .07 .20
454 Phil Plantier .07 .20
455 Ernie Young .07 .20
456 Pete Harnisch .07 .20
457 Roberto Kelly .07 .20
458 Mark Portugal .07 .20
459 Mark Leiter .07 .20
460 Tony Pena .07 .20
461 Roger Pavlik .07 .20
462 Jeff King .07 .20
463 Bryan Rekar .07 .20
464 Al Leiter .07 .20
465 Phil Nevin .07 .20
466 Jose Lima .07 .20
467 Mike Stanley .07 .20
468 David McCarty .07 .20
469 Herb Perry .07 .20
470 Geronimo Berroa .07 .20
471 David Wells .07 .20
472 Vaughn Eshelman .07 .20
473 Greg Swindell .07 .20
474 Steve Sparks .07 .20
475 Luis Sojo .07 .20
476 Derrick May .07 .20
477 Joe Oliver .07 .20
478 Alex Arias .07 .20
479 Brad Ausmus .07 .20
480 Gabe White .07 .20
481 Pat Rapp .07 .20
482 Damon Buford .07 .20
483 Turk Wendell .07 .20
484 Jeff Brantley .07 .20
485 Curtis Leskanic .07 .20
486 Robb Nen .07 .20
487 Lou Whitaker .07 .20
488 Melido Perez .07 .20
489 Luis Polonia .07 .20
490 Scott Brosius .07 .20
491 Robert Perez .07 .20
492 Mike Sweeney RC .30 .75
493 Mark Loretta .07 .20
494 Alex Ochoa .07 .20
495 Matt Lawton RC .07 .20
496 Shawn Estes .07 .20
497 John Wasdin .07 .20
498 Marc Kroon .07 .20
499 Chris Snopek .07 .20
500 Jeff Suppan .07 .20
501 Terrell Wade .07 .20
502 Marvin Benard RC .07 .20
503 Chris Widger .07 .20
504 Quinton McCracken .07 .20
505 Bob Wolcott .07 .20
506 C.J. Nitkowski .07 .20
507 Aaron Ledesma .07 .20
508 Scott Hatteberg .07 .20
509 Jimmy Haynes .07 .20
510 Howard Battle .07 .20
511 Marty Cordova CL .07 .20
512 Randy Johnson CL .10 .30
513 Mo Vaughn CL .07 .20
514 Hideo Nomo CL .07 .20
515 Greg Maddux CL .20 .50
516 Barry Larkin CL .07 .20
517 Tom Glavine CL .07 .20
NNO Cal Ripken 2131 8.00 20.00

1996 Score All-Stars

Randomly inserted in second series jumbo packs at a rate of one in nine, this 20-card set was printed in rainbow holographic prismatic foil.

COMPLETE SET (20) 25.00 60.00
1 Frank Thomas 1.25 3.00
2 Albert Belle .50 1.25
3 Ken Griffey Jr. 2.00 5.00
4 Cal Ripken 4.00 10.00
5 Mo Vaughn .50 1.25
6 Matt Williams .50 1.25
7 Barry Bonds 4.00 10.00
8 Dante Bichette .50 1.25
9 Tony Gwynn 1.50 4.00
10 Greg Maddux 2.00 5.00
11 Randy Johnson 1.25 3.00
12 Hideo Nomo 1.25 3.00
13 Tim Salmon .75 2.00
14 Jeff Bagwell .75 2.00
15 Edgar Martinez .75 2.00
16 Reggie Sanders .50 1.25
17 Larry Walker .50 1.25
18 Chipper Jones 1.25 3.00
19 Manny Ramirez .75 2.00
20 Eddie Murray 1.25 3.00

1996 Score Big Bats

This 20-card set was randomly inserted in retail packs at a rate of approximately one in 31. The cards are numbered "X" of 20 in the upper left corner.

COMPLETE SET (20) 40.00 100.00
1 Cal Ripken 6.00 15.00
2 Ken Griffey Jr. 3.00 8.00
3 Frank Thomas 2.00 5.00
4 Jeff Bagwell 1.25 3.00
5 Mike Piazza 3.00 8.00
6 Barry Bonds 6.00 15.00
7 Matt Williams .75 2.00
8 Raul Mondesi .75 2.00
9 Tony Gwynn 2.50 6.00
10 Albert Belle .75 2.00
11 Manny Ramirez 1.25 3.00
12 Carlos Baerga .75 2.00
13 Mo Vaughn .75 2.00
14 Derek Bell .75 2.00
15 Larry Walker .75 2.00
16 Kenny Lofton .75 2.00
17 Edgar Martinez 1.25 3.00
18 Reggie Sanders .75 2.00
19 Eddie Murray 2.00 5.00
20 Chipper Jones 2.00 5.00

1996 Score Diamond Aces

This 30-card set features some of baseball's best players. These cards were inserted approximately one every eight jumbo packs.

COMPLETE SET (30)	50.00	120.00
1 Hideo Nomo	2.00	5.00
2 Brian L.Hunter	.75	2.00
3 Ray Durham	.75	2.00
4 Frank Thomas	2.00	5.00
5 Cal Ripken	6.00	15.00
6 Barry Bonds	6.00	15.00
7 Greg Maddux	3.00	8.00
8 Chipper Jones	2.00	5.00
9 Raul Mondesi	.75	2.00
10 Mike Piazza	3.00	8.00
11 Derek Jeter	5.00	12.00
12 Bill Pulsipher	.75	2.00
13 Larry Walker	.75	2.00
14 Ken Griffey Jr.	3.00	8.00
15 Alex Rodriguez	4.00	10.00
16 Manny Ramirez	1.25	3.00
17 Mo Vaughn	.75	2.00
18 Reggie Sanders	.75	2.00
19 Derek Bell	.75	2.00
20 Jim Edmonds	.75	2.00
21 Albert Belle	.75	2.00
22 Eddie Murray	2.00	5.00
23 Tony Gwynn	2.50	6.00
24 Jeff Bagwell	1.25	3.00
25 Carlos Baerga	.75	2.00
26 Matt Williams	.75	2.00
27 Garret Anderson	.75	2.00
28 Todd Hollandsworth	.75	2.00
29 Johnny Damon	.75	2.00
30 Tim Salmon	1.25	3.00

1996 Score Dream Team

This nine-card set was randomly inserted in approximately one in 72 packs. This set features a leading player at each position. The cards are numbered in the upper right as "X" of nine.

COMPLETE SET (9)	25.00	60.00
1 Cal Ripken	6.00	15.00
2 Frank Thomas	2.00	5.00
3 Carlos Baerga	.75	2.00
4 Matt Williams	.75	2.00
5 Mike Piazza	3.00	8.00
6 Barry Bonds	6.00	15.00
7 Ken Griffey Jr.	3.00	8.00
8 Manny Ramirez	1.25	3.00
9 Greg Maddux	3.00	8.00

1996 Score Dugout Collection

This set is a mini-parallel to the regular issue. Only 110 cards of each Series 1 and Series 2 were selected. Randomly inserted approximately one in every three packs, these cards have all gold foil printing that gives them a shiny copper cast. The words "Dugout Collection" are printed on the back.

COMP. SERIES 1 (110)	20.00	50.00
COMP. SERIES 2 (110)	20.00	50.00

*DUGOUT: 1.5X TO 4X BASIC
STATED ODDS 1:3 HOB/RET
*AP DUGOUT: 10X TO 25X BASIC
AP STATED ODDS 1:36 HOB/RET

1996 Score Dugout Collection Artist's Proofs

This set is a parallel to the Dugout Collection set. These cards are different from the regular Dugout Collection as they have the words Artist Proof printed on the front. Randomly inserted one in every 36 packs, this set was printed using Gold Rush all gold-foil card technology.

*STARS: 2.5X TO 6X BASIC DUGOUT

1996 Score Future Franchise

Randomly inserted in retail packs at a rate of one in 72, this 16-card set honors young stars of the game.

COMPLETE SET (16)	40.00	100.00
1 Jason Isringhausen	1.50	4.00
2 Chipper Jones	4.00	10.00
3 Derek Jeter	10.00	25.00
4 Alex Rodriguez	8.00	20.00
5 Alex Ochoa	1.50	4.00
6 Manny Ramirez	2.50	6.00
7 Johnny Damon	1.50	4.00
8 Ruben Rivera	1.50	4.00
9 Karim Garcia	1.50	4.00
10 Garret Anderson	1.50	4.00
11 Marty Cordova	1.50	4.00
12 Bill Pulsipher	1.50	4.00
13 Hideo Nomo	4.00	10.00
14 Marc Newfield	1.50	4.00
15 Charles Johnson	1.50	4.00
16 Raul Mondesi	1.50	4.00

1996 Score Gold Stars

Randomly inserted in packs at a rate of one in 15, this 30-card set features borderless color action player photos with a special sepia player cutout inserted behind a gold foil stamp designating the star player.

COMPLETE SET (30)	20.00	50.00
1 Ken Griffey Jr.	1.50	4.00
2 Frank Thomas	1.00	2.50
3 Reggie Sanders	.40	1.00
4 Tim Salmon	.60	1.50
5 Mike Piazza	1.50	4.00
6 Tony Gwynn	1.25	3.00
7 Gary Sheffield	.40	1.00
8 Matt Williams	.40	1.00
9 Bernie Williams	.60	1.50
10 Jason Isringhausen	.40	1.00
11 Albert Belle	.40	1.00
12 Chipper Jones	1.00	2.50
13 Edgar Martinez	.60	1.50
14 Barry Larkin	.60	1.50
15 Barry Bonds	3.00	8.00
16 Jeff Bagwell	.60	1.50
17 Greg Maddux	1.50	4.00
18 Mo Vaughn	.40	1.00
19 Ryan Klesko	.40	1.00
20 Sammy Sosa	1.00	2.50
21 Darren Daulton	.40	1.00
22 Ivan Rodriguez	.60	1.50
23 Dante Bichette	.40	1.00
24 Hideo Nomo	1.00	2.50
25 Cal Ripken	3.00	8.00
26 Rafael Palmeiro	.60	1.50
27 Larry Walker	.40	1.00
28 Carlos Baerga	.40	1.00
29 Randy Johnson	1.00	2.50
30 Manny Ramirez	.60	1.50

1996 Score Numbers Game

This 30-card set was inserted approximately one in every 15 packs. The cards are numbered as "X" of 30 in the upper left corner.

COMPLETE SET (30)	25.00	60.00
1 Cal Ripken	3.00	8.00
2 Frank Thomas	1.00	2.50
3 Ken Griffey Jr.	1.50	4.00
4 Mike Piazza	1.50	4.00
5 Barry Bonds	3.00	8.00
6 Greg Maddux	1.50	4.00
7 Jeff Bagwell	.60	1.50
8 Derek Bell	.40	1.00
9 Tony Gwynn	1.25	3.00
10 Hideo Nomo	1.00	2.50
11 Raul Mondesi	.40	1.00
12 Manny Ramirez	.60	1.50
13 Albert Belle	.40	1.00
14 Matt Williams	.40	1.00
15 Jim Edmonds	.40	1.00
16 Edgar Martinez	.60	1.50
17 Mo Vaughn	.40	1.00
18 Reggie Sanders	.40	1.00
19 Chipper Jones	1.00	2.50
20 Larry Walker	.40	1.00
21 Juan Gonzalez	.40	1.00
22 Kenny Lofton	.40	1.00
23 Don Mattingly	2.50	6.00
24 Ivan Rodriguez	.60	1.50
25 Randy Johnson	1.00	2.50
26 Derek Jeter	2.50	6.00
27 J.T. Snow	.40	1.00
28 Will Clark	.60	1.50
29 Rafael Palmeiro	.60	1.50
30 Alex Rodriguez	2.00	5.00

1996 Score Power Pace

Randomly inserted in retail packs at a rate of one in 31, this 18-card set features homerun hitters.

COMPLETE SET (18)	25.00	60.00
1 Mark McGwire	4.00	10.00
2 Albert Belle	.60	1.50
3 Jay Buhner	.60	1.50
4 Frank Thomas	1.50	4.00
5 Matt Williams	.60	1.50
6 Gary Sheffield	.60	1.50
7 Mike Piazza	2.50	6.00
8 Larry Walker	.60	1.50
9 Mo Vaughn	.60	1.50
10 Rafael Palmeiro	1.00	2.50
11 Dante Bichette	.60	1.50
12 Ken Griffey Jr.	2.50	6.00
13 Barry Bonds	5.00	12.00
14 Manny Ramirez	1.00	2.50
15 Sammy Sosa	1.50	4.00
16 Tim Salmon	1.00	2.50
17 Dave Justice	.60	1.50
18 Eric Karros	.60	1.50

1996 Score Reflextions

This 20-card set was randomly inserted approximately one in every 31 hobby packs. Two players per card are featured, a veteran player and a younger star playing the same position.

COMPLETE SET (20)	40.00	100.00
1 Cal Ripken Chipper Jones	6.00	15.00
2 Ken Griffey Jr. Alex Rodriguez	3.00	8.00
3 Frank Thomas Mo Vaughn	2.00	5.00
4 Kenny Lofton Brian L.Hunter	.75	2.00
5 Don Mattingly J.T.Snow	5.00	12.00
6 Manny Ramirez Raul Mondesi	1.25	3.00
7 Tony Gwynn Garret Anderson	2.50	6.00
8 Roberto Alomar Carlos Baerga	1.25	3.00
9 Andre Dawson Larry Walker	.75	2.00
10 Barry Larkin Derek Jeter	5.00	12.00
11 Barry Bonds Reggie Sanders	6.00	15.00
12 Mike Piazza Albert Belle	3.00	8.00
13 Wade Boggs Edgar Martinez	1.25	3.00
14 David Cone John Smoltz	.75	2.00
15 Will Clark Jeff Bagwell	1.25	3.00
16 Mark McGwire Cecil Fielder	5.00	12.00
17 Greg Maddux Mike Mussina	3.00	8.00
18 Randy Johnson Hideo Nomo	2.00	5.00
19 Jim Thome Dean Palmer	1.25	3.00
20 Chuck Knoblauch Craig Biggio	1.25	3.00

1996 Score Titanic Taters

Randomly inserted in hobby packs at a rate of one in 31, this 18-card set features long home run hitters.

COMPLETE SET (18)	30.00	80.00
1 Albert Belle	.75	2.00
2 Frank Thomas	2.00	5.00
3 Mo Vaughn	.75	2.00
4 Ken Griffey Jr.	3.00	8.00
5 Matt Williams	.75	2.00
6 Mark McGwire	5.00	12.00
7 Dante Bichette	.75	2.00
8 Tim Salmon	1.25	3.00
9 Jeff Bagwell	1.25	3.00
10 Rafael Palmeiro	1.25	3.00
11 Mike Piazza	3.00	8.00
12 Cecil Fielder	.75	2.00
13 Larry Walker	.75	2.00
14 Sammy Sosa	2.00	5.00
15 Manny Ramirez	1.25	3.00
16 Gary Sheffield	.75	2.00
17 Barry Bonds	6.00	15.00
18 Jay Buhner	.75	2.00

1997 Score

The 1997 Score set has a total of 550 cards. With cards 1-330 distributed in series one packs and cards 331-550 in series two packs. The 10-card Series one packs and the 12-card Series two packs carried a suggested retail price of $.99 each and were distributed exclusively to retail outlets. The fronts feature color player action photos in a white border. The backs carry player information and career statistics. The Hideki Irabu card (551A and B) is shortprinted (about twice as tough to pull as a basic card). One final note on the Irabu card, in the retail packs and factory sets, the card text is in English. In the Hobby Reserve packs, text is in Japanese. Notable Rookie Cards include Brian Giles.

COMPLETE SET (551)	15.00	40.00
COMP.FACT.SET (551)	15.00	40.00
COMP.SERIES 1 (330)	6.00	15.00
COMP.SERIES 2 (221)	10.00	25.00
1 Jeff Bagwell	.10	.30
2 Mickey Tettleton	.07	.20
3 Johnny Damon	.10	.30
4 Jeff Conine	.07	.20
5 Bernie Williams	.10	.30
6 Will Clark	.10	.30
7 Ryan Klesko	.07	.20
8 Cecil Fielder	.07	.20
9 Paul Wilson	.07	.20
10 Gregg Jefferies	.07	.20
11 Chili Davis	.07	.20
12 Albert Belle	.07	.20
13 Ken Hill	.07	.20
14 Cliff Floyd	.07	.20
15 Jaime Navarro	.07	.20
16 Ismael Valdes	.07	.20
17 Jeff King	.07	.20
18 Chris Bosio	.07	.20
19 Reggie Sanders	.07	.20
20 Darren Daulton	.07	.20
21 Ken Caminiti	.07	.20
22 Mike Piazza	.30	.75
23 Chad Mottola	.07	.20
24 Darin Erstad	.07	.20
25 Dante Bichette	.07	.20
26 Frank Thomas	.20	.50
27 Ben McDonald	.07	.20
28 Raul Casanova	.07	.20
29 Kevin Ritz	.07	.20
30 Garret Anderson	.07	.20
31 Jason Kendall	.07	.20
32 Billy Wagner	.07	.20
33 Dave Justice	.07	.20
34 Marty Cordova	.07	.20
35 Derek Jeter	.50	1.25
36 Trevor Hoffman	.07	.20
37 Geronimo Berroa	.07	.20
38 Walt Weiss	.07	.20
39 Kirt Manwaring	.07	.20
40 Alex Gonzalez	.07	.20
41 Sean Berry	.07	.20
42 Kevin Appier	.07	.20
43 Rusty Greer	.07	.20
44 Pete Incaviglia	.07	.20
45 Rafael Palmeiro	.10	.30
46 Eddie Murray	.20	.50
47 Moises Alou	.07	.20
48 Mark Lewis	.07	.20
49 Hal Morris	.07	.20
50 Edgar Renteria	.07	.20
51 Rickey Henderson	.20	.50
52 Pat Listach	.07	.20
53 John Wasdin	.07	.20
54 James Baldwin	.07	.20
55 Brian Jordan	.07	.20
56 Edgar Martinez	.10	.30
57 Wil Cordero	.07	.20
58 Danny Tartabull	.07	.20
59 Keith Lockhart	.07	.20
60 Rico Brogna	.07	.20
61 Ricky Bottalico	.07	.20
62 Terry Pendleton	.07	.20
63 Bret Boone	.07	.20
64 Charlie Hayes	.07	.20
65 Marc Newfield	.07	.20
66 Sterling Hitchcock	.07	.20
67 Roberto Alomar	.10	.30
68 John Jaha	.07	.20
69 Greg Colbrunn	.07	.20
70 Sal Fasano	.07	.20
71 Brooks Kieschnick	.07	.20
72 Pedro Martinez	.10	.30
73 Kevin Elster	.07	.20
74 Ellis Burks	.07	.20
75 Chuck Finley	.07	.20
76 John Olerud	.07	.20
77 Jay Bell	.07	.20
78 Allen Watson	.07	.20
79 Darryl Strawberry	.07	.20
80 Orlando Miller	.07	.20
81 Jose Herrera	.07	.20
82 Andy Pettitte	.10	.30
83 Juan Guzman	.07	.20
84 Alan Benes	.07	.20
85 Jack McDowell	.07	.20
86 Ugueth Urbina	.07	.20
87 Rocky Coppinger	.07	.20
88 Jeff Cirillo	.07	.20
89 Tom Glavine	.10	.30
90 Robby Thompson	.07	.20
91 Barry Bonds	.60	1.50
92 Carlos Delgado	.07	.20
93 Mo Vaughn	.07	.20
94 Ryne Sandberg	.30	.75
95 Alex Rodriguez	.30	.75
96 Brady Anderson	.07	.20
97 Scott Brosius	.07	.20
98 Dennis Eckersley	.07	.20
99 Brian McRae	.07	.20
100 Rey Ordonez	.07	.20
101 John Valentin	.07	.20
102 Brett Butler	.07	.20
103 Eric Karros	.07	.20
104 Harold Baines	.07	.20
105 Javier Lopez	.07	.20
106 Alan Trammell	.07	.20
107 Jim Thome	.10	.30
108 Frank Rodriguez	.07	.20
109 Bernard Gilkey	.07	.20
110 Reggie Jefferson	.07	.20
111 Scott Stahoviak	.07	.20
112 Steve Gibralter	.07	.20
113 Todd Hollandsworth	.07	.20
114 Ruben Rivera	.07	.20
115 Dennis Martinez	.07	.20
116 Mariano Rivera	.20	.50
117 John Smoltz	.10	.30
118 John Mabry	.07	.20
119 Tom Gordon	.07	.20
120 Alex Ochoa	.07	.20
121 Jamey Wright	.07	.20
122 Dave Nilsson	.07	.20
123 Bobby Bonilla	.07	.20
124 Al Leiter	.07	.20
125 Rick Aguilera	.07	.20
126 Jeff Brantley	.07	.20
127 Kevin Brown	.07	.20
128 George Arias	.07	.20
129 Darren Oliver	.07	.20
130 Bill Pulsipher	.07	.20
131 Roberto Hernandez	.07	.20
132 Delino DeShields	.07	.20
133 Mark Grudzielanek	.07	.20
134 John Wetteland	.07	.20
135 Carlos Baerga	.07	.20
136 Paul Sorrento	.07	.20
137 Leo Gomez	.07	.20
138 Andy Ashby	.07	.20
139 Julio Franco	.07	.20
140 Brian Hunter	.07	.20
141 Jermaine Dye	.07	.20
142 Tony Clark	.07	.20
143 Ruben Sierra	.07	.20
144 Donovan Osborne	.07	.20
145 Mark McLemore	.07	.20
146 Terry Steinbach	.07	.20
147 Bob Wells	.07	.20
148 Chan Ho Park	.07	.20
149 Tim Salmon	.10	.30
150 Paul O'Neill	.10	.30
151 Cal Ripken	.60	1.50
152 Wally Joyner	.07	.20
153 Omar Vizquel	.10	.30
154 Mike Mussina	.10	.30
155 Andres Galarraga	.07	.20
156 Ken Griffey Jr.	.30	.75
157 Kenny Lofton	.07	.20
158 Ray Durham	.07	.20
159 Hideo Nomo	.20	.50
160 Ozzie Guillen	.07	.20
161 Roger Pavlik	.07	.20
162 Manny Ramirez	.10	.30
163 Mark Lemke	.07	.20
164 Mike Stanley	.07	.20
165 Chuck Knoblauch	.07	.20
166 Kimera Bartee	.07	.20
167 Wade Boggs	.10	.30
168 Jay Buhner	.07	.20
169 Eric Young	.07	.20
170 Jose Canseco	.10	.30
171 Dwight Gooden	.07	.20
172 Fred McGriff	.10	.30
173 Sandy Alomar Jr.	.07	.20
174 Andy Benes	.07	.20
175 Dean Palmer	.07	.20
176 Larry Walker	.07	.20
177 Charles Nagy	.07	.20
178 David Cone	.07	.20
179 Mark Grace	.10	.30
180 Robin Ventura	.07	.20
181 Roger Clemens	.40	1.00
182 Bobby Witt	.07	.20
183 Vinny Castilla	.07	.20
184 Gary Sheffield	.07	.20
185 Dan Wilson	.07	.20
186 Roger Cedeno	.07	.20
187 Mark McGwire	.50	1.25
188 Darren Bragg	.07	.20
189 Quinton McCracken	.07	.20
190 Randy Myers	.07	.20
191 Jeromy Burnitz	.07	.20
192 Randy Johnson	.20	.50
193 Chipper Jones	.20	.50
194 Greg Vaughn	.07	.20
195 Travis Fryman	.07	.20
196 Tim Naehring	.07	.20
197 B.J. Surhoff	.07	.20
198 Juan Gonzalez	.07	.20
199 Terrell Wade	.07	.20
200 Jeff Frye	.07	.20
201 Joey Cora	.07	.20
202 Raul Mondesi	.07	.20
203 Ivan Rodriguez	.10	.30
204 Armando Reynoso	.07	.20
205 Jeffrey Hammonds	.07	.20
206 Darren Dreifort	.07	.20
207 Kevin Seitzer	.07	.20
208 Tino Martinez	.10	.30
209 Jim Bruske	.07	.20
210 Jeff Suppan	.07	.20
211 Mark Carreon	.07	.20
212 Wilson Alvarez	.07	.20
213 John Burkett	.07	.20
214 Tony Phillips	.07	.20
215 Greg Maddux	.30	.75
216 Mark Whiten	.07	.20
217 Curtis Pride	.07	.20
218 Lyle Mouton	.07	.20
219 Todd Hundley	.07	.20
220 Greg Gagne	.07	.20
221 Rich Amaral	.07	.20
222 Tom Goodwin	.07	.20
223 Chris Hoiles	.07	.20
224 Jayhawk Owens	.07	.20
225 Kenny Rogers	.07	.20
226 Mike Greenwell	.07	.20
227 Mark Wohlers	.07	.20
228 Henry Rodriguez	.07	.20
229 Robert Perez	.07	.20
230 Jeff Kent	.07	.20
231 Darryl Hamilton	.07	.20
232 Alex Fernandez	.07	.20
233 Ron Karkovice	.07	.20
234 Jimmy Haynes	.07	.20
235 Craig Biggio	.10	.30
236 Ray Lankford	.07	.20
237 Lance Johnson	.07	.20
238 Matt Williams	.07	.20
239 Chad Curtis	.07	.20
240 Mark Thompson	.07	.20
241 Jason Giambi	.07	.20
242 Barry Larkin	.10	.30
243 Paul Molitor	.07	.20
244 Sammy Sosa	.20	.50
245 Kevin Tapani	.07	.20
246 Marquis Grissom	.07	.20
247 Joe Carter	.07	.20
248 Ramon Martinez	.07	.20
249 Tony Gwynn	.25	.60
250 Andy Fox	.07	.20
251 Troy O'Leary	.07	.20
252 Warren Newson	.07	.20
253 Troy Percival	.07	.20
254 Jamie Moyer	.07	.20
255 Danny Graves	.07	.20
256 David Wells	.07	.20
257 Todd Zeile	.07	.20
258 Raul Ibanez	.07	.20
259 Tyler Houston	.07	.20
260 LaTroy Hawkins	.07	.20
261 Joey Hamilton	.07	.20
262 Mike Sweeney	.07	.20
263 Brant Brown	.07	.20
264 Pat Hentgen	.07	.20
265 Mark Johnson	.07	.20
266 Robb Nen	.07	.20
267 Justin Thompson	.07	.20
268 Ron Gant	.07	.20
269 Jeff D'Amico	.07	.20
270 Shawn Estes	.07	.20
271 Derek Bell	.07	.20
272 Fernando Valenzuela	.07	.20
273 Tom Pagnozzi	.07	.20
274 John Burke	.07	.20
275 Ed Sprague	.07	.20
276 F.P. Santangelo	.07	.20
277 Todd Greene	.07	.20
278 Butch Huskey	.07	.20
279 Steve Finley	.07	.20
280 Eric Davis	.07	.20
281 Shawn Green	.07	.20
282 Al Martin	.07	.20
283 Michael Tucker	.07	.20
284 Shane Reynolds	.07	.20
285 Matt Mieske	.07	.20
286 Jose Rosado	.07	.20
287 Mark Langston	.07	.20
288 Ralph Milliard	.07	.20
289 Mike Lansing	.07	.20
290 Scott Servais	.07	.20
291 Royce Clayton	.07	.20
292 Mike Grace	.07	.20
293 James Mouton	.07	.20
294 Charles Johnson	.07	.20
295 Gary Gaetti	.07	.20
296 Kevin Mitchell	.07	.20
297 Carlos Garcia	.07	.20
298 Desi Relaford	.07	.20
299 Jason Thompson	.07	.20
300 Osvaldo Fernandez	.07	.20
301 Fernando Vina	.07	.20
302 Jose Offerman	.07	.20
303 Yamil Benitez	.07	.20
304 J.T. Snow	.07	.20
305 Rafael Bournigal	.07	.20
306 Jason Isringhausen	.07	.20
307 Bobby Higginson	.07	.20
308 Nerio Rodriguez RC	.07	.20
309 Brian Giles RC	.40	1.00
310 Andruw Jones	.10	.30
311 Tony Graffanino	.07	.20
312 Arquimedez Pozo	.07	.20
313 Jermaine Allensworth	.07	.20
314 Jeff Darwin	.07	.20
315 George Williams	.07	.20
316 Karim Garcia	.07	.20
317 Trey Beamon	.07	.20
318 Mac Suzuki	.07	.20
319 Robin Jennings	.07	.20
320 Danny Patterson	.07	.20
321 Damon Mashore	.07	.20
322 Wendell Magee	.07	.20
323 Dax Jones	.07	.20
324 Todd Walker	.07	.20
325 Marvin Benard	.07	.20
326 Mike Cameron	.07	.20
327 Marcus Jensen	.07	.20
328 Eddie Murray CL	.10	.30
329 Paul Molitor CL	.07	.20
330 Todd Hundley CL	.07	.20
331 Norm Charlton	.07	.20
332 Bruce Ruffin	.07	.20
333 John Wetteland	.07	.20
334 Marquis Grissom	.07	.20
335 Sterling Hitchcock	.07	.20
336 John Olerud	.07	.20
337 David Wells	.07	.20
338 Chili Davis	.07	.20
339 Mark Lewis	.07	.20
340 Kenny Lofton	.07	.20

341 Alex Fernandez .07 .20
342 Ruben Sierra .07 .20
343 Delino DeShields .07 .20
344 John Wasdin .07 .20
345 Dennis Martinez .07 .20
346 Kevin Elster .07 .20
347 Bobby Bonilla .07 .20
348 Jaime Navarro .07 .20
349 Chad Curtis .07 .20
350 Terry Steinbach .07 .20
351 Ariel Prieto .07 .20
352 Jeff Kent .07 .20
353 Carlos Garcia .07 .20
354 Mark Whiten .07 .20
355 Todd Zeile .07 .20
356 Eric Davis .07 .20
357 Greg Colbrunn .07 .20
358 Moises Alou .07 .20
359 Allen Watson .07 .20
360 Jose Canseco .10 .30
361 Matt Williams .07 .20
362 Jeff King .07 .20
363 Darryl Hamilton .07 .20
364 Mark Clark .07 .20
365 J.T. Snow .07 .20
366 Kevin Mitchell .07 .20
367 Orlando Miller .07 .20
368 Rico Brogna .07 .20
369 Mike James .07 .20
370 Brad Ausmus .07 .20
371 Darryl Kile .07 .20
372 Edgardo Alfonzo .07 .20
373 Julian Tavarez .07 .20
374 Darren Lewis .07 .20
375 Steve Karsay .07 .20
376 Lee Stevens .07 .20
377 Albie Lopez .07 .20
378 Orel Hershiser .07 .20
379 Lee Smith .07 .20
380 Rick Helling .07 .20
381 Carlos Perez .07 .20
382 Tony Tarasco .07 .20
383 Melvin Nieves .07 .20
384 Benji Gil .07 .20
385 Devon White .07 .20
386 Armando Benitez .07 .20
387 Bill Swift .07 .20
388 John Smiley .07 .20
389 Midre Cummings .07 .20
390 Tim Belcher .07 .20
391 Tim Raines .07 .20
392 Todd Worrell .07 .20
393 Quilvio Veras .07 .20
394 Matt Lawton .07 .20
395 Aaron Sele .07 .20
396 Bip Roberts .07 .20
397 Denny Neagle .07 .20
398 Tyler Green .07 .20
399 Hipolito Pichardo .07 .20
400 Scott Erickson .07 .20
401 Bobby Jones .07 .20
402 Jim Edmonds .07 .20
403 Chad Ogea .07 .20
404 Cal Eldred .07 .20
405 Pat Listach .07 .20
406 Todd Stottlemyre .07 .20
407 Phil Nevin .07 .20
408 Otis Nixon .07 .20
409 Billy Ashley .07 .20
410 Jimmy Key .07 .20
411 Mike Timlin .07 .20
412 Joe Vitiello .07 .20
413 Rondell White .07 .20
414 Jeff Fassero .07 .20
415 Rex Hudler .07 .20
416 Curt Schilling .07 .20
417 Rich Becker .07 .20
418 W.Van Landingham .07 .20
419 Chris Snopek .07 .20
420 David Segui .07 .20
421 Eddie Murray .20 .50
422 Shane Andrews .07 .20
423 Gary DiSarcina .07 .20
424 Brian Hunter .07 .20
425 Willie Greene .07 .20
426 Felipe Crespo .07 .20
427 Jason Bates .07 .20
428 Albert Belle .07 .20
429 Rey Sanchez .07 .20
430 Roger Clemens .40 1.00
431 Deion Sanders .10 .30
432 Ernie Young .07 .20
433 Jay Bell .07 .20
434 Jeff Blauser .07 .20
435 Lenny Dykstra .07 .20
436 Chuck Carr .07 .20
437 Russ Davis .07 .20
438 Carl Everett .07 .20
439 Damion Easley .07 .20
440 Pat Kelly .07 .20
441 Pat Rapp .07 .20
442 Dave Justice .07 .20
443 Graeme Lloyd .07 .20
444 Damon Buford .07 .20
445 Jose Valentin .07 .20
446 Jason Schmidt .07 .20
447 Dave Martinez .07 .20
448 Danny Tartabull .07 .20
449 Jose Vizcaino .07 .20
450 Steve Avery .07 .20
451 Mike Devereaux .07 .20
452 Jim Eisenreich .07 .20
453 Mark Leiter .07 .20
454 Roberto Kelly .07 .20
455 Benito Santiago .07 .20
456 Steve Trachsel .07 .20
457 Gerald Williams .07 .20
458 Pete Schourek .07 .20
459 Esteban Loaiza .07 .20
460 Mel Rojas .07 .20
461 Tim Wakefield .07 .20
462 Tony Fernandez .07 .20
463 Doug Drabek .07 .20
464 Joe Girardi .07 .20
465 Mike Bordick .07 .20
466 Jim Leyritz .07 .20
467 Erik Hanson .07 .20
468 Michael Tucker .07 .20
469 Tony Womack RC .07 .20
470 Doug Glanville .07 .20
471 Rudy Pemberton .07 .20
472 Keith Lockhart .07 .20
473 Nomar Garciaparra .30 .75
474 Scott Rolen .10 .30
475 Jason Dickson .07 .20
476 Glendon Rusch .07 .20
477 Todd Walker .07 .20
478 Dmitri Young .07 .20
479 Rod Myers .07 .20
480 Wilton Guerrero .07 .20
481 Jorge Posada .10 .30
482 Brant Brown .07 .20
483 Bubba Trammell RC .07 .20
484 Jose Guillen .07 .20
485 Scott Spiezio .07 .20
486 Bob Abreu .10 .30
487 Chris Holt .07 .20
488 Deivi Cruz RC .07 .20
489 Vladimir Guerrero .20 .50
490 Julio Santana .07 .20
491 Ray Montgomery RC .07 .20
492 Kevin Orie .07 .20
493 Todd Hundley GY .07 .20
494 Tim Salmon GY .07 .20
495 Albert Belle GY .07 .20
496 Manny Ramirez GY .07 .20
497 Rafael Palmeiro GY .07 .20
498 Juan Gonzalez GY .07 .20
499 Ken Griffey Jr. GY .20 .50
500 Andruw Jones GY .10 .30
501 Mike Piazza GY .20 .50
502 Jeff Bagwell GY .07 .20
503 Bernie Williams GY .07 .20
504 Barry Bonds GY .30 .75
505 Ken Caminiti GY .07 .20
506 Darin Erstad GY .07 .20
507 Alex Rodriguez GY .20 .50
508 Frank Thomas GY .10 .30
509 Chipper Jones GY .10 .30
510 Mo Vaughn GY .07 .20
511 Mark McGwire GY .25 .60
512 Fred McGriff GY .07 .20
513 Jay Buhner GY .07 .20
514 Jim Thome GY .07 .20
515 Gary Sheffield GY .07 .20
516 Dean Palmer GY .07 .20
517 Henry Rodriguez GY .07 .20
518 Andy Pettitte RF .07 .20
519 Mike Mussina RF .07 .20
520 Greg Maddux RF .20 .50
521 John Smoltz RF .07 .20
522 Hideo Nomo RF .07 .20
523 Troy Percival RF .07 .20
524 John Wetteland RF .07 .20
525 Roger Clemens RF .20 .50
526 Charles Nagy RF .07 .20
527 Mariano Rivera RF .10 .30
528 Tom Glavine RF .07 .20
529 Randy Johnson RF .10 .30
530 J.Isringhausen RF .07 .20
531 Alex Fernandez RF .07 .20
532 Kevin Brown RF .07 .20
533 Chuck Knoblauch TG .07 .20
534 Rusty Greer TG .07 .20
535 Tony Gwynn TG .10 .30
536 Ryan Klesko TG .07 .20
537 Ryne Sandberg TG .20 .50
538 Barry Larkin TG .07 .20
539 Will Clark TG .07 .20
540 Kenny Lofton TG .07 .20
541 Paul Molitor TG .07 .20
542 Roberto Alomar TG .07 .20
543 Rey Ordonez TG .07 .20
544 Jason Giambi TG .07 .20
545 Derek Jeter TG .25 .60
546 Cal Ripken TG .30 .75
547 Ivan Rodriguez TG .07 .20
548 Ken Griffey Jr. CL .20 .50
549 Frank Thomas CL .10 .30
550 Mike Piazza CL .20 .50
551A Hideki Irabu SP 1.00 2.50
551B Hideki Irabu Japenese SP 1.00 2.50

1997 Score Artist's Proofs White Border

Artist's Proofs White Border cards were randomly inserted exclusively into Score Series 1 retail packs. The cards share the similar "Artist's Proof" logo as seen on the more commonly traded Showcase Series Artist's Proofs. Unlike the silver-foiled Showcase Series Artist's Proofs, however, the White Border cards have plain white stock card fronts - making them easy to misidentify with a basic issue Score card. Please note that Series 2 Artist Proofs do not exist.

*STARS: 12.5X TO 30X BASIC CARDS
*ROOKIES: 4X TO 10X BASIC CARDS

1997 Score Premium Stock

A special Premium Stock version of the base series one set was produced exclusively for hobby outlets. The cards parallel the regular issue set except for a grey border, thicker card stock and a prominent gold foil "Premium Stock" logo on front. The cards were distributed in Premium Stock hobby packs. Second series Premium Stock cards were called "Hobby Reserve."

COMPLETE SET (551) 30.00 80.00
COMP.SERIES 1 (330) 15.00 40.00
COMP.SERIES 2 (221) 15.00 40.00
*STARS: .75X TO 2X BASIC CARDS
*ROOKIES: .6X TO 1.5X BASIC CARDS
*IRABU: .4X TO 1X BASIC IRABU

1997 Score Reserve Collection

Randomly inserted in second series hobby reserve packs only at a rate of one in 11, this set is parallel to the regular second series set. The cards are printed on thick 20 pt. foil card stock with screen printing for a raised ink effect. A large grey "Reserve Collection" logo is printed on each card back.

*STARS: 5X TO 12X BASIC CARDS
*ROOKIES: 2.5X TO 6X BASIC CARDS
*IRABU: 1.5X TO 3X BASIC IRABU

1997 Score Showcase Series

Randomly inserted in first series packs at a rate of one in seven hobby packs, one in two jumbo packs, one in four magazine and one in seven retail packs, and second series packs at a rate of one in five hobby packs and one in seven retail packs, cards from this set are silver-coated parallel versions of the regular Score set.

*STARS: 3X TO 8X BASIC CARDS
*ROOKIES: 1.5X TO 4X BASIC CARDS
*IRABU: .5X TO 1.2X BASIC IRABU

1997 Score Showcase Series Artist's Proofs

Randomly inserted in first series hobby and retail packs at a rate of one in 35, and second series hobby 1:23 and second series retail 1:35, cards from this 551-card set are parallel to the more common Showcase Series set. The cards are printed on holographic laminated card stock with a prismatic foil background and stamped with an Artist's Proof logo on front.

*STARS: 10X TO 25X BASIC CARDS
*ROOKIES: 4X TO 10X BASIC CARDS
*IRABU: 2X TO 5X BASIC IRABU

1997 Score All-Star Fanfest

This 20-card insert set features players that were involved in the 1996 All-Star game. The cards were available at a rate of 1:29 in special retail Score I boxes.

COMPLETE SET (20) 40.00 80.00
1 Frank Thomas 1.50 4.00
2 Jeff Bagwell 2.00 5.00
3 Chuck Knoblauch .75 2.00
4 Ryne Sandberg 2.00 5.00
5 Alex Rodriguez 4.00 10.00
6 Chipper Jones 3.00 8.00
7 Jim Thome 1.25 3.00
8 Ken Caminiti .60 1.50
9 Albert Belle .60 1.50
10 Tony Gwynn 3.00 8.00
11 Ken Griffey Jr. 4.00 10.00
12 Andruw Jones 2.50 6.00
13 Juan Gonzalez 1.25 3.00
14 Brian Jordan .60 1.50
15 Ivan Rodriguez 2.00 5.00
16 Mike Piazza 4.00 10.00
17 Andy Pettitte .75 2.00
18 John Smoltz 1.25 3.00
19 John Wetteland .60 1.50
20 Mark Wohlers .40 1.00

1997 Score Blast Masters

Randomly inserted in second series packs at a rate of 1:35 (retail) and 1:23 (hobby reserve), this 18-card set features color player photos on a gold prismatic foil card.

COMPLETE SET (18) 40.00 100.00
1 Mo Vaughn .75 2.00
2 Mark McGwire 5.00 12.00
3 Juan Gonzalez .75 2.00
4 Albert Belle .75 2.00
5 Barry Bonds 6.00 15.00
6 Ken Griffey Jr. 3.00 8.00
7 Andruw Jones 1.25 3.00
8 Chipper Jones 2.00 5.00
9 Mike Piazza 3.00 8.00
10 Jeff Bagwell 1.25 3.00
11 Dante Bichette .75 2.00
12 Alex Rodriguez 3.00 8.00
13 Gary Sheffield .75 2.00
14 Ken Caminiti .75 2.00
15 Sammy Sosa 2.00 5.00
16 Vladimir Guerrero 2.00 5.00
17 Brian Jordan .75 2.00
18 Tim Salmon 1.25 3.00

1997 Score Franchise

Randomly inserted in series one hobby packs only at a rate of one in 72, this nine-card set honors superstar players for their irreplaceable contribution to their team. The fronts display sepia player portraits on a white baseball replica background. The backs carry an action player photo with a sentence about the player which explains why he was selected for this set.

COMPLETE SET (9) 8.00 20.00
*GLOWING: 1.25X TO 3X BASIC FRANCHISE
GLOW.SER.1 ODDS 1:240H/R, 1:79J, 1:120M
1 Ken Griffey Jr. .75 2.00
2 John Smoltz .30 .75
3 Cal Ripken 1.50 4.00
4 Chipper Jones .50 1.25
5 Mike Piazza .75 2.00
6 Albert Belle .20 .50
7 Frank Thomas .50 1.25
8 Sammy Sosa .50 1.25
9 Roberto Alomar .30 .75

1997 Score Heart of the Order

Randomly inserted in packs at a rate of 1:23 (retail) and 1:15 (hobby reserve), this 36-card set features color photos of players on six teams with a panorama of the stadium in the background. Each team's three cards form one collectible unit. Eighteen of these cards are found in retail packs, and eighteen in Hobby Reserve packs.

COMPLETE SET (36) 40.00 100.00
1 Will Clark 1.00 2.50
2 Ivan Rodriguez 1.00 2.50
3 Juan Gonzalez .60 1.50
4 Frank Thomas 1.50 4.00
5 Albert Belle .60 1.50
6 Robin Ventura .60 1.50
7 Alex Rodriguez 2.50 6.00
8 Jay Buhner .60 1.50
9 Ken Griffey Jr. 2.50 6.00
10 Rafael Palmeiro 1.00 2.50
11 Roberto Alomar 1.00 2.50
12 Cal Ripken 5.00 12.00
13 Manny Ramirez 1.00 2.50
14 Matt Williams .60 1.50
15 Jim Thome 1.00 2.50
16 Derek Jeter 4.00 10.00
17 Wade Boggs 1.00 2.50
18 Bernie Williams 1.00 2.50
19 Chipper Jones 1.50 4.00
20 Andruw Jones 1.00 2.50
21 Ryan Klesko .60 1.50
22 Mike Piazza 2.50 6.00
23 Wilton Guerrero .60 1.50
24 Raul Mondesi .60 1.50
25 Tony Gwynn 2.00 5.00
26 Greg Vaughn .60 1.50
27 Ken Caminiti .60 1.50
28 Brian Jordan .60 1.50
29 Ron Gant .60 1.50
30 Dmitri Young .60 1.50
31 Darin Erstad .60 1.50
32 Tim Salmon 1.00 2.50
33 Jim Edmonds .60 1.50
34 Chuck Knoblauch .60 1.50
35 Paul Molitor .60 1.50
36 Todd Walker .60 1.50

1997 Score Highlight Zone

Randomly inserted in series one hobby packs only at a rate of one in 35, this 18-card set honors those mega-stars who have the incredible ability to consistently make the highlight films. The set is printed on thicker card stock with special foil stamping and a dot matrix holographic background.

COMPLETE SET (18) 60.00 150.00
1 Frank Thomas 2.50 6.00
2 Ken Griffey Jr. 4.00 10.00
3 Mo Vaughn 1.00 2.50
4 Albert Belle 1.00 2.50
5 Mike Piazza 4.00 10.00
6 Barry Bonds 8.00 20.00
7 Greg Maddux 4.00 10.00
8 Sammy Sosa 2.50 6.00
9 Jeff Bagwell 1.50 4.00
10 Alex Rodriguez 4.00 10.00
11 Chipper Jones 2.50 6.00
12 Brady Anderson 1.00 2.50
13 Ozzie Smith 1.00 2.50
14 Edgar Martinez 1.50 4.00
15 Cal Ripken 8.00 20.00
16 Ryan Klesko 1.00 2.50
17 Randy Johnson 2.50 6.00
18 Eddie Murray 2.50 6.00

1997 Score Pitcher Perfect

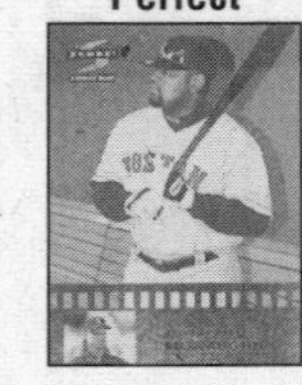

Randomly inserted in series one packs at a rate of one in 23, this 15-card set features players photographed by Randy Johnson in unique poses and foil stamping. The backs carry player information.

COMPLETE SET (15) 2.00 5.00
1 Cal Ripken .60 1.50
2 Alex Rodriguez .30 .75
3 Alex Rodriguez Cal Ripken 1.25 3.00
4 Edgar Martinez .10 .30
5 Ivan Rodriguez .10 .30
6 Mark McGwire .50 1.25
7 Tim Salmon .10 .30
8 Chili Davis .07 .20
9 Joe Carter .07 .20
10 Frank Thomas .20 .50
11 Will Clark .10 .30
12 Mo Vaughn .07 .20
13 Wade Boggs .10 .30
14 Ken Griffey Jr. .30 .75
15 Randy Johnson .20 .50

1997 Score Stand and Deliver

Randomly inserted in series two packs at a rate of 1:71 (retail) and 1:47 (hobby reserve), this 24-card set features color player photos printed on silver foil card stock. The set is broken into six separate 4-card groupings. Groups contain players from the following teams: 1-4 (Braves), 5-8 (Mariners), 9-12 (Yankees), 13-16 (Dodgers), 17-20 (Indians) and 21-24 (Wild Card). The four players featured within the Wild Card group are from "lesser" teams not given a shot at winning the World Series. Each of these cards, unlike cards 1-20, has a "Wild Card" logo stamped on front. Collectors were then supposed to gather up the particular group that won the 1997 World Series, in this case - the Florida Marlins. Since none of the featured teams won, the 4-card Wild Card group was designated as the winner. The winning cards could then be mailed into Pinnacle for a special gold upgrade version of the set, framed in glass.

COMPLETE SET (24) 100.00 250.00
1 Andruw Jones 2.50 6.00
2 Greg Maddux 6.00 15.00
3 Chipper Jones 4.00 10.00
4 John Smoltz 2.50 6.00
5 Ken Griffey Jr. 6.00 15.00
6 Alex Rodriguez 6.00 15.00
7 Jay Buhner 1.50 4.00
8 Randy Johnson 4.00 10.00
9 Derek Jeter 10.00 25.00
10 Andy Pettitte 2.50 6.00
11 Bernie Williams 2.50 6.00
12 Mariano Rivera 4.00 10.00
13 Mike Piazza 6.00 15.00
14 Hideo Nomo 4.00 10.00
15 Raul Mondesi 1.50 4.00
16 Todd Hollandsworth 1.50 4.00
17 Manny Ramirez 2.50 6.00
18 Jim Thome 2.50 6.00
19 Dave Justice 1.50 4.00
20 Matt Williams 1.50 4.00
21 Juan Gonzalez W 1.50 4.00
22 Jeff Bagwell W 2.50 6.00
23 Cal Ripken W 12.50 30.00
24 Frank Thomas W 4.00 10.00

1997 Score Stellar Season

Randomly inserted in series one pre-priced magazine packs only at a rate of one in 35, this 18-card set features players who had a star season. The cards are printed using dot matrix holographic printing.

COMPLETE SET (18) 25.00 60.00
1 Juan Gonzalez .60 1.50
2 Chuck Knoblauch .60 1.50
3 Jeff Bagwell 1.00 2.50
4 John Smoltz 1.00 2.50
5 Mark McGwire 4.00 10.00
6 Ken Griffey Jr. 2.50 6.00
7 Frank Thomas 1.50 4.00
8 Alex Rodriguez 2.50 6.00
9 Mike Piazza 2.50 6.00
10 Albert Belle .60 1.50
11 Roberto Alomar 1.00 2.50
12 Sammy Sosa 1.50 4.00
13 Mo Vaughn .60 1.50
14 Brady Anderson .60 1.50
15 Henry Rodriguez .60 1.50
16 Eric Young .60 1.50
17 Gary Sheffield .60 1.50
18 Ryan Klesko .60 1.50

1997 Score Titanic Taters

Randomly inserted in series one retail packs only at a rate of one in 35, this 18-card set honors the long-ball ability of some of the league's top sluggers and uses dot matrix holographic printing.

COMPLETE SET (18) 50.00 120.00
1 Mark McGwire 6.00 15.00
2 Mike Piazza 4.00 10.00
3 Ken Griffey Jr. 4.00 10.00
4 Juan Gonzalez 1.00 2.50
5 Frank Thomas 2.50 6.00
6 Albert Belle 1.00 2.50
7 Sammy Sosa 2.50 6.00
8 Jeff Bagwell 1.50 4.00
9 Todd Hundley 1.00 2.50
10 Ryan Klesko 1.00 2.50
11 Brady Anderson 1.00 2.50
12 Mo Vaughn 1.00 2.50
13 Jay Buhner 1.00 2.50
14 Chipper Jones 2.50 6.00
15 Barry Bonds 8.00 20.00
16 Gary Sheffield 1.00 2.50
17 Alex Rodriguez 4.00 10.00
18 Cecil Fielder 1.00 2.50

1998 Score

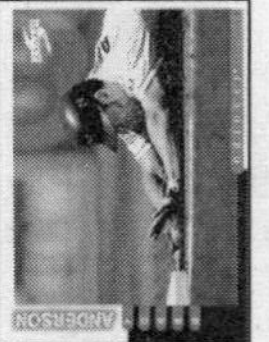

This 270-card set was distributed in 10-card packs exclusively to retail outlets with a suggested retail price of $.99. The fronts feature color player photos in a thin white border. The backs carry player information and statistics. In addition, two unnumbered checklist cards were created. The first card was available only in regular issue packs and provided listings for the standard 270-card set. A blank-backed checklist card was randomly seeded exclusively into All-Star Edition packs (released about three months after the regular packs went live). This checklist card provided listings only for the three insert sets exclusively distributed in All-Star Edition packs (First Pitch, Loaded Lineup and New Season).

COMPLETE SET (270) 15.00 40.00
1 Andruw Jones .10 .30
2 Dan Wilson .07 .20
3 Hideo Nomo .20 .50
4 Chuck Carr .07 .20
5 Barry Bonds .60 1.50
6 Jack McDowell .07 .20
7 Albert Belle .07 .20
8 Francisco Cordova .07 .20
9 Greg Maddux .30 .75
10 Alex Rodriguez .30 .75
11 Steve Avery .07 .20
12 Chuck McElroy .07 .20
13 Larry Walker .07 .20
14 Hideki Irabu .07 .20
15 Roberto Alomar .10 .30
16 Neifi Perez .07 .20
17 Jim Thome .10 .30
18 Rickey Henderson .20 .50
19 Andres Galarraga .07 .20
20 Jeff Fassero .07 .20
21 Kevin Young .07 .20
22 Derek Jeter .50 1.25
23 Andy Benes .07 .20
24 Mike Piazza .30 .75
25 Todd Stottlemyre .07 .20
26 Michael Tucker .07 .20
27 Denny Neagle .07 .20
28 Javier Lopez .07 .20
29 Aaron Sele .07 .20
30 Ryan Klesko .07 .20
31 Dennis Eckersley .07 .20
32 Quinton McCracken .07 .20
33 Brian Anderson .07 .20
34 Ken Griffey Jr. .30 .75
35 Shawn Estes .07 .20
36 Tim Wakefield .07 .20
37 Jimmy Key .07 .20
38 Jeff Bagwell .10 .30
39 Edgardo Alfonzo .07 .20
40 Mike Cameron .07 .20
41 Mark McGwire .50 1.25
42 Tino Martinez .10 .30
43 Cal Ripken .60 1.50
44 Curtis Goodwin .07 .20
45 Bobby Ayala .07 .20
46 Sandy Alomar Jr. .07 .20
47 Bobby Jones .07 .20
48 Omar Vizquel .10 .30
49 Roger Clemens .40 1.00
50 Tony Gwynn .25 .60
51 Chipper Jones .20 .50
52 Ron Coomer .07 .20
53 Dmitri Young .07 .20
54 Brian Giles .07 .20
55 Steve Finley .07 .20
56 David Cone .07 .20
57 Andy Pettitte .10 .30
58 Wilton Guerrero .07 .20
59 Deion Sanders .10 .30
60 Carlos Delgado .07 .20
61 Jason Giambi .07 .20
62 Ozzie Guillen .07 .20
63 Jay Bell .07 .20
64 Barry Larkin .10 .30
65 Sammy Sosa .20 .50
66 Bernie Williams .10 .30
67 Terry Steinbach .07 .20
68 Scott Rolen .10 .30
69 Melvin Nieves .07 .20
70 Craig Biggio .10 .30
71 Todd Greene .07 .20
72 Greg Gagne .07 .20
73 Shigetoshi Hasegawa .07 .20
74 Mark McLemore .07 .20
75 Darren Bragg .07 .20
76 Brett Butler .07 .20
77 Ron Gant .07 .20
78 Mike Difelice RC .07 .20
79 Charles Nagy .07 .20
80 Scott Hatteberg .07 .20
81 Brady Anderson .07 .20
82 Jay Buhner .07 .20
83 Todd Hollandsworth .07 .20
84 Geronimo Berroa .07 .20
85 Jeff Suppan .07 .20
86 Pedro Martinez .10 .30
87 Roger Cedeno .07 .20
88 Ivan Rodriguez .10 .30
89 Jaime Navarro .07 .20
90 Chris Hoiles .07 .20
91 Nomar Garciaparra .30 .75
92 Rafael Palmeiro .10 .30
93 Darin Erstad .07 .20
94 Kenny Lofton .07 .20
95 Mike Timlin .07 .20
96 Chris Clemons .07 .20
97 Vinny Castilla .07 .20
98 Charlie Hayes .07 .20
99 Lyle Mouton .07 .20
100 Jason Dickson .07 .20
101 Justin Thompson .07 .20
102 Pat Kelly .07 .20
103 Chan Ho Park .07 .20
104 Ray Lankford .07 .20
105 Frank Thomas .20 .50
106 Jermaine Allensworth .07 .20
107 Doug Drabek .07 .20
108 Todd Hundley .07 .20
109 Carl Everett .07 .20
110 Edgar Martinez .10 .30
111 Robin Ventura .07 .20
112 John Wetteland .07 .20
113 Mariano Rivera .20 .50
114 Jose Rosado .07 .20
115 Ken Caminiti .07 .20
116 Paul O'Neill .10 .30
117 Tim Salmon .10 .30
118 Eduardo Perez .07 .20
119 Mike Jackson .07 .20
120 John Smoltz .10 .30
121 Brant Brown .07 .20
122 John Mabry .07 .20
123 Chuck Knoblauch .07 .20
124 Reggie Sanders .07 .20
125 Ken Hill .07 .20
126 Mike Mussina .10 .30
127 Chad Curtis .07 .20
128 Todd Worrell .07 .20
129 Chris Widger .07 .20
130 Damon Mashore .07 .20
131 Kevin Brown .10 .30
132 Bip Roberts .07 .20
133 Tim Naehring .07 .20
134 Dave Martinez .07 .20
135 Jeff Blauser .07 .20
136 David Justice .07 .20
137 Dave Hollins .07 .20
138 Pat Hentgen .07 .20
139 Darren Daulton .07 .20
140 Ramon Martinez .07 .20
141 Raul Casanova .07 .20
142 Tom Glavine .10 .30
143 J.T. Snow .07 .20
144 Tony Graffanino .07 .20
145 Randy Johnson .20 .50
146 Orlando Merced .07 .20
147 Jeff Juden .07 .20
148 Darryl Kile .07 .20
149 Ray Durham .07 .20
150 Alex Fernandez .07 .20
151 Joey Cora .07 .20
152 Royce Clayton .07 .20
153 Randy Myers .07 .20
154 Charles Johnson .07 .20
155 Alan Benes .07 .20
156 Mike Bordick .07 .20
157 Heathcliff Slocumb .07 .20
158 Roger Bailey .07 .20
159 Reggie Jefferson .07 .20
160 Ricky Bottalico .07 .20
161 Scott Erickson .07 .20
162 Matt Williams .07 .20
163 Robb Nen .07 .20
164 Matt Stairs .07 .20
165 Ismael Valdes .07 .20
166 Lee Stevens .07 .20
167 Gary DiSarcina .07 .20
168 Brad Radke .07 .20
169 Mike Lansing .07 .20
170 Armando Benitez .07 .20
171 Mike James .07 .20
172 Russ Davis .07 .20
173 Lance Johnson .07 .20
174 Joey Hamilton .07 .20
175 John Valentin .07 .20
176 David Segui .07 .20
177 David Wells .07 .20
178 Delino DeShields .07 .20
179 Eric Karros .07 .20
180 Jim Leyritz .07 .20
181 Raul Mondesi .07 .20
182 Travis Fryman .07 .20
183 Todd Zeile .07 .20
184 Brian Jordan .07 .20
185 Rey Ordonez .07 .20
186 Jim Edmonds .07 .20
187 Terrell Wade .07 .20
188 Marquis Grissom .07 .20
189 Chris Snopek .07 .20
190 Shane Reynolds .07 .20
191 Jeff Frye .07 .20
192 Paul Sorrento .07 .20
193 James Baldwin .07 .20
194 Brian McRae .07 .20
195 Fred McGriff .10 .30
196 Troy Percival .07 .20
197 Rich Amaral .07 .20
198 Juan Guzman .07 .20
199 Cecil Fielder .07 .20
200 Willie Blair .07 .20
201 Chili Davis .07 .20
202 Gary Gaetti .07 .20
203 B.J. Surhoff .07 .20
204 Steve Cooke .07 .20
205 Chuck Finley .07 .20
206 Jeff Kent .07 .20
207 Ben McDonald .07 .20
208 Jeffrey Hammonds .07 .20
209 Tom Goodwin .07 .20
210 Billy Ashley .07 .20
211 Wil Cordero .07 .20
212 Shawon Dunston .07 .20
213 Tony Phillips .07 .20
214 Jamie Moyer .07 .20
215 John Jaha .07 .20
216 Troy O'Leary .07 .20
217 Brad Ausmus .07 .20
218 Garret Anderson .07 .20
219 Wilson Alvarez .07 .20
220 Kent Mercker .07 .20
221 Wade Boggs .10 .30
222 Mark Wohlers .07 .20
223 Kevin Appier .07 .20
224 Tony Fernandez .07 .20
225 Ugueth Urbina .07 .20
226 Gregg Jefferies .07 .20
227 Mo Vaughn .07 .20
228 Arthur Rhodes .07 .20
229 Jorge Fabregas .07 .20
230 Mark Gardner .07 .20
231 Shane Mack .07 .20
232 Jorge Posada .10 .30
233 Jose Cruz Jr. .07 .20
234 Paul Konerko .07 .20
235 Derrek Lee .10 .30
236 Steve Woodard .07 .20
237 Todd Dunwoody .07 .20
238 Fernando Tatis .07 .20
239 Jacob Cruz .07 .20
240 Pokey Reese .07 .20
241 Mark Kotsay .07 .20
242 Matt Morris .07 .20
243 Antone Williamson .07 .20
244 Ben Grieve .07 .20
245 Ryan McGuire .07 .20
246 Lou Collier .07 .20
247 Shannon Stewart .07 .20
248 Brett Tomko .07 .20
249 Bobby Estalella .07 .20
250 Livan Hernandez .07 .20
251 Todd Helton .10 .30
252 Jaret Wright .07 .20
253 Darryl Hamilton IM .07 .20
254 Stan Javier IM .07 .20
255 Glenallen Hill IM .07 .20
256 Mark Gardner IM .07 .20
257 Cal Ripken IM .30 .75
258 Mike Mussina IM .07 .20
259 Mike Piazza IM .20 .50
260 Sammy Sosa IM .10 .30
261 Todd Hundley IM .07 .20
262 Eric Karros IM .07 .20
263 Denny Neagle IM .07 .20
264 Jeromy Burnitz IM .07 .20
265 Greg Maddux IM .20 .50
266 Tony Clark IM .07 .20
267 Vladimir Guerrero IM .10 .30
268 Cal Ripken CL UER .30 .75
269 Ken Griffey Jr. CL .20 .50
270 Mark McGwire CL .25 .60
NNO CL Regular Issue .07 .20
NNO CL All-Star Edition .10 .30

1998 Score Showcase Series

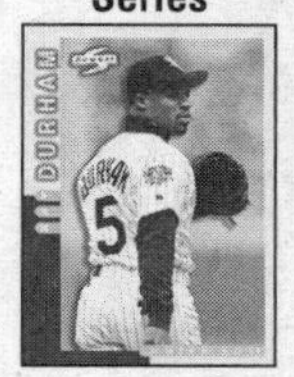

Randomly inserted in packs at the rate of one in seven, this 160-card set is an all silver-foil partial parallel rendition of the base set.

*SHOWCASE: 2X TO 5X BASIC CARDS
STATED ODDS 1:7

1998 Score Showcase Series Artist's Proofs

Randomly inserted in packs at the rate of one in 35, this 160-card set is a partial parallel to the base set and features color player photos printed on full prismatic foil with the "Artist Proof" stamp on the fronts.

*STARS: 1.5X TO 4X BASIC SHOWCASE
STATED ODDS 1:35

1998 Score All Score Team

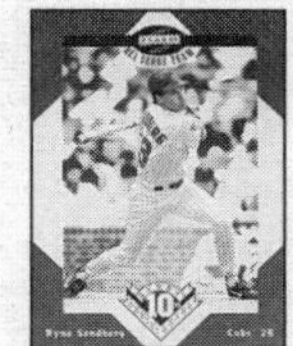

Randomly inserted in packs at the rate of one in 35, this 20-card set features color player images on a metallic foil background. The backs carry a small player head photo with information stating why the player was selected to this appear in this set.

COMPLETE SET (20) 40.00 100.00
1 Mike Piazza 3.00 8.00
2 Ivan Rodriguez 1.25 3.00
3 Frank Thomas 2.00 5.00
4 Mark McGwire 5.00 12.00
5 Ryne Sandberg 2.00 5.00
6 Roberto Alomar 1.25 3.00
7 Cal Ripken 6.00 15.00
8 Barry Larkin 1.25 3.00
9 Paul Molitor 2.00 5.00
10 Travis Fryman .75 2.00
11 Kirby Puckett 4.00 10.00
12 Tony Gwynn 2.50 6.00
13 Ken Griffey Jr. 3.00 8.00
14 Juan Gonzalez 2.00 5.00
15 Barry Bonds 6.00 15.00
16 Andruw Jones 1.25 3.00
17 Roger Clemens 4.00 10.00
18 Randy Johnson 2.00 5.00
19 Greg Maddux 3.00 8.00
20 Dennis Eckersley .75 2.00

1998 Score All-Score Team Gold Jones Autograph

This special autographed card was created as a prize for Pinnacle's 1998 "Score with Score" hobby shop promotion. Dealers that ordered 1998 Score 1 baseball direct from Pinnacle or through one of their distributors were automatically entered into Pinnacle's hobby shop locator program. In December of 1997, all eligible shops were mailed a "Score with Score" contest ballot box and collector entry forms. Over the next several months, store customers could then fill out and submit forms. In the Spring of 1998, 600 lucky collectors were randomly selected winners. 100 people won actual Interleague game-used baseballs and 500 people won this special Andruw Jones autographed All-Score Team Gold card. The card is easy to differentiate from the more common All-Score Team inserts by it's bold gold (rather than silver) foil front and Jones' black ink signature.

1 Andruw Jones Gold AU/500 * 20.00 50.00

1998 Score Complete Players

Randomly inserted in packs at the rate of one in 23, this 30-card set features three photos of each of the ten listed players with full holographic foil stamping.

COMPLETE SET (30) 60.00 150.00
*GOLD: .4X TO 1X BASIC COMP.PLAY.
GOLD: RANDOM IN SCORE TEAM SETS
1A Ken Griffey Jr. 2.50 6.00
2A Mark McGwire 4.00 10.00
3A Derek Jeter 4.00 10.00
4A Cal Ripken 5.00 12.00
5A Mike Piazza 2.50 6.00
6A Darin Erstad .60 1.50
7A Frank Thomas 1.50 4.00
8A Andruw Jones 1.00 2.50
9A Nomar Garciaparra 2.50 6.00
10A Manny Ramirez 1.50 4.00

1998 Score First Pitch

This 20 card insert set features star players anxiously awaiting opening day. The player's name is at top with the "First Pitch" words on the bottom of the card. These cards were inserted one every 11 All-Star Edition packs.

COMPLETE SET (20) 25.00 60.00
1 Ken Griffey Jr. 1.50 4.00
2 Frank Thomas 1.00 2.50
3 Alex Rodriguez 1.50 4.00
4 Cal Ripken 3.00 8.00
5 Chipper Jones 1.00 2.50
6 Juan Gonzalez 1.00 2.50
7 Derek Jeter 2.50 6.00
8 Mike Piazza 1.50 4.00
9 Andruw Jones .60 1.50
10 Nomar Garciaparra 1.50 4.00
11 Barry Bonds 3.00 8.00
12 Jeff Bagwell .60 1.50
13 Scott Rolen .60 1.50
14 Hideo Nomo 1.00 2.50
15 Roger Clemens 2.00 5.00
16 Mark McGwire 2.50 6.00
17 Greg Maddux 1.50 4.00
18 Albert Belle .40 1.00
19 Ivan Rodriguez .60 1.50
20 Mo Vaughn .40 1.00

1998 Score Andruw Jones Icon Order Card

This one-card set features a white bordered color photo of Andruw Jones kneeling with his right arm resting on his bat. The card was always inserted on the top of the prepriced 1998 Score 27-card blister packs. The backs carry instructions on how to order a Pinnacle Icon display.

1 Andruw Jones .40 1.00

1998 Score Loaded Lineup

This 10-card set was inserted one every 45 Score All-Star Edition packs. The cards feature a player for each position and the cards are printed on all-foil micro etched cards.

COMPLETE SET (10) 25.00 60.00
LL1 Chuck Knoblauch .75 2.00
LL2 Tony Gwynn 2.50 6.00
LL3 Frank Thomas 2.00 5.00
LL4 Ken Griffey Jr. 3.00 8.00
LL5 Mike Piazza 3.00 8.00
LL6 Barry Bonds 6.00 15.00
LL7 Cal Ripken 6.00 15.00
LL8 Paul Molitor 2.00 5.00
LL9 Nomar Garciaparra 3.00 8.00
LL10 Greg Maddux 3.00 8.00

1998 Score New Season

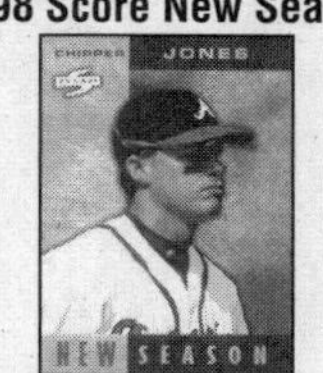

This 15 card insert set features a mix of young and veteran players waiting for the new season to begin. The players photo take up most of the borderless cards with his name on top and the words "New Season" on the bottom.

COMPLETE SET (15) 20.00 50.00
NS1 Kenny Lofton .75 2.00
NS2 Nomar Garciaparra 2.50 6.00
NS3 Todd Helton 1.00 2.50
NS4 Miguel Tejada 1.25 3.00
NS5 Jaret Wright .60 1.50
NS6 Alex Rodriguez 2.50 6.00
NS7 Vladimir Guerrero 1.25 3.00
NS8 Ken Griffey Jr. 3.00 8.00
NS9 Ben Grieve .60 1.50
NS10 Travis Lee .60 1.50
NS11 Jose Cruz Jr. .60 1.50
NS12 Paul Konerko .75 2.00
NS13 Frank Thomas 1.25 3.00
NS14 Chipper Jones 1.25 3.00
NS15 Cal Ripken 5.00 12.00

1998 Score Rookie Traded

The 1998 Score Rookie and Traded set was issued in one series totalling 270 cards. The 10-card packs retail for $.99 each. The set contains the subset: Spring Training (253-267). Cards numbered one through 50 were inserted one per pack making them short prints compared to the other cards in the set. Paul Konerko signed 500 cards which were also randomly seeded into packs. Notable Rookie Cards include Magglio Ordonez.

COMPLETE SET (270) 15.00 40.00
COMMON SP (1-50) .10 .30
COMMON CARD (51-270) .07 .20
COMMON RC (51-270) .07 .20
1 Tony Clark .10 .30
2 Juan Gonzalez .10 .30
3 Frank Thomas .30 .75
4 Greg Maddux .50 1.25
5 Barry Larkin .20 .50
6 Derek Jeter .75 2.00
7 Randy Johnson .30 .75
8 Roger Clemens .60 1.50
9 Tony Gwynn .40 1.00
10 Barry Bonds .75 2.00
11 Jim Edmonds .10 .30
12 Bernie Williams .20 .50
13 Ken Griffey Jr. .50 1.25
14 Tim Salmon .20 .50
15 Mo Vaughn .10 .30
16 David Justice .10 .30
17 Jose Cruz Jr. .10 .30
18 Andruw Jones .20 .50
19 Sammy Sosa .30 .75
20 Jeff Bagwell .20 .50
21 Scott Rolen .20 .50
22 Darin Erstad .10 .30
23 Andy Pettitte .20 .50
24 Mike Mussina .20 .50
25 Mark McGwire .75 2.00
26 Hideo Nomo .30 .75
27 Chipper Jones .30 .75
28 Cal Ripken 1.00 2.50
29 Chuck Knoblauch .10 .30
30 Alex Rodriguez .50 1.25
31 Jim Thome .20 .50
32 Mike Piazza .50 1.25
33 Ivan Rodriguez .20 .50
34 Roberto Alomar .20 .50
35 Nomar Garciaparra .50 1.25
36 Albert Belle .10 .30
37 Vladimir Guerrero .30 .75
38 Raul Mondesi .10 .30
39 Larry Walker .10 .30
40 Manny Ramirez .20 .50
41 Tino Martinez .20 .50
42 Craig Biggio .20 .50
43 Jay Buhner .10 .30
44 Kenny Lofton .10 .30
45 Pedro Martinez .20 .50
46 Edgar Martinez .20 .50
47 Gary Sheffield .10 .30
48 Jose Guillen .10 .30
49 Ken Caminiti .10 .30
50 Bobby Higginson .10 .30
51 Alan Benes .07 .20
52 Shawn Green .07 .20
53 Ron Coomer .07 .20
54 Charles Nagy .07 .20
55 Steve Karsay .07 .20
56 Matt Morris .07 .20
57 Bobby Jones .07 .20
58 Jason Kendall .07 .20
59 Jeff Conine .07 .20
60 Joe Girardi .07 .20
61 Mark Kotsay .07 .20
62 Eric Karros .07 .20
63 Bartolo Colon .07 .20
64 Mariano Rivera .20 .50
65 Alex Gonzalez .07 .20
66 Scott Spiezio .07 .20
67 Luis Castillo .07 .20
68 Joey Cora .07 .20
69 Mark McLemore .07 .20
70 Reggie Jefferson .07 .20
71 Lance Johnson .07 .20
72 Damian Jackson .07 .20
73 Jeff D'Amico .07 .20
74 David Ortiz .30 .75
75 J.T. Snow .07 .20
76 Todd Hundley .07 .20
77 Billy Wagner .07 .20
78 Vinny Castilla .07 .20
79 Ismael Valdes .07 .20
80 Neifi Perez .07 .20
81 Derek Bell .07 .20
82 Ryan Klesko .07 .20
83 Rey Ordonez .07 .20
84 Carlos Garcia .07 .20
85 Curt Schilling .07 .20
86 Robin Ventura .07 .20
87 Pat Hentgen .07 .20
88 Glendon Rusch .07 .20
89 Hideki Irabu .07 .20
90 Antone Williamson .07 .20
91 Denny Neagle .07 .20
92 Kevin Orie .07 .20
93 Reggie Sanders .07 .20
94 Brady Anderson .07 .20
95 Andy Benes .07 .20
96 John Valentin .07 .20
97 Bobby Bonilla .07 .20
98 Walt Weiss .07 .20
99 Robin Jennings .07 .20
100 Marty Cordova .07 .20
101 Brad Ausmus .07 .20
102 Brian Rose .07 .20
103 Calvin Maduro .07 .20
104 Raul Casanova .07 .20
105 Jeff King .07 .20
106 Sandy Alomar Jr. .07 .20
107 Tim Naehring .07 .20
108 Mike Cameron .07 .20
109 Omar Vizquel .10 .30
110 Brad Radke .07 .20
111 Jeff Fassero .07 .20
112 Deivi Cruz .07 .20
113 Dave Hollins .07 .20
114 Dean Palmer .07 .20
115 Esteban Loaiza .07 .20
116 Brian Giles .07 .20
117 Steve Finley .07 .20
118 Jose Canseco .10 .30
119 Al Martin .07 .20
120 Eric Young .07 .20
121 Curtis Goodwin .07 .20
122 Ellis Burks .07 .20
123 Mike Hampton .07 .20
124 Lou Collier .07 .20
125 John Olerud .07 .20
126 Ramon Martinez .07 .20
127 Todd Dunwoody .07 .20
128 Jermaine Allensworth .07 .20
129 Eduardo Perez .07 .20
130 Dante Bichette .07 .20
131 Edgar Renteria .07 .20
132 Bob Abreu .07 .20
133 Rondell White .07 .20
134 Michael Coleman .07 .20
135 Jason Giambi .07 .20
136 Brant Brown .07 .20
137 Michael Tucker .07 .20
138 Dave Nilsson .07 .20
139 Benito Santiago .07 .20
140 Ray Durham .07 .20
141 Jeff Kent .07 .20
142 Matt Stairs .07 .20
143 Kevin Young .07 .20
144 Eric Davis .07 .20
145 John Wetteland .07 .20
146 Esteban Yan RC .10 .30
147 Wilton Guerrero .07 .20
148 Moises Alou .07 .20
149 Edgardo Alfonzo .07 .20
150 Andy Ashby .07 .20
151 Todd Walker .07 .20
152 Jermaine Dye .07 .20
153 Brian Hunter .07 .20
154 Shawn Estes .07 .20
155 Bernard Gilkey .07 .20
156 Tony Womack .07 .20
157 John Smoltz .10 .30
158 Delino DeShields .07 .20
159 Jacob Cruz .07 .20
160 Javier Valentin .07 .20
161 Chris Hoiles .07 .20
162 Garret Anderson .07 .20
163 Dan Wilson .07 .20
164 Paul O'Neill .10 .30
165 Matt Williams .07 .20
166 Travis Fryman .07 .20
167 Javier Lopez .07 .20
168 Ray Lankford .07 .20
169 Bobby Estalella .07 .20
170 Henry Rodriguez .07 .20
171 Quinton McCracken .07 .20
172 Jaret Wright .07 .20
173 Darryl Kile .07 .20
174 Wade Boggs .10 .30
175 Orel Hershiser .07 .20
176 B.J. Surhoff .07 .20
177 Fernando Tatis .07 .20
178 Carlos Delgado .07 .20
179 Jorge Fabregas .07 .20
180 Tony Saunders .07 .20
181 Devon White .07 .20
182 Dmitri Young .07 .20
183 Ryan McGuire .07 .20
184 Mark Bellhorn .07 .20

185 Joe Carter .07 .20
186 Kevin Stocker .07 .20
187 Mike Lansing .07 .20
188 Jason Dickson .07 .20
189 Charles Johnson .07 .20
190 Will Clark .10 .30
191 Shannon Stewart .07 .20
192 Johnny Damon .10 .30
193 Todd Greene .07 .20
194 Carlos Baerga .07 .20
195 David Cone .07 .20
196 Pokey Reese .07 .20
197 Livan Hernandez .07 .20
198 Tom Glavine .10 .30
199 Geronimo Berroa .07 .20
200 Darryl Hamilton .07 .20
201 Terry Steinbach .07 .20
202 Robb Nen .07 .20
203 Ron Gant .07 .20
204 Rafael Palmeiro .10 .30
205 Rickey Henderson .20 .50
206 Justin Thompson .07 .20
207 Jeff Suppan .07 .20
208 Kevin Brown .10 .30
209 Jimmy Key .07 .20
210 Brian Jordan .07 .20
211 Aaron Sele .07 .20
212 Fred McGriff .10 .30
213 Jay Bell .07 .20
214 Andres Galarraga .07 .20
215 Mark Grace .10 .30
216 Brett Tomko .07 .20
217 Francisco Cordova .07 .20
218 Rusty Greer .07 .20
219 Bubba Trammell .07 .20
220 Derrek Lee .10 .30
221 Brian Anderson .07 .20
222 Mark Grudzielanek .07 .20
223 Marquis Grissom .07 .20
224 Gary DiSarcina .07 .20
225 Jim Leyritz .07 .20
226 Jeffrey Hammonds .07 .20
227 Karim Garcia .07 .20
228 Chan Ho Park .07 .20
229 Brooks Kieschnick .07 .20
230 Trey Beamon .07 .20
231 Kevin Appier .07 .20
232 Wally Joyner .07 .20
233 Richie Sexson .07 .20
234 Frank Catalanotto RC .20 .50
235 Rafael Medina .07 .20
236 Travis Lee .07 .20
237 Eli Marrero .07 .20
238 Carl Pavano .07 .20
239 Enrique Wilson .07 .20
240 Richard Hidalgo .07 .20
241 Todd Helton .10 .30
242 Ben Grieve .07 .20
243 Mario Valdez .07 .20
244 Magglio Ordonez RC .60 1.50
245 Juan Encarnacion .07 .20
246 Russell Branyan .07 .20
247 Sean Casey .07 .20
248 Abraham Nunez .07 .20
249 Brad Fullmer .07 .20
250 Paul Konerko .07 .20
251 Miguel Tejada .20 .50
252 Mike Lowell RC .40 1.00
253 Ken Griffey Jr. ST .20 .50
254 Frank Thomas ST .10 .30
255 Alex Rodriguez ST .20 .50
256 Jose Cruz Jr. ST .07 .20
257 Jeff Bagwell ST .20 .50
258 Chipper Jones ST .10 .30
259 Mo Vaughn ST .07 .20
260 Nomar Garciaparra ST .20 .50
261 Jim Thome ST .07 .20
262 Derek Jeter ST .25 .60
263 Mike Piazza ST .20 .50
264 Tony Gwynn ST .10 .30
265 Scott Rolen ST .10 .30
266 Andruw Jones ST .10 .30
267 Cal Ripken ST .30 .75
268 Checklist 1 .07 .20
269 Checklist 2 .07 .20
270 Checklist 3 .07 .20
S250 Paul Konerko AU/500 4.00 10.00

1998 Score Rookie Traded Showcase Series

Randomly inserted in packs at a rate of one in seven, this 160-card set is a parallel to the Score Rookie Traded base set.

*STARS 1-50: 1.25X TO 3X BASIC CARDS
*SHOWCASE 51-270: 2X TO 5X BASIC
*SHOWCASE RC'S 51-270: 1.5X TO 4X BASIC
STATED ODDS 1:7

1998 Score Rookie Traded Showcase Series Artist's Proofs

Randomly inserted in packs at a rate of one in 35, this 160-card set is a parallel to the Score Rookie Traded base set.

*SHOWCASE AP 1-50: 5X TO 12X BASIC
*SHOWCASE AP 51-270: 8X TO 20X BASIC
*SHOWCASE AP RC'S 51-270: 3X TO 8X BASIC
STATED ODDS 1:35

1998 Score Rookie Traded Showcase Series Artist's Proofs 1 of 1's

These extremely scarce parallel Artist's Proofs cards were randomly seeded into Rookie Traded hobby packs. Only one of each card was produced. They're easy to spot due to the gold foil circular logo directly on the middle of the card front that says "SCORE ONE OF ONE . . . 001/001". Due to scarcity no pricing is provided.

RANDOM INSERTS IN HOBBY PACKS
STATED PRINT RUN 1 SET
NO PRICING DUE TO SCARCITY

1998 Score Rookie Traded Complete Players Samples

These cards were issued to preview the Score Rookie Traded Complete Players set. The cards have the word sample written on them so they can be easily differentiated from the regular Complete Player cards.

COMPLETE SET (30) 20.00 50.00
THREE CARDS PER PLAYER
1A Ken Griffey Jr. 1.50 4.00
2A Larry Walker .40 1.00
3A Alex Rodriguez 1.00 2.50
4A Jose Cruz Jr. .20 .50
5A Jeff Bagwell .50 1.25
6A Greg Maddux 1.25 3.00
7A Ivan Rodriguez .50 1.25
8A Roger Clemens 1.00 2.50
9A Chipper Jones 1.00 2.50
10A Hideo Nomo .40 1.00

1998 Score Rookie Traded Complete Players

Randomly inserted in packs at a rate of one in 11, this 30-card set is an insert to the Score Rookie Traded base set. The card fronts feature special holographic foil stamping. Each player has three different cards highlighting his own power, speed and approach to the game. Put them together and form the Complete Player.

COMPLETE SET (30) 20.00 50.00
1A Ken Griffey Jr. 1.25 3.00
2A Larry Walker .30 .75
3A Alex Rodriguez 1.25 3.00
4A Jose Cruz Jr. .30 .75
5A Jeff Bagwell .50 1.25
6A Greg Maddux 1.25 3.00
7A Ivan Rodriguez .50 1.25
8A Roger Clemens 1.50 4.00
9A Chipper Jones .75 2.00
10A Hideo Nomo .75 2.00

1998 Score Rookie Traded Star Gazing

Randomly inserted in packs at a rate of one in 35, this 20-card set is an insert to the Score Rookie Traded base set. The fronts feature color action photos printed on a diamond-shaped star-gazing background. The player's name sits atop the player photo with the Score logo in the upper right corner.

COMPLETE SET (20) 10.00 25.00
1 Ken Griffey Jr. 1.00 2.50
2 Frank Thomas .60 1.50
3 Chipper Jones .60 1.50
4 Mark McGwire 1.50 4.00
5 Cal Ripken 2.00 5.00
6 Mike Piazza 1.00 2.50
7 Nomar Garciaparra 1.00 2.50
8 Derek Jeter 1.50 4.00
9 Juan Gonzalez .25 .60
10 Vladimir Guerrero .60 1.50
11 Alex Rodriguez 1.00 2.50
12 Tony Gwynn .75 2.00
13 Andruw Jones .40 1.00
14 Scott Rolen .40 1.00
15 Jose Cruz Jr. .25 .60
16 Mo Vaughn .25 .60
17 Bernie Williams .40 1.00
18 Greg Maddux 1.00 2.50
19 Tony Clark .25 .60
20 Ben Grieve .15 .40

1993 SP

This 290-card standard-size set, produced by Upper Deck, features fronts with action color player photos. Special subsets include All Star players (1-18) and Foil Prospects (271-290). Cards 19-270 are in alphabetical order by team nickname. Notable Rookie Cards include Johnny Damon and Derek Jeter.

COMPLETE SET (290) 40.00 80.00
COMMON CARD (1-270) .20 .50
COMMON FOIL (271-290) .40 1.00
1 Roberto Alomar AS .50 1.25
2 Wade Boggs AS .50 1.25
3 Joe Carter AS .20 .50
4 Ken Griffey Jr. AS 1.25 3.00
5 Mark Langston AS .20 .50
6 John Olerud AS .30 .75
7 Kirby Puckett AS .75 2.00
8 Cal Ripken Jr. AS 2.50 6.00
9 Ivan Rodriguez AS .50 1.25
10 Barry Bonds AS 2.00 5.00
11 Darren Daulton AS .30 .75
12 Marquis Grissom AS .30 .75
13 David Justice AS .30 .75
14 John Kruk AS .30 .75
15 Barry Larkin AS .50 1.25
16 Terry Mulholland AS .20 .50
17 Ryne Sandberg AS 1.25 3.00
18 Gary Sheffield AS .30 .75
19 Chad Curtis .20 .50
20 Chili Davis .30 .75
21 Gary DiSarcina .20 .50
22 Damion Easley .20 .50
23 Chuck Finley .30 .75
24 Luis Polonia .20 .50
25 Tim Salmon .50 1.25
26 J.T. Snow RC .50 1.25
27 Russ Springer .20 .50
28 Jeff Bagwell .50 1.25
29 Craig Biggio .50 1.25
30 Ken Caminiti .30 .75
31 Andujar Cedeno .20 .50
32 Doug Drabek .20 .50
33 Steve Finley .30 .75
34 Luis Gonzalez .30 .75
35 Pete Harnisch .20 .50
36 Darryl Kile .30 .75
37 Mike Bordick .20 .50
38 Dennis Eckersley .30 .75
39 Brent Gates .20 .50
40 Rickey Henderson .75 2.00
41 Mark McGwire 2.00 5.00
42 Craig Paquette .20 .50
43 Ruben Sierra .30 .75
44 Terry Steinbach .20 .50
45 Todd Van Poppel .20 .50
46 Pat Borders .20 .50
47 Tony Fernandez .20 .50
48 Juan Guzman .20 .50
49 Pat Hentgen .20 .50
50 Paul Molitor .30 .75
51 Jack Morris .30 .75
52 Ed Sprague .20 .50
53 Duane Ward .20 .50
54 Devon White .30 .75
55 Steve Avery .20 .50
56 Jeff Blauser .20 .50
57 Ron Gant .30 .75
58 Tom Glavine .50 1.25
59 Greg Maddux 1.25 3.00
60 Fred McGriff .50 1.25
61 Terry Pendleton .30 .75
62 Deion Sanders .50 1.25
63 John Smoltz .50 1.25
64 Cal Eldred .20 .50
65 Darryl Hamilton .20 .50
66 John Jaha .20 .50
67 Pat Listach .20 .50
68 Jaime Navarro .20 .50
69 Kevin Reimer .20 .50
70 B.J. Surhoff .30 .75
71 Greg Vaughn .20 .50
72 Robin Yount 1.25 3.00
73 Rene Arocha RC .30 .75
74 Bernard Gilkey .20 .50
75 Gregg Jefferies .20 .50
76 Ray Lankford .30 .75
77 Tom Pagnozzi .20 .50
78 Lee Smith .30 .75
79 Ozzie Smith 1.25 3.00
80 Bob Tewksbury .20 .50
81 Mark Whiten .20 .50
82 Steve Buechele .20 .50
83 Mark Grace .50 1.25
84 Jose Guzman .20 .50
85 Derrick May .20 .50
86 Mike Morgan .20 .50
87 Randy Myers .20 .50
88 Kevin Roberson RC .20 .50
89 Sammy Sosa .75 2.00
90 Rick Wilkins .20 .50
91 Brett Butler .30 .75
92 Eric Davis .30 .75
93 Orel Hershiser .30 .75
94 Eric Karros .30 .75
95 Ramon Martinez .20 .50
96 Raul Mondesi .30 .75
97 Jose Offerman .20 .50
98 Mike Piazza 2.00 5.00
99 Darryl Strawberry .30 .75
100 Moises Alou .30 .75
101 Wil Cordero .20 .50
102 Delino DeShields .20 .50
103 Darrin Fletcher .20 .50
104 Ken Hill .20 .50
105 Mike Lansing RC .30 .75
106 Dennis Martinez .30 .75
107 Larry Walker .30 .75
108 John Wetteland .30 .75
109 Rod Beck .20 .50
110 John Burkett .20 .50
111 Will Clark .50 1.25
112 Royce Clayton .20 .50
113 Darren Lewis .20 .50
114 Willie McGee .30 .75
115 Bill Swift .20 .50
116 Robby Thompson .20 .50
117 Matt Williams .30 .75
118 Sandy Alomar Jr. .20 .50
119 Carlos Baerga .20 .50
120 Albert Belle .30 .75
121 Reggie Jefferson .20 .50
122 Wayne Kirby .20 .50
123 Kenny Lofton .30 .75
124 Carlos Martinez .20 .50
125 Charles Nagy .20 .50
126 Paul Sorrento .20 .50
127 Rich Amaral .20 .50
128 Jay Buhner .30 .75
129 Norm Charlton .20 .50
130 Dave Fleming .20 .50
131 Erik Hanson .20 .50
132 Randy Johnson .75 2.00
133 Edgar Martinez .50 1.25
134 Tino Martinez .50 1.25
135 Omar Vizquel .50 1.25
136 Bret Barberie .20 .50
137 Chuck Carr .20 .50
138 Jeff Conine .30 .75
139 Orestes Destrade .20 .50
140 Chris Hammond .20 .50
141 Bryan Harvey .20 .50
142 Benito Santiago .30 .75
143 Walt Weiss .20 .50
144 Darrell Whitmore RC .20 .50
145 Tim Bogar RC .20 .50
146 Bobby Bonilla .30 .75
147 Jeromy Burnitz .30 .75
148 Vince Coleman .20 .50
149 Dwight Gooden .30 .75
150 Todd Hundley .20 .50
151 Howard Johnson .20 .50
152 Eddie Murray .75 2.00
153 Bret Saberhagen .30 .75
154 Brady Anderson .30 .75
155 Mike Devereaux .20 .50
156 Jeffrey Hammonds .20 .50
157 Chris Hoiles .20 .50
158 Ben McDonald .20 .50
159 Mark McLemore .20 .50
160 Mike Mussina .50 1.25
161 Gregg Olson .20 .50
162 David Segui .20 .50
163 Derek Bell .20 .50
164 Andy Benes .20 .50
165 Archi Cianfrocco .20 .50
166 Ricky Gutierrez .20 .50
167 Tony Gwynn UER 1.00 2.50
Photo is Tracy Sanders
168 Gene Harris .20 .50
169 Trevor Hoffman .75 2.00
170 Ray McDavid RC .20 .50
171 Phil Plantier .20 .50
172 Mariano Duncan .20 .50
173 Len Dykstra .30 .75
174 Tommy Greene .20 .50
175 Dave Hollins .20 .50
176 Pete Incaviglia .20 .50
177 Mickey Morandini .20 .50
178 Curt Schilling .30 .75
179 Kevin Stocker .20 .50
180 Mitch Williams .20 .50
181 Stan Belinda .20 .50
182 Jay Bell .30 .75
183 Steve Cooke .20 .50
184 Carlos Garcia .20 .50
185 Jeff King .20 .50
186 Orlando Merced .20 .50
187 Don Slaught .20 .50
188 Andy Van Slyke .50 1.25
189 Kevin Young .30 .75
190 Kevin Brown .30 .75
191 Jose Canseco .50 1.25
192 Julio Franco .30 .75
193 Benji Gil .20 .50
194 Juan Gonzalez .30 .75
195 Tom Henke .20 .50
196 Rafael Palmeiro .50 1.25
197 Dean Palmer .30 .75
198 Nolan Ryan 3.00 8.00
199 Roger Clemens 1.50 4.00
200 Scott Cooper .20 .50
201 Andre Dawson .30 .75
202 Mike Greenwell .20 .50
203 Carlos Quintana .20 .50
204 Jeff Russell .20 .50
205 Aaron Sele .20 .50
206 Mo Vaughn .30 .75
207 Frank Viola .30 .75
208 Rob Dibble .30 .75
209 Roberto Kelly .20 .50
210 Kevin Mitchell .20 .50
211 Hal Morris .20 .50
212 Joe Oliver .20 .50
213 Jose Rijo .20 .50
214 Bip Roberts .20 .50
215 Chris Sabo .20 .50
216 Reggie Sanders .30 .75
217 Dante Bichette .30 .75
218 Jerald Clark .20 .50
219 Alex Cole .20 .50
220 Andres Galarraga .30 .75
221 Joe Girardi .20 .50
222 Charlie Hayes .20 .50
223 Roberto Mejia RC .20 .50
224 Armando Reynoso .20 .50
225 Eric Young .20 .50
226 Kevin Appier .30 .75
227 George Brett 2.00 5.00
228 David Cone .30 .75
229 Phil Hiatt .20 .50
230 Felix Jose .20 .50
231 Wally Joyner .30 .75
232 Mike Macfarlane .20 .50
233 Brian McRae .20 .50
234 Jeff Montgomery .20 .50
235 Rob Deer .20 .50
236 Cecil Fielder .30 .75
237 Travis Fryman .30 .75
238 Mike Henneman .20 .50
239 Tony Phillips .20 .50
240 Mickey Tettleton .20 .50
241 Alan Trammell .30 .75
242 David Wells .30 .75
243 Lou Whitaker .30 .75
244 Rick Aguilera .20 .50
245 Scott Erickson .20 .50
246 Brian Harper .20 .50
247 Kent Hrbek .30 .75
248 Chuck Knoblauch .30 .75
249 Shane Mack .20 .50
250 David McCarty .20 .50
251 Pedro Munoz .20 .50
252 Dave Winfield .30 .75
253 Alex Fernandez .20 .50
254 Ozzie Guillen .30 .75
255 Bo Jackson .75 2.00
256 Lance Johnson .20 .50
257 Ron Karkovice .20 .50
258 Jack McDowell .20 .50
259 Tim Raines .30 .75
260 Frank Thomas .75 2.00
261 Robin Ventura .30 .75
262 Jim Abbott .50 1.25
263 Steve Farr .20 .50
264 Jimmy Key .30 .75
265 Don Mattingly 2.00 5.00
266 Paul O'Neill .50 1.25
267 Mike Stanley .20 .50
268 Danny Tartabull .20 .50
269 Bob Wickman .20 .50
270 Bernie Williams .50 1.25
271 Jason Bere FOIL .40 1.00
272 R.Cedeno FOIL RC .60 1.50
273 J.Damon FOIL RC 5.00 12.00
274 Russ Davis FOIL RC .60 1.50
275 Carlos Delgado FOIL 1.50 4.00
276 Carl Everett FOIL .60 1.50
277 Cliff Floyd FOIL .30 .75
278 Alex Gonzalez FOIL .40 1.00
279 Derek Jeter FOIL RC 50.00 100.00
280 Chipper Jones FOIL 1.50 4.00
281 Javier Lopez FOIL .50 1.25
282 Chad Mottola FOIL RC .40 1.00
283 Marc Newfield FOIL .40 1.00
284 Eduardo Perez FOIL .40 1.00
285 Manny Ramirez FOIL 2.00 5.00
286 T.Steverson FOIL RC .40 1.00
287 Michael Tucker FOIL .40 1.00
288 Allen Watson FOIL .40 1.00
289 Rondell White FOIL .60 1.50
290 Dmitri Young FOIL .60 1.50

1993 SP Platinum Power

Cards from this 20-card standard-size were inserted one every nine packs and feature power hitters from the American and National Leagues.

COMPLETE SET (20) 30.00 80.00
PP1 Albert Belle .75 2.00
PP2 Barry Bonds 5.00 12.00
PP3 Joe Carter .50 1.25
PP4 Will Clark 1.25 3.00
PP5 Darren Daulton .75 2.00
PP6 Cecil Fielder .75 2.00
PP7 Ron Gant .75 2.00
PP8 Juan Gonzalez .75 2.00
PP9 Ken Griffey Jr. 3.00 8.00
PP10 Dave Hollins .50 1.25
PP11 David Justice .75 2.00
PP12 Fred McGriff 1.25 3.00
PP13 Mark McGwire 5.00 12.00
PP14 Dean Palmer .75 2.00
PP15 Mike Piazza 5.00 12.00
PP16 Tim Salmon 1.25 3.00
PP17 Ryne Sandberg 3.00 8.00
PP18 Gary Sheffield .75 2.00
PP19 Frank Thomas 2.00 5.00
PP20 Matt Williams .75 2.00

1994 SP

This 200-card standard-size set distributed in foil packs contains the game's top players and prospects. The first 20 cards in the set are Foil Prospects which are brighter and more metallic than the rest of the set. These cards therefore are highly condition sensitive. Cards 21-200 are in alphabetical order by team nickname. Rookie Cards include Brad Fullmer, Derrek Lee, Chan Ho Park and Alex Rodriguez.

COMPLETE SET (200) 125.00 250.00
COMMON CARD (21-200) .07 .20
COMMON FOIL (1-20) .20 .50
1 Mike Bell FOIL RC .20 .50
2 D.J. Boston FOIL RC .20 .50
3 Johnny Damon FOIL .75 2.00
4 Brad Fullmer FOIL RC .40 1.00
5 Joey Hamilton FOIL .20 .50
6 T.Hollandsworth FOIL .20 .50
7 Brian L. Hunter FOIL .20 .50
8 L.Hawkins FOIL RC .40 1.00
9 B.Kieschnick FOIL RC .20 .50
10 Derrek Lee FOIL RC 4.00 10.00
11 Trot Nixon FOIL RC 1.50 4.00
12 Alex Ochoa FOIL .20 .50
13 Chan Ho Park FOIL RC .75 2.00
14 Kirk Presley FOIL RC .20 .50
15 A.Rodriguez FOIL RC 75.00 150.00
16 Jose Silva FOIL RC .20 .50
17 Terrell Wade FOIL RC .20 .50
18 Billy Wagner FOIL RC 1.50 4.00
19 G.Williams FOIL RC .20 .50
20 Preston Wilson FOIL .40 1.00
21 Brian Anderson RC .15 .40
22 Chad Curtis .07 .20
23 Chili Davis .15 .40
24 Bo Jackson .40 1.00
25 Mark Langston .07 .20
26 Tim Salmon .25 .60
27 Jeff Bagwell .25 .60
28 Craig Biggio .25 .60
29 Ken Caminiti .15 .40
30 Doug Drabek .07 .20
31 John Hudek RC .07 .20
32 Greg Swindell .07 .20
33 Brent Gates .07 .20
34 Rickey Henderson .40 1.00
35 Steve Karsay .07 .20
36 Mark McGwire 1.00 2.50
37 Ruben Sierra .15 .40
38 Terry Steinbach .07 .20
39 Roberto Alomar .25 .60
40 Joe Carter .15 .40
41 Carlos Delgado .25 .60
42 Alex Gonzalez .07 .20
43 Juan Guzman .07 .20
44 Paul Molitor .15 .40
45 John Olerud .15 .40
46 Devon White .15 .40
47 Steve Avery .07 .20
48 Jeff Blauser .07 .20
49 Tom Glavine .25 .60
50 David Justice .15 .40
51 Roberto Kelly .07 .20
52 Ryan Klesko .15 .40
53 Javier Lopez .15 .40
54 Greg Maddux .60 1.50
55 Fred McGriff .25 .60
56 Ricky Bones .07 .20
57 Cal Eldred .07 .20
58 Brian Harper .07 .20
59 Pat Listach .07 .20
60 B.J. Surhoff .15 .40
61 Greg Vaughn .07 .20
62 Bernard Gilkey .07 .20
63 Gregg Jefferies .07 .20
64 Ray Lankford .15 .40
65 Ozzie Smith .60 1.50
66 Bob Tewksbury .07 .20
67 Mark Whiten .07 .20
68 Todd Zeile .07 .20
69 Mark Grace .25 .60
70 Randy Myers .07 .20
71 Ryne Sandberg .60 1.50
72 Sammy Sosa .40 1.00
73 Steve Trachsel .07 .20
74 Rick Wilkins .07 .20
75 Brett Butler .15 .40
76 Delino DeShields .07 .20
77 Orel Hershiser .15 .40
78 Eric Karros .15 .40
79 Raul Mondesi .15 .40
80 Mike Piazza .75 2.00
81 Tim Wallach .07 .20
82 Moises Alou .15 .40
83 Cliff Floyd .15 .40
84 Marquis Grissom .15 .40
85 Pedro Martinez .40 1.00
86 Larry Walker .15 .40
87 John Wetteland .15 .40
88 Rondell White .15 .40
89 Rod Beck .07 .20
90 Barry Bonds 1.00 2.50
91 John Burkett .07 .20
92 Royce Clayton .07 .20
93 Billy Swift .07 .20
94 Robby Thompson .07 .20
95 Matt Williams .15 .40
96 Carlos Baerga .07 .20
97 Albert Belle .15 .40
98 Kenny Lofton .15 .40
99 Dennis Martinez .15 .40
100 Eddie Murray .40 1.00
101 Manny Ramirez .40 1.00
102 Eric Anthony .07 .20
103 Chris Bosio .07 .20
104 Jay Buhner .15 .40
105 Ken Griffey Jr. .60 1.50
106 Randy Johnson .40 1.00
107 Edgar Martinez .25 .60
108 Chuck Carr .07 .20
109 Jeff Conine .15 .40
110 Carl Everett .15 .40
111 Chris Hammond .07 .20
112 Bryan Harvey .07 .20
113 Charles Johnson .15 .40
114 Gary Sheffield .15 .40
115 Bobby Bonilla .15 .40
116 Dwight Gooden .15 .40
117 Todd Hundley .07 .20
118 Bobby Jones .07 .20
119 Jeff Kent .25 .60
120 Bret Saberhagen .15 .40
121 Jeffrey Hammonds .07 .20
122 Chris Hoiles .07 .20
123 Ben McDonald .07 .20
124 Mike Mussina .25 .60
125 Rafael Palmeiro .25 .60
126 Cal Ripken Jr. 1.25 3.00
127 Lee Smith .15 .40
128 Derek Bell .07 .20

129 Andy Benes .07 .20
130 Tony Gwynn .50 1.25
131 Trevor Hoffman .25 .60
132 Phil Plantier .07 .20
133 Bip Roberts .07 .20
134 Darren Daulton .15 .40
135 Lenny Dykstra .15 .40
136 Dave Hollins .07 .20
137 Danny Jackson .07 .20
138 John Kruk .15 .40
139 Kevin Stocker .07 .20
140 Jay Bell .15 .40
141 Carlos Garcia .07 .20
142 Jeff King .07 .20
143 Orlando Merced .07 .20
144 Andy Van Slyke .25 .60
145 Rick White .07 .20
146 Jose Canseco .25 .60
147 Will Clark .25 .60
148 Juan Gonzalez .15 .40
149 Rick Helling .07 .20
150 Dean Palmer .15 .40
151 Ivan Rodriguez .25 .60
152 Roger Clemens .75 2.00
153 Scott Cooper .07 .20
154 Andre Dawson .15 .40
155 Mike Greenwell .07 .20
156 Aaron Sele .07 .20
157 Mo Vaughn .15 .40
158 Bret Boone .15 .40
159 Barry Larkin .25 .60
160 Kevin Mitchell .07 .20
161 Jose Rijo .07 .20
162 Deion Sanders .25 .60
163 Reggie Sanders .15 .40
164 Dante Bichette .15 .40
165 Ellis Burks .15 .40
166 Andres Galarraga .15 .40
167 Charlie Hayes .07 .20
168 David Nied .07 .20
169 Walt Weiss .07 .20
170 Kevin Appier .15 .40
171 David Cone .15 .40
172 Jeff Granger .07 .20
173 Felix Jose .07 .20
174 Wally Joyner .15 .40
175 Brian McRae .07 .20
176 Cecil Fielder .15 .40
177 Travis Fryman .15 .40
178 Mike Henneman .07 .20
179 Tony Phillips .07 .20
180 Mickey Tettleton .07 .20
181 Alan Trammell .15 .40
182 Rick Aguilera .07 .20
183 Rich Becker .07 .20
184 Scott Erickson .07 .20
185 Chuck Knoblauch .15 .40
186 Kirby Puckett .40 1.00
187 Dave Winfield .15 .40
188 Wilson Alvarez .07 .20
189 Jason Bere .07 .20
190 Alex Fernandez .07 .20
191 Julio Franco .15 .40
192 Jack McDowell .07 .20
193 Frank Thomas .40 1.00
194 Robin Ventura .15 .40
195 Jim Abbott .25 .60
196 Wade Boggs .25 .60
197 Jimmy Key .15 .40
198 Don Mattingly 1.00 2.50
199 Paul O'Neill .25 .60
200 Danny Tartabull .07 .20
P24 Ken Griffey Jr. Promo .75 2.00

1994 SP Die Cuts

This 200-card die-cut set is parallel to that of the basic SP issue. The cards were inserted one per SP pack. The difference, of course, is the unique die-cut shape. The backs have a silver Upper Deck hologram as opposed to gold on the basic issue.

COMPLETE SET (200) 75.00 150.00
*STARS: .75X TO 2X BASIC CARDS
*ROOKIES: .6X TO 1.5X BASIC CARDS
10 Derrek Lee FOIL 6.00 15.00
15 Alex Rodriguez FOIL 100.00 200.00

1994 SP Holoviews

Randomly inserted in SP foil packs at a rate of one in five, this 38-card set contains top stars and prospects.

1 Roberto Alomar 1.25 3.00
2 Kevin Appier .75 2.00
3 Jeff Bagwell 1.25 3.00
4 Jose Canseco 1.25 3.00
5 Roger Clemens 4.00 10.00
6 Carlos Delgado 1.25 3.00
7 Cecil Fielder .75 2.00
8 Cliff Floyd .75 2.00
9 Travis Fryman .75 2.00
10 Andres Galarraga .75 2.00
11 Juan Gonzalez .75 2.00
12 Ken Griffey Jr. 3.00 8.00
13 Tony Gwynn 2.50 6.00
14 Jeffrey Hammonds .60 1.50
15 Bo Jackson 2.00 5.00
16 Michael Jordan 6.00 15.00
17 David Justice .75 2.00
18 Steve Karsay .60 1.50
19 Jeff Kent 1.25 3.00
20 Brooks Kieschnick .60 1.50
21 Ryan Klesko .75 2.00
22 John Kruk .75 2.00
23 Barry Larkin 1.25 3.00
24 Pat Listach .60 1.50
25 Don Mattingly 5.00 12.00
26 Mark McGwire 5.00 12.00
27 Raul Mondesi .75 2.00
28 Trot Nixon 2.50 6.00
29 Mike Piazza 3.00 8.00
30 Kirby Puckett 2.00 5.00
31 Manny Ramirez 2.00 5.00
32 Cal Ripken 6.00 15.00
33 Alex Rodriguez 40.00 80.00
34 Tim Salmon 1.25 3.00
35 Gary Sheffield .75 2.00
36 Ozzie Smith 3.00 8.00
37 Sammy Sosa 2.00 5.00
38 Andy Van Slyke 1.25 3.00

1994 SP Holoviews Die Cuts

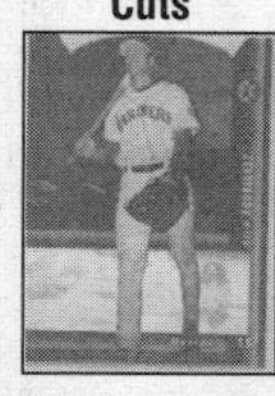

Parallel to the blue Holoview set, this 38-card red-bordered issue was also randomly inserted in SP packs. They are much more difficult to pull than the blue version with an insertion rate of one in 75.

*DIE CUTS: 4X TO 10X BASIC HOLO
*DIE CUTS: 2.5X TO 6X BASIC HOLO RC YR
16 Michael Jordan 75.00 150.00
28 Trot Nixon 15.00 40.00
33 Alex Rodriguez 800.00 1200.00

1995 SP

This set consists of 207 cards being sold in eight-card, hobby-only packs with a suggested retail price of $3.99. Subsets featured are Salute (1-4) and Premier Prospects (5-24). The only notable Rookie Card in this set is Hideo Nomo. Dealers who ordered a certain quantity of Upper Deck baseball cases received as a bonus, a certified autographed SP card of Ken Griffey Jr.

COMPLETE SET (207) 15.00 40.00
COMMON CARD (1-207) .07 .20
COMMON FOIL (5-24) .20 .50
GRIFFEY AU SENT TO DEALERS AS BONUS
1 Cal Ripken Salute 1.25 3.00
2 Nolan Ryan Salute 1.50 4.00
3 George Brett Salute 1.00 2.50
4 Mike Schmidt Salute .60 1.50
5 Dustin Hermanson FOIL .20 .50
6 Antonio Osuna FOIL .20 .50
7 M.Grudzielanek FOIL RC .50 1.25
8 Ray Durham FOIL .30 .75
9 Ugueth Urbina FOIL .20 .50
10 Ruben Rivera FOIL .20 .50
11 Curtis Goodwin FOIL .20 .50
12 Jimmy Hurst FOIL .20 .50
13 Jose Malave FOIL .20 .50
14 Hideo Nomo FOIL RC 1.50 4.00
15 Juan Acevedo RC FOIL .20 .50
16 Tony Clark FOIL .20 .50
17 Jim Pittsley FOIL .20 .50
18 Freddy A. Garcia RC FOIL .20 .50
19 Carlos Perez RC FOIL .30 .75
20 R.Casanova FOIL RC .20 .50
21 Quilvio Veras FOIL .20 .50
22 Edgardo Alfonzo FOIL .20 .50
23 Marty Cordova FOIL .20 .50
24 C.J. Nitkowski FOIL .20 .50
25 Wade Boggs CL .15 .40
26 Dave Winfield CL .07 .20
27 Eddie Murray CL .25 .60
28 David Justice .15 .40
29 Marquis Grissom .15 .40
30 Fred McGriff .25 .60
31 Greg Maddux .60 1.50
32 Tom Glavine .25 .60
33 Steve Avery .07 .20
34 Chipper Jones .40 1.00
35 Sammy Sosa .40 1.00
36 Jaime Navarro .07 .20
37 Randy Myers .07 .20
38 Mark Grace .25 .60
39 Todd Zeile .07 .20
40 Brian McRae .07 .20
41 Reggie Sanders .15 .40
42 Ron Gant .15 .40
43 Deion Sanders .25 .60
44 Bret Boone .15 .40
45 Barry Larkin .25 .60
46 Jose Rijo .07 .20
47 Jason Bates .07 .20
48 Andres Galarraga .15 .40
49 Bill Swift .07 .20
50 Larry Walker .15 .40
51 Vinny Castilla .15 .40
52 Dante Bichette .15 .40
53 Jeff Conine .15 .40
54 John Burkett .07 .20
55 Gary Sheffield .15 .40
56 Andre Dawson .15 .40
57 Terry Pendleton .15 .40
58 Charles Johnson .15 .40
59 Brian L. Hunter .07 .20
60 Jeff Bagwell .25 .60
61 Craig Biggio .25 .60
62 Phil Nevin .15 .40
63 Doug Drabek .07 .20
64 Derek Bell .07 .20
65 Raul Mondesi .15 .40
66 Eric Karros .15 .40
67 Roger Cedeno .07 .20
68 Delino DeShields .07 .20
69 Ramon Martinez .07 .20
70 Mike Piazza .60 1.50
71 Billy Ashley .07 .20
72 Jeff Fassero .07 .20
73 Shane Andrews .07 .20
74 Wil Cordero .07 .20
75 Tony Tarasco .07 .20
76 Rondell White .15 .40
77 Pedro Martinez .25 .60
78 Moises Alou .15 .40
79 Rico Brogna .07 .20
80 Bobby Bonilla .15 .40
81 Jeff Kent .15 .40
82 Brett Butler .15 .40
83 Bobby Jones .07 .20
84 Bill Pulsipher .07 .20
85 Bret Saberhagen .15 .40
86 Gregg Jefferies .07 .20
87 Lenny Dykstra .15 .40
88 Dave Hollins .07 .20
89 Charlie Hayes .07 .20
90 Darren Daulton .15 .40
91 Curt Schilling .15 .40
92 Heathcliff Slocumb .07 .20
93 Carlos Garcia .07 .20
94 Denny Neagle .15 .40
95 Jay Bell .15 .40
96 Orlando Merced .07 .20
97 Dave Clark .07 .20
98 Bernard Gilkey .07 .20
99 Scott Cooper .07 .20
100 Ozzie Smith .60 1.50
101 Tom Henke .07 .20
102 Ken Hill .07 .20
103 Brian Jordan .15 .40
104 Ray Lankford .15 .40
105 Tony Gwynn .50 1.25
106 Andy Benes .07 .20
107 Ken Caminiti .15 .40
108 Steve Finley .15 .40
109 Joey Hamilton .07 .20
110 Bip Roberts .07 .20
111 Eddie Williams .07 .20
112 Rod Beck .07 .20
113 Matt Williams .15 .40
114 Glenallen Hill .07 .20
115 Barry Bonds 1.00 2.50
116 Robby Thompson .07 .20
117 Mark Portugal .07 .20
118 Brady Anderson .15 .40
119 Mike Mussina .25 .60
120 Rafael Palmeiro .25 .60
121 Chris Hoiles .07 .20
122 Harold Baines .15 .40
123 Jeffrey Hammonds .07 .20
124 Tim Naehring .07 .20
125 Mo Vaughn .15 .40
126 Mike Macfarlane .07 .20
127 Roger Clemens .75 2.00
128 John Valentin .07 .20
129 Aaron Sele .07 .20
130 Jose Canseco .25 .60
131 J.T. Snow .15 .40
132 Mark Langston .07 .20
133 Chili Davis .15 .40
134 Chuck Finley .15 .40
135 Tim Salmon .25 .60
136 Tony Phillips .07 .20
137 Jason Bere .07 .20
138 Robin Ventura .15 .40
139 Tim Raines .15 .40
140 Frank Thomas COR .40 1.00
Career stats correct, example is RBI career total is 484
140A Frank Thomas ERR .40 1.00
Career stats alll messed up
141 Alex Fernandez .07 .20
142 Jim Abbott .25 .60
143 Wilson Alvarez .07 .20
144 Carlos Baerga .07 .20
145 Albert Belle .15 .40
146 Jim Thome .25 .60
147 Dennis Martinez .15 .40
148 Eddie Murray .40 1.00
149 Dave Winfield .15 .40
150 Kenny Lofton .15 .40
151 Manny Ramirez .25 .60
152 Chad Curtis .07 .20
153 Lou Whitaker .15 .40
154 Alan Trammell .15 .40
155 Cecil Fielder .15 .40
156 Kirk Gibson .15 .40
157 Michael Tucker .07 .20
158 Jon Nunnally .07 .20
159 Wally Joyner .15 .40
160 Kevin Appier .15 .40
161 Jeff Montgomery .07 .20
162 Greg Gagne .07 .20
163 Ricky Bones .07 .20
164 Cal Eldred .07 .20
165 Greg Vaughn .07 .20
166 Kevin Seitzer .07 .20
167 Jose Valentin .07 .20
168 Joe Oliver .07 .20
169 Rick Aguilera .07 .20
170 Kirby Puckett .40 1.00
171 Scott Stahoviak .07 .20
172 Kevin Tapani .07 .20
173 Chuck Knoblauch .15 .40
174 Rich Becker .07 .20
175 Don Mattingly 1.00 2.50
176 Jack McDowell .07 .20
177 Jimmy Key .15 .40
178 Paul O'Neill .25 .60
179 John Wetteland .15 .40
180 Wade Boggs .25 .60
181 Derek Jeter 1.00 2.50
182 Rickey Henderson .40 1.00
183 Terry Steinbach .07 .20
184 Ruben Sierra .15 .40
185 Mark McGwire 1.00 2.50
186 Todd Stottlemyre .07 .20
187 Dennis Eckersley .15 .40
188 Alex Rodriguez 1.00 2.50
189 Randy Johnson .40 1.00
190 Ken Griffey Jr. .60 1.50
191 Tino Martinez UER .25 .60
Mike Blowers pictured on back
192 Jay Buhner .15 .40
193 Edgar Martinez .25 .60
194 Mickey Tettleton .07 .20
195 Juan Gonzalez .15 .40
196 Benji Gil .07 .20
197 Dean Palmer .15 .40
198 Ivan Rodriguez .25 .60
199 Kenny Rogers .15 .40
200 Will Clark .25 .60
201 Roberto Alomar .25 .60
202 David Cone .15 .40
203 Paul Molitor .15 .40
204 Shawn Green .15 .40
205 Joe Carter .15 .40
206 Alex Gonzalez .07 .20
207 Pat Hentgen .07 .20
P100 K.Griffey Jr. Promo .75 2.00
AU190 Ken Griffey Jr. AU 100.00 175.00

1995 SP Silver

This 207-card set parallels that of the regular SP set and was inserted one per pack. The only difference between the regular 180 cards in the two sets is that the chevron of the parallel version on the left side of the front uses rainbow-colored foil instead of blue or red. The subset cards have a die-cut design to differentiate them from the regular edition cards. The only other difference is the silver (rather than gold) hologram on the back.

COMPLETE SET (207) 50.00 100.00
*STARS: 1X to 2.5X BASIC CARDS
*ROOKIES: .6X to 1.5X BASIC CARDS

1995 SP Platinum Power

This 20-card set was randomly inserted in packs at a rate of one in five. This die-cut set is comprised of the top home run hitters in baseball.

COMPLETE SET (20) 8.00 20.00
PP1 Jeff Bagwell .30 .75
PP2 Barry Bonds 1.25 3.00
PP3 Ron Gant .20 .50
PP4 Fred McGriff .30 .75
PP5 Raul Mondesi .20 .50
PP6 Mike Piazza .75 2.00
PP7 Larry Walker .20 .50
PP8 Matt Williams .20 .50
PP9 Albert Belle .20 .50
PP10 Cecil Fielder .20 .50
PP11 Juan Gonzalez .20 .50
PP12 Ken Griffey Jr. .75 2.00
PP13 Mark McGwire 1.25 3.00
PP14 Eddie Murray .50 1.25
PP15 Manny Ramirez .30 .75
PP16 Cal Ripken 1.50 4.00
PP17 Tim Salmon .30 .75
PP18 Frank Thomas .50 1.25
PP19 Jim Thome .30 .75
PP20 Mo Vaughn .20 .50

1995 SP Special FX

This 48-card set was randomly inserted in packs at a rate of one in 75. The set is comprised of the top names in baseball. The cards are numbered on the back "X/48."

COMPLETE SET (48) 125.00 300.00
1 Jose Canseco 4.00 10.00
2 Roger Clemens 12.50 30.00
3 Mo Vaughn 2.50 6.00
4 Tim Salmon 4.00 10.00
5 Chuck Finley 2.50 6.00
6 Robin Ventura 2.50 6.00
7 Jason Bere 1.25 3.00
8 Carlos Baerga 1.25 3.00
9 Albert Belle 2.50 6.00
10 Kenny Lofton 2.50 6.00
11 Manny Ramirez 4.00 10.00
12 Jeff Montgomery 1.25 3.00
13 Kirby Puckett 6.00 15.00
14 Wade Boggs 4.00 10.00
15 Don Mattingly 15.00 40.00
16 Cal Ripken 20.00 50.00
17 Ruben Sierra 2.50 6.00
18 Ken Griffey Jr. 10.00 25.00
19 Randy Johnson 6.00 15.00
20 Alex Rodriguez 15.00 40.00
21 Will Clark 4.00 10.00
22 Juan Gonzalez 2.50 6.00
23 Roberto Alomar 4.00 10.00
24 Joe Carter 2.50 6.00
25 Alex Gonzalez 1.25 3.00
26 Paul Molitor 2.50 6.00
27 Ryan Klesko 2.50 6.00
28 Fred McGriff 4.00 10.00
29 Greg Maddux 10.00 25.00
30 Sammy Sosa 6.00 15.00
31 Bret Boone 2.50 6.00
32 Barry Larkin 4.00 10.00
33 Reggie Sanders 2.50 6.00
34 Dante Bichette 2.50 6.00
35 Andres Galarraga 2.50 6.00
36 Charles Johnson 2.50 6.00
37 Gary Sheffield 2.50 6.00
38 Jeff Bagwell 4.00 10.00
39 Craig Biggio 4.00 10.00
40 Eric Karros 2.50 6.00
41 Billy Ashley 1.25 3.00
42 Raul Mondesi 2.50 6.00
43 Mike Piazza 10.00 25.00
44 Rondell White 2.50 6.00
45 Bret Saberhagen 2.50 6.00
46 Tony Gwynn 8.00 20.00
47 Melvin Nieves 1.25 3.00
48 Matt Williams 2.50 6.00

1996 SP

The 1996 SP set was issued in one series totalling 188 cards. The eight-card packs retailed for $4.19 each. Cards number 1-20 feature color action player photos with "Premier Prospects" printed in silver foil across the top and the player's name and team at the bottom in the border. The backs carry player information and statistics. Cards number 21-185 display unique player photos with an outer wood-grain border and inner thin platinum foil border as well as a small inset player shot. The only notable Rookie Card in this set is Darin Erstad.

COMPLETE SET (188) 15.00 40.00
1 Rey Ordonez FOIL .15 .40
2 George Arias FOIL .15 .40
3 Osvaldo Fernandez FOIL .15 .40
4 Darin Erstad FOIL RC 2.00 5.00
5 Paul Wilson FOIL .15 .40
6 Richard Hidalgo FOIL .15 .40
7 Justin Thompson FOIL .15 .40
8 Jimmy Haynes FOIL .15 .40
9 Edgar Renteria FOIL .15 .40
10 Ruben Rivera FOIL .15 .40
11 Chris Snopek FOIL .15 .40
12 Billy Wagner FOIL .15 .40
13 Mike Grace FOIL RC .15 .40
14 Todd Greene FOIL .15 .40
15 Karim Garcia FOIL .15 .40
16 John Wasdin FOIL .15 .40
17 Jason Kendall FOIL .15 .40
18 Bob Abreu FOIL .40 1.00
19 Jermaine Dye FOIL .15 .40
20 Jason Schmidt FOIL .25 .60
21 Javy Lopez .15 .40
22 Ryan Klesko .15 .40
23 Tom Glavine .25 .60
24 John Smoltz .25 .60
25 Greg Maddux .60 1.50
26 Chipper Jones .40 1.00
27 Fred McGriff .25 .60
28 David Justice .15 .40
29 Roberto Alomar .25 .60
30 Cal Ripken 1.25 3.00
31 B.J. Surhoff .15 .40
32 Bobby Bonilla .15 .40
33 Mike Mussina .25 .60
34 Randy Myers .15 .40
35 Rafael Palmeiro .25 .60
36 Brady Anderson .15 .40
37 Tim Naehring .15 .40
38 Jose Canseco .25 .60
39 Roger Clemens .75 2.00
40 Mo Vaughn .15 .40
41 John Valentin .15 .40
42 Kevin Mitchell .15 .40
43 Chili Davis .15 .40
44 Garret Anderson .15 .40
45 Tim Salmon .25 .60
46 Chuck Finley .15 .40
47 Troy Percival .15 .40
48 Jim Abbott .25 .60
49 J.T. Snow .15 .40
50 Jim Edmonds .15 .40
51 Sammy Sosa .40 1.00
52 Brian McRae .15 .40
53 Ryne Sandberg .60 1.50
54 Jaime Navarro .15 .40
55 Mark Grace .25 .60
56 Harold Baines .15 .40
57 Robin Ventura .15 .40
58 Tony Phillips .15 .40
59 Alex Fernandez .15 .40
60 Frank Thomas .40 1.00
61 Ray Durham .15 .40
62 Bret Boone .15 .40
63 Reggie Sanders .15 .40
64 Pete Schourek .15 .40
65 Barry Larkin .25 .60
66 John Smiley .15 .40
67 Carlos Baerga .15 .40
68 Jim Thome .25 .60
69 Eddie Murray .40 1.00
70 Albert Belle .15 .40
71 Dennis Martinez .15 .40
72 Jack McDowell .15 .40
73 Kenny Lofton .15 .40
74 Manny Ramirez .25 .60
75 Dante Bichette .15 .40
76 Vinny Castilla .15 .40
77 Andres Galarraga .15 .40
78 Walt Weiss .15 .40
79 Ellis Burks .15 .40
80 Larry Walker .15 .40
81 Cecil Fielder .15 .40
82 Melvin Nieves .15 .40
83 Travis Fryman .15 .40
84 Chad Curtis .15 .40
85 Alan Trammell .15 .40
86 Gary Sheffield .15 .40
87 Charles Johnson .15 .40
88 Andre Dawson .15 .40
89 Jeff Conine .15 .40
90 Greg Colbrunn .15 .40
91 Derek Bell .15 .40
92 Brian L.Hunter .15 .40
93 Doug Drabek .15 .40
94 Craig Biggio .25 .60
95 Jeff Bagwell .25 .60
96 Kevin Appier .15 .40
97 Jeff Montgomery .15 .40
98 Michael Tucker .15 .40
99 Bip Roberts .15 .40
100 Johnny Damon .25 .60
101 Eric Karros .15 .40
102 Raul Mondesi .15 .40
103 Ramon Martinez .15 .40
104 Ismael Valdes .15 .40
105 Mike Piazza .60 1.50
106 Hideo Nomo .40 1.00
107 Chan Ho Park .15 .40
108 Ben McDonald .15 .40
109 Kevin Seitzer .15 .40
110 Greg Vaughn .15 .40
111 Jose Valentin .15 .40
112 Rick Aguilera .15 .40
113 Marty Cordova .15 .40
114 Brad Radke .15 .40
115 Kirby Puckett .40 1.00
116 Chuck Knoblauch .15 .40
117 Paul Molitor .15 .40
118 Pedro Martinez .25 .60
119 Mike Lansing .15 .40
120 Rondell White .15 .40
121 Moises Alou .15 .40
122 Mark Grudzielanek .15 .40
123 Jeff Fassero .15 .40
124 Rico Brogna .15 .40
125 Jason Isringhausen .15 .40
126 Jeff Kent .15 .40
127 Bernard Gilkey .15 .40
128 Todd Hundley .15 .40
129 David Cone .15 .40
130 Andy Pettitte .25 .60
131 Wade Boggs .25 .60
132 Paul O'Neill .25 .60
133 Ruben Sierra .15 .40
134 John Wetteland .15 .40
135 Derek Jeter 1.00 2.50
136 Geronimo Berroa .15 .40
137 Terry Steinbach .15 .40
138 Ariel Prieto .15 .40
139 Scott Brosius .15 .40
140 Mark McGwire 1.00 2.50
141 Lenny Dykstra .15 .40
142 Todd Zeile .15 .40
143 Benito Santiago .15 .40
144 Mickey Morandini .15 .40
145 Gregg Jefferies .15 .40
146 Denny Neagle .15 .40
147 Orlando Merced .15 .40
148 Charlie Hayes .15 .40
149 Carlos Garcia .15 .40
150 Jay Bell .15 .40
151 Ray Lankford .15 .40
152 Alan Benes .15 .40
Andy Benes
153 Dennis Eckersley .15 .40
154 Gary Gaetti .15 .40
155 Ozzie Smith .60 1.50
156 Ron Gant .15 .40
157 Brian Jordan .15 .40
158 Ken Caminiti .15 .40
159 Rickey Henderson .40 1.00
160 Tony Gwynn .50 1.25
161 Wally Joyner .15 .40
162 Andy Ashby .15 .40
163 Steve Finley .15 .40
164 Glenallen Hill .15 .40
165 Matt Williams .15 .40
166 Barry Bonds 1.00 2.50
167 W. VanLandingham .15 .40
168 Rod Beck .15 .40
169 Randy Johnson .40 1.00
170 Ken Griffey Jr. .60 1.50
171 Alex Rodriguez .75 2.00
172 Edgar Martinez .25 .60
173 Jay Buhner .15 .40
174 Russ Davis .15 .40
175 Juan Gonzalez .15 .40
176 Mickey Tettleton .15 .40
177 Will Clark .25 .60
178 Ken Hill .15 .40
179 Dean Palmer .15 .40
180 Ivan Rodriguez .25 .60
181 Carlos Delgado .15 .40
182 Alex Gonzalez .15 .40
183 Shawn Green .15 .40
184 Juan Guzman .15 .40
185 Joe Carter .15 .40
186 Hideo Nomo CL UER .25 .60
Checklist lists Livan Hernandez as #4
187 Cal Ripken CL .60 1.50
188 Ken Griffey Jr. CL .40 1.00

1996 SP Baseball Heroes

This 10-card set was randomly inserted at the rate of one in 96 packs. It continues the insert set that was started in 1990 featuring ten of the top players in baseball. Please note these cards are condition sensitive and trade for premiums in Mint.

COMPLETE SET (10)	60.00	150.00
82 Frank Thomas	5.00	12.00
83 Albert Belle	2.00	5.00
84 Barry Bonds	12.50	30.00
85 Chipper Jones	5.00	12.00
86 Hideo Nomo	5.00	12.00
87 Mike Piazza	8.00	20.00
88 Manny Ramirez	3.00	8.00
89 Greg Maddux	8.00	20.00
90 Ken Griffey Jr.	8.00	20.00
NNO Ken Griffey Jr. HDR	8.00	20.00

1996 SP Marquee Matchups

Randomly inserted at the rate of one in five packs, this 20-card set highlights two superstars' cards with a common matching stadium background photograph in a blue border.

COMPLETE SET (20)	15.00	40.00
*DIE CUTS: 2X TO 5X BASIC MARQUEE		
DC STATED ODDS 1:61		
MM1 Ken Griffey Jr.	1.25	3.00
MM2 Hideo Nomo	.75	2.00
MM3 Derek Jeter	2.00	5.00
MM4 Rey Ordonez	.30	.75
MM5 Tim Salmon	.50	1.25
MM6 Mike Piazza	1.25	3.00
MM7 Mark McGwire	2.00	5.00
MM8 Barry Bonds	2.00	5.00
MM9 Cal Ripken	2.50	6.00
MM10 Greg Maddux	1.25	3.00
MM11 Albert Belle	.30	.75
MM12 Barry Larkin	.50	1.25
MM13 Jeff Bagwell	.50	1.25
MM14 Juan Gonzalez	.30	.75
MM15 Frank Thomas	.75	2.00
MM16 Sammy Sosa	.75	2.00
MM17 Mike Mussina	.50	1.25
MM18 Chipper Jones	.75	2.00
MM19 Roger Clemens	1.50	4.00
MM20 Fred McGriff	.50	1.25

1996 SP Special FX

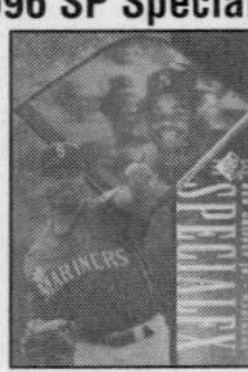

Randomly inserted at the rate of one in five packs, this 48-card set features a color action player cutout on a gold foil background with a holoview diamond shaped insert containing a black-and-white player portrait.

COMPLETE SET (48)	60.00	150.00
*DIE CUTS: 2X TO 5X BASIC SPECIAL FX		
DIE CUTS STATED ODDS 1:75		
1 Greg Maddux	3.00	8.00
2 Eric Karros	.75	2.00
3 Mike Piazza	3.00	8.00
4 Raul Mondesi	.75	2.00
5 Hideo Nomo	2.00	5.00
6 Jim Edmonds	.75	2.00
7 Jason Isringhausen	.75	2.00
8 Jay Buhner	.75	2.00
9 Barry Larkin	1.25	3.00
10 Ken Griffey Jr.	3.00	8.00
11 Gary Sheffield	.75	2.00
12 Craig Biggio	1.25	3.00
13 Paul Wilson	.75	2.00
14 Rondell White	.75	2.00
15 Chipper Jones	2.00	5.00
16 Kirby Puckett	2.00	5.00
17 Ron Gant	.75	2.00
18 Wade Boggs	1.25	3.00
19 Fred McGriff	1.25	3.00
20 Cal Ripken	6.00	15.00
21 Jason Kendall	.75	2.00
22 Johnny Damon	1.25	3.00
23 Kenny Lofton	.75	2.00
24 Roberto Alomar	1.25	3.00
25 Barry Bonds	5.00	12.00
26 Dante Bichette	.75	2.00
27 Mark McGwire	5.00	12.00
28 Rafael Palmeiro	1.25	3.00
29 Juan Gonzalez	.75	2.00
30 Albert Belle	.75	2.00
31 Randy Johnson	2.00	5.00
32 Jose Canseco	1.25	3.00
33 Sammy Sosa	2.00	5.00
34 Eddie Murray	2.00	5.00
35 Frank Thomas	2.00	5.00
36 Tom Glavine	1.25	3.00
37 Matt Williams	.75	2.00
38 Roger Clemens	4.00	10.00
39 Paul Molitor	.75	2.00
40 Tony Gwynn	2.50	6.00
41 Mo Vaughn	.75	2.00
42 Tim Salmon	1.25	3.00
43 Manny Ramirez	1.25	3.00
44 Jeff Bagwell	1.25	3.00
45 Edgar Martinez	1.25	3.00
46 Rey Ordonez	.75	2.00
47 Osvaldo Fernandez	.75	2.00
48 Derek Jeter	5.00	12.00

1997 SP

The 1997 SP set was issued in one series totalling 183 cards and was distributed in eight-card packs with a suggested retail of $4.39. Although unconfirmed by the manufacturer, it is perceived in some circles that cards numbered between 160 and 180 are in slightly shorter supply. Notable Rookie Cards include Jose Cruz Jr. and Hideki Irabu.

COMPLETE SET (184)	15.00	40.00
1 Andruw Jones FOIL	.40	1.00
2 Kevin Orie FOIL	.20	.50
3 Nomar Garciaparra FOIL	1.00	2.50
4 Jose Guillen FOIL	.30	.75
5 Todd Walker FOIL	.20	.50
6 Derrick Gibson FOIL	.20	.50
7 Aaron Boone FOIL	.30	.75
8 Bartolo Colon FOIL	.30	.75
9 Derrek Lee FOIL	.40	1.00
10 Vladimir Guerrero FOIL	.60	1.50
11 Wilton Guerrero FOIL	.20	.50
12 Luis Castillo FOIL	.20	.50
13 Jason Dickson FOIL	.20	.50
14 B.Trammell FOIL RC	.30	.75
15 Jose Cruz Jr. FOIL RC	.30	.75
16 Eddie Murray	.40	1.00
17 Darin Erstad	.15	.40
18 Garret Anderson	.15	.40
19 Jim Edmonds	.15	.40
20 Tim Salmon	.25	.60
21 Chuck Finley	.15	.40
22 John Smoltz	.25	.60
23 Greg Maddux	.60	1.50
24 Kenny Lofton	.15	.40
25 Chipper Jones	.40	1.00
26 Ryan Klesko	.15	.40
27 Javy Lopez	.15	.40
28 Fred McGriff	.25	.60
29 Roberto Alomar	.25	.60
30 Rafael Palmeiro	.25	.60
31 Mike Mussina	.25	.60
32 Brady Anderson	.15	.40
33 Rocky Coppinger	.15	.40
34 Cal Ripken	1.25	3.00
35 Mo Vaughn	.15	.40
36 Steve Avery	.15	.40
37 Tom Gordon	.15	.40
38 Tim Naehring	.15	.40
39 Troy O'Leary	.15	.40
40 Sammy Sosa	.40	1.00
41 Brian McRae	.15	.40
42 Mel Rojas	.15	.40
43 Ryne Sandberg	.60	1.50
44 Mark Grace	.25	.60
45 Albert Belle	.15	.40
46 Robin Ventura	.15	.40
47 Roberto Hernandez	.15	.40
48 Ray Durham	.15	.40
49 Harold Baines	.15	.40
50 Frank Thomas	.40	1.00
51 Bret Boone	.15	.40
52 Reggie Sanders	.15	.40
53 Deion Sanders	.25	.60
54 Hal Morris	.15	.40
55 Barry Larkin	.25	.60
56 Jim Thome	.25	.60
57 Marquis Grissom	.15	.40
58 David Justice	.15	.40
59 Charles Nagy	.15	.40
60 Manny Ramirez	.25	.60
61 Matt Williams	.15	.40
62 Jack McDowell	.15	.40
63 Vinny Castilla	.15	.40
64 Dante Bichette	.15	.40
65 Andres Galarraga	.15	.40
66 Ellis Burks	.15	.40
67 Larry Walker	.15	.40
68 Eric Young	.15	.40
69 Brian L. Hunter	.15	.40
70 Travis Fryman	.15	.40
71 Tony Clark	.15	.40
72 Bobby Higginson	.15	.40
73 Melvin Nieves	.15	.40
74 Jeff Conine	.15	.40
75 Gary Sheffield	.15	.40
76 Moises Alou	.15	.40
77 Edgar Renteria	.15	.40
78 Alex Fernandez	.15	.40
79 Charles Johnson	.15	.40
80 Bobby Bonilla	.15	.40
81 Darryl Kile	.15	.40
82 Derek Bell	.15	.40
83 Shane Reynolds	.15	.40
84 Craig Biggio	.25	.60
85 Jeff Bagwell	.25	.60
86 Billy Wagner	.15	.40
87 Chili Davis	.15	.40
88 Kevin Appier	.15	.40
89 Jay Bell	.15	.40
90 Johnny Damon	.25	.60
91 Jeff King	.15	.40
92 Hideo Nomo	.40	1.00
93 Todd Hollandsworth	.15	.40
94 Eric Karros	.15	.40
95 Mike Piazza	.60	1.50
96 Ramon Martinez	.15	.40
97 Todd Worrell	.15	.40
98 Raul Mondesi	.15	.40
99 Dave Nilsson	.15	.40
100 John Jaha	.15	.40
101 Jose Valentin	.15	.40
102 Jeff Cirillo	.15	.40
103 Jeff D'Amico	.15	.40
104 Ben McDonald	.15	.40
105 Paul Molitor	.15	.40
106 Rich Becker	.15	.40
107 Frank Rodriguez	.15	.40
108 Marty Cordova	.15	.40
109 Terry Steinbach	.15	.40
110 Chuck Knoblauch	.15	.40
111 Mark Grudzielanek	.15	.40
112 Mike Lansing	.15	.40
113 Pedro Martinez	.25	.60
114 Henry Rodriguez	.15	.40
115 Rondell White	.15	.40
116 Rey Ordonez	.15	.40
117 Carlos Baerga	.15	.40
118 Lance Johnson	.15	.40
119 Bernard Gilkey	.15	.40
120 Todd Hundley	.15	.40
121 John Franco	.15	.40
122 Bernie Williams	.25	.60
123 David Cone	.15	.40
124 Cecil Fielder	.15	.40
125 Derek Jeter	1.00	2.50
126 Tino Martinez	.25	.60
127 Mariano Rivera	.40	1.00
128 Andy Pettitte	.25	.60
129 Wade Boggs	.25	.60
130 Mark McGwire	1.00	2.50
131 Jose Canseco	.25	.60
132 Geronimo Berroa	.15	.40
133 Jason Giambi	.15	.40
134 Ernie Young	.15	.40
135 Scott Rolen	.25	.60
136 Ricky Bottalico	.15	.40
137 Curt Schilling	.15	.40
138 Gregg Jefferies	.15	.40
139 Mickey Morandini	.15	.40
140 Jason Kendall	.15	.40
141 Kevin Elster	.15	.40
142 Al Martin	.15	.40
143 Joe Randa	.15	.40
144 Jason Schmidt	.15	.40
145 Ray Lankford	.15	.40
146 Brian Jordan	.15	.40
147 Andy Benes	.15	.40
148 Alan Benes	.15	.40
149 Gary Gaetti	.15	.40
150 Ron Gant	.15	.40
151 Dennis Eckersley	.15	.40
152 Rickey Henderson	.40	1.00
153 Joey Hamilton	.15	.40
154 Ken Caminiti	.15	.40
155 Tony Gwynn	.50	1.25
156 Steve Finley	.15	.40
157 Trevor Hoffman	.15	.40
158 Greg Vaughn	.15	.40
159 J.T.Snow	.15	.40
160 Barry Bonds	1.00	2.50
161 Glenallen Hill	.15	.40
162 Bill Van Landingham	.15	.40
163 Jeff Kent	.15	.40
164 Jay Buhner	.15	.40
165 Ken Griffey Jr.	.60	1.50
166 Alex Rodriguez	.60	1.50
167 Randy Johnson	.40	1.00
168 Edgar Martinez	.25	.60
169 Dan Wilson	.15	.40
170 Ivan Rodriguez	.25	.60
171 Roger Pavlik	.15	.40
172 Will Clark	.25	.60
173 Dean Palmer	.15	.40
174 Rusty Greer	.15	.40
175 Juan Gonzalez	.15	.40
176 John Wetteland	.15	.40
177 Joe Carter	.15	.40
178 Ed Sprague	.15	.40
179 Carlos Delgado	.15	.40
180 Roger Clemens	.75	2.00
181 Juan Guzman	.15	.40
182 Pat Hentgen	.15	.40
183 Ken Griffey Jr. CL	.40	1.00
184 Hideki Irabu RC	.15	.40

1997 SP Game Film

Randomly inserted in packs, this 10-card set features actual game film that highlights the accomplishments of some of the League's greatest players. Only 500 of each card in this crash numbered, limited edition set were produced.

COMPLETE SET (10)	75.00	200.00
GF1 Alex Rodriguez	10.00	25.00
GF2 Frank Thomas	6.00	15.00
GF3 Andruw Jones	6.00	15.00
GF4 Cal Ripken	20.00	50.00
GF5 Mike Piazza	10.00	25.00
GF6 Derek Jeter	15.00	40.00
GF7 Mark McGwire	15.00	40.00
GF8 Chipper Jones	6.00	15.00
GF9 Barry Bonds	15.00	40.00
GF10 Ken Griffey Jr.	10.00	25.00

1997 SP Griffey Heroes

This 10-card continuation insert set pays special tribute to one of the game's most talented players and features color photos of Ken Griffey Jr. Only 2,000 of each card in this crash numbered, limited edition set were produced.

COMPLETE SET (10)	20.00	50.00
COMMON CARD (91-100)	3.00	8.00

1997 SP Inside Info

Inserted one in every 30-pack box, this 25-card set features color player photos on original cards with an exclusive pull-out panel that details the accomplishments of the League's brightest stars. Please note these cards are condition sensitive and trade for premium values in Mint condition.

COMPLETE SET (25)	60.00	150.00
1 Ken Griffey Jr.	4.00	10.00
2 Mark McGwire	6.00	15.00
3 Kenny Lofton	1.00	2.50
4 Paul Molitor	1.00	2.50
5 Frank Thomas	2.50	6.00
6 Greg Maddux	4.00	10.00
7 Mo Vaughn	1.00	2.50
8 Cal Ripken	8.00	20.00
9 Jeff Bagwell	1.50	4.00
10 Alex Rodriguez	4.00	10.00
11 John Smoltz	1.50	4.00
12 Manny Ramirez	1.50	4.00
13 Sammy Sosa	2.50	6.00
14 Vladimir Guerrero	4.00	10.00
15 Albert Belle	1.00	2.50
16 Mike Piazza	4.00	10.00
17 Derek Jeter	6.00	15.00
18 Scott Rolen	1.50	4.00
19 Tony Gwynn	3.00	8.00
20 Barry Bonds	6.00	15.00
21 Ken Caminiti	1.00	2.50
22 Chipper Jones	2.50	6.00
23 Juan Gonzalez	1.00	2.50
24 Roger Clemens	5.00	12.00
25 Andruw Jones	2.50	6.00

1997 SP Marquee Matchups

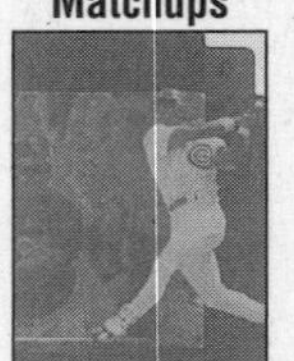

Randomly inserted in packs at a rate of one in five, this 20-card set features color player images on die-cut cards that match-up the best pitchers and hitters from around the League.

COMPLETE SET (20)	20.00	50.00
MM1 Ken Griffey Jr.	1.25	3.00
MM2 Andres Galarraga	.30	.75
MM3 Barry Bonds	2.00	5.00
MM4 Mark McGwire	2.00	5.00
MM5 Mike Piazza	1.25	3.00
MM6 Tim Salmon	.50	1.25
MM7 Tony Gwynn	1.00	2.50
MM8 Alex Rodriguez	1.25	3.00
MM9 Chipper Jones	.75	2.00
MM10 Derek Jeter	2.00	5.00
MM11 Manny Ramirez	.50	1.25
MM12 Jeff Bagwell	.50	1.25
MM13 Greg Maddux	1.25	3.00
MM14 Cal Ripken	2.50	6.00
MM15 Mo Vaughn	.30	.75
MM16 Gary Sheffield	.30	.75
MM17 Jim Thome	.50	1.25
MM18 Barry Larkin	.50	1.25
MM19 Frank Thomas	.75	2.00
MM20 Sammy Sosa	.75	2.00

1997 SP Special FX

Randomly inserted in packs at a rate of one in nine, this 48-card set features color player photos on Holoview cards with the Special F/X die-cut design. Cards numbers 1-47 are from 1997 with card number 49 featuring a design from 1996. There is no card number 48.

COMPLETE SET (48)	80.00	200.00
1 Ken Griffey Jr.	3.00	8.00
2 Frank Thomas	2.00	5.00
3 Barry Bonds	5.00	12.00
4 Albert Belle	.75	2.00
5 Mike Piazza	3.00	8.00
6 Greg Maddux	3.00	8.00
7 Chipper Jones	2.00	5.00
8 Cal Ripken	6.00	15.00
9 Jeff Bagwell	1.25	3.00
10 Alex Rodriguez	3.00	8.00
11 Mark McGwire	5.00	12.00
12 Kenny Lofton	.75	2.00
13 Juan Gonzalez	.75	2.00
14 Mo Vaughn	.75	2.00
15 John Smoltz	1.25	3.00
16 Derek Jeter	5.00	12.00
17 Tony Gwynn	2.50	6.00
18 Ivan Rodriguez	1.25	3.00
19 Barry Larkin	1.25	3.00
20 Sammy Sosa	2.00	5.00
21 Mike Mussina	1.25	3.00
22 Gary Sheffield	.75	2.00
23 Brady Anderson	.75	2.00
24 Roger Clemens	4.00	10.00
25 Ken Caminiti	.75	2.00
26 Roberto Alomar	1.25	3.00
27 Hideo Nomo	2.00	5.00
28 Bernie Williams	1.25	3.00
29 Todd Hundley	.75	2.00
30 Manny Ramirez	1.25	3.00
31 Eric Karros	.75	2.00
32 Tim Salmon	1.25	3.00
33 Jay Buhner	.75	2.00
34 Andy Pettitte	1.25	3.00
35 Jim Thome	1.25	3.00
36 Ryne Sandberg	3.00	8.00
37 Matt Williams	.75	2.00
38 Ryan Klesko	.75	2.00
39 Jose Canseco	1.25	3.00
40 Paul Molitor	.75	2.00
41 Eddie Murray	2.00	5.00
42 Darin Erstad	.75	2.00
43 Todd Walker	1.00	2.50
44 Wade Boggs	1.25	3.00
45 Andruw Jones	2.00	5.00
46 Scott Rolen	1.25	3.00
47 Vladimir Guerrero	3.00	8.00
49 Alex Rodriguez '96	4.00	10.00

1997 SP SPx Force

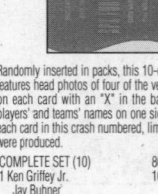

Randomly inserted in packs, this 10-card die-cut set features head photos of four of the very best players on each card with an "X" in the background and players' and teams' names on one side. Only 500 of each card in this crash numbered, limited edition set were produced.

COMPLETE SET (10)	80.00	200.00
1 Ken Griffey Jr.	10.00	25.00
Jay Buhner		
Andres Galarraga		
Dante Bichette		
2 Albert Belle	15.00	40.00
Brady Anderson		
Mark McGwire		
Cecil Fielder		
3 Mo Vaughn	6.00	15.00
Ken Caminiti		
Frank Thomas		
Jeff Bagwell		
4 Gary Sheffield	6.00	15.00
Sammy Sosa		
Barry Bonds		
Jose Canseco		
5 Greg Maddux	10.00	25.00
Roger Clemens		
John Smoltz		
Randy Johnson		
6 Alex Rodriguez	15.00	40.00
Derek Jeter		
Chipper Jones		
Rey Ordonez		
7 Todd Hollandsworth	10.00	25.00
Mike Piazza		
Raul Mondesi		
Hideo Nomo		
8 Juan Gonzalez	4.00	10.00
Manny Ramirez		
Roberto Alomar		
Ivan Rodriguez		
9 Tony Gwynn	8.00	20.00
Wade Boggs		
Eddie Murray		
Paul Molitor		
10 Andruw Jones	10.00	25.00
Vladimir Guerrero		
Todd Walker		
Scott Rolen		

1997 SP SPx Force Autographs

Randomly inserted in packs, this 10-card set is an autographed parallel version of the regular SPx Force set. Only 100 of each card in this crash numbered, limited edition set were produced. Mo Vaughn packed out as an exchange card.

Card	Low	High
1 Ken Griffey Jr.	75.00	150.00
2 Albert Belle	15.00	40.00
3 Mo Vaughn	15.00	40.00
4 Gary Sheffield	20.00	50.00
5 Greg Maddux	75.00	150.00
6 Alex Rodriguez	125.00	200.00
7 Todd Hollandsworth	10.00	25.00
8 Roberto Alomar	20.00	50.00
9 Tony Gwynn	40.00	80.00
10 Andruw Jones	20.00	50.00

1997 SP Vintage Autographs

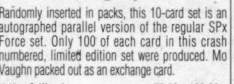

Randomly inserted in packs, this set features authenticated original 1993-1996 SP cards that have been autographed by the pictured player. The print runs are listed after year following the player's name in our checklist. Some of the very short printed autographs are listed but not priced. Each card came in the pack along with a standard size certificate of authenticity. These certificates are usually included when these autographed cards are traded. The 1997 Mo Vaughn card was available only as a mail-in exchange. Upper Deck seeded 250 '97 SP Vaughn cards into packs each carrying a large circular sticker on front. UD sent Mo 300 cards to sign, hoping that he'd sign at least 250 cards and actually received 293 cards back. The additional 43 cards were sent to UD's Quality Assurance area. An additional Mo Vaughn card, hailing from 1995, surfaced in early 2001. This set now stands as one of the most important issues of the 1990's in that it was the first to feature the popular "buy-back" concept widely used in the 2000's.

Card	Low	High
1 Jeff Bagwell 93/7		
2 Jeff Bagwell 95/173	30.00	60.00
3 Jeff Bagwell 96/292	20.00	50.00
4 Jeff Bagwell 96 MM/23		
5 Jay Buhner 95/57	15.00	40.00
6 Jay Buhner 96/79	15.00	40.00
7 Jay Buhner 96 FX/27	20.00	50.00
8 Ken Griffey Jr. 93/16		
9 Ken Griffey Jr. 93 PP/5		
10 Ken Griffey Jr. 94/103	40.00	80.00
11 Ken Griffey Jr. 95/38	75.00	150.00
12 Ken Griffey Jr. 96/312	40.00	80.00
13 Tony Gwynn 93/17		
14 Tony Gwynn 94/367	15.00	40.00
15 Tony Gwynn 94 HV/31	60.00	120.00
16 Tony Gwynn 95/64	30.00	60.00
17 Tony Gwynn 96/20		
18 Todd Hollandsworth 94/167	6.00	15.00
19 Chipper Jones 93/34	50.00	100.00
20 Chipper Jones 95/60	40.00	80.00
21 Chipper Jones 96/102	30.00	60.00
22 Rey Ordonez 96/111	6.00	15.00
23 R.Ordonez '96 MM/40	10.00	25.00
24 Alex Rodriguez 94/94	1000.00	1600.00
25 Alex Rodriguez 95/63	75.00	150.00
26 Alex Rodriguez 96/73	75.00	150.00
27 Gary Sheffield 94/130	15.00	40.00
28 Gary Sheffield 94 HVDC/4		
29 Gary Sheffield 95/221	10.00	25.00
30 Gary Sheffield 96/58	30.00	60.00
31 Mo Vaughn 95/75	15.00	40.00
32 Mo Vaughn 97/293	6.00	15.00

1998 SP Authentic

The 1998 SP Authentic set was issued in one series totalling 198 cards. The five-card packs retailed for $4.99 each. The set contains the topical subset: Future Watch (1-30). Rookie Cards include Maggio Ordonez. A sample card featuring Ken Griffey Jr. was issued prior to the product's release and distributed along with dealer order forms. The card is identical to the basic issue Griffey Jr. card (number 123) except for the term "SAMPLE" in red print running diagonally against the card back.

COMPLETE SET (198)	15.00	40.00
1 Travis Lee FOIL	.15	.40
2 Mike Caruso FOIL	.15	.40
3 Kerry Wood FOIL	.20	.50
4 Mark Kotsay FOIL	.15	.40
5 Magglio Ordonez FOIL RC	5.00	12.00
6 Scott Elarton FOIL	.15	.40
7 Carl Pavano FOIL	.15	.40
8 A.J. Hinch FOIL	.15	.40
9 Rolando Arrojo FOIL RC	.15	.40
10 Ben Grieve FOIL	.15	.40
11 Gabe Alvarez FOIL	.15	.40
12 Mike Kinkade FOIL RC	.15	.40
13 Bruce Chen FOIL	.15	.40
14 Juan Encarnacion FOIL	.15	.40
15 Todd Helton FOIL	.25	.60
16 Aaron Boone FOIL	.15	.40
17 Sean Casey FOIL	.15	.40
18 R.Hernandez FOIL	.15	.40
19 Daryle Ward FOIL	.15	.40
20 Paul Konerko FOIL	.15	.40
21 David Ortiz FOIL	.50	1.25
22 Derrek Lee FOIL	.25	.60
23 Brad Fullmer FOIL	.15	.40
24 Javier Vazquez FOIL	.15	.40
25 Miguel Tejada FOIL	.40	1.00
26 Dave Dellucci FOIL RC	.25	.60
27 Alex Gonzalez FOIL	.15	.40
28 Matt Clement FOIL	.15	.40
29 Masato Yoshii FOIL RC	.15	.40
30 Russell Branyan FOIL	.15	.40
31 Chuck Finley	.15	.40
32 Jim Edmonds	.15	.40
33 Darin Erstad	.15	.40
34 Jason Dickson	.15	.40
35 Tim Salmon	.25	.60
36 Cecil Fielder	.15	.40
37 Todd Greene	.15	.40
38 Andy Benes	.15	.40
39 Jay Bell	.15	.40
40 Matt Williams	.15	.40
41 Brian Anderson	.15	.40
42 Karim Garcia	.15	.40
43 Javy Lopez	.15	.40
44 Tom Glavine	.25	.60
45 Greg Maddux	.60	1.50
46 Andruw Jones	.25	.60
47 Chipper Jones	.40	1.00
48 Ryan Klesko	.15	.40
49 John Smoltz	.25	.60
50 Andres Galarraga	.15	.40
51 Rafael Palmeiro	.25	.60
52 Mike Mussina	.25	.60
53 Roberto Alomar	.25	.60

54 Joe Carter .15 .40
55 Cal Ripken 1.25 3.00
56 Brady Anderson .15 .40
57 Mo Vaughn .15 .40
58 John Valentin .15 .40
59 Dennis Eckersley .15 .40
60 Nomar Garciaparra .60 1.50
61 Pedro Martinez .25 .60
62 Jeff Blauser .15 .40
63 Kevin Orie .15 .40
64 Henry Rodriguez .15 .40
65 Mark Grace .25 .60
66 Albert Belle .15 .40
67 Mike Cameron .15 .40
68 Robin Ventura .15 .40
69 Frank Thomas .40 1.00
70 Barry Larkin .25 .60
71 Brett Tomko UER .15 .40
1 Yr Total is Wrong
72 Willie Greene .15 .40
73 Reggie Sanders .15 .40
74 Sandy Alomar Jr. .15 .40
75 Kenny Lofton .15 .40
76 Jaret Wright .15 .40
77 David Justice .15 .40
78 Omar Vizquel .25 .60
79 Manny Ramirez .25 .60
80 Jim Thome .25 .60
81 Travis Fryman .15 .40
82 Neifi Perez .15 .40
83 Mike Lansing .15 .40
84 Vinny Castilla .15 .40
85 Larry Walker .15 .40
86 Dante Bichette .15 .40
87 Darryl Kile .15 .40
88 Justin Thompson .15 .40
89 Damion Easley .15 .40
90 Tony Clark .15 .40
91 Bobby Higginson .15 .40
92 Brian Hunter .15 .40
93 Edgar Renteria .15 .40
94 Craig Counsell .15 .40
95 Mike Piazza .60 1.50
96 Livan Hernandez .15 .40
97 Todd Zeile .15 .40
98 Richard Hidalgo .15 .40
99 Moises Alou .15 .40
100 Jeff Bagwell .25 .60
101 Mike Hampton .15 .40
102 Craig Biggio .25 .60
103 Dean Palmer .15 .40
104 Tim Belcher .15 .40
105 Jeff King .15 .40
106 Jeff Conine .15 .40
107 Johnny Damon .25 .60
108 Hideo Nomo .40 1.00
109 Raul Mondesi .15 .40
110 Gary Sheffield .15 .40
111 Ramon Martinez .15 .40
112 Chan Ho Park .15 .40
113 Eric Young .15 .40
114 Charles Johnson .15 .40
115 Eric Karros .15 .40
116 Bobby Bonilla .15 .40
117 Jeromy Burnitz .15 .40
118 Cal Eldred .15 .40
119 Jeff D'Amico .15 .40
120 Marquis Grissom .15 .40
121 Dave Nilsson .15 .40
122 Brad Radke .15 .40
123 Marty Cordova .15 .40
124 Ron Coomer .15 .40
125 Paul Molitor .15 .40
126 Todd Walker .15 .40
127 Rondell White .15 .40
128 Mark Grudzielanek .15 .40
129 Carlos Perez .15 .40
130 Vladimir Guerrero .40 1.00
131 Dustin Hermanson .15 .40
132 Butch Huskey .15 .40
133 John Franco .15 .40
134 Rey Ordonez .15 .40
135 Todd Hundley .15 .40
136 Edgardo Alfonzo .15 .40
137 Bobby Jones .15 .40
138 John Olerud .15 .40
139 Chili Davis .15 .40
140 Tino Martinez .25 .60
141 Andy Pettitte .25 .60
142 Chuck Knoblauch .15 .40
143 Bernie Williams .25 .60
144 David Cone .15 .40
145 Derek Jeter 1.00 2.50
146 Paul O'Neill .25 .60
147 Rickey Henderson .40 1.00
148 Jason Giambi .15 .40
149 Kenny Rogers .15 .40
150 Scott Rolen .25 .60
151 Curt Schilling .15 .40
152 Ricky Bottalico .15 .40
153 Mike Lieberthal .15 .40
154 Francisco Cordova .15 .40
155 Jose Guillen .15 .40
156 Jason Schmidt .15 .40
157 Jason Kendall .15 .40
158 Kevin Young .15 .40
159 Delino DeShields .15 .40
160 Mark McGwire 1.00 2.50
161 Ray Lankford .15 .40
162 Brian Jordan .15 .40
163 Ron Gant .15 .40
164 Todd Stottlemyre .15 .40
165 Ken Caminiti .15 .40
166 Kevin Brown .25 .60
167 Trevor Hoffman .15 .40
168 Steve Finley .15 .40
169 Wally Joyner .15 .40
170 Tony Gwynn .50 1.25
171 Shawn Estes .15 .40
172 J.T. Snow .15 .40
173 Jeff Kent .15 .40
174 Robb Nen .15 .40
175 Barry Bonds 1.00 2.50
176 Randy Johnson .40 1.00
177 Edgar Martinez .25 .60
178 Jay Buhner .15 .40
179 Alex Rodriguez .60 1.50
180 Ken Griffey Jr. .60 1.50
181 Ken Cloude .15 .40
182 Wade Boggs .25 .60
183 Tony Saunders .15 .40
184 Wilson Alvarez .15 .40
185 Fred McGriff .25 .60
186 Roberto Hernandez .15 .40
187 Kevin Stocker .15 .40
188 Fernando Tatis .15 .40
189 Will Clark .25 .60
190 Juan Gonzalez .15 .40
191 Rusty Greer .15 .40
192 Ivan Rodriguez .25 .60
193 Jose Canseco .25 .60
194 Carlos Delgado .15 .40
195 Roger Clemens .75 2.00
196 Pat Hentgen .15 .40
197 Randy Myers .15 .40
198 Ken Griffey Jr. CL .40 1.00
S123 Ken Griffey Jr. Sample .75 2.00

1998 SP Authentic Chirography

Randomly inserted in packs at a rate of one in 25, this 31-card set is autographed by the league's top players. The Ken Griffey Jr. card was actually not available in packs. Instead, an exchange card was printed and seeded into packs. Collectors had until July 27th, 1999 to redeem these Griffey exchange cards. A selection of players were short-printed to 400 or 800 copies. These cards, however, are not serial numbered.

AJ Andruw Jones 10.00 25.00
AR Alex Rodriguez SP/800 60.00 120.00
BG Ben Grieve 6.00 15.00
CJ Charles Johnson 6.00 15.00
CP Chipper Jones SP/800 20.00 50.00
DE Darin Erstad 6.00 15.00
GS Gary Sheffield 10.00 25.00
IR Ivan Rodriguez 15.00 40.00
JC Jose Cruz Jr. 6.00 15.00
JW Jaret Wright 6.00 15.00
KG Ken Griffey Jr. SP/400 50.00 100.00
KGEX K.Griffey Jr. EXCH 6.00 15.00
LH Livan Hernandez 6.00 15.00
MK Mark Kotsay 6.00 15.00
MM Mike Mussina 10.00 25.00
MT Miguel Tejada 15.00 40.00
MV Mo Vaughn SP800 6.00 15.00
NG N. Garciaparra SP400 60.00 120.00
PK Paul Konerko 10.00 25.00
PM Paul Molitor SP/800 6.00 15.00
RA R. Alomar SP/800 10.00 25.00
RB Russell Branyan 6.00 15.00
RC R. Clemens SP/400 60.00 120.00
RL Ray Lankford 6.00 15.00
SC Sean Casey 6.00 15.00
SR Scott Rolen 10.00 25.00
TC Tony Clark 6.00 15.00
TG Tony Gwynn SP/850 15.00 40.00
TH Todd Helton 10.00 25.00
TL Travis Lee 6.00 15.00
VG Vladimir Guerrero 8.00 20.00

1998 SP Authentic Griffey 300th HR Redemption

This 5" by 7" card is the redemption one received for mailing in the Ken Griffey Jr. 300 Home Run card available in the SP Authentic packs.

300 Ken Griffey Jr. 12.50 30.00

1998 SP Authentic Game Jersey 5 x 7

These attractive 5" by 7" memorabilia cards are the items one received when redeeming the SP Authentic Trade Cards (of which were randomly seeded into 1998 SP Authentic packs at a rate of 1:291). The 5 x 7 cards feature a larger swatch of the jersey on them as compared to a standard size Game Jersey card. The exchange deadline expired back on August 1st, 1999.

1 Ken Griffey Jr./125 75.00 150.00
2 Gary Sheffield/125 10.00 25.00
3 Greg Maddux/125 40.00 80.00
4 Alex Rodriguez/125 40.00 80.00
5 Tony Gwynn/415 20.00 50.00
6 Jay Buhner/125 10.00 25.00

1998 SP Authentic Sheer Dominance

Randomly inserted in packs at a rate of one in three, this 42-card set has a mix of stars and young players and were issued in three different versions.

COMPLETE SET (42) 40.00 100.00
*GOLD: 1.25X TO 3X BASIC DOMINANCE
GOLD: RANDOM INSERTS IN PACKS
GOLD PRINT RUN 2000 SERIAL #'d SETS 1.00 2.50
*TITANIUM: 3X TO 8X BASIC DOMINANCE
TITANIUM: RANDOM INSERTS IN PACKS
TITANIUM PRINT RUN 100 SERIAL #'d SETS
SD1 Ken Griffey Jr. 1.50 4.00
SD2 Rickey Henderson 1.00 2.50
SD3 Jaret Wright .40 1.00
SD4 Craig Biggio .60 1.50
SD5 Travis Lee .40 1.00
SD6 Kenny Lofton .40 1.00
SD7 Raul Mondesi .40 1.00
SD8 Cal Ripken 3.00 8.00
SD9 Matt Williams .40 1.00
SD10 Mark McGwire 2.50 6.00
SD11 Alex Rodriguez 1.50 4.00
SD12 Fred McGriff .60 1.50
SD13 Scott Rolen .60 1.50
SD14 Paul Molitor .40 1.00
SD15 Nomar Garciaparra 1.50 4.00
SD16 Vladimir Guerrero 1.00 2.50
SD17 Andruw Jones .60 1.50
SD18 Manny Ramirez .60 1.50
SD19 Tony Gwynn 1.25 3.00
SD20 Barry Bonds 2.50 6.00
SD21 Ben Grieve .40 1.00
SD22 Ivan Rodriguez .60 1.50
SD23 Jose Cruz Jr. 1.00 2.50
SD24 Pedro Martinez .60 1.50
SD25 Chipper Jones 1.00 2.50
SD26 Albert Belle .40 1.00
SD27 Todd Helton .60 1.50
SD28 Paul Konerko .40 1.00
SD29 Sammy Sosa 1.00 2.50
SD30 Frank Thomas 1.00 2.50
SD31 Greg Maddux 1.50 4.00
SD32 Randy Johnson 1.00 2.50
SD33 Larry Walker .40 1.00
SD34 Roberto Alomar .60 1.50
SD35 Roger Clemens 2.00 5.00
SD36 Mo Vaughn .40 1.00
SD37 Jim Thome .60 1.50
SD38 Jeff Bagwell .60 1.50
SD39 Tino Martinez .60 1.50
SD40 Mike Piazza 1.50 4.00
SD41 Derek Jeter 2.50 6.00
SD42 Juan Gonzalez .40 1.00

1998 SP Authentic Trade Cards

Randomly seeded into packs at a rate of 1:291, these fifteen different trade cards could be redeemed for an assortion of UDA material. Specific quantities for each item are detailed below after each player name. The deadline to redeem these cards was August 1st, 1999. It is important to note that the redemption items came from UDA back stock and in many cases the card is far mor valuable than the redemption prize.

COMMON CARD (B1-B5) 6.00 15.00
COMMON CARD (J1-J6) 6.00 15.00
COMMON CARD (KG1-KG4) 6.00 15.00
B1 Roberto Alomar 10.00 25.00
Ball 100
B2 Albert Belle 6.00 15.00
Ball 100
B3 Brian Jordan 6.00 15.00
Ball 50
B4 Raul Mondesi 6.00 15.00
Ball 100
B5 Robin Ventura 10.00 25.00
Ball 50
J1 Jay Buhner 6.00 15.00
Jersey Card 125
J2 Ken Griffey Jr. 25.00 60.00
Jersey Card 125
J3 Tony Gwynn 10.00 25.00
Jersey Card 415
J4 Greg Maddux 25.00 60.00
Jersey Card 125
J5 Alex Rodriguez 20.00 50.00
Jersey Card 125
J6 Gary Sheffield 6.00 15.00
Jersey Card 125
KG1 Ken Griffey Jr. 6.00 15.00
300 Card 1000 made
KG2 Ken Griffey Jr.
Auto Glove 30
KG3 Ken Griffey Jr.
Auto Jersey 30
KG4 Ken Griffey Jr. 10.00 25.00
Standee 200

1999 SP Authentic

The 1999 SP Authentic set was issued in one series totalling 135 cards and distributed in five-card packs with a suggested retail price of $4.99. The fronts feature color action player photos with player information printed on the backs. The set features the following limited edition subsets: Future Watch (91-120) serially numbered to 2700 and Season to Remember (121-135) numbered to 2700 also. 350 Ernie Banks A Piece of History 500 Club bat cards were randomly seeded into packs. Also, Banks signed and numbered twenty additional copies. Pricing for these bat cards can be referenced under 1999 Upper Deck A Piece of History 500 Club.

COMP.SET w/o SP's (90) 10.00 25.00
COMMON CARD (1-90) .15 .40
COMMON FW (91-120) 4.00 10.00
COMMON STR (121-135) 1.25 3.00
1 Mo Vaughn .15 .40
2 Jim Edmonds .15 .40
3 Darin Erstad .15 .40
4 Travis Lee .15 .40
5 Matt Williams .15 .40
6 Randy Johnson .40 1.00
7 Chipper Jones .40 1.00
8 Greg Maddux .60 1.50
9 Andruw Jones .25 .60
10 Andres Galarraga .15 .40
11 Tom Glavine .25 .60
12 Cal Ripken 1.25 3.00
13 Brady Anderson .15 .40
14 Albert Belle .15 .40
15 Nomar Garciaparra .60 1.50
16 Donnie Sadler .15 .40
17 Pedro Martinez .25 .60
18 Sammy Sosa .40 1.00
19 Kerry Wood .15 .40
20 Mark Grace .25 .60
21 Mike Caruso .15 .40
22 Frank Thomas .40 1.00
23 Paul Konerko .15 .40
24 Sean Casey .15 .40
25 Barry Larkin .25 .60
26 Kenny Lofton .15 .40
27 Manny Ramirez .25 .60
28 Jim Thome .25 .60
29 Bartolo Colon .15 .40
30 Jaret Wright .15 .40
31 Larry Walker .15 .40
32 Todd Helton .25 .60
33 Tony Clark .15 .40
34 Dean Palmer .15 .40
35 Mark Kotsay .15 .40
36 Cliff Floyd .15 .40
37 Ken Caminiti .15 .40
38 Craig Biggio .25 .60
39 Jeff Bagwell .25 .60
40 Moises Alou .15 .40
41 Johnny Damon .25 .60
42 Larry Sutton .15 .40
43 Kevin Brown .25 .60
44 Gary Sheffield .15 .40
45 Raul Mondesi .15 .40
46 Jeromy Burnitz .15 .40
47 Jeff Cirillo .15 .40
48 Todd Walker .15 .40
49 David Ortiz .40 1.00
50 Brad Radke .15 .40
51 Vladimir Guerrero .40 1.00
52 Rondell White .15 .40
53 Brad Fullmer .15 .40
54 Mike Piazza .60 1.50
55 Robin Ventura .15 .40
56 John Olerud .15 .40
57 Derek Jeter 1.00 2.50
58 Tino Martinez .25 .60
59 Bernie Williams .25 .60
60 Roger Clemens .75 2.00
61 Ben Grieve .15 .40
62 Miguel Tejada .15 .40
63 A.J. Hinch .15 .40
64 Scott Rolen .25 .60
65 Curt Schilling .15 .40
66 Doug Glanville .15 .40
67 Aramis Ramirez .15 .40
68 Tony Womack .15 .40
69 Jason Kendall .15 .40
70 Tony Gwynn .50 1.25
71 Wally Joyner .15 .40
72 Greg Vaughn .15 .40
73 Barry Bonds 1.00 2.50
74 Ellis Burks .15 .40
75 Jeff Kent .15 .40
76 Ken Griffey Jr. .60 1.50
77 Alex Rodriguez .60 1.50
78 Edgar Martinez .25 .60
79 Mark McGwire 1.00 2.50
80 Eli Marrero .15 .40
81 Matt Morris .15 .40
82 Rolando Arrojo .15 .40
83 Quinton McCracken .15 .40
84 Jose Canseco .25 .60
85 Ivan Rodriguez .25 .60
86 Juan Gonzalez .15 .40
87 Royce Clayton .15 .40
88 Shawn Green .15 .40
89 Jose Cruz Jr. .15 .40
90 Carlos Delgado .15 .40
91 Troy Glaus FW 5.00 12.00
92 George Lombard FW 4.00 10.00
93 Ryan Minor FW 4.00 10.00
94 Calvin Pickering FW 4.00 10.00
95 Jin Ho Cho FW 4.00 10.00
96 Russ Branyan FW 4.00 10.00
97 Derrick Gibson FW 4.00 10.00
98 Gabe Kapler FW 4.00 10.00
99 Matt Anderson FW 4.00 10.00
100 Preston Wilson FW 4.00 10.00
101 Alex Gonzalez FW 4.00 10.00
102 Carlos Beltran FW 4.00 10.00
103 Dee Brown FW 4.00 10.00
104 Jeremy Giambi FW 4.00 10.00
105 Angel Pena FW 4.00 10.00
106 Geoff Jenkins FW 4.00 10.00
107 Corey Koskie FW 4.00 10.00
108 A.J. Pierzynski FW 4.00 10.00
109 Michael Barrett FW 4.00 10.00
110 F.Seguignol FW 4.00 10.00
111 Mike Kinkade FW 4.00 10.00
112 Ricky Ledee FW 4.00 10.00
113 Mike Lowell FW 4.00 10.00
114 Eric Chavez FW 4.00 10.00
115 Matt Clement FW 4.00 10.00
116 Shane Monahan FW 4.00 10.00
117 J.D. Drew FW 4.00 10.00
118 Bubba Trammell FW 4.00 10.00
119 Kevin Witt FW 4.00 10.00
120 Roy Halladay FW 4.00 10.00
121 Mark McGwire STR 5.00 12.00
122 Mark McGwire STR 4.00 10.00
Sammy Sosa
123 Sammy Sosa STR 2.00 5.00
124 Ken Griffey Jr. STR 3.00 8.00
125 Cal Ripken STR 6.00 15.00
126 Juan Gonzalez STR 1.25 3.00
127 Kerry Wood STR 1.25 3.00
128 Trevor Hoffman STR 1.25 3.00
129 Barry Bonds STR 5.00 12.00
130 Alex Rodriguez STR 3.00 8.00
131 Ben Grieve STR 1.25 3.00
132 Tom Glavine STR 1.25 3.00
133 David Wells STR 1.25 3.00
134 Mike Piazza STR 3.00 8.00
135 Scott Brosius STR 1.25 3.00

1999 SP Authentic Chirography

Randomly inserted in packs at the rate of one in 24, this 39-card set features color player photos with the pictured player's autograph at the bottom of the photo. Exchange cards for Ken Griffey Jr., Cal Ripken, Ruben Rivera and Scott Rolen were seeded into packs. The expiration date for the exchange cards was February 24th, 2000. Prices in our checklist refer to the actual autograph cards.

AG Alex Gonzalez 3.00 8.00
BC Bruce Chen 3.00 8.00
BF Brad Fullmer 3.00 8.00
BG Ben Grieve 3.00 8.00
CB Carlos Beltran 10.00 25.00
CJ Chipper Jones 30.00 60.00
CK Corey Koskie 4.00 10.00
CP Calvin Pickering 3.00 8.00
CR Cal Ripken 60.00 120.00
EC Eric Chavez 4.00 10.00
GK Gabe Kapler 4.00 10.00
GL George Lombard 3.00 8.00
GM Greg Maddux 75.00 150.00
GMJ Gary Matthews Jr. 3.00 8.00
GV Greg Vaughn 3.00 8.00
IR Ivan Rodriguez 15.00 40.00
JD J.D. Drew 4.00 10.00
JG Jeremy Giambi 3.00 8.00
JR Ken Griffey Jr. 50.00 100.00
JT Jim Thome 15.00 40.00
KW Kevin Witt 3.00 8.00
KW Kerry Wood 10.00 25.00
MA Matt Anderson 3.00 8.00
MK Mike Kinkade 3.00 8.00
ML Mike Lowell 5.00 12.00
NG Nomar Garciaparra 20.00 50.00
RB Russell Branyan 3.00 8.00
RH Richard Hidalgo 3.00 8.00
RL Ricky Ledee 3.00 8.00
RM Ryan Minor 3.00 8.00
RR Ruben Rivera 3.00 8.00
SM Shane Monahan 3.00 8.00
SR Scott Rolen 10.00 25.00
TG Tony Gwynn 15.00 40.00
TGL Troy Glaus 5.00 12.00
TH Todd Helton 8.00 20.00
TL Travis Lee 3.00 8.00
TW Todd Walker 4.00 10.00
VG Vladimir Guerrero 15.00 40.00
CRX Cal Ripken EXCH 4.00 10.00
JRX Ken Griffey Jr. EXCH 5.00 12.00
RRX Ruben Rivera EXCH .40 1.00
SRX Scott Rolen EXCH 1.00 2.50

1999 SP Authentic Chirography Gold

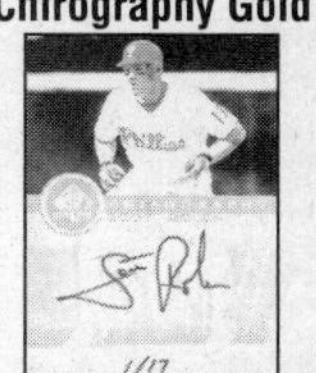

These scarce parallel versions of the Chirography cards were all serial numbered to the featured player's jersey number. The serial numbering was done by hand and is on the front of the card. In addition, gold ink was used on the card fronts (a flat grey front was used on the more common basic Chirography cards). While we only have pricing on some of the cards in this set, we are printing the checklist so collectors can know how many cards are available of each player. The same four players featured on exchange cards in the basic chirography (Griffey, Ripken, Rivera and Rolen) also had exchange cards in this set. The deadline for redeeming these cards was February 24th, 2000. Our listed price refers to the actual autograph cards.

AG Alex Gonzalez/22
BC Bruce Chen/48 10.00 25.00
BF Brad Fullmer/20
BG Ben Grieve/14
CB Carlos Beltran/36 30.00 60.00
CJ Chipper Jones/10
CK Corey Koskie/47 15.00 40.00
CP Calvin Pickering/6
CR Cal Ripken/8
EC Eric Chavez/30 15.00 40.00
GK Gabe Kapler/51 15.00 40.00
GL George Lombard/26 10.00 25.00
GM Greg Maddux/31 125.00 250.00
GMJ G.Matthews Jr./68 10.00 25.00
GV Greg Vaughn/23
IR Ivan Rodriguez/7
JD J.D. Drew/8
JG Jeremy Giambi/15
JR Ken Griffey Jr./24
JT Jim Thome/25
KW Kevin Witt/6
KW Kerry Wood/34 30.00 60.00
MA Matt Anderson/14
MK Mike Kinkade/33 10.00 25.00
ML Mike Lowell/60 20.00 50.00
NG Nomar Garciaparra/5
RB Russ Branyan/66 10.00 25.00
RH Richard Hidalgo/15
RL Ricky Ledee/38 10.00 25.00
RM Ryan Minor/10
RR Ruben Rivera/28 10.00 25.00
SM Shane Monahan/12
SR Scott Rolen/17
TG Tony Gwynn/19
TGL Troy Glaus/14
TH Todd Helton/17
TL Travis Lee/16
TW Todd Walker/12
VG Vladimir Guerrero/27 60.00 120.00
CRX Cal Ripken EXCH
JRX Ken Griffey Jr. EXCH
RRX Ruben Rivera EXCH
SRX Scott Rolen EXCH

1999 SP Authentic Epic Figures

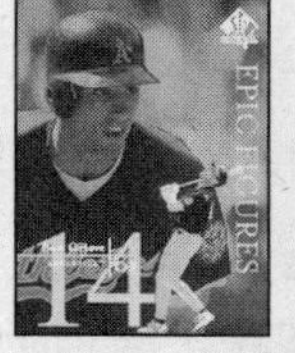

Randomly inserted in packs at the rate of one in seven, this 30-card set features action color photos of some of the game's most impressive players.

COMPLETE SET (30) 40.00 100.00
E1 Mo Vaughn .60 1.50
E2 Travis Lee .60 1.50
E3 Andres Galarraga .60 1.50
E4 Andruw Jones 1.00 2.50
E5 Chipper Jones 1.50 4.00
E6 Greg Maddux 2.50 6.00
E7 Cal Ripken 5.00 12.00
E8 Nomar Garciaparra 2.50 6.00
E9 Sammy Sosa 1.50 4.00
E10 Frank Thomas 1.50 4.00
E11 Kerry Wood .60 1.50
E12 Kenny Lofton .60 1.50
E13 Manny Ramirez 1.00 2.50
E14 Larry Walker .60 1.50
E15 Jeff Bagwell 1.00 2.50
E16 Paul Molitor 1.50 4.00
E17 Vladimir Guerrero 1.50 4.00
E18 Derek Jeter 4.00 10.00
E19 Tino Martinez 1.00 2.50
E20 Mike Piazza 2.50 6.00
E21 Ben Grieve .60 1.50
E22 Scott Rolen 1.00 2.50
E23 Mark McGwire 4.00 10.00
E24 Tony Gwynn 2.00 5.00
E25 Barry Bonds 4.00 10.00
E26 Ken Griffey Jr. 2.50 6.00
E27 Alex Rodriguez 2.50 6.00
E28 J.D. Drew .60 1.50
E29 Juan Gonzalez .60 1.50
E30 Kevin Brown 1.00 2.50

1999 SP Authentic Home Run Chronicles

Inserted one per pack, this 70-card set features action color photos of players who were the leading sluggers of the 1998 season.

COMPLETE SET (70) 30.00 60.00
*DIE CUTS: 5X TO 12X BASIC HR CHRON.
DIE CUTS RANDOM INSERTS IN PACKS
DIE CUT PRINT RUN 70 SERIAL #'d SETS
HR1 Mark McGwire 1.50 4.00
HR2 Sammy Sosa .40 1.00
HR3 Ken Griffey Jr. .60 1.50
HR4 Mark McGwire 1.00 2.50
HR5 Mark McGwire 1.00 2.50
HR6 Albert Belle .15 .40

HR7 Jose Canseco .25 .60
HR8 Juan Gonzalez .15 .40
HR9 Manny Ramirez .25 .60
HR10 Rafael Palmeiro .40 1.00
HR11 Mo Vaughn .15 .40
HR12 Carlos Delgado .15 .40
HR13 Nomar Garciaparra .60 1.50
HR14 Barry Bonds 1.00 2.50
HR15 Alex Rodriguez .60 1.50
HR16 Tony Clark .15 .40
HR17 Jim Thome .25 .60
HR18 Edgar Martinez .25 .60
HR19 Frank Thomas .40 1.00
HR20 Greg Vaughn .15 .40
HR21 Vinny Castilla .15 .40
HR22 Andres Galarraga .15 .40
HR23 Moises Alou .15 .40
HR24 Jeromy Burnitz .15 .40
HR25 Vladimir Guerrero .40 1.00
HR26 Jeff Bagwell .25 .60
HR27 Chipper Jones .40 1.00
HR28 Javier Lopez .15 .40
HR29 Mike Piazza .60 1.50
HR30 Andruw Jones .25 .60
HR31 Henry Rodriguez .15 .40
HR32 Jeff Kent .15 .40
HR33 Ray Lankford .15 .40
HR34 Scott Rolen .25 .60
HR35 Raul Mondesi .15 .40
HR36 Ken Caminiti .15 .40
HR37 J.D. Drew .15 .40
HR38 Troy Glaus .25 .60
HR39 Gabe Kapler .15 .40
HR40 Alex Rodriguez .60 1.50
HR41 Ken Griffey Jr. .60 1.50
HR42 Sammy Sosa .40 1.00
HR43 Mark McGwire 1.00 2.50
HR44 Sammy Sosa .40 1.00
HR45 Mark McGwire 1.00 2.50
HR46 Vinny Castilla .15 .40
HR47 Sammy Sosa .40 1.00
HR48 Mark McGwire 1.00 2.50
HR49 Sammy Sosa .40 1.00
HR50 Greg Vaughn .15 .40
HR51 Sammy Sosa .40 1.00
HR52 Mark McGwire 1.00 2.50
HR53 Sammy Sosa .40 1.00
HR54 Mark McGwire 1.00 2.50
HR55 Sammy Sosa .40 1.00
HR56 Ken Griffey Jr. .60 1.50
HR57 Sammy Sosa .40 1.00
HR58 Mark McGwire 1.00 2.50
HR59 Sammy Sosa .40 1.00
HR60 Mark McGwire 1.00 2.50
HR61 Mark McGwire 1.50 4.00
HR62 Mark McGwire 2.00 5.00
HR63 Mark McGwire 1.00 2.50
HR64 Mark McGwire 1.00 2.50
HR65 Mark McGwire 1.00 2.50
HR66 Sammy Sosa 2.00 5.00
HR67 Mark McGwire 1.00 2.50
HR68 Mark McGwire 1.00 2.50
HR69 Mark McGwire 1.00 2.50
HR70 Mark McGwire 4.00 10.00

1999 SP Authentic Redemption Cards

Randomly inserted in packs at the rate of one in 864, this 10-card set features hand-numbered cards that could be redeemed for various items autographed by the player named on the card. The expiration date for these cards was March 1st, 2000.

1 K.Griffey Jr. AU Jersey/25
2 K.Griffey Jr. AU Baseball/75
3 K.Griffey Jr. AU SI Cover/75
4 K.Griffey Jr. AU Mini Helmet/75
5 M.McGwire AU 62 Ticket/1
6 M.McGwire AU 70 Ticket/3
7 Ken Griffey Jr. Standee/300 5.00 12.00
8 Ken Griffey Jr. Glove Card/200 15.00 40.00
9 Ken Griffey Jr. HE Cel Card/346 10.00 25.00
10 Ken Griffey Jr. SI Cover/200 8.00 20.00

1999 SP Authentic Reflections

Randomly inserted in packs at the rate of one in 23, this 30-card set features color action photos of some of the game's best players and printed using Dot Matrix technology.

COMPLETE SET (30) 150.00 300.00
R1 Mo Vaughn 1.25 3.00
R2 Travis Lee 1.25 3.00
R3 Andres Galarraga 1.25 3.00
R4 Andruw Jones 2.00 5.00
R5 Chipper Jones 3.00 8.00
R6 Greg Maddux 5.00 12.00
R7 Cal Ripken 10.00 25.00
R8 Nomar Garciaparra 5.00 12.00
R9 Sammy Sosa 3.00 8.00
R10 Frank Thomas 3.00 8.00
R11 Kerry Wood 1.25 3.00
R12 Kenny Lofton 1.25 3.00
R13 Manny Ramirez 2.00 5.00
R14 Larry Walker 1.25 3.00
R15 Jeff Bagwell 2.00 5.00
R16 Paul Molitor 3.00 8.00
R17 Vladimir Guerrero 3.00 8.00
R18 Derek Jeter 8.00 20.00
R19 Tino Martinez 2.00 5.00
R20 Mike Piazza 5.00 12.00
R21 Ben Grieve 1.25 3.00
R22 Scott Rolen 2.00 5.00
R23 Mark McGwire 8.00 20.00
R24 Tony Gwynn 4.00 10.00
R25 Barry Bonds 8.00 20.00
R26 Ken Griffey Jr 5.00 12.00
R27 Alex Rodriguez 5.00 12.00
R28 J.D. Drew 1.25 3.00
R29 Juan Gonzalez 1.25 3.00
R30 Roger Clemens 6.00 15.00

2000 SP Authentic

The 2000 SP Authentic product was initially released in late July, 2000 as a 135-card set. Each pack contained five cards and carried a suggested retail price of $4.99. The basic set features 90 veteran players, a 15-card SP Superstars subset serial numbered to 2500, and a 30-card Future Watch subset also serial numbered to 2500. In late December, Upper Deck released their UD Rookie Update brand, which contained a selection of cards to append the 2000 SP Authentic, SPx and UD Pros and Prospects brands. For SP Authentic, sixty new cards were intended, but card number 165 was never created due to problems at the manufacturer. Cards 136-164 are devoted to an extension of the Future Watch prospect subset established in the basic set. Similar to the basic set's FW cards, these Update cards are serial numbered, but only 1,700 copies of each card were produced (as compared to the 2,500 print run for the "first series" cards). Cards 166-195 feature a selection of established veterans either initially not included in the basic set or traded to new teams. Notable Rookie Cards include Xavier Nady, Kazuhiro Sasaki and Barry-Zito. Also, a selection of A Piece of History 3000 Club Tris Speaker and Paul Waner memorabilia cards were randomly seeded into packs. 350 bat cards and five hand-numbered, combination bat chip and autograph cut cards for each player were produced. Pricing for these memorabilia cards can be referenced under 2000 Upper Deck A Piece of History 3000 Club. Finally, a Ken Griffey Jr. sample card was distributed to dealers and hobby media in June, 2000 (several weeks prior to the basic product's national release). The card can be readily distinguished by the large "SAMPLE" text running diagonally across the back.

COMP.BASIC w/o SP's (90) 10.00 25.00
COMP.UPDATE w/o SP'S (30) 4.00 10.00
COMMON CARD (1-90) .15 .40
COMMON SUP (91-105) 1.25 3.00
COMMON FW (106-135) 2.00 5.00
COMMON FW (136-164) 2.00 5.00
COMMON (166-195) .25 .60
1 Mo Vaughn .15 .40
2 Troy Glaus .25 .60
3 Jason Giambi .15 .40
4 Tim Hudson .15 .40
5 Eric Chavez .15 .40
6 Shannon Stewart .15 .40
7 Raul Mondesi .15 .40
8 Carlos Delgado .15 .40
9 Jose Canseco .25 .60
10 Vinny Castilla .15 .40
11 Greg Vaughn .15 .40
12 Manny Ramirez .25 .60
13 Roberto Alomar .25 .60
14 Jim Thome .25 .60
15 Richie Sexson .15 .40
16 Alex Rodriguez .60 1.50
17 Freddy Garcia .15 .40
18 John Olerud .15 .40
19 Albert Belle .15 .40
20 Cal Ripken 1.25 3.00
21 Mike Mussina .25 .60
22 Ivan Rodriguez .25 .60
23 Gabe Kapler .15 .40
24 Rafael Palmeiro .25 .60
25 Nomar Garciaparra .60 1.50
26 Pedro Martinez .25 .60
27 Carl Everett .15 .40
28 Carlos Beltran .15 .40
29 Jermaine Dye .15 .40
30 Juan Gonzalez .15 .40
31 Dean Palmer .15 .40
32 Corey Koskie .15 .40
33 Jacque Jones .15 .40
34 Frank Thomas .40 1.00
35 Paul Konerko .15 .40
36 Magglio Ordonez .15 .40
37 Bernie Williams .25 .60
38 Derek Jeter 1.00 2.50
39 Roger Clemens .75 2.00
40 Mariano Rivera .40 1.00
41 Jeff Bagwell .25 .60
42 Craig Biggio .25 .60
43 Jose Lima .15 .40
44 Moises Alou .15 .40
45 Chipper Jones .40 1.00
46 Greg Maddux .60 1.50
47 Andruw Jones .25 .60
48 Andres Galarraga .15 .40
49 Jeromy Burnitz .15 .40
50 Geoff Jenkins .15 .40
51 Mark McGwire 1.00 2.50
52 Fernando Tatis .15 .40
53 J.D. Drew .15 .40
54 Sammy Sosa .40 1.00
55 Kerry Wood .15 .40
56 Mark Grace .25 .60
57 Matt Williams .15 .40
58 Randy Johnson .40 1.00
59 Erubiel Durazo .15 .40
60 Gary Sheffield .15 .40
61 Kevin Brown .25 .60
62 Shawn Green .15 .40
63 Vladimir Guerrero .40 1.00
64 Michael Barrett .15 .40
65 Barry Bonds 1.00 2.50
66 Jeff Kent .15 .40
67 Russ Ortiz .15 .40
68 Preston Wilson .15 .40
69 Mike Lowell .15 .40
70 Mike Piazza .60 1.50
71 Mike Hampton .15 .40
72 Robin Ventura .15 .40
73 Edgardo Alfonzo .15 .40
74 Tony Gwynn .50 1.25
75 Ryan Klesko .15 .40
76 Trevor Hoffman .15 .40
77 Scott Rolen .25 .60
78 Bob Abreu .15 .40
79 Mike Lieberthal .15 .40
80 Curt Schilling .15 .40
81 Jason Kendall .15 .40
82 Brian Giles .15 .40
83 Kris Benson .15 .40
84 Ken Griffey Jr. .60 1.50
85 Sean Casey .15 .40
86 Pokey Reese .15 .40
87 Barry Larkin .25 .60
88 Larry Walker .15 .40
89 Todd Helton .25 .60
90 Jeff Cirillo .15 .40
91 Ken Griffey Jr. SUP 3.00 8.00
92 Mark McGwire SUP 5.00 12.00
93 Chipper Jones SUP 2.00 5.00
94 Derek Jeter SUP 5.00 12.00
95 Shawn Green SUP 1.25 3.00
96 Pedro Martinez SUP 1.25 3.00
97 Mike Piazza SUP 3.00 8.00
98 Alex Rodriguez SUP 3.00 8.00
99 Jeff Bagwell SUP 1.25 3.00
100 Cal Ripken SUP 6.00 15.00
101 Sammy Sosa SUP 2.00 5.00
102 Barry Bonds SUP 5.00 12.00
103 Jose Canseco SUP 1.25 3.00
104 N.Garciaparra SUP 3.00 8.00
105 Ivan Rodriguez SUP 1.25 3.00
106 Rick Ankiel FW 3.00 8.00
107 Pat Burrell FW 1.25 3.00
108 Vernon Wells FW 2.00 5.00
109 Nick Johnson FW 2.00 5.00
110 Kip Wells FW 2.00 5.00
111 Matt Riley FW 2.00 5.00
112 Alfonso Soriano FW 3.00 8.00
113 Josh Beckett FW 3.00 8.00
114 Danys Baez FW RC 2.00 5.00
115 Travis Dawkins FW 2.00 5.00
116 Eric Gagne FW 3.00 8.00
117 Mike Lamb FW RC 3.00 8.00
118 Eric Munson FW 2.00 5.00
119 W.Rodriguez FW RC 2.00 5.00
120 K.Sasaki FW RC 3.00 8.00
121 Chad Hutchinson FW 2.00 5.00
122 Peter Bergeron FW 2.00 5.00
123 W.Serrano FW RC 2.00 5.00
124 Tony Armas Jr. FW 2.00 5.00
125 Ramon Ortiz FW 2.00 5.00
126 Adam Kennedy FW 2.00 5.00
127 Joe Crede FW 4.00 10.00
128 Roosevelt Brown FW 2.00 5.00
129 Mark Mulder FW 2.00 5.00
130 Brad Penny FW 2.00 5.00
131 Terrence Long FW 2.00 5.00
132 Ruben Mateo FW 2.00 5.00
133 Wily Mo Pena FW 2.00 5.00
134 Rafael Furcal FW 2.00 5.00
135 M.Encarnacion FW 2.00 5.00
136 Barry Zito FW RC 8.00 20.00
137 Aaron McNeal FW RC 2.00 5.00
138 Timo Perez FW RC 2.00 5.00
139 Sun Woo Kim FW RC 2.00 5.00
140 Xavier Nady FW RC 4.00 10.00
141 M.Wheatland FW RC 2.00 5.00
142 B.Abernathy FW RC 2.00 5.00
143 Cory Vance FW RC 2.00 5.00
144 Scott Heard FW RC 2.00 5.00
145 Mike Meyers FW RC 2.00 5.00
146 Ben Diggins FW RC 2.00 5.00
147 Luis Matos FW RC 2.00 5.00
148 Ben Sheets FW RC 5.00 12.00
149 K.Ainsworth FW RC 2.00 5.00
150 Dave Krynzel FW RC 2.00 5.00
151 Alex Cabrera FW RC 2.00 5.00
152 Mike Tonis FW RC 2.00 5.00
153 Dane Sardinha FW RC 2.00 5.00
154 Keith Ginter FW RC 2.00 5.00
155 D.Espinosa FW RC 2.00 5.00
156 Joe Torres FW RC 2.00 5.00
157 Daylan Holt FW RC 2.00 5.00
158 Koyie Hill FW RC 2.00 5.00
159 B.Wilkerson FW RC 3.00 8.00
160 Juan Pierre FW RC 3.00 8.00
161 Matt Ginter FW RC 2.00 5.00
162 Dane Artman FW RC 2.00 5.00
163 Jon Rauch FW RC 2.00 5.00
164 Sean Burnett FW RC 2.00 5.00
165 Does Not Exist
166 Darin Erstad .25 .60
167 Ben Grieve .25 .60
168 David Wells .25 .60
169 Fred McGriff .40 1.00
170 Bob Wickman .25 .60
171 Al Martin .25 .60
172 Melvin Mora .25 .60
173 Ricky Ledee .25 .60
174 Dante Bichette .25 .60
175 Mike Sweeney .25 .60
176 Bobby Higginson .25 .60
177 Matt Lawton .25 .60
178 Charles Johnson .25 .60
179 David Justice .25 .60
180 Richard Hidalgo .25 .60
181 B.J. Surhoff .25 .60
182 Richie Sexson .25 .60
183 Jim Edmonds .25 .60
184 Rondell White .25 .60
185 Curt Schilling .25 .60
186 Tom Goodwin .25 .60
187 Jose Vidro .25 .60
188 Ellis Burks .25 .60
189 Henry Rodriguez .25 .60
190 Mike Bordick .25 .60
191 Eric Owens .25 .60
192 Travis Lee .25 .60
193 Kevin Young .25 .60
194 Aaron Boone .25 .60
195 Todd Hollandsworth .25 .60
SPA K.Griffey Jr. Sample .75 2.00

2000 SP Authentic Limited

Randomly inserted into packs, this 135-card set is a complete parallel of the 2000 SP Authentic base set. These cards are individually serial numbered to 100.

*STARS 1-90: 8X TO 20X BASIC CARDS
*SUP 91-105: 1.25X TO 3X BASIC SUP
*FW 106-135: 1X TO 2.5X BASIC FW
*FW 106-135 RC: 1X TO 2.5X BASIC FW RC

2000 SP Authentic Buybacks

Representatives at Upper Deck purchased back a selection of vintage SP brand trading cards from 1993-1999, featuring 29 different players. The "vintage" cards were all purchased in 2000 through hobby dealers. Each card was then hand-numbered in blue ink sharpie on front (please see listings for print runs), affixed with a serial numbered UDA hologram on back and packaged with a 2 1/2" by 3 1/2" UDA Certificate of Authenticity (of which had a hologram with a matching serial number of the signed card). The Certificate of Authenticity and the signed card were placed together in a soft plastic "penny" sleeve and then randomly seeded into 2000 SP Authentic packs at a rate of 1:95. Jeff Bagwell, Ken Griffey, Andruw Jones, Chipper Jones, Manny Ramirez and Alex Rodriguez did not manage to sign their cards in time for packout, thus exchange cards were created and seeded into packs for these players. The exchange cards did NOT specify the actual vintage card that the bearer would receive back in the mail. The deadline to redeem the exchange cards was March 30th, 2001. Pricing for cards with production of 25 or fewer cards is not provided due to scarcity.

1 Jeff Bagwell 93/58 20.00 50.00
2 Jeff Bagwell 94/46 20.00 50.00
3 Jeff Bagwell 95/60 20.00 50.00
4 Jeff Bagwell 96/74 20.00 50.00
5 Jeff Bagwell 97/53 20.00 50.00
6 Jeff Bagwell 98/38 20.00 50.00
7 Jeff Bagwell 99/539 20.00 50.00
8 Jeff Bagwell EXCH
9 Craig Biggio 93/59 15.00 40.00
10 Craig Biggio 94/69 15.00 40.00
11 Craig Biggio 95/171 10.00 25.00
12 Craig Biggio 96/71 15.00 40.00
13 Craig Biggio 97/46 15.00 40.00
14 Craig Biggio 98/40 15.00 40.00
15 Craig Biggio 99/125 10.00 25.00
16 Barry Bonds 93/12
17 Barry Bonds 94/12
18 Barry Bonds 95/21
19 Barry Bonds 96/9
20 Barry Bonds 97/5
21 Barry Bonds 98/22
22 Barry Bonds 99/520 100.00 175.00
23 Jose Canseco 93/29 20.00 50.00
24 Jose Canseco 94/20
25 Jose Canseco 95/6
26 Jose Canseco 96/23
27 Jose Canseco 97/23
28 Jose Canseco 98/24
29 Jose Canseco 99/502 10.00 25.00
30 Sean Casey 98/5
31 Sean Casey 99/139 6.00 15.00
32 Roger Clemens 93/68 60.00 120.00
33 Roger Clemens 94/60 60.00 120.00
34 Roger Clemens 95/68 60.00 120.00
35 Roger Clemens 96/68 60.00 120.00
36 Roger Clemens 97/7
37 Roger Clemens 98/25
38 Roger Clemens 99/134 50.00 100.00
39 Jason Giambi 97/34 20.00 50.00
40 Jason Giambi 98/25
41 Tom Glavine 93/99 15.00 40.00
42 Tom Glavine 94/107 15.00 40.00
43 Tom Glavine 95/97 15.00 40.00
44 Tom Glavine 96/42 20.00 50.00
45 Tom Glavine 98/40 20.00 50.00
46 Tom Glavine 99/138 15.00 40.00
47 Shawn Green 96/55 15.00 40.00
48 Shawn Green 99/530 10.00 25.00
49 Ken Griffey Jr. 93/19
50 Ken Griffey Jr. 94/8
51 Ken Griffey Jr. 95/9
52 Ken Griffey Jr. 96/12
53 Ken Griffey Jr. 97/10
54 Ken Griffey Jr. 98/22
55 Ken Griffey Jr. 99/403 40.00 80.00
56 Ken Griffey Jr. EXCH
57 Tony Gwynn 93/17
58 Tony Gwynn 94/7
59 Tony Gwynn 95/11
60 Tony Gwynn 96/11
61 Tony Gwynn 97/24
62 Tony Gwynn 98/21
63 Tony Gwynn 99/129 15.00 40.00
64 Tony Gwynn 99/369 15.00 40.00
65 Derek Jeter 93/5
66 Derek Jeter 95/17
67 Derek Jeter 96/10
68 Derek Jeter 97/12
69 Derek Jeter 98/11
70 Derek Jeter 99/119 100.00 200.00
71 Randy Johnson 93/60 40.00 80.00
72 Randy Johnson 94/45 40.00 80.00
73 Randy Johnson 95/70 40.00 80.00
74 Randy Johnson 96/60 40.00 80.00
75 Randy Johnson 97/10
76 Randy Johnson 98/21
77 Randy Johnson 99/113 40.00 80.00
78 Andruw Jones 97/70 10.00 25.00
79 Andruw Jones 98/56 15.00 40.00
80 Andruw Jones 99/531 10.00 25.00
81 Andruw Jones EXCH
82 Chipper Jones 93/3
83 Chipper Jones 95/9
84 Chipper Jones 96/17
85 Chipper Jones 97/63 30.00 60.00
86 Chipper Jones 98/23
87 Chipper Jones 99/541 15.00 40.00
88 Chipper Jones EXCH
89 Kenny Lofton 94/100 10.00 25.00
90 Kenny Lofton 95/84 10.00 25.00
91 Kenny Lofton 96/34 20.00 50.00
92 Kenny Lofton 97/82 10.00 25.00
93 Kenny Lofton 98/21
94 Kenny Lofton 99/99 10.00 25.00
95 Javy Lopez 93/106 6.00 15.00
96 Javy Lopez 94/160 6.00 15.00
97 Javy Lopez 96/99 6.00 15.00
98 Javy Lopez 97/61 10.00 25.00
99 Javy Lopez 98/26 12.50 30.00
100 Greg Maddux 93/22
101 Greg Maddux 94/19
102 Greg Maddux 95/14
103 Greg Maddux 96/13
104 Greg Maddux 97/8
105 Greg Maddux 98/11
106 Greg Maddux 99/504 40.00 80.00
107 Paul O'Neill 93/110 10.00 25.00
108 Paul O'Neill 94/97 10.00 25.00
109 Paul O'Neill 95/142 10.00 25.00
110 Paul O'Neill 96/70 10.00 25.00
111 Paul O'Neill 98/23
112 Manny Ramirez 93/6
113 Manny Ramirez 94/7
114 Manny Ramirez 95/22
115 Manny Ramirez 96/13
116 Manny Ramirez 97/42 20.00 50.00
117 Manny Ramirez 98/36 20.00 50.00
118 M. Ramirez 99/532 20.00 50.00
119 Manny Ramirez EXCH
120 Cal Ripken 93/7
121 Cal Ripken 94/22
122 Cal Ripken 95/10
123 Cal Ripken 96/12
124 Cal Ripken 97/12
125 Cal Ripken 98/13
126 Cal Ripken 99/510 50.00 100.00
127 Alex Rodriguez 94/5
128 Alex Rodriguez 95/57 75.00 150.00
129 Alex Rodriguez 96/37 75.00 150.00
130 Alex Rodriguez 97/10
131 Alex Rodriguez 98/22
132 A.Rodriguez 99/408 60.00 120.00
133 Alex Rodriguez EXCH
134 Ivan Rodriguez 93/29 30.00 60.00
135 Ivan Rodriguez 94/16
136 Ivan Rodriguez 95/18
137 Ivan Rodriguez 96/22
138 Ivan Rodriguez 97/14
139 Ivan Rodriguez 98/27 30.00 60.00
140 Ivan Rodriguez 99/2
141 Scott Rolen 95/23
142 Scott Rolen 98/31 20.00 50.00
143 Frank Thomas 93/1
144 Frank Thomas 94/20
145 Frank Thomas 95/5
146 Frank Thomas 96/10
147 Frank Thomas 97/20
148 Frank Thomas 98/29 30.00 60.00
149 F.Thomas 99/100 15.00 40.00
150 Greg Vaughn 93/79 4.00 10.00
151 Greg Vaughn 94/75 4.00 10.00
152 Greg Vaughn 95/155 4.00 10.00
153 Greg Vaughn 96/113 4.00 10.00
154 Greg Vaughn 97/29 8.00 20.00
155 Greg Vaughn 99/527 4.00 10.00
156 Mo Vaughn 93/119 6.00 15.00
157 Mo Vaughn 94/96 6.00 15.00
158 Mo Vaughn 95/121 6.00 15.00
159 Mo Vaughn 96/114 6.00 15.00
160 Mo Vaughn 97/61 10.00 25.00
161 Mo Vaughn 98/29 12.50 30.00
162 Mo Vaughn 99/537 6.00 15.00
163 Robin Ventura 93/59 10.00 25.00
164 Robin Ventura 94/49 10.00 25.00
165 R.Ventura 95/125 6.00 15.00
166 Robin Ventura 96/55 10.00 25.00
167 Robin Ventura 97/44 10.00 25.00
168 Robin Ventura 98/28 12.50 30.00
169 R.Ventura 99/370 6.00 15.00
170 Matt Williams 93/55 15.00 40.00
171 Matt Williams 94/50 15.00 40.00
172 Matt Williams 95/137 10.00 25.00
173 Matt Williams 96/77 10.00 25.00
174 Matt Williams 97/54 15.00 40.00
175 Matt Williams 98/29 20.00 50.00
176 Matt Williams 99/529 10.00 25.00
177 P.Wilson 94/249 6.00 15.00
178 P.Wilson 99/195 6.00 15.00
179 Authentication Card .20 .50

2000 SP Authentic Chirography

Randomly inserted into packs at one in 23, this 42-card insert features autographed cards of modern superstar players. Please note that there were also autographs of Sandy Koufax inserted into this set. There were a number of cards in this set that packed out as exchange cards, the exchange cards must be sent to Upper Deck by 03/30/01.

AJ Andruw Jones 10.00 25.00
AR Alex Rodriguez 60.00 120.00
AS Alfonso Soriano 15.00 40.00
BB Barry Bonds 100.00 175.00
BP Ben Petrick 4.00 10.00
CBE Carlos Beltran 6.00 15.00
CJ Chipper Jones 20.00 50.00
CR Cal Ripken 60.00 120.00
DJ Derek Jeter 75.00 150.00
EC Eric Chavez 6.00 15.00
ED Erubiel Durazo 4.00 10.00
EM Eric Munson 4.00 10.00
EY Ed Yarnall 4.00 10.00
IR Ivan Rodriguez 15.00 40.00
JB Jeff Bagwell 20.00 50.00
JC Jose Canseco 10.00 25.00
JD J.D. Drew 6.00 15.00
JG Jason Giambi 10.00 25.00
JK Josh Kalinowski 4.00 10.00
JL Jose Lima 6.00 15.00
JMA Joe Mays 4.00 10.00
JMO Jim Morris 10.00 25.00
JOB John Bale 4.00 10.00
KL Kenny Lofton 10.00 25.00
MQ Mark Quinn 4.00 10.00
MR Manny Ramirez 12.50 30.00
MRI Matt Riley 4.00 10.00
MV Mo Vaughn 6.00 15.00
NJ Nick Johnson 6.00 15.00
PB Pat Burrell 6.00 15.00
RA Rick Ankiel 10.00 25.00
RC Roger Clemens 60.00 120.00
RF Rafael Furcal 6.00 15.00
RP Robert Person 4.00 10.00
SC Sean Casey 6.00 15.00
SK Sandy Koufax 175.00 300.00
SR Scott Rolen 10.00 25.00
TG Tony Gwynn 20.00 50.00
TGL Troy Glaus 10.00 25.00
VG Vladimir Guerrero 15.00 40.00
VW Vernon Wells 6.00 15.00
WG Wilton Guerrero 4.00 10.00

2000 SP Authentic Chirography Gold

Randomly inserted into packs, this 42-card insert is a complete parallel of the SP Authentic Chirography set. All Gold cards have a G suffix on the card number (for example Rick Ankiel's card is number G-RA). For the handful of exchange cards that were seeded into packs, this was the key manner to differentiate them from basic Chirography cards. Please note exchange cards (with a redemtpion deadline of 03/30/01) were seeded into packs for Andruw Jones, Alex Rodriguez, Chipper Jones, Jeff Bagwell, Manny Ramirez, Pat Burrell, Rick Ankiel and Scott Rolen. In addition, about 50% of Jose Lima's cards went into packs as real autographs and the remainder packed out as exchange cards.

GAJ Andruw Jones/25
GAR Alex Rodriguez/3
GAS Alfonso Soriano/53 20.00 50.00
GBB Barry Bonds/25
GBP Ben Petrick/15
GCBE Carlos Beltran/15
GCJ Cal Ripken/8
GCR Chipper Jones/10
GDJ Derek Jeter/2
GEC Eric Chavez/3
GED Erubiel Durazo/44 6.00 15.00
GEM Eric Munson/17
GEY Ed Yarnall/41 6.00 15.00
GIR Ivan Rodriguez/7
GJB Jeff Bagwell/5
GJC Jose Canseco/33 30.00 60.00
GJD J.D. Drew/7
GJG Jason Giambi/16
GJK Josh Kalinowski/62 6.00 15.00
GJL Jose Lima/42 10.00 25.00
GJMA Joe Mays/53 6.00 15.00
GJMO Jim Morris/63 15.00 40.00
GJOB John Bale/49 6.00 15.00
GKL Kenny Lofton/7
GMQ Mark Quinn/14
GMR Manny Ramirez/24
GMRI Matt Riley/25
GMV Mo Vaughn/42 10.00 25.00
GNJ Nick Johnson/63 10.00 25.00
GPB Pat Burrell/33 15.00 40.00
GRA Rick Ankiel/66 10.00 25.00
GRC Roger Clemens/22
GRF Rafael Furcal/1
GRP Robert Person/31 10.00 25.00

GSC Sean Casey/21		
GSK Sandy Koufax/32		
GSR Scott Rolen/17		
GTG Tony Gwynn/19		
GTGL Troy Glaus/14		
GVG V.Guerrero/27	60.00	120.00
GVW Vernon Wells/10		
GWG Wilton Guerrero/4		

2000 SP Authentic Cornerstones

Randomly inserted into packs at one in 23, this seven-card insert features players that are the cornerstones of their teams. Card backs carry a "C" prefix.

COMPLETE SET (7)	25.00	60.00
C1 Ken Griffey Jr	2.50	6.00
C2 Cal Ripken	5.00	12.00
C3 Mike Piazza	2.50	6.00
C4 Derek Jeter	4.00	10.00
C5 Mark McGwire	4.00	10.00
C6 Nomar Garciaparra	2.50	6.00
C7 Sammy Sosa	1.50	4.00

2000 SP Authentic DiMaggio Memorabilia

Randomly inserted into packs, this three-card insert features game-used memorabilia cards of Joe DiMaggio. This set features a Game-Used Jersey card (numbered to 500), a Game-Used Jersey card Gold (numbered to 56), and a Game-Used Jersey/Cut Autograph card (numbered to 5).

1 Joe DiMaggio Jsy/500	60.00	120.00
2 Joe DiMaggio Jsy Gold/56	100.00	200.00
3 Joe DiMaggio Jsy-Cut AU/5		

2000 SP Authentic Midsummer Classics

Randomly inserted into packs at one in 12, this 10-card insert features perennial All-Stars. Card backs carry a "MC" prefix.

COMPLETE SET (10)	12.50	30.00
MC1 Cal Ripken	3.00	8.00
MC2 Roger Clemens	2.00	5.00
MC3 Jeff Bagwell	.60	1.50
MC4 Barry Bonds	2.50	6.00
MC5 Jose Canseco	.60	1.50
MC6 Frank Thomas	1.00	2.50
MC7 Mike Piazza	1.50	4.00
MC8 Tony Gwynn	1.25	3.00
MC9 Juan Gonzalez	.40	1.00
MC10 Greg Maddux	1.50	4.00

2000 SP Authentic Premier Performers

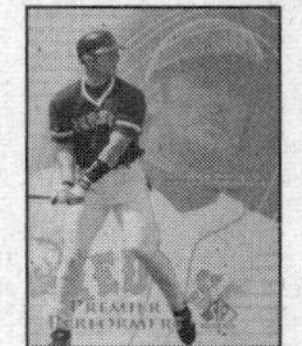

Randomly inserted into packs at one in 12, this 10-card insert features prime-time players that leave it all on the field and hold nothing back. Card backs carry a "PP" prefix.

COMPLETE SET (10)	20.00	50.00
PP1 Mark McGwire	2.50	6.00
PP2 Alex Rodriguez	1.50	4.00
PP3 Cal Ripken	3.00	8.00
PP4 Nomar Garciaparra	1.50	4.00
PP5 Ken Griffey Jr.	1.50	4.00
PP6 Chipper Jones	1.00	2.50
PP7 Derek Jeter	2.50	6.00
PP8 Ivan Rodriguez	.60	1.50
PP9 Vladimir Guerrero	1.00	2.50
PP10 Sammy Sosa	1.00	2.50

2000 SP Authentic Supremacy

Randomly inserted into packs at one in 23, this seven-card insert features players that any team would like to have. Card backs carry a "S" prefix.

COMPLETE SET (7)	12.50	30.00
S1 Alex Rodriguez	2.50	6.00
S2 Shawn Green	.60	1.50
S3 Pedro Martinez	1.00	2.50
S4 Chipper Jones	1.50	4.00
S5 Tony Gwynn	2.00	5.00
S6 Ivan Rodriguez	1.00	2.50
S7 Jeff Bagwell	1.00	2.50

2000 SP Authentic United Nations

Randomly inserted into packs at one in four, this 10-card insert features players that have come from other countries to play in the Major Leagues. Card backs carry a "UN" prefix.

COMPLETE SET (10)	4.00	10.00
UN1 Sammy Sosa	.50	1.25
UN2 Ken Griffey Jr.	.75	2.00
UN3 Orlando Hernandez	.20	.50
UN4 Andres Galarraga	.20	.50
UN5 Kazuhiro Sasaki	.30	.75
UN6 Larry Walker	.20	.50
UN7 Vinny Castilla	.20	.50
UN8 Andruw Jones	.30	.75
UN9 Ivan Rodriguez	.30	.75
UN10 Chan Ho Park	.20	.50

2001 SP Authentic

SP Authentic was initially released as a 180-card set in September, 2001. An additional 60-card Update set was distributed within Upper Deck Rookie Update packs in late December, 2001. Each basic sealed box contained 24 packs plus two three-card bonus packs (one entitled Stars of Japan and another entitled Mantle Pinstripe Exclusives). Each basic pack of SP Authentic contained five cards and carried a suggested retail price of $4.99. Upper Deck Rookie Update packs contained four cards and carried an SRP of $4.99. The basic set is broken into the following components: basic veterans (1-90), Future Watch (91-135) and Superstars (136-180). Each Future Watch and Superstar subset card from the first series is serial numbered to 1250 copies. Though odds were not released by the manufacturer, information supplied by dealers breaking several cases indicate on average one in every 18 basic packs contains one of these serial-numbered cards. The Update set is broken down as follows: basic veterans (181-210) and Future Watch (211-240). Each Update Future Watch is serial numbered to 1500 copies. Notable Rookie Cards in the basic set include Albert Pujols, Tsuyoshi Shinjo and Ichiro Suzuki. Notable Rookie Cards in the Update set include Mark Prior and Mark Teixeira.

COMP.BASIC w/o SP's (90)	10.00	25.00
COMP.UPDATE w/o SP's (30)	4.00	10.00
COMMON CARD (1-90)	.15	.40
COMMON FW (91-135)	3.00	8.00
COMMON SS (136-180)	2.00	5.00
COMMON (181-210)	.25	.60
COMMON (211-240)	2.50	6.00
1 Troy Glaus	.15	.40
2 Darin Erstad	.15	.40
3 Jason Giambi	.15	.40
4 Tim Hudson	.15	.40
5 Eric Chavez	.15	.40
6 Miguel Tejada	.15	.40
7 Jose Ortiz	.15	.40
8 Carlos Delgado	.15	.40
9 Tony Batista	.15	.40
10 Raul Mondesi	.15	.40
11 Aubrey Huff	.15	.40
12 Greg Vaughn	.15	.40
13 Roberto Alomar	.25	.60
14 Juan Gonzalez	.15	.40
15 Jim Thome	.25	.60
16 Omar Vizquel	.25	.60
17 Edgar Martinez	.25	.60
18 Freddy Garcia	.15	.40
19 Cal Ripken	1.25	3.00
20 Ivan Rodriguez	.25	.60
21 Rafael Palmeiro	.25	.60
22 Alex Rodriguez	.60	1.50
23 Manny Ramirez Sox	.25	.60
24 Pedro Martinez	.25	.60
25 Nomar Garciaparra	.60	1.50
26 Mike Sweeney	.15	.40
27 Jermaine Dye	.15	.40
28 Bobby Higginson	.15	.40
29 Dean Palmer	.15	.40
30 Matt Lawton	.15	.40
31 Eric Milton	.15	.40
32 Frank Thomas	.40	1.00
33 Magglio Ordonez	.15	.40
34 David Wells	.15	.40
35 Paul Konerko	.15	.40
36 Derek Jeter	1.00	2.50
37 Bernie Williams	.25	.60
38 Roger Clemens	.75	2.00
39 Mike Mussina	.25	.60
40 Jorge Posada	.25	.60
41 Jeff Bagwell	.25	.60
42 Richard Hidalgo	.15	.40
43 Craig Biggio	.25	.60
44 Greg Maddux	.60	1.50
45 Chipper Jones	.40	1.00
46 Andruw Jones	.25	.60
47 Rafael Furcal	.15	.40
48 Tom Glavine	.25	.60
49 Jeromy Burnitz	.15	.40
50 Jeffrey Hammonds	.15	.40
51 Mark McGwire	1.00	2.50
52 Jim Edmonds	.15	.40
53 Rick Ankiel	.15	.40
54 J.D. Drew	.15	.40
55 Sammy Sosa	.40	1.00
56 Corey Patterson	.15	.40
57 Kerry Wood	.15	.40
58 Randy Johnson	.40	1.00
59 Luis Gonzalez	.15	.40
60 Curt Schilling	.15	.40
61 Gary Sheffield	.15	.40
62 Shawn Green	.15	.40
63 Kevin Brown	.15	.40
64 Vladimir Guerrero	.40	1.00
65 Jose Vidro	.15	.40
66 Barry Bonds	1.00	2.50
67 Jeff Kent	.15	.40
68 Livan Hernandez	.15	.40
69 Preston Wilson	.15	.40
70 Charles Johnson	.15	.40
71 Ryan Dempster	.15	.40
72 Mike Piazza	.60	1.50
73 Al Leiter	.15	.40
74 Edgardo Alfonzo	.15	.40
75 Robin Ventura	.15	.40
76 Tony Gwynn	.50	1.25
77 Phil Nevin	.15	.40
78 Trevor Hoffman	.15	.40
79 Scott Rolen	.25	.60
80 Pat Burrell	.15	.40
81 Bob Abreu	.15	.40
82 Jason Kendall	.15	.40
83 Brian Giles	.15	.40
84 Kris Benson	.15	.40
85 Ken Griffey Jr.	.60	1.50
86 Barry Larkin	.25	.60
87 Sean Casey	.15	.40
88 Todd Helton	.25	.60
89 Mike Hampton	.15	.40
90 Larry Walker	.15	.40
91 Ichiro Suzuki FW RC	60.00	120.00
92 Wilson Betemit FW RC	6.00	15.00
93 A. Hernandez FW RC	3.00	8.00
94 Juan Uribe FW RC	4.00	10.00
95 Travis Hafner FW RC	20.00	50.00
96 M. Ensberg FW RC	6.00	15.00
97 Sean Douglass FW RC	3.00	8.00
98 Juan Diaz FW RC	3.00	8.00
99 Erick Almonte FW RC	3.00	8.00
100 Ryan Freel FW RC	3.00	8.00
101 E. Guzman FW RC	3.00	8.00
102 C. Parker FW RC	3.00	8.00
103 Josh Fogg FW RC	3.00	8.00
104 Bert Snow FW RC	3.00	8.00
105 H. Ramirez FW RC	4.00	10.00
106 R. Rodriguez FW RC	3.00	8.00
107 Tyler Walker FW RC	3.00	8.00
108 Jose Mieses FW RC	3.00	8.00
109 Billy Sylvester FW RC	3.00	8.00
110 Martin Vargas FW RC	3.00	8.00
111 Andres Torres FW RC	3.00	8.00
112 Greg Miller FW RC	3.00	8.00
113 Alexis Gomez FW RC	3.00	8.00
114 Grant Balfour FW RC	3.00	8.00
115 Henry Mateo FW RC	3.00	8.00
116 Esix Snead FW RC	3.00	8.00
117 J. Melian FW RC	3.00	8.00
118 Nate Teut FW RC	3.00	8.00
119 T. Shinjo FW RC	4.00	10.00
120 C. Valderrama FW RC	3.00	8.00
121 J. Estrada FW RC	4.00	10.00
122 J. Michaels FW RC	3.00	8.00
123 William Ortega FW RC	3.00	8.00
124 Jason Smith FW RC	3.00	8.00
125 B. Lawrence FW RC	3.00	8.00
126 Albert Pujols FW RC	200.00	300.00
127 Wilkin Ruan FW RC	3.00	8.00
128 Josh Towers FW RC	4.00	10.00
129 Kris Keller FW RC	3.00	8.00
130 Nick Maness FW RC	3.00	8.00
131 Jack Wilson FW RC	4.00	10.00
132 B. Duckworth FW RC	3.00	8.00
133 Mike Penney FW RC	3.00	8.00
134 Jay Gibbons FW RC	4.00	10.00
135 Cesar Crespo FW RC	3.00	8.00
136 Ken Griffey Jr. SS	4.00	10.00
137 Mark McGwire SS	6.00	15.00
138 Derek Jeter SS	6.00	15.00
139 Alex Rodriguez SS	4.00	10.00
140 Sammy Sosa SS	2.50	6.00
141 Carlos Delgado SS	2.00	5.00
142 Cal Ripken SS	8.00	20.00
143 Pedro Martinez SS	2.00	5.00
144 Frank Thomas SS	2.50	6.00
145 Juan Gonzalez SS	2.00	5.00
146 Troy Glaus SS	2.00	5.00
147 Jason Giambi SS	2.00	5.00
148 Ivan Rodriguez SS	2.00	5.00
149 Chipper Jones SS	2.50	6.00
150 Vladimir Guerrero SS	2.50	6.00
151 Mike Piazza SS	4.00	10.00
152 Jeff Bagwell SS	2.00	5.00
153 Randy Johnson SS	2.50	6.00
154 Todd Helton SS	2.00	5.00
155 Gary Sheffield SS	2.00	5.00
156 Tony Gwynn SS	3.00	8.00
157 Barry Bonds SS	6.00	15.00
158 N. Garciaparra SS	4.00	10.00
159 Bernie Williams SS	2.00	5.00
160 Greg Vaughn SS	2.00	5.00
161 David Wells SS	2.00	5.00
162 Roberto Alomar SS	2.00	5.00
163 Jermaine Dye SS	2.00	5.00
164 Rafael Palmeiro SS	2.00	5.00
165 Andruw Jones SS	2.00	5.00
166 Preston Wilson SS	2.00	5.00
167 Edgardo Alfonzo SS	2.00	5.00
168 Pat Burrell SS	2.00	5.00
169 Jim Edmonds SS	2.00	5.00
170 Mike Hampton SS	2.00	5.00
171 Jeff Kent SS	2.00	5.00
172 Kevin Brown SS	2.00	5.00
173 Manny Ramirez Sox SS	2.00	5.00
174 Magglio Ordonez SS	2.00	5.00
175 Roger Clemens SS	5.00	12.00
176 Jim Thome SS	2.00	5.00
177 Barry Zito SS	2.00	5.00
178 Brian Giles SS	2.00	5.00
179 Rick Ankiel SS	2.00	5.00
180 Corey Patterson SS	2.00	5.00
181 Garret Anderson	.25	.60
182 Jermaine Dye	.25	.60
183 Shannon Stewart	.25	.60
184 Ben Grieve	.25	.60
185 Ellis Burks	.25	.60
186 John Olerud	.25	.60
187 Tony Batista	.25	.60
188 Ruben Sierra	.25	.60
189 Carl Everett	.25	.60
190 Neifi Perez	.25	.60
191 Tony Clark	.25	.60
192 Doug Mientkiewicz	.25	.60
193 Carlos Lee	.25	.60
194 Jorge Posada	.40	1.00
195 Lance Berkman	2.00	5.00
196 Ken Caminiti	.25	.60
197 Ben Sheets	.40	1.00
198 Matt Morris	.25	.60
199 Fred McGriff	.40	1.00
200 Mark Grace	.40	1.00
201 Paul LoDuca	.25	.60
202 Tony Armas Jr.	.25	.60
203 Andres Galarraga	.25	.60
204 Cliff Floyd	.25	.60
205 Matt Lawton	.25	.60
206 Ryan Klesko	.25	.60
207 Jimmy Rollins	.25	.60
208 Aramis Ramirez	.25	.60
209 Aaron Boone	.25	.60
210 Jose Ortiz	.25	.60
211 Mark Prior FW RC	6.00	15.00
212 Mark Teixeira FW RC	20.00	50.00
213 Bud Smith FW RC	2.50	6.00
214 W.Caceres FW RC	2.50	6.00
215 Dave Williams FW RC	2.50	6.00
216 Delvin James FW RC	2.50	6.00
217 Endy Chavez FW RC	2.50	6.00
218 Doug Nickle FW RC	2.50	6.00
219 Bret Prinz FW RC	2.50	6.00
220 Troy Mattes FW RC	2.50	6.00
221 D.Sanchez FW RC	2.50	6.00
222 D.Brazelton FW RC	2.50	6.00
223 Brian Bowles FW RC	2.50	6.00
224 D.Mendez FW RC	2.50	6.00
225 Jorge Julio FW RC	2.50	6.00
226 Matt White FW RC	2.50	6.00
227 Casey Fossum FW RC	2.50	6.00
228 Mike Rivera FW RC	2.50	6.00
229 Joe Kennedy FW RC	3.00	8.00
230 Kyle Lohse FW RC	3.00	8.00
231 Juan Cruz FW RC	2.50	6.00
232 Jeremy Affeldt FW RC	2.50	6.00
233 Brandon Lyon FW RC	2.50	6.00
234 Brian Roberts FW RC	8.00	20.00
235 Willie Harris FW RC	2.50	6.00
236 Pedro Santana FW RC	2.50	6.00
237 Rafael Soriano FW RC	2.50	6.00
238 Steve Green FW RC	2.50	6.00
239 Junior Spivey FW RC	3.00	8.00
240 R.Mackowiak FW RC	3.00	8.00
NNO K.Griffey Jr. Promo	.75	2.00

2001 SP Authentic Limited

This 180-card set is a straight parallel of the basic set. Only fifty sets were produced and each card features serial-numbering in thin gold foil on front and a gold foil brand logo (basic cards feature silver foil brand logos).

*STARS 1-90: 10X TO 25X BASIC 1-90
*FW 91-135: 1X TO 2.5X BASIC 91-135
*SS 136-180: 1.5X TO 4X BASIC 136-180

91 Ichiro Suzuki FW	175.00	300.00
126 Albert Pujols FW	600.00	800.00

2001 SP Authentic BuyBacks

For the third time in the history of the brand (including 1997 and 2000), Upper Deck incorporated Buyback cards into SP Authentic packs. Representatives from UD purchased varying quantities of actual previously released SP Authentic cards ranging from 1993 to 2000. The cards were then signed by the featured ballplayer, hand-numbered in blue ink on front and affixed with a serial-numbered hologram sticker on back (note: it's believed all 2001 hologram sticker numbers begin with the letters "AAA"). In addition to the actual signed card, each Buyback was distributed with a 2 1/2" by 3 1/2" Authenticity Guarantee card. Each of these cards featured a hologram with a matching serial-number and a note of congratulations from Upper Deck's CEO Richard McWilliam. Our listings for these cards feature the year of the card followed by the quantity produced. Thus, "Edgardo Alfonzo 95/77" indicates a 1995 SP Authentic Edgardo Alfonzo card of which 77 copies were made. Please note that several Buyback cards are too scarce for us to provide accurate pricing. Please see our magazine or website for pricing information on these cards as it's made available. The following players were seeded into packs as exchange cards: Roger Clemens, Cal Ripken and Frank Thomas. Collectors did not know which card of these players they would receive until it was mailed to them. Exchange deadline was 8/30/04.

1 Edgardo Alfonzo 95/77	10.00	25.00
2 Edgardo Alfonzo 98/15		
3 Edgardo Alfonzo 00/280	6.00	15.00
4 Barry Bonds 93/75	100.00	175.00
5 Barry Bonds 94/103	100.00	175.00
6 Barry Bonds 95/31	100.00	175.00
7 Barry Bonds 95 Silver/2		
8 Barry Bonds 96/49	100.00	175.00
9 Barry Bonds 97/15		
10 Barry Bonds 98/15		
11 Barry Bonds 00/146	100.00	175.00
12 Roger Clemens 00/145	50.00	100.00
13 R.Clemens 99/150 EXCH	50.00	100.00
15 Carlos Delgado 93/24		
16 Carlos Delgado 94/272	6.00	15.00
17 Carlos Delgado 96/81	10.00	25.00
18 Carlos Delgado 97/8		
19 Carlos Delgado 98/29	20.00	50.00
20 Carlos Delgado 00/169	6.00	15.00
21 Jim Edmonds 96/72	15.00	40.00
22 Jim Edmonds 97/38	30.00	60.00
23 Jim Edmonds 98/23		
24 Jason Giambi 97/14		
25 Jason Giambi 98/6		
26 Jason Giambi 00/290	6.00	15.00
27 Troy Glaus 00/340	10.00	25.00
28 Shawn Green 00/340	10.00	25.00
29 Ken Griffey Jr. 93/34	75.00	150.00
30 Ken Griffey Jr. 94/182	40.00	80.00
31 Ken Griffey Jr. 95/116	40.00	80.00
32 Ken Griffey Jr. 95 Silver/2		
33 Ken Griffey Jr. 96/53	60.00	120.00
34 Ken Griffey Jr. 97/7		
35 Ken Griffey Jr. 98/8		
36 Ken Griffey Jr. 00/333	40.00	80.00
37 Tony Gwynn 93/101	30.00	60.00
38 Tony Gwynn 94/88	30.00	60.00
39 Tony Gwynn 95/179	20.00	50.00
40 Tony Gwynn 96/92	30.00	60.00
41 Tony Gwynn 97/9		
42 Tony Gwynn 98/16		
43 Tony Gwynn 00/95	30.00	60.00
44 Todd Helton 00/194	10.00	25.00
45 Tim Hudson 00/291	10.00	25.00
46 Randy Johnson 93/97	50.00	100.00
47 Randy Johnson 94/146	30.00	60.00
48 Randy Johnson 95/121	30.00	60.00
49 Randy Johnson 95 Silver/6		
50 Randy Johnson 96/78	50.00	100.00
51 Randy Johnson 97/8		
52 Randy Johnson 98/12		
53 Randy Johnson 00/213	30.00	60.00
54 Andruw Jones 97/20		
55 Andruw Jones 98/12		
56 Andruw Jones 00/336	10.00	25.00
57 Chipper Jones 93/13		
58 Chipper Jones 95/118	20.00	50.00
59 Chipper Jones 96/72	30.00	60.00
60 Chipper Jones 97/15		
61 Chipper Jones 98/11		
62 Chipper Jones 00/303	20.00	50.00
63 Cal Ripken 93/22		
64 Cal Ripken 94/99	60.00	120.00
65 Cal Ripken 95/37	75.00	150.00
66 Cal Ripken 96/16		
67 Cal Ripken 96 CL/10		
68 Cal Ripken 97/23		
69 Cal Ripken 98/11		
70 Cal Ripken 00/266	60.00	120.00
72 Alex Rodriguez 95/117	100.00	200.00
73 Alex Rodriguez 95 Silver/2		
74 Alex Rodriguez 96/72	100.00	200.00
75 Alex Rodriguez 97/14		
76 Alex Rodriguez 98/11		
77 Alex Rodriguez 00/332	100.00	200.00
78 Ivan Rodriguez 93/89	20.00	50.00
79 Ivan Rodriguez 95/16		
80 Ivan Rodriguez 95 Silver/2		
81 Ivan Rodriguez 96/64	40.00	80.00
82 Ivan Rodriguez 97/8		
83 Ivan Rodriguez 98/13		
84 Ivan Rodriguez 00/163	15.00	40.00
85 Gary Sheffield 93/82	15.00	40.00
86 Gary Sheffield 94/3		
87 Gary Sheffield 95/70	15.00	40.00
88 Gary Sheffield 96/67	15.00	40.00
89 Gary Sheffield 97/43	30.00	60.00
90 Gary Sheffield 98/27	40.00	80.00
91 Gary Sheffield 00/146	10.00	25.00
92 Sammy Sosa 93/73	50.00	100.00
93 Sammy Sosa 94/19		
94 Sammy Sosa 95/30	50.00	100.00
95 Sammy Sosa 96/9		
96 Sammy Sosa 97/14		
97 Fernando Tatis 00/267	4.00	10.00
98 Frank Thomas 93/79	30.00	60.00
99 Frank Thomas 94/165	15.00	40.00
100 Frank Thomas 95/3		
101 Frank Thomas 97/34	50.00	100.00
102 Frank Thomas 98/10		
103 Frank Thomas 00/302	15.00	40.00
105 Mo Vaughn 93/94	10.00	25.00
106 Mo Vaughn 94/102	10.00	25.00
107 Mo Vaughn 95/129	6.00	15.00
108 Mo Vaughn 95 Silver/3		
109 Mo Vaughn 96/81	10.00	25.00
110 Mo Vaughn 97/36	15.00	40.00
111 Mo Vaughn 98/23		
112 Mo Vaughn 00/309	6.00	15.00
113 Robin Ventura 00/340	6.00	15.00
114 Matt Williams 00/340	10.00	25.00
115 Authentication Card		

2001 SP Authentic Chirography

Signed Chirography inserts were brought back for the fourth straight year within SP Authentic. Over 40 players were featured in the 2001 issue, with announced odds of 1:72 packs. Each card features a horizontal design and a small black and white action photo of the player at the side to allow the maximum amount of room for the featured player's autograph (of which is typically found signed in blue ink). Quantities produced for each card varied dramatically and shortly after the product was released, representatives at Upper Deck publicly announced print runs on a selection of the toughest cards to obtain. Those quantities have been added to our checklist following the featured player's name.

AB Albert Belle	6.00	15.00
AJ Andruw Jones	10.00	25.00
AP Albert Pujols	250.00	400.00
AR Alex Rodriguez SP/229	60.00	120.00
BS Ben Sheets	10.00	25.00
CB Carlos Beltran	12.50	30.00
CD Carlos Delgado	12.50	30.00
CF Cliff Floyd	6.00	15.00
CJ Chipper Jones SP/184	20.00	50.00
CR Cal Ripken SP/109	60.00	120.00
DD Darren Dreifort SP/206	4.00	10.00
DER Darin Erstad	6.00	15.00
DES David Espinosa	4.00	10.00
DJ David Justice	6.00	15.00
DS Dane Sardinha	4.00	10.00
DW David Wells	6.00	15.00
EA Edgardo Alfonzo	6.00	15.00
JC Jose Canseco	10.00	25.00
JD J.D. Drew	8.00	20.00
JE Jim Edmonds	10.00	25.00
JG Jason Giambi	6.00	15.00
KG Ken Griffey Jr. SP/126	50.00	100.00
LG Luis Gonzalez SP/271	10.00	25.00
MB Milton Bradley	6.00	15.00
MK Mark Kotsay SP/228	6.00	15.00
MS Mike Sweeney	6.00	15.00
MV Mo Vaughn SP/103	6.00	15.00
MW Matt Williams	10.00	25.00
PB Pat Burrell	6.00	15.00
RF Rafael Furcal SP/222	6.00	15.00
RH Rick Helling SP/211	4.00	10.00
RJ R. Johnson SP/143	30.00	60.00
RV Robin Ventura SP/92		
RW Rondell White	6.00	15.00
SG Shawn Green SP/82	15.00	40.00
SS Sammy Sosa SP/76	50.00	100.00
TIH Tim Hudson	10.00	25.00
TL Travis Lee SP/226	4.00	10.00
TOG Tony Gwynn SP/76	20.00	50.00
TOH Todd Helton SP/152	10.00	25.00
TRG Troy Glaus	10.00	25.00

2001 SP Authentic Chirography Gold

These scarce autograph cards are a straight parallel of the more commonly available Chirography cards. The Gold cards, however, were all produced to quantities mirroring the featured player's uniform number. Furthermore, the cards are individually numbered on front in blue ink and the imagery and design accents are printed in a subdued gold color (rather than the black and white design used on the basic Chirography cards). Many of these cards are too scarce for us to provide accurate pricing on.

GAB Albert Belle/88	20.00	50.00
GAJ Andruw Jones/25		
GAP Albert Pujols/5		
GAR Alex Rodriguez/3		
GBS Ben Sheets/15		
GCB Carlos Beltran/15		
GCD Carlos Delgado/25		
GCF Cliff Floyd/30		
GCJ Chipper Jones/10		
GCR Cal Ripken/8		
GDD Darren Dreifort/37	10.00	25.00
GDER Darin Erstad/17		
GDES David Espinosa/79	10.00	25.00
GDJ David Justice/28	20.00	50.00
GDS Dane Sardinha/50	10.00	25.00
GDW David Wells/33	20.00	50.00
GEA Edgardo Alfonzo/13		
GJD J.D. Drew/7		

Card	Low	High
GJE Jim Edmonds/15		
GJG Jason Giambi/16		
GKG Ken Griffey Jr./30	75.00	150.00
GLG Luis Gonzalez/20		
GMB Milton Bradley/24		
GMK Mark Kotsay/14		
GMS Mike Sweeney/29	20.00	50.00
GMV Mo Vaughn/42	20.00	50.00
GMW Matt Williams/9		
GPB Pat Burrell/5		
GRF Rafael Furcal/1		
GRH Rick Helling/32	10.00	25.00
GRJ Randy Johnson/51	50.00	100.00
GRV Robin Ventura/4		
GRW Rondell White/22		
GSG Shawn Green/15		
GSS Sammy Sosa/21		
GTIH Tim Hudson/15		
GTL Travis Lee/16		
GTOG Tony Gwynn/21		
GTOH Todd Helton/17		
GTRG Troy Glaus/25		

2001 SP Authentic Chirography Update

Randomly inserted into Upper Deck Rookie Update packs, thse eight cards feature autographs from leading players in the game. Cal Ripken and Ichiro Suuzki did not return their cards in time for inclusion in these packs and these cards are available as exchange cards. Those cards could be redeemed until September 13th, 2004. These cards are serial numbered to 250.

Card	Low	High
SPCR Cal Ripken	75.00	150.00
SPDM Doug Mientkiewicz	6.00	15.00
SPIS Ichiro Suzuki	250.00	400.00
SPJP Jorge Posada	15.00	40.00
SPKG Ken Griffey Jr.	40.00	80.00
SPLB Lance Berkman	10.00	25.00
SPMS Mike Sweeney	6.00	15.00
SPTG Tony Gwynn	15.00	40.00

2001 SP Authentic Chirography Update Silver

Randomly inserted into Upper Deck Rookie Update packs, thse eight cards parallel the Chirography Update insert set and feature autographs from leading players in the game. Cal Ripken Jr. and Ichiro Suuzki did not return their cards in time for inclusion in these packs and these cards are available as exchange cards. These cards are serial numbered to 100.

Card	Low	High
SPCR Cal Ripken		
SPDM Doug Mientkiewicz	10.00	25.00
SPIS Ichiro Suzuki		
SPJP Jorge Posada	15.00	40.00
SPKG Ken Griffey Jr.	60.00	120.00
SPLB Lance Berkman	15.00	40.00
SPMS Mike Sweeney	10.00	25.00
SPTG Tony Gwynn	30.00	60.00

2001 SP Authentic Cooperstown Calling Game Jersey

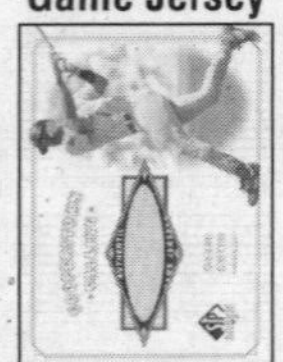

This 22-card set features a selection of players that were voted in (or were soon to be voted in) to the baseball Hall of Fame in Cooperstown, NY. Each card features a swatch of game-used jersey incorporated into an attractive horizontal design. Though specific odds per pack were not released for this set, Upper Deck did release cumulative odds of 1:24 packs for finding a game-used jersey card from either of the Cooperstown Calling, UD Exclusives or UD Exclusives Combos sets within the SP Authentic product.

Card	Low	High
CCAD Andre Dawson	4.00	10.00
CCBM Bill Mazeroski	6.00	15.00
CCCR Cal Ripken	15.00	40.00
CCDM Don Mattingly	15.00	40.00
CCDW Dave Winfield	4.00	10.00
CCEM Eddie Murray	6.00	15.00
CCGC Gary Carter	4.00	10.00
CCGG Goose Gossage	4.00	10.00
CCJB Jeff Bagwell	6.00	15.00
CCKP Kirby Puckett	6.00	15.00
CCKS Kazuhiro Sasaki	4.00	10.00
CCMP Mike Piazza SP	10.00	25.00
CCMR M. Ramirez Sox SP	6.00	15.00
CCOS Ozzie Smith	6.00	15.00
CCPM Pedro Martinez SP	6.00	15.00
CCPM Paul Molitor	4.00	10.00
CCRC Roger Clemens	15.00	40.00
CCRM R. Maris SP/243	40.00	80.00
CCRS Ryne Sandberg	12.50	30.00
CCSG Steve Garvey	4.00	10.00
CCTG Tony Gwynn	8.00	20.00
CCWB Wade Boggs	6.00	15.00

2001 SP Authentic Stars of Japan

This 30-card dual player set features a selection of Japanese stars active in Major League baseball at the time of issue. The cards were distributed in special Stars of Japan packs of which were available as a bonus pack within each sealed box of 2001 SP Authentic baseball. Each Stars of Japan pack contained three cards and one in every 12 packs contained a memorabilia card.

Card	Low	High
COMPLETE SET (30)	20.00	50.00
RS1 Ichiro Suzuki / Tsuyoshi Shinjo	3.00	8.00
RS2 Shigetoshi Hasegawa / Hideki Irabu	.75	2.00
RS3 Tomo Ohka / Mac Suzuki	.75	2.00
RS4 Tsuyoshi Shinjo / Hideki Irabu	.75	2.00
RS5 Ichiro Suzuki / Hideo Nomo	4.00	10.00
RS6 Tsuyoshi Shinjo / Mac Suzuki	.75	2.00
RS7 Tsuyoshi Shinjo / Kazuhiro Sasaki	.75	2.00
RS8 Hideo Nomo / Tomo Ohka	.75	2.00
RS9 Ichiro Suzuki / Mac Suzuki	3.00	8.00
RS10 Hideo Nomo / Shigetoshi Hasegawa	.75	2.00
RS11 Hideo Nomo / Masato Yoshii	.75	2.00
RS12 Hideo Nomo / Hideki Irabu	.75	2.00
RS13 Shig. Hasegawa / Kazuhiro Sasaki	.75	2.00
RS14 Shig. Hasegawa / Mac Suzuki	.75	2.00
RS15 Tsuyoshi Shinjo / Hideo Nomo	.75	2.00
RS16 Tsuyoshi Shinjo / Tomo Ohka	.75	2.00
RS17 Ichiro Suzuki / Kazuhiro Sasaki	4.00	10.00
RS18 Masato Yoshii / Hideki Irabu	.75	2.00
RS19 Ichiro Suzuki / Tomo Ohka	3.00	8.00
RS20 Hideki Irabu / Kazuhiro Sasaki	.75	2.00
RS21 Tsuyoshi Shinjo / Masato Yoshii	.75	2.00
RS22 Ichiro Suzuki / Shigetoshi Hasegawa	3.00	8.00
RS23 Mac Suzuki / Kazuhiro Sasaki	.75	2.00
RS24 Ichiro Suzuki / Hideki Irabu	3.00	8.00
RS25 Tomo Ohka / Kazuhiro Sasaki	.75	2.00
RS26 Tsuyoshi Shinjo / Shigetoshi Hasegawa	.75	2.00
RS27 Masato Yoshii / Kazuhiro Sasaki	.75	2.00
RS28 Hideo Nomo / Kazuhiro Sasaki	.75	2.00
RS29 Ichiro Suzuki / Masato Yoshii	3.00	8.00
RS30 Hideo Nomo / Mac Suzuki	.75	2.00

2001 SP Authentic Stars of Japan Game Ball

This six-card set features a selection of Japanese stars actively playing in the Major Leagues at the time of issue. Each card features a patch of game-used baseball. The cards were distributed in special Stars of Japan packs. Each sealed box of 2001 SP Authentic contained one three-card Stars of Japan pack inside. Though individual Jersey card odds were not announced, the cumulative odds of finding a memorabilia card (ball, base, bat or jersey) from a Stars of Japan packs was 1:12.

GOLD RANDOM INSERTS IN PACKS
GOLD PRINT RUN 25 SERIAL #'d SETS
GOLD NO PRICING DUE TO SCARCITY

Card	Low	High
BBHI Hideki Irabu	4.00	10.00
BBIS Ichiro Suzuki	40.00	80.00
BBKS Kazuhiro Sasaki	4.00	10.00
BBMY Masato Yoshii	4.00	10.00
BBSH Shig. Hasegawa SP/30		
BBTS T. Shinjo SP/50	6.00	15.00

2001 SP Authentic Stars of Japan Game Ball-Base Combos

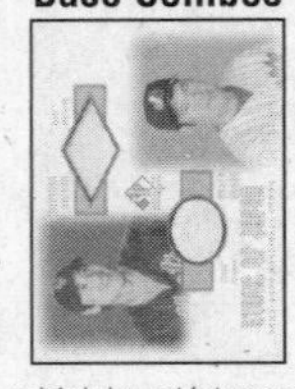

This 14-card dual player set features a selection of Japanese stars actively playing in the Major Leagues at the time of issue. Each card features a piece of a game-used baseball coupled with a piece of game-used base. The cards were distributed in special Stars of Japan packs. Each sealed box of 2001 SP Authentic contained one three-card Stars of Japan pack inside.Though individual Jersey card odds were not announced, the cumulative odds of finding a memorabilia card (ball, base, bat or jersey) from a Stars of Japan packs was 1:12.

GOLD RANDOM INSERTS IN PACKS
GOLD PRINT RUN 25 SERIAL #'d SETS
GOLD NO PRICING DUE TO SCARCITY

Card	Low	High
HIKS Hideki Irabu / Kazuhiro Sasaki SP/30		
HNKS Hideo Nomo / Kazuhiro Sasaki SP/50	40.00	80.00
HNSH Hideo Nomo / Shigetosi Hasegawa	10.00	25.00
ISKS Ichiro Suzuki / Kazuhiro Sasaki SP/30		
ISMY Ichiro Suzuki / Masato Yoshii	40.00	80.00
ISSH Ichiro Suzuki / Shigestosi Hasegawa SP/72	60.00	120.00
ISTS Ichiro Suzuki / Tsuyoshi Shinjo SP/40		
MSKS Mac Suzuki / Kazuhiro Sasaki SP/30		
MYKS Masato Yoshii / Kazuhiro Sasaki SP/30		
SHKS S. Hasegawa / Kazuhiro Sasaki SP/30		
TOKS Tomokazu Ohka / Kazuhiro Sasaki	4.00	10.00
TSHI Tsuyoshi Shinjo / Hideki Irabu SP/30		
TSKS Tsuyoshi Shinjo / Kazuhiro Sasaki SP/30		
TSSH Tsuyoshi Shinjo / Shigetosi Hasegawa SP/30		

2001 SP Authentic Stars of Japan Game Ball-Base Trio

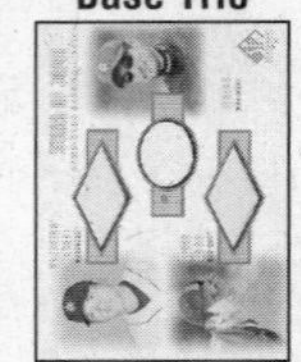

This card features the three greatest Japanese stars actively playing in the Major Leagues at the time of issue. The card features two pieces of game-used bases and one piece of a game-used baseball from the highlighted players. The card was distributed in special Stars of Japan packs. Each sealed box of 2001 SP Authentic contained one three-card Stars of Japan pack inside.Though individual Jersey card odds were not announced, the cumulative odds of finding a memorabilia card (ball, base, bat or jersey) from a Stars of Japan packs was 1:12.

GOLD RANDOM INSERTS IN PACKS
GOLD PRINT RUN 25 SERIAL #'d SETS
GOLD NO PRICING DUE TO SCARCITY

RS Kazuhiro Sasaki / Ichiro Suzuki / Hideo Nomo SP/30

2001 SP Authentic Stars of Japan Game Base

This eight-card set features a selection of Japanese stars actively playing in the Major Leagues at the time of issue. Each card features a piece of game used base. The cards were distributed in special Stars of Japan packs. Each sealed box of 2001 SP Authentic contained one three-card Stars of Japan pack inside. Though individual Jersey card odds were not announced, the cumulative odds of finding a memorabilia card (ball, base, bat or jersey) from a Stars of Japan packs was 1:12.

OVERALL MEMORABILIA ODDS 1:12 SOJ
SP PRINT RUNS PROVIDED BY UD
NO PRICING ON QTY OF 40 OR LESS
GOLD RANDOM INSERTS IN PACKS
GOLD PRINT RUN 25 SERIAL #'d SETS
GOLD NO PRICING DUE TO SCARCITY

HI Hideki Irabu SP/33
IS Ichiro Suzuki SP/23
KS Kazuhiro Sasaki SP/33
MS Mac Suzuki SP/23
MY Masato Yoshii SP/33
SH S. Hasegawa SP/23
TO Tomokazu Ohka SP/33
TS Tsuyoshi Shinjo SP/33

2001 SP Authentic Stars of Japan Game Bat

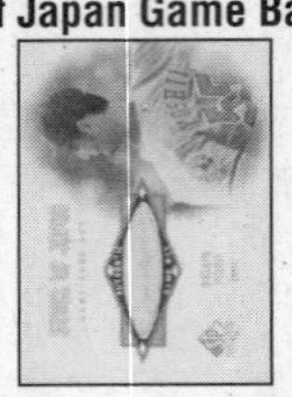

This three-card set features a selection of Japanese stars actively playing in the Major Leagues at the time of issue. Each card features a piece of game-used bat. The cards were distributed in special Stars of Japan packs. Each sealed box of 2001 SP Authentic contained one three-card Stars of Japan pack inside.Though individual Jersey card odds were not announced, the cumulative odds of finding a memorabilia card (ball, base, bat or jersey) from a Stars of Japan packs was 1:12.

GOLD RANDOM INSERTS IN PACKS
GOLD PRINT RUN 25 SERIAL #'d SETS
GOLD NO PRICING DUE TO SCARCITY

Card	Low	High
BHN Hideo Nomo SP/30		
BMY Masato Yoshii	4.00	10.00
BTS T. Shinjo SP/30		

2001 SP Authentic Stars of Japan Game Bat-Jersey Combos

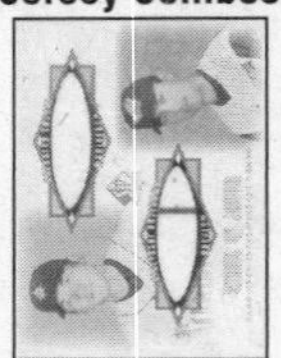

This 4-card dual player set features a selection of Japanese stars actively playing in the Major Leagues at the time of issue. Each card features a combination of a game-used bat chip or game-used jersey swatch from the featured players. The cards were distributed in special Stars of Japan packs. Each sealed box of 2001 SP Authentic contained one 3-card Stars of Japan pack inside.Though individual Jersey card odds were not announced, the cumulative odds of finding a memorabilia card (ball, base, bat or jersey) from a Stars of Japan packs was 1:12.

GOLD RANDOM INSERTS IN PACKS
GOLD PRINT RUN 25 SERIAL #'d SETS
GOLD NO PRICING DUE TO SCARCITY

Card	Low	High
BBHS S. Hasegawa / Tsuyoshi Shinjo	10.00	25.00
JBNN Hideo Nomo / Hideo Nomo	30.00	60.00
JBSN Kazuhiro Sasaki / Hideo Nomo	10.00	25.00
JJSH Kazuhiro Sasaki / Shigetosi Hasegawa	6.00	15.00

2001 SP Authentic Stars of Japan Game Jersey

This six-card set features a selection of Japanese stars actively playing in the Major Leagues at the time of issue. Each card features a swatch of game-used jersey. The cards were distributed in special Stars of Japan packs. Each sealed box of 2001 SP Authentic contained one three-card Stars of Japan pack inside. Though individual Jersey card odds were not announced, the cumulative odds of finding a memorabilia card (ball, base, bat or jersey) from a Stars of Japan packs was 1:12. Ichiro Suzuki's jersey card was not available at time of packout and an exchange card was seeded into packs in it's place. The exchange card had a redemption deadline of August 30th, 2004. Though not serial-numbered, officials at Upper Deck announced that only 260 copies of Ichiro's jersey card were produced.

GOLD RANDOM INSERTS IN PACKS
GOLD PRINT RUN 25 SERIAL #'d SETS
NO GOLD PRICING DUE TO SCARCITY

Card	Low	High
JHN Hideo Nomo	6.00	15.00
JIS Ichiro Suzuki SP/260	50.00	100.00
JKS Kazuhiro Sasaki	4.00	10.00
JMY Masato Yoshii	4.00	10.00
JSH S. Hasegawa	4.00	10.00
JTS Tsuyoshi Shinjo	6.00	15.00

2001 SP Authentic Stars of Japan Game Jersey Gold

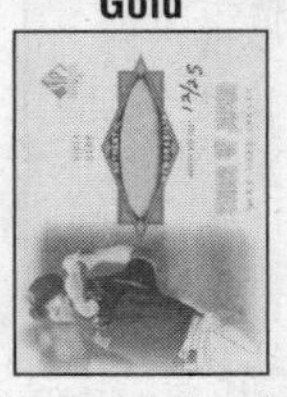

These Gold cards are straight parallels to the standard Stars of Japan Game Jersey inserts. However, only 25 Gold sets were produced and each card carries gold-foil serial-numbering "XX/25" on front. In addition, gold ink design highlights on the card fronts and backs replace the silver ink highlights seen on the standard Stars of Japan memorabilia cards. The cards were randomly inserted into Stars of Japan packs at an unspecified ratio. No Ichiro Suzuki game jersey gold card was issued.

JHN Hideo Nomo
JKS Kazuhiro Sasaki
JMY Masato Yoshii
JSH S. Hasegawa
JTS Tsuyoshi Shinjo

2001 SP Authentic Sultan of Swatch Memorabilia

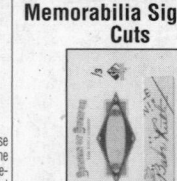

This 21-card set features a selection of significant achievements from legendary slugger Babe Ruth's storied career. Each card features a swatch of game-used uniform (most likely pants) and is hand-numbered in blue ink on front to the year or statisitical figure of the featured event (i.e. card SOS3 highlights Ruth's 94 career wins as a pitcher, thus only 94 hand-numbered copies of that card were produced). Quantities on each card vary from as many as 94 copies to as few as 14 copies. The cards were randomly inserted into packs at an unspecified ratio.

Card	Low	High
SOS1 B.Ruth Red Sox/14		
SOS2 B.Ruth 29.2 Inn/29	250.00	400.00
SOS3 B.Ruth 94 Wins/94	250.00	400.00
SOS4 B.Ruth 54 HRs/54	250.00	400.00
SOS5 B.Ruth 59 HRs/59	250.00	400.00
SOS6 Babe Ruth 3 HRs WS/26	250.00	400.00
SOS7 B.Ruth 60 HRs/27	250.00	400.00
SOS8 Babe Ruth Called Shot/32	250.00	400.00
SOS9 B.Ruth HR Title/20		
SOS10 B.Ruth HR Title/21		
SOS11 B.Ruth Christens/23		
SOS12 B.Ruth 46 HRs/24		
SOS13 B.Ruth 40 HRs/26	250.00	400.00
SOS14 B.Ruth HR Title/27	250.00	400.00
SOS15 B.Ruth 50 HRs/28	250.00	400.00
SOS16 Babe Ruth Leads Way/29	250.00	400.00
SOS17 B.Ruth 49 HRs/30	250.00	400.00
SOS18 Babe Ruth Last Title/31	250.00	400.00
SOS19 Babe Ruth 1st AS/33	250.00	400.00
SOS20 B.Ruth 1st HOF/36	250.00	400.00
SOS21 B.Ruth House/48	250.00	400.00

2001 SP Authentic Sultan of Swatch Memorabilia Signature Cuts

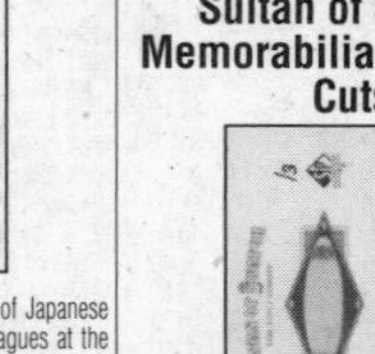

Each of these cards features an actual Babe Ruth autograph taken from an autographed "cut" (an industry term for a signed piece of paper - often old checks or 3 x 5 note cards) incorporated directly into the card through a window of cardboard. Though only one copy of each card was made for this set, three cards are actually identical parallels of each other save for the SOS-prefixed card numbering on back and the variations in the cut signatures used for each. The signature on card SOS2 has been verified as "Babe Ruth" and for card SOS3 as "G.H. Ruth". Due to the extreme scarcity of these cards, we cannot provide an accurate value as they rarely are seen for public sale.

JC1 Babe Ruth Jsy-Cut AU/1
JC2 Babe Ruth Jsy-Cut AU
Cut signed as Babe Ruth
JC3 Babe Ruth Jsy-Cut AU
Cut signed as G.H. Ruth

2001 SP Authentic UD Exclusives Game Jersey

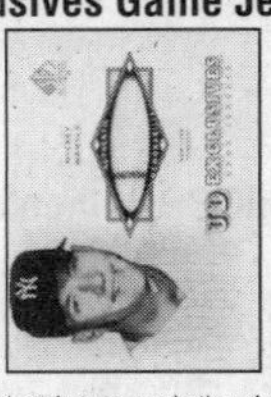

This 6-card set features a selection of superstars signed exclusively to Upper Deck for the rights to produce game-used jersey cards. Each card features a swatch of game-used jersey incorporated into an attractive horizontal design. Though specific odds per pack were not released for this set, Upper Deck did release cumulative odds of 1:24 packs for finding a game-used jersey card from either of the Cooperstown Calling, UD Exclusives or UD Exclusives Combos sets within the SP Authentic product. Shortly after release, representatives at Upper Deck publicly released print run information on several short prints. These quantities have been added to the end of the card description within our checklist.

Card	Low	High
AR Alex Rodriguez	6.00	15.00
GS Gary Sheffield	4.00	10.00
JD J.DiMaggio SP/243	50.00	100.00
KG Ken Griffey Jr.	6.00	15.00
MM M.Mantle SP/243	75.00	150.00
SS Sammy Sosa	6.00	15.00

2001 SP Authentic UD Exclusives Game Jersey Combos

This six-card set features a selection of superstars signed exclusively to Upper Deck for the rights to produce game-used jersey cards. Each card features a swatch of game-used jersey from each featured player incorporated into an attractive horizontal design. Though specific odds per pack were not released for this set, Upper Deck did release cumulative odds of 1:24 packs for finding a game-used jersey card from either of the Cooperstown Calling, UD Exclusives or UD Exclusives Combos sets within the SP Authentic product. Shortly after release, representatives at Upper Deck publicly released print run information on several short prints. These quantities have been added to the end of the card description within our checklist.

Card	Low	High
GD Ken Griffey Jr. / Joe DiMaggio SP/98	100.00	175.00
MD Mickey Mantle / Joe DiMaggio SP/98	175.00	300.00
MG Mickey Mantle / Ken Griffey Jr. SP/98	75.00	150.00
RS Alex Rodriguez / Ozzie Smith	20.00	50.00
SD Sammy Sosa / Andre Dawson	10.00	25.00
SW Gary Sheffiel / Dave Winfield	10.00	25.00

2002 SP Authentic

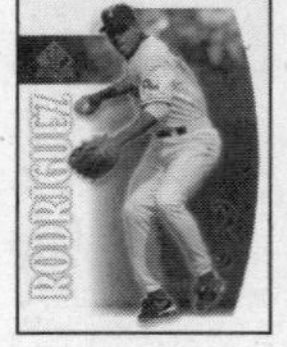

This 230 card set was released in two separate series. The basic SP Authentic product (containing cards 1-170) was issued in September, 2002. Update cards 171-230 were distributed within packs of 2002 Upper Deck Rookie Update in mid-December, 2002. SP Authentic packs were issued in five card packs with a $5 SRP. Boxes contained 24 packs and were packed five to a case. Cards numbered 1 through 90 featured veterans while cards number 91 through 135 were part of the Future Watch subset and were printed to a stated print run of 1999 serial numbered sets. Cards numbered 136 through 170 were signed by the player and most of the cards were printed to a stated print run of 999 serial numbered sets. Cards number 146, 152 and 157 were printed to a stated print run of 249 serial numbered sets. Update cards 201-230 continued the Future Watch subset (focusing on rookies and prospects) and each card was serial numbered to 1999. Though pack odds for these cards was never released, we estimate the cards were seeded at an approximate rate of 1:7 Rookie Update packs. In addition, an exchange card with a redemption deadline of August 8th, 2005, good for a signed Joe DiMaggio poster was randomly inserted into SP Authentic packs.

Card	Low	High
COMP.LOW w/o SP's (90)	6.00	15.00
COMP.UPDATE w/o SP's (30)	4.00	10.00
COMMON CARD (1-90)	.15	.40
COMMON (91-135/201-230)	2.00	5.00
COMMON CARD (136-170)	4.00	10.00
COMMON CARD (171-200)	.25	.60

1 Troy Glaus .15 .40
2 Darin Erstad .15 .40
3 Barry Zito .15 .40
4 Eric Chavez .15 .40
5 Tim Hudson .15 .40
6 Miguel Tejada .15 .40
7 Carlos Delgado .15 .40
8 Shannon Stewart .15 .40
9 Ben Grieve .15 .40
10 Jim Thome .25 .60
11 C.C. Sabathia .15 .40
12 Ichiro Suzuki .75 2.00
13 Freddy Garcia .15 .40
14 Edgar Martinez .25 .60
15 Bret Boone .15 .40
16 Jeff Conine .15 .40
17 Alex Rodriguez .60 1.50
18 Juan Gonzalez .15 .40
19 Ivan Rodriguez .25 .60
20 Rafael Palmeiro .25 .60
21 Hank Blalock .25 .60
22 Pedro Martinez .25 .60
23 Manny Ramirez .25 .60
24 Nomar Garciaparra .60 1.50
25 Carlos Beltran .15 .40
26 Mike Sweeney .15 .40
27 Randall Simon .15 .40
28 Dmitri Young .15 .40
29 Bobby Higginson .15 .40
30 Corey Koskie .15 .40
31 Eric Milton .15 .40
32 Torii Hunter .15 .40
33 Joe Mays .15 .40
34 Frank Thomas .40 1.00
35 Mark Buehrle .15 .40
36 Magglio Ordonez .15 .40
37 Kenny Lofton .15 .40
38 Roger Clemens .75 2.00
39 Derek Jeter 1.00 2.50
40 Jason Giambi .15 .40
41 Bernie Williams .25 .60
42 Alfonso Soriano .15 .40
43 Lance Berkman .15 .40
44 Roy Oswalt .15 .40
45 Jeff Bagwell .25 .60
46 Craig Biggio .25 .60
47 Chipper Jones .40 1.00
48 Greg Maddux .60 1.50
49 Gary Sheffield .15 .40
50 Andruw Jones .25 .60
51 Ben Sheets .15 .40
52 Richie Sexson .15 .40
53 Albert Pujols .75 2.00
54 Matt Morris .15 .40
55 J.D. Drew .15 .40
56 Sammy Sosa .40 1.00
57 Kerry Wood .15 .40
58 Corey Patterson .15 .40
59 Mark Prior .25 .60
60 Randy Johnson .40 1.00
61 Luis Gonzalez .15 .40
62 Curt Schilling .15 .40
63 Shawn Green .15 .40
64 Kevin Brown .15 .40
65 Hideo Nomo .40 1.00
66 Vladimir Guerrero .40 1.00
67 Jose Vidro .15 .40
68 Barry Bonds 1.00 2.50
69 Jeff Kent .15 .40
70 Rich Aurilia .15 .40
71 Preston Wilson .15 .40
72 Josh Beckett .15 .40
73 Mike Lowell .15 .40
74 Roberto Alomar .25 .60
75 Mo Vaughn .15 .40
76 Jeromy Burnitz .15 .40
77 Mike Piazza .60 1.50
78 Sean Burroughs .15 .40
79 Phil Nevin .15 .40
80 Bobby Abreu .15 .40
81 Pat Burrell .15 .40
82 Scott Rolen .25 .60
83 Jason Kendall .15 .40
84 Brian Giles .15 .40
85 Ken Griffey Jr. .60 1.50
86 Adam Dunn .15 .40
87 Sean Casey .15 .40
88 Todd Helton .25 .60
89 Larry Walker .15 .40
90 Mike Hampton .15 .40
91 Brandon Puffer FW 2.00 5.00
92 Tom Shearn FW RC 2.00 5.00
93 Chris Baker FW RC 2.00 5.00
94 Gustavo Chacin FW RC 3.00 8.00
95 Joe Orloski FW RC 2.00 5.00
96 Mike Smith FW RC 2.00 5.00
97 John Ennis FW RC 2.00 5.00
98 John Foster FW RC 2.00 5.00
99 Kevin Gryboski FW RC 2.00 5.00
100 Brian Mallette FW RC 2.00 5.00
101 Takahito Nomura FW RC 2.00 5.00
102 So Taguchi FW RC 3.00 8.00
103 Jeremy Lambert FW RC 2.00 5.00
104 J.Simontacchi FW RC 2.00 5.00
105 Jorge Sosa FW RC 3.00 8.00
106 Brandon Backe FW RC 3.00 8.00
107 P.J. Bevis FW RC 2.00 5.00
108 Jeremy Ward FW RC 2.00 5.00
109 Doug Devore FW RC 2.00 5.00
110 Ron Chiavacci FW 2.00 5.00
111 Ron Calloway FW RC 2.00 5.00
112 Nelson Castro FW RC 2.00 5.00
113 Deivis Santos FW 2.00 5.00
114 Earl Snyder FW RC 2.00 5.00
115 Julio Mateo FW RC 2.00 5.00
116 J.J. Putz FW RC 2.00 5.00
117 Allan Simpson FW RC 2.00 5.00
118 Satoru Komiyama FW RC 2.00 5.00
119 Adam Walker FW RC 2.00 5.00
120 Oliver Perez FW RC 3.00 8.00
121 Cliff Bartosh FW RC 2.00 5.00
122 Todd Donovan FW RC 2.00 5.00
123 Elio Serrano FW RC 2.00 5.00
124 Pete Zamora FW RC 2.00 5.00
125 Mike Gonzalez FW RC 2.00 5.00
126 Travis Hughes FW RC 2.00 5.00
127 J.De La Rosa FW RC 2.00 5.00
128 An.Martinez FW RC 2.00 5.00
129 Colin Young FW RC 2.00 5.00
130 Nate Field FW RC 2.00 5.00
131 Tim Kalita FW RC 2.00 5.00
132 Julius Matos FW RC 2.00 5.00
133 Terry Pearson FW RC 2.00 5.00
134 Kyle Kane FW RC 2.00 5.00
135 Mitch Wylie FW RC 2.00 5.00
136 Rodrigo Rosario AU RC 4.00 10.00
137 Franklyn German AU RC 4.00 10.00
138 Reed Johnson AU RC 8.00 20.00
139 Luis Martinez AU RC 4.00 10.00
140 Michael Crudale AU RC 4.00 10.00
141 Francis Beltran AU RC 4.00 10.00
142 Steve Kent AU RC 4.00 10.00
143 Felix Escalona AU RC 4.00 10.00
144 Jose Valverde AU RC 4.00 10.00
145 Victor Alvarez AU RC 4.00 10.00
146 Kazuhisa Ishii AU/249 RC 15.00 40.00
147 Jorge Nunez AU RC 4.00 10.00
148 Eric Good AU RC 4.00 10.00
149 Luis Ugueto AU RC 4.00 10.00
150 Matt Thornton AU RC 4.00 10.00
151 Wilson Valdez AU RC 4.00 10.00
152 Han Izquierdo AU/249 RC 15.00 40.00
153 Jaime Cerda AU RC 4.00 10.00
154 Mark Corey AU RC 4.00 10.00
155 Tyler Yates AU RC 4.00 10.00
156 Steve Bechler AU RC 4.00 10.00
157 Ben Howard AU/249 RC 15.00 40.00
158 And. Machado AU RC 4.00 10.00
159 Jorge Padilla AU RC 4.00 10.00
160 Eric Junge AU RC 4.00 10.00
161 Adrian Burnside AU RC 4.00 10.00
162 Josh Hancock AU RC 8.00 20.00
163 Chris Booker AU RC 4.00 10.00
164 Cam Esslinger AU RC 4.00 10.00
165 Rene Reyes AU RC 4.00 10.00
166 Aaron Cook AU RC 6.00 15.00
167 Juan Brito AU RC 4.00 10.00
168 Miguel Ascencio AU RC 4.00 10.00
169 Kevin Frederick AU RC 4.00 10.00
170 Edwin Almonte AU RC 4.00 10.00
171 Erubiel Durazo .25 .60
172 Junior Spivey .25 .60
173 Geronimo Gil .25 .60
174 Cliff Floyd .25 .60
175 Brandon Larson .25 .60
176 Aaron Boone .25 .60
177 Shawn Estes .25 .60
178 Austin Kearns .25 .60
179 Joe Borchard .25 .60
180 Russell Branyan .25 .60
181 Jay Payton .25 .60
182 Andres Torres .25 .60
183 Andy Van Hekken .25 .60
184 Alex Sanchez .25 .60
185 Endy Chavez .25 .60
186 Bartolo Colon .25 .60
187 Raul Mondesi .25 .60
188 Robin Ventura .25 .60
189 Mike Mussina .40 1.00
190 Jorge Posada .40 1.00
191 Ted Lilly .25 .60
192 Ray Durham .25 .60
193 Brett Myers .25 .60
194 Marlon Byrd .25 .60
195 Vicente Padilla .25 .60
196 Josh Fogg .25 .60
197 Kenny Lofton .25 .60
198 Scott Rolen .40 1.00
199 Jason Lane .25 .60
200 Josh Phelps .25 .60
201 Travis Driskill FW RC 2.00 5.00
202 Howie Clark FW RC 2.00 5.00
203 Mike Mahoney FW 2.00 5.00
204 Brian Tallet FW RC 2.00 5.00
205 Kirk Saarloos FW RC 2.00 5.00
206 Barry Wesson FW RC 2.00 5.00
207 Aaron Guiel FW RC 2.00 5.00
208 Shawn Sedlacek FW RC 2.00 5.00
209 Jose Diaz FW RC 2.00 5.00
210 Jorge Nunez FW 2.00 5.00
211 Danny Mota FW RC 2.00 5.00
212 David Ross FW RC 3.00 8.00
213 Jayson Durocher FW RC 2.00 5.00
214 Shane Nance FW RC 2.00 5.00
215 Wil Nieves FW RC 2.00 5.00
216 Freddy Sanchez FW RC 4.00 10.00
217 Alex Pelaez FW RC 2.00 5.00
218 Jamey Carroll FW RC 3.00 8.00
219 J.J. Trujillo FW RC 2.00 5.00
220 Kevin Pickford FW RC 2.00 5.00
221 Clay Condrey FW RC 2.00 5.00
222 Chris Snelling FW RC 2.50 6.00
223 Cliff Lee FW RC 5.00 12.00
224 Jeremy Hill FW RC 2.00 5.00
225 Jose Rodriguez FW RC 2.00 5.00
226 Lance Carter FW RC 2.00 5.00
227 Ken Huckaby FW RC 2.00 5.00
228 Scott Wiggins FW RC 2.00 5.00
229 Corey Thurman FW RC 2.00 5.00
230 Kevin Cash FW RC 2.00 5.00
RJD Joe DiMaggio AU Poster 125.00 200.00

2002 SP Authentic Limited

Randomly inserted into packs, this is a parallel to the basic 170-card SP Authentic first series set. These cards have a stated print run of 125 serial numbered sets.

*LTD 1-90: 5X TO 12X BASIC
*LTD 91-135: .6X TO 1.5X BASIC
*LTD 136-170: .4X TO 1X BASIC
*LTD 146/152/157: .3X TO .8X BASIC
146 Kazuhisa Ishii FW AU 15.00 40.00

2002 SP Authentic Limited Gold

Randomly inserted into packs, this is a parallel to the basic 170-card SP Authentic first series set. These cards have a stated print run of 50 serial numbered sets.

*GOLD 1-90: 10X TO 25X BASIC
*GOLD 91-135: 1X TO 2.5X BASIC
*GOLD 136-170: .6X TO 1.5X BASIC
*GOLD 146/152/157: .5X TO 1.2X BASIC
146 Kazuhisa Ishii FW AU 30.00 60.00

2002 SP Authentic Big Mac Missing Link

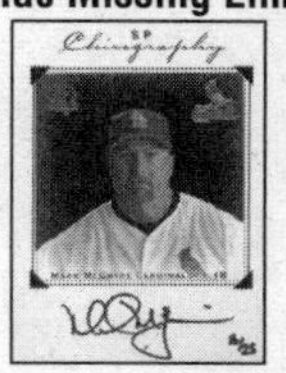

Randomly inserted into packs, these five cards feature autographs of Mark McGwire. Each card was issued to a stated print run of 25 serial numbered sets and thus no pricing is available due to market scarcity.

MMC Mark McGwire 98
MM Mark McGwire 99
MAM Mark McGwire 00
SPMM Mark McGwire 01
MAMC Mark McGwire 02

2002 SP Authentic Chirography

Bret Boone and Tony Gwynn are available only in the basic Chirography set. No Gold parallels were created for them. The following players packed out as redemption cards: Alex Rodriguez, Bret Boone, Sammy Sosa and Tony Gwynn. The deadline for exchange cards to be received by Upper Deck was September 10th, 2005.

AD Adam Dunn/348 10.00 25.00
AG Alex Graman/418 4.00 10.00
AR Alex Rodriguez/391 60.00 120.00
BB Barry Bonds/112 100.00 175.00
BBo Bret Boone/500 6.00 15.00
BZ Barry Zito/419 10.00 25.00
CF Cliff Floyd/313 6.00 15.00
CS C.C. Sabathia/442 6.00 15.00
DE Darin Erstad/80 6.00 15.00
DM Doug Mientkiewicz/478 6.00 15.00
FG Freddy Garcia/456 6.00 15.00
HB Hank Blalock/282 6.00 15.00
IS Ichiro Suzuki/78 300.00 500.00
JB John Buck/427 4.00 10.00
JG Jason Giambi/244 6.00 15.00
JL Jon Lieber/462 6.00 15.00
JM Joe Mays/469 4.00 10.00
KG Ken Griffey Jr./238 50.00 100.00
MBr Milton Bradley/470 6.00 15.00
MBu Mark Buehrle/438 10.00 25.00
MM Mark McGwire/50 175.00 300.00
MS Mike Sweeney/265 6.00 15.00
RS Richie Sexson/483 6.00 15.00
SB Sean Burroughs/275 4.00 10.00
SS Sammy Sosa/247 50.00 100.00
TG Tom Glavine/376 15.00 40.00
TGw Tony Gwynn/75 20.00 50.00

2002 SP Authentic Chirography Gold

Gold parallel cards were not created for Tony Gwynn and Bret Boone. Sammy Sosa and Alex Rodriguez packed out as exchange cards with a redemption deadline of September 10th, 2005.

AD Adam Dunn/44 20.00 50.00
AG Alex Graman/76 6.00 15.00
AR Alex Rodriguez/3
BB Barry Bonds/25
BZ Barry Zito/75 15.00 40.00
CF Cliff Floyd/30 15.00 40.00
CS C.C. Sabathia/52 12.50 30.00
DE Darin Erstad/17
DM Doug Mientkiewicz/16
FG Freddy Garcia/34 15.00 40.00
HB Hank Blalock/12
IS Ichiro Suzuki/51 300.00 500.00
JB John Buck/67
JG Jason Giambi/25
JL Jon Lieber/32 15.00 40.00
JM Joe Mays/25
KG Ken Griffey Jr./30 100.00 200.00
MBr Milton Bradley/24
MBu Mark Buehrle/56 20.00 50.00
MM Mark McGwire/25
MS Mike Sweeney/29 15.00 40.00
RS Richie Sexson/11
SB Sean Burroughs/21
SS Sammy Sosa/21
TG Tom Glavine/47 30.00 60.00

2002 SP Authentic Excellence

Randomly inserted into packs, theis card features signatures of many of Upper Deck's spokespeople. This card was issued to a stated print run of 25 serial numbered sets and no pricing is available due to market scarcity. Please note that this card was issued as an exchange card and was redeemable until September 10, 2005.

AE Ken Griffey Jr.
Sammy Sosa
Cal Ripken
Jason Giambi
Mark McGwire
Ichiro Suzuki

2002 SP Authentic Game Jersey

Inserted into packs at stated odds of one in 24, these 38 cards feature some of the leading players along with a game-used memorabilia swatch. A few cards were issued in shorter supply and we have notated that in our checklist along with a stated print run when available.

JAJ Andruw Jones 6.00 15.00
JAP Andy Pettitte 6.00 15.00
JAR Alex Rodriguez 8.00 20.00
JBW Bernie Williams 6.00 15.00
JBZ Barry Zito 4.00 10.00
JCC C.C. Sabathia 4.00 10.00
JCD Carlos Delgado 4.00 10.00
JCJ Chipper Jones 6.00 15.00
JCS Curt Schilling 4.00 10.00
JDE Darin Erstad 4.00 10.00
JGM Greg Maddux 6.00 15.00
JGS Gary Sheffield 4.00 10.00
JIR Ivan Rodriguez 6.00 15.00
JIS Ichiro Suzuki SP 30.00 60.00
JJBA Jeff Bagwell 6.00 15.00
JJBU Jeromy Burnitz SP 6.00 15.00
JJE Jim Edmonds 4.00 10.00
JJGO Juan Gonzalez 4.00 10.00
JJGR Jason Giambi 4.00 10.00
JJK Jason Kendall 4.00 10.00
JJT Jim Thome 6.00 15.00
JKG Ken Griffey Jr. SP/95 15.00 40.00
JKI Kazuhisa Ishii 6.00 15.00
JMM Mark McGwire SP 75.00 150.00
JMO Magglio Ordonez 4.00 10.00
JMP Mike Piazza 6.00 15.00
JMR Manny Ramirez 6.00 15.00
JOV Omar Vizquel 6.00 15.00
JPW Preston Wilson 4.00 10.00
JRA Roberto Alomar 6.00 15.00
JRC Roger Clemens 8.00 20.00
JRJ Randy Johnson 6.00 15.00
JRV Robin Ventura 4.00 10.00
JSG Shawn Green 4.00 10.00
JSR Scott Rolen 6.00 15.00
JSS Sammy Sosa 6.00 15.00
JTH Todd Helton 6.00 15.00
JTS Tsuyoshi Shinjo 4.00 10.00

2002 SP Authentic Game Jersey Gold

Randomly inserted into packs, this is a parallel to the Game Jersey insert set. Each of these cards have a stated print run which matches the featured player's uniform number and we have notated that information in our checklist. If a card was issued to a stated print run of 25 or fewer, it is not priced due to market scarcity.

JAJ Andruw Jones/25
JAP Andy Pettitte/46 12.50 30.00
JAR Alex Rodriguez/3
JBW Bernie Williams/51 12.50 30.00
JBZ Barry Zito/75 8.00 20.00
JCC C.C. Sabathia/52 8.00 20.00
JCD Carlos Delgado/25
JCJ Chipper Jones/10
JCS Curt Schilling/38 10.00 25.00
JDE Darin Erstad/17
JGM Greg Maddux/31 40.00 80.00
JGS Gary Sheffield/11
JIR Ivan Rodriguez/7
JIS Ichiro Suzuki/51 60.00 120.00
JJBA Jeff Bagwell/5
JJBU Jeromy Burnitz/20
JJE Jim Edmonds/15
JJGO Juan Gonzalez/19
JJGR Jason Giambi/25
JJK Jason Kendall/18
JJT Jim Thome/25
JKG Ken Griffey Jr./30 40.00 80.00
JKI Kazuhisa Ishii/17
JMM Mark McGwire/25
JMO Magglio Ordonez/30 10.00 25.00
JMP Mike Piazza/31 40.00 80.00
JMR Manny Ramirez/24
JOV Omar Vizquel/13
JPW Preston Wilson/44 8.00 20.00
JRA Roberto Alomar/12
JRC Roger Clemens/22
JRJ Randy Johnson/51 15.00 40.00
JRV Robin Ventura/19
JSG Shawn Green/15
JSR Scott Rolen/17
JSS Sammy Sosa/21
JTH Todd Helton/17
JTS Tsuyoshi Shinjo/5

2002 SP Authentic Prospects Signatures

Inserted into packs at a stated rate of one in 36, these 12 cards feature signed cards of some leading baseball prospects.

PAG Alex Graman 3.00 8.00
PBH Bill Hall 4.00 10.00
PDM Dustan Mohr 3.00 8.00
PDW Danny Wright 3.00 8.00
PJC Jose Cueto 3.00 8.00
PJDE Jeff Deardorff 3.00 8.00
PJDI Jose Diaz 3.00 8.00
PKH Ken Huckaby 3.00 8.00
PMG Matt Guerrier 3.00 8.00
PMS Marcos Scutaro 3.00 8.00
PST Steve Torrealba 3.00 8.00
PXN Xavier Nady 3.00 8.00

2002 SP Authentic Signed Big Mac

Randomly inserted into packs, these 10 cards feature authentic autographs of retired superstar Mark McGwire. Each of these cards were signed to a different stated print run and we have notated that information in our checklist. If a card was signed to 25 or fewer copies, there is no pricing provided due to market scarcity.

MM1 Mark McGwire/1
MM2 Mark McGwire/25
MM3 Mark McGwire/5
MM4 Mark McGwire/4
MM5 Mark McGwire/12
MM6 Mark McGwire/70 200.00 350.00
MM7 Mark McGwire/4
MM8 Mark McGwire/7
MM9 Mark McGwire/5
MM10 Mark McGwire/16

2002 SP Authentic Signs of Greatness

Randomly inserted into packs, this card features five autographs and only one copy was produced. An exchange card with a redemption deadline of September 10th, 2005 was placed into packs whereby the lucky collector received the actual signed card directly from Upper Deck via mail. There is no pricing due to scarcity.

SOG Babe Ruth
Joe DiMaggio
Mickey Mantle
Ken Griffey Jr.
Sammy Sosa
Mark McGwire

2002 SP Authentic USA Future Watch

Randomly inserted into packs, these 22 cards feature players from the USA National Team. Each card was issued to a stated print run of 1999 serial numbered sets.

USA1 Chad Cordero 4.00 10.00
USA2 Philip Humber 3.00 8.00
USA3 Grant Johnson 2.00 5.00
USA4 Wes Littleton 2.00 5.00
USA5 Kyle Sleeth 2.00 5.00
USA6 Huston Street 4.00 10.00
USA7 Brad Sullivan 2.00 5.00
USA8 Bob Zimmermann 2.00 5.00
USA9 Abe Alvarez 2.00 5.00
USA10 Kyle Bakker 2.00 5.00
USA11 Landon Powell 2.00 5.00
USA12 Clint Sammons 2.00 5.00
USA13 Michael Aubrey 3.00 8.00
USA14 Aaron Hill 4.00 10.00
USA15 Conor Jackson 6.00 15.00
USA16 Eric Patterson 3.00 8.00
USA17 Dustin Pedroia 10.00 25.00
USA18 Rickie Weeks 10.00 25.00
USA19 Shane Costa 2.00 5.00
USA20 Mark Jurich 2.00 5.00
USA21 Sam Fuld 2.00 5.00
USA22 Carlos Quentin 6.00 15.00

2002 SP Authentic Hawaii Sign of the Times Duke Snider

This card was distributed on February 27th, 2002 at Upper Deck's poolside reception during the Hawaii Trade Conference. Each attendee received either this signed Duke Snider card or a signed card of NFL legend John Riggins, both of which were hand-numbered to 500 copies in blue ink. Snider signed each card in blue ink sharpie across the front.

DS Duke Snider/500 8.00 20.00

2003 SP Authentic

This 239-card set was distributed in two separate series. The primary SP Authentic product was originally issued as a 189-card set released in May, 2003. These cards were issued in five card packs with an $5 SRP which were issued 24 packs to a box and 12 boxes to a case. Update cards 190-239 were issued randomly within packs of 2003 Upper Deck Finite and released in December, 2003. Cards numbered 1-90 featured commonly seeded veterans while cards 91-123 featured what was titled SP Rookie Archives (RA) and those cards were issued to a stated print run of 2500 serial numbered sets. Cards numbered 124 to 150 feature a subset called Back to 93 and those cards were issued to a stated print run of 1993 serial numbered sets. Cards numbered 151 through 189 feature Future Watch prospects (with 181 to 189 being autographed). Please note that cards numbered 151-180 were also issued to a stated print run of 2003 serial numbered sets and cards numbered 181-189 were issued to a stated print run of 500 serial numbered sets. The Jose Contreras signed card was issued either as a live card or an exchange card. The Contreras exchange card could be redeemed until May 21, 2006. Cards 190-239 (released at year's end) continued the Future Watch subset but each card was serial numbered to 699 copies.

COMP.LO SET w/o SP's (90) 6.00 15.00
COMMON CARD (1-90) .15 .40
COMMON CARD (91-123) 1.25 3.00
COMMON CARD (124-150) 1.25 3.00
COMMON CARD (151-180) 2.00 5.00
COMMON CARD (181-189) 6.00 15.00
91-189 RANDOM INSERTS IN PACKS
COMMON CARD (190-239) 2.00 5.00
190-239 RANDOM IN 03 UD FINITE PACKS
190-239 PRINT RUN 699 SERIAL #'d SETS
1 Darin Erstad .15 .40

Card		
2 Garret Anderson	.15	.40
3 Troy Glaus	.15	.40
4 Eric Chavez	.15	.40
5 Barry Zito	.15	.40
6 Miguel Tejada	.15	.40
7 Eric Hinske	.15	.40
8 Carlos Delgado	.15	.40
9 Josh Phelps	.15	.40
10 Ben Grieve	.15	.40
11 Carl Crawford	.15	.40
12 Omar Vizquel	.25	.60
13 Matt Lawton	.15	.40
14 C.C. Sabathia	.15	.40
15 Ichiro Suzuki	.75	2.00
16 John Olerud	.15	.40
17 Freddy Garcia	.15	.40
18 Jay Gibbons	.15	.40
19 Tony Batista	.15	.40
20 Melvin Mora	.15	.40
21 Alex Rodriguez	.60	1.50
22 Rafael Palmeiro	.25	.60
23 Hank Blalock	.15	.40
24 Nomar Garciaparra	.60	1.50
25 Pedro Martinez	.25	.60
26 Johnny Damon	.25	.60
27 Mike Sweeney	.15	.40
28 Carlos Febles	.15	.40
29 Carlos Beltran	.15	.40
30 Carlos Pena	.15	.40
31 Eric Munson	.15	.40
32 Bobby Higginson	.15	.40
33 Torii Hunter	.15	.40
34 Doug Mientkiewicz	.15	.40
35 Jacque Jones	.15	.40
36 Paul Konerko	.15	.40
37 Bartolo Colon	.15	.40
38 Magglio Ordonez	.15	.40
39 Derek Jeter	1.00	2.50
40 Bernie Williams	.25	.60
41 Jason Giambi	.15	.40
42 Alfonso Soriano	.15	.40
43 Roger Clemens	.75	2.00
44 Jeff Bagwell	.25	.60
45 Jeff Kent	.15	.40
46 Lance Berkman	.15	.40
47 Chipper Jones	.40	1.00
48 Andruw Jones	.25	.60
49 Gary Sheffield	.15	.40
50 Ben Sheets	.15	.40
51 Richie Sexson	.15	.40
52 Geoff Jenkins	.15	.40
53 Jim Edmonds	.15	.40
54 Albert Pujols	.75	2.00
55 Scott Rolen	.25	.60
56 Sammy Sosa	.40	1.00
57 Kerry Wood	.15	.40
58 Eric Karros	.15	.40
59 Luis Gonzalez	.15	.40
60 Randy Johnson	.40	1.00
61 Curt Schilling	.15	.40
62 Fred McGriff	.25	.60
63 Shawn Green	.15	.40
64 Paul Lo Duca	.15	.40
65 Vladimir Guerrero	.40	1.00
66 Jose Vidro	.15	.40
67 Barry Bonds	1.00	2.50
68 Rich Aurilia	.15	.40
69 Edgardo Alfonzo	.15	.40
70 Ivan Rodriguez	.25	.60
71 Mike Lowell	.15	.40
72 Derrek Lee	.25	.60
73 Tom Glavine	.25	.60
74 Mike Piazza	.60	1.50
75 Roberto Alomar	.25	.60
76 Ryan Klesko	.15	.40
77 Phil Nevin	.15	.40
78 Mark Kotsay	.15	.40
79 Jim Thome	.25	.60
80 Pat Burrell	.15	.40
81 Bobby Abreu	.15	.40
82 Jason Kendall	.15	.40
83 Brian Giles	.15	.40
84 Aramis Ramirez	.15	.40
85 Austin Kearns	.15	.40
86 Ken Griffey Jr.	.60	1.50
87 Adam Dunn	.15	.40
88 Larry Walker	.15	.40
89 Todd Helton	.25	.60
90 Preston Wilson	.15	.40
91 Derek Jeter RA	3.00	8.00
92 Johnny Damon RA	1.25	3.00
93 Chipper Jones RA	1.25	3.00
94 Manny Ramirez RA	1.25	3.00
95 Trot Nixon RA	1.25	3.00
96 Alex Rodriguez RA	2.00	5.00
97 Chan Ho Park RA	1.25	3.00
98 Brad Fullmer RA	1.25	3.00
99 Billy Wagner RA	1.25	3.00
100 Hideo Nomo RA	1.25	3.00
101 Freddy Garcia RA	1.25	3.00
102 Darin Erstad RA	1.25	3.00
103 Jose Cruz Jr. RA	1.25	3.00
104 Nomar Garciaparra RA	2.00	5.00
105 Magglio Ordonez RA	1.25	3.00
106 Kerry Wood RA	1.25	3.00
107 Troy Glaus RA	1.25	3.00
108 J.D. Drew RA	1.25	3.00
109 Alfonso Soriano RA	1.25	3.00
110 Danys Baez RA	1.25	3.00
111 Kazuhiro Sasaki RA	1.25	3.00
112 Barry Zito RA	1.25	3.00
113 Brent Abernathy RA	1.25	3.00
114 Ben Diggins RA	1.25	3.00
115 Ben Sheets RA	1.25	3.00
116 Brad Wilkerson RA	1.25	3.00
117 Juan Pierre RA	1.25	3.00
118 Jon Rauch RA	1.25	3.00
119 Ichiro Suzuki RA	2.50	6.00
120 Albert Pujols RA	2.50	6.00
121 Mark Prior RA	1.25	3.00
122 Mark Teixeira RA	1.25	3.00
123 Kazuhisa Ishii RA	1.25	3.00
124 Troy Glaus B93	1.25	3.00
125 Randy Johnson B93	1.25	3.00
126 Curt Schilling B93	1.25	3.00
127 Chipper Jones B93	1.25	3.00
128 Greg Maddux B93	2.00	5.00
129 Nomar Garciaparra B93	2.00	5.00
130 Pedro Martinez B93	1.25	3.00
131 Sammy Sosa B93	1.25	3.00
132 Mark Prior B93	1.25	3.00
133 Ken Griffey Jr. B93	2.00	5.00
134 Adam Dunn B93	1.25	3.00
135 Jeff Bagwell B93	1.25	3.00
136 Vladimir Guerrero B93	1.25	3.00
137 Mike Piazza B93	2.00	5.00
138 Tom Glavine B93	1.25	3.00
139 Derek Jeter B93	3.00	8.00
140 Roger Clemens B93	2.50	6.00
141 Jason Giambi B93	1.25	3.00
142 Alfonso Soriano B93	1.25	3.00
143 Miguel Tejada B93	1.25	3.00
144 Barry Zito B93	1.25	3.00
145 Jim Thome B93	1.25	3.00
146 Barry Bonds B93	3.00	8.00
147 Ichiro Suzuki B93	2.50	6.00
148 Albert Pujols B93	2.50	6.00
149 Alex Rodriguez B93	2.00	5.00
150 Carlos Delgado B93	1.25	3.00
151 Rich Fischer FW RC	2.00	5.00
152 Brandon Webb FW RC	10.00	25.00
153 Rob Hammock FW RC	2.00	5.00
154 Matt Kata FW RC	2.00	5.00
155 Tim Olson FW RC	2.00	5.00
156 Oscar Villarreal FW RC	2.00	5.00
157 Michael Hessman FW RC	2.00	5.00
158 Daniel Cabrera FW RC	3.00	8.00
159 Jon Leicester FW RC	2.00	5.00
160 Todd Wellemeyer FW RC	2.00	5.00
161 Felix Sanchez FW RC	2.00	5.00
162 David Sanders FW RC	2.00	5.00
163 Josh Stewart FW RC	2.00	5.00
164 Arnie Munoz FW RC	2.00	5.00
165 Ryan Cameron FW RC	2.00	5.00
166 Clint Barmes FW RC	2.00	5.00
167 Josh Willingham FW RC	4.00	10.00
169 Willie Eyre FW RC	2.00	5.00
170 Brent Hoard FW RC	2.00	5.00
171 Terrmel Sledge FW RC	2.00	5.00
172 Phil Seibel FW RC	2.00	5.00
173 Craig Brazell FW RC	2.00	5.00
174 Jeff Duncan FW RC	2.00	5.00
176 Bernie Castro FW RC	2.00	5.00
177 Mike Nicolas FW RC	2.00	5.00
178 Rett Johnson FW RC	2.00	5.00
179 Bobby Madritsch FW RC	2.00	5.00
180 Chris Capuano FW RC	10.00	25.00
181 Hid Matsui FW AU RC	175.00	300.00
182 J.Contreras FW AU RC	12.50	30.00
183 Lew Ford FW AU RC	10.00	25.00
184 Jer. Griffiths FW AU RC	6.00	15.00
185 G.Quiroz FW AU RC	6.00	15.00
186 Alej Machado FW AU RC	6.00	15.00
187 Fran Cruceta FW AU RC	6.00	15.00
188 Pr. Redman FW AU RC	6.00	15.00
189 S.Bazzell FW AU RC	6.00	15.00
190 Aaron Looper FW RC	2.00	5.00
191 Alex Prieto FW RC	2.00	5.00
192 Alfredo Gonzalez FW RC	2.00	5.00
193 Andrew Brown FW RC	3.00	8.00
194 Anthony Ferrari FW RC	2.00	5.00
195 Aquilino Lopez FW RC	2.00	5.00
196 Beau Kemp FW RC	2.00	5.00
197 Bo Hart FW RC	2.00	5.00
198 Chad Gaudin FW RC	2.00	5.00
199 Colin Porter FW RC	2.00	5.00
200 D.J. Carrasco FW RC	2.00	5.00
201 Dan Haren FW RC	3.00	8.00
202 Danny Garcia FW RC	2.00	5.00
203 Jon Switzer FW	2.00	5.00
204 Edwin Jackson FW RC	3.00	8.00
205 Fernando Cabrera FW RC	2.00	5.00
206 Garrett Atkins FW	2.00	5.00
207 Gerald Laird FW	2.00	5.00
208 Greg Jones FW RC	2.00	5.00
209 Ian Ferguson FW RC	2.00	5.00
210 Jason Roach FW RC	2.00	5.00
211 Jason Shiell FW RC	2.00	5.00
212 Jeremy Bonderman FW RC	10.00	25.00
213 Jeremy Wedel FW RC	2.00	5.00
214 Jhonny Peralta FW	3.00	8.00
215 Delmon Young FW RC	25.00	50.00
216 Jorge DePaula FW	2.00	5.00
217 Josh Hall FW RC	2.00	5.00
218 Julio Manon FW RC	2.00	5.00
219 Kevin Correia FW RC	2.00	5.00
220 Kevin Ohme FW RC	2.00	5.00
221 Kevin Tolar FW RC	2.00	5.00
222 Luis Ayala FW RC	2.00	5.00
223 Luis De Los Santos FW	2.00	5.00
224 Chad Cordero FW RC	4.00	10.00
225 Mark Malaska FW RC	2.00	5.00
226 Khalil Greene FW	3.00	8.00
227 Michael Nakamura FW RC	2.00	5.00
228 Michel Hernandez FW RC	2.00	5.00
229 Miguel Ojeda FW RC	2.00	5.00
230 Mike Neu FW RC	2.00	5.00
231 Nate Bland FW RC	2.00	5.00
232 Pete LaForest FW RC	2.00	5.00
233 Rickie Weeks FW RC	8.00	20.00
234 Rosman Garcia FW RC	2.00	5.00
235 Ryan Wagner FW RC	2.00	5.00
236 Lance Niekro FW	2.00	5.00
237 Tom Gregorio FW RC	2.00	5.00
238 Tommy Phelps FW	2.00	5.00
239 Wilfredo Ledezma FW RC	2.00	5.00

2003 SP Authentic Matsui Future Watch Autograph Parallel

RANDOM INSERTS IN PACKS
PRINT RUNS B/WN 10-75 COPIES PER
NO PRICING ON QTY OF 25 OR LESS

Card		
181A H.Matsui Bronze/75	175.00	300.00
181B H.Matsui Silver/25		
181C H.Matsui Gold/10		

2003 SP Authentic 500 HR Club

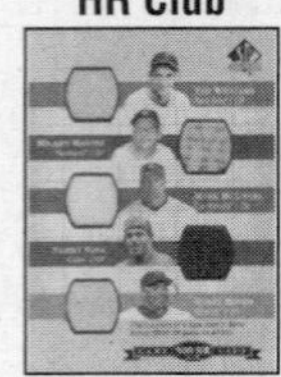

Randomly inserted into packs, this card featured members of the 500 homer club along with a game-used memorablia piece from each player. A gold parallel was also issued for this card and that card was issued to a stated print run of 25 serial numbered sets. The gold version is not priced due to market scarcity.

Card		
500 Sammy Sosa Jsy/Pants	125.00	250.00
Ted Williams Pants		
Mickey Mantle Jsy/Pants		
Mark McGwire Jsy/Pants		
Barry Bonds Base		
500G Sammy Sosa Jsy/Pants		
Ted Williams Pants		
Mickey Mantle Jsy/Pants		
Mark McGwire Jsy/Pants		
Barry Bonds Base Gold/25		

2003 SP Authentic Chirography

Randomly inserted into packs, these cards feature authentic autographs from the player pictured on the card. These cards marked the debut of Upper Deck using the "Band-Aid" approach to putting autographs on cards. What that means is that the player does not actually sign the card, instead the player signs a sticker which is then attached to the card. Please note that since these cards were issued to varying print runs, we have notated the stated print run next to the player's name in our checklist. Several players did not get their cards signed in time for inclusion in this product and those exchange cards could be redeemed until April 21, 2006. Please note that many cards in the various sets have notations but neither Mark Prior nor Corey Patterson used whatever notations they were supposed to throughout the course of this product.

Card		
AD Adam Dunn/170	10.00	25.00
BA Jeff Bagwell/175	30.00	60.00
CR Cal Ripken/250	60.00	120.00
FC Rafael Furcal/150	6.00	15.00
FG Freddy Garcia/345	6.00	15.00
FL Cliff Floyd/125	6.00	15.00
GA1 Garret Anderson/350	6.00	15.00
GI Jason Giambi/250	6.00	15.00
GJ Ken Griffey Jr./350	40.00	80.00
GL Brian Giles/225	6.00	15.00
IC Ichiro Suzuki/85	350.00	500.00
IS Ichiro Suzuki/75	350.00	500.00
JD Johnny Damon/245	15.00	40.00
JE2 Jim Edmonds/350	10.00	25.00
JM Joe Mays/245	4.00	10.00
JR Ken Griffey Jr./350	40.00	80.00
JT1 Jim Thome/250	15.00	40.00
KE Jason Kendall/145	6.00	15.00
LG1 Luis Gonzalez/195	6.00	15.00
MM Mark McGwire/50	175.00	300.00
RO Scott Rolen/345	15.00	40.00
RS Richie Sexson/245	6.00	15.00
SA Sammy Sosa/335	40.00	80.00
SO Sammy Sosa/335	40.00	80.00
SW Mike Sweeney/125	6.00	15.00
TO Torii Hunter/245	6.00	15.00
TS Tim Salmon/350	10.00	25.00

2003 SP Authentic Chirography Bronze

Randomly inserted into packs, this is a partial parallel to the Chirography insert set. A few of these cards have special notations and we have noted that information in our checklist. Again, a few cards were issued as exchange cards and those cards could be redeemed until May 21, 2006.

Card		
AD Adam Dunn/50	15.00	40.00
BA Jeff Bagwell/50	40.00	100.00
CR Cal Ripken/75	75.00	150.00
FC Rafael Furcal/50	10.00	25.00
FG Freddy Garcia/100	10.00	25.00
FL Cliff Floyd/50	10.00	25.00
GI Jason Giambi/50	10.00	25.00
GJ Ken Griffey Jr./100	50.00	100.00
GL Brian Giles/50	10.00	25.00
IC Ichiro Suzuki ROY/50	400.00	600.00
IS Ichiro Suzuki MVP/50	400.00	600.00
JD Johnny Damon/100	25.00	60.00
JM Joe Mays/100	6.00	15.00
JR Ken Griffey Jr./100	50.00	100.00
KE Jason Kendall/50	10.00	25.00
MM Mark McGwire/25		
RO Scott Rolen/100	25.00	60.00
RS Richie Sexson	10.00	25.00
Milwaukee Notation/100		
SA Sammy Sosa/100	50.00	100.00
SO Sammy Sosa/100	50.00	100.00
SW Mike Sweeney/75	10.00	25.00
TO Torii Hunter/100	10.00	25.00
Gold Glove Notation		

2003 SP Authentic Chirography Silver

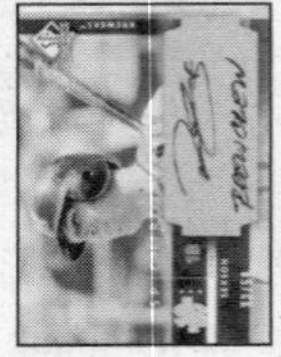

Card		
AD Adam Dunn/25		
BA Jeff Bagwell/25		
CR Cal Ripken/25		
FC Rafael Furcal/25		
FG Freddy Garcia/50	15.00	40.00
FL Cliff Floyd/25		
GI Jason Giambi/25		
GJ Ken Griffey Jr./25		
GL Brian Giles/25		
IC Ichiro Suzuki/25		
IS Ichiro Suzuki/25		
JD Johnny Damon/50	40.00	100.00
JM Joe Mays/50	10.00	25.00
JR Ken Griffey Jr./25		
KE Jason Kendall/25		
MM Mark McGwire/15		
RO Scott Rolen/50	40.00	100.00
RS Richie Sexson/50	15.00	40.00
SA Sammy Sosa/50	50.00	100.00
SO Sammy Sosa/50	50.00	100.00
SW Mike Sweeney/25		
TO Torii Hunter/50	15.00	40.00

2003 SP Authentic Chirography Dodgers Stars

Randomly inserted in packs, these 11 cards feature retired Dodger stars and were issued to varying print runs. We have noted the stated print run in our checklist next to the player's name.

Card		
BB Bill Buckner/245	6.00	15.00
BI Bill Russell/245	6.00	15.00
CE Ron Cey/345	6.00	15.00
DL Davey Lopes/245	6.00	15.00
DN Don Newcombe/345	6.00	15.00
DS Duke Snider/345	15.00	40.00
JN Tommy John/170	6.00	15.00
MW Maury Wills/320	6.00	15.00
SG Steve Garvey/320	10.00	25.00
SU Don Sutton/245	6.00	15.00
SY Steve Yeager/345	6.00	15.00

2003 SP Authentic Chirography Dodgers Stars Bronze

Randomly inserted in packs, this is a partial parallel to the Dodgers Stars insert set. Please note that all of these cards have the word "Dodgers" as an inscription.

*BRONZE: .6X TO 1.5X BASIC DODGER

2003 SP Authentic Chirography Dodgers Stars Silver

Randomly inserted into packs, this is a partial parallel to the Dodgers Stars insert set. Each of these cards were issued to a stated print run of 50 serial numbered sets and most of these cards had a 1981 WS Champs Notation. Please note that the player's who signed cards for this set and were not on the 81 Dodgers used different notations which we have identified in our checklist.

*SILVER: .75X TO 2X BASIC DODGER

2003 SP Authentic Chirography Doubles

Randomly inserted into packs, these 15 cards feature signatures from two different players, who had a reason for commonality. These cards were issued to a stated print run of anywhere from 10 to 150 copies and we have placed that information next to the player's name in our checklist. Please note that cards with a stated print run of 25 or fewer are not priced due to market scarcity. In addition, a few cards were issued as exchange cards and those cards could be redeemed until May 21, 2006.

Card		
FB Whitey Ford	75.00	150.00
Yogi Berra/75		
FE Carlton Fisk	40.00	80.00
Dwight Evans/75		
FM Carlton Fisk	30.00	60.00
Bill Mazeroski/75		
GG Ken Griffey Jr.	60.00	120.00
Jason Giambi/75		
GR Steve Garvey	30.00	60.00
Ron Cey/75		
JI Ken Griffey Jr.	300.00	500.00
Ichiro Suzuki/125		
KR Tony Kubek	50.00	100.00
Bobby Richardson/75		
KT Jerry Koosman	40.00	80.00
Tom Seaver/75		
MG Don Mattingly		
Jason Giambi/25		
MJ Mark McGwire		
Ken Griffey Jr./10		
MS Mark McGwire		
Sammy Sosa/15		
RT Nolan Ryan		
Tom Seaver/25		
SE Tim Salmon		
Darin Erstad/25		
SJ Sammy Sosa	60.00	120.00
Jason Giambi/75		
WB Mookie Wilson	20.00	50.00
Bill Buckner/150		

2003 SP Authentic Chirography Flashback

Randomly inserted into packs, these cards feature an important moment from the player's career as well as authentic autograph. Most of these cards were issued to a stated print run of 350 copies but a few were issued to differing amounts so we have noted the print run information next to the player's name in our checklist. In addition, some players did not return their autograph in time and those cards could be exchanged until May 21, 2006.

Card		
BN Brian Giles/245	6.00	15.00
CF1 Cliff Floyd/350	6.00	15.00
GM Ken Griffey Jr./350	40.00	80.00
JA Jason Giambi/350	6.00	15.00
JE1 Jim Edmonds/350	10.00	25.00
LA Luis Gonzalez/200	8.00	20.00
MA Mark McGwire/55	150.00	300.00
SR Sammy Sosa/245	50.00	100.00

2003 SP Authentic Chirography Flashback Bronze

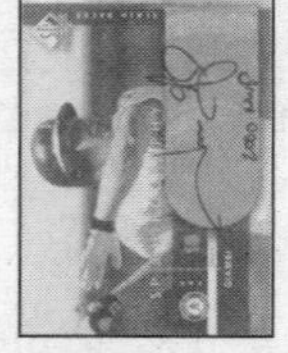

Randomly inserted in packs, this is a partial parallel to the Flashback insert set. All of the cards live at the time of issue had special notations and we have noted those notations in our checklist. These cards were issued to varying print runs and we have identified the stated print runs in our checklist. Ken Griffey Jr and Sammy Sosa did not return their autographs in time for inclusion and those exchange cards could be redeemed until May 21, 2006.

Card		
BN Brian Giles/50	10.00	25.00
GM Ken Griffey Jr./100	50.00	100.00
JA Jason Giambi	10.00	25.00
2000 MVP/100		
LA Luis Gonzalez	12.50	30.00
2001 Champs/75		
MA Mark McGwire		
500 HR Club/25		
SR Sammy Sosa/100	50.00	100.00

2003 SP Authentic Chirography Flashback Silver

Randomly inserted into packs, this is a partial parallel to the Flashback insert set. These cards were issued to stated print runs of between 15 and 50 copies and for those copies with stated print runs fo 25 or fewer, no pricing is provided due to market scarcity.

Card		
BN Brian Giles/25		
GM Ken Griffey Jr./25		
JA0 Jason Giambi A's/50	12.50	30.00
LA Luis Gonzalez 25		
MA Mark McGwire/15		
SR Sammy Sosa/50	60.00	120.00

2003 SP Authentic Chirography Hall of Famers

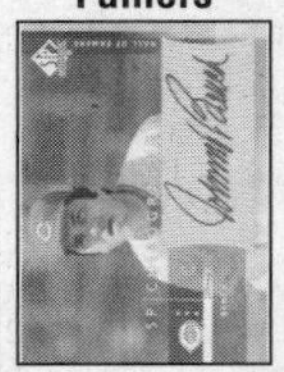

Randomly inserted into packs, these 14 cards feature autographs of Hall of Famers. Since these cards were issued to varying print runs, we have identified the stated print run next to the player's name in our checklist.

Card		
BG Bob Gibson/245	15.00	40.00
CF Carlton Fisk/240	15.00	40.00
DS Duke Snider/250	15.00	40.00
DW2 Dave Winfield/350	10.00	25.00
GC1 Gary Carter/350	10.00	25.00
JB1 Johnny Bench/350	20.00	50.00
NR Nolan Ryan/170	75.00	150.00
OC Orlando Cepeda/245	10.00	25.00
RF Rollie Fingers/170	10.00	25.00
RR Robin Roberts/170	15.00	40.00
RY Robin Yount/350	20.00	50.00
TP Tony Perez/320	10.00	25.00
TS Tom Seaver/170	15.00	40.00
WF Whitey Ford/150	15.00	40.00

2003 SP Authentic Chirography Hall of Famers Bronze

Randomly inserted into packs, this is a partial parallel to the Hall of Famers insert set. These cards all feature an HOF (or some close variation) notation as part of the autograph. These cards were issued to stated print runs between 50 and 100 copies and we have noted the specific information next to the player's name in our checklist.

Card		
BG Bob Gibson/100	25.00	60.00
CF Carlton Fisk/100	25.00	60.00
DS Duke Snider/100	25.00	60.00
NR Nolan Ryan/50	100.00	200.00
OC Orlando Cepeda/100	15.00	40.00
RF Rollie Fingers/50	15.00	40.00
RR Robin Roberts/50	25.00	60.00
TP Tony Perez/100	15.00	40.00
TS Tom Seaver/75	25.00	60.00
WF Whitey Ford/75	25.00	60.00

2003 SP Authentic Chirography Hall of Famers Silver

Randomly inserted into packs, this is a partial parallel to the Hall of Famers insert set. All of these cards have the HOF (and specific year of the player's induction) notation. These cards were issued to a stated print run of either 25 or 50 copies. Please note that for cards with a stated print run of 25 copies there is no pricing due to market scarcity.

BG Bob Gibson/50 30.00 80.00
CF Carlton Fisk/50 30.00 80.00
DS Duke Snider/50 30.00 80.00
NR Nolan Ryan/25
OC Orlando Cepeda/50 20.00 50.00
RF Rollie Fingers/25
RR Robin Roberts/25
TP Tony Perez/50 20.00 50.00
TS Tom Seaver/50 30.00 80.00
WF Whitey Ford/25

2003 SP Authentic Chirography Triples

Randomly inserted in packs, these 12 cards feature autographs from three leading players. These cards were issued to stated print runs of anywhere from 10 to 75 copies and we are only providing pricing for cards with a stated print run of more than 10 copies. The following cards were available only as an exchange and those cards could be redeemed until May 21, 2006: Berra/Kubek/Richardson, Fisk/Carter/Gibson, Griffey Jr./Ichiro/Sosa, Griffey Jr./Sosa/Giambi, Giambi/Sosa/Griffey Jr., Ichiro/Sosa/Giambi, McGwire/Sosa/Griffey Jr., McGwire/Sosa/Ichiro and Seaver/Koosman/McGraw.

BKR Yogi Berra 100.00 200.00
Tony Kubek
Bobby Richardson/75
FCG Carlton Fisk 60.00 120.00
Gary Carter
Kirk Gibson/75 EXCH
GIS Ken Griffey Jr. 300.00 500.00
Ichiro Suzuki
Sammy Sosa/75 EXCH
GLC Steve Garvey 50.00 100.00
Davy Lopes
Ron Cey/75
GRC Steve Garvey 50.00 100.00
Bill Russell
Ron Cey/75
GSG Ken Griffey Jr. 150.00 250.00
Sammy Sosa
Jason Giambi/75 EXCH
GSJ Jason Giambi 75.00 150.00
Sammy Sosa
Ken Griffey Jr./75
ISG Ichiro Suzuki 250.00 500.00
Sammy Sosa
Jason Giambi/75
MSG Mark McGwire
Sammy Sosa
Ken Griffey Jr./10
MSI Mark McGwire
Sammy Sosa
Ichiro Suzuki/10
SEA Tim Salmon 60.00 120.00
Darin Erstad
Garret Anderson/75
SKM Tom Seaver 75.00 150.00
Jerry Koosman
Tug McGraw/75 EXCH

2003 SP Authentic Chirography World Series Heroes

Randomly inserted into packs, these 17 cards feature players who were leading players in at least one World Series. Each of these cards were issued to varying print runs and we have identified the stated print run next to the player's name in our checklist. Andruw Jones did not return his cards in time for inclusion in this product so those exchange cards could be redeemed until May 21, 2006.

AJ1 Andruw Jones/350 10.00 25.00
BM Bill Mazeroski/245 10.00 25.00
CF Carlton Fisk/200 15.00 40.00
CR Cal Ripken/295 60.00 120.00
CS Curt Schilling/345 15.00 40.00
DE Darin Erstad/245 8.00 20.00
DJ David Justice/170 10.00 25.00
ER Edgar Renteria/220 8.00 20.00
GA Garret Anderson/245 10.00 25.00
GC Gary Carter/345 8.00 20.00
GO Luis Gonzalez/225 8.00 20.00
GS Ken Griffey Sr./295 8.00 20.00
JK Jerry Koosman/170 10.00 25.00
JP Jorge Posada/350 15.00 40.00
KG Kirk Gibson/145 10.00 25.00
TI Tim Salmon/245 10.00 25.00
TM Tug McGraw/170 20.00 50.00

2003 SP Authentic Chirography World Series Heroes Bronze

Randomly inserted into packs, this is a partial parallel to the World Series Heroes insert set. Each of these cards have not only an autograph but a notation identifying a key world series this player's

career. Each of these cards were issued to a stated print run of between 50 and 100 copies.

BM Bill Mazeroski/100 15.00 40.00
CF Carlton Fisk/75 25.00 60.00
CS Curt Schilling/100 25.00 60.00
DE Darin Erstad/100 12.50 30.00
DJ David Justice/75 15.00 40.00
ER Edgar Renteria/75 12.50 30.00
GA Garret Anderson/100 15.00 40.00
GC Gary Carter/100 12.50 30.00
GO Luis Gonzalez/100 12.50 30.00
GS Ken Griffey Sr./100 12.50 30.00
JK Jerry Koosman/75 15.00 40.00
KG Kirk Gibson/50 15.00 40.00
TI Tim Salmon/100 15.00 40.00
TM Tug McGraw/100 30.00 80.00

2003 SP Authentic Chirography World Series Heroes Silver

Randomly inserted into packs, this is a partial parallel to the World Series Heroes insert set. These cards feature not only the player's autograph but also in most cases a notation which we have identified in our checklist. Please note that these cards have stated print runs of either 25 or 50 cards. Cards with stated print runs of 25 are not printed due to market scarcity. Of note, Tug McGraw's card, inscribed "Ya Gotta Believe" took on a much deeper meaning after his unfortunate death less than a year after the card was issued.

BM Bill Mazeroski 20.00 50.00
Buc's 60/50
CF Carlton Fisk
Home Run/25
CS Curt Schilling/50 30.00 80.00
DE Darin Erstad/50 15.00 40.00
DJ David Justice/50 20.00 50.00
ER Edgar Renteria
Marlins 97/25
GA Garret Anderson/50 20.00 50.00
GC Gary Carter 15.00 40.00
Mets Champs/50
GO Luis Gonzalez 15.00 40.00
D-Backs 01/50
GS Ken Griffey Sr. 15.00 40.00
Big Red Machine/50
JK Jerry Koosman/50 20.00 50.00
KG Kirk Gibson
Home Run/25
TI Tim Salmon 20.00 50.00
2002 Champs/50
TM Tug McGraw 50.00 100.00
Ya Gotta Believe/50

2003 SP Authentic Chirography Yankees Stars

Randomly inserted into packs, these 14 cards feature not only Yankee stars of the past and present but also authentic autographs of the featured players. Since these cards were issued to varying print runs, we have identified the stated print run next to the player's name in our checklist.

BR Bobby Richardson/320 10.00 25.00
DM Don Mattingly/295 30.00 60.00
DW1 Dave Winfield/350 10.00 25.00
HK Ralph Houk/245 6.00 15.00
JB Jim Bouton/345 6.00 15.00
JG Jason Giambi/275 6.00 15.00
KS Ken Griffey Sr./350 6.00 15.00
RC Roger Clemens/210 50.00 100.00
SL Sparky Lyle/345 6.00 15.00
ST Mel Stottlemyre/345 6.00 15.00
TH Tommy Henrich/345 6.00 15.00
TJ Tommy John/345 6.00 15.00
TK Tony Kubek/345 10.00 25.00
YB Yogi Berra/320 15.00 40.00

2003 SP Authentic Chirography Yankees Stars Bronze

Randomly inserted into packs, this is a partial parallel to the Yankee Stars insert set. Most of these cards were issued to a stated print run of 100 copies and most have an "Yankees" inscription. Please note that for the few players who did not put an Yankees

inscription we put a NO next to the player's name. In addition, since a few cards have a print run of fewer than 100 copies we have noted all print runs in our checklist.

BR Bobby Richardson/100 15.00 40.00
DM Don Mattingly NO/100 40.00 100.00
HK Ralph Houk/100 10.00 25.00
JB Jim Bouton/100 10.00 25.00
JG Jason Giambi/60 10.00 25.00
KS Ken Griffey Sr./100 10.00 25.00
RC Roger Clemens NO/75 60.00 120.00
SL Sparky Lyle/100 10.00 25.00
ST Mel Stottlemyre/100 10.00 25.00
TH Tommy Henrich/100 10.00 25.00
TJ Tommy John/100 10.00 25.00
TK Tony Kubek/100 15.00 40.00
YB Yogi Berra NO/100 25.00 60.00

2003 SP Authentic Chirography Yankees Stars Silver

Randomly inserted into packs, this is a partial parallel to the Yankee Stars insert set. Each of these cards were issued to a stated print run of either 25 or 50 copies and we have noted that information in our checklist. Since there is a mix in this set about cards with notations, what the notations are -- we have put the notation information, when it exists, in our checklist.

BR Bobby Richardson 20.00 50.00
New York/50
DM Don Mattingly/50 50.00 120.00
HK Ralph Houk 12.50 30.00
New York/50
JB Jim Bouton 12.50 30.00
New York/50
JG Jason Giambi/25
KS Ken Griffey Sr./25
RC Roger Clemens/50 60.00 120.00
SL Sparky Lyle/50 12.50 30.00
ST Mel Stottlemyre/50 12.50 30.00
TH Tommy Henrich 12.50 30.00
Yankees/50
TJ Tommy John/50 12.50 30.00
TK Tony Kubek 20.00 50.00
New York/50
YB Yogi Berra/75 30.00 80.00

2003 SP Authentic Chirography Young Stars

Randomly inserted into packs, these 25 cards feature autographs of some of the leading young stars in baseball. These cards were issued to stated print runs of between 150 and 350 cards and we have notated that information in our checklist. Please note that Hee Seop Choi did not return his autographs in time for pack out and those exchange cards could be redeemed until May 21, 2006.

AP A.J. Pierzynski/245 6.00 15.00
BO Joe Borchard/245 4.00 10.00
BP1 Brandon Phillips/350 4.00 10.00
BZ Barry Zito/350 10.00 25.00
CP Corey Patterson/245 4.00 10.00
DH Drew Henson/245 4.00 10.00
DI1 Ben Diggins/350 4.00 10.00
EH Eric Hinske/245 4.00 10.00
FS Freddy Sanchez/350 6.00 15.00
HB Hank Blalock/245 6.00 15.00
JJ Jacque Jones/245 6.00 15.00
JJ1 Jimmy Journell/350 4.00 10.00
JL Jason Lane/245 6.00 15.00
JP Josh Phelps/245 4.00 10.00
JS Jayson Werth/350 4.00 10.00
MB Marlon Byrd/245 4.00 10.00
MI Doug Mientkiewicz/245 6.00 15.00
MP Mark Prior/150 10.00 25.00
MY Brett Myers/245 6.00 15.00
OH Orlando Hudson/245 4.00 10.00
OP Oliver Perez/245 6.00 15.00
PE Carlos Pena/245 4.00 10.00
SB Sean Burroughs/245 4.00 10.00
TX Mark Teixeira/245 10.00 25.00

2003 SP Authentic Chirography Young Stars Bronze

Randomly inserted into packs, this is a partial parallel to the Young Stars insert set. Please note that most of these cards (with the exception of the Mark Prior card) were issued to a stated print run of 100 serial numbered sets and most of these cards had a notation of what city the player was playing in at the time of issue for this set. We have put the city information when applicable in our checklist.

*BRONZE: .6X TO 1.5X BASIC YS
*BRONZE PRIOR: .75X TO 2X BASIC YS

2003 SP Authentic Chirography Young Stars Silver

Randomly inserted into packs, this is a partial parallel to the Young Stars insert set. Most of these cards have a team notation and we have put that information next to the players name in our checklist. Please note that most of these cards, with the exception of Mark Prior was issued to a stated print run of 50 serial numbered sets. The Prior card was issued to a stated print run of 25 serial numbered sets and there is no pricing due to market scarcity on that card.

*SILVER: .75X TO 2X BASIC YS

2003 SP Authentic Simply Splendid

COMMON CARD (TW1-TW30) 3.00 8.00
RANDOM INSERTS IN PACKS
STATED PRINT RUN 406 SERIAL #'d SETS

2003 SP Authentic Splendid Jerseys

RANDOM INSERTS IN PACKS
STATED PRINT RUN 406 SERIAL #'d SETS
SJTW Ted Williams 50.00 100.00

2003 SP Authentic Splendid Signatures

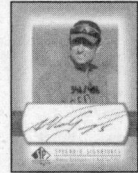

Randomly inserted in packs, these two cards feature autographs of current Red Sox star Nomar Garciaparra and retired Red Sox legend Ted Williams. Please note, that since these cards were issued after Williams passed on, that the Williams autographs are "cuts" while the Nomar autographs were signed for this product. Since the Williams card was issued to a stated print run of five serial numbered copies, no pricing is available for that card.

GA Nomar Garciaparra/406 30.00 60.00
TWSIG Ted Williams/5

2003 SP Authentic Splendid Signatures Pairs

Randomly inserted into packs, these six cards feature a Ted Williams autograph "cut" to go with an autograph of an modern star. Each of these cards were issued to a stated print run of 3 serial numbered copies and no pricing is available due to market scarcity. Of note, all three copies of the Ken Griffey Jr./Ted Williams combo signature actually packed erroneously featuring Ken Griffey Sr. signatures. It's been verified that at least one of the three copies was returned to Upper Deck by a dealer and a Griffey Jr. signature was switched out.

IS2 Ted Williams
Ichiro Suzuki
JG2 Ted Williams
Jason Giambi
KG2 Ted Williams
Ken Griffey Jr.
MM2 Ted Williams
Mark McGwire
NM3 Ted Williams
Nomar Garciaparra
SS2 Ted Williams
Sammy Sosa

2003 SP Authentic Splendid Swatches Pairs

Randomly inserted into packs, these nine cards feature a game-worn jersey swatch of retired Red Sox legend Ted Williams along with a game-used jersey swatch of another star. Each of these cards were issued to a stated print run of 406 serial numbered sets. The two Williams/Nomar cards were not ready for pack-out and those were issued as a exchange cards with a redemption date of May 21, 2006.

IS Ted Williams 50.00 100.00
Ichiro Suzuki
JG Ted Williams 30.00 60.00
Jason Giambi
KG Ted Williams 40.00 80.00
Ken Griffey Jr.
MM Ted Williams 60.00 120.00
Mark McGwire
NM1 Ted Williams 30.00 60.00
Nomar Garciaparra
NM2 Ted Williams 30.00 60.00
Nomar Garciaparra
SS Ted Williams 40.00 80.00
Sammy Sosa
TW Ted Williams 100.00 200.00
Mickey Mantle

2003 SP Authentic Superstar Flashback

RANDOM INSERTS IN PACKS
STATED PRINT RUN 2003 SERIAL #'d SETS
SF1 Tim Salmon 1.25 3.00
SF2 Darin Erstad 1.25 3.00
SF3 Troy Glaus 1.25 3.00
SF4 Randy Johnson 1.25 3.00
SF5 Curt Schilling 1.25 3.00
SF6 Steve Finley 1.25 3.00
SF7 Greg Maddux 2.00 5.00
SF8 Chipper Jones 1.25 3.00
SF9 Andruw Jones 1.25 3.00
SF10 Gary Sheffield 1.25 3.00
SF11 Manny Ramirez 1.25 3.00
SF12 Pedro Martinez 1.25 3.00
SF13 Nomar Garciaparra 2.00 5.00
SF14 Sammy Sosa 1.25 3.00
SF15 Frank Thomas 1.25 3.00
SF16 Kerry Wood 1.25 3.00
SF17 Paul Konerko 1.25 3.00
SF18 Corey Patterson 1.25 3.00
SF19 Mark Prior 1.25 3.00
SF20 Ken Griffey Jr. 2.00 5.00
SF21 Adam Dunn 1.25 3.00
SF22 Larry Walker 1.25 3.00
SF23 Preston Wilson 1.25 3.00
SF24 Todd Helton 1.25 3.00
SF25 Ivan Rodriguez 1.25 3.00
SF26 Josh Beckett 1.25 3.00
SF27 Jeff Bagwell 1.25 3.00
SF28 Jeff Kent 1.25 3.00
SF29 Lance Berkman 1.25 3.00
SF30 Carlos Beltran 1.25 3.00
SF31 Shawn Green 1.25 3.00
SF32 Richie Sexson 1.25 3.00
SF33 Vladimir Guerrero 1.25 3.00
SF34 Mike Piazza 2.00 5.00
SF35 Roberto Alomar 1.25 3.00
SF36 Roger Clemens 2.50 6.00
SF37 Derek Jeter 3.00 8.00
SF38 Jason Giambi 1.25 3.00
SF39 Bernie Williams 1.25 3.00
SF40 Nick Johnson 1.25 3.00
SF41 Alfonso Soriano 1.25 3.00
SF42 Miguel Tejada 1.25 3.00
SF43 Eric Chavez 1.25 3.00
SF44 Barry Zito 1.25 3.00
SF45 Jim Thome 1.25 3.00
SF46 Pat Burrell 1.25 3.00
SF47 Marlon Byrd 1.25 3.00
SF48 Jason Kendall 1.25 3.00
SF49 Aramis Ramirez 1.25 3.00
SF50 Brian Giles 1.25 3.00
SF51 Phil Nevin 1.25 3.00
SF52 Barry Bonds 3.00 8.00
SF53 Ichiro Suzuki 2.50 6.00
SF54 Scott Rolen 1.25 3.00
SF55 J.D. Drew 1.25 3.00
SF56 Albert Pujols 2.50 6.00
SF57 Mark Teixeira 1.25 3.00
SF58 Hank Blalock 1.25 3.00
SF59 Carlos Delgado 1.25 3.00
SF60 Roy Halladay 1.25 3.00

2004 SP Authentic

This 191 card set was released in June, 2004. The set was issued in five card packs with an $5 SRP which came 24 packs to a box and 12 boxes to a case. Cards numbered 1 through 90 featured veterans while cards numbered 91 through 132 and 178 through 191 feature rookies. With the exception of card 180, there were parallel versions issued of these cards and those cards all begin their serial numbering with 296. Card number 180 featuring Kazuo Matsui has a straight serial print run of card 1 through 999. Cards numbered 133 through 177 feature a mix of active and retired players with All-Star game memories and those cards were inserted at a stated rate of one in 24 with a stated print run of 999 serial numbered sets.

COMP.SET w/o SP's (90) 6.00 15.00
COMMON CARD (1-90) .15 .40
COMMON (91-132/178-191) 2.00 5.00
91-132/178-191 OVERALL FW ODDS 1:24
91-132/178-179/181-191 PRINT 704 #'d SETS
91-132/178-179/181-191 #'d FROM 296-999
CARD 180 PRINT RUN 999 #'d COPIES
CARD 180 #'d FROM 1-999
COMMON CARD (133-177) 1.25 3.00
133-177 STATED ODDS 1:24
133-177 PRINT RUN 999 SERIAL #'d SETS
1 Bret Boone .15 .40
2 Gary Sheffield .15 .40
3 Rafael Palmeiro .25 .60
4 Jorge Posada .25 .60
5 Derek Jeter .75 2.00
6 Garret Anderson .15 .40
7 Bartolo Colon .15 .40
8 Kevin Brown .15 .40
9 Shea Hillenbrand .15 .40
10 Ryan Klesko .15 .40
11 Bobby Abreu .15 .40
12 Scott Rolen .25 .60
13 Alfonso Soriano .15 .40
14 Jason Giambi .15 .40
15 Tom Glavine .25 .60
16 Hideo Nomo .40 1.00
17 Johan Santana .40 1.00
18 Sammy Sosa .40 1.00
19 Rickie Weeks .15 .40
20 Barry Zito .15 .40
21 Kerry Wood .15 .40
22 Austin Kearns .15 .40
23 Shawn Green .15 .40
24 Miguel Cabrera .25 .60
25 Richard Hidalgo .15 .40
26 Andruw Jones .25 .60
27 Randy Wolf .15 .40
28 David Ortiz .40 1.00
29 Roy Oswalt .15 .40
30 Vernon Wells .15 .40
31 Ben Sheets .15 .40
32 Mike Lowell .15 .40
33 Todd Helton .25 .60
34 Jacque Jones .15 .40
35 Mike Sweeney .15 .40
36 Hank Blalock .15 .40
37 Jason Schmidt .15 .40
38 Jeff Kent .15 .40
39 Josh Beckett .15 .40
40 Manny Ramirez .25 .60
41 Torii Hunter .15 .40
42 Brian Giles .15 .40
43 Javier Vazquez .15 .40
44 Jim Edmonds .15 .40
45 Dmitri Young .15 .40
46 Preston Wilson .15 .40
47 Jeff Bagwell .25 .60
48 Pedro Martinez .25 .60
49 Eric Chavez .15 .40
50 Ken Griffey Jr. .60 1.50
51 Shannon Stewart .15 .40
52 Rafael Furcal .15 .40
53 Brandon Webb .15 .40
54 Juan Pierre .15 .40
55 Roger Clemens .75 2.00
56 Geoff Jenkins .15 .40

57 Lance Berkman .15 .40
58 Albert Pujols .75 2.00
59 Frank Thomas .40 1.00
60 Edgar Martinez .25 .60
61 Tim Hudson .15 .40
62 Eric Gagne .15 .40
63 Richie Sexson .15 .40
64 Corey Patterson .15 .40
65 Nomar Garciaparra .60 1.50
66 Hideki Matsui .60 1.50
67 Mark Teixeira .25 .60
68 Troy Glaus .15 .40
69 Carlos Lee .15 .40
70 Mike Mussina .25 .60
71 Magglio Ordonez .15 .40
72 Roy Halladay .15 .40
73 Ichiro Suzuki .75 2.00
74 Randy Johnson .40 1.00
75 Luis Gonzalez .15 .40
76 Mark Prior .25 .60
77 Carlos Beltran .15 .40
78 Ivan Rodriguez .25 .60
79 Alex Rodriguez .60 1.50
80 Dontrelle Willis .25 .60
81 Mike Piazza .60 1.50
82 Curt Schilling .25 .60
83 Vladimir Guerrero .40 1.00
84 Greg Maddux .60 1.50
85 Jim Thome .25 .60
86 Miguel Tejada .15 .40
87 Carlos Delgado .15 .40
88 Jose Reyes .15 .40
89 Matt Morris .15 .40
90 Mark Mulder .15 .40
91 Angel Chavez FW RC 2.00 5.00
92 Brandon Medders FW RC 2.00 5.00
93 Carlos Vasquez FW RC 2.00 5.00
94 Chris Aguila FW RC 2.00 5.00
95 Colby Miller FW RC 2.00 5.00
96 Dave Crouthers FW RC 2.00 5.00
97 Dennis Sarfate FW RC 2.00 5.00
98 Donnie Kelly FW RC 2.00 5.00
99 Merkin Valdez FW RC 2.00 5.00
100 Eddy Rodriguez FW RC 2.00 5.00
101 Edwin Moreno FW RC 2.00 5.00
102 Enemencio Pacheco FW RC 2.00 5.00
103 Roberto Novoa FW RC 2.00 5.00
104 Greg Dobbs FW RC 2.00 5.00
105 Hector Gimenez FW RC 2.00 5.00
106 Ian Snell FW RC 3.00 8.00
107 Jake Woods FW RC 2.00 5.00
108 Jamie Brown FW RC 2.00 5.00
109 Jason Frasor FW RC 2.00 5.00
110 Jerome Gamble FW RC 2.00 5.00
111 Jerry Gil FW RC 2.00 5.00
112 Jesse Harper FW RC 2.00 5.00
113 Jorge Vasquez FW RC 2.00 5.00
114 Jose Capellan FW RC 2.00 5.00
115 Josh Labandeira FW RC 2.00 5.00
116 Justin Hampson FW RC 2.00 5.00
117 Justin Huisman FW RC 2.00 5.00
118 Justin Leone FW RC 2.00 5.00
119 Lincoln Holdzkom FW RC 2.00 5.00
120 Lino Urdaneta FW RC 2.00 5.00
121 Mike Gosling FW RC 2.00 5.00
122 Mike Johnston FW RC 2.00 5.00
123 Mike Rouse FW RC 2.00 5.00
124 Scott Proctor FW RC 2.00 5.00
125 Roman Colon FW RC 2.00 5.00
126 Ronny Cedeno FW RC 3.00 8.00
127 Ryan Meaux FW RC 2.00 5.00
128 Scott Dohmann FW RC 2.00 5.00
129 Sean Henn FW RC 2.00 5.00
130 Tim Bausher FW RC 2.00 5.00
131 Tim Bittner FW RC 2.00 5.00
132 William Bergolla FW RC 2.00 5.00
133 Rick Ferrell ASM 1.25 3.00
134 Joe DiMaggio ASM 2.00 5.00
135 Bob Feller ASM 1.25 3.00
136 Ted Williams ASM 3.00 8.00
137 Stan Musial ASM 2.00 5.00
138 Larry Doby ASM 1.25 3.00
139 Red Schoendienst ASM 1.25 3.00
140 Enos Slaughter ASM 1.25 3.00
141 Stan Musial ASM 2.00 5.00
142 Mickey Mantle ASM 4.00 10.00
143 Ted Williams ASM 3.00 8.00
144 Mickey Mantle ASM 4.00 10.00
145 Stan Musial ASM 2.00 5.00
146 Tom Seaver ASM 1.50 4.00
147 Willie McCovey ASM 1.50 4.00
148 Bob Gibson ASM 1.50 4.00
149 Frank Robinson ASM 1.25 3.00
150 Joe Morgan ASM 1.25 3.00
151 Billy Williams ASM 1.25 3.00
152 Catfish Hunter ASM 1.50 4.00
153 Joe Morgan ASM 1.25 3.00
154 Joe Morgan ASM 1.25 3.00
155 Mike Schmidt ASM 3.00 8.00
156 Tommy Lasorda ASM 1.25 3.00
157 Robin Yount ASM 1.50 4.00
158 Nolan Ryan ASM 4.00 10.00
159 John Franco ASM 1.25 3.00
160 Nolan Ryan ASM 4.00 10.00
161 Ken Griffey Jr. ASM 2.00 5.00
162 Cal Ripken ASM 4.00 10.00
163 Ken Griffey Jr. ASM 2.00 5.00
164 Gary Sheffield ASM 1.25 3.00
165 Fred McGriff ASM 1.50 4.00
166 Hideo Nomo ASM 1.50 4.00
167 Mike Piazza ASM 2.00 5.00
168 Sandy Alomar Jr. ASM 1.25 3.00
169 Roberto Alomar ASM 1.50 4.00
170 Ted Williams ASM 3.00 8.00
171 Pedro Martinez ASM 1.50 4.00
172 Derek Jeter ASM 2.50 6.00
173 Cal Ripken ASM 4.00 10.00
174 Torii Hunter ASM 1.25 3.00
175 Alfonso Soriano ASM 1.25 3.00
176 Hank Blalock ASM 1.25 3.00
177 Ichiro Suzuki ASM 2.50 6.00
178 Orlando Rodriguez FW RC 2.00 5.00
179 Ramon Ramirez FW RC 2.00 5.00
180 Kazuo Matsui FW RC 2.00 5.00
181 Kevin Cave FW RC 2.00 5.00
182 John Gall FW RC 2.00 5.00
183 Freddy Guzman FW RC 2.00 5.00
184 Chris Oxspring FW RC 2.00 5.00
185 Rusty Tucker FW RC 2.00 5.00
186 Jorge Sequea FW RC 2.00 5.00
187 Carlos Hines FW RC 2.00 5.00
188 Michael Vento FW RC 2.00 5.00
189 Ryan Wing FW RC 2.00 5.00
190 Jeff Bennett FW RC 2.00 5.00
191 Luis A. Gonzalez FW RC 2.00 5.00

2004 SP Authentic 199/99

*199/99 1-90: 3X TO 8X BASIC
*199/99 91-132/178-191: .75X TO 2X BASIC
1-132/178-191 PRINT RUN SER. 99 #'d SETS
*199/99 133-177: .75X TO 2X BASIC
133-177 PRINT RUN 199 SERIAL #'d SETS
OVERALL PARALLEL ODDS 1:8

2004 SP Authentic 499/249

*499/249 1-90: 1.25X TO 3X BASIC
*499/249 133-177: .6X TO 1.5X BASIC
1-90/133-177 PRINT RUN 499 #'d SETS
*499/249 91-132/178-191: .5X TO 1.2X BASIC
91-132/178-191 PRINT RUN 249 #'d SETS
OVERALL PARALLEL ODDS 1:8

2004 SP Authentic Future Watch Autograph

STATED PRINT RUN 295 SERIAL #'d SETS
*AUTO 195: .5X TO 1.2X BASIC
AUTO 195 PRINT RUN 195 SERIAL #'d SETS
OVERALL FUTURE WATCH ODDS 1:24
91 Angel Chavez FW 4.00 10.00
92 Brandon Medders FW 4.00 10.00
93 Carlos Vasquez FW 6.00 15.00
94 Chris Aguila FW 4.00 10.00
95 Colby Miller FW 4.00 10.00
96 Dave Crouthers FW 4.00 10.00
97 Dennis Sarfate FW 4.00 10.00
98 Donnie Kelly FW 4.00 10.00
99 Merkin Valdez FW 4.00 10.00
100 Eddy Rodriguez FW 6.00 15.00
101 Edwin Moreno FW 4.00 10.00
102 Enemencio Pacheco FW 4.00 10.00
103 Roberto Novoa FW 4.00 10.00
104 Greg Dobbs FW 4.00 10.00
105 Hector Gimenez FW 4.00 10.00
106 Ian Snell FW 10.00 25.00
107 Jake Woods FW 4.00 10.00
108 Jamie Brown FW 4.00 10.00
109 Jason Frasor FW 4.00 10.00
110 Jerome Gamble FW 4.00 10.00
111 Jerry Gil FW 4.00 10.00
112 Jesse Harper FW 4.00 10.00
113 Jorge Vasquez FW 4.00 10.00
114 Jose Capellan FW 4.00 10.00
115 Josh Labandeira FW 4.00 10.00
116 Justin Hampson FW 4.00 10.00
117 Justin Huisman FW 4.00 10.00
118 Justin Leone FW 6.00 15.00
119 Lincoln Holdzkom FW 4.00 10.00
120 Lino Urdaneta FW 4.00 10.00
121 Mike Gosling FW 4.00 10.00
122 Mike Johnston FW 4.00 10.00
123 Mike Rouse FW 4.00 10.00
124 Scott Proctor FW 6.00 15.00
125 Roman Colon FW 4.00 10.00
126 Ronny Cedeno FW 6.00 15.00
127 Ryan Meaux FW 4.00 10.00
128 Scott Dohmann FW 4.00 10.00
129 Sean Henn FW 4.00 10.00
130 Tim Bausher FW 4.00 10.00
131 Tim Bittner FW 4.00 10.00
132 William Bergolla FW 4.00 10.00
178 Orlando Rodriguez FW 4.00 10.00
179 Ramon Ramirez FW 4.00 10.00
181 Kevin Cave FW 4.00 10.00
182 John Gall FW 6.00 15.00
183 Freddy Guzman FW 4.00 10.00
184 Chris Oxspring FW 4.00 10.00
185 Rusty Tucker FW 6.00 15.00
186 Jorge Sequea FW 4.00 10.00
187 Carlos Hines FW 4.00 10.00
188 Michael Vento FW 6.00 15.00
189 Ryan Wing FW 4.00 10.00
190 Jeff Bennett FW 4.00 10.00
191 Luis A. Gonzalez FW 6.00 15.00

2004 SP Authentic Game-Dated

OVERALL GAME DATED ODDS 1:288
STATED PRINT RUN 1 SERIAL #'d SET

MULTIPLE VERSIONS OF EACH CARD EXIST
NO PRICING DUE TO SCARCITY

2004 SP Authentic Game-Dated Autographs

OVERALL GAME DATED ODDS 1:288
STATED PRINT RUN 1 SERIAL #'d SET
CL: 1/5/6/10/11/19-20/22/24-25/27/29
CL: 31/34/36/43/49-50/59-60/62/67/69
CL: 72/76/78/80/86-88
MULTIPLE VERSIONS OF EACH CARD EXIST
NO PRICING DUE TO SCARCITY

2004 SP Authentic Buybacks

Jorge Posada did not return his cards in time for pack out and those cards could be redeemed until June 4, 2007.

OVERALL AUTO INSERT ODDS 1:12
PRINT RUNS B/WN 1-105 COPIES PER
NO PRICING ON QTY OF 14 OR LESS
AB1 Angel Berroa 04 VIN/70 4.00 10.00
AD1 Andre Dawson 04 SSC/50 6.00 15.00
AKE1 Austin Kearns 03 40M/5
AKE2 Austin Kearns 03 CP/1
AKE3 Austin Kearns 03 PC/1
AKE4 Austin Kearns 03 SPx/1
AKE5 Austin Kearns 03 SS/5
AKE6 Austin Kearns 03 UDA/1
AKE7 Austin Kearns 04 DAS/1
AKE8 Austin Kearns 04 VIN/5
AK1 Al Kaline 03 SP LC/20 30.00 60.00
AK2 Al Kaline 04 SSC/70 20.00 50.00
AL1 Al Leiter 04 FP/80 6.00 15.00
AL2 Al Leiter 04 UD/60 6.00 15.00
BA1 Bobby Abreu 03 CP/63 6.00 15.00
BA2 Bobby Abreu 03 HR/53
BA3 Bobby Abreu 03 SPx/63 6.00 15.00
BA4 Bobby Abreu 03 SS/64 6.00 15.00
BA5 Bobby Abreu 03 UDA/63 6.00 15.00
BA6 Bobby Abreu 04 DAS/53 6.00 15.00
BA7 Bobby Abreu 04 FP/53 6.00 15.00
BA8 Bobby Abreu 04 UD/65 6.00 15.00
BA9 Bobby Abreu 04 VIN/53 6.00 15.00
BB1 Bret Boone 03 CP/66 15.00 40.00
BB2 Bret Boone 03 PC/15 30.00 60.00
BB3 Bret Boone 03 SPx/29 20.00 50.00
BB4 Bret Boone 03 SS/44 15.00 40.00
BB5 Bret Boone 03 UDA/63 15.00 40.00
BB6 Bret Boone 04 DAS/57 15.00 40.00
BB7 Bret Boone 04 VIN/53 15.00 40.00
BD1 Bobby Doerr 03 SP LCB/50 6.00 15.00
BD2 Bobby Doerr 04 SSC/73 6.00 15.00
BG1 Bob Gibson 04 SSC/23 15.00 40.00
BHI1 Bobby Hill 03 40M/40 4.00 10.00
BHI2 Bobby Hill 03 UDA/17 8.00 20.00
BHI3 Bobby Hill 04 FP/17 8.00 20.00
BHI4 Bobby Hill 04 UD/17 8.00 20.00
BHI5 Bobby Hill 04 VIN/34 6.00 15.00
BH1 Bo Hart 03 SPx/50 4.00 10.00
BH2 Bo Hart 04 VIN/45 4.00 10.00
BL1 Barry Larkin 03 FP/10
BR1 B.Robinson 03 SP LC/50 10.00 25.00
BR2 B.Robinson 04 SSC/70 10.00 25.00
BS1 Ben Sheets 03 40M/25 10.00 25.00
BS2 Ben Sheets 03 CP/15 12.50 30.00
BS3 Ben Sheets 03 PC/15 12.50 30.00
BS4 Ben Sheets 03 SPx/15 12.50 30.00
BS5 Ben Sheets 04 DAS/15 12.50 30.00
BS6 Ben Sheets 04 FP/15
BS7 Ben Sheets 04 UD/25 10.00 25.00
BS8 Ben Sheets 04 VIN/15 12.50 30.00
BW1 Brandon Webb 03 SPx/20 6.00 15.00
BW2 Brandon Webb 03 UD/65 4.00 10.00
BW3 Brandon Webb 03 UDA/10
BW4 Brandon Webb 04 DAS/50 4.00 10.00
BW5 Brandon Webb 04 FP/30 6.00 15.00
BW6 Brandon Webb 04 VIN/85 4.00 10.00
BZ1 Barry Zito 03 40M/30 15.00 40.00
BZ2 Barry Zito 03 CP/41 10.00 25.00
BZ3 Barry Zito 03 HR/60 10.00 25.00
BZ4 Barry Zito 03 PC/15 20.00 50.00
BZ5 Barry Zito 03 SPx/46 10.00 25.00
BZ6 Barry Zito 03 SS/63 10.00 25.00
BZ7 Barry Zito 03 UDA/40 10.00 25.00
BZ8 Barry Zito 04 FP/69 10.00 25.00
BZ9 Barry Zito 04 UD/61 10.00 25.00
BZ10 Barry Zito 04 VIN/50 10.00 25.00
CB1 Carlos Beltran 03 40M/25
CB2 Carlos Beltran 03 CP/15 12.50 30.00
CB3 Carlos Beltran 03 PC/15 12.50 30.00
CB4 Carlos Beltran 03 SPx/15 12.50 30.00
CB5 Carlos Beltran 03 SS/15 12.50 30.00
CB6 Carlos Beltran 04 DAS/15 12.50 30.00
CB7 Carlos Beltran 04 VIN/15 12.50 30.00
CD1 Carlos Delgado 03 CP/1
CD2 Carlos Delgado 03 HR/1
CD3 Carlos Delgado 03 SPx/1
CD4 Carlos Delgado 03 SS/1
CD5 C.Delgado 03 UDA/43 6.00 15.00
CD6 Carlos Delgado 04 DAS/1
CD7 Carlos Delgado 04 VIN/1
CF1 C.Fisk 03 SP LC/38 15.00 40.00
CF2 C.Fisk 03 SP LCB/55 15.00 40.00
CLL1 Cliff Lee 04 FP/40 4.00 10.00
CLL2 Cliff Lee 04 UD/50 4.00 10.00
CL1 Carlos Lee 04 FP/70 6.00 15.00
CL2 Carlos Lee 04 UD/70 6.00 15.00
CL3 Carlos Lee 04 VIN/70 6.00 15.00
CPO1 Colin Porter 03 CP/60 4.00 10.00
CPO2 Colin Porter 03 SS/10
CPO3 Colin Porter 04 FP/70 4.00 10.00
CP1 C.Patterson 03 40M/20 6.00 15.00
CP2 C.Patterson 03 PC/20 6.00 15.00
CP3 C.Patterson 03 SPx/20 6.00 15.00
CP4 C.Patterson 03 SS/20 6.00 15.00
CP5 C.Patterson 04 FP/20 6.00 15.00
CP6 C.Patterson 04 UD/20 6.00 15.00
CP7 C.Patterson 04 VIN/20 6.00 15.00
CR1 Cal Ripken 04 SSC/45 75.00 150.00
CW1 C.Wang 04 FP/26 75.00 150.00
CY1 C.Yastrzemski 04 SSC/22 40.00 80.00
CZ1 C.Zambrano 04 VIN/70 10.00 25.00
DJ1 Derek Jeter 03 40M/30 90.00 180.00
DJ2 Derek Jeter 03 CP/2
DJ3 Derek Jeter 03 HR/25 100.00 200.00
DJ4 Derek Jeter 03 PC/25 100.00 200.00
DJ5 Derek Jeter 03 SPx/2
DJ6 Derek Jeter 03 SS/30 90.00 180.00
DJ7 Derek Jeter 03 UDA/2
DJ8 Derek Jeter 04 DAS/12
DJ9 Derek Jeter 04 FP/12
DJ10 Derek Jeter 04 UD/25 100.00 200.00
DJ11 Derek Jeter 04 VIN/25 100.00 200.00
DS1 Duke Snider 04 SSC/23 15.00 40.00
DW1 D.Willis 04 DAS/70 10.00 25.00
DW2 D.Willis 04 FP/80 10.00 25.00
DW3 D.Willis 04 UD SR/45 10.00 25.00
DW4 D.Willis 04 VIN/105 10.00 25.00
DY1 Delmon Young 04 DAS/5
DY2 Delmon Young 04 FP/5
DY3 Delmon Young 04 VIN/35 15.00 40.00
EC1 Eric Chavez 03 40M/30 10.00 25.00
EC2 Eric Chavez 03 CP/3
EC3 Eric Chavez 03 HR/3
EC4 Eric Chavez 03 SPx/3
EC5 Eric Chavez 03 SS/25 10.00 25.00
EC6 Eric Chavez 04 FP/3
EC7 Eric Chavez 04 DAS/2
EC8 Eric Chavez 04 UD/3
EC9 Eric Chavez 04 VIN/3
EG1 Eric Gagne 03 40M/38 10.00 25.00
EG2 Eric Gagne 04 FP/26 15.00 40.00
EG3 Eric Gagne 04 UD/38 10.00 25.00
EG4 Eric Gagne 04 VIN/38 10.00 25.00
EM1 E.Martinez 04 DAS/70 15.00 40.00
GA1 G.Anderson 03 40M/30 10.00 25.00
GA2 G.Anderson 03 CP/16
GA3 G.Anderson 03 SPx/2
GA4 G.Anderson 03 SS/20 10.00 25.00
GA5 G.Anderson 04 DAS/16 12.50 30.00
GA6 G.Anderson 04 VIN/16 12.50 30.00
HB1 Hank Blalock 03 40M/20 10.00 25.00
HB2 Hank Blalock 03 CP/9
HB3 Hank Blalock 03 PC/9
HB4 Hank Blalock 03 SPx/9
HB5 Hank Blalock 03 SS/15 12.50 30.00
HB6 Hank Blalock 04 FP/10
HB7 Hank Blalock 04 UD/9
HB8 Hank Blalock 04 VIN/9
HK1 H.Killebrew 03 SP LC/20 30.00 60.00
HK2 Harmon Killebrew 04 SSC/3
HR1 H.Ramirez 03 40M/25 6.00 15.00
HR2 Horacio Ramirez 04 FP/5
HR3 Horacio Ramirez 04 UD/15 8.00 20.00
JB1 Josh Beckett 03 40M/21 15.00 40.00
JB2 Josh Beckett 03 CP/5
JB3 Josh Beckett 03 HR/21 15.00 40.00
JB4 Josh Beckett 03 PC/12
JB5 Josh Beckett 03 SPx/5
JB6 Josh Beckett 03 SS/21 15.00 40.00
JB7 Josh Beckett 04 VIN/5
JE1 Jim Edmonds 03 CP/25 15.00 40.00
JE2 Jim Edmonds 03 HR/15 20.00 50.00
JE3 Jim Edmonds 03 SPx/25 15.00 40.00
JE4 Jim Edmonds 03 SS/45 10.00 25.00
JE5 Jim Edmonds 03 UDA/25 15.00 40.00
JE6 Jim Edmonds 04 DAS/15 20.00 50.00
JE7 Jim Edmonds 04 FP/15 20.00 50.00
JE8 Jim Edmonds 04 UD/25 15.00 40.00
JE9 Jim Edmonds 04 VIN/15 20.00 50.00
JGE1 Jody Gerut 04 DAS/70 4.00 10.00
JGE2 Jody Gerut 04 VIN/70 4.00 10.00
JG1 Juan Gonzalez 03 40M/19 12.50 30.00
JG2 Juan Gonzalez 03 CP/19
JG3 Juan Gonzalez 03 PC/19 12.50 30.00
JG4 Juan Gonzalez 03 SS/19 12.50 30.00
JG5 Juan Gonzalez 04 FP/5
JG6 Juan Gonzalez 04 UD/19 12.50 30.00
JG7 Juan Gonzalez 04 VIN/20 10.00 25.00
JJ1 Jacque Jones 03 40M/40 6.00 15.00
JJ2 Jacque Jones 03 CP/11
JJ3 Jacque Jones 03 SPx/35 10.00 25.00
JJ4 Jacque Jones 03 SS/35 10.00 25.00
JJ5 Jacque Jones 03 UDA/11
JJ6 Jacque Jones 04 DAS/2
JJ7 Jacque Jones 04 VIN/11
JL1 Javy Lopez 03 40M/30 10.00 25.00
JL2 Javy Lopez 04 FP/18 12.50 30.00
JL3 Javy Lopez 04 UD/29 10.00 25.00
JL4 Javy Lopez 04 VIN/18 12.50 30.00
JO1 John Olerud 03 CP/50 10.00 25.00
JO2 John Olerud 03 SS/45 10.00 25.00
JO3 John Olerud 04 VIN/70 10.00 25.00
JP1 Jorge Posada 03 40M/20 EXCH
JP2 Jorge Posada 03 CP/5 EXCH
JP3 Jorge Posada 03 SPx/5 EXCH
JP4 Jorge Posada 03 SS/20 EXCH
JP5 Jorge Posada 04 FP/5 EXCH
JP6 Jorge Posada 04 UD/20 EXCH
JP7 Jorge Posada 04 VIN/20 EXCH
JP8 Jorge Posada EXCH 20.00 50.00
JR1 Jose Reyes 04 DAS/7
JS1 John Smoltz 04 FP/67 30.00 60.00
JS2 John Smoltz 04 UD/67 30.00 60.00
JS3 John Smoltz 04 VIN/70 30.00 60.00
JT1 Joe Torre 04 SSC/70 10.00 25.00
JV1 Javier Vazquez 04 DAS/70 6.00 15.00
JV2 Javier Vazquez 04 VIN/70 6.00 15.00
JWS1 Jae Seo 03 SS/10
JWS2 Jae Seo 04 FP/5
JWS3 Jae Seo 04 UD/15 12.50 30.00
JWS4 Jae Seo 04 VIN/15 12.50 30.00
JW1 Jer.Williams 04 UD/70 4.00 10.00
JW2 Jer.Williams 04 VIN/60 4.00 10.00
KG1 K.Grif 02 SUP Silv/45 50.00 100.00
KG2 K.Grif 02 SUP SK 92 AS/6
KG3 K.Grif 02 SUP SK Blue/19 75.00 150.00
KG4 K.Grif 03 40M Blue/20 60.00 120.00
KG5 K.Grif 03 40M Red/10
KG6 K.Grif 03 40M 92 AS/18 75.00 150.00
KG7 K.Grif 03 40M 97 AL/18 75.00 150.00
KG8 K.Grif 03 40MHR94 Blk/31 60.00 120.00
KG9 K.Grif 03 40MHR94 Blu/27 60.00 120.00
KG10 K.Grif 03 40MHR98 Sil/28 60.00 120.00
KG11 K.Grif 03 40M HR98 AS/12
KG12 K.Grif 03 40M HR98 GG/14
KG13 K.Grif 03 40M HR99 Sil/48 50.00 100.00
KG14 K.Grif 03 40M T40 Blu/35 60.00 120.00
KG15 K.Grif 03 40M T40 AL/29 50.00 100.00
KG16 K.Grif 03 GF Black/40 50.00 100.00
KG17 K.Grif 03 GF Blue/23 60.00 120.00
KG18 K.Grif 03 GF Red/10
KG19 K.Grif 03 GF 92AS/19 75.00 150.00
KG20 K.Grif 03 HR 92AS/15 75.00 150.00
KG21 K.Grif 03 HR 97AL/37 60.00 120.00
KG22 K.Grif 03 HR Red/10
KG23 K.Grif 03 MVP Blk/56 50.00 100.00
KG24 K.Grif 03 MVP Red/10
KG25 K.Grif 03 MVP GG/15 75.00 150.00
KG26 K.Grif 03 MVP GG92/1
KG27 K.Grif 03 PC Black/27 60.00 120.00
KG28 K.Grif 03 PC Blue/7
KG29 K.Grif 03 PC 92 AS/8
KG30 K.Grif 03 PB Black/15 75.00 150.00
KG31 K.Grif 03 PB Blue/SSC/10
KG32 K.Grif 03 PB 56 HR/15 75.00 150.00
KG33 K.Grif 03 PB 92 AS/9
KG34 K.Grif 03 SPA 56 HR/15 75.00 150.00
KG35 K.Grif 03 SPA 92 AS/20 60.00 120.00
KG36 K.Grif 03 SPA B93 AS/20 60.00 120.00
KG37 K.Grif 03 SPA B93 AS MVP/1
KG38 K.Grif 03 SPA Red/5
KG39 K.Grif 03 SPx 97 AL/26 60.00 120.00
KG40 K.Grif 03 SS 97 AL/32 50.00 120.00
KG41 K.Grif 03 UDA Red/5
KG42 K.Grif 03 VIC Blk/57 50.00 100.00
KG43 K.Grif 03 VIC 92 AS/18 75.00 150.00
KW1 Kerry Wood 03 40M/34 15.00 40.00
KW2 Kerry Wood 03 40M RWB/13
KW3 Kerry Wood 03 CP/1
KW4 Kerry Wood 03 PC/1
KW5 Kerry Wood 03 SPx/5
KW6 Kerry Wood 03 SS/34 15.00 40.00
KW7 Kerry Wood 03 UDA/5
KW8 Kerry Wood 04 DAS/1
KW9 Kerry Wood 04 VIN/5
LA1 L.Aparicio 03 SP LC/20 10.00 25.00
LA2 Luis Aparicio 04 SSC/3
LG1 L.Gonzalez 03 40M HR/25 10.00 25.00
LG2 Luis Gonzalez 03 CP/20
LG3 Luis Gonzalez 03 HR/20 10.00 25.00
LG4 Luis Gonzalez 03 SPx/1
LG5 Luis Gonzalez 03 SS/40 6.00 15.00
LG6 Luis Gonzalez 03 UDA/1
LG7 Luis Gonzalez 04 FP/20
LG8 Luis Gonzalez 04 UD/10
LG9 Luis Gonzalez 04 VIN/20 10.00 25.00
MB1 Marlon Byrd 04 VIN/70 4.00 10.00
MC1 M.Cabrera 03 SPx/25 15.00 40.00
MC2 M.Cabrera 04 DAS/20 15.00 40.00
MC3 M.Cabrera 04 FP/20 15.00 40.00
MC4 M.Cabrera 04 VIN/20 15.00 40.00
ME1 M.Ensberg 04 FP/70 6.00 15.00
ME2 M.Ensberg 04 UD/70 6.00 15.00
ME3 M.Ensberg 04 VIN/70 6.00 15.00
MG1 Marcus Giles 04 VIN/70 6.00 15.00
MH1 Mike Hampton 03 UDA/60 4.00 10.00
MH2 Mike Hampton 04 FP/34 6.00 15.00
MH3 Mike Hampton 04 UD/47 4.00 10.00
MI1 Monte Irvin 03 SP LC/20 10.00 25.00
MI2 Monte Irvin 04 SSC/3
ML1 Mike Lowell 03 40M/19 8.00 20.00
ML2 Mike Lowell 04 DAS/19 8.00 20.00
ML3 Mike Lowell 04 FP/19 8.00 20.00
ML4 Mike Lowell 04 UD/19 8.00 20.00
ML5 Mike Lowell 04 VIN/19 8.00 20.00
MM1 Mike Mussina 03 CP/45
MM2 Mike Mussina 03 HR/20 15.00 40.00
MM3 Mike Mussina 03 HR/25 15.00 40.00
MM4 Mike Mussina 03 SPx/45
MM5 Mike Mussina 03 SS/60 10.00 25.00
MM6 Mike Mussina 03 UDA/45 10.00 25.00
MM7 Mike Mussina 04 FP/58 10.00 25.00
MM8 Mike Mussina 04 UD/45 10.00 25.00
MM9 Mike Mussina 04 VIN/45 10.00 25.00
MPI1 Mike Piazza 03 40M/5
MPI2 Mike Piazza 03 CP/1
MPI3 Mike Piazza 03 HR/1
MPI4 Mike Piazza 03 PC/1
MPI5 Mike Piazza 03 SPx/1
MPI6 Mike Piazza 03 SS/1
MPI7 Mike Piazza 03 UDA/1
MPI8 Mike Piazza 04 DAS/1
MPI9 Mike Piazza 04 FP/2
MPI10 Mike Piazza 04 UD/5
MPI11 Mike Piazza 04 VIN/1
MP1 Mark Prior 03 40M/22 12.50 30.00
MP2 Mark Prior 03 40M RWB/5
MP3 Mark Prior 03 CP/5
MP4 Mark Prior 03 HR/22 12.50 30.00
MP5 Mark Prior 03 PC/22 12.50 30.00
MP6 Mark Prior 03 SPx/22 12.50 30.00
MP7 Mark Prior 03 SS/22 12.50 30.00
MP8 Mark Prior 03 UDA/10
MP9 Mark Prior 04 DAS/4
MP10 Mark Prior 04 FP/22 12.50 30.00
MP11 Mark Prior 04 UD/22 12.50 30.00
MP12 Mark Prior 04 VIN/22 12.50 30.00
MS1 M.Schmidt 03 SP LC/20 50.00 100.00
MS2 Mike Schmidt 04 SSC/3
MTE1 Miguel Tejada 03 CP/38 10.00 25.00
MTE2 Miguel Tejada 03 HR/36 10.00 25.00
MTE3 M.Tejada 03 SPx/30 15.00 40.00
MTE4 M.Tejada 03 UDA/58 10.00 25.00
MTE5 Miguel Tejada 04 DAS/37 10.00 25.00
MTE6 Miguel Tejada 04 VIN/70 6.00 15.00
MT1 M.Teix 03 40M RWB/45 10.00 25.00
MT2 Mark Teixeira 03 CP/23
MT3 Mark Teixeira 03 PC/3
MT4 Mark Teixeira 03 SPx/40 10.00 25.00
MT5 Mark Teixeira 03 SS/23 15.00 40.00
MT6 Mark Teixeira 03 SS/25 15.00 40.00
MT7 Mark Teixeira 03 UDA/21 15.00 40.00
MT8 Mark Teixeira 04 DAS/5
MT9 Mark Teixeira 04 FP/10
MT10 Mark Teixeira 04 UD/23 15.00 40.00
MT11 Mark Teixeira 04 VIN/23
MW1 Maury Wills 04 SSC/70 6.00 15.00
NR1 Nolan Ryan 03 UDA/20 75.00 150.00
NR2 Nolan Ryan 04 SSC/3
OD1 Octavio Dotel 04 FP/70 4.00 10.00
OD2 Octavio Dotel 04 UD/70 4.00 10.00
OD3 Octavio Dotel 04 VIN/70 4.00 10.00
PB1 Pat Burrell 03 CP/50 6.00 15.00
PB2 Pat Burrell 03 HR/25 10.00 25.00
PB3 Pat Burrell 03 SS/50 6.00 15.00
PB4 Pat Burrell 03 UDA/50 6.00 15.00
PB5 Pat Burrell 04 VIN/68 6.00 15.00
PL1 P.LoDuca 03 40M RWB/60 6.00 15.00
PL2 Paul Lo Duca 04 VIN/60 6.00 15.00
PL3 P.Lo Duca 04 VIN BW/20 10.00 25.00
PR1 Phil Rizzuto 03 SP LC/21 15.00 40.00
PR2 Phil Rizzuto 04 SSC/2
RB1 Rocco Baldelli 03 40M/20
RB2 Rocco Baldelli 03 PC/20
RB3 Rocco Baldelli 03 SPx/15 12.50 30.00
RB4 Rocco Baldelli 03 UDA/10
RB5 Rocco Baldelli 04 DAS/5
RB6 Rocco Baldelli 04 FP/10
RB7 R.Baldelli 04 PB Red/25 10.00 25.00
RB8 R.Baldelli 04 PB Blue/25 10.00 25.00
RB9 Rocco Baldelli 04 UD/5
RB10 Rocco Baldelli 04 VIN/5
RF1 Rollie Fingers 03 SP LC/1
RF2 Rollie Fingers 03 UDA/5
RF3 Rollie Fingers 04 SSC/10
RHL1 Roy Halladay 03 40M/32 10.00 25.00
RHL2 Roy Halladay 03 HR/10
RHL3 Roy Halladay 04 DAS/10
RHL4 Roy Halladay 04 FP/10
RHL5 Roy Halladay 04 UD/32 10.00 25.00
RHL6 Roy Halladay 04 VIN/1
RHM1 R.Hammock 03 40M/35 6.00 15.00
RHM2 R.Hammock 03 PC/15 8.00 20.00
RHM3 R.Hammock 03 UDA/5
RHM4 R.Hammock 04 UD/30 6.00 15.00
RHM5 R.Hammock 04 VIN/7
RHR1 R.Hernandez 03 40M/55 4.00 10.00
RHR2 R.Hernandez 03 UDA/40 4.00 10.00
RI1 Raul Ibanez 04 FP/70 4.00 10.00
RI2 Raul Ibanez 04 UD/65 4.00 10.00
RI3 Raul Ibanez 04 VIN/70 4.00 10.00
RK1 Ralph Kiner 03 SP LC/20 15.00 40.00
RK2 Ralph Kiner 04 SSC/3
RO1 Roy Oswalt 03 40M/44 6.00 15.00
RO2 Roy Oswalt 03 HR/55 6.00 15.00
RO3 Roy Oswalt 03 SS/20 10.00 25.00
RO4 Roy Oswalt 04 UD/52 6.00 15.00
RR1 R.Roberts 03 SP LC/15 12.50 30.00
RR2 Robin Roberts 03 UDA/5
RR3 Robin Roberts 04 SSC/3
RW1 Rickie Weeks 03 UD/30 15.00 40.00
RW2 Rickie Weeks 04 FP/15 12.50 30.00
RW3 Rickie Weeks 04 VIN/50 6.00 15.00
RY1 Robin Yount 03 SP LC/20 50.00 100.00
RY2 Robin Yount 04 SSC/3
SG1 Shawn Green 03 CP/2
SG2 Shawn Green 03 HR/10
SG3 Shawn Green 03 SS/15 20.00 50.00
SG4 Shawn Green 03 UDA/5
SG5 Shawn Green 04 DAS/5
SG6 Shawn Green 04 FP/15 20.00 50.00
SG7 Shawn Green 04 UD/1
SG8 Shawn Green 04 VIN/15 20.00 50.00
SM1 S.Musial 03 SP LC/16 50.00 100.00
SM2 Stan Musial 03 UDA/6
SM3 Stan Musial 04 SSC/1
THO1 T.Hoffman 04 FP/67 10.00 25.00
THO2 T.Hoffman 04 UD/51 10.00 25.00
TH1 Travis Hafner 03 40M/32 6.00 15.00
TH2 Travis Hafner 03 HR/10
TH3 Travis Hafner 03 SPx/1
TH4 Travis Hafner 03 SS/32 6.00 15.00
TH5 Travis Hafner 03 UDA/5
TH6 Travis Hafner 04 VIN/10
TP1 Tony Perez 03 SP LC/20
TP2 Tony Perez 04 SSC/3
TS1 Tom Seaver 03 SP LC/15 30.00 60.00
TS2 Tom Seaver 03 UDA/6
TS3 Tom Seaver 04 SSC/2
VG1 Vlad Guerrero 03 CP/20 20.00 50.00
VG2 Vlad Guerrero 03 HR/27
VG3 Vlad Guerrero 03 SPx/34 20.00 50.00
VG4 Vlad Guerrero 03 SS/27 20.00 50.00
VG5 Vlad Guerrero 03 UDA/54 15.00 40.00
VG6 Vlad Guerrero 04 DAS/27 20.00 50.00
VG7 Vlad Guerrero 04 FP/28 20.00 50.00
VG8 Vlad Guerrero 04 UD/27
VG9 Vlad Guerrero 04 VIN/27 20.00 50.00
VW1 Vernon Wells 03 40M/15 12.50 30.00
VW2 Vernon Wells 03 CP/10
VW3 Vernon Wells 03 PC/10
VW4 Vernon Wells 03 SPx/10
VW5 Vernon Wells 03 SS/10
VW6 Vernon Wells 04 DAS/10
VW7 Vernon Wells 04 FP/10
VW8 Vernon Wells 04 UD/10
VW9 Vernon Wells 04 VIN/10
WE1 Willie Eyre 03 40M/45 4.00 10.00
WE2 W.Eyre 03 40M RWB/45 4.00 10.00
YB1 Yogi Berra 03 SP LC/23 30.00 60.00

2004 SP Authentic Chirography

Jorge Posada and Ken Griffey Jr. did not return their cards in time for pack out and those cards could be redeemed until June 4, 2007. It is interesting to note that Griffey did return his buy-backed cards in time for inclusion in this product.

STATED PRINT RUN 75 SERIAL #'d SETS

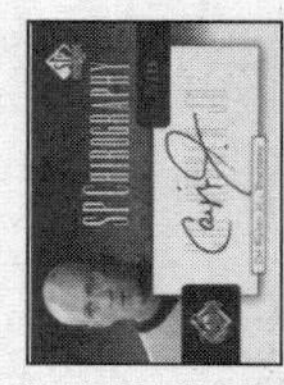

BASIC CHIRO. HAVE RED BACKGROUNDS
*DT w/NOTE: .5X TO 1.2X BASIC
*DT w/o NOTE: .4X TO 1X BASIC
DUO TONE PRINT RUN 75 SERIAL #'d SETS
MOST DT FEATURE UNIFORM # NOTATION
*BRONZE: .4X TO 1X BASIC
BRONZE PRINT RUN 65 SERIAL #'d SETS
*BRONZE DT w/NOTE: .5X TO 1.2X BASIC
*BRONZE DT w/o NOTE: .4X TO 1X BASIC
BRONZE DUO TONE PRINT RUN 60 #'d SETS
MOST BRONZE DT FEATURE TEAM NAMES
*SILVER: .4X TO 1X BASIC
SILVER PRINT RUN 60 SERIAL #'d SETS
*SILVER DT w/NOTE: .6X TO 1.5X BASIC
*SILVER DT w/o NOTE: .5X TO 1.2X BASIC
SILVER DT PRINT RUN 30 SERIAL #'d SETS
MOST SILVER DT HAVE KEY ACHIEVEMENT
OVERALL AUTO INSERT ODDS 1:12
AK Austin Kearns 5.00 12.00
BA Bobby Abreu 8.00 20.00
BB Bret Boone 12.50 30.00
BH Bo Hart 5.00 12.00
BS Ben Sheets 8.00 20.00
BW Brandon Webb 6.00 15.00
BZ Barry Zito 12.50 30.00
CB Carlos Beltran 8.00 20.00
CL Cliff Lee 5.00 12.00
CP Colin Porter 5.00 12.00
CR Cal Ripken 60.00 120.00
CW Chien-Ming Wang 75.00 150.00
DE Dennis Eckersley 12.50 30.00
DJ Derek Jeter 75.00 150.00
DW Dontrelle Willis 12.50 30.00
DY Delmon Young 12.50 30.00
EC Eric Chavez 8.00 20.00
EG Eric Gagne 12.50 30.00
GA Garret Anderson 8.00 20.00
HA Robby Hammock 5.00 12.00
HB Hank Blalock 8.00 20.00
HE Runelvys Hernandez 5.00 12.00
HI Bobby Hill 5.00 12.00
HR Horacio Ramirez 5.00 12.00
HY Roy Halladay 8.00 20.00
JB Josh Beckett 12.50 30.00
JG Juan Gonzalez 8.00 20.00
JJ Jacque Jones 11 8.00 20.00
JL Javy Lopez 12.50 30.00
JP Jorge Posada EXCH 12.50 30.00
JR Jose Reyes 8.00 20.00
JS Jae Weong Seo 8.00 20.00
JV Javier Vazquez 8.00 20.00
JW Jerome Williams 5.00 12.00
KG Ken Griffey Jr. EXCH 60.00 120.00
KW Kerry Wood 12.50 30.00
MC Miguel Cabrera 12.50 30.00
ML Mike Lowell 8.00 20.00
MP Mark Prior 12.50 30.00
MT Mark Teixeira 12.50 30.00
PA Corey Patterson 5.00 12.00
PI Mike Piazza 90.00 180.00
PL Paul Lo Duca 8.00 20.00
RB Rocco Baldelli 8.00 20.00
RO Roy Oswalt 8.00 20.00
RW Rickie Weeks 8.00 20.00
TH Travis Hafner 5.00 12.00
VW Vernon Wells 8.00 20.00
WE Willie Eyre 5.00 12.00

2004 SP Authentic Chirography Gold

*GOLD p/r 40: .5X TO 1.2X BASIC
STATED PRINT RUN 40 SERIAL #'d SETS
EDGAR/LEITER/SMOLTZ 75 #'d COPIES PER
*GLD DT p/r 20 w/NOTE: .6X TO 1.5X p/r 40
*GLD DT p/r20 w/o NOTE: .5X TO 1.2X p/r 40
*GOLD DT p/r 75: .4X TO 1X GOLD p/r 75
GOLD DT PRINT RUN 20 SERIAL #'d SETS
MOST GOLD DT HAVE KEY ACHIEVEMENT
OVERALL AUTO INSERT ODDS 1:12
EXCHANGE DEADLINE 06/04/07
AL Al Leiter/75 8.00 20.00
AR Alex Rodriguez 100.00 200.00
EM Edgar Martinez/75 12.50 30.00
SM John Smoltz/75 20.00 50.00

2004 SP Authentic Chirography Dual

A few cards were not ready in time for pack out and those cards could be exchanged until June 4, 2007.
OVERALL AUTO INSERT ODDS 1:12
STATED PRINT RUN 50 SERIAL #'d SETS
BC Bret Boone 30.00 60.00
Eric Chavez
BL Josh Beckett 30.00 60.00
Mike Lowell
BP Carlos Beltran 20.00 50.00
Corey Patterson
BT Hank Blalock 30.00 60.00
Mark Teixeira
EG Dennis Eckersley 30.00 60.00
Eric Gagne
HW Roy Halladay 20.00 50.00
Vernon Wells
JM Johnny Bench 175.00 300.00
Mike Piazza
KG Austin Kearns 60.00 120.00
Ken Griffey Jr. EXCH
PB Jorge Posada 60.00 120.00
Yogi Berra
RR Alex Rodriguez 300.00 500.00
Cal Ripken
SG Ichiro Suzuki 300.00 500.00
Ken Griffey Jr. EXCH
SM Ozzie Smith 125.00 200.00
Stan Musial
WC Dontrelle Willis 40.00 80.00
Miguel Cabrera
WJ Chien-Ming Wang 300.00 500.00
Derek Jeter
WR Kerry Wood 175.00 300.00
Nolan Ryan
WW Brandon Webb 30.00 60.00
Dontrelle Willis
YW Delmon Young 20.00 50.00
Rickie Weeks EXCH
ZC Barry Zito 30.00 60.00
Eric Chavez

2004 SP Authentic Chirography Hall of Famers

STATED PRINT RUN 40 SERIAL #'d SETS
*DUO TONE: .5X TO 1.2X BASIC
DUO TONE PRINT RUN 25 SERIAL #'d SETS
SOME DT FEATURE HOF NOTATION
OVERALL AUTO INSERT ODDS 1:12
AK Al Kaline 30.00 60.00
BD Bobby Doerr 10.00 25.00
BG Bob Gibson 15.00 40.00
BR B.Robinson UER B/W 15.00 40.00
CF Carlton Fisk 15.00 40.00
CY Carl Yastrzemski HOF 89 50.00 100.00
DE Dennis Eckersley 15.00 40.00
DS Duke Snider 15.00 40.00
HK Harmon Killebrew 30.00 60.00
JB Johnny Bench 30.00 60.00
KP Kirby Puckett 50.00 100.00
LA Luis Aparicio Hall of Famer 10.00 25.00
MI Monte Irvin 10.00 25.00
MS Mike Schmidt 60.00 120.00
NR Nolan Ryan 75.00 150.00
OS Ozzie Smith 50.00 100.00
PM Paul Molitor 10.00 25.00
PR Phil Rizzuto Hall of Famer 15.00 40.00
RK Ralph Kiner HOF 1975 10.00 25.00
RR Robin Roberts Hall of Famer 15.00 40.00
RY Robin Yount 50.00 100.00
SM Stan Musial 60.00 120.00
TP Tony Perez Hall of Famer 10.00 25.00
TS Tom Seaver 15.00 40.00
YB Yogi Berra 30.00 60.00

2004 SP Authentic Chirography Quad

OVERALL AUTO INSERT ODDS 1:12
STATED PRINT RUN 10 SERIAL #'d SETS
NO PRICING DUE TO SCARCITY
EXCHANGE DEADLINE 06/04/07
GRRS Bob Gibson
Nolan Ryan
Robin Roberts
Tom Seaver
RRRS Alex Rodriguez
Cal Ripken
Jose Reyes
Ozzie Smith
RTCW Jose Reyes
Mark Teixeira
Miguel Cabrera
Rickie Weeks EXCH
RYYM Cal Ripken
Carl Yastrzemski
Robin Yount
Stan Musial
SIRB Duke Snider
Monte Irvin
Nolan Ryan
Yogi Berra
WBCL Dontrelle Willis
Josh Beckett
Miguel Cabrera
Mike Lowell
WBWP Dontrelle Willis
Josh Beckett
Kerry Wood
Mark Prior
WJVP Chien-Ming Wang
Derek Jeter
Javier Vazquez
Jorge Posada
WPRS Kerry Wood
Mark Prior
Nolan Ryan
Tom Seaver
WWRW Brandon Webb
Dontrelle Willis
Horacio Ramirez
Jerome Williams

2004 SP Authentic Chirography Triple

A couple of cards were not totally ready at pack-out time and those cards could be exchanged until June 4, 2007.
OVERALL AUTO INSERT ODDS 1:12
STATED PRINT RUN 25 SERIAL #'d SETS
BWR Josh Beckett 150.00 250.00
Kerry Wood
Nolan Ryan EXCH
FBB Carlton Fisk 200.00 350.00
Johnny Bench
Yogi Berra
GSM Bob Gibson 175.00 300.00
Ozzie Smith
Stan Musial
JVB Derek Jeter 250.00 400.00
Javier Vazquez
Yogi Berra
PRC Colin Porter 75.00 150.00
Jose Reyes
Miguel Cabrera
RBT Alex Rodriguez 175.00 300.00
Hank Blalock
Mark Teixeira
RRR Alex Rodriguez 400.00 600.00
Cal Ripken
Phil Rizzuto EXCH
SJB Ichiro Suzuki 250.00 400.00
Jacque Jones
Rocco Baldelli
WLE Chien-Ming Wang 250.00 400.00
Cliff Lee
Willie Eyre
WPB Brandon Webb 75.00 150.00
Mark Prior
Josh Beckett
YYM Carl Yastrzemski 250.00 400.00
Robin Yount
Stan Musial
ZHO Barry Zito 150.00 250.00
Roy Halladay
Roy Oswalt

2004 SP Authentic USA Signatures 445

STATED PRINT RUN 445 SERIAL #'d SETS
*USA SIG 50: .6X TO 1.5X BASIC
USA SIG 50 PRINT RUN 50 #'d SETS
OVERALL AUTO INSERT ODDS 1:12
1 Ernie Young 4.00 10.00
2 Chris Burke 6.00 15.00
3 Jesse Crain 6.00 15.00
4 Justin Duchscherer 6.00 15.00
5 J.D. Durbin 4.00 10.00
6 Gerald Laird 6.00 15.00
7 John Grabow 4.00 10.00
8 Gabe Gross 6.00 15.00
9 J.J. Hardy 15.00 40.00
10 Jeremy Reed 6.00 15.00
11 Graham Koonce 4.00 10.00
12 Mike Lamb 4.00 10.00
13 Justin Leone 6.00 15.00
14 Ryan Madson 6.00 15.00
15 Joe Mauer 12.50 30.00
16 Todd Williams 4.00 10.00
17 Horacio Ramirez 4.00 10.00
18 Mike Rouse 4.00 10.00
19 Jason Stanford 4.00 10.00
20 John Van Benschoten 4.00 10.00
21 Grady Sizemore 12.50 30.00

2004 SP Authentic USA Signatures 50

9 J.J. Hardy 40.00 80.00

2005 SP Authentic

This set was released within two separate products . . SP Collection in October, 2005 (containing cards 1-100) and Upper Deck Update in February, 2006 (containing cards 101-186) . The SP Collection packs had five cards in each pack with an $6 SRP and those packs came 20 packs to a box and 16 boxes to a case. Upper Deck Update packs

contained 5 cards and carried a $4.99 SRP. 24 packs were issued in each box. Of note, cards 105, 115, 118-119, 142, 154, 161, 180, 183 and 186 do not exist.

COMP.BASIC SET (100) 10.00 25.00
COMMON CARD (1-100) .15 .40
COMMON RETIRED 1-100 .15 .40
1-100 ISSUED IN 05 SP COLLECTION PACKS
COMMON AUTO (101-186) 4.00 10.00
101-186 ODDS APPX 1:8 '05 UD UPDATE
101-186 PRINT RUN 185 SERIAL #'d SETS
105, 115, 118-119, 142, 154 DO NOT EXIST
161, 180, 183, 186 DO NOT EXIST
1 A.J. Burnett .15 .40
2 Aaron Rowand .15 .40
3 Adam Dunn .15 .40
4 Adrian Beltre .15 .40
5 Adrian Gonzalez .15 .40
6 Akinori Otsuka .15 .40
7 Albert Pujols .75 2.00
8 Andre Dawson .15 .40
9 Andruw Jones .25 .60
10 Aramis Ramirez .15 .40
11 Barry Larkin .25 .60
12 Ben Sheets .15 .40
13 Bo Jackson .40 1.00
14 Bobby Abreu .15 .40
15 Bobby Crosby .15 .40
16 Bronson Arroyo .15 .40
17 Cal Ripken 1.25 3.00
18 Carl Crawford .15 .40
19 Carlos Zambrano .15 .40
20 Casey Kotchman .15 .40
21 Cesar Izturis .15 .40
22 Chone Figgins .15 .40
23 Corey Patterson .15 .40
24 Craig Biggio .25 .60
25 Dale Murphy .25 .60
26 Dallas McPherson .15 .40
27 Danny Haren .15 .40
28 Darryl Strawberry .15 .40
29 David Ortiz .25 .60
30 David Wright .60 1.50
31 Derek Jeter .75 2.00
32 Derrek Lee .25 .60
33 Don Mattingly .75 2.00
34 Dwight Gooden .15 .40
35 Edgar Renteria .15 .40
36 Eric Chavez .15 .40
37 Eric Gagne .15 .40
38 Gary Sheffield .15 .40
39 Gavin Floyd .15 .40
40 Pedro Martinez .25 .60
41 Greg Maddux .60 1.50
42 Hank Blalock .15 .40
43 Huston Street .25 .60
44 J.D. Drew .15 .40
45 Jake Peavy .15 .40
46 Jake Westbrook .15 .40
47 Jason Bay .15 .40
48 Austin Kearns .15 .40
49 Jeremy Reed .15 .40
50 Jim Rice .15 .40
51 Jimmy Rollins .15 .40
52 Joe Blanton .15 .40
53 Joe Mauer .40 1.00
54 Johan Santana .40 1.00
55 John Smoltz .25 .60
56 Johnny Estrada .15 .40
57 Jose Reyes .15 .40
58 Ken Griffey Jr. .60 1.50
59 Kerry Wood .15 .40
60 Khalil Greene .25 .60
61 Marcus Giles .15 .40
62 Melvin Mora .15 .40
63 Mark Grace .25 .60
64 Mark Mulder .15 .40
65 Mark Prior .25 .60
66 Mark Teixeira .25 .60
67 Matt Clement .15 .40
68 Michael Young .15 .40
69 Miguel Cabrera .25 .60
70 Miguel Tejada .15 .40
71 Mike Piazza .40 1.00
72 Mike Schmidt .75 2.00
73 Nolan Ryan 1.00 2.50
74 Oliver Perez .15 .40
75 Nick Johnson .15 .40
76 Paul Molitor .15 .40
77 Rafael Palmeiro .25 .60
78 Randy Johnson .40 1.00
79 Reggie Jackson .25 .60
80 Rich Harden .15 .40
81 Rickie Weeks .15 .40
82 Robin Yount .40 1.00
83 Roger Clemens .60 1.50
84 Roy Oswalt .15 .40
85 Ryan Howard 1.00 2.50
86 Ryne Sandberg .75 2.00
87 Scott Kazmir .15 .40
88 Scott Rolen .25 .60
89 Sean Burroughs .15 .40
90 Sean Casey .15 .40
91 Shingo Takatsu .15 .40
92 Tim Hudson .15 .40
93 Tony Gwynn .50 1.25
94 Torii Hunter .15 .40
95 Travis Hafner .15 .40
96 Victor Martinez .15 .40
97 Vladimir Guerrero .40 1.00
98 Wade Boggs .25 .60
99 Will Clark .25 .60
100 Yadier Molina .15 .40
101 Adam Shabala AU RC 4.00 10.00
102 Ambiorix Burgos AU RC 4.00 10.00
103 Ambiorix Concepcion AU RC 4.00 10.00
104 Anibal Sanchez AU RC 15.00 40.00
106 Brandon McCarthy AU RC 15.00 40.00
107 Brian Burres AU RC 4.00 10.00
108 Carlos Ruiz AU RC 10.00 25.00
109 Casey Rogowski AU RC 6.00 15.00
110 Chad Orvella AU RC 4.00 10.00
111 Chris Resop AU RC 6.00 15.00
112 Chris Roberson AU RC 4.00 10.00
113 Chris Seddon AU RC 4.00 10.00
114 Colter Bean AU RC 6.00 15.00
116 Dave Gassner AU RC 4.00 10.00
117 Brian Anderson AU RC 15.00 40.00
120 Devon Lowery AU RC 4.00 10.00
121 Enrique Gonzalez AU RC 6.00 15.00
122 Eude Brito AU RC 4.00 10.00
123 Francisco Butto AU RC 4.00 10.00
124 Franquelis Osoria AU RC 4.00 10.00
125 Garrett Jones AU RC 4.00 10.00
126 Geovany Soto AU RC 75.00 150.00
127 Hayden Penn AU RC 10.00 25.00
128 Ismael Ramirez AU RC 4.00 10.00
129 Jared Gothreaux AU RC 4.00 10.00
130 Jason Hammel AU RC 4.00 10.00
131 Jeff Miller AU RC 4.00 10.00
132 Jeff Niemann AU RC 12.50 30.00
133 Joel Peralta AU RC 4.00 10.00
134 John Hattig AU RC 4.00 10.00
135 Jorge Campillo AU RC 4.00 10.00
136 Juan Morillo AU RC 4.00 10.00
137 Justin Verlander AU RC 90.00 150.00
138 Ryan Garko AU RC 25.00 50.00
139 Keiichi Yabu AU RC 6.00 15.00
140 Kendry Morales AU RC 30.00 60.00
141 Luis Hernandez AU RC 4.00 10.00
143 Luis O.Rodriguez AU RC 4.00 10.00
144 Luke Scott AU RC 30.00 60.00
145 Marcos Carvajal AU RC 4.00 10.00
146 Mark Woodyard AU RC 4.00 10.00
147 Matt A.Smith AU RC 4.00 10.00
148 Matthew Lindstrom AU RC 4.00 10.00
149 Miguel Negron AU RC 6.00 15.00
150 Mike Morse AU RC 8.00 20.00
151 Nate McLouth AU RC 50.00 100.00
152 Nelson Cruz AU RC 25.00 50.00
153 Nick Masset AU RC 4.00 10.00
155 Paulino Reynoso AU RC 4.00 10.00
156 Pedro Lopez AU RC 4.00 10.00
157 Pete Orr AU RC 4.00 10.00
158 Philip Humber AU RC 12.50 30.00
159 Prince Fielder AU RC 225.00 300.00
160 Randy Messenger AU RC 4.00 10.00
162 Raul Tablado AU RC 4.00 10.00
163 Ronny Paulino AU RC 10.00 25.00
164 Russ Rohlicek AU RC 4.00 10.00
165 Russell Martin AU RC 60.00 120.00
166 Scott Baker AU RC 6.00 15.00
167 Scott Munter AU RC 4.00 10.00
168 Sean Thompson AU RC 4.00 10.00
169 Sean Tracey AU RC 4.00 10.00
170 Shane Costa AU RC 4.00 10.00
171 Stephen Drew AU RC 30.00 60.00
172 Steve Schmoll AU RC 4.00 10.00
173 Tadahito Iguchi AU RC 20.00 50.00
174 Tony Giarratano AU RC 4.00 10.00
175 Tony Pena AU RC 4.00 10.00
176 Travis Bowyer AU RC 4.00 10.00
177 Ubaldo Jimenez AU RC 20.00 50.00
178 Wladimir Balentien AU RC 50.00 100.00
179 Yorman Bazardo AU RC 4.00 10.00
181 Ryan Zimmerman AU RC 150.00 225.00
182 Chris Denorfia AU RC 10.00 25.00
184 Jermaine Van Buren AU 4.00 10.00
185 Mark McLemore AU RC 4.00 10.00

2005 SP Authentic Gold

APPX AU ODDS 1:8 '05 UD UPDATE
STATED PRINT RUN 10 SERIAL #'d SETS
105, 115, 118-119, 142, 154 DO NOT EXIST
161, 180, 183, 186 DO NOT EXIST
NO PRICING DUE TO SCARCITY

2005 SP Authentic Jersey

STATED PRINT RUN 199 SERIAL #'d SETS
*GOLD: .5X TO 1.2X BASIC
GOLD PRINT RUN 99 SERIAL #'d SETS
ISSUED IN 05 SP COLLECTION PACKS
OVERALL GAME-USED ODDS 1:10
1 A.J. Burnett 2.00 5.00
2 Aaron Rowand 2.00 5.00
3 Adam Dunn 2.00 5.00
4 Adrian Beltre 2.00 5.00
5 Adrian Gonzalez 2.00 5.00
6 Akinori Otsuka 2.00 5.00
7 Albert Pujols 6.00 15.00
8 Andre Dawson 3.00 8.00
9 Andruw Jones 3.00 8.00
10 Aramis Ramirez 2.00 5.00
11 Barry Larkin 3.00 8.00
12 Ben Sheets 2.00 5.00
13 Bo Jackson 4.00 10.00
14 Bobby Abreu 2.00 5.00
15 Bobby Crosby 2.00 5.00
16 Bronson Arroyo 2.00 5.00
17 Cal Ripken Pants 8.00 20.00
18 Carl Crawford 2.00 5.00
19 Carlos Zambrano 2.00 5.00
20 Casey Kotchman 2.00 5.00
21 Cesar Izturis 2.00 5.00
22 Chone Figgins 2.00 5.00
23 Corey Patterson 2.00 5.00
24 Craig Biggio 3.00 8.00
25 Dale Murphy 4.00 10.00
26 Dallas McPherson 2.00 5.00
27 Danny Haren 2.00 5.00
28 Darryl Strawberry 3.00 8.00
29 David Ortiz 3.00 8.00
30 David Wright 4.00 10.00
31 Derek Jeter Pants 8.00 20.00
32 Derrek Lee 3.00 8.00
33 Don Mattingly 6.00 15.00
34 Dwight Gooden 3.00 8.00
35 Edgar Renteria 2.00 5.00
36 Eric Chavez 2.00 5.00
37 Eric Gagne 2.00 5.00
38 Gary Sheffield 2.00 5.00
39 Gavin Floyd 2.00 5.00
40 Pedro Martinez 3.00 8.00
41 Greg Maddux 4.00 10.00
42 Hank Blalock 2.00 5.00
43 Huston Street 3.00 8.00
44 J.D. Drew 2.00 5.00
45 Jake Peavy 2.00 5.00
46 Jake Westbrook 2.00 5.00
47 Jason Bay 2.00 5.00
48 Austin Kearns 2.00 5.00
49 Jeremy Reed 2.00 5.00
50 Jim Rice 3.00 8.00
51 Jimmy Rollins 2.00 5.00
52 Joe Blanton 2.00 5.00
53 Joe Mauer 4.00 10.00
54 Johan Santana 4.00 10.00
55 John Smoltz 3.00 8.00
56 Johnny Estrada 2.00 5.00
57 Jose Reyes 2.00 5.00
58 Ken Griffey Jr. 6.00 15.00
59 Kerry Wood 2.00 5.00
60 Khalil Greene 3.00 8.00
61 Marcus Giles 2.00 5.00
62 Melvin Mora 2.00 5.00
63 Mark Grace 4.00 10.00
64 Mark Mulder 2.00 5.00
65 Mark Prior 3.00 8.00
66 Mark Teixeira 3.00 8.00
67 Matt Clement 2.00 5.00
68 Michael Young 2.00 5.00
69 Miguel Cabrera 3.00 8.00
70 Miguel Tejada 2.00 5.00
71 Mike Piazza 4.00 10.00
72 Mike Schmidt 6.00 15.00
73 Nolan Ryan Pants 8.00 20.00
74 Oliver Perez 2.00 5.00
75 Nick Johnson 2.00 5.00
76 Paul Molitor 3.00 8.00
77 Rafael Palmeiro 4.00 10.00
78 Randy Johnson 4.00 10.00
79 Reggie Jackson 4.00 10.00
80 Rich Harden 2.00 5.00
81 Rickie Weeks 2.00 5.00
82 Robin Yount 4.00 10.00
83 Roger Clemens Pants 4.00 10.00
84 Roy Oswalt 2.00 5.00
85 Ryan Howard 10.00 25.00
86 Ryne Sandberg 6.00 15.00
87 Scott Kazmir 2.00 5.00
88 Scott Rolen 3.00 8.00
89 Sean Burroughs 2.00 5.00
90 Sean Casey 2.00 5.00
91 Shingo Takatsu 2.00 5.00
92 Tim Hudson 2.00 5.00
93 Tony Gwynn 4.00 10.00
94 Torii Hunter 2.00 5.00
95 Travis Hafner 2.00 5.00
96 Victor Martinez 2.00 5.00
97 Vladimir Guerrero 4.00 10.00
98 Wade Boggs 4.00 10.00
99 Will Clark 4.00 10.00
100 Yadier Molina 2.00 5.00

2005 SP Authentic Signature

PRINT RUNS B/WN 25-550 COPIES PER
GOLD PRINT RUN 10 SERIAL #'d SETS
NO GOLD PRICING DUE TO SCARCITY
ISSUED IN 05 SP COLLECTION PACKS
OVERALL AUTO ODDS 1:10
2 Aaron Rowand/550 10.00 25.00
3 Adam Dunn/25 10.00 25.00
4 Adrian Beltre/125 6.00 15.00
5 Adrian Gonzalez/550 4.00 10.00
6 Akinori Otsuka/475 6.00 15.00
7 Albert Pujols/25 150.00 250.00
8 Andre Dawson/125 6.00 15.00
9 Andruw Jones/25 20.00 50.00
10 Aramis Ramirez/475 6.00 15.00
11 Barry Larkin/125 15.00 40.00
12 Ben Sheets/350 6.00 15.00
13 Bo Jackson/25 40.00 80.00
15 Bobby Crosby/350 6.00 15.00
16 Bronson Arroyo/550 6.00 15.00
18 Carl Crawford/475 6.00 15.00
20 Casey Kotchman/550 6.00 15.00
21 Cesar Izturis/550 4.00 10.00
22 Chone Figgins/550 6.00 15.00
23 Corey Patterson/350 4.00 10.00
24 Craig Biggio/125 15.00 40.00
25 Dale Murphy/350 10.00 25.00
26 Dallas McPherson/550 4.00 10.00
27 Danny Haren/550 4.00 10.00
28 Darryl Strawberry/125 6.00 15.00
30 David Wright/350 20.00 50.00
31 Derek Jeter/150 90.00 150.00

32 Derrek Lee/350 10.00 25.00
33 Don Mattingly/25 40.00 80.00
34 Dwight Gooden/475 6.00 15.00
36 Eric Chavez/75 8.00 20.00
38 Gary Sheffield/25 15.00 40.00
39 Gavin Floyd/550 4.00 10.00
42 Hank Blalock/25 10.00 25.00
43 Huston Street/550 10.00 25.00
45 Jake Peavy/475 6.00 15.00
46 Jake Westbrook/550 4.00 10.00
47 Jason Bay/475 6.00 15.00
48 Austin Kearns/75 5.00 12.00
49 Jeremy Reed/550 4.00 10.00
50 Jim Rice/350 6.00 15.00
52 Joe Blanton/550 4.00 10.00
53 Joe Mauer/350 12.50 30.00
55 John Smoltz/25 20.00 50.00
57 Jose Reyes/475 6.00 15.00
59 Kerry Wood/25 10.00 25.00
60 Khalil Greene/350 10.00 25.00
62 Melvin Mora/475 6.00 15.00
63 Mark Grace/25 15.00 40.00
64 Mark Mulder/350 6.00 15.00
65 Mark Prior/25 10.00 25.00
66 Mark Teixeira/125 10.00 25.00
67 Matt Clement/350 6.00 15.00
68 Michael Young/475 6.00 15.00
69 Miguel Cabrera/125 10.00 25.00
70 Miguel Tejada/25 10.00 25.00
71 Mike Piazza/25 50.00 100.00
72 Mike Schmidt/25 40.00 80.00
73 Nolan Ryan/25 50.00 100.00
74 Oliver Perez/475 4.00 10.00
75 Nick Johnson/550 6.00 15.00
76 Paul Molitor/25 10.00 25.00
77 Rafael Palmeiro/25 15.00 40.00
78 Randy Johnson/25 50.00 100.00
79 Reggie Jackson/25 15.00 40.00
83 Roger Clemens/25 125.00 200.00
84 Roy Oswalt/125 6.00 15.00
85 Ryan Howard/550 20.00 50.00
86 Ryne Sandberg/25 40.00 80.00
87 Scott Kazmir/475 10.00 25.00
89 Sean Burroughs/475 4.00 10.00
91 Shingo Takatsu/550 6.00 15.00
92 Tim Hudson/25 10.00 25.00
93 Tony Gwynn/25 30.00 60.00
94 Torii Hunter/125 6.00 15.00
97 Vladimir Guerrero/25 40.00 80.00
98 Wade Boggs/25 15.00 40.00
99 Will Clark/25 20.00 50.00

2005 SP Authentic Signature Jersey Gold

ISSUED IN 05 SP COLLECTION PACKS
OVERALL PREMIUM AU-GU ODDS 1:20
STATED PRINT RUN 10 SERIAL #'d SETS
NO PRICING DUE TO SCARCITY

2005 SP Authentic Chirography

ISSUED IN 05 SP COLLECTION
OVERALL AUTO ODDS 1:10
STATED PRINT RUN 15 SERIAL #'d SETS
NO PRICING DUE TO SCARCITY
AB Adrian Beltre
AD Adam Dunn
AG Adrian Gonzalez
AK Austin Kearns
AO Akinori Otsuka
AP Albert Pujols
AR Aaron Rowand
BA Bronson Arroyo
BC Bobby Crosby
BJ Bo Jackson
BL Joe Blanton
BS Ben Sheets
CA Miguel Cabrera
CB Craig Biggio
CC Carl Crawford
CF Chone Figgins
CI Cesar Izturis
CK Casey Kotchman
CL Matt Clement
CP Corey Patterson
DA Andre Dawson
DG Dwight Gooden
DH Danny Haren
DJ Derek Jeter
DL Derrek Lee
DM Dale Murphy
DS Darryl Strawberry
DW David Wright
EC Eric Chavez
GF Gavin Floyd
GM Greg Maddux
GR Mark Grace
GS Gary Sheffield
HA Travis Hafner
HB Hank Blalock
HO Ryan Howard
HS Huston Street
HU Tim Hudson
JA Reggie Jackson
JB Jason Bay
JD J.D. Drew
JE Johnny Estrada
JM Joe Mauer
JO Andruw Jones
JP Jake Peavy
JR Jeremy Reed
JW Jake Westbrook
KH Khalil Greene
KW Kerry Wood
LA Barry Larkin
MA Don Mattingly
MC Dallas McPherson
MM Mark Mulder
MO Melvin Mora
MP Mark Prior
MS Mike Schmidt
MT Mark Teixeira
MY Michael Young
NJ Nick Johnson
NR Nolan Ryan
OP Oliver Perez
OS Roy Oswalt
PI Mike Piazza
PM Paul Molitor
RA Aramis Ramirez
RC Roger Clemens
RE Jose Reyes
RH Rich Harden
RI Jim Rice
RJ Randy Johnson
RP Rafael Palmeiro
RS Ryne Sandberg
SB Sean Burroughs
SK Scott Kazmir
SM John Smoltz
SR Scott Rolen
ST Shingo Takatsu
TE Miguel Tejada
TG Tony Gwynn
TH Torii Hunter
VG Vladimir Guerrero
WB Wade Boggs
WC Will Clark

2005 SP Authentic Chirography Triple

ISSUED IN 05 SP COLLECTION PACKS
OVERALL PREMIUM AU-GU ODDS 1:20
STATED PRINT RUN 5 SERIAL #'d SETS
NO PRICING DUE TO SCARCITY
BCB Adrian Beltre
Eric Chavez
Hank Blalock
BTY Hank Blalock
Mark Teixeira
Michael Young
DMR Andre Dawson
Dale Murphy
Jim Rice
JSG Bo Jackson
Darryl Strawberry
Tony Gwynn
JSH Andruw Jones
John Smoltz
Tim Hudson
JSJ Derek Jeter
Gary Sheffield
Randy Johnson
MGC Don Mattingly
Mark Grace
Will Clark
PJG Albert Pujols
Derek Jeter
Vladimir Guerrero
RJC Nolan Ryan
Randy Johnson
Roger Clemens
RPL Aramis Ramirez
Corey Patterson
Derrek Lee
RWR Aramis Ramirez
David Wright
Scott Rolen
SPP Ben Sheets
Jake Peavy
Oliver Perez
WSR David Wright
Mike Schmidt
Scott Rolen
WTC David Wright
Mark Teixeira
Miguel Cabrera

2005 SP Authentic Honors

ISSUED IN 05 SP COLLECTION PACKS
OVERALL INSERT ODDS 1:10
STATED PRINT RUN 299 SERIAL #'d SETS
AB Adrian Beltre 1.25 3.00
AP Albert Pujols 4.00 10.00
AR Aramis Ramirez 1.25 3.00
BC Bobby Crosby 1.25 3.00
BJ Bo Jackson 1.50 4.00
BL Barry Larkin 1.50 4.00
BO Jeremy Bonderman 1.25 3.00
BS Ben Sheets 1.25 3.00
BU B.J. Upton 1.25 3.00
CA Miguel Cabrera 1.50 4.00
CC Carl Crawford 1.25 3.00
CP Corey Patterson 1.25 3.00
CR Cal Ripken 6.00 15.00
CZ Carlos Zambrano 1.25 3.00
DG Dwight Gooden 1.25 3.00
DJ Derek Jeter 4.00 10.00
DM Dale Murphy 1.50 4.00
DO David Ortiz 1.50 4.00
DW David Wright 3.00 8.00
GR Khalil Greene 1.50 4.00
JB Jason Bay 1.25 3.00
JM Joe Mauer 1.50 4.00
JP Jake Peavy 1.25 3.00
JR Jimmy Rollins 1.25 3.00
JS Johan Santana 1.50 4.00
JW Jake Westbrook 1.25 3.00
KG Ken Griffey Jr. 3.00 8.00
MC Dallas McPherson 1.25 3.00
MG Marcus Giles 1.25 3.00
MO Justin Morneau 1.25 3.00
MS Mike Schmidt 3.00 8.00
MT Mark Teixeira 1.50 4.00
MY Michael Young 1.25 3.00
NR Nolan Ryan 4.00 10.00
OP Oliver Perez 1.25 3.00
PM Paul Molitor 1.25 3.00
RC Roger Clemens 3.00 8.00
RE Jose Reyes 1.25 3.00
RH Rich Harden 1.25 3.00
RS Ryne Sandberg 4.00 10.00
SK Scott Kazmir 1.25 3.00
SM John Smoltz 1.50 4.00
ST Shingo Takatsu 1.25 3.00
TE Miguel Tejada 1.25 3.00
TG Tony Gwynn 3.00 8.00
TH Travis Hafner 1.25 3.00
VM Victor Martinez 1.25 3.00
WB Wade Boggs 1.50 4.00
WC Will Clark 1.50 4.00
ZG Zack Greinke 1.25 3.00

2005 SP Authentic Honors Jersey

ISSUED IN 05 SP COLLECTION PACKS
OVERALL PREMIUM AU-GU ODDS 1:20
STATED PRINT RUN 130 SERIAL #'d SETS
AB Adrian Beltre 2.00 5.00
AP Albert Pujols 6.00 15.00
AR Aramis Ramirez 2.00 5.00
BC Bobby Crosby 2.00 5.00
BJ Bo Jackson 4.00 10.00
BL Barry Larkin 3.00 8.00
BO Jeremy Bonderman 2.00 5.00
BS Ben Sheets 2.00 5.00
BU B.J. Upton 2.00 5.00
CA Miguel Cabrera 3.00 8.00
CC Carl Crawford 2.00 5.00
CP Corey Patterson 2.00 5.00
CR Cal Ripken Pants 8.00 20.00
CZ Carlos Zambrano 2.00 5.00
DG Dwight Gooden 3.00 8.00
DJ Derek Jeter Pants 8.00 20.00
DM Dale Murphy 4.00 10.00
DO David Ortiz 3.00 8.00
DW David Wright 4.00 10.00
GR Khalil Greene 3.00 8.00
JB Jason Bay 2.00 5.00
JM Joe Mauer 4.00 10.00
JP Jake Peavy 2.00 5.00
JR Jimmy Rollins 2.00 5.00
JS Johan Santana 4.00 10.00
JW Jake Westbrook 2.00 5.00
KG Ken Griffey Jr. 6.00 15.00
MC Dallas McPherson 2.00 5.00
MG Marcus Giles 2.00 5.00
MO Justin Morneau 2.00 5.00
MS Mike Schmidt 6.00 15.00
MT Mark Teixeira 3.00 8.00
MY Michael Young 2.00 5.00
NR Nolan Ryan Pants 8.00 20.00
OP Oliver Perez 2.00 5.00
PM Paul Molitor 3.00 8.00
RC Roger Clemens Pants 4.00 10.00
RE Jose Reyes 2.00 5.00
RH Rich Harden 2.00 5.00
RS Ryne Sandberg 6.00 15.00
SK Scott Kazmir 2.00 5.00
SM John Smoltz 3.00 8.00
ST Shingo Takatsu 2.00 5.00
TE Miguel Tejada 2.00 5.00
TG Tony Gwynn 4.00 10.00
TH Travis Hafner 2.00 5.00
VM Victor Martinez 2.00 5.00
WB Wade Boggs 4.00 10.00
WC Will Clark 4.00 10.00
ZG Zack Greinke 2.00 5.00

2005 SP Authentic Honors Signature

ISSUED IN 05 SP COLLECTION PACKS
OVERALL PREMIUM AU-GU ODDS 1:20
STATED PRINT RUN 5 SERIAL #'d SETS
NO PRICING DUE TO SCARCITY
AB Adrian Beltre
AP Albert Pujols
AR Aramis Ramirez
BC Bobby Crosby
BJ Bo Jackson
BL Barry Larkin

BS Ben Sheets
BU B.J. Upton
CA Miguel Cabrera
CC Carl Crawford
CP Corey Patterson
DG Dwight Gooden
DJ Derek Jeter
DM Dale Murphy
DW David Wright
GR Khalil Greene
JB Jason Bay
JM Joe Mauer
JP Jake Peavy
JS Johan Santana
JW Jake Westbrook
MC Dallas McPherson
MO Justin Morneau
MS Mike Schmidt
MT Mark Teixeira
MY Michael Young
NR Nolan Ryan
OP Oliver Perez
PM Paul Molitor
RC Roger Clemens
RE Jose Reyes
RH Rich Harden
RS Ryne Sandberg
SK Scott Kazmir
SM John Smoltz
ST Shingo Takatsu
TE Miguel Tejada
TG Tony Gwynn
TH Travis Hafner
WB Wade Boggs
WC Will Clark
ZG Zack Greinke

2006 SP Authentic

This 300-card set was released in December, 2006. The set was issued in five-card packs, with an $4.99 SRP, which came 24 packs to a box and 12 boxes to a case. The first 100 cards of the set all feature veterans while cards 101-200 were inserted at a stated rate of one in eight and were issued to a stated print run of 899 serial numbered cards. The final 100-cards in this set all feature 2006 rookies and had between 125 and 899 serial numbered copies produced. These autograph cards were issued at a stated rate of one in 16. A few players did not return their signatures in time for pack out and those autographs could be redeemed until December 5, 2009.

COMP.SET w/o SP's (100) 6.00 15.00
101-200 STATED ODDS 1:8
101-200 PRINT RUN 899 #'d SETS
201-300 AU STATED ODDS 1:16
201-300 AU PRINTS B/WN 125-899 PER
EXCH: 214/235/242/247/249/253/277
EXCH: 279/280/291
EXCHANGE DEADLINE 12/05/09
1 Erik Bedard .15 .40
2 Corey Patterson .15 .40
3 Ramon Hernandez .15 .40
4 Kris Benson .15 .40
5 Miguel Batista .15 .40
6 Orlando Hudson .15 .40
7 Shawn Green .15 .40
8 Jeff Francoeur .40 1.00
9 Marcus Giles .15 .40
10 Edgar Renteria .15 .40
11 Tim Hudson .15 .40
12 Tim Wakefield .15 .40
13 Mark Loretta .15 .40
14 Kevin Youkilis .15 .40
15 Mike Lowell .15 .40
16 Coco Crisp .15 .40
17 Tadahito Iguchi .15 .40
18 Scott Podsednik .15 .40
19 Jermaine Dye .15 .40
20 Jose Contreras .15 .40
21 Carlos Zambrano .15 .40
22 Aramis Ramirez .15 .40
23 Jacque Jones .15 .40
24 Austin Kearns .15 .40
25 Felipe Lopez .15 .40
26 Brandon Phillips .15 .40
27 Aaron Harang .15 .40
28 Cliff Lee .15 .40
29 Jhonny Peralta .15 .40
30 Jason Michaels .15 .40
31 Clint Barmes .15 .40
32 Brad Hawpe .15 .40
33 Aaron Cook .15 .40
34 Kenny Rogers .15 .40
35 Carlos Guillen .15 .40
36 Brian Moehler .15 .40
37 Andy Pettitte .25 .60
38 Wandy Rodriguez .15 .40
39 Morgan Ensberg .15 .40
40 Preston Wilson .15 .40
41 Mark Grudzielanek .15 .40
42 Angel Berroa .15 .40
43 Jeremy Affeldt .15 .40
44 Zack Greinke .15 .40
45 Orlando Cabrera .15 .40
46 Garret Anderson .15 .40
47 Ervin Santana .15 .40
48 Derek Lowe .15 .40
49 Nomar Garciaparra .40 1.00
50 J.D. Drew .15 .40
51 Rafael Furcal .15 .40
52 Rickie Weeks .15 .40
53 Geoff Jenkins .15 .40
54 Bill Hall .15 .40
55 Chris Capuano .15 .40
56 Derrick Turnbow .15 .40
57 Justin Morneau .15 .40
58 Michael Cuddyer .15 .40
59 Luis Castillo .15 .40
60 Hideki Matsui .40 1.00
61 Jason Giambi .15 .40
62 Jorge Posada .25 .60
63 Mariano Rivera .40 1.00
64 Billy Wagner .15 .40
65 Carlos Delgado .15 .40
66 Jose Reyes .40 1.00
67 Nick Swisher .15 .40
68 Bobby Crosby .15 .40
69 Frank Thomas .40 1.00
70 Ryan Howard .60 1.50
71 Pat Burrell .15 .40
72 Jimmy Rollins .15 .40
73 Craig Wilson .15 .40
74 Freddy Sanchez .15 .40
75 Sean Casey .15 .40
76 Mike Piazza .40 1.00
77 Dave Roberts .15 .40
78 Chris Young .15 .40
79 Noah Lowry .15 .40
80 Armando Benitez .15 .40
81 Pedro Feliz .15 .40
82 Jose Lopez .15 .40
83 Adrian Beltre .15 .40
84 Jamie Moyer .15 .40
85 Jason Isringhausen .15 .40
86 Jason Marquis .15 .40
87 David Eckstein .15 .40
88 Juan Encarnacion .15 .40
89 Julio Lugo .15 .40
90 Ty Wigginton .15 .40
91 Jorge Cantu .15 .40
92 Akinori Otsuka .15 .40
93 Hank Blalock .15 .40
94 Kevin Mench .15 .40
95 Lyle Overbay .15 .40
96 Shea Hillenbrand .15 .40
97 B.J. Ryan .15 .40
98 Tony Armas .15 .40
99 Chad Cordero .15 .40
100 Jose Guillen .15 .40
101 Miguel Tejada 1.50 4.00
102 Brian Roberts 1.50 4.00
103 Melvin Mora 1.50 4.00
104 Brandon Webb 1.50 4.00
105 Chad Tracy 1.50 4.00
106 Luis Gonzalez 1.50 4.00
107 Andruw Jones 2.00 5.00
108 Chipper Jones 2.00 5.00
109 John Smoltz 2.00 5.00
110 Curt Schilling 2.00 5.00
111 Josh Beckett 1.50 4.00
112 David Ortiz 2.00 5.00
113 Manny Ramirez 2.00 5.00
114 Jason Varitek 2.00 5.00
115 Jim Thome 2.00 5.00
116 Paul Konerko 1.50 4.00
117 Javier Vazquez 1.50 4.00
118 Mark Prior 1.50 4.00
119 Derrek Lee 1.50 4.00
120 Greg Maddux 3.00 8.00
121 Ken Griffey Jr. 3.00 8.00
122 Adam Dunn 1.50 4.00
123 Bronson Arroyo 2.00 5.00
124 Travis Hafner 1.50 4.00
125 Victor Martinez 1.50 4.00
126 Grady Sizemore 2.00 5.00
127 C.C. Sabathia 1.50 4.00
128 Todd Helton 2.00 5.00
129 Matt Holliday 2.00 5.00
130 Garrett Atkins 1.50 4.00
131 Jeff Francis 1.50 4.00
132 Jeremy Bonderman 1.50 4.00
133 Ivan Rodriguez 2.00 5.00
134 Chris Shelton 1.50 4.00
135 Magglio Ordonez 1.50 4.00
136 Dontrelle Willis 1.50 4.00
137 Miguel Cabrera 2.00 5.00
138 Roger Clemens 3.00 8.00
139 Roy Oswalt 1.50 4.00
140 Lance Berkman 1.50 4.00
141 Reggie Sanders 1.50 4.00
142 Vladimir Guerrero 2.00 5.00
143 Bartolo Colon 1.50 4.00
144 Chone Figgins 1.50 4.00
145 Francisco Rodriguez 1.50 4.00
146 Brad Penny 1.50 4.00
147 Jeff Kent 1.50 4.00
148 Eric Gagne 1.50 4.00
149 Carlos Lee 1.50 4.00
150 Ben Sheets 1.50 4.00
151 Johan Santana 2.00 5.00
152 Torii Hunter 1.50 4.00
153 Joe Nathan 1.50 4.00
154 Alex Rodriguez 3.00 8.00
155 Derek Jeter 4.00 10.00
156 Randy Johnson 2.00 5.00
157 Johnny Damon 2.00 5.00
158 Mike Mussina 2.00 5.00
159 Pedro Martinez 2.00 5.00
160 Tom Glavine 2.00 5.00
161 David Wright 3.00 8.00
162 Carlos Beltran 1.50 4.00
163 Rich Harden 1.50 4.00
164 Barry Zito 1.50 4.00
165 Eric Chavez 1.50 4.00
166 Huston Street 1.50 4.00
167 Bobby Abreu 1.50 4.00
168 Chase Utley 2.00 5.00
169 Brett Myers 1.50 4.00
170 Jason Bay 1.50 4.00
171 Zach Duke 1.50 4.00
172 Jake Peavy 1.50 4.00
173 Brian Giles 1.50 4.00
174 Khalil Greene 2.00 5.00
175 Trevor Hoffman 1.50 4.00
176 Jason Schmidt 1.50 4.00
177 Randy Winn 1.50 4.00
178 Omar Vizquel 2.00 5.00
179 Kenji Johjima 3.00 8.00
180 Ichiro Suzuki 3.00 8.00
181 Richie Sexson 1.50 4.00
182 Felix Hernandez 2.00 5.00
183 Albert Pujols 4.00 10.00
184 Chris Carpenter 2.00 5.00
185 Jim Edmonds 2.00 5.00
186 Scott Rolen 2.00 5.00
187 Carl Crawford 1.50 4.00
188 Scott Kazmir 1.50 4.00
189 Jonny Gomes 1.50 4.00
190 Mark Teixeira 2.00 5.00
191 Michael Young 1.50 4.00
192 Kevin Millwood 1.50 4.00
193 Vernon Wells 1.50 4.00
194 Troy Glaus 1.50 4.00
195 Roy Halladay 1.50 4.00
196 Alex Rios 1.50 4.00
197 Nick Johnson 1.50 4.00
198 Livan Hernandez 1.50 4.00
199 Alfonso Soriano 1.50 4.00
200 Jose Vidro 1.50 4.00
201 Aaron Rakers AU/399 (RC) 3.00 8.00
202 Angel Pagan AU/399 (RC) 6.00 15.00
203 Ben Hendrickson AU/399 (RC) 3.00 8.00
204 Bobby Livingston AU/399 (RC) 3.00 8.00
205 Darrell Rasner AU/399 (RC) 3.00 8.00
206 Brian Bannister AU/399 (RC) 12.50 30.00
207 Brian Wilson AU/899 RC 3.00 8.00
208 Bobby Keppel AU/199 (RC) 6.00 15.00
209 Choo Freeman AU/399 (RC) 3.00 8.00
210 Chris Booker AU/899 (RC) 3.00 8.00
211 Chris Britton AU/399 (RC) 4.00 10.00
212 Chris Demaria AU/329 RC 4.00 10.00
213 Chris Resop AU/899 (RC) 3.00 8.00
214 Tony Gwynn Jr. AU/399 (RC) 30.00 60.00
215 Eric Reed AU/399 (RC) 3.00 8.00
216 Fabio Castro AU/399 RC 8.00 20.00
217 Fernando Nieve AU/299 (RC) 4.00 10.00
218 Freddie Bynum AU/399 (RC) 3.00 8.00
219 Guillermo Quiroz AU/399 (RC) 3.00 8.00
220 Hong-Chih Kuo AU/899 (RC) 30.00 60.00
221 Ryan Theriot AU/399 RC 30.00 60.00
222 Jack Taschner AU/899 (RC) 3.00 8.00
223 Jason Bergmann AU/899 (RC) 3.00 8.00
224 Jason Hammel AU/899 (RC) 3.00 8.00
225 Jeff Harris AU/399 RC 3.00 8.00
226 Jeremy Accardo AU/399 RC 4.00 10.00
227 Ty Taubenheim AU/399 RC 12.50 30.00
228 Joel Zumaya AU/399 (RC) 15.00 40.00
229 John Koronka AU/399 (RC) 3.00 8.00
230 Erick Aybar AU/399 (RC) 3.00 8.00
231 Jordan Tata AU/399 RC 6.00 15.00
232 Russell Martin AU/399 (RC) 15.00 40.00
233 Josh Rupe AU/399 (RC) 3.00 8.00
234 Kevin Frandsen AU/399 (RC) 6.00 15.00
235 Martin Prado AU/399 (RC) 6.00 15.00
236 Matt Capps AU/399 (RC) 3.00 8.00
237 Agustin Montero AU/199 (RC) 4.00 10.00
238 Mike Thompson AU/399 RC 3.00 8.00
239 Nate McLouth AU/399 (RC) 8.00 20.00
240 Peter Moylan AU/399 RC 3.00 8.00
241 Reggie Abercrombie AU/399 (RC) 3.00 8.00
242 Carlos Quentin AU/399 (RC) 8.00 20.00
243 Ron Flores AU/399 RC 3.00 8.00
244 Ryan Shealy AU/399 (RC) 8.00 20.00
245 Mike Rouse AU/399 (RC) 3.00 8.00
246 Santiago Ramirez AU/399 (RC) 3.00 8.00
247 Clay Hensley AU/399 (RC) 3.00 8.00
248 Skip Schumaker AU/399 (RC) 4.00 10.00
249 Eliezer Alfonzo AU/899 RC 3.00 8.00
250 Steve Stemle AU/399 RC 3.00 8.00
251 Tim Hamulack AU/399 (RC) 3.00 8.00
252 Tony Pena Jr. AU/399 (RC) 4.00 10.00
253 Emiliano Fruto AU/899 RC 3.00 8.00
254 Wil Nieves AU/399 (RC) 4.00 10.00
255 Joey Devine AU/399 RC 4.00 10.00
256 Adam Wainwright AU/399 (RC) 10.00 25.00
257 Andre Ethier AU/399 (RC) 10.00 25.00
258 Ben Johnson AU/399 (RC) 3.00 8.00
259 Boone Logan AU/399 RC 6.00 15.00
260 Chris Denorfia AU/899 (RC) 4.00 10.00
261 Alay Soler AU/299 RC 6.00 15.00
262 Cody Ross AU/899 (RC) 3.00 8.00
263 David Gassner AU/399 (RC) 3.00 8.00
264 Fausto Carmona AU/399 (RC) 15.00 40.00
265 Jeremy Sowers AU/299 (RC) 10.00 25.00
266 Jason Kubel AU/399 (RC) 4.00 10.00
267 John Van Benschoten AU/399 (RC) 3.00 8.00
268 Jose Capellan AU/399 (RC) 3.00 8.00
269 Josh Wilson AU/399 (RC) 3.00 8.00
270 Kelly Shoppach AU/399 (RC) 3.00 8.00
271 Macay McBride AU/399 (RC) 4.00 10.00
272 Matt Cain AU/399 (RC) 10.00 25.00
273 Mike Jacobs AU/399 (RC) 6.00 15.00
274 Paul Maholm AU/399 (RC) 4.00 10.00
275 Chad Billingsley AU/399 (RC) 10.00 25.00
276 Ruddy Lugo AU/399 (RC) 3.00 8.00
277 Jon Lester AU/399 RC 30.00 60.00
278 Sean Marshall AU/383 (RC) 10.00 25.00
279 Melky Cabrera AU/399 (RC) 15.00 40.00
280 Yusmeiro Petit AU/399 (RC) 4.00 10.00
281 Anderson Hernandez AU/299 (RC) 4.00 10.00
282 Brian Anderson AU/699 (RC) 4.00 10.00
283 Cole Hamels AU/299 (RC) 60.00 120.00
284 Boof Bonser AU/299 (RC) 6.00 15.00
285 Dan Uggla AU/199 (RC) 20.00 50.00
286 Francisco Liriano AU/299 (RC) 15.00 40.00
287 Hanley Ramirez AU/199 (RC) 30.00 60.00
288 Ian Kinsler AU/299 (RC) 6.00 15.00
289 Jeremy Hermida AU/299 (RC) 6.00 15.00
290 Jonathan Papelbon AU/199 (RC) 30.00 60.00
291 Jered Weaver AU/199 (RC) 15.00 40.00
292 Josh Johnson AU/299 (RC) 6.00 15.00
293 Josh Willingham AU/199 (RC) 6.00 15.00
294 Justin Verlander AU/199 (RC) 40.00 80.00
295 Stephen Drew AU/299 (RC) 12.50 30.00
296 Prince Fielder AU/125 (RC) 60.00 120.00
297 Ryan Zimmerman AU/199 (RC) 40.00 70.00
298 Takashi Saito AU/283 RC 15.00 40.00
299 Taylor Buchholz AU/299 (RC) 4.00 10.00
300 Conor Jackson AU/299 (RC) 6.00 15.00

2006 SP Authentic Rookie Signatures Platinum

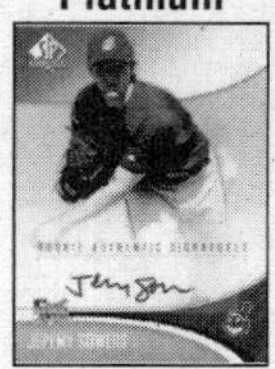

RANDOM INSERTS IN PACKS
STATED PRINT RUN 1 SERIAL #'d SET
NO PRICING DUE TO SCARCITY
CARD 242 DOES NOT EXIST

2006 SP Authentic Baseball Heroes

COMPLETE SET (70) 50.00 100.00
STATED ODDS 1:4
1 Albert Pujols 2.00 5.00
2 Andruw Jones 1.00 2.50
3 Aramis Ramirez .60 1.50
4 Brian Roberts .60 1.50
5 Carl Crawford .60 1.50
6 Carlos Lee .60 1.50
7 Vladimir Guerrero 1.00 2.50
8 Chris Carpenter .60 1.50
9 Craig Biggio 1.00 2.50
10 David Ortiz 1.00 2.50
11 David Wright 1.50 4.00
12 Derrek Lee .60 1.50
13 Dontrelle Willis .60 1.50
14 Felix Hernandez 1.00 2.50
15 Garrett Atkins .60 1.50
16 Grady Sizemore 1.00 2.50
17 Huston Street .60 1.50
18 Jake Peavy .60 1.50
19 Jason Bay .60 1.50
20 Joe Mauer 1.00 2.50
21 John Smoltz 1.00 2.50
22 Jonny Gomes .60 1.50
23 Jorge Cantu .60 1.50
24 Ken Griffey Jr. 1.50 4.00
25 Marcus Giles .60 1.50
26 Mark Teixeira 1.00 2.50
27 Matt Cain .60 1.50
28 Michael Young .60 1.50
29 Miguel Cabrera 1.00 2.50
30 Johan Santana 1.00 2.50
31 Nick Swisher .60 1.50
32 Prince Fielder 1.50 4.00
33 Joe Blanton .60 1.50
34 Roy Oswalt .60 1.50
35 Ryan Howard 1.50 4.00
36 Scott Kazmir .60 1.50
37 Tadahito Iguchi .60 1.50
38 Travis Hafner .60 1.50
39 Victor Martinez .60 1.50
40 Jose Reyes .60 1.50
41 Chris Carpenter 2.00 5.00
Albert Pujols
42 Albert Pujols 2.00 5.00
Miguel Cabrera
43 Ken Griffey Jr. 1.50 4.00
Andruw Jones
44 Derrek Lee .60 1.50
Aramis Ramirez
45 Ryan Howard 1.50 4.00
Prince Fielder
46 Roy Oswalt .60 1.50
Jake Peavy
47 Craig Biggio .60 1.50
Morgan Ensberg
48 Travis Hafner 1.00 2.50
David Ortiz
49 Derek Jeter 2.00 5.00
David Wright
50 Ken Griffey Jr. 2.00 5.00
Derek Jeter
51 Derek Jeter 2.00 5.00
Michael Young
52 Scott Kazmir .60 1.50
Dontrelle Willis
53 Grady Sizemore 1.00 2.50
Jason Bay
54 Michael Young 1.00 2.50
Mark Teixeira
55 Brian Roberts .60 1.50
Tadahito Iguchi
56 Chien-Ming Wang 1.50 4.00
Matt Cain
Felix Hernandez
57 Derrek Lee 2.00 5.00
Albert Pujols
Mark Teixeira
58 Ken Griffey Jr. 2.00 5.00
Albert Pujols
Miguel Cabrera
59 Andruw Jones 1.00 2.50
John Smoltz
Marcus Giles
60 Kerry Wood .60 1.50
Derrek Lee
Aramis Ramirez
61 Aramis Ramirez 1.50 4.00
Morgan Ensberg
David Wright
62 Carl Crawford .60 1.50
Jorge Cantu
Jonny Gomes
63 John Smoltz 1.00 2.50
Chris Carpenter
Jake Peavy
64 Travis Hafner 1.00 2.50
Victor Martinez
Grady Sizemore
65 David Ortiz 1.50 4.00
Ryan Howard
Prince Fielder
66 John Smoltz 1.00 2.50
Chris Carpenter
Jake Peavy
Dontrelle Willis
67 Ken Griffey Jr. 2.00 5.00
Derek Jeter
David Ortiz
Albert Pujols
68 Andruw Jones 1.00 2.50
Derrek Lee
David Ortiz
Mark Teixeira
69 Craig Biggio .60 1.50
Brian Roberts
Marcus Giles
Tadahito Iguchi
70 David Wright 1.50 4.00
Mark Teixeira
Miguel Cabrera
Jason Bay

2006 SP Authentic By the Letter

STATED ODDS 1:24
PRINT RUNS B/WN 4-400 COPIES PER
EXCH: AJ, AR, CS, CZ, FH, FH2, GM, HO
EXCH: HU, JM, JR, JV, JW, KG, KG2, KG3
EXCH: KG4, KM, KW, MT, SM, TE
EXCHANGE DEADLINE 12/05/09
ABB A.J. Burnett B/50 20.00 40.00
ABE A.J. Burnett E/50 20.00 40.00
ABN A.J. Burnett N/50 20.00 40.00
ABR A.J. Burnett R/50 20.00 40.00
ABT A.J. Burnett T/100 20.00 40.00
ABU A.J. Burnett U/50 20.00 40.00
ADD Adam Dunn D/50 30.00 60.00
ADN Adam Dunn N/100 30.00 60.00
ADU Adam Dunn U/50 30.00 60.00
AGG Tony Gwynn Jr. G/150 20.00 40.00
AGN Tony Gwynn Jr. N/300 20.00 40.00
AGW Tony Gwynn Jr. W/150 20.00 40.00
AGY Tony Gwynn Jr. Y/150 20.00 40.00
AJE Andruw Jones E/20 60.00 120.00
AJJ Andruw Jones J/20 60.00 120.00
AJN Andruw Jones N/20 60.00 120.00
AJO Andruw Jones O/20 60.00 120.00
AJS Andruw Jones S/20 60.00 120.00
APJ Albert Pujols J/5 350.00 500.00
APL Albert Pujols L/5 350.00 500.00
APO Albert Pujols O/5 350.00 500.00
APP Albert Pujols P/5 350.00 500.00
APS Albert Pujols S/5 350.00 500.00
APU Albert Pujols U/5 350.00 500.00
AP2M Albert Pujols MVP M/10 350.00 500.00
AP2P Albert Pujols MVP P/10 350.00 500.00
AP2V Albert Pujols MVP V/10 350.00 500.00
ARI Alex Rios I/100 20.00 40.00
ARO Alex Rios O/100 20.00 40.00
ARR Alex Rios R/100 20.00 40.00
ARS Alex Rios S/100 20.00 40.00
BAA Bronson Arroyo A/80 20.00 40.00
BAO Bronson Arroyo O/160 20.00 40.00
BAR Bronson Arroyo R/160 20.00 40.00
BAY Bronson Arroyo Y/80 20.00 40.00
BIB Chad Billingsley B/75 20.00 40.00
BIE Chad Billingsley E/75 20.00 40.00
BIG Chad Billingsley G/75 20.00 40.00
BII Chad Billingsley I/150 20.00 40.00
BIL Chad Billingsley L/225 20.00 40.00
BIN Chad Billingsley N/75 20.00 40.00
BIS Chad Billingsley S/75 20.00 40.00
BIY Chad Billingsley Y/75 20.00 40.00
BRB Brian Roberts B/14 40.00 80.00
BRE Brian Roberts E/14 40.00 80.00
BRO Brian Roberts O/14 40.00 80.00
BRR Brian Roberts R/28 40.00 80.00
BRS Brian Roberts S/14 40.00 80.00
BRT Brian Roberts T/14 40.00 80.00
BSE Ben Sheets E/250 20.00 40.00
BSH Ben Sheets H/125 20.00 40.00
BSS Ben Sheets S/250 20.00 40.00
BST Ben Sheets T/125 20.00 40.00
BUN B.J. Upton N/20 25.00 50.00
BUO B.J. Upton O/20 25.00 50.00
BUP B.J. Upton P/20 25.00 50.00
BUT B.J. Upton T/20 25.00 50.00
BUU B.J. Upton U/20 25.00 50.00
CBB Craig Biggio B/55 40.00 80.00
CBG Craig Biggio G/110 40.00 80.00
CBI Craig Biggio I/110 40.00 80.00
CBO Craig Biggio O/55 40.00 80.00
CCA Chris Carpenter A/4 40.00 80.00
CCC Chris Carpenter C/4 40.00 80.00
CCE Chris Carpenter E/8 40.00 80.00
CCN Chris Carpenter N/4 40.00 80.00
CCP Chris Carpenter P/4 40.00 80.00
CCR Chris Carpenter R/8 40.00 80.00
CCT Chris Carpenter T/4 40.00 80.00
CC2C Chris Carpenter CY C/8 40.00 80.00
CC2G Chris Carpenter CY G/8 40.00 80.00
CC2N Chris Carpenter CY N/8 40.00 80.00
CC2O Chris Carpenter CY O/8 40.00 80.00
CC2U Chris Carpenter CY U/8 40.00 80.00
CC2Y Chris Carpenter CY Y/16 40.00 80.00
CHA Craig Hansen A/30 30.00 60.00
CHE Craig Hansen E/30 30.00 60.00
CHH Craig Hansen H/30 30.00 60.00
CHN Craig Hansen N/60 30.00 60.00
CHS Craig Hansen S/30 30.00 60.00
COA Cole Hamels A/120 40.00 80.00
COE Cole Hamels E/120 40.00 80.00
COH Cole Hamels H/120 40.00 80.00
COL Cole Hamels L/120 40.00 80.00
COM Cole Hamels M/120 40.00 80.00
COS Cole Hamels S/120 40.00 80.00
CSA C.C. Sabathia A/120 20.00 40.00
CSB C.C. Sabathia B/40 20.00 40.00
CSH C.C. Sabathia H/40 20.00 40.00
CSI C.C. Sabathia I/40 20.00 40.00
CSS C.C. Sabathia S/40 20.00 40.00
CST C.C. Sabathia T/40 20.00 40.00
CUE Chase Utley E/25 75.00 150.00
CUL Chase Utley L/25 75.00 150.00
CUT Chase Utley T/25 75.00 150.00
CUU Chase Utley U/25 75.00 150.00
CUY Chase Utley Y/25 75.00 150.00
CZA Carlos Zambrano A/34 50.00 100.00
CZB Carlos Zambrano B/17 50.00 100.00
CZM Carlos Zambrano M/17 50.00 100.00
CZN Carlos Zambrano N/17 50.00 100.00
CZO Carlos Zambrano O/17 50.00 100.00
CZR Carlos Zambrano R/17 50.00 100.00
CZZ Carlos Zambrano Z/17 50.00 100.00
DHA Danny Haren A/180 15.00 30.00
DHE Danny Haren E/180 15.00 30.00
DHH Danny Haren H/180 15.00 30.00
DHN Danny Haren N/180 15.00 30.00
DHR Danny Haren R/180 15.00 30.00
DJE Derek Jeter E/12 300.00 500.00
DJJ Derek Jeter J/6 300.00 500.00
DJR Derek Jeter R/6 300.00 500.00
DJT Derek Jeter T/6 300.00 500.00
DJ2A Derek Jeter Captain A/10 300.00 500.00
DJ2C Derek Jeter Captain C/5 300.00 500.00
DJ2I Derek Jeter Captain I/5 300.00 500.00
DJ2N Derek Jeter Captain N/5 300.00 500.00
DJ2P Derek Jeter Captain P/5 300.00 500.00
DJ2T Derek Jeter Captain T/5 300.00 500.00
DLE Derrek Lee E/400 25.00 50.00
DLL Derrek Lee L/200 25.00 50.00
DUA Dan Uggla A/100 12.50 30.00
DUG Dan Uggla G/200 12.50 30.00
DUL Dan Uggla L/100 12.50 30.00
DUU Dan Uggla U/100 12.50 30.00
DWI Dontrelle Willis I/300 15.00 30.00
DWL Dontrelle Willis L/300 15.00 30.00
DWS Dontrelle Willis S/150 15.00 30.00
DWW Dontrelle Willis W/150 15.00 30.00
ECA Eric Chavez A/75 20.00 40.00
ECC Eric Chavez C/75 20.00 40.00
ECE Eric Chavez E/75 20.00 40.00
ECH Eric Chavez H/75 20.00 40.00
ECV Eric Chavez V/75 20.00 40.00
ECZ Eric Chavez Z/75 20.00 40.00
FHA Felix Hernandez A/40 30.00 60.00
FHD Felix Hernandez D/40 30.00 60.00
FHE Felix Hernandez E/80 30.00 60.00
FHH Felix Hernandez H/40 30.00 60.00
FHN Felix Hernandez N/80 30.00 60.00
FHR Felix Hernandez R/40 30.00 60.00
FHZ Felix Hernandez Z/40 30.00 60.00
FH2G Felix Hernandez King G/75 40.00 80.00
FH2I Felix Hernandez King I/75 40.00 80.00
FH2K Felix Hernandez King K/75 40.00 80.00
FH2N Felix Hernandez King N/75 40.00 80.00
FLA Francisco Liriano A/100 25.00 50.00
FLI Francisco Liriano I/200 25.00 50.00
FLL Francisco Liriano L/100 25.00 50.00
FLN Francisco Liriano N/100 25.00 50.00
FLO Francisco Liriano O/100 25.00 50.00
FLR Francisco Liriano R/100 25.00 50.00
GMA Greg Maddux A/25 75.00 150.00
GMD Greg Maddux D/50 75.00 150.00
GMM Greg Maddux M/25 75.00 150.00
GMU Greg Maddux U/25 75.00 150.00
GMX Greg Maddux X/25 75.00 150.00
HBA Hank Blalock A/50 20.00 40.00
HBB Hank Blalock B/50 20.00 40.00
HBC Hank Blalock C/50 20.00 40.00
HBK Hank Blalock K/50 20.00 40.00
HBL Hank Blalock L/100 20.00 40.00
HBO Hank Blalock O/50 20.00 40.00
HKC Howie Kendrick C/75 25.00 50.00
HKD Howie Kendrick D/75 25.00 50.00
HKE Howie Kendrick E/75 25.00 50.00
HKI Howie Kendrick I/75 25.00 50.00
HKK Howie Kendrick K/150 25.00 50.00
HKN Howie Kendrick N/75 25.00 50.00
HKR Howie Kendrick R/75 25.00 50.00
HOA Trevor Hoffman A/8 40.00 80.00
HOF Trevor Hoffman F/16 40.00 80.00
HOH Trevor Hoffman H/8 40.00 80.00
HOM Trevor Hoffman M/8 40.00 80.00
HON Trevor Hoffman N/8 40.00 80.00
HOO Trevor Hoffman O/8 40.00 80.00
HRA Hanley Ramirez A/125 30.00 60.00
HRE Hanley Ramirez E/125 30.00 60.00
HRI Hanley Ramirez I/125 30.00 60.00
HRM Hanley Ramirez M/125 30.00 60.00
HRR Hanley Ramirez R/250 30.00 60.00
HRZ Hanley Ramirez Z/125 30.00 60.00
HSE Huston Street E/150 20.00 40.00
HSR Huston Street R/75 20.00 40.00
HSS Huston Street S/75 20.00 40.00
HST Huston Street T/150 20.00 40.00
HUD Tim Hudson D/50 20.00 40.00
HUH Tim Hudson H/50 20.00 40.00
HUN Tim Hudson N/50 20.00 40.00
HUO Tim Hudson O/50 20.00 40.00
HUS Tim Hudson S/50 20.00 40.00
HUU Tim Hudson U/50 20.00 40.00
IKE Ian Kinsler E/125 12.50 30.00
IKI Ian Kinsler I/125 12.50 30.00
IKK Ian Kinsler K/125 12.50 30.00
IKL Ian Kinsler L/125 12.50 30.00
IKN Ian Kinsler N/125 12.50 30.00
IKR Ian Kinsler R/125 12.50 30.00
IKS Ian Kinsler S/125 12.50 30.00
JBA Jason Bay A/110 25.00 50.00
JBB Jason Bay B/110 25.00 50.00
JBY Jason Bay Y/110 25.00 50.00
JB2O Jason Bay ROY O/50 25.00 50.00
JB2R Jason Bay ROY R/50 25.00 50.00
JB2Y Jason Bay ROY Y/50 25.00 50.00
JGE Jonny Gomes E/175 15.00 30.00
JGG Jonny Gomes G/175 15.00 30.00
JGM Jonny Gomes M/175 15.00 30.00
JGO Jonny Gomes O/175 15.00 30.00
JGS Jonny Gomes S/175 15.00 30.00
JHA Jeremy Hermida A/125 15.00 30.00
JHD Jeremy Hermida D/125 15.00 30.00
JHE Jeremy Hermida E/125 15.00 30.00
JHH Jeremy Hermida H/125 15.00 30.00
JHI Jeremy Hermida I/125 15.00 30.00
JHM Jeremy Hermida M/125 15.00 30.00
JHR Jeremy Hermida R/125 15.00 30.00
JMA Joe Mauer A/25 30.00 60.00
JME Joe Mauer E/25 30.00 60.00
JMM Joe Mauer M/25 30.00 60.00
JMR Joe Mauer R/25 30.00 60.00
JMU Joe Mauer U/25 30.00 60.00
JNA Joe Nathan A/200 15.00 30.00
JNH Joe Nathan H/100 15.00 30.00
JNN Joe Nathan N/200 15.00 30.00
JNT Joe Nathan T/100 15.00 30.00
JPA Jonathan Papelbon A/100 40.00 80.00
JPB Jonathan Papelbon B/100 40.00 80.00
JPE Jonathan Papelbon E/100 40.00 80.00
JPL Jonathan Papelbon L/100 40.00 80.00
JPN Jonathan Papelbon N/100 40.00 80.00
JPO Jonathan Papelbon O/100 40.00 80.00
JPP Jonathan Papelbon P/200 40.00 80.00
JRE Jose Reyes E/150 40.00 80.00
JRR Jose Reyes R/75 40.00 80.00
JRS Jose Reyes S/75 40.00 80.00
JRY Jose Reyes Y/75 40.00 80.00
JSE Jeremy Sowers E/50 25.00 50.00
JSO Jeremy Sowers O/50 25.00 50.00
JSR Jeremy Sowers R/50 25.00 50.00
JSS Jeremy Sowers S/100 25.00 50.00
JSW Jeremy Sowers W/50 25.00 50.00
JTE Jim Thome E/30 50.00 100.00
JTH Jim Thome H/30 50.00 100.00
JTM Jim Thome M/30 50.00 100.00
JTO Jim Thome O/30 50.00 100.00
JTT Jim Thome T/30 50.00 100.00
JVA Justin Verlander A/20 40.00 80.00
JVD Justin Verlander D/20 40.00 80.00
JVE Justin Verlander E/40 40.00 80.00
JVL Justin Verlander L/20 40.00 80.00
JVN Justin Verlander N/20 40.00 80.00
JVR Justin Verlander R/40 40.00 80.00
JVV Justin Verlander V/20 40.00 80.00
JWA Jered Weaver A/40 30.00 60.00
JWE Jered Weaver E/80 30.00 60.00
JWR Jered Weaver R/40 30.00 60.00
JWV Jered Weaver V/40 30.00 60.00
JWW Jered Weaver W/40 30.00 60.00
JZA Joel Zumaya A/250 25.00 50.00
JZM Joel Zumaya M/125 25.00 50.00
JZU Joel Zumaya U/125 25.00 50.00
JZY Joel Zumaya Y/125 25.00 50.00
JZZ Joel Zumaya Z/125 25.00 50.00
KGE Ken Griffey Jr. Reds E/25 90.00 150.00
KGF Ken Griffey Jr. Reds F/50 90.00 150.00
KGG Ken Griffey Jr. Reds G/25 90.00 150.00
KGI Ken Griffey Jr. Reds I/25 90.00 150.00
KGR Ken Griffey Jr. Reds R/25 90.00 150.00
KGY Ken Griffey Jr. Reds Y/25 90.00 150.00
KG2I Ken Griffey Jr. Junior I/25 90.00 150.00
KG2J Ken Griffey Jr. Junior J/25 90.00 150.00
KG2N Ken Griffey Jr. Junior N/25 90.00 150.00
KG2O Ken Griffey Jr. Junior O/25 90.00 150.00
KG2R Ken Griffey Jr. Junior R/25 90.00 150.00
KG2U Ken Griffey Jr. Junior U/25 90.00 150.00
KG3E Ken Griffey Jr. M's E/25 90.00 150.00
KG3F Ken Griffey Jr. M's F/50 90.00 150.00
KG3G Ken Griffey Jr. M's G/25 90.00 150.00
KG3I Ken Griffey Jr. M's I/25 90.00 150.00
KG3R Ken Griffey Jr. M's R/25 90.00 150.00
KG3Y Ken Griffey Jr. M's Y/25 90.00 150.00
KG4D Ken Griffey Jr. The Kid D/25 90.00 150.00
KG4E Ken Griffey Jr. The Kid E/25 90.00 150.00
KG4H Ken Griffey Jr. The Kid H/25 90.00 150.00
KG4I Ken Griffey Jr. The Kid I/25 90.00 150.00
KG4K Ken Griffey Jr. The Kid K/25 90.00 150.00
KG4T Ken Griffey Jr. The Kid T/25 90.00 150.00
KHE Khalil Greene E/225 15.00 30.00
KHG Khalil Greene G/75 15.00 30.00
KHN Khalil Greene N/75 15.00 30.00
KHR Khalil Greene R/75 15.00 30.00
KMA Kendry Morales A/20 25.00 50.00
KME Kendry Morales E/20 25.00 50.00
KML Kendry Morales L/20 25.00 50.00
KMM Kendry Morales M/20 25.00 50.00
KMO Kendry Morales O/20 25.00 50.00
KMR Kendry Morales R/20 25.00 50.00
KMS Kendry Morales S/20 25.00 50.00
KWD Kerry Wood D/10 40.00 80.00
KWO Kerry Wood O/20 40.00 80.00
KWW Kerry Wood W/10 40.00 80.00
LEE Carlos Lee E/50 20.00 40.00
LEL Carlos Lee L/25 20.00 40.00
MCA Miguel Cabrera A/70 40.00 80.00
MCB Miguel Cabrera B/35 40.00 80.00
MCC Miguel Cabrera C/35 40.00 80.00
MCE Miguel Cabrera E/35 40.00 80.00
MCR Miguel Cabrera R/70 40.00 80.00
MGE Marcus Giles E/136 15.00 30.00
MGG Marcus Giles G/136 15.00 30.00
MGI Marcus Giles I/136 15.00 30.00
MGL Marcus Giles L/136 15.00 30.00
MGS Marcus Giles S/136 15.00 30.00
MHA Matt Holliday A/37 40.00 80.00
MHD Matt Holliday D/37 40.00 80.00
MHH Matt Holliday H/37 40.00 80.00
MHI Matt Holliday I/37 40.00 80.00
MHL Matt Holliday L/74 40.00 80.00
MHO Matt Holliday O/37 40.00 80.00
MHY Matt Holliday Y/37 40.00 80.00
MMD Mark Mulder D/50 20.00 40.00
MME Mark Mulder E/50 20.00 40.00
MML Mark Mulder L/50 20.00 40.00
MMM Mark Mulder M/50 20.00 40.00
MMR Mark Mulder R/50 20.00 40.00
MMU Mark Mulder U/50 20.00 40.00
MOA Justin Morneau A/75 30.00 60.00
MOE Justin Morneau E/75 30.00 60.00
MOM Justin Morneau M/75 30.00 60.00
MON Justin Morneau N/75 30.00 60.00
MOO Justin Morneau O/75 30.00 60.00
MOR Justin Morneau R/75 30.00 60.00
MOU Justin Morneau U/75 30.00 60.00
MTA Mark Teixeira A/5 50.00 100.00
MTE Mark Teixeira E/10 50.00 100.00
MTI Mark Teixeira I/10 50.00 100.00
MTR Mark Teixeira R/5 50.00 100.00
MTT Mark Teixeira T/5 50.00 100.00
MTX Mark Teixeira X/5 50.00 100.00
MYG Michael Young G/50 25.00 50.00
MYN Michael Young N/50 25.00 50.00
MYO Michael Young O/50 25.00 50.00
MYU Michael Young U/50 25.00 50.00
MYY Michael Young Y/50 25.00 50.00
NSE Nick Swisher E/170 15.00 30.00
NSH Nick Swisher H/170 15.00 30.00
NSI Nick Swisher I/170 15.00 30.00
NSR Nick Swisher R/170 15.00 30.00
NSS Nick Swisher S/340 15.00 30.00
NSW Nick Swisher W/170 15.00 30.00
PEA Jake Peavy A/20 30.00 60.00
PEE Jake Peavy E/20 30.00 60.00
PEP Jake Peavy P/20 30.00 60.00
PEV Jake Peavy V/20 30.00 60.00
PEY Jake Peavy Y/20 30.00 60.00
RCC Roger Clemens C/15 100.00 150.00
RCE Roger Clemens E/30 100.00 150.00
RCL Roger Clemens L/15 100.00 150.00
RCM Roger Clemens M/15 100.00 150.00
RCN Roger Clemens N/15 100.00 150.00
RCS Roger Clemens S/15 100.00 150.00
RC2C Roger Clemens The Rocket C/15 100.00 150.00
RC2E Roger Clemens The Rocket E/30 100.00 150.00
RC2H Roger Clemens The Rocket H/15 100.00 150.00
RC2K Roger Clemens The Rocket K/15 100.00 150.00
RC2O Roger Clemens The Rocket O/15 100.00 150.00
RC2R Roger Clemens The Rocket R/15 100.00 150.00
RC2T Roger Clemens The Rocket T/30 100.00 150.00
ROA Roy Oswalt A/50 30.00 60.00
ROL Roy Oswalt L/50 30.00 60.00
ROO Roy Oswalt O/50 30.00 60.00
ROS Roy Oswalt S/50 30.00 60.00
ROT Roy Oswalt T/50 30.00 60.00
ROW Roy Oswalt W/50 30.00 60.00
RWE Rickie Weeks E/200 20.00 40.00
RWK Rickie Weeks K/100 20.00 40.00
RWS Rickie Weeks S/100 20.00 40.00
RWW Rickie Weeks W/100 20.00 40.00
RZA Ryan Zimmerman A/17 50.00 100.00
RZE Ryan Zimmerman E/17 50.00 100.00
RZI Ryan Zimmerman I/17 50.00 100.00
RZM Ryan Zimmerman M/51 50.00 100.00
RZN Ryan Zimmerman N/17 50.00 100.00
RZR Ryan Zimmerman R/17 50.00 100.00
RZZ Ryan Zimmerman Z/17 50.00 100.00
SKA Scott Kazmir A/6 50.00 100.00
SKI Scott Kazmir I/6 50.00 100.00
SKK Scott Kazmir K/6 50.00 100.00
SKM Scott Kazmir M/6 50.00 100.00
SKR Scott Kazmir R/6 50.00 100.00
SKZ Scott Kazmir Z/6 50.00 100.00
SML John Smoltz L/75 40.00 80.00
SMM John Smoltz M/75 40.00 80.00
SMO John Smoltz O/75 40.00 80.00
SMS John Smoltz S/75 40.00 80.00
SMT John Smoltz T/75 40.00 80.00
SMZ John Smoltz Z/75 40.00 80.00
TEA Miguel Tejada A/50 30.00 60.00
TED Miguel Tejada D/25 30.00 60.00
TEE Miguel Tejada E/25 30.00 60.00
TEJ Miguel Tejada J/25 30.00 60.00
TET Miguel Tejada T/25 30.00 60.00
THA Travis Hafner A/10 50.00 100.00
THE Travis Hafner E/10 50.00 100.00
THF Travis Hafner F/10 50.00 100.00
THH Travis Hafner H/10 50.00 100.00
THN Travis Hafner N/10 50.00 100.00
THR Travis Hafner R/10 50.00 100.00
TH2K Travis Hafner Pronk K/8 50.00 100.00
TH2N Travis Hafner Pronk N/8 50.00 100.00
TH2O Travis Hafner Pronk O/8 50.00 100.00
TH2P Travis Hafner Pronk P/8 50.00 100.00
TH2R Travis Hafner Pronk R/8 50.00 100.00
TIC Tadahito Iguchi C/20 30.00 60.00
TIG Tadahito Iguchi G/20 30.00 60.00
TIH Tadahito Iguchi H/20 30.00 60.00
TII Tadahito Iguchi I/40 30.00 60.00
TIU Tadahito Iguchi U/20 30.00 60.00
VGE Vladimir Guerrero E/50 40.00 80.00
VGG Vladimir Guerrero G/25 40.00 80.00
VGO Vladimir Guerrero O/25 40.00 80.00
VGR Vladimir Guerrero R/75 40.00 80.00
VGU Vladimir Guerrero U/25 40.00 80.00
VMA Victor Martinez A/75 20.00 40.00
VME Victor Martinez E/75 20.00 40.00
VMI Victor Martinez I/75 20.00 40.00
VMM Victor Martinez M/75 20.00 40.00
VMN Victor Martinez N/75 20.00 40.00
VMR Victor Martinez R/75 20.00 40.00
VMT Victor Martinez T/75 20.00 40.00
VMZ Victor Martinez Z/75 20.00 40.00
WIA Josh Willingham A/75 15.00 30.00
WIG Josh Willingham G/75 15.00 30.00
WIH Josh Willingham H/150 15.00 30.00
WII Josh Willingham I/150 15.00 30.00
WIL Josh Willingham L/150 15.00 30.00
WIM Josh Willingham M/75 15.00 30.00
WIN Josh Willingham N/75 15.00 30.00
WIW Josh Willingham W/75 15.00 30.00

2006 SP Authentic Chirography

STATED ODDS 1:96
PRINT RUNS B/WN 25-75 COPIES PER
NO PRICING ON QTY OF 25
EXCHANGE DEADLINE 12/05/09.
AE Andre Ethier/75 15.00 40.00
AG Tony Gwynn Jr./75 15.00 40.00
AH Anderson Hernandez/75 4.00 10.00
AN Brian Anderson/75 4.00 10.00
AR Alex Rios/75 EXCH 6.00 15.00
AS Alfonso Soriano/75 20.00 50.00
AW Adam Wainwright/75 10.00 25.00
BA Brian Bannister/75 6.00 15.00
BB Brandon Backe/75 4.00 10.00
BC Bobby Crosby/75 6.00 15.00
BI Chad Billingsley/75 10.00 25.00
BL Boone Logan/75 4.00 10.00
BO Boof Bonser/75 6.00 15.00
BS Ben Sheets/75 10.00 25.00
CB Craig Biggio/75 30.00 60.00
CD Chris Denorfia/75 4.00 10.00
CF Choo Freeman/75 4.00 10.00
CG Carlos Guillen/75 10.00 25.00
CH Cole Hamels/75 20.00 50.00
CJ Conor Jackson/75 6.00 15.00
CK Casey Kotchman/75 4.00 10.00
CL Cliff Lee/75 4.00 10.00
CP Corey Patterson/75 6.00 15.00
CR Cody Ross/75 4.00 10.00
CS C.C. Sabathia/75 6.00 15.00
CU Chase Utley/25
DB Denny Bautista/75 4.00 10.00
DD David DeJesus/75 6.00 15.00
DG David Gassner/75 4.00 10.00
DJ Derek Jeter/75 100.00 175.00
DU Dan Uggla/75 6.00 15.00
DW Dontrelle Willis/75 10.00 25.00
ER Edgar Renteria/75 EXCH 6.00 15.00
FC Fausto Carmona/75 4.00 10.00
FH Felix Hernandez/25
FL Felipe Lopez/75 4.00 10.00
FT Frank Thomas/75 40.00 80.00
GA Garret Anderson/75 6.00 15.00
GR Ken Griffey Jr./75 60.00 120.00
HA Jeff Harris/75 4.00 10.00
HB Hank Blalock/75 6.00 15.00
HK Hong-Chih Kuo/75 50.00 100.00
HR Hanley Ramirez/75 10.00 25.00
IK Ian Kinsler/75 6.00 15.00
IR Ivan Rodriguez/75 EXCH 15.00 40.00
JB Joe Blanton/75 6.00 15.00
JC Jose Capellan/75 4.00 10.00
JD Joey Devine/75 4.00 10.00
JE Johnny Estrada/75 4.00 10.00
JF Jeff Francis/75 10.00 25.00
JH Jeremy Hermida/75 6.00 15.00
JJ Josh Johnson/75 6.00 15.00
JK Jason Kubel/75 4.00 10.00
JL Jon Lester/75 20.00 50.00
JN Joe Nathan/75 6.00 15.00
JP Jonathan Papelbon/75 20.00 50.00
JQ Jacque Jones/75 EXCH 6.00 15.00
JR Josh Rupe/75 4.00 10.00
JS Jeremy Sowers/75 6.00 15.00
JV Jason Varitek/75 EXCH 20.00 50.00
JW Josh Willingham/75 4.00 10.00
KF Keith Foulke/75 6.00 15.00
KG Khalil Greene/75 10.00 25.00
KM Kevin Mench/75 6.00 15.00
KS Kelly Shoppach/75 6.00 15.00
KY Kevin Youkilis/75 6.00 15.00
LI Francisco Liriano/75 15.00 40.00
LO Lyle Overbay/40 6.00 15.00
MC Matt Cain/75 10.00 25.00
ML Mark Loretta/75 EXCH 4.00 10.00
MM Macay McBride/75 4.00 10.00
MP Mark Prior/55 EXCH 10.00 25.00
NS Nick Swisher/75 6.00 15.00
OP Oliver Perez/75 6.00 15.00
PM Paul Maholm/75 4.00 10.00
RE Eric Reed/75 4.00 10.00
RH Rich Harden/75 6.00 15.00
RZ Ryan Zimmerman/75 20.00 50.00
SC Sean Casey/75 10.00 25.00
SD Stephen Drew/75 20.00 50.00
SH Chris Shelton/75 4.00 10.00
SK Scott Kazmir/25
SM Sean Marshall/75 12.50 30.00
SO Alay Soler/75 6.00 15.00
TB Taylor Buchholz/75 6.00 15.00
TH Travis Hafner/75 10.00 25.00
TP Tony Pena Jr./75 4.00 10.00
TS Takashi Saito/75 20.00 50.00
VA John Van Benschoten/75 4.00 10.00
VE Justin Verlander/75 15.00 40.00
VM Victor Martinez/75 10.00 25.00
VP Vicente Padilla/75 EXCH 6.00 15.00
WE Jered Weaver/75 15.00 40.00
WI Josh Wilson/75 4.00 10.00
WM Wily Mo Pena/75 6.00 15.00
YP Yusmeiro Petit/75 EXCH 6.00 15.00

2006 SP Authentic Chirography Dual

RANDOM INSERTS IN PACKS
STATED PRINT RUN 25 SERIAL #'d SETS
NO PRICING DUE TO SCARCITY
EXCHANGE DEADLINE 12/05/09
BN Taylor Buchholz
Fernando Nieve
CE Cody Ross
Eric Reed
EL James Loney
Andre Ethier
FJ Conor Jackson
Prince Fielder
GB Khalil Greene
Josh Barfield
GJ Ken Griffey Jr.
Derek Jeter
HA Reggie Abercrombie
Jeremy Hermida
HK Scott Kazmir
Cole Hamels
KH Ian Kinsler
Anderson Hernandez
KS Hong-Chih Kuo
Takashi Saito
LB Boof Bonser
Francisco Liriano
MH Rich Hill
Sean Marshall

MW Victor Martinez
Josh Willingham
PB Freddie Bynum
Angel Pagan
PG Ken Griffey Jr.
Albert Pujols
PO Roy Oswalt
Jake Peavy
PP Tony Pena Jr.
Martin Prado
RC Hanley Ramirez
Miguel Cabrera
RR Jose Reyes
Hanley Ramirez
SC Ben Sheets
Jose Capellan
SP Curt Schilling
Jonathan Papelbon
TL Derrek Lee
Mark Teixeira
UH Chase Utley
Cole Hamels
VJ Josh Johnson
Justin Verlander
WS Josh Wilson
Ryan Shealy

2006 SP Authentic Chirography Triple

RANDOM INSERTS IN PACKS
STATED PRINT RUN 15 SERIAL #'d SETS
NO PRICING DUE TO SCARCITY
EXCHANGE DEADLINE 12/05/09
BCB Taylor Buchholz
Matt Cain
Brian Bannister
BGL Boof Bonser
Francisco Liriano
Dave Gassner
BUK Josh Barfield
Dan Uggla
Howie Kendrick
CMS Carl Crawford
Grady Sizemore
Lastings Milledge
CVC Roger Clemens
Justin Verlander
Matt Cain
CVL Francisco Liriano
Justin Verlander
Matt Cain
CZU Miguel Cabrera
Ryan Zimmerman
BJ Upton
FHJ Travis Hafner
Conor Jackson
Prince Fielder
GHK Ken Griffey Jr.
Jason Kubel
Jeremy Hermida
GJP Ken Griffey Jr.
Derek Jeter
Albert Pujols
GPH Eric Gagne
Trevor Hoffman
Jonathan Papelbon
HCW Miguel Cabrera
Josh Willingham
Jeremy Hermida
HOP Roy Oswalt
Jake Peavy
Rich Harden
JCS Derek Jeter
Gary Sheffield
Melky Cabrera
KSI Hong-Chih Kuo
Takashi Saito
Travis Ishikawa
KTB Mark Teixeira
Hank Blalock
Ian Kinsler
LKH Francisco Liriano
Scott Kazmir
Cole Hamels
POV Roy Oswalt
Jake Peavy
Justin Verlander
RGR Khalil Greene
Jose Reyes
Hanley Ramirez
RHW Josh Willingham
Hanley Ramirez
Jeremy Hermida
URK Brian Roberts
Chase Utley
Ian Kinsler
URW Josh Willingham
Hanley Ramirez
Dan Uggla
WKK Rickie Weeks
Ian Kinsler
Howie Kendrick
WMK Kendry Morales
Howie Kendrick
Jered Weaver
WVJ Josh Johnson
Justin Verlander
Jered Weaver

2006 SP Authentic Sign of the Times

STATED ODDS 1:96
PRINT RUNS B/WN 25-75 COPIES PER
NO PRICING ON QTY OF 25
EXCHANGE DEADLINE 12/05/09
AB Adrian Beltre/75 EXCH 6.00 15.00

AE Andre Ethier/75 15.00 40.00
AG Tony Gwynn Jr./75 EXCH 15.00 40.00
AH Anderson Hernandez/75 4.00 10.00
AJ Andruw Jones/75 15.00 40.00
AN Brian Anderson/75 4.00 10.00
AR Aramis Ramirez/75 6.00 15.00
AS Alay Soler/75 6.00 15.00
AW Adam Wainwright/75 10.00 25.00
BA Bobby Abreu/75 30.00 60.00
BB Boof Bonser/75 6.00 15.00
BI Chad Billingsley/75 10.00 25.00
BJ Ben Johnson/75 4.00 10.00
BL Boone Logan/75 4.00 10.00
BR Brian Bannister/75 6.00 15.00
CA Matt Cain/75 10.00 25.00
CB Chris Booker/75 4.00 10.00
CC Carl Crawford/75 6.00 15.00
CD Chris Demaria/75 4.00 10.00
CH Cole Hamels/75 20.00 50.00
CL Carlos Lee/25
CR Cody Ross/75 4.00 10.00
CS Curt Schilling/75 20.00 50.00
CY Clay Hensley/75 4.00 10.00
DE Chris Denorfia/75 4.00 10.00
DG David Gassner/75 4.00 10.00
DJ Derek Jeter/75 100.00 175.00
DL Derrek Lee/75 10.00 25.00
DU Dan Uggla/75 12.50 30.00
EG Eric Gagne/75 10.00 25.00
ER Eric Reed/75 4.00 10.00
FC Fausto Carmona/75 10.00 25.00
FL Francisco Liriano/75 15.00 40.00
FR Ron Flores/75 4.00 10.00
GM Greg Maddux/75 60.00 120.00
HA Tim Hamulack/75 4.00 10.00
HE Jeremy Hermida/75 6.00 15.00
HR Hanley Ramirez/75 10.00 25.00
IK Ian Kinsler/75 6.00 15.00
JA Conor Jackson/75 6.00 15.00
JC Jose Capellan/75 4.00 10.00
JD J.D. Drew/75 10.00 25.00
JE Jered Weaver/75 15.00 40.00
JG Jose Guillen/75 4.00 10.00
JH Jason Hammel/75 4.00 10.00
JJ Josh Johnson/75 6.00 15.00
JK Jason Kendall/75 6.00 15.00
JM Joe Mauer/75 EXCH 10.00 25.00
JP Jake Peavy/75 6.00 15.00
JR Jose Reyes/75 EXCH 15.00 40.00
JS John Smoltz/75 EXCH 15.00 40.00
JV John Van Benschoten/75 4.00 10.00
JW Josh Willingham/75 4.00 10.00
JY Jeremy Sowers/75 6.00 15.00
KG Ken Griffey Jr./75 60.00 120.00
KU Jason Kubel/75 4.00 10.00
LO Derek Lowe/75 EXCH 10.00 25.00
MA Macay McBride/75 4.00 10.00
MC Miguel Cabrera/75 15.00 40.00
ME Melky Cabrera/75 EXCH 10.00 25.00
MI Mike Thompson/75 4.00 10.00
MJ Mike Jacobs/75 6.00 15.00
MK Mark Kotsay/75 6.00 15.00
MM Mark Mulder/75 6.00 15.00
MO Justin Morneau/75 6.00 15.00
MT Mark Teixeira/75 10.00 25.00
PA Jonathan Papelbon/75 20.00 50.00
PE Joel Peralta/75 4.00 10.00
PM Paul Maholm/75 4.00 10.00
RA Reggie Abercrombie/75 4.00 10.00
RF Rafael Furcal/75 6.00 15.00
RH Ramon Hernandez/75 10.00 25.00
RJ Randy Johnson/75 30.00 60.00
RM Russell Martin/75 6.00 15.00
RS Ryan Shealy/75 6.00 15.00
RW Rickie Weeks/75 10.00 25.00
RZ Ryan Zimmerman/75 20.00 50.00
SA Santiago Ramirez/75 4.00 10.00
SD Stephen Drew/75 20.00 50.00
SM Sean Marshall/75 10.00 25.00
SP Scott Podsednik/75 6.00 15.00
SR Scott Rolen/75 EXCH 15.00 40.00
SS Skip Schumaker/75 4.00 10.00
ST Steve Stemle/75 4.00 10.00
TB Taylor Buchholz/75 4.00 10.00
TE Miguel Tejada/75 10.00 25.00
TH Tim Hudson/75 10.00 25.00
TP Tony Pena Jr./75 4.00 10.00
TS Takashi Saito/75 20.00 50.00
VE Justin Verlander/75 15.00 40.00
VG Vladimir Guerrero/75 20.00 50.00
VW Vernon Wells/75 6.00 15.00
WI Josh Wilson/75 4.00 10.00
YB Yuniesky Betancourt/75 6.00 15.00
YP Yusmeiro Petit/75 EXCH 6.00 15.00
ZG Zack Greinke/75 4.00 10.00

2006 SP Authentic Sign of the Times Dual

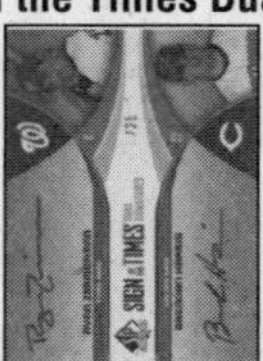

RANDOM INSERTS IN PACKS
STATED PRINT RUN 25 SERIAL #'d SETS
NO PRICING DUE TO SCARCITY
EXCHANGE DEADLINE 12/05/09
BM Jason Bay
Nate McLouth
CH Ben Hendrickson
Jose Capellan
FW Rickie Weeks
Prince Fielder
GP Ken Griffey Jr.
Albert Pujols
HD Tim Hudson
Joey Devine
HF Rich Harden
Ron Flores
HM Lastings Milledge
Jeremy Hermida
HW Felix Hernandez
Jered Weaver
JS Jose Reyes
Stephen Drew
KN Howie Kendrick
Mike Napoli
LG Francisco Liriano
Dave Gassner
MF Prince Fielder
Kendry Morales
MM Greg Maddux
Sean Marshall
MS Victor Martinez
Kelly Shoppach
OB Roy Oswalt
Taylor Buchholz
OW Dontrelle Willis
Scott Olsen
PB Freddie Bynum
Angel Pagan
PT Jake Peavy
Mike Thompson
PV Justin Verlander
Jonathan Papelbon
RW Josh Willingham
Hanley Ramirez
SC Fausto Carmona
C.C. Sabathia
UK Ian Kinsler
Dan Uggla
UZ B.J. Upton
Ryan Zimmerman
WM Kendry Morales
Jered Weaver
ZH Ryan Zimmerman
Brendan Harris

2006 SP Authentic Sign of the Times Triple

RANDOM INSERTS IN PACKS
STATED PRINT RUN 15 SERIAL #'d SETS
NO PRICING DUE TO SCARCITY
EXCHANGE DEADLINE 12/05/09
AHM Rich Hill
David Aardsma
Sean Marshall
BMD Jason Bay
Chris Duffy
Nate McLouth
BOR Jason Bergmann
Michael O'Connor
Saul Rivera
BUK Craig Biggio
Chase Utley
Howie Kendrick
FHJ Travis Hafner
Conor Jackson
Prince Fielder
FWS Ben Sheets
Rickie Weeks
Prince Fielder
HBH Boof Bonser
Jason Hammel
Cole Hamels
HLD Ruddy Lugo
Scott Dunn
Jason Hammel
HMC Travis Hafner
Victor Martinez
Fausto Carmona
HMM Lastings Milledge
Nick Markakis
Jeremy Hermida
ICF Kevin Frandsen
Matt Cain
Travis Ishikawa
JRR Derek Jeter
Jose Reyes
Hanley Ramirez
LFJ Derrek Lee
Conor Jackson
Prince Fielder
MCH Lastings Milledge
Melky Cabrera
Jeremy Hermida
MFJ Conor Jackson
Prince Fielder
Kendry Morales
OBN Roy Oswalt
Taylor Buchholz
Fernando Nieve
OJP Josh Johnson
Scott Olsen
Yusmeiro Petit
PAD Jermaine Dye
Brian Anderson
Scott Podsednik
PPJ Andruw Jones
Tony Pena Jr.
Martin Prado
SHG Ken Griffey Jr.
Nick Swisher
Jeremy Hermida
VMP Oliver Perez
John Van Benschoten
Paul Maholm
WKC Adam Wainwright
Fausto Carmona
John Koronka
WOJ Josh Johnson
Dontrelle Willis
Scott Olsen
WVC Justin Verlander
Matt Cain
Jered Weaver
ZPN Joe Nathan
Jonathan Papelbon
Joel Zumaya

2006 SP Authentic WBC Future Watch

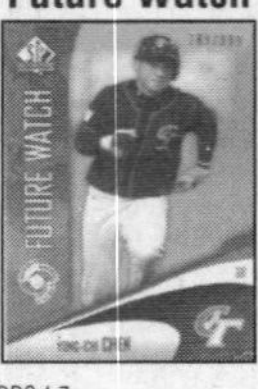

STATED ODDS 1:7
STATED PRINT RUN 999 SERIAL #'d SETS
1 Adrian Burnside 2.00 5.00
2 Gavin Fingleson 2.00 5.00
3 Bradley Harman 2.00 5.00
4 Brendan Kingman 2.00 5.00
5 Brett Roneberg 2.00 5.00
6 Paul Rutgers 2.00 5.00
7 Phil Stockman 2.00 5.00
8 Stubby Clapp 2.00 5.00
9 Steve Green 2.00 5.00
10 Pete LaForest 2.00 5.00
11 Adam Loewen 2.00 5.00
12 Ryan Radmanovich 2.00 5.00
13 Chenhao Li 2.00 5.00
14 Guangbiao Liu 2.00 5.00
15 Guogan Yang 2.00 5.00
16 Jingchao Wang 2.00 5.00
17 Lei Li 2.00 5.00
18 Lingfeng Sun 2.00 5.00
19 Nan Wang 2.00 5.00
20 Shuo Yang 2.00 5.00
21 Tao Bu 2.00 5.00
22 Wei Wang 2.00 5.00
23 Yi Feng 2.00 5.00
24 Chien-Ming Chiang 4.00 10.00
25 Yung-Chi Chen 6.00 15.00
26 Chia-Hsien Hseih 4.00 10.00
27 Chin-Lung Hu 6.00 15.00
28 En-Yu Lin 6.00 15.00
29 Wei-Lun Pan 4.00 10.00
30 Ariel Borrero 2.00 5.00
31 Yadel Marti 2.00 5.00
32 Yulieski Gourriel 4.00 10.00
33 Frederich Cepeda 2.00 5.00
34 Yadiel Pedroso 2.00 5.00
35 Pedro Luis Lazo 2.00 5.00
36 Elier Sanchez 2.00 5.00
37 Norberto Gonzalez 2.00 5.00
38 Carlos Tabares 2.00 5.00
39 Eduardo Paret 2.00 5.00
40 Osmany Urrutia 2.00 5.00
41 Alexi Ramirez 20.00 50.00
42 Yoandy Garlobo 2.00 5.00
43 Vicyohandry Odelin 2.00 5.00
44 Michel Enriquez 2.00 5.00
45 Ormari Romero 2.00 5.00
46 Ariel Pestano 2.00 5.00
47 Francisco Liriano 2.00 5.00
48 Dustin Delucchi 2.00 5.00
49 Tony Giarratano 2.00 5.00
50 Tom Gregorio 2.00 5.00
51 Mark Saccomanno 2.00 5.00
52 Takahiro Arai 3.00 8.00
53 Akinori Iwamura 6.00 15.00
54 Munenori Kawaski 4.00 10.00
55 Nobuhiko Matsunaka 3.00 8.00
56 Daisuke Matsuzaka 12.50 30.00
57 Shinya Miyamoto 3.00 8.00
58 Tsuyoshi Nishioka 4.00 10.00
59 Tomoya Satozaki 3.00 8.00
60 Koji Uehara 4.00 10.00
61 Shunsuke Watanabe 3.00 8.00
62 Sadaharu Oh 6.00 15.00
63 Byung Kyu Lee 2.00 5.00
64 Ji Man Song 2.00 5.00
65 Jin Man Park 2.00 5.00
66 Jong Beom Lee 2.00 5.00
67 Jong Kook Kim 2.00 5.00
68 Min Han Son 2.00 5.00
69 Min Jae Kim 2.00 5.00
70 Seung Yeop Lee 3.00 8.00
71 Luis A. Garcia 2.00 5.00
72 Mario Valenzuela 2.00 5.00
73 Sharnol Adriana 2.00 5.00
74 Rob Cordemans 2.00 5.00
75 Michael Duursma 2.00 5.00
76 Percy Isenia 2.00 5.00
77 Sidney de Jong 2.00 5.00
78 Dirk Klooster 2.00 5.00
79 Raylinoe Legito 2.00 5.00
80 Shairon Martis 2.00 5.00
81 Harvey Monte 2.00 5.00
82 Hainley Statia 2.00 5.00
83 Roger Deago 2.00 5.00
84 Audes De Leon 2.00 5.00
85 Freddy Herrera 2.00 5.00
86 Yoni Lasso 2.00 5.00
87 Orlando Miller 2.00 5.00
88 Len Pecota 2.00 5.00
89 Federico Baez 2.00 5.00
90 Dicky Gonzalez 2.00 5.00
91 Josue Matos 2.00 5.00
92 Orlando Roman 2.00 5.00
93 Paul Bell 2.00 5.00
94 Kyle Botha 2.00 5.00
95 Jason Cook 2.00 5.00
96 Nicholas Dempsey 2.00 5.00
97 Victor Moreno 2.00 5.00
98 Ricardo Palma 2.00 5.00
99 Huston Street 2.00 5.00
100 Chase Utley 3.00 8.00

2007 SP Authentic

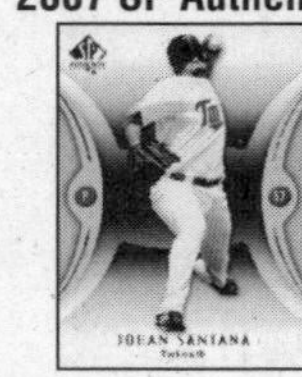

COMP.SET w/o RCs (100) 6.00 15.00
COMMON CARD (1-100) .15 .40
COMMON AU RC (101-158) 5.00 12.00
OVERALL BY THE LETTER AUTOS 1:12
AU RC PRINT RUN B/WN 20-120 COPIES PER
EXCHANGE DEADLINE 11/08/2008
1 Chipper Jones .40 1.00
2 Andruw Jones .25 .60
3 John Smoltz .25 .60
4 Carlos Quentin .15 .40
5 Randy Johnson .40 1.00
6 Brandon Webb .15 .40
7 Alfonso Soriano .15 .40
8 Derrek Lee .15 .40
9 Aramis Ramirez .15 .40
10 Carlos Zambrano .15 .40
11 Ken Griffey Jr. .60 1.50
12 Adam Dunn .15 .40
13 Josh Hamilton .40 1.00
14 Todd Helton .25 .60
15 Jeff Francis .15 .40
16 Matt Holliday .40 1.00
17 Hanley Ramirez .25 .60
18 Dontrelle Willis .15 .40
19 Miguel Cabrera .25 .60
20 Lance Berkman .15 .40
21 Roy Oswalt .15 .40
22 Carlos Lee .15 .40
23 Nomar Garciaparra .40 1.00
24 Derek Lowe .15 .40
25 Juan Pierre .15 .40
26 Rafael Furcal .15 .40
27 Rickie Weeks .15 .40
28 Prince Fielder .40 1.00
29 Ben Sheets .15 .40
30 David Wright .60 1.50
31 Jose Reyes .40 1.00
32 Tom Glavine .25 .60
33 Carlos Beltran .15 .40
34 Cole Hamels .40 1.00
35 Jimmy Rollins .15 .40
36 Ryan Howard .60 1.50
37 Jason Bay .15 .40
38 Freddy Sanchez .15 .40
39 Ian Snell .15 .40
40 Jake Peavy .15 .40
41 Greg Maddux .60 1.50
42 Trevor Hoffman .15 .40
43 Matt Cain .25 .60
44 Barry Zito .15 .40
45 Ray Durham .15 .40
46 Albert Pujols .75 2.00
47 Chris Carpenter .15 .40
48 Jim Edmonds .25 .60
49 Scott Rolen .25 .60
50 Ryan Zimmerman .40 1.00
51 Felipe Lopez .15 .40
52 Austin Kearns .15 .40
53 Miguel Tejada .15 .40
54 Erik Bedard .15 .40
55 Daniel Cabrera .15 .40
56 David Ortiz .40 1.00
57 Curt Schilling .25 .60
58 Manny Ramirez .25 .60
59 Jonathan Papelbon .40 1.00
60 Jim Thome .25 .60
61 Paul Konerko .15 .40
62 Bobby Jenks .15 .40
63 Grady Sizemore .25 .60
64 Victor Martinez .15 .40
65 Travis Hafner .15 .40
66 Ivan Rodriguez .25 .60
67 Justin Verlander .40 1.00
68 Joel Zumaya .25 .60
69 Jeremy Bonderman .15 .40
70 Gil Meche .15 .40
71 Mike Sweeney .15 .40
72 Mark Teahen .15 .40
73 Vladimir Guerrero .40 1.00
74 Howie Kendrick .15 .40
75 Francisco Rodriguez .15 .40
76 Johan Santana .25 .60
77 Justin Morneau .15 .40
78 Joe Mauer .25 .60
79 Joe Nathan .15 .40
80a Alex Rodriguez .60 1.50
80b Alex Rodriguez
Angels Logo
80c Alex Rodriguez
Cubs Logo
80d Alex Rodriguez
Dodgers Logo
80e Alex Rodriguez
Mets Logo
80f Alex Rodriguez
Red Sox Logo
81 Derek Jeter 1.00 2.50
82 Johnny Damon .25 .60
83 Chien-Ming Wang .60 1.50
84 Rich Harden .15 .40
85 Mike Piazza .40 1.00
86 Dan Haren .15 .40
87 Ichiro Suzuki .60 1.50
88 Felix Hernandez .25 .60
89 Kenji Johjima .40 1.00
90 Adrian Beltre .15 .40
91 Carl Crawford .15 .40
92 Scott Kazmir .25 .60
93 Delmon Young .25 .60
94 Michael Young .15 .40
95 Mark Teixeira .25 .60
96 Eric Gagne .15 .40
97 Hank Blalock .15 .40
98 Vernon Wells .15 .40
99 Roy Halladay .15 .40
100 Frank Thomas .40 1.00
101 Joaquin Arias AU/75 (RC) 5.00 12.00
102 Jeff Baker AU (RC) EXCH 5.00 12.00
103 Michael Bourn AU/75 (RC) 6.00 15.00
104 Brian Burres AU/75 (RC) 6.00 15.00
105 Jared Burton AU/75 RC 6.00 15.00
106 Ryan Braun AU/50 (RC) 60.00 150.00
109 Alex Gordon AU/50 RC 40.00 80.00
112 Sean Henn AU/75 (RC) 10.00 25.00
113 Phil Hughes AU (RC) EXCH 40.00 80.00
114 Kei Igawa AU/25 RC 30.00 60.00
115 Akinori Iwamura AU/20 RC 40.00 80.00
119 Adam Lind AU/75 (RC) 10.00 25.00
123 Brad Salmon AU/75 RC 5.00 12.00
127 Cesar Jimenez AU RC EXCH 5.00 12.00
129 Troy Tulowitzki AU (RC) EXCH 30.00 60.00
130 Chasé Wright AU/75 RC 12.50 30.00
131 Delmon Young AU/20 (RC) 20.00 50.00
133 Brian Barden AU/75 RC 5.00 12.00
137 Billy Butler AU/75 (RC) 20.00 50.00
139 Kory Casto AU/75 (RC) 6.00 15.00
140 Matt Chico AU/75 (RC) 6.00 15.00
141 John Danks AU/75 RC 10.00 25.00
142 Andrew Miller AU/50 RC 20.00 50.00
145 Devern Hansack AU RC EXCH 6.00 15.00
146 Mike Rabelo AU/75 RC 8.00 20.00
150a Daisuke Matsuzaka AU/20 RC 175.00300.00
152 Micah Owings AU/75 (RC) 20.00 50.00
153 Hunter Pence AU/75 (RC) 40.00 80.00
156 Danny Putnam AU/75 (RC) 6.00 15.00
159 Doug Slaten AU/75 RC 6.00 15.00
160 Joe Smith AU/75 RC 8.00 20.00
161 Justin Upton AU/120 RC 50.00 100.00
162 Joba Chamberlain AU/60 RC 100.00 200.00
107a Yovani Gallardo AU/75 (RC) 20.00 50.00
107b Yovani Gallardo AU/35 (RC) 30.00 60.00
108a Hector Gimenez AU/75 (RC) 6.00 15.00
108b Hector Gimenez AU/50 (RC) 6.00 15.00
110a Josh Hamilton AU/50 (RC) 30.00 60.00
110b Josh Hamilton AU/35 (RC) 40.00 80.00
111a Justin Hampson AU/75 (RC) 5.00 12.00
111b Justin Hampson AU/50 (RC) 5.00 12.00
116a Mark Reynolds AU/75 RC 40.00 80.00
116b Mark Reynolds AU/35 (RC) 50.00 100.00
117a Homer Bailey AU/75 (RC) 10.00 25.00
117b Homer Bailey AU/50 (RC) 10.00 25.00
118a Kevin Kouzmanoff AU/75 (RC) 8.00 20.00
118b Kevin Kouzmanoff AU/40 (RC) 8.00 20.00
120a Carlos Gomez AU/75 RC 20.00 50.00
120b Carlos Gomez AU/50 (RC) 20.00 50.00
121a Glen Perkins AU/75 (RC) 6.00 15.00
121b Glen Perkins AU/50 (RC) 6.00 15.00
122a Rick Vanden Hurk AU/75 RC 10.00 25.00
122b Rick Vanden Hurk AU/35 (RC) 12.50 30.00
124a Zack Segovia AU/75 (RC) 5.00 12.00
124b Zack Segovia AU/50 (RC) 5.00 12.00
125a Kurt Suzuki AU/75 (RC) 12.50 30.00
125b Kurt Suzuki AU/50 (RC) 12.50 30.00
126a Chris Stewart AU/75 RC 5.00 12.00
126b Chris Stewart AU/50 (RC) 5.00 12.00
128a Ryan Sweeney AU/50 (RC) 6.00 15.00
128b Ryan Sweeney AU/40 (RC) 6.00 15.00
132a Tony Abreu AU/75 RC 10.00 25.00
132b Tony Abreu AU/57 (RC) 10.00 25.00
132c Tony Abreu AU/50 (RC) 10.00 25.00
134a Curtis Thigpen AU/75 (RC) 10.00 25.00
134b Curtis Thigpen AU/40 (RC) 10.00 25.00
135a Jon Coutlangus AU/75 (RC) 5.00 12.00
135b Jon Coutlangus AU/55 (RC) 5.00 12.00
136a Kevin Cameron AU/75 RC 5.00 12.00
136b Kevin Cameron AU/50 (RC) 5.00 12.00
138a Alexi Casilla AU/75 RC 6.00 15.00
138b Alexi Casilla AU/50 (RC) 6.00 15.00
143a Ben Francisco AU/75 (RC) 6.00 15.00
143b Ben Francisco AU/40 (RC) 6.00 15.00
144a Andy Gonzalez AU/75 RC 5.00 12.00
144b Andy Gonzalez AU/50 RC 5.00 12.00
147a Tim Lincecum AU/50 RC 60.00 120.00
147b Tim Lincecum AU/25 (RC) 100.00 200.00
148a Matt Lindstrom AU/75 (RC) 6.00 15.00
148b Matt Lindstrom AU/40 (RC) 6.00 15.00
149a Jay Marshall AU/75 RC 5.00 12.00
149b Jay Marshall AU/50 (RC) 5.00 12.00
150b Daisuke Matsuzaka AU/10 RC
151a Miguel Montero AU/75 (RC) 6.00 15.00
151b Miguel Montero AU/60 (RC) 6.00 15.00
154a Brandon Wood AU/75 (RC) 6.00 15.00
155a Felix Pie AU/75 (RC) 12.50 30.00
155b Felix Pie AU/70 (RC) 12.50 30.00
157a Andy LaRoche AU/50 (RC) 6.00 15.00
157b Andy LaRoche AU/40 (RC) 6.00 15.00
158a Jarrod Saltalamacchia AU/75 (RC) 10.0025.00
158b Jarrod Saltalamacchia AU/25 (RC) 12.50 30.00

2007 SP Authentic Autograph Parallel

RANDOM INSERTS IN PACKS
STATED PRINT RUN 5 SER.#'d SETS
NO PRICING DUE TO SCARCITY
EXCHANGE DEADLINE 11/8/2008

2007 SP Authentic By the Letter Rookie Signatures Full Name Redemptions

RANDOM INSERTS IN PACKS
PRINT RUNS B/WN 1-5 COPIES PER
REDEMPTION CARDS ARE NOT SERIAL #'d
PRINT RUNS PROVIDED BY UPPER DECK
NO PRICING DUE TO SCARCITY
EXCHANGE DEADLINE 12/31/08
101 Joaquin Arias/5

102 Jeff Baker/5
103 Michael Bourn/5
104 Brian Burres/3
105 Jared Burton/3
106 Ryan Braun/2
107 Yovani Gallardo/2
108 Hector Gimenez/3
109 Alex Gordon/3
110 Josh Hamilton/2
111 Justin Hampson/3
112 Sean Henn/5
113 Phil Hughes/3
114 Kei Igawa/2
115 Akinori Iwamura/2
116 Mark Reynolds/2
117 Homer Bailey/3
118 Kevin Kouzmanoff/2
119 Adam Lind/5
120 Carlos Gomez/3
121 Glen Perkins/3
122 Rick Vanden Hurk/2
123 Brad Salmon/3
124 Zack Segovia/3
125 Kurt Suzuki/3
126 Chris Stewart/3
127 Cesar Jimenez/3
128 Ryan Sweeney/2
129 Troy Tulowitzki/3
130 Chase Wright/2
131 Delmon Young/3
132 Tony Abreu/3
133 Brian Barden/3
134 Curtis Thigpen/3
136 Kevin Cameron/3
137 Billy Butler/2
138 Alexi Casilla/5
139 Kory Casto/5
140 Matt Chico/5
141 John Danks/3
142 Andrew Miller/2
143 Ben Francisco/2
144 Andy Gonzalez/3
145 Devern Hansack/3
146 Mike Rabelo/1
147 Tim Lincecum/2
148 Matt Lindstrom/2
149 Jay Marshall/2
150 Daisuke Matsuzaka/2
151 Miguel Montero/5
153 Hunter Pence/5
154 Brandon Wood/3
155 Felix Pie/2
156 Danny Putnam/2
157 Andy LaRoche/3
158 Jarrod Saltalamacchia/5
159 Doug Slaten/3
160 Joe Smith/3

2007 SP Authentic By the Letter Signatures

OVERALL BY THE LETTER AUTOS 1:12
PRINT RUNS B/WN 5-199 COPIES PER
NO PRICING ON SOME DUE TO SCARCITY
EXCHANGE DEADLINE 11/08/2008
1 Derek Jeter EXCH 200.00 300.00
8 Josh Beckett/15 60.00 120.00
10 Aramis Ramirez/25 20.00 50.00
11 Austin Kearns/50 6.00 15.00
16 Felix Pie/75 12.50 30.00
17 Alex Gordon/25 50.00 100.00
22 Adam Lind/75 10.00 25.00
25 Dan Haren/25 8.00 20.00
26 David Ortiz/10 75.00 150.00
27 Felix Hernandez/10 40.00 80.00
2a Ken Griffey Jr./25 100.00 250.00
2b Ken Griffey Jr./20 100.00 250.00
31 Khalil Greene/25 10.00 25.00
36 Ian Kinsler EXCH 8.00 20.00
41 Jonathan Papelbon/40 20.00 50.00
44 Victor Martinez/25 15.00 40.00
45 Roger Clemens/5 100.00 200.00
46 Ryan Zimmerman/25 30.00 60.00
48 Travis Hafner/25 30.00 60.00
4a Justin Verlander/25 20.00 50.00
4b Justin Verlander/15 20.00 50.00
51 Billy Butler/50 20.00 50.00
55 Hunter Pence/50 40.00 80.00
5a Adrian Gonzalez/60 8.00 20.00
5b Adrian Gonzalez/50 8.00 20.00
9a Carlos Quentin/75 10.00 25.00
9b Carlos Quentin/50 10.00 25.00
12a B.J. Upton/25 20.00 50.00
12b B.J. Upton/15 20.00 50.00
13a Boof Bonser/75 6.00 15.00
13b Boof Bonser/50 6.00 15.00
14a Bronson Arroyo/75 8.00 20.00
14b Bronson Arroyo/10 12.50 30.00
15a Troy Tulowitzki EXCH 30.00 60.00
15b Troy Tulowitzki EXCH 30.00 60.00
18a Chris Duffy/75 6.00 15.00
18b Chris Duffy EXCH 6.00 15.00
19a Chris Young/75 6.00 15.00
19b Chris Young/50 6.00 15.00
20a Cliff Lee/75 8.00 20.00
20b Cliff Lee/50 8.00 20.00
21a Cole Hamels/25 20.00 50.00
21b Cole Hamels/15 20.00 50.00
23a Akinori Iwamura/25 30.00 60.00
23b Akinori Iwamura/15 30.00 60.00
24a Dan Uggla/25 12.50 30.00
24b Dan Uggla/21 12.50 30.00
28a Tony Gwynn Jr. EXCH 10.00 25.00
28b Tony Gwynn Jr. EXCH 10.00 25.00
29a Josh Hamilton/75 20.00 50.00
29b Josh Hamilton/50 20.00 50.00
29c Josh Hamilton/10 40.00 80.00
30a Phil Hughes EXCH 30.00 60.00
30b Phil Hughes EXCH 30.00 60.00
32a Dontrelle Willis/25 6.00 15.00
32b Dontrelle Willis/20 6.00 15.00
33a Hanley Ramirez/50 15.00 40.00
33b Hanley Ramirez/25 20.00 50.00
34a Howie Kendrick/60 8.00 20.00
34b Howie Kendrick/50 8.00 20.00
35a Huston Street/50 6.00 15.00
35b Huston Street/25 8.00 20.00
37a Jason Bay/50 8.00 20.00
37b Jason Bay/25 10.00 25.00
40a Joe Mauer EXCH 20.00 50.00
40b Joe Mauer EXCH 20.00 50.00
42a Tim Lincecum/50 60.00 120.00
42b Tim Lincecum/40 60.00 120.00
43a Matt Cain/75 30.00 60.00
43b Matt Cain/40 30.00 60.00
47a Stephen Drew/25 12.50 30.00
47b Stephen Drew/10 15.00 40.00
49a Josh Willingham EXCH 6.00 15.00
49b Josh Willingham/50 6.00 15.00
50a Torii Hunter/25 12.50 30.00
52a Justin Morneau/25 30.00 60.00
52b Justin Morneau/15 30.00 60.00
53a Andy LaRoche/75 6.00 15.00
53b Andy LaRoche/60 6.00 15.00
53c Andy LaRoche/50 6.00 15.00
54a Brandon Wood/75 6.00 15.00
54b Brandon Wood/50 6.00 15.00
56a Devern Hansack EXCH 6.00 15.00
56b Devern Hansack/75 6.00 15.00
56c Devern Hansack EXCH 6.00 15.00
58a Derrek Lee/25 30.00 60.00
58b Derrek Lee/10 40.00 80.00
59a Prince Fielder/25 40.00 80.00
59b Prince Fielder/10 75.00 150.00
60a Kevin Kouzmanoff/50 8.00 20.00

2007 SP Authentic By the Letter Signatures Full Name Redemptions

RANDOM INSERTS IN PACKS
PRINT RUNS B/WN 2-5 COPIES PER
REDEMPTION CARDS ARE NOT SERIAL #'d
PRINT RUNS PROVIDED BY UPPER DECK
NO PRICING DUE TO SCARCITY
EXCHANGE DEADLINE 12/31/08
1 Derek Jeter/2
2 Ken Griffey Jr./3
4 Justin Verlander/2
5 Adrian Gonzalez/5
8 Josh Beckett/5
10 Aramis Ramirez/3
11 Austin Kearns/5
12 B.J. Upton/5
13 Boof Bonser/5
14 Bronson Arroyo/5
15 Troy Tulowitzki/2
16 Felix Pie/5
17 Alex Gordon/3
18 Chris Duffy/5
19 Chris Young/5
20 Cliff Lee/5
21 Cole Hamels/3
22 Adam Lind/5
23 Akinori Iwamura/2
24 Dan Uggla/2
25 Dan Haren/5
26 David Ortiz/2
27 Felix Hernandez/2
28 Tony Gwynn Jr./5
29 Josh Hamilton/3
30 Phil Hughes/3
31 Khalil Greene/3
32 Dontrelle Willis/3
33 Hanley Ramirez/2
34 Howie Kendrick/2
35 Huston Street/3
36 Ian Kinsler/3
37 Jason Bay/5
40 Joe Mauer/2
41 Jonathan Papelbon/2
42 Tim Lincecum/2
43 Matt Cain/5
44 Victor Martinez/2
45 Roger Clemens/2
46 Ryan Zimmerman/2
47 Stephen Drew/5
48 Travis Hafner/3
49 Josh Willingham/2
50 Torii Hunter/3
51 Billy Butler/5
52 Justin Morneau/2
53 Andy LaRoche/3
54 Brandon Wood/5
55 Hunter Pence/3
58 Derrek Lee/5
59 Prince Fielder/3
60 Kevin Kouzmanoff/2

2007 SP Authentic Authentic Power

COMPLETE SET (50) 8.00 20.00
STATED ODDS 1:2
AP1 Adam Dunn .20 .50
AP2 Albert Pujols 1.00 2.50
AP3 Alex Rodriguez .75 2.00
AP4 Alfonso Soriano .20 .50
AP5 Andruw Jones .30 .75
AP6 Aramis Ramirez .20 .50
AP7 Bill Hall .20 .50
AP8 Carlos Beltran .20 .50
AP9 Carlos Delgado .20 .50
AP10 Carlos Lee .20 .50
AP11 Chase Utley .50 1.25
AP12 Chipper Jones .50 1.25
AP13 Dan Uggla .30 .75
AP14 David Ortiz .50 1.25
AP15 David Wright .75 2.00
AP16 Derrek Lee .20 .50
AP17 Eric Chavez .20 .50
AP18 Frank Thomas .50 1.25
AP19 Garrett Atkins .20 .50
AP20 Gary Sheffield .20 .50
AP21 Hideki Matsui .50 1.25
AP22 J.D. Drew .20 .50
AP23 Jason Bay .20 .50
AP24 Jason Giambi .20 .50
AP25 Jeff Francoeur .50 1.25
AP26 Jermaine Dye .20 .50
AP27 Jim Thome .30 .75
AP28 Justin Morneau .20 .50
AP29 Ken Griffey Jr. .75 2.00
AP30 Lance Berkman .20 .50
AP31 Magglio Ordonez .20 .50
AP32 Manny Ramirez .30 .75
AP33 Mark Teixeira .30 .75
AP34 Matt Holliday .50 1.25
AP35 Miguel Cabrera .30 .75
AP36 Miguel Tejada .20 .50
AP37 Mike Piazza .50 1.25
AP38 Nick Swisher .20 .50
AP39 Pat Burrell .20 .50
AP40 Paul Konerko .20 .50
AP41 Prince Fielder .50 1.25
AP42 Richie Sexson .20 .50
AP43 Ryan Howard .75 2.00
AP44 Sammy Sosa .50 1.25
AP45 Todd Helton .30 .75
AP46 Travis Hafner .20 .50
AP47 Troy Glaus .20 .50
AP48 Vernon Wells .20 .50
AP49 Victor Martinez .20 .50
AP50 Vladimir Guerrero .50 1.25

2007 SP Authentic Authentic Speed

COMPLETE SET (50) 8.00 20.00
STATED ODDS 1:2
AS1 Alex Rios .20 .50
AS2 Alex Rodriguez .75 2.00
AS3 Alfonso Soriano .20 .50
AS4 B.J. Upton .20 .50
AS5 Bobby Abreu .20 .50
AS6 Brandon Phillips .20 .50
AS7 Brian Roberts .20 .50
AS8 Carl Crawford .20 .50
AS9 Carlos Beltran .20 .50
AS10 Chase Utley .50 1.25
AS11 Chone Figgins .20 .50
AS12 Chris Burke .20 .50
AS13 Chris Duffy .20 .50
AS14 Coco Crisp .20 .50
AS15 Corey Patterson .20 .50
AS16 Dave Roberts .20 .50
AS17 David Wright .75 2.00
AS18 Derek Jeter 1.25 3.00
AS19 Edgar Renteria .20 .50
AS20 Eric Byrnes .20 .50
AS21 Felipe Lopez .20 .50
AS22 Gary Matthews .20 .50
AS23 Grady Sizemore .30 .75
AS24 Hanley Ramirez .30 .75
AS25 Ian Kinsler .20 .50
AS26 Ichiro Suzuki .75 2.00
AS27 Jacque Jones .20 .50
AS28 Jimmy Rollins .20 .50
AS29 Johnny Damon .30 .75
AS30 Jose Reyes .50 1.25
AS31 Juan Pierre .20 .50
AS32 Julio Lugo .20 .50
AS33 Kenny Lofton .20 .50
AS34 Luis Castillo .20 .50
AS35 Marcus Giles .20 .50
AS36 Melky Cabrera .20 .50
AS37 Mike Cameron .20 .50
AS38 Orlando Cabrera .20 .50
AS39 Rafael Furcal .20 .50
AS40 Randy Winn .20 .50
AS41 Rickie Weeks .20 .50
AS42 Rocco Baldelli .20 .50
AS43 Ryan Freel .20 .50
AS44 Ryan Theriot .20 .50
AS45 Scott Podsednik .20 .50
AS46 Shane Victorino .20 .50
AS47 Tadahito Iguchi .20 .50
AS48 Torii Hunter .20 .50
AS49 Vernon Wells .20 .50
AS50 Willy Taveras .20 .50

2007 SP Authentic Chirography Dual

RANDOM INSERTS IN PACKS
PRINT RUNS B/WN 75-175 COPIES PER
EXCHANGE DEADLINE 11/05/2008
CG Eric Chavez 30.00 60.00
Alex Gordon/75 EXCH
CL Tim Lincecum 30.00 60.00

Matt Cain/175 EXCH
DR Hanley Ramirez 20.00 50.00
Stephen Drew/75 EXCH
HD Adam Dunn 12.50 30.00
Travis Hafner/75
HW Dan Haren 12.50 30.00
Jered Weaver/175 EXCH
KH Cole Hamels 20.00 50.00
Scott Kazmir/175 EXCH
MI Daisuke Matsuzaka 150.00 250.00
Akinori Iwamura/75
ML Andrew Miller 40.00 80.00
Tim Lincecum/175 EXCH
MZ Nick Markakis 20.00 50.00
Ryan Zimmerman/75
RJ Cal Ripken Jr. 150.00 200.00
Derek Jeter/75 EXCH
VH Felix Hernandez/Justin Verlander
/175 EXCH 20.00 50.00
WH Torii Hunter
Vernon Wells/75 EXCH
WK Rickie Weeks 8.00 20.00
Ian Kinsler/175 EXCH

2007 SP Authentic Chirography Quad

RANDOM INSERTS IN PACKS
STATED PRINT RUN 5 SER.#'d SETS
NO PRICING DUE TO SCARCITY
EXCHANGE DEADLINE 11/05/2008
AHBT Matt Holliday
Garrett Atkins
Troy Tulowitzki
Jeff Baker/5 EXCH
CJIH Roger Clemens
Derek Jeter
Phil Hughes
Kei Igawa/5 EXCH
CKJY Carl Crawford
Delmon Young
Scott Kazmir
B.J. Upton/5 EXCH
JQYD Stephen Drew
Conor Jackson
Carlos Quentin
Chris B. Young/5 EXCH
RMCM Cal Ripken Jr.
Nick Markakis
Daniel Cabrera
Melvin Mora/5 EXCH
SWGB Ben Sheets
Rickie Weeks
Tony Gwynn Jr.
Ryan Braun/5 EXCH

2007 SP Authentic Sign of the Times Dual

RANDOM INSERTS IN PACKS
PRINT RUNS B/WN 75-175 COPIES PER
EXCHANGE DEADLINE 11/05/2008
BP Josh Beckett 75.00 150.00
Jonathan Papelbon/75 EXCH
CH Eric Chavez 8.00 20.00
Rich Harden/75 EXCH
CJ Roger Clemens 200.00 250.00
Derek Jeter/75 EXCH
CL Matt Cain 50.00 100.00
Tim Lincecum/175 EXCH
FL Rafael Furcal 8.00 20.00
Andy LaRoche/175 EXCH
GD Ken Griffey Jr. 60.00 120.00
Adam Dunn/75 EXCH
HM Travis Hafner 20.00 50.00
Victor Martinez/75 EXCH
SW Ben Sheets 8.00 20.00
Rickie Weeks/75 EXCH
TK Mark Teixeira 8.00 20.00
Ian Kinsler/75
UY Delmon Young 12.50 30.00
B.J. Upton/75 EXCH
VM Justin Verlander 30.00 60.00
Andrew Miller/75 EXCH

2007 SP Authentic Sign of the Times Triple

RANDOM INSERTS IN PACKS
PRINT RUNS B/WN 25-75 COPIES PER
NO PRICING ON QTY OF 25 DUE TO SCARCITY
EXCHANGE DEADLINE 11/05/2008
CBK Roger Clemens
Josh Beckett
Scott Kazmir/25 EXCH
FLR Rafael Furcal 30.00 60.00
Felipe Lopez
Hanley Ramirez/75 EXCH
GHY Ken Griffey Jr.
Torii Hunter
Chris B. Young/25 EXCH
HHM Cole Hamels
Felix Hernandez
Andrew Miller/25 EXCH
KKL Ian Kinsler 15.00 40.00
Howie Kendrick
Adam Lind/75 EXCH
MII Daisuke Matsuzaka
Akinori Iwamura
Kei Igawa/25 EXCH
NZP Joe Nathan
Joel Zumaya
Jonathan Papelbon/25 EXCH
RJD Cal Ripken Jr.
Derek Jeter
Stephen Drew/25 EXCH
TOH Jim Thome
David Ortiz
Travis Hafner/25 EXCH

2007 SP Authentic Sign of the Times Quad

RANDOM INSERTS IN PACKS
STATED PRINT RUN 5 SER.#'d SETS
NO PRICING DUE TO SCARCITY
EXCHANGE DEADLINE 11/05/2008
GKIB Alex Gordon
Ryan Braun
Kevin Kouzmanoff
Akinori Iwamura/5 EXCH
GWHY Ken Griffey Jr.
Torii Hunter
Vernon Wells
Chris B. Young/5 EXCH
OMMH Daisuke Matsuzaka
Andrew Miller
Phil Hughes
Micah Owings/5 EXCH
THOT David Ortiz
Jim Thome
Travis Hafner
Mark Teixeira/5 EXCH

2008 SP Authentic

This set was released on October 14, 2008. The base set consists of 191 cards. Cards 1-100 feature veterans, and cards 101-191 are rookies serial numbered of various quantities. Some rookie cards feature autographs, jerseys, or both.

COMP.SET w/o RCs (100) 8.00 20.00
COMMON CARD .15 .40
COMMON AU RC (101-191) 3.00 8.00
AU PRINT RUNS 149-999 PER
OVERALL AU ODDS 1:8 HOBBY
COMMON JSY AU RC (101-191) 4.00 10.00
JSY AU PRINT RUN 299-999 PER
OVERALL AU ODDS 1:8 HOBBY
EXCH DEADLINE 9/18/2010
1 Ken Griffey Jr. .60 1.50
2 Derek Jeter 1.00 2.50
3 Albert Pujols .75 2.00
4 Ichiro Suzuki .60 1.50
5 Daisuke Matsuzaka .60 1.50
6 Vladimir Guerrero .40 1.00
7 Magglio Ordonez .25 .60
8 Eric Chavez .15 .40
9 Randy Johnson .40 1.00
10 Ryan Braun .50 1.25
11 Phil Hughes .40 1.00
12 Joba Chamberlain .50 1.25
13 B.J. Upton .25 .60
14 Frank Thomas .40 1.00
15 Greg Maddux .50 1.25
16 Delmon Young .25 .60
17 Carlos Beltran .15 .40
18 Derrek Lee .25 .60
19 Aramis Ramirez .15 .40
20 Miguel Tejada .15 .40
21 Manny Ramirez .40 1.00
22 Justin Upton .40 1.00
23 Miguel Cabrera .25 .60
24 Prince Fielder .40 1.00
25 Adam Dunn .15 .40
26 Jose Reyes .25 .60
27 Chase Utley .40 1.00
28 Jimmy Rollins .25 .60
29 Joe Blanton .15 .40
30 Mark Teixeira .25 .60
31 Brian McCann .25 .60
32 Russell Martin .15 .40
33 Ian Kinsler .25 .60
34 Travis Hafner .15 .40
35 Victor Martinez .15 .40
36 Grady Sizemore .25 .60
37 Alex Rodriguez .60 1.50
38 David Wright .50 1.25
39 Ryan Howard .50 1.25
40 Carlos Lee .15 .40
41 Lance Berkman .25 .60
42 Hunter Pence .40 1.00
43 John Lackey .15 .40
44 C.C. Sabathia .15 .40
45 Michael Young .15 .40
46 Carl Crawford .15 .40
47 Carlos Pena .40 1.00
48 Justin Verlander .25 .60
49 Cole Hamels .40 1.00
50 Carlos Zambrano .15 .40
51 Jake Peavy .25 .60
52 Khalil Greene .25 .60
53 Chris Young .15 .40
54 Vernon Wells .15 .40
55 Alex Rios .15 .40
56 Roy Halladay .15 .40
57 Roy Oswalt .15 .40
58 Ben Sheets .25 .60
59 J.J. Hardy .15 .40
60 Pedro Martinez .25 .60
61 Nick Swisher .15 .40
62 Curtis Granderson .15 .40
63 Johnny Damon .25 .60
64 Mariano Rivera .40 1.00
65 Josh Beckett .25 .60
66 Erik Bedard .15 .40
67 Johan Santana .25 .60
68 Joe Mauer .25 .60
69 Justin Morneau .25 .60
70 Torii Hunter .15 .40
71 Alex Gordon .40 1.00
72 Jose Guillen .15 .40
73 Jim Thome .25 .60
74 Paul Konerko .15 .40
75 Josh Hamilton .50 1.25
76 Hanley Ramirez .40 1.00
77 Dontrelle Willis .15 .40
78 Dan Uggla .25 .60
79 Brandon Phillips .15 .40
80 Rick Ankiel .15 .40
81 Nick Markakis .25 .60
82 Ryan Zimmerman .25 .60
83 Brian Roberts .25 .60
84 Lastings Milledge .15 .40
85 Freddy Sanchez .15 .40
86 Barry Zito .15 .40
87 Matt Cain .15 .40
88 Andruw Jones .15 .40
89 Dan Haren .15 .40
90 Chien-Ming Wang .50 1.25
91 Jonathan Papelbon .25 .60
92 Felix Hernandez .25 .60
93 David Ortiz .40 1.00
94 Jason Bay .15 .40
95 Matt Holliday .25 .60
96 Troy Tulowitzki .25 .60
97 Hideki Matsui .40 1.00
98 Jeff Francoeur .25 .60
99 Alfonso Soriano .25 .60
100 Curt Schilling .25 .60
101 Alex Romero Jsy AU/799 (RC) 4.00 10.00
102 Matt Tolbert Jsy/699 RC 5.00 12.00
103 Bobby Wilson AU/699 (RC) 6.00 15.00
104 Brent Lillibridge AU/599 (RC) 5.00 12.00
105 Brian Barton AU/698 RC 6.00 15.00
106 Brian Bass Jsy AU/799 (RC) 8.00 20.00
107 Brian Bixler AU/698 (RC) 3.00 8.00
108 Brian Bocock Jsy AU/599 RC 4.00 10.00
109 Burke Badenhop AU/797 RC 3.00 8.00
110 Chin-Lung Hu Jsy AU/999 (RC) 10.00 25.00
111 Chris Perez AU/699 RC 5.00 12.00
112 Clay Buchholz Jsy AU/699 (RC) 8.00 20.00
113 Clayton Kershaw Jsy AU/699 RC EXCH 12.50 30.00
114 Colt Morton Jsy AU/574 RC 4.00 10.00
115 Daric Barton Jsy AU/799 (RC) 4.00 10.00
116 Darren O'Day AU/798 RC 3.00 8.00
117 David Purcey AU/599 (RC) 3.00 8.00
118 Denard Span Jsy AU/299 (RC) EXCH 8.00 20.00
119 Elliot Johnson AU/798 (RC) 3.00 8.00
120 Emmanuel Burriss AU/299 RC EXCH 4.00 10.00
121 Evan Longoria Jsy AU/499 RC 50.00 100.00
122 Evan Meek Jsy AU/649 RC 5.00 12.00
123 Felipe Paulino Jsy AU/799 RC 4.00 10.00
124 Carlos Gonzalez Jsy AU/599 (RC) EXCH 10.00 25.00
125 German Duran AU/699 RC 3.00 8.00
126 Greg Reynolds AU/149 RC 3.00 8.00
127 Greg Smith Jsy AU/799 RC 5.00 12.00
128 Harvey Garcia Jsy AU/799 (RC) 4.00 10.00
129 Hernan Iribarren Jsy AU/799 (RC) 4.00 10.00
130 Ian Kennedy Jsy AU/699 RC 10.00 25.00
131 J.R. Towles Jsy AU/499 RC 4.00 10.00
132 Jay Bruce Jsy AU/549 (RC) 20.00 50.00
133 Jayson Nix Jsy AU/299 (RC) EXCH 4.00 10.00
134 Jed Lowrie AU/499 (RC) 10.00 25.00
135 Jeff Clement AU/399 (RC) 6.00 15.00
136 Jonathan Herrera AU/699 RC 3.00 8.00
137 Joey Votto Jsy AU/999 (RC) 10.00 25.00
138 Johnny Cueto Jsy AU/999 RC 8.00 20.00
139 Jonathan Albaladejo Jsy AU/799 RC 4.00 10.00
140 Justin Masterson AU/699 RC 20.00 50.00
141 Justin Ruggiano AU/149 RC 3.00 8.00
142 Kevin Hart Jsy AU/749 (RC) 4.00 10.00
143 Kosuke Fukudome Jsy/799 RC 12.50 30.00
144 Luis Mendoza Jsy AU/299 (RC) 4.00 10.00
145 Luke Carlin AU/699 RC 6.00 15.00
146 Luke Hochevar AU/798 RC 4.00 10.00
147 Max Scherzer Jsy AU/799 RC EXCH 12.50 30.00
148 Micah Hoffpauir AU/699 RC 8.00 20.00
149 Mike Parisi AU/699 RC 8.00 20.00
150 Nick Adenhart AU/599 (RC) 5.00 12.00
151 Nick Blackburn Jsy AU/799 RC 8.00 20.00
152 Nyjer Morgan Jsy AU/999 (RC) 4.00 10.00
153 Ramon Troncoso Jsy AU/399 RC 5.00 12.00
154 Randor Bierd Jsy AU/799 RC 4.00 10.00
155 Rich Thompson AU/398 RC 5.00 12.00
156 Rico Washington Jsy AU/799 (RC) 4.00 10.00
157 Ross Ohlendorf Jsy AU/999 RC 4.00 10.00
158 Steve Holm Jsy AU/999 RC 4.00 10.00
159 Wesley Wright Jsy AU/849 RC 4.00 10.00
160 Wladimir Balentien AU/599 (RC) 3.00 8.00
161 Alex Hinshaw AU/699 RC EXCH 5.00 12.00
162 Bobby Korecky AU/999 RC 5.00 12.00
163 Brad Harman AU/999 RC 5.00 12.00
164 Brandon Boggs AU/999 (RC) 3.00 8.00
165 Callix Crabbe AU/325 (RC) 3.00 8.00
166 Clay Timpner AU/849 (RC) 3.00 8.00
167 Clete Thomas AU/850 RC 6.00 15.00
168 Cory Wade AU/999 (RC) 3.00 8.00
169 Doug Mathis AU/999 RC 3.00 8.00
170 Eider Torres AU/999 RC 5.00 12.00
171 Gregorio Petit AU/999 RC 4.00 10.00
172 Michael Aubrey AU/699 RC EXCH 4.00 10.00
173 Jesse Carlson AU/999 RC 8.00 20.00
174 Billy Buckner AU/999 (RC) 3.00 8.00
175 Josh Newman AU/699 RC 3.00 8.00
176 Matt Tupman AU/999 RC 5.00 12.00
177 Matt Joyce AU/999 RC 8.00 20.00
178 Paul Janish AU/999 (RC) 5.00 12.00
179 Robinzon Diaz AU/999 (RC) 3.00 8.00
180 Fernando Hernandez AU/999 RC 3.00 8.00
181 Brandon Jones AU/999 RC 3.00 8.00
182 Eddie Bonine AU/899 RC 3.00 8.00
183 Chris Smith AU/384 (RC) 6.00 15.00
184 Jonathan Van Every AU/999 RC 4.00 10.00
185 Marino Salas AU/999 RC 4.00 10.00
186 Mike Aviles AU/899 RC 6.00 15.00
187 Mitchell Boggs AU/699 (RC) EXCH 6.00 15.00
188 Chris Carter AU/699 (RC) EXCH 5.00 12.00
189 Travis Denker AU/699 RC EXCH 3.00 8.00
190 Carlos Rosa AU/699 RC 5.00 12.00
191 Evan Longoria Jsy AU/350 (RC) 50.00 100.00

2008 SP Authentic Gold

*GOLD 1-100: 5X TO 12X BASIC
*GLD AU RC: .75X TO 2X BASIC
*GLD JSY AU RC: .75X TO 2X BASIC
RANDOM INSERTS IN PACKS
PRINT RUN B/WN 10-50 SER.#'d SETS
NO VOTTO PRICING AVAILABLE
EXCH DEADLINE 9/18/2010
2 Derek Jeter 20.00 50.00
4 Ichiro Suzuki 20.00 50.00
110 Chin-Lung Hu Jsy AU/50 40.00 80.00
112 Clay Buchholz Jsy AU/50 20.00 50.00
121 Evan Longoria Jsy AU/50 400.00 600.00

147 Max Scherzer Jsy AU/50 40.00 80.00
151 Nick Blackburn Jsy AU/50 20.00 50.00
191 Evan Longoria AU/50 250.00 350.00

2008 SP Authentic Authentic Achievements

STATED ODDS 1:2 HOBBY
AA1 Derek Jeter 2.00 5.00
AA2 Ken Griffey Jr. 1.25 3.00
AA3 Randy Johnson .75 2.00
AA4 Frank Thomas .75 2.00
AA5 Tom Glavine .50 1.25
AA6 Matt Holliday .50 1.25
AA7 Justin Verlander .50 1.25
AA8 Manny Ramirez .75 2.00
AA9 Scott Rolen .50 1.25
AA10 Brandon Webb .50 1.25
AA11 Erik Bedard .30 .75
AA12 Daisuke Matsuzaka 1.25 3.00
AA13 Johan Santana .50 1.25
AA14 Carlos Lee .30 .75
AA15 Alfonso Soriano .50 1.25
AA16 Grady Sizemore .50 1.25
AA17 Jose Reyes .50 1.25
AA18 Chase Utley .75 2.00
AA19 Roy Oswalt .30 .75
AA20 David Ortiz .75 2.00
AA21 Jake Peavy .50 1.25
AA22 Hanley Ramirez .75 2.00
AA23 Alex Rodriguez 1.25 3.00
AA24 Ryan Howard 1.00 2.50
AA25 David Wright 1.00 2.50
AA26 Trevor Hoffman .30 .75
AA27 Prince Fielder .75 2.00
AA28 Ichiro Suzuki 1.25 3.00
AA29 Jimmy Rollins .50 1.25
AA30 Mariano Rivera .75 2.00
AA31 Pedro Martinez .50 1.25
AA32 Torii Hunter .30 .75
AA33 Ivan Rodriguez .50 1.25
AA34 Jim Thome .50 1.25
AA35 Chipper Jones 1.00 2.50
AA36 John Smoltz .75 2.00
AA37 Jeff Kent .30 .75
AA38 Albert Pujols 1.50 4.00
AA39 Lance Berkman .50 1.25
AA40 Justin Morneau .50 1.25
AA41 Andruw Jones .30 .75
AA42 Adam Dunn .30 .75
AA43 Greg Maddux 1.00 2.50
AA44 Billy Wagner .30 .75
AA45 Vladimir Guerrero .75 2.00
AA46 C.C. Sabathia .30 .75
AA47 Mark Teixeira .50 1.25
AA48 Mark Buehrle .30 .75
AA49 Miguel Cabrera .50 1.25
AA50 Josh Beckett .50 1.25

2008 SP Authentic By The Letter Signatures

OVERALL AU ODDS 1:8 HOBBY
ANNCD PRINT RUNS LISTED
SER.# ON CARDS ARE DIFFERENT
EXCH DEADLINE 9/18/2010
AD Adam Dunn/140 * 10.00 25.00
Spells Dunn and Reds
AG Adrian Gonzalez/110 * 8.00 20.00
Spells Gonzalez and Padres
AS Alfonso Soriano/90 *
Spells Soriano and Cubs
BH Bill Hall/1570 * 8.00 20.00
Spells Bill Hall and Milwaukee Brewers
BP Brandon Phillips/1259 * 12.50 30.00
Spells Brandon Phillips and Cincinnati Reds
BR Brandon Webb/30 *
Spells Webb
BW Billy Wagner/125 * 20.00 50.00
Spells Wagner and New York Mets
CB Chad Billingsley/1306 * 10.00 25.00
Spells Chad Billingsley and Los Angeles Dodgers
CD Chris Duncan/480 *
Spells Chris Duncan and St Louis Cardinals
CJ Chipper Jones/100 * 75.00 150.00
Spells Chipper and Braves
CL Carlos Lee/160 * 10.00 25.00
Spells Lee and Houston Astros
CW Chien-Ming Wang/80 * 200.00 300.00
Spells Wang and Yankees
DA David Murphy/1837 * 10.00 26.00
Spells David Murphy and Texas Rangers
DE David Eckstein/10 *
Spells David Eckstein and Toronto Blue Jays
DJ Derek Jeter/240 * 100.00 175.00
Spells Jeter and Yankees EXCH
DM Daisuke Matsuzaka/125 * 175.00 300.00
Spells Matsuzaka and Red Sox
EE Edwin Encarnacion/1570 * 5.00 12.00
Spells Edwin Encarnacion and Cincinnati Reds
FC Fausto Carmona/844 * 8.00 20.00
Spells Fausto Carmona and Cleveland Indians
GA Garrett Atkins/588 * 10.00 25.00
Spells Garrett Atkins and Colorado Rockies
GJ Geoff Jenkins/1200 * 8.00 20.00
Spells Geoff Jenkins and Philadelphia Phillies
GM Gil Meche/380 *
Spells Gil Meche and Kansas City Royals
GS Grady Sizemore/240 * 40.00 80.00
Spells Sizemore and Indians
HK Howie Kendrick/175 *
Spells Howie Kendrick and Anaheim Angels
JB Joe Blanton/580 * 6.00 15.00
Spells Joe Blanton and Oakland Athletics
JE Jeff Francoeur/275 * 15.00 40.00
Spells Jeff Francoeur and Atlanta Braves
JF Jeff Francis/335 * 8.00 20.00
Spells Jeff Francis and Colorado Rockies
JG Jeremy Guthrie/985 * 12.50 30.00
Spells Jeremy Guthrie and Baltimore Orioles
JH Jeremy Hermida/505 *
Spells Jeremy Hermida and Florida Marlins
JL James Loney/1275 * 10.00 25.00
Spells James Loney and Los Angeles Dodgers EXCH
JN Joe Nathan/365 * 10.00 25.00
Spells Joe Nathan and Minnesota Twins
JO John Lackey/187 * 12.50 30.00
Spells John Lackey and Anaheim Angels
JP Jonathan Papelbon/550 * 20.00 50.00
Spells Papelbon and Red Sox
JS Jon Lester/235 * 60.00 120.00
Spells Jon Lester and Boston Red Sox
JT Jim Thome/35 *
Spells Thome and White Sox
JV Jason Varitek/110 *
Spells Varitek and Red Sox
KE Kevin Youkilis/365 * 50.00 100.00
Spells Kevin Youkilis and Boston Red Sox
KG Ken Griffey Jr./275 * 100.00 175.00
Spells Griffey and Reds EXCH
KJ Kelly Johnson/1399 * 5.00 12.00
Spells Kelly Johnson and Atlanta Braves
LB Lance Berkman/165 * 30.00 60.00
Spells Berkman and Astros
MC Miguel Cabrera/35 *
Spells Cabrera and Tigers
ME Mark Ellis/995 * 5.00 12.00
Spells Mark Ellis and Oakland Athletics
MG Matt Garza/235 * 20.00 50.00
Spells Matt Garza and Tampa Bay Rays
MK Matt Kemp/1369 * 10.00 25.00
Spells Matt Kemp and Los Angeles Dodgers EXCH
MM Melvin Mora/490 * 8.00 20.00
Spells Melvin Mora and Baltimore Orioles EXCH
NL Noah Lowry/1440 * 10.00 25.00
Spells Noah Lowry and San Francisco Giants
NM Nick Markakis/1100 *
Spells Nick Markakis and Baltimore Orioles
NS Nick Swisher/1150 * 10.00 25.00
Spells Nick Swisher and Chicago White Sox
PF Prince Fielder/245 * 20.00 50.00
Spells Fielder and Brewers EXCH
PH Phil Hughes/385 * 12.50 30.00
Spells Phil Hughes and New York Yankees
PK Paul Konerko/175 * 15.00 40.00
Spells Konerko and White Sox
RH Rich Hill/220 * 10.00 25.00
Spells Hill and Cubs
RM Russell Martin/265 * 40.00 80.00
Spells Martin and Dodgers
RO Roy Halladay/160 * 40.00 80.00
Spells Halladay and Blue Jays
SB Scott Baker/1248 * 6.00 15.00
Spells Scott Baker and Minnesota Twins
TG Tom Gorzelanny/1082 * 5.00 12.00
Spells Tom Gorzelanny and Pittsburgh Pirates
TH Tim Hudson/170 *
Spells Hudson and Braves
TT Troy Tulowitzki/252 * 20.00 50.00
Spells Tulowitzki and Rockies
YE Yunel Escobar/1342 *
Spells Yunel Escobar and Atlanta Braves

2008 SP Authentic Chirography Signatures Dual

OVERALL AU ODDS 1:8 HOBBY
PRINT RUNS B/WN 10-99 COPIES PER
NO PRICING ON MOST CARDS
EXCH DEADLINE 9/18/2010
BH Joe Blanton
Rich Harden/99
GB Tom Gorzelanny 10.00 25.00
Chad Billingsley/96
GJ Ken Griffey Jr.
Derek Jeter/25
HF Bill Hall
Prince Fielder/25
HK Phil Hughes 20.00 50.00
Ian Kennedy/99 EXCH
KF Howie Kendrick
Chone Figgins/99
KW Ian Kennedy
Chien-Ming Wang/15
MH David Murphy
Josh Hamilton/99
MK Nick Markakis
Matt Kemp/99
MM Russell Martin
Victor Martinez/99
PE Brandon Phillips 6.00 15.00
Edwin Encarnacion/99
SD Nick Swisher
Chris Duncan/99
TS Jim Thome
Alfonso Soriano/10
WH Brandon Webb
Dan Haren/25
WJ Chien-Ming Wang
Derek Jeter/15

2008 SP Authentic Chirography Signatures Triple

OVERALL AU ODDS 1:8 HOBBY
PRINT RUNS B/WN 25-50 COPIES PER
NO PRICING DUE TO SCARCITY
EXCH DEADLINE 9/18/2010
EPE David Eckstein
Placido Polanco
Mark Ellis/50
GMM Jeremy Guthrie
Melvin Mora
Nick Markakis/50
HHK Jeremy Hermida
Corey Hart
Matt Kemp/50
HHM Felix Hernandez
Cole Hamels
John Maine/25 EXCH
JEF Kelly Johnson
Yunel Escobar
Jeff Francoeur/50
KEH Howie Kendrick
Edwin Encarnacion
Chin-Lung Hu/50
KFL Howie Kendrick
Chone Figgins
John Lackey/25
KHZ Ian Kinsler
Bill Hall
Ryan Zimmerman/50
LPH Derrek Lee
Felix Pie
Rich Hill/25
PBT Hunter Pence
Michael Bourn
J.R. Towles/25

2008 SP Authentic Chirography Signatures Quad

OVERALL AU ODDS 1:8 HOBBY
PRINT RUNS B/WN 5-15 COPIES PER
NO PRICING DUE TO SCARCITY
EXCH DEADLINE 9/18/2010
CHMS Fausto Carmona
Travis Hafner
Victor Martinez
Grady Sizemore/10
GPED Ken Griffey Jr.
Brandon Phillips
Edwin Encarnacion
Adam Dunn/5
HBLK Chin-Lung Hu
Chad Billingsley
James Loney
Matt Kemp/10
JEFJ Kelly Johnson
Yunel Escobar
Jeff Francoeur
Chipper Jones/10
PFJG Albert Pujols
Prince Fielder
Derek Jeter
Ken Griffey Jr./15

2008 SP Authentic Marquee Matchups

STATED ODDS 1:2 HOBBY
MM1 Derek Jeter 2.00 5.00
Curt Schilling
MM2 Josh Beckett 2.00 5.00
Derek Jeter
MM3 Albert Pujols 1.50 4.00
Brad Lidge
MM4 Daisuke Matsuzaka 1.25 3.00
Alex Rodriguez
MM5 Ken Griffey Jr. 1.25 3.00
John Smoltz
MM6 John Smoltz 1.00 2.50
David Wright
MM7 Jonathan Papelbon .50 1.25
Gary Sheffield
MM8 Ryan Braun 1.00 2.50
Roy Oswalt
MM9 Mariano Rivera .75 2.00
David Ortiz
MM10 Carlos Zambrano 1.50 4.00
Albert Pujols
MM11 Dontrelle Willis .30 .75
Travis Hafner
MM12 Felix Hernandez .50 1.25
Victor Martinez
MM13 Carlos Zambrano .30 .75
Carlos Lee
MM14 Chien-Ming Wang 1.00 2.50
Manny Ramirez
MM15 Felix Hernandez .50 1.25
Justin Morneau
MM16 Ichiro Suzuki 1.25 3.00
Francisco Rodriguez
MM17 Grady Sizemore .50 1.25
Erik Bedard
MM18 Vladimir Guerrero .75 2.00
Justin Verlander
MM19 Daisuke Matsuzaka 1.25 3.00
Ichiro Suzuki
MM20 Alfonso Soriano .50 1.25
Chris Carpenter
MM21 Hanley Ramirez .75 2.00
Pedro Martinez
MM22 Chase Utley .75 2.00
Randy Johnson
MM23 Ken Griffey Jr. 1.25 3.00
Roy Oswalt
MM24 Randy Johnson 1.25 3.00
Ken Griffey Jr.
MM25 Jimmy Rollins .50 1.25
Johan Santana
MM26 Matt Cain .30 .75
Andruw Jones
MM27 Pedro Martinez 1.00 2.50
Ryan Howard
MM28 Cole Hamels .75 2.00
David Wright
MM29 Chipper Jones .50 1.25
Johan Santana
MM30 Billy Wagner .50 1.25
Mark Teixeira
MM31 C.C. Sabathia .50 1.25
Magglio Ordonez
MM32 Jose Reyes .50 1.25
Tom Glavine
MM33 Derek Jeter 2.00 5.00
Jonathan Papelbon
MM34 Johan Santana .50 1.25
Alex Rodriguez
MM35 Alfonso Soriano .50 1.25
Jake Peavy
MM36 Johan Santana .50 1.25
Ryan Howard
MM37 Jake Peavy .50 1.25
Russell Martin
MM38 Carlos Zambrano .75 2.00
Prince Fielder
MM39 Cole Hamels .75 2.00
Carlos Beltran
MM40 Josh Beckett 1.25 3.00
Alex Rodriguez
MM41 Roy Halladay 2.00 5.00
Derek Jeter
MM42 Hideki Matsui 1.25 3.00
Daisuke Matsuzaka
MM43 C.C. Sabathia .50 1.25
Joe Mauer
MM44 Francisco Rodriguez .75 2.00
Manny Ramirez
MM45 Jered Weaver .50 1.25
Miguel Cabrera
MM46 David Wright .50 1.25
Jake Peavy
MM47 Greg Maddux 1.25 3.00
Ken Griffey Jr.
MM48 John Smoltz .75 2.00
Hanley Ramirez
MM49 Pedro Martinez 1.25 3.00
Alex Rodriguez
MM50 Trevor Hoffman .50 1.25
Matt Holliday

2008 SP Authentic Rookie Exclusives

RANDOM INSERTS IN PACKS
AH Alex Hinshaw 1.25 3.00
AR Alex Romero 1.25 3.00
BA Brian Barton 1.25 3.00
BB Brandon Boggs 1.25 3.00
BH Brad Harman 1.25 3.00
BI Brian Bixler .75 2.00
BK Bobby Korecky .75 2.00
BO Brian Bocock .75 2.00
BR Brian Bass .75 2.00
BU Burke Badenhop 1.25 3.00
BW Bobby Wilson .75 2.00
CB Clay Buchholz 2.00 5.00
CC Callix Crabbe .75 2.00
CM Colt Morton .75 2.00
CT Clay Timpner .75 2.00
CU Johnny Cueto 1.25 3.00
CW Cory Wade .75 2.00
DB Daric Barton .75 2.00
DM Doug Mathis .75 2.00
DS Denard Span 1.25 3.00
EB Emmanuel Burriss 1.25 3.00
EJ Elliot Johnson .75 2.00
EM Evan Meek .75 2.00
ET Eider Torres 1.25 3.00
FH Fernando Hernandez .75 2.00
FP Felipe Paulino 1.25 3.00
GD German Duran 1.25 3.00
GP Gregorio Petit 1.25 3.00
GS Greg Smith .75 2.00
HI Hernan Iribarren .75 2.00
IK Ian Kennedy 2.00 5.00
JA Jonathan Albaladejo 1.25 3.00
JB Jay Bruce 3.00 8.00
JC Jesse Carlson 1.25 3.00
JH Jonathan Herrera 1.25 3.00
JL Jed Lowrie 2.00 5.00
JN Jayson Nix .75 2.00
JT J.R. Towles 2.00 5.00
KH Kevin Hart .75 2.00
LC Luke Carlin .75 2.00
LM Luis Mendoza .75 2.00
MA Matt Tolbert 1.25 3.00
MH Micah Hoffpauir 1.25 3.00
MJ Matt Joyce 2.00 5.00
MP Mike Parisi 1.25 3.00
MT Matt Tupman .75 2.00
NA Nick Adenhart .75 2.00
NB Nick Blackburn 1.25 3.00
NE Josh Newman 1.25 3.00
NM Nyjer Morgan .75 2.00
RB Randor Bierd .75 2.00
RD Robinzon Diaz .75 2.00
RI Rich Thompson 1.25 3.00
RO Ross Ohlendorf 1.25 3.00
RT Ramon Troncoso .75 2.00
RW Rico Washington .75 2.00
SH Steve Holm .75 2.00
TH Clete Thomas 1.25 3.00
WB Wladimir Balentien .75 2.00
WW Wesley Wright .75 2.00

2008 SP Authentic Rookie Exclusives Autographs

OVERALL AU ODDS 1:8 HOBBY
NO PRICING DUE TO SCARCITY
EXCH DEADLINE 9/18/2010

2008 SP Authentic Sign of the Times Dual

OVERALL AU ODDS 1:8 HOBBY
PRINT RUNS B/WN 10-99 COPIES PER
MOST CARDS NOT PRICED
EXCH DEADLINE 9/18/2010
BB Clay Buchholz
Chad Billingsley/99 EXCH
DC Daisuke Matsuzaka
Chien-Ming Wang/10
FZ Jeff Francoeur
Ryan Zimmerman/25
GL Yovani Gallardo
Tim Lincecum/99
GM Alex Gordon
Gil Meche/99
HL Phil Hughes
Jon Lester/25
JE Kelly Johnson
Yunel Escobar/99
JH Derek Jeter
Phil Hughes/25
JT Derek Jeter
Troy Tulowitzki/25
KR Ian Kinsler
Mark Reynolds/99
NW Joe Nathan 20.00 50.00
Billy Wagner/74
PK Brandon Phillips
Howie Kendrick/99
PW Felix Pie 6.00 15.00
Josh Willingham/99
RJ Rich Hill
Jon Lester/99
UR B.J. Upton
Hanley Ramirez/25

2008 SP Authentic Sign of the Times Triple

OVERALL AU ODDS 1:8 HOBBY
PRINT RUNS B/WN 10-50 COPIES PER
NO PRICING DUE TO SCARCITY
EXCH DEADLINE 9/18/2010
BEB Joe Blanton
Mark Ellis
Daric Barton/50
BLK Chad Billingsley
James Loney
Matt Kemp/50
BTL Lance Berkman
J.R. Towles
Carlos Lee/15
FTL Prince Fielder
Jim Thome
Derrek Lee/14
HCM Travis Hafner
Fausto Carmona
Victor Martinez/50
HGK Jeremy Hermida
Carlos Gomez
Matt Kemp/50
HHM Roy Halladay
Felix Hernandez
Daisuke Matsuzaka/10
JKK Kelly Johnson
Kevin Kouzmanoff
Ian Kinsler/50
TAF Troy Tulowitzki
Garrett Atkins
Jeff Francis/50
WYE Josh Willingham
Chris B. Young
Andre Ethier/50

2008 SP Authentic USA Junior National Team Jersey Autographs

OVERALL AU ODDS 1:8 HOBBY
STATED PRINT RUN 120 SER.#'d SETS
AA Andrew Aplin 10.00 25.00
AM Austin Maddox 15.00 40.00
CC Colton Cain 4.00 10.00
CG Cameron Garfield 5.00 12.00
CT Cecil Tanner 4.00 10.00
DN David Nick 4.00 10.00
DT Donovan Tate 10.00 25.00
FR Nick Franklin 5.00 12.00
HM Harold Martinez 10.00 25.00
JB Jake Barrett 6.00 15.00
MA Jeff Malm 6.00 15.00
ME Jonathan Meyer 8.00 20.00
MP Matthew Purke 8.00 20.00
MS Max Stassi 6.00 15.00
NF Nolan Fontana
RW Ryan Weber
TU Jacob Turner 8.00 20.00
WH Wes Hatton 10.00 25.00

2008 SP Authentic USA Junior National Team Patch Autographs

OVERALL AU ODDS 1:8 HOBBY
STATED PRINT RUN 50 SER.#'d SETS
AA Andrew Aplin 10.00 25.00
AM Austin Maddox
CC Colton Cain 10.00 25.00
CG Cameron Garfield
CT Cecil Tanner
DN David Nick 6.00 15.00
DT Donovan Tate
FR Nick Franklin
HM Harold Martinez
JB Jake Barrett 6.00 15.00
MA Jeff Malm
ME Jonathan Meyer
MP Matthew Purke
MS Max Stassi 30.00 60.00
NF Nolan Fontana 12.50 30.00
RW Ryan Weber 12.50 30.00
TU Jacob Turner 15.00 40.00
WH Wes Hatton 15.00 40.00

2008 SP Authentic USA National Team By the Letter Autographs

OVERALL AU ODDS 1:8 HOBBY
PRINT RUNS BW/N 50-181 PER
AG A.J. Griffin/105 6.00 15.00
AO Andrew Oliver/105
BS Blake Smith/105 8.00 20.00
CC Christian Colon/105 8.00 20.00
CH Chris Hernandez/180 12.50 30.00
DD Derek Dietrich/105 12.50 30.00
HM Hunter Morris/106
KD Kentrail Davis/103 20.00 50.00
KG Kyle Gibson/181 10.00 25.00
KR Kevin Rhoderick/172 6.00 15.00
KV Kendal Volz/105 8.00 20.00
MD Matt den Dekker/105 8.00 20.00
MG Micah Gibbs/180 6.00 15.00
ML Mike Leake/180 6.00 15.00
MM Mike Minor/105 8.00 20.00
RJ Ryan Jackson/104 8.00 20.00
RL Ryan Lipkin/50
SS Stephen Strasberg/105
TL Tyler Lyons/104 6.00 15.00

2001 SP Game Used Edition

This 90-card set was distributed in three-card packs with a suggested retail value of $29.99 and features color action player photos. The set includes the following subset: Super Prospects (61-90).

COMP.SET w/o SP's (60) 30.00 80.00
COMMON CARD (1-60) .50 1.25
COMMON CARD (61-90) 3.00 8.00
1 Garret Anderson .50 1.25
2 Troy Glaus .50 1.25
3 Darin Erstad .50 1.25
4 Jason Giambi .50 1.25
5 Tim Hudson .50 1.25
6 Johnny Damon .75 2.00
7 Carlos Delgado .50 1.25
8 Greg Vaughn .50 1.25
9 Juan Gonzalez .50 1.25
10 Roberto Alomar .75 2.00
11 Jim Thome .75 2.00
12 Edgar Martinez .75 2.00
13 Cal Ripken 4.00 10.00
14 Andres Galarraga .50 1.25
15 Alex Rodriguez 2.00 5.00
16 Rafael Palmeiro .75 2.00
17 Ivan Rodriguez .75 2.00
18 Manny Ramirez Sox .75 2.00
19 Nomar Garciaparra 2.00 5.00
20 Pedro Martinez .75 2.00
21 Jermaine Dye .50 1.25
22 Dean Palmer .50 1.25
23 Matt Lawton .50 1.25
24 Frank Thomas 1.25 3.00
25 David Wells .50 1.25
26 Magglio Ordonez .50 1.25
27 Derek Jeter 3.00 8.00
28 Bernie Williams .75 2.00
29 Roger Clemens 2.50 6.00
30 Jeff Bagwell .75 2.00
31 Richard Hidalgo .50 1.25
32 Chipper Jones 1.25 3.00
33 Andruw Jones .75 2.00
34 Greg Maddux 2.00 5.00
35 Jeffrey Hammonds .50 1.25
36 Mark McGwire 3.00 8.00
37 Jim Edmonds .50 1.25
38 Sammy Sosa 1.25 3.00
39 Corey Patterson .50 1.25
40 Randy Johnson 1.25 3.00
41 Luis Gonzalez .50 1.25
42 Gary Sheffield .50 1.25
43 Shawn Green .50 1.25
44 Kevin Brown .50 1.25
45 Vladimir Guerrero 1.25 3.00
46 Barry Bonds 3.00 8.00
47 Jeff Kent .50 1.25
48 Preston Wilson .50 1.25
49 Charles Johnson .50 1.25
50 Mike Piazza 2.00 5.00
51 Edgardo Alfonzo .50 1.25
52 Tony Gwynn 1.50 4.00
53 Scott Rolen .75 2.00
54 Pat Burrell .50 1.25
55 Brian Giles .50 1.25
56 Jason Kendall .50 1.25
57 Ken Griffey Jr. 2.00 5.00
58 Mike Hampton .50 1.25
59 Todd Helton .75 2.00
60 Larry Walker .50 1.25
61 Wilson Betemit RC 6.00 15.00
62 Travis Hafner RC 12.50 30.00
63 Ichiro Suzuki RC 40.00 80.00
64 Juan Diaz RC 3.00 8.00
65 Morgan Ensberg RC 6.00 15.00
66 Horacio Ramirez RC 4.00 10.00
67 Ricardo Rodriguez RC 3.00 8.00
68 Sean Douglass RC 3.00 8.00
69 Brandon Duckworth RC 3.00 8.00
70 Jackson Melian RC 3.00 8.00
71 Adrian Hernandez RC 3.00 8.00
72 Kyle Kessel RC 3.00 8.00
73 Jason Michaels RC 3.00 8.00
74 Esix Snead RC 3.00 8.00
75 Jason Smith RC 3.00 8.00
76 Tyler Walker RC 3.00 8.00
77 Juan Uribe RC 4.00 10.00
78 Adam Pettyjohn RC 3.00 8.00
79 Tsuyoshi Shinjo RC 4.00 10.00
80 Mike Penney RC 3.00 8.00
81 Josh Towers RC 4.00 10.00
82 Erick Almonte RC 3.00 8.00
83 Ryan Freel RC 4.00 10.00
84 Juan Pena 3.00 8.00
85 Albert Pujols RC 40.00 80.00
86 Henry Mateo RC 3.00 8.00
87 Greg Miller RC 3.00 8.00
88 Jose Mieses RC 3.00 8.00
89 Jack Wilson RC 4.00 10.00
90 Carlos Valderrama RC 3.00 8.00

2001 SP Game Used Edition Authentic Fabric

Randomly inserted one in every pack, this 82-card set features color player portraits with a swatch of a game-used jersey embedded in the card.

Card	Low	High
AH Aubrey Huff	4.00	10.00
AJ Andruw Jones	6.00	15.00
AL Al Leiter	4.00	10.00
AP Adam Piatt	4.00	10.00
ARH A.Rodriguez Rangers	6.00	15.00
ARM Alex Rodriguez Mariners DP	6.00	15.00
BB Barry Bonds	10.00	25.00
BG Brian Giles SP	10.00	25.00
BL Barry Larkin	6.00	15.00
CD Carlos Delgado SP	10.00	25.00
CJ Chipper Jones	6.00	15.00
CJO Charles Johnson	4.00	10.00
CR Cal Ripken	15.00	40.00
DE Darin Erstad	4.00	10.00
DW David Wells SP	10.00	25.00
DY Dmitri Young	4.00	10.00
EA Edgardo Alfonzo	4.00	10.00
EC Eric Chavez	4.00	10.00
EM Edgar Martinez DP	6.00	15.00
FM Fred McGriff	6.00	15.00
FTA Fernando Tatis	4.00	10.00
FTH Frank Thomas	6.00	15.00
GM Greg Maddux DP	6.00	15.00
GS Gary Sheffield	4.00	10.00
GV Greg Vaughn	4.00	10.00
IR Ivan Rodriguez	6.00	15.00
JB Jeromy Burnitz	4.00	10.00
JCB Jose Canseco BLC		
JCH Jose Canseco	6.00	15.00
JCI Jeff Cirillo	4.00	10.00
JDI Joe DiMaggio SP/50 *	75.00	150.00
JDR J.D. Drew DP	4.00	10.00
JDY Jermaine Dye SP	10.00	25.00
JE Jim Edmonds DP	4.00	10.00
JG Jason Giambi	4.00	10.00
JI Jason Isringhausen SP	10.00	25.00
JK Jason Kendall	4.00	10.00
JK Jeff Kent	4.00	10.00
JO John Olerud	4.00	10.00
JT Jim Thome	6.00	15.00
JV Jose Vidro	4.00	10.00
KB Kevin Brown	4.00	10.00
KGH Ken Griffey Jr. Reds	6.00	15.00
KGM Ken Griffey Jr. Mariners DP	6.00	15.00
KGR Ken Griffey Jr. Road		
KL Kenny Lofton	4.00	10.00
KM Kevin Millwood	4.00	10.00
LG Luis Gonzalez	4.00	10.00
MG Mark Grace	6.00	15.00
MH Mike Hampton	4.00	10.00
MM Mickey Mantle SP/50 *	150.00	250.00
MO Magglio Ordonez	4.00	10.00
MR Mariano Rivera	6.00	15.00
MT Miguel Tejada	4.00	10.00
MW Matt Williams	4.00	10.00
NR Nolan Ryan Rangers SP/50 *	40.00	80.00
NRA Nolan Ryan Astros SP/50 *	40.00	80.00
PB Pat Burrell	4.00	10.00
PN Phil Nevin	4.00	10.00
PW Preston Wilson	4.00	10.00
RA Rick Ankiel DP	4.00	10.00
RAL Roberto Alomar	6.00	15.00
RC Roger Clemens	6.00	15.00
RJ Randy Johnson	6.00	15.00
RM Roger Maris SP	40.00	80.00
RV Robin Ventura	4.00	10.00
SG Shawn Green	4.00	10.00
SR Scott Rolen	6.00	15.00
SSH Sammy Sosa Home	6.00	15.00
SSR Sammy Sosa Road	6.00	15.00
TB Tony Batista SP	6.00	15.00
TGL Troy Glaus	4.00	10.00
TGW Tony Gwynn DP	6.00	15.00
TH Tim Hudson	4.00	10.00
THE Todd Helton	6.00	15.00
TL Terrence Long	4.00	10.00
TM Tino Martinez	6.00	15.00
TOG Tom Glavine	6.00	15.00
TRH Trevor Hoffman	4.00	10.00
TS Tom Seaver Mets SP/50 *	15.00	40.00
TSR Tom Seaver Reds SP/50 *	15.00	40.00
TZ Todd Zeile	4.00	10.00

2001 SP Game Used Edition Authentic Fabric Autographs

Randomly inserted in packs, this 21-card set is an autographed, partial parallel version of the regular insert set. Only 50 serially numbered sets were produced. An exchange card was seeded into packs for Alex Rodriguez.

Card	Low	High
SAJ Andruw Jones	40.00	80.00
SAR Alex Rodriguez	100.00	200.00
SBB Barry Bonds	125.00	200.00
SCD Carlos Delgado	20.00	50.00
SCJ Chipper Jones	60.00	120.00
SCR Cal Ripken	125.00	200.00
SDW David Wells	20.00	50.00
SEA Edgardo Alfonzo	20.00	50.00
SFTH Frank Thomas	60.00	120.00
SIR Ivan Rodriguez	60.00	120.00
SJC Jose Canseco	40.00	80.00
SJDR J.D. Drew	20.00	50.00
SJG Jason Giambi	20.00	50.00
SKG Ken Griffey Jr.	75.00	150.00
SNR Nolan Ryan	125.00	200.00
SRA Rick Ankiel	30.00	60.00
SRJ Randy Johnson	60.00	120.00
SSS Sammy Sosa	50.00	100.00
STGL Troy Glaus	40.00	80.00
STH Tim Hudson	40.00	80.00
STS Tom Seaver Mets		

2001 SP Game Used Edition Authentic Fabric Duos

Randomly inserted in packs, this 14-card set features color photos of two players to a card with two game jersey swatches embedded in each card. Only 50 serially numbered sets were produced.

Card	Low	High
BC Barry Bonds / Jose Canseco	40.00	80.00
CW Roger Clemens / Bernie Williams	20.00	50.00
GR Ken Griffey Jr. / Alex Rodriguez	30.00	60.00
GS Ken Griffey Jr. / Sammy Sosa	30.00	60.00
HG Tim Hudson / Jason Giambi	15.00	40.00
JJ Chipper Jones / Andruw Jones	20.00	50.00
JR Randy Johnson / Nolan Ryan	50.00	100.00
MD Mickey Mantle / Joe DiMaggio	250.00	400.00
MM Mickey Mantle / Roger Maris	250.00	400.00
RR Alex Rodriguez / Ivan Rodriguez	30.00	60.00
RS Nolan Ryan / Tom Seaver	60.00	120.00
SG Gary Sheffield / Shawn Green	15.00	40.00
SR Sammy Sosa / Alex Rodriguez	30.00	60.00
ST Sammy Sosa / Frank Thomas	20.00	50.00

2001 SP Game Used Edition Authentic Fabric Trios

Randomly inserted in packs, this six-card set features color photos of three players to a card with three game jersey swatches embedded in each card. Only 25 serially numbered sets were produced. Due to market scarcity, no pricing is provided for these cards.

DGS Joe DiMaggio / Ken Griffey Jr. / Sammy Sosa
DMM Joe DiMaggio / Mickey Mantle / Roger Maris
GRS Ken Griffey Jr. / Alex Rodriguez / Sammy Sosa
JBS Andruw Jones / Barry Bonds / Sammy Sosa
JSM Randy Johnson / Tom Seaver / Greg Maddux
MJJ Greg Maddux / Chipper Jones / Andruw Jones

2004 SP Game Used Patch

The initial 119 card set was released in April, 2004. This set was issued in three-card pack with an $150 SRP which came one pack to box and 12 boxes to a case. Cards numbered 1 through 60 feature active veterans while cards 61 through 90 feature veterans in a significant number subset in which cards were issued to an important number of their career. Cards numbered 91 through 119 feature rookies and those cards were issued to a stated print run of 375 serial numbered sets. Cards 121-170 were issued as a complete sealed factory set randomly seeded into one in every 48 hobby boxes of 2004 Upper Deck Series 2 baseball in June, 2004. Please note, card 120 was never produced, thus the set is complete at 169 cards despite being checklisted from 1-170.

	Low	High
COMP.UPDATE SET (50)	40.00	100.00
COMMON CARD 1-60	1.50	4.00
61-90 PRINT RUN B/WN 86-684 COPIES PER		
COMMON CARD (91-119)	3.00	8.00
COMMON CARD (121-135)	1.00	2.50
COMMON CARD (136-170)	1.00	2.50
ONE UPDATE SET PER 48 UD2 HOB.BOXES		
1 Miguel Cabrera	1.50	4.00
2 Alex Rodriguez Yanks	3.00	8.00
3 Edgar Renteria	1.50	4.00
4 Juan Gonzalez	1.50	4.00
5 Mike Lowell	1.50	4.00
6 Andruw Jones	1.50	4.00
7 Eric Chavez	1.50	4.00
8 Jim Edmonds	1.50	4.00
9 Mike Piazza	3.00	8.00
10 Angel Berroa	1.50	4.00
11 Eric Gagne	1.50	4.00
12 Jody Gerut	1.50	4.00
13 Orlando Cabrera	1.50	4.00
14 Austin Kearns	1.50	4.00
15 Frank Thomas	2.00	5.00
16 Johan Santana	2.00	5.00
17 Randy Johnson	2.00	5.00
18 Preston Wilson	1.50	4.00
19 Garret Anderson	1.50	4.00
20 Jorge Posada	1.50	4.00
21 Rich Harden	1.50	4.00
22 Barry Zito	1.50	4.00
23 Gary Sheffield	1.50	4.00
24 Jose Reyes	1.50	4.00
25 Roy Halladay	1.50	4.00
26 Ben Sheets	1.50	4.00
27 Geoff Jenkins	1.50	4.00
28 Josh Beckett	1.50	4.00
29 Roy Oswalt	1.50	4.00
30 Bobby Abreu	1.50	4.00
31 Hank Blalock	1.50	4.00
32 Kerry Wood	1.50	4.00
33 Ryan Klesko	1.50	4.00
34 Rafael Furcal	1.50	4.00
35 Tom Glavine	1.50	4.00
36 Kevin Brown	1.50	4.00
37 Scott Rolen	1.50	4.00
38 Bret Boone	1.50	4.00
39 Ichiro Suzuki	4.00	10.00
40 Lance Berkman	1.50	4.00
41 Tim Hudson	1.50	4.00
42 Carlos Delgado	1.50	4.00
43 Ivan Rodriguez	1.50	4.00
44 Luis Gonzalez	1.50	4.00
45 Torii Hunter	1.50	4.00
46 Carlos Lee	1.50	4.00
47 Jacque Jones	1.50	4.00
48 Manny Ramirez	1.50	4.00
49 Troy Glaus	1.50	4.00
50 Corey Patterson	1.50	4.00
51 Jason Schmidt	1.50	4.00
52 Mark Mulder	1.50	4.00
53 Vernon Wells	1.50	4.00
54 Curt Schilling	1.50	4.00
55 Javy Lopez	1.50	4.00
56 Mark Prior	1.50	4.00
57 Dontrelle Willis	1.50	4.00
58 Derek Jeter	4.00	10.00
59 Jeff Bagwell	1.50	4.00
60 Marlon Byrd	1.50	4.00
61 Rafael Palmeiro SN/500	2.00	5.00
62 Kevin Millwood SN/165	2.00	5.00
63 Greg Maddux SN/273	4.00	10.00
64 Adam Dunn SN/400	2.00	5.00
65 Richie Sexson SN/469	2.00	5.00
66 Magglio Ordonez SN/567	2.00	5.00
67 Hideo Nomo SN/236	2.50	6.00
68 Albert Pujols SN/194	5.00	12.00
69 Rocco Baldelli SN/368	2.00	5.00
70 Mark Teixeira SN/86	2.50	6.00
71 Jason Giambi SN/660	2.00	5.00
72 Alfonso Soriano SN/230	2.00	5.00
73 Roger Clemens SN/300	5.00	12.00
74 Miguel Tejada SN/359	2.00	5.00
75 Jeff Kent SN/684	2.00	5.00
76 Bernie Williams SN/342	2.00	5.00
77 Sammy Sosa SN/470	2.50	6.00
78 Mike Mussina SN/641	2.00	5.00
79 Jim Thome SN/334	2.00	5.00
80 Brian Giles SN/506	2.00	5.00
81 Shawn Green SN/234	2.00	5.00
82 Mike Sweeney SN/340	2.00	5.00
83 John Smoltz SN/262	2.00	5.00
84 Carlos Beltran SN/319	2.00	5.00
85 Todd Helton SN/384	2.00	5.00
86 Nomar Garciaparra SN/372	4.00	10.00
87 Ken Griffey Jr. SN/481	4.00	10.00
88 Chipper Jones SN/633	2.50	6.00
89 Vladimir Guerrero SN/226	2.50	6.00
90 Pedro Martinez SN/313	2.00	5.00
91 Brandon Medders RD RC	3.00	8.00
92 Colby Miller RD RC	3.00	8.00
93 Dave Crouthers RD RC	3.00	8.00
94 Dennis Sarfate RD RC	3.00	8.00
95 Donald Kelly RD RC	3.00	8.00
96 Alec Zumwalt RD RC	3.00	8.00
97 Chris Aguila RD RC	3.00	8.00
98 Greg Dobbs RD RC	3.00	8.00
99 Ian Snell RD RC	4.00	10.00
100 Jake Woods RD RC	3.00	8.00
101 Jamie Brown RD RC	3.00	8.00
102 Jason Frasor RD RC	3.00	8.00
103 Jerome Gamble RD RC	3.00	8.00
104 Jesse Harper RD RC	3.00	8.00
105 Josh Labandeira RD RC	3.00	8.00
106 Justin Hampson RD RC	3.00	8.00
107 Justin Huisman RD RC	3.00	8.00
108 Justin Leone RD RC	4.00	10.00
109 Lincoln Holdzkom RD RC	3.00	8.00
110 Mike Bumatay RD RC	3.00	8.00
111 Mike Gosling RD RC	3.00	8.00
112 Mike Johnston RD RC	3.00	8.00
113 Mike Rouse RD RC	3.00	8.00
114 Nick Regilio RD RC	3.00	8.00
115 Ryan Meaux RD RC	3.00	8.00
116 Scott Dohmann RD RC	3.00	8.00
117 Sean Henn RD RC	3.00	8.00
118 Tim Bausher RD RC	3.00	8.00
119 Tim Bittner RD RC	3.00	8.00
121 Richie Sexson	1.00	2.50
122 Javier Vazquez	1.00	2.50
123 Alex Rodriguez Yanks	3.00	8.00
124 Javy Lopez	1.00	2.50
125 Miguel Tejada	1.00	2.50
126 Bartolo Colon	1.00	2.50
127 Ivan Rodriguez	1.50	4.00
128 Rafael Palmeiro	1.50	4.00
129 Kevin Brown	1.00	2.50
130 Gary Sheffield	1.00	2.50
131 Greg Maddux	3.00	8.00
132 Curt Schilling	1.50	4.00
133 Roger Clemens	4.00	10.00
134 Alfonso Soriano	1.00	2.50
135 Vladimir Guerrero	2.00	5.00
136 Carlos Vasquez RC	1.00	2.50
137 Roman Colon RC	1.00	2.50
138 William Bergolla RC	1.00	2.50
139 Jason Bartlett RC	1.25	3.00
140 Casey Daigle RC	1.00	2.50
141 Ryan Wing RC	1.00	2.50
142 Chris Saenz RC	1.00	2.50
143 Edwin Moreno RC	1.00	2.50
144 Shawn Hill RC	1.00	2.50
145 Eddy Rodriguez RC	1.25	3.00
146 Justin Knoedler RC	1.00	2.50
147 Renyel Pinto RC	1.25	3.00
148 Kevin Cave RC	1.00	2.50
149 Carlos Hines RC	1.00	2.50
150 Merkin Valdez RC	1.25	3.00
151 Tim Hamulack RC	1.00	2.50
152 Hector Gimenez RC	1.00	2.50
153 Mike Vento RC	1.25	3.00
154 Scott Proctor RC	1.25	3.00
155 Rusty Tucker RC	1.25	3.00
156 Akinori Otsuka RC	1.00	2.50
157 Ronny Cedeno RC	2.00	5.00
158 Jose Capellan RC	1.25	3.00
159 Justin Germano RC	1.00	2.50
160 Shingo Takatsu RC	2.00	5.00
161 Fernando Nieve RC	2.00	5.00
162 Michael Wuertz RC	1.25	3.00
163 Jerry Gil RC	1.00	2.50
164 Jorge Vasquez RC	1.00	2.50
165 Chad Bentz RC	1.00	2.50
166 Luis A. Gonzalez RC	1.25	3.00
167 Ivan Ochoa RC	1.00	2.50
168 Onil Joseph RC	1.00	2.50
169 Enemencio Pacheco RC	1.00	2.50
170 Kazuo Matsui RC	1.25	3.00

2004 SP Game Used Patch 1 of 1

RANDOM INSERTS IN PACKS
STATED PRINT RUN 1 SERIAL #'d SET
NO PRICING DUE TO SCARCITY

2004 SP Game Used Patch 300 Win Club

RANDOM INSERTS IN PACKS
STATED PRINT RUN 10 SERIAL #'d SETS
NO PRICING DUE TO SCARCITY
DS Don Sutton
LG Lefty Grove
NR Nolan Ryan
RC Roger Clemens
SC Steve Carlton
TS Tom Seaver
WS Warren Spahn

2004 SP Game Used Patch 300 Win Club Autograph

RANDOM INSERTS IN PACKS
STATED PRINT RUN 10 SERIAL #'d SETS
NO PRICING DUE TO SCARCITY
DS Don Sutton
GP Gaylord Perry
NR Nolan Ryan Astros
NR1 Nolan Ryan Mets
NR2 Nolan Ryan Angels
NR3 Nolan Ryan Rgr
PN Phil Niekro
SC Steve Carlton
TS Tom Seaver Mets
TS1 Tom Seaver W.Sox

2004 SP Game Used Patch 3000 Hit Club

RANDOM INSERTS IN PACKS
STATED PRINT RUN 10 SERIAL #'d SETS
NO PRICING DUE TO SCARCITY
CR Cal Ripken
CY Carl Yastrzemski
SM Stan Musial
TG Tony Gwynn

2004 SP Game Used Patch 3000 Hit Club Autograph

RANDOM INSERTS IN PACKS
STATED PRINT RUN 10 SERIAL #'d SETS
NO PRICING DUE TO SCARCITY
CR Cal Ripken
CY Carl Yastrzemski
LB Lou Brock Cards
LB1 Lou Brock Cubs
PM Paul Molitor Brewers
PM1 Paul Molitor Jays
PM2 Paul Molitor Twins
RY Robin Yount
TG Tony Gwynn
WB Wade Boggs

2004 SP Game Used Patch 500 HR Club

RANDOM INSERTS IN PACKS
STATED PRINT RUN 10 SERIAL #'d SETS
NO PRICING DUE TO SCARCITY
EM Eddie Mathews
FR Frank Robinson
HK Harmon Killebrew
MS Mike Schmidt
RP Rafael Palmeiro
SS Sammy Sosa
TW Ted Williams

2004 SP Game Used Patch 500 HR Club Autograph

RANDOM INSERTS IN PACKS
STATED PRINT RUN 10 SERIAL #'d SETS
NO PRICING DUE TO SCARCITY
FR Frank Robinson Reds
FR1 Frank Robinson O's
HK Harmon Killebrew Twins
HK1 Harmon Killebrew Royals
HK2 Harmon Killebrew Senators
RP Rafael Palmeiro Rgr
RP1 Rafael Palmeiro O's

2004 SP Game Used Patch 500 HR Club Triple

RANDOM INSERTS IN PACKS
STATED PRINT RUN 10 SERIAL #'d SETS
NO PRICING DUE TO SCARCITY
MSW Eddie Mathews / Sammy Sosa / Ted Williams
RKS Frank Robinson / Harmon Killebrew / Mike Schmidt

2004 SP Game Used Patch All-Star

Card	Low	High
RANDOM INSERTS IN PACKS		
STATED PRINT RUN 50 SERIAL #'d SETS		
AP Albert Pujols	40.00	80.00
AR Alex Rodriguez	30.00	60.00
AS Alfonso Soriano	10.00	25.00
BZ Barry Zito	10.00	25.00
CD Carlos Delgado	10.00	25.00
CJ Chipper Jones	15.00	40.00
CS Curt Schilling	15.00	40.00
DJ Derek Jeter	50.00	100.00
EC Eric Chavez	10.00	25.00
FT Frank Thomas	15.00	40.00
GS Gary Sheffield	10.00	25.00
HE Todd Helton	15.00	40.00
HN Hideo Nomo	40.00	80.00
IS Ichiro Suzuki	50.00	100.00
JG Juan Gonzalez	10.00	25.00
JT Jim Thome	15.00	40.00
KG Ken Griffey Jr.	30.00	60.00
MP Mark Prior	15.00	40.00
SS Sammy Sosa	15.00	40.00
TH Tim Hudson	10.00	25.00
VW Vernon Wells	10.00	25.00

2004 SP Game Used Patch All-Star Number

Card	Low	High
RANDOM INSERTS IN PACKS		
PRINT RUNS B/WN 3-50 COPIES PER		
NO PRICING ON QTY OF 12 OR LESS		
AJ Andruw Jones/25	20.00	50.00
AP Andy Pettitte/42	15.00	40.00
AR Alex Rodriguez/3		
AS Alfonso Soriano/12		
BZ Barry Zito/50	10.00	25.00
CD Carlos Delgado/25	15.00	40.00
CD1 Carlos Delgado/25	15.00	40.00
CJ Chipper Jones/10		
CS Curt Schilling Sox/38	15.00	40.00
CS1 Curt Schilling D'backs/38	10.00	25.00
CY Carl Yastrzemski/8		
EC Eric Chavez/3		
EC1 Eric Chavez/3		
FT Frank Thomas/35	15.00	40.00
GA Garret Anderson/16	15.00	40.00
GM Greg Maddux Braves/31	30.00	60.00
GM1 Greg Maddux Cubs/31	30.00	60.00
GS Gary Sheffield/11		
HE Todd Helton/17	20.00	50.00
HN Hideo Nomo/10		
IR Ivan Rodriguez/7		
IS Ichiro Suzuki/50	50.00	100.00
JG Juan Gonzalez/19	15.00	40.00
JP Jorge Posada/20	20.00	50.00
JT Jim Thome/25	20.00	50.00
KG Ken Griffey Jr./30	40.00	80.00
MM Mike Mussina/35	15.00	40.00
MO Magglio Ordonez/30	10.00	25.00
MP Mark Prior/5		
MT Miguel Tejada/4		
PM Pedro Martinez/45	15.00	40.00
PU Albert Pujols/7		
RC Roger Clemens/22	40.00	80.00
RH Roy Halladay/32	10.00	25.00
RP Rafael Palmeiro/25	20.00	50.00
SG Shawn Green/15	15.00	40.00
SR Scott Rolen/27	15.00	40.00
SS Sammy Sosa Cubs/21	20.00	50.00
SS1 Sammy Sosa Sox/21	20.00	50.00
TH Tim Hudson/15	15.00	40.00
TH1 Tim Hudson/15	15.00	40.00
VW Vernon Wells/10		

2004 SP Game Used Patch All-Star Autograph

RANDOM INSERTS IN PACKS
STATED PRINT RUN 10 SERIAL #'d SETS
NO PRICING DUE TO SCARCITY

2004 SP Game Used Patch All-Star Autograph Dual

RANDOM INSERTS IN PACKS
STATED PRINT RUN 10 SERIAL #'d SETS
NO PRICING DUE TO SCARCITY

2004 SP Game Used Patch Cut Signatures

RANDOM INSERTS IN PACKS
PRINT RUNS B/WN 1-2 COPIES PER
NO PRICING DUE TO SCARCITY
AD John Adams/1
AE Albert Einstein/1
DE1 Dwight Eisenhower/1
HH Herbert Hoover/1
JA James Monroe/1
JPG Jean Paul Getty/2
MLK Martin Luther King Jr./1
OW Orville Wright/1
REL Robert E. Lee/1
SH William Sherman/1
TE Thomas Edison/1

2004 SP Game Used Patch Famous Nicknames

RANDOM INSERTS IN PACKS
PRINT RUNS B/WN 1-27 COPIES PER
NO PRICING ON QTY OF 14 OR LESS
AR Alex Rodriguez/10
BM Bill Mazeroski/1
BR Brooks Robinson/23 20.00 50.00
CR Cal Ripken Glove Down/21 100.00 200.00
CR1 Cal Ripken Glove Up/21 100.00 200.00
CY Carl Yastrzemski/23 40.00 80.00
DM Don Mattingly/14
DS Darryl Strawberry/17 15.00 40.00
DW Dontrelle Willis/1
ES Duke Snider/18 20.00 50.00
FT Frank Thomas/14
GA Sparky Anderson/27 10.00 25.00
GC Gary Carter/19 15.00 40.00
HK Harmon Killebrew/22 50.00 100.00
HM Hideki Matsui/1
IR Ivan Rodriguez/13
JB Jeff Bagwell/13
JD Joe DiMaggio/13
JF Nellie Fox/19 100.00 200.00
JG Juan Gonzalez/15 15.00 40.00
JH Catfish Hunter/15 20.00 50.00
KG Ken Griffey Jr./15 60.00 120.00
LB Yogi Berra/19 50.00 100.00
LJ Chipper Jones Hand Up/10
LJ1 Chipper Jones Arms Out/10
MU Mike Mussina Yanks/13
MU1 Mike Mussina O's/13
NR Nolan Ryan Astros/27 50.00 100.00
NR1 Nolan Ryan Rgr/27 50.00 100.00
OC Orlando Cepeda/17 15.00 40.00
OS Ozzie Smith/19 40.00 80.00
PN Phil Niekro/24 15.00 40.00
RC Roger Clemens/20 40.00 80.00
RI Phil Rizzuto/13
RJ Randy Johnson/16 20.00 50.00
RR Red Rolfe/10
RY Robin Yount/20 20.00 50.00
SM Stan Musial/22 75.00 150.00
SS Sammy Sosa Cubs/15 20.00 50.00
SS1 Sammy Sosa Sox/15 20.00 50.00
TS Tom Seaver/20 20.00 50.00
WS Willie Stargell/21 20.00 50.00

2004 SP Game Used Patch Famous Nicknames Autograph

RANDOM INSERTS IN PACKS
STATED PRINT RUN 50 SERIAL #'d SETS
AD Andre Dawson 30.00 60.00
AR Alex Rodriguez Rgr 125.00 200.00
AR1 Alex Rodriguez M's 125.00 200.00
BM Bill Mazeroski 40.00 80.00
BR Brooks Robinson 40.00 80.00
DM Don Mattingly 75.00 150.00
FT Frank Thomas 50.00 100.00
HK Harmon Killebrew 50.00 100.00
HM Hideki Matsui 250.00 400.00
JB Jeff Bagwell 60.00 120.00
JG Juan Gonzalez 30.00 60.00
KG Ken Griffey Jr. 100.00 200.00
LJ Chipper Jones Hand Up 50.00 100.00
MM Mike Mussina 40.00 80.00
NR Nolan Ryan 125.00 200.00
OS Ozzie Smith 60.00 120.00
PN Phil Niekro 30.00 60.00
RC Roger Clemens 100.00 175.00
RY Robin Yount 60.00 120.00
TS Tom Seaver 40.00 80.00
WI Dontrelle Willis 40.00 80.00

2004 SP Game Used Patch HOF Numbers

RANDOM INSERTS IN PACKS
PRINT RUNS B/WN 1-50 COPIES PER
NO PRICING ON QTY OF 11 OR LESS
AJ Andruw Jones/25 20.00 50.00
AP Albert Pujols/5
AR Alex Rodriguez/3
BE Johnny Bench/5
BG Bob Gibson/45 15.00 40.00
BM Bill Mazeroski/1
BR Brooks Robinson/5
BW Billy Williams/26 15.00 40.00
CD Carlos Delgado/25 15.00 40.00
CH Catfish Hunter/27 15.00 40.00
CJ Chipper Jones/10
CL Roger Clemens/22 40.00 80.00
CR Cal Ripken/8
CS Curt Schilling/38 15.00 40.00
CY Carl Yastrzemski/8
DD Don Drysdale/50 30.00 60.00
DJ Derek Jeter Cap/2
DJ1 Derek Jeter No Cap/2
DS Don Sutton/20 15.00 40.00
EC Eric Chavez/3
EG Eric Gagne/38 10.00 25.00
EM Eddie Mathews/41 40.00 80.00
FR Frank Robinson/20 15.00 40.00
FT Frank Thomas/35 15.00 40.00
GC Gary Carter/8
GL Tom Glavine/47 15.00 40.00
GM Greg Maddux/31 30.00 60.00
GO Juan Gonzalez Royals/19 15.00 40.00
GO1 Juan Gonzalez Rgr/19 15.00 40.00
GP Gaylord Perry/36 10.00 25.00
GS Gary Sheffield/11
HE Todd Helton/17 20.00 50.00
HK Harmon Killebrew/3
HN Hideo Nomo/10
IR Ivan Rodriguez/7
IS Ichiro Suzuki/50 50.00 100.00
JB Jeff Bagwell/5
JC Jose Canseco/33 15.00 40.00
JD Joe DiMaggio/5
JG Jason Giambi/25 15.00 40.00
JI Jim Thome/25 20.00 50.00
JM Joe Morgan/8
JP Jim Palmer/22 15.00 40.00
JT Joe Torre/9
KG Ken Griffey Jr./30 40.00 80.00
LA Luis Aparicio/11
LD Leo Durocher/2
MA Juan Marichal/27 15.00 40.00
MP Mike Piazza/31 30.00 60.00
MR Manny Ramirez/24 20.00 50.00
MS Mike Schmidt/20 40.00 80.00
MZ Pedro Martinez/45 15.00 40.00
NF Nellie Fox/2
NG Nomar Garciaparra/5
NR Nolan Ryan/34 40.00 80.00
OC Orlando Cepeda/30 10.00 25.00
OS Ozzie Smith/1
PI Mark Prior Look Right/22 15.00 40.00
PI1 Mark Prior Look Left/22 15.00 40.00
PM Paul Molitor/4
PR Phil Rizzuto/10
RC Roberto Clemente/21 200.00 350.00
RF Rollie Fingers/34 10.00 25.00
RH Rickey Henderson/25 20.00 50.00
RP Rafael Palmeiro O's/25 20.00 50.00
RP1 Rafael Palmeiro Rgr/25 20.00 50.00
RY Robin Yount/19 20.00 50.00
SA Sparky Anderson/2
SC Steve Carlton/32 10.00 25.00
SG Shawn Green/15 15.00 40.00
SM Stan Musial/6
SN Duke Snider/4
SR Scott Rolen/27 15.00 40.00
SS Sammy Sosa Cubs/21 20.00 50.00
SS1 Sammy Sosa Sox/21 20.00 50.00
ST Willie Stargell/8
TG Tony Gwynn/19
TH Tim Hudson/15 15.00 40.00
TS Tom Seaver/41 15.00 40.00
WB Wade Boggs/26 15.00 40.00
WS Warren Spahn/21 40.00 80.00
YB Yogi Berra/8

2004 SP Game Used Patch HOF Numbers Autograph

RANDOM INSERTS IN PACKS
STATED PRINT RUN 10 SERIAL #'d SETS
PUCKETT PRINT RUN 3 SERIAL #'d CARDS
NO PRICING DUE TO SCARCITY

2004 SP Game Used Patch HOF Numbers Autograph Dual

RANDOM INSERTS IN PACKS
STATED PRINT RUN 10 SERIAL #'d SETS
NO PRICING DUE TO SCARCITY

2004 SP Game Used Patch Legendary Combo Cuts

RANDOM INSERTS IN PACKS
STATED PRINT RUN 1 SERIAL #'d SET
NO PRICING DUE TO SCARCITY
AECL Amelia Earhart
Charles Lindbergh
BRMM Babe Ruth
Mickey Mantle
ERFR Eleanor Roosevelt
Franklin D.Roosevelt
GWTJ George Washington
Thomas Jefferson
JKRK John F. Kennedy
Robert Kennedy

2004 SP Game Used Patch Legendary Fabrics

RANDOM INSERTS IN PACKS
PRINT RUNS B/WN 6-50 COPIES PER
NO PRICING ON QTY OF 10 OR LESS
BE Johnny Bench w/Mask/50 15.00 40.00
BE1 Johnny Bench Hitting/50 15.00 40.00
BG Bob Gibson/50 15.00 40.00
BR Brooks Robinson/9
BR1 Brooks Robinson/10
BW Billy Williams/50 10.00 25.00
CH Catfish Hunter/50 15.00 40.00
CR Cal Ripken Fielding/50 50.00 100.00
CR1 Cal Ripken Running/50 50.00 100.00
CY Carl Yastrzemski/31 30.00 60.00
EM Eddie Mathews/50 40.00 80.00
FR Frank Robinson O's/50 15.00 40.00
FR1 Frank Robinson Reds/50 15.00 40.00
GP Gaylord Perry/50 10.00 25.00
HK Harmon Killebrew Twins/50 40.00 80.00
HK1 H.Killebrew Senators/50 40.00 80.00
JC Jose Canseco/50 15.00 40.00
JM Joe Morgan Reds/50 10.00 25.00
JM1 Joe Morgan Giants/50 10.00 25.00
JP Jim Palmer/6
JP1 Jim Palmer/7
JT Joe Torre/50 10.00 25.00
LA Luis Aparicio/50 10.00 25.00
LD Leo Durocher/50 15.00 40.00
MS Mike Schmidt Bat Hand/50 30.00 60.00
MS1 Mike Schmidt Swing/50 30.00 60.00
NR Nolan Ryan Astros/50 30.00 60.00
NR1 Nolan Ryan Rgr/50 30.00 60.00
OC Orlando Cepeda/50 10.00 25.00
OS Ozzie Smith/50 20.00 50.00
PO Paul O'Neill/50 15.00 40.00
RF Rollie Fingers/50 10.00 25.00
RY Robin Yount Bat Up/50 15.00 40.00
RY1 Robin Yount Bat Down/50 15.00 40.00
SC Steve Carlton/50 10.00 25.00
TS Tom Seaver Mets/50 15.00 40.00
TS1 Tom Seaver Reds/50 15.00 40.00
WS W.Spahn Arms Down/50 20.00 50.00
WS1 W.Spahn Arms Up/50 20.00 50.00

2004 SP Game Used Patch Legendary Fabrics Autograph Dual

RANDOM INSERTS IN PACKS
PRINT RUNS B/WN 10-25 COPIES PER
NO PRICING ON QTY OF 13 OR LESS
AD Andre Dawson/25 50.00 100.00
BE Johnny Bench/25 75.00 150.00
BM Bill Mazeroski/10
BR Brooks Robinson/25 60.00 120.00
BW Billy Williams/25 60.00 120.00
CR Cal Ripken/25 200.00 350.00
CY Carl Yastrzemski/17 125.00 200.00
DE Dwight Evans/25 60.00 120.00
DM Don Mattingly/25 150.00 250.00
DS Don Sutton/25 40.00 80.00
FL Fred Lynn/25 40.00 80.00
FR Frank Robinson/25 60.00 120.00
GP Gaylord Perry/25 40.00 80.00
HK Harmon Killebrew/25 75.00 150.00
JC Jose Canseco/25 60.00 120.00
JM Joe Morgan/25 50.00 100.00
JP Jim Palmer/25 50.00 100.00
JT Joe Torre Cards/25 50.00 100.00
JT1 Joe Torre Braves/25 50.00 100.00
KP Kirby Puckett/25 75.00 150.00
KP1 Kirby Puckett/12
LA Luis Aparicio/25 40.00 80.00
LB Lou Brock/13
NR Nolan Ryan Astros/25 150.00 250.00
NR1 Nolan Ryan Rgr/25 150.00 250.00
OC Orlando Cepeda/25 50.00 100.00
OS Ozzie Smith/25 100.00 175.00
PM Paul Molitor/25 50.00 100.00
PO Paul O'Neill/25 60.00 120.00
RC Roger Clemens/25 150.00 250.00
RF Rollie Fingers/25 50.00 100.00
RY Robin Yount Look Ahead/25 100.00 175.00
SG Steve Garvey/25 50.00 100.00
ST Darryl Strawberry/25 50.00 100.00
TG Tony Gwynn Look Left/25 75.00 150.00
TG1 Tony Gwynn Look Right/25 75.00 150.00
TS Tom Seaver Mets/25 60.00 120.00
TS1 Tom Seaver Reds/25 60.00 120.00
WB Wade Boggs Yanks/25 60.00 120.00
WB1 Wade Boggs Sox/25 60.00 120.00
WI Maury Wills/25 40.00 80.00
YO Robin Yount Look Right/25 100.00 175.00

2004 SP Game Used Patch Logo Threads

RANDOM INSERTS IN PACKS
STATED PRINT RUN 1 SERIAL #'d SET
NO PRICING DUE TO SCARCITY

2004 SP Game Used Patch Logo Threads Autograph

RANDOM INSERTS IN PACKS
STATED PRINT RUN 1 SERIAL #'d SET
NO PRICING DUE TO SCARCITY

2004 SP Game Used Patch Logo Threads Autograph Dual

RANDOM INSERTS IN PACKS
STATED PRINT RUN 1 SERIAL #'d SET
NO PRICING DUE TO SCARCITY

2004 SP Game Used Patch MLB Masters

RANDOM INSERTS IN PACKS
PRINT RUNS B/WN 3-50 COPIES PER
NO PRICING ON QTY OF 12 OR LESS
AJ Andruw Jones/25 20.00 50.00
AP Albert Pujols/5
AR Alex Rodriguez/3
AS Alfonso Soriano/12
BE Josh Beckett/25 15.00 40.00
CD Carlos Delgado/25 15.00 40.00
CJ Chipper Jones/10
CS Curt Schilling/38 15.00 40.00
EC Eric Chavez/3
FT Frank Thomas/35 15.00 40.00
GM Greg Maddux Braves/31 30.00 60.00
GM1 Greg Maddux Cubs/31 30.00 60.00
GO Juan Gonzalez/19 15.00 40.00
GS Gary Sheffield/11
HE Todd Helton/17 20.00 50.00
HN Hideo Nomo Dodgers/10
HN1 Hideo Nomo Sox/10
IR Ivan Rodriguez/7
IS Ichiro Suzuki/50 50.00 100.00
JB Jeff Bagwell/5
JG Jason Giambi/25 15.00 40.00
JP Jorge Posada/20 20.00 50.00
JT Jim Thome Phils/25 20.00 50.00
JT1 Jim Thome Indians/25 20.00 50.00
KG Ken Griffey Jr./30 40.00 80.00
MO Magglio Ordonez/30 10.00 25.00
MP Mark Prior/22 20.00 50.00
MR Manny Ramirez/24 20.00 50.00
PI Mike Piazza/31 30.00 60.00
PM Pedro Martinez/45 15.00 40.00
RC Roger Clemens/22 40.00 80.00
RH Roy Halladay/32 10.00 25.00
SG Shawn Green/15 15.00 40.00
SR Scott Rolen/27 15.00 40.00
SS Sammy Sosa/21 20.00 50.00
TH Tim Hudson Glove Up/15 15.00 40.00
TH1 Tim Hudson Glove Down/15 15.00 40.00
VW Vernon Wells/10

2004 SP Game Used Patch MVP

RANDOM INSERTS IN PACKS
STATED PRINT RUN 25 SERIAL #'d SETS
AR Alex Rodriguez 30.00 60.00
BR Brooks Robinson 20.00 50.00
BW Bernie Williams 20.00 50.00
CJ Chipper Jones 20.00 50.00
CR Cal Ripken 75.00 150.00
CS Curt Schilling 20.00 50.00
DJ Derek Jeter 60.00 120.00
FT Frank Thomas 20.00 50.00
GA Garret Anderson 15.00 40.00
IS Ichiro Suzuki 60.00 120.00
IV Ivan Rodriguez 20.00 50.00
JB Josh Beckett 15.00 40.00
JG Jason Giambi 15.00 40.00
KG Ken Griffey Jr. 40.00 80.00
MP Mike Piazza 30.00 60.00
MT Miguel Tejada 15.00 40.00
PM Pedro Martinez 20.00 50.00
RC Roger Clemens 40.00 80.00
RJ Randy Johnson 20.00 50.00
SS Sammy Sosa 20.00 50.00
TG Troy Glaus 15.00 40.00

2004 SP Game Used Patch Premium

RANDOM INSERTS IN PACKS
STATED PRINT RUN 50 SERIAL #'d SETS
GARCIAPARRA PRINT RUN 11 #'d CARDS
MATSUI PRINT RUN 17 #'d CARDS
SORIANO PRINT RUN 34 #'d CARDS
NO PRICING ON QTY OF 11 OR LESS
AD Adam Dunn 10.00 25.00
AP Albert Pujols 40.00 80.00
AR Alex Rodriguez Rgr 30.00 60.00
AR1 A.Rodriguez Yanks Cap 40.00 80.00
AR2 A.Rodriguez Yanks Helmet 40.00 80.00
AS Alfonso Soriano/34 10.00 25.00
BE Josh Beckett 10.00 25.00
BW Bernie Williams 15.00 40.00
BZ Barry Zito 10.00 25.00
CD Carlos Delgado 10.00 25.00
CJ Chipper Jones 15.00 40.00
CS Curt Schilling Glove Up 15.00 40.00
CS1 Curt Schilling Hand in Air 15.00 40.00
DJ Derek Jeter 40.00 100.00
DW Dontrelle Willis 15.00 40.00
EC Eric Chavez 10.00 25.00
FT Frank Thomas 15.00 40.00
GM Greg Maddux Braves 20.00 50.00
GM1 Greg Maddux Cubs 20.00 50.00
GO Juan Gonzalez 10.00 25.00
HM Hideki Matsui/17 125.00 200.00
IR Ivan Rodriguez 15.00 40.00
IS Ichiro Suzuki Profile 50.00 100.00
IS1 Ichiro Suzuki Arm Out 50.00 100.00
JB Jeff Bagwell 15.00 40.00
JG Jason Giambi 10.00 25.00
JP Jorge Posada 15.00 40.00
JT Jim Thome 15.00 40.00
KB Kevin Brown 10.00 25.00
KG Ken Griffey Jr. Arm Out 30.00 60.00
KG1 K.Griffey Jr. Red Helmet 30.00 60.00
MO Magglio Ordonez 10.00 25.00
MP Mark Prior 15.00 40.00
MR Manny Ramirez 15.00 40.00
MT Miguel Tejada 10.00 25.00
NG Nomar Garciaparra/11
NR Nolan Ryan 30.00 60.00
PI Mike Piazza 20.00 50.00
PM Pedro Martinez 15.00 40.00
RC Roger Clemens 20.00 50.00
RH Roy Halladay 10.00 25.00
RI Mariano Rivera 15.00 40.00
RJ Randy Johnson 15.00 40.00
RP Rafael Palmeiro 15.00 40.00
SG Shawn Green 10.00 25.00
SR Scott Rolen 15.00 40.00
SS Sammy Sosa Swing 15.00 40.00
SS1 Sammy Sosa Bat Down 15.00 40.00
TE Mark Teixeira 15.00 40.00
TG Tom Glavine 15.00 40.00
TH Tim Hudson 10.00 25.00

2004 SP Game Used Patch Premium Update

ONE PER SPGU UPDATE FACTORY SET
ONE UPDATE SET PER 48 UD2 HOB.BOXES
STATED PRINT RUN 20 SERIAL #'d SETS
V.WELLS PRINT RUN 21 SERIAL #'d CARDS
AK Austin Kearns 15.00 40.00
BA Bobby Abreu 15.00 40.00
BB Bret Boone 15.00 40.00
BC Bartolo Colon 15.00 40.00
BW Brandon Webb 15.00 40.00
CP Corey Patterson 15.00 40.00
EG Eric Gagne 15.00 40.00
EM Edgar Martinez 30.00 60.00
GA Garret Anderson 15.00 40.00
HB Hank Blalock 15.00 40.00
HN Hideo Nomo 40.00 80.00
JE Jim Edmonds 15.00 40.00
JJ Jacque Jones 15.00 40.00
JK Jeff Kent 15.00 40.00
JR Jose Reyes 15.00 40.00
KM Kevin Millwood 15.00 40.00
KW Kerry Wood 15.00 40.00
LB Lance Berkman 15.00 40.00
MM Mark Mulder 15.00 40.00
MS Mike Sweeney 15.00 40.00
RB Rocco Baldelli 15.00 40.00
RK Ryan Klesko 15.00 40.00
RO Roy Oswalt 15.00 40.00
RS Richie Sexson 15.00 40.00
TG Troy Glaus 15.00 40.00
TH Torii Hunter 15.00 40.00
VG Vladimir Guerrero 40.00 80.00
VW Vernon Wells /21 15.00 40.00

2004 SP Game Used Patch Premium Autograph

RANDOM INSERTS IN PACKS
STATED PRINT RUN 50 SERIAL #'d SETS
GARCIAPARRA PRINT 33 SERIAL #'d CARDS
AK Austin Kearns 30.00 60.00
AR Alex Rodriguez 125.00 200.00
BZ Barry Zito 40.00 80.00
CD Carlos Delgado 30.00 60.00
DW Dontrelle Willis 30.00 60.00
EC Eric Chavez 40.00 80.00
EG Eric Gagne 40.00 80.00
HM Hideki Matsui 250.00 400.00
IR Ivan Rodriguez 50.00 100.00
IS Ichiro Suzuki 300.00 450.00
KB Kevin Brown 30.00 60.00
KG Ken Griffey Jr. Reds 100.00 200.00
KG1 Ken Griffey Jr. M's 175.00 350.00
MP Mark Prior 30.00 60.00
MT Miguel Tejada 40.00 80.00
NG Nomar Garciaparra/33 75.00 150.00
RC Roger Clemens 100.00 175.00
SG Shawn Green 40.00 80.00
TG Troy Glaus 40.00 80.00
TH Tim Hudson 40.00 80.00
VG Vladimir Guerrero 50.00 100.00

2004 SP Game Used Patch Significant Numbers

RANDOM INSERTS IN PACKS
PRINT RUNS B/WN 1-27 COPIES PER
NO PRICING ON QTY OF 14 OR LESS
AJ Andruw Jones/8
AP Albert Pujols/3
AR Alex Rodriguez/10
BE Josh Beckett/3
BW Brandon Webb/1
CD Carlos Delgado/11
CJ Chipper Jones/10
CR Cal Ripken/21 100.00 200.00
CS Curt Schilling/16 20.00 50.00
CY Carl Yastrzemski/23 40.00 80.00
DJ Derek Jeter/9
DS Darryl Strawberry/17 15.00 40.00
EC Eric Chavez/6
EG Eric Gagne/5
EM Eddie Mathews/17 60.00 120.00

FT Frank Thomas/14
GM Greg Maddux/18 40.00 80.00
GO Juan Gonzalez/15 15.00 40.00
GS Gary Sheffield/16 15.00 40.00
HM Hideki Matsui/1
IS Ichiro Suzuki/3
JB Jeff Bagwell/13
JG Jason Giambi/9
KG Ken Griffey Jr./15 60.00 120.00
MM Mike Mussina/13
MP Mike Piazza/12
MR Manny Ramirez/11
MT Mark Teixeira/1
NR Nolan Ryan/27 50.00 100.00
PM Pedro Martinez/12
PO Paul O'Neill/17 20.00 50.00
PR Mark Prior/2
RC Roger Clemens/20 40.00 80.00
RF Rollie Fingers/17 15.00 40.00
RH Roy Halladay/6
RJ Randy Johnson/16 20.00 50.00
RP Rafael Palmeiro/18 20.00 50.00
SG Shawn Green/11
SN Duke Snider/18 20.00 50.00
SS Sammy Sosa/15 20.00 50.00
TG Tom Glavine/17 20.00 50.00
TS Tom Seaver/20 20.00 50.00

2004 SP Game Used Patch Significant Numbers Autograph

RANDOM INSERTS IN PACKS
STATED PRINT RUN 50 SERIAL #'d SETS
BROCK PRINT RUN 16 SERIAL #'d CARDS
PUCKETT PRINT RUN 3 SERIAL #'d CARDS
NO PUCKETT PRICING DUE TO SCARCITY
AR Alex Rodriguez Rgr 125.00 200.00
AR1 Alex Rodriguez M's 125.00 200.00
BA Bobby Abreu 30.00 60.00
BG Brian Giles 30.00 60.00
BW Bernie Williams 60.00 120.00
BZ Barry Zito 40.00 80.00
CD Carlos Delgado 30.00 60.00
CJ Chipper Jones 50.00 100.00
EC Eric Chavez 30.00 60.00
EG Eric Gagne 40.00 80.00
GM Greg Maddux 75.00 150.00
HE Todd Helton 40.00 80.00
HM Hideki Matsui 250.00 400.00
JG Juan Gonzalez Royals 30.00 60.00
JG1 Juan Gonzalez Rgr 30.00 60.00
KB Kevin Brown 30.00 60.00
KG Ken Griffey Jr. Reds 100.00 200.00
KG1 Ken Griffey Jr. M's 100.00 200.00
KP Kirby Puckett/3
LB Lou Brock/16 50.00 100.00
LG Luis Gonzalez 30.00 60.00
MM Mike Mussina Yanks 40.00 80.00
MM1 Mike Mussina O's 40.00 80.00
MP Mike Piazza 150.00 250.00
MS Mike Schmidt 60.00 120.00
MT Miguel Tejada O's 40.00 80.00
MT1 Miguel Tejada A's 40.00 80.00
NR Nolan Ryan 125.00 200.00
PB Pat Burrell 30.00 60.00
PO Paul O'Neill 40.00 80.00
PR Mark Prior 30.00 60.00
RA Roberto Alomar 40.00 80.00
RB Rocco Baldelli 30.00 60.00
RF Rollie Fingers 30.00 60.00
RO Roy Oswalt Arm Up 30.00 60.00
RO1 Roy Oswalt Elbow Out 30.00 60.00
RP Rafael Palmeiro 50.00 100.00
RS Ryne Sandberg 60.00 120.00
SG Shawn Green 40.00 80.00
TG Tom Glavine 40.00 80.00
TH Tim Hudson 40.00 80.00
VG Vladimir Guerrero 50.00 100.00

2004 SP Game Used Patch Significant Numbers Autograph Dual

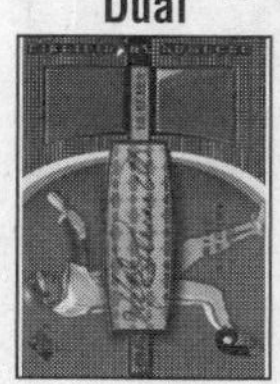

RANDOM INSERTS IN PACKS
STATED PRINT RUN 25 SERIAL #'d SETS
BROCK PRINT RUN 14 SERIAL #'d CARDS
NO BROCK PRICING DUE TO SCARCITY
AR Alex Rodriguez Rgr 175.00 300.00
BA Bobby Abreu 50.00 100.00
BG Brian Giles 40.00 80.00
BW Bernie Williams 125.00 200.00
BZ Barry Zito 60.00 120.00
CD Carlos Delgado 50.00 100.00
CJ Chipper Jones 75.00 150.00
DW Dontrelle Willis 60.00 120.00
EC Eric Chavez 50.00 100.00
EG Eric Gagne 60.00 120.00
GI Bob Gibson 60.00 120.00
GM Greg Maddux 125.00 200.00
HE Todd Helton 60.00 120.00
HM Hideki Matsui 400.00 600.00
JG Juan Gonzalez Royals 50.00 100.00
JG1 Juan Gonzalez Rgr 50.00 100.00
KB Kevin Brown 50.00 100.00
KG Ken Griffey Jr. Reds 150.00 250.00
KP Kirby Puckett 75.00 150.00
LB Lou Brock/14
LG Luis Gonzalez 40.00 80.00
MM Mike Mussina Yanks 60.00 120.00
MM1 Mike Mussina O's 60.00 120.00
MP Mike Piazza 200.00 350.00
MR Troy Glaus 60.00 120.00
MS Mike Schmidt 150.00 250.00
MT Miguel Tejada O's 40.00 80.00
MT1 Miguel Tejada A's 40.00 80.00
NR Nolan Ryan 150.00 250.00
PB Pat Burrell 50.00 100.00
PO Paul O'Neill 60.00 120.00
RA Roberto Alomar 60.00 120.00
RF Rollie Fingers 50.00 100.00
RP Rafael Palmeiro 75.00 150.00
RS Ryne Sandberg 150.00 250.00
SG Shawn Green Dodgers 60.00 120.00
SG1 Shawn Green Jays 60.00 120.00
TG Tom Glavine 60.00 120.00
TH Tim Hudson 60.00 120.00
TO Tony Gwynn 75.00 150.00
TS Tom Seaver 60.00 120.00
VG Vladimir Guerrero 75.00 150.00

2004 SP Game Used Patch Star Potential

RANDOM INSERTS IN PACKS
PRINT RUNS B/WN 3-50 COPIES PER
NO PRICING ON QTY OF 12 OR LESS
AS Alfonso Soriano/12
BW Brandon Webb/50 10.00 25.00
CP Corey Patterson/20 15.00 40.00
DW0 D.Willis Arm Up/35 15.00 40.00
DW1 D.Willis Arm Down/35 15.00 40.00
EC Eric Chavez/3
HA Roy Halladay/32 10.00 25.00
HB Hank Blalock/9
IS Ichiro Suzuki/50 50.00 100.00
JB Josh Beckett/21 15.00 40.00
JR Jose Reyes/7
LB Lance Berkman/17 15.00 40.00
MM Mark Mulder/20 15.00 40.00
MP0 M.Prior Hand in Glove/22 20.00 50.00
MP1 Mark Prior Throwing/22 20.00 50.00
MT M.Teixeira Hands Back/23 20.00 50.00
MT1 M.Teixeira Hands Fwd/23 20.00 50.00
RB Rocco Baldelli/5
RH Rich Harden/40 10.00 25.00
RO Roy Oswalt/44 10.00 25.00
RS Richie Sexson/11
RW Rickie Weeks/23 15.00 40.00
TE Miguel Tejada/4
TG Troy Glaus/25 15.00 40.00
TH Tim Hudson/15 15.00 40.00
VW Vernon Wells/10

2004 SP Game Used Patch Stellar Combos Dual

RANDOM INSERTS IN PACKS
PRINT RUNS B/WN 1-25 COPIES PER
NO PRICING ON QTY OF 8 OR LESS
AD Alfonso Soriano 60.00 120.00
Derek Jeter/8
AJ Alex Rodriguez 40.00 80.00
Juan Gonzalez/25
AT Bobby Abreu 30.00 60.00
Jim Thome/25
BK Jeff Bagwell 30.00 60.00
Jeff Kent/25
BT Hank Blalock 30.00 60.00
Mark Teixeira/25
CA Joe Carter 30.00 60.00
Roberto Alomar/25
CO Roger Clemens 40.00 80.00
Roy Oswalt/25
CR Curt Schilling 30.00 60.00
Randy Johnson/25
DG Carlos Delgado 20.00 50.00
Jason Giambi/25
DK Adam Dunn 20.00 50.00
Austin Kearns/25
DL Derek Jeter
Lou Gehrig/25
GH Eric Gagne 20.00 50.00
Trevor Hoffman/25
GT Greg Maddux 50.00 100.00
Tom Glavine/25
JD Derek Jeter
Joe DiMaggio/10
JG Derek Jeter
Nomar Garciaparra/3
JJ Andruw Jones 30.00 60.00
Chipper Jones/25
KR Jerry Koosman 100.00 175.00
Nolan Ryan/25
LP Al Leiter 40.00 80.00
Mike Piazza/25
LS Fred Lynn 60.00 120.00
Ichiro Suzuki/25
MG Don Mattingly 50.00 100.00
Jason Giambi/25
MM Hideki Matsui
Mickey Mantle/1
MN Hideki Matsui
Hideo Nomo/5
MT Edgar Martinez 30.00 60.00
Frank Thomas/25
MY Paul Molitor 30.00 60.00
Robin Yount/25
NB Hideo Nomo 30.00 60.00
Kevin Brown/25
NY Alfonso Soriano 20.00 50.00
Jose Reyes/25
PC Mark Prior 50.00 100.00
Roger Clemens/25
PE Albert Pujols 60.00 120.00
Jim Edmonds/25
PM Andy Pettitte 30.00 60.00
Mike Mussina/25
PP Jorge Posada 40.00 80.00
Mike Piazza/25
PS Rafael Palmeiro 30.00 60.00
Sammy Sosa/25
RB Ivan Rodriguez 30.00 60.00
Josh Beckett/25
RG1 Manny Ramirez
Nomar Garciaparra/3
RG2 Cal Ripken 300.00 500.00
Lou Gehrig/25
RJ1 Alex Rodriguez Rgr 75.00 150.00
Derek Jeter/25
RJ2 Alex Rodriguez Yanks 100.00 200.00
Derek Jeter/25
RR Alex Rodriguez 150.00 250.00
Cal Ripken/25
RS Brooks Robinson 75.00 150.00
Mike Schmidt/25
SC Ichiro Suzuki 150.00 250.00
Ty Cobb Pants/25
SG Duke Snider 30.00 60.00
Shawn Green/25
SJ Gary Sheffield 30.00 60.00
Randy Johnson/25
SM Curt Schilling 30.00 60.00
Pedro Martinez/25
SR Curt Schilling 50.00 100.00
Nolan Ryan/25
TO Frank Thomas 30.00 60.00
Magglio Ordonez/25
WC David Wells 40.00 80.00
Roger Clemens/25
WH Larry Walker 30.00 60.00
Todd Helton/25
WS Billy Williams 30.00 60.00
Sammy Sosa/25
WW Honus Wagner Pants
Ted Williams/1
ZH Barry Zito 20.00 50.00
Tim Hudson/25

2004 SP Game Used Patch Team Threads Triple

RANDOM INSERTS IN PACKS
STATED PRINT RUN 10 SERIAL #'d SETS
MANNY/NOMAR/PEDRO PRINT 3 #'d CARDS
A.ROD/JETER/MATSUI PRINT 5 #'d CARDS
NO PRICING DUE TO SCARCITY
AB Andruw Jones
Chipper Jones
Gary Sheffield
AD Curt Schilling
Luis Gonzalez
Randy Johnson
BR Manny Ramirez
Nomar Garciaparra
Pedro Martinez/3
CC Kerry Wood
Mark Prior
Sammy Sosa
CW Frank Thomas
Magglio Ordonez
Roberto Alomar
HA Craig Biggio
Jeff Bagwell
Lance Berkman
NY Bernie Williams
Hideki Matsui
Jason Giambi
PP Bobby Abreu
Jim Thome
Kevin Millwood
RJG Alex Rodriguez
Derek Jeter
Jason Giambi
RJM Alex Rodriguez
Derek Jeter
Hideki Matsui/5
RSB Alex Rodriguez
Gary Sheffield
Kevin Brown
SC Albert Pujols
Jim Edmonds
Scott Rolen
SM Bret Boone
Edgar Martinez
Ichiro Suzuki
WSM Honus Wagner Pants
Ichiro Suzuki
Mickey Mantle

2004 SP Game Used Patch Triple Authentic

RANDOM INSERTS IN PACKS
STATED PRINT RUN 10 SERIAL #'d SETS
A.ROD/JETER/NOMAR PRINT 3 #'d CARDS
A.ROD/MANNY/NOMAR PRINT 3 #'d CARDS
NO PRICING DUE TO SCARCITY
BTH Jeff Bagwell
Jim Thome
Todd Helton
CBG Eric Chavez
Hank Blalock
Troy Glaus
CRB Eric Chavez
Scott Rolen
Tony Batista
DGP Carlos Delgado
Jason Giambi
Rafael Palmeiro
DHW Carlos Delgado
Roy Halladay
Vernon Wells
DKG Adam Dunn
Austin Kearns
Ken Griffey Jr.
FCB Carlton Fisk
Gary Carter
Johnny Bench
GNG Eric Gagne
Hideo Nomo
Shawn Green
GPS Ken Griffey Jr.
Rafael Palmeiro
Sammy Sosa
JAB Andruw Jones
Bobby Abreu
Pat Burrell
JBJ Jason Jennings
Kevin Brown
Randy Johnson
JJP Randy Johnson
Jacque Jones
Mark Prior
KSB Adam Kennedy
Alfonso Soriano
Bret Boone
LHG Al Leiter
Mike Hampton
Tom Glavine
LTP Javy Lopez
Miguel Tejada
Rafael Palmeiro
MMG Greg Maddux
Kevin Millwood
Tom Glavine
MYW Paul Molitor
Robin Yount
Rickie Weeks
PBS Albert Pujols
Lance Berkman
Sammy Sosa
PDH Albert Pujols
Carlos Delgado
Todd Helton
PMO Mark Prior
Matt Morris
Roy Oswalt
RJG Alex Rodriguez
Derek Jeter
Nomar Garciaparra/3
RPP Ivan Rodriguez
Jorge Posada
Mike Piazza
RRG Alex Rodriguez
Manny Ramirez
Nomar Garciaparra/3
RVS Cal Ripken
Omar Vizquel
Ozzie Smith
SCM Ichiro Suzuki
Roberto Clemente
Stan Musial
SJM Alfonso Soriano
Derek Jeter
Hideki Matsui
SSB Curt Schilling
Gary Sheffield
Kevin Brown
WWP Brandon Webb
Dontrelle Willis
Mark Prior
ZMC Barry Zito
Pedro Martinez
Roger Clemens
ZMH Barry Zito
Mark Mulder
Tim Hudson

2004 SP Game Used Patch World Series

RANDOM INSERTS IN PACKS
PRINT RUNS B/WN 15-50 COPIES PER
AJ Andruw Jones/50 15.00 40.00
AP Andy Pettitte/15 20.00 50.00
AS0 A.Soriano Hands on Bat/15 15.00 40.00
AS1 A.Soriano Hands Apart/15 15.00 40.00
BL Barry Larkin/50 15.00 40.00
BW Bernie Williams/50 15.00 40.00
CA Jose Canseco/50 15.00 40.00
CJ Chipper Jones/50 15.00 40.00
CS Curt Schilling D'backs/50 10.00 25.00
CS1 Curt Schilling Sox/50 15.00 40.00
CY Carl Yastrzemski/31 30.00 60.00
DW Dontrelle Willis/50 15.00 40.00
GA Garret Anderson/50 10.00 25.00
GL Troy Glaus Run/50 10.00 25.00
GL1 Troy Glaus Walk/50 10.00 25.00
GM Greg Maddux Arm Up/50 20.00 50.00
GM1 Greg Maddux Cubs/50 20.00 50.00
GM2 G.Maddux Glove Out/50 20.00 50.00
HM Hideki Matsui/17 125.00 200.00
IR Ivan Rodriguez/50 15.00 40.00
JB Josh Beckett Leaning/50 10.00 25.00
JB1 Josh Beckett Leg Kick/50 10.00 25.00
JE Derek Jeter Gray/50 40.00 100.00
JE1 Derek Jeter Stripes/50 40.00 100.00
JM Joe Morgan/50 10.00 25.00
JP Jorge Posada/50 15.00 40.00
JT Jim Thome Indians/50 15.00 40.00
JT1 Jim Thome Phils/50 15.00 40.00
KB Kevin Brown/50 10.00 25.00
MM Mike Mussina Yanks/50 15.00 40.00
MM1 Mike Mussina O's/43 15.00 40.00
MP Mike Piazza Mets/50 20.00 50.00
MP1 Mike Piazza Dodgers/50 20.00 50.00
MR Mariano Rivera/50 15.00 40.00
MS Mike Schmidt/50 30.00 60.00
PM Paul Molitor/50 10.00 25.00
PO Paul O'Neill/50 15.00 40.00
RC Roger Clemens/50 20.00 50.00
RF Rollie Fingers/50 15.00 40.00
RJ Randy Johnson/50 15.00 40.00
TG Tom Glavine/50 15.00 40.00

2004 SP Game Used Patch World Series Autograph

RANDOM INSERTS IN PACKS
STATED PRINT RUN 1 SERIAL #'d SET
NO PRICING DUE TO SCARCITY

2004 SP Game Used Patch World Series Autograph Dual

RANDOM INSERTS IN PACKS
STATED PRINT RUN 1 SERIAL #'d SET
NO PRICING DUE TO SCARCITY

2001 SP Legendary Cuts

The SP Lengendary Cuts product was released in October, 2001 and featured a 90-card base set. Each pack contained four cards and carried a suggested retail price of $9.99.

COMPLETE SET (90) 10.00 25.00
1 Al Simmons .10 .30
2 Jimmie Foxx .30 .75
3 Mickey Cochrane .20 .50
4 Phil Niekro .10 .30
5 Eddie Mathews .30 .75
6 Gary Matthews .10 .30
7 Hank Aaron .60 1.50
8 Joe Adcock .10 .30
9 Warren Spahn .20 .50
10 George Sisler .10 .30
11 Stan Musial .50 1.25
12 Dizzy Dean .30 .75
13 Frankie Frisch .30 .75
14 Harvey Haddix .10 .30
15 Johnny Mize .20 .50
16 Ken Boyer .10 .30
17 Rogers Hornsby .30 .75
18 Cap Anson .30 .75
19 Andre Dawson .10 .30
20 Billy Williams .10 .30
21 Billy Herman .10 .30
22 Hack Wilson .20 .50
23 Ron Santo .20 .50
24 Ryne Sandberg .50 1.25
25 Ernie Banks .30 .75
26 Burleigh Grimes .10 .30
27 Don Drysdale .20 .50
28 Gil Hodges .30 .75
29 Jackie Robinson .30 .75
30 Tommy Lasorda .10 .30
31 Pee Wee Reese .30 .75
32 Roy Campanella .30 .75
33 Tommy Davis .10 .30
34 Branch Rickey .10 .30
35 Leo Durocher .20 .50
36 Walt Alston .10 .30
37 Bill Terry .10 .30
38 Carl Hubbell .20 .50
39 Eddie Stanky .10 .30
40 George Kelly .10 .30
41 Mel Ott .30 .75
42 Juan Marichal .10 .30
43 Rube Marquard .10 .30
44 Travis Jackson .10 .30
45 Bob Feller .10 .30
46 Earl Averill .10 .30
47 Elmer Flick .10 .30
48 Ken Keltner .10 .30
49 Lou Boudreau .20 .50
50 Early Wynn .20 .50
51 Satchel Paige .30 .75
52 Ron Hunt .10 .30
53 Tom Seaver .20 .50
54 Richie Ashburn .20 .50
55 Mike Schmidt .60 1.50
56 Honus Wagner .40 1.00
57 Lloyd Waner .20 .50
58 Max Carey .10 .30
59 Paul Waner .20 .50
60 Roberto Clemente .75 2.00
61 Nolan Ryan .75 2.00
62 Bobby Doerr .20 .50
63 Carlton Fisk .20 .50
64 Joe Cronin .10 .30
65 Joe Wood .20 .50
66 Tony Conigliaro .20 .50
67 Edd Roush .10 .30
68 Johnny VanderMeer .10 .30
69 Walter Johnson .30 .75
70 Charlie Gehringer .10 .30
71 Al Kaline .30 .75
72 Ty Cobb .50 1.25
73 Tony Oliva .10 .30
74 Luke Appling .10 .30
75 Minnie Minoso .10 .30
76 Nellie Fox .20 .50
77 Joe Jackson .60 1.50
78 Babe Ruth 1.00 2.50
79 Bill Dickey .20 .50
80 Elston Howard .20 .50
81 Joe DiMaggio .60 1.50
82 Lefty Gomez .30 .75
83 Lou Gehrig .60 1.50
84 Mickey Mantle 1.25 3.00
85 Reggie Jackson .20 .50
86 Roger Maris .30 .75
87 Whitey Ford .20 .50
88 Waite Hoyt .10 .30
89 Yogi Berra .30 .75
90 Casey Stengel .30 .75

2001 SP Legendary Cuts Autographs

Randomly inserted into packs at a rate of one in 252 (a.k.a. - one per case), this 85-card set features more than 3,300 autographs of deceased legends that were cut off of checks, contracts, letters, etc that Upper Deck purchased on the secondary market. The card backs carry the players initials as numbering. Cards with a print run of less than 25 are not priced due to scarcity. A couple of players, Joe DiMaggio and Ted Lyons, were printed to different quantities.

CBD Bill Dickey/28 300.00 450.00
CBG Burleigh Grimes/18
CBHA Bucky Harris/10
CBHE Billy Herman/88 75.00 150.00
CBL Bob Lemon/23
CBM Bob Meusel/23
CBRI Branch Rickey/16
CBRU Babe Ruth/7
CBS Bob Shawkey/39 150.00 250.00
CBT Bill Terry/184 150.00 250.00
CBW Bucky Walters/13
CCA Cap Anson/2
CCH Carl Hubbell/30 250.00 400.00
CCK Charlie Keller/16
CCS Casey Stengel/10
CDDE Dizzy Dean/56 400.00 800.00
CDDR Don Drysdale/12
CEA Earl Averill/189 60.00 120.00
CEB Ed Barrow/16
CEF Elmer Flick/22
CEL Eddie Lopat/22
CER Edd Roush/83 75.00 150.00
CFF Ford Frick/21
CFF Frankie Frisch/3
CFL Freddy Lindstrom/2
CGA Grover Alexander/1
CGH Gabby Hartnett/32 175.00 300.00
CGH Gil Hodges/6
CGK George Kelly/52 125.00 200.00
CGS George Selkirk/15
CGS George Sisler/1
CHH Harvey Haddix/4
CHH Harry Hooper/14
CHM Heinie Manush/50 175.00 300.00
CHW Honus Wagner/24
CHW Hack Wilson/4
CJC Jocko Conlan/26 250.00 400.00
CJC Joe Cronin/12
CJD1 Joe DiMaggio/25
CJD2 Joe DiMaggio/50 400.00 600.00

CJD3 Joe DiMaggio/150	300.00	500.00
CJD4 Joe DiMaggio/275	300.00	500.00
CJF Jimmie Foxx/16		
CJJ Judy Johnson/9		
CJM Joe Medwick/18		
CJMC Joe McCarthy/40	300.00	500.00
CJMI Johnny Mize/84	150.00	250.00
CJR Jackie Robinson/147	1200.00	1600.00
CJS Joe Sewell/55	150.00	250.00
CJW Joe Wood/43	300.00	500.00
CKC Kiki Cuyler/6		
CKK Ken Keltner/11		
CKL Kenesaw Landis/4		
CLA Luke Appling/45	125.00	200.00
CLD Leo Durocher/45	175.00	300.00
CLG Lefty Grove/34	300.00	500.00
CLGE Lou Gehrig/7		
CLGO Lefty Gomez/85	175.00	300.00
CLW Lloyd Waner/217	125.00	250.00
CMC Max Carey/73	150.00	250.00
CMK Mark Koenig/30	250.00	400.00
CMM Mickey Mantle/8		
CMO Mel Ott/8		
CNF Nellie Fox/9		
CPW Paul Waner/4		
CRC Roberto Clemente/4		
CRF Rick Ferrell/8		
CRH Rogers Hornsby/4		
CROM Roger Maris/73	1000.00	1500.00
CRP R.Peckinpaugh/45	150.00	250.00
CRR Red Ruffing/5		
CRS Rip Sewell/39	150.00	250.00
CRUM Rube Marquard/23		
CSC Stanley Coveleski/42	125.00	200.00
CSM Sal Maglie/19		
CSP Satchel Paige/36	1200.00	1700.00
CTC Ty Cobb/24		
CTJ Travis Jackson/35	175.00	300.00
CTL1 Ted Lyons/2		
CTL2 Ted Lyons/59	125.00	200.00
CVM J. VanderMeer/65	150.00	250.00
CVR Vic Raschi/26	175.00	300.00
CWA Walt Alston/34	250.00	400.00
CWG Warren Giles/10		
CWH Waite Hoyt/38	150.00	250.00
CWJ Walter Johnson/113	2000.00	3000.00

2001 SP Legendary Cuts Debut Game Bat

Randomly inserted into packs at one in 18, this 35-card set features the first game-used pieces of bat cards for each player. Card backs carry the player's intials as numbering. Cards with a perceived larger supply carry an asterisk and all short-print cards carry an SP designation.

BAT Alan Trammell *	4.00	10.00
BBB Bobby Bonds	4.00	10.00
BBF Bill Freehan	4.00	10.00
BGL Greg Luzinski	4.00	10.00
BLW Lou Whitaker	4.00	10.00
BSS Steve Sax *	4.00	10.00
BSY Steve Yeager	4.00	10.00
BWH Willie Horton	4.00	10.00
BWP Wes Parker *	4.00	10.00
DBB Bill Buckner *	4.00	10.00
DBD Bobby Doerr SP	10.00	25.00
DBF Bob Feller SP	15.00	40.00
DBH Billy Herman SP	10.00	25.00
DBM Bill Mazeroski	6.00	15.00
DBR B.Richardson SP	10.00	25.00
DCG Charlie Gehringer	20.00	50.00
DEH Elston Howard SP	10.00	25.00
DES Eddie Stanky	4.00	10.00
DFF Frankie Frisch SP	10.00	25.00
DGM Gary Matthews	4.00	10.00
DGS George Sisler	10.00	25.00
DHW Hack Wilson SP	50.00	100.00
DJA Joe Adcock SP	10.00	25.00
DJC Joe Cronin	6.00	15.00
DJJ Joe Jackson	350.00	450.00
DKB Ken Boyer SP	10.00	25.00
DLA Luke Appling SP	15.00	40.00
DLB Lou Boudreau	6.00	15.00
DMC Mickey Cochrane	40.00	80.00
DMM Minnie Minoso SP	10.00	25.00
DPW Paul Waner SP	30.00	60.00
DRA Richie Ashburn SP	15.00	40.00
DRH Ron Hunt	4.00	10.00
DTC Tony Conigliaro SP	10.00	25.00
DTO Tony Oliva	4.00	10.00

2001 SP Legendary Cuts Game Bat

Randomly inserted into packs at one in 18, this 36-card set features game-used pieces of bat cards for each player. Card backs carry the player's intials as numbering. Cards with a perceived larger supply carry an asterisk and all short-print cards carry an SP designation.

BAD Andre Dawson *	4.00	10.00
BAS Al Simmons SP	75.00	150.00
BBR Babe Ruth SP	125.00	200.00
BBT Bill Terry SP	30.00	60.00
BCF Carlton Fisk	6.00	15.00
BDD Don Drysdale SP	15.00	40.00
BDJ Davey Johnson	4.00	10.00
BEM Eddie Mathews	6.00	15.00
BGB George Brett *	6.00	15.00
BGH Gil Hodges SP	30.00	60.00
BHA Hank Aaron SP	20.00	50.00
BJD Joe DiMaggio SP	60.00	120.00
BJF Jimmie Foxx	30.00	60.00
BJR Jackie Robinson SP	30.00	60.00
BKC Kiki Cuyler	30.00	60.00
BMM Mickey Mantle SP	75.00	150.00
BMM Manny Mota	4.00	10.00
BMO Mel Ott SP	40.00	80.00
BMW Maury Wills *	4.00	10.00
BNF Nellie Fox	6.00	15.00
BNR Nolan Ryan SP	15.00	40.00
BPM Paul Molitor	4.00	10.00
BRC Rico Carty	4.00	10.00
BRCA R.Campanella SP	20.00	50.00
BRCL Roberto Clemente	30.00	60.00
BRJ Reggie Jackson *	6.00	15.00
BRM Roger Maris SP	40.00	80.00
BRS Ryne Sandberg *	10.00	25.00
BRY Robin Yount *	6.00	15.00
BTC Ty Cobb SP	75.00	150.00
BTD Tommy Davis SP	40.00	80.00
BTHO Tommy Holmes UER	4.00	10.00
Eddie Mathews pictured		
BVP Vada Pinson	4.00	10.00
BWB Wade Boggs *	6.00	15.00
BWMC Willie McCovey *	4.00	10.00
BYB Yogi Berra	6.00	15.00

2001 SP Legendary Cuts Game Bat Combo

Randomly inserted into packs, these 24 cards feature dual player game-used bat pieces from some of the games greatest stars. Card backs carry both players' initials as numbering. Please note that there were only 25 serial numbered sets produced. Due to market scarcity, no pricing is provided for these cards.

BMRC Bill Mazeroski
Roberto Clemente
BRMM Babe Ruth
Mickey Mantle
GSBT George Sisler
Bill Terry
HABR Hank Aaron
Babe Ruth
HWBH Hack Wilson
Billy Herman
JCBD Joe Cronin
Bobby Doerr
JDMM Joe DiMaggio
Mickey Mantle
JFAS Jimmie Foxx
Al Simmons
JFBR Jimmie Foxx
Babe Ruth
JRRC Jackie Robinson
Roy Campanella
LBBF Lou Boudreau
Bob Feller
MMNF Minnie Minoso
Nellie Fox
MOBT Mel Ott
Bill Terry
MOJD Mel Ott
Joe DiMaggio
NRBF Nolan Ryan
Bob Feller
RJMM Reggie Jackson
Mickey Mantle
RMMM Roger Maris
Mickey Mantle
RSAD Ryne Sandberg
Andre Dawson
SJPW Joe Jackson
Paul Waner
TCBR Ty Cobb
Babe Ruth
TCCG Ty Cobb
Charlie Gehringer
TDDD Tommy Davis
Don Drysdale
TORC Tony Oliva
Roberto Clemente
YBEH Yogi Berra
Elston Howard

2001 SP Legendary Cuts Game Jersey

Randomly inserted into packs at one in 18, this 35-card set features game-worn jersey or uniform pieces for each player. Card backs carry the player's intials as numbering. Cards with a perceived larger supply carry an asterisk and all short-print cards carry an SP designation.

SP'S NOT PRICED DUE TO SCARCITY

JBD Bill Dickey Uni	15.00	40.00
JBL Bob Lemon Uni	6.00	15.00
JBM B.Mazeroski Uni SP		
JBR B.Richardson Uni	4.00	10.00
JBR Babe Ruth Uni SP		
JBRO B.Robinson Uni	6.00	15.00
JBT Bobby Thomson Uni	6.00	15.00
JBW Billy Williams Jsy	4.00	10.00
JCS Casey Stengel Uni	6.00	15.00
JGH Gil Hodges Jsy	6.00	15.00
JGP Gaylord Perry Jsy	4.00	10.00
JHW H.Wagner Uni SP		
JJD Joe DiMaggio Uni SP		
JJF Jim Fregosi Jsy	4.00	10.00
JJM Juan Marichal Jsy *	4.00	10.00
JJN Joe Nuxhall Jsy	6.00	15.00
JLD Leo Durocher Jsy	6.00	15.00
JMM M. Mantle Uni SP		
JMW Maury Wills Jsy	4.00	10.00
JNF Nellie Fox Uni	6.00	15.00
JNR Nolan Ryan Jsy	15.00	40.00
JRC R. Clemente Jsy	50.00	100.00
JRJ Reggie Jackson Jsy	6.00	15.00
JRM Roger Maris Uni SP		
JRY Robin Yount Jsy	6.00	15.00
JTC Tony Conigliaro Jsy	6.00	15.00
JTC Ty Cobb Uni SP		
JTHO T.Holmes Uni*	4.00	10.00
JTK Ted Kluszewski Jsy	6.00	15.00
JTS Tom Seaver Jsy SP		
JVL Vic Lombardi Jsy	4.00	10.00
JWB Wade Boggs Jsy	6.00	15.00
JWF Whitey Ford Uni	6.00	15.00
JWM Willie McCovey Uni*	4.00	10.00
JYB Yogi Berra Uni	6.00	15.00

2002 SP Legendary Cuts

This 90 card set was released in October, 2002. The set was issued in four card packs which came 12 packs to a box and 16 boxes to a case. In addition to these basic cards, an exchange card for a Mark McGwire "private signings" card was randomly inserted into packs. That card has a stated print run of 100 copies inserted and a redemption deadline of 09/12/03.

COMPLETE SET (90)	10.00	25.00
1 Al Kaline	.60	1.50
2 Alvin Dark	.25	.60
3 Andre Dawson	.25	.60
4 Babe Ruth	2.00	5.00
5 Ernie Banks	.60	1.50
6 Bob Lemon	.40	1.00
7 Bobby Bonds	.25	.60
8 Carl Erskine	.25	.60
9 Carl Hubbell	.40	1.00
10 Casey Stengel	.60	1.50
11 Charlie Gehringer	.40	1.00
12 Christy Mathewson	.60	1.50
13 Dale Murphy	.40	1.00
14 Dave Concepcion	.25	.60
15 Dave Parker	.25	.60
16 Dazzy Vance	.25	.60
17 Dizzy Dean	.40	1.00
18 Don Baylor	.25	.60
19 Don Drysdale	.40	1.00
20 Duke Snider	.40	1.00
21 Earl Averill	.25	.60
22 Early Wynn	.25	.60
23 Edd Roush	.25	.60
24 Elston Howard	.25	.60
25 Ferguson Jenkins	.25	.60
26 Frank Crosetti	.25	.60
27 Frankie Frisch	.25	.60
28 Gaylord Perry	.25	.60
29 George Foster	.25	.60
30 George Kell	.25	.60
31 Gil Hodges	.40	1.00
32 Hank Greenberg	.60	1.50
33 Phil Niekro	.25	.60
34 Harvey Haddix	.25	.60
35 Harvey Kuenn	.25	.60
36 Honus Wagner	1.00	2.50
37 Jackie Robinson	.60	1.50
38 Orlando Cepeda	.25	.60
39 Joe Adcock	.25	.60
40 Joe Cronin	.25	.60
41 Joe DiMaggio	1.00	2.50
42 Joe Morgan	.25	.60
43 Johnny Mize	.25	.60
44 Lefty Gomez	.40	1.00
45 Lefty Grove	.40	1.00
46 Jim Palmer	.25	.60
47 Lou Boudreau	.25	.60
48 Lou Gehrig	1.00	2.50
49 Luke Appling	.25	.60
50 Mark McGwire	2.00	5.00
51 Mel Ott	.60	1.50
52 Mickey Cochrane	.40	1.00
53 Mickey Mantle	2.00	5.00
54 Minnie Minoso	.25	.60
55 Brooks Robinson	.40	1.00
56 Nellie Fox	.40	1.00
57 Nolan Ryan	1.50	4.00
58 Rollie Fingers	.25	.60
59 Pee Wee Reese	.40	1.00
60 Phil Rizzuto	.40	1.00
61 Ralph Kiner	.25	.60
62 Ray Dandridge	.25	.60
63 Richie Ashburn	.40	1.00
64 Robin Yount	.60	1.50
65 Rocky Colavito	.40	1.00
66 Roger Maris	.60	1.50
67 Rogers Hornsby	.60	1.50
68 Ron Santo	.25	.60
69 Ryne Sandberg	1.25	3.00
70 Stan Musial	1.00	2.50
71 Sam McDowell	.25	.60
72 Satchel Paige	.60	1.50
73 Willie McCovey	.25	.60
74 Steve Garvey	.25	.60
75 Ted Kluszewski	.40	1.00
76 Catfish Hunter	.40	1.00
77 Terry Moore	.15	.40
78 Thurman Munson	.60	1.50
79 Tom Seaver	.40	1.00
80 Tommy John	.25	.60
81 Tony Gwynn	.75	2.00
82 Tony Kubek	.40	1.00
83 Tony Lazzeri	.25	.60
84 Ty Cobb	1.00	2.50
85 Wade Boggs	.40	1.00
86 Waite Hoyt	.25	.60
87 Walter Johnson	.60	1.50
88 Willie Stargell	.40	1.00
89 Yogi Berra	.60	1.50
90 Zack Wheat	.25	.60
MM M.McGwire AU/100 EX		

2002 SP Legendary Cuts Autographs

Inserted in packs at stated odds of one in 128, these 97 cards feature "cut" autographs of a mix of retired greats and tough to track down early players dating back to the 1910's. Each card has a different stated serial numbered print run and we have notated that information next to the player's name in our checklist. Edd Roush has two different varieties issued. Also, if a player has a stated print run of 25 or fewer copies, there is no pricing provided due to market scarcity.

BDA Babe Dahlgren/51	125.00	200.00
BFA Bibb Falk/44	75.00	150.00
BGO Bill Goodman/53	75.00	150.00
BHA Buddy Hassett/56	75.00	150.00
BIL Bill Lee/40	75.00	150.00
BKA Bob Kahle/53	60.00	120.00
BOL Bob Lemon/91	75.00	150.00
BRU Babe Ruth/3		
BSC Bob Scheffing/19		
BSE Bill Serena/16		
BSH Bill Sherdel/10		
BSH Bob Shawkey/118	75.00	150.00
BSZ Billy Shantz/17		
BVE Bill Veeck/11		
BWA Bucky Walters/31	150.00	250.00
CGE Charlie Gehringer/3		
CHM Chet Morgan/27	125.00	200.00
CHRM Christy Mathewson/2		
CHU Carl Hubbell/17		
CKE Charlie Keller/29	150.00	250.00
CLA Cookie Lavagetto/22		
CST Casey Stengel/8		
DDE Dizzy Dean/4		
DDO Dick Donovan/23		
DDR Don Drysdale/14		
DVA Dazzy Vance/5		
EAV Earl Averill/22		
EJO Earl Johnson/31	125.00	200.00
ELO Ed Lopat/58	60.00	120.00
ERO Edd Roush/101	60.00	120.00
ERO2 Edd Roush/155	60.00	120.00
EWY Early Wynn/4		
FFR Frankie Frisch/35	250.00	400.00
FOF Ford Frick/1		
GBU Guy Bush/38	75.00	150.00
GCA George Case/35	125.00	200.00
GHO Gil Hodges/1		
GPI George Pipgras/34	125.00	200.00
HCH Happy Chandler/96	75.00	150.00
HGR Hank Greenberg/94	200.00	400.00
HHA Harvey Haddix/37	125.00	200.00
HKU Harvey Kuenn/23		
HMA Hank Majeski/21		
HNE Hal Newhouser/81	60.00	120.00
HSC Hal Schumacher/17		
HWA Honus Wagner/6		
JAD Joe Adcock/48	100.00	175.00
JBE Johnny Berardino/12		
JCO Johnny Cooney/64	60.00	120.00
JCR Joe Cronin/185	75.00	150.00
JDI Joe DiMaggio/103	350.00	500.00
JDU Joe Dugan/39	125.00	200.00
JJO Judy Johnson/86	125.00	200.00
JMI Johnny Mize/3		
JMO Johnny Moore/22		
JSE Joe Sewell/136	60.00	120.00
KKE Ken Keltner/11		
LAP Luke Appling/53	75.00	150.00
LBO Lou Boudreau/85	75.00	150.00
LGE Lou Gehrig/3		
LGO Lefty Gomez/3		
LGR Lefty Grove/194	150.00	250.00
LJA Larry Jackson/37	75.00	150.00
LRI Lance Richbourg/3		
LSE Luke Sewell/2		
MCO Mickey Cochrane/2		
MKO Mark Koenig/22		
MMA Mickey Mantle/2		
NFO Nellie Fox/1		
NJA Bucky Jacobs/44	125.00	200.00
ORO Oscar Roettger/9		
PRE Pete Reiser/73	100.00	175.00
PWE Pee Wee Reese/23		
PWI Pete Whisenant/13		
RAS Richie Ashburn/10		
RDA Ray Dandridge/179	60.00	120.00
RFE Rick Ferrell/19		
RHO Rogers Hornsby/1		
RMA Roger Maris/1		
RMC Roy McMillan/18		
RRE Rip Repulski/19		
SCH Spud Chandler/17		
SCO Stan Coveleski/85	75.00	150.00
SHA Stan Hack/36	150.00	250.00
SMA Sal Maglie/29	125.00	200.00
TDO Taylor Douthit/60	75.00	150.00
TKL Ted Kluszewski/23		
TMO Terry Moore/86	60.00	120.00
TYC Ty Cobb/2		
VRA Vic Raschi/98	75.00	150.00
VWE Vic Wertz/17		
WHO Waite Hoyt/61	75.00	150.00
WJO Walter Johnson/20		
WKA Willie Kamm/57	60.00	120.00
WSC Willard Schmidt/10		
WST Willie Stargell/153	75.00	150.00
ZWH Zack Wheat/127	200.00	300.00

2002 SP Legendary Cuts Bat Barrel

Randomly inserted into packs, these 26 cards feature "barrel" pieces of the featured player. Each card has a stated print run of 11 or fewer and there is no pricing provided due to market scarcity.

BBADA Alvin Dark/4
BBAND Andre Dawson/4
BBBBO Bobby Bonds/3
BBBRU Babe Ruth/3
BBDBA Don Baylor/5
BBDMU Dale Murphy/3
BBDPA Dave Parker/6
BBDSN Duke Snider/2
BBEWY Early Wynn/1
BBGFO George Foster/5
BBHGR Hank Greenberg/1
BBJAR Jackie Robinson/1
BBJMI Johnny Mize/2
BBLGR Lefty Grove/1
BBMMA Mickey Mantle/7
BBMMC Mark McGwire/4
BBNRY Nolan Ryan/9
BBPWE Pee Wee Reese/4
BBRCO Rocky Colavito/2
BBRMA Roger Maris/1
BBRSA Ryne Sandberg/3
BBRYO Robin Yount/8
BBTGW Tony Gwynn/11
BBTLA Tony Lazzeri/1
BBTMU Thurman Munson/4
BBWST Willie Stargell/5

2002 SP Legendary Cuts Buybacks

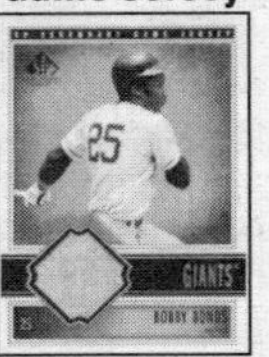

Randomly inserted into packs, this is a one card set featuring signed cards from the 1992 Upper Deck Ted Williams Heroes insert set. These Buyback cards have a stated print run of nine copies based upon information provided by the manufacturer and there is no pricing due to market scarcity. It's believed these Buyback cards have a rectangular foil sticker with a tracking code running verically along the back of the card on the right hand side. In addition, each Buyback comes with an additional certificate of Authenticity card.

NNO Ted Williams 92 Heroes AU/9

2002 SP Legendary Cuts Game Bat

Inserted in packs at a stated rate of one in eight, these 36 cards feature game-used bat chips of some leading retired superstars. A few cards were issued in shorter supply and we have either notated that information with an SP next to the players name or an asterisk.

BADA Alvin Dark DP	4.00	10.00
BAND Andre Dawson DP	3.00	8.00
BBBO Bobby Bonds DP	3.00	8.00
BBRU Babe Ruth SP	100.00	175.00
BCRI Cal Ripken	12.50	30.00
BDBA Don Baylor DP	3.00	8.00
BDMU Dale Murphy DP	4.00	10.00
BDPA Dave Parker DP	3.00	8.00
BDSN Duke Snider	6.00	15.00
BEHO Elston Howard SP *	6.00	15.00
BEWY Early Wynn	4.00	10.00
BGFO George Foster DP	3.00	8.00
BGKE George Kell	4.00	10.00
BGPE Gaylord Perry	3.00	8.00
BHGR Hank Greenberg SP	20.00	50.00
BJAR Jackie Robinson SP *	20.00	50.00
BJMI Johnny Mize SP *	6.00	15.00
BLGR Lefty Grove	15.00	40.00
BMMA Mickey Mantle SP	100.00	175.00
BMMC Mark McGwire DP	30.00	60.00
BNFO Nellie Fox	6.00	15.00
BNRY Nolan Ryan	15.00	40.00
BPWE Pee Wee Reese DP	6.00	15.00
BRCO Rocky Colavito DP	6.00	15.00
BRKI Ralph Kiner	4.00	10.00
BRMA Roger Maris SP *	40.00	80.00
BRSA Ryne Sandberg DP	6.00	15.00
BRYO Robin Yount DP	6.00	15.00
BSGA Steve Garvey	3.00	8.00
BTGW Tony Gwynn SP *	8.00	20.00
BTKU Tony Kubek UER	6.00	15.00
Name spelled Tonk on the front		
BTLA Tony Lazzeri	4.00	10.00
BTMU Thurman Munson	10.00	25.00
BTSE Tom Seaver SP	8.00	20.00
BWST Willie Stargell	4.00	10.00
BYBE Yogi Berra SP	10.00	25.00

2002 SP Legendary Cuts Game Jersey

Inserted in packs at stated odds of one in 24, these 15 cards feature pieces of game-worn jerseys. A few players cards actually feature pant pieces and we have notated that next to their name in our checklist. In addition, a few cards were issued in shorter supply and we have notated that information in our checklist as well.

JAND Andre Dawson	3.00	8.00
JBBO Bobby Bonds Pants	3.00	8.00
JDBA Don Baylor	3.00	8.00
JDPA Dave Parker Pants DP	3.00	8.00
JFCR Frank Crosetti	4.00	10.00
JGFO George Foster	3.00	8.00
JJRO J.Robinson Pants SP *	20.00	50.00
JMMA M.Mantle Pants SP *	60.00	120.00
JNRY Nolan Ryan Pants	15.00	40.00
JPWE Pee Wee Reese	6.00	15.00
JRMA Roger Maris Pants	20.00	50.00
JRSA Ryne Sandberg SP *	10.00	25.00
JSGA Steve Garvey	3.00	8.00
JTSE Tom Seaver	4.00	10.00
JYBE Yogi Berra Pants DP	10.00	25.00

2002 SP Legendary Cuts Game Swatches

Inserted in packs at stated odds of one in 24, these 15 cards feature game-used memorabilia swatches of the featured players.

SCER Carl Erskine Pants	4.00	10.00
SCRJ Cal Ripken	10.00	25.00
SDBA Don Baylor	3.00	8.00
SDDR Don Drysdale Pants	10.00	25.00
SDPA Dave Parker	3.00	8.00
SFCR Frank Crosetti	4.00	10.00
SFJE Ferguson Jenkins Pants	3.00	8.00
SJMO Joe Morgan	3.00	8.00
SMMI Minnie Minoso	4.00	10.00
SMOT Mel Ott Pants	15.00	40.00
SRSA Ron Santo	6.00	15.00
SSMC Sam McDowell	3.00	8.00
STGW Tony Gwynn	6.00	15.00
STJO Tommy John	3.00	8.00
SWBO Wade Boggs	4.00	10.00

2003 SP Legendary Cuts

This 130-card set was released in December, 2003. This set was issued in four-card packs with an $10 SRP which came 12 packs to a box and 16 boxes to a case. Thirty cards in this set were short printed and each of those cards were issued to a stated print run of 1299 serial numbered sets and were inserted at a stated rate of one in 12.

COMP.SET w/o SP's (100)	15.00	40.00
COMMON CARD	.15	.40
COMMON SP	3.00	8.00
1 Luis Aparicio	.25	.60
2 Al Barlick	.15	.40
3 Al Lopez	.25	.60
4 Ernie Banks	.60	1.50
5 Alexander Cartwright	.25	.60
6 Lou Brock	.40	1.00
7 Babe Ruth/1299	6.00	15.00
8 Bill Dickey	.40	1.00
9 Bill Mazeroski	.40	1.00
10 Bob Feller	.25	.60
11 Billy Herman	.25	.60

12 Billy Williams .25 .60
13 Bob Gibson/1299 4.00 10.00
14 Bob Lemon .25 .60
15 Bobby Doerr .25 .60
16 Branch Rickey .25 .60
17 Gary Carter .25 .60
18 Burleigh Grimes .25 .60
19 Cap Anson .40 1.00
20 Carl Hubbell .40 1.00
21 Carlton Fisk .40 1.00
22 Casey Stengel .40 1.00
23 Charlie Gehringer .25 .60
24 Chief Bender .25 .60
25 Christy Mathewson/1299 4.00 10.00
26 Cy Young .60 1.50
27 Dave Winfield .25 .60
28 Dazzy Vance .25 .60
29 Dizzy Dean/1299 4.00 10.00
30 Don Drysdale/1299 4.00 10.00
31 Duke Snider/1299 4.00 10.00
32 Earl Averill .25 .60
33 Earle Combs .25 .60
34 Edd Roush .25 .60
35 Earl Weaver .25 .60
36 Eddie Collins .25 .60
37 Eddie Plank .25 .60
38 Elmer Flick .25 .60
39 Enos Slaughter .25 .60
40 Ernie Lombardi .25 .60
41 Ford Frick .15 .40
42 Jim Hunter .40 1.00
43 Frankie Frisch .25 .60
44 Gabby Hartnett .25 .60
45 George Kell .25 .60
46 Early Wynn .25 .60
47 Ferguson Jenkins .25 .60
48 Al Kaline .60 1.50
49 Harmon Killebrew .60 1.50
50 Hal Newhouser .25 .60
51 Hank Greenberg/1299 4.00 10.00
52 Harry Caray .40 1.00
53 Tommy Lasorda .25 .60
54 Honus Wagner/1299 4.00 10.00
55 Hoyt Wilhelm/1299 3.00 8.00
56 Jackie Robinson/1299 4.00 10.00
57 Jim Bottomley .25 .60
58 Jim Bunning/1299 4.00 10.00
59 Jimmie Foxx/1299 4.00 10.00
60 Eddie Mathews .60 1.50
61 Joe Cronin .25 .60
62 Joe DiMaggio/1299 4.00 10.00
63 Joe McCarthy/1299 3.00 8.00
64 Joe Morgan/1299 3.00 8.00
65 Willie McCovey .25 .60
66 Joe Tinker .25 .60
67 Johnny Bench/1299 4.00 10.00
68 Johnny Evers/1299 3.00 8.00
69 Johnny Mize/1299 3.00 8.00
70 Josh Gibson/1299 4.00 10.00
71 Juan Marichal .25 .60
72 Judy Johnson .25 .60
73 Stan Musial 1.00 2.50
74 Kiki Cuyler .25 .60
75 Larry Doby .25 .60
76 Nap Lajoie .40 1.00
77 Larry MacPhail .15 .40
78 Phil Niekro .25 .60
79 Lefty Gomez/1299 4.00 10.00
80 Lefty Grove/1299 4.00 10.00
81 Leo Durocher/1299 3.00 8.00
82 Leon Day .25 .60
83 Gaylord Perry/1299 3.00 8.00
84 Lou Boudreau .25 .60
85 Lou Gehrig 1.00 2.50
86 Luke Appling .25 .60
87 Max Carey .25 .60
88 Mel Allen/1299 3.00 8.00
89 Mel Ott/1299 4.00 10.00
90 Mickey Cochrane .25 .60
91 Mickey Mantle 2.00 5.00
92 Brooks Robinson .40 1.00
93 Monte Irvin .25 .60
94 Nellie Fox .40 1.00
95 Nolan Ryan/1299 5.00 12.00
96 Ozzie Smith/1299 4.00 10.00
97 Mike Schmidt 1.25 3.00
98 Pee Wee Reese/1299 4.00 10.00
99 Phil Rizzuto .40 1.00
100 Ralph Kiner .25 .60
101 Ray Dandridge .25 .60
102 Richie Ashburn .40 1.00
103 Rick Ferrell .25 .60
104 Roberto Clemente 1.50 4.00
105 Robin Roberts .25 .60
106 Robin Yount .60 1.50
107 Rogers Hornsby .60 1.50
108 Rollie Fingers .25 .60
109 Roy Campanella .60 1.50
110 Rube Marquard .25 .60
111 Sam Crawford .25 .60
112 Steve Carlton .25 .60
113 Satchel Paige/1299 4.00 10.00
114 Sparky Anderson .25 .60
115 Stan Coveleski .25 .60
116 Red Schoendienst .40 1.00
117 Ted Williams 1.25 3.00
118 Tom Seaver .40 1.00
119 Tom Yawkey .15 .40
120 Tony Lazzeri .25 .60
121 Tony Perez .25 .60
122 Tris Speaker .60 1.50
123 Ty Cobb 1.00 2.50
124 Waite Hoyt/1299 3.00 8.00
125 Walter Alston .25 .60
126 Walter Johnson .60 1.50
127 Warren Spahn .40 1.00
128 Whitey Ford .40 1.00
129 Willie Stargell .40 1.00
130 Yogi Berra .60 1.50

2003 SP Legendary Cuts Blue

*BLUE POST-WAR: 2X TO 5X BASIC
*BLUE PRE-WAR: 1.5X TO 4X BASIC
*BLUE POST-WAR: .6X TO 1.5X BASIC SP
*BLUE PRE-WAR: .5X TO 1.2X BASIC SP
RANDOM INSERTS IN PACKS
STATED PRINT RUN 275 SERIAL #'d SETS

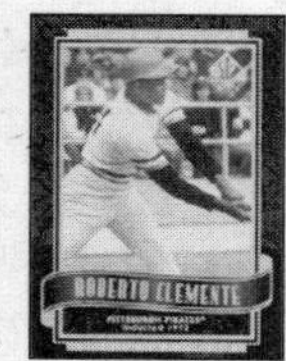

2003 SP Legendary Cuts Green

RANDOM INSERTS IN PACKS
STATED PRINT RUN 25 SERIAL #'d SETS
NO PRICING DUE TO SCARCITY

2003 SP Legendary Cuts Autographs

All the autograph cards in this insert set feature HOFers. After having a mix in 2002 of HOFers and retired players of varying note, Upper Deck decided that this product was better off with only HOFers involved in the cut signature insert set. Please note that several players: Bob Lemon, Charlie Gehringer, Carl Hubbell, Hal Newhouser, Joe DiMaggio and Ray Dandridge had two different varities in the main autograph set. In addition, for the first time, Upper Deck made some "color" variations in the autograph cut insert set. This set includes a "cut" signature of Alexander Cartwright who is believed by most historians to be the true founder of baseball.

OVERALL CUT SIG ODDS 1:196
PRINT RUNS B/WN 1-96 COPIES PER
NO PRICING ON QTY OF 25 OR LESS
AL Alexander Cartwright/1
BD Bill Dickey/25
BG Burleigh Grimes/34 175.00 300.00
BI Billy Herman/30 75.00 150.00
BL Bob Lemon/34 75.00 150.00
BL1 Bob Lemon/41 75.00 150.00
CG Charlie Gehringer/17
CG1 Charlie Gehringer/20
CH Carl Hubbell/47 150.00 250.00
CH1 Carl Hubbell/63 150.00 250.00
CS Casey Stengel/3
CY Cy Young/2
DD Dizzy Dean/8
DO Don Drysdale/12
DV Dazzy Vance/2
EA Earl Averill/96 60.00 120.00
EC Earle Combs/45 150.00 250.00
EF Elmer Flick/6
EL Ernie Lombardi/1
ER Edd Roush/15
ER1 Edd Roush/14
ES Enos Slaughter/30 100.00 200.00
FF Ford Frick/10
FR Frankie Frisch/4
GH Gabby Hartnett/20
HC Harry Caray/29 175.00 300.00
HC1 Harry Caray/35 175.00 300.00
HG Hank Greenberg/30 250.00 400.00
HN Hal Newhouser TC/22
HN1 Hal Newhouser B2B/22
HW Honus Wagner/1
JB Jim Bottomley/2
JC Joe Cronin/15
JD Joe DiMaggio/30 300.00 500.00
JD1 Joe DiMaggio/28 350.00 550.00
JF Jimmie Foxx/3
JJ Judy Johnson/23
JM Johnny Mize/18
JM1 Johnny Mize/12
JO Joe McCarthy/22
JR Jackie Robinson/4
LA Leon Day/6
LB Lou Boudreau/82 60.00 120.00
LB1 Lou Boudreau/49 75.00 150.00
LD Leo Durocher/20
LE Lefty Grove/9
LG Lefty Gomez/21
LM Larry MacPhail/2
LU Luke Appling/52 75.00 150.00
MA Mel Allen/2
MC Max Carey/18
MI Mickey Cochrane/3
MM Mickey Mantle/2
NF Nellie Fox/5
NL Nap Lajoie/2
RA Richie Ashburn/10
RD Ray Dandridge Hands/20
RD1 Ray Dandridge MVP/20
RH Rogers Hornsby/1
RM Rube Marquard/40 150.00 250.00
RO Roy Campanella/1
SC Sam Crawford/3
SP Satchel Paige/11
ST Stan Coveleski/20
ST1 Stan Coveleski/20
TC Ty Cobb/6
TJ Travis Jackson/19
TO Tony Lazzeri/8
TS Tris Speaker/2
TW Ted Williams/7
TY Tom Yawkey/1
WA Walter Alston/30 100.00 200.00
WJ Walter Johnson/1
WS Willie Stargell/4
ZW Zack Wheat/19

2003 SP Legendary Cuts Autographs Blue

OVERALL CUT SIG ODDS 1:196
PRINT RUNS B/WN 1-50 COPIES PER
NO PRICING ON QTY OF 25 OR LESS
BD Bill Dickey/12
BG Burleigh Grimes/22
BI Billy Herman/15
BL1 Bob Lemon/25
BR Branch Rickey/1
CG1 Charlie Gehringer/4
CH1 Carl Hubbell/25
CS Casey Stengel/1
CY Cy Young/1
DD Dizzy Dean/4
DO Don Drysdale/6
DV Dazzy Vance/1
EA Earl Averill/50 75.00 150.00
EC Earle Combs/16
ED Eddie Collins/1
EF Elmer Flick/4
EL Ernie Lombardi/1
ER Edd Roush/15
ES Enos Slaughter/11
FF Ford Frick/7
FR Frankie Frisch/2
GH Gabby Hartnett/5
HC1 Harry Caray/35 175.00 300.00
HG Hank Greenberg/15
HN1 Hal Newhouser B2B/29 75.00 150.00
HW Honus Wagner/1
JB Jim Bottomley/2
JC Joe Cronin/5
JD1 Joe DiMaggio/40 300.00 500.00
JE Johnny Evers/1
JF Jimmie Foxx/2
JJ Judy Johnson/8
JM Johnny Mize/15
JO Joe McCarthy/15
JR Jackie Robinson/2
JT Joe Tinker/1
LA Leon Day/5
LB Lou Boudreau/25
LD Leo Durocher/5
LE Lefty Grove/4
LG Lefty Gomez/14
LM Larry MacPhail/1
LO Lou Gehrig/1
LU Luke Appling/18
MA Mel Allen/1
MC Max Carey/5
MI Mickey Cochrane/2
MM Mickey Mantle/1
MO Mel Ott/1
NF Nellie Fox/1
NL Nap Lajoie/1
RA Richie Ashburn/5
RC Roberto Clemente/1
RD1 Ray Dandridge MVP/9
RH Rogers Hornsby/1
RM Rube Marquard/16
RO Roy Campanella/1
SC Sam Crawford/2
SP Satchel Paige/4
ST1 Stan Coveleski/20
TC Ty Cobb/2
TJ Travis Jackson/5
TO Tony Lazzeri/3
TS Tris Speaker/1
TW Ted Williams/1
TY Tom Yawkey/1
WA Walter Alston/10
WJ Walter Johnson/1
WS Willie Stargell/2
ZW Zack Wheat/5

2003 SP Legendary Cuts Autographs Green

OVERALL CUT SIG ODDS 1:196
PRINT RUNS B/WN 1-5 COPIES PER
NO PRICING DUE TO SCARCITY

2003 SP Legendary Cuts Combo Cuts

OVERALL CUT SIG ODDS 1:196
STATED PRINT RUN 1 SERIAL #'d SET
NO PRICING DUE TO SCARCITY
BJ Branch Rickey
Jackie Robinson
BL Babe Ruth
Lou Gehrig

HM Harry Caray
Mel Allen
HT Honus Wagner
Ty Cobb
JC Jackie Robinson
Roy Campanella
JM Joe DiMaggio
Mickey Mantle
JT Joe DiMaggio
Ted Williams
SJ Satchel Paige
Jackie Robinson

2003 SP Legendary Cuts Etched in Time 400

STATED PRINT RUN 400 SERIAL #'d SETS
*ETCHED 300: .4X TO 1X BASIC 400
ETCHED 300 PRINT RUN 300 #'d SETS
*ETCHED 175: .5X TO 1.2X BASIC 400
ETCHED 175 PRINT RUN 175 #'d SETS
OVERALL ETCHED ODDS 1:12
AB Al Barlick 2.00 5.00
AC Alexander Cartwright 2.00 5.00
BR Babe Ruth 6.00 15.00
CG Charlie Gehringer 2.00 5.00
CH Carl Hubbell 3.00 8.00
CM Christy Mathewson 3.00 8.00
CS Casey Stengel 3.00 8.00
CY Cy Young 3.00 8.00
DD Dizzy Dean 3.00 8.00
DO Don Drysdale 3.00 8.00
EC Eddie Collins 2.00 5.00
EL Ernie Lombardi 2.00 5.00
GH Gabby Hartnett 2.00 5.00
HC Harry Caray 3.00 8.00
HG Hank Greenberg 3.00 8.00
HW Honus Wagner 3.00 8.00
JD Joe DiMaggio 4.00 10.00
JF Jimmie Foxx 3.00 8.00
JG Josh Gibson 3.00 8.00
JM Joe McCarthy 2.00 5.00
JO Johnny Mize 2.00 5.00
JR Jackie Robinson 3.00 8.00
LB Lou Boudreau 2.00 5.00
LD Leo Durocher 2.00 5.00
LE Lefty Grove 3.00 8.00
LG Lefty Gomez 3.00 8.00
LO Lou Gehrig 5.00 12.00
ME Mel Allen 2.00 5.00
MM Mickey Mantle 10.00 25.00
MO Mel Ott 3.00 8.00
PR Pee Wee Reese 3.00 8.00
RA Richie Ashburn 3.00 8.00
RC Roberto Clemente 6.00 15.00
RH Rogers Hornsby 3.00 8.00
RO Roy Campanella 3.00 8.00
SP Satchel Paige 3.00 8.00
TC Ty Cobb 4.00 10.00
TL Tony Lazzeri 2.00 5.00
TS Tris Speaker 3.00 8.00
TW Ted Williams 4.00 10.00

2003 SP Legendary Cuts Hall Marks Autographs

OVERALL HALL MARKS ODDS 1:196
BLACK INK PRINTS B/WN 10-99 COPIES PER
BLUE INK PRINTS B/WN 10-15 COPIES PER
RED INK PRINT RUN 5 #'d SETS
NO PRICING ON QTY OF 15 OR LESS
BD1 Bobby Doerr Black/50 15.00 40.00
BD2 Bobby Doerr Blue/15
BD3 Bobby Doerr Red/5
BG1 Bob Gibson Black/30
BG2 Bob Gibson Blue/15
BG3 Bob Gibson Red/5
BM1 Bill Mazeroski Black/50 30.00 60.00
BM2 Bill Mazeroski Blue/15
BM3 Bill Mazeroski Red/5
CF1 Carlton Fisk Black/50 30.00 60.00
CF2 Carlton Fisk Blue/15
CF3 Carlton Fisk Red/5
CY1 Carl Yastrzemski Black/45 50.00 100.00
CY2 Carl Yastrzemski Blue/15
CY3 Carl Yastrzemski Red/5
DS1 Duke Snider Black/50 30.00 60.00
DS2 Duke Snider Blue/15
DS3 Duke Snider Red/5
DW1 Dave Winfield Black/10
DW2 Dave Winfield Blue/15
DW3 Dave Winfield Red/5
GC1 Gary Carter Black/50 15.00 40.00
GC2 Gary Carter Blue/15
GC3 Gary Carter Red/5
GK1 George Kell Black/50 15.00 40.00
GK2 George Kell Blue/15
GK3 George Kell Red/5
JB2 Johnny Bench Blue/10
JB3 Johnny Bench Red/5
JM1 Juan Marichal Black/50 15.00 40.00
JM2 Juan Marichal Blue/15
JM3 Juan Marichal Red/5
JO1 Joe Morgan Black/75 15.00 40.00
JO2 Joe Morgan Blue/15
JO3 Joe Morgan Red/5
LA1 Luis Aparicio Black/45 15.00 40.00
LA2 Luis Aparicio Blue/15
LA3 Luis Aparicio Red/5
MI1 Monte Irvin Black/85 20.00 50.00
MI2 Monte Irvin Blue/15
MI3 Monte Irvin Red/5
NR3 Nolan Ryan Red/5
OS1 Ozzie Smith Black/45 50.00 100.00
OS2 Ozzie Smith Blue/15
OS3 Ozzie Smith Red/5
PR1 Phil Rizzuto Black/50 30.00 60.00
PR2 Phil Rizzuto Blue/15
PR3 Phil Rizzuto Red/5
RF1 Rollie Fingers Black/99 10.00 25.00
RF2 Rollie Fingers Blue/15
RF3 Rollie Fingers Red/5
RK1 Ralph Kiner Black/50 15.00 40.00
RK2 Ralph Kiner Blue/15
RK3 Ralph Kiner Red/5
RR1 Robin Roberts Black/65 30.00 60.00
RR2 Robin Roberts Blue/15
RR3 Robin Roberts Red/5
RY1 Robin Yount Black/45 50.00 100.00
RY2 Robin Yount Blue/15
RY3 Robin Yount Red/5
SA1 Sparky Anderson Black/30 15.00 40.00
SA2 Sparky Anderson Blue/15
SA3 Sparky Anderson Red/5
TP1 Tony Perez Black/50 15.00 40.00
TP2 Tony Perez Blue/15
TP3 Tony Perez Red/5
TS2 Tom Seaver Blue/10
TS3 Tom Seaver Red/5
WS1 Warren Spahn Black/35 40.00 80.00
WS2 Warren Spahn Blue/15
WS3 Warren Spahn Red/5
YB1 Yogi Berra Black/50 40.00 80.00
YB2 Yogi Berra Blue/15
YB3 Yogi Berra Red/5

2003 SP Legendary Cuts Hall Marks Autographs Blue

OVERALL HALL MARKS ODD 1:196
STATED PRINT RUN 25 SERIAL #'d SETS
NO PRICING DUE TO SCARCITY

2003 SP Legendary Cuts Hall Marks Autographs Green

OVERALL HALL MARKS ODDS 1:196
STATED PRINT RUN 10 SERIAL #'d SETS
NO PRICING DUE TO SCARCITY

2003 SP Legendary Cuts Historic Lumber

OVERALL GAME USED ODDS 1:12
PRINT RUNS B/WN 50-350 COPIES PER
BR Babe Ruth Away/150 75.00 150.00
BR1 Babe Ruth Home/150 75.00 150.00
CF Carlton Fisk R.Sox/50 10.00 25.00
CF1 Carlton Fisk W.Sox/50 10.00 25.00
CY C.Yastrzemski w/Bat/300 12.50 30.00
CY1 C.Yastrzemski w/Cap/350 12.50 30.00
CY2 C.Yaz w/Helmet/350 12.50 30.00
DW Dave Winfield Padres/350 4.00 10.00
DW1 Dave Winfield Yanks/350 4.00 10.00
FR Frank Robinson O's/300 6.00 15.00
FR1 Frank Robinson Reds/350 6.00 15.00
FR2 Frank Robinson Angels/350 6.00 15.00
GC Gary Carter Mets/300 4.00 10.00
GC1 G.Carter Helmet Expos/100 4.00 10.00
GC2 G.Carter Cap Expos/100 4.00 10.00
HK Harmon Killebrew/350 6.00 15.00
JB Johnny Bench w/Bat/350 6.00 15.00
JB1 Johnny Bench Swing/350 6.00 15.00
JM Joe Morgan Reds/350 4.00 10.00
JM1 Joe Morgan Astros/350 4.00 10.00
MM Mickey Mantle/300 60.00 120.00
NR Nolan Ryan Rgr/225 12.50 30.00
OS Ozzie Smith Cards/300 10.00 25.00
OS1 Ozzie Smith Padres/350 10.00 25.00
RS R.Schoen Look Right/165 6.00 15.00
RS1 R.Schoen Look Left/165 6.00 15.00
SC Steve Carlton/350 4.00 10.00
TP Tony Perez Swing/350 4.00 10.00
TP1 Tony Perez Portrait/350 4.00 10.00
TS Tom Seaver/100 6.00 15.00
TW Ted Williams w/3 Bats/150 40.00 80.00
TW1 Ted Williams Portrait/150 40.00 80.00
WS W.Stargell Arms Down/150 6.00 15.00
WS1 W.Stargell Arms Up/150 6.00 15.00
YB Yogi Berra Shout/350 6.00 15.00
YB1 Yogi Berra w/Bat/350 6.00 15.00

2003 SP Legendary Cuts Historic Lumber Green

OVERALL GAME USED ODDS 1:12
PRINT RUNS BETWEEN 50-125 COPIES PER
BR Babe Ruth Away/75 100.00 200.00
BR1 Babe Ruth Home/75 100.00 200.00
CY C.Yastrzemski w/Bat/125 15.00 40.00
CY1 C.Yastrzemski w/Cap/125 15.00 40.00
CY2 C.Yaz w/Helmet/125 15.00 40.00
DW Dave Winfield Padres/125 4.00 10.00
DW1 Dave Winfield Yanks/125 4.00 10.00
FR Frank Robinson O's/125 6.00 15.00
FR1 Frank Robinson Reds/125 6.00 15.00
FR2 Frank Robinson Angels/125 6.00 15.00
GC Gary Carter Mets/125 4.00 10.00
GC1 G.Carter Helmet Expos/125 4.00 10.00
GC2 G.Carter Cap Expos/125 4.00 10.00
HK Harmon Killebrew/125 6.00 15.00
JB Johnny Bench w/Bat/125 6.00 15.00
JB1 Johnny Bench Swing/125 6.00 15.00
JM Joe Morgan Reds/125 4.00 10.00
JM1 Joe Morgan Astros/125 4.00 10.00
MM Mickey Mantle/75 75.00 150.00
NR Nolan Ryan Astros/50 30.00 60.00
OS Ozzie Smith Cards/125 12.50 30.00
OS1 Ozzie Smith Padres/125 12.50 30.00
RS R.Schoen Look Right/125 6.00 15.00
RS1 R.Schoen Look Left/125 6.00 15.00
SC Steve Carlton/125 4.00 10.00
TP Tony Perez Swing/125 4.00 10.00
TP1 Tony Perez Portrait/125 4.00 10.00
TS Tom Seaver/50 10.00 25.00
TW Ted Williams w/3 Bats/75 50.00 100.00
TW1 Ted Williams Portrait/75 50.00 100.00
WS W.Stargell Arms Down/125 6.00 15.00
WS1 W.Stargell Arms Up/125 6.00 15.00
YB Yogi Berra Shout/125 6.00 15.00
YB1 Yogi Berra w/Bat/125 6.00 15.00

2003 SP Legendary Cuts Historic Swatches

OVERALL GAME USED ODDS 1:12
PRINT RUNS B/WN 48-350 COPIES PER
BG Bob Gibson CO Jsy/350 6.00 15.00
BM Bill Mazeroski Pants/50 10.00 25.00
BW Billy Williams Jsy/190 4.00 10.00
CF Carlton Fisk Pants/350 6.00 15.00
CM C.Mathewson Pants/300 75.00 150.00
CS Casey Stengel Jsy/275 6.00 15.00
CY Carl Yastrzemski Jsy/350 10.00 25.00
CY1 Carl Yastrzemski Pants/350 10.00 25.00
DS Duke Snider Jsy/350 6.00 15.00
DW1 D.Winfield Twins Jsy/300 4.00 10.00
FR F.Robinson O's Jsy/350 6.00 15.00
FR1 F.Robinson Angels Jsy/350 6.00 15.00
GC G.Carter Mets Jsy/350 4.00 10.00
GC1 G.Carter Expos Jsy/350 4.00 10.00
HW Honus Wagner Pants/275 75.00 150.00
JB Johnny Bench Jsy/150 6.00 15.00
JM Joe Morgan Jsy/350 4.00 10.00
JN Juan Marichal Pants/225 4.00 10.00
JN1 Juan Marichal Jsy/48 6.00 15.00
LA Luis Aparicio Jsy/230 4.00 10.00
LB Lou Boudreau Jsy/265 4.00 10.00
MM Mickey Mantle Pants/350 60.00 120.00
NR N.Ryan Rgr Pants/350 12.50 30.00
NR1 N.Ryan Astros Pants/350 12.50 30.00
OS Ozzie Smith Jsy/85 15.00 40.00
RF Rollie Fingers Jsy/105 4.00 10.00
RY R.Yount Portrait Jsy/350 6.00 15.00
RY1 R.Yount Swing Jsy/350 6.00 15.00
SA Sparky Anderson Jsy/350 4.00 10.00
SC Steve Carlton Jsy/350 4.00 10.00
SM Stan Musial Jsy/350 15.00 40.00
TC Ty Cobb Pants/300 50.00 100.00
TP Tony Perez Jsy/350 4.00 10.00
TS Tom Seaver Jsy/350 6.00 15.00
TS1 Tom Seaver Pants/350 6.00 15.00
TW Ted Williams Jsy/250 40.00 80.00
WA W.Alston Look Left Jsy/350 4.00 10.00
WA1 W.Alston Ahead Jsy/350 4.00 10.00
WI Willie Stargell Jsy/55 10.00 25.00

WS Warren Spahn CO Jsy/350 6.00 15.00
YB Yogi Berra Jsy/300 6.00 15.00

2003 SP Legendary Cuts Historic Swatches Blue

*BLUE: .6X TO 1.5X BASIC p/r 225-350
*BLUE: .6X TO 1.5X BASIC p/r 150-190
OVERALL GAME USED ODDS 1:12
STATED PRINT RUN 50 SERIAL #'d SETS

2003 SP Legendary Cuts Historic Swatches Green

*GREEN: .5X TO 1.2X BASIC SWATCH
OVERALL GAME USED ODDS 1:12
PRINT RUNS B/WN 160-250 COPIES PER
DW D.Winfield Yanks Jsy/160 4.00 10.00

2003 SP Legendary Cuts Historic Swatches Purple

*PURPLE p/r 150: .5X TO 1.2X BASIC
*PURPLE p/r 75-100: .6X TO 1.5X BASIC
OVERALL GAME USED ODDS 1:12
PRINT RUNS B/WN 75-150 COPIES PER

2003 SP Legendary Cuts Historical Impressions

STATED PRINT RUN 350 SERIAL #'d SETS
*GOLD 200: .6X TO 1.5X BASIC
GOLD 200 PRINT RUN 200 SERIAL #'d SETS
*GOLD 75: 1.25X TO 3X BASIC
GOLD 75 PRINT RUN 75 SERIAL #'d SETS
*SILVER: .75X TO 2X BASIC
SILVER PRINT RUN 250 SERIAL #'d SETS
OVERALL HIST.IMP.ODDS 1:12
AC Alexander Cartwright 3.00 8.00
BR Babe Ruth 8.00 20.00
CG Charlie Gehringer 3.00 8.00
CH Carl Hubbell 4.00 10.00
CM Christy Mathewson 4.00 10.00
CS Casey Stengel 4.00 10.00
CY Cy Young 4.00 10.00
DD Dizzy Dean 4.00 10.00
DO Don Drysdale 4.00 10.00
EC Eddie Collins 3.00 8.00
ES Enos Slaughter 3.00 8.00
GH Gabby Hartnett 3.00 8.00
HC Harry Caray 4.00 10.00
HG Hank Greenberg 4.00 10.00
HO Hoyt Wilhelm 3.00 8.00
HW Honus Wagner 4.00 10.00
JD Joe DiMaggio 5.00 12.00
JF Jimmie Foxx 4.00 10.00
JM Johnny Mize 3.00 8.00
JQ Joe McCarthy 3.00 8.00
JR Jackie Robinson 4.00 10.00
LB Lou Boudreau 3.00 8.00
LD Leo Durocher 3.00 8.00
LE Lefty Grove 4.00 10.00
LG Lefty Gomez 4.00 10.00
LO Lou Gehrig 5.00 12.00
MA Mel Allen 3.00 8.00
MC Mickey Cochrane 3.00 8.00
MM Mickey Mantle 12.50 30.00
MO Mel Ott 4.00 10.00
PR Pee Wee Reese 4.00 10.00
RA Richie Ashburn 4.00 10.00
RC Roberto Clemente 8.00 20.00
RH Rogers Hornsby 4.00 10.00
RO Roy Campanella 4.00 10.00
SP Satchel Paige 4.00 10.00
TL Tony Lazzeri 3.00 8.00
TS Tris Speaker 4.00 10.00
TW Ted Williams 5.00 12.00
TY Ty Cobb 5.00 12.00

2003 SP Legendary Cuts Presidential Cut Signatures

Randomly inserted into packs, these cards featured autographs of deceased United States Presidents. It is believed that these cards were originally supposed to be included in the 2003 Upper Deck "American History" set which was never produced. We have put the stated print runs for these cards next to the President's name in our checklist. Please note that due to market scarcity, no pricing is provided for these cards. Many collectors were somewhat dismayed to discover that Upper Deck actually put their serial numbering on the cut itself.

AJ Andrew Johnson/2
BH Benjamin Harrison/2
CA Chester Arthur/3
CC Calvin Coolidge/2
DE Dwight Eisenhower/2
FDR Franklin D. Roosevelt/3
GW George Washington /1
HT Harry Truman/2
JK John F. Kennedy /2
LJ Lyndon Johnson/2
RN Richard Nixon/2
UG Ulysses S. Grant/2
WT William Taft/2
WW Woodrow Wilson/2

2004 SP Legendary Cuts

This 126-card set was released in November, 2004. The set was issued in four card packs with an $10 SRP which came 12 packs to a box and 16 boxes to a case. The arrangement of this set was by first name of each player.

COMPLETE SET (126) 15.00 40.00
1 Al Kaline .60 1.50
2 Al Lopez .25 .60
3 Alan Trammell .25 .60
4 Andre Dawson .25 .60
5 Babe Ruth 2.00 5.00
6 Bert Campaneris .15 .40
7 Bill Mazeroski .40 1.00
8 Bill Russell .15 .40
9 Billy Williams .25 .60
10 Bob Feller .40 1.00
11 Bob Gibson .40 1.00
12 Bob Lemon .25 .60
13 Bobby Doerr .25 .60
14 Brooks Robinson .40 1.00
15 Cal Ripken 2.00 5.00
16 Carl Yastrzemski 1.00 2.50
17 Carlton Fisk .40 1.00
18 Catfish Hunter .25 .60
19 Dale Murphy .40 1.00
20 Darryl Strawberry .25 .60
21 Dave Concepcion .25 .60
22 Dave Winfield .25 .60
23 Dennis Eckersley .25 .60
24 Denny McLain .25 .60
25 Don Drysdale .40 1.00
26 Don Larsen .25 .60
27 Don Mattingly 1.25 3.00
28 Don Sutton .25 .60
29 Duke Snider UER .40 1.00
Tris Speaker's stats are on the back
30 Dusty Baker .25 .60
31 Dwight Gooden .25 .60
32 Earl Weaver .15 .40
33 Early Wynn .25 .60
34 Eddie Mathews .60 1.50
35 Eddie Murray .60 1.50
36 Enos Slaughter .25 .60
37 Ernie Banks .60 1.50
38 Fergie Jenkins .25 .60
39 Frank Robinson .25 .60
40 Fred Lynn .15 .40
41 Gary Carter .25 .60
42 Gaylord Perry .25 .60
43 George Brett 1.25 3.00
44 George Foster .15 .40
45 George Kell .25 .60
46 Greg Luzinski .25 .60
47 Hal Newhouser .25 .60
48 Hank Greenberg .60 1.50
49 Harmon Killebrew .60 1.50
50 Honus Wagner .60 1.50
51 Hoyt Wilhelm .25 .60
52 Jackie Robinson .60 1.50
53 Jim Bunning .40 1.00
54 Jim Palmer .25 .60
55 Jimmie Foxx .60 1.50
56 Joe Carter .25 .60
57 Joe DiMaggio 1.00 2.50
58 Joe Morgan .25 .60
59 Joe Torre .40 1.00
60 Johnny Bench .60 1.50
61 Johnny Podres .25 .60
62 Johnny Roseboro .15 .40
63 Johnny Sain .25 .60
64 Juan Marichal .25 .60
65 Keith Hernandez .25 .60
66 Kirby Puckett .60 1.50
67 Kirk Gibson .25 .60
68 Will Clark .40 1.00
69 Jim Rice .25 .60
70 Larry Doby .25 .60
71 Lou Boudreau .25 .60
72 Lou Brock .40 1.00
73 Lou Gehrig 1.00 2.50
74 Lou Piniella .25 .60
75 Luis Aparicio .25 .60
76 Mark Grace .40 1.00
77 Mel Ott .60 1.50
78 Mickey Lolich .25 .60
79 Mickey Mantle 3.00 8.00
80 Mike Greenwell .15 .40
81 Mike Schmidt 1.25 3.00
82 Monte Irvin .25 .60
83 Nellie Fox .40 1.00
84 Nolan Ryan 1.50 4.00
85 Orlando Cepeda .25 .60
86 Ozzie Smith 1.00 2.50
87 Paul Molitor .25 .60
88 Pee Wee Reese .40 1.00
89 Phil Niekro .25 .60
90 Phil Rizzuto .40 1.00
91 Ralph Kiner .40 1.00
92 Red Rolfe .15 .40
93 Red Schoendienst .25 .60
94 Reggie Smith .15 .40
95 Rich Gossage .25 .60
96 Richie Ashburn .40 1.00
97 Rick Ferrell .25 .60
98 Elston Howard .25 .60
99 Roberto Clemente 1.50 4.00
100 Robin Roberts .25 .60
101 Robin Yount .60 1.50
102 Roger Maris .60 1.50
103 Rollie Fingers .25 .60
104 Ron Santo .40 1.00
105 Roy Campanella .60 1.50
106 Ryne Sandberg 1.25 3.00
107 Sparky Anderson .25 .60
108 Sparky Lyle .15 .40
109 Stan Musial 1.00 2.50
110 Steve Carlton .25 .60
111 Steve Garvey .25 .60
112 Ted Williams 1.25 3.00
113 Thurman Munson .60 1.50
114 Tom Seaver .40 1.00
115 Tommy Henrich .25 .60
116 Tommy Lasorda .25 .60
117 Tony Gwynn .75 2.00
118 Tony Perez .25 .60
119 Ty Cobb .75 2.00
120 Wade Boggs .40 1.00
121 Warren Spahn .40 1.00
122 Whitey Ford .40 1.00
123 Willie McCovey .40 1.00
124 Willie Randolph .25 .60
125 Willie Stargell .40 1.00
126 Yogi Berra .60 1.50

2004 SP Legendary Cuts Significant Fact Memorabilia

COMMON CARD p/r 50-61 15.00 40.00
MINOR STARS p/r 50-61 15.00 40.00
SEMISTARS p/r 50-61 20.00 50.00
UNLISTED STARS p/r 50-61 30.00 60.00
STATED ODDS 1:96
B/WN 5-99 VARIATIONS PER CARD EXIST
VARIATION PRINT RUNS PROVIDED BY UD
DIFT.FACTS FEATURED ON EACH CARD
EACH VARIATION SERIAL #'d AS 1 OF 1
NO PRICING ON QTY OF 10 OR LESS
SEE BECKETT.COM FOR ALL PRINT RUNS
1 Al Kaline Bat/50 * 30.00 60.00
3 Alan Trammell Jsy/25 * 20.00 50.00
4 Andre Dawson Jsy/25 * 20.00 50.00
5 Babe Ruth Bat/10 *
7 Bill Mazeroski Bat/50 * 20.00 50.00
8 Bill Russell Pants/25 * 20.00 50.00
9 Billy Williams Jsy/99 * 10.00 25.00
11 Bob Gibson Jsy/99 * 15.00 40.00
13 Bobby Doerr Pants/99 * 10.00 25.00
14 Brooks Robinson Bat/99 * 15.00 40.00
15 Cal Ripken Jsy/99 * 125.00 200.00
16 Carl Yastrzemski Pants/99 * 30.00 60.00
17 Carlton Fisk Bat/99 * 15.00 40.00
18 Catfish Hunter Jsy/99 * 15.00 40.00
19 Dale Murphy Jsy/99 * 15.00 40.00
20 Darryl Strawberry Jsy/25 * 20.00 50.00
21 Dave Concepcion Jsy/99 * 10.00 25.00
22 Dave Winfield Jsy/99 * 10.00 25.00
23 Dennis Eckersley Jsy/25 * 20.00 50.00
25 Don Drysdale Jsy/99 * 20.00 50.00
26 Don Larsen Pants/50 * 20.00 50.00
27 Don Mattingly Jsy/99 * 75.00 150.00
28 Don Sutton Jsy/99 * 10.00 25.00
29 Duke Snider Jsy/99 * 15.00 40.00
30 Dusty Baker Jsy/50 * 15.00 40.00
31 Dwight Gooden Jsy/25 * 20.00 50.00
32 Earl Weaver Jsy/25 * 20.00 50.00
34 Eddie Mathews Jsy/99 * 20.00 50.00
35 Eddie Murray Jsy/99 * 75.00 150.00
36 Enos Slaughter Bat/10 *
37 Ernie Banks Jsy/99 * 20.00 50.00
38 Fergie Jenkins Pants/99 * 10.00 25.00
39 Frank Robinson Jsy/99 * 10.00 25.00
40 Fred Lynn Jsy/25 * 20.00 50.00
41 Gary Carter Jsy/99 * 10.00 25.00
42 Gaylord Perry Jsy/99 * 10.00 25.00
43 George Brett Jsy/99 * 60.00 120.00
49 Harmon Killebrew Jsy/99 * 20.00 50.00
50 Honus Wagner Pants/10 *
51 Hoyt Wilhelm Pants/99 * 15.00 40.00
52 Jackie Robinson Jsy/99 * 75.00 150.00
53 Jim Bunning Pants/25 * 20.00 50.00
54 Jim Palmer Jsy/25 * 20.00 50.00
55 Jimmie Foxx Bat/10 *
56 Joe Carter Jsy/99 * 50.00 100.00
57 Joe DiMaggio Pants/10 *
58 Joe Morgan Bat/50 * 15.00 40.00
59 Joe Torre Jsy/25 * 30.00 60.00
60 Johnny Bench Jsy/99 * 20.00 50.00
61 Johnny Podres Jsy/99 * 10.00 25.00
62 Johnny Roseboro Bat/50 * 15.00 40.00
63 Johnny Sain Jsy/25 * 20.00 50.00
64 Juan Marichal Jsy/99 * 10.00 25.00
66 Kirby Puckett Bat/50 * 50.00 100.00
69 Jim Rice Jsy/99 * 10.00 25.00
71 Lou Boudreau Bat/25 * 30.00 60.00
72 Lou Brock Bat/99 * 15.00 40.00
73 Lou Gehrig Pants/10 *
74 Lou Piniella Jsy/25 * 20.00 50.00
75 Luis Aparicio Jsy/25 * 20.00 50.00
76 Mark Grace Jsy/25 * 30.00 60.00
77 Mel Ott Pants/5 *
78 Mickey Lolich Jsy/25 * 20.00 50.00
79 Mickey Mantle Bat/25 * 200.00 350.00
81 Mike Schmidt Jsy/99 * 75.00 150.00
83 Nellie Fox Jsy/99 * 60.00 120.00
84 Nolan Ryan Pants/99 * 75.00 150.00
85 Orlando Cepeda Pants/99 * 10.00 25.00
86 Ozzie Smith Bat/99 * 40.00 80.00
87 Paul Molitor Pants/99 * 10.00 25.00
88 Pee Wee Reese Jsy/99 * 15.00 40.00
89 Phil Niekro Jsy/99 * 10.00 25.00
90 Phil Rizzuto Jsy/99 * 15.00 40.00
92 Red Rolfe Bat/25 * 20.00 50.00
94 Reggie Smith Jsy/10 *
95 Rich Gossage Jsy/50 * 15.00 40.00
98 Elston Howard Jsy/99 * 15.00 40.00
99 Roberto Clemente Jsy/10 *
101 Robin Yount Jsy/99 * 20.00 50.00
102 Roger Maris Pants/50 * 75.00 150.00
103 Rollie Fingers Jsy/99 * 10.00 25.00
104 Ron Santo Bat/10 *
105 Roy Campanella Pants/50 * 20.00 50.00
106 Ryne Sandberg Jsy/50 * 40.00 80.00
107 Sparky Anderson Jsy/50 * 15.00 40.00
108 Sparky Lyle Jsy/50 * 15.00 40.00
109 Stan Musial Pants/99 * 50.00 100.00
110 Steve Carlton Bat/99 * 10.00 25.00
111 Steve Garvey Jsy/99 * 10.00 25.00
112 Ted Williams Pants/10 *
113 Thurman Munson Jsy/99 * 20.00 50.00
114 Tom Seaver Jsy/61 * 20.00 50.00
115 Tommy Henrich Jsy/10 *
116 Tommy Lasorda Jsy/25 * 20.00 50.00
117 Tony Gwynn Jsy/99 * 30.00 60.00
118 Tony Perez Jsy/99 * 10.00 25.00
120 Wade Boggs Jsy/99 * 15.00 40.00
121 Warren Spahn Jsy/99 * 20.00 50.00
123 Willie McCovey Pants/99 * 15.00 40.00
124 Willie Randolph Jsy/25 * 20.00 50.00
125 Willie Stargell Jsy/99 * 15.00 40.00
126 Yogi Berra Jsy/99 * 20.00 50.00

2004 SP Legendary Cuts All-Time Autos

OVERALL AU ODDS 1:64
STATED PRINT RUN 50 SERIAL #'d SETS
EXCHANGE DEADLINE 11/19/07
AK Al Kaline 20.00 50.00
BD Bobby Doerr 10.00 25.00
BM Bill Mazeroski 15.00 40.00
BW Billy Williams EXCH 10.00 25.00
CF Carlton Fisk 15.00 40.00
CR Cal Ripken 75.00 150.00
DE Dennis Eckersley 15.00 40.00
DM Dale Murphy 15.00 40.00
DN Don Newcombe 10.00 25.00
DS Don Sutton 10.00 25.00
FJ Fergie Jenkins 10.00 25.00
FL Fred Lynn 6.00 15.00
GC Gary Carter 10.00 25.00
GK George Kell 10.00 25.00
GP Gaylord Perry 10.00 25.00
HK Harmon Killebrew 20.00 50.00
JC Joe Carter 10.00 25.00
JP Johnny Podres 6.00 15.00
LA Luis Aparicio 10.00 25.00
MA Don Mattingly 40.00 80.00
MC Denny McLain 10.00 25.00
MI Monte Irvin 15.00 40.00
MW Maury Wills 10.00 25.00
NR Nolan Ryan 60.00 120.00
OC Orlando Cepeda 10.00 25.00
PN Phil Niekro 10.00 25.00
RF Rollie Fingers 10.00 25.00
RR Robin Roberts 10.00 25.00
RS Red Schoendienst 10.00 25.00
RY Robin Yount 30.00 60.00
SA Ryne Sandberg 40.00 80.00
SC Steve Carlton EXCH 10.00 25.00
SM Stan Musial 40.00 80.00
TG Tony Gwynn 20.00 50.00
TP Tony Perez 15.00 40.00
TS Tom Seaver 20.00 50.00
WB Wade Boggs 15.00 40.00
WC Will Clark 15.00 40.00
WF Whitey Ford 15.00 40.00
WM Willie McCovey 15.00 40.00
YB Yogi Berra 20.00 50.00

2004 SP Legendary Cuts Autographs

Some of the key players in this set include Adrian "Cap" Anson, "Gettysburg" Eddie Plank, Frank Chance, "Bullet" Joe Bush, Christy Mathewson and the original "Sad" Sam Jones. Many of these

autographs, which were inserted at a stated rate of one in 128 are very tough to obtain.

OVERALL CUT AU ODDS 1:128
PRINT RUNS B/WN 1-199 COPIES PER
NO PRICING ON QTY OF 19 OR LESS
EXCHANGE DEADLINE 11/19/07
AN Cap Anson/1
AR Allie Reynolds/25 200.00 350.00
AS Al Simmons/10
AV Arky Vaughan/4
BD Bill Dickey/82 100.00 200.00
BG A. Bartlett Giamatti/2
BH Billy Herman/134 60.00 120.00
BJ Bob Johnson/32 150.00 250.00
BL Bob Lemon/199 60.00 120.00
BM Billy Martin/7
BO Jim Bottomley/2
BR Babe Ruth/13
BU Burleigh Grimes/83 100.00 200.00
BW Bobby Wallace/2
CA Max Carey/72 75.00 150.00
CB Chief Bender/6
CC Charlie Comiskey/2
CG Charlie Gehringer/171 100.00 200.00
CH Carl Hubbell/199 100.00 200.00
CJ Jack Coombs/1
CK Chuck Klein/5
CL Fred Clarke/2
CM Carl Mays/2
CO Eddie Collins/6
CR Joe Cronin/84 100.00 200.00
CS Casey Stengel/38 300.00 500.00
CY Cy Young/5
DD Dizzy Dean/33 500.00 800.00
DO Larry Doby/14
DR Don Drysdale/66 175.00 300.00
DU Joe Dugan/9
DV Dazzy Vance/5
EC Earle Combs/27 175.00 300.00
ED Ed Walsh/5
EH Elston Howard/2
EL Ernie Lombardi/39 175.00 300.00
EM Eddie Mathews/27 175.00 300.00
EP0 Eddie Plank/1 UER
Signature was of the Eddie Plank who played in the 1970's
ER Edd Roush/129 75.00 150.00
ES Enos Slaughter/147 60.00 120.00
EW Early Wynn/54 150.00 250.00
FB Frank Baker/3
FC Frank Chance/1
FF Frankie Frisch/57 200.00 350.00
GA Grover Alexander/2
GE Lou Gehrig/7
GH Gaby Hartnett/19
GI Gil Hodges/9
GP George Pipgras/46 100.00 200.00
GR Lefty Grove/75 125.00 250.00
GS George Sisler/32 300.00 600.00
HG Hank Greenberg/37 250.00 400.00
HH Harry Heilmann/3
HK Harvey Kuenn/49 100.00 200.00
HM Heinie Manush/16
HN Hal Newhouser/51 75.00 150.00
HP Herb Pennock/2
HW Honus Wagner/17
JA Jack Buck/2
JB Joe Bush/1
JD Joe DiMaggio/111 350.00 500.00
JF Jimmie Foxx/15
JH Jim Hunter/25 150.00 250.00
JM Joe Medwick/32 250.00 400.00
JR Jackie Robinson/19
JS Joe Sewell/199 60.00 120.00
KC Kiki Cuyler/4
KN Kid Nichols/4
LA Tony Lazzeri/5
LB Lou Boudreau/199 50.00 100.00
LD Leo Durocher/75 150.00 300.00
LG Lefty Gomez/98 100.00 200.00
LU Luke Appling/108 60.00 120.00
MA Roger Maris/6
MB Mordecai Brown/2
MC Mickey Cochrane/7
MI Johnny Mize/118 75.00 150.00
MK Connie Mack/9
MM Mickey Mantle/19
MO Mel Ott/17
MW Christy Mathewson/1
NF Nellie Fox/14
NL Nap LaJoie/2
PB James Cool Papa Bell/47 350.00 500.00
PR Pee Wee Reese/35 175.00 300.00
PT Pie Traynor/6
PW Paul Waner/9
RA Richie Ashburn/31 175.00 300.00
RC Roy Campanella/3
RD Ray Dandridge/199 50.00 100.00
RF Rick Ferrell/43 60.00 120.00
RH Rogers Hornsby/5
RM Rabbit Maranville/5
RO Roberto Clemente/9
RR Red Ruffing/30 175.00 300.00
RU Rube Marquard/59 150.00 250.00
SC Sam Crawford/9
SJ Sam Jones/4
SM Stuffy McInnis/2
SP Satchel Paige/28 900.00 1300.00
SR Sam Rice/28 175.00 300.00
ST Stan Coveleski/102 75.00 150.00
SW Joe Wood/79 175.00 300.00
TC Ty Cobb/18
TL Ted Lyons/199 60.00 120.00
TM Thurman Munson/2
TS Tris Speaker/4
TW Ted Williams/28 1000.00 1200.00
WA Walter Alston/74 100.00 200.00
WF Wes Ferrell/36 150.00 250.00
WH Waite Hoyt/106 150.00 250.00
WI Hack Wilson/5
WJ Walter Johnson/14
WM Hoyt Wilhelm/115 60.00 120.00
WS Willie Stargell/39 100.00 200.00

2004 SP Legendary Cuts Game Graphs Memorabilia 25

OVERALL AU ODDS 1:64
STATED PRINT RUN 25 SERIAL #'d SETS
GRAPH 10 PRINT RUN 10 SERIAL #'d SETS
NO GRAPH 10 PRICING DUE TO SCARCITY
EXCHANGE DEADLINE 11/19/07
AK Al Kaline Bat 40.00 80.00
BG Bob Gibson Jsy 20.00 50.00
BM Bill Mazeroski Bat 20.00 50.00
BR Brooks Robinson Bat 20.00 50.00
BW Billy Williams Jsy EXCH 15.00 40.00
CF Carlton Fisk Jsy 20.00 50.00
CR Cal Ripken Jsy 125.00 200.00
CY Carl Yastrzemski Jsy 50.00 100.00
DM Dale Murphy Jsy 20.00 50.00
DS Don Sutton Jsy 12.50 30.00
DW Dave Winfield Pants 20.00 50.00
EB Ernie Banks Jsy 40.00 80.00
EM Eddie Murray Jsy 50.00 100.00
FR Frank Robinson Jsy 20.00 50.00
GB George Brett Jsy 60.00 120.00
GC Gary Carter Jsy 15.00 40.00
HK Harmon Killebrew Jsy 40.00 80.00
JB Johnny Bench Jsy 40.00 80.00
JC Joe Carter Jsy 15.00 40.00
JM Juan Marichal Jsy 15.00 40.00
KP Kirby Puckett Bat 50.00 100.00
LA Luis Aparicio Jsy 15.00 40.00
LB Lou Brock Jsy 20.00 50.00
MA Don Mattingly Jsy 60.00 120.00
MO Joe Morgan Bat 15.00 40.00
MS Mike Schmidt Jsy 50.00 100.00
NR Nolan Ryan Jsy 75.00 150.00
OS Ozzie Smith Jsy 40.00 80.00
PM Paul Molitor Jsy 15.00 40.00
PN Phil Niekro Jsy 15.00 40.00
PR Phil Rizzuto Jsy 20.00 50.00
RF Rollie Fingers Jsy 12.50 30.00
RS Ryne Sandberg Jsy 60.00 120.00
RY Robin Yount Jsy 40.00 80.00
SC Steve Carlton Bat EXCH 15.00 40.00
SM Stan Musial Jsy 50.00 100.00
SN Duke Snider Jsy 20.00 50.00
TG Tony Gwynn Jsy 40.00 80.00
TS Tom Seaver Jsy EXCH 40.00 80.00
WB Wade Boggs Jsy 40.00 80.00
WM Willie McCovey Pants 20.00 50.00
YB Yogi Berra Jsy 40.00 80.00

2004 SP Legendary Cuts Historic Patches

OVERALL GU ODDS 1:4
STATED PRINT RUN 25 SERIAL #'d SETS
BG Bob Gibson 15.00 40.00
CR Cal Ripken 60.00 120.00
CY Carl Yastrzemski 20.00 50.00
DD Don Drysdale 15.00 40.00
DS Duke Snider 15.00 40.00
EB Ernie Banks 30.00 60.00
EM Eddie Mathews 40.00 80.00
GB George Brett 20.00 50.00
JB Johnny Bench 15.00 40.00
MS Mike Schmidt 20.00 50.00
NR Nolan Ryan 40.00 80.00
RY Robin Yount 15.00 40.00
SM Stan Musial 40.00 80.00
TG Tony Gwynn 15.00 40.00
TS Tom Seaver 15.00 40.00

2004 SP Legendary Cuts Historic Quads Memorabilia

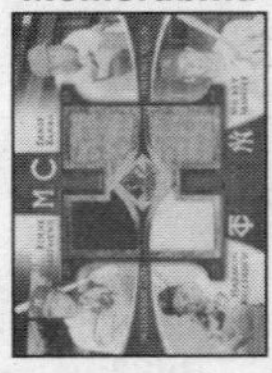

OVERALL GU ODDS 1:4
STATED PRINT RUN 10 SERIAL #'d SETS
NO PRICING DUE TO SCARCITY
B ='s BAT, J ='s JSY, P ='s PANTS
FCBM Carlton Fisk Pants
Gary Carter Jsy
Johnny Bench Jsy

Thurman Munson Jsy
MBKM Eddie Mathews Jsy
Ernie Banks Jsy
Harmon Killebrew Jsy
Mickey Mantle Pants
MPGB Don Mattingly Jsy
Kirby Puckett Bat
Tony Gwynn Jsy
Wade Boggs Jsy
RMBM Cal Ripken Jsy
Eddie Murray Jsy
George Brett Jsy
Paul Molitor Jsy
SMMW Duke Snider Jsy
Mickey Mantle Jsy
Stan Musial Jsy
Ted Williams Jsy
SRCS Don Sutton Jsy
Nolan Ryan Jsy
Steve Carlton Bat
Tom Seaver Jsy

2004 SP Legendary Cuts Historic Quads Patch

OVERALL GU ODDS 1:4
STATED PRINT RUN 5 SERIAL #'d SETS
NO PRICING DUE TO SCARCITY
BCBM Yogi Berra
Gary Carter
Johnny Bench
Thurman Munson
MBKS Eddie Mathews
Ernie Banks
Harmon Killebrew
Mike Schmidt
MYGB Don Mattingly
Robin Yount
Tony Gwynn
Wade Boggs
RMBM Cal Ripken
Eddie Murray
George Brett
Paul Molitor
SMMB Duke Snider
Eddie Mathews
Stan Musial
Ernie Banks
SRSS Don Sutton
Nolan Ryan
Warren Spahn
Tom Seaver

2004 SP Legendary Cuts Historic Swatches

OVERALL GU ODDS 1:4
SP INFO PROVIDED BY UPPER DECK
AN Sparky Anderson Jsy 3.00 8.00
BR Brooks Robinson Bat 4.00 10.00
CF Carlton Fisk Pants 4.00 10.00
CH Catfish Hunter Pants 4.00 10.00
CR Cal Ripken Jsy 10.00 25.00
DC Dave Concepcion Jsy 3.00 8.00
DD Don Drysdale Pants 4.00 10.00
DL Don Larsen Pants SP 6.00 15.00
DM Don Mattingly Jsy 6.00 15.00
DS Don Sutton Jsy 3.00 8.00
DW Dave Winfield Pants 3.00 8.00
EM Eddie Murray Jsy SP 6.00 15.00
FJ Fergie Jenkins Pants 3.00 8.00
GB George Brett Jsy 6.00 15.00
GC Gary Carter Pants 3.00 8.00
GF George Foster Bat 3.00 8.00
GP Gaylord Perry Jsy 3.00 8.00
HK Harmon Killebrew Jsy 4.00 10.00
HW Hoyt Wilhelm Pants 3.00 8.00
JB Johnny Bench Pants SP 6.00 15.00
JC Joe Carter Jsy 3.00 8.00
JM Joe Morgan Bat 3.00 8.00
JP Johnny Podres Jsy 3.00 8.00
JR Jim Rice Jsy 3.00 8.00
KP Kirby Puckett Bat 4.00 10.00
LB Lou Brock Jsy 4.00 10.00
MA Eddie Mathews Jsy 4.00 10.00
ML Mickey Lolich Jsy 3.00 8.00
MU Dale Murphy Jsy 4.00 10.00
NR Nolan Ryan Jsy 10.00 25.00
OS Ozzie Smith Jsy 6.00 15.00
PM Paul Molitor Jsy 3.00 8.00
PN Phil Niekro Jsy 3.00 8.00
RF Rollie Fingers Pants 3.00 8.00
RY Robin Yount Pants 4.00 10.00
SG Steve Garvey Jsy 3.00 8.00
SL Sparky Lyle Jsy 3.00 8.00
SM Stan Musial Pants 8.00 20.00
TM Thurman Munson Jsy 4.00 10.00
TS Tom Seaver Pants 4.00 10.00

2004 SP Legendary Cuts Historic Swatches 25

*SWATCH 25: .75X TO 2X BASIC
*SWATCH 25: .75X TO 2X BASIC SP
OVERALL GU ODDS 1:4

STATED PRINT RUN 25 SERIAL #'d SETS
CR Cal Ripken Jsy 40.00 80.00
PR Phil Rizzuto Jsy 8.00 20.00

2004 SP Legendary Cuts Historical Cuts

OVERALL CUT AU ODDS 1:128
PRINT RUNS B/WN
NO PRICING DUE TO SCARCITY
AC Alexander Cartwright/1
AD John Adams/1
AL Abraham Lincoln/1
DE Dwight D. Eisenhower/1
DM Douglass MacArthur/3
DO Abner Doubleday/2
FD Frederick Douglass/1
FDR Franklyn D. Roosevelt/1
FLW Frank Lloyd Wright/1
HA John Hancock/1
HT Howard Taft/1
JD James Doolittle/1
LP Louis Pasteur/1
PG Pat Garrett/1
SF Sigmund Freud/1
TE Thomas Edison/2
TJ Thomas Jefferson/1
WC Winston Churchill/2
WF William Faulkner/2

2004 SP Legendary Cuts Legendary Duels Memorabilia

OVERALL GU ODDS 1:4
STATED PRINT RUN 25 SERIAL #'d SETS
BG George Brett Jsy 30.00 60.00
Rich Gossage Jsy
DW Joe DiMaggio Jsy 100.00 200.00
Ted Williams Jsy
EG Dennis Eckersley Jsy 15.00 40.00
Kirk Gibson Bat
FM Carlton Fisk Pants 15.00 40.00
Joe Morgan Bat
GL Bob Gibson Jsy 15.00 40.00
Mickey Lolich Jsy
MW Mickey Mantle Pants 150.00 250.00
Ted Williams Jsy
PL Johnny Podres Jsy 15.00 40.00
Don Larsen Jsy
RM John Roseboro Bat 10.00 25.00
Juan Marichal Pants
RR Pee Wee Reese Jsy 15.00 40.00
Phil Rizzuto Pants
SM Duke Snider Jsy 100.00 200.00
Mickey Mantle Pants
SS Ozzie Smith Jsy 40.00 80.00
Ryne Sandberg Jsy
WB Honus Wagner Pants 75.00 150.00
Ernie Banks Jsy

2004 SP Legendary Cuts Legendary Duels Patch

OVERALL GU ODDS 1:4
STATED PRINT RUN 15 SERIAL #'d SETS
NO PRICING DUE TO SCARCITY
BS George Brett
Mike Schmidt
GB Tony Gwynn
Wade Boggs
MD Juan Marichal
Don Drysdale
SG Warren Spahn
Bob Gibson
SM Duke Snider
Stan Musial

2004 SP Legendary Cuts Legendary Duos Memorabilia

OVERALL GU ODDS 1:4
STATED PRINT RUN 25 SERIAL #'d SETS
CM Dave Concepcion Jsy 10.00 25.00
Joe Morgan Bat
DM Joe DiMaggio Jsy 175.00 300.00
Mickey Mantle Pants
LB Don Larsen Jsy 40.00 80.00
Yogi Berra Jsy
MB Mickey Mantle Pants 150.00 250.00
Yogi Berra Jsy
MM Mickey Mantle Pants 175.00 300.00
Roger Maris Jsy
MY Paul Molitor Jsy 20.00 50.00
Robin Yount Jsy
PJ Pee Wee Reese Jsy 40.00 80.00
Jackie Robinson Jsy
RR Brooks Robinson Bat 40.00 80.00
Cal Ripken Jsy
RS Nolan Ryan Jsy 75.00 150.00
Tom Seaver Jsy
SC Duke Snider Jsy 30.00 60.00
Roy Campanella Pants
SS Johnny Sain Jsy 20.00 50.00
Warren Spahn Jsy
WB Billy Williams Jsy 20.00 50.00
Ernie Banks Jsy

2004 SP Legendary Cuts Legendary Duos Patch

OVERALL GU ODDS 1:4
STATED PRINT RUN 15 SERIAL #'d SETS
NO PRICING DUE TO SCARCITY
BM Yogi Berra
Roger Maris
CB Dave Concepcion
Johnny Bench
MS Eddie Mathews
Warren Spahn
MY Paul Molitor
Robin Yount
RS Nolan Ryan
Tom Seaver

2004 SP Legendary Cuts Legendary Sigs

OVERALL AU ODDS 1:64
STATED PRINT RUN 50 SERIAL #'d SETS
AK Al Kaline 20.00 50.00
BD Bobby Doerr 10.00 25.00
BF Bob Feller 10.00 25.00
BG Bob Gibson 15.00 40.00
BR Brooks Robinson 15.00 40.00
CR Cal Ripken 75.00 150.00
CY Carl Yastrzemski 30.00 60.00
DE Dennis Eckersley 15.00 40.00
DM Dale Murphy 15.00 40.00
DN Don Newcombe 10.00 25.00
DS Don Sutton 10.00 25.00
EB Ernie Banks 30.00 60.00
EM Eddie Murray 50.00 100.00
FL Fred Lynn 6.00 15.00
GC Gary Carter 10.00 25.00
GK George Kell 10.00 25.00
GP Gaylord Perry 10.00 25.00
HK Harmon Killebrew UER 10.00 25.00
Killebrew misspelled Killewbrew on front)
JB Johnny Bench 30.00 60.00
JC Joe Carter 10.00 25.00
JM Juan Marichal 10.00 25.00
JP Johnny Podres 6.00 15.00
LA Luis Aparicio 10.00 25.00
MA Don Mattingly 40.00 80.00
MC Denny McLain 10.00 25.00
MI Monte Irvin 15.00 40.00
MS Mike Schmidt 40.00 80.00
MW Maury Wills 10.00 25.00
OS Ozzie Smith 30.00 60.00
PA Jim Palmer 10.00 25.00
PR Phil Rizzuto 15.00 40.00
RF Rollie Fingers 10.00 25.00
RK Ralph Kiner 15.00 40.00
RR Robin Roberts 10.00 25.00
RS Red Schoendienst 10.00 25.00
SA Ryne Sandberg 40.00 80.00
SN Duke Snider 15.00 40.00

TG Tony Gwynn 20.00 50.00
WB Wade Boggs 15.00 40.00
WC Will Clark 15.00 40.00
WM Willie McCovey 15.00 40.00

2004 SP Legendary Cuts Legendary Swatches

SP INFO PROVIDED BY UPPER DECK
SWATCH 15 PRINT RUN 15 #'d SETS
NO SWATCH 15 PRICING DUE TO SCARCITY
OVERALL GU ODDS 1:4
AK Al Kaline Bat 4.00 10.00
BD Bobby Doerr Pants 3.00 8.00
BG Bob Gibson Jsy 4.00 10.00
BW Billy Williams Jsy 3.00 8.00
CF Carlton Fisk Pants 4.00 10.00
CH Catfish Hunter Jsy 4.00 10.00
CR Cal Ripken Jsy 10.00 25.00
CY Carl Yastrzemski Jsy 6.00 15.00
DD Don Drysdale Pants 4.00 10.00
DM Don Mattingly Jsy 6.00 15.00
DS Duke Snider Pants 4.00 10.00
DW Dave Winfield Jsy 3.00 8.00
EB Ernie Banks Jsy SP 6.00 15.00
EH Elston Howard Jsy 4.00 10.00
EM Eddie Mathews Jsy 4.00 10.00
FR Frank Robinson Pants 3.00 8.00
GB George Brett Jsy 6.00 15.00
HK Harmon Killebrew Jsy 4.00 10.00
JB Johnny Bench Jsy 4.00 10.00
JR Jim Rice Jsy 3.00 8.00
MA Juan Marichal Pants 3.00 8.00
MS Mike Schmidt Jsy 6.00 15.00
NF Nellie Fox Jsy 4.00 10.00
NR Nolan Ryan Jsy 10.00 25.00
OC Orlando Cepeda Pants 3.00 8.00
PO Johnny Podres Jsy 3.00 8.00
PR Pee Wee Reese Jsy 4.00 10.00
RC Roy Campanella Pants 4.00 10.00
RI Phil Rizzuto Pants 4.00 10.00
RY Robin Yount Pants 4.00 10.00
SC Steve Carlton Bat 3.00 8.00
SM Stan Musial Jsy 8.00 20.00
ST Willie Stargell Jsy 4.00 10.00
TG Tony Gwynn Pants 4.00 10.00
TM Thurman Munson Jsy 4.00 10.00
TP Tony Perez Jsy 3.00 8.00
TS Tom Seaver Jsy 4.00 10.00
WB Wade Boggs Pants 4.00 10.00
WM Willie McCovey Pants 4.00 10.00
WS Warren Spahn Jsy 4.00 10.00
YB Yogi Berra Jsy 4.00 10.00

2004 SP Legendary Cuts Marked for the Hall Autos

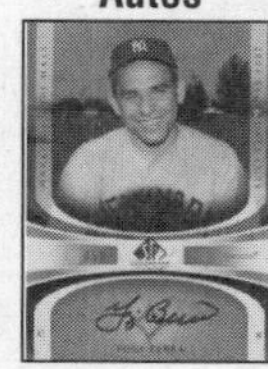

OVERALL AU ODDS 1:64
STATED PRINT RUN 50 SERIAL #'d SETS
EXCHANGE DEADLINE 11/19/07
AK Al Kaline 20.00 50.00
BD Bobby Doerr 10.00 25.00
BF Bob Feller 10.00 25.00
BG Bob Gibson 15.00 40.00
BM Bill Mazeroski 15.00 40.00
BR Brooks Robinson 15.00 40.00
BW Billy Williams EXCH 10.00 25.00
CF Carlton Fisk 15.00 40.00
CY Carl Yastrzemski 30.00 60.00
DS Duke Snider 15.00 40.00
DW Dave Winfield 15.00 40.00
EB Ernie Banks 30.00 60.00
EM Eddie Murray 50.00 100.00
FR Frank Robinson 15.00 40.00
GB George Brett 40.00 80.00
GC Gary Carter 10.00 25.00
GP Gaylord Perry 10.00 25.00
HK Harmon Killebrew 20.00 50.00
JB Johnny Bench 30.00 60.00
JM Joe Morgan 10.00 25.00
JP Jim Palmer 10.00 25.00
KP Kirby Puckett 50.00 100.00
LA Luis Aparicio 10.00 25.00
LB Lou Brock 15.00 40.00
MA Juan Marichal 10.00 25.00
MS Mike Schmidt 40.00 80.00
NR Nolan Ryan 60.00 120.00
OC Orlando Cepeda 10.00 25.00
OS Ozzie Smith 30.00 60.00
PM Paul Molitor 10.00 25.00
PN Phil Niekro 10.00 25.00
PR Phil Rizzuto 10.00 25.00
RK Ralph Kiner 15.00 40.00
RR Robin Roberts 15.00 40.00
RY Robin Yount 30.00 60.00
SC Steve Carlton EXCH 15.00 40.00
SM Stan Musial 40.00 80.00
TP Tony Perez 15.00 40.00
TS Tom Seaver 20.00 50.00
WF Whitey Ford 15.00 40.00
WM Willie McCovey 15.00 40.00
YB Yogi Berra 20.00 50.00

2004 SP Legendary Cuts Marks of Greatness Autos

OVERALL AU ODDS 1:64
STATED PRINT RUN 50 SERIAL #'d SETS
EXCHANGE DEADLINE 11/19/07
AK Al Kaline 20.00 50.00
BG Bob Gibson 15.00 40.00
BR Brooks Robinson 15.00 40.00
BW Billy Williams EXCH 10.00 25.00
CF Carlton Fisk 15.00 40.00
CR Cal Ripken 75.00 150.00
DM Dale Murphy 15.00 40.00
DN Don Newcombe 10.00 25.00
DS Duke Snider 15.00 40.00
DW Dave Winfield 15.00 40.00
EB Ernie Banks 30.00 60.00
FJ Fergie Jenkins 10.00 25.00
FL Fred Lynn 6.00 15.00
FR Frank Robinson 15.00 40.00
GB George Brett 40.00 80.00
HK Harmon Killebrew 20.00 50.00
JB Johnny Bench 30.00 60.00
JC Joe Carter 10.00 25.00
JM Joe Morgan 10.00 25.00
JP Jim Palmer 10.00 25.00
KP Kirby Puckett 50.00 100.00
LB Lou Brock 15.00 40.00
MA Don Mattingly 40.00 80.00
MC Denny McLain 10.00 25.00
MS Mike Schmidt 40.00 80.00
NR Nolan Ryan 60.00 120.00
OC Orlando Cepeda 10.00 25.00
OZ Ozzie Smith 30.00 60.00
PM Paul Molitor 10.00 25.00
PN Phil Niekro 10.00 25.00
RF Rollie Fingers 10.00 25.00
RS Ryne Sandberg 40.00 80.00
RY Robin Yount 30.00 60.00
SC Steve Carlton EXCH 10.00 25.00
SM Stan Musial 40.00 80.00
TG Tony Gwynn 20.00 50.00
TP Tony Perez 15.00 40.00
TS Tom Seaver 20.00 50.00
WB Wade Boggs 15.00 40.00
WC Will Clark 15.00 40.00
WF Whitey Ford 15.00 40.00
YB Yogi Berra 20.00 50.00

2004 SP Legendary Cuts Significant Swatches

OVERALL GU ODDS 1:4
SP INFO PROVIDED BY UPPER DECK
BD Bobby Doerr Pants 3.00 8.00
BM Bill Mazeroski Bat 4.00 10.00
CF Carlton Fisk Pants 4.00 10.00
CH Catfish Hunter Pants 4.00 10.00
CR Cal Ripken Jsy 10.00 25.00
CY Carl Yastrzemski Jsy 6.00 15.00
DC Dave Concepcion Jsy 3.00 8.00
DD Don Drysdale Jsy 4.00 10.00
DM Dale Murphy Bat 4.00 10.00
DS Don Sutton Jsy 3.00 8.00
DW Dave Winfield Pants 3.00 8.00
EB Ernie Banks Pants SP 6.00 15.00
ED Eddie Mathews Jsy 4.00 10.00
EM Eddie Murray Jsy SP 6.00 15.00
FJ Fergie Jenkins Pants 3.00 8.00
FR Frank Robinson Jsy 3.00 8.00
GC Gary Carter Jsy 3.00 8.00
GF George Foster Bat 3.00 8.00
GP Gaylord Perry Jsy 3.00 8.00
HW Hoyt Wilhelm Pants 3.00 8.00
JC Joe Carter Jsy 3.00 8.00
JP Johnny Podres Jsy 3.00 8.00
LB Lou Brock Jsy SP 6.00 15.00
MA Don Mattingly Jsy 6.00 15.00
MS Mike Schmidt Pants 6.00 15.00
NR Nolan Ryan Jsy 10.00 25.00
OC Orlando Cepeda Pants 3.00 8.00
PM Paul Molitor Bat 3.00 8.00
PN Phil Niekro Jsy SP 4.00 10.00
RF Rollie Fingers Pants 3.00 8.00
RM Roger Maris Pants 12.50 30.00
RY Robin Yount Bat 4.00 10.00
SA Sparky Anderson Jsy 3.00 8.00
SG Steve Garvey Jsy 3.00 8.00
SL Sparky Lyle Jsy 3.00 8.00
SN Duke Snider Pants 4.00 10.00
ST Willie Stargell Jsy SP 6.00 15.00
TM Thurman Munson Pants 4.00 10.00
TP Tony Perez Jsy 3.00 8.00
TS Tom Seaver Pants 4.00 10.00
WM Willie McCovey Pants 4.00 10.00
WS Warren Spahn Jsy 4.00 10.00

2004 SP Legendary Cuts Significant Swatches 25

*SWATCH 25: .75X TO 2X BASIC
*SWATCH 25: .75X TO 2X BASIC SP
OVERALL GU ODDS 1:4

STATED PRINT RUN 25 SERIAL #'d SETS
CR Cal Ripken Jsy 40.00 80.00

2004 SP Legendary Cuts Significant Trips Memorabilia

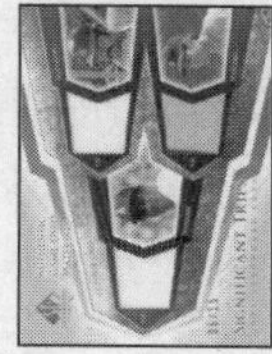

OVERALL GU ODDS 1:4
STATED PRINT RUN 15 SERIAL #'d SETS
NO PRICING DUE TO SCARCITY
B ='s BAT, J ='s JSY, P ='s PANTS
BSG Dusty Baker Jsy
Reggie Smith Jsy
Steve Garvey Jsy
DFW Bobby Doerr Pants
Jimmie Foxx Bat
Ted Williams Jsy
DGS Andre Dawson Jsy
Mark Grace Jsy
Ryne Sandberg Jsy
DMB Joe DiMaggio Jsy
Mickey Mantle Pants
Yogi Berra Jsy
MBP Joe Morgan Bat
Johnny Bench Jsy
Tony Perez Jsy
MMB Mickey Mantle Pants
Roger Maris Jsy
Yogi Berra Jsy
SCH Darryl Strawberry Jsy
Gary Carter Jsy
Keith Hernandez Bat
SCR Duke Snider Jsy
Roy Campanella Pants
Pee Wee Reese Jsy
SRC Duke Snider Jsy
Jackie Robinson Jsy
Roy Campanella Pants
SSM Enos Slaughter Bat
Red Schoendienst Bat
Stan Musial Jsy
WBS Billy Williams Jsy
Ernie Banks Jsy
Ron Santo Jsy
WMG Dave Winfield Jsy
Don Mattingly Jsy
Ken Griffey Sr. Jsy

2004 SP Legendary Cuts Significant Trips Patch

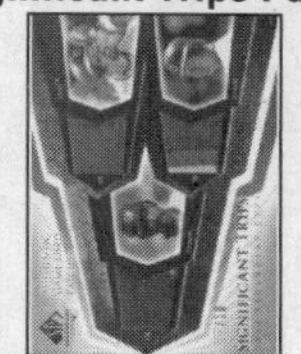

OVERALL GU ODDS 1:4
STATED PRINT RUN 10 SERIAL #'d SETS
NO PRICING DUE TO SCARCITY
BPG Johnny Bench
Tony Perez
Ken Griffey Sr.
CBP Dave Concepcion
Johnny Bench
Tony Perez
DGS Andre Dawson
Mark Grace
Ryne Sandberg
HMB Elston Howard
Roger Maris
Yogi Berra
MBG Roger Maris
Lou Brock
Bob Gibson
MYF Paul Molitor
Robin Yount
Rollie Fingers
SRD Duke Snider
Pee Wee Reese
Don Drysdale
SRR Duke Snider
Jackie Robinson
Pee Wee Reese
YBR Carl Yastrzemski
Wade Boggs
Jim Rice

2004 SP Legendary Cuts Ultimate Autos

OVERALL AU ODDS 1:64
STATED PRINT RUN 25 SERIAL #'d SETS
EXCHANGE DEADLINE 11/19/07
AK Al Kaline 30.00 60.00
BF Bob Feller 12.50 30.00
BG Bob Gibson 15.00 40.00

BM Bill Mazeroski 15.00 40.00
BR Brooks Robinson 15.00 40.00
CY Carl Yastrzemski 40.00 80.00
DE Dennis Eckersley 15.00 40.00
DM Don Mattingly 50.00 100.00
DS Don Sutton 10.00 25.00
DW Dave Winfield 15.00 40.00
EB Ernie Banks 30.00 60.00
EM Eddie Murray 40.00 80.00
FJ Fergie Jenkins 12.50 30.00
FR Frank Robinson 15.00 40.00
GB George Brett 50.00 100.00
GK George Kell 12.50 30.00
HK Harmon Killebrew 30.00 60.00
JB Johnny Bench 30.00 60.00
JM Joe Morgan 12.50 30.00
JP Johnny Podres 10.00 25.00
KP Kirby Puckett 50.00 100.00
LB Lou Brock 15.00 40.00
MA Juan Marichal 12.50 30.00
MI Monte Irvin 15.00 40.00
MS Mike Schmidt 40.00 80.00
MW Maury Wills 12.50 30.00
NR Nolan Ryan 60.00 120.00
OS Ozzie Smith 30.00 60.00
PA Jim Palmer 12.50 30.00
PM Paul Molitor 12.50 30.00
PR Phil Rizzuto 15.00 40.00
RK Ralph Kiner 15.00 40.00
RS Red Schoendienst 12.50 30.00
RY Robin Yount 30.00 60.00
SA Ryne Sandberg 50.00 100.00
SC Steve Carlton EXCH 12.50 30.00
SM Stan Musial 40.00 80.00
SN Duke Snider 15.00 40.00
TS Tom Seaver 30.00 60.00
WF Whitey Ford 15.00 40.00
YB Yogi Berra 30.00 60.00

2004 SP Legendary Cuts Ultimate Swatches

SP INFO PROVIDED BY UPPER DECK
SWATCH 10 PRINT RUN 10 #'d SETS
NO SWATCH 10 PRICING DUE TO SCARCITY
OVERALL GU ODDS 1:4
BG Bob Gibson Jsy 4.00 10.00
BR Brooks Robinson Bat 4.00 10.00
BW Billy Williams Jsy 3.00 8.00
CH Catfish Hunter Jsy 4.00 10.00
CR Cal Ripken Jsy 10.00 25.00
CY Carl Yastrzemski Jsy 6.00 15.00
DD Don Drysdale Jsy 4.00 10.00
DM Don Mattingly Jsy 6.00 15.00
DS Duke Snider Jsy SP 6.00 15.00
DW Dave Winfield Jsy 3.00 8.00
EB Ernie Banks Jsy 4.00 10.00
EM Eddie Mathews Jsy 4.00 10.00
FR Frank Robinson Pants 3.00 8.00
GB George Brett Jsy 6.00 15.00
HG Hank Greenberg Bat 10.00 25.00
HK Harmon Killebrew Jsy 4.00 10.00
HW Honus Wagner Pants SP 75.00 150.00
JB Johnny Bench Jsy 4.00 10.00
JD Joe DiMaggio Jsy SP 40.00 80.00
JR Jackie Robinson Jsy 15.00 40.00
KP Kirby Puckett Bat 4.00 10.00
MA Juan Marichal Jsy 3.00 8.00
MM Mickey Mantle Pants SP 75.00 150.00
MS Mike Schmidt Jsy 6.00 15.00
NF Nellie Fox Jsy 4.00 10.00
NR Nolan Ryan Jsy 10.00 25.00
OS Ozzie Smith Jsy 6.00 15.00
PR Pee Wee Reese Jsy 4.00 10.00
RC Roy Campanella Pants 4.00 10.00
RM Roger Maris Jsy 12.50 30.00
RY Robin Yount Jsy 4.00 10.00
SC Steve Carlton Bat 3.00 8.00
SM Stan Musial Jsy 8.00 20.00
TG Tony Gwynn Jsy 4.00 10.00
TM Thurman Munson Jsy 4.00 10.00
TS Tom Seaver Jsy SP 6.00 15.00
TW Ted Williams Pants SP 20.00 50.00
WB Wade Boggs Jsy 4.00 10.00
WM Willie McCovey Pants 4.00 10.00
WS Warren Spahn Jsy 4.00 10.00
YB Yogi Berra Pants 4.00 10.00

2005 SP Legendary Cuts

This 90-card set was released in November, 2005. The set was issued in four-card packs with an $10 SRP which came 12 packs to a box and 16 boxes to a case. Interestingly this set was sequenced in alphabetical order by the player's first name.

COMPLETE SET (90) 10.00 25.00
COMMON CARD (1-90) .15 .40
1 Al Kaline .60 1.50
2 Babe Ruth 2.00 5.00
3 Bill Mazeroski .40 1.00
4 Billy Williams .25 .60
5 Bob Feller .40 1.00
6 Bob Gibson .40 1.00
7 Bob Lemon .25 .60
8 Bobby Doerr .25 .60
9 Brooks Robinson .40 1.00
10 Carl Yastrzemski 1.00 2.50
11 Carlton Fisk .40 1.00
12 Casey Stengel .40 1.00
13 Catfish Hunter .25 .60
14 Christy Mathewson .60 1.50
15 Cy Young .60 1.50
16 Dennis Eckersley .25 .60
17 Dizzy Dean .40 1.00
18 Don Drysdale .40 1.00
19 Don Sutton .25 .60
20 Duke Snider .40 1.00
21 Early Wynn .25 .60
22 Eddie Mathews .60 1.50
23 Eddie Murray .60 1.50
24 Enos Slaughter .25 .60
25 Ernie Banks .60 1.50
26 Fergie Jenkins .25 .60
27 Frank Robinson .25 .60
28 Gary Carter .25 .60
29 Gaylord Perry .25 .60
30 Reggie Jackson .40 1.00
31 George Kell .25 .60
32 George Sisler .25 .60
33 Hal Newhouser .25 .60
34 Harmon Killebrew .60 1.50
35 Honus Wagner .60 1.50
36 Jackie Robinson .60 1.50
37 Jim Bunning .40 1.00
38 Jim Palmer .25 .60
39 Jimmie Foxx .60 1.50
40 Joe DiMaggio 1.00 2.50
41 Joe Morgan .25 .60
42 Johnny Bench .60 1.50
43 Johnny Mize .25 .60
44 Juan Marichal .25 .60
45 Kirby Puckett .60 1.50
46 Larry Doby .25 .60
47 Lefty Grove .25 .60
48 Lou Boudreau .25 .60
49 Lou Brock .40 1.00
50 Lou Gehrig 1.00 2.50
51 Luis Aparicio .25 .60
52 Mel Ott .60 1.50
53 Mickey Cochrane .25 .60
54 Mickey Mantle 3.00 8.00
55 Mike Schmidt 1.25 3.00
56 Monte Irvin .25 .60
57 Nolan Ryan 1.50 4.00
58 Orlando Cepeda .25 .60
59 Ozzie Smith 1.00 2.50
60 Paul Molitor .25 .60
61 Pee Wee Reese .40 1.00
62 Phil Niekro .25 .60
63 Phil Rizzuto .40 1.00
64 Ralph Kiner .40 1.00
65 Red Schoendienst .25 .60
66 Richie Ashburn .40 1.00
67 Rick Ferrell .25 .60
68 Robin Roberts .25 .60
69 Robin Yount .60 1.50
70 Rod Carew .40 1.00
71 Rogers Hornsby .40 1.00
72 Rollie Fingers .25 .60
73 Roy Campanella .60 1.50
74 Ryne Sandberg 1.25 3.00
75 Satchel Paige .60 1.50
76 Stan Musial 1.00 2.50
77 Steve Carlton .25 .60
78 Ted Williams 1.25 3.00
79 Thurman Munson .60 1.50
80 Tom Seaver .40 1.00
81 Tony Gwynn .75 2.00
82 Tony Perez .25 .60
83 Ty Cobb .75 2.00
84 Wade Boggs .40 1.00
85 Walter Johnson .60 1.50
86 Warren Spahn .40 1.00
87 Whitey Ford .40 1.00
88 Willie McCovey .40 1.00
89 Willie Stargell .40 1.00
90 Yogi Berra .60 1.50

2005 SP Legendary Cuts HoloFoil

*HOLOFOIL: 2X TO 5X BASIC
RANDOM INSERTS IN PACKS
STATED PRINT RUN 50 SERIAL #'d SETS
54 Mickey Mantle 20.00 50.00

2005 SP Legendary Cuts Autograph Cuts

OVERALL CUT AU ODDS 1:196
PRINT RUNS B/WN 1-108 COPIES PER
NO PRICING ON QTY OF 19 OR LESS
AN Cap Anson/1
AS Al Simmons/7
AV Arky Vaughan/1
BC Ben Chapman/7
BD Bill Dickey/95 75.00 150.00
BG A. Bartlett Giamatti/1
BH Billy Herman/99 50.00 100.00
BJ Indian Bob Johnson/13

BL Bob Lemon/108 50.00 100.00
BM Billy Martin/10
BN Bill Nicholson/8
BR Babe Ruth/3
BU Burleigh Grimes/99 75.00 150.00
BW Bucky Walters/34 75.00 150.00
CA Roy Campanella/4
CB Chief Bender/2
CF Carl Furillo/25 150.00 250.00
CG Charlie Gehringer/97 60.00 120.00
CH Carl Hubbell/99 75.00 150.00
CJ Colby Jack Coombs/1
CK Charlie Keller/98 75.00 150.00
CM Christy Mathewson/1
CP Claude Passeau/1
CR Joe Cronin/76 75.00 150.00
CS Casey Stengel/61 200.00 400.00
CY Cy Young/2
DD Don Drysdale/50 100.00 175.00
DE Dizzy Dean/21 450.00 600.00
DM Dale Mitchell/7
DU Leo Durocher/57 75.00 150.00
DV Dazzy Vance/2
EA Earl Averill/91 50.00 100.00
EC Earle Combs/5
EL Ed Lopat/11
EM Eddie Mathews/80 100.00 175.00
ER Edd Roush/99 60.00 120.00
ES Enos Slaughter/99 60.00 120.00
EW Early Wynn/89 50.00 100.00
FE Rick Ferrell/60 75.00 150.00
FF Frankie Frisch/18
FL Curt Flood/7
FM Frank McCormick/15
GA Gene Autry/1
GH Gabby Hartnett/50 125.00 200.00
GO Lefty Gomez/68 100.00 175.00
GP George Pipgras/12
GR Lefty Grove/41 150.00 250.00
GS George Selkirk/5
HA Chick Hafey/52 100.00 175.00
HC Happy Chandler/39 60.00 120.00
HE Harry Heilmann/1
HG Hank Greenberg/44 250.00 400.00
HK Harvey Kuenn/33 75.00 150.00
HM Heinie Manush/25 125.00 200.00
HN Hal Newhouser/96 50.00 100.00
HO Gil Hodges/8
HU Catfish Hunter/65 60.00 120.00
HW Honus Wagner/1
JB Cool Papa Bell/78 200.00 350.00
JC Jocko Conlan/40 100.00 175.00
JD Joe DiMaggio/56 350.00 500.00
JF Jimmie Foxx/1
JG Joe Gordon/5
JH Jesse Haines/90 125.00 200.00
JJ Jackie Jensen/48 125.00 200.00
JM Joe Medwick/19
JO Judy Johnson/39 100.00 175.00
JR Jackie Robinson/4
JS Joe Sewell/76 75.00 150.00
JV Johnny Vander Meer/17
JW Hoyt Wilhelm/48 60.00 120.00
KC Kiki Cuyler/2
KL Chuck Klein/2
KN Kid Nichols/1
LA Luke Appling/55 60.00 120.00
LB Lou Boudreau/99 50.00 100.00
LD Larry Doby/32 100.00 200.00
LE Buck Leonard/71 100.00 175.00
LG Lou Gehrig/4
LI Fred Lindstrom/19
LO Ernie Lombardi/29 125.00 200.00
MA Connie Mack/6
MB Mordecai Brown/1
MC Max Carey/84 60.00 120.00
MI Johnny Mize/90 60.00 120.00
MM Mickey Mantle/7
MO Mel Ott/1
NF Nellie Fox/12
NL Nap Lajoie/1
PD Paul Derringer/3
PM Pepper Martin/3
PR Pee Wee Reese/69 100.00 175.00
PT Pie Traynor/9
PW Paul Waner/4
RA Rabbit Maranville/2
RC Roberto Clemente/5
RD1 Ray Dandridge/23 75.00 150.00
RD2 Ray Dandridge/76 60.00 120.00
RE Red Ruffing/22 250.00 400.00
RF Red Faber/5
RH Rogers Hornsby/1
RI Richie Ashburn/83 125.00 200.00
RM Roger Maris/9
RO Roy McMillan/23 75.00 150.00
RR Red Rolfe/8
RU Rube Marquard/80 100.00 175.00
RY Rudy York/4
SC Spud Chandler/14
SH Stan Hack/15
SI George Sisler/21 450.00 600.00
SJ Smokey Joe Wood/11
SP Satchel Paige/14
SR Sam Rice/41 125.00 200.00
ST Stan Coveleski/71 60.00 120.00
TC Ty Cobb/1
TJ Travis Jackson/16
TK Ted Kluszewski/50 150.00 250.00
TL Tony Lazzeri/1
TM Thurman Munson/2
TS Tris Speaker/1
TW Ted Williams/10
TY Tom Yawkey/3
VR Vic Raschi/21 75.00 150.00
VS Vern Stephens/10
WA Warren Spahn/92 60.00 120.00
WC Wahoo Sam Crawford/6
WF Wes Ferrell/1
WH Waite Hoyt/99 60.00 120.00
WI Hack Wilson/1
WJ Walter Johnson/1
WS Willie Stargell/63 75.00 150.00
ZV Zoilo Versalles/13
ZW Zack Wheat/15

2005 SP Legendary Cuts Autograph Dual Cuts

OVERALL CUT AU ODDS 1:196
PRINT RUNS B/WN 1-10 COPIES PER
NO PRICING DUE TO SCARCITY
EXCHANGE DEADLINE 11/10/08
CM Mickey Cochrane
Mickey Mantle /7
CW Roberto Clemente
Paul Waner /5
DD Dizzy Dean
Paul 'Daffy' Dean /10
DI Vince DiMaggio
Joe DiMaggio/10
DW Joe DiMaggio
Ted Williams /9
FG Jimmie Foxx
Lou Gehrig /1
GG Charlie Gehringer
Hank Greenberg /10
HC Harry Heilmann
Ty Cobb/1
MA Mickey Mantle
Roger Maris /7
MM Billy Martin
Thurman Munson/2
MW Mickey Mantle
Ted Williams/4 EXCH
RC Jackie Robinson
Roy Campanella/5
RF Babe Ruth
Harry Frazee/1
RG Babe Ruth
Lou Gehrig/1
RP Jackie Robinson
Satchel Paige /4
RR Branch Rickey
Jackie Robinson/2
SC Tris Speaker
Ty Cobb/1
WC Honus Wagner
Ty Cobb/1

2005 SP Legendary Cuts Autograph Quad Cuts

OVERALL CUT AU ODDS 1:196
STATED PRINT RUN 1 SERIAL #'d SET
NO PRICING DUE TO SCARCITY
CRWJ Ty Cobb
Babe Ruth
Honus Wagner
Walter Johnson
MCBB John 'Stuffy' McInnis
Eddie Collins
John Barry
Frank 'Home Run' Baker
MYGJ Christy Mathewson
Cy Young
Lefty Grove
Walter Johnson
RMFW Babe Ruth
Mickey Mantle
Jimmie Foxx
Ted Williams

2005 SP Legendary Cuts Battery Cuts

OVERALL CUT AU ODDS 1:196
PRINT RUNS B/WN 6-99 COPIES PER
NO PRICING ON QTY OF 9 OR LESS
BD Bill Dickey/22 125.00 200.00
CH Carl Hubbell/99 75.00 150.00
DD Don Drysdale/31 125.00 200.00
EL Ernie Lombardi/9
EW Early Wynn/32 75.00 150.00
GH Gabby Hartnett/9
HN Hal Newhouser/32 75.00 150.00
JH Jesse Haines/28 175.00 300.00
JV Johnny Vander Meer/8
LG Lefty Gomez/77 125.00 200.00
RR Red Ruffing/6
SC Stan Coveleski/25 100.00 175.00
WH Waite Hoyt/58 60.00 120.00
WS Warren Spahn/43 75.00 150.00

2005 SP Legendary Cuts Classic Careers

STATED PRINT RUN 399 SERIAL #'d SETS
*GOLD: .6X TO 1.5X BASIC
GOLD PRINT RUN 75 SERIAL #'d SETS
PLATINUM PRINT RUN 1 SERIAL #'d SET
NO PLATINUM PRICING DUE TO SCARCITY
OVERALL INSERT ODDS 1:6
AD Andre Dawson 1.25 3.00
AR Al Rosen 1.50 4.00
AV Andy Van Slyke 1.50 4.00
BD Bobby Doerr 1.25 3.00
BF Bill Freehan 1.25 3.00
BH Bob Horner 1.25 3.00
BL Barry Larkin 1.50 4.00
BM Bill Madlock 1.25 3.00
CA Jose Canseco 1.50 4.00
CE Carl Erskine 1.25 3.00
CF Carlton Fisk 1.50 4.00
CR Cal Ripken 4.00 10.00
CY Carl Yastrzemski 2.00 5.00
DC David Cone 1.25 3.00
DE Dennis Martinez 1.25 3.00
DG Dwight Gooden 1.25 3.00
DM Dale Murphy 1.50 4.00
DO Don Sutton 1.25 3.00
DS Darryl Strawberry 1.25 3.00
FJ Fergie Jenkins 1.25 3.00
GC Gary Carter 1.25 3.00
GF George Foster 1.25 3.00
GG Goose Gossage 1.25 3.00
GM Gary Matthews 1.25 3.00
GN Graig Nettles 1.25 3.00
GP Gaylord Perry 1.25 3.00
GU Don Gullett 1.25 3.00
HB Harold Baines 1.25 3.00
JB Jay Buhner 1.25 3.00
JC Jack Clark 1.25 3.00
JM Jack Morris 1.25 3.00
JP Johnny Podres 1.25 3.00
JR Jim Rice 1.25 3.00
KH Keith Hernandez 1.25 3.00
LA Luis Aparicio 1.25 3.00
LD Lenny Dykstra 1.25 3.00
LT Luis Tiant 1.25 3.00
MA Don Mattingly 3.00 8.00
MG Mark Grace 1.50 4.00
MU Bobby Murcer 1.50 4.00
OC Orlando Cepeda 1.25 3.00
PN Phil Niekro 1.25 3.00
RG Ron Guidry 1.25 3.00
SF Sid Fernandez 1.25 3.00
SL Sparky Lyle 1.25 3.00
ST Dave Stewart 1.25 3.00
SU Bruce Sutter 1.25 3.00
TO Tony Oliva 1.25 3.00
TR Tim Raines 1.25 3.00
WC Will Clark 1.50 4.00

2005 SP Legendary Cuts Classic Careers Material

OVERALL GAME-USED ODDS 1:6
*GOLD: .5X TO 1.2X BASIC
GOLD PRINT RUN 75 SERIAL #'d SETS
PLATINUM PRINT RUN 1 SERIAL #'d SET
NO PLATINUM PRICING DUE TO SCARCITY
OVERALL #'d GAME-USED ODDS 1:40
AD Andre Dawson Jsy 2.00 5.00
AR Al Rosen Pants 3.00 8.00
AV Andy Van Slyke Jsy 3.00 8.00
BD Bobby Doerr Jsy 2.00 5.00
BF Bill Freehan Jsy 2.00 5.00
BH Bob Horner Jsy 2.00 5.00
BL Barry Larkin Jsy 3.00 8.00
BM Bill Madlock Jsy 2.00 5.00
CA Jose Canseco Jsy 3.00 8.00
CE Carl Erskine Pants 3.00 8.00
CF Carlton Fisk Jsy 3.00 8.00
CR Cal Ripken Jsy 8.00 20.00
CY Carl Yastrzemski Jsy 4.00 10.00
DC David Cone Jsy 2.00 5.00
DE Dennis Martinez Jsy 2.00 5.00
DG Dwight Gooden Jsy 2.00 5.00
DM Dale Murphy Jsy 3.00 8.00
DO Don Sutton Jsy 2.00 5.00
DS Darryl Strawberry Jsy 2.00 5.00
FJ Fergie Jenkins Jsy 2.00 5.00
GC Gary Carter Jsy 2.00 5.00
GF George Foster Jsy 2.00 5.00
GG Goose Gossage Jsy 2.00 5.00
GM Gary Matthews Jsy 2.00 5.00
GN Graig Nettles Jsy 2.00 5.00
GP Gaylord Perry Jsy 2.00 5.00
GU Don Gullett Jsy 2.00 5.00
HB Harold Baines Jsy 2.00 5.00
JB Jay Buhner Jsy 3.00 8.00
JC Jack Clark Jsy 2.00 5.00
JM Jack Morris Jsy 2.00 5.00
JP Johnny Podres Jsy 3.00 8.00
JR Jim Rice Jsy 2.00 5.00
KH Keith Hernandez Jsy 2.00 5.00
LA Luis Aparicio Jsy 2.00 5.00
LD Lenny Dykstra Jsy 2.00 5.00
LT Luis Tiant Jsy 2.00 5.00
MA Don Mattingly Jsy 5.00 12.00
MG Mark Grace Jsy 3.00 8.00
MU Bobby Murcer Pants 3.00 8.00
OC Orlando Cepeda Jsy 2.00 5.00
PN Phil Niekro Jsy 2.00 5.00
RG Ron Guidry Pants 3.00 8.00
SF Sid Fernandez Jsy 2.00 5.00
SL Sparky Lyle Pants 2.00 5.00
ST Dave Stewart Jsy 2.00 5.00
SU Bruce Sutter Jsy 2.00 5.00
TO Tony Oliva Jsy 2.00 5.00
TR Tim Raines Jsy 2.00 5.00
WC Will Clark Jsy 3.00 8.00

2005 SP Legendary Cuts Classic Careers Patch

*PATCH p/r 50: 1X TO 2.5X MATERIAL
*PATCH p/r 20: 1.25X TO 3X MATERIAL
STATED PRINT RUN 50 SERIAL #'d SETS
J.BUHNER PRINT RUN 14 CARDS
D.MARTINEZ PRINT RUN 20 CARDS
NO BUHNER PRICING AVAILABLE
GOLD PRINT RUN 10 SERIAL #'d SETS
NO GOLD PRICING DUE TO SCARCITY
PLATINUM PRINT RUN 1 SERIAL #'d SET
NO PLATINUM PRICING DUE TO SCARCITY
OVERALL PATCH ODDS 1:96

2005 SP Legendary Cuts Classic Careers Autograph

STATED PRINT RUN 25 SERIAL #'d SETS
GOLD PRINT RUN 10 SERIAL #'d SETS
NO GOLD PRICING DUE TO SCARCITY
PLATINUM PRINT RUN 1 SERIAL #'d SET
NO PLATINUM PRICING DUE TO SCARCITY
OVERALL AUTO ODDS 1:96
EXCHANGE DEADLINE 11/10/08
AD Andre Dawson 10.00 25.00
AR Al Rosen 10.00 25.00
AV Andy Van Slyke 15.00 40.00
BD Bobby Doerr 6.00 15.00
BF Bill Freehan 10.00 25.00
BH Bob Horner 6.00 15.00
BL Barry Larkin 15.00 40.00
BM Bill Madlock 10.00 25.00
CA Jose Canseco 20.00 50.00
CE Carl Erskine 10.00 25.00
CF Carlton Fisk 15.00 40.00
CR Cal Ripken EXCH 60.00 120.00
CY Carl Yastrzemski 20.00 50.00
DC David Cone 6.00 15.00
DE Dennis Martinez 6.00 15.00
DG Dwight Gooden 6.00 15.00
DM Dale Murphy 15.00 40.00
DO Don Sutton 10.00 25.00
DS Darryl Strawberry 10.00 25.00
FJ Fergie Jenkins 10.00 25.00
GC Gary Carter 10.00 25.00
GF George Foster 10.00 25.00
GG Goose Gossage 10.00 25.00
GM Gary Matthews 6.00 15.00
GN Graig Nettles 10.00 25.00
GP Gaylord Perry 10.00 25.00
GU Don Gullett 6.00 15.00
HB Harold Baines 6.00 15.00
JB Jay Buhner 15.00 40.00
JC Jack Clark 10.00 25.00
JM Jack Morris 6.00 15.00
JP Johnny Podres 10.00 25.00
JR Jim Rice 10.00 25.00
KH Keith Hernandez 6.00 15.00
LA Luis Aparicio 10.00 25.00
LD Lenny Dykstra 6.00 15.00
LT Luis Tiant 6.00 15.00
MA Don Mattingly 30.00 60.00
MG Mark Grace 15.00 40.00
MU Bobby Murcer EXCH 15.00 40.00
OC Orlando Cepeda 10.00 25.00
PN Phil Niekro 10.00 25.00
RG Ron Guidry 15.00 40.00
SF Sid Fernandez 6.00 15.00
SL Sparky Lyle 6.00 15.00
ST Dave Stewart 6.00 15.00
SU Bruce Sutter 15.00 40.00
TO Tony Oliva 10.00 25.00
TR Tim Raines 10.00 25.00
WC Will Clark 15.00 40.00

2005 SP Legendary Cuts Classic Careers Autograph Material

*AUTO MAT: .4X TO 1X AUTO
STATED PRINT RUN 25 SERIAL #'d SETS
GOLD PRINT RUN 10 SERIAL #'d SETS
NO GOLD PRICING DUE TO SCARCITY

PLATINUM PRINT RUN 1 SERIAL #'d SET
NO PLATINUM PRICING DUE TO SCARCITY
OVERALL AU-GU ODDS 1:96
EXCHANGE DEADLINE 11/10/08

2005 SP Legendary Cuts Classic Careers Autograph Patch

*AUTO PATCH: .6X TO 1.5X AUTO
STATED PRINT RUN 25 SERIAL #'d SETS
GOLD PRINT RUN 5 SERIAL #'d SETS
NO GOLD PRICING DUE TO SCARCITY
PLATINUM PRINT RUN 1 SERIAL #'d SET
NO PLATINUM PRICING DUE TO SCARCITY
OVERALL AU-PATCH ODDS 1:196
EXCHANGE DEADLINE 11/10/08

2005 SP Legendary Cuts Cornerstone Cuts

OVERALL CUT AU ODDS 1:196
PRINT RUNS B/WN 1-79 COPIES PER
NO PRICING ON QTY OF 16 OR LESS
BL Buck Leonard/15
DC Dolph Camilli/79 75.00 150.00
EM Eddie Mathews/50 125.00 200.00
GH Gil Hodges/8
GS George Sisler/6
HG Hank Greenberg/10
JF Jimmie Foxx/1
JJ Judy Johnson/16
JM Johnny Mize/44 75.00 150.00
PT Pie Traynor/1
RD Ray Dandridge/27 75.00 150.00
RY Rudy York/5
TK Ted Kluszewski/16
WP Wally Pipp/1
WS Willie Stargell/36 100.00 175.00

2005 SP Legendary Cuts Glory Days

STATED PRINT RUN 399 SERIAL #'d SETS
*GOLD: .6X TO 1.5X BASIC
GOLD PRINT RUN 75 SERIAL #'d SETS
PLATINUM PRINT RUN 1 SERIAL #'d SET
NO PLATINUM PRICING DUE TO SCARCITY
OVERALL INSERT ODDS 1:6
AD Andre Dawson 1.25 3.00
AR Al Rosen 1.25 3.00
AV Andy Van Slyke 1.25 3.00
BD Bobby Doerr 1.25 3.00
BF Bill Freehan 1.25 3.00
BH Bob Horner 1.25 3.00
BL Barry Larkin 1.25 3.00
BM Bill Madlock 1.25 3.00
BS Bruce Sutter 1.25 3.00
CA Jose Canseco 1.50 4.00
CR Cal Ripken 4.00 10.00
DC David Cone 1.25 3.00
DE Dennis Martinez 1.25 3.00
DG Dwight Gooden 1.25 3.00
DM Dale Murphy 1.50 4.00
DS Darryl Strawberry 1.25 3.00
FJ Fergie Jenkins 1.25 3.00
FL Fred Lynn 1.25 3.00
GF George Foster 1.25 3.00
GM Gary Matthews 1.25 3.00
GN Graig Nettles 1.25 3.00
GU Don Gullett 1.25 3.00
HB Harold Baines 1.25 3.00
JB Jay Buhner 1.25 3.00
JC Jack Clark 1.25 3.00
JM Jack Morris 1.25 3.00
JP Jim Palmer 1.25 3.00
JR Jim Rice 1.25 3.00
KG Kirk Gibson 1.25 3.00
KH Keith Hernandez 1.25 3.00
LB Lou Brock 1.50 4.00
LD Lenny Dykstra 1.25 3.00
LT Luis Tiant 1.25 3.00
MA Juan Marichal 1.25 3.00
MU Bobby Murcer 1.50 4.00
NR Nolan Ryan 3.00 8.00
PM Paul Molitor 1.25 3.00
RG Ron Guidry 1.25 3.00
RS Red Schoendienst 1.25 3.00
RY Robin Yount 1.50 4.00
SF Sid Fernandez 1.25 3.00
SL Sparky Lyle UER 1.25 3.00
Name misspelled as Sparly
SN Duke Snider 1.50 4.00
ST Dave Stewart 1.25 3.00
TG Tony Gwynn 2.00 5.00
TO Tony Oliva 1.25 3.00
TR Tim Raines 1.25 3.00
WC Will Clark 1.50 4.00
WF Whitey Ford 1.50 4.00
YB Yogi Berra 1.50 4.00

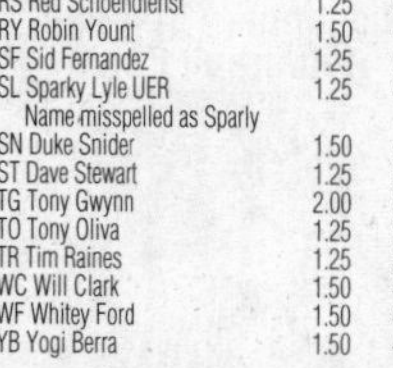

2005 SP Legendary Cuts Glory Days Material

OVERALL GAME-USED ODDS 1:6
*GOLD: .5X TO 1.2X BASIC
GOLD PRINT RUN 75 SERIAL #'d SETS
PLATINUM PRINT RUN 1 SERIAL #'d SET
NO PLATINUM PRICING DUE TO SCARCITY
OVERALL #'d GAME-USED ODDS 1:40
AD Andre Dawson Jsy 2.00 5.00
AR Al Rosen Pants 3.00 8.00
AV Andy Van Slyke Jsy 3.00 8.00
BD Bobby Doerr Jsy 2.00 5.00
BF Bill Freehan Jsy 2.00 5.00
BH Bob Horner Jsy 2.00 5.00
BL Barry Larkin Jsy 3.00 8.00
BM Bill Madlock Jsy 2.00 5.00
BS Bruce Sutter Jsy 2.00 5.00
CA Jose Canseco Jsy 3.00 8.00
CR Cal Ripken Jsy 8.00 20.00
DC David Cone Jsy 2.00 5.00
DE Dennis Martinez Jsy 2.00 5.00
DG Dwight Gooden Jsy 2.00 5.00
DM Dale Murphy Jsy 3.00 8.00
DS Darryl Strawberry Jsy 2.00 5.00
FJ Fergie Jenkins Jsy 2.00 5.00
FL Fred Lynn Bat 2.00 5.00
GF George Foster Jsy 2.00 5.00
GM Gary Matthews Jsy 2.00 5.00
GN Graig Nettles Jsy 2.00 5.00
GU Don Gullett Jsy 2.00 5.00
HB Harold Baines Jsy 2.00 5.00
JB Jay Buhner Jsy 3.00 8.00
JC Jack Clark Jsy 2.00 5.00
JM Jack Morris Jsy 2.00 5.00
JP Jim Palmer Jsy 2.00 5.00
JR Jim Rice Jsy 2.00 5.00
KG Kirk Gibson Jsy 2.00 5.00
KH Keith Hernandez Jsy 2.00 5.00
LB Lou Brock Jsy * 3.00 8.00
LD Lenny Dykstra Jsy 2.00 5.00
LT Luis Tiant Jsy 2.00 5.00
MA Juan Marichal Jsy 3.00 8.00
MU Bobby Murcer Pants 3.00 8.00
NR Nolan Ryan Jsy 6.00 15.00
PM Paul Molitor Bat 2.00 5.00
RG Ron Guidry Pants 3.00 8.00
RS Red Schoendienst Jsy 3.00 8.00
RY Robin Yount Jsy 4.00 10.00
SF Sid Fernandez Jsy 2.00 5.00
SL Sparky Lyle Pants 2.00 5.00
SN Duke Snider Pants 4.00 10.00
ST Dave Stewart Jsy 2.00 5.00
TG Tony Gwynn Jsy 4.00 10.00
TO Tony Oliva Jsy 2.00 5.00
TR Tim Raines Jsy 2.00 5.00
WC Will Clark Jsy 3.00 8.00
WF Whitey Ford Jsy 5.00 12.00
YB Yogi Berra Pants 5.00 12.00

2005 SP Legendary Cuts Glory Days Patch

*PATCH: 1X TO 2.5X MATERIAL
STATED PRINT RUN 50 SERIAL #'d SETS
K.HERNANDEZ PRINT RUN 37 CARDS
L.TIANT PRINT RUN 40 CARDS
GOLD PRINT RUN 10 SERIAL #'d SETS
NO GOLD PRICING DUE TO SCARCITY
PLATINUM PRINT RUN 1 SERIAL #'d SET
NO PLATINUM PRICING DUE TO SCARCITY
OVERALL PATCH ODDS 1:96

2005 SP Legendary Cuts Glory Days Autograph

STATED PRINT RUN 25 SERIAL #'d SETS
GOLD PRINT RUN 10 SERIAL #'d SETS
NO GOLD PRICING DUE TO SCARCITY
PLATINUM PRINT RUN 1 SERIAL #'d SET
NO PLATINUM PRICING DUE TO SCARCITY
OVERALL AUTO ODDS 1:96
EXCHANGE DEADLINE 11/10/08

AD Andre Dawson 10.00 25.00
AR Al Rosen 10.00 25.00
AV Andy Van Slyke 15.00 40.00
BD Bobby Doerr 6.00 15.00
BF Bill Freehan 10.00 25.00
BH Bob Horner 6.00 15.00
BL Barry Larkin 15.00 40.00
BM Bill Madlock 10.00 25.00
BS Bruce Sutter 15.00 40.00
CA Jose Canseco 20.00 50.00
CR Cal Ripken EXCH 60.00 120.00
DC David Cone 6.00 15.00
DE Dennis Martinez 6.00 15.00
DG Dwight Gooden 6.00 15.00
DM Dale Murphy 15.00 40.00
DS Darryl Strawberry 10.00 25.00
FJ Fergie Jenkins 10.00 25.00
FL Fred Lynn 10.00 25.00
GF George Foster 10.00 25.00
GM Gary Matthews 6.00 15.00
GN Graig Nettles 10.00 25.00
GU Don Gullett 6.00 15.00
HB Harold Baines 10.00 25.00
JB Jay Buhner 15.00 40.00
JC Jack Clark 10.00 25.00
JM Jack Morris 6.00 15.00
JP Jim Palmer 10.00 25.00
JR Jim Rice 10.00 25.00
KG Kirk Gibson 10.00 25.00
KH Keith Hernandez 6.00 15.00
LB Lou Brock 15.00 40.00
LD Lenny Dykstra 6.00 15.00
LT Luis Tiant 6.00 15.00
MA Juan Marichal 10.00 25.00
MU Bobby Murcer EXCH 15.00 40.00
NR Nolan Ryan 50.00 100.00
PM Paul Molitor 10.00 25.00
RG Ron Guidry 15.00 40.00
RS Red Schoendienst 10.00 25.00
RY Robin Yount 20.00 50.00
SF Sid Fernandez 6.00 15.00
SL Sparky Lyle 6.00 15.00
SN Duke Snider 20.00 50.00
ST Dave Stewart 6.00 15.00
TG Tony Gwynn 20.00 50.00
TO Tony Oliva 10.00 25.00
TR Tim Raines 10.00 25.00
WC Will Clark 15.00 40.00
WF Whitey Ford 15.00 40.00
YB Yogi Berra 30.00 60.00

2005 SP Legendary Cuts Glory Days Autograph Material

*AUTO MAT: .4X TO 1X AUTO
STATED PRINT RUN 25 SERIAL #'d SETS
GOLD PRINT RUN 10 SERIAL #'d SETS
NO GOLD PRICING DUE TO SCARCITY
PLATINUM PRINT RUN 1 SERIAL #'d SET
NO PLATINUM PRICING DUE TO SCARCITY
OVERALL AU-GU ODDS 1:96
EXCHANGE DEADLINE 11/10/08

2005 SP Legendary Cuts Glory Days Autograph Patch

*AUTO PATCH: .6X TO 1.5X AUTO
STATED PRINT RUN 25 SERIAL #'d SETS
D.GULLETT PRINT RUN 7 CARDS
NO D.GULLETT PRICING DUE TO SCARCITY
GOLD PRINT RUN 5 SERIAL #'d SETS
NO GOLD PRICING DUE TO SCARCITY
PLATINUM PRINT RUN 1 SERIAL #'d SET
NO PLATINUM PRICING DUE TO SCARCITY
OVERALL AU-PATCH ODDS 1:196

2005 SP Legendary Cuts Glovemen Cuts

OVERALL CUT AU ODDS 1:196
PRINT RUNS B/WN 1-75 COPIES PER
NO PRICING ON QTY OF 19 OR LESS
CK Chuck Klein/1
CP Cool Papa Bell/29 300.00 400.00
EA Earl Averill/39 60.00 120.00
EC Earle Combs/12
ES Enos Slaughter/65 60.00 120.00
FL Fred Lindstrom/5
HM Heinie Manush/17

JD Joe DiMaggio/75 350.00 450.00
JM Joe Medwick/8
LD Larry Doby/16
MC Max Carey/50 75.00 150.00
MM Mickey Mantle/19
RA Richie Ashburn/20 150.00 250.00
TW Ted Williams/9

2005 SP Legendary Cuts Historic Cuts

OVERALL CUT AU ODDS 1:196
STATED PRINT RUN 1 SERIAL #'d SET
NO PRICING DUE TO SCARCITY
CD Charles Dickens
JH John Hancock
JPM J.P. Morgan
MT Mark Twain
SA Samuel Adams

2005 SP Legendary Cuts Historic Quads Autograph

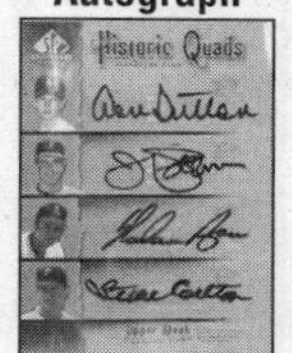

OVERALL AUTO ODDS 1:96
STATED PRINT RUN 5 SERIAL #'d SETS
NO PRICING DUE TO SCARCITY
EXCHANGE DEADLINE 11/10/08
DMSC Andre Dawson
Dale Murphy
Darryl Strawberry
Jose Canseco
FCBB Carlton Fisk
Gary Carter
Johnny Bench
Yogi Berra
LRSY Barry Larkin
Cal Ripken
Ozzie Smith
Robin Yount EXCH
MMHC Don Mattingly
Eddie Murray
Keith Hernandez
Will Clark EXCH
RRSB Cal Ripken
Brooks Robinson
Mike Schmidt
Wade Boggs EXCH
SPRC Don Sutton
Jim Palmer
Nolan Ryan
Steve Carlton

2005 SP Legendary Cuts Historic Quads Material

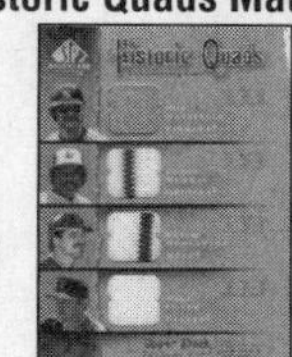

OVERALL #'d GAME-USED ODDS 1:40
STATED PRINT RUN 5 SERIAL #'d SETS
OVERALL PATCH ODDS 1:96
PATCH PRINT RUN 1 SERIAL #'d SET
NO PRICING DUE TO SCARCITY
DMSC Andre Dawson Jsy
Dale Murphy Jsy
Darryl Strawberry Jsy
Jose Canseco Jsy
FCBB Carlton Fisk Jsy
Gary Carter Jsy
Johnny Bench Jsy
Yogi Berra Pants
LRSY Barry Larkin Jsy
Cal Ripken Jsy
Ozzie Smith Jsy
Robin Yount Jsy
MMHC Don Mattingly Jsy
Eddie Murray Jsy
Keith Hernandez Jsy
Will Clark Jsy
RRSB Cal Ripken Jsy
Brooks Robinson Jsy
Mike Schmidt Jsy
Wade Boggs Jsy *
SPRC Don Sutton Jsy
Jim Palmer Jsy
Nolan Ryan Jsy
Steve Carlton Jsy

2005 SP Legendary Cuts Lasting Legends

STATED PRINT RUN 399 SERIAL #'d SETS
*GOLD: .6X TO 1.5X BASIC
GOLD PRINT RUN 75 SERIAL #'d SETS
PLATINUM PRINT RUN 1 SERIAL #'d SET
NO PLATINUM PRICING DUE TO SCARCITY
OVERALL INSERT ODDS 1:6
AK Al Kaline 1.50 4.00
BD Bobby Doerr 1.25 3.00
BE Johnny Bench 1.50 4.00
BG Bob Gibson 1.50 4.00
BL Barry Larkin 1.50 4.00
BM Bill Mazeroski 1.50 4.00
BR Brooks Robinson 1.50 4.00
BS Bruce Sutter 1.25 3.00
CF Carlton Fisk 1.50 4.00
CR Cal Ripken 4.00 10.00
CY Carl Yastrzemski 2.00 5.00
DE Dennis Eckersley 1.25 3.00
DG Dwight Gooden 1.25 3.00
DM Don Mattingly 3.00 8.00
DS Don Sutton 1.25 3.00
EB Ernie Banks 1.50 4.00
EM Eddie Murray 1.50 4.00
FJ Fergie Jenkins 1.25 3.00
FR Frank Robinson 1.25 3.00
GC Gary Carter 1.25 3.00
GN Graig Nettles 1.25 3.00
GP Gaylord Perry 1.25 3.00
JM Joe Morgan 1.25 3.00
JP Jim Palmer 1.25 3.00
JR Jim Rice 1.25 3.00
KH Keith Hernandez 1.25 3.00
KP Kirby Puckett 1.50 4.00
LA Luis Aparicio 1.25 3.00
LB Lou Brock 1.50 4.00
MA Juan Marichal 1.25 3.00
MS Mike Schmidt 3.00 8.00
MU Dale Murphy 1.50 4.00
NR Nolan Ryan 3.00 8.00
OC Orlando Cepeda 1.25 3.00
OS Ozzie Smith 2.00 5.00
PM Paul Molitor 1.25 3.00
PN Phil Niekro 1.25 3.00
RC Rod Carew 1.25 3.00
RF Rollie Fingers 1.25 3.00
RS Red Schoendienst 1.25 3.00
RY Robin Yount 1.50 4.00
SA Ryne Sandberg 3.00 8.00
SC Steve Carlton 1.25 3.00
SM Stan Musial 2.00 5.00
SN Duke Snider 1.50 4.00
TG Tony Gwynn 2.00 5.00
TP Tony Perez 1.25 3.00
WB Wade Boggs 1.50 4.00
WF Whitey Ford 1.50 4.00
YB Yogi Berra 1.50 4.00

2005 SP Legendary Cuts Lasting Legends Material

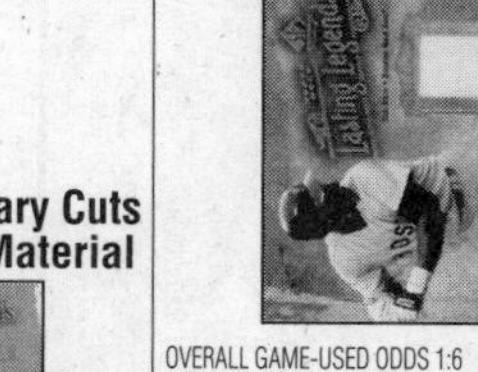

OVERALL GAME-USED ODDS 1:6
*GOLD: .5X TO 1.2X BASIC
GOLD PRINT RUN 75 SERIAL #'d SETS
PLATINUM PRINT RUN 1 SERIAL #'d SET
NO PLATINUM PRICING DUE TO SCARCITY
OVERALL #'d GAME-USED ODDS 1:40
AK Al Kaline Bat 4.00 10.00
BD Bobby Doerr Pants 2.00 5.00
BE Johnny Bench Jsy 4.00 10.00
BG Bob Gibson Jsy 3.00 8.00
BL Barry Larkin Jsy 3.00 8.00
BM Bill Mazeroski Jsy 3.00 8.00
BR Brooks Robinson Jsy 3.00 8.00
BS Bruce Sutter Jsy 2.00 5.00
CF Carlton Fisk Jsy 3.00 8.00
CR Cal Ripken Jsy 8.00 20.00
CY Carl Yastrzemski Jsy 4.00 10.00
DE Dennis Eckersley Jsy 2.00 5.00
DG Dwight Gooden Jsy 2.00 5.00
DM Don Mattingly Jsy 5.00 12.00
DS Don Sutton Jsy 2.00 5.00
EB Ernie Banks Pants 4.00 10.00
EM Eddie Murray Jsy 4.00 10.00
FJ Fergie Jenkins Jsy 2.00 5.00
FR Frank Robinson Jsy 3.00 8.00
GC Gary Carter Jsy 2.00 5.00
GN Graig Nettles Jsy 2.00 5.00
GP Gaylord Perry Jsy 2.00 5.00
JM Joe Morgan Jsy 2.00 5.00
JP Jim Palmer Jsy 2.00 5.00
JR Jim Rice Jsy 2.00 5.00
KH Keith Hernandez Jsy 2.00 5.00
KP Kirby Puckett Jsy 4.00 10.00
LA Luis Aparicio Jsy 2.00 5.00
LB Lou Brock Jsy * 3.00 8.00
MA Juan Marichal Jsy 3.00 8.00
MS Mike Schmidt Jsy 5.00 12.00
MU Dale Murphy Jsy 3.00 8.00
NR Nolan Ryan Jsy 6.00 15.00
OC Orlando Cepeda Jsy 2.00 5.00
OS Ozzie Smith Jsy 4.00 10.00
PM Paul Molitor Bat 2.00 5.00
PN Phil Niekro Jsy 2.00 5.00
RC Rod Carew Jsy 3.00 8.00
RF Rollie Fingers Jsy 2.00 5.00
RS Red Schoendienst Jsy 3.00 8.00
RY Robin Yount Jsy 4.00 10.00
SA Ryne Sandberg Jsy 5.00 12.00
SC Steve Carlton Jsy 2.00 5.00
SM Stan Musial Jsy 6.00 15.00
SN Duke Snider Pants 4.00 10.00
TG Tony Gwynn Jsy 4.00 10.00
TP Tony Perez Jsy 2.00 5.00
WB Wade Boggs Jsy 3.00 8.00
WF Whitey Ford Jsy 5.00 12.00
YB Yogi Berra Pants 5.00 12.00

2005 SP Legendary Cuts Lasting Legends Patch

*PATCH: 1X TO 2.5X MATERIAL
STATED PRINT RUN 50 SERIAL #'d SETS
P.MOLITOR PRINT RUN 2 CARDS
B.ROBINSON PRINT RUN 43 CARDS
N.RYAN PRINT RUN 11 CARDS
NO MOLITOR/RYAN PRICING AVAILABLE
GOLD PRINT RUN 10 SERIAL #'d SETS
NO GOLD PRICING DUE TO SCARCITY
PLATINUM PRINT RUN 1 SERIAL #'d SET
NO PLATINUM PRICING DUE TO SCARCITY
OVERALL PATCH ODDS 1:96

2005 SP Legendary Cuts Lasting Legends Autograph

STATED PRINT RUN 25 SERIAL #'d SETS
GOLD PRINT RUN 10 SERIAL #'d SETS
NO GOLD PRICING DUE TO SCARCITY
PLATINUM PRINT RUN 1 SERIAL #'d SET
NO PLATINUM PRICING DUE TO SCARCITY
OVERALL AUTO ODDS 1:96
EXCHANGE DEADLINE 11/10/08
AK Al Kaline 20.00 50.00
BD Bobby Doerr 6.00 15.00
BE Johnny Bench 20.00 50.00
BG Bob Gibson 15.00 40.00
BL Barry Larkin 15.00 40.00
BM Bill Mazeroski 15.00 40.00
BR Brooks Robinson 15.00 40.00
BS Bruce Sutter 15.00 40.00
CF Carlton Fisk 15.00 40.00
CR Cal Ripken EXCH 60.00 120.00
CY Carl Yastrzemski 20.00 50.00
DE Dennis Eckersley 10.00 25.00
DG Dwight Gooden 6.00 15.00
DM Don Mattingly 30.00 60.00
DS Don Sutton 10.00 25.00
EB Ernie Banks 30.00 60.00
EM Eddie Murray EXCH 30.00 60.00
FJ Fergie Jenkins 10.00 25.00
FR Frank Robinson 10.00 25.00
GC Gary Carter 10.00 25.00
GN Graig Nettles 10.00 25.00
GP Gaylord Perry 10.00 25.00
JM Joe Morgan 10.00 25.00
JP Jim Palmer 10.00 25.00
JR Jim Rice 10.00 25.00
KH Keith Hernandez 6.00 15.00
KP Kirby Puckett 50.00 100.00
LA Luis Aparicio 10.00 25.00
LB Lou Brock 15.00 40.00
MA Juan Marichal 10.00 25.00
MS Mike Schmidt 30.00 60.00
MU Dale Murphy 15.00 40.00
NR Nolan Ryan 50.00 100.00
OC Orlando Cepeda 10.00 25.00
OS Ozzie Smith 20.00 50.00
PM Paul Molitor 10.00 25.00
PN Phil Niekro 10.00 25.00
RC Rod Carew 15.00 40.00
RF Rollie Fingers 10.00 25.00
RS Red Schoendienst 10.00 25.00
RY Robin Yount 20.00 50.00
SA Ryne Sandberg 30.00 60.00
SC Steve Carlton 10.00 25.00
SM Stan Musial 30.00 60.00
SN Duke Snider 20.00 50.00
TG Tony Gwynn 20.00 50.00
TP Tony Perez 10.00 25.00
WB Wade Boggs 15.00 40.00
WF Whitey Ford 15.00 40.00
YB Yogi Berra 30.00 60.00

2005 SP Legendary Cuts Lasting Legends Autograph Material

*AUTO MAT: .4X TO 1X AUTO
STATED PRINT RUN 25 SERIAL #'d SETS
C.FISK PRINT RUN 21 CARDS
GOLD PRINT RUN 10 SERIAL #'d SETS
NO GOLD PRICING DUE TO SCARCITY
PLATINUM PRINT RUN 1 SERIAL #'d SET
NO PLATINUM PRICING DUE TO SCARCITY
OVERALL AU-GU ODDS 1:96
EXCHANGE DEADLINE 11/10/08

2005 SP Legendary Cuts Lasting Legends Autograph Patch

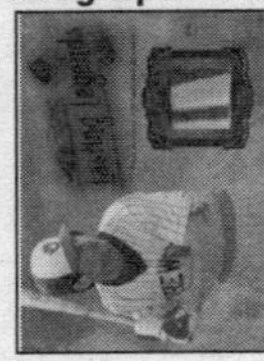

*AUTO PATCH: .6X TO 1.5X AUTO
STATED PRINT RUN 25 SERIAL #'d SETS
L.BROCK PRINT RUN 6 CARDS
K.PUCKETT PRINT RUN 6 CARDS
NO BROCK/PUCKETT PRICING AVAILABLE
GOLD PRINT RUN 5 SERIAL #'d SETS
NO GOLD PRICING DUE TO SCARCITY
PLATINUM PRINT RUN 1 SERIAL #'d SET
NO PLATINUM PRICING DUE TO SCARCITY
OVERALL AU-PATCH ODDS 1:196

2005 SP Legendary Cuts Legendary Duels Autograph

OVERALL AUTO ODDS 1:96
STATED PRINT RUN 15 SERIAL #'d SETS
NO PRICING DUE TO SCARCITY
BM Ernie Banks
Stan Musial
CC Jose Canseco
Will Clark
DM Lenny Dykstra
Paul Molitor
EG Dennis Eckersley
Kirk Gibson
FB Carlton Fisk
Johnny Bench
FR George Foster
Jim Rice
JY Reggie Jackson
Carl Yastrzemski
MC Paul Molitor
Rod Carew
MH Don Mattingly
Keith Hernandez
SF Duke Snider
Whitey Ford
SG Don Sutton
Ron Guidry
SS Ozzie Smith
Ryne Sandberg
YS Robin Yount
Mike Schmidt

2005 SP Legendary Cuts Legendary Duels Material

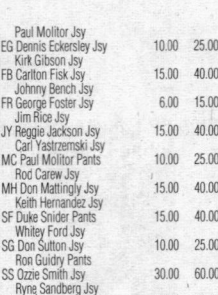

OVERALL #'d GAME-USED ODDS 1:40
STATED PRINT RUN 25 SERIAL #'d SETS
OVERALL PATCH ODDS 1:96
PATCH PRINT RUN 10 SERIAL #'d SETS
NO PATCH PRICING DUE TO SCARCITY
BM Ernie Banks Pants 30.00 60.00
Stan Musial Jsy
CC Jose Canseco Jsy 15.00 40.00
Will Clark Jsy
DM Lenny Dykstra Jsy 6.00 15.00
Paul Molitor Jsy
EG Dennis Eckersley Jsy 10.00 25.00
Kirk Gibson Jsy
FB Carlton Fisk Jsy 15.00 40.00
Johnny Bench Jsy
FR George Foster Jsy 6.00 15.00
Jim Rice Jsy
JY Reggie Jackson Jsy 15.00 40.00
Carl Yastrzemski Jsy
MC Paul Molitor Pants 10.00 25.00
Rod Carew Jsy
MH Don Mattingly Jsy 15.00 40.00
Keith Hernandez Jsy
SF Duke Snider Pants 15.00 40.00
Whitey Ford Jsy
SG Don Sutton Jsy 10.00 25.00
Ron Guidry Pants
SS Ozzie Smith Jsy 30.00 60.00
Ryne Sandberg Jsy
YS Robin Yount Jsy 15.00 40.00
Mike Schmidt Jsy

2005 SP Legendary Cuts Legendary Duos Autograph

OVERALL AUTO ODDS 1:96
STATED PRINT RUN 15 SERIAL #'d SETS
NO PRICING DUE TO SCARCITY
EXCHANGE DEADLINE 11/10/08
CO Rod Carew
Tony Oliva
ES Carl Erskine
Duke Snider
FB Whitey Ford
Yogi Berra
GS Mark Grace
Ryne Sandberg
JG Reggie Jackson
Ron Guidry
MB Joe Morgan
Johnny Bench
MY Paul Molitor
Robin Yount
RB Jim Rice
Wade Boggs
RC Cal Ripken
Will Clark
RM Cal Ripken
Eddie Murray EXCH
RR Brooks Robinson
Frank Robinson
SC Mike Schmidt
Steve Carlton
SG Darryl Strawberry
Dwight Gooden

2005 SP Legendary Cuts Legendary Duos Material

OVERALL #'d GAME-USED ODDS 1:40
STATED PRINT RUN 25 SERIAL #'d SETS
OVERALL PATCH ODDS 1:96
PATCH PRINT RUN 10 SERIAL #'d SETS
NO PATCH PRICING DUE TO SCARCITY
CO Rod Carew Jsy 10.00 25.00
Tony Oliva Jsy
ES Carl Erskine Jsy 10.00 25.00
Duke Snider Jsy
FB Whitey Ford Jsy 15.00 40.00
Yogi Berra Pants
GS Mark Grace Jsy 20.00 50.00
Ryne Sandberg Jsy
JG Reggie Jackson Jsy 10.00 25.00
Ron Guidry Pants
MB Joe Morgan Jsy 15.00 40.00
Johnny Bench Jsy
MY Paul Molitor Pants 15.00 40.00
Robin Yount Jsy
RB Jim Rice Jsy 10.00 25.00
Wade Boggs Jsy
RC Cal Ripken Jsy 20.00 50.00
Will Clark Jsy
RM Cal Ripken Jsy 30.00 60.00
Eddie Murray Jsy
RR Brooks Robinson Jsy 10.00 25.00
Frank Robinson Jsy
SC Mike Schmidt Jsy 15.00 40.00
Steve Carlton Jsy
SG Darryl Strawberry Jsy 6.00 15.00
Dwight Gooden Jsy

2005 SP Legendary Cuts Legendary Lineage

STATED PRINT RUN 399 SERIAL #'d SETS
*GOLD: .6X TO 1.5X BASIC
GOLD PRINT RUN 75 SERIAL #'d SETS
PLATINUM PRINT RUN 1 SERIAL #'d SET
NO PLATINUM PRICING DUE TO SCARCITY
OVERALL INSERT ODDS 1:6
AD Andre Dawson 1.25 3.00
AR Al Rosen 1.50 4.00

AV Andy Van Slyke 1.50 4.00
BD Bobby Doerr 1.25 3.00
BF Bill Freehan 1.25 3.00
BH Bob Horner 1.25 3.00
BL Barry Larkin 1.50 4.00
BM Bill Madlock 1.25 3.00
BR Brooks Robinson 1.50 4.00
CA Jose Canseco 1.50 4.00
CR Cal Ripken 4.00 10.00
DC David Cone 1.25 3.00
DE Dennis Martinez 1.25 3.00
DG Dwight Gooden 1.25 3.00
DM Dale Murphy 1.50 4.00
DS Dave Stewart 1.25 3.00
EC Dennis Eckersley 1.25 3.00
FJ Fergie Jenkins 1.25 3.00
GG Goose Gossage 1.25 3.00
GM Gary Matthews 1.25 3.00
GN Graig Nettles 1.25 3.00
GU Don Gullett 1.25 3.00
HB Harold Baines 1.25 3.00
JB Jay Buhner 1.25 3.00
JC Jack Clark 1.25 3.00
JM Jack Morris 1.25 3.00
JP Jim Palmer 1.25 3.00
JR Jim Rice 1.25 3.00
KH Keith Hernandez 1.25 3.00
KP Kirby Puckett 1.50 4.00
LD Lenny Dykstra 1.25 3.00
LT Luis Tiant 1.25 3.00
MA Don Mattingly 3.00 8.00
MG Mark Grace 1.50 4.00
MS Mike Schmidt 3.00 8.00
MU Bobby Murcer 1.50 4.00
OS Ozzie Smith 2.00 5.00
PM Paul Molitor 1.25 3.00
RG Ron Guidry 1.25 3.00
RJ Reggie Jackson 1.50 4.00
SC Steve Carlton 1.25 3.00
SF Sid Fernandez 1.25 3.00
SL Sparky Lyle 1.25 3.00
SN Duke Snider 1.50 4.00
ST Darryl Strawberry 1.25 3.00
SU Bruce Sutter 1.25 3.00
TG Tony Gwynn 2.00 5.00
TO Tony Oliva 1.25 3.00
TR Tim Raines 1.25 3.00
WC Will Clark 1.50 4.00

2005 SP Legendary Cuts Legendary Lineage Material

OVERALL GAME-USED ODDS 1:6
*GOLD: .5X TO 1.2X BASIC
GOLD PRINT RUN 75 SERIAL #'d SETS
PLATINUM PRINT RUN 1 SERIAL #'d SET
NO PLATINUM PRICING DUE TO SCARCITY
OVERALL #'d GAME-USED ODDS 1:40
AD Andre Dawson Jsy 2.00 5.00
AR Al Rosen Pants 3.00 8.00
AV Andy Van Slyke Jsy 3.00 8.00
BD Bobby Doerr Jsy 2.00 5.00
BF Bill Freehan Jsy 2.00 5.00
BH Bob Horner Jsy 2.00 5.00
BL Barry Larkin Jsy 3.00 8.00
BM Bill Madlock Jsy 2.00 5.00
BR Brooks Robinson Jsy 3.00 8.00
CA Jose Canseco Jsy 3.00 8.00
CR Cal Ripken Jsy 8.00 20.00
DC David Cone Jsy 2.00 5.00
DE Dennis Martinez Jsy 2.00 5.00
DG Dwight Gooden Jsy 2.00 5.00
DM Dale Murphy Jsy 3.00 8.00
DS Dave Stewart Jsy 2.00 5.00
EC Dennis Eckersley Jsy 2.00 5.00
FJ Fergie Jenkins Jsy 2.00 5.00
GG Goose Gossage Jsy 2.00 5.00
GM Gary Matthews Jsy 2.00 5.00
GN Graig Nettles Jsy 2.00 5.00
GU Don Gullett Jsy 2.00 5.00
HB Harold Baines Jsy 2.00 5.00
JB Jay Buhner Jsy 3.00 8.00
JC Jack Clark Jsy 2.00 5.00
JM Jack Morris Jsy 2.00 5.00
JP Jim Palmer Jsy 2.00 5.00
JR Jim Rice Jsy 2.00 5.00
KH Keith Hernandez Jsy 2.00 5.00
KP Kirby Puckett Jsy 4.00 10.00
LD Lenny Dykstra Jsy 2.00 5.00
LT Luis Tiant Jsy 2.00 5.00
MA Don Mattingly Jsy 5.00 12.00
MG Mark Grace Jsy 3.00 8.00
MS Mike Schmidt Jsy 5.00 12.00
MU Bobby Murcer Pants 3.00 8.00
OS Ozzie Smith Jsy 4.00 10.00
PM Paul Molitor Bat 2.00 5.00
RG Ron Guidry Pants 2.00 5.00
RJ Reggie Jackson Jsy 3.00 8.00
SC Steve Carlton Jsy 2.00 5.00
SF Sid Fernandez Jsy 2.00 5.00
SL Sparky Lyle Pants 2.00 5.00
SN Duke Snider Pants 4.00 10.00
ST Darryl Strawberry Jsy 2.00 5.00
SU Bruce Sutter Jsy 2.00 5.00
TG Tony Gwynn Jsy 4.00 10.00
TO Tony Oliva Jsy 2.00 5.00
TR Tim Raines Jsy 2.00 5.00
WC Will Clark Jsy 3.00 8.00

2005 SP Legendary Cuts Legendary Lineage Patch

*PATCH: 1X TO 2.5X MATERIAL
STATED PRINT RUN 50 SERIAL #'d SETS
K.HERNANDEZ PRINT RUN 39 CARDS
B.MADLOCK PRINT RUN 43 CARDS
P.MOLITOR PRINT RUN 5 CARDS
J.RICE PRINT RUN 12 CARDS
NO MOLITOR/RICE PRICING AVAILABLE
GOLD PRINT RUN 10 SERIAL #'d SETS
NO GOLD PRICING DUE TO SCARCITY
PLATINUM PRINT RUN 1 SERIAL #'d SET
NO PLATINUM PRICING DUE TO SCARCITY
OVERALL PATCH ODDS 1:96

2005 SP Legendary Cuts Legendary Lineage Autograph

STATED PRINT RUN 25 SERIAL #'d SETS
GOLD PRINT RUN 10 SERIAL #'d SETS
NO GOLD PRICING DUE TO SCARCITY
PLATINUM PRINT RUN 1 SERIAL #'d SET
NO PLATINUM PRICING DUE TO SCARCITY
OVERALL AUTO ODDS 1:96
EXCHANGE DEADLINE 11/10/08
AD Andre Dawson 10.00 25.00
AR Al Rosen 10.00 25.00
AV Andy Van Slyke 15.00 40.00
BD Bobby Doerr 6.00 15.00
BF Bill Freehan 10.00 25.00
BH Bob Horner 6.00 15.00
BL Barry Larkin 15.00 40.00
BM Bill Madlock 10.00 25.00
BR Brooks Robinson 15.00 40.00
CA Jose Canseco 20.00 50.00
CR Cal Ripken EXCH 60.00 120.00
DC David Cone 6.00 15.00
DE Dennis Martinez 6.00 15.00
DG Dwight Gooden 6.00 15.00
DM Dale Murphy 15.00 40.00
DS Dave Stewart 6.00 15.00
EC Dennis Eckersley 10.00 25.00
FJ Fergie Jenkins 10.00 25.00
GG Goose Gossage 10.00 25.00
GM Gary Matthews 6.00 15.00
GN Graig Nettles 10.00 25.00
GU Don Gullett 6.00 15.00
HB Harold Baines 10.00 25.00
JB Jay Buhner 15.00 40.00
JC Jack Clark 10.00 25.00
JM Jack Morris 6.00 15.00
JP Jim Palmer 10.00 25.00
JR Jim Rice 10.00 25.00
KH Keith Hernandez 6.00 15.00
KP Kirby Puckett 50.00 100.00
LD Lenny Dykstra 6.00 15.00
LT Luis Tiant 6.00 15.00
MA Don Mattingly 30.00 60.00
MG Mark Grace 15.00 40.00
MS Mike Schmidt 30.00 60.00
MU Bobby Murcer EXCH 15.00 40.00
OS Ozzie Smith 20.00 50.00
PM Paul Molitor 10.00 25.00
RG Ron Guidry 15.00 40.00
RJ Reggie Jackson 20.00 50.00
SC Steve Carlton 10.00 25.00
SF Sid Fernandez 6.00 15.00
SL Sparky Lyle 6.00 15.00
SN Duke Snider 20.00 50.00
ST Darryl Strawberry 10.00 25.00
SU Bruce Sutter 15.00 40.00
TG Tony Gwynn 20.00 50.00
TO Tony Oliva 10.00 25.00
TR Tim Raines 10.00 25.00
WC Will Clark 15.00 40.00

2005 SP Legendary Cuts Legendary Lineage Autograph Material

*AUTO MAT: .4X TO 1X AUTO
STATED PRINT RUN 25 SERIAL #'d SETS
GOLD PRINT RUN 10 SERIAL #'d SETS
NO GOLD PRICING DUE TO SCARCITY
PLATINUM PRINT RUN 1 SERIAL #'d SET
NO PLATINUM PRICING DUE TO SCARCITY
OVERALL AU-GU ODDS 1:96
EXCHANGE DEADLINE 11/10/08

2005 SP Legendary Cuts Legendary Lineage Autograph Patch

*AUTO PATCH: .6X TO 1.5X AUTO
STATED PRINT RUN 25 SERIAL #'d SETS
T.OLIVA PRINT RUN 16 CARDS
NO T.OLIVA PRICING DUE TO SCARCITY
GOLD PRINT RUN 5 SERIAL #'d SETS
NO GOLD PRICING DUE TO SCARCITY
PLATINUM PRINT RUN 1 SERIAL #'d SET
NO PLATINUM PRICING DUE TO SCARCITY
OVERALL AU-PATCH ODDS 1:196
EXCHANGE DEADLINE 11/10/08

2005 SP Legendary Cuts Material

STATED PRINT RUN 75 SERIAL #'d SETS
H.WAGNER PRINT RUN 22 CARDS
GOLD PRINT RUN 15 SERIAL #'d SETS
GOLD H.WAGNER PRINT RUN 5 CARDS
NO GOLD PRICING DUE TO SCARCITY
OVERALL MATERIAL ODDS 1:196
BD Bill Dickey Jsy 15.00 40.00
BL Bob Lemon Jsy 10.00 25.00
BR Babe Ruth Bat 150.00 250.00
CA Roy Campanella Pants 15.00 40.00
CM Christy Mathewson Pants 75.00 150.00
CO Mickey Cochrane Bat 15.00 40.00
CR Joe Cronin Bat 10.00 25.00
CS Casey Stengel Jsy 15.00 40.00
DD Don Drysdale Pants 10.00 25.00
DE Dizzy Dean Jsy 40.00 80.00
EM Eddie Mathews Jsy 15.00 40.00
ES Enos Slaughter Bat 10.00 25.00
EW Early Wynn Pants 6.00 15.00
HG Hank Greenberg Bat 20.00 50.00
HO Gil Hodges Bat 20.00 50.00
HU Catfish Hunter Jsy 6.00 15.00
HW Honus Wagner Pants/22 90.00 150.00
JD Joe DiMaggio Jsy 60.00 120.00
JF Jimmie Foxx Bat 30.00 60.00
JR Jackie Robinson Pants 30.00 60.00
JW Hoyt Wilhelm Jsy 10.00 25.00
LG Lou Gehrig Pants 125.00 200.00
MI Johnny Mize Pants 10.00 25.00
MM Mickey Mantle Pants 100.00 175.00
MO Mel Ott Jsy 15.00 40.00
PR Pee Wee Reese Jsy 10.00 25.00
RC Roberto Clemente Pants 40.00 80.00
RH Rogers Hornsby Jkt 40.00 80.00
RM Roger Maris Pants 30.00 60.00
SI George Sisler Bat 15.00 40.00
SP Satchel Paige Pants 30.00 60.00
TC Ty Cobb Bat 75.00 150.00
TK Ted Kluszewski Jsy 10.00 25.00
TL Tony Lazzeri Bat 15.00 40.00
TM Thurman Munson Pants 15.00 40.00
TW Ted Williams Pants 40.00 80.00
WS Warren Spahn Jsy 15.00 40.00

2005 SP Legendary Cuts Middlemen Cuts

OVERALL CUT AU ODDS 1:196
PRINT RUNS B/WN 2-99 COPIES PER
NO PRICING ON QTY OF 18 OR LESS
AV Arky Vaughan/2
BH Billy Herman/90 60.00 120.00
CG Charlie Gehringer/95 75.00 150.00
FF Frankie Frisch/23 125.00 200.00
JC Joe Cronin/30 125.00 200.00
JS Joe Sewell/76 75.00 150.00
LA Luke Appling/32 100.00 175.00
LB Lou Boudreau/99 50.00 100.00
LD Leo Durocher/18
MC Roy McMillan/5
NF Nellie Fox/3
PW Pee Wee Reese/39 125.00 200.00
RM Rabbit Maranville/5
ZV Zoilo Versalles/4

2005 SP Legendary Cuts Significant Trips Autograph

OVERALL AUTO ODDS 1:96
STATED PRINT RUN 10 SERIAL #'d SETS
NO PRICING DUE TO SCARCITY
EXCHANGE DEADLINE 11/10/08
CSV Jack Clark
Ozzie Smith
Andy Van Slyke
DCR Andre Dawson
Gary Carter
Tim Raines
DGS Andre Dawson
Mark Grace
Ryne Sandberg
FLR Carlton Fisk
Fred Lynn
Jim Rice
HMM Bob Horner
Dale Murphy
Gary Matthews
MBP Joe Morgan
Johnny Bench
Tony Perez
RMP Cal Ripken
Eddie Murray
Jim Palmer
RRA Brooks Robinson
Frank Robinson
Luis Aparicio
SCH Keith Hernandez
Gary Carter
Darryl Strawberry
SEC Dave Stewart
Dennis Eckersley
Jose Canseco

2005 SP Legendary Cuts Significant Trips Material

OVERALL #'d GAME-USED ODDS 1:40
STATED PRINT RUN 10 SERIAL #'d SETS
OVERALL PATCH ODDS 1:96
PATCH PRINT RUN 5 SERIAL #'d SETS
NO PRICING DUE TO SCARCITY
CSV Jack Clark Jsy
Ozzie Smith Jsy
Andy Van Slyke Jsy
DCR Andre Dawson Jsy
Gary Carter Jsy
Tim Raines Jsy
DGS Andre Dawson Jsy
Mark Grace Jsy
Ryne Sandberg Jsy
FLR Carlton Fisk Jsy
Fred Lynn Bat
Jim Rice Jsy
HMM Bob Horner Jsy
Dale Murphy Jsy
Gary Matthews Jsy
MBP Joe Morgan Jsy
Johnny Bench Jsy
Tony Perez Jsy
RMP Cal Ripken Jsy
Eddie Murray Jsy
Jim Palmer Jsy
RRA Brooks Robinson Jsy
Frank Robinson Jsy
Luis Aparicio Jsy
SCH Keith Hernandez Jsy
Gary Carter Jsy
Darryl Strawberry Jsy
SEC Dave Stewart Jsy
Dennis Eckersley Jsy
Jose Canseco Jsy

2006 SP Legendary Cuts

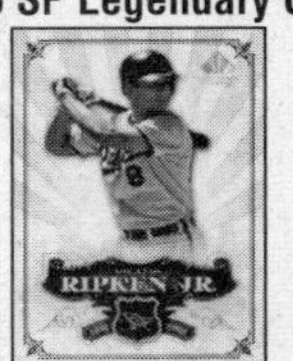

This 200-card set was released in August, 2006. The product was issued in four-card packs with an $10 SRP, which came 12 packs to a box and 16 boxes to a case.

COMP.SET w/o SP's (100) 10.00 25.00
COMMON CARD (1-100) .25 .60
COMMON CARD (101-200) 2.00 5.00
101-200: ONE BASIC OR BRONZE PER BOX
101-200 PRINT RUN 550 SERIAL #'d SETS
EXQUISITE EXCH ODDS 1:60

EXQUISITE EXCH DEADLINE 07/27/07
1 Juan Marichal .25 .60
2 Monte Irvin .25 .60
3 Will Clark .40 1.00
4 Willie McCovey .40 1.00
5 Eddie Gaedel .25 .60
6 Ken Williams .25 .60
7 Earl Battey .25 .60
8 Rick Ferrell .25 .60
9 Bob Gibson .40 1.00
10 Elmer Flick .25 .60
11 Joe Medwick .25 .60
12 Lou Brock .40 1.00
13 Ozzie Smith 1.00 2.50
14 Red Schoendienst .25 .60
15 Stan Musial 1.00 2.50
16 Tony Oliva .25 .60
17 Phil Niekro .25 .60
18 Boog Powell .25 .60
19 Brooks Robinson .40 1.00
20 Cal Ripken 2.50 6.00
21 Eddie Murray .60 1.50
22 Frank Robinson .25 .60
23 Jim Palmer .25 .60
24 Jocko Conlon .25 .60
25 Carlton Fisk .40 1.00
26 Dwight Evans .25 .60
27 Fred Lynn .25 .60
28 Jim Rice .25 .60
29 Ted Williams 1.50 4.00
30 Wade Boggs .40 1.00
31 Hugh Duffy .25 .60
32 Kid Nichols .25 .60
33 Johnny Vander Meer .25 .60
34 Dolph Camilli .25 .60
35 Carl Yastrzemski 1.00 2.50
36 Chick Hafey .25 .60
37 Kirby Higbe .25 .60
38 Pee Wee Reese .40 1.00
39 Pete Reiser .25 .60
40 Don Sutton .25 .60
41 Rod Carew .40 1.00
42 Andre Dawson .25 .60
43 Billy Herman .25 .60
44 Billy Williams .25 .60
45 Charley Root .25 .60
46 Hack Wilson .40 1.00
47 Ernie Banks .60 1.50
48 Fergie Jenkins .25 .60
49 Gabby Hartnett .25 .60
50 Ken Hubbs .25 .60
51 Kiki Cuyler .25 .60
52 Mark Grace .40 1.00
53 Ryne Sandberg 1.25 3.00
54 Harold Newhouser .25 .60
55 Charlie Robertson .25 .60
56 Harold Baines .25 .60
57 Luis Aparicio .25 .60
58 Luke Appling .25 .60
59 Nellie Fox .40 1.00
60 Ray Schalk .25 .60
61 Red Faber .25 .60
62 Sloppy Thurston .25 .60
63 Freddie Lindstrom .25 .60
64 Vern Kennedy .25 .60
65 Barry Larkin .40 1.00
66 Bucky Walters .25 .60
67 Dolf Luque .25 .60
68 Al Campanis .25 .60
69 Ernie Lombardi .25 .60
70 George Foster .25 .60
71 Joe Morgan .25 .60
72 Johnny Bench .60 1.50
73 Ken Griffey Sr. .25 .60
74 Ted Kluszewski .40 1.00
75 Tony Perez .25 .60
76 Wally Post .25 .60
77 Bob Feller .25 .60
78 Bob Lemon .25 .60
79 Earl Averill .25 .60
80 Joe Sewell .25 .60
81 Johnny Hodapp .25 .60
82 Larry Doby .25 .60
83 Lou Boudreau .25 .60
84 Rocky Colavito .40 1.00
85 Stan Coveleski .25 .60
86 Nap Lajoie .40 1.00
87 Al Kaline .60 1.50
88 Alan Trammell .25 .60
89 Charlie Gehringer .25 .60
90 Denny McLain .25 .60
91 Hank Greenberg .60 1.50
92 Jack Morris .25 .60
93 Mark Fidrych .25 .60
94 Ray Boone .25 .60
95 Rudy York .25 .60
96 Buck Leonard .25 .60
97 Bo Jackson .60 1.50
98 Zoilo Versalles .25 .60
99 John Kruk .25 .60
100 Don Drysdale .40 1.00
101 Cecil Cooper 2.00 5.00
102 Vic Wertz 2.00 5.00
103 Kirk Gibson 2.00 5.00
104 Maury Wills 2.00 5.00
105 Steve Garvey 2.00 5.00
106 Warren Spahn 3.00 8.00
107 Paul Molitor 2.00 5.00
108 Robin Yount 3.00 8.00
109 Rollie Fingers 2.00 5.00
110 Bob Allison 2.00 5.00
111 Kirby Puckett 3.00 8.00
112 Tim Raines 2.00 5.00
113 George Pipgras 2.00 5.00
114 Eddie Grant 2.00 5.00
115 Hoyt Wilhelm 2.00 5.00
116 Sal Maglie 2.00 5.00
117 Ron Santo 3.00 8.00
118 Wally Joyner 2.00 5.00
119 Tom Seaver 3.00 8.00
120 Tommie Agee 2.00 5.00
121 Harmon Killebrew 3.00 8.00
122 Bill Dickey 2.00 5.00
123 Early Wynn 2.00 5.00
124 Bobby Murcer 3.00 8.00
125 Bucky Dent 2.00 5.00
126 Dave Winfield 2.00 5.00
127 Don Larsen 2.00 5.00
128 Don Mattingly 4.00 10.00
129 Earle Combs 2.00 5.00
130 Ed Lopat 2.00 5.00
131 Elston Howard 2.00 5.00
132 Everett Scott 2.00 5.00
133 Goose Gossage 2.00 5.00
134 Graig Nettles 2.00 5.00
135 Joe DiMaggio 4.00 10.00
136 Lou Piniella 2.00 5.00
137 Bill Skowron 2.00 5.00
138 Phil Rizzuto 3.00 8.00
139 Red Ruffing 2.00 5.00
140 Reggie Jackson 3.00 8.00
141 Roger Maris 3.00 8.00
142 Ron Guidry 2.00 5.00
143 Tiny Bonham 2.00 5.00
144 Bruce Sutter 2.00 5.00
145 Tony Lazzeri 2.00 5.00
146 Waite Hoyt 2.00 5.00
147 Whitey Ford 3.00 8.00
148 Steve Sax 2.00 5.00
149 Yogi Berra 3.00 8.00
150 Enos Slaughter 2.00 5.00
151 Catfish Hunter 2.00 5.00
152 Dennis Eckersley 2.00 5.00
153 Jose Canseco 3.00 8.00
154 Al Rosen 2.00 5.00
155 Al Simmons 2.00 5.00
156 Chief Bender 2.00 5.00
157 Cy Williams 2.00 5.00
158 Mike Schmidt 4.00 10.00
159 Richie Ashburn 3.00 8.00
160 Robin Roberts 2.00 5.00
161 Steve Carlton 2.00 5.00
162 Judy Johnson 2.00 5.00
163 Al Oliver 2.00 5.00
164 Bill Mazeroski 3.00 8.00
165 Dave Parker 2.00 5.00
166 Max Carey 2.00 5.00
167 Pie Traynor 2.00 5.00
168 Ralph Kiner 2.00 5.00
169 Roberto Clemente 6.00 15.00
170 Willie Stargell 2.00 5.00
171 Gaylord Perry 2.00 5.00
172 Tony Gwynn 3.00 8.00
173 Nolan Ryan 4.00 10.00
174 Joe Carter 2.00 5.00
175 Frank Howard 2.00 5.00
176 George Kell 2.00 5.00
177 Heinie Manush 2.00 5.00
178 Sam Rice 2.00 5.00
179 Babe Ruth 6.00 15.00
180 Casey Stengel 3.00 8.00
181 Christy Mathewson 3.00 8.00
182 Cy Young 3.00 8.00
183 Dizzy Dean 3.00 8.00
184 Eddie Mathews 3.00 8.00
185 George Sisler 2.00 5.00
186 Honus Wagner 3.00 8.00
187 Jackie Robinson 3.00 8.00
188 Jimmie Foxx 3.00 8.00
189 Johnny Mize 2.00 5.00
190 Lefty Gomez 2.00 5.00
191 Lou Gehrig 4.00 10.00
192 Mel Ott 3.00 8.00
193 Mickey Cochrane 2.00 5.00
194 Rogers Hornsby 3.00 8.00
195 Roy Campanella 3.00 8.00
196 Satchel Paige 3.00 8.00
197 Thurman Munson 3.00 8.00
198 Ty Cobb 4.00 10.00
199 Walter Johnson 3.00 8.00
200 Lefty Grove 2.00 5.00
NNO Exquisite Redemption

2006 SP Legendary Cuts Bronze

*101-200 BRONZE: .6X TO 1.5X BASIC
101-200: ONE BASIC OR BRONZE PER BOX
STATED PRINT RUN 99 SERIAL #'d SETS

2006 SP Legendary Cuts A Place in History Cuts

OVERALL CUT AU ODDS 1:96
PRINT RUNS B/WN 1-98 COPIES PER
NO PRICING ON QTY OF 25 OR LESS
AD Abner Doubleday/1
BA Bob Allison/94 75.00 150.00
BD Bill Dickey/29 125.00 250.00
BG Burleigh Grimes/43 75.00 150.00
BL Bob Lemon/47 60.00 120.00
BR Babe Ruth/1
CA Roy Campanella/5
CG Charlie Gehringer/57 60.00 120.00
CH Carl Hubbell/32 125.00 200.00
CM Connie Mack/7
CO Chuck Connors/25
CR Charley Root/1
CW Cy Williams/29 150.00 250.00
CY Cy Young/1
DD Don Drysdale/19
DH Dick Howser/28 75.00 150.00
DL Leo Durocher/42 60.00 120.00
DU Joe Dugan/25
EA Earl Averill/75 50.00 100.00
EM Eddie Mathews/34 60.00 120.00
ER Edd Roush/98 50.00 100.00
ES Everett Scott/1
EW Early Wynn/36 60.00 120.00
FF Ford Frick/30 100.00 175.00
GB Garland Braxton/1
GE Lou Gehrig/2
GH Gabby Hartnett/15
GS George Sisler/42 300.00 500.00
HC Happy Chandler/61 50.00 100.00
HG Hank Greenberg/31 125.00 250.00
HI Kirby Higbe/59 75.00 150.00
HM Heinie Manush/16
HW Honus Wagner/2
JC Joe Cronin/30 75.00 150.00
JD Joe DiMaggio/17
JF Jimmie Foxx/8
JH Johnny Hodapp/26 50.00 100.00
JJ Judy Johnson/20
JM Joe McCarthy/58 125.00 250.00
JR Jackie Robinson/4
JS Joe Sewell/87 50.00 100.00
KH Ken Hubbs/3
KL Kenesaw Landis/2
KW Ken Williams/3
LA Luke Appling/94 60.00 120.00
LB Lou Boudreau/88 50.00 100.00
LG Lefty Gomez/30 100.00 175.00
LU Dolf Luque/1
ME Joe Medwick/60 125.00 200.00
MO Mel Ott/5
PR Pee Wee Reese/57 125.00 200.00
RA Richie Ashburn/3
RC Roberto Clemente/3
RD Ray Dandridge/43 60.00 120.00
RE Pete Reiser/75 75.00 150.00
RH Rogers Hornsby/3
RM Roger Maris/11
RO Charlie Robertson/42 75.00 150.00
RR Red Ruffing/16
RS Ray Schalk Best/37 200.00 400.00
RS2 Ray Schalk/75 175.00 300.00
SM Sal Maglie/73 50.00 100.00
SP Satchel Paige/12
ST Sloppy Thurston/15
TA Tommie Agee/20
TB Tiny Bonham/1
TK Ted Kluszewski/24
TL Tony Lazzeri/3
TM Thurman Munson/1
TS Tris Speaker/1
TW Ted Williams/7
TY Ty Cobb/2
VK Vern Kennedy/61 60.00 120.00
WG Warren Giles/45 75.00 150.00
WI Hoyt Wilhelm/65 50.00 100.00
WS Warren Spahn/41 75.00 150.00
YO Rudy York/3

2006 SP Legendary Cuts Baseball Chronology Gold

STATED PRINT RUN 550 SERIAL #'d SETS
*PLATINUM: .6X TO 1.5X BASIC
PLATINUM PRINT RUN 99 SERIAL #'d SETS
OVERALL CHRONOLOGY ODDS 1:12
AD Andre Dawson 1.25 3.00
AK Al Kaline 2.00 5.00
AT Alan Trammell 1.25 3.00
BD Bucky Dent 1.25 3.00
BF Bob Feller 2.00 5.00
BG Bob Gibson 2.00 5.00
BL Bob Lemon 1.25 3.00
BM Bill Mazeroski 2.00 5.00
BO Bo Jackson 2.00 5.00
BR Babe Ruth 4.00 10.00
BR2 Babe Ruth 4.00 10.00
BR3 Babe Ruth 4.00 10.00
BW Billy Williams 1.25 3.00
CA Rod Carew 2.00 5.00
CF Carlton Fisk 2.00 5.00
CH Catfish Hunter 1.25 3.00
CL Roberto Clemente 4.00 10.00
CM Christy Mathewson 2.00 5.00
CN Joe Cronin 1.25 3.00
CR Cal Ripken 6.00 15.00
CS Casey Stengel Yanks 2.00 5.00
CS2 Casey Stengel Mets 2.00 5.00
CY Cy Young 2.00 5.00
DD Don Drysdale 2.00 5.00
DE Dennis Eckersley 1.25 3.00
DL Don Larsen 1.25 3.00
DM Don Mattingly 3.00 8.00
DS Don Sutton 1.25 3.00
DZ Dizzy Dean 2.00 5.00
EB Ernie Banks 2.00 5.00
EB2 Ernie Banks 2.00 5.00
EM Eddie Murray 2.00 5.00
ES Enos Slaughter 1.25 3.00
FL Fred Lynn 1.25 3.00
FR Frank Robinson 1.25 3.00
GH Gil Hodges 2.00 5.00
GP Gaylord Perry 1.25 3.00
GS George Sisler 1.25 3.00
HG Hank Greenberg 2.00 5.00
HW Honus Wagner 2.00 5.00
HY Hoyt Wilhelm 1.25 3.00
JB Johnny Bench 2.00 5.00
JC Joe Carter 1.25 3.00
JD Joe DiMaggio 3.00 8.00
JF Jimmie Foxx A's 2.00 5.00
JF2 Jimmie Foxx Sox 2.00 5.00
JM Johnny Mize 1.25 3.00
JO Joe Morgan 1.25 3.00
JR Jackie Robinson 2.00 5.00
KG Kirk Gibson 1.25 3.00
KP Kirby Puckett 2.00 5.00
LB Lou Boudreau 1.25 3.00
LG Lou Gehrig 3.00 8.00
LG2 Lou Gehrig 3.00 8.00
LO Lou Brock 2.00 5.00
MC Mickey Cochrane 1.25 3.00
MF Mark Fidrych 1.25 3.00
MO Mel Ott 2.00 5.00
MS Mike Schmidt 3.00 8.00
MW Maury Wills 1.25 3.00
NL Nap Lajoie 1.25 3.00
NR Nolan Ryan Angels 3.00 8.00
NR2 Nolan Ryan Rgr 3.00 8.00
NR3 Nolan Ryan Rgr 3.00 8.00
OS Ozzie Smith 2.00 5.00
PM Paul Molitor 1.25 3.00
PN Phil Niekro 1.25 3.00
PW Pee Wee Reese 2.00 5.00
RC Roy Campanella 2.00 5.00
RF Rollie Fingers 1.25 3.00
RH Rogers Hornsby 2.00 5.00
RI Jim Rice 1.25 3.00
RJ Reggie Jackson 2.00 5.00
RK Ralph Kiner 1.25 3.00
RM Roger Maris 2.00 5.00
RO Brooks Robinson 2.00 5.00
RS Ryne Sandberg 3.00 8.00
RY Robin Yount 2.00 5.00
SC Steve Carlton Cards 1.25 3.00
SC2 Steve Carlton Phils 1.25 3.00
SG Steve Garvey 1.25 3.00
SM Stan Musial 2.00 5.00
SP Satchel Paige 2.00 5.00
ST Willie Stargell 1.25 3.00
TC Ty Cobb Tigers 3.00 8.00
TC2 Ty Cobb A's 3.00 8.00
TG Tony Gwynn 2.00 5.00
TM Thurman Munson 2.00 5.00
TS Tom Seaver 2.00 5.00
TW Ted Williams 3.00 8.00
TW2 Ted Williams 3.00 8.00
WB Wade Boggs Sox 1.25 3.00
WB2 Wade Boggs Rays 1.25 3.00
WC Will Clark 2.00 5.00
WF Whitey Ford 2.00 5.00
WJ Walter Johnson 2.00 5.00
WM Willie McCovey 2.00 5.00
WS Warren Spahn 2.00 5.00
YB Yogi Berra 2.00 5.00
YZ Carl Yastrzemski 2.00 5.00

2006 SP Legendary Cuts Baseball Chronology Materials

STATED ODDS 1:12
SP PRINT RUNS PROVIDED BY UD
NO PRICING ON QTY OF 25 OR LESS
AD Andre Dawson Pants 3.00 8.00
AK Al Kaline Bat 4.00 10.00
AT Alan Trammell Bat 3.00 8.00
BD Bucky Dent Jsy 3.00 8.00
BF Bob Feller Pants 4.00 10.00
BG Bob Gibson Jsy 3.00 8.00
BL Bob Lemon Jsy 3.00 8.00
BM Bill Mazeroski Bat SP/59 * 6.00 15.00
BO Bo Jackson Jsy 4.00 10.00
BR Babe Ruth Sox Pants SP/10 *
BR2 B.Ruth 60 HR Pants SP/20 *
BR3 B.Ruth 500 HR Pants SP/20 *
BW Billy Williams Bat 3.00 8.00
CA Rod Carew Bat 3.00 8.00
CF Carlton Fisk Bat 3.00 8.00
CH Catfish Hunter Jsy 3.00 8.00
CL Roberto Clemente Pants SP/100 * 30.00 60.00
CM Christy Mathewson Pants SP/49 * 60.00 120.00
CN Joe Cronin Bat 4.00 10.00
CR Cal Ripken Pants 6.00 15.00
CS Casey Stengel Yanks Jsy SP/199 * 10.00 25.00
CS2 Casey Stengel Mets Jsy SP/100 * 10.00 25.00
DD Don Drysdale Jsy SP/94 * 10.00 25.00
DE Dennis Eckersley Jsy 3.00 8.00
DL Don Larsen Pants 3.00 8.00
DM Don Mattingly Pants 4.00 10.00
DS Don Sutton Jsy 3.00 8.00
DZ Dizzy Dean Jsy SP/100 * 30.00 60.00
EB Ernie Banks MVP Jsy 4.00 10.00
EB2 Ernie Banks 500 Jsy SP/100 * 6.00 15.00
EM Eddie Murray Jsy 4.00 10.00
ES Enos Slaughter Bat SP/100 * 6.00 15.00
FL Fred Lynn Bat 3.00 8.00
FR Frank Robinson Jsy 3.00 8.00
GH Gil Hodges Bat SP/50 * 10.00 25.00
GP Gaylord Perry Jsy 3.00 8.00
GS George Sisler Bat SP/100 * 8.00 20.00
HG Hank Greenberg Bat SP/198 * 10.00 25.00
HW Honus Wagner Pants SP/10 *
HY Hoyt Wilhelm Jsy SP/46 * 4.00 10.00
JB Johnny Bench Jsy 4.00 10.00
JC Joe Carter Jsy 3.00 8.00
JD Joe DiMaggio Jsy SP/100 * 40.00 80.00
JF Jimmie Foxx A's Bat SP/50 * 30.00 60.00
JF2 Jimmie Foxx Sox Bat SP/100 * 30.00 60.00
JM Johnny Mize Pants 4.00 10.00
JO Joe Morgan Jsy 3.00 8.00
JR Jackie Robinson Pants SP/10 *
KG Kirk Gibson Jsy 3.00 8.00
KP Kirby Puckett Bat 4.00 10.00
LB Lou Boudreau Jsy 4.00 10.00
LG L.Gehrig Speech Bat SP/20 *
LG2 L.Gehrig MVP Bat SP/20 *
LO Lou Brock Jsy 3.00 8.00
MF Mark Fidrych Jsy 3.00 8.00
MO Mel Ott Jsy SP/100 * 15.00 40.00
MS Mike Schmidt Bat 4.00 10.00
MW Maury Wills Bat 3.00 8.00
NR Nolan Ryan Angels Jsy SP/109 * 6.00 15.00
NR2 Nolan Ryan 5000 Jsy 6.00 15.00
NR3 Nolan Ryan 7th No-Hitter Jsy 6.00 15.00
OS Ozzie Smith Jkt-Jsy 4.00 10.00
PM Paul Molitor Bat 3.00 8.00
PN Phil Niekro Jsy 3.00 8.00
PW Pee Wee Reese Bat 4.00 10.00
RC Roy Campanella Pants SP/154 * 6.00 15.00
RF Rollie Fingers Jsy 3.00 8.00
RH Rogers Hornsby Bat SP/10 *
RI Jim Rice Bat 3.00 8.00
RJ Reggie Jackson Jsy 4.00 10.00
RK Ralph Kiner Bat SP/154 * 4.00 10.00
RM Roger Maris Jsy 12.50 30.00
RO Brooks Robinson Bat 4.00 10.00
RS Ryne Sandberg Jsy 4.00 10.00
RY Robin Yount Pants 3.00 8.00
SC Steve Carlton Cards Bat 3.00 8.00
SC2 Steve Carlton Phils Bat 3.00 8.00
SG Steve Garvey Jsy 3.00 8.00
SM Stan Musial Bat 6.00 15.00
SP Satchel Paige Pants SP/50 * 30.00 60.00
ST Willie Stargell Bat 4.00 10.00
TC Ty Cobb Tigers Bat SP/25 *
TC2 Ty Cobb A's Bat SP/25 *
TG Tony Gwynn Jsy 3.00 8.00
TM Thurman Munson Jsy 8.00 20.00
TS Tom Seaver Jsy 3.00 8.00
TW Ted Williams Pants SP/198 * 20.00 50.00
TW2 Ted Williams Bat 20.00 50.00
WB Wade Boggs Jsy 3.00 8.00
WB2 Wade Boggs Bat 3.00 8.00
WC Will Clark Jsy 3.00 8.00
WM Willie McCovey Jsy 3.00 8.00
WS Warren Spahn Jsy 6.00 15.00
YB Yogi Berra Jsy 6.00 15.00
YZ Carl Yastrzemski Jsy 4.00 10.00

2006 SP Legendary Cuts Historical Cuts

OVERALL CUT AU ODDS 1:96
STATED PRINT RUN 1 SERIAL #'d SET
NO PRICING DUE TO SCARCITY
AE Amelia Earhart
AS Albert Schweitzer
CC Calvin Coolidge
GC Grover Cleveland
HH Herbert Hoover
JFK John F. Kennedy
JL Jack London
JPG J. Paul Getty
OW Orville Wright
RN Richard Nixon
TE Thomas Edison
TJ Thomas Jefferson

2006 SP Legendary Cuts Legendary Materials Gold

PRINT RUNS B/WN 99-225 COPIES PER
*BRONZE: .5X TO 1.2X GOLD
BRONZE PRINT RUNS B/WN 25-99 PER
NO BRONZE PRICING ON QTY OF 25
PLATINUM PRINT RUNS B/WN 5-15 PER
NO PLATINUM PRICING DUE TO SCARCITY
*SILVER: .4X TO 1X GOLD
SILVER PRINT RUNS B/WN 50-199 PER
OVERALL #'d GU ODDS 1:12
AD Andre Dawson Pants/225 3.00 8.00
AK Al Kaline Bat/225 4.00 10.00
AO Al Oliver Bat/225 3.00 8.00
AR Al Rosen Bat/225 3.00 8.00
BD Bucky Dent Jsy/225 3.00 8.00
BF Bob Feller Pants/225 4.00 10.00
BG Bob Gibson Jsy/225 3.00 8.00
BL Barry Larkin Bat/225 3.00 8.00
BM Bill Mazeroski Bat/225 4.00 10.00
BO Bo Jackson Bat/225 4.00 10.00
BP Boog Powell Bat/225 3.00 8.00
BR Babe Ruth Pants/99 150.00 250.00
BS Bruce Sutter Pants/225 3.00 8.00
BW Billy Williams Bat/225 3.00 8.00
CC Cecil Cooper Pants/225 3.00 8.00
CF Carlton Fisk Pants/225 3.00 8.00
CR Cal Ripken Pants/225 6.00 15.00
CW Rod Carew Pants/225 3.00 8.00
CY Carl Yastrzemski Pants/225 4.00 10.00
DC Dave Concepcion Bat/225 3.00 8.00
DE Dennis Eckersley Bat/225 3.00 8.00
DE2 Dennis Eckersley Jsy/225 3.00 8.00
DL Don Larsen Pants/225 3.00 8.00
DP Dave Parker Jsy/225 3.00 8.00
DW Dave Winfield Bat/225 3.00 8.00
EB Ernie Banks Jsy/225 4.00 10.00
EM Eddie Murray Jsy/225 3.00 8.00
EV Dwight Evans Jsy/225 3.00 8.00
FH Frank Howard Bat/225 3.00 8.00
FJ Fergie Jenkins Jsy/225 3.00 8.00
FL Fred Lynn Pants/225 3.00 8.00
FR Frank Robinson Pants/225 3.00 8.00
FR2 Frank Robinson Bat/225 3.00 8.00
GF George Foster Bat/225 3.00 8.00
GG Goose Gossage Jsy/225 3.00 8.00
GN Graig Nettles Jsy/225 3.00 8.00
GP Gaylord Perry Jsy/225 3.00 8.00
GP2 Gaylord Perry Jsy/225 3.00 8.00
GU Ron Guidry Pants/225 3.00 8.00
HB Harold Baines Bat/225 3.00 8.00
JB Johnny Bench Jsy/225 4.00 10.00
JC Jose Canseco Jsy/225 4.00 10.00
JD Joe DiMaggio Jsy/99 40.00 80.00
JK John Kruk Bat/225 3.00 8.00
JM Jack Morris Jsy/225 3.00 8.00
JO Joe Morgan Jsy/225 3.00 8.00
JP Jim Palmer Jsy/225 3.00 8.00
JP2 Jim Palmer Jsy/225 3.00 8.00
JR Jim Rice Pants/225 3.00 8.00
JT Joe Torre Bat/225 4.00 10.00
JU Juan Marichal Jsy/225 3.00 8.00
KG Ken Griffey Sr. Pants/225 3.00 8.00
KI Kirk Gibson Jsy/225 3.00 8.00
KP Kirby Puckett Jsy/225 4.00 10.00
LB Lou Brock Jsy/225 3.00 8.00
LB2 Lou Brock Jsy/225 3.00 8.00
LP Lou Piniella Jsy/225 3.00 8.00
MA Don Mattingly Pants/225 4.00 10.00
MG Mark Grace Bat/225 3.00 8.00
MS Mike Schmidt Jsy/225 4.00 10.00
MU Bobby Murcer Bat/225 3.00 8.00
MW Maury Wills Bat/225 3.00 8.00
NR Nolan Ryan Jkt/225 6.00 15.00
OS Ozzie Smith Jsy/225 4.00 10.00
PM Paul Molitor Bat/225 3.00 8.00
PN Phil Niekro Jsy/225 3.00 8.00
PN2 Phil Niekro Jsy/225 3.00 8.00
PR Phil Rizzuto Jsy/99 5.00 12.00
RC Rocky Colavito Bat/225 6.00 15.00
RE Red Schoendienst Jsy/99 5.00 12.00
RF Rollie Fingers Jsy/225 3.00 8.00
RJ Reggie Jackson Bat/225 4.00 10.00
RK Ralph Kiner Bat/225 4.00 10.00
RN Ron Santo Jsy/125 4.00 10.00
RN2 Ron Santo Jsy/125 4.00 10.00
RO Brooks Robinson Jsy/175 4.00 10.00
RR Robin Roberts Pants/225 4.00 10.00
RS Ryne Sandberg Jsy/225 4.00 10.00
RY Robin Yount Jsy/225 3.00 8.00
SC Steve Carlton Bat/225 3.00 8.00
SC2 Steve Carlton Bat/225 3.00 8.00
SG Steve Garvey Jsy/225 3.00 8.00
SK Bill Skowron Bat/225 3.00 8.00
SM Stan Musial Bat/225 6.00 15.00
SS Steve Sax Jsy/225 3.00 8.00
SU Don Sutton Jsy/225 3.00 8.00
TG Tony Gwynn Jsy/225 3.00 8.00
TO Tony Oliva Bat/225 3.00 8.00
TP Tony Perez Pants/225 3.00 8.00
TS Tom Seaver Jsy/225 3.00 8.00
WB Wade Boggs Jsy/225 3.00 8.00
WC Will Clark Jsy/225 3.00 8.00
WC2 Will Clark Jsy/99 3.00 8.00
WJ Wally Joyner Jsy/225 3.00 8.00
WM Willie McCovey Jsy/225 3.00 8.00
YB Yogi Berra Bat/225 6.00 15.00

2006 SP Legendary Cuts Legendary Signature Cuts

OVERALL CUT AU ODDS 1:96
PRINT RUNS B/WN 1-90 COPIES PER
NO PRICING ON QTY OF 25 OR LESS
AS Al Simmons/4
BD Bill Dickey/34 125.00 250.00
BG Burleigh Grimes/33 75.00 150.00
BL Bob Lemon/77 50.00 100.00
BR Babe Ruth/3
BW Bucky Walters/52 60.00 120.00
CA Roy Campanella/6
CB Chief Bender/1
CG Charlie Gehringer/76 50.00 100.00
CH Catfish Hunter/24
CM Mickey Cochrane/10
CO Eddie Collins/3
CR Charley Root/12
CS Casey Stengel/35 250.00 400.00
CY Cy Young/1
DC Dolph Camilli/58 60.00 120.00
DD Dizzy Dean/21
DL Leo Durocher/22
DR Don Drysdale/45 125.00 200.00
DU Joe Dugan/25
EA Earl Averill/50 60.00 120.00
EB Ed Barrow/35 150.00 250.00
EC Earle Combs/65 150.00 250.00
EH Elston Howard/7
EL Ed Lopat/32 100.00 175.00
EM Eddie Mathews/59 75.00 150.00
ER Edd Roush/90 50.00 100.00
EW Early Wynn/15
FF Ford Frick/7
GA Grover Alexander/1
GE Lou Gehrig/1
GH Gabby Hartnett/15
GS George Sisler/14
HD Hugh Duffy/2
HE Billy Herman/87 50.00 100.00
HG Hank Greenberg/60 175.00 300.00
HK Harvey Kuehn/89 60.00 120.00
HM Heinie Manush/22
HO Gil Hodges/3
HW Honus Wagner/1
JA Joe Adcock/47 75.00 150.00
JC Jocko Conlon/76 50.00 100.00
JD Joe DiMaggio/5
JE Johnny Evers/1
JF Jimmie Foxx/1
JJ Judy Johnson/40 75.00 150.00
JM Joe McCarthy/67 100.00 200.00
JO Joe Cronin/30 50.00 100.00
JR Jackie Robinson/5

JS Joe Sewell/83 50.00 100.00
KC Kiki Cuyler/6
KN Kid Nichols/2
LA Luke Appling/84 60.00 120.00
LB Lou Boudreau/86 50.00 100.00
LG Lefty Gomez/44 75.00 150.00
LO Ernie Lombardi/25
MA Mel Allen/67 125.00 200.00
MC Max Carey/79 75.00 150.00
ME Joe Medwick/82 100.00 175.00
MH Miller Huggins/1
MI Johnny Mize/90 60.00 120.00
MO Mel Ott/1
NF Nellie Fox/12
PR Pee Wee Reese/47 125.00 200.00
PT Pie Traynor/26 400.00 600.00
RA Richie Ashburn/22
RB Ray Boone/51 60.00 120.00
RC Roberto Clemente/3
RD Ray Dandridge/35 60.00 120.00
RF Red Faber/18
RH Rogers Hornsby/4
RM Rabbit Maranville/2
RO Roger Maris/13
RR Red Ruffing/72 125.00 200.00
SC Sam Crawford/8
SP Satchel Paige/7
SR Sam Rice/31 75.00 150.00
ST Stan Coveleski/81 60.00 120.00
TC Ty Cobb/1
TK Ted Kluszewski/19
TM Thurman Munson/2
TO Tony Lazzeri/1
TS Tris Speaker/1
TW Ted Williams/9
WA Walter Alston/27 100.00 175.00
WH Waite Hoyt/45 75.00 150.00
WI Hoyt Wilhelm/47 50.00 100.00
WJ Walter Johnson/1
WP Wally Post/66 60.00 120.00
WS Warren Spahn/52 75.00 150.00

2006 SP Legendary Cuts Legendary Dual Cuts

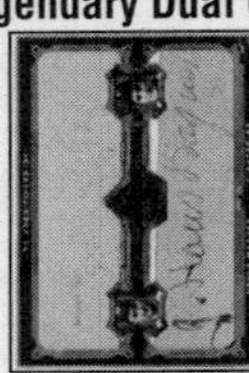

OVERALL CUT AU ODDS 1:96
STATED PRINT RUN 1 SERIAL #'d SET
NO PRICING DUE TO SCARCITY
BR Branch Rickey
Jackie Robinson
CD Bill Dickey
Mickey Cochrane
CH Elston Howard
Roy Campanella
CS Roberto Clemente
Willie Stargell
CW Honus Wagner
Ty Cobb
DJ Don Drysdale
Walter Johnson
DM Joe DiMaggio
Thurman Munson
GM Hank Greenberg
Johnny Mize
GO Lou Gehrig
Mel Ott
HR Gil Hodges
Pee Wee Reese
RF Jimmie Foxx
Babe Ruth
RR Jackie Robinson
Pee Wee Reese
SM Casey Stengel
Joe McCarthy
WM Hack Wilson
Roger Maris
WS Ted Williams
George Sisler
YH Carl Hubbell
Cy Young

2006 SP Legendary Cuts Legendary Quad Cuts

OVERALL CUT AU ODDS 1:96
STATED PRINT RUN 1 SERIAL #'d SET
NO PRICING DUE TO SCARCITY
CDHL Bill Dickey
Elston Howard
Ernie Lombardi
Mickey Cochrane
CWST Honus Wagner
Roberto Clemente
Willie Stargell
Pie Traynor
GFSG Jimmie Foxx
Lou Gehrig
Hank Greenberg
George Sisler
PRCD Ray Dandridge
Jackie Robinson
Satchel Paige
Roy Campanella
RDMM Babe Ruth
Joe DiMaggio
Roger Maris
Thurman Munson
RRHD Gil Hodges
Leo Durocher
Jackie Robinson
Pee Wee Reese
WCOS Al Simmons
Ted Williams
Ty Cobb
Mel Ott
YJDS Don Drysdale
Walter Johnson
Cy Young
Warren Spahn

2006 SP Legendary Cuts Memorable Moments Autographs

OVERALL AU STATED ODDS 1:192
PRINT RUNS B/WN 1-99 COPIES PER
NO PRICING ON QTY OF 25 OR LESS
AD Andre Dawson/99 6.00 15.00
BF Bob Feller/25
BJ Bo Jackson/25
BL Barry Larkin/50 20.00 50.00
BM Bobby Murcer/50
BS Bruce Sutter/50
CC Cesar Cedeno/99 6.00 15.00
CE Cecil Cooper/99 5.00 12.00
CF Carlton Fisk/25
DC David Cone/99 6.00 15.00
DE Dwight Evans/25
DM Don Mattingly/50 60.00 120.00
DP Dave Parker/25
DS Don Sutton/26
GF George Foster/25
GG Goose Gossage/10
GP Gaylord Perry/99 6.00 15.00
JB Johnny Bench/10
JK John Kruk/99 6.00 15.00
KG Kirk Gibson/25
MA Juan Marichal/25
MO Joe Morgan/20
MS Mike Schmidt/15
OS Ozzie Smith/25
PO Paul O'Neill/1
PR Phil Rizzuto/99 15.00 40.00
RC Rocky Colavito/25
RF Rollie Fingers/47 8.00 20.00
RG Ron Guidry/25
RJ Reggie Jackson/15
RS Ron Santo/25
RY Robin Yount/25
SG Steve Garvey/25
SM Stan Musial/30
SS Steve Sax/20
TG Tony Gwynn/25
TR Tim Raines/50 20.00 50.00
TS Tom Seaver/44 30.00 60.00

2006 SP Legendary Cuts Memorable Moments Materials

OVERALL #'d GU ODDS 1:12
PRINT RUNS B/WN 223-225 COPIES PER
AD Andre Dawson Pants/225 3.00 8.00
BF Bob Feller Pants/225 4.00 10.00
BJ Bo Jackson Bat/225 4.00 10.00
BL Barry Larkin Pants/225 4.00 10.00
BM Bobby Murcer Pants/225 3.00 8.00
BS Bruce Sutter Pants/225 3.00 8.00
CC Cesar Cedeno Pants/225 3.00 8.00
CE Cecil Cooper Jsy/225 3.00 8.00
CF Carlton Fisk Pants/225 3.00 8.00
DC David Cone Jsy/225 3.00 8.00
DE Dwight Evans Jsy/225 3.00 8.00
DM Don Mattingly Pants/225 4.00 10.00
DP Dave Parker Jsy/225 3.00 8.00
DS Don Sutton Jsy/225 3.00 8.00
EM Eddie Mathews Pants/225 6.00 15.00
GF George Foster Bat/225 3.00 8.00
GG Goose Gossage Jsy/225 3.00 8.00
GP Gaylord Perry Bat/225 3.00 8.00
JB Johnny Bench Jsy/225 4.00 10.00
JK John Kruk Bat/225 3.00 8.00
JM Johnny Mize Pants/225 4.00 10.00
KG Kirk Gibson Jsy/225 3.00 8.00
MA Juan Marichal Jsy/225 3.00 8.00
MO Joe Morgan Jsy/225 3.00 8.00
MS Mike Schmidt Jsy/225 4.00 10.00
MU Eddie Murray Jsy/225 3.00 8.00
OS Ozzie Smith Jsy/225 4.00 10.00
PO Paul O'Neill Jsy/225 3.00 8.00
PR Phil Rizzuto Jsy/225 4.00 10.00
RC Rocky Colavito Bat/225 6.00 15.00
RF Rollie Fingers Jsy/225 3.00 8.00
RG Ron Guidry Jsy/223 3.00 8.00
RJ Reggie Jackson Jsy/225 4.00 10.00
RS Ron Santo Bat/225 4.00 10.00
RY Robin Yount Jsy/225 3.00 8.00
SG Steve Garvey Jsy/225 3.00 8.00
SM Stan Musial Bat/225 6.00 15.00
SS Steve Sax Jsy/223 3.00 8.00
TG Tony Gwynn Pants/225 3.00 8.00
TR Tim Raines Jsy/225 3.00 8.00
TS Tom Seaver Jsy/225 3.00 8.00

2006 SP Legendary Cuts Place in History Autographs

OVERALL AU STATED ODDS 1:192
PRINT RUNS B/WN 6-99 COPIES PER
NO PRICING ON QTY OF 25 OR LESS
AD Andre Dawson/99 6.00 15.00
AK Al Kaline/24
AR Al Rosen/99 6.00 15.00
BD Bucky Dent/99 6.00 15.00
BF Bob Feller/35 15.00 40.00
BG Bob Gibson/25
BL Barry Larkin/49 20.00 50.00
BM Bill Mazeroski/99 15.00 40.00
BO Bo Jackson/99 20.00 50.00
BP Boog Powell/99 6.00 15.00
BR Brooks Robinson/35 15.00 40.00
BR2 Brooks Robinson/35 15.00 40.00
BS Bruce Sutter/99 6.00 15.00
BW Billy Williams/99 6.00 15.00
CA Rod Carew/50
CC Cecil Cooper/99 5.00 12.00
CF Carlton Fisk/99 10.00 25.00
CR Cal Ripken/35 100.00 175.00
CY Carl Yastrzemski/45 20.00 50.00
DE Dennis Eckersley/99 6.00 15.00
DE2 Dennis Eckersley/99 6.00 15.00
DL Don Larsen/20
DP Dave Parker/20
DW Dave Winfield/12
EB Ernie Banks/25
EV Dwight Evans/99 10.00 25.00
FH Frank Howard/99 10.00 25.00
FJ Fergie Jenkins/99 6.00 15.00
FL Fred Lynn/99 6.00 15.00
FR Frank Robinson Reds/45 15.00 40.00
FR2 Frank Robinson O's/45 15.00 40.00
GF George Foster/56 6.00 15.00
GG Goose Gossage/25
GN Graig Nettles/99 6.00 15.00
GP Gaylord Perry Rgr/99 6.00 15.00
GP2 Gaylord Perry Giants/99 6.00 15.00
GU Ron Guidry/17
HB Harold Baines/45 8.00 20.00
JB Johnny Bench/42 30.00 60.00
JC Jose Canseco/99 20.00 50.00
JM Jack Morris/82 6.00 15.00
JO Joe Morgan/50 12.50 30.00
JP Jim Palmer/99 10.00 25.00
JR Jim Rice/75 10.00 25.00
JT Joe Torre/99 15.00 40.00
JU Juan Marichal/29 10.00 25.00
JY Johnny Podres/38 12.50 30.00
KG Ken Griffey Sr./99 6.00 15.00
KI Kirk Gibson/25
KP Kirby Puckett/99 40.00 80.00
LA Luis Aparicio/99 10.00 25.00
LA2 Luis Aparicio/99 10.00 25.00
LB Lou Brock/99 10.00 25.00
LB2 Lou Brock/99 10.00 25.00
LP Lou Piniella/99 10.00 25.00
MA Don Mattingly/50 60.00 120.00
MC Denny McLain/31 10.00 25.00
MG Mark Grace/99 10.00 25.00
MS Mike Schmidt/25
MU Bobby Murcer/6
MW Maury Wills/96 6.00 15.00
NR Nolan Ryan/21
OS Ozzie Smith/99 30.00 60.00
PM Paul Molitor/99 10.00 25.00
PN Phil Niekro/52 8.00 20.00
PN2 Phil Niekro/52 8.00 20.00
PR Phil Rizzuto/99 15.00 40.00
RD Red Schoendienst/99 15.00 40.00
RF Rollie Fingers/23
RJ Reggie Jackson/25
RK Ralph Kiner/99 15.00 40.00
RO Ron Santo/99 20.00 50.00
RO2 Ron Santo/99 20.00 50.00
RR Robin Roberts/55 12.50 30.00
RS Ryne Sandberg/25
RY Robin Yount/99 15.00 40.00
SC Steve Carlton/99 10.00 25.00
SC2 Steve Carlton/99 10.00 25.00
SG Steve Garvey/99 10.00 25.00
SM Stan Musial/45 30.00 60.00
SS Steve Sax/99 5.00 12.00
SU Don Sutton/24
TG Tony Gwynn/26 40.00 80.00
TO Tony Oliva/99 6.00 15.00
TO2 Tony Oliva/99 6.00 15.00
TP Tony Perez/24
TR Tim Raines/97 10.00 25.00
TS Tom Seaver/55 30.00 60.00
WB Wade Boggs/50 20.00 50.00
WC Will Clark/92 10.00 25.00
WC2 Will Clark/92 10.00 25.00
WF Whitey Ford/35 30.00 60.00
WJ Wally Joyner/99 10.00 25.00
WM Willie McCovey/25
YB Yogi Berra/25

2006 SP Legendary Cuts When It Was A Game Silver

STATED PRINT RUN 550 SERIAL #'d SETS
*GOLD: .6X TO 1.5X BASIC
GOLD PRINT RUN 99 SERIAL #'d SETS
OVERALL WIWAG ODDS 1:12

AD Andre Dawson 1.25 3.00
AK Al Kaline 2.00 5.00
AR Al Rosen 1.25 3.00
BF Bob Feller 2.00 5.00
BG Bob Gibson 2.00 5.00
BM Bill Mazeroski 2.00 5.00
BR Babe Ruth 4.00 10.00
BS Bruce Sutter 1.25 3.00
BW Billy Williams 1.25 3.00
CA Rod Carew 2.00 5.00
CF Carlton Fisk 2.00 5.00
CO Rocky Colavito 2.00 5.00
CR Cal Ripken 6.00 15.00
CY Cy Young 2.00 5.00
DD Don Drysdale 2.00 5.00
DE Dennis Eckersley 1.25 3.00
DL Don Larsen 1.25 3.00
DP Dave Parker 1.25 3.00
DY Denny McLain 1.25 3.00
EB Ernie Banks 2.00 5.00
ED Eddie Murray 2.00 5.00
EM Eddie Mathews 2.00 5.00
EV Dwight Evans 1.25 3.00
FH Frank Howard 1.25 3.00
FJ Fergie Jenkins 1.25 3.00
FL Fred Lynn 1.25 3.00
FR Frank Robinson Reds 1.25 3.00
FR2 Frank Robinson O's 1.25 3.00
GG Goose Gossage 1.25 3.00
GN Graig Nettles 1.25 3.00
GP Gaylord Perry 1.25 3.00
GS George Sisler 1.25 3.00
GU Ron Guidry 1.25 3.00
HB Harold Baines 1.25 3.00
HG Hank Greenberg 2.00 5.00
HO Rogers Hornsby 2.00 5.00
HW Honus Wagner 2.00 5.00
JB Johnny Bench 2.00 5.00
JD Joe DiMaggio 3.00 8.00
JF Jimmie Foxx 2.00 5.00
JK John Kruk 1.25 3.00
JM Jack Morris 1.25 3.00
JO Joe Morgan 1.25 3.00
JP Jim Palmer 1.25 3.00
JR Jackie Robinson 2.00 5.00
JT Joe Torre 1.25 3.00
JU Juan Marichal 1.25 3.00
KG Ken Griffey Sr. 1.25 3.00
KI Kirk Gibson 1.25 3.00
KP Kirby Puckett 2.00 5.00
LA Luis Aparicio 1.25 3.00
LB Lou Brock 2.00 5.00
LG Lou Gehrig 3.00 8.00
LP Lou Piniella 1.25 3.00
MA Don Mattingly 3.00 8.00
MC Mickey Cochrane 1.25 3.00
MO Mel Ott 2.00 5.00
MS Mike Schmidt 3.00 8.00
MU Bobby Murcer 2.00 5.00
MW Maury Wills 1.25 3.00
MZ Johnny Mize 1.25 3.00
NR Nolan Ryan 3.00 8.00
OS Ozzie Smith 2.00 5.00
PM Paul Molitor 2.00 5.00
PN Phil Niekro 1.25 3.00
PR Phil Rizzuto 2.00 5.00
PS Johnny Podres 1.25 3.00
RC Roberto Clemente 4.00 10.00
RF Rollie Fingers 1.25 3.00
RI Jim Rice 1.25 3.00
RJ Reggie Jackson 2.00 5.00
RK Ralph Kiner 2.00 5.00
RN Ron Santo 2.00 5.00
RO Brooks Robinson 2.00 5.00
RO2 Brooks Robinson 2.00 5.00
RR Robin Roberts 1.25 3.00
RS Red Schoendienst 1.25 3.00
RY Robin Yount 2.00 5.00
SA Ryne Sandberg 3.00 8.00
SC Steve Carlton 1.25 3.00
SC2 Steve Carlton 1.25 3.00
SG Steve Garvey 1.25 3.00
SK Bill Skowron 1.25 3.00
SM Stan Musial 2.00 5.00
SP Satchel Paige 2.00 5.00
SU Don Sutton 1.25 3.00
TG Tony Gwynn 2.00 5.00
TM Thurman Munson 2.00 5.00
TO Tony Oliva 1.25 3.00
TO2 Tony Oliva 1.25 3.00
TP Tony Perez 1.25 3.00
TR Tim Raines 1.25 3.00
TS Tom Seaver 2.00 5.00
WB Wade Boggs 2.00 5.00
WC Will Clark 1.25 3.00
WF Whitey Ford 2.00 5.00
WJ Wally Joyner 1.25 3.00
WM Willie McCovey 2.00 5.00
YB Yogi Berra 2.00 5.00
YZ Carl Yastrzemski 2.00 5.00

2006 SP Legendary Cuts When It Was A Game Materials

OVERALL #'d GU ODDS 1:12
PRINT RUNS B/WN 5-75 COPIES PER
NO PRICING ON QTY OF 25 OR LESS
AD Andre Dawson Pants/75 4.00 10.00
AK Al Kaline Pants/25
AR Al Rosen Pants/75 4.00 10.00
BF Bob Feller Pants/75 5.00 12.00
BG Bob Gibson Jsy/75 4.00 10.00
BM Bill Mazeroski Jsy/75 5.00 12.00
BR Babe Ruth Pants/25
BS Bruce Sutter Pants/75 4.00 10.00
BW Billy Williams Jsy/75 4.00 10.00
CA Rod Carew Jsy/75 4.00 10.00
CF Carlton Fisk Pants/75 4.00 10.00
CO Rocky Colavito Jsy/75 8.00 20.00
CR Cal Ripken Pants/75 8.00 20.00
DD Don Drysdale Pants/75 10.00 25.00
DE Dennis Eckersley Jsy/75 4.00 10.00
DL Don Larsen Pants/75 4.00 10.00
DP Dave Parker Jsy/75 4.00 10.00
EB Ernie Banks Jsy/75 5.00 12.00
ED Eddie Murray Jsy/75 4.00 10.00
EM Eddie Mathews Pants/75 8.00 20.00
EV Dwight Evans Jsy/25
FH Frank Howard Jsy/25
FJ Fergie Jenkins Jsy/75 4.00 10.00
FL Fred Lynn Jsy/75 4.00 10.00
FR Frank Robinson Reds Bat/75 4.00 10.00
FR2 Frank Robinson O's Bat/75 4.00 10.00
GG Goose Gossage Jsy/25
GN Graig Nettles Jsy/75 4.00 10.00
GP Gaylord Perry Bat/75 4.00 10.00
GS George Sisler Bat/75 10.00 25.00
GU Ron Guidry Jsy/75 4.00 10.00
HB Harold Baines Jsy/25
HG Hank Greenberg Bat/75 15.00 40.00
HO Rogers Hornsby Bat/75 15.00 40.00
JB Johnny Bench Jsy/75 5.00 12.00
JD Joe DiMaggio Jsy/75 40.00 80.00
JF Jimmie Foxx Bat/75 15.00 40.00
JK John Kruk Bat/75 4.00 10.00
JM Jack Morris Jsy/25
JO Joe Morgan Jsy/75 4.00 10.00
JP Jim Palmer Jsy/75 4.00 10.00
JR Jackie Robinson Jsy/75 20.00 50.00
JT Joe Torre Bat/75 5.00 12.00
JU Juan Marichal Jsy/75 5.00 12.00
KG Ken Griffey Sr. Jsy/75 4.00 10.00
KI Kirk Gibson Jsy/75 4.00 10.00
KP Kirby Puckett Jsy/75 5.00 12.00
LA Luis Aparicio Jsy/25
LB Lou Brock Jsy/25
LG Lou Gehrig Bat/75 75.00 150.00
LP Lou Piniella Jsy 4.00 10.00
MA Don Mattingly Pants/75 5.00 12.00
MC Mickey Cochrane Bat/25
MO Mel Ott Jsy/75 15.00 40.00
MS Mike Schmidt Jsy/75 5.00 12.00
MU Bobby Murcer Pants/75 4.00 10.00
MW Maury Wills Jsy/75 4.00 10.00
MZ Johnny Mize Pants/75 5.00 12.00
NR Nolan Ryan Jsy/25
OS Ozzie Smith Jkt-Jsy/75 5.00 12.00
PM Paul Molitor Bat/75 4.00 10.00
PN Phil Niekro Jsy/75 4.00 10.00
PR Phil Rizzuto Jsy/25
RC Roberto Clemente Jsy/75 40.00 80.00
RF Rollie Fingers Pants/75 4.00 10.00
RI Jim Rice Jsy-Pants/75 4.00 10.00
RJ Reggie Jackson Jsy/25
RK Ralph Kiner Bat/75 5.00 12.00
RN Ron Santo Jsy/75 5.00 12.00
RO Brooks Robinson Pants/25
RO2 Brooks Robinson Pants/25
RR Robin Roberts Pants/75 5.00 12.00
RS Red Schoendienst Jsy/75 5.00 12.00
RY Robin Yount Jsy/75 4.00 10.00
SA Ryne Sandberg Jsy/25
SC Steve Carlton Pants/75 4.00 10.00
SC2 Steve Carlton Pants/75 4.00 10.00
SG Steve Garvey Jsy/75 4.00 10.00
SK Bill Skowron Bat/75 4.00 10.00
SM Stan Musial Bat/75 8.00 20.00
SP Satchel Paige Pants/5
SU Don Sutton Jsy/75 4.00 10.00
TG Tony Gwynn Jsy/75 4.00 10.00
TM Thurman Munson Pants/75 10.00 25.00
TO Tony Oliva Jsy/75 4.00 10.00
TO2 Tony Oliva Jsy/75 4.00 10.00
TP Tony Perez Pants/75 4.00 10.00
TR Tim Raines Jsy/75 4.00 10.00
TS Tom Seaver Jsy/75 4.00 10.00
WB Wade Boggs Jsy/75 4.00 10.00
WC Will Clark Jsy/75 4.00 10.00
WJ Wally Joyner Jsy/75 4.00 10.00
WM Willie McCovey Jsy/75 4.00 10.00
YB Yogi Berra Pants/75 8.00 20.00
YZ Carl Yastrzemski Jsy-Pants/75 5.00 12.00

2006 SP Legendary Cuts When It Was A Game Cuts

OVERALL CUT AU ODDS 1:96
PRINT RUNS B/WN 2-99 COPIES PER
NO PRICING ON QTY OF 25 OR LESS
AC Al Campanis/30 150.00 250.00
BD Bill Dickey/24
BG Burleigh Grimes/56 50.00 100.00
BL Bob Lemon/79 50.00 100.00
CG Charlie Gehringer/64 30.00 60.00
CH Carl Hubbell/80 75.00 150.00
CR Joe Cronin/34 75.00 150.00
DC Dolph Camilli/2
DD Dizzy Dean/4
DR Don Drysdale/6
DU Leo Durocher/25
EA Earl Averill/67 50.00 100.00
EB Earl Battey/25
EF Elmer Flick/25
EL Ernie Lombardi/24
EM Eddie Mathews/33 100.00 175.00
ER Edd Roush/98 50.00 100.00
ES Enos Slaughter/8
EW Early Wynn/40 60.00 120.00
FF Ford Frick/30 100.00 175.00
FL Freddie Lindstrom/25
GH Gabby Hartnett/6
GP George Pipgras/25
GS George Sisler/37 300.00 500.00
HA Chick Hafey/12
HC Happy Chandler/64 50.00 100.00
HE Billy Herman/99 50.00 100.00
HG Hank Greenberg/21
HM Heinie Manush/29 125.00 250.00
HO Gil Hodges/5
HU Catfish Hunter/34 75.00 150.00
HW Hoyt Wilhelm/56 50.00 100.00
JA Joe Adcock/18
JC Jocko Conlon/73 50.00 100.00
JD Joe Dugan/30 125.00 200.00
JH Johnny Hodapp/17
JJ Judy Johnson/20
JM Joe McCarthy/51 125.00 250.00
JS Joe Sewell/78 50.00 100.00
JV Johnny Vander Meer/45 75.00 150.00
LA Luke Appling/83 60.00 120.00
LB Lou Boudreau/50 60.00 120.00
LG Lefty Gomez/36 100.00 200.00
LO Ed Lopat/28 100.00 175.00
MC Max Carey/71 75.00 150.00
ME Joe Medwick/57 125.00 200.00
MI Johnny Mize/70 60.00 120.00
PR Pee Wee Reese/52 125.00 200.00
RA Richie Ashburn/12
RB Ray Boone/68 60.00 120.00
RD Ray Dandridge/75 50.00 100.00
RF Rick Ferrell/25
RR Red Ruffing/44 150.00 250.00
SC Stan Coveleski/91 60.00 120.00
SE George Selkirk/30 125.00 200.00
SM Sal Maglie/68 60.00 120.00
SR Sam Rice/33 100.00 200.00
ST Willie Stargell/27 100.00 200.00
TA Tommie Agee/12
TK Ted Kluszewski/50 100.00 175.00
VK Vern Kennedy/58 60.00 120.00
VW Vic Wertz/30 125.00 200.00
WA Walter Alston/16
WH Waite Hoyt/70 60.00 120.00
WP Wally Post/66 60.00 120.00
WS Warren Spahn/78 60.00 120.00
ZV Zoilo Versalles/5

2007 SP Legendary Cuts

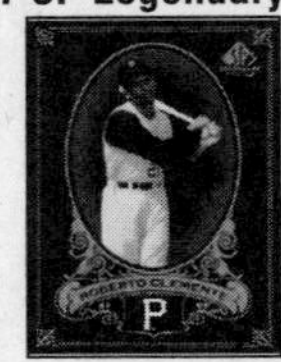

This 200-card set was released in September, 2007. The set was issued in four-card packs, with an $10 SRP, which came 12 packs per box and 16 boxes per case. While all cards in this set feature veterans, cards numbered 101-200 are a league leader subset and those cards were issued to a stated print run of 550 serial numbered sets.

COMP.SET w/o SP's (100) 10.00 25.00
COMMON CARD (1-100) .25 .60
COMMON CARD (101-200) 2.00 5.00
101-200 RANDOMLY INSERTED
101-200 PRINT RUN 550 SERIAL #'d SETS
1 Phil Niekro .25 .60
2 Brooks Robinson .40 1.00
3 Frank Robinson .25 .60
4 Jim Palmer .25 .60
5 Cal Ripken Jr. 2.50 6.00
6 Warren Spahn .40 1.00
7 Cy Young .60 1.50
8 Carl Yastrzemski 1.00 2.50
9 Wade Boggs .40 1.00
10 Carlton Fisk .40 1.00
11 Joe Cronin .25 .60
12 Bobby Doerr .25 .60
13 Roy Campanella .60 1.50
14 Pee Wee Reese .40 1.00
15 Rod Carew .40 1.00
16 Ernie Banks .60 1.50
17 Fergie Jenkins .25 .60
18 Billy Williams .25 .60
19 Gabby Hartnett .25 .60
20 Luis Aparicio .25 .60
21 Nellie Fox .40 1.00
22 Luke Appling .25 .60
23 Joe Morgan .25 .60
24 Johnny Bench .60 1.50
25 Tony Perez .25 .60
26 George Foster .25 .60
27 Johnny Vander Meer .25 .60
28 Bob Feller .25 .60
29 Bob Lemon .25 .60
30 Lou Boudreau .25 .60
31 Early Wynn .25 .60
32 Charlie Gehringer .25 .60
33 George Kell .25 .60
34 Hal Newhouser .25 .60
35 Al Kaline .60 1.50
36 Ted Kluszewski .40 1.00
37 Harvey Kuenn .25 .60
38 Maury Wills .25 .60
39 Don Drysdale .40 1.00
40 Don Sutton .25 .60
41 Eddie Mathews .60 1.50
42 Joe Adcock .25 .60
43 Paul Molitor .25 .60
44 Kirby Puckett .60 1.50
45 Harmon Killebrew .60 1.50
46 Monte Irvin .25 .60
47 Ralph Kiner .40 1.00

48 Christy Mathewson .60 1.50
49 Hoyt Wilhelm .25 .60
50 Tom Seaver .40 1.00
51 Allie Reynolds .25 .60
52 Joe DiMaggio 1.25 3.00
53 Lou Gehrig 1.25 3.00
54 Babe Ruth 1.50 4.00
55 Casey Stengel .25 .60
56 Phil Rizzuto .40 1.00
57 Thurman Munson .60 1.50
58 Johnny Mize .25 .60
59 Yogi Berra .60 1.50
60 Rube Marquard .25 .60
61 Don Mattingly 1.25 3.00
62 Ray Dandridge .25 .60
63 Rollie Fingers .25 .60
64 Roberto Clemente 2.00 5.00
65 Reggie Jackson .40 1.00
66 Dennis Eckersley .25 .60
67 Robin Yount .60 1.50
68 Jimmie Foxx .60 1.50
69 Lefty Grove .25 .60
70 Richie Ashburn .40 1.00
71 Jim Bunning .25 .60
72 Steve Carlton .25 .60
73 Robin Roberts .25 .60
74 Mike Schmidt 1.00 2.50
75 Willie Stargell .40 1.00
76 Ozzie Smith 1.00 2.50
77 Bill Mazeroski .40 1.00
78 Honus Wagner .60 1.50
79 Pie Traynor .25 .60
80 Tony Gwynn .60 1.50
81 Willie McCovey .40 1.00
82 Gaylord Perry .25 .60
83 Juan Marichal .25 .60
84 Orlando Cepeda .25 .60
85 Satchel Paige .60 1.50
86 George Sisler .25 .60
87 Ken Boyer .25 .60
88 Joe Medwick .25 .60
89 Travis Jackson .25 .60
90 Stan Musial 1.00 2.50
91 Dizzy Dean .40 1.00
92 Bob Gibson .40 1.00
93 Red Schoendienst .25 .60
94 Lou Brock .40 1.00
95 Enos Slaughter .25 .60
96 Nolan Ryan 1.50 4.00
97 Smokey Burgess .25 .60
98 Mickey Vernon .25 .60
99 Vern Stephens .25 .60
100 Rick Ferrell .25 .60
101 Phil Niekro LL 2.00 5.00
102 Brooks Robinson LL 3.00 8.00
103 Frank Robinson LL 2.00 5.00
104 Jim Palmer LL 2.00 5.00
105 Cal Ripken Jr. LL 5.00 12.00
106 Warren Spahn LL 3.00 8.00
107 Cy Young LL 3.00 8.00
108 Nellie Fox LL 3.00 8.00
109 Carl Yastrzemski LL 3.00 8.00
110 Joe Sewell LL 2.00 5.00
111 Wade Boggs LL 3.00 8.00
112 Carlton Fisk LL 3.00 8.00
113 Jackie Robinson LL 3.00 8.00
114 Roy Campanella LL 3.00 8.00
115 Pee Wee Reese LL 3.00 8.00
116 Earl Averill LL 2.00 5.00
117 Rod Carew LL 3.00 8.00
118 Ernie Banks LL 3.00 8.00
119 Fergie Jenkins LL 2.00 5.00
120 Billy Williams LL 2.00 5.00
121 Al Lopez LL 2.00 5.00
122 Luis Aparicio LL 2.00 5.00
123 Luke Appling LL 2.00 5.00
124 Joe Morgan LL 2.00 5.00
125 Johnny Bench LL 3.00 8.00
126 Tony Perez LL 2.00 5.00
127 George Foster LL 2.00 5.00
128 Bob Feller LL 2.00 5.00
129 Bob Lemon LL 2.00 5.00
130 Larry Doby LL 2.00 5.00
131 Lou Boudreau LL 2.00 5.00
132 George Kell LL 2.00 5.00
133 Hal Newhouser LL 2.00 5.00
134 Al Kaline LL 3.00 8.00
135 Ty Cobb LL 4.00 10.00
136 Charlie Keller LL 2.00 5.00
137 Buck Leonard LL 2.00 5.00
138 Maury Wills LL 2.00 5.00
139 Don Drysdale LL 3.00 8.00
140 Don Sutton LL 2.00 5.00
141 Eddie Mathews LL 3.00 8.00
142 Paul Molitor LL 2.00 5.00
143 Kirby Puckett LL 4.00 10.00
144 Harmon Killebrew LL 3.00 8.00
145 Monte Irvin LL 2.00 5.00
146 Mel Ott LL 2.00 5.00
147 Charlie Gehringer LL 2.00 5.00
148 Hoyt Wilhelm LL 2.00 5.00
149 Tom Seaver LL 3.00 8.00
150 Ted Kluszewski LL 3.00 8.00
151 Joe DiMaggio LL 4.00 10.00
152 Lou Gehrig LL 4.00 10.00
153 Babe Ruth LL 5.00 12.00
154 Casey Stengel LL 2.00 5.00
155 Phil Rizzuto LL 3.00 8.00
156 Thurman Munson LL 3.00 8.00
157 Johnny Mize LL 2.00 5.00
158 Yogi Berra LL 3.00 8.00
159 Roger Maris LL 3.00 8.00
160 Early Wynn LL 2.00 5.00
161 Bobby Doerr LL 2.00 5.00
162 Joe Cronin LL 2.00 5.00
163 Don Mattingly LL 4.00 10.00
164 Ray Dandridge LL 2.00 5.00
165 Rollie Fingers LL 2.00 5.00
166 Christy Mathewson LL 3.00 8.00
167 Reggie Jackson LL 3.00 8.00
168 Dennis Eckersley LL 2.00 5.00
169 Mickey Cochrane LL 2.00 5.00
170 Jimmie Foxx LL 3.00 8.00
171 Lefty Gomez LL 2.00 5.00
172 Jim Bunning LL 2.00 5.00
173 Steve Carlton LL 2.00 5.00
174 Robin Roberts LL 2.00 5.00
175 Richie Ashburn LL 3.00 8.00
176 Mike Schmidt LL 3.00 8.00
177 Ralph Kiner LL 3.00 8.00
178 Willie Stargell LL 3.00 8.00
179 Roberto Clemente LL 6.00 15.00
180 Bill Mazeroski LL 3.00 8.00
181 Honus Wagner LL 3.00 8.00
182 Pie Traynor LL 2.00 5.00
183 Tony Gwynn LL 3.00 8.00
184 Willie McCovey LL 3.00 8.00
185 Gaylord Perry LL 2.00 5.00
186 Juan Marichal LL 2.00 5.00
187 Orlando Cepeda LL 2.00 5.00
188 Satchel Paige LL 3.00 8.00
189 George Sisler LL 2.00 5.00
190 Rogers Hornsby LL 3.00 8.00
191 Stan Musial LL 3.00 8.00
192 Dizzy Dean LL 3.00 8.00
193 Bob Gibson LL 3.00 8.00
194 Red Schoendienst LL 2.00 5.00
195 Lou Brock LL 3.00 8.00
196 Enos Slaughter LL 2.00 5.00
197 Nolan Ryan LL 5.00 12.00
198 Mickey Vernon LL 2.00 5.00
199 Walter Johnson LL 3.00 8.00
200 Rick Ferrell LL 2.00 5.00

2007 SP Legendary Cuts A Stitch in Time Memorabilia

OVERALL AU-GU ODDS 1:12
BG Bob Gibson 3.00 8.00
BR Brooks Robinson 4.00 10.00
BW Billy Williams 3.00 8.00
CR Cal Ripken Jr. 6.00 15.00
DE Dwight Evans 3.00 8.00
DM Don Mattingly 4.00 10.00
EM Eddie Murray 3.00 8.00
GP Gaylord Perry 3.00 8.00
HK Harmon Killebrew 4.00 10.00
JB Johnny Bench 4.00 10.00
JR Jim Rice 3.00 8.00
KP Kirby Puckett 6.00 15.00
MS Mike Schmidt 5.00 12.00
PM Paul Molitor 3.00 8.00
RC Rod Carew 3.00 8.00
RJ Reggie Jackson 4.00 10.00
TG Tony Gwynn 4.00 10.00

2007 SP Legendary Cuts Enshrinement Cuts

OVERALL CUT ODDS 1:96
PRINT RUNS B/WN 1-86 COPIES PER
NO PRICING ON QTY 25 OR LESS
AB Al Barlick/44 50.00 100.00
BD Bill Dickey/5
BL Bob Lemon/53 30.00 60.00
BR Babe Ruth/1
CG Charlie Gehringer/65 40.00 80.00
CH Carl Hubbell/31 100.00 200.00
EA Earl Averill/6
EC Earle Combs/27 200.00 250.00
ER Edd Roush/65 30.00 60.00
EW Early Wynn/15
FF Frankie Frisch/2
GH Gabby Hartnett/31 90.00 150.00
HM Heinie Manush/10
HN Hal Newhouser/40 30.00 60.00
HU Catfish Hunter/17
HW Honus Wagner/1
JC Joe Cronin/86 40.00 80.00
JD Joe DiMaggio/19
JF Jimmie Foxx/1
LA Luke Appling/45 30.00 60.00
LB Lou Boudreau/30 30.00 60.00
MO Mel Ott/4
RH Rogers Hornsby/1
ST Willie Stargell/15
TC Ty Cobb/1
WH Waite Hoyt/33 50.00 100.00
WS Warren Spahn/35 60.00 120.00

2007 SP Legendary Cuts Historical Cuts

OVERALL CUT ODDS 1:96
STATED PRINT RUN 1 SER.#'d SET
NO PRICING DUE TO SCARCITY
AD Abner Doubleday
BR Babe Ruth
CL Charles Lindbergh

2007 SP Legendary Cuts Inside the Numbers Cuts

OVERALL CUT ODDS 1:96
PRINT RUNS B/WN 4-119 COPIES PER
NO PRICING ON QTY 25 OR LESS
BD Bill Dickey/28 60.00 120.00
BH Babe Herman/99 40.00 80.00
BL Bob Lemon/75 30.00 60.00
CG Charlie Gehringer/60 40.00 80.00
CH Carl Hubbell/70 50.00 100.00
CK Charlie Keller/38 50.00 100.00
EA Earl Averill/57 30.00 60.00
EL Ernie Lombardi/38 175.00 250.00

EM Eddie Mathews/70 60.00 120.00
ES Enos Slaughter/69 30.00 60.00
EW Early Wynn/34 40.00 80.00
FS Fred Snodgrass/75 75.00 150.00
GH Gabby Hartnett/25
GR Lefty Grove/73 150.00 200.00
HG Hank Greenberg/25
JC Joe Cronin/29 60.00 120.00
JM Joe Medwick/119 60.00 120.00
JV Johnny Vander Meer/39 60.00 120.00
LA Luke Appling/59
LB Lou Boudreau/13
LG Lefty Gomez/75 75.00 150.00
MC Max Carey/8
RA Richie Ashburn/4
RD Ray Dandridge/5
RH Rogers Hornsby/6
RM Rube Marquard/33 75.00 150.00
SC Stan Coveleski/72 50.00 100.00
ST Willie Stargell/6
VK Vern Kennedy/45
VS Vern Stephens/10
WH Waite Hoyt/65 40.00 80.00
WI Hoyt Wilhelm/55 40.00 80.00
WS Warren Spahn/55 50.00 100.00

2007 SP Legendary Cuts Legendary Americana

RANDOM INSERTS IN PACKS
STATED PRINT RUN 550 SER.#'d SETS
1 George Washington Carver 1.25 3.00
2 George Custer 1.25 3.00
3 Frederick Douglass 1.25 3.00
4 Crazy Horse UER 1.25 3.00
Photo is not Crazy Horse
5 William Cody 1.25 3.00
6 Abraham Lincoln 2.00 5.00
7 Thomas Edison 1.25 3.00
8 Andrew Carnegie 1.25 3.00
9 Eli Whitney 1.25 3.00
10 Harriet Tubman 1.25 3.00
11 Davy Crockett 1.25 3.00
12 Robert E. Lee 2.00 5.00
13 John D. Rockefeller 1.25 3.00
14 Billy the Kid 1.25 3.00
15 Ulysses S. Grant 2.00 5.00
16 Doc Holliday 1.25 3.00
17 Annie Oakley 1.25 3.00
18 Kit Carson 1.25 3.00
19 Francis Scott Key 1.25 3.00
20 Franklin Delano Roosevelt 1.25 3.00
21 Mark Twain 1.25 3.00
22 Thomas Paine 1.25 3.00
23 Walt Whitman 1.25 3.00
24 Alexander Graham Bell 1.25 3.00
25 Susan B. Anthony 1.25 3.00
26 Harriet Beecher Stowe 1.25 3.00
27 Eleanor Roosevelt 1.25 3.00
28 John F. Kennedy 2.00 5.00
29 P.T. Barnum 1.25 3.00
30 Frank Lloyd Wright 1.25 3.00
31 Wilbur Wright 1.25 3.00
32 Casey Jones 1.25 3.00
33 Theodore Roosevelt 1.25 3.00
34 Henry Ford 1.25 3.00
35 Dwight D. Eisenhower 1.25 3.00
36 Daniel Boone 1.25 3.00
37 Florence Nightingale 1.25 3.00
38 William Randolph Hearst 1.25 3.00
39 Charles Lindbergh 1.25 3.00
40 Wild Bill Hickok 1.25 3.00
41 William T. Sherman 2.00 5.00
42 Wyatt Earp 2.00 5.00
43 Jesse James 1.25 3.00
44 Boss Tweed 1.25 3.00
45 Daniel Webster 1.25 3.00
46 Joseph Pulitzer 1.25 3.00
47 Abner Doubleday 1.25 3.00
48 Harry Truman 1.25 3.00
49 Amelia Earhart 1.25 3.00
50 Eugene V. Debs 1.25 3.00
51 Bat Masterson 1.25 3.00
52 Will Rogers 1.25 3.00
53 Orville Wright 1.25 3.00
54 Johnny Appleseed 1.25 3.00
55 Jack London 1.25 3.00
56 Washington Irving 1.25 3.00
57 F. Scott Fitzgerald 1.25 3.00
58 Geronimo 4.00 10.00
59 Andrew Jackson 1.25 3.00
60 Zachary Taylor 1.25 3.00
61 George Eastman 1.25 3.00
62 Jefferson Davis 2.00 5.00
63 Sitting Bull 4.00 10.00
64 Clara Barton 1.25 3.00
65 Dorothea Dix 1.25 3.00
66 Booker T. Washington 1.25 3.00
67 Al Capone 4.00 10.00
68 Samuel F.B. Morse 1.25 3.00
69 Alexander Cartwright 1.25 3.00
70 John Marshall 1.25 3.00
71 William Seward 1.25 3.00
72 Andrew Johnson 1.25 3.00
73 Rutherford B. Hayes 1.25 3.00
74 James A. Garfield 1.25 3.00
75 Chester Arthur 1.25 3.00
76 Grover Cleveland 1.25 3.00
77 Benjamin Harrison 1.25 3.00
78 William McKinley 1.25 3.00
79 William H. Taft 1.25 3.00
80 Woodrow Wilson 1.25 3.00
81 Warren G. Harding 1.25 3.00
82 Calvin Coolidge 1.25 3.00
83 Herbert Hoover 1.25 3.00
84 Lyndon B. Johnson 1.25 3.00
85 Richard M. Nixon 1.25 3.00
86 Gerald Ford 1.25 3.00
87 Robert Johnson 1.25 3.00
88 Ronald Reagan 1.25 3.00
89 Chief Joseph 3.00 8.00
90 Butch Cassidy 2.00 5.00
91 Sundance Kid 2.00 5.00
92 Babe Ruth 5.00 12.00
93 Jackie Robinson 3.00 8.00
94 Frederick Winslow Taylor 1.25 3.00
95 Sojourner Truth 1.25 3.00
96 William Lloyd Garrison 1.25 3.00
97 Ira Hayes 1.25 3.00
98 Calamity Jane 1.25 3.00
99 Stonewall Jackson 2.00 5.00
100 Mary Harris Jones 1.25 3.00

2007 SP Legendary Cuts Legendary Cut Signatures

OVERALL CUT ODDS 1:96
PRINT RUNS B/WN 4-119 COPIES PER
NO PRICING ON QTY 25 OR LESS
AB Al Barlick/49 50.00 100.00
AH Happy Chandler/44 40.00 80.00
AR Allie Reynolds/40 60.00 120.00
BA Bob Allison/31 50.00 100.00
BD Bill Dickey/50 50.00 100.00
BG Burleigh Grimes/52 50.00 100.00
BH Babe Herman/99 40.00 80.00
BL Bob Lemon/23
BR Babe Ruth/1
BU Lew Burdette/50 30.00 60.00
BV Bill Veeck/47 200.00 300.00
CA Max Carey/40 50.00 100.00
CG Charlie Gehringer/50 40.00 80.00
CH Carl Hubbell/54 60.00 120.00
CM Connie Mack/6
CR Joe Cronin/28 60.00 120.00
CS Casey Stengel/20
CY Cy Young/1
DC Dolph Camilli/25
DD Dizzy Dean/11
DI Joe DiMaggio/52 400.00 500.00
DU Leo Durocher/84 60.00 120.00
EA Earl Averill/50 40.00 80.00
EB Ewell Blackwell/50 60.00 120.00
EC Earle Combs/11
EL Ed Lopat/66 60.00 120.00
EM Eddie Mathews/69 60.00 120.00
ER Edd Roush/50 30.00 60.00
ES Enos Slaughter/47 40.00 80.00
EW Early Wynn/40 40.00 80.00
FF Ford Frick/88 75.00 150.00
FL Freddy Lindstrom/45 125.00 175.00
GH Gabby Hartnett/50 75.00 150.00
GK George Kelly/95 40.00 80.00
GO Lefty Gomez/5
GP George Pipgras/70 50.00 100.00
GR Lefty Grove/66 150.00 200.00
GS George Sisler/18
HA Chick Hafey/10
HC Harry Caray/10
HG Hank Greenberg/59 175.00 250.00
HH Harvey Haddix/44 75.00 150.00
HK Harvey Kuenn/10
HN Hal Newhouser/14
HO Gil Hodges/25
HU Catfish Hunter/26 75.00 150.00
HW Honus Wagner/2
JA Joe Adcock/49 50.00 100.00
JC Jocko Conlan/54 30.00 60.00
JD Joe Dugan/46 60.00 120.00
JF Jimmie Foxx/4
JH Jesse Haines/25
JJ Jackie Jensen/19
JO Judy Johnson/54 60.00 120.00
JR Jackie Robinson/5
JS Joe Sewell/100 40.00 80.00
JV Johnny Vander Meer/49 60.00 120.00
KB Ken Boyer/19
KH Ken Hubbs/3
LA Luke Appling/92 40.00 80.00
LB Lou Boudreau/5
LD Larry Doby/50 50.00 100.00
LG Lou Gehrig/2
LO Ernie Lombardi/2
MC Mickey Cochrane/7
MI Johnny Mize/133 30.00 60.00
MO Mel Ott/2
NC Norm Cash/5
NF Nellie Fox/5
NL Nap Lajoie/2
PR Pee Wee Reese/39 100.00 150.00
PT Pie Traynor/2
RA Richie Ashburn/50 75.00 150.00
RC Roberto Clemente/3
RD Ray Dandridge/50 40.00 80.00
RF Rick Ferrell/7
RH Rogers Hornsby/3
RI Branch Rickey/3
RM Rube Marquard/52 75.00 150.00
RS Ray Schalk/44 250.00 300.00
SC Stan Coveleski/84 50.00 100.00
SP Satchel Paige/15
SW Warren Spahn/95 30.00 60.00
TC Ty Cobb/2
TJ Travis Jackson/88 40.00 80.00
VD Vince DiMaggio/34 100.00 175.00
VS Vern Stephens/17
WA Walter Alston/48 40.00 80.00
WH Waite Hoyt/79 40.00 80.00
WI Hoyt Wilhelm/60 40.00 80.00
WJ Walter Johnson/1
WO Walter O'Malley/8
WS Willie Stargell/71 75.00 200.00

2007 SP Legendary Cuts Legendary Cut Signatures Dual

OVERALL CUT ODDS 1:96
STATED PRINT RUN 1 SER.#'d SET
NO PRICING DUE TO SCARCITY
AS Walter Alston
Casey Stengel
BS Lou Boudreau
Vern Stephens
DC Joe Dugan
Earle Combs
DD Joe DiMaggio
Vince DiMaggio
DJ Judy Johnson
Ray Dandridge
DL Bill Dickey
Ernie Lombardi
GF Nellie Fox
Charlie Gehringer
GR Lefty Gomez
Red Ruffing
HA Gil Hodges
Walter Alston
HM Thurman Munson
Elston Howard
HS Carl Hubbell
Warren Spahn
MG Johnny Mize
Hank Greenberg
MM Billy Martin
Thurman Munson
RG Babe Ruth
Hank Greenberg
SS Warren Spahn
Johnny Sain
WC Max Carey
Honus Wagner

2007 SP Legendary Cuts Legendary Cut Signatures Quad

OVERALL CUT ODDS 1:96
STATED PRINT RUN 1 SER.#'d SET
NO PRICING DUE TO SCARCITY
DJBR Jackie Robinson
Judy Johnson
Satchel Paige
Ray Dandridge
FGBS Nellie Fox
Charlie Gehringer
Lou Boudreau
Vern Stephens
FRGO Babe Ruth
Jimmie Foxx
Mel Ott
Hank Greenberg
GCGH Ty Cobb
Charlie Gehringer
Hank Greenberg
Harry Heilmann Jr.
HRRC Jackie Robinson
Roy Campanella
Gil Hodges
Pee Wee Reese
MDLS Thurman Munson
Bill Dickey
Ernie Lombardi
Ray Schalk
MHJY Walter Johnson
Cy Young
Carl Hubbell
Rube Marquard

2007 SP Legendary Cuts Legendary Materials

OVERALL AU-GU ODDS 1:12
PRINT RUN B/WN 189-199 COPIES PER
AD1 Andre Dawson/199 3.00 8.00
AD2 Andre Dawson/199 3.00 8.00
AK1 Al Kaline/189 4.00 10.00
AK2 Al Kaline/199 4.00 10.00
AO Al Oliver/199 3.00 8.00
BJ Bo Jackson/199 4.00 10.00
BL Barry Larkin/199 4.00 10.00
BR1 Brooks Robinson/199 4.00 10.00
BR2 Brooks Robinson/199 4.00 10.00
BS Bruce Sutter/199 3.00 8.00
BW Billy Williams/199 3.00 8.00
CA Roy Campanella/199 4.00 10.00
CF1 Carlton Fisk/199 3.00 8.00
CF2 Carlton Fisk/199 3.00 8.00
CR1 Cal Ripken Jr./199 8.00 20.00
CR2 Cal Ripken Jr./199 8.00 20.00
CY1 Carl Yastrzemski/199 4.00 10.00
CY2 Carl Yastrzemski/199 4.00 10.00
DD Don Drysdale/199 4.00 10.00
DE Dwight Evans/199 3.00 8.00
DM1 Don Mattingly/199 4.00 10.00
DM2 Don Mattingly/199 4.00 10.00
DP Dave Parker/199 3.00 8.00
DS Don Sutton/199 3.00 8.00
DW1 Dave Winfield/199 3.00 8.00
DW2 Dave Winfield/199 3.00 8.00
EC Dennis Eckersley/199 3.00 8.00
EM1 Eddie Murray/199 3.00 8.00
EM2 Eddie Murray/199 3.00 8.00
FJ Fergie Jenkins/199 3.00 8.00
FL1 Fred Lynn/199 3.00 8.00
FL2 Fred Lynn/199 3.00 8.00
FR Frank Robinson/199 3.00 8.00
GF George Foster/199 3.00 8.00
GG Goose Gossage/199 3.00 8.00
GP1 Gaylord Perry/199 3.00 8.00
GP2 Gaylord Perry/199 3.00 8.00
HB Harold Baines/199 3.00 8.00
HK1 Harmon Killebrew/199 4.00 10.00
HK2 Harmon Killebrew/199 4.00 10.00
HU Catfish Hunter/199 3.00 8.00
JB1 Johnny Bench/199 4.00 10.00
JB2 Johnny Bench/199 4.00 10.00
JM1 Jack Morris/199 3.00 8.00
JM2 Jack Morris/199 3.00 8.00
JP Jim Palmer/199 3.00 8.00
JR1 Jim Rice/199 3.00 8.00
JR2 Jim Rice/199 3.00 8.00
JT Joe Torre/199 4.00 10.00
KG Ken Griffey Sr./199 3.00 8.00
KG1 Kirk Gibson/199 3.00 8.00
KG2 Kirk Gibson/199 3.00 8.00
KP1 Kirby Puckett/199 10.00 25.00
KP2 Kirby Puckett/199 10.00 25.00
LA Luis Aparicio/199 3.00 8.00
LB1 Lou Brock/199 3.00 8.00
LB2 Lou Brock/199 3.00 8.00
MA Bill Madlock/199 3.00 8.00
MG Mark Grace/199 3.00 8.00
MS1 Mike Schmidt/199 5.00 12.00
MS2 Mike Schmidt/199 5.00 12.00
NR1 Nolan Ryan/199 8.00 20.00
NR2 Nolan Ryan/199 8.00 20.00
OS1 Ozzie Smith/199 5.00 12.00
OS2 Ozzie Smith/199 5.00 12.00
PM1 Paul Molitor/199 3.00 8.00
PM2 Paul Molitor/199 3.00 8.00
PN Phil Niekro/199 3.00 8.00
PO Paul O'Neill/199 3.00 8.00
PW Pee Wee Reese/199 5.00 12.00
RA Roberto Alomar/199 3.00 8.00
RC Roberto Clemente/199 20.00 50.00
RC1 Rod Carew/199 3.00 8.00
RC2 Rod Carew/199 3.00 8.00
RF Rollie Fingers/199 3.00 8.00
RG Ron Guidry/199 6.00 15.00
RJ1 Reggie Jackson/199 3.00 8.00
RJ2 Reggie Jackson/199 3.00 8.00
RM Roger Maris/199 10.00 25.00
RS Ryne Sandberg/199 5.00 12.00
RY1 Robin Yount/199 5.00 12.00
RY2 Robin Yount/199 5.00 12.00
SC Red Schoendienst/199 4.00 10.00
SC1 Steve Carlton/199 3.00 8.00
SC2 Steve Carlton/199 3.00 8.00
SG1 Steve Garvey/199 3.00 8.00
SG2 Steve Garvey/199 3.00 8.00
TG1 Tony Gwynn/199 4.00 10.00
TG2 Tony Gwynn/199 4.00 10.00
TO Tony Oliva/199 3.00 8.00
TP Tony Perez/199 3.00 8.00
WB1 Wade Boggs/199 3.00 8.00
WB2 Wade Boggs/199 3.00 8.00
WC1 Will Clark/199 3.00 8.00
WC2 Will Clark/199 3.00 8.00
WS Willie Stargell/199

2007 SP Legendary Cuts Legendary Materials Dual

*DUAL: .5X TO 1.2X BASIC
OVERALL AU-GU ODDS 1:12
PRINT RUN B/WN 63-125 COPIES PER
AK1 Al Kaline/125 8.00 20.00
AK2 Al Kaline/125 8.00 20.00
BJ Bo Jackson/125 8.00 20.00
CR1 Cal Ripken Jr./125 8.00 20.00
CR2 Cal Ripken Jr./125 8.00 20.00
EM Eddie Mathews/125 8.00 20.00
HK2 Harmon Killebrew/63 6.00 15.00
KP1 Kirby Puckett/125 10.00 25.00
KP2 Kirby Puckett/125 10.00 25.00

2007 SP Legendary Cuts Legendary Materials Triple

*TRIPLE: .6X TO 1.5X BASIC
OVERALL AU-GU ODDS 1:12
PRINT RUN B/WN 9-99 COPIES PER
NO PRICING ON QTY 25 OR LESS
AK1 Al Kaline/32 10.00 25.00
BJ Bo Jackson/99 10.00 25.00
CR1 Cal Ripken Jr./99 10.00 25.00
CR2 Cal Ripken Jr./99 10.00 25.00
KP1 Kirby Puckett/99 12.50 30.00
KP2 Kirby Puckett/99 12.50 30.00
RC Roberto Clemente/99 30.00 60.00

2007 SP Legendary Cuts Legendary Materials Quad

OVERALL AU-GU ODDS 1:12
PRINT RUNS B/WN 13-25 COPIES PER
NO PRICING DUE TO SCARCITY

2007 SP Legendary Cuts Legendary Signatures

OVERALL AU-GU ODDS 1:12
PRINT RUN B/WN 15-199 COPIES PER
NO PRICING ON QTY 25 OR LESS
ASTERISK EQUALS PARTIAL EXCH
EXCH DEADLINE 8/22/2010
AD1 Andre Dawson/199 6.00 15.00
AD2 Andre Dawson/199 6.00 15.00
AK1 Al Kaline/199 10.00 25.00
AK2 Al Kaline/199 10.00 25.00
BF1 Bob Feller/199 8.00 20.00
BF2 Bob Feller/199 8.00 20.00
BF3 Bob Feller/189 8.00 20.00
BG1 Bob Gibson/50 10.00 25.00
BG2 Bob Gibson/50 10.00 25.00
BG3 Bob Gibson/40 10.00 25.00
BJ1 Bo Jackson/100 20.00 50.00
BJ2 Bo Jackson/100 20.00 50.00
BM1 Bill Mazeroski/189 10.00 25.00
BM2 Bill Mazeroski/199 10.00 25.00
BR1 Brooks Robinson/150 10.00 25.00
BR2 Brooks Robinson/140 10.00 25.00
BW1 Billy Williams/199 5.00 12.00
BW2 Billy Williams/189 5.00 12.00
CF1 Carlton Fisk/75 8.00 20.00
CF2 Carlton Fisk/75 8.00 20.00
CF3 Carlton Fisk/65 8.00 20.00
CR1 Cal Ripken Jr./99 EXCH * 50.00 100.00
CR2 Cal Ripken Jr./50 EXCH * 50.00 100.00
CR3 Cal Ripken Jr./25
CY1 Carl Yastrzemski/25
CY2 Carl Yastrzemski/15
DM1 Don Mattingly/25
DM2 Don Mattingly/25
DM3 Don Mattingly/15
DW1 Dave Winfield/25
DW2 Dave Winfield/15
EB1 Ernie Banks/35 EXCH 20.00 50.00
EB2 Ernie Banks/35 EXCH 20.00 50.00
EB3 Ernie Banks/25
EM1 Eddie Murray/25
EM2 Eddie Murray/25
FJ1 Fergie Jenkins/125 5.00 12.00
FJ2 Fergie Jenkins/125 5.00 12.00
FJ3 Fergie Jenkins/125 5.00 12.00
FR1 Frank Robinson/50 8.00 20.00
FR2 Frank Robinson/50 8.00 20.00
FR3 Frank Robinson/40 8.00 20.00
GP1 Gaylord Perry/199 4.00 10.00
GP2 Gaylord Perry/199 4.00 10.00
HK1 Harmon Killebrew/100 20.00 50.00
HK2 Harmon Killebrew/90 20.00 50.00
JB1 Johnny Bench/25
JB2 Johnny Bench/25
JB3 Johnny Bench/15
JM1 Juan Marichal/199 5.00 12.00
JM2 Juan Marichal/199 5.00 12.00
JM3 Juan Marichal/189 5.00 12.00
JP1 Jim Palmer/199 6.00 15.00
JP2 Jim Palmer/199 6.00 15.00
JP3 Jim Palmer/199 6.00 15.00
JT Joe Torre/99 20.00 50.00
KG Kirk Gibson/199 4.00 10.00
LA1 Luis Aparicio/199 6.00 15.00
LA2 Luis Aparicio/186 6.00 15.00
MS1 Mike Schmidt/35 20.00 50.00
MS2 Mike Schmidt/35 20.00 50.00
MS3 Mike Schmidt/25
NR1 Nolan Ryan/25
NR2 Nolan Ryan/25
NR3 Nolan Ryan/15
OS1 Ozzie Smith/100 15.00 40.00
OS2 Ozzie Smith/100 15.00 40.00
OS3 Ozzie Smith/100 15.00 40.00
PM1 Paul Molitor/100 10.00 25.00
PM2 Paul Molitor/90 10.00 25.00
RC1 Rod Carew/35 20.00 50.00
RC2 Rod Carew/35 20.00 50.00
RJ1 Reggie Jackson/25
RJ2 Reggie Jackson/15
RS1 Ryne Sandberg/25
RS2 Ryne Sandberg/25
RS3 Ryne Sandberg/25
RY1 Robin Yount/35 20.00 50.00
RY2 Robin Yount/35 20.00 50.00
RY3 Robin Yount/25
SC1 Steve Carlton/199 6.00 15.00
SC2 Steve Carlton/199 6.00 15.00
SC3 Steve Carlton/189 6.00 15.00
SM1 Stan Musial/25
SM2 Stan Musial/25
TG1 Tony Gwynn/25
TG2 Tony Gwynn/15
TP1 Tony Perez/199 5.00 12.00
TP2 Tony Perez/199 5.00 12.00
WB1 Wade Boggs/35 15.00 40.00
WB2 Wade Boggs/35 15.00 40.00
WB3 Wade Boggs/35 15.00 40.00
WC1 Will Clark/199 6.00 15.00
WC2 Will Clark/199 EXCH 6.00 15.00
WM1 Willie McCovey/25
WM2 Willie McCovey/25
WM3 Willie McCovey/15
YB1 Yogi Berra/25
YB2 Yogi Berra/25
YB3 Yogi Berra/15

2007 SP Legendary Cuts Legendary Signatures Dual

OVERALL AU-GU ODDS 1:12
STATED PRINT RUN 1 SER.#'d SET
NO PRICING DUE TO SCARCITY
BH Johnny Bench
Gabby Hartnett
BS Mike Schmidt
Ken Boyer
CS Steve Carlton
Warren Spahn
DG Bob Gibson
Dizzy Dean
DK Sandy Koufax
Don Drysdale
FL Bob Feller
Bob Lemon
FM Carlton Fisk
Thurman Munson
GK Sandy Koufax
Hank Greenberg
JM Reggie Jackson
Billy Martin
KG Al Kaline
Charlie Gehringer
MJ Reggie Jackson
Thurman Munson
RB Reggie Jackson
Babe Ruth
RW Cal Ripken Jr.
Honus Wagner
SG Ryne Sandberg
Charlie Gehringer

2007 SP Legendary Cuts Legendary Team Cuts

OVERALL CUT ODDS 1:96
STATED PRINT RUN 1 SER.#'d SET
NO PRICING DUE TO SCARCITY
BD Bill Dickey
BG Burleigh Grimes
BR Babe Ruth
CK Charlie Keller
CM Connie Mack
DD Dizzy Dean
DU Joe Dugan
EC Earle Combs
FF Frankie Frisch
GE Lou Gehrig
GH Gil Hodges
JD Joe DiMaggio
JF Jimmie Foxx
JH Jesse Haines
JR Jackie Robinson
LD Leo Durocher
LG Lefty Gomez
LO Lou Gehrig
MC Mickey Cochrane
PD Paul Dean
PR Pee Wee Reese
RC Roy Campanella
TL Tony Lazzeri
WA Walter Alston

2007 SP Legendary Cuts Masterful Materials

OVERALL AU-GU ODDS 1:12
AD Andre Dawson 3.00 8.00
BJ Bo Jackson 4.00 10.00
BL Barry Larkin 3.00 8.00
BM Bill Madlock 3.00 8.00
BR Brooks Robinson 4.00 10.00
BS Bruce Sutter 3.00 8.00
CF Carlton Fisk 3.00 8.00
CR Cal Ripken Jr. 6.00 15.00
CY Carl Yastrzemski 4.00 10.00
DE Dwight Evans 3.00 8.00
DM Don Mattingly 4.00 10.00
DP Dave Parker 3.00 8.00
DS Don Sutton 3.00 8.00
DW Dave Winfield 3.00 8.00
EM Eddie Mathews 4.00 10.00
FL Fred Lynn 3.00 8.00
FR Frank Robinson 3.00 8.00
GP Gaylord Perry 3.00 8.00
JB Johnny Bench 4.00 10.00
JR Jim Rice 3.00 8.00
KG Ken Griffey Sr. 3.00 8.00
KP Kirby Puckett 6.00 15.00
MS Mike Schmidt 5.00 12.00
MU Eddie Murray 3.00 8.00
NR Nolan Ryan 8.00 20.00
PM Paul Molitor 3.00 8.00
RJ Reggie Jackson 4.00 10.00
RS Ryne Sandberg 4.00 10.00
RY Robin Yount 4.00 10.00
SC Steve Carlton 3.00 8.00
SG Steve Garvey 3.00 8.00
TG Tony Gwynn 4.00 10.00
WB Wade Boggs 3.00 8.00
WC Will Clark 3.00 8.00
WM Willie McCovey 4.00 10.00
YB Yogi Berra 5.00 12.00

2007 SP Legendary Cuts Material Cuts

OVERALL CUT ODDS 1:96
PRINT RUNS B/WN 1-5 COPIES PER
NO PRICING DUE TO SCARCITY
BD Bill Dickey/5
CA Roy Campanella/5
CS Casey Stengel/5
DD Don Drysdale/5
EA Earl Averill/5
EM Eddie Mathews/1
ES Enos Slaughter/5
EW Early Wynn/5
GE Lou Gehrig/1
GS George Sisler/3
HG Hank Greenberg/5
HW Hoyt Wilhelm/5
JD Joe DiMaggio/5
JM Johnny Mize/5
JR Jackie Robinson/5
LB Lou Boudreau/4
LG Lefty Grove/5
MO Mel Ott/5
PR Pee Wee Reese/5
RC Roberto Clemente/2
RH Rogers Hornsby/5
ST Willie Stargell/5
TC Ty Cobb/1
TM Thurman Munson/2
WS Warren Spahn/5

2007 SP Legendary Cuts Material Signatures

OVERALL AU-GU ODDS 1:12
PRINT RUNS B/WN 5-10 COPIES PER
NO PRICING DUE TO SCARCITY
AK Al Kaline
BF Bob Feller
BG Bob Gibson/5
BM Bill Mazeroski
BW Billy Williams
CF Carlton Fisk
DM Don Mattingly
EM Eddie Murray
FJ Fergie Jenkins
HK Harmon Killebrew
JP Jim Palmer
LA Luis Aparicio
MS Mike Schmidt
NR Nolan Ryan
RY Robin Yount
WM Willie McCovey
YB Yogi Berra

2007 SP Legendary Cuts Quotation Cuts

OVERALL CUT ODDS 1:96
PRINT RUNS B/WN 1-109 COPIES PER
NO PRICING ON QTY 25 OR LESS
BL Bob Lemon/80 30.00 60.00
BM Billy Martin/8
BR Branch Rickey/5
BV Bill Veeck/20
CA Harry Caray/25
CH Carl Hubbell/65 50.00 100.00
CK Charlie Keller/45 50.00 100.00
CM Connie Mack/5
CS Casey Stengel/36 200.00 300.00
DD Dizzy Dean/16
EL Ernie Lombardi/13
EW Early Wynn/9
HC Happy Chandler/44 40.00 80.00
HH Harvey Haddix/30 50.00 100.00
JD Joe Dugan/2
JF Jimmie Foxx/2
JM Joe McCarthy/109 60.00 120.00
JR Jackie Robinson/2
KB Ken Boyer/10
LB Lou Boudreau/28 30.00 60.00
MI Johnny Mize/45 60.00 120.00
RA Richie Ashburn/48 75.00 150.00
RC Roberto Clemente/5
RD Ray Dandridge/72 40.00 80.00
RM Rube Marquard/35 75.00 150.00
SC Stan Coveleski/71 50.00 100.00
SP Satchel Paige/3
ST Willie Stargell/25
TC Ty Cobb/1
VS Vern Stephens/2
WA Walter Alston/31 40.00 80.00
WI Hoyt Wilhelm/37 50.00 100.00
WS Warren Spahn/60 40.00 80.00

2007 SP Legendary Cuts Reel History Film Frame

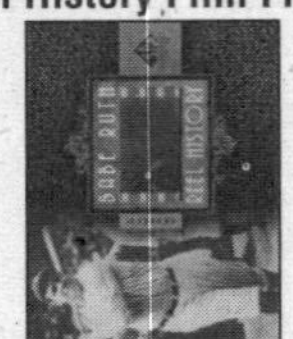

STATED ODDS 1:576
CARDS SERIAL #'d TO ONE
BR Babe Ruth/785 * 60.00 120.00
LG Lou Gehrig/473 * 50.00 100.00

2007 SP Legendary Cuts When it Was a Game Memorabilia

OVERALL AU-GU ODDS 1:12
AT Alan Trammell 3.00 8.00
BF Bob Feller 3.00 8.00
BG Bob Gibson 3.00 8.00
BM Bill Mazeroski 4.00 10.00
BW Billy Williams 3.00 8.00
CF Carlton Fisk 3.00 8.00
CY Carl Yastrzemski 4.00 10.00
DE Dennis Eckersley 3.00 8.00
DM Don Mattingly 4.00 10.00
DW Dave Winfield 3.00 8.00
EM Eddie Murray 3.00 8.00
FJ Fergie Jenkins 3.00 8.00
FL Fred Lynn 3.00 8.00
FR Frank Robinson 3.00 8.00
GP Gaylord Perry 3.00 8.00
HK Harmon Killebrew 4.00 10.00
JP Jim Palmer 3.00 8.00
JR Jim Rice 3.00 8.00
KG Kirk Gibson 3.00 8.00
KP Kirby Puckett 6.00 15.00
LB Lou Brock 4.00 10.00
MS Mike Schmidt 5.00 12.00
NR Nolan Ryan 8.00 20.00
PM Paul Molitor 3.00 8.00
PW Pee Wee Reese 4.00 10.00
RF Rollie Fingers 3.00 8.00
RJ Reggie Jackson 4.00 10.00
RM Roger Maris 10.00 25.00
RS Red Schoendienst 3.00 8.00
TG Tony Gwynn 4.00 10.00

2008 SP Legendary Cuts

COMP.SET w/o SP's (100) 8.00 20.00
COMMON CARD (1-100) .20 .50
COMMON CARD (101-146) 2.00 5.00
COMMON CARD (147-200) 2.00 5.00
101-200 RANDOMLY INSERTED
101-200 PRINT RUN 550 SERIAL #'d SETS
1 Ken Griffey Jr. .75 2.00
2 Derek Jeter 1.25 3.00
3 Albert Pujols 1.00 2.50
4 Ichiro Suzuki .75 2.00
5 Ryan Braun .60 1.50
6 Manny Ramirez .50 1.25
7 David Ortiz .50 1.25
8 Greg Maddux .60 1.50
9 Roger Clemens .60 1.50
10 Chase Utley .50 1.25
11 Vladimir Guerrero .50 1.25
12 Johan Santana .30 .75
13 Chipper Jones .60 1.50
14 Tom Glavine .30 .75
15 Ryan Howard .60 1.50
16 Hunter Pence .50 1.25
17 Prince Fielder .50 1.25
18 Jeff Francoeur .30 .75
19 David Wright .60 1.50
20 Carlos Beltran .20 .50
21 Carlos Lee .20 .50
22 Cole Hamels .50 1.25
23 Jered Weaver .20 .50
24 B.J. Upton .30 .75
25 Akinori Iwamura .20 .50
26 Daisuke Matsuzaka .75 2.00
27 Curt Schilling .30 .75
28 Adam Dunn .20 .50
29 Jose Reyes .30 .75
30 Nomar Garciaparra .50 1.25
31 Hideki Matsui .50 1.25
32 Matt Holliday .30 .75
33 Jason Bay .20 .50
34 Grady Sizemore .30 .75
35 Travis Hafner .20 .50
36 Victor Martinez .20 .50
37 C.C. Sabathia .20 .50
38 Justin Morneau .30 .75
39 Torii Hunter .20 .50
40 Joe Mauer .30 .75
41 Russell Martin .20 .50
42 Frank Thomas .50 1.25
43 Miguel Tejada .20 .50
44 Brian Roberts .30 .75
45 Justin Verlander .30 .75
46 Gary Sheffield .20 .50
47 Magglio Ordonez .30 .75
48 Alex Rodriguez .75 2.00
49 Bobby Abreu .20 .50
50 Mark Teixeira .30 .75
51 Andruw Jones .20 .50
52 Derrek Lee .30 .75
53 Aramis Ramirez .20 .50
54 Carlos Zambrano .20 .50
55 Alfonso Soriano .30 .75
56 Omar Vizquel .20 .50
57 Lance Berkman .30 .75
58 Roy Oswalt .20 .50
59 Jake Peavy .30 .75
60 Chris R. Young .20 .50
61 Khalil Greene .30 .75
62 Troy Tulowitzki .30 .75
63 Todd Helton .30 .75
64 Josh Beckett .30 .75
65 Miguel Cabrera .30 .75
66 Hanley Ramirez .50 1.25
67 Dan Uggla .30 .75
68 Scott Kazmir .30 .75
69 Delmon Young .30 .75
70 Erik Bedard .20 .50
71 Alex Gordon .50 1.25
72 Felix Hernandez .30 .75
73 Kenji Johjima .20 .50
74 John Lackey .20 .50
75 Ryan Zimmerman .30 .75
76 Jeremy Bonderman .20 .50
77 Chien-Ming Wang .60 1.50
78 Jim Thome .30 .75
79 Jimmy Rollins .30 .75
80 Mariano Rivera .50 1.25
81 Curtis Granderson .20 .50
82 Nick Markakis .30 .75
83 Trevor Hoffman .20 .50
84 Barry Zito .20 .50
85 Yovani Gallardo .20 .50
86 Dan Haren .20 .50
87 Vernon Wells .20 .50
88 Ian Kennedy RC .50 1.25
89 Phil Hughes .50 1.25
90 Brian McCann .30 .75
91 J.J. Hardy .20 .50
92 Roy Halladay .20 .50
93 Mike Piazza .50 1.25
94 Ivan Rodriguez .30 .75
95 Dontrelle Willis .20 .50
96 Brandon Webb .30 .75
97 Carl Crawford .20 .50
98 Tim Lincecum .50 1.25
99 Jason Varitek .50 1.25
100 Freddy Sanchez .20 .50
101 Abraham Lincoln 4.00 10.00
102 Ulysses S. Grant 3.00 8.00
103 Andrew Johnson 2.00 5.00
104 George Washington 3.00 8.00
105 Thomas Jefferson 2.00 5.00
106 Andrew Jackson 3.00 8.00
107 James Madison 2.00 5.00
108 James Monroe 2.00 5.00
109 Benjamin Franklin 2.50 6.00
110 Alexander Graham Bell 2.00 5.00
111 Thomas Edison 2.00 5.00
112 Red Baron 2.00 5.00
113 Robert E. Lee 3.00 8.00
114 Mark Twain 2.00 5.00
115 Arthur Conan Doyle 2.00 5.00
116 Bram Stoker 2.00 5.00
117 Jules Verne 2.00 5.00
118 Billy the Kid 2.50 6.00
119 Harriet Beecher Stowe 2.00 5.00
120 Andrew Carnegie 2.00 5.00
121 Lewis Carroll 2.00 5.00
122 Cornelius Vanderbilt 2.00 5.00
123 Brigham Young 2.00 5.00
124 Charles Dickens 2.00 5.00
125 Vincent Van Gogh 2.00 5.00
126 Claude Monet 2.00 5.00
127 Jesse James 2.50 6.00
128 John D. Rockefeller 2.00 5.00
129 Harry Longabaugh 2.00 5.00
130 John F. Kennedy 4.00 10.00
131 Richard Nixon 2.50 6.00
132 Lyndon B. Johnson 2.50 6.00
133 Dwight D. Eisenhower 2.00 5.00
134 Franklin D. Roosevelt 2.00 5.00
135 Harry Truman 2.00 5.00
136 Ronald Reagan 4.00 10.00
137 Bill Clinton 2.50 6.00
138 George H.W. Bush 2.50 6.00
139 Jimmy Carter 2.50 6.00
140 Gerald Ford 2.50 6.00
141 Herbert Hoover 2.00 5.00
142 Calvin Coolidge 2.00 5.00
143 Warren G. Harding 2.00 5.00
144 Woodrow Wilson 2.00 5.00
145 William Taft 2.00 5.00
146 Theodore Roosevelt 2.50 6.00
147 Phil Niekro 2.00 5.00
148 Brooks Robinson 3.00 8.00
149 Cal Ripken Jr. 6.00 15.00
150 Eddie Murray 3.00 8.00
151 Jim Palmer 2.00 5.00
152 Abner Doubleday 2.00 5.00
153 Wade Boggs 3.00 8.00
154 Carl Yastrzemski 5.00 12.00
155 Bobby Doerr 2.00 5.00
156 Carlton Fisk 3.00 8.00
157 Pee Wee Reese 3.00 8.00
158 Ernie Banks 3.00 8.00
159 Fergie Jenkins 2.00 5.00
160 Billy Williams 2.00 5.00
161 Ryne Sandberg 4.00 10.00
162 Luis Aparicio 2.00 5.00
163 Joe Morgan 2.00 5.00
164 Johnny Bench 3.00 8.00
165 Tony Perez 2.00 5.00
166 Bob Feller 2.00 5.00
167 Larry Doby 2.00 5.00
168 Bob Lemon 2.00 5.00
169 Al Kaline 3.00 8.00
170 Warren Spahn 3.00 8.00
171 Robin Yount 3.00 8.00
172 Rollie Fingers 2.00 5.00
173 Harmon Killebrew 3.00 8.00
174 Rod Carew 3.00 8.00
175 Babe Ruth 5.00 12.00
176 Monte Irvin 2.00 5.00
177 Tom Seaver 3.00 8.00
178 Phil Rizzuto 3.00 8.00
179 Jack Chesbro 2.00 5.00
180 Catfish Hunter 2.00 5.00
181 Babe Ruth 5.00 12.00
182 Reggie Jackson 3.00 8.00
183 Dennis Eckersley 2.00 5.00
184 Steve Carlton 2.00 5.00
185 Ed Delahanty 2.00 5.00
186 Mike Schmidt 4.00 10.00
187 Jim Bunning 2.00 5.00
188 Robin Roberts 2.00 5.00
189 Willie Stargell 3.00 8.00
190 Bill Mazeroski 3.00 8.00
191 Ralph Kiner 3.00 8.00
192 Tony Gwynn 2.00 5.00
193 Juan Marichal 2.00 5.00
194 Willie McCovey 3.00 8.00
195 Orlando Cepeda 2.00 5.00
196 Stan Musial 4.00 10.00
197 Ozzie Smith 4.00 10.00
198 Bob Gibson 3.00 8.00
199 Bruce Sutter 2.00 5.00
200 Nolan Ryan 5.00 12.00

2008 SP Legendary Cuts Memorable Moments

RANDOM INSERTS IN PACKS
STATED PRINT RUN 1 SER.#'d SET
MULTIPLE VERSIONS OF EACH CARD
NO PRICING DUE TO SCARCITY

2008 SP Legendary Cuts Baseball Headlines Cut Signatures

RANDOM INSERTS IN PACKS
NO PRICING DUE TO SCARCITY
BR Babe Ruth
CH Catfish Hunter
HG Hank Greenberg
JD Joe DiMaggio/15
JV Johnny Vander Meer/8
SC Stan Coveleski
WS Willie Stargell
WS Warren Spahn

2008 SP Legendary Cuts Classic Signatures

RANDOM INSERTS IN PACKS
STATED PRINT RUN 25 SER.#'d SETS
NO PRICING DUE TO SCARCITY
BD Bucky Dent
BD Bobby Doerr
BR Brooks Robinson
BT Bobby Thomson
BW Billy Williams
CF Carlton Fisk
DL Don Larsen
DM Don Mattingly
EB Ernie Banks
EM Edgar Martinez
FL Fred Lynn
JB Johnny Bench
JC Joe Carter
JP Johnny Pesky
JP2 Jim Palmer
JR Jim Rice
JR J.R. Richard
LB Lou Brock
MS Mike Schmidt
NR Nolan Ryan
OS Ozzie Smith
PM Paul Molitor
RA Roberto Alomar
RC Rod Carew
RS Ryne Sandberg
RS2 Ron Santo
RY Robin Yount
SC Steve Carlton
TG Tony Gwynn
TM Tino Martinez
TP Tony Perez
WB Wade Boggs
WC Will Clark

2008 SP Legendary Cuts Destination Stardom Memorabilia

RANDOM INSERTS IN PACKS
AG Alex Gordon 4.00 10.00
AI Akinori Iwamura 3.00 8.00
AM Andrew Miller 3.00 8.00
AR Alex Rios 3.00 8.00
BB Billy Butler 3.00 8.00
BM Brian McCann 3.00 8.00

BU B.J. Upton 3.00 8.00
CB Chad Billingsley 3.00 8.00
CD Chris Duncan 3.00 8.00
CG Curtis Granderson 3.00 8.00
CH Cole Hamels 3.00 8.00
DH Dan Haren 3.00 8.00
DM Daisuke Matsuzaka 5.00 12.00
DU Dan Uggla 3.00 8.00
DY Delmon Young 3.00 8.00
FH Felix Hernandez 3.00 8.00
FI Josh Fields 3.00 8.00
GA Garrett Atkins 3.00 8.00
GS Grady Sizemore 3.00 8.00
HA Corey Hart 3.00 8.00
HK Howie Kendrick 3.00 8.00
HP Hunter Pence 3.00 8.00
HR Hanley Ramirez 4.00 10.00
JF Jeff Francoeur 3.00 8.00
JH J.J. Hardy 3.00 8.00
JL James Loney 3.00 8.00
JM John Maine 3.00 8.00
JO Josh Hamilton 10.00 25.00
JP Jon Papelbon 4.00 10.00
JV Justin Verlander 3.00 8.00
JW Jered Weaver 3.00 8.00
KG Khalil Greene 3.00 8.00
LE Jon Lester 3.00 8.00
MH Matt Holliday 3.00 8.00
NM Nick Markakis 3.00 8.00
PF Prince Fielder 4.00 10.00
PH Phil Hughes 4.00 10.00
RB Ryan Braun 4.00 10.00
RG Ryan Garko 3.00 8.00
RH Rich Hill 3.00 8.00
RM Russell Martin 3.00 8.00
RZ Ryan Zimmerman 3.00 8.00
SD Stephen Drew 3.00 8.00
TB Travis Buck 3.00 8.00
TL Tim Lincecum 4.00 10.00
TT Troy Tulowitzki 3.00 8.00
YG Yovani Gallardo 3.00 8.00

2008 SP Legendary Cuts Destined for History Memorabilia

RANDOM INSERTS IN PACKS
AD Adam Dunn 3.00 8.00
AJ Andruw Jones 3.00 8.00
AP Albert Pujols 6.00 15.00
AP Andy Pettitte 3.00 8.00
AR Alex Rodriguez 6.00 15.00
AS Alfonso Soriano 3.00 8.00
BW Brandon Webb 3.00 8.00
CB Carlos Beltran 3.00 8.00
CD Carlos Delgado 3.00 8.00
CJ Chipper Jones 4.00 10.00
CL Carlos Lee 3.00 8.00
CM Chien-Ming Wang 5.00 12.00
CS Curt Schilling 3.00 8.00
CZ Carlos Zambrano 3.00 8.00
DJ Derek Jeter 8.00 20.00
DL Derrek Lee 3.00 8.00
DO David Ortiz 4.00 10.00
DW Dontrelle Willis 3.00 8.00
FT Frank Thomas 4.00 10.00
GM Greg Maddux 4.00 10.00
GS Gary Sheffield 3.00 8.00
HA Travis Hafner 3.00 8.00
IR Ivan Rodriguez 3.00 8.00
JM Justin Morneau 3.00 8.00
JP Jake Peavy
JR Jimmy Rollins 3.00 8.00
JS John Smoltz 3.00 8.00
JT Jim Thome 3.00 8.00
MC Miguel Cabrera 3.00 8.00
MO Magglio Ordonez 3.00 8.00
MP Mike Piazza 4.00 10.00
MR Manny Ramirez 4.00 10.00
MT Mark Teixeira 3.00 8.00
MY Michael Young 3.00 8.00
OV Omar Vizquel 3.00 8.00
PM Pedro Martinez 3.00 8.00
RA Aramis Ramirez 3.00 8.00
RC Roger Clemens 4.00 10.00
RE Jose Reyes 3.00 8.00
RH Roy Halladay 3.00 8.00
RJ Randy Johnson 4.00 10.00
RO Roy Oswalt 3.00 8.00
SA Johan Santana 3.00 8.00
SS Sammy Sosa 3.00 8.00
TE Miguel Tejada 3.00 8.00
TG Tom Glavine 3.00 8.00
TH Todd Helton 3.00 8.00
TH Trevor Hoffman 3.00 8.00
VG Vladimir Guerrero 3.00 8.00

2008 SP Legendary Cuts Fall Classic Cut Signatures

RANDOM INSERTS IN PACKS
NO PRICING DUE TO SCARCITY
BL Bob Lemon/15
CH Carl Hubbell/15
CH Catfish Hunter
CK Charlie Keller/15
DD Don Drysdale/15
HG Hank Greenberg/15
JD Joe DiMaggio/12
LB Lou Boudreau/15
LG Lefty Grove
LG Lefty Gomez
NF Nellie Fox/15
RR Red Ruffing/14
SC Stan Coveleski/15
TK Ted Kluszewski/7
WH Waite Hoyt/15
WS Warren Spahn

2008 SP Legendary Cuts Future Legends Signatures

RANDOM INSERTS IN PACKS
STATED PRINT RUN 99 SER.#'d SETS
BM Brian McCann 10.00 25.00
BU B.J. Upton 8.00 20.00
BW Brandon Wood 5.00 12.00
CB Clay Buchholz 10.00 25.00
CB Chad Billingsley 6.00 15.00
CD Chris Duncan 6.00 15.00
CH Chin-Lung Hu 15.00 40.00
CH Cole Hamels 15.00 40.00
CH Corey Hart 12.50 30.00
DB Daric Barton 5.00 12.00
DJ Derek Jeter
DU Dan Uggla 6.00 15.00
FC Fausto Carmona 5.00 12.00
FH Felix Hernandez 10.00 25.00
GA Garrett Atkins 5.00 12.00
HK Hong-Chih Kuo 50.00 100.00
HR Hanley Ramirez 10.00 25.00
IK Ian Kennedy 10.00 25.00
IK2 Ian Kinsler 8.00 20.00
JF Jeff Francis 5.00 12.00
JH Josh Hamilton 15.00 40.00
JL Jon Lester 10.00 25.00
JM John Maine 6.00 15.00
JP Jonathan Papelbon 10.00 25.00
KG Ken Griffey Jr. 40.00 80.00
KY Kevin Youkilis 10.00 25.00
LH Luke Hochevar 6.00 15.00
MC Matt Cain 6.00 15.00
MG Matt Garza 5.00 12.00
NM Nick Markakis 8.00 20.00
PH Phil Hughes 10.00 25.00
RH Rich Hill 5.00 12.00
TH Travis Hafner 6.00 15.00
YG Yovani Gallardo 6.00 15.00

2008 SP Legendary Cuts Generations Dual Autographs

RANDOM INSERTS IN PACKS
ASTERISK EQUALS PARTIAL EXCHANGE
NO PRICING ON SOME DUE TO SCARCITY
EXCHANGE DEADLINE 5/22/2010
AR Luis Aparicio 20.00 50.00
Hanley Ramirez EXCH *
BC Johnny Bench
Mickey Cochrane/2
BM Johnny Bench 30.00 60.00
Russ Martin
CH Steve Carlton 30.00 60.00
Cole Hamels
DR Larry Doby
Frank Robinson/5
GC Lefty Grove
Steve Carlton/1
GG Tony Gwynn 30.00 60.00
Tony Gwynn Jr.
GM Ken Griffey Jr. 150.00 250.00
Stan Musial
JJ Derek Jeter 125.00 250.00
Reggie Jackson EXCH
MB Willie McCovey 30.00 60.00
Lance Berkman
MH Paul Molitor 15.00 40.00
Travis Hafner
PC Gaylord Perry 12.50 30.00
Fausto Carmona
PK Jim Palmer 12.50 30.00
Ian Kennedy
RC Brooks Robinson 12.50 30.00
Eric Chavez
RG Cal Ripken Jr.
Lou Gehrig/3
RM Nolan Ryan
Daisuke Matsuzaka
YH Robin Yount 20.00 50.00
Corey Hart EXCH *

2008 SP Legendary Cuts Generations Dual Memorabilia

RANDOM INSERTS IN PACKS
AR Luis Aparicio 5.00 12.00
Hanley Ramirez
BC Lou Brock 4.00 10.00
Carl Crawford
BL Ernie Banks 8.00 20.00
Derrek Lee
BM Johnny Bench 5.00 12.00
Victor Martinez
BM Johnny Bench 4.00 10.00
Joe Mauer
BP Lance Berkman 4.00 10.00
Hunter Pence
BY Wade Boggs 5.00 12.00
Kevin Youkilis
CD Cal Ripken 12.50 30.00
Derek Jeter
CG Roberto Clemente 15.00 40.00
Vladimir Guerrero
CH Roger Clemens 4.00 10.00
Philip Hughes
CK Rod Carew 4.00 10.00
Howie Kendrick
CM Will Clark 4.00 10.00
Justin Morneau
CP Orlando Cepeda 5.00 12.00
Albert Pujols
CS Steve Carlton 4.00 10.00
Johan Santana
DC Don Sutton 4.00 10.00
Chad Billingsley
DD Don Mattingly 10.00 25.00
Derek Jeter
DJ Joe DiMaggio 50.00 100.00
Derek Jeter
DP Bill Dickey 10.00 25.00
Jorge Posada
DS Andre Dawson 6.00 15.00
Alfonso Soriano
DT Don Mattingly 4.00 10.00
Todd Helton
EA Enos Slaughter 8.00 20.00
Albert Pujols
EC Eddie Murray 4.00 10.00
Chipper Jones
FF Frank Robinson 5.00 12.00
Frank Thomas
FP Carlton Fisk 4.00 10.00
Mike Piazza
FS Rollie Fingers 4.00 10.00
Huston Street
FV Carlton Fisk 4.00 10.00
Jason Varitek
GC Bob Gibson 5.00 12.00
Chris Carpenter
GF Tony Gwynn 5.00 12.00
Prince Fielder
GG Gaylord Perry 4.00 10.00
Greg Maddux
GH Ken Griffey Jr. 20.00 50.00
Josh Hamilton
GL Tom Glavine 4.00 10.00
Jon Lester
GP Goose Gossage 4.00 10.00
Jon Papelbon
GR Goose Gossage 5.00 12.00
Mariano Rivera
HH Catfish Hunter 5.00 12.00
Philip Hughes
HU Rogers Hornsby 20.00 50.00
Chase Utley
JD Jim Rice 5.00 12.00
David Ortiz
JG Frank Robinson 8.00 20.00
Ken Griffey Jr.
JG Reggie Jackson 20.00 50.00
Ken Griffey Jr.
JH Reggie Jackson 4.00 10.00
Travis Hafner
JJ Reggie Jackson 15.00 40.00
Derek Jeter
KB Ralph Kiner 10.00 25.00
Jason Bay
KD Ted Kluszewski 5.00 12.00
Adam Dunn
KH Harmon Killebrew 4.00 10.00
Travis Hafner
KK Ken Griffey Sr. 12.50 30.00
Ken Griffey Jr.
KT Harmon Killebrew 5.00 12.00
Frank Thomas
LM Fred Lynn 4.00 10.00
Nick Markakis
MA Mike Schmidt 6.00 15.00
Albert Pujols
MB Paul Molitor 8.00 20.00
Ryan Braun
MG Stan Musial
Ken Griffey Jr.
MJ Roger Maris 15.00 40.00
Derek Jeter
MM Juan Marichal 4.00 10.00
Pedro Martinez
MS Bill Mazeroski 8.00 20.00
Ryne Sandberg
NW Phil Niekro 4.00 10.00
Tim Wakefield
OJ Ozzie Smith 5.00 12.00
Jose Reyes
PB Jim Palmer 4.00 10.00
Erik Bedard
PH Gaylord Perry 4.00 10.00
Roy Halladay
PL Gaylord Perry 5.00 12.00
Tim Lincecum
PM Mike Piazza 4.00 10.00
Russell Martin
PO Dave Parker 5.00 12.00
David Ortiz
PY Gaylord Perry 4.00 10.00
Chris Young
RC Nolan Ryan 6.00 15.00
Roger Clemens
RD Ryne Sandberg 4.00 10.00
Dan Uggla
RJ Phil Rizzuto 12.50 30.00
Derek Jeter
RM Cal Ripken 8.00 20.00
Nick Markakis
RM Babe Ruth 100.00 200.00
Roger Maris
RO Nolan Ryan 5.00 12.00
Roy Oswalt
RR Randy Johnson 4.00 10.00
Rich Hill
RT Cal Ripken 6.00 15.00
Troy Tulowitzki
RV Nolan Ryan 5.00 12.00
Justin Verlander
RW Nolan Ryan 5.00 12.00
Jered Weaver
SA Stan Musial 15.00 40.00
Albert Pujols
SB Mike Schmidt 8.00 20.00
Ryan Braun
SC Steve Carlton 5.00 12.00
Cole Hamels
SG Ben Sheets 4.00 10.00
Yovani Gallardo
SJ Mike Schmidt 5.00 12.00
Chipper Jones
SL John Smoltz 5.00 12.00
Tim Lincecum
SM Tom Seaver 5.00 12.00
John Maine
SP Tom Seaver 4.00 10.00
Jake Peavy
SR Ron Santo 6.00 15.00
Aramis Ramirez
SU Ryne Sandberg 6.00 15.00
Chase Utley
SY Gary Sheffield 4.00 10.00
Delmon Young
SZ Mike Schmidt 5.00 12.00
Ryan Zimmerman
TM Todd Helton 5.00 12.00
Matt Holliday
TR Cal Ripken 5.00 12.00
Miguel Tejada
YH Robin Yount 5.00 12.00
J.J. Hardy
YJ Robin Yount 8.00 20.00
Derek Jeter
YO Carl Yastrzemski 6.00 15.00
David Ortiz

2008 SP Legendary Cuts Headliners and Heroes Cut Signatures

RANDOM INSERTS IN PACKS
NO PRICING ON MOST DUE TO SCARCITY
AB Al Barlick/32 30.00 60.00
AL Al Lopez/45 30.00 60.00
BC Ben Chapman/28 100.00 200.00
BH Bucky Harris/18
BH Babe Herman/44 30.00 60.00
BH Billy Herman/76 30.00 60.00
BO Buck O'Neil/10
BT Bill Terry/94 75.00 150.00
CC Chuck Connors/9
CG Charlie Gehringer/40 30.00 60.00
EB Ed Barrow
EF Elmer Flick
EL Ed Lopat/46 40.00 80.00
ER Edd Roush/122 30.00 60.00
ES Enos Slaughter/36 30.00 60.00
EW Eugene Woodling/72 30.00 60.00
FC Frank Crosetti/24
FF Ford Frick
FL Freddie Lindstrom/21
FM Frank McCormick
GK George Kelly/77 30.00 60.00
GS George Selkirk
HC Happy Chandler/75 20.00 50.00
HH Harry Hooper/34 125.00 250.00
JA Joe Adcock
JB James Cool Papa Bell/23
JC Jocko Conlan/43
JD Joe DiMaggio
JH Jesse Haines/37 50.00 100.00
JJ Judy Johnson/38 40.00 80.00
JM Johnny Mize/41 40.00 80.00
JS Joe Sewell/59 30.00 60.00
JS Johnny Sain/50 50.00 100.00
KK Ken Keltner/10
LA Luke Appling/45 30.00 60.00
LB Lou Boudreau/52 30.00 60.00
LW Lloyd Waner
MC Max Carey/31 50.00 100.00
NL Nap Lajoie
PR Pee Wee Reese/52 75.00 150.00
RC Roy Campanella/37 300.00 600.00
RD Ray Dandridge/38 30.00 60.00
RF Red Faber
RM Rube Marquard
SB Smoky Burgess
SC Stan Coveleski/34
SH Stan Hack/10 60.00 120.00
SM Sal Maglie
TC Tony Conigliaro
TJ Travis Jackson/39 60.00 120.00
TL Ted Lyons/34 40.00 80.00
TS Tris Speaker/4
WG Warren Giles/9
ZW Zach Wheat/8
BL1 Buck Leonard/68 30.00 60.00
BL2 Buck Leonard/58 30.00 60.00
BL3 Bob Lemon/39 30.00 60.00

2008 SP Legendary Cuts Legendary Cut Signatures

RANDOM INSERTS IN PACKS
NO PRICING ON MOST DUE TO SCARCITY
AB Al Barlick/52 30.00 60.00
BD Bill Dickey/16
BH Babe Herman/30 40.00 80.00
BH Billy Herman/79 30.00 60.00
BL Bob Lemon 20.00 50.00
BL Buck Leonard 30.00 60.00
BR Babe Ruth/8
CF Curt Flood/26 175.00 300.00
CG Charlie Gehringer/45 30.00 60.00
CH Carl Hubbell/31 20.00 50.00
CK Charlie Keller/34 30.00 60.00
CM Connie Mack
CS Casey Stengel/10
DD Don Drysdale/2
DD Dizzy Dean/10
DH Dick Howser/3
EA Earl Averill/44 30.00 60.00
EL Ernie Lombardi/5
EM Eddie Mathews
ES Enos Slaughter
EW Early Wynn
GH Gabby Hartnett
HC Happy Chandler/55 30.00 60.00
HH Harvey Haddix/15
HN Hal Newhouser/52 30.00 60.00
HU Catfish Hunter/37 40.00 80.00
HW Hoyt Wilhelm 30.00 60.00
HW Honus Wagner/6
JC Jocko Conlan/40 20.00 50.00
JD Joe DiMaggio
JF Jimmie Foxx/3
JH Jesse Haines/40 40.00 80.00
JJ Judy Johnson/29 40.00 80.00
JM Johnny Mize
JM Joe McCarthy/27 40.00 80.00
JS Joe Sewell 30.00 60.00
LA Luke Appling 20.00 50.00
LB Lyman Bostock/15
LB Lou Boudreau/54 30.00 60.00
LB Lou Boudreau/50 30.00 60.00
LD Larry Doby/4
LD Leo Durocher/11
LG Lefty Gomez/20
LG Lou Gehrig/3
LW Lloyd Waner/60 60.00 120.00
PT Pie Traynor/6
RA Richie Ashburn/7
RC Roy Campanella/26 300.00 600.00
RF Rick Ferrell/108 30.00 60.00
RM Roger Maris/8
RM Rube Marquard/40
RR Red Ruffing
RS Ray Schalk/5
SB Smoky Burgess/28 40.00 80.00
SC Stan Coveleski/45 30.00 60.00
SP Satchel Paige/17
TL Ted Lyons 40.00 80.00
WH Waite Hoyt/18
WS Warren Spahn 40.00 80.00

2008 SP Legendary Cuts Legendary Cut Signatures Dual

RANDOM INSERTS IN PACKS
STATED PRINT RUN 1 SER.#'d SET
NO PRICING DUE TO SCARCITY
CB Harry Carey
Jack Buck
LC Kenesaw Landis
Charles Comiskey

2008 SP Legendary Cuts Legendary Memorabilia 99

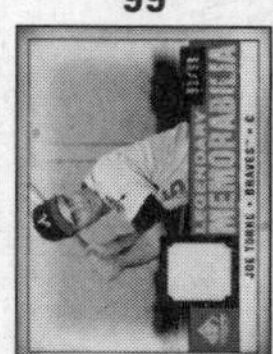

RANDOM INSERTS IN PACKS
STATED PRINT RUN 99 SER.#'d SETS
AD Andre Dawson 4.00 10.00
BF Bob Feller 6.00 15.00
BR Brooks Robinson 4.00 10.00
BS Bruce Sutter 3.00 8.00
BW Billy Williams 4.00 10.00
CA Rod Carew 3.00 8.00
CF2 Carlton Fisk 4.00 10.00
CR Cal Ripken Jr. 6.00 15.00
CY Carl Yastrzemski 5.00 12.00
DM Don Mattingly 5.00 12.00
DP2 Dave Parker 3.00 8.00
DP2 Dave Parker 3.00 8.00
DS Don Sutton 3.00 8.00
DW Dave Winfield 3.00 8.00
EB Ernie Banks 5.00 12.00
EH Elston Howard 3.00 8.00
EM Eddie Murray 3.00 8.00
EW Early Wynn 3.00 8.00
FJ Fergie Jenkins 3.00 8.00
FL Fred Lynn 3.00 8.00
FR Frank Robinson 3.00 8.00
GG Goose Gossage 3.00 8.00
GP Gaylord Perry 3.00 8.00
HK Harmon Killebrew 5.00 12.00
JB Johnny Bench 3.00 8.00
JB2 Jim Bunning 3.00 8.00
JC Joe Carter 4.00 10.00
JM Joe Morgan 3.00 8.00
JM Juan Marichal 3.00 8.00
JT Joe Torre 4.00 10.00
LA Luis Aparicio 3.00 8.00
LE Bob Lemon 3.00 8.00
MA Edgar Martinez 4.00 10.00
MG Mark Grace 3.00 8.00
MS Mike Schmidt 4.00 10.00
NR Nolan Ryan 6.00 15.00
OS Ozzie Smith 4.00 10.00
OS2 Ozzie Smith 4.00 10.00
PM2 Paul Molitor 4.00 10.00
PN Phil Niekro 3.00 8.00
PO Paul O'Neill 3.00 8.00
RC Roberto Clemente 20.00 50.00
RF Rollie Fingers 3.00 8.00
RG Ron Guidry 4.00 10.00
RI Jim Rice 3.00 8.00
RJ Reggie Jackson 5.00 12.00
RM Roger Maris 12.50 30.00
RS Red Schoendienst 3.00 8.00
RS Ryne Sandberg 5.00 12.00
RY Robin Yount 4.00 10.00
SA Ron Santo 5.00 12.00
SM Stan Musial 6.00 15.00
ST Steve Carlton 3.00 8.00
TG2 Tony Gwynn 4.00 10.00
TP Tony Perez 3.00 8.00
TR Tim Raines 3.00 8.00
TS Tom Seaver 3.00 8.00
WB Wade Boggs 3.00 8.00
WC Will Clark 4.00 10.00
WF Whitey Ford 5.00 12.00

2008 SP Legendary Cuts Legendary Memorabilia 75

*MEM 75: .4X TO 1X MEM 99
RANDOM INSERTS IN PACKS
STATED PRINT RUN 75 SER.#'d SETS
BJ Bo Jackson 4.00 10.00
OC Orlando Cepeda 3.00 8.00

2008 SP Legendary Cuts Legendary Memorabilia 50

*MEM 50: .4X TO 1X MEM 99
RANDOM INSERTS IN PACKS
STATED PRINT RUN 50 SER.#'d SETS
BD Bill Dickey 5.00 12.00
BJ Bo Jackson 6.00 15.00
BM Bill Mazeroski 5.00 12.00
FM Fred McGriff 4.00 10.00
JD Joe DiMaggio 20.00 50.00
OC Orlando Cepeda 3.00 8.00

2008 SP Legendary Cuts Legendary Memorabilia 35

*MEM 35: .6X TO 1.5X MEM 99
RANDOM INSERTS IN PACKS
STATED PRINT RUN 35 SER.#'d SETS

2008 SP Legendary Cuts Legendary Memorabilia 25

RANDOM INSERTS IN PACKS
STATED PRINT RUN 25 SER.#'d SETS
NO PRICING DUE TO SCARCITY

2008 SP Legendary Cuts Legendary Memorabilia 15

RANDOM INSERTS IN PACKS
STATED PRINT RUN 15 SER.#'d SETS
NO PRICING DUE TO SCARCITY

2008 SP Legendary Cuts Legendary Memorabilia 10

RANDOM INSERTS IN PACKS
STATED PRINT RUN 10 SER.#'d SETS
NO PRICING DUE TO SCARCITY

2008 SP Legendary Cuts Midsummer Classic Cut Signatures

RANDOM INSERTS IN PACKS
NO PRICING DUE TO SCARCITY
BD Bill Dickey/15
BH Billy Herman/15
CG Charlie Gehringer/15
CH Carl Hubbell/15
EL Ernie Lombardi
EM Eddie Mathews
HN Hal Newhouser/15
JM Joe Medwick
LD Larry Doby/14
LG Lefty Gomez/10
RA Richie Ashburn/15
TW Ted Williams/16

2008 SP Legendary Cuts Mystery Cut Signatures

COMMON CARD 250.00 400.00
RANDOM INSERTS IN PACKS
EXCHANGE DEADLINE 12/31/2010
NNO Mystery EXCH 250.00 400.00

2004 SP Prospects

This 437-card set was released in December, 2004. The set was issued in five card packs with an $5 SRP which came 24 packs to a box and 12 boxes to a case. The first 90 cards feature active veterans while cards 91 through 190 feature rookies. Cards numbere 191 through 290 feature players who were drafted and signed from the 2004 amateur draft and cards 291 through 447 feature players who were not only drafted and signed but also signed autographs for this product. SP Prospects was the Upper Deck product in which they put in those players who were involved in the 2004 amateur draft.

COMP.ROOKIES SET (198) 20.00 50.00
COMMON CARD (1-90) .40 1.00
1-90 APPX. 2X TOUGHER THAN 91-290
COMMON CARD (91-190) .40 1.00
91-190 ODDS TWO PER PACK
COMMON CARD (191-290) .40 1.00
191-290 APPX.TWO PER PACK
OVERALL AU ODDS 1:5
AU PRINT RUNS B/WN 400-600 PER
233/237/345/436-443/445 DO NOT EXIST
1 Roger Clemens 2.00 5.00
2 Melvin Mora .40 1.00
3 Dontrelle Willis .60 1.50
4 Jose Vidro .40 1.00
5 Oliver Perez .40 1.00

6 Carlos Zambrano .40 1.00
7 Chipper Jones 1.00 2.50
8 Greg Maddux 1.50 4.00
9 Curt Schilling .60 1.50
10 Jose Reyes .40 1.00
11 David Ortiz 1.00 2.50
12 Mike Piazza 1.50 4.00
13 Jason Schmidt .40 1.00
14 Randy Johnson 1.00 2.50
15 Magglio Ordonez .40 1.00
16 Mike Mussina .60 1.50
17 Jake Peavy .40 1.00
18 Jim Edmonds .40 1.00
19 Ken Griffey Jr. 1.50 4.00
20 Jason Giambi .40 1.00
21 Mike Sweeney .40 1.00
22 Carlos Lee .40 1.00
23 Craig Wilson .40 1.00
24 Pedro Martinez .60 1.50
25 Bobby Abreu .40 1.00
26 Mike Lowell .40 1.00
27 Miguel Cabrera .60 1.50
28 Hank Blalock .40 1.00
29 Frank Thomas 1.00 2.50
30 Manny Ramirez .60 1.50
31 Mark Mulder .40 1.00
32 Scott Podsednik .40 1.00
33 Albert Pujols 2.00 5.00
34 Preston Wilson .40 1.00
35 Todd Helton .60 1.50
36 Victor Martinéz .40 1.00
37 Kerry Wood .40 1.00
38 Carlos Beltran .40 1.00
39 Vernon Wells .40 1.00
40 Sammy Sosa 1.00 2.50
41 Pat Burrell .40 1.00
42 Tim Hudson .40 1.00
43 Eric Gagne .40 1.00
44 Jim Thome .60 1.50
45 Vladimir Guerrero 1.00 2.50
46 Travis Hafner .40 1.00
47 Rickie Weeks .40 1.00
48 Miguel Tejada .40 1.00
49 Ivan Rodriguez .60 1.50
50 J.D. Drew .40 1.00
51 Ben Sheets .40 1.00
52 Garret Anderson .40 1.00
53 Aubrey Huff .40 1.00
54 Nomar Garciaparra 1.50 4.00
55 Luis Gonzalez .40 1.00
56 Lance Berkman .40 1.00
57 Ichiro Suzuki 2.00 5.00
58 Torii Hunter .40 1.00
59 Adam Dunn .40 1.00
60 Mark Teixeira .60 1.50
61 Bret Boone .40 1.00
62 Roy Oswalt .40 1.00
63 Joe Mauer .50 1.25
64 Scott Rolen .60 1.50
65 Hideki Matsui 1.50 4.00
66 Richie Sexson .40 1.00
67 Jeff Kent .40 1.00
68 Barry Zito .40 1.00
69 C.C. Sabathia .40 1.00
70 Carlos Delgado .40 1.00
71 Gary Sheffield .40 1.00
72 Shawn Green .40 1.00
73 Jason Bay .40 1.00
74 Andruw Jones .60 1.50
75 Jeff Bagwell .60 1.50
76 Rafael Palmeiro .60 1.50
77 Alex Rodriguez 1.50 4.00
78 Adrian Beltre .40 1.00
79 Troy Glaus .40 1.00
80 Tom Glavine .60 1.50
81 Paul Konerko .40 1.00
82 Alfonso Soriano .40 1.00
83 Roy Halladay .40 1.00
84 Derek Jeter 2.00 5.00
85 Josh Beckett .40 1.00
86 Delmon Young .60 1.50
87 Brian Giles .40 1.00
88 Eric Chavez .40 1.00
89 Lyle Overbay .40 1.00
90 Mark Prior .60 1.50
91 Shawn Camp RC .40 1.00
92 Travis Smith .40 1.00
93 Juan Padilla RC .40 1.00
94 Brad Halsey RC .60 1.50
95 Scott Kazmir RC 2.50 6.00
96 Sam Narron RC .40 1.00
97 Frank Francisco RC .40 1.00
98 Mike Johnston RC .40 1.00
99 Sam McConnell RC .40 1.00
100 Josh Labandeira RC .40 1.00
101 Kazuhito Tadano RC .60 1.50
102 Hector Gimenez RC .40 1.00
103 David Aardsma RC .60 1.50
104 Charles Thomas RC .40 1.00
105 Ian Snell RC .75 2.00
106 Jeff Keppinger RC 1.25 3.00
107 Michael Vento RC .60 1.50
108 Jerry Gil RC .40 1.00
109 Marty McLeary RC .40 1.00
110 Donnie Kelly RC .40 1.00
111 Roman Colon RC .40 1.00
112 Travis Blackley RC .40 1.00
113 Edwardo Sierra RC .60 1.50
114 Chris Shelton RC .75 2.00
115 Bartolome Fortunato RC .40 1.00
116 Brandon Medders RC .40 1.00
117 Merkin Valdez RC .60 1.50
118 Carlos Vasquez RC .60 1.50
119 Shingo Takatsu RC .60 1.50
120 Aarom Baldiris RC .60 1.50
121 Chris Aguila RC .40 1.00
122 Jimmy Serrano RC .40 1.00
123 Mike Gosling RC .40 1.00
124 Brian Dallimore RC .40 1.00
125 Ronald Belisario RC .40 1.00
126 George Sherrill RC .40 1.00
127 Fernando Nieve RC .60 1.50
128 Abe Alvarez RC .40 1.00
129 Jeff Bennett RC .40 1.00
130 Ryan Meaux RC .40 1.00
131 Edwin Moreno RC .60 1.50
132 Jesse Crain RC .60 1.50
133 Scott Dohmann RC .40 1.00
134 Ronny Cedeno RC .75 2.00
135 Orlando Rodriguez RC .40 1.00
136 Michael Wuertz RC .60 1.50
137 Justin Hampson RC .40 1.00
138 Matt Treanor RC .40 1.00
139 Andy Green RC .40 1.00
140 Yadier Molina RC 1.00 2.50
141 Joe Nelson RC .40 1.00
142 Justin Lehr RC .40 1.00
143 Ryan Wing RC .40 1.00
144 Kevin Cave RC .40 1.00
145 Evan Rust RC .40 1.00
146 Mike Rouse RC .40 1.00
147 Lance Cormier RC .40 1.00
148 Eduardo Villacis RC .40 1.00
149 Justin Knoedler RC .40 1.00
150 Freddy Guzman RC .40 1.00
151 Casey Daigle RC .40 1.00
152 Joey Gathright RC .75 2.00
153 Tim Bittner RC .40 1.00
154 Scott Atchison RC .40 1.00
155 Ivan Ochoa RC .40 1.00
156 Lincoln Holdzkom RC .40 1.00
157 Onil Joseph RC .40 1.00
158 Jason Bartlett RC .60 1.50
159 Jon Knott RC .40 1.00
160 Jake Woods RC .40 1.00
161 Jerome Gamble RC .40 1.00
162 Sean Henn RC .40 1.00
163 Kazuo Matsui RC .60 1.50
164 Roberto Novoa RC .60 1.50
165 Eddy Rodriguez RC .60 1.50
166 Ramon Ramirez RC .40 1.00
167 Enemencio Pacheco RC .40 1.00
168 Chad Bentz RC .40 1.00
169 Chris Oxspring RC .40 1.00
170 Justin Leone RC .60 1.50
171 Joe Horgan RC .40 1.00
172 Jose Capellan RC .60 1.50
173 Greg Dobbs RC .60 1.50
174 Jason Frasor RC .40 1.00
175 Shawn Hill RC .40 1.00
176 Carlos Hines RC .40 1.00
177 John Gall RC .60 1.50
178 Steve Andrade RC .40 1.00
179 Scott Proctor RC .60 1.50
180 Rusty Tucker RC .60 1.50
181 Dave Crouthers RC .40 1.00
182 Franklyn Gracesqui RC .40 1.00
183 Justin Germano RC .40 1.00
184 Alfredo Simon RC .40 1.00
185 Jorge Sequea RC .40 1.00
186 Nick Regilio RC .40 1.00
187 Justin Huisman RC .40 1.00
188 Akinori Otsuka RC .40 1.00
189 Luis Gonzalez RC .40 1.00
190 Renyel Pinto RC .60 1.50
191 Joshua Leblanc RC .60 1.50
192 Devin Ivany RC .75 2.00
193 Chad Blackwell RC .60 1.50
194 Brandon Burgess RC .60 1.50
195 Cory Patton RC .60 1.50
196 Daniel Batz RC .60 1.50
197 Adam Russell RC .60 1.50
198 Jarrett Hoffpauir RC .75 2.00
199 Patrick Bryant RC .60 1.50
200 Sean Gamble RC .75 2.00
201 Jermaine Brock RC .75 2.00
202 Ben Zobrist RC .75 2.00
203 Clay Meredith RC .75 2.00
204 Derek Tharpe RC .60 1.50
205 Bradley McCann RC 1.00 2.50
206 Justin Hedrick RC .60 1.50
207 Clint Sammons RC .75 2.00
208 Richard Steik RC .60 1.50
209 Fernando Perez RC .75 2.00
210 Mark Jecmen RC .75 2.00
211 Benjamin Harrison RC .60 1.50
212 Jason Quarles RC .60 1.50
213 William Layman RC .60 1.50
214 Koley Kolberg RC .60 1.50
215 Randy Dicken RC .40 1.00
216 Barry Richmond RC .60 1.50
217 Timothy Murphey RC .60 1.50
218 John Hardy RC .60 1.50
219 Sebastien Boucher RC .75 2.00
220 Andrew Alvarado RC .60 1.50
221 Patrick Perry RC .75 2.00
222 Jarod McAuliff RC .60 1.50
223 Jared Gaston RC .60 1.50
224 William Thompson RC .60 1.50
225 Lucas French RC .60 1.50
226 Brandon Parillo RC .75 2.00
227 Gregory Goetz RC .60 1.50
228 David Haehnel RC .75 2.00
229 James Miller RC .60 1.50
230 Mark Roberts RC .60 1.50
231 Eric Ridener RC .60 1.50
232 Freddy Sandoval RC .60 1.50
234 Carlos Medero-Stullz RC .60 1.50
235 Matthew Shepherd RC .60 1.50
236 Thomas Hubbard RC .60 1.50
238 Kyle Bono RC .75 2.00
239 Craig Moldrem RC .40 1.00
240 Brandon Timm RC UER .75 2.00
Photo is Cory Middleton
241 Mike Carp RC 1.00 2.50
242 Joseph Muro RC .60 1.50
243 Derek Decarlo RC .60 1.50
244 Christopher Niesel RC .75 2.00
245 Trevor Lawhorn RC .75 2.00
246 Joey Howell RC .75 2.00
247 Dustin Hahn RC .60 1.50
248 James Fasano RC .75 2.00
249 Hainley Statia RC .60 1.50
250 Brandon Conway RC .60 1.50
251 Christopher McConnell RC 1.00 2.50
252 Austin Shappi RC .75 2.00
253 Joseph Metropoulos RC .75 2.00
254 David Nicholson RC .75 2.00
255 Ryan McCarthy RC .75 2.00
256 Michael Parisi RC .60 1.50
257 Andrew Macfarlane RC .60 1.50
258 Jeffrey Dominguez RC .60 1.50
259 Troy Patton RC 2.00 5.00
260 Ryan Norwood RC 1.00 2.50
261 Chad Boyd RC .60 1.50
262 Grant Plumley RC .60 1.50
263 Jeffrey Katz RC .75 2.00
264 Cory Middleton RC .60 1.50
265 Andrew Moffitt RC .40 1.00
266 Jarrett Grube RC .75 2.00
267 Derek Hankins RC .60 1.50
268 Douglas Reinhardt RC .60 1.50
269 Duron Legrande RC .60 1.50
270 Steven Jackson RC .40 1.00
271 Brian Hall RC .75 2.00
272 Cory Wade RC .75 2.00
273 John Grogan RC .60 1.50
274 Robert Asanovich RC .75 2.00
275 Kevin Hart RC .75 2.00
276 Matthew Guillory RC .60 1.50
277 Clifton Remole RC .60 1.50
278 David Trahan RC .60 1.50
279 Kristian Bell RC .40 1.00
280 Christopher Westervelt RC .60 1.50
281 Garry Bakker RC .60 1.50
282 Jonathan Ash RC .75 2.00
283 Ryan Phillips RC .60 1.50
284 Wesley Letson RC UER .60 1.50
Name spelled Lesly on the back
285 Jeffrey Landing RC .60 1.50
286 Mark Worrell RC .60 1.50
287 Sean Gallagher RC 2.00 5.00
288 Nicholas Blasi RC .60 1.50
289 Kevin Frandsen RC 1.25 3.00
290 Richard Mercado RC .60 1.50
291 Matt Bush AU 400/RC 6.00 15.00
292 Mark Rogers AU 400/RC 10.00 25.00
293 Homer Bailey AU 400/RC 30.00 60.00
294 Chris Nelson AU 400/RC 30.00 60.00
295 T.Diamond AU 400/RC 3.00 8.00
296 Neil Walker AU 400/RC 15.00 40.00
297 Bill Bray AU 400/RC 4.00 10.00
298 David Purcey AU 400/RC 10.00 25.00
299 Scott Elbert AU 400/RC 15.00 40.00
300 Josh Fields AU 400/RC 30.00 60.00
301 Chris Lambert AU 400/RC 3.00 8.00
302 Trevor Plouffe AU 400/RC 12.50 30.00
303 Greg Golson AU 400/RC 12.50 30.00
304 Phillip Hughes AU 400/RC 50.00 100.00
305 Kyle Waldrop AU 400/RC 3.00 8.00
306 Richie Robnett AU 350/RC 8.00 20.00
307 T.Tankersley AU 400/RC 6.00 15.00
308 Blake Dewitt AU 400/RC 12.50 30.00
309 Eric Hurley AU 400/RC 8.00 20.00
310 J.Howell AU 400/RC EX * 5.00 12.00
311 Zachary Jackson AU 400/RC 6.00 15.00
312 Justin Orenduff AU 400/RC 10.00 25.00
313 Tyler Lumsden AU 400/RC 6.00 15.00
314 Matthew Fox AU 600/RC 3.00 8.00
315 Danny Putnam AU 450/RC 6.00 15.00
316 Jon Poterson AU 400/RC 6.00 15.00
317 Gio Gonzalez AU 400/RC 20.00 50.00
318 Jay Rainville AU 475/RC 6.00 15.00
319 Huston Street AU 400/RC 15.00 40.00
320 Jeff Marquez AU 400/RC 20.00 50.00
321 Eric Beattie AU 500/RC 6.00 15.00
322 Reid Brignac AU 325/RC 60.00 120.00
323 Y.Gallardo AU 400/RC 60.00 120.00
324 Justin Hoyman AU 400/RC 3.00 8.00
325 B.J. Szymanski AU 400/RC 8.00 20.00
326 Seth Smith AU 600/RC 12.50 30.00
327 Karl Herren AU 600/RC 6.00 15.00
328 Brian Bixler AU 600/RC 3.00 8.00
329 Wesley Whisler AU 600/RC 3.00 8.00
330 E.San Pedro AU 400/RC 6.00 15.00
331 Billy Buckner AU 400/RC 3.00 8.00
332 Jon Zeringue AU 400/RC 4.00 10.00
333 Curtis Thigpen AU 400/RC 5.00 12.00
334 Blake Johnson AU 400/RC 6.00 15.00
335 Donald Lucy AU 400/RC 3.00 8.00
336 Michael Ferris AU 600/RC 5.00 12.00
337 A.Swarzak AU 600/RC 8.00 20.00
338 Jason Jaramillo AU 400/RC 6.00 15.00
339 Hunter Pence AU 600/RC 75.00 150.00
340 Dustin Pedroia AU 400/RC 100.00 175.00
341 Grant Johnson AU 400/RC 6.00 15.00
342 Kurt Suzuki AU 400/RC 8.00 20.00
343 Jason Vargas AU 600/RC 4.00 10.00
344 Raymond Liotta AU 400/RC 15.00 30.00
346 Eric Campbell AU 400/RC 6.00 15.00
347 Jeffrey Frazier AU 600/RC 3.00 8.00
348 G.Hernandez AU 400/RC 10.00 25.00
349 Wade Davis AU 600/RC 20.00 50.00
350 J.Wahpepah AU 400/RC 4.00 10.00
351 Scott Lewis AU 400/RC 12.50 30.00
352 Jeff Fiorentino AU 400/RC 4.00 10.00
353 S.Register AU 600/RC 3.00 8.00
354 Michael Schlact AU 400/RC 4.00 10.00
355 Eddie Prasch AU 400/RC 6.00 15.00
356 Adam Lind AU 400/RC 40.00 80.00
357 Ian Desmond AU 400/RC 10.00 25.00
358 Josh Johnson AU 575/RC 5.00 12.00
359 Garrett Mock AU 600/RC 3.00 8.00
360 Danny Hill AU 400/RC 3.00 8.00
361 Cory Dunlap AU 600/RC 4.00 10.00
362 Grant Hansen AU 600/RC 3.00 8.00
363 Eric Haberer AU 400/RC 3.00 8.00
364 E.Morlan AU 400/RC 10.00 25.00
365 James Happ AU 600/RC 10.00 25.00
366 M.Tuiasosopo AU 600/RC 20.00 50.00
367 Jordan Parraz AU 400/RC 6.00 15.00
368 Andrew Dobies AU 400/RC 8.00 20.00
369 Mark Reed AU 400/RC 10.00 25.00
370 Jason Windsor AU 400/RC 4.00 10.00
371 Gregory Burns AU 600/RC 3.00 8.00
372 Christian Garcia AU 600/RC 8.00 20.00
373 John Bowker AU 575/RC 6.00 15.00
374 J.C. Holt AU 550/RC 5.00 12.00
375 Daryl Jones AU 400/RC 3.00 8.00
376 Collin Mahoney AU 400/RC 6.00 15.00
377 A.Hathaway AU 400/RC 6.00 15.00
378 Matthew Spring AU 400/RC 3.00 8.00
379 Joshua Baker AU 400/RC 4.00 10.00
380 Charles Lofgren AU 400/RC 20.00 50.00
381 Raf Gonzalez AU 400/RC 10.00 25.00
382 Brad Bergesen AU 575/RC 5.00 12.00
383 Brandon Boggs AU 400/RC 5.00 12.00
384 J.Bauserman AU 400/RC 3.00 8.00
385 Collin Balester AU 500/RC 6.00 15.00
386 James Moore AU 400/RC 3.00 8.00
387 Robert Janssen AU 400/RC 10.00 25.00
388 Luis Guerra AU 400/RC 6.00 15.00
389 Lucas Harrell AU 550/RC 3.00 8.00
390 Donnie Smith AU 500/RC 5.00 12.00
391 Mark Robinson AU 525/RC 5.00 12.00
392 Louis Marson AU 550/RC 6.00 15.00
393 Rob Johnson AU 600/RC 3.00 8.00
394 L.Santangelo AU 600/RC 5.00 12.00
395 T.Hottovy AU 400/RC 3.00 8.00
396 Ryan Webb AU 400/RC 6.00 15.00
397 Jamar Walton AU 400/RC 4.00 10.00
398 Jason Jones AU 400/RC 10.00 25.00
399 Clay Timpner AU 400/RC 5.00 12.00
400 James Parr AU 400/RC 8.00 20.00
401 Sean Kazmar AU 400/RC 4.00 10.00
402 Andrew Kown AU 400/RC 6.00 15.00
403 Jacob McGee AU 400/RC 20.00 50.00
404 Michael Butia AU 600/RC 3.00 8.00
405 Paul Janish AU 500/RC 6.00 15.00
406 Matthew Macri AU 400/RC 10.00 25.00
407 Mike Nickeas AU 500/RC 3.00 8.00
408 Kyle Bloom AU 550/RC 4.00 10.00
409 Luis Rivera AU 500/RC 5.00 12.00
410 William Bunn AU 600/RC 10.00 25.00
411 Enrique Barrera AU 400/RC 10.00 25.00
412 R.Klosterman AU 400/RC 4.00 10.00
413 John Raglani AU 515/RC 8.00 20.00
414 Brandon Allen AU 500/RC 8.00 20.00
415 A.Baldwin AU 600/RC 3.00 8.00
416 Mark Lowe AU 400/RC 20.00 50.00
417 Mitch Einertson AU 400/RC 12.50 30.00
418 Ryan Schroyer AU 600/RC 5.00 12.00
419 Bradley Davis AU 400/RC 4.00 10.00
420 Jesse Hoover AU 500/RC 5.00 12.00
421 G.Broshuis AU 400/RC 8.00 20.00
422 Peter Pope AU 400/RC 8.00 20.00
423 Brent Dlugach AU 400/RC 6.00 15.00
424 Ryan Coultas AU 400/RC 6.00 15.00
425 Ryan Royster AU 400/RC 40.00 80.00
426 S.Chapman AU 400/RC 6.00 15.00
427 B.Chamberlin AU 400/RC 8.00 20.00
428 J.Koshansky AU 550/RC 12.50 30.00
429 William Susdorf AU 400/RC 3.00 8.00
430 A.J. Johnson AU 400/RC 8.00 20.00
431 Jeremy Sowers AU 400/RC 30.00 60.00
432 Justin Pekarek AU 400/RC 6.00 15.00
433 Brett Smith AU 400/RC 12.50 30.00
434 Matt Durkin AU 400/RC 6.00 15.00
435 Daniel Barone AU 400/RC 4.00 10.00
436 Scott Hyde AU 400/RC 6.00 15.00
437 T.Everidge AU 400/RC 20.00 50.00
444 Mark Trumbo AU 400/RC 12.50 30.00
446 Eric Patterson AU 400/RC 5.00 12.00
447 Michael Rozier AU 400/RC 6.00 15.00

2004 SP Prospects Gold

OVERALL AU ODDS 1:5
STATED PRINT RUN 10 SERIAL #'d SETS
NO PRICING DUE TO SCARCITY

2004 SP Prospects Platinum

OVERALL AU ODDS 1:5
STATED PRINT RUN 1 SERIAL #'d SET
NO PRICING DUE TO SCARCITY

2004 SP Prospects Autograph Bonus

OVERALL AU ODDS 1:5
PRINT RUNS B/WN 325-600 COPIES PER
AA Andrew Alvarado/400 4.00 10.00
AM Andrew Moffitt/400 4.00 10.00
AR Adam Russell/550 3.00 8.00
AS Austin Shappi/475 6.00 15.00
BB Brandon Burgess/400 6.00 15.00
BC Brandon Conway/400 3.00 8.00
BE Benjamin Harrison/387 3.00 8.00
BH Brian Hall/400 6.00 15.00
BL Chad Blackwell/400 3.00 8.00
BM Bradley McCann/400 10.00 25.00
BO Kyle Bono/400 3.00 8.00
BP Brandon Parillo/475 6.00 15.00
BR Barry Richmond/400 6.00 15.00
BT Brandon Timm/475 6.00 15.00
BZ Ben Zobrist/600 10.00 25.00
CA Mike Carp/400 15.00 40.00
CB Chad Boyd/475 4.00 10.00
CH Christopher McConnell/400 3.00 8.00
CL Clay Meredith/400 4.00 10.00
CM Cory Middleton/400 4.00 10.00
CN Christopher Niesel/475 6.00 15.00
CP Cory Patton/400 4.00 10.00
CR Clifton Remole/400 4.00 10.00
CS Clint Sammons/400 3.00 8.00
CW Cory Wade/400 6.00 15.00
DA David Haehnel/475 6.00 15.00
DB Daniel Batz/400 3.00 8.00
DD Derek Decarlo/400 4.00 10.00
DH Derek Hankins/400 4.00 10.00
DI Devin Ivany/550 3.00 8.00
DL Duron Legrande/400 4.00 10.00
DN David Nicholson/475 3.00 8.00
DR Douglas Reinhardt/400 4.00 10.00
DT Derek Tharpe/400 4.00 10.00
ER Eric Ridener/475 4.00 10.00
FP Fernando Perez/400 20.00 50.00
FS Freddy Sandoval/400 6.00 15.00
GA Jared Gaston/400 4.00 10.00
GB Garry Bakker/400 4.00 10.00
GG Gregory Goetz/400 4.00 10.00
GP Grant Plumley/475 3.00 8.00
GR John Grogan/400 4.00 10.00
HA Dustin Hahn/400 4.00 10.00
HE Justin Hedrick/400 4.00 10.00
HO Joey Howell/400 5.00 12.00
HS Hainley Statia/400 5.00 12.00
JA Jonathan Ash/400 8.00 20.00
JB Jermaine Brock/400 6.00 15.00
JD Jeffrey Dominguez/400 3.00 8.00
JF James Fasano/400 6.00 15.00
JG Jarrett Grube/400 4.00 10.00
JH Jarrett Hoffpauir/400 10.00 25.00
JK Jeffrey Katz/400 6.00 15.00
JL Joshua Leblanc/400 4.00 10.00
JM Joseph Metropoulos/400 6.00 15.00
JO John Hardy/475 4.00 10.00
JQ Jason Quarles/400 4.00 10.00
KB Kristian Bell/400 4.00 10.00
KF Kevin Frandsen/400 10.00 25.00
KH Kevin Hart/400 5.00 12.00
KK Koley Kolberg/400 4.00 10.00
LA Jeffrey Landing/400 4.00 10.00
LE Wesley Letson/400 4.00 10.00
LF Lucas French/400 3.00 8.00
MA Andrew Macfarlane/400 4.00 10.00
MC Jarod McAuliff/400 4.00 10.00
ME Carlos Medero-Stullz/400 4.00 10.00
MG Matthew Guillory/400 3.00 8.00
MI James Miller/475 4.00 10.00
MJ Mark Jecmen/600 3.00 8.00
MO Craig Moldrem/400 3.00 8.00
MP Michael Parisi/475 4.00 10.00
MR Mark Roberts/400 4.00 10.00
MS Matthew Shepherd/400 4.00 10.00
MU Joseph Muro/400 4.00 10.00
MW Mark Worrell/400 6.00 15.00
NB Nicholas Blasi/400 4.00 10.00
PB Patrick Bryant/400 4.00 10.00
PP Patrick Perry/475 6.00 15.00
RA Robert Asanovich/400 6.00 15.00
RD Randy Dicken/475 3.00 8.00
RI Richard Mercado/400 4.00 10.00
RM Ryan McCarthy/400 8.00 20.00
RN Ryan Norwood/400 10.00 25.00
RP Ryan Phillips/400 4.00 10.00
RS Richard Steik/400 4.00 10.00
SB Sebastien Boucher/325 6.00 15.00
SE Sean Gallagher/400 30.00 60.00
SG Sean Gamble/400 6.00 15.00
SJ Steven Jackson/475 4.00 10.00
TH Thomas Hubbard/400 4.00 10.00
TL Trevor Lawhorn/475 6.00 15.00
TM Timothy Murphey/400 4.00 10.00
TP Troy Patton/400 40.00 80.00
TR David Trahan/400 4.00 10.00
WE Christopher Westervelt/400 4.00 10.00
WL William Layman/400 4.00 10.00
WT William Thompson/475 4.00 10.00

2004 SP Prospects Autograph Bonus Gold

OVERALL AU ODDS 1:5
STATED PRINT RUN 10 SERIAL #'d SETS
NO PRICING DUE TO SCARCITY

2004 SP Prospects Autograph Bonus Platinum

OVERALL AU ODDS 1:5
STATED PRINT RUN 1 SERIAL #'d SET
NO PRICING DUE TO SCARCITY

2004 SP Prospects Draft Class Quad Autographs

OVERALL AU ODDS 1:5
STATED PRINT RUN 10 SERIAL #'d SETS
NO PRICING DUE TO SCARCITY
BZSR Josh Beckett
Barry Zito
Ben Sheets
Alex Rios
CGFC Joe Carter
Tony Gwynn
Sid Fernandez
David Cone
CLJP Will Clark
John Smoltz
Randy Johnson
Rafael Palmeiro
MPTK Joe Mauer
Mark Prior
Mark Teixeira
Casey Kotchman
RBGS Jim Rice
George Brett
Ron Guidry
Mike Schmidt
SRSG Steve Sax
Cal Ripken
Ryne Sandberg
Kirk Gibson
TVOB Frank Thomas
Mo Vaughn
John Olerud
Jeff Bagwell
WHJB Kerry Wood
Todd Helton
Geoff Jenkins
Carlos Beltran
YWLM Robin Yount
Dave Winfield
Fred Lynn
Eddie Murray

2004 SP Prospects Draft Duos Dual Autographs

OVERALL AU ODDS 1:5
STATED PRINT RUN 175 SERIAL #'d SETS
BB Bill Bray 10.00 25.00
Collin Balester
BG Homer Bailey 15.00 40.00
Rafael Gonzalez
BH Matt Bush 20.00 50.00
Philip Hughes
BI Bill Bray 12.50 30.00
Ian Desmond
BJ Matt Bush 6.00 15.00
Daryl Jones
BK Matt Bush 6.00 15.00
Sean Kazmar
BM Billy Buckner 8.00 20.00
James Moore
BN Matt Bush 15.00 40.00
Chris Nelson
BP Matt Bush 10.00 25.00
Trevor Plouffe
BR Reid Brignac 8.00 20.00
Ryan Royster
BS Homer Bailey 15.00 40.00
B.J. Szymanski
BT Thomas Diamond 6.00 15.00
Brandon Boggs
CF Bryce Chamberlin 10.00 25.00
Jeff Fiorentino
CH Ryan Coultas 8.00 20.00
Aaron Hathaway
CL Justin Hoyman 12.50 30.00
Jeremy Sowers
CO Steven Register 10.00 25.00
Seth Smith
DB Blake Dewitt 6.00 15.00
Daniel Batz
DG Cory Dunlap 8.00 20.00
Luis Guerra
DH Thomas Diamond 10.00 25.00
Eric Hurley
DR Blake Dewitt 8.00 20.00
John Raglani
DZ David Purcey 6.00 15.00
Zachary Jackson
EA Eric Beattie 8.00 20.00
Andrew Kown
EC Eric Beattie 8.00 20.00
Collin Mahoney
ED Scott Elbert 10.00 25.00
Blake Dewitt
EJ Eric Campbell 15.00 40.00
J.C. Holt
EM Eric Hurley 10.00 25.00
Michael Nickeas
ER Scott Elbert 8.00 20.00
John Raglani
FB Jeff Fiorentino 10.00 25.00
Brad Bergesen
FH Josh Fields 15.00 40.00
Lucas Harrell
FM Jeffrey Frazier 8.00 20.00
Collin Mahoney
FW Josh Fields 6.00 15.00
Wesley Whisler
GB Homer Bailey 15.00 40.00
Gregory Goetz
GG Greg Golson 10.00 25.00
Sean Gamble
GH Greg Golson 8.00 20.00
James Happ
GM Giovanny Gonzalez 6.00 15.00
Timothy Murphey
GW Yovani Gallardo 15.00 40.00
Joshua Wahpepah
HB James Howell 6.00 15.00
Chad Blackwell
HG Philip Hughes 20.00 50.00
Christian Garcia
HH Gaby Hernandez 12.50 30.00
Aaron Hathaway
HJ Hunter Pence 30.00 60.00
Jordan Parraz
HM Jeff Marquez 20.00 50.00
Philip Hughes
HP Philip Hughes 20.00 50.00
Jonathan Poterson
HS Karl Herren 8.00 20.00
Michael Schlact
JB Billy Buckner 6.00 15.00
Joshua Johnson
JE Jeffrey Frazier 8.00 20.00
Eric Beattie
JH James Howell 8.00 20.00
Joshua Johnson
JJ Jonathan Poterson 8.00 20.00
Jason Jones
JK Zachary Jackson 8.00 20.00
Ryan Klosterman
JM Jason Jaramillo 8.00 20.00
Louis Marson
JP Jay Rainville 10.00 25.00
Patrick Bryant
JR Grant Johnson 10.00 25.00
Mark Reed
JS Jeremy Sowers 8.00 20.00
Scott Lewis
KB Kyle Waldrop 8.00 20.00

Patrick Bryant
KH Matthew Durkin 6.00 15.00
Aaron Hathaway
LA Raymond Liotta 8.00 20.00
Brandon Allen
LF Chris Lambert 8.00 20.00
Michael Ferris
LG Tyler Lumsden 6.00 15.00
Giovanny Gonzalez
LH Donald Lucy 6.00 15.00
Grant Hansen
LK Adam Lind 15.00 40.00
Ryan Klosterman
LR Tyler Lumsden 8.00 20.00
Adam Russell
LS Chris Lambert 8.00 20.00
Donnie Smith
MH Jeff Marquez 8.00 20.00
Jesse Hoover
MR Eduardo Morlan 8.00 20.00
Mark Robinson
MS Jeff Marquez 8.00 20.00
Brett Smith
NB Neil Walker 10.00 25.00
Brian Bixler
NK Neil Walker 12.50 30.00
Kyle Bloom
NM Chris Nelson 12.50 30.00
Matthew Macri
NS Chris Nelson 10.00 25.00
Seth Smith
OG Justin Orenduff 8.00 20.00
Luis Guerra
OJ Justin Orenduff 8.00 20.00
Blake Johnson
PB Eddie Prasch 8.00 20.00
Joseph Bauserman
PD Dustin Pedroia 50.00 100.00
Andrew Dobies
PI Erick San Pedro 8.00 20.00
Devin Ivany
PJ David Purcey 8.00 20.00
Robert Janssen
PR Trevor Plouffe 6.00 15.00
Mark Robinson
PT Danny Putnam 8.00 20.00
Derek Tharpe
PW Trevor Plouffe 10.00 25.00
Kyle Waldrop
PZ Jordan Parraz 8.00 20.00
Ben Zobrist
RB Mark Rogers 10.00 25.00
Joshua Baker
RD Cory Dunlap 8.00 20.00
John Raglani
RG Mark Rogers 15.00 40.00
Yovani Gallardo
RH Richie Robnett 12.50 30.00
Huston Street
RL Luis Rivera 8.00 20.00
William Layman
RP Richie Robnett 8.00 20.00
Danny Putnam
RS Jay Rainville 12.50 30.00
Anthony Swarzak
RW Richie Robnett 8.00 20.00
Jason Windsor
SB Jeremy Sowers 12.50 30.00
Homer Bailey
SH Brett Smith 15.00 40.00
Phillip Hughes
SJ B.J. Szymanski 8.00 20.00
Paul Janish
SK Seth Smith 15.00 40.00
Joseph Koshansky
SL Jeremy Sowers 15.00 40.00
Charles Lofgren
SR Richie Robnett 10.00 25.00
Kurt Suzuki
SS Huston Street 12.50 30.00
Kurt Suzuki
SW Huston Street 12.50 30.00
Ryan Webb
TD Taylor Tankersley 6.00 15.00
Bradley Davis
TH Curtis Thigpen 8.00 20.00
Danny Hill UER(Photo of Thigpen is not him
TV Taylor Tankersley 6.00 15.00
Jason Vargas
WB Joshua Wahpepah 6.00 15.00
Joshua Baker
WE Billy Buckner 8.00 20.00
Enrique Barrera
WF Kyle Waldrop 8.00 20.00
Matthew Fox
WJ Billy Buckner 6.00 15.00
James Howell
WR Reid Brignac 15.00 40.00
Wade Davis
ZM Jonathan Zeringue 10.00 25.00
Garrett Mock
ZP Hunter Pence 30.00 60.00
Ben Zobrist

2004 SP Prospects Draft Generations Triple Autographs

OVERALL AU ODDS 1:5
STATED PRINT RUN 25 SERIAL #'d SETS
NO PRICING DUE TO SCARCITY

2004 SP Prospects Link to the Future Dual Autographs

COMMON CARD 6.00 15.00
OVERALL AU ODDS 1:5
STATED PRINT RUN 100 SERIAL #'d SETS
BD Adrian Beltre 15.00 40.00
Blake Dewitt
BG Carlos Beltran 6.00 15.00
Greg Golson
BH Angel Berroa 10.00 25.00
James Howell
CD Roger Clemens 60.00 120.00
Thomas Diamond
CF Matt Clement 6.00 15.00
Matthew Fox
EJ Eric Chavez 15.00 40.00
Josh Fields
GB Nomar Garciaparra 30.00 60.00
Matt Bush
GP Brian Giles 10.00 25.00
Danny Putnam
GS Ken Griffey Jr. 30.00 60.00
B.J. Szymanski
GZ Luis Gonzalez 10.00 25.00
Jonathan Zeringue
HS Todd Helton 15.00 40.00
Seth Smith
HW Rich Harden 10.00 25.00
Kyle Waldrop
JB Jason Kendall 10.00 25.00
Brian Bixler
JJ Edwin Jackson 6.00 15.00
Blake Johnson
JR Andruw Jones 15.00 40.00
Richie Robnett
KB Scott Kazmir 25.00 50.00
Reid Brignac
KW Jason Kendall 15.00 40.00
Neil Walker
LS Paul LoDuca 10.00 25.00
Erick San Pedro
MB Mark Mulder 10.00 25.00
Bill Bray
MH Mike Mussina 50.00 100.00
Philip Hughes
MP Joe Mauer 20.00 50.00
Trevor Plouffe
MS Mike Mussina 6.00 15.00
Brett Smith
OH Magglio Ordonez 10.00 25.00
Karl Herren
PE Odalis Perez 10.00 25.00
Scott Elbert
PJ Mark Prior 15.00 40.00
Grant Johnson
QT Guillermo Quiroz 6.00 15.00
Curtis Thigpen
RE Roy Oswalt 10.00 25.00
Eric Hurley
RF Scott Rolen 15.00 40.00
Michael Ferris
RL Scott Rolen 15.00 40.00
Chris Lambert
RP Alexis Rios 10.00 25.00
David Purcey
SJ Johan Santana 15.00 40.00
Jay Rainville
SR Ben Sheets 20.00 40.00
Mark Rogers
SW Johan Santana 15.00 40.00
Kyle Waldrop
TJ Tom Glavine 15.00 40.00
Jeremy Sowers
TN Miguel Tejada 30.00 60.00
Chris Nelson
TS Tim Hudson 15.00 40.00
Huston Street
VD Victor Martinez 10.00 25.00
Donald Lucy
VM Javier Vazquez 10.00 25.00
Jeff Marquez
VP Javier Vazquez 6.00 15.00
Jonathan Poterson
WB Kerry Wood 25.00 50.00
Homer Bailey
WT Dontrelle Willis 10.00 25.00
Taylor Tankersley

2004 SP Prospects Link to the Future Triple Autographs

OVERALL AU ODDS 1:5
STATED PRINT RUN 50 SERIAL #'d SETS
PRICING UNAVAILABLE AT THIS TIME

2004 SP Prospects Link to the Past Dual Autographs

OVERALL AU ODDS 1:5
STATED PRINT RUN 50 SERIAL #'d SETS
NO PRICING DUE TO LOW VOLUME

2004 SP Prospects National Honors USA Jersey

STATED ODDS 1:12
AG Alex Gordon 10.00 25.00
BC J. Brent Cox 3.00 8.00
BH Brett Hayes 3.00 8.00
CR Cesar Ramos 3.00 8.00
CV Chris Valaika 3.00 8.00
DB Daniel Bard 3.00 8.00
DS Drew Stubbs 3.00 8.00
IK Ian Kennedy 6.00 15.00
JC Jeff Clement 4.00 10.00
JD Joey Devine 3.00 8.00
JL Jed Lowrie 3.00 8.00
JM John Mayberry Jr. 4.00 10.00
LH Luke Hochevar 3.00 8.00
MP Mike Pelfrey 6.00 15.00
MR Mark Romanczuk 3.00 8.00
RR Ricky Romero 3.00 8.00
RZ Ryan Zimmerman 6.00 15.00
SK Stephen Kahn 3.00 8.00
TB Travis Buck 3.00 8.00
TC Trevor Crowe 3.00 8.00
TE Taylor Teagarden 3.00 8.00
TT Troy Tulowitzki 8.00 20.00

1999 SP Signature

The 1999 SP Signature set was issued in one series totalling 180 cards and distributed in three card packs with a suggested retail price of $19.99. The expensive SRP was due to the fact that there is one autograph card per pack. The set features color action player photos with player information on the cardback. Rookie Cards include A.J. Burnett and Pat Burrell. 350 Mel Ott A Piece of History 500 Club bat cards were randomly seeded into packs. Pricing for these bat cards can be referenced under 1999 Upper Deck A Piece of History 500 Club.

COMPLETE SET (180) 60.00 150.00
1 Nomar Garciaparra 1.50 4.00
2 Ken Griffey Jr. 1.50 4.00
3 J.D. Drew .40 1.00
4 Alex Rodriguez 1.50 4.00
5 Juan Gonzalez .40 1.00
6 Mo Vaughn .40 1.00
7 Greg Maddux 1.50 4.00
8 Chipper Jones 1.00 2.50
9 Frank Thomas 1.00 2.50
10 Vladimir Guerrero 1.00 2.50
11 Mike Piazza 1.50 4.00
12 Eric Chavez .40 1.00
13 Tony Gwynn 1.25 3.00
14 Orlando Hernandez .40 1.00
15 Pat Burrell RC 3.00 8.00
16 Darin Erstad .40 1.00
17 Greg Vaughn .30 .75
18 Russ Branyan .30 .75
19 Gabe Kapler .40 1.00
20 Craig Biggio .60 1.50
21 Troy Glaus .60 1.50
22 Pedro Martinez .60 1.50
23 Carlos Beltran .60 1.50
24 Derrek Lee .60 1.50
25 Manny Ramirez .60 1.50
26 Shea Hillenbrand RC 1.50 4.00
27 Carlos Lee .40 1.00
28 Angel Pena .30 .75
29 Rafael Roque RC .40 1.00
30 Octavio Dotel .30 .75
31 Jeromy Burnitz .40 1.00
32 Jeremy Giambi .30 .75
33 Andruw Jones .60 1.50
34 Todd Helton .60 1.50
35 Scott Rolen .60 1.50
36 Jason Kendall .40 1.00
37 Trevor Hoffman .40 1.00
38 Barry Bonds 2.50 6.00
39 Ivan Rodriguez .60 1.50
40 Roy Halladay .40 1.00
41 Rickey Henderson 1.00 2.50
42 Ryan Minor .30 .75
43 Brian Jordan .40 1.00
44 Alex Gonzalez .30 .75
45 Raul Mondesi .40 1.00
46 Corey Koskie .30 .75
47 Paul O'Neill .60 1.50
48 Todd Walker .30 .75
49 Carlos Febles .30 .75
50 Travis Fryman .40 1.00
51 Albert Belle .40 1.00
52 Travis Lee .30 .75
53 Bruce Chen .30 .75
54 Reggie Taylor .30 .75
55 Jerry Hairston Jr. .30 .75
56 Carlos Guillen .40 1.00
57 Michael Barrett .30 .75
58 Jason Conti .30 .75
59 Joe Lawrence .30 .75
60 Jeff Cirillo .30 .75
61 Juan Melo .30 .75
62 Chad Hermansen .30 .75
63 Ruben Mateo .30 .75
64 Ben Davis .30 .75
65 Mike Caruso .30 .75
66 Jason Giambi .40 1.00
67 Jose Canseco .60 1.50
68 Chad Hutchinson RC .60 1.50
69 Mitch Meluskey .30 .75
70 Adrian Beltre .40 1.00
71 Mark Kotsay .40 1.00
72 Juan Encarnacion .30 .75
73 Dermal Brown .30 .75
74 Kevin Witt .30 .75
75 Vinny Castilla .40 1.00
76 Aramis Ramirez .40 1.00
77 Marlon Anderson .30 .75
78 Mike Kinkade .30 .75
79 Kevin Barker .30 .75
80 Ron Belliard .30 .75
81 Chris Haas .30 .75
82 Bob Henley .30 .75
83 Fernando Seguignol .30 .75
84 Damon Minor .30 .75
85 A.J. Burnett RC 1.50 4.00
86 Calvin Pickering .30 .75
87 Mike Darr .30 .75
88 Cesar King .30 .75
89 Rob Bell .30 .75
90 Derrick Gibson .30 .75
91 Orber Moreno RC .40 1.00
92 Robert Fick .30 .75
93 Doug Mientkiewicz RC 1.00 2.50
94 A.J. Pierzynski .40 1.00
95 Orlando Palmeiro .30 .75
96 Sidney Ponson .30 .75
97 Ivanon Coffie RC .40 1.00
98 Juan Pena RC .40 1.00
99 Matt Karchner .30 .75
100 Carlos Castillo .30 .75
101 Bryan Ward RC .40 1.00
102 Mario Valdez .30 .75
103 Billy Wagner .40 1.00
104 Miguel Tejada .40 1.00
105 Jose Cruz Jr. .30 .75
106 George Lombard .30 .75
107 Geoff Jenkins .30 .75
108 Ray Lankford .40 1.00
109 Todd Stottlemyre .30 .75
110 Mike Lowell .40 1.00
111 Matt Clement .40 1.00
112 Scott Brosius .40 1.00
113 Preston Wilson .40 1.00
114 Bartolo Colon .40 1.00
115 Rolando Arrojo .30 .75
116 Jose Guillen .40 1.00
117 Ron Gant .40 1.00
118 Ricky Ledee .30 .75
119 Carlos Delgado .40 1.00
120 Abraham Nunez .30 .75
121 John Olerud .40 1.00
122 Chan Ho Park .40 1.00
123 Brad Radke .40 1.00
124 Al Leiter .40 1.00
125 Gary Matthews Jr. .30 .75
126 F.P. Santangelo .30 .75
127 Brad Fullmer .30 .75
128 Matt Anderson .30 .75
129 A.J. Hinch .30 .75
130 Sterling Hitchcock .30 .75
131 Edgar Martinez .60 1.50
132 Fernando Tatis .30 .75
133 Bobby Smith .30 .75
134 Paul Konerko .40 1.00
135 Sean Casey .40 1.00
136 Donnie Sadler .30 .75
137 Denny Neagle .30 .75
138 Sandy Alomar Jr. .30 .75
139 Mariano Rivera 1.00 2.50
140 Emil Brown .30 .75
141 J.T. Snow .40 1.00
142 Eli Marrero .30 .75
143 Rusty Greer .40 1.00
144 Johnny Damon .60 1.50
145 Damion Easley .30 .75
146 Eric Milton .30 .75
147 Rico Brogna .30 .75
148 Ray Durham .40 1.00
149 Wally Joyner .40 1.00
150 Royce Clayton .30 .75
151 David Ortiz 1.00 2.50
152 Wade Boggs .60 1.50
153 Ugueth Urbina .30 .75
154 Richard Hidalgo .30 .75
155 Bob Abreu .40 1.00
156 Robb Nen .40 1.00
157 David Segui .30 .75
158 Sean Berry .30 .75
159 Kevin Tapani .30 .75
160 Jason Varitek 1.00 2.50
161 Fernando Vina .30 .75
162 Jim Leyritz .30 .75
163 Enrique Wilson .30 .75
164 Jim Parque .30 .75
165 Doug Glanville .30 .75
166 Jesus Sanchez .30 .75
167 Nolan Ryan 2.50 6.00
168 Robin Yount 1.50 4.00
169 Stan Musial 1.50 4.00
170 Tom Seaver .60 1.50
171 Mike Schmidt 2.00 5.00
172 Willie Stargell .60 1.50
173 Rollie Fingers .40 1.00
174 Willie McCovey .40 1.00
175 Harmon Killebrew 1.00 2.50
176 Eddie Mathews 1.00 2.50
177 Reggie Jackson .60 1.50
178 Frank Robinson .60 1.50
179 Ken Griffey Sr. .40 1.00
180 Eddie Murray 1.00 2.50
S1 Ken Griffey Jr. Sample .75 2.00

1999 SP Signature Autographs

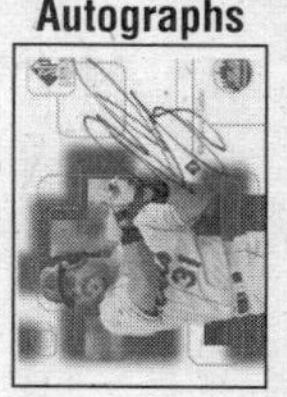

Inserted one per pack, this 150-card set is a partial parallel autographed version of the base set. Though print runs were not released, the amount of cards each player signed varied greatly. Many of the active veteran stars are noticeably tougher to find than the other cards in the set. In addition, several players had exchange cards of which expired on May 12th, 2000. The following players originally packed out as exchange cards: A.J. Burnett, Sean Casey, Vinny Castilla, Bartolo Colon, Pedro Martinez, Ruben Mateo, Jim Parque, Mike Piazza, Scott Rolen, J.T. Snow and Willie Stargell.

AB Albert Belle 6.00 15.00
ABE Adrian Beltre 6.00 15.00
AG Alex Gonzalez 3.00 8.00
AJ Andruw Jones 10.00 25.00
AJB A.J. Burnett 10.00 25.00
AJP A.J. Pierzynski 6.00 15.00
AL Al Leiter 6.00 15.00
AN Abraham Nunez 3.00 8.00
AP Angel Pena 3.00 8.00
AR Alex Rodriguez 75.00 150.00
ARA Aramis Ramirez 6.00 15.00
BA Bob Abreu 6.00 15.00
BB Barry Bonds 100.00 200.00
BC Bruce Chen 3.00 8.00
BCO Bartolo Colon 6.00 15.00
BD Ben Davis 3.00 8.00
BF Brad Fullmer 3.00 8.00
BH Bob Henley 3.00 8.00
BR Brad Radke 6.00 15.00
BS Bobby Smith 3.00 8.00
BW Bryan Ward 3.00 8.00
BWA Billy Wagner 10.00 25.00
CBE Carlos Beltran 6.00 15.00
CC Carlos Castillo 3.00 8.00
CD Carlos Delgado 6.00 15.00
CF Carlos Febles 3.00 8.00
CH Chad Hermansen 3.00 8.00
CHA Chris Haas 3.00 8.00
CHU Chad Hutchinson 3.00 8.00
CJ Chipper Jones 30.00 60.00
CK Corey Koskie 6.00 15.00
CKI Cesar King 3.00 8.00
CL Carlos Lee 6.00 15.00
CP Calvin Pickering 3.00 8.00
DAM Damon Minor 3.00 8.00
DB Dermal Brown 3.00 8.00
DE Darin Erstad 6.00 15.00
DEA Damion Easley 3.00 8.00
DG Derrick Gibson 3.00 8.00
DGL Doug Glanville 6.00 15.00
DL Derrek Lee 10.00 25.00
DO David Ortiz 15.00 40.00
DOM Doug Mientkiewicz 4.00 10.00
DS Donnie Sadler 3.00 8.00
DSE David Segui 6.00 15.00
EB Emil Brown 3.00 8.00
EC Eric Chavez 6.00 15.00
ED Orlando Hernandez SP 60.00 120.00
ELI Eli Marrero 3.00 8.00
EM Edgar Martinez 10.00 25.00
EMA Eddie Mathews 50.00 100.00
EMI Eric Milton 3.00 8.00
EW Enrique Wilson 3.00 8.00
FR Frank Robinson 10.00 25.00
FS Fernando Seguignol 3.00 8.00
FT Frank Thomas 30.00 60.00
FTA Fernando Tatis 3.00 8.00
FV Fernando Vina 3.00 8.00
GJ Geoff Jenkins 6.00 15.00
GK Gabe Kapler 6.00 15.00
GM Greg Maddux 60.00 120.00
GMJ Gary Matthews Jr. 3.00 8.00
GV Greg Vaughn 3.00 8.00
HK Harmon Killebrew 15.00 40.00
IC Ivanon Coffie 3.00 8.00
JAG Jason Giambi 10.00 25.00
JC Jason Conti 3.00 8.00
JCI Jeff Cirillo 6.00 15.00
JD J.D. Drew 12.50 30.00
JDA Johnny Damon 15.00 40.00
JE Juan Encarnacion 6.00 15.00
JEG Jeremy Giambi 3.00 8.00
JG Jose Guillen 6.00 15.00
JHJ Jerry Hairston Jr. 3.00 8.00
JK Jason Kendall 6.00 15.00
JLA Joe Lawrence 3.00 8.00
JLE Jim Leyritz 3.00 8.00
JM Juan Melo 3.00 8.00
JO John Olerud 6.00 15.00
JOC Jose Canseco 10.00 25.00
JP Jim Parque 3.00 8.00
JR Ken Griffey Jr. 60.00 120.00
JS Jesus Sanchez 3.00 8.00
JT J.T. Snow 6.00 15.00
JV Jason Varitek 30.00 60.00
KB Kevin Barker 3.00 8.00
KW Kevin Witt 3.00 8.00
MA Marlon Anderson 3.00 8.00
MB Michael Barrett 3.00 8.00
MC Mike Caruso 3.00 8.00
MCL Matt Clement 6.00 15.00
MK Mark Kotsay 6.00 15.00
MKA Matt Karchner 3.00 8.00
MKI Mike Kinkade 3.00 8.00
MME Mitch Meluskey 3.00 8.00
MO Mo Vaughn 6.00 15.00
MP Mike Piazza 100.00 200.00
MR Manny Ramirez 30.00 60.00
MRI Mariano Rivera 40.00 80.00
MS Mike Schmidt 20.00 50.00
MT Miguel Tejada 6.00 15.00
MV Mario Valdez 3.00 8.00
NG Nomar Garciaparra 20.00 50.00
NR Nolan Ryan 75.00 150.00
OD Octavio Dotel 3.00 8.00
OP Orlando Palmeiro 3.00 8.00
PB Pat Burrell 10.00 25.00
PG Ivan Rodriguez 15.00 40.00
PK Paul Konerko 10.00 25.00
PM Pedro Martinez 60.00 120.00
PO Paul O'Neill 10.00 25.00
POP Willie Stargell 40.00 80.00
RB Russ Branyan 3.00 8.00
RBE Ron Belliard 3.00 8.00
RC Royce Clayton 3.00 8.00
RD Ray Durham 6.00 15.00
RGA Ron Gant SP 40.00 80.00
RGR Rusty Greer 6.00 15.00
RH Roy Halladay 6.00 15.00
RJ Reggie Jackson SP 60.00 120.00
RL Ray Lankford 6.00 15.00
RM Ryan Minor 3.00 8.00
RMA Ruben Mateo 3.00 8.00
RN Robb Nen 6.00 15.00
ROB Rob Bell 3.00 8.00
ROB Robert Fick 3.00 8.00
ROL Rollie Fingers 6.00 15.00
RR Rafael Roque 3.00 8.00
RT Reggie Taylor 3.00 8.00
RY Robin Yount 20.00 50.00
SA Sandy Alomar Jr. 3.00 8.00
SB Scott Brosius SP 60.00 120.00
SC Sean Casey 6.00 15.00
SHH Shea Hillenbrand 6.00 15.00
SM Stan Musial 30.00 60.00
SP Sidney Ponson 3.00 8.00
SR Ken Griffey Sr. 6.00 15.00
SR Scott Rolen 10.00 25.00
STH Sterling Hitchcock 3.00 8.00
TG Tony Gwynn 15.00 40.00
TGL Troy Glaus 10.00 25.00
THE Todd Helton 10.00 25.00
THO Trevor Hoffman 10.00 25.00
TSE Tom Seaver 15.00 40.00
TST Todd Stottlemyre 3.00 8.00
TW Todd Walker 6.00 15.00
VC Vinny Castilla 6.00 15.00
VG Vladimir Guerrero 12.50 30.00
WJ Wally Joyner 6.00 15.00
WMC Willie McCovey 15.00 40.00

1999 SP Signature Autographs Gold

Randomly inserted into packs, this 90-card set is a gold signature style partial parallel version of the base set. The only difference in design is a thin strip of gold foil squares on the card front. According to Upper Deck, 11 players did not sign their cards and are marked "NO AU" in the checklist below. Only 50 serial-numbered sets were produced. In addition, the following players had exchange cards of which expired on May 12th, 2000: Mike Piazza, Pedro Martinez, Scott Rolen and Vinny Castilla. Finally, a mere 20 copies of A.J. Burnett's cards packed out. All twenty made their way into packs as exchange cards with a May 12th, 2000 deadline. The Burnett card is not priced due to scarcity.

AB Albert Belle 30.00 60.00
ABE Adrian Beltre 30.00 60.00
AG Alex Gonzalez 20.00 50.00
AJ Andruw Jones 50.00 100.00
AJB A.J. Burnett SP/20
AP Angel Pena 20.00 50.00
AR Alex Rodriguez 175.00 300.00
ARA Aramis Ramirez 30.00 60.00
BB Barry Bonds 225.00 350.00
BC Bruce Chen 20.00 50.00
BD Ben Davis 15.00 40.00
BH Bob Henley 20.00 50.00
BJ Brian Jordan NO AU
CB Craig Biggio NO AU
CBE Carlos Beltran 20.00 50.00
CF Carlos Febles 15.00 40.00
CG Carlos Guillen NO AU
CH Chad Hermansen 20.00 50.00
CHA Chris Haas 20.00 50.00
CHU Chad Hutchinson 20.00 50.00
CJ Chipper Jones 75.00 150.00
CK Corey Koskie 30.00 60.00
CKI Cesar King 20.00 50.00
CL Carlos Lee 30.00 60.00
CP Calvin Pickering 20.00 50.00
DAM Damon Minor 20.00 50.00
DB Dermal Brown 20.00 50.00
DE Darin Erstad 30.00 60.00
DG Derrick Gibson 20.00 50.00
DL Derrek Lee 50.00 100.00
EC Eric Chavez 30.00 60.00
ED Orlando Hernandez 125.00 200.00
FS Fernando Seguignol 20.00 50.00
FT Frank Thomas 125.00 200.00
GK Gabe Kapler 30.00 60.00
GM Greg Maddux 175.00 300.00
GV Greg Vaughn 20.00 50.00
JAG Jason Giambi 50.00 100.00
JB Jeromy Burnitz NO AU
JC Jason Conti 20.00 50.00
JCI Jeff Cirillo 30.00 60.00
JD J.D. Drew 30.00 60.00
JE Juan Encarnacion 30.00 60.00
JEG Jeremy Giambi NO AU
JHJ Jerry Hairston Jr. 20.00 50.00
JK Jason Kendall 30.00 60.00
JLA Joe Lawrence 20.00 50.00
JM Juan Melo 20.00 50.00
JOC Jose Canseco 50.00 100.00
JR Ken Griffey Jr. 150.00 250.00
JUG Juan Gonzalez NO AU
KB Kevin Barker 20.00 50.00
KW Kevin Witt 20.00 50.00

MA Marlon Anderson 20.00 50.00
MB Michael Barrett 20.00 50.00
MC Mike Caruso 20.00 50.00
MD Mike Darr NO AU
MK Mark Kotsay 30.00 60.00
MKI Mike Kinkade 20.00 50.00
MME Mitch Meluskey 20.00 50.00
MO Mo Vaughn 30.00 60.00
MP Mike Piazza 175.00 300.00
MR Manny Ramirez 75.00 150.00
NG Nomar Garciaparra 75.00 150.00
OD Octavio Dotel 20.00 50.00
PB Pat Burrell 50.00 100.00
PG Ivan Rodriguez 75.00 150.00
PM Pedro Martinez 175.00 300.00
PO Paul O'Neill 50.00 100.00
RB Russ Branyan 20.00 50.00
RBE Ron Belliard 15.00 40.00
RH Roy Halladay 30.00 60.00
RHE R. Henderson NO AU
RM Ryan Minor 20.00 50.00
RMA Ruben Mateo 20.00 50.00
RMO R.Mondesi NO AU
ROB Rob Bell 20.00 50.00
RR Rafael Roque 20.00 50.00
RT Reggie Taylor 20.00 50.00
SHH Shea Hillenbrand 40.00 80.00
SR Scott Rolen 50.00 100.00
TF Travis Fryman NO AU
TG Tony Gwynn 75.00 150.00
TGL Troy Glaus 50.00 100.00
THE Todd Helton 50.00 100.00
THO Trevor Hoffman 50.00 100.00
TL Travis Lee NO AU
TW Todd Walker 30.00 60.00
VC Vinny Castilla 30.00 60.00
VG Vladimir Guerrero 75.00 150.00

1999 SP Signature Legendary Cuts

Randomly inserted into packs, this eight-card set features a "cut" signature from one of baseball's legends. Only one of each card was produced. No pricing is available due to scarcity but a checklist is provided.

ROY Roy Campanella
XX Jimmie Foxx
LG Lefty Grove
W Walter Johnson
MEL1 Mel Ott
MEL2 Mel Ott
BR Babe Ruth
CY Cy Young

2007 SP Rookie Edition

COMP.SET w/o RC's (100) 6.00 15.00
COMMON CARD (1-100) .12 .30
COMMON RC (101-142) .25 .60
COMMON SP (143-234) .40 1.00
SP ODDS 1:2
COMMON CARD (235-284) .25 .60
1 Chipper Jones .30 .75
2 Andruw Jones .20 .50
3 Jeff Francoeur .30 .75
4 Stephen Drew .20 .50
5 Randy Johnson .30 .75
6 Brandon Webb .12 .30
7 Alfonso Soriano .12 .30
8 Derrek Lee .12 .30
9 Aramis Ramirez .12 .30
10 Carlos Zambrano .12 .30
11 Ken Griffey Jr. .50 1.25
12 Adam Dunn .12 .30
13 Bronson Arroyo .12 .30
14 Todd Helton .20 .50
15 Jeff Francis .12 .30
16 Matt Holliday .30 .75
17 Hanley Ramirez .20 .50
18 Dontrelle Willis .12 .30
19 Miguel Cabrera .20 .50
20 Lance Berkman .12 .30
21 Roy Oswalt .12 .30
22 Carlos Lee .12 .30
23 Nomar Garciaparra .30 .75
24 Jason Schmidt .12 .30
25 Juan Pierre .12 .30
26 Rafael Furcal .12 .30
27 Rickie Weeks .12 .30
28 Prince Fielder .30 .75
29 Ben Sheets .12 .30
30 David Wright .50 1.25
31 Jose Reyes .30 .75
32 Pedro Martinez .20 .50
33 Carlos Beltran .20 .50
34 Cole Hamels .30 .75
35 Jimmy Rollins .12 .30
36 Ryan Howard .50 1.25
37 Jason Bay .12 .30
38 Freddy Sanchez .12 .30
39 Zach Duke .12 .30
40 Jake Peavy .12 .30
41 Greg Maddux .50 1.25
42 Trevor Hoffman .12 .30
43 Matt Cain .20 .50
44 Barry Zito .12 .30
45 Omar Vizquel .20 .50
46 Albert Pujols .60 1.50
47 Chris Carpenter .12 .30
48 Jim Edmonds .20 .50
49 Scott Rolen .20 .50
50 Ryan Zimmerman .30 .75
51 Felipe Lopez .12 .30
52 Austin Kearns .12 .30
53 Miguel Tejada .12 .30
54 Erik Bedard .12 .30
55 Chris Ray .12 .30
56 David Ortiz .30 .75
57 Curt Schilling .20 .50
58 Manny Ramirez .20 .50
59 Jonathan Papelbon .30 .75
60 Jim Thome .20 .50
61 Paul Konerko .12 .30
62 Bobby Jenks .12 .30
63 Grady Sizemore .20 .50
64 Victor Martinez .20 .50
65 C.C. Sabathia .12 .30
66 Ivan Rodriguez .20 .50
67 Justin Verlander .30 .75
68 Joel Zumaya .20 .50
69 Jeremy Bonderman .12 .30
70 Gil Meche .12 .30
71 Mike Sweeney .12 .30
72 Mark Teahen .12 .30
73 Vladimir Guerrero .30 .75
74 Howie Kendrick .12 .30
75 Francisco Rodriguez .12 .30
76 Johan Santana .20 .50
77 Justin Morneau .12 .30
78 Joe Mauer .20 .50
79 Joe Nathan .12 .30
80 Alex Rodriguez .50 1.25
81 Derek Jeter .75 2.00
82 Johnny Damon .20 .50
83 Mariano Rivera .30 .75
84 Rich Harden .12 .30
85 Mike Piazza .30 .75
86 Nick Swisher .12 .30
87 Ichiro Suzuki .50 1.25
88 Felix Hernandez .20 .50
89 Kenji Johjima .30 .75
90 Richie Sexson .12 .30
91 Carl Crawford .12 .30
92 Scott Kazmir .20 .50
93 B.J. Upton .12 .30
94 Michael Young .12 .30
95 Mark Teixeira .20 .50
96 Eric Gagne .12 .30
97 Hank Blalock .12 .30
98 Vernon Wells .12 .30
99 Roy Halladay .12 .30
100 Frank Thomas .30 .75
101 Joaquin Arias (RC) .25 .60
102 Jeff Baker (RC) .25 .60
103 Brian Barden RC .25 .60
104 Michael Bourn (RC) .25 .60
105 Kevin Slowey (RC) .60 1.50
106 Chase Wright RC .60 1.50
107 Kory Casto (RC) .25 .60
108 Matt Chico (RC) .25 .60
109 Matt DeSalvo (RC) .25 .60
110 Homer Bailey (RC) .40 1.00
111 Ryan Braun (RC) 1.50 4.00
112 Felix Pie (RC) .25 .60
113 Jesus Flores RC .25 .60
114 Ryan Sweeney (RC) .25 .60
115 Ryan Z. Braun RC .25 .60
116 Alex Gordon RC 1.25 3.00
117 Josh Hamilton (RC) .60 1.50
118 Sean Henn (RC) .25 .60
119 Kei Igawa RC .60 1.50
120 Akinori Iwamura RC .60 1.50
121 Andy LaRoche (RC) .25 .60
122 Kevin Kouzmanoff (RC) .25 .60
123 Matt Lindstrom (RC) .25 .60
124 Tim Lincecum RC 2.00 5.00
125 Daisuke Matsuzaka RC 2.50 6.00
126 Gustavo Molina RC .25 .60
127 Miguel Montero (RC) .25 .60
128 Brandon Morrow RC .60 1.50
129 Hideki Okajima RC 1.25 3.00
130 Adam Lind (RC) .25 .60
131 Mike Rabelo RC .25 .60
132 Micah Owings (RC) .25 .60
133 Brandon Wood (RC) .25 .60
134 Alexi Casilla RC .40 1.00
135 Joe Smith RC .25 .60
136 Hunter Pence (RC) 1.25 3.00
137 Glen Perkins (RC) .25 .60
138 Chris Stewart RC .25 .60
139 Troy Tulowitzki (RC) .60 1.50
140 Billy Butler (RC) .40 1.00
141 Delmon Young (RC) .40 1.00
142 Phil Hughes (RC) 1.25 3.00
143 Joaquin Arias 95 .40 1.00
144 Jeff Baker 95 .40 1.00
145 Brian Barden 95 .40 1.00
146 Michael Bourn 95 .40 1.00
147 Kevin Slowey 95 1.00 2.50
148 Chase Wright 95 1.00 2.50
149 Kory Casto 95 .40 1.00
150 Matt Chico 95 .40 1.00
151 Shawn Riggans 95 .40 1.00
152 Juan Salas 95 .40 1.00
153 Ryan Braun 95 2.50 6.00
154 Felix Pie 95 .40 1.00
155 Jesus Flores 95 .40 1.00
156 Ryan Sweeney 95 .40 1.00
157 Ryan Z. Braun 95 .40 1.00
158 Alex Gordon 95 2.00 5.00
159 Josh Hamilton 95 1.00 2.50
160 Sean Henn 95 .40 1.00
161 Kei Igawa 95 1.00 2.50
162 Akinori Iwamura 95 1.00 2.50
163 Andy LaRoche 95 .40 1.00
164 Kevin Kouzmanoff 95 .40 1.00
165 Matt Lindstrom 95 .40 1.00
166 Tim Lincecum 95 3.00 8.00
167 Daisuke Matsuzaka 95 4.00 10.00
168 Gustavo Molina 95 .40 1.00
169 Miguel Montero 95 .40 1.00
170 Brandon Morrow 95 1.00 2.50
171 Hideki Okajima 95 2.00 5.00
172 Adam Lind 95 .40 1.00
173 Mike Rabelo 95 .40 1.00
174 Micah Owings 95 .40 1.00
175 Brandon Wood 95 .40 1.00
176 Alexi Casilla 95 .60 1.50
177 Joe Smith 95 .40 1.00
178 Hunter Pence 95 2.50 6.00
179 Glen Perkins 95 .40 1.00
180 Chris Stewart 95 .40 1.00
181 Troy Tulowitzki 95 1.00 2.50
182 Billy Butler 95 .60 1.50
183 Delmon Young 95 .60 1.50
184 Phil Hughes 95 2.00 5.00
185 Joaquin Arias 93 .40 1.00
186 Jeff Baker 93 .40 1.00
187 Mark Reynolds 93 1.50 4.00
188 Joseph Bisenius 93 .40 1.00
189 Michael Bourn 93 .40 1.00
190 Zack Segovia 93 .40 1.00
191 Kevin Slowey 93 1.00 2.50
192 Chase Wright 93 1.00 2.50
193 Rocky Cherry 93 1.00 2.50
194 Danny Putnam 93 .40 1.00
195 Kory Casto 93 .40 1.00
196 Matt Chico 93 .40 1.00
197 John Danks 93 .40 1.00
198 Homer Bailey 93 .60 1.50
199 Ryan Braun 93 2.50 6.00
200 Felix Pie 93 .40 1.00
201 Jesus Flores 93 .40 1.00
202 Andy Gonzalez 93 .40 1.00
203 Ryan Sweeney 93 .40 1.00
204 Jarrod Saltalamacchia 93 .60 1.50
205 Alex Gordon 93 2.00 5.00
206 Josh Hamilton 93 1.00 2.50
207 Sean Henn 93 .40 1.00
208 Kei Igawa 93 1.00 2.50
209 Akinori Iwamura 93 1.00 2.50
210 Andy LaRoche 93 .40 1.00
211 Rick Vanden Hurk 93 .60 1.50
212 Kevin Kouzmanoff 93 .40 1.00
213 Matt Lindstrom 93 .40 1.00
214 Tim Lincecum 93 3.00 8.00
215 Daisuke Matsuzaka 93 4.00 10.00
216 Gustavo Molina 93 .40 1.00
217 Miguel Montero 93 .40 1.00
218 Brandon Morrow 93 1.00 2.50
219 Hideki Okajima 93 2.00 5.00
220 Adam Lind 93 .40 1.00
221 Mike Rabelo 93 .40 1.00
222 Brian Burres 93 .40 1.00
223 Micah Owings 93 .40 1.00
224 Brandon Wood 93 .40 1.00
225 Alexi Casilla 93 .60 1.50
226 Joe Smith 93 .40 1.00
227 Hunter Pence 93 2.50 6.00
228 Glen Perkins 93 .40 1.00
229 Chris Stewart 93 .40 1.00
230 Ben Francisco 93 .40 1.00
231 Troy Tulowitzki 93 1.00 2.50
232 Billy Butler 93 .60 1.50
233 Delmon Young 93 .60 1.50
234 Phil Hughes 93 2.00 5.00
235 Joaquin Arias 96 .25 .60
236 Jeff Baker 96 .25 .60
237 Mark Reynolds 96 1.00 2.50
238 Joseph Bisenius 96 .25 .60
239 Michael Bourn 96 .25 .60
240 Zack Segovia 96 .25 .60
241 Travis Buck 96 .25 .60
242 Chase Wright 96 .60 1.50
243 Rocky Cherry 96 .60 1.50
244 Danny Putnam 96 .25 .60
245 Kory Casto 96 .25 .60
246 Matt Chico 96 .25 .60
247 John Danks 96 .25 .60
248 Juan Salas 96 .25 .60
249 Ryan Braun 96 1.50 4.00
250 Felix Pie 96 .25 .60
251 Jesus Flores 96 .25 .60
252 Andy Gonzalez 96 .25 .60
253 Ryan Sweeney 96 .25 .60
254 Jarrod Saltalamacchia 96 .40 1.00
255 Alex Gordon 96 1.25 3.00
256 Josh Hamilton 96 .60 1.50
257 Sean Henn 96 .25 .60
258 Kei Igawa 96 .60 1.50
259 Akinori Iwamura 96 .60 1.50
260 Andy LaRoche 96 .25 .60
261 Rick Vanden Hurk 96 .40 1.00
262 Kevin Kouzmanoff 96 .25 .60
263 Matt Lindstrom 96 .25 .60
264 Tim Lincecum 96 2.00 5.00
265 Daisuke Matsuzaka 96 2.50 6.00
266 Gustavo Molina 96 .25 .60
267 Miguel Montero 96 .25 .60
268 Brandon Morrow 96 .60 1.50
269 Hideki Okajima 96 1.25 3.00
270 Adam Lind 96 .25 .60
271 Mike Rabelo 96 .25 .60
272 Brian Burres 96 .25 .60
273 Micah Owings 96 .25 .60
274 Brandon Wood 96 .25 .60
275 Alexi Casilla 96 .40 1.00
276 Joe Smith 96 .25 .60
277 Hunter Pence 96 1.25 3.00
278 Glen Perkins 96 .25 .60
279 Chris Stewart 96 .25 .60
280 Ben Francisco 96 .25 .60
281 Troy Tulowitzki 96 .60 1.50
282 Billy Butler 96 .40 1.00
283 Delmon Young 96 .40 1.00
284 Phil Hughes 96 1.25 3.00

2007 SP Rookie Edition Autographs

STATED ODDS 1:7
EXCH DEADLINE 8/17/2009
NO SP PRICING DUE TO SCARCITY

101 Joaquin Arias 3.00 8.00
102 Jeff Baker 3.00 8.00
103 Brian Barden 3.00 8.00
104 Michael Bourn 3.00 8.00
105 Kevin Slowey 6.00 15.00
106 Chase Wright 6.00 15.00
107 Kory Casto 3.00 8.00
108 Matt Chico 3.00 8.00
109 Matt DeSalvo 5.00 12.00
110 Homer Bailey 6.00 15.00
111 Ryan Braun 40.00 80.00
112 Felix Pie 5.00 12.00
113 Jesus Flores 4.00 10.00
114 Ryan Sweeney 4.00 10.00
115 Ryan Z. Braun 5.00 12.00
116 Alex Gordon SP
117 Josh Hamilton 10.00 25.00
118 Sean Henn 3.00 8.00
119 Kei Igawa SP
120 Akinori Iwamura SP
121 Andy LaRoche 4.00 10.00
122 Kevin Kouzmanoff 4.00 10.00
123 Matt Lindstrom 3.00 8.00
124 Tim Lincecum SP
125 Daisuke Matsuzaka SP
126 Gustavo Molina 4.00 10.00
127 Miguel Montero 3.00 8.00
128 Brandon Morrow 5.00 12.00
130 Adam Lind 4.00 10.00
131 Mike Rabelo 3.00 8.00
132 Micah Owings EXCH 4.00 10.00
133 Brandon Wood 6.00 15.00
134 Alexi Casilla 4.00 10.00
135 Joe Smith 4.00 10.00
136 Hunter Pence SP
137 Glen Perkins 3.00 8.00
138 Chris Stewart 3.00 8.00
139 Troy Tulowitzki SP
140 Billy Butler 10.00 25.00
141 Delmon Young SP
142 Phil Hughes SP
143 Joaquin Arias 95 3.00 8.00
144 Jeff Baker 95 3.00 8.00
145 Brian Barden 95 3.00 8.00
146 Michael Bourn 95 3.00 8.00
147 Kevin Slowey 95 6.00 15.00
148 Chase Wright 95 6.00 15.00
149 Kory Casto 95 3.00 8.00
150 Matt Chico 95 3.00 8.00
151 Shawn Riggans 95 3.00 8.00
152 Juan Salas 95 EXCH 3.00 8.00
153 Ryan Braun 95 30.00 60.00
154 Felix Pie 95 5.00 12.00
155 Jesus Flores 95 4.00 10.00
156 Ryan Sweeney 95 4.00 10.00
157 Ryan Z. Braun 95 5.00 12.00
158 Alex Gordon 95 SP
159 Josh Hamilton 95 10.00 25.00
160 Sean Henn 95 3.00 8.00
161 Kei Igawa 95 SP
162 Akinori Iwamura 95 SP
163 Andy LaRoche 95 4.00 10.00
164 Kevin Kouzmanoff 95 4.00 10.00
165 Matt Lindstrom 95 EXCH 3.00 8.00
166 Tim Lincecum 95 SP
167 Daisuke Matsuzaka 95 SP EXCH
168 Gustavo Molina 95 4.00 10.00
169 Miguel Montero 95 3.00 8.00
170 Brandon Morrow 95 5.00 12.00
172 Adam Lind 95 4.00 10.00
173 Mike Rabelo 95 3.00 8.00
174 Micah Owings 95 4.00 10.00
175 Brandon Wood 95 6.00 15.00
176 Alexi Casilla 95 4.00 10.00
177 Joe Smith 95 4.00 10.00
178 Hunter Pence 95 20.00 50.00
179 Glen Perkins 95 3.00 8.00
180 Chris Stewart 95 3.00 8.00
181 Troy Tulowitzki 95 15.00 40.00
182 Billy Butler 95 10.00 25.00
183 Delmon Young 95 SP
184 Phil Hughes 95 SP
185 Joaquin Arias 93 3.00 8.00
186 Jeff Baker 93 3.00 8.00
187 Mark Reynolds 93
188 Joseph Bisenius 93 3.00 8.00
189 Michael Bourn 93 3.00 8.00
190 Zack Segovia 93 3.00 8.00
191 Kevin Slowey 93 6.00 15.00
192 Chase Wright 93 6.00 15.00
193 Rocky Cherry 93 10.00 25.00
194 Danny Putnam 93 8.00 20.00
195 Kory Casto 93 3.00 8.00
196 Matt Chico 93 3.00 8.00
197 John Danks 93 3.00 8.00
198 Homer Bailey 93 6.00 15.00
199 Ryan Braun 93 SP
200 Felix Pie 93 5.00 12.00
201 Jesus Flores 93 4.00 10.00
202 Andy Gonzalez 93 4.00 10.00
203 Ryan Sweeney 93 SP
204 Jarrod Saltalamacchia 93 5.00 12.00
205 Alex Gordon 93 SP
206 Josh Hamilton 93 SP
207 Sean Henn 93 3.00 8.00
208 Kei Igawa 93 SP
209 Akinori Iwamura 93 SP
210 Andy LaRoche 93 4.00 10.00
211 Rick Vanden Hurk 93 3.00 8.00
212 Kevin Kouzmanoff 93 4.00 10.00
213 Matt Lindstrom 93 3.00 8.00
214 Tim Lincecum 93 SP
215 Daisuke Matsuzaka 93
216 Gustavo Molina 93 4.00 10.00
217 Miguel Montero 93 3.00 8.00
218 Brandon Morrow 93 5.00 12.00
220 Adam Lind 93 4.00 10.00
221 Mike Rabelo 93 3.00 8.00
222 Brian Burres 93 3.00 8.00
223 Micah Owings 93 4.00 10.00
224 Brandon Wood 93 SP
225 Alexi Casilla 93 4.00 10.00
226 Joe Smith 93 4.00 10.00
227 Hunter Pence 93 SP
228 Glen Perkins 93 3.00 8.00
229 Chris Stewart 93 3.00 8.00
230 Ben Francisco 93 3.00 8.00
231 Troy Tulowitzki 93 SP
232 Billy Butler 93 SP
233 Delmon Young 93 SP
234 Phil Hughes 93 SP
235 Joaquin Arias 96 3.00 8.00
236 Jeff Baker 96 3.00 8.00
237 Mark Reynolds 96
238 Joseph Bisenius 96 3.00 8.00
239 Michael Bourn 96 3.00 8.00
240 Zack Segovia 96 3.00 8.00
241 Travis Buck 96 SP
242 Chase Wright 96 6.00 15.00
243 Rocky Cherry 96 10.00 25.00
244 Danny Putnam 96 8.00 20.00
245 Kory Casto 96 3.00 8.00
246 Matt Chico 96 3.00 8.00
247 John Danks 96 3.00 8.00
248 Juan Salas 96 3.00 8.00
249 Ryan Braun 96 SP
250 Felix Pie 96 5.00 12.00
251 Jesus Flores 96 4.00 10.00
252 Andy Gonzalez 96 4.00 10.00
253 Ryan Sweeney 96 4.00 10.00
254 Jarrod Saltalamacchia 96 SP
255 Alex Gordon 96 SP
256 Josh Hamilton 96 10.00 25.00
257 Sean Henn 96 3.00 8.00
258 Kei Igawa 96 SP
259 Akinori Iwamura 96 SP
260 Andy LaRoche 96 4.00 10.00
261 Rick Vanden Hurk 96 3.00 8.00
262 Kevin Kouzmanoff 96 4.00 10.00
263 Matt Lindstrom 96 3.00 8.00
264 Tim Lincecum 96 SP
265 Daisuke Matsuzaka 96 EXCH
266 Gustavo Molina 96 4.00 10.00
267 Miguel Montero 96 3.00 8.00
268 Brandon Morrow 96 5.00 12.00
270 Adam Lind 96 4.00 10.00
271 Mike Rabelo 96 3.00 8.00
272 Brian Burres 96 3.00 8.00
273 Micah Owings 96 4.00 10.00
274 Brandon Wood 96 6.00 15.00
275 Alexi Casilla 96 4.00 10.00
276 Joe Smith 96 4.00 10.00
277 Hunter Pence 96 SP
278 Glen Perkins 96 3.00 8.00
279 Chris Stewart 96 3.00 8.00
280 Ben Francisco 96 3.00 8.00
281 Troy Tulowitzki 96 SP
282 Billy Butler 96 SP
283 Delmon Young 96 SP
284 Phil Hughes 96 SP

1996 SPx

This 1996 SPx set (produced by Upper Deck) was issued in one series totalling 60 cards. The one-card packs had a suggested retail price of $3.49. Printed on 32 pt. card stock with Holoview technology and a perimeter diecut design, the set features color player photos with a Holography background on the fronts and decorative foil stamping on the back. Two special cards are included in the set: a Ken Griffey Jr. Commemorative card was inserted one in every 75 packs and a Mike Piazza Tribute card inserted one in every 95 packs. An autographed version of each of these cards was inserted at the rate of one in 2,000.

COMPLETE SET (60) 20.00 50.00
1 Greg Maddux 1.25 3.00
2 Chipper Jones .75 2.00
3 Fred McGriff .50 1.25
4 Tom Glavine .50 1.25
5 Cal Ripken 2.50 6.00
6 Roberto Alomar .50 1.25
7 Rafael Palmeiro .50 1.25
8 Jose Canseco .50 1.25
9 Roger Clemens 1.50 4.00
10 Mo Vaughn .30 .75
11 Jim Edmonds .30 .75
12 Tim Salmon .50 1.25
13 Sammy Sosa .75 2.00
14 Ryne Sandberg 1.25 3.00
15 Mark Grace .50 1.25
16 Frank Thomas .75 2.00
17 Barry Larkin .50 1.25
18 Kenny Lofton .30 .75
19 Albert Belle .30 .75
20 Eddie Murray .75 2.00
21 Manny Ramirez .50 1.25
22 Dante Bichette .30 .75
23 Larry Walker .30 .75
24 Vinny Castilla .30 .75
25 Andres Galarraga .30 .75
26 Cecil Fielder .30 .75
27 Gary Sheffield .30 .75
28 Craig Biggio .50 1.25
29 Jeff Bagwell .50 1.25
30 Derek Bell .30 .75
31 Johnny Damon .50 1.25
32 Eric Karros .30 .75
33 Mike Piazza 1.25 3.00
34 Raul Mondesi .30 .75
35 Hideo Nomo .75 2.00
36 Kirby Puckett .75 2.00
37 Paul Molitor .30 .75
38 Marty Cordova .30 .75
39 Rondell White .30 .75
40 Jason Isringhausen .30 .75
41 Paul Wilson .30 .75
42 Rey Ordonez .30 .75
43 Derek Jeter 2.00 5.00
44 Wade Boggs .50 1.25
45 Mark McGwire 2.00 5.00
46 Jason Kendall .30 .75
47 Ron Gant .30 .75
48 Ozzie Smith 1.25 3.00
49 Tony Gwynn 1.00 2.50
50 Ken Caminiti .30 .75
51 Barry Bonds 2.00 5.00
52 Matt Williams .30 .75
53 Osvaldo Fernandez .30 .75
54 Jay Buhner .30 .75
55 Ken Griffey Jr. 1.25 3.00
56 Randy Johnson .75 2.00
57 Alex Rodriguez 1.50 4.00
58 Juan Gonzalez .30 .75
59 Joe Carter .30 .75
60 Carlos Delgado .30 .75
KG1 K.Griffey Jr. Comm. 2.00 5.00
MP1 Mike Piazza Trib. 2.00 5.00
KGA1 Ken Griffey Jr. Auto. 150.00 250.00
MPA1 Mike Piazza Auto. 125.00 200.00

1996 SPx Gold

Parallel to the regular version, this 60-card set was randomly inserted in hobby packs only at a rate of one in seven. The design is similar to the regular set with the exception being the gold foil borders on front.

*STARS: 1.25X TO 3X BASIC CARDS

1996 SPx Bound for Glory

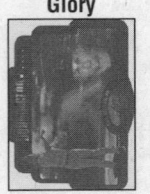

Randomly inserted in packs at a rate of one in 24, this 10-card set features players with a chance to be long remembered.

COMPLETE SET (10) 30.00 80.00
1 Ken Griffey Jr. 3.00 8.00
2 Frank Thomas 2.00 5.00
3 Barry Bonds 5.00 12.00
4 Cal Ripken 6.00 15.00
5 Greg Maddux 3.00 8.00
6 Chipper Jones 2.00 5.00
7 Roberto Alomar 1.25 3.00
8 Manny Ramirez 1.25 3.00
9 Tony Gwynn 2.50 6.00
10 Mike Piazza 3.00 8.00

1997 SPx

The 1997 SPx set (produced by Upper Deck) was issued in one series totalling 50 cards and was distributed in three-card hobby only packs with a suggested retail price of $5.99. The fronts feature color player images on a Holoview perimeter die cut design. The backs carry a player photo, player information, and career statistics. A sample card featuring Ken Griffey Jr. was distribued to dealers and hobby media several weeks prior to the products release.

COMPLETE SET (50) 25.00 60.00
1 Eddie Murray .60 1.50
2 Darin Erstad .25 .60
3 Tim Salmon .40 1.00
4 Andruw Jones .40 1.00
5 Chipper Jones .60 1.50
6 John Smoltz .40 1.00
7 Greg Maddux 1.00 2.50
8 Kenny Lofton .25 .60
9 Roberto Alomar .40 1.00
10 Rafael Palmeiro .40 1.00
11 Brady Anderson .25 .60
12 Cal Ripken 2.00 5.00
13 Nomar Garciaparra 1.00 2.50
14 Mo Vaughn .25 .60
15 Ryne Sandberg 1.00 2.50
16 Sammy Sosa .60 1.50
17 Frank Thomas .60 1.50
18 Albert Belle .25 .60
19 Barry Larkin .40 1.00
20 Deion Sanders .40 1.00
21 Manny Ramirez .40 1.00
22 Jim Thome .40 1.00
23 Dante Bichette .25 .60
24 Andres Galarraga .25 .60
25 Larry Walker .25 .60
26 Gary Sheffield .25 .60
27 Jeff Bagwell .40 1.00
28 Raul Mondesi .25 .60
29 Hideo Nomo .60 1.50
30 Mike Piazza 1.00 2.50
31 Paul Molitor .25 .60
32 Todd Walker .25 .60
33 Vladimir Guerrero .60 1.50
34 Todd Hundley .25 .60
35 Andy Pettitte .40 1.00
36 Derek Jeter 1.50 4.00
37 Jose Canseco .40 1.00
38 Mark McGwire 1.50 4.00
39 Scott Rolen .40 1.00

40 Ron Gant .25 .60
41 Ken Caminiti .25 .60
42 Tony Gwynn .75 2.00
43 Barry Bonds 1.50 4.00
44 Jay Buhner .25 .60
45 Ken Griffey Jr. 1.00 2.50
46 Alex Rodriguez 1.00 2.50
47 Jose Cruz Jr. RC .40 1.00
48 Juan Gonzalez .25 .60
49 Ivan Rodriguez .40 1.00
50 Roger Clemens 1.25 3.00
S45 Ken Griffey Jr. Sample .75 2.00

1997 SPx Bronze

Randomly inserted in packs at the approximate rate of one in three, cards from this 50-card set are a parallel version of the base set with bronze etched foil enhancements.

*STARS: 1X TO 2.5X BASIC CARDS
*ROOKIES: .6X TO 1.5X BASIC CARDS

1997 SPx Gold

Randomly inserted in packs at the rate of one in 17. This 50-card set is parallel to the base set and features etched gold foil enhancements.

*STARS: 2.5X TO 6X BASIC CARDS
*ROOKIES: 1.5X TO 4X BASIC CARDS

1997 SPx Grand Finale

Randomly inserted in packs, cards from this 50-card set are an extremely limited edition parallel version of the base set and features an all gold holoview image. Only 50 of each card was produced. The set was entitled Grand Finale to signify the fact that this would be the last baseball product Upper Deck would ever use the holoview technology on.

*STARS: 12.5X TO 30X BASIC CARDS
*ROOKIES: 5X TO 12X BASIC CARDS

1997 SPx Silver

Randomly inserted in packs at an approximate rate of one in six, cards from this 50-card set are a parallel version of the base set with etched silver foil enhancements.

*STARS: 1.5X TO 4X BASIC CARDS
*ROOKIES: 1X TO 2.5X BASIC CARDS

1997 SPx Steel

Randomly inserted one in approximately one in every two packs, cards from this 50-card set are a parallel version of the base set. Many dealers and collectors believe that cards numbered 25-50 were printed in shorter supply. These cards can be distinguished from the similar looking silver cards by the holographic background behind the SPx logo and the player's number. Silvers lack the holographic background behind the SPx logo.

*STARS: .6X TO 1.5X BASIC CARDS
*ROOKIES: .5X TO 1.2X BASIC CARDS

1997 SPx Bound for Glory

Randomly inserted in packs, this 20-card set features color photos of promising great players on a Holoview die cut card design. Only 1,500 of each card was produced and are sequentially numbered.

COMPLETE SET (20) 100.00 250.00
1 Andruw Jones 2.50 6.00
2 Chipper Jones 4.00 10.00
3 Greg Maddux 6.00 15.00
4 Kenny Lofton 1.50 4.00
5 Cal Ripken 12.50 30.00
6 Mo Vaughn 1.50 4.00
7 Frank Thomas 4.00 10.00
8 Albert Belle 1.50 4.00
9 Manny Ramirez 2.50 6.00
10 Gary Sheffield 1.50 4.00
11 Jeff Bagwell 2.50 6.00
12 Mike Piazza 6.00 15.00
13 Derek Jeter 10.00 25.00
14 Mark McGwire 10.00 25.00
15 Tony Gwynn 5.00 12.00
16 Ken Caminiti 1.50 4.00
17 Barry Bonds 10.00 25.00
18 Alex Rodriguez 6.00 15.00
19 Ken Griffey Jr. 6.00 15.00
20 Juan Gonzalez 1.50 4.00

1997 SPx Bound for Glory Supreme Signatures

Randomly inserted in packs, this five-card set features unnumbered autographed Bound for Glory cards. Only 250 of each card was produced and signed and are sequentially numbered. The cards are checklisted below in alphabetical order.

1 Jeff Bagwell 30.00 60.00
2 Ken Griffey Jr. 100.00 175.00
3 Andruw Jones 10.00 25.00
4 Alex Rodriguez 150.00 250.00
5 Gary Sheffield 10.00 25.00

1997 SPx Cornerstones of the Game

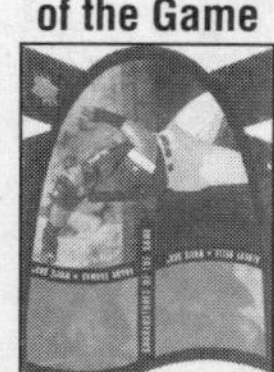

Randomly inserted in packs, cards from this 10-card set display color photos of 20 top players. Two players are featured on each card using double Holoview technology. Only 500 of each card was produced and each is sequentially numbered on back.

COMPLETE SET (10) 100.00 250.00
1 Ken Griffey Jr. 10.00 25.00
Barry Bonds
2 Frank Thomas 6.00 15.00
Albert Belle
3 Chipper Jones 10.00 25.00
Greg Maddux
4 Tony Gwynn 8.00 20.00
Paul Molitor
5 Andruw Jones 6.00 15.00
Vladimir Guerrero
6 Jeff Bagwell 10.00 25.00
Ryne Sandberg
7 Mike Piazza 10.00 25.00
Ivan Rodriguez
8 Cal Ripken 20.00 50.00
Eddie Murray
9 Mo Vaughn 15.00 40.00
Mark McGwire
10 Alex Rodriguez 15.00 40.00
Derek Jeter

1998 SPx Finite

The 1998 SPx Finite set contains a total of 180 cards, all serial numbered based upon specific subsets. The three-card packs retailed for $5.99 each and hit the market in June, 1998. The subsets and serial numbering are as follows: Youth Movement (1-30) - 5000 of each card, Power Explosion (31-50) - 4000 of each card, Basic Cards (51-140) - 9000 of each card, Star Focus (141-170) - 7000 of each card, Heroes of the Game (171-180) - 2000 of each card, Youth Movement (181-210) - 5000 of each card, Power Passion (211-240) - 7000 of each card, Basic Cards (241-330) - 9000 of each card, Tradewinds (331-350) - 4000 of each card and Cornerstones of the Game (351-360) -2000 of each card. Notable Rookie Cards include Kevin Millwood and Magglio Ordonez.

COMP.YM SER.1 (30) 15.00 40.00
COMMON YM (1-30) .60 1.50
COMP.PE SER.1 (20) 50.00 120.00
COMMON PE (31-50) 1.00 2.50
COMP.BASIC SER.1 (90) 30.00 80.00
COMMON CARD (51-140) .40 1.00
COMP.SF SER.1 (30) 40.00 100.00
COMMON SF (141-170) .50 1.25
COMP.HG SER.1 (10) 60.00 150.00
COMMON HG (171-180) 1.50 4.00
COMP.YM SER.2 (30) 25.00 60.00
COMMON YM (181-210) .60 1.50
COMP.PP SER.2 (30) 30.00 80.00
COMMON PP (211-240) .50 1.25
COMP.BASIC SER.2 (90) 20.00 50.00
COMMON (241-330) .40 1.00
COMP.TW SER.2 (20) 12.50 30.00
COMMON TW (331-350) 1.00 2.50
COMP.CG SER.2 (10) 60.00 150.00
COMMON CG (351-360) 1.50 4.00
1 Nomar Garciaparra YM 2.50 6.00
2 Miguel Tejada YM 1.50 4.00
3 Mike Cameron YM .60 1.50
4 Ken Cloude YM .60 1.50
5 Jaret Wright YM .60 1.50
6 Mark Kotsay YM .60 1.50
7 Craig Counsell YM .60 1.50
8 Jose Guillen YM .60 1.50
9 Neifi Perez YM .60 1.50
10 Jose Cruz Jr. YM .60 1.50
11 Brett Tomko YM .60 1.50
12 Matt Morris YM .60 1.50
13 Justin Thompson YM .60 1.50
14 Jeremi Gonzalez YM .60 1.50
15 Scott Rolen YM 1.00 2.50
16 Vladimir Guerrero YM 1.50 4.00
17 Brad Fullmer YM .60 1.50
18 Brian Giles YM .60 1.50
19 Todd Dunwoody YM .60 1.50
20 Ben Grieve YM .60 1.50
21 Juan Encarnacion YM .60 1.50
22 Aaron Boone YM .60 1.50
23 Richie Sexson YM .60 1.50
24 Richard Hidalgo YM .60 1.50
25 Andruw Jones YM 1.00 2.50
26 Todd Helton YM 1.00 2.50
27 Paul Konerko YM .60 1.50
28 Dante Powell YM .60 1.50
29 Eli Marrero YM .60 1.50
30 Derek Jeter YM 4.00 10.00
31 Mike Piazza PE 4.00 10.00
32 Tony Clark PE 1.00 2.50
33 Larry Walker PE 1.00 2.50
34 Jim Thome PE 1.50 4.00
35 Juan Gonzalez PE 2.00 5.00
36 Jeff Bagwell PE 1.50 4.00
37 Jay Buhner PE 1.00 2.50
38 Tim Salmon PE 1.50 4.00
39 Albert Belle PE 1.00 2.50
40 Mark McGwire PE 6.00 15.00
41 Sammy Sosa PE 2.50 6.00
42 Mo Vaughn PE 1.00 2.50
43 Manny Ramirez PE 1.50 4.00
44 Tino Martinez PE 1.50 4.00
45 Frank Thomas PE 2.50 6.00
46 Nomar Garciaparra PE 4.00 10.00
47 Alex Rodriguez PE 4.00 10.00
48 Chipper Jones PE 2.50 6.00
49 Barry Bonds PE 6.00 15.00
50 Ken Griffey Jr. PE 4.00 10.00
51 Jason Dickson .40 1.00
52 Jim Edmonds .40 1.00
53 Darin Erstad .40 1.00
54 Tim Salmon .60 1.50
55 Chipper Jones 1.00 2.50
56 Ryan Klesko .40 1.00
57 Tom Glavine .60 1.50
58 Denny Neagle .40 1.00
59 John Smoltz .60 1.50
60 Javy Lopez .40 1.00
61 Roberto Alomar .60 1.50
62 Rafael Palmeiro .60 1.50
63 Mike Mussina .60 1.50
64 Cal Ripken 3.00 8.00
65 Mo Vaughn .40 1.00
66 Tim Naehring .40 1.00
67 John Valentin .40 1.00
68 Mark Grace .60 1.50
69 Kevin Orie .40 1.00
70 Sammy Sosa 1.00 2.50
71 Albert Belle .40 1.00
72 Frank Thomas 1.00 2.50
73 Robin Ventura .40 1.00
74 David Justice .40 1.00
75 Kenny Lofton .40 1.00
76 Omar Vizquel .60 1.50
77 Manny Ramirez .60 1.50
78 Jim Thome .60 1.50
79 Dante Bichette .40 1.00
80 Larry Walker .40 1.00
81 Vinny Castilla .40 1.00
82 Ellis Burks .40 1.00
83 Bobby Higginson .40 1.00
84 Brian Hunter .40 1.00
85 Tony Clark .40 1.00
86 Mike Hampton .40 1.00
87 Jeff Bagwell .60 1.50
88 Craig Biggio .60 1.50
89 Derek Bell .40 1.00
90 Mike Piazza 1.50 4.00
91 Ramon Martinez .40 1.00
92 Raul Mondesi .40 1.00
93 Hideo Nomo 1.00 2.50
94 Eric Karros .40 1.00
95 Paul Molitor .40 1.00
96 Marty Cordova .40 1.00
97 Brad Radke .40 1.00
98 Mark Grudzielanek .40 1.00
99 Carlos Perez .40 1.00
100 Rondell White .40 1.00
101 Todd Hundley .40 1.00
102 Edgardo Alfonzo .40 1.00
103 John Franco .40 1.00
104 John Olerud .40 1.00
105 Tino Martinez .60 1.50
106 David Cone .40 1.00
107 Paul O'Neill .60 1.50
108 Andy Pettitte .60 1.50
109 Bernie Williams .60 1.50
110 Rickey Henderson 1.50 4.00
111 Jason Giambi .40 1.00
112 Matt Stairs .40 1.00
113 Gregg Jefferies .40 1.00
114 Rico Brogna .40 1.00
115 Curt Schilling .40 1.00
116 Jason Schmidt .40 1.00
117 Jose Guillen .40 1.00
118 Kevin Young .40 1.00
119 Ray Lankford .40 1.00
120 Mark McGwire 2.50 6.00
121 Delino DeShields .40 1.00
122 Ken Caminiti .40 1.00
123 Tony Gwynn 1.25 3.00
124 Trevor Hoffman .40 1.00
125 Barry Bonds 2.50 6.00
126 Jeff Kent .40 1.00
127 Shawn Estes .40 1.00
128 J.T. Snow .40 1.00
129 Jay Buhner .40 1.00
130 Ken Griffey Jr. 1.50 4.00
131 Dan Wilson .40 1.00
132 Edgar Martinez .60 1.50
133 Alex Rodriguez 1.50 4.00
134 Rusty Greer .40 1.00
135 Juan Gonzalez .40 1.00
136 Fernando Tatis .40 1.00
137 Ivan Rodriguez .60 1.50
138 Carlos Delgado .40 1.00
139 Pat Hentgen .40 1.00
140 Roger Clemens 2.00 5.00
141 Chipper Jones SF 1.25 3.00
142 Greg Maddux SF 2.00 5.00
143 Rafael Palmeiro SF .75 2.00
144 Mike Mussina SF .75 2.00
145 Cal Ripken SF 4.00 10.00
146 Nomar Garciaparra SF 2.00 5.00
147 Mo Vaughn SF .50 1.25
148 Sammy Sosa SF 1.25 3.00
149 Albert Belle SF .50 1.25
150 Frank Thomas SF 1.25 3.00
151 Jim Thome SF .75 2.00
152 Kenny Lofton SF .50 1.25
153 Manny Ramirez SF .75 2.00
154 Larry Walker SF .50 1.25
155 Jeff Bagwell SF .75 2.00
156 Craig Biggio SF .75 2.00
157 Mike Piazza SF 2.00 5.00
158 Paul Molitor SF .50 1.25
159 Derek Jeter SF 3.00 8.00
160 Tino Martinez SF .75 2.00
161 Curt Schilling SF .50 1.25
162 Mark McGwire SF 3.00 8.00
163 Tony Gwynn SF 1.50 4.00
164 Barry Bonds SF 3.00 8.00
165 Ken Griffey Jr. SF 2.00 5.00
166 Randy Johnson SF 1.25 3.00
167 Alex Rodriguez SF 2.00 5.00
168 Juan Gonzalez SF .50 1.25
169 Ivan Rodriguez SF .75 2.00
170 Roger Clemens SF 2.50 6.00
171 Greg Maddux HG 6.00 15.00
172 Cal Ripken HG 12.50 30.00
173 Frank Thomas HG 4.00 10.00
174 Jeff Bagwell HG 2.50 6.00
175 Mike Piazza HG 6.00 15.00
176 Mark McGwire HG 10.00 25.00
177 Barry Bonds HG 10.00 25.00
178 Ken Griffey Jr. HG 6.00 15.00
179 Alex Rodriguez HG 6.00 15.00
180 Roger Clemens HG 8.00 20.00
181 Mike Caruso YM .60 1.50
182 David Ortiz YM 2.00 5.00
183 Gabe Alvarez YM .60 1.50
184 G.Matthews Jr. YM RC 1.00 2.50
185 Kerry Wood YM .75 2.00
186 Carl Pavano YM .60 1.50
187 Alex Gonzalez YM .60 1.50
188 Masato Yoshii YM RC .60 1.50
189 Larry Sutton YM .60 1.50
190 Russell Branyan YM .60 1.50
191 Bruce Chen YM .60 1.50
192 R. Arrojo YM RC .60 1.50
193 R.Christenson YM RC .60 1.50
194 Cliff Politte YM .60 1.50
195 A.J. Hinch YM .60 1.50
196 Kevin Witt YM .60 1.50
197 Daryle Ward YM .60 1.50
198 Corey Koskie YM RC 1.00 2.50
199 Mike Lowell YM RC 4.00 10.00
200 Travis Lee YM .60 1.50
201 K.Millwood YM RC 2.00 5.00
202 Robert Smith YM .60 1.50
203 Magglio Ordonez YM RC 6.00 15.00
204 Eric Milton YM .60 1.50
205 Geoff Jenkins YM .60 1.50
206 Rich Butler YM RC .60 1.50
207 Mike Kinkade YM RC .60 1.50
208 Braden Looper YM .60 1.50
209 Matt Clement YM .60 1.50
210 Derrek Lee YM 1.00 2.50
211 Randy Johnson PP 1.25 3.00
212 John Smoltz PP .75 2.00
213 Roger Clemens PP 2.50 6.00
214 Curt Schilling PP .50 1.25
215 Pedro Martinez PP .75 2.00
216 Vinny Castilla PP .50 1.25
217 Jose Cruz Jr. PP .50 1.25
218 Jim Thome PP .75 2.00
219 Alex Rodriguez PP 2.00 5.00
220 Frank Thomas PP 1.25 3.00
221 Tim Salmon PP .75 2.00
222 Larry Walker PP .50 1.25
223 Albert Belle PP .50 1.25
224 Manny Ramirez PP .75 2.00
225 Mark McGwire PP 3.00 8.00
226 Mo Vaughn PP .50 1.25
227 Andres Galarraga PP .50 1.25
228 Scott Rolen PP .75 2.00
229 Travis Lee PP .50 1.25
230 Mike Piazza PP 2.00 5.00
231 N.Garciaparra PP 2.00 5.00
232 Andruw Jones PP .75 2.00
233 Barry Bonds PP 3.00 8.00
234 Jeff Bagwell PP .75 2.00
235 Juan Gonzalez PP .50 1.25
236 Tino Martinez PP .75 2.00
237 Vladimir Guerrero PP 1.25 3.00
238 Rafael Palmeiro PP .75 2.00
239 Russell Branyan PP .50 1.25
240 Ken Griffey Jr. PP 2.00 5.00
241 Cecil Fielder .40 1.00
242 Chuck Finley .40 1.00
243 Jay Bell .40 1.00
244 Andy Benes .40 1.00
245 Matt Williams .40 1.00
246 Brian Anderson .40 1.00
247 Dave Dellucci RC .60 1.50
248 Andres Galarraga .40 1.00
249 Andruw Jones .60 1.50
250 Greg Maddux 1.50 4.00
251 Brady Anderson .40 1.00
252 Joe Carter .40 1.00
253 Eric Davis .40 1.00
254 Pedro Martinez .60 1.50
255 Nomar Garciaparra 1.50 4.00
256 Dennis Eckersley .40 1.00
257 Henry Rodriguez .40 1.00
258 Jeff Blauser .40 1.00
259 Jaime Navarro .40 1.00
260 Ray Durham .40 1.00
261 Chris Stynes .40 1.00
262 Willie Greene .40 1.00
263 Reggie Sanders .40 1.00
264 Bret Boone .40 1.00
265 Barry Larkin .60 1.50
266 Travis Fryman .40 1.00
267 Charles Nagy .40 1.00
268 Sandy Alomar Jr. .40 1.00
269 Darryl Kile .40 1.00
270 Mike Lansing .40 1.00
271 Pedro Astacio .40 1.00
272 Damion Easley .40 1.00
273 Joe Randa .40 1.00
274 Luis Gonzalez .40 1.00
275 Mike Piazza 1.50 4.00
276 Todd Zeile .40 1.00
277 Edgar Renteria .40 1.00
278 Livan Hernandez .40 1.00
279 Cliff Floyd .40 1.00
280 Moises Alou .40 1.00
281 Billy Wagner .40 1.00
282 Jeff King .40 1.00
283 Hal Morris .40 1.00
284 Johnny Damon .60 1.50
285 Dean Palmer .40 1.00
286 Tim Belcher .40 1.00
287 Eric Young .40 1.00
288 Bobby Bonilla .40 1.00
289 Gary Sheffield .40 1.00
290 Chan Ho Park .40 1.00
291 Charles Johnson .40 1.00
292 Jeff Cirillo .40 1.00
293 Jeromy Burnitz .40 1.00
294 Jose Valentin .40 1.00
295 Marquis Grissom .40 1.00
296 Todd Walker .40 1.00
297 Terry Steinbach .40 1.00
298 Rick Aguilera .40 1.00
299 Vladimir Guerrero 1.00 2.50
300 Rey Ordonez .40 1.00
301 Butch Huskey .40 1.00
302 Bernard Gilkey .40 1.00
303 Mariano Rivera 1.00 2.50
304 Chuck Knoblauch .40 1.00
305 Derek Jeter 2.50 6.00
306 Ricky Bottalico .40 1.00
307 Bob Abreu .40 1.00
308 Scott Rolen .60 1.50
309 Al Martin .40 1.00
310 Jason Kendall .40 1.00
311 Brian Jordan .40 1.00
312 Ron Gant .40 1.00
313 Todd Stottlemyre .40 1.00
314 Greg Vaughn .40 1.00
315 Kevin Brown .60 1.50
316 Wally Joyner .40 1.00
317 Robb Nen .40 1.00
318 Orel Hershiser .40 1.00
319 Russ Davis .40 1.00
320 Randy Johnson 1.00 2.50
321 Quinton McCracken .40 1.00
322 Tony Saunders .40 1.00
323 Wilson Alvarez .40 1.00
324 Wade Boggs .60 1.50
325 Fred McGriff .60 1.50
326 Lee Stevens .40 1.00
327 John Wetteland .40 1.00
328 Jose Canseco .60 1.50
329 Randy Myers .40 1.00
330 Jose Cruz Jr. .40 1.00
331 Matt Williams TW 1.00 2.50
332 Andres Galarraga TW 1.00 2.50
333 Walt Weiss TW 1.00 2.50
334 Joe Carter TW 1.00 2.50
335 Pedro Martinez TW 1.50 4.00
336 Henry Rodriguez TW 1.00 2.50
337 Travis Fryman TW 1.00 2.50
338 Darryl Kile TW 1.00 2.50
339 Mike Lansing TW 1.00 2.50
340 Mike Piazza TW 4.00 10.00
341 Moises Alou TW 1.00 2.50
342 Charles Johnson TW 1.00 2.50
343 Chuck Knoblauch TW 1.00 2.50
344 Rickey Henderson TW 2.50 6.00
345 Kevin Brown TW 1.50 4.00
346 Orel Hershiser TW 1.00 2.50
347 Wade Boggs TW 1.50 4.00
348 Fred McGriff TW 1.50 4.00
349 Jose Canseco TW 1.50 4.00
350 Gary Sheffield TW 1.00 2.50
351 Travis Lee CG 1.50 4.00
352 N.Garciaparra CG 6.00 15.00
353 Frank Thomas CG 4.00 10.00
354 Cal Ripken CG 12.50 30.00
355 Mark McGwire CG 10.00 25.00
356 Mike Piazza CG 6.00 15.00
357 Alex Rodriguez CG 6.00 15.00
358 Barry Bonds CG 10.00 25.00
359 Tony Gwynn CG 5.00 12.00
360 Ken Griffey Jr. CG 6.00 15.00

1998 SPx Finite Radiance

Randomly inserted in packs, this 360-card set is a parallel to the SPx Finite base set. Due to problems in the manufacturing process, exchange cards had to be inserted into packs for Power Explosion cards 40, 41 and 45. The deadline to redeem these exchange cards was June 2nd, 1999. Serial numbering of the various subsets is as follows: Youth Movement (1-30) - 2500 of each card, Power Explosion (31-50) - 1000 of each card, Basic Cards (51-140) - 4500 of each card, Star Focus (141-170) - 3500 of each card, Heroes of the Game (171-180) - 100 of each card, Youth Movement (181-210) - 2500 of each card, Power Passion (211-240) - 3500 of each card, Basic Cards (241-330) - 4500 of each card, Tradewinds (331-350) -1000 of each card, Cornerstones of the Game (351-360) -100 of each card.

*YOUTH: .6X TO 1.5X BASIC YOUTH
*PE RADIANCE: 1.25X TO 3X BASIC POW.EXP.
*BASIC RADIANCE: .75X TO 2X BASIC CARDS
*SF RADIANCE: .75X TO 2X BASIC SF
*HG RADIANCE: 2X TO 5X BASIC HG
*YM RADIANCE: .6X TO 1.5X BASIC YM
*YM RADIANCE RC's: .3X TO .8X BASIC YM
*PP RADIANCE: .6X TO 1.5X BASIC PP
*BASIC RADIANCE: .75X TO 2X BASIC CARDS
*TW RADIANCE: 1.25X TO 3X BASIC TW
*CG RADIANCE: 2X TO 5X BASIC CG

1998 SPx Finite Spectrum

Randomly inserted in packs, this 360-card set is a parallel to the SPx Finite base set. Due to problems in the manufacturing process, exchange cards had to be inserted into packs for Power Explosion cards 40, 41 and 45. The deadline to redeem these exchange cards was June 2nd, 1999. This version is the most difficult to obtain of the three varieties of SPx Finite. Serial numbering for the various subsets is as follows: Youth Movement (1-30) - 1250 of each card, Power Explosion (31-50) - 50 of each card, Basic Cards (51-140) - 2250 of each card, Star Focus (141-170) - 1750 of each card, Heroes of the Game (171-180) - 1 of each card, Youth Movement (181-210) - 1250 of each card, Power Passion (211-240) -1750 of each card, Basic Cards (241-330) - 2250 of each card, Tradewinds (331-350) - 50 of each card and Cornerstones of the Game (351-360) - 1 of each card. Neither the Heroes of the Game nor the Cornerstones of the Game subsets are priced due to scarcity.

*YM SPECTRUM: 1X TO 2.5X BASIC YM
*PE SPECTRUM: 5X TO 12X BASIC PE
*BASIC SPECTRUM: 1.25X TO 3X BASIC
*SF SPECTRUM: 1.25X TO 3X BASIC SF
*YM SPECTRUM: .75X TO 2X BASIC YM
*YM SPECTRUM RC's: .5X TO 1.2X BASIC YM
*PP SPECTRUM: 1.25X TO 3X BASIC PP
*BASIC SPECTRUM: 1.25X TO 3X BASIC
*TW SPECTRUM: 5X TO 12X BASIC TW

1998 SPx Finite Home Run Hysteria

Randomly seeded exclusively into second series packs, these ten different inserts chronicle the epic home run race of the 1998 season. Each card is serial numbered to 62 on back.

HR1 Ken Griffey Jr. 40.00 100.00
HR2 Mark McGwire 40.00 100.00
HR3 Sammy Sosa 20.00 50.00
HR4 Albert Belle 8.00 20.00
HR5 Alex Rodriguez 40.00 100.00
HR6 Greg Vaughn 8.00 20.00
HR7 Andres Galarraga 8.00 20.00
HR8 Vinny Castilla 8.00 20.00
HR9 Juan Gonzalez 8.00 20.00
HR10 Chipper Jones 20.00 50.00

1999 SPx

The 1999 SPx set (produced by Upper Deck) was issued in one series for a total of 120 cards and distributed in thee-card packs with a suggested retail price of $5.99. The set features color photos of 80 MLB verteran players (1-80) with 40 top rookies on subset cards (81-120) numbered to 1,999. J.D.

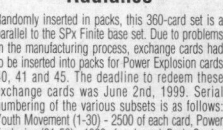

Drew and Gabe Kapler autographed all 1,999 of their respective rookie cards. A Ken Griffey Jr. Sample card was distributed to dealers and hobby media several weeks prior to the product's release. This card is serial numbered "0000/0000" on front, has the word "SAMPLE" pasted across the back in red ink and is oddly numbered "24 East" on back (even though the basic cards have no regional references). Also, 350 Willie Mays A Piece of History 500 Home Run bat cards were randomly seeded into packs. Mays personally signed an additional 24 cards (matching his jersey number) - all of which were then serial numbered by hand and randomly seeded into packs. Pricing for these bat cards can be referenced under 1999 Upper Deck A Piece of History 500 Club.

Card	Low	High
COMP.SET w/o SP's (80)	10.00	25.00
COMMON (1-10)	.60	1.50
COMMON CARD (11-80)	.20	.50
COMMON SP (81-120)	4.00	10.00
1 Mark McGwire 61	1.25	3.00
2 Mark McGwire 62	1.25	3.00
3 Mark McGwire 63	.60	1.50
4 Mark McGwire 64	.60	1.50
5 Mark McGwire 65	.60	1.50
6 Mark McGwire 66	.60	1.50
7 Mark McGwire 67	.60	1.50
8 Mark McGwire 68	.60	1.50
9 Mark McGwire 69	.60	1.50
10 Mark McGwire 70	1.50	4.00
11 Mo Vaughn	.20	.50
12 Darin Erstad	.20	.50
13 Travis Lee	.20	.50
14 Randy Johnson	.50	1.25
15 Matt Williams	.20	.50
16 Chipper Jones	.50	1.25
17 Greg Maddux	.75	2.00
18 Andruw Jones	.30	.75
19 Andres Galarraga	.20	.50
20 Cal Ripken	1.50	4.00
21 Albert Belle	.20	.50
22 Mike Mussina	.30	.75
23 Nomar Garciaparra	.75	2.00
24 Pedro Martinez	.30	.75
25 John Valentin	.20	.50
26 Kerry Wood	.20	.50
27 Sammy Sosa	.50	1.25
28 Mark Grace	.30	.75
29 Frank Thomas	.50	1.25
30 Mike Caruso	.20	.50
31 Barry Larkin	.30	.75
32 Sean Casey	.20	.50
33 Jim Thome	.30	.75
34 Kenny Lofton	.20	.50
35 Manny Ramirez	.30	.75
36 Larry Walker	.20	.50
37 Todd Helton	.30	.75
38 Vinny Castilla	.20	.50
39 Tony Clark	.20	.50
40 Derek Lee	.30	.75
41 Mark Kotsay	.20	.50
42 Jeff Bagwell	.30	.75
43 Craig Biggio	.30	.75
44 Moises Alou	.20	.50
45 Larry Sutton	.20	.50
46 Johnny Damon	.30	.75
47 Gary Sheffield	.20	.50
48 Raul Mondesi	.20	.50
49 Jeromy Burnitz	.20	.50
50 Todd Walker	.20	.50
51 David Ortiz	.50	1.25
52 Vladimir Guerrero	.50	1.25
53 Rondell White	.20	.50
54 Mike Piazza	.75	2.00
55 Derek Jeter	1.25	3.00
56 Tino Martinez	.30	.75
57 Roger Clemens	1.00	2.50
58 Ben Grieve	.20	.50
59 A.J. Hinch	.20	.50
60 Scott Rolen	.30	.75
61 Doug Glanville	.20	.50
62 Aramis Ramirez	.20	.50
63 Jose Guillen	.20	.50
64 Tony Gwynn	.60	1.50
65 Greg Vaughn	.20	.50
66 Ruben Rivera	.20	.50
67 Barry Bonds	1.25	3.00
68 J.T. Snow	.20	.50
69 Alex Rodriguez	.75	2.00
70 Ken Griffey Jr.	.75	2.00
71 Jay Buhner	.20	.50
72 Mark McGwire	1.25	3.00
73 Fernando Tatis	.20	.50
74 Quinton McCracken	.20	.50
75 Wade Boggs	.30	.75
76 Ivan Rodriguez	.30	.75
77 Juan Gonzalez	.30	.75
78 Rafael Palmeiro	.30	.75
79 Jose Cruz Jr.	.20	.50
80 Carlos Delgado	.20	.50
81 Troy Glaus SP	6.00	15.00
82 Vladimir Nunez SP	4.00	10.00
83 George Lombard SP	4.00	10.00
84 Bruce Chen SP	4.00	10.00
85 Ryan Minor SP	4.00	10.00
86 Calvin Pickering SP	4.00	10.00
87 Jin Ho Cho SP	4.00	10.00
88 Russ Branyan SP	4.00	10.00
89 Derrick Gibson SP	4.00	10.00
90 Gabe Kapler SP AU	6.00	15.00
91 Matt Anderson SP	4.00	10.00
92 Robert Fick SP	4.00	10.00
93 Juan Encarnacion SP	4.00	10.00
94 Preston Wilson SP	4.00	10.00
95 Alex Gonzalez SP	4.00	10.00
96 Carlos Beltran SP	6.00	15.00
97 Jeremy Giambi SP	4.00	10.00
98 Dee Brown SP	4.00	10.00
99 Adrian Beltre SP	4.00	10.00
100 Alex Cora SP	4.00	10.00
101 Angel Pena SP	4.00	10.00
102 Geoff Jenkins SP	4.00	10.00
103 Ronnie Belliard SP	4.00	10.00
104 Corey Koskie SP	4.00	10.00
105 A.J. Pierzynski SP	4.00	10.00
106 Michael Barrett SP	4.00	10.00
107 Fern.Seguignol SP	4.00	10.00
108 Mike Kinkade SP	4.00	10.00
109 Mike Lowell SP	4.00	10.00
110 Ricky Ledee SP	4.00	10.00
111 Eric Chavez SP	4.00	10.00
112 Abraham Nunez SP	4.00	10.00
113 Matt Clement SP	4.00	10.00
114 Ben Davis SP	4.00	10.00
115 Mike Darr SP	4.00	10.00
116 Ramon E.Martinez SP RC	4.00	10.00
117 Carlos Guillen SP	4.00	10.00
118 Shane Monahan SP	4.00	10.00
119 J.D. Drew SP AU	6.00	15.00
120 Kevin Witt SP	4.00	10.00
24EAST K.Griffey Jr. SAMP	.75	2.00

1999 SPx Finite Radiance

Randomly inserted in Finite Radiance Hot Packs only, this 120-card set is parallel to the SPx base set. Only 100 serial-numbered sets were produced.

*RADIANCE 1-10: 5X TO 12X BASIC 1-10
*RADIANCE 11-80: 8X TO 20X BASIC 11-80
*RADIANCE 81-120: .75X TO 2X BASIC 81-120

Card	Low	High
90 Gabe Kapler AU	10.00	25.00
119 J.D. Drew AU	10.00	25.00

1999 SPx Dominance

Randomly inserted into packs at the rate of one in 17, this 20-card set features color photos of some of the most dominant MLB superstars.

Card	Low	High
COMPLETE SET (20)	50.00	120.00
FB1 Chipper Jones	2.50	6.00
FB2 Greg Maddux	4.00	10.00
FB3 Cal Ripken	8.00	20.00
FB4 Nomar Garciaparra	4.00	10.00
FB5 Mo Vaughn	1.00	2.50
FB6 Sammy Sosa	2.50	6.00
FB7 Albert Belle	1.00	2.50
FB8 Frank Thomas	2.50	6.00
FB9 Jim Thome	1.50	4.00
FB10 Jeff Bagwell	1.50	4.00
FB11 Vladimir Guerrero	2.50	6.00
FB12 Mike Piazza	4.00	10.00
FB13 Derek Jeter	6.00	15.00
FB14 Tony Gwynn	50.00	120.00
FB15 Barry Bonds	6.00	15.00
FB16 Ken Griffey Jr.	4.00	10.00
FB17 Alex Rodriguez	4.00	10.00
FB18 Mark McGwire	6.00	15.00
FB19 J.D. Drew	1.00	2.50
FB20 Juan Gonzalez	1.00	2.50

1999 SPx Power Explosion

Randomly inserted in packs at the rate of one in three, this 30-card set features color action photos of some of the top power hitters of the game.

Card	Low	High
COMPLETE SET (30)	15.00	40.00
PE1 Troy Glaus	.50	1.25
PE2 Mo Vaughn	.30	.75
PE3 Travis Lee	.30	.75
PE4 Chipper Jones	.75	2.00
PE5 Andres Galarraga	.30	.75
PE6 Brady Anderson	.30	.75
PE7 Albert Belle	.30	.75
PE8 Nomar Garciaparra	1.25	3.00
PE9 Sammy Sosa	.75	2.00
PE10 Frank Thomas	.75	2.00
PE11 Jim Thome	.50	1.25
PE12 Manny Ramirez	.50	1.25
PE13 Larry Walker	.30	.75
PE14 Tony Clark	.30	.75
PE15 Jeff Bagwell	.50	1.25
PE16 Moises Alou	.30	.75
PE17 Ken Caminiti	.30	.75
PE18 Vladimir Guerrero	.75	2.00
PE19 Mike Piazza	1.25	3.00
PE20 Tino Martinez	.50	1.25
PE21 Ben Grieve	.30	.75
PE22 Scott Rolen	.50	1.25
PE23 Greg Vaughn	.30	.75
PE24 Barry Bonds	2.00	5.00
PE25 Ken Griffey Jr.	1.25	3.00
PE26 Alex Rodriguez	1.25	3.00
PE27 Mark McGwire	2.00	5.00
PE28 J.D. Drew	.30	.75
PE29 Juan Gonzalez	.30	.75
PE30 Ivan Rodriguez	.50	1.25

1999 SPx Premier Stars

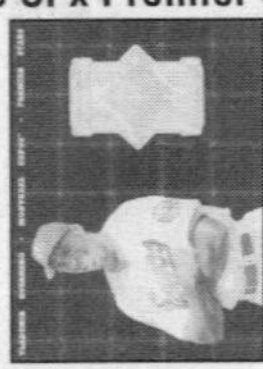

Randomly inserted in packs at the rate of one in 17, this 30-card set features color action photos of some of the game's most powerful players captured on cards with a unique rainbow-foil design.

Card	Low	High
PS1 Mark McGwire	8.00	20.00
PS2 Sammy Sosa	3.00	8.00
PS3 Frank Thomas	3.00	8.00
PS4 J.D. Drew	1.25	3.00
PS5 Kerry Wood	1.25	3.00
PS6 Moises Alou	1.25	3.00
PS7 Kenny Lofton	1.25	3.00
PS8 Jeff Bagwell	2.00	5.00
PS9 Tony Clark	1.25	3.00
PS10 Roberto Alomar	3.00	8.00
PS11 Cal Ripken	10.00	25.00
PS12 Derek Jeter	8.00	20.00
PS13 Mike Piazza	5.00	12.00
PS14 Jose Cruz Jr.	1.25	3.00
PS15 Chipper Jones	3.00	8.00
PS16 Nomar Garciaparra	5.00	12.00
PS17 Greg Maddux	5.00	12.00
PS18 Scott Rolen	2.00	5.00
PS19 Vladimir Guerrero	3.00	8.00
PS20 Albert Belle	1.25	3.00
PS21 Ken Griffey Jr.	5.00	12.00
PS22 Alex Rodriguez	5.00	12.00
PS23 Ben Grieve	1.25	3.00
PS24 Juan Gonzalez	1.25	3.00
PS25 Barry Bonds	8.00	20.00
PS26 Roger Clemens	6.00	15.00
PS27 Tony Gwynn	4.00	10.00
PS28 Randy Johnson	3.00	8.00
PS29 Travis Lee	1.25	3.00
PS30 Mo Vaughn	1.25	3.00

1999 SPx Star Focus

Randomly inserted in packs at the rate of one in eight, this 30-card set features action color photos of some of the brightest stars in the game beside a black-and-white portrait of the player.

Card	Low	High
COMPLETE SET (30)	50.00	120.00
SF1 Chipper Jones	2.00	5.00
SF2 Greg Maddux	3.00	8.00
SF3 Cal Ripken	6.00	15.00
SF4 Nomar Garciaparra	3.00	8.00
SF5 Mo Vaughn	.75	2.00
SF6 Sammy Sosa	2.00	5.00
SF7 Albert Belle	.75	2.00
SF8 Frank Thomas	2.00	5.00
SF9 Jim Thome	1.25	3.00
SF10 Kenny Lofton	.75	2.00
SF11 Manny Ramirez	1.25	3.00
SF12 Larry Walker	.75	2.00
SF13 Jeff Bagwell	1.25	3.00
SF14 Craig Biggio	1.25	3.00
SF15 Randy Johnson	2.00	5.00
SF16 Vladimir Guerrero	2.00	5.00
SF17 Mike Piazza	3.00	8.00
SF18 Derek Jeter	5.00	12.00
SF19 Tino Martinez	1.25	3.00
SF20 Bernie Williams	2.00	5.00
SF21 Curt Schilling	.75	2.00
SF22 Tony Gwynn	2.50	6.00
SF23 Barry Bonds	5.00	12.00
SF24 Ken Griffey Jr.	3.00	8.00
SF25 Alex Rodriguez	3.00	8.00
SF26 Mark McGwire	5.00	12.00
SF27 J.D. Drew	.75	2.00
SF28 Juan Gonzalez	.75	2.00
SF29 Ivan Rodriguez	1.25	3.00
SF30 Ben Grieve	.75	2.00

1999 SPx Winning Materials

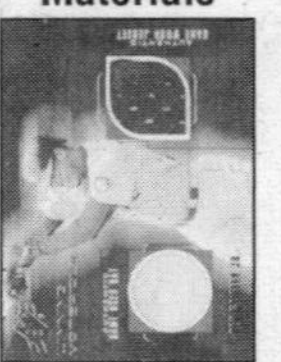

Randomly inserted into packs at the rate of one in 251, this eight-card set features color photos of top players with a piece of the player's game-worn jersey and game-used bat embedded in the card.

Card	Low	High
IR Ivan Rodriguez	10.00	25.00
JD J.D. Drew	6.00	15.00
JR Ken Griffey Jr.	20.00	50.00
TG Tony Gwynn	15.00	40.00
TH Todd Helton	10.00	25.00
TL Travis Lee	4.00	10.00
VC Vinny Castilla	6.00	15.00
VG Vladimir Guerrero	10.00	25.00

2000 SPx

The 2000 SPx (produced by Upper Deck) set was initially released in May, 2000 as a 120-card set. Each pack contained four cards and carried a suggested retail price of $5.99. The set featured 90-player cards, and a 30-card "Young Stars" subset. There are three tiers within the Young Stars subset. Tier one cards are serial numbered to 1000, Tier two cards are serial numbered to 1500 and autographed by the player and Tier three cards are serial numbered to 500 and autographed by the player. Redemption cards were issued for several of the autograph cards and they were to be postmarked by 1/24/01 and received by 2/3/01 to be valid for exchange. In late December, 2000, Upper Deck issued a new product called Rookie Update which contained a selection of new cards for SP Authentic, SPx and UD Pros and Prospects. Rookie Update packs contained four cards and the collector was guaranteed one card from each featured brand, plus a fourth card. For SPx, these "high series" cards were numbered 121-196. The Young Stars subset was extended with cards 121-151 and cards 182-196. Cards 121-135 and 182-196 featured a selection of prospects each serial numbered to 1600. Cards 136-151 featured a selection of prospect cards signed by the player and each serial numbered to 1500. Cards 152-181 contained a selection of veteran players that were either initially not included in the basic 120-card "first series" set or traded to new teams. Notable Rookie Cards include Xavier Nady, Kazuhiro Sasaki, Ben Sheets and Barry Zito. Also, a selection of A Piece of History 3000 Club Ty Cobb memorabilia cards were randomly seeded into packs. 350 bat cards, three hand-numbered autograph cut cards and one hand-numbered, combination bat chip and autograph cut card were produced. Pricing for these memorabilia cards can be referenced under 2000 Upper Deck A Piece of History 3000 Club.

Card	Low	High
COMP.BASIC w/o SP's (90)	10.00	25.00
COMP.UPDATE w/o SP's (30)	4.00	10.00
COMMON CARD (1-90)	.20	.50
COMMON AU/1500 (91-120)	4.00	10.00
COMMON (121-135/182-196)	3.00	8.00
COMMON (136-151)	4.00	10.00
COMMON (152-181)	.30	.75
1 Troy Glaus	.20	.50
2 Mo Vaughn	.20	.50
3 Ramon Ortiz	.20	.50
4 Jeff Bagwell	.30	.75
5 Moises Alou	.20	.50
6 Craig Biggio	.30	.75
7 Jose Lima	.20	.50
8 Jason Giambi	.20	.50
9 John Jaha	.20	.50
10 Matt Stairs	.20	.50
11 Chipper Jones	.50	1.25
12 Greg Maddux	.75	2.00
13 Andres Galarraga	.20	.50
14 Andruw Jones	.30	.75
15 Jeromy Burnitz	.20	.50
16 Ron Belliard	.20	.50
17 Carlos Delgado	.20	.50
18 David Wells	.20	.50
19 Tony Batista	.20	.50
20 Shannon Stewart	.20	.50
21 Sammy Sosa	.50	1.25
22 Mark Grace	.30	.75
23 Henry Rodriguez	.20	.50
24 Mark McGwire	1.25	3.00
25 J.D. Drew	.20	.50
26 Luis Gonzalez	.20	.50
27 Randy Johnson	.50	1.25
28 Matt Williams	.20	.50
29 Steve Finley	.20	.50
30 Shawn Green	.20	.50
31 Kevin Brown	.30	.75
32 Gary Sheffield	.20	.50
33 Jose Canseco	.30	.75
34 Greg Vaughn	.20	.50
35 Vladimir Guerrero	.50	1.25
36 Michael Barrett	.20	.50
37 Russ Ortiz	.20	.50
38 Barry Bonds	1.25	3.00
39 Jeff Kent	.20	.50
40 Richie Sexson	.20	.50
41 Manny Ramirez	.30	.75
42 Jim Thome	.30	.75
43 Roberto Alomar	.30	.75
44 Edgar Martinez	.30	.75
45 Alex Rodriguez	.75	2.00
46 John Olerud	.20	.50
47 Alex Gonzalez	.20	.50
48 Cliff Floyd	.20	.50
49 Mike Piazza	.75	2.00
50 Al Leiter	.20	.50
51 Robin Ventura	.30	.75
52 Edgardo Alfonzo	.20	.50
53 Albert Belle	.20	.50
54 Cal Ripken	1.50	4.00
55 B.J. Surhoff	.20	.50
56 Tony Gwynn	.60	1.50
57 Trevor Hoffman	.20	.50
58 Brian Giles	.20	.50
59 Jason Kendall	.20	.50
60 Kris Benson	.20	.50
61 Bob Abreu	.20	.50
62 Scott Rolen	.30	.75
63 Curt Schilling	.20	.50
64 Mike Lieberthal	.20	.50
65 Sean Casey	.20	.50
66 Dante Bichette	.20	.50
67 Ken Griffey Jr.	.75	2.00
68 Pokey Reese	.20	.50
69 Mike Sweeney	.20	.50
70 Carlos Febles	.20	.50
71 Ivan Rodriguez	.30	.75
72 Ruben Mateo	.20	.50
73 Rafael Palmeiro	.30	.75
74 Larry Walker	.20	.50
75 Todd Helton	.30	.75
76 Nomar Garciaparra	.75	2.00
77 Pedro Martinez	.30	.75
78 Troy O'Leary	.20	.50
79 Jacque Jones	.20	.50
80 Corey Koskie	.20	.50
81 Juan Gonzalez	.20	.50
82 Dean Palmer	.20	.50
83 Juan Encarnacion	.20	.50
84 Frank Thomas	.50	1.25
85 Magglio Ordonez	.20	.50
86 Paul Konerko	.20	.50
87 Bernie Williams	.30	.75
88 Derek Jeter	1.25	3.00
89 Roger Clemens	1.00	2.50
90 Orlando Hernandez	.20	.50
91 Vernon Wells AU/1500	10.00	25.00
92 Rick Ankiel AU/1500	40.00	80.00
93 Eric Chavez AU/1500	10.00	25.00
94 A.Soriano/1500 AU	30.00	60.00
95 Eric Gagne AU/1500	30.00	60.00
96 Rob Bell AU/1500	4.00	10.00
97 Matt Riley AU/1500	4.00	10.00
98 Josh Beckett AU/1500	50.00	100.00
99 Ben Petrick AU/1500	4.00	10.00
100 Rob Ramsay AU/1500	4.00	10.00
101 Scott Williamson 1500 AU	4.00	10.00
102 Doug Davis AU/1500	6.00	15.00
103 E.Munson/1500 AU*	4.00	10.00
104 Pat Burrell AU/500	30.00	60.00
105 Jim Morris AU/1500	10.00	25.00
106 Gabe Kapler AU/500	15.00	40.00
107 Lance Berkman/1000	3.00	8.00
108 E.Durazo/1500 AU	4.00	10.00
109 Tim Hudson AU/1500	15.00	40.00
110 Ben Davis AU/1500	4.00	10.00
111 N.Johnson/1500 AU	6.00	15.00
112 O.Dotel/1500 AU	4.00	10.00
113 Jerry Hairston/1000	3.00	8.00
114 Ruben Mateo/1000	3.00	8.00
115 Chris Singleton/1000	3.00	8.00
116 Bruce Chen AU/1500	4.00	10.00
117 Derrick Gibson/1000	3.00	8.00
118 Carlos Beltran AU/500	75.00	125.00
119 F.Garcia/1500 AU	6.00	15.00
120 P.Wilson/1500 AU	6.00	15.00
121 B.Wilkerson/1600 RC	4.00	10.00
122 Roy Oswalt/1600 RC	60.00	120.00
123 W.Serrano/1600 RC	3.00	8.00
124 Sean Burnett/1600 RC	3.00	8.00
125 Alex Cabrera/1600 RC	3.00	8.00
126 Timo Perez/1600 RC	3.00	8.00
127 Juan Pierre/1600 RC	4.00	10.00
128 Daylan Holt/1600 RC	3.00	8.00
129 T.Ohka/1600 RC	3.00	8.00
130 K.Sasaki/1600 RC	4.00	10.00
131 K.Ainsworth/1600 RC	3.00	8.00
132 B.Abernathy/1600 RC	3.00	8.00
133 Danys Baez/1600 RC	3.00	8.00
134 Brad Cresse/1600 RC	3.00	8.00
135 R.Franklin/1600 RC	3.00	8.00
136 M.Lamb/1500 AU RC	6.00	15.00
137 David Espinosa 1500 AU RC	4.00	10.00
138 Matt Wheatland 1500 AU RC	4.00	10.00
139 X.Nady/1500 AU RC	15.00	40.00
140 S.Heard/1500 AU RC	4.00	10.00
141 P.Coco/1500 AU RC	4.00	10.00
Card erroneously numbered 54 instead of 141		
142 J.Miller/1500 AU RC	4.00	10.00
143 Dave Krynzel 1500 AU RC	4.00	10.00
144 Dane Sardinha 1500 AU RC	4.00	10.00
145 B.Sheets/1500 AU RC	30.00	60.00
146 L.Estrella/1500 AU RC	4.00	10.00
147 Ben Diggins 1500 AU RC	4.00	10.00
148 B.Zito/1500 AU RC	20.00	50.00
149 J.Torres/1500 AU RC	4.00	10.00
150 Mike Meyers 1500 AU RC	4.00	10.00
151 K.Wilson/1500 AU RC	4.00	10.00
152 Darin Erstad	.30	.75
153 Richard Hidalgo	.30	.75
154 Eric Chavez	.30	.75
155 B.J. Surhoff	.30	.75
156 Richie Sexson	.30	.75
157 Raul Mondesi	.30	.75
158 Rondell White	.30	.75
159 Jim Edmonds	.30	.75
160 Curt Schilling	.30	.75
161 Tom Goodwin	.30	.75
162 Fred McGriff	.50	1.25
163 Jose Vidro	.30	.75
164 Ellis Burks	.30	.75
165 David Segui	.30	.75
166 Aaron Sele	.30	.75
167 Henry Rodriguez	.30	.75
168 Mike Bordick	.30	.75
169 Mike Mussina	.50	1.25
170 Ryan Klesko	.30	.75
171 Kevin Young	.30	.75
172 Travis Lee	.30	.75
173 Aaron Boone	.30	.75
174 Jermaine Dye	.30	.75
175 Ricky Ledee	.30	.75
176 Jeffrey Hammonds	.30	.75
177 Carl Everett	.30	.75
178 Matt Lawton	.30	.75
179 Bobby Higginson	.30	.75
180 Charles Johnson	.30	.75
181 David Justice	.30	.75
182 Joey Nation/1600 RC	3.00	8.00
183 Rico Washington 1600 RC	3.00	8.00
184 Luis Matos/1600 RC	3.00	8.00
185 C.Wakeland/1600 RC	3.00	8.00
186 SW Kim/1600 RC	3.00	8.00
187 Keith Ginter/1600 RC	3.00	8.00
188 G.Guzman/1600 RC	3.00	8.00
189 J.Spurgeon/1600 RC	3.00	8.00
190 Jace Brewer/1600 RC	3.00	8.00
191 J.Guzman/1600 RC	3.00	8.00
192 Ross Gload/1600 RC	3.00	8.00
193 P.Crawford/1600 RC	3.00	8.00
194 R.Kohlmeier/1600 RC	3.00	8.00
195 Julio Zuleta/1600 RC	3.00	8.00
196 Matt Ginter/1600 RC	3.00	8.00

2000 SPx Radiance

Randomly inserted into packs, this 135-card insert is a parallel of the SPx base set. Each card in the set is individually serial numbered to 100. Please note the cards with asterisks next to their name were not issued in the basic set but were prepared and accidentally issued in the 2000 SPx packs. They are numbered and packed out to 100 just like the other Radiance cards.

Card	Low	High
COMMON CARD (1-90)	1.50	4.00
*STARS 1-90: 6X TO 15X BASIC CARDS		
COMMON CARD (91-120)	3.00	8.00
91 Vernon Wells	3.00	8.00
92 Rick Ankiel	3.00	8.00
93 Eric Chavez	3.00	8.00
94 Alfonso Soriano	6.00	15.00
95 Eric Gagne	10.00	25.00
96 Rob Bell	3.00	8.00
97 Matt Riley	3.00	8.00
98 Josh Beckett	6.00	15.00
98A John Bale *	3.00	8.00
98B Alex Escobar *	3.00	8.00
98C Joe Mays *	3.00	8.00
98D Calvin Pickering *	3.00	8.00
98E Dave Roberts *	3.00	8.00
98F Jared Sandberg *	3.00	8.00
98G Dernell Stenson *	3.00	8.00
98H Reggie Taylor *	3.00	8.00
98I Ed Yarnall *	3.00	8.00
99 Ben Petrick	3.00	8.00
100 Rob Ramsay	3.00	8.00
101 Scott Williamson	3.00	8.00
102 Doug Davis	3.00	8.00
103 Eric Munson	3.00	8.00
103A Tony Armas Jr. *	3.00	8.00
103B Travis Dawkins *	3.00	8.00
103C Mike Lamb *	4.00	10.00
103D Rico Washington *	3.00	8.00
104 Pat Burrell	3.00	8.00
105 Jim Morris	6.00	15.00
106 Gabe Kapler	3.00	8.00
106A Adam Piatt *	3.00	8.00
106B Mark Quinn *	3.00	8.00
107 Lance Berkman	3.00	8.00
108 Erubiel Durazo	3.00	8.00
109 Tim Hudson	3.00	8.00
110 Ben Davis	3.00	8.00
111 Nick Johnson	3.00	8.00
112 Octavio Dotel	3.00	8.00
113 Jerry Hairston	3.00	8.00
114 Ruben Mateo	3.00	8.00
115 Chris Singleton	3.00	8.00
116 Bruce Chen	3.00	8.00
117 Derrick Gibson	3.00	8.00
118 Carlos Beltran	3.00	8.00
119 Freddy Garcia	3.00	8.00
120 Preston Wilson	3.00	8.00

2000 SPx Foundations

Randomly inserted into packs at one 32, this 10-card insert features players that are the cornerstones teams build around. Card backs carry a "F" prefix.

Card	Low	High
COMPLETE SET (10)	40.00	100.00
F1 Ken Griffey Jr.	4.00	10.00
F2 Nomar Garciaparra	4.00	10.00
F3 Cal Ripken	8.00	20.00
F4 Chipper Jones	2.50	6.00
F5 Mike Piazza	4.00	10.00
F6 Derek Jeter	6.00	15.00
F7 Manny Ramirez	1.50	4.00
F8 Jeff Bagwell	1.50	4.00
F9 Tony Gwynn	3.00	8.00
F10 Larry Walker	1.00	2.50

2000 SPx Heart of the Order

Randomly inserted into packs at one in eight, this 20-card insert features players that can lift their teams to victory with one swing of the bat. Card backs carry a "H" prefix.

Card	Low	High
COMPLETE SET (20)	25.00	60.00
H1 Bernie Williams	.75	2.00
H2 Mike Piazza	2.00	5.00
H3 Ivan Rodriguez	.75	2.00

Card	Low	High
H4 Mark McGwire	3.00	8.00
H5 Manny Ramirez	.75	2.00
H6 Ken Griffey Jr.	2.00	5.00
H7 Matt Williams	.50	1.25
H8 Sammy Sosa	1.25	3.00
H9 Mo Vaughn	.50	1.25
H10 Carlos Delgado	.50	1.25
H11 Brian Giles	.50	1.25
H12 Chipper Jones	1.25	3.00
H13 Sean Casey	.50	1.25
H14 Tony Gwynn	1.50	4.00
H15 Barry Bonds	3.00	8.00
H16 Carlos Beltran	.50	1.25
H17 Scott Rolen	.75	2.00
H18 Juan Gonzalez	.50	1.25
H19 Larry Walker	.50	1.25
H20 Vladimir Guerrero	1.25	3.00

2000 SPx Highlight Heroes

Randomly inserted into packs at one in 16, this 10-card insert features players that have a flair for heroics. Card backs carry a "HH" prefix.

Card	Low	High
COMPLETE SET (10)	12.50	30.00
HH1 Pedro Martinez	.75	2.00
HH2 Ivan Rodriguez	.75	2.00
HH3 Carlos Beltran	.50	1.25
HH4 Nomar Garciaparra	2.00	5.00
HH5 Ken Griffey Jr.	2.00	5.00
HH6 Randy Johnson	1.25	3.00
HH7 Chipper Jones	1.25	3.00
HH8 Scott Williamson	.40	1.00
HH9 Larry Walker	.50	1.25
HH10 Mark McGwire	3.00	8.00

2000 SPx Power Brokers

Randomly inserted into packs at one in eight, this 20-card insert features some of the greatest power hitters of all time. Card backs carry a "PB" prefix.

Card	Low	High
COMPLETE SET (20)	25.00	60.00
PB1 Rafael Palmeiro	.75	2.00
PB2 Carlos Delgado	.50	1.25
PB3 Ken Griffey Jr.	2.00	5.00
PB4 Matt Stairs	.50	1.25
PB5 Mike Piazza	2.00	5.00
PB6 Vladimir Guerrero	1.25	3.00
PB7 Chipper Jones	1.25	3.00
PB8 Mark McGwire	3.00	8.00
PB9 Matt Williams	.50	1.25
PB10 Juan Gonzalez	.50	1.25
PB11 Shawn Green	.50	1.25
PB12 Sammy Sosa	1.25	3.00
PB13 Brian Giles	.50	1.25
PB14 Jeff Bagwell	.75	2.00
PB15 Alex Rodriguez	2.00	5.00
PB16 Frank Thomas	1.25	3.00
PB17 Larry Walker	.50	1.25
PB18 Albert Belle	.50	1.25
PB19 Dean Palmer	.50	1.25
PB20 Mo Vaughn	.50	1.25

2000 SPx Signatures

Randomly inserted into packs at one in 179, this 15-card insert features autographed cards of some of the hottest players in major league baseball. The following players went out as stickered exchange cards: Jeff Bagwell (100 percent), Ken Griffey Jr. (100 percent), Tony Gwynn (25 percent), Vladimir Guerrero (50 percent), Manny Ramirez (100 percent) and Ivan Rodriguez (25 percent). The exchange deadline for the stickered cards was February 3rd, 2001. Card backs carry a "X" prefix followed by the players initials.

Card	Low	High
XBB Barry Bonds	100.00	175.00
XCJ Chipper Jones	20.00	50.00
XCR Cal Ripken	75.00	150.00
XDJ Derek Jeter	75.00	150.00
XIR I.Rodriguez EXCH *	15.00	40.00
XJB Jeff Bagwell	20.00	50.00
XJC Jose Canseco	10.00	25.00
XKG Ken Griffey Jr.	75.00	150.00
XMR M.Ramirez EXCH	15.00	40.00
XOH Orlando Hernandez	60.00	120.00
XRC Roger Clemens	60.00	120.00
XSC Sean Casey	6.00	15.00
XSR Scott Rolen	10.00	25.00
XTG Tony Gwynn	20.00	50.00
XVG V.Guerrero EXCH *	15.00	40.00

2000 SPx SPXcitement

Randomly inserted into packs at one in four, this 20-card insert features some of the most exciting players in the major leagues. Card backs carry a "XC" prefix.

Card	Low	High
COMPLETE SET (20)	12.50	30.00
XC1 Nomar Garciaparra	1.00	2.50
XC2 Mark McGwire	1.50	4.00
XC3 Derek Jeter	1.50	4.00
XC4 Cal Ripken	2.00	5.00
XC5 Barry Bonds	1.50	4.00
XC6 Alex Rodriguez	1.00	2.50
XC7 Scott Rolen	.40	1.00
XC8 Pedro Martinez	.40	1.00
XC9 Sean Casey	.25	.60
XC10 Sammy Sosa	.60	1.50
XC11 Randy Johnson	.60	1.50
XC12 Ivan Rodriguez	.40	1.00
XC13 Frank Thomas	.60	1.50
XC14 Greg Maddux	1.00	2.50
XC15 Tony Gwynn	.75	2.00
XC16 Ken Griffey Jr.	1.00	2.50
XC17 Carlos Beltran	.25	.60
XC18 Mike Piazza	1.00	2.50
XC19 Chipper Jones	.60	1.50
XC20 Craig Biggio	.40	1.00

2000 SPx Untouchable Talents

Randomly inserted into packs at one in 96, this 10-card insert features players that have skills that are unmatched. Card backs carry a "UT" prefix.

Card	Low	High
COMPLETE SET (10)	80.00	200.00
UT1 Mark McGwire	15.00	40.00
UT2 Ken Griffey Jr.	10.00	25.00
UT3 Shawn Green	2.50	6.00
UT4 Ivan Rodriguez	4.00	10.00
UT5 Sammy Sosa	6.00	15.00
UT6 Derek Jeter	15.00	40.00
UT7 Sean Casey	2.50	6.00
UT8 Chipper Jones	6.00	15.00
UT9 Pedro Martinez	4.00	10.00
UT10 Vladimir Guerrero	6.00	15.00

2000 SPx Winning Materials

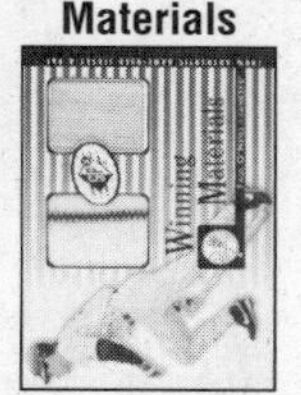

Randomly inserted into first series packs, this 30-card insert features game-used memorabilia cards from some of the top names in baseball. The set includes Bat/Jersey cards, Cap/Jersey cards, Ball/Jersey cards, and autographed Bat/Jersey cards. Card backs carry the players initals. Please note that the Ken Griffey Jr. autographed Bat/Jersey cards, and the Manny Ramirez autographed Bat/Jersey cards were both redemptions with an exchang deadline of 12/31/2000.

Card	Low	High
AR1 Alex Rodriguez Bat-Jsy	10.00	25.00
AR2 Alex Rodriguez Cap-Jsy/100	20.00	50.00
AR3 Alex Rodriguez Ball-Jsy/50	30.00	60.00
BB1 Barry Bonds Bat-Jsy	15.00	40.00
BB2 Barry Bonds Cap-Jsy/100	30.00	60.00
BB3 Barry Bonds Bat-Jsy AU/25		
BW Bernie Williams Bat-Jsy	6.00	15.00
DJ1 Derek Jeter Bat-Jsy	20.00	50.00
DJ2 Derek Jeter Ball-Jsy/50	50.00	100.00
DJ3 Derek Jeter Bat-Jsy AU/2		
EC1 Eric Chavez Bat-Jsy	4.00	10.00
EC2 Eric Chavez Cap-Jsy/100	6.00	15.00
GM Greg Maddux Bat-Jsy	10.00	25.00
IR Ivan Rodriguez Bat-Jsy	6.00	15.00
JB1 Jeff Bagwell Bat-Jsy	6.00	15.00
JB2 Jeff Bagwell Ball-Jsy/50	15.00	40.00
JC Jose Canseco Bat-Jsy	6.00	15.00
JL1 Javy Lopez Bat-Jsy	4.00	10.00
JL2 Javy Lopez Cap-Jsy	6.00	15.00
KG1 Ken Griffey Jr. Bat-Jsy	10.00	25.00
KG2 Ken Griffey Jr. Ball-Jsy/50	30.00	60.00
KG3 Ken Griffey Jr. Bat-Jsy AU/24		
MM1 Mark McGwire Ball-Base/250	30.00	60.00
MM2 Mark McGwire Ball-Base/250	30.00	60.00
MR1 Manny Ramirez Bat-Jsy	6.00	15.00
MR2 Manny Ramirez Bat-Jsy AU/24		
MW Matt Williams Bat-Jsy	4.00	10.00
PM Pedro Martinez Cap-Jsy/100	10.00	25.00
PO Paul O'Neill Bat-Jsy	6.00	15.00
VG1 Vladimir Guerrero Bat-Jsy	6.00	15.00
VG2 Vladimir Guerrero Cap-Jsy/100	10.00	25.00
VG3 Vladimir Guerrero Ball-Jsy/50	15.00	40.00
TGL Troy Glaus Bat-Jsy	4.00	10.00
TGW1 Tony Gwynn Bat-Jsy	6.00	15.00
TGW2 Tony Gwynn Ball-Jsy/50	20.00	50.00
TGW3 Tony Gwynn Cap-Jsy/100	12.50	30.00

2000 SPx Winning Materials Update

Randomly inserted into packs of 2000 Upper Deck Rookie Update (at an approximate rate of one per box), this 28-card insert features game-used memorabilia cards from some of baseball's top athletes. The set also includes a few members of the 2000 USA Olympic Baseball team. Card backs carry the player's initials as numbering.

Card	Low	High
MKGD Travis Dawkins Mike Kinkade Bat-Bat	3.00	8.00
BAAE Brent Abernathy Adam Everett Bat-Bat	3.00	8.00
BWEY Brad Wilkerson Ernie Young Bat-Bat	4.00	10.00
CRTG Cal Ripken Tony Gwynn Base-Base	15.00	40.00
DJAR Derek Jeter Alex Rodriguez Base-Bat	15.00	40.00
DJNG Derek Jeter Nomar Garciaparra Base-Bat	20.00	50.00
FTMO Frank Thomas Magglio Ordonez Base-Base	4.00	10.00
GSR Ken Griffey Jr. Sammy Sosa Alex Rodriguez Jsy-Jsy-Jsy	20.00	50.00
GWBS Ben Sheets Ball-Jsy	3.00	8.00
GWDM D.Mientkiewicz Bat-Base	3.00	8.00
GWEY Ernie Young Bat-Base	3.00	8.00
GWJC John Cotton Bat-Jsy	3.00	8.00
GWMN Mike Neill Bat-Jsy	3.00	8.00
GWSB Sean Burroughs Bat-Jsy	3.00	8.00
IRRP Ivan Rodriguez Rafael Palmeiro Ball-Ball	4.00	10.00
JGR Derek Jeter Nomar Garciaparra Alex Rodriguez Base-Ball-Bat	60.00	120.00
JBCB Jeff Bagwell Craig Biggio Base-Base	4.00	10.00
JCBB Jose Canseco Barry Bonds Ball-Ball	12.50	30.00
KGSS Ken Griffey Jr. Sammy Sosa Bat-Bat	12.50	30.00
MMKG Mark McGwire Ken Griffey Jr. Ball-Bat	15.00	40.00
MMRA Mark McGwire Rick Ankiel Base-Base	15.00	40.00
MMSS Mark McGwire Sammy Sosa Ball-Ball	20.00	50.00
MPRV Mike Piazza Robin Ventura Ball-Ball	10.00	25.00
NGPM N.Garciaparra Pedro Martinez Ball-Ball	12.50	30.00
RCPM Roger Clemens Pedro Martinez Ball-Ball	15.00	40.00
SBBS Sean Burroughs Ben Sheets Bat-Base	3.00	8.00

2000 SPx Winning Materials Update Numbered

Randomly inserted into 2001 Rookie Update packs, this 3-card insert features game-used memorabilia from three different major leaguers on the same card. These rare gems are individually serial numbered to 50. Card backs carry the players initials as numbering

Card	Low	High
CBG Jose Canseco Barry Bonds Ken Griffey Jr Ball-Ball-Bat	60.00	120.00
GSM Ken Griffey Jr. Sammy Sosa Mark McGwire Bat-Ball-Base	50.00	100.00
JGR Derek Jeter Nomar Garciaparra Alex Rodriguez Base-Ball-Bat	50.00	100.00

2001 SPx

The 2001 SPx product was initially released in early May, 2001, and featured a 150-card base set. 60 additional update cards (151-210) were distributed within Upper Deck Rookie Update packs in late December, 2001. The base set is broken into tiers as follows: Base Veterans (1-90), Young Stars (91-120) serial numbered to 2000, Rookie Jerseys (121-135), and Jersey Autographs (136-150). The Rookie Update SPx cards were broken into tiers as follows: base veterans (151-180) and Young Stars (181-210) serial numbered to 1500. Cards 206-210, in addition to being serial-numbered of 1,500 copies per, also feature on-card autographs. Each basic pack contained four cards and carried a suggested retail price of $6.99. Rookie Update packs contained four cards with an SRP of $4.99.

Card	Low	High
COMP.BASIC w/o SP's (90)	10.00	25.00
COMP.UPDATE w/o SP's (30)	4.00	10.00
COMMON CARD (1-90)	.20	.50
COMMON YS (91-120)	2.00	5.00
COMMON JSY (121-135)	3.00	8.00
COMMON (136-150)	6.00	15.00
COMMON (151-180)	.30	.75
COMMON (181-210)	2.00	5.00
1 Darin Erstad	.20	.50
2 Troy Glaus	.20	.50
3 Mo Vaughn	.20	.50
4 Johnny Damon	.30	.75
5 Jason Giambi	.20	.50
6 Tim Hudson	.20	.50
7 Miguel Tejada	.20	.50
8 Carlos Delgado	.20	.50
9 Raul Mondesi	.20	.50
10 Tony Batista	.20	.50
11 Ben Grieve	.20	.50
12 Greg Vaughn	.20	.50
13 Juan Gonzalez	.20	.50
14 Jim Thome	.30	.75
15 Roberto Alomar	.30	.75
16 John Olerud	.20	.50
17 Edgar Martinez	.30	.75
18 Albert Belle	.20	.50
19 Cal Ripken	1.50	4.00
20 Ivan Rodriguez	.30	.75
21 Rafael Palmeiro	.30	.75
22 Alex Rodriguez	.75	2.00
23 Nomar Garciaparra	.75	2.00
24 Pedro Martinez	.30	.75
25 Manny Ramirez Sox	.30	.75
26 Jermaine Dye	.20	.50
27 Mark Quinn	.20	.50
28 Carlos Beltran	.20	.50
29 Tony Clark	.20	.50
30 Bobby Higginson	.20	.50
31 Eric Milton	.20	.50
32 Matt Lawton	.20	.50
33 Frank Thomas	.50	1.25
34 Magglio Ordonez	.20	.50
35 Ray Durham	.20	.50
36 David Wells	.20	.50
37 Derek Jeter	1.25	3.00
38 Bernie Williams	.30	.75
39 Roger Clemens UER Wrong uniform number on card	1.00	2.50
40 David Justice	.20	.50
41 Jeff Bagwell	.30	.75
42 Richard Hidalgo	.20	.50
43 Moises Alou	.20	.50
44 Chipper Jones	.50	1.25
45 Andruw Jones	.30	.75
46 Greg Maddux	.75	2.00
47 Rafael Furcal	.20	.50
48 Jeromy Burnitz	.20	.50
49 Geoff Jenkins	.20	.50
50 Mark McGwire	1.25	3.00
51 Jim Edmonds	.20	.50
52 Rick Ankiel	.20	.50
53 Edgar Renteria	.20	.50
54 Sammy Sosa	.50	1.25
55 Kerry Wood	.20	.50
56 Rondell White	.20	.50
57 Randy Johnson	.50	1.25
58 Steve Finley	.20	.50
59 Matt Williams	.20	.50
60 Luis Gonzalez	.20	.50
61 Kevin Brown	.20	.50
62 Gary Sheffield	.20	.50
63 Shawn Green	.20	.50
64 Vladimir Guerrero	.50	1.25
65 Jose Vidro	.20	.50
66 Barry Bonds	1.25	3.00
67 Jeff Kent	.20	.50
68 Livan Hernandez	.20	.50
69 Preston Wilson	.20	.50
70 Charles Johnson	.20	.50
71 Cliff Floyd	.20	.50
72 Mike Piazza	.75	2.00
73 Edgardo Alfonzo	.20	.50
74 Jay Payton	.20	.50
75 Robin Ventura	.20	.50
76 Tony Gwynn	.60	1.50
77 Phil Nevin	.20	.50
78 Ryan Klesko	.20	.50
79 Scott Rolen	.30	.75
80 Pat Burrell	.20	.50
81 Bob Abreu	.20	.50
82 Brian Giles	.20	.50
83 Kris Benson	.20	.50
84 Jason Kendall	.20	.50
85 Ken Griffey Jr.	.75	2.00
86 Barry Larkin	.30	.75
87 Sean Casey	.20	.50
88 Todd Helton	.30	.75
89 Larry Walker	.20	.50
90 Mike Hampton	.20	.50
91 Billy Sylvester YS RC	2.00	5.00
92 Josh Towers YS RC	3.00	8.00
93 Zach Day YS RC	2.00	5.00
94 Martin Vargas YS RC	2.00	5.00
95 Adam Pettyjohn YS RC	2.00	5.00
96 Andres Torres YS RC	2.00	5.00
97 Kris Keller YS RC	2.00	5.00
98 Blaine Neal YS RC	2.00	5.00
99 Kyle Kessel YS RC	2.00	5.00
100 Greg Miller YS RC	2.00	5.00
101 Shawn Sonnier YS	2.00	5.00
102 Alexis Gomez YS RC	2.00	5.00
103 Grant Balfour YS RC	2.00	5.00
104 Henry Mateo YS RC	2.00	5.00
105 Wilken Ruan YS RC	2.00	5.00
106 Nick Maness YS RC	2.00	5.00
107 J. Michaels YS RC	2.00	5.00
108 Esix Snead YS RC	2.00	5.00
109 William Ortega YS RC	2.00	5.00
110 David Elder YS RC	2.00	5.00
111 J. Melian YS RC	2.00	5.00
112 Nate Teut YS RC	2.00	5.00
113 Jason Smith YS RC	2.00	5.00
114 Mike Penney YS RC	2.00	5.00
115 Jose Mieses YS RC	2.00	5.00
116 Juan Pena YS	2.00	5.00
117 B. Lawrence YS RC	2.00	5.00
118 Jeremy Owens YS RC	2.00	5.00
119 C. Valderrama YS RC	2.00	5.00
120 Rafael Soriano YS RC	2.00	5.00
121 H. Ramirez JSY RC	4.00	10.00
122 R. Rodriguez JSY RC	3.00	8.00
123 Juan Diaz JSY RC	3.00	8.00
124 Donnie Bridges JSY	3.00	8.00
125 Tyler Walker JSY RC	3.00	8.00
126 Erick Almonte JSY RC	3.00	8.00
127 Jesus Colome JSY	3.00	8.00
128 Ryan Freel JSY RC	4.00	10.00
129 Elpidio Guzman JSY RC	3.00	8.00
130 Jack Cust JSY	3.00	8.00
131 Eric Hinske JSY RC	4.00	10.00
132 Josh Fogg JSY RC	3.00	8.00
133 Juan Uribe JSY RC	4.00	10.00
134 Bert Snow JSY RC	3.00	8.00
135 Pedro Feliz JSY	3.00	8.00
136 W. Betemit JSY AU RC	15.00	40.00
137 S. Douglass JSY AU RC	6.00	15.00
138 D. Stenson JSY AU	6.00	15.00
139 Brandon Inge JSY AU	6.00	15.00
140 M. Ensberg JSY AU RC	15.00	40.00
141 Brian Cole JSY AU	6.00	15.00
142 A. Hernandez JSY AU RC	6.00	15.00
143 Brandon Duckworth JSY AU RC	6.00	15.00
144 J. Wilson JSY AU RC	10.00	25.00
145 T. Hafner JSY AU RC	40.00	80.00
146 Carlos Pena JSY AU	8.00	20.00
147 C. Patterson JSY AU	6.00	15.00
148 Xavier Nady JSY AU	6.00	15.00
149 Jason Hart JSY AU	6.00	15.00
150 I.Suzuki JSY AU RC	600.00	800.00
151 Garret Anderson	.30	.75
152 Jermaine Dye	.30	.75
153 Shannon Stewart	.30	.75
154 Toby Hall	.30	.75
155 C.C. Sabathia	.30	.75
156 Bret Boone	.30	.75
157 Tony Batista	.30	.75
158 Gabe Kapler	.30	.75
159 Carl Everett	.30	.75
160 Mike Sweeney	.30	.75
161 Dean Palmer	.30	.75
162 Doug Mientkiewicz	.30	.75
163 Carlos Lee	.30	.75
164 Mike Mussina	.50	1.25
165 Lance Berkman	.30	.75
166 Ken Caminiti	.30	.75
167 Ben Sheets	.50	1.25
168 Matt Morris	.30	.75
169 Fred McGriff	.50	1.25
170 Curt Schilling	.30	.75
171 Paul LoDuca	.30	.75
172 Javier Vazquez	.30	.75
173 Rich Aurilia	.30	.75
174 A.J. Burnett	.30	.75
175 Al Leiter	.30	.75
176 Mark Kotsay	.30	.75
177 Jimmy Rollins	.30	.75
178 Aramis Ramirez	.30	.75
179 Aaron Boone	.30	.75
180 Jeff Cirillo	.30	.75
181 J.Estrada YS RC	3.00	8.00
182 Dave Williams YS RC	2.00	5.00
183 D.Mendez YS RC	2.00	5.00
184 Junior Spivey YS RC	3.00	8.00
185 Jay Gibbons YS RC	3.00	8.00
186 Kyle Lohse YS RC	3.00	8.00
187 Willie Harris YS RC	2.00	5.00
188 Juan Cruz YS RC	2.00	5.00
189 Joe Kennedy YS RC	3.00	8.00
190 D.Sanchez YS RC	2.00	5.00
191 Jorge Julio YS RC	2.00	5.00
192 Cesar Crespo YS RC	2.00	5.00
193 Casey Fossum YS RC	2.00	5.00
194 Brian Roberts YS RC	6.00	15.00
195 Troy Mattes YS RC	2.00	5.00
196 R.Mackowiak YS RC	3.00	8.00
197 T.Shinjo YS RC	3.00	8.00
198 Nick Punto YS RC	2.00	5.00
199 Wilmy Caceres YS RC	2.00	5.00
200 Jeremy Affeldt YS RC	2.00	5.00
201 Bret Prinz YS RC	2.00	5.00
202 Delvin James YS RC	2.00	5.00
203 Luis Pineda YS RC	2.00	5.00
204 Matt White YS RC	2.00	5.00
205 B.Knight YS RC	2.00	5.00
206 Albert Pujols YS AU RC	300.00	400.00
207 M.Teixeira YS AU RC	40.00	80.00
208 Mark Prior YS AU RC	30.00	60.00
209 D.Brazelton YS AU RC	6.00	15.00
210 Bud Smith YS AU RC	6.00	15.00

2001 SPx Spectrum

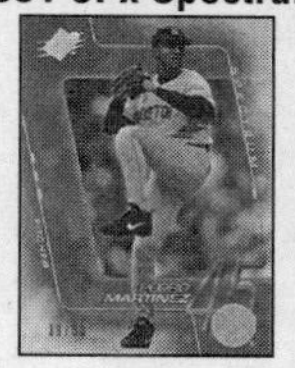

Randomly inserted into packs, this 120-card insert is a partial parallel of the 2001 SPx base set. Please note that each card is individually serial numbered to 50.

*STARS 1-90: 12.5X TO 30X BASIC CARDS
*YS 91-120: 1X TO 2.5X BASIC CARDS

2001 SPx Foundations

Randomly inserted into packs at one in eight, this 12-card insert features players that are the major foundation that keeps their respective ballclubs together. Card backs carry a "F" prefix.

Card	Low	High
COMPLETE SET (12)	20.00	50.00
F1 Mark McGwire	3.00	8.00
F2 Jeff Bagwell	.75	2.00
F3 Alex Rodriguez	2.00	5.00
F4 Ken Griffey Jr.	2.00	5.00
F5 Andruw Jones	.75	2.00
F6 Cal Ripken	4.00	10.00
F7 Barry Bonds	3.00	8.00
F8 Derek Jeter	3.00	8.00
F9 Frank Thomas	1.25	3.00
F10 Sammy Sosa	1.25	3.00
F11 Tony Gwynn	1.50	4.00
F12 Vladimir Guerrero	1.25	3.00

2001 SPx SPXcitement

Randomly inserted into packs at one in eight, this 12-card insert features players that are known for bringing excitement to the game. Card backs carry an "X" prefix.

Card	Low	High
COMPLETE SET (12)	20.00	50.00
X1 Alex Rodriguez	2.00	5.00
X2 Jason Giambi	.75	2.00
X3 Ken Griffey Jr.	2.00	5.00
X4 Sammy Sosa	1.25	3.00
X5 Frank Thomas	1.25	3.00
X6 Todd Helton	.75	2.00
X7 Mark McGwire	3.00	8.00
X8 Mike Piazza	2.00	5.00
X9 Derek Jeter	3.00	8.00
X10 Vladimir Guerrero	1.25	3.00
X11 Carlos Delgado	.75	2.00
X12 Chipper Jones	1.25	3.00

2001 SPx Untouchable Talents

Randomly inserted into packs at one in 15, this six-card insert features players whose skills are unmatched. Card backs carry a "UT" prefix.

Card	Low	High
COMPLETE SET (6)	15.00	40.00
UT1 Ken Griffey Jr.	2.00	5.00
UT2 Mike Piazza	2.00	5.00
UT3 Mark McGwire	3.00	8.00
UT4 Alex Rodriguez	2.00	5.00
UT5 Sammy Sosa	2.00	5.00
UT6 Derek Jeter	3.00	8.00

2001 SPx Winning Materials Ball-Base

Randomly inserted into packs, this 13-card insert features actual swatches of both game-used baseball and base. Card backs carry a "B" prefix followed by the player's initials. Each card is individually serial numbered to 250.

BAJ Andruw Jones	10.00	25.00
BAR Alex Rodriguez	10.00	25.00
BBB Barry Bonds	20.00	50.00
BCJ Chipper Jones	10.00	25.00
BDJ Derek Jeter	20.00	50.00
BFT Frank Thomas	10.00	25.00
BKG Ken Griffey Jr.	15.00	40.00
BMM Mark McGwire	40.00	80.00
BMP Mike Piazza	10.00	25.00
BNG Nomar Garciaparra	10.00	25.00
BPM Pedro Martinez	10.00	25.00
BSS Sammy Sosa	10.00	25.00
BVG Vladimir Guerrero	10.00	25.00

2001 SPx Winning Materials Base Duos

Randomly inserted into packs, this 10-card insert features actual swatches of game-used bases. Card backs carry a "B2" prefix followed by the player's initials. Each card is individually serial numbered to 50.

B2GJ Nomar Garciaparra	50.00	100.00
Derek Jeter		
B2JG Derek Jeter	40.00	80.00
Jason Giambi		
B2JP Derek Jeter	50.00	100.00
Mike Piazza		
B2MG Mark McGwire	40.00	80.00
Ken Griffey Jr.		
B2MR Mark McGwire	40.00	80.00
Alex Rodriguez		
B2MS Mark McGwire	50.00	100.00
Sammy Sosa		
B2PB Mike Piazza	50.00	100.00
Barry Bonds		
B2PM Mike Piazza	40.00	80.00
Mark McGwire		
B2RJ Alex Rodriguez	50.00	100.00
Derek Jeter		
B2TR Frank Thomas	40.00	80.00
Alex Rodriguez		

2001 SPx Winning Materials Base Trios

Randomly inserted into packs, this five-card insert set features actual swatches of game-used bases. Card backs carry a "B3" prefix followed by the player's initials. Each card is individually serial numbered to 25. Due to market scarcity, no pricing is provided.

B3BMS Barry Bonds
Mark McGwire
Sammy Sosa
B3GJR Ken Griffey Jr.
Derek Jeter
Alex Rodriguez
B3JRG Derek Jeter
Alex Rodriguez
Nomar Garciaparra
B3MGS Mark McGwire
Ken Griffey Jr.
Sammy Sosa
B3PJW Mike Piazza
Derek Jeter
Bernie Williams

2001 SPx Winning Materials Bat-Jersey

Randomly inserted into packs, this 21-card insert features actual swatches of both game-used bats and jerseys. Card backs carry the player's initials as numbering.

AJ1 Andruw Jones AS	6.00	15.00
AJ2 Andruw Jones	6.00	15.00
AR1 Alex Rodriguez AS	6.00	15.00
AR2 Alex Rodriguez	6.00	15.00
BB1 Barry Bonds AS	10.00	25.00
BB2 Barry Bonds	10.00	25.00
CD Carlos Delgado AS *	4.00	10.00
CJ1 Chipper Jones AS	6.00	15.00
CJ2 Chipper Jones	6.00	15.00
CR Cal Ripken	15.00	40.00
FT Frank Thomas	6.00	15.00
IR1 Ivan Rodriguez AS	6.00	15.00
IR2 Ivan Rodriguez	6.00	15.00
JD Joe DiMaggio	75.00	150.00
JE Jim Edmonds *	4.00	10.00
KG1 Ken Griffey Jr. AS	6.00	15.00
KG2 Ken Griffey Jr.	6.00	15.00
RA Rick Ankiel *	4.00	10.00
RJ1 Randy Johnson AS	6.00	15.00
RJ2 Randy Johnson	6.00	15.00
SS Sammy Sosa	6.00	15.00

2001 SPx Winning Materials Jersey Duos

Randomly inserted into packs, this 13-card insert features actual swatches of game-used jerseys. Card backs carry both player's initials as numbering. Each card is individually serial numbered to 50.

AJCJ Andruw Jones	15.00	40.00
Chipper Jones		
ARCR Alex Rodriguez	50.00	100.00
Cal Ripken		
BBSS Barry Bonds	50.00	100.00
Sammy Sosa		
CJDW Chipper Jones	15.00	40.00
David Wells		
IRAR Ivan Rodriguez	40.00	80.00
Alex Rodriguez		
KGAR Ken Griffey Jr.	40.00	80.00
Alex Rodriguez AS		
KGBB Ken Griffey Jr.	50.00	100.00
Barry Bonds AS		
KGJD Ken Griffey Jr.	75.00	150.00
Joe DiMaggio		
KGKG Ken Griffey Jr.	40.00	80.00
Ken Griffey Jr. AS		
KGRJ Ken Griffey Jr.	40.00	80.00
Randy Johnson AS		
KGSS Ken Griffey Jr.	40.00	80.00
Sammy Sosa		
SSCD Sammy Sosa	15.00	40.00
Carlos Delgado		
SSFT Sammy Sosa	15.00	40.00
Frank Thomas		

2001 SPx Winning Materials Jersey Trios

Randomly inserted into packs, this seven-card insert set features actual swatches of game-used jerseys. Card backs carry the first letter of each player's last name as numbering. Each card is individually serial numbered to 25. Due to market scarcity, no pricing is provided for these cards.

BGJ Barry Bonds
Ken Griffey Jr.
Andruw Jones
DBS Carlos Delgado
Barry Bonds
Sammy Sosa
DGJ Joe DiMaggio
Ken Griffey Jr.
Andruw Jones
GRB Ken Griffey Jr.
Alex Rodriguez
Barry Bonds
RJD Cal Ripken
Chipper Jones
Carlos Delgado
RRD Alex Rodriguez
Ivan Rodriguez
Carlos Delgado
SGC Sammy Sosa
Ken Griffey Jr.
Chipper Jones

2001 SPx Winning Materials Update Duos

Inserted into 2001 Upper Deck Rookie Update packs at a rate of one in 15, these cards feature two players and a memorabilia piece from each of them.

GOLD RANDOM INSERTS IN PACKS
GOLD PRINT RUN 25 SERIAL #'d SETS
NO GOLD PRICING DUE TO SCARCITY
EACH CARD FEATURES DUAL JSY SWATCH

APJE Albert Pujols	30.00	60.00
Jim Edmonds		
ASKS Aaron Sele	4.00	10.00
Kazuhiro Sasaki		
BBLG Barry Bonds	10.00	25.00
Luis Gonzalez		
BWMR Bernie Williams	6.00	15.00
Mariano Rivera		
BWRJ Bernie Williams	6.00	15.00
Reggie Jackson		
CPBK Chan Ho Park	4.00	10.00
Byung-Hyun Kim		
CPFV Chan Ho Park	6.00	15.00
Fernando Valenzuela		
CREM Cal Ripken	15.00	40.00
Eddie Murray		
CRX2 Cal Ripken	15.00	40.00
Cal Ripken		
CSRJ Curt Schilling	6.00	15.00
Randy Johnson		
EMJM Eric Milton	4.00	10.00
Joe Mays		
FTMO Frank Thomas	6.00	15.00
Magglio Ordonez		
GSSG Gary Sheffield	4.00	10.00
Shawn Green		
HNMY Hideo Nomo	6.00	15.00
Masato Yoshii		
IRAR Ivan Rodriguez	6.00	15.00
Alex Rodriguez		
JBCB Jeff Bagwell	6.00	15.00
Craig Biggio		
JBRY Jeromy Burnitz	6.00	15.00
Robin Yount		
JGBB Jason Giambi	10.00	25.00
Barry Bonds		
KGSC Ken Griffey Jr.	6.00	15.00
Sean Casey		
LWTH Larry Walker	6.00	15.00
Todd Helton		
MPEA Mike Piazza	6.00	15.00
Edgardo Alfonzo		
MRJG Manny Ramirez Sox	6.00	15.00
Juan Gonzalez		
PMGM Pedro Martinez	6.00	15.00
Greg Maddux		
PMRJ Pedro Martinez	6.00	15.00
Randy Johnson		
SRBA Scott Rolen	6.00	15.00
Bobby Abreu		
SSEB Sammy Sosa	10.00	25.00
Ernie Banks		
SSJG Sammy Sosa	6.00	15.00
Jason Giambi		
TGCR Tony Gwynn	15.00	40.00
Cal Ripken		
TGDW Tony Gwynn	6.00	15.00
Dave Winfield		
TGX2 Tony Gwynn	6.00	15.00
Tony Gwynn		
TSHN Tsuyoshi Shinjo	6.00	15.00
Hideo Nomo		

2001 SPx Winning Materials Update Trios

Inserted into 2001 Upper Deck Rookie Update Packs at a rate of one in 15, these 22 cards feature three players as well as a piece of game-worn jersey memorabilia from each one.

GOLD RANDOM INSERTS IN PACKS
GOLD PRINT RUN 25 SERIAL #'d SETS
NO GOLD PRICING DUE TO SCARCITY
ALL FEATURE THREE JSY SWATCHES

BGG Barry Bonds	15.00	40.00
Luis Gonzalez		
Ken Griffey Jr.		
BTD Jeff Bagwell	6.00	15.00
Frank Thomas		
Carlos Delgado		
CHN Roger Clemens	10.00	25.00
Tim Hudson		
Hideo Nomo		
DEA J.D. Drew	4.00	10.00
Jim Edmonds		
Bobby Abreu		
DOP Carlos Delgado	30.00	60.00
Magglio Ordonez		
Albert Pujols		
GWS Luis Gonzalez	4.00	10.00
Matt Williams		
Curt Schilling		
GZH Jason Giambi	4.00	10.00
Barry Zito		
Tim Hudson		
HDG Todd Helton	6.00	15.00
Carlos Delgado		
Jason Giambi		
JAF Chipper Jones	6.00	15.00
Andruw Jones		
Rafael Furcal		
KBA Jeff Kent	10.00	25.00
Barry Bonds		
Rich Aurilia		
MGJ Greg Maddux	10.00	25.00
Tom Glavine		
Andruw Jones		
PPV Jay Payton	8.00	20.00
Mike Piazza		
Robin Ventura		
PWO Andy Pettitte	6.00	15.00
Bernie Williams		
Paul O'Neill		
RPK Ivan Rodriguez	8.00	20.00
Mike Piazza		
Jason Kendall		
RRK Alex Rodriguez	8.00	20.00
Ivan Rodriguez		
Gabe Kapler		
SJC Curt Schilling	15.00	40.00
Randy Johnson		
Roger Clemens		
SKB Gary Sheffield	4.00	10.00
Eric Karros		
Kevin Brown		
SSM Aaron Sele	15.00	40.00
Ichiro Suzuki		
Edgar Martinez		
SYN Kazuhiro Sasaki	6.00	15.00
Masato Yoshii		
Hideo Nomo		
TDK Frank Thomas	6.00	15.00
Ray Durham		
Paul Konerko		
TGA Jim Thome	4.00	10.00
Juan Gonzalez		
Roberto Alomar		
VRF Omar Vizquel	8.00	20.00
Alex Rodriguez		
Rafael Furcal		

2002 SPx

This 280-card set was issued in two separate brands. The SPx product itself was released in late April, 2002 and contained cards 1-250. These cards were issued in four card packs of which were distributed at a rate of 18 packs per box and 14 boxes per case. Cards numbered from 91 through 120 feature either a portrait or an action shot of a prospect. Both the portrait and the action shot were issued with separate stated print runs of 1800 serial numbered cards (for a total of 3,600 of each player in the subset). Cards 121-150 were not serial-numbered but instead feature autographs and were seeded into packs at a rate of 1:18. Cards numbered 151 through 190 were issued and featured jersey swatches of leading major league players. These cards had a stated print run of either 700 or 800 serial numbered cards. High series cards 191-250 were distributed in mid-December, 2002 within packs of 2002 Upper Deck Rookie Update. Cards 191-220 feature veterans on new teams and were commonly distributed in all packs. Cards 221-250 feature prospects and were signed by the player. In addition, the card were serial numbered to 825 copies. Though stated pack odds were not released by the manufacturer, we believe these signed cards were seeded at an approximate rate of 1:16 Upper Deck Rookie Update packs.

COMP.LOW w/o SP's (90)	10.00	25.00
COMP.UPDATE w/o SP's (30)	4.00	10.00
COMMON CARD (1-90)	.20	.50
COMMON ROOKIE (91-120)	3.00	8.00
COMMON CARD (121-150)	6.00	15.00
COMMON CARD (151-190)	3.00	8.00
COMMON CARD (191-220)	.30	.75
COMMON CARD (221-250)	4.00	10.00
1 Troy Glaus	.20	.50
2 Darin Erstad	.20	.50
3 David Justice	.20	.50
4 Tim Hudson	.20	.50
5 Miguel Tejada	.20	.50
6 Barry Zito	.20	.50
7 Carlos Delgado	.20	.50
8 Shannon Stewart	.20	.50
9 Greg Vaughn	.20	.50
10 Toby Hall	.20	.50
11 Jim Thome	.30	.75
12 C.C. Sabathia	.20	.50
13 Ichiro Suzuki	1.00	2.50
14 Edgar Martinez	.30	.75
15 Freddy Garcia	.20	.50
16 Mike Cameron	.20	.50
17 Jeff Conine	.20	.50
18 Tony Batista	.20	.50
19 Alex Rodriguez	.75	2.00
20 Rafael Palmeiro	.30	.75
21 Ivan Rodriguez	.30	.75
22 Carl Everett	.20	.50
23 Pedro Martinez	.30	.75
24 Manny Ramirez	.30	.75
25 Nomar Garciaparra	.75	2.00
26 Johnny Damon Sox	.30	.75
27 Mike Sweeney	.20	.50
28 Carlos Beltran	.20	.50
29 Dmitri Young	.20	.50
30 Joe Mays	.20	.50
31 Doug Mientkiewicz	.20	.50
32 Cristian Guzman	.20	.50
33 Corey Koskie	.20	.50
34 Frank Thomas	.50	1.25
35 Magglio Ordonez	.20	.50
36 Mark Buehrle	.20	.50
37 Bernie Williams	.30	.75
38 Roger Clemens	1.00	2.50
39 Derek Jeter	1.25	3.00
40 Jason Giambi	.20	.50
41 Mike Mussina	.30	.75
42 Lance Berkman	.20	.50
43 Jeff Bagwell	.30	.75
44 Roy Oswalt	.20	.50
45 Greg Maddux	.75	2.00
46 Chipper Jones	.50	1.25
47 Andruw Jones	.30	.75
48 Gary Sheffield	.20	.50
49 Geoff Jenkins	.20	.50
50 Richie Sexson	.20	.50
51 Ben Sheets	.20	.50
52 Albert Pujols	1.00	2.50
53 J.D. Drew	.20	.50
54 Jim Edmonds	.20	.50
55 Sammy Sosa	.50	1.25
56 Moises Alou	.20	.50
57 Kerry Wood	.20	.50
58 Jon Lieber	.20	.50
59 Fred McGriff	.30	.75
60 Randy Johnson	.50	1.25
61 Luis Gonzalez	.20	.50
62 Curt Schilling	.20	.50
63 Kevin Brown	.20	.50
64 Hideo Nomo	.50	1.25
65 Shawn Green	.20	.50
66 Vladimir Guerrero	.50	1.25
67 Jose Vidro	.20	.50
68 Barry Bonds	1.25	3.00
69 Jeff Kent	.20	.50
70 Rich Aurilia	.20	.50
71 Cliff Floyd	.20	.50
72 Josh Beckett	.20	.50
73 Preston Wilson	.20	.50
74 Mike Piazza	.75	2.00
75 Mo Vaughn	.20	.50
76 Jeromy Burnitz	.20	.50
77 Roberto Alomar	.30	.75
78 Phil Nevin	.20	.50
79 Ryan Klesko	.20	.50
80 Scott Rolen	.30	.75
81 Bobby Abreu	.20	.50
82 Jimmy Rollins	.20	.50
83 Brian Giles	.20	.50
84 Aramis Ramirez	.20	.50
85 Ken Griffey Jr.	.75	2.00
86 Sean Casey	.20	.50
87 Barry Larkin	.30	.75
88 Mike Hampton	.20	.50
89 Larry Walker	.20	.50
90 Todd Helton	.30	.75
91A Ron Calloway YS RC	3.00	8.00
91P Ron Calloway YS RC	3.00	8.00
92A Joe Orloski YS RC	3.00	8.00
92P Joe Orloski YS RC	3.00	8.00
93A An. Machado YS RC	3.00	8.00
93P An. Machado YS RC	3.00	8.00
94A Eric Good YS RC	3.00	8.00
94P Eric Good YS RC	3.00	8.00
95A Reed Johnson YS RC	4.00	10.00
95P Reed Johnson YS RC	4.00	10.00
96A Brendan Donnelly YS RC	3.00	8.00
96P Brendan Donnelly YS RC	3.00	8.00
97A Chris Baker YS RC	3.00	8.00
97P Chris Baker YS RC	3.00	8.00
98A Wilson Valdez YS RC	3.00	8.00
98P Wilson Valdez YS RC	3.00	8.00
99A Scotty Layfield YS RC	3.00	8.00
99P Scotty Layfield YS RC	3.00	8.00
100A P.J. Bevis YS RC	3.00	8.00
100P P.J. Bevis YS RC	3.00	8.00
101A Edwin Almonte YS RC	3.00	8.00
101P Edwin Almonte YS RC	3.00	8.00
102A Francis Beltran YS RC	3.00	8.00
102P Francis Beltran YS RC	3.00	8.00
103A Val Pascucci YS	3.00	8.00
103P Val Pascucci YS	3.00	8.00
104A Nelson Castro YS RC	3.00	8.00
104P Nelson Castro YS RC	3.00	8.00
105A Michael Crudale YS RC	3.00	8.00
105P Michael Crudale YS RC	3.00	8.00
106A Colin Young YS RC	3.00	8.00
106P Colin Young YS RC	3.00	8.00
107A Todd Donovan YS RC	3.00	8.00
107P Todd Donovan YS RC	3.00	8.00
108A Felix Escalona YS RC	3.00	8.00
108P Felix Escalona YS RC	3.00	8.00
109A Brandon Backe YS RC	4.00	10.00
109P Brandon Backe YS RC	4.00	10.00
110A Corey Thurman YS RC	3.00	8.00
110P Corey Thurman YS RC	3.00	8.00
111A Kyle Kane YS RC	3.00	8.00
111P Kyle Kane YS RC	3.00	8.00
112A Allan Simpson YS RC	3.00	8.00
112P Allan Simpson YS RC	3.00	8.00
113A Jose Valverde YS RC	3.00	8.00
113P Jose Valverde YS RC	3.00	8.00
114A Chris Booker YS RC	3.00	8.00
114P Chris Booker YS RC	3.00	8.00
115A Brandon Puffer YS RC	3.00	8.00
115P Brandon Puffer YS RC	3.00	8.00
116A John Foster YS RC	3.00	8.00
116P John Foster YS RC	3.00	8.00
117A Cliff Bartosh YS RC	3.00	8.00
117P Cliff Bartosh YS RC	3.00	8.00
118A Gustavo Chacin YS RC	4.00	10.00
118P Gustavo Chacin YS RC	4.00	10.00
119A Steve Kenf YS RC	3.00	8.00
119P Steve Kent YS RC	3.00	8.00
120A Nate Field YS RC	3.00	8.00
120P Nate Field YS RC	3.00	8.00
121 Victor Alvarez AU RC	4.00	10.00
122 Steve Bechler AU RC	4.00	10.00
123 Adrian Burnside AU RC	4.00	10.00
124 Marlon Byrd AU	6.00	15.00
125 Jaime Cerda AU RC	4.00	10.00
126 Brandon Claussen AU	6.00	15.00
127 Mark Corey AU RC	4.00	10.00
128 Doug Devore AU RC	4.00	10.00
129 Kazuhisa Ishii AU SP RC	30.00	60.00
130 John Ennis AU RC	4.00	10.00
131 Kevin Frederick AU RC	4.00	10.00
132 Josh Hancock AU RC	8.00	20.00
133 Ben Howard AU RC	4.00	10.00
134 Orlando Hudson AU	6.00	15.00
135 Hansel Izquierdo AU RC	4.00	10.00
136 Eric Junge AU RC	4.00	10.00
137 Austin Kearns AU	6.00	15.00
138 Victor Martinez AU	10.00	25.00
139 Luis Martinez AU RC	4.00	10.00
140 Danny Mota AU RC	4.00	10.00
141 Jorge Padilla AU RC	4.00	10.00
142 Andy Pratt AU RC	4.00	10.00
143 Rene Reyes AU RC	4.00	10.00
144 Rodrigo Rosario AU RC	4.00	10.00
145 Tom Shearn AU RC	4.00	10.00
146 So Taguchi AU SP RC	10.00	25.00
147 Dennis Tankersley AU	6.00	15.00
148 Matt Thornton AU RC	4.00	10.00
149 Jeremy Ward AU RC	4.00	10.00
150 Mitch Wylie AU RC	4.00	10.00
151 Pedro Martinez JSY/800	4.00	10.00
152 Cal Ripken JSY/800	10.00	25.00
153 Roger Clemens JSY/800	6.00	15.00
154 Bernie Williams JSY/800	4.00	10.00
155 Jason Giambi JSY/700	3.00	8.00
156 Robin Ventura JSY/800	3.00	8.00
157 Carlos Delgado JSY/800	3.00	8.00
158 Frank Thomas JSY/800	4.00	10.00
159 Mag. Ordonez JSY/800	3.00	8.00
160 Jim Thome JSY/800	4.00	10.00
161 Darin Erstad JSY/800	3.00	8.00
162 Tim Salmon JSY/800	4.00	10.00
163 Tim Hudson JSY/800	3.00	8.00
164 Barry Zito JSY/800	3.00	8.00
165 Ichiro Suzuki JSY/800	10.00	25.00
166 Edgar Martinez JSY/800	4.00	10.00
167 Alex Rodriguez JSY/800	6.00	15.00
168 Ivan Rodriguez JSY/800	4.00	10.00
169 Juan Gonzalez JSY/800	3.00	8.00
170 Greg Maddux JSY/800	6.00	15.00
171 Chipper Jones JSY/800	4.00	10.00
172 Andruw Jones JSY/800	4.00	10.00
173 Tom Glavine JSY/800	4.00	10.00
174 Mike Piazza JSY/800	6.00	15.00
175 Roberto Alomar JSY/800	4.00	10.00
176 Scott Rolen JSY/800	4.00	10.00
177 Sammy Sosa JSY/800	4.00	10.00
178 Moises Alou JSY/800	3.00	8.00
179 Ken Griffey Jr. JSY/700	8.00	20.00
180 Jeff Bagwell JSY/800	4.00	10.00
181 Jim Edmonds JSY/800	3.00	8.00
182 J.D. Drew JSY/800	3.00	8.00
183 Brian Giles JSY/800	3.00	8.00
184 Randy Johnson JSY/800	4.00	10.00
185 Curt Schilling JSY/800	3.00	8.00
186 Luis Gonzalez JSY/800	3.00	8.00
187 Todd Helton JSY/800	4.00	10.00
188 Shawn Green JSY/800	3.00	8.00
189 David Wells JSY/800	3.00	8.00
190 Jeff Kent JSY/800	3.00	8.00
191 Tom Glavine	.50	1.25
192 Cliff Floyd	.30	.75
193 Mark Prior	.50	1.25
194 Corey Patterson	.30	.75
195 Paul Konerko	.30	.75
196 Adam Dunn	.30	.75
197 Joe Borchard	.30	.75
198 Carlos Pena	.30	.75
199 Juan Encarnacion	.30	.75
200 Luis Castillo	.30	.75
201 Torii Hunter	.30	.75
202 Hee Seop Choi	.30	.75
203 Bartolo Colon	.30	.75
204 Raul Mondesi	.30	.75
205 Jeff Weaver	.30	.75
206 Eric Munson	.30	.75
207 Alfonso Soriano	.30	.75
208 Ray Durham	.30	.75
209 Eric Chavez	.30	.75
210 Brett Myers	.30	.75
211 Jeremy Giambi	.30	.75
212 Vicente Padilla	.30	.75
213 Felipe Lopez	.30	.75
214 Sean Burroughs	.30	.75
215 Kenny Lofton	.30	.75
216 Scott Rolen	.50	1.25
217 Carl Crawford	.30	.75
218 Juan Gonzalez	.30	.75
219 Orlando Hudson	.30	.75
220 Eric Hinske	.30	.75
221 Adam Walker AU RC	4.00	10.00
222 Aaron Cook AU RC	6.00	15.00
223 Cam Esslinger AU RC	4.00	10.00
224 Kirk Saarloos AU RC	4.00	10.00
225 Jose Diaz AU RC	4.00	10.00
226 David Ross AU RC	10.00	25.00
227 Jayson Durocher AU RC	4.00	10.00
228 Brian Mallette AU RC	4.00	10.00
229 Aaron Guiel AU RC	4.00	10.00
230 Jorge Nunez AU RC	4.00	10.00
231 Satoru Komiyama AU RC	10.00	25.00
232 Tyler Yates AU RC	4.00	10.00
233 Pete Zamora AU RC	4.00	10.00
234 Mike Gonzalez AU RC	4.00	10.00
235 Oliver Perez AU RC	12.50	30.00
236 Julius Matos AU RC	4.00	10.00
237 Andy Shibilo AU RC	4.00	10.00
238 J.Simontacchi AU RC	4.00	10.00
239 Ron Chiavacci AU	4.00	10.00
240 Deivis Santos AU	4.00	10.00
241 Travis Driskill AU RC	4.00	10.00
242 Jorge De La Rosa AU RC	4.00	10.00
243 An. Martinez AU RC	4.00	10.00
244 Earl Snyder AU RC	4.00	10.00
245 Freddy Sanchez AU RC	12.50	30.00
246 Miguel Asencio AU RC	4.00	10.00
247 Juan Brito AU RC	4.00	10.00
248 Franklyn German AU RC	4.00	10.00
249 Chris Snelling AU RC	6.00	15.00
250 Ken Huckaby AU RC	4.00	10.00

2002 SPx SuperStars Swatches Gold

Randomly inserted in packs, these cards parallel the final forty cards of the base set. These cards were printed to a stated print run of 150 serial numbered sets.

*GOLD JSY: .6X TO 1.5X BASIC JSY

2002 SPx SuperStars Swatches Silver

Randomly inserted in packs, these cards parallel the final forty cards of the base set. These cards were printed to a stated print run of 400 serial numbered sets.

*SILVER JSY: .4X TO 1X BASIC JSY

2002 SPx Sweet Spot Preview Bat Barrel

Randomly inserted in packs, these cards feature bat "barrel" cards of leading players. Each card was printed to a different amount and we have notated that information next to their name in our checklist.

Due to market scarcity, no pricing is provided for these cards.

BBAJ Andruw Jones/5
BBAR Alex Rodriguez/5
BBCB Carlos Beltran/1
BBCD Carlos Delgado/1
BBCJ Chipper Jones/5
BBEC Eric Chavez/1
BBEM Edgar Martinez/2
BBFT Frank Thomas/8
BBGM Greg Maddux/5
BBGS Gary Sheffield/5
BBIR Ivan Rodriguez/7
BBIS Ichiro Suzuki/2
BBJD J.D. Drew/1
BBJE Jim Edmonds/1
BBJG Jason Giambi/1
BBJT Jim Thome/1
BBKG Ken Griffey Jr./6
BBKW Kerry Wood/1
BBMP Mike Piazza/7
BBMR Manny Ramirez/4
BBMW Matt Williams/5
BBPW Preston Wilson/1
BBRA Roberto Alomar/3
BBRC Roger Clemens/1
BBRP Rafael Palmeiro/1
BBSG Shawn Green/7
BBSS Sammy Sosa/5
BBTG Tom Glavine/5
BBTH Todd Helton/3

2002 SPx Winning Materials 2-Player Base Combos

Randomly inserted into packs, these cards include bases used by both players featured on the card. These cards were issued to a stated print run of 200 serial numbered sets.

BBG Barry Bonds	15.00	40.00
Shawn Green		
BGR Troy Glaus	12.50	30.00
Alex Rodriguez		
BGS Ken Griffey Jr.	15.00	40.00
Sammy Sosa		
BIM Ichiro Suzuki	30.00	60.00
Edgar Martinez		
BPE Mike Piazza	10.00	25.00
Jim Edmonds		
BPI Albert Pujols	50.00	100.00
Ichiro Suzuki		
BRJ Alex Rodriguez	30.00	60.00
Derek Jeter		
BSG Sammy Sosa	10.00	25.00
Luis Gonzalez		
BSR Kazuhiro Sasaki	10.00	25.00
Mariano Rivera		
BWJ Bernie Williams	20.00	50.00
Derek Jeter		

2002 SPx Winning Materials 2-Player Jersey Combos

Inserted at stated odds of one in 18, these 29 cards feature not only the players but a jersey swatch from each player. A few players were issued in lesser quantities and we have notated that with an SP in our checklist. Other players were issued in larger quantities and we have notated that with an asterisk next to the player's name.

WMAR Alex Rodriguez	8.00	20.00
Ivan Rodriguez		
WMBA Jeromy Burnitz	4.00	10.00
Edgardo Alfonzo		
WMBG Jeff Bagwell	6.00	15.00
Juan Gonzalez		
WMBR Jeff Bagwell	6.00	15.00
Alex Rodriguez DP		
WMDH Jermaine Dye	4.00	10.00
Tim Hudson		
WMDS Carlos Delgado	4.00	10.00
Shannon Stewart		
WMED Jim Edmonds	4.00	10.00
J.D. Drew		
WMGC Ken Griffey Jr.	8.00	20.00
Sean Casey SP		
WMGK Shawn Green	4.00	10.00
Eric Karros		
WMGR Juan Gonzalez	6.00	15.00
Ivan Rodriguez		
WMHW Mike Hampton	4.00	10.00
Larry Walker		
WMJJ Chipper Jones	6.00	15.00
Andruw Jones		
WMJS Randy Johnson	6.00	15.00
Curt Schilling		
WMKG Jason Kendall	4.00	10.00
Brian Giles		
WMLH Al Leiter	4.00	10.00
Mike Hampton		
WMMC Edgar Martinez	6.00	15.00
Mike Cameron		
WMMJ Greg Maddux	10.00	25.00
Chipper Jones		
WMNM Hideo Nomo	10.00	25.00
Pedro Martinez SP		
WMPA Mike Piazza	6.00	15.00
Roberto Alomar DP		
WMRA Scott Rolen	6.00	15.00
Bob Abreu		
WMRP Ivan Rodriguez	6.00	15.00
Chan Ho Park		
WMSE Aaron Sele	4.00	10.00
Darin Erstad		
WMSH Kazuhiro Sasaki	4.00	10.00
Shigetoshi Hasegawa		
WMSP Sammy Sosa	6.00	15.00
Corey Patterson		
WMTO Frank Thomas	6.00	15.00
Magglio Ordonez		
WMTS Jim Thome	6.00	15.00
C.C. Sabathia DP		
WMVR Omar Vizquel	8.00	20.00
Alex Rodriguez		
WMWG Bernie Williams	6.00	15.00
Jason Giambi DP		
WMWP David Wells	6.00	15.00
Jorge PosadaDP		

2002 SPx Winning Materials Ball Patch Combos

Randomly inserted into packs, these nine cards feature both a ball piece along with a jersey patch of the featured players. Each of these cards were issued to a stated print run of 25 serial numbered sets and we are not pricing these cards due to market scarcity.

PCAR Alex Rodriguez
PCCJ Chipper Jones
PCIS Ichiro Suzuki
PCKG Ken Griffey Jr.
PCMP Mike Piazza
PCRC Roger Clemens
PCSG Shawn Green
PCSS Sammy Sosa
PCTH Todd Helton

2002 SPx Winning Materials Base Patch Combos

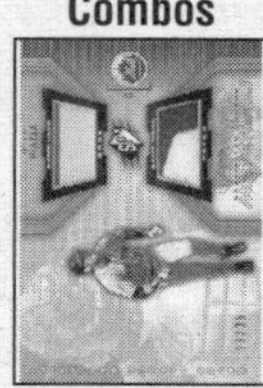

Randomly inserted into packs, these eight cards feature both a base piece along with a jersey patch of the featured players. Each of these cards were issued to a stated print run of 25 serial numbered sets and we are not pricing these cards due to market scarcity.

BPAR Alex Rodriguez
BPBW Bernie Williams
BPIS Ichiro Suzuki
BPJG Jason Giambi
BPKG Ken Griffey Jr.
BPLG Luis Gonzalez
BPMP Mike Piazza
BPSS Sammy Sosa

2002 SPx Winning Materials USA Jersey Combos

Randomly inserted into packs, these 23 cards feature two uniform swatches from players who played for the USA National team. These cards had a stated print run of 150 serial numbered sets.

USAAH Brent Abernathy	6.00	15.00
Orlando Hudson		
USAAW Matt Anderson	6.00	15.00
Jeff Weaver		
USABT Sean Burroughs	10.00	25.00
MarkTeixeira		
USAGB Jason Giambi	6.00	15.00
Sean Burroughs		
USAGT Jason Giambi	10.00	25.00
Mark Teixeira		
USAHD Orlando Hudson	6.00	15.00
Jeff Deardorff		
USAHP Dustin Hermanson	6.00	15.00
Mark Prior		
USAJC Jacques Jones	6.00	15.00
Michael Cuddyer		
USAKB Austin Kearns	6.00	15.00
Sean Burroughs		
USAKC Aaron Kearns	6.00	15.00
Michael Cuddyer		
USAMG Doug Mientkiewicz	6.00	15.00
Jason Giambi		
USAMO Matt Morris	6.00	15.00
Roy Oswalt		
USAMP Matt Morris	6.00	15.00
Mark Prior		
USAMW Matt Morris	6.00	15.00
Jeff Weaver		
USAPB Mark Prior	6.00	15.00
Dewon Brazelton		
USARE Brian Roberts	6.00	15.00
Adam Everett		
USASD Mark Kotsay	6.00	15.00
Sean Burroughs		
USATB Brent Abernathy	6.00	15.00
Dewon Brazelton		
USATP Mark Teixeira	10.00	25.00
Mark Prior		
USAWB Jeff Weaver	6.00	15.00
Dewon Brazelton		
USAWH Jeff Weaver	6.00	15.00
Dustin Hermanson		
USAHOU Roy Oswalt	6.00	15.00
Adam Everett		
USAMIN Doug Mientkiewicz	6.00	15.00
Michael Cuddyer		

2003 SPx

This 199 card set was released in two series. The primary 178-card set was issued in August, 2003 followed up with 21 Update cards randomly seeded within a special rookie pack within sealed boxes of 2003 Upper Deck Finite baseball (of which was released in December, 2003). The primary SPx product was distributed in four card packs carrying an SRP of $7. Each sealed box contained 18 packs and each sealed case contained 14 boxes. Cards numbered 1 to 125 featured veterans with 25 short print cards inserted. Cards numbered 126 through 160 featured rookie cards which were issued to a stated print run of 999 serial numbered sets. Cards 161 and 162 featured New York Yankees rookies Hideki Matsui and Jose Contreras. The Matsui card was issued to a serial numbered print run of 864 copies while the Contreras was issued to a serial numbered print run of 800 copies. Both cards were signed while the Matsui also included a game-used jersey swatch. Cards numbered 163 through 178 featured both autographs and jersey swatches of the featured player and those cards were issued to a stated print run of 1224 cards. The Update cards 179-193 featured a selection of prospects and each card was serial numbered to 150 copies. For reasons unknown to us, the set then skipped to cards 381-387, of which featured additional prospects on cards enriched with both certified autographs and game jersey swatches. These "high number" cards were printed to a serial numbered quantity of 355 copies each.

COMP.LO SET w/o SP's (100)	10.00	25.00
COMP.LO SET w/ SP's (125)	50.00	100.00
COMMON CARD (1-125)	.20	.50
COMMON SP (1-125)	1.50	4.00
COMMON CARD (126-160)	3.00	8.00
COMMON CARD (161-178)	6.00	15.00
163-178 PRINT RUN 1224 SERIAL #'d SETS		
126-178 RANDOM INSERTS IN SPx PACKS		
COMMON CARD (179-193)	6.00	15.00
COMMON CARD (381-387)	6.00	15.00
1 Darin Erstad	.20	.50
2 Garret Anderson	.20	.50
3 Tim Salmon	.30	.75
4 Troy Glaus SP	1.50	4.00
5 Luis Gonzalez	.20	.50
6 Randy Johnson	.50	1.25
7 Curt Schilling	.20	.50
8 Lyle Overbay	.20	.50
9 Andruw Jones SP	1.50	4.00
10 Gary Sheffield	.20	.50
11 Rafael Furcal	.20	.50
12 Greg Maddux	.75	2.00
13 Chipper Jones SP	2.00	5.00
14 Tony Batista	.20	.50
15 Rodrigo Lopez	.20	.50
16 Jay Gibbons	.20	.50
17 Byung-Hyun Kim	.20	.50
18 Johnny Damon	.30	.75
19 Derek Lowe	.20	.50
20 Nomar Garciaparra SP	3.00	8.00
21 Pedro Martinez	.30	.75
22 Manny Ramirez SP	1.50	4.00
23 Mark Prior	.30	.75
24 Kerry Wood	.20	.50
25 Corey Patterson	.20	.50
26 Sammy Sosa SP	2.00	5.00
27 Moises Alou	.20	.50
28 Magglio Ordonez	.20	.50
29 Frank Thomas	.50	1.25
30 Paul Konerko	.20	.50
31 Bartolo Colon	.20	.50
32 Adam Dunn	.20	.50
33 Austin Kearns	.20	.50
34 Aaron Boone	.20	.50
35 Ken Griffey Jr. SP	3.00	8.00
36 Omar Vizquel	.30	.75
37 C.C. Sabathia	.20	.50
38 Jason Davis	.20	.50
39 Travis Hafner	.20	.50
40 Brandon Phillips	.20	.50
41 Larry Walker	.20	.50
42 Preston Wilson	.20	.50
43 Jay Payton	.20	.50
44 Todd Helton	.30	.75
45 Carlos Pena	.20	.50
46 Eric Munson	.20	.50
47 Ivan Rodriguez	.30	.75
48 Josh Beckett	.20	.50
49 Alex Gonzalez	.20	.50
50 Roy Oswalt	.20	.50
51 Craig Biggio	.30	.75
52 Jeff Bagwell	.30	.75
53 Dontrelle Willis SP	2.00	5.00
54 Mike Sweeney	.20	.50
55 Carlos Beltran	.20	.50
56 Brent Mayne	.20	.50
57 Hideo Nomo	.50	1.25
58 Rickey Henderson	.50	1.25
59 Adrian Beltre	.20	.50
60 Miguel Cabrera SP	2.00	5.00
61 Kazuhisa Ishii	.20	.50
62 Ben Sheets	.20	.50
63 Richie Sexson	.20	.50
64 Torii Hunter SP	1.50	4.00
65 Jacque Jones	.20	.50
66 Joe Mays	.20	.50
67 Corey Koskie	.20	.50
68 A.J. Pierzynski	.20	.50
69 Jose Vidro	.20	.50
70 Vladimir Guerrero SP	2.00	5.00
71 Tom Glavine	.30	.75
72 Jose Reyes SP	1.50	4.00
73 Aaron Heilman	.20	.50
74 Mike Piazza	.75	2.00
75 Jorge Posada	.30	.75
76 Mike Mussina	.30	.75
77 Robin Ventura	.20	.50
78 Mariano Rivera	.50	1.25
79 Roger Clemens SP	4.00	10.00
80 Jason Giambi	.20	.50
81 Bernie Williams	.30	.75
82 Alfonso Soriano SP	1.50	4.00
83 Derek Jeter SP	5.00	12.00
84 Miguel Tejada SP	1.50	4.00
85 Eric Chavez	.20	.50
86 Tim Hudson	.20	.50
87 Barry Zito	.20	.50
88 Mark Mulder	.20	.50
89 Erubiel Durazo	.20	.50
90 Pat Burrell	.20	.50
91 Jim Thome SP	1.50	4.00
92 Bobby Abreu	.20	.50
93 Brian Giles	.20	.50
94 Reggie Sanders SP	1.50	4.00
95 Kenny Lofton	.20	.50
96 Ryan Klesko	.20	.50
97 Sean Burroughs	.20	.50
98 Edgardo Alfonzo	.20	.50
99 Rich Aurilia	.20	.50
100 Jose Cruz Jr.	.20	.50
101 Barry Bonds SP	5.00	12.00
102 Mike Cameron	.20	.50
103 Kazuhiro Sasaki	.20	.50
104 Bret Boone	.20	.50
105 Ichiro Suzuki SP	4.00	10.00
106 J.D. Drew	.20	.50
107 Jim Edmonds	.20	.50
108 Scott Rolen SP	1.50	4.00
109 Matt Morris	.20	.50
110 Tino Martinez	.30	.75
111 Albert Pujols SP	4.00	10.00
112 Damian Rolls	.20	.50
113 Carl Crawford	.20	.50
114 Rocco Baldelli SP	1.50	4.00
115 Hank Blalock	.20	.50
116 Alex Rodriguez SP	3.00	8.00
117 Kevin Mench	.20	.50
118 Rafael Palmeiro	.30	.75
119 Mark Teixeira	.30	.75
120 Shannon Stewart	.20	.50
121 Vernon Wells	.20	.50
122 Josh Phelps	.20	.50
123 Eric Hinske	.20	.50
124 Orlando Hudson	.20	.50
125 Carlos Delgado SP	1.50	4.00
126 Jason Roach ROO RC	3.00	8.00
127 Dan Haren ROO RC	4.00	10.00
128 Luis Ayala ROO RC	3.00	8.00
129 Bo Hart ROO RC	3.00	8.00
130 Wil. Ledezma ROO RC	3.00	8.00
131 Rick Roberts ROO RC	3.00	8.00
132 Miguel Ojeda ROO RC	3.00	8.00
133 Aquilino Lopez ROO RC	3.00	8.00
134 Roger Deago ROO RC	3.00	8.00
135 Arnie Munoz ROO RC	3.00	8.00
136 Brent Hoard ROO RC	3.00	8.00
137 Termel Sledge ROO RC	3.00	8.00
138 Ryan Cameron ROO RC	3.00	8.00
139 Pr. Redman ROO RC	3.00	8.00
140 Clint Barmes ROO RC	2.50	6.00
141 Jeremy Griffiths ROO RC	3.00	8.00
142 Jon Leicester ROO RC	3.00	8.00
143 Brandon Webb ROO RC	5.00	12.00
144 T.Wellemeyer ROO RC	3.00	8.00
145 Felix Sanchez ROO RC	3.00	8.00
146 Anthony Ferrari ROO RC	3.00	8.00
147 Ian Ferguson ROO RC	3.00	8.00
148 Mi. Nakamura ROO RC	3.00	8.00
149 Lew Ford ROO RC	4.00	10.00
150 Nate Bland ROO RC	3.00	8.00
151 David Matranga ROO RC	3.00	8.00
152 Edgar Gonzalez ROO RC	3.00	8.00
153 Carlos Mendez ROO RC	3.00	8.00
154 Jason Gilfillan ROO RC	3.00	8.00
155 Mike Neu ROO RC	3.00	8.00
156 Jason Shiell ROO RC	3.00	8.00
157 Jeff Duncan ROO RC	3.00	8.00
158 Oscar Villarreal ROO RC	3.00	8.00
159 D.Markwell ROO RC	3.00	8.00
160 Joe Valentine ROO RC	3.00	8.00
161 H.Matsui AU JSY RC	150.00	250.00
162 Jose Contreras AU RC	20.00	40.00
163 Willie Eyre AU JSY RC	6.00	15.00
164 Matt Bruback AU JSY RC	6.00	15.00
165 Rett Johnson AU JSY RC	6.00	15.00
166 Jeremy Griffiths AU JSY	6.00	15.00
167 Fran Cruceta AU JSY RC	6.00	15.00
168 Fern Cabrera AU JSY RC	6.00	15.00
169 J.Peralta AU JSY	6.00	15.00
170 S.Bazzell AU JSY RC	6.00	15.00
171 B.Madritsch AU JSY RC	10.00	25.00
172 Phil Seibel AU JSY RC	6.00	15.00
173 J.Willingham AU JSY RC	25.00	50.00
174 R.Hammock AU JSY RC	6.00	15.00
175 A.Machado AU JSY RC	6.00	15.00
176 D.Sanders AU JSY RC	6.00	15.00
177 Matt Kata AU JSY RC	6.00	15.00
178 Heath Bell AU JSY RC	6.00	15.00
179 Chad Gaudin ROO RC	6.00	15.00
180 Chris Capuano ROO RC	10.00	25.00
181 Danny Garcia ROO RC	6.00	15.00
182 Delmon Young ROO RC	50.00	80.00
183 Edwin Jackson ROO RC	8.00	20.00
184 Greg Jones ROO RC	6.00	15.00
185 Jeremy Bonderman ROO RC	20.00	50.00
186 Jorge DePaula ROO	6.00	15.00
187 Khalil Greene ROO	8.00	20.00
188 Chad Cordero ROO RC	10.00	25.00
189 Miguel Cabrera ROO	8.00	20.00
190 Rich Harden ROO	8.00	20.00
191 Rickie Weeks ROO	15.00	40.00
192 Rosman Garcia ROO RC	6.00	15.00
193 Tom Gregorio ROO RC	6.00	15.00
381 Andrew Brown AU JSY RC	6.00	15.00
382 Delm Young AU JSY RC	350.00	450.00
383 Colin Porter AU JSY RC	6.00	15.00
385 Rickie Weeks AU JSY RC	40.00	80.00
386 David Matranga AU JSY RC	6.00	15.00
387 Bo Hart AU JSY	6.00	15.00

2003 SPx Spectrum

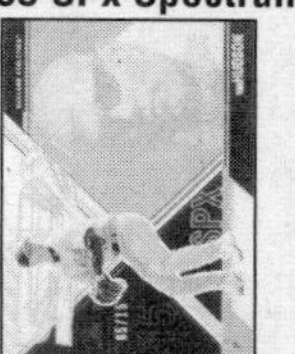

*SPECTRUM 1-125 p/r 51-75: 5X TO 12X
*SPECTRUM 1-125 p/r 36-50: 6X TO 15X
*SPECTRUM 1-125 p/r 26-35: 8X TO 20X
*SPECTRUM 1-125 p/r 51-75: 1.25X TO 3X SP
*SPECTRUM 1-125 p/r 36-50: 1.5X TO 4X SP
*SPECTRUM 1-125 p/r 26-35: 2X TO 5X SP
1-125 PRINT RUNS B/WN 1-75 COPIES PER
*SPECTRUM 126-160: .6X TO 1.5X BASIC
126-160 PRINT RUN 125 SERIAL #'d SETS
161-178 PRINT RUN 25 SERIAL #'d SETS
161-178 NO PRICING DUE TO SCARCITY
RANDOM INSERTS IN PACKS

143 Brandon Webb ROO	15.00	40.00

2003 SPx Game Used Combos

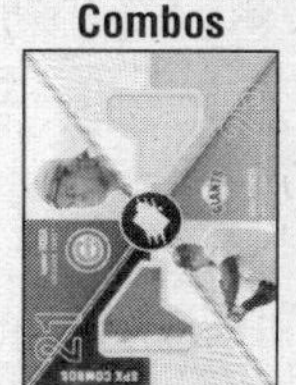

Randomly inserted into packs, these 42 cards feature two players along with game-used memorabilia of each player. Since these cards were issued in varying quantities, we have notated the print run next to the card in our checklist. Please note that if a card was issued to a print run of 25 or fewer copies, no pricing is provided due to market scarcity.

BK Jeff Bagwell Patch	15.00	40.00
Jeff Kent Patch/90		
BM Barry Bonds Base	60.00	120.00
Roger Maris Jsy/50		
BT Barry Bonds Base	150.00	250.00
Ted Williams Patch/50		
CA Cal Ripken Patch	125.00	200.00
Alex Rodriguez Patch/50		
CC Jose Contreras Base	20.00	50.00
Roger Clemens Patch/50		
CL Cal Ripken Patch	200.00	400.00
Lou Gehrig Pants/90		
CM Jose Contreras Base	15.00	40.00
Pedro Martinez Patch/90		
EG Darin Erstad Patch	10.00	25.00
Troy Glaus Patch/90		
FC Carlton Fisk Patch	15.00	40.00
Gary Carter Patch/90		
GC Greg Maddux Patch	20.00	50.00
Chipper Jones Patch/90		
GD Ken Griffey Jr. Patch	30.00	60.00
Adam Dunn Patch/90		
GR Ken Griffey Jr. Patch	30.00	60.00
Sammy Sosa Patch/90		
GS Jason Giambi Patch	10.00	25.00
Alfonso Soriano Patch/90		
HJ Hideki Matsui Patch	50.00	100.00
Jason Giambi Patch/50		
HM Hideki Matsui Patch		
Mickey Mantle Bat/10		
IA Ichiro Suzuki Patch	150.00	250.00
Albert Pujols Patch/50		
JJ Chipper Jones Patch	15.00	40.00
Andruw Jones Patch/90		
MB Mickey Mantle Bat	125.00	200.00
Barry Bonds Base/50		
MC Hideki Matsui Patch		
Jose Contreras Base/10		
MD Mickey Mantle Bat	150.00	250.00
Derek Jeter Base/50		
MG Pedro Martinez Patch	30.00	60.00
Nomar Garciaparra Base/90		
MJ Hideki Matsui Patch	60.00	120.00
Derek Jeter Base/90		
MR Mickey Mantle Bat		
Roger Maris Jsy/10		
MS Hideki Matsui Patch	250.00	400.00
Ichiro Suzuki Patch/50		
MW Mickey Mantle Bat	250.00	400.00
Ted Williams Jsy/50		
NI Hideo Nomo Patch	40.00	80.00
Kazuhisa Ishii Patch/50		
PM Rafael Palmeiro Patch	15.00	40.00
Fred McGriff Patch/90		
PS Rafael Palmeiro Patch		
Sammy Sosa Patch/10		
RC Nolan Ryan Patch	75.00	150.00
Roger Clemens Patch/90		
RG Alex Rodriguez Patch	30.00	60.00
Nomar Garciaparra Base/90		
RM Babe Ruth Bat		
Hideki Matsui Patch/10		
RR Cal Ripken Patch	50.00	100.00
Scott Rolen Patch/90		
RS Nolan Ryan Patch	75.00	150.00
Tom Seaver Patch/90		
RT Alex Rodriguez Patch	20.00	50.00
Miguel Tejada Patch/90		
RY Nolan Ryan Patch		
Pedro Martinez Patch/10		
SB Sammy Sosa Patch	30.00	60.00
Barry Bonds Base/90		
SJ Curt Schilling Patch	15.00	40.00
Randy Johnson Patch/90		
SN Ichiro Suzuki Patch	125.00	200.00
Hideo Nomo Patch/90		
SP Sammy Sosa Patch	15.00	40.00
Rafael Palmeiro Patch/90		
TB Thurman Munson Patch		
Yogi Berra Bat/10		
WG Ted Williams Patch		
Nomar Garciaparra Base/10		
WM Ted Williams Patch		
Pedro Martinez Patch/10		

2003 SPx Stars Autograph Jersey

Randomly inserted in packs, these cards feature both a game-used jersey swatch as well as an authentic signature. Since these cards were issued in varying print runs, we have notated the stated print run next to their name in our checklist.

SPECTRUM PRINT RUN 1 SERIAL #'d SET
NO SPECTRUM PRICING DUE TO SCARCITY
RANDOM INSERTS IN PACKS

CJ0 Chipper Jones/195	40.00	80.00
CS Curt Schilling/490	20.00	50.00
JG Jason Giambi/315	15.00	40.00
KG Ken Griffey Jr./690	50.00	100.00
LB Lance Berkman/590	12.50	30.00
LG Luis Gonzalez/790	10.00	25.00
MP Mark Prior/490	15.00	40.00
NM Nomar Garciaparra/195	40.00	80.00
PB Pat Burrell/590	10.00	25.00
TG Troy Glaus/490	15.00	40.00
VG Vladimir Guerrero/390	30.00	60.00

2003 SPx Winning Materials 375

LOGO'S CONSECUTIVELY #'d FROM 41-375
NUMBERS CONSECUTIVELY #'d FROM 1-40
CARDS CUMULATIVELY SERIAL #'d TO 375
*WIN.MAT.250: .5X TO 1.2X WIN.MAT.375
NUMBERS CONSECUTIVELY #'d FROM 1-28
LOGOS CONSECUTIVELY #'d FROM 29-250
WM 250 CUMULATIVELY SERIAL #'d TO 250
LOGO/NUMBER PRINTS PROVIDED BY UD
RANDOM INSERTS IN PACKS

AJ1A Andruw Jones Logo	4.00	10.00
AJ1B Andruw Jones Num	8.00	20.00
AP1A Albert Pujols Logo	10.00	25.00
AP1B Albert Pujols Num	20.00	50.00
AR1A Alex Rodriguez Logo	6.00	15.00
AR1B Alex Rodriguez Num	12.50	30.00
AS1A Alfonso Soriano Logo	3.00	8.00
AS1B Alfonso Soriano Num	6.00	15.00
BW1A Bernie Williams Logo	4.00	10.00
BW1B Bernie Williams Num	8.00	20.00
BZ1A Barry Zito Logo	3.00	8.00
BZ1B Barry Zito Num	6.00	15.00
CD1A Carlos Delgado Logo	3.00	8.00
CD1B Carlos Delgado Num	6.00	15.00
CJ1A Chipper Jones Logo	4.00	10.00
CJ1B Chipper Jones Num	8.00	20.00
CS1A Curt Schilling Logo	3.00	8.00
CS1B Curt Schilling Num	6.00	15.00
FT1A Frank Thomas Logo	4.00	10.00
FT1B Frank Thomas Num	8.00	20.00
GM1A Greg Maddux Logo	6.00	15.00
GM1B Greg Maddux Num	12.50	30.00
GS1A Gary Sheffield Logo	3.00	8.00
GS1B Gary Sheffield Num	6.00	15.00

HM1A Hideki Matsui Logo 10.00 25.00
HM1B Hideki Matsui Num 15.00 40.00
HN1A Hideo Nomo Logo 10.00 25.00
HN1B Hideo Nomo Num 20.00 50.00
IR1A Ivan Rodriguez Logo 4.00 10.00
IR1B Ivan Rodriguez Num 8.00 20.00
IS1A Ichiro Suzuki Logo 15.00 40.00
IS1B Ichiro Suzuki Num 40.00 80.00
JB1A Jeff Bagwell Logo 4.00 10.00
JB1B Jeff Bagwell Num 8.00 20.00
JG1A Jason Giambi Logo 3.00 8.00
JG1B Jason Giambi Num 6.00 15.00
JK1A Jeff Kent Logo 3.00 8.00
JK1B Jeff Kent Num 6.00 15.00
JT1A Jim Thome Logo 4.00 10.00
JT1B Jim Thome Num 8.00 20.00
KG1A Ken Griffey Jr. Logo 8.00 20.00
KG1B Ken Griffey Jr. Num 15.00 40.00
LB1A Lance Berkman Logo 3.00 8.00
LB1B Lance Berkman Num 6.00 15.00
LG1A Luis Gonzalez Logo 3.00 8.00
LG1B Luis Gonzalez Num 6.00 15.00
MA1A Mark Prior Logo 4.00 10.00
MA1B Mark Prior Num 8.00 20.00
MP1A Mike Piazza Logo 6.00 15.00
MP1B Mike Piazza Num 12.50 30.00
MR1A Manny Ramirez Logo 4.00 10.00
MR1B Manny Ramirez Num 8.00 20.00
MT1A Miguel Tejada Logo 3.00 8.00
MT1B Miguel Tejada Num 6.00 15.00
PB1A Pat Burrell Logo 3.00 8.00
PB1B Pat Burrell Num 6.00 15.00
PM1A Pedro Martinez Logo 4.00 10.00
PM1B Pedro Martinez Num 8.00 20.00
RA1A Roberto Alomar Logo 4.00 10.00
RA1B Roberto Alomar Num 8.00 20.00
RC1A Roger Clemens Logo 8.00 20.00
RC1B Roger Clemens Num 15.00 40.00
RF1A Rafael Furcal Logo 3.00 8.00
RF1B Rafael Furcal Num 6.00 15.00
RJ1A Randy Johnson Logo 4.00 10.00
RJ1B Randy Johnson Num 8.00 20.00
SG1A Shawn Green Logo 3.00 8.00
SG1B Shawn Green Num 6.00 15.00
SS1A Sammy Sosa Logo 4.00 10.00
SS1B Sammy Sosa Num 8.00 20.00
TG1A Tom Glavine Logo 4.00 10.00
TG1B Tom Glavine Num 8.00 20.00
TH1A Torii Hunter Logo 3.00 8.00
TH1B Torii Hunter Num 6.00 15.00
TO1A Todd Helton Logo 4.00 10.00
TO1B Todd Helton Num 8.00 20.00
TR1A Troy Glaus Logo 3.00 8.00
TR1B Troy Glaus Num 6.00 15.00
VG1A Vladimir Guerrero Logo 4.00 10.00
VG1B Vladimir Guerrero Num 8.00 20.00

2003 SPx Winning Materials 175

NUMBERS CONSECUTIVELY #'d FROM 1-20
LOGOS CONSECUTIVELY #'d FROM 21-175
CARDS CUMULATIVELY SERIAL #'d TO 175
*WM LOGO 50: .75X TO 2X WM LOGO 175
WM 50 NUMBERS CONSECUTIVELY #'d 1-10
WM 50 LOGOS CONSECUTIVELY #'d 11-50
WM 50 CUMULATIVELY SERIAL #'d TO 50
NO NUMBER PRICING DUE TO SCARCITY
LOGO/NUMBER PRINTS PROVIDED BY UD
AJ2A Andruw Jones Logo 5.00 12.00
AP2A Albert Pujols Logo 12.50 30.00
AR2A Alex Rodriguez Logo 8.00 20.00
AS2A Alfonso Soriano Logo 4.00 10.00
BW2A Bernie Williams Logo 5.00 12.00
BZ2A Barry Zito Logo 4.00 10.00
CD2A Carlos Delgado Logo 4.00 10.00
CJ2A Chipper Jones Logo 5.00 12.00
CS2A Curt Schilling Logo 4.00 10.00
FT2A Frank Thomas Logo 5.00 12.00
GM2A Greg Maddux Logo 8.00 20.00
GS2A Gary Sheffield Logo 4.00 10.00
HM2A Hideki Matsui Logo 12.50 30.00
HN2A Hideo Nomo Logo 12.50 30.00
IR2A Ivan Rodriguez Logo 5.00 12.00
IS2A Ichiro Suzuki Logo 20.00 50.00
JB2A Jeff Bagwell Logo 5.00 12.00
JG2A Jason Giambi Logo 4.00 10.00
JK2A Jeff Kent Logo 4.00 10.00
JT2A Jim Thome Logo 5.00 12.00
KG2A Ken Griffey Jr. Logo 10.00 25.00
LB2A Lance Berkman Logo 4.00 10.00
LG2A Luis Gonzalez Logo 4.00 10.00
MM2A M.Mantle Pants Logo 75.00 150.00
MP2RA Mark Prior Logo 5.00 12.00
MP2A Mike Piazza Logo 8.00 20.00
MR2A Manny Ramirez Logo 5.00 12.00
MT2A Miguel Tejada Logo 4.00 10.00
PB2A Pat Burrell Logo 4.00 10.00
PM2A Pedro Martinez Logo 5.00 12.00
RA2A Roberto Alomar Logo 5.00 12.00
RC2A Roger Clemens Logo 10.00 25.00
RF2A Rafael Furcal Logo 4.00 10.00
RJ2A Randy Johnson Logo 5.00 12.00
SG2A Shawn Green Logo 4.00 10.00
SS2A Sammy Sosa Logo 5.00 12.00
TGL2A Troy Glaus Logo 4.00 10.00
TG2A Tom Glavine Logo 5.00 12.00
THE2A Todd Helton Logo 5.00 12.00
TH2A Torii Hunter Logo 4.00 10.00
TW2A T.Williams Pants Logo 40.00 80.00
VG2A Vladimir Guerrero Logo 5.00 12.00

2003 SPx Young Stars Autograph Jersey

20 of the 23 cards within this set were randomly inserted in 2003 SPx packs (released in August, 2003). Serial #'d print runs for the 20 low series

cards range between 964-1460 copies each. An additional three cards (all of which are much scarcer with serial #'d print runs of only 355 copies per), were randomly seeded in packs of 2003 Upper Deck Finite of which was released in December, 2003. These cards feature game-used jersey swatches and authentic autographs from each player. Since these cards were issued in varying quantities, we have noted the stated print run next to the player's name in our checklist. Rocco Baldelli did not return his autographs prior to packout thus an exchange card with a redemption deadline of August 15th, 2006 was placed into packs.

SPECTRUM PRINT RUN 25 SERIAL #'d SETS
NO SPECTRUM PRICING DUE TO SCARCITY
AD Adam Dunn/1295 10.00 25.00
AK Austin Kearns/964 6.00 15.00
BM Brett Myers/1295 6.00 15.00
BP Brandon Phillips/1295 6.00 15.00
CG Chris George/1260 6.00 15.00
DW Dontrelle Willis/355 30.00 60.00
EH Eric Hinske/1295 6.00 15.00
HB Hank Blalock/1295 6.00 15.00
JA Jason Jennings/1295 6.00 15.00
JBA Josh Bard/1295 6.00 15.00
JJ Jacque Jones/1260 6.00 15.00
JP Josh Phelps/1295 6.00 15.00
KA Kurt Ainsworth/1460 6.00 15.00
KG Khalil Greene/355 20.00 50.00
KS Kirk Saarloos/1295 6.00 15.00
MD Michael Cuddyer/1156 6.00 15.00
MK Mike Kinkade/1295 6.00 15.00
MT Mark Teixeira/1295 10.00 25.00
NJ Nick Johnson/1295 6.00 15.00
RB Rocco Baldelli/1295 6.00 15.00
RH Rich Harden/355 20.00 50.00
RO Roy Oswalt/1295 6.00 15.00
SB Sean Burroughs/1295 6.00 15.00

2004 SPx

This 202-card set was released in December, 2004. The set was issued in four-card packs with an $7 SRP which came 18 packs to a box and 14 boxes to a case. The first 100 cards of this set feature active veterans while cards 101 through 110 feature retired greats. Cards 111 through 202 feature rookies either issued to different tiers or with both a jersey swatch and an autograph.

COMP.SET w/o SP's (100) 10.00 25.00
COMMON CARD (1-100) .20 .50
COMMON CARD (101-110) 3.00 8.00
101-110 STATED ODDS 1:18
COMMON CARD (111-145) 2.00 5.00
111-145 PRINT RUN 1599 SERIAL #'d SETS
COMMON CARD (146-154) 3.00 8.00
146-154 PRINT RUN 499 SERIAL #'d SETS
COMMON CARD (155-160) 3.00 8.00
155-160 PRINT RUN 299 SERIAL #'d SETS
111-160 ODDS W/SPECTRUM 1:9
161-202 ODDS W/SPECTRUM 1:18
161-202 PRINT RUN 799 SERIAL #'d SETS
EXCHANGE DEADLINE 12/03/07
MASTER PLATE ODDS 1:2500
MASTER PLATE PRINT RUN 1 #'d SET
NO PLATE PRICING DUE TO SCARCITY
1 Alfonso Soriano .20 .50
2 Todd Helton .30 .75
3 Andruw Jones .30 .75
4 Eric Gagne .20 .50
5 Craig Wilson .20 .50
6 Brian Giles .20 .50
7 Miguel Tejada .20 .50
8 Kevin Brown .20 .50
9 Shawn Green .20 .50
10 Ben Sheets .20 .50
11 John Smoltz .30 .75
12 Tim Hudson .20 .50
13 Jason Schmidt .20 .50
14 Paul Konerko .20 .50
15 Randy Johnson .50 1.25
16 Roy Oswalt .20 .50
17 Mike Lowell .20 .50
18 Carlos Lee .20 .50
19 Sean Burroughs .20 .50
20 Edgar Renteria .20 .50
21 Michael Young .20 .50
22 Jose Vidro .20 .50
23 Scott Rolen .30 .75
24 Rafael Furcal .20 .50
25 Tom Glavine .30 .75
26 Scott Podsednik .20 .50
27 Gary Sheffield .20 .50
28 Eric Chavez .20 .50
29 Mark Prior .30 .75
30 Chipper Jones .50 1.25
31 Frank Thomas .50 1.25
32 Victor Martinez .20 .50
33 Jake Peavy .20 .50
34 Carlos Beltran .20 .50
35 Roy Halladay .20 .50
36 Mark Teixeira .30 .75
37 Jacque Jones .20 .50
38 Mike Sweeney .20 .50
39 Troy Glaus .20 .50
40 Pat Burrell .20 .50
41 Ichiro Suzuki 1.00 2.50
42 Vladimir Guerrero .50 1.25
43 Bobby Abreu .20 .50
44 Jim Edmonds .20 .50
45 Garret Anderson .20 .50
46 J.D. Drew .20 .50
47 C.C. Sabathia .20 .50
48 Joe Mauer .50 1.25
49 Phil Nevin .20 .50
50 Hank Blalock .20 .50
51 Carlos Zambrano .20 .50
52 Mike Piazza .75 2.00
53 Manny Ramirez .30 .75
54 Lance Berkman .20 .50
55 Delmon Young .30 .75
56 Nomar Garciaparra .75 2.00
57 Alex Rodriguez .75 2.00
58 Rickie Weeks .20 .50
59 Adrian Beltre .20 .50
60 Albert Pujols 1.00 2.50
61 Richie Sexson .20 .50
62 Magglio Ordonez .20 .50
63 Derrek Lee .30 .75
64 Sammy Sosa .50 1.25
65 Jason Giambi .20 .50
66 Curt Schilling .30 .75
67 Jorge Posada .30 .75
68 Rafael Palmeiro .30 .75
69 Jeff Kent .20 .50
70 Jose Reyes .20 .50
71 David Ortiz .50 1.25
72 Aubrey Huff .20 .50
73 Jim Thome .30 .75
74 Andy Pettitte .30 .75
75 Barry Zito .20 .50
76 Carlos Delgado .20 .50
77 Hideki Matsui .75 2.00
78 Sean Casey .20 .50
79 Luis Gonzalez .20 .50
80 Marcus Giles .20 .50
81 Preston Wilson .20 .50
82 Javy Lopez .20 .50
83 Mark Mulder .20 .50
84 Derek Jeter 1.00 2.50
85 Miguel Cabrera .30 .75
86 Vernon Wells .20 .50
87 Roger Clemens 1.00 2.50
88 Lyle Overbay .20 .50
89 Bret Boone .20 .50
90 Melvin Mora .20 .50
91 Greg Maddux .75 2.00
92 Kerry Wood .20 .50
93 Ivan Rodriguez .30 .75
94 Pedro Martinez .30 .75
95 Jeff Bagwell .30 .75
96 Torii Hunter .20 .50
97 Ken Griffey Jr. .75 2.00
98 Mike Mussina .30 .75
99 Oliver Perez .20 .50
100 Josh Beckett .20 .50
101 Bob Gibson LGD 3.00 8.00
102 Cal Ripken LGD 6.00 15.00
103 Ted Williams LGD 3.00 8.00
104 Nolan Ryan LGD 4.00 10.00
105 Mickey Mantle LGD 6.00 15.00
106 Ernie Banks LGD 3.00 8.00
107 Joe DiMaggio LGD 3.00 8.00
108 Stan Musial LGD 3.00 8.00
109 Tom Seaver LGD 3.00 8.00
110 Mike Schmidt LGD 4.00 10.00
111 Jerry Gil T1 RC 2.00 5.00
112 Dioner Navarro T1 RC 3.00 8.00
113 Bartolome Fortunato T1 RC 2.00 5.00
114 Carlos Hines T1 RC 2.00 5.00
115 Franklyn Gracesqui T1 RC 2.00 5.00
116 Aarom Baldiris T1 RC 3.00 8.00
117 Casey Daigle T1 RC 2.00 5.00
118 Joey Gathright T1 RC 3.00 8.00
119 William Bergolla T1 RC 2.00 5.00
120 Jeff Bennett T1 RC 2.00 5.00
121 Lincoln Holdzkom T1 RC 2.00 5.00
122 Jorge Vasquez T1 RC 2.00 5.00
123 Donnie Kelly T1 RC 2.00 5.00
124 Yadier Molina T1 RC 3.00 8.00
125 Ryan Wing T1 RC 2.00 5.00
126 Justin Germano T1 RC 2.00 5.00
127 Freddy Guzman T1 RC 2.00 5.00
128 Onil Joseph T1 RC 2.00 5.00
129 Roman Colon T1 RC 2.00 5.00
130 Roberto Novoa T1 RC 3.00 8.00
131 Renyel Pinto T1 RC 3.00 8.00
132 Evan Rust T1 RC 2.00 5.00
133 Orlando Rodriguez T1 RC 2.00 5.00
134 Edwardo Sierra T1 RC 3.00 8.00
135 Mike Rose T1 RC 2.00 5.00
136 Phil Stockman T1 RC 2.00 5.00
137 Greg Dobbs T1 RC 2.00 5.00
138 Brad Halsey T1 RC 3.00 8.00
139 David Aardsma T1 RC 3.00 8.00
140 Joe Hietpas T1 RC 2.00 5.00
141 Josh Labandeira T1 RC 2.00 5.00
142 Mariano Gomez T1 RC 2.00 5.00
143 Jeff Bajenaru T1 RC 2.00 5.00
144 Travis Blackley T1 RC 2.00 5.00
145 Abe Alvarez T1 RC 3.00 8.00
146 Ramon Ramirez T2 RC 3.00 8.00
147 Edwin Moreno T2 RC 4.00 10.00
148 Ronny Cedeno T2 RC 4.00 10.00
149 Hector Gimenez T2 RC 3.00 8.00
150 Carlos Vasquez T2 RC 4.00 10.00
151 Jesse Crain T2 RC 6.00 15.00
152 Logan Kensing T2 RC 3.00 8.00
153 Sean Henn T2 RC 3.00 8.00
154 Rusty Tucker T2 RC 4.00 10.00
155 Justin Lehr T3 RC 3.00 8.00
156 Ian Snell T3 RC 4.00 10.00
157 Merkin Valdez T3 RC 3.00 8.00
158 Scott Proctor T3 RC 4.00 10.00
159 Jose Capellan T3 RC 4.00 10.00
160 Kazuo Matsui T3 RC 3.00 8.00
161 Chris Oxspring AU JSY RC 6.00 15.00
162 Jimmy Serrano AU JSY RC 6.00 15.00
163 Jeff Keppinger AU JSY RC 8.00 20.00
164 B.Medders AU JSY RC 6.00 15.00
165 Brian Dallimore AU JSY RC 6.00 15.00
166 Chad Bentz AU JSY RC 6.00 15.00
167 Chris Aguila AU JSY RC 6.00 15.00
168 Chris Saenz AU JSY RC 6.00 15.00
169 Frank Francisco AU JSY RC 6.00 15.00
170 Colby Miller AU JSY RC 6.00 15.00
171 D.Crouth AU JSY RC EXCH 6.00 15.00
172 Charles Thomas AU JSY RC 6.00 15.00
173 Dennis Sarfate AU JSY RC 6.00 15.00
174 Lance Cormier AU JSY RC 6.00 15.00
175 Joe Horgan AU JSY RC 6.00 15.00
176 Fernando Nieve AU JSY RC 6.00 15.00
177 Jake Woods AU JSY RC 6.00 15.00
178 Matt Treanor AU JSY RC 6.00 15.00
179 Jerome Gamble AU JSY RC 6.00 15.00
180 John Gall AU JSY RC 10.00 25.00
181 Jorge Sequea AU JSY RC 6.00 15.00
182 Justin Hampson AU JSY RC 6.00 15.00
183 Justin Huisman AU JSY RC 6.00 15.00
184 Justin Knoedler AU JSY RC 6.00 15.00
185 Justin Leone AU JSY RC 10.00 25.00
186 Scott Atchison AU JSY RC 6.00 15.00
187 Jon Knott AU JSY RC 6.00 15.00
188 Kevin Cave AU JSY RC 6.00 15.00
189 Jason Frasor AU JSY RC 6.00 15.00
190 George Sherrill AU JSY RC 6.00 15.00
191 Mike Gosling AU JSY RC 6.00 15.00
192 Mike Johnston AU JSY RC 6.00 15.00
193 Mike Rouse AU JSY RC 6.00 15.00
194 Nick Regilio AU JSY RC 6.00 15.00
195 Ryan Meaux AU JSY RC 6.00 15.00
196 Scott Dohmann AU JSY RC 6.00 15.00
197 Shawn Camp AU JSY RC 6.00 15.00
198 Shawn Hill AU JSY RC 6.00 15.00
199 Shingo Takatsu AU JSY RC 6.00 15.00
200 Tim Bausher AU JSY RC 6.00 15.00
201 Tim Bittner AU JSY RC 6.00 15.00
202 Scott Kazmir AU JSY RC 12.50 30.00

2004 SPx Spectrum

*SPEC 1-100: 8X TO 20X BASIC
*SPEC 101/106/109: 1.25X TO 3X
*SPEC 102-105/107-108/110: 2X TO 5X
1-110 STATED ODDS 1:252
111-160 W/BASIC OVERALL ODDS 1:9
161-202 W/BASIC OVERALL ODDS 1:18
STATED PRINT RUN 25 SERIAL #'d SETS
111-202 NO PRICING DUE TO SCARCITY
EXCHANGE DEADLINE 12/03/07

2004 SPx SuperScripts Rookies

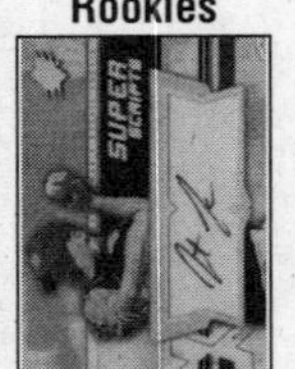

OVERALL SUPERSCRIPT ODDS 1:18
EXCHANGE DEADLINE 12/03/07
AS Alfredo Simon 4.00 10.00
BF Bartolome Fortunato EXCH 4.00 10.00
CH Carlos Hines 4.00 10.00
CV Carlos Vasquez 6.00 15.00
DK Donnie Kelly 4.00 10.00
ES Edwardo Sierra 6.00 15.00
IO Ivan Ochoa 4.00 10.00
IS Ian Snell 8.00 20.00
JL Justin Lehr 4.00 10.00
LA Josh Labandeira 4.00 10.00
LH Lincoln Holdzkom 4.00 10.00
MG Mariano Gomez 4.00 10.00
MV Merkin Valdez 4.00 10.00
PS Phil Stockman 4.00 10.00
RR Ramon Ramirez 4.00 10.00
RU Evan Rust 4.00 10.00
SH Sean Henn 4.00 10.00
SP Scott Proctor 6.00 15.00
VE Michael Vento 6.00 15.00

2004 SPx SuperScripts Stars

OVERALL SUPERSCRIPT ODDS 1:18
SP INFO PROVIDED BY UPPER DECK
AP Albert Pujols SP 150.00 250.00
CR Cal Ripken SP 75.00 150.00
DJ Derek Jeter SP 125.00 200.00
EC Eric Chavez 10.00 25.00
JB Josh Beckett 15.00 40.00
KG Ken Griffey Jr. 40.00 80.00
MP Mark Prior 15.00 40.00
NG Nomar Garciaparra SP 50.00 100.00
NR Nolan Ryan SP
TE Miguel Tejada 15.00 40.00

2004 SPx SuperScripts Young Stars

OVERALL SUPERSCRIPT ODDS 1:18
BC Bobby Crosby 6.00 15.00
BW Brandon Webb 12.50 30.00
DW Dontrelle Willis 10.00 25.00
DY Delmon Young 12.50 30.00
EJ Edwin Jackson 4.00 10.00
JM Joe Mauer 12.50 30.00
JR Jose Reyes 6.00 15.00
MC Miguel Cabrera 10.00 25.00
MT Mark Teixeira 10.00 25.00
RH Rich Harden 6.00 15.00
RO Roy Oswalt 6.00 15.00
RW Rickie Weeks 6.00 15.00

2004 SPx Swatch Supremacy Cut Signatures Material

RANDOM INSERTS IN PACKS
PRINT RUNS B/WN 1-9 COPIES PER
NO PRICING DUE TO SCARCITY
BR Babe Ruth Pants/3
HW Honus Wagner Pants/1
JD Joe DiMaggio Jsy/5
LG Lou Gehrig Pants/4
MM Mickey Mantle Pants/7
TC Ty Cobb Pants/1
TW Ted Williams Jsy/9

2004 SPx Swatch Supremacy Signatures Stars

STATED PRINT RUN 275 SERIAL #'d SETS
*SPECTRUM: .75X TO 1.5X BASIC
SPECTRUM PRINT RUN 25 #'d SETS
OVERALL SWATCH SUP.ODDS 1:18
AP Albert Pujols 150.00 250.00
CR Cal Ripken 75.00 150.00
DJ Derek Jeter 100.00 200.00
DL Derrek Lee 15.00 40.00
EC Eric Chavez 10.00 25.00
GA Garret Anderson 10.00 25.00
KG Ken Griffey Jr. 50.00 100.00
MP Mark Prior 15.00 40.00
NG Nomar Garciaparra 30.00 60.00
NR Nolan Ryan 60.00 120.00

2004 SPx Swatch Supremacy Signatures Young Stars

STATED PRINT RUN 999 SERIAL #'d SETS
*SPECTRUM: .75X TO 1.5X BASIC
SPECTRUM PRINT RUN 25 #'d SETS
OVERALL SWATCH SUP.ODDS 1:18
AB Angel Berroa 6.00 15.00
AE Adam Eaton 6.00 15.00
BC Bobby Crosby 6.00 15.00
BS Ben Sheets 6.00 15.00
BW Brandon Webb 12.50 30.00
CC Chad Cordero 6.00 15.00
CK Casey Kotchman 10.00 25.00
CL Cliff Lee 8.00 20.00
CP Corey Patterson 6.00 15.00
DW Dontrelle Willis 15.00 40.00
GR Khalil Greene 15.00 40.00
HB Hank Blalock 10.00 25.00
HR Horacio Ramirez 6.00 15.00
JB Josh Beckett 15.00 40.00
JM Joe Mauer 15.00 40.00
JP Jake Peavy 10.00 25.00
JR Jose Reyes 15.00 40.00
JW Jerome Williams 6.00 15.00
LO Lyle Overbay 6.00 15.00
MC Miguel Cabrera 15.00 40.00
MG Marcus Giles 10.00 25.00
MT Mark Teixeira 15.00 40.00
MY Michael Young 6.00 15.00
RB Rocco Baldelli 6.00 15.00
RH Rich Harden 6.00 15.00
RO Roy Oswalt 6.00 15.00
RW Rickie Weeks 10.00 25.00
SB Sean Burroughs 6.00 15.00
SP Scott Podsednik 15.00 40.00

2004 SPx Winning Materials Dual Jersey

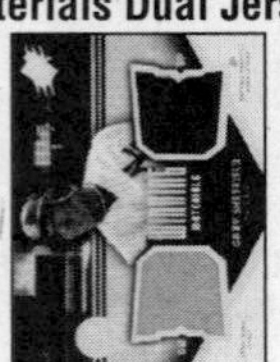

*SPECTRUM: .6X TO 1.5X BASIC
SPECTRUM PRINT RUN 25 #'d SETS
OVERALL WINNING MTL.ODDS 1:18
ALL HAVE GAME-WORN & BP SWATCHES
AP Albert Pujols 15.00 40.00
BE Josh Beckett 4.00 10.00
CD Carlos Delgado 4.00 10.00
CJ Chipper Jones 6.00 15.00
DJ Derek Jeter 15.00 40.00
EC Eric Chavez 4.00 10.00
GM Greg Maddux 10.00 25.00
GS Gary Sheffield 4.00 10.00
HB Hank Blalock 4.00 10.00
HM Hideki Matsui 20.00 50.00
IS Ichiro Suzuki 20.00 50.00
JB Jeff Bagwell 6.00 15.00
JG Jason Giambi 4.00 10.00
JP Jorge Posada 6.00 15.00
JR Jose Reyes 4.00 10.00
JT Jim Thome 6.00 15.00
KB Kevin Brown 4.00 10.00
MM Mike Mussina 6.00 15.00
MP Mark Prior 6.00 15.00
MR Manny Ramirez 6.00 15.00
PI Mike Piazza 10.00 25.00
RC Roger Clemens 10.00 25.00
RP Rafael Palmeiro 6.00 15.00
SG Shawn Green 4.00 10.00
SR Scott Rolen 6.00 15.00
SS Sammy Sosa 6.00 15.00
TE Miguel Tejada 4.00 10.00
TG Troy Glaus 4.00 10.00
VG Vladimir Guerrero 6.00 15.00

2005 SPx

These cards were issued as part of the SP Collection packs. For details on those packs, please see the write-up for SP Authentic.

COMP.BASIC SET (100) 10.00 25.00
COMMON CARD (1-100) .15 .40
COMMON RC (1-100) .15 .40
1-100 ISSUED IN 05 SP COLLECTION PACKS
COMMON AUTO (101-180) 4.00 10.00
101-180 ODDS APPX 1:8 '05 UD UPDATE
101-180 PRINT RUN 185 SERIAL #'d SETS
105, 117, 139, 149, 155, 172 DO NOT EXIST
175, 178, 180 DO NOT EXIST
1 Aaron Harang .15 .40
2 Aaron Rowand .15 .40
3 Aaron Miles .15 .40
4 Adrian Gonzalez .15 .40
5 Alex Rios .15 .40
6 Angel Berroa .15 .40
7 B.J. Upton .15 .40
8 Brandon Claussen .15 .40
9 Andy Marte .15 .40
10 Brandon Webb .15 .40
11 Bronson Arroyo .15 .40
12 Casey Kotchman .15 .40
13 Cesar Izturis .15 .40
14 Chad Cordero .15 .40
15 Chad Tracy .15 .40
16 Charles Thomas .15 .40
17 Chase Utley .25 .60
18 Chone Figgins .15 .40
19 Chris Burke .15 .40
20 Cliff Lee .15 .40
21 Clint Barmes .15 .40
22 Coco Crisp .15 .40
23 Bill Hall .15 .40
24 Dallas McPherson .15 .40
25 Brad Halsey .15 .40
26 Daniel Cabrera .15 .40
27 Danny Haren .15 .40
28 Dave Bush .15 .40
29 David DeJesus .15 .40
30 D.J. Houlton RC .25 .60
31 Derek Jeter .75 2.00
32 Dewon Brazelton .15 .40
33 Edwin Jackson .15 .40
34 Brad Hawpe .15 .40
35 Brandon Inge .15 .40
36 Brett Myers .15 .40
37 Garrett Atkins .15 .40
38 Gavin Floyd .15 .40
39 Grady Sizemore .25 .60
40 Guillermo Mota .15 .40
41 Carlos Guillen .15 .40
42 Gustavo Chacin .15 .40
43 Huston Street .25 .60
44 Chris Duffy .15 .40
45 J.D. Closser .15 .40
46 J.J. Hardy .15 .40
47 Jason Bartlett .15 .40
48 Jason DuBois .15 .40
49 Chris Shelton .25 .60
50 Jason Lane .15 .40
51 Jayson Werth .15 .40
52 Jeff Baker .15 .40
53 Jeff Francis .15 .40
54 Jeremy Bonderman .15 .40
55 Jeremy Reed .15 .40
56 Jerome Williams .15 .40
57 Jesse Crain .15 .40
58 Chris Young .15 .40
59 Jhonny Peralta .15 .40
60 Joe Blanton .15 .40
61 Joe Crede .15 .40
62 Joel Pineiro .15 .40
63 Joey Gathright .15 .40
64 John Buck .15 .40
65 Jonny Gomes .15 .40
66 Jorge Cantu .15 .40
67 Dan Johnson .15 .40
68 Jose Valverde .15 .40
69 Ervin Santana .15 .40
70 Justin Morneau .15 .40
71 Keiichi Yabu RC .25 .60
72 Ken Griffey Jr. .60 1.50
73 Jason Repko .15 .40
74 Kevin Youkilis .15 .40
75 Koyie Hill .15 .40
76 Laynce Nix .15 .40
77 Luke Scott RC .75 2.00
78 Juan Rivera .15 .40
79 Justin Duchscherer .15 .40
80 Mark Teahen .15 .40
81 Lance Niekro .15 .40
82 Michael Cuddyer .15 .40
83 Nick Swisher .15 .40
84 Noah Lowry .15 .40
85 Matt Holliday .20 .50
86 Reed Johnson .15 .40
87 Rich Harden .15 .40
88 Robb Quinlan .15 .40

89 Nick Johnson .15 .40
90 Ryan Howard 1.00 2.50
91 Nook Logan .15 .40
92 Steve Schmoll RC .25 .60
93 Tadahito Iguchi RC 1.50 4.00
94 Willy Taveras .15 .40
95 Wily Mo Pena .15 .40
96 Xavier Nady .15 .40
97 Yadier Molina .15 .40
98 Yhency Brazoban .15 .40
99 Ryan Freel .15 .40
100 Zack Greinke .15 .40
101 Adam Shabala AU RC 4.00 10.00
102 Ambiorix Burgos AU RC 4.00 10.00
103 Ambiorix Concepcion AU RC 4.00 10.00
104 Anibal Sanchez AU RC 15.00 40.00
106 Brandon McCarthy AU RC 12.50 30.00
107 Brian Burres AU RC 4.00 10.00
108 Carlos Ruiz AU RC 6.00 15.00
109 Casey Rogowski AU RC 6.00 15.00
110 Chad Orvella AU RC 4.00 10.00
111 Chris Resop AU RC 6.00 15.00
112 Chris Roberson AU RC 4.00 10.00
113 Chris Seddon AU RC 4.00 10.00
114 Colter Bean AU RC 6.00 15.00
115 Dave Gassner AU RC 4.00 10.00
116 Brian Anderson AU RC 15.00 40.00
118 Devon Lowery AU RC 4.00 10.00
119 Enrique Gonzalez AU RC 6.00 15.00
120 Eude Brito AU RC 4.00 10.00
121 Francisco Butto AU RC 4.00 10.00
122 Franquelis Osoria AU RC 4.00 10.00
123 Garrett Jones AU RC 4.00 10.00
124 Geovany Soto AU RC 60.00 120.00
125 Hayden Penn AU RC 8.00 20.00
126 Ismael Ramirez AU RC 4.00 10.00
127 Jared Gothreaux AU RC 4.00 10.00
128 Jason Hammel AU RC 4.00 10.00
129 Jeff Miller AU RC 4.00 10.00
130 Jeff Niemann AU RC 12.50 30.00
131 Joel Peralta AU RC 4.00 10.00
132 John Hattig AU RC 4.00 10.00
133 Jorge Campillo AU RC 4.00 10.00
134 Juan Morillo AU RC 4.00 10.00
135 Justin Verlander AU RC 125.00 200.00
136 Ryan Garko AU RC 15.00 40.00
137 Kendry Morales AU RC 30.00 60.00
138 Luis Hernandez AU RC 4.00 10.00
140 Luis O.Rodriguez AU RC 4.00 10.00
141 Mark Woodyard AU RC 4.00 10.00
142 Matt A.Smith AU RC 4.00 10.00
143 Matthew Lindstrom AU RC 4.00 10.00
144 Miguel Negron AU RC 6.00 15.00
145 Mike Morse AU RC 8.00 20.00
146 Nate McLouth AU RC 20.00 50.00
147 Nelson Cruz AU RC 15.00 40.00
148 Nick Masset AU RC 4.00 10.00
150 Paulino Reynoso AU RC 4.00 10.00
151 Pedro Lopez AU RC 4.00 10.00
152 Philip Humber AU RC 12.50 30.00
153 Prince Fielder AU RC 125.00 200.00
154 Randy Messenger AU RC 4.00 10.00
156 Raul Tablado AU RC 4.00 10.00
157 Ronny Paulino AU RC 6.00 15.00
158 Russ Rohlicek AU RC 4.00 10.00
159 Russell Martin AU RC 30.00 60.00
160 Scott Baker AU RC 6.00 15.00
161 Scott Munter AU RC 4.00 10.00
162 Sean Thompson AU RC 4.00 10.00
163 Sean Tracey AU RC 4.00 10.00
164 Shane Costa AU RC 4.00 10.00
165 Stephen Drew AU RC 30.00 60.00
166 Tony Giarratano AU RC 4.00 10.00
167 Tony Pena AU RC 4.00 10.00
168 Travis Bowyer AU RC 4.00 10.00
169 Ubaldo Jimenez AU RC 20.00 50.00
170 Wladimir Balentien AU RC 40.00 80.00
171 Yorman Bazardo AU RC 4.00 10.00
173 Ryan Zimmerman AU RC 75.00 150.00
174 Chris Denorfia AU RC 6.00 15.00
176 Jermaine Van Buren AU 4.00 10.00
177 Mark McLemore AU RC 4.00 10.00
179 Ryan Speier AU RC 4.00 10.00

2005 SPx Silver

APPX AU ODDS 1:8 '05 UD UPDATE
STATED PRINT RUN 10 SERIAL #'d SETS
NO PRICING DUE TO SCARCITY

2005 SPx Jersey

STATED PRINT RUN 199 SERIAL #'d SETS
*SPECTRUM: .5X TO 1.2X BASIC
SPECTRUM PRINT RUN 99 SERIAL #'d SETS
ISSUED IN 05 SP COLLECTION PACKS
OVERALL GAME-USED ODDS 1:10
1 Aaron Harang 2.00 5.00
2 Aaron Rowand 2.00 5.00
3 Aaron Miles 2.00 5.00
4 Adrian Gonzalez 2.00 5.00
5 Alex Rios 2.00 5.00
6 Angel Berroa 2.00 5.00
7 B.J. Upton 2.00 5.00
8 Brandon Claussen 2.00 5.00
9 Andy Marte 2.00 5.00
10 Brandon Webb 2.00 5.00
11 Bronson Arroyo 2.00 5.00
12 Casey Kotchman 2.00 5.00
13 Cesar Izturis 2.00 5.00
14 Chad Cordero 2.00 5.00
15 Chad Tracy 2.00 5.00
16 Charles Thomas 2.00 5.00
17 Chase Utley 3.00 8.00
18 Chone Figgins 2.00 5.00
19 Chris Burke 2.00 5.00
20 Cliff Lee 2.00 5.00
21 Clint Barmes 2.00 5.00
22 Coco Crisp 2.00 5.00
23 Bill Hall 2.00 5.00
24 Dallas McPherson 2.00 5.00
25 Brad Halsey 2.00 5.00
26 Daniel Cabrera 2.00 5.00
27 Danny Haren 2.00 5.00
28 Dave Bush 2.00 5.00
29 David DeJesus 2.00 5.00
30 D.J. Houlton 2.00 5.00
31 Derek Jeter Pants 8.00 20.00
32 Dewon Brazelton 2.00 5.00
33 Edwin Jackson 2.00 5.00
34 Brad Hawpe 2.00 5.00
35 Brandon Inge 2.00 5.00
36 Brett Myers 2.00 5.00
37 Garrett Atkins 2.00 5.00
38 Gavin Floyd 2.00 5.00
39 Grady Sizemore 3.00 8.00
40 Guillermo Mota 2.00 5.00
41 Carlos Guillen 2.00 5.00
42 Gustavo Chacin 2.00 5.00
43 Huston Street 3.00 8.00
44 Chris Duffy 2.00 5.00
45 J.D. Closser 2.00 5.00
46 J.J. Hardy 2.00 5.00
47 Jason Bartlett 2.00 5.00
48 Jason DuBois 2.00 5.00
49 Chris Shelton 4.00 10.00
50 Jason Lane 2.00 5.00
51 Jayson Werth 2.00 5.00
52 Jeff Baker 2.00 5.00
53 Jeff Francis 2.00 5.00
54 Jeremy Bonderman 2.00 5.00
55 Jeremy Reed 2.00 5.00
56 Jerome Williams 2.00 5.00
57 Jesse Crain 2.00 5.00
58 Chris Young 2.00 5.00
59 Jhonny Peralta 2.00 5.00
60 Joe Blanton 2.00 5.00
61 Joe Crede 2.00 5.00
62 Joel Pineiro 2.00 5.00
63 Joey Gathright 2.00 5.00
64 John Buck 2.00 5.00
65 Jonny Gomes 2.00 5.00
66 Jorge Cantu 2.00 5.00
67 Dan Johnson 2.00 5.00
68 Jose Valverde 2.00 5.00
69 Ervin Santana 2.00 5.00
70 Justin Morneau 2.00 5.00
71 Keiichi Yabu 2.00 5.00
72 Ken Griffey Jr. 6.00 15.00
73 Jason Repko 2.00 5.00
74 Kevin Youkilis 2.00 5.00
75 Koyie Hill 2.00 5.00
76 Laynce Nix 2.00 5.00
77 Luke Scott 4.00 10.00
78 Juan Rivera 2.00 5.00
79 Justin Duchscherer 2.00 5.00
80 Mark Teahen 2.00 5.00
81 Lance Niekro 2.00 5.00
82 Michael Cuddyer 2.00 5.00
83 Nick Swisher 2.00 5.00
84 Noah Lowry 2.00 5.00
85 Matt Holliday 2.50 6.00
86 Reed Johnson 2.00 5.00
87 Rich Harden 2.00 5.00
88 Robb Quinlan 2.00 5.00
89 Nick Johnson 2.00 5.00
90 Ryan Howard 10.00 25.00
91 Nook Logan 2.00 5.00
92 Steve Schmoll 2.00 5.00
93 Tadahito Iguchi 12.50 30.00
94 Willy Taveras 2.00 5.00
95 Wily Mo Pena 2.00 5.00
96 Xavier Nady 2.00 5.00
97 Yadier Molina 2.00 5.00
98 Yhency Brazoban 2.00 5.00
99 Ryan Freel 2.00 5.00
100 Zack Greinke 2.00 5.00

2005 SPx Signature

PRINT RUNS B/WN 50-350 COPIES PER
SPECTRUM PRINT RUN 10 SERIAL #'d SETS
NO SPECTRUM PRICING DUE TO SCARCITY
OVERALL AUTO ODDS 1:10
1 Aaron Harang/350 6.00 15.00
2 Aaron Rowand/150 10.00 25.00
4 Adrian Gonzalez/225 4.00 10.00
6 Angel Berroa/150 4.00 10.00
7 B.J. Upton/50 8.00 20.00
8 Brandon Claussen/350 4.00 10.00
9 Andy Marte/350 6.00 15.00
11 Bronson Arroyo/350 6.00 15.00
12 Casey Kotchman/225 6.00 15.00
13 Cesar Izturis/150 4.00 10.00
14 Chad Cordero/350 6.00 15.00
15 Chad Tracy/350 4.00 10.00
16 Charles Thomas/350 4.00 10.00
17 Chase Utley/50 20.00 50.00
18 Chone Figgins/150 6.00 15.00
19 Chris Burke/350 4.00 10.00
20 Cliff Lee/225 6.00 15.00
21 Clint Barmes/350 6.00 15.00
22 Coco Crisp/225 10.00 25.00
23 Bill Hall/350 4.00 10.00
24 Dallas McPherson/150 4.00 10.00
25 Brad Halsey/350 4.00 10.00
26 Daniel Cabrera/350 4.00 10.00
27 Danny Haren/225 4.00 10.00
28 Dave Bush/350 4.00 10.00
29 David DeJesus/225 4.00 10.00
30 D.J. Houlton/350 4.00 10.00
31 Derek Jeter/50 90.00 150.00
32 Dewon Brazelton/225 4.00 10.00
33 Edwin Jackson/150 4.00 10.00
34 Brad Hawpe/350 10.00 25.00
35 Brandon Inge/350 4.00 10.00
36 Brett Myers/150 6.00 15.00
37 Garrett Atkins/350 4.00 10.00
38 Gavin Floyd/150 4.00 10.00
39 Grady Sizemore/350 12.50 30.00
40 Guillermo Mota/225 4.00 10.00
41 Carlos Guillen/150 6.00 15.00
42 Gustavo Chacin/350 6.00 15.00
43 Huston Street/350 10.00 25.00
44 Chris Duffy/225 4.00 10.00
45 J.D. Closser/350 4.00 10.00
46 J.J. Hardy/350 20.00 50.00
47 Jason Bartlett/350 4.00 10.00
48 Jason DuBois/350 4.00 10.00
50 Jason Lane/350 4.00 10.00
51 Jayson Werth/350 4.00 10.00
52 Jeff Baker/350 4.00 10.00
53 Jeff Francis/150 4.00 10.00
54 Jeremy Bonderman/50 8.00 20.00
55 Jeremy Reed/150 6.00 15.00
56 Jerome Williams/50 8.00 20.00
57 Jesse Crain/350 4.00 10.00
59 Jhonny Peralta/350 6.00 15.00
60 Joe Blanton/350 4.00 10.00
61 Joe Crede/350 10.00 25.00
62 Joel Pineiro/150 6.00 15.00
63 Joey Gathright/350 4.00 10.00
64 John Buck/350 4.00 10.00
65 Jonny Gomes/350 6.00 15.00
66 Jorge Cantu/350 6.00 15.00
67 Dan Johnson/350 6.00 15.00
68 Jose Valverde/350 4.00 10.00
69 Ervin Santana/350 6.00 15.00
70 Justin Morneau/50 8.00 20.00
71 Keiichi Yabu/350 6.00 15.00
73 Jason Repko/350 10.00 25.00
74 Kevin Youkilis/225 8.00 20.00
75 Koyie Hill/350 4.00 10.00
76 Laynce Nix/150 4.00 10.00
77 Luke Scott/350 20.00 50.00
78 Juan Rivera/225 4.00 10.00
79 Justin Duchscherer/350 4.00 10.00
80 Mark Teahen/350 4.00 10.00
81 Lance Niekro/350 4.00 10.00
82 Michael Cuddyer/350 4.00 10.00
84 Noah Lowry/150 6.00 15.00
85 Matt Holliday/225 10.00 25.00
86 Reed Johnson/350 4.00 10.00
88 Robb Quinlan/350 4.00 10.00
89 Nick Johnson/150 6.00 15.00
90 Ryan Howard/225 20.00 50.00
91 Nook Logan/350 4.00 10.00
92 Steve Schmoll/350 4.00 10.00
93 Tadahito Iguchi/50 125.00 200.00
95 Wily Mo Pena/150 6.00 15.00
96 Xavier Nady/150 4.00 10.00
98 Yhency Brazoban/350 4.00 10.00
100 Zack Greinke/150 4.00 10.00

2005 SPx Signature Jersey Spectrum

ISSUED IN 05 SP COLLECTION PACKS
OVERALL PREMIUM AU-GU ODDS 1:20
STATED PRINT RUN 10 SERIAL #'d SETS
NO PRICING DUE TO SCARCITY

2005 SPx SPxtreme Stats

ISSUED IN 05 SP COLLECTION PACKS
OVERALL INSERT ODDS 1:10
STATED PRINT RUN 299 SERIAL #'d SETS
AB Adrian Beltre 1.25 3.00
AD Adam Dunn 1.25 3.00
AJ Andruw Jones 1.50 4.00
AP Albert Pujols 4.00 10.00
AR Aramis Ramirez 1.25 3.00
BA Bobby Abreu 1.25 3.00
BC Bobby Crosby 1.25 3.00
BS Ben Sheets 1.25 3.00
CB Craig Biggio 1.50 4.00
CC Carl Crawford 1.25 3.00
CP Corey Patterson 1.25 3.00
CZ Carlos Zambrano 1.25 3.00
DJ Derek Jeter 4.00 10.00
DL Derrek Lee 1.50 4.00
DO David Ortiz 1.50 4.00
DW David Wright 3.00 8.00
EC Eric Chavez 1.25 3.00
EG Eric Gagne 1.25 3.00
ER Edgar Renteria 1.25 3.00
GM Greg Maddux 3.00 8.00
GR Khalil Greene 1.50 4.00
GS Gary Sheffield 1.25 3.00
HB Hank Blalock 1.25 3.00
HU Torii Hunter 1.25 3.00
JD J.D. Drew 1.25 3.00
JM Joe Mauer 1.50 4.00
JP Jake Peavy 1.25 3.00
JR Jose Reyes 1.25 3.00
KG Ken Griffey Jr. 3.00 8.00
KW Kerry Wood 1.25 3.00
MC Miguel Cabrera 1.50 4.00
MM Mark Mulder 1.25 3.00
MO Melvin Mora 1.25 3.00
MP Mark Prior 1.50 4.00
MT Mark Teixeira 1.50 4.00
MY Michael Young 1.25 3.00
OP Oliver Perez 1.25 3.00
PI Mike Piazza 1.50 4.00
RC Roger Clemens 3.00 8.00
RJ Randy Johnson 1.50 4.00
RO Roy Oswalt 1.25 3.00
RP Rafael Palmeiro 1.50 4.00
SA Johan Santana 1.50 4.00
SC Sean Casey 1.25 3.00
SM John Smoltz 1.50 4.00
SR Scott Rolen 1.50 4.00
TE Miguel Tejada 1.25 3.00
TH Tim Hudson 1.25 3.00
VG Vladimir Guerrero 1.50 4.00
VM Victor Martinez 1.25 3.00

2005 SPx SPxtreme Stats Jersey

ISSUED IN 05 SP COLLECTION PACKS
OVERALL PREMIUM AU-GU ODDS 1:20
STATED PRINT RUN 130 SERIAL #'d SETS
AB Adrian Beltre 2.00 5.00
AD Adam Dunn 2.00 5.00
AJ Andruw Jones 3.00 8.00
AP Albert Pujols 6.00 15.00
AR Aramis Ramirez 2.00 5.00
BA Bobby Abreu 2.00 5.00
BC Bobby Crosby 2.00 5.00
BS Ben Sheets 2.00 5.00
CB Craig Biggio 3.00 8.00
CC Carl Crawford 2.00 5.00
CP Corey Patterson 2.00 5.00
CZ Carlos Zambrano 2.00 5.00
DJ Derek Jeter Pants 8.00 20.00
DL Derrek Lee 3.00 8.00
DO David Ortiz 3.00 8.00
DW David Wright 4.00 10.00
EC Eric Chavez 2.00 5.00
EG Eric Gagne 2.00 5.00
ER Edgar Renteria 2.00 5.00
GM Greg Maddux 4.00 10.00
GR Khalil Greene 3.00 8.00
GS Gary Sheffield 2.00 5.00
HB Hank Blalock 2.00 5.00
HU Torii Hunter 2.00 5.00
JD J.D. Drew 2.00 5.00
JM Joe Mauer 4.00 10.00
JP Jake Peavy 2.00 5.00
JR Jose Reyes 2.00 5.00
KG Ken Griffey Jr. 6.00 15.00
KW Kerry Wood 2.00 5.00
MC Miguel Cabrera 3.00 8.00
MM Mark Mulder 2.00 5.00
MO Melvin Mora 2.00 5.00
MP Mark Prior 3.00 8.00
MT Mark Teixeira 3.00 8.00
MY Michael Young 2.00 5.00
OP Oliver Perez 2.00 5.00
PI Mike Piazza 4.00 10.00
RC Roger Clemens Pants 4.00 10.00
RJ Randy Johnson 4.00 10.00
RO Roy Oswalt 2.00 5.00
RP Rafael Palmeiro 3.00 8.00
SA Johan Santana 4.00 10.00
SC Sean Casey 2.00 5.00
SM John Smoltz 3.00 8.00
SR Scott Rolen 3.00 8.00
TE Miguel Tejada 2.00 5.00
TH Tim Hudson 2.00 5.00
VG Vladimir Guerrero 4.00 10.00
VM Victor Martinez 2.00 5.00

2005 SPx SPxtreme Stats Signature

ISSUED IN 05 SP COLLECTION PACKS
OVERALL PREMIUM AU-GU ODDS 1:20
STATED PRINT RUN 5 SERIAL #'d SETS
NO PRICING DUE TO SCARCITY
AB Adrian Beltre
AD Adam Dunn
AJ Andruw Jones
AP Albert Pujols
AR Aramis Ramirez
BC Bobby Crosby
BS Ben Sheets
CB Craig Biggio
CC Carl Crawford
CP Corey Patterson
DJ Derek Jeter
DL Derrek Lee
DW David Wright
EC Eric Chavez
EG Eric Gagne
GM Greg Maddux
GR Khalil Greene
GS Gary Sheffield
HB Hank Blalock
HU Torii Hunter
JM Joe Mauer
JP Jake Peavy
JR Jose Reyes
KW Kerry Wood
MC Miguel Cabrera
MM Mark Mulder
MO Melvin Mora
MP Mark Prior
MT Mark Teixeira
MY Michael Young
OP Oliver Perez
PI Mike Piazza
RC Roger Clemens
RJ Randy Johnson
RO Roy Oswalt
RP Rafael Palmeiro
SM John Smoltz
TE Miguel Tejada
TH Tim Hudson
VG Vladimir Guerrero

2005 SPx Superscripts

ISSUED IN 05 SP COLLECTION PACKS
OVERALL AUTO ODDS 1:10
STATED PRINT RUN 15 SERIAL #'d SETS
NO PRICING DUE TO SCARCITY
AB Angel Berroa
AG Adrian Gonzalez
AH Aaron Harang
AM Aaron Miles
AR Aaron Rowand
BA Clint Barmes
BC Brandon Claussen
BH Brad Halsey
BI Bill Hall
BL Joe Blanton
BO Jeremy Bonderman
BR Bronson Arroyo
BU B.J. Upton
CA Jorge Cantu
CB Chris Burke
CC Chad Cordero
CD Chris Duffy
CF Chone Figgins
CG Carlos Guillen
CI Cesar Izturis
CK Casey Kotchman
CL Cliff Lee
CO Coco Crisp
CR Jesse Crain
CS Chris Shelton
CT Chad Tracy
CU Michael Cuddyer
CY Chris Young
DB Dave Bush
DC Daniel Cabrera
DD David DeJesus
DE Dewon Brazelton
DH Danny Haren
DJ Derek Jeter
DM Dallas McPherson
DS Justin Duchscherer
DU Jason DuBois
EJ Edwin Jackson
ES Ervin Santana
GA Garrett Atkins
GC Gustavo Chacin
GF Gavin Floyd
GM Guillermo Mota
GO Jonny Gomes
GS Grady Sizemore
HA Brad Hawpe
HO D.J. Houlton
HS Huston Street
IN Brandon Inge
JB Jason Bartlett
JC Joe Crede
JD J.D. Closser
JE Jeff Baker
JF Jeff Francis
JG Joey Gathright
JH J.J. Hardy
JL Jason Lane
JM Justin Morneau
JO Dan Johnson
JP Jhonny Peralta
JR Jeremy Reed
JU Juan Rivera
JV Jose Valverde
JW Jayson Werth
KH Koyie Hill
KY Kevin Youkilis
LN Laynce Nix
LO Nook Logan
LS Luke Scott
MA Andy Marte
MH Matt Holliday
MT Mark Teahen
NI Lance Niekro
NJ Nick Johnson
NL Noah Lowry
NS Nick Swisher
PI Joel Pineiro
RE Jason Repko
RH Rich Harden
RI Alex Rios
RJ Reed Johnson
RQ Robb Quinlan
RY Ryan Howard
SK Scott Kazmir
SS Steve Schmoll
TH Charles Thomas
TI Tadahito Iguchi
UT Chase Utley
WI Jerome Williams
WM Wily Mo Pena
XN Xavier Nady
YA Keiichi Yabu
YB Yhency Brazoban
YM Yadier Molina
ZG Zack Greinke

2005 SPx Superscripts Triple

ISSUED IN 05 SP COLLECTION PACKS
OVERALL PREMIUM AU-GU ODDS 1:20
STATED PRINT RUN 5 SERIAL #'d SETS
NO PRICING DUE TO SCARCITY
ACB Garrett Atkins
J.D. Closser
Jeff Baker
BDT Angel Berroa
David DeJesus
Mark Teahen
BMC Jason Bartlett
Justin Morneau
Michael Cuddyer
CSC Chad Cordero
Huston Street
Jesse Crain
CSP Coco Crisp
Grady Sizemore
Jhonny Peralta
FKG Gavin Floyd
Scott Kazmir
Zack Greinke
GYN Adrian Gonzalez
Chris Young
Laynce Nix
HCP Aaron Harang
Brandon Claussen
Wily Mo Pena
HHB Rich Harden
Danny Haren
Joe Blanton
HML Brad Halsey
Brett Myers
Noah Lowry
HTH Brad Halsey
Chad Tracy
Koyie Hill
IWD Cesar Izturis
Jayson Werth
J.D. Drew
KMQ Casey Kotchman
Dallas McPherson
Robb Quinlan
LBC Brandon League
Dave Bush
Gustavo Chacin
LST Jason Lane
Luke Scott
Willy Taveras
MIM Andy Marte
Brandon Inge
Melvin Mora
MWT Dallas McPherson
David Wright
Mark Teahen
NGB Xavier Nady
Khalil Greene
Sean Burroughs
RCI Aaron Rowand
Joe Crede
Tadahito Iguchi
RCJ Alex Rios
Gustavo Chacin
Reed Johnson
RRR Aaron Rowand
Jeremy Reed
Alex Rios
UGC B.J. Upton
Joey Gathright
Jorge Cantu

2005 SPx Winning Materials Dual Jersey

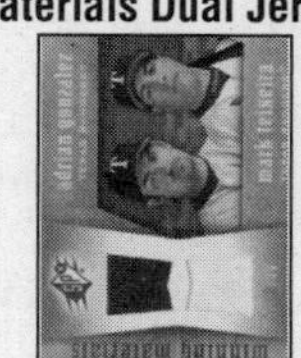

ISSUED IN 05 SP COLLECTION PACKS
OVERALL PREMIUM AU-GU ODDS 1:20
STATED PRINT RUN 20 SERIAL #'d SETS
NO PRICING DUE TO SCARCITY
AB Garrett Atkins
Jeff Baker
AC Bronson Arroyo
Matt Clement
AG Bobby Abreu
Ken Griffey Jr.
AJ A.J. Burnett
Jeremy Bonderman
AM Albert Pujols
Miguel Cabrera

AY Jason Bay
Matt Holliday
BA A.J. Burnett
Bronson Arroyo
BB Chris Burke
Craig Biggio
BC Jason Bartlett
Michael Cuddyer
BH Jason Bartlett
J.J. Hardy
BJ Ben Sheets
Jake Peavy
BM John Buck
Yadier Molina
BS A.J. Burnett
Ben Sheets
BY Hank Blalock
Michael Young
CB Dave Bush
Gustavo Chacin
CC Carl Crawford
Coco Crisp
CD David DeJesus
Chris Duffy
CG Carl Crawford
Joey Gathright
CH Brandon Claussen
Aaron Harang
CJ Clint Barmes
J.D. Closser
CP Coco Crisp
Corey Patterson
CR Craig Biggio
Ryne Sandberg
CS Chad Cordero
Huston Street
DC Adam Dunn
Sean Casey
DD Dave Bush
Dewon Brazelton
DG Adam Dunn
Ken Griffey Jr.
DJ Derek Jeter Pants
Jason Bartlett
DR Alex Rios
Chris Duffy
DT David DeJesus
Mark Teahen
EM Johnny Estrada
Yadier Molina
FC Chone Figgins
Coco Crisp
FK Jeff Francis
Scott Kazmir
FQ Chone Figgins
Robb Quinlan
GC Ken Griffey Jr.
Sean Casey
GE Gustavo Chacin
Ervin Santana
GH Brad Halsey
Zack Greinke
GK Adrian Gonzalez
Casey Kotchman
GP Ken Griffey Jr.
Wily Mo Pena
GT Adrian Gonzalez
Mark Teixeira
HB Jeremy Bonderman
Rich Harden
HG Danny Haren
Zack Greinke
HH Danny Haren
Rich Harden
HJ Huston Street
Joe Blanton
HK Brad Halsey
Scott Kazmir
HP Ryan Howard
Wily Mo Pena
HR J.J. Hardy
Jose Reyes
HT Brad Halsey
Chad Tracy
HY J.J. Hardy
Robin Yount
JB Jeremy Bonderman
Joe Blanton
JC Chad Cordero
Nick Johnson
JG Derek Jeter Pants
Ken Griffey Jr.
JH Nick Johnson
Travis Hafner
JJ John Buck
J.D. Closser
JK Dan Johnson
Casey Kotchman
JM Andruw Jones
Dale Murphy
JR Reggie Jackson
Jim Rice
JS Dan Johnson
Nick Swisher
JT Bo Jackson
Mark Teahen
JY Derek Jeter Pants
Robin Yount
KG Casey Kotchman
Mark Grace
KL Noah Lowry
Scott Kazmir
KM Casey Kotchman
Justin Morneau
LS Jason Lane
Luke Scott
LW Cliff Lee
Jake Westbrook
MC Justin Morneau
Michael Cuddyer
MJ Reggie Jackson
Don Mattingly
MM Joe Mauer
Victor Martinez
MR Mike Piazza
Roger Clemens Pants
MS Joe Mauer
Johan Santana
MT Dallas McPherson
Mark Teahen
MW Dallas McPherson
David Wright
PC Jhonny Peralta
Jorge Cantu
PG Albert Pujols
Vladimir Guerrero
PH Jake Peavy
Rich Harden
PS Ervin Santana
Oliver Perez
RC Aaron Rowand
Joe Crede
RD Aaron Rowand
Jason DuBois
RJ Nolan Ryan Pants
Randy Johnson Pants
RL Aramis Ramirez
Derrek Lee
RM Jimmy Rollins
Brett Myers
RR Aaron Rowand
Jeremy Reed
RS Alex Rios
Nick Swisher
RT Cal Ripken Pants
Miguel Tejada
RW Jose Reyes
Rickie Weeks
SC Gary Sheffield
Miguel Cabrera
SH John Smoltz
Tim Hudson
SP Johan Santana
Oliver Perez
SR Mike Schmidt
Cal Ripken Pants
SS Grady Sizemore
Nick Swisher
ST Luke Scott
Willy Taveras
TC Mark Teixeira
Will Clark
TD David DeJesus
Willy Taveras
TW David Wright
Mark Teahen
UB Chase Utley
Craig Biggio
UC B.J. Upton
Carl Crawford
UG Chase Utley
Marcus Giles
WL Jerome Williams
Noah Lowry
WP Kerry Wood
Mark Prior
WR David Wright
Jose Reyes
ZC Carlos Zambrano
Gustavo Chacin

2005 SPx Winning Materials Dual Jersey Signature

ISSUED IN 05 SP COLLECTION PACKS
OVERALL PREMIUM AU-GU ODDS 1:20
STATED PRINT RUN 5 SERIAL #'d SETS
NO PRICING DUE TO SCARCITY
AB Garrett Atkins
Jeff Baker
AC Bronson Arroyo
Matt Clement
AM Albert Pujols
Miguel Cabrera
AY Jason Bay
Matt Holliday
BB Chris Burke
Craig Biggio
BC Jason Bartlett
Michael Cuddyer
BH Jason Bartlett
J.J. Hardy
BJ Ben Sheets
Jake Peavy
BY Hank Blalock
Michael Young
CB Dave Bush
Gustavo Chacin
CC Carl Crawford
Coco Crisp
CD David DeJesus
Chris Duffy
CG Carl Crawford
Joey Gathright
CH Brandon Claussen
Aaron Harang
CJ Clint Barmes
J.D. Closser
CP Coco Crisp
Corey Patterson
CR Craig Biggio
Ryne Sandberg
CS Chad Cordero
Huston Street
DD Dave Bush
Dewon Brazelton
DJ Derek Jeter Pants
Jason Bartlett
DT David DeJesus
Mark Teahen
FC Chone Figgins
Coco Crisp
FK Jeff Francis
Scott Kazmir
FQ Chone Figgins
Robb Quinlan
GE Gustavo Chacin
Ervin Santana
GH Brad Halsey
Zack Greinke
GK Adrian Gonzalez
Casey Kotchman
GT Adrian Gonzalez
Mark Teixeira
HB Jeremy Bonderman
Rich Harden
HG Danny Haren
Zack Greinke
HH Danny Haren
Rich Harden
HJ Huston Street
Joe Blanton
HK Brad Halsey
Scott Kazmir
HP Ryan Howard
Wily Mo Pena
HR J.J. Hardy
Jose Reyes
HT Brad Halsey
Chad Tracy
JB Jeremy Bonderman
Joe Blanton
JC Chad Cordero
Nick Johnson
JH Nick Johnson
Travis Hafner
JJ John Buck
J.D. Closser
JK Dan Johnson
Casey Kotchman
JM Andruw Jones
Dale Murphy
JR Reggie Jackson
Jim Rice
JT Bo Jackson
Mark Teahen
KG Casey Kotchman
Mark Grace
KL Noah Lowry
Scott Kazmir
KM Casey Kotchman
Justin Morneau
LS Jason Lane
Luke Scott
LW Cliff Lee
Jake Westbrook
MC Justin Morneau
Michael Cuddyer
MJ Reggie Jackson
Don Mattingly
MR Mike Piazza
Roger Clemens Pants
MT Dallas McPherson
Mark Teahen
MW Dallas McPherson
David Wright
PC Jhonny Peralta
Jorge Cantu
PG Albert Pujols
Vladimir Guerrero
PH Jake Peavy
Rich Harden
PS Ervin Santana
Oliver Perez
RC Aaron Rowand
Joe Crede
RD Aaron Rowand
Jason DuBois
RJ Nolan Ryan Pants
Randy Johnson Pants
RL Aramis Ramirez
Derrek Lee
RR Aaron Rowand
Jeremy Reed
SC Gary Sheffield
Miguel Cabrera
SH John Smoltz
Tim Hudson
TC Mark Teixeira
Will Clark
TW David Wright
Mark Teahen
UB Chase Utley
Craig Biggio
UC B.J. Upton
Carl Crawford
WL Jerome Williams
Noah Lowry
WP Kerry Wood
Mark Prior
WR David Wright
Jose Reyes

2006 SPx

This 160-card set was released in September, 2006. The set was issued in four-card packs, which came 18 packs per box and 14 boxes per case. The first 100 cards feature veteran players which were sequenced in alphabetical order by team while the final 60 cards feature signed cards of 2006 rookies. Those cards were issued to stated print runs beteen 190 and 999 serial numbered copies and were inserted into packs at a stated rate of one in nine. A few players did not sign their cards in time for pack out and those autographs could be redeemed until September 7, 2008.

COMP.BASIC SET (100) 10.00 25.00
COMMON CARD (1-100) .15 .40
COMMON AU p/r 659-999 4.00 10.00
COMMON AU p/r 350-500 4.00 10.00
OVERALL 101-161 AU ODDS 1:9
101-161 AU EXCH DEADLINE 09/07/08
101-161 AU PRINT RUN B/WN 190-999 PER
101-161 PRINTING PLATE ODDS 1:224
101-161 PLATES PRINT RUN 1 SET PER CLR
101-161 PLATES FEATURE AUTOS
BLACK-CYAN-MAGENTA-YELLOW ISSUED
NO PLATE PRICING DUE TO SCARCITY
EXQUISITE EXCH ODDS 1:36
EXQUISITE EXCH DEADLINE 07/27/07
1 Luis Gonzalez .15 .40
2 Chad Tracy .15 .40
3 Brandon Webb .15 .40
4 Andruw Jones .25 .60
5 Chipper Jones .40 1.00
6 John Smoltz .25 .60
7 Tim Hudson .15 .40
8 Miguel Tejada .15 .40
9 Brian Roberts .15 .40
10 Ramon Hernandez .15 .40
11 Curt Schilling .25 .60
12 David Ortiz .40 1.00
13 Manny Ramirez .25 .60
14 Jason Varitek .40 1.00
15 Josh Beckett .15 .40
16 Greg Maddux .60 1.50
17 Derrek Lee .15 .40
18 Mark Prior .25 .60
19 Aramis Ramirez .15 .40
20 Jim Thome .25 .60
21 Paul Konerko .15 .40
22 Scott Podsednik .15 .40
23 Jose Contreras .15 .40
24 Ken Griffey Jr. .60 1.50
25 Adam Dunn .15 .40
26 Felipe Lopez .15 .40
27 Travis Hafner .15 .40
28 Victor Martinez .15 .40
29 Grady Sizemore .25 .60
30 Jhonny Peralta .15 .40
31 Todd Helton .25 .60
32 Garrett Atkins .15 .40
33 Clint Barmes .15 .40
34 Ivan Rodriguez .25 .60
35 Chris Shelton .15 .40
36 Jeremy Bonderman .15 .40
37 Miguel Cabrera .25 .60
38 Dontrelle Willis .15 .40
39 Lance Berkman .15 .40
40 Morgan Ensberg .15 .40
41 Roy Oswalt .15 .40
42 Reggie Sanders .15 .40
43 Mike Sweeney .15 .40
44 Vladimir Guerrero .40 1.00
45 Bartolo Colon .15 .40
46 Chone Figgins .15 .40
47 Nomar Garciaparra .40 1.00
48 Jeff Kent .15 .40
49 J.D. Drew .15 .40
50 Carlos Lee .15 .40
51 Ben Sheets .15 .40
52 Rickie Weeks .15 .40
53 Johan Santana .25 .60
54 Torii Hunter .15 .40
55 Joe Mauer .25 .60
56 Pedro Martinez .25 .60
57 David Wright .60 1.50
58 Carlos Beltran .15 .40
59 Carlos Delgado .15 .40
60 Jose Reyes .40 1.00
61 Derek Jeter 1.00 2.50
62 Alex Rodriguez .60 1.50
63 Randy Johnson .40 1.00
64 Hideki Matsui .40 1.00
65 Gary Sheffield .15 .40
66 Rich Harden .15 .40
67 Eric Chavez .15 .40
68 Huston Street .15 .40
69 Bobby Crosby .15 .40
70 Bobby Abreu .15 .40
71 Ryan Howard .60 1.50
72 Chase Utley .40 1.00
73 Pat Burrell .15 .40
74 Jason Bay .15 .40
75 Sean Casey .15 .40
76 Mike Piazza .40 1.00
77 Jake Peavy .15 .40
78 Brian Giles .15 .40
79 Milton Bradley .15 .40
80 Omar Vizquel .25 .60
81 Jason Schmidt .15 .40
82 Ichiro Suzuki .60 1.50
83 Felix Hernandez .25 .60
84 Richie Sexson .15 .40
85 Albert Pujols .75 2.00
86 Chris Carpenter .15 .40
87 Scott Rolen .25 .60
88 Jim Edmonds .25 .60
89 Carl Crawford .15 .40
90 Jonny Gomes .15 .40
91 Scott Kazmir .25 .60
92 Mark Teixeira .25 .60
93 Michael Young .15 .40
94 Phil Nevin .15 .40
95 Vernon Wells .15 .40
96 Roy Halladay .15 .40
97 Troy Glaus .15 .40
98 Alfonso Soriano .15 .40
99 Nick Johnson .15 .40
100 Jose Vidro .15 .40
101 Conor Jackson AU/999 (RC) 6.00 15.00
102 Jered Weaver AU/299 (RC) EXCH 15.00 40.00
103 Macay McBride AU/999 (RC) 4.00 10.00
104 Aaron Rakers AU/499 (RC) 4.00 10.00
105 Jonathan Papelbon AU/499 (RC) 12.50 30.00
106 Jason Bergmann AU/999 RC 4.00 10.00
107 Stephen Drew AU/350 (RC) 12.50 30.00
108 Chris Denorfia AU/999 (RC) 4.00 10.00
109 Kelly Shoppach AU/999 (RC) 4.00 10.00
110 Ryan Shealy AU/999 (RC) 4.00 10.00
111 Josh Wilson AU/999 (RC) 4.00 10.00
112 Brian Anderson AU/999 (RC) 4.00 10.00
113 Justin Verlander AU/749 (RC) 20.00 50.00
114 Jeremy Hermida AU/999 (RC) 6.00 15.00
115 Mike Jacobs AU/999 (RC) 6.00 15.00
116 Josh Johnson AU/999 (RC) 6.00 15.00
117 Hanley Ramirez AU/659 (RC) 20.00 50.00
118 Chris Resop AU/999 (RC) 4.00 10.00
119 Josh Willingham AU/999 (RC) 4.00 10.00
120 Cole Hamels AU/499 (RC) 20.00 50.00
121 Matt Cain AU/999 (RC) 8.00 20.00
122 Steve Stemle AU/999 RC 4.00 10.00
123 Tim Hamulack AU/999 (RC) 4.00 10.00
124 Choo Freeman AU/999 (RC) 4.00 10.00
125 Hong-Chih Kuo AU/999 (RC) 20.00 50.00
126 Cody Ross AU/999 (RC) 4.00 10.00
127 Jose Capellan AU/999 (RC) 4.00 10.00
128 Prince Fielder AU/190 (RC) 60.00 120.00
129 David Gassner AU/999 (RC) 4.00 10.00
130 Jason Kubel AU/999 (RC) 4.00 10.00
131 Francisco Liriano AU/299 (RC) 20.00 50.00
132 Anderson Hernandez AU/999 (RC) 6.00 15.00
133 Joey Devine AU/499 RC 4.00 10.00
134 Chris Booker AU/999 (RC) 4.00 10.00
135 Matt Capps AU/999 (RC) 4.00 10.00
136 Paul Maholm AU/999 (RC) 4.00 10.00
137 Nate McLouth AU/999 (RC) 8.00 20.00
138 John Van Benschoten AU/999 (RC) 4.00 10.00
139 Jeff Harris AU/999 RC 4.00 10.00
140 Ben Johnson AU/999 (RC) 4.00 10.00
141 Wil Nieves AU/999 (RC) 4.00 10.00
142 Guillermo Quiroz AU/999 (RC) 4.00 10.00
143 Josh Rupe AU/500 (RC) 4.00 10.00
144 Skip Schumaker AU/999 (RC) 4.00 10.00
145 Jack Taschner AU/999 (RC) 4.00 10.00
146 Adam Wainwright AU/999 (RC) 10.00 25.00
147 Alay Soler AU/499 RC 10.00 25.00
148 Kendry Morales AU/999 (RC) 6.00 15.00
149 Ian Kinsler AU/999 (RC) 8.00 20.00
150 Jason Hammel AU/999 (RC) 4.00 10.00
151 Chad Billingsley AU/499 (RC) 10.00 25.00
152 Boof Bonser AU/999 (RC) 6.00 15.00
153 Peter Moylan AU/999 RC 4.00 10.00
154 Chris Britton AU/999 RC 4.00 10.00
155 Takashi Saito AU/999 RC 12.50 30.00
156 Scott Dunn AU/999 (RC) 4.00 10.00
157 Joel Zumaya AU/299 (RC) EXCH 12.50 30.00
158 Dan Uggla AU/999 (RC) 10.00 25.00
159 Taylor Buchholz AU/999 (RC) 4.00 10.00
160 Melky Cabrera AU/499 (RC) EXCH 15.00 40.00
NNO Exquisite Redemption

2006 SPx Spectrum

*SPECTRUM 1-100: 2X TO 5X BASIC
STATED ODDS 1:3

2006 SPx Rookie Signature Gold

RANDOM INSERTS IN PACKS
STATED PRINT RUN 5 SERIAL #'d SETS
NO PRICING DUE TO SCARCITY
EXCH DEADLINE 09/07/08

2006 SPx Rookie Signature Platinum

RANDOM INSERTS IN PACKS
STATED PRINT RUN 1 SERIAL #'d SET
NO PRICING DUE TO SCARCITY
EXCH DEADLINE 09/07/08

2006 SPx Next In Line

STATED ODDS 1:9
AW Adam Wainwright 1.00 2.50
BA Brian Anderson 1.00 2.50
BB Brian Bannister 1.00 2.50
BJ Ben Johnson 1.00 2.50
CJ Conor Jackson 1.50 4.00
DU Dan Uggla 2.50 6.00
FH Felix Hernandez 1.50 4.00
FL Francisco Liriano 4.00 10.00
HR Hanley Ramirez 2.00 5.00
HS Huston Street 1.00 2.50
IK Ian Kinsler 1.50 4.00
JB Josh Barfield 1.00 2.50
JE Jered Weaver 3.00 8.00
JH Jeremy Hermida 1.50 4.00
JL James Loney 1.50 4.00
JP Jonathan Papelbon 4.00 10.00
JS Jeremy Sowers 1.00 2.50
JV Justin Verlander 3.00 8.00
JW Josh Willingham 1.00 2.50
LE Jon Lester 3.00 8.00
MC Matt Cain 1.50 4.00
MJ Mike Jacobs 1.00 2.50
AS Alay Soler 1.00 2.50
PF Prince Fielder 3.00 8.00
RC Ryan Church 1.00 2.50
RH Ryan Howard 3.00 8.00
RZ Ryan Zimmerman 4.00 10.00
SO Scott Olsen 1.00 2.50
TB Taylor Buchholz 1.00 2.50
TI Travis Ishikawa 1.00 2.50

2006 SPx SPxtra Info

STATED ODDS 1:9
AJ Andruw Jones 1.50 4.00
AP Albert Pujols 4.00 10.00
BA Bobby Abreu 1.00 2.50
BG Brian Giles 1.00 2.50
CC Carl Crawford 1.00 2.50
CL Carlos Lee 1.00 2.50
DJ Derek Jeter 5.00 12.00
DL Derrek Lee 1.00 2.50
DO David Ortiz 2.50 6.00
DW Dontrelle Willis 1.00 2.50
EC Eric Chavez 1.00 2.50
HE Todd Helton 1.50 4.00
IR Ivan Rodriguez 1.50 4.00
IS Ichiro Suzuki 3.00 8.00
JB Jason Bay 1.00 2.50
JK Jeff Kent 1.00 2.50
JS Johan Santana 1.50 4.00
JT Jim Thome 1.50 4.00
KG Ken Griffey Jr. 3.00 8.00
LG Luis Gonzalez 1.00 2.50
MT Miguel Tejada 1.00 2.50
NJ Nick Johnson 1.00 2.50
PM Pedro Martinez 1.50 4.00
RO Roy Oswalt 1.00 2.50
RS Reggie Sanders 1.00 2.50
SC Jason Schmidt 1.00 2.50
TE Mark Teixeira 1.50 4.00
TH Travis Hafner 1.00 2.50
VG Vladimir Guerrero 2.50 6.00
VW Vernon Wells 1.00 2.50

2006 SPx SPxciting Signature

RANDOM INSERTS IN PACKS
PRINT RUNS B/WN 10-30 COPIES PER
NO PRICING DUE TO SCARCITY
AB Adrian Beltre/30
AJ Andruw Jones/10
AP Albert Pujols/10
AR Aaron Rakers/30
AS Alay Soler/30
AW Adam Wainwright/30
BA Brian Anderson/30
BG Brian Giles/30
BI Craig Biggio/30
BJ Ben Johnson/30
BR Chris Britton/30
BY Jason Bay/30
CA Matt Capps/30
CB Chris Booker/30
CF Choo Freeman/30
CH Chad Billingsley/30
CJ Conor Jackson/30
CL Cliff Lee/30
CP Corey Patterson/30
CR Chris Resop/30
CW Carl Crawford/30
DG Dave Gassner/30
DJ Derek Jeter/10
DL Derrek Lee/30
DO David Ortiz/10
DU Dan Uggla/30
EC Eric Chavez/30
EG Eric Gagne/30
GR Khalil Greene/30
HA Jason Hammel/30
HB Hank Blalock/30
HE Jeremy Hermida/30
HK Hong-Chih Kuo/30
HR Hanley Ramirez/30
HT Travis Hafner/30
IK Ian Kinsler/30
JA Jeremy Accardo/30
JH Jeff Harris/30
JJ Josh Johnson/30
JP Jonathan Papelbon/30
JV John Van Benschoten/30
JW Josh Willingham/30
KG Ken Griffey Jr./30
KS Kelly Shoppach/30
KU Jason Kubel/30
MC Matt Cain/30
MI Miguel Cabrera/30
MM Macay McBride/30
MU Mark Mulder/30
NM Nate McLouth/30
OP Oliver Perez/30
PE Jake Peavy/30
PM Paul Maholm/30
RC Roger Clemens/30
RO Cody Ross/30

RS Ryan Shealy/30
SD Scott Dunn/30
SS Skip Schumaker/30
TB Taylor Buchholz/30
TH Tim Hamulack/30
TR Trevor Hoffman/30
TS Takashi Saito/30
VE Justin Verlander/30
VM Victor Martinez/30
WI Josh Wilson/30
WN Wil Nieves/30

2006 SPx SPxtreme Team

STATED ODDS 1:9
AD Adam Dunn 1.00 2.50
AJ Andruw Jones 1.50 4.00
AP Albert Pujols 4.00 10.00
AR Alex Rodriguez 3.00 8.00
AS Alfonso Soriano 1.00 2.50
BA Bobby Abreu 1.00 2.50
CC Chris Carpenter 1.00 2.50
CD Carlos Delgado 1.00 2.50
CL Carlos Lee 1.00 2.50
CR Carl Crawford 1.00 2.50
DJ Derek Jeter 5.00 12.00
DL Derrek Lee 1.00 2.50
DO David Ortiz 2.50 6.00
DW David Wright 3.00 8.00
GS Grady Sizemore 1.50 4.00
HA Travis Hafner 1.00 2.50
HM Hideki Matsui 2.50 6.00
HO Ryan Howard 3.00 8.00
IS Ichiro Suzuki 3.00 8.00
JB Jason Bay 1.00 2.50
JK Jeff Kent 1.00 2.50
JP Jake Peavy 1.00 2.50
JR Jose Reyes 1.00 2.50
JS Johan Santana 1.50 4.00
JT Jim Thome 1.50 4.00
KG Ken Griffey Jr. 3.00 8.00
LB Lance Berkman 1.00 2.50
MC Miguel Cabrera 1.50 4.00
MR Manny Ramirez 1.50 4.00
MT Mark Teixeira 1.50 4.00
MY Michael Young 1.00 2.50
PF Prince Fielder 3.00 8.00
PK Paul Konerko 1.00 2.50
PM Pedro Martinez 1.50 4.00
RH Rich Harden 1.00 2.50
TE Miguel Tejada 1.00 2.50
TH Todd Helton 1.50 4.00
VG Vladimir Guerrero 2.50 6.00
VM Victor Martinez 1.00 2.50
VW Vernon Wells 1.00 2.50

2006 SPx WBC All-World Team

STATED ODDS 1:9
1 Brett Willemburg 1.00 2.50
2 Bradley Harman 1.50 4.00
3 Adam Stern 1.50 4.00
4 Jason Bay 1.00 2.50
5 Adam Loewen 1.00 2.50
6 Wei Wang 1.50 4.00
7 Yi Feng 1.50 4.00
8 Yung Chi Chen 4.00 10.00
9 Chin-Lung Hu 2.50 6.00
10 Wei-Lun Pan 2.50 6.00
11 Yoandy Garlobo 1.50 4.00
12 Frederich Cepeda 1.00 2.50
13 Osmany Urrutia 1.00 2.50
14 Yulieski Gourriel 1.00 2.50
15 Yadel Marti 1.00 2.50
16 Pedro Luis Lazo 1.00 2.50
17 Adrian Beltre 1.00 2.50
18 David Ortiz 2.50 6.00
19 Albert Pujols 4.00 10.00
20 Bartolo Colon 1.00 2.50
21 Miguel Tejada 1.00 2.50
22 Mike Piazza 2.50 6.00
23 Jason Grilli 1.00 2.50
24 Nobuhiko Matsunaka 1.50 4.00
25 Tomoya Satozaki 1.50 4.00
26 Ichiro Suzuki 3.00 8.00
27 Hitoshi Tamura 1.50 4.00
28 Daisuke Matsuzaka 10.00 25.00
29 Koji Uehara 2.50 6.00
30 Jong Beom Lee 1.50 4.00
31 Seung Yeop Lee 1.50 4.00
32 Jae Seo 1.00 2.50
33 Min Han Son 1.50 4.00
34 Chan Ho Park 1.00 2.50
35 Jorge Cantu 1.00 2.50
36 Miguel Ojeda 1.00 2.50
37 Andruw Jones 1.50 4.00
38 Shairon Martis 1.00 2.50
39 Carlos Lee 1.00 2.50
40 Carlos Beltran 1.00 2.50
41 Javy Lopez 1.00 2.50
42 Javier Vazquez 1.00 2.50
43 Ken Griffey Jr. 3.00 8.00
44 Derek Jeter 5.00 12.00
45 Alex Rodriguez 3.00 8.00
46 Derrek Lee 1.00 2.50
47 Roger Clemens 4.00 10.00
48 Miguel Cabrera 1.50 4.00
49 Victor Martinez 1.00 2.50
50 Johan Santana 1.50 4.00

2006 SPx Winning Big Materials

STATED ODDS 1:252
PRINT RUNS B/WN 5-40 COPIES PER
NO PRICING ON QTY 26 OR LESS
PRICING IS FOR 2-3 CLR PATCHES
AB Adrian Beltre/40 50.00 100.00
AI Akinori Iwamura/30 200.00 300.00
AJ Andruw Jones/40 50.00 100.00
AP Ariel Pestano/30 50.00 100.00
AR Alex Rios/55 30.00 60.00
AS Alfonso Soriano/40 50.00 100.00
BA Bobby Abreu/40 50.00 100.00
BW Bernie Williams/40 75.00 120.00
CB Carlos Beltran/40 50.00 100.00
CD Carlos Delgado/40 30.00 60.00
CH Chin-Lung Hu/26
CL Carlos Lee/40 30.00 60.00
CZ Carlos Zambrano/40 75.00 150.00
DL Derrek Lee/40 50.00 100.00
DO David Ortiz/30 75.00 150.00
EB Erik Bedard/40 30.00 60.00
EP Eduardo Paret/30 30.00 60.00
FC Frederich Cepeda/30 50.00 100.00
GY Guogan Yang/52 30.00 60.00
HC Hee Seop Choi/32 50.00 100.00
HT Hitoshi Tamura/30 200.00 300.00
IR Ivan Rodriguez/40 30.00 60.00
IS Ichiro Suzuki/5
JB Jason Bay/40 50.00 100.00
JD Johnny Damon/40 50.00 100.00
JF Jeff Francis/40 30.00 60.00
JL Jong Beom Lee/20
JM Justin Morneau/25
JP Jin Man Park/22
JS Johan Santana/40 50.00 100.00
JV Jason Varitek/40 50.00 100.00
KG Ken Griffey Jr./5
KU Koji Uehara/30 250.00 400.00
LO Javy Lopez/40 30.00 60.00
MA Moises Alou/53 30.00 60.00
MC Miguel Cabrera/40 50.00 100.00
ME Michel Enriquez/30 50.00 100.00
MF Maikel Folch/30 50.00 100.00
MK Munenori Kawasaki/30 250.00 400.00
MO Michihiro Ogasawara/30 300.00 400.00
MP Mike Piazza/40 60.00 150.00
MS Min Han Son/24
MT Miguel Tejada/40 50.00 100.00
NM Nobuhiko Matsunaka/30 225.00 350.00
NS Naoyuki Shimizu/30 150.00 300.00
OU Osmany Urrutia/30 30.00 60.00
PE Wily Mo Pena/60 30.00 60.00
PL Pedro Luis Lazo/30 50.00 100.00
PU Albert Pujols/20
RO Alex Rodriguez/5
SW Shunsuke Watanabe/30 200.00 300.00
TN Tsuyoshi Nishioka/30 250.00 400.00
TW Tsuyoshi Wada/30 150.00 300.00
VM Victor Martinez/40 50.00 100.00
VO Vicyohandry Odelin/30 50.00 100.00
WL Wei-Chu Lin/45 200.00 400.00
WP Wei-Lun Pan/38 200.00 300.00
YG Yulieski Gourriel/30 50.00 100.00
YM Yunieski Maya/30 50.00 100.00

2006 SPx Winning Materials

STATED ODDS 1:18
AI Akinori Iwamura 8.00 20.00
AJ Andruw Jones 4.00 10.00
AP Ariel Pestano 3.00 8.00
AR Alex Rodriguez 6.00 15.00
AS Alfonso Soriano 3.00 8.00
BA Bobby Abreu 3.00 8.00
CB Carlos Beltran 3.00 8.00
CD Carlos Delgado 3.00 8.00
DL Derrek Lee 3.00 8.00
DO David Ortiz 4.00 10.00
EP Eduardo Paret 3.00 8.00
FC Frederich Cepeda 3.00 8.00
HC Hee Seop Choi 3.00 8.00
HT Hitoshi Tamura 8.00 20.00
IS Ichiro Suzuki 40.00 80.00
JB Jason Bay 3.00 8.00
JD Johnny Damon 3.00 8.00
JL Jong Beom Lee 3.00 8.00
JS Johan Santana 4.00 10.00
KG Ken Griffey Jr. 6.00 15.00
KU Koji Uehara 8.00 20.00
MC Miguel Cabrera 4.00 10.00
ME Michel Enriquez 3.00 8.00
MF Maikel Folch 3.00 8.00
MK Munenori Kawasaki 8.00 20.00
MO Michihiro Ogasawara 8.00 20.00
MP Mike Piazza 4.00 10.00
MS Min Han Son 4.00 10.00
MT Miguel Tejada 3.00 8.00
NM Nobuhiko Matsunaka 6.00 15.00
NS Naoyuki Shimizu 6.00 15.00
OU Osmany Urrutia 3.00 8.00
PL Pedro Luis Lazo 4.00 10.00
PU Albert Pujols 8.00 20.00
RC Roger Clemens 6.00 15.00
SW Shunsuke Watanabe 8.00 20.00
TN Tsuyoshi Nishioka 8.00 20.00
TW Tsuyoshi Wada 6.00 15.00
VM Victor Martinez 3.00 8.00
VO Vicyohandry Odelin 4.00 10.00
YG Yulieski Gourriel 3.00 8.00
YM Yunieski Maya 3.00 8.00

2007 SPx

This 150-card set was released in May, 2007. The set was issued in the hobby in three-card packs which came 10 packs per box and 10 boxes per case. Cards numbered 1-100 feature veterans while cards 101-150 (with the exception of Daisuke Matsuzaka (card #128) are signed rookie cards. The stated odds for the signed rookie cards were one in three packs. A few players did not return their signatures in time for pack out and those cards could be redeemed until May 10, 2010. The veteran cards were sequenced in alphabetical order by team.

COMMON CARD (1-100) .30 .75
COMMON AU RC (101-150) 3.00 8.00
OVERALL 101-150 AU RC ODDS 1:3
101-150 AU RC EXCH DEADLINE 05/10/2010
ASTERISK EQUALS PARTIAL EXCH
APPX.PRINTING PLATE ODDS 2 PER CASE
PLATES PRINT RUN 1 SET PER COLOR
BLACK-CYAN-MAGENTA-YELLOW ISSUED
NO PLATE PRICING DUE TO SCARCITY
1 Miguel Tejada .30 .75
2 Brian Roberts .30 .75
3 Melvin Mora .30 .75
4 David Ortiz .75 2.00
5 Manny Ramirez .50 1.25
6 Jason Varitek .75 2.00
7 Curt Schilling .50 1.25
8 Jim Thome .50 1.25
9 Paul Konerko .30 .75
10 Jermaine Dye .30 .75
11 Travis Hafner .30 .75
12 Victor Martinez .30 .75
13 Grady Sizemore .50 1.25
14 C.C. Sabathia .30 .75
15 Ivan Rodriguez .50 1.25
16 Magglio Ordonez .30 .75
17 Carlos Guillen .30 .75
18 Justin Verlander .75 2.00
19 Shane Costa .30 .75
20 Emil Brown .30 .75
21 Mark Teahen .30 .75
22 Vladimir Guerrero .75 2.00
23 Jered Weaver .50 1.25
24 Juan Rivera .30 .75
25 Justin Morneau .30 .75
26 Joe Mauer .50 1.25
27 Torii Hunter .30 .75
28 Johan Santana .50 1.25
29 Derek Jeter 2.00 5.00
30 Alex Rodriguez 1.25 3.00
31 Johnny Damon .50 1.25
32 Jason Giambi .30 .75
33 Bobby Crosby .30 .75
34 Nick Swisher .30 .75
35 Eric Chavez .30 .75
36 Ichiro Suzuki 1.25 3.00
37 Raul Ibanez .30 .75
38 Richie Sexson .30 .75
39 Carl Crawford .30 .75
40 Rocco Baldelli .30 .75
41 Scott Kazmir .50 1.25
42 Michael Young .30 .75
43 Mark Teixeira .50 1.25
44 Ian Kinsler .30 .75
45 Troy Glaus .30 .75
46 Vernon Wells .30 .75
47 Roy Halladay .30 .75
48 Lyle Overbay .30 .75
49 Brandon Webb .30 .75
50 Conor Jackson .30 .75
51 Stephen Drew .30 .75
52 Chipper Jones .75 2.00
53 Andruw Jones .50 1.25
54 Adam LaRoche .30 .75
55 John Smoltz .50 1.25
56 Derrek Lee .30 .75
57 Aramis Ramirez .30 .75
58 Carlos Zambrano .30 .75
59 Ken Griffey Jr. 1.25 3.00
60 Adam Dunn .30 .75
61 Aaron Harang .30 .75
62 Todd Helton .50 1.25
63 Matt Holliday .40 1.00
64 Garrett Atkins .30 .75
65 Miguel Cabrera .50 1.25
66 Hanley Ramirez .50 1.25
67 Dontrelle Willis .30 .75
68 Lance Berkman .30 .75
69 Roy Oswalt .30 .75
70 Craig Biggio .50 1.25
71 J.D. Drew .30 .75
72 Nomar Garciaparra .75 2.00
73 Rafael Furcal .30 .75
74 Jeff Kent .30 .75
75 Prince Fielder .75 2.00
76 Bill Hall .30 .75
77 Rickie Weeks .30 .75
78 Jose Reyes .30 .75
79 David Wright 1.25 3.00
80 Carlos Delgado .30 .75
81 Carlos Beltran .30 .75
82 Ryan Howard 1.25 3.00
83 Chase Utley .75 2.00
84 Jimmy Rollins .30 .75
85 Jason Bay .30 .75
86 Freddy Sanchez .30 .75
87 Zach Duke .30 .75
88 Trevor Hoffman .30 .75
89 Adrian Gonzalez .30 .75
90 Chris Young .30 .75
91 Ray Durham .30 .75
92 Omar Vizquel .50 1.25
93 Jason Schmidt .30 .75
94 Albert Pujols 1.50 4.00
95 Scott Rolen .50 1.25
96 Jim Edmonds .50 1.25
97 Chris Carpenter .30 .75
98 Alfonso Soriano .30 .75
99 Ryan Zimmerman .75 2.00
100 Nick Johnson .30 .75
101 Delmon Young AU (RC) 10.00 25.00
102 Andrew Miller AU RC 10.00 25.00
103 Troy Tulowitzki AU (RC) 12.50 30.00
104 Jeff Fiorentino AU (RC) 3.00 8.00
105 David Murphy AU (RC) 3.00 8.00
106 Tim Lincecum AU RC 50.00 100.00
107 Philip Hughes AU (RC) EXCH 15.00 40.00
108 Kevin Kouzmanoff AU (RC) 6.00 15.00
109 Adam Lind AU (RC) 6.00 15.00
110 Mark Reynolds AU RC EXCH 20.00 50.00
111 Kevin Hooper AU (RC) 3.00 8.00
112 Mitch Maier AU RC 3.00 8.00
113 Homey Bailey AU (RC) EXCH 10.00 25.00
114 Dennis Sarfate AU (RC) 3.00 8.00
115 Drew Anderson AU RC 3.00 8.00
116 Miguel Montero AU (RC) 3.00 8.00
117 Glen Perkins AU (RC) 3.00 8.00
118 Kevin Slowey AU (RC) EXCH 10.00 25.00
119 Tim Gradoville AU RC 3.00 8.00
120 Ryan Braun AU (RC) 30.00 60.00
121 Chris Narveson AU (RC) 3.00 8.00
122 Patrick Misch AU (RC) 3.00 8.00
123 Juan Salas AU (RC) 3.00 8.00
124 Beltran Perez AU (RC) 3.00 8.00
125 Joaquin Arias AU (RC) 3.00 8.00
126 Philip Humber AU (RC) 6.00 15.00
127 Kei Igawa AU RC 30.00 60.00
128 Daisuke Matsuzaka AU RC 90.00 150.00
129 Andy Cannizaro AU RC 6.00 15.00
130 Ubaldo Jimenez AU (RC) 6.00 15.00
131 Fred Lewis AU (RC) 6.00 15.00
132 Ryan Sweeney AU (RC) 3.00 8.00
133 Jeff Baker AU (RC) 3.00 8.00
134 Michael Bourn AU (RC) 3.00 8.00
135 Akinori Iwamura AU RC 6.00 15.00
136 Oswaldo Navarro AU RC 3.00 8.00
137 Hunter Pence AU (RC) 15.00 40.00
138 Jon Knott AU (RC) 3.00 8.00
139 Justin Hampson AU (RC) 3.00 8.00
140 Jeff Salazar AU (RC) 3.00 8.00
141 Juan Morillo AU (RC) 3.00 8.00
142 Delwyn Young AU (RC) 3.00 8.00
143 Brian Burres AU (RC) 5.00 12.00
144 Chris Stewart AU RC 3.00 8.00
145 Eric Stults AU RC 3.00 8.00
146 Carlos Maldonado AU (RC) 3.00 8.00
147 Angel Sanchez AU RC 3.00 8.00
148 Cesar Jimenez AU RC 3.00 8.00
149 Shawn Riggans AU (RC) 3.00 8.00
150 John Nelson AU (RC) 3.00 8.00

2007 SPx Spectrum

RANDOM INSERTS IN PACKS
STATED PRINT RUN 25 SER.#'d SETS
EXCH DEADLINE 05/10/2010
NO PRICING DUE TO SCARCITY

2007 SPx Autofacts Preview

ONE PER HOBBY BOX TOPPER
EXCH DEADLINE 05/10/2010
AI Akinori Iwamura 15.00 40.00
AL Adam Lind 5.00 12.00
AM Andrew Miller SP
AS Angel Sanchez 3.00 8.00
BP Beltran Perez 3.00 8.00
BR Jeremy Brown 3.00 8.00
CM Carlos Maldonado 3.00 8.00
CN Chris Narveson 3.00 8.00
CR Cal Ripken SP
CS C.C. Sabathia
DJ Derek Jeter
DM Daisuke Matsuzaka
DS Dennis Sarfate 3.00 8.00
DW Dewayne Wise 5.00 12.00
DY Delmon Young 6.00 15.00
ES Eric Stults 3.00 8.00
FL Fred Lewis 5.00 12.00
GP Glen Perkins 3.00 8.00
HG Hector Gimenez
HU Jon Huber
JA Joaquin Arias 3.00 8.00
JB Jeff Baker 3.00 8.00
JH Justin Hampson 3.00 8.00
JK Jon Knott 3.00 8.00
JM Juan Morillo 3.00 8.00
JN John Nelson 3.00 8.00
JS Juan Salas 3.00 8.00
JW Jason Wood 3.00 8.00
KG Ken Griffey Jr. SP
KH Kevin Hooper 3.00 8.00
KI Kei Igawa 6.00 15.00
KK Kevin Kouzmanoff 5.00 12.00
MB Michael Bourn 5.00 12.00
MM Miguel Montero 3.00 8.00
PH Philip Humber 5.00 12.00
PM Patrick Misch 3.00 8.00
RB Ryan Braun
SA Jeff Salazar 3.00 8.00
SR Shawn Riggans 3.00 8.00
ST Chris Stewart 3.00 8.00
TT Troy Tulowitzki 10.00 25.00
YO Delwyn Young 3.00 8.00

2007 SPx Iron Man

COMMON CARD 1.50 4.00
APPX.ODDS 1:3
STATED PRINT RUN 699 SER.#'d SETS
APPX.PRINTING PLATE ODDS 2 PER CASE
PLATES PRINT RUN 1 SET PER COLOR
BLACK-CYAN-MAGENTA-YELLOW ISSUED
NO PLATE PRICING DUE TO SCARCITY

2007 SPx Iron Man Platinum

COMMON CARD 15.00 40.00
RANDOM INSERTS IN PACKS
STATED PRINT RUN 1 SER.#'d SET

2007 SPx Iron Man Memorabilia

COMMON CARD 20.00 50.00
APPX. SIX GAME-USED PER BOX
STATED PRINT RUN 25 SER.#'d SETS

2007 SPx Iron Man Signatures

COMMON CARD 150.00 300.00
RANDOM INSERTS IN PACKS
STATED PRINT RUN 1 SER.#'d SET

2007 SPx Winning Materials 199 Bronze

APPX. SIX GAME-USED PER BOX
STATED PRINT RUN 199 SER.#'d SETS
APPX.PRINTING PLATE ODDS 2 PER CASE
PLATES PRINT RUN 1 SET PER COLOR
BLACK-CYAN-MAGENTA-YELLOW ISSUED
NO PLATE PRICING DUE TO SCARCITY
AB A.J. Burnett/199 3.00 8.00
AD Adam Dunn/199 3.00 8.00
AE Andre Ethier/199 3.00 8.00
AJ Andruw Jones/199 3.00 8.00
AL Adam LaRoche/199 3.00 8.00
AP Albert Pujols/199 6.00 15.00
AR Aramis Ramirez/199 3.00 8.00
AS Anibal Sanchez/199 3.00 8.00
BA Bobby Abreu/199 4.00 10.00
BG Brian Giles/199 3.00 8.00
BL Joe Blanton/199 3.00 8.00
BM Brian McCann/199 3.00 8.00
BO Jeremy Bonderman/199 3.00 8.00
BR Brian Roberts/199 3.00 8.00
BS Ben Sheets/199 3.00 8.00
BU B.J. Upton/199 3.00 8.00
CA Miguel Cabrera/199 3.00 8.00
CB Craig Biggio/199 4.00 10.00
CC Chris Carpenter/199 3.00 8.00
CF Chone Figgins/199 3.00 8.00
CH Cole Hamels/199 4.00 10.00
CJ Chipper Jones/199 4.00 10.00
CL Roger Clemens/199 6.00 15.00
CN Robinson Cano/199 4.00 10.00
CR Carl Crawford/199 3.00 8.00
CU Chase Utley/199 4.00 10.00
CW Chien-Ming Wang/199 15.00 40.00
DJ Derek Jeter/199 8.00 20.00
DJ2 Derek Jeter/199 8.00 20.00
DL Derrek Lee/199 3.00 8.00
DO David Ortiz/199 4.00 10.00
DU Dan Uggla/199 3.00 8.00
DW Dontrelle Willis/199 3.00 8.00
EC Eric Chavez/199 3.00 8.00
FH Felix Hernandez/199 4.00 10.00
FL Francisco Liriano/199 3.00 8.00
FS Freddy Sanchez/199 3.00 8.00
FT Frank Thomas/199 4.00 10.00
GA Garrett Atkins/199 3.00 8.00
HA Travis Hafner/199 3.00 8.00
HE Todd Helton/199 4.00 10.00
HI Rich Hill/199 3.00 8.00
HK Howie Kendrick/199 3.00 8.00
HN Rich Harden/199 3.00 8.00
HR Hanley Ramirez/199 4.00 10.00
HS Huston Street/199 3.00 8.00
IK Ian Kinsler/199 3.00 8.00
IR Ivan Rodriguez/199 4.00 10.00
JB Jason Bay/199 3.00 8.00
JE Jim Edmonds/199 3.00 8.00
JF Jeff Francoeur/199 4.00 10.00
JJ Josh Johnson/199 3.00 8.00
JL Chad Billingsley/199 3.00 8.00
JM Joe Mauer/199 4.00 10.00
JN Joe Nathan/199 3.00 8.00
JP Jake Peavy/199 3.00 8.00
JR Jose Reyes/199 3.00 8.00
JS Jeremy Sowers/199 3.00 8.00
JT Jim Thome/199 3.00 8.00
JV Justin Verlander/199 4.00 10.00
JW Jered Weaver/199 3.00 8.00
JZ Joel Zumaya/199 3.00 8.00
KG Ken Griffey Jr./199 6.00 15.00
KG2 Ken Griffey Jr./199 6.00 15.00
KH Khalil Greene/199 4.00 10.00
KU Hong-Chih Kuo/199 8.00 20.00
LE Jon Lester/199 4.00 10.00
LG Luis Gonzalez/199 3.00 8.00
MC Matt Cain/199 3.00 8.00
ME Melky Cabrera/199 3.00 8.00
MH Matt Holliday/199 4.00 10.00
MO Justin Morneau/199 3.00 8.00
MT Mark Teixeira/199 3.00 8.00
NM Nick Markakis/199 4.00 10.00
NS Nick Swisher/199 3.00 8.00
PA Jonathan Papelbon/199 4.00 10.00
PF Prince Fielder/199 4.00 10.00
PL Paul LoDuca/199 3.00 8.00
RC Cal Ripken /199 6.00 15.00
RI Alex Rios/199 3.00 8.00
RJ Randy Johnson/199 3.00 8.00
RO Roy Oswalt/199 3.00 8.00
RW Rickie Weeks/199 3.00 8.00
RZ Ryan Zimmerman/199 3.00 8.00
SA Alfonso Soriano/199 3.00 8.00
SD Stephen Drew/199 3.00 8.00
SH James Shields/199 3.00 8.00
SK Scott Kazmir/199 3.00 8.00
SM John Smoltz/199 4.00 10.00
SO Scott Olsen/199 3.00 8.00
SR Scott Rolen/199 4.00 10.00
TE Miguel Tejada/199 3.00 8.00
TG Tom Glavine/199 4.00 10.00
TH Trevor Hoffman/199 3.00 8.00
TO Torii Hunter/199 3.00 8.00
VG Vladimir Guerrero/199 4.00 10.00
VM Victor Martinez/199 3.00 8.00
WE David Wells/199 3.00 8.00
WI Josh Willingham/199 3.00 8.00
YB Yuniesky Betancourt/199 3.00 8.00

2007 SPx Winning Materials 199 Gold

*199 GOLD: .4X TO 1X 199 BRONZE
APPX. SIX GAME-USED PER BOX
STATED PRINT RUN 199 SER.#'d SETS

2007 SPx Winning Materials 199 Silver

*199 SILVER: .4X TO 1X 199 BRONZE
APPX. SIX GAME-USED PER BOX
STATED PRINT RUN 199 SER.#'d SETS

2007 SPx Winning Materials 175 Blue

*175 BLUE: .4X TO 1X 199 BRONZE
APPX. SIX GAME-USED PER BOX
STATED PRINT RUN 175 SER.#'d SETS

2007 SPx Winning Materials 175 Green

*175 GREEN: .4X TO 1X 199 BRONZE
APPX. SIX GAME-USED PER BOX
STATED PRINT RUN 175 SER.#'d SETS

2007 SPx Winning Materials 99 Gold

*99 GOLD: .5X TO 1.2X 199 BRONZE
APPX. SIX GAME-USED PER BOX
STATED PRINT RUN 99 SER.#'d SETS

2007 SPx Winning Materials 99 Silver

*99 SILVER: .5X TO 1.2X 199 BRONZE
APPX. SIX GAME-USED PER BOX
STATED PRINT RUN 99 SER.#'d SETS

2007 SPx Winning Materials Dual Gold

APPX. SIX GAME-USED PER BOX
STATED PRINT RUN 50 SER.#'d SETS
AB A.J. Burnett/50 5.00 12.00
AD Adam Dunn/50 5.00 12.00
AE Andre Ethier/50 5.00 12.00
AJ Andruw Jones/50 5.00 12.00
AL Adam LaRoche/50 5.00 12.00
AP Albert Pujols/50 10.00 25.00
AR Aramis Ramirez/50 5.00 12.00
AS Anibal Sanchez/50 5.00 12.00
BA Bobby Abreu/50 6.00 15.00
BG Brian Giles/50 5.00 12.00
BL Joe Blanton/50 5.00 12.00
BM Brian McCann/50 5.00 12.00
BO Jeremy Bonderman/50 5.00 12.00
BR Brian Roberts/50 5.00 12.00
BS Ben Sheets/50 5.00 12.00
BU B.J. Upton/50 5.00 12.00
CA Miguel Cabrera/50 5.00 12.00
CB Craig Biggio/50 6.00 15.00
CC Chris Carpenter/50 5.00 12.00
CF Chone Figgins/50 5.00 12.00
CH Cole Hamels/50 6.00 15.00
CJ Chipper Jones/50 6.00 15.00
CL Roger Clemens/50 10.00 25.00
CN Robinson Cano/50 6.00 15.00
CR Carl Crawford/50 5.00 12.00
CU Chase Utley/50 6.00 15.00
CW Chien-Ming Wang/50 30.00 60.00
DJ Derek Jeter/50 12.50 30.00
DJ2 Derek Jeter/50 12.50 30.00
DL Derrek Lee/50 5.00 12.00
DO David Ortiz/50 6.00 15.00
DU Dan Uggla/50 6.00 15.00
DW Dontrelle Willis/50 5.00 12.00
EC Eric Chavez/50 5.00 12.00
FH Felix Hernandez/50 6.00 15.00
FL Francisco Liriano/50 5.00 12.00
FS Freddy Sanchez/50 5.00 12.00
FT Frank Thomas/50 6.00 15.00
GA Garrett Atkins/50 5.00 12.00
HA Travis Hafner/50 5.00 12.00
HE Todd Helton/50 6.00 15.00
HI Rich Hill/50 5.00 12.00
HK Howie Kendrick/50 5.00 12.00
HN Rich Harden/50 5.00 12.00
HR Hanley Ramirez/50 6.00 15.00
HS Huston Street/50 5.00 12.00
IK Ian Kinsler/50 5.00 12.00
IR Ivan Rodriguez/50 6.00 15.00
JB Jason Bay/50 5.00 12.00
JE Jim Edmonds/50 5.00 12.00
JF Jeff Francoeur/50 6.00 15.00
JJ Josh Johnson/50 5.00 12.00
JL Chad Billingsley/50 5.00 12.00
JM Joe Mauer/50 6.00 15.00
JN Joe Nathan/50 5.00 12.00
JP Jake Peavy/50 5.00 12.00
JR Jose Reyes/50 5.00 12.00
JS Jeremy Sowers/50 5.00 12.00
JT Jim Thome/50 5.00 12.00
JV Justin Verlander/50 6.00 15.00
JW Jered Weaver/50 5.00 12.00
JZ Joel Zumaya/50 5.00 12.00
KG Ken Griffey Jr./50 10.00 25.00
KG2 Ken Griffey Jr./50 10.00 25.00
KH Khalil Greene/50 6.00 15.00
KU Hong-Chih Kuo/50 12.50 30.00
LE Jon Lester/50 6.00 15.00
LG Luis Gonzalez/50 5.00 12.00
MC Matt Cain/50 5.00 12.00
ME Melky Cabrera/50 5.00 12.00
MH Matt Holliday/50 6.00 15.00
MO Justin Morneau/50 5.00 12.00
MT Mark Teixeira/50 5.00 12.00
NM Nick Markakis/50 6.00 15.00
NS Nick Swisher/50 5.00 12.00
PA Jonathan Papelbon/50 6.00 15.00
PF Prince Fielder/50 6.00 15.00
PL Paul LoDuca/50 5.00 12.00
RC Cal Ripken /50 10.00 25.00
RI Alex Rios/50 5.00 12.00
RJ Randy Johnson/50 5.00 12.00
RO Roy Oswalt/50 5.00 12.00
RW Rickie Weeks/50 5.00 12.00
RZ Ryan Zimmerman/50 5.00 12.00
SA Alfonso Soriano/50 5.00 12.00
SD Stephen Drew/50 5.00 12.00
SH James Shields/50 5.00 12.00
SK Scott Kazmir/50 5.00 12.00
SM John Smoltz/50 5.00 12.00
SO Scott Olsen/50 5.00 12.00
SR Scott Rolen/50 5.00 12.00
TE Miguel Tejada/50 5.00 12.00
TG Tom Glavine/50 5.00 12.00
TH Trevor Hoffman/50 5.00 12.00
TO Torii Hunter/50 5.00 12.00
VG Vladimir Guerrero/50 6.00 15.00
VM Victor Martinez/50 5.00 12.00
WE David Wells/50 5.00 12.00
WI Josh Willingham/50 5.00 12.00
YB Yuniesky Betancourt/50 5.00 12.00

2007 SPx Winning Materials Dual Silver

*DUAL SILVER: .4X TO 1X DUAL GOLD
APPX. SIX GAME-USED PER BOX
STATED PRINT RUN 50 SER.#'d SETS

2007 SPx Winning Materials Dual Bronze

APPX. SIX GAME-USED PER BOX
STATED PRINT RUN 25 SER.#'d SETS
NO PRICING DUE TO SCARCITY

2007 SPx Winning Materials Dual Green

APPX. SIX GAME-USED PER BOX
STATED PRINT RUN 15 SER.#'d SETS
NO PRICING DUE TO SCARCITY

2007 SPx Winning Materials Patches Gold

APPX. SIX GAME-USED PER BOX
PRINT RUNS B/WN 3-99 COPIES PER
NO VERLANDER PRICING DUE TO SCARCITY
AB A.J. Burnett/99 4.00 10.00
AD Adam Dunn/99 4.00 10.00
AE Andre Ethier/99 5.00 12.00
AJ Andruw Jones/99 5.00 12.00
AL Adam LaRoche/99 4.00 10.00
AP Albert Pujols/99 15.00 40.00
AR Aramis Ramirez/99 4.00 10.00
AS Anibal Sanchez/54 4.00 10.00
BA Bobby Abreu/99 6.00 15.00
BG Brian Giles/99 4.00 10.00
BL Joe Blanton/99 4.00 10.00
BM Brian McCann/99 6.00 15.00
BO Jeremy Bonderman/99 6.00 15.00
BR Brian Roberts/99 4.00 10.00
BS Ben Sheets/99 4.00 10.00
BU B.J. Upton/99 10.00 25.00
CA Miguel Cabrera/99 5.00 12.00
CB Craig Biggio/99 6.00 15.00
CC Chris Carpenter/99 5.00 12.00
CF Chone Figgins/99 4.00 10.00
CH Cole Hamels/99 6.00 15.00
CJ Chipper Jones/99 6.00 15.00
CL Roger Clemens/99 15.00 40.00
CN Robinson Cano/99 6.00 15.00
CR Carl Crawford/99 5.00 12.00
CU Chase Utley/99 6.00 15.00
CW Chien-Ming Wang/99 30.00 60.00
DJ Derek Jeter/99 20.00 50.00
DJ2 Derek Jeter/99 20.00 50.00
DL Derrek Lee/99 4.00 10.00
DO David Ortiz/99 6.00 15.00
DU Dan Uggla/99 4.00 10.00
DW Dontrelle Willis/99 4.00 10.00
EC Eric Chavez/99 4.00 10.00
FH Felix Hernandez/99 5.00 12.00
FL Francisco Liriano/99 6.00 15.00
FS Freddy Sanchez/99 4.00 10.00
FT Frank Thomas/99 10.00 25.00
GA Garrett Atkins/99 4.00 10.00
HA Travis Hafner/99 4.00 10.00
HE Todd Helton/99 5.00 12.00
HI Rich Hill/99 4.00 10.00
HK Howie Kendrick/34 6.00 15.00
HN Rich Harden/99 4.00 10.00
HR Hanley Ramirez/99 5.00 12.00
HS Huston Street/99 4.00 10.00
IK Ian Kinsler/99 4.00 10.00
IR Ivan Rodriguez/99 5.00 12.00
JB Jason Bay/99 5.00 12.00
JE Jim Edmonds/99 5.00 12.00
JF Jeff Francoeur/99 10.00 25.00
JJ Josh Johnson/99 4.00 10.00
JL Chad Billingsley/99 4.00 10.00
JM Joe Mauer/99 5.00 12.00
JN Joe Nathan/99 4.00 10.00
JP Jake Peavy/99 4.00 10.00
JR Jose Reyes/99 6.00 15.00
JS Jeremy Sowers/99 4.00 10.00
JT Jim Thome/99 5.00 12.00
JV Justin Verlander/3
JW Jered Weaver/99 5.00 12.00
JZ Joel Zumaya/99 5.00 12.00
KG Ken Griffey Jr./99 12.50 30.00
KG2 Ken Griffey Jr./99 12.50 30.00
KH Khalil Greene/99 5.00 12.00
KU Hong-Chih Kuo/99 5.00 12.00
LE Jon Lester/99 5.00 12.00
LG Luis Gonzalez/99 4.00 10.00
MC Matt Cain/99 5.00 12.00
ME Melky Cabrera/99 4.00 10.00
MH Matt Holliday/99 5.00 12.00
MO Justin Morneau/99 4.00 10.00
MT Mark Teixeira/99 5.00 12.00
NM Nick Markakis/99 10.00 25.00
NS Nick Swisher/99 6.00 15.00
PA Jonathan Papelbon/99 6.00 15.00
PF Prince Fielder/99 6.00 15.00
PL Paul LoDuca/99 5.00 12.00
RC Cal Ripken /99 15.00 40.00
RI Alex Rios/99 4.00 10.00
RJ Randy Johnson/99 6.00 15.00
RO Roy Oswalt/99 5.00 12.00
RW Rickie Weeks/99 4.00 10.00
RZ Ryan Zimmerman/99 10.00 25.00
SA Alfonso Soriano/99 5.00 12.00
SD Stephen Drew/99 5.00 12.00
SH James Shields/99 4.00 10.00
SK Scott Kazmir/99 5.00 12.00
SM John Smoltz/99 10.00 25.00
SO Scott Olsen/99 4.00 10.00
SR Scott Rolen/99 10.00 25.00
TE Miguel Tejada/99 4.00 10.00
TG Tom Glavine/99 6.00 15.00
TH Trevor Hoffman/99 5.00 12.00
TO Torii Hunter/99 5.00 12.00
VG Vladimir Guerrero/99 10.00 25.00
VM Victor Martinez/99 4.00 10.00
WE David Wells/99 4.00 10.00
WI Josh Willingham/99 4.00 10.00
YB Yuniesky Betancourt/99 4.00 10.00

2007 SPx Winning Materials Patches Silver

*PATCH SILVER: .4X TO 1X PATCH GOLD
APPX. SIX GAME-USED PER BOX
PRINT RUN B/WN 3-99 COPIES PER
NO PRICING ON QTY 27 OR LESS
JV Justin Verlander/99 6.00 15.00
LE Jon Lester/37 6.00 15.00

2007 SPx Winning Materials Patches Bronze

*PATCH BRONZE: .5X TO 1.2X PATCH GOLD
APPX. SIX GAME-USED PER BOX
STATED PRINT RUN 50 SER.#'d SETS
AR Aramis Ramirez/50 4.00 10.00
JM Joe Mauer/50
LE Jon Lester/50 6.00 15.00
MH Matt Holliday/50 5.00 12.00
RI Alex Rios/50

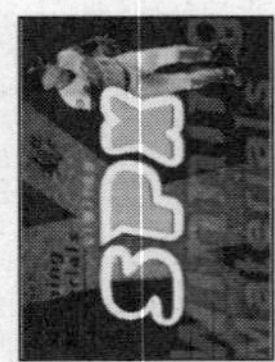

2007 SPx Winning Materials Patches Triple

APPX. SIX GAME-USED PER BOX
STATED PRINT RUN 25 SER.#'d SETS
NO PRICING DUE TO SCARCITY

2007 SPx Winning Materials Triple Signatures

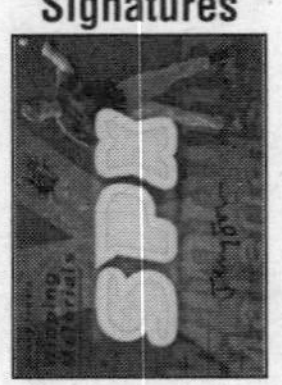

APPX. FOUR AUTOS PER BOX
PRINT RUNS B/WN 15-35
EXCH DEADLINE 05/10/2010
NO PRICING DUE TO SCARCITY

2007 SPx Winning Materials Triple Signatures Platinum

APPX. FOUR AUTOS PER BOX
PRINT RUNS B/WN 4-10 COPIES PER
EXCH DEADLINE 05/10/2010
NO PRICING DUE TO SCARCITY

2007 SPx Winning Trios Bronze

*BRONZE: .5X TO 1.2X GOLD
APPX. SIX GAME-USED PER BOX
STATED PRINT RUN 30 SER.#'d SETS

2007 SPx Winning Trios Gold

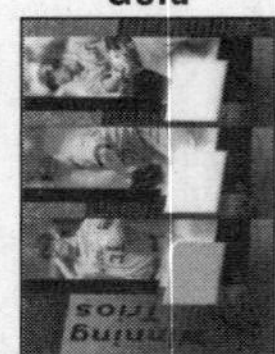

APPX. SIX GAME-USED PER BOX
STATED PRINT RUN 75 SER.#'d SETS
WT1 Ken Griffey Jr. 20.00 50.00
Albert Pujols
Derek Jeter
WT2 Dan Uggla 10.00 25.00
Hanley Ramirez
Josh Willingham
WT3 Dontrelle Willis 6.00 15.00
Josh Johnson
Anibal Sanchez
WT4 Lance Berkman 10.00 25.00
David Ortiz
Travis Hafner
WT5 Jake Peavy 6.00 15.00
Roy Oswalt
Ben Sheets
WT6 Justin Verlander 10.00 25.00
Jeremy Bonderman
Ivan Rodriguez
WT7 Jose Reyes 10.00 25.00
Hanley Ramirez
Stephen Drew
WT8 Miguel Cabrera 10.00 25.00
Ryan Zimmerman
B.J. Upton
WT9 Jered Weaver 10.00 25.00
Justin Verlander
Jonathan Papelbon
WT10 Derek Jeter 20.00 50.00
Randy Johnson
Bobby Abreu
WT11 Morgan Ensberg 6.00 15.00
Craig Biggio
Lance Berkman
WT12 Jeff Francoeur 10.00 25.00
Adam LaRoche
Brian McCann
WT13 Joe Mauer 10.00 25.00
Brian McCann
Victor Martinez
WT14 Carl Crawford 10.00 25.00
Grady Sizemore
Jose Reyes
WT15 Freddy Garcia 6.00 15.00
Carlos Zambrano
Johan Santana
WT16 Vladimir Guerrero 10.00 25.00
Bobby Abreu
Alfonso Soriano
WT17 Justin Morneau 10.00 25.00
Joe Mauer
Johan Santana
WT18 Carlos Delgado 6.00 15.00
Jose Reyes
Carlos Beltran
WT19 Chad Billingsley 10.00 25.00
Andre Ethier
Matt Kemp
WT20 Jim Thome 10.00 25.00
Jermaine Dye
Tadahito Iguchi
WT21 Chase Utley 10.00 25.00
Aaron Rowand
Jimmy Rollins
WT22 Magglio Ordonez 15.00 40.00
Ivan Rodriguez
Curtis Granderson
WT23 Albert Pujols 15.00 40.00
Chris Carpenter
Scott Rolen
WT24 James Shields 6.00 15.00
B.J. Upton
Carl Crawford
WT25 Howie Kendrick 6.00 15.00
Jered Weaver
Mike Napoli
WT26 Dan Uggla 6.00 15.00
Howie Kendrick
Ian Kinsler
WT27 Brian Roberts 10.00 25.00
Miguel Tejada
Nick Markakis
WT28 Jered Weaver 10.00 25.00
Justin Verlander
Mike Pelfrey
WT29 Cole Hamels 10.00 25.00
Rich Hill
Francisco Liriano
WT30 Anibal Sanchez 6.00 15.00
Derek Lowe
Randy Johnson
WT31 Ryan Zimmerman 10.00 25.00
Prince Fielder
Dan Uggla
WT32 Trevor Hoffman 6.00 15.00
Joe Nathan
Huston Street
WT33 A.J. Burnett 6.00 15.00
Alex Rios
Vernon Wells
WT34 Rickie Weeks 10.00 25.00
Prince Fielder
Ben Sheets
WT35 Yuniesky Betancourt 10.00 25.00
Adrian Beltre
Felix Hernandez
WT36 Justin Verlander 10.00 25.00
Joel Zumaya
Jeremy Bonderman
WT37 Billy Wagner 6.00 15.00
Jose Reyes
Paul LoDuca
WT38 Jeremy Sowers 6.00 15.00
C.C. Sabathia
Victor Martinez
WT39 Stephen Drew 6.00 15.00
Brandon Webb
Conor Jackson
WT40 Felix Hernandez 10.00 25.00
Jered Weaver
Justin Verlander
WT41 Ken Griffey Jr. 15.00 40.00
Frank Thomas
Ivan Rodriguez
WT42 Derek Jeter 30.00 60.00
Cal Ripken
Jose Reyes

2007 SPx Winning Trios Silver

*SILVER: .4X TO 1X GOLD
APPX. SIX GAME-USED PER BOX
STATED PRINT RUN 50 SER.#'d SETS

2007 SPx Winning Trios Patches

APPX. SIX GAME-USED PER BOX
PRINT RUNS B/WN 8-25 COPIES PER
NO PRICING DUE TO SCARCITY

2007 SPx Young Stars Signatures

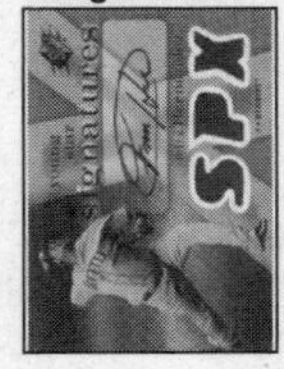

STATED ODDS 1:12
EXCH DEADLINE 05/10/2010
APPX.PRINTING PLATE ODDS 2 PER CASE
PLATES PRINT RUN 1 SET PER COLOR
BLACK-CYAN-MAGENTA-YELLOW ISSUED
NO PLATE PRICING DUE TO SCARCITY
AE Andre Ethier 5.00 12.00
AG Adrian Gonzalez 6.00 15.00
AM Andrew Miller 15.00 40.00
AS Anibal Sanchez 3.00 8.00
BH Bill Hall
BU B.J. Upton 6.00 15.00
CA Matt Cain 6.00 15.00
CH Cole Hamels 20.00 50.00
CQ Carlos Quentin 8.00 20.00
CU Chase Utley
DJ Derek Jeter 75.00 150.00
DU Dan Uggla 10.00 25.00
DY Delmon Young 6.00 15.00
FH Felix Hernandez 8.00 20.00
FL Francisco Liriano 6.00 15.00
FS Freddy Sanchez
HA Rich Harden 5.00 12.00
HI Rich Hill 6.00 15.00
HK Howie Kendrick 6.00 15.00
HR Hanley Ramirez 6.00 15.00
HS Huston Street
IK Ian Kinsler
JB Jeremy Brown 3.00 8.00
JF Jeff Francoeur
JJ Josh Johnson 3.00 8.00
JL Jon Lester 10.00 25.00
JM Joe Mauer 10.00 25.00
JP Jonathan Papelbon 12.50 30.00
JR Jose Reyes 20.00 50.00
JS Jeremy Sowers 3.00 8.00
JV Justin Verlander 12.50 30.00
JW Jered Weaver 10.00 25.00
JZ Joel Zumaya 8.00 20.00
KG Ken Griffey Jr. 40.00 80.00
KU Hong-Chih Kuo 10.00 25.00
LO James Loney 10.00 25.00
MC Melky Cabrera
MO Justin Morneau 10.00 25.00
NM Nick Markakis 10.00 25.00
PF Prince Fielder
PH Philip Humber 5.00 12.00
RW Rickie Weeks 5.00 12.00
RY Jae Kuk Ryu
RZ Ryan Zimmerman 10.00 25.00
SC Shin-Soo Choo
SD Stephen Drew 5.00 12.00
SO Scott Olsen
ST Scott Thorman 5.00 12.00
TT Troy Tulowitzki 15.00 40.00
WI Josh Willingham 3.00 8.00

2007 SPx Young Stars Signatures Spectrum

APPX. FOUR AUTOS PER BOX
STATED PRINT RUN 25 SER.#'d SETS
EXCH DEADLINE 05/10/2010

2008 SPx

COMMON CARD (1-100) .25 .60
COMMON AU RC (101-150) 3.00 8.00
OVERALL AU ODDS FOUR PER BOX
1 Brandon Webb .40 1.00
2 Chris B. Young .25 .60
3 Eric Byrnes .25 .60
4 Dan Haren .25 .60
5 Mark Teixeira .40 1.00
6 Chipper Jones .75 2.00
7 John Smoltz .60 1.50
8 Erik Bedard .25 .60
9 Nick Markakis .40 1.00
10 Brian Roberts .40 1.00
11 David Ortiz .60 1.50
12 Curt Schilling .40 1.00
13 Manny Ramirez .60 1.50

14 Daisuke Matsuzaka 1.00 2.50
15 Josh Beckett .40 1.00
16 Derrek Lee .40 1.00
17 Alfonso Soriano .40 1.00
18 Carlos Zambrano .25 .60
19 Aramis Ramirez .25 .60
20 Jermaine Dye .25 .60
21 Jim Thome .40 1.00
22 Nick Swisher .25 .60
23 Ken Griffey Jr. 1.00 2.50
24 Adam Dunn .25 .60
25 Brandon Phillips .25 .60
26 Grady Sizemore .40 1.00
27 Victor Martinez .25 .60
28 C.C. Sabathia .25 .60
29 Travis Hafner .25 .60
30 Matt Holliday .40 1.00
31 Todd Helton .40 1.00
32 Troy Tulowitzki .40 1.00
33 Magglio Ordonez .40 1.00
34 Gary Sheffield .25 .60
35 Justin Verlander .40 1.00
36 Curtis Granderson .25 .60
37 Miguel Cabrera .40 1.00
38 Hanley Ramirez .60 1.50
39 Dan Uggla .40 1.00
40 Miguel Tejada .25 .60
41 Lance Berkman .40 1.00
42 Hunter Pence .60 1.50
43 Carlos Lee .25 .60
44 Alex Gordon .60 1.50
45 David DeJesus .25 .60
46 Vladimir Guerrero .60 1.50
47 Jered Weaver .25 .60
48 Torii Hunter .25 .60
49 Andruw Jones .25 .60
50 Rafael Furcal .25 .60
51 Russell Martin .25 .60
52 Brad Penny .25 .60
53 Ryan Braun .75 2.00
54 Prince Fielder .60 1.50
55 J.J. Hardy .25 .60
56 Justin Morneau .25 .60
57 Johan Santana .40 1.00
58 Joe Mauer .40 1.00
59 Delmon Young .40 1.00
60 Jose Reyes .40 1.00
61 David Wright .75 2.00
62 Carlos Beltran .25 .60
63 Pedro Martinez .40 1.00
64 Chien-Ming Wang 1.00 2.50
65 Alex Rodriguez 1.00 2.50
66 Derek Jeter 1.50 4.00
67 Robinson Cano .40 1.00
68 Hideki Matsui .60 1.50
69 Joe Blanton .25 .60
70 Jack Cust .25 .60
71 Cole Hamels .60 1.50
72 Jimmy Rollins .40 1.00
73 Ryan Howard .75 2.00
74 Chase Utley .60 1.50
75 Jason Bay .25 .60
76 Freddy Sanchez .25 .60
77 Jake Peavy .40 1.00
78 Greg Maddux .75 2.00
79 Adrian Gonzalez .40 1.00
80 Barry Zito .25 .60
81 Omar Vizquel .25 .60
82 Tim Lincecum .60 1.50
83 Ichiro Suzuki 1.00 2.50
84 Felix Hernandez .40 1.00
85 Kenji Johjima .25 .60
86 Albert Pujols 1.25 3.00
87 Scott Rolen .40 1.00
88 Chris Carpenter .25 .60
89 Rick Ankiel .25 .60
90 Scott Kazmir .40 1.00
91 Carl Crawford .25 .60
92 B.J. Upton .40 1.00
93 Michael Young .25 .60
94 Josh Hamilton .75 2.00
95 Hank Blalock .25 .60
96 Roy Halladay .25 .60
97 Vernon Wells .25 .60
98 Alex Rios .25 .60
99 Ryan Zimmerman .40 1.00
100 Dmitri Young .25 .60
101 Bill Murphy AU (RC) 3.00 8.00
102 Emilio Bonifacio AU RC 3.00 8.00
103 Brandon Jones AU RC 3.00 8.00
104 Clint Sammons AU (RC) 3.00 8.00
105 Clay Buchholz AU (RC) 10.00 25.00
106 Kevin Hart AU (RC) 3.00 8.00
107 Donny Lucy AU (RC) 3.00 8.00
108 Lance Broadway AU (RC) 3.00 8.00
109 Joey Votto AU (RC) 10.00 25.00
110 Ryan Hanigan AU RC 3.00 8.00
111 Joe Koshansky AU (RC) 3.00 8.00
112 Josh Newman AU RC 3.00 8.00
113 Seth Smith AU (RC) 3.00 8.00
114 Chris Seddon AU (RC) 3.00 8.00
115 Harvey Garcia AU (RC) 3.00 8.00
116 Felipe Paulino AU RC 3.00 8.00
117 J.R. Towles AU RC 4.00 10.00
118 Josh Anderson AU (RC) 3.00 8.00
119 Troy Patton AU (RC) 3.00 8.00
120 Billy Buckner AU (RC) 3.00 8.00
121 Luke Hochevar AU RC 3.00 8.00
122 Chin-Lung Hu AU (RC) 6.00 15.00
123 Jonathan Meloan AU RC
124 Jose Morales AU (RC) 6.00 15.00
125 Carlos Muniz AU RC
126 Alberto Gonzalez AU RC 3.00 8.00
127 Bronson Sardinha AU (RC) 3.00 8.00
128 Ian Kennedy AU RC 10.00 25.00
129 Ross Ohlendorf AU RC 3.00 8.00
130 Daric Barton AU (RC) 6.00 15.00
131 Jerry Blevins AU RC 3.00 8.00
132 Dave Davidson AU RC 3.00 8.00
133 Nyjer Morgan AU (RC) 3.00 8.00
134 Steve Pearce AU RC 3.00 8.00
135 Colt Morton AU RC 3.00 8.00
136 Eugenio Velez AU RC 3.00 8.00
137 Jeff Clement AU (RC)
138 Rob Johnson AU (RC) 3.00 8.00
139 Wladimir Balentien AU (RC) 3.00 8.00
140 Justin Ruggiano AU RC 3.00 8.00
141 Bill White AU RC 3.00 8.00
142 Luis Mendoza AU (RC) 3.00 8.00
143 Jonathan Albaladejo AU RC 3.00 8.00
144 Justin Maxwell AU RC
145 Ross Detwiler AU RC 6.00 15.00
146 Jay Bruce AU (RC) EXCH
147 Carlos Gonzalez AU (RC) EXCH
148 Evan Longoria AU RC EXCH 60.00 120.00
149 Collin Balester AU (RC) EXCH
150 Max Scherzer AU RC EXCH
151 Clayton Kershaw AU RC EXCH
152 Alexei Ramirez AU RC EXCH

2008 SPx Silver

*SILVER AU: .4X TO 1X BASIC AU RC
RANDOM INSERT IN BOX TOPPER PACK
CARDS 146-150 DO NOT EXIST

2008 SPx Babe Ruth American Legend

COMMON RUTH 20.00 50.00
OVERALL ODDS ONE PER CASE
STATED PRINT RUN 1 SER.#'d SET

2008 SPx Ken Griffey Jr. American Hero

RANDOM INSERTS IN PACKS
STATED PRINT RUN 725 SER.#'d SETS
KG1 Ken Griffey Jr. 1.25 3.00
KG2 Ken Griffey Jr. 1.25 3.00
KG3 Ken Griffey Jr. 1.25 3.00
KG4 Ken Griffey Jr. 1.25 3.00
KG5 Ken Griffey Jr. 1.25 3.00
KG6 Ken Griffey Jr. 1.25 3.00
KG7 Ken Griffey Jr. 1.25 3.00
KG8 Ken Griffey Jr. 1.25 3.00
KG9 Ken Griffey Jr. 1.25 3.00
KG10 Ken Griffey Jr. 1.25 3.00
KG11 Ken Griffey Jr. 1.25 3.00
KG12 Ken Griffey Jr. 1.25 3.00
KG13 Ken Griffey Jr. 1.25 3.00
KG14 Ken Griffey Jr. 1.25 3.00
KG15 Ken Griffey Jr. 1.25 3.00
KG16 Ken Griffey Jr. 1.25 3.00
KG17 Ken Griffey Jr. 1.25 3.00
KG18 Ken Griffey Jr. 1.25 3.00
KG19 Ken Griffey Jr. 1.25 3.00
KG20 Ken Griffey Jr. 1.25 3.00
KG21 Ken Griffey Jr. 1.25 3.00
KG22 Ken Griffey Jr. 1.25 3.00
KG23 Ken Griffey Jr. 1.25 3.00
KG24 Ken Griffey Jr. 1.25 3.00
KG25 Ken Griffey Jr. 1.25 3.00
KG26 Ken Griffey Jr. 1.25 3.00
KG27 Ken Griffey Jr. 1.25 3.00
KG28 Ken Griffey Jr. 1.25 3.00
KG29 Ken Griffey Jr. 1.25 3.00
KG30 Ken Griffey Jr. 1.25 3.00
KG31 Ken Griffey Jr. 1.25 3.00
KG32 Ken Griffey Jr. 1.25 3.00
KG33 Ken Griffey Jr. 1.25 3.00
KG34 Ken Griffey Jr. 1.25 3.00
KG35 Ken Griffey Jr. 1.25 3.00
KG36 Ken Griffey Jr. 1.25 3.00
KG37 Ken Griffey Jr. 1.25 3.00
KG38 Ken Griffey Jr. 1.25 3.00
KG39 Ken Griffey Jr. 1.25 3.00
KG40 Ken Griffey Jr. 1.25 3.00
KG41 Ken Griffey Jr. 1.25 3.00
KG42 Ken Griffey Jr. 1.25 3.00
KG43 Ken Griffey Jr. 1.25 3.00
KG44 Ken Griffey Jr. 1.25 3.00
KG45 Ken Griffey Jr. 1.25 3.00
KG46 Ken Griffey Jr. 1.25 3.00
KG47 Ken Griffey Jr. 1.25 3.00
KG48 Ken Griffey Jr. 1.25 3.00
KG49 Ken Griffey Jr. 1.25 3.00
KG50 Ken Griffey Jr. 1.25 3.00
KG51 Ken Griffey Jr. 1.25 3.00
KG52 Ken Griffey Jr. 1.25 3.00
KG53 Ken Griffey Jr. 1.25 3.00
KG54 Ken Griffey Jr. 1.25 3.00
KG55 Ken Griffey Jr. 1.25 3.00
KG56 Ken Griffey Jr. 1.25 3.00
KG57 Ken Griffey Jr. 1.25 3.00
KG58 Ken Griffey Jr. 1.25 3.00
KG59 Ken Griffey Jr. 1.25 3.00
KG60 Ken Griffey Jr. 1.25 3.00
KG61 Ken Griffey Jr. 1.25 3.00
KG62 Ken Griffey Jr. 1.25 3.00
KG63 Ken Griffey Jr. 1.25 3.00
KG64 Ken Griffey Jr. 1.25 3.00
KG65 Ken Griffey Jr. 1.25 3.00
KG66 Ken Griffey Jr. 1.25 3.00
KG67 Ken Griffey Jr. 1.25 3.00
KG68 Ken Griffey Jr. 1.25 3.00
KG69 Ken Griffey Jr. 1.25 3.00
KG70 Ken Griffey Jr. 1.25 3.00
KG71 Ken Griffey Jr. 1.25 3.00
KG72 Ken Griffey Jr. 1.25 3.00
KG73 Ken Griffey Jr. 1.25 3.00
KG74 Ken Griffey Jr. 1.25 3.00
KG75 Ken Griffey Jr. 1.25 3.00
KG76 Ken Griffey Jr. 1.25 3.00
KG77 Ken Griffey Jr. 1.25 3.00
KG78 Ken Griffey Jr. 1.25 3.00
KG79 Ken Griffey Jr. 1.25 3.00
KG80 Ken Griffey Jr. 1.25 3.00
KG81 Ken Griffey Jr. 1.25 3.00
KG82 Ken Griffey Jr. 1.25 3.00
KG83 Ken Griffey Jr. 1.25 3.00
KG84 Ken Griffey Jr. 1.25 3.00
KG85 Ken Griffey Jr. 1.25 3.00
KG86 Ken Griffey Jr. 1.25 3.00
KG87 Ken Griffey Jr. 1.25 3.00
KG88 Ken Griffey Jr. 1.25 3.00
KG89 Ken Griffey Jr. 1.25 3.00
KG90 Ken Griffey Jr. 1.25 3.00
KG91 Ken Griffey Jr. 1.25 3.00
KG92 Ken Griffey Jr. 1.25 3.00
KG93 Ken Griffey Jr. 1.25 3.00
KG94 Ken Griffey Jr. 1.25 3.00
KG95 Ken Griffey Jr. 1.25 3.00
KG96 Ken Griffey Jr. 1.25 3.00
KG97 Ken Griffey Jr. 1.25 3.00
KG98 Ken Griffey Jr. 1.25 3.00
KG99 Ken Griffey Jr. 1.25 3.00
KG100 Ken Griffey Jr. 1.25 3.00

2008 SPx Ken Griffey Jr. American Hero Boxscore

OVERALL ODDS ONE PER CASE
STATED PRINT RUN 1 SER.#'d SET
KG1 Ken Griffey Jr. 40.00 80.00
KG2 Ken Griffey Jr. 40.00 80.00
KG3 Ken Griffey Jr. 40.00 80.00
KG4 Ken Griffey Jr. 40.00 80.00
KG5 Ken Griffey Jr. 40.00 80.00
KG6 Ken Griffey Jr. 40.00 80.00
KG7 Ken Griffey Jr. 40.00 80.00
KG8 Ken Griffey Jr. 40.00 80.00
KG9 Ken Griffey Jr. 40.00 80.00
KG10 Ken Griffey Jr. 40.00 80.00
KG11 Ken Griffey Jr. 40.00 80.00
KG12 Ken Griffey Jr. 40.00 80.00
KG13 Ken Griffey Jr. 40.00 80.00
KG14 Ken Griffey Jr. 40.00 80.00
KG15 Ken Griffey Jr. 40.00 80.00
KG16 Ken Griffey Jr. 40.00 80.00
KG17 Ken Griffey Jr. 40.00 80.00
KG18 Ken Griffey Jr. 40.00 80.00
KG19 Ken Griffey Jr. 40.00 80.00
KG20 Ken Griffey Jr. 40.00 80.00
KG21 Ken Griffey Jr. 40.00 80.00
KG22 Ken Griffey Jr. 40.00 80.00
KG23 Ken Griffey Jr. 40.00 80.00
KG24 Ken Griffey Jr. 40.00 80.00
KG25 Ken Griffey Jr. 40.00 80.00
KG26 Ken Griffey Jr. 40.00 80.00
KG27 Ken Griffey Jr. 40.00 80.00
KG28 Ken Griffey Jr. 40.00 80.00
KG29 Ken Griffey Jr. 40.00 80.00
KG30 Ken Griffey Jr. 40.00 80.00
KG31 Ken Griffey Jr. 40.00 80.00
KG32 Ken Griffey Jr. 40.00 80.00
KG33 Ken Griffey Jr. 40.00 80.00
KG34 Ken Griffey Jr. 40.00 80.00
KG35 Ken Griffey Jr. 40.00 80.00
KG36 Ken Griffey Jr. 40.00 80.00
KG37 Ken Griffey Jr. 40.00 80.00
KG38 Ken Griffey Jr. 40.00 80.00
KG39 Ken Griffey Jr. 40.00 80.00
KG40 Ken Griffey Jr. 40.00 80.00
KG41 Ken Griffey Jr. 40.00 80.00
KG42 Ken Griffey Jr. 40.00 80.00
KG43 Ken Griffey Jr. 40.00 80.00
KG44 Ken Griffey Jr. 40.00 80.00
KG45 Ken Griffey Jr. 40.00 80.00
KG46 Ken Griffey Jr. 40.00 80.00
KG47 Ken Griffey Jr. 40.00 80.00
KG48 Ken Griffey Jr. 40.00 80.00
KG49 Ken Griffey Jr. 40.00 80.00
KG50 Ken Griffey Jr. 40.00 80.00
KG51 Ken Griffey Jr. 40.00 80.00
KG52 Ken Griffey Jr. 40.00 80.00
KG53 Ken Griffey Jr. 40.00 80.00
KG54 Ken Griffey Jr. 40.00 80.00
KG55 Ken Griffey Jr. 40.00 80.00
KG56 Ken Griffey Jr. 40.00 80.00
KG57 Ken Griffey Jr. 40.00 80.00
KG58 Ken Griffey Jr. 40.00 80.00
KG59 Ken Griffey Jr. 40.00 80.00
KG60 Ken Griffey Jr. 40.00 80.00
KG61 Ken Griffey Jr. 40.00 80.00
KG62 Ken Griffey Jr. 40.00 80.00
KG63 Ken Griffey Jr. 40.00 80.00
KG64 Ken Griffey Jr. 40.00 80.00
KG65 Ken Griffey Jr. 40.00 80.00
KG66 Ken Griffey Jr. 40.00 80.00
KG67 Ken Griffey Jr. 40.00 80.00
KG68 Ken Griffey Jr. 40.00 80.00
KG69 Ken Griffey Jr. 40.00 80.00
KG70 Ken Griffey Jr. 40.00 80.00
KG71 Ken Griffey Jr. 40.00 80.00
KG72 Ken Griffey Jr. 40.00 80.00
KG73 Ken Griffey Jr. 40.00 80.00
KG74 Ken Griffey Jr. 40.00 80.00
KG75 Ken Griffey Jr. 40.00 80.00
KG76 Ken Griffey Jr. 40.00 80.00
KG77 Ken Griffey Jr. 40.00 80.00
KG78 Ken Griffey Jr. 40.00 80.00
KG79 Ken Griffey Jr. 40.00 80.00
KG80 Ken Griffey Jr. 40.00 80.00
KG81 Ken Griffey Jr. 40.00 80.00
KG82 Ken Griffey Jr. 40.00 80.00
KG83 Ken Griffey Jr. 40.00 80.00
KG84 Ken Griffey Jr. 40.00 80.00
KG85 Ken Griffey Jr. 40.00 80.00
KG86 Ken Griffey Jr. 40.00 80.00
KG87 Ken Griffey Jr. 40.00 80.00
KG88 Ken Griffey Jr. 40.00 80.00
KG89 Ken Griffey Jr. 40.00 80.00
KG90 Ken Griffey Jr. 40.00 80.00
KG91 Ken Griffey Jr. 40.00 80.00
KG92 Ken Griffey Jr. 40.00 80.00
KG93 Ken Griffey Jr. 40.00 80.00
KG94 Ken Griffey Jr. 40.00 80.00
KG95 Ken Griffey Jr. 40.00 80.00
KG96 Ken Griffey Jr. 40.00 80.00
KG97 Ken Griffey Jr. 40.00 80.00
KG98 Ken Griffey Jr. 40.00 80.00
KG99 Ken Griffey Jr. 40.00 80.00
KG100 Ken Griffey Jr. 40.00 80.00

2008 SPx Ken Griffey Jr. American Hero Memorabilia

COMMON GRIFFEY 20.00 50.00
OVERALL MEM ODDS SIX PER BOX
STATED PRINT RUN 25 SER.#'d SETS
KG1 Ken Griffey Jr. 20.00 50.00
KG2 Ken Griffey Jr. 20.00 50.00
KG3 Ken Griffey Jr. 20.00 50.00
KG4 Ken Griffey Jr. 20.00 50.00
KG5 Ken Griffey Jr. 20.00 50.00
KG6 Ken Griffey Jr. 20.00 50.00
KG7 Ken Griffey Jr. 20.00 50.00
KG8 Ken Griffey Jr. 20.00 50.00
KG9 Ken Griffey Jr. 20.00 50.00
KG10 Ken Griffey Jr. 20.00 50.00
KG11 Ken Griffey Jr. 20.00 50.00
KG12 Ken Griffey Jr. 20.00 50.00
KG13 Ken Griffey Jr. 20.00 50.00
KG14 Ken Griffey Jr. 20.00 50.00
KG15 Ken Griffey Jr. 20.00 50.00
KG16 Ken Griffey Jr. 20.00 50.00
KG17 Ken Griffey Jr. 20.00 50.00
KG18 Ken Griffey Jr. 20.00 50.00
KG19 Ken Griffey Jr. 20.00 50.00
KG20 Ken Griffey Jr. 20.00 50.00
KG21 Ken Griffey Jr. 20.00 50.00
KG22 Ken Griffey Jr. 20.00 50.00
KG23 Ken Griffey Jr. 20.00 50.00
KG24 Ken Griffey Jr. 20.00 50.00
KG25 Ken Griffey Jr. 20.00 50.00
KG26 Ken Griffey Jr. 20.00 50.00
KG27 Ken Griffey Jr. 20.00 50.00
KG28 Ken Griffey Jr. 20.00 50.00
KG29 Ken Griffey Jr. 20.00 50.00
KG30 Ken Griffey Jr. 20.00 50.00
KG31 Ken Griffey Jr. 20.00 50.00
KG32 Ken Griffey Jr. 20.00 50.00
KG33 Ken Griffey Jr. 20.00 50.00
KG34 Ken Griffey Jr. 20.00 50.00
KG35 Ken Griffey Jr. 20.00 50.00
KG36 Ken Griffey Jr. 20.00 50.00
KG37 Ken Griffey Jr. 20.00 50.00
KG38 Ken Griffey Jr. 20.00 50.00
KG39 Ken Griffey Jr. 20.00 50.00
KG40 Ken Griffey Jr. 20.00 50.00
KG41 Ken Griffey Jr. 20.00 50.00
KG42 Ken Griffey Jr. 20.00 50.00
KG43 Ken Griffey Jr. 20.00 50.00
KG44 Ken Griffey Jr. 20.00 50.00
KG45 Ken Griffey Jr. 20.00 50.00
KG46 Ken Griffey Jr. 20.00 50.00
KG47 Ken Griffey Jr. 20.00 50.00
KG48 Ken Griffey Jr. 20.00 50.00
KG49 Ken Griffey Jr. 20.00 50.00
KG50 Ken Griffey Jr. 20.00 50.00
KG51 Ken Griffey Jr. 20.00 50.00
KG52 Ken Griffey Jr. 20.00 50.00
KG53 Ken Griffey Jr. 20.00 50.00
KG54 Ken Griffey Jr. 20.00 50.00
KG55 Ken Griffey Jr. 20.00 50.00
KG56 Ken Griffey Jr. 20.00 50.00
KG57 Ken Griffey Jr. 20.00 50.00
KG58 Ken Griffey Jr. 20.00 50.00
KG59 Ken Griffey Jr. 20.00 50.00
KG60 Ken Griffey Jr. 20.00 50.00
KG61 Ken Griffey Jr. 20.00 50.00
KG62 Ken Griffey Jr. 20.00 50.00
KG63 Ken Griffey Jr. 20.00 50.00
KG64 Ken Griffey Jr. 20.00 50.00
KG65 Ken Griffey Jr. 20.00 50.00
KG66 Ken Griffey Jr. 20.00 50.00
KG67 Ken Griffey Jr. 20.00 50.00
KG68 Ken Griffey Jr. 20.00 50.00
KG69 Ken Griffey Jr. 20.00 50.00
KG70 Ken Griffey Jr. 20.00 50.00
KG71 Ken Griffey Jr. 20.00 50.00
KG72 Ken Griffey Jr. 20.00 50.00
KG73 Ken Griffey Jr. 20.00 50.00
KG74 Ken Griffey Jr. 20.00 50.00
KG75 Ken Griffey Jr. 20.00 50.00
KG76 Ken Griffey Jr. 20.00 50.00
KG77 Ken Griffey Jr. 20.00 50.00
KG78 Ken Griffey Jr. 20.00 50.00
KG79 Ken Griffey Jr. 20.00 50.00
KG80 Ken Griffey Jr. 20.00 50.00
KG81 Ken Griffey Jr. 20.00 50.00
KG82 Ken Griffey Jr. 20.00 50.00
KG83 Ken Griffey Jr. 20.00 50.00
KG84 Ken Griffey Jr. 20.00 50.00
KG85 Ken Griffey Jr. 20.00 50.00
KG86 Ken Griffey Jr. 20.00 50.00
KG87 Ken Griffey Jr. 20.00 50.00
KG88 Ken Griffey Jr. 20.00 50.00
KG89 Ken Griffey Jr. 20.00 50.00
KG90 Ken Griffey Jr. 20.00 50.00
KG91 Ken Griffey Jr. 20.00 50.00
KG92 Ken Griffey Jr. 20.00 50.00
KG93 Ken Griffey Jr. 20.00 50.00
KG94 Ken Griffey Jr. 20.00 50.00
KG95 Ken Griffey Jr. 20.00 50.00
KG96 Ken Griffey Jr. 20.00 50.00
KG97 Ken Griffey Jr. 20.00 50.00
KG98 Ken Griffey Jr. 20.00 50.00
KG99 Ken Griffey Jr. 20.00 50.00
KG100 Ken Griffey Jr. 20.00 50.00

2008 SPx Ken Griffey Jr. American Hero Signature

OVERALL AU ODDS FOUR PER BOX
STATED PRINT RUN 3 SER.#'d SETS
KG1 Ken Griffey Jr. 250.00 350.00
KG2 Ken Griffey Jr. 250.00 350.00
KG3 Ken Griffey Jr. 250.00 350.00
KG4 Ken Griffey Jr. 250.00 350.00
KG5 Ken Griffey Jr. 250.00 350.00
KG6 Ken Griffey Jr. 250.00 350.00
KG7 Ken Griffey Jr. 250.00 350.00
KG8 Ken Griffey Jr. 250.00 350.00
KG9 Ken Griffey Jr. 250.00 350.00
KG10 Ken Griffey Jr. 250.00 350.00
KG11 Ken Griffey Jr. 250.00 350.00
KG12 Ken Griffey Jr. 250.00 350.00
KG13 Ken Griffey Jr. 250.00 350.00
KG14 Ken Griffey Jr. 250.00 350.00
KG15 Ken Griffey Jr. 250.00 350.00
KG16 Ken Griffey Jr. 250.00 350.00
KG17 Ken Griffey Jr. 250.00 350.00
KG18 Ken Griffey Jr. 250.00 350.00
KG19 Ken Griffey Jr. 250.00 350.00
KG20 Ken Griffey Jr. 250.00 350.00
KG21 Ken Griffey Jr. 250.00 350.00
KG22 Ken Griffey Jr. 250.00 350.00
KG23 Ken Griffey Jr. 250.00 350.00
KG24 Ken Griffey Jr. 250.00 350.00
KG25 Ken Griffey Jr. 250.00 350.00
KG26 Ken Griffey Jr. 250.00 350.00
KG27 Ken Griffey Jr. 250.00 350.00
KG28 Ken Griffey Jr. 250.00 350.00
KG29 Ken Griffey Jr. 250.00 350.00
KG30 Ken Griffey Jr. 250.00 350.00
KG31 Ken Griffey Jr. 250.00 350.00
KG32 Ken Griffey Jr. 250.00 350.00
KG33 Ken Griffey Jr. 250.00 350.00
KG34 Ken Griffey Jr. 250.00 350.00
KG35 Ken Griffey Jr. 250.00 350.00
KG36 Ken Griffey Jr. 250.00 350.00
KG37 Ken Griffey Jr. 250.00 350.00
KG38 Ken Griffey Jr. 250.00 350.00
KG39 Ken Griffey Jr. 250.00 350.00
KG40 Ken Griffey Jr. 250.00 350.00
KG41 Ken Griffey Jr. 250.00 350.00
KG42 Ken Griffey Jr. 250.00 350.00
KG43 Ken Griffey Jr. 250.00 350.00
KG44 Ken Griffey Jr. 250.00 350.00
KG45 Ken Griffey Jr. 250.00 350.00
KG46 Ken Griffey Jr. 250.00 350.00
KG47 Ken Griffey Jr. 250.00 350.00
KG48 Ken Griffey Jr. 250.00 350.00
KG49 Ken Griffey Jr. 250.00 350.00
KG50 Ken Griffey Jr. 250.00 350.00
KG51 Ken Griffey Jr. 250.00 350.00
KG52 Ken Griffey Jr. 250.00 350.00
KG53 Ken Griffey Jr. 250.00 350.00
KG54 Ken Griffey Jr. 250.00 350.00
KG55 Ken Griffey Jr. 250.00 350.00
KG56 Ken Griffey Jr. 250.00 350.00
KG57 Ken Griffey Jr. 250.00 350.00
KG58 Ken Griffey Jr. 250.00 350.00
KG59 Ken Griffey Jr. 250.00 350.00
KG60 Ken Griffey Jr. 250.00 350.00
KG61 Ken Griffey Jr. 250.00 350.00
KG62 Ken Griffey Jr. 250.00 350.00
KG63 Ken Griffey Jr. 250.00 350.00
KG64 Ken Griffey Jr. 250.00 350.00
KG65 Ken Griffey Jr. 250.00 350.00
KG66 Ken Griffey Jr. 250.00 350.00
KG67 Ken Griffey Jr. 250.00 350.00
KG68 Ken Griffey Jr. 250.00 350.00
KG69 Ken Griffey Jr. 250.00 350.00
KG70 Ken Griffey Jr. 250.00 350.00
KG71 Ken Griffey Jr. 250.00 350.00
KG72 Ken Griffey Jr. 250.00 350.00
KG73 Ken Griffey Jr. 250.00 350.00
KG74 Ken Griffey Jr. 250.00 350.00
KG75 Ken Griffey Jr. 250.00 350.00
KG76 Ken Griffey Jr. 250.00 350.00
KG77 Ken Griffey Jr. 250.00 350.00
KG78 Ken Griffey Jr. 250.00 350.00
KG79 Ken Griffey Jr. 250.00 350.00
KG80 Ken Griffey Jr. 250.00 350.00
KG81 Ken Griffey Jr. 250.00 350.00
KG82 Ken Griffey Jr. 250.00 350.00
KG83 Ken Griffey Jr. 250.00 350.00
KG84 Ken Griffey Jr. 250.00 350.00
KG85 Ken Griffey Jr. 250.00 350.00
KG86 Ken Griffey Jr. 250.00 350.00
KG87 Ken Griffey Jr. 250.00 350.00
KG88 Ken Griffey Jr. 250.00 350.00
KG89 Ken Griffey Jr. 250.00 350.00
KG90 Ken Griffey Jr. 250.00 350.00
KG91 Ken Griffey Jr. 250.00 350.00
KG92 Ken Griffey Jr. 250.00 350.00
KG93 Ken Griffey Jr. 250.00 350.00
KG94 Ken Griffey Jr. 250.00 350.00
KG95 Ken Griffey Jr. 250.00 350.00
KG96 Ken Griffey Jr. 250.00 350.00
KG97 Ken Griffey Jr. 250.00 350.00
KG98 Ken Griffey Jr. 250.00 350.00
KG99 Ken Griffey Jr. 250.00 350.00
KG100 Ken Griffey Jr. 250.00 350.00

2008 SPx Mystery Rookie Redemptions

OVERALL ODDS TWO PER CASE
REDEEMABLE FOR BASE SET AU RC
EXCHANGE DEADLINE 6/30/2010
RR1 Jay Bruce #146 AU (RC) 50.00 100.00
RR2 Carlos Gonzalez #147 AU (RC) 30.00 60.00
RR3 Evan Longoria #148 AU RC 100.00 200.00
RR4 Collin Balester #149 AU (RC) 30.00 60.00
RR5 Max Scherzer #150 AU RC 40.00 80.00
RR6 Clayton Kershaw #151 AU RC 30.00 60.00
RR7 Alexei Ramirez #152 AU RC 40.00 80.00

2008 SPx Superstar Signatures

OVERALL AU ODDS FOUR PER BOX
EXCHANGE DEADLINE 4/28/2010
BW Brandon Webb 12.50 30.00
DJ Derek Jeter EXCH 75.00 150.00
DM Daisuke Matsuzaka EXCH 75.00 150.00
DU Dan Uggla 6.00 15.00
HR Hanley Ramirez 8.00 20.00
KG Ken Griffey Jr. 50.00 100.00
MH Matt Holliday 8.00 20.00
MT Mark Teixeira 10.00 25.00
PF Prince Fielder 12.50 30.00
PM Pedro Martinez
SR Scott Rolen 10.00 25.00
TG Tom Glavine 15.00 40.00
TH Travis Hafner 4.00 10.00
VG Vladimir Guerrero 15.00 40.00
VM Victor Martinez 6.00 15.00

2008 SPx Superstar Signatures Silver

RANDOM INSERT IN BOX TOPPER PACK
NO PRICING DUE TO SCARCITY
EXCHANGE DEADLINE 4/28/2010

2008 SPx Winning Materials SPx 150

OVERALL GU ODDS SIX PER BOX
STATED PRINT RUN 150 SER.#'d SETS
AB A.J. Burnett 3.00 8.00
AE Andre Ethier 3.00 8.00
AG Adrian Gonzalez 3.00 8.00
AH Aaron Harang 3.00 8.00
AJ Andruw Jones 3.00 8.00
AK Austin Kearns 3.00 8.00
AL Adam LaRoche 3.00 8.00
AP Albert Pujols 5.00 12.00
AP Andy Pettitte 4.00 10.00
AR Aaron Rowand 3.00 8.00
AS Alfonso Soriano 3.00 8.00
BA Bobby Abreu 3.00 8.00
BC Bartolo Colon 3.00 8.00
BE Adrian Beltre 3.00 8.00
BG Brian Giles 3.00 8.00
BM Brian McCann 3.00 8.00
BS Ben Sheets 3.00 8.00
BU B.J. Upton 3.00 8.00
BW Billy Wagner 4.00 10.00
CA Chris Carpenter 3.00 8.00
CB Carlos Beltran 3.00 8.00
CC Chad Cordero 3.00 8.00
CD Carlos Delgado 3.00 8.00
CG Carlos Guillen 3.00 8.00
CH Chris Burke 3.00 8.00
CJ Chipper Jones
CK Casey Kotchman 3.00 8.00
CL Carlos Lee 3.00 8.00
CS Curt Schilling 3.00 8.00
CU Chase Utley 5.00 12.00
CZ Carlos Zambrano 3.00 8.00
DH Dan Haren 3.00 8.00
DJ Derek Jeter 6.00 15.00
DL Derrek Lee 3.00 8.00
DO David Ortiz 3.00 8.00
DU Dan Uggla 3.00 8.00
DW Dontrelle Willis 3.00 8.00
DY Jermaine Dye 3.00 8.00
EC Eric Chavez 3.00 8.00
FH Felix Hernandez 3.00 8.00
FL Francisco Liriano 3.00 8.00
GA Garret Anderson 3.00 8.00
GA Garrett Atkins 3.00 8.00
GJ Geoff Jenkins 3.00 8.00
GM Greg Maddux 5.00 12.00
GO Alex Gordon 5.00 12.00
GR Curtis Granderson 3.00 8.00
GS Grady Sizemore 3.00 8.00
HA Cole Hamels 3.00 8.00
HB Hank Blalock 3.00 8.00
HE Todd Helton 3.00 8.00
HO Trevor Hoffman 3.00 8.00
HR Hanley Ramirez 3.00 8.00
HU Torii Hunter 3.00 8.00
IR Ivan Rodriguez 4.00 10.00
JA Conor Jackson 3.00 8.00
JB Josh Barfield 3.00 8.00
JD J.D. Drew 3.00 8.00
JE Jim Edmonds 4.00 10.00
JF Jeff Francoeur 4.00 10.00
JG Jason Giambi 3.00 8.00
JH Jhonny Peralta 3.00 8.00
JJ J.J. Hardy 3.00 8.00
JK Jeff Kent 3.00 8.00
JM Joe Mauer 3.00 8.00
JN Joe Nathan 3.00 8.00
JO Josh Beckett 4.00 10.00
JP Jake Peavy 3.00 8.00
JR Jose Reyes 3.00 8.00
JS Johan Santana 3.00 8.00
JT Jim Thome 3.00 8.00
JV Jason Varitek 4.00 10.00
KG Ken Griffey Jr.
KJ Kenji Johjima 3.00 8.00
KY Kevin Youkilis 4.00 10.00
LB Lance Berkman 3.00 8.00
LG Luis Gonzalez 3.00 8.00
MC Miguel Cabrera 3.00 8.00
MH Matt Holliday 3.00 8.00
MO Justin Morneau 3.00 8.00
MR Manny Ramirez 4.00 10.00
MT Mark Teixeira 3.00 8.00
MY Michael Young 3.00 8.00
OR Magglio Ordonez 3.00 8.00
PA Jonathan Papelbon 4.00 10.00
PF Prince Fielder 4.00 10.00
PM Pedro Martinez 3.00 8.00
PO Jorge Posada 3.00 8.00
RA Aramis Ramirez 3.00 8.00
RF Rafael Furcal
RH Roy Halladay 3.00 8.00
RJ Randy Johnson 3.00 8.00
RO Roy Oswalt 3.00 8.00
SM John Smoltz 4.00 10.00
TE Miguel Tejada 3.00 8.00
TH Tim Hudson 3.00 8.00
TR Travis Hafner 3.00 8.00
VE Justin Verlander 3.00 8.00
VG Vladimir Guerrero 3.00 8.00
VW Vernon Wells 3.00 8.00

2008 SPx Winning Materials Autographs

OVERALL AU ODDS FOUR PER BOX
STATED PRINT RUN 20 SER.#'d SETS
VERLAN.PRINT RUN 10 SER.#'d SETS
NO PRICING DUE TO SCARCITY
EXCHANGE DEADLINE 4/28/2010

2008 SPx Winning Materials Baseball 99

*BB 99: .4X TO 1X WM SPX 150
OVERALL GU ODDS SIX PER BOX
STATED PRINT RUN 99 SER.#'d SETS
KG Ken Griffey Jr. 5.00 12.00
RF Rafael Furcal 3.00 8.00

2008 SPx Winning Materials Dual Jersey Number

*DUAL JN: .5X TO 1.2X WM SPX 150
OVERALL GU ODDS SIX PER BOX
PRINT RUNS B/WN 35-46 COPIES PER
CJ Chipper Jones/46 5.00 12.00

2008 SPx Winning Materials Dual Limited Patch SPx

*DUAL LTD PATCH: .6X TO 1.5X LTD PATCH SPX
OVERALL GU ODDS SIX PER BOX
PRINT RUNS B/WN 23-50 COPIES PER
NO PRICING ON QTY 25 OR LESS
KG Ken Griffey Jr. 15.00 40.00

2008 SPx Winning Materials Dual Limited Patch Team Initials

OVERALL GU ODDS SIX PER BOX
STATED PRINT RUN 25 SER.#'d SETS
HANLEY PRINT RUN 5 SER.#'d SETS
NO PRICING DUE TO SCARCITY

2008 SPx Winning Materials Dual MLB 20

OVERALL GU ODDS SIX PER BOX
STATED PRINT RUN 20 SER.#'d SETS
NO PRICING DUE TO SCARCITY

2008 SPx Winning Materials Dual Position 20

OVERALL GU ODDS SIX PER BOX
STATED PRINT RUN 20 SER.#'d SETS
NO PRICING DUE TO SCARCITY

2008 SPx Winning Materials Dual SPx

*DUAL SPX: .5X TO 1.2X WM SPX 150
OVERALL GU ODDS SIX PER BOX
STATED PRINT RUN 50 SER.#'d SETS

2008 SPx Winning Materials Dual Team Initials 25

OVERALL GU ODDS SIX PER BOX
STATED PRINT RUN 25 SER.#'d SETS
NO PRICING DUE TO SCARCITY

2008 SPx Winning Materials Jersey Number 125

*JN 125: .4X TO 1X WM SPX 150
OVERALL GU ODDS SIX PER BOX
STATED PRINT RUN 125 SER.#'d SETS
RF Rafael Furcal 3.00 8.00

2008 SPx Winning Materials Limited Patch SPx

OVERALL GU ODDS SIX PER BOX
PRINT RUNS B/WN 72-99 COPIES PER
AB A.J. Burnett 4.00 10.00
AE Andre Ethier 4.00 10.00
AG Adrian Gonzalez 4.00 10.00
AH Aaron Harang 4.00 10.00
AJ Andruw Jones 4.00 10.00
AK Austin Kearns 4.00 10.00
AL Adam LaRoche 4.00 10.00
AP Albert Pujols 10.00 25.00
AR Aaron Rowand 4.00 10.00
AS Alfonso Soriano 4.00 10.00
AT Garrett Atkins 4.00 10.00
BA Bobby Abreu 4.00 10.00
BC Bartolo Colon 4.00 10.00
BE Adrian Beltre 4.00 10.00
BG Brian Giles 4.00 10.00
BM Brian McCann/72 4.00 10.00
BS Ben Sheets/97 4.00 10.00
BU B.J. Upton 4.00 10.00
BW Billy Wagner 5.00 12.00
CA Chris Carpenter 4.00 10.00
CB Carlos Beltran 4.00 10.00
CC Chad Cordero 4.00 10.00
CD Carlos Delgado 4.00 10.00
CG Carlos Guillen 4.00 10.00
CH Chris Burke 4.00 10.00
CJ Chipper Jones 5.00 12.00
CK Casey Kotchman 4.00 10.00
CL Carlos Lee 4.00 10.00
CS Curt Schilling 4.00 10.00
CU Chase Utley 5.00 12.00
CZ Carlos Zambrano 4.00 10.00
DH Dan Haren 4.00 10.00
DJ Derek Jeter/76 10.00 25.00
DL Derrek Lee 4.00 10.00
DO David Ortiz 5.00 12.00
DU Dan Uggla 4.00 10.00
DW Dontrelle Willis 4.00 10.00
DY Jermaine Dye 4.00 10.00
EC Eric Chavez 4.00 10.00
FH Felix Hernandez 4.00 10.00
FL Francisco Liriano 4.00 10.00
GA Garret Anderson 4.00 10.00
GJ Geoff Jenkins 4.00 10.00
GM Greg Maddux 6.00 15.00
GO Alex Gordon 6.00 15.00
GR Curtis Granderson 4.00 10.00
GS Grady Sizemore 4.00 10.00
HA Cole Hamels 4.00 10.00
HB Hank Blalock 4.00 10.00
HE Todd Helton 4.00 10.00
HO Trevor Hoffman 4.00 10.00
HR Hanley Ramirez 4.00 10.00
HU Torii Hunter 4.00 10.00
IR Ivan Rodriguez 5.00 12.00
JA Conor Jackson/80 4.00 10.00
JB Josh Barfield 4.00 10.00
JD J.D. Drew 4.00 10.00
JE Jim Edmonds 5.00 12.00
JF Jeff Francoeur 5.00 12.00
JG Jason Giambi 4.00 10.00
JH Jhonny Peralta 4.00 10.00
JJ J.J. Hardy 4.00 10.00
JK Jeff Kent 4.00 10.00
JM Joe Mauer 4.00 10.00
JN Joe Nathan 4.00 10.00
JO Josh Beckett 5.00 12.00
JP Jake Peavy 4.00 10.00
JR Jose Reyes 4.00 10.00
JS Johan Santana 4.00 10.00
JT Jim Thome 4.00 10.00
JV Jason Varitek 5.00 12.00
KG Ken Griffey Jr. 6.00 15.00
KJ Kenji Johjima 4.00 10.00
KY Kevin Youkilis 5.00 12.00
LB Lance Berkman 4.00 10.00
LG Luis Gonzalez 4.00 10.00
MC Miguel Cabrera 4.00 10.00
MH Matt Holliday 4.00 10.00
MO Justin Morneau 4.00 10.00
MR Manny Ramirez 5.00 12.00
MT Mark Teixeira 4.00 10.00
MY Michael Young 4.00 10.00
OR Magglio Ordonez 4.00 10.00
PA Jonathan Papelbon 5.00 12.00
PE Andy Pettitte 4.00 10.00
PF Prince Fielder 5.00 12.00
PM Pedro Martinez 4.00 10.00
PO Jorge Posada 4.00 10.00
RA Aramis Ramirez 4.00 10.00
RF Rafael Furcal 4.00 10.00
RH Roy Halladay 4.00 10.00
RJ Randy Johnson 4.00 10.00
RO Roy Oswalt 4.00 10.00
SM John Smoltz 5.00 12.00
TE Miguel Tejada/83 4.00 10.00
TH Tim Hudson 4.00 10.00
TR Travis Hafner 4.00 10.00
VE Justin Verlander 4.00 10.00
VG Vladimir Guerrero 4.00 10.00
VW Vernon Wells 4.00 10.00

2008 SPx Winning Materials Limited Patch Team Initials

*LTD PATCH TI: .5X TO 1.2X LTD PATCH SPX
OVERALL GU ODDS SIX PER BOX
PRINT RUNS B/WN 40-50 COPIES PER

2008 SPx Winning Materials MLB 125

*MLB 125: .4X TO 1X WM SPX 150
OVERALL GU ODDS SIX PER BOX
STATED PRINT RUN 125 SER.#'d SETS
RF Rafael Furcal 3.00 8.00

2008 SPx Winning Materials Position 75

*POS 75: .4X TO 1X WM SPX 150
OVERALL GU ODDS SIX PER BOX
STATED PRINT RUN 75 SER.#'d SETS

2008 SPx Winning Materials SPx Die Cut 150

*SPX DC 150: .4X TO 1X SPX 150
OVERALL GU ODDS SIX PER BOX
STATED PRINT RUN 150 SER.#'d SETS

2008 SPx Winning Materials Team Initials 99

*TI 99: .4X TO 1X WM SPX 150
OVERALL GU ODDS SIX PER BOX
STATED PRINT RUN 99 SER.#'d SETS
KG Ken Griffey Jr. 5.00 12.00
RF Rafael Furcal 3.00 8.00

2008 SPx Winning Materials Triple Limited Patch 15

OVERALL GU ODDS SIX PER BOX
STATED PRINT RUN 15 SER.#'d SETS
NO PRICING DUE TO SCARCITY

2008 SPx Winning Materials Triple SPx 15

OVERALL GU ODDS SIX PER BOX
STATED PRINT RUN 15 SER.#'d SETS
NO PRICING DUE TO SCARCITY

2008 SPx Winning Materials Triple Swatch Autographs

OVERALL AU ODDS FOUR PER BOX
STATED PRINT RUN 5 SER.#'d SETS
NO PRICING DUE TO SCARCITY
EXCHANGE DEADLINE 4/28/2010

2008 SPx Winning Materials Triple Team Initials 10

OVERALL GU ODDS SIX PER BOX
STATED PRINT RUN 10 SER.#'d SETS
NO PRICING DUE TO SCARCITY

2008 SPx Winning Materials UD Logo

*LOGO 99: .4X TO 1X WM SPX 150
OVERALL GU ODDS SIX PER BOX
PRINT RUNS B/WN 26-99 COPIES PER
KG Ken Griffey Jr./26 8.00 20.00
RF Rafael Furcal 3.00 8.00

2008 SPx Winning Trios

OVERALL GU ODDS SIX PER BOX
STATED PRINT RUN 75 SER.#'d SETS
GOLD 25 PRINT RUN 25 SER.#'d SETS
NO GOLD 25 PRICING DUE TO SCARCITY
GOLD 15 PRINT RUN 15 SER.#'d SETS
NO GOLD 15 PRICING DUE TO SCARCITY
LTD.PATCH PRINT RUN 25 SER.#'d SETS
NO LTD.PATCH PRICING DUE TO SCARCITY
AGK Garret Anderson 4.00 10.00
Vladimir Guerrero
Casey Kotchman
BHJ Adrian Beltre 4.00 10.00
Felix Hernandez
Kenji Johjima
BSS Josh Beckett 4.00 10.00
Johan Santana
C.C. Sabathia
CRP Chris Carpenter 6.00 15.00
Scott Rolen
Albert Pujols
CRU Miguel Cabrera 4.00 10.00
Hanley Ramirez
Dan Uggla
DBR Carlos Delgado 4.00 10.00
Carlos Beltran
Jose Reyes
DOP Carlos Delgado 8.00 20.00
David Ortiz
Albert Pujols
GHL Yovani Gallardo 6.00 15.00
Phil Hughes
Tim Lincecum
GIB Alex Gordon 20.00 50.00
Akinori Iwamura
Ryan Braun
GJP Ken Griffey Jr. 15.00 40.00
Derek Jeter
Albert Pujols
GMW Tom Glavine 8.00 20.00
Pedro Martinez
Billy Wagner
HAH Todd Helton 5.00 12.00
Garrett Atkins
Matt Holliday
HDF Travis Hafner 5.00 12.00
Adam Dunn
Prince Fielder
HFB J.J. Hardy 8.00 20.00
Prince Fielder
Ryan Braun
HRR J.J. Hardy 4.00 10.00
Jose Reyes
Hanley Ramirez
HSS Travis Hafner 4.00 10.00
Grady Sizemore
C.C. Sabathia
JBH Andruw Jones 4.00 10.00
Carlos Beltran
Torii Hunter
JDY Conor Jackson 4.00 10.00
Stephen Drew
Chris B. Young
JRR Chipper Jones 5.00 12.00
Scott Rolen
Aramis Ramirez
JST Chipper Jones 6.00 15.00
John Smoltz
Mark Teixeira
KFE Jeff Kent 5.00 12.00
Rafael Furcal
Andre Ethier
KUY Scott Kazmir 4.00 10.00
B.J. Upton
Delmon Young
LBO Carlos Lee 4.00 10.00
Lance Berkman
Roy Oswalt
LCL Noah Lowry 6.00 15.00
Matt Cain
Tim Lincecum
LSZ Derrek Lee 6.00 15.00
Alfonso Soriano
Carlos Zambrano
MGS Greg Maddux 15.00 40.00
Tom Glavine
John Smoltz
MHP Greg Maddux 6.00 15.00
Trevor Hoffman
Jake Peavy
MPB Victor Martinez 4.00 10.00
Jhonny Peralta
Josh Barfield
MSM Justin Morneau 5.00 12.00
Johan Santana
Joe Mauer
OGV Magglio Ordonez 10.00 25.00
Curtis Granderson
Justin Verlander
PJP Andy Pettitte 30.00 60.00
Derek Jeter
Jorge Posada
RJC Alex Rodriguez 30.00 60.00
Derek Jeter
Robinson Cano
RMM Ivan Rodriguez 5.00 12.00
Victor Martinez
Joe Mauer
SBP Curt Schilling 6.00 15.00
Josh Beckett
Jonathan Papelbon
SOH Ben Sheets 4.00 10.00
Roy Oswalt
Aaron Harang
SRG Gary Sheffield 6.00 15.00
Ivan Rodriguez
Carlos Guillen
TDB Jim Thome 5.00 12.00
Jermaine Dye
Mark Buehrle
UHR Chase Utley 6.00 15.00
Cole Hamels
Aaron Rowand
UKU Chase Utley 4.00 10.00
Ian Kinsler
Dan Uggla
VOY Jason Varitek 12.50 30.00
David Ortiz
Kevin Youkilis
WHB Vernon Wells 5.00 12.00
Roy Halladay
A.J. Burnett
ZPH Carlos Zambrano 4.00 10.00
Jake Peavy
Aaron Harang

2008 SPx Young Star Signatures

OVERALL AU ODDS FOUR PER BOX
EXCHANGE DEADLINE 4/28/2010
AC Alexi Casilla 3.00 8.00
AE Andre Ethier 4.00 10.00
BB Brian Bannister 4.00 10.00
BM Brian McCann 10.00 25.00
BU Brian Burres 4.00 10.00
CD Chris Duncan 10.00 25.00
CH Cole Hamels 10.00 25.00
CY Chris B. Young 5.00 12.00
FC Fausto Carmona 4.00 10.00
FL Francisco Liriano 4.00 10.00
IK Ian Kinsler 6.00 15.00
JA Joaquin Arias 3.00 8.00
JD John Danks 3.00 8.00
JJ Josh Johnson 3.00 8.00
JL James Loney 6.00 15.00
JS Jarrod Saltalamacchia 3.00 8.00
JV Justin Verlander 8.00 20.00
JW Josh Willingham 3.00 8.00
JZ Joel Zumaya 3.00 8.00
KK Kevin Kouzmanoff 3.00 8.00
MA Nick Markakis 6.00 15.00
MC Matt Chico 3.00 8.00
MF Mike Fontenot 5.00 12.00
MO Micah Owings 4.00 10.00
MR Mark Reynolds 5.00 12.00
NM Nate McLouth 5.00 12.00
PH Phil Hughes 6.00 15.00
RB Ryan Braun 12.50 30.00
RG Ryan Garko 3.00 8.00
RM Russell Martin 6.00 15.00
SD Stephen Drew 4.00 10.00
SH James Shields 5.00 12.00
TB Travis Buck 4.00 10.00
TG Tom Gorzelanny 3.00 8.00
TT Troy Tulowitzki 8.00 20.00

2008 SPx Young Star Signatures Silver

RANDOM INSERT IN BOX TOPPER PACK
NO PRICING DUE TO SCARCITY
EXCHANGE DEADLINE 4/28/2010

1991 Stadium Club

This 600-card standard size set marked Topps first premium quality set. The set was issued in two separate series of 300 cards each. Cards were distributed in plastic wrapped packs. Series II cards were also available at McDonald's restaurants in the Northeast at three cards per pack. The set created a stir in the hobby upon release with dazzling full-color borderless photos and slick, glossy card stock. The back of each card has the basic biographical information as well as making use of the Fastball BARS system and an inset photo of the player's Topps rookie card. Notable Rookie Cards include Jeff Bagwell.

COMPLETE SET (600) 25.00 60.00
COMP.SERIES 1 (300) 15.00 40.00
COMP.SERIES 2 (300) 8.00 20.00
1 Dave Stewart Tuxedo .20 .50
2 Wally Joyner .20 .50
3 Shawon Dunston .08 .25
4 Darren Daulton .08 .25
5 Will Clark .30 .75
6 Sammy Sosa .50 1.25
7 Dan Plesac .08 .25
8 Marquis Grissom .20 .50
9 Erik Hanson .08 .25
10 Geno Petralli .08 .25
11 Jose Rijo .08 .25
12 Carlos Quintana .08 .25
13 Junior Ortiz .08 .25
14 Bob Walk .08 .25
15 Mike Macfarlane .08 .25
16 Eric Yelding .08 .25
17 Bryn Smith .08 .25
18 Bip Roberts .08 .25
19 Mike Scioscia .08 .25
20 Mark Williamson .08 .25
21 Don Mattingly 1.25 3.00
22 John Franco .20 .50
23 Chet Lemon .08 .25
24 Tom Henke .08 .25
25 Jerry Browne .08 .25
26 Dave Justice .20 .50
27 Mark Langston .08 .25
28 Damon Berryhill .08 .25
29 Kevin Bass .08 .25
30 Scott Fletcher .08 .25
31 Moises Alou .20 .50
32 Dave Valle .08 .25
33 Jody Reed .08 .25
34 Dave West .08 .25
35 Kevin McReynolds .08 .25
36 Pat Combs .08 .25
37 Eric Davis .20 .50
38 Bret Saberhagen .20 .50
39 Stan Javier .08 .25
40 Chuck Cary .08 .25
41 Tony Phillips .08 .25
42 Lee Smith .20 .50
43 Tim Teufel .08 .25
44 Lance Dickson RC .15 .40
45 Greg Litton .08 .25
46 Ted Higuera .08 .25
47 Edgar Martinez .30 .75
48 Steve Avery .08 .25
49 Walt Weiss .08 .25
50 David Segui .20 .50
51 Andy Benes .08 .25
52 Karl Rhodes .08 .25
53 Neal Heaton .08 .25
54 Danny Gladden .08 .25
55 Luis Rivera .08 .25
56 Kevin Brown .20 .50
57 Frank Thomas .50 1.25
58 Terry Mulholland .08 .25
59 Dick Schofield .08 .25
60 Ron Darling .08 .25
61 Sandy Alomar Jr. .08 .25
62 Dave Stieb .08 .25
63 Alan Trammell .20 .50
64 Matt Nokes .08 .25
65 Lenny Harris .08 .25
66 Milt Thompson .08 .25
67 Storm Davis .08 .25
68 Joe Oliver .08 .25
69 Andres Galarraga .20 .50
70 Ozzie Guillen .20 .50
71 Ken Howell .08 .25
72 Garry Templeton .08 .25
73 Derrick May .08 .25
74 Xavier Hernandez .08 .25
75 Dave Parker .20 .50
76 Rick Aguilera .20 .50
77 Robby Thompson .08 .25
78 Pete Incaviglia .08 .25
79 Bob Welch .08 .25
80 Randy Milligan .08 .25
81 Chuck Finley .20 .50
82 Alvin Davis .08 .25
83 Tim Naehring .08 .25
84 Jay Bell .20 .50
85 Joe Magrane .08 .25
86 Howard Johnson .08 .25
87 Jack McDowell .08 .25
88 Kevin Seitzer .08 .25
89 Bruce Ruffin .08 .25
90 Fernando Valenzuela .20 .50
91 Terry Kennedy .08 .25
92 Barry Larkin .30 .75
93 Larry Walker .50 1.25
94 Luis Salazar .08 .25
95 Gary Sheffield .20 .50
96 Bobby Witt .08 .25
97 Lonnie Smith .08 .25
98 Bryan Harvey .08 .25
99 Mookie Wilson .20 .50
100 Dwight Gooden .20 .50
101 Lou Whitaker .20 .50
102 Ron Karkovice .08 .25
103 Jesse Barfield .08 .25
104 Jose DeJesus .08 .25
105 Benito Santiago .20 .50
106 Brian Holman .08 .25
107 Rafael Ramirez .08 .25
108 Ellis Burks .20 .50
109 Mike Bielecki .08 .25
110 Kirby Puckett .50 1.25
111 Terry Shumpert .08 .25
112 Chuck Crim .08 .25
113 Todd Benzinger .08 .25
114 Brian Barnes RC .15 .40
115 Carlos Baerga .08 .25
116 Kal Daniels .08 .25
117 Dave Johnson .08 .25
118 Andy Van Slyke .30 .75
119 John Burkett .08 .25
120 Rickey Henderson .50 1.25
121 Tim Jones .08 .25
122 Daryl Irvine RC .08 .25
123 Ruben Sierra .20 .50
124 Jim Abbott .30 .75
125 Daryl Boston .08 .25
126 Greg Maddux .75 2.00
127 Von Hayes .08 .25
128 Mike Fitzgerald .08 .25
129 Wayne Edwards .08 .25
130 Greg Briley .08 .25
131 Rob Dibble .20 .50
132 Gene Larkin .08 .25
133 David Wells .20 .50
134 Steve Balboni .08 .25
135 Greg Vaughn .08 .25
136 Mark Davis .08 .25
137 Dave Rhode .08 .25
138 Eric Show .08 .25
139 Bobby Bonilla .20 .50
140 Dana Kiecker .08 .25
141 Gary Pettis .08 .25
142 Dennis Boyd .08 .25
143 Mike Benjamin .08 .25
144 Luis Polonia .08 .25
145 Doug Jones .08 .25
146 Al Newman .08 .25
147 Alex Fernandez .08 .25
148 Bill Doran .08 .25
149 Kevin Elster .08 .25
150 Len Dykstra .20 .50
151 Mike Gallego .08 .25
152 Tim Belcher .08 .25
153 Jay Buhner .20 .50
154 Ozzie Smith UER .75 2.00
(Rookie card is 1979, but card back says '78)
155 Jose Canseco .30 .75
156 Gregg Olson .08 .25
157 Charlie O'Brien .08 .25
158 Frank Tanana .08 .25
159 George Brett 1.25 3.00
160 Jeff Huson .08 .25
161 Kevin Tapani .08 .25
162 Jerome Walton .08 .25
163 Charlie Hayes .08 .25
164 Chris Bosio .08 .25
165 Chris Sabo .08 .25
166 Lance Parrish .20 .50
167 Don Robinson .08 .25
168 Manny Lee .08 .25
169 Dennis Rasmussen .08 .25
170 Wade Boggs .30 .75
171 Bob Geren .08 .25
172 Mackey Sasser .08 .25
173 Julio Franco .20 .50
174 Otis Nixon .08 .25
175 Bert Blyleven .20 .50
176 Craig Biggio .30 .75
177 Eddie Murray .50 1.25
178 Randy Tomlin RC .15 .40
179 Tino Martinez .50 1.25
180 Carlton Fisk .30 .75
181 Dwight Smith .08 .25
182 Scott Garrelts .08 .25
183 Jim Gantner .08 .25
184 Dickie Thon .08 .25
185 John Farrell .08 .25
186 Cecil Fielder .20 .50
187 Glenn Braggs .08 .25
188 Allan Anderson .08 .25
189 Kurt Stillwell .08 .25
190 Jose Oquendo .08 .25
191 Joe Orsulak .08 .25
192 Ricky Jordan .08 .25
193 Kelly Downs .08 .25
194 Delino DeShields .08 .25
195 Omar Vizquel .30 .75
196 Mark Carreon .08 .25
197 Mike Harkey .08 .25
198 Jack Howell .08 .25
199 Lance Johnson .08 .25
200 Nolan Ryan TUX 2.00 5.00
201 John Marzano .08 .25
202 Doug Drabek .08 .25
203 Mark Lemke .08 .25
204 Steve Sax .08 .25
205 Greg Harris .08 .25
206 B.J. Surhoff .20 .50
207 Todd Burns .08 .25
208 Jose Gonzalez .08 .25
209 Mike Scott .08 .25
210 Dave Magadan .08 .25
211 Dante Bichette .20 .50
212 Trevor Wilson .08 .25
213 Hector Villanueva .08 .25
214 Dan Pasqua .08 .25
215 Greg Colbrunn RC .25 .60
216 Mike Jeffcoat .08 .25
217 Harold Reynolds .20 .50
218 Paul O'Neill .30 .75
219 Mark Guthrie .08 .25
220 Barry Bonds 1.50 4.00
221 Jimmy Key .20 .50
222 Billy Ripken .08 .25
223 Tom Pagnozzi .08 .25
224 Bo Jackson .50 1.25
225 Sid Fernandez .08 .25
226 Mike Marshall .08 .25
227 John Kruk .20 .50
228 Mike Fetters .08 .25
229 Eric Anthony .08 .25
230 Ryne Sandberg .75 2.00
231 Carney Lansford .20 .50
232 Melido Perez .08 .25
233 Jose Lind .08 .25
234 Darryl Hamilton .08 .25
235 Tom Browning .08 .25
236 Spike Owen .08 .25
237 Juan Gonzalez .50 1.25
238 Felix Fermin .08 .25
239 Keith Miller .08 .25
240 Mark Gubicza .08 .25
241 Kent Anderson .08 .25
242 Alvaro Espinoza .08 .25
243 Dale Murphy .30 .75
244 Orel Hershiser .20 .50
245 Paul Molitor .20 .50
246 Eddie Whitson .08 .25
247 Joe Girardi .08 .25
248 Kent Hrbek .20 .50
249 Bill Sampen .08 .25
250 Kevin Mitchell .08 .25
251 Mariano Duncan .08 .25
252 Scott Bradley .08 .25
253 Mike Greenwell .08 .25
254 Tom Gordon .08 .25
255 Todd Zeile .08 .25
256 Bobby Thigpen .08 .25
257 Gregg Jefferies .08 .25
258 Kenny Rogers .20 .50
259 Shane Mack .08 .25
260 Zane Smith .08 .25
261 Mitch Williams .08 .25
262 Jim Deshaies .08 .25
263 Dave Winfield .20 .50
264 Ben McDonald .08 .25
265 Randy Ready .08 .25
266 Pat Borders .08 .25
267 Jose Uribe .08 .25
268 Derek Lilliquist .08 .25
269 Greg Brock .08 .25
270 Ken Griffey Jr. 1.00 2.50
271 Jeff Gray RC .08 .25
272 Danny Tartabull .08 .25
273 Dennis Martinez .20 .50
274 Robin Ventura .20 .50
275 Randy Myers .08 .25
276 Jack Daugherty .08 .25
277 Greg Gagne .08 .25
278 Jay Howell .08 .25
279 Mike LaValliere .08 .25
280 Rex Hudler .08 .25
281 Mike Simms RC .08 .25
282 Kevin Maas .08 .25
283 Jeff Ballard .08 .25
284 Dave Henderson .08 .25
285 Pete O'Brien .08 .25
286 Brook Jacoby .08 .25
287 Mike Henneman .08 .25
288 Greg Olson .08 .25
289 Greg Myers .08 .25
290 Mark Grace .30 .75
291 Shawn Abner .08 .25
292 Frank Viola .20 .50
293 Lee Stevens .08 .25
294 Jason Grimsley .08 .25
295 Matt Williams .20 .50
296 Ron Robinson .08 .25
297 Tom Brunansky .08 .25
298 Checklist 1-100 .08 .25
299 Checklist 101-200 .08 .25
300 Checklist 201-300 .08 .25
301 Darryl Strawberry .20 .50
302 Bud Black .08 .25
303 Harold Baines .20 .50
304 Roberto Alomar .30 .75
305 Norm Charlton .08 .25
306 Gary Thurman .08 .25
307 Mike Felder .08 .25
308 Tony Gwynn .60 1.50
309 Roger Clemens 1.50 4.00
310 Andre Dawson .20 .50
311 Scott Radinsky .08 .25
312 Bob Melvin .08 .25
313 Kirk McCaskill .08 .25
314 Pedro Guerrero .20 .50
315 Walt Terrell .08 .25
316 Sam Horn .08 .25
317 W.Chamberlain RC UER .25 .60
Card listed as 1989
Debut card, should be 1990)
318 Pedro Munoz RC .15 .40
319 Roberto Kelly .08 .25
320 Mark Portugal .08 .25
321 Tim McIntosh .08 .25
322 Jesse Orosco .08 .25
323 Gary Green .08 .25
324 Greg Harris .08 .25
325 Hubie Brooks .08 .25
326 Chris Nabholz .08 .25
327 Terry Pendleton .20 .50
328 Eric King .08 .25

Card	Low	High
329 Chili Davis	.20	.50
330 Anthony Telford RC	.08	.25
331 Kelly Gruber	.08	.25
332 Dennis Eckersley	.20	.50
333 Mel Hall	.08	.25
334 Bob Kipper	.08	.25
335 Willie McGee	.20	.50
336 Steve Olin	.08	.25
337 Steve Buechele	.08	.25
338 Scott Leius	.08	.25
339 Hal Morris	.08	.25
340 Jose Offerman	.08	.25
341 Kent Mercker	.08	.25
342 Ken Griffey Sr.	.20	.50
343 Pete Harnisch	.08	.25
344 Kirk Gibson	.20	.50
345 Dave Smith	.08	.25
346 Dave Martinez	.08	.25
347 Atlee Hammaker	.08	.25
348 Brian Downing	.08	.25
349 Todd Hundley	.08	.25
350 Candy Maldonado	.08	.25
351 Dwight Evans	.30	.75
352 Steve Searcy	.08	.25
353 Gary Gaetti	.20	.50
354 Jeff Reardon	.20	.50
355 Travis Fryman	.20	.50
356 Dave Righetti	.20	.50
357 Fred McGriff	.30	.75
358 Don Slaught	.08	.25
359 Gene Nelson	.08	.25
360 Billy Spiers	.08	.25
361 Lee Guetterman	.08	.25
362 Darren Lewis	.08	.25
363 Duane Ward	.08	.25
364 Lloyd Moseby	.08	.25
365 John Smoltz	.30	.75
366 Felix Jose	.08	.25
367 David Cone	.20	.50
368 Wally Backman	.08	.25
369 Jeff Montgomery	.08	.25
370 Rich Garces RC	.15	.40
371 Billy Hatcher	.08	.25
372 Bill Swift	.08	.25
373 Jim Eisenreich	.08	.25
374 Rob Ducey	.08	.25
375 Tim Crews	.08	.25
376 Steve Finley	.20	.50
377 Jeff Blauser	.08	.25
378 Willie Wilson	.08	.25
379 Gerald Perry	.08	.25
380 Jose Mesa	.08	.25
381 Pat Kelly RC	.25	.60
382 Matt Merullo	.08	.25
383 Ivan Calderon	.08	.25
384 Scott Chiamparino	.08	.25
385 Lloyd McClendon	.08	.25
386 Dave Bergman	.08	.25
387 Ed Sprague	.08	.25
388 Jeff Bagwell RC	1.25	3.00
389 Brett Butler	.20	.50
390 Larry Andersen	.08	.25
391 Glenn Davis	.08	.25
392 Alex Cole UER (Front photo actually Otis Nixon)	.08	.25
393 Mike Heath	.08	.25
394 Danny Darwin	.08	.25
395 Steve Lake	.08	.25
396 Tim Layana	.08	.25
397 Terry Leach	.08	.25
398 Bill Wegman	.08	.25
399 Mark McGwire	1.50	4.00
400 Mike Boddicker	.08	.25
401 Steve Howe	.08	.25
402 Bernard Gilkey	.08	.25
403 Thomas Howard	.08	.25
404 Rafael Belliard	.08	.25
405 Tom Candiotti	.08	.25
406 Rene Gonzales	.08	.25
407 Chuck McElroy	.08	.25
408 Paul Sorrento	.08	.25
409 Randy Johnson	.60	1.50
410 Brady Anderson	.20	.50
411 Dennis Cook	.08	.25
412 Mickey Tettleton	.08	.25
413 Mike Stanton	.08	.25
414 Ken Oberkfell	.08	.25
415 Rick Honeycutt	.08	.25
416 Nelson Santovenia	.08	.25
417 Bob Tewksbury	.08	.25
418 Brent Mayne	.08	.25
419 Steve Farr	.08	.25
420 Phil Stephenson	.08	.25
421 Jeff Russell	.08	.25
422 Chris James	.08	.25
423 Tim Leary	.08	.25
424 Gary Carter	.20	.50
425 Glenallen Hill	.08	.25
426 Matt Young UER Card mentions 83T/Tr as RC, but 84T shown)	.08	.25
427 Sid Bream	.08	.25
428 Greg Swindell	.08	.25
429 Scott Aldred	.08	.25
430 Cal Ripken	1.50	4.00
431 Bill Landrum	.08	.25
432 Earnest Riles	.08	.25
433 Danny Jackson	.08	.25
434 Casey Candaele	.08	.25
435 Ken Hill	.08	.25
436 Jaime Navarro	.08	.25
437 Lance Blankenship	.08	.25
438 Randy Velarde	.08	.25
439 Frank DiPino	.08	.25
440 Carl Nichols	.08	.25
441 Jeff M. Robinson	.08	.25
442 Deion Sanders	.30	.75
443 Vicente Palacios	.08	.25
444 Devon White	.20	.50
445 John Cerutti	.08	.25
446 Tracy Jones	.08	.25
447 Jack Morris	.20	.50
448 Mitch Webster	.08	.25
449 Bob Ojeda	.08	.25
450 Oscar Azocar	.08	.25
451 Luis Aquino	.08	.25
452 Mark Whiten	.08	.25
453 Stan Belinda	.08	.25
454 Ron Gant	.20	.50
455 Jose DeLeon	.08	.25
456 Mark Salas UER Back has 85T photo, but calls it 86T	.08	.25
457 Junior Felix	.08	.25
458 Wally Whitehurst	.08	.25
459 Phil Plantier RC	.25	.60
460 Juan Berenguer	.08	.25
461 Franklin Stubbs	.08	.25
462 Joe Boever	.08	.25
463 Tim Wallach	.08	.25
464 Mike Moore	.08	.25
465 Albert Belle	.20	.50
466 Mike Witt	.08	.25
467 Craig Worthington	.08	.25
468 Jerald Clark	.08	.25
469 Scott Terry	.08	.25
470 Milt Cuyler	.08	.25
471 John Smiley	.08	.25
472 Charles Nagy	.08	.25
473 Alan Mills	.08	.25
474 John Russell	.08	.25
475 Bruce Hurst	.08	.25
476 Andujar Cedeno	.08	.25
477 Dave Eiland	.08	.25
478 Brian McRae RC	.25	.60
479 Mike LaCoss	.08	.25
480 Chris Gwynn	.08	.25
481 Jamie Moyer	.20	.50
482 John Olerud	.20	.50
483 Efrain Valdez RC	.08	.25
484 Sil Campusano	.08	.25
485 Pascual Perez	.08	.25
486 Gary Redus	.08	.25
487 Andy Hawkins	.08	.25
488 Cory Snyder	.08	.25
489 Chris Hoiles	.08	.25
490 Ron Hassey	.08	.25
491 Gary Wayne	.08	.25
492 Mark Lewis	.08	.25
493 Scott Coolbaugh	.08	.25
494 Gerald Young	.08	.25
495 Juan Samuel	.08	.25
496 Willie Fraser	.08	.25
497 Jeff Treadway	.08	.25
498 Vince Coleman	.08	.25
499 Cris Carpenter	.08	.25
500 Jack Clark	.20	.50
501 Kevin Appier	.20	.50
502 Rafael Palmeiro	.30	.75
503 Hensley Meulens	.08	.25
504 George Bell	.08	.25
505 Tony Pena	.08	.25
506 Roger McDowell	.08	.25
507 Luis Sojo	.08	.25
508 Mike Schooler	.08	.25
509 Robin Yount	.75	2.00
510 Jack Armstrong	.08	.25
511 Rick Cerone	.08	.25
512 Curt Wilkerson	.08	.25
513 Joe Carter	.20	.50
514 Tim Burke	.08	.25
515 Tony Fernandez	.08	.25
516 Ramon Martinez	.08	.25
517 Tim Hulett	.08	.25
518 Terry Steinbach	.08	.25
519 Pete Smith	.08	.25
520 Ken Caminiti	.20	.50
521 Shawn Boskie	.08	.25
522 Mike Pagliarulo	.08	.25
523 Tim Raines	.20	.50
524 Alfredo Griffin	.08	.25
525 Henry Cotto	.08	.25
526 Mike Stanley	.08	.25
527 Charlie Leibrandt	.08	.25
528 Jeff King	.08	.25
529 Eric Plunk	.08	.25
530 Tom Lampkin	.08	.25
531 Steve Bedrosian	.08	.25
532 Tom Herr	.08	.25
533 Craig Lefferts	.08	.25
534 Jeff Reed	.08	.25
535 Mickey Morandini	.08	.25
536 Greg Cadaret	.08	.25
537 Ray Lankford	.20	.50
538 John Candelaria	.08	.25
539 Rob Deer	.08	.25
540 Brad Arnsberg	.08	.25
541 Mike Sharperson	.08	.25
542 Jeff D. Robinson	.08	.25
543 Mo Vaughn	.20	.50
544 Jeff Parrett	.08	.25
545 Willie Randolph	.20	.50
546 Herm Winningham	.08	.25
547 Jeff Innis	.08	.25
548 Chuck Knoblauch	.20	.50
549 Tommy Greene UER (Born in North Carolina, not South Carolina)	.08	.25
550 Jeff Hamilton	.08	.25
551 Barry Jones	.08	.25
552 Ken Dayley	.08	.25
553 Rick Dempsey	.08	.25
554 Greg Smith	.08	.25
555 Mike Devereaux	.08	.25
556 Keith Comstock	.08	.25
557 Paul Faries RC	.08	.25
558 Tom Glavine	.30	.75
559 Craig Grebeck	.08	.25
560 Scott Erickson	.08	.25
561 Joel Skinner	.08	.25
562 Mike Morgan	.08	.25
563 Dave Gallagher	.08	.25
564 Todd Stottlemyre	.08	.25
565 Rich Rodriguez RC	.08	.25
566 Craig Wilson RC	.08	.25
567 Jeff Brantley	.08	.25
568 Scott Kamieniecki RC	.25	.60
569 Steve Decker RC	.15	.40
570 Juan Agosto	.08	.25
571 Tommy Gregg	.08	.25
572 Kevin Wickander	.08	.25
573 Jamie Quirk UER (Rookie card is 1976, but card back is 1990)	.08	.25
574 Jerry Don Gleaton	.08	.25
575 Chris Hammond	.08	.25
576 Luis Gonzalez RC	.60	1.50
577 Russ Swan	.08	.25
578 Jeff Conine RC	.40	1.00
579 Charlie Hough	.20	.50
580 Jeff Kunkel	.08	.25
581 Darrel Akerfelds	.08	.25
582 Jeff Manto	.08	.25
583 Alejandro Pena	.08	.25
584 Mark Davidson	.08	.25
585 Bob MacDonald RC	.15	.40
586 Paul Assenmacher	.08	.25
587 Dan Wilson RC	.25	.60
588 Tom Bolton	.08	.25
589 Brian Harper	.08	.25
590 John Habyan	.08	.25
591 John Orton	.08	.25
592 Mark Gardner	.08	.25
593 Turner Ward RC	.25	.60
594 Bob Patterson	.08	.25
595 Ed Nunez	.08	.25
596 Gary Scott UER RC (Major League Batting Record should be Minor League)	.15	.40
597 Scott Bankhead	.08	.25
598 Checklist 301-400	.08	.25
599 Checklist 401-500	.08	.25
600 Checklist 501-600	.08	.25

1992 Stadium Club Dome

The 1992 Stadium Club Dome set (issued by Topps) features 100 top draft picks, 56 1991 All-Star Game cards, 25 1991 Team U.S.A. cards, and 19 1991 Championship and World Series cards, all packaged in a factory set box inside a molded-plastic SkyDome display. Topps actually references this set as a 1991 set and the copyright lines on the card backs say 1991, but the set was released well into 1992. Rookie Cards in this set include Shawn Green and Manny Ramirez.

Card	Low	High
COMP.FACT.SET (200)	5.00	12.00
1 Terry Adams RC	.20	.50
2 Tommy Adams RC	.08	.25
3 Rick Aguilera	.05	.15
4 Ron Allen RC	.08	.25
5 Roberto Alomar	.08	.25
6 Sandy Alomar Jr.	.02	.10
7 Greg Anthony RC	.08	.25
8 James Austin RC	.08	.25
9 Steve Avery	.02	.10
10 Harold Baines	.05	.15
11 Brian Barber RC	.08	.25
12 Jon Barnes RC	.08	.25
13 George Bell	.02	.10
14 Doug Bennett RC	.08	.25
15 Sean Bergman RC	.20	.50
16 Craig Biggio	.08	.25
17 Bill Bliss RC	.08	.25
18 Wade Boggs	.08	.25
19 Bobby Bonilla	.05	.15
20 Russell Brock RC	.08	.25
21 Tarrik Brock RC	.08	.25
22 Tom Browning	.02	.10
23 Brett Butler	.05	.15
24 Ivan Calderon	.02	.10
25 Joe Carter	.05	.15
26 Joe Caruso RC	.08	.25
27 Dan Cholowsky RC	.08	.25
28 Will Clark	.08	.25
29 Roger Clemens	.40	1.00
30 Shawn Curran RC	.08	.25
31 Chris Curtis RC	.08	.25
32 Chili Davis	.05	.15
33 Andre Dawson	.05	.15
34 Joe DeBerry RC	.08	.25
35 John Dettmer	.02	.10
36 Rob Dibble	.05	.15
37 John Donati RC	.08	.25
38 Dave Doorneweerd RC	.08	.25
39 Darren Dreifort	.02	.10
40 Mike Durant RC	.08	.25
41 Chris Durkin RC	.08	.25
42 Dennis Eckersley	.05	.15
43 Brian Edmondson RC	.08	.25
44 Vaughn Eshelman RC	.08	.25
45 Shawn Estes RC	.20	.50
46 Jorge Fabregas RC	.20	.50
47 Jon Farrell RC	.08	.25
48 Cecil Fielder	.05	.15
49 Carlton Fisk	.08	.25
50 Tim Flannelly RC	.08	.25
51 Cliff Floyd RC	.60	1.50
52 Julio Franco	.05	.15
53 Greg Gagne	.02	.10
54 Chris Gambs RC	.08	.25
55 Ron Gant	.05	.15
56 Brent Gates RC	.08	.25
57 Dwayne Gerald RC	.08	.25
58 Jason Giambi	.40	1.00
59 Benji Gil RC	.20	.50
60 Mark Gipner RC	.08	.25
61 Danny Gladden	.02	.10
62 Tom Glavine	.08	.25
63 Jimmy Gonzalez RC	.08	.25
64 Jeff Granger	.02	.10
65 Dan Grapenthien RC	.08	.25
66 Dennis Gray RC	.08	.25
67 Shawn Green RC	.75	2.00
68 Tyler Green RC	.08	.25
69 Todd Greene	.02	.10
70 Ken Griffey Jr.	.30	.75
71 Kelly Gruber	.02	.10
72 Ozzie Guillen	.05	.15
73 Tony Gwynn	.25	.60
74 Shane Halter RC	.08	.25
75 Jeffrey Hammonds	.05	.15
76 Larry Hanlon RC	.08	.25
77 Pete Harnisch	.02	.10
78 Mike Harrison RC	.08	.25
79 Bryan Harvey	.02	.10
80 Scott Hatteberg RC	.20	.50
81 Rick Helling	.02	.10
82 Dave Henderson	.02	.10
83 Rickey Henderson	.20	.50
84 Tyrone Hill RC	.08	.25
85 T.Hollandsworth RC	.20	.50
86 Brian Holliday RC	.08	.25
87 Terry Horn RC	.08	.25
88 Jeff Hostetler RC	.08	.25
89 Kent Hrbek	.05	.15
90 Mark Hubbard RC	.08	.25
91 Charles Johnson	.05	.15
92 Howard Johnson	.02	.10
93 Todd Johnson	.02	.10
94 Bobby Jones RC	.20	.50
95 Dan Jones RC	.08	.25
96 Felix Jose	.02	.10
97 David Justice	.02	.10
98 Jimmy Key	.05	.15
99 Marc Kroon RC	.08	.25
100 John Kruk	.05	.15
101 Mark Langston	.02	.10
102 Barry Larkin	.08	.25
103 Mike LaValliere	.02	.10
104 Scott Leius	.02	.10
105 Mark Lemke	.02	.10
106 Donnie Leshnock	.02	.10
107 Jimmy Lewis RC	.08	.25
108 Shane Livesy RC	.08	.25
109 Ryan Long RC	.08	.25
110 Trevor Mallory RC	.08	.25
111 Dennis Martinez	.05	.15
112 Justin Mashore RC	.08	.25
113 Jason McDonald	.02	.10
114 Jack McDowell	.02	.10
115 Tom McKinnon RC	.08	.25
116 Billy McMillon	.02	.10
117 Buck McNabb RC	.08	.25
118 Jim Mecir RC	.08	.25
119 Dan Melendez	.08	.25
120 Shawn Miller RC	.08	.25
121 Trever Miller RC	.08	.25
122 Paul Molitor	.05	.15
123 Vincent Moore RC	.08	.25
124 Mike Morgan	.02	.10
125 Jack Morris WS	.02	.10
126 Jack Morris AS	.02	.10
127 Sean Mulligan RC	.08	.25
128 Eddie Murray AS	.20	.50
129 Mike Neill RC	.20	.50
130 Phil Nevin	.40	1.00
131 Mark O'Brien RC	.08	.25
132 Alex Ochoa RC	.08	.25
133 Chad Ogea RC	.08	.25
134 Greg Olson	.02	.10
135 Paul O'Neill	.08	.25
136 Jared Osentowski RC	.08	.25
137 Mike Pagliarulo	.02	.10
138 Rafael Palmeiro	.08	.25
139 Rodney Pedraza RC	.08	.25
140 Tony Phillips (P)	.02	.10
141 Scott Pisciotta RC	.08	.25
142 C.Pritchett RC	.08	.25
143 Jason Pruitt RC	.08	.25
144 K.Puckett WS UER Championship series AB and BA is wrong	.20	.50
145 Kirby Puckett AS	.20	.50
146 Manny Ramirez RC	3.00	8.00
147 Eddie Ramos RC	.08	.25
148 Mark Ratekin RC	.08	.25
149 Jeff Reardon	.05	.15
150 Sean Rees RC	.08	.25
151 Pokey Reese RC	.20	.50
152 Desmond Relaford RC	.08	.25
153 Eric Richardson RC	.08	.25
154 Cal Ripken	.60	1.50
155 Chris Roberts	.02	.10
156 Mike Robertson RC	.08	.25
157 Steve Rodriguez	.02	.10
158 Mike Rossiter RC	.08	.25
159 Scott Ruffcorn RC	.08	.25
160 Chris Sabo	.02	.10
161 Juan Samuel	.02	.10
162 Ryne Sandberg UER (On 5th line, prior misspelled as prilor)	.30	.75
163 Scott Sanderson	.02	.10
164 Benny Santiago	.05	.15
165 Gene Schall RC	.08	.25
166 Chad Schoenvogel RC	.08	.25
167 Chris Seelbach RC	.08	.25
168 Aaron Sele RC	.20	.50
169 Basil Shabazz RC	.08	.25
170 Al Shirley RC	.08	.25
171 Paul Shuey	.02	.10
172 Ruben Sierra	.02	.10
173 John Smiley	.02	.10
174 Lee Smith	.05	.15
175 Ozzie Smith	.30	.75
176 Tim Smith RC	.08	.25
177 Zane Smith	.02	.10
178 John Smoltz	.08	.25
179 Scott Stahoviak RC	.08	.25
180 Kennie Steenstra	.02	.10
181 Kevin Stocker RC	.08	.25
182 Chris Stynes RC	.20	.50
183 Danny Tartabull	.02	.10
184 Brien Taylor RC	.20	.50
185 Todd Taylor	.02	.10
186 Larry Thomas RC	.08	.25
187 Ozzie Timmons RC (See also 188)	.08	.25
188 David Tuttle UER (Mistakenly numbered as 187 on card)	.02	.10
189 Andy Van Slyke	.08	.25
190 Frank Viola	.05	.15
191 Michael Walkden RC	.08	.25
192 Jeff Ware	.02	.10
193 Allen Watson RC	.08	.25
194 Steve Whitaker RC	.08	.25
195 Jerry Willard	.02	.10
196 Craig Wilson	.02	.10
197 Chris Wimmer	.02	.10
198 S.Wojciechowski RC	.08	.25
199 Joel Wolfe RC	.08	.25
200 Ivan Zweig	.02	.10

1992 Stadium Club

The 1992 Stadium Club baseball card set consists of 900 standard-size cards issued in three series of 300 cards each. Cards were issued in plastic wrapped packs. A card-like application form for membership in Topps Stadium Club was inserted in each pack. Card numbers 591-610 form a "Members Choice" subset.

Card	Low	High
COMPLETE SET (900)	18.00	45.00
COMP.SERIES 1 (300)	6.00	15.00
COMP.SERIES 2 (300)	6.00	15.00
COMP.SERIES 3 (300)	6.00	15.00
1 Cal Ripken UER (Misspelled Ripkin on card back)	.60	1.50
2 Eric Yelding	.02	.10
3 Geno Petralli	.02	.10
4 Wally Backman	.02	.10
5 Milt Cuyler	.02	.10
6 Kevin Bass	.02	.10
7 Dante Bichette	.05	.15
8 Ray Lankford	.05	.15
9 Mel Hall	.02	.10
10 Joe Carter	.05	.15
11 Juan Samuel	.02	.10
12 Jeff Montgomery	.02	.10
13 Glenn Braggs	.02	.10
14 Henry Cotto	.02	.10
15 Deion Sanders	.08	.25
16 Dick Schofield	.02	.10
17 David Cone	.05	.15
18 Chili Davis	.05	.15
19 Tom Foley	.02	.10
20 Ozzie Guillen	.05	.15
21 Luis Salazar	.02	.10
22 Terry Steinbach	.02	.10
23 Chris James	.02	.10
24 Jeff King	.02	.10
25 Carlos Quintana	.02	.10
26 Mike Maddux	.02	.10
27 Tommy Greene	.02	.10
28 Jeff Russell	.02	.10
29 Steve Finley	.05	.15
30 Mike Flanagan	.02	.10
31 Darren Lewis	.02	.10
32 Mark Lee	.02	.10
33 Willie Fraser	.02	.10
34 Mike Henneman	.02	.10
35 Kevin Maas	.02	.10
36 Dave Hansen	.02	.10
37 Erik Hanson	.02	.10
38 Bill Doran	.02	.10
39 Mike Boddicker	.02	.10
40 Vince Coleman	.02	.10
41 Devon White	.05	.15
42 Mark Gardner	.02	.10
43 Scott Lewis	.02	.10
44 Juan Berenguer	.02	.10
45 Carney Lansford	.05	.15
46 Curt Wilkerson	.02	.10
47 Shane Mack	.02	.10
48 Bip Roberts	.02	.10
49 Greg A. Harris	.02	.10
50 Ryne Sandberg	.30	.75
51 Mark Whiten	.02	.10
52 Jack McDowell	.02	.10
53 Jimmy Jones	.02	.10
54 Steve Lake	.02	.10
55 Bud Black	.02	.10
56 Dave Valle	.02	.10
57 Kevin Reimer	.02	.10
58 Rich Gedman UER (Wrong BARS chart used)	.02	.10
59 Travis Fryman	.05	.15
60 Steve Avery	.02	.10
61 Francisco de la Rosa	.02	.10
62 Scott Hemond	.02	.10
63 Hal Morris	.02	.10
64 Hensley Meulens	.02	.10
65 Frank Castillo	.02	.10
66 Gene Larkin	.02	.10
67 Jose DeLeon	.02	.10
68 Al Osuna	.02	.10
69 Dave Cochrane	.02	.10
70 Robin Ventura	.05	.15
71 John Cerutti	.02	.10
72 Kevin Gross	.02	.10
73 Ivan Calderon	.02	.10
74 Mike Macfarlane	.02	.10
75 Stan Belinda	.02	.10
76 Shawn Hillegas	.02	.10
77 Pat Borders	.02	.10
78 Jim Vatcher	.02	.10
79 Bobby Rose	.02	.10
80 Roger Clemens	.40	1.00
81 Craig Worthington	.02	.10
82 Jeff Treadway	.02	.10
83 Jamie Quirk	.02	.10
84 Randy Bush	.02	.10
85 Anthony Young	.02	.10
86 Trevor Wilson	.02	.10
87 Jaime Navarro	.02	.10
88 Les Lancaster	.02	.10
89 Pat Kelly	.02	.10
90 Alvin Davis	.02	.10
91 Larry Andersen	.02	.10
92 Rob Deer	.02	.10
93 Mike Sharperson	.02	.10
94 Lance Parrish	.05	.15
95 Cecil Espy	.02	.10
96 Tim Spehr	.02	.10
97 Dave Stieb	.02	.10
98 Terry Mulholland	.02	.10
99 Dennis Boyd	.02	.10
100 Barry Larkin	.08	.25
101 Ryan Bowen	.02	.10
102 Felix Fermin	.02	.10
103 Luis Alicea	.02	.10
104 Tim Hulett	.02	.10
105 Rafael Belliard	.02	.10
106 Mike Gallego	.02	.10
107 Dave Righetti	.05	.15
108 Jeff Schaefer	.02	.10
109 Ricky Bones	.02	.10
110 Scott Erickson	.02	.10
111 Matt Nokes	.02	.10
112 Bob Scanlan	.02	.10
113 Tom Candiotti	.02	.10
114 Sean Berry	.02	.10
115 Kevin Morton	.02	.10
116 Scott Fletcher	.02	.10
117 B.J. Surhoff	.05	.15
118 Dave Magadan UER (Born Tampa, not Tamps)	.02	.10
119 Bill Gullickson	.02	.10
120 Marquis Grissom	.05	.15
121 Lenny Harris	.02	.10
122 Wally Joyner	.05	.15
123 Kevin Brown	.02	.10
124 Braulio Castillo	.02	.10
125 Eric King	.02	.10
126 Mark Portugal	.02	.10
127 Calvin Jones	.02	.10
128 Mike Heath	.02	.10
129 Todd Van Poppel	.02	.10
130 Benny Santiago	.05	.15
131 Gary Thurman	.02	.10
132 Joe Girardi	.02	.10
133 Dave Eiland	.02	.10
134 Orlando Merced	.02	.10
135 Joe Orsulak	.02	.10
136 John Burkett	.02	.10
137 Ken Dayley	.02	.10
138 Ken Hill	.02	.10
139 Walt Terrell	.02	.10
140 Mike Scioscia	.02	.10
141 Junior Felix	.02	.10
142 Ken Caminiti	.05	.15
143 Carlos Baerga	.02	.10
144 Tony Fossas	.02	.10
145 Craig Grebeck	.02	.10
146 Scott Bradley	.02	.10
147 Kent Mercker	.02	.10
148 Derrick May	.02	.10
149 Jerald Clark	.02	.10
150 George Brett	.50	1.25
151 Luis Quinones	.02	.10
152 Mike Pagliarulo	.02	.10
153 Jose Guzman	.02	.10
154 Charlie O'Brien	.02	.10
155 Darren Holmes	.02	.10
156 Joe Boever	.02	.10
157 Rich Monteleone	.02	.10
158 Reggie Harris	.02	.10
159 Roberto Alomar	.08	.25
160 Robby Thompson	.02	.10
161 Chris Hoiles	.02	.10
162 Tom Pagnozzi	.02	.10
163 Omar Vizquel	.08	.25
164 John Candelaria	.02	.10
165 Terry Shumpert	.02	.10
166 Andy Mota	.02	.10
167 Scott Bailes	.02	.10
168 Jeff Blauser	.02	.10
169 Steve Olin	.02	.10
170 Doug Drabek	.02	.10
171 Dave Bergman	.02	.10
172 Eddie Whitson	.02	.10
173 Gilberto Reyes	.02	.10
174 Mark Grace	.08	.25
175 Paul O'Neill	.08	.25
176 Greg Cadaret	.02	.10
177 Mark Williamson	.02	.10
178 Casey Candaele	.02	.10
179 Candy Maldonado	.02	.10
180 Lee Smith	.05	.15
181 Harold Reynolds	.05	.15
182 David Justice	.05	.15
183 Lenny Webster	.02	.10
184 Donn Pall	.02	.10
185 Gerald Alexander	.02	.10
186 Jack Clark	.05	.15
187 Stan Javier	.02	.10
188 Ricky Jordan	.02	.10
189 Franklin Stubbs	.02	.10
190 Dennis Eckersley	.05	.15
191 Danny Tartabull	.02	.10
192 Pete O'Brien	.02	.10
193 Mark Lewis	.02	.10
194 Mike Felder	.02	.10
195 Mickey Tettleton	.02	.10
196 Dwight Smith	.02	.10
197 Shawn Abner	.02	.10
198 Jim Leyritz UER (Career totals less than 1991 totals)	.02	.10
199 Mike Devereaux	.02	.10
200 Craig Biggio	.08	.25
201 Kevin Elster	.02	.10
202 Rance Mulliniks	.02	.10
203 Tony Fernandez	.02	.10
204 Allan Anderson	.02	.10
205 Herm Winningham	.02	.10
206 Tim Jones	.02	.10
207 Ramon Martinez	.02	.10
208 Teddy Higuera	.02	.10
209 John Kruk	.05	.15
210 Jim Abbott	.08	.25
211 Dean Palmer	.05	.15
212 Mark Davis	.02	.10
213 Jay Buhner	.05	.15
214 Jesse Barfield	.02	.10
215 Kevin Mitchell	.02	.10
216 Mike LaValliere	.02	.10
217 Mark Wohlers	.02	.10
218 Dave Henderson	.02	.10
219 Dave Smith	.02	.10
220 Albert Belle	.05	.15
221 Spike Owen	.02	.10
222 Jeff Gray	.02	.10
223 Paul Gibson	.02	.10
224 Bobby Thigpen	.02	.10
225 Mike Mussina	.20	.50
226 Darrin Jackson	.02	.10
227 Luis Gonzalez	.05	.15
228 Greg Briley	.02	.10
229 Brent Mayne	.02	.10
230 Paul Molitor	.05	.15

231 Al Leiter .05 .15
232 Andy Van Slyke .08 .25
233 Ron Tingley .02 .10
234 Bernard Gilkey .02 .10
235 Kent Hrbek .05 .15
236 Eric Karros .05 .15
237 Randy Velarde .02 .10
238 Andy Allanson .02 .10
239 Willie McGee .05 .15
240 Juan Gonzalez .08 .25
241 Karl Rhodes .02 .10
242 Luis Mercedes .02 .10
243 Bill Swift .02 .10
244 Tommy Gregg .02 .10
245 David Howard .02 .10
246 Dave Hollins .02 .10
247 Kip Gross .02 .10
248 Walt Weiss .02 .10
249 Mackey Sasser .02 .10
250 Cecil Fielder .05 .15
251 Jerry Browne .02 .10
252 Doug Dascenzo .02 .10
253 Darryl Hamilton .02 .10
254 Dann Bilardello .02 .10
255 Luis Rivera .02 .10
256 Larry Walker .08 .25
257 Ron Karkovice .02 .10
258 Bob Tewksbury .05 .15
259 Jimmy Key .05 .15
260 Bernie Williams .08 .25
261 Gary Wayne .02 .10
262 Mike Simms UER .02 .10
(Reversed negative)
263 John Orton .02 .10
264 Marvin Freeman .02 .10
265 Mike Jeffcoat .02 .10
266 Roger Mason .02 .10
267 Edgar Martinez .08 .25
268 Henry Rodriguez .02 .10
269 Sam Horn .02 .10
270 Brian McRae .02 .10
271 Kirt Manwaring .02 .10
272 Mike Bordick .02 .10
273 Chris Sabo .02 .10
274 Jim Olander .02 .10
275 Greg W. Harris .02 .10
276 Dan Gakeler .02 .10
277 Bill Sampen .02 .10
278 Joel Skinner .02 .10
279 Curt Schilling .08 .25
280 Dale Murphy .08 .25
281 Lee Stevens .02 .10
282 Lonnie Smith .02 .10
283 Manuel Lee .02 .10
284 Shawn Boskie .02 .10
285 Kevin Seitzer .02 .10
286 Stan Royer .02 .10
287 John Dopson .02 .10
288 Scott Bullett RC .02 .10
289 Ken Patterson .02 .10
290 Todd Hundley .02 .10
291 Tim Leary .02 .10
292 Brett Butler .05 .15
293 Gregg Olson .02 .10
294 Jeff Brantley .02 .10
295 Brian Holman .02 .10
296 Brian Harper .02 .10
297 Brian Bohanon .02 .10
298 Checklist 1-100 .02 .10
299 Checklist 101-200 .02 .10
300 Checklist 201-300 .02 .10
301 Frank Thomas .20 .50
302 Lloyd McClendon .02 .10
303 Brady Anderson .05 .15
304 Julio Valera .02 .10
305 Mike Aldrete .02 .10
306 Joe Oliver .02 .10
307 Todd Stottlemyre .02 .10
308 Rey Sanchez RC .05 .15
309 Gary Sheffield UER .05 .15
310 Andujar Cedeno .02 .10
311 Kenny Rogers .05 .15
312 Bruce Hurst .02 .10
313 Mike Schooler .02 .10
314 Mike Benjamin .02 .10
315 Chuck Finley .05 .15
316 Mark Lemke .02 .10
317 Scott Livingstone .02 .10
318 Chris Nabholz .02 .10
319 Mike Humphreys .02 .10
320 Pedro Guerrero .05 .15
321 Willie Banks .02 .10
322 Tom Goodwin .02 .10
323 Hector Wagner .02 .10
324 Wally Ritchie .02 .10
325 Mo Vaughn .05 .15
326 Joe Klink .02 .10
327 Cal Eldred .02 .10
328 Daryl Boston .02 .10
329 Mike Huff .02 .10
330 Jeff Bagwell .20 .50
331 Bob Milacki .02 .10
332 Tom Prince .02 .10
333 Pat Tabler .02 .10
334 Ced Landrum .02 .10
335 Reggie Jefferson .02 .10
336 Mo Sanford .02 .10
337 Kevin Ritz .02 .10
338 Gerald Perry .02 .10
339 Jeff Hamilton .02 .10
340 Tim Wallach .02 .10
341 Jeff Huson .02 .10
342 Jose Melendez .02 .10
343 Willie Wilson .02 .10
344 Mike Stanton .02 .10
345 Joel Johnston .02 .10
346 Lee Guetterman .02 .10
347 Francisco Oliveras .02 .10
348 Dave Burba .02 .10
349 Tim Crews .02 .10
350 Scott Leius .02 .10
351 Danny Cox .02 .10
352 Wayne Housie .02 .10
353 Chris Donnels .02 .10
354 Chris George .02 .10
355 Gerald Young .02 .10
356 Roberto Hernandez .02 .10
357 Neal Heaton .02 .10
358 Todd Frohwirth .02 .10
359 Jose Vizcaino .02 .10
360 Jim Thome .20 .50
361 Craig Wilson .02 .10
362 Dave Haas .02 .10
363 Billy Hatcher .02 .10
364 John Barfield .02 .10
365 Luis Aquino .02 .10
366 Charlie Leibrandt .02 .10
367 Howard Farmer .02 .10
368 Bryn Smith .02 .10
369 Mickey Morandini .02 .10
370 Jose Canseco .08 .25
(See also 597)
371 Jose Uribe .02 .10
372 Bob MacDonald .02 .10
373 Luis Sojo .02 .10
374 Craig Shipley .02 .10
375 Scott Bankhead .02 .10
376 Greg Gagne .02 .10
377 Scott Cooper .02 .10
378 Jose Offerman .02 .10
379 Bill Spiers .02 .10
380 John Smiley .02 .10
381 Jeff Carter .02 .10
382 Heathcliff Slocumb .02 .10
383 Jeff Tackett .02 .10
384 John Kiely .02 .10
385 John Vander Wal .02 .10
386 Omar Olivares .02 .10
387 Ruben Sierra .05 .15
388 Tom Gordon .02 .10
389 Charles Nagy .02 .10
390 Dave Stewart .05 .15
391 Pete Harnisch .02 .10
392 Tim Burke .02 .10
393 Roberto Kelly .02 .10
394 Freddie Benavides .02 .10
395 Tom Glavine .08 .25
396 Wes Chamberlain .02 .10
397 Eric Gunderson .02 .10
398 Dave West .02 .10
399 Ellis Burks .05 .15
400 Ken Griffey Jr. .30 .75
401 Thomas Howard .02 .10
402 Juan Guzman .02 .10
403 Mitch Webster .02 .10
404 Matt Merullo .02 .10
405 Steve Buechele .02 .10
406 Danny Jackson .02 .10
407 Felix Jose .02 .10
408 Doug Piatt .02 .10
409 Jim Eisenreich .02 .10
410 Bryan Harvey .02 .10
411 Jim Austin .02 .10
412 Jim Poole .02 .10
413 Glenallen Hill .02 .10
414 Gene Nelson .02 .10
415 Ivan Rodriguez .20 .50
416 Frank Tanana .02 .10
417 Steve Decker .02 .10
418 Jason Grimsley .02 .10
419 Tim Layana .02 .10
420 Don Mattingly .50 1.25
421 Jerome Walton .02 .10
422 Rob Ducey .02 .10
423 Andy Benes .02 .10
424 John Marzano .02 .10
425 Gene Harris .02 .10
426 Tim Raines .05 .15
427 Bret Barberie .02 .10
428 Harvey Pulliam .02 .10
429 Cris Carpenter .02 .10
430 Howard Johnson .02 .10
431 Orel Hershiser .05 .15
432 Brian Hunter .02 .10
433 Kevin Tapani .02 .10
434 Rick Reed .02 .10
435 Ron Witmeyer RC .02 .10
436 Gary Gaetti .05 .15
437 Alex Cole .02 .10
438 Chito Martinez .02 .10
439 Greg Litton .02 .10
440 Julio Franco .05 .15
441 Mike Munoz .02 .10
442 Erik Pappas .02 .10
443 Pat Combs .02 .10
444 Lance Johnson .02 .10
445 Ed Sprague .02 .10
446 Mike Greenwell .02 .10
447 Milt Thompson .02 .10
448 Mike Magnante RC .02 .10
449 Chris Haney .02 .10
450 Robin Yount .30 .75
451 Rafael Ramirez .02 .10
452 Gino Minutelli .02 .10
453 Tom Lampkin .02 .10
454 Tony Perezchica .02 .10
455 Dwight Gooden .05 .15
456 Mark Guthrie .02 .10
457 Jay Howell .02 .10
458 Gary DiSarcina .02 .10
459 John Smoltz .08 .25
460 Will Clark .08 .25
461 Dave Otto .02 .10
462 Rob Maurer .02 .10
463 Dwight Evans .08 .25
464 Tom Brunansky .02 .10
465 Shawn Hare RC .02 .10
466 Geronimo Pena .02 .10
467 Alex Fernandez .02 .10
468 Greg Myers .02 .10
469 Jeff Fassero .02 .10
470 Len Dykstra .05 .15
471 Jeff Johnson .02 .10
472 Russ Swan .02 .10
473 Archie Corbin .02 .10
474 Chuck McElroy .02 .10
475 Mark McGwire .50 1.25
476 Wally Whitehurst .02 .10
477 Tim McIntosh .02 .10
478 Sid Bream .02 .10
479 Jeff Juden .02 .10
480 Carlton Fisk .08 .25
481 Jeff Plympton .02 .10
482 Carlos Martinez .02 .10
483 Jim Gott .02 .10
484 Bob McClure .02 .10
485 Tim Teufel .02 .10
486 Vicente Palacios .02 .10
487 Jeff Reed .02 .10
488 Tony Phillips .02 .10
489 Mel Rojas .02 .10
490 Ben McDonald .02 .10
491 Andres Santana .02 .10
492 Chris Beasley .02 .10
493 Mike Timlin .02 .10
494 Brian Downing .02 .10
495 Kirk Gibson .05 .15
496 Scott Sanderson .02 .10
497 Nick Esasky .02 .10
498 Johnny Guzman RC .02 .10
499 Mitch Williams .02 .10
500 Kirby Puckett .20 .50
501 Mike Harkey .02 .10
502 Jim Gantner .02 .10
503 Bruce Egloff .02 .10
504 Josias Manzanillo RC .02 .10
505 Delino DeShields .02 .10
506 Rheal Cormier .02 .10
507 Jay Bell .05 .15
508 Rich Rowland RC .02 .10
509 Scott Servais .02 .10
510 Terry Pendleton .05 .15
511 Rich DeLucia .02 .10
512 Warren Newson .02 .10
513 Paul Faries .02 .10
514 Kal Daniels .02 .10
515 Jarvis Brown .02 .10
516 Rafael Palmeiro .08 .25
517 Kelly Downs .02 .10
518 Steve Chitren .05 .15
519 Moises Alou .05 .15
520 Wade Boggs .08 .25
521 Pete Schourek .02 .10
522 Scott Terry .02 .10
523 Kevin Appier .05 .15
524 Gary Redus .02 .10
525 George Bell .02 .10
526 Jeff Kaiser .02 .10
527 Alvaro Espinoza .02 .10
528 Luis Polonia .02 .10
529 Darren Daulton .05 .15
530 Norm Charlton .02 .10
531 John Olerud .05 .15
532 Dan Plesac .02 .10
533 Billy Ripken .02 .10
534 Rod Nichols .02 .10
535 Joey Cora .02 .10
536 Harold Baines .05 .15
537 Bob Ojeda .02 .10
538 Mark Leonard .02 .10
539 Danny Darwin .02 .10
540 Shawon Dunston .02 .10
541 Pedro Munoz .02 .10
542 Mark Gubicza .02 .10
543 Kevin Baez .02 .10
544 Todd Zeile .02 .10
545 Don Slaught .02 .10
546 Tony Eusebio .05 .15
547 Alonzo Powell .02 .10
548 Gary Pettis .02 .10
549 Brian Barnes .02 .10
550 Lou Whitaker .05 .15
551 Keith Mitchell .02 .10
552 Oscar Azocar .02 .10
553 Stu Cole RC .02 .10
554 Steve Wapnick .02 .10
555 Derek Bell .05 .15
556 Luis Lopez .02 .10
557 Anthony Telford .02 .10
558 Tim Mauser .02 .10
559 Glen Sutko .02 .10
560 Darryl Strawberry .05 .15
561 Tom Bolton .02 .10
562 Cliff Young .02 .10
563 Bruce Walton .02 .10
564 Chico Walker .02 .10
565 John Franco .05 .15
566 Paul McClellan .02 .10
567 Paul Abbott .02 .10
568 Gary Varsho .02 .10
569 Carlos Maldonado RC .02 .10
570 Kelly Gruber .02 .10
571 Jose Oquendo .02 .10
572 Steve Frey .02 .10
573 Tino Martinez .08 .25
574 Bill Haselman .02 .10
575 Eric Anthony .02 .10
576 John Habyan .02 .10
577 Jeff McNeely .02 .10
578 Chris Bosio .02 .10
579 Joe Grahe .02 .10
580 Fred McGriff .08 .25
581 Rick Honeycutt .02 .10
582 Matt Williams .05 .15
583 Cliff Brantley .02 .10
584 Rob Dibble .05 .15
585 Skeeter Barnes .02 .10
586 Greg Hibbard .02 .10
587 Randy Milligan .02 .10
588 Checklist 301-400 .02 .10
589 Checklist 401-500 .02 .10
590 Checklist 501-600 .02 .10
591 Frank Thomas MC .08 .25
592 David Justice MC .02 .10
593 Roger Clemens MC .20 .50
594 Steve Avery MC .02 .10
595 Cal Ripken MC .30 .75
596 Barry Larkin MC UER .05 .15
(Ranked in AL,
should be NL)
597 J.Canseco MC UER .05 .15
Mistakenly numbered
370 on card back
598 Will Clark MC .05 .15
599 Cecil Fielder MC .02 .10
600 Ryne Sandberg MC .20 .50
601 Chuck Knoblauch MC .02 .10
602 Dwight Gooden MC .02 .10
603 Ken Griffey Jr. MC .20 .50
604 Barry Bonds MC .40 1.00
605 Nolan Ryan MC .30 .75
606 Jeff Bagwell MC .08 .25
607 Robin Yount MC .20 .50
608 Bobby Bonilla MC .02 .10
609 George Brett MC .25 .60
610 Howard Johnson MC .02 .10
611 Esteban Beltre .02 .10
612 Mike Christopher .02 .10
613 Troy Afenir .02 .10
614 Mariano Duncan .02 .10
615 Doug Henry RC .02 .10
616 Doug Jones .02 .10
617 Alvin Davis .02 .10
618 Craig Lefferts .02 .10
619 Kevin McReynolds .02 .10
620 Barry Bonds .60 1.50
621 Turner Ward .02 .10
622 Joe Magrane .02 .10
623 Mark Parent .02 .10
624 Tom Browning .02 .10
625 John Smiley .02 .10
626 Steve Wilson .02 .10
627 Mike Gallego .02 .10
628 Sammy Sosa .20 .50
629 Rico Rossy .02 .10
630 Royce Clayton .02 .10
631 Clay Parker .02 .10
632 Pete Smith .02 .10
633 Jeff McKnight .02 .10
634 Jack Daugherty .02 .10
635 Steve Sax .02 .10
636 Joe Hesketh .02 .10
637 Vince Horsman .02 .10
638 Eric King .02 .10
639 Joe Boever .02 .10
640 Jack Morris .05 .15
641 Arthur Rhodes .02 .10
642 Bob Melvin .02 .10
643 Rick Wilkins .02 .10
644 Scott Scudder .02 .10
645 Bip Roberts .02 .10
646 Julio Valera .02 .10
647 Kevin Campbell .02 .10
648 Steve Searcy .02 .10
649 Scott Kamieniecki .02 .10
650 Kurt Stillwell .02 .10
651 Bob Welch .02 .10
652 Andres Galarraga .05 .15
653 Mike Jackson .02 .10
654 Bo Jackson .20 .50
655 Sid Fernandez .02 .10
656 Mike Bielecki .02 .10
657 Jeff Reardon .05 .15
658 Wayne Rosenthal .02 .10
659 Eric Bullock .02 .10
660 Eric Davis .05 .15
661 Randy Tomlin .02 .10
662 Tom Edens .02 .10
663 Rob Murphy .02 .10
664 Leo Gomez .02 .10
665 Greg Maddux .30 .75
666 Greg Vaughn .02 .10
667 Wade Taylor .02 .10
668 Brad Arnsberg .02 .10
669 Mike Moore .02 .10
670 Mark Langston .02 .10
671 Barry Jones .02 .10
672 Bill Landrum .02 .10
673 Greg Swindell .02 .10
674 Wayne Edwards .02 .10
675 Greg Olson .02 .10
676 Bill Pulsipher RC .02 .10
677 Bobby Witt .02 .10
678 Mark Carreon .02 .10
679 Patrick Lennon .02 .10
680 Ozzie Smith .30 .75
681 John Briscoe .02 .10
682 Matt Young .02 .10
683 Jeff Conine .05 .15
684 Phil Stephenson .02 .10
685 Ron Darling .02 .10
686 Bryan Hickerson RC .02 .10
687 Dale Sveum .02 .10
688 Kirk McCaskill .02 .10
689 Rich Amaral .02 .10
690 Danny Tartabull .02 .10
691 Donald Harris .02 .10
692 Doug Davis .02 .10
693 John Farrell .02 .10
694 Paul Gibson .02 .10
695 Kenny Lofton .08 .25
696 Mike Fetters .02 .10
697 Rosario Rodriguez .02 .10
698 Chris Jones .02 .10
699 Jeff Manto .02 .10
700 Rick Sutcliffe .05 .15
701 Scott Bankhead .02 .10
702 Donnie Hill .02 .10
703 Todd Worrell .02 .10
704 Rene Gonzales .02 .10
705 Rick Cerone .02 .10
706 Tony Pena .02 .10
707 Paul Sorrento .02 .10
708 Gary Scott .02 .10
709 Junior Noboa .02 .10
710 Wally Joyner .05 .15
711 Charlie Hayes .02 .10
712 Rich Rodriguez .02 .10
713 Rudy Seanez .02 .10
714 Jim Bullinger .02 .10
715 Jeff M. Robinson .02 .10
716 Jeff Branson .02 .10
717 Andy Ashby .02 .10
718 Dave Burba .02 .10
719 Rich Gossage .05 .15
720 Randy Johnson .20 .50
721 David Wells .05 .15
722 Paul Kilgus .02 .10
723 Dave Martinez .02 .10
724 Denny Neagle .05 .15
725 Andy Stankiewicz .02 .10
726 Rick Aguilera .05 .15
727 Junior Ortiz .02 .10
728 Storm Davis .02 .10
729 Don Robinson .02 .10
730 Ron Gant .05 .15
731 Paul Assenmacher .02 .10
732 Mike Gardiner .02 .10
733 Milt Hill .02 .10
734 Jeremy Hernandez RC .02 .10
735 Ken Hill .02 .10
736 Xavier Hernandez .02 .10
737 Gregg Jefferies .02 .10
738 Dick Schofield .02 .10
739 Ron Robinson .02 .10
740 Sandy Alomar Jr. .02 .10
741 Mike Stanley .02 .10
742 Butch Henry RC .02 .10
743 Floyd Bannister .02 .10
744 Brian Drahman .02 .10
745 Dave Winfield .05 .15
746 Bob Walk .02 .10
747 Chris James .02 .10
748 Don Prybylinski RC .02 .10
749 Dennis Rasmussen .02 .10
750 Rickey Henderson .20 .50
751 Chris Hammond .02 .10
752 Bob Kipper .02 .10
753 Dave Rohde .02 .10
754 Hubie Brooks .02 .10
755 Bret Saberhagen .05 .15
756 Jeff D. Robinson .02 .10
757 Pat Listach RC .05 .15
758 Bill Wegman .02 .10
759 John Wetteland .05 .15
760 Phil Plantier .02 .10
761 Wilson Alvarez .02 .10
762 Scott Aldred .02 .10
763 Armando Reynoso RC .05 .15
764 Todd Benzinger .02 .10
765 Kevin Mitchell .02 .10
766 Gary Sheffield .05 .15
767 Allan Anderson .02 .10
768 Rusty Meacham .02 .10
769 Rick Parker .02 .10
770 Nolan Ryan .75 2.00
771 Jeff Ballard .02 .10
772 Cory Snyder .02 .10
773 Denis Boucher .02 .10
774 Jose Gonzalez .02 .10
775 Juan Guerrero .02 .10
776 Ed Nunez .02 .10
777 Scott Ruskin .02 .10
778 Terry Leach .02 .10
779 Carl Willis .02 .10
780 Bobby Bonilla .05 .15
781 Duane Ward .02 .10
782 Joe Slusarski .02 .10
783 David Segui .02 .10
784 Kirk Gibson .05 .15
785 Frank Viola .05 .15
786 Keith Miller .02 .10
787 Mike Morgan .02 .10
788 Kim Batiste .02 .10
789 Sergio Valdez .02 .10
790 Eddie Taubensee RC .05 .15
791 Jack Armstrong .02 .10
792 Scott Fletcher .02 .10
793 Steve Farr .02 .10
794 Dan Pasqua .02 .10
795 Eddie Murray .20 .50
796 John Morris .02 .10
797 Francisco Cabrera .02 .10
798 Mike Perez .02 .10
799 Ted Wood .02 .10
800 Jose Rijo .02 .10
801 Danny Gladden .02 .10
802 Archi Cianfrocco RC .02 .10
803 Monty Fariss .02 .10
804 Roger McDowell .02 .10
805 Randy Myers .02 .10
806 Kirk Dressendorfer .02 .10
807 Zane Smith .02 .10
808 Glenn Davis .02 .10
809 Torey Lovullo .02 .10
810 Andre Dawson .05 .15
811 Bill Pecota .02 .10
812 Ted Power .02 .10
813 Willie Blair .02 .10
814 Dave Fleming .02 .10
815 Chris Gwynn .02 .10
816 Jody Reed .02 .10
817 Mark Dewey .02 .10
818 Kyle Abbott .02 .10
819 Tom Henke .02 .10
820 Kevin Seitzer .02 .10
821 Al Newman .02 .10
822 Tim Sherrill .02 .10
823 Chuck Crim .02 .10
824 Darren Reed .02 .10
825 Tony Gwynn .25 .60
826 Steve Foster .02 .10
827 Steve Howe .02 .10
828 Brook Jacoby .02 .10
829 Rodney McCray .02 .10
830 Chuck Knoblauch .05 .15
831 John Wehner .02 .10
832 Scott Garrelts .02 .10
833 Alejandro Pena .02 .10
834 Jeff Parrett UER .02 .10
(Kentucy)
835 Juan Bell .02 .10
836 Lance Dickson .02 .10
837 Darryl Kile .05 .15
838 Efrain Valdez .02 .10
839 Bob Zupcic RC .02 .10
840 George Bell .02 .10
841 Dave Gallagher .02 .10
842 Tim Belcher .02 .10
843 Jeff Shaw .02 .10
844 Mike Fitzgerald .02 .10
845 Gary Carter .05 .15
846 John Russell .02 .10
847 Eric Hillman RC .02 .10
848 Mike Witt .02 .10
849 Curt Wilkerson .02 .10
850 Alan Trammell .05 .15
851 Rex Hudler .02 .10
852 Mike Walkden RC .02 .10
853 Kevin Ward .02 .10
854 Tim Naehring .02 .10
855 Bill Swift .02 .10
856 Damon Berryhill .02 .10
857 Mark Eichhorn .02 .10
858 Hector Villanueva .02 .10
859 Jose Lind .02 .10
860 Dennis Martinez .05 .15
861 Bill Krueger .02 .10
862 Mike Kingery .02 .10
863 Jeff Innis .02 .10
864 Derek Lilliquist .02 .10
865 Reggie Sanders .05 .15
866 Ramon Garcia .02 .10
867 Bruce Ruffin .02 .10
868 Dickie Thon .02 .10
869 Melido Perez .02 .10
870 Ruben Amaro .02 .10
871 Alan Mills .02 .10
872 Matt Sinatro .02 .10
873 Eddie Zosky .02 .10
874 Pete Incaviglia .02 .10
875 Tom Candiotti .02 .10
876 Bob Patterson .02 .10
877 Neal Heaton .02 .10
878 Terrel Hansen RC .02 .10
879 Dave Eiland .02 .10
880 Von Hayes .02 .10
881 Tim Scott .02 .10
882 Otis Nixon .02 .10
883 Herm Winningham .02 .10
884 Dion James .02 .10
885 Dave Wainhouse .02 .10
886 Frank DiPino .02 .10
887 Dennis Cook .02 .10
888 Jose Mesa .02 .10
889 Mark Leiter .02 .10
890 Willie Randolph .05 .15
891 Craig Colbert .02 .10
892 Dwayne Henry .02 .10
893 Jim Lindeman .02 .10
894 Charlie Hough .05 .15
895 Gil Heredia RC .05 .15
896 Scott Chiamparino .02 .10
897 Lance Blankenship .02 .10
898 Checklist 601-700 .02 .10
899 Checklist 701-800 .02 .10
900 Checklist 801-900 .02 .10

1992 Stadium Club First Draft Picks

This three-card standard-size set, featuring Major League Baseball's Number 1 draft pick for 1990, 1991, and 1992, was randomly inserted into 1992 Stadium Club Series III packs at an approximate rate of 1:72. One card also was mailed to each member of Topps Stadium Club.

1 Chipper Jones 2.00 5.00
2 Brien Taylor .75 2.00
3 Phil Nevin .75 2.00

1992 Stadium Club Master Photos

In the first package of materials sent to 1992 Topps Stadium Club members, along with an 11-card boxed set, members received a randomly chosen "Master Photo" printed on (approximately) 5" by 7" white card stock to demonstrate how the photos are cropped to create a borderless design. Each master photo has the Topps Stadium Club logo and the words "Master Photo" above a gold foil picture frame enclosing the color player photo. The backs are blank. The cards are unnumbered and checklisted below alphabetically. Master photos were also available through a special promotion at Walmart as an insert one-per-box in specially marked wax boxes of regular Topps Stadium Club cards.

COMPLETE SET (15) 8.00 20.00
1 Wade Boggs .50 1.25
2 Barry Bonds .75 2.00
3 Jose Canseco .50 1.25
4 Will Clark .40 1.00
5 Cecil Fielder .20 .50
6 Dwight Gooden .20 .50
7 Ken Griffey Jr. 1.00 2.50
8 Rickey Henderson .60 1.50
9 Lance Johnson .08 .25
10 Cal Ripken 2.00 5.00
11 Nolan Ryan 2.00 5.00
12 Deion Sanders .40 1.00
13 Darryl Strawberry .20 .50
14 Danny Tartabull .08 .25
15 Frank Thomas .60 1.50

1993 Stadium Club Murphy

This 200-card boxed set features 1992 All-Star Game cards, 1992 Team USA cards, and 1992 Championship and World Series cards. Topps actually refers to this set as a 1992 issue, but the set was released in 1993. This set is housed in a replica of San Diego's Jack Murphy Stadium, site of the 1992 All-Star Game. Production was limited to 8,000 cases, with 16 boxes per case. The set includes 100 Draft Pick cards, 56 All-Star cards, 25 Team USA cards, and 19 cards commemorating the 1992 National and American League Championship Series and the World Series. Notable Rookie Cards in this set include Derek Jeter, Jason Kendall, Shannon Stewart and Preston Wilson. A second year Team USA Nomar Garciaparra is featured in this set as well.

COMP.FACT.SET (212) 15.00 40.00

COMPLETE SET (200) 12.00 30.00
COMMON CARD (1-200) .05 .15
COMMON RC .05 .15
STATED PRINT RUN 128,000 SETS
1 Dave Winfield .05 .15
2 Juan Guzman .05 .15
3 Tony Gwynn .40 1.00
4 Chris Roberts .05 .15
5 Benny Santiago .10 .30
6 Sherard Clinkscales RC .05 .15
7 Jon Nunnally RC .20 .50
8 Chuck Knoblauch .10 .30
9 Bob Wolcott RC .05 .15
10 Steve Rodriguez .05 .15
11 Mark Williams RC .05 .15
12 Danny Clyburn RC .05 .15
13 Darren Dreifort .05 .15
14 Andy Van Slyke .20 .50
15 Wade Boggs .20 .50
16 Scott Patton RC .05 .15
17 Gary Sheffield .10 .30
18 Ron Villone .05 .15
19 Roberto Alomar .20 .50
20 Marc Valdes .05 .15
21 Daron Kirkreit .05 .15
22 Jeff Granger .05 .15
23 Levon Largusa RC .05 .15
24 Jimmy Key .10 .30
25 Kevin Pearson RC .05 .15
26 Michael Moore RC .05 .15
27 Preston Wilson RC .60 1.50
28 Kirby Puckett .30 .75
29 Tim Crabtree RC .05 .15
30 Bip Roberts .05 .15
31 Kelly Gruber .05 .15
32 Tony Fernandez .05 .15
33 Jason Angel RC .05 .15
34 Calvin Murray .05 .15
35 Chad McConnell .05 .15
36 Jason Moler .05 .15
37 Mark Lemke .05 .15
38 Tom Knauss RC .05 .15
39 Larry Mitchell RC .05 .15
40 Doug Mirabelli RC .20 .50
41 Everett Stull II RC .05 .15
42 Chris Wimmer .05 .15
43 Dan Serafini RC .05 .15
44 Ryne Sandberg .50 1.25
45 Steve Lyons RC .10 .30
46 Ryan Freeburg RC .05 .15
47 Ruben Sierra .10 .30
48 David Mysel RC .05 .15
49 Joe Hamilton RC .05 .15
50 Steve Rodriguez .05 .15
51 Tim Wakefield .30 .75
52 Scott Gentile RC .05 .15
53 Doug Jones .05 .15
54 Willie Brown RC .05 .15
55 Chad Mottola RC .20 .50
56 Ken Griffey Jr. .50 1.25
57 Jon Lieber RC 1.00 2.50
58 Dennis Martinez .10 .30
59 Joe Petcka RC .05 .15
60 Benji Simonton RC .05 .15
61 Brett Backlund RC .05 .15
62 Damon Berryhill .05 .15
63 Juan Guzman .05 .15
64 Doug Hecker RC .05 .15
65 Jamie Arnold RC .05 .15
66 Bob Tewksbury .05 .15
67 Tim Leger RC .05 .15
68 Todd Etler RC .05 .15
69 Lloyd McClendon .05 .15
70 Kurt Ehmann RC .05 .15
71 Rick Magdaleno RC .05 .15
72 Tom Pagnozzi .05 .15
73 Jeffrey Hammonds .05 .15
74 Joe Carter .10 .30
75 Chris Holt RC .10 .30
76 Charles Johnson .10 .30
77 Bob Walk .05 .15
78 Fred McGriff .20 .50
79 Tom Evans RC .05 .15
80 Scott Klingenbeck RC .05 .15
81 Chad McConnell .05 .15
82 Chris Eddy RC .05 .15
83 Phil Nevin .10 .30
84 John Kruk .10 .30
85 Tony Sheffield RC .05 .15
86 John Smoltz .20 .50
87 Trevor Humphry RC .05 .15
88 Charles Nagy .05 .15
89 Sean Runyan RC .05 .15
90 Mike Gulan RC .05 .15
91 Darren Daulton .10 .30
92 Otis Nixon .05 .15
93 Nomar Garciaparra 2.00 5.00
94 Larry Walker .10 .30
95 Hut Smith RC .05 .15
96 Rick Helling .05 .15
97 Roger Clemens .60 1.50
98 Ron Gant .10 .30
99 Kenny Felder RC .05 .15
100 Steve Murphy RC .05 .15
101 Mike Smith RC .05 .15
102 Terry Pendleton .10 .30
103 Tim Davis .05 .15
104 Jeff Patzke RC .05 .15
105 Craig Wilson .05 .15
106 Tom Glavine .20 .50
107 Mark Langston .05 .15
108 Mark Thompson RC .05 .15
109 Eric Owens RC .05 .15
110 Keith Johnson RC .05 .15
111 Robin Ventura .10 .30
112 Ed Sprague .05 .15
113 Jeff Schmidt RC .05 .15
114 Don Wengert RC .05 .15
115 Craig Biggio .20 .50
116 Kenny Carlyle RC .05 .15
117 Derek Jeter RC 12.50 30.00
118 Manuel Lee .05 .15
119 Jeff Haas RC .05 .15
120 Roger Bailey RC .05 .15
121 Sean Lowe RC .05 .15
122 Rick Aguilera .05 .15
123 Sandy Alomar Jr. .05 .15
124 Derek Wallace RC .05 .15
125 B.J. Wallace .05 .15
126 Greg Maddux .50 1.25
127 Tim Moore RC .05 .15
128 Lee Smith .10 .30
129 Todd Steverson RC .05 .15
130 Chris Widger RC .20 .50
131 Paul Molitor .10 .30
132 Chris Smith RC .05 .15
133 Chris Gomez RC .20 .50
134 Jimmy Baron RC .05 .15
135 John Smoltz .20 .50
136 Pat Borders .05 .15
137 Donnie Leshnock .05 .15
138 Gus Gandarillos RC .05 .15
139 Will Clark .20 .50
140 Ryan Luzinski RC .05 .15
141 Cal Ripken 1.00 2.50
142 B.J. Wallace .05 .15
143 Trey Beamon RC .20 .50
144 Norm Charlton .05 .15
145 Mike Mussina .20 .50
146 Billy Owens RC .05 .15
147 Ozzie Smith .50 1.25
148 Jason Kendall RC .60 1.50
149 Mike Matthews RC .05 .15
150 David Spykstra RC .05 .15
151 Benji Grigsby RC .05 .15
152 Sean Smith RC .05 .15
153 Mark McGwire .75 2.00
154 David Cone .10 .30
155 Shon Walker RC .05 .15
156 Jason Giambi .40 1.00
157 Jack McDowell .05 .15
158 Paxton Briley RC .05 .15
159 Edgar Martinez .20 .50
160 Brian Sackinsky RC .05 .15
161 Barry Bonds .75 2.00
162 Roberto Kelly .05 .15
163 Jeff Alkire .05 .15
164 Mike Sharperson .05 .15
165 Jamie Taylor RC .05 .15
166 John Saffer UER RC .05 .15
167 Jerry Browne .05 .15
168 Travis Fryman .10 .30
169 Brady Anderson .10 .30
170 Chris Roberts .05 .15
171 Lloyd Peever RC .05 .15
172 Francisco Cabrera .05 .15
173 Ramiro Martinez RC .05 .15
174 Jeff Alkire .05 .15
175 Ivan Rodriguez .20 .50
176 Kevin Brown .10 .30
177 Chad Roper RC .05 .15
178 Rod Henderson RC .05 .15
179 Dennis Eckersley .10 .30
180 Shannon Stewart RC .60 1.50
181 DeShawn Warren RC .05 .15
182 Lonnie Smith .05 .15
183 Willie Adams .05 .15
184 Jeff Montgomery .05 .15
185 Damon Hollins RC .20 .50
186 Byron Mathews RC .05 .15
187 Harold Baines .10 .30
188 Rick Greene .05 .15
189 Carlos Baerga .05 .15
190 Brandon Cromer RC .05 .15
191 Roberto Alomar .20 .50
192 Rich Ireland RC .05 .15
193 S.Montgomery RC .05 .15
194 Brant Brown RC .05 .15
195 Ritchie Moody RC .05 .15
196 Michael Tucker .05 .15
197 Jason Varitek 2.00 5.00
198 David Manning RC .05 .15
199 Marquis Riley RC .05 .15
200 Jason Giambi .40 1.00

1993 Stadium Club Murphy Master Photos

One Murphy Master Photo was included in each 1993 Stadium Club Murphy Special factory set. Each of these twelve uncropped Murphy Master Photos is inlaid in a 5" by 7" white frame and bordered with a prismatic foil trim. The photo within parallels the corresponding player's regular issue Murphy card. The cards are unnumbered and checklisted below in alphabetical order.

COMPLETE SET (12) 2.00 5.00
1 Sandy Alomar Jr. AS .05 .15
2 Tom Glavine AS .20 .50
3 Ken Griffey Jr. AS .50 1.25
4 Tony Gwynn AS .40 1.00
5 Chuck Knoblauch AS .10 .30
6 Chad Mottola .20 .50
7 Kirby Puckett AS .30 .75
8 Chris Roberts USA .05 .15
9 Ryne Sandberg AS .50 1.25
10 Gary Sheffield AS .10 .30
11 Larry Walker AS .10 .30
12 Preston Wilson .75 2.00

1993 Stadium Club

The 1993 Stadium Club baseball set consists of 750 standard-size cards issued in three series of 300, 300, and 150 cards respectively. Each series closes with a Members Choice subset (291-300, 591-600, and 746-750.

COMPLETE SET (750) 20.00 50.00
COMP.SERIES 1 (300) 6.00 15.00
COMP.SERIES 2 (300) 8.00 20.00
COMP.SERIES 3 (150) 6.00 15.00
1 Pat Borders .05 .15
2 Greg Maddux .50 1.25
3 Daryl Boston .05 .15
4 Bob Ayrault .05 .15
5 Tony Phillips IF .05 .15
6 Damion Easley .05 .15
7 Kip Gross .05 .15
8 Jim Thome .20 .50
9 Tim Belcher .05 .15
10 Gary Wayne .05 .15
11 Sam Militello .05 .15
12 Mike Magnante .05 .15
13 Tim Wakefield .30 .75
14 Tim Hulett .05 .15
15 Rheal Cormier .05 .15
16 Juan Guerrero .05 .15
17 Rich Gossage .10 .30
18 Tim Laker RC .05 .15
19 Darrin Jackson .05 .15
20 Jack Clark .10 .30
21 Roberto Hernandez .05 .15
22 Dean Palmer .10 .30
23 Harold Reynolds .10 .30
24 Dan Plesac .05 .15
25 Brent Mayne .05 .15
26 Pat Hentgen .05 .15
27 Luis Sojo .05 .15
28 Ron Gant .10 .30
29 Paul Gibson .05 .15
30 Bip Roberts .05 .15
31 Mickey Tettleton .05 .15
32 Randy Velarde .05 .15
33 Brian McRae .05 .15
34 Wes Chamberlain .05 .15
35 Wayne Kirby .05 .15
36 Rey Sanchez .05 .15
37 Jesse Orosco .05 .15
38 Mike Stanton .05 .15
39 Royce Clayton .05 .15
40 Cal Ripken UER 1.00 2.50
(Place of birth Havre de Grave; should be Havre de Grace)
41 John Dopson .05 .15
42 Gene Larkin .05 .15
43 Tim Raines .10 .30
44 Randy Myers .05 .15
45 Clay Parker .05 .15
46 Mike Scioscia .05 .15
47 Pete Incaviglia .05 .15
48 Todd Van Poppel .05 .15
49 Ray Lankford .10 .30
50 Eddie Murray .30 .75
51 Barry Bonds COR .75 2.00
51A Barry Bonds ERR .75 2.00
(Missing four stars over name to indicate NL MVP)
52 Gary Thurman .05 .15
53 Bob Wickman .05 .15
54 Joey Cora .05 .15
55 Kenny Rogers .10 .30
56 Mike Devereaux .05 .15
57 Kevin Seitzer .05 .15
58 Rafael Belliard .05 .15
59 David Wells .10 .30
60 Mark Clark .05 .15
61 Carlos Baerga .05 .15
62 Scott Brosius .10 .30
63 Jeff Grotewold .05 .15
64 Rick Wrona .05 .15
65 Kurt Knudsen .05 .15
66 Lloyd McClendon .05 .15
67 Omar Vizquel .20 .50
68 Jose Vizcaino .05 .15
69 Rob Ducey .05 .15
70 Casey Candaele .05 .15
71 Ramon Martinez .05 .15
72 Todd Hundley .05 .15
73 John Marzano .05 .15
74 Derek Parks .05 .15
75 Jack McDowell .05 .15
76 Tim Scott .05 .15
77 Mike Mussina .20 .50
78 Delino DeShields .05 .15
79 Chris Bosio .05 .15
80 Mike Bordick .05 .15
81 Rod Beck .05 .15
82 Ted Power .05 .15
83 John Kruk .10 .30
84 Steve Shifflett .05 .15
85 Danny Tartabull .05 .15
86 Mike Greenwell .05 .15
87 Jose Melendez .05 .15
88 Craig Wilson .05 .15
89 Melvin Nieves .05 .15
90 Ed Sprague .05 .15
91 Willie McGee .10 .30
92 Joe Orsulak .05 .15
93 Jeff King .05 .15
94 Dan Pasqua .05 .15
95 Brian Harper .05 .15
96 Joe Oliver .05 .15
97 Shane Turner .05 .15
98 Lenny Harris .05 .15
99 Jeff Parrett .05 .15
100 Luis Polonia .05 .15
101 Kent Bottenfield .05 .15
102 Albert Belle .10 .30
103 Mike Maddux .05 .15
104 Randy Tomlin .05 .15
105 Andy Stankiewicz .05 .15
106 Rico Rossy .05 .15
107 Joe Hesketh .05 .15
108 Dennis Powell .05 .15
109 Derrick May .05 .15
110 Pete Harnisch .05 .15
111 Kent Mercker .05 .15
112 Scott Fletcher .05 .15
113 Rex Hudler .05 .15
114 Chico Walker .05 .15
115 Rafael Palmeiro .20 .50
116 Mark Leiter .05 .15
117 Pedro Munoz .05 .15
118 Jim Bullinger .05 .15
119 Ivan Calderon .05 .15
120 Mike Timlin .05 .15
121 Rene Gonzales .05 .15
122 Greg Vaughn .05 .15
123 Mike Flanagan .05 .15
124 Mike Hartley .05 .15
125 Jeff Montgomery .05 .15
126 Mike Gallego .05 .15
127 Don Slaught .05 .15
128 Charlie O'Brien .05 .15
129 Jose Offerman .05 .15
(Can be found with home town missing on back)
130 Mark Wohlers .05 .15
131 Eric Fox .05 .15
132 Doug Strange .05 .15
133 Jeff Frye .05 .15
134 Wade Boggs UER .20 .50
(Redundantly lists lefty breakdown)
135 Lou Whitaker .10 .30
136 Craig Grebeck .05 .15
137 Rich Rodriguez .05 .15
138 Jay Bell .10 .30
139 Felix Fermin .05 .15
140 Dennis Martinez .10 .30
141 Eric Anthony .05 .15
142 Roberto Alomar .20 .50
143 Darren Lewis .05 .15
144 Mike Blowers .05 .15
145 Scott Bankhead .05 .15
146 Jeff Reboulet .05 .15
147 Frank Viola .10 .30
148 Bill Pecota .05 .15
149 Carlos Hernandez .05 .15
150 Bobby Witt .05 .15
151 Sid Bream .05 .15
152 Todd Zeile .05 .15
153 Dennis Cook .05 .15
154 Brian Bohanon .05 .15
155 Pat Kelly .05 .15
156 Milt Cuyler .05 .15
157 Juan Bell .05 .15
158 Randy Milligan .05 .15
159 Mark Gardner .05 .15
160 Pat Tabler .05 .15
161 Jeff Reardon .10 .30
162 Ken Patterson .05 .15
163 Bobby Bonilla .10 .30
164 Tony Pena .05 .15
165 Greg Swindell .05 .15
166 Kirk McCaskill .05 .15
167 Doug Drabek .05 .15
168 Franklin Stubbs .05 .15
169 Ron Tingley .05 .15
170 Willie Banks .05 .15
171 Sergio Valdez .05 .15
172 Mark Lemke .05 .15
173 Robin Yount .50 1.25
174 Storm Davis .05 .15
175 Dan Walters .05 .15
176 Steve Farr .05 .15
177 Curt Wilkerson .05 .15
178 Luis Alicea .05 .15
179 Russ Swan .05 .15
180 Mitch Williams .05 .15
181 Wilson Alvarez .05 .15
182 Carl Willis .05 .15
183 Craig Biggio .20 .50
184 Sean Berry .05 .15
185 Trevor Wilson .05 .15
186 Jeff Tackett .05 .15
187 Ellis Burks .10 .30
188 Jeff Branson .05 .15
189 Matt Nokes .05 .15
190 John Smiley .05 .15
191 Danny Gladden .05 .15
192 Mike Boddicker .05 .15
193 Roger Pavlik .05 .15
194 Paul Sorrento .05 .15
195 Vince Coleman .05 .15
196 Gary DiSarcina .05 .15
197 Rafael Bournigal .05 .15
198 Mike Schooler .05 .15
199 Scott Ruskin .05 .15
200 Frank Thomas .30 .75
201 Kyle Abbott .05 .15
202 Mike Perez .05 .15
203 Andre Dawson .10 .30
204 Bill Swift .05 .15
205 Alejandro Pena .05 .15
206 Dave Winfield .10 .30
207 Andujar Cedeno .05 .15
208 Terry Steinbach .05 .15
209 Chris Hammond .05 .15
210 Todd Burns .05 .15
211 Hipolito Pichardo .05 .15
212 John Kiely .05 .15
213 Tim Teufel .05 .15
214 Lee Guetterman .05 .15
215 Geronimo Pena .05 .15
216 Brett Butler .10 .30
217 Bryan Hickerson .05 .15
218 Rick Trlicek .05 .15
219 Lee Stevens .05 .15
220 Roger Clemens .60 1.50
221 Carlton Fisk .20 .50
222 Chili Davis .10 .30
223 Walt Terrell .05 .15
224 Jim Eisenreich .05 .15
225 Ricky Bones .05 .15
226 Henry Rodriguez .05 .15
227 Ken Hill .05 .15
228 Rick Wilkins .05 .15
229 Ricky Jordan .05 .15
230 Bernard Gilkey .05 .15
231 Tim Fortugno .05 .15
232 Geno Petralli .05 .15
233 Jose Rijo .05 .15
234 Jim Leyritz .05 .15
235 Kevin Campbell .05 .15
236 Al Osuna .05 .15
237 Pete Smith .05 .15
238 Pete Schourek .05 .15
239 Moises Alou .10 .30
240 Donn Pall .05 .15
241 Denny Neagle .10 .30
242 Dan Peltier .05 .15
243 Scott Scudder .05 .15
244 Juan Guzman .05 .15
245 Dave Burba .05 .15
246 Rick Sutcliffe .10 .30
247 Tony Fossas .05 .15
248 Mike Munoz .05 .15
249 Tim Salmon .20 .50
250 Rob Murphy .05 .15
251 Roger McDowell .05 .15
252 Lance Parrish .10 .30
253 Cliff Brantley .05 .15
254 Scott Leius .05 .15
255 Carlos Martinez .05 .15
256 Vince Horsman .05 .15
257 Oscar Azocar .05 .15
258 Craig Shipley .05 .15
259 Ben McDonald .05 .15
260 Jeff Brantley .05 .15
261 Damon Berryhill .05 .15
262 Joe Grahe .05 .15
263 Dave Hansen .05 .15
264 Rich Amaral .05 .15
265 Tim Pugh RC .05 .15
266 Dion James .05 .15
267 Frank Tanana .05 .15
268 Stan Belinda .05 .15
269 Jeff Kent .30 .75
270 Bruce Ruffin .05 .15
271 Xavier Hernandez .05 .15
272 Darrin Fletcher .05 .15
273 Tino Martinez .20 .50
274 Benny Santiago .10 .30
275 Scott Radinsky .05 .15
276 Mariano Duncan .05 .15
277 Kenny Lofton .10 .30
278 Dwight Smith .05 .15
279 Joe Carter .10 .30
280 Tim Jones .05 .15
281 Jeff Huson .05 .15
282 Phil Plantier .05 .15
283 Kirby Puckett .30 .75
284 Johnny Guzman .05 .15
285 Mike Morgan .05 .15
286 Chris Sabo .05 .15
287 Matt Williams .10 .30
288 Checklist 1-100 .05 .15
289 Checklist 101-200 .05 .15
290 Checklist 201-300 .05 .15
291 Dennis Eckersley MC .10 .30
292 Eric Karros MC .05 .15
293 Pat Listach MC .05 .15
294 Andy Van Slyke MC .10 .30
295 Robin Ventura MC .05 .15
296 Tom Glavine MC .10 .30
297 J.Gonzalez MC UER .05 .15
Misspelled Gonzales
298 Travis Fryman MC .05 .15
299 Larry Walker MC .10 .30
300 Gary Sheffield MC .05 .15
301 Chuck Finley .10 .30
302 Luis Gonzalez .10 .30
303 Darryl Hamilton .05 .15
304 Bien Figueroa .05 .15
305 Ron Darling .05 .15
306 Jonathan Hurst .05 .15
307 Mike Sharperson .05 .15
308 Mike Christopher .05 .15
309 Marvin Freeman .05 .15
310 Jay Buhner .10 .30
311 Butch Henry .05 .15
312 Greg W. Harris .05 .15
313 Darren Daulton .10 .30
314 Chuck Knoblauch .10 .30
315 Greg A. Harris .05 .15
316 John Franco .10 .30
317 John Wehner .05 .15
318 Donald Harris .05 .15
319 Benny Santiago .10 .30
320 Larry Walker .10 .30
321 Randy Knorr .05 .15
322 Ramon Martinez RC .05 .15
323 Mike Stanley .05 .15
324 Bill Wegman .05 .15
325 Tom Candiotti .05 .15
326 Glenn Davis .05 .15
327 Chuck Crim .05 .15
328 Scott Livingstone .05 .15
329 Eddie Taubensee .05 .15
330 George Bell .05 .15
331 Edgar Martinez .20 .50
332 Paul Assenmacher .05 .15
333 Steve Hosey .05 .15
334 Mo Vaughn .10 .30
335 Bret Saberhagen .10 .30
336 Mike Trombley .05 .15
337 Mark Lewis .05 .15
338 Terry Pendleton .10 .30
339 Dave Hollins .05 .15
340 Jeff Conine .10 .30
341 Bob Tewksbury .05 .15
342 Billy Ashley .05 .15
343 Zane Smith .05 .15
344 John Wetteland .10 .30
345 Chris Hoiles .05 .15
346 Frank Castillo .05 .15
347 Bruce Hurst .05 .15
348 Kevin McReynolds .05 .15
349 Dave Henderson .05 .15
350 Ryan Bowen .05 .15
351 Sid Fernandez .05 .15
352 Mark Whiten .05 .15
353 Nolan Ryan 1.25 3.00
354 Rick Aguilera .05 .15
355 Mark Langston .05 .15
356 Jack Morris .10 .30
357 Rob Deer .05 .15
358 Dave Fleming .05 .15
359 Lance Johnson .05 .15
360 Joe Millette .05 .15
361 Wil Cordero .05 .15
362 Chito Martinez .05 .15
363 Scott Servais .05 .15
364 Bernie Williams .20 .50
365 Pedro Martinez .60 1.50
366 Ryne Sandberg .50 1.25
367 Brad Ausmus .30 .75
368 Scott Cooper .05 .15
369 Rob Dibble .10 .30
370 Walt Weiss .05 .15
371 Mark Davis .05 .15
372 Orlando Merced .05 .15
373 Mike Jackson .05 .15
374 Kevin Appier .10 .30
375 Esteban Beltre .05 .15
376 Joe Slusarski .05 .15
377 William Suero .05 .15
378 Pete O'Brien .05 .15
379 Alan Embree .05 .15
380 Lenny Webster .05 .15
381 Eric Davis .10 .30
382 Duane Ward .05 .15
383 John Habyan .05 .15
384 Jeff Bagwell .20 .50
385 Ruben Amaro .05 .15
386 Julio Valera .05 .15
387 Robin Ventura .10 .30
388 Archi Cianfrocco .05 .15
389 Skeeter Barnes .05 .15
390 Tim Costo .05 .15
391 Luis Mercedes .05 .15
392 Jeremy Hernandez .05 .15
393 Shawon Dunston .05 .15
394 Andy Van Slyke .20 .50
395 Kevin Maas .05 .15
396 Kevin Brown .10 .30
397 J.T. Bruett .05 .15
398 Darryl Strawberry .10 .30
399 Tom Pagnozzi .05 .15
400 Sandy Alomar Jr. .05 .15
401 Keith Miller .05 .15
402 Rich DeLucia .05 .15
403 Shawn Abner .05 .15
404 Howard Johnson .05 .15
405 Mike Benjamin .05 .15
406 Roberto Mejia RC .05 .15
407 Mike Butcher .05 .15
408 Deion Sanders UER .20 .50
(Braves on front and Yankees on back)
409 Todd Stottlemyre .05 .15
410 Scott Kamieniecki .05 .15
411 Doug Jones .05 .15
412 John Burkett .05 .15
413 Lance Blankenship .05 .15
414 Jeff Parrett .05 .15
415 Barry Larkin .20 .50
416 Alan Trammell .10 .30
417 Mark Kiefer .05 .15
418 Gregg Olson .05 .15
419 Mark Grace .20 .50
420 Shane Mack .05 .15
421 Bob Walk .05 .15
422 Curt Schilling .10 .30
423 Erik Hanson .05 .15
424 George Brett .75 2.00
425 Reggie Jefferson .05 .15
426 Mark Portugal .05 .15
427 Ron Karkovice .05 .15
428 Matt Young .05 .15
429 Troy Neel .05 .15
430 Hector Fajardo .05 .15
431 Dave Righetti .10 .30
432 Pat Listach .05 .15
433 Jeff Innis .05 .15
434 Bob MacDonald .05 .15
435 Brian Jordan .10 .30
436 Jeff Blauser .05 .15
437 Mike Myers RC .05 .15
438 Frank Seminara .05 .15
439 Rusty Meacham .05 .15
440 Greg Briley .05 .15
441 Derek Lilliquist .05 .15
442 John Vander Wal .05 .15
443 Scott Erickson .05 .15
444 Bob Scanlan .05 .15
445 Todd Frohwirth .05 .15
446 Tom Goodwin .05 .15
447 William Pennyfeather .05 .15
448 Travis Fryman .10 .30
449 Mickey Morandini .05 .15
450 Greg Olson .05 .15
451 Trevor Hoffman .30 .75
452 Dave Magadan .05 .15
453 Shawn Jeter .05 .15
454 Andres Galarraga .10 .30
455 Ted Wood .05 .15
456 Freddie Benavides .05 .15
457 Junior Felix .05 .15
458 Alex Cole .05 .15
459 John Orton .05 .15
460 Eddie Zosky .05 .15
461 Dennis Eckersley .10 .30
462 Lee Smith .10 .30
463 John Smoltz .20 .50
464 Ken Caminiti .10 .30
465 Melido Perez .05 .15
466 Tom Marsh .05 .15
467 Jeff Nelson .05 .15
468 Jesse Levis .05 .15
469 Chris Nabholz .05 .15
470 Mike Macfarlane .05 .15
471 Reggie Sanders .10 .30
472 Chuck McElroy .05 .15
473 Kevin Gross .05 .15
474 Matt Whiteside RC .05 .15
475 Cal Eldred .05 .15
476 Dave Gallagher .05 .15
477 Len Dykstra .10 .30
478 Mark McGwire .75 2.00
479 David Segui .05 .15
480 Mike Henneman .05 .15
481 Bret Barberie .05 .15
482 Steve Sax .05 .15
483 Dave Valle .05 .15
484 Danny Darwin .05 .15
485 Devon White .10 .30
486 Eric Plunk .05 .15
487 Jim Gott .05 .15
488 Scooter Tucker .05 .15
489 Omar Olivares .05 .15
490 Greg Myers .05 .15
491 Brian Hunter .05 .15
492 Kevin Tapani .05 .15
493 Rich Monteleone .05 .15
494 Steve Buechele .05 .15
495 Bo Jackson .30 .75
496 Mike LaValliere .05 .15
497 Mark Leonard .05 .15
498 Daryl Boston .05 .15
499 Jose Canseco .20 .50
500 Brian Barnes .05 .15
501 Randy Johnson .30 .75
502 Tim McIntosh .05 .15
503 Cecil Fielder .10 .30
504 Derek Bell .05 .15
505 Kevin Koslofski .05 .15
506 Darren Holmes .05 .15
507 Brady Anderson .10 .30

508 John Valentin .05 .15
509 Jerry Browne .05 .15
510 Fred McGriff .20 .50
511 Pedro Astacio .05 .15
512 Gary Gaetti .10 .30
513 John Burke RC .05 .15
514 Dwight Gooden .10 .30
515 Thomas Howard .05 .15
516 D.Whitmore RC UER .05 .15
11 games played in 1992; should be 121
517 Ozzie Guillen .10 .30
518 Darryl Kile .10 .30
519 Rich Rowland .05 .15
520 Carlos Delgado .30 .75
521 Doug Henry .05 .15
522 Greg Colbrunn .05 .15
523 Tom Gordon .05 .15
524 Ivan Rodriguez .20 .50
525 Kent Hrbek .10 .30
526 Eric Young .05 .15
527 Rod Brewer .05 .15
528 Eric Karros .10 .30
529 Marquis Grissom .10 .30
530 Rico Brogna .05 .15
531 Sammy Sosa .30 .75
532 Bret Boone .10 .30
533 Luis Rivera .05 .15
534 Hal Morris .05 .15
535 Monty Fariss .05 .15
536 Leo Gomez .05 .15
537 Wally Joyner .10 .30
538 Tony Gwynn .40 1.00
539 Mike Williams .05 .15
540 Juan Gonzalez .10 .30
541 Ryan Klesko .10 .30
542 Ryan Thompson .05 .15
543 Chad Curtis .05 .15
544 Orel Hershiser .10 .30
545 Carlos Garcia .05 .15
546 Bob Welch .05 .15
547 Vinny Castilla .30 .75
548 Ozzie Smith .50 1.25
549 Luis Salazar .05 .15
550 Mark Guthrie .05 .15
551 Charles Nagy .05 .15
552 Alex Fernandez .05 .15
553 Mel Rojas .05 .15
554 Orestes Destrade .05 .15
555 Mark Gubicza .05 .15
556 Steve Finley .10 .30
557 Don Mattingly .75 2.00
558 Rickey Henderson .30 .75
559 Tommy Greene .05 .15
560 Arthur Rhodes .05 .15
561 Alfredo Griffin .05 .15
562 Will Clark .20 .50
563 Bob Zupcic .05 .15
564 Chuck Carr .05 .15
565 Henry Cotto .05 .15
566 Billy Spiers .05 .15
567 Jack Armstrong .05 .15
568 Kurt Stillwell .05 .15
569 David McCarty .05 .15
570 Joe Vitiello .05 .15
571 Gerald Williams .05 .15
572 Dale Murphy .20 .50
573 Scott Aldred .05 .15
574 Bill Gullickson .05 .15
575 Bobby Thigpen .05 .15
576 Glenallen Hill .05 .15
577 Dwayne Henry .05 .15
578 Calvin Jones .05 .15
579 Al Martin .05 .15
580 Ruben Sierra .10 .30
581 Andy Benes .05 .15
582 Anthony Young .05 .15
583 Shawn Boskie .05 .15
584 Scott Pose RC .05 .15
585 Mike Piazza 1.25 3.00
586 Donovan Osborne .05 .15
587 Jim Austin .05 .15
588 Checklist 301-400 .05 .15
589 Checklist 401-500 .05 .15
590 Checklist 501-600 .05 .15
591 Ken Griffey Jr. MC .30 .75
592 Ivan Rodriguez MC .10 .30
593 Carlos Baerga MC .05 .15
594 Fred McGriff MC .10 .30
595 Mark McGwire MC .40 1.00
596 Roberto Alomar MC .10 .30
597 Kirby Puckett MC .20 .50
598 Marquis Grissom MC .05 .15
599 John Smoltz MC .10 .30
600 Ryne Sandberg MC .30 .75
601 Wade Boggs .20 .50
602 Jeff Reardon .10 .30
603 Billy Ripken .05 .15
604 Bryan Harvey .05 .15
605 Carlos Quintana .05 .15
606 Greg Hibbard .05 .15
607 Ellis Burks .10 .30
608 Greg Swindell .05 .15
609 Dave Winfield .10 .30
610 Charlie Hough .10 .30
611 Chili Davis .10 .30
612 Jody Reed .05 .15
613 Mark Williamson .05 .15
614 Phil Plantier .05 .15
615 Jim Abbott .20 .50
616 Dante Bichette .10 .30
617 Mark Eichhorn .05 .15
618 Gary Sheffield .10 .30
619 Richie Lewis RC .05 .15
620 Joe Girardi .05 .15
621 Jaime Navarro .05 .15
622 Willie Wilson .05 .15
623 Scott Fletcher .05 .15
624 Bud Black .05 .15
625 Tom Brunansky .05 .15
626 Steve Avery .05 .15
627 Paul Molitor .10 .30
628 Gregg Jefferies .05 .15
629 Dave Stewart .10 .30
630 Javier Lopez .20 .50
631 Greg Gagne .05 .15
632 Roberto Kelly .05 .15
633 Mike Fetters .05 .15
634 Ozzie Canseco .05 .15
635 Jeff Russell .05 .15
636 Pete Incaviglia .05 .15
637 Tom Henke .05 .15
638 Chipper Jones .30 .75
639 Jimmy Key .10 .30
640 Dave Martinez .05 .15
641 Dave Stieb .05 .15
642 Milt Thompson .05 .15
643 Alan Mills .05 .15
644 Tony Fernandez .05 .15
645 Randy Bush .05 .15
646 Joe Magrane .05 .15
647 Ivan Calderon .05 .15
648 Jose Guzman .05 .15
649 John Olerud .10 .30
650 Tom Glavine .20 .50
651 Julio Franco .10 .30
652 Armando Reynoso .05 .15
653 Felix Jose .05 .15
654 Ben Rivera .05 .15
655 Andre Dawson .10 .30
656 Mike Harkey .05 .15
657 Kevin Seitzer .05 .15
658 Lonnie Smith .05 .15
659 Norm Charlton .05 .15
660 David Justice .10 .30
661 Fernando Valenzuela .10 .30
662 Dan Wilson .10 .30
663 Mark Gardner .05 .15
664 Doug Dascenzo .05 .15
665 Greg Maddux .50 1.25
666 Harold Baines .10 .30
667 Randy Myers .05 .15
668 Harold Reynolds .10 .30
669 Candy Maldonado .05 .15
670 Al Leiter .10 .30
671 Jerald Clark .05 .15
672 Doug Drabek .05 .15
673 Kirk Gibson .10 .30
674 Steve Reed RC .05 .15
675 Mike Felder .05 .15
676 Ricky Gutierrez .05 .15
677 Spike Owen .05 .15
678 Otis Nixon .05 .15
679 Scott Sanderson .05 .15
680 Mark Carreon .05 .15
681 Troy Percival .20 .50
682 Kevin Stocker .05 .15
683 Jim Converse RC .05 .15
684 Barry Bonds .75 2.00
685 Greg Gohr .05 .15
686 Tim Wallach .05 .15
687 Matt Mieske .05 .15
688 Robby Thompson .05 .15
689 Brien Taylor .05 .15
690 Kirt Manwaring .05 .15
691 Mike Lansing RC .10 .30
692 Steve Decker .05 .15
693 Mike Moore .05 .15
694 Kevin Mitchell .05 .15
695 Phil Hiatt .05 .15
696 Tony Tarasco RC .05 .15
697 Benji Gil .05 .15
698 Jeff Juden .05 .15
699 Kevin Reimer .05 .15
700 Andy Ashby .05 .15
701 John Jaha .05 .15
702 Tim Bogar RC .05 .15
703 David Cone .10 .30
704 Willie Greene .05 .15
705 David Hulse RC .05 .15
706 Cris Carpenter .05 .15
707 Ken Griffey Jr. .50 1.25
708 Steve Bedrosian .05 .15
709 Dave Nilsson .05 .15
710 Paul Wagner .05 .15
711 B.J. Surhoff .10 .30
712 Rene Arocha RC .10 .30
713 Manuel Lee .05 .15
714 Brian Williams .05 .15
715 Sherman Obando RC .05 .15
716 Terry Mulholland .05 .15
717 Paul O'Neill .20 .50
718 David Nied .05 .15
719 J.T. Snow RC .20 .50
720 Nigel Wilson .05 .15
721 Mike Bielecki .05 .15
722 Kevin Young .10 .30
723 Charlie Leibrandt .05 .15
724 Frank Bolick .05 .15
725 Jon Shave RC .05 .15
726 Steve Cooke .05 .15
727 Domingo Martinez RC .05 .15
728 Todd Worrell .05 .15
729 Jose Lind .05 .15
730 Jim Tatum RC .05 .15
731 Mike Hampton .10 .30
732 Mike Draper .05 .15
733 Henry Mercedes .05 .15
734 John Johnstone RC .05 .15
735 Mitch Webster .05 .15
736 Russ Springer .05 .15
737 Rob Natal .05 .15
738 Steve Howe .05 .15
739 Darrell Sherman RC .05 .15
740 Pat Mahomes .05 .15
741 Alex Arias .05 .15
742 Damon Buford .05 .15
743 Charlie Hayes .05 .15
744 Guillermo Velasquez .05 .15
745 CL 601-750 UER .05 .15
650 Tom Glavine
746 Frank Thomas MC .20 .50
747 Barry Bonds MC .40 1.00
748 Roger Clemens MC .30 .75
749 Joe Carter MC .05 .15
750 Greg Maddux MC .30 .75

1993 Stadium Club First Day Issue

Two thousand of each 1993 Stadium Club baseball card were produced on the first day and then randomly inserted in packs at a rate of 1:24. These standard-size cards are identical to the regular-issue 1993 Stadium Club cards, except for the embossed prismatic-foil "1st Day Production" logo stamped in an upper corner. Some of the logos have been transferred from "common" 1st day cards to the fronts of better players.

*STARS: 8X TO 20X BASIC CARDS

1993 Stadium Club Members Only Parallel

These standard-sized cards were issued in complete set form only through Topps' Stadium Club. These cards are the same as the regular Stadium Club cards except they are imprinted with the Stadium Club logo on the front. The set includes parallel versions of both the basic cards and the insert cards. Only the inserts cards have been priced below. Please use the multiplier for values on the basic cards. These sets were issued at an approximate cost of $200 to Stadium Club members. Even though, the set was issued at $200, the current market conditions makes this set available at less than original issue cost.

COMP.FACT.SET (760) 35.00 150.00
COMMON CARD (1-750) .02 .25
*STARS: 2X TO 4X BASIC CARDS
*ROOKIES: 1.5X TO 3X BASIC CARDS
MA1 Robin Yount 1.50 4.00
MA2 George Brett 3.00 8.00
MA3 David Nied .40 1.00
MA4 Nigel Wilson .40 1.00
MB1 Will Clark 3.00 8.00
Mark McGwire
MB2 Dwight Gooden 1.50 4.00
Don Mattingly
MB3 Ryne Sandberg 2.00 5.00
Frank Thomas
MB4 Darryl Strawberry 2.00 5.00
Ken Griffey
MC1 David Nied .40 1.00
MC2 Charlie Hough .60 1.50

1993 Stadium Club Inserts

This 10-card set was randomly inserted in all series of Stadium Club packs, the first four in series 1, the second four in series 2 and the last two in series 3. The themes of the standard-size cards differ from series to series, but the basic design -- borderless color action shots on the fronts -- remains the same throughout. The series 1 and 3 cards are numbered on the back, the series 2 cards are unnumbered. No matter what series, all of these inserts were included one every 15 packs.

COMPLETE SERIES 1 (4) .75 2.00
COMPLETE SERIES 2 (4) 4.00 10.00
COMPLETE SERIES 3 (2) .20 .50
COMMON SER.1 (A1-A4) .10 .30
COMMON SER.2 (B1-B4) .10 .30
COMMON SER.3 (C1-C2) .10 .30
A1 Robin Yount 1.00 2.50
A2 George Brett 1.50 4.00
A3 David Nied FDP .10 .30
A4 Nigel Wilson FDP .10 .30
B1 Will Clark 1.50 4.00
Mark McGwire
B2 Dwight Gooden 1.50 4.00
Don Mattingly
B3 Ryne Sandberg .60 1.50
Frank Thomas
B4 Darryl Strawberry 1.00 2.50
Ken Griffey Jr.
C1 David Nied UER .10 .30
Colorado Rockies Firsts
(Misspelled pitch-
hitter on back)
C2 Charlie Hough .25 .60

1993 Stadium Club Master Photos

Each of the three Stadium Club series features Master Photos, uncropped versions of the regular Stadium Club cards. Each Master Photo is inlaid in a 5" by 7" white frame and bordered with a prismatic foil trim. The Master Photos were made available to the public in two ways. First, one in every 24 packs included a Master Photo winner card redeemable for a group of three Master Photos until Jan. 31, 1994. Second, each hobby box contained one Master Photo. The cards are unnumbered and checklisted below in alphabetical order within series I (1-12), II (13-24), and III (25-30). Two different versions of these master photos were issued, one with and one without the "Members Only" gold foil seal at the upper right corner. The "Members Only" Master Photos were only available with the direct-mail solicited 750-card Stadium Club Members Only set.

COMPLETE SERIES 1 (12) 2.50 6.00
COMPLETE SERIES 2 (12) 3.00 8.00
COMPLETE SERIES 3 (6) 4.00 10.00
1 Carlos Baerga .08 .25
2 Delino DeShields .08 .25
3 Brian McRae .08 .25
4 Sam Militello .08 .25
5 Joe Oliver .08 .25
6 Kirby Puckett .50 1.25
7 Cal Ripken 1.50 4.00
8 Bip Roberts .08 .25
9 Mike Scioscia .08 .25
10 Rick Sutcliffe .20 .50
11 Danny Tartabull .08 .25
12 Tim Wakefield .50 1.25
13 George Brett 1.25 3.00
14 Jose Canseco .30 .75
15 Will Clark .30 .75
16 Travis Fryman .20 .50
17 Dwight Gooden .20 .50
18 Mark Grace .30 .75
19 Rickey Henderson .50 1.25
20 Mark McGwire MC 1.25 3.00
21 Nolan Ryan 2.00 5.00
22 Ruben Sierra .20 .50
23 Darryl Strawberry .20 .50
24 Larry Walker .20 .50
25 Barry Bonds 1.25 3.00
26 Ken Griffey Jr. .75 2.00
27 Greg Maddux .75 2.00
28 David Nied .08 .25
29 J.T. Snow .30 .75
30 Brien Taylor .08 .25

1993 Stadium Club Ultra-Pro

The ten cards in this set measure the standard size and were available singly as limited edition random inserts in the Topps Stadium Club Ultra-Pro Platinum collector pages refill packs (1-6) and individual semi-rigid card protector packs (7-10). In light of a marketing partnership with the Rembrandt Company, this ten-card set was produced by Stadium Club to mark the launch of a new accessory line of premium card storage accessory products. Reportedly no more than 150,000 sets were produced. Willie Mays is Barry Bonds' godfather.

COMPLETE SET (10) 8.00 20.00
1 Barry Bonds 1.00 2.50
Willie Mays
Bobby Bonds
2 Willie Mays 1.25 3.00
3 Bobby Bonds .40 1.00
4 Barry Bonds .75 2.00
5 Barry Bonds .75 2.00
Bobby Bonds
6 Willie Mays 1.25 3.00
7 Barry Bonds .75 2.00
8 Bobby Bonds .75 2.00
Willie Mays
9 Willie Mays 1.25 3.00
10 Barry Bonds .75 2.00

1994 Stadium Club

The 720 standard-size cards comprising this set were issued two series of 270 and a third series of 180. There are a number of subsets including Home Run Club (258-268), Tale of Two Players (525/526), Division Leaders (527-532), Quick Starts (533-538), Career Contributors (541-543), Rookie Rocker (626-630), Rookie Rocket (631-634) and Fantastic Finishes (714-719). Rookie Cards include Jeff Cirillo and Chan Ho Park.

COMPLETE SET (720) 22.00 55.00
COMP.SERIES 1 (270) 8.00 20.00
COMP.SERIES 2 (270) 8.00 20.00
COMP.SERIES 3 (180) 6.00 15.00
1 Robin Yount .50 1.25
2 Rick Wilkins .05 .15
3 Steve Scarsone .05 .15
4 Gary Sheffield .10 .30
5 George Brett UER .75 2.00
(birthdate listed as 1963;
should be 1953)
6 Al Martin .05 .15
7 Joe Oliver .05 .15
8 Stan Belinda .05 .15
9 Denny Hocking .05 .15
10 Roberto Alomar .20 .50
11 Luis Polonia .05 .15
12 Scott Hemond .05 .15
13 Jody Reed .05 .15
14 Mel Rojas .05 .15
15 Junior Ortiz .05 .15
16 Harold Baines .10 .30
17 Brad Pennington .05 .15
18 Jay Bell .10 .30
19 Tom Henke .05 .15
20 Jeff Branson .05 .15
21 Roberto Mejia .05 .15
22 Pedro Munoz .05 .15
23 Matt Nokes .05 .15
24 Jack McDowell .05 .15
25 Cecil Fielder .10 .30
26 Tony Fossas .05 .15
27 Jim Eisenreich .05 .15
28 Anthony Young .05 .15
29 Chuck Carr .05 .15
30 Jeff Treadway .05 .15
31 Chris Nabholz .05 .15
32 Tom Candiotti .05 .15
33 Mike Maddux .05 .15
34 Nolan Ryan 1.25 3.00
35 Luis Gonzalez .10 .30
36 Tim Salmon .20 .50
37 Mark Whiten .05 .15
38 Roger McDowell .05 .15
39 Royce Clayton .05 .15
40 Troy Neel .05 .15
41 Mike Harkey .05 .15
42 Darrin Fletcher .05 .15
43 Wayne Kirby .05 .15
44 Rich Amaral .05 .15
45 Robb Nen UER .10 .30
(Nenn on back)
46 Tim Teufel .05 .15
47 Steve Cooke .05 .15
48 Jeff McNeely .05 .15
49 Jeff Montgomery .05 .15
50 Skeeter Barnes .05 .15
51 Scott Stahoviak .05 .15
52 Pat Kelly .05 .15
53 Brady Anderson .10 .30
54 Mariano Duncan .05 .15
55 Brian Bohanon .05 .15
56 Jerry Spradlin .05 .15
57 Ron Karkovice .05 .15
58 Jeff Gardner .05 .15
59 Bobby Bonilla .10 .30
60 Tino Martinez .20 .50
61 Todd Benzinger .05 .15
62 Steve Trachsel .05 .15
63 Brian Jordan .10 .30
64 Steve Bedrosian .05 .15
65 Brent Gates .05 .15
66 Shawn Green .30 .75
67 Sean Berry .05 .15
68 Joe Klink .05 .15
69 Fernando Valenzuela .10 .30
70 Andy Tomberlin .05 .15
71 Tony Pena .05 .15
72 Eric Young .05 .15
73 Chris Gomez .05 .15
74 Paul O'Neill .20 .50
75 Ricky Gutierrez .05 .15
76 Brad Holman .05 .15
77 Lance Painter .05 .15
78 Mike Butcher .05 .15
79 Sid Bream .05 .15
80 Sammy Sosa .30 .75
81 Felix Fermin .05 .15
82 Todd Hundley .05 .15
83 Kevin Higgins .05 .15
84 Todd Pratt .05 .15
85 Ken Griffey Jr. .50 1.25
86 John O'Donoghue .05 .15
87 Rick Renteria .05 .15
88 John Burkett .05 .15
89 Jose Vizcaino .05 .15
90 Kevin Seitzer .05 .15
91 Bobby Witt .05 .15
92 Chris Turner .05 .15
93 Omar Vizquel .20 .50
94 David Justice .10 .30
95 David Segui .05 .15
96 Dave Hollins .05 .15
97 Doug Strange .05 .15
98 Jerald Clark .05 .15
99 Mike Moore .05 .15
100 Joey Cora .05 .15
101 Scott Kamieniecki .05 .15
102 Andy Benes .05 .15
103 Chris Bosio .05 .15
104 Rey Sanchez .05 .15
105 John Jaha .05 .15
106 Otis Nixon .05 .15
107 Rickey Henderson .30 .75
108 Jeff Bagwell .20 .50
109 Gregg Jefferies .05 .15
110 Roberto Alomar .10 .30
Paul Molitor
John Olerud
111 Ron Gant .10 .30
David Justice
Fred McGriff
112 Juan Gonzalez .20 .50
Rafael Palmeiro
Dean Palmer
113 Greg Swindell .05 .15
114 Bill Haselman .05 .15
115 Phil Plantier .05 .15
116 Ivan Rodriguez .20 .50
117 Kevin Tapani .05 .15
118 Mike LaValliere .05 .15
119 Tim Costo .05 .15
120 Mickey Morandini .05 .15
121 Brett Butler .10 .30
122 Tom Pagnozzi .05 .15
123 Ron Gant .10 .30
124 Damion Easley .05 .15
125 Dennis Eckersley .10 .30
126 Matt Mieske .05 .15
127 Cliff Floyd .10 .30
128 Julian Tavarez RC .10 .30
129 Arthur Rhodes .05 .15
130 Dave West .05 .15
131 Tim Naehring .05 .15
132 Freddie Benavides .05 .15
133 Paul Assenmacher .05 .15
134 David McCarty .05 .15
135 Jose Lind .05 .15
136 Reggie Sanders .10 .30
137 Don Slaught .05 .15
138 Andujar Cedeno .05 .15
139 Rob Deer .05 .15
140 Mike Piazza UER .60 1.50
(listed as outfielder)
141 Moises Alou .10 .30
142 Tom Foley .05 .15
143 Benito Santiago .10 .30
144 Sandy Alomar Jr. .05 .15
145 Carlos Hernandez .05 .15
146 Luis Alicea .05 .15
147 Tom Lampkin .05 .15
148 Ryan Klesko .10 .30
149 Juan Guzman .05 .15
150 Scott Servais .05 .15
151 Tony Gwynn .40 1.00
152 Tim Wakefield .20 .50
153 David Nied .05 .15
154 Chris Haney .05 .15
155 Danny Bautista .05 .15
156 Randy Velarde .05 .15
157 Darrin Jackson .05 .15
158 J.R. Phillips .05 .15
159 Greg Gagne .05 .15
160 Luis Aquino .05 .15
161 John Vander Wal .05 .15
162 Randy Myers .05 .15
163 Ted Power .05 .15
164 Scott Brosius .10 .30
165 Len Dykstra .10 .30
166 Jacob Brumfield .05 .15
167 Bo Jackson .30 .75
168 Eddie Taubensee .05 .15
169 Carlos Baerga .05 .15
170 Tim Bogar .05 .15
171 Jose Canseco .20 .50
172 Greg Blosser UER .05 .15
(Gregg on front)
173 Chili Davis .10 .30
174 Randy Knorr .05 .15
175 Mike Perez .05 .15
176 Henry Rodriguez .05 .15
177 Brian Turang RC .05 .15
178 Roger Pavlik .05 .15
179 Aaron Sele .05 .15
180 Fred McGriff .20 .50
Gary Sheffield
181 J.T. Snow .20 .50
Tim Salmon
182 Roberto Hernandez .05 .15
183 Jeff Reboulet .05 .15
184 John Doherty .05 .15
185 Danny Sheaffer .05 .15
186 Bip Roberts .05 .15
187 Dennis Martinez .10 .30
188 Darryl Hamilton .05 .15
189 Eduardo Perez .05 .15
190 Pete Harnisch .05 .15
191 Rich Gossage .10 .30
192 Mickey Tettleton .05 .15
193 Lenny Webster .05 .15
194 Lance Johnson .05 .15
195 Don Mattingly .75 2.00
196 Gregg Olson .05 .15
197 Mark Gubicza .05 .15
198 Scott Fletcher .05 .15
199 Jon Shave .05 .15
200 Tim Mauser .05 .15
201 Jeromy Burnitz .10 .30
202 Rob Dibble .10 .30
203 Will Clark .20 .50
204 Steve Buechele .05 .15
205 Brian Williams .05 .15
206 Carlos Garcia .05 .15
207 Mark Clark .05 .15
208 Rafael Palmeiro .20 .50
209 Eric Davis .10 .30
210 Pat Meares .05 .15
211 Chuck Finley .10 .30
212 Jason Bere .05 .15
213 Gary DiSarcina .05 .15
214 Tony Fernandez .05 .15
215 B.J. Surhoff .10 .30
216 Lee Guetterman .05 .15
217 Tim Wallach .05 .15
218 Kirt Manwaring .05 .15
219 Albert Belle .10 .30
220 Dwight Gooden .10 .30
221 Archi Cianfrocco .05 .15
222 Terry Mulholland .05 .15
223 Hipolito Pichardo .05 .15
224 Kent Hrbek .10 .30
225 Craig Grebeck .05 .15
226 Todd Jones .05 .15
227 Mike Bordick .05 .15
228 John Olerud .10 .30
229 Jeff Blauser .05 .15
230 Alex Arias .05 .15
231 Bernard Gilkey .05 .15
232 Denny Neagle .10 .30
233 Pedro Borbon .05 .15
234 Dick Schofield .05 .15
235 Matias Carrillo .05 .15
236 Juan Bell .05 .15
237 Mike Hampton .10 .30
238 Barry Bonds .75 2.00
239 Cris Carpenter .05 .15
240 Eric Karros .10 .30
241 Greg McMichael .05 .15
242 Pat Hentgen .05 .15
243 Tim Pugh .05 .15
244 Vinny Castilla .10 .30
245 Charlie Hough .10 .30
246 Bobby Munoz .05 .15
247 Kevin Baez .05 .15
248 Todd Frohwirth .05 .15
249 Charlie Hayes .05 .15
250 Mike Macfarlane .05 .15
251 Danny Darwin .05 .15
252 Ben Rivera .05 .15
253 Dave Henderson .05 .15
254 Steve Avery .05 .15
255 Tim Belcher .05 .15
256 Dan Plesac .05 .15
257 Jim Thome .20 .50
258 Albert Belle HR .05 .15
259 Barry Bonds HR .40 1.00
260 Ron Gant HR .05 .15

261 Juan Gonzalez HR .05 .15
262 Ken Griffey Jr. HR .30 .75
263 David Justice HR .05 .15
264 Fred McGriff HR .10 .30
265 Rafael Palmeiro HR .10 .30
266 Mike Piazza HR .30 .75
267 Frank Thomas HR .20 .50
268 Matt Williams HR .05 .15
269 Checklist 1-135 .05 .15
270 Checklist 136-270 .05 .15
271 Mike Stanley .05 .15
272 Tony Tarasco .05 .15
273 Teddy Higuera .05 .15
274 Ryan Thompson .05 .15
275 Rick Aguilera .05 .15
276 Ramon Martinez .05 .15
277 Orlando Merced .05 .15
278 Guillermo Velasquez .05 .15
279 Mark Hutton .05 .15
280 Larry Walker .10 .30
281 Kevin Gross .05 .15
282 Jose Offerman .05 .15
283 Jim Leyritz .05 .15
284 Jamie Moyer .10 .30
285 Frank Thomas .30 .75
286 Derek Bell .05 .15
287 Derrick May .05 .15
288 Dave Winfield .10 .30
289 Curt Schilling .10 .30
290 Carlos Quintana .05 .15
291 Bob Natal .05 .15
292 David Cone .10 .30
293 Al Osuna .05 .15
294 Bob Hamelin .05 .15
295 Chad Curtis .05 .15
296 Danny Jackson .05 .15
297 Bob Welch .05 .15
298 Felix Jose .05 .15
299 Jay Buhner .10 .30
300 Joe Carter .10 .30
301 Kenny Lofton .10 .30
302 Kirk Rueter .05 .15
303 Kim Batiste .05 .15
304 Mike Morgan .05 .15
305 Pat Borders .05 .15
306 Rene Arocha .05 .15
307 Ruben Sierra .10 .30
308 Steve Finley .10 .30
309 Travis Fryman .10 .30
310 Zane Smith .05 .15
311 Willie Wilson .05 .15
312 Trevor Hoffman .20 .50
313 Terry Pendleton .10 .30
314 Salomon Torres .05 .15
315 Robin Ventura .10 .30
316 Randy Tomlin .05 .15
317 Dave Stewart .10 .30
318 Mike Benjamin .05 .15
319 Matt Turner .05 .15
320 Manny Ramirez .30 .75
321 Kevin Young .05 .15
322 Ken Caminiti .10 .30
323 Joe Girardi .05 .15
324 Jeff McKnight .05 .15
325 Gene Harris .05 .15
326 Devon White .10 .30
327 Darryl Kile .10 .30
328 Craig Paquette .05 .15
329 Cal Eldred .05 .15
330 Bill Swift .05 .15
331 Alan Trammell .10 .30
332 Armando Reynoso .05 .15
333 Brent Mayne .05 .15
334 Chris Donnels .05 .15
335 Darryl Strawberry .10 .30
336 Dean Palmer .10 .30
337 Frank Castillo .05 .15
338 Jeff King .05 .15
339 John Franco .10 .30
340 Kevin Appier .10 .30
341 Lance Blankenship .05 .15
342 Mark McLemore .05 .15
343 Pedro Astacio .05 .15
344 Rich Batchelor .05 .15
345 Ryan Bowen .05 .15
346 Terry Steinbach .05 .15
347 Troy O'Leary .05 .15
348 Willie Blair .05 .15
349 Wade Boggs .20 .50
350 Tim Raines .10 .30
351 Scott Livingstone .05 .15
352 Rod Correia .05 .15
353 Ray Lankford .10 .30
354 Pat Listach .05 .15
355 Milt Thompson .05 .15
356 Miguel Jimenez .05 .15
357 Marc Newfield .05 .15
358 Mark McGwire .75 2.00
359 Kirby Puckett .30 .75
360 Kent Mercker .05 .15
361 John Kruk .10 .30
362 Jeff Kent .20 .50
363 Hal Morris .05 .15
364 Edgar Martinez .20 .50
365 Dave Magadan .05 .15
366 Dante Bichette .10 .30
367 Chris Hammond .05 .15
368 Bret Saberhagen .10 .30
369 Billy Ripken .05 .15
370 Bill Gullickson .05 .15
371 Andre Dawson .10 .30
372 Roberto Kelly .05 .15
373 Cal Ripken 1.00 2.50
374 Craig Biggio .20 .50
375 Dan Pasqua .05 .15
376 Dave Nilsson .05 .15
377 Duane Ward .05 .15
378 Greg Vaughn .05 .15
379 Jeff Fassero .05 .15
380 Jerry DiPoto .05 .15
381 John Patterson .05 .15
382 Kevin Brown .10 .30
383 Kevin Roberson .05 .15
384 Joe Orsulak .05 .15
385 Hilly Hathaway .05 .15
386 Mike Greenwell .05 .15
387 Orestes Destrade .05 .15
388 Mike Gallego .05 .15
389 Ozzie Guillen .10 .30
390 Raul Mondesi .10 .30
391 Scott Lydy .05 .15
392 Tom Urbani .05 .15
393 Wil Cordero .05 .15
394 Tony Longmire .05 .15
395 Todd Zeile .05 .15
396 Scott Cooper .05 .15
397 Ryne Sandberg .50 1.25
398 Ricky Bones .05 .15
399 Phil Clark .05 .15
400 Orel Hershiser .10 .30
401 Mike Henneman .05 .15
402 Mark Lemke .05 .15
403 Mark Grace .20 .50
404 Ken Ryan .05 .15
405 John Smoltz .20 .50
406 Jeff Conine .10 .30
407 Greg Harris .05 .15
408 Doug Drabek .05 .15
409 Dave Fleming .05 .15
410 Danny Tartabull .05 .15
411 Chad Kreuter .05 .15
412 Brad Ausmus .20 .50
413 Ben McDonald .05 .15
414 Barry Larkin .20 .50
415 Bret Barberie .05 .15
416 Chuck Knoblauch .10 .30
417 Ozzie Smith .50 1.25
418 Ed Sprague .05 .15
419 Matt Williams .10 .30
420 Jeremy Hernandez .05 .15
421 Jose Bautista .05 .15
422 Kevin Mitchell .05 .15
423 Manuel Lee .05 .15
424 Mike Devereaux .05 .15
425 Omar Olivares .05 .15
426 Rafael Belliard .05 .15
427 Richie Lewis .05 .15
428 Ron Darling .05 .15
429 Shane Mack .05 .15
430 Tim Hulett .05 .15
431 Wally Joyner .10 .30
432 Wes Chamberlain .05 .15
433 Tom Browning .05 .15
434 Scott Radinsky .05 .15
435 Rondell White .10 .30
436 Rod Beck .05 .15
437 Rheal Cormier .05 .15
438 Randy Johnson .30 .75
439 Pete Schourek .05 .15
440 Mo Vaughn .10 .30
441 Mike Timlin .05 .15
442 Mark Langston .05 .15
443 Lou Whitaker .10 .30
444 Kevin Stocker .05 .15
445 Ken Hill .05 .15
446 John Wetteland .10 .30
447 J.T. Snow .10 .30
448 Erik Pappas .05 .15
449 David Hulse .05 .15
450 Darren Daulton .10 .30
451 Chris Hoiles .05 .15
452 Bryan Harvey .05 .15
453 Darren Lewis .05 .15
454 Andres Galarraga .10 .30
455 Joe Hesketh .05 .15
456 Jose Valentin .05 .15
457 Dan Peltier .05 .15
458 Joe Boever .05 .15
459 Kevin Rogers .05 .15
460 Craig Shipley .05 .15
461 Alvaro Espinoza .05 .15
462 Wilson Alvarez .05 .15
463 Cory Snyder .05 .15
464 Candy Maldonado .05 .15
465 Blas Minor .05 .15
466 Rod Bolton .05 .15
467 Kenny Rogers .10 .30
468 Greg Myers .05 .15
469 Jimmy Key .10 .30
470 Tony Castillo .05 .15
471 Mike Stanton .05 .15
472 Deion Sanders .20 .50
473 Tito Navarro .05 .15
474 Mike Gardiner .05 .15
475 Steve Reed .05 .15
476 John Roper .05 .15
477 Mike Trombley .05 .15
478 Charles Nagy .05 .15
479 Larry Casian .05 .15
480 Eric Hillman .05 .15
481 Bill Wertz .05 .15
482 Jeff Schwarz .05 .15
483 John Valentin .05 .15
484 Carl Willis .05 .15
485 Gary Gaetti .10 .30
486 Bill Pecota .05 .15
487 John Smiley .05 .15
488 Mike Mussina .20 .50
489 Mike Ignasiak .05 .15
490 Billy Brewer .05 .15
491 Jack Voigt .05 .15
492 Mike Munoz .05 .15
493 Lee Tinsley .05 .15
494 Bob Wickman .05 .15
495 Roger Salkeld .05 .15
496 Thomas Howard .05 .15
497 Mark Davis .05 .15
498 Dave Clark .05 .15
499 Turk Wendell .05 .15
500 Rafael Bournigal .05 .15
501 Chip Hale .05 .15
502 Matt Whiteside .05 .15
503 Brian Koelling .05 .15
504 Jeff Reed .05 .15
505 Paul Wagner .05 .15
506 Torey Lovullo .05 .15
507 Curt Leskanic .05 .15
508 Derek Lilliquist .05 .15
509 Joe Magrane .05 .15
510 Mackey Sasser .05 .15
511 Lloyd McClendon .05 .15
512 Jayhawk Owens .05 .15
513 Woody Williams .05 .15
514 Gary Redus .05 .15
515 Tim Spehr .05 .15
516 Jim Abbott .20 .50
517 Lou Frazier .05 .15
518 Erik Plantenberg RC .05 .15
519 Tim Worrell .05 .15
520 Brian McRae .05 .15
521 Chan Ho Park RC .30 .75
522 Mark Wohlers .05 .15
523 Geronimo Pena .05 .15
524 Andy Ashby .05 .15
525 Tim Raines .05 .15
Andre Dawson TALE
526 Paul Molitor TALE .05 .15
527 Joe Carter DL .05 .15
528 F.Thomas DL UER .20 .50
listed as third in RBI in 1993; was actually second
529 Ken Griffey Jr. DL .30 .75
530 David Justice DL .05 .15
531 Gregg Jefferies DL .05 .15
532 Barry Bonds DL .40 1.00
533 John Kruk QS .05 .15
534 Roger Clemens QS .30 .75
535 Cecil Fielder QS .05 .15
536 Ruben Sierra QS .05 .15
537 Tony Gwynn QS .20 .50
538 Tom Glavine QS .10 .30
539 CL 271-405 UER .05 .15
number on back is 269
540 CL 406-540 UER .05 .15
numbered 270 on back
541 Ozzie Smith ATL .30 .75
542 Eddie Murray ATL .20 .50
543 Lee Smith ATL .05 .15
544 Greg Maddux .50 1.25
545 Denis Boucher .05 .15
546 Mark Gardner .05 .15
547 Bo Jackson .30 .75
548 Eric Anthony .05 .15
549 Delino DeShields .05 .15
550 Turner Ward .05 .15
551 Scott Sanderson .05 .15
552 Hector Carrasco .05 .15
553 Tony Phillips .05 .15
554 Melido Perez .05 .15
555 Mike Felder .05 .15
556 Jack Morris .10 .30
557 Rafael Palmeiro .20 .50
558 Shane Reynolds .05 .15
559 Pete Incaviglia .05 .15
560 Greg Harris .05 .15
561 Matt Walbeck .05 .15
562 Todd Van Poppel .05 .15
563 Todd Stottlemyre .05 .15
564 Ricky Bones .05 .15
565 Mike Jackson .05 .15
566 Kevin McReynolds .05 .15
567 Melvin Nieves .05 .15
568 Juan Gonzalez .10 .30
569 Frank Viola .10 .30
570 Vince Coleman .05 .15
571 Brian Anderson RC .10 .30
572 Omar Vizquel .20 .50
573 Bernie Williams .20 .50
574 Tom Glavine .20 .50
575 Mitch Williams .05 .15
576 Shawon Dunston .05 .15
577 Mike Lansing .05 .15
578 Greg Pirkl .05 .15
579 Sid Fernandez .05 .15
580 Doug Jones .05 .15
581 Walt Weiss .05 .15
582 Tim Belcher .05 .15
583 Alex Fernandez .05 .15
584 Alex Cole .05 .15
585 Greg Cadaret .05 .15
586 Bob Tewksbury .05 .15
587 Dave Hansen .05 .15
588 Kurt Abbott RC .05 .15
589 Rick White RC .05 .15
590 Kevin Bass .05 .15
591 Geronimo Berroa .05 .15
592 Jaime Navarro .05 .15
593 Steve Farr .05 .15
594 Jack Armstrong .05 .15
595 Steve Howe .05 .15
596 Jose Rijo .05 .15
597 Otis Nixon .05 .15
598 Robby Thompson .05 .15
599 Kelly Stinnett RC .10 .30
600 Carlos Delgado .20 .50
601 Brian Johnson RC .05 .15
602 Gregg Olson .05 .15
603 Jim Edmonds .30 .75
604 Mike Blowers .05 .15
605 Lee Smith .10 .30
606 Pat Rapp .05 .15
607 Mike Magnante .05 .15
608 Karl Rhodes .05 .15
609 Jeff Juden .05 .15
610 Rusty Meacham .05 .15
611 Pedro Martinez .30 .75
612 Todd Worrell .05 .15
613 Stan Javier .05 .15
614 Mike Hampton .10 .30
615 Jose Guzman .05 .15
616 Xavier Hernandez .05 .15
617 David Wells .10 .30
618 John Habyan .05 .15
619 Chris Nabholz .05 .15
620 Bobby Jones .05 .15
621 Chris James .05 .15
622 Ellis Burks .10 .30
623 Erik Hanson .05 .15
624 Pat Meares .05 .15
625 Harold Reynolds .10 .30
626 Bob Hamelin RR .05 .15
627 Manny Ramirez RR .20 .50
628 Ryan Klesko RR .10 .30
629 Carlos Delgado RR .10 .30
630 Javier Lopez RR .10 .30
631 Steve Karsay RR .05 .15
632 Rick Helling RR .05 .15
633 Steve Trachsel RR .05 .15
634 Hector Carrasco RR .05 .15
635 Andy Stankiewicz .05 .15
636 Paul Sorrento .05 .15
637 Scott Erickson .05 .15
638 Chipper Jones .30 .75
639 Luis Polonia .05 .15
640 Howard Johnson .05 .15
641 John Dopson .05 .15
642 Jody Reed .05 .15
643 Lonnie Smith UER .05 .15
Card numbered 543
644 Mark Portugal .05 .15
645 Paul Molitor .10 .30
646 Paul Assenmacher .05 .15
647 Hubie Brooks .05 .15
648 Gary Wayne .05 .15
649 Sean Berry .05 .15
650 Roger Clemens .60 1.50
651 Brian R. Hunter .05 .15
652 Wally Whitehurst .05 .15
653 Allen Watson .05 .15
654 Rickey Henderson .30 .75
655 Sid Bream .05 .15
656 Dan Wilson .05 .15
657 Ricky Jordan .05 .15
658 Sterling Hitchcock .05 .15
659 Darrin Jackson .05 .15
660 Junior Felix .05 .15
661 Tom Brunansky .05 .15
662 Jose Vizcaino .05 .15
663 Mark Leiter .05 .15
664 Gil Heredia .05 .15
665 Fred McGriff .20 .50
666 Will Clark .20 .50
667 Al Leiter .10 .30
668 James Mouton .05 .15
669 Billy Bean .05 .15
670 Scott Leius .05 .15
671 Bret Boone .10 .30
672 Darren Holmes .05 .15
673 Dave Weathers .05 .15
674 Eddie Murray .30 .75
675 Felix Fermin .05 .15
676 Chris Sabo .05 .15
677 Billy Spiers .05 .15
678 Aaron Sele .05 .15
679 Juan Samuel .05 .15
680 Julio Franco .10 .30
681 Heathcliff Slocumb .05 .15
682 Dennis Martinez .10 .30
683 Jerry Browne .05 .15
684 Pedro Martinez RC .05 .15
685 Rex Hudler .05 .15
686 Willie McGee .10 .30
687 Andy Van Slyke .20 .50
688 Pat Mahomes .05 .15
689 Dave Henderson .05 .15
690 Tony Eusebio .05 .15
691 Rick Sutcliffe .10 .30
692 Willie Banks .05 .15
693 Alan Mills .05 .15
694 Jeff Treadway .05 .15
695 Alex Gonzalez .05 .15
696 David Segui .05 .15
697 Rick Helling .05 .15
698 Bip Roberts .05 .15
699 Jeff Cirillo RC .10 .30
700 Terry Mulholland .05 .15
701 Marvin Freeman .05 .15
702 Jason Bere .05 .15
703 Javier Lopez .10 .30
704 Greg Hibbard .05 .15
705 Tommy Greene .05 .15
706 Marquis Grissom .10 .30
707 Brian Harper .05 .15
708 Steve Karsay .05 .15
709 Jeff Brantley .05 .15
710 Jeff Russell .05 .15
711 Bryan Hickerson .05 .15
712 Jim Pittsley RC .05 .15
713 Bobby Ayala .05 .15
714 John Smoltz .20 .50
715 Jose Rijo .05 .15
716 Greg Maddux .30 .75
717 Matt Williams .05 .15
718 Frank Thomas .20 .50
719 Ryne Sandberg .30 .75
720 Checklist .05 .15

1994 Stadium Club First Day Issue

Randomly inserted in one of every 24 packs, these First Day Production cards are identical to the regular issues except for a special 1st Day foil stamp engraved on the front of each card. No more than 2,000 of each Stadium Club card was issued as First Day Issue. Some FDI logos have been transferred from "common" players to the front of "star" players.

*STARS: 8X TO 20X BASIC CARDS
*ROOKIES: 6X to 15X BASIC CARDS

1994 Stadium Club Golden Rainbow

Parallel to the basic Stadium Club set, Golden Rainbows differ in that the player's last name on front has gold refracting foil over it. The cards were inserted one per Stadium Club foil pack and two per jumbo.

COMPLETE SET (720) 75.00 160.00
COMP.SERIES 1 (270) 25.00 60.00
COMP.SERIES 2 (270) 25.00 60.00
COMP.SERIES 3 (180) 15.00 40.00
*STARS: 1.25X TO 3X BASIC CARDS
*ROOKIES: 1X TO 2.5X BASIC CARDS

1994 Stadium Club Members Only Parallel

This set, issued only to Topps Stadium Club Members, is a parallel of the regular Stadium Club set. This set was issued in factory set form only and includes parallel versions of both the basic issue and insert cards from the 1994 Stadium Club set. According to Topps, 5,000 sets were produced. However, some dealers believe less cards than that were actually produced. Only the insert cards have been listed below. Please use the multiplier for values on the basic issue cards.

COMP.FACT.SET (770) 27.50 200.00
*1ST SERIES MEMBERS ONLY: 4X BASIC CARDS

2ND AND 3RD SERIES MEMBERS ONLY STARS: 6X BASIC CARDS
F1 Jeff Bagwell 1.50 4.00
F2 Albert Belle .60 1.50
F3 Barry Bonds 3.00 8.00
F4 Juan Gonzalez 1.25 3.00
F5 Ken Griffey Jr. 5.00 12.00
F6 Marquis Grissom .40 1.00
F7 David Justice 1.25 3.00
F8 Mike Piazza 3.00 8.00
F9 Tim Salmon 1.25 3.00
F10 Frank Thomas 2.50 6.00
DD1 Mike Piazza 3.00 8.00
DD2 Dave Winfield 1.25 3.00
DD3 John Kruk .60 1.50
DD4 Cal Ripken 6.00 15.00
DD5 Jack McDowell 2.50 6.00
DD6 Barry Bonds 3.00 8.00
DD7 Ken Griffey Jr. 5.00 12.00
DD8 Tim Salmon 1.25 3.00
DD9 Frank Thomas 2.00 5.00
DD10 Jeff Kent 1.25 3.00
DD11 Randy Johnson 1.50 4.00
DD12 Darren Daulton .60 1.50
ST1 Jeff Blauser .30 .75
Terry Pendleton
ST2 Sammy Sosa .60 1.50
Derrick May
ST3 Reggie Sanders .40 1.00
Barry Larkin
ST4 Vinny Castilla .20 .50
Eric Young
ST5 Alex Arias .20 .50
ST6 Eric Anthony .30 .75
Steve Finley
ST7 Mike Piazza 2.00 5.00
ST8 Marquis Grissom .30 .75
ST9 Bobby Bonilla .20 .50
ST10 Mickey Morandini .20 .50
ST11 Andy Van Slyke .30 .75
Jay Bell
ST12 Todd Zeile .20 .50
Gregg Jefferies
ST13 Ricky Gutierrez .20 .50
ST14 Matt Williams .40 1.00
Kirt Manwaring
ST15 Cal Ripken 2.50 6.00
ST16 Luis Rivera .20 .50
John Valentin
ST17 Tim Salmon .60 1.50
ST18 Ozzie Guillen .20 .50
ST19 Kenny Lofton .40 1.00
Carlos Baerga
Albert Belle
ST20 Alan Trammell .30 .75
Tony Phillips
ST21 Jose Lind .20 .50
Curt Wilkerson
ST22 Pat Listach .20 .50
John Jaha
Cal Eldred
ST23 Kirby Puckett 1.25 3.00
Kent Hrbek
ST24 Don Mattingly 1.25 3.00
Bernie Williams
ST25 Mike Bordick .20 .50
Brent Gates
ST26 Jay Buhner .40 1.00
Mike Blowers
ST27 Ivan Rodriguez .60 1.50
Dean Palmer
Jose Canseco
Juan Gonzalez
ST28 John Olerud .20 .50

1994 Stadium Club Dugout Dirt

Randomly inserted at a rate of one per six packs, these standard-size cards feature some of baseball's most popular and colorful players by sports cartoonists Daniel Guidera and Steve Benson. The cards resemble basic Stadium Club cards except for a Dugout Dirt logo at the bottom. Backs contain a cartoon. Cards 1-4 were found in first series packs with cards 5-8 and 9-12 were inserted in second series and third series packs respectively.

COMPLETE SERIES 1 (4) 2.00 5.00
COMPLETE SERIES 2 (4) 1.25 3.00
COMPLETE SERIES 3 (4) 1.25 3.00
DD1 Mike Piazza .60 1.50
DD2 Dave Winfield .10 .30
DD3 John Kruk .10 .30
DD4 Cal Ripken 1.00 2.50
DD5 Jack McDowell .05 .15
DD6 Barry Bonds .75 2.00
DD7 Ken Griffey Jr. .50 1.25
DD8 Tim Salmon .20 .50
DD9 Frank Thomas .30 .75
DD10 Jeff Kent .20 .50
DD11 Randy Johnson .30 .75
DD12 Darren Daulton .10 .30

1994 Stadium Club Finest

This set contains 10 standard-size metallic cards of top players. They were randomly inserted one in six third series packs. Jumbo versions measuring approximately five inches by seven inches were issued for retail repacks.

COMPLETE SET (10) 10.00 25.00
*JUMBOS: .6X TO 1.5X BASIC SC FINEST
JUMBOS DISTRIBUTED IN RETAIL PACKS
F1 Jeff Bagwell .60 1.50
F2 Albert Belle .40 1.00
F3 Barry Bonds 2.50 6.00
F4 Juan Gonzalez .40 1.00
F5 Ken Griffey Jr. 1.50 4.00
F6 Marquis Grissom .40 1.00
F7 David Justice .40 1.00
F8 Mike Piazza 2.00 5.00
F9 Tim Salmon .60 1.50
F10 Frank Thomas 1.00 2.50

1994 Stadium Club Super Teams

Randomly inserted at a rate of one per 24 first series packs only, this 28-card standard-size features one card for each of the 28 MLB teams. Collectors holding team cards could redeem them for special prizes if those teams won a division title, a league championship, or the World Series. But, since the strike affected the 1994 season, Topps postponed the promotion until the 1995 season. The expiration was pushed back to January 31, 1996.

COMPLETE SET (28) 20.00 50.00
ST1 Jeff Blauser 1.00 2.50
Terry Pendleton
ST2 Sammy Sosa .40 1.00
Derrick May
ST3 Reggie Sanders .60 1.50
Barry Larkin
ST4 Vinny Castilla .40 1.00
Eric Young
ST5 Alex Arias .40 1.00
ST6 Eric Anthony .40 1.00
Steve Finley
ST7 Mike Piazza 2.00 5.00
ST8 Marquis Grissom .40 1.00
ST9 Bobby Bonilla .40 1.00
ST10 Mickey Morandini .40 1.00
ST11 Andy Van Slyke .60 1.50
Jay Bell
ST12 Todd Zeile .40 1.00
Gregg Jefferies
ST13 Ricky Gutierrez .40 1.00
ST14 Matt Williams .40 1.00
Kirt Manwaring
ST15 Cal Ripken 3.00 8.00
ST16 Luis Rivera .40 1.00
John Valentin
ST17 Tim Salmon .40 1.00
ST18 Joey Cora .40 1.00
ST19 Kenny Lofton .40 1.00
Carlos Baerga
Albert Belle
ST20 (Alan Trammell .40 1.00
Tony Phillips
ST21 Jose Lind .40 1.00
Curt Wilkerson
ST22 Pat Listach .40 1.00
John Jaha
Cal Eldred
ST23 Kirby Puckett 1.00 2.50
Kent Hrbek
ST24 Don Mattingly 2.50 6.00
Bernie Williams
ST25 Mike Bordick .40 1.00
Brent Gates
ST26 Jay Buhner .40 1.00
Mike Blowers
ST27 Ivan Rodriguez .40 1.00
Dean Palmer
Jose Canseco
Juan Gonzalez
ST28 John Olerud .40 1.00

1994 Stadium Club Special

This 12-card set is standard sized and borderless. The fronts carry full color action shots. The Topps logo is in the upper left-hand corner. The featured player's name is in the bottom center with the first name typed in lower case and the last name typed in upper case. The backs have a small bio of the player along with his career stats.

COMPLETE SET (12)
COMMON CARD (1-12)
1 InfoCard
· Rookie Rockers
543 Lee Smith
558 Shane Reynolds
568 Juan Gonzalez
572 Omar Vizquel
574 Tom Glavine
611 Pedro Martinez
647 Hubie Brooks
674 Eddie Murray
675 Felix Fermin
677 Billy Spiers
678 Aaron Sele
694 Jeff Treadway

1994 Stadium Club Members Only

Issued to Stadium Club members, this 50-card standard-size set features 45 regular Stadium Club cards as well as five Stadium Club Finest cards.

COMP. FACT SET (50) 8.00 20.00
1 Juan Gonzalez .30 .75
2 Tom Henke .02 .10
3 John Kruk .08 .25
4 Paul Molitor .30 .75
5 David Justice .08 .25
6 Rafael Palmeiro .25 .60
7 John Smoltz .25 .60
8 Matt Williams .15 .40
9 John Olerud .08 .25
10 Mark Grace .15 .40
11 Joe Carter .08 .25
12 Wilson Alvarez .08 .25
13 Len Dykstra .08 .25
14 Kevin Appier .08 .25
15 Andres Galarraga .25 .60
16 Mark Langston .02 .10
17 Ken Griffey Jr. .75 2.00
18 Albert Belle .08 .25
19 Gregg Jefferies .02 .10
20 Duane Ward .02 .10
21 Jack McDowell .02 .10
22 Randy Johnson .30 .75
23 Tom Glavine .25 .60
24 Barry Bonds .60 1.50
25 Chuck Carr .02 .10
26 Ron Gant .08 .25
27 Kenny Lofton .15 .40
28 Mike Piazza .60 1.50
29 Frank Thomas .40 1.00
30 Fred McGriff .15 .40
31 Bryan Harvey .02 .10
32 John Burkett .02 .10
33 Roberto Alomar .25 .60
34 Cecil Fielder .08 .25
35 Marquis Grissom .08 .25
36 Randy Myers .02 .10
37 Tony Phillips .02 .10
38 Rickey Henderson .30 .75
39 Luis Polonia .02 .10
40 Jose Rijo .02 .10
41 Jeff Montgomery .02 .10
42 Greg Maddux .75 2.00
43 Tony Gwynn .60 1.50
44 Rod Beck .02 .10
45 Carlos Baerga .08 .25
46 Wil Cordero FIN .20 .50
47 Tim Salmon FIN .75 2.00
48 Mike Lansing FIN .20 .50
49 J.T. Snow FIN .20 .50
50 Jeff Conine FIN .30 .75

1994 Stadium Club Team

This 360-card standard-size set features 30 players from 12 teams. The cards are checklisted alphabetically according to teams.

COMPLETE SET (360) 16.00 40.00
1 Barry Bonds .75 2.00
2 Royce Clayton .02 .10
3 Kirt Manwaring .02 .10
4 J.R. Phillips .02 .10
5 Robby Thompson .02 .10
6 Willie McGee .07 .20
7 Steve Hosey .02 .10
8 Dave Burba .02 .10
9 Steve Scarsone .02 .10
10 Salomon Torres .02 .10
11 Bryan Hickerson .02 .10
12 Mike Benjamin .02 .10
13 Mark Carreon .02 .10
14 Rich Monteleone .02 .10
15 Dave Martinez .07 .20
16 Bill Swift .02 .10
17 Jeff Reed .02 .10
18 John Patterson .02 .10
19 Darren Lewis .02 .10
20 Mark Portugal .02 .10
21 Trevor Wilson .02 .10
22 Matt Williams .15 .40
23 Kevin Rogers .02 .10
24 Luis Mercedes .02 .10
25 Mike Jackson .02 .10
26 Steve Frey .02 .10
27 Tony Menendez .02 .10
28 John Burkett .02 .10
29 Todd Benzinger .02 .10
30 Rod Beck .02 .10
31 Greg Maddux 1.00 2.50
32 Steve Avery .02 .10
33 Milt Hill .02 .10
34 Charlie O'Brien .02 .10
35 John Smoltz .07 .20
36 Jarvis Brown .02 .10
37 Dave Gallagher .02 .10
Wearing Mets Uniform
38 Ryan Klesko .15 .40
39 Kent Mercker .02 .10
40 Terry Pendleton .02 .10
41 Ron Gant .07 .20
42 Pedro Borbon Jr. .02 .10
43 Steve Bedrosian .02 .10
44 Ramon Caraballo .02 .10
45 Tyler Houston .02 .10
46 Mark Lemke .02 .10
47 Fred McGriff .15 .40
48 Jose Oliva .02 .10
49 David Justice .25 .60
50 Chipper Jones .75 2.00
51 Tony Tarasco .02 .10
52 Javier Lopez .15 .40
53 Mark Wohlers .02 .10
54 Deion Sanders .25 .60
55 Greg McMichael .02 .10
56 Tom Glavine .40 1.00
57 Bill Pecota .02 .10
58 Mike Stanton .02 .10
59 Rafael Belliard .02 .10
60 Jeff Blauser .02 .10
61 Bryan Harvey .02 .10
62 Bret Barberie .02 .10
63 Rick Renteria .02 .10
64 Chris Hammond .02 .10
65 Pat Rapp .02 .10
66 Nigel Wilson .02 .10
67 Gary Sheffield .40 1.00
68 Jerry Browne .02 .10
69 Charlie Hough .02 .10
70 Orestes Destrade .02 .10
71 Mario Diaz .02 .10
72 Ryan Bowen .02 .10
73 Carl Everett .07 .20
74 Richie Lewis .02 .10
75 Bob Natal .02 .10
76 Rich Rodriguez .02 .10
77 Darrell Whitmore .02 .10
78 Matt Turner .02 .10
79 Benito Santiago .07 .20
80 Robb Nen .07 .20
81 Dave Magadan .02 .10
82 Brian Drahman .02 .10
83 Mark Gardner .02 .10
84 Chuck Carr .02 .10
85 Alex Arias .02 .10
86 Kurt Abbott .02 .10
87 Joe Klink .02 .10
88 Jeff Mutis .02 .10
89 Dave Weathers .02 .10
90 Jeff Conine .07 .20
91 Andres Galarraga .25 .60
92 Vinny Castilla .07 .20
93 Roberto Mejia .02 .10
94 Darrell Sherman .02 .10
95 Mike Harkey .02 .10
96 Danny Sheaffer .02 .10
97 Pedro Castellano .02 .10
98 Walt Weiss .02 .10
99 Greg W. Harris .02 .10
100 Jayhawk Owens .02 .10
101 Bruce Ruffin .02 .10
102 Mike Munoz .02 .10
103 Armando Reynoso .02 .10
104 Eric Young .07 .20
105 Dante Bichette .07 .20
106 Marvin Freeman .02 .10
107 Joe Girardi .07 .20
108 Kent Bottenfield .02 .10
109 Howard Johnson .02 .10
110 Nelson Liriano .02 .10
111 David Nied .02 .10
112 Steve Reed .02 .10
113 Eric Wedge .07 .20
114 Charlie Hayes .02 .10
115 Ellis Burks .15 .40
116 Willie Blair .02 .10
117 Darren Holmes .02 .10
118 Curtis Leskanic .02 .10
119 Lance Painter .02 .10
120 Jim Tatum .02 .10
121 Frank Thomas .50 1.25
122 Jack McDowell .02 .10
123 Ron Karkovice .02 .10
124 Mike LaValliere .02 .10
125 Scott Radinsky .02 .10
126 Robin Ventura .15 .40
127 Scott Ruffcorn .02 .10
128 Steve Sax .02 .10
129 Roberto Hernandez .07 .20
130 Jose DeLeon .02 .10
131 Rod Bolton .02 .10
132 Wilson Alvarez .02 .10
133 Craig Grebeck .02 .10
134 Lance Johnson .02 .10
135 Kirk McCaskill .02 .10
136 Tim Raines .07 .20
137 Jeff Schwarz .02 .10
138 Warren Newson .02 .10
139 Norberto Martin .02 .10
140 Mike Huff .02 .10
141 Ozzie Guillen .15 .40
142 Alex Fernandez .02 .10
143 Joey Cora .02 .10
144 Jason Bere .02 .10
145 James Baldwin .07 .20
146 Esteban Beltre .02 .10
147 Julio Franco .07 .20
148 Matt Merullo .02 .10
149 Dan Pasqua .02 .10
150 Darrin Jackson .02 .10
151 Joe Carter .07 .20
152 Danny Cox .02 .10
153 Roberto Alomar .25 .60
154 Woody Williams .15 .40
155 Duane Ward .02 .10
156 Ed Sprague .02 .10
157 Domingo Martinez .02 .10
158 Pat Hentgen .07 .20
159 Shawn Green .40 1.00
160 Dick Schofield .02 .10
161 Paul Molitor .40 1.00
162 Darnell Coles .02 .10
163 Willie Canate .02 .10
164 Domingo Cedeno .02 .10
165 Pat Borders .02 .10
166 Greg Cadaret .02 .10
167 Tony Castillo .02 .10
168 Carlos Delgado .40 1.00
169 Scott Brow .02 .10
170 Juan Guzman .02 .10
171 Al Leiter .07 .20
172 John Olerud .15 .40
173 Todd Stottlemyre .02 .10
174 Devon White .07 .20
175 Paul Spoljaric .02 .10
176 Randy Knorr .02 .10
177 Huck Flener .02 .10
178 Rob Butler .02 .10
179 Dave Stewart .07 .20
180 Mike Timlin .02 .10
181 Don Mattingly .75 2.00
182 Mark Hutton .02 .10
183 Mike Gallego .02 .10
184 Jim Abbott .07 .20
185 Paul Gibson .02 .10
186 Scott Kamieniecki .02 .10
187 Sam Horn .02 .10
188 Melido Perez .02 .10
189 Randy Velarde .02 .10
190 Gerald Williams .02 .10
191 Dave Silvestri .02 .10
192 Jim Leyritz .02 .10
193 Steve Howe .02 .10
194 Russ Davis .02 .10
195 Paul Assenmacher .02 .10
196 Pat Kelly .02 .10
197 Mike Stanley .02 .10
198 Bernie Williams .30 .75
199 Paul O'Neill .25 .60
200 Donn Pall .02 .10
201 Xavier Hernandez .02 .10
202 Jim Austin .02 .10
203 Sterling Hitchcock .07 .20
204 Wade Boggs .40 1.00
205 Jimmy Key .07 .20
206 Matt Nokes .02 .10
207 Terry Mulholland .02 .10
208 Luis Polonia .02 .10
209 Danny Tartabull .07 .20
210 Bob Wickman .07 .20
211 Len Dykstra .07 .20
212 Kim Batiste .02 .10
213 Tony Longmire .02 .10
214 Bobby Munoz .02 .10
215 Pete Incaviglia .02 .10
216 Doug Jones .07 .20
217 Mariano Duncan .02 .10
218 Jeff Juden .02 .10
219 Milt Thompson .02 .10
220 Dave West .02 .10
221 Roger Mason .02 .10
222 Tommy Greene .02 .10
223 Larry Andersen .02 .10
224 Jim Eisenreich .02 .10
225 Dave Hollins .02 .10
226 John Kruk .07 .20
227 Todd Pratt .02 .10
228 Ricky Jordan .02 .10
229 Curt Schilling .60 1.50
230 Mike Williams .02 .10
231 Heathcliff Slocumb .02 .10
232 Ben Rivera .02 .10
233 Mike Lieberthal .07 .20
234 Mickey Morandini .02 .10
235 Danny Jackson .02 .10
236 Kevin Foster .02 .10
237 Darren Daulton .07 .20
238 Wes Chamberlain .02 .10
239 Tyler Green .02 .10
240 Kevin Stocker .02 .10
241 Juan Gonzalez .30 .75
242 Rick Honeycutt .02 .10
243 Bruce Hurst .02 .10
244 Steve Dreyer .02 .10
245 Brian Bohanon .02 .10
246 Benji Gil .02 .10
247 Jon Shave .02 .10
248 Manuel Lee .02 .10
249 Donald Harris .02 .10
250 Jose Canseco .30 .75
251 David Hulse .02 .10
252 Kenny Rogers .07 .20
253 Jeff Huson .02 .10
254 Dan Peltier .02 .10
255 Mike Scioscia .07 .20
256 Jack Armstrong .02 .10
257 Rob Ducey .02 .10
258 Will Clark .25 .60
259 Cris Carpenter .02 .10
260 Kevin Brown .15 .40
261 Jeff Frye .02 .10
262 Jay Howell .02 .10
263 Roger Pavlik .02 .10
264 Gary Redus .02 .10
265 Ivan Rodriguez .40 1.00
266 Matt Whiteside .02 .10
267 Doug Strange .02 .10
268 Billy Ripken .02 .10
269 Dean Palmer .07 .20
270 Tom Henke .02 .10
271 Cal Ripken 1.50 4.00
272 Mark McLemore .07 .20
273 Sid Fernandez .07 .20
274 Sherman Obando .02 .10
275 Paul Carey .02 .10
276 Mike Oquist .02 .10
277 Alan Mills .02 .10
278 Harold Baines .07 .20
279 Mike Mussina .40 1.00
280 Arthur Rhodes .02 .10
281 Kevin McGehee .02 .10
282 Mark Eichhorn .02 .10
283 Damon Buford .02 .10
284 Ben McDonald .02 .10
285 David Segui .02 .10
286 Brad Pennington .02 .10
287 Jamie Moyer .15 .40
288 Chris Hoiles .02 .10
289 Mike Cook .02 .10
290 Brady Anderson .07 .20
291 Chris Sabo .02 .10
292 Jack Voigt .02 .10
293 Jim Poole .02 .10
294 Jeff Tackett .02 .10
295 Rafael Palmeiro .30 .75
296 Alex Ochoa .02 .10
297 John O'Donoghue .02 .10
298 Tim Hulett .02 .10
299 Mike Devereaux .02 .10
300 Manny Alexander .02 .10
301 Ozzie Smith .40 1.00
302 Omar Olivares .02 .10
303 Rheal Cormier .02 .10
304 Donovan Osborne .02 .10
305 Mark Whiten .02 .10
306 Todd Zeile .07 .20
307 Geronimo Pena .02 .10
308 Brian Jordan .07 .20
309 Luis Alicea .02 .10
310 Ray Lankford .07 .20
311 Stan Royer .02 .10
312 Bob Tewksbury .02 .10
313 Jose Oquendo .02 .10
314 Steve Dixon .02 .10
315 Rene Arocha .02 .10
316 Bernard Gilkey .02 .10
317 Gregg Jefferies .02 .10
318 Rob Murphy .02 .10
319 Tom Pagnozzi .02 .10
320 Mike Perez .02 .10
321 Tom Urbani .02 .10
322 Allen Watson .02 .10
323 Erik Pappas .02 .10
324 Paul Kilgus .02 .10
325 John Habyan .02 .10
326 Rod Brewer .02 .10
327 Rich Batchelor .02 .10
328 Tripp Cromer .02 .10
329 Gerald Perry .02 .10
330 Les Lancaster .02 .10
331 Ryne Sandberg .75 2.00
332 Derrick May .02 .10
333 Steve Buechele .02 .10
334 Willie Banks .02 .10
335 Larry Luebbers .02 .10
336 Tommy Shields .02 .10
337 Eric Yelding .02 .10
338 Rey Sanchez .02 .10
339 Mark Grace .15 .40
340 Jose Bautista .02 .10
341 Frank Castillo .02 .10
342 Jose Guzman .02 .10
343 Rafael Novoa .02 .10
Wearing Milwaukee Brewer uniform
344 Karl Rhodes .02 .10
345 Steve Trachsel .02 .10
346 Rick Wilkins .07 .20
347 Sammy Sosa .60 1.50
348 Kevin Roberson .02 .10
349 Mark Parent .02 .10
350 Randy Myers .07 .20
351 Glenallen Hill .02 .10
352 Lance Dickson .02 .10
353 Shawn Boskie .02 .10
354 Shawon Dunston .07 .20
355 Dan Plesac .02 .10
356 Jose Vizcaino .02 .10
357 Willie Wilson .02 .10
358 Turk Wendell .02 .10
359 Mike Morgan .02 .10
360 Jim Bullinger .02 .10

1994 Stadium Club Team First Day Issue

This 360-card standard-size set features 30 players from 12 teams. First Day Issue cards were randomly packed one in every six 12-card packs; the odds of finding these insert cards in 20-card jumbo packs are one in three. Also one 1st Day Issue card was included in the 30-card team sets sold in blister packs. They are identical in design with the regular Stadium Club Team cards except for a holographic "1st Day Issue" emblem on the fronts.

*STARS: 10X to 20X BASIC CARDS

1994 Stadium Club Team Finest

This 12-card standard-size set consists of one player from each of the 12 teams featured in the 1994 Stadium Club team series. The cards were randomly inserted in 12-card foil packs. Also one card was included in the 30-card team sets sold in blister packs. The cards are identical in design with the regular series, except for the metallic sheen characteristic of the Finest series.

COMPLETE SET (12) 12.00 30.00
1 Roberto Alomar .75 2.00

2 Barry Bonds 2.00 5.00
3 Len Dykstra .40 1.00
4 Andres Galarraga .75 2.00
5 Juan Gonzalez .75 2.00
6 David Justice .75 2.00
7 Don Mattingly 1.50 4.00
8 Cal Ripken 4.00 10.00
9 Ryne Sandberg 2.00 5.00
10 Gary Sheffield 1.00 2.50
11 Ozzie Smith 1.50 4.00
12 Frank Thomas .75 2.00

1994 Stadium Club Draft Picks

This 90-card standard-size set features players chosen in the June 1994 MLB draft and photographed in their major league uniforms. Each 24-pack box included four First Day Issue Draft Pick cards randomly packed, one in every six packs. Early cards of Nomar Garciaparra, Ben Grieve and Terrence Long are featured in this set.

COMPLETE SET (90) 4.00 10.00
1 Jacob Shumate XRC .08 .25
2 C.J. Nitkowski XRC .08 .25
3 Doug Million XRC .08 .25
4 Matt Smith XRC .08 .25
5 Kevin Lovinger XRC .08 .25
6 Alberto Castillo XRC .08 .25
7 Mike Russell XRC .08 .25
8 Dan Lock XRC .08 .25
9 Tom Szimanski XRC .08 .25
10 Aaron Boone XRC .20 .50
11 Jayson Peterson XRC .08 .25
12 Mark Johnson XRC .08 .25
13 Cade Gaspar XRC .08 .25
14 George Lombard XRC .08 .25
15 Russ Johnson .08 .25
16 Travis Miller XRC .08 .25
17 Jay Payton XRC .20 .50
18 Brian Buchanan XRC .08 .25
19 Jacob Cruz XRC .15 .40
20 Gary Rath XRC .08 .25
21 Ramon Castro XRC .08 .25
22 Tommy Davis XRC .08 .25
23 Tony Terry XRC .08 .25
24 Jerry Whittaker XRC .08 .25
25 Mike Darr XRC .08 .25
26 Doug Webb XRC .08 .25
27 Jason Camilli XRC .08 .25
28 Brad Rigby XRC .08 .25
29 Ryan Nye XRC .08 .25
30 Carl Dale XRC .08 .25
31 Andy Taulbee XRC .08 .25
32 Trey Moore XRC .08 .25
33 John Crowther XRC .08 .25
34 Joe Giuliano XRC .08 .25
35 Brian Rose XRC .08 .25
36 Paul Failla XRC .08 .25
37 Brian Meadows XRC .08 .25
38 Oscar Robles XRC .15 .40
39 Mike Metcalfe XRC .08 .25
40 Larry Barnes XRC .08 .25
41 Paul Ottavinia XRC .08 .25
42 Chris McBride XRC .08 .25
43 Ricky Stone XRC .08 .25
44 Billy Blythe XRC .08 .25
45 Eddie Priest XRC .08 .25
46 Scott Forster XRC .08 .25
47 Eric Pickett XRC .08 .25
48 Matt Beaumont .08 .25
49 Darrell Nicholas XRC .08 .25
50 Mike A. Hampton XRC .08 .25
51 Paul O'Malley XRC .08 .25
52 Steve Shoemaker XRC .08 .25
53 Jason Sikes XRC .08 .25
54 Bryan Farson XRC .08 .25
55 Yates Hall XRC .08 .25
56 Troy Brohawn XRC .08 .25
57 Dan Hower XRC .08 .25
58 Clay Caruthers XRC .08 .25
59 Pepe McNeal XRC .08 .25
60 Ray Ricken XRC .08 .25
61 Scott Shores XRC .08 .25
62 Eddie Brooks XRC .08 .25
63 Dave Kauflin XRC .08 .25
64 David Meyer XRC .08 .25
65 Geoff Blum XRC .20 .50
66 Roy Marsh XRC .08 .25
67 Ryan Beeney XRC .08 .25
68 Derek Dukart XRC .08 .25
69 Nomar Garciaparra 1.25 3.00
70 Jason Kelly XRC .08 .25
71 Jesse Ibarra XRC .08 .25
72 Bucky Buckles XRC .08 .25
73 Mark Little XRC .08 .25
74 Heath Murray XRC .08 .25
75 Greg Morris XRC .08 .25
76 Mike Halperlin XRC .08 .25
77 Wes Helms XRC .15 .40
78 Ray Brown XRC .08 .25
79 Kevin L.Brown XRC .15 .40
80 Paul Konerko XRC 2.00 5.00
81 Mike Thurman XRC .08 .25
82 Paul Wilson .08 .25
83 Terrence Long XRC .15 .40
84 Ben Grieve XRC .15 .40
85 Mark Farris XRC .08 .25
86 Bret Wagner .08 .25
87 Dustin Hermanson .08 .25
88 Kevin Witt XRC .15 .40
89 Corey Pointer XRC .08 .25
90 Tim Grieve XRC .08 .25

1994 Stadium Club Draft Picks First Day Issue

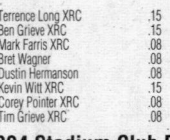

Randomly inserted in packs, this 90-card standard-size set is identical in design with the regular Stadium Club Draft Picks cards except for a holographic "1st Day Issue" emblem on the fronts.

*FIRST DAY: 1.25X TO 3X BASIC CARDS

1994 Stadium Club Draft Picks Members Only

This parallel to the Stadium Club Draft Pick set was issued only in Factory set form and features a special "Members Only" logo on the card.

*MEMBERS ONLY: 1.25X TO 3X BASIC CARD

1995 Stadium Club

The 1995 Stadium Club baseball card set was issued in three series of 270, 225 and 135 standard-size cards for a total of 630. The cards were distributed in 14-card packs at a suggested retail price of $2.50 and contained 24 packs per box. Notable Rookie Cards include Mark Grudzielanek, Bobby Higginson and Hideo Nomo.

COMPLETE SET (630) 25.00 60.00
COMP.SERIES 1 (270) 10.00 25.00
COMP.SERIES 2 (225) 8.00 20.00
COMP.SERIES 3 (135) 6.00 15.00
1 Cal Ripken 1.00 2.50
2 Bo Jackson .30 .75
3 Bryan Harvey .05 .15
4 Curt Schilling .10 .30
5 Bruce Ruffin .05 .15
6 Travis Fryman .10 .30
7 Jim Abbott .20 .50
8 David McCarty .05 .15
9 Gary Gaetti .10 .30
10 Roger Clemens .60 1.50
11 Carlos Garcia .05 .15
12 Lee Smith .10 .30
13 Bobby Ayala .05 .15
14 Charles Nagy .05 .15
15 Lou Frazier .05 .15
16 Rene Arocha .05 .15
17 Carlos Delgado .10 .30
18 Steve Finley .10 .30
19 Ryan Klesko .10 .30
20 Cal Eldred .05 .15
21 Rey Sanchez .05 .15
22 Ken Hill .05 .15
23 Benito Santiago .10 .30
24 Julian Tavarez .05 .15
25 Jose Vizcaino .05 .15
26 Andy Benes .05 .15
27 Mariano Duncan .05 .15
28 Checklist A .05 .15
29 Shawon Dunston .05 .15
30 Rafael Palmeiro .20 .50
31 Dean Palmer .10 .30
32 Andres Galarraga .10 .30
33 Joey Cora .05 .15
34 Mickey Tettleton .05 .15
35 Barry Larkin .20 .50
36 Carlos Baerga .05 .15
37 Orel Hershiser .10 .30
38 Jody Reed .05 .15
39 Paul Molitor .10 .30
40 Jim Edmonds .20 .50
41 Bob Tewksbury .05 .15
42 John Patterson .05 .15
43 Ray McDavid .05 .15
44 Zane Smith .05 .15
45 Bret Saberhagen SE .05 .15
46 Greg Maddux SE .30 .75
47 Frank Thomas SE .20 .50
48 Carlos Baerga SE .05 .15
49 Billy Spiers .05 .15
50 Stan Javier .05 .15
51 Rex Hudler .05 .15
52 Denny Hocking .05 .15
53 Todd Worrell .05 .15
54 Mark Clark .05 .15
55 Hipolito Pichardo .05 .15
56 Bob Wickman .05 .15
57 Raul Mondesi .10 .30
58 Steve Cooke .05 .15
59 Rod Beck .05 .15
60 Tim Davis .05 .15
61 Jeff Kent .10 .30
62 John Valentin .05 .15
63 Alex Arias .05 .15
64 Steve Reed .05 .15
65 Ozzie Smith .50 1.25

66 Terry Pendleton .10 .30
67 Kenny Rogers .10 .30
68 Vince Coleman .05 .15
69 Tom Pagnozzi .05 .15
70 Roberto Alomar .20 .50
71 Darrin Jackson .05 .15
72 Dennis Eckersley .10 .30
73 Jay Buhner .10 .30
74 Darren Lewis .05 .15
75 Dave Weathers .05 .15
76 Matt Walbeck .05 .15
77 Brad Ausmus .10 .30
78 Danny Bautista .05 .15
79 Bob Hamelin .05 .15
80 Steve Trachsel .05 .15
81 Ken Ryan .05 .15
82 Chris Turner .05 .15
83 David Segui .05 .15
84 Ben McDonald .05 .15
85 Wade Boggs .20 .50
86 John Vander Wal .05 .15
87 Sandy Alomar Jr. .05 .15
88 Ron Karkovice .05 .15
89 Doug Jones .05 .15
90 Gary Sheffield .10 .30
91 Ken Caminiti .10 .30
92 Chris Bosio .05 .15
93 Kevin Tapani .05 .15
94 Walt Weiss .05 .15
95 Erik Hanson .05 .15
96 Ruben Sierra .10 .30
97 Nomar Garciaparra .75 2.00
98 Terrence Long .05 .15
99 Jacob Shumate .05 .15
100 Paul Wilson .05 .15
101 Kevin Witt .05 .15
102 Paul Konerko .40 1.00
103 Ben Grieve .05 .15
104 Mark Johnson RC .15 .40
105 Cade Gaspar RC .05 .15
106 Mark Farris .05 .15
107 Dustin Hermanson .05 .15
108 Scott Elarton RC .15 .40
109 Doug Million .05 .15
110 Matt Smith .05 .15
111 Brian Buchanan RC .05 .15
112 Jayson Peterson RC .05 .15
113 Bret Wagner .05 .15
114 C.J. Nitkowski RC .15 .40
115 Ramon Castro RC .15 .40
116 Rafael Bournigal .05 .15
117 Jeff Fassero .05 .15
118 Bobby Bonilla .10 .30
119 Ricky Gutierrez .05 .15
120 Roger Pavlik .05 .15
121 Mike Greenwell .05 .15
122 Deion Sanders .20 .50
123 Charlie Hayes .05 .15
124 Paul O'Neill .20 .50
125 Jay Bell .10 .30
126 Royce Clayton .05 .15
127 Willie Banks .05 .15
128 Mark Wohlers .05 .15
129 Todd Jones .05 .15
130 Todd Stottlemyre .05 .15
131 Will Clark .20 .50
132 Wilson Alvarez .05 .15
133 Chili Davis .10 .30
134 Dave Burba .05 .15
135 Chris Hoiles .05 .15
136 Jeff Blauser .05 .15
137 Jeff Reboulet .05 .15
138 Bret Saberhagen .10 .30
139 Kirk Rueter .05 .15
140 Dave Nilsson .05 .15
141 Pat Borders .05 .15
142 Ron Darling .05 .15
143 Derek Bell .05 .15
144 Dave Hollins .05 .15
145 Juan Gonzalez .10 .30
146 Andre Dawson .10 .30
147 Jim Thome .20 .50
148 Larry Walker .10 .30
149 Mike Piazza .50 1.25
150 Mike Perez .05 .15
151 Steve Avery .05 .15
152 Dan Wilson .05 .15
153 Andy Van Slyke .20 .50
154 Junior Felix .05 .15
155 Jack McDowell .05 .15
156 Danny Tartabull .05 .15
157 Willie Blair .05 .15
158 Wm.VanLandingham .05 .15
159 Robb Nen .10 .30
160 Lee Tinsley .05 .15
161 Ismael Valdes .05 .15
162 Juan Guzman .05 .15
163 Scott Servais .05 .15
164 Cliff Floyd .10 .30
165 Allen Watson .05 .15
166 Eddie Taubensee .05 .15
167 Scott Hemond .05 .15
168 Jeff Tackett .05 .15
169 Chad Curtis .05 .15
170 Rico Brogna .05 .15
171 Luis Polonia .05 .15
172 Checklist B .05 .15
173 Lance Johnson .05 .15
174 Sammy Sosa .30 .75
175 Mike Macfarlane .05 .15
176 Darryl Hamilton .05 .15
177 Rick Aguilera .05 .15
178 Dave West .05 .15
179 Mike Gallego .05 .15
180 Marc Newfield .05 .15
181 Steve Buechele .05 .15
182 David Wells .10 .30
183 Tom Glavine .20 .50
184 Joe Girardi .05 .15
185 Craig Biggio .20 .50
186 Eddie Murray .30 .75
187 Kevin Gross .05 .15
188 Sid Fernandez .05 .15
189 John Franco .10 .30
190 Bernard Gilkey .05 .15
191 Matt Williams .10 .30
192 Darrin Fletcher .05 .15
193 Jeff Conine .10 .30
194 Ed Sprague .05 .15
195 Eduardo Perez .05 .15
196 Scott Livingstone .05 .15
197 Ivan Rodriguez .20 .50
198 Orlando Merced .05 .15
199 Ricky Bones .05 .15
200 Javier Lopez .10 .30
201 Miguel Jimenez .05 .15
202 Terry McGriff .05 .15
203 Mike Lieberthal .10 .30
204 David Cone .10 .30
205 Todd Hundley .05 .15
206 Ozzie Guillen .10 .30
207 Alex Cole .05 .15
208 Tony Phillips .05 .15
209 Jim Eisenreich .05 .15
210 Greg Vaughn BES .05 .15
211 Barry Larkin BES .10 .30
212 Don Mattingly BES .40 1.00
213 Mark Grace BES .10 .30
214 Jose Canseco BES .10 .30
215 Joe Carter BES .05 .15
216 David Cone BES .05 .15
217 Sandy Alomar Jr. BES .05 .15
218 Al Martin BES .05 .15
219 Roberto Kelly BES .05 .15
220 Paul Sorrento .05 .15
221 Tony Fernandez .05 .15
222 Stan Belinda .05 .15
223 Mike Stanley .05 .15
224 Doug Drabek .05 .15
225 Todd Van Poppel .05 .15
226 Matt Mieske .05 .15
227 Tino Martinez .20 .50
228 Andy Ashby .05 .15
229 Midre Cummings .05 .15
230 Jeff Frye .05 .15
231 Hal Morris .05 .15
232 Jose Lind .05 .15
233 Shawn Green .10 .30
234 Rafael Belliard .05 .15
235 Randy Myers .05 .15
236 Frank Thomas CE .20 .50
237 Darren Daulton CE .05 .15
238 Sammy Sosa CE .20 .50
239 Cal Ripken CE .50 1.25
240 Jeff Bagwell CE .10 .30
241 Ken Griffey Jr. .50 1.25
242 Brett Butler .10 .30
243 Derrick May .05 .15
244 Pat Listach .05 .15
245 Mike Bordick .05 .15
246 Mark Langston .05 .15
247 Randy Velarde .05 .15
248 Julio Franco .10 .30
249 Chuck Knoblauch .10 .30
250 Bill Gullickson .05 .15
251 Dave Henderson .05 .15
252 Bret Boone .10 .30
253 Al Martin .05 .15
254 Armando Benitez .05 .15
255 Wil Cordero .05 .15
256 Al Leiter .10 .30
257 Luis Gonzalez .10 .30
258 Charlie O'Brien .05 .15
259 Tim Wallach .05 .15
260 Scott Sanders .05 .15
261 Tom Henke .05 .15
262 Otis Nixon .05 .15
263 Darren Daulton .10 .30
264 Manny Ramirez .20 .50
265 Bret Barberie .05 .15
266 Mel Rojas .05 .15
267 John Burkett .05 .15
268 Brady Anderson .10 .30
269 John Roper .05 .15
270 Shane Reynolds .05 .15
271 Barry Bonds .75 2.00
272 Alex Fernandez .05 .15
273 Brian McRae .05 .15
274 Todd Zeile .05 .15
275 Greg Swindell .05 .15
276 Johnny Ruffin .05 .15
277 Troy Neel .05 .15
278 Eric Karros .10 .30
279 John Hudek .05 .15
280 Thomas Howard .05 .15
281 Joe Carter .10 .30
282 Mike Devereaux .05 .15
283 Butch Henry .05 .15
284 Reggie Jefferson .05 .15
285 Mark Lemke .05 .15
286 Jeff Montgomery .05 .15
287 Ryan Thompson .05 .15
288 Paul Shuey .05 .15
289 Mark McGwire .75 2.00
290 Bernie Williams .20 .50
291 Mickey Morandini .05 .15
292 Scott Leius .05 .15
293 David Hulse .05 .15
294 Greg Gagne .05 .15
295 Moises Alou .10 .30
296 Geronimo Berroa .05 .15
297 Eddie Zambrano .05 .15
298 Alan Trammell .10 .30
299 Don Slaught .05 .15
300 Jose Rijo .05 .15
301 Joe Ausanio .05 .15
302 Tim Raines .10 .30
303 Melido Perez .05 .15
304 Kent Mercker .05 .15
305 James Mouton .05 .15
306 Luis Lopez .05 .15
307 Mike Kingery .05 .15
308 Willie Greene .05 .15
309 Cecil Fielder .10 .30
310 Scott Kamieniecki .05 .15
311 Mike Greenwell BES .05 .15
312 Bobby Bonilla BES .05 .15
313 A.Galarraga BES .05 .15
314 Cal Ripken BES .50 1.25
315 Matt Williams BES .05 .15
316 Tom Pagnozzi BES .05 .15
317 Len Dykstra BES .05 .15
318 Frank Thomas BES .20 .50
319 Kirby Puckett BES .30 .75
320 Mike Piazza BES .30 .75
321 Jason Jacome .05 .15
322 Brian Hunter .05 .15
323 Brent Gates .05 .15
324 Jim Converse .05 .15
325 Damion Easley .05 .15
326 Dante Bichette .10 .30
327 Kurt Abbott .05 .15
328 Scott Cooper .05 .15
329 Mike Henneman .05 .15
330 Orlando Miller .05 .15
331 John Kruk .10 .30
332 Jose Oliva .05 .15
333 Reggie Sanders .10 .30
334 Omar Vizquel .20 .50
335 Devon White .10 .30
336 Mike Morgan .05 .15
337 J.R. Phillips .05 .15
338 Gary DiSarcina .05 .15
339 Joey Hamilton .05 .15
340 Randy Johnson .30 .75
341 Jim Leyritz .05 .15
342 Bobby Jones .05 .15
343 Jaime Navarro .05 .15
344 Bip Roberts .05 .15
345 Steve Karsay .05 .15
346 Kevin Stocker .05 .15
347 Jose Canseco .20 .50
348 Bill Wegman .05 .15
349 Rondell White .10 .30
350 Mo Vaughn .10 .30
351 Joe Orsulak .05 .15
352 Pat Meares .05 .15
353 Albie Lopez .05 .15
354 Edgar Martinez .20 .50
355 Brian Jordan .10 .30
356 Tommy Greene .05 .15
357 Chuck Carr .05 .15
358 Pedro Astacio .05 .15
359 Russ Davis .05 .15
360 Chris Hammond .05 .15
361 Gregg Jefferies .05 .15
362 Shane Mack .05 .15
363 Fred McGriff .20 .50
364 Pat Rapp .05 .15
365 Bill Swift .05 .15
366 Checklist .05 .15
367 Robin Ventura .10 .30
368 Bobby Witt .05 .15
369 Karl Rhodes .05 .15
370 Eddie Williams .05 .15
371 John Jaha .05 .15
372 Steve Howe .05 .15
373 Leo Gomez .05 .15
374 Hector Fajardo .05 .15
375 Jeff Bagwell .20 .50
376 Mark Acre .05 .15
377 Wayne Kirby .05 .15
378 Mark Portugal .05 .15
379 Jesus Tavarez .05 .15
380 Jim Lindeman .05 .15
381 Don Mattingly .75 2.00
382 Trevor Hoffman .10 .30
383 Chris Gomez .05 .15
384 Garret Anderson .10 .30
385 Bobby Munoz .05 .15
386 Jon Lieber .05 .15
387 Rick Helling .05 .15
388 Marvin Freeman .05 .15
389 Juan Castillo .05 .15
390 Jeff Cirillo .05 .15
391 Sean Berry .05 .15
392 Hector Carrasco .05 .15
393 Mark Grace .20 .50
394 Pat Kelly .05 .15
395 Tim Naehring .05 .15
396 Greg Pirkl .05 .15
397 John Smoltz .20 .50
398 Robby Thompson .05 .15
399 Rick White .05 .15
400 Frank Thomas .30 .75
401 Jeff Conine CS .05 .15
402 Jose Valentin CS .05 .15
403 Carlos Baerga CS .05 .15
404 Rick Aguilera CS .05 .15
405 Wilson Alvarez CS .05 .15
406 Juan Gonzalez CS .05 .15
407 Barry Larkin CS .10 .30
408 Ken Hill CS .05 .15
409 Chuck Carr CS .05 .15
410 Tim Raines CS .05 .15
411 Bryan Eversgerd .05 .15
412 Phil Plantier .05 .15
413 Josias Manzanillo .05 .15
414 Roberto Kelly .05 .15
415 Rickey Henderson .30 .75
416 John Smiley .05 .15
417 Kevin Brown .10 .30
418 Jimmy Key .10 .30
419 Wally Joyner .10 .30
420 Roberto Hernandez .05 .15
421 Felix Fermin .05 .15
422 Checklist .05 .15
423 Greg Vaughn .05 .15
424 Ray Lankford .10 .30
425 Greg Maddux .50 1.25
426 Mike Mussina .20 .50
427 Geronimo Pena .05 .15
428 David Nied .05 .15
429 Scott Erickson .05 .15
430 Kevin Mitchell .05 .15
431 Mike Lansing .05 .15
432 Brian Anderson .05 .15
433 Jeff King .05 .15
434 Ramon Martinez .05 .15
435 Kevin Seitzer .05 .15
436 Salomon Torres .05 .15
437 Brian L.Hunter .05 .15
438 Melvin Nieves .05 .15
439 Mike Kelly .05 .15
440 Marquis Grissom .10 .30
441 Chuck Finley .10 .30
442 Len Dykstra .10 .30
443 Ellis Burks .10 .30
444 Harold Baines .10 .30
445 Kevin Appier .10 .30
446 David Justice .10 .30
447 Darryl Kile .10 .30
448 John Olerud .10 .30
449 Greg McMichael .05 .15
450 Kirby Puckett .30 .75
451 Jose Valentin .05 .15
452 Rick Wilkins .05 .15
453 Arthur Rhodes .05 .15
454 Pat Hentgen .05 .15
455 Tom Gordon .05 .15
456 Tom Candiotti .05 .15
457 Jason Bere .05 .15
458 Wes Chamberlain .05 .15
459 Greg Colbrunn .05 .15
460 John Doherty .05 .15
461 Kevin Foster .05 .15
462 Mark Whiten .05 .15
463 Terry Steinbach .05 .15
464 Aaron Sele .05 .15
465 Kirt Manwaring .05 .15
466 Darren Hall .05 .15
467 Delino DeShields .05 .15
468 Andujar Cedeno .05 .15
469 Billy Ashley .05 .15
470 Kenny Lofton .10 .30
471 Pedro Munoz .05 .15
472 John Wetteland .10 .30
473 Tim Salmon .20 .50
474 Denny Neagle .10 .30
475 Tony Gwynn .40 1.00
476 Vinny Castilla .10 .30
477 Steve Dreyer .05 .15
478 Jeff Shaw .05 .15
479 Chad Ogea .05 .15
480 Scott Ruffcorn .05 .15
481 Lou Whitaker .10 .30
482 J.T. Snow .10 .30
483 Rich Rowland .05 .15
484 Denny Martinez .10 .30
485 Pedro Martinez .20 .50
486 Rusty Greer .10 .30
487 Dave Fleming .05 .15
488 John Dettmer .05 .15
489 Albert Belle .10 .30
490 Ravelo Manzanillo .05 .15
491 Henry Rodriguez .05 .15
492 Andrew Lorraine .05 .15
493 Dwayne Hosey .05 .15
494 Mike Blowers .05 .15
495 Turner Ward .05 .15
496 Fred McGriff EC .10 .30
497 Sammy Sosa EC .20 .50
498 Barry Larkin EC .10 .30
499 Andres Galarraga EC .05 .15
500 Gary Sheffield EC .05 .15
501 Jeff Bagwell EC .10 .30
502 Mike Piazza EC .30 .75
503 Moises Alou EC .05 .15
504 Bobby Bonilla EC .05 .15
505 Darren Daulton EC .05 .15
506 Jeff King EC .05 .15
507 Ray Lankford EC .05 .15
508 Tony Gwynn EC .20 .50
509 Barry Bonds EC .40 1.00
510 Cal Ripken EC .50 1.25
511 Mo Vaughn EC .05 .15
512 Tim Salmon EC .10 .30
513 Frank Thomas EC .20 .50
514 Albert Belle EC .05 .15
515 Cecil Fielder EC .05 .15
516 Kevin Appier EC .05 .15
517 Greg Vaughn EC .05 .15
518 Kirby Puckett EC .20 .50
519 Paul O'Neill EC .10 .30
520 Ruben Sierra EC .05 .15
521 Ken Griffey Jr. EC .30 .75
522 Will Clark EC .10 .30
523 Joe Carter EC .05 .15
524 Antonio Osuna .05 .15
525 Glenallen Hill .05 .15
526 Alex Gonzalez .05 .15
527 Dave Stewart .10 .30
528 Ron Gant .10 .30
529 Jason Bates .05 .15
530 Mike Macfarlane .05 .15
531 Esteban Loaiza .05 .15
532 Joe Randa .10 .30
533 Dave Winfield .10 .30
534 Danny Darwin .05 .15
535 Pete Harnisch .05 .15
536 Joey Cora .05 .15
537 Jaime Navarro .05 .15
538 Marty Cordova .05 .15
539 Andujar Cedeno .05 .15
540 Mickey Tettleton .05 .15
541 Andy Van Slyke .20 .50
542 Carlos Perez RC .15 .40
543 Chipper Jones .30 .75
544 Tony Fernandez .05 .15
545 Tom Henke .05 .15
546 Pat Borders .05 .15
547 Chad Curtis .05 .15
548 Ray Durham .10 .30
549 Joe Oliver .05 .15
550 Jose Mesa .05 .15
551 Steve Finley .10 .30
552 Otis Nixon .05 .15
553 Jacob Brumfield .05 .15
554 Bill Swift .05 .15
555 Quilvio Veras .05 .15
556 Hideo Nomo RC UER 1.00 2.50
Wins and IP totals reversed
557 Joe Vitiello .05 .15
558 Mike Perez .05 .15
559 Charlie Hayes .05 .15
560 Brad Radke RC .30 .75
561 Darren Bragg .05 .15
562 Orel Hershiser .10 .30
563 Edgardo Alfonzo .05 .15
564 Doug Jones .05 .15
565 Andy Pettitte .20 .50
566 Benito Santiago .10 .30
567 John Burkett .05 .15
568 Brad Clontz .05 .15
569 Jim Abbott .20 .50
570 Joe Rosselli .05 .15
571 Mark Grudzielanek RC .30 .75
572 Dustin Hermanson .05 .15
573 Benji Gil .05 .15
574 Mark Whiten .05 .15
575 Mike Ignasiak .05 .15
576 Kevin Ritz .05 .15
577 Paul Quantrill .05 .15
578 Andre Dawson .10 .30
579 Jerald Clark .05 .15
580 Frank Rodriguez .05 .15
581 Mark Kiefer .05 .15
582 Trevor Wilson .05 .15
583 Gary Wilson RC .05 .15
584 Andy Stankiewicz .05 .15
585 Felipe Lira .05 .15
586 Mike Mimbs RC .05 .15
587 Jon Nunnally .05 .15
588 Tomas Perez RC .05 .15
589 Chad Fonville .05 .15
590 John Hollandsworth .05 .15
591 Roberto Petagine .05 .15
592 Mariano Rivera .40 1.00
593 Mark McLemore .05 .15
594 Bobby Witt .05 .15
595 Jose Offerman .05 .15
596 J.Christiansen RC .05 .15
597 Jeff Manto .05 .15
598 Jim Dougherty RC .05 .15
599 Juan Acevedo RC .05 .15
600 Troy O'Leary .05 .15
601 Ron Villone .05 .15
602 Tripp Cromer .05 .15
603 Steve Scarsone .05 .15
604 Lance Parrish .10 .30
605 Ozzie Timmons .05 .15
606 Ray Holbert .05 .15
607 Tony Phillips .05 .15
608 Phil Plantier .05 .15
609 Shane Andrews .05 .15
610 Heathcliff Slocumb .05 .15
611 Bobby Higginson RC .30 .75
612 Bob Tewksbury .05 .15
613 Terry Pendleton .10 .30
614 Scott Cooper TA .05 .15
615 John Wetteland TA .05 .15
616 Ken Hill TA .05 .15
617 Marquis Grissom TA .05 .15
618 Larry Walker TA .05 .15
619 Derek Bell TA .05 .15
620 David Cone TA .05 .15
621 Ken Caminiti TA .05 .15
622 Jack McDowell TA .05 .15
623 Vaughn Eshelman TA .05 .15
624 Brian McRae TA .05 .15
625 Gregg Jefferies TA .05 .15
626 Kevin Brown TA .05 .15
627 Lee Smith TA .05 .15
628 Tony Tarasco TA .05 .15
629 Brett Butler TA .05 .15
630 Jose Canseco TA .10 .30

1995 Stadium Club First Day Issue

Parallel to the basic first series Stadium Club issue, these cards, were primarily inserted in second series Topps packs. They were also inserted at a rate of ten per Topps factory set. Nine double printed cards were issued in both first and second series Topps packs. Those cards are as follows: 29, 39, 79, 96, 131, 149, 153, 168 and 197. Limited instances of duplicitous parties transferring the FDI foil logos from "common" players to the fronts of "star" players were chronicled shortly after release - thus it's recommended for collectors to take a close look at the logo on front before purchasing these cards.

COMPLETE SET (270) 125.00 250.00
COMMON CARD (1-270) .75 2.00
*STARS: 5X TO 12X BASIC CARDS
*ROOKIES: 3X TO 8X BASIC CARDS
*DP STARS: 1.25X TO 3X BASIC CARDS

1995 Stadium Club Members Only Parallel

This set is a parallel to the regular 1995 Stadium Club set.These cards are identical to their regular issue counterparts except for the distinctive "Members Only" logo. According to Topps, only 4,000 factory sets were issued through the Topps Stadium Club at a price of $200 each. A certificate of authenticity carrying the serial number accompanied each set. In addition to the 630 regular cards, the factory set includes Members Only versions of the following inserts: Crystal Ball, Clear Cut, Power Zone, Ring Leaders, Super Skills, Virtual Extremists and Virtual Reality (listed separately). Only the insert cards are listed below. Please use the multipliers for values on the basic cards.

COMP.SET w/o VR (755) 27.50 250.00
*MEM.ONLY 1-630: 1.5X TO 4X BASIC CARDS
CB1 Chipper Jones 3.00 8.00
CB2 Dustin Hermanson .30 .75
CB3 Ray Durham .60 1.50
CB4 Phil Nevin .30 .75
CB5 Billy Ashley .08 .25
CB6 Shawn Green .75 2.00
CB7 Jason Bates .08 .25
CB8 Benji Gil .08 .25
CB9 Marty Cordova .08 .25
CB10 Quilvio Veras .30 .75
CB11 Mark Grudzielanek .30 .75
CB12 Ruben Rivera .08 .25
CB13 Bill Pulsipher .08 .25
CB14 Derek Jeter 6.00 15.00
CB15 LaTroy Hawkins .08 .25
CC1 Mike Piazza 3.00 8.00
CC2 Ruben Sierra .08 .25
CC3 Tony Gwynn 3.00 8.00
CC4 Frank Thomas 2.50 6.00
CC5 Fred McGriff .60 1.50
CC6 Rafael Palmeiro .75 2.00
CC7 Bobby Bonilla .08 .25
CC8 Chili Davis .30 .75
CC9 Hal Morris .08 .25
CC10 Jose Canseco 1.25 3.00
CC11 Jay Bell .30 .75
CC12 Kirby Puckett 2.50 6.00
CC13 Gary Sheffield .75 2.00
CC14 Bob Hamelin .08 .25
CC15 Jeff Bagwell 1.25 3.00
CC16 Albert Belle .30 .75
CC17 Sammy Sosa 3.00 8.00
CC18 Ken Griffey Jr. 5.00 12.00
CC19 Todd Zeile .30 .75
CC20 Mo Vaughn .30 .75
CC21 Moises Alou .30 .75
CC22 Paul O'Neill .30 .75
CC23 Andres Galarraga .75 2.00
CC24 Greg Vaughn .30 .75
CC25 Len Dykstra .30 .75
CC26 Joe Carter .30 .75
CC27 Barry Bonds 3.00 8.00
CC28 Cecil Fielder .30 .75
PZ1 Jeff Bagwell 1.25 3.00
PZ2 Albert Belle .30 .75
PZ3 Barry Bonds 3.00 8.00
PZ4 Joe Carter .30 .75
PZ5 Cecil Fielder .30 .75
PZ6 Andres Galarraga .75 2.00
PZ7 Ken Griffey Jr. 5.00 12.00
PZ8 Paul Molitor .75 2.00
PZ9 Fred McGriff .60 1.50
PZ10 Rafael Palmeiro .75 2.00
PZ11 Frank Thomas 2.50 6.00
PZ12 Matt Williams .60 1.50
RL1 Jeff Bagwell 1.25 3.00
RL2 Mark McGwire 5.00 12.00
RL3 Ozzie Smith 2.50 6.00
RL4 Paul Molitor .75 2.00
RL5 Darryl Strawberry .08 .25
RL6 Eddie Murray .75 2.00
RL7 Tony Gwynn 3.00 8.00
RL8 Jose Canseco 1.25 3.00
RL9 Howard Johnson .08 .25
RL10 Andre Dawson .60 1.50
RL11 Matt Williams .60 1.50
RL12 Tim Raines .30 .75
RL13 Fred McGriff .60 1.50
RL14 Ken Griffey Jr. 5.00 12.00
RL15 Gary Sheffield .75 2.00
RL16 Dennis Eckersley .30 .75
RL17 Kevin Mitchell .08 .25
RL18 Will Clark .75 2.00
RL19 Darren Daulton .30 .75
RL20 Paul O'Neill .75 2.00
RL21 Julio Franco .08 .25
RL22 Albert Belle .30 .75
RL23 Juan Gonzalez 1.25 3.00
RL24 Kirby Puckett 2.50 6.00
RL25 Joe Carter .30 .75
RL26 Frank Thomas 2.50 6.00
RL27 Cal Ripken 6.00 15.00
RL28 John Olerud .30 .75
RL29 Ruben Sierra .30 .75
RL30 Barry Bonds 3.00 8.00
RL31 Cecil Fielder .30 .75
RL32 Roger Clemens 3.00 8.00
RL33 Don Mattingly 3.00 8.00
RL34 Terry Pendleton .08 .25
RL35 Rickey Henderson 1.25 3.00
RL36 Dave Winfield 1.25 3.00
RL37 Edgar Martinez .60 1.50
RL38 Wade Boggs 1.25 3.00
RL39 Willie McGee .30 .75
RL40 Andres Galarraga .75 2.00
SS1 Roberto Alomar .75 2.00
SS2 Barry Bonds 3.00 8.00
SS3 Jay Buhner .30 .75
SS4 Chuck Carr .08 .25
SS5 Don Mattingly 3.00 8.00
SS6 Raul Mondesi .60 1.50
SS7 Tim Salmon .75 2.00
SS8 Deion Sanders .30 .75
SS9 Devon White .08 .25
SS10 Mark Whiten .08 .25
SS11 Ken Griffey Jr. 5.00 12.00
SS12 Marquis Grissom .08 .25
SS13 Paul O'Neill .30 .75
SS14 Kenny Lofton .08 .25
SS15 Larry Walker .75 2.00
SS16 Scott Cooper .08 .25
SS17 Barry Larkin .75 2.00
SS18 Matt Williams .60 1.50
SS19 John Wetteland .30 .75
SS20 Randy Johnson 1.25 3.00
VRE1 Barry Bonds 3.00 8.00
VRE2 Ken Griffey Jr. 5.00 12.00
VRE3 Jeff Bagwell 1.25 3.00
VRE4 Albert Belle .30 .75
VRE5 Frank Thomas 2.50 6.00
VRE6 Tony Gwynn 3.00 8.00
VRE7 Kenny Lofton .30 .75
VRE8 Deion Sanders .75 2.00
VRE9 Ken Hill .08 .25
VRE10 Jimmy Key .30 .75

1995 Stadium Club Super Team Division Winners

Each of these six team sets was available exclusively by mailing in the corresponding winning 1994 Super Team card. Each team set was distributed in a clear plastic sealed wrapper and included ten player cards and a Super Team card (of which was stamped "REDEEMED" on back). The card design and numbering for the player cards parallels regular issue 1995 Stadium Club cards. In fact, the only way to tell these cards apart is by the gold foil "Division Winner" logo on each card front. The cards are listed below alphabetically by team; the prefixes B, D, I, M, R and RS have been added to denote Braves, Dodgers, Indians, Mariners, Reds and Red Sox.

COMP.BRAVES SET (11) 3.00 8.00
COMP.DODGERS (11) 3.00 8.00
COMP.INDIANS SET (11) 2.50 6.00
COMP.MARINERS (11) 3.00 8.00
COMP.REDS SET (11) 1.25 3.00
COMP.RED SOX SET (11) 2.50 6.00
COMMON SUPER TEAM .40 1.00
B1T Braves DW .40 1.00
Super Team
Jeff Blauser
Terry Pendleton
B19 Ryan Klesko .25 .60
B128 Mark Wohlers .10 .30
B151 Steve Avery .10 .30
B183 Tom Glavine .40 1.00
B200 Javy Lopez .25 .60
B393 Fred McGriff .40 1.00
B397 John Smoltz .40 1.00
B425 Greg Maddux 1.00 2.50
B446 Dave Justice .25 .60
B543 Chipper Jones .60 1.50
D7T Dodgers DW .40 1.00
Super Team
Mike Piazza
D57 Raul Mondesi .25 .60
D149 Mike Piazza 1.00 2.50
D161 Ismael Valdes .10 .30
D242 Brett Butler .25 .60
D259 Tim Wallach .10 .30
D278 Eric Karros .25 .60
D434 Ramon Martinez .10 .30
D456 Tom Candiotti .10 .30
D467 Delino DeShields .10 .30
D556 Hideo Nomo 2.00 5.00
I19T Indians DW .40 1.00
Super Team
Carlos Baerga
Albert Belle
Kenny Lofton
I36 Carlos Baerga .10 .30
I147 Jim Thome .40 1.00
I186 Eddie Murray .60 1.50
I264 Manny Ramirez .40 1.00
I334 Omar Vizquel .40 1.00
I470 Kenny Lofton .25 .60
I484 Dennis Martinez .25 .60
I489 Albert Belle .25 .60
I550 Jose Mesa .10 .30
I562 Orel Hershiser .25 .60
M26T Mariners DW .40 1.00
Super Team
Mike Blowers
Jay Buhner
M73 Jay Buhner .25 .60
M92 Chris Bosio .10 .30
M152 Dan Wilson .10 .30
M227 Tino Martinez .40 1.00
M241 Ken Griffey Jr. 1.00 2.50
M340 Randy Johnson .60 1.50
M354 Edgar Martinez .40 1.00
M421 Felix Fermin .10 .30
M494 Mike Blowers .10 .30
M536 Joey Cora .10 .30
RE3T Reds DW
Super Team
Barry Larkin
Reggie Sanders
RE35 Barry Larkin .40 1.00
RE231 Hal Morris .10 .30
RE252 Bret Boone .25 .60
RE280 Thomas Howard .10 .30
RE300 Jose Rijo .10 .30
RE333 Reggie Sanders .25 .60
RE392 Hector Carrasco .10 .30
RE416 John Smiley .10 .30
RE528 Ron Gant .25 .60
RE566 Benito Santiago .25 .60
RS1T Red Sox DW .40 1.00
Super Team
Luis Rivera
John Valentin
RS10 Roger Clemens 1.25 3.00
RS62 John Valentin .10 .30
RS121 Mike Greenwell .10 .30
RS160 Lee Tinsley .10 .30
RS347 Jose Canseco .40 1.00
RS350 Mo Vaughn .25 .60
RS395 Tim Naehring .10 .30
RS464 Aaron Sele .10 .30
RS530 Mike Macfarlane .10 .30
RS600 Troy O'Leary .10 .30

1995 Stadium Club Super Team Master Photos

This 20-card set was distributed in two separate 10-card sealed team bags. The cards were available exclusively by mailing in a Braves or Indians 1994 Super Team card. These oversized cards (5" by 7") feature a reproduction of the player's standard 1995 Stadium Club card enframed around a shining blue background. Unlike the standard issue cards they parallel, these are numbered X of 20.

COMP.BRAVES SET (10) 4.00 10.00
COMP.INDIANS SET (10) 3.00 8.00
1 Steve Avery .15 .40
2 Tom Glavine .50 1.25
3 Chipper Jones .75 2.00
4 Dave Justice .30 .75
5 Ryan Klesko .30 .75
6 Javy Lopez .30 .75
7 Greg Maddux 1.25 3.00
8 Fred McGriff .50 1.25
9 John Smoltz .50 1.25
10 Mark Wohlers .15 .40
11 Carlos Baerga .15 .40
12 Albert Belle .30 .75
13 Orel Hershiser .30 .75
14 Kenny Lofton .30 .75
15 Dennis Martinez .30 .75
16 Jose Mesa .15 .40
17 Eddie Murray .75 2.00
18 Manny Ramirez .50 1.25
19 Jim Thome .50 1.25
20 Omar Vizquel .50 1.25

1995 Stadium Club Super Team World Series

Because of the strike-interrupted season, the 1994 Stadium Club Super Team insert program had to be finished up with the 1995 product. Collectors who redeemed the 1994 Atlanta Braves Super Team card received: 1) a complete 630-card 1995 Stadium Club parallel set stamped with a special gold foil World Series logo (of which was mailed in two separate series of 585 and 45 cards) 2) a Division Winner parallel Braves team set along with the winner card stamped "redeemed" on its back 3) a jumbo-sized (3" by 5") parallel Master Photo Braves team set. Collectors who redeemed the 1994 Cleveland Indians Super Team card got parallel Indians Division Winner and Master Photo team sets. Collectors who redeemed the 1994 Super Team card of a division winner (Dodgers, Mariners, Red Sox and Reds) received a Division Winner parallel team set of the respective team that they sent in. All of these winner cards parallel the 1995 Stadium Club regular series cards.

COMP.WS SET (585) 50.00 120.00
COMP.EC/TA SET (45) 6.00 15.00
*STARS: .6X TO 1.5X BASIC CARDS
*ROOKIES: .6X TO 1.5X BASIC CARDS

1995 Stadium Club Virtual Reality

This 270-card standard-size set parallels a selection of cards from the regular 1995 Stadium Club set. Differences include the words "Virtual Reality" printed above the player's name and the numbering on the back. These cards were inserted in the first two Stadium Club series on a one per pack, two per rack pack basis.

COMPLETE SET (270) 40.00 100.00
COMP.SERIES 1 (135) 20.00 50.00
COMP.SERIES 2 (135) 20.00 50.00
*STARS: .75X TO 2X BASIC CARDS

1995 Stadium Club Virtual Reality Members Only

These cards parallel the regular 1995 Stadium Club Stadium Club Virtual Reality cards. The only difference is that they all have a Stadium Club Members Only logo imprinted on the front. These cards were distributed as part of the package of material that members of the "Stadium Club Members Only" club received when they ordered the 1995 parallel master set.

COMP.FACT.SET (270) 40.00 100.00
*MEMBERS ONLY: 2X BASIC VIRTUAL REALITY

1995 Stadium Club Clear Cut

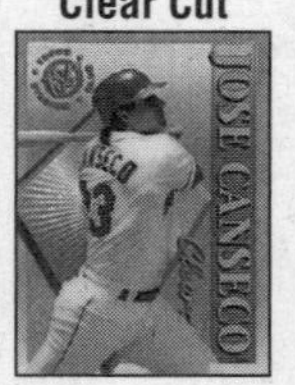

Randomly inserted at a rate of one in 24 hobby and retail packs, this 28-card set features a full color action photo of the player against a clear acetate background with the player's name printed vertically.

COMPLETE SET (28) 30.00 80.00
COMPLETE SERIES 1 (14) 15.00 40.00
COMP.SERIES 2 (14) 15.00 40.00
CC1 Mike Piazza 4.00 10.00
CC2 Ruben Sierra 1.00 2.50
CC3 Tony Gwynn 3.00 8.00
CC4 Frank Thomas 2.50 6.00
CC5 Fred McGriff 1.50 4.00
CC6 Rafael Palmeiro 1.50 4.00
CC7 Bobby Bonilla 1.00 2.50
CC8 Chili Davis 1.00 2.50
CC9 Hal Morris .50 1.25
CC10 Jose Canseco 1.50 4.00
CC11 Jay Bell 1.00 2.50
CC12 Kirby Puckett 2.50 6.00
CC13 Gary Sheffield 1.00 2.50
CC14 Bob Hamelin .50 1.25
CC15 Jeff Bagwell 1.50 4.00
CC16 Albert Belle 1.00 2.50
CC17 Sammy Sosa 2.50 6.00
CC18 Ken Griffey Jr. 4.00 10.00
CC19 Todd Zeile .50 1.25
CC20 Mo Vaughn 1.00 2.50
CC21 Moises Alou 1.00 2.50
CC22 Paul O'Neill 1.50 4.00
CC23 Andres Galarraga 1.00 2.50
CC24 Greg Vaughn .50 1.25
CC25 Len Dykstra 1.00 2.50
CC26 Joe Carter 1.00 2.50
CC27 Barry Bonds 6.00 15.00
CC28 Cecil Fielder 1.00 2.50

1995 Stadium Club Crunch Time

This 20-card standard-size set features home run hitters and was randomly inserted in first series rack packs. The cards are numbered as "X" of 20 in the upper right corner.

COMPLETE SET (20) 20.00 50.00
1 Jeff Bagwell .75 2.00
2 Kirby Puckett 1.25 3.00
3 Frank Thomas 1.25 3.00
4 Albert Belle .50 1.25
5 Julio Franco .50 1.25
6 Jose Canseco .75 2.00
7 Paul Molitor .50 1.25
8 Joe Carter .50 1.25
9 Ken Griffey Jr. 2.00 5.00
10 Larry Walker .50 1.25
11 Dante Bichette .50 1.25
12 Carlos Baerga .25 .60
13 Fred McGriff .75 2.00
14 Ruben Sierra .50 1.25
15 Will Clark .75 2.00
16 Moises Alou .50 1.25
17 Rafael Palmeiro .75 2.00
18 Travis Fryman .50 1.25
19 Barry Bonds 3.00 8.00
20 Cal Ripken 4.00 10.00

1995 Stadium Club Crystal Ball

This 15-card standard-size set was inserted into series three packs at a rate of one in 24. Fifteen leading 1995 rookies and prospects were featured in this set. The player is identified on the top and the cards are numbered with a "CB" prefix in the upper left corner.

COMPLETE SET (15) 50.00 80.00
CB1 Chipper Jones 4.00 10.00
CB2 Dustin Hermanson .75 2.00
CB3 Ray Durham 1.50 4.00
CB4 Phil Nevin 1.50 4.00
CB5 Billy Ashley .75 2.00
CB6 Shawn Green 1.50 4.00
CB7 Jason Bates .75 2.00
CB8 Benji Gil .75 2.00
CB9 Marty Cordova .75 2.00
CB10 Quilvio Veras .75 2.00
CB11 Mark Grudzielanek 2.50 6.00
CB12 Ruben Rivera .75 2.00
CB13 Bill Pulsipher .75 2.00
CB14 Derek Jeter 8.00 20.00
CB15 LaTroy Hawkins .75 2.00

1995 Stadium Club Phone Cards

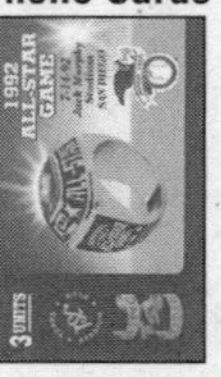

These phone cards were randomly inserted into packs. The prizes for these cards were as follows. The Gold Winner card was redeemable for the ring depicted on the front of the card. The silver winner card was redeemable for a set of all 39 phone cards. The regular winner card was redeemable for a Ring Leaders set. The fronts feature a photo of a specific ring while the backs have game information. If the card was not a winner for any of the prizes, it was still good for three minutes of time. The phone cards expired on January 1, 1996. If the PIN number is revealed the value is a percentage of an untouched card.

COMP.REGULAR (13) 10.00 20.00
COMMON REGULAR 1.00 2.00
COMP.SILVER SET (13) 15.00 30.00
COMMON SILVER CARD 2.00 4.00
COMP.GOLD SET (13) 30.00 75.00
COMMON GOLD CARD 4.00 8.00
*PIN NUMBER REVEALED: .25X to .50X BASIC CARDS

1995 Stadium Club Power Zone

This 12-card standard-size set was inserted into series three packs at a rate of one in 24. The cards are numbered in the upper right corner with a "PZ" prefix.

COMPLETE SET (12) 20.00 50.00
PZ1 Jeff Bagwell 1.50 4.00
PZ2 Albert Belle 1.00 2.50
PZ3 Barry Bonds 6.00 15.00
PZ4 Joe Carter 1.00 2.50
PZ5 Cecil Fielder 1.00 2.50
PZ6 Andres Galarraga 1.00 2.50
PZ7 Ken Griffey Jr. 4.00 10.00
PZ8 Paul Molitor 1.00 2.50
PZ9 Fred McGriff 1.50 4.00
PZ10 Rafael Palmeiro 1.50 4.00
PZ11 Frank Thomas 2.50 6.00
PZ12 Matt Williams 1.00 2.50

1995 Stadium Club Ring Leaders

Randomly inserted in packs, this set features players who have won various awards or titles. This set was also redeemable as a prize with winning regular phone cards. This set features Stadium Club's "Power Matrix Technology," which makes the cards shine and glow. The horizontal fronts feature a player photo, rings in both upper corners as well as other designs that make for a very busy front. The backs have information on how the player earned his rings, along with a player photo and some other pertinent information.

COMPLETE SET (40) 40.00 100.00
COMPLETE SERIES 1 (20) 20.00 50.00
COMP.SERIES 2 (20) 20.00 50.00
RL1 Jeff Bagwell 2.00 5.00
RL2 Mark McGwire 8.00 20.00
RL3 Ozzie Smith 5.00 12.00
RL4 Paul Molitor 1.25 3.00
RL5 Darryl Strawberry .60 1.50
RL6 Eddie Murray 3.00 8.00
RL7 Tony Gwynn 4.00 10.00
RL8 Jose Canseco 2.00 5.00
RL9 Howard Johnson .60 1.50
RL10 Andre Dawson 1.25 3.00
RL11 Matt Williams 1.25 3.00
RL12 Tim Raines 1.25 3.00
RL13 Fred McGriff 2.00 5.00
RL14 Ken Griffey Jr. 5.00 12.00
RL15 Gary Sheffield 1.25 3.00
RL16 Dennis Eckersley 1.25 3.00
RL17 Kevin Mitchell .60 1.50
RL18 Will Clark 2.00 5.00
RL19 Darren Daulton 1.25 3.00
RL20 Paul O'Neill 2.00 5.00
RL21 Julio Franco 1.25 3.00
RL22 Albert Belle 1.25 3.00
RL23 Juan Gonzalez 1.25 3.00
RL24 Kirby Puckett 3.00 8.00
RL25 Joe Carter 1.25 3.00
RL26 Frank Thomas 3.00 8.00
RL27 Cal Ripken 10.00 25.00
RL28 John Olerud 1.25 3.00
RL29 Ruben Sierra 1.25 3.00
RL30 Barry Bonds 8.00 20.00
RL31 Cecil Fielder 1.25 3.00
RL32 Roger Clemens 6.00 15.00
RL33 Don Mattingly 8.00 20.00
RL34 Terry Pendleton 1.25 3.00
RL35 Rickey Henderson 3.00 8.00
RL36 Dave Winfield 1.25 3.00
RL37 Edgar Martinez 2.00 5.00
RL38 Wade Boggs 2.00 5.00
RL39 Willie McGee 1.25 3.00
RL40 Andres Galarraga 1.25 3.00

1995 Stadium Club Super Skills

This 20-card set was randomly inserted into hobby packs. The cards are numbered in the upper left as "X" of 9.

COMPLETE SERIES 1 (9) 12.50 30.00
COMP.SERIES 2 (11) 15.00 40.00
SS1 Roberto Alomar 1.50 4.00
SS2 Barry Bonds 6.00 15.00
SS3 Jay Buhner 1.00 2.50
SS4 Chuck Carr .50 1.25

SS5 Don Mattingly 6.00 15.00
SS6 Raul Mondesi 1.00 2.50
SS7 Tim Salmon 1.50 4.00
SS8 Deion Sanders 1.50 4.00
SS9 Devon White 1.00 2.50
SS10 Mark Whiten .50 1.25
SS11 Ken Griffey Jr. 4.00 10.00
SS12 Marquis Grissom 1.00 2.50
SS13 Paul O'Neill 1.50 4.00
SS14 Kenny Lofton 1.00 2.50
SS15 Larry Walker 1.00 2.50
SS16 Scott Cooper .50 1.25
SS17 Barry Larkin 1.50 4.00
SS18 Matt Williams 1.00 2.50
SS19 John Wetteland 1.00 2.50
SS20 Randy Johnson 2.50 6.00

1995 Stadium Club Virtual Extremists

This 10-card set was inserted randomly into second series rack packs. The fronts feature a player photo against a baseball backdrop. The words "VR Extremist" are spelled vertically down the right side while the player name is in silver foil on the bottom. All of this is surrounded by blue and purple borders. The horizontal backs feature projected full-season 1994 stats. The cards are numbered with a "VRE" prefix in the upper right corner.

COMPLETE SET (10) 30.00 80.00
VRE1 Barry Bonds 10.00 25.00
VRE2 Ken Griffey Jr. 6.00 15.00
VRE3 Jeff Bagwell 2.50 6.00
VRE4 Albert Belle 1.50 4.00
VRE5 Frank Thomas 4.00 10.00
VRE6 Tony Gwynn 5.00 12.00
VRE7 Kenny Lofton 1.50 4.00
VRE8 Deion Sanders 2.50 6.00
VRE9 Ken Hill .75 2.00
VRE10 Jimmy Key 1.50 4.00

1995 Stadium Club Members Only

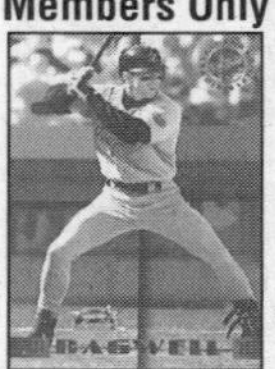

Topps produced a 50-card boxed set for each of the four major sports. With their club membership, members received one set of their choice and had the option of purchasing additional sets for $10.00 each. Player section was based on 1994 leaders from both leagues in various statistical categories. The five Finest cards (46-50) represent Topps' selection of the top rookies of 1994. The color action photos on the fronts have brightly-colored backgrounds and carry the distinctive Topps Stadium Club Members Only gold foil seal. The backs present a second color photo and player profile.

COMP. FACT SET (50) 8.00 20.00
1 Moises Alou .08 .25
2 Jeff Bagwell .40 1.00
3 Albert Belle .08 .25
4 Andy Benes .02 .10
5 Dante Bichette .08 .25
6 Craig Biggio .20 .50
7 Wade Boggs .40 1.00
8 Barry Bonds .60 1.50
9 Brett Butler .08 .25
10 Jose Canseco .40 1.00
11 Joe Carter .08 .25
12 Vince Coleman .02 .10
13 Jeff Conine .02 .10
14 Cecil Fielder .08 .25
15 John Franco .08 .25
16 Julio Franco .08 .25
17 Travis Fryman .08 .25
18 Andres Galarraga .30 .75
19 Ken Griffey Jr. 1.00 2.50
20 Marquis Grissom .02 .10
21 Tony Gwynn .75 2.00
22 Ken Hill .02 .10
23 Randy Johnson .50 1.25
24 Lance Johnson .02 .10
25 Jimmy Key .08 .25
26 Chuck Knoblauch .20 .50
27 Ray Lankford .08 .25
28 Darren Lewis .02 .10
29 Kenny Lofton .20 .50
30 Greg Maddux 1.00 2.50
31 Fred McGriff .20 .50
32 Kevin Mitchell .02 .10
33 Paul Molitor .40 1.00
34 Hal Morris .02 .10
35 Paul O'Neill .08 .25
36 Rafael Palmeiro .30 .75
37 Tony Phillips .02 .10
38 Mike Piazza 1.00 2.50
39 Kirby Puckett .50 1.25
40 Cal Ripken 1.50 4.00
41 Deion Sanders .30 .75
42 Lee Smith .08 .25
43 Frank Thomas .50 1.25
44 Larry Walker .30 .75
45 Matt Williams .20 .50
46 Manny Ramirez .40 1.00
47 Joey Hamilton .02 .10
48 Raul Mondesi .20 .50
49 Bob Hamelin .02 .10
50 Ryan Klesko .08 .25

1995 Stadium Club Members Only Finest Bronze

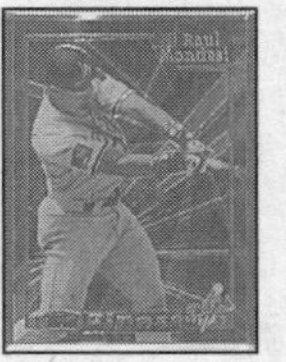

As a special bonus along with the complete 1995 Stadium Club Members Only factory set, members received these four cards featuring the 1994 Rookie of the Year and Cy Young Award Winners. The first shipment included series 1 and 2 cards as well as two of the Finest Bronze cards. The second shipment included series 3 cards and the remaining two Finest Bronze cards. The cards feature chromium metallized graphics, mounted on bronze and factory sealed in clear resin. Also, collectors got one of thsese cards if they only ordered one series. Bob Hamelin (series 1), Greg Maddux (Series 2) and David Cone (series 3). Mondesi was only available if one bought a complete set.

COMPLETE SET (4) 20.00 50.00
1 Bob Hamelin 1.25 3.00
2 Greg Maddux 15.00 40.00
3 David Cone 2.00 5.00
4 Raul Mondesi 2.00 5.00

1996 Stadium Club

The 1996 Stadium Club set consists of 450 cards with cards 1-225 in first series packs and 226-450 in second series packs. The product was primarily distributed in first and second series foil-wrapped packs. There was also a factory set, which included the Mantle insert cards, packaged in mini-cereal box type cartons and made available through retail outlets. The set includes a Team TSC subset (181-270). These subset cards were slightly shortprinted in comparison to the other cards in the set. Though not confirmed by the manufacturer, it is believed that card number 22 (Roberto Hernandez) is a short-print.

COMPLETE SET (450) 40.00 80.00
COMP.CEREAL SET (454) 40.00 80.00
COMP.SERIES 1 (225) 20.00 40.00
COMP.SERIES 2 (225) 20.00 40.00
COMMON (1-180/271-450) .10 .30
COMMON SP (181-270) .20 .50
1 Hideo Nomo .30 .75
2 Paul Molitor .10 .30
3 Garret Anderson .10 .30
4 Jose Mesa .10 .30
5 Vinny Castilla .10 .30
6 Mike Mussina .20 .50
7 Ray Durham .10 .30
8 Jack McDowell .10 .30
9 Juan Gonzalez .10 .30
10 Chipper Jones .30 .75
11 Deion Sanders .20 .50
12 Rondell White .10 .30
13 Tom Henke .10 .30
14 Derek Bell .10 .30
15 Randy Myers .10 .30
16 Randy Johnson .30 .75
17 Len Dykstra .10 .30
18 Bill Pulsipher .10 .30
19 Greg Colbrunn .10 .30
20 David Wells .10 .30
21 Chad Curtis .10 .30
22 Roberto Hernandez SP 2.00 5.00
23 Kirby Puckett .30 .75
24 Joe Vitiello .10 .30
25 Roger Clemens .60 1.50
26 Al Martin .10 .30
27 Chad Ogea .10 .30
28 David Segui .10 .30
29 Joey Hamilton .10 .30
30 Dan Wilson .10 .30
31 Chad Fonville .10 .30
32 Bernard Gilkey .10 .30
33 Kevin Seitzer .10 .30
34 Shawn Green .10 .30
35 Rick Aguilera .10 .30
36 Gary DiSarcina .10 .30
37 Jaime Navarro .10 .30
38 Doug Jones .10 .30
39 Brent Gates .10 .30
40 Dean Palmer .10 .30
41 Pat Rapp .10 .30

42 Tony Clark	.10	.30
43 Bill Swift	.10	.30
44 Randy Velarde	.10	.30
45 Matt Williams	.10	.30
46 John Mabry	.10	.30
47 Mike Fetters	.10	.30
48 Orlando Miller	.10	.30
49 Tom Glavine	.20	.50
50 Delino DeShields	.10	.30
51 Scott Erickson	.10	.30
52 Andy Van Slyke	.20	.50
53 Jim Bullinger	.10	.30
54 Lyle Mouton	.10	.30
55 Bret Saberhagen	.10	.30
56 Benito Santiago	.10	.30
57 Dan Miceli	.10	.30
58 Carl Everett	.10	.30
59 Rod Beck	.10	.30
60 Phil Nevin	.10	.30
61 Jason Giambi	.10	.30
62 Paul Menhart	.10	.30
63 Eric Karros	.10	.30
64 Allen Watson	.10	.30
65 Jeff Cirillo	.10	.30
66 Lee Smith	.10	.30
67 Sean Berry	.10	.30
68 Luis Sojo	.10	.30
69 Jeff Montgomery	.10	.30
70 Todd Hundley	.10	.30
71 John Burkett	.10	.30
72 Mark Gubicza	.10	.30
73 Don Mattingly	.75	2.00
74 Jeff Brantley	.10	.30
75 Matt Walbeck	.10	.30
76 Steve Parris	.10	.30
77 Ken Caminiti	.10	.30
78 Kirt Manwaring	.10	.30
79 Greg Vaughn	.10	.30
80 Pedro Martinez	.20	.50
81 Benji Gil	.10	.30
82 Heathcliff Slocumb	.10	.30
83 Joe Girardi	.10	.30
84 Sean Bergman	.10	.30
85 Matt Karchner	.10	.30
86 Butch Huskey	.10	.30
87 Mike Morgan	.10	.30
88 Todd Worrell	.10	.30
89 Mike Bordick	.10	.30
90 Bip Roberts	.10	.30
91 Mike Hampton	.10	.30
92 Troy O'Leary	.10	.30
93 Wally Joyner	.10	.30
94 Dave Stevens	.10	.30
95 Cecil Fielder	.10	.30
96 Wade Boggs	.20	.50
97 Hal Morris	.10	.30
98 Mickey Tettleton	.10	.30
99 Jeff Kent	.10	.30
100 Denny Martinez	.10	.30
101 Luis Gonzalez	.10	.30
102 John Jaha	.10	.30
103 Javier Lopez	.10	.30
104 Mark McGwire	.75	2.00
105 Ken Griffey Jr.	.50	1.25
106 Darren Daulton	.10	.30
107 Bryan Rekar	.10	.30
108 Mike Macfarlane	.10	.30
109 Gary Gaetti	.10	.30
110 Shane Reynolds	.10	.30
111 Pat Meares	.10	.30
112 Jason Schmidt	.20	.50
113 Otis Nixon	.10	.30
114 John Franco	.10	.30
115 Marc Newfield	.10	.30
116 Andy Benes	.10	.30
117 Ozzie Guillen	.10	.30
118 Brian Jordan	.10	.30
119 Terry Pendleton	.10	.30
120 Chuck Finley	.10	.30
121 Scott Stahoviak	.10	.30
122 Sid Fernandez	.10	.30
123 Derek Jeter	.75	2.00
124 John Smiley	.10	.30
125 David Bell	.10	.30
126 Brett Butler	.10	.30
127 Doug Drabek	.10	.30
128 J.T. Snow	.10	.30
129 Joe Carter	.10	.30
130 Dennis Eckersley	.10	.30
131 Marty Cordova	.10	.30
132 Greg Maddux	.50	1.25
133 Tom Goodwin	.10	.30
134 Andy Ashby	.10	.30
135 Paul Sorrento	.10	.30
136 Ricky Bones	.10	.30
137 Shawon Dunston	.10	.30
138 Moises Alou	.10	.30
139 Mickey Morandini	.10	.30
140 Ramon Martinez	.10	.30
141 Royce Clayton	.10	.30
142 Brad Ausmus	.10	.30
143 Kenny Rogers	.10	.30
144 Tim Naehring	.10	.30
145 Chris Gomez	.10	.30
146 Bobby Bonilla	.10	.30
147 Wilson Alvarez	.10	.30
148 Johnny Damon	.20	.50
149 Pat Hentgen	.10	.30
150 Andres Galarraga	.10	.30
151 David Cone	.10	.30
152 Lance Johnson	.10	.30
153 Carlos Garcia	.10	.30
154 Doug Johns	.10	.30
155 Midre Cummings	.10	.30
156 Steve Sparks	.10	.30
157 Sandy Martinez	.10	.30
158 Wm. Van Landingham	.10	.30
159 David Justice	.10	.30
160 Mark Grace	.20	.50
161 Robb Nen	.10	.30
162 Mike Greenwell	.10	.30
163 Brad Radke	.10	.30
164 Edgardo Alfonzo	.10	.30
165 Mark Leiter	.10	.30
166 Walt Weiss	.10	.30
167 Mel Rojas	.10	.30
168 Bret Boone	.10	.30
169 Ricky Bottalico	.10	.30
170 Bobby Higginson	.10	.30
171 Trevor Hoffman	.10	.30
172 Jay Bell	.10	.30
173 Gabe White	.10	.30
174 Curtis Goodwin	.10	.30
175 Tyler Green	.10	.30
176 Roberto Alomar	.20	.50
177 Sterling Hitchcock	.10	.30
178 Ryan Klesko	.10	.30
179 Donne Wall	.10	.30
180 Brian McRae	.10	.30
181 Will Clark TSC SP	.30	.75
182 F.Thomas TSC SP	.40	1.00
183 Jeff Bagwell TSC SP	.20	.50
184 Mo Vaughn TSC SP	.20	.50
185 Tino Martinez TSC SP	.30	.75
186 Craig Biggio TSC SP	.30	.75
187 C. Knoblauch TSC SP	.20	.50
188 Carlos Baerga TSC SP	.20	.50
189 Quilvio Veras TSC SP	.20	.50
190 Luis Alicea TSC SP	.20	.50
191 Jim Thome TSC SP	.30	.75
192 Mike Blowers TSC SP	.20	.50
193 R.Ventura TSC SP	.20	.50
194 Jeff King TSC SP	.20	.50
195 Tony Phillips TSC SP	.20	.50
196 John Valentin TSC SP	.20	.50
197 Barry Larkin TSC SP	.30	.75
198 Cal Ripken TSC SP	1.25	3.00
199 Omar Vizquel TSC SP	.30	.75
200 Kurt Abbott TSC SP	.20	.50
201 Albert Belle TSC SP	.20	.50
202 Barry Bonds TSC SP	1.00	2.50
203 Ron Gant TSC SP	.20	.50
204 D.Bichette TSC SP	.20	.50
205 Jeff Conine TSC SP	.20	.50
206 Jim Edmonds TSC SP UER Greg Myers pictured on front	.20	.50
207 Stan Javier TSC SP	.20	.50
208 Kenny Lofton TSC SP	.20	.50
209 Ray Lankford TSC SP	.20	.50
210 B.Williams TSC SP	.30	.75
211 Jay Buhner TSC SP	.20	.50
212 Paul O'Neill TSC SP	.30	.75
213 Tim Salmon TSC SP	.30	.75
214 R.Sanders TSC SP	.20	.50
215 M.Ramirez TSC SP	.30	.75
216 Mike Piazza TSC SP	.60	1.50
217 Mike Stanley TSC SP	.20	.50
218 Tony Eusebio TSC SP	.20	.50
219 Chris Hoiles TSC SP	.20	.50
220 R.Karkovice TSC SP	.20	.50
221 E.Martinez TSC SP	.30	.75
222 Chili Davis TSC SP	.20	.50
223 Jose Canseco TSC SP	.30	.75
224 Eddie Murray TSC SP	.40	1.00
225 G.Berroa TSC SP	.20	.50
226 C.Jones TSC SP	.40	1.00
227 G.Anderson TSC SP	.20	.50
228 M.Cordova TSC SP	.20	.50
229 Jon Nunnally TSC SP	.20	.50
230 Brian L.Hunter TSC SP	.20	.50
231 Shawn Green TSC SP	.20	.50
232 Ray Durham TSC SP	.20	.50
233 Alex Gonzalez TSC SP	.20	.50
234 B.Higginson TSC SP	.20	.50
235 R.Johnson TSC SP	.40	1.00
236 Al Leiter TSC SP	.20	.50
237 Tom Glavine TSC SP	.30	.75
238 Kenny Rogers TSC SP	.20	.50
239 M.Hampton TSC SP	.20	.50
240 David Wells TSC SP	.20	.50
241 Jim Abbott TSC SP	.30	.75
242 Denny Neagle TSC SP	.20	.50
243 W.Alvarez TSC SP	.20	.50
244 John Smiley TSC SP	.20	.50
245 Greg Maddux TSC SP	.30	.75
246 Andy Ashby TSC SP	.20	.50
247 Hideo Nomo TSC SP	.40	1.00
248 Pat Rapp TSC SP	.20	.50
249 T.Wakefield TSC SP	.20	.50
250 John Smoltz TSC SP	.30	.75
251 J.Hamilton TSC SP	.20	.50
252 Frank Castillo TSC SP	.20	.50
253 D.Martinez TSC SP	.20	.50
254 J.Navarro TSC SP	.20	.50
255 Karim Garcia TSC SP	.20	.50
256 Bob Abreu TSC SP	.40	1.00
257 Butch Huskey TSC SP	.20	.50
258 Ruben Rivera TSC SP	.20	.50
259 J.Damon TSC SP	.30	.75
260 Derek Jeter TSC SP	1.00	2.50
261 D. Eckersley TSC SP	.20	.50
262 Jose Mesa TSC SP	.20	.50
263 Tom Henke TSC SP	.20	.50
264 Rick Aguilera TSC SP	.20	.50
265 Randy Myers TSC SP	.20	.50
266 John Franco TSC SP	.20	.50
267 Jeff Brantley TSC SP	.20	.50
268 J.Wetteland TSC SP	.20	.50
269 Mark Wohlers TSC SP	.20	.50
270 Rod Beck TSC SP	.20	.50
271 Barry Larkin	.20	.50
272 Paul O'Neill	.20	.50
273 Bobby Jones	.10	.30
274 Will Clark	.20	.50
275 Steve Avery	.10	.30
276 Jim Edmonds	.10	.30
277 John Olerud	.10	.30
278 Carlos Perez	.10	.30
279 Chris Hoiles	.10	.30
280 Jeff Conine	.10	.30
281 Jim Eisenreich	.10	.30
282 Jason Jacome	.10	.30
283 Ray Lankford	.10	.30
284 John Wasdin	.10	.30
285 Frank Thomas	.30	.75
286 Jason Isringhausen	.10	.30
287 Glenallen Hill	.10	.30
288 Esteban Loaiza	.10	.30
289 Bernie Williams	.20	.50
290 Curtis Leskanic	.10	.30
291 Scott Cooper	.10	.30
292 Curt Schilling	.10	.30
293 Eddie Murray	.30	.75
294 Rick Krivda	.10	.30
295 Domingo Cedeno	.10	.30
296 Jeff Fassero	.10	.30
297 Albert Belle	.10	.30
298 Craig Biggio	.20	.50
299 Fernando Vina	.10	.30
300 Edgar Martinez	.20	.50
301 Tony Gwynn	.40	1.00
302 Felipe Lira	.10	.30
303 Mo Vaughn	.10	.30
304 Alex Fernandez	.10	.30
305 Keith Lockhart	.10	.30
306 Roger Pavlik	.10	.30
307 Lee Tinsley	.10	.30
308 Omar Vizquel	.20	.50
309 Scott Servais	.10	.30
310 Danny Tartabull	.10	.30
311 Chili Davis	.10	.30
312 Cal Eldred	.10	.30
313 Roger Cedeno	.10	.30
314 Chris Hammond	.10	.30
315 Rusty Greer	.10	.30
316 Brady Anderson	.10	.30
317 Ron Villone	.10	.30
318 Mark Carreon	.10	.30
319 Larry Walker	.10	.30
320 Pete Harnisch	.10	.30
321 Robin Ventura	.10	.30
322 Tim Belcher	.10	.30
323 Tony Tarasco	.10	.30
324 Juan Guzman	.10	.30
325 Kenny Lofton	.10	.30
326 Kevin Foster	.10	.30
327 Wil Cordero	.10	.30
328 Troy Percival	.10	.30
329 Turk Wendell	.10	.30
330 Thomas Howard	.10	.30
331 Carlos Baerga	.10	.30
332 B.J. Surhoff	.10	.30
333 Jay Buhner	.10	.30
334 Andujar Cedeno	.10	.30
335 Jeff King	.10	.30
336 Dante Bichette	.10	.30
337 Alan Trammell	.10	.30
338 Scott Leius	.10	.30
339 Chris Snopek	.10	.30
340 Roger Bailey	.10	.30
341 Jacob Brumfield	.10	.30
342 Jose Canseco	.20	.50
343 Rafael Palmeiro	.20	.50
344 Quilvio Veras	.10	.30
345 Darrin Fletcher	.10	.30
346 Carlos Delgado	.10	.30
347 Tony Eusebio	.10	.30
348 Ismael Valdes	.10	.30
349 Terry Steinbach	.10	.30
350 Orel Hershiser	.10	.30
351 Kurt Abbott	.10	.30
352 Jody Reed	.10	.30
353 David Howard	.10	.30
354 Ruben Sierra	.10	.30
355 John Ericks	.10	.30
356 Buck Showalter MG	.10	.30
357 Jim Thome	.20	.50
358 Geronimo Berroa	.10	.30
359 Robby Thompson	.10	.30
360 Jose Vizcaino	.10	.30
361 Jeff Frye	.10	.30
362 Kevin Appier	.10	.30
363 Pat Kelly	.10	.30
364 Ron Gant	.10	.30
365 Luis Alicea	.10	.30
366 Armando Benitez	.10	.30
367 Rico Brogna	.10	.30
368 Manny Ramirez	.20	.50
369 Mike Lansing	.10	.30
370 Sammy Sosa	.30	.75
371 Don Wengert	.10	.30
372 Dave Nilsson	.10	.30
373 Sandy Alomar Jr.	.10	.30
374 Joey Cora	.10	.30
375 Larry Thomas	.10	.30
376 John Valentin	.10	.30
377 Kevin Ritz	.10	.30
378 Steve Finley	.10	.30
379 Frank Rodriguez	.10	.30
380 Ivan Rodriguez	.20	.50
381 Alex Ochoa	.10	.30
382 Mark Lemke	.10	.30
383 Scott Brosius	.10	.30
384 James Mouton	.10	.30
385 Mark Langston	.10	.30
386 Ed Sprague	.10	.30
387 Joe Oliver	.10	.30
388 Steve Ontiveros	.10	.30
389 Rey Sanchez	.10	.30
390 Mike Henneman	.10	.30
391 Jose Valentin	.10	.30
392 Tom Candiotti	.10	.30
393 Damon Buford	.10	.30
394 Erik Hanson	.10	.30
395 Mark Smith	.10	.30
396 Pete Schourek	.10	.30
397 John Flaherty	.10	.30
398 Dave Martinez	.10	.30
399 Tommy Greene	.10	.30
400 Gary Sheffield	.10	.30
401 Glenn Dishman	.10	.30
402 Barry Bonds	.75	2.00
403 Tom Pagnozzi	.10	.30
404 Todd Stottlemyre	.10	.30
405 Tim Salmon	.20	.50
406 John Hudek	.10	.30
407 Fred McGriff	.20	.50
408 Orlando Merced	.10	.30
409 Brian Barber	.10	.30
410 Ryan Thompson	.10	.30
411 Mariano Rivera	.30	.75
412 Eric Young	.10	.30
413 Chris Bosio	.10	.30
414 Chuck Knoblauch	.10	.30
415 Jamie Moyer	.10	.30
416 Chan Ho Park	.10	.30
417 Mark Portugal	.10	.30
418 Tim Raines	.10	.30
419 Antonio Osuna	.10	.30
420 Todd Zeile	.10	.30
421 Steve Wojciechowski	.10	.30
422 Marquis Grissom	.10	.30
423 Norm Charlton	.10	.30
424 Cal Ripken	1.00	2.50
425 Gregg Jefferies	.10	.30
426 Mike Stanton	.10	.30
427 Tony Fernandez	.10	.30
428 Jose Rijo	.10	.30
429 Jeff Bagwell	.20	.50
430 Raul Mondesi	.10	.30
431 Travis Fryman	.10	.30
432 Ron Karkovice	.10	.30
433 Alan Benes	.10	.30
434 Tony Phillips	.10	.30
435 Reggie Sanders	.10	.30
436 Andy Pettitte	.20	.50
437 Matt Lawton RC	.10	.30
438 Jeff Blauser	.10	.30
439 Michael Tucker	.10	.30
440 Mark Loretta	.10	.30
441 Charlie Hayes	.10	.30
442 Mike Piazza	.50	1.25
443 Shane Andrews	.10	.30
444 Jeff Suppan	.10	.30
445 Steve Rodriguez	.10	.30
446 Mike Matheny	.10	.30
447 Trenidad Hubbard	.10	.30
448 Denny Hocking	.10	.30
449 Mark Grudzielanek	.10	.30
450 Joe Randa	.10	.30
NNO Roger Clemens Extreme Gold PROMO	2.00	5.00

1996 Stadium Club Members Only Parallel

This set, of which only 750 were produced is a parallel to the regular 1996 Stadium Club set. The cards are embossed with a "Members Only" logo and were available only to members of Topps' Stadium Club. The set includes a parallel of the complete 450-card basic set plus the following inserts: Bash and Burn, Mickey Mantle Heroes, Megaheroes, Metalists, Midsummer Matchups, Power Packed, Power Streak, Prime Cuts and TSC Awards. Only the inserts cards are priced below. Please refer to the multiplier for value on parallels to the basic issue cards.

COMP.SET W/INSERTS (555)	200.00	500.00
COMP.BASE SET (450)	80.00	200.00
COMMON CARD (1-450)	.10	.25
COMMON (M1-M19)	2.00	5.00
*MEMBERS ONLY: 6X BASIC CARDS		
M1 Jeff Bagwell	1.50	4.00
M2 Barry Bonds	4.00	10.00
M3 Jose Canseco	1.50	4.00
M4 Roger Clemens	4.00	10.00
M5 Dennis Eckersley	.60	1.50
M6 Greg Maddux	5.00	12.00
M7 Cal Ripken	8.00	20.00
M8 Frank Thomas	3.00	8.00
BB1 Sammy Sosa	4.00	10.00
BB2 Barry Bonds	4.00	10.00
BB3 Reggie Sanders	.40	1.00
BB4 Craig Biggio	.75	2.00
BB5 Raul Mondesi	.75	2.00
BB6 Ron Gant	.40	1.00
BB7 Ray Lankford	.60	1.50
BB8 Glenallen Hill	.40	1.00
BB9 Chad Curtis	.40	1.00
BB10 John Valentin	.60	1.50
MH1 Frank Thomas	3.00	8.00
MH2 Ken Griffey Jr.	6.00	15.00
MH3 Hideo Nomo	1.50	4.00
MH4 Ozzie Smith	1.50	4.00
MH5 Will Clark	1.25	3.00
MH6 Jack McDowell	.40	1.00
MH7 Andres Galarraga	1.25	3.00
MH8 Roger Clemens	4.00	10.00
MH9 Deion Sanders	.60	1.50
MH10 Mo Vaughn	.60	1.50
MM1 Hideo Nomo Randy Johnson	2.00	5.00
MM2 Mike Piazza Ivan Rodriguez	5.00	12.00
MM3 Fred McGriff Frank Thomas	3.00	8.00
MM4 Craig Biggio Carlos Baerga	.75	2.00
MM5 Vinny Castilla Wade Boggs	1.50	4.00
MM6 Barry Larkin Cal Ripken	8.00	20.00
MM7 Barry Bonds Albert Belle	3.00	8.00
MM8 Len Dykstra Kenny Lofton	.60	1.50
MM9 Tony Gwynn Kirby Puckett	4.00	10.00
MM10 Ron Gant Edgar Martinez	.75	2.00
PC1 Albert Belle	.60	1.50
PC2 Barry Bonds	1.50	4.00
PC3 Ken Griffey Jr.	6.00	15.00
PC4 Tony Gwynn	4.00	10.00
PC5 Edgar Martinez	.75	2.00
PC6 Rafael Palmeiro	1.25	3.00
PC7 Mike Piazza	4.00	10.00
PC8 Frank Thomas	3.00	8.00
PP1 Albert Belle	.60	1.50
PP2 Mark McGwire	6.00	15.00
PP3 Jose Canseco	1.50	4.00
PP4 Mike Piazza	4.00	10.00
PP5 Ron Gant	.60	1.50
PP6 Ken Griffey Jr.	6.00	15.00
PP7 Mo Vaughn	.60	1.50
PP8 Cecil Fielder	.60	1.50
PP9 Tim Salmon	1.25	3.00
PP10 Frank Thomas	3.00	8.00
PP11 Juan Gonzalez	1.50	4.00
PP12 Andres Galarraga	1.25	3.00
PP13 Fred McGriff	.75	2.00
PP14 Jay Buhner	.60	1.50
PP15 Dante Bichette	.60	1.50
PS1 Randy Johnson	1.50	4.00
PS2 Hideo Nomo	2.00	5.00
PS3 Albert Belle	.60	1.50
PS4 Dante Bichette	.60	1.50
PS5 Jay Buhner	.60	1.50
PS6 Frank Thomas	3.00	8.00
PS7 Mark McGwire	6.00	15.00
PS8 Rafael Palmeiro	1.25	3.00
PS9 Mo Vaughn	.60	1.50
PS10 Sammy Sosa	4.00	10.00
PS11 Larry Walker	1.25	3.00
PS12 Gary Gaetti	.60	1.50
PS13 Tim Salmon	1.25	3.00
PS14 Barry Bonds	4.00	10.00
PS15 Jim Edmonds	1.25	3.00
TSCA1 Cal Ripken	8.00	20.00
TSCA2 Albert Belle	.60	1.50
TSCA3 Tom Glavine	1.25	3.00
TSCA4 Jeff Conine	.40	1.00
TSCA5 Ken Griffey Jr.	6.00	15.00
TSCA6 Hideo Nomo	1.50	4.00
TSCA7 Greg Maddux	4.00	10.00
TSCA8 Chipper Jones	4.00	10.00
TSCA9 Randy Johnson	1.50	4.00
TSCA10 Jose Mesa	.40	1.00

1996 Stadium Club Bash and Burn

Randomly inserted in packs at a rate of one in 24 (retail) and one in 48 (hobby), this ten card set features power/speed players.

COMPLETE SET (10)	15.00	40.00
BB1 Sammy Sosa	4.00	10.00
BB2 Barry Bonds	10.00	25.00
BB3 Reggie Sanders	1.50	4.00
BB4 Craig Biggio	2.50	6.00
BB5 Raul Mondesi	1.50	4.00
BB6 Ron Gant	1.50	4.00
BB7 Ray Lankford	1.50	4.00
BB8 Glenallen Hill	1.50	4.00
BB9 Chad Curtis	1.50	4.00
BB10 John Valentin	1.50	4.00

1996 Stadium Club Extreme Players Bronze

One hundred and seventy nine different players were featured on Extreme Player game cards randomly issued in 1996 Stadium Club first and second series packs. Each player has three versions: Bronze, Silver and Gold. All of these cards parallel their corresponding regular issue card except for the Bronze foil "Extreme Players" logo on each card front and the "EP" suffix on the card number, thus creating a skip-numbered set. The Bronze cards listed below were seeded at a rate of 1:12 packs. At the conclusion of the 1996 regular season, an Extreme Player from each of ten positions was identified as a winner based on scores calculated from their actual playing statistics. The 10 winning players are noted with a "W" below. Prior to the December 31st, 1996 deadline, each of the ten winning Extreme Players Bronze cards was redeemable for a 10-card set of Extreme Winners Bronze. Unredeemed winners are now in much shorter supply than other cards in this set and carry premium values.

COMP.BRONZE SER.1 (90)	50.00	120.00
COMP.BRONZE SER.2 (90)	50.00	120.00
*BRONZE: 2X TO 5X BASE CARD HI		
*SILVER SINGLES: .6X TO 1.5X BRONZE	1.50	4.00
*SILVER WIN: .6X TO 1.5X BRONZE WIN		
*GOLD SINGLES: 1.25X TO 3X BRONZE		
*GOLD WIN: 1.25X TO 3X BRONZE WIN		
GOLD STATED ODDS 1:48		
SKIP-NUMBERED 179-CARD SET		
77 Ken Caminiti W	1.50	4.00
88 Todd Worrell W	.60	1.50
105 Ken Griffey Jr. W	5.00	12.00
132 Greg Maddux W	5.00	12.00
150 Andres Galarraga W	1.50	4.00
271 Barry Larkin W	1.50	4.00
400 Gary Sheffield W	2.00	5.00
402 Barry Bonds W	8.00	20.00
414 Chuck Knoblauch W	1.25	3.00
442 Mike Piazza W	5.00	12.00

1996 Stadium Club Extreme Winners Bronze

This 10-card skip-numbered set was only available to collectors who redeemed one of the ten winning Bronze Extreme Players cards before the December 31st, 1996 deadline. The cards parallel the Extreme Players cards inserted in Stadium Club packs except for their distinctive diffraction foil fronts.

COMPLETE SET (10)	10.00	25.00
*SILVER: 1.25X TO 3X BRONZE WINNERS		
ONE SILV.SET VIA MAIL PER SILV.WINNER		
*GOLD: 5X TO 12X BRONZE WINNERS		
ONE GOLD CARD VIA MAIL PER GOLD WNR.		
EW1 Greg Maddux	1.50	4.00
EW2 Mike Piazza	1.50	4.00
EW3 Andres Galarraga	.40	1.00
EW4 Chuck Knoblauch	.40	1.00
EW5 Ken Caminiti	.40	1.00
EW6 Barry Larkin	.60	1.50
EW7 Barry Bonds	2.50	6.00
EW8 Ken Griffey Jr.	1.50	4.00
EW9 Gary Sheffield	.40	1.00
EW10 Todd Worrell	.40	1.00

1996 Stadium Club Mantle

Randomly inserted at a rate of one card in every 24 packs in series one, one in 12 packs in series two, this 19-card retrospective set chronicles Mantle's career with classic photography, celebrity quotes and highlights from each year. The cards are double foil-stamped. The series one cards feature black-and-white photos, series two color photos. Mantle's name is printed across a silver foil facade of Yankee Stadium on each card top. Cereal Box factory sets include these cards with gold foil. They are valued the same as the pack inserts.

COMPLETE SET (19)	50.00	120.00
COMMON (MM1-MM9)	4.00	10.00
COMMON (MM10-MM19)	2.50	6.00

1996 Stadium Club Megaheroes

Randomly inserted at a rate of one in every 48 hobby and 24 retail packs, this 10-card set features super-heroic players matched with a comic book-style illustration depicting their nicknames.

COMPLETE SET (10)	15.00	40.00
MH1 Frank Thomas	2.00	5.00
MH2 Ken Griffey Jr.	3.00	8.00
MH3 Hideo Nomo	2.00	5.00
MH4 Ozzie Smith	2.00	5.00
MH5 Will Clark	1.25	3.00
MH6 Jack McDowell	.75	2.00
MH7 Andres Galarraga	.75	2.00
MH8 Roger Clemens	4.00	10.00
MH9 Deion Sanders	1.25	3.00
MH10 Mo Vaughn	.75	2.00

1996 Stadium Club Metalists

Randomly inserted in packs at a rate of one in 96 (retail) and one in 48 (hobby), this eight-card set features players with two or more MLB awards and is printed on laser-cut foil board.

COMPLETE SET (8)	15.00	40.00
M1 Jeff Bagwell	1.00	2.50
M2 Barry Bonds	4.00	10.00
M3 Jose Canseco	1.00	2.50
M4 Roger Clemens	3.00	8.00
M5 Dennis Eckersley	.60	1.50
M6 Greg Maddux	2.50	6.00
M7 Cal Ripken	5.00	12.00
M8 Frank Thomas	1.50	4.00

1996 Stadium Club Midsummer Matchups

Randomly inserted at a rate of one in every 48 hobby and 24 retail packs, this 10-card set salutes 1995 National League and American League All-Stars as they are matched back-to-back by position on these two-sided etched foil cards.

COMPLETE SET (10)	25.00	60.00
M1 Hideo Nomo Randy Johnson	2.00	5.00
M2 Mike Piazza Ivan Rodriguez	3.00	8.00
M3 Fred McGriff Frank Thomas	2.00	5.00
M4 Craig Biggio Carlos Baerga	1.25	3.00
M5 Vinny Castilla Wade Boggs	1.25	3.00
M6 Barry Larkin Cal Ripken	6.00	15.00
M7 Barry Bonds Albert Belle	5.00	12.00
M8 Len Dykstra Kenny Lofton	.75	2.00
M9 Tony Gwynn Kirby Puckett	2.50	6.00
M10 Ron Gant Edgar Martinez	1.25	3.00

1996 Stadium Club Power Packed

Randomly inserted in packs at a rate of one in 48, this 15-card set features the biggest, most powerful hitters in the League. Printed on Power Matrix, the cards carry diagrams showing where the players hit the ball over the fence and how far.

COMPLETE SET (15)	25.00	60.00
PP1 Albert Belle	1.00	2.50
PP2 Mark McGwire	6.00	15.00
PP3 Jose Canseco	1.50	4.00
PP4 Mike Piazza	4.00	10.00
PP5 Ron Gant	1.00	2.50
PP6 Ken Griffey Jr.	4.00	10.00
PP7 Mo Vaughn	1.00	2.50
PP8 Cecil Fielder	1.00	2.50
PP9 Tim Salmon	1.50	4.00
PP10 Frank Thomas	2.50	6.00
PP11 Juan Gonzalez	1.00	2.50
PP12 Andres Galarraga	1.00	2.50
PP13 Fred McGriff	1.50	4.00
PP14 Jay Buhner	1.00	2.50
PP15 Dante Bichette	1.00	2.50

1996 Stadium Club Power Streak

Randomly inserted at a rate of one in every 24 hobby packs and 48 retail packs, this 15-card set spotlights baseball's most awesome power hitters and strikeout artists.

COMPLETE SET (15)	25.00	60.00
PS1 Randy Johnson	2.50	6.00
PS2 Hideo Nomo	2.50	6.00
PS3 Albert Belle	1.00	2.50
PS4 Dante Bichette	1.00	2.50
PS5 Jay Buhner	1.00	2.50
PS6 Frank Thomas	2.50	6.00
PS7 Mark McGwire	6.00	15.00
PS8 Rafael Palmeiro	1.50	4.00
PS9 Mo Vaughn	1.00	2.50
PS10 Sammy Sosa	2.50	6.00
PS11 Larry Walker	1.00	2.50
PS12 Gary Gaetti	1.00	2.50
PS13 Tim Salmon	1.50	4.00
PS14 Barry Bonds	6.00	15.00
PS15 Jim Edmonds	1.00	2.50

1996 Stadium Club Prime Cuts

Randomly inserted at a rate of one in every 36 hobby and 72 retail packs, this eight card set this set highlights hitters with the purest swings. The cards are numbered on the back with a "PC" prefix.

COMPLETE SET (8)	20.00	50.00
PC1 Albert Belle	.75	2.00
PC2 Barry Bonds	5.00	12.00
PC3 Ken Griffey Jr.	3.00	8.00
PC4 Tony Gwynn	2.50	6.00
PC5 Edgar Martinez	1.25	3.00
PC6 Rafael Palmeiro	1.25	3.00
PC7 Mike Piazza	3.00	8.00
PC8 Frank Thomas	2.00	5.00

1996 Stadium Club TSC Awards

Randomly inserted in packs at a rate of one in 24 (retail) and one in 48 (hobby), this ten-card set features players whom TSC baseball experts voted to win various awards and is printed on diffraction foil.

COMPLETE SET (10)	15.00	40.00
1 Cal Ripken	5.00	12.00
2 Albert Belle	.60	1.50
3 Tom Glavine	1.00	2.50
4 Jeff Conine	.60	1.50
5 Ken Griffey Jr.	2.50	6.00
6 Hideo Nomo	1.50	4.00
7 Greg Maddux	2.50	6.00
8 Chipper Jones	1.50	4.00
9 Randy Johnson	1.50	4.00
10 Jose Mesa	.60	1.50

1996 Stadium Club Members Only

This 50-card set features color player photos of Topps' selection of 45 (numbers 1-45) of the top 1995 American and National League players. The set includes five Finest Cards (numbers 46-50) which represent Topps' selection of the top rookies from 1995. The backs carry information about the player.

COMP. FACT SET (50)	8.00	20.00
1 Carlos Baerga	.02	.10
2 Derek Bell	.02	.10
3 Albert Belle	.08	.25
4 Dante Bichette	.08	.25
5 Craig Biggio	.15	.40
6 Wade Boggs	.30	.75
7 Barry Bonds	.50	1.25
8 Jay Buhner	.08	.25
9 Vinny Castilla	.08	.25
10 Jeff Conine	.02	.10
11 Jim Edmonds	.25	.60
12 Steve Finley	.08	.25
13 Andres Galarraga	.25	.60
14 Mark Grace	.15	.40
15 Tony Gwynn	.60	1.50
16 Lance Johnson	.02	.10
17 Randy Johnson	.30	.75
18 Eric Karros	.08	.25
19 Chuck Knoblauch	.15	.40
20 Barry Larkin	.25	.60
21 Kenny Lofton	.15	.40
22 Greg Maddux	.75	2.00
23 Edgar Martinez	.15	.40
24 Tino Martinez	.08	.25
25 Mark McGwire	.60	1.50
26 Brian McRae	.02	.10
27 Jose Mesa	.02	.10
28 Eddie Murray	.30	.75
29 Mike Mussina	.25	.60
30 Randy Myers	.02	.10
31 Hideo Nomo	.30	.75
32 Rafael Palmeiro	.30	.75
33 Tony Phillips	.02	.10
34 Mike Piazza	.75	2.00
35 Kirby Puckett	.40	1.00
36 Manny Ramirez	.30	.75
37 Tim Salmon	.15	.40
38 Reggie Sanders	.02	.10
39 Sammy Sosa	.50	1.25
40 Frank Thomas	.30	.75
41 Jim Thome	.30	.75
42 John Valentin	.02	.10
43 Mo Vaughn	.08	.25
44 Quilvio Veras	.02	.10
45 Larry Walker	.30	.75
46 Hideo Nomo FIN	.60	1.50
47 Marty Cordova FIN	.08	.25
48 Chipper Jones FIN	1.25	3.00
49 Garret Anderson FIN	.40	1.00
50 Andy Pettitte FIN	.25	.60

1997 Stadium Club

Cards from this 390 card set were distributed in eight-card hobby and retail packs (SRP $3) and 13-card hobby collector packs (SRP $5). Card fronts feature color action player photos printed on 20 pt. card stock with Topps Super Color processing, Hi-gloss laminating, embossing and double foil stamping. The backs carry player information and statistics. In addition to the standard selection of major leaguers, the set contains a 15-card TSC 2000 subset (181-195) featuring a selection of top young prospects. These subset cards were inserted one in every two eight-card first series packs and one per 13-card first series pack. First series cards were released in February, 1997. The 195-card Series two set was issued in six-card retail packs with a suggested retail price of $2 and in nine-card hobby packs with a suggested retail price of $3. The second series set features a 15-card Stadium Sluggers subset (376-390) with an insertion rate of one in every two hobby and three retail Series 2 packs. Second series cards were released in April, 1997. Please note that cards 361 and 374 do not exist. Due to an error at the manufacturer both Mike Sweeney and Tom Pagnozzi had their cards numbered as 274. In addition, Jermaine Dye and Brant Brown both had their cards numbered as 351. These numbering errors were never corrected and no premiums in value are associated.

COMPLETE SET (390)	30.00	80.00
COMP.SERIES 1 (195)	15.00	40.00
COMP.SERIES 2 (195)	15.00	40.00
COMMON (1-180/196-375)	.10	.30
COM.SP (181-195/376-390)	.30	.75
1 Chipper Jones	.30	.75
2 Gary Sheffield	.10	.30
3 Kenny Lofton	.10	.30
4 Brian Jordan	.10	.30
5 Mark McGwire	.75	2.00
6 Charles Nagy	.10	.30
7 Tim Salmon	.20	.50
8 Cal Ripken	1.00	2.50
9 Jeff Conine	.10	.30
10 Paul Molitor	.10	.30
11 Mariano Rivera	.30	.75
12 Pedro Martinez	.20	.50
13 Jeff Bagwell	.20	.50
14 Bobby Bonilla	.10	.30
15 Barry Bonds	.75	2.00
16 Ryan Klesko	.10	.30
17 Barry Larkin	.20	.50
18 Jim Thome	.20	.50
19 Jay Buhner	.10	.30
20 Juan Gonzalez	.10	.30
21 Mike Mussina	.20	.50
22 Kevin Appier	.10	.30
23 Eric Karros	.10	.30
24 Steve Finley	.10	.30
25 Ed Sprague	.10	.30
26 Bernard Gilkey	.10	.30
27 Tony Phillips	.10	.30
28 Henry Rodriguez	.10	.30
29 John Smoltz	.20	.50
30 Dante Bichette	.10	.30
31 Mike Piazza	.50	1.25
32 Paul O'Neill	.20	.50
33 Billy Wagner	.10	.30
34 Reggie Sanders	.10	.30
35 John Jaha	.10	.30
36 Eddie Murray	.30	.75
37 Eric Young	.10	.30
38 Roberto Hernandez	.10	.30
39 Pat Hentgen	.10	.30
40 Sammy Sosa	.30	.75
41 Todd Hundley	.10	.30
42 Mo Vaughn	.10	.30
43 Robin Ventura	.10	.30
44 Mark Grudzielanek	.10	.30
45 Shane Reynolds	.10	.30
46 Andy Pettitte	.20	.50
47 Fred McGriff	.20	.50
48 Rey Ordonez	.10	.30
49 Will Clark	.20	.50
50 Ken Griffey Jr.	.50	1.25
51 Todd Worrell	.10	.30
52 Rusty Greer	.10	.30
53 Mark Grace	.20	.50
54 Tom Glavine	.20	.50
55 Derek Jeter	.75	2.00
56 Rafael Palmeiro	.20	.50
57 Bernie Williams	.20	.50
58 Marty Cordova	.10	.30
59 Andres Galarraga	.10	.30
60 Ken Caminiti	.10	.30
61 Garret Anderson	.10	.30
62 Denny Martinez	.10	.30
63 Mike Greenwell	.10	.30
64 David Segui	.10	.30
65 Julio Franco	.10	.30
66 Rickey Henderson	.30	.75
67 Ozzie Guillen	.10	.30
68 Pete Harnisch	.10	.30
69 Chan Ho Park	.10	.30
70 Harold Baines	.10	.30
71 Mark Clark	.10	.30
72 Steve Avery	.10	.30
73 Brian Hunter	.10	.30
74 Pedro Astacio	.10	.30
75 Jack McDowell	.10	.30
76 Gregg Jefferies	.10	.30
77 Jason Kendall	.10	.30
78 Todd Walker	.10	.30
79 B.J. Surhoff	.10	.30
80 Moises Alou	.10	.30
81 Fernando Vina	.10	.30
82 Darryl Strawberry	.10	.30
83 Jose Rosado	.10	.30
84 Chris Gomez	.10	.30
85 Chili Davis	.10	.30
86 Alan Benes	.10	.30
87 Todd Hollandsworth	.10	.30
88 Jose Vizcaino	.10	.30
89 Edgardo Alfonzo	.10	.30
90 Ruben Rivera	.10	.30
91 Donovan Osborne	.10	.30
92 Doug Glanville	.10	.30
93 Gary DiSarcina	.10	.30
94 Brooks Kieschnick	.10	.30
95 Bobby Jones	.10	.30
96 Raul Casanova	.10	.30
97 Jermaine Allensworth	.10	.30
98 Kenny Rogers	.10	.30
99 Mark McLemore	.10	.30
100 Jeff Fassero	.10	.30
101 Sandy Alomar Jr.	.10	.30
102 Chuck Finley	.10	.30
103 Eric Owens	.10	.30
104 Billy McMillon	.10	.30
105 Dwight Gooden	.10	.30
106 Sterling Hitchcock	.10	.30
107 Doug Drabek	.10	.30
108 Paul Wilson	.10	.30
109 Chris Snopek	.10	.30
110 Al Leiter	.10	.30
111 Bob Tewksbury	.10	.30
112 Todd Greene	.10	.30
113 Jose Valentin	.10	.30
114 Delino DeShields	.10	.30
115 Mike Bordick	.10	.30
116 Pat Meares	.10	.30
117 Mariano Duncan	.10	.30
118 Steve Trachsel	.10	.30
119 Luis Castillo	.10	.30
120 Andy Benes	.10	.30
121 Donne Wall	.10	.30
122 Alex Gonzalez	.10	.30
123 Dan Wilson	.10	.30
124 Omar Vizquel	.20	.50
125 Devon White	.10	.30
126 Darryl Hamilton	.10	.30
127 Orlando Merced	.10	.30
128 Royce Clayton	.10	.30
129 W.VanLandingham	.10	.30
130 Terry Steinbach	.10	.30
131 Jeff Blauser	.10	.30
132 Jeff Cirillo	.10	.30
133 Roger Pavlik	.10	.30
134 Danny Tartabull	.10	.30
135 Jeff Montgomery	.10	.30
136 Bobby Higginson	.10	.30
137 Mike Grace	.10	.30
138 Kevin Elster	.10	.30
139 Brian Giles RC	.60	1.50
140 Rod Beck	.10	.30
141 Ismael Valdes	.10	.30
142 Scott Brosius	.10	.30
143 Mike Fetters	.10	.30
144 Gary Gaetti	.10	.30
145 Mike Lansing	.10	.30
146 Glenallen Hill	.10	.30
147 Shawn Green	.10	.30
148 Mel Rojas	.10	.30
149 Joey Cora	.10	.30
150 John Smiley	.10	.30
151 Marvin Benard	.10	.30
152 Curt Schilling	.10	.30
153 Dave Nilsson	.10	.30
154 Edgar Renteria	.10	.30
155 Joey Hamilton	.10	.30
156 Carlos Garcia	.10	.30
157 Nomar Garciaparra	.50	1.25
158 Kevin Ritz	.10	.30
159 Keith Lockhart	.10	.30
160 Justin Thompson	.10	.30
161 Terry Adams	.10	.30
162 Jamey Wright	.10	.30
163 Otis Nixon	.10	.30
164 Michael Tucker	.10	.30
165 Mike Stanley	.10	.30
166 Ben McDonald	.10	.30
167 John Mabry	.10	.30
168 Troy O'Leary	.10	.30
169 Mel Nieves	.10	.30
170 Bret Boone	.10	.30
171 Mike Timlin	.10	.30
172 Scott Rolen	.20	.50
173 Reggie Jefferson	.10	.30
174 Neifi Perez	.10	.30
175 Brian McRae	.10	.30
176 Tom Goodwin	.10	.30
177 Aaron Sele	.10	.30
178 Benito Santiago	.10	.30
179 Frank Rodriguez	.10	.30
180 Eric Davis	.10	.30
181 A.Jones 2000 SP	.30	.75
182 Todd Walker 2000 SP	.30	.75
183 Wes Helms 2000 SP	.30	.75
184 Nelson Figueroa 2000 SP RC	.30	.75
185 V. Guerrero 2000 SP	.50	1.25
186 B.McMillon 2000 SP	.30	.75
187 Todd Helton 2000 SP	.50	1.25
188 Nomar Garciaparra 2000 SP	1.00	2.50
189 K. Maeda 2000 SP	.30	.75
190 R.Branyan 2000 SP	.30	.75
191 G.Rusch 2000 SP	.30	.75
192 B.Colon 2000 SP	.30	.75
193 Scott Rolen 2000 SP	.30	.75
194 A. Echevarria 2000 SP	.30	.75
195 Bob Abreu 2000 SP	.30	.75
196 Greg Maddux	.50	1.25
197 Joe Carter	.10	.30
198 Alex Ochoa	.10	.30
199 Ellis Burks	.10	.30
200 Ivan Rodriguez	.20	.50
201 Marquis Grissom	.10	.30
202 Trevor Hoffman	.10	.30
203 Matt Williams	.10	.30
204 Carlos Delgado	.10	.30
205 Ramon Martinez	.10	.30
206 Chuck Knoblauch	.10	.30
207 Juan Guzman	.10	.30
208 Derek Bell	.10	.30
209 Roger Clemens	.60	1.50
210 Vladimir Guerrero	.30	.75
211 Cecil Fielder	.10	.30
212 Hideo Nomo	.30	.75
213 Frank Thomas	.30	.75
214 Greg Vaughn	.10	.30
215 Javy Lopez	.10	.30
216 Raul Mondesi	.10	.30
217 Wade Boggs	.20	.50
218 Carlos Baerga	.10	.30
219 Tony Gwynn	.40	1.00
220 Tino Martinez	.20	.50
221 Vinny Castilla	.10	.30
222 Lance Johnson	.10	.30
223 David Justice	.10	.30
224 Rondell White	.10	.30
225 Dean Palmer	.10	.30
226 Jim Edmonds	.10	.30
227 Albert Belle	.10	.30
228 Alex Fernandez	.10	.30
229 Ryne Sandberg	.50	1.25
230 Jose Mesa	.10	.30
231 David Cone	.10	.30
232 Troy Percival	.10	.30
233 Edgar Martinez	.20	.50
234 Jose Canseco	.20	.50
235 Kevin Brown	.10	.30
236 Ray Lankford	.10	.30
237 Karim Garcia	.10	.30
238 J.T. Snow	.10	.30
239 Dennis Eckersley	.10	.30
240 Roberto Alomar	.20	.50
241 John Valentin	.10	.30
242 Ron Gant	.10	.30
243 Geronimo Berroa	.10	.30
244 Manny Ramirez	.20	.50
245 Travis Fryman	.10	.30
246 Denny Neagle	.10	.30
247 Randy Johnson	.30	.75
248 Darin Erstad	.10	.30
249 Mark Wohlers	.10	.30
250 Ken Hill	.10	.30
251 Larry Walker	.10	.30
252 Craig Biggio	.20	.50
253 Brady Anderson	.10	.30
254 John Wetteland	.10	.30
255 Andruw Jones	.20	.50
256 Turk Wendell	.10	.30
257 Jason Isringhausen	.10	.30
258 Jaime Navarro	.10	.30
259 Sean Berry	.10	.30
260 Albie Lopez	.10	.30
261 Jay Bell	.10	.30
262 Bobby Witt	.10	.30
263 Tony Clark	.10	.30
264 Tim Wakefield	.10	.30
265 Brad Radke	.10	.30
266 Tim Belcher	.10	.30
267 Nerio Rodriguez RC	.10	.30
268 Roger Cedeno	.10	.30
269 Tim Naehring	.10	.30
270 Kevin Tapani	.10	.30
271 Joe Randa	.10	.30
272 Randy Myers	.10	.30
273 Dave Burba	.10	.30
274 Mike Sweeney	.10	.30
275 Danny Graves	.10	.30
276 Chad Mottola	.10	.30
277 Ruben Sierra	.10	.30
278 Norm Charlton	.10	.30
279 Scott Servais	.10	.30
280 Jacob Cruz	.10	.30
281 Mike Macfarlane	.10	.30
282 Rich Becker	.10	.30
283 Shannon Stewart	.10	.30
284 Gerald Williams	.10	.30
285 Jody Reed	.10	.30
286 Jeff D'Amico	.10	.30
287 Walt Weiss	.10	.30
288 Jim Leyritz	.10	.30
289 Francisco Cordova	.10	.30
290 F.P. Santangelo	.10	.30
291 Scott Erickson	.10	.30
292 Hal Morris	.10	.30
293 Ray Durham	.10	.30
294 Andy Ashby	.10	.30
295 Darryl Kile	.10	.30
296 Jose Paniagua	.10	.30
297 Mickey Tettleton	.10	.30
298 Joe Girardi	.10	.30
299 Rocky Coppinger	.10	.30
300 Bob Abreu	.20	.50
301 John Olerud	.10	.30
302 Paul Shuey	.10	.30
303 Jeff Brantley	.10	.30
304 Bob Wells	.10	.30
305 Kevin Seitzer	.10	.30
306 Shawon Dunston	.10	.30
307 Jose Herrera	.10	.30
308 Butch Huskey	.10	.30
309 Jose Offerman	.10	.30
310 Rick Aguilera	.10	.30
311 Greg Gagne	.10	.30
312 John Burkett	.10	.30
313 Mark Thompson	.10	.30
314 Alvaro Espinoza	.10	.30
315 Todd Stottlemyre	.10	.30
316 Al Martin	.10	.30
317 James Baldwin	.10	.30
318 Cal Eldred	.10	.30
319 Sid Fernandez	.10	.30
320 Mickey Morandini	.10	.30
321 Robb Nen	.10	.30
322 Mark Lemke	.10	.30
323 Pete Schourek	.10	.30
324 Marcus Jensen	.10	.30
325 Rich Aurilia	.10	.30
326 Jeff King	.10	.30
327 Scott Stahoviak	.10	.30
328 Ricky Otero	.10	.30
329 Antonio Osuna	.10	.30
330 Chris Hoiles	.10	.30
331 Luis Gonzalez	.10	.30
332 Wil Cordero	.10	.30
333 Johnny Damon	.20	.50
334 Mark Langston	.10	.30
335 Orlando Miller	.10	.30
336 Jason Giambi	.10	.30
337 Damian Jackson	.10	.30
338 David Wells	.10	.30
339 Bip Roberts	.10	.30
340 Matt Ruebel	.10	.30
341 Tom Candiotti	.10	.30
342 Wally Joyner	.10	.30
343 Jimmy Key	.10	.30
344 Tony Batista	.10	.30
345 Paul Sorrento	.10	.30
346 Ron Karkovice	.10	.30
347 Wilson Alvarez	.10	.30
348 John Flaherty	.10	.30
349 Rey Sanchez	.10	.30
350 John Vander Wal	.10	.30
351 Jermaine Dye	.10	.30
352 Mike Hampton	.10	.30
353 Greg Colbrunn	.10	.30
354 Heathcliff Slocumb	.10	.30
355 Ricky Bottalico	.10	.30
356 Marty Janzen	.10	.30
357 Orel Hershiser	.10	.30
358 Rex Hudler	.10	.30
359 Amaury Telemaco	.10	.30
360 Darrin Fletcher	.10	.30
361 Brant Brown UER Card numbered 351	.10	.30
362 Russ Davis	.10	.30
363 Allen Watson	.10	.30
364 Mike Lieberthal	.10	.30
365 Dave Stevens	.10	.30
366 Jay Powell	.10	.30
367 Tony Fossas	.10	.30
368 Bob Wolcott	.10	.30
369 Mark Loretta	.10	.30
370 Shawn Estes	.10	.30
371 Sandy Martinez	.10	.30
372 Wendell Magee Jr.	.10	.30
373 John Franco	.10	.30
374 Tom Pagnozzi UER misnumbered as 274	.10	.30
375 Willie Adams	.10	.30
376 Chipper Jones SS SP	.50	1.25
377 Mo Vaughn SS SP	.30	.75
378 Frank Thomas SS SP	.50	1.25
379 Albert Belle SS SP	.30	.75
380 A.Galarraga SS SP	.30	.75
381 Gary Sheffield SS SP	.30	.75
382 Jeff Bagwell SS SP	.30	.75
383 Mike Piazza SS SP	1.00	2.50
384 Mark McGwire SS SP	1.50	4.00
385 Ken Griffey Jr. SS SP	1.00	2.50
386 Barry Bonds SS SP	1.50	4.00
387 Juan Gonzalez SS SP	.30	.75
388 B.Anderson SS SP	.30	.75
389 Ken Caminiti SS SP	.30	.75
390 Jay Buhner SS SP	.30	.75

1997 Stadium Club Matrix

Randomly inserted in first and second series eight-card packs at a rate of one in 12 and in 13-card packs at a rate of one in six, this 120-card set is parallel to the first 60 cards of both the series one and series two of the regular set. Each Matrix card was reproduced with Power Matrix technology, giving the card fronts a glittering effect.

*STARS: 4X TO 10X BASIC CARDS

1997 Stadium Club Members Only Parallel

These cards are a parallel issue to the 1997 Stadium Club Series one and Series two sets and the following insert sets: Millennium, Instavision, Firebrand, and Pure Gold. No first series Co-Signers insert cards are in this set, but it does contain the second series Patent Leather insert set. The only difference between the regular issue cards and these parallels are the words "TSC Members Only" printed lightly in the background. The cards all come together in factory set form and one must be a member of Topps Stadium Club to order these cards.

COMP.FACT SET (497)	160.00	400.00
COMP.SERIES 1 (235)	80.00	200.00
COMP.SERIES 2 (242)	80.00	200.00
COMMON CARD (1-390)	.10	.25
*MEMBERS ONLY: 6X BASIC CARDS		
I1 Eddie Murray	1.50	4.00
I2 Paul Molitor	1.50	4.00
I3 Todd Hundley	.75	2.00
I4 Roger Clemens	4.00	10.00
I5 Barry Bonds	2.00	5.00
I6 Mark McGwire	10.00	25.00
I7 Brady Anderson	.75	2.00
I8 Barry Larkin	1.50	4.00
I9 Ken Caminiti	1.25	3.00
I10 Hideo Nomo	1.50	4.00
I11 Bernie Williams	1.50	4.00
I12 Juan Gonzalez	1.50	4.00
I13 Andy Pettitte	1.25	3.00
I14 Albert Belle	.75	2.00
I15 John Smoltz	.75	2.00
I16 Brian Jordan	.40	1.00
I17 Derek Jeter	10.00	25.00
I18 Ken Caminiti	.75	2.00
I19 John Wetteland	.75	2.00
I20 Brady Anderson	.75	2.00
I21 Andruw Jones	2.00	5.00
I22 Jim Leyritz	.40	1.00
M1 Derek Jeter	10.00	25.00
M2 Mark Grudzielanek	.75	2.00
M3 Jacob Cruz	.40	1.00
M4 Ray Durham	1.25	3.00
M5 Tony Clark	.75	2.00
M6 Chipper Jones	5.00	12.00
M7 Luis Castillo	.75	2.00
M8 Carlos Delgado	2.00	5.00
M9 Brant Brown	.40	1.00
M10 Jason Kendall	1.25	3.00
M11 Alan Benes	.40	1.00
M12 Rey Ordonez	.40	1.00
M13 Justin Thompson	.40	1.00
M14 J.Allensworth	.40	1.00
M15 Brian L. Hunter	.40	1.00
M16 Marty Cordova	.40	1.00
M17 Edgar Renteria	.40	1.00
M18 Karim Garcia	.40	1.00
M19 Todd Greene	.40	1.00
M20 Paul Wilson	.40	1.00
M21 Andruw Jones	2.00	5.00
M22 Todd Walker	.40	1.00
M23 Alex Ochoa	.40	1.00

M24 Bartolo Colon 1.50 4.00
M25 Wendell Magee Jr. .40 1.00
M26 Jose Rosado .40 1.00
M27 Katsuhiro Maeda .40 1.00
M28 Bob Abreu 1.50 4.00
M29 Brooks Kieschnick .40 1.00
M30 Derrick Gibson .40 1.00
M31 Mike Sweeney 2.00 5.00
M32 Jeff D'Amico .40 1.00
M33 Chad Mottola .40 1.00
M34 Chris Snopek .40 1.00
M35 Jaime Bluma .40 1.00
M36 Vladimir Guerrero 3.00 8.00
M37 Nomar Garciaparra 6.00 15.00
M38 Scott Rolen 1.50 4.00
M39 Dmitri Young .75 2.00
M40 Neifi Perez .40 1.00
FB1 Jeff Bagwell 2.00 5.00
FB2 Albert Belle .75 2.00
FB3 Barry Bonds 5.00 12.00
FB4 Andres Galarraga 1.50 4.00
FB5 Ken Griffey Jr. 8.00 20.00
FB6 Brady Anderson .75 2.00
FB7 Mark McGwire 8.00 20.00
FB8 Chipper Jones 5.00 12.00
FB9 Frank Thomas 3.00 8.00
FB10 Mike Piazza 6.00 15.00
FB11 Mo Vaughn .75 2.00
FB12 Juan Gonzalez 2.00 5.00
PG1 Brady Anderson .75 2.00
PG2 Albert Belle .75 2.00
PG3 Dante Bichette .75 2.00
PG4 Barry Bonds 5.00 12.00
PG5 Jay Buhner .75 2.00
PG6 Tony Gwynn 5.00 12.00
PG7 Chipper Jones 5.00 12.00
PG8 Mark McGwire 8.00 20.00
PG9 Gary Sheffield 1.50 4.00
PG10 Frank Thomas 4.00 10.00
PG11 Juan Gonzalez 2.00 5.00
PG12 Ken Caminiti .75 2.00
PG13 Kenny Lofton .75 2.00
PG14 Jeff Bagwell 2.00 5.00
PG15 Ken Griffey Jr. 8.00 20.00
PG16 Cal Ripken 10.00 25.00
PG17 Mo Vaughn .75 2.00
PG18 Mike Piazza 5.00 12.00
PG19 Derek Jeter 10.00 25.00
PG20 Andres Galarraga 1.50 4.00
PL1 Ivan Rodriguez 2.00 5.00
PL2 Ken Caminiti .75 2.00
PL3 Barry Bonds 5.00 12.00
PL4 Ken Griffey Jr. 8.00 20.00
PL5 Greg Maddux 6.00 15.00
PL6 Craig Biggio 1.25 3.00
PL7 Andres Galarraga 1.50 4.00
PL8 Kenny Lofton .75 2.00
PL9 Barry Larkin 1.50 4.00
PL10 Mark Grace 1.50 4.00
PL11 Rey Ordonez .40 1.00
PL12 Roberto Alomar 1.50 4.00
PL13 Derek Jeter 10.00 25.00

1997 Stadium Club Co-Signers

Randomly inserted in first series eight-card hobby packs at a rate of one in 168 and first series 13-card hobby collector packs at a rate of one in 96, cards (CO1-CO5) from this dual-sided, dual-player set feature color action player photos printed on 20pt. card stock with authentic signatures of two major league stand-outs per card. The last five cards (CO6-CO10) were randomly inserted in second series 10-card hobby packs with a rate of one in 168 and inserted with a rate of one in 96 Hobby Collector packs.

CO1 Andy Pettitte 75.00 150.00
Derek Jeter
CO2 Paul Wilson 6.00 15.00
Todd Hundley
CO3 Jermaine Dye 6.00 15.00
Mark Wohlers
CO4 Scott Rolen 8.00 20.00
Gregg Jefferies
CO5 Todd Hollandsworth 6.00 15.00
Jason Kendall
CO6 Alan Benes 6.00 15.00
Robin Ventura
CO7 Eric Karros 6.00 15.00
Raul Mondesi
CO8 Rey Ordonez 40.00 80.00
Nomar Garciaparra
CO9 Rondell White 6.00 15.00
Marty Cordova
CO10 Tony Gwynn 12.50 30.00
Karim Garcia

1997 Stadium Club Firebrand Redemption

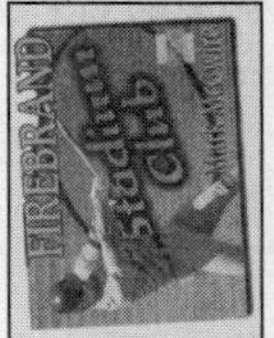

Randomly inserted exclusively into first series eight-card retail packs at a rate of one in 36, these redemption cards feature a selection of the leagues top sluggers. Due to circumstances beyond the manufacturers control, they were not able to insert the actual etched-wood cards into packs and had to resort to these redemption cards.

*WOOD: 5X TO 1.2X BASIC FIREBRAND
ONE WOOD CARD VIA MAIL PER EXCH.CARD
F1 Jeff Bagwell 1.50 4.00
F2 Albert Belle 1.00 2.50
F3 Barry Bonds 6.00 15.00
F4 Andres Galarraga 1.00 2.50
F5 Ken Griffey Jr. 4.00 10.00
F6 Brady Anderson 1.00 2.50
F7 Mark McGwire 6.00 15.00
F8 Chipper Jones 2.50 6.00
F9 Frank Thomas 2.50 6.00
F10 Mike Piazza 4.00 10.00
F11 Mo Vaughn 1.00 2.50
F12 Juan Gonzalez 1.00 2.50

1997 Stadium Club Instavision

The first ten cards of this 22-card set were randomly inserted in first series eight-card packs at a rate of one in 24 and first series 13-card packs at a rate of 1:12. The last 12 cards were inserted in series two packs at the rate of one in 24 and one in 12 in hobby collector packs. The set highlights some of the 1996 season's most exciting moments through exclusive holographic video action.

COMPLETE SET (22) 20.00 50.00
COMPLETE SERIES 1 (10) 10.00 25.00
COMPLETE SERIES 2 (12) 10.00 25.00
I1 Eddie Murray 1.50 4.00
I2 Paul Molitor .60 1.50
I3 Todd Hundley .60 1.50
I4 Roger Clemens 3.00 8.00
I5 Barry Bonds 4.00 10.00
I6 Mark McGwire 4.00 10.00
I7 Brady Anderson .60 1.50
I8 Barry Larkin 1.00 2.50
I9 Ken Caminiti .60 1.50
I10 Hideo Nomo 1.50 4.00
I11 Bernie Williams 1.00 2.50
I12 Juan Gonzalez .60 1.50
I13 Andy Pettitte 1.00 2.50
I14 Albert Belle .60 1.50
I15 John Smoltz 1.00 2.50
I16 Brian Jordan .60 1.50
I17 Derek Jeter 4.00 10.00
I18 Ken Caminiti .60 1.50
I19 John Wetteland .60 1.50
I20 Brady Anderson .60 1.50
I21 Andruw Jones 1.00 2.50
I22 Jim Leyritz .60 1.50

1997 Stadium Club Millennium

Randomly inserted in first and second series eight-card packs at a rate of one in 24 and 13-card packs at a rate of 1:12, this 40-card set features color player photos of breakthrough stars of Major League Baseball reproduced using state-of-the-art advanced embossed holographic technology.

COMPLETE SET (40) 50.00 130.00
COMPLETE SERIES 1 (20) 20.00 50.00
COMPLETE SERIES 2 (20) 30.00 80.00
M1 Derek Jeter 8.00 20.00
M2 Mark Grudzielanek .60 1.50
M3 Jacob Cruz .60 1.50
M4 Ray Durham 1.00 2.50
M5 Tony Clark .60 1.50
M6 Chipper Jones 2.50 6.00
M7 Luis Castillo .60 1.50
M8 Carlos Delgado 1.00 2.50
M9 Brant Brown .60 1.50
M10 Jason Kendall 1.00 2.50
M11 Alan Benes .60 1.50
M12 Rey Ordonez .60 1.50
M13 Justin Thompson .60 1.50
M14 J.Allensworth .60 1.50
M15 Brian Hunter .60 1.50
M16 Marty Cordova .60 1.50
M17 Edgar Renteria 1.00 2.50
M18 Karim Garcia .60 1.50
M19 Todd Greene .60 1.50
M20 Paul Wilson .60 1.50
M21 Andruw Jones 1.50 4.00
M22 Todd Walker .60 1.50
M23 Alex Ochoa .60 1.50
M24 Bartolo Colon 1.00 2.50
M25 Wendell Magee Jr. .60 1.50
M26 Jose Rosado .60 1.50
M27 Katsuhiro Maeda .60 1.50
M28 Bob Abreu .60 1.50
M29 Brooks Kieschnick .60 1.50
M30 Derrick Gibson .60 1.50
M31 Mike Sweeney 1.00 2.50
M32 Jeff D'Amico .60 1.50
M33 Chad Mottola .60 1.50
M34 Chris Snopek .60 1.50
M35 Jaime Bluma .60 1.50
M36 Vladimir Guerrero 2.50 6.00
M37 Nomar Garciaparra 5.00 12.00
M38 Scott Rolen 1.50 4.00
M39 Dmitri Young 1.00 2.50
M40 Neifi Perez .60 1.50

1997 Stadium Club Patent Leather

Randomly inserted in second series retail packs only at a rate of one in 36, this 13-card set features action player images standing in a baseball glove and with an inner die-cut glove background printed on leather card stock.

COMPLETE SET (13) 50.00 120.00
PL1 Ivan Rodriguez 2.50 6.00
PL2 Ken Caminiti 1.50 4.00
PL3 Barry Bonds 10.00 25.00
PL4 Ken Griffey Jr. 6.00 15.00
PL5 Greg Maddux 6.00 15.00
PL6 Craig Biggio 2.50 6.00
PL7 Andres Galarraga 1.50 4.00
PL8 Kenny Lofton 1.50 4.00
PL9 Barry Larkin 2.50 6.00
PL10 Mark Grace 2.50 6.00
PL11 Rey Ordonez 1.50 4.00
PL12 Roberto Alomar 2.50 6.00
PL13 Derek Jeter 10.00 25.00

1997 Stadium Club Pure Gold

Randomly inserted in first and second series eight-card packs at a rate of one in 72 and 13-card packs at a rate of one in 36, this 20-card set features color action star player photos reproduced on 20 pt. embossed gold mirror foilboard.

COMPLETE SERIES 1 (10) 50.00 120.00
COMPLETE SERIES 2 (10) 80.00 200.00
PG1 Brady Anderson 1.25 3.00
PG2 Albert Belle 1.25 3.00
PG3 Dante Bichette 1.25 3.00
PG4 Barry Bonds 8.00 20.00
PG5 Jay Buhner 1.25 3.00
PG6 Tony Gwynn 4.00 10.00
PG7 Chipper Jones 3.00 8.00
PG8 Mark McGwire 8.00 20.00
PG9 Gary Sheffield 1.25 3.00
PG10 Frank Thomas 3.00 8.00
PG11 Juan Gonzalez 1.25 3.00
PG12 Ken Caminiti 1.25 3.00
PG13 Kenny Lofton 1.25 3.00
PG14 Jeff Bagwell 2.00 5.00
PG15 Ken Griffey Jr. 5.00 12.00
PG16 Cal Ripken 10.00 25.00
PG17 Mo Vaughn 1.25 3.00
PG18 Mike Piazza 5.00 12.00
PG19 Derek Jeter 8.00 20.00
PG20 Andres Galarraga 1.25 3.00

1998 Stadium Club

The 1998 Stadium Club set was issued in two separate 200-card series and distributed in six-card retail packs for $2, nine-card hobby packs for $3, and 15-card Home Team Advantage packs for $5. The card fronts feature action color player photos with player information displayed on the backs. The series one set included odd numbered cards only and series two included even numbered cards only. The set contains the topical subsets: Future Stars (odd-numbered 361-379), Draft Picks (odd-numbered 381-399) and Traded (even-numbered 356-400). Two separate Cal Ripken Sound Chip cards were distributed as chiptoppers in Home Team Advantage boxes. The second series features a 23-card Transaction subset (356-400). Second series cards were released in April, 1998. Rookie Cards include Jack Cust, Kevin Millwood and Magglio Ordonez.

COMPLETE SET (400) 30.00 80.00
COMP.SERIES 1 (200) 15.00 40.00
COMP.SERIES 2 (200) 15.00 40.00
1 Chipper Jones .30 .75
2 Frank Thomas .30 .75
3 Vladimir Guerrero .30 .75
4 Ellis Burks .10 .30
5 John Franco .10 .30
6 Paul Molitor .10 .30
7 Rusty Greer .10 .30
8 Todd Hundley .10 .30
9 Brett Tomko .10 .30
10 Eric Karros .10 .30
11 Mike Cameron .10 .30
12 Jim Edmonds .10 .30
13 Bernie Williams .20 .50
14 Denny Neagle .10 .30
15 Jason Dickson .10 .30
16 Sammy Sosa .30 .75
17 Brian Jordan .10 .30
18 Jose Vidro .10 .30
19 Scott Spiezio .10 .30
20 Jay Buhner .10 .30
21 Jim Thome .20 .50
22 Sandy Alomar Jr. .10 .30
23 Livan Hernandez .10 .30
24 Roberto Alomar .20 .50
25 Chris Gomez .10 .30
26 John Wetteland .10 .30
27 Willie Greene .10 .30
28 Gregg Jefferies .10 .30
29 Johnny Damon .20 .50
30 Barry Larkin .20 .50
31 Chuck Knoblauch .10 .30
32 Mo Vaughn .10 .30
33 Tony Clark .10 .30
34 Marty Cordova .10 .30
35 Vinny Castilla .10 .30
36 Jeff King .10 .30
37 Reggie Jefferson .10 .30
38 Mariano Rivera .30 .75
39 Jermaine Allensworth .10 .30
40 Livan Hernandez .10 .30
41 Heathcliff Slocumb .10 .30
42 Jacob Cruz .10 .30
43 Barry Bonds .75 2.00
44 Dave Magadan .10 .30
45 Chan Ho Park .10 .30
46 Jeremi Gonzalez .10 .30
47 Jeff Cirillo .10 .30
48 Delino DeShields .10 .30
49 Craig Biggio .20 .50
50 Benito Santiago .10 .30
51 Mark Clark .10 .30
52 Fernando Vina .10 .30
53 F.P. Santangelo .10 .30
54 Pep Harris .10 .30
55 Edgar Renteria .10 .30
56 Jeff Bagwell .20 .50
57 Jimmy Key .10 .30
58 Bartolo Colon .10 .30
59 Curt Schilling .10 .30
60 Steve Finley .10 .30
61 Andy Ashby .10 .30
62 John Burkett .10 .30
63 Orel Hershiser .10 .30
64 Pokey Reese .10 .30
65 Scott Servais .10 .30
66 Todd Jones .10 .30
67 Javy Lopez .10 .30
68 Robin Ventura .10 .30
69 Miguel Tejada .30 .75
70 Raul Casanova .10 .30
71 Reggie Sanders .10 .30
72 Edgardo Alfonzo .10 .30
73 Dean Palmer .10 .30
74 Todd Stottlemyre .10 .30
75 David Wells .10 .30
76 Troy Percival .10 .30
77 Albert Belle .10 .30
78 Pat Hentgen .10 .30
79 Brian Hunter .10 .30
80 Richard Hidalgo .10 .30
81 Darren Oliver .10 .30
82 Mark Wohlers .10 .30
83 Cal Ripken 1.00 2.50
84 Hideo Nomo .30 .75
85 Derrek Lee .20 .50
86 Stan Javier .10 .30
87 Rey Ordonez .10 .30
88 Randy Johnson .30 .75
89 Jeff Kent .10 .30
90 Brian McRae .10 .30
91 Manny Ramirez .20 .50
92 Trevor Hoffman .10 .30
93 Doug Glanville .10 .30
94 Todd Walker .10 .30
95 Andy Benes .10 .30
96 Jason Schmidt .10 .30
97 Mike Matheny .10 .30
98 Tim Naehring .10 .30
99 Keith Lockhart .10 .30
100 Jose Rosado .10 .30
101 Roger Clemens .60 1.50
102 Pedro Astacio .10 .30
103 Mark Bellhorn .10 .30
104 Paul O'Neill .20 .50
105 Darin Erstad .10 .30
106 Mike Lieberthal .10 .30
107 Wilson Alvarez .10 .30
108 Mike Mussina .20 .50
109 George Williams .10 .30
110 Cliff Floyd .10 .30
111 Shawn Estes .10 .30
112 Mark Grudzielanek .10 .30
113 Tony Gwynn .40 1.00
114 Alan Benes .10 .30
115 Terry Steinbach .10 .30
116 Greg Maddux .50 1.25
117 Andy Pettitte .20 .50
118 Dave Nilsson .10 .30
119 Deivi Cruz .10 .30
120 Carlos Delgado .10 .30
121 Scott Hatteberg .10 .30
122 John Olerud .10 .30
123 Todd Dunwoody .10 .30
124 Garret Anderson .10 .30
125 Royce Clayton .10 .30
126 Dante Powell .10 .30
127 Tom Glavine .20 .50
128 Gary DiSarcina .10 .30
129 Terry Adams .10 .30
130 Raul Mondesi .10 .30
131 Dan Wilson .10 .30
132 Al Martin .10 .30
133 Mickey Morandini .10 .30
134 Rafael Palmeiro .20 .50
135 Juan Encarnacion .10 .30
136 Jim Pittsley .10 .30
137 Magglio Ordonez RC 1.25 3.00
138 Will Clark .20 .50
139 Todd Helton .20 .50
140 Kelvim Escobar .10 .30
141 Esteban Loaiza .10 .30
142 John Jaha .10 .30
143 Jeff Fassero .10 .30
144 Harold Baines .10 .30
145 Butch Huskey .10 .30
146 Pat Meares .10 .30
147 Brian Giles .10 .30
148 Ramiro Mendoza .10 .30
149 John Smoltz .20 .50
150 Felix Martinez .10 .30
151 Jose Valentin .10 .30
152 Brad Rigby .10 .30
153 Ed Sprague .10 .30
154 Mike Hampton .10 .30
155 Carlos Perez .10 .30
156 Ray Lankford .10 .30
157 Bobby Bonilla .10 .30
158 Bill Mueller .10 .30
159 Jeffrey Hammonds .10 .30
160 Charles Nagy .10 .30
161 Rich Loiselle RC .10 .30
162 Al Leiter .10 .30
163 Larry Walker .10 .30
164 Chris Hoiles .10 .30
165 Jeff Montgomery .10 .30
166 Francisco Cordova .10 .30
167 James Baldwin .10 .30
168 Mark McLemore .10 .30
169 Kevin Appier .10 .30
170 Jamey Wright .10 .30
171 Nomar Garciaparra .50 1.25
172 Matt Franco .10 .30
173 Armando Benitez .10 .30
174 Jeromy Burnitz .10 .30
175 Ismael Valdes .10 .30
176 Lance Johnson .10 .30
177 Paul Sorrento .10 .30
178 Rondell White .10 .30
179 Kevin Elster .10 .30
180 Jason Giambi .10 .30
181 Carlos Baerga .10 .30
182 Russ Davis .10 .30
183 Ryan McGuire .10 .30
184 Eric Young .10 .30
185 Ron Gant .10 .30
186 Manny Alexander .10 .30
187 Scott Karl .10 .30
188 Brady Anderson .10 .30
189 Randall Simon .10 .30
190 Tim Belcher .10 .30
191 Jaret Wright .10 .30
192 Dante Bichette .10 .30
193 John Valentin .10 .30
194 Darren Bragg .10 .30
195 Mike Sweeney .10 .30
196 Craig Counsell .10 .30
197 Jaime Navarro .10 .30
198 Todd Dunn .10 .30
199 Ken Griffey Jr. .50 1.25
200 Juan Gonzalez .10 .30
201 Billy Wagner .10 .30
202 Tino Martinez .20 .50
203 Mark McGwire .75 2.00
204 Jeff D'Amico .10 .30
205 Rico Brogna .10 .30
206 Todd Hollandsworth .10 .30
207 Chad Curtis .10 .30
208 Tom Goodwin .10 .30
209 Neifi Perez .10 .30
210 Derek Bell .10 .30
211 Quilvio Veras .10 .30
212 Greg Vaughn .10 .30
213 Kirk Rueter .10 .30
214 Arthur Rhodes .10 .30
215 Cal Eldred .10 .30
216 Bill Taylor .10 .30
217 Todd Greene .10 .30
218 Mario Valdez .10 .30
219 Ricky Bottalico .10 .30
220 Frank Rodriguez .10 .30
221 Rich Becker .10 .30
222 Roberto Duran RC .10 .30
223 Ivan Rodriguez .20 .50
224 Mike Jackson .10 .30
225 Deion Sanders .20 .50
226 Tony Womack .10 .30
227 Mark Kotsay .10 .30
228 Steve Trachsel .10 .30
229 Ryan Klesko .10 .30
230 Ken Cloude .10 .30
231 Luis Gonzalez .10 .30
232 Gary Gaetti .10 .30
233 Michael Tucker .10 .30
234 Shawn Green .10 .30
235 Ariel Prieto .10 .30
236 Kirt Manwaring .10 .30
237 Omar Vizquel .20 .50
238 Matt Beech .10 .30
239 Justin Thompson .10 .30
240 Bret Boone .10 .30
241 Derek Jeter .75 2.00
242 Ken Caminiti .10 .30
243 Jose Offerman .10 .30
244 Kevin Tapani .10 .30
245 Jason Kendall .10 .30
246 Jose Guillen .10 .30
247 Mike Bordick .10 .30
248 Dustin Hermanson .10 .30
249 Darrin Fletcher .10 .30
250 Dave Hollins .10 .30
251 Ramon Martinez .10 .30
252 Hideki Irabu .10 .30
253 Mark Grace .20 .50
254 Jason Isringhausen .10 .30
255 Jose Cruz Jr. .10 .30
256 Brian Johnson .10 .30
257 Brad Ausmus .10 .30
258 Andruw Jones .20 .50
259 Doug Jones .10 .30
260 Jeff Shaw .10 .30
261 Chuck Finley .10 .30
262 Gary Sheffield .10 .30
263 David Segui .10 .30
264 John Smiley .10 .30
265 Tim Salmon .20 .50
266 J.T. Snow .10 .30
267 Alex Fernandez .10 .30
268 Matt Stairs .10 .30
269 B.J. Surhoff .10 .30
270 Keith Foulke .10 .30
271 Edgar Martinez .20 .50
272 Shannon Stewart .10 .30
273 Eduardo Perez .10 .30
274 Wally Joyner .10 .30
275 Kevin Young .10 .30
276 Eli Marrero .10 .30
277 Brad Radke .10 .30
278 Jamie Moyer .10 .30
279 Joe Girardi .10 .30
280 Troy O'Leary .10 .30
281 Jeff Frye .10 .30
282 Jose Offerman .10 .30
283 Scott Erickson .10 .30
284 Sean Berry .10 .30
285 Shigetoshi Hasegawa .10 .30
286 Felix Heredia .10 .30
287 Willie McGee .10 .30
288 Alex Rodriguez .50 1.25
289 Ugueth Urbina .10 .30
290 Jon Lieber .10 .30
291 Fernando Tatis .10 .30
292 Chris Stynes .10 .30
293 Bernard Gilkey .10 .30
294 Joey Hamilton .10 .30
295 Matt Karchner .10 .30
296 Paul Wilson .10 .30
297 Damion Easley .10 .30
298 Kevin Millwood RC .40 1.00
299 Ellis Burks .10 .30
300 Jerry DiPoto .10 .30
301 Jermaine Dye .10 .30
302 Travis Lee .10 .30
303 Ron Coomer .10 .30
304 Matt Williams .10 .30
305 Bobby Higginson .10 .30
306 Jorge Fabregas .10 .30
307 Jon Nunnally .10 .30
308 Jay Bell .10 .30
309 Jason Schmidt .10 .30
310 Andy Benes .10 .30
311 Sterling Hitchcock .10 .30
312 Jeff Suppan .10 .30
313 Shane Reynolds .10 .30
314 Willie Blair .10 .30
315 Scott Rolen .20 .50
316 Wilson Alvarez .10 .30
317 David Justice .10 .30
318 Fred McGriff .20 .50
319 Bobby Jones .10 .30
320 Wade Boggs .20 .50
321 Tim Wakefield .10 .30
322 Tony Saunders .10 .30
323 David Cone .10 .30
324 Roberto Hernandez .10 .30
325 Jose Canseco .20 .50
326 Kevin Stocker .10 .30
327 Gerald Williams .10 .30
328 Quinton McCracken .10 .30
329 Mark Gardner .10 .30
330 Ben Grieve .10 .30
331 Kevin Brown .20 .50
332 Mike Lowell RC .60 1.50
333 Jed Hansen .10 .30
334 Abraham Nunez .10 .30
335 John Thomson .10 .30
336 Masato Yoshii RC .15 .40
337 Mike Piazza .50 1.25
338 Brad Fullmer .10 .30
339 Ray Durham .10 .30
340 Kerry Wood .15 .40
341 Kevin Polcovich .10 .30
342 Russ Johnson .10 .30
343 Darryl Hamilton .10 .30
344 David Ortiz .40 1.00
345 Kevin Orie .10 .30
346 Mike Caruso .10 .30
347 Juan Guzman .10 .30
348 Ruben Rivera .10 .30
349 Rick Aguilera .10 .30
350 Bobby Estalella .10 .30
351 Bobby Witt .10 .30
352 Paul Konerko .10 .30
353 Matt Morris .10 .30
354 Carl Pavano .10 .30
355 Todd Zeile .10 .30
356 Kevin Brown TR .20 .50
357 Alex Gonzalez .10 .30
358 Chuck Knoblauch TR .10 .30
359 Joey Cora .10 .30
360 Mike Lansing TR .10 .30
361 Adrian Beltre .10 .30
362 Dennis Eckersley TR .10 .30
363 A.J. Hinch .10 .30
364 Kenny Lofton TR .10 .30
365 Alex Gonzalez .10 .30
366 Henry Rodriguez TR .10 .30
367 Mike Stoner RC .10 .30
368 Darryl Kile TR .10 .30
369 Kevin McGlinchy .10 .30
370 Walt Weiss TR .10 .30
371 Kris Benson .10 .30
372 Cecil Fielder TR .10 .30
373 Dermal Brown .10 .30
374 Rod Beck TR .10 .30
375 Eric Milton .10 .30
376 Travis Fryman TR .10 .30
377 Preston Wilson .10 .30
378 Chili Davis TR .10 .30
379 Travis Lee .10 .30
380 Jim Leyritz TR .10 .30
381 Vernon Wells .10 .30
382 Joe Carter TR .10 .30
383 J.J. Davis .10 .30
384 Marquis Grissom TR .10 .30
385 Mike Cuddyer RC .40 1.00
386 Rickey Henderson TR .30 .75
387 Chris Enochs RC .10 .30
388 Andres Galarraga TR .10 .30
389 Jason Dellaero .10 .30
390 Robb Nen TR .10 .30
391 Mark Mangum .10 .30
392 Jeff Blauser TR .10 .30
393 Adam Kennedy .10 .30
394 Bob Abreu TR .10 .30
395 Jack Cust RC .75 2.00
396 Jose Vizcaino TR .10 .30
397 Jon Garland .10 .30
398 Pedro Martinez TR .20 .50
399 Aaron Akin .10 .30
400 Jeff Conine TR .10 .30
NNO Cal Ripken 6.00 15.00
Sound Chip 1
NNO Cal Ripken 6.00 15.00
Sound Chip 2

1998 Stadium Club First Day Issue

Randomly inserted in first series retail packs at the rate of one in 42 and second series retail packs at the rate of one in 47, this 400-card set parallels the 1998 Stadium Club base set and features a "First Day Issue" foil stamp on the front. Each card is serial numbered out of 200 on back.

*STARS: 6X TO 15X BASIC CARDS
*ROOKIES: 6X TO 15X BASIC CARDS

1998 Stadium Club One Of A Kind

Randomly inserted in first and second series hobby and Home Team Advantage packs this 400-card set parallels the 1998 Stadium Club base set. First series cards were seeded at 1:21 hobby and 1:13 HTA packs. Series 2 cards were seeded at 1:24 hobby and 1:14 HTA packs. Each card front features a special metalized foil treatment coupled with a "One of a Kind" logo. In addition, each card is serial numbered out of 150 on back.

*STARS: 8X TO 20X BASIC CARDS
*ROOKIES: 8X TO 20X BASIC CARDS

1998 Stadium Club Co-Signers

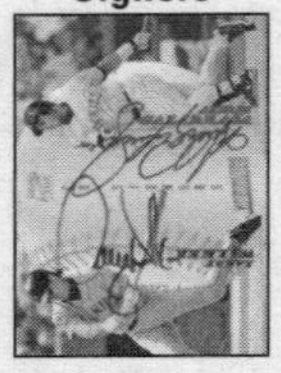

Randomly inserted exclusively in first and second series hobby and Home Team Advantage packs, this 36-card set features color photos of two top players on each card along with their autographs. These cards were released in three different levels of scarcity: A, B and C. Seeding rates are as follows: Series 1 Group A 1:4372 hobby and 1:2623 HTA, Series 1 Group B 1:1457 hobby and 1:874 HTA, Series 1 Group C 1:121 hobby and 1:73 HTA, Series 2 Group A 1:4702 hobby and 1:2821 HTA, Series 2 Group B 1:1567 hobby and 1:940 HTA and Series 2 Group C 1:131 hobby and 1:78 HTA. The scarce group A cards (rumored to be only 25 of each made) are the most difficult to obtain.

CS1 Nomar Garciaparra A	60.00	120.00
Scott Rolen		
CS2 Nomar Garciaparra B	175.00	300.00
Derek Jeter		
CS3 Nomar Garciaparra C	15.00	40.00
Eric Karros		
CS4 Scott Rolen C	60.00	120.00
Derek Jeter		
CS5 Scott Rolen B	20.00	50.00
Eric Karros		
CS6 Derek Jeter A	75.00	150.00
Eric Karros		
CS7 Travis Lee B	6.00	15.00
Jose Cruz Jr.		
CS8 Travis Lee C	6.00	15.00
Mark Kotsay		
CS9 Travis Lee A	40.00	80.00
Paul Konerko		
CS10 Jose Cruz Jr. A	20.00	50.00
Mark Kotsay		
CS11 Jose Cruz Jr. C	15.00	40.00
Paul Konerko		
CS12 Mark Kotsay B	20.00	50.00
Paul Konerko		
CS13 Tony Gwynn A	60.00	120.00
Larry Walker		
CS14 Tony Gwynn C	15.00	40.00
Mark Grudzielanek		
CS15 Tony Gwynn B	60.00	120.00
Andres Galarraga		
CS16 Larry Walker B	40.00	80.00
Mark Grudzielanek		
CS17 Larry Walker C	20.00	50.00
Andres Galarraga		
CS18 Mark Grudzielanek A	20.00	50.00
Andres Galarraga		
CS19 Sandy Alomar A	15.00	40.00
Roberto Alomar		
CS20 Sandy Alomar C	15.00	40.00
Andy Pettitte		
CS21 Sandy Alomar B	30.00	60.00
Tino Martinez		
CS22 Roberto Alomar B	30.00	60.00
Andy Pettitte		
CS23 Roberto Alomar C	20.00	50.00
Tino Martinez		
CS24 Andy Pettitte A	60.00	120.00
Tino Martinez		
CS25 Tony Clark A	20.00	50.00
Todd Hundley		
CS26 Tony Clark B	20.00	50.00
Tim Salmon		
CS27 Tony Clark C	6.00	15.00
Robin Ventura		
CS28 Todd Hundley C	6.00	15.00
Tim Salmon		
CS29 Todd Hundley B	15.00	40.00
Robin Ventura		
CS30 Tim Salmon A	40.00	80.00
Robin Ventura		
CS31 Roger Clemens B	100.00	200.00
Randy Johnson		
CS32 Roger Clemens A	75.00	150.00
Jaret Wright		
CS33 Roger Clemens C	50.00	100.00
Matt Morris		
CS34 Randy Johnson C	20.00	50.00
Jaret Wright		
CS35 Randy Johnson A	60.00	120.00
Matt Morris		
CS36 Jaret Wright B	15.00	40.00
Matt Morris		

1998 Stadium Club In The Wings

Randomly inserted in first series hobby and retail packs at the rate of one in 36 and first series Home Team Advantage packs at a rate of one in 12, this 15-card set features color photos of some of the top young players in the league.

COMPLETE SET (15)	15.00	40.00
W1 Juan Encarnacion	1.50	4.00
W2 Brad Fullmer	1.50	4.00
W3 Ben Grieve	1.50	4.00
W4 Todd Helton	2.50	6.00
W5 Richard Hidalgo	1.50	4.00
W6 Russ Johnson	1.50	4.00
W7 Paul Konerko	1.50	4.00
W8 Mark Kotsay	1.50	4.00
W9 Derrek Lee	2.50	6.00
W10 Travis Lee	1.50	4.00
W11 Eli Marrero	1.50	4.00
W12 David Ortiz	5.00	12.00
W13 Randall Simon	1.50	4.00
W14 Shannon Stewart	1.50	4.00
W15 Fernando Tatis	1.50	4.00

1998 Stadium Club Never Compromise

Randomly inserted in first series hobby and retail packs at the rate of one in 12 and first series HTA packs at the rate of one in four, this 20-card set features color photos of top players who never compromise in their game play.

COMPLETE SET (20)	30.00	80.00
NC1 Cal Ripken	4.00	10.00
NC2 Ivan Rodriguez	.75	2.00
NC3 Ken Griffey Jr.	2.00	5.00
NC4 Frank Thomas	1.25	3.00
NC5 Tony Gwynn	1.50	4.00
NC6 Mike Piazza	2.00	5.00
NC7 Randy Johnson	1.25	3.00
NC8 Greg Maddux	2.00	5.00
NC9 Roger Clemens	2.50	6.00
NC10 Derek Jeter	3.00	8.00
NC11 Chipper Jones	1.25	3.00
NC12 Barry Bonds	3.00	8.00
NC13 Larry Walker	.50	1.25
NC14 Jeff Bagwell	.75	2.00
NC15 Barry Larkin	.75	2.00
NC16 Ken Caminiti	.50	1.25
NC17 Mark McGwire	3.00	8.00
NC18 Manny Ramirez	.75	2.00
NC19 Tim Salmon	.75	2.00
NC20 Paul Molitor	.50	1.25

1998 Stadium Club Playing With Passion

Randomly seeded into second series hobby and retail packs at a rate of one in 12 and second series Home Team Advantage packs at a rate of one in four, cards from this 10-card set feature a selection of players who've got true fire in their hearts and the burning desire to win.

COMPLETE SET (10)	10.00	25.00
P1 Bernie Williams	.60	1.50
P2 Jim Edmonds	.40	1.00
P3 Chipper Jones	1.00	2.50
P4 Cal Ripken	3.00	8.00
P5 Craig Biggio	.60	1.50
P6 Juan Gonzalez	.40	1.00
P7 Alex Rodriguez	1.50	4.00
P8 Tino Martinez	.60	1.50
P9 Mike Piazza	1.50	4.00
P10 Ken Griffey Jr.	1.50	4.00

1998 Stadium Club Royal Court

Randomly seeded into second series hobby and retail packs at a rate of one in 36 and second series Home Team Advantage packs at a rate of one in 12, cards from this 15-card set feature a selection of players that have proven their talent and dedication that they've got what it takes to achieve royalty. Players are broken into groups of ten Kings (veterans) and five Princes (rookies). Each card features a special Uniluster technology on front.

COMPLETE SET (15)	50.00	120.00
RC1 Ken Griffey Jr.	5.00	12.00
RC2 Frank Thomas	3.00	8.00
RC3 Mike Piazza	5.00	12.00
RC4 Chipper Jones	3.00	8.00
RC5 Mark McGwire	8.00	20.00
RC6 Cal Ripken	10.00	25.00
RC7 Jeff Bagwell	2.00	5.00
RC8 Barry Bonds	8.00	20.00
RC9 Juan Gonzalez	1.25	3.00
RC10 Alex Rodriguez	5.00	12.00
RC11 Travis Lee	1.25	3.00
RC12 Paul Konerko	1.25	3.00
RC13 Todd Helton	2.00	5.00
RC14 Ben Grieve	1.25	3.00
RC15 Mark Kotsay	1.25	3.00

1998 Stadium Club Triumvirate Luminous

Randomly inserted in first and second series retail packs at the rate of one in 48, the cards of this 54-card set feature color photos of three teammates that can be fused together to make one big card. These laser cut cards use Luminous technology.

*LUMINESCENT: 1.25X TO 3X LUMINOUS
LUMINESCENT STATED ODDS 1:192 RETAIL
*ILLUMINATOR: 2X TO 5X LUMINOUS
ILLUMINATOR STATED ODDS 1:384 RETAIL

T1A Chipper Jones	2.50	6.00
T1B Andruw Jones	1.50	4.00
T1C Kenny Lofton	1.00	2.50
T2A Derek Jeter	6.00	15.00
T2B Bernie Williams	1.50	4.00
T2C Tino Martinez	1.50	4.00
T3A Jay Buhner	1.00	2.50
T3B Edgar Martinez	1.50	4.00
T3C Ken Griffey Jr.	4.00	10.00
T4A Albert Belle	1.00	2.50
T4B Robin Ventura	1.00	2.50
T4C Frank Thomas	2.50	6.00
T5A Brady Anderson	1.00	2.50
T5B Cal Ripken	8.00	20.00
T5C Rafael Palmeiro	1.50	4.00
T6A Mike Piazza	4.00	10.00
T6B Raul Mondesi	1.00	2.50
T6C Eric Karros	1.00	2.50
T7A Vinny Castilla	1.00	2.50
T7B Andres Galarraga	1.00	2.50
T7C Larry Walker	1.00	2.50
T8A Jim Thome	1.50	4.00
T8B Manny Ramirez	1.50	4.00
T8C David Justice	1.00	2.50
T9A Mike Mussina	1.50	4.00
T9B Greg Maddux	4.00	10.00
T9C Randy Johnson	2.50	6.00
T10A Mike Piazza	4.00	10.00
T10B Sandy Alomar Jr.	1.00	2.50
T10C Ivan Rodriguez	1.50	4.00
T11A Mark McGwire	6.00	15.00
T11B Tino Martinez	1.50	4.00
T11C Frank Thomas	2.50	6.00
T12A Roberto Alomar	1.50	4.00
T12B Chuck Knoblauch	1.00	2.50
T12C Craig Biggio	1.50	4.00
T13A Cal Ripken	8.00	20.00
T13B Chipper Jones	2.50	6.00
T13C Ken Caminiti	1.00	2.50
T14A Derek Jeter	6.00	15.00
T14B Nomar Garciaparra	4.00	10.00
T14C Alex Rodriguez	4.00	10.00
T15A Barry Bonds	6.00	15.00
T15B David Justice	1.00	2.50
T15C Albert Belle	1.00	2.50
T16A Bernie Williams	1.50	4.00
T16B Ken Griffey Jr.	4.00	10.00
T16C Ray Lankford	1.00	2.50
T17A Tim Salmon	1.50	4.00
T17B Larry Walker	1.00	2.50
T17C Tony Gwynn	3.00	8.00
T18A Paul Molitor	1.00	2.50
T18B Edgar Martinez	1.50	4.00
T18C Juan Gonzalez	1.00	2.50

1999 Stadium Club

This 355-card set of 1999 Stadium Club cards was distributed in two separate series of 170 and 185 cards respectively. Six-card hobby and six-card retail packs each carried a suggested retail price of $2. 15-card Home Team Advantage packs (SRP of $5) were also distributed. All pack types contained a trifold/checklist info card. The card fronts feature color action player photos printed on 20 pt. card stock. The backs carry player information and career statistics. Draft Pick and Future Stars cards 141-160 and 336-355 were shortprinted at the following rates: 1:3 hobby/retail packs, one per HTA pack. Key Rookie Cards include Pat Burrell, Nick Johnson and Austin Kearns.

COMPLETE SET (355)	40.00	100.00
COMP.SERIES 1 (170)	20.00	50.00
COMP.SER.1 w/o SP's (150)	10.00	25.00
COMP.SERIES 2 (185)	20.00	50.00
COMP.SER.2 w/o SP's (165)	10.00	25.00
COMMON (1-140/161-170)	.10	.30
COMMON (171-335)	.10	.30
COMMON (141-160/336-355)	.75	2.00
1 Alex Rodriguez	.50	1.25
2 Chipper Jones	.30	.75
3 Rusty Greer	.10	.30
4 Jim Edmonds	.10	.30
5 Ron Gant	.10	.30
6 Kevin Polcovich	.10	.30
7 Darryl Strawberry	.10	.30
8 Bill Mueller	.10	.30
9 Vinny Castilla	.10	.30
10 Wade Boggs	.20	.50
11 Jose Lima	.10	.30
12 Darren Dreifort	.10	.30
13 Jay Bell	.10	.30
14 Ben Grieve	.10	.30
15 Shawn Green	.10	.30
16 Andres Galarraga	.10	.30
17 Bartolo Colon	.10	.30
18 Francisco Cordova	.10	.30
19 Paul O'Neill	.20	.50
20 Trevor Hoffman	.10	.30
21 Darren Oliver	.10	.30
22 John Franco	.10	.30
23 Eli Marrero	.10	.30
24 Roberto Hernandez	.10	.30
25 Craig Biggio	.20	.50
26 Brad Fullmer	.10	.30
27 Scott Erickson	.10	.30
28 Tom Gordon	.10	.30
29 Brian Hunter	.10	.30
30 Raul Mondesi	.10	.30
31 Rick Reed	.10	.30
32 Jose Canseco	.20	.50
33 Robb Nen	.10	.30
34 Turner Ward	.10	.30
35 Orlando Hernandez	.10	.30
36 Jeff Shaw	.10	.30
37 Matt Lawton	.10	.30
38 David Wells	.10	.30
39 Bob Abreu	.10	.30
40 Jeromy Burnitz	.10	.30
41 Deivi Cruz	.10	.30
42 Derek Bell	.10	.30
43 Rico Brogna	.10	.30
44 Dmitri Young	.10	.30
45 Chuck Knoblauch	.10	.30
46 Johnny Damon	.20	.50
47 Brian Meadows	.10	.30
48 Jeremi Gonzalez	.10	.30
49 Gary DiSarcina	.10	.30
50 Frank Thomas	.30	.75
51 F.P. Santangelo	.10	.30
52 Tom Candiotti	.10	.30
53 Shane Reynolds	.10	.30
54 Rod Beck	.10	.30
55 Rey Ordonez	.10	.30
56 Todd Helton	.20	.50
57 Mickey Morandini	.10	.30
58 Jorge Posada	.20	.50
59 Mike Mussina	.20	.50
60 Al Leiter	.10	.30
61 David Segui	.10	.30
62 Brian McRae	.10	.30
63 Fred McGriff	.20	.50
64 Brett Tomko	.10	.30
65 Derek Jeter	.75	2.00
66 Sammy Sosa	.30	.75
67 Kenny Rogers	.10	.30
68 Dave Nilsson	.10	.30
69 Eric Young	.10	.30
70 Mark McGwire	.75	2.00
71 Kenny Lofton	.10	.30
72 Tom Glavine	.20	.50
73 Joey Hamilton	.10	.30
74 John Valentin	.10	.30
75 Mariano Rivera	.30	.75
76 Ray Durham	.10	.30
77 Tony Clark	.10	.30
78 Livan Hernandez	.10	.30
79 Rickey Henderson	.30	.75
80 Vladimir Guerrero	.30	.75
81 J.T. Snow	.10	.30
82 Juan Guzman	.10	.30
83 Darryl Hamilton	.10	.30
84 Matt Anderson	.10	.30
85 Travis Lee	.10	.30
86 Joe Randa	.10	.30
87 Dave Dellucci	.10	.30
88 Moises Alou	.10	.30
89 Alex Gonzalez	.10	.30
90 Tony Womack	.10	.30
91 Neifi Perez	.10	.30

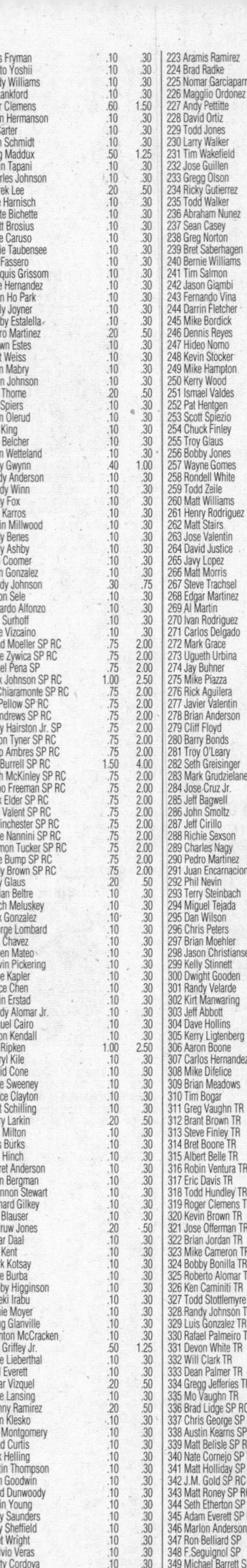

92 Travis Fryman	.10	.30
93 Masato Yoshii	.10	.30
94 Woody Williams	.10	.30
95 Ray Lankford	.10	.30
96 Roger Clemens	.60	1.50
97 Dustin Hermanson	.10	.30
98 Joe Carter	.10	.30
99 Jason Schmidt	.10	.30
100 Greg Maddux	.50	1.25
101 Kevin Tapani	.10	.30
102 Charles Johnson	.10	.30
103 Derrek Lee	.20	.50
104 Pete Harnisch	.10	.30
105 Dante Bichette	.10	.30
106 Scott Brosius	.10	.30
107 Mike Caruso	.10	.30
108 Eddie Taubensee	.10	.30
109 Jeff Fassero	.10	.30
110 Marquis Grissom	.10	.30
111 Jose Hernandez	.10	.30
112 Chan Ho Park	.10	.30
113 Wally Joyner	.10	.30
114 Bobby Estalella	.10	.30
115 Pedro Martinez	.20	.50
116 Shawn Estes	.10	.30
117 Walt Weiss	.10	.30
118 John Mabry	.10	.30
119 Brian Johnson	.10	.30
120 Jim Thome	.20	.50
121 Bill Spiers	.10	.30
122 John Olerud	.10	.30
123 Jeff King	.10	.30
124 Tim Belcher	.10	.30
125 John Wetteland	.10	.30
126 Tony Gwynn	.40	1.00
127 Brady Anderson	.10	.30
128 Randy Winn	.10	.30
129 Andy Fox	.10	.30
130 Eric Karros	.10	.30
131 Kevin Millwood	.10	.30
132 Andy Benes	.10	.30
133 Andy Ashby	.10	.30
134 Ron Coomer	.10	.30
135 Juan Gonzalez	.10	.30
136 Randy Johnson	.30	.75
137 Aaron Sele	.10	.30
138 Edgardo Alfonzo	.10	.30
139 B.J. Surhoff	.10	.30
140 Jose Vizcaino	.10	.30
141 Chad Moeller SP RC	.75	2.00
142 Mike Zywica SP RC	.75	2.00
143 Angel Pena SP	.75	2.00
144 Nick Johnson SP RC	1.00	2.50
145 G. Chiaramonte SP RC	.75	2.00
146 Kit Pellow SP RC	.75	2.00
147 C.Andrews SP RC	.75	2.00
148 Jerry Hairston Jr. SP	.75	2.00
149 Jason Tyner SP RC	.75	2.00
150 Chip Ambres SP RC	.75	2.00
151 Pat Burrell SP RC	1.50	4.00
152 Josh McKinley SP RC	.75	2.00
153 Choo Freeman SP RC	.75	2.00
154 Rick Elder SP RC	.75	2.00
155 Eric Valent SP RC	.75	2.00
156 J.Winchester SP RC	.75	2.00
157 Mike Nannini SP RC	.75	2.00
158 Mamon Tucker SP RC	.75	2.00
159 Nate Bump SP RC	.75	2.00
160 Andy Brown SP RC	.75	2.00
161 Troy Glaus	.20	.50
162 Adrian Beltre	.10	.30
163 Mitch Meluskey	.10	.30
164 Alex Gonzalez	.10	.30
165 George Lombard	.10	.30
166 Eric Chavez	.10	.30
167 Ruben Mateo	.10	.30
168 Calvin Pickering	.10	.30
169 Gabe Kapler	.10	.30
170 Bruce Chen	.10	.30
171 Darin Erstad	.10	.30
172 Sandy Alomar Jr.	.10	.30
173 Miguel Cairo	.10	.30
174 Jason Kendall	.10	.30
175 Cal Ripken	1.00	2.50
176 Darryl Kile	.10	.30
177 David Cone	.10	.30
178 Mike Sweeney	.10	.30
179 Royce Clayton	.10	.30
180 Curt Schilling	.10	.30
181 Barry Larkin	.20	.50
182 Eric Milton	.10	.30
183 Ellis Burks	.10	.30
184 A.J. Hinch	.10	.30
185 Garret Anderson	.10	.30
186 Sean Bergman	.10	.30
187 Shannon Stewart	.10	.30
188 Bernard Gilkey	.10	.30
189 Jeff Blauser	.10	.30
190 Andruw Jones	.20	.50
191 Omar Daal	.10	.30
192 Jeff Kent	.10	.30
193 Mark Kotsay	.10	.30
194 Dave Burba	.10	.30
195 Bobby Higginson	.10	.30
196 Hideki Irabu	.10	.30
197 Jamie Moyer	.10	.30
198 Doug Glanville	.10	.30
199 Quinton McCracken	.10	.30
200 Ken Griffey Jr.	.50	1.25
201 Mike Lieberthal	.10	.30
202 Carl Everett	.10	.30
203 Omar Vizquel	.20	.50
204 Mike Lansing	.10	.30
205 Manny Ramirez	.20	.50
206 Ryan Klesko	.10	.30
207 Jeff Montgomery	.10	.30
208 Chad Curtis	.10	.30
209 Rick Helling	.10	.30
210 Justin Thompson	.10	.30
211 Tom Goodwin	.10	.30
212 Todd Dunwoody	.10	.30
213 Kevin Young	.10	.30
214 Tony Saunders	.10	.30
215 Gary Sheffield	.10	.30
216 Jaret Wright	.10	.30
217 Quilvio Veras	.10	.30
218 Marty Cordova	.10	.30
219 Tino Martinez	.20	.50
220 Scott Rolen	.20	.50
221 Fernando Tatis	.10	.30
222 Damion Easley	.10	.30
223 Aramis Ramirez	.10	.30
224 Brad Radke	.10	.30
225 Nomar Garciaparra	.50	1.25
226 Magglio Ordonez	.10	.30
227 Andy Pettitte	.20	.50
228 David Ortiz	.30	.75
229 Todd Jones	.10	.30
230 Larry Walker	.10	.30
231 Tim Wakefield	.10	.30
232 Jose Guillen	.10	.30
233 Gregg Olson	.10	.30
234 Ricky Gutierrez	.10	.30
235 Todd Walker	.10	.30
236 Abraham Nunez	.10	.30
237 Sean Casey	.10	.30
238 Greg Norton	.10	.30
239 Bret Saberhagen	.10	.30
240 Bernie Williams	.20	.50
241 Tim Salmon	.20	.50
242 Jason Giambi	.10	.30
243 Fernando Vina	.10	.30
244 Darrin Fletcher	.10	.30
245 Mike Bordick	.10	.30
246 Dennis Reyes	.10	.30
247 Hideo Nomo	.30	.75
248 Kevin Stocker	.10	.30
249 Mike Hampton	.10	.30
250 Kerry Wood	.10	.30
251 Ismael Valdes	.10	.30
252 Pat Hentgen	.10	.30
253 Scott Spiezio	.10	.30
254 Chuck Finley	.10	.30
255 Troy Glaus	.20	.50
256 Bobby Jones	.10	.30
257 Wayne Gomes	.10	.30
258 Rondell White	.10	.30
259 Todd Zeile	.10	.30
260 Matt Williams	.10	.30
261 Henry Rodriguez	.10	.30
262 Matt Stairs	.10	.30
263 Jose Valentin	.10	.30
264 David Justice	.10	.30
265 Javy Lopez	.10	.30
266 Matt Morris	.10	.30
267 Steve Trachsel	.10	.30
268 Edgar Martinez	.20	.50
269 Al Martin	.10	.30
270 Ivan Rodriguez	.20	.50
271 Carlos Delgado	.10	.30
272 Mark Grace	.20	.50
273 Ugueth Urbina	.10	.30
274 Jay Buhner	.10	.30
275 Mike Piazza	.50	1.25
276 Rick Aguilera	.10	.30
277 Javier Valentin	.10	.30
278 Brian Anderson	.10	.30
279 Cliff Floyd	.10	.30
280 Barry Bonds	.75	2.00
281 Troy O'Leary	.10	.30
282 Seth Greisinger	.10	.30
283 Mark Grudzielanek	.10	.30
284 Jose Cruz Jr.	.10	.30
285 Jeff Bagwell	.20	.50
286 John Smoltz	.20	.50
287 Jeff Cirillo	.10	.30
288 Richie Sexson	.10	.30
289 Charles Nagy	.10	.30
290 Pedro Martinez	.20	.50
291 Juan Encarnacion	.10	.30
292 Phil Nevin	.10	.30
293 Terry Steinbach	.10	.30
294 Miguel Tejada	.10	.30
295 Dan Wilson	.10	.30
296 Chris Peters	.10	.30
297 Brian Moehler	.10	.30
298 Jason Christiansen	.10	.30
299 Kelly Stinnett	.10	.30
300 Dwight Gooden	.10	.30
301 Randy Velarde	.10	.30
302 Kirt Manwaring	.10	.30
303 Jeff Abbott	.10	.30
304 Dave Hollins	.10	.30
305 Kerry Ligtenberg	.10	.30
306 Aaron Boone	.10	.30
307 Carlos Hernandez	.10	.30
308 Mike Difelice	.10	.30
309 Brian Meadows	.10	.30
310 Tim Bogar	.10	.30
311 Greg Vaughn TR	.10	.30
312 Brant Brown TR	.10	.30
313 Steve Finley TR	.10	.30
314 Bret Boone TR	.10	.30
315 Albert Belle TR	.10	.30
316 Robin Ventura TR	.10	.30
317 Eric Davis TR	.10	.30
318 Todd Hundley TR	.10	.30
319 Roger Clemens TR	.60	1.50
320 Kevin Brown TR	.10	.30
321 Jose Offerman TR	.10	.30
322 Brian Jordan TR	.10	.30
323 Mike Cameron TR	.10	.30
324 Bobby Bonilla TR	.10	.30
325 Roberto Alomar TR	.20	.50
326 Ken Caminiti TR	.10	.30
327 Todd Stottlemyre TR	.10	.30
328 Randy Johnson TR	.30	.75
329 Luis Gonzalez TR	.10	.30
330 Rafael Palmeiro TR	.20	.50
331 Devon White TR	.10	.30
332 Will Clark TR	.20	.50
333 Dean Palmer TR	.10	.30
334 Gregg Jefferies TR	.10	.30
335 Mo Vaughn TR	.10	.30
336 Brad Lidge SP RC	1.50	4.00
337 Chris George SP RC	.75	2.00
338 Austin Kearns SP RC	1.50	4.00
339 Matt Belisle SP RC	.75	2.00
340 Nate Cornejo SP RC	.75	2.00
341 Matt Holliday SP RC	3.00	8.00
342 J.M. Gold SP RC	.75	2.00
343 Matt Roney SP RC	.75	2.00
344 Seth Etherton SP RC	.75	2.00
345 Adam Everett SP RC	.75	2.00
346 Marlon Anderson SP	.75	2.00
347 Ron Belliard SP	.75	2.00
348 F.Seguignol SP	.75	2.00
349 Michael Barrett SP	.75	2.00
350 Dernell Stenson SP	.75	2.00
351 Ryan Anderson SP	.75	2.00
352 Ramon Hernandez SP	.75	2.00
353 Jeremy Giambi SP	.75	2.00

354 Ricky Ledee SP	.75	2.00
355 Carlos Lee SP	.75	2.00

1999 Stadium Club First Day Issue

Randomly inserted in retail packs only at the rate of 1:75 series one packs and 1:60 series two packs, this 355-card set is parallel to Stadium Club Series one base set. Only 170 serially numbered series one sets were produced and 200 serial numbered series two sets were produced.

*STARS: 6X TO 15X BASIC CARDS
*SP 141-160/336-355: 2X TO 5X BASIC SP

1999 Stadium Club One of a Kind

This set is a parallel version of the regular issue printed on mirrorboard and sequentially numbered to 150. The cards were randomly inserted packs at the rate of 1:53 first series hobby packs, 1:21 first series HTA packs, 1:48 second series retail packs and 1:19 second series HTA packs.

*STARS: 6X TO 15X BASIC CARDS
*SP'S 141-160/336-355: 2X TO 5X BASIC

1999 Stadium Club Autographs

This 10-card set features color player photos with the pictured player's autograph and a gold-foil Topps Certified Autograph Issue stamp on the card front. They were inserted exclusively into retail packs as follows: series 1 1:1107, series 2 1:877.

SCA1 Alex Rodriguez	75.00	150.00
SCA2 Chipper Jones	20.00	50.00
SCA3 Barry Bonds	100.00	175.00
SCA4 Tino Martinez	10.00	25.00
SCA5 Ben Grieve	6.00	15.00
SCA6 Juan Gonzalez	6.00	15.00
SCA7 Vladimir Guerrero	15.00	40.00
SCA8 Albert Belle	6.00	15.00
SCA9 Kerry Wood	10.00	25.00
SCA10 Todd Helton	10.00	25.00

1999 Stadium Club Chrome

Randomly inserted in packs at the rate of one in 24 hobby and retail packs and one in six HTA packs, this 40-card set features color player photos printed using chromium technology which gives the cards the shimmering metallic light of fresh steel.

COMPLETE SERIES 1 (20)	30.00	60.00
COMPLETE SERIES 2 (20)	30.00	60.00
*REFRACTORS: 1X TO 2.5X BASIC CHROME		
REFRACTOR ODDS 1:96 HOB/RET, 1:24 HTA		
SCC1 Nomar Garciaparra	2.50	6.00
SCC2 Kerry Wood	.60	1.50
SCC3 Jeff Bagwell	1.00	2.50
SCC4 Ivan Rodriguez	1.00	2.50
SCC5 Albert Belle	.60	1.50
SCC6 Gary Sheffield	.60	1.50
SCC7 Andruw Jones	1.00	2.50
SCC8 Kevin Brown	.60	1.50
SCC9 David Cone	.60	1.50
SCC10 Darin Erstad	.60	1.50
SCC11 Manny Ramirez	1.00	2.50
SCC12 Larry Walker	.60	1.50
SCC13 Mike Piazza	2.50	6.00
SCC14 Cal Ripken	5.00	12.00
SCC15 Pedro Martinez	1.00	2.50
SCC16 Greg Vaughn	.60	1.50
SCC17 Barry Bonds	4.00	10.00
SCC18 Mo Vaughn	.60	1.50
SCC19 Bernie Williams	1.00	2.50
SCC20 Ken Griffey Jr.	2.50	6.00
SCC21 Alex Rodriguez	2.50	6.00
SCC22 Chipper Jones	1.50	4.00
SCC23 Ben Grieve	.60	1.50
SCC24 Frank Thomas	1.50	4.00
SCC25 Derek Jeter	4.00	10.00
SCC26 Sammy Sosa	1.50	4.00
SCC27 Mark McGwire	4.00	10.00
SCC28 Vladimir Guerrero	1.50	4.00
SCC29 Greg Maddux	2.50	6.00
SCC30 Juan Gonzalez	.60	1.50
SCC31 Troy Glaus	1.00	2.50
SCC32 Adrian Beltre	.60	1.50
SCC33 Mitch Meluskey	.60	1.50
SCC34 Alex Gonzalez	.60	1.50
SCC35 George Lombard	.60	1.50
SCC36 Eric Chavez	.60	1.50
SCC37 Ruben Mateo	.60	1.50
SCC38 Calvin Pickering	.60	1.50
SCC39 Gabe Kapler	.60	1.50
SCC40 Bruce Chen	.60	1.50

1999 Stadium Club Co-Signers

Randomly inserted in hobby packs only, this 42-card set features color player photos with their autographs and Topps "Certified Autograph Issue" stamp. Cards 1-21 were seeded in first series packs and 22-42 in second series. The cards are divided into four groups. Group A was signed by all four players appearing on the cards. Groups B-D are dual player cards featuring two autographs. Series 1 hobby pack insertion rates are as follows: Group A 1:45,213, Group B 1:3617, Group C 1:1006, and Group D 1:102. Series 2 hobby pack insertion rates are as follows: Group A 1:43,369, Group B 1:8984, Group C 1:2975 and Group D 1:251. Series 2 HTA pack insertion rates are as follows: Group A 1:18,171, Group B 1:3533, Group C 1:1189 and Group D 1:100. Pricing is available for all cards where possible.

CS1 Ben Grieve	8.00	20.00
Richie Sexson D		
CS2 Todd Helton	30.00	60.00
Troy Glaus D		
CS3 Alex Rodriguez	75.00	150.00
Scott Rolen D		
CS4 Derek Jeter	150.00	300.00
Chipper Jones D		
CS5 Cliff Floyd	8.00	20.00
Eli Marrero D		
CS6 Jay Buhner	8.00	20.00
Kevin Young D		
CS7 Ben Grieve	15.00	40.00
Troy Glaus C		
CS8 Todd Helton	15.00	40.00
Richie Sexson C		
CS9 Alex Rodriguez	100.00	175.00
Chipper Jones C		
CS10 Derek Jeter	100.00	175.00
Scott Rolen C		
CS11 Cliff Floyd	8.00	20.00
Kevin Young C		
CS12 Jay Buhner	8.00	20.00
Eli Marrero B		
CS13 Ben Grieve	30.00	60.00
Todd Helton B		
CS14 Richie Sexson	30.00	60.00
Troy Glaus B		
CS15 Alex Rodriguez	300.00	500.00
Derek Jeter B		
CS16 Chipper Jones	60.00	120.00
Scott Rolen B		
CS17 Cliff Floyd	15.00	40.00
Jay Buhner B		
CS18 Eli Marrero	8.00	20.00
Kevin Young B		
CS19 Ben Grieve		
Todd Helton		
Richie Sexson		
Troy Glaus A		
CS20 Alex Rodriguez		
Derek Jeter		
Chipper Jones		
Scott Rolen A		
CS21 Cliff Floyd		
Jay Buhner		
Eli Marrero		
Kevin Young A		
CS22 Edgardo Alfonzo	8.00	20.00
Jose Guillen D		
CS23 Mike Lowell	8.00	20.00
Ricardo Rincon D		
CS24 Juan Gonzalez	8.00	20.00
Vinny Castilla D		
CS25 Moises Alou	20.00	50.00
Roger Clemens D		
CS26 Scott Spiezio	6.00	15.00
Tony Womack D		
CS27 Fernando Vina	6.00	15.00
Quilvio Veras D		
CS28 Edgardo Alfonzo	8.00	20.00
Ricardo Rincon C		
CS29 Jose Guillen	8.00	20.00
Mike Lowell C		
CS30 Juan Gonzalez	8.00	20.00
Moises Alou C		
CS31 Roger Clemens	30.00	60.00
Vinny Castilla C		
CS32 Scott Spiezio	6.00	15.00
Fernando Vina C		
CS33 Tony Womack	8.00	20.00
Quilvio Veras B		
CS34 Edgardo Alfonzo	15.00	40.00
Mike Lowell B		
CS35 Jose Guillen	15.00	40.00
Ricardo Rincon B		
CS36 Juan Gonzalez	150.00	250.00
Roger Clemens B		
CS37 Moises Alou	30.00	60.00
Vinny Castilla B		
CS38 Scott Spiezio	8.00	20.00
Quilvio Veras B		
CS39 Tony Womack	8.00	20.00
Fernando Vina B		
CS40 Edgardo Alfonzo		
Jose Guillen		
Mike Lowell		
Ricardo Rincon A		
CS41 Juan Gonzalez		
Moises Alou		
Roger Clemens		
Vinny Castilla A		
CS42 Scott Spiezio		
Tony Womack		
Fernando Vina		
Quilvio Veras A		

1999 Stadium Club Never Compromise

Randomly inserted in packs at the rate of one in 12 hobby and retail packs and one in four HTA packs, this 10-card set features color action photos of top players.

COMPLETE SET (20)	25.00	50.00
COMPLETE SERIES 1 (10)	15.00	30.00
COMPLETE SERIES 2 (10)	10.00	20.00
NC1 Mark McGwire	2.00	5.00
NC2 Sammy Sosa	.75	2.00
NC3 Ken Griffey Jr.	1.25	3.00
NC4 Greg Maddux	1.25	3.00
NC5 Barry Bonds	2.00	5.00
NC6 Alex Rodriguez	1.25	3.00
NC7 Darin Erstad	.30	.75
NC8 Roger Clemens	1.50	4.00
NC9 Nomar Garciaparra	1.25	3.00
NC10 Derek Jeter	2.00	5.00
NC11 Cal Ripken	2.50	6.00
NC12 Mike Piazza	1.25	3.00
NC13 Kerry Wood	.30	.75
NC14 Andres Galarraga	.30	.75
NC15 Vinny Castilla	.30	.75
NC16 Jeff Bagwell	.50	1.25
NC17 Chipper Jones	.75	2.00
NC18 Eric Chavez	.30	.75
NC19 Orlando Hernandez	.30	.75
NC20 Troy Glaus	.50	1.25

1999 Stadium Club Triumvirate Luminous

Randomly inserted in hobby packs at the rate of one in 36 and in retail packs at the rate of one in 48, this 24-card set features color player photos printed on cards made to fit together to form eight different long cards.

COMPLETE SERIES 1 (24)	60.00	120.00
COMPLETE SERIES 2 (24)	75.00	150.00
*ILLUMINATOR: 2X TO 5X LUMINOUS		
ILLUM.ODDS 1:288 H, 1:384 R, 1:144 HTA		
*LUMINESCENT: 1X TO 2.5X LUMINOUS		
L'SCENT.ODDS 1:144 H, 1:192 R, 1:72 HTA		
T1A Greg Vaughn	.75	2.00
T1B Ken Caminiti	.75	2.00
T1C Tony Gwynn	2.50	6.00
T2A Andruw Jones	1.25	3.00
T2B Chipper Jones	2.00	5.00
T2C Andres Galarraga	.75	2.00
T3A Jay Buhner	.75	2.00
T3B Ken Griffey Jr.	3.00	8.00
T3C Alex Rodriguez	3.00	8.00
T4A Derek Jeter	5.00	12.00
T4B Tino Martinez	1.25	3.00
T4C Bernie Williams	1.25	3.00
T5A Brian Jordan	.75	2.00
T5B Ray Lankford	.75	2.00
T5C Mark McGwire	5.00	12.00
T6A Jeff Bagwell	1.25	3.00
T6B Craig Biggio	1.25	3.00
T6C Randy Johnson	2.00	5.00
T7A Nomar Garciaparra	3.00	8.00
T7B Pedro Martinez	1.25	3.00
T7C Mo Vaughn	.75	2.00
T8A Sammy Sosa	2.00	5.00
T8B Mark Grace	1.25	3.00
T8C Kerry Wood	.75	2.00
T9A Alex Rodriguez	3.00	8.00
T9B Nomar Garciaparra	3.00	8.00
T9C Derek Jeter	5.00	12.00
T10A Todd Helton	1.25	3.00
T10B Travis Lee	.75	2.00
T10C Pat Burrell	1.25	3.00
T11A Greg Maddux	3.00	8.00
T11B Kerry Wood	.75	2.00
T11C Tom Glavine	1.25	3.00
T12A Chipper Jones	2.00	5.00
T12B Vinny Castilla	.75	2.00
T12C Scott Rolen	1.25	3.00
T13A Juan Gonzalez	.75	2.00
T13B Ken Griffey Jr.	3.00	8.00
T13C Ben Grieve	.75	2.00
T14A Sammy Sosa	2.00	5.00
T14B Vladimir Guerrero	2.00	5.00
T14C Barry Bonds	5.00	12.00
T15A Frank Thomas	2.00	5.00
T15B Jim Thome	1.25	3.00
T15C Tino Martinez	1.25	3.00
T16A Mark McGwire	5.00	12.00
T16B Andres Galarraga	.75	2.00
T16C Jeff Bagwell	1.25	3.00

1999 Stadium Club Video Replay

Randomly inserted in Series two hobby and retail packs at the rate of one in 12 and HTA packs at the rate of one in four, this five-card set features live-action video images of top players on lenticular cards.

COMPLETE SET (5)	5.00	12.00
VR1 Mark McGwire	1.50	4.00
VR2 Sammy Sosa	.60	1.50
VR3 Ken Griffey Jr.	1.00	2.50
VR4 Kerry Wood	.25	.60
VR5 Alex Rodriguez	1.00	2.50

2000 Stadium Club

This 250-card single series set was released in February, 2000. Six-card hobby and retail packs carried an SRP of $2.00. There was also a HTC (Home Team Collector) fourteen card pack issued with a SRP of $5.00. The last 50 cards were printed in shorter supply the first 200 cards. These cards were inserted one in five packs and one per HTC pack. This was the first time the Stadium Club set was issued in a single series. Notable Rookie Cards include Rick Asadoorian and Bobby Bradley.

COMPLETE SET (250)	50.00	120.00
COMP.SET w/o SP'S (200)	12.50	30.00
COMMON CARD (1-200)	.10	.30
COMMON SP (201-250)	1.25	3.00
1 Nomar Garciaparra	.50	1.25
2 Brian Jordan	.10	.30
3 Mark Grace	.20	.50
4 Jeromy Burnitz	.10	.30
5 Shane Reynolds	.10	.30
6 Alex Gonzalez	.10	.30
7 Jose Offerman	.10	.30
8 Orlando Hernandez	.10	.30
9 Mike Caruso	.10	.30
10 Tony Clark	.10	.30
11 Sean Casey	.10	.30
12 Johnny Damon	.20	.50
13 Dante Bichette	.10	.30
14 Kevin Young	.10	.30
15 Juan Gonzalez	.10	.30
16 Chipper Jones	.30	.75
17 Quilvio Veras	.10	.30
18 Trevor Hoffman	.10	.30
19 Roger Cedeno	.10	.30
20 Ellis Burks	.10	.30
21 Richie Sexson	.10	.30
22 Gary Sheffield	.10	.30
23 Delino DeShields	.10	.30
24 Wade Boggs	.20	.50
25 Ray Lankford	.10	.30
26 Kevin Appier	.10	.30
27 Roy Halladay	.10	.30
28 Harold Baines	.10	.30
29 Todd Zeile	.10	.30
30 Barry Larkin	.20	.50
31 Ron Coomer	.10	.30
32 Jorge Posada	.20	.50
33 Magglio Ordonez	.10	.30
34 Brian Giles	.10	.30
35 Jeff Kent	.10	.30
36 Henry Rodriguez	.10	.30
37 Fred McGriff	.20	.50
38 Shawn Green	.10	.30
39 Derek Bell	.10	.30
40 Ben Grieve	.10	.30
41 Dave Nilsson	.10	.30
42 Mo Vaughn	.10	.30
43 Rondell White	.10	.30
44 Doug Glanville	.10	.30
45 Paul O'Neill	.20	.50
46 Carlos Lee	.10	.30
47 Vinny Castilla	.10	.30
48 Mike Sweeney	.10	.30
49 Rico Brogna	.10	.30
50 Alex Rodriguez	.50	1.25
51 Luis Castillo	.10	.30
52 Kevin Brown	.20	.50
53 Jose Vidro	.10	.30
54 John Smoltz	.20	.50
55 Garret Anderson	.10	.30
56 Matt Stairs	.10	.30
57 Omar Vizquel	.20	.50
58 Tom Goodwin	.10	.30
59 Scott Brosius	.10	.30
60 Robin Ventura	.20	.50
61 B.J. Surhoff	.10	.30
62 Andy Ashby	.10	.30
63 Chris Widger	.10	.30
64 Tim Hudson	.10	.30
65 Javy Lopez	.10	.30
66 Tim Salmon	.20	.50
67 Warren Morris	.10	.30
68 John Wetteland	.10	.30
69 Gabe Kapler	.10	.30
70 Bernie Williams	.20	.50
71 Rickey Henderson	.30	.75
72 Andruw Jones	.20	.50
73 Eric Young	.10	.30
74 Bob Abreu	.10	.30
75 David Cone	.10	.30
76 Rusty Greer	.10	.30
77 Ron Belliard	.10	.30
78 Troy Glaus	.10	.30
79 Mike Hampton	.10	.30
80 Miguel Tejada	.10	.30
81 Jeff Cirillo	.10	.30
82 Todd Hundley	.10	.30
83 Roberto Alomar	.20	.50
84 Charles Johnson	.10	.30
85 Rafael Palmeiro	.20	.50
86 Doug Mientkiewicz	.10	.30
87 Mariano Rivera	.30	.75
88 Neifi Perez	.10	.30
89 Jermiane Dye	.10	.30
90 Ivan Rodriguez	.20	.50
91 Jay Buhner	.10	.30
92 Pokey Reese	.10	.30
93 John Olerud	.10	.30
94 Brady Anderson	.10	.30
95 Manny Ramirez	.20	.50
96 Keith Osik RC	.10	.30
97 Mickey Morandini	.10	.30
98 Matt Williams	.10	.30
99 Eric Karros	.10	.30
100 Ken Griffey Jr.	.50	1.25
101 Bret Boone	.10	.30
102 Ryan Klesko	.10	.30
103 Craig Biggio	.20	.50
104 John Jaha	.10	.30
105 Vladimir Guerrero	.30	.75
106 Devon White	.10	.30
107 Tony Womack	.10	.30
108 Marvin Benard	.10	.30
109 Kenny Lofton	.10	.30
110 Preston Wilson	.10	.30
111 Al Leiter	.10	.30
112 Reggie Sanders	.10	.30
113 Scott Williamson	.10	.30
114 Deivi Cruz	.10	.30
115 Carlos Beltran	.10	.30
116 Ray Durham	.10	.30
117 Ricky Ledee	.10	.30
118 Torii Hunter	.10	.30
119 John Valentin	.10	.30
120 Scott Rolen	.20	.50
121 Jason Kendall	.10	.30
122 Dave Martinez	.10	.30
123 Jim Thome	.20	.50
124 David Bell	.10	.30
125 Jose Canseco	.20	.50
126 Jose Lima	.10	.30
127 Carl Everett	.10	.30
128 Kevin Millwood	.10	.30
129 Bill Spiers	.10	.30
130 Omar Daal	.10	.30
131 Miguel Cairo	.10	.30
132 Mark Grudzielanek	.10	.30
133 David Justice	.10	.30
134 Russ Ortiz	.10	.30
135 Mike Piazza	.50	1.25
136 Brian Meadows	.10	.30
137 Tony Gwynn	.40	1.00
138 Cal Ripken	1.00	2.50
139 Kris Benson	.10	.30
140 Larry Walker	.10	.30
141 Cristian Guzman	.10	.30
142 Tino Martinez	.20	.50
143 Chris Singleton	.10	.30
144 Lee Stevens	.10	.30
145 Rey Ordonez	.10	.30
146 Russ Davis	.10	.30
147 J.T. Snow	.10	.30
148 Luis Gonzalez	.10	.30
149 Marquis Grissom	.10	.30
150 Greg Maddux	.50	1.25
151 Fernando Tatis	.10	.30
152 Jason Giambi	.10	.30
153 Carlos Delgado	.10	.30
154 Joe McEwing	.10	.30
155 Raul Mondesi	.10	.30
156 Rich Aurilia	.10	.30
157 Alex Fernandez	.10	.30
158 Albert Belle	.10	.30
159 Pat Meares	.10	.30
160 Mike Lieberthal	.10	.30
161 Mike Cameron	.10	.30
162 Juan Encarnacion	.10	.30
163 Chuck Knoblauch	.10	.30
164 Pedro Martinez	.20	.50
165 Randy Johnson	.30	.75
166 Shannon Stewart	.10	.30
167 Jeff Bagwell	.20	.50
168 Edgar Renteria	.10	.30
169 Barry Bonds	.75	2.00
170 Steve Finley	.10	.30
171 Brian Hunter	.10	.30
172 Tom Glavine	.20	.50
173 Mark Kotsay	.10	.30
174 Tony Fernandez	.10	.30
175 Sammy Sosa	.30	.75
176 Geoff Jenkins	.10	.30
177 Adrian Beltre	.10	.30
178 Jay Bell	.10	.30
179 Mike Bordick	.10	.30
180 Ed Sprague	.10	.30
181 Dave Roberts	.10	.30
182 Greg Vaughn	.10	.30
183 Brian Daubach	.10	.30
184 Damion Easley	.10	.30
185 Carlos Febles	.10	.30
186 Kevin Tapani	.10	.30
187 Frank Thomas	.30	.75
188 Roger Clemens	.60	1.50
189 Mike Benjamin	.10	.30
190 Curt Schilling	.10	.30
191 Edgardo Alfonzo	.10	.30
192 Mike Mussina	.20	.50
193 Todd Helton	.20	.50
194 Todd Jones	.10	.30
195 Dean Palmer	.10	.30
196 John Flaherty	.10	.30
197 Derek Jeter	.75	2.00
198 Todd Walker	.10	.30
199 Brad Ausmus	.10	.30
200 Mark McGwire	.75	2.00
201 Erubiel Durazo SP	1.25	3.00
202 Nick Johnson SP	1.25	3.00
203 Ruben Mateo SP	1.25	3.00
204 Lance Berkman SP	1.25	3.00
205 Pat Burrell SP	1.25	3.00
206 Pablo Ozuna SP	1.25	3.00
207 Roosevelt Brown SP	1.25	3.00
208 Alfonso Soriano SP	1.50	4.00
209 A.J. Burnett SP	1.25	3.00
210 Rafael Furcal SP	1.25	3.00
211 Scott Morgan SP	1.25	3.00
212 Adam Piatt SP	1.25	3.00
213 Dee Brown SP	1.25	3.00
214 Corey Patterson SP	1.25	3.00
215 Mickey Lopez SP	1.25	3.00
216 Rob Ryan SP	1.25	3.00
217 Sean Burroughs SP	1.25	3.00
218 Jack Cust SP	1.25	3.00
219 John Patterson SP	1.25	3.00
220 Kit Pellow SP	1.25	3.00
221 Chad Hermansen SP	1.25	3.00
222 Daryle Ward SP	1.25	3.00
223 Jayson Werth SP	1.25	3.00
224 Jason Standridge SP	1.25	3.00
225 Mark Mulder SP	1.25	3.00
226 Peter Bergeron SP	1.25	3.00
227 Willi Mo Pena SP	1.25	3.00
228 Aramis Ramirez SP	1.25	3.00
229 John Sneed SP RC	1.25	3.00
230 Wilton Veras SP	1.25	3.00
231 Josh Hamilton SP	3.00	8.00
232 Eric Munson SP	1.25	3.00
233 Bobby Bradley SP RC	1.25	3.00
234 Larry Bigbie SP RC	1.50	4.00
235 B.J. Garbe SP RC	1.25	3.00
236 Brett Myers SP RC	1.50	4.00
237 Jason Stumm SP RC	1.25	3.00
238 Corey Myers SP RC	1.25	3.00
239 R.Christianson SP RC	1.25	3.00
240 David Walling SP	1.25	3.00
241 Josh Girdley SP	1.25	3.00
242 Omar Ortiz SP	1.25	3.00
243 Jason Jennings SP	1.25	3.00
244 Kyle Snyder SP	1.25	3.00
245 Jay Gehrke SP	1.25	3.00
246 Mike Paradis SP	1.25	3.00
247 Chance Caple SP RC	1.25	3.00
248 B.Christensen SP RC	1.25	3.00
249 Brad Baker SP RC	1.25	3.00
250 R.Asadoorian SP RC	1.25	3.00

2000 Stadium Club First Day Issue

This parallel to the Stadium Club set was inserted at a rate of one in 36 retail packs and were serial numbered to 150. These cards can be identified by the first day issue stamp on the front.

*STARS: 10X TO 25X BASIC CARDS
*SP'S 201-250: 1X TO 2.5X BASIC
*SP RC'S 201-250: 1.25X TO 3X BASIC

2000 Stadium Club One of a Kind

This parallel set was issued at a rate of one in 27 hobby and one in 11 HTC packs. The cards are serial numbered to 150 as well. These cards are differentiated from the regular cards by the mirrorboard technology.

*STARS 1-250: 10X TO 25X BASIC CARDS
*SP'S 201-250: 1X TO 2.5X BASIC
*SP RC'S 201-250: 1.25X TO 3X BASIC

2000 Stadium Club Bats of Brilliance

Issued at a rate of one in 12 hobby packs, one in 15 retail packs and one in six HTC packs these 10 cards feature some of the best clutch hitters in the game.

COMPLETE SET (10)	8.00	20.00
*DIE CUTS: 1.25X TO 3X BASIC BATS	.60	1.50
DIE CUT ODDS 1:60 HOB, 1:75 RET, 1:30 HTC		
BB1 Mark McGwire	1.50	4.00

BB2 Sammy Sosa .60 1.50
BB3 Jose Canseco .40 1.00
BB4 Jeff Bagwell .40 1.00
BB5 Ken Griffey Jr. 1.00 2.50
BB6 Nomar Garciaparra 1.00 2.50
BB7 Mike Piazza 1.00 2.50
BB8 Alex Rodriguez 1.00 2.50
BB9 Vladimir Guerrero .60 1.50
BB10 Chipper Jones .60 1.50

2000 Stadium Club Capture the Action

Inserted one in 12 hobby and retail packs and one in six HTC packs, these 20 cards feature players who continually hustle when on the field. This set is broken up into three groups: Rookies (CA1 through CA5); Stars (CA6 through CA14) and Legends (CA15 through CA20).

COMPLETE SET (20) 25.00 60.00
*GAME VIEW 1-5: 5X TO 12X BASIC CAPT 1.00 2.50
*GAME VIEW: 5X TO 12X BASIC CAPTURE 1.00 2.50
GAME VIEW ODDS 1:508 HOB, 1:203 HTC
GAME VIEW PRINT RUN 100 SERIAL #'d SETS
CA1 Josh Hamilton 1.25 3.00
CA2 Pat Burrell .40 1.00
CA3 Erubiel Durazo .40 1.00
CA4 Alfonso Soriano .50 1.25
CA5 A.J. Burnett .40 1.00
CA6 Alex Rodriguez 1.50 4.00
CA7 Sean Casey .40 1.00
CA8 Derek Jeter 2.50 6.00
CA9 Vladimir Guerrero 1.00 2.50
CA10 Nomar Garciaparra 1.50 4.00
CA11 Mike Piazza 1.50 4.00
CA12 Ken Griffey Jr. 1.50 4.00
CA13 Sammy Sosa 1.00 2.50
CA14 Juan Gonzalez .40 1.00
CA15 Mark McGwire 2.50 6.00
CA16 Ivan Rodriguez .60 1.50
CA17 Barry Bonds 2.50 6.00
CA18 Wade Boggs .60 1.50
CA19 Tony Gwynn 1.25 3.00
CA20 Cal Ripken 3.00 8.00

2000 Stadium Club Chrome Preview

Inserted at a rate of one in 24 for hobby and retail and one in 12 HTC packs, these 20 cards preview the "Chrome" set. These cards carry a "SCC" prefix.

COMPLETE SET (20) 50.00 100.00
*REFRACTOR: 1.25X TO 3X BASIC CHR.PREV.
REFRACTOR ODDS 1:120 HOB/RET, 1:60 HTC
SCC1 Nomar Garciaparra 2.50 6.00
SCC2 Juan Gonzalez 1.50 4.00
SCC3 Chipper Jones 1.50 4.00
SCC4 Alex Rodriguez 2.50 6.00
SCC5 Ivan Rodriguez 1.00 2.50
SCC6 Manny Ramirez 1.00 2.50
SCC7 Ken Griffey Jr. 2.50 6.00
SCC8 Vladimir Guerrero 1.50 4.00
SCC9 Mike Piazza 2.50 6.00
SCC10 Pedro Martinez 1.00 2.50
SCC11 Jeff Bagwell 1.00 2.50
SCC12 Barry Bonds 4.00 10.00
SCC13 Sammy Sosa 1.50 4.00
SCC14 Derek Jeter 4.00 10.00
SCC15 Mark McGwire 4.00 10.00
SCC16 Erubiel Durazo .60 1.50
SCC17 Nick Johnson .60 1.50
SCC18 Pat Burrell .60 1.50
SCC19 Alfonso Soriano 1.50 4.00
SCC20 Adam Piatt .60 1.50

2000 Stadium Club Co-Signers

Inserted in hobby packs only at different rates, these 15 cards feature a pair of players who have signed these cards. The odds are broken down like this: Group A was issued one every 10,184 hobby packs and one every 4060 HTC packs. Group B was issued one every 5092 hobby packs and one every 2032 HTC packs. Group C was issued one every 508 hobby packs and one every 203 HTC packs.

CO1 Alex Rodriguez 600.00 1000.00
Derek Jeter A
CO2 Derek Jeter 125.00 200.00
Omar Vizquel B
CO3 Alex Rodriguez 100.00 175.00
Rey Ordonez B
CO4 Derek Jeter 100.00 175.00
Rey Ordonez B
CO5 Omar Vizquel 100.00 175.00
Alex Rodriguez B
CO6 Rey Ordonez 15.00 40.00
Omar Vizquel C
CO7 Wade Boggs 15.00 40.00
Robin Ventura C
CO8 Randy Johnson 75.00 150.00
Mike Mussina C
CO9 Pat Burrell 10.00 25.00
Magglio Ordonez C
CO10 Chad Hermansen 10.00 25.00
Pat Burrell C
CO11 Magglio Ordonez 10.00 25.00
Chad Hermansen C
CO12 Josh Hamilton 15.00 40.00
Corey Myers C
CO13 B.J.Garbe 15.00 40.00
Josh Hamilton C
CO14 Corey Myers 6.00 15.00
B.J. Garbe C
CO15 Tino Martinez 75.00 150.00
Fred McGriff C

2000 Stadium Club Lone Star Signatures

Issued at different rates throughout the various packaging, these 16 cards feature signed cards of various stars. The cards were inserted at these rates: Group 1 was inserted at a rate of one in 1981 retail packs, one in 1979 hobby packs and one in 792 HTC packs. Group 2 was inserted at a rate of one in 2421 retail packs, one in 2374 hobby packs and one in 946 HTC packs. Group 3 was issued at the same rate as Group 1 (1:1979 hobby, 1:1981 retail; 1:792 HTC packs). Group 4 were issued at a rate of one in 424 hobby packs, one in 423 retail packs and one in 169 HTC packs. These cards are authenticated with a "Topps Certified Autograph" stamp as well as a "Topps3M" sticker.

LS1 Derek Jeter G1 75.00 150.00
LS2 Alex Rodriguez G1 100.00 175.00
LS3 Wade Boggs G1 15.00 40.00
LS4 Robin Ventura G1 6.00 15.00
LS5 Randy Johnson G2 40.00 80.00
LS6 Mike Mussina G2 10.00 25.00
LS7 Tino Martinez G3 20.00 50.00
LS8 Fred McGriff G3 20.00 50.00
LS9 Omar Vizquel G4 10.00 25.00
LS10 Rey Ordonez G4 4.00 10.00
LS11 Pat Burrell G4 6.00 15.00
LS12 Chad Hermansen G4 4.00 10.00
LS13 Magglio Ordonez G4 6.00 15.00
LS14 Josh Hamilton G4 15.00 40.00
LS15 Corey Myers G4 4.00 10.00
LS16 B.J. Garbe G4 4.00 10.00

2000 Stadium Club Onyx Extreme

Inserted at a rate of one in 12 hobby, one in 15 retail and one in six HTC packs, these 10 cards feature 10 cards printed using black styrene technology with silver foil stamping.

COMPLETE SET (10) 10.00 25.00
*DIE CUTS: 1.25X TO 3X BASIC ONYX
DIE CUT ODDS 1:60 HOB, 1:75 RET, 1:30 HTC
OE1 Ken Griffey Jr. 1.00 2.50
OE2 Derek Jeter 1.50 4.00
OE3 Vladimir Guerrero .60 1.50
OE4 Nomar Garciaparra 1.00 2.50
OE5 Barry Bonds 1.50 4.00
OE6 Alex Rodriguez 1.00 2.50
OE7 Sammy Sosa .60 1.50
OE8 Ivan Rodriguez .40 1.00
OE9 Larry Walker .25 .60
OE10 Andruw Jones .40 1.00

2000 Stadium Club Scenes

Inserted as a box-topper in hobby and HTC boxes, these eight cards which measure 2 1/2" by 4 11/16" feature superstar players in a special "widevision" format.

COMPLETE SET (8) 10.00 25.00
SCS1 Mark McGwire 2.00 5.00
SCS2 Alex Rodriguez 1.25 3.00
SCS3 Cal Ripken 2.50 6.00
SCS4 Sammy Sosa .75 2.00
SCS5 Derek Jeter 2.00 5.00
SCS6 Ken Griffey Jr. 1.25 3.00
SCS7 Nomar Garciaparra 1.25 3.00
SCS8 Chipper Jones .75 2.00

2000 Stadium Club Souvenir

Inserted exclusively into hobby packs at a rate of one in 339 hobby packs and one in 136 HTC packs, these cards feature die-cut technology which incorporates an actual piece of a game-used uniform.

S1 Wade Boggs 10.00 25.00
S2 Edgardo Alfonzo 4.00 10.00
S3 Robin Ventura 6.00 15.00

2000 Stadium Club 3 X 3 Luminous

Inserted at a rate of one in 18 hobby, one in 24 retail and one in nine HTC packs, these 30 cards can be fused together to form one very oversized card. The luminous variety is the most common of the three forms used (Luminous, Luminescent and Illuminator).

COMPLETE SET (30) 60.00 120.00
*ILLUMINATOR: 1.5X TO 4X LUMINOUS
ILLUM ODDS 1:144 HOB, 1:192 RET, 1:72 HTC
*L'SCENT: .75X TO 2X LUMINOUS
L'SCENT ODDS 1:72 HOB, 1:96 RET, 1:36 HTC
1A Randy Johnson 1.50 4.00
1B Pedro Martinez 1.00 2.50
1C Greg Maddux 2.50 6.00
2A Mike Piazza 2.50 6.00
2B Ivan Rodriguez 1.00 2.50
2C Mike Lieberthal .60 1.50
3A Mark McGwire 4.00 10.00
3B Jeff Bagwell 1.00 2.50
3C Sean Casey .60 1.50
4A Craig Biggio 1.00 2.50
4B Roberto Alomar 1.00 2.50
4C Jay Bell .60 1.50
5A Chipper Jones 1.50 4.00
5B Matt Williams .60 1.50
5C Robin Ventura 1.00 2.50
6A Alex Rodriguez 2.50 6.00
6B Derek Jeter 4.00 10.00
6C Nomar Garciaparra 2.50 6.00
7A Barry Bonds 4.00 10.00
7B Luis Gonzalez .60 1.50
7C Dante Bichette .60 1.50
8A Ken Griffey Jr. 2.50 6.00
8B Bernie Williams 1.00 2.50
8C Andruw Jones 1.00 2.50
9A Manny Ramirez 1.00 2.50
9B Sammy Sosa 1.50 4.00
9C Juan Gonzalez .60 1.50
10A Jose Canseco 1.00 2.50
10B Frank Thomas 1.50 4.00
10C Rafael Palmeiro 1.00 2.50

2001 Stadium Club

The 2001 Stadium Club product was released in late December, 2000 and features a 200-card base set. The set is broken into tiers as follows: 175 Base Veterans and 25 Prospects (1:6). Each pack contained seven cards and carried a suggested retail price of $1.99.

COMPLETE SET (200) 50.00 120.00
COMP.SET w/o SP's (175) 10.00 25.00
COMMON CARD (1-150) .10 .30
COMMON SP (151-200) 1.25 3.00
1 Nomar Garciaparra .50 1.25
2 Chipper Jones .30 .75
3 Jeff Bagwell .20 .50
4 Chad Kreuter .10 .30
5 Randy Johnson .30 .75
6 Mike Hampton .10 .30
7 Barry Larkin .20 .50
8 Bernie Williams .20 .50
9 Chris Singleton .10 .30
10 Larry Walker .10 .30
11 Brad Ausmus .10 .30
12 Ron Coomer .10 .30
13 Edgardo Alfonzo .10 .30
14 Delino DeShields .10 .30
15 Tony Gwynn .40 1.00
16 Andruw Jones .20 .50
17 Raul Mondesi .10 .30
18 Troy Glaus .10 .30
19 Ben Grieve .10 .30
20 Sammy Sosa .30 .75
21 Fernando Vina .10 .30
22 Jeromy Burnitz .10 .30
23 Jay Bell .10 .30
24 Pete Harnisch .10 .30
25 Barry Bonds .75 2.00
26 Eric Karros .10 .30
27 Alex Gonzalez .10 .30
28 Mike Lieberthal .10 .30
29 Juan Encarnacion .10 .30
30 Derek Jeter .75 2.00
31 Luis Sojo .10 .30
32 Eric Milton .10 .30
33 Aaron Boone .10 .30
34 Roberto Alomar .20 .50
35 John Olerud .10 .30
36 Orlando Cabrera .10 .30
37 Shawn Green .10 .30
38 Roger Cedeno .10 .30
39 Garret Anderson .10 .30
40 Jim Thome .20 .50
41 Gabe Kapler .10 .30
42 Mo Vaughn .10 .30
43 Sean Casey .10 .30
44 Preston Wilson .10 .30
45 Javy Lopez .10 .30
46 Ryan Klesko .10 .30
47 Ray Durham .10 .30
48 Dean Palmer .10 .30
49 Jorge Posada .20 .50
50 Alex Rodriguez .50 1.25
51 Tom Glavine .20 .50
52 Ray Lankford .10 .30
53 Jose Canseco .20 .50
54 Tim Salmon .20 .50
55 Cal Ripken 1.00 2.50
56 Bob Abreu .10 .30
57 Robin Ventura .10 .30
58 Damion Easley .10 .30
59 Paul O'Neill .20 .50
60 Ivan Rodriguez .20 .50
61 Carl Everett .10 .30
62 Doug Glanville .10 .30
63 Jeff Kent .10 .30
64 Jay Buhner .10 .30
65 Cliff Floyd .10 .30
66 Rick Ankiel .10 .30
67 Mark Grace .20 .50
68 Brian Jordan .10 .30
69 Craig Biggio .20 .50
70 Carlos Delgado .10 .30
71 Brad Radke .10 .30
72 Greg Maddux .50 1.25
73 Al Leiter .10 .30
74 Pokey Reese .10 .30
75 Todd Helton .20 .50
76 Mariano Rivera .30 .75
77 Shane Spencer .10 .30
78 Jason Kendall .10 .30
79 Chuck Knoblauch .10 .30
80 Scott Rolen .20 .50
81 Jose Offerman .10 .30
82 J.T. Snow .10 .30
83 Pat Meares .10 .30
84 Quilvio Veras .10 .30
85 Edgar Renteria .10 .30
86 Luis Matos .10 .30
87 Adrian Beltre .10 .30
88 Luis Gonzalez .10 .30
89 Rickey Henderson .30 .75
90 Brian Giles .10 .30
91 Carlos Febles .10 .30
92 Tino Martinez .20 .50
93 Magglio Ordonez .10 .30
94 Rafael Furcal .10 .30
95 Mike Mussina .20 .50
96 Gary Sheffield .10 .30
97 Kenny Lofton .10 .30
98 Fred McGriff .20 .50
99 Ken Caminiti .10 .30
100 Mark McGwire .75 2.00
101 Tom Goodwin .10 .30
102 Mark Grudzielanek .10 .30
103 Derek Bell .10 .30
104 Mike Lowell .10 .30
105 Jeff Cirillo .10 .30
106 Orlando Hernandez .10 .30
107 Jose Valentin .10 .30
108 Warren Morris .10 .30
109 Mike Williams .10 .30
110 Greg Zaun .10 .30
111 Jose Vidro .10 .30
112 Omar Vizquel .20 .50
113 Vinny Castilla .10 .30
114 Gregg Jefferies .10 .30
115 Kevin Brown .10 .30
116 Shannon Stewart .10 .30
117 Marquis Grissom .10 .30
118 Manny Ramirez .20 .50
119 Albert Belle .10 .30
120 Bret Boone .10 .30
121 Johnny Damon .20 .50
122 Juan Gonzalez .10 .30
123 David Justice .10 .30
124 Jeffrey Hammonds .10 .30
125 Ken Griffey Jr. .50 1.25
126 Mike Sweeney .10 .30
127 Tony Clark .10 .30
128 Todd Zeile .10 .30
129 Mark Johnson .10 .30
130 Matt Williams .10 .30
131 Geoff Jenkins .10 .30
132 Jason Giambi .10 .30
133 Steve Finley .10 .30
134 Derrek Lee .20 .50
135 Royce Clayton .10 .30
136 Joe Randa .10 .30
137 Rafael Palmeiro .20 .50
138 Kevin Young .10 .30
139 Mike Redmond .10 .30
140 Vladimir Guerrero .30 .75
141 Greg Vaughn .10 .30
142 Jermaine Dye .10 .30
143 Roger Clemens .60 1.50
144 Denny Hocking .10 .30
145 Frank Thomas .30 .75
146 Carlos Beltran .10 .30
147 Eric Young .10 .30
148 Pat Burrell .10 .30
149 Pedro Martinez .20 .50
150 Mike Piazza .50 1.25
151 Adrian Gonzalez .20 .50
152 Adam Johnson .20 .50
153 Luis Montanez SP RC 1.25 3.00
154 Mike Stodolka .20 .50
155 Phil Dumatrait .20 .50
156 Sean Burnett SP 1.25 3.00
157 Dominic Rich SP RC 1.25 3.00
158 Adam Wainwright .20 .50
159 Scott Thorman .20 .50
160 Scott Heard SP 1.25 3.00
161 Chad Petty SP RC 1.25 3.00
162 Matt Wheatland .20 .50
163 Bryan Digby .20 .50
164 Rocco Baldelli .20 .50
165 Grady Sizemore .75 2.00
166 Brian Sellier SP RC 1.25 3.00
167 Rick Brosseau SP RC 1.25 3.00
168 Shawn Fagan SP RC 1.25 3.00
169 Sean Smith SP 1.25 3.00
170 Chris Bass SP RC 1.25 3.00
171 Corey Patterson .20 .50
172 Sean Burroughs .20 .50
173 Ben Petrick .20 .50
174 Mike Glendenning .20 .50
175 Barry Zito .30 .75
176 Milton Bradley .20 .50
177 Bobby Bradley .20 .50
178 Jason Hart .20 .50
179 Ryan Anderson .20 .50
180 Ben Sheets .30 .75
181 Adam Everett .20 .50
182 Alfonso Soriano .20 .50
183 Josh Hamilton .40 1.00
184 Eric Munson .20 .50
185 Chin-Feng Chen .20 .50
186 Tim Christman SP RC 1.25 3.00
187 J.R. House SP 1.25 3.00
188 B.Parker SP RC 1.25 3.00
189 Sean Fesh SP RC 1.25 3.00
190 Joel Pineiro SP 1.25 3.00
191 Oscar Ramirez SP RC 1.25 3.00
192 Alex Santos SP RC 1.25 3.00
193 Eddy Reyes SP RC 1.25 3.00
194 Mike Jacobs SP RC 6.00 15.00
195 Erick Almonte SP RC 1.25 3.00
196 B.Claussen SP RC 1.25 3.00
197 Kris Keller SP RC 1.25 3.00
198 Wilson Betemit SP RC 3.00 8.00
199 Andy Phillips SP RC 6.00 15.00
200 A.Pettyjohn SP RC 1.25 3.00

2001 Stadium Club Beam Team

Randomly inserted into packs at one in 175 Hobby, and one in 68 HTA, this 30-card die-cut insert set features players who possess unparalleled style to accompany their world-class talent. Please note that these cards are individually serial numbered to 500, and that the card backs carry a "BT" prefix.

BT1 Sammy Sosa 5.00 12.00
BT2 Mark McGwire 12.50 30.00
BT3 Vladimir Guerrero 5.00 12.00
BT4 Chipper Jones 5.00 12.00
BT5 Manny Ramirez 3.00 8.00
BT6 Derek Jeter 12.50 30.00
BT7 Alex Rodriguez 8.00 20.00
BT8 Cal Ripken 15.00 40.00
BT9 Ken Griffey Jr. 8.00 20.00
BT10 Greg Maddux 8.00 20.00
BT11 Barry Bonds 12.50 30.00
BT12 Pedro Martinez 3.00 8.00
BT13 Nomar Garciaparra 8.00 20.00
BT14 Randy Johnson 5.00 12.00
BT15 Frank Thomas 5.00 12.00
BT16 Ivan Rodriguez 3.00 8.00
BT17 Jeff Bagwell 3.00 8.00
BT18 Mike Piazza 8.00 20.00
BT19 Todd Helton 3.00 8.00
BT20 Shawn Green 2.00 5.00
BT21 Juan Gonzalez 2.00 5.00
BT22 Larry Walker 2.00 5.00
BT23 Tony Gwynn 8.00 20.00
BT24 Pat Burrell 2.00 5.00
BT25 Rafael Furcal 2.00 5.00
BT26 Corey Patterson 2.00 5.00
BT27 Chin-Feng Chen 2.00 5.00
BT28 Sean Burroughs 2.00 5.00
BT29 Ryan Anderson 2.00 5.00
BT30 Josh Hamilton 4.00 10.00

2001 Stadium Club Capture the Action

Randomly inserted into packs at one in eight HOB/RET and one in two HTA, this 15-card insert features transformer technology that open up to enlarged action photos of ballplayers at the top of their game. Card backs carry a "CA" prefix.

COMPLETE SET (15) 12.50 30.00
*GAME VIEW: 10X TO 25X BASIC CAPTURE
GAME VIEW ODDS 1:577 HOBBY, 1:224 HTA
GAME VIEW PRINT RUN 100 SERIAL #'d SETS
CA1 Cal Ripken 1.50 4.00
CA2 Alex Rodriguez .75 2.00
CA3 Mike Piazza .75 2.00
CA4 Mark McGwire 1.25 3.00
CA5 Greg Maddux .75 2.00
CA6 Derek Jeter 1.25 3.00
CA7 Chipper Jones .50 1.25
CA8 Pedro Martinez .40 1.00
CA9 Ken Griffey Jr. .75 2.00
CA10 Nomar Garciaparra .75 2.00
CA11 Randy Johnson .50 1.25
CA12 Sammy Sosa .50 1.25
CA13 Vladimir Guerrero .50 1.25
CA14 Barry Bonds 1.25 3.00
CA15 Ivan Rodriguez .40 1.00

2001 Stadium Club Co-Signers

Randomly inserted into packs at one in 962 Hobby and one in 374 HTA packs, this nine-card insert features authenticated autographs of two players on the same card. Please note that the Chipper Jones/Troy Glaus and the Corey Patterson/Nick Johnson cards packed out as exchange cards, and must be redeemed by 11/30/01.

CO1 Nomar Garciaparra 300.00 500.00
Derek Jeter
CO2 Roberto Alomar 20.00 50.00
Edgardo Alfonzo
CO3 Rick Ankiel 15.00 40.00
Kevin Millwood
CO4 Chipper Jones 40.00 80.00
Troy Glaus
CO5 Magglio Ordonez 15.00 40.00
Bob Abreu
CO6 Adam Piatt 10.00 25.00
Sean Burroughs
CO7 Corey Patterson 15.00 40.00
Nick Johnson
CO8 Adrian Gonzalez 15.00 40.00
Rocco Baldelli
CO9 Adam Johnson 10.00 25.00
Mike Stodolka

2001 Stadium Club Diamond Pearls

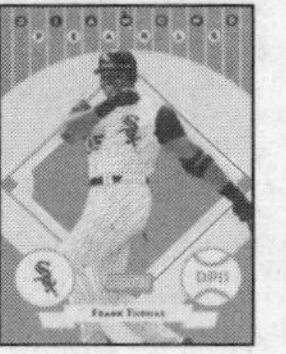

Randomly inserted into packs at one in eight HOB/RET packs, and one in 3 HTA packs; this 20-card insert features players that are the most sought after treasures in the game today. Card backs carry a "DP" prefix.

COMPLETE SET (20) 20.00 50.00
DP1 Ken Griffey Jr. 1.25 3.00
DP2 Alex Rodriguez 1.25 3.00
DP3 Derek Jeter 2.00 5.00
DP4 Chipper Jones .75 2.00
DP5 Nomar Garciaparra 1.25 3.00
DP6 Vladimir Guerrero .75 2.00
DP7 Jeff Bagwell .60 1.50
DP8 Cal Ripken 2.50 6.00
DP9 Sammy Sosa .75 2.00
DP10 Mark McGwire 2.00 5.00
DP11 Frank Thomas .75 2.00
DP12 Pedro Martinez .60 1.50
DP13 Manny Ramirez .60 1.50
DP14 Randy Johnson .75 2.00
DP15 Barry Bonds 2.00 5.00
DP16 Ivan Rodriguez .60 1.50
DP17 Greg Maddux 1.25 3.00
DP18 Mike Piazza 1.25 3.00
DP19 Todd Helton .60 1.50
DP20 Shawn Green .60 1.50

2001 Stadium Club King of the Hill Dirt Relic

Randomly inserted into packs at one in 20 HTA, this five-card insert features game-used dirt cards from the pitchers mound of today's top pitchers. The Topps Company announced that the ten exchange subjects from Stadium Club Play at the Plate, King of the Hill, and Souvenirs contain the wrong card back stating that they were autographed. None of these cards are actually autographed. Also note that these cards were inserted into packs with a white "waxpaper" covering to protect the cards. Card backs carry a "KH" prefix. Please note that Greg Maddux and Rick Ankiel both packed out as exchange cards and must be returned to Topps by 11/30/01.

KH1 Pedro Martinez 4.00 10.00
KH2 Randy Johnson 4.00 10.00
KH3 G.Maddux ERR 4.00 10.00
KH4 R.Ankiel ERR 3.00 8.00
KH5 Kevin Brown 3.00 8.00

2001 Stadium Club Lone Star Signatures

Randomly inserted into packs, this 18-card insert features authentic autographs from some of the Major Leagues most prolific players. Please note that this insert was broken into four tiers as follows: Group A (1:937 HOB/RET, 1:364 HTA), Group B (1:1010 HOB/RET, 1:392 HTA), Group C (1:1541 HOB/RET, 1:600 HTA), and Group D (1:354 HOB/RET, 1:138 HTA). The overall odds for pulling an autograph was one in 181 HOB/RET and one in 70 HTA.

LS1 Nomar Garciaparra A 50.00 100.00
LS2 Derek Jeter A 75.00 150.00
LS3 Edgardo Alfonzo A 10.00 25.00
LS4 Roberto Alomar A 30.00 60.00
LS5 Magglio Ordonez A 10.00 25.00
LS6 Bobby Abreu A 15.00 40.00
LS7 Chipper Jones A 20.00 50.00
LS8 Troy Glaus A 15.00 40.00
LS9 Nick Johnson B 6.00 15.00
LS10 Adam Piatt B 6.00 15.00
LS11 Sean Burroughs B 4.00 10.00
LS12 Corey Patterson B 4.00 10.00
LS13 Rick Ankiel C 10.00 25.00
LS14 Kevin Millwood C 6.00 15.00
LS15 Adrian Gonzalez D 15.00 40.00
LS16 Adam Johnson D 4.00 10.00
LS17 Rocco Baldelli D 6.00 15.00
LS18 Mike Stodolka D 4.00 10.00

2001 Stadium Club Play at the Plate Dirt Relic

Randomly inserted into packs at one in 10 HTA, this nine-card insert features game-used dirt from the batter's box in which these top players played in. The Topps Company announced that the ten exchange subjects from Stadium Club Play at the Plate, King of the Hill, and Souvenirs contain the wrong card back stating that they were autographed. None of these cards are actually autographed. Please note that both Chipper Jones and Jeff Bagwell are numbered PP6. Also note that these cards were inserted into packs with a white "waxpaper" covering to protect the cards. The exchange deadline for these cards was 11/30/01.

PP1 Mark McGwire ERR 15.00 40.00
PP2 S.Sosa ERR 4.00 10.00
PP3 Vladimir Guerrero 4.00 10.00
PP4 Ken Griffey Jr. ERR 6.00 15.00
PP5 Mike Piazza 4.00 10.00
PP6 J.Bagwell ERR 4.00 10.00
PP6 C.Jones ERR 4.00 10.00
PP7 Barry Bonds 10.00 25.00
PP8 Alex Rodriguez 6.00 15.00
PP10 Nomar Garciaparra ERR 6.00 15.00

2001 Stadium Club Prospect Performance

Randomly inserted into packs at one in 262 HOB/RET and one in 102 HTA, this 20-card insert features game-used jersey cards from some of the hottest young players in the Major Leagues. Card backs carry a "PRP" prefix.

PRP1 Chin-Feng Chen 40.00 80.00
PRP2 Bobby Bradley 3.00 8.00
PRP3 Tomokazu Ohka 4.00 10.00
PRP4 Kurt Ainsworth 3.00 8.00
PRP5 Craig Anderson 3.00 8.00
PRP6 Josh Hamilton 6.00 15.00
PRP7 Felipe Lopez 4.00 10.00
PRP8 Ryan Anderson 3.00 8.00
PRP9 Alex Escobar 3.00 8.00
PRP10 Ben Sheets 6.00 15.00
PRP11 Ntema Ndungidi 3.00 8.00
PRP12 Eric Munson 3.00 8.00
PRP13 Aaron Myette 3.00 8.00
PRP14 Jack Cust 3.00 8.00
PRP15 Julio Zuleta 3.00 8.00
PRP16 Corey Patterson 3.00 8.00
PRP17 Carlos Pena 3.00 8.00
PRP18 Marcus Giles 4.00 10.00
PRP19 Travis Wilson 3.00 8.00
PRP20 Barry Zito 6.00 15.00

2001 Stadium Club Souvenirs

Randomly inserted into HTA packs, this eight-card insert features game-used bat cards and game-used jersey cards of modern superstars. Card backs carry a "SCS" prefix. Please note that the Topps Company announced that the ten exchange subjects from Stadium Club Play at the Plate, King of the Hill, and Souvenirs contain the wrong card back stating that they were autographed. None of these cards are actually autographed. Also note that cards of Scott Rolen, Matt Lawton, Jose Vidro, and Pat Burrell all packed out as exchange cards. These cards needed to have been returned to Topps by 11/30/01.

SCS1 Scott Rolen Bat A ERR 6.00 15.00
SCS2 Larry Walker Bat B 6.00 15.00
SCS3 Rafael Furcal Bat A 6.00 15.00
SCS4 Darin Erstad Bat A 6.00 15.00
SCS5 Mike Sweeney Jsy 4.00 10.00
SCS6 Matt Lawton Jsy ERR 4.00 10.00
SCS7 Jose Vidro Jsy ERR 4.00 10.00
SCS8 Pat Burrell Jsy ERR 4.00 10.00

2002 Stadium Club

This 125 card set was issued in late 2001. The set was issued in either six card regular packs or 15 card HTA packs. Cards numbered 101-125 were short printed and are serial numbered to 2999.

COMP.SET w/o SP's (100) 12.50 30.00
COMMON CARD (1-100) .10 .30
COMMON (101-125) 10.00 25.00
1 Pedro Martinez .20 .50
2 Derek Jeter .75 2.00
3 Chipper Jones .30 .75
4 Roberto Alomar .20 .50
5 Albert Pujols 4.00 10.00
6 Bret Boone .10 .30
7 Alex Rodriguez .50 1.25
8 Jose Cruz Jr. .10 .30
9 Mike Hampton .10 .30
10 Vladimir Guerrero .30 .75
11 Jim Edmonds .10 .30
12 Luis Gonzalez .10 .30
13 Jeff Kent .10 .30
14 Mike Piazza .50 1.25
15 Ben Sheets .10 .30
16 Tsuyoshi Shinjo .10 .30
17 Pat Burrell UER .10 .30
Card has a photo of Scott Rolen
18 Jermaine Dye .10 .30
19 Rafael Furcal .10 .30
20 Randy Johnson .30 .75
21 Carlos Delgado .10 .30
22 Roger Clemens .60 1.50
23 Eric Chavez .10 .30
24 Nomar Garciaparra .50 1.25
25 Ivan Rodriguez .20 .50
26 Juan Gonzalez .10 .30
27 Reggie Sanders .10 .30
28 Jeff Bagwell .20 .50
29 Kazuhiro Sasaki .10 .30
30 Larry Walker .10 .30
31 Ben Grieve .10 .30
32 David Justice .10 .30
33 David Wells .10 .30
34 Kevin Brown .10 .30
35 Miguel Tejada .10 .30
36 Jorge Posada .20 .50
37 Javy Lopez .10 .30
38 Cliff Floyd .10 .30
39 Carlos Lee .10 .30
40 Manny Ramirez .20 .50
41 Jim Thome .20 .50
42 Pokey Reese .10 .30
43 Scott Rolen .20 .50
44 Richie Sexson .10 .30
45 Dean Palmer .10 .30
46 Rafael Palmeiro .20 .50
47 Alfonso Soriano .10 .30
48 Craig Biggio .20 .50
49 Troy Glaus .10 .30
50 Andruw Jones .20 .50
51 Ichiro Suzuki .60 1.50
52 Kenny Lofton .10 .30
53 Hideo Nomo .30 .75
54 Magglio Ordonez .10 .30
55 Brad Penny .10 .30
56 Omar Vizquel .20 .50
57 Mike Sweeney .10 .30
58 Gary Sheffield .10 .30
59 Ken Griffey Jr. .50 1.25
60 Curt Schilling .10 .30
61 Bobby Higginson .10 .30
62 Terrence Long .10 .30
63 Moises Alou .10 .30
64 Sandy Alomar Jr. .10 .30
65 Cristian Guzman .10 .30
66 Sammy Sosa .30 .75
67 Jose Vidro .10 .30
68 Edgar Martinez .20 .50
69 Jason Giambi .10 .30
70 Mark McGwire .75 2.00
71 Barry Bonds .75 2.00
72 Greg Vaughn .10 .30
73 Phil Nevin .10 .30
74 Jason Kendall .10 .30
75 Greg Maddux .50 1.25
76 Jeromy Burnitz .10 .30
77 Mike Mussina .20 .50
78 Johnny Damon .20 .50
79 Shawn Green .10 .30
80 Jimmy Rollins .10 .30
81 Edgardo Alfonzo .10 .30
82 Barry Larkin .20 .50
83 Raul Mondesi .10 .30
84 Preston Wilson .10 .30
85 Mike Lieberthal .10 .30
86 J.D. Drew .10 .30
87 Ryan Klesko .10 .30
88 David Segui .10 .30
89 Derek Bell .10 .30
90 Bernie Williams .20 .50
91 Doug Mientkiewicz .10 .30
92 Rich Aurilia .10 .30
93 Ellis Burks .10 .30
94 Placido Polanco .10 .30
95 Darin Erstad .10 .30
96 Brian Giles .10 .30
97 Geoff Jenkins .10 .30
98 Kerry Wood .10 .30
99 Mariano Rivera .30 .75
100 Todd Helton .20 .50
101 Adam Dunn FS 10.00 25.00
102 Grant Balfour FS 10.00 25.00
103 Jae Seo FS 10.00 25.00
104 Hank Blalock FS 10.00 25.00
105 Chris George FS 10.00 25.00
106 Jack Cust FS 10.00 25.00
107 Juan Cruz FS 10.00 25.00
108 Adrian Gonzalez FS 10.00 25.00
109 Nick Johnson FS 10.00 25.00
110 Jeff DaVanon FS 10.00 25.00
111 Juan Diaz FS 10.00 25.00
112 B. Duckworth FS 10.00 25.00
113 Jason Lane FS 10.00 25.00
114 Seung Song FS 10.00 25.00
115 Morgan Ensberg FS 10.00 25.00
116 Marlyn Tisdale FY RC 10.00 25.00
117 Jason Botts FY RC 6.00 15.00
118 Henry Pichardo FY RC 10.00 25.00
119 J. Rodriguez FY RC 10.00 25.00
120 Mike Peeples FY RC 10.00 25.00
121 Rob Bowen EFY RC 10.00 25.00
122 Jeremy Affeldt EFY 10.00 25.00
123 Jorge Buret EFY RC 10.00 25.00
124 Manny Ravelo EFY RC 10.00 25.00
125 Eudy Lajara EFY RC 10.00 25.00
NNO B.Bonds AU Ball 150.00 250.00

2002 Stadium Club All-Star Relics

Randomly inserted in packs, these 28 cards feature relics of players who participated in the All-Star game. Depending on which group the player belonged to there could be between 400 and 4800 of each card printed.

GROUP 1 ODDS 1:477 H, 1:548 R, 1:80 HTA
GROUP 1 PRINT RUN 400 SERIAL #'d SETS
GROUP 2 ODDS 1:795 H, 1:915 R, 1:133 HTA
GROUP 2 PRINT RUN 800 SERIAL #'d SETS
GROUP 3 ODDS 1:199 H, 1:247 R, 1:33 HTA
GROUP 3 PRINT RUN 1200 SERIAL #'d SETS
GROUP 4 ODDS 1:199 H, 1:247 R, 1:33 HTA
GROUP 4 PRINT RUN 2400 SERIAL #'d SETS
GROUP 5 ODDS 1:265 H, 1:305 R, 1:44 HTA
GROUP 5 PRINT RUN 3600 SERIAL #'d SETS
GROUP 6 ODDS 1:397 H, 1:457 R, 1:67 HTA
GROUP 6 PRINT RUN 4800 SERIAL #'d SETS
SCASAP Albert Pujols Bat/800 G2 15.00 40.00
SCASBB Barry Bonds Uni/4800 G6 12.50 30.00
SCASBG Brian Giles Bat/800 G2 4.00 10.00
SCASCF Cliff Floyd Bat/400 G1 4.00 10.00
SCASCG C.Guzman Bat/400 G1 4.00 10.00
SCASCJ Chipper Jones Jsy/1200 G3 6.00 15.00
SCASEM Edgar Martinez Jsy/1200 G3 6.00 15.00
SCASIR Ivan Rodriguez Uni/2400 G4 6.00 15.00
SCASJG Juan Gonzalez Bat/400 G1 4.00 10.00
SCASJK Jeff Kent Bat/400 G1 4.00 10.00
SCASJO John Olerud Jsy/1200 G3 4.00 10.00
SCASJP Jorge Posada Bat/400 G1 6.00 15.00
SCASKS Kaz Sasaki Jsy/1200 G3 4.00 10.00
SCASLW Larry Walker Jsy/2400 G4 4.00 10.00
SCASMA Moises Alou Bat/400 G1 4.00 10.00
SCASMC Mike Cameron Bat/400 G1 4.00 10.00
SCASMO M. Ordonez Bat/400 G1 4.00 10.00
SCASMP Mike Piazza Uni/1200 G3 15.00 40.00
SCASMR Manny Ramirez Uni/3600 G5 6.00 15.00
SCASMS Mike Sweeney Bat/400 G1 4.00 10.00
SCASRA Roberto Alomar Uni/3600 G5 6.00 15.00
SCASRJ Randy Johnson Jsy/2400 G4 6.00 15.00
SCASRK Ryan Klesko Jsy/1200 G3 4.00 10.00
SCASSC Sean Casey Bat/400 G1 4.00 10.00
SCASTG Tony Gwynn Jsy/2400 G4 8.00 20.00
SCASTH Todd Helton Jsy/1200 G3 6.00 15.00
SCASBRB Bret Boone Bat/1200 G3 4.00 10.00
SCASLG3 Luis Gonzalez Bat/800 G2 4.00 10.00

2002 Stadium Club Chasing 500-500

Randomly inserted in packs, these three cards feature memorabilia from Barry Bonds as he chases becoming the first member of the 500 homer, 500 stolen base club.

C55BB1 Barry Bonds Dual 20.00 50.00
C55BB2 Barry Bonds Jsy/600 15.00 40.00
C55BB3 Barry Bonds Multiple/200 50.00 100.00

2002 Stadium Club Passport to the Majors

Randomly inserted in packs, these cards feature foreign players as well as a game-used relic. The jersey relics are serial numbered to 1200 while the bats are printed to differing amounts. The specific print information is notated in our checklist.

PTMAG Andres Galarraga Jsy/1200 4.00 10.00
PTMAJ Andruw Jones Jsy/1200 6.00 15.00
PTMAP Albert Pujols Bat/450 20.00 50.00
PTMAS Alfonso Soriano Bat/400 4.00 10.00
PTMBA Bob Abreu Bat/450 4.00 10.00
PTMBC Bartolo Colon Uni/1200 4.00 10.00
PTMCL Carlos Lee Jsy/1200 4.00 10.00
PTMCP Chan Ho Park Jsy/1200 4.00 10.00
PTMEA Edgardo Alfonzo Jsy/1200 4.00 10.00
PTMIR Ivan Rodriguez Uni/1200 6.00 15.00
PTMJG Juan Gonzalez Jsy/1200 4.00 10.00
PTMJL Javier Lopez Jsy/1200 4.00 10.00
PTMKS Kazuhiro Sasaki Jsy/1200 4.00 10.00
PTMLW Larry Walker Jsy/1200 4.00 10.00
PTMMO Magglio Ordonez Jsy/1200 4.00 10.00
PTMMR Manny Ramirez Jsy/1200 6.00 15.00
PTMMT Miguel Tejada Bat/375 4.00 10.00
PTMPM Pedro Martinez Jsy/1200 6.00 15.00
PTMRA Roberto Alomar Uni/1200 6.00 15.00
PTMRF Rafael Furcal Jsy/1200 4.00 10.00
PTMRM Raul Mondesi Jsy/1200 4.00 10.00
PTMRP Rafael Palmeiro Jsy/1200 6.00 15.00
PTMSH Shig Hasegawa Jsy/1200 4.00 10.00
PTMTS Tsuyoshi Shinjo Bat/400 4.00 10.00
PTMWB Wilson Betemit Bat/325 4.00 10.00

2002 Stadium Club Reel Time

Inserted at a rate of one in eight hobby/retail packs and one in four HTA packs this 20 card set features players who constantly make the highlight reel.

COMPLETE SET (20) 30.00 60.00
RT1 Luis Gonzalez .75 2.00
RT2 Derek Jeter 2.50 6.00
RT3 Ken Griffey Jr. 1.50 4.00
RT4 Alex Rodriguez 1.50 4.00
RT5 Barry Bonds 2.50 6.00
RT6 Ichiro Suzuki 2.00 5.00
RT7 Carlos Delgado .75 2.00
RT8 Manny Ramirez .75 2.00
RT9 Mike Piazza 1.50 4.00
RT10 Mark McGwire 2.50 6.00
RT11 Todd Helton .75 2.00
RT12 Vladimir Guerrero 1.00 2.50
RT13 Jim Thome .75 2.00
RT14 Rich Aurilia .75 2.00
RT15 Bret Boone .75 2.00
RT16 Roberto Alomar .75 2.00
RT17 Jason Giambi .75 2.00
RT18 Chipper Jones 1.00 2.50
RT19 Albert Pujols 2.00 5.00
RT20 Sammy Sosa 1.00 2.50

2002 Stadium Club Stadium Shots

Inserted at a rate of one in 12 hobby/retail packs and one in six HTA packs, these 10 cards feature 10 sluggers known for their long homers.

COMPLETE SET (10) 10.00 25.00
SS1 Sammy Sosa 1.00 2.50
SS2 Manny Ramirez 1.00 2.50
SS3 Jason Giambi 1.00 2.50
SS4 Mike Piazza 1.50 4.00
SS5 Barry Bonds 2.50 6.00
SS6 Ken Griffey Jr. 1.50 4.00
SS7 Juan Gonzalez 1.00 2.50
SS8 Jeff Bagwell 1.00 2.50
SS9 Jim Thome 1.00 2.50
SS10 Mark McGwire 2.50 6.00

2002 Stadium Club Stadium Slices Barrel Relics

These five cards were inserted in packs and feature bat slices cut from the barrel of the bat. Each card is printed to a different amount and that information is notated in our checklist.

GROUP A ODDS 1:4289 HOBBY, 1:1700 HTA
GROUP B ODDS 1:6768 HOBBY, 1:2680 HTA
GROUP C ODDS 1:6465 HOBBY, 1:2581 HTA
GROUP D ODDS 1:6101 HOBBY, 1:2489 HTA
SCSSAP Albert Pujols B/95 50.00 100.00
SCSSBB Barry Bonds C/100 50.00 100.00
SCSSBW Bern Williams A/100 12.50 30.00
SCSSIR Ivan Rodriguez D/105 12.50 30.00
SCSSLG Luis Gonzalez A/75 12.50 30.00

2002 Stadium Club Stadium Slices Handle Relics

These five cards were inserted in packs and feature bat slices cut from the handle of the bat. Each card is printed to a different amount and that information is notated in our checklist.

GROUP A ODDS 1:3671 HOBBY, 1:1483 HTA
GROUP B ODDS 1:3580 HOBBY, 1:1422 HTA
GROUP C ODDS 1:3384 HOBBY, 1:1366 HTA
GROUP D ODDS 1:3209 HOBBY, 1:1290 HTA
GROUP E ODDS 1:3050 HOBBY, 1:1222 HTA
SCSSAP Albert Pujols C/190 30.00 60.00
SCSSBB Barry Bonds A/175 25.00 60.00
SCSSBW Bernie Williams E/210 8.00 20.00
SCSSIR Ivan Rodriguez B/180 8.00 20.00
SCSSLG Luis Gonzalez D/200 8.00 20.00

2002 Stadium Club Stadium Slices Trademark Relics

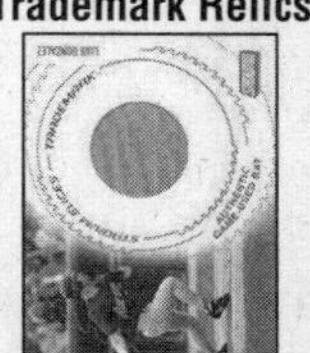

These five cards were inserted in packs and feature bat slices cut from the middle of the bat. Each card is printed to a different amount and that information is notated in our checklist.

SCSSAP Albert Pujols C/130 40.00 80.00
SCSSBB Barry Bonds A/105 40.00 80.00
SCSSBW Bernie Williams B/110 10.00 25.00
SCSSIR Ivan Rodriguez E/170 10.00 25.00
SCSSLG Luis Gonzalez D/140 10.00 25.00

2002 Stadium Club World Champion Relics

Inserted at different odds depending on what type of relic, these 69 cards feature game-used relics from World Series ring holders. The Rickey Henderson card was short printed and we have notated this information in our checklist.

BAT ODDS 1:94 H, 1:108 R, 1:16 HTA
JERSEY ODDS 1:106 H, 1:122 R, 1:18 HTA
PANTS ODDS 1:795 H, 1:1022 R, 1:133 HTA
SPIKES 1:38,400 H, 1:51,696 R, 1:6335 HTA
WCAB Al Bumbry Bat 4.00 10.00
WCAL Al Leiter Jsy 6.00 15.00
WCAT Alan Trammell Bat 6.00 15.00
WCBB Bert Blyleven Jsy 6.00 15.00
WCBD Bucky Dent Bat 6.00 15.00
WCBM Bill Madlock Bat 6.00 15.00
WCBW B.Williams Bat 8.00 20.00
WCBRB Bob Boone Jsy 6.00 15.00
WCCC C.Chambliss Bat 6.00 15.00
WCCJ Chipper Jones Bat 10.00 25.00
WCCK C.Knoblauch Bat 6.00 15.00
WCDB Don Baylor Bat 6.00 15.00
WCDC D.Concepcion Bat 6.00 15.00
WCDJ David Justice Bat 6.00 15.00
WCDL Dave Lopes Bat 6.00 15.00
WCDP Dave Parker Bat 6.00 15.00
WCDW Dave Winfield Bat 6.00 15.00
WCED Eric Davis Bat 6.00 15.00
WCES Ed Sprague Jsy 4.00 10.00
WCEM1 Eddie Murray Bat 10.00 25.00
WCEM2 Ed. Murray Jsy 10.00 25.00
WCFM Fred McGriff Jsy 8.00 20.00
WCFV F. Valenzuela Bat 6.00 15.00
WCGB George Brett Bat 20.00 50.00
WCGF George Foster Bat 6.00 15.00
WCGH G. Hendrick Bat 6.00 15.00
WCGL Greg Luzinski Bat 6.00 15.00
WCGM Greg Maddux Jsy 15.00 40.00
WCGC1 Gary Carter Bat 6.00 15.00
WCGC2 Gary Carter Jsy 6.00 15.00
WCHM Hal McRae Bat 6.00 15.00
WCJB Johnny Bench Bat 10.00 25.00
WCJC Joe Carter Jsy 6.00 15.00
WCJL Javy Lopez Bat 6.00 15.00
WCJO John Olerud Jsy 6.00 15.00
WCJP Jorge Posada Bat 8.00 20.00
WCJS John Smoltz Jsy 8.00 20.00
WCJV Jose Vizcaino Bat 4.00 10.00
WCJC1 Jose Canseco Yankees Bat 8.00 20.00
WCJC2 Jose Canseco A's Bat 8.00 20.00
WCKG Ken Griffey Sr. Bat 8.00 20.00
WCKH K. Hernandez Bat 6.00 15.00
WCKP Kirby Puckett Bat 10.00 25.00
WCKG1 Kirk Gibson Bat 6.00 15.00
WCKG2 Kirk Gibson Jsy 6.00 15.00
WCLW Lou Whitaker Bat 6.00 15.00
WCLVP Lou Piniella Bat 6.00 15.00
WCMA Moises Alou Bat 6.00 15.00
WCMS Mike Scioscia Bat 6.00 15.00
WCMW M. Wilson Bat 6.00 15.00
WCMJS M. Schmidt Bat 20.00 50.00
WCOH Orel Hershiser Jsy 6.00 15.00
WCOS Ozzie Smith Bat 15.00 40.00
WCPG Phil Garner Bat 6.00 15.00
WCPM Paul Molitor Bat 6.00 15.00
WCPO Paul O'Neill Pants 8.00 20.00
WCRA R. Alomar Pants 8.00 20.00
WCRC Ron Cey Bat 6.00 15.00
WCRH R.Henderson Spikes SP/50 *
WCRJ R. Jackson Bat 8.00 20.00
WCSB Scott Brosius Bat 6.00 15.00
WCTG Tom Glavine Jsy 8.00 20.00
WCTM T. Munson Bat 30.00 60.00
WCTP Tony Perez Bat 6.00 15.00
WCTLM T. Martinez Bat 8.00 20.00
WCWB Wade Boggs Bat 8.00 20.00
WCWH W. Hernandez Jsy 6.00 15.00
WCWR W. Randolph Bat 6.00 15.00
WCWS Willie Stargell Bat 8.00 20.00

2003 Stadium Club

This 125 card set was released in November, 2002. This set marked the conclusion of the 13 year run of Stadium Club product being released as a baseball brand by Topps. This set was issued in either 10 card packs or 20 card HTA packs. The 10-card packs were issued 10 cards to a pack with 24 packs to a box and 12 boxes to a case with an SRP of $3 per pack. The 20-card HTA packs were issued 10 packs to a box and eight boxes to a case with an SRP of $10 per pack. Cards numbered from 101 through 113 featured future stars while cards numbered 114 through 125 feature players in their first year on a Stadium Club card. Cards numbered

101 through 125 were issued with different photos depending on whether or not they came from hobby or retail packs. These cards have two different varieties in all the parallel sets as well. Sets are considered complete at 125 cards - with one copy of either the hobby or retail versions of cards 101-125.

COMP.MASTER SET (150) 30.00 60.00
COMPLETE SET (125) 20.00 40.00
COMMON CARD (1-100) .10 .30
COMMON CARD (101-115) .20 .50
COMMON CARD (116-125) .40 1.00
1 Rafael Furcal .10 .30
2 Randy Winn .10 .30
3 Eric Chavez .10 .30
4 Fernando Vina .10 .30
5 Pat Burrell .10 .30
6 Derek Jeter .75 2.00
7 Ivan Rodriguez .20 .50
8 Eric Hinske .10 .30
9 Roberto Alomar .20 .50
10 Tony Batista .10 .30
11 Jacque Jones .10 .30
12 Alfonso Soriano .10 .30
13 Omar Vizquel .20 .50
14 Paul Konerko .10 .30
15 Shawn Green .10 .30
16 Garret Anderson .10 .30
17 Darin Erstad .10 .30
18 Johnny Damon .20 .50
19 Juan Gonzalez .10 .30
20 Luis Gonzalez .10 .30
21 Sean Burroughs .10 .30
22 Mark Prior .20 .50
23 Javier Vazquez .10 .30
24 Shannon Stewart .10 .30
25 Jay Gibbons .10 .30
26 A.J. Pierzynski .10 .30
27 Vladimir Guerrero .30 .75
28 Austin Kearns .10 .30
29 Shea Hillenbrand .10 .30
30 Magglio Ordonez .10 .30
31 Mike Cameron .10 .30
32 Tim Salmon .20 .50
33 Brian Jordan .10 .30
34 Moises Alou .10 .30
35 Rich Aurilia .10 .30
36 Nick Johnson .10 .30
37 Junior Spivey .10 .30
38 Curt Schilling .10 .30
39 Jose Vidro .10 .30
40 Orlando Cabrera .10 .30
41 Jeff Bagwell .20 .50
42 Mo Vaughn .10 .30
43 Luis Castillo .10 .30
44 Vicente Padilla .10 .30
45 Pedro Martinez .20 .50
46 John Olerud .10 .30
47 Tom Glavine .20 .50
48 Torii Hunter .10 .30
49 J.D. Drew .10 .30
50 Alex Rodriguez .50 1.25
51 Randy Johnson .30 .75
52 Richie Sexson .10 .30
53 Jimmy Rollins .10 .30
54 Cristian Guzman .10 .30
55 Tim Hudson .10 .30
56 Mark Buehrle .10 .30
57 Paul Lo Duca .10 .30
58 Aramis Ramirez .10 .30
59 Todd Helton .20 .50
60 Lance Berkman .10 .30
61 Josh Beckett .10 .30
62 Bret Boone .10 .30
63 Miguel Tejada .10 .30
64 Nomar Garciaparra .50 1.25
65 Albert Pujols .60 1.50
66 Chipper Jones .30 .75
67 Scott Rolen .20 .50
68 Kerry Wood .10 .30
69 Jorge Posada .20 .50
70 Ichiro Suzuki .60 1.50
71 Jeff Kent .10 .30
72 David Eckstein .10 .30
73 Phil Nevin .10 .30
74 Brian Giles .10 .30
75 Barry Zito .10 .30
76 Andruw Jones .20 .50
77 Jim Thome .20 .50
78 Robert Fick .10 .30
79 Rafael Palmeiro .20 .50
80 Barry Bonds .75 2.00
81 Gary Sheffield .10 .30
82 Jim Edmonds .10 .30
83 Kazuhisa Ishii .10 .30
84 Jose Hernandez .10 .30
85 Jason Giambi .10 .30
86 Mark Mulder .10 .30
87 Roger Clemens .60 1.50
88 Troy Glaus .10 .30
89 Carlos Delgado .10 .30
90 Mike Sweeney .10 .30
91 Ken Griffey Jr. .50 1.25
92 Manny Ramirez .20 .50
93 Ryan Klesko .10 .30
94 Larry Walker .10 .30
95 Adam Dunn .10 .30
96 Raul Ibanez .10 .30
97 Preston Wilson .10 .30
98 Roy Oswalt .10 .30
99 Sammy Sosa .30 .75
100 Mike Piazza .50 1.25
101H Jose Reyes FS .30 .75
101R Jose Reyes FS .30 .75
102H Ed Rogers FS .20 .50
102R Ed Rogers FS .20 .50
103H Hank Blalock FS .30 .75
103R Hank Blalock FS .30 .75
104H Mark Teixeira FS .40 1.00
104R Mark Teixeira FS .40 1.00
105H Orlando Hudson FS .20 .50
105R Orlando Hudson FS .20 .50
106H Drew Henson FS .20 .50
106R Drew Henson FS .20 .50
107H Joe Mauer FS .60 1.50
107R Joe Mauer FS .60 1.50
108H Carl Crawford FS .30 .75
108R Carl Crawford FS .30 .75
109H Marlon Byrd FS .20 .50
109R Marlon Byrd FS .20 .50
110H Jason Stokes FS .20 .50
110R Jason Stokes FS .20 .50
111H Miguel Cabrera FS .60 1.50
111R Miguel Cabrera FS .60 1.50
112H Wilson Betemit FS .20 .50
112R Wilson Betemit FS .20 .50
113H Jerome Williams FS .20 .50
113R Jerome Williams FS .20 .50
114H Walter Young FYP .40 1.00
114R Walter Young FYP .40 1.00
115H Juan Camacho FYP RC .40 1.00
115R Juan Camacho FYP RC .40 1.00
116H Chris Duncan FYP RC 2.00 5.00
116R Chris Duncan FYP RC 2.00 5.00
117H F.Gutierrez FYP RC .75 2.00
117R F.Gutierrez FYP RC .75 2.00
118H Adam LaRoche FYP .40 1.00
118R Adam LaRoche FYP .40 1.00
119H M.Ramirez FYP RC .60 1.50
119R M.Ramirez FYP RC .60 1.50
120H Il Kim FYP RC .40 1.00
120R Il Kim FYP RC .40 1.00
121H Wayne Lydon FYP RC .40 1.00
121R Wayne Lydon FYP RC .40 1.00
122H Daryl Clark FYP RC .40 1.00
122R Daryl Clark FYP RC .40 1.00
123H Sean Pierce FYP .40 1.00
123R Sean Pierce FYP .40 1.00
124H Andy Marte FYP RC 1.50 4.00
124R Andy Marte FYP RC 1.50 4.00
125H Mat.Peterson FYP RC .40 1.00
125R Mat.Peterson FYP RC .40 1.00

2003 Stadium Club Photographer's Proof

Randomly inserted into packs:, this is a parallel to the Stadium Club set. These cards were issued to a stated print run of 299 serial numbered sets.

*PROOF 1-100: 4X TO 10X BASIC
*PROOF 101-115: 2X TO 5X BASIC
*PROOF 116-125: 1.5X TO 4X BASIC
1-100 ODDS 1:39 H, 1:23 HTA, 1:34 R
101-125 ODDS 1:61 H, 1:17 HTA, 1:92 R

2003 Stadium Club Royal Gold

Inserted one per pack, this is a parallel to the Stadium Club set. These cards can be differentiated by their thickness compared to the regular cards. Photo variations were created for cards 101-125 whereby hobby and retail packs each had exclusive distribution on one image per player.

*GOLD 1-100: 1X TO 2.5X BASIC
*GOLD 101-115: 1X TO 2.5X BASIC
*GOLD 116-125: .75X TO 2X BASIC

2003 Stadium Club Beam Team

Inserted into packs at a stated rate of one in 12 hobby, one in 12 retail and one in two HTA, these 20 cards feature some of the hottest talents in baseball.

BT1 Lance Berkman .75 2.00
BT2 Barry Bonds 3.00 8.00
BT3 Carlos Delgado .75 2.00
BT4 Adam Dunn .75 2.00
BT5 Nomar Garciaparra 2.00 5.00
BT6 Jason Giambi .75 2.00
BT7 Brian Giles .75 2.00
BT8 Shawn Green .75 2.00
BT9 Vladimir Guerrero 1.25 3.00
BT10 Todd Helton 1.25 3.00
BT11 Derek Jeter 3.00 8.00
BT12 Chipper Jones 1.25 3.00
BT13 Jeff Kent .75 2.00
BT14 Mike Piazza 2.00 5.00
BT15 Alex Rodriguez 2.00 5.00
BT16 Ivan Rodriguez 1.25 3.00
BT17 Sammy Sosa 1.25 3.00
BT18 Ichiro Suzuki 2.50 6.00
BT19 Miguel Tejada .75 2.00
BT20 Larry Walker .75 2.00

2003 Stadium Club Born in the USA Relics

Inserted into packs at different odds depending on what type of game-used memorabilia piece was used, these 50 cards feature those memorabilia pieces cut into the shape of the player's home state.

BAT ODDS 1:76 H, 1:23 HTA, 1:89 R
JERSEY ODDS 1:52 H, 1:15 HTA, 1:61 R
UNIFORM ODDS 1:413 H, 1:126 HTA, 1:484 R
AB A.J. Burnett Jsy 4.00 10.00
AD Adam Dunn Bat 4.00 10.00
AR Alex Rodriguez Bat 10.00 25.00
BB Bret Boone Jsy 4.00 10.00
BF Brad Fullmer Bat 4.00 10.00
BL Barry Larkin Jsy 6.00 15.00
CB Craig Biggio Jsy 6.00 15.00
CF Cliff Floyd Bat 4.00 10.00
CJ Chipper Jones Jsy 6.00 15.00
CP Corey Patterson Bat 4.00 10.00
EC Eric Chavez Uni 4.00 10.00
EM Eric Milton Jsy 4.00 10.00
FT Frank Thomas Bat 6.00 15.00
GM Greg Maddux Jsy 6.00 15.00
GS Gary Sheffield Bat 4.00 10.00
JB Jeff Bagwell Jsy 6.00 15.00
JD Johnny Damon Bat 6.00 15.00
JDD J.D. Drew Bat 4.00 10.00
JE Jim Edmonds Jsy 4.00 10.00
JH Josh Hamilton Bat 8.00 20.00
JNB Jeromy Burnitz Bat 4.00 10.00
JO John Olerud Jsy 4.00 10.00
JS John Smoltz Jsy 6.00 15.00
JT Jim Thome Jsy 6.00 15.00
KW Kerry Wood Bat 4.00 10.00
LG Luis Gonzalez Bat 4.00 10.00
MG Mark Grace Jsy 6.00 15.00
MP Mike Piazza Jsy 6.00 15.00
MV Mo Vaughn Bat 4.00 10.00
MW Matt Williams Bat 4.00 10.00
NG Nomar Garciaparra Bat 10.00 25.00
PB Pat Burrell Bat 4.00 10.00
PK Paul Konerko Bat 4.00 10.00
PW Preston Wilson Jsy 4.00 10.00
RA Rich Aurilia Jsy 4.00 10.00
RH Rickey Henderson Bat 6.00 15.00
RJ Randy Johnson Bat 6.00 15.00
RK Ryan Klesko Bat 4.00 10.00
RS Richie Sexson Bat 4.00 10.00
RV Robin Ventura Bat 4.00 10.00
SB Sean Burroughs Bat 4.00 10.00
SG Shawn Green Bat 4.00 10.00
SR Scott Rolen Bat 6.00 15.00
TC Tony Clark Bat 4.00 10.00
TH Todd Helton Bat 6.00 15.00
TJH Toby Hall Bat 4.00 10.00
TL Terrence Long Uni 4.00 10.00
TM Tino Martinez Bat 6.00 15.00
TRL Travis Lee Bat 4.00 10.00
WM Willie Mays Bat 30.00 60.00

2003 Stadium Club Clubhouse Exclusive

Inserted into packs at a different rate depending on how many memorabilia pieces are used, these four cards feature game-worn memorabilia pieces of Cardinals star Albert Pujols.

JSY ODDS 1:488 H, 1:178 HTA
BAT-JSY ODDS 1:2073 H, 1:758 HTA
BAT-JSY-SPK ODDS 1:2750 H, 1:1016 HTA
BAT-HAT-JSY-SPK ODDS 1:1016 HTA
CE1 Albert Pujols Jsy 8.00 20.00
CE2 Albert Pujols Bat-Jsy 15.00 40.00
CE3 Albert Pujols Bat-Jsy-Spike 50.00 100.00
CE4 Albert Pujols Bat-Hat-Jsy-Spike

2003 Stadium Club Co-Signers

Randomly inserted into packs, these two cards featue a pair of important baseball players who each signed cards for this set. This set features the first Masanori Murakami (the first Japanese player to play in the majors) certified signed cards. Murakami, to honor his heritage, signed an equivalent amount of cards in English and Japanese.

GROUP A STATED ODDS 1:339 HTA
GROUP B STATED ODDS 1:1016 HTA
AM Hank Aaron 300.00 500.00
Willie Mays A
MI Masanori Murakami 175.00 300.00
Kazuhisa Ishii B

2003 Stadium Club License to Drive Bat Relics

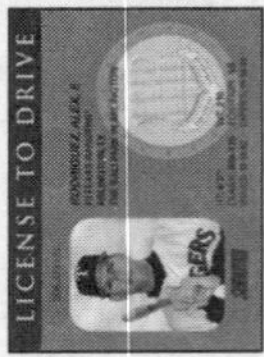

Inserted into packs at a stated rate of one in 98 hobby, one in 114 retail and one in 29 HTA, these 25 cards feature game-used bat relics of players who have driven in 100 runs in a season.

AB Adrian Beltre 4.00 10.00
AD Adam Dunn 4.00 10.00
AJ Andruw Jones 6.00 15.00
ANR Aramis Ramirez 4.00 10.00
AP Albert Pujols 8.00 20.00
AR Alex Rodriguez 10.00 25.00
BW Bernie Williams 6.00 15.00
CJ Chipper Jones 6.00 15.00
EC Eric Chavez 4.00 10.00
FT Frank Thomas 6.00 15.00
GS Gary Sheffield 4.00 10.00
IR Ivan Rodriguez 6.00 15.00
JG Juan Gonzalez 4.00 10.00
LB Lance Berkman 4.00 10.00
LG Luis Gonzalez 4.00 10.00
LW Larry Walker 4.00 10.00
MA Moises Alou 4.00 10.00
MP Mike Piazza 10.00 25.00
NG Nomar Garciaparra 10.00 25.00
RA Roberto Alomar 6.00 15.00
RP Rafael Palmeiro 6.00 15.00
SG Shawn Green 4.00 10.00
SR Scott Rolen 6.00 15.00
TH Todd Helton 6.00 15.00
TM Tino Martinez 6.00 15.00

2003 Stadium Club MLB Match-Up Dual Relics

Inserted into hobby packs at a stated rate of one in 485, one in 570 retail and HTA packs at one in 148, these five cards feature both a game-worn jersey swatch as well as a game-used bat relic of the featured players.

AJ Andruw Jones 10.00 25.00
AP Albert Pujols 15.00 40.00
BB Bret Boone 8.00 20.00
GM Greg Maddux 12.50 30.00
TH Todd Helton 10.00 25.00

2003 Stadium Club Shots

Inserted into hobby packs at a stated rate of one in 24, retail packs at one in 24 and HTA packs at a stated rate of one in four, these 10 cards feature players who are known for their long distance slugging.

SS1 Lance Berkman .75 2.00
SS2 Barry Bonds 3.00 8.00
SS3 Jason Giambi .75 2.00
SS4 Shawn Green .75 2.00
SS5 Miguel Tejada .75 2.00
SS6 Paul Konerko .75 2.00
SS7 Mike Piazza 2.00 5.00
SS8 Alex Rodriguez 2.00 5.00
SS9 Sammy Sosa 1.25 3.00
SS10 Gary Sheffield .75 2.00

2003 Stadium Club Stadium Slices Barrel Relics

Inserted into hobby packs at a stated rate of one in 550 and HTA packs at a stated rate of one in 204, these 10 cards feature game-used bat pieces taken from the barrel.

AJ Andruw Jones 15.00 40.00
AP Albert Pujols 20.00 50.00
AR Alex Rodriguez 30.00 60.00
CD Carlos Delgado 10.00 25.00
GS Gary Sheffield 10.00 25.00
MP Mike Piazza 30.00 60.00
NG Nomar Garciaparra 40.00 80.00
RA Roberto Alomar 15.00 40.00
RP Rafael Palmeiro 15.00 40.00
TH Todd Helton 15.00 40.00

2003 Stadium Club Stadium Slices Handle Relics

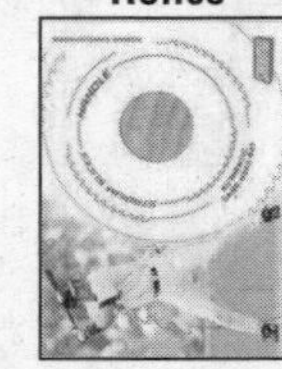

Inserted into hobby packs at a stated rate of one in 237 and HTA packs at a stated rate of one in 86, these 10 cards feature game-used bat pieces taken from the handle.

AJ Andruw Jones 8.00 20.00
AP Albert Pujols 10.00 25.00
AR Alex Rodriguez 12.50 30.00
CD Carlos Delgado 5.00 12.00
GS Gary Sheffield 5.00 12.00
MP Mike Piazza 12.50 30.00
NG Nomar Garciaparra 15.00 40.00
RA Roberto Alomar 8.00 20.00
RP Rafael Palmeiro 8.00 20.00
TH Todd Helton 8.00 20.00

2003 Stadium Club Stadium Slices Trademark Relics

Inserted into hobby packs at a stated rate of one in 415 and HTA packs at a stated rate of one in 151, these 10 cards feature game-used bat pieces taken from the middle of the bat.

AJ Andruw Jones 10.00 25.00
AP Albert Pujols 12.50 30.00
AR Alex Rodriguez 15.00 40.00
CD Carlos Delgado 6.00 15.00
GS Gary Sheffield 6.00 15.00
MP Mike Piazza 15.00 40.00
NG Nomar Garciaparra 20.00 50.00
RA Roberto Alomar 10.00 25.00
RP Rafael Palmeiro 10.00 25.00
TH Todd Helton 10.00 25.00

2003 Stadium Club World Stage Relics

Inserted into packs at a different rate depending on whether or not it is a bat or a jersey, these 10 cards feature game-used memorabilia pieces of players born outside the continental U.S.

BAT ODDS 1:809 H, 1:246 HTA, 1:950 R
JSY ODDS 1:118 H, 1:36 HTA, 1:138 R
AB Adrian Beltre Jsy 3.00 8.00
AP Albert Pujols Jsy 8.00 20.00
AS Alfonso Soriano Bat 4.00 10.00
BK Byung-Hyun Kim Jsy 4.00 10.00
HN Hideo Nomo Bat 10.00 25.00
IR Ivan Rodriguez Jsy 4.00 10.00
KI Kazuhisa Ishii Jsy 3.00 8.00
KS Kazuhiro Sasaki Jsy 3.00 8.00
MT Miguel Tejada Jsy 3.00 8.00
TS Tsuyoshi Shinjo Bat 4.00 10.00

2008 Stadium Club

This set was released on November 5, 2008.

COMMON CARD(1-100) .40 1.00
COMMON 999 (1-100) .75 2.00
COMMON RC (1-150) .40 1.00
COMMON RC 999 (1-150) .60 1.50
COMMON AU RC (151-185) 4.00 10.00
AU RC A ODDS 1:3
AU RC B ODDS 1:8
EXCHANGE DEADLINE 10/31/2010
PRINTING PLATE ODDS 1:85 HOBBY
PRINT PLATE AUTO ODDS 1:198 HOBBY
PLATE PRINT RUN 1 SET PER COLOR
BLACK-CYAN-MAGENTA-YELLOW ISSUED
NO PLATE PRICING DUE TO SCARCITY
1 Chase Utley 1.00 2.50
2 Tim Lincecum 1.00 2.50
3 Ryan Zimmerman/999 1.00 2.50
4 Todd Helton .60 1.50
5 Russell Martin .40 1.00
6 Curtis Granderson/999 .60 1.50
7 Torii Hunter .40 1.00
8 Mark Teixeira .60 1.50
9 Alfonso Soriano/999 1.00 2.50
10 C.C. Sabathia .40 1.00
11 David Ortiz 1.00 2.50
12 Miguel Tejada/999 .60 1.50
13 Alex Rodriguez 1.50 4.00
14 Prince Fielder 1.00 2.50
15 Alex Gordon/999 1.50 4.00
16 Jake Peavy .60 1.50
17 B.J. Upton .60 1.50
18 Michael Young/999 .60 1.50
19 Jason Bay .40 1.00
20 Jorge Posada .60 1.50
21 Jacoby Ellsbury/999 2.50 6.00
22 Nick Markakis .60 1.50
23 Tom Glavine .60 1.50
24 Justin Upton/999 1.50 4.00
25 Edinson Volquez .40 1.00
26 Miguel Cabrera .60 1.50
27 Carlos Lee/999 .60 1.50
28 Ryan Church .40 1.00
29 Delmon Young .60 1.50
30 Carlos Quentin/999 .60 1.50
31 Carl Crawford .40 1.00
32 Roy Halladay .40 1.00
33 Brandon Webb/999 1.00 2.50
34 Brian Roberts .60 1.50
35 Ken Griffey Jr. 1.50 4.00
36 Troy Tulowitzki/999 1.00 2.50
37 Hanley Ramirez 1.00 2.50
38 Hunter Pence 1.00 2.50
39 Johnny Damon/999 1.00 2.50
40 Eric Chavez .40 1.00
41 Adrian Gonzalez .60 1.50
42 Carlos Pena/999 1.50 4.00
43 Felix Hernandez .60 1.50
44 Magglio Ordonez .60 1.50
45 Josh Beckett/999 1.00 2.50
46 Fausto Carmona .40 1.00
47 Chris Young .40 1.00
48 John Lackey/999 .60 1.50
49 John Smoltz 1.00 2.50
50 David Wright 1.25 3.00
51 Ichiro Suzuki/999 2.50 6.00
52 Vernon Wells .40 1.00
53 Josh Hamilton 1.25 3.00
54 Albert Pujols/999 3.00 8.00
55 Dustin Pedroia 1.50 4.00
56 Garrett Atkins .40 1.00
57 Roy Oswalt/999 .60 1.50
58 Jose Reyes .60 1.50
59 Derek Jeter 2.50 6.00
60 Scott Kazmir/999 1.00 2.50
61 Vladimir Guerrero 1.00 2.50
62 Joba Chamberlain 1.25 3.00
63 Kevin Youkilis/999 1.00 2.50
64 Victor Martinez .40 1.00
65 Nick Swisher .40 1.00
66 Carlos Beltran/999 .60 1.50
67 Joe Mauer .60 1.50
68 Gary Sheffield .40 1.00
69 Cole Hamels/999 1.50 4.00
70 Brian McCann .60 1.50
71 Grady Sizemore .60 1.50
72 Robinson Cano/999 1.00 2.50
73 Greg Maddux 1.25 3.00
74 Rich Harden .40 1.00
75 Ryan Howard/999 2.00 5.00
76 Johan Santana .60 1.50
77 Dan Uggla .60 1.50
78 Justin Verlander/999 1.00 2.50
79 Derrek Lee .60 1.50
80 Ryan Braun 1.25 3.00
81 Lance Berkman/999 1.00 2.50
82 Manny Ramirez 1.00 2.50
83 Chipper Jones 1.25 3.00
84 Daisuke Matsuzaka/999 2.50 6.00
85 Matt Holliday .60 1.50
86 Justin Morneau .60 1.50
87 Jimmy Rollins/999 1.00 2.50
88 Hideki Matsui 1.00 2.50
89 Pedro Martinez .60 1.50
90 Carlos Zambrano/999 .60 1.50
91 Jackie Robinson 1.00 2.50
92 Mickey Mantle 4.00 10.00
93 Ty Cobb/999 2.50 6.00
94 Joe DiMaggio
Cut Out
95 Honus Wagner 1.00 2.50
96 Babe Ruth/999 4.00 10.00
97 Nolan Ryan 3.00 8.00
98 Roberto Clemente 2.00 5.00
99 Ted Williams/999 4.00 10.00
100 Tom Seaver .60 1.50
101a Luke Hochevar RC 1.00 2.50
101b Luke Hochevar VAR/999 (RC) 1.50 4.00
Pitching
102a Daric Barton/999 (RC) .60 1.50
102b Daric Barton VAR/999 (RC) .60 1.50
Swinging away hit down the 3rd base line
103a Nick Adenhart (RC) .40 1.00
103b Nick Adenhart VAR/999 (RC) .60 1.50
Photoday shot in the dugout
104a Gregor Blanco (RC) .40 1.00
104b Gregor Blanco VAR/999 (RC) .60 1.50
Hitting
105a Chris Carter/999 (RC) 1.00 2.50
105b Chris Carter VAR/999 (RC) 1.00 2.50
Hitting
106a Eric Hurley (RC) .40 1.00
106b Eric Hurley VAR/999 (RC) .60 1.50
Starting his windup
107a Clayton Kershaw RC 1.25 3.00
107b Clayton Kershaw VAR/999 (RC) 2.00 5.00
Throwing fastball to home
108a Evan Longoria/999 RC 5.00 12.00
108b Evan Longoria VAR/999 RC 5.00 12.00
Photoday shot
109a Garrett Mock (RC) .40 1.00

109b Garrett Mock VAR/999 (RC) .60 1.50
In mid windup
110a David Purcey (RC) .40 1.00
110b David Purcey VAR/999 (RC) .60 1.50
Ready to release a pitch
111a Ryan Tucker/999 (RC) .60 1.50
111b Ryan Tucker VAR/999 (RC) .60 1.50
Photoday shot throwing up baseball
112a Joey Votto (RC) 1.00 2.50
112b Joey Votto VAR/999 (RC) 1.50 4.00
Flipping ball to pitcher for an out
113a Jeff Clement (RC) .40 1.00
113b Jeff Clement VAR/999 (RC) .60 1.50
Running back to homeplate
114a Michael Aubrey/999 RC 1.00 2.50
114b Michael Aubrey VAR/999 RC 1.00 2.50
Just got a basehit
115a Brandon Boggs (RC) .60 1.50
115b Brandon Boggs VAR/999 (RC) 1.00 2.50
Throwing someone out in the outfield
116a Johnny Cueto RC .60 1.50
116b Johnny Cueto VAR/999 (RC) 1.00 2.50
Delivering a pitch
117a Hernan Iribarren/999 (RC) 1.00 2.50
117b Hernan Iribarren VAR/999 (RC) 1.00 2.50
Throwing in the outfield
118a Masahide Kobayashi RC .60 1.50
118b Masahide Kobayashi VAR/999 (RC) 1.00 2.50
Photoday shot
119a Jed Lowrie (RC) 1.00 2.50
119b Jed Lowrie VAR/999 (RC) 1.50 4.00
Tagging someone out at 3rd base
120a Greg Reynolds/999 RC 1.00 2.50
120b Greg Reynolds VAR/999 RC 1.00 2.50
Delivering a pitch towards home
121a Matt Tolbert RC .60 1.50
121b Matt Tolbert VAR/999 (RC) 1.00 2.50
Turning a double play
122a Jonathan Herrera RC .60 1.50
122b Jonathan Herrera VAR/999 (RC) 1.00 2.50
Safe at home
123a J.R. Towles/999 RC 1.50 4.00
123b J.R. Towles VAR/999 RC 1.50 4.00
Single up the middle
124a Armando Galarraga RC .60 1.50
124b Armando Galarraga VAR/999 (RC) 1.00 2.50
Delivering a pitch
125a Josh Banks (RC) .40 1.00
125b Josh Banks VAR/999 (RC) .60 1.50
Delivering a pitch
126a Mitch Boggs/999 (RC) .60 1.50
126b Mitch Boggs VAR/999 (RC) .60 1.50
Delivering a pitch
127a Blake DeWitt (RC) 1.00 2.50
127b Blake DeWitt VAR/999 (RC) 1.50 4.00
Getting ready for a pitch
128a Carlos Gonzalez (RC) .40 1.00
128b Carlos Gonzalez VAR/999 (RC) .60 1.50
Walking to home with bat in hand
129a Elliot Johnson/999 (RC) .60 1.50
129b Elliot Johnson VAR/999 (RC) .60 1.50
Throwing to first base
130a Brian Barton RC .60 1.50
130b Brian Barton VAR/999 (RC) 1.00 2.50
Getting ready to crush a pitch
131a Sean Rodriguez (RC) .40 1.00
131b Sean Rodriguez VAR/999 (RC) .60 1.50
Making a sweet double play
132a Kosuke Fukudome/999 RC 2.50 6.00
132b Kosuke Fukudome VAR/999 RC 2.50 6.00
Throwing someone out in the outfield
133a Chin-Lung Hu (RC) .60 1.50
133b Chin-Lung Hu VAR/999 (RC) 1.00 2.50
Catching the ball at second base
134a Wladimir Balentien (RC) .40 1.00
134b Wladimir Balentien VAR/999 (RC) .60 1.50
Tagging someone out at home!
135a Jeff Niemann/999 (RC) .60 1.50
135b Jeff Niemann VAR/999 (RC) .60 1.50
Warming up in the bullpen
136a Jay Bruce (RC) 1.50 4.00
136b Jay Bruce VAR/999 (RC) 2.50 6.00
Taking a massive cut
137a Brandon Jones RC 1.00 2.50
137b Brandon Jones VAR/999 (RC) 1.50 4.00
Ready for the pitch
138a Justin Masterson/999 RC 3.00 8.00
138b Justin Masterson VAR/999 RC 3.00 8.00
3/4 body shot pitching
139a Jayson Nix (RC) .40 1.00
139b Jayson Nix VAR/999 (RC) .60 1.50
Throwing to home
140a Max Scherzer RC 1.00 2.50
140b Max Scherzer VAR/999 (RC) 1.50 4.00
Unloading a pitch to home
141a Mike Aviles/999 RC 1.00 2.50
141b Mike Aviles VAR/999 RC 1.00 2.50
Connecting on a fastball
142a Greg Smith RC .40 1.00
142b Greg Smith VAR/999 (RC) .60 1.50
Delivering a pitch
143a Nick Blackburn RC .60 1.50
143b Nick Blackburn VAR/999 (RC) 1.00 2.50
Warming up on the mound
144a Justin Ruggiano/999 RC 1.00 2.50
144b Justin Ruggiano VAR/999 RC 1.00 2.50
Relaxing before taking another cut
145a Clay Buchholz (RC) 1.00 2.50
145b Clay Buchholz VAR/999 (RC) 1.50 4.00
Throwing a nasty breaking ball
146a German Duran RC .60 1.50
146b German Duran VAR/999 (RC) 1.00 2.50
Turning a sweet double play
147a Radhames Liz/999 RC 1.00 2.50
147b Radhames Liz VAR/999 RC 1.00 2.50
Throwing a pitch to home
148a Chris Perez RC .60 1.50
148b Chris Perez VAR/999 (RC) 1.00 2.50
Delivering a pitch
149a Hiroki Kuroda RC .60 1.50
149b Hiroki Kuroda VAR/999 (RC) 1.00 2.50
Delivering an unorthodox pitch to home
150a Gregorio Petit RC .60 1.50
150b Gregorio Petit VAR/999 (RC) 1.00 2.50
Getting ready to field one in the hole
151 Emmanuel Burriss AU RC EXCH A 4.00 10.00
152 Elliot Johnson AU (RC) A 4.00 10.00
153 Jonathan Van Every AU RC A 4.00 10.00
154 Darren O'Day AU RC A 4.00 10.00
155 Matt Joyce AU RC A 6.00 15.00
156 Burke Badenhop AU RC A 4.00 10.00
157 Brent Lillibridge AU (RC) A 4.00 10.00
158 Johnny Cueto AU (RC) EXCH A 5.00 12.00
159 Jeff Niemann AU (RC) A 4.00 10.00
160 John Bowker AU (RC) A 4.00 10.00
161 Brandon Boggs AU (RC) A 4.00 10.00
162 Justin Masterson AU (RC) A 12.50 30.00
163 Masahide Kobayashi AU (RC) A 5.00 12.00
164 Nick Adenhart AU (RC) A 4.00 10.00
165 Chris Perez AU (RC) EXCH A 4.00 10.00
166 Gregor Blanco AU (RC) A 4.00 10.00
167 Travis Denker AU RC A 4.00 10.00
168 Jeff Clement AU (RC) EXCH A 4.00 10.00
169 Evan Longoria AU (RC) A 30.00 60.00
170 Greg Smith AU (RC) A 4.00 10.00
171 Jay Bruce AU (RC) B 12.50 30.00
172 Brian Barton AU RC B 6.00 15.00
173 Max Scherzer AU (RC) B 6.00 15.00
174 Blake DeWitt AU (RC) B 6.00 15.00
175 Jed Lowrie AU (RC) EXCH B 6.00 15.00
176 Clayton Kershaw AU (RC) B 8.00 20.00
177 Jonathan Albaladejo AU RC B 4.00 10.00
178 Josh Banks AU (RC) B 4.00 10.00
179 Brian Horwitz AU RC B 4.00 10.00
180 Micah Hoffpauir AU RC B 6.00 15.00
181 Robinzon Diaz AU (RC) B 4.00 10.00
182 Nick Evans AU RC B 6.00 15.00
183 Joe Mather AU RC EXCH B 5.00 12.00
184 Danny Herrera AU RC B 4.00 10.00
185 Eugenio Velez AU RC B 4.00 10.00

2008 Stadium Club First Day Issue

*1ST DAY VET 1-100: .6X TO 1.5X BASIC
*1ST DAY RC 101-150: .6X TO 1.5X BASIC
*1ST DAY RC 999 101-150: .4X TO 1X BASIC
APPX. ODDS TEN PER HOBBY BOX
STATED PRINT RUN 599 SER.#'d SETS

2008 Stadium Club Photographer's Proof Blue

*BLUE VET 1-100: 1X TO 2.5X BASIC
*BLUE 999 1-100: .6X TO 1.5X BASIC
*BLUE RC 101-150: 1X TO 2.5X BASIC
*BLUE 999 101-150: .6X TO 1.5X BASIC
NON-AU BLUE ODDS 1:5 HOBBY
*BLUE AU: .5X TO 1.2X BASIC
AU BLUE ODDS 1:29 HOBBY
BLUE PRINT RUN 99 SER.#'d SETS
162 Justin Masterson AU 40.00 80.00

2008 Stadium Club Photographer's Proof Gold

*GLD VET 1-100: 1.2X TO 3X BASIC
*GLD 999 1-100: .75X TO 2X BASIC
*GLD RC 101-150: 1.2X TO 3X BASIC
*GLD 999 101-150: .75X TO 2X BASIC
NON-AU GOLD ODDS 1:9 HOBBY
*GLD AU: .6X TO 1.5X BASIC
AU GOLD ODDS 1:62 HOBBY
GOLD PRINT RUN 50 SER.#'d SETS

2008 Stadium Club Photographer's Proof Platinum

STATED ODDS 1:340 HOBBY
STATED AUTO ODDS 1:1970 HOBBY
STATED PRINT RUN 1 SER.#'d SET
NO PRICING DUE TO SCARCITY

2008 Stadium Club Beam Team Autographs

GROUP A ODDS 1:13 HOBBY
GROUP B ODDS 1:6 HOBBY
GROUP C ODDS 1:11 HOBBY
PRINTING PLATE ODDS 1:198 HOBBY
PLATE PRINT RUN 1 SET PER COLOR
BLACK-CYAN-MAGENTA-YELLOW ISSUED
NO PLATE PRICING DUE TO SCARCITY
EXCHANGE DEADLINE 10/31/2010
AG Adrian Gonzalez C 5.00 12.00
BH Brad Hawpe C 4.00 10.00
BP Brandon Phillips B 5.00 12.00
BT Brad Thompson C 8.00 20.00
CC Carl Crawford C 5.00 12.00
CCR Callix Crabbe C 4.00 10.00
CD Carlos Delgado C 8.00 20.00
CF Chone Figgins B 4.00 10.00
CM Carlos Marmol C 8.00 20.00
CMO Craig Monroe B 4.00 10.00
CP Carlos Pena C 8.00 20.00
CV Claudio Vargas C 4.00 10.00
CVI Carlos Villanueva B 4.00 10.00
CW C.J. Wilson B 4.00 10.00
DH Dan Haren C 4.00 10.00
DS Darryl Strawberry B 6.00 15.00
DY Delwyn Young A 4.00 10.00
ER Edwar Ramirez C 4.00 10.00
FL Francisco Liriano C 6.00 15.00
FP Felix Pie B 4.00 10.00
FS Freddy Sanchez C 4.00 10.00
GC Gary Carter C 6.00 15.00
GD German Duran B 4.00 10.00
GP Glen Perkins B 4.00 10.00
GS Gary Sheffield C 6.00 15.00
GSM Greg Smith C 4.00 10.00
JB Jason Bartlett C 4.00 10.00
JC Jack Cust C 5.00 12.00
JCR Jesse Crain A 4.00 10.00
JGA Joey Gathright C 4.00 10.00
JGU Jeremy Guthrie C 4.00 10.00
JH Josh Hamilton B 12.50 30.00
JJ Jair Jurrjens C 5.00 12.00
JL John Lackey B 4.00 10.00
JN Jayson Nix A 4.00 10.00
JP Jonathan Papelbon C 8.00 20.00
JPO Johnny Podres B 5.00 12.00
JR Jose Reyes C 12.50 30.00
JS Jeff Salazar B 4.00 10.00
KS Kevin Slowey B 5.00 12.00
LM Lastings Milledge B 4.00 10.00
ME Mark Ellis C 4.00 10.00
MK Mark Kotsay C 4.00 10.00
MN Mike Napoli C 4.00 10.00
MT Marcus Thames C 4.00 10.00
MTO Matt Tolbert A 4.00 10.00
NR Nate Robertson B 4.00 10.00
RC Robinson Cano B 5.00 12.00
RP Ronny Paulino B 4.00 10.00
TG Tom Gorzelanny C 4.00 10.00
TJ Todd Jones B 4.00 10.00
YP Yusmeiro Petit A 4.00 10.00

2008 Stadium Club Beam Team Autographs Black and White

*B AND W: .5X TO 1.2X BASIC
STATED ODDS 1:19 HOBBY
STATED PRINT RUN 99 SER.#'d SETS
EXCHANGE DEADLINE 10/31/2010

2008 Stadium Club Beam Team Autographs Gold

*GOLD: .5X TO 1.2X BASIC
STATED ODDS 1:40 HOBBY
STATED PRINT RUN 50 SER.#'d SETS
EXCHANGE DEADLINE 10/31/2010

2008 Stadium Club Beam Team Autographs Platinum

STATED ODDS 1:1327 HOBBY
STATED PRINT RUN 1 SER.#'d SET
NO PRICING DUE TO SCARCITY
EXCHANGE DEADLINE 10/31/2010

2008 Stadium Club Ceremonial Cuts

STATED ODDS 1:34 HOBBY
STATED PRINT RUN 199 SER.#'d SETS
BR Babe Ruth 15.00 40.00
GB George Bush 10.00 25.00
JF Jimmie Foxx 8.00 20.00
JR Jackie Robinson 12.50 30.00
LG Lou Gehrig 15.00 40.00
MO Mel Ott 8.00 20.00
RH Rogers Hornsby 8.00 20.00
TC Ty Cobb 12.50 30.00
TW Ted Williams 12.50 30.00

2008 Stadium Club Ceremonial Cuts Photographer's Proof Blue

*BLUE: .5X TO 1.2X BASIC
STATED ODDS 1:28 HOBBY
STATED PRINT RUN 99 SER.#'d SETS

2008 Stadium Club Ceremonial Cuts Photographer's Proof Platinum

STATED ODDS 1:2710 HOBBY
STATED PRINT RUN 1 SER.#'d SET
NO PRICING DUE TO SCARCITY

2008 Stadium Club Sketch Cards

STATED ODDS 1:28 HOBBY
ANNCD PRINT RUN 1 SET
MULTIPLE VERSIONS OF EACH CARD
NO PRICING DUE TO SCARCITY

2008 Stadium Club Stadium Slices

STATED ODDS 1:23 HOBBY
PRINT RUNS B/WN 89-428 COPIES PER
AP Albert Pujols/428 10.00 25.00
AR Alex Rodriguez/89 30.00 60.00
DM Daisuke Matsuzaka/428 10.00 25.00
DO David Ortiz/428 4.00 10.00
GG Goose Gossage/89 15.00 40.00
HM Hideki Matsui/428 12.50 30.00
IS Ichiro Suzuki/428 10.00 25.00
JT Joe Torre/89 15.00 40.00
LP Lou Piniella/89 8.00 20.00
MM Mickey Mantle/89 40.00 80.00
MR Mariano Rivera/428 12.50 30.00
RJ Reggie Jackson/89 15.00 40.00
TM Thurman Munson/89 30.00 60.00
WF Whitey Ford/89 20.00 50.00
YB Yogi Berra/89 20.00 50.00

2008 Stadium Club Stadium Slices Photographer's Proof Blue

*BLUE: .5X TO 1.2X BASIC
STATED ODDS 1:28 HOBBY
PRINT RUNS B/WN 25-99 SER.#'d SETS
NO PRICING ON QTY 25 OR LESS

2008 Stadium Club Stadium Slices Photographer's Proof Gold

*GOLD: .5X TO 1.2X BASIC
STATED ODDS 1:55 HOBBY
PRINT RUNS B/WN 5-50 SER.#'d SETS
NO PRICING ON QTY 5 OR LESS

2008 Stadium Club Stadium Slices Photographer's Proof Platinum

STATED ODDS 1:2710 HOBBY
STATED PRINT RUN 1 SER.#'d SET
NO PRICING DUE TO SCARCITY

2008 Stadium Club Triumvirate Memorabilia Autographs

STATED ODDS 1:26 HOBBY
PRINT RUNS B/WN 49-99 SER.#'d SETS
EXCHANGE DEADLINE 10/31/2010
AD Adam Dunn 10.00 25.00
AP Albert Pujols 100.00 200.00
AR Aramis Ramirez 12.50 30.00
ARI Alex Rios 12.50 30.00
AS Alfonso Soriano 15.00 40.00
BU B.J. Upton 10.00 25.00
CC Carl Crawford 12.50 30.00
CL Carlos Lee 6.00 15.00
CW Chien-Ming Wang 60.00 120.00
DL Derrek Lee 12.50 30.00
DO David Ortiz 30.00 60.00
HR Hanley Ramirez 12.50 30.00
JF Jeff Francoeur 10.00 25.00
JM Justin Morneau 15.00 40.00
JP Jake Peavy 15.00 40.00
JPA Jonathan Papelbon 15.00 40.00
JU Justin Upton 12.50 30.00
MH Matt Holliday 15.00 40.00
MO Magglio Ordonez/49 6.00 15.00
MR Mariano Rivera 60.00 120.00
MT Miguel Tejada 6.00 15.00
RM Russ Martin 8.00 20.00
SK Scott Kazmir 15.00 40.00
TH Torii Hunter 12.50 30.00
TLH Todd Helton 10.00 25.00
TT Troy Tulowitzki 8.00 20.00
VG Vladimir Guerrero 20.00 50.00
VW Vernon Wells 10.00 25.00

2008 Stadium Club Triumvirate Memorabilia Autographs Black

STATED ODDS 1:2501 HOBBY
STATED PRINT RUN 1 SER.#'d SET
NO PRICING DUE TO SCARCITY
EXCHANGE DEADLINE 10/31/2010

2000 Stadium Club Chrome

The 2000 Stadium Club Chrome set was released in May, 2000 as a 250-card set. The set features 200 Player cards, 30 Future Star cards, and 20 Draft Pick cards. Each pack contained five cards and carried a suggested retail price of $4.00. Notable Rookie Cards include Rick Asadoorian and Bobby Bradley.

COMPLETE SET (250) 20.00 50.00
COMMON CARD (1-250) .20 .50
COMMON RC .30 .75
1 Nomar Garciaparra .75 2.00
2 Brian Jordan .20 .50
3 Mark Grace .30 .75
4 Jeromy Burnitz .20 .50
5 Shane Reynolds .20 .50
6 Alex Gonzalez .20 .50
7 Jose Offerman .20 .50
8 Orlando Hernandez .20 .50
9 Mike Caruso .20 .50
10 Tony Clark .20 .50
11 Sean Casey .20 .50
12 Johnny Damon .30 .75
13 Dante Bichette .20 .50
14 Kevin Young .20 .50
15 Juan Gonzalez .20 .50
16 Chipper Jones .50 1.25
17 Quilvio Veras .20 .50
18 Trevor Hoffman .20 .50
19 Roger Cedeno .20 .50
20 Ellis Burks .20 .50
21 Richie Sexson .20 .50
22 Gary Sheffield .20 .50
23 Delino DeShields .20 .50
24 Wade Boggs .30 .75
25 Ray Lankford .20 .50
26 Kevin Appier .20 .50
27 Roy Halladay .20 .50
28 Harold Baines .20 .50
29 Todd Zeile .20 .50
30 Barry Larkin .30 .75
31 Ron Coomer .20 .50
32 Jorge Posada .30 .75
33 Magglio Ordonez .20 .50
34 Brian Giles .20 .50
35 Jeff Kent .20 .50
36 Henry Rodriguez .20 .50
37 Fred McGriff .30 .75
38 Shawn Green .20 .50
39 Derek Bell .20 .50
40 Ben Grieve .20 .50
41 Dave Nilsson .20 .50
42 Mo Vaughn .20 .50
43 Rondell White .20 .50
44 Doug Glanville .20 .50
45 Paul O'Neill .30 .75
46 Carlos Lee .20 .50
47 Vinny Castilla .20 .50
48 Mike Sweeney .20 .50
49 Rico Brogna .20 .50
50 Alex Rodriguez .75 2.00
51 Luis Castillo .20 .50
52 Kevin Brown .30 .75
53 Jose Vidro .20 .50
54 John Smoltz .30 .75
55 Garret Anderson .20 .50
56 Matt Stairs .20 .50
57 Omar Vizquel .30 .75
58 Tom Goodwin .20 .50
59 Scott Brosius .20 .50
60 Robin Ventura .30 .75
61 B.J. Surhoff .20 .50
62 Andy Ashby .20 .50
63 Chris Widger .20 .50
64 Tim Hudson .30 .75
65 Javy Lopez .20 .50
66 Tim Salmon .30 .75
67 Warren Morris .20 .50
68 John Wetteland .20 .50
69 Gabe Kapler .20 .50
70 Bernie Williams .30 .75
71 Rickey Henderson .50 1.25
72 Andruw Jones .30 .75
73 Eric Young .20 .50
74 Bob Abreu .20 .50
75 David Cone .20 .50
76 Rusty Greer .20 .50
77 Ron Belliard .20 .50
78 Troy Glaus .20 .50
79 Mike Hampton .20 .50
80 Miguel Tejada .20 .50
81 Jeff Cirillo .20 .50
82 Todd Hundley .20 .50
83 Roberto Alomar .30 .75
84 Charles Johnson .20 .50
85 Rafael Palmeiro .30 .75
86 Doug Mientkiewicz .20 .50
87 Mariano Rivera .50 1.25
88 Neifi Perez .20 .50
89 Jermaine Dye .20 .50
90 Ivan Rodriguez .30 .75
91 Jay Buhner .20 .50
92 Pokey Reese .20 .50
93 John Olerud .20 .50
94 Brady Anderson .20 .50
95 Manny Ramirez .30 .75
96 Keith Osik RC .30 .75
97 Mickey Morandini .20 .50
98 Matt Williams .20 .50
99 Eric Karros .20 .50
100 Ken Griffey Jr. .75 2.00
101 Bret Boone .20 .50
102 Ryan Klesko .20 .50
103 Craig Biggio .30 .75
104 John Jaha .20 .50
105 Vladimir Guerrero .50 1.25
106 Devon White .20 .50
107 Tony Womack .20 .50
108 Marvin Benard .20 .50
109 Kenny Lofton .20 .50
110 Preston Wilson .20 .50
111 Al Leiter .20 .50
112 Reggie Sanders .20 .50
113 Scott Williamson .20 .50
114 Deivi Cruz .20 .50
115 Carlos Beltran .30 .75
116 Ray Durham .20 .50
117 Ricky Ledee .20 .50
118 Torii Hunter .20 .50
119 John Valentin .20 .50
120 Scott Rolen .30 .75
121 Jason Kendall .20 .50
122 Dave Martinez .20 .50
123 Jim Thome .30 .75
124 David Bell .20 .50
125 Jose Canseco .30 .75
126 Jose Lima .20 .50
127 Carl Everett .20 .50
128 Kevin Millwood .20 .50
129 Bill Spiers .20 .50
130 Omar Daal .20 .50
131 Miguel Cairo .20 .50
132 Mark Grudzielanek .20 .50
133 David Justice .20 .50
134 Russ Ortiz .20 .50
135 Mike Piazza .75 2.00
136 Brian Meadows .20 .50
137 Tony Gwynn .60 1.50
138 Cal Ripken 1.50 4.00
139 Kris Benson .20 .50
140 Larry Walker .20 .50
141 Cristian Guzman .20 .50
142 Tino Martinez .30 .75
143 Chris Singleton .20 .50
144 Lee Stevens .20 .50
145 Rey Ordonez .20 .50
146 Russ Davis .20 .50
147 J.T. Snow .20 .50
148 Luis Gonzalez .20 .50
149 Marquis Grissom .20 .50
150 Greg Maddux .75 2.00
151 Fernando Tatis .20 .50
152 Jason Giambi .20 .50
153 Carlos Delgado .20 .50
154 Joe McEwing .20 .50
155 Raul Mondesi .20 .50
156 Rich Aurilia .20 .50
157 Alex Fernandez .20 .50
158 Albert Belle .20 .50
159 Pat Meares .20 .50
160 Mike Lieberthal .20 .50
161 Mike Cameron .20 .50
162 Juan Encarnacion .20 .50
163 Chuck Knoblauch .20 .50
164 Pedro Martinez .30 .75
165 Randy Johnson .50 1.25
166 Shannon Stewart .20 .50
167 Jeff Bagwell .30 .75
168 Edgar Renteria .20 .50
169 Barry Bonds 1.25 3.00
170 Steve Finley .20 .50
171 Brian Hunter .20 .50
172 Tom Glavine .30 .75
173 Mark Kotsay .20 .50
174 Tony Fernandez .20 .50
175 Sammy Sosa .50 1.25
176 Geoff Jenkins .20 .50
177 Adrian Beltre .20 .50
178 Jay Bell .20 .50
179 Mike Bordick .20 .50
180 Ed Sprague .20 .50
181 Dave Roberts .20 .50
182 Greg Vaughn .20 .50
183 Brian Daubach .20 .50
184 Damion Easley .20 .50
185 Carlos Febles .20 .50
186 Kevin Tapani .20 .50
187 Frank Thomas .50 1.25
188 Roger Clemens 1.00 2.50
189 Mike Benjamin .20 .50
190 Curt Schilling .20 .50
191 Edgardo Alfonzo .20 .50
192 Mike Mussina .30 .75
193 Todd Helton .30 .75
194 Todd Jones .20 .50
195 Dean Palmer .20 .50
196 John Flaherty .20 .50
197 Derek Jeter 1.25 3.00
198 Todd Walker .20 .50
199 Brad Ausmus .20 .50
200 Mark McGwire 1.25 3.00
201 Erubiel Durazo .20 .50
202 Nick Johnson .20 .50
203 Ruben Mateo .20 .50
204 Lance Berkman .20 .50
205 Pat Burrell .20 .50
206 Pablo Ozuna .20 .50
207 Roosevelt Brown .20 .50
208 Alfonso Soriano .50 1.25
209 A.J. Burnett .20 .50
210 Rafael Furcal .20 .50
211 Scott Morgan .20 .50
212 Adam Piatt .20 .50
213 Dee Brown .20 .50
214 Corey Patterson .20 .50
215 Mickey Lopez .20 .50
216 Rob Ryan .20 .50
217 Sean Burroughs .20 .50
218 Jack Cust .20 .50
219 John Patterson .20 .50
220 Kit Pellow .20 .50
221 Chad Hermansen .20 .50
222 Daryle Ward .20 .50
223 Jayson Werth .20 .50
224 Jason Standridge .20 .50
225 Mark Mulder .20 .50
226 Peter Bergeron .20 .50
227 Willi Mo Pena .20 .50
228 Aramis Ramirez .20 .50
229 John Sneed RC .30 .75
230 Wilton Veras .20 .50
231 Josh Hamilton .75 2.00
232 Eric Munson .20 .50
233 Bobby Bradley RC .30 .75
234 Larry Bigbie RC .50 1.25
235 B.J. Garbe RC .30 .75
236 Brett Myers RC 1.00 2.50
237 Jason Stumm RC .30 .75
238 Corey Myers RC .30 .75
239 Ryan Christianson RC .30 .75
240 David Walling .20 .50
241 Josh Girdley .20 .50
242 Omar Ortiz .20 .50
243 Jason Jennings .20 .50
244 Kyle Snyder .20 .50
245 Jay Gehrke .20 .50
246 Mike Paradis .20 .50
247 Chance Caple RC .30 .75
248 Ben Christensen RC .30 .75
249 Brad Baker RC .30 .75
250 Rick Asadoorian RC .30 .75

2000 Stadium Club Chrome First Day Issue

Randomly inserted into packs at one in 33, this 250-card insert is a complete parallel of the Stadium Club Chrome base set. Each card is individually serial numbered to 100.

*STARS: 6X TO 15X BASIC CARDS
*ROOKIES: 2.5X TO 6X BASIC CARDS

2000 Stadium Club Chrome First Day Issue Refractors

Randomly inserted into packs at one in 131, this 250-card insert is a complete parallel of the Stadium Club Chrome base set. Each card features Topps' 'refractor' technology. Each card is also individually serial numbered to 25.

*STARS: 15X TO 40X BASIC CARDS

2000 Stadium Club Chrome Refractors

Randomly inserted into packs at one in 12, this 250-card insert is a complete parallel of the Stadium Club Chrome base set. Each card features Topps' 'refractor' technology.

*STARS: 4X TO 10X BASIC CARDS
*ROOKIES: 1.5X TO 4X BASIC CARDS

2000 Stadium Club Chrome Capture the Action

Randomly inserted into packs at one in 18, this 20-card insert features some of the major league's top prospects and veteran players. Card backs carry a "CA" prefix.

COMPLETE SET (20) 75.00 150.00
*REFRACTORS: 1X TO 2.5X BASIC CAPTURE
REFRACTOR STATED ODDS 1:90
CA1 Josh Hamilton 1.25 3.00
CA2 Pat Burrell .50 1.25
CA3 Erubiel Durazo .50 1.25
CA4 Alfonso Soriano 1.25 3.00
CA5 A.J. Burnett .50 1.25
CA6 Alex Rodriguez 2.00 5.00
CA7 Sean Casey .50 1.25
CA8 Derek Jeter 3.00 8.00
CA9 Vladimir Guerrero 1.25 3.00
CA10 Nomar Garciaparra 2.00 5.00
CA11 Mike Piazza 2.00 5.00
CA12 Ken Griffey Jr. 2.00 5.00
CA13 Sammy Sosa 1.25 3.00
CA14 Juan Gonzalez .50 1.25
CA15 Mark McGwire 3.00 8.00
CA16 Ivan Rodriguez .75 2.00
CA17 Barry Bonds 3.00 8.00
CA18 Wade Boggs .75 2.00
CA19 Tony Gwynn 1.50 4.00
CA20 Cal Ripken 4.00 10.00

2000 Stadium Club Chrome Clear Shots

Randomly inserted into packs at one in 24, this insert features ten of the major leagues most famous stars from both front and back angles at the same time. Card backs carry a "CS" prefix.

COMPLETE SET (10) 12.50 30.00
*REFRACTORS: 1X TO 2.5X BASIC CLEAR
REFRACTOR ODDS 1:120
CS1 Derek Jeter 2.50 6.00
CS2 Bernie Williams .60 1.50
CS3 Roger Clemens 2.00 5.00
CS4 Chipper Jones 1.00 2.50
CS5 Greg Maddux 1.50 4.00
CS6 Andruw Jones .60 1.50
CS7 Juan Gonzalez .40 1.00
CS8 Manny Ramirez .60 1.50
CS9 Ken Griffey Jr. 1.50 4.00
CS10 Josh Hamilton 1.25 3.00

2000 Stadium Club Chrome Eyes of the Game

Randomly inserted into packs at one in 16, this 10-card insert features players who have an "eye" for the game. Card backs carry an "EG" prefix.

COMPLETE SET (10) 12.50 30.00
*REFRACTORS: 1X TO 2.5X BASIC EYES .75
2.00
REFRACTOR ODDS 1:80
EG1 Randy Johnson .75 2.00
EG2 Mike Piazza 1.25 3.00
EG3 Nomar Garciaparra 1.25 3.00
EG4 Mark McGwire 2.00 5.00
EG5 Alex Rodriguez 1.25 3.00
EG6 Derek Jeter 2.00 5.00
EG7 Tony Gwynn 1.00 2.50
EG8 Sammy Sosa .75 2.00
EG9 Larry Walker .30 .75
EG10 Ken Griffey Jr. 1.25 3.00

2000 Stadium Club Chrome True Colors

Randomly inserted into packs at one in 32, this 10-card insert features players that rise to the occasion when the game's on the line. Card backs carry a "TC" prefix.

COMPLETE SET (10) 20.00 50.00
*REFRACTORS: 1X TO 2.5X BASIC TRUE
REFRACTOR ODDS 1:160
TC1 Sammy Sosa 1.25 3.00
TC2 Nomar Garciaparra 2.00 5.00
TC3 Alex Rodriguez 2.00 5.00
TC4 Derek Jeter 3.00 8.00
TC5 Mark McGwire 3.00 8.00
TC6 Chipper Jones 1.25 3.00
TC7 Mike Piazza 2.00 5.00
TC8 Ken Griffey Jr. 2.00 5.00
TC9 Manny Ramirez .75 2.00
TC10 Vladimir Guerrero 1.25 3.00

2000 Stadium Club Chrome Visionaries

Randomly inserted into packs at one in 18, this 20-card insert features some of the major league's most talented prospects. Card backs carry a "V" prefix.

COMPLETE SET (20) 25.00 60.00
*REF: .75X TO 2X BASIC VISIONARIES 1.25 3.00
REFRACTOR ODDS 1:90
V1 Alfonso Soriano 1.25 3.00
V2 Josh Hamilton 1.25 3.00
V3 A.J. Burnett .50 1.25
V4 Pat Burrell .50 1.25
V5 Ruben Salazar .50 1.25
V6 Aaron Rowand 1.50 4.00
V7 Adam Piatt .50 1.25
V8 Nick Johnson .50 1.25
V9 Brett Myers 1.25 3.00
V10 Jack Cust .50 1.25
V11 Corey Patterson .50 1.25
V12 Sean Burroughs .50 1.25
V13 Pablo Ozuna .50 1.25
V14 Dee Brown .50 1.25
V15 John Patterson .50 1.25
V16 Willi Mo Pena .50 1.25
V17 Mark Mulder .50 1.25
V18 Eric Munson .50 1.25
V19 Alex Escobar 1.25 3.00
V20 Rick Asadoorian .50 1.25

2001 Studio

This 200 card set was issued in six-card packs with 18 packs per box. Cards numbered 151-200 were shorter printed than cards 1-150. Each of the cards from 151-200 were serial numbered to 700.

COMP.SET w/o SP's (150) 15.00 40.00
COMMON CARD (1-150) .20 .50
COMMON (151-200) 3.00 8.00
1 Alex Rodriguez .75 2.00
2 Barry Bonds 1.25 3.00
3 Cal Ripken 1.50 4.00
4 Chipper Jones .50 1.25
5 Derek Jeter 1.25 3.00
6 Troy Glaus .20 .50
7 Frank Thomas .50 1.25
8 Greg Maddux .75 2.00
9 Ivan Rodriguez .30 .75
10 Jeff Bagwell .30 .75
11 Mark Quinn .20 .50
12 Todd Helton .30 .75
13 Ken Griffey Jr. .75 2.00
14 Manny Ramirez Sox .30 .75
15 Mark McGwire 1.25 3.00
16 Mike Piazza .75 2.00
17 Nomar Garciaparra .75 2.00
18 Robin Ventura .20 .50
19 Aramis Ramirez .20 .50
20 J.T. Snow .20 .50
21 Pat Burrell .20 .50
22 Curt Schilling .20 .50
23 Carlos Delgado .20 .50
24 J.D. Drew .20 .50
25 Cliff Floyd .20 .50
26 Brian Jordan .20 .50
27 Roberto Alomar .30 .75
28 Barry Zito .30 .75
29 Harold Baines .20 .50
30 Brad Penny .20 .50
31 Jose Cruz Jr. .20 .50
32 Andy Pettitte .30 .75
33 Jim Edmonds .20 .50
34 Darin Erstad .20 .50
35 Jason Giambi .20 .50
36 Tom Glavine .30 .75
37 Juan Gonzalez .20 .50
38 Mark Grace .30 .75
39 Shawn Green .20 .50
40 Tim Hudson .20 .50
41 Andruw Jones .30 .75
42 Jeff Kent .20 .50
43 Barry Larkin .30 .75
44 Rafael Furcal .20 .50
45 Mike Mussina .30 .75
46 Hideo Nomo .50 1.25
47 Rafael Palmeiro .30 .75
48 Scott Rolen .30 .75
49 Gary Sheffield .20 .50
50 Bernie Williams .30 .75
51 Bob Abreu .20 .50
52 Edgardo Alfonzo .20 .50
53 Edgar Martinez .30 .75
54 Magglio Ordonez .20 .50
55 Kerry Wood .20 .50
56 Matt Morris .20 .50
57 Lance Berkman .20 .50
58 Kevin Brown .20 .50
59 Sean Casey .20 .50
60 Eric Chavez .20 .50
61 Bartolo Colon .20 .50
62 Johnny Damon .30 .75
63 Jermaine Dye .20 .50
64 Juan Encarnacion .20 .50
65 Carl Everett .20 .50
66 Brian Giles .20 .50
67 Mike Hampton .20 .50
68 Richard Hidalgo .20 .50
69 Geoff Jenkins .20 .50
70 Jacque Jones .20 .50
71 Jason Kendall .20 .50
72 Ryan Klesko .20 .50
73 Chan Ho Park .20 .50
74 Richie Sexson .20 .50
75 Mike Sweeney .20 .50
76 Fernando Tatis .20 .50
77 Miguel Tejada .20 .50
78 Jose Vidro .20 .50
79 Larry Walker .75 2.00
80 Preston Wilson .20 .50
81 Craig Biggio .30 .75
82 Fred McGriff .30 .75
83 Jim Thome .30 .75
84 Garret Anderson .20 .50
85 Mark Mulder .20 .50
86 Tony Batista .20 .50
87 Terrence Long .20 .50
88 Brad Fullmer .20 .50
89 Rusty Greer .20 .50
90 Orlando Hernandez .20 .50
91 Gabe Kapler .20 .50
92 Paul Konerko .20 .50
93 Carlos Lee .20 .50
94 Kenny Lofton .20 .50
95 Raul Mondesi .20 .50
96 Jorge Posada .30 .75
97 Tim Salmon .30 .75
98 Greg Vaughn .20 .50
99 Mo Vaughn .20 .50
100 Omar Vizquel .30 .75
101 Ben Grieve .20 .50
102 Luis Gonzalez .20 .50
103 Ray Durham .20 .50
104 Ryan Dempster .20 .50
105 Eric Karros .20 .50
106 David Justice .20 .50
107 Pedro Martinez .30 .75
108 Randy Johnson .50 1.25
109 Rick Ankiel .20 .50
110 Rickey Henderson .50 1.25
111 Roger Clemens 1.00 2.50
112 Sammy Sosa .50 1.25
113 Tony Gwynn .60 1.50
114 Vladimir Guerrero .50 1.25
115 Kazuhiro Sasaki .20 .50
116 Phil Nevin .20 .50
117 Ruben Mateo .20 .50
118 Shannon Stewart .20 .50
119 Matt Williams .20 .50
120 Tino Martinez .30 .75
121 Ken Caminiti .20 .50
122 Edgar Renteria .20 .50
123 Charles Johnson .20 .50
124 Aaron Sele .20 .50
125 Javy Lopez .20 .50
126 Mariano Rivera .50 1.25
127 Shea Hillenbrand .20 .50
128 Jeff D'Amico .20 .50
129 Brady Anderson .20 .50
130 Kevin Millwood .20 .50
131 Trot Nixon .20 .50
132 Mike Lieberthal .20 .50
133 Juan Pierre .20 .50
134 Russ Ortiz .20 .50
135 Jose Macias .20 .50
136 John Smoltz .30 .75
137 Jason Varitek .50 1.25
138 Dean Palmer .20 .50
139 Jeff Cirillo .20 .50
140 Paul O'Neill .30 .75
141 Andres Galarraga .20 .50
142 David Wells .20 .50
143 Brad Radke .20 .50
144 Wade Miller .20 .50
145 John Olerud .20 .50
146 Moises Alou .20 .50
147 Carlos Beltran .20 .50
148 Jeromy Burnitz .20 .50
149 Steve Finley .20 .50
150 Joe Mays .20 .50
151 Alex Escobar ROO 3.00 8.00
152 J. Estrada ROO RC 4.00 10.00
153 Pedro Feliz ROO 3.00 8.00
154 Nate Frese ROO RC 3.00 8.00
155 Dee Brown ROO 3.00 8.00
156 B. Larson ROO RC 3.00 8.00
157 A. Gomez ROO RC 3.00 8.00
158 Jason Hart ROO 3.00 8.00
159 C.C. Sabathia ROO 3.00 8.00
160 Josh Towers ROO RC 4.00 10.00
161 C. Parker ROO RC 3.00 8.00
162 J. Melian ROO RC 3.00 8.00
163 Joe Kennedy ROO RC 4.00 10.00
164 A. Hernandez ROO RC 3.00 8.00
165 Jimmy Rollins ROO 3.00 8.00
166 Jose Mieses ROO RC 3.00 8.00
167 Roy Oswalt ROO 4.00 10.00
168 Eric Munson ROO 3.00 8.00
169 Xavier Nady ROO 3.00 8.00
170 H. Ramirez ROO RC 4.00 10.00
171 Abraham Nunez ROO 3.00 8.00
172 Jose Ortiz ROO 3.00 8.00
173 Jeremy Owens ROO RC UER 3.00 8.00
Eric Owens pictured on front
174 C. Vargas ROO RC 3.00 8.00
175 Corey Patterson ROO 3.00 8.00
176 Carlos Pena ROO 3.00 8.00
177 Bud Smith ROO RC 3.00 8.00
178 Adam Dunn ROO 4.00 10.00
179 A. Pettyjohn ROO RC 3.00 8.00
180 E. Guzman ROO RC 3.00 8.00
181 Jay Gibbons ROO RC 4.00 10.00
182 Wilkin Ruan ROO RC 3.00 8.00
183 T. Shinjo ROO RC 4.00 10.00
184 Alfonso Soriano ROO 4.00 10.00
185 Marcus Giles ROO 3.00 8.00
186 Ichiro Suzuki ROO RC 40.00 80.00
187 Juan Uribe ROO RC 4.00 10.00
188 D. Williams ROO RC 3.00 8.00
189 Carlos Valderrama ROO RC 3.00 8.00
190 Matt White ROO RC 3.00 8.00
191 Albert Pujols ROO RC 150.00 225.00
192 D. Mendez ROO RC 3.00 8.00
193 C. Aldridge ROO RC 3.00 8.00
194 Endy Chavez ROO RC 3.00 8.00
195 Josh Beckett ROO 4.00 10.00
196 W. Betemit ROO RC 4.00 10.00
197 Ben Sheets ROO 4.00 10.00
198 A. Torres ROO RC 3.00 8.00
199 Aubrey Huff ROO 3.00 8.00
200 Jack Wilson ROO RC 4.00 10.00

2001 Studio Diamond Collection

Randomly inserted in packs, these 47 cards feature each of these players along with a game-worn jersey swatch. Cards numbered 24, 35 and 44 were not printed for this set.

DC1 Vladimir Guerrero 6.00 15.00
DC2 Barry Bonds 10.00 25.00
DC3 Cal Ripken 15.00 40.00
DC4 Nomar Garciaparra 6.00 15.00
DC5 Greg Maddux 6.00 15.00
DC6 Frank Thomas 6.00 15.00
DC7 Roger Clemens 10.00 25.00
DC8 Luis Gonzalez SP 6.00 15.00
DC9 Tony Gwynn 6.00 15.00
DC10 Carlos Lee SP 6.00 15.00
DC11 Troy Glaus 4.00 10.00
DC12 Randy Johnson 6.00 15.00
DC13 Manny Ramirez SP 10.00 25.00
DC14 Pedro Martinez 6.00 15.00
DC15 Todd Helton 6.00 15.00
DC16 Jeff Bagwell 6.00 15.00
DC17 Rickey Henderson 6.00 15.00
DC18 Kazuhiro Sasaki 4.00 10.00
DC19 Albert Pujols SP 30.00 60.00
DC20 Ivan Rodriguez 6.00 15.00
DC21 Darin Erstad 4.00 10.00
DC22 Andruw Jones 6.00 15.00
DC23 Roberto Alomar 6.00 15.00
DC25 Juan Gonzalez 4.00 10.00
DC26 Shawn Green 4.00 10.00
DC27 Lance Berkman 4.00 10.00
DC28 Scott Rolen 6.00 15.00
DC29 Rafael Palmeiro 6.00 15.00
DC30 J.D. Drew 4.00 10.00
DC31 Kerry Wood 4.00 10.00
DC32 Jim Edmonds 4.00 10.00
DC33 Tom Glavine SP 10.00 25.00
DC34 Hideo Nomo SP 10.00 25.00
DC36 Tim Hudson 4.00 10.00
DC37 Miguel Tejada 4.00 10.00
DC38 Chipper Jones 6.00 15.00
DC39 Edgar Martinez SP 10.00 25.00
DC40 Chan Ho Park 4.00 10.00
DC41 Magglio Ordonez 4.00 10.00
DC42 Sean Casey 4.00 10.00
DC43 Larry Walker 4.00 10.00
DC45 Cliff Floyd 4.00 10.00
DC46 Mike Sweeney 4.00 10.00
DC47 Kevin Brown 4.00 10.00
DC48 Richie Sexson 4.00 10.00
DC49 Jermaine Dye 4.00 10.00
DC50 Craig Biggio 6.00 15.00

2001 Studio Diamond Cut Collection

This parallel to the Diamond Cut insert set was randomly inserted in packs. Each card was serial numbered to 75 and features an upgraded patch swatch of fabric (as averse to the standard jersey swatch used for the more readily available Diamond Collection inserts). Six player signed 25 of their cards, thus creating an Autograph parallel set. Please note, the six players have been tagged as "SP/50" in our checklist for this set.

1/8/19/26-28 PRINT RUN 50 #'d OF EACH

2001 Studio Leather and Lumber

Randomly inserted in packs, these 47 cards feature player cards along with one swatch of a game-used bat. A few players were printed in lesser quantity and we have notated those players with an SP. Also, cards numbered 4,22 and 39 do not exist.

COMBOS PRINT RUN 25 #'d SETS
NO COMBO PRICING DUE TO SCARCITY
LL1 Barry Bonds 10.00 25.00
LL2 Cal Ripken 15.00 40.00
LL3 Miguel Tejada 4.00 10.00
LL5 Frank Thomas 6.00 15.00
LL6 Greg Maddux 6.00 15.00
LL7 Ivan Rodriguez 6.00 15.00
LL8 Jeff Bagwell SP 10.00 25.00
LL9 Sean Casey SP 6.00 15.00
LL10 Todd Helton 6.00 15.00
LL11 Cliff Floyd 4.00 10.00
LL12 Hideo Nomo 6.00 15.00
LL13 Chipper Jones 6.00 15.00
LL14 Rickey Henderson 6.00 15.00
LL15 Richard Hidalgo 4.00 10.00
LL16 Mike Piazza 6.00 15.00
LL17 Larry Walker 4.00 10.00
LL18 Tony Gwynn 6.00 15.00
LL19 Vladimir Guerrero 6.00 15.00
LL20 Rafael Furcal 4.00 10.00
LL21 Roberto Alomar SP 10.00 25.00
LL23 Albert Pujols 30.00 60.00
LL24 Raul Mondesi 4.00 10.00
LL25 J.D. Drew 4.00 10.00
LL26 Jim Edmonds 4.00 10.00
LL27 Darin Erstad SP 6.00 15.00
LL28 Craig Biggio 6.00 15.00
LL29 Kenny Lofton 4.00 10.00
LL30 Juan Gonzalez 4.00 10.00
LL31 John Olerud 4.00 10.00
LL32 Shawn Green 4.00 10.00
LL33 Andruw Jones SP 10.00 25.00
LL34 Moises Alou 4.00 10.00
LL35 Jeff Kent 4.00 10.00
LL36 Ryan Klesko 4.00 10.00
LL37 Luis Gonzalez 4.00 10.00
LL38 Rafael Palmeiro 6.00 15.00
LL40 Scott Rolen 6.00 15.00
LL41 Carlos Lee 4.00 10.00
LL42 Bob Abreu 4.00 10.00
LL43 Edgardo Alfonzo 4.00 10.00
LL44 Bernie Williams 6.00 15.00
LL45 Brian Giles 4.00 10.00
LL46 Jermaine Dye 4.00 10.00
LL47 Lance Berkman 4.00 10.00
LL48 Edgar Martinez 6.00 15.00
LL49 Richie Sexson 4.00 10.00
LL50 Magglio Ordonez 4.00 10.00

2001 Studio Masterstrokes

Randomly inserted in packs, these 30 cards feature the player along with both a swatch of game-used bat and a game-used jersey. These cards are serial numbered to 200 and cards numbered 13 and 15 were not issued.

MS1 Tony Gwynn 10.00 25.00
MS2 Ivan Rodriguez 10.00 25.00
MS3 J.D. Drew 6.00 15.00
MS4 Cal Ripken 30.00 60.00
MS5 Hideo Nomo 10.00 25.00
MS6 Darin Erstad 6.00 15.00
MS7 Frank Thomas 10.00 25.00
MS8 Andruw Jones 10.00 25.00
MS9 Roberto Alomar 10.00 25.00
MS10 Larry Walker 6.00 15.00
MS11 Vladimir Guerrero 10.00 25.00
MS12 Barry Bonds 20.00 50.00
MS14 Luis Gonzalez 6.00 15.00
MS16 Juan Gonzalez 6.00 15.00
MS17 Todd Helton 10.00 25.00
MS18 Jeff Bagwell 10.00 25.00
MS19 Albert Pujols 75.00 150.00
MS20 Shawn Green 6.00 15.00
MS21 Magglio Ordonez 6.00 15.00
MS22 Scott Rolen 10.00 25.00
MS23 Rafael Palmeiro 10.00 25.00
MS24 Sean Casey 6.00 15.00
MS25 Jim Edmonds 6.00 15.00
MS26 Chipper Jones 10.00 25.00
MS27 Cliff Floyd 6.00 15.00
MS28 Carlos Lee 6.00 15.00
MS29 Edgar Martinez 10.00 25.00
MS30 Lance Berkman

2001 Studio Masterstrokes Artist's Proofs

This parallel to the Studio Masterstroke set was issued to a print run of 25 sets. A few of the players signed their cards for inclusion in the set.

2/11/14/19-20/24 ARE AUTO CARDS

2001 Studio Private Signings 5 x 7

Issued one per sealed box, these cards measure 5" by 7" and were signed by the players. A few cards were issued in shorter supply and we have notated them with an SP and print run information supplied by Donruss/Playoff.

1 Bob Abreu 6.00 15.00
2 Roberto Alomar SP/200 10.00 25.00
3 Rick Ankiel 10.00 25.00
4 Josh Beckett 10.00 25.00
5 Lance Berkman 15.00 40.00
6 Wilson Betemit 10.00 25.00
7 Barry Bonds SP/95 100.00 175.00
8 Sean Casey 6.00 15.00
9 Roger Clemens SP/200 60.00 120.00
10 Adam Dunn 10.00 25.00
11 Darin Erstad SP/25
12 Alex Escobar 4.00 10.00
13 Cliff Floyd 6.00 15.00
14 Jason Giambi SP/250 6.00 15.00
15 Brian Giles 6.00 15.00
16 Troy Glaus 10.00 25.00
17 Tom Glavine 15.00 40.00
18 Luis Gonzalez 6.00 15.00
19 Shawn Green SP/190 10.00 25.00
20 Vladimir Guerrero 15.00 40.00
21 Tony Gwynn SP/190 50.00 100.00
22 Todd Helton SP/125 10.00 25.00
23 Andruw Jones SP/250 10.00 25.00
24 Gabe Kapler 6.00 15.00
25 Ryan Klesko 6.00 15.00
26 Carlos Lee 6.00 15.00
27 Greg Maddux SP/200 50.00 100.00
28 Edgar Martinez 15.00 40.00
29 Mike Mussina SP/144 15.00 40.00
30 Magglio Ordonez 6.00 15.00
31 R. Palmeiro SP/250 20.00 50.00
32 Corey Patterson 4.00 10.00
33 Brad Penny 4.00 10.00
34 Albert Pujols SP/50 600.00 1000.00
35 Manny Ramirez Sox SP/115 30.00 60.00
36 Cal Ripken SP/50 150.00 250.00
37 Alex Rodriguez 60.00 120.00
38 Ivan Rodriguez SP/150 15.00 40.00
39 Scott Rolen 10.00 25.00
40 C.C. Sabathia 6.00 15.00
41 Curt Schilling 20.00 50.00
42 Ben Sheets 10.00 25.00
43 Alfonso Soriano 10.00 25.00
44 Mike Sweeney 6.00 15.00
45 Miguel Tejada 10.00 25.00
46 Frank Thomas 15.00 40.00
47 Kerry Wood 10.00 25.00
48 Barry Zito 10.00 25.00

2001 Studio Warning Track

Randomly inserted in packs, these 35 cards feature the player along with a swatch from an outfield-wall. Card number 26 does not exist in this set.

OFF THE WALL 25 SERIAL #'D SETS
OFF THE WALL: NO PRICING DUE TO SCARCITY

WT1 Andruw Jones	4.00	10.00
WT2 Rafael Palmeiro	4.00	10.00
WT3 Gary Sheffield	3.00	8.00
WT4 Larry Walker	3.00	8.00
WT5 Shawn Green	3.00	8.00
WT6 Mike Piazza	6.00	15.00
WT7 Barry Bonds	10.00	25.00
WT8 J.D. Drew	3.00	8.00
WT9 Magglio Ordonez	3.00	8.00
WT10 Todd Helton	4.00	10.00
WT11 Juan Gonzalez	3.00	8.00
WT12 Pat Burrell	3.00	8.00
WT13 Mark McGwire	12.50	30.00
WT14 Frank Robinson	4.00	10.00
WT15 Manny Ramirez	4.00	10.00
WT16 Lance Berkman	3.00	8.00
WT17 Kirby Puckett	4.00	10.00
WT18 Johnny Bench	4.00	10.00
WT19 Chipper Jones	4.00	10.00
WT20 Mike Schmidt	8.00	20.00
WT21 Vladimir Guerrero	4.00	10.00
WT22 Sammy Sosa	4.00	10.00
WT23 Cal Ripken	12.50	30.00
WT24 Roberto Alomar	4.00	10.00
WT25 Willie Stargell	4.00	10.00
WT27 Scott Rolen	4.00	10.00
WT28 R. Clemente SP	30.00	60.00
WT29 Tony Gwynn	6.00	15.00
WT30 Ivan Rodriguez	4.00	10.00
WT31 Sean Casey	3.00	8.00
WT32 Frank Thomas	4.00	10.00
WT33 Jeff Bagwell	4.00	10.00
WT34 Jeff Kent	3.00	8.00
WT35 Reggie Jackson	4.00	10.00

2001-02 Studio Chicago Collection

These cards were among the first in a project in which Donruss/Playoff unveiled a show-exclusive program. At the March 2002 Chicago Sun-Times Show, if a collector opened a box at the Donruss/Playoff booth -- they received a card from what Donruss/Playoff called the "Chicago Collection". Donruss/Playoff created a limited amount of singles from selected products and sequentially numbered each card to 5. The cards were distributed on a strict product-specific basis. For example, collectors who opened 2001 Donruss packs or boxes in front of a Donruss representative were be rewarded with the appropriate number of 2001

NO PRICING DUE TO SCARCITY

2002 Studio Samples

This 200 card set, which previewed the veteran players from the Studio set, was issued one per Beckett Baseball Card Monthly issue number 210. These cards are valued at a multiple of the regular Studio cards. These cards can be differentiated from the regular cards with the "Sample" verbiage in the back.

*SAMPLES: 1.5X TO 4X BASIC CARDS
ONE PER ICHIRO BBCM 210
*GOLD: 1.5X TO 4X BASIC SAMPLES
GOLD: ISSUED IN 10% OF TOTAL RUN

2002 Studio

This 275 card set was issued in two separate series. The Studio product, containing cards 1-250, was released in July, 2002. The product was issued in five card packs which came 18 packs to a box and 16 boxes to a case. Cards numbered 1 through 200 feature veterans while cards 201 through 250 feature rookies and prospects and have a stated print run of 1500 serial numbered sets. Cards 251-275 were distributed in 2002 Donruss the Rookies packs in mid-December 2002. Like cards 201-250, these update cards featured a selection of prospects and were each serial-numbered to 1500 copies.

COMP.LOW SET w/o SP's (200)	20.00	50.00
COMMON CARD (1-200)	.20	.50
COMMON ROOKIE (1-200)	.20	.50
COMMON CARD (201-275)	1.50	4.00
1 Vladimir Guerrero	.50	1.25
2 Chipper Jones	.50	1.25
3 Bob Abreu	.20	.50
4 Barry Zito	.20	.50
5 Larry Walker	.20	.50
6 Miguel Tejada	.20	.50
7 Mike Sweeney	.20	.50
8 Shannon Stewart	.20	.50
9 Sammy Sosa	.50	1.25
10 Bud Smith	.20	.50
11 Wilson Betemit	.20	.50
12 Kevin Brown	.20	.50
13 Ellis Burks	.20	.50
14 Pat Burrell	.20	.50
15 Cliff Floyd	.20	.50
16 Marcus Giles	.20	.50
17 Troy Glaus	.20	.50
18 Barry Larkin	.30	.75
19 Carlos Lee	.20	.50
20 Brian Lawrence	.20	.50
21 Paul Lo Duca	.20	.50
22 Ben Grieve	.20	.50
23 Shawn Green	.20	.50
24 Mike Cameron	.20	.50
25 Roger Clemens	1.00	2.50
26 Joe Crede	.20	.50
27 Jose Cruz Jr.	.20	.50
28 Jeremy Affeldt	.20	.50
29 Adrian Beltre	.20	.50
30 Josh Beckett	.20	.50
31 Roberto Alomar	.30	.75
32 Toby Hall	.20	.50
33 Mike Hampton	.20	.50
34 Eric Milton	.20	.50
35 Eric Munson	.20	.50
36 Trot Nixon	.20	.50
37 Roy Oswalt	.20	.50
38 Chan Ho Park	.20	.50
39 Charles Johnson	.20	.50
40 Nick Johnson	.20	.50
41 Tim Hudson	.20	.50
42 Cristian Guzman	.20	.50
43 Drew Henson	.20	.50
44 Mark Grace	.30	.75
45 Luis Gonzalez	.20	.50
46 Pedro Martinez	.30	.75
47 Joe Mays	.20	.50
48 Jorge Posada	.30	.75
49 Aramis Ramirez	.20	.50
50 Kip Wells	.20	.50
51 Moises Alou	.20	.50
52 Omar Vizquel	.30	.75
53 Ichiro Suzuki	1.00	2.50
54 Jimmy Rollins	.20	.50
55 Freddy Garcia	.20	.50
56 Steve Green	.20	.50
57 Brian Jordan	.20	.50
58 Paul Konerko	.20	.50
59 Jack Cust	.20	.50
60 Sean Casey	.20	.50
61 Bret Boone	.20	.50
62 Hideo Nomo	.50	1.25
63 Magglio Ordonez	.20	.50
64 Frank Thomas	.50	1.25
65 Josh Towers	.20	.50
66 Javier Vazquez	.20	.50
67 Robin Ventura	.20	.50
68 Aubrey Huff	.20	.50
69 Richard Hidalgo	.20	.50
70 Brandon Claussen	.20	.50
71 Bartolo Colon	.20	.50
72 John Buck	.20	.50
73 Dee Brown	.20	.50
74 Barry Bonds	1.25	3.00
75 Jason Giambi	.20	.50
76 Erick Almonte	.20	.50
77 Ryan Dempster	.20	.50
78 Jim Edmonds	.20	.50
79 Jay Gibbons	.20	.50
80 Shigetoshi Hasegawa	.20	.50
81 Todd Helton	.30	.75
82 Erik Bedard	.20	.50
83 Carlos Beltran	.20	.50
84 Rafael Soriano	.20	.50
85 Gary Sheffield	.20	.50
86 Richie Sexson	.20	.50
87 Mike Rivera	.20	.50
88 Jose Ortiz	.20	.50
89 Abraham Nunez	.20	.50
90 Dave Williams	.20	.50
91 Preston Wilson	.20	.50
92 Jason Jennings	.20	.50
93 Juan Diaz	.20	.50
94 Steve Smyth	.20	.50
95 Phil Nevin	.20	.50
96 John Olerud	.20	.50
97 Brad Penny	.20	.50
98 Andy Pettitte	.30	.75
99 Juan Pierre	.20	.50
100 Manny Ramirez	.30	.75
101 Edgardo Alfonzo	.20	.50
102 Michael Cuddyer	.20	.50
103 Johnny Damon Sox	.30	.75
104 Carlos Zambrano	.20	.50
105 Jose Vidro	.20	.50
106 Tsuyoshi Shinjo	.20	.50
107 Ed Rogers	.20	.50
108 Scott Rolen	.30	.75
109 Mariano Rivera	.50	1.25
110 Tim Redding	.20	.50
111 Josh Phelps	.20	.50
112 Gabe Kapler	.20	.50
113 Edgar Martinez	.30	.75
114 Fred McGriff	.30	.75
115 Raul Mondesi	.20	.50
116 Wade Miller	.20	.50
117 Mike Mussina	.30	.75
118 Rafael Palmeiro	.30	.75
119 Adam Johnson	.20	.50
120 Rickey Henderson	.50	1.25
121 Bill Hall	.20	.50
122 Ken Griffey Jr.	.75	2.00
123 Geronimo Gil	.20	.50
124 Robert Fick	.20	.50
125 Darin Erstad	.20	.50
126 Brandon Duckworth	.20	.50
127 Garret Anderson	.20	.50
128 Pedro Feliz	.20	.50
129 Jeff Cirillo	.20	.50
130 Brian Giles	.20	.50
131 Craig Biggio	.30	.75
132 Willie Harris	.20	.50
133 Doug Davis	.20	.50
134 Jeff Kent	.20	.50
135 Terrence Long	.20	.50
136 Carlos Delgado	.20	.50
137 Tino Martinez	.30	.75
138 Donaldo Mendez	.20	.50
139 Sean Douglass	.20	.50
140 Eric Chavez	.20	.50
141 Rick Ankiel	.20	.50
142 Jeremy Giambi	.20	.50
143 Juan Pena	.20	.50
144 Bernie Williams	.30	.75
145 Craig Wilson	.20	.50
146 Ricardo Rodriguez	.20	.50
147 Albert Pujols	1.00	2.50
148 Antonio Perez	.20	.50
149 Russ Ortiz	.20	.50
150 Corky Miller	.20	.50
151 Rich Aurilia	.20	.50
152 Kerry Wood	.20	.50
153 Joe Thurston	.20	.50
154 Jeff Deardorff	.20	.50
155 Jermaine Dye	.20	.50
156 Andruw Jones	.30	.75
157 Victor Martinez	.50	1.25
158 Nick Neugebauer	.20	.50
159 Matt Morris	.20	.50
160 Casey Fossum	.20	.50
161 J.D. Drew	.20	.50
162 Matt Childers	.20	.50
163 Mark Buehrle	.20	.50
164 Jeff Bagwell	.30	.75
165 Kazuhiro Sasaki	.20	.50
166 Ben Sheets	.20	.50
167 Alex Rodriguez	.75	2.00
168 Adam Pettyjohn	.20	.50
169 Chris Snelling RC	.50	1.25
170 Robert Person	.20	.50
171 Juan Uribe	.20	.50
172 Mo Vaughn	.20	.50
173 Alfredo Amezaga	.20	.50
174 Ryan Drese	.20	.50
175 Corey Thurman RC	.20	.50
176 Jim Thome	.30	.75
177 Orlando Cabrera	.20	.50
178 Eric Cyr	.20	.50
179 Greg Maddux	.75	2.00
180 Earl Snyder RC	.20	.50
181 C.C. Sabathia	.20	.50
182 Mark Mulder	.20	.50
183 Jose Mieses	.20	.50
184 Joe Kennedy	.20	.50
185 Randy Johnson	.50	1.25
186 Tom Glavine	.30	.75
187 Eric Junge RC	.20	.50
188 Mike Piazza	.75	2.00
189 Corey Patterson	.20	.50
190 Carlos Pena	.20	.50
191 Curt Schilling	.20	.50
192 Nomar Garciaparra	.75	2.00
193 Lance Berkman	.20	.50
194 Ryan Klesko	.20	.50
195 Ivan Rodriguez	.30	.75
196 Alfonso Soriano	.20	.50
197 Derek Jeter	1.25	3.00
198 David Justice	.20	.50
199 Juan Gonzalez	.20	.50
200 Adam Dunn	.20	.50
201 Victor Alvarez ROO RC	1.50	4.00
202 Miguel Asencio ROO RC	1.50	4.00
203 Brandon Backe ROO RC	2.00	5.00
204 Chris Baker ROO RC	1.50	4.00
205 Steve Bechler ROO RC	1.50	4.00
206 Francis Beltran ROO RC	1.50	4.00
207 Angel Berroa ROO	1.50	4.00
208 Hank Blalock ROO	2.00	5.00
209 Dewon Brazelton ROO	1.50	4.00
210 Sean Burroughs ROO	1.50	4.00
211 Marlon Byrd ROO	1.50	4.00
212 Raul Chavez ROO RC	1.50	4.00
213 Juan Cruz ROO	1.50	4.00
214 J.De La Rosa ROO RC	1.50	4.00
215 Doug Devore ROO RC	1.50	4.00
216 John Ennis ROO RC	1.50	4.00
217 Felix Escalona ROO RC	1.50	4.00
218 Morgan Ensberg ROO	1.50	4.00
219 Cam Esslinger ROO RC	1.50	4.00
220 Kevin Frederick ROO RC	1.50	4.00
221 Fr.German ROO RC	1.50	4.00
222 Eric Hinske ROO	1.50	4.00
223 Ben Howard ROO RC	1.50	4.00
224 Orlando Hudson ROO	1.50	4.00
225 Travis Hughes ROO RC	1.50	4.00
226 Kazuhisa Ishii ROO RC	2.00	5.00
227 Ryan Jamison ROO	1.50	4.00
228 Reed Johnson ROO RC	2.00	5.00
229 Kyle Kane ROO RC	1.50	4.00
230 Austin Kearns ROO	1.50	4.00
231 Sat.Komiyama ROO RC	1.50	4.00
232 Jason Lane ROO	1.50	4.00
233 Jeremy Lambert ROO RC	1.50	4.00
234 And. Machado ROO RC	1.50	4.00
235 Brian Mallette ROO RC	1.50	4.00
236 Tak. Nomura ROO RC	1.50	4.00
237 Jorge Padilla ROO RC	1.50	4.00
238 Luis Ugueto ROO RC	1.50	4.00
239 Mark Prior ROO	2.00	5.00
240 Rene Reyes ROO RC	1.50	4.00
241 Deivis Santos ROO	1.50	4.00
242 Elio Serrano ROO RC	1.50	4.00
243 Tom Shearn ROO RC	1.50	4.00
244 Allan Simpson ROO RC	1.50	4.00
245 So Taguchi ROO RC	2.00	5.00
246 Dennis Tankersley ROO	1.50	4.00
247 Mark Teixeira ROO	2.00	5.00
248 Matt Thornton ROO RC	1.50	4.00
249 Bobby Hill ROO	1.50	4.00
250 Ramon Vazquez ROO	1.50	4.00
251 Freddy Sanchez ROO RC	2.00	5.00
252 Josh Bard ROO RC	1.50	4.00
253 Trey Hodges ROO RC	1.50	4.00
254 Jorge Sosa ROO RC	2.00	5.00
255 Ben Kozlowski ROO RC	1.50	4.00
256 Eric Good ROO RC	1.50	4.00
257 Brian Tallet ROO RC	1.50	4.00
258 P.J. Bevis ROO RC	1.50	4.00
259 Rodrigo Rosario ROO RC	1.50	4.00
260 Kirk Saarloos ROO RC	1.50	4.00
261 Run. Hernandez ROO RC	1.50	4.00
262 Josh Hancock ROO RC	2.00	5.00
263 Tim Kalita ROO RC	1.50	4.00
264 J.Simontacchi ROO RC	1.50	4.00
265 Clay Condrey ROO RC	1.50	4.00
266 Cliff Lee ROO RC	2.50	6.00
267 Aaron Guiel ROO RC	1.50	4.00
268 Andy Pratt ROO RC	1.50	4.00
269 Wilson Valdez ROO RC	1.50	4.00
270 Oliver Perez ROO RC	2.00	5.00
271 Joe Borchard ROO	1.50	4.00
272 J.Robertson ROO RC	1.50	4.00
273 Aaron Cook ROO RC	1.50	4.00
274 Kevin Cash ROO RC	1.50	4.00
275 Chone Figgins ROO RC	2.00	5.00

2002 Studio Private Signings

Randomly inserted in packs of Studio and Donruss the Rookies, these 210 cards partially parallel the 2002 Studio set. Since these cards are signed to a variable amount of cards, we have listed the print run next to the player's name. Those players who signed 25 or fewer cards are not priced due to market scarcity.

1 Vladimir Guerrero/25		
2 Chipper Jones/15		
3 Bob Abreu/50	10.00	25.00
4 Barry Zito/25		
6 Miguel Tejada/50	15.00	40.00
7 Mike Sweeney/50	10.00	25.00
8 Shannon Stewart/50	10.00	25.00
10 Bud Smith/100	6.00	15.00
11 Wilson Betemit/250	4.00	10.00
12 Kevin Brown/25		
15 Cliff Floyd/50	10.00	25.00
16 Marcus Giles/250	6.00	15.00
17 Troy Glaus/50	15.00	40.00
18 Barry Larkin/25		
19 Carlos Lee/25		
20 Brian Lawrence/250	4.00	10.00
21 Paul Lo Duca/50	10.00	25.00
25 Roger Clemens/15		
26 Joe Crede/250	6.00	15.00
28 Jeremy Affeldt/250	4.00	10.00
29 Adrian Beltre/25		
30 Josh Beckett/25		
31 Roberto Alomar/25		
32 Toby Hall/250	4.00	10.00
35 Eric Munson/25		
37 Roy Oswalt/50	10.00	25.00
40 Nick Johnson/250	6.00	15.00
41 Tim Hudson/25		
43 Drew Henson/150	4.00	10.00
45 Luis Gonzalez/15		
46 Pedro Martinez/15		
47 Joe Mays/100	6.00	15.00
49 Aramis Ramirez/50	10.00	25.00
50 Kip Wells/250	4.00	10.00
51 Moises Alou/15		
55 Freddy Garcia/50	10.00	25.00
56 Steve Green/250	4.00	10.00
59 Jack Cust/250	4.00	10.00
60 Sean Casey/50	10.00	25.00
63 Magglio Ordonez/15		
64 Frank Thomas/15		
65 Josh Towers/250	4.00	10.00
66 Javier Vazquez/100	8.00	20.00
68 Aubrey Huff/250	6.00	15.00
69 Richard Hidalgo/25		
70 Brandon Claussen/250	4.00	10.00
72 John Buck/250	4.00	10.00
73 Dee Brown/250	4.00	10.00
75 Jason Giambi/25		
76 Erick Almonte/250	4.00	10.00
79 Jay Gibbons/250	4.00	10.00
81 Todd Helton/15		
82 Erik Bedard/250	6.00	15.00
83 Carlos Beltran/15		
84 Rafael Soriano/250	4.00	10.00
85 Gary Sheffield/15		
86 Richie Sexson/50	10.00	25.00
87 Mike Rivera/250	4.00	10.00
88 Jose Ortiz/250	4.00	10.00
89 Abraham Nunez/250	4.00	10.00
90 Dave Williams/250	4.00	10.00
92 Jason Jennings/250	4.00	10.00
93 Juan Diaz/250	4.00	10.00
94 Steve Smyth/250	4.00	10.00
97 Brad Penny/80	6.00	15.00
99 Juan Pierre/100	8.00	20.00
100 Manny Ramirez/15		
102 Michael Cuddyer/250	4.00	10.00
104 Carlos Zambrano/250	10.00	25.00
105 Jose Vidro/100	6.00	15.00
107 Ed Rogers/250	4.00	10.00
108 Scott Rolen/15		
110 Tim Redding/250	4.00	10.00
111 Josh Phelps/250	4.00	10.00
112 Gabe Kapler/100	8.00	20.00
113 Edgar Martinez/50	20.00	50.00
116 Wade Miller/250	4.00	10.00
117 Mike Mussina/15		
118 Rafael Palmeiro/25		
120 Rickey Henderson/15		
121 Bill Hall/250	6.00	15.00
123 Geronimo Gil/250	4.00	10.00
124 Robert Fick/150	4.00	10.00
125 Darin Erstad/15		
126 Brandon Duckworth/250	4.00	10.00
128 Pedro Feliz/250	4.00	10.00
130 Brian Giles/15		
131 Craig Biggio/15		
132 Willie Harris/250	4.00	10.00
133 Doug Davis/250	4.00	10.00
135 Terrence Long/50	10.00	25.00
138 Donaldo Mendez/250	4.00	10.00
139 Sean Douglass/250	4.00	10.00
140 Eric Chavez/15		
141 Rick Ankiel/250	12.50	30.00
142 Jeremy Giambi/100	6.00	15.00
143 Juan Pena/250	4.00	10.00
144 Bernie Williams/15		
145 Craig Wilson/250	4.00	10.00
146 Ricardo Rodriguez/250	4.00	10.00
147 Albert Pujols/25		
148 Antonio Perez/250	4.00	10.00
150 Corky Miller/250	4.00	10.00
151 Rich Aurilia/25		
152 Kerry Wood/25		
153 Joe Thurston/250	4.00	10.00
154 Jeff Deardorff/250	4.00	10.00
155 Jermaine Dye/15		
156 Andruw Jones/15		
157 Victor Martinez/250	15.00	40.00
158 Nick Neugebauer/150	4.00	10.00
160 Casey Fossum/250	4.00	10.00
161 J.D. Drew/25		
162 Matt Childers/250	4.00	10.00
163 Mark Buehrle/150	10.00	25.00
164 Jeff Bagwell/15		
166 Ben Sheets/100	8.00	20.00
167 Alex Rodriguez/15		
168 Adam Pettyjohn/250	4.00	10.00
169 Chris Snelling/250	5.00	12.00
170 Robert Person/250	4.00	10.00
171 Juan Uribe/250	4.00	10.00
173 Alfredo Amezaga/250	4.00	10.00
175 Corey Thurman/250	4.00	10.00
176 Jim Thome/15		
178 Eric Cyr/250	4.00	10.00
179 Greg Maddux/15		
180 Earl Snyder/250	4.00	10.00
181 C.C. Sabathia/50	10.00	25.00
182 Mark Mulder/50	10.00	25.00
183 Jose Mieses/250	4.00	10.00
184 Joe Kennedy/250	4.00	10.00
186 Tom Glavine/15		
187 Eric Junge/250	4.00	10.00
189 Corey Patterson/205	4.00	10.00
190 Carlos Pena/200	4.00	10.00
191 Curt Schilling/15		
192 Nomar Garciaparra/15		
193 Lance Berkman/15		
194 Ryan Klesko/15		
195 Ivan Rodriguez/15		
196 Alfonso Soriano/50	15.00	40.00
198 David Justice/15		
199 Juan Gonzalez/15		
200 Adam Dunn/25		
201 Victor Alvarez ROO/250	4.00	10.00
203 Brandon Backe ROO/250	6.00	15.00
204 Chris Baker ROO/250	4.00	10.00
205 Steve Bechler ROO/250	4.00	10.00
206 Francis Beltran ROO/250	4.00	10.00
207 Angel Berroa ROO/250	4.00	10.00
208 Hank Blalock ROO/100	8.00	20.00
209 Dewon Brazelton ROO/200	4.00	10.00
210 Sean Burroughs ROO/50	10.00	25.00
211 Marlon Byrd ROO/200	4.00	10.00
212 Raul Chavez ROO/250	4.00	10.00
213 Juan Cruz ROO/50	10.00	25.00
214 Jorge De La Rosa ROO/250	4.00	10.00
215 Doug Devore ROO/250	4.00	10.00
216 John Ennis ROO/250	4.00	10.00
217 Felix Escalona ROO/250	4.00	10.00
218 Morgan Ensberg ROO/250	6.00	15.00
219 Cam Esslinger ROO/250	4.00	10.00
220 Kevin Frederick ROO/250	4.00	10.00
221 Franklyn German ROO/250	4.00	10.00
222 Eric Hinske ROO/250	4.00	10.00
223 Ben Howard ROO/250	4.00	10.00
224 Orlando Hudson ROO/250	4.00	10.00
225 Travis Hughes ROO/250	4.00	10.00
226 Kazuhisa Ishii ROO/50	15.00	40.00
227 Ryan Jamison ROO/250	4.00	10.00
228 Reed Johnson ROO/250	6.00	15.00
229 Kyle Kane ROO/250	4.00	10.00
230 Austin Kearns ROO/250	4.00	10.00
231 Satoru Komiyama ROO/50	15.00	40.00
232 Jason Lane ROO/200	6.00	15.00
233 Jeremy Lambert ROO/250	4.00	10.00
234 And Machado ROO/200	4.00	10.00
235 Brian Mallette ROO/250	4.00	10.00
236 Takahito Nomura ROO/100	10.00	25.00
237 Jorge Padilla ROO/200	4.00	10.00
238 Luis Ugueto ROO/250	4.00	10.00
239 Mark Prior ROO/100	8.00	20.00
240 Rene Reyes ROO/250	4.00	10.00
241 Deivis Santos ROO/250	4.00	10.00
242 Elio Serrano ROO/250	4.00	10.00
243 Tom Shearn ROO/250	4.00	10.00
244 Allan Simpson ROO/250	4.00	10.00
245 So Taguchi ROO/100	10.00	25.00
246 Dennis Tankersley ROO/100	6.00	15.00
247 Mark Teixeira ROO/50	20.00	50.00
248 Matt Thornton ROO/250	4.00	10.00
249 Bobby Hill ROO/100	6.00	15.00
250 Ramon Vazquez ROO/250	4.00	10.00
252 Josh Bard ROO/100	4.00	10.00
253 Trey Hodges ROO/250	4.00	10.00
255 Ben Kozlowski ROO/200	4.00	10.00
256 Eric Good ROO/200	4.00	10.00
257 Brian Tallet ROO/100	4.00	10.00
258 P.J. Bevis ROO/50	10.00	25.00
259 Rodrigo Rosario ROO/250	4.00	10.00
260 Kirk Saarloos ROO/100	4.00	10.00
263 Tim Kalita ROO/50	6.00	15.00
266 Cliff Lee ROO/100	20.00	50.00
268 Andy Pratt ROO/250	4.00	10.00
269 Wilson Valdez ROO/200	4.00	10.00
270 Oliver Perez ROO/25		
271 Joe Borchard ROO/100	6.00	15.00
274 Kevin Cash ROO/100	4.00	10.00
275 Chone Figgins ROO/100	10.00	25.00

2002 Studio Proofs

Randomly issued in Studio and Donruss the Rookies packs, this is a complete parallel of the 2002 Studio set. Cards 1-250 were distributed in Studio packs and 251-275 in Donruss the Rookies. These cards were printed to a stated print run of 100 serial numbered sets.

*PROOFS 1-200: 4X TO 10X BASIC
*PROOFS RC'S 1-200: 3X TO 8X BASIC
*PROOFS 201-275: .75X TO 2X BASIC

201 Victor Alvarez ROO	3.00	8.00
202 Miguel Asencio ROO	3.00	8.00
203 Brandon Backe ROO	4.00	10.00
204 Chris Baker ROO	3.00	8.00
205 Steve Bechler ROO	3.00	8.00
206 Francis Beltran ROO	3.00	8.00
207 Angel Berroa ROO	3.00	8.00
208 Hank Blalock ROO	4.00	10.00
209 Dewon Brazelton ROO	3.00	8.00
210 Sean Burroughs ROO	3.00	8.00
211 Marlon Byrd ROO	3.00	8.00
212 Raul Chavez ROO	3.00	8.00
213 Juan Cruz ROO	3.00	8.00
214 Jorge De La Rosa ROO	3.00	8.00
215 Doug Devore ROO	3.00	8.00
216 John Ennis ROO	3.00	8.00
217 Felix Escalona ROO	3.00	8.00
218 Morgan Ensberg ROO	3.00	8.00
219 Cam Esslinger ROO	3.00	8.00
220 Kevin Frederick ROO	3.00	8.00
221 Franklyn German ROO	3.00	8.00
222 Eric Hinske ROO	3.00	8.00
223 Ben Howard ROO	3.00	8.00
224 Orlando Hudson ROO	3.00	8.00
225 Travis Hughes ROO	3.00	8.00
226 Kazuhisa Ishii ROO	4.00	10.00
227 Ryan Jamison ROO	3.00	8.00
228 Reed Johnson ROO	4.00	10.00
229 Kyle Kane ROO	3.00	8.00
230 Austin Kearns ROO	3.00	8.00
231 Satoru Komiyama ROO	3.00	8.00
232 Jason Lane ROO	3.00	8.00
233 Jeremy Lambert ROO	3.00	8.00
234 Anderson Machado ROO	3.00	8.00
235 Brian Mallette ROO	3.00	8.00
236 Takahito Nomura ROO	3.00	8.00
237 Jorge Padilla ROO	3.00	8.00
238 Luis Ugueto ROO	3.00	8.00
239 Mark Prior ROO	4.00	10.00
240 Rene Reyes ROO	3.00	8.00
241 Deivis Santos ROO	3.00	8.00
242 Elio Serrano ROO	3.00	8.00
243 Tom Shearn ROO	3.00	8.00
244 Allan Simpson ROO	3.00	8.00
245 So Taguchi ROO	4.00	10.00
246 Dennis Tankersley ROO	3.00	8.00
247 Mark Teixeira ROO	4.00	10.00
248 Matt Thornton ROO	3.00	8.00
249 Bobby Hill ROO	3.00	8.00
250 Ramon Vazquez ROO	3.00	8.00
251 Freddy Sanchez ROO	4.00	10.00
252 Josh Bard ROO	3.00	8.00
253 Trey Hodges ROO	3.00	8.00
254 Jorge Sosa ROO	4.00	10.00
255 Ben Kozlowski ROO	3.00	8.00
256 Eric Good ROO	3.00	8.00
257 Brian Tallet ROO	3.00	8.00
258 P.J. Bevis ROO	3.00	8.00
259 Rodrigo Rosario ROO	3.00	8.00
260 Kirk Saarloos ROO	3.00	8.00
261 Runelvys Hernandez ROO	3.00	8.00
262 Josh Hancock ROO	4.00	10.00
263 Tim Kalita ROO	3.00	8.00
264 Jason Simontacchi ROO	3.00	8.00
265 Clay Condrey ROO	3.00	8.00
266 Cliff Lee ROO	4.00	10.00
267 Aaron Guiel ROO	3.00	8.00
268 Andy Pratt ROO	3.00	8.00
269 Wilson Valdez ROO	3.00	8.00
270 Oliver Perez ROO	4.00	10.00
271 Joe Borchard ROO	3.00	8.00
272 Jeriome Robertson ROO	3.00	8.00
273 Aaron Cook ROO	3.00	8.00
274 Kevin Cash ROO	3.00	8.00
275 Chone Figgins ROO	4.00	10.00

2002 Studio Classic

Randomly inserted in packs, these 25 card feature players elected to the Hall of Fame on the first ballot and have a stated print run of 1,000 serial numbered sets.

COMPLETE SET (25)	75.00	150.00
*1ST BALLOT: 2X TO 5X BASIC CLASSIC		
1ST BALLOT RANDOM IN PACKS		
1ST BALLOT PRINT RUN BASED ON HOF YR		
1 Kirby Puckett	3.00	8.00
2 George Brett	5.00	12.00
3 Nolan Ryan	6.00	15.00
4 Mike Schmidt	5.00	12.00
5 Steve Carlton	2.00	5.00
6 Reggie Jackson	2.00	5.00
7 Tom Seaver	2.00	5.00
8 Joe Morgan	2.00	5.00
9 Jim Palmer	2.00	5.00
10 Johnny Bench	3.00	8.00
11 Willie McCovey	2.00	5.00
12 Brooks Robinson	2.00	5.00
13 Al Kaline	3.00	8.00
14 Stan Musial	4.00	10.00
15 Ozzie Smith	4.00	10.00
16 Dave Winfield	2.00	5.00
17 Robin Yount	3.00	8.00
18 Rod Carew	2.00	5.00
19 Willie Stargell	2.00	5.00
20 Lou Brock	2.00	5.00
21 Ernie Banks	3.00	8.00

22 Ted Williams 5.00 12.00
23 Jackie Robinson 3.00 8.00
24 Roberto Clemente 6.00 15.00
25 Lou Gehrig 6.00 15.00

2002 Studio Classic Autographs

Randomly inserted in packs, these 19 cards partially parallel the Studio Classic insert set. We have listed the stated print runs next to the player's name and since no player signed more than 20 cards there is no pricing due to market scarcity.

1 Kirby Puckett/15
2 George Brett/15
3 Nolan Ryan/15
4 Mike Schmidt/20
5 Steve Carlton/20
6 Reggie Jackson/15
7 Tom Seaver/15
8 Joe Morgan/20
10 Johnny Bench/20
11 Willie McCovey/15
12 Brooks Robinson/20
13 Al Kaline/20
14 Stan Musial/15
15 Ozzie Smith/15
16 Dave Winfield/15
17 Robin Yount/15
18 Rod Carew/25
20 Lou Brock/20
21 Ernie Banks/20

2002 Studio Diamond Collection

Inserted in packs at stated odds of one in 17, these 25 cards feature some of the most popular players in baseball.

COMPLETE SET (25) 60.00 120.00
1 Todd Helton 1.50 4.00
2 Chipper Jones 1.50 4.00
3 Lance Berkman 1.50 4.00
4 Derek Jeter 4.00 10.00
5 Hideo Nomo 1.50 4.00
6 Kazuhisa Ishii 1.50 4.00
7 Barry Bonds 4.00 10.00
8 Alex Rodriguez 2.50 6.00
9 Ichiro Suzuki 3.00 8.00
10 Mike Piazza 2.50 6.00
11 Jim Thome 1.50 4.00
12 Greg Maddux 2.50 6.00
13 Jeff Bagwell 1.50 4.00
14 Vladimir Guerrero 1.50 4.00
15 Ken Griffey Jr. 2.50 6.00
16 Jason Giambi 1.50 4.00
17 Nomar Garciaparra 2.50 6.00
18 Albert Pujols 3.00 8.00
19 Manny Ramirez 1.50 4.00
20 Pedro Martinez 1.50 4.00
21 Roger Clemens 3.00 8.00
22 Randy Johnson 1.50 4.00
23 Mark Prior 1.50 4.00
24 So Taguchi 1.50 4.00
25 Sammy Sosa 1.50 4.00

2002 Studio Diamond Collection Artist's Proofs

Randomly inserted in packs, these cards partially parallel the Diamond Collection insert set. Each card features a memorabilia piece and we have notated both the information as to what type of piece along with the stated print run next to the player's name in our checklist.

1 Todd Helton Jsy/200 6.00 15.00
2 Chipper Jones Jsy/150 6.00 15.00
3 Lance Berkman Jsy/200 4.00 10.00
4 Derek Jeter Base/200 10.00 25.00
5 Hideo Nomo Jsy/150 30.00 80.00
6 Kazuhisa Ishii Jsy/150 6.00 15.00
7 Barry Bonds Base/200 10.00 25.00
8 Alex Rodriguez Jsy/150 8.00 20.00
9 Ichiro Suzuki Base/200 10.00 25.00
10 Mike Piazza Jsy/150 6.00 15.00
11 Jim Thome Jsy/150 6.00 15.00
12 Greg Maddux Jsy/150 6.00 15.00
13 Jeff Bagwell Jsy/150 6.00 15.00
14 Vladimir Guerrero Jsy/200 6.00 15.00
15 Ken Griffey Jr. Base/200 6.00 15.00
16 Jason Giambi Base/200 4.00 10.00
17 Nomar Garciaparra Jsy/150 8.00 20.00
18 Albert Pujols Base/200 6.00 15.00
19 Manny Ramirez Jsy/150 6.00 15.00
20 Pedro Martinez Jsy/150 6.00 15.00
21 Roger Clemens Jsy/150 10.00 25.00
22 Randy Johnson Jsy/150 6.00 15.00
24 So Taguchi Jsy/200 6.00 15.00
25 Sammy Sosa Base/200 6.00 15.00

2002 Studio Heroes Icons Texans

Randomly inserted in packs, these four cards honor that Texas sports legend, Nolan Ryan. There are four stated print runs with the highlight being an autograph card numbered to a stated print run of 32 serial numbered cards.

HIT2 Nolan Ryan 4.00 10.00
HIT2 Nolan Ryan/500 6.00 15.00
HIT2 Nolan Ryan/100 20.00 50.00
HIT2 Nolan Ryan AU/32 150.00 250.00

2002 Studio Leather and Lumber

Randomly inserted in packs, these 25 cards feature some of the game's most dominating batsmen. Each card contains one game-used bat piece. And since there are different print runs, we have put that information next to the player's name in our checklist.

1 Nomar Garciaparra/200 10.00 25.00
2 Jeff Bagwell/150 6.00 15.00
3 Alex Rodriguez/200 8.00 20.00
4 Vladimir Guerrero/100 8.00 20.00
5 Luis Gonzalez/200 4.00 10.00
6 Chipper Jones/200 6.00 15.00
7 Shawn Green/200 4.00 10.00
8 Kirby Puckett/100 8.00 20.00
9 Juan Gonzalez/200 4.00 10.00
10 Troy Glaus/200 4.00 10.00
11 Don Mattingly/100 15.00 40.00
12 Todd Helton/200 6.00 15.00
13 Jim Thome/200 6.00 15.00
14 Rickey Henderson/200 6.00 15.00
15 Mike Schmidt/100 15.00 40.00
16 Adam Dunn/100 6.00 15.00
17 Ivan Rodriguez/200 6.00 15.00
18 Manny Ramirez/150 6.00 15.00
19 Tsuyoshi Shinjo/200 4.00 10.00
20 Andruw Jones/150 6.00 15.00
21 Roberto Alomar/200 6.00 15.00
22 Lance Berkman/200 4.00 10.00
23 Derek Jeter Ball/50 30.00 80.00
24 Ichiro Suzuki Ball/50 30.00 80.00
25 Mike Piazza/200 6.00 15.00

2002 Studio Leather and Lumber Artist's Proofs

Randomly inserted in packs, these cards parallel the Leather and Lumber insert set. These cards have a stated print run of 50 serial numbered sets which included a combination of a bat chip and a ball swatch. Of note, the cards for Derek Jeter and Ichiro feature two ball swatches.

5 Luis Gonzalez SP/25

2002 Studio Masterstrokes

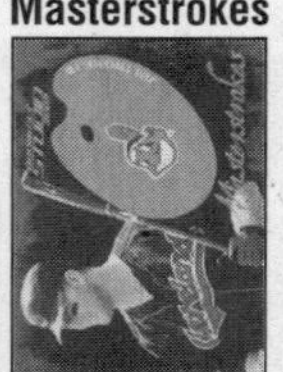

Inserted in packs at stated odds of one in 17, these 25 cards feature baseball's most skilled hitters.

COMPLETE SET (25) 50.00 100.00
1 Vladimir Guerrero 1.50 4.00
2 Frank Thomas 1.50 4.00
3 Alex Rodriguez 2.50 6.00
4 Manny Ramirez 1.50 4.00
5 Jeff Bagwell 1.50 4.00
6 Jim Thome 1.50 4.00
7 Ichiro Suzuki 3.00 8.00
8 Andruw Jones 1.50 4.00
9 Troy Glaus 1.50 4.00
10 Chipper Jones 1.50 4.00
11 Juan Gonzalez 1.50 4.00
12 Lance Berkman 1.50 4.00
13 Mike Piazza 2.50 6.00
14 Darin Erstad 1.50 4.00
15 Albert Pujols 3.00 8.00
16 Kazuhisa Ishii 1.50 4.00
17 Shawn Green 1.50 4.00
18 Rafael Palmeiro 1.50 4.00
19 Todd Helton 1.50 4.00
20 Carlos Delgado 1.50 4.00
21 Ivan Rodriguez 1.50 4.00
22 Luis Gonzalez 1.50 4.00
23 Derek Jeter 4.00 10.00
24 Nomar Garciaparra 2.50 6.00
25 J.D. Drew 1.50 4.00

2002 Studio Masterstrokes Artist's Proofs

Randomly inserted in packs, these 25 cards are a parallel to the Masterstrokes insert set and most of them feature a bat-jersey combo. The Ichiro Suzuki, Derek Jeter and J.D. Drew cards feature a ball-base combo.

1 Vladimir Guerrero/200 8.00 20.00
2 Frank Thomas/200 8.00 20.00
3 Alex Rodriguez/100 15.00 40.00
4 Manny Ramirez/200 8.00 20.00
5 Jeff Bagwell/150 8.00 20.00
6 Jim Thome/200 8.00 20.00
7 Ichiro Suzuki/100 30.00 60.00
8 Andruw Jones/200 8.00 20.00
9 Troy Glaus/200 6.00 15.00
10 Chipper Jones/200 8.00 20.00
11 Juan Gonzalez/200 6.00 15.00
12 Lance Berkman/200 6.00 15.00
13 Mike Piazza/200 15.00 40.00
14 Darin Erstad/200 6.00 15.00
15 Albert Pujols/150 15.00 40.00
16 Kazuhisa Ishii/150 8.00 20.00
17 Shawn Green/200 6.00 15.00
18 Rafael Palmeiro/200 8.00 20.00
19 Todd Helton/200 8.00 20.00
20 Carlos Delgado/200 6.00 15.00
21 Ivan Rodriguez/200 8.00 20.00
22 Luis Gonzalez/200 6.00 15.00
23 Derek Jeter/100 25.00 60.00
24 Nomar Garciaparra/150 15.00 40.00
25 J.D. Drew/150 6.00 15.00

2002 Studio Spirit of the Game

Inserted in packs at a stated odds of one in nine, these 50 cards highlight players who play the game with a real passion.

COMPLETE SET (50) 60.00 120.00
1 Alex Rodriguez 2.50 6.00
2 Curt Schilling 1.00 2.50
3 Hideo Nomo 1.50 4.00
4 Derek Jeter 4.00 10.00
5 Mike Sweeney 1.00 2.50
6 Mike Piazza 2.50 6.00
7 Roger Clemens 3.00 8.00
8 Shawn Green 1.00 2.50
9 Vladimir Guerrero 1.50 4.00
10 Carlos Lee 1.00 2.50
11 Edgar Martinez 1.00 2.50
12 Albert Pujols 3.00 8.00
13 Mark Prior 1.00 2.50
14 Mark Buehrle 1.00 2.50
15 Chipper Jones 1.50 4.00
16 Paul Lo Duca 1.00 2.50
17 Frank Thomas 1.50 4.00
18 Randy Johnson 1.50 4.00
19 Cliff Floyd 1.00 2.50
20 Todd Helton 1.00 2.50
21 Luis Gonzalez 1.00 2.50
22 Brandon Duckworth 1.00 2.50
23 Jason Giambi 1.00 2.50
24 Juan Uribe 1.00 2.50
25 Dewon Brazelton 1.00 2.50
26 J.D. Drew 1.00 2.50
27 Troy Glaus 1.00 2.50
28 Wade Miller 1.00 2.50
29 Darin Erstad 1.00 2.50
30 Brian Giles 1.00 2.50
31 Lance Berkman 1.00 2.50
32 Shannon Stewart 1.00 2.50
33 Kazuhisa Ishii 1.00 2.50
34 Corey Patterson 1.00 2.50
35 Rafael Palmeiro 1.00 2.50
36 Roy Oswalt 1.00 2.50
37 Jason Lane 1.00 2.50
38 Andruw Jones 1.00 2.50
39 Brad Penny 1.00 2.50
40 Bud Smith 1.00 2.50
41 Carlos Beltran 1.00 2.50
42 Magglio Ordonez 1.00 2.50
43 Craig Biggio 1.00 2.50
44 Hank Blalock 1.00 2.50
45 Jeff Bagwell 1.00 2.50
46 Josh Beckett 1.00 2.50
47 Juan Cruz 1.00 2.50
48 Kerry Wood 1.00 2.50
49 Brandon Berger 1.00 2.50
50 Juan Pierre 1.00 2.50

2002 Studio Spirit of the Game Hats Off

Randomly inserted in packs, these 24 cards form a partial parallel to the Spirit of the Game insert set. These cards feature pieces of game-used hats and most are serial numbered to 100. The Kazuishi Ishii card has a stated print run of 50 serial numbered sets.

MLB LOGO PRINT RUN 1 SERIAL #'d SET
NO MLB LOGO PRICING DUE TO SCARCITY
USA FLAG PRINT RUN 1 SERIAL #'d SET
NO USA FLAG PRICING DUE TO SCARCITY
10 Carlos Lee 10.00 25.00
14 Mark Buehrle 10.00 25.00
16 Paul Lo Duca 10.00 25.00
22 Brandon Duckworth 6.00 15.00
26 J.D. Drew 10.00 25.00
28 Wade Miller 6.00 15.00
30 Brian Giles 10.00 25.00
31 Lance Berkman 10.00 25.00
32 Shannon Stewart 10.00 25.00
33 Kazuhisa Ishii SP/50 10.00 25.00
35 Rafael Palmeiro 15.00 40.00
36 Roy Oswalt 10.00 25.00
37 Jason Lane 10.00 25.00
38 Andruw Jones 15.00 40.00
39 Brad Penny 6.00 15.00
40 Bud Smith 6.00 15.00
41 Carlos Beltran 10.00 25.00
42 Magglio Ordonez 10.00 25.00
43 Craig Biggio 15.00 40.00
45 Jeff Bagwell 15.00 40.00
47 Juan Cruz 6.00 15.00
48 Kerry Wood 10.00 25.00
49 Brandon Berger 6.00 15.00
50 Juan Pierre 6.00 15.00

2002 Studio Stars

Randomly inserted in packs, these 50 cards feature leading players in a credit charge design. These cards have some key statistics for the players listed across the front of their cards.

COMPLETE SET (50) 50.00 100.00
1 Mike Piazza 1.50 4.00
2 Ivan Rodriguez .75 2.00
3 Albert Pujols 2.00 5.00
4 Scott Rolen .75 2.00
5 Alex Rodriguez 1.50 4.00
6 Curt Schilling .75 2.00
7 Vladimir Guerrero .75 2.00
8 Jim Thome .75 2.00
9 Derek Jeter 2.50 6.00
10 C.C. Sabathia .75 2.00
11 Sammy Sosa .75 2.00
12 Adam Dunn .75 2.00
13 Bernie Williams .75 2.00
14 Ichiro Suzuki 2.00 5.00
15 Barry Bonds 2.50 6.00
16 Rickey Henderson .75 2.00
17 Ken Griffey Jr. 1.50 4.00
18 Kazuhisa Ishii .75 2.00
19 Kerry Wood .75 2.00
20 Todd Helton .75 2.00
21 Hideo Nomo .75 2.00
22 Frank Thomas .75 2.00
23 Manny Ramirez .75 2.00
24 Luis Gonzalez .75 2.00
25 Rafael Palmeiro .75 2.00
26 Mike Mussina .75 2.00
27 Roy Oswalt .75 2.00
28 Darin Erstad .75 2.00
29 Barry Larkin .75 2.00
30 Randy Johnson .75 2.00
31 Tom Glavine .75 2.00
32 Lance Berkman .75 2.00
33 Juan Gonzalez .75 2.00
34 Shawn Green .75 2.00
35 Nomar Garciaparra 1.50 4.00
36 Troy Glaus .75 2.00
37 Tim Hudson .75 2.00
38 Carlos Delgado .75 2.00
39 Jason Giambi .75 2.00
40 Andruw Jones .75 2.00
41 Roberto Alomar .75 2.00
42 Greg Maddux 1.50 4.00
43 Pedro Martinez .75 2.00
44 Tony Gwynn 1.25 3.00
45 Alfonso Soriano .75 2.00
46 Chipper Jones .75 2.00
47 J.D. Drew .75 2.00
48 Roger Clemens 2.00 5.00
49 Barry Zito .75 2.00
50 Jeff Bagwell .75 2.00

2003 Studio

This 210-card set was issued in two separate series. The primary Studio product - containing cards 1-200 from the basic set - was released in June, 2003. The set was issued in six card packs with an $4 SRP which came packed 20 packs to a box and 16 boxes to a case. The first 190 cards feature just one player while the final 10 cards portray two teammates. Cards 201-211 were randomly seeded into packs of DLP Rookies and Traded of which was distributed in December, 2003. Each of these update cards featured a top prospect and was serial numbered to 1500 copies.

COMP.LO SET (200) 20.00 50.00
COMMON CARD (1-190) .20 .50
COMMON RC (1-190) .15 .40
COMMON CARD (191-200) .40 1.00
COMMON CARD (201-211) 1.50 4.00
1 Darin Erstad .20 .50
2 David Eckstein .20 .50
3 Garret Anderson .20 .50
4 Jarrod Washburn .20 .50
5 Tim Salmon .30 .75
6 Troy Glaus .20 .50
7 Jay Gibbons .20 .50
8 Melvin Mora .20 .50
9 Rodrigo Lopez .20 .50
10 Tony Batista .20 .50
11 Freddy Sanchez .20 .50
12 Derek Lowe .20 .50
13 Johnny Damon .30 .75
14 Manny Ramirez .30 .75
15 Nomar Garciaparra .75 2.00
16 Pedro Martinez .30 .75
17 Rickey Henderson .50 1.25
18 Shea Hillenbrand .20 .50
19 Carlos Lee .20 .50
20 Frank Thomas .50 1.25
21 Magglio Ordonez .20 .50
22 Bartolo Colon .20 .50
23 Paul Konerko .20 .50
24 Josh Stewart RC .15 .40
25 C.C. Sabathia .20 .50
26 Jeremy Guthrie .20 .50
27 Ellis Burks .20 .50
28 Omar Vizquel .30 .75
29 Victor Martinez .30 .75
30 Cliff Lee .20 .50
31 Jhonny Peralta .50 1.25
32 Brian Tallet .20 .50
33 Bobby Higginson .20 .50
34 Carlos Pena .20 .50
35 Nook Logan RC .20 .50
36 Steve Sparks .20 .50
37 Travis Chapman .20 .50
38 Carlos Beltran .20 .50
39 Joe Randa .20 .50
40 Mike Sweeney .20 .50
41 Jimmy Gobble .20 .50
42 Michael Tucker .20 .50
43 Runelvys Hernandez .20 .50
44 Brad Radke .20 .50
45 Corey Koskie .20 .50
46 Cristian Guzman .20 .50
47 J.C. Romero .20 .50
48 Doug Mientkiewicz .20 .50
49 Lew Ford RC .20 .50
50 Jacque Jones .20 .50
51 Torii Hunter .20 .50
52 Alfonso Soriano .20 .50
53 Nick Johnson .20 .50
54 Bernie Williams .30 .75
55 Jose Contreras RC .30 .75
56 Derek Jeter 1.25 3.00
57 Jason Giambi .20 .50
58 Brandon Claussen .20 .50
59 Jorge Posada .30 .75
60 Mike Mussina .30 .75
61 Roger Clemens 1.00 2.50
62 Hideki Matsui RC 2.00 5.00
63 Barry Zito .20 .50
64 Adam Morrissey .20 .50
65 Eric Chavez .20 .50
66 Jermaine Dye .20 .50
67 Mark Mulder .20 .50
68 Miguel Tejada .20 .50
69 Joe Valentine RC .15 .40
70 Tim Hudson .20 .50
71 Bret Boone .20 .50
72 Chris Snelling .20 .50
73 Edgar Martinez .30 .75
74 Freddy Garcia .20 .50
75 Ichiro Suzuki 1.00 2.50
76 Jamie Moyer .20 .50
77 John Olerud .20 .50
78 Kazuhiro Sasaki .20 .50
79 Aubrey Huff .20 .50
80 Joe Kennedy .20 .50
81 Dewon Brazelton .20 .50
82 Pete LaForest RC .15 .40
83 Alex Rodriguez .75 2.00
84 Chan Ho Park .20 .50
85 Hank Blalock .20 .50
86 Juan Gonzalez .20 .50
87 Kevin Mench .20 .50
88 Rafael Palmeiro .30 .75
89 Carlos Delgado .20 .50
90 Eric Hinske .20 .50
91 Josh Phelps .20 .50
92 Roy Halladay .20 .50
93 Shannon Stewart .20 .50
94 Vernon Wells .20 .50
95 Vinny Chulk .20 .50
96 Curt Schilling .20 .50
97 Junior Spivey .20 .50
98 Luis Gonzalez .20 .50
99 Mark Grace .30 .75
100 Randy Johnson .50 1.25
101 Andruw Jones .30 .75
102 Chipper Jones .50 1.25
103 Gary Sheffield .20 .50
104 Greg Maddux .75 2.00
105 John Smoltz .30 .75
106 Mike Hampton .20 .50
107 Adam LaRoche .20 .50
108 Michael Hessman RC .15 .40
109 Corey Patterson .20 .50
110 Kerry Wood .20 .50
111 Mark Prior .30 .75
112 Moises Alou .20 .50
113 Sammy Sosa .50 1.25
114 Adam Dunn .20 .50
115 Austin Kearns .20 .50
116 Barry Larkin .30 .75
117 Ken Griffey Jr. .75 2.00
118 Sean Casey .20 .50
119 Jason Jennings .20 .50
120 Jay Payton .20 .50
121 Larry Walker .20 .50
122 Todd Helton .30 .75
123 Jeff Baker .20 .50
124 Clint Barmes RC .40 1.00
125 Ivan Rodriguez .30 .75
126 Josh Beckett .20 .50
127 Juan Encarnacion .20 .50
128 Mike Lowell .20 .50
129 Craig Biggio .30 .75
130 Jason Lane .20 .50
131 Jeff Bagwell .30 .75
132 Lance Berkman .20 .50
133 Roy Oswalt .20 .50
134 Jeff Kent .20 .50
135 Hideo Nomo .50 1.25
136 Kazuhisa Ishii .20 .50
137 Kevin Brown .20 .50
138 Odalis Perez .20 .50
139 Paul Lo Duca .20 .50
140 Shawn Green .20 .50
141 Adrian Beltre .20 .50
142 Ben Sheets .20 .50
143 Bill Hall .20 .50
144 Jeffrey Hammonds .20 .50
145 Richie Sexson .20 .50
146 Termel Sledge RC .15 .40
147 Brad Wilkerson .20 .50
148 Javier Vazquez .20 .50
149 Jose Vidro .20 .50
150 Michael Barrett .20 .50
151 Vladimir Guerrero .50 1.25
152 Al Leiter .20 .50
153 Mike Piazza .75 2.00
154 Mo Vaughn .20 .50
155 Cliff Floyd .20 .50
156 Roberto Alomar .30 .75
157 Roger Cedeno .20 .50
158 Tom Glavine .30 .75
159 Prentice Redman RC .15 .40
160 Bobby Abreu .20 .50
161 Jimmy Rollins .20 .50
162 Mike Lieberthal .20 .50
163 Pat Burrell .20 .50
164 Vicente Padilla .20 .50
165 Jim Thome .30 .75
166 Kevin Millwood .20 .50
167 Aramis Ramirez .20 .50
168 Brian Giles .20 .50
169 Jason Kendall .20 .50
170 Josh Fogg .20 .50
171 Kip Wells .20 .50
172 Jose Castillo .20 .50
173 Mark Kotsay .20 .50
174 Oliver Perez .20 .50
175 Phil Nevin .20 .50
176 Ryan Klesko .20 .50
177 Sean Burroughs .20 .50
178 Brian Lawrence .20 .50
179 Shane Victorino RC .40 1.00
180 Barry Bonds 1.25 3.00
181 Benito Santiago .20 .50
182 Ray Durham .20 .50
183 Rich Aurilia .20 .50
184 Damian Moss .20 .50
185 Albert Pujols 1.00 2.50
186 J.D. Drew .20 .50
187 Jim Edmonds .20 .50
188 Matt Morris .20 .50
189 Tino Martinez .30 .75
190 Scott Rolen .30 .75
191 Troy Glaus .60 1.50
Tim Salmon
192 Barry Zito .40 1.00
Tim Hudson
193 Carlos Lee .60 1.50
Frank Thomas
194 Lance Berkman .40 1.00
Jeff Kent
195 Jose Contreras .60 1.50
Mariano Rivera
196 Alex Rodriguez .60 1.50
Juan Gonzalez
197 Andy Pettitte .60 1.50
David Wells
198 Shawn Green .40 1.00
Dave Roberts
199 Mike Lieberthal .40 1.00
Jimmy Rollins
200 Mike Mussina .75 2.00
Hideki Matsui
201 Adam Loewen ROO RC 2.00 5.00
202 Jeremy Bonderman ROO RC 4.00 10.00
203 Brandon Webb ROO RC 4.00 10.00
204 Chien-Ming Wang ROO RC 8.00 20.00
205 Chad Gaudin ROO RC 1.50 4.00
206 Ryan Wagner ROO RC 1.50 4.00
207 Hong-Chih Kuo ROO RC 4.00 10.00
208 Dan Haren ROO RC 2.00 5.00
209 Rickie Weeks ROO RC 2.50 6.00
210 Ramon Nivar ROO RC 1.50 4.00
211 Delmon Young ROO RC 4.00 10.00

2003 Studio Private Signings

1-200 RANDOM INSERTS IN PACKS
201-211 RANDOM IN DLP R/T PACKS

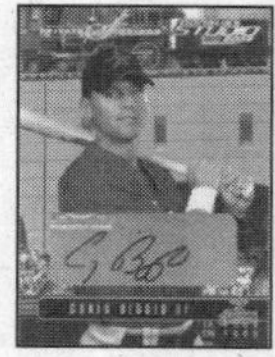

PRINT RUNS B/WN 5-200 COPIES PER
NO PRICING ON QTY OF 35 OR LESS
1 Darin Erstad/5
6 Troy Glaus/15
7 Jay Gibbons/100 6.00 15.00
11 Freddy Sanchez/150 6.00 15.00
16 Pedro Martinez/5
17 Rickey Henderson/10
19 Carlos Lee/25
20 Frank Thomas/5
22 Mark Buehrle/50
24 Josh Stewart/200 4.00 10.00
25 C.C. Sabathia/10
26 Jeremy Guthrie/125 4.00 10.00
29 Victor Martinez/200 10.00 25.00
30 Cliff Lee/150 4.00 10.00
31 Jhonny Peralta/200 6.00 15.00
32 Brian Tallet/35
35 Nook Logan/100 6.00 15.00
37 Travis Chapman/150 4.00 10.00
38 Carlos Beltran/25
40 Mike Sweeney/25
41 Jimmy Gobble/200 4.00 10.00
47 J.C. Romero/200 4.00 10.00
49 Lew Ford/200 6.00 15.00
51 Torii Hunter/50 10.00 25.00
52 Alfonso Soriano/5
53 Nick Johnson/100 8.00 20.00
54 Bernie Williams/5
55 Jose Contreras/100 12.50 30.00
58 Brandon Claussen/200 4.00 10.00
60 Mike Mussina/5
61 Roger Clemens/5
63 Barry Zito/25
64 Adam Morrissey/100
66 Jermaine Dye/25
67 Mark Mulder/15
69 Joe Valentine/200 4.00 10.00
70 Tim Hudson/15
72 Chris Snelling/25
73 Edgar Martinez/15
74 Freddy Garcia/5
79 Aubrey Huff/50 10.00 25.00
80 Joe Kennedy/25
81 Dewon Brazelton/75 6.00 15.00
82 Pete LaForest/200 4.00 10.00
83 Alex Rodriguez/5
85 Hank Blalock/50 10.00 25.00
87 Kevin Mench/200 6.00 15.00
90 Eric Hinske/125 4.00 10.00
95 Vinny Chulk/100 6.00 15.00
97 Junior Spivey/50 6.00 15.00
98 Luis Gonzalez/5
101 Andruw Jones/15
102 Chipper Jones/5
103 Gary Sheffield/10
104 Greg Maddux/10
107 Adam LaRoche/200 4.00 10.00
108 Michael Hessman/200 4.00 10.00
109 Corey Patterson/20
110 Kerry Wood/15
111 Mark Prior/50 15.00 40.00
114 Adam Dunn/25
115 Austin Kearns/25
116 Barry Larkin/15
119 Jason Jennings/50 6.00 15.00
123 Jeff Baker/75 6.00 15.00
124 Clint Barmes/200 6.00 15.00
125 Ivan Rodriguez/5
126 Josh Beckett/10
129 Craig Biggio/10
130 Jason Lane/100 8.00 20.00
132 Lance Berkman/10
133 Roy Oswalt/25
136 Kazuhisa Ishii/10
139 Paul Lo Duca/75 8.00 20.00
140 Shawn Green/5
143 Bill Hall/50 6.00 15.00
145 Richie Sexson/15
146 Termel Sledge/125 4.00 10.00
148 Javier Vazquez/25
149 Jose Vidro/50 6.00 15.00
151 Vladimir Guerrero/15
156 Roberto Alomar/20
158 Tom Glavine/15
159 Prentice Redman/200 4.00 10.00
160 Bobby Abreu/50 10.00 25.00
163 Pat Burrell/10
165 Jim Thome/10
167 Aramis Ramirez/15
168 Brian Giles/25
171 Kip Wells/100 6.00 15.00
172 Jose Castillo/175 4.00 10.00
176 Ryan Klesko/20
178 Brian Lawrence/100 6.00 15.00
179 Shane Victorino/200 20.00 50.00
185 Albert Pujols/15
187 Jim Edmonds/5
201 Adam Loewen ROO/100 10.00 25.00
202 Jeremy Bonderman ROO/50 30.00 60.00
203 Brandon Webb ROO/100 20.00 50.00
204 C.Wang ROO/50 150.00 250.00
205 Chad Gaudin ROO/25
206 Ryan Wagner ROO/100 4.00 10.00
207 Hong-Chih Kuo ROO/25
208 Dan Haren ROO/100 10.00 25.00
209 Rickie Weeks ROO/10
210 Ramon Nivar ROO/100 4.00 10.00
211 Delmon Young ROO/25

2003 Studio Proofs

*PROOFS 1-190: 4X TO 10X BASIC
*PROOFS RC's 1-190: 2X TO 5X BASIC
*PROOFS 191-200: 1.5X TO 4X BASIC
*PROOFS 201-211: .6X TO 1.5X BASIC
1-200 RANDOM INSERTS IN PACKS
201-211 RANDOM IN DLP R/T PACKS

STATED PRINT RUN 100 SERIAL #'d SETS
204 Chien-Ming Wang ROO 30.00 60.00
207 Hong-Chih Kuo ROO 20.00 50.00

2003 Studio Big League Challenge

STATED PRINT RUN 400 SERIAL #'d SETS
*PROOFS: 1.5X TO 4X BASIC BLC
PROOFS PRINT RUN 25 SERIAL #'d SETS
NO PROOFS PRICING DUE TO SCARCITY
1 Jose Canseco 00 WIN 3.00 8.00
2 Magglio Ordonez 03 WIN 2.00 5.00
3 Alex Rodriguez 03 4.00 10.00
4 Lance Berkman 03 2.00 5.00
5 Rafael Palmeiro 03 3.00 8.00
6 Nomar Garciaparra 00 4.00 10.00
7 Nomar Garciaparra 00 4.00 10.00
8 Nomar Garciaparra 00 4.00 10.00
9 Troy Glaus 02 WIN 2.00 5.00
10 Mark McGwire 00 6.00 15.00
11 Mark McGwire 00 6.00 15.00
12 Mark McGwire 00 6.00 15.00
13 Jim Thome 02 3.00 8.00
14 Chipper Jones 00 3.00 8.00
15 Shawn Green 02 2.00 5.00
16 Alex Rodriguez 00 4.00 10.00
17 Alex Rodriguez 00 4.00 10.00
18 Alex Rodriguez 00 4.00 10.00
19 Alex Rodriguez 00 4.00 10.00
20 Jason Giambi 01 2.00 5.00
21 Pat Burrell 01 2.00 5.00
22 Mike Piazza 01 4.00 10.00
23 Mike Piazza 01 4.00 10.00
24 Mike Piazza 01 4.00 10.00
25 Frank Thomas 01 3.00 8.00
26 Rafael Palmeiro 01 WIN 3.00 8.00
27 Todd Helton 01 3.00 8.00
28 Jose Canseco 01 3.00 8.00
29 Albert Pujols 03 4.00 10.00
30 Troy Glaus 01 2.00 5.00
31 Barry Bonds 01 4.00 10.00
32 Barry Bonds 01 4.00 10.00
33 Barry Bonds 01 4.00 10.00
34 Todd Helton 02 3.00 8.00
35 Rafael Palmeiro 02 3.00 8.00
36 Jim Thome 02 3.00 8.00
37 Ozzie Smith 02 6.00 15.00
38 Troy Glaus 02 WIN 2.00 5.00
39 Shawn Green 02 2.00 5.00
40 Barry Bonds 02 4.00 10.00
41 Barry Bonds 02 4.00 10.00
42 Barry Bonds 02 4.00 10.00
43 Magglio Ordonez 03 WIN 2.00 5.00
44 Alex Rodriguez 03 4.00 10.00
45 Alex Rodriguez 03 4.00 10.00
46 Alex Rodriguez 03 4.00 10.00
47 Lance Berkman 03 2.00 5.00
48 Rafael Palmeiro 03 3.00 8.00
49 Pat Burrell 03 2.00 5.00
50 Albert Pujols 03 4.00 10.00

2003 Studio Big League Challenge Materials

STATED ODDS 1:20
*PRIME 100: 1X TO 2.5X BASIC MATERIAL
*PRIME 50: 1.5X TO 4X BASIC MATERIAL
PRIME RANDOM INSERTS IN PACKS
PRIME PRINT RUN B/WN 50-100 COPIES PER
2 Magglio Ordonez 03 BP Jsy 3.00 8.00
3 Alex Rodriguez 03 BP Jsy 6.00 15.00
4 Lance Berkman 03 Jsy 3.00 8.00
15 Shawn Green 02 BP Jsy 3.00 8.00
29 Albert Pujols 03 Jsy 10.00 25.00
36 Jim Thome 02 BP Jsy 6.00 15.00
39 Shawn Green 02 Pants 3.00 8.00
40 Barry Bonds 02 Base 6.00 15.00
41 Barry Bonds 02 Base 6.00 15.00
42 Barry Bonds 02 Plate 6.00 15.00
43 Magglio Ordonez 03 Jsy 3.00 8.00
45 Alex Rodriguez 03 Jsy 6.00 15.00
46 Alex Rodriguez 03 Pants 6.00 15.00
47 Lance Berkman 03 BP Jsy 3.00 8.00
48 Rafael Palmeiro 03 BP Jsy 3.00 8.00
50 Albert Pujols 03 Pants 6.00 15.00

2003 Studio Enshrinement

STATED PRINT RUN 750 SERIAL #'d SETS
PROOFS PRINT RUN B/WN 20-21 COPIES PER

NO PROOFS PRICING DUE TO SCARCITY
RANDOM INSERTS IN PACKS
1 Gary Carter 2.00 5.00
2 Ozzie Smith 4.00 10.00
3 Kirby Puckett 3.00 8.00
4 Carlton Fisk 3.00 8.00
5 Tony Perez 2.00 5.00
6 Nolan Ryan 6.00 15.00
7 George Brett 5.00 12.00
8 Robin Yount 3.00 8.00
9 Orlando Cepeda 2.00 5.00
10 Phil Niekro 2.00 5.00
11 Mike Schmidt 5.00 12.00
12 Richie Ashburn 3.00 8.00
13 Steve Carlton 2.00 5.00
14 Phil Rizzuto 3.00 8.00
15 Reggie Jackson 3.00 8.00
16 Tom Seaver 3.00 8.00
17 Rollie Fingers 2.00 5.00
18 Rod Carew 3.00 8.00
19 Gaylord Perry 2.00 5.00
20 Fergie Jenkins 2.00 5.00
21 Jim Palmer 2.00 5.00
22 Joe Morgan 2.00 5.00
23 Johnny Bench 3.00 8.00
24 Willie Stargell 3.00 8.00
25 Billy Williams 2.00 5.00
26 Catfish Hunter 3.00 8.00
27 Willie McCovey 2.00 5.00
28 Bobby Doerr 2.00 5.00
29 Lou Brock 3.00 8.00
30 Enos Slaughter 2.00 5.00
31 Hoyt Wilhelm 2.00 5.00
32 Harmon Killebrew 3.00 8.00
33 Pee Wee Reese 3.00 8.00
34 Luis Aparicio 2.00 5.00
35 Brooks Robinson 3.00 8.00
36 Juan Marichal 2.00 5.00
37 Frank Robinson 3.00 8.00
38 Bob Gibson 3.00 8.00
39 Al Kaline 3.00 8.00
40 Duke Snider 3.00 8.00
41 Eddie Mathews 3.00 8.00
42 Robin Roberts 2.00 5.00
43 Ralph Kiner 2.00 5.00
44 Whitey Ford 3.00 8.00
45 Roberto Clemente 5.00 12.00
46 Warren Spahn 3.00 8.00
47 Yogi Berra 3.00 8.00
48 Early Wynn 2.00 5.00
49 Stan Musial 4.00 10.00
50 Bob Feller 2.00 5.00

2003 Studio Enshrinement Autographs

Randomly inserted into packs, this is a partial parallel to the Enshrinement insert set. Each of these cards is signed to beween one and 100 copies and we have notated the print run in our checklist. If a card was printed to 25 or fewer copies there is no pricing available due to market scarcity.

1 Gary Carter/50 12.50 30.00
2 Ozzie Smith/5
3 Kirby Puckett/5
4 Carlton Fisk/5
5 Tony Perez/50 20.00 50.00
6 Nolan Ryan/5
7 George Brett/5
8 Robin Yount/5
9 Orlando Cepeda/50 12.50 30.00
10 Phil Niekro/50 12.50 30.00
11 Mike Schmidt/5
13 Steve Carlton/50 12.50 30.00
14 Phil Rizzuto/15
15 Reggie Jackson/5
16 Tom Seaver/5
20 Fergie Jenkins/50 12.50 30.00
21 Jim Palmer/25
22 Joe Morgan/10
23 Johnny Bench/10
27 Willie McCovey/10
28 Bobby Doerr/100 10.00 25.00
29 Lou Brock/25
31 Hoyt Wilhelm/50 20.00 50.00
32 Harmon Killebrew/10
34 Luis Aparicio/100 10.00 25.00
35 Brooks Robinson/25
37 Frank Robinson/25
39 Al Kaline/25
40 Duke Snider/10
43 Ralph Kiner/25
46 Warren Spahn/1
47 Yogi Berra/10
49 Stan Musial/5
50 Bob Feller/100 10.00 25.00

2003 Studio Leather and Lumber

COMMON CARD p/r 300-400 3.00 8.00
RANDOM INSERTS IN PACKS
PRINT RUNS B/WN 100-400 COPIES PER

1 Adam Dunn Bat/400 3.00 8.00
2 Alex Rodriguez Bat/250 8.00 20.00
3 Alfonso Soriano Bat/250 4.00 10.00
4 Andruw Jones Bat/400 4.00 10.00
5 Austin Kearns Bat/400 3.00 8.00
6 Chipper Jones Bat/400 4.00 10.00
7 Derek Jeter Ball/100 15.00 40.00
8 Don Mattingly Bat/100 15.00 40.00
9 Edgar Martinez Bat/400 4.00 10.00
10 Frank Thomas Bat/400 4.00 10.00
11 Fred McGriff Bat/400 4.00 10.00
12 Garret Anderson Bat/400
13 Greg Maddux Bat/150 6.00 15.00
14 Hideki Matsui Ball/100 15.00 40.00
15 Hideo Nomo Bat/150 8.00 20.00
16 Ichiro Suzuki Ball/100 15.00 40.00
17 Ivan Rodriguez Bat/250 6.00 15.00
18 Jason Giambi Bat/400 3.00 8.00
19 Jeff Bagwell Bat/400 4.00 10.00
20 Jim Edmonds Bat/150 4.00 10.00
21 Jim Thome Bat/400 4.00 10.00
22 Juan Gonzalez Bat/400 3.00 8.00
23 Kerry Wood Bat/250 4.00 10.00
24 Kirby Puckett Bat/100 10.00 25.00
25 Lance Berkman Bat/400 3.00 8.00
26 Magglio Ordonez Bat/400 3.00 8.00
27 Manny Ramirez Bat/250 6.00 15.00
28 Mark Prior Bat/400 4.00 10.00
29 Miguel Tejada Bat/200 4.00 10.00
30 Mike Piazza Bat/400 4.00 10.00
31 Mike Schmidt Bat/200 15.00 40.00
32 Nomar Garciaparra Bat/400 6.00 15.00
33 Pat Burrell Bat/400 3.00 8.00
34 Pedro Martinez Bat/150 6.00 15.00
35 Rafael Palmeiro Bat/400
36 Randy Johnson Bat/250 6.00 15.00
37 Rickey Henderson Bat/175 6.00 15.00
38 Sammy Sosa Bat/300 4.00 10.00
39 Shawn Green Bat/400 3.00 8.00
40 Vladimir Guerrero Bat/400 4.00 10.00

2003 Studio Leather and Lumber Combos

RANDOM INSERTS IN PACKS
PRINT RUNS B/WN 25-50 COPIES PER
NO PRICING ON QTY OF 25 OR LESS
1 Adam Dunn Bat-Btg Glv/50 10.00 25.00
2 Alex Rodriguez Bat-Fld Glv/50 20.00 50.00
3 Alfonso Soriano Bat-Ball/25
4 Andruw Jones Bat-Fld Glv/50 15.00 40.00
5 Austin Kearns Bat-Shoe/50 10.00 25.00
6 Chipper Jones Bat-Ball/25
7 Derek Jeter Ball-Ball/25
8 Don Mattingly Bat-Btg Glv/25
9 Edgar Martinez Bat-Ball/25
10 Frank Thomas Bat-Btg Glv/50 15.00 40.00
11 Fred McGriff Bat-Ball/25
12 Garret Anderson Bat-Ball/25
13 Greg Maddux Bat-Shoe/50 15.00 40.00
14 Hideki Matsui Ball-Ball/25
15 Hideo Nomo Bat-Ball/25
16 Ichiro Suzuki Ball-Ball/25
17 Ivan Rodriguez Bat-Btg Glv/50 15.00 40.00
18 Jason Giambi Bat-Ball/25
19 Jeff Bagwell Bat-Ball/25
20 Jim Edmonds Bat-Shoe/50 10.00 25.00
21 Jim Thome Bat-Ball/25
22 Juan Gonzalez Bat-Ball/25
23 Kerry Wood Bat-Fld Glv/50 10.00 25.00
24 Kirby Puckett Bat-Btg Glv/25
25 Lance Berkman Bat-Fld Glv/50 10.00 25.00
26 Magglio Ordonez Bat-Shoe/25
27 Manny Ramirez Bat-Ball/25
28 Mark Prior Bat-Shoe/25
29 Miguel Tejada Bat-Ball/25
30 Mike Piazza Bat-Shoe/25
31 Mike Schmidt Bat-Btg Glv/25
32 Nomar Garciaparra Bat-Ball/25
33 Pat Burrell Bat-Ball/25
34 Pedro Martinez Bat-Ball/25
35 Rafael Palmeiro Bat-Fld Glv/25
36 Randy Johnson Bat-Ball/25
37 Rickey Henderson Bat-Ball/25
38 Sammy Sosa Bat-Shoe/25
39 Shawn Green Bat-Ball/25
40 Vladimir Guerrero Bat-Ball/25

2003 Studio Masterstrokes

RANDOM INSERTS IN PACKS
STATED PRINT RUN 1000 SERIAL #'d SETS
1 Adam Dunn 1.25 3.00
2 Albert Pujols 4.00 10.00
3 Alex Rodriguez 3.00 8.00
4 Alfonso Soriano 1.25 3.00
5 Andruw Jones 2.00 5.00
6 Chipper Jones 2.00 5.00
7 Derek Jeter 5.00 12.00
8 Greg Maddux 3.00 8.00
9 Hideki Matsui 4.00 10.00
10 Hideo Nomo 2.00 5.00
11 Ivan Rodriguez 2.00 5.00
12 Jason Giambi 1.25 3.00
13 Jeff Bagwell 2.00 5.00
14 Juan Gonzalez 1.25 3.00
15 Ken Griffey Jr. 3.00 8.00
16 Lance Berkman 1.25 3.00
17 Magglio Ordonez 1.25 3.00
18 Manny Ramirez 2.00 5.00
19 Mark Prior 2.00 5.00
20 Miguel Tejada 1.25 3.00
21 Mike Piazza 3.00 8.00
22 Nomar Garciaparra 3.00 8.00
23 Pat Burrell 1.25 3.00
24 Sammy Sosa 2.00 5.00
25 Vladimir Guerrero 2.00 5.00

2003 Studio Masterstrokes Proofs

RANDOM INSERTS IN PACKS
STATED PRINT RUN 50 SERIAL #'d SETS
1 Adam Dunn Bat-Jsy 8.00 20.00
2 Albert Pujols Bat-Jsy 25.00 60.00
3 Alex Rodriguez Bat-Jsy 25.00 60.00
4 Alfonso Soriano Bat-Jsy 8.00 20.00
5 Andruw Jones Bat-Jsy 12.50 30.00
6 Chipper Jones Bat-Jsy 12.50 30.00
7 Derek Jeter Base-Ball 30.00 80.00
8 Greg Maddux Bat-Jsy 15.00 40.00
9 Hideki Matsui Base-Ball 40.00 80.00
10 Hideo Nomo Bat-Jsy 60.00 120.00
11 Ivan Rodriguez Bat-Jsy 12.50 30.00
12 Jason Giambi Bat-Jsy 8.00 20.00
13 Jeff Bagwell Bat-Jsy 12.50 30.00
14 Juan Gonzalez Bat-Jsy 8.00 20.00
15 Ken Griffey Jr. Base-Base 20.00 50.00
16 Lance Berkman Bat-Jsy 8.00 20.00
17 Magglio Ordonez Bat-Jsy 8.00 20.00
18 Manny Ramirez Bat-Jsy 12.50 30.00
19 Mark Prior Bat-Jsy 12.50 30.00
20 Miguel Tejada Bat-Jsy 8.00 20.00
21 Mike Piazza Bat-Jsy 15.00 40.00
22 Nomar Garciaparra Bat-Jsy 20.00 50.00
23 Pat Burrell Bat-Jsy 8.00 20.00
24 Sammy Sosa Bat-Jsy 12.50 30.00
25 Vladimir Guerrero Bat-Jsy 12.50 30.00

2003 Studio Recollection Autographs 5 x 7

Inserted at a stated rate of one per sealed hobby case, these 27 cards feature authentic autographs of the featured players. Please note that these cards are alll 2001 Studio buybacks and we have put the stated print run next to the player's name in our checklist. In addition, if a card has a print run of 25 or fewer copies, there is no pricing due to market scarcity.

1 Josh Beckett/3
2 Lance Berkman/13
3 Sean Casey/125 8.00 20.00
4 Adam Dunn/12
5 Troy Glaus/82 12.50 30.00
6 Tom Glavine/3
7 Shawn Green/3
8 Vladimir Guerrero/125 15.00 40.00
9 Tony Gwynn/13
10 Todd Helton/55 15.00 40.00
11 Andruw Jones/3
12 Ryan Klesko/75 8.00 20.00
13 Greg Maddux/25
14 Edgar Martinez/11
15 Magglio Ordonez/6
16 Cal Ripken/4
17 Alex Rodriguez/3
18 Ivan Rodriguez/50 20.00 50.00
19 C.C. Sabathia/50 10.00 25.00
20 Curt Schilling/75 20.00 50.00
21 Ben Sheets/1
22 Alfonso Soriano/8
23 Mike Sweeney/42 10.00 25.00
24 Miguel Tejada/44 15.00 40.00
25 Frank Thomas/11
26 Kerry Wood/200 10.00 25.00
27 Barry Zito/200 10.00 25.00

2003 Studio Spirit of the Game

RANDOM INSERTS IN PACKS
STATED PRINT RUN 1250 SERIAL #'d SETS

1 Garret Anderson 1.00 2.50
2 Nomar Garciaparra 2.50 6.00
3 Pedro Martinez 1.50 4.00
4 Rickey Henderson 1.50 4.00
5 Magglio Ordonez 1.00 2.50
6 Torii Hunter 1.00 2.50
7 Alfonso Soriano 1.00 2.50
8 Jose Contreras 1.50 4.00
9 Derek Jeter 4.00 10.00
10 Jason Giambi 1.00 2.50
11 Roger Clemens 3.00 8.00
12 Hideki Matsui 3.00 8.00
13 Barry Zito 1.00 2.50
14 Ichiro Suzuki 3.00 8.00
15 Alex Rodriguez 2.50 6.00
16 Curt Schilling 1.00 2.50
17 Randy Johnson 1.50 4.00
18 Andruw Jones 1.50 4.00
19 Chipper Jones 1.50 4.00
20 Greg Maddux 2.50 6.00
21 Sammy Sosa 1.50 4.00
22 Adam Dunn 1.00 2.50
23 Ken Griffey Jr. 2.50 6.00
24 Todd Helton 1.50 4.00
25 Ivan Rodriguez 1.50 4.00
26 Lance Berkman 1.00 2.50
27 Hideo Nomo 1.50 4.00
28 Shawn Green 1.00 2.50
29 Vladimir Guerrero 1.50 4.00
30 Mike Piazza 2.50 6.00
31 Roberto Alomar 1.50 4.00
32 Jim Thome 1.50 4.00
33 Barry Bonds 4.00 10.00
34 Albert Pujols 3.00 8.00
35 Scott Rolen 1.50 4.00

2003 Studio Spirit of MLB

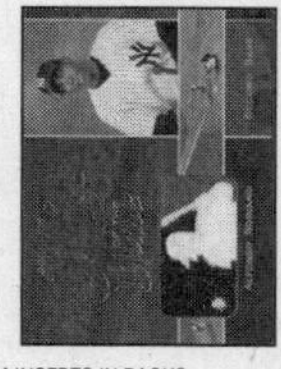

RANDOM INSERTS IN PACKS
STATED PRINT RUN 1 SERIAL #'d SET

2003 Studio Stars

STATED ODDS 1:5
*GOLD: 1X TO 2.5X BASIC STARS
GOLD PRINT RUN 100 SERIAL #'d SETS
PLATINUM PRINT RUN 25 SERIAL #'d SETS
NO PLATINUM PRICING DUE TO SCARCITY
GOLD/PLATINUM RANDOM IN PACKS
1 Troy Glaus .75 2.00
2 Manny Ramirez .75 2.00
3 Nomar Garciaparra 2.00 5.00
4 Pedro Martinez .75 2.00
5 Rickey Henderson 1.25 3.00
6 Torii Hunter .75 2.00
7 Frank Thomas 1.25 3.00
8 Magglio Ordonez .75 2.00
9 Alfonso Soriano .75 2.00
10 Jose Contreras 1.25 3.00
11 Derek Jeter 3.00 8.00
12 Jason Giambi .75 2.00
13 Roger Clemens 2.50 6.00
14 Mike Mussina .75 2.00
15 Barry Zito .75 2.00
16 Miguel Tejada .75 2.00
17 Ichiro Suzuki 2.50 6.00
18 Alex Rodriguez 2.00 5.00
19 Juan Gonzalez .75 2.00
20 Rafael Palmeiro .75 2.00
21 Hank Blalock .75 2.00
22 Curt Schilling .75 2.00
23 Randy Johnson 1.25 3.00
24 Junior Spivey .75 2.00
25 Andruw Jones .75 2.00
26 Chipper Jones 1.25 3.00
27 Greg Maddux 2.00 5.00
28 Kerry Wood .75 2.00
29 Mark Prior .75 2.00
30 Sammy Sosa 1.25 3.00
31 Adam Dunn .75 2.00
32 Ken Griffey Jr. 2.00 5.00
33 Austin Kearns .75 2.00
34 Larry Walker .75 2.00
35 Todd Helton .75 2.00
36 Ivan Rodriguez .75 2.00
37 Jeff Bagwell .75 2.00
38 Lance Berkman .75 2.00
39 Craig Biggio .75 2.00
40 Hideo Nomo 1.25 3.00
41 Shawn Green .75 2.00
42 Vladimir Guerrero 1.25 3.00

43 Mike Piazza 2.00 5.00
44 Tom Glavine .75 2.00
45 Roberto Alomar .75 2.00
46 Pat Burrell .75 2.00
47 Jim Thome .75 2.00
48 Barry Bonds 3.00 8.00
49 Albert Pujols 2.50 6.00
50 Scott Rolen .75 2.00

2004 Studio

This 275 card was actually issued twice during the 2004 year. The first 225 cards of this set were relased in June. Those cards were issued in six-card packs with an $3 SRP which came 24 packs to a box and 12 boxes to a case. Cards numbered 201-225 featured signed Rookie Cards issued to varying print runs. Cards numbered 226-275 were issued as part of the 2005 Donruss released and those cards were issued at a stated rate of one in 23. Please note that cards 220 and 222-225 were not issued.

COMP.SET w/o SP's (200) 20.00 50.00
COMMON ACTIVE (1-200) .15 .40
COMMON RETIRED (1-200) .20 .50
COMMON RC (1-200) .15 .40
AU'S RANDOM INSERTS IN PACKS
AU PRINT RUNS B/WN 400-800 COPIES PER
COMMON CARD (226-241) 1.25 3.00
COMMON CARD (242-275) 1.25 3.00
226-275 ODDS 1:23 '05 DONRUSS
CARDS 220/222-225 DO NOT EXIST
1 Bartolo Colon .15 .40
2 Garret Anderson .15 .40
3 Tim Salmon .25 .60
4 Troy Glaus .15 .40
5 Vladimir Guerrero .40 1.00
6 Brandon Webb .15 .40
7 Brian Bruney .15 .40
8 Casey Fossum .15 .40
9 Luis Gonzalez .15 .40
10 Randy Johnson .40 1.00
11 Richie Sexson .15 .40
12 Robby Hammock .15 .40
13 Roberto Alomar .25 .60
14 Shea Hillenbrand .15 .40
15 Steve Finley .15 .40
16 Adam LaRoche .15 .40
17 Andruw Jones .25 .60
18 Bubba Nelson .15 .40
19 Chipper Jones .40 1.00
20 Dale Murphy .25 .60
21 J.D. Drew .15 .40
22 Marcus Giles .15 .40
23 Michael Hessman .15 .40
24 Rafael Furcal .15 .40
25 Warren Spahn .25 .60
26 Adam Loewen .15 .40
27 Cal Ripken 1.50 4.00
28 Javy Lopez .15 .40
29 Jay Gibbons .15 .40
30 Luis Matos .15 .40
31 Miguel Tejada .15 .40
32 Rafael Palmeiro .25 .60
33 Curt Schilling .25 .60
34 Jason Varitek .40 1.00
35 Kevin Youkilis .15 .40
36 Manny Ramirez .25 .60
37 Nomar Garciaparra .60 1.50
38 Pedro Martinez .25 .60
39 Trot Nixon .15 .40
40 Aramis Ramirez .15 .40
41 Brendan Harris .15 .40
42 Derrek Lee .25 .60
43 Ernie Banks .50 1.25
44 Greg Maddux .60 1.50
45 Kerry Wood .15 .40
46 Mark Prior .25 .60
47 Ryne Sandberg 1.00 2.50
48 Sammy Sosa .40 1.00
49 Todd Wellemeyer .15 .40
50 Carlos Lee .15 .40
51 Edwin Almonte .15 .40
52 Frank Thomas .40 1.00
53 Joe Borchard .15 .40
54 Joe Crede .15 .40
55 Magglio Ordonez .15 .40
56 Adam Dunn .15 .40
57 Austin Kearns .15 .40
58 Barry Larkin .25 .60
59 Brandon Larson .15 .40
60 Ken Griffey Jr. .60 1.50
61 Ryan Wagner .15 .40
62 Sean Casey .15 .40
63 Brian Tallet .15 .40
64 C.C. Sabathia .15 .40
65 Jeremy Guthrie .15 .40
66 Jody Gerut .15 .40
67 Travis Hafner .15 .40
68 Clint Barmes .15 .40
69 Jeff Baker .15 .40
70 Joe Kennedy .15 .40
71 Larry Walker .15 .40
72 Preston Wilson .15 .40
73 Todd Helton .25 .60
74 Dmitri Young .15 .40
75 Ivan Rodriguez .25 .60
76 Jeremy Bonderman .15 .40
77 Preston Larrison .15 .40
78 Dontrelle Willis .25 .60
79 Josh Beckett .15 .40
80 Juan Pierre .15 .40
81 Luis Castillo .15 .40
82 Miguel Cabrera .25 .60
83 Mike Lowell .15 .40
84 Andy Pettitte .25 .60
85 Chris Burke .15 .40
86 Craig Biggio .25 .60
87 Jeff Bagwell .25 .60
88 Jeff Kent .15 .40
89 Lance Berkman .15 .40
90 Morgan Ensberg .15 .40
91 Richard Hidalgo .15 .40
92 Roger Clemens .75 2.00
93 Roy Oswalt .15 .40
94 Wade Miller .15 .40
95 Angel Berroa .15 .40
96 Byron Gettis .15 .40
97 Carlos Beltran .15 .40
98 Juan Gonzalez .15 .40
99 Mike Sweeney .15 .40
100 Duke Snider .30 .75
101 Edwin Jackson .15 .40
102 Eric Gagne .15 .40
103 Hideo Nomo .40 1.00
104 Hong-Chih Kuo .15 .40
105 Kazuhisa Ishii .15 .40
106 Paul Lo Duca .15 .40
107 Robin Ventura .15 .40
108 Shawn Green .15 .40
109 Junior Spivey .15 .40
110 Lyle Overbay .15 .40
111 Rickie Weeks .15 .40
112 Scott Podsednik .15 .40
113 J.D. Durbin .15 .40
114 Jacque Jones .15 .40
115 Jason Kubel .15 .40
116 Johan Santana .40 1.00
117 Shannon Stewart .15 .40
118 Torii Hunter .15 .40
119 Brad Wilkerson .15 .40
120 Jose Vidro .15 .40
121 Nick Johnson .15 .40
122 Orlando Cabrera .15 .40
123 Zach Day .15 .40
124 Gary Carter .20 .50
125 Jae Weong Seo .15 .40
126 Kazuo Matsui RC .40 1.00
127 Mike Piazza .60 1.50
128 Tom Glavine .25 .60
129 Alex Rodriguez Yanks .60 1.50
130 Bernie Williams .25 .60
131 Chien-Ming Wang .60 1.50
132 Derek Jeter .75 2.00
133 Don Mattingly 1.00 2.50
134 Gary Sheffield .15 .40
135 Hideki Matsui .60 1.50
136 Jason Giambi .15 .40
137 Javier Vazquez .15 .40
138 Jorge Posada .25 .60
139 Jose Contreras .15 .40
140 Kevin Brown .15 .40
141 Mariano Rivera .40 1.00
142 Mike Mussina .25 .60
143 Whitey Ford .30 .75
144 Barry Zito .15 .40
145 Eric Chavez .15 .40
146 Mark Mulder .15 .40
147 Rich Harden .15 .40
148 Tim Hudson .15 .40
149 Bobby Abreu .15 .40
150 Jim Thome .25 .60
151 Kevin Millwood .15 .40
152 Marlon Byrd .15 .40
153 Mike Schmidt 1.00 2.50
154 Ryan Howard 2.00 5.00
155 Jack Wilson .15 .40
156 Jason Kendall .15 .40
157 Akinori Otsuka RC .15 .40
158 Brian Giles .15 .40
159 David Wells .15 .40
160 Jay Payton .15 .40
161 Phil Nevin .15 .40
162 Ryan Klesko .15 .40
163 Sean Burroughs .15 .40
164 A.J. Pierzynski .15 .40
165 J.T. Snow .15 .40
166 Jason Schmidt .15 .40
167 Jerome Williams .15 .40
168 Merkin Valdez RC .25 .60
169 Will Clark .30 .75
170 Bret Boone .15 .40
171 Chris Snelling .15 .40
172 Edgar Martinez .25 .60
173 Ichiro Suzuki .75 2.00
174 Jamie Moyer .15 .40
175 Randy Winn .15 .40
176 Rich Aurilia .15 .40
177 Shigetoshi Hasegawa .15 .40
178 Albert Pujols .75 2.00
179 Dan Haren .15 .40
180 Edgar Renteria .15 .40
181 Jim Edmonds .15 .40
182 Matt Morris .15 .40
183 Scott Rolen .25 .60
184 Stan Musial .75 2.00
185 Aubrey Huff .15 .40
186 Chad Gaudin .15 .40
187 Delmon Young .25 .60
188 Fred McGriff .25 .60
189 Rocco Baldelli .15 .40
190 Alfonso Soriano .25 .60
191 Hank Blalock .15 .40
192 Mark Teixeira .25 .60
193 Nolan Ryan 1.25 3.00
194 Alexis Rios .15 .40
195 Carlos Delgado .15 .40
196 Dustin McGowan .15 .40
197 Guillermo Quiroz .15 .40
198 Josh Phelps .15 .40
199 Roy Halladay .15 .40
200 Vernon Wells .15 .40
201 Mike Gosling AU/400 RC 4.00 10.00
202 Ronny Cedeno AU/766 RC 6.00 15.00
203 Ron Belisario AU/400 RC 4.00 10.00
204 Justin Hampson AU/800 RC 3.00 8.00
205 Carlos Vasquez AU/800 RC 3.00 8.00
206 Linc.Holdzkom AU/800 RC 3.00 8.00
207 Casey Daigle AU/550 RC 4.00 10.00
208 Jason Bartlett AU/800 RC 4.00 10.00
209 Mariano Gomez AU/800 RC 3.00 8.00
210 Mike Rouse AU/800 RC 3.00 8.00
211 Chris Shelton AU/800 RC 8.00 20.00
212 Dennis Sarfate AU/800 RC 3.00 8.00
213 Shingo Takatsu AU/400 RC 6.00 15.00
214 Justin Leone AU/800 RC 4.00 10.00
215 Cory Sullivan AU/800 RC 3.00 8.00
216 Michael Wuertz AU/800 RC 4.00 10.00
217 Tim Bausher AU/800 RC 3.00 8.00
218 Jesse Harper AU/800 RC 3.00 8.00
219 Ryan Meaux AU/800 RC 3.00 8.00
221 Kevin Cave AU/800 RC 3.00 8.00
226 Abe Alvarez XRC 3.00 8.00
227 Carlos Hines XRC 2.00 5.00
228 Charles Thomas XRC 2.00 5.00
229 Frankie Francisco XRC 2.00 5.00
230 Greg Dobbs XRC 2.00 5.00
231 Hector Gimenez XRC 1.25 3.00
232 Jesse Crain XRC 3.00 8.00
233 Joey Gathright XRC 3.00 8.00
234 Justin Knoedler XRC 2.00 5.00
235 Kazuhito Tadano XRC 3.00 8.00
236 Lance Cormier XRC 2.00 5.00
237 Scott Proctor XRC 3.00 8.00
238 Tim Bittner XRC 2.00 5.00
239 Travis Blackley XRC 2.00 5.00
240 Mike Johnston XRC 2.00 5.00
241 Yadier Molina XRC 3.00 8.00
242 B.J. Upton 3.00 8.00
243 Ben Sheets 2.00 5.00
244 Bobby Crosby 2.00 5.00
245 Brad Penny 1.25 3.00
246 Carl Crawford 2.00 5.00
247 Carlos Beltran 2.00 5.00
248 Carlos Guillen 2.00 5.00
249 Carlos Zambrano 2.00 5.00
250 Casey Kotchman 2.00 5.00
251 Chase Utley 3.00 8.00
252 Craig Wilson 1.25 3.00
253 Danny Graves 1.25 3.00
254 Danny Kolb 1.25 3.00
255 David Wright 8.00 20.00
256 Eric Milton 1.25 3.00
257 Esteban Loaiza 1.25 3.00
258 Francisco Cordero 1.25 3.00
259 Francisco Rodriguez 2.00 5.00
260 Jake Peavy 2.00 5.00
261 Jason Bay 2.00 5.00
262 Jermaine Dye 2.00 5.00
263 Joe Nathan 2.00 5.00
264 John Lackey 1.25 3.00
265 Ken Harvey 1.25 3.00
266 Khalil Greene 3.00 8.00
267 Lew Ford 1.25 3.00
268 Livan Hernandez 2.00 5.00
269 Milton Bradley 2.00 5.00
270 Nomar Garciaparra 4.00 10.00
271 Orlando Cabrera Sox 2.00 5.00
272 Paul Lo Duca 2.00 5.00
273 Richard Hidalgo 1.25 3.00
274 Steve Finley 2.00 5.00
275 Victor Martinez 2.00 5.00

2004 Studio Proofs Gold

*GOLD 1-200: 5X TO 12X BASIC ACTIVE
*GOLD 1-200: 5X TO 12X BASIC RETIRED
*GOLD 1-200: 2.5X TO 6X BASIC RC'S
*GOLD 201-225: .25X TO .6X AU p/r 766-800
*GOLD 201-225: .2X TO .5X AU p/r 400-550
1-225 RANDOM INSERTS IN PACKS
220/222-225 EXIST ONLY IN PARALLEL SET
*GOLD 226-241: .75X TO 2X BASIC
*GOLD 242-275: .75X TO 2X BASIC
226-275 RANDOM IN '05 DONRUSS
STATED PRINT RUN 50 SERIAL #'d SETS
220 David Aardsma 3.00 8.00
222 Mike Johnston 2.00 5.00
223 Jason Szuminski 2.00 5.00
224 Shawn Camp 2.00 5.00
225 Colby Miller 2.00 5.00

2004 Studio Proofs Platinum

1-225 RANDOM INSERTS IN PACKS
226-275 RANDOM IN '05 DONRUSS
STATED PRINT RUN 10 SERIAL #'d SETS
NO PRICING DUE TO SCARCITY

2004 Studio Proofs Silver

*SILVER 1-200: 3X TO 8X BASIC ACTIVE
*SILVER 1-200: 3X TO 8X BASIC RETIRED
*SILVER 1-200: 1.5X TO 4X BASIC RC'S
*SILVER 201-225: .15X TO .4X AU p/r 766-800
*SILVER 201-225: .12X TO .3X AU p/r 400-550
1-225 RANDOM INSERTS IN PACKS
*SILVER 226-241: .5X TO 1.2X BASIC
*SILVER 242-275: .5X TO 1.2X BASIC
226-275 RANDOM IN '05 DONRUSS
STATED PRINT RUN 100 SERIAL #'d SETS
220/222-225 EXIST ONLY IN PARALLEL SET
220 David Aardsma 2.00 5.00
222 Mike Johnston 1.25 3.00
223 Jason Szuminski 1.25 3.00
224 Shawn Camp 1.25 3.00
225 Colby Miller 1.25 3.00

2004 Studio Private Signings Gold

RANDOM INSERTS IN PACKS
PRINT RUNS B/WN 1-100 COPIES PER
NO PRICING ON QTY OF 12 OR LESS
NO RC YR PRICING ON QTY OF 25 OR LESS
2 Garret Anderson/16 15.00 40.00
5 Vladimir Guerrero/10
6 Brandon Webb/55 6.00 15.00
7 Brian Bruney/100 4.00 10.00
8 Casey Fossum/5
10 Randy Johnson/5
11 Richie Sexson/5
12 Robby Hammock/7
14 Shea Hillenbrand/28 10.00 25.00
15 Steve Finley/12
16 Adam LaRoche/25 8.00 20.00
17 Andruw Jones/5
18 Bubba Nelson/100 4.00 10.00
19 Chipper Jones/10
20 Dale Murphy/5
21 J.D. Drew/7
22 Marcus Giles/25 12.50 30.00
23 Michael Hessman/25 8.00 20.00
24 Rafael Furcal/1
25 Warren Spahn/5
26 Adam Loewen/1
27 Cal Ripken/10
29 Jay Gibbons/25 8.00 20.00
30 Luis Matos/100 4.00 10.00
32 Rafael Palmeiro/5
33 Curt Schilling/5
34 Jason Varitek/33 30.00 60.00
35 Kevin Youkilis/100 4.00 10.00
36 Manny Ramirez/1
39 Trot Nixon/7
40 Aramis Ramirez/16 15.00 40.00
41 Brendan Harris/75 4.00 10.00
43 Ernie Banks/5
45 Kerry Wood/5
46 Mark Prior/22 15.00 40.00
47 Ryne Sandberg/1
48 Sammy Sosa/10
49 Todd Wellemeyer/50 5.00 12.00
50 Carlos Lee/45 8.00 20.00
51 Edwin Almonte/56 5.00 12.00
52 Frank Thomas/5
53 Joe Borchard/25 8.00 20.00
54 Joe Crede/24 12.50 30.00
55 Magglio Ordonez/10
57 Austin Kearns/28 6.00 15.00
58 Barry Larkin/11
59 Brandon Larson/16 10.00 25.00
61 Ryan Wagner/38 5.00 12.00
63 Brian Tallet/50 5.00 12.00
65 Jeremy Guthrie/67 4.00 10.00
66 Jody Gerut/25 8.00 20.00
67 Travis Hafner/34 10.00 25.00
68 Clint Barmes/36 8.00 20.00
69 Jeff Baker/62 4.00 10.00
70 Joe Kennedy/37 5.00 12.00
72 Preston Wilson/10
73 Todd Helton/17 30.00 60.00
77 Preston Larrison/56 5.00 12.00
78 Dontrelle Willis/35 15.00 40.00
79 Josh Beckett/1
81 Luis Castillo/1
82 Miguel Cabrera/24 20.00 50.00
84 Andy Pettitte/5
85 Chris Burke/46 8.00 20.00
86 Craig Biggio/7
87 Jeff Bagwell/5
89 Lance Berkman/17 30.00 60.00
90 Morgan Ensberg/25 12.50 30.00
93 Roy Oswalt/5
94 Wade Miller/10
95 Angel Berroa/4
96 Byron Gettis/100 4.00 10.00
97 Carlos Beltran/25 12.50 30.00
98 Juan Gonzalez/22 12.50 30.00
100 Duke Snider/25 20.00 50.00
101 Edwin Jackson/50 5.00 12.00
103 Hideo Nomo/1
104 Hong-Chih Kuo/100 20.00 50.00
105 Kazuhisa Ishii/17 15.00 40.00
106 Paul Lo Duca/16 15.00 40.00
107 Robin Ventura/25 20.00 50.00
108 Shawn Green/15 30.00 60.00
109 Junior Spivey/37 5.00 12.00
110 Lyle Overbay/10
111 Rickie Weeks/1
112 Scott Podsednik/20 20.00 50.00
113 J.D. Durbin/31 6.00 15.00
114 Jacque Jones/25 12.50 30.00
116 Johan Santana/57 12.50 30.00
117 Shannon Stewart/23 8.00 20.00
118 Torii Hunter/10
120 Jose Vidro/3
121 Nick Johnson/21 12.50 30.00
122 Orlando Cabrera/18 15.00 40.00
123 Zach Day/1
124 Gary Carter/25 12.50 30.00
125 Jae Weong Seo/25 12.50 30.00
127 Mike Piazza/1
128 Tom Glavine/1
129 Alex Rodriguez Yanks/3
130 Bernie Williams/1
131 Chien-Ming Wang/100 75.00 150.00
133 Don Mattingly/5
134 Gary Sheffield/11
137 Javier Vazquez/5
138 Jorge Posada/10
139 Jose Contreras/5
142 Mike Mussina/1
143 Whitey Ford/5
144 Barry Zito/1
146 Mark Mulder/10
147 Rich Harden/53 8.00 20.00
148 Tim Hudson/5
149 Bobby Abreu/5
152 Marlon Byrd/29 6.00 15.00
153 Mike Schmidt/5
154 Ryan Howard/100 40.00 80.00
157 Akinori Otsuka/16
160 Jay Payton/17 10.00 25.00
165 J.T. Snow/10
167 Jerome Williams/50 5.00 12.00
168 Merkin Valdez/100 4.00 10.00
169 Will Clark/10
171 Chris Snelling/32 6.00 15.00
172 Edgar Martinez/11
174 Jamie Moyer/1
176 Rich Aurilia/10
177 Shigetoshi Hasegawa/17 60.00 120.00
178 Albert Pujols/5
179 Dan Haren/100 4.00 10.00
181 Jim Edmonds/10
183 Scott Rolen/10
184 Stan Musial/25 40.00 80.00
185 Aubrey Huff/19 15.00 40.00
186 Chad Gaudin/100 4.00 10.00
187 Delmon Young/73 10.00 25.00
188 Fred McGriff/5
189 Rocco Baldelli/5
191 Hank Blalock/5
192 Mark Teixeira/25 20.00 50.00
193 Nolan Ryan/10
194 Alexis Rios/50 8.00 20.00
196 Dustin McGowan/50 5.00 12.00
197 Guillermo Quiroz/12
198 Josh Phelps/17 10.00 25.00
199 Roy Halladay/5
226 Abe Alvarez/50 6.00 15.00
227 Carlos Hines/50 4.00 10.00
228 Charles Thomas/50 5.00 12.00
229 Frankie Francisco/50 4.00 10.00
231 Hector Gimenez/50 4.00 10.00
232 Jesse Crain/50 8.00 20.00
233 Joey Gathright/50 6.00 15.00
234 Justin Knoedler/50 4.00 10.00
236 Lance Cormier/50 4.00 10.00
237 Scott Proctor/50 6.00 15.00
238 Tim Bittner/50 4.00 10.00
239 Travis Blackley/50 4.00 10.00
240 Mike Johnston/50 4.00 10.00
241 Yadier Molina/50 12.50 30.00
244 Bobby Crosby/5
245 Brad Penny/5
246 Carl Crawford/5
247 Carlos Beltran/5
252 Craig Wilson/5
255 David Wright/5
257 Esteban Loaiza/5
260 Jake Peavy/5
261 Jason Bay/5
262 Jermaine Dye/5
263 Joe Nathan/5
264 John Lackey/5
265 Ken Harvey/5
267 Lew Ford/5
269 Milton Bradley/5
271 Orlando Cabrera/5
272 Paul Lo Duca/5
275 Victor Martinez/5

2004 Studio Private Signings Platinum

RANDOM INSERTS IN PACKS
PRINT RUNS B/WN 1-10 COPIES PER
NO PRICING DUE TO SCARCITY

2004 Studio Private Signings Silver

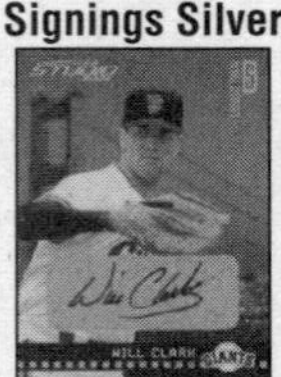

RANDOM INSERTS IN PACKS
PRINT RUNS B/WN 1-250 COPIES PER
NO PRICING ON QTY OF 10 OR LESS
NO RC YR PRICING ON QTY OF 25 OR LESS
2 Garret Anderson/25 12.50 30.00
5 Vladimir Guerrero/5
6 Brandon Webb/25 10.00 25.00
7 Brian Bruney/200 4.00 10.00
8 Casey Fossum/63 4.00 10.00
10 Randy Johnson/5
11 Richie Sexson/5
13 Roberto Alomar/5
14 Shea Hillenbrand/25 12.50 30.00
15 Steve Finley/10
16 Adam LaRoche/26 6.00 15.00
17 Andruw Jones/10
18 Bubba Nelson/250 4.00 10.00
19 Chipper Jones/1
21 J.D. Drew/1
22 Marcus Giles/25 12.50 30.00
23 Michael Hessman/95 4.00 10.00
24 Rafael Furcal/25 12.50 30.00
25 Warren Spahn/10
26 Adam Loewen/25 8.00 20.00
27 Cal Ripken/10
29 Jay Gibbons/50 5.00 12.00
30 Luis Matos/250 4.00 10.00
32 Rafael Palmeiro/5
33 Curt Schilling/5
34 Jason Varitek/10
35 Kevin Youkilis/250 4.00 10.00
36 Manny Ramirez/1
39 Trot Nixon/25 12.50 30.00
40 Aramis Ramirez/25 12.50 30.00
41 Brendan Harris/100 4.00 10.00
43 Ernie Banks/25 40.00 80.00
45 Kerry Wood/5
46 Mark Prior/10
48 Sammy Sosa/21 50.00 100.00
49 Todd Wellemeyer/92 4.00 10.00
50 Carlos Lee/25 12.50 30.00
51 Edwin Almonte/227 4.00 10.00
52 Frank Thomas/5
53 Joe Borchard/100 4.00 10.00
54 Joe Crede/10
55 Magglio Ordonez/10
57 Austin Kearns/10
58 Barry Larkin/5
59 Brandon Larson/100 4.00 10.00
61 Ryan Wagner/50 5.00 12.00
63 Brian Tallet/250 4.00 10.00
65 Jeremy Guthrie/89 4.00 10.00
66 Jody Gerut/100 4.00 10.00
67 Travis Hafner/100 6.00 15.00
68 Clint Barmes/100 6.00 15.00
69 Jeff Baker/50 5.00 12.00
70 Joe Kennedy/100 4.00 10.00
72 Preston Wilson/25 12.50 30.00
73 Todd Helton/5
77 Preston Larrison/100 4.00 10.00
78 Dontrelle Willis/10
79 Josh Beckett/1
81 Luis Castillo/25 8.00 20.00
82 Miguel Cabrera/25 20.00 50.00
84 Andy Pettitte/5
85 Chris Burke/100 4.00 10.00
86 Craig Biggio/5
87 Jeff Bagwell/5
89 Lance Berkman/10
90 Morgan Ensberg/50 8.00 20.00
93 Roy Oswalt/10
94 Wade Miller/10
95 Angel Berroa/10
96 Byron Gettis/250 4.00 10.00
97 Carlos Beltran/50 8.00 20.00
98 Juan Gonzalez/10
100 Duke Snider/50 12.50 30.00
101 Edwin Jackson/100 4.00 10.00
103 Hideo Nomo/1
104 Hong-Chih Kuo/250 20.00 50.00
105 Kazuhisa Ishii/5
106 Paul Lo Duca/25 12.50 30.00
107 Robin Ventura/25 20.00 50.00
108 Shawn Green/1
109 Junior Spivey/50 5.00 12.00
111 Rickie Weeks/1
112 Scott Podsednik/100 10.00 25.00
113 J.D. Durbin/250 4.00 10.00
114 Jacque Jones/50 8.00 20.00
115 Jason Kubel/100 4.00 10.00
116 Johan Santana/25 20.00 50.00
117 Shannon Stewart/25 8.00 20.00
118 Torii Hunter/10
120 Jose Vidro/15 10.00 25.00
121 Nick Johnson/5
122 Orlando Cabrera/15 15.00 40.00
123 Zach Day/6
124 Gary Carter/50 8.00 20.00
127 Mike Piazza/1
128 Tom Glavine/1
129 Alex Rodriguez Yanks/3
130 Bernie Williams/1
131 Chien-Ming Wang/243 60.00 120.00
133 Don Mattingly/25 50.00 100.00
134 Gary Sheffield/25 20.00 50.00
137 Javier Vazquez/5
138 Jorge Posada/10
139 Jose Contreras/5
143 Whitey Ford/5
144 Barry Zito/5
146 Mark Mulder/5
147 Rich Harden/200 6.00 15.00
148 Tim Hudson/5
149 Bobby Abreu/5
152 Marlon Byrd/10
153 Mike Schmidt/10
154 Ryan Howard/250 30.00 60.00
157 Akinori Otsuka/5
160 Jay Payton/50 5.00 12.00
165 J.T. Snow/10
167 Jerome Williams/57 5.00 12.00
168 Merkin Valdez/250 3.00 8.00
169 Will Clark/25 60.00 120.00
171 Chris Snelling/200 4.00 10.00
172 Edgar Martinez/7
176 Rich Aurilia/8
177 Shigetoshi Hasegawa/25 60.00 120.00
178 Albert Pujols/5
179 Dan Haren/250 4.00 10.00
181 Jim Edmonds/5
183 Scott Rolen/10
184 Stan Musial/25 40.00 80.00
185 Aubrey Huff/250 6.00 15.00
186 Chad Gaudin/100 4.00 10.00
187 Delmon Young/25 20.00 50.00
188 Fred McGriff/5
189 Rocco Baldelli/10
191 Hank Blalock/5
192 Mark Teixeira/25 20.00 50.00
193 Nolan Ryan/34 60.00 120.00
194 Alexis Rios/250 6.00 15.00
196 Dustin McGowan/115 4.00 10.00
197 Guillermo Quiroz/120 4.00 10.00
198 Josh Phelps/10
199 Roy Halladay/5
226 Abe Alvarez/100 5.00 12.00
227 Carlos Hines/100 3.00 8.00
228 Charles Thomas/100 4.00 10.00
229 Frankie Francisco/100 3.00 8.00
230 Greg Dobbs/40 3.00 8.00
231 Hector Gimenez/100 3.00 8.00

232 Jesse Crain/100 6.00 15.00
233 Joey Gathright/100 5.00 12.00
234 Justin Knoedler/100 3.00 8.00
236 Lance Cormier/100 3.00 8.00
237 Scott Proctor/100 5.00 12.00
238 Tim Bittner/100 3.00 8.00
239 Travis Blackley/100 3.00 8.00
240 Mike Johnston/100 3.00 8.00
241 Yadier Molina/100 10.00 25.00
244 Bobby Crosby/10
245 Brad Penny/10
246 Carl Crawford/10
247 Carlos Beltran/10
252 Craig Wilson/10
255 David Wright/10
257 Esteban Loaiza/10
260 Jake Peavy/10
261 Jason Bay/10
262 Jermaine Dye/10
263 Joe Nathan/10
264 John Lackey/10
265 Ken Harvey/10
267 Lew Ford/10
269 Milton Bradley/10
271 Orlando Cabrera/10
272 Paul Lo Duca/10
275 Victor Martinez/10

2004 Studio Big League Challenge

STATED PRINT RUN 999 SERIAL #'d SETS
*DIE CUT: .6X TO 1.5X BASIC
DIE CUT PRINT RUN 500 SERIAL #'d SETS
*GOLD: .6X TO 1.5X BASIC
GOLD PRINT RUN 499 SERIAL #'d SETS
RANDOM INSERTS IN PACKS
1 Albert Pujols Left 2.50 6.00
2 Albert Pujols Right 2.50 6.00
3 Alex Rodriguez Rgr Left 2.00 5.00
4 Alex Rodriguez Rgr Right 2.00 5.00
5 Magglio Ordonez 1.25 3.00
6 Rafael Palmeiro 1.50 4.00
7 Troy Glaus Follow 1.25 3.00
8 Troy Glaus Start 1.25 3.00
9 Albert Pujols Bat Up 2.50 6.00
10 Alex Rodriguez Rgr Bat Up 2.00 5.00

2004 Studio Big League Challenge Material

STATED PRINT RUN 100 SERIAL #'d SETS
*COMBO: .75X TO 2X BASIC
COMBO PRINT RUN 50 SERIAL #'d SETS
RANDOM INSERTS IN PACKS
1 Albert Pujols Jsy 6.00 15.00
2 Albert Pujols Pants 6.00 15.00
3 Alex Rodriguez Rgr Jsy 4.00 10.00
4 Alex Rodriguez Rgr Pants 4.00 10.00
5 Magglio Ordonez Jsy 3.00 8.00
6 Rafael Palmeiro Jsy 4.00 10.00
7 Troy Glaus Jsy 3.00 8.00
8 Troy Glaus Pants 3.00 8.00
9 Albert Pujols Hat 8.00 20.00
10 Alex Rodriguez Rgr Hat 6.00 15.00

2004 Studio Diamond Cuts Material Bat

RANDOM INSERTS IN PACKS
PRINT RUNS B/WN 100-200 COPIES PER
1 Derek Jeter/100 10.00 25.00
2 Greg Maddux/100 5.00 12.00
3 Nomar Garciaparra/200 4.00 10.00
4 Miguel Cabrera/200 3.00 8.00
5 Mark Mulder/200 2.00 5.00
6 Rafael Furcal/200 2.00 5.00
7 Mark Prior/200 3.00 8.00
8 Roy Oswalt/200 2.00 5.00
9 Dontrelle Willis/200 4.00 10.00
10 Jay Gibbons/200 2.00 5.00
11 Josh Beckett/200 2.00 5.00
12 Angel Berroa/200 2.00 5.00
13 Adam Dunn/200 2.00 5.00
14 Hank Blalock/200 2.00 5.00
15 Carlos Beltran/200 2.00 5.00
16 Shannon Stewart/200 2.00 5.00
17 Aubrey Huff/200 2.00 5.00
18 Jeff Bagwell/200 3.00 8.00
19 Trot Nixon/200 2.00 5.00
21 Tony Gwynn/200 5.00 12.00
22 Andre Dawson/200 3.00 8.00
23 Don Mattingly/200 6.00 15.00
24 Dale Murphy/200 4.00 10.00
25 Gary Carter/200 3.00 8.00

2004 Studio Diamond Cuts Material Jersey

PRINT RUNS B/WN 200-250 COPIES PER
PRIME PRINT RUN B/WN 5-10 COPIES PER
NO PRIME PRICING DUE TO SCARCITY
RANDOM INSERTS IN PACKS
1 Derek Jeter/250 8.00 20.00
2 Greg Maddux/250 4.00 10.00
3 Nomar Garciaparra/200 4.00 10.00
4 Miguel Cabrera/250 3.00 8.00
5 Mark Mulder/250 2.00 5.00
6 Rafael Furcal/250 2.00 5.00
7 Mark Prior/250 3.00 8.00
8 Roy Oswalt/250 2.00 5.00
9 Dontrelle Willis/250 3.00 8.00
10 Jay Gibbons/250 2.00 5.00
11 Josh Beckett/250 2.00 5.00
12 Angel Berroa/250 2.00 5.00
13 Adam Dunn/250 2.00 5.00
14 Hank Blalock/250 2.00 5.00
15 Carlos Beltran/250 2.00 5.00
16 Shannon Stewart/250 2.00 5.00
17 Aubrey Huff/250 2.00 5.00
18 Jeff Bagwell/250 3.00 8.00
19 Trot Nixon/250 2.00 5.00
20 Nolan Ryan Jacket/250 10.00 25.00
21 Tony Gwynn/250 6.00 15.00
22 Andre Dawson/250 3.00 8.00
23 Don Mattingly Jacket/250 6.00 15.00
24 Dale Murphy/250 4.00 10.00
25 Gary Carter/250 3.00 8.00

2004 Studio Diamond Cuts Combo Material

PRINT RUNS B/WN 25-50 COPIES PER
PRIME PRINT RUN 5 SERIAL #'d SETS
NO PRIME PRICING DUE TO SCARCITY
RANDOM INSERTS IN PACKS
1 Derek Jeter Bat-Jsy/50 20.00 50.00
2 Greg Maddux Bat-Jsy/50 12.50 30.00
3 N.Garciaparra Bat-Jsy/25
4 Miguel Cabrera Bat-Jsy/50 8.00 20.00
5 Mark Mulder Bat-Jsy/50 5.00 12.00
6 Rafael Furcal Bat-Jsy/50 5.00 12.00
7 Mark Prior Bat-Jsy/50 8.00 20.00
8 Roy Oswalt Bat-Jsy/50 5.00 12.00
9 Dontrelle Willis Bat-Jsy/25
10 Jay Gibbons Bat-Jsy/50 5.00 12.00
11 Josh Beckett Bat-Jsy/50 5.00 12.00
12 Angel Berroa Bat-Jsy/50 5.00 12.00
13 Adam Dunn Bat-Jsy/50 5.00 12.00
14 Hank Blalock Bat-Jsy/50 5.00 12.00
15 Carlos Beltran Bat-Jsy/50 5.00 12.00
16 Shannon Stewart Bat-Jsy/50 5.00 12.00
17 Aubrey Huff Bat-Jsy/50 5.00 12.00
18 Jeff Bagwell Bat-Jsy/50 8.00 20.00
19 Trot Nixon Bat-Jsy/50 5.00 12.00
20 Nolan Ryan Jacket-Jsy/50 15.00 40.00
21 Tony Gwynn Bat-Jsy/50 15.00 40.00
22 Andre Dawson Bat-Jsy/50 6.00 15.00
23 D.Mattingly Bat-Jacket/50 20.00 50.00
24 Dale Murphy Bat-Jsy/50 10.00 25.00
25 Gary Carter Bat-Jsy/50 6.00 15.00

2004 Studio Diamond Cuts Combo Material Signature

PRINT RUNS B/WN 1-5 COPIES PER
PRIME PRINT RUNS B/WN 1-5 COPIES PER
RANDOM INSERTS IN PACKS
NO PRICING DUE TO SCARCITY

2004 Studio Fans of the Game

RANDOM INSERTS IN PACKS
216 Regis Philbin 1.50 4.00
217 Denis Leary 1.25 3.00
218 Bode Miller .75 2.00
219 Steve Schirripa .75 2.00
220 Adam Mesh .75 2.00

2004 Studio Fans of the Game Autographs

RANDOM INSERTS IN PACKS
SP PRINT RUNS PROVIDED BY DONRUSS
SP'S ARE NOT SERIAL-NUMBERED
216 Regis Philbin 20.00 50.00
217 Denis Leary 20.00 50.00
218 Bode Miller SP/250 10.00 25.00
219 Steve Schirripa 6.00 15.00
220 Adam Mesh SP/300 10.00 25.00

2004 Studio Game Day Souvenirs

These cards were distributed by the MLB Player's Association and MLB Properties for a sepcial promotion. Donruss-Playoff printed the cards and provided them to the league's after packout and distribution for the standard 2004 Studio product. These promotional cards can be easily differentiated from the Number and Position Game Day memorabilia cards issued in '04 Studio packs by the home plate shaped cut out housing the jersey fabric coupled with the lack of any serial-numbering. Of note, representatives at D/P have confirmed that all 80 cards from this promotional set were issued in equal quantity.

*SOUV: .4X TO 1X NUMBER p/r 150-300
*SOUV: .25X TO .6X NUMBER p/r 75-100
*SOUV: .2X TO .5X NUMBER p/r 50
*SOUV: .12X TO .3X NUMBER p/r 25
DISTRIBUTED BY MLBPA AND PROPERTIES

2004 Studio Game Day Souvenirs Number

PRINT RUNS B/WN 25-300 COPIES PER
*POSITION: .4X TO 1X BASIC
POSITION PRINT B/WN 25-300 COPIES PER
RANDOM INSERTS IN PACKS
1 Garret Anderson Jsy/300 2.00 5.00
2 Troy Glaus Jsy/300 2.00 5.00
3 Vladimir Guerrero Jsy/300 3.00 8.00
4 Steve Finley Jsy/250 2.00 5.00
5 Luis Gonzalez Jsy/25 6.00 15.00
6 Richie Sexson Jsy/250 2.00 5.00
7 Andruw Jones Jsy/300 3.00 8.00
8 Chipper Jones Jsy/250 3.00 8.00
9 Rafael Furcal Jsy/250 2.00 5.00
13 Curt Schilling Jsy/300 3.00 8.00
14 Pedro Martinez Jsy/300 3.00 8.00
15 David Ortiz Jsy/300 3.00 8.00
16 Sammy Sosa Jsy/300 3.00 8.00
17 Corey Patterson Jsy/250 2.00 5.00
18 Moises Alou Jsy/300 2.00 5.00
19 Magglio Ordonez Jsy/250 2.00 5.00
20 Paul Konerko Jsy/300 2.00 5.00
21 Frank Thomas Jsy/300 3.00 8.00
22 Austin Kearns Jsy/50 4.00 10.00
23 Sean Casey Jsy/200 2.00 5.00
24 Adam Dunn Jsy/200 2.00 5.00
25 Omar Vizquel Jsy/250 3.00 8.00
26 C.C. Sabathia Jsy/300 2.00 5.00
27 Jody Gerut Jsy/250 2.00 5.00
28 Todd Helton Jsy/300 3.00 8.00
29 Vinny Castilla Jsy/300 2.00 5.00
30 Jeromy Burnitz Jsy/300 2.00 5.00
31 Fernando Vina Jsy/150 2.00 5.00
32 Ivan Rodriguez Jsy/300 3.00 8.00
33 Jeremy Bonderman Jsy/300 2.00 5.00
34 Mike Lowell Jsy/225 2.00 5.00
35 Luis Castillo Jsy/250 2.00 5.00
36 Miguel Cabrera Jsy/250 3.00 8.00
37 Roger Clemens Jsy/300 4.00 10.00
38 Andy Pettitte Jsy/300 3.00 8.00
39 Jeff Bagwell Jsy/300 3.00 8.00
40 Mike Sweeney Jsy/150 2.00 5.00
41 Carlos Beltran Jsy/200 2.00 5.00
42 Angel Berroa Jsy/100 3.00 8.00
43 Paul Lo Duca Jsy/75 3.00 8.00
44 Shawn Green Jsy/300 2.00 5.00
45 Adrian Beltre Jsy/150 2.00 5.00
46 Ben Sheets Jsy/300 2.00 5.00
47 Geoff Jenkins Jsy/250 2.00 5.00
48 Junior Spivey Jsy/300 2.00 5.00
49 Doug Mientkiewicz Jsy/100 3.00 8.00
50 Shannon Stewart Jsy/100 3.00 8.00
51 Torii Hunter Jsy/300 2.00 5.00
52 Livan Hernandez Jsy/300 2.00 5.00
53 Jose Vidro Jsy/200 2.00 5.00
54 Orlando Cabrera Jsy/300 2.00 5.00
55 Mike Piazza Jsy/250 3.00 8.00
56 Mike Cameron Jsy/250 2.00 5.00
57 Kazuo Matsui Jsy/200 3.00 8.00
58 Derek Jeter Jsy/50 10.00 25.00
59 Jason Giambi Jsy/50 4.00 10.00
61 Barry Zito Jsy/200 2.00 5.00
62 Eric Chavez Jsy/150 2.00 5.00
63 Eric Byrnes Jsy/150 2.00 5.00
65 Jim Thome Jsy/300 3.00 8.00
66 Jimmy Rollins Jsy/250 2.00 5.00
67 Jason Kendall Jsy/250 2.00 5.00
68 Craig Wilson Jsy/250 2.00 5.00
69 Jack Wilson Jsy/250 2.00 5.00
70 Ryan Klesko Jsy/300 2.00 5.00
71 Brian Giles Jsy/300 2.00 5.00
72 Sean Burroughs Jsy/300 2.00 5.00
73 A.J. Pierzynski Jsy/300 2.00 5.00
74 J.T. Snow Jsy/300 2.00 5.00
75 Michael Tucker Jsy/300 2.00 5.00
77 Edgar Martinez Jsy/50 6.00 15.00
79 Scott Rolen Jsy/300 3.00 8.00
80 Albert Pujols Jsy/300 6.00 15.00
81 Jim Edmonds Jsy/300 2.00 5.00
82 Aubrey Huff Jsy/100 3.00 8.00
83 Tino Martinez Jsy/100 5.00 12.00
84 Rocco Baldelli Jsy/100 2.00 5.00
85 Alfonso Soriano Jsy/200 2.00 5.00
86 Michael Young Jsy/250 2.00 5.00
87 Hank Blalock Jsy/200 2.00 5.00
88 Eric Hinske Jsy/200 2.00 5.00
89 Carlos Delgado Jsy/300 2.00 5.00
90 Vernon Wells Jsy/250 2.00 5.00

2004 Studio Game Day Souvenirs Signature Number

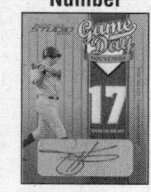

STATED PRINT RUN 5 SERIAL #'d SETS
POSITION PRINT RUN 5 SERIAL #'d SETS
RANDOM INSERTS IN PACKS
NO PRICING DUE TO SCARCITY

2004 Studio Heritage

STATED PRINT RUN 999 SERIAL #'d SETS
*DIE CUT: 1.25X TO 3X BASIC
DIE CUT PRINT RUN 100 SERIAL #'d SETS
*GOLD: .6X TO 1.5X BASIC
GOLD PRINT RUN 499 SERIAL #'d SETS
RANDOM INSERTS IN PACKS
1 George Brett 2.50 6.00
2 Nolan Ryan 3.00 8.00
3 Cal Ripken 4.00 10.00
4 Mike Schmidt 2.50 6.00
5 Roberto Clemente 3.00 8.00
6 Don Mattingly 2.50 6.00
7 Dale Murphy 1.50 4.00
8 Ryne Sandberg 2.50 6.00
9 Harmon Killebrew 1.50 4.00
10 Stan Musial 2.00 5.00

2004 Studio Heritage Material Bat

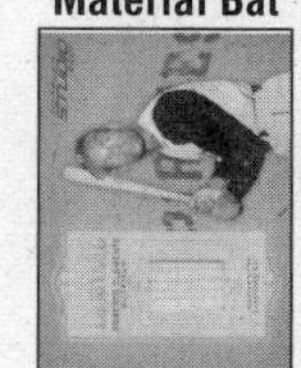

RANDOM INSERTS IN PACKS
STATED PRINT RUN 50 SERIAL #'d SETS
1 George Brett 10.00 25.00
3 Cal Ripken 30.00 60.00
4 Mike Schmidt 10.00 25.00
5 Roberto Clemente 50.00 100.00
6 Don Mattingly 10.00 25.00
7 Dale Murphy 8.00 20.00
8 Ryne Sandberg 15.00 40.00
9 Harmon Killebrew 8.00 20.00
10 Stan Musial 15.00 40.00

2004 Studio Heritage Material Jersey

PRINT RUNS B/WN 50-200 COPIES PER
PRIME PRINT RUN B/WN 3-10 COPIES PER
NO PRIME PRICING DUE TO SCARCITY
RANDOM INSERTS IN PACKS
1 George Brett/200 6.00 15.00
2 Nolan Ryan Jacket/200 10.00 25.00
3 Cal Ripken/200 15.00 40.00
4 Mike Schmidt Pants/200 6.00 15.00
5 Roberto Clemente/50 50.00 100.00
6 Don Mattingly Jacket/200 6.00 15.00
7 Dale Murphy/200 4.00 10.00
8 Ryne Sandberg/200 10.00 25.00
9 Harmon Killebrew Pants/200 6.00 15.00
10 Stan Musial/100 10.00 25.00

2004 Studio Heritage Material Signature Jersey

RANDOM INSERTS IN PACKS
STATED PRINT RUN 5 SERIAL #'d SETS
NO PRICING DUE TO SCARCITY

2004 Studio Heroes of the Hall

STATED PRINT RUN 999 SERIAL #'d SETS
*DIE CUT: .6X TO 1.5X BASIC
DIE CUT PRINT RUN 500 SERIAL #'d SETS
*GOLD: .6X TO 1.5X BASIC
GOLD PRINT RUN 499 SERIAL #'d SETS
RANDOM INSERTS IN PACKS
1 Fergie Jenkins 1.25 3.00
2 Gary Carter 1.25 3.00
3 Gaylord Perry 1.25 3.00
4 George Brett 3.00 8.00
5 Jim Palmer 1.25 3.00
6 Nolan Ryan 3.00 8.00
7 Paul Molitor 1.25 3.00
8 Rod Carew 1.50 4.00
9 Steve Carlton 1.25 3.00
10 Robin Yount 1.50 4.00

2004 Studio Heroes of the Hall Material Bat

RANDOM INSERTS IN PACKS
STATED PRINT RUN 100 SERIAL #'d SETS
2 Gary Carter 3.00 8.00
4 George Brett 10.00 25.00
7 Paul Molitor 3.00 8.00
8 Rod Carew 4.00 10.00
9 Steve Carlton 3.00 8.00
10 Robin Yount 4.00 10.00

2004 Studio Heroes of the Hall Material Jersey

STATED PRINT RUN 200 SERIAL #'d SETS
PRIME PRINT RUN 10 SERIAL #'d SETS
NO PRIME PRICING DUE TO SCARCITY
RANDOM INSERTS IN PACKS
1 Fergie Jenkins Pants/200 3.00 8.00
2 Gary Carter/200 3.00 8.00
3 Gaylord Perry/100 3.00 8.00
4 George Brett/200 6.00 15.00
5 Jim Palmer/200 3.00 8.00
6 Nolan Ryan/200 10.00 25.00
7 Paul Molitor/200 3.00 8.00
8 Rod Carew/200 4.00 10.00
9 Steve Carlton/200 3.00 8.00
10 Robin Yount/200 4.00 10.00

2004 Studio Heroes of the Hall Material Signature Jersey

RANDOM INSERTS IN PACKS
PRINT RUNS B/WN 1-10 COPIES PER
NO PRICING DUE TO SCARCITY

2004 Studio Masterstrokes Material Bat

RANDOM INSERTS IN PACKS
STATED PRINT RUN 200 SERIAL #'d SETS
1 Todd Helton 3.00 8.00
2 Jose Vidro .75 2.00
3 Edgar Renteria 2.00 5.00
4 Mike Lowell 2.00 5.00
5 Gary Sheffield 2.00 5.00
6 Albert Pujols 6.00 15.00
7 Javy Lopez 2.00 5.00
8 Carlos Delgado 2.00 5.00
9 Bret Boone 2.00 5.00
10 Alex Rodriguez Rgr 4.00 10.00
11 Vernon Wells 2.00 5.00
12 Manny Ramirez 3.00 8.00
13 Jorge Posada 3.00 8.00
14 Edgar Martinez 3.00 8.00
15 Bernie Williams 3.00 8.00
16 Magglio Ordonez 2.00 5.00
17 Garret Anderson 2.00 5.00
18 Eric Chavez 2.00 5.00
19 Alfonso Soriano 2.00 5.00
20 Jason Giambi 2.00 5.00
21 Jeff Kent 2.00 5.00
22 Scott Rolen 3.00 8.00
23 Vladimir Guerrero 3.00 8.00
24 Sammy Sosa 3.00 8.00
25 Mike Piazza 4.00 10.00

2004 Studio Masterstrokes Material Jersey

PRINT RUNS B/WN 150-250 COPIES PER
PRIME PRINT RUN 5 SERIAL #'d SETS
NO PRIME PRICING DUE TO SCARCITY
RANDOM INSERTS IN PACKS
1 Todd Helton/250 3.00 8.00
2 Jose Vidro/250 2.00 5.00
3 Edgar Renteria/250 2.00 5.00
4 Mike Lowell/250 2.00 5.00
5 Gary Sheffield/250 2.00 5.00
6 Albert Pujols/250 6.00 15.00
7 Javy Lopez/250 2.00 5.00
8 Carlos Delgado/250 2.00 5.00
9 Bret Boone/250 2.00 5.00
10 Alex Rodriguez Rgr/250 4.00 10.00
11 Vernon Wells/250 2.00 5.00
12 Manny Ramirez/250 3.00 8.00
13 Jorge Posada/250 3.00 8.00
14 Edgar Martinez/250 3.00 8.00
15 Bernie Williams/250 3.00 8.00
16 Magglio Ordonez/250 2.00 5.00
17 Garret Anderson/250 2.00 5.00
18 Eric Chavez/250 2.00 5.00
19 Alfonso Soriano/150 2.00 5.00
20 Jason Giambi/250 2.00 5.00
21 Jeff Kent/250 2.00 5.00
22 Scott Rolen/250 3.00 8.00
23 Vladimir Guerrero/250 3.00 8.00
24 Sammy Sosa/250 3.00 8.00
25 Mike Piazza/250 4.00 10.00

2004 Studio Masterstrokes Combo Material

STATED PRINT RUN 50 SERIAL #'d SETS
PRIME PRINT RUN 5 SERIAL #'d SETS
NO PRIME PRICING DUE TO SCARCITY
RANDOM INSERTS IN PACKS
1 Todd Helton Bat-Jsy/50 8.00 20.00
2 Jose Vidro Bat-Jsy/50 5.00 12.00
3 Edgar Renteria Bat-Jsy/50 5.00 12.00
4 Mike Lowell Bat-Jsy/50 5.00 12.00
5 Gary Sheffield Bat-Jsy/50 5.00 12.00
6 Albert Pujols Bat-Jsy/50 15.00 40.00
7 Javy Lopez Bat-Jsy/50 5.00 12.00
8 Carlos Delgado Bat-Jsy/50 5.00 12.00
9 Bret Boone Bat-Jsy/50 5.00 12.00
10 A.Rodriguez Rgr Bat-Jsy/50 10.00 25.00
11 Vernon Wells Bat-Jsy/50 5.00 12.00
12 Manny Ramirez Bat-Jsy/50 8.00 20.00
13 Jorge Posada Bat-Jsy/50 8.00 20.00
14 Edgar Martinez Bat-Jsy/50 8.00 20.00
15 Bernie Williams Bat-Jsy/50 8.00 20.00
16 Magglio Ordonez Bat-Jsy/50 5.00 12.00
17 Garret Anderson Bat-Jsy/50 5.00 12.00
18 Eric Chavez Bat-Jsy/50 5.00 12.00
19 Alfonso Soriano Bat-Jsy/50 5.00 12.00
20 Jason Giambi Bat-Jsy/50 5.00 12.00
21 Jeff Kent Bat-Jsy/50
22 Scott Rolen Bat-Jsy/50 8.00 20.00
23 Vladimir Guerrero Bat-Jsy/50 8.00 20.00
24 Sammy Sosa Bat-Jsy/50 8.00 20.00
25 Mike Piazza Bat-Jsy/50 12.50 30.00

2004 Studio Masterstrokes Combo Material Signature

PRINT RUNS B/WN 1-10 COPIES PER
PRIME PRINT RUNS B/WN 1-5 COPIES PER
RANDOM INSERTS IN PACKS
NO PRICING DUE TO SCARCITY

2004 Studio Players Collection Jersey

*STUDIO PC: .4X TO 1X PRESTIGE PC
STATED PRINT RUN 150 SERIAL #'d SETS
*STUDIO PC PLAT: .75X TO 2X PRESTIGE PC
PLATINUM PRINT RUN 50 SERIAL #'d SETS
RANDOM INSERTS IN PACKS

2004 Studio Rally Caps

STATED PRINT RUN 999 SERIAL #'d SETS
*DIE CUT: .6X TO 1.5X BASIC
DIE CUT PRINT RUN 500 SERIAL #'d SETS
*GOLD: .6X TO 1.5X BASIC
GOLD PRINT RUN 499 SERIAL #'d SETS
RANDOM INSERTS IN PACKS
1 Adam Dunn 1.25 3.00
2 Adrian Beltre 1.25 3.00
3 Albert Pujols 2.50 6.00
4 Alex Rodriguez 2.50 6.00
5 Andruw Jones 1.50 4.00
6 Angel Berroa 1.25 3.00
7 Aubrey Huff 1.25 3.00
8 Austin Kearns 1.25 3.00
9 Ben Sheets 1.25 3.00
10 Brad Penny 1.25 3.00
11 Carlos Beltran 1.25 3.00
12 Carlos Lee 1.25 3.00
13 Casey Fossum 1.25 3.00
14 Eric Hinske 1.25 3.00
15 Geoff Jenkins 1.25 3.00
16 Jack Wilson 1.25 3.00
17 Jason Jennings 1.25 3.00
18 Joe Kennedy 1.25 3.00
19 Lance Berkman 1.25 3.00
20 Magglio Ordonez 1.25 3.00
21 Kerry Wood 1.25 3.00
22 Mark Buehrle 1.25 3.00
23 Mark Prior 1.50 4.00
24 Mark Teixeira 1.50 4.00
25 Michael Cuddyer 1.25 3.00
26 Jeff Conine 1.25 3.00
27 Mike Mussina 1.50 4.00
28 Mike Piazza 2.00 5.00
29 Jose Reyes 1.25 3.00
30 Paul Lo Duca 1.25 3.00
31 Pedro Martinez 1.50 4.00
32 Roy Oswalt 1.25 3.00
33 Ryan Klesko 1.25 3.00
34 Sammy Sosa 1.50 4.00
35 Tim Hudson 1.25 3.00
36 Todd Helton 1.50 4.00
37 Torii Hunter 1.25 3.00
38 Vernon Wells 1.25 3.00
39 Craig Wilson 1.25 3.00
40 Edgar Renteria 1.25 3.00

2004 Studio Spirit of the Game

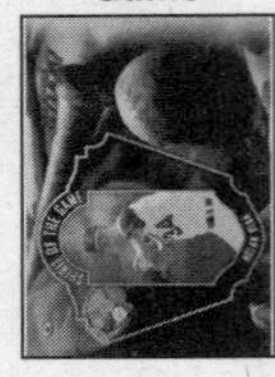

STATED PRINT RUN 999 SERIAL #'d SETS
*DIE CUT: .6X TO 1.5X BASIC
DIE CUT PRINT RUN 500 SERIAL #'d SETS
RANDOM INSERTS IN PACKS
1 Sammy Sosa 1.50 4.00
2 Alex Rodriguez Rgr 2.00 5.00
3 Nomar Garciaparra 2.00 5.00
4 Derek Jeter 2.50 6.00
5 Albert Pujols 2.50 6.00
6 Roger Clemens 2.50 6.00
7 Mark Prior 1.50 4.00
8 Randy Johnson 1.50 4.00
9 Pedro Martinez 1.50 4.00
10 Vladimir Guerrero 1.50 4.00
11 Todd Helton 1.50 4.00
12 Jeff Bagwell 1.50 4.00
13 Mike Mussina 1.50 4.00
14 Josh Beckett 1.25 3.00
15 Hideo Nomo 1.50 4.00
16 Mike Piazza 2.00 5.00
17 Don Mattingly 3.00 8.00
18 George Brett 3.00 8.00
19 Nolan Ryan 3.00 8.00
20 Cal Ripken 4.00 10.00

2004 Studio Spirit of the Game Material Bat

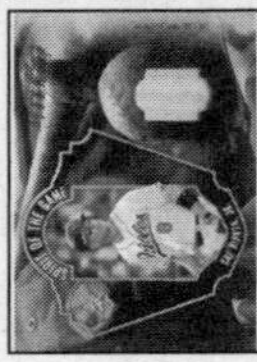

RANDOM INSERTS IN PACKS
PRINT RUNS B/WN 10-100 COPIES PER
NO PRICING ON QTY OF 10 OR LESS
1 Sammy Sosa/100 4.00 10.00
2 Alex Rodriguez Rgr/100 5.00 12.00
3 Nomar Garciaparra/100 5.00 12.00
4 Derek Jeter/100 10.00 25.00
5 Albert Pujols/100 8.00 20.00
6 Roger Clemens/50 10.00 25.00
7 Mark Prior/100 4.00 10.00
8 Randy Johnson/100 4.00 10.00
9 Pedro Martinez/100
10 Vladimir Guerrero/100 4.00 10.00
11 Todd Helton/100 4.00 10.00
12 Jeff Bagwell/100 4.00 10.00
13 Mike Mussina/50 4.00 10.00
14 Josh Beckett/100 3.00 8.00
15 Hideo Nomo/100 4.00 10.00
16 Mike Piazza/100 5.00 12.00
17 Don Mattingly/100 10.00 25.00
18 George Brett/100 10.00 25.00
19 Nolan Ryan/10
20 Cal Ripken/50 30.00 60.00

2004 Studio Spirit of the Game Material Jersey

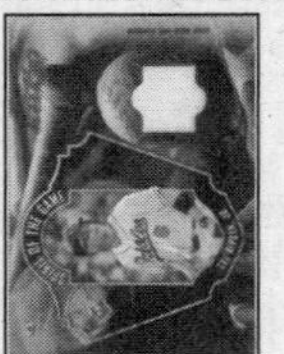

PRINT RUNS B/WN 100-200 COPIES PER
PRIME PRINT RUNS B/WN 1-5 COPIES PER
NO PRIME PRICING DUE TO SCARCITY
RANDOM INSERTS IN PACKS
1 Sammy Sosa/200 3.00 8.00
2 Alex Rodriguez Rgr/200 4.00 10.00
3 Nomar Garciaparra/100 5.00 12.00
4 Derek Jeter/200 8.00 20.00
5 Albert Pujols/100 8.00 20.00
7 Mark Prior/100 3.00 8.00
8 Randy Johnson/100 4.00 10.00
9 Pedro Martinez/200 3.00 8.00
11 Todd Helton/100 4.00 10.00
12 Jeff Bagwell/200 3.00 8.00
13 Mike Mussina/200 3.00 8.00
14 Josh Beckett/200 2.00 5.00
15 Hideo Nomo/200 3.00 8.00
16 Mike Piazza/200 4.00 10.00
17 Don Mattingly Jacket/200 6.00 15.00
18 George Brett/200 6.00 15.00
19 Nolan Ryan/100 15.00 40.00
20 Cal Ripken/100 20.00 50.00

2004 Studio Spirit of the Game Material Signature Jersey

RANDOM INSERTS IN PACKS
PRINT RUNS B/WN 1-5 COPIES PER
NO PRICING DUE TO SCARCITY

2004 Studio Stars

STATED ODDS 1:5
*GOLD: 1.25X TO 3X BASIC
*GOLD K.MATSUI: 1.25X TO 3X BASIC
GOLD PRINT RUN 100 SERIAL #'d SETS
*PLAT: 2.5X TO 6X BASIC
*PLAT K.MATSUI: 4X TO 10X BASIC
PLATINUM PRINT RUN 25 SERIAL #'d SETS
GOLD/PLATINUM RANDOM IN PACKS
1 Albert Pujols 2.00 5.00
2 Alex Rodriguez Yanks 1.50 4.00
3 Alfonso Soriano .60 1.50
4 Andy Pettitte 1.00 2.50
5 Angel Berroa .60 1.50
6 Aubrey Huff .60 1.50
7 Austin Kearns .60 1.50
8 Barry Zito .60 1.50
9 Brian Giles .60 1.50
10 Carlos Delgado .60 1.50
11 Chipper Jones 1.00 2.50
12 Craig Biggio 1.00 2.50
13 Curt Schilling 1.00 2.50
14 Derek Jeter 2.00 5.00
15 Edgar Martinez 1.00 2.50
16 Eric Gagne .60 1.50
17 Frank Thomas 1.00 2.50
18 Hank Blalock .60 1.50
19 Hideki Matsui 1.50 4.00
20 Hideo Nomo 1.00 2.50
21 Ichiro Suzuki 2.00 5.00
22 Ivan Rodriguez 1.00 2.50
23 Jason Kendall .60 1.50
24 Jason Schmidt .60 1.50
25 Jeff Bagwell 1.00 2.50
26 Jim Edmonds .60 1.50
27 Jim Thome 1.00 2.50
28 Josh Beckett .60 1.50
29 Kazuo Matsui 1.00 2.50
30 Ken Griffey Jr. 1.50 4.00
31 Larry Walker .60 1.50
32 Magglio Ordonez .60 1.50
33 Manny Ramirez 1.00 2.50
34 Mark Mulder .60 1.50
35 Mark Prior 1.00 2.50
36 Mark Teixeira 1.00 2.50
37 Miguel Tejada .60 1.50
38 Mike Mussina 1.00 2.50
39 Mike Piazza 1.50 4.00
40 Pedro Martinez 1.00 2.50
41 Randy Johnson 1.00 2.50
42 Roger Clemens 2.00 5.00
43 Roy Halladay .60 1.50
44 Russ Ortiz .60 1.50
45 Sammy Sosa 1.00 2.50
46 Scott Podsednik .60 1.50
47 Tim Hudson .60 1.50
48 Todd Helton 1.00 2.50
49 Vernon Wells .60 1.50
50 Vladimir Guerrero 1.00 2.50

2005 Studio

This 300-card set was released in June, 2005. The set was issued in six-card packs with an $4 SRP which came 24 packs in a box and 12 boxes in a case.

COMPLETE SET (300) 30.00 60.00
COMMON CARD (1-300) .15 .40
COMMON RC .15 .40
1 Casey Kotchman .15 .40
2 Chone Figgins .15 .40
3 Dallas McPherson .15 .40
4 Darin Erstad .15 .40
5 Ervin Santana .15 .40
6 Garret Anderson .15 .40
7 Norihiro Nakamura RC .50 1.25
8 John Lackey .15 .40
9 Orlando Cabrera .15 .40
10 Robb Quinlan .15 .40
11 Steve Finley .15 .40
12 Tim Salmon .25 .60
13 Vladimir Guerrero .40 1.00
14 Brandon Webb .15 .40
15 Craig Counsell .15 .40
16 Javier Vazquez .15 .40
17 Luis Gonzalez .15 .40
18 Tony Pena RC .15 .40
19 Russ Ortiz .15 .40
20 Scott Hairston .15 .40
21 Shawn Green .15 .40
22 Jose Cruz Jr. .15 .40
23 Troy Glaus .15 .40
24 Adam LaRoche .15 .40
25 Andruw Jones .25 .60
26 Chipper Jones .40 1.00
27 Danny Kolb .15 .40
28 John Smoltz .25 .60
29 Johnny Estrada .15 .40
30 Marcus Giles .15 .40
31 Nick Green .15 .40
32 Rafael Furcal .15 .40
33 Tim Hudson .15 .40
34 Brian Roberts .15 .40
35 Javy Lopez .15 .40
36 Jay Gibbons .15 .40
37 Melvin Mora .15 .40
38 Miguel Tejada .15 .40
39 Rafael Palmeiro .25 .60
40 Rodrigo Lopez .15 .40
41 Sidney Ponson .15 .40
42 Abe Alvarez .15 .40
43 Bill Mueller .15 .40
44 Curt Schilling .25 .60
45 David Ortiz .25 .60
46 David Wells .15 .40
47 Edgar Renteria .15 .40
48 Jason Varitek .40 1.00
49 Jay Payton .15 .40
50 Johnny Damon .25 .60
51 Juan Cedeno .15 .40
52 Manny Ramirez .25 .60
53 Matt Clement .15 .40
54 Trot Nixon .15 .40
55 Wade Miller .15 .40
56 Aramis Ramirez .15 .40
57 Carlos Zambrano .15 .40
58 Corey Patterson .15 .40
59 Derrek Lee .25 .60
60 Greg Maddux .60 1.50
61 Kerry Wood .15 .40
62 Mark Prior .25 .60
63 Nomar Garciaparra .40 1.00
64 Sammy Sosa .40 1.00
65 Todd Walker .15 .40
66 A.J. Pierzynski .15 .40
67 Aaron Rowand .15 .40
68 Frank Thomas .40 1.00
69 Freddy Garcia .15 .40
70 Jermaine Dye .15 .40
71 Mark Buehrle .15 .40
72 Paul Konerko .15 .40
73 Tadahito Iguchi RC .75 2.00
74 Pedro Lopez RC .15 .40
75 Scott Podsednik .15 .40
76 Shingo Takatsu .15 .40
77 Adam Dunn .15 .40
78 Austin Kearns .15 .40
79 Barry Larkin .25 .60
80 Bubba Nelson .15 .40
81 Danny Graves .15 .40
82 Eric Milton .15 .40
83 Ken Griffey Jr. .60 1.50
84 Ryan Wagner .15 .40
85 Sean Casey .15 .40
86 C.C. Sabathia .15 .40
87 Cliff Lee .15 .40
88 Fausto Carmona .15 .40
89 Grady Sizemore .25 .60
90 Jake Westbrook .15 .40
91 Jody Gerut .15 .40
92 Juan Gonzalez .15 .40
93 Kazuhito Tadano .15 .40
94 Travis Hafner .15 .40
95 Victor Martinez .15 .40
96 Charles Johnson .15 .40
97 Clint Barmes .15 .40
98 Cory Sullivan .15 .40
99 Jeff Baker .15 .40
100 Jeff Francis .15 .40
101 Jeff Salazar .15 .40
102 Jeromy Burnitz .15 .40
103 Joe Kennedy .15 .40
104 Matt Holliday .20 .50
105 Preston Wilson .15 .40
106 Todd Helton .25 .60
107 Ubaldo Jimenez RC .60 1.50
108 Brandon Inge .15 .40
109 Carlos Guillen .15 .40
110 Carlos Pena .15 .40
111 Craig Monroe .15 .40
112 Ivan Rodriguez .25 .60
113 Jeremy Bonderman .15 .40
114 Justin Verlander RC 1.50 4.00
115 Magglio Ordonez .15 .40
116 Troy Percival .15 .40
117 Vance Wilson .15 .40
118 A.J. Burnett .15 .40
119 Al Leiter .15 .40
120 Dontrelle Willis .15 .40
121 Josh Beckett .15 .40
122 Juan Pierre .15 .40
123 Miguel Cabrera .25 .60
124 Mike Lowell .15 .40
125 Paul Lo Duca .15 .40
126 Randy Messenger RC .15 .40
127 Yorman Bazardo RC .15 .40
128 Andy Pettitte .25 .60
129 Brad Lidge .15 .40
130 Chris Burke .15 .40
131 Craig Biggio .25 .60
132 Fernando Nieve .15 .40
133 Jason Lane .15 .40
134 Jeff Bagwell .25 .60
135 Lance Berkman .15 .40
136 Morgan Ensberg .15 .40
137 Roger Clemens .60 1.50
138 Roy Oswalt .15 .40
139 Ambiorix Burgos RC .15 .40
140 David DeJesus .15 .40
141 Jeremy Affeldt .15 .40
142 Jose Lima .15 .40
143 Ken Harvey .15 .40
144 Mike MacDougal .15 .40
145 Mike Sweeney .15 .40
146 Terrence Long .15 .40
147 Zack Greinke .15 .40
148 Brad Penny .15 .40
149 Derek Lowe .15 .40
150 Dioner Navarro .15 .40
151 Edwin Jackson .15 .40
152 Eric Gagne .15 .40
153 Hee Seop Choi .15 .40
154 Hideo Nomo .40 1.00
155 J.D. Drew .15 .40
156 Jeff Kent .15 .40
157 Jeff Weaver .15 .40
158 Milton Bradley .15 .40
159 Yhency Brazoban .15 .40
160 Ben Sheets .15 .40
161 Bill Hall .15 .40
162 Carlos Lee .15 .40
163 Gustavo Chacin .15 .40
164 Geoff Jenkins .15 .40
165 Jose Capellan .15 .40
166 Lyle Overbay .15 .40
167 Rickie Weeks .15 .40
168 Jacque Jones .15 .40
169 Joe Mauer .40 1.00
170 Joe Nathan .15 .40
171 Johan Santana .40 1.00
172 Justin Morneau .15 .40
173 Lew Ford .15 .40
174 Michael Cuddyer .15 .40
175 Shannon Stewart .15 .40
176 Torii Hunter .15 .40
177 Brad Radke .15 .40
178 Ambiorix Concepcion RC .15 .40
179 Carlos Beltran .15 .40
180 David Wright .60 1.50
181 Jose Reyes .15 .40
182 Kazuo Matsui .15 .40
183 Kris Benson .15 .40
184 Mike Piazza .40 1.00
185 Pedro Martinez .25 .60
186 Phil Humber RC .40 1.00
187 Tom Glavine .25 .60
188 Alex Rodriguez .60 1.50
189 Carl Pavano .15 .40
190 Derek Jeter .75 2.00
191 Yuniesky Betancourt RC .75 2.00
192 Hideki Matsui .60 1.50
193 Jorge Posada .25 .60
194 Kevin Brown .15 .40
195 Mariano Rivera .40 1.00
196 Mike Mussina .25 .60
197 Randy Johnson .40 1.00
198 Scott Proctor .15 .40
199 Tom Gordon .15 .40
200 Barry Zito .15 .40
201 Bobby Crosby .15 .40
202 Dan Haren .15 .40
203 Eric Chavez .15 .40
204 Keiichi Yabu RC .15 .40
205 Jason Kendall .15 .40
206 Joe Blanton .15 .40
207 Mark Kotsay .15 .40
208 Nick Swisher .15 .40
209 Octavio Dotel .15 .40
210 Rich Harden .15 .40
211 Billy Wagner .15 .40
212 Bobby Abreu .15 .40
213 Chase Utley .25 .60
214 Gavin Floyd .15 .40
215 Jim Thome .25 .60
216 Jimmy Rollins .15 .40
217 Jon Lieber UER .15 .40
Name misspelled in text in Back
218 Kenny Lofton .15 .40
219 Mike Lieberthal .15 .40
220 Pat Burrell .15 .40
221 Randy Wolf .15 .40
222 Craig Wilson .15 .40
223 Jack Wilson .15 .40
224 Jason Bay .15 .40
225 John Van Benschoten .15 .40
226 Jose Castillo .15 .40
227 Kip Wells .15 .40
228 Matt Lawton .15 .40
229 Akinori Otsuka .15 .40
230 Brian Giles .15 .40
231 Freddy Guzman .15 .40
232 Jake Peavy .15 .40
233 Khalil Greene .25 .60
234 Mark Loretta .15 .40
235 Sean Burroughs .15 .40
236 Trevor Hoffman .15 .40
237 Woody Williams .15 .40
238 Armando Benitez .15 .40
239 Edgardo Alfonzo .15 .40
240 Erick Threets RC .15 .40
241 Jason Schmidt .15 .40
242 Marquis Grissom .15 .40
243 Merkin Valdez .15 .40
244 Michael Tucker .15 .40
245 Moises Alou .15 .40
246 Omar Vizquel .25 .60
247 Adrian Beltre .15 .40
248 Bret Boone .15 .40
249 Bucky Jacobsen .15 .40
250 Clint Nageotte .15 .40
251 Ichiro Suzuki .75 2.00
252 J.J. Putz .15 .40
253 Jeremy Reed .15 .40
254 Miguel Olivo .15 .40
255 Mike Morse RC .30 .75
256 Richie Sexson .15 .40
257 Wladimir Balentien RC .40 1.00
258 Albert Pujols .75 2.00
259 Jason Isringhausen .15 .40
260 Jeff Suppan .15 .40
261 Jim Edmonds .15 .40
262 Larry Walker .25 .60
263 Mark Mulder .15 .40
264 Rick Ankiel .15 .40
265 Scott Rolen .25 .60
266 Yadier Molina .15 .40
267 Aubrey Huff .15 .40
268 B.J. Upton .15 .40
269 Carl Crawford .15 .40
270 Chris Seddon RC .15 .40
271 Delmon Young .25 .60
272 Dewon Brazelton .15 .40
273 Jeff Niemann RC .40 1.00
274 Rocco Baldelli .15 .40
275 Scott Kazmir .15 .40
276 Adrian Gonzalez .15 .40
277 Alfonso Soriano .15 .40
278 Francisco Cordero .15 .40
279 Hank Blalock .15 .40
280 Kameron Loe .15 .40
281 Kenny Rogers .15 .40
282 Laynce Nix .15 .40
283 Mark Teixeira .25 .60
284 Michael Young .15 .40
285 Corey Koskie .15 .40
286 Dave Bush .15 .40
287 Frank Catalanotto .15 .40
288 Gabe Gross .15 .40
289 Raul Tablado RC .15 .40
290 Roy Halladay .15 .40
291 Shea Hillenbrand .15 .40
292 Vernon Wells .15 .40
293 Chad Cordero .15 .40
294 Cristian Guzman .15 .40
295 Jose Guillen .15 .40
296 Jose Vidro .15 .40
297 Josh Karp .15 .40
298 Livan Hernandez .15 .40
299 Nick Johnson .15 .40
300 Vinny Castilla .15 .40

2005 Studio Proofs Gold

*GOLD: 6X TO 15X BASIC
OVERALL INSERT ODDS 1:1 HOBBY
STATED PRINT RUN 25 SERIAL #'d SETS
NO RC YR PRICING DUE TO SCARCITY

2005 Studio Proofs Platinum

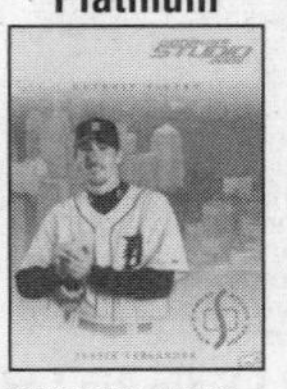

OVERALL INSERT ODDS 1:1 HOBBY
STATED PRINT RUN 10 SERIAL #'d SETS
NO PRICING DUE TO SCARCITY

2005 Studio Proofs Silver

*SILVER: 2.5X TO 6X BASIC
*SILVER: 2X TO 5X BASIC RC's
OVERALL INSERT ODDS 1:1 HOBBY
STATED PRINT RUN 100 SERIAL #'d SETS

2005 Studio Autographs

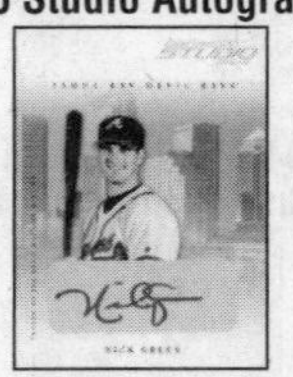

OVERALL AU-GU ODDS 1:8 HOBBY
NO SP PRICING DUE TO SCARCITY
CARDS LACK PRIVATE SIGNINGS LOGO
1 Casey Kotchman 4.00 10.00
3 Dallas McPherson 4.00 10.00
5 Ervin Santana 4.00 10.00
8 John Lackey 4.00 10.00
18 Tony Pena 4.00 10.00
31 Nick Green 4.00 10.00
51 Juan Cedeno 4.00 10.00
80 Bubba Nelson 4.00 10.00
88 Fausto Carmona 6.00 15.00
93 Kazuhito Tadano 6.00 15.00
101 Jeff Salazar 4.00 10.00
103 Joe Kennedy 4.00 10.00
108 Brandon Inge 4.00 10.00
111 Craig Monroe 4.00 10.00
113 Jeremy Bonderman 6.00 15.00
117 Vance Wilson 4.00 10.00
126 Randy Messenger 4.00 10.00
127 Yorman Bazardo 4.00 10.00
150 Dioner Navarro 4.00 10.00
159 Yhency Brazoban 4.00 10.00
161 Bill Hall 4.00 10.00
170 Joe Nathan 6.00 15.00
178 Ambiorix Concepcion 4.00 10.00
191 Yuniesky Betancourt 15.00 30.00
198 Scott Proctor 4.00 10.00
223 Jack Wilson 6.00 15.00
226 Jose Castillo 4.00 10.00
231 Freddy Guzman 4.00 10.00

240 Erick Threets SP
250 Clint Nageotte 4.00 10.00
252 J.J. Putz 4.00 10.00
254 Miguel Olivo SP
257 Wladimir Balentien 6.00 15.00
260 Jeff Suppan 6.00 15.00
266 Yadier Molina SP
276 Adrian Gonzalez 4.00 10.00
280 Kameron Loe 4.00 10.00
282 Laynce Nix 4.00 10.00
293 Chad Cordero SP
297 Josh Karp 4.00 10.00

2005 Studio Private Signings Gold

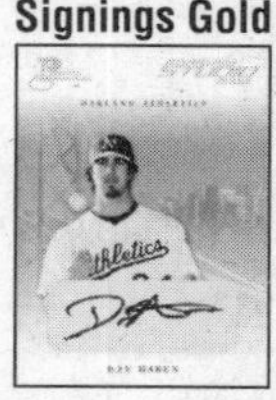

*GOLD: .5X TO 1.2X SILVER
*GOLD RC YR: .5X TO 1.2X SILVER RC YR
OVERALL AU-GU ODDS 1:8 HOBBY
STATED PRINT RUN 50 SERIAL #'d SETS
6 Garret Anderson 8.00 20.00
10 Robb Quinlan 5.00 12.00
11 Steve Finley 8.00 20.00
14 Brandon Webb 5.00 12.00
29 Johnny Estrada 5.00 12.00
32 Rafael Furcal 8.00 20.00
40 Rodrigo Lopez 5.00 12.00
47 Edgar Renteria 8.00 20.00
53 Matt Clement 8.00 20.00
54 Trot Nixon 8.00 20.00
59 Derrek Lee 20.00 50.00
71 Mark Buehrle 12.50 30.00
72 Paul Konerko 12.50 30.00
76 Shingo Takatsu 8.00 20.00
78 Austin Kearns 5.00 12.00
93 Kazuhito Tadano 8.00 20.00
116 Troy Percival 8.00 20.00
123 Miguel Cabrera 12.50 30.00
148 Brad Penny 5.00 12.00
168 Jacque Jones 8.00 20.00
175 Shannon Stewart 8.00 20.00
199 Tom Gordon 5.00 12.00
229 Akinori Otsuka 8.00 20.00
235 Sean Burroughs 5.00 12.00
243 Merkin Valdez 5.00 12.00
246 Omar Vizquel 12.50 30.00
249 Bucky Jacobsen 5.00 12.00
254 Miguel Olivo 5.00 12.00
266 Yadier Molina 5.00 12.00
267 Aubrey Huff 8.00 20.00
268 B.J. Upton 8.00 20.00
269 Carl Crawford 8.00 20.00
271 Delmon Young 12.50 30.00
272 Dewon Brazelton 5.00 12.00
284 Michael Young 8.00 20.00
299 Nick Johnson 8.00 20.00

2005 Studio Private Signings Platinum

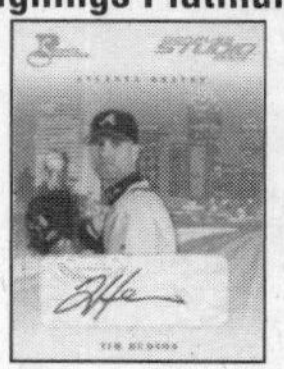

OVERALL AU-GU ODDS 1:8 HOBBY
STATED PRINT RUN 10 SERIAL #'d SETS
NO PRICING DUE TO SCARCITY

2005 Studio Private Signings Silver

OVERALL AU-GU ODDS 1:8 HOBBY
STATED PRINT RUN 100 SERIAL #'d SETS
1 Casey Kotchman 6.00 15.00
2 Chone Figgins 4.00 10.00
5 Ervin Santana 4.00 10.00
9 Orlando Cabrera 6.00 15.00
12 Tim Salmon 10.00 25.00
18 Tony Pena 4.00 10.00
19 Russ Ortiz 4.00 10.00
24 Adam LaRoche 4.00 10.00
27 Danny Kolb 4.00 10.00
31 Nick Green 4.00 10.00
34 Brian Roberts 6.00 15.00
36 Jay Gibbons 4.00 10.00
49 Jay Payton 4.00 10.00
51 Juan Cedeno 4.00 10.00
55 Wade Miller 4.00 10.00
57 Carlos Zambrano 10.00 25.00
65 Todd Walker 6.00 15.00
70 Jermaine Dye 6.00 15.00
80 Bubba Nelson 4.00 10.00
81 Danny Graves 4.00 10.00
84 Ryan Wagner 4.00 10.00
87 Cliff Lee 4.00 10.00
88 Fausto Carmona 10.00 25.00
91 Jody Gerut 4.00 10.00
94 Travis Hafner 6.00 15.00
98 Cory Sullivan 4.00 10.00
101 Jeff Salazar 4.00 10.00
103 Joe Kennedy 4.00 10.00
108 Brandon Inge 6.00 15.00
111 Craig Monroe 4.00 10.00
113 Jeremy Bonderman 6.00 15.00
117 Vance Wilson 4.00 10.00
127 Yorman Bazardo 4.00 10.00
133 Jason Lane 6.00 15.00
136 Morgan Ensberg 6.00 15.00
141 Jeremy Affeldt 4.00 10.00
143 Ken Harvey 4.00 10.00
150 Dioner Navarro 6.00 15.00
151 Edwin Jackson 4.00 10.00
158 Milton Bradley 6.00 15.00
159 Yhency Brazoban 4.00 10.00
161 Bill Hall 4.00 10.00
162 Carlos Lee 6.00 15.00
166 Lyle Overbay 4.00 10.00
170 Joe Nathan 6.00 15.00
173 Lew Ford 4.00 10.00
191 Yuniesky Betancourt 20.00 40.00
198 Scott Proctor 4.00 10.00
201 Bobby Crosby 6.00 15.00
202 Dan Haren 4.00 10.00
209 Octavio Dotel 4.00 10.00
210 Rich Harden 6.00 15.00
219 Mike Lieberthal 6.00 15.00
221 Randy Wolf 4.00 10.00
222 Craig Wilson 4.00 10.00
223 Jack Wilson 6.00 15.00
224 Jason Bay 6.00 15.00
226 Jose Castillo 4.00 10.00
231 Freddy Guzman 4.00 10.00
232 Jake Peavy 10.00 25.00
234 Mark Loretta 4.00 10.00
250 Clint Nageotte 4.00 10.00
252 J.J. Putz 4.00 10.00
260 Jeff Suppan 6.00 15.00
276 Adrian Gonzalez 4.00 10.00
278 Francisco Cordero 6.00 15.00
280 Kameron Loe 4.00 10.00
282 Laynce Nix 4.00 10.00
291 Shea Hillenbrand 4.00 10.00
293 Chad Cordero 6.00 15.00
295 Jose Guillen 6.00 15.00
297 Josh Karp 4.00 10.00
298 Livan Hernandez 10.00 25.00

2005 Studio Diamond Cuts

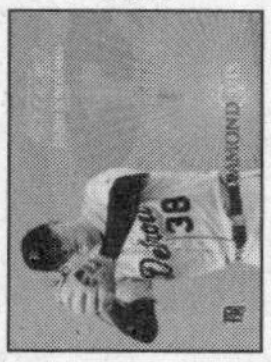

STATED PRINT RUN 1250 SERIAL #'d SETS
*DIE CUT: .6X TO 1.5X BASIC
DIE CUT PRINT RUN 250 #'d SETS
*DC GOLD: 1X TO 2.5X BASIC
DC GOLD PRINT RUN 75 #'d SETS
OVERALL INSERT ODDS 1:1 HOBBY
1 Roger Clemens 2.00 5.00
2 Manny Ramirez 1.25 3.00
3 Francisco Rodriguez .75 2.00
4 Brian Roberts .75 2.00
5 Javy Lopez .75 2.00
6 Vernon Wells .75 2.00
7 Johan Santana 1.25 3.00
8 Torii Hunter .75 2.00
9 Mike Mussina 1.25 3.00
10 Sammy Sosa 1.25 3.00
11 Ryan Wagner .75 2.00
12 Jack Wilson .75 2.00
13 Ichiro Suzuki 2.50 6.00
14 Greg Maddux 2.00 5.00
15 Albert Pujols 2.50 6.00
16 Jeremy Bonderman .75 2.00
17 Johnny Estrada .75 2.00
18 Mark Buehrle .75 2.00
19 Jorge Posada 1.25 3.00
20 Carl Crawford .75 2.00
21 Paul Konerko .75 2.00
22 Victor Martinez .75 2.00
23 Jose Vidro .75 2.00
24 Jim Thome 1.25 3.00
25 Andruw Jones 1.25 3.00

2005 Studio Diamond Cuts Bat

*BAT p/r 200-300: .4X TO 1X JSY p/r 175-250
*BAT p/r 200-300: .15X TO .4X JSY p/r 15
*BAT p/r 50: .6X TO 1.5X JSY p/r 175-250
*BAT p/r 50: .5X TO 1.2X JSY p/r 125
*BAT p/r 25: .75X TO 2X JSY p/r 175-250
OVERALL AU-GU ODDS 1:8 HOBBY
PRINT RUNS B/WN 5-300 COPIES PER
NO PRICING ON QTY OF 10 OR LESS

2005 Studio Diamond Cuts Jersey

PRINT RUNS B/WN 15-250 COPIES PER
PRIME PRINT RUNS B/WN 5-10 COPIES PER
NO PRIME PRICING DUE TO SCARCITY
OVERALL AU-GU ODDS 1:8 HOBBY
1 Roger Clemens/125 5.00 12.00
2 Manny Ramirez/250 2.50 6.00
3 Francisco Rodriguez/250 2.00 5.00
4 Brian Roberts/250 2.00 5.00
5 Javy Lopez/250 2.00 5.00
6 Vernon Wells/250 2.00 5.00
7 Johan Santana/175 3.00 8.00
8 Torii Hunter/250 2.00 5.00
9 Mike Mussina/250 2.50 6.00
10 Sammy Sosa/250 3.00 8.00
11 Ryan Wagner/250 2.00 5.00
12 Jack Wilson/15 5.00 12.00
14 Greg Maddux/250 4.00 10.00
15 Albert Pujols/250 6.00 15.00
16 Jeremy Bonderman/250 2.00 5.00
17 Johnny Estrada/250 2.00 5.00
18 Mark Buehrle/250 2.00 5.00
19 Jorge Posada/250 2.50 6.00
20 Carl Crawford/250 2.00 5.00
21 Paul Konerko/250 2.00 5.00
22 Victor Martinez/250 2.00 5.00
23 Jose Vidro/175 2.00 5.00
24 Jim Thome/250 2.50 6.00
25 Andruw Jones/250 2.50 6.00

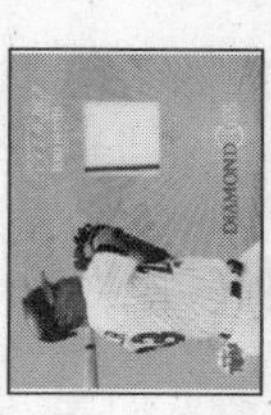

2005 Studio Diamond Cuts Combo

*COMBO p/r 50: .75X TO 2X JSY p/r 175-250
*COMBO p/r 50: .6X TO 1.5X JSY p/r 125
*COMBO p/r 50: .3X TO .8X JSY p/r 15
PRINT RUNS B/WN 5-50 COPIES PER
PRIME PRINT RUN 10 SERIAL #'d SETS
NO PRIME PRICING DUE TO SCARCITY
OVERALL AU-GU ODDS 1:8 HOBBY

2005 Studio Diamond Cuts Signature Combo

PRINT RUNS B/WN 25-50 COPIES PER
PRIME PRINT 10 SERIAL #'d SETS
NO PRIME PRICING DUE TO SCARCITY
OVERALL AU-GU ODDS 1:8 HOBBY
3 F.Rodriguez Jsy-Jsy/25 20.00 50.00
6 Vernon Wells Jsy-Jsy/25 12.50 30.00
8 Torii Hunter Bat-Jsy/50 10.00 25.00
11 Ryan Wagner Jsy-Jsy/50 6.00 15.00
12 Jack Wilson Bat-Jsy/50 10.00 25.00
16 J.Bonderman Jsy-Jsy/50 10.00 25.00
17 J.Estrada Fld Glv-Jsy/50 6.00 15.00
21 Paul Konerko Jsy-Jsy/25 20.00 50.00

2005 Studio Heritage

STATED PRINT RUN 1000 SERIAL #'d SETS
*DIE CUT: .6X TO 1.5X BASIC
DIE CUT PRINT RUN 200 #'d SETS
*DC GOLD: 1.25X TO 3X BASIC
DC GOLD PRINT RUN 50 #'d SETS
OVERALL INSERT ODDS 1:1 HOBBY
1 Rickey Henderson 1.50 4.00
2 Jeff Bagwell 1.25 3.00
3 Steve Garvey 1.00 2.50
4 Albert Pujols 2.50 6.00
5 Don Mattingly 3.00 8.00
6 Frank Thomas 1.25 3.00
7 Tony Gwynn 2.00 5.00
8 Gary Sheffield .75 2.00
9 Dale Murphy 1.50 4.00
10 Kerry Wood .75 2.00
11 Cal Ripken 5.00 12.00
12 Miguel Cabrera 1.25 3.00
13 Dwight Gooden 1.00 2.50
14 Barry Zito .75 2.00
15 Darryl Strawberry 1.00 2.50

2005 Studio Heritage Bat

*BAT: .4X TO 1X JSY p/r 250
*BAT: .25X TO .6X JSY p/r 50
OVERALL AU-GU ODDS 1:8 HOBBY
STATED PRINT RUN 150 SERIAL #'d SETS
8 Gary Sheffield 2.00 5.00

2005 Studio Heritage Jersey

PRINT RUNS B/WN 50-250 COPIES PER
PRIME PRINT RUN 10 SERIAL #'d SETS
NO PRIME PRICING DUE TO SCARCITY
OVERALL AU-GU ODDS 1:8 HOBBY
1 Rickey Henderson/250 4.00 10.00
2 Jeff Bagwell/250 2.50 6.00
3 Steve Garvey/250 2.50 6.00
4 Albert Pujols/250 6.00 15.00
5 Don Mattingly/250 5.00 12.00
6 Frank Thomas/250 3.00 8.00
7 Tony Gwynn/250 4.00 10.00
9 Dale Murphy/250 3.00 8.00
10 Kerry Wood/250 2.00 5.00
11 Cal Ripken/250 10.00 25.00
12 Miguel Cabrera/50 4.00 10.00
13 Dwight Gooden/250 2.50 6.00
14 Barry Zito/250 2.00 5.00
15 Darryl Strawberry/250 2.50 6.00

2005 Studio Heritage Combo

*COMBO p/r 50: .75X TO 2X JSY p/r 250
*COMBO p/r 50: .5X TO 1.2X JSY p/r 50
*COMBO p/r 25: 1X TO 2.5X JSY p/r 250
PRINT RUNS B/WN 10-50 COPIES PER
NO PRICING ON QTY OF 10
PRIME PRINT RUN 10 SERIAL #'d SETS
NO PRIME PRICING DUE TO SCARCITY
OVERALL AU-GU ODDS 1:8 HOBBY
8 Gary Sheffield Bat-Jsy/50 4.00 10.00

2005 Studio Heritage Signature Combo

PRINT RUNS B/WN 10-50 COPIES PER
NO PRICING ON QTY OF 10
PRIME PRINT RUNS B/WN 5-10 COPIES PER
NO PRIME PRICING DUE TO SCARCITY
OVERALL AU-GU ODDS 1:8 HOBBY
3 Steve Garvey Bat-Jsy/50 10.00 25.00
5 Don Mattingly Bat-Jsy/25 40.00 80.00
6 Frank Thomas Bat-Jsy/10
7 Tony Gwynn Bat-Jsy/15 50.00 100.00
9 Dale Murphy Bat-Jsy/25 20.00 50.00
11 Cal Ripken Bat-Jsy/25 100.00 175.00
12 Miguel Cabrera Bat-Jsy/25 20.00 50.00
13 Dwight Gooden Bat-Jsy/25 12.50 30.00
15 D.Strawberry Bat-Jsy/25 12.50 30.00

2005 Studio Heroes of the Hall

STATED PRINT RUN 350 SERIAL #'d SETS
*DIE CUT: .6X TO 1.5X BASIC
DIE CUT PRINT RUN 75 #'d SETS
*DC GOLD: 1.25X TO 3X BASIC
DC GOLD PRINT RUN 25 #'d SETS
OVERALL INSERT ODDS 1:1 HOBBY
1 Luis Aparicio 1.25 3.00
2 Dennis Eckersley 1.25 3.00
3 Brooks Robinson 2.00 5.00
4 Carlton Fisk 2.00 5.00
5 Tom Seaver 2.00 5.00
6 Paul Molitor 1.25 3.00
7 Rod Carew 2.00 5.00
8 George Brett 5.00 12.00
9 Nolan Ryan 6.00 15.00
10 Mike Schmidt 5.00 12.00
11 Willie Mays 5.00 12.00
12 Gary Carter 1.25 3.00
13 Lou Brock 2.00 5.00
14 Steve Carlton 1.25 3.00
15 Harmon Killebrew 2.00 5.00

2005 Studio Heroes of the Hall Bat

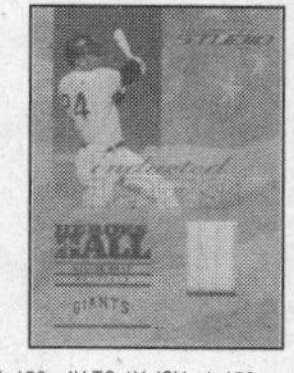

*BAT p/r 150: .4X TO 1X JSY p/r 150
*BAT p/r 150: .25X TO .6X JSY p/r 50
*BAT p/r 100-125: .5X TO 1.2X JSY p/r 150
*BAT p/r 100-125: .4X TO 1X JSY p/r 100
*BAT p/r 100-125: .3X TO .8X JSY p/r 50
OVERALL AU-GU ODDS 1:8 HOBBY
PRINT RUNS B/WN 100-150 COPIES PER
13 Lou Brock/150 3.00 8.00

2005 Studio Heroes of the Hall Jersey

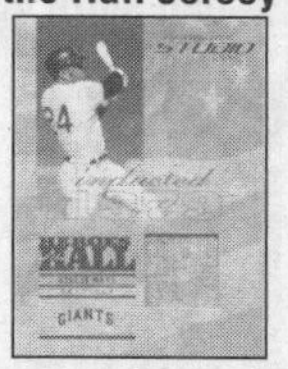

PRINT RUNS B/WN 50-150 COPIES PER
PRIME PRINT RUNS B/WN 5-10 COPIES PER
NO PRIME PRICING DUE TO SCARCITY
OVERALL AU-GU ODDS 1:8 HOBBY
1 Luis Aparicio/150 2.50 6.00
2 Dennis Eckersley/150 2.50 6.00
3 Brooks Robinson/50 5.00 12.00
4 Carlton Fisk/150 3.00 8.00
5 Tom Seaver/150 3.00 8.00
6 Paul Molitor/150 2.50 6.00
7 Rod Carew/150 3.00 8.00
8 George Brett/150 5.00 12.00
9 Nolan Ryan/100 8.00 20.00
10 Mike Schmidt/100 6.00 15.00
11 Willie Mays/50 20.00 50.00
12 Gary Carter/150 2.50 6.00
14 Steve Carlton/150 2.50 6.00
15 Harmon Killebrew/150 4.00 10.00

2005 Studio Heroes of the Hall Combo

*COMBO p/r 50: .75X TO 2X JSY p/r 150
*COMBO p/r 50: .6X TO 1.5X JSY p/r 100
*COMBO p/r 25: .6X TO 1.5X JSY p/r 50
PRINT RUNS B/WN 25-50 COPIES PER
PRIME PRINT RUNS B/WN 5-10 COPIES PER
NO PRIME PRICING DUE TO SCARCITY
OVERALL AU-GU ODDS 1:8 HOBBY
13 Lou Brock Bat-Jkt/50 6.00 15.00

2005 Studio Heroes of the Hall Signature Combo

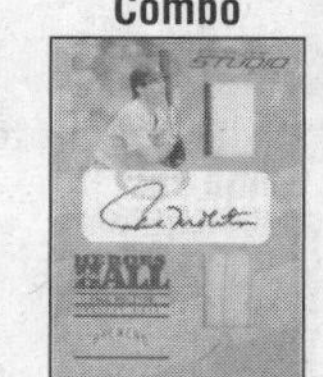

PRINT RUNS B/WN 5-50 COPIES PER
NO PRICING ON QTY OF 10 OR LESS
PRIME PRINT RUNS B/WN 5-10 COPIES PER
NO PRIME PRICING DUE TO SCARCITY
OVERALL AU-GU ODDS 1:8 HOBBY
1 Luis Aparicio Bat-Jsy/50 10.00 25.00
2 D.Eckersley Jsy-Pants/25 12.50 30.00
3 B.Robinson Bat-Jsy/10
4 Carlton Fisk Bat-Jsy/25 20.00 50.00
5 Tom Seaver Jsy-Pants/15 40.00 80.00
6 Paul Molitor Bat-Jsy/25 12.50 30.00
11 Willie Mays Bat-Jsy/5
12 Gary Carter Jsy-Pants/15 15.00 40.00
14 Steve Carlton Bat-Jsy/25 12.50 30.00
15 H.Killebrew Bat-Jsy/25 30.00 60.00

2005 Studio Masterstrokes

STATED PRINT RUN 750 SERIAL #'d SETS
*DIE CUT: .6X TO 1.5X BASIC
DIE CUT PRINT RUN 150 #'d SETS
*DC GOLD: 1X TO 2.5X BASIC
DC GOLD PRINT RUN 50 #'d SETS
OVERALL INSERT ODDS 1:1 HOBBY
1 Hideki Matsui 2.50 6.00
2 David Ortiz 1.50 4.00
3 Aramis Ramirez 1.00 2.50
4 Lance Berkman 1.00 2.50
5 Ichiro Suzuki 3.00 8.00
6 Mike Piazza 1.50 4.00
7 Ivan Rodriguez 1.50 4.00
8 Hideo Nomo 1.50 4.00
9 Jeff Bagwell 1.50 4.00
10 Travis Hafner 1.00 2.50
11 Casey Kotchman 1.00 2.50
12 Jim Edmonds 1.00 2.50
13 Michael Young 1.00 2.50
14 Lyle Overbay 1.00 2.50
15 Eric Chavez 1.00 2.50
16 Jason Bay 1.00 2.50
17 Hank Blalock 1.00 2.50
18 Frank Thomas 1.50 4.00
19 Craig Biggio 1.50 4.00
20 Miguel Cabrera 1.50 4.00
21 Vladimir Guerrero 1.50 4.00
22 Sammy Sosa 1.50 4.00
23 Chipper Jones 1.50 4.00
24 Rafael Palmeiro 1.50 4.00
25 Adam Dunn 1.00 2.50

2005 Studio Masterstrokes Bat

*BAT p/r 200-250: .4X TO 1X JSY p/r 150-250
*BAT p/r 200-250: .25X TO .6X JSY p/r 40-50
*BAT p/r 100: .5X TO 1.2X JSY p/r 150-250
*BAT p/r 50: .6X TO 1.5X JSY p/r 150-250
*BAT p/r 25: .75X TO 2X JSY p/r 150-250
OVERALL AU-GU ODDS 1:8 HOBBY
PRINT RUNS B/WN 25-250 COPIES PER

2005 Studio Masterstrokes Jersey

PRINT RUNS B/WN 40-250 COPIES PER
PRIME PRINT RUN 10 SERIAL #'d SETS
NO PRIME PRICING DUE TO SCARCITY
OVERALL AU-GU ODDS 1:8 HOBBY
1 Hideki Matsui/250 10.00 25.00
2 David Ortiz/250 2.50 6.00
3 Aramis Ramirez/250 2.00 5.00
4 Lance Berkman/250 2.00 5.00
6 Mike Piazza/250 3.00 8.00
7 Ivan Rodriguez/250 2.50 6.00
8 Hideo Nomo/250 3.00 8.00
9 Jeff Bagwell/250 2.50 6.00
10 Travis Hafner/200 2.00 5.00
11 Casey Kotchman/250 2.00 5.00
12 Jim Edmonds/250 2.00 5.00
13 Michael Young/150 2.00 5.00
14 Lyle Overbay/250 2.00 5.00
15 Eric Chavez/250 2.00 5.00
16 Jason Bay/150 2.00 5.00
17 Hank Blalock/250 2.00 5.00
18 Frank Thomas/250 3.00 8.00
19 Craig Biggio/250 2.50 6.00
20 Miguel Cabrera/250 2.50 6.00
21 Vladimir Guerrero/50 5.00 12.00
22 Sammy Sosa/250 3.00 8.00
23 Chipper Jones/225 3.00 8.00
24 Rafael Palmeiro/40 4.00 10.00
25 Adam Dunn/250 2.00 5.00

2005 Studio Masterstrokes Combo

*COMBO p/r 50: .75X TO 2X JSY p/r 150-250
*COMBO p/r 50: .5X TO 1.2X JSY p/r 40-50
*COMBO p/r 15: 1.25X TO 3X JSY p/r 150-250
PRINT RUNS B/WN 15-50 COPIES PER

PRIME PRINT RUN 10 SERIAL #'d SETS
NO PRIME PRICING DUE TO SCARCITY
OVERALL AU-GU ODDS 1:8 HOBBY

2005 Studio Masterstrokes Signature Combo

PRINT RUNS B/WN 5-50 COPIES PER
NO PRICING ON QTY OF 10 OR LESS
PRIME PRINT RUNS B/WN 5-10 COPIES PER
NO PRIME PRICING DUE TO SCARCITY
OVERALL AU-GU ODDS 1:8 HOBBY
10 Travis Hafner Bat-Jsy/50 10.00 25.00
11 C.Kotchman Bat-Jsy/50 10.00 25.00
12 Jim Edmonds Jsy-Jsy/5
13 Michael Young Bat-Jsy/10
14 Lyle Overbay Bat-Jsy/50 6.00 15.00
15 Eric Chavez Bat-Jsy/25 12.50 30.00
16 Jason Bay Bat-Jsy/50 10.00 25.00
17 Hank Blalock Jsy-Jsy/25 12.50 30.00
18 Frank Thomas Bat-Jsy/10
20 Miguel Cabrera Bat-Jsy/25 20.00 50.00
23 Chipper Jones Bat-Jsy/5
25 Adam Dunn Bat-Jsy/10

2005 Studio Portraits Zenith White

STATED PRINT RUN 70 SERIAL #'d SETS
*PARALLEL #'d OF 50-60: .4X TO 1X
*PARALLEL #'d OF 40-45: .5X TO 1.2X
*PARALLEL #'d OF 30-35: .6X TO 1.5X
*PARALLEL #'d OF 20-25: .75X TO 2X
*PARALLEL #'d OF 15: 1X TO 2.5X
PARALLELS #'d FROM 5-60 COPIES PER
NO PRICING ON QTY OF 10 OR LESS
OVERALL PORTRAITS ODDS 1:3 HOBBY
1 Ozzie Smith 2.50 6.00
2 Derek Jeter 3.00 8.00
3 Eric Chavez 1.25 3.00
4 Duke Snider 1.50 4.00
5 Albert Pujols 3.00 8.00
6 Stan Musial 2.50 6.00
7 Ivan Rodriguez 1.50 4.00
8 Cal Ripken 6.00 15.00
9 Hank Blalock 1.25 3.00
10 Chipper Jones 1.50 4.00
11 Gary Sheffield 1.25 3.00
12 Alfonso Soriano 1.25 3.00
13 Carl Crawford 1.25 3.00
14 Lou Brock 1.50 4.00
15 Jim Edmonds 1.25 3.00
16 Bo Jackson 1.50 4.00
17 Todd Helton 1.50 4.00
18 Javy Lopez 1.25 3.00
19 Tony Gwynn 2.00 5.00
20 Mark Mulder 1.25 3.00
21 Sammy Sosa 1.50 4.00
22 Roger Clemens 3.00 8.00
23 Don Mattingly 3.00 8.00
24 Willie Mays 3.00 8.00
25 Andruw Jones 1.50 4.00
26 Steve Garvey 1.25 3.00
27 Scott Rolen 1.50 4.00
28 George Brett 3.00 8.00
29 Rod Carew 1.50 4.00
30 Ken Griffey Jr. 2.50 6.00
31 Mike Piazza 1.50 4.00
32 Steve Carlton 1.25 3.00
33 Larry Walker 1.50 4.00
34 Kerry Wood 1.25 3.00
35 Frank Thomas 1.50 4.00
36 Lance Berkman 1.25 3.00
37 Nomar Garciaparra 1.50 4.00
38 Curt Schilling 1.50 4.00
39 Carl Yastrzemski 2.50 6.00
40 Mark Grace 1.50 4.00
41 Tom Seaver 1.50 4.00
42 Mariano Rivera 1.50 4.00
43 Carlos Beltran 1.25 3.00
44 Reggie Jackson 1.50 4.00
45 Pedro Martinez 1.50 4.00
46 Richie Sexson 1.25 3.00
47 Tom Glavine 1.50 4.00
48 Torii Hunter 1.25 3.00
49 Ron Guidry 1.25 3.00
50 Michael Young 1.25 3.00
51 Ichiro Suzuki 3.00 8.00
52 C.C. Sabathia 1.25 3.00
53 Johnny Bench 1.50 4.00
54 Mark Teixeira 1.50 4.00
55 Hideki Matsui 2.50 6.00
56 Mike Mussina 1.50 4.00
57 Johan Santana 1.50 4.00
58 Fergie Jenkins 1.25 3.00
59 Hideo Nomo 1.50 4.00
60 Nolan Ryan 4.00 10.00
61 Whitey Ford 1.50 4.00
62 Jim Thome 1.50 4.00
63 Gary Carter 1.25 3.00
64 Randy Johnson 1.50 4.00
65 Vladimir Guerrero 1.50 4.00
66 Harmon Killebrew 1.50 4.00
67 Tim Hudson 1.25 3.00
68 Josh Beckett 1.25 3.00
69 Eddie Murray 1.50 4.00
70 Greg Maddux 2.50 6.00
71 J.D. Drew 1.25 3.00
72 Bob Feller 1.50 4.00
73 Adrian Beltre 1.25 3.00
74 Wade Boggs 1.50 4.00
75 Barry Zito 1.25 3.00
76 David Ortiz 1.50 4.00
77 Mike Schmidt 3.00 8.00
78 Miguel Cabrera 1.50 4.00
79 Carlos Delgado 1.25 3.00
80 Andre Dawson 1.25 3.00
81 Garret Anderson 1.25 3.00
82 Rickey Henderson 1.50 4.00
83 Shawn Green 1.25 3.00
84 Dale Murphy 1.50 4.00
85 Alex Rodriguez 2.50 6.00
86 Mark Prior 1.50 4.00
87 Paul Molitor 1.25 3.00
88 Jeff Bagwell 1.50 4.00
89 Eric Gagne 1.25 3.00
90 Troy Glaus 1.25 3.00
91 Robin Yount 1.50 4.00
92 Miguel Tejada 1.25 3.00
93 Kirk Gibson 1.25 3.00
94 Manny Ramirez 1.50 4.00
95 Rafael Palmeiro 1.50 4.00
96 Maury Wills 1.25 3.00
97 Craig Biggio 1.50 4.00
98 Jim Palmer 1.25 3.00
99 Adam Dunn 1.25 3.00
100 Carlton Fisk 1.50 4.00

2005 Studio Spirit of the Game

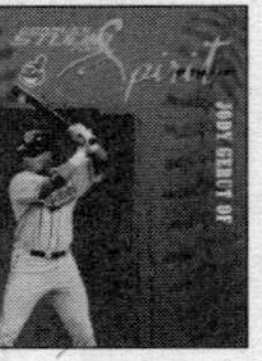

STATED PRINT RUN 600 SERIAL #'d SETS
*DIE CUT: .6X TO 1.5X BASIC
DIE CUT PRINT RUN 125 #'d SETS
*DC GOLD: 1.5X TO 4X BASIC
DC GOLD PRINT RUN 25 #'d SETS
OVERALL INSERT ODDS 1:1 HOBBY
1 Mark Prior 1.50 4.00
2 Sean Casey 1.00 2.50
3 Ichiro Suzuki 3.00 8.00
4 Andruw Jones 1.50 4.00
5 Francisco Cordero 1.50 4.00
6 Ben Sheets 1.00 2.50
7 Rocco Baldelli 1.00 2.50
8 Rafael Furcal 1.00 2.50
9 Angel Berroa 1.00 2.50
10 Roy Oswalt 1.00 2.50
11 Jose Reyes 1.00 2.50
12 Shannon Stewart 1.00 2.50
13 Greg Maddux 2.50 6.00
14 Alfonso Soriano 1.00 2.50
15 Curt Schilling 1.50 4.00
16 Jody Gerut 1.00 2.50
17 Brandon Webb 1.00 2.50
18 Josh Beckett 1.00 2.50
19 Laynce Nix 1.00 2.50
20 Scott Rolen 1.50 4.00

2005 Studio Spirit of the Game Bat

*BAT p/r 225-300: .4X TO 1X JSY p/r 250
*BAT p/r 225-300: .3X TO .8X JSY p/r 125
*BAT p/r 75: .5X TO 1.2X JSY p/r 250
OVERALL AU-GU ODDS 1:8 HOBBY
PRINT RUNS B/WN 75-300 COPIES PER

2005 Studio Spirit of the Game Jersey

PRINT RUNS B/WN 125-250 COPIES PER
PRIME PRINT RUN 10 SERIAL #'d SETS
NO PRIME PRICING DUE TO SCARCITY
OVERALL AU-GU ODDS 1:8 HOBBY
1 Mark Prior/250 2.50 6.00
2 Sean Casey/250 2.00 5.00
4 Andruw Jones/250 2.50 6.00
5 Francisco Cordero/250 2.50 6.00
6 Ben Sheets/250 2.00 5.00
7 Rocco Baldelli/250 2.00 5.00
8 Rafael Furcal/250 2.00 5.00
10 Roy Oswalt/250 2.00 5.00
11 Jose Reyes/250 2.00 5.00
12 Shannon Stewart/250 2.00 5.00
13 Greg Maddux/250 4.00 10.00
14 Alfonso Soriano/250 2.00 5.00
15 Curt Schilling/250 2.50 6.00
16 Jody Gerut/125 2.50 6.00
18 Josh Beckett/250 2.00 5.00
19 Laynce Nix/250 2.00 5.00
20 Scott Rolen/250 2.50 6.00

2005 Studio Spirit of the Game Combo

*COMBO: .75X TO 2X JSY p/r 250
*COMBO: .6X TO 1.5X JSY p/r 125
STATED PRINT RUN 50 SERIAL #'d SETS
PRIME PRINT RUN 10 SERIAL #'d SETS
NO PRIME PRICING DUE TO SCARCITY
OVERALL AU-GU ODDS 1:8 HOBBY

2005 Studio Spirit of the Game Signature Combo

PRINT RUNS B/WN 10-25 COPIES PER
NO PRICING ON QTY OF 10
PRIME PRINT RUNS B/WN 5-10 COPIES PER
NO PRIME PRICING DUE TO SCARCITY
OVERALL AU-GU ODDS 1:8 HOBBY
1 Mark Prior Bat-Jsy/15 20.00 50.00
2 Sean Casey Jsy-Jsy/25 12.50 30.00
6 Ben Sheets Bat-Jsy/10
8 Rafael Furcal Bat-Jsy/25 12.50 30.00
12 S.Stewart Jsy-Jsy/25 12.50 30.00
14 A.Soriano Jsy-Jsy/15 15.00 40.00
16 Jody Gerut Bat-Jsy/25 8.00 20.00
19 Laynce Nix Bat-Jsy/25 8.00 20.00
20 Scott Rolen Jsy-Jsy/10

2005 Studio Stars

STATED ODDS 1:6
*GOLD: .75X TO 2X BASIC
GOLD PRINT RUN 500 #'d SETS
*PLATINUM: 1.5X TO 4X BASIC
PLATINUM PRINT RUN 50 #'d SETS
OVERALL INSERT ODDS 1:1 HOBBY
1 Carlos Beltran .60 1.50
2 Sean Casey .60 1.50
3 Ichiro Suzuki 2.00 5.00
4 Vladimir Guerrero 1.00 2.50
5 Tim Hudson .60 1.50
6 Alex Rodriguez 1.50 4.00
7 Miguel Tejada .60 1.50
8 Curt Schilling 1.00 2.50
9 Roger Clemens 1.50 4.00
10 Ben Sheets .60 1.50
11 Todd Helton 1.00 2.50
12 Mark Mulder .60 1.50
13 Scott Podsednik .60 1.50
14 Victor Martinez .60 1.50
15 Mark Prior 1.00 2.50
16 Ivan Rodriguez 1.00 2.50
17 Dontrelle Willis .60 1.50
18 Andy Pettitte 1.00 2.50
19 Khalil Greene 1.00 2.50
20 Jeff Kent .60 1.50
21 Paul Konerko 1.00 2.50
22 Joe Mauer 1.00 2.50
23 Bobby Crosby .60 1.50
24 Pedro Martinez 1.00 2.50
25 John Smoltz 1.00 2.50
26 Derek Jeter 2.00 5.00
27 Moises Alou .60 1.50
28 Rich Harden .60 1.50
29 Jim Thome 1.00 2.50
30 Jason Bay .60 1.50
31 Aramis Ramirez .60 1.50
32 Carlos Lee .60 1.50
33 B.J. Upton .60 1.50
34 Nomar Garciaparra 1.00 2.50
35 Ken Griffey Jr. 1.50 4.00
36 Darin Erstad .60 1.50
37 Larry Walker 1.00 2.50
38 Jose Vidro .60 1.50
39 Zack Greinke .60 1.50
40 Michael Young .60 1.50
41 David Wright 1.50 4.00
42 Albert Pujols 2.00 5.00
43 Vernon Wells .60 1.50
44 Mark Teixeira 1.00 2.50
45 Jacque Jones .60 1.50
46 Brian Giles .60 1.50
47 Austin Kearns .60 1.50
48 Omar Vizquel 1.00 2.50
49 Randy Johnson 1.00 2.50
50 Jason Varitek 1.00 2.50

2001 Sweet Spot

The 2001 Upper Deck Sweet Spot product was initially released in February, 2001 and offered a 90-card base set. An additional 60-card Update set was distributed within Upper Deck Rookie Update packs in late December, 2001. The basic 90-card set is broken into tiers as follows: 60 basic veterans (1-60), and 30 Sweet Beginning subset cards (each individually serial numbered to 1000). The Update set was composed of 30 basic veterans (91-120) and 30 Sweet Beginnings subset cards (121-150) each serial numbered to 1500. Basic packs contained four cards and carried a suggested retail price of $2.99. Rookie Update packs contained four cards and carried a suggested retail price of $4.99.

COMP.BASIC w/o SP's (60) 8.00 20.00
COMP.UPDATE w/o SP's (30) 4.00 10.00
COMMON CARD (1-60) .15 .40
COMMON CARD (61-90) 4.00 10.00
COMMON CARD (91-120) .25 .60
COMMON (121-150) 2.00 5.00
1 Troy Glaus .15 .40
2 Darin Erstad .15 .40
3 Jason Giambi .15 .40
4 Tim Hudson .15 .40
5 Ben Grieve .15 .40
6 Carlos Delgado .15 .40
7 David Wells .15 .40
8 Greg Vaughn .15 .40
9 Roberto Alomar .25 .60
10 Jim Thome .25 .60
11 John Olerud .15 .40
12 Edgar Martinez .25 .60
13 Cal Ripken 1.25 3.00
14 Albert Belle .15 .40
15 Ivan Rodriguez .25 .60
16 Alex Rodriguez Rangers 1.25 3.00
17 Pedro Martinez .25 .60
18 Nomar Garciaparra .60 1.50
19 Manny Ramirez .25 .60
20 Jermaine Dye .15 .40
21 Juan Gonzalez .15 .40
22 Dean Palmer .15 .40
23 Matt Lawton .15 .40
24 Eric Milton .15 .40
25 Frank Thomas .40 1.00
26 Magglio Ordonez .15 .40
27 Derek Jeter 1.00 2.50
28 Bernie Williams .25 .60
29 Roger Clemens .75 2.00
30 Jeff Bagwell .25 .60
31 Richard Hidalgo .15 .40
32 Chipper Jones .40 1.00
33 Greg Maddux .60 1.50
34 Richie Sexson .15 .40
35 Jeromy Burnitz .15 .40
36 Mark McGwire 1.00 2.50
37 Jim Edmonds .15 .40
38 Sammy Sosa .40 1.00
39 Randy Johnson .40 1.00
40 Steve Finley .15 .40
41 Gary Sheffield .15 .40
42 Shawn Green .15 .40
43 Vladimir Guerrero .40 1.00
44 Jose Vidro .15 .40
45 Barry Bonds 1.00 2.50
46 Jeff Kent .15 .40
47 Preston Wilson .15 .40
48 Luis Castillo .15 .40
49 Mike Piazza .60 1.50
50 Edgardo Alfonzo .15 .40
51 Tony Gwynn .50 1.25
52 Ryan Klesko .15 .40
53 Scott Rolen .25 .60
54 Bob Abreu .15 .40
55 Jason Kendall .15 .40
56 Brian Giles .15 .40
57 Ken Griffey Jr. .60 1.50
58 Barry Larkin .25 .60
59 Todd Helton .25 .60
60 Mike Hampton .15 .40
Card back has batting header lines UER
61 Corey Patterson SB 4.00 10.00
62 Ichiro Suzuki SB RC 125.00 200.00
63 Jason Grilli SB 4.00 10.00
64 Brian Cole SB 4.00 10.00
65 Juan Pierre SB 4.00 10.00
66 Matt Ginter SB 4.00 10.00
67 Jimmy Rollins SB 4.00 10.00
68 Jason Smith SB RC 4.00 10.00
69 Israel Alcantara SB 4.00 10.00
70 Adam Pettyjohn SB RC 4.00 10.00
71 Luke Prokopec SB 4.00 10.00
72 Barry Zito SB 5.00 12.00
73 Keith Ginter SB 4.00 10.00
74 Sun Woo Kim SB 4.00 10.00
75 Ross Gload SB 4.00 10.00
76 Matt Wise SB 4.00 10.00
77 Aubrey Huff SB 4.00 10.00
78 Ryan Franklin SB 4.00 10.00
79 Brandon Inge SB 4.00 10.00
80 Wes Helms SB 4.00 10.00
81 Junior Spivey SB RC 5.00 12.00
82 Ryan Vogelsong SB 4.00 10.00
83 John Parrish SB 4.00 10.00
84 Joe Crede SB 5.00 12.00
85 Damian Rolls SB 4.00 10.00
86 Esix Snead SB RC 4.00 10.00
87 Rocky Biddle SB 4.00 10.00
88 Brady Clark SB 4.00 10.00
89 Timo Perez SB 4.00 10.00
90 Jay Spurgeon SB 4.00 10.00
91 Garret Anderson .25 .60
92 Jermaine Dye .25 .60
93 Shannon Stewart .25 .60
94 Ben Grieve .25 .60
95 Juan Gonzalez .25 .60
96 Brett Boone .25 .60
97 Tony Batista .25 .60
98 Rafael Palmeiro .40 1.00
99 Carl Everett .25 .60
100 Mike Sweeney .25 .60
101 Tony Clark .25 .60
102 Doug Mientkiewicz .25 .60
103 Jose Canseco .40 1.00
104 Mike Mussina .40 1.00
105 Lance Berkman .25 .60
106 Andruw Jones .40 1.00
107 Geoff Jenkins .25 .60
108 Matt Morris .25 .60
109 Fred McGriff .40 1.00
110 Luis Gonzalez .25 .60
111 Kevin Brown .25 .60
112 Tony Armas Jr. .25 .60
113 John Vander Wal .25 .60
114 Cliff Floyd .25 .60
115 Matt Lawton .25 .60
116 Phil Nevin .25 .60
117 Pat Burrell .25 .60
118 Aramis Ramirez .25 .60
119 Sean Casey .25 .60
120 Larry Walker .25 .60
121 Albert Pujols SB RC 60.00 120.00
122 J.Estrada SB RC 2.00 5.00
123 Wilson Betemit SB RC 3.00 8.00
124 A.Hernandez SB RC 2.00 5.00
125 M.Ensberg SB RC 3.00 8.00
126 H.Ramirez SB RC 2.00 5.00
127 Josh Towers SB RC 2.00 5.00
128 Juan Uribe SB RC 2.00 5.00
129 Wilken Ruan SB RC 2.00 5.00
130 Andres Torres SB RC 2.00 5.00
131 B.Lawrence SB RC 2.00 5.00
132 Ryan Freel SB RC 2.00 5.00
133 B.Duckworth SB RC 2.00 5.00
134 Juan Diaz SB RC 2.00 5.00
135 Rafael Soriano SB RC 2.00 5.00
136 R.Rodriguez SB RC 2.00 5.00
137 Bud Smith SB RC 2.00 5.00
138 Mark Teixeira SB RC 12.50 30.00
139 Mark Prior SB RC 6.00 15.00
140 J.Melian SB RC 2.00 5.00
141 D.Brazelton SB RC 2.00 5.00
142 Greg Miller SB RC 2.00 5.00
143 Billy Sylvester SB RC 2.00 5.00
144 E.Guzman SB RC 2.00 5.00
145 Jack Wilson SB RC 2.00 5.00
146 Jose Mieses SB RC 2.00 5.00
147 Brandon Lyon SB RC 2.00 5.00
148 T.Shinjo SB RC 2.00 5.00
149 Juan Cruz SB RC 2.00 5.00
150 Jay Gibbons SB RC 2.00 5.00

2001 Sweet Spot Big League Challenge

Randomly inserted into packs at one in six, this 20-card insert features the top power-hitting players in the league. Card backs carry a "BL" prefix.

COMPLETE SET (20) 30.00 60.00
BL1 Mark McGwire 3.00 8.00
BL2 Richard Hidalgo .75 2.00
BL3 Alex Rodriguez 2.00 5.00
BL4 Shawn Green .75 2.00
BL5 Frank Thomas 1.25 3.00
BL6 Chipper Jones 1.25 3.00
BL7 Rafael Palmeiro .75 2.00
BL8 Troy Glaus .75 2.00
BL9 Mike Piazza 2.00 5.00
BL10 Andruw Jones .75 2.00
BL11 Todd Helton .75 2.00
BL12 Jason Giambi .75 2.00
BL13 Sammy Sosa 1.25 3.00
BL14 Carlos Delgado .75 2.00
BL15 Barry Bonds 3.00 8.00
BL16 Jose Canseco .75 2.00
BL17 Jim Edmonds .75 2.00
BL18 Manny Ramirez .75 2.00
BL19 Gary Sheffield .75 2.00
BL20 Nomar Garciaparra 2.00 5.00

2001 Sweet Spot Game Base Duos

Randomly inserted into packs at one in 18, this 16-card insert set features dual-player cards with a swatch of an actual game-used base. Card backs carry a "B1" prefix followed by the player's initials.

B1BD Jeff Bagwell 6.00 15.00
Jermaine Dye
B1BH Barry Bonds 10.00 25.00
Todd Helton
B1CP Roger Clemens 6.00 15.00
Mike Piazza
B1GD Vladimir Guerrero 6.00 15.00
Carlos Delgado
B1HG Jeffrey Hammonds 4.00 10.00
Troy Glaus
B1JG Chipper Jones 6.00 15.00
Nomar Garciaparra
B1JP Mike Piazza 15.00 40.00
Derek Jeter
B1MG Mark McGwire 30.00 60.00
Ken Griffey Jr.
B1MP Mark McGwire 20.00 50.00
Timo Perez
B1RJ Alex Rodriguez 15.00 40.00
Derek Jeter
B1RR Scott Rolen 10.00 25.00
Cal Ripken
B1SR Gary Sheffield 6.00 15.00
Alex Rodriguez
B1ST Sammy Sosa 6.00 15.00
Frank Thomas
B1GRA Ken Griffey Jr. 6.00 15.00
Manny Ramirez
B1GRO Tony Gwynn 4.00 10.00
Ivan Rodriguez
B1JGI Randy Johnson 6.00 15.00
Jason Giambi

2001 Sweet Spot Game Base Trios

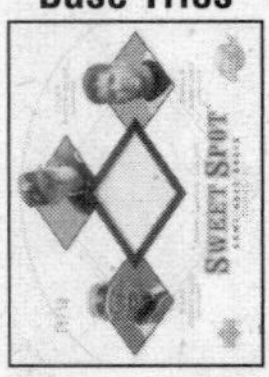

Randomly inserted into packs, this 13-card insert set features three players on one card with a swatch of an actual game-used base. Card backs carry a "B2" prefix followed by the player's initials. Please note that there were only 50 serial numbered sets produced.

BDH Jef Bagwell 15.00 40.00
Jermaine Dye
Richard Hidalgo
BHK Barry Bonds 40.00 80.00
Todd Helton
Jeff Kent
GDM V. Guerrero 15.00 40.00
Carlos Delgado
Raul Mondesi
GRP Tony Gwynn 15.00 40.00
Ivan Rodriguez
Rafael Palmeiro
GRT Ken Griffey Jr. 15.00 40.00
Manny Ramirez
Jim Thome
HGH Jeffrey Hammonds 15.00 40.00
Troy Glaus
Todd Helton
JGC Randy Johnson 15.00 40.00
Jason Giambi
Eric Chavez
JGJ Chipper Jones 20.00 50.00
Nomar Garciaparra
Andruw Jones
MGE Mark McGwire 50.00 100.00
Ken Griffey Jr.
Jim Edmonds
PJW Mike Piazza 40.00 80.00
Derek Jeter
Bernie Williams
RRB Scott Rolen 30.00 60.00
Cal Ripken
Albert Belle
SRM Gary Sheffield 15.00 40.00
Alex Rodriguez
Edgar Martinez
STO Sammy Sosa 15.00 40.00
Frank Thomas
Magglio Ordonez

2001 Sweet Spot Game Bat

Randomly inserted into packs at one in 18, this 19-card insert set features a swatch of actual game-used bat. Card backs carry a "B" prefix followed by the player's initials.

BAJ Andruw Jones 6.00 15.00
BAR Alex Rodriguez 6.00 15.00
BBB Barry Bonds 10.00 25.00
BCR Cal Ripken 15.00 40.00
BFT Frank Thomas 6.00 15.00
BGS Gary Sheffield 4.00 10.00
BHA Hank Aaron 15.00 40.00
BIR Ivan Rodriguez 6.00 15.00
BJC Jose Canseco 6.00 15.00
BJD Joe DiMaggio 40.00 80.00
BKG Ken Griffey Jr. 6.00 15.00
BMM Mickey Mantle 75.00 150.00
BNR Nolan Ryan 15.00 40.00
BRA Rick Ankiel 6.00 15.00
BRJ Reggie Jackson 6.00 15.00

BSM Stan Musial 15.00 40.00
BSS Sammy Sosa 6.00 15.00
BTC Ty Cobb 75.00 150.00
BWM Willie Mays 15.00 40.00

2001 Sweet Spot Game Jersey

Randomly inserted into packs at one in 18, this 20-card insert set features a swatch from an actual game-used jersey. Card backs carry a "J" prefix followed by the player's initials. The Ichiro jersey actually was not major league regular-season game worn, but was worn in an spring training game in 1999.

JAJ Andruw Jones 6.00 15.00
JAR Alex Rodriguez 6.00 15.00
JBB Barry Bonds 10.00 25.00
JCJ Chipper Jones 6.00 15.00
JCR Cal Ripken 15.00 40.00
JDS Duke Snider 6.00 15.00
JFT Frank Thomas 6.00 15.00
JIR Ivan Rodriguez 6.00 15.00
JIS Ichiro Suzuki 50.00 100.00
JJC Jose Canseco 6.00 15.00
JJD Joe DiMaggio 40.00 80.00
JKG Ken Griffey Jr. 6.00 15.00
JMM Mickey Mantle 75.00 150.00
JNR Nolan Ryan 15.00 40.00
JRC Roberto Clemente 40.00 80.00
JRC Roger Clemens 6.00 15.00
JRJ Randy Johnson 6.00 15.00
JSM Stan Musial 20.00 50.00
JSS Sammy Sosa 6.00 15.00
JWM Willie Mays 20.00 50.00

2001 Sweet Spot Players Party

Inserted at a rate of one in 12 packs, these 10 cards feature some of Baseball's leading players. These cards have a "PP" prefix.

COMPLETE SET (10) 25.00 50.00
PP1 Derek Jeter 3.00 8.00
PP2 Randy Johnson 1.25 3.00
PP3 Frank Thomas 1.25 3.00
PP4 Nomar Garciaparra 2.00 5.00
PP5 Ken Griffey Jr. 2.00 5.00
PP6 Carlos Delgado .75 2.00
PP7 Mike Piazza 2.00 5.00
PP8 Barry Bonds 3.00 8.00
PP9 Sammy Sosa 1.25 3.00
PP10 Pedro Martinez .75 2.00

2001 Sweet Spot Signatures

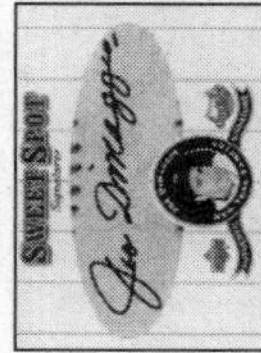

This 52-card insert set features authentic autographs from some of the Major League's top active and retired players. These cards incorporate the leather sweet spots from actual baseballs, whereby the featured athlete signed the leather swatch. The stunning design of these cards made them one of the most popular autograph inserts of the modern era. One in every eighteen packs of Sweet Spot contained either a Game Base insert or one of these Signatures inserts. Please note the following players packed out as exchange cards with a redemption deadline of November 8th, 2001: Roger Clemens and Willie Mays. In addition, the following players packed out as 50% exchange cards and 50% actual signed cards: Albert Belle, Pat Burrell and Rafael Furcal. Though the cards lack actual serial-numbering, representatives at Upper Deck publicly announced specific print runs on several short-printed cards within this set. That information is listed within our checklist. Forty of the 150 serial numbered Joe DiMaggio cards were actually inscribed by DiMaggio as "Joe DiMaggio - Yankee Clipper".Card backs carry a "S" prefix followed by the player's initials.

NO PRICING ON QTY OF 10 OR LESS
SAB Albert Belle 15.00 40.00
SAH Art Howe 10.00 25.00
SAJ Andruw Jones 30.00 60.00
SAR A. Rodriguez SP/154 150.00 250.00
SAT Alan Trammell 15.00 40.00
SBB Buddy Bell 15.00 40.00
SBM Bill Madlock 15.00 40.00
SBR Babe Ruth SP/1
SBV Bobby Valentine 15.00 40.00
SCB Chris Chambliss 15.00 40.00
SCD Carlos Delgado 15.00 40.00
SCJ Chipper Jones 50.00 100.00
SDB Dusty Baker 30.00 60.00
SDB Don Baylor 15.00 40.00
SDE Darin Erstad 15.00 40.00
SDJ Davey Johnson 15.00 40.00
SDL Davey Lopes 15.00 40.00
SFT Frank Thomas 50.00 100.00
SGS Gary Sheffield 30.00 60.00
SHM Hal McRae 15.00 40.00
SIR I. Rodriguez SP/150 60.00 120.00
SJB Jeff Bagwell SP/214 90.00 150.00
SJC Jose Canseco 30.00 60.00
SJD J.DiMaggio SP/110 450.00 600.00
SJDa DiMag Clipper SP/40 600.00 1000.00
SJG Joe Garagiola 40.00 80.00
SJG Jason Giambi 15.00 40.00
SJR Jim Rice 15.00 40.00
SKG Ken Griffey Jr. SP/100 200.00 300.00
SLP Lou Piniella 15.00 40.00
SMB Milton Bradley 15.00 40.00
SML Mike Lamb 10.00 25.00
SMM Mickey Mantle SP/10
SMW Matt Williams 30.00 60.00
SNR Nolan Ryan 90.00 150.00
SPB Pat Burrell 8.00 20.00
SPO Paul O'Neill 30.00 60.00
SRAI Roberto Alomar 30.00 60.00
SRAN Rick Ankiel 20.00 50.00
SRC R. Clemens EXCH 50.00 100.00
SRF Rafael Furcal 15.00 40.00
SRJ Randy Johnson 60.00 120.00
SRV Robin Ventura 30.00 60.00
SSG Shawn Green 30.00 60.00
SSM Stan Musial 90.00 150.00
SSS S. Sosa SP/148 90.00 150.00
STC Ty Cobb SP/1
STGL Troy Glaus 30.00 60.00
STGW Tony Gwynn 50.00 100.00
STH Tim Hudson 30.00 60.00
STL Tony LaRussa 15.00 40.00
SWM Willie Mays 150.00 250.00

2002 Sweet Spot

This 175 card set was released in October, 2002. The four card packs were issued 12 packs to a box and 16 boxes to a case with an $10 SRP per pack. Cards numbered 1 through 90 feature veterans while cards numbered 91 through 145 feature rookies and cards numbered 146-175 feature veterans as part of the "Game Face" subset. Cards numbered 91 through 130 were issued to a stated print run of 1300 serial numbered sets while cards 131 through 145 were issued to either a stated print run of 750 or 100 serial numbered sets. Cards numbered 146 through 175 were issued at stated odds of one in 24. Also randomly inserted in packs were redemptions for Mark McGwire autographs which had an exchange deadline of September 12, 2003. These McGwire exchange cards entitled the bearer to send in a item for McGwire to sign.

COMP.SET w/o SP's (90) 8.00 20.00
COMMON CARD (1-90) .15 .40
COMMON CARD (91-130) 1.50 4.00
COMMON TIER 1 AU (131-145) 6.00 15.00
COMMON TIER 2 AU (131-145) 10.00 25.00
COMMON CARD (146-175) 4.00 10.00
1 Troy Glaus .15 .40
2 Darin Erstad .15 .40
3 Tim Hudson .15 .40
4 Eric Chavez .15 .40
5 Barry Zito .15 .40
6 Miguel Tejada .15 .40
7 Carlos Delgado .15 .40
8 Eric Hinske .15 .40
9 Ben Grieve .15 .40
10 Jim Thome .25 .60
11 C.C. Sabathia .15 .40
12 Omar Vizquel .25 .60
13 Ichiro Suzuki .75 2.00
14 Edgar Martinez .25 .60
15 Bret Boone .15 .40
16 Freddy Garcia .15 .40
17 Tony Batista .15 .40
18 Geronimo Gil .15 .40
19 Alex Rodriguez .60 1.50
20 Rafael Palmeiro .25 .60
21 Ivan Rodriguez .25 .60
22 Hank Blalock .25 .60
23 Juan Gonzalez .15 .40
24 Nomar Garciaparra .60 1.50
25 Pedro Martinez .25 .60
26 Manny Ramirez .25 .60
27 Mike Sweeney .15 .40
28 Carlos Beltran .15 .40
29 Dmitri Young .15 .40
30 Torii Hunter .15 .40
31 Eric Milton .15 .40
32 Corey Koskie .15 .40
33 Frank Thomas .40 1.00
34 Mark Buehrle .15 .40
35 Magglio Ordonez .15 .40
36 Roger Clemens .75 2.00
37 Derek Jeter 1.00 2.50
38 Jason Giambi .15 .40
39 Alfonso Soriano .15 .40
40 Bernie Williams .25 .60
41 Jeff Bagwell .25 .60
42 Roy Oswalt .15 .40
43 Lance Berkman .15 .40
44 Greg Maddux .60 1.50
45 Chipper Jones .40 1.00
46 Gary Sheffield .15 .40
47 Andruw Jones .25 .60
48 Richie Sexson .15 .40
49 Ben Sheets .15 .40
50 Albert Pujols .75 2.00
51 Matt Morris .15 .40
52 J.D. Drew .15 .40
53 Sammy Sosa .40 1.00
54 Kerry Wood .15 .40
55 Mark Prior .25 .60
56 Moises Alou .15 .40
57 Corey Patterson .15 .40
58 Randy Johnson .40 1.00
59 Luis Gonzalez .15 .40
60 Curt Schilling .15 .40
61 Shawn Green .15 .40
62 Kevin Brown .15 .40
63 Paul Lo Duca .15 .40
64 Adrian Beltre .15 .40
65 Vladimir Guerrero .40 1.00
66 Jose Vidro .15 .40
67 Javier Vazquez .15 .40
68 Barry Bonds 1.00 2.50
69 Jeff Kent .15 .40
70 Rich Aurilia .15 .40
71 Mike Lowell .15 .40
72 Josh Beckett .15 .40
73 Brad Penny .15 .40
74 Roberto Alomar .25 .60
75 Mike Piazza .60 1.50
76 Jeromy Burnitz .15 .40
77 Mo Vaughn .15 .40
78 Phil Nevin .15 .40
79 Sean Burroughs .15 .40
80 Jeremy Giambi .15 .40
81 Bobby Abreu .15 .40
82 Jimmy Rollins .15 .40
83 Pat Burrell .15 .40
84 Brian Giles .15 .40
85 Aramis Ramirez .15 .40
86 Ken Griffey Jr. .60 1.50
87 Adam Dunn .15 .40
88 Austin Kearns .15 .40
89 Todd Helton .25 .60
90 Larry Walker .15 .40
91 Earl Snyder SB RC 1.50 4.00
92 Jorge Padilla SB RC 1.50 4.00
93 Felix Escalona SB RC 1.50 4.00
94 John Foster SB RC 1.50 4.00
95 Brandon Puffer SB RC 1.50 4.00
96 Steve Bechler SB RC 1.50 4.00
97 Hansel Izquierdo SB RC 1.50 4.00
98 Chris Baker SB RC 1.50 4.00
99 Jeremy Ward SB RC 1.50 4.00
100 Kevin Frederick SB RC 1.50 4.00
101 Josh Hancock SB RC 2.00 5.00
102 Allan Simpson SB RC 1.50 4.00
103 Mitch Wylie SB RC 1.50 4.00
104 Mark Corey SB RC 1.50 4.00
105 Victor Alvarez SB RC 1.50 4.00
106 Todd Donovan SB RC 1.50 4.00
107 Nelson Castro SB RC 1.50 4.00
108 Chris Booker SB RC 1.50 4.00
109 Corey Thurman SB RC 1.50 4.00
110 Kirk Saarloos SB RC 1.50 4.00
111 Michael Crudale SB RC 1.50 4.00
112 J.Simontacchi SB RC 1.50 4.00
113 Ron Calloway SB RC 1.50 4.00
114 Brandon Backe SB RC 2.00 5.00
115 Tom Shearn SB RC 1.50 4.00
116 Oliver Perez SB RC 2.00 5.00
117 Kyle Kane SB RC 1.50 4.00
118 Francis Beltran SB RC 1.50 4.00
119 So Taguchi SB RC 2.00 5.00
120 Doug Devore SB RC 1.50 4.00
121 Juan Brito SB RC 1.50 4.00
122 Cliff Bartosh SB RC 1.50 4.00
123 Eric Junge SB RC 1.50 4.00
124 Joe Orloski SB RC 1.50 4.00
125 Scotty Layfield SB RC 1.50 4.00
126 Jorge Sosa SB RC 2.00 5.00
127 Satoru Komiyama SB RC 1.50 4.00
128 Edwin Almonte SB RC 1.50 4.00
129 Takahito Nomura SB RC 1.50 4.00
130 John Ennis SB RC 1.50 4.00
131 Kazuhisa Ishii T2 AU RC 40.00 80.00
132 Ben Howard T2 AU RC 10.00 25.00
133 Aaron Cook T1 AU RC 8.00 20.00
134 Andy Machado T1 AU RC 6.00 15.00
135 Luis Ugueto T1 AU RC 6.00 15.00
136 Tyler Yates T1 AU RC 6.00 15.00
137 Rod. Rosario T1 AU RC 6.00 15.00
138 Jaime Cerda T1 AU RC 6.00 15.00
139 Luis Martinez T1 AU RC 6.00 15.00
140 Rene Reyes T1 AU RC 6.00 15.00
141 Eric Good T1 AU RC 6.00 15.00
142 Matt Thornton T2 AU RC 10.00 25.00
143 Steve Kent T1 AU RC 6.00 15.00
144 Jose Valverde T1 AU RC 6.00 15.00
145 A.Burnside T1 AU RC 6.00 15.00
146 Barry Bonds GF 10.00 25.00
147 Ken Griffey Jr. GF 6.00 15.00
148 Alex Rodriguez GF 6.00 15.00
149 Jason Giambi GF 1.50 4.00
150 Chipper Jones GF 4.00 10.00
151 Nomar Garciaparra GF 6.00 15.00
152 Mike Piazza GF 6.00 15.00
153 Sammy Sosa GF 4.00 10.00
154 Derek Jeter GF 10.00 25.00
155 Jeff Bagwell GF 4.00 10.00
156 Albert Pujols GF 6.00 15.00
157 Ichiro Suzuki GF 6.00 15.00
158 Randy Johnson GF 4.00 10.00
159 Frank Thomas GF 4.00 10.00
160 Greg Maddux GF 6.00 15.00
161 Jim Thome GF 4.00 10.00
162 Scott Rolen GF 4.00 10.00
163 Shawn Green GF 4.00 10.00
164 Vladimir Guerrero GF 4.00 10.00
165 Troy Glaus GF 4.00 10.00
166 Carlos Delgado GF 4.00 10.00
167 Luis Gonzalez GF 4.00 10.00
168 Roger Clemens GF 8.00 20.00
169 Todd Helton GF 4.00 10.00
170 Eric Chavez GF 4.00 10.00
171 Rafael Palmeiro GF 4.00 10.00
172 Pedro Martinez GF 4.00 10.00
173 Lance Berkman GF 4.00 10.00
174 Josh Beckett GF 4.00 10.00
175 Sean Burroughs GF 4.00 10.00
MM Mark McGwire AU EXCH/100

2002 Sweet Spot Game Face Blue Portraits

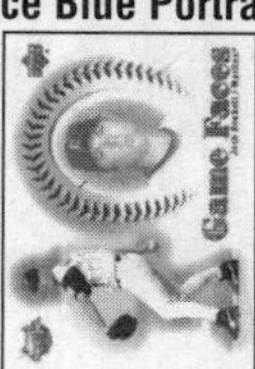

Randomly inserted in packs, this is a parallel to the Game Face subset. These cards can be differentiated from the regular card by their "blue" tint and were issued to a stated print run of 100 serial numbered sets.

*GAME FACE: .6X TO 1.5X BASIC CARDS

2002 Sweet Spot Legendary Signatures

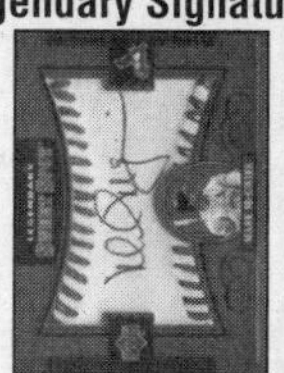

Inserted at stated odds of one in 72, these 16 cards feature signatures of retired greats. Since each player signed a different amount of cards we have notated that stated print run information next to their name in our checklist.

PRINT RUN INFO PROVIDED BY UD
AK Al Kaline/835 * 20.00 50.00
AT Alan Trammell/843 * 10.00 25.00
BP Boog Powell/944 * 12.50 30.00
BR Brooks Robinson 12.50 30.00
CR Cal Ripken/194 * 75.00 150.00
FJ Ferguson Jenkins/857 * 10.00 25.00
FL Fred Lynn/853 * 10.00 25.00
GP Gaylord Perry/921 * 10.00 25.00
JD Joe DiMaggio/50 * 500.00 800.00
KH Keith Hernandez/906 * 10.00 25.00
LA Luis Aparicio/485 * 10.00 25.00
MM Mark McGwire/90 * 300.00 500.00
PM Paul Molitor/852 * 10.00 25.00
RF Rollie Fingers/866 * 10.00 25.00
SG Steve Garvey/871 * 10.00 25.00
SK Sandy Koufax/485 * 175.00 300.00

2002 Sweet Spot Signatures

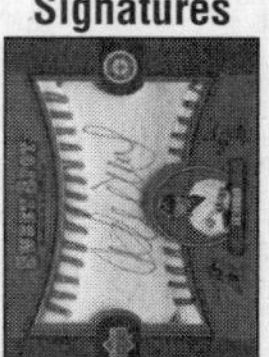

Inserted at stated odds of one in 72, these 25 cards feature signatures of some of today's leading players. Since each player signed a different amount of cards we have notated that stated print run information next to their name in our checklist. The Barry Bonds cards were not returned in time for inclusion in packs and those cards could be redeemed until October 23rd, 2005.

AD Adam Dunn/291 15.00 40.00
AJ Andruw Jones/291 15.00 40.00
AR Alex Rodriguez/291 125.00 200.00
BB Barry Bonds/380 100.00 200.00
BG Brian Giles/291 10.00 25.00
BZ Barry Zito/291 15.00 40.00
CD Carlos Delgado/291 10.00 25.00
FG Freddy Garcia/145 10.00 25.00
FT Frank Thomas/291 40.00 80.00
HB Hank Blalock/291 10.00 25.00
IS Ichiro Suzuki/145 400.00 500.00
JB Jeromy Burnitz/291 10.00 25.00
JG Jason Giambi/291 10.00 25.00
JT Jim Thome/291 20.00 50.00
KG Ken Griffey Jr./291 75.00 150.00
LB Lance Berkman/291 15.00 40.00
LG Luis Gonzalez/291 10.00 25.00
MPr Mark Prior/291 10.00 25.00
MS Mike Sweeney/291 10.00 25.00
RC Roger Clemens/194 100.00 175.00
RO Roy Oswalt/291 10.00 25.00
SB Sean Burroughs/291 10.00 25.00
SR Scott Rolen/291 15.00 40.00
SS Sammy Sosa/145 60.00 120.00
TG Tom Glavine/291 20.00 50.00

2002 Sweet Spot Swatches

Inserted at stated odds of one in 12, these 25 cards feature game-used swatches of the featured players.

AR Alex Rodriguez 6.00 15.00
BG Brian Giles 4.00 10.00
BW Bernie Williams 4.00 10.00
CJ Chipper Jones 4.00 10.00
DE Darin Erstad 4.00 10.00
EC Eric Chavez 4.00 10.00
FT Frank Thomas 4.00 10.00
GM Greg Maddux 6.00 15.00
IR Ivan Rodriguez 4.00 10.00
IS Ichiro Suzuki 20.00 50.00
JBa Jeff Bagwell 4.00 10.00
JBe Josh Beckett 4.00 10.00
JE Jim Edmonds 4.00 10.00
JGi Jason Giambi 4.00 10.00
JGo Juan Gonzalez 4.00 10.00
KG Ken Griffey Jr. 6.00 15.00
KI Kazuhisa Ishii 4.00 10.00
LG Luis Gonzalez 4.00 10.00
MP Mike Piazza 6.00 15.00
OV Omar Vizquel 4.00 10.00
PM Pedro Martinez 4.00 10.00
SB Sean Burroughs 4.00 10.00
SG Shawn Green 4.00 10.00
SR Scott Rolen 4.00 10.00
SS Sammy Sosa 4.00 10.00

2002 Sweet Spot USA Jerseys

Issued at a stated rate of one in 12, these 17 cards feature jersey swatches from players who represented the USA team in International competition.

AE Adam Everett 3.00 8.00
AK Adam Kennedy 3.00 8.00
BA Brent Abernathy 3.00 8.00
DB Dewon Brazelton 3.00 8.00
DG Danny Graves 3.00 8.00
DM Doug Mientkiewicz 3.00 8.00
EM Eric Munson 3.00 8.00
JG Jake Gautreau 3.00 8.00
JK Josh Karp 3.00 8.00
JM Joe Mauer 6.00 15.00
JR Jon Rauch 3.00 8.00
JW Justin Wayne 3.00 8.00
MP Mark Prior 4.00 10.00
MT Mark Teixeira 4.00 10.00
RO Roy Oswalt 3.00 8.00
TB Tagg Bozied 4.00 10.00
XN Xavier Nady 3.00 8.00

2003 Sweet Spot

This 231 card set was released in September, 2003. The set was issued in four card packs with an $10 SRP which were issued in 12 pack boxes which came 16 boxes to a case. Thirty of the first 130 cards were issued at a stated rate of one in four packs and we have notated those cards with an SP in our checklist. Cards number 131 through 190 are part of the Sweet Beginning subset and those cards were issued at a stated rate of one in three. Cards numbered 191 through 232 were issued at an overall stated rate of one in nine and those cards were issued in three different tiers. Card number 217 was not issued.

COMP.SET w/o SP's (100) 8.00 20.00
COMP.SET w/SP's (130) 60.00 120.00
COMMON CARD (1-130) .20 .50
COMMON SP (1-130) 1.25 3.00
COMMON CARD (131-190) 1.25 3.00
131-190 PRINT RUN 2003 SERIAL #'d SETS
COMMON P1 (191-232) 1.50 4.00
P1 191-232 PRINT RUN 500 SERIAL #'d SETS
COMMON P2-P3 (191-232) 1.25 3.00
P2 191-232 PRINT RUN 1200 SERIAL #'d SETS
P3 191-232 PRINT RUN 1430 SERIAL #'d SETS
1 Darin Erstad .20 .50
2 Garret Anderson .20 .50
3 Tim Salmon .30 .75
4 Troy Glaus .20 .50
5 Luis Gonzalez .20 .50
6 Randy Johnson .50 1.25
7 Curt Schilling .20 .50
8 Lyle Overbay .20 .50
9 Andruw Jones SP 1.50 4.00
10 Gary Sheffield SP 1.25 3.00
11 Rafael Furcal SP 1.25 3.00
12 Greg Maddux SP 2.50 6.00
13 Chipper Jones SP 1.50 4.00
14 Tony Batista .20 .50
15 Rodrigo Lopez .20 .50
16 Jay Gibbons .20 .50
17 Jason Johnson .20 .50
18 Byung-Hyun Kim SP 1.25 3.00
19 Johnny Damon SP 1.50 4.00
20 Derek Lowe SP 1.25 3.00
21 Nomar Garciaparra SP 2.50 6.00
22 Pedro Martinez SP 1.50 4.00
23 Manny Ramirez SP 1.50 4.00
24 Mark Prior .30 .75
25 Kerry Wood .20 .50
26 Corey Patterson .20 .50
27 Sammy Sosa .50 1.25
28 Moises Alou .20 .50
29 Magglio Ordonez .20 .50
30 Frank Thomas .50 1.25
31 Paul Konerko .20 .50
32 Roberto Alomar .30 .75
33 Adam Dunn .20 .50
34 Austin Kearns .20 .50
35 Ryan Wagner RC .20 .50
36 Ken Griffey Jr. .75 2.00
37 Sean Casey .20 .50
38 Omar Vizquel .30 .75
39 C.C. Sabathia .20 .50
40 Jason Davis .20 .50
41 Travis Hafner .20 .50
42 Brandon Phillips .20 .50
43 Larry Walker .20 .50
44 Preston Wilson .20 .50
45 Jay Payton .20 .50
46 Todd Helton .30 .75
47 Carlos Pena .20 .50
48 Eric Munson .20 .50
49 Ivan Rodriguez .30 .75
50 Josh Beckett .20 .50
51 Alex Gonzalez .20 .50
52 Roy Oswalt .20 .50
53 Craig Biggio .30 .75
54 Jeff Bagwell .30 .75
55 Lance Berkman .20 .50
56 Mike Sweeney .20 .50
57 Carlos Beltran .20 .50
58 Brent Mayne .20 .50
59 Mike MacDougal .20 .50
60 Hideo Nomo .50 1.25
61 Dave Roberts .20 .50
62 Adrian Beltre .20 .50
63 Shawn Green .20 .50
64 Kazuhisa Ishii .20 .50
65 Rickey Henderson .50 1.25
66 Richie Sexson .20 .50
67 Torii Hunter .20 .50
68 Jacque Jones .20 .50
69 Joe Mays .20 .50
70 Corey Koskie .20 .50
71 A.J. Pierzynski .20 .50
72 Jose Vidro .20 .50
73 Vladimir Guerrero .50 1.25
74 Tom Glavine .30 .75
75 Mike Piazza .75 2.00
76 Jose Reyes .20 .50
77 Jae Weong Seo .20 .50
78 Jorge Posada SP 1.50 4.00
79 Mike Mussina SP 1.50 4.00
80 Robin Ventura SP 1.25 3.00
81 Mariano Rivera SP 1.50 4.00
82 Roger Clemens SP 3.00 8.00
83 Jason Giambi SP 1.25 3.00
84 Bernie Williams SP 1.50 4.00
85 Alfonso Soriano SP 1.25 3.00
86 Derek Jeter 1.25 3.00
87 Miguel Tejada .20 .50
88 Eric Chavez .20 .50
89 Tim Hudson .20 .50
90 Barry Zito .20 .50
91 Mark Mulder .20 .50
92 Erubiel Durazo .20 .50
93 Pat Burrell .20 .50
94 Jim Thome .30 .75
95 Bobby Abreu .20 .50
96 Brian Giles .20 .50
97 Reggie Sanders .20 .50
98 Jose Hernandez .20 .50
99 Ryan Klesko .20 .50
100 Sean Burroughs .20 .50
101 Edgardo Alfonzo SP 1.25 3.00
102 Rich Aurilia SP 1.25 3.00
103 Jose Cruz Jr. SP 1.25 3.00
104 Barry Bonds SP 4.00 10.00
105 Andres Galarraga SP 1.25 3.00
106 Mike Cameron .20 .50
107 Kazuhiro Sasaki .20 .50
108 Bret Boone .20 .50
109 Ichiro Suzuki 1.00 2.50
110 John Olerud .20 .50
111 J.D. Drew SP 1.25 3.00
112 Jim Edmonds SP 1.25 3.00
113 Scott Rolen SP 1.50 4.00
114 Matt Morris SP 1.25 3.00
115 Tino Martinez SP 1.50 4.00
116 Albert Pujols SP 3.00 8.00
117 Jared Sandberg .20 .50
118 Carl Crawford .20 .50
119 Rafael Palmeiro .30 .75
120 Hank Blalock .20 .50
121 Alex Rodriguez SP 2.50 6.00
122 Kevin Mench .20 .50
123 Juan Gonzalez .20 .50
124 Mark Teixeira .30 .75
125 Shannon Stewart .20 .50
126 Vernon Wells .20 .50
127 Josh Phelps .20 .50
128 Eric Hinske .20 .50
129 Orlando Hudson .20 .50
130 Carlos Delgado .20 .50
131 Jason Shiell SB RC 1.25 3.00
132 Kevin Tolar SB RC 1.25 3.00
133 Nathan Bland SB RC 1.25 3.00
134 Brent Hoard SB RC 1.25 3.00
135 Jon Pridie SB RC 1.25 3.00
136 Mike Ryan SB RC 1.25 3.00
137 Francisco Rosario SB RC 1.25 3.00
138 Runelvys Hernandez SB 1.25 3.00
139 Guillermo Quiroz SB RC 1.25 3.00
140 Chin-Hui Tsao SB 1.25 3.00
141 Rett Johnson SB RC 1.25 3.00
142 Colin Porter SB RC 1.25 3.00
143 Jose Castillo SB 1.25 3.00
144 Chris Waters SB RC 1.25 3.00
145 Jeremy Guthrie SB 1.25 3.00
146 Pedro Liriano SB 1.25 3.00
147 Joe Borowski SB 1.25 3.00
148 Felix Sanchez SB RC 1.25 3.00
149 Todd Wellemeyer SB RC 1.25 3.00
150 Gerald Laird SB 1.25 3.00
151 Brandon Webb SB RC 3.00 8.00
152 Tommy Whiteman SB 1.25 3.00
153 Carlos Rivera SB 1.25 3.00
154 Rick Roberts SB RC 1.25 3.00
155 Termel Sledge SB RC 1.25 3.00
156 Jeff Duncan SB RC 1.25 3.00
157 Craig Brazell SB RC 1.25 3.00
158 Bernie Castro SB RC 1.25 3.00
159 Cory Stewart SB RC 1.25 3.00

160 Brandon Villafuerte SB 1.25 3.00
161 Tommy Phelps SB 1.25 3.00
162 Josh Hall SB RC 1.25 3.00
163 Ryan Cameron SB RC 1.25 3.00
164 Garret Atkins SB 1.25 3.00
165 Brian Stokes SB RC 1.25 3.00
166 Rafael Betancourt SB RC 1.50 4.00
167 Jaime Cerda SB 1.25 3.00
168 D.J. Carrasco SB RC 1.25 3.00
169 Ian Ferguson SB RC 1.25 3.00
170 Jorge Cordova SB RC 1.25 3.00
171 Eric Munson SB 1.25 3.00
172 Nook Logan SB RC 1.50 4.00
173 Jeremy Bonderman SB RC 5.00 12.00
174 Kyle Snyder SB 1.25 3.00
175 Rich Harden SB 1.50 4.00
176 Kevin Ohme SB RC 1.25 3.00
177 Roger Deago SB RC 1.25 3.00
178 Marlon Byrd SB 1.25 3.00
179 Dontrelle Willis SB 1.50 4.00
180 Bobby Hill SB 1.25 3.00
181 Jesse Foppert SB 1.25 3.00
182 Andrew Good SB 1.25 3.00
183 Chase Utley SB 1.50 4.00
184 Bo Hart SB RC 1.25 3.00
185 Dan Haren SB RC 1.50 4.00
186 Tim Olson SB RC 1.25 3.00
187 Joe Thurston SB 1.25 3.00
188 Jason Anderson SB 1.25 3.00
189 Jason Gilfillan SB RC 1.25 3.00
190 Rickie Weeks SB RC 3.00 8.00
191 Hideki Matsui SB P1 RC 10.00 25.00
192 J.Contreras SB P3 RC 1.50 4.00
193 Willie Eyre SB P3 RC 1.25 3.00
194 Matt Bruback SB P3 RC 1.25 3.00
195 Heath Bell SB P3 RC 1.25 3.00
196 Lew Ford SB P3 RC 1.50 4.00
197 J.Griffiths SB P3 RC 1.25 3.00
198 O.Villarreal SB P1 RC 1.50 4.00
199 Fr. Cruceta SB P3 RC 1.25 3.00
200 Fern Cabrera SB P3 RC 1.25 3.00
201 Jhonny Peralta SB P3 1.50 4.00
202 Shane Bazzell SB P3 RC 1.25 3.00
203 B.Madritsch SB P1 RC 1.50 4.00
204 Phil Seibel SB P3 RC 1.25 3.00
205 J.Willingham SB P3 RC 2.00 5.00
206 Rob Hammock SB P1 RC 1.50 4.00
207 Al. Machado SB P3 RC 1.25 3.00
208 David Sanders SB P3 RC 1.25 3.00
209 Mike Neu SB P1 RC 1.50 4.00
210 Andrew Brown SB P3 RC 1.50 4.00
211 N. Robertson SB P3 RC 2.00 5.00
212 Miguel Ojeda SB P3 RC 1.25 3.00
213 Beau Kemp SB P3 RC 1.25 3.00
214 Aaron Looper SB P3 RC 1.25 3.00
215 Alf.Gonzalez SB P3 RC 1.25 3.00
216 Rich Fischer SB P1 RC 1.50 4.00
218 Jeremy Wedel SB P3 RC 1.25 3.00
219 Pr.Redman SB P3 RC 1.25 3.00
220 Mi.Hernandez SB P3 RC 1.25 3.00
221 Rocco Baldelli SB P1 1.50 4.00
222 Luis Ayala SB P3 RC 1.25 3.00
223 Arnaldo Munoz SB P3 RC 1.25 3.00
224 Wil.Ledezma SB P3 RC 1.25 3.00
225 Chris Capuano SB P3 RC 1.50 4.00
226 Aquilino Lopez SB P3 RC 1.25 3.00
227 Joe Valentine SB P1 RC 1.50 4.00
228 Matt Kata SB P2 RC 1.25 3.00
229 D.Markwell SB P2 RC 1.25 3.00
230 Clint Barmes SB P2 RC 1.25 3.00
231 Mike Nicolas SB P1 RC 1.50 4.00
232 Jon Leicester SB P2 RC 1.25 3.00

2003 Sweet Spot Sweet Beginnings 75

*SB 75: .6X TO 1.5X BASIC P1
*SB 75 MATSUI: .75X TO 1.5X BASIC MATSUI
*SB 75: .75X TO 2X BASIC P2-P3
RANDOM INSERTS IN PACKS
STATED PRINT RUN 75 SERIAL #'d SETS
CARDS ARE NOT GAME-USED MATERIAL

2003 Sweet Spot Sweet Beginnings Game Used 25

RANDOM INSERTS IN PACKS
STATED PRINT RUN 25 SERIAL #'d SETS
NO PRICING DUE TO SCARCITY
191 Hideki Matsui
193 Willie Eyre
194 Matt Bruback
195 Heath Bell
197 Jeremy Griffiths

2003 Sweet Spot Sweet Beginnings Game Used 10

RANDOM INSERTS IN PACKS
STATED PRINT RUN 10 SERIAL #'d SETS
NO PRICING DUE TO SCARCITY
191 Hideki Matsui

202 Shane Bazzell
203 Bobby Madritsch
204 Phil Seibel
206 Robby Hammock
207 Alejandro Machado

2003 Sweet Spot Bat Barrels

STATED ODDS 1:6000
NO PRICING DUE TO SCARCITY

2003 Sweet Spot Instant Win Redemptions

Randomly inserted into packs, these cards enabled a lucky collector to receive a prize from the Upper Deck Company.

ONE OR MORE CARDS PER CASE
PRINT RUNS B/WN 1-350 COPIES PER
NO PRICING ON QTY OF 28 OR LESS
EXCHANGE DEADLINE 09/16/06

2003 Sweet Spot Patches

*PATCH 75: 1X TO 2.5X BASIC
PATCH 75 PRINT RUN 75 SERIAL #'d SETS
CUMULATIVE PATCHES ODDS 1:8
CARDS ARE NOT GAME-USED MATERIAL
AD1 Adam Dunn 3.00 8.00
AJ1 Andruw Jones 4.00 10.00
AP1 Albert Pujols 6.00 15.00
AR1 Alex Rodriguez 6.00 15.00
AS1 Alfonso Soriano 3.00 8.00
BB1 Barry Bonds 8.00 20.00
BW1 Bernie Williams 4.00 10.00
BZ1 Barry Zito 3.00 8.00
CD1 Carlos Delgado 3.00 8.00
CJ1 Chipper Jones 4.00 10.00
CP1 Corey Patterson 3.00 8.00
CS1 Curt Schilling 3.00 8.00
DE1 Darin Erstad 3.00 8.00
DJ1 Derek Jeter 8.00 20.00
GM1 Greg Maddux 6.00 15.00
GS1 Gary Sheffield 3.00 8.00
HN1 Hideo Nomo 4.00 10.00
IS1 Ichiro Suzuki 6.00 15.00
JB1 Jeff Bagwell 4.00 10.00
JE1 Jim Edmonds 3.00 8.00
JG1 Jason Giambi 3.00 8.00
JK1 Jeff Kent 3.00 8.00
JT1 Jim Thome 4.00 10.00
KG1 Ken Griffey Jr. 6.00 15.00
KI1 Kazuhisa Ishii 3.00 8.00
LB1 Lance Berkman 3.00 8.00
LG1 Luis Gonzalez 3.00 8.00
MA1 Mark Prior 4.00 10.00
MO1 Magglio Ordonez 3.00 8.00
MP1 Mike Piazza 6.00 15.00
MT1 Miguel Tejada 3.00 8.00
NG1 Nomar Garciaparra 6.00 15.00
PB1 Pat Burrell 3.00 8.00
PM1 Pedro Martinez 4.00 10.00
RC1 Roger Clemens 6.00 15.00
RJ1 Randy Johnson 4.00 10.00
SG1 Shawn Green 3.00 8.00
SS1 Sammy Sosa 4.00 10.00
TG1 Troy Glaus 3.00 8.00
TH1 Torii Hunter 3.00 8.00
TO1 Tom Glavine 4.00 10.00
VG1 Vladimir Guerrero 4.00 10.00

2003 Sweet Spot Patches Game Used 25

RANDOM INSERTS IN PACKS
STATED PRINT RUN 25 SERIAL #'d SETS
NO PRICING DUE TO SCARCITY

AS3 Alfonso Soriano
KG3 Ken Griffey Jr.
MP3 Mike Piazza
NG3 Nomar Garciaparra
SS3 Sammy Sosa
TG3 Troy Glaus

2003 Sweet Spot Patches Game Used 10

RANDOM INSERTS IN PACKS
STATED PRINT RUN 10 SERIAL #'d SETS
NO PRICING DUE TO SCARCITY
AP3 Albert Pujols
AR3 Alex Rodriguez
IS3 Ichiro Suzuki
JG3 Jason Giambi
JT3 Jim Thome
RC3 Roger Clemens

2003 Sweet Spot Signatures Black Ink

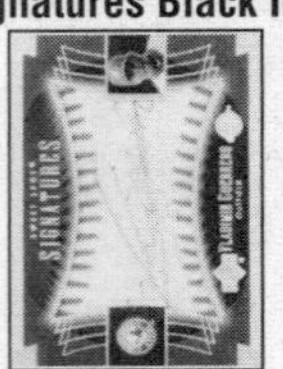

CUMULATIVE AUTO ODDS 1:24
SP PRINT RUNS PROVIDED BY UPPER DECK
SP'S ARE NOT SERIAL-NUMBERED
AD Adam Dunn 15.00 40.00
AK Austin Kearns 6.00 15.00
BH Bo Hart 6.00 15.00
BP Brandon Phillips 6.00 15.00
BW Brandon Webb 30.00 60.00
CR Cal Ripken SP/122 125.00 200.00
CS Curt Schilling 20.00 50.00
DH Drew Henson 6.00 15.00
DW Dontrelle Willis 20.00 50.00
GL Tom Glavine 20.00 50.00
GS Gary Sheffield 15.00 40.00
HA Travis Hafner 10.00 25.00
HB Hank Blalock 10.00 25.00
HM Hideki Matsui SP/147 175.00 300.00
JC Jose Contreras 15.00 40.00
JG Jason Giambi SP 20.00 50.00
JR Jose Reyes 10.00 25.00
JT Jim Thome 20.00 50.00
JW Jerome Williams 6.00 15.00
KGJ Ken Griffey Jr. 50.00 100.00
KGS Ken Griffey Sr. 10.00 25.00
KI Kazuhisa Ishii SP 20.00 50.00
LO Lyle Overbay 6.00 15.00
MP Mark Prior 12.50 30.00
MT Mark Teixeira 15.00 40.00
NG Nomar Garciaparra 50.00 100.00
NR Nolan Ryan SP 75.00 150.00
PB Pat Burrell 10.00 25.00
RC Roger Clemens SP/73 75.00 150.00
RO Roy Oswalt 10.00 25.00
TH Todd Helton SP/45 40.00 80.00
TR Troy Glaus 15.00 40.00
TS Tim Salmon 15.00 40.00
VG Vladimir Guerrero 30.00 60.00

2003 Sweet Spot Signatures Black Ink Holo-Foil

CUMULATIVE AUTO ODDS 1:24
STATED PRINT RUN 25 SERIAL #'d SETS
SOSA PRINT RUN 7 SERIAL #'d CARDS
NO PRICING DUE TO SCARCITY

2003 Sweet Spot Signatures Blue Ink

Rickie Weeks did not return his cards in time for inclusion in this product. Those cards were issued as exchange cards and were redeemable until September 16, 2006.

CUMULATIVE AUTO ODDS 1:24

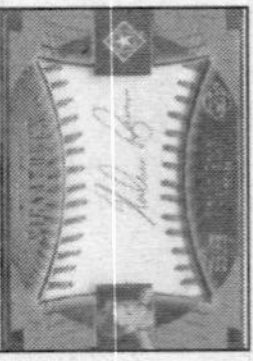

STATED PRINT RUN 40 SERIAL #'d SETS
T.GWYNN CARD NOT SERIAL-NUMBERED
T.GWYNN AU IN FAR GREATER SUPPLY
AD Adam Dunn 30.00 60.00
AK Austin Kearns 10.00 25.00
BH Bo Hart 10.00 25.00
BP Brandon Phillips 10.00 25.00
BW Brandon Webb 40.00 80.00
CR Cal Ripken 150.00 250.00
CS Curt Schilling 40.00 80.00
DH Drew Henson 10.00 25.00
DW Dontrelle Willis 40.00 80.00
GL Tom Glavine 40.00 80.00
GS Gary Sheffield 30.00 60.00
HA Travis Hafner 15.00 40.00
HB Hank Blalock 15.00 40.00
HM Hideki Matsui 250.00 400.00
IS Ichiro Suzuki 400.00 600.00
JC Jose Contreras 20.00 50.00
JG Jason Giambi 15.00 40.00
JR Jose Reyes 15.00 40.00
JT Jim Thome 40.00 80.00
JW Jerome Williams 10.00 25.00
KGJ Ken Griffey Jr. 75.00 150.00
KGS Ken Griffey Sr. 15.00 40.00
KI Kazuhisa Ishii 15.00 40.00
LO Lyle Overbay 10.00 25.00
MM Mickey Mantle/7
MP Mark Prior 20.00 50.00
MT Mark Teixeira 30.00 60.00
NG Nomar Garciaparra 60.00 120.00
NR Nolan Ryan 125.00 200.00
PB Pat Burrell 15.00 40.00
RC Roger Clemens 125.00 200.00
RO Roy Oswalt 15.00 40.00
RW Rickie Weeks/100 40.00 80.00
SS Sammy Sosa 60.00 120.00
TG Tony Gwynn NNO 20.00 50.00
TH Todd Helton 30.00 60.00
TR Troy Glaus 30.00 60.00
TS Tim Salmon 15.00 40.00
TW Ted Williams/9
VG Vladimir Guerrero 40.00 80.00

2003 Sweet Spot Signatures Red Ink

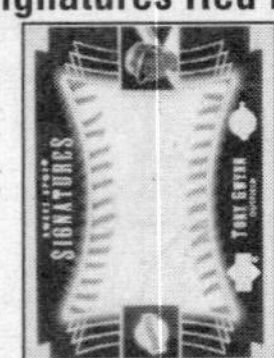

CUMULATIVE AUTO ODDS 1:24
PRINT RUNS B/WN 9-35 COPIES PER
GWYNN CARD NOT SERIAL-NUMBERED
NO PRICING ON QTY OF 10 OR LESS

2003 Sweet Spot Signatures Barrel

CUMULATIVE AUTO ODDS 1:24
PRINT RUNS B/WN 49-445 COPIES PER
CARDS ARE NOT GAME-USED MATERIAL
AD Adam Dunn/345 20.00 50.00
CR Cal Ripken/149 125.00 200.00
HB Hank Blalock/420 15.00 40.00
HM Hideki Matsui/124 250.00 400.00
JT Jim Thome/345 30.00 60.00
KG Ken Griffey Jr./295 60.00 120.00
NR Nolan Ryan/445 75.00 150.00
PB Pat Burrell/445 15.00 40.00
RC Roger Clemens/49 150.00 250.00
TG Tom Glavine/345 30.00 60.00
TR Troy Glaus/345 20.00 50.00

2003 Sweet Spot Swatches

SP INFO PROVIDED BY UPPER DECK
SP'S ARE NOT SERIAL-NUMBERED
*SWATCH 75: .6X TO 1.5X BASIC
*SWATCH 75: .5X TO 1.2X BASIC SP
*SWATCH 75: .4X TO 1X BASIC SP p/r 75-100
*SWATCH 75 MATSUI: .5X TO 1.2X BASIC
SWATCH 75 PRINT RUN 75 #'d SETS
CUMULATIVE SWATCHES ODDS 1:20
AJ Andruw Jones 3.00 8.00
AK Austin Kearns 2.00 5.00
AP Albert Pujols 8.00 20.00
AR Alex Rodriguez 4.00 10.00
AS Alfonso Soriano SP/81 4.00 10.00
BW Bernie Williams SP 6.00 15.00
BZ Barry Zito SP 4.00 10.00
CJ Chipper Jones 3.00 8.00
CS Curt Schilling 2.00 5.00
FT Frank Thomas 3.00 8.00
GM Greg Maddux 4.00 10.00
GS Gary Sheffield SP 4.00 10.00
HM Hideki Matsui SP/150 15.00 40.00
IS Ichiro Suzuki 10.00 25.00
JG Jason Giambi 2.00 5.00
JT Jim Thome 3.00 8.00
KG Ken Griffey Jr. 6.00 15.00
LG Luis Gonzalez 2.00 5.00
MM M.Mantle Pants UER SP/100 75.00 150.00
Card erroneously states Game Used Jersey
MP Mike Piazza 4.00 10.00
MP Mark Prior SP 6.00 15.00
MT Miguel Tejada 2.00 5.00
NG Nomar Garciaparra SP/75
PB Pat Burrell 2.00 5.00
RA Roberto Alomar SP 6.00 15.00
RC Roger Clemens 4.00 10.00
RJ Randy Johnson SP 6.00 15.00
RO Roy Oswalt 2.00 5.00
SS Sammy Sosa 3.00 8.00
TG Troy Glaus 2.00 5.00
TG Tom Glavine SP 6.00 15.00
TH Torii Hunter 2.00 5.00
TW Ted Williams Pants SP/100 50.00 100.00
VG Vladimir Guerrero 3.00 8.00

2004 Sweet Spot

This 262 card set was released in October, 2004. The set was issued in three card packs with an $10 SRP which came 12 packs to a box and 10 boxes to a case. The first 90 cards in this set feature veterans while cards 91 through 170 and 261-262 feature Rookie Cards. Those cards were issued at a stated rate of one in two. Cards numbered 91 through 170 and 261-262 were issued to a stated print run of 799 serial numnbered sets. Cards numbered 171 through 205 comprise a swinging for the fences subset and cards numbered 206 through 230 are season leader subset cards. Those cards were issued to a stated print run of 399 serial numbered sets. Cards numbered 231 through 250 is a pennant drive subset and those cards were issued to a stated print run of 299 serial numbered sets. Cards numbered 251 through 260 comprise a diamond duo subset and those cards were issued to a stated print run of 199 serial numbered sets.

COMP.SET w/o SP's (90) 8.00 20.00
COMMON CARD (1-90) .20 .50
COMMON (91-170/261-262) 1.50 4.00
91-170/261-262 STATED ODDS 1:12
91-170/261-262 PRINT RUN 799 #'d SETS
COMMON CARD (171-230) 1.50 4.00
171-230 PRINT RUN 399 SERIAL #'d SETS
COMMON CARD (231-250) 1.50 4.00
231-250 PRINT RUN 299 SERIAL #'d SETS
COMMON CARD (251-260) 2.50 6.00
251-260 PRINT RUN 199 SERIAL #'d SETS
171-260/Ltd 10/W99 OVERALL ODDS 1:12
OVERALL PLATES ODDS 1:360 HOBBY
PLATES PRINT RUN 1 SET PER COLOR
BLACK-CYAN-MAGENTA-YELLOW ISSUED
NO PLATES PRICING DUE TO SACRCITY
1 Albert Pujols 1.00 2.50
2 Alex Rodriguez .75 2.00
3 Alfonso Soriano .30 .75
4 Andruw Jones .30 .75
5 Andy Pettitte .30 .75
6 Aubrey Huff .20 .50
7 Austin Kearns .20 .50
8 Barry Zito .20 .50
9 Bobby Abreu .20 .50
10 Brandon Webb .20 .50
11 Bret Boone .20 .50
12 Brian Giles .20 .50
13 C.C. Sabathia .20 .50
14 Carlos Beltran .20 .50
15 Carlos Delgado .20 .50
16 Chipper Jones .50 1.25
17 Cliff Floyd .20 .50
18 Curt Schilling .30 .75
19 Delmon Young .30 .75
20 Derek Jeter 1.00 2.50
21 Dontrelle Willis .30 .75
22 Edgar Martinez .30 .75
23 Edgar Renteria .20 .50
24 Eric Chavez .20 .50
25 Eric Gagne .20 .50
26 Frank Thomas .50 1.25
27 Garret Anderson .20 .50
28 Gary Sheffield .20 .50
29 Geoff Jenkins .20 .50
30 Greg Maddux .75 2.00
31 Hank Blalock .20 .50
32 Hideo Nomo .50 1.25
33 Ichiro Suzuki 1.00 2.50
34 Ivan Rodriguez .30 .75
35 Jacque Jones .20 .50
36 Jason Giambi .20 .50
37 Jason Schmidt .20 .50
38 Javier Vazquez .20 .50
39 Javy Lopez .20 .50
40 Jeff Bagwell .30 .75
41 Jim Edmonds .20 .50
42 Jim Thome .30 .75
43 Joe Mauer .50 1.25
44 John Smoltz .20 .50
45 Jose Cruz Jr. .20 .50
46 Jose Reyes .20 .50
47 Jose Vidro .20 .50
48 Josh Beckett .20 .50
49 Ken Griffey Jr. .75 2.00
50 Kerry Wood .20 .50
51 Kevin Brown .20 .50
52 Larry Walker .20 .50
53 Magglio Ordonez .20 .50
54 Manny Ramirez .30 .75
55 Mark Mulder .20 .50
56 Mark Prior .30 .75
57 Mark Teixeira .30 .75
58 Miguel Cabrera .30 .75
59 Miguel Tejada .20 .50
60 Mike Lowell .20 .50
61 Mike Mussina .30 .75
62 Mike Piazza .75 2.00
63 Nomar Garciaparra .75 2.00
64 Orlando Cabrera .20 .50
65 Pat Burrell .20 .50
66 Pedro Martinez .30 .75
67 Phil Nevin .20 .50
68 Preston Wilson .20 .50
69 Rafael Furcal .20 .50
70 Rafael Palmeiro .30 .75
71 Randy Johnson .50 1.25
72 Craig Wilson .20 .50
73 Rich Harden .20 .50
74 Richie Sexson .20 .50
75 Rickie Weeks .20 .50
76 Rocco Baldelli .20 .50
77 Roger Clemens 1.00 2.50
78 Roy Halladay .20 .50
79 Roy Oswalt .20 .50
80 Ryan Klesko .20 .50
81 Sammy Sosa .50 1.25
82 Scott Podsednik .20 .50
83 Scott Rolen .30 .75
84 Shawn Green .20 .50
85 Tim Hudson .20 .50
86 Todd Helton .30 .75
87 Torii Hunter .20 .50
88 Troy Glaus .20 .50
89 Vernon Wells .20 .50
90 Vladimir Guerrero .50 1.25
91 Aarom Baldiris SB RC 2.00 5.00
92 Akinori Otsuka SB RC 1.50 4.00
93 Andres Blanco SB RC 1.50 4.00
94 Angel Chavez SB RC 1.50 4.00
95 Brian Dallimore SB RC 1.50 4.00
96 Carlos Hines SB RC 1.50 4.00
97 Carlos Vasquez SB RC 2.00 5.00
98 Casey Daigle SB RC 1.50 4.00
99 Chad Bentz SB RC 1.50 4.00
100 Chris Aguila SB RC 1.50 4.00
101 Chris Oxspring SB RC 1.50 4.00
102 Chris Saenz SB RC 1.50 4.00
103 Chris Shelton SB RC 2.00 5.00
104 Colby Miller SB RC 1.50 4.00
105 Dave Crouthers SB RC 1.50 4.00
106 David Aardsma SB RC 2.00 5.00
107 Dennis Sarfate SB RC 1.50 4.00
108 Donnie Kelly SB RC 1.50 4.00
109 Eddy Rodriguez SB RC 2.00 5.00
110 Eduardo Villacis SB RC 1.50 4.00
111 Edwin Moreno SB RC 2.00 5.00
112 Enemencio Pacheco SB RC 1.50 4.00
113 Fernando Nieve SB RC 2.00 5.00
114 Franklyn Gracesqui SB RC 1.50 4.00
115 Freddy Guzman SB RC 1.50 4.00
116 Greg Dobbs SB RC 1.50 4.00
117 Hector Gimenez SB RC 1.50 4.00
118 Ian Snell SB RC 2.00 5.00
119 Ivan Ochoa SB RC 1.50 4.00
120 Jake Woods SB RC 1.50 4.00
121 Jamie Brown SB RC 1.50 4.00
122 Jason Bartlett SB RC 2.00 5.00
123 Jason Frasor SB RC 1.50 4.00
124 Jeff Bennett SB RC 1.50 4.00
125 Jerome Gamble SB RC 1.50 4.00
126 Jerry Gil SB RC 1.50 4.00
127 Brandon Medders SB RC 1.50 4.00
128 Ryan Meaux SB RC 1.50 4.00
129 John Gall SB RC 2.00 5.00
130 Jorge Sequea SB RC 1.50 4.00
131 Jorge Vasquez SB RC 1.50 4.00
132 Jose Capellan SB RC 2.00 5.00
133 Josh Labandeira SB RC 1.50 4.00
134 Justin Germano SB RC 1.50 4.00
135 Justin Hampson SB RC 1.50 4.00
136 Justin Huisman SB RC 1.50 4.00
137 Justin Knoedler SB RC 1.50 4.00
138 Justin Leone SB RC 2.00 5.00
139 Kazuhito Tadano SB RC 2.00 5.00
140 Kazuo Matsui SB RC 2.00 5.00
141 Kevin Cave SB RC 1.50 4.00
142 Lincoln Holdzkom SB RC 1.50 4.00
143 Lino Urdaneta SB RC 1.50 4.00
144 Luis A. Gonzalez SB RC 1.50 4.00
145 Mariano Gomez SB RC 1.50 4.00
146 Merkin Valdez SB RC 2.00 5.00
147 Michael Vento SB RC 2.00 5.00
148 Michael Wuertz SB RC 2.00 5.00
149 Mike Gosling SB RC 1.50 4.00
150 Mike Johnston SB RC 1.50 4.00
151 Mike Rouse SB RC 1.50 4.00
152 Nick Regilio SB RC 1.50 4.00
153 Onil Joseph SB RC 1.50 4.00
154 Orlando Rodriguez SB RC 1.50 4.00
155 Ramon Ramirez SB RC 1.50 4.00
156 Renyel Pinto SB RC 2.00 5.00
157 Roberto Novoa SB RC 2.00 5.00
158 Roman Colon SB RC 1.50 4.00
159 Ronald Belisario SB RC 1.50 4.00
160 Ronny Cedeno SB RC 2.00 5.00
161 Rusty Tucker SB RC 2.00 5.00
162 Ryan Wing SB RC 1.50 4.00
163 Scott Dohmann SB RC 1.50 4.00
164 Scott Proctor SB RC 2.00 5.00
165 Sean Henn SB RC 1.50 4.00
166 Shawn Camp SB RC 1.50 4.00
167 Shawn Hill SB RC 1.50 4.00
168 Shingo Takatsu SB RC 2.00 5.00
169 Tim Hamulack SB RC 1.50 4.00
170 William Bergolla SB RC 1.50 4.00
171 Adam Dunn SF 1.50 4.00
172 Albert Pujols SF 4.00 10.00
173 Alex Rodriguez SF 3.00 8.00
174 Alfonso Soriano SF 1.50 4.00

175 Andruw Jones SF 2.00 5.00
176 Bret Boone SF 1.50 4.00
177 Brian Giles SF 1.50 4.00
178 Carlos Delgado SF 1.50 4.00
179 Derrek Lee SF 2.00 5.00
180 Eric Chavez SF 1.50 4.00
181 Frank Thomas SF 2.00 5.00
182 Garret Anderson SF 1.50 4.00
183 Gary Sheffield SF 1.50 4.00
184 Hank Blalock SF 1.50 4.00
185 Jason Giambi SF 1.50 4.00
186 Javy Lopez SF 1.50 4.00
187 Jeff Bagwell SF 2.00 5.00
188 Jim Edmonds SF 1.50 4.00
189 Jim Thome SF 2.00 5.00
190 Ken Griffey Jr. SF 3.00 8.00
191 Lance Berkman SF 1.50 4.00
192 Magglio Ordonez SF 1.50 4.00
193 Manny Ramirez SF 2.00 5.00
194 Mike Lowell SF 1.50 4.00
195 Mike Piazza SF 3.00 8.00
196 Preston Wilson SF 1.50 4.00
197 Rafael Palmeiro SF 2.00 5.00
198 Richie Sexson SF 1.50 4.00
199 Sammy Sosa SF 2.00 5.00
200 Scott Rolen SF 2.00 5.00
201 Shawn Green SF 1.50 4.00
202 Todd Helton SF 2.00 5.00
203 Troy Glaus SF 1.50 4.00
204 Vernon Wells SF 1.50 4.00
205 Vladimir Guerrero SF 2.00 5.00
206 Garret Anderson 2.00 5.00
Vladimir Guerrero SL
207 Luis Gonzalez 1.50 4.00
Richie Sexson SL
208 Andruw Jones 2.00 5.00
Chipper Jones SL
209 Javy Lopez 1.50 4.00
Miguel Tejada SL
210 Manny Ramirez 2.00 5.00
David Ortiz SL
211 Derrek Lee 2.00 5.00
Sammy Sosa SL
212 Frank Thomas 2.00 5.00
Magglio Ordonez SL
213 Austin Kearns 3.00 8.00
Ken Griffey Jr. SL
214 Preston Wilson 2.00 5.00
Todd Helton SL
215 Dmitri Young 2.00 5.00
Ivan Rodriguez SL
216 Miguel Cabrera 2.00 5.00
Mike Lowell SL
217 Jeff Bagwell 2.00 5.00
Lance Berkman SL
218 Lyle Overbay 1.50 4.00
Geoff Jenkins SL
219 Adrian Beltre 1.50 4.00
Shawn Green SL
220 Jacque Jones 1.50 4.00
Torii Hunter SL
221 Jose Vidro 1.50 4.00
Nick Johnson SL
222 Kazuo Matsui 3.00 8.00
Mike Piazza SL
223 Alex Rodriguez 3.00 8.00
Jason Giambi SL
224 Eric Chavez 1.50 4.00
Jermaine Dye SL
225 Jim Thome 2.00 5.00
Pat Burrell SL
226 Brian Giles 1.50 4.00
Phil Nevin SL
227 Bret Boone 4.00 10.00
Ichiro Suzuki SL
228 Albert Pujols 4.00 10.00
Scott Rolen SL
229 Hank Blalock 2.00 5.00
Mark Teixeira SL
230 Carlos Delgado 1.50 4.00
Vernon Wells SL
231 Albert Pujols PD 4.00 10.00
232 Alex Rodriguez PD 3.00 8.00
233 Chipper Jones PD 2.00 5.00
234 Craig Biggio PD 2.00 5.00
235 Curt Schilling PD 2.00 5.00
236 Derek Jeter PD 4.00 10.00
237 Ivan Rodriguez PD 2.00 5.00
238 Jeff Bagwell PD 2.00 5.00
239 Jim Edmonds PD 1.50 4.00
240 Jim Thome PD 2.00 5.00
241 Josh Beckett PD 1.50 4.00
242 Kerry Wood PD 1.50 4.00
243 Kevin Brown PD 1.50 4.00
244 Mark Prior PD 2.00 5.00
245 Miguel Tejada PD 1.50 4.00
246 Mike Mussina PD 2.00 5.00
247 Nomar Garciaparra PD 3.00 8.00
248 Pedro Martinez PD 2.00 5.00
249 Randy Johnson PD 2.00 5.00
250 Roger Clemens PD 4.00 10.00
251 Alex Rodriguez 6.00 15.00
Derek Jeter DD
252 Alfonso Soriano 2.50 6.00
Hank Blalock DD
253 Bobby Abreu 2.50 6.00
Pat Burrell DD
254 Edgar Renteria 3.00 8.00
Scott Rolen DD
255 Garret Anderson 3.00 8.00
Vladimir Guerrero DD
256 Jeff Bagwell 3.00 8.00
Jeff Kent DD
257 Jose Reyes 3.00 8.00
Kazuo Matsui DD
258 Khalil Greene 3.00 8.00
Sean Burroughs DD
259 Marcus Giles 2.50 6.00
Rafael Furcal DD
260 Manny Ramirez 3.00 8.00
Johnny Damon DD
261 Tim Bausher SB RC 1.50 4.00
262 Tim Bittner SB RC 1.50 4.00

2004 Sweet Spot Limited

Basic 171-260/Ltd 10/Wood 99 ODDS 1:12
STATED PRINT RUN 10 SERIAL #'d SETS
NO PRICING DUE TO SCARCITY

2004 Sweet Spot Wood

*WOOD 91-170/261-262: .6X TO 1.5X BASIC
*WOOD 171-230: .6X TO 1.5X BASIC
*WOOD 231-250: .6X TO 1.5X BASIC
*WOOD 251-260: .5X TO 1.2X BASIC
Wood 99/Basic 171-260/Ltd 10 ODDS 1:12
STATED PRINT RUN 99 SERIAL #'d SETS
OVERALL PLATES ODDS 1:360 HOBBY
PLATES PRINT RUN 1 SET PER COLOR
BLACK-CYAN-MAGENTA-YELLOW ISSUED
NO PLATES PRICING DUE TO SCARCITY

2004 Sweet Spot Diamond Champs Jersey

STATED PRINT RUN 150 SERIAL #'d SETS
PATCH PRINT RUN 10 SERIAL #'d SETS
A-ROD PATCH PRINT RUN 1 #'d CARD
NO PATCH PRICING DUE TO SCARCITY
OVERALL GAME-USED ODDS 1:6
AP Albert Pujols 8.00 20.00
AR Alex Rodriguez Yanks 6.00 15.00
BZ Barry Zito 3.00 8.00
CJ Chipper Jones 4.00 10.00
CS Curt Schilling 6.00 15.00
DJ Derek Jeter 10.00 25.00
EG Eric Gagne 3.00 8.00
GA Garret Anderson 3.00 8.00
GM Greg Maddux 6.00 15.00
IR Ivan Rodriguez 4.00 10.00
IS Ichiro Suzuki 12.50 30.00
JB Josh Beckett 3.00 8.00
KG Ken Griffey Jr. 6.00 15.00
MP Mike Piazza 6.00 15.00
MT Miguel Tejada 3.00 8.00
PE Andy Pettitte 4.00 10.00
PM Pedro Martinez 4.00 10.00
RC Roger Clemens 6.00 15.00
RH Roy Halladay 4.00 10.00
RJ Randy Johnson 4.00 10.00

2004 Sweet Spot Home Run Heroes Jersey

STATED PRINT RUN 199 SERIAL #'d SETS
*1-2 COLOR PATCH: .75X TO 2X BASIC
*3-4 COLOR PATCH: 1.25X TO 3X BASIC
PATCH PRINT RUN 55 SERIAL #'d SETS
A-ROD PATCH PRINT RUN 10 #'d CARDS
NO A-ROD PATCH PRICING AVAILABLE
OVERALL GAME-USED ODDS 1:6
AB Adrian Beltre 3.00 8.00
AD Adam Dunn 3.00 8.00
AJ Andruw Jones 4.00 10.00
AP Albert Pujols 8.00 20.00
AR A.Rod Yanks Bat Up 6.00 15.00
AR1 A.Rod Yanks Swing 6.00 15.00
AS Alfonso Soriano 3.00 8.00
BB Bret Boone 3.00 8.00
BG Brian Giles 3.00 8.00
BW Bernie Williams 4.00 10.00
CB Carlos Beltran 3.00 8.00
CD Carlos Delgado 3.00 8.00
CJ Chipper Jones 4.00 10.00
DJ Derek Jeter 10.00 25.00
DL Derrek Lee 4.00 10.00
DO David Ortiz 4.00 10.00
EC Eric Chavez 3.00 8.00
FM Fred McGriff 4.00 10.00
FT Frank Thomas 4.00 10.00
GA Garret Anderson 3.00 8.00
GS Gary Sheffield 3.00 8.00
HA Travis Hafner 3.00 8.00
HB Hank Blalock 3.00 8.00
HM Hideki Matsui 12.50 30.00
IR Ivan Rodriguez 4.00 10.00
JB Jeff Bagwell 4.00 10.00
JD J.D. Drew 3.00 8.00
JE Jim Edmonds 3.00 8.00
JG Jason Giambi 3.00 8.00
JK Jeff Kent 3.00 8.00
JM Joe Mauer 4.00 10.00
JP Jorge Posada 4.00 10.00
JT Jim Thome 4.00 10.00
KG Ken Griffey Jr. 6.00 15.00
KG1 Ken Griffey Jr. 6.00 15.00
LB Lance Berkman 3.00 8.00
LG Luis Gonzalez 3.00 8.00
MC Miguel Cabrera 4.00 10.00
ML Mike Lowell 3.00 8.00
MO Magglio Ordonez 3.00 8.00
MP Mike Piazza 6.00 15.00
MR Manny Ramirez 4.00 10.00
MT Mark Teixeira 4.00 10.00
PB Pat Burrell 3.00 8.00
PW Preston Wilson 3.00 8.00
RP Rafael Palmeiro 4.00 10.00
RS Richie Sexson 3.00 8.00
SG Shawn Green 3.00 8.00
SR Scott Rolen 4.00 10.00
SS Sammy Sosa 4.00 10.00
TE Miguel Tejada 3.00 8.00
TG Troy Glaus 3.00 8.00
TH Todd Helton 4.00 10.00
VG Vladimir Guerrero 4.00 10.00
VW Vernon Wells 3.00 8.00

2004 Sweet Spot Marquee Attractions Jersey

STATED PRINT RUN 199 SERIAL #'d SETS
*1-2 COLOR PATCH: 1X TO 2.5X BASIC
*3-4 COLOR PATCH: 1.5X TO 4X BASIC
*5+ COLOR PATCH: 2X TO 5X BASIC
PATCH PRINT RUN 35 SERIAL #'d SETS
A-ROD PATCH PRINT RUN 5 #'d CARDS
NO A-ROD PATCH PRICING AVAILABLE
OVERALL GAME-USED ODDS 1:6
AJ Andruw Jones 4.00 10.00
AP Albert Pujols 8.00 20.00
AR Alex Rodriguez Yanks 6.00 15.00
BG Brian Giles 3.00 8.00
BS Ben Sheets 3.00 8.00
CD Carlos Delgado 3.00 8.00
CS Curt Schilling 4.00 10.00
DJ Derek Jeter 10.00 25.00
EC Eric Chavez 3.00 8.00
EG Eric Gagne 3.00 8.00
FT Frank Thomas 4.00 10.00
HB Hank Blalock 3.00 8.00
HU Torii Hunter 3.00 8.00
IR Ivan Rodriguez 4.00 10.00
IS Ichiro Suzuki 12.50 30.00
JS Jason Schmidt 3.00 8.00
JT Jim Thome 4.00 10.00
KG Ken Griffey Jr. 6.00 15.00
MC Miguel Cabrera 4.00 10.00
MP Mark Prior 4.00 10.00
MS Mike Sweeney 3.00 8.00
MT Miguel Tejada 3.00 8.00
PI Mike Piazza 6.00 15.00
RC Roger Clemens 6.00 15.00
RJ Randy Johnson 4.00 10.00
TH Todd Helton 4.00 10.00
VG Vladimir Guerrero 4.00 10.00

2004 Sweet Spot Signatures

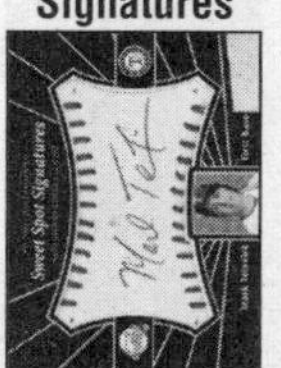

TIER 4 PRINT RUNS 201 COPIES AND UP
TIER 3 PRINT RUNS B/WN 101-200 PER
TIER 2 PRINT RUNS B/WN 51-100 PER
TIER 1 PRINT RUNS B/WN 27-34 PER
TIER 1 PRINT RUNS PROVIDED BY UD
OVERALL AU ODDS 1:12
TIER INFO PROVIDED BY UPPER DECK
CARDS ARE NOT SERIAL-NUMBERED
BASIC SIGNATURES FEATURE RED STITCH
EXCHANGE DEADLINE 11/22/07
AB Angel Berroa T4 6.00 15.00
AD Adam Dunn T4 10.00 25.00
AK Austin Kearns T4 6.00 15.00
AP Albert Pujols T3 150.00 250.00
AR Alex Rodriguez T1/27 *
BB Bret Boone T4 10.00 25.00
BE Josh Beckett T3 15.00 40.00
BG Brian Giles T4 6.00 15.00
BS Ben Sheets T4 6.00 15.00
BW Brandon Webb T4 6.00 15.00
CB Carlos Beltran T3 10.00 25.00
CL Carlos Lee T4 6.00 15.00
CP Corey Patterson T2 EXCH 10.00 25.00
CR Cal Ripken T2 EXCH * 125.00 200.00
CZ Carlos Zambrano T3 15.00 40.00
DJ Derek Jeter T2 125.00 200.00
DL Derrek Lee T4 10.00 25.00
DM Don Mattingly T4 30.00 60.00
DW Dontrelle Willis T4 10.00 25.00
DY Delmon Young T4 10.00 25.00
EC Eric Chavez T4 6.00 15.00
EJ Edwin Jackson T2 EXCH
EL Esteban Loaiza T4 6.00 15.00
EM Edgar Martinez T3 30.00 60.00
FT Frank Thomas T3 30.00 60.00
GA Garret Anderson T4 6.00 15.00
GJ Geoff Jenkins T4 6.00 15.00
GL Tom Glavine T2 20.00 50.00
GS Gary Sheffield T4 15.00 40.00
HA Roy Halladay T3 10.00 25.00
HB Hank Blalock T4 6.00 15.00
HI Richard Hidalgo T4 6.00 15.00
HO Trevor Hoffman T4 6.00 15.00
HU Torii Hunter T4 6.00 15.00
IR Ivan Rodriguez T2 EXCH 40.00 80.00
IS Ichiro Suzuki T4 150.00 250.00
JD J.D. Drew T3 10.00 25.00
JG Juan Gonzalez T2 12.50 30.00
JJ Jacque Jones T4 6.00 15.00
JM Joe Mauer T4 12.50 30.00
JR Jose Reyes T4 20.00 50.00
JS Jason Schmidt T4 6.00 15.00
JV Javier Vazquez T4 6.00 15.00
KG Ken Griffey Jr. T4 40.00 80.00
KW Kerry Wood T4 10.00 25.00
LG Luis Gonzalez T2 12.50 30.00
LO Mike Lowell T3 10.00 25.00
MA Mike Marshall T1/34 *
MC Miguel Cabrera T4 10.00 25.00
MG Marcus Giles T4 6.00 15.00
ML Mike Lieberthal T4 6.00 15.00
MM Mike Mussina T3 15.00 40.00
MP Mark Prior T3 15.00 40.00
MR Manny Ramirez T2 40.00 80.00
MT Mark Teixeira T4 10.00 25.00
MU Mark Mulder T4 6.00 15.00
NG Nomar Garciaparra T4 30.00 60.00
NR Nolan Ryan T2 EXCH * 125.00 200.00
OP Odalis Perez T4 6.00 15.00
PB Pat Burrell T2 12.50 30.00
PI Mike Piazza T2 125.00 200.00
RB Rocco Baldelli T2 12.50 30.00
RC Roger Clemens T2 75.00 150.00
RH Rich Harden T4 6.00 15.00
RK Ryan Klesko T4 6.00 15.00
RO Roy Oswalt T4 6.00 15.00
RS Ryne Sandberg T2 40.00 80.00
RW Randy Wolf T4 6.00 15.00
SA Johan Santana T4 30.00 60.00
SB Sean Burroughs T4 6.00 15.00
SM John Smoltz T3 30.00 60.00
SP Scott Podsednik T4 10.00 25.00
SR Scott Rolen T4 20.00 50.00
TE Miguel Tejada T3 15.00 40.00
TG Tony Gwynn T3 30.00 60.00
TH Todd Helton T2 20.00 50.00
TI Tim Hudson T2 20.00 50.00
TS Tom Seaver T3 30.00 60.00
VG Vladimir Guerrero T2 30.00 60.00
VW Vernon Wells T1/30 *
WA Billy Wagner T4 10.00 25.00
WC Will Clark T4 10.00 25.00
WE Rickie Weeks T4 6.00 15.00

2004 Sweet Spot Signatures Black Stitch

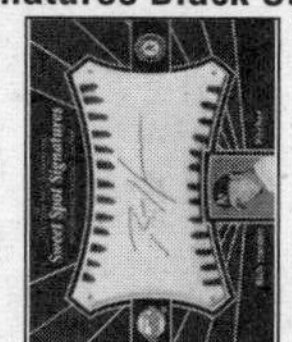

BLK/RED-BLUE/DUAL/HIST AU ODDS 1:180
STATED PRINT RUN 1 SERIAL #'d SET
NO PRICING DUE TO SCARCITY
EXCHANGE DEADLINE 11/22/07

2004 Sweet Spot Signatures Red-Blue Stitch

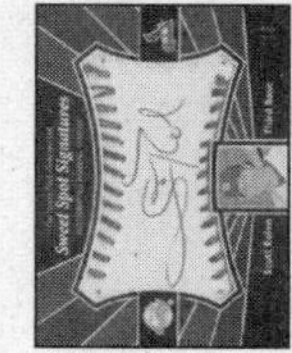

*R/B p/r 40-55: .6X TO 1.5X TIER 4
*R/B p/r 40-55: .5X TO 1.2X TIER 3
*R/B p/r 40-55: .5X TO 1.2X TIER 2
*R/B p/r 20-35: .6X TO 1.5X TIER 3
*R/B p/r 20-35: .5X TO 1.2X TIER 2
*R/B p/r 15: .75X TO 2X TIER 4
BLK/RED-BLUE/DUAL/HIST AU ODDS 1:180
PRINT RUNS B/WN 10-55 COPIES PER
NO PRICING ON QTY OF 10 OR LESS
EXCHANGE DEADLINE 11/22/07
AP Albert Pujols/45 200.00 300.00
CR Cal Ripken/35 EXCH * 175.00 300.00
DJ Derek Jeter/35 200.00 350.00
IS Ichiro Suzuki/25 400.00 600.00
NR Nolan Ryan/40 EXCH 125.00 200.00
PI Mike Piazza/20 150.00 250.00
RC Roger Clemens/30 EXCH * 125.00 200.00

2004 Sweet Spot Signatures Barrel

OVERALL AU ODDS 1:12
PRINT RUNS B/WN 13-74 COPIES PER
CARDS ARE NOT SERIAL-NUMBERED
PRINT RUNS PROVIDED BY UPPER DECK
NO PRICING ON QTY OF 14 OR LESS
EXCHANGE DEADLINE 11/22/07
AB Angel Berroa/64 * 12.50 30.00

AD Adam Dunn/74 * 20.00 50.00
AK Austin Kearns/64 * 12.50 30.00
AP Albert Pujols/64 * 150.00 250.00
AR Alex Rodriguez/28 * 250.00 350.00
BB Bret Boone/64 * 20.00 50.00
BE Josh Beckett/65 * 20.00 50.00
BG Brian Giles/64 * 15.00 40.00
BS Ben Sheets/64 * 15.00 40.00
BW Brandon Webb/64 * 12.50 30.00
CB Carlos Beltran/55 * 15.00 40.00
CL Carlos Lee/64 * 15.00 40.00
CP Corey Patterson/74 EXCH * 12.50 30.00
CR Cal Ripken/38 * 150.00 250.00
CZ Carlos Zambrano/38 * 30.00 60.00
DJ Derek Jeter/53 * 175.00 300.00
DL Derrek Lee/64 * 20.00 50.00
DM Don Mattingly/38 * 75.00 150.00
DW Dontrelle Willis/64 * 20.00 50.00
DY Delmon Young/74 * 20.00 50.00
EC Eric Chavez/74 * 15.00 40.00
EJ Edwin Jackson/64 EXCH * 12.50 30.00
EL Esteban Loaiza/64 * 12.50 30.00
EM Edgar Martinez/64 * 40.00 80.00
FT Frank Thomas/13 *
GA Garret Anderson/74 * 15.00 40.00
GJ Geoff Jenkins/64 * 15.00 40.00
GL Tom Glavine/64 * 20.00 50.00
GS Gary Sheffield/38 * 40.00 80.00
HA Roy Halladay/64 * 15.00 40.00
HB Hank Blalock/74 * 15.00 40.00
HI Richard Hidalgo/64 * 12.50 30.00
HO Trevor Hoffman/68 * 15.00 40.00
HU Torii Hunter/64 * 15.00 40.00
IR Ivan Rodriguez/64 * 40.00 80.00
IS Ichiro Suzuki/64 * 400.00 600.00
JD J.D. Drew/13 *
JG Juan Gonzalez/13 *
JJ Jacque Jones/64 * 15.00 40.00
JM Joe Mauer/72 * 30.00 60.00
JR Jose Reyes/49 * 15.00 40.00
JS Jason Schmidt/64 * 15.00 40.00
JV Javier Vazquez/64 * 15.00 40.00
KG Ken Griffey Jr./64 * 75.00 150.00
KW Kerry Wood/64 * 20.00 50.00
LG Luis Gonzalez/13 *
LO Mike Lowell/64 * 15.00 40.00
MA Mike Marshall/13 *
MC Miguel Cabrera/64 * 20.00 50.00
MG Marcus Giles/64 * 15.00 40.00
ML Mike Lieberthal/64 * 15.00 40.00
MM Mike Mussina/64 * 30.00 60.00
MP Mark Prior/64 * 15.00 40.00
MR Manny Ramirez/63 * 60.00 120.00
MT Mark Teixeira/64 * 20.00 50.00
MU Mark Mulder/64 * 15.00 40.00
NG Nomar Garciaparra/38 * 50.00 100.00
NR Nolan Ryan/38 * 125.00 200.00
OP Odalis Perez/64 * 12.50 30.00
PB Pat Burrell/13 *
PI Mike Piazza/38 * 100.00 175.00
RB Rocco Baldelli/19 * 30.00 60.00
RH Rich Harden/64 * 15.00 40.00
RK Ryan Klesko/64 * 15.00 40.00
RO Roy Oswalt/64 * 15.00 40.00
RS Ryne Sandberg/14 *
RW Randy Wolf/64 * 12.50 30.00
SA Johan Santana/64 * 30.00 60.00
SB Sean Burroughs/64 * 12.50 30.00
SM John Smoltz/13 *
SP Scott Podsednik/64 * 20.00 50.00
TE Miguel Tejada/64 * 20.00 50.00
TG Tony Gwynn/15 *
TH Todd Helton/38 * 30.00 60.00
TI Tim Hudson/64 * 20.00 50.00
TS Tom Seaver/38 * 40.00 80.00
VG Vladimir Guerrero/38 * 40.00 80.00
VW Vernon Wells/33 * 20.00 50.00
WA Billy Wagner/64 * 20.00 50.00
WC Will Clark/13 *
WE Rickie Weeks/64 * 15.00 40.00

2004 Sweet Spot Signatures Glove

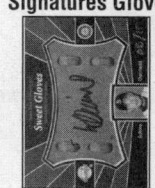

OVERALL AU ODDS 1:12
PRINT RUNS B/WN 5-25 #'d COPIES PER
NO PRICING ON QTY OF 5 OR LESS
EXCHANGE DEADLINE 11/22/07
AB Angel Berroa/25 20.00 50.00
AD Adam Dunn/25 40.00 80.00
AK Austin Kearns/25 20.00 50.00
AP Albert Pujols/25 250.00 400.00
AR Alex Rodriguez/5
BB Bret Boone/25 40.00 80.00
BE Josh Beckett/25 40.00 80.00
BG Brian Giles/25 30.00 60.00
BS Ben Sheets/25 30.00 60.00
BW Brandon Webb/25 20.00 50.00
CB Carlos Beltran/25 30.00 60.00
CL Carlos Lee/25 30.00 60.00
CP Corey Patterson/25 EXCH 20.00 50.00
CR Cal Ripken/25 225.00 350.00
CZ Carlos Zambrano/15 50.00 100.00
DJ Derek Jeter/5
DL Derrek Lee/25 40.00 80.00
DM Don Mattingly/25 125.00 200.00
DW Dontrelle Willis/25 40.00 80.00
DY Delmon Young/25 40.00 80.00
EC Eric Chavez/25 30.00 60.00
EJ Edwin Jackson/25 EXCH 20.00 50.00
EL Esteban Loaiza/25 20.00 50.00
EM Edgar Martinez/25 60.00 120.00
FT Frank Thomas/15 75.00 150.00
GA Garret Anderson/25 30.00 60.00
GJ Geoff Jenkins/25 30.00 60.00
GL Tom Glavine/25 40.00 80.00
GS Gary Sheffield/20 50.00 100.00
HA Roy Halladay/24 30.00 60.00
HB Hank Blalock/25 30.00 60.00
HI Richard Hidalgo/15 30.00 60.00
HO Trevor Hoffman/15 40.00 80.00
HU Torii Hunter/25 30.00 60.00
IR Ivan Rodriguez/25 EXCH * 60.00 120.00
IS Ichiro Suzuki/15
JD J.D. Drew/5
JG Juan Gonzalez/25 30.00 60.00
JJ Jacque Jones/25 30.00 60.00
JM Joe Mauer/25 30.00 60.00
JR Jose Reyes/25 30.00 60.00
JS Jason Schmidt/25 30.00 60.00
JV Javier Vazquez/25 30.00 60.00
KG Ken Griffey Jr./25 150.00 250.00
KW Kerry Wood/25 40.00 80.00
LG Luis Gonzalez/25 30.00 60.00
LO Mike Lowell/5
MA Mike Marshall/25 40.00 80.00
MC Miguel Cabrera/25 40.00 80.00
MG Marcus Giles/25 30.00 60.00
ML Mike Lieberthal/25 30.00 60.00
MM Mike Mussina/25 50.00 100.00
MP Mark Prior/25 30.00 60.00
MR Manny Ramirez/25 60.00 120.00
MT Mark Teixeira/25 40.00 80.00
MU Mark Mulder/25 30.00 60.00
NG Nomar Garciaparra/25 75.00 150.00
NR Nolan Ryan/25 175.00 300.00
OP Odalis Perez/25 20.00 50.00
PB Pat Burrell/15 40.00 80.00
PI Mike Piazza/5
RB Rocco Baldelli/25 30.00 60.00
RH Rich Harden/25 30.00 60.00
RK Ryan Klesko/15 40.00 80.00
RO Roy Oswalt/25 30.00 60.00
RS Ryne Sandberg/20 75.00 150.00
RW Randy Wolf/15 30.00 60.00
SA Johan Santana/25 60.00 120.00
SB Sean Burroughs/25 20.00 50.00
SM John Smoltz/5
SP Scott Podsednik/25 40.00 80.00
TE Miguel Tejada/25 40.00 80.00
TG Tony Gwynn/25 60.00 120.00
TH Todd Helton/25 30.00 60.00
TI Tim Hudson/25 40.00 80.00
TS Tom Seaver/15 60.00 120.00
VG Vladimir Guerrero/25 60.00 120.00
VW Vernon Wells/5
WA Billy Wagner/25 40.00 80.00
WC Will Clark/25 75.00 150.00
WE Rickie Weeks/25 30.00 60.00

2004 Sweet Spot Signatures Dual

BLK/RED-BLUE/DUAL/HIST AU ODDS 1:180
STATED PRINT RUN 10 SERIAL #'d SETS
NO PRICING DUE TO SCARCITY
EXCHANGE DEADLINE 11/22/07

2004 Sweet Spot Signatures Historical Ball

BLK/RED-BLUE/DUAL/HIST AU ODDS 1:180
STATED PRINT RUN 1 SERIAL #'d SET
NO PRICING DUE TO SCARCITY

2004 Sweet Spot Sweet Sticks

OVERALL GAME-USED ODDS 1:6
STATED PRINT RUN 199 SERIAL #'d SETS
AB Adrian Beltre 3.00 8.00
AD Adam Dunn 3.00 8.00
AJ Andruw Jones 4.00 10.00
AP Albert Pujols 8.00 20.00
AR Alex Rodriguez 6.00 15.00
AS Alfonso Soriano 3.00 8.00

BA Bobby Abreu 3.00 8.00
BB Bret Boone 3.00 8.00
BE Carlos Beltran 3.00 8.00
BG Brian Giles 3.00 8.00
CB Craig Biggio 4.00 10.00
CD Carlos Delgado 3.00 8.00
CJ Chipper Jones 4.00 10.00
CR Cal Ripken 12.50 30.00
CS Curt Schilling 4.00 10.00
DJ Derek Jeter 10.00 25.00
DL Derrek Lee 4.00 10.00
EC Eric Chavez 3.00 8.00
ER Edgar Renteria 3.00 8.00
FT Frank Thomas 4.00 10.00
GA Garret Anderson 3.00 8.00
GL Tom Glavine 4.00 10.00
GM Greg Maddux 6.00 15.00
GS Gary Sheffield 3.00 8.00
HB Hank Blalock 3.00 8.00
HM Hideki Matsui 12.50 30.00
IR Ivan Rodriguez 4.00 10.00
IS Ichiro Suzuki 12.50 30.00
JB Jeff Bagwell 4.00 10.00
JD J.D. Drew 3.00 8.00
JE Jim Edmonds 3.00 8.00
JG Jason Giambi 3.00 8.00
JK Jeff Kent 3.00 8.00
JR Jose Reyes 3.00 8.00
JT Jim Thome 4.00 10.00
KG Ken Griffey Jr. 6.00 15.00
KM Kazuo Matsui 3.00 8.00
LB Lance Berkman 4.00 10.00
LG Luis Gonzalez 3.00 8.00
LW Larry Walker Cards 4.00 10.00
MA Moises Alou 3.00 8.00
MC Miguel Cabrera 4.00 10.00
MG Marcus Giles 3.00 8.00
ML Mike Lowell 3.00 8.00
MO Magglio Ordonez 3.00 8.00
MP Mike Piazza 6.00 15.00
MR Manny Ramirez 4.00 10.00
MT Mark Teixeira 4.00 10.00
NG Nomar Garciaparra 6.00 15.00
PB Pat Burrell 3.00 8.00
PR Mark Prior 4.00 10.00
PW Preston Wilson 3.00 8.00
RC Roger Clemens 6.00 15.00
RF Rafael Furcal 3.00 8.00
RJ Randy Johnson 4.00 10.00
RP Rafael Palmeiro 4.00 10.00
RS Richie Sexson 3.00 8.00
SG Shawn Green 3.00 8.00
SR Scott Rolen 4.00 10.00
SS Sammy Sosa 4.00 10.00
TE Miguel Tejada 3.00 8.00
TG Troy Glaus 3.00 8.00
TH Todd Helton 4.00 10.00
TW Ted Williams 20.00 50.00
VG Vladimir Guerrero 4.00 10.00

2004 Sweet Spot Sweet Sticks Dual

OVERALL GAME-USED ODDS 1:6
STATED PRINT RUN 100 SERIAL #'d SETS
BT Hank Blalock 6.00 15.00
Mark Teixeira
CL Miguel Cabera 6.00 15.00
Mike Lowell
JC Randy Johnson 12.50 30.00
Roger Clemens
JG Derek Jeter 15.00 40.00
Nomar Garciaparra
JM Jose Reyes 6.00 15.00
Kazuo Matsui
MM Hideki Matsui 30.00 60.00
Kazuo Matsui
PR Albert Pujols 15.00 40.00
Scott Rolen
RG Manny Ramirez 6.00 15.00
Nomar Garciaparra
RJ Alex Rodriguez 30.00 60.00
Derek Jeter
RP Ivan Rodriguez 6.00 15.00
Mike Piazza
TB Jim Thome 6.00 15.00
Pat Burrell
WP Kerry Wood 6.00 15.00
Mark Prior

2004 Sweet Spot Sweet Sticks Triple

OVERALL GAME-USED ODDS 1:6
STATED PRINT RUN 50 SERIAL #'d SETS
GPS Ken Griffey Jr. 20.00 50.00
Rafael Palmeiro
Sammy Sosa
JJD Andruw Jones 12.50 30.00
Chipper Jones
J.D. Drew
JSG Derek Jeter 75.00 150.00
Ichiro Suzuki
Ken Griffey Jr.
MWP Greg Maddux 20.00 50.00
Kerry Wood
Mark Prior
RJG Alex Rodriguez 40.00 80.00
Derek Jeter
Jason Giambi

2004 Sweet Spot Sweet Sticks Quad

OVERALL GAME-USED ODDS 1:6
STATED PRINT RUN 25 SERIAL #'d SETS
PRSG Albert Pujols 75.00 150.00
Alex Rodriguez
Ichiro Suzuki
Ken Griffey Jr.
RGDM Babe Ruth 600.00 1000.00
Lou Gehrig
Joe DiMaggio
Mickey Mantle

2004 Sweet Spot Sweet Threads

*1-2 COLOR PATCH: .75X TO 2X BASIC
*3-4 COLOR PATCH: 1.25X TO 3X BASIC
*1-2 COLOR PATCH: .6X TO 1.5X BASIC SP
*3-4 COLOR PATCH: 1X TO 2.5X BASIC SP
PATCH PRINT RUN 85 SERIAL #'d SETS
MAUER PATCH PRINT RUN 70 #'d CARDS
OVERALL GAME-USED ODDS 1:6
PLATES PRINT RUN 4 SERIAL #'d SETS
BLACK-CYAN-MAGENTA-YELLOW EXIST
NO PLATES PRICING DUE TO SCARCITY
AS Alfonso Soriano 2.00 5.00
BB Bret Boone 2.00 5.00
BC Bartolo Colon 2.00 5.00
BG Brian Giles 2.00 5.00
CB Carlos Beltran 2.00 5.00
CD Carlos Delgado 2.00 5.00
DW Dontrelle Willis 3.00 8.00
DY Delmon Young 3.00 8.00
EC Eric Chavez 2.00 5.00
EM Edgar Martinez 3.00 8.00
FT Frank Thomas 3.00 8.00
GS Gary Sheffield 2.00 5.00
HB Hank Blalock 2.00 5.00
HE Todd Helton 3.00 8.00
HN Hideo Nomo 3.00 8.00
JB Jeff Bagwell 3.00 8.00
JG Jason Giambi 2.00 5.00
JM Joe Mauer 3.00 8.00
JR Jose Reyes 2.00 5.00
JS Jason Schmidt 2.00 5.00
JT Jim Thome 3.00 8.00
KM Kazuo Matsui SP 4.00 10.00
KW Kerry Wood 2.00 5.00
LB Lance Berkman 2.00 5.00
MC Miguel Cabrera 3.00 8.00
ML Mike Lowell 2.00 5.00
MM Mark Mulder 2.00 5.00
MO Magglio Ordonez 2.00 5.00
MP Mark Prior 3.00 8.00
MR Manny Ramirez 3.00 8.00
MT Mark Teixeira 3.00 8.00
PW Preston Wilson 2.00 5.00
RH Rich Harden 2.00 5.00
RO Roy Oswalt 2.00 5.00
RS Richie Sexson 2.00 5.00
RW Rickie Weeks 2.00 5.00
SG Shawn Green 2.00 5.00
SS Sammy Sosa 3.00 8.00
TG Troy Glaus 2.00 5.00
TH Tim Hudson 2.00 5.00
VG Vladimir Guerrero 3.00 8.00
VW Vernon Wells 2.00 5.00

2004 Sweet Spot Sweet Threads Dual

OVERALL GAME-USED ODDS 1:6
STATED PRINT RUN 150 SERIAL #'d SETS
BP Angel Berroa 4.00 10.00
Scott Podsednik
BT Hank Blalock 6.00 15.00
Mark Teixeira
CK Curt Schilling 6.00 15.00
Kevin Brown
CS Roger Clemens 8.00 20.00
Sammy Sosa
DT Carlos Delgado 6.00 15.00
Jim Thome
GH Eric Gagne 4.00 10.00
Roy Halladay
HG Tim Hudson 4.00 10.00
Vladimir Guerrero
JC Randy Johnson 10.00 25.00
Roger Clemens
JH Andruw Jones 6.00 15.00
Torii Hunter
JJ Andruw Jones 6.00 15.00
Chipper Jones
MM Hideki Matsui 20.00 50.00
Kazuo Matsui
MP Joe Mauer 6.00 15.00
Mark Prior
PC Andy Pettitte 8.00 20.00
Roger Clemens
PP Jorge Posada 6.00 15.00
Mike Piazza
PS Albert Pujols 20.00 50.00
Ichiro Suzuki
PW Albert Pujols 8.00 20.00
Kerry Wood
RJ Alex Rodriguez 20.00 50.00
Derek Jeter
RM Jose Reyes 6.00 15.00
Kazuo Matsui
SB Alfonso Soriano 4.00 10.00
Bret Boone
SM Gary Sheffield 6.00 15.00
Pedro Martinez
WP Kerry Wood 6.00 15.00
Mark Prior
YW Delmon Young 6.00 15.00
Rickie Weeks

2004 Sweet Spot Sweet Threads Dual Patch

*PATCHES: 1X TO 2.5X BASIC
OVERALL GAME-USED ODDS 1:6
STATED PRINT RUN 60 SERIAL #'d SETS
A.ROD-JETER PRINT RUN 10 #'d CARDS
NO A.ROD-JETER PRICING AVAILABLE
MM Hideki Matsui 75.00 150.00
Kazuo Matsui
PS Albert Pujols 100.00 175.00
Ichiro Suzuki

2004 Sweet Spot Sweet Threads Triple

OVERALL GAME-USED ODDS 1:6
STATED PRINT RUN 99 SERIAL #'d SETS
AGG Garret Anderson 10.00 25.00
Troy Glaus
Vladimir Guerrero
BKE Jeff Bagwell 6.00 15.00
Jeff Kent
Morgan Ensberg
BLR Adrian Beltre 6.00 15.00
Mike Lowell
Scott Rolen
BMS Bret Boone 30.00 60.00
Edgar Martinez
Ichiro Suzuki
BWC Josh Beckett 12.50 30.00
Kerry Wood
Roger Clemens
CMM Bobby Crosby 10.00 25.00
Joe Mauer
Kazuo Matsui
DHW Carlos Delgado 6.00 15.00
Roy Halladay
Vernon Wells
DKG Adam Dunn 10.00 25.00
Austin Kearns
Ken Griffey Jr.
DMJ Joe DiMaggio 175.00 300.00
Mickey Mantle
Derek Jeter
DMW Joe DiMaggio 200.00 350.00
Mickey Mantle
Ted Williams
DRN Johnny Damon 20.00 50.00
Manny Ramirez
Trot Nixon
FRP Keith Foulke 10.00 25.00
Mariano Rivera
Troy Percival
GPS Ken Griffey Jr. 15.00 40.00
Rafael Palmeiro
Sammy Sosa
JJD Andruw Jones 10.00 25.00
Chipper Jones
J.D. Drew
JTG Derek Jeter 12.50 30.00
Miguel Tejada
Nomar Garciaparra
JWH Edwin Jackson 6.00 15.00
Jerome Williams
Rich Harden
KVG Jeff Kent 6.00 15.00
Jose Vidro
Marcus Giles
LTO Carlos Lee 10.00 25.00
Frank Thomas
Magglio Ordonez
LTP Javy Lopez 6.00 15.00
Miguel Tejada
Rafael Palmeiro
MCF Kazuo Matsui 10.00 25.00
Orlando Cabrera
Rafael Furcal
MMH Mike Mussina 10.00 25.00
Pedro Martinez
Tim Hudson
MSH Joe Mauer 15.00 40.00
Johan Santana
Torii Hunter
MWP Greg Maddux 15.00 40.00
Kerry Wood
Mark Prior
PAS Corey Patterson 10.00 25.00
Moises Alou
Sammy Sosa
PCO Andy Pettitte 12.50 30.00
Roger Clemens
Roy Oswalt
PRR Albert Pujols 15.00 40.00
Edgar Renteria
Scott Rolen
PTH Albert Pujols 12.50 30.00
Jim Thome
Todd Helton
RCB Alex Rodriguez 10.00 25.00
Eric Chavez
Hank Blalock
RGJ Alex Rodriguez 15.00 40.00
Ken Griffey Jr.
Randy Johnson
RGW Jose Reyes 10.00 25.00
Khalil Greene
Rickie Weeks
RJG Alex Rodriguez 30.00 60.00
Derek Jeter
Jason Giambi
RMP Jose Reyes 15.00 40.00
Kazuo Matsui
Mike Piazza
SBK Alfonso Soriano 6.00 15.00
Bret Boone
Adam Kennedy
SBP Jason Schmidt 10.00 25.00
Josh Beckett
Mark Prior
SBT Alfonso Soriano 10.00 25.00
Hank Blalock
Mark Teixeira
SLM Curt Schilling 20.00 50.00
Derek Lowe
Pedro Martinez
VBM Javier Vazquez 6.00 15.00
Kevin Brown
Mike Mussina
WBP Brandon Webb 10.00 25.00
Josh Beckett
Mark Prior
WGS Billy Wagner 10.00 25.00
Eric Gagne
John Smoltz
WRC Kerry Wood 40.00 80.00
Nolan Ryan
Roger Clemens
YCW Delmon Young 10.00 25.00
Miguel Cabrera
Rickie Weeks
ZMH Barry Zito 6.00 15.00
Mark Mulder
Tim Hudson

2004 Sweet Spot Sweet Threads Triple Patch

*PATCH p/r 20-25: 1.5X TO 3X BASIC
OVERALL GAME-USED ODDS 1:6
PRINT RUNS B/WN 5-25 COPIES PER
NO PRICING ON QTY OF 5 OR LESS
FRP Keith Foulke 30.00 60.00
Mariano Rivera
Troy Percival/25
GPS Ken Griffey Jr. 40.00 80.00
Rafael Palmeiro
Sammy Sosa/25
JTG Derek Jeter 40.00 80.00
Miguel Tejada
Nomar Garciaparra/25
MSH Joe Mauer 40.00 80.00
Johan Santana
Torii Hunter/20
WRC Kerry Wood 100.00 200.00
Nolan Ryan
Roger Clemens/25

2004 Sweet Spot Sweet Threads Quad

OVERALL GAME-USED ODDS 1:6
STATED PRINT RUN 99 SERIAL #'d SETS
BADH Carlos Beltran 15.00 40.00
Garret Anderson
Johnny Damon
Torii Hunter
BBGS Angel Berroa 10.00 25.00
Carlos Beltran
Juan Gonzalez
Mike Sweeney
BPJC Josh Beckett 20.00 50.00
Mark Prior
Randy Johnson
Roger Clemens
BWRC Josh Beckett 40.00 80.00
Kerry Wood
Nolan Ryan
Roger Clemens
CAGG Bartolo Colon 15.00 40.00
Garret Anderson
Troy Glaus
Vladimir Guerrero
DHHW Carlos Delgado 10.00 25.00
Eric Hinske
Roy Halladay
Vernon Wells
DOGP Carlos Delgado 15.00 40.00
David Ortiz
Jason Giambi
Rafael Palmeiro
GNKB Brian Giles 10.00 25.00
Phil Nevin
Ryan Klesko
Sean Burroughs
GNLG Eric Gagne 15.00 40.00
Hideo Nomo
Paul LoDuca
Shawn Green
JBGB Chipper Jones 10.00 25.00
Lance Berkman
Luis Gonzalez
Pat Burrell
JEGW Andruw Jones 15.00 40.00
Jim Edmonds
Ken Griffey Jr.
Preston Wilson
JJDF Andruw Jones 15.00 40.00
Chipper Jones
J.D. Drew
Rafael Furcal
JMSH Jacque Jones 12.50 30.00
Joe Mauer
Shannon Stewart
Torii Hunter
JRMT Derek Jeter 20.00 50.00
Edgar Renteria
Kazuo Matsui
Miguel Tejada
KGCS Austin Kearns 15.00 40.00
Brian Giles
Miguel Cabrera
Sammy Sosa
LMRS Carlos Lee 30.00 60.00
Hideki Matsui
Manny Ramirez
Shannon Stewart
LTOK Carlos Lee 15.00 40.00
Frank Thomas
Magglio Ordonez
Paul Konerko
LTPP Javy Lopez 15.00 40.00
Miguel Tejada
Rafael Palmeiro
Sidney Ponson
MMMH Mark Mulder 10.00 25.00
Mike Mussina
Pedro Martinez
Roy Halladay
MTTS Edgar Martinez 15.00 40.00
Frank Thomas
Mark Teixeira
Mike Sweeney
NSGH Phil Nevin 10.00 25.00
Richie Sexson
Shawn Green
Todd Helton
PBBC Andy Pettitte 20.00 50.00
Craig Biggio
Jeff Bagwell
Roger Clemens
PLBT Albert Pujols 15.00 40.00
Derrek Lee
Jeff Bagwell
Jim Thome
PRER Albert Pujols 40.00 80.00
Edgar Renteria
Jim Edmonds
Scott Rolen
PWPS Corey Patterson 15.00 40.00
Kerry Wood
Mark Prior
Sammy Sosa
RCBG Alex Rodriguez 15.00 40.00
Eric Chavez
Hank Blalock
Troy Glaus
RDRW Alex Rodriguez 100.00 200.00
Joe DiMaggio
Manny Ramirez
Ted Williams
RJDM Alex Rodriguez 250.00 400.00
Derek Jeter
Joe DiMaggio
Mickey Mantle
RJGP Alex Rodriguez 50.00 100.00
Derek Jeter
Jason Giambi
Jorge Posada
RLPM Ivan Rodriguez 15.00 40.00
Javy Lopez
Jorge Posada
Joe Mauer
RMPG Jose Reyes 15.00 40.00
Kazuo Matsui
Mike Piazza
Tom Glavine
SBKV Alfonso Soriano 10.00 25.00
Bret Boone
Jeff Kent
Jose Vidro
SBMM Curt Schilling 15.00 40.00
Kevin Brown
Mike Mussina
Pedro Martinez
SDRM Curt Schilling 50.00 100.00
Johnny Damon
Manny Ramirez
Pedro Martinez
SSOG Gary Sheffield 30.00 60.00
Ichiro Suzuki
Magglio Ordonez
Vladimir Guerrero
VCBM Javier Vazquez 10.00 25.00
Jose Contreras
Kevin Brown
Mike Mussina
WATM Billy Wagner 15.00 40.00
Bobby Abreu
Jim Thome
Kevin Millwood
WBCL Dontrelle Willis 15.00 40.00
Josh Beckett
Miguel Cabrera
Mike Lowell
WGJS Brandon Webb 10.00 25.00
Luis Gonzalez
Randy Johnson
Richie Sexson
ZMHH Barry Zito 15.00 40.00
Mark Mulder
Rich Harden
Tim Hudson

2004 Sweet Spot Sweet Threads Quad Patch

*PATCH: 1.5X TO 3X BASIC
OVERALL GAME-USED ODDS 1:6
PRINT RUNS B/WN 1-15 #'d COPIES PER
NO PRICING ON QTY OF 10 OR LESS
BWRC Josh Beckett 250.00 400.00
Kerry Wood
Nolan Ryan
Roger Clemens/15
LMRS Carlos Lee 125.00 200.00
Hideki Matsui
Manny Ramirez
Shannon Stewart/15
PRER Albert Pujols 125.00 200.00
Edgar Renteria
Jim Edmonds
Scott Rolen/15
PWPS Corey Patterson 60.00 120.00
Kerry Wood
Mark Prior
Sammy Sosa/15
SBMM Curt Schilling 40.00 80.00
Kevin Brown
Mike Mussina
Pedro Martinez/15
SDRM Curt Schilling 175.00 300.00
Johnny Damon
Manny Ramirez
Pedro Martinez/15

2005 Sweet Spot

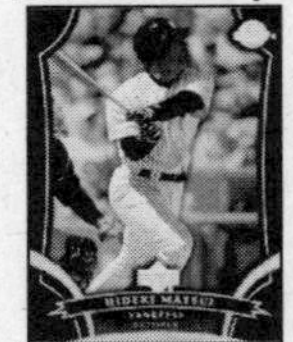

This product was released in September, 2005. The product was issued in five-card packs with an $10 SRP which came 12 packs to a box and 16 boxes to a case. Of note, cards 1-90 from the basic set were issued in standard '05 Sweet Spot packs. Cards 91-174 were distributed within packs of '05 Upper Deck Update in February, 2006. Each 5-card pack of UD Update contained one Sweet Spot card.

COMP.BASIC SET (90) 8.00 20.00
COMP.UPDATE SET (84) 10.00 25.00
COMMON CARD (1-90) .20 .50
COMMON CARD (91-174) .40 1.00
91-174 ONE PER '05 UD UPDATE PACK
1 Magglio Ordonez .20 .50
2 Craig Biggio .30 .75
3 Hank Blalock .20 .50
4 Nomar Garciaparra .50 1.25
5 Ken Griffey Jr. .75 2.00
6 Khalil Greene .30 .75
7 Andruw Jones .20 .50
8 Ichiro Suzuki 1.00 2.50
9 Philip Humber RC .50 1.25
10 Vladimir Guerrero .50 1.25
11 Carlos Delgado .20 .50
12 Jeff Niemann RC .50 1.25
13 Chipper Jones .50 1.25
14 Jose Vidro .20 .50
15 Miguel Cabrera .30 .75
16 Albert Pujols 1.00 2.50
17 Tadahito Iguchi RC .75 2.00
18 Norihiro Nakamura RC .60 1.50
19 Jeff Bagwell .30 .75
20 Troy Glaus .20 .50
21 Scott Rolen .30 .75
22 Derek Lowe .20 .50
23 Mark Prior .30 .75
24 Bobby Abreu .20 .50
25 David Wright .75 2.00
26 Barry Zito .20 .50
27 Livan Hernandez .20 .50
28 Mark Teixeira .30 .75
29 Manny Ramirez .30 .75
30 Paul Konerko .20 .50
31 Victor Martinez .20 .50

32 Greg Maddux .75 2.00
33 Jim Thome .30 .75
34 Miguel Tejada .20 .50
35 Ivan Rodriguez .30 .75
36 Carlos Beltran .20 .50
37 Steve Finley .20 .50
38 Torii Hunter .20 .50
39 Bobby Crosby .20 .50
40 Jorge Posada .30 .75
41 Ben Sheets .20 .50
42 Mike Piazza .50 1.25
43 Luis Gonzalez .20 .50
44 Joe Mauer .50 1.25
45 Shawn Green .20 .50
46 Eric Gagne .20 .50
47 Kerry Wood .20 .50
48 Derek Jeter 1.25 3.00
49 Josh Beckett .20 .50
50 Alex Rodriguez .75 2.00
51 Aubrey Huff .20 .50
52 Eric Chavez .20 .50
53 Sammy Sosa .50 1.25
54 Roger Clemens .75 2.00
55 Mike Mussina .30 .75
56 Mike Sweeney .20 .50
57 Oliver Perez .20 .50
58 Tim Hudson .20 .50
59 Justin Verlander RC 1.50 4.00
60 Johan Santana .50 1.25
61 Hideki Matsui .75 2.00
62 Mark Mulder .20 .50
63 Jake Peavy .20 .50
64 Adam Dunn .20 .50
65 Dallas McPherson .20 .50
66 Jeff Kent .20 .50
67 Pedro Martinez .30 .75
68 J.D. Drew .20 .50
69 Frank Thomas .50 1.25
70 Kazuo Matsui .20 .50
71 Travis Hafner .20 .50
72 John Smoltz .30 .75
73 Jason Schmidt .20 .50
74 Carlos Lee .20 .50
75 Todd Helton .30 .75
76 David Ortiz .50 1.25
77 Roy Oswalt .20 .50
78 Brian Giles .20 .50
79 Gary Sheffield .20 .50
80 Jason Bay .20 .50
81 Alfonso Soriano .20 .50
82 Randy Johnson .50 1.25
83 Tom Glavine .30 .75
84 Richie Sexson .20 .50
85 Curt Schilling .30 .75
86 Adrian Beltre .20 .50
87 Jim Edmonds .20 .50
88 Roy Halladay .20 .50
89 Johnny Damon .30 .75
90 Lance Berkman .20 .50
91 Adam Shabala SB RC .40 1.00
92 Ambiorix Burgos SB RC .40 1.00
93 Ambiorix Concepcion SB RC .40 1.00
94 Anibal Sanchez SB RC 1.25 3.00
95 Bill McCarthy SB RC .40 1.00
96 Brandon McCarthy SB RC .60 1.50
97 Brian Burres SB RC .40 1.00
98 Carlos Ruiz SB RC .40 1.00
99 Casey Rogowski SB RC .50 1.25
100 Chad Orvella SB RC .40 1.00
101 Chris Resop SB RC .40 1.00
102 Chris Roberson SB RC .40 1.00
103 Chris Seddon SB RC .40 1.00
104 Colter Bean SB RC .40 1.00
105 Dae-Sung Koo SB RC .40 1.00
106 Ryan Zimmerman SB RC 3.00 8.00
107 Dave Gassner SB RC .40 1.00
108 Brian Anderson SB RC .60 1.50
109 D.J. Houlton SB RC .40 1.00
110 Derek Wathan SB RC .40 1.00
111 Devon Lowery SB RC .40 1.00
112 Enrique Gonzalez SB RC .40 1.00
113 Chris Denorfia SB RC .50 1.25
114 Eude Brito SB RC .40 1.00
115 Francisco Butto SB RC .40 1.00
116 Franquelis Osoria SB RC .40 1.00
117 Garrett Jones SB RC .40 1.00
118 Geovany Soto SB RC 1.50 4.00
119 Hayden Penn SB RC .50 1.25
120 Ismael Ramirez SB RC .40 1.00
121 Jared Gothreaux SB RC .40 1.00
122 Jason Hammel SB RC .40 1.00
123 Dana Eveland SB RC .40 1.00
124 Jeff Miller SB RC .40 1.00
125 Jermaine Van Buren SB .40 1.00
126 Joel Peralta SB RC .40 1.00
127 John Hattig SB RC .40 1.00
128 Jorge Campillo SB RC .40 1.00
129 Juan Morillo SB RC .40 1.00
130 Ryan Garko SB RC .75 2.00
131 Keiichi Yabu SB RC .40 1.00
132 Kendry Morales SB RC 1.00 2.50
133 Luis Hernandez SB RC .40 1.00
134 Mark McLemore SB RC .40 1.00
135 Luis Pena SB RC .40 1.00
136 Luis O.Rodriguez SB RC .40 1.00
137 Luke Scott SB RC .75 2.00
138 Marcos Carvajal SB RC .40 1.00
139 Mark Woodyard SB RC .40 1.00
140 Matt A.Smith SB RC .40 1.00
141 Matthew Lindstrom SB RC .40 1.00
142 Miguel Negron SB RC .50 1.25
143 Mike Morse SB RC .50 1.25
144 Nate McLouth SB RC .50 1.25
145 Nelson Cruz SB RC .75 2.00
146 Nick Masset SB RC .40 1.00
147 Ryan Spilborghs SB RC .50 1.25
148 Oscar Robles SB RC .40 1.00
149 Paulino Reynoso SB RC .40 1.00
150 Pedro Lopez SB RC .40 1.00
151 Pete Orr SB RC .40 1.00
152 Prince Fielder SB RC 1.50 4.00
153 Randy Messenger SB RC .40 1.00
154 Randy Williams SB RC .40 1.00
155 Raul Tablado SB RC .40 1.00
156 Ronny Paulino SB RC .50 1.25
157 Russ Rohlicek SB RC .40 1.00
158 Russell Martin SB RC .75 2.00
159 Scott Baker SB RC .50 1.25
160 Scott Munter SB RC .40 1.00
161 Sean Thompson SB RC .40 1.00
162 Sean Tracey SB RC .40 1.00
163 Shane Costa SB RC .40 1.00
164 Stephen Drew SB RC 2.00 5.00
165 Steve Schmoll SB RC .40 1.00
166 Ryan Speier SB RC .40 1.00
167 Tadahito Iguchi SB .75 2.00
168 Tony Giarratano SB RC .40 1.00
169 Tony Pena SB RC .40 1.00
170 Travis Bowyer SB RC .40 1.00
171 Ubaldo Jimenez SB RC .75 2.00
172 Wladimir Balentien SB RC .50 1.25
173 Yorman Bazardo SB RC .40 1.00
174 Yuniesky Betancourt SB RC .75 2.00

2005 Sweet Spot Gold

*GOLD 1-90: 1.25X TO 3X BASIC
*GOLD 1-90: 1X TO 2.5X BASIC RC
1-90 OVERALL PARALLEL ODDS 1:6
1-90 PRINT RUN 599 SERIAL #'d SETS
*GOLD 91-174: 1X TO 2.5X BASIC
91-174 ISSUED IN '05 UD UPDATE PACKS
91-174 ONE #'d CARD OR AU PER PACK
91-174 PRINT RUN 399 SERIAL #'d SETS
1 Magglio Ordonez .60 1.50

2005 Sweet Spot Platinum

*PLATINUM 1-90: 2X TO 5X BASIC
*PLATINUM 1-90: 1.25X TO 3X BASIC RC
1-90 OVERALL PARALLEL ODDS 1:6
*PLATINUM 91-174: 1.5X TO 4X BASIC
91-174 ISSUED IN '05 UD UPDATE PACKS
91-174 ONE #'d CARD OR AU PER PACK
STATED PRINT RUN 99 SERIAL #'d SETS
1 Magglio Ordonez 1.00 2.50

2005 Sweet Spot Plutonium

1-90 OVERALL PARALLEL ODDS 1:6
91-174 ISSUED IN '05 UD UPDATE PACKS
91-174 ONE #'d CARD OR AU PER PACK
STATED PRINT RUN 1 SERIAL #'d SET
NO PRICING DUE TO SCARCITY
1 Magglio Ordonez

2005 Sweet Spot Majestic Materials

*GOLD: .6X TO 1.5X BASIC
GOLD PRINT RUN 75 SERIAL #'d SETS
PLATINUM PRINT RUN 10 SERIAL #'d SETS
NO PLATINUM PRICING DUE TO SCARCITY
PLUTONIUM PRINT RUN 1 SERIAL #'d SET
NO PLUTONIUM PRICING DUE TO SCARCITY
OVERALL 1-PIECE GU ODDS 1:6
*PATCH: 1.5X TO 4X BASIC
OVERALL PATCH ODDS 1:96
PATCH PRINT RUN 35 SERIAL #'d SETS
PRICES ARE FOR 2-3 COLOR PATCHES
REDUCE 20% FOR 1-COLOR PATCH
ADD 20% FOR 4-COLOR PATCH
ADD 50% FOR 5-COLOR+ PATCH
AD Adam Dunn 2.00 5.00
AJ Andruw Jones 3.00 8.00
AP Andy Pettitte 3.00 8.00
BA Bobby Abreu 2.00 5.00
BB Bret Boone 2.00 5.00
BC Bobby Crosby 2.00 5.00
BE Josh Beckett 2.00 5.00
BG Brian Giles 2.00 5.00
BS Ben Sheets 2.00 5.00
BU B.J. Upton 2.00 5.00
BZ Barry Zito 2.00 5.00
CB Craig Biggio 3.00 8.00
CD Carlos Delgado 2.00 5.00
DM Dallas McPherson 2.00 5.00
DW David Wright 4.00 10.00
ER Edgar Renteria 2.00 5.00
GS Gary Sheffield 2.00 5.00
HA Travis Hafner 2.00 5.00
HU Torii Hunter 2.00 5.00
JB Jason Bay 2.00 5.00
JD J.D. Drew 2.00 5.00
JE Jim Edmonds 2.00 5.00
JG Jason Giambi 2.00 5.00
JK Jeff Kent 2.00 5.00
JM Joe Mauer 3.00 8.00
JP Jake Peavy 2.00 5.00
JR Jose Reyes 2.00 5.00
JS Jason Schmidt 2.00 5.00
JV Jose Vidro 2.00 5.00
KG Khalil Greene 3.00 8.00
KM Kazuo Matsui 2.00 5.00
LB Lance Berkman 2.00 5.00
LG Luis Gonzalez 2.00 5.00
MA Moises Alou 2.00 5.00
MM Mark Mulder 2.00 5.00
MO Magglio Ordonez 2.00 5.00
MU Mike Mussina 3.00 8.00
OP Oliver Perez 2.00 5.00
PO Jorge Posada 3.00 8.00
RH Roy Halladay 2.00 5.00
RO Roy Oswalt 2.00 5.00
RS Richie Sexson 2.00 5.00
SG Shawn Green 2.00 5.00
SK Scott Kazmir 2.00 5.00
ST Shingo Takatsu 2.00 5.00
TG Troy Glaus 2.00 5.00
TH Tim Hudson 2.00 5.00
TI Tadahito Iguchi 6.00 15.00
VM Victor Martinez 2.00 5.00
VW Vernon Wells 2.00 5.00

2005 Sweet Spot Majestic Materials Dual

STATED PRINT RUN 25 SERIAL #'d SETS
GOLD PRINT RUN 5 SERIAL #'d SETS
NO GOLD PRICING DUE TO SCARCITY
PLUTONIUM PRINT RUN 1 SERIAL #'d SET
NO PLUTONIUM PRICING DUE TO SCARCITY
OVERALL COMBO GU ODDS 1:192
OVERALL PATCH ODDS 1:96
PATCH PRINT RUN 5 SERIAL #'d SETS
NO PATCH PRICING DUE TO SCARCITY
BB Craig Biggio 8.00 20.00
Jeff Bagwell
BP Jason Bay 6.00 15.00
Oliver Perez
BS Adrian Beltre 6.00 15.00
Richie Sexson
BT Hank Blalock 8.00 20.00
Mark Teixeira
CC Bobby Crosby 6.00 15.00
Eric Chavez
DG Adam Dunn 15.00 40.00
Ken Griffey Jr.
DK J.D. Drew 6.00 15.00
Jeff Kent
DR Johnny Damon 8.00 20.00
Manny Ramirez
GG Shawn Green 6.00 15.00
Troy Glaus
GR Eric Gagne 10.00 25.00
Mariano Rivera
HM Travis Hafner 6.00 15.00
Victor Martinez
JJ Andruw Jones 10.00 25.00
Chipper Jones
MC Don Mattingly 15.00 40.00
Will Clark
MW Dallas McPherson 10.00 25.00
David Wright
PC Albert Pujols 15.00 40.00
Miguel Cabrera
PG Jake Peavy 8.00 20.00
Khalil Greene
PL Albert Pujols 15.00 40.00
Derrek Lee
RM Jose Reyes 6.00 15.00
Kazuo Matsui
RO Ivan Rodriguez 8.00 20.00
Magglio Ordonez
RT Brian Roberts 6.00 15.00
Miguel Tejada
SH John Smoltz 8.00 20.00
Tim Hudson
SM Joe Mauer 8.00 20.00
Johan Santana
TI Shingo Takatsu 12.50 30.00
Tadahito Iguchi
UK B.J. Upton 6.00 15.00
Scott Kazmir
WC David Wright 12.50 30.00
Miguel Cabrera

2005 Sweet Spot Majestic Materials Triple

STATED PRINT RUN 25 SERIAL #'d SETS
GOLD PRINT RUN 5 SERIAL #'d SETS
NO GOLD PRICING DUE TO SCARCITY
PLUTONIUM PRINT RUN 1 SERIAL #'d SET
NO PLUTONIUM PRICING DUE TO SCARCITY
OVERALL COMBO GU ODDS 1:192
OVERALL PATCH ODDS 1:96
PATCH PRINT RUN 5 SERIAL #'d SETS
NO PATCH PRICING DUE TO SCARCITY
BPO Josh Beckett 10.00 25.00
Mark Prior
Roy Oswalt
BSB George Brett 30.00 60.00
Mike Schmidt
Wade Boggs
BTH Jeff Bagwell 10.00 25.00
Jim Thome
Todd Helton
HRG Torii Hunter 10.00 25.00
Manny Ramirez
Vladimir Guerrero
JCG Andruw Jones 10.00 25.00
Miguel Cabrera
Vladimir Guerrero
JRT Derek Jeter 15.00 40.00
Edgar Renteria
Miguel Tejada
MMP Greg Maddux 15.00 40.00
Pedro Martinez
Jake Peavy
MSG Greg Maddux 30.00 60.00
John Smoltz
Tom Glavine
OGP David Ortiz 10.00 25.00
Jason Giambi
Rafael Palmeiro
PBC Albert Pujols 15.00 40.00
Carlos Beltran
Miguel Cabrera
RBW Nolan Ryan 30.00 60.00
Josh Beckett
Kerry Wood
RGB Cal Ripken 40.00 80.00
Tony Gwynn
Wade Boggs
SSJ Curt Schilling 10.00 25.00
Johan Santana
Randy Johnson
VPP Jason Varitek 10.00 25.00
Jorge Posada
Mike Piazza
WRG David Wright 12.50 30.00
Scott Rolen
Troy Glaus

2005 Sweet Spot Majestic Materials Quad

STATED PRINT RUN 25 SERIAL #'d SETS
GOLD PRINT RUN 5 SERIAL #'d SETS
NO GOLD PRICING DUE TO SCARCITY
PLUTONIUM PRINT RUN 1 SERIAL #'d SET
NO PLUTONIUM PRICING DUE TO SCARCITY
OVERALL COMBO GU ODDS 1:192
OVERALL PATCH ODDS 1:96
PATCH PRINT RUN 5 SERIAL #'d SETS
NO PATCH PRICING DUE TO SCARCITY
JJSH Andruw Jones 20.00 50.00
Chipper Jones
John Smoltz
Tim Hudson
JSJP Derek Jeter 50.00 100.00
Gary Sheffield
Randy Johnson
Jorge Posada
OVDR David Ortiz 30.00 60.00
Jason Varitek
Johnny Damon
Manny Ramirez
PEWR Albert Pujols 40.00 80.00
Jim Edmonds
Larry Walker
Scott Rolen
ZMWP Carlos Zambrano 20.00 50.00
Greg Maddux
Kerry Wood
Mark Prior

2005 Sweet Spot Signatures Black Stitch Black Ink

OVERALL AU ODDS 1:12
STATED PRINT RUN 1 SERIAL #'d SET
NO PRICING DUE TO SCARCITY

2005 Sweet Spot Signatures Black Stitch Blue Ink

OVERALL AU ODDS 1:12
STATED PRINT RUN 1 SERIAL #'d SET
NO PRICING DUE TO SCARCITY

2005 Sweet Spot Signatures Black Stitch Red Ink

OVERALL AU ODDS 1:12
STATED PRINT RUN 1 SERIAL #'d SET
NO PRICING DUE TO SCARCITY

2005 Sweet Spot Signatures Red Stitch Black Ink

OVERALL AU ODDS 1:12
PRINT RUNS B/WN 58-350 COPIES PER
EXCHANGE DEADLINE 09/15/08
AD Adam Dunn/175 12.50 30.00
AH Aubrey Huff/350 6.00 15.00
AJ Andruw Jones/175 20.00 50.00
AP Albert Pujols/175 150.00 250.00
AR Aramis Ramirez/350 6.00 15.00
BC Bobby Crosby/350 6.00 15.00
BJ Bo Jackson/175 30.00 60.00
BL Barry Larkin/175 12.50 30.00
BU B.J. Upton/350 8.00 20.00
CA Miguel Cabrera/175 20.00 50.00
CC Carl Crawford/350 6.00 15.00
CR Cal Ripken/175 75.00 125.00
CZ Carlos Zambrano/350 10.00 25.00
DA Andre Dawson/175 8.00 20.00
DJ Derek Jeter/175 110.00 175.00
DW David Wright/350 30.00 60.00
EM Edgar Martinez/175 12.50 30.00
GF Gavin Floyd/350 6.00 15.00
GR Khalil Greene/350 10.00 25.00
HB Hank Blalock/175 8.00 20.00
HO Ryan Howard/350 30.00 60.00
JB Jason Bay/350 6.00 15.00
JN Jeff Niemann/350 8.00 20.00
JP Jake Peavy/350 10.00 25.00
JV Justin Verlander/350 25.00 50.00
KG Ken Griffey Jr./175 50.00 100.00
KH Keith Hernandez/350 6.00 15.00
LO Lyle Overbay/350 6.00 15.00
MA Don Mattingly/175 40.00 80.00
MG Marcus Giles/350 6.00 15.00
MM Mark Mulder/350 6.00 15.00
MO Justin Morneau/350 6.00 15.00
MP Mark Prior/175 12.50 30.00
MS Mike Schmidt/175 30.00 60.00
MT Mark Teixeira/175 12.50 30.00
NG Nomar Garciaparra/175 40.00 80.00
NR Nolan Ryan/175 50.00 100.00
PH Philip Humber/350 8.00 20.00
PI Mike Piazza/175 50.00 100.00
PM Paul Molitor/175 8.00 20.00
RC Roger Clemens/175 60.00 120.00
RE Jose Reyes/350 EXCH 10.00 25.00
RH Rich Harden/350 6.00 15.00
RJ Randy Johnson/175 50.00 100.00
RO Roy Oswalt/350 6.00 15.00
RS Ryne Sandberg/175 30.00 60.00
RY Robin Yount/175 20.00 50.00
SC Steve Carlton/58 10.00 25.00
SE Sean Casey/350 6.00 15.00
SK Scott Kazmir/350 8.00 20.00
WB Wade Boggs/175 12.50 30.00
WC Will Clark/175 12.50 30.00

2005 Sweet Spot Signatures Red Stitch Blue Ink

*BLUE p/r 135: .5X TO 1.2X BLK p/r 350
*BLUEp/r135: .5X TO 1.2X BLK RC YRp/r350
*BLUE p/r 75: .5X TO 1.2X BLK p/r 175
*BLUE p/r 75: .4X TO 1X BLK p/r 58
OVERALL AU ODDS 1:12
PRINT RUNS B/WN 75-135 COPIES PER
EXCHANGE DEADLINE 09/15/08
AP Albert Pujols/75 150.00 250.00
CP Corey Patterson/135 8.00 20.00
CR Cal Ripken/75 90.00 150.00
DJ Derek Jeter/75 125.00 200.00
GL Tom Glavine/135 12.50 30.00
HA Travis Hafner/135 8.00 20.00
NR Nolan Ryan/75 50.00 100.00
PI Mike Piazza/75 60.00 120.00
RC Roger Clemens/75 75.00 150.00

2005 Sweet Spot Signatures Red Stitch Red Ink

*RED p/r 35: .75X TO 2X BLK p/r 350
*RED p/r 35: .75X TO 2X BLK RC YR p/r 350
*RED p/r 15: .75X TO 2X BLK p/r 175
*RED p/r 15: .6X TO 1.5X BLK p/r 58
OVERALL AU ODDS 1:12
PRINT RUNS B/WN 15-35 COPIES PER
EXCHANGE DEADLINE 09/15/08
AP Albert Pujols/15 175.00 300.00
CP Corey Patterson/35 12.50 30.00
CR Cal Ripken/15 150.00 250.00
DJ Derek Jeter/15 250.00 400.00
GL Tom Glavine/35 20.00 50.00
HA Travis Hafner/35 12.50 30.00
NR Nolan Ryan/15 90.00 150.00
PI Mike Piazza/15 110.00 175.00
RC Roger Clemens/15 100.00 200.00

2005 Sweet Spot Signatures Red-Blue Stitch Black Ink

*BLK p/r 50: .6X TO 1.5X BLK p/r 350
*BLK p/r 50: .6X TO 1.5X BLK RC YR p/r 350
*BLK p/r 25: .6X TO 1.5X BLK p/r 175
*BLK p/r 25: .5X TO 1.2X BLK p/r 58
OVERALL AU ODDS 1:12
PRINT RUNS B/WN 25-50 COPIES PER
EXCHANGE DEADLINE 09/15/08
AP Albert Pujols/25 150.00 250.00
CR Cal Ripken/25 125.00 200.00
DJ Derek Jeter/25 175.00 300.00
JS Johan Santana/25 40.00 80.00
NR Nolan Ryan/25 75.00 125.00
PI Mike Piazza/25 90.00 150.00
RC Roger Clemens/25 90.00 150.00

2005 Sweet Spot Signatures Red-Blue Stitch Blue Ink

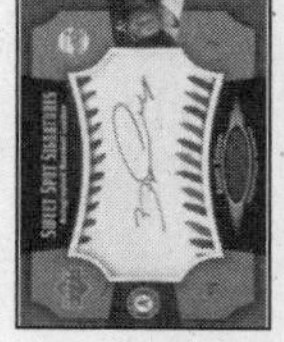

*BLUE p/r 30: .75X TO 2X BLK p/r 350
*BLUE p/r 30: .75X TO 2X BLK RC YR p/r 350
*BLUE p/r 15: .75X TO 2X BLK p/r 175
*BLUE p/r 15: .6X TO 1.5X BLK p/r 58
OVERALL AU ODDS 1:12
PRINT RUNS B/WN 15-30 COPIES PER
EXCHANGE DEADLINE 09/15/08
AP Albert Pujols/15 250.00 400.00
CP Corey Patterson/30 EXCH 12.50 30.00
CR Cal Ripken/15 150.00 250.00
GL Tom Glavine/30 20.00 50.00
HA Travis Hafner/30 12.50 30.00
JS Johan Santana/15 40.00 80.00
NR Nolan Ryan/15 90.00 150.00
PI Mike Piazza/15 EXCH 110.00 175.00
RC Roger Clemens/15 100.00 200.00

2005 Sweet Spot Signatures Red-Blue Stitch Red Ink

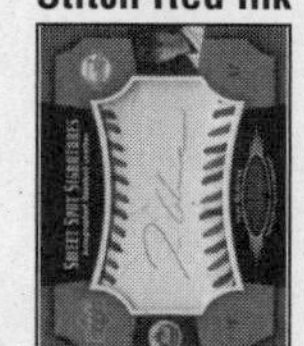

OVERALL AU ODDS 1:12
PRINT RUNS B/WN 5-10 SERIAL #'d SETS
NO PRICING DUE TO SCARCITY
EXCHANGE DEADLINE 09/15/08

2005 Sweet Spot Signatures Barrel Black Ink

*BLK p/r 50: .6X TO 1.5X BLK p/r 350
*BLK p/r 50: .6X TO 1.5X BLK RC YR p/r 350
*BLK p/r 25: .6X TO 1.5X BLK p/r 175

*BLK p/r 25: .5X TO 1.2X BLK p/r 58
OVERALL AU ODDS 1:12
PRINT RUNS B/WN 25-50 COPIES PER
EXCHANGE DEADLINE 09/15/08
AP Albert Pujols/25 150.00 250.00
CR Cal Ripken/25 EXCH 125.00 200.00
DJ Derek Jeter/25 175.00 300.00
GL Tom Glavine/50 15.00 40.00
HA Travis Hafner/50 10.00 25.00
NR Nolan Ryan/25 EXCH 75.00 125.00
PI Mike Piazza/25 EXCH 90.00 150.00

2005 Sweet Spot Signatures Barrel Blue Ink

*BLUE p/r 30: .75X TO 2X BLK p/r 350
*BLUE p/r 30: .75X TO 2X BLK RC YR p/r 350
*BLUE p/r 15: .75X TO 2X BLK p/r 175
*BLUE p/r 15: .6X TO 1.5X BLK p/r 58
OVERALL AU ODDS 1:12
PRINT RUNS B/WN 15-30 COPIES PER
EXCHANGE DEADLINE 09/15/08
AP Albert Pujols/15 175.00 300.00
CP Corey Patterson/30 12.50 30.00
CR Cal Ripken/15 150.00 250.00
DJ Derek Jeter/15 250.00 400.00
GL Tom Glavine/30 20.00 50.00
HA Travis Hafner/30 12.50 30.00
NR Nolan Ryan/15 90.00 150.00
PH Philip Humber/30 20.00 50.00
PI Mike Piazza/15 110.00 175.00
RC Roger Clemens/15 125.00 200.00

2005 Sweet Spot Signatures Barrel Red Ink

OVERALL AU ODDS 1:12
PRINT RUNS B/WN 5-10 COPIES PER
NO PRICING DUE TO SCARCITY
EXCHANGE DEADLINE 09/15/08

2005 Sweet Spot Signatures Glove Black Ink

*BLK p/r 30: 1X TO 2.5X BLK p/r 350
*BLK p/r 30: 1X TO 2.5X BLK RC YR p/r 350
*BLK p/r 15: 1X TO 2.5X BLK p/r 175
*BLK p/r 15: .75X TO 2X BLK p/r 58
OVERALL AU ODDS 1:12
PRINT RUNS B/WN 15-30 COPIES PER
EXCHANGE DEADLINE 09/15/08
AP Albert Pujols/15 250.00 400.00
BJ Bo Jackson/15 125.00 200.00
CP Corey Patterson/30 15.00 40.00
CR Cal Ripken/15 175.00 300.00
DJ Derek Jeter/15 300.00 500.00
GL Tom Glavine/30 25.00 60.00
HA Travis Hafner/30 15.00 40.00
NR Nolan Ryan/15 125.00 200.00
PI Mike Piazza/15 150.00 250.00

2005 Sweet Spot Signatures Glove Blue Ink

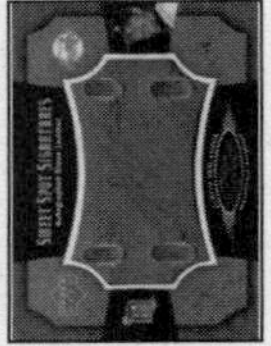

OVERALL AU ODDS 1:12
PRINT RUNS B/WN 5-10 COPIES PER
NO PRICING DUE TO SCARCITY

2005 Sweet Spot Signatures Glove Red Ink

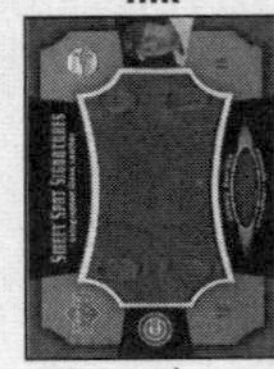

OVERALL AU ODDS 1:12
PRINT RUNS B/WN 2-5 COPIES PER
NO PRICING DUE TO SCARCITY

2005 Sweet Spot Signatures Dual Black Stitch

OVERALL AU ODDS 1:12
STATED PRINT RUN 1 SERIAL #'d SET
NO PRICING DUE TO SCARCITY

2005 Sweet Spot Signatures Dual Red Stitch

OVERALL DUAL AU ODDS 1:196
STATED PRINT RUN 25 SERIAL #'d SETS
EXCHANGE DEADLINE 09/15/08
BJ Bobby Crosby 30.00 60.00
Jason Bay
BW Adrian Beltre 60.00 120.00
David Wright EXCH
CG Bobby Crosby 40.00 80.00
Khalil Greene EXCH
DC Adam Dunn 30.00 60.00
Sean Casey
FH Gavin Floyd 75.00 150.00
Ryan Howard EXCH
GC Ken Griffey Jr. 90.00 150.00
Miguel Cabrera EXCH
GL Khalil Greene 40.00 80.00
Mark Loretta
GS Eric Gagne
John Smoltz EXCH
GT Eric Gagne
Shingo Takatsu EXCH
JC Randy Johnson 175.00 300.00
Roger Clemens EXCH
JG Andruw Jones 125.00 200.00
Ken Griffey Jr. EXCH
JM Derek Jeter 250.00 400.00
Don Mattingly EXCH
LG Barry Larkin 90.00 150.00
Ken Griffey Jr. EXCH
LR Barry Larkin 125.00 200.00
Cal Ripken EXCH
MG Greg Maddux 125.00 200.00
Tom Glavine EXCH
MJ Pedro Martinez 90.00 150.00
Randy Johnson EXCH
NH Jeff Niemann 40.00 80.00
Philip Humber
PB Jason Bay 30.00 60.00
Oliver Perez
PC Albert Pujols 250.00 400.00
Miguel Cabrera
PO Jake Peavy 30.00 60.00
Roy Oswalt
RJ Cal Ripken 250.00 400.00
Derek Jeter EXCH
RP Aramis Ramirez
Corey Patterson EXCH
SB Ryne Sandberg 60.00 120.00
Wade Boggs
SG Nomar Garciaparra 125.00 200.00
Ryne Sandberg
SP Ben Sheets 30.00 60.00
Jake Peavy
WC David Wright 90.00 150.00
Miguel Cabrera
WR David Wright 150.00 250.00
Jose Reyes

2005 Sweet Spot Signatures Dual Red-Blue Stitch

OVERALL DUAL AU ODDS 1:196
STATED PRINT RUN 15 SERIAL #'d SETS
NO PRICING DUE TO SCARCITY
EXCHANGE DEADLINE 09/15/08

2005 Sweet Spot Signatures Dual Barrel

OVERALL DUAL AU ODDS 1:196
STATED PRINT RUN 15 SERIAL #'d SETS
NO PRICING DUE TO SCARCITY
EXCHANGE DEADLINE 09/15/08

2005 Sweet Spot Signatures Dual Glove

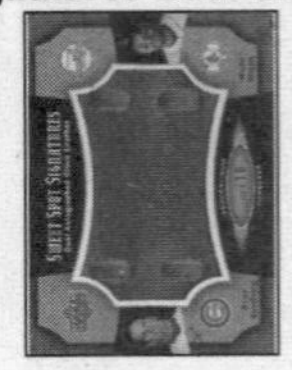

OVERALL DUAL AU ODDS 1:196
STATED PRINT RUN 10 SERIAL #'d SETS
NO PRICING DUE TO SCARCITY
EXCHANGE DEADLINE 09/15/08

2005 Sweet Spot Signatures Game Used Ball

OVERALL AU ODDS 1:12
STATED PRINT RUN 1 SERIAL #'d SET
NO PRICING DUE TO SCARCITY
EXCHANGE DEADLINE 09/15/08

2005 Sweet Spot Signatures Game Used Barrel

OVERALL AU ODDS 1:12
PRINT RUNS B/WN 1-10 COPIES PER
NO PRICING DUE TO SCARCITY

2005 Sweet Spot Signatures Game Used Fielding Glove

OVERALL AU ODDS 1:12
PRINT RUNS B/WN 9-10 COPIES PER
NO PRICING DUE TO SCARCITY

2005 Sweet Spot Sweet Threads

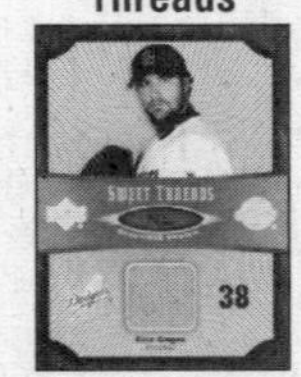

*GOLD: .6X TO 1.5X BASIC
GOLD PRINT RUN 75 SERIAL #'d SETS
PLATINUM PRINT RUN 10 SERIAL #'d SETS
NO PLATINUM PRICING DUE TO SCARCITY
PLUTONIUM PRINT RUN 1 SERIAL #'d SET
NO PLUTONIUM PRICING DUE TO SCARCITY
OVERALL 1-PIECE GU ODDS 1:6
*PATCH: 1.5X TO 4X BASIC
OVERALL PATCH ODDS 1:96
PATCH PRINT RUN 35 SERIAL #'d SETS
PRICES ARE FOR 2-3 COLOR PATCHES
REDUCE 20% FOR 1-COLOR PATCH
ADD 20% FOR 4-COLOR PATCH
ADD 50% FOR 5-COLOR+ PATCH
AB Adrian Beltre 2.00 5.00
AP Albert Pujols 6.00 15.00
AS Alfonso Soriano 2.00 5.00
BC Bartolo Colon 2.00 5.00
BJ Bo Jackson 4.00 10.00
BW Bernie Williams 3.00 8.00
CB Carlos Beltran 2.00 5.00
CJ Chipper Jones 4.00 10.00
CL Carlos Lee 2.00 5.00
CR Cal Ripken 8.00 20.00
CS Curt Schilling 3.00 8.00
DJ Derek Jeter 10.00 25.00
DM Don Mattingly 5.00 12.00
DO David Ortiz 4.00 10.00
EC Eric Chavez 2.00 5.00
EG Eric Gagne 2.00 5.00
FT Frank Thomas 4.00 10.00
GB George Brett 5.00 12.00
GM Greg Maddux 4.00 10.00
GW Tony Gwynn 4.00 10.00
HB Hank Blalock 2.00 5.00
HO Trevor Hoffman 2.00 5.00
IR Ivan Rodriguez 3.00 8.00
JB Jeff Bagwell 3.00 8.00
JD Johnny Damon 3.00 8.00
JS Johan Santana 4.00 10.00
JT Jim Thome 3.00 8.00
JV Jason Varitek 6.00 15.00
KG Ken Griffey Jr. 6.00 15.00
KW Kerry Wood 2.00 5.00
MC Miguel Cabrera 3.00 8.00
MP Mark Prior 3.00 8.00
MR Manny Ramirez 3.00 8.00
MS Mike Schmidt 5.00 12.00
MT Mark Teixeira 3.00 8.00
NR Nolan Ryan 6.00 15.00
PI Mike Piazza 4.00 10.00
PM Pedro Martinez 3.00 8.00
RJ Randy Johnson 4.00 10.00
RP Rafael Palmeiro 3.00 8.00
RS Ryne Sandberg 5.00 12.00
SM John Smoltz 3.00 8.00
SR Scott Rolen 3.00 8.00
SS Sammy Sosa 4.00 10.00
TE Miguel Tejada 2.00 5.00
TG Tom Glavine 3.00 8.00
TH Todd Helton 3.00 8.00
VG Vladimir Guerrero 4.00 10.00
WB Wade Boggs 3.00 8.00
WC Will Clark 3.00 8.00

2005 Sweet Spot Sweet Threads Dual

STATED PRINT RUN 25 SERIAL #'d SETS
GOLD PRINT RUN 5 SERIAL #'d SETS
NO GOLD PRICING DUE TO SCARCITY
PLUTONIUM PRINT RUN 1 SERIAL #'d SET
NO PLUTONIUM PRICING DUE TO SCARCITY
OVERALL COMBO GU ODDS 1:192
OVERALL PATCH ODDS 1:96
PATCH PRINT RUN 5 SERIAL #'d SETS
NO PATCH PRICING DUE TO SCARCITY
BG Carlos Beltran 15.00 40.00
Ken Griffey Jr.
BM Carlos Beltran 8.00 20.00
Pedro Martinez
DC Carlos Delgado 8.00 20.00
Miguel Cabrera
GC Ken Griffey Jr. 15.00 40.00
Miguel Cabrera
GM Dallas McPherson 10.00 25.00
Vladimir Guerrero
JB Bo Jackson 15.00 40.00
George Brett
JJ Randy Johnson 20.00 50.00
Derek Jeter
JM Derek Jeter 30.00 60.00
Don Mattingly
JS Jim Thome 15.00 40.00
Mike Schmidt
MG Greg Maddux 15.00 40.00
Tom Glavine
MJ Mike Mussina 10.00 25.00
Randy Johnson
MP Greg Maddux 15.00 40.00
Mark Prior
OR David Ortiz 8.00 20.00
Manny Ramirez
PO Andy Pettitte 8.00 20.00
Roy Oswalt
PR Pedro Martinez 10.00 25.00
Randy Johnson
PS Rafael Palmeiro 10.00 25.00
Sammy Sosa
PW David Wright 15.00 40.00
Mike Piazza
RJ Cal Ripken 40.00 80.00
Derek Jeter
RP Albert Pujols 15.00 40.00
Scott Rolen
RT Cal Ripken 30.00 60.00
Miguel Tejada
SB Ryne Sandberg 15.00 40.00
Wade Boggs
SJ Curt Schilling 10.00 25.00
Randy Johnson
SV Curt Schilling 10.00 25.00
Jason Varitek
WP Kerry Wood 8.00 20.00
Mark Prior

2005 Sweet Spot Sweet Threads Triple

STATED PRINT RUN 25 SERIAL #'d SETS
GOLD PRINT RUN 5 SERIAL #'d SETS
NO GOLD PRICING DUE TO SCARCITY
PLUTONIUM PRINT RUN 1 SERIAL #'d SET
NO PLUTONIUM PRICING DUE TO SCARCITY
OVERALL COMBO GU ODDS 1:192
OVERALL PATCH ODDS 1:96
PATCH PRINT RUN 5 SERIAL #'d SETS
NO PATCH PRICING DUE TO SCARCITY
BBB Craig Biggio 10.00 25.00
Jeff Bagwell
Lance Berkman
BWP Carlos Beltran 15.00 40.00
David Wright
Mike Piazza
GGG Luis Gonzalez 8.00 20.00
Shawn Green
Troy Glaus
JMB Randy Johnson 10.00 25.00
Mike Mussina
Kevin Brown
JWS Derek Jeter 30.00 60.00
Bernie Williams
Gary Sheffield
KGD Austin Kearns 15.00 40.00
Ken Griffey Jr.
Adam Dunn
LOP Brad Lidge 10.00 25.00
Roy Oswalt
Andy Pettitte
ODR David Ortiz 10.00 25.00
Johnny Damon
Manny Ramirez
PER Albert Pujols 15.00 40.00
Jim Edmonds
Scott Rolen
PWM Mark Prior 15.00 40.00
Kerry Wood
Greg Maddux
RDN Manny Ramirez 15.00 40.00
Johnny Damon
Trot Nixon
SBT Alfonso Soriano 10.00 25.00
Hank Blalock
Mark Teixeira
SMJ Curt Schilling 10.00 25.00
Pedro Martinez
Randy Johnson
TPS Miguel Tejada 10.00 25.00
Rafael Palmeiro
Sammy Sosa

2005 Sweet Spot Sweet Threads Quad

STATED PRINT RUN 25 SERIAL #'d SETS
GOLD PRINT RUN 5 SERIAL #'d SETS
NO GOLD PRICING DUE TO SCARCITY
PLUTONIUM PRINT RUN 1 SERIAL #'d SET
NO PLUTONIUM PRICING DUE TO SCARCITY
OVERALL COMBO GU ODDS 1:192
OVERALL PATCH ODDS 1:96
PATCH PRINT RUN 5 SERIAL #'d SETS
NO PATCH PRICING DUE TO SCARCITY
BMCB Adrian Beltre 15.00 40.00
Dallas McPherson
Eric Chavez
Hank Blalock
BRGG Carlos Beltran 30.00 60.00
Manny Ramirez
Ken Griffey Jr.
Vladimir Guerrero
POTH Albert Pujols 30.00 60.00
David Ortiz
Jim Thome
Todd Helton
RBGB Cal Ripken 60.00 120.00
George Brett
Tony Gwynn
Wade Boggs
RVMP Ivan Rodriguez 20.00 50.00
Jason Varitek
Joe Mauer
Jorge Posada

2006 Sweet Spot

This 183-card set was released in June, 2006. The set was issued in five-card hobby packs with an $10 SRP and those packs were issued 12 packs per box and 12 boxes per case. Cards numbered 1-100 feature veterans while cards 101-184 were all signed. These cards were issued to stated print runs between 86 and 275 copies. A few players did not return their signatures in time for pack out and those cards could be redeemed until May 25, 2008.

COMP.SET w/o AU's (100) 10.00 25.00
COMMON CARD (1-100) .20 .50
OVERALL AU ODDS 1:12
AU PRINT RUNS B/WN 45-275 PER
EXCHANGE DEADLINE 05/25/08
ASTERISK = PARTIAL EXCHANGE
1 Bartolo Colon .20 .50
2 Garret Anderson .20 .50
3 Francisco Rodriguez .20 .50
4 Dallas McPherson .20 .50
5 Andy Pettitte .30 .75
6 Lance Berkman .20 .50
7 Willy Taveras .20 .50
8 Bobby Crosby .20 .50
9 Dan Haren .20 .50
10 Nick Swisher .20 .50
11 Vernon Wells .20 .50
12 Orlando Hudson .20 .50
13 Roy Halladay .20 .50
14 Andruw Jones .30 .75
15 Chipper Jones .50 1.25
16 Jeff Francoeur .50 1.25
17 John Smoltz .30 .75
18 Carlos Lee .20 .50
19 Rickie Weeks .20 .50
20 Bill Hall .20 .50
21 Jim Edmonds .30 .75
22 David Eckstein .20 .50
23 Mark Mulder .20 .50
24 Aramis Ramirez .20 .50
25 Greg Maddux .75 2.00
26 Nomar Garciaparra .50 1.25
27 Carlos Zambrano .20 .50
28 Scott Kazmir .30 .75
29 Jorge Cantu .20 .50
30 Carl Crawford .20 .50
31 Luis Gonzalez .20 .50
32 Troy Glaus .20 .50
33 Shawn Green .20 .50
34 Jeff Kent .20 .50
35 Milton Bradley .20 .50
36 Cesar Izturis .20 .50
37 Omar Vizquel .30 .75
38 Moises Alou .20 .50
39 Randy Winn .20 .50
40 Jason Schmidt .20 .50
41 Coco Crisp .20 .50
42 C.C. Sabathia .20 .50
43 Cliff Lee .20 .50
44 Ichiro Suzuki .75 2.00
45 Richie Sexson .20 .50
46 Jeremy Reed .20 .50
47 Carlos Delgado .20 .50
48 Miguel Cabrera .30 .75
49 Luis Castillo .20 .50
50 Carlos Beltran .20 .50
51 Tom Glavine .30 .75
52 David Wright .75 2.00
53 Cliff Floyd .20 .50
54 Chad Cordero .20 .50
55 Jose Vidro .20 .50
56 Jose Guillen .20 .50
57 Nick Johnson .20 .50
58 Miguel Tejada .20 .50
59 Melvin Mora .20 .50
60 Javy Lopez .20 .50
61 Khalil Greene .30 .75
62 Brian Giles .20 .50
63 Trevor Hoffman .20 .50
64 Bobby Abreu .20 .50
65 Jimmy Rollins .20 .50
66 Pat Burrell .20 .50
67 Billy Wagner .20 .50
68 Jack Wilson .20 .50
69 Zach Duke .20 .50
70 Craig Wilson .20 .50
71 Mark Teixeira .30 .75
72 Hank Blalock .20 .50
73 David Dellucci .20 .50
74 Manny Ramirez .30 .75
75 Johnny Damon .30 .75
76 Jason Varitek .50 1.25
77 Trot Nixon .20 .50
78 Adam Dunn .20 .50
79 Felipe Lopez .20 .50
80 Brandon Claussen .20 .50
81 Sean Casey .20 .50
82 Todd Helton .30 .75
83 Clint Barmes .20 .50
84 Matt Holliday .50 1.25
85 Mike Sweeney .20 .50
86 Zack Greinke .20 .50
87 David DeJesus .20 .50
88 Ivan Rodriguez .30 .75
89 Jeremy Bonderman .20 .50
90 Magglio Ordonez .20 .50
91 Torii Hunter .20 .50
92 Joe Nathan .20 .50
93 Michael Cuddyer .20 .50
94 Paul Konerko .20 .50
95 Jermaine Dye .20 .50
96 Jon Garland .20 .50
97 Alex Rodriguez .75 2.00
98 Hideki Matsui .50 1.25
99 Jason Giambi .20 .50
100 Mariano Rivera .50 1.25
101 Adrian Beltre AU/99 15.00 40.00
102 Matt Cain AU/275 (RC) 15.00 40.00
103 Craig Biggio AU/99 30.00 60.00
104 Eric Chavez AU/99 12.50 30.00
105 J.D. Drew AU/99 12.50 30.00
106 Eric Gagne AU/99 20.00 50.00
107 Tim Hudson AU/99 15.00 40.00
108 Tom Glavine AU/275 20.00 50.00
109 David Ortiz AU/99 40.00 80.00
110 Scott Rolen AU/275 15.00 40.00
111 Johan Santana AU/99 20.00 50.00
112 Curt Schilling AU/96 40.00 80.00
113 John Smoltz AU/99 30.00 60.00
114 Alfonso Soriano AU/99 30.00 60.00
115 Kerry Wood AU/99 12.50 30.00
116 Edwin Jackson AU/99 8.00 20.00
117 Felix Hernandez AU/125 20.00 50.00
118 Prince Fielder AU/99 (RC) 60.00 120.00
119 Vladimir Guerrero AU/86 30.00 60.00

120 Roger Clemens AU/99 30.00 60.00
121 Albert Pujols AU/45 175.00 300.00
122 Chris Carpenter AU/99 20.00 50.00
123 Derrek Lee AU/99 15.00 40.00
124 Dontrelle Willis AU/99 12.50 30.00
125 Roy Oswalt AU/99 15.00 40.00
126 Ryan Garko AU/275 (RC) 10.00 25.00
127 Tadahito Iguchi AU/275 20.00 50.00
128 Mark Loretta AU/275 10.00 25.00
129 Joe Mauer AU/275 20.00 50.00
130 Victor Martinez AU/275 10.00 25.00
131 Wily Mo Pena AU/275 10.00 25.00
132 Oliver Perez AU/274 6.00 15.00
133 Corey Patterson AU/275 EXCH 10.00 25.00
134 Ben Sheets AU/275 10.00 25.00
135 Michael Young AU/275 10.00 25.00
136 Jonny Gomes AU/275 6.00 15.00
137 Derek Jeter AU/99 125.00 200.00
138 Ken Griffey Jr. AU/275 EXCH * 30.00 60.00
139 Ryan Zimmerman AU/275 (RC) 30.00 60.00
140 Scott Baker AU/275 (RC) 6.00 15.00
141 Huston Street AU/275 10.00 25.00
142 Jason Bay AU/275 EXCH 10.00 25.00
143 Ryan Howard AU/275 40.00 80.00
145 Travis Hafner AU/275 10.00 25.00
146 Brian Myrow AU/275 RC 6.00 15.00
147 Scott Podsednik AU/275 10.00 25.00
148 Brian Roberts AU/275 10.00 25.00
149 Grady Sizemore AU/135 15.00 40.00
150 Chris Demaria AU/275 RC 6.00 15.00
151 Jonah Bayliss AU/275 RC 6.00 15.00
152 Geovany Soto AU/275 (RC) 15.00 40.00
153 Lyle Overbay AU/275 6.00 15.00
154 Joey Devine AU/275 RC 6.00 15.00
155 Alejandro Freire AU/275 RC 6.00 15.00
156 Conor Jackson AU/275 (RC) 10.00 25.00
157 Danny Sandoval AU/275 RC 6.00 15.00
158 Chase Utley AU/275 20.00 50.00
159 Jeff Harris AU/275 RC 6.00 15.00
160 Ron Flores AU/275 RC 6.00 15.00
161 Scott Feldman AU/275 RC 6.00 15.00
162 Yadier Molina AU/275 10.00 25.00
163 Tim Corcoran AU/275 RC 6.00 15.00
164 Craig Hansen AU/275 RC 15.00 40.00
165 Jason Bergmann AU/275 RC 6.00 15.00
166 Craig Breslow AU/275 RC 6.00 15.00
167 Jhonny Peralta AU/275 6.00 15.00
168 Jeremy Hermida AU/275 (RC) 10.00 25.00
169 Scott Kazmir AU/275 10.00 25.00
170 Bobby Crosby AU/99 12.50 30.00
171 Rich Harden AU/275 6.00 15.00
172 Casey Kotchman AU/275 6.00 15.00
173 Tim Hamulack AU/275 (RC) 6.00 15.00
174 Justin Morneau AU/275 10.00 25.00
175 Jake Peavy AU/275 10.00 25.00
176 Yuniesky Betancourt AU/275 10.00 25.00
177 Jeremy Accardo AU/275 RC 6.00 15.00
178 Jorge Cantu AU/200 10.00 25.00
179 Marlon Byrd AU/275 6.00 15.00
180 Ryan Jorgensen AU/275 RC 6.00 15.00
181 Chris Denorfia AU/275 (RC) 6.00 15.00
182 Steve Stemle AU/275 RC 6.00 15.00
183 Robert Andino AU/275 RC 6.00 15.00
184 Chris Heintz AU/275 RC 6.00 15.00

2006 Sweet Spot Signatures Red Stitch Blue Ink

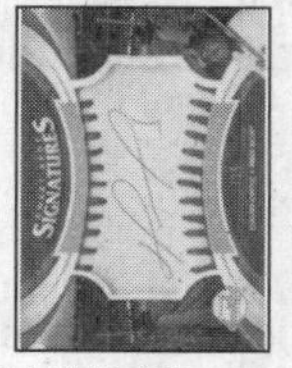

*RS BLUE p/r 114-150: .4X TO 1X p/r 125-275
*RS BLUE p/r 114-150: .3X TO .8X p/r 99
*RS BLUE p/r 75-100: .5X TO 1.2X p/r 125-275
*RS BLUE p/r 40: .6X TO 1.5X p/r 125-275
OVERALL AUTO ODDS 1:12
PRINT RUNS B/WN 15-150 COPIES PER
NO PRICING ON QTY OF 25 OR LESS
EXCHANGE DEADLINE 05/25/08
144 Mike Piazza/100 50.00 100.00

2006 Sweet Spot Signatures Black Stitch Black Ink

OVERALL AUTO ODDS 1:12
STATED PRINT RUN 1 SERIAL #'d SET
NO PRICING DUE TO SCARCITY
EXCHANGE DEADLINE 05/25/08

2006 Sweet Spot Signatures Black Stitch Blue Ink

OVERALL AUTO ODDS 1:12
STATED PRINT RUN 1 SERIAL #'d SET
NO PRICING DUE TO SCARCITY
EXCHANGE DEADLINE 05/25/08

2006 Sweet Spot Signatures Red-Blue Stitch Black Ink

*RBS BLK p/r 50-99: .5X TO 1.2X p/r 125-275
*RBS BLACK p/r 50-99: .4X TO 1X p/r 86-99
*RBS BLACK p/r 45-49: .5X TO 1.2X p/r 86-99
OVERALL AUTO ODDS 1:12
PRINT RUNS B/WN 25-99 COPIES PER
NO PRICING ON QTY OF 25 OR LESS
EXCHANGE DEADLINE 05/25/08

2006 Sweet Spot Signatures Red-Blue Stitch Blue Ink

*RBS BLUE p/r 50: .5X TO 1.2X p/r 125-275
*RBS BLUE p/r 50: .4X TO 1X p/r 86-99
*RBS BLUE p/r 30-49: .6X TO 1.5X p/r 125-275
OVERALL AUTO ODDS 1:12
PRINT RUNS B/WN 5-50 COPIES PER
NO PRICING ON QTY OF 25 OR LESS
EXCHANGE DEADLINE 05/25/08
144 Mike Piazza/50 60.00 120.00

2006 Sweet Spot Signatures Bat Barrel Black Ink

OVERALL AU ODDS 1:12
PRINT RUNS B/WN 13-25 COPIES PER
NO PRICING DUE TO SCARCITY
EXCHANGE DEADLINE 05/25/08

2006 Sweet Spot Signatures Bat Barrel Blue Ink

OVERALL AU ODDS 1:12
STATED PRINT RUN 5 SERIAL #'d SETS
FELDMAN PRINT RUN 3 SER. #'d SETS
NO PRICING DUE TO SCARCITY
EXCHANGE DEADLINE 05/25/08

2006 Sweet Spot Signatures Glove Leather Black Ink

OVERALL AU ODDS 1:12
PRINT RUNS B/WN 5-15 COPIES PER
NO PRICING DUE TO SCARCITY
EXCHANGE DEADLINE 05/25/08

2006 Sweet Spot Signatures Glove Leather Blue Ink

OVERALL AU ODDS 1:12
STATED PRINT RUN 5 SERIAL #'d SETS

HARDEN PRINT RUN 4 SER. #'d SETS
NO PRICING DUE TO SCARCITY
EXCHANGE DEADLINE 05/25/08

2006 Sweet Spot Super Sweet Swatch

OVERALL GU ODDS 1:12
PRINT RUNS B/WN 5-299 COPIES PER
NO PRICING ON QTY OF 9 OR LESS
AD Adam Dunn Jsy/299 4.00 10.00
AE Adam Eaton Jsy/299 3.00 8.00
AJ Andruw Jones Jsy/299 5.00 12.00
AN Andy Pettitte Jsy/299 5.00 12.00
AP Albert Pujols Jsy/299 12.50 30.00
AT Garrett Atkins Jsy/299 3.00 8.00
BA Bobby Abreu Jsy/299 4.00 10.00
BC Brandon Claussen Jsy/299 3.00 8.00
BE Josh Beckett Jsy/299 4.00 10.00
BG Brian Giles Jsy/299 3.00 8.00
BS Ben Sheets Jsy/299 4.00 10.00
BW Bernie Williams Bat/299 5.00 12.00
BZ Barry Zito Jsy/299 4.00 10.00
CB Craig Biggio Jsy/299 4.00 10.00
CD Carlos Delgado Bat/299 5.00 12.00
CJ Chipper Jones Jsy/299 6.00 15.00
CR Bobby Crosby Bat/136 4.00 10.00
CS Curt Schilling Jsy/299 5.00 12.00
DJ Derek Jeter Bat/299 15.00 40.00
DL Derrek Lee Jsy/299 4.00 10.00
DO David Ortiz Jsy/299 6.00 15.00
DW Dontrelle Willis Jsy/299 4.00 10.00
DY Jermaine Dye Jsy/299 4.00 10.00
EC Eric Chavez Jsy/299 4.00 10.00
ED Jim Edmonds Bat/257 5.00 12.00
EG Eric Gagne Jsy/299 4.00 10.00
FG Freddy Garcia Jsy/299 3.00 8.00
FH Felix Hernandez Jsy/299 4.00 10.00
FR Jeff Francoeur Jsy/299 10.00 25.00
FT Frank Thomas Jsy/299 6.00 15.00
GA Garret Anderson Jsy/299 4.00 10.00
GL Tom Glavine Jsy/299 5.00 12.00
GR Grady Sizemore Jsy/299 5.00 12.00
GS Gary Sheffield Bat/189 4.00 10.00
HA Travis Hafner Jsy/299 4.00 10.00
HB Hank Blalock Jsy/299 4.00 10.00
HE Ramon Hernandez Bat/272 3.00 8.00
HO Trevor Hoffman Jsy/299 4.00 10.00
HU Torii Hunter Bat/287 4.00 10.00
HY Roy Halladay Jsy/299 4.00 10.00
IR Ivan Rodriguez Jsy/299 5.00 12.00
JA Jay Payton Bat/193 3.00 8.00
JB Jason Bay Jsy/299 4.00 10.00
JE Johnny Estrada Jsy/299 3.00 8.00
JG Jason Giambi Jsy/299 6.00 15.00
JJ Jacque Jones Jsy/299 4.00 10.00
JL Jeff Bagwell Jsy/299 5.00 12.00
JM Joe Mauer Jsy/299 5.00 12.00
JO John Smoltz Jsy/299 5.00 12.00
JP Jorge Posada Jsy/299 8.00 20.00
JR Jose Reyes Jsy/299 4.00 10.00
JS Jason Schmidt Jsy/299 4.00 10.00
JU Justin Morneau Jsy/299 4.00 10.00
JV Jason Varitek Jsy/299 6.00 15.00
JW Jack Wilson Jsy/299 3.00 8.00
KG Ken Griffey Jr. Jsy/299 15.00 40.00
KO Paul Konerko Jsy/299 4.00 10.00
KW Kerry Wood Jsy/299 4.00 10.00
LB Lance Berkman Bat/299 4.00 10.00
MA Matt Cain Jsy/299 5.00 12.00
MC Matt Clement Jsy/299 4.00 10.00
MG Marcus Giles Jsy/299 3.00 8.00
MI Miguel Cabrera Jsy/299 5.00 12.00
ML Mark Loretta Bat/267 3.00 8.00
MM Mark Mulder Jsy/299 4.00 10.00
MO Maggio Ordonez Bat/9
MP Mark Prior Jsy/299 4.00 10.00
MR Manny Ramirez Jsy/299 5.00 12.00
MS Mike Sweeney Jsy/299 3.00 8.00
MT Miguel Tejada Jsy/299 4.00 10.00
MY Michael Young Bat/221 4.00 10.00
NJ Nick Johnson Jsy/299 3.00 8.00
NL Noah Lowry Jsy/299 3.00 8.00
NS Nick Swisher Jsy/299 4.00 10.00
PE Jake Peavy Jsy/299 4.00 10.00
PF Prince Fielder Jsy/299 8.00 20.00
PI Mike Piazza Jsy/299 6.00 15.00
PM Pedro Martinez Jsy/299 5.00 12.00
RB Rocco Baldelli Jsy/299 3.00 8.00
RH Ryan Howard Jsy/299 12.50 30.00
RK Ryan Klesko Jsy/299 3.00 8.00
RO Roy Oswalt Jsy/299 4.00 10.00
RS Richie Sexson Jsy/299 3.00 8.00
RW Rickie Weeks Jsy/299 4.00 10.00
RZ Ryan Zimmerman Jsy/299 10.00 25.00
SA Johan Santana Jsy/299 5.00 12.00
SF Steve Finley Bat/5
SK Scott Kazmir Jsy/299 4.00 10.00
SR Scott Rolen Jsy/299 5.00 12.00
ST Huston Street Jsy/299 4.00 10.00
TG Troy Glaus Bat/160 4.00 10.00
TH Tim Hudson Jsy/299 4.00 10.00
TN Trot Nixon Jsy/299 5.00 12.00
TO Todd Helton Bat/232 5.00 12.00
TX Mark Teixeira Jsy/299 4.00 10.00
VG Vladimir Guerrero Jsy/299 6.00 15.00
VM Victor Martinez Jsy/299 4.00 10.00
VW Vernon Wells Jsy/299 4.00 10.00
WE David Wells Jsy/299 3.00 8.00
ZD Zach Duke Jsy/299 3.00 8.00

2006 Sweet Spot Super Sweet Swatch Gold

*GOLD: .5X TO 1.2X BASIC
OVERALL GU ODDS 1:12
STATED PRINT RUN 75 SERIAL #'d SETS
MO Maggio Ordonez Bat 5.00 12.00
SF Steve Finley Bat 5.00 12.00

2006 Sweet Spot Super Sweet Swatch Platinum

*PLATINUM: .6X TO 1.5X BASIC
OVERALL GU ODDS 1:12
STATED PRINT RUN 45 SERIAL #'d SETS
MO Maggio Ordonez Bat 6.00 15.00
SF Steve Finley Bat 6.00 15.00

2007 Sweet Spot

COMMON CARD (1-100) .75 2.00
STATED PRINT RUN 850 SER.#'d SETS
TWO BASE CARDS PER TIN
COMMON AU RC (101-142) 3.00 8.00
OVERALL AU ODDS ONE PER TIN
EXCHANGE DEADLINE 11/9/2009
1 Adam Dunn .75 2.00
2 Adrian Beltre .75 2.00
3 Albert Pujols 4.00 10.00
4 Alex Rios .75 2.00
5 Alex Rodriguez 3.00 8.00
6 Alfonso Soriano .75 2.00
7 Andruw Jones 1.25 3.00
8 Aramis Ramirez .75 2.00
9 B.J. Upton .75 2.00
10 Barry Zito .75 2.00
11 Bartolo Colon .75 2.00
12 Ben Sheets .75 2.00
13 Bill Hall .75 2.00
14 Brad Penny .75 2.00
15 Brandon Webb .75 2.00
16 C.C. Sabathia .75 2.00
17 Carl Crawford .75 2.00
18 Carlos Beltran .75 2.00
19 Carlos Guillen .75 2.00
20 Carlos Lee .75 2.00
21 Chase Utley 2.00 5.00
22 Chien-Ming Wang 3.00 8.00
23 Chipper Jones 2.00 5.00
24 Chris Carpenter .75 2.00
25 Cole Hamels 2.00 5.00
26 Craig Biggio 1.25 3.00
27 Curt Schilling 1.25 3.00
28 Dan Haren .75 2.00
29 David Ortiz 2.00 5.00
30 David Wright 3.00 8.00
31 Delmon Young 1.25 3.00
32 Derek Jeter 5.00 12.00
33 Derrek Lee .75 2.00
34 Dontrelle Willis .75 2.00
35 Felix Hernandez 1.25 3.00
36 Frank Thomas 2.00 5.00
37 Gil Meche .75 2.00
38 Grady Sizemore 1.25 3.00
39 Greg Maddux 3.00 8.00
40 Ian Kinsler .75 2.00
41 Ichiro Suzuki 3.00 8.00
42 Ivan Rodriguez 1.25 3.00
43 Jake Peavy .75 2.00
44 Jason Bay .75 2.00
45 Jason Varitek 2.00 5.00
46 Jeff Kent .75 2.00
47 Jermaine Dye .75 2.00
48 Jim Edmonds 1.25 3.00
49 Jim Thome 1.25 3.00
50 Jimmy Rollins 1.25 3.00
51 Joe Mauer 1.25 3.00
52 Johan Santana 1.25 3.00
53 John Smoltz 1.25 3.00
54 Jonathan Papelbon 2.00 5.00
55 Jorge Posada 1.25 3.00
56 Jose Reyes 2.00 5.00
57 Josh Beckett 1.25 3.00
58 Justin Morneau .75 2.00
59 Justin Verlander 2.00 5.00
60 Ken Griffey Jr. 3.00 8.00
61 Kenji Johjima 2.00 5.00
62 Lance Berkman .75 2.00
63 Magglio Ordonez .75 2.00
64 Manny Ramirez 1.25 3.00
65 Mariano Rivera 2.00 5.00
66 Mark Buehrle .75 2.00
67 Mark Teixeira 1.25 3.00
68 Matt Holliday 2.00 5.00
69 Matt Morris .75 2.00
70 Melvin Mora .75 2.00
71 Michael Young .75 2.00
72 Miguel Cabrera 1.25 3.00
73 Miguel Tejada .75 2.00
74 Mike Lowell .75 2.00
75 Mike Mussina 1.25 3.00
76 Mike Piazza 2.00 5.00
77 Nick Swisher .75 2.00
78 Orlando Hudson .75 2.00
79 Paul Konerko .75 2.00
80 Paul Lo Duca .75 2.00
81 Pedro Martinez 1.25 3.00
82 Prince Fielder 2.00 5.00
83 Randy Johnson 2.00 5.00
84 Rickie Weeks .75 2.00
85 Roger Clemens 3.00 8.00
86 Roy Halladay .75 2.00
87 Roy Oswalt .75 2.00
88 Russell Martin .75 2.00
89 Ryan Howard 3.00 8.00
90 Ryan Zimmerman 2.00 5.00
91 Sammy Sosa 2.00 5.00
92 Scott Rolen 1.25 3.00
93 Shawn Green .75 2.00
94 Todd Helton 1.25 3.00
95 Tom Glavine 1.25 3.00
96 Torii Hunter .75 2.00
97 Travis Hafner .75 2.00
98 Vernon Wells .75 2.00
99 Victor Martinez .75 2.00
100 Vladimir Guerrero 2.00 5.00
101 Adam Lind AU (RC) 3.00 8.00
102 Akinori Iwamura AU SP RC 10.00 25.00
103 Alex Gordon AU RC 40.00 80.00
104 Alexi Casilla AU RC 6.00 15.00
105 Andy LaRoche AU (RC) 6.00 15.00
106 Billy Butler AU (RC) 6.00 15.00
107 Ryan Rowland-Smith AU RC 3.00 8.00
108 Brandon Wood AU (RC) 6.00 15.00
109 Brian Burres AU (RC) 3.00 8.00
110 Chase Wright AU RC 4.00 10.00
111 Chris Stewart AU RC 3.00 8.00
112 Daisuke Matsuzaka AU SP RC 150.00 250.00
113 Delmon Young AU SP (RC) 6.00 15.00
114 Andy Sonnanstine AU RC 6.00 15.00
115 Andrew Miller AU RC
116 Fred Lewis AU (RC) 4.00 10.00
117 Glen Perkins AU SP (RC) 10.00 25.00
118 David Murphy AU (RC) 3.00 8.00
119 Hunter Pence AU (RC) 12.50 30.00
120 Jarrod Saltalamacchia AU (RC) 6.00 15.00
121 Jeff Baker AU SP (RC) 4.00 10.00
122 Jesus Flores AU SP RC 10.00 25.00
123 Joakim Soria AU SP RC 10.00 25.00
124 Joe Smith AU RC 4.00 10.00
125 Jon Knott AU (RC) 3.00 8.00
126 Josh Hamilton AU (RC) 15.00 40.00
127 Justin Hampson AU (RC) 3.00 8.00
128 Kei Igawa AU SP RC 10.00 25.00
129 Kevin Cameron AU RC 3.00 8.00
130 Matt Chico AU (RC) 4.00 10.00
131 Matt DeSalvo AU (RC) 4.00 10.00
132 Micah Owings AU SP (RC) 10.00 25.00
133 Michael Bourn AU (RC) 4.00 10.00
134 Miguel Montero AU (RC) 3.00 8.00
135 Phil Hughes AU SP (RC) 20.00 50.00
136 Rick Vanden Hurk AU RC 3.00 8.00
137 Ryan Sweeney AU SP (RC)
138 Tim Lincecum AU RC
139 Travis Buck AU (RC) 4.00 10.00
140 Troy Tulowitzki AU SP (RC) 20.00 50.00
141 Sean Henn AU (RC) 4.00 10.00
142 Zack Segovia AU (RC) 4.00 10.00
NNO Michael Buysner 15.00 40.00

2007 Sweet Spot Sweet Swatch Memorabilia

OVERALL MEM ODDS TWO PER TIN
AD Adam Dunn 3.00 8.00
AJ Andruw Jones 3.00 8.00
AP Albert Pujols 6.00 15.00
AS Alfonso Soriano 3.00 8.00
AT Garrett Atkins 3.00 8.00
BA Bobby Abreu 3.00 8.00
BE Josh Beckett 4.00 10.00
BG Brian Giles 3.00 8.00
BI Craig Biggio 3.00 8.00
BO Jeremy Bonderman 3.00 8.00
BR Brian Roberts 3.00 8.00
BU B.J. Upton 3.00 8.00
BW Billy Wagner 3.00 8.00
CA Chris Carpenter 3.00 8.00
CB Carlos Beltran 3.00 8.00
CC Carl Crawford 3.00 8.00
CD Carlos Delgado 3.00 8.00
CH Cole Hamels 3.00 8.00
CJ Chipper Jones 4.00 10.00
CL Carlos Lee 3.00 8.00
CS Curt Schilling 4.00 10.00
CU Chase Utley 4.00 10.00
DA Johnny Damon
DJ Derek Jeter 8.00 20.00
DM Daisuke Matsuzaka 10.00 25.00
DO David Ortiz 5.00 12.00
DW Dontrelle Willis 3.00 8.00
EB Erik Bedard 3.00 8.00
EC Eric Chavez 3.00 8.00
FG Freddy Garcia 3.00 8.00
FH Felix Hernandez 3.00 8.00
FL Francisco Liriano 3.00 8.00
FT Frank Thomas 5.00 12.00
GA Garret Anderson 3.00 8.00
GM Greg Maddux 5.00 12.00
GR Khalil Greene 3.00 8.00
GS Grady Sizemore 3.00 8.00
HA Roy Halladay 3.00 8.00
HB Hank Blalock 3.00 8.00
HE Todd Helton 3.00 8.00
HO Trevor Hoffman 3.00 8.00
HR Hanley Ramirez 3.00 8.00
HS Huston Street 3.00 8.00
HU Torii Hunter 3.00 8.00
IK Ian Kinsler 3.00 8.00
IR Ivan Rodriguez 3.00 8.00
JB Jason Bay 3.00 8.00
JD Jermaine Dye 3.00 8.00
JE Jim Edmonds 4.00 10.00
JF Jeff Francoeur 4.00 10.00
JG Jason Giambi 3.00 8.00
JK Jeff Kent 3.00 8.00
JM Joe Mauer 3.00 8.00
JN Joe Nathan 3.00 8.00
JP Jake Peavy 3.00 8.00
JR Jimmy Rollins 3.00 8.00
JS Jason Schmidt 3.00 8.00
JT Jim Thome 3.00 8.00
JV Jason Varitek 5.00 12.00
JW Jered Weaver 3.00 8.00
JZ Joel Zumaya 3.00 8.00
KG Ken Griffey Jr. 6.00 15.00
KM Kendry Morales 3.00 8.00
LB Lance Berkman 3.00 8.00
LG Luis Gonzalez 3.00 8.00
MC Miguel Cabrera 3.00 8.00
MM Mike Mussina 3.00 8.00
MO Justin Morneau 3.00 8.00
MR Manny Ramirez 4.00 10.00
MT Mark Teixeira 3.00 8.00
MY Michael Young 3.00 8.00
OR Magglio Ordonez 3.00 8.00
OS Roy Oswalt 3.00 8.00
PA Jonathan Papelbon 5.00 12.00
PB Pat Burrell 3.00 8.00
PE Jhonny Peralta 3.00 8.00
PF Prince Fielder 3.00 8.00
PM Pedro Martinez 3.00 8.00
PO Jorge Posada 3.00 8.00
RC Robinson Cano 4.00 10.00
RE Jose Reyes 5.00 12.00
RH Rich Harden 3.00 8.00
RI Mariano Rivera 3.00 8.00
RJ Randy Johnson 3.00 8.00
RO Roger Clemens 6.00 15.00
RW Rickie Weeks 3.00 8.00
RZ Ryan Zimmerman 5.00 12.00
SA Johan Santana 3.00 8.00
SD Stephen Drew 3.00 8.00
SK Scott Kazmir 3.00 8.00
SM John Smoltz 4.00 10.00
SR Scott Rolen 3.00 8.00
TE Miguel Tejada 3.00 8.00
TG Tom Glavine 3.00 8.00
TH Tim Hudson 3.00 8.00
TR Travis Hafner 3.00 8.00
VE Justin Verlander 4.00 10.00
VG Vladimir Guerrero 3.00 8.00
VM Victor Martinez 3.00 8.00
VW Vernon Wells 3.00 8.00

2007 Sweet Spot Sweet Swatch Memorabilia Patch

OVERALL MEM ODDS TWO PER TIN
STATED PRINT RUN 25 SER.#'d SETS
NO PRICING DUE TO SCARCITY

2007 Sweet Spot Signatures Red Stitch Blue Ink

OVERALL AU ODDS ONE PER TIN
PRINT RUNS B/WN 99-350 COPIES PER
EXCHANGE DEADLINE 11/9/2009
AD Adam Dunn/99 12.50 30.00
AG Adrian Gonzalez/350 8.00 20.00
AI Akinori Iwamura/99 15.00 40.00
AK Austin Kearns/299 4.00 10.00
AL Adam LaRoche/350 4.00 10.00
AM Andrew Miller/99 15.00 40.00
AX Alex Gordon/99 40.00 80.00
BB Boof Bonser/299 4.00 10.00
BP Brandon Phillips/99 10.00 25.00
BR Brian Bruney/299 4.00 10.00
BW Brandon Wood/350 6.00 15.00
CA Carl Crawford/99 6.00 15.00
CB Chad Billingsley/299 6.00 15.00
CC Chris Capuano/299 4.00 10.00
CH Cole Hamels/99 15.00 40.00
CJ Conor Jackson/299 4.00 10.00
CK Casey Kotchman/99 6.00 15.00

CL Cliff Lee/299 6.00 15.00
CQ Carlos Quentin/299 5.00 12.00
CY Chris Young/350 4.00 10.00
DC Daniel Cabrera/299 4.00 10.00
DH Dan Haren/299 6.00 15.00
DR Darrel Rasner/299 4.00 10.00
DY Delmon Young/99 10.00 25.00
EA Erick Aybar/299 4.00 10.00
FH Felix Hernandez/99 15.00 40.00
FP Felix Pie/99 10.00 25.00
GP Glen Perkins/350 4.00 10.00
HA Travis Hafner/99 6.00 15.00
HK Howie Kendrick/350 4.00 10.00
HP Hunter Pence/350 20.00 50.00
HS Huston Street/99 6.00 15.00
JH Josh Hamilton/350 20.00 50.00
JK Jason Kubel/299 4.00 10.00
JL Jon Lester/99 10.00 25.00
JN Joe Nathan/299 4.00 10.00
JP Jonathan Papelbon/99 20.00 50.00
JS Jeremy Sowers/99 6.00 15.00
JV Jason Varitek/99 20.00 50.00
JW Josh Willingham/299 4.00 10.00
KA Jeff Karstens/299 4.00 10.00
KS Kurt Suzuki/299 4.00 10.00
LI Adam Lind/299 4.00 10.00
LO Lyle Overbay/299 4.00 10.00
MC Matt Cain/299 6.00 15.00
MH Matt Holliday/99 EXCH 12.50 30.00
MM Melvin Mora/99 6.00 15.00
NS Nick Swisher/299 6.00 15.00
PH Phil Hughes/99 30.00 60.00
PK Paul Konerko/99 10.00 25.00
RC Roger Clemens/99 50.00 100.00
RH Rich Hill/299 6.00 15.00
RI Rich Harden/99 6.00 15.00
RM Russell Martin/299 EXCH 10.00 25.00
RW Rickie Weeks/99 6.00 15.00
RZ Ryan Zimmerman/99 12.50 30.00
SE Sergio Mitre/299 4.00 10.00
SK Scott Kazmir/99 10.00 25.00
TB Travis Buck/299 6.00 15.00
TG Tom Glavine/99 15.00 40.00
TH Torii Hunter/99 EXCH 6.00 15.00
TL Tim Lincecum/99 40.00 80.00
VE Justin Verlander/99 15.00 40.00
VM Victor Martinez/99 10.00 25.00
YG Chris B. Young/299 6.00 15.00
NNO 756

2007 Sweet Spot Signatures Red-Blue Stitch Red Ink

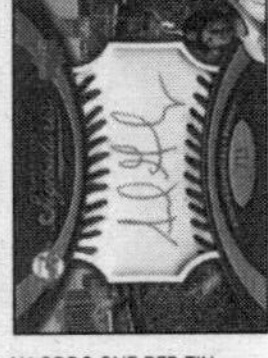

OVERALL AU ODDS ONE PER TIN
PRINT RUNS B/WN 5-15 COPIES PER
NO PRICING DUE TO SCARCITY
EXCHANGE DEADLINE 11/9/2009

2007 Sweet Spot Signatures Black Stitch Black Ink

OVERALL AU ODDS ONE PER TIN
STATED PRINT RUN 1 SER.#'d SET
NO PRICING DUE TO SCARCITY
EXCHANGE DEADLINE 11/9/2009

2007 Sweet Spot Signatures Black-Silver Stitch Silver Ink

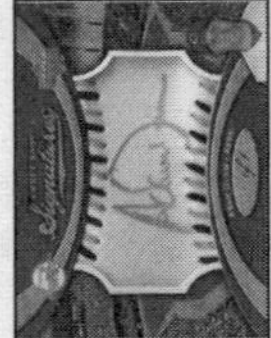

OVERALL AU ODDS ONE PER TIN
STATED PRINT RUN 1 SER.#'d SET
NO PRICING DUE TO SCARCITY
EXCHANGE DEADLINE 11/9/2009

2007 Sweet Spot Signatures Gold Stitch Gold Ink

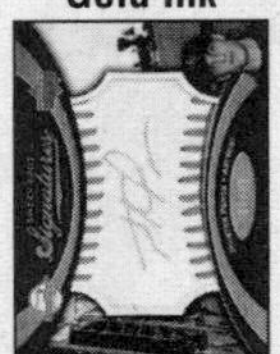

OVERALL AU ODDS ONE PER TIN
PRINT RUNS B/WN 25-99 COPIES PER
NO PRICING ON QTY 25 OR LESS
EXCHANGE DEADLINE 11/9/2009
AD Adam Dunn/25
AG Adrian Gonzalez/99 12.50 30.00
AI Akinori Iwamura/25
AK Austin Kearns/99 6.00 15.00
AL Adam LaRoche/99 6.00 15.00
AM Andrew Miller/25
AX Alex Gordon/25
BB Boof Bonser/99 6.00 15.00
BP Brandon Phillips/25
BR Brian Bruney/99 6.00 15.00
BW Brandon Wood/99 10.00 25.00
CA Carl Crawford/25
CB Chad Billingsley/99 10.00 25.00
CC Chris Capuano/99 6.00 15.00
CH Cole Hamels/25
CJ Conor Jackson/99 6.00 15.00
CK Casey Kotchman/25
CL Cliff Lee/99 10.00 25.00
CQ Carlos Quentin/99 8.00 20.00
CY Chris Young/99 6.00 15.00
DC Daniel Cabrera/99 6.00 15.00
DH Dan Haren/99 6.00 15.00
DR Darrel Rasner/99 6.00 15.00
DY Delmon Young/25
EA Erick Aybar/99 6.00 15.00
FH Felix Hernandez/25
FP Felix Pie/25
GP Glen Perkins/99 6.00 15.00
HA Travis Hafner/25
HK Howie Kendrick/99 6.00 15.00
HP Hunter Pence/99 40.00 80.00
HS Huston Street/25
JH Josh Hamilton/99 30.00 60.00
JK Jason Kubel/99 6.00 15.00
JL Jon Lester/25
JN Joe Nathan/99 6.00 15.00
JP Jonathan Papelbon/25
JS Jeremy Sowers/25
JV Jason Varitek/25
JW Josh Willingham/99 6.00 15.00
KA Jeff Karstens/99 6.00 15.00
KS Kurt Suzuki/99 6.00 15.00
LI Adam Lind/99 6.00 15.00
LO Lyle Overbay/99 6.00 15.00
MC Matt Cain/99 10.00 25.00
MH Matt Holliday/25
MM Melvin Mora/25
NS Nick Swisher/99 10.00 25.00
PH Phil Hughes/25
PK Paul Konerko/25
RC Roger Clemens/25
RH Rich Hill/99 10.00 25.00
RI Rich Harden/25
RM Russell Martin/99 EXCH 15.00 40.00
RW Rickie Weeks/25
RZ Ryan Zimmerman/25
SE Sergio Mitre/99 6.00 15.00
SK Scott Kazmir/25
TB Travis Buck/99 10.00 25.00
TG Tom Glavine/25
TH Torii Hunter/25
TL Tim Lincecum/25
VE Justin Verlander/25
VM Victor Martinez/25
YG Chris B. Young/99 10.00 25.00

2007 Sweet Spot Signatures Silver Stitch Silver Ink

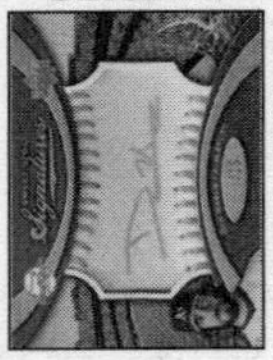

OVERALL AU ODDS ONE PER TIN
PRINT RUNS B/WN 1-99 COPIES PER
NO PRICING ON QTY 25 OR LESS
EXCHANGE DEADLINE 11/9/2009
AD Adam Dunn/44 15.00 40.00
AG Adrian Gonzalez/23
AI Akinori Iwamura/1
AK Austin Kearns/25
AL Adam LaRoche/25
AM Andrew Miller/48 20.00 50.00
AX Alex Gordon/7
BB Boof Bonser/26 8.00 20.00
BP Brandon Phillips/99 10.00 25.00
BR Brian Bruney/99 6.00 15.00
BW Brandon Wood/3
CA Carl Crawford/13
CB Chad Billingsley/58 10.00 25.00
CC Chris Capuano/39 8.00 20.00
CH Cole Hamels/35 20.00 50.00
CJ Conor Jackson/16
CK Casey Kotchman/99 6.00 15.00
CL Cliff Lee/31 12.50 30.00
CQ Carlos Quentin/7
CY Chris Young/32 8.00 20.00
DC Daniel Cabrera/35 8.00 20.00
DH Dan Haren/15
DJ Derek Jeter/2
DJ2 Derek Jeter/2
DR Darrel Rasner/27 8.00 20.00
DY Delmon Young/26 12.50 30.00
EA Erick Aybar/32 8.00 20.00
FH Felix Hernandez/34 20.00 50.00
FP Felix Pie/99 10.00 25.00
GP Glen Perkins/60 6.00 15.00
HA Travis Hafner/48 8.00 20.00
HK Howie Kendrick/47 8.00 20.00
HP Hunter Pence/9
HS Huston Street/20
JH Josh Hamilton/33 30.00 60.00
JK Jason Kubel/16
JL Jon Lester/31 12.50 30.00
JN Joe Nathan/36 8.00 20.00
JP Jonathan Papelbon/58 20.00 50.00
JS Jeremy Sowers/45 8.00 20.00
JV Jason Varitek/33 30.00 60.00
JW Josh Willingham/14
KG Ken Griffey Jr./3
KG2 Ken Griffey Jr./3
KS Kurt Suzuki/99 6.00 15.00
LI Adam Lind/99 6.00 15.00
LO Lyle Overbay/17
MC Matt Cain/18
MH Matt Holliday/5
MM Melvin Mora/6
NS Nick Swisher/33 12.50 30.00
PH Phil Hughes/65 30.00 60.00
PK Paul Konerko/99 10.00 25.00
RC Roger Clemens/22
RH Rich Hill/51 10.00 25.00
RI Rich Harden/40 8.00 20.00
RM Russell Martin/55 EXCH 15.00 40.00
RW Rickie Weeks/23
RZ Ryan Zimmerman/11
SE Sergio Mitre/99 6.00 15.00
SK Scott Kazmir/19
TB Travis Buck/6
TG Tom Glavine/47 20.00 50.00
TH Torii Hunter/48 8.00 20.00
TL Tim Lincecum/55 50.00 100.00
VE Justin Verlander/35 20.00 50.00
VM Victor Martinez/41 12.50 30.00
YG Chris B. Young/24

2007 Sweet Spot Signatures Bat Barrel Blue Ink

OVERALL AU ODDS ONE PER TIN
PRINT RUNS B/WN 1-99 COPIES PER
NO PRICING ON QTY 25 OR LESS
EXCHANGE DEADLINE 11/9/2009
AD Adam Dunn/44 15.00 40.00
AG Adrian Gonzalez/23
AI Akinori Iwamura/1
AK Austin Kearns/25
AL Adam LaRoche/25
AM Andrew Miller/48 20.00 50.00
AX Alex Gordon/7
BB Boof Bonser/26 8.00 20.00
BP Brandon Phillips/99 10.00 25.00
BR Brian Bruney/99 6.00 15.00
BW Brandon Wood/3
CA Carl Crawford/13
CB Chad Billingsley/58 10.00 25.00
CC Chris Capuano/39 8.00 20.00
CH Cole Hamels/35 20.00 50.00
CJ Conor Jackson/16
CK Casey Kotchman/99 6.00 15.00
CL Cliff Lee/31 12.50 30.00
CQ Carlos Quentin/7
CY Chris Young/32 8.00 20.00
DC Daniel Cabrera/35 8.00 20.00
DH Dan Haren/15
DJ Derek Jeter/2
DJ2 Derek Jeter/2
DR Darrel Rasner/27 8.00 20.00
DY Delmon Young/26 12.50 30.00
EA Erick Aybar/23
FH Felix Hernandez/34 20.00 50.00
FP Felix Pie/99 10.00 25.00
GP Glen Perkins/60 6.00 15.00
HA Travis Hafner/48 8.00 20.00
HK Howie Kendrick/47 8.00 20.00
HP Hunter Pence/9
HS Huston Street/20
JH Josh Hamilton/33 30.00 60.00
JK Jason Kubel/16
JL Jon Lester/31 12.50 30.00
JN Joe Nathan/36 8.00 20.00
JP Jonathan Papelbon/58 20.00 50.00
JS Jeremy Sowers/45 8.00 20.00
JV Jason Varitek/33 30.00 60.00
JW Josh Willingham/14
KA Jeff Karstens/17
KG Ken Griffey Jr./3 EXCH
KG2 Ken Griffey Jr./3 EXCH
KS Kurt Suzuki/99 6.00 15.00
LI Adam Lind/99 6.00 15.00
LO Lyle Overbay/17
MC Matt Cain/18
MH Matt Holliday/5
MM Melvin Mora/6
NS Nick Swisher/33 12.50 30.00
PH Phil Hughes/65 30.00 60.00
PK Paul Konerko/99 10.00 25.00
RC Roger Clemens/22
RH Rich Hill/53 10.00 25.00
RI Rich Harden/40 EXCH 8.00 20.00
RM Russell Martin/55 EXCH 15.00 40.00
RW Rickie Weeks/23
RZ Ryan Zimmerman/11
SE Sergio Mitre/99 6.00 15.00
SK Scott Kazmir/19
TB Travis Buck/6
TG Tom Glavine/47 20.00 50.00
TH Torii Hunter/48 EXCH 8.00 20.00
TL Tim Lincecum/55 50.00 100.00
VE Justin Verlander/35 20.00 50.00
VM Victor Martinez/41 12.50 30.00
YG Chris B. Young/24

2007 Sweet Spot Signatures Bat Barrel Gold Ink

OVERALL AU ODDS ONE PER TIN
STATED PRINT RUN 1 SER.#'d SET
NO PRICING DUE TO SCARCITY
EXCHANGE DEADLINE 11/9/2009

2007 Sweet Spot Signatures Bat Barrel Red Ink

OVERALL AU ODDS ONE PER TIN
STATED PRINT RUN 5 SER.#'d SETS
NO PRICING DUE TO SCARCITY
EXCHANGE DEADLINE 11/9/2009

2007 Sweet Spot Signatures Bat Barrel Silver Ink

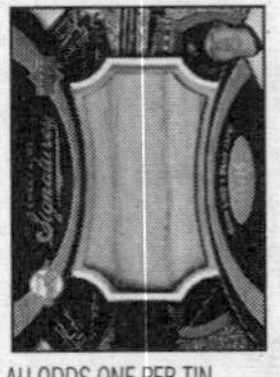

OVERALL AU ODDS ONE PER TIN
PRINT RUNS B/WN 5-25 COPIES PER
NO PRICING DUE TO SCARCITY
EXCHANGE DEADLINE 11/9/2009

2007 Sweet Spot Signatures Black Bat Barrel Gold Ink

OVERALL AU ODDS ONE PER TIN
STATED PRINT RUN 1 SER.#'d SET
NO PRICING DUE TO SCARCITY
EXCHANGE DEADLINE 11/9/2009

2007 Sweet Spot Signatures Black Bat Barrel Red Ink

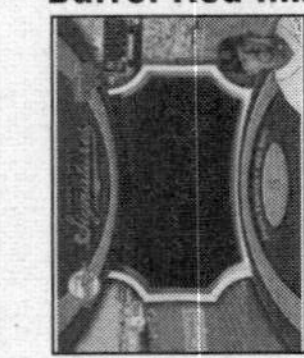

OVERALL AU ODDS ONE PER TIN
STATED PRINT RUN 5 SER.#'d SETS
NO PRICING DUE TO SCARCITY
EXCHANGE DEADLINE 11/9/2009

2007 Sweet Spot Signatures Black Bat Barrel Silver Ink

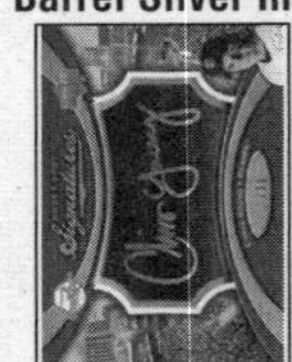

OVERALL AU ODDS ONE PER TIN
PRINT RUNS B/WN 5-15 COPIES PER
NO PRICING DUE TO SCARCITY
EXCHANGE DEADLINE 11/9/2009

2007 Sweet Spot Signatures Glove Leather Black Ink

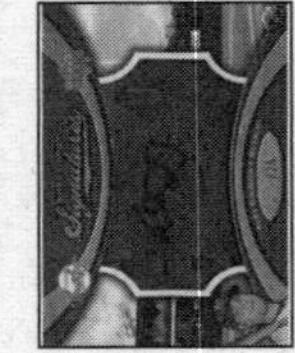

OVERALL AU ODDS ONE PER TIN
PRINT RUNS B/WN 25-75 COPIES PER
NO PRICING DUE TO SCARCITY
EXCHANGE DEADLINE 11/9/2009
AD Adam Dunn/25
AG Adrian Gonzalez/75 12.50 30.00
AI Akinori Iwamura/25
AK Austin Kearns/75 6.00 15.00
AL Adam LaRoche/75 6.00 15.00
AM Andrew Miller/25
AX Alex Gordon/25

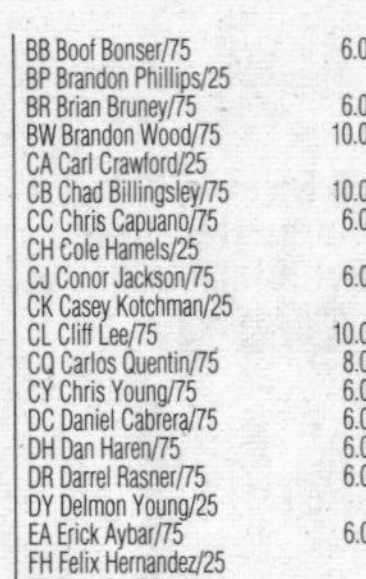

BB Boof Bonser/75 6.00 15.00
BP Brandon Phillips/25
BR Brian Bruney/75 6.00 15.00
BW Brandon Wood/75 10.00 25.00
CA Carl Crawford/25
CB Chad Billingsley/75 10.00 25.00
CC Chris Capuano/75 6.00 15.00
CH Cole Hamels/25
CJ Conor Jackson/75 6.00 15.00
CK Casey Kotchman/25
CL Cliff Lee/75 10.00 25.00
CQ Carlos Quentin/75 8.00 20.00
CY Chris Young/75 6.00 15.00
DC Daniel Cabrera/75 6.00 15.00
DH Dan Haren/75 6.00 15.00
DR Darrel Rasner/75 6.00 15.00
DY Delmon Young/25
EA Erick Aybar/75 6.00 15.00
FH Felix Hernandez/25
FP Felix Pie/25
GP Glen Perkins/75 6.00 15.00
HA Travis Hafner/25
HK Howie Kendrick/75 6.00 15.00
HP Hunter Pence/75 40.00 80.00
HS Huston Street/25
JH Josh Hamilton/75 30.00 60.00
JK Jason Kubel/75 6.00 15.00
JL Jon Lester/25
JN Joe Nathan/75 6.00 15.00
JP Jonathan Papelbon/25
JS Jeremy Sowers/25
JV Jason Varitek/25
JW Josh Willingham/75 EXCH 6.00 15.00
KA Jeff Karstens/75 6.00 15.00
KS Kurt Suzuki/75 6.00 15.00
LO Lyle Overbay/75 6.00 15.00
MC Matt Cain/75 10.00 25.00
MH Matt Holliday/25 EXCH
MM Melvin Mora/25
NS Nick Swisher/75 10.00 25.00
PH Phil Hughes/25
PK Paul Konerko/25
RC Roger Clemens/25
RH Rich Hill/75 10.00 25.00
RI Rich Harden/25
RM Russell Martin/75 15.00 40.00
RW Rickie Weeks/25
RZ Ryan Zimmerman/25
SE Sergio Mitre/75 6.00 15.00
SK Scott Kazmir/25
TB Travis Buck/75 10.00 25.00
TG Tom Glavine/25
TH Torii Hunter/25 EXCH
TL Tim Lincecum/25
VE Justin Verlander/25
VM Victor Martinez/25
YG Chris B. Young/75 10.00 25.00

2007 Sweet Spot Signatures Glove Leather Green Ink

OVERALL AU ODDS ONE PER TIN
STATED PRINT RUN 1 SER.#'d SET
NO PRICING DUE TO SCARCITY
EXCHANGE DEADLINE 11/9/2009

2007 Sweet Spot Signatures Glove Leather Silver Ink

OVERALL AU ODDS ONE PER TIN
PRINT RUNS B/WN 5-25 COPIES PER
NO PRICING DUE TO SCARCITY
EXCHANGE DEADLINE 11/9/2009

2007 Sweet Spot Signatures Black Glove Leather Gold Ink

OVERALL AU ODDS ONE PER TIN
STATED PRINT RUN 5 SER.#'d SETS
NO PRICING DUE TO SCARCITY
EXCHANGE DEADLINE 11/9/2009

2007 Sweet Spot Signatures Black Glove Leather Metallic Blue Ink

OVERALL AU ODDS ONE PER TIN
STATED PRINT RUN 1 SER.#'d SET
NO PRICING DUE TO SCARCITY
EXCHANGE DEADLINE 11/9/2009

2007 Sweet Spot Signatures Black Glove Leather Silver Ink

OVERALL AU ODDS ONE PER TIN
PRINT RUNS B/WN 5-25 COPIES PER
NO PRICING DUE TO SCARCITY
EXCHANGE DEADLINE 11/9/2009

2007 Sweet Spot Dual Signatures Red Stitch Blue Ink

OVERALL AU ODDS ONE PER TIN
PRINT RUNS B/WN 5-15 COPIES PER
NO PRICING DUE TO SCARCITY
EXCHANGE DEADLINE 11/9/2009

2007 Sweet Spot Dual Signatures Black Stitch Black Ink

OVERALL AU ODDS ONE PER TIN
STATED PRINT RUN 1 SER.#'d SET
NO PRICING DUE TO SCARCITY
EXCHANGE DEADLINE 11/9/2009

2007 Sweet Spot Dual Signatures Gold Stitch Gold Ink

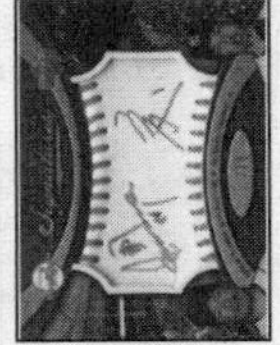

OVERALL AU ODDS ONE PER TIN
PRINT RUNS B/WN 5-10 COPIES PER
NO PRICING DUE TO SCARCITY
EXCHANGE DEADLINE 11/9/2009

2007 Sweet Spot Dual Signatures Silver Stitch Silver Ink

OVERALL AU ODDS ONE PER TIN
STATED PRINT RUN 5 SER.#'d SETS
NO PRICING DUE TO SCARCITY
EXCHANGE DEADLINE 11/9/2009

2007 Sweet Spot Dual Signatures Glove Leather Black Ink

OVERALL AU ODDS ONE PER TIN
PRINT RUNS B/WN 5-15 COPIES PER
NO PRICING DUE TO SCARCITY
EXCHANGE DEADLINE 11/9/2009

2007 Sweet Spot Dual Signatures Glove Leather Silver Ink

OVERALL AU ODDS ONE PER TIN
STATED PRINT RUN 1 SER.#'d SET
NO PRICING DUE TO SCARCITY
EXCHANGE DEADLINE 11/9/2009

2007 Sweet Spot Dual Signatures Black Glove Leather Gold Ink

OVERALL AU ODDS ONE PER TIN
PRINT RUNS B/WN 5-10 COPIES PER
NO PRICING DUE TO SCARCITY
EXCHANGE DEADLINE 11/9/2009

2007 Sweet Spot Dual Signatures Black Glove Leather Silver Ink

OVERALL AU ODDS ONE PER TIN
STATED PRINT RUN 1 SER.#'d SET
NO PRICING DUE TO SCARCITY
EXCHANGE DEADLINE 11/9/2009

2002 Sweet Spot Classics

This 90 card set was issued in February, 2002. These cards were issued in four card packs which came 12 packs to a box and eight boxes to a case.

COMPLETE SET (90) 15.00 40.00
1 Mickey Mantle 2.50 6.00
2 Joe DiMaggio 1.25 3.00
3 Babe Ruth 2.00 5.00
4 Ty Cobb 1.00 2.50
5 Nolan Ryan 1.50 4.00

6 Sandy Koufax 1.25 3.00
7 Cy Young .60 1.50
8 Roberto Clemente 1.50 4.00
9 Lefty Grove .40 1.00
10 Lou Gehrig 1.25 3.00
11 Walter Johnson .60 1.50
12 Honus Wagner .75 2.00
13 Christy Mathewson .60 1.50
14 Jackie Robinson .60 1.50
15 Joe Morgan .40 1.00
16 Reggie Jackson .40 1.00
17 Eddie Collins .40 1.00
18 Cal Ripken 2.00 5.00
19 Hank Greenberg .60 1.50
20 Harmon Killebrew .60 1.50
21 Johnny Bench .60 1.50
22 Ernie Banks .60 1.50
23 Willie McCovey .40 1.00
24 Mel Ott .60 1.50
25 Tom Seaver .40 1.00
26 Tony Gwynn .75 2.00
27 Dave Winfield .40 1.00
28 Willie Stargell .40 1.00
29 Mark McGwire 1.50 4.00
30 Al Kaline .60 1.50
31 Jimmie Foxx .60 1.50
32 Satchel Paige .60 1.50
33 Eddie Murray .60 1.50
34 Lou Boudreau .40 1.00
35 Joe Jackson 1.25 3.00
36 Luke Appling .40 1.00
37 Ralph Kiner .40 1.00
38 Robin Yount .60 1.50
39 Paul Molitor .40 1.00
40 Juan Marichal .40 1.00
41 Brooks Robinson .40 1.00
42 Wade Boggs .40 1.00
43 Kirby Puckett .60 1.50
44 Yogi Berra .60 1.50
45 George Sisler .40 1.00
46 Buck Leonard .40 1.00
47 Billy Williams .40 1.00
48 Duke Snider .40 1.00
49 Don Drysdale .40 1.00
50 Bill Mazeroski .40 1.00
51 Tony Oliva .40 1.00
52 Luis Aparicio .40 1.00
53 Carlton Fisk .40 1.00
54 Kirk Gibson .40 1.00
55 Catfish Hunter .40 1.00
56 Joe Carter .40 1.00
57 Gaylord Perry .40 1.00
58 Don Mattingly 1.25 3.00
59 Eddie Mathews .60 1.50
60 Fergie Jenkins .40 1.00
61 Roy Campanella .60 1.50
62 Orlando Cepeda .40 1.00
63 Tony Perez .40 1.00
64 Dave Parker .40 1.00
65 Richie Ashburn .40 1.00
66 Andre Dawson .40 1.00
67 Dwight Evans .40 1.00
68 Rollie Fingers .40 1.00
69 Dale Murphy .40 1.00
70 Ron Santo .40 1.00
71 Steve Garvey .40 1.00
72 Monte Irvin .40 1.00
73 Alan Trammell .40 1.00
74 Ryne Sandberg 1.00 2.50
75 Gary Carter .40 1.00
76 Fred Lynn .40 1.00
77 Maury Wills .40 1.00
78 Ozzie Smith 1.00 2.50
79 Bobby Bonds .40 1.00
80 Mickey Cochrane .40 1.00
81 Dizzy Dean .60 1.50
82 Graig Nettles .40 1.00
83 Keith Hernandez .40 1.00
84 Boog Powell .40 1.00
85 Jack Clark .40 1.00
86 Dave Stewart .40 1.00
87 Tommy Lasorda .40 1.00
88 Dennis Eckersley .40 1.00
89 Ken Griffey Sr. .40 1.00
90 Bucky Dent .40 1.00

2002 Sweet Spot Classics Game Bat

Inserted at stated odds of one in eight, these cards feature the most notable tools of the trade. Please note that if the player has a DP next to their name than that card is perceived to be in larger supply. Also note that some player have shorter print runs and that information is notated in our checklist along with a stated print run from the company.

GOLD RANDOM INSERTS IN PACKS
GOLD PRINT RUN 25 SERIAL #'d SETS
GOLD NO PRICING DUE TO SCARCITY

BAK Al Kaline 6.00 15.00
BBBO Bob Boone 4.00 10.00
BBBU Bill Buckner 4.00 10.00
BBD Bucky Dent 4.00 10.00
BBM Bill Madlock 4.00 10.00
BBR Brooks Robinson 6.00 15.00
BBW Billy Williams 4.00 10.00
BCR Cal Ripken DP 10.00 25.00
BDE Dwight Evans 6.00 15.00
BDM Don Mattingly 10.00 25.00
BDP Dave Parker 4.00 10.00
BDW Dave Winfield DP 4.00 10.00
BFJ Fergie Jenkins 4.00 10.00
BFL Fred Lynn 4.00 10.00
BGC Gary Carter 4.00 10.00
BGN Graig Nettles 4.00 10.00
BHG Hank Greenberg SP 30.00 60.00
BJB Johnny Bench 6.00 15.00
BJD Joe DiMaggio SP/40 *
BKG Ken Griffey Sr. DP 4.00 10.00
BKP Kirby Puckett DP 6.00 15.00
BNR Nolan Ryan 15.00 40.00
BPM Paul Molitor 4.00 10.00
BRC Roberto Clemente 30.00 60.00
BRJ Reggie Jackson 6.00 15.00
BSG Steve Garvey 4.00 10.00
BTG Tony Gwynn DP 6.00 15.00
BTM Thurman Munson 15.00 40.00
BWB Wade Boggs DP 6.00 15.00
BYB Yogi Berra 6.00 15.00

2002 Sweet Spot Classics Game Jersey

Inserted at stated odds of one in eight, these cards feature memorabilia from the featured player. Please note that if the player has a DP next to their name than that card is perceived to be in larger supply. Also note that some player have shorter print runs and that information is notated in our checklist along with a stated print run from the company if available.

GOLD RANDOM INSERTS IN PACKS
GOLD PRINT RUN 25 SERIAL #'d SETS
GOLD NO PRICING DUE TO SCARCITY

JBM Bill Madlock 4.00 10.00
JBW Billy Williams 4.00 10.00
JCR Cal Ripken DP 10.00 25.00
JDM Don Mattingly DP 10.00 25.00
JDP Dave Parker 4.00 10.00
JDSN Duke Snider SP/53 * 50.00 100.00
JDST Dave Stewart 4.00 10.00
JEM Eddie Murray 6.00 15.00
JGC Gary Carter 4.00 10.00
JGN Graig Nettles 4.00 10.00
JJC Joe Carter 4.00 10.00
JJD Joe DiMaggio SP/53 * 100.00 200.00
JJMA Juan Marichal 4.00 10.00
JMM Mickey Mantle SP/53 * 150.00 250.00
JNR Nolan Ryan DP 15.00 40.00
JOS Ozzie Smith 6.00 15.00
JPM Paul Molitor DP 4.00 10.00
JRF Rollie Fingers 4.00 10.00
JRJ Reggie Jackson 6.00 15.00
JRS Ryne Sandberg 6.00 15.00
JRY Robin Yount DP 6.00 15.00
JSG Steve Garvey 4.00 10.00
JSK Sandy Koufax SP 75.00 150.00
JTG Tony Gwynn DP 6.00 15.00
JTS Tom Seaver 6.00 15.00
JWB Wade Boggs 6.00 15.00
JWS Willie Stargell 6.00 15.00

2002 Sweet Spot Classics Signatures

Inserted at stated odds of one in 24, these cards feature the top stars of yesterday with their signature on a "sweet spot". Though UD refused to comment on the matter, it's believed that Don Mattingly's card is in larger supply than others from this set. Also note that some players, as verified by UD, have shorter print runs and that information is notated in our checklist along with a stated print run from the company. Though not stated as SP's by Upper Deck, our own research provided solid evidence that Reggie Jackson, Sandy Koufax and Willie McCovey were also seeded in shorter supply than the typical allotment for this set. These cards have been tagged with an "SP *" in our checklist below. Finally, the Kirk Gibson card was detailed as an SP by Upper Deck, but a specific print run for the card was not divulged. That card is simpl tagged as an SP (bereft of the asterisk - indicating it's verified status by Upper Deck).

GOLD RANDOM INSERTS IN PACKS
GOLD PRINT RUN 25 SERIAL #'d SETS
GOLD NO PRICING DUE TO SCARCITY

SAD Andre Dawson SP/100 * 60.00 120.00
SAK Al Kaline 20.00 50.00
SAT Alan Trammell 10.00 25.00
SBD Bucky Dent 10.00 25.00
SBM Bill Mazeroski 20.00 50.00
SBP Boog Powell 10.00 25.00
SBR Brooks Robinson 15.00 40.00
SCF Carlton Fisk SP/100 * 75.00 150.00
SCR Cal Ripken 100.00 175.00
SDAM Dale Murphy 15.00 40.00
SDAS Dave Stewart 10.00 25.00
SDEE Dennis Eckersley 15.00 40.00
SDOM Don Mattingly DP 50.00 100.00
SDW Dave Winfield SP/70 * 60.00 120.00
SEB Ernie Banks 40.00 80.00
SFJ Fergie Jenkins 10.00 25.00
SFL Fred Lynn 10.00 25.00
SGP Gaylord Perry 10.00 25.00
SJB Johnny Bench 40.00 80.00
SJM Joe Morgan 10.00 25.00
SKG Kirk Gibson/SP 30.00 60.00
SKH Keith Hernandez 10.00 25.00
SKP Kirby Puckett SP/74 * 75.00 150.00
SNR Nolan Ryan SP/74 * 225.00 350.00
SOS Ozzie Smith SP/137 * 75.00 150.00
SPM Paul Molitor 10.00 25.00
SRF Rollie Fingers 10.00 25.00
SRJ Reggie Jackson SP * 60.00 120.00
SSG Steve Garvey 10.00 25.00
SSK Sandy Koufax SP * 200.00 350.00
STL Tommy Lasorda 40.00 80.00
STS Tom Seaver 30.00 60.00
SWM Willie McCovey SP * 50.00 100.00
SYB Yogi Berra SP/100 * 100.00 175.00

2003 Sweet Spot Classics

This 150 card set was issued in March, 2003. It was issued in five-card packs with an $10 SRP. The packs were issued in 12 pack boxes which came 16 boxes to a case. The following subsets are included: Ted Williams Ball Game (91-120) and Yankee Heritage (121-150). The Williams's cards were printed to a stated print run of 1941 and the Yankee Heritage cards were printed to a stated print run of 1500 serial numbered sets. While this set features mainly retired players, a special Hideki Matsui card (75) was issued. That card was issued to a stated print run of 1999 serial numbered sets. Originally that card was supposed to be Rod Carew and a few Carew cards made it through the production process. However, at this time no pricing information is available on the Carew card which was supposed to be card number 75 originally.

COMP.SET w/o SP's (89) 15.00 40.00
COMMON (1-74/76-90) .30 .75
COMMON CARD (91-120) 3.00 8.00
COMMON CARD (121-150) 2.00 5.00
1 Al Hrabosky .30 .75
2 Al Lopez .30 .75
3 Andre Dawson .30 .75
4 Bill Buckner .30 .75
5 Billy Williams .30 .75
6 Bob Feller .30 .75
7 Bob Lemon .30 .75
8 Bobby Doerr .30 .75
9 Cecil Cooper .30 .75
10 Cal Ripken 2.50 6.00
11 Carlton Fisk .50 1.25
12 Catfish Hunter .50 1.25
13 Chris Chambliss .30 .75
14 Dale Murphy .50 1.25
15 Gaylord Perry .30 .75
16 Dave Kingman .30 .75
17 Dave Parker .30 .75
18 Dave Stewart .30 .75
19 David Cone .30 .75
20 Dennis Eckersley .30 .75
21 Don Baylor .30 .75
22 Don Sutton .30 .75
23 Duke Snider .50 1.25
24 Dwight Evans .50 1.25
25 Dwight Gooden .30 .75
26 Earl Weaver MG .30 .75
27 Early Wynn .30 .75
28 Eddie Mathews .75 2.00
29 Enos Slaughter .30 .75
30 Ernie Banks .75 2.00
31 Fred Lynn .30 .75
32 Fred Stanley .30 .75
33 Gary Carter .30 .75
34 George Foster .30 .75
35 Hal Newhouser .30 .75
36 George Kell .30 .75
37 Harmon Killebrew .75 2.00
38 Hoyt Wilhelm .30 .75
39 Jack Morris .30 .75
40 Jim Bunning .30 .75
41 Jim Gilliam .30 .75
42 Jim Leyritz .30 .75
43 Jimmy Key .30 .75
44 Joe Carter .30 .75
45 Joe Morgan .30 .75
46 John Montefusco .30 .75
47 Johnny Bench .75 2.00
48 Johnny Podres .30 .75
49 Jose Canseco .50 1.25
50 Juan Marichal .30 .75
51 Keith Hernandez .30 .75
52 Ken Griffey Sr. .30 .75
53 Kirby Puckett .75 2.00
54 Kirk Gibson .30 .75
55 Larry Doby .30 .75
56 Lee May .30 .75
57 Lee Mazzilli .30 .75
58 Lou Boudreau .30 .75
59 Mark McGwire 2.00 5.00
60 Maury Wills .30 .75
61 Mike Pagliarulo .30 .75
62 Monte Irvin .30 .75
63 Nolan Ryan 2.00 5.00
64 Orlando Cepeda .30 .75
65 Ozzie Smith 1.25 3.00
66 Paul O'Neill .50 1.25
67 Pee Wee Reese .50 1.25
68 Phil Niekro .30 .75
69 Ralph Kiner .30 .75
70 Red Schoendienst .30 .75
71 Richie Ashburn .50 1.25
72 Rick Ferrell .30 .75
73 Robin Roberts .30 .75
74 Robin Yount .75 2.00
75 Hideki Matsui/1999 XRC 6.00 15.00
75B Rod Carew ERR
Not Intended for Public Release
76 Rollie Fingers .30 .75
77 Ron Cey .30 .75
78 Tom Seaver .50 1.25
79 Sparky Anderson MG .30 .75
80 Stan Musial 1.25 3.00
81 Steve Garvey .30 .75
82 Ted Williams 1.50 4.00
83 Tommy Lasorda .30 .75
84 Tony Gwynn 1.00 2.50
85 Tony Perez .30 .75
86 Vida Blue .30 .75
87 Warren Spahn .50 1.25
88 Bob Gibson .50 1.25
89 Willie McCovey .30 .75
90 Willie Stargell .50 1.25
91 Ted Williams TB 3.00 8.00
92 Ted Williams TB 3.00 8.00
93 Ted Williams TB 3.00 8.00
94 Ted Williams TB 3.00 8.00
95 Ted Williams TB 3.00 8.00
96 Ted Williams TB 3.00 8.00
97 Ted Williams TB 3.00 8.00
98 Ted Williams TB 3.00 8.00
99 Ted Williams TB 3.00 8.00
100 Ted Williams TB 3.00 8.00
101 Ted Williams TB 3.00 8.00
102 Ted Williams TB 3.00 8.00
103 Ted Williams TB 3.00 8.00
104 Ted Williams TB 3.00 8.00
105 Ted Williams TB 3.00 8.00
106 Ted Williams TB 3.00 8.00
106B Ted Williams TB UER 116 3.00 8.00
107 Ted Williams TB 3.00 8.00
108 Ted Williams TB 3.00 8.00
109 Ted Williams TB 3.00 8.00
110 Ted Williams TB 3.00 8.00
111 Ted Williams TB 3.00 8.00
112 Ted Williams TB 3.00 8.00
113 Ted Williams TB 3.00 8.00
114 Ted Williams TB 3.00 8.00
115 Ted Williams TB 3.00 8.00
117 Ted Williams TB 3.00 8.00
118 Ted Williams TB 3.00 8.00
119 Ted Williams TB 3.00 8.00
120 Ted Williams TB 3.00 8.00
121 Babe Ruth YH 6.00 15.00
122 Bucky Dent YH 2.00 5.00
123 Casey Stengel YH 2.00 5.00
124 Dave Righetti YH 2.00 5.00
125 Dave Winfield YH 2.00 5.00
126 Dick Tidrow YH 2.00 5.00
127 Dock Ellis YH 2.00 5.00
128 Don Mattingly YH 5.00 12.00
129 Hank Bauer YH 2.00 5.00
130 Jim Bouton YH 2.00 5.00
131 Jim Kaat YH 2.00 5.00
132 Joe DiMaggio YH 4.00 10.00
133 Joe Torre YH 2.00 5.00
134 Lou Piniella YH 2.00 5.00
135 Mel Stottlemyre YH 2.00 5.00
136 Mickey Mantle YH 8.00 20.00
137 Mickey Rivers YH 2.00 5.00
138 Phil Rizzuto YH 2.00 5.00
139 Ralph Branca YH 2.00 5.00
140 Ralph Houk YH 2.00 5.00
141 Roger Maris YH 3.00 8.00
142 Ron Guidry YH 2.00 5.00
143 Ruben Amaro Sr. YH 2.00 5.00
144 Sparky Lyle YH 2.00 5.00
145 Thurman Munson YH 3.00 8.00
146 Tommy Henrich YH 2.00 5.00
147 Tommy John YH 2.00 5.00
148 Tony Kubek YH 2.00 5.00
149 Whitey Ford YH 2.00 5.00
150 Yogi Berra YH 3.00 8.00

2003 Sweet Spot Classics Matsui Parallel

Randomly inserted into packs, these cards parallel the Hideki Matsui base card. There are three different versions of this card and they were all issued to different stated print runs. Please note the silver version (75C) was issued to a stated print run of 25 serial numbered sets and there is no pricing due to market scarcity.

75A Hideki Matsui Red/500 6.00 15.00
75B Hideki Matsui Blue/250 8.00 20.00
75C Hideki Matsui Silver/25

2003 Sweet Spot Classics Autographs Black Ink

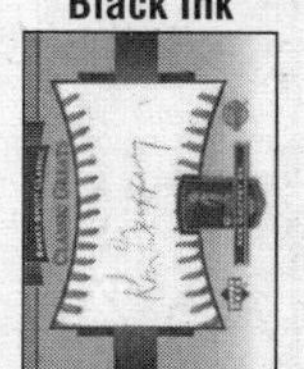

Randomly inserted into packs, these cards feature the players signing in black ink. These autograph cards were in packs at overall rate of one in 24. Each card was printed to a different amount and we have noted that information next to the player's name in our checklist. All the Mark McGwire autos are inscribed "Maris '61"

AD Andre Dawson/75 20.00 50.00
AH Al Hrabosky/100 15.00 40.00
AT Alan Trammell/173 15.00 40.00
BB Bill Buckner/85 15.00 40.00
BW Billy Williams/173 15.00 40.00
CR Cal Ripken/38
DB Don Baylor/50 20.00 50.00
DE Dwight Evans/100 40.00 80.00
DP Dave Parker/113 15.00 40.00
DS Don Sutton/123 15.00 40.00
EB Ernie Banks/73 60.00 120.00
GC Gary Carter/173 15.00 40.00
GF George Foster/173 15.00 40.00
GI Kirk Gibson/173 15.00 40.00
HK Harmon Killebrew/73 60.00 120.00
JB Johnny Bench/73 75.00 150.00
JC Joe Carter/123 15.00 40.00
JM Joe Morgan/169 15.00 40.00
JM Jack Morris/123 15.00 40.00
JP Johnny Podres/173 15.00 40.00
KG Ken Griffey Sr./100 20.00 50.00
KH Keith Hernandez/173 15.00 40.00
KP Kirby Puckett/174 60.00 120.00
MM Mark McGwire/73 300.00 500.00
MW Maury Wills/173 15.00 40.00
OC Orlando Cepeda/34
PN Phil Niekro/173 15.00 40.00
RF Rollie Fingers/73 20.00 50.00
RR Robin Roberts/173 20.00 50.00
RY Robin Yount/73 75.00 150.00
SG Steve Garvey/173 15.00 40.00
SN Duke Snider/100 40.00 80.00
TG Tony Gwynn/101 40.00 80.00
TP Tony Perez/51 40.00 80.00
TS Tom Seaver/74 40.00 80.00

2003 Sweet Spot Classics Autographs Blue Ink

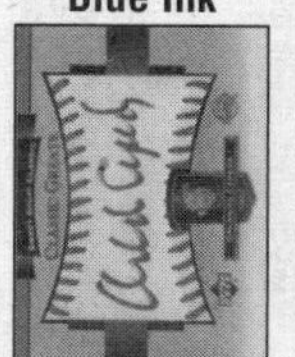

Randomly inserted in packs, these cards feature the players signing their cards in black ink. A few players were issued in shorter quantity and we have notated that information with an SP next to their name in our checklist. In addition, Upper Deck purchased nine Ted Williams cuts and issued nine of these cards to match his uniform number.

AD Andre Dawson 10.00 25.00
AH Al Hrabosky SP 10.00 25.00
BB Bill Buckner SP 10.00 25.00
CF Carlton Fisk 30.00 60.00
CR Cal Ripken 100.00 200.00
DB Don Baylor SP 10.00 25.00
DE Dennis Eckersley 10.00 25.00
DE Dwight Evans * 10.00 25.00
DM Dale Murphy 12.50 30.00
DS Dave Stewart 10.00 25.00
KG Ken Griffey Sr. 10.00 25.00
KP Kirby Puckett 50.00 100.00
OC Orlando Cepeda * 10.00 25.00
SN Duke Snider 20.00 50.00
TG Tony Gwynn 20.00 50.00
TW Ted Williams/9

2003 Sweet Spot Classics Autographs Yankee Greats Black Ink

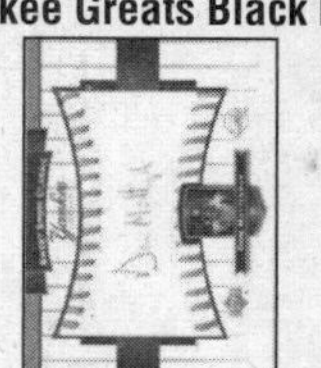

Randomly inserted in packs, these cards feature former New York Yankees who signed their card in black ink. We have notated the stated print run information next to the player's name in our checklist. Please note that the Hideki Matsui card was issued as an exchange card and has an exchange deadline of March 13, 2006.

CC Chris Chambliss/101 30.00 60.00
DC David Cone/74 40.00 80.00
DE Dock Ellis/174 15.00 40.00
DG Dwight Gooden/74 30.00 60.00
DK Dave Kingman/100 30.00 60.00
DM Don Mattingly/74 75.00 150.00
DR Dave Righetti/173 30.00 60.00
DT Dick Tidrow/101 15.00 40.00
DW Dave Winfield/25
FS Fred Stanley/101 15.00 40.00
GU Ron Guidry/100 40.00 80.00
HB Hank Bauer/75 30.00 60.00
HM Hideki Matsui/25
JB Jim Bouton/100 15.00 40.00
JC Jose Canseco/73 40.00 80.00
JD Joe DiMaggio/5
JK Jim Kaat/100 15.00 40.00
JK Jimmy Key/100 15.00 40.00
JL Jim Leyritz/100 15.00 40.00
JM John Montefusco/100 15.00 40.00
JT Joe Torre/73 40.00 80.00
LM Lee Mazzilli/100 15.00 40.00
LP Lou Piniella/100 15.00 40.00
MP Mike Pagliarulo/99 15.00 40.00
MR Mickey Rivers/73 30.00 60.00
MS Mel Stottlemyre/73 30.00 60.00
PO Paul O'Neill/100 40.00 80.00
PR Phil Rizzuto/173 40.00 80.00
RA Ruben Amaro Sr./100 15.00 40.00
RB Ralph Branca/100 15.00 40.00
RH Ralph Houk/100 15.00 40.00
SL Sparky Lyle/100 15.00 40.00
TH Tommy Henrich/100 15.00 40.00
TJ Tommy John/100 15.00 40.00
TK Tony Kubek/123 30.00 60.00
YB Yogi Berra/73 60.00 120.00

2003 Sweet Spot Classics Autographs Yankee Greats Blue Ink

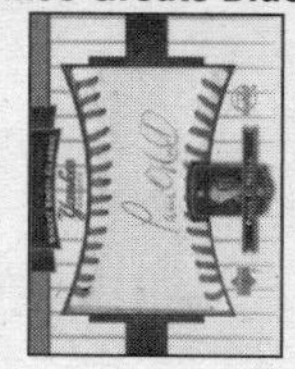

Randomly inserted in packs, these cards feature former New York Yankees who signed their card in blue ink. A few cards were issued in lesser quantity and we have notated those cards with an SP in our checklist. In addition, the Bucky Dent card seems to be in larger supply and we have notated that with an asterisk in our checklist. Also, Upper Deck purchased seven Mickey Mantle autographs and used those as scarce cuts in this product.

BD Bucky Dent * 10.00 25.00
CC Chris Chambliss SP 15.00 40.00
DK Dave Kingman 15.00 40.00
DT Dick Tidrow 10.00 25.00
FS Fred Stanley 10.00 25.00
GU Ron Guidry 20.00 50.00
HB Hank Bauer SP 15.00 40.00
JB Jim Bouton 10.00 25.00
JK Jim Kaat 10.00 25.00
JK Jimmy Key 15.00 40.00
JL Jim Leyritz 10.00 25.00
JM John Montefusco 10.00 25.00
LM Lee Mazzilli 10.00 25.00
LP Lou Piniella SP 15.00 40.00
MM Mickey Mantle/7
MP Mike Pagliarulo 10.00 25.00
PO Paul O'Neill 20.00 50.00
RA Ruben Amaro Sr. 10.00 25.00
RB Ralph Branca 10.00 25.00
RH Ralph Houk 10.00 25.00
SL Sparky Lyle SP 15.00 40.00
TH Tommy Henrich SP 15.00 40.00
TJ Tommy John 10.00 25.00

2003 Sweet Spot Classics Game Jersey

Issued at a stated rate of one in 16, these 30 cards feature game-worn jersey swatches on the card. A few cards were issued in smaller quantities and we have notated those cards with an SP in our checklist.

AD Andre Dawson SP 4.00 10.00
CC Cecil Cooper 4.00 10.00
CF Carlton Fisk 6.00 15.00
CR Cal Ripken 10.00 25.00
DM Dale Murphy 6.00 15.00
DPO Dave Parker Pants 4.00 10.00
DS Duke Snider SP 6.00 15.00
EB Ernie Banks SP 6.00 15.00
FL Fred Lynn 4.00 10.00
GC Gary Carter SP 4.00 10.00
GF George Foster 4.00 10.00
HK Harmon Killebrew 6.00 15.00
JB Johnny Bench 6.00 15.00
JC Jose Canseco 6.00 15.00
JG Jim Gilliam 4.00 10.00
JMO Joe Morgan Pants 4.00 10.00
JP Johnny Podres 4.00 10.00
KP Kirby Puckett 6.00 15.00
LM Lee May 4.00 10.00
MM Mark McGwire 20.00 50.00
NR Nolan Ryan 15.00 40.00
OS Ozzie Smith 6.00 15.00
RC Ron Cey 4.00 10.00
RF Rollie Fingers 4.00 10.00
RY Robin Yount 6.00 15.00
SG Steve Garvey 4.00 10.00
SM Stan Musial SP 15.00 40.00
TG Tony Gwynn 6.00 15.00
TW Ted Williams SP 50.00 100.00
WS Willie Stargell SP 6.00 15.00

2003 Sweet Spot Classics Patch Cards

Inserted at a stated rate of one in six, these 83 cards feature special patch-type pieces. These cards honor different highlights in many player's career and we have notated that information next to their name in our checklist.

BR1 Babe Ruth Red Sox/350 15.00 40.00
BR2 Babe Ruth Yankees 12.50 30.00
BR3 Babe Ruth 27 WS/150 20.00 50.00
BW1 Billy Williams 4.00 10.00
CF1 Carlton Fisk Red Sox 6.00 15.00
CF2 Carlton Fisk White Sox/150 10.00 25.00
CH1 Catfish Hunter A's/350 6.00 15.00
CH2 Catfish Hunter Yankees 6.00 15.00
CH3 Catfish Hunter A's GU/39 30.00 60.00
CH4 Catfish Hunter 72 WS/50 15.00 40.00
CR1 Cal Ripken 10.00 25.00
CR2 Cal Ripken GU/75 75.00 150.00
CR3 Cal Ripken 83 WS/150 30.00 60.00
DS1 Duke Snider 6.00 15.00
DS2 Duke Snider LA/150 10.00 25.00
DS3 Duke Snider Mets/350 6.00 15.00
DS4 Duke Snider Dodgers GU/25
DS5 Duke Snider Brooklyn/150 10.00 25.00
DS6 Duke Snider 59 WS/150 10.00 25.00
EB1 Ernie Banks 6.00 15.00
FL1 Fred Lynn Red Sox 4.00 10.00
FL2 Fred Lynn Angels/350 4.00 10.00
FL3 Fred Lynn O's/150 6.00 15.00
FL4 Fred Lynn Tigers/50 10.00 25.00
GF1 George Foster Mets/350 4.00 10.00
GF2 George Foster Reds 4.00 10.00
HM1 Hideki Matsui 10.00 25.00
JB1 Johnny Bench 6.00 15.00
JB2 Johnny Bench GU/150 30.00 60.00
JB3 Johnny Bench 76 WS/150 15.00 40.00
JD1 Joe DiMaggio 6.00 15.00
JD2 Joe DiMaggio 47 WS/50 50.00 100.00
JD3 Joe DiMaggio 37 WS/350 12.50 30.00
JD4 Joe DiMaggio 39 WS/150 15.00 40.00
JM1 Joe Morgan Reds 4.00 10.00
JM2 Joe Morgan Astros/350 4.00 10.00
JM3 Joe Morgan Giants/150 6.00 15.00
JM4 Joe Morgan Reds GU/150 15.00 40.00
JM5 Joe Morgan 76 WS/100 6.00 15.00
KG1 Kirk Gibson Dodgers 4.00 10.00
KG2 Kirk Gibson Tigers/350 4.00 10.00
KP1 Kirby Puckett 6.00 15.00
KP2 Kirby Puckett GU/40 50.00 100.00
MC1 Mark McGwire A's 10.00 25.00
MC2 Mark McGwire Cards/350 20.00 50.00
MC3 Mark McGwire Cards GU/9
MM1 Mickey Mantle 15.00 40.00
MM2 M.Mantle 52 WS/150 60.00 120.00
MM3 M.Mantle 56 WS/150 60.00 120.00
MM4 M.Mantle 60 WS/150 60.00 120.00
MM5 Mickey Mantle Logo/7
NR1 Nolan Ryan Astros 10.00 25.00
NR2 Nolan Ryan Rangers/350 20.00 50.00
NR3 Nolan Ryan Angels/150 30.00 60.00
NR4 N.Ryan Astros GU/105 60.00 120.00
OS1 Ozzie Smith Cards 6.00 15.00
OS2 Ozzie Smith Padres/350 10.00 25.00
OS3 Ozzie Smith Cards GU/150 30.00 60.00
OS4 Ozzie Smith 82 WS/100 15.00 40.00
OS5 Ozzie Smith 85 WS/100 15.00 40.00
RM1 Roger Maris Yankees 6.00 15.00
RM2 Roger Maris Cards/350 10.00 25.00
RM3 Roger Maris 62 WS/150 15.00 40.00
RM4 Roger Maris 67 WS/50 20.00 50.00
RY1 Robin Yount 6.00 15.00
RY2 Robin Yount GU/150 15.00 40.00
RY3 Robin Yount 82 WS/350 10.00 25.00
SG1 Steve Garvey Dodgers 4.00 10.00
SG2 Steve Garvey Padres/350 4.00 10.00
SG3 S.Garvey Dodgers GU/150 15.00 40.00
SG4 Steve Garvey 77 WS/50 10.00 25.00
SG5 Steve Garvey 81 WS/50 10.00 25.00
TG1 Tony Gwynn 6.00 15.00
TG2 Tony Gwynn GU/150 40.00 80.00
TG3 Tony Gwynn 84 WS/350 10.00 25.00
TW1 Ted Williams 8.00 20.00
TW2 Ted Williams 46 WS/350 15.00 40.00
WS1 Willie Stargell 6.00 15.00
WS2 Willie Stargell GU/137 20.00 50.00
WS3 Willie Stargell 71 WS/150 10.00 25.00
WS4 Willie Stargell 79 WS/50 15.00 40.00
YB1 Yogi Berra 6.00 15.00
YB2 Yogi Berra 53 WS/350 10.00 25.00
YB3 Yogi Berra 56 WS/150 15.00 40.00

2003 Sweet Spot Classics Pinstripes

Inserted at a stated rate of one in 40, these 12 cards feature authentic game-used pieces of New York Yankee uniforms. Please note that a few cards were issued in shorter supply and we have notated that information with an SP notation in our checklist.

BR0 Babe Ruth Pants SP 150.00 250.00
CS Casey Stengel 6.00 15.00
DE Bucky Dent 4.00 10.00
DG0 Dwight Gooden Pants 4.00 10.00
DM0 Don Mattingly Pants 15.00 40.00
DR Dave Righetti 4.00 10.00
JB Jim Bouton 4.00 10.00
JD Joe DiMaggio SP 60.00 120.00
MM Mickey Mantle SP 90.00 180.00
PR Phil Rizzuto 6.00 15.00
TM Thurman Munson SP 15.00 40.00
YB Yogi Berra 8.00 20.00

2004 Sweet Spot Classic

This 159 card standard-size set was released in February, 2004. The set was issued in four card packs which came 12 packs to a box and 8 boxes to a case. Cards numbered 1-90 were issued in higher quantity than cards 91-161. The cards 91 through 161 feature "famous firsts" in players careers. Each of these cards are numbered to that year in issue. Cards numbered 143 and 148 which were supposed to feature Roger Clemens were removed from the set when Clemens came out of a very short retirement to sign with the Houston Astros.

COMP.SET w/o SP'S (90) 15.00 40.00
COMMON CARD (1-90) .30 .75
COMMON CARD (91-161) 2.00 5.00
91-161 STATED ODDS 1:3
1 Al Kaline .75 2.00
2 Andre Dawson .30 .75
3 Bert Blyleven .30 .75
4 Bill Dickey .50 1.25
5 Bill Mazeroski .50 1.25
6 Billy Martin .50 1.25
7 Bob Feller .30 .75
8 Bob Gibson .50 1.25
9 Bob Lemon .30 .75
10 George Kell .30 .75
11 Bobby Doerr .30 .75
12 Brooks Robinson .50 1.25
13 Cal Ripken 2.50 6.00
14 Carl Hubbell .50 1.25
15 Carl Yastrzemski 1.25 3.00
16 Charlie Keller .30 .75
17 Chuck Dressen .30 .75
18 Cy Young .75 2.00
19 Dave Winfield .30 .75
20 Dizzy Dean .50 1.25
21 Don Drysdale .50 1.25
22 Don Larsen .30 .75
23 Don Mattingly 1.50 4.00
24 Don Newcombe .30 .75
25 Duke Snider .50 1.25
26 Early Wynn .30 .75
27 Eddie Mathews .75 2.00
28 Elston Howard .30 .75
29 Frank Robinson .30 .75
30 Gary Carter .30 .75
31 Gil Hodges .50 1.25
32 Gil McDougald .50 1.25
33 Hank Greenberg .75 2.00
34 Harmon Killebrew .75 2.00
35 Harry Caray .30 .75
36 Honus Wagner .75 2.00
37 Hoyt Wilhelm .30 .75
38 Jackie Robinson .75 2.00
39 Jim Bunning .30 .75
40 Jim Palmer .30 .75
41 Jimmie Foxx .75 2.00
42 Jimmy Wynn .30 .75
43 Joe DiMaggio 1.50 4.00
44 Joe Torre .50 1.25
45 Johnny Mize .30 .75
46 Juan Marichal .30 .75
47 Larry Doby .30 .75
48 Lefty Gomez .50 1.25
49 Lefty Grove .50 1.25
50 Leo Durocher .30 .75
51 Lou Boudreau .30 .75
52 Lou Brock .50 1.25
53 Lou Gehrig 1.50 4.00
54 Luis Aparicio .30 .75
55 Maury Wills .30 .75
56 Mel Allen .30 .75
57 Mel Ott .75 2.00
58 Mickey Cochrane .30 .75
59 Mickey Mantle 3.00 8.00
60 Mike Schmidt 1.50 4.00
61 Monte Irvin .30 .75
62 Nolan Ryan 2.00 5.00
63 Pee Wee Reese .50 1.25
64 Phil Rizzuto .50 1.25
65 Ralph Kiner .30 .75
66 Richie Ashburn .50 1.25
67 Rick Ferrell .30 .75
68 Roberto Clemente 2.00 5.00
69 Robin Roberts .30 .75
70 Robin Yount .75 2.00
71 Rogers Hornsby .75 2.00
72 Rollie Fingers .30 .75
73 Roy Campanella .75 2.00
74 Ryne Sandberg 1.50 4.00
75 Tony Gwynn 1.00 2.50
76 Satchel Paige .75 2.00
77 Shoeless Joe Jackson 1.25 3.00
78 Stan Musial 1.25 3.00
79 Ted Williams 1.50 4.00
80 Thurman Munson .75 2.00
81 Tom Seaver .30 .75
82 Tommy Henrich .30 .75
83 Tony Perez .30 .75
84 Tris Speaker .50 1.25
85 Vida Blue .30 .75
86 Wade Boggs .50 1.25
87 Walter Johnson .75 2.00
88 Warren Spahn .50 1.25
89 Whitey Ford .50 1.25
90 Willie McCovey .30 .75
91 Andre Dawson FF/1987 2.00 5.00
92 Andre Dawson FF/1990 2.00 5.00
93 Ernie Banks FF/1958 3.00 8.00
94 Bob Lemon FF/1948 2.00 5.00
95 Cal Ripken FF/1982 6.00 15.00
96 Cal Ripken FF/1995 6.00 15.00
97 Carl Yastrzemski FF/1979 3.00 8.00
98 Carlton Fisk FF/1972 3.00 8.00
99 Cy Young FF/1910 3.00 8.00
100 Don Larsen FF/1956 2.00 5.00
101 Don Newcombe FF/1949 2.00 5.00
102 Don Newcombe FF/1956 2.00 5.00
103 Dwight Evans FF/1986 3.00 8.00
104 Elston Howard FF/1955 2.00 5.00
105 Frank Robinson FF/1956 2.00 5.00
106 Frank Robinson FF/1966 2.00 5.00
107 Frank Robinson FF/1973 2.00 5.00
108 Gil McDougald FF/1951 3.00 8.00
109 Hank Greenberg FF/1941 3.00 8.00
110 Harmon Killebrew FF/1964 3.00 8.00
111 Hoyt Wilhelm FF/1952 2.00 5.00
112 Hoyt Wilhelm FF/1958 2.00 5.00
113 Jackie Robinson FF/1946 3.00 8.00
114 J.Robinson FF Black/1947 3.00 8.00
115 J.Robinson FF ROY/1947 3.00 8.00
116 Jackie Robinson FF/1997 3.00 8.00
117 Jim Bunning FF/1964 2.00 5.00
118 J.DiMaggio FF Bench/1950 4.00 10.00
119 Joe Morgan FF/1976 2.00 5.00
120 Johnny Mize FF/1939 2.00 5.00
121 Johnny Mize FF/1947 2.00 5.00
122 Juan Marichal FF/1968 2.00 5.00
123 Ken Griffey Sr. FF/1990 2.00 5.00
124 Larry Doby FF/1947 2.00 5.00
125 Lefty Gomez FF/1933 3.00 8.00
126 Lou Boudreau FF/1946 2.00 5.00
127 Lou Gehrig FF Lineup/1939 4.00 10.00
128 Lou Gehrig FF Number/1939 4.00 10.00
129 Mark McGwire FF/1989 5.00 12.00
130 Mark McGwire FF/1998 5.00 12.00
131 Maury Wills FF/1962 2.00 5.00
132 Mel Ott FF/1946 3.00 8.00
133 Mike Schmidt FF/1980 4.00 10.00
134 Nolan Ryan FF/1973 5.00 12.00
135 Nolan Ryan FF/1989 5.00 12.00
136 Pee Wee Reese FF/1955 3.00 8.00
137 Nolan Ryan FF/1979 5.00 12.00
138 Richie Ashburn FF/1962 3.00 8.00
139 Roberto Clemente FF/1971 5.00 12.00
140 Roberto Clemente FF/1973 5.00 12.00
141 Robin Roberts FF/1956 2.00 5.00
142 Robin Yount FF/1982 3.00 8.00
144 Rollie Fingers FF/1975 2.00 5.00
145 Rollie Fingers FF/1981 2.00 5.00
146 Roy Campanella FF/1953 3.00 8.00
147 Ryne Sandberg FF/1990 4.00 10.00
149 Satchel Paige FF/1948 3.00 8.00
150 Stan Musial FF/1952 3.00 8.00
151 Stan Musial FF/1954 3.00 8.00
152 Stan Musial FF/1963 3.00 8.00
153 Ted Williams FF/1947 4.00 10.00
154 Ted Williams FF/1957 4.00 10.00
155 Tom Seaver FF/1970 3.00 8.00
156 Tom Seaver FF/1975 3.00 8.00
157 Wade Boggs FF/1999 3.00 8.00
158 Warren Spahn FF/1957 3.00 8.00
159 Warren Spahn FF/1958 3.00 8.00
160 Joe DiMaggio FF AS/1950 4.00 10.00
161 Yogi Berra FF/1947 3.00 8.00

2004 Sweet Spot Classic Barrel Signatures

Lou Brock did not return his cards in time for inclusion in this product. Those cards could be redeemed until January 27, 2004. A few cards have been seen on the secondary market with Duke Snider's photo used on Wade Boggs' card.

OVERALL AUTO ODDS 1:24
PRINT RUNS B/WN 24-203 COPIES PER
NO PRICING ON QTY OF 25 OR LESS
BM Bill Mazeroski/24
BW Billy Williams/200 20.00 50.00
CR Cal Ripken/25
HB Harold Baines/200 20.00 50.00
JB Johnny Bench/50
LB Lou Brock/50 EXCH
NR Nolan Ryan/25
RS Ron Santo/203 20.00 50.00
SM Stan Musial/25
TS Tom Seaver/25
WB Wade Boggs/200 40.00 80.00

2004 Sweet Spot Classic Game Used Memorabilia

OVERALL GU MEMORABILIA ODDS 1:24
STATED PRINT RUN 275 SERIAL #'d SETS
AD Andre Dawson Expos Jsy 4.00 10.00
AD1 Andre Dawson Cubs Jsy 4.00 10.00
BB Bert Blyleven Jsy 4.00 10.00
BM Billy Martin Pants 6.00 15.00
CD Chuck Dressen Pants 4.00 10.00
CK Charlie Keller Jsy 4.00 10.00
CR Cal Ripken Jsy 15.00 40.00
CY Carl Yastrzemski Jsy 10.00 25.00
DM Don Mattingly Jsy 10.00 25.00
EH Elston Howard Jsy 6.00 15.00
EM Eddie Mathews Jsy 6.00 15.00
FR Frank Robinson Jsy 4.00 10.00
GC Gary Carter Pants 4.00 10.00
GM Gil McDougald Jsy 6.00 15.00
JB Jim Bunning Pants 6.00 15.00
JD Joe DiMaggio Pants 40.00 80.00
JM Juan Marichal Pants 4.00 10.00
JO Johnny Mize Pants 6.00 15.00
JP Jim Palmer Jsy 4.00 10.00
JR Jackie Robinson Pants 15.00 40.00
JT Joe Torre Jsy 6.00 15.00
KG Ken Griffey Sr. Jsy 4.00 10.00
ML Mickey Lolich Jsy 4.00 10.00
MM Mickey Mantle Pants 60.00 120.00
MW Maury Wills Pants 4.00 10.00
NR Nolan Ryan Jsy 15.00 40.00
OS Ozzie Smith Jsy 6.00 15.00
PR Phil Rizzuto Pants 6.00 15.00
RB Ron Blomberg Jsy 4.00 10.00
RC Roberto Clemente Pants 40.00 80.00
RM Roger Maris Pants 30.00 60.00
RY Robin Yount Jsy 6.00 15.00
SA Sparky Anderson Jsy 4.00 10.00
SB Sal Bando Jsy 4.00 10.00
SM Stan Musial Pants 15.00 40.00
TG Tony Gwynn Pants 6.00 15.00
TM Thurman Munson Jsy 12.50 30.00
TS Tom Seaver Pants 6.00 15.00
TW Ted Williams Pants 30.00 60.00
WB Wade Boggs Sox Pants 6.00 15.00
WB1 Wade Boggs Yanks Pants 6.00 15.00

2004 Sweet Spot Classic Game Used Memorabilia Silver Rainbow

*SILVER RBW: .75X TO 2X BASIC SWATCH
OVERALL GU MEMORABILIA ODDS 1:24
STATED PRINT RUN 50 SERIAL #'d SETS
JD Joe DiMaggio Pants 50.00 100.00
MM Mickey Mantle Pants 125.00 200.00
RC Roberto Clemente Pants 50.00 100.00
TW Ted Williams Pants 40.00 80.00

2004 Sweet Spot Classic Game Used Patch

PRINT RUNS B/WN 17-176 COPIES PER
NO PRICING ON QTY OF 23 OR LESS
SILVER RAINBOW PRINT RUN 10 #'d SETS
NO SILV.RAIN.PRICING DUE TO SCARCITY
RANDOM INSERTS IN PACKS
AD Andre Dawson/100 10.00 25.00
BB Bert Blyleven/113 10.00 25.00
CK Charlie Keller/55 15.00 40.00
CR Cal Ripken/17
CY Carl Yastrzemski/20
DM Don Mattingly/176 30.00 60.00
EH Elston Howard/23
FR Frank Robinson/50 15.00 40.00
GM Gil McDougald/31 20.00 50.00
ML Mickey Lolich/115 10.00 25.00
MW Maury Wills/78 10.00 25.00
NR Nolan Ryan/96 50.00 100.00
RY Robin Yount/100 20.00 50.00
TG Tony Gwynn/100 30.00 60.00
TM Thurman Munson/100 30.00 60.00
TS Tom Seaver/94 15.00 40.00
WB Wade Boggs/90 15.00 40.00

2004 Sweet Spot Classic Patch 300

STATED PRINT RUN 300 SERIAL #'d SETS
*PATCH 230: .4X TO 1X BASIC
PATCH 230 PRINT RUN 230 SERIAL #'d SETS
*PATCH 200: .4X TO 1X BASIC
PATCH 200 PRINT RUN 200 SERIAL #'d SETS
*PATCH 150: .5X TO 1.2X BASIC
PATCH 150 PRINT RUN 150 SERIAL #'d SETS
*PATCH 125: .5X TO 1.2X BASIC
PATCH 125 PRINT RUN 125 SERIAL #'d SETS
*PATCH 75: .6X TO 1.5X BASIC
PATCH 75 PRINT RUN 75 SERIAL #'d SETS
*PATCH 50: .75X TO 2X BASIC
PATCH 50 PRINT RUN 50 SERIAL #'d SETS
PATCH 25 PRINT RUN 25 SERIAL #'d SETS
NO PATCH 25 PRICING DUE TO SCARCITY
PATCH 10 PRINT RUN 10 SERIAL #'d SETS
NO PATCH 10 PRICING DUE TO SCARCITY
OVERALL PATCH ODDS 1:3
AD Andre Dawson Cubs 4.00 10.00
AK Al Kaline Tigers 8.00 20.00
AL Mel Allen Yanks 4.00 10.00
BD Bill Dickey Yanks 6.00 15.00
BF Bob Feller Indians 4.00 10.00
BG Bob Gibson Cards 6.00 15.00
BL Bob Lemon Indians 4.00 10.00
BM Billy Martin Yanks 6.00 15.00
BR Lou Brock Cards 6.00 15.00
CA Roy Campanella Dodgers 6.00 15.00
CG Charlie Gehringer Tigers 4.00 10.00
CH Carl Hubbell Giants 6.00 15.00
CM Christy Mathewson Giants 6.00 15.00
CO Mickey Cochrane Tigers 4.00 10.00
CR Cal Ripken AS 15.00 40.00
CY Cy Young Indians 6.00 15.00
DD Dizzy Dean Cards 6.00 15.00
DL Don Larsen Yanks 4.00 10.00
DM Don Mattingly Yanks 10.00 25.00
DN Don Newcombe Dodgers 4.00 10.00
DO Bobby Doerr Red Sox 4.00 10.00
DR Don Drysdale Dodgers 6.00 15.00
DS Duke Snider AS 6.00 15.00
DU Leo Durocher Dodgers 4.00 10.00
DW Dave Winfield Yanks 4.00 10.00
EM Eddie Mathews Braves 6.00 15.00
ES Enos Slaughter Cards 4.00 10.00
EW Early Wynn Indians 4.00 10.00
FF Frankie Frisch Cards 4.00 10.00
FI Rollie Fingers A's 4.00 10.00
FJ Ferguson Jenkins Cubs 4.00 10.00
FR Frank Robinson Reds 4.00 10.00
GC Gary Carter Mets 4.00 10.00
GE Lou Gehrig Yanks 8.00 20.00
GH Gil Hodges Dodgers 6.00 15.00
GP Gaylord Perry Giants 4.00 10.00
GR Lefty Grove A's 6.00 15.00
HC Harry Caray Cubs 4.00 10.00
HG Hank Greenberg Tigers 6.00 15.00
HK Harmon Killebrew Twins 8.00 20.00
HW Honus Wagner Pirates 6.00 15.00
IR Monte Irvin Giants 4.00 10.00
JB Jim Bunning Phils 6.00 15.00
JD Joe DiMaggio AS 8.00 20.00
JF Jimmie Foxx A's 6.00 15.00
JJ Shoeless Joe Jackson Sox 8.00 20.00
JM Johnny Mize Cards 4.00 10.00
JP Jim Palmer O's 4.00 10.00
JR Jackie Robinson Dodgers 6.00 15.00
JT Joe Torre Braves 4.00 10.00
LA Luis Aparicio White Sox 4.00 10.00
LB Lou Boudreau Indians 4.00 10.00
LD Larry Doby Indians 4.00 10.00
LG Lefty Gomez Yanks 6.00 15.00
MA Juan Marichal Giants 4.00 10.00
MI Mickey Mantle AS 20.00 50.00
ML Mickey Lolich Tigers 4.00 10.00
MO Mel Ott Giants 6.00 15.00
MS Mike Schmidt Phils 10.00 25.00
MW Maury Wills Dodgers 4.00 10.00
NR Nolan Ryan Mets 12.50 30.00
PR Pee Wee Reese Dodgers 6.00 15.00
RA Richie Ashburn Phils 6.00 15.00
RC Roberto Clemente Pirates 12.50 30.00
RF Rick Ferrell Red Sox 4.00 10.00
RH Rogers Hornsby Cards 6.00 15.00
RI Phil Rizzuto Yanks 6.00 15.00
RK Ralph Kiner Pirates 4.00 10.00
RO Brooks Robinson O's 6.00 15.00
RR Robin Roberts Phils 4.00 10.00
RS Ryne Sandberg Cubs 10.00 25.00
RU Babe Ruth AS 12.50 30.00
SK Bill Skowron Yanks 4.00 10.00
SM Stan Musial Cards 8.00 20.00
SP Satchel Paige Indians 6.00 15.00
TC Ty Cobb Tigers 8.00 20.00
TH Tommy Henrich Yanks 4.00 10.00
TL Tommy Lasorda Dodgers 4.00 10.00
TM Thurman Munson Yanks 6.00 15.00
TP Tony Perez Reds 4.00 10.00
TR Tris Speaker Red Sox 6.00 15.00
TS Tom Seaver Mets 6.00 15.00
TW Ted Williams AS 10.00 25.00
WB Wade Boggs Red Sox 6.00 15.00
WF Whitey Ford Yanks 6.00 15.00
WI Hoyt Wilhelm White Sox 4.00 10.00
WJ Walter Johnson Senators 6.00 15.00
WM Willie McCovey Giants 4.00 10.00
WS Warren Spahn Braves 6.00 15.00
YA Carl Yastrzemski Red Sox 10.00 25.00

2004 Sweet Spot Classic Signatures Black

Randomly inserted in packs, these cards feature signatures from the noted personages in black ink. Several people including long-time Phillies announcer Harry Kalas and one time NL consecutive-games played leader Gus Suhr have their 1st certified autograph card in this set. Please note that several people did not return their cards in time for inclusion in pack out and those cards could be redeemed until January 27, 2004. Please note that for players with 25 or fewer signatures that no pricing is provided due to market scarcity.

OVERALL AUTO ODDS 1:24
PRINT RUNS B/WN 25-275 COPIES PER
2 Preacher Roe/225 15.00 40.00
4 Bob Feller/65 20.00 50.00
5 Bob Gibson/50 40.00 80.00
6 Harry Kalas/100 30.00 60.00
7 Bobby Doerr/100 15.00 40.00
8 Cal Ripken/50 100.00 175.00
9 Carl Yastrzemski/35
10 Carlton Fisk/100 30.00 60.00
11 Chuck Tanner/150 10.00 25.00
12 Cito Gaston/150 10.00 25.00
13 Danny Ozark/150 10.00 25.00
14 Dave Winfield/80 40.00 80.00
15 Davey Johnson/175 15.00 40.00
16 Ernie Harwell/100 EXCH 30.00 60.00
17 Dick Williams/150 10.00 25.00
18 Don Mattingly/40
19 Don Newcombe/40 20.00 50.00
20 Duke Snider/35 40.00 80.00
21 Steve Carlton/150 15.00 40.00
22 Felipe Alou/175 10.00 25.00
23 Frank Robinson/65 40.00 80.00
24 Gary Carter/100 15.00 40.00
25 Gene Mauch/225 10.00 25.00
26 George Bamberger/225 10.00 25.00
28 Gus Suhr/100 15.00 40.00
30 Harmon Killebrew/50 50.00 100.00
31 Jack McKeon/225 15.00 40.00
32 Jim Bunning/100 40.00 80.00
33 Jimmy Piersall/212 15.00 40.00
35 Johnny Bench/50 50.00 100.00
36 Juan Marichal/50 20.00 50.00
37 Lou Brock/50 EXCH 40.00 80.00
38 George Kell/40 20.00 50.00
39 Maury Wills/40 20.00 50.00
41 Mike Schmidt/40 EXCH
42 Nolan Ryan/50
43 Ozzie Smith/65 50.00 100.00
44 Eddie Mayo/140 10.00 25.00
45 Phil Rizzuto/50 40.00 80.00
46 Ralph Kiner/40 EXCH 20.00 50.00
47 Lonny Frey/114 10.00 25.00
48 Bill Mazeroski/50 40.00 80.00
49 Robin Roberts/40 40.00 80.00
50 Robin Yount/40 50.00 100.00
52 Roger Craig/175 15.00 40.00
55 Tony Perez/40 20.00 50.00
56 Sparky Anderson/175 15.00 40.00
57 Stan Musial/40
58 Ted Radcliffe/225 40.00 80.00
60 Tom Seaver/25
61 Tony Gwynn/65
62 Tony LaRussa/275 10.00 25.00
63 Tony Oliva/150 15.00 40.00
64 Tony Pena/150 10.00 25.00
66 Whitey Ford/45 40.00 80.00
67 Yogi Berra/65 50.00 100.00

2004 Sweet Spot Classic Signatures Black Holo-Foil

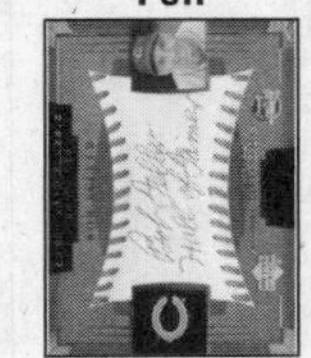

For those people who did not return their cards in time for inclusion in this product, those exchange cards could be returned until January 27, 2007.

OVERALL AUTO ODDS 1:24
PRINT RUNS B/WN 10-100 COPIES PER
NO PRICING ON QTY OF 25 OR LESS
MOST CARDS FEATURE INSCRIPTIONS
11 Chuck Tanner/100 10.00 25.00
12 Cito Gaston/100 10.00 25.00
13 Danny Ozark/100 10.00 25.00
15 Davey Johnson/50 20.00 50.00
17 Dick Williams/100 10.00 25.00
22 Felipe Alou/50 12.50 30.00
24 Gary Carter/50 20.00 50.00
52 Roger Craig/50 20.00 50.00
56 Sparky Anderson/50 20.00 50.00
62 Tony LaRussa/50 12.50 30.00
63 Tony Oliva/100 15.00 40.00
64 Tony Pena/100 10.00 25.00

2004 Sweet Spot Classic Signatures Blue

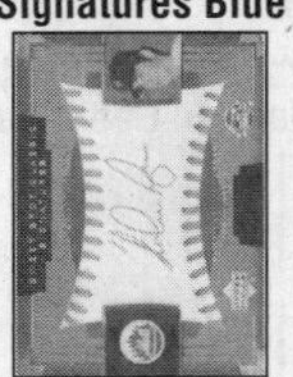

A few people did not return their cards in time for inclusion in packs, those signed cards could be redeemed until January 27, 2004.

OVERALL AUTO ODDS 1:24
PRINT RUNS B/WN 15-150 COPIES PER
NO PRICING ON QTY OF 25 OR LESS
2 Preacher Roe/150 15.00 40.00
4 Bob Feller/50 20.00 50.00
5 Bob Gibson/25
6 Harry Kalas/50 40.00 80.00
7 Bobby Doerr/50 20.00 50.00
8 Cal Ripken/25
9 Carl Yastrzemski/15
10 Carlton Fisk/50 40.00 80.00
11 Chuck Tanner/125 10.00 25.00
12 Cito Gaston/125 10.00 25.00
13 Danny Ozark/125 10.00 25.00
14 Dave Winfield/35 40.00 80.00
15 Davey Johnson/150 15.00 40.00

16 Ernie Harwell/50 EXCH 40.00 80.00
17 Dick Williams/125 10.00 25.00
18 Don Mattingly/25
19 Don Newcombe/25
20 Duke Snider/25
21 Steve Carlton/100 15.00 40.00
22 Felipe Alou/150 10.00 25.00
23 Frank Robinson/50 40.00 80.00
24 Gary Carter/75 20.00 50.00
25 Gene Mauch/150 10.00 25.00
26 George Bamberger/150 10.00 25.00
28 Gus Suhr/85 20.00 50.00
30 Harmon Killebrew/25
31 Jack McKeon/150 15.00 40.00
32 Jim Bunning/65 50.00 100.00
33 Jimmy Piersall/150 15.00 40.00
35 Johnny Bench/20
36 Juan Marichal/25
37 Lou Brock/20 EXCH
38 George Kell/25
39 Maury Wills/25
41 Mike Schmidt/25 EXCH
42 Nolan Ryan/25
43 Ozzie Smith/50 50.00 100.00
44 Eddie Mayo/50 12.50 30.00
45 Phil Rizzuto/25
46 Ralph Kiner/25 EXCH
47 Lonny Frey/75 12.50 30.00
48 Bill Mazeroski/25
49 Robin Roberts/25
50 Robin Yount/25
52 Roger Craig/150 15.00 40.00
55 Tony Perez/25
56 Sparky Anderson/150 15.00 40.00
57 Stan Musial/25
58 Ted Radcliffe/150 40.00 80.00
60 Tom Seaver/15
61 Tony Gwynn/25
62 Tony LaRussa/145 10.00 25.00
63 Tony Oliva/125 15.00 40.00
64 Tony Pena/115 10.00 25.00
66 Whitey Ford/20
67 Yogi Berra/50 50.00 100.00

2004 Sweet Spot Classic Signatures Red

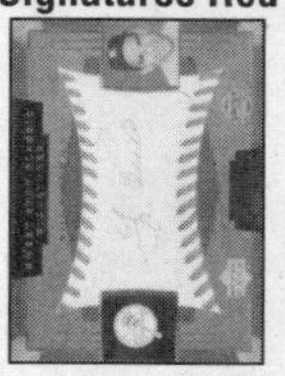

Ernie Harwell, Lou Brock, Mike Schmidt and Ralph Kiner did not return their cards in time for inclusion in packs. Redemption cards with an expiration date of January 27th, 2007 were seeded into packs for these aforementioned athletes. The Joe DiMaggio and Ted Williams cards from this set feature blue ink signed leather baseball patches (as averse to the red ink featured on the other cards). Representatives at Upper Deck have confirmed that they estimate approximately 25% of the Joe DiMaggio cards actually feature the added notation "Yankee Clipper".

OVERALL AUTO ODDS 1:24
PRINT RUNS B/WN 2-86 COPIES PER
NO PRICING ON QTY OF 25 OR LESS
34 Joe DiMaggio/86 500.00 800.00

2005 Sweet Spot Classic

COMPLETE SET (100) 15.00 40.00
1 Al Kaline .75 2.00
2 Al Rosen .30 .75
3 Babe Ruth 2.50 6.00
4 Bill Mazeroski .50 1.25
5 Billy Williams .30 .75
6 Bob Feller .50 1.25
7 Bob Gibson .50 1.25
8 Bobby Doerr .30 .75
9 Brooks Robinson .50 1.25
10 Cal Ripken 2.50 6.00
11 Carl Yastrzemski 1.25 3.00
12 Carlton Fisk .50 1.25
13 Casey Stengel .50 1.25
14 Christy Mathewson .75 2.00
15 Cy Young .75 2.00
16 Dale Murphy .50 1.25
17 Dave Winfield .30 .75
18 Dennis Eckersley .30 .75
19 Dizzy Dean .50 1.25
20 Don Drysdale .50 1.25
21 Don Mattingly 1.50 4.00
22 Don Newcombe .30 .75
23 Don Sutton .30 .75
24 Duke Snider .50 1.25
25 Dwight Evans .50 1.25
26 Eddie Mathews .75 2.00
27 Eddie Murray .75 2.00
28 Enos Slaughter .30 .75
29 Ernie Banks .75 2.00
30 Frank Howard .30 .75
31 Frank Robinson .30 .75
32 Gary Carter .30 .75
33 Gaylord Perry .30 .75
34 George Brett 1.50 4.00
35 George Kell .30 .75
36 George Sisler .30 .75
37 Larry Doby .30 .75
38 Harmon Killebrew .75 2.00
39 Honus Wagner .75 2.00
40 Jackie Robinson .75 2.00
41 Jim Bunning .30 .75
42 Jim Palmer .30 .75
43 Jim Rice .30 .75
44 Jimmie Foxx .75 2.00
45 Joe DiMaggio 1.50 4.00
46 Joe Morgan .30 .75
47 Johnny Bench .75 2.00
48 Johnny Mize .30 .75
49 Johnny Podres .30 .75
50 Juan Marichal .30 .75
51 Keith Hernandez .30 .75
52 Kirby Puckett .75 2.00
53 Lefty Grove .30 .75
54 Lou Brock .50 1.25
55 Lou Gehrig 1.50 4.00
56 Luis Aparicio .30 .75
57 Fergie Jenkins .30 .75
58 Maury Wills .30 .75
59 Mel Ott .75 2.00
60 Mickey Cochrane .30 .75
61 Mickey Mantle 3.00 8.00
62 Mike Schmidt 1.50 4.00
63 Monte Irvin .30 .75
64 Nolan Ryan UER 2.00 5.00
Ryan led his league in strikeouts 11 times; not 12
65 Orlando Cepeda .30 .75
66 Ozzie Smith 1.25 3.00
67 Paul Molitor .30 .75
68 Pee Wee Reese .50 1.25
69 Phil Niekro .30 .75
70 Phil Rizzuto .50 1.25
71 Ralph Kiner .50 1.25
72 Richie Ashburn .50 1.25
73 Roberto Clemente 2.00 5.00
74 Robin Roberts .30 .75
75 Robin Yount .75 2.00
76 Rocky Colavito .50 1.25
77 Rod Carew .50 1.25
78 Rogers Hornsby .75 2.00
79 Rollie Fingers .30 .75
80 Roy Campanella .75 2.00
81 Bob Lemon .30 .75
82 Red Schoendienst .30 .75
83 Satchel Paige .75 2.00
84 Stan Musial 1.25 3.00
85 Steve Carlton .30 .75
86 Ted Williams 1.50 4.00
87 Thurman Munson .75 2.00
88 Tom Seaver .50 1.25
89 Tony Gwynn 1.00 2.50
90 Tony Perez .50 1.25
91 Ty Cobb 1.25 3.00
92 Wade Boggs .50 1.25
93 Walter Johnson .75 2.00
94 Warren Spahn .50 1.25
95 Whitey Ford .50 1.25
96 Will Clark .50 1.25
97 Catfish Hunter .50 1.25
98 Willie McCovey .50 1.25
99 Willie Stargell .50 1.25
100 Yogi Berra .75 2.00

2005 Sweet Spot Classic Gold

*GOLD: 2.5X TO 6X BASIC
STATED ODDS 1:120 HOBBY
STATED PRINT RUN 50 SERIAL #'d SETS

2005 Sweet Spot Classic Materials

OVERALL GAME-USED ODDS 1:6
SP INFO PROVIDED BY UPPER DECK
STARGELL PRINT RUN PROVIDED BY UD
NO STARGELL PRICING DUE TO SCARCITY
AD Andre Dawson Jsy 3.00 8.00
AK Al Kaline Jsy 6.00 15.00
BE Johnny Bench Jsy 6.00 15.00
BF Bob Feller Jsy 4.00 10.00
BG Bob Gibson Jsy 4.00 10.00
BM Bill Mazeroski Jsy 4.00 10.00
BR Babe Ruth Pants SP 175.00 300.00
CA Rod Carew Jsy 4.00 10.00
CF Carlton Fisk Jsy 4.00 10.00
CH Catfish Hunter Pants 4.00 10.00
CO Rocky Colavito Jsy 10.00 25.00
CP Roy Campanella Pants 6.00 15.00
CR C.Ripken Hitting Jsy 8.00 20.00
CR1 C.Ripken Fielding Pants 8.00 20.00
CY Carl Yastrzemski Jsy 6.00 15.00
DC David Cone Jsy 3.00 8.00
DD Don Drysdale Pants 6.00 15.00
DM D.Mattingly Pose Jsy 6.00 15.00
DM1 D.Mattingly Hitting Jsy 6.00 15.00
DS Don Sutton Dgr Jsy 3.00 8.00
DS1 Don Sutton Astros Jsy 3.00 8.00
DW D.Winfield Yanks Jsy 3.00 8.00
DW1 D.Winfield Padres Jsy 3.00 8.00
ED Eddie Murray O's Jsy 6.00 15.00
ED1 Eddie Murray Dgr Jsy 6.00 15.00
EM Eddie Mathews Pants 6.00 15.00
EW Early Wynn Pants 4.00 10.00
FJ Fergie Jenkins Jsy 3.00 8.00
FR Frank Robinson Jsy 4.00 10.00
FV Fernando Valenzuela Jsy 4.00 10.00
GB G.Brett Sunglass Jsy 6.00 15.00
GB1 G.Brett Hitting Jsy 6.00 15.00
GC Gary Carter Expos Jsy 3.00 8.00
GP Gaylord Perry Jsy 3.00 8.00
HK Harmon Killebrew Jsy 6.00 15.00
JB Jim Bunning Jsy 4.00 10.00
JD Joe DiMaggio Jsy 40.00 80.00
JM Joe Morgan Reds Pants 3.00 8.00
JM1 Joe Morgan Astros Jsy 3.00 8.00
JP Jim Palmer Jsy 3.00 8.00
JR Jackie Robinson Jsy 15.00 40.00
LB Lou Brock Jsy 4.00 10.00
LG Lou Gehrig Pants SP 100.00 175.00
MA Juan Marichal Jsy 3.00 8.00
MG Mark Grace Jsy 4.00 10.00
MM Mickey Mantle Jsy SP 75.00 150.00
MS M.Schmidt Hitting Jsy 6.00 15.00
MS1 M.Schmidt Running Jsy 6.00 15.00
MU Dale Murphy Jsy 4.00 10.00
MW Maury Wills Dgr Jsy 3.00 8.00
MW1 Maury Wills Pirates Jsy 3.00 8.00
NR Nolan Ryan Astros Jsy 12.50 30.00
NR1 Nolan Ryan Rgr Jsy 12.50 30.00
OC Orlando Cepeda Jsy 3.00 8.00
OS Ozzie Smith Jsy SP 10.00 25.00
PM Paul Molitor Brewers Jsy 3.00 8.00
PN Phil Niekro Jsy 3.00 8.00
PR Phil Rizzuto Pants 4.00 10.00
RC Roberto Clemente Pants 30.00 60.00
RE Pee Wee Reese Jsy SP 6.00 15.00
RG Ron Guidry Jsy 3.00 8.00
RI Jim Rice Jsy 3.00 8.00
RO Brooks Robinson Jsy 6.00 15.00
RR Robin Roberts Pants 4.00 10.00
RY Robin Yount Jsy 6.00 15.00
SC Steve Carlton Pants 3.00 8.00
SD Red Schoendienst Jsy 3.00 8.00
SM Stan Musial Pants SP 10.00 25.00
SN Duke Snider Pants 6.00 15.00
SP Satchel Paige Pants 30.00 60.00
ST Willie Stargell Jsy SP/18
TC Ty Cobb Pants SP 300.00 600.00
TG Tony Gwynn Jsy 6.00 15.00
TM Thurman Munson Jsy SP 10.00 25.00
TP Tony Perez Jsy 4.00 10.00
TS Tom Seaver Reds Jsy 4.00 10.00
TW Ted Williams Jsy SP 40.00 80.00
WB Wade Boggs Jsy 4.00 10.00
WC Will Clark Giants Jsy 4.00 10.00
WC1 Will Clark Rgr Jsy 4.00 10.00
WI Willie McCovey Jsy 4.00 10.00
WS Warren Spahn Jsy 6.00 15.00
YB Yogi Berra Pants 6.00 15.00

2005 Sweet Spot Classic Patches

OVERALL GAME-USED ODDS 1:6
PRINT RUNS B/WN 1-50 COPIES PER
NO PRICING ON QTY OF 19 OR LESS
LISTED PRICES ARE 2-3 COLOR PATCH
*1-COLOR PATCH: DROP 20-50% DISCOUNT
*4-5-COLOR PATCH: ADD 20-50% PREMIUM
LOGO PATCHES TOO VOLATILE TO PRICE
AD Andre Dawson/7
BE Johnny Bench/32 75.00 150.00
BG Bob Gibson/1
BS Bruce Sutter/50 20.00 50.00
CF1 Carlton Fisk/50 30.00 60.00
CR C.Ripken Hitting/34 60.00 120.00
CR1 C.Ripken Fielding/34 60.00 120.00
CY Carl Yastrzemski/35 60.00 120.00
DC David Cone/39 30.00 60.00
DM D.Mattingly Pose/9
DM1 D.Mattingly Hitting/9
DS Don Sutton Dgr/34 50.00 100.00
DS1 Don Sutton Astros/50 50.00 100.00
DW D.Winfield Yanks/3
DW1 D.Winfield Padres/50 30.00 60.00
ED Eddie Murray O's/34 50.00 100.00
ED1 Eddie Murray Dgr/50 50.00 100.00
FH Frank Howard/34 50.00 100.00
FJ Fergie Jenkins/34 30.00 60.00
FR Frank Robinson/34 40.00 80.00
GB G.Brett Pose/38 30.00 60.00
GB1 G.Brett Action/50 30.00 60.00
GC Gary Carter Expos/47 20.00 50.00
GC1 Gary Carter Mets/34 20.00 50.00
GP Gaylord Perry/34 20.00 50.00
JD Joe DiMaggio/38 175.00 300.00
JM Joe Morgan Reds/50 40.00 80.00
JR Jackie Robinson/12
LA Luis Aparicio/19
LB Lou Brock/34 40.00 80.00
MM Mickey Mantle/19
MS M.Schmidt Hitting/6
MS1 M.Schmidt Running/5
MU Dale Murphy/34 30.00 60.00
MW Maury Wills Dgr/50 30.00 60.00
MW1 Maury Wills Pirates/47 30.00 60.00
NR Nolan Ryan Astros/16
NR1 Nolan Ryan Rgr/3
NR2 Nolan Ryan Angels/15
OC Orlando Cepeda/40 20.00 50.00
OS Ozzie Smith/34 60.00 120.00
PM Paul Molitor Brewers/13
PM1 Paul Molitor Twins/12
PN Phil Niekro/44 20.00 50.00
PO Johnny Podres/50 30.00 60.00
RE Pee Wee Reese/10
RG Ron Guidry/30 20.00 50.00
RI Jim Rice/34 30.00 60.00
RO B.Robinson Color/50 50.00 100.00
RO1 B.Robinson B/W/43 50.00 100.00
RY R.Yount Bat Back/34 40.00 80.00
RY1 R.Yount Bat Out/19
SC Steve Carlton/50 30.00 60.00
SD Red Schoendienst/42 20.00 50.00
SM Stan Musial/3
ST Willie Stargell/50 30.00 60.00
TG T.Gwynn Blue Uni/34 40.00 80.00
TG1 T.Gwynn Camo Uni/30 40.00 80.00
TP Tony Perez/34 40.00 80.00
TS Tom Seaver Reds/50 30.00 60.00
TS1 Tom Seaver Mets/50 30.00 60.00
WB Wade Boggs Sox/25 30.00 60.00
WB1 Wade Boggs Yanks/34 30.00 60.00
WI Willie McCovey/50 30.00 60.00

2005 Sweet Spot Classic Signatures

OVERALL AUTO ODDS 1:12
TIER 1 PRINT RUNS B/WN 25-99 PER
TIER 2 PRINT RUNS B/WN 125-230 PER
TIER 3 PRINT RUNS 250 OR MORE PER
CARDS ARE NOT SERIAL-NUMBERED
TIER 1-3 INFO PROVIDED BY UPPER DECK
NO DIMAGGIO PRICING DUE TO SCARCITY
EXCHANGE DEADLINE 01/28/08
AD Andre Dawson T3 10.00 25.00
AK Al Kaline T3 20.00 50.00
AR Al Rosen T3 10.00 25.00
BD Bobby Doerr T3 10.00 25.00
BE Johnny Bench T2 30.00 60.00
BF Bob Feller T3 15.00 40.00
BG Bob Gibson T3 20.00 50.00
BJ Bo Jackson T2 50.00 100.00
BM Bill Mazeroski T3 20.00 50.00
BR Brooks Robinson T3 15.00 40.00
BW Billy Williams T3 10.00 25.00
CA Rod Carew T2 20.00 50.00
CF Carlton Fisk T2 20.00 50.00
CR Cal Ripken T2 100.00 175.00
CY Carl Yastrzemski T2 30.00 60.00
DC David Cone T3 10.00 25.00
DE Dennis Eckersley T3 10.00 25.00
DJ Dave Justice T3 10.00 25.00
DM Don Mattingly T2 40.00 80.00
DN Don Newcombe T2 12.50 30.00
DS Don Sutton T2 12.50 30.00
EB Ernie Banks T2 30.00 60.00
EH Ernie Harwell T1/56 EXCH 20.00 50.00
EV Dwight Evans T3 15.00 40.00
FH Frank Howard T3 10.00 25.00
FR Frank Robinson T2 12.50 30.00
FV Fernando Valenzuela T3 15.00 40.00
GB George Brett T2 75.00 150.00
GC Gary Carter T3 10.00 25.00
GK George Kell T3 10.00 25.00
GP Gaylord Perry T3 10.00 25.00
HB Harold Baines T3 6.00 15.00
HK Harmon Killebrew T3 20.00 50.00
JB Jim Bunning T3 10.00 25.00
JC Jose Canseco T2 30.00 60.00
JD Joe DiMaggio T1/25
JM Joe Morgan T1/99 15.00 40.00
JP Jim Palmer T3 10.00 25.00
JR Jim Rice T3 10.00 25.00
KA Harry Kalas T3 15.00 40.00
KH Keith Hernandez T3 10.00 25.00
KP Kirby Puckett T1/50 EXCH 60.00 120.00
LA Luis Aparicio T3 10.00 25.00
LT Luis Tiant T3 6.00 15.00
MA Juan Marichal T3 15.00 40.00
MC Willie McCovey T1/99 30.00 60.00
MG Mark Grace T3 20.00 50.00
MI Monte Irvin T3 10.00 25.00
MS Mike Schmidt T2 50.00 100.00
MU Dale Murphy T3 10.00 25.00
MW Matt Williams T3 15.00 40.00
NR Nolan Ryan T2 75.00 150.00
OC Orlando Cepeda T3 10.00 25.00
OS Ozzie Smith T2 30.00 60.00
PM Paul Molitor T3 10.00 25.00
PN Phil Niekro T2 12.50 30.00
PO Johnny Podres T3 10.00 25.00
PR Phil Rizzuto T2 20.00 50.00
RC R.Colavito T1/50 EXCH * 50.00 100.00
RE Red Schoendienst T2 12.50 30.00
RF Rollie Fingers T3 10.00 25.00
RK Ralph Kiner T1/99 15.00 40.00
RR Robin Roberts T2 12.50 30.00
RS Ron Santo T3 15.00 40.00
RY Robin Yount T1/50 EXCH 50.00 100.00
SC Steve Carlton T2 12.50 30.00
SM Stan Musial T2 50.00 100.00
SN Duke Snider T2 20.00 50.00
ST Rusty Staub T3 6.00 15.00
SU Bruce Sutter T3 15.00 40.00
TG Tony Gwynn T2 20.00 50.00
TP Tony Perez T2 12.50 30.00
TS Tom Seaver T2 30.00 60.00
WB Wade Boggs T2 20.00 50.00
WC Will Clark T3 15.00 40.00
WF Whitey Ford T2 20.00 50.00
WI Maury Wills T3 10.00 25.00
YB Yogi Berra T1/99 30.00 60.00

2005 Sweet Spot Classic Signatures Black Stitch

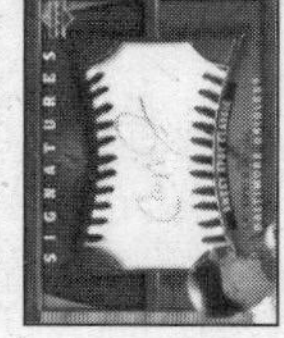

OVERALL AUTO ODDS 1:12
STATED PRINT RUN 1 SERIAL #'d SET
NO PRICING DUE TO SCARCITY
EXCHANGE DEADLINE 01/28/08

2005 Sweet Spot Classic Signatures Red-Blue Stitch

*R/B: .6X TO 1.5X TIER 3
*R/B: .5X TO 1.2X TIER 2
*R/B: .5X TO 1.2X TIER 1 p/r 99
*R/B: .4X TO 1X TIER 1 p/r 50-56
OVERALL AUTO ODDS 1:12
STATED PRINT RUN 40 SERIAL #'d SETS
BO JACKSON PRINT RUN 36 #'d CARDS
EXCHANGE DEADLINE 01/28/08
BJ Bo Jackson/36 75.00 150.00
CR Cal Ripken 100.00 200.00
DM Don Mattingly 60.00 120.00
GB George Brett 60.00 120.00
HB Harold Baines 15.00 40.00
JC Jose Canseco 30.00 80.00
JD Joe DiMaggio
KP Kirby Puckett EXCH 50.00 100.00
LT Luis Tiant 15.00 40.00
MS Mike Schmidt 60.00 120.00
MU Dale Murphy 25.00 60.00
NR Nolan Ryan 90.00 180.00
SM Stan Musial 60.00 120.00
ST Rusty Staub 15.00 40.00
SU Bruce Sutter 25.00 60.00

2005 Sweet Spot Classic Signature Sticks

*STICKS: .75X TO 2X TIER 3
*STICKS: .6X TO 1.5X TIER 2
*STICKS: .6X TO 1.5X TIER 1 p/r 99
*STICKS: .5X TO 1.2X TIER 1 p/r 50-56
OVERALL AUTO ODDS 1:12
STATED PRINT RUN 35 SERIAL #'d SETS
BJ Bo Jackson 90.00 180.00
CR Cal Ripken 175.00 300.00
DA Darryl Strawberry
DM Don Mattingly 75.00 150.00
GB George Brett 75.00 150.00
HB Harold Baines 20.00 50.00
JC Jose Canseco 40.00 100.00
KP Kirby Puckett EXCH 75.00 150.00
LT Luis Tiant 20.00 50.00
MS Mike Schmidt 75.00 150.00
MU Dale Murphy 30.00 80.00
NR Nolan Ryan 100.00 200.00
RC Rocky Colavito 75.00 150.00
SM Stan Musial 75.00 150.00
ST Rusty Staub 20.00 50.00
SU Bruce Sutter 30.00 80.00

2005 Sweet Spot Classic Signatures Sweet Leather

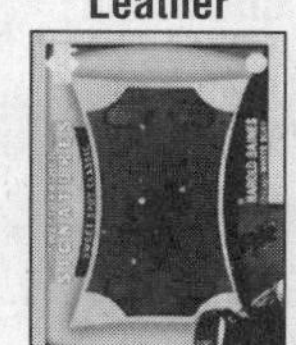

*LEATHER: 1.25X TO 2.5X TIER 3
*LEATHER: 1X TO 2X TIER 2
*LEATHER: 1X TO 2X TIER 1 p/r 99
*LEATHER: .75X TO 1.5X TIER 1 p/r 50-56
OVERALL AUTO ODDS 1:12
STATED PRINT RUN 25 SERIAL #'d SETS
EXCHANGE DEADLINE 01/28/08
BJ Bo Jackson 100.00 200.00
CR Cal Ripken 200.00 350.00
DA Darryl Strawberry
DM Don Mattingly 90.00 180.00
GB George Brett 90.00 180.00
HB Harold Baines 30.00 60.00
JC Jose Canseco 60.00 120.00
KP Kirby Puckett EXCH
LT Luis Tiant 30.00 60.00
MS Mike Schmidt 90.00 180.00
MU Dale Murphy 50.00 100.00
NR Nolan Ryan 150.00 250.00
SM Stan Musial 90.00 180.00
ST Rusty Staub 30.00 60.00
SU Bruce Sutter 50.00 100.00

2005 Sweet Spot Classic Signatures Dual

OVERALL AUTO ODDS 1:12
STATED PRINT RUN 15 SERIAL #'d SETS

CARLTON/SCHMIDT PRINT 14 #'d CARDS
NO PRICING DUE TO SCARCITY
EXCHANGE DEADLINE 01/28/08

2005 Sweet Spot Classic Wingfield Classics Collection

ONE PER SEALED HOBBY BOX
1 Al Kaline 4.00 10.00
2 Pee Wee Reese 4.00 10.00
3 Stan Musial 4.00 10.00
Ted Williams
4 Bill Dickey 4.00 10.00
5 Frank Robinson 3.00 8.00
6 Billy Martin 4.00 10.00
7 Joe DiMaggio 6.00 15.00
Casey Stengel
8 Dwight D. Eisenhower 4.00 10.00
Bob Feller
9 Duke Snider 4.00 10.00
10 Carl Yastrzemski 4.00 10.00
11 Honus Wagner 4.00 10.00
12 Clark Griffith 3.00 8.00
Dwight D. Eisenhower
13 Mickey Mantle 12.50 30.00
Joe DiMaggio
14 Don Drysdale 4.00 10.00
15 Ted Williams 6.00 15.00
16 Mickey Mantle 12.50 30.00
Al Kaline
17 Ernie Banks 4.00 10.00
18 Lou Boudreau 3.00 8.00
19 George Sisler 4.00 10.00
Harmon Killebrew
20 Gil Hodges 4.00 10.00
21 Rogers Hornsby 4.00 10.00
22 Luis Aparicio 3.00 8.00
23 Jackie Robinson 4.00 10.00
24 Joe Morgan 3.00 8.00
25 Enos Slaughter 3.00 8.00
26 Joe DiMaggio 6.00 15.00
27 Mickey Mantle 15.00 40.00
Ted Kluszewski
28 John F. Kennedy 4.00 10.00
29 Johnny Bench 4.00 10.00
30 Juan Marichal 3.00 8.00
31 Larry Doby 3.00 8.00
32 Don Newcombe 3.00 8.00
Elston Howard
33 Dwight D. Eisenhower 4.00 10.00
Harmon Killebrew
34 Roger Maris 12.50 30.00
Mickey Mantle
35 Stan Musial 12.50 30.00
Mickey Mantle
36 Ted Williams 12.50 30.00
Yogi Berra
Mickey Mantle
37 Nellie Fox 6.00 15.00
38 Richie Ashburn 6.00 15.00
39 Roberto Clemente 8.00 20.00
40 Stan Musial 4.00 10.00
Robin Roberts
41 Joe DiMaggio 4.00 10.00
Tommy Henrich
42 Roy Campanella 4.00 10.00
43 Rocky Colavito 4.00 10.00
Harmon Killebrew
44 Steve Carlton 3.00 8.00
45 Thurman Munson 4.00 10.00
46 Ernie Banks 4.00 10.00
Luis Aparicio
47 Dwight D. Eisenhower 4.00 10.00
Gil Hodges
Yogi Berra
48 Whitey Ford 4.00 10.00
49 Yogi Berra 12.50 30.00
Mickey Mantle
Joe DiMaggio
50 Yogi Berra 4.00 10.00

2007 Sweet Spot Classic

This 197-card set was released in August, 2007. The set was issued in five-card "tins" which came 20 tins to a box. All cards in this set were issued to a stated print run of 575 serial numbered cards. Cards numbered 35, 75 and 164 were never issued.

COMMON CARD .60 1.50
STATED PRINT RUN 575 SER.#'d SETS
1 Phil Niekro .60 1.50

Card	Low	High
2 Fred McGriff	1.00	2.50
3 Bob Horner	.60	1.50
4 Earl Weaver	.60	1.50
5 Boog Powell	.60	1.50
6 Eddie Murray	1.50	4.00
7 Fred Lynn	.60	1.50
8 Dwight Evans	.60	1.50
9 Jim Rice	.60	1.50
10 Carlton Fisk	1.00	2.50
11 Luis Tiant	.60	1.50
12 Robin Yount	1.50	4.00
13 Bobby Doerr	.60	1.50
14 Ryne Sandberg	3.00	8.00
15 Billy Williams	.60	1.50
16 Andre Dawson	.60	1.50
17 Mark Grace	1.00	2.50
18 Ron Santo	1.00	2.50
19 Shawon Dunston	.60	1.50
20 Harold Baines	.60	1.50
21 Carlton Fisk	1.00	2.50
22 Sparky Anderson	.60	1.50
23 George Foster	.60	1.50
24 Dave Parker	.60	1.50
25 Ken Griffey Sr.	.60	1.50
26 Dave Concepcion	.60	1.50
27 Rafael Palmeiro	1.00	2.50
28 Al Rosen	.60	1.50
29 Kirk Gibson	.60	1.50
30 Alan Trammell	.60	1.50
31 Jack Morris	.60	1.50
32 Willie Horton	.60	1.50
33 JR Richard	.60	1.50
34 Jose Cruz	.60	1.50
36 Willie Wilson	.60	1.50
37 Bo Jackson	1.50	4.00
38 Nolan Ryan	4.00	10.00
39 Don Baylor	.60	1.50
40 Maury Wills	.60	1.50
41 Tommy John	.60	1.50
42 Ron Cey	.60	1.50
43 Davey Lopes	.60	1.50
44 Tommy Lasorda	.60	1.50
45 Burt Hooton	.60	1.50
46 Reggie Smith	.60	1.50
47 Rollie Fingers	.60	1.50
48 Cecil Cooper	.60	1.50
49 Paul Molitor	.60	1.50
50 Vern Stephens	.60	1.50
51 Tony Oliva	.60	1.50
52 Andres Galarraga	.60	1.50
53 Tim Raines	.60	1.50
54 Dennis Martinez	.60	1.50
55 Lee Mazzilli	.60	1.50
56 Rusty Staub	.60	1.50
57 David Cone	.60	1.50
58 Reggie Jackson	1.00	2.50
59 Ron Guidry	.60	1.50
60 Tino Martinez	.60	1.50
61 Don Mattingly	3.00	8.00
62 Chris Chambliss	.60	1.50
63 Sparky Lyle	.60	1.50
64 Goose Gossage	.60	1.50
65 Dave Righetti	.60	1.50
66 Phil Garner	.60	1.50
67 Bill Madlock	.60	1.50
68 Kent Hrbek	.60	1.50
69 Al Oliver	.60	1.50
70 John Kruk	.60	1.50
71 Greg Luzinski	.60	1.50
72 Dick Allen	.60	1.50
73 Richie Ashburn	1.00	2.50
74 Gary Matthews	.60	1.50
76 Mike Schmidt	2.50	6.00
77 Waite Hoyt	.60	1.50
78 Bruce Sutter	.60	1.50
79 Roger Maris	1.50	4.00
80 Joe Torre	1.00	2.50
81 Kevin Mitchell	.60	1.50
82 John Montefusco	.60	1.50
83 Rick Reuschel	.60	1.50
84 Will Clark	1.00	2.50
85 Jack Clark	.60	1.50
86 Matt Williams	.60	1.50
87 Steve Garvey	.60	1.50
88 Dave Winfield	.60	1.50
89 Jay Buhner	.60	1.50
90 Edgar Martinez	1.00	2.50
91 Carney Lansford	.60	1.50
92 Sal Bando	.60	1.50
93 Dave Stewart	.60	1.50
94 Dennis Eckersley	.60	1.50
95 Jose Canseco	1.00	2.50
96 Dennis Eckersley	.60	1.50
97 Roberto Alomar	1.00	2.50
98 George Bell	.60	1.50
99 Joe Carter	.60	1.50
100 Frank Howard	.60	1.50
101 Brooks Robinson	1.00	2.50
102 Frank Robinson	.60	1.50
103 Jim Palmer	.60	1.50
104 Cal Ripken Jr.	6.00	15.00
105 Warren Spahn	1.00	2.50
106 Cy Young	1.50	4.00
107 Waite Hoyt	.60	1.50
108 Carl Yastrzemski	2.50	6.00
109 Johnny Pesky	.60	1.50
110 Wade Boggs	1.00	2.50
111 Jackie Robinson	1.50	4.00
112 Roy Campanella	1.50	4.00
113 Pee Wee Reese	1.00	2.50
114 Don Newcombe	.60	1.50
115 Rod Carew	1.00	2.50
116 Ernie Banks	1.50	4.00
117 Fergie Jenkins	.60	1.50
118 Al Lopez	.60	1.50
119 Luis Aparicio	.60	1.50
120 Toby Harrah	.60	1.50
121 Joe Morgan	.60	1.50
122 Johnny Bench	1.50	4.00
123 Tony Perez	.60	1.50
124 Ted Kluszewski	1.00	2.50
125 Bob Feller	.60	1.50
126 Bob Lemon	.60	1.50
127 Larry Doby	.60	1.50
128 Lou Boudreau	.60	1.50
129 George Kell	.60	1.50
130 Hal Newhouser	.60	1.50
131 Al Kaline	1.50	4.00
132 Ty Cobb	2.50	6.00
133 Denny McLain	.60	1.50
134 Buck Leonard	.60	1.50
135 Dean Chance	.60	1.50
136 Don Drysdale	1.00	2.50
137 Don Sutton	.60	1.50
138 Eddie Mathews	1.50	4.00
139 Paul Molitor	.60	1.50
140 Kirby Puckett	1.50	4.00
141 Rod Carew	1.00	2.50
142 Harmon Killebrew	1.50	4.00
143 Monte Irvin	.60	1.50
144 Mel Ott	.60	1.50
145 Christy Mathewson	1.50	4.00
146 Hoyt Wilhelm	.60	1.50
147 Tom Seaver	1.00	2.50
148 Joe McCarthy	.60	1.50
149 Joe DiMaggio	3.00	8.00
150 Lou Gehrig	3.00	8.00
151 Babe Ruth	4.00	10.00
152 Casey Stengel	.60	1.50
153 Phil Rizzuto	1.00	2.50
154 Thurman Munson	1.50	4.00
155 Johnny Mize	.60	1.50
156 Yogi Berra	1.50	4.00
157 Roger Maris	1.50	4.00
158 Don Larsen	.60	1.50
159 Bill Skowron	.60	1.50
160 Lou Piniella	.60	1.50
161 Joe Pepitone	.60	1.50
162 Ray Dandridge	.60	1.50
163 Rollie Fingers	.60	1.50
165 Reggie Jackson	1.00	2.50
166 Mickey Cochrane	.60	1.50
167 Jimmie Foxx	1.50	4.00
168 Lefty Grove	.60	1.50
169 Gus Zernial	.60	1.50
170 Jim Bunning	.60	1.50
171 Steve Carlton	.60	1.50
172 Robin Roberts	.60	1.50
173 Ralph Kiner	1.00	2.50
174 Willie Stargell	1.00	2.50
175 Roberto Clemente	5.00	12.00
176 Bill Mazeroski	1.00	2.50
177 Honus Wagner	1.50	4.00
178 Pie Traynor	.60	1.50
179 Elroy Face	.60	1.50
180 Dick Groat	.60	1.50
181 Tony Gwynn	1.50	4.00
182 Willie McCovey	1.00	2.50
183 Gaylord Perry	.60	1.50
184 Juan Marichal	.60	1.50
185 Orlando Cepeda	.60	1.50
186 Satchel Paige	1.50	4.00
187 George Sisler	.60	1.50
188 Rogers Hornsby	1.00	2.50
189 Stan Musial	2.50	6.00
190 Dizzy Dean	1.00	2.50
191 Bob Gibson	1.00	2.50
192 Red Schoendienst	.60	1.50
193 Lou Brock	1.00	2.50
194 Enos Slaughter	.60	1.50
195 Nolan Ryan	4.00	10.00
196 Mickey Vernon	.60	1.50
197 Walter Johnson	1.50	4.00
198 Rick Ferrell	.60	1.50
199 Roy Sievers	.60	1.50
200 Judy Johnson	.60	1.50

2007 Sweet Spot Classic Cal Ripken Immortal Membership

RANDOM INSERTS IN TINS
STATED PRINT RUN 1 SER.#'d SET
NO PRICING DUE TO SCARCITY

IM1 Cal Ripken Jr.
Lou Gehrig
IM2 Cal Ripken Jr.
Pee Wee Reese
IM3 Cal Ripken Jr.
Lou Boudreau
IM4 Cal Ripken Jr.
Charlie Gehringer
IM5 Cal Ripken Jr.
Joe DiMaggio

2007 Sweet Spot Classic Classic Cuts

RANDOM INSERTS IN TINS
PRINT RUNS B/WN 1-103
NO PRICING ON MOST DUE TO SCARCITY
CARDS LISTED ALPHABETICALLY
CHECKLIST MAY BE INCOMPLETE
MYSTERY EXCHANGE RANDOMLY INSERTED
EXCHANGE DEADLINE 8/3/2009

Card	Low	High
AC Art Carney/34	150.00	250.00
AH Alex Haley/108	60.00	100.00
GF Gerald Ford/61	200.00	400.00
PB Pappy Boyington/52	100.00	200.00
NNO Mystery EXCH	650.00	750.00

2007 Sweet Spot Classic Classic Memorabilia

RANDOM INSERTS IN TINS

Card	Low	High
AD Andre Dawson Pants	3.00	8.00
AK Al Kaline	4.00	10.00
AO Al Oliver	3.00	8.00
BE Johnny Bench Pants	5.00	12.00
BJ Bo Jackson	5.00	12.00
BM Bill Madlock Bat	3.00	8.00
BO Wade Boggs Yanks	4.00	10.00
BR Babe Ruth Bat	200.00	300.00
BS Bruce Sutter Cubs Pants	3.00	8.00
CF1 Carlton Fisk Red Sox	4.00	10.00
CF2 Carlton Fisk ChiSox	4.00	10.00
CL Roberto Clemente	15.00	40.00
CM Christy Mathewson Pants	70.00	100.00
CR Cal Ripken Jr.	6.00	15.00
CS Casey Stengel	6.00	15.00
CY Carl Yastrzemski	4.00	10.00
DD Dizzy Dean	12.50	30.00
DE Dennis Eckersley	3.00	8.00
DM Don Mattingly	5.00	12.00
DP Dave Parker Reds	3.00	8.00
DR Don Drysdale Pants	4.00	10.00
DS Don Sutton	3.00	8.00
DW Dave Winfield	3.00	8.00
ED Eddie Murray Pants	3.00	8.00
EM Eddie Mathews Pants	5.00	12.00
EV Dwight Evans	3.00	8.00
EW Early Wynn Pants	4.00	10.00
FG Fred McGriff Bat	3.00	8.00
FI Rollie Fingers Mil	3.00	8.00
FR Frank Robinson Cle Jsy	6.00	15.00
FR1 Frank Robinson Giants Pants	6.00	15.00
GF George Foster	3.00	8.00
GG Goose Gossage	3.00	8.00
GI Kirk Gibson	3.00	8.00
GP Gaylord Perry	3.00	8.00
GW Tony Gwynn	5.00	12.00
HB Harold Baines Bat	3.00	8.00
HK Harmon Killebrew	15.00	40.00
JB Jim Bunning Pants	3.00	8.00
JD Joe DiMaggio Pants	30.00	60.00
JI Jim Rice Bat	3.00	8.00
JM Jack Morris	3.00	8.00
JP Jim Palmer	3.00	8.00
JU Juan Marichal	5.00	12.00
KG Ken Griffey Sr.	3.00	8.00
KH Kent Hrbek	3.00	8.00
KP Kirby Puckett	5.00	12.00
LA Luis Aparicio	3.00	8.00
LB Lou Brock	4.00	10.00
LG Lou Gehrig Pants	75.00	150.00
MA Don Mattingly Pants	5.00	12.00
ME Eddie Murray Pants	3.00	8.00
MG Mark Grace	3.00	8.00
MI1 Johnny Mize NYG Pants	4.00	10.00
MI2 Johnny Mize Yanks Bat	4.00	10.00
MO1 Mel Ott	6.00	15.00
MO2 Mel Ott Bat		
MP Paul Molitor Mil	3.00	8.00
MR Edgar Martinez	3.00	8.00
MS Mike Schmidt	5.00	12.00
MW Maury Wills Pants	3.00	8.00
NR Nolan Ryan Hou	8.00	20.00
PA Dave Parker Brewers	3.00	8.00
PE Tony Perez Sox	3.00	8.00
PM Paul Molitor Twins Pants	3.00	8.00
PN Phil Niekro	3.00	8.00
PR Pee Wee Reese Bat	5.00	12.00
RC1 Rod Carew Twins	3.00	8.00
RC2 Rod Carew Angels Pants	3.00	8.00
RF Rollie Fingers Oak	3.00	8.00
RG Ron Guidry Pants	3.00	8.00
RH Rogers Hornsby Pants	20.00	50.00
RJ1 Reggie Jackson Oak	4.00	10.00
RJ2 Reggie Jackson Cal	4.00	10.00
RJ3 Reggie Jackson	4.00	10.00
RK Ralph Kiner Bat	4.00	10.00
RM Roger Maris Pants	12.50	30.00
RO Roy Campanella Pants	6.00	15.00
RS Ron Santo Bat	8.00	20.00
RY Nolan Ryan Tex	8.00	20.00
SC Red Schoendienst Bat	3.00	8.00
SG Steve Garvey	3.00	8.00
ST Steve Carlton Bat	3.00	8.00
SU Bruce Sutter Cards	3.00	8.00
TG Tony Gwynn Bat	4.00	10.00
TM Thurman Munson Pants	6.00	15.00
TO Tony Oliva	3.00	8.00
TP Tony Perez Reds	3.00	8.00
TR Tim Raines	3.00	8.00
WB Wade Boggs Sox	4.00	10.00
WC1 Will Clark Bat	3.00	8.00
WM Willie McCovey Pants	4.00	10.00
WS Willie Stargell Bat	4.00	10.00
YO Robin Yount Pants	4.00	10.00
WC2 Will Clark Jsy	4.00	10.00

2007 Sweet Spot Classic Classic Memorabilia Patch

RANDOM INSERTS IN TINS
STATED PRINT RUNS B/WN 10-55 COPIES PER
NO PRICING ON QTY UNDER 28
PRICING FOR NON-PREMIUM PATCHES

Card	Low	High
AD Andre Dawson/55	12.50	30.00
AK Al Kaline/55	20.00	50.00
AO Al Oliver/55	5.00	12.00
BE Johnny Bench/55	30.00	60.00
BJ Bo Jackson/55	10.00	25.00
BM Bill Madlock/55	5.00	12.00
BO Wade Boggs/55	15.00	40.00
BS Bruce Sutter/55	8.00	20.00
CF1 Carlton Fisk/55	8.00	20.00
CF2 Carlton Fisk/55	8.00	20.00
CL Roberto Clemente/55	75.00	150.00
CR Cal Ripken Jr./55	30.00	60.00
CS Casey Stengel/55	20.00	50.00
CY Carl Yastrzemski/55	12.50	30.00
DE Dennis Eckersley/55	5.00	12.00
DM Don Mattingly/55	12.50	30.00
DP Dave Parker/55	5.00	12.00
DR Don Drysdale/55	40.00	80.00
DS Don Sutton/55	6.00	15.00
DW Dave Winfield/55	10.00	25.00
ED Eddie Murray/55	6.00	15.00
EV Dwight Evans/55	8.00	20.00
FI Rollie Fingers/55	8.00	20.00
FR Frank Robinson/28	15.00	40.00
FR1 Frank Robinson/28	15.00	40.00
GF George Foster/55	5.00	12.00
GG Goose Gossage/55	5.00	12.00
GI Kirk Gibson/55	8.00	20.00
GP Gaylord Perry/55	5.00	12.00
GW Tony Gwynn/55	10.00	25.00
HB Harold Baines/55	6.00	15.00
JI Jim Rice/55	10.00	25.00
JM Jack Morris/55	6.00	15.00
JP Jim Palmer/55	6.00	15.00
JU Juan Marichal/15		
KG Ken Griffey Sr./55	5.00	12.00
KP Kirby Puckett/55	15.00	40.00
LA Luis Aparicio/55	12.50	30.00
LB Lou Brock/55	10.00	25.00
MA Don Mattingly/55	12.50	30.00
ME Eddie Murray/55	6.00	15.00
MG Mark Grace/55	10.00	25.00
MP Paul Molitor/55	15.00	40.00
MS Mike Schmidt/55	10.00	25.00
MW Maury Wills/55	6.00	15.00
PA Dave Parker/55	5.00	12.00
PE Tony Perez/55	10.00	25.00
PM Paul Molitor/55	15.00	40.00
PN Phil Niekro/55	8.00	20.00
PR Pee Wee Reese/55	40.00	80.00
RA Roberto Alomar/55	6.00	15.00
RC1 Rod Carew/55	5.00	12.00
RC2 Rod Carew/55	5.00	12.00
RF Rollie Fingers/55	8.00	20.00
RG Ron Guidry/55	15.00	40.00
RI Cal Ripken Jr./25		
RJ1 Reggie Jackson/55	50.00	100.00
RJ2 Reggie Jackson/55	8.00	20.00
RJ3 Reggie Jackson/55	12.50	30.00
RM Roger Maris/55	40.00	80.00
RY Nolan Ryan/55	30.00	60.00
SC Red Schoendienst/55	20.00	50.00
SG Steve Garvey/55	6.00	15.00
SU Bruce Sutter/55	8.00	20.00
TG Tony Gwynn/55	10.00	25.00
TO Tony Oliva/55	6.00	15.00
TP Tony Perez/55	10.00	25.00
TR Tim Raines/55	8.00	20.00
WC Will Clark/55	8.00	20.00
WI Dave Winfield/55	10.00	25.00
WM Willie McCovey/55	40.00	80.00
WS Willie Stargell/10		
YO Robin Yount/55	12.50	30.00

2007 Sweet Spot Classic Dual Signatures Red Stitch Blue Ink

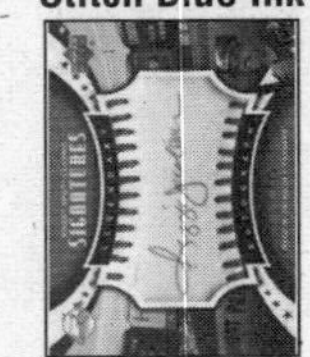

RANDOM INSERTS IN TINS
STATED PRINT RUN 50 SER.#'d SETS
EXCHANGE DEADLINE 8/3/2009

Card	Low	High
AG Luis Aparicio Ozzie Guillen	30.00	60.00
BC Brooks Robinson Cal Ripken Jr.	100.00	150.00
BF Carlton Fisk Johnny Bench	50.00	100.00
BG Harold Baines Ozzie Guillen	20.00	50.00
BR Jim Bunning Robin Roberts	30.00	60.00
CG Rod Carew Tony Gwynn EXCH	50.00	100.00
CO Rod Carew Tony Oliva	30.00	60.00
FE Rollie Fingers Dennis Eckersley	30.00	60.00
FG Elroy Face Dick Groat	20.00	50.00
FM Frank Robinson Mike Schmidt	40.00	80.00
FR Carlton Fisk Jim Rice	40.00	80.00
GR Bob Gibson JR Richard	40.00	80.00
GS Steve Garvey Reggie Smith	20.00	50.00
GW Tony Gwynn Dave Winfield	40.00	80.00
HK Willie Horton Al Kaline	40.00	80.00
JS Reggie Jackson Reggie Smith EXCH	30.00	60.00
KM Ralph Kiner Bill Mazeroski	40.00	80.00
LT Lou Brock Tim Raines EXCH	40.00	80.00
MC Willie McCovey Jack Clark	40.00	80.00
MG Juan Marichal Bob Gibson	30.00	60.00
MK Stan Musial Al Kaline	60.00	120.00
MM Don Mattingly Tino Martinez	50.00	100.00
MR Edgar Martinez Harold Reynolds EXCH	40.00	80.00
OH Tony Oliva Kent Hrbek	20.00	50.00
RG Cal Ripken Jr. Tony Gwynn EXCH	150.00	200.00
RR JR Richard Nolan Ryan	60.00	120.00
RS Cal Ripken Jr. Mike Schmidt EXCH	150.00	200.00
SB Ron Santo Ernie Banks EXCH	60.00	120.00
SC Mike Schmidt Steve Carlton	50.00	100.00
SD Ryne Sandberg Shawon Dunston	50.00	100.00
SF Bruce Sutter Rollie Fingers EXCH	20.00	50.00
SS Ron Santo Ryne Sandberg EXCH	60.00	120.00
SV Roy Sievers Mickey Vernon	20.00	50.00
WC Wade Boggs Cal Ripken Jr. EXCH	90.00	150.00
YP Carl Yastrzemski Johnny Pesky EXCH	40.00	80.00

2007 Sweet Spot Classic Dual Signatures Black Stitch Red Ink

RANDOM INSERTS IN TINS
STATED PRINT RUN 1 SER.#'d SET
NO PRICING DUE TO SCARCITY
EXCHANGE DEADLINE 8/3/2009

2007 Sweet Spot Classic Dual Signatures Gold Stitch Black Ink

RANDOM INSERTS IN TINS
STATED PRINT RUN 15 SER.#'d SETS
NO PRICING DUE TO SCARCITY
EXCHANGE DEADLINE 8/3/2009

2007 Sweet Spot Classic Immortal Signatures

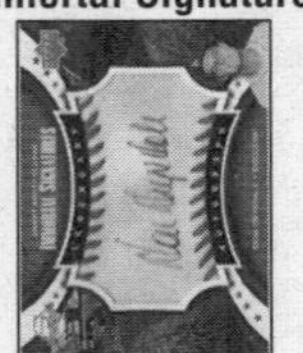

RANDOM INSERTS IN TINS
PRINT RUNS B/WN 1-126 COPIES PER
NO PRICING ON QTY 25 OR LESS
EXCHANGE DEADLINE 8/3/2009

Card	Low	High
AB Al Barlick/43	60.00	100.00
AL Al Lopez/9		
AR Allie Reynolds/1		
BB Bo Belinsky/6		
BD Bill Dickey/10		
BH Billy Herman/49	60.00	100.00
BL Bob Lemon/58	60.00	100.00
BM Billy Martin/1		
BO Buck O'Neil/126	60.00	100.00
BR Babe Ruth/1		
CG Charlie Gehringer/7		
CH Carl Hubbell/1		
DC Dolph Camilli/13		
DD Don Drysdale/18		
DI Joe DiMaggio/2		
DU Leo Durocher/4		
EM Eddie Mathews/35	150.00	200.00
ES Enos Slaughter/80	60.00	100.00
EW Early Wynn/26	75.00	120.00
HC Happy Chandler/29	60.00	100.00
HN Hal Newhouser/33	60.00	100.00
HW Hoyt Wilhelm/33	60.00	100.00
JA Joe Adcock/6		
JD Joe DiMaggio/2		
JM Johnny Mize/48	60.00	100.00
JO Johnny Oates/1		
JS Joe Sewell/23		
JV Johnny Vander Meer/49	75.00	120.00
LA Luke Appling/31	75.00	120.00
LB Lou Boudreau/47	75.00	120.00
LD Larry Doby/7		
MH Mel Harder/37	60.00	100.00
PR Pee Wee Reese/37	150.00	200.00
RA Richie Ashburn/29	100.00	150.00
RD Ray Dandridge/20		
RF Rick Ferrell/52	60.00	100.00
ST Willie Stargell/30	150.00	200.00
TA Tommie Agee/2		
WS Warren Spahn/102	60.00	100.00

2007 Sweet Spot Classic Legendary Lettermen

Card	Low	High
E.BANKS p/r 25	30.00	60.00
E.BANKS TWO p/r 15	20.00	50.00
J.BENCH p/r 25	30.00	60.00
R.CAMPANELLA p/r 10	30.00	60.00
T.COBB p/r 25	40.00	80.00
T.COBB PEACH p/r 5	50.00	100.00
D.DEAN p/r 25	30.00	60.00
D.DRYSDALE p/r 25	15.00	40.00
C.FISK p/r 20	30.00	60.00
J.FOXX p/r 25	30.00	60.00
L.GEHRIG p/r 15	100.00	150.00
B.GIBSON p/r 25	15.00	40.00
T.GWYNN p/r 25	15.00	40.00
R.HORNSBY p/r 25	30.00	60.00
R.JACKSON p/r 25	20.00	50.00
B.JACKSON p/r 25	20.00	50.00
B.JACKSON KNOWS p/r 15	20.00	50.00
W.JOHNSON p/r 15	30.00	60.00
W.JOHNSON TRAIN p/r 10	40.00	80.00
A.KALINE p/r 25	20.00	50.00
S.KOUFAX p/r 25	225.00	300.00
C.MATHEWSON p/r 10	30.00	60.00
D.MATTINGLY p/r 15	50.00	100.00
B.MAZEROSKI p/r 15	15.00	40.00
T.MUNSON p/r 25	30.00	60.00
T.MUNSON CAPTAIN p/r 10	40.00	80.00
S.MUSIAL p/r 25	20.00	50.00
S.MUSIAL MAN p/r 25	20.00	50.00
M.OTT p/r 25	15.00	40.00
S.PAIGE p/r 25	30.00	60.00
C.RIPKEN p/r 25	50.00	100.00
C.RIPKEN IRON p/r 25	50.00	100.00
J.ROBINSON p/r 10	30.00	60.00
J.ROBINSON PIONEER p/r 10	30.00	60.00
B.RUTH p/r 25	100.00	175.00
B.RUTH SULTAN p/r 15	100.00	200.00
N.RYAN p/r 20	30.00	60.00
N.RYAN EXPRESS p/r 15	30.00	60.00
R.SANDBERG p/r 25	60.00	120.00
M.SCHMIDT p/r 25	30.00	60.00
H.WAGNER p/r 25	20.00	50.00
C.YASTRZEMSKI p/r 15	30.00	60.00

RANDOM INSERTS IN TINS
PRINT RUNS B/WN 5-25 COPIES PER

Card	Low	High
LL1H Babe Ruth H/25	100.00	175.00
LL1R Babe Ruth R/25	100.00	175.00
LL1T Babe Ruth T/25	100.00	175.00
LL1U Babe Ruth U/25	100.00	175.00
LL2B Ty Cobb B/25	40.00	80.00
LL2B Ty Cobb B/25	40.00	80.00
LL2C Ty Cobb C/25	40.00	80.00
LL2O Ty Cobb O/25	40.00	80.00
LL3A Christy Mathewson A/10	30.00	60.00
LL3E Christy Mathewson E/10	30.00	60.00
LL3H Christy Mathewson H/10	30.00	60.00
LL3M Christy Mathewson M/10	30.00	60.00
LL3N Christy Mathewson N/10	30.00	60.00
LL3O Christy Mathewson O/10	30.00	60.00
LL3S Christy Mathewson S/10	30.00	60.00
LL3T Christy Mathewson T/10	30.00	60.00
LL3W Christy Mathewson W/10	30.00	60.00
LL4B Jackie Robinson B/10	30.00	60.00
LL4I Jackie Robinson I/10	30.00	60.00
LL4N Jackie Robinson N/10	30.00	60.00
LL4N Jackie Robinson N/10	30.00	60.00
LL4O Jackie Robinson O/10	30.00	60.00
LL4O Jackie Robinson O/10	30.00	60.00
LL4R Jackie Robinson R/10	30.00	60.00
LL4S Jackie Robinson S/10	30.00	60.00
LL5A Roy Campanella A/10	30.00	60.00
LL5A Roy Campanella A/10	30.00	60.00
LL5A Roy Campanella A/10	30.00	60.00
LL5C Roy Campanella C/10	30.00	60.00
LL5E Roy Campanella E/10	30.00	60.00
LL5L Roy Campanella L/10	30.00	60.00
LL5L Roy Campanella L/10	30.00	60.00
LL5M Roy Campanella M/10	30.00	60.00
LL5N Roy Campanella N/10	30.00	60.00
LL5P Roy Campanella P/10	30.00	60.00
LL6E Lou Gehrig E/15	100.00	150.00
LL6G Lou Gehrig G/15	100.00	150.00
LL6G Lou Gehrig G/15	100.00	150.00
LL6H Lou Gehrig H/15	100.00	150.00
LL6I Lou Gehrig I/15	100.00	150.00
LL6R Lou Gehrig R/15	100.00	150.00
LL7O Mel Ott O/25	15.00	40.00
LL7T Mel Ott T/25	15.00	40.00
LL7T Mel Ott T/25	15.00	40.00
LL8F Jimmie Foxx F/25	30.00	60.00
LL8O Jimmie Foxx O/25	30.00	60.00
LL8X Jimmie Foxx X/25	30.00	60.00
LL8X Jimmie Foxx X/25	30.00	60.00
LL9A Satchel Paige A/25	30.00	60.00
LL9E Satchel Paige E/25	30.00	60.00
LL9G Satchel Paige G/25	30.00	60.00
LL9I Satchel Paige I/25	30.00	60.00
LL9P Satchel Paige P/25	30.00	60.00
LL10A Don Drysdale A/25	15.00	40.00
LL10D Don Drysdale D/25	15.00	40.00
LL10D Don Drysdale D/25	15.00	40.00
LL10E Don Drysdale E/25	15.00	40.00
LL10L Don Drysdale L/25	15.00	40.00
LL10R Don Drysdale R/25	15.00	40.00
LL10S Don Drysdale S/25	15.00	40.00
LL10Y Don Drysdale Y/25	15.00	40.00
LL11B Rogers Hornsby B/25	30.00	60.00
LL11H Rogers Hornsby H/25	30.00	60.00
LL11N Rogers Hornsby N/25	30.00	60.00
LL11O Rogers Hornsby O/25	30.00	60.00
LL11R Rogers Hornsby R/25	30.00	60.00
LL11S Rogers Hornsby S/25	30.00	60.00
LL11Y Rogers Hornsby Y/25	30.00	60.00
LL12A Honus Wagner A/25	20.00	50.00
LL12E Honus Wagner E/25	20.00	50.00
LL12G Honus Wagner G/25	20.00	50.00
LL12N Honus Wagner N/25	20.00	50.00
LL12R Honus Wagner R/25	20.00	50.00
LL12W Honus Wagner W/25	20.00	50.00
LL13A Babe Ruth A/15	100.00	200.00
LL13B Babe Ruth B/15	100.00	200.00
LL13B Babe Ruth B/15	100.00	200.00
LL13I Babe Ruth I/15	100.00	200.00
LL13M Babe Ruth M/15	100.00	200.00
LL13N Babe Ruth N/15	100.00	200.00
LL13O Babe Ruth O/15	100.00	200.00
LL14A Dizzy Dean A/25	30.00	60.00
LL14D Dizzy Dean D/25	30.00	60.00
LL14E Dizzy Dean E/25	30.00	60.00
LL14N Dizzy Dean N/25	30.00	60.00
LL15A Ty Cobb A/5	50.00	100.00
LL15A Ty Cobb A/5	50.00	100.00

LL15C Ty Cobb C/5 50.00 100.00
LL15E Ty Cobb E/5 50.00 100.00
LL15E Ty Cobb E/5 50.00 100.00
LL15G Ty Cobb G/5 50.00 100.00
LL15G Ty Cobb G/5 50.00 100.00
LL15H Ty Cobb H/5 50.00 100.00
LL15I Ty Cobb I/5 50.00 100.00
LL15O Ty Cobb O/5 50.00 100.00
LL15P Ty Cobb P/5 50.00 100.00
LL15R Ty Cobb R/5 50.00 100.00
LL16H Walter Johnson H/15 30.00 60.00
LL16J Walter Johnson J/15 30.00 60.00
LL16N Walter Johnson N/15 30.00 60.00
LL16N Walter Johnson N/15 30.00 60.00
LL16O Walter Johnson O/15 30.00 60.00
LL16O Walter Johnson O/15 30.00 60.00
LL16S Walter Johnson S/15 30.00 60.00
LL17A Walter Johnson A/10 40.00 80.00
LL17B Walter Johnson B/10 40.00 80.00
LL17B Walter Johnson G/10 40.00 80.00
LL17I Walter Johnson I/10 40.00 80.00
LL17I Walter Johnson I/10 40.00 80.00
LL17N Walter Johnson N/10 40.00 80.00
LL17R Walter Johnson R/10 40.00 80.00
LL17T Walter Johnson T/10 40.00 80.00
LL18E Cal Ripken Jr. E/25 50.00 100.00
LL18I Cal Ripken Jr. I/25 50.00 100.00
LL18K Cal Ripken Jr. K/25 50.00 100.00
LL18N Cal Ripken Jr. N/25 50.00 100.00
LL18P Cal Ripken Jr. P/25 50.00 100.00
LL18R Cal Ripken Jr. R/25 50.00 100.00
LL19A Sandy Koufax A/25 225.00 300.00
LL19F Sandy Koufax F/25 225.00 300.00
LL19K Sandy Koufax K/25 225.00 300.00
LL19O Sandy Koufax O/25 225.00 300.00
LL19U Sandy Koufax U/25 225.00 300.00
LL19X Sandy Koufax X/25 225.00 300.00
LL20M Thurman Munson M/25 30.00 60.00
LL20N Thurman Munson N/25 30.00 60.00
LL20N Thurman Munson N/25 30.00 60.00
LL20O Thurman Munson O/25 30.00 60.00
LL20S Thurman Munson S/25 30.00 60.00
LL20U Thurman Munson U/25 30.00 60.00
LL21A Thurman Munson A/10 40.00 80.00
LL21A Thurman Munson A/10 40.00 80.00
LL21C Thurman Munson C/10 40.00 80.00
LL21I Thurman Munson I/10 40.00 80.00
LL21N Thurman Munson N/10 40.00 80.00
LL21P Thurman Munson P/10 40.00 80.00
LL21T Thurman Munson T/10 40.00 80.00
LL22A Cal Ripken Jr. A/25 50.00 100.00
LL22I Cal Ripken Jr. I/25 50.00 100.00
LL22M Cal Ripken Jr. M/25 50.00 100.00
LL22N Cal Ripken Jr. N/25 50.00 100.00
LL22N Cal Ripken Jr. N/25 50.00 100.00
LL22O Cal Ripken Jr. O/25 50.00 100.00
LL22R Cal Ripken Jr. R/25 50.00 100.00
LL23G Tony Gwynn G/25 15.00 40.00
LL23N Tony Gwynn N/25 15.00 40.00
LL23N Tony Gwynn N/25 15.00 40.00
LL23W Tony Gwynn W/25 15.00 40.00
LL23Y Tony Gwynn Y/25 15.00 40.00
LL24A Nolan Ryan A/20 30.00 60.00
LL24N Nolan Ryan N/20 30.00 60.00
LL24R Nolan Ryan R/20 30.00 60.00
LL24Y Nolan Ryan Y/20 30.00 60.00
LL25A Nolan Ryan A/15 30.00 60.00
LL25E Nolan Ryan E/15 30.00 60.00
LL25E Nolan Ryan E/15 30.00 60.00
LL25N Nolan Ryan N/15 30.00 60.00
LL25P Nolan Ryan P/15 30.00 60.00
LL25R Nolan Ryan R/15 30.00 60.00
LL25R Nolan Ryan R/15 30.00 60.00
LL25S Nolan Ryan S/15 30.00 60.00
LL25S Nolan Ryan S/15 30.00 60.00
LL25X Nolan Ryan X/15 30.00 60.00
LL25Y Nolan Ryan Y/15 30.00 60.00
LL26E Jackie Robinson E/10 30.00 60.00
LL26E Jackie Robinson E/10 30.00 60.00
LL26I Jackie Robinson I/10 30.00 60.00
LL26N Jackie Robinson N/10 30.00 60.00
LL26O Jackie Robinson O/10 30.00 60.00
LL26P Jackie Robinson P/10 30.00 60.00
LL26R Jackie Robinson R/10 30.00 60.00
LL27F Carlton Fisk F/20 30.00 60.00
LL27I Carlton Fisk I/20 30.00 60.00
LL27K Carlton Fisk K/20 30.00 60.00
LL27S Carlton Fisk S/20 30.00 60.00
LL28A Carl Yastrzemski A/15 30.00 60.00
LL28E Carl Yastrzemski E/15 30.00 60.00
LL28I Carl Yastrzemski I/15 30.00 60.00
LL28K Carl Yastrzemski K/15 30.00 60.00
LL28M Carl Yastrzemski M/15 30.00 60.00
LL28R Carl Yastrzemski R/15 30.00 60.00
LL28S Carl Yastrzemski S/15 30.00 60.00
LL28S Carl Yastrzemski S/15 30.00 60.00
LL28T Carl Yastrzemski T/15 30.00 60.00
LL28Y Carl Yastrzemski Y/15 30.00 60.00
LL28Z Carl Yastrzemski Z/15 30.00 60.00
LL29B Johnny Bench B/25 30.00 60.00
LL29C Johnny Bench C/25 30.00 60.00
LL29E Johnny Bench E/25 30.00 60.00
LL29H Johnny Bench H/25 30.00 60.00
LL29N Johnny Bench N/25 30.00 60.00
LL30A Ryne Sandberg A/25 60.00 120.00
LL30B Ryne Sandberg B/25 60.00 120.00
LL30D Ryne Sandberg D/25 60.00 120.00
LL30E Ryne Sandberg E/25 60.00 120.00
LL30G Ryne Sandberg G/25 60.00 120.00
LL30N Ryne Sandberg N/25 60.00 120.00
LL30R Ryne Sandberg R/25 60.00 120.00
LL30S Ryne Sandberg S/25 60.00 120.00
LL31A Don Mattingly A/15 50.00 100.00
LL31G Don Mattingly G/15 50.00 100.00
LL31I Don Mattingly I/15 50.00 100.00
LL31L Don Mattingly L/15 50.00 100.00
LL31M Don Mattingly M/15 50.00 100.00
LL31N Don Mattingly N/15 50.00 100.00
LL31T Don Mattingly T/15 50.00 100.00
LL31T Don Mattingly T/15 50.00 100.00
LL31Y Don Mattingly Y/15 50.00 100.00
LL32A Ernie Banks A/25 30.00 60.00
LL32B Ernie Banks B/25 30.00 60.00
LL32K Ernie Banks K/25 30.00 60.00
LL32N Ernie Banks N/25 30.00 60.00
LL32S Ernie Banks S/25 30.00 60.00
LL33A Bill Mazeroski A/15 15.00 40.00
LL33E Bill Mazeroski E/15 15.00 40.00
LL33I Bill Mazeroski I/15 15.00 40.00
LL33K Bill Mazeroski K/15 15.00 40.00
LL33M Bill Mazeroski M/15 15.00 40.00
LL33O Bill Mazeroski O/15 15.00 40.00
LL33R Bill Mazeroski R/15 15.00 40.00
LL33S Bill Mazeroski S/15 15.00 40.00
LL33Z Bill Mazeroski Z/15 15.00 40.00
LL34A Ernie Banks A/15 20.00 50.00
LL34E Ernie Banks E/15 20.00 50.00
LL34L Ernie Banks L/15 20.00 50.00
LL34L Ernie Banks L/15 20.00 50.00
LL34O Ernie Banks O/15 20.00 50.00
LL34P Ernie Banks P/15 20.00 50.00
LL34S Ernie Banks S/15 20.00 50.00
LL34T Ernie Banks T/15 20.00 50.00
LL34T Ernie Banks T/15 20.00 50.00
LL34W Ernie Banks W/15 20.00 50.00
LL34Y Ernie Banks Y/15 20.00 50.00
LL35B Bob Gibson B/25 15.00 40.00
LL35G Bob Gibson G/25 15.00 40.00
LL35I Bob Gibson I/25 15.00 40.00
LL35N Bob Gibson N/25 15.00 40.00
LL35O Bob Gibson O/25 15.00 40.00
LL35S Bob Gibson S/25 15.00 40.00
LL36C Mike Schmidt C/25 30.00 60.00
LL36D Mike Schmidt D/25 30.00 60.00
LL36H Mike Schmidt H/25 30.00 60.00
LL36I Mike Schmidt I/25 30.00 60.00
LL36M Mike Schmidt M/25 30.00 60.00
LL36S Mike Schmidt S/25 30.00 60.00
LL36T Mike Schmidt T/25 30.00 60.00
LL37A Al Kaline A/25 20.00 50.00
LL37E Al Kaline E/25 20.00 50.00
LL37I Al Kaline I/25 20.00 50.00
LL37K Al Kaline K/25 20.00 50.00
LL37L Al Kaline L/25 20.00 50.00
LL37N Al Kaline N/25 20.00 50.00
LL38A Reggie Jackson A/25 20.00 50.00
LL38C Reggie Jackson C/25 20.00 50.00
LL38J Reggie Jackson J/25 20.00 50.00
LL38K Reggie Jackson K/25 20.00 50.00
LL38N Reggie Jackson N/25 20.00 50.00
LL38O Reggie Jackson O/25 20.00 50.00
LL38S Reggie Jackson S/25 20.00 50.00
LL39A Stan Musial A/25 20.00 50.00
LL39I Stan Musial I/25 20.00 50.00
LL39L Stan Musial L/25 20.00 50.00
LL39M Stan Musial M/25 20.00 50.00
LL39S Stan Musial S/25 20.00 50.00
LL39U Stan Musial U/25 20.00 50.00
LL40A Bo Jackson A/25 20.00 50.00
LL40C Bo Jackson C/25 20.00 50.00
LL40J Bo Jackson J/25 20.00 50.00
LL40K Bo Jackson K/25 20.00 50.00
LL40N Bo Jackson N/25 20.00 50.00
LL40O Bo Jackson O/25 20.00 50.00
LL40S Bo Jackson S/25 20.00 50.00
LL41B Bo Jackson B/15 20.00 50.00
LL41K Bo Jackson K/15 20.00 50.00
LL41N Bo Jackson N/15 20.00 50.00
LL41O Bo Jackson O/15 20.00 50.00
LL41O Bo Jackson O/15 20.00 50.00
LL41S Bo Jackson S/15 20.00 50.00
LL41W Bo Jackson W/15 20.00 50.00
LL42A Stan Musial A/25 20.00 50.00
LL42E Stan Musial E/25 20.00 50.00
LL42H Stan Musial H/25 20.00 50.00
LL42M Stan Musial M/25 20.00 50.00
LL42N Stan Musial N/25 20.00 50.00
LL42T Stan Musial T/25 20.00 50.00

2007 Sweet Spot Classic Signatures Red Stitch Black Ink

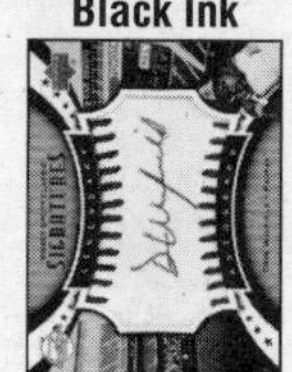

RANDOM INSERTS IN TINS
PRINT RUNS B/WN 35-175 COPIES PER
EXCHANGE DEADLINE 8/3/2009

AG Andres Galarraga/175 6.00 15.00
AK Al Kaline/175 12.50 30.00
AO Al Oliver/175 6.00 15.00
BJ Bo Jackson/175 20.00 50.00
BM Bill Mazeroski/175 15.00 40.00
BO Wade Boggs/75 15.00 40.00
BR Brooks Robinson/175 10.00 25.00
BS Bruce Sutter/75 12.50 30.00
BW Billy Williams/175 6.00 15.00
CF Carlton Fisk/75 15.00 40.00
CL Carney Lansford/175 6.00 15.00
CO Dave Concepcion/175 10.00 25.00
CY Carl Yastrzemski/75 30.00 60.00
DA Dick Allen/175 6.00 15.00
DG Dick Groat/175 10.00 25.00
DL Don Larsen/175 10.00 25.00
DM Don Mattingly/75 30.00 60.00
DS Don Sutton/175 6.00 15.00
DW Dave Winfield/75 15.00 40.00
EB Ernie Banks/75 30.00 60.00
EC Dennis Eckersley/175 10.00 25.00
EF Elroy Face/175 6.00 15.00
EM Edgar Martinez/175 12.50 30.00
EV Dwight Evans/175 6.00 15.00
FL Fred Lynn/175 6.00 15.00
FM Fred McGriff/175 10.00 25.00
FR Frank Robinson Blue/75 15.00 40.00
GI Bob Gibson/175 12.50 30.00
GP Gaylord Perry/175 6.00 15.00
HB Harold Baines/175 6.00 15.00
JB Johnny Bench/75 20.00 50.00
JI Jim Bunning/175 10.00 25.00
JK John Kruk/175 6.00 15.00
JP Johnny Pesky/175 10.00 25.00
JR Jim Rice/175 6.00 15.00
KG Ken Griffey Sr./175 6.00 15.00
LA Luis Aparicio/175 6.00 15.00
LB Lou Brock/175 15.00 40.00
MA Juan Marichal/175 10.00 25.00
MG Mark Grace/175 12.50 30.00
MO Jack Morris/175 6.00 15.00
MS Mike Schmidt/75 30.00 60.00
MU Stan Musial/75 40.00 80.00
MV Mickey Vernon/75 12.50 30.00
NR Nolan Ryan/75 50.00 100.00
OG Ozzie Guillen/175 6.00 15.00
OS Ozzie Smith/75 20.00 50.00
PN Phil Niekro/175 6.00 15.00
RA Roberto Alomar/75 10.00 25.00
RC Rod Carew/75 12.50 30.00
RF Rollie Fingers/175 6.00 15.00
RI Jim Rice/175 6.00 15.00
RJ Reggie Jackson/75 30.00 60.00
RK Ralph Kiner/75 15.00 40.00
RR Robin Roberts/175 6.00 15.00
RS Ryne Sandberg/75 20.00 50.00
RY Robin Yount/75 15.00 40.00
SA Ron Santo/75 12.50 30.00
SC Steve Carlton/175 10.00 25.00
SD Shawon Dunston/175 6.00 15.00
SG Steve Garvey/175 6.00 15.00
SK Bill Skowron/175 6.00 15.00
SM Reggie Smith/175 6.00 15.00
TG Tony Gwynn/75 30.00 60.00
TH Toby Harrah/175 6.00 15.00
TM Tino Martinez/175 10.00 25.00
TO Tony Oliva/175 6.00 15.00
TP Tony Perez/175 6.00 15.00
TR Tim Raines/175 6.00 15.00
WB Wade Boggs/75 15.00 40.00
WD Willie Davis/75 10.00 25.00
WH Willie Horton/175 6.00 15.00
WM Willie McCovey/75 15.00 40.00
YB Yogi Berra/75 40.00 80.00

2007 Sweet Spot Classic Signatures Red Stitch Blue Ink

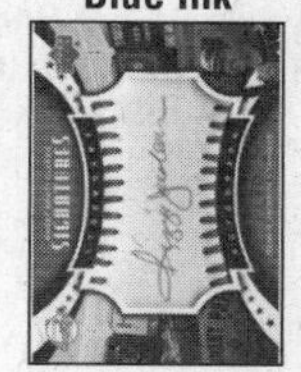

*BLUE p/r 75-125: .5X TO 1.2X BLK p/r 175
*BLUE p/r 75-125: .4X TO 1X BLK p/r 75
*BLUE p/r 35: .6X TO 1.5X BLK p/r 175
*BLUE p/r 35: .5X TO 1.2X BLK p/r 75
RANDOM INSERTS IN TINS
PRINT RUNS B/WN 35-125 COPIES PER
EXCHANGE DEADLINE 8/3/2009

2007 Sweet Spot Classic Signatures Black Stitch Blue Ink

RANDOM INSERTS IN TINS
STATED PRINT RUN 1 SER.#'d SET
NO PRICING DUE TO SCARCITY
EXCHANGE DEADLINE 8/3/2009

2007 Sweet Spot Classic Signatures Black Stitch Red Ink

RANDOM INSERTS IN TINS
STATED PRINT RUN 1 SER.#'d SET
NO PRICING DUE TO SCARCITY
EXCHANGE DEADLINE 8/3/2009

2007 Sweet Spot Classic Signatures Gold Stitch Black Ink

RANDOM INSERTS IN TINS
PRINT RUNS B/WN 25-99 COPIES PER
NO PRICING ON QTY 25 OR LESS
EXCHANGE DEADLINE 8/3/2009

AG Andres Galarraga/99 6.00 15.00
AK Al Kaline/99 10.00 25.00
AO Al Oliver/99 6.00 15.00
BJ Bo Jackson/99 30.00 60.00
BM Bill Mazeroski/99 15.00 40.00
BR Brooks Robinson/99 15.00 40.00
BW Billy Williams/99 10.00 25.00
CL Carney Lansford/99 6.00 15.00
CO Dave Concepcion/99 10.00 25.00
DA Dick Allen/99 10.00 25.00
DG Dick Groat/99 10.00 25.00
DL Don Larsen/99 10.00 25.00
DS Don Sutton/99 10.00 25.00
EB Ernie Banks/99 40.00 80.00
EC Dennis Eckersley/99 10.00 25.00
EF Elroy Face/99 10.00 25.00
EM Edgar Martinez/99 15.00 40.00
EV Dwight Evans/99 6.00 15.00
FL Fred Lynn/99 10.00 25.00
FM Fred McGriff/99 15.00 40.00
GI Bob Gibson/99 20.00 50.00
GP Gaylord Perry/99 6.00 15.00
HB Harold Baines/99 10.00 25.00
JI Jim Bunning/99 10.00 25.00
JK John Kruk/99 6.00 15.00
JP Johnny Pesky/99 6.00 15.00
JR Jim Rice/99 10.00 25.00
KG Ken Griffey Sr./99 6.00 15.00
LA Luis Aparicio/99 10.00 25.00
MA Juan Marichal/99 15.00 40.00
MG Mark Grace/99 15.00 40.00
MO Jack Morris/99 10.00 25.00
MV Mickey Vernon/99 10.00 25.00
OG Ozzie Guillen/99 10.00 25.00
PN Phil Niekro/99 10.00 25.00
RA Roberto Alomar/99 15.00 40.00
RF Rollie Fingers/99 10.00 25.00
RI Jim Rice/99 10.00 25.00
RR Robin Roberts/99 10.00 25.00
SA Ron Santo/99 20.00 50.00
SC Steve Carlton/99 10.00 25.00
SD Shawon Dunston/99 10.00 25.00
SG Steve Garvey/99 10.00 25.00
SK Bill Skowron/99 6.00 15.00
SM Reggie Smith/99 6.00 15.00
TH Toby Harrah/99 6.00 15.00
TM Tino Martinez/99 15.00 40.00
TO Tony Oliva/99 6.00 15.00
TP Tony Perez/99 10.00 25.00
TR Tim Raines/99 10.00 25.00
WH Willie Horton/99 10.00 25.00

2007 Sweet Spot Classic Signatures Gold Stitch Blue Ink

*BLUE: .5X TO 1.2X BLACK INK
RANDOM INSERTS IN TINS
PRINT RUNS B/WN 15-50 COPIES PER
NO PRICING ON QTY 25 OR LESS
EXCHANGE DEADLINE 8/3/2009

CY Carl Yastrzemski/50 30.00 60.00
DW Dave Winfield/50 12.50 30.00
MU Stan Musial/50 40.00 80.00
RY Robin Yount/50 20.00 50.00

2007 Sweet Spot Classic Signatures Sepia Black Ink

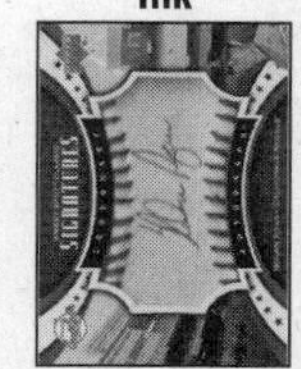

RANDOM INSERTS IN TINS
PRINT RUNS B/WN 16-199 COPIES PER
NO PRICING ON QTY 25 OR LESS
EXCHANGE DEADLINE 8/3/2009

CF Carlton Fisk/124 12.50 30.00
CY Carl Yastrzemski/124 20.00 50.00
DM Don Mattingly/124 20.00 50.00
DS Duke Snider/30 30.00 60.00
JM Juan Marichal/124 10.00 25.00
JR Jim Rice/85 10.00 25.00
KH Keith Hernandez/16
MU Dale Murphy/183 12.50 30.00
NR Nolan Ryan/123 50.00 100.00
OS Ozzie Smith/183 20.00 50.00
RS Ryne Sandberg/199 20.00 50.00
TG Tony Gwynn/199 20.00 50.00
TS Tom Seaver/16

2007 Sweet Spot Classic Signatures Sepia Blue Ink

RANDOM INSERTS IN TINS
PRINT RUNS B/WN 15-200 COPIES PER
NO PRICING ON QTY 25 OR LESS
EXCHANGE DEADLINE 8/3/2009

AK Al Kaline/199 10.00 25.00
BR Brooks Robinson/200 10.00 25.00
BW Billy Williams/199 10.00 25.00
CF Carlton Fisk/78 15.00 40.00
CR Cal Ripken Jr./199 60.00 100.00
CY Carl Yastrzemski/90 30.00 60.00
DE Dennis Eckersley/15
DM Don Mattingly/78 30.00 60.00
DS Duke Snider/199 12.50 30.00
EM Edgar Martinez/74 30.00 60.00
JM Juan Marichal/84 12.50 30.00
JP Jim Palmer/200 10.00 25.00
JR Jim Rice/75 10.00 25.00
LM Lee Mazzilli/199 10.00 25.00
MU Dale Murphy/75 15.00 40.00
NR Nolan Ryan/80 60.00 120.00
OS Ozzie Smith/75 30.00 60.00
RC Rocky Colavito/199 30.00 60.00
RY Robin Yount/35 30.00 60.00
TG Tony Gwynn/199 20.00 50.00
WC Will Clark/199 12.50 30.00
WF Whitey Ford/15

2007 Sweet Spot Classic Signatures Sepia Red Ink

RANDOM INSERTS IN TINS
STATED PRINT RUN 15 SER.#'d SETS
NO PRICING DUE TO SCARCITY
EXCHANGE DEADLINE 8/3/2009

2007 Sweet Spot Classic Signatures Silver Stitch Black Ink

RANDOM INSERTS IN TINS
PRINT RUNS B/WN 15-25 COPIES PER
NO PRICING DUE TO SCARCITY
EXCHANGE DEADLINE 8/3/2009

2007 Sweet Spot Classic Signatures Silver Stitch Blue Ink

RANDOM INSERTS IN TINS
PRINT RUNS B/WN 16-199 COPIES PER
NO PRICING ON QTY 25 OR LESS
EXCHANGE DEADLINE 8/3/2009

AG Andres Galarraga/14
AK Al Kaline/6
AO Al Oliver/16
BJ Bo Jackson/16
BM Bill Mazeroski/9
BO Wade Boggs/12
BR Brooks Robinson/5
BS Bruce Sutter/42 EXCH 10.00 25.00
BW Billy Williams/26 12.50 30.00
CF Carlton Fisk/15
CL Carney Lansford/4
CO Dave Concepcion/13
CY Carl Yastrzemski/8
DA Dick Allen/15
DG Dick Groat/24
DL Don Larsen/18
DM Don Mattingly/23
DS Don Sutton/20
DW Dave Winfield/31 30.00 60.00
EB Ernie Banks/14
EC Dennis Eckersley/43 10.00 25.00
EF Elroy Face/25
EM Edgar Martinez/11
EV Dwight Evans/24
FL Fred Lynn/19
FM Fred McGriff/27 30.00 60.00
FR Frank Robinson/20
GI Bob Gibson/45 30.00 60.00
GP Gaylord Perry/36 12.50 30.00
HB Harold Baines/3
JB Johnny Bench/5
JI Jim Bunning/14
JK John Kruk/29 12.50 30.00
JP Johnny Pesky/6
JR Jim Rice/14
KG Ken Griffey Sr./30 12.50 30.00
KO Sandy Koufax/32
LA Luis Aparicio/11
LB Lou Brock/5
MA Juan Marichal/27 12.50 30.00
MG Mark Grace/17
MO Jack Morris/47 10.00 25.00
MS Mike Schmidt/20
MU Stan Musial/6
MV Mickey Vernon/3
NR Nolan Ryan/30 60.00 150.00
OG Ozzie Guillen/13
OS Ozzie Smith/1
PN Phil Niekro/35 12.50 30.00
RA Roberto Alomar/12
RC Rod Carew/29 12.50 30.00
RF Rollie Fingers/34 10.00 25.00
RI Jim Rice/14
RJ Reggie Jackson/44 30.00 60.00
RK Ralph Kiner/4
RR Robin Roberts/36 12.50 30.00
RS Ryne Sandberg/23
RY Robin Yount/19
SA Ron Santo/11
SC Steve Carlton/32 12.50 30.00
SD Shawon Dunston/12
SG Steve Garvey/6
SK Bill Skowron/14
SM Reggie Smith/8
TG Tony Gwynn/19
TH Toby Harrah/11
TM Tino Martinez/24
TO Tony Oliva/6
TP Tony Perez/24
TR Tim Raines/30 40.00 80.00
WB Wade Boggs/26 40.00 80.00
WD Willie Davis/3
WH Willie Horton/23
WM Willie McCovey/44 30.00 60.00
YB Yogi Berra/8

2007 Sweet Spot Classic Signatures Barrel Black Ink

*BLUE: .5X TO 1.2X BLACK INK
RANDOM INSERTS IN TINS
STATED PRINT RUN B/WN 15-50 PER
NO BLUE PRICING ON QTY 25 OR LESS
EXCHANGE DEADLINE 8/3/2009

RR Robin Roberts Blue/50 10.00 25.00

2007 Sweet Spot Classic Signatures Barrel Blue Ink

RANDOM INSERTS IN TINS
PRINT RUNS B/WN 25-75 COPIES PER
NO PRICING ON QTY 25 OR LESS
*BLUE: .5X TO 1.2X BLACK INK
BLUE RANDOMLY INSERTED IN TINS
BLUE PRINT RUN B/WN 15-50 PER
NO BLUE PRICING ON QTY 25 OR LESS
EXCHANGE DEADLINE 8/3/2009

AG Andres Galarraga/75 6.00 15.00
AK Al Kaline/75 15.00 40.00
AO Al Oliver/75 8.00 20.00
BJ Bo Jackson/75 30.00 60.00
BM Bill Mazeroski/75 20.00 50.00
BR Brooks Robinson/75 30.00 60.00
BW Billy Williams/75 12.50 30.00
CL Carney Lansford/75 8.00 20.00
DA Dick Allen/75 10.00 25.00
DG Dick Groat/75 10.00 25.00
DL Don Larsen/75 10.00 25.00
DS Don Sutton/75 10.00 25.00
EC Dennis Eckersley/75 10.00 25.00
EF Elroy Face/75 12.50 30.00
EM Edgar Martinez/75 20.00 50.00
EV Dwight Evans/75 10.00 25.00
FL Fred Lynn/75 8.00 20.00
FM Fred McGriff/75 15.00 40.00
GP Gaylord Perry/75 10.00 25.00
HB Harold Baines/75 10.00 25.00
JI Jim Bunning/75 10.00 25.00
JK John Kruk/75 8.00 20.00
JP Johnny Pesky/75 12.50 30.00
KG Ken Griffey Sr./75 10.00 25.00
LA Luis Aparicio/75 10.00 25.00
MA Juan Marichal/75 15.00 40.00
MG Mark Grace/75 15.00 40.00
MO Jack Morris/75 8.00 20.00
MV Mickey Vernon/75 12.50 30.00
OG Ozzie Guillen/75 10.00 25.00
PN Phil Niekro/75 10.00 25.00
RA Roberto Alomar/75 30.00 60.00
RF Rollie Fingers/75 8.00 20.00
RI Jim Rice/75 10.00 25.00
RR Robin Roberts/50 10.00 25.00
SA Ron Santo/75 20.00 50.00
SC Steve Carlton/75 20.00 50.00
SD Shawon Dunston/75 10.00 25.00
SG Steve Garvey/75 10.00 25.00
SK Bill Skowron/75 10.00 25.00
SM Reggie Smith/75 6.00 15.00
TH Toby Harrah/75 6.00 15.00
TM Tino Martinez/75 12.50 30.00
TO Tony Oliva/75 10.00 25.00
TP Tony Perez/75 12.50 30.00
TR Tim Raines/75 10.00 25.00
WH Willie Horton/75 10.00 25.00

2007 Sweet Spot Classic Signatures Black Barrel Gold Ink

RANDOM INSERTS IN TINS
STATED PRINT RUN 1 SER.#'d SET
NO PRICING DUE TO SCARCITY
EXCHANGE DEADLINE 8/3/2009

2007 Sweet Spot Classic Signatures Black Barrel Silver Ink

RANDOM INSERTS IN TINS
PRINT RUNS B/WN 1-47 COPIES PER
NO PRICING ON QTY 25 OR LESS
EXCHANGE DEADLINE 8/3/2009
BW Billy Williams/26 20.00 50.00
EC Dennis Eckersley/43 12.50 30.00
EF Elroy Face/26 20.00 50.00
FM Fred McGriff/27 30.00 60.00
GP Gaylord Perry/36 10.00 25.00
JK John Kruk/29 12.50 30.00
KG Ken Griffey Sr./30 15.00 40.00
MA Juan Marichal/27 10.00 25.00
MO Jack Morris/47 10.00 25.00
PN Phil Niekro/35 15.00 40.00
RF Rollie Fingers/34 10.00 25.00
RR Robin Roberts/36 12.50 30.00
SC Steve Carlton/32 40.00 80.00
TR Tim Raines/30 30.00 60.00

2007 Sweet Spot Classic Signatures Black Leather Green Ink

RANDOM INSERTS IN TINS
STATED PRINT RUN 1 SER.#'d SET
NO PRICING DUE TO SCARCITY
EXCHANGE DEADLINE 8/3/2009

2007 Sweet Spot Classic Signatures Black Leather Silver Ink

RANDOM INSERTS IN TINS
PRINT RUNS B/WN 1-47 COPIES PER
NO PRICING ON QTY 25 OR LESS
EXCHANGE DEADLINE 8/3/2009
BS Bruce Sutter/42 12.50 30.00
BW Billy Williams/26 20.00 50.00
CF Carlton Fisk/27 20.00 50.00
DW Dave Winfield/31 20.00 50.00
EC Dennis Eckersley/43 12.50 30.00
EF Elroy Face/26 20.00 50.00
FM Fred McGriff/27 30.00 60.00
GI Bob Gibson/45 40.00 80.00
GP Gaylord Perry/36 10.00 25.00
JK John Kruk/29 12.50 30.00
KG Ken Griffey Sr./30 15.00 40.00
MA Juan Marichal/27 30.00 60.00
MO Jack Morris/47 10.00 25.00
NR Nolan Ryan/30 60.00 120.00
PN Phil Niekro/35 15.00 40.00
RC Rod Carew/29 20.00 50.00
RF Rollie Fingers/34 12.50 30.00
RJ Reggie Jackson/44 30.00 60.00
RR Robin Roberts/36 12.50 30.00
SC Steve Carlton/32 40.00 80.00
TR Tim Raines/30 30.00 60.00
WB Wade Boggs/26 30.00 60.00
WM Willie McCovey/44 30.00 60.00

2007 Sweet Spot Classic Signatures Leather Blue Ink

RANDOM INSERTS IN TINS
PRINT RUNS B/WN 25-75 COPIES PER
NO PRICING ON QTY 25 OR LESS
EXCHANGE DEADLINE 8/3/2009
AG Andres Galarraga/75 6.00 15.00
AK Al Kaline/75 15.00 40.00
AO Al Oliver/75 8.00 20.00
BJ Bo Jackson/75 30.00 60.00
BM Bill Mazeroski/75 20.00 50.00
BR Brooks Robinson/75 30.00 60.00
BW Billy Williams/75 12.50 30.00
CL Carney Lansford/75 8.00 20.00
DA Dick Allen/75 10.00 25.00
DG Dick Groat/75 10.00 25.00
DL Don Larsen/75 10.00 25.00
EC Dennis Eckersley/75 10.00 25.00
EF Elroy Face/75 12.50 30.00
EM Edgar Martinez/75 20.00 50.00
EV Dwight Evans/75 10.00 25.00
FL Fred Lynn/75 8.00 20.00
FM Fred McGriff/75 15.00 40.00
GP Gaylord Perry/75 10.00 25.00
HB Harold Baines/75 10.00 25.00
JI Jim Bunning/75 10.00 25.00
JK John Kruk/75 8.00 20.00
JP Johnny Pesky/75 12.50 30.00
KG Ken Griffey Sr./75 10.00 25.00
LA Luis Aparicio/75 10.00 25.00
LB Lou Brock/75 15.00 40.00
MA Juan Marichal/75 15.00 40.00
MG Mark Grace/75 15.00 40.00
MO Jack Morris/75 8.00 20.00
MV Mickey Vernon/75 12.50 30.00
OG Ozzie Guillen/75 10.00 25.00
RA Roberto Alomar/75 30.00 60.00
RC Rod Carew/75 12.50 30.00
RF Rollie Fingers/75 8.00 20.00
RI Jim Rice/75 10.00 25.00
RR Robin Roberts/75 8.00 20.00
RS Ryne Sandberg/75 20.00 50.00
SA Ron Santo/75 20.00 50.00
SC Steve Carlton/75 20.00 50.00
SD Shawon Dunston/75 10.00 25.00
SG Steve Garvey/75 10.00 25.00
SK Bill Skowron/75 10.00 25.00
SM Reggie Smith/75 6.00 15.00
TH Toby Harrah/75 6.00 15.00
TM Tino Martinez/75 12.50 30.00
TO Tony Oliva/75 10.00 25.00
TP Tony Perez/75 12.50 30.00
TR Tim Raines/75 10.00 25.00
WH Willie Horton/75 10.00 25.00

2007 Sweet Spot Classic Signatures Leather Gold Ink

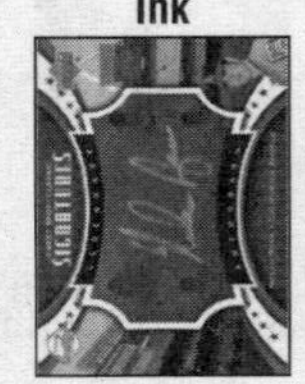

*GOLD: .5X TO 1.2X BLUE INK
GOLD RANDOMLY INSERTED IN TINS
GOLD PRINT RUN B/WN 15-50 PER
NO GOLD PRICING ON QTY 25 OR LESS
EXCHANGE DEADLINE 8/3/2009
PN Phil Niekro/50 12.50 30.00

2006 Sweet Spot Update

This 182-card set was released in December, 2006. The set was issued in five-card packs with an $9.99 SRP and those packs came 12 to a box and 16 boxes to a case. Cards numbered 1-100 feature veteran players while cards 101-182 feature signed cards of 2006 rookies. Those cards, which were issued to a stated print run range between 98 and 499 serial numbered copies, were inserted at a stated rate of one in six. A few players did not return their signatures in time for pack out and those cards could be redeemed until December 19, 2009.

COMP.SET w/o AU's (100) 10.00 25.00
COMMON CARD (1-100) .20 .50
COMMON AU p/r 399-499 3.00 8.00
COMMON AU p/r 150-240 4.00 10.00
COMMON AU p/r 98-125 4.00 10.00
OVERALL AU ODDS 1:6
AU PRINT RUNS B/WN 98-499 PER
EXCHANGE DEADLINE 12/19/09
1 Luis Gonzalez .20 .50
2 Chad Tracy .20 .50
3 Brandon Webb .20 .50
4 Andruw Jones .30 .75
5 Chipper Jones .50 1.25
6 John Smoltz .30 .75
7 Tim Hudson .20 .50
8 Miguel Tejada .20 .50
9 Brian Roberts .20 .50
10 Ramon Hernandez .20 .50
11 Curt Schilling .30 .75
12 David Ortiz .50 1.25
13 Manny Ramirez .30 .75
14 Jason Varitek .50 1.25
15 Josh Beckett .20 .50
16 Greg Maddux .75 2.00
17 Derrek Lee .20 .50
18 Mark Prior .30 .75
19 Aramis Ramirez .20 .50
20 Jim Thome .30 .75
21 Paul Konerko .20 .50
22 Scott Podsednik .20 .50
23 Jose Contreras .20 .50
24 Ken Griffey Jr. .75 2.00
25 Adam Dunn .20 .50
26 Felipe Lopez .20 .50
27 Travis Hafner .20 .50
28 Victor Martinez .20 .50
29 Grady Sizemore .30 .75
30 Jhonny Peralta .20 .50
31 Todd Helton .30 .75
32 Garrett Atkins .20 .50
33 Clint Barmes .20 .50
34 Ivan Rodriguez .30 .75
35 Chris Shelton .20 .50
36 Jeremy Bonderman .20 .50
37 Miguel Cabrera .30 .75
38 Dontrelle Willis .20 .50
39 Lance Berkman .20 .50
40 Morgan Ensberg .20 .50
41 Roy Oswalt .20 .50
42 Reggie Sanders .20 .50
43 Mike Sweeney .20 .50
44 Vladimir Guerrero .50 1.25
45 Bartolo Colon .20 .50
46 Chone Figgins .20 .50
47 Nomar Garciaparra .50 1.25
48 Jeff Kent .20 .50
49 J.D. Drew .20 .50
50 Carlos Lee .20 .50
51 Ben Sheets .20 .50
52 Rickie Weeks .20 .50
53 Johan Santana .30 .75
54 Torii Hunter .20 .50
55 Joe Mauer .30 .75
56 Pedro Martinez .30 .75
57 David Wright .75 2.00
58 Carlos Beltran .20 .50
59 Carlos Delgado .20 .50
60 Jose Reyes .50 1.25
61 Derek Jeter 1.25 3.00
62 Alex Rodriguez .75 2.00
63 Randy Johnson .50 1.25
64 Hideki Matsui .50 1.25
65 Gary Sheffield .20 .50
66 Rich Harden .20 .50
67 Eric Chavez .20 .50
68 Huston Street .20 .50
69 Bobby Crosby .20 .50
70 Bobby Abreu .20 .50
71 Ryan Howard .75 2.00
72 Chase Utley .50 1.25
73 Pat Burrell .20 .50
74 Jason Bay .20 .50
75 Sean Casey .20 .50
76 Mike Piazza .50 1.25
77 Jake Peavy .20 .50
78 Brian Giles .20 .50
79 Milton Bradley .20 .50
80 Omar Vizquel .30 .75
81 Jason Schmidt .20 .50
82 Ichiro Suzuki .75 2.00
83 Felix Hernandez .30 .75
84 Kenji Johjima RC 1.00 2.50
85 Albert Pujols 1.00 2.50
86 Chris Carpenter .20 .50
87 Scott Rolen .30 .75
88 Jim Edmonds .30 .75
89 Carl Crawford .20 .50
90 Jonny Gomes .20 .50
91 Scott Kazmir .30 .75
92 Mark Teixeira .30 .75
93 Michael Young .20 .50
94 Phil Nevin .20 .50
95 Vernon Wells .20 .50
96 Roy Halladay .20 .50
97 Troy Glaus .20 .50
98 Alfonso Soriano .20 .50
99 Nick Johnson .20 .50
100 Jose Vidro .20 .50
101 Adam Wainwright AU/100 (RC) 15.00 40.00
102 Anderson Hernandez AU/100 (RC) EXCH 6.00 15.00
103 Andre Ethier AU/150 (RC) 12.50 30.00
104 Jason Botts AU/100 (RC) EXCH 6.00 15.00
105 Ben Johnson AU/400 (RC) 3.00 8.00
106 Boof Bonser AU/100 (RC) 6.00 15.00
107 Boone Logan AU/200 RC 4.00 10.00
108 Brian Anderson AU/200 (RC) 4.00 10.00
109 Brian Bannister AU/100 (RC) 8.00 20.00
110 Chris Denorfia AU/100 (RC) 4.00 10.00
111 Agustin Montero AU/100 (RC) 6.00 15.00
112 Cody Ross AU/100 (RC) 4.00 10.00
113 Cole Hamels AU/399 (RC) 20.00 50.00
114 Conor Jackson AU/400 (RC) 4.00 10.00
115 Dan Uggla AU/125 (RC) 12.50 30.00
116 Dave Gassner AU/100 (RC) 4.00 10.00
117 C.J. Wilson AU/150 (RC) 4.00 10.00
118 Eric Reed AU/150 (RC) 4.00 10.00
119 Fausto Carmona AU/99 (RC) 10.00 25.00
120 Fernando Nieve AU/100 (RC) 4.00 10.00
121 Francisco Liriano AU/499 (RC) 10.00 25.00
122 Freddie Bynum AU/100 (RC) 4.00 10.00
123 Hanley Ramirez AU/100 (RC) 15.00 40.00
124 Hong-Chih Kuo AU/100 (RC) 75.00 150.00
125 Ian Kinsler AU/100 (RC) 6.00 15.00
126 Carlos Marmol AU/100 RC 6.00 15.00
127 Bobby Keppel AU/200 (RC) 4.00 10.00
128 Jason Kubel AU/100 (RC) 6.00 15.00
129 Jeff Harris AU/100 RC 4.00 10.00
130 Alay Soler AU/100 RC 6.00 15.00
131 Jered Weaver AU/100 (RC) EXCH 10.00 25.00
132 Carlos Quentin AU/100 (RC) 12.50 30.00
133 Jeremy Hermida AU/100 (RC) 6.00 15.00
134 Joel Zumaya AU/100 (RC) 20.00 50.00
135 Joey Devine AU/100 RC 6.00 15.00
136 John Koronka AU/98 (RC) 4.00 10.00
137 Jonathan Papelbon AU/399 (RC) 15.00 40.00
138 Jose Capellan AU/240 (RC) 4.00 10.00
139 Josh Johnson AU/100 (RC) 6.00 15.00
140 Josh Rupe AU/100 (RC) EXCH 4.00 10.00
141 Josh Willingham AU/100 (RC) 4.00 10.00
143 Justin Verlander AU/100 (RC) 15.00 40.00
144 Kelly Shoppach AU/100 (RC) 6.00 15.00
145 Kendry Morales AU/100 (RC) EXCH 4.00 10.00
146 Kevin Thompson AU/100 (RC) 4.00 10.00
147 Macay McBride AU/100 (RC) 4.00 10.00
148 Martin Prado AU/100 (RC) EXCH 4.00 10.00
149 Matt Cain AU/150 (RC) EXCH 6.00 15.00
150 Clay Hensley AU/100 (RC) 4.00 10.00
151 Ty Taubenheim AU/100 RC 10.00 25.00
152 Mike Jacobs AU/200 (RC) 4.00 10.00
153 Saul Rivera AU/100 (RC) 4.00 10.00
154 Mike Thompson AU/100 RC 4.00 10.00
155 Nate McLouth AU/100 (RC) 10.00 25.00
156 Mike Vento AU/100 (RC) 4.00 10.00
157 Paul Maholm AU/200 (RC) 4.00 10.00
159 Reggie Abercrombie AU/100 (RC) 4.00 10.00
160 Mike Rouse AU/100 (RC) 4.00 10.00
161 Ken Ray AU/100 (RC) 4.00 10.00
162 Ron Flores AU/100 RC 4.00 10.00
163 Ryan Zimmerman AU/100 (RC) 30.00 60.00
164 Erick Aybar AU/100 (RC) 6.00 15.00
165 Sean Marshall AU/150 (RC) 8.00 20.00
166 Takashi Saito AU/100 RC EXCH
167 Taylor Buchholz AU/100 (RC) 4.00 10.00
168 Matt Murton AU/100 (RC) 12.50 30.00
169 Luis Figueroa AU/100 RC EXCH 6.00 15.00
170 Wil Nieves AU/100 (RC) 6.00 15.00
171 James Shields AU/100 RC 6.00 15.00
172 Jon Lester AU/399 RC 20.00 50.00
173 Craig Hansen AU/100 RC EXCH 12.50 30.00
174 Aaron Rakers AU/100 (RC) 4.00 10.00
175 Bobby Livingston AU/100 (RC) 6.00 15.00
176 Brendan Harris AU/100 (RC) 4.00 10.00
177 Zach Jackson AU/100 (RC) 6.00 15.00
178 Chris Britton AU/100 RC 4.00 10.00
179 Howie Kendrick AU/399 (RC) 10.00 25.00
180 Zach Miner AU/100 (RC) 6.00 15.00
181 Kevin Frandsen AU/100 (RC) 4.00 10.00
182 Matt Capps AU/100 (RC) 4.00 10.00
183 Peter Moylan AU/100 RC 4.00 10.00
184 Melky Cabrera AU/100 (RC) EXCH 20.00 50.00

2006 Sweet Spot Update Rookie Signatures Black Stitch Black Ink

OVERALL AUTO ODDS 1:6
STATED PRINT RUN 1 SERIAL #'d SET
NO PRICING DUE TO SCARCITY
EXCHANGE DEADLINE 12/19/09

2006 Sweet Spot Update Rookie Signatures Red-Blue Stitch Red Ink

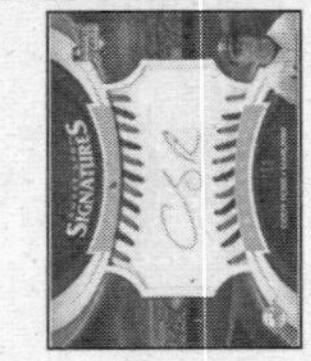

*RB p/r 175-225: .5X TO 1.2X RC p/r 399-499
*RB p/r 100: .6X TO 1.5X RC p/r 399-499
*RB p/r 100: .5X TO 1.2X RC p/r 150-240
*RB p/r 100: .4X TO 1X RC p/r 98-125
*RB p/r 50: .6X TO 1.5X RC p/r 150-240
*RB p/r 50: .5X TO 1.2X RC p/r 98-125
OVERALL AUTO ODDS 1:6
PRINT RUNS B/WN 50-225 COPIES PER
EXCHANGE DEADLINE 12/19/09
ASTERISK = PARTIAL EXCHANGE
124 Hong-Chih Kuo/50 150.00 250.00
164 Erick Aybar/50 10.00 25.00

2006 Sweet Spot Update Rookie Signatures Bat Barrel Black Ink

*BLK p/r 34-35: 1X TO 2.5X RC p/r 399-499
*BLK p/r 70: .5X TO 1.2X RC p/r 150-240
*BLK p/r 34-35: .75X TO 2X RC p/r 150-240
*BLK p/r 70: .6X TO 1.5X RC p/r 399-499
*BLK p/r 34-35: .6X TO 1.5X RC p/r 98-125
OVERALL AUTO ODDS 1:6
PRINT RUNS B/WN 34-70 COPIES PER
EXCHANGE DEADLINE 12/19/09
101 Adam Wainwright/35 20.00 50.00
103 Andre Ethier/35 EXCH 20.00 50.00
119 Fausto Carmona/35 20.00 50.00
124 Hong-Chih Kuo/35 200.00 250.00
137 Jonathan Papelbon/70 30.00 60.00

2006 Sweet Spot Update Rookie Signatures Bat Barrel Blue Ink

OVERALL AUTO ODDS 1:6
PRINT RUNS B/WN 9-20 PER
NO PRICING DUE TO SCARCITY
EXCHANGE DEADLINE 12/19/09

2006 Sweet Spot Update Rookie Signatures Bat Barrel Silver Ink

OVERALL AUTO ODDS 1:6
STATED PRINT RUN 1 SERIAL #'d SET
NO PRICING DUE TO SCARCITY
EXCHANGE DEADLINE 12/19/09

2006 Sweet Spot Update Rookie Signatures Glove Leather Black Ink

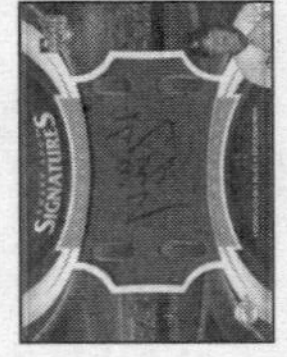

OVERALL AUTO ODDS 1:6
PRINT RUNS B/WN 20-40 PER
NO PRICING ON QTY OF 25 OR LESS
EXCHANGE DEADLINE 12/19/09
ASTERISK = PARTIAL EXCHANGE
113 Cole Hamels/40 EXCH * 30.00 60.00
121 Francisco Liriano/40 30.00 60.00
137 Jonathan Papelbon/40 40.00 80.00
172 Jon Lester/40 50.00 100.00
179 Howie Kendrick/40 15.00 40.00

2006 Sweet Spot Update Rookie Signatures Glove Leather Blue Ink

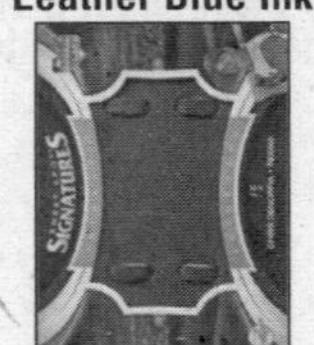

OVERALL AUTO ODDS 1:6
PRINT RUNS B/WN 5-10 PER
NO PRICING DUE TO SCARCITY
EXCHANGE DEADLINE 12/19/09

2006 Sweet Spot Update Rookie Signatures Glove Leather Silver Ink

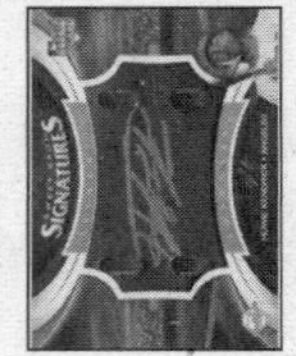

OVERALL AUTO ODDS 1:6
STATED PRINT RUN 1 SERIAL #'d SET
NO PRICING DUE TO SCARCITY
EXCHANGE DEADLINE 12/19/09

2006 Sweet Spot Update Announcer Signatures

OVERALL AUTO ODDS 1:6
PRINT RUNS B/WN 25-50 PER
CB Chris Berman/50 20.00 50.00
DP Dan Patrick/50 30.00 60.00
LC Linda Cohn/50 15.00 40.00
PG Peter Gammons/25 30.00 60.00
SS Stuart Scott/50 15.00 40.00

2006 Sweet Spot Update Dual Signatures

OVERALL AUTO ODDS 1:6
PRINT RUNS B/WN 1-55 PER
NO PRICING ON QTY OF 25 OR LESS
EXCHANGE DEADLINE 12/19/09
BL Boof Bonser
Francisco Liriano/5 EXCH
BN Taylor Buchholz 15.00 40.00
Fernando Nieve/55
CK Carl Crawford 15.00 40.00
Scott Kazmir/55 EXCH
CU Carl Crawford 15.00 40.00
B.J. Upton/45 EXCH
CV Roger Clemens
Justin Verlander/5
CW Chris Carpenter 30.00 60.00
Dontrelle Willis/35 EXCH
CZ Miguel Cabrera 40.00 80.00
Ryan Zimmerman/35 EXCH
EG Andre Ethier 15.00 40.00
Tony Gwynn Jr./35
GG Ken Griffey Jr. 75.00 150.00
Vladimir Guerrero/35 EXCH
GJ Ken Griffey Jr.
Michael Jordan/1
GT Ken Griffey Jr. 75.00 150.00
Jim Thome/35 EXCH
HC Jeremy Hermida
Melky Cabrera/5 EXCH
HD Howie Kendrick 15.00 40.00
Dan Uggla/35 EXCH
HJ Howie Kendrick
Jered Weaver/25
HK Jason Kubel 15.00 40.00
Jeremy Hermida/55
HL Francisco Liriano
Cole Hamels/15
HM Travis Hafner
Victor Martinez/35
HS Cole Hamels
Jeremy Sowers/35
HW Josh Willingham 15.00 40.00
Jeremy Hermida/55
ID Ian Kinsler
Dan Uggla/5 EXCH
IU Tadahito Iguchi
Chase Utley/35
JB Derek Jeter
Reggie Bush/5
JG Ken Griffey Jr.
Derek Jeter/5
JQ Conor Jackson
Carlos Quentin/5 EXCH
JS Josh Johnson
Alay Soler/5 EXCH
JW Josh Johnson
Dontrelle Willis/55 EXCH
KL Ken Griffey Jr.
LeBron James/5
KR Howie Kendrick
Brian Roberts/35
KU Scott Kazmir 15.00 40.00
B.J. Upton/55
KW Scott Kazmir 15.00 40.00
Dontrelle Willis/35
LN Francisco Liriano 40.00 80.00
Joe Nathan/35
MK Kendry Morales
Howie Kendrick/5 EXCH
ML Joe Mauer
Francisco Liriano/15
MM Justin Morneau 40.00 80.00
Joe Mauer/35 EXCH
MO Justin Morneau 20.00 50.00
Lyle Overbay/35 EXCH
MW Kendry Morales
Jered Weaver/5 EXCH
PL Jon Lester
Jonathan Papelbon/5 EXCH
PO Jake Peavy 15.00 40.00
Roy Oswalt/35 EXCH
PZ Jonathan Papelbon 50.00 100.00
Joel Zumaya/35
RO Alex Rios 15.00 40.00
Lyle Overbay/35 EXCH
RR Jose Reyes 30.00 60.00
Hanley Ramirez/35 EXCH
RU Hanley Ramirez
Dan Uggla/5 EXCH
SJ Josh Johnson
Jamie Shields/5 EXCH
SN Huston Street 15.00 40.00
Joe Nathan/35
TI Jim Thome 60.00 120.00
Tadahito Iguchi/35 EXCH
TJ Travis Hafner 20.00 50.00
Jeremy Sowers/35 EXCH
UD B.J. Upton 30.00 60.00
Stephen Drew/35 EXCH
UH Chase Utley 125.00 250.00
Cole Hamels/35
UU Chase Utley 40.00 80.00
Dan Uggla/35
UW Dan Uggla 15.00 40.00
Josh Willingham/55 EXCH
WL Jered Weaver
Francisco Liriano/10
ZJ Conor Jackson
Ryan Zimmerman/5 EXCH
ZU Ryan Zimmerman 30.00 60.00
B.J. Upton/35 EXCH

2006 Sweet Spot Update Spokesmen Signatures

OVERALL AUTO ODDS 1:6
PRINT RUNS B/WN 5-20 PER
NO PRICING DUE TO SCARCITY
EXCHANGE DEADLINE 12/19/09
1 Ken Griffey Jr. EXCH
2 Derek Jeter/15
5 Michael Jordan
Derek Jeter/5
6 Ken Griffey Jr.
Michael Jordan/5
7 Ken Griffey Jr.
Derek Jeter/5
8 Derek Jeter
LeBron James/5
9 Ken Griffey Jr.
LeBron James/5 EXCH
12 Derek Jeter
Reggie Bush/5 EXCH
13 Ken Griffey Jr.
Reggie Bush/5 EXCH
SP1 Ken Griffey Jr./20

2006 Sweet Spot Update Sweet Beginnings Swatches

OVERALL GU ODDS 1:12
NO SP PRICING DUE TO SCARCITY
AB Adrian Beltre 3.00 8.00
AE Andre Ethier SP
AI Akinori Iwamura 12.50 30.00
AJ Andruw Jones 4.00 10.00
AP Ariel Pestano 3.00 8.00
AR Alex Rios 3.00 8.00
AS Alfonso Soriano 3.00 8.00
BA Bobby Abreu 4.00 10.00
BB Brian Bannister 3.00 8.00
BI Chad Billingsley 4.00 10.00
BW Bernie Williams 4.00 10.00
CA Miguel Cabrera 6.00 15.00
CB Carlos Beltran 4.00 10.00
CD Carlos Delgado 3.00 8.00
CH Chin-Lung Hu 20.00 50.00
CJ Conor Jackson 4.00 10.00
CL Carlos Lee 3.00 8.00
CM Matt Cain 4.00 10.00
CR Craig Hansen SP
CU Chris Duncan 4.00 10.00
CZ Carlos Zambrano 3.00 8.00
DL Derrek Lee 3.00 8.00
DO David Ortiz 6.00 15.00
DU Dan Uggla SP
EB Erik Bedard 3.00 8.00
EP Eduardo Paret 3.00 8.00
FA Fausto Carmona 3.00 8.00
FC Frederich Cepeda 3.00 8.00
FL Francisco Liriano SP
GY Guogang Yang 3.00 8.00
HA Cole Hamels 6.00 15.00
HC Hee Seop Choi 3.00 8.00
HK Hong-Chih Kuo SP
HR Hanley Ramirez SP
HT Hitoshi Tamura 12.50 30.00
IK Ian Kinsler 6.00 15.00
IR Ivan Rodriguez 6.00 15.00
IS Ichiro Suzuki 100.00 200.00
JB Jason Bay 6.00 15.00
JD Johnny Damon 4.00 10.00
JF Jeff Francis 3.00 8.00
JH Jeremy Hermida 3.00 8.00
JJ Josh Johnson SP
JK Jason Kubel SP
JL Jong Beom Lee 3.00 8.00
JM Justin Morneau 6.00 15.00
JO Josh Barfield SP
JP Jin Man Park 3.00 8.00
JS Johan Santana 6.00 15.00
JV Jason Varitek 10.00 25.00
JZ Joel Zumaya 10.00 25.00
KE Matt Kemp 4.00 10.00
KG Ken Griffey Jr. 10.00 25.00
KJ Kenji Johjima SP
KM Kendry Morales SP
KU Koji Uehara 12.50 30.00
LE Jon Lester SP
LM Lastings Milledge SP
LO Javy Lopez 3.00 8.00
MA Moises Alou 3.00 8.00
MC Michael Collins 4.00 10.00
ME Michel Enriquez 3.00 8.00
MF Maikel Folch 3.00 8.00
MJ Mike Jacobs 3.00 8.00
MK Munenori Kawasaki 20.00 50.00
MN Mike Napoli 3.00 8.00
MO Michihiro Ogasawara 12.50 30.00
MP Mike Piazza 8.00 20.00
MS Min Han Son 4.00 10.00
MT Miguel Tejada 3.00 8.00
NI Nick Markakis SP
NM Nobuhiko Matsunaka 12.50 30.00
NS Naoyuki Shimizu 12.50 30.00
OU Osmany Urrutia 3.00 8.00
PA Jonathan Papelbon SP
PE Mike Pelfrey SP
PF Prince Fielder SP
PL Pedro Luis Lazo 3.00 8.00
PU Albert Pujols 12.50 30.00
RM Russell Martin SP
RN Ricky Nolasco SP
RO Alex Rodriguez 8.00 20.00
RZ Ryan Zimmerman SP
SH James Shields 3.00 8.00
SW Shunsuke Watanabe 12.50 30.00
TN Tsuyoshi Nishioka 15.00 40.00
TW Tsuyoshi Wada 15.00 40.00
VE Justin Verlander 6.00 15.00
VM Victor Martinez 6.00 15.00
VO Vicyohandry Odelin 3.00 8.00
WE Jered Weaver SP
WI Josh Willingham 3.00 8.00
WL Wei-Chu Lin 30.00 60.00
YG Yulieski Gourriel 6.00 15.00
YM Yunieski Maya 3.00 8.00

2006 Sweet Spot Update Sweet Beginnings Patches

OVERALL GU ODDS 1:12
PRICING FOR NON-LOGO PATCHES
NO SP PRICING DUE TO SCARCITY
AB Adrian Beltre 30.00 60.00
AE Andre Ethier 20.00 50.00
AI Akinori Iwamura SP
AJ Andruw Jones 20.00 50.00
AP Ariel Pestano 20.00 50.00
AR Alex Rios SP
AS Alfonso Soriano 60.00 120.00
BA Bobby Abreu 30.00 60.00
BB Brian Bannister 20.00 50.00
BI Chad Billingsley 20.00 50.00
BW Bernie Williams 60.00 120.00
CA Miguel Cabrera 30.00 60.00
CB Carlos Beltran 30.00 60.00
CD Carlos Delgado 40.00 80.00
CJ Conor Jackson 30.00 60.00
CL Carlos Lee 20.00 50.00
CM Matt Cain 40.00 80.00
CU Chris Duncan 20.00 50.00
CZ Carlos Zambrano 40.00 80.00
DL Derrek Lee 40.00 80.00
DO David Ortiz 40.00 80.00
DU Dan Uggla 20.00 50.00
EB Erik Bedard 30.00 60.00
EP Eduardo Paret 20.00 50.00
FA Fausto Carmona 20.00 50.00
FC Frederich Cepeda 20.00 50.00
FL Francisco Liriano 20.00 50.00
GY Guogan Yang SP
HA Cole Hamels 20.00 50.00
HK Hong-Chih Kuo 175.00 300.00
HT Hitoshi Tamura
IK Ian Kinsler
IR Ivan Rodriguez SP
IS Ichiro Suzuki
JB Jason Bay 20.00 50.00
JD Johnny Damon 20.00 50.00
JF Jeff Francis 20.00 50.00
JH Jeremy Hermida 20.00 50.00
JJ Josh Johnson 20.00 50.00
JL Jong Beom Lee SP
JM Justin Morneau
JO Josh Barfield 20.00 50.00
JP Jin Man Park SP
JS Johan Santana 50.00 100.00
JV Jason Varitek 20.00 50.00
JZ Joel Zumaya 30.00 60.00
KE Matt Kemp 20.00 50.00
KG Ken Griffey Jr. SP
KJ Kenji Johjima 125.00 250.00
KU Koji Uehara
LE Jon Lester 30.00 60.00
LM Lastings Milledge SP
LO Javy Lopez 20.00 50.00
MA Moises Alou SP
MC Michael Collins 20.00 50.00
ME Michel Enriquez 20.00 50.00
MF Maikel Folch 20.00 50.00
MJ Mike Jacobs 20.00 50.00
MK Munenori Kawasaki 200.00 300.00
MN Mike Napoli 20.00 50.00
MO Michihiro Ogasawara 150.00 250.00
MP Mike Piazza 60.00 120.00
MS Min Han Son SP
MT Miguel Tejada
NI Nick Markakis 30.00 60.00
NM Nobuhiko Matsunaka 40.00 80.00
NS Naoyuki Shimizu
OU Osmany Urrutia 30.00 60.00
PA Jonathan Papelbon 50.00 100.00
PE Mike Pelfrey 50.00 100.00
PF Prince Fielder SP
PL Pedro Luis Lazo 30.00 60.00
PU Albert Pujols
RM Russell Martin 30.00 60.00
RN Ricky Nolasco 20.00 50.00
RZ Ryan Zimmerman 30.00 60.00
SW Shunsuke Watanabe
TN Tsuyoshi Nishioka
TW Tsuyoshi Wada 150.00 300.00
VE Justin Verlander 30.00 60.00
VM Victor Martinez 30.00 60.00
VO Vicyohandry Odelin 20.00 50.00
WE Jered Weaver 20.00 50.00
WI Josh Willingham 20.00 50.00
WL Wei-Chu Lin SP
YG Yulieski Gourriel 50.00 100.00
YM Yunieski Maya 20.00 50.00

2006 Sweet Spot Update Veteran Signatures Red Stitch Blue Ink

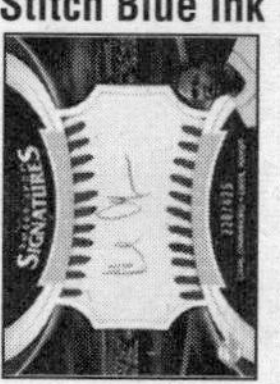

OVERALL AUTO ODDS 1:6
PRINT RUNS B/WN 30-525 COPIES PER
EXCHANGE DEADLINE 12/19/09
ASTERISK = PARTIAL EXCHANGE
AG Tony Gwynn Jr./425 6.00 15.00
AH Aaron Harang/425 5.00 12.00
AP Albert Pujols/30 175.00 300.00
AZ Aramis Ramirez/225 6.00 15.00
BJ B.J. Upton/193 10.00 25.00
BR Brian Roberts/300 6.00 15.00
CC Carl Crawford/425 6.00 15.00
CU Chase Utley/425 30.00 60.00
DJ Derek Jeter/75 125.00 250.00
DW Dontrelle Willis/125 8.00 20.00
HS Huston Street/200 6.00 15.00
JB Jason Bay/425 8.00 20.00
JM Joe Mauer/57 EXCH 15.00 40.00
JN Joe Nathan/200 6.00 15.00
JS Jeremy Sowers/425 6.00 15.00
JT Jim Thome/75 30.00 60.00
KG Ken Griffey Jr./50 60.00 120.00
KG2 Ken Griffey Jr./358 EXCH 30.00 60.00
KY Kevin Youkilis/425 8.00 20.00
LO Lyle Overbay/525 EXCH * 5.00 12.00
MC Miguel Cabrera/525 10.00 25.00
MO Justin Morneau/425 10.00 25.00
RC Roger Clemens/30 75.00 150.00
SD Stephen Drew/525 10.00 25.00
SK Scott Kazmir/522 8.00 20.00
SM John Smoltz/507 EXCH * 12.50 30.00
SP Scott Podsednik/247 5.00 12.00
SS Mark Mulder/300 5.00 12.00
TH Travis Hafner/525 6.00 15.00
TI Tadahito Iguchi/425 12.50 30.00
VM Victor Martinez/71 EXCH 10.00 25.00

2006 Sweet Spot Update Veteran Signatures Red-Blue Stitch Red Ink

*RBS: .5X TO 1.2X RED STITCH AU
OVERALL AUTO ODDS 1:6
PRINT RUNS B/WN 5-299 COPIES PER
NO PRICING ON QTY OF 25 OR LESS
EXCHANGE DEADLINE 12/19/09
ASTERISK = PARTIAL EXCHANGE
KG Ken Griffey Jr./38 50.00 100.00
KG2 Ken Griffey Jr./37 50.00 100.00

2006 Sweet Spot Update Veteran Signatures Black and White

APPX. ODDS 1 PER CASE
NO PRICING DUE TO SCARCITY
EXCHANGE DEADLINE 12/19/09

2006 Sweet Spot Update Veteran Signatures Black Stitch Black Ink

OVERALL AUTO ODDS 1:6
STATED PRINT RUN 1 SERIAL #'d SET
NO PRICING DUE TO SCARCITY
EXCHANGE DEADLINE 12/19/09

2006 Sweet Spot Update Veteran Signatures Bat Barrel Black Ink

COMMON CARD 12.50 30.00
OVERALL AUTO ODDS 1:6
PRINT RUNS B/WN 10-35 COPIES PER
NO PRICING ON QTY OF 25 OR LESS
EXCHANGE DEADLINE 12/19/09
BJ B.J. Upton/35 20.00 50.00
CU Chase Utley/35 60.00 120.00
KG Ken Griffey Jr./28 50.00 100.00
KG2 Ken Griffey Jr./27 EXCH 50.00 100.00
KY Kevin Youkilis/35 20.00 50.00
MC Miguel Cabrera/35 20.00 50.00
SD Stephen Drew/35 30.00 60.00
SM John Smoltz/35 20.00 50.00
TH Travis Hafner/35 20.00 50.00
TI Tadahito Iguchi/35 30.00 60.00

2006 Sweet Spot Update Veteran Signatures Bat Barrel Blue Ink

OVERALL AUTO ODDS 1:6
PRINT RUNS B/WN 1-20 PER
NO PRICING DUE TO SCARCITY
EXCHANGE DEADLINE 12/19/09

2006 Sweet Spot Update Veteran Signatures Bat Barrel Silver Ink

OVERALL AUTO ODDS 1:6
STATED PRINT RUN 1 SERIAL #'d SET
NO PRICING DUE TO SCARCITY
EXCHANGE DEADLINE 12/19/09

2006 Sweet Spot Update Veteran Signatures Glove Leather Black Ink

OVERALL AUTO ODDS 1:6
PRINT RUNS B/WN 5-20 PER
NO PRICING DUE TO SCARCITY
EXCHANGE DEADLINE 12/19/09

2006 Sweet Spot Update Veteran Signatures Glove Leather Blue Ink

OVERALL AUTO ODDS 1:6
PRINT RUNS B/WN 1-5 PER
NO PRICING DUE TO SCARCITY
EXCHANGE DEADLINE 12/19/09

2006 Sweet Spot Update Veteran Signatures Glove Leather Silver Ink

OVERALL AUTO ODDS 1:6
STATED PRINT RUN 1 SERIAL #'d SET
NO PRICING DUE TO SCARCITY
EXCHANGE DEADLINE 12/19/09

1911 T205 Gold Border

The cards in this 218-card set measure approximately 1 1/2" by 2 5/8". The T205 set (catalog designation), also known as the "Gold Border" set, was issued in 1911 in packages of the following cigarette brands: American Beauty, Broadleaf, Cycle, Drum, Hassan, Honest Long Cut, Piedmont, Polar Bear, Sovereign and Sweet Caporal. All the above were products of the American Tobacco Company, and the ads for the various brands appear below the biographical section on the back of each card. There are pose variations noted in the checklist (which is alphabetized and numbered for reference) and there are 12 minor league cards of a more ornate design which are somewhat scarce. The numbers below correspond to alphabetical order within category, i.e., major leaguers and minor leaguers are alphabetized separately. The gold borders of T205 cards chip easily and they are hard to find in "Mint" or even "Near Mint" condition, due to this there is a high premium on these high condition cards. Listed pricing for raw cards references "EX" condition.

COMPLETE SET (218) 25000.00 50000.00
COMMON (1-186) 90.00 150.00
COMMON (187-198) 150.00 300.00
1 Ed Abbaticchio 60.00 100.00
2 Doc Adkins 125.00 200.00
3 Red Ames 60.00 100.00
4 Jimmy Archer 60.00 100.00
5 Jimmy Austin 60.00 100.00
6 Bill Bailey 60.00 100.00
7 Home Run Baker 175.00 300.00
8 Neal Ball 60.00 100.00
9 Cy Barger 60.00 100.00
(Full B)
10 Cy Barger 250.00 400.00
Part B
11 Jack Barry 60.00 100.00
12 Emil Batch 125.00 200.00
13 Johnny Bates 60.00 100.00
14 Fred Beck 60.00 100.00
15 Beals Becker 60.00 100.00
16 George Bell 60.00 100.00
17 Chief Bender 175.00 300.00
18 Bill Bergen 60.00 100.00
19 Bob Bescher 60.00 100.00
20 Joe Birmingham 60.00 100.00
21 Russ Blackburne 60.00 100.00
22 Kitty Bransfield 60.00 100.00
23 Roger Bresnahan 175.00 300.00
(Mouth closed)
24 Roger Bresnahan 300.00 500.00
(Mouth open)
25 Al Bridwell 60.00 100.00
26 Mordecai Brown 175.00 300.00
27 Bobby Byrne 60.00 100.00
28 Hick Cady 150.00 250.00
29 Howie Camnitz 60.00 100.00
30 Bill Carrigan 60.00 100.00
31 Frank Chance 175.00 300.00
32A Hal Chase Both Ears 125.00 200.00
Border Ends at Shoulders
32B Hal Chase Both Ears 125.00 200.00
Border Extends Beyond Shoulders
33 Hal Chase Left Ear 300.00 500.00
34 Eddie Cicotte 250.00 400.00
35 Fred Clarke 150.00 250.00
36 Ty Cobb 2500.00 4000.00
37 Edward T. Collins 175.00 300.00
(Mouth closed)
38 Edward T. Collins 350.00 600.00
(Mouth open)
39 Jimmy Collins 250.00 400.00
40 Frank Corridon 60.00 100.00
41A Otis Crandall 150.00 250.00
T Crossed in name
41B Otis Crandall 90.00 150.00
T Not Crossed in Name
42 Lou Criger 60.00 100.00
43 Bill Dahlen 250.00 400.00
44 Jake Daubert 60.00 100.00
45 Jim Delahanty 60.00 100.00
46 Art Devlin 60.00 100.00
47 Josh Devore 60.00 100.00
48 Walt Dickson 60.00 100.00
49 Jiggs Donahue UER 250.00 400.00
(Misspelled Donohue on card)
50 Red Dooin 60.00 100.00
51 Mickey Doolan 60.00 100.00
52A Patsy Dougherty 150.00 250.00
(Red stocking)
52B Patsy Dougherty 150.00 250.00
(White stocking)
53 Tom Downey 60.00 100.00
54 Larry Doyle 60.00 100.00
55 Hugh Duffy 175.00 300.00
56 Jack Dunn 175.00 300.00
57 Jimmy Dygert 60.00 100.00
58 Dick Egan 60.00 100.00
59 Kid Elberfeld 60.00 100.00
60 Clyde Engle 60.00 100.00
61 Steve Evans 60.00 100.00
62 Johnny Evers 300.00 500.00
63 Bob Ewing 60.00 100.00
64 George Ferguson 60.00 100.00
65 Ray Fisher 175.00 300.00
66 Art Fletcher 60.00 100.00
67 John Flynn 60.00 100.00
68 Russell Ford 60.00 100.00
(Dark cap)
69 Russell Ford 250.00 400.00
(Light cap)
70 Bill Foxen 60.00 100.00
71 James Frick 150.00 250.00
72 Art Fromme 60.00 100.00
73 Earl Gardner 60.00 100.00
74 Harry Gaspar 60.00 100.00
75 George Gibson 60.00 100.00
76 William Goode 60.00 100.00
UER (Sic Good)
77 George F. Graham 250.00 400.00
(Chicago Cubs)
78 George F. Graham 60.00 100.00
(Boston Rustlers)
79 Eddie Grant 250.00 400.00
80A Dolly Gray 150.00 250.00
Stats on Back
80B Dolly Gray 600.00 1000.00
No stats on back
81 Clark Griffith 175.00 300.00
82 Bob Groom 60.00 100.00
83 Charles Hanford 150.00 250.00
84 Robert Harmon 60.00 100.00
(Both ears)
85 Robert Harmon 250.00 400.00
(Left ear only)
86 Topsy Hartsel 60.00 100.00
87 Arnold Hauser 60.00 100.00
88 Charlie Hemphill 60.00 100.00
89 Buck Herzog 60.00 100.00
90A Dick Hoblitzell 7000.00 12000.00
No Stats
90B Dick Hoblitzell 90.00 150.00
CIN after second 1908
90C Dick Hoblitzell 350.00 600.00
sic.Hoblitzel
90D Dick Hoblitzell 350.00 600.00
No CIN after second 1908
91 Danny Hoffman 60.00 100.00
92 Miller Huggins 175.00 300.00
93 John Hummell 60.00 100.00
94 Fred Jacklitsch 60.00 100.00
95 Hughie Jennings MG 175.00 300.00
96 Walter Johnson 1000.00 1800.00
97 Davy Jones 60.00 100.00
98 Tom Jones 60.00 100.00
99 Addie Joss 900.00 1500.00
100 Ed Karger 250.00 400.00
101 Ed Killian 60.00 100.00
102 Red Kleinow 250.00 400.00
103 John Kling 60.00 100.00
104 John Knight 60.00 100.00
105 Ed Konetchy 60.00 100.00
106 Harry Krause 60.00 100.00
107 Rube Kroh 60.00 100.00
108 Frank Lang 60.00 100.00
109 Frank LaPorte 60.00 100.00
110A Arlie Latham 125.00 200.00
A. Latham on back
110B Arlie Latham 250.00 400.00
Back says W.A. Latham
111 Tommy Leach 60.00 100.00
112 Wyatt Lee 90.00 150.00
113 Sam Leever 60.00 100.00
114A Lefty Leifield 150.00 250.00
A.Leifield on front
114B Lefty Leifield 250.00 400.00
A.P.Leifield on front
115 Ed Lennox 60.00 100.00
116 Paddy Livingston 60.00 100.00
117 Hans Lobert 60.00 100.00
118 Bris Lord 60.00 100.00
119 Harry Lord 60.00 100.00
120 John Lush 60.00 100.00
121 Nick Maddox 60.00 100.00
122 Sherry Magee 60.00 100.00
123 Rube Marquard 175.00 300.00
124 Christy Mathewson 1000.00 1800.00
125 Al Mattern 60.00 100.00
126 Lewis McAllister 90.00 150.00
127 George McBride 60.00 100.00
128 Amby McConnell 60.00 100.00
129 Pryor McElveen 60.00 100.00
130 John McGraw 175.00 300.00
131 Harry McIntire 60.00 100.00
132 Matty McIntyre 60.00 100.00
133 Larry McLean 60.00 100.00
134 Fred Merkle 60.00 100.00
135 George Merritt 150.00 250.00
136 Chief Meyers 60.00 100.00
137 Clyde Milan 60.00 100.00
138 Dots Miller 60.00 100.00
139 Mike Mitchell 60.00 100.00
140A Pat Moran 900.00 1500.00
Stray Line Under Stats
140B Pat Moran 60.00 100.00
No Stray Line
141 George Moriarity 60.00 100.00
142 George Mullin 60.00 100.00
143 Danny Murphy 60.00 100.00
144 Jack Murray 60.00 100.00
145 John Nee 150.00 250.00
146 Tom Needham 60.00 100.00
147 Rebel Oakes 60.00 100.00
148 Rube Oldring 60.00 100.00
149 Charley O'Leary 60.00 100.00
150 Fred Olmstead 60.00 100.00
151 Orval Overall 60.00 100.00
152 Freddy Parent 60.00 100.00
153 Dode Paskert 60.00 100.00
154 Fred Payne 60.00 100.00
155 Barney Pelty 60.00 100.00
156 Jack Pfiester 60.00 100.00
157 James Phelan 150.00 250.00
158 Ed Phelps 60.00 100.00
159 Decon Phillippe 60.00 100.00
160 Jack Quinn 60.00 100.00
161 Bugs Raymond 250.00 400.00
162 Ed Reulbach 60.00 100.00
163 Lewis Richie 60.00 100.00
164 Jack Rowan 175.00 300.00
165 George Rucker 60.00 100.00
166 W.D. Scanlan 250.00 400.00
167 Germany Schaefer 60.00 100.00
168 Admiral Schlei 60.00 100.00
169 Boss Schmidt 60.00 100.00
170 F.M. Schulte 60.00 100.00
171 Jim Scott 60.00 100.00
172 Bayard Sharpe 60.00 100.00
173 David Shean 175.00 300.00
(Chicago Cubs)
174 David Shean 60.00 100.00
(Boston Rustlers)
175 Jimmy Sheckard 60.00 100.00
176 Hack Simmons 60.00 100.00
177 Tony Smith 60.00 100.00
178 Fred Snodgrass 60.00 100.00
179 Tris Speaker 500.00 800.00
180 Jake Stahl 60.00 100.00
181 Oscar Stanage 60.00 100.00
182 Harry Steinfeldt 60.00 100.00
183 George Stone 60.00 100.00
184 George Stovall 60.00 100.00
185 Gabby Street 60.00 100.00
186 George Suggs 250.00 400.00
187 Ed Summers 60.00 100.00
188 Jeff Sweeney 250.00 400.00
189 Lee Tannehill 60.00 100.00
190 Ira Thomas 60.00 100.00
191 Joe Tinker 175.00 300.00
192 John Titus 60.00 100.00
193 Terry Turner 250.00 400.00
194 Hippo Vaughn 300.00 500.00
195 Heinie Wagner 175.00 300.00
196 Bobby Wallace 150.00 250.00
(With cap)
197A Bobby Wallace 1200.00 2000.00
no cap 1 line/1910
197B Bobby Wallace 700.00 1200.00
no cap 2 lines/1910
198 Ed Walsh 500.00 800.00
199 Zach Wheat 175.00 300.00
200 Doc White 60.00 100.00
201 Kirby White 250.00 400.00
202A Irvin K. Wilhelm 350.00 600.00
202B Irvin K. Wilhelm 175.00 300.00
Suffe ed in Bio
203 Ed Willett 60.00 100.00
204 Owen Wilson 60.00 100.00
205 Hooks Wiltse 60.00 100.00
(Both ears)
206 Hooks Wiltse 250.00 400.00
(Right ear only)
207 Harry Wolter 60.00 100.00
208 Cy Young 1000.00 1800.00

1909-11 T206

The T206 set was and is the most popular of all the tobacco issues. The set was issued from 1909 to 1911 with sixteen different brands of cigarettes: American Beauty, Broadleaf, Cycle, Carolina Brights, Drum, El Principe de Gales, Hindu, Lenox, Old Mill, Piedmont, Polar Bear, Sovereign, Sweet Caporal, Tolstoi, and Uzit. There was also an extremely rare Ty Cobb back version for the Ty Cobb Red Portrait that it's believed was issued as a promotional card. Pricing for the Cobb back card is unavailable and it's typically not considered part of the complete 524-card set. The minor league cards are supposedly slightly more difficult to obtain than the cards of the major leaguers, with the Southern League player cards being definitively more difficult. Minor League players were obtained from the American Association and the Eastern league. Southern League players were obtained from a variety of leagues including the following: South Atlantic League, Southern League, Texas League, and Virginia League. Series 150 (notated as such on the card backs) was issued between February 1909 thru the end of May, 1909. Series 350 was issued from the end of May, 1909 thru April, 1910. The last series 350 to 460 was issued in late December 1910 through early 1911. The set price below does not include ultra-expensive Wagner, Plank, Magie error, or Doyle variation. The Wagner card is one of the most sought after cards in the hobby. This card was pulled from circulation almost immediately after being issued. Estimates of how many Wagners are in existence generally settle on around 50 to 60 copies. The backs vary in scarcity as follows: Exceedingly Rare: Ty Cobb; Rare: Drum, Uzit, Lenox, Broadleaf 460 and Hindu; Scarce: Broadleaf 350, Carolina brights, Hindu Red; Less Common: American Beauty, Cycle and Tolstoi; Readily Available: El Principe de Gales, Old Mill, Polar Bear and Sovereign and Common: Piedmont and Sweet Caporal. Listed prices refer to the Piedmont and Sweet caporal backs in raw "EX" condition. Of note, the O'Hara St. Louis and Demmitt St. Louis cards were only issued with Polar Bear backs and are are priced as such. Pricing is unavailable for the unbelieveably rare Joe Doyle Nat'l variation (perhaps a dozen or fewer copies exist) in addition to the Bud Shappe and Fred nodgrass printing variaitons. Finally, unlike the other cards in this set, listed raw pricing for the famed Honus Wagner references "Good" condition insetad of "EX".

COMPLETE SET (520) 30000.00 55000.00
COMMON (1-389) 50.00 100.00
COMMON (390-475) 50.00 100.00
COMMON (476-523) 125.00 250.00
CARDS PRICED IN EXMT CONDITION
HONUS WAGNER PRICED IN GOOD CONDITION

1 Ed Abbaticchio 85.00 135.00
Blue Sleeves
2 Ed Abbaticchio 85.00 135.00
Brown Sleeves
3 Fred Abbott ML 60.00 100.00
4 Bill Abstein 60.00 100.00
5 Doc Adkins ML 125.00 200.00
6 Whitey Alperman 60.00 100.00
7 Red Ames 150.00 250.00
Hands at Chest
8 Red Ames 60.00 100.00
Hands over Head
9 Red Ames 60.00 100.00
Portrait
10 John Anderson ML 60.00 100.00
11 Frank Arellanes 60.00 100.00
12 Herman Armbruster ML 60.00 100.00
13 Harry Arndt ML 70.00 120.00
14 Jake Atz 60.00 100.00
15 Home Run Baker 250.00 400.00
16 Neal Ball 60.00 100.00
Cleveland
17 Neal Ball 60.00 100.00
New York
18 Jap Barbeau 60.00 100.00
19 Cy Barger ML 60.00 100.00
20 Jack Barry 60.00 100.00
21 Shad Barry ML 60.00 100.00
22 Jack Bastian SL 175.00 300.00
23 Emil Batch ML 60.00 100.00
24 Johnny Bates 60.00 100.00
25 Harry Bay SL 175.00 300.00
26 Ginger Beaumont 60.00 100.00
27 Fred Beck 60.00 100.00
28 Beals Becker 60.00 100.00
29 Jake Beckley ML 175.00 300.00
30 George Bell 60.00 100.00
Follow Through
31 George Bell 60.00 100.00
Hands above Head
32 Chief Bender 250.00 400.00
Pitching No Trees
33 Chief Bender 250.00 400.00
Pitching Trees in Back
34 Chief Bender 300.00 500.00
Portrait
35 Bill Bergen 60.00 100.00
Batting
36 Bill Bergen 60.00 100.00
Catching
37 Heinie Berger 60.00 100.00
38 Bill Bernhard SL 175.00 300.00
39 Bob Bescher 60.00 100.00
Hands in Air
40 Bob Bescher 60.00 100.00
Portrait
41 Joe Birmingham 90.00 150.00
Horizontal
42 Lena Blackburne ML 60.00 100.00
43 Jack Bliss 60.00 100.00
44 Frank Bowerman 60.00 100.00
45 Bill Bradley 60.00 100.00
with Bat
46 Bill Bradley 60.00 100.00
Portrait
47 Dave Brain ML 60.00 100.00
48 Kitty Bransfield 60.00 100.00
49 Roy Brashear ML 60.00 100.00
50 Ted Breitenstein SL 175.00 300.00
51 Roger Bresnahan 175.00 300.00
Portrait
52 Roger Bresnahan 175.00 300.00
with Bat
53 Al Bridwell 60.00 100.00
No Cap
54 Al Bridwell 60.00 100.00
with Cap
55 George Brown 125.00 200.00
Chicago
56 George Brown 300.00 500.00
Washington
57 Mordecai Brown 200.00 350.00
Chicago Shirt
58 Mordecai Brown 350.00 600.00
Cubs Shirt
59 Mordecai Brown 300.00 500.00
Portrait
60 Al Burch 125.00 200.00
Batting
61 Al Burch 60.00 100.00
Fielding
62 Fred Burchell ML 60.00 100.00
63 Jimmy Burke ML 60.00 100.00
64 Bill Burns 60.00 100.00
65 Donie Bush 60.00 100.00
66 John Butler ML 60.00 100.00
67 Bobby Byrne 60.00 100.00
68 Howie Camnitz 60.00 100.00
Arm at Side
69 Howie Camnitz 60.00 100.00
Arms Folded
70 Howie Camnitz 60.00 100.00
Hands above Head
71 Billy Campbell 60.00 100.00
72 Scoops Carey SL 175.00 300.00
73 Charley Carr ML 60.00 100.00
74 Bill Carrigan 60.00 100.00
75 Doc Casey ML 60.00 100.00
76 Peter Cassidy ML 60.00 100.00
77 Frank Chance 250.00 400.00
Batting
78 Frank Chance 300.00 500.00
Portrait Red
79 Frank Chance 250.00 400.00
Portrait Yellow
80 Bill Chappelle ML 60.00 100.00
81 Chappie Charles 60.00 100.00
82 Hal Chase 90.00 150.00
Throwing Dark Cap
83 Hal Chase 150.00 250.00
Holding Trophy
84 Hal Chase 90.00 150.00
Portrait Blue
85 Hal Chase 250.00 400.00
Portrait Pink
86 Hal Chase 125.00 200.00
Throwing White Cap
87 Jack Chesbro 250.00 400.00
88 Ed Cicotte 175.00 300.00
89 Bill Clancy (Clancey) ML 60.00 100.00
90 Fred Clarke 250.00 400.00
Holding Bat
91 Fred Clarke 250.00 400.00
Portrait
92 Josh Clark (Clarke) ML 60.00 100.00
93 J.J. (Nig) Clarke 60.00 100.00
94 Bill Clymer ML 60.00 100.00
95 Ty Cobb 1500.00 2500.00
Bat off Shoulder
96 Ty Cobb 1500.00 2500.00
Bat on Shoulder
97 Ty Cobb 3500.00 5000.00
Portrait Green
98 Ty Cobb 1200.00 2000.00
Portrait Red
99 Cad Coles 175.00 300.00
100 Eddie Collins 200.00 350.00
Philadelphia
101 Jimmy Collins 175.00 300.00
Minneapolis ML
102 Bunk Congalton ML 60.00 100.00
103 Wid Conroy 60.00 100.00
Fielding
104 Wid Conroy 60.00 100.00
with Bat
105 Harry Covaleski (Coveleski) 60.00 100.00
106 Doc Crandall 60.00 100.00
No Cap
107 Doc Crandall 60.00 100.00
with Cap
108 Bill Cranston SL 175.00 300.00
109 Gavvy Cravath ML 60.00 100.00
110 Sam Crawford 250.00 400.00
Throwing
111 Sam Crawford 250.00 400.00
with Bat
112 Birdie Cree 60.00 100.00
113 Lou Criger 60.00 100.00
114 Dode Criss 60.00 100.00
115 Monte Cross 60.00 100.00
116 Bill Dahlen 90.00 150.00
Boston
117 Bill Dahlen 300.00 500.00
Brooklyn
118 Paul Davidson ML 60.00 100.00
119 George Davis 175.00 300.00
120 Harry Davis 60.00 100.00
Davis on Front
121 Harry Davis 60.00 100.00
H.Davis on Front
122 Frank Delehanty 60.00 100.00
(Delahanty) ML
123 Jim Delehanty 60.00 100.00
124 Ray Demmitt 70.00 120.00
New York
125 Ray Demmitt 6000.00 10000.00
St. Louis
126 Rube Dessau ML 85.00 135.00
127 Art Devlin 60.00 100.00
128 Josh Devore 60.00 100.00
129 Bill Dineen 60.00 100.00
130 Mike Donlin 125.00 200.00
Fielding
131 Mike Donlin 60.00 100.00
Seated
132 Mike Donlin 60.00 100.00
with Bat
133 Jiggs Donahue (Donohue) 60.00 100.00
134 Wild Bill Donovan 60.00 100.00
Portrait
135 Wild Bill Donovan 60.00 100.00
Throwing
136 Red Dooin 60.00 100.00
137 Mickey Doolan 60.00 100.00
Batting
138 Mickey Doolan 60.00 100.00
Fielding
139 Mickey Doolin 60.00 100.00
Portrait (Doolan)
140 Gus Dorner ML 60.00 100.00
141 Gus Dorner
Card Spelled Dopner on Back
142 Patsy Dougherty
Arm in Air
143 Patsy Dougherty 60.00 100.00
Portrait
144 Tom Downey 60.00 100.00
Batting
145 Tom Downey 60.00 100.00
Fielding
146 Jerry Downs ML 60.00 100.00
147 Joe Doyle 350.00 600.00
Hands Above Head
148 Joe Doyle
Hands Above Head Nat'l
149 Larry Doyle Portrait 60.00 100.00
150 Larry Doyle 60.00 100.00
Throwing
151 Larry Doyle 60.00 100.00
with Bat
152 Jean Dubuc 60.00 100.00
153 Hugh Duffy 175.00 300.00
154 Jack Dunn 60.00 100.00
Baltimore ML
155 Joe Dunn 60.00 100.00
Brooklyn
156 Bull Durham 60.00 100.00
157 Jimmy Dygert 60.00 100.00
158 Ted Easterly 60.00 100.00
159 Dick Egan 90.00 150.00
160 Kid Elberfeld 60.00 100.00
Fielding
161 Kid Elberfeld 60.00 100.00
Portrait New York
162 Kid Elberfeld 1800.00 3000.00
Portrait Washington
163 Roy Ellam SL 175.00 300.00
164 Clyde Engle 60.00 100.00
165 Steve Evans 60.00 100.00
166 Johnny Evers 350.00 600.00
Portrait
167 Johnny Evers 250.00 400.00
with Bat Chicago Shirt
168 Johnny Evers 500.00 800.00
with Bat Cubs Shirt
169 Bob Ewing 60.00 100.00
170 Cecil Ferguson 60.00 100.00
171 Hobe Ferris 60.00 100.00
172 Lou Fiene 60.00 100.00
Portrait
173 Lou Fiene 60.00 100.00
Throwing
174 Steamer Flanagan ML 60.00 100.00
175 Art Fletcher 60.00 100.00
176 Elmer Flick 175.00 300.00
177 Russ Ford 60.00 100.00
178 Ed Foster SL 175.00 300.00
179 Jerry Freeman ML 60.00 100.00
180 John Frill 60.00 100.00
181 Charlie Fritz SL 175.00 300.00
182 Art Fromme 60.00 100.00
183 Chick Gandil 175.00 300.00
184 Bob Ganley 60.00 100.00
185 John Ganzel ML 60.00 100.00
186 Harry Gasper (Gaspar) 60.00 100.00
187 Rube Geyer 60.00 100.00
188 George Gibson 60.00 100.00
189 Billy Gilbert 60.00 100.00
190 Wilbur Goode (Good) 60.00 100.00
191 Bill Graham 60.00 100.00
St. Louis
192 Peaches Graham 70.00 120.00
Boston
193 Dolly Gray 60.00 100.00
194 Ed Greminger SL 175.00 300.00
195 Clark Griffith 175.00 300.00
Batting
196 Clark Griffith 175.00 300.00
Portrait
197 Moose Grimshaw ML 60.00 100.00
198 Bob Groom 60.00 100.00
199 Tom Guiheen SL 175.00 300.00
200 Ed Hahn 60.00 100.00
201 Bob Hall ML 60.00 100.00
202 Bill Hallman ML 60.00 100.00
203 Jack Hannifan 60.00 100.00
(Hannifin) ML
204 Bill Hart 175.00 300.00
Little Rock SL
205 Jimmy Hart 175.00 300.00
Montgomery SL
206 Topsy Hartsel 60.00 100.00
207 Jack Hayden ML 60.00 100.00
208 J.Ross Helm SL 175.00 300.00
209 Charlie Hemphill 60.00 100.00
210 Buck Herzog 60.00 100.00
Boston
211 Buck Herzog 60.00 100.00
New York
212 Gordon Hickman SL 175.00 300.00
213 Bill Hinchman 60.00 100.00
Cleveland
214 Harry Hinchman 60.00 100.00
Toledo ML
215 Doc Hoblitzell 60.00 100.00
216 Danny Hoffman 60.00 100.00
St. Louis
217 Izzy Hoffman 60.00 100.00
Providence ML
218 Solly Hofman 60.00 100.00
219 Bock Hooker SL 175.00 300.00
220 Del Howard 60.00 100.00
Chicago
221 Ernie Howard 175.00 300.00
Savannah SL
222 Harry Howell 60.00 100.00
Hand at Waist
223 Harry Howell 60.00 100.00
Portrait
224 Miller Huggins 175.00 300.00
Hands at Mouth
225 Miller Huggins 175.00 300.00
Portrait
226 Rudy Hulswitt 60.00 100.00
227 John Hummel 60.00 100.00
228 George Hunter 60.00 100.00
229 Frank Isbell 60.00 100.00
230 Fred Jacklitsch 60.00 100.00
231 Jimmy Jackson ML 60.00 100.00
232 Hughie Jennings 175.00 300.00
Both Hands Showing
233 Hughie Jennings 175.00 300.00
One Hand Showing
234 Hughie Jennings 175.00 300.00
Portrait
235 Walter Johnson 700.00 1200.00
Hands at Chest
236 Walter Johnson 1000.00 1800.00
Portrait
237 Davy Jones 60.00 100.00
Detroit
238 Fielder Jones 60.00 100.00
Hands at Hips
239 Fielder Jones 60.00 100.00
Portrait
240 Tom Jones 60.00 100.00
St. Louis
241 Dutch Jordan 175.00 300.00
Atlanta SL
242 Tim Jordan 60.00 100.00
Brooklyn Batting
243 Tim Jordan 60.00 100.00
Brooklyn Portrait
244 Addie Joss 175.00 300.00
Pitching
245 Addie Joss 250.00 400.00
Portrait
246 Ed Karger 60.00 100.00
247 Willie Keeler 350.00 600.00
Portrait
248 Willie Keeler 350.00 600.00
with Bat
249 Joe Kelley ML 150.00 250.00
250 J.F. Kiernan SL 300.00 500.00
251 Ed Killian 60.00 100.00
Pitching
252 Ed Killian 60.00 100.00
Portrait
253 Frank King SL 175.00 300.00
254 Rube Kisinger 60.00 100.00
(Kissinger) ML
255 Red Kleinow 300.00 500.00
Boston
256 Red Kleinow 60.00 100.00
New York Catching
257 Red Kleinow 60.00 100.00
New York with Bat
258 Johnny Kling 60.00 100.00
259 Otto Knabe 60.00 100.00
260 Jack Knight 60.00 100.00
Portrait
261 Jack Knight 60.00 100.00
with Bat
262 Ed Konetchy 60.00 100.00
Glove Near Ground
263 Ed Konetchy 60.00 100.00
Glove Above Head
264 Harry Krause 60.00 100.00
Pitching
265 Harry Krause 60.00 100.00
Portrait
266 Rube Kroh 60.00 100.00
267 Otto Kruger 60.00 100.00
(Krueger) ML
268 James LaFitte SL 175.00 300.00
269 Nap Lajoie 500.00 800.00
Portrait
270 Nap Lajoie 400.00 700.00
Throwing
271 Nap Lajoie 400.00 700.00
with Bat
272 Joe Lake 60.00 100.00
New York
273 Joe Lake 60.00 100.00
St. Louis No Ball
274 Joe Lake 60.00 100.00
St. Louis with Ball
275 Frank LaPorte 60.00 100.00
276 Arlie Latham 60.00 100.00
277 Bill Lattimore ML 60.00 100.00
278 Jimmy Lavender ML 60.00 100.00
279 Tommy Leach 60.00 100.00
Bending Over
280 Tommy Leach 60.00 100.00
Portrait
281 Lefty Leifield 60.00 100.00
Batting
282 Lefty Leifield 60.00 100.00
Pitching
283 Ed Lennox 60.00 100.00
284 Harry Lentz 250.00 400.00
(Sentz) SL
285 Glenn Liebhardt 60.00 100.00
286 Vive Lindaman 60.00 100.00
287 Perry Lipe SL 175.00 300.00
288 Paddy Livingstone 60.00 100.00
(Livingston)
289 Hans Lobert 60.00 100.00
290 Harry Lord 60.00 100.00
291 Harry Lumley 60.00 100.00
292 Carl Lundgren 500.00 800.00
Chicago
293 Carl Lundgren 125.00 200.00
Kansas City ML
294 Nick Maddox 60.00 100.00
294 Sherry Magie 15000.00 25000.00
Portrait ERR (Magee)
295 Sherry Magee 60.00 100.00
with Bat
296 Sherry Magee 150.00 250.00
Portrait
298 Bill Malarkey ML 60.00 100.00
299 Billy Maloney ML 60.00 100.00
300 George Manion SL 175.00 300.00
301 Rube Manning 60.00 100.00
Batting
302 Rube Manning 60.00 100.00
Pitching
303 Rube Marquard 175.00 300.00
Follow Through
304 Rube Marquard 175.00 300.00
Hands at Thighs
305 Rube Marquard 200.00 350.00
Portrait
306 Doc Marshall 60.00 100.00
307 Christy Mathewson 700.00 1200.00
Dark Cap
308 Christy Mathewson 900.00 1500.00
Portrait
309 Christy Mathewson 900.00 1500.00
White Cap
310 Al Mattern 60.00 100.00
311 John McAleese 60.00 100.00
312 George McBride 60.00 100.00
313 Pat McCauley SL 175.00 300.00
314 Moose McCormick 60.00 100.00
315 Pryor McElveen 60.00 100.00
316 Dan McGann ML 60.00 100.00
317 Jim McGinley ML 60.00 100.00
318 Iron Man McGinnity ML 175.00 300.00
319 Stoney McGlynn ML 60.00 100.00
320 John McGraw 250.00 400.00
Finger in Air
321 John McGraw 250.00 400.00
Glove at Hip
322 John McGraw 250.00 400.00
Portrait No Cap
323 John McGraw 250.00 400.00
Portrait with Cap
324 Harry McIntyre 60.00 100.00
Brooklyn
325 Harry McIntyre 60.00 100.00
Brooklyn-Chicago
326 Matty McIntyre 60.00 100.00
Detroit
327 Larry McLean 60.00 100.00
328 George McQuillan 60.00 100.00
Ball in Hand
329 George McQuillan 60.00 100.00
with Bat
330 Fred Merkle Portrait 70.00 120.00
331 Fred Merkle Throwing 90.00 150.00
332 George Merritt ML 60.00 100.00
333 Chief Meyers 60.00 100.00
334 Chief Myers 70.00 120.00
Batting (Meyers)
335 Chief Myers 60.00 100.00
Fielding (Meyers)
336 Clyde Milan 60.00 100.00
337 Molly Miller 175.00 300.00
Dallas SL
338 Dots Miller 60.00 100.00
Pittsburgh
339 Bill Milligan ML 60.00 100.00
340 Fred Mitchell 60.00 100.00
Toronto ML
341 Mike Mitchell 60.00 100.00
Cincinnati
342 Dan Moeller ML 60.00 100.00
343 Carleton Molesworth SL 175.00 300.00
344 Herbie Moran 60.00 100.00
Providence ML
345 Pat Moran 60.00 100.00
Chicago
346 George Moriarty 60.00 100.00
347 Mike Mowrey 60.00 100.00
348 Dom Mullaney SL 175.00 300.00
349 George Mullen 60.00 100.00
(Mullin)
350 George Mullin 60.00 100.00
with Bat
351 George Mullin 60.00 100.00
Throwing Horizontal
352 Danny Murphy 60.00 100.00
Batting
353 Danny Murphy 60.00 100.00
Throwing
354 Red Murray 60.00 100.00
Batting
355 Red Murray 60.00 100.00
Portrait
356 Billy Nattress ML 60.00 100.00
357 Tom Needham 60.00 100.00
358 Simon Nicholls 60.00 100.00
Hands on Knees
359 Simon Nichols 60.00 100.00
Batting (Nicholls)
360 Harry Niles 60.00 100.00
361 Rebel Oakes 60.00 100.00
362 Frank Oberlin ML 60.00 100.00
363 Peter O'Brien ML 60.00 100.00
364 Bill O'Hara 60.00 100.00
New York
365 Bill O'Hara 6000.00 10000.00
St. Louis
366 Rube Oldring 60.00 100.00
Batting
367 Rube Oldring 60.00 100.00
Fielding
368 Charley O'Leary 60.00 100.00
Hands on Knees
369 Charley O'Leary 60.00 100.00
Portrait
370 William O'Neil ML 150.00 250.00
371 Al Orth SL 175.00 300.00
372 William Otey SL 175.00 300.00
373 Orval Overall 60.00 100.00
Hand at Face
374 Orval Overall 60.00 100.00
Hands at Waist
375 Orval Overall 60.00 100.00
Portrait
376 Frank Owen (Owens) 60.00 100.00
377 George Paige SL 175.00 300.00
378 Freddy Parent 60.00 100.00
379 Dode Paskert 60.00 100.00
380 Jim Pastorius 60.00 100.00
381 Harry Pattee 60.00 100.00
382 Fred Payne 60.00 100.00
383 Barney Pelty 60.00 100.00
Horizontal
384 Barney Pelty 60.00 100.00
Vertical
385 Hub Perdue SL 175.00 300.00
386 George Perring 60.00 100.00
387 Arch Persons SL 175.00 300.00
388 Jeff Pfeffer 60.00 100.00
389 Jake Pfeister 60.00 100.00
Seated (Pfiester)
390 Jake Pfeister 60.00 100.00
Throwing (Pfiester)
391 Jimmy Phelan ML 60.00 100.00
392 Ed Phelps 60.00 100.00
393 Deacon Phillippe. 60.00 100.00
394 Ollie Pickering ML 60.00 100.00
395 Eddie Plank 45000.00 60000.00
396 Phil Poland ML 60.00 100.00
397 Jack Powell 60.00 100.00
Horizontal
398 Mike Powers 60.00 100.00
399 Billy Purtell 60.00 100.00
400 Ambrose Puttman 85.00 135.00
(Puttmann) ML
401 Lee Quillen 60.00 100.00
(Quillin) ML
402 Jack Quinn 60.00 100.00
403 Newt Randall ML 60.00 100.00
404 Bugs Raymond 60.00 100.00
405 Ed Reagan SL 175.00 300.00
406 Ed Reulbach 60.00 100.00
Glove Showing
407 Ed Reulbach 70.00 120.00
No Glove
408 Dutch Revelle SL 175.00 300.00
409 Bob Rhoades 60.00 100.00
Hands at Chest
410 Bob Rhoades 60.00 100.00
Right Arm Out
411 Charlie Rhodes 60.00 100.00
412 Claude Ritchey 60.00 100.00
413 Lou Ritter ML 60.00 100.00
414 Ike Rockenfeld SL 175.00 300.00
415 Claude Rossman 60.00 100.00
416 Nap Rucker 60.00 100.00
Portrait
417 Nap Rucker 60.00 100.00
Throwing
418 Dick Rudolph ML 60.00 100.00
419 Ray Ryan SL 175.00 300.00
420 Germany Schaefer 60.00 100.00
Detroit
421 Germany Schaefer 60.00 100.00
Washington
422 George Schirm ML 85.00 135.00
423 Larry Schlafly ML 60.00 100.00
424 Admiral Schlei 60.00 100.00
Batting
425 Admiral Schlei 60.00 100.00
Catching
426 Admiral Schlei 60.00 100.00
Portrait
427 Boss Schmidt 60.00 100.00
Portrait
428 Boss Schmidt 60.00 100.00
Throwing
429 Ossee Schreck 70.00 120.00
(Schreckengost) ML
430 Wildfire Schulte 60.00 100.00
Back View
431 Wildfire Schulte 175.00 300.00
Front View
432 Jim Scott 60.00 100.00
433 Charles Seitz SL 175.00 300.00
434 Cy Seymour 60.00 100.00
Batting
435 Cy Seymour 60.00 100.00
Portrait
436 Cy Seymour 60.00 100.00
Throwing
437 Spike Shannon ML 60.00 100.00
438 Bud Sharpe ML 60.00 100.00
439 Bud Shappe ERR
(Sharpe) ML
440 Frank Shaughnessy SL 175.00 300.00
441 Al Shaw 60.00 100.00
St. Louis
442 Hunky Shaw 60.00 100.00
Providence ML
443 Jimmy Sheckard 60.00 100.00
Glove Showing
444 Jimmy Sheckard 60.00 100.00
No Glove
445 Bill Shipke 60.00 100.00
446 Jimmy Slagle ML 60.00 100.00
447 Carlos Smith 175.00 300.00
Shreveport SL
448 Frank Smith 350.00 600.00
Chicago-Boston
449 Frank Smith 60.00 100.00
Chicago
Listed as F.Smith
450 Frank Smith 60.00 100.00
Chicago
Listed as Smith
White Cap
451 Heinie Smith 60.00 100.00
Buffalo ML
452 Happy Smith 60.00 100.00
Brooklyn
453 Sid Smith 175.00 300.00
Atlanta SL
454 Fred Snodgrass 60.00 100.00
Batting
455 Fred nodgrass
Batting ERR (Missing S)
456 Fred Snodgrass 60.00 100.00
Catching
457 Bob Spade 60.00 100.00
458 Tris Speaker 600.00 1000.00
459 Tubby Spencer 60.00 100.00
460 Jake Stahl 85.00 135.00
Glove Shows
461 Jake Stahl 60.00 100.00
No Glove Shows
462 Oscar Stanage 60.00 100.00
463 Dolly Stark SL 175.00 300.00
464 Charlie Starr 60.00 100.00
465 Harry Steinfeldt 60.00 100.00
with Bat
466 Harry Steinfeldt 60.00 100.00
Portrait
467 Jim Stephens 60.00 100.00
468 George Stone 60.00 100.00
469 George Stovall 60.00 100.00
Batting
470 George Stovall 60.00 100.00
Portrait
471 Sam Strang ML 60.00 100.00
472 Gabby Street 60.00 100.00
Catching
473 Gabby Street 60.00 100.00
Portrait
474 Billy Sullivan 60.00 100.00
475 Ed Summers 60.00 100.00
476 Bill Sweeney 60.00 100.00
Boston
477 Jeff Sweeney 60.00 100.00
New York
478 Jesse Tannehill 60.00 100.00

Card	Low	High
Washington		
479 Lee Tannehill Chicago L.Tannehill	60.00	100.00
480 Lee Tannehill Chicago Tannehill	60.00	100.00
481 Dummy Taylor ML	60.00	100.00
482 Fred Tenney	60.00	100.00
483 Tony Thebo SL	175.00	300.00
484 Jake Thielman ML	90.00	150.00
485 Ira Thomas	60.00	100.00
486 Woodie Thornton SL	175.00	300.00
487 Joe Tinker Bat off Shoulder	250.00	400.00
488 Joe Tinker Bat on Shoulder	400.00	400.00
489 Joe Tinker Hands on Knees	350.00	600.00
490 Joe Tinker Portrait	350.00	600.00
491 John Titus	60.00	100.00
492 Terry Turner	60.00	100.00
493 Bob Unglaub	60.00	100.00
494 Juan Violat (Viola) SL	175.00	300.00
495 Rube Waddell Portrait	250.00	400.00
496 Rube Waddell Throwing	250.00	400.00
497 Heinie Wagner Bat on Left Shoulder	60.00	100.00
498 Heinie Wagner Bat on Right Shoulder	60.00	100.00
499 Honus Wagner	200000.00	300000.00
500 Bobby Wallace	175.00	300.00
501 Ed Walsh	250.00	400.00
502 Jack Warhop	60.00	100.00
503 Jake Weimer	60.00	100.00
504 James Westlake SL	175.00	300.00
505 Zack Wheat	200.00	350.00
506 Doc White Chicago Pitching	60.00	100.00
507 Doc White Chicago Portrait	60.00	100.00
509 Jack White Buffalo ML	60.00	100.00
510 Kaiser Wilhelm Hands at Chest	60.00	100.00
511 Kaiser Wilhelm with Bat	60.00	100.00
512 Ed Willett with Bat	60.00	100.00
513 Ed Willetts Throwing (Willett)	60.00	100.00
514 Jimmy Williams	60.00	100.00
515 Vic Willis Pittsburgh Portrait	200.00	350.00
516 Vic Willis St. Louis Throwing	175.00	300.00
517 Vic Willis St. Louis with Bat	175.00	300.00
518 Owen Wilson	60.00	100.00
519 Hooks Wiltse Pitching	60.00	100.00
520 Hooks Wiltse Portrait No Cap	60.00	100.00
521 Hooks Wiltse Portrait with Cap	60.00	100.00
522 Lucky Wright ML	60.00	100.00
523 Cy Young Bare Hand Shows	700.00	1200.00
524 Cy Young Glove Shows	700.00	1200.00
525 Cy Young Portrait	1000.00	1800.00
526 Irv Young Minneapolis ML	70.00	120.00
527 Heinie Zimmerman:	60.00	100.00
527 Foley White Houston SL	175.00	300.00

2004 Throwback Threads

This 250-card set was released in August, 2004. The set was issued in five-card packs with an $4 SRP which came 24 packs to a box and 20 boxes to a case. Cards numbered 1-200 feature active veterans while cards numbered 201 through 224 feature retired players and cards 225 through 250 feature a mix of Rookie Cards and leading prospects. All cards numbered 201 through 250 were random inserts in packs and were issued to a stated print run of 1000 serial numbered sets.

Card	Low	High
COMP.SET w/o SP's (200)	15.00	40.00
COMMON CARD (1-200)	.10	.30
COMMON RETIRED (201-224)	.75	2.00
COMMON ROOKIE (225-250)	1.25	3.00
1 Bartolo Colon	.10	.30
2 Darin Erstad	.10	.30
3 David Eckstein	.10	.30
4 Garret Anderson	.10	.30
5 Tim Salmon	.20	.50
6 Troy Glaus	.10	.30
7 Vladimir Guerrero	.30	.75
8 Brandon Webb	.10	.30
9 Luis Gonzalez	.10	.30
10 Randy Johnson	.30	.75
11 Richie Sexson	.10	.30
12 Roberto Alomar	.20	.50
13 Shea Hillenbrand	.10	.30
14 Steve Finley	.10	.30
15 Adam LaRoche	.10	.30
16 Andruw Jones	.20	.50
17 Chipper Jones	.30	.75
18 J.D. Drew	.10	.30
19 John Smoltz	.20	.50
20 Rafael Furcal	.10	.30
21 Russ Ortiz	.10	.30
22 Javy Lopez	.10	.30
23 Jay Gibbons	.10	.30
24 Larry Bigbie	.10	.30
25 Luis Matos	.10	.30
26 Melvin Mora	.10	.30
27 Miguel Tejada	.20	.50
28 Rafael Palmeiro	.20	.50
29 Curt Schilling	.20	.50
30 David Ortiz	.30	.75
31 Derek Lowe	.10	.30
32 Jason Varitek	.30	.75
33 Johnny Damon	.20	.50
34 Manny Ramirez	.20	.50
35 Nomar Garciaparra	.30	.75
36 Pedro Martinez	.20	.50
37 Trot Nixon	.10	.30
38 Aramis Ramirez	.10	.30
39 Corey Patterson	.10	.30
40 Derrek Lee	.20	.50
41 Greg Maddux	.50	1.25
42 Kerry Wood	.10	.30
43 Mark Prior	.20	.50
44 Sammy Sosa	.30	.75
45 Carlos Lee	.10	.30
46 Esteban Loaiza	.10	.30
47 Frank Thomas	.30	.75
48 Joe Borchard	.10	.30
49 Magglio Ordonez	.10	.30
50 Mark Buehrle	.10	.30
51 Paul Konerko	.10	.30
52 Adam Dunn	.10	.30
53 Austin Kearns	.10	.30
54 Barry Larkin	.20	.50
55 Brandon Larson	.10	.30
56 Ken Griffey Jr.	.50	1.25
57 Ryan Wagner	.10	.30
58 Sean Casey	.10	.30
59 C.C. Sabathia	.10	.30
60 Jody Gerut	.10	.30
61 Omar Vizquel	.20	.50
62 Travis Hafner	.10	.30
63 Victor Martinez	.10	.30
64 Charles Johnson	.10	.30
65 Garrett Atkins	.10	.30
66 Jason Jennings	.10	.30
67 Joe Kennedy	.10	.30
68 Larry Walker	.20	.50
69 Preston Wilson	.10	.30
70 Todd Helton	.20	.50
71 Ivan Rodriguez	.20	.50
72 Jeremy Bonderman	.10	.30
73 A.J. Burnett	.10	.30
74 Brad Penny	.10	.30
75 Dontrelle Willis	.20	.50
76 Josh Beckett	.10	.30
77 Juan Pierre	.10	.30
78 Luis Castillo	.10	.30
79 Miguel Cabrera	.20	.50
80 Mike Lowell	.10	.30
81 Andy Pettitte	.20	.50
82 Craig Biggio	.20	.50
83 Jeff Bagwell	.20	.50
84 Jeff Kent	.10	.30
85 Lance Berkman	.10	.30
86 Morgan Ensberg	.10	.30
87 Richard Hidalgo	.10	.30
88 Roger Clemens	.50	1.25
89 Roy Oswalt	.10	.30
90 Wade Miller	.10	.30
91 Angel Berroa	.10	.30
92 Carlos Beltran	.10	.30
93 Juan Gonzalez	.10	.30
94 Ken Harvey	.10	.30
95 Mike Sweeney	.10	.30
96 Runelvys Hernandez	.10	.30
97 Adrian Beltre	.10	.30
98 Edwin Jackson	.10	.30
99 Eric Gagne	.10	.30
100 Hideo Nomo	.30	.75
101 Hong-Chih Kuo	.10	.30
102 Kazuhisa Ishii	.10	.30
103 Paul Lo Duca	.10	.30
104 Shawn Green	.10	.30
105 Ben Sheets	.10	.30
106 Geoff Jenkins	.10	.30
107 Junior Spivey	.10	.30
108 Rickie Weeks	.10	.30
109 Scott Podsednik	.10	.30
110 Corey Koskie	.10	.30
111 Doug Mientkiewicz	.10	.30
112 Jacque Jones	.10	.30
113 Joe Mays	.10	.30
114 Johan Santana	.30	.75
115 Shannon Stewart	.10	.30
116 Torii Hunter	.10	.30
117 Brad Wilkerson	.10	.30
118 Carl Everett	.10	.30
119 Chad Cordero	.10	.30
120 Jose Vidro	.10	.30
121 Nick Johnson	.10	.30
122 Orlando Cabrera	.10	.30
123 Al Leiter	.10	.30
124 Cliff Floyd	.10	.30
125 Jae Weong Seo	.10	.30
126 Jose Reyes	.10	.30
127 Mike Cameron	.10	.30
128 Mike Piazza	.30	.75
129 Tom Glavine	.20	.50
130 Alex Rodriguez	.50	1.25
131 Bernie Williams	.20	.50
132 Chien-Ming Wang	.50	1.25
133 Derek Jeter	.60	1.50
134 Gary Sheffield	.10	.30
135 Hideki Matsui	.50	1.25
136 Jason Giambi	.10	.30
137 Javier Vazquez	.10	.30
138 Jorge Posada	.20	.50
139 Jose Contreras	.10	.30
140 Kevin Brown	.10	.30
141 Mariano Rivera	.30	.75
142 Mike Mussina	.20	.50
143 Barry Zito	.10	.30
144 Bobby Crosby	.10	.30
145 Eric Chavez	.10	.30
146 Erubial Durazo	.10	.30
147 Jermaine Dye	.10	.30
148 Mark Kotsay	.10	.30
149 Mark Mulder	.10	.30
150 Rich Harden	.10	.30
151 Tim Hudson	.10	.30
152 Billy Wagner	.10	.30
153 Bobby Abreu	.10	.30
154 Brett Myers	.10	.30
155 Jim Thome	.20	.50
156 Jimmy Rollins	.10	.30
157 Kevin Millwood	.10	.30
158 Marlon Byrd	.10	.30
159 Pat Burrell	.10	.30
160 Jason Bay	.10	.30
161 Jason Kendall	.10	.30
162 Brian Giles	.10	.30
163 Jay Payton	.10	.30
164 Ryan Klesko	.10	.30
165 Edgardo Alfonzo	.10	.30
166 Jason Schmidt	.10	.30
167 Jerome Williams	.10	.30
168 Todd Linden	.10	.30
169 Bret Boone	.10	.30
170 Edgar Martinez	.20	.50
171 Freddy Garcia	.10	.30
172 Ichiro Suzuki	.60	1.50
173 Jamie Moyer	.10	.30
174 John Olerud	.10	.30
175 Shigetoshi Hasegawa	.10	.30
176 Albert Pujols	.60	1.50
177 Dan Haren	.10	.30
178 Edgar Renteria	.10	.30
179 Jim Edmonds	.10	.30
180 Matt Morris	.10	.30
181 Scott Rolen	.20	.50
182 Aubrey Huff	.10	.30
183 Carl Crawford	.10	.30
184 Chad Gaudin	.10	.30
185 Delmon Young	.20	.50
186 Dewon Brazelton	.10	.30
187 Fred McGriff	.20	.50
188 Rocco Baldelli	.10	.30
189 Alfonso Soriano	.10	.30
190 Hank Blalock	.10	.30
191 Laynce Nix	.10	.30
192 Mark Teixeira	.20	.50
193 Michael Young	.10	.30
194 Carlos Delgado	.10	.30
195 Eric Hinske	.10	.30
196 Frank Catalanotto	.10	.30
197 Josh Phelps	.10	.30
198 Orlando Hudson	.10	.30
199 Roy Halladay	.10	.30
200 Vernon Wells	.10	.30
201 Dale Murphy RET	1.25	3.00
202 Cal Ripken RET	5.00	12.00
203 Fred Lynn RET	.75	2.00
204 Wade Boggs RET	1.25	3.00
205 Nolan Ryan RET	3.00	8.00
206 Rod Carew RET	1.25	3.00
207 Andre Dawson RET	.75	2.00
208 Ernie Banks RET	1.25	3.00
209 Ryne Sandberg RET	2.50	6.00
210 Bo Jackson RET	1.25	3.00
211 Carlton Fisk RET	1.25	3.00
212 Dave Concepcion RET	.75	2.00
213 Alan Trammell RET	.75	2.00
214 George Brett RET	2.50	6.00
215 Robin Yount RET	1.25	3.00
216 Gary Carter RET	.75	2.00
217 Darryl Strawberry RET	.75	2.00
218 Dwight Gooden RET	.75	2.00
219 Babe Ruth RET	2.50	6.00
220 Don Mattingly RET	2.50	6.00
221 Reggie Jackson RET	1.25	3.00
222 Mike Schmidt RET	2.50	6.00
223 Tony Gwynn RET	2.00	5.00
224 Keith Hernandez RET	.75	2.00
225 Hector Gimenez ROO RC	1.25	3.00
226 Graham Koonce ROO	1.25	3.00
227 John Gall ROO RC	2.00	5.00
228 Jerry Gil ROO RC	1.25	3.00
229 Jason Frasor ROO RC	1.25	3.00
230 Justin Knoedler ROO RC	1.25	3.00
231 Ivan Ochoa ROO RC	1.25	3.00
232 Greg Dobbs ROO RC	1.25	3.00
233 Ronald Belisario ROO RC	1.25	3.00
234 Jerome Gamble ROO RC	1.25	3.00
235 Roberto Novoa ROO RC	1.25	3.00
236 Sean Henn ROO RC	1.25	3.00
237 Willy Taveras ROO RC	2.00	5.00
238 Ramon Ramirez ROO RC	1.25	3.00
239 Kazuo Matsui ROO RC	2.00	5.00
240 Akinori Otsuka ROO RC	1.25	3.00
241 Jason Bartlett ROO RC	2.00	5.00
242 Fernando Nieve ROO RC	2.00	5.00
243 Freddy Guzman ROO RC	1.25	3.00
244 Aarom Baldiris ROO RC	2.00	5.00
245 Merkin Valdez ROO RC	2.00	5.00
246 Mike Gosling ROO RC	1.25	3.00
247 Shingo Takatsu ROO RC	2.00	5.00
248 William Bergolla ROO RC	1.25	3.00
249 Shawn Hill ROO RC	1.25	3.00
250 Justin Germano ROO RC	1.25	3.00

2004 Throwback Threads Gold Proof

*GOLD 1-200: 3X TO 8X BASIC
*GOLD 201-224: .75X TO 2X BASIC
*GOLD 225-250: .5X TO 1.2X BASIC
RANDOM INSERTS IN PACKS
STATED PRINT RUN 100 SERIAL #'d SETS

2004 Throwback Threads Green Proof

*GREEN 1-200: 8X TO 20X BASIC
*GREEN 201-224: 2.5X TO 6X BASIC
RANDOM INSERTS IN RETAIL PACKS
STATED PRINT RUN 25 SERIAL #'d SETS
NO PRICING ON 225-250 DUE TO SCARCITY

2004 Throwback Threads Platinum Proof

RANDOM INSERTS IN PACKS
STATED PRINT RUN 10 SERIAL #'d SETS
NO PRICING DUE TO SCARCITY

2004 Throwback Threads Silver Proof

*SILVER 1-200: 3X TO 8X BASIC
*SILVER 201-224: .75X TO 2X BASIC
*SILVER 225-250: .5X TO 1.2X BASIC
RANDOM INSERTS IN RETAIL PACKS
STATED PRINT RUN 100 SERIAL #'d SETS

2004 Throwback Threads Material

OVERALL AU-GU ODDS 1:8
PRINT RUNS B/WN 25-100 COPIES PER

Card	Low	High
2 Darin Erstad Jsy/100	2.00	5.00
4 Garret Anderson Jsy/100	2.00	5.00
5 Tim Salmon Jsy/100	3.00	8.00
6 Troy Glaus Jsy/100	2.00	5.00
7 Vladimir Guerrero Bat/100	4.00	10.00
8 Brandon Webb Pants/100	2.00	5.00
9 Luis Gonzalez Jsy/100	2.00	5.00
10 Randy Johnson Jsy/100	4.00	10.00
11 Richie Sexson Bat/50	3.00	8.00
12 Roberto Alomar Bat/100	3.00	8.00
14 Steve Finley Jsy/100	2.00	5.00
15 Adam LaRoche Bat/100	2.00	5.00
16 Andruw Jones Jsy/100	3.00	8.00
17 Chipper Jones Jsy/100	4.00	10.00
18 J.D. Drew Bat/100	2.00	5.00
19 John Smoltz Jsy/100	3.00	8.00
20 Rafael Furcal Jsy/100	2.00	5.00
22 Javy Lopez Bat/100	2.00	5.00
23 Jay Gibbons Jsy/100	2.00	5.00
24 Larry Bigbie Jsy/100	2.00	5.00
25 Luis Matos Jsy/100	2.00	5.00
26 Melvin Mora Jsy/100	2.00	5.00
27 Miguel Tejada Bat/100	2.00	5.00
28 Rafael Palmeiro Jsy/100	3.00	8.00
29 Curt Schilling Bat/100	3.00	8.00
30 David Ortiz Bat/100	4.00	10.00
32 Jason Varitek Jsy/100	4.00	10.00
33 Johnny Damon Bat/100	3.00	8.00
34 Manny Ramirez Jsy/100	3.00	8.00
35 Nomar Garciaparra Jsy/100	5.00	12.00
36 Pedro Martinez Jsy/100	3.00	8.00
37 Trot Nixon Bat/100	2.00	5.00
38 Aramis Ramirez Jsy/100	2.00	5.00
39 Corey Patterson Pants/100	2.00	5.00
41 Greg Maddux Bat/100	5.00	12.00
42 Kerry Wood Pants/100	2.00	5.00
43 Mark Prior Jsy/100	2.00	5.00
44 Sammy Sosa Jsy/100	4.00	10.00
45 Carlos Lee Jsy/100	2.00	5.00
47 Frank Thomas Pants/100	4.00	10.00
48 Joe Borchard Jsy/100	2.00	5.00
49 Magglio Ordonez Jsy/100	2.00	5.00
50 Mark Buehrle Jsy/100	2.00	5.00
51 Paul Konerko Jsy/100	2.00	5.00
52 Adam Dunn Jsy/100	2.00	5.00
53 Austin Kearns Jsy/100	2.00	5.00
54 Barry Larkin Jsy/100	3.00	8.00
55 Brandon Larson Fld Glv/100	2.00	5.00
58 Sean Casey Jsy/100	2.00	5.00
59 C.C. Sabathia Jsy/100	2.00	5.00
60 Jody Gerut Jsy/100	2.00	5.00
61 Omar Vizquel Jsy/100	3.00	8.00
62 Travis Hafner Jsy/100	2.00	5.00
63 Victor Martinez Bat/100	2.00	5.00
64 Charles Johnson Bat/100	2.00	5.00
65 Garrett Atkins Jsy/100	2.00	5.00
66 Jason Jennings Jsy/100	2.00	5.00
67 Joe Kennedy Bat/100	2.00	5.00
68 Larry Walker Jsy/100	2.00	5.00
69 Preston Wilson Jsy/100	2.00	5.00
70 Todd Helton Jsy/100	3.00	8.00
71 Ivan Rodriguez Bat/100	3.00	8.00
72 Jeremy Bonderman Jsy/100	2.00	5.00
73 A.J. Burnett Jsy/100	2.00	5.00
74 Brad Penny Jsy/100	2.00	5.00
75 Dontrelle Willis Jsy/100	3.00	8.00
76 Josh Beckett Jsy/100	2.00	5.00
77 Juan Pierre Bat/100	2.00	5.00
78 Luis Castillo Jsy/100	2.00	5.00
79 Miguel Cabrera Jsy/100	3.00	8.00
80 Mike Lowell Jsy/50	3.00	8.00
81 Andy Pettitte Bat/100	3.00	8.00
82 Craig Biggio Jsy/100	3.00	8.00
83 Jeff Bagwell Jsy/100	3.00	8.00
84 Jeff Kent Jsy/100	2.00	5.00
85 Lance Berkman Jsy/100	2.00	5.00
86 Morgan Ensberg Jsy/100	2.00	5.00
87 Richard Hidalgo Pants/100	2.00	5.00
88 Roger Clemens Bat/50	8.00	20.00
89 Roy Oswalt Jsy/100	2.00	5.00
90 Wade Miller Jsy/100	2.00	5.00
91 Angel Berroa Pants/100	2.00	5.00
92 Carlos Beltran Jsy/100	2.00	5.00
93 Juan Gonzalez Bat/100	2.00	5.00
94 Ken Harvey Bat/100	2.00	5.00
95 Mike Sweeney Jsy/100	2.00	5.00
96 Runelvys Hernandez Jsy/100	2.00	5.00
97 Adrian Beltre Jsy/100	2.00	5.00
98 Edwin Jackson Jsy/100	2.00	5.00
100 Hideo Nomo Jsy/100	4.00	10.00
101 Hong-Chih Kuo Bat/100	2.00	5.00
102 Kazuhisa Ishii Jsy/100	2.00	5.00
103 Paul Lo Duca Jsy/100	2.00	5.00
104 Shawn Green Jsy/100	2.00	5.00
105 Ben Sheets Jsy/100	2.00	5.00
106 Geoff Jenkins Jsy/100	2.00	5.00
107 Junior Spivey Bat/50	3.00	8.00
108 Rickie Weeks Bat/50	3.00	8.00
111 Doug Mientkiewicz Bat/100	2.00	5.00
112 Jacque Jones Jsy/100	2.00	5.00
113 Joe Mays Jsy/100	2.00	5.00
114 Johan Santana Jsy/100	3.00	8.00
115 Shannon Stewart Jsy/100	2.00	5.00
116 Torii Hunter Jsy/100	2.00	5.00
117 Brad Wilkerson Bat/100	2.00	5.00
118 Carl Everett Bat/100	2.00	5.00
120 Jose Vidro Jsy/100	2.00	5.00
121 Nick Johnson Bat/100	2.00	5.00
122 Orlando Cabrera Jsy/100	2.00	5.00
123 Al Leiter Jsy/100	2.00	5.00
124 Cliff Floyd Bat/100	2.00	5.00
125 Jae Weong Seo Jsy/100	2.00	5.00
126 Jose Reyes Jsy/100	2.00	5.00
128 Mike Piazza Jsy/100	5.00	12.00
129 Tom Glavine Jsy/100	3.00	8.00
130 Alex Rodriguez Bat/100	5.00	12.00
131 Bernie Williams Jsy/100	3.00	8.00
133 Derek Jeter Jsy/100	10.00	25.00
134 Gary Sheffield Bat/100	2.00	5.00
135 Hideki Matsui Jsy/100	12.50	30.00
136 Jason Giambi Jsy/100	2.00	5.00
138 Jorge Posada Jsy/100	3.00	8.00
141 Mariano Rivera Jsy/50	6.00	15.00
142 Mike Mussina Jsy/100	3.00	8.00
143 Barry Zito Jsy/100	2.00	5.00
145 Eric Chavez Jsy/100	2.00	5.00
146 Erubial Durazo Bat/100	2.00	5.00
147 Jermaine Dye Bat/100	2.00	5.00
149 Mark Mulder Jsy/100	2.00	5.00
150 Rich Harden Jsy/100	2.00	5.00
151 Tim Hudson Jsy/100	2.00	5.00
153 Bobby Abreu Jsy/100	2.00	5.00
154 Brett Myers Jsy/100	2.00	5.00
155 Jim Thome Jsy/100	3.00	8.00
157 Kevin Millwood Jsy/100	2.00	5.00
158 Marlon Byrd Jsy/100	2.00	5.00
159 Pat Burrell Jsy/100	2.00	5.00
161 Jason Kendall Jsy/100	2.00	5.00
162 Brian Giles Bat/100	2.00	5.00
164 Ryan Klesko Jsy/100	2.00	5.00
165 Edgardo Alfonzo Bat/100	2.00	5.00
167 Jerome Williams Jsy/100	2.00	5.00
169 Bret Boone Jsy/29		
170 Edgar Martinez Jsy/100	3.00	8.00
171 Freddy Garcia Jsy/100	2.00	5.00
173 Jamie Moyer Jsy/100	2.00	5.00
174 John Olerud Jsy/100	2.00	5.00
176 Albert Pujols Jsy/100	8.00	20.00
177 Dan Haren Jsy/100	2.00	5.00
178 Edgar Renteria Jsy/100	2.00	5.00
179 Jim Edmonds Jsy/100	2.00	5.00
180 Matt Morris Jsy/100	2.00	5.00
181 Scott Rolen Jsy/100	3.00	8.00
182 Aubrey Huff Jsy/100	2.00	5.00
183 Carl Crawford Jsy/100	2.00	5.00
184 Chad Gaudin Jsy/100	2.00	5.00
185 Delmon Young Bat/100	3.00	8.00
186 Dewon Brazelton Jsy/100	2.00	5.00
187 Fred McGriff Jsy/100	3.00	8.00
188 Rocco Baldelli Jsy/100	2.00	5.00
189 Alfonso Soriano Bat/100	2.00	5.00
190 Hank Blalock Jsy/100	2.00	5.00
191 Laynce Nix Bat/100	2.00	5.00
192 Mark Teixeira Jsy/23	8.00	20.00
193 Michael Young Bat/100	2.00	5.00
194 Carlos Delgado Jsy/100	2.00	5.00
195 Eric Hinske Jsy/100	2.00	5.00
196 Frank Catalanotto Jsy/100	2.00	5.00
197 Josh Phelps Jsy/100	2.00	5.00
198 Orlando Hudson Jsy/100	2.00	5.00
199 Roy Halladay Jsy/100	2.00	5.00
200 Vernon Wells Jsy/100	2.00	5.00
201 Dale Murphy RET Jsy/100	5.00	12.00
202 Cal Ripken RET Jsy/100	15.00	40.00
203 Fred Lynn RET Bat/100	3.00	8.00
204 Wade Boggs RET Jsy/100	5.00	12.00
205 Nolan Ryan RET Jkt/100	10.00	25.00
206 Rod Carew RET Jkt/100	5.00	12.00
207 A.Dawson RET Pants/100	3.00	8.00
208 Ernie Banks RET Pants/50	8.00	20.00
209 Ryne Sandberg RET Jsy/50	12.50	30.00
210 Bo Jackson RET Jsy/100	6.00	15.00
211 Carlton Fisk RET Jkt/100	5.00	12.00
212 D.Concepcion RET Jsy/100	3.00	8.00
213 Alan Trammell RET Bat/100	3.00	8.00
214 George Brett RET Jsy/100	8.00	20.00
215 Robin Yount RET Jsy/100	4.00	10.00
216 Gary Carter RET Jsy/100	3.00	8.00
217 D.Straw RET Pants/100	3.00	8.00
218 Dwight Gooden RET Jsy/50	4.00	10.00
219 Babe Ruth RET Jsy/25	450.00	600.00
220 Don Mattingly RET Jkt/100	6.00	15.00
221 R.Jackson RET Jkt/100	5.00	12.00
222 Mike Schmidt RET Jkt/100	8.00	20.00
223 Tony Gwynn RET Jsy/100	6.00	15.00
224 K.Hernandez RET Jsy/100	3.00	8.00

2004 Throwback Threads Material Prime

*PRIME p/r 25: 1.25X TO 3X BASIC p/r 100
*PRIME p/r 25: .75X TO 2X BASIC p/r 50
OVERALL AU-GU ODDS 1:8
PRINT RUNS B/WN 5-25 COPIES PER
NO PRICING ON QTY OF 10 OR LESS
156 Jimmy Rollins Jsy/25

2004 Throwback Threads Material Combo

*COMBO p/r 50: .75X TO 2X BASIC p/r 100
*COMBO p/r 50: .6X TO 1.5X BASIC p/r 50
*COMBO p/r 50: .4X TO 1X BASIC p/r 23-29
*COMBO p/r 25: 1X TO 2.5X BASIC p/r 100
*COMBO p/r 25: .75X TO 2X BASIC p/r 50
OVERALL AU-GU ODDS 1:8
PRINT RUNS B/WN 10-50 COPIES PER
NO PRICING ON QTY OF 10 OR LESS
MOST COMBOS FEATURE BAT-JSY

2004 Throwback Threads Material Combo Prime

*COMBO PR p/r 24-25: 1.5X TO 4X p/r 100
*COMBO PR p/r 24-25: 1X TO 2.5X p/r 23
*COMBO PR p/r 15-17: 2X TO 5X p/r 100
OVERALL AU-GU ODDS 1:8
PRINT RUNS B/WN 5-25 COPIES PER
NO PRICING ON QTY OF 12 OR LESS

2004 Throwback Threads Signature Marks

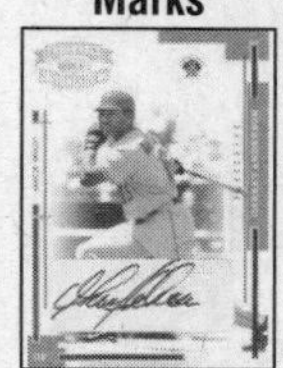

OVERALL AU-GU ODDS 1:8
PRINT RUNS B/WN 5-200 COPIES PER
1-224 NO PRICING ON QTY OF 10 OR LESS
225-250 NO PRICING ON QTY OF 25 OR LESS

Card	Low	High
4 Garret Anderson/25	10.00	25.00
7 Vladimir Guerrero/5		
8 Brandon Webb/50	5.00	12.00
10 Randy Johnson/5		
12 Roberto Alomar/5		
13 Shea Hillenbrand/50	8.00	20.00
14 Steve Finley/5		
15 Adam LaRoche/50	5.00	12.00
16 Andruw Jones/5		
17 Chipper Jones/5		
20 Rafael Furcal/25	10.00	25.00
23 Jay Gibbons/50	5.00	12.00
24 Larry Bigbie/50	8.00	20.00
25 Luis Matos/50	5.00	12.00
26 Melvin Mora/50	8.00	20.00
29 Curt Schilling/5		
30 David Ortiz/25	30.00	60.00
32 Jason Varitek/5		
34 Manny Ramirez/5		
37 Trot Nixon/5		
38 Aramis Ramirez/5		
40 Derrek Lee/25	15.00	40.00
42 Kerry Wood/5		
43 Mark Prior/25	12.50	30.00
44 Sammy Sosa/5		
45 Carlos Lee/50	8.00	20.00
46 Esteban Loaiza/50	5.00	12.00

47 Frank Thomas/5
48 Joe Borchard/25 6.00 15.00
49 Magglio Ordonez/5
50 Mark Buehrle/25 15.00 40.00
52 Adam Dunn/5
53 Austin Kearns/25 6.00 15.00
54 Barry Larkin/5
55 Brandon Larson/25 6.00 15.00
57 Ryan Wagner/5
60 Jody Gerut/50 5.00 12.00
62 Travis Hafner/50 8.00 20.00
63 Victor Martinez/50 8.00 20.00
67 Joe Kennedy/5
69 Preston Wilson/50 8.00 20.00
70 Todd Helton/5
74 Brad Penny/50 5.00 12.00
75 Dontrelle Willis/5
76 Josh Beckett/5
78 Luis Castillo/5
79 Miguel Cabrera/25 15.00 40.00
80 Mike Lowell/25 10.00 25.00
81 Andy Pettitte/5
82 Craig Biggio/5
83 Jeff Bagwell/5
85 Lance Berkman/5
86 Morgan Ensberg/50 8.00 20.00
89 Roy Oswalt/25
91 Angel Berroa/25 6.00 15.00
92 Carlos Beltran/25 10.00 25.00
93 Juan Gonzalez/5
98 Edwin Jackson/50 5.00 12.00
100 Hideo Nomo/5
101 Hong-Chih Kuo/50 20.00 50.00
102 Kazuhisa Ishii/5
103 Paul Lo Duca/10
104 Shawn Green/5
107 Junior Spivey/10
109 Scott Podsednik/50 12.50 30.00
112 Jacque Jones/50 8.00 20.00
114 Johan Santana/25 15.00 40.00
115 Shannon Stewart/25 10.00 25.00
116 Torii Hunter/25 10.00 25.00
119 Chad Cordero/50 8.00 20.00
120 Jose Vidro/25 6.00 15.00
121 Nick Johnson/5
122 Orlando Cabrera/50 8.00 20.00
125 Jae Weong Seo/5
126 Jose Reyes/10
128 Mike Piazza/5
130 Alex Rodriguez/5
131 Bernie Williams/5
132 Chien-Ming Wang/25 125.00 200.00
134 Gary Sheffield/5
137 Javier Vazquez/5
138 Jorge Posada/5
139 Jose Contreras/5
143 Barry Zito/5
145 Eric Chavez/5
147 Jermaine Dye/50 8.00 20.00
149 Mark Mulder/10
150 Rich Harden/5
151 Tim Hudson/5
154 Brett Myers/5
160 Jason Bay/50 8.00 20.00
163 Jay Payton/50 5.00 12.00
167 Jerome Williams/5
168 Todd Linden/50 5.00 12.00
170 Edgar Martinez/5
175 Shigetoshi Hasegawa/25 40.00 80.00
176 Albert Pujols/5
177 Dan Haren/50
179 Jim Edmonds/5
181 Scott Rolen/25 15.00 40.00
182 Aubrey Huff/50 8.00 20.00
184 Chad Gaudin/50 5.00 12.00
185 Delmon Young/5
186 Dewon Brazelton/50 5.00 12.00
187 Fred McGriff/25 30.00 60.00
188 Rocco Baldelli/5
189 Alfonso Soriano/25 15.00 40.00
190 Hank Blalock/25
192 Mark Teixeira/5
193 Michael Young/50 8.00 20.00
197 Josh Phelps/5
198 Orlando Hudson/5
199 Roy Halladay/5
200 Vernon Wells/10
202 Cal Ripken RET/5
203 Fred Lynn RET/50 5.00 12.00
204 Wade Boggs RET/5
205 Nolan Ryan RET/5
206 Rod Carew RET/5
207 Andre Dawson RET/50 8.00 20.00
208 Ernie Banks RET/5
209 Ryne Sandberg RET/5
210 Bo Jackson RET/5
211 Carlton Fisk RET/5
212 Dave Concepcion RET/10
213 Alan Trammell RET/25
214 George Brett RET/5
215 Robin Yount RET/5
216 Gary Carter RET/25 10.00 25.00
217 Darryl Strawberry RET/50 8.00 20.00
218 Dwight Gooden RET/50 8.00 20.00
220 Don Mattingly RET/5
221 Reggie Jackson RET/5
222 Mike Schmidt RET/5
223 Tony Gwynn RET/5
224 Keith Hernandez RET/50 8.00 20.00
225 Hector Gimenez ROO/100 3.00 8.00
226 Graham Koonce ROO/100 3.00 8.00
227 John Gall ROO/25
228 Jerry Gil ROO/100 4.00 10.00
229 Jason Frasor ROO/100 4.00 10.00
230 Justin Knoedler ROO/50 6.00 15.00
231 Ivan Ochoa ROO/25
232 Greg Dobbs ROO/25
233 Ronald Belisario ROO/200 4.00 10.00
234 Jerome Gamble ROO/200 3.00 8.00
235 Roberto Novoa ROO/200 3.00 8.00
236 Sean Henn ROO/200 4.00 10.00
237 Willy Taveras ROO/100 12.50 30.00
238 Ramon Ramirez ROO/200 4.00 10.00
241 Jason Bartlett ROO/25
242 Fernando Nieve ROO/25
243 Freddy Guzman ROO/25
244 Aarom Baldiris ROO/25
245 Merkin Valdez ROO/25
246 Mike Gosling ROO/25
247 Shingo Takatsu ROO/25
248 William Bergolla ROO/100 4.00 10.00
249 Shawn Hill ROO/100 4.00 10.00
250 Justin Germano ROO/100 4.00 10.00

2004 Throwback Threads Blast From the Past

STATED PRINT RUN 1500 SERIAL #'d SETS
*SPECTRUM: .75X TO 2X BASIC
SPECTRUM PRINT RUN 100 #'d SETS
RANDOM INSERTS IN PACKS
1 Albert Pujols 2.50 6.00
2 Alex Rodriguez 2.00 5.00
3 Babe Ruth 2.50 6.00
4 Cal Ripken 4.00 10.00
5 Carlton Fisk 1.25 3.00
6 Eddie Mathews 1.25 3.00
7 Eddie Murray 1.25 3.00
8 Ernie Banks 1.25 3.00
9 Frank Robinson .75 2.00
10 George Foster .75 2.00
11 Harmon Killebrew 1.25 3.00
12 Jim Rice .75 2.00
13 Jim Thome 1.25 3.00
14 Johnny Bench 1.25 3.00
15 Jose Canseco 1.25 3.00
16 Juan Gonzalez .75 2.00
17 Ken Griffey Jr. 2.00 5.00
18 Mike Piazza 2.00 5.00
19 Mike Schmidt 2.50 6.00
20 Reggie Jackson 1.25 3.00
21 Roger Maris 1.25 3.00
22 Sammy Sosa 1.25 3.00
23 Stan Musial 2.00 5.00
24 Willie McCovey 1.25 3.00
25 Willie Stargell 1.25 3.00

2004 Throwback Threads Blast From the Past Material Bat

OVERALL AU-GU ODDS 1:8
PRINT RUNS B/WN 50-250 COPIES PER
1 Albert Pujols/250 6.00 15.00
2 Alex Rodriguez/250 4.00 10.00
3 Babe Ruth/50 100.00 200.00
4 Cal Ripken/250 12.50 30.00
5 Carlton Fisk/250 4.00 10.00
6 Eddie Mathews/250 4.00 10.00
7 Eddie Murray/250 4.00 10.00
8 Ernie Banks/250 4.00 10.00
9 Frank Robinson/250 3.00 8.00
10 George Foster/250 3.00 8.00
11 Harmon Killebrew/250 4.00 10.00
12 Jim Rice/250 3.00 8.00
13 Jim Thome/250 3.00 8.00
14 Johnny Bench/250 4.00 10.00
15 Jose Canseco/100 5.00 12.00
16 Juan Gonzalez/250 2.00 5.00
18 Mike Piazza/250 4.00 10.00
19 Mike Schmidt/250 6.00 15.00
20 Reggie Jackson/250 4.00 10.00
21 Roger Maris/250 10.00 25.00
22 Sammy Sosa/250 4.00 10.00
23 Stan Musial/250 8.00 20.00
24 Willie McCovey/250 4.00 10.00
25 Willie Stargell/250 4.00 10.00

2004 Throwback Threads Century Collection Material

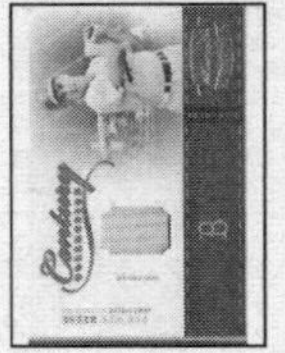

PRINT RUNS B/WN 25-250 COPIES PER
*COMBO p/r 50: .75X TO 2X p/r 150-250
*COMBO p/r 50: .75X TO 2X p/r 100
*COMBO p/r 50: .6X TO 1.5X p/r 50
*COMBO p/r 50: .4X TO 1X p/r 25
*COMBO p/r 20-25: 1X TO 2.5X p/r 250
*COMBO p/r 20-25: .5X TO 1.2X p/r 25
*COMBO p/r 15: 1.25X TO 3X p/r 250
COMBO PRINT RUNS B/WN 5-50 PER
NO COMBO PRICING ON QTY OF 5 OR LESS
OVERALL AU-GU ODDS 1:8
1 Alan Trammell Jsy/250 3.00 8.00
2 Alex Rodriguez Jsy/250 4.00 10.00
3 Alfonso Soriano Jsy/250 2.00 5.00
4 Andre Dawson Jsy/250 3.00 8.00
5 Andy Pettitte Jsy/250 3.00 8.00
6 Bert Blyleven Jsy/250 3.00 8.00
7 Bo Jackson Jsy/250 6.00 15.00
8 Bobby Doerr Jsy/250 3.00 8.00
9 Brooks Robinson Jsy/25 10.00 25.00
10 Carl Yastrzemski Jsy/250 8.00 20.00
11 Carlos Delgado Jsy/250 2.00 5.00
12 Carlton Fisk Jkt/250 4.00 10.00
13 Curt Schilling Jsy/250 2.00 5.00
14 Darryl Strawberry Jsy/250 3.00 8.00
15 Dave Concepcion Jsy/250 3.00 8.00
16 Dave Parker Jsy/100 3.00 8.00
17 Dennis Eckersley Jsy/250 4.00 10.00
18 Don Sutton Jsy/250 3.00 8.00
19 Duke Snider Jsy/250 4.00 10.00
20 Dwight Gooden Jsy/250 3.00 8.00
21 Eddie Mathews Jsy/25 15.00 40.00
22 Enos Slaughter Jsy/100 6.00 15.00
23 Ernie Banks Pants/250 4.00 10.00
24 Frankie Frisch Jkt/250 6.00 15.00
25 Frank Robinson Jsy/50 4.00 10.00
26 Frank Thomas Jsy/250 4.00 10.00
27 Garret Anderson Jsy/250 2.00 5.00
28 Gary Carter Jsy/250 3.00 8.00
29 Gary Sheffield Jsy/250 2.00 5.00
30 Harmon Killebrew Jsy/50 8.00 20.00
31 Harold Baines Jsy/250 3.00 8.00
32 Hideo Nomo Jsy/250 4.00 10.00
33 Jack Morris Jsy/250 3.00 8.00
34 Jason Giambi Jsy/250 2.00 5.00
35 Jeff Kent Jsy/250 2.00 5.00
36 Catfish Hunter Jsy/250 4.00 10.00
37 Jim Palmer Jsy/50 4.00 10.00
38 Jim Rice Jsy/250 3.00 8.00
39 Jim Thome Jsy/250 3.00 8.00
40 John Smoltz Jsy/250 3.00 8.00
41 Johnny Mize Pants/250 4.00 10.00
42 Jose Canseco Jsy/250 4.00 10.00
43 Juan Gonzalez Jsy/250 2.00 5.00
44 Juan Marichal Jsy/250 3.00 8.00
45 Keith Hernandez Jsy/250 3.00 8.00
46 Kerry Wood Jsy/250 2.00 5.00
47 Kevin Brown Jsy/250 2.00 5.00
48 Lance Berkman Jsy/250 2.00 5.00
49 Larry Walker Jsy/250 2.00 5.00
50 Lee Smith Jsy/250 3.00 8.00
51 Lenny Dykstra Bat/250 3.00 8.00
52 Luis Tiant Jsy/250 3.00 8.00
53 Magglio Ordonez Jsy/250 2.00 5.00
54 Manny Ramirez Jsy/250 3.00 8.00
55 Mariano Rivera Jsy/100 4.00 10.00
56 Mark Grace Jsy/250 4.00 10.00
57 Mark Mulder Jsy/250 2.00 5.00
58 Mark Teixeira Jsy/150 3.00 8.00
59 Marty Marion Jsy/25 6.00 15.00
60 Mike Mussina Pants/250 3.00 8.00
61 Mike Piazza Jsy/250 4.00 10.00
62 Nellie Fox Bat/250 8.00 20.00
63 Nolan Ryan Jkt/250 10.00 25.00
65 Ozzie Smith Jsy/250 5.00 12.00
66 Pedro Martinez Jsy/250 3.00 8.00
67 Pee Wee Reese Bat/250 4.00 10.00
68 Phil Niekro Jsy/250 3.00 8.00
69 Phil Rizzuto Pants/250 4.00 10.00
70 Rafael Palmeiro Jsy/250 3.00 8.00
71 Ralph Kiner Bat/250 4.00 10.00
72 Randy Johnson Jsy/250 4.00 10.00
73 Reggie Jackson Jkt/250 4.00 10.00
74 Rickey Henderson Jsy/250 4.00 10.00
75 Roberto Alomar Jsy/250 3.00 8.00
76 Robin Ventura Jsy/250 2.00 5.00
77 Rod Carew Jsy/250 4.00 10.00
78 Roger Clemens Jsy/250 4.00 10.00
79 Ron Santo Bat/250 4.00 10.00
80 Scott Rolen Jsy/250 3.00 8.00
81 Shawn Green Jsy/250 2.00 5.00
82 Steve Garvey Jsy/250 3.00 8.00
83 Tim Hudson Jsy/250 2.00 5.00
84 Tom Glavine Jsy/250 3.00 8.00
85 Tom Seaver Jsy/25 10.00 25.00
86 Adam Dunn Jsy/250 2.00 5.00
87 Tommy John Jsy/250 3.00 8.00
88 Tommy Lasorda Jsy/250 3.00 8.00
89 Tony Oliva Jsy/250 3.00 8.00
90 Tony Perez Bat/250 3.00 8.00
91 Torii Hunter Jsy/250 2.00 5.00
92 Troy Glaus Jsy/250 2.00 5.00
93 Vernon Wells Jsy/250 2.00 5.00
94 Vladimir Guerrero Jsy/250 4.00 10.00
95 Wade Boggs Jsy/250 4.00 10.00
96 Warren Spahn Jsy/100 6.00 15.00
97 Will Clark Bat/250 4.00 10.00
98 Willie McCovey Jsy/250 4.00 10.00
99 Willie Stargell Jsy/250 4.00 10.00
100 George Foster Jsy/250 3.00 8.00

2004 Throwback Threads Century Collection Material Prime

*PRIME p/r 20-25: 1.25X TO 3X p/r 150-250
*PRIME p/r 20-25: 1.25X TO 3X p/r 100
*PATCH p/r 20-25: .75X TO 2X BASIC p/r 50
*PRIME p/r 15: 1.5X TO 4X BASIC p/r 250
OVERALL AU-GU ODDS 1:8
PRINT RUNS B/WN 10-25 COPIES PER
NO PRICING ON QTY OF 10 OR LESS
7 Bo Jackson Jsy/25 30.00 60.00
63 Nolan Ryan Jkt/25 50.00 100.00
65 Ozzie Smith Jsy/25 30.00 60.00

2004 Throwback Threads Century Collection Material Combo Prime

*COMBO PR p/r 25: 1.5X TO 4X p/r 150-250
*COMBO PR p/r 25: 1.5X TO 4X p/r 100
*COMBO PR p/r 25: 1X TO 2.5X p/r 50

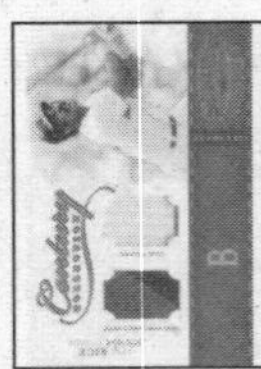

*COMBO PR p/r 15: 2X TO 5X p/r 250
OVERALL AU-GU ODDS 1:8
PRINT RUNS B/WN 4-25 COPIES PER
NO PRICING ON QTY OF 10 OR LESS
7 Bo Jackson Bat-Jsy/25 30.00 60.00
32 Hideo Nomo Bat-Jsy/25 15.00 40.00
63 Nolan Ryan Jkt-Jsy/25 50.00 100.00
65 Ozzie Smith Bat-Jsy/25 30.00 60.00

2004 Throwback Threads Century Collection Signature Material

PRINT RUNS B/WN 10-50 COPIES PER
NO PRICING ON QTY OF 10 OR LESS
PRIME PRINT RUNS B/WN 5-10 COPIES PER
NO PRIME PRICING DUE TO SCARCITY
*COMBO p/r 25: .5X TO 1.2X BASIC p/r 50
*COMBO p/r 25: .5X TO 1.2X BASIC p/r 25
COMBO PRINT RUN B/WN 5-25 COPIES PER
NO COMBO PRICE ON QTY OF 10 OR LESS
COMBO PRIME PRINT RUN B/WN 4-10 PER
NO COMBO PR PRICING DUE TO SCARCITY
OVERALL AU-GU ODDS 1:8
1 Alan Trammell Jsy/50 10.00 25.00
3 Alfonso Soriano Jsy/50 15.00 40.00
4 Andre Dawson Jsy/50 10.00 25.00
6 Bert Blyleven Jsy/50 6.00 15.00
7 Bo Jackson Jsy/10
8 Bobby Doerr Jsy/50 10.00 25.00
12 Carlton Fisk Jkt/10
14 Darryl Strawberry Jsy/50 10.00 25.00
15 Dave Concepcion Jsy/50 10.00 25.00
16 Dave Parker Jsy/50 10.00 25.00
17 Dennis Eckersley Jsy/50 15.00 40.00
18 Don Sutton Jsy/50 10.00 25.00
19 Duke Snider Jsy/25 20.00 50.00
20 Dwight Gooden Jsy/50 10.00 25.00
23 Ernie Banks Pants/10
25 Frank Robinson Jsy/10
26 Frank Thomas Jsy/10
27 Garret Anderson Jsy/50 10.00 25.00
28 Gary Carter Jsy/50 10.00 25.00
29 Gary Sheffield Jsy/25 20.00 50.00
31 Harold Baines Jsy/50 10.00 25.00
33 Jack Morris Jsy/50 6.00 15.00
37 Jim Palmer Jsy/25 12.50 30.00
38 Jim Rice Jsy/50 10.00 25.00
42 Jose Canseco Jsy/25 20.00 50.00
44 Juan Marichal Jsy/50 10.00 25.00
45 Keith Hernandez Jsy/50 10.00 25.00
50 Lee Smith Jsy/50 6.00 15.00
51 Lenny Dykstra Bat/50 10.00 25.00
52 Luis Tiant Jsy/50 6.00 15.00
53 Magglio Ordonez Jsy/50 10.00 25.00
56 Mark Grace Jsy/50 15.00 40.00
57 Mark Mulder Jsy/25 12.50 30.00
58 Mark Teixeira Jsy/25 20.00 50.00
59 Marty Marion Jsy/50 6.00 15.00
63 Nolan Ryan Jkt/10
68 Phil Niekro Jsy/50 10.00 25.00
71 Ralph Kiner Bat/50 15.00 40.00
75 Roberto Alomar Jsy/25 20.00 50.00
76 Robin Ventura Jsy/50 10.00 25.00
82 Steve Garvey Jsy/50 15.00 40.00
86 Adam Dunn Jsy/10
87 Tommy John Jsy/50 6.00 15.00
90 Tony Perez Bat/25 30.00 60.00
91 Torii Hunter Jsy/25 12.50 30.00
93 Vernon Wells Jsy/25 12.50 30.00
94 Vladimir Guerrero Jsy/50 20.00 50.00
100 George Foster Jsy/50 6.00 15.00

2004 Throwback Threads Century Stars

STATED PRINT RUN 1500 SERIAL #'d SETS
*SPECTRUM: .75X TO 2X BASIC
SPECTRUM PRINT RUN 100 #'d SETS
RANDOM INSERTS IN PACKS
1 Al Kaline 1.25 3.00
2 Albert Pujols 2.50 6.00
3 Alex Rodriguez 2.00 5.00
4 Barry Larkin 1.25 3.00
5 Barry Zito .75 2.00
6 Billy Williams .75 2.00
7 Bob Feller .75 2.00
8 Bob Gibson 1.25 3.00
9 Cal Ripken 4.00 10.00
10 Chipper Jones 1.25 3.00
11 Curt Schilling .75 2.00
12 Dale Murphy 1.25 3.00
13 Dave Parker .75 2.00
14 Derek Jeter 2.50 6.00
15 Don Drysdale 1.25 3.00
16 Don Mattingly 2.50 6.00
17 Eddie Murray 1.25 3.00
18 Fergie Jenkins .75 2.00
19 Gary Carter .75 2.00
20 George Brett 2.50 6.00
21 Greg Maddux 2.00 5.00
22 Ivan Rodriguez 1.25 3.00
23 Jeff Bagwell 1.25 3.00
24 Joe Morgan .75 2.00
25 Johnny Bench 1.25 3.00
26 Kirby Puckett 1.25 3.00
27 Lou Boudreau .75 2.00
28 Lou Brock 1.25 3.00
29 Luis Aparicio .75 2.00
30 Manny Ramirez 1.25 3.00
31 Mark Prior 1.25 3.00
32 Miguel Tejada .75 2.00
33 Mike Mussina 1.25 3.00
34 Mike Piazza 2.00 5.00
35 Mike Schmidt 2.50 6.00
36 Nolan Ryan 3.00 8.00
37 Nomar Garciaparra 2.00 5.00
38 Ozzie Smith 2.00 5.00
39 Paul Molitor .75 2.00
40 Pedro Martinez 1.25 3.00
41 Rafael Palmeiro 1.25 3.00
42 Randy Johnson 1.25 3.00
43 Red Schoendienst .75 2.00
44 Reggie Jackson 1.25 3.00
45 Rickey Henderson 1.25 3.00
46 Roberto Alomar 1.25 3.00
47 Roberto Clemente 3.00 8.00
48 Robin Yount 1.25 3.00
49 Rod Carew 1.25 3.00
50 Roger Clemens 2.50 6.00
51 Ryne Sandberg 2.50 6.00
52 Sammy Sosa 1.25 3.00
53 Stan Musial 2.00 5.00
54 Steve Carlton .75 2.00
55 Todd Helton 1.25 3.00
56 Tom Glavine 1.25 3.00
57 Tom Seaver 1.25 3.00
58 Tony Gwynn 2.00 5.00
59 Wade Boggs 1.25 3.00
60 Whitey Ford 1.25 3.00

2004 Throwback Threads Century Stars Material

PRINT RUNS B/WN 10-50 COPIES PER
NO PRICING ON QTY OF 10 OR LESS
PRIME PRINT RUN 5 SERIAL #'d SETS
NO PRIME PRICING DUE TO SCARCITY
OVERALL AU-GU ODDS 1:8
1 Al Kaline Pants/25 15.00 40.00
2 Albert Pujols Jsy/50 12.50 30.00
4 Barry Larkin Jsy/50 5.00 12.00
5 Barry Zito Jsy/50 3.00 8.00
6 Billy Williams Jsy/50 4.00 10.00
7 Bob Feller Jsy/10
8 Bob Gibson Jsy/25 10.00 25.00
9 Cal Ripken Jsy/50 25.00 60.00
10 Chipper Jones Jsy/50 6.00 15.00
11 Curt Schilling Jsy/50 3.00 8.00
12 Dale Murphy Jsy/50 6.00 15.00
13 Dave Parker Jsy/50 4.00 10.00
14 Derek Jeter Jsy/50 15.00 40.00
15 Don Drysdale Jsy/50 8.00 20.00
16 Don Mattingly Jkt/50 12.50 30.00
17 Eddie Murray Jsy/50 8.00 20.00
18 Fergie Jenkins Pants/25 6.00 15.00
19 Gary Carter Pants/50 4.00 10.00
20 George Brett Jsy/50 12.50 30.00
21 Greg Maddux Jsy/50 8.00 20.00
22 Ivan Rodriguez Jsy/50 5.00 12.00
23 Jeff Bagwell Jsy/50 5.00 12.00
24 Joe Morgan Jsy/25 6.00 15.00
25 Johnny Bench Jsy/50 8.00 20.00
26 Kirby Puckett Jsy/50 8.00 20.00
27 Lou Boudreau Jsy/50 4.00 10.00
28 Lou Brock Jsy/25 10.00 25.00
29 Luis Aparicio Pants/50 4.00 10.00
30 Manny Ramirez Jsy/50 5.00 12.00
31 Mark Prior Jsy/50 5.00 12.00
32 Miguel Tejada Jsy/50 3.00 8.00
33 Mike Mussina Jsy/50 5.00 12.00
34 Mike Piazza Jsy/50 8.00 20.00
35 Mike Schmidt Jsy/50 12.50 30.00
36 Nolan Ryan Jsy/50 15.00 40.00
37 Nomar Garciaparra Jsy/50 8.00 20.00
38 Ozzie Smith Jsy/50 10.00 25.00
40 Pedro Martinez Jsy/50 5.00 12.00
41 Rafael Palmeiro Jsy/25 8.00 20.00
42 Randy Johnson Jsy/50 6.00 15.00
43 Red Schoendienst Jsy/50 4.00 10.00
44 Reggie Jackson Pants/50 6.00 15.00
45 Rickey Henderson Jsy/50 8.00 20.00
46 Roberto Alomar Jsy/50 5.00 12.00
47 Roberto Clemente Jsy/10
48 Robin Yount Jsy/50 8.00 20.00
49 Rod Carew Jkt/50 6.00 15.00
50 Roger Clemens Jsy/50 8.00 20.00
51 Ryne Sandberg Jsy/50 12.50 30.00
52 Sammy Sosa Jsy/50 6.00 15.00
53 Stan Musial Jsy/10
54 Steve Carlton Jsy/25 6.00 15.00
55 Todd Helton Jsy/50 5.00 12.00
56 Tom Glavine Jsy/50 5.00 12.00
57 Tom Seaver Jsy/50 6.00 15.00
58 Tony Gwynn Jsy/50 8.00 20.00
59 Wade Boggs Jsy/50 6.00 15.00
60 Whitey Ford Pants/10

2004 Throwback Threads Century Stars Signature

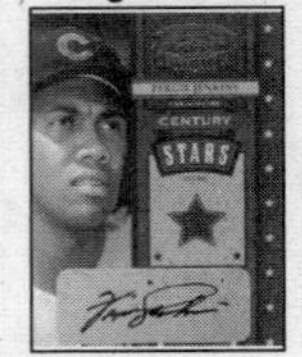

PRINT RUNS B/WN 5-25 COPIES PER
NO PRICING ON QTY OF 10 OR LESS
SIG.MATERIAL PRINT RUN 5 #'d SETS
NO SIG.MTL.PRICING DUE TO SCARCITY
SIG.MATERIAL PRIME PRINT RUN 5 #'d SETS
NO SIG.MTL.PR.PRICING DUE TO SCARCITY
OVERALL AU-GU ODDS 1:8
1 Al Kaline/25 30.00 60.00
2 Albert Pujols/5
3 Alex Rodriguez/5
4 Barry Larkin/10
5 Barry Zito/5
6 Billy Williams/25 15.00 40.00
7 Bob Feller/25 15.00 40.00
8 Bob Gibson/25 15.00 40.00
9 Cal Ripken/5
10 Chipper Jones/5
12 Dale Murphy/25 15.00 40.00
13 Dave Parker/25 10.00 25.00
16 Don Mattingly/10
17 Eddie Murray/5
18 Fergie Jenkins/25 10.00 25.00
19 Gary Carter/25 10.00 25.00
20 George Brett/5
23 Jeff Bagwell/5
24 Joe Morgan/25 10.00 25.00
25 Johnny Bench/5
26 Kirby Puckett/5
28 Lou Brock/25 15.00 40.00
29 Luis Aparicio/25 10.00 25.00
30 Manny Ramirez/5
31 Mark Prior/25 12.50 30.00
33 Mike Mussina/5
35 Mike Schmidt/25 50.00 100.00
36 Nolan Ryan/10
38 Ozzie Smith/25 40.00 80.00
39 Paul Molitor/10
41 Rafael Palmeiro/10
44 Reggie Jackson/10
45 Rickey Henderson/10
46 Roberto Alomar/10
48 Robin Yount/10
49 Rod Carew/10
51 Ryne Sandberg/10
52 Sammy Sosa/5
53 Stan Musial/25 40.00 80.00
54 Steve Carlton/10
55 Todd Helton/5
57 Tom Seaver/5
58 Tony Gwynn/10
59 Wade Boggs/10
60 Whitey Ford/5

2004 Throwback Threads Dynasty

STATED PRINT RUN 1500 SERIAL #'d SETS
*SPECTRUM: .75X TO 2X BASIC
SPECTRUM PRINT RUN 100 #'d SETS
RANDOM INSERTS IN PACKS
1 Phil Rizzuto 1.25 3.00
Whitey Ford
2 Pee Wee Reese 1.25 3.00
Duke Snider
Tommy Lasorda
3 Catfish Hunter 1.25 3.00
Reggie Jackson
4 Roger Maris 1.25 3.00
Whitey Ford
5 Enos Slaughter 2.00 5.00
Marty Marion
Stan Musial
6 Dwight Gooden .75 2.00
Gary Carter
Darryl Strawberry
Keith Hernandez
7 Johnny Bench 1.25 3.00
Tony Perez
Joe Morgan
George Foster
8 Derek Jeter 2.50 6.00
Jorge Posada
Bernie Williams
Andy Pettitte
9 Frank Robinson 1.25 3.00
Brooks Robinson
Jim Palmer
10 Willie Stargell 1.25 3.00
Dave Parker
Bill Madlock
11 Bob Gibson 1.25 3.00
Lou Brock
Ken Boyer
12 Rickey Henderson 1.25 3.00
Paul Molitor
Joe Carter
Roberto Alomar

2004 Throwback Threads Dynasty Material

PRINT RUNS B/WN 5-50 COPIES PER
NO PRICING ON QTY OF 10 OR LESS
ALL ARE JSY SWATCHES UNLESS NOTED
PRIME PRINT RUN 5 SERIAL #'d SETS
NO PRIME PRICING DUE TO SCARCITY
OVERALL AU-GU ODDS 1:8
1 Phil Rizzuto Pants
Whitey Ford Jsy/10
2 Pee Wee Reese Jsy
Duke Snider Jsy
Tommy Lasorda Jsy/5
3 Catfish Hunter Jsy 10.00 25.00
Reggie Jackson Jsy/25
4 Roger Maris Jsy
Whitey Ford Pants/10
5 Enos Slaughter Jsy
Marty Marion Jsy
Stan Musial Jsy/10
6 Dwight Gooden Jsy 10.00 25.00
Gary Carter Jsy
Darryl Strawberry Pants
Keith Hernandez Bat/50
7 Johnny Bench Jsy 60.00 120.00
Tony Perez Bat
Joe Morgan Jsy
George Foster Jsy/25
8 Derek Jeter Jsy 30.00 60.00
Jorge Posada Jsy
Bernie Williams Jsy
Andy Pettitte Jsy/50
9 Frank Robinson Jsy
Brooks Robinson Jsy
Jim Palmer Jsy/10
10 Willie Stargell Jsy 15.00 40.00
Dave Parker Jsy
Bill Madlock Bat/25
11 Bob Gibson Jsy 15.00 40.00
Lou Brock Jsy
Ken Boyer Jsy/25
12 Rickey Henderson Jsy 20.00 50.00
Paul Molitor Bat
Joe Carter Jsy
Roberto Alomar Bat/25

2004 Throwback Threads Fans of the Game

STATED ODDS 1:24
1 Emilio Estevez 1.25 3.00
2 Shannon Elizabeth 1.25 3.00
3 Joe Mantegna UER .75 2.00
Incorrectly spelled Montegna
4 Jamie-Lynn DiScala 1.25 3.00
5 Jonathan Silverman .75 2.00

2004 Throwback Threads Fans of the Game Autographs

RANDOM INSERTS IN PACKS
1 Emilio Estevez 15.00 40.00
2 Shannon Elizabeth 40.00 80.00
3 Joe Mantegna UER 10.00 25.00
Incorrectly spelled Montegna
4 Jamie-Lynn DiScala 40.00 80.00
5 Jonathan Silverman 6.00 15.00

2004 Throwback Threads Generations

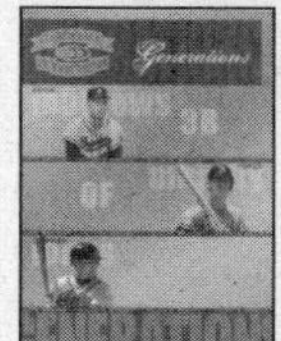

STATED PRINT RUN 1500 SERIAL #'d SETS
*SPECTRUM: .75X TO 2X BASIC
SPECTRUM PRINT RUN 100 #'d SETS
RANDOM INSERTS IN PACKS
1 George Brett 2.50 6.00
Albert Pujols
2 Wade Boggs 1.25 3.00
Aubrey Huff
3 Catfish Hunter 1.25 3.00
Tim Hudson
4 Steve Garvey .75 2.00
Shawn Green
5 Tony Gwynn 2.00 5.00
Garret Anderson
6 Fergie Jenkins 1.25 3.00
Mark Prior
7 Robin Yount 1.25 3.00
Rickie Weeks
8 Warren Spahn 2.00 5.00
Greg Maddux
9 Brooks Robinson 4.00 10.00
Cal Ripken
Miguel Tejada
10 Bobby Doerr 2.00 5.00
Carl Yastrzemski
Manny Ramirez
11 Al Kaline 1.25 3.00
Alan Trammell
Ivan Rodriguez
12 Tom Seaver 1.25 3.00
Dwight Gooden
Tom Glavine
13 Stan Musial 2.00 5.00
Lou Brock
Jim Edmonds
14 George Foster .75 2.00
Dave Parker
Austin Kearns
15 Eddie Mathews 1.25 3.00
Dale Murphy
Chipper Jones
16 Don Sutton 3.00 8.00
Nolan Ryan
Roger Clemens
17 Billy Williams 1.25 3.00
Andre Dawson
Sammy Sosa
18 Whitey Ford 1.25 3.00
Tommy John
Andy Pettitte
19 Carlton Fisk 2.50 6.00
Roger Clemens
Nomar Garciaparra
20 Marty Marion 2.00 5.00
Ozzie Smith
Edgar Renteria
21 Reggie Jackson 1.25 3.00
Rickey Henderson
Eric Chavez
22 Babe Ruth 2.50 6.00
Don Mattingly
Derek Jeter
23 Roberto Clemente 3.00 8.00
Reggie Jackson
Sammy Sosa
24 Bob Feller 2.50 6.00
Tom Seaver
Roger Clemens
25 Ernie Banks 4.00 10.00
Cal Ripken
Alex Rodriguez
26 Pee Wee Reese 2.50 6.00
Ozzie Smith
Derek Jeter
27 Harmon Killebrew 2.50 6.00
Mike Schmidt
Alex Rodriguez
28 Bob Gibson 1.25 3.00
Dwight Gooden
Josh Beckett

2004 Throwback Threads Generations Material

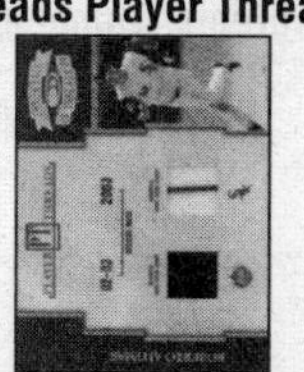

PRINT RUNS B/WN 5-50 COPIES PER
NO PRICING ON QTY OF 10 OR LESS
ALL ARE JSY SWATCHES UNLESS NOTED
PRIME PRINT RUN 5 SERIAL #'d SETS
NO PRIME PRICING DUE TO SCARCITY
OVERALL AU-GU ODDS 1:8
1 George Brett Jsy 15.00 40.00
Albert Pujols Jsy/50
2 Wade Boggs Jsy 6.00 15.00
Aubrey Huff Jsy/50
3 Catfish Hunter Jsy 8.00 20.00
Tim Hudson Jsy/25
4 Steve Garvey Jsy
Shawn Green Jsy/5
5 Tony Gwynn Jsy 10.00 25.00
Garret Anderson Jsy/50
6 Fergie Jenkins Pants 8.00 20.00
Mark Prior Jsy/25
7 Robin Yount Jsy 8.00 20.00
Rickie Weeks Bat/50
8 Warren Spahn Pants 15.00 40.00
Greg Maddux Jsy/25
9 Brooks Robinson Jsy
Cal Ripken Jsy
Miguel Tejada Bat/10
10 Bobby Doerr Bat
Carl Yastrzemski Jsy
Manny Ramirez Jsy/10
11 Al Kaline Pants 20.00 50.00
Alan Trammell Jsy
Ivan Rodriguez Bat/25
12 Tom Seaver Jsy
Dwight Gooden Jsy
Tom Glavine Jsy/5
13 Stan Musial Jsy
Lou Brock Jsy
Jim Edmonds Jsy/10
14 George Foster Jsy 10.00 25.00
Dave Parker Jsy
Austin Kearns Jsy/25
15 Eddie Mathews Jsy
Dale Murphy Jsy
Chipper Jones Jsy/10
16 Don Sutton Jsy 20.00 50.00
Nolan Ryan Jkt
Roger Clemens Bat/50
17 Billy Williams Jsy 10.00 25.00
Andre Dawson Jsy
Sammy Sosa Jsy/50
18 Whitey Ford Jsy 15.00 40.00
Tommy John Jsy
Andy Pettitte Jsy/25
19 Carlton Fisk Jsy 15.00 40.00
Roger Clemens Jsy
Nomar Garciaparra Jsy/50
20 Marty Marion Jsy 30.00 60.00
Ozzie Smith Jsy
Edgar Renteria Jsy/25
21 Reggie Jackson Jkt 15.00 40.00
Rickey Henderson Jsy
Eric Chavez Jsy/50
22 Babe Ruth Jsy
Don Mattingly Jsy
Derek Jeter Jsy/10
23 Roberto Clemente Jsy
Reggie Jackson Jsy
Sammy Sosa Jsy/10
24 Bob Feller Jsy 15.00 40.00
Tom Seaver Jsy
Roger Clemens Jsy/25
25 Ernie Banks Pants 40.00 80.00
Cal Ripken Jsy
Alex Rodriguez Jsy/50
26 Pee Wee Reese Jsy 30.00 60.00
Ozzie Smith Jsy
Derek Jeter Jsy/25
27 Harmon Killebrew Jsy 30.00 60.00
Mike Schmidt Jsy
Alex Rodriguez Bat/25
28 Bob Gibson Jsy 15.00 40.00
Dwight Gooden Jsy
Josh Beckett Jsy/25

2004 Throwback Threads Player Threads

STATED PRINT RUN 250 SERIAL #'d SETS
CARD 57 PRINT RUN 25 SERIAL #'d COPIES
ALL ARE JSY SWATCHES UNLESS NOTED
*PRIME p/r 25: 1.25X TO 3X BASIC
PRIME PRINT RUNS B/WN 10-25 PER
NO PRIME PRICING ON QTY OF 10 OR LESS
OVERALL AU-GU ODDS 1:8
1 Aaron Boone 2.00 5.00
2 Alex Rodriguez M's-Rgr 6.00 15.00
3 A.Gala Braves-Giants-Rgr 6.00 15.00
4 Aramis Ramirez 2.00 5.00
5 Bartolo Colon 2.00 5.00
6 Ben Grieve A's-D'Rays 3.00 8.00
7 Brad Fullmer 2.00 5.00
8 Bret Boone Braves-M's 3.00 8.00
9 Brian Giles 2.00 5.00
10 Brian Jordan 2.00 5.00
11 Byung-Hyun Kim 2.00 5.00
12 Casey Fossum 2.00 5.00
13 Cesar Izturis Pants 2.00 5.00
14 Chan Ho Park 2.00 5.00
15 Charles Johnson 2.00 5.00
16 Cliff Floyd 2.00 5.00
17 D.Straw Dgr-Met-Ynk Pant 4.00 10.00
18 David Ortiz 5.00 12.00
19 David Wells Jays-Yanks 3.00 8.00
20 Derrek Lee 3.00 8.00
21 Dmitri Young 2.00 5.00
22 Edgardo Alfonzo 2.00 5.00
23 Ellis Burks 2.00 5.00
24 G.Shef Braves-Brew-Dgr 4.00 10.00
25 Hee Seop Choi 2.00 5.00
26 I.Rodriguez Marlins-Rgr 4.00 10.00
27 J.D. Drew 2.00 5.00
28 Javier Vazquez 2.00 5.00
29 Jay Payton 2.00 5.00
30 Jeff Kent Astros-Giants-Jays 4.00 10.00
31 Jeromy Burnitz 2.00 5.00
32 Jim Thome Indians-Phils 4.00 10.00
33 Joe Kennedy 2.00 5.00
34 Joe Torre 3.00 8.00
35 Jose Cruz Jr. 2.00 5.00
36 Juan Encarnacion 2.00 5.00
37 Juan Gonzalez Indians-Rgr 3.00 8.00
38 Juan Pierre 2.00 5.00
39 Junior Spivey 2.00 5.00
40 K.Loft Brave Fld Glv-Tribe Hat 4.00 10.00
41 Kevin Millwood Braves-Phils 3.00 8.00
42 Manny Ramirez Indians-Sox 4.00 10.00
43 Mark Grace Cubs-D'backs 4.00 10.00
44 Mike Hampton 2.00 5.00
45 M.Piazza Dgr-Marlins-Mets 8.00 20.00
46 Milton Bradley 2.00 5.00
47 Moises Alou 2.00 5.00
48 Nick Johnson 2.00 5.00
49 N.Ryan Ang Jkt-Ast Jkt-Rgr 20.00 50.00
50 P.Wilson Marlins-Rockies 3.00 8.00
51 Rafael Palmeiro O's-Rgr 4.00 10.00
52 Ray Durham 2.00 5.00
53 R.Jack A's Jkt-Ang-Yank 6.00 15.00
54 Reggie Sanders 2.00 5.00
55 Rich Aurilia 2.00 5.00
56 Richie Sexson 2.00 5.00
57 R.Hend A's-M's-Yanks/25 20.00 50.00
58 R.Hend Dgr-Mets-Padres 6.00 15.00
59 Robert Fick 2.00 5.00
60 Roberto Alomar Mets-Sox 4.00 10.00
61 Roberto Alomar Indians-O's 4.00 10.00
62 R.Ventura Mets-Sox-Yanks 4.00 10.00
63 Rondell White Cubs-Expos 3.00 8.00
64 Ryan Klesko Braves-Padres 3.00 8.00
65 Sean Casey 2.00 5.00
66 S.Stewart Jays-Twins 3.00 8.00
67 Shawn Green Jays-Dgr 3.00 8.00
68 Shea Hillenbrand 2.00 5.00
69 Steve Carlton Giants-Sox 3.00 8.00
70 Terrence Long 2.00 5.00
71 Tony Batista 2.00 5.00
72 Travis Hafner Indians-Rgr 3.00 8.00
73 Travis Lee 2.00 5.00
74 Vladimir Guerrero 4.00 10.00
75 Wes Helms 2.00 5.00

2004 Throwback Threads Player Threads Signature

OVERALL AU-GU ODDS 1:8
PRINT RUNS B/WN 3-25 COPIES PER
NO PRICING ON QTY OF 11 OR LESS
ALL ARE JSY SWATCHES UNLESS NOTED
2 Alex Rodriguez M's-Rgr/5
4 Aramis Ramirez/25 12.50 30.00
17 D.Straw Dgr-Met-Ynk Pnt/25 20.00 50.00
24 G.Shef Brave-Brw-Dgr/25 20.00 50.00
28 Javier Vazquez/25 12.50 30.00
29 Jay Payton/25 8.00 20.00
33 Joe Kennedy/11
37 J.Gonzalez Indians-Rgr/25 15.00 40.00
39 Junior Spivey/25 8.00 20.00
42 M.Ramirez Indians-Sox/10
43 M.Grace Cubs-D'backs/5
45 M.Piazza Dgr-Marlins-Mets/5
49 N.Ryan Ang Jkt-Ast Jkt-Rgr/5
50 P.Wilson Marlins-Rockies/25 15.00 40.00
51 Rafael Palmeiro O's-Rgr/5
53 R.Jack A's Jkt-Ang-Yank/5
55 Rich Aurilia/25 8.00 20.00
57 R.Hend A's-M's-Yanks/5
58 R.Hend Dgr-Mets-Padres/5
60 Roberto Alomar Mets-Sox/5
61 Roberto Alomar Indians-O's/5
62 R.Vent Mets-Sox-Yanks/25 20.00 50.00
66 S.Stewart Jays-Twins/10
67 Shawn Green Jays-Dgr/5
68 Shea Hillenbrand/25
69 Steve Carlton Giants-Sox/5
72 Travis Hafner Indians-Rgr/3
74 Vladimir Guerrero/25 30.00 60.00

2005 Throwback Threads

This 300-card set was released in August, 2005. The set was issued in five-card packs with an $4 SRP which came 24 packs to a box and 12 boxes to a case. Cards numbered 1-277 feature a mix of active veterans and Rookie Cards while cards numbered 278 through 299 feature retired stars. Card number of Babe Ruth was printed to a shorter quantity than the rest of the set and that card was inserted randomly into packs.

COMP.SET w/o RUTH (299) 35.00 60.00
COMMON CARD (1-277) .10 .30
COMMON RET (278-299) .20 .50
1 Luis Castillo .10 .30
2 Derek Jeter .60 1.50
3 Eric Chavez .10 .30
4 Angel Berroa .10 .30
5 Jeff Bagwell .20 .50
6 J.T. Snow .10 .30
7 Craig Biggio .20 .50
8 Michael Barrett .10 .30
9 Hank Blalock .10 .30
10 Chipper Jones .30 .75
11 Jacque Jones .10 .30
12 Mark Teixeira .20 .50
13 Omar Vizquel .20 .50
14 Paul Lo Duca .10 .30
15 Jim Edmonds .10 .30
16 Aramis Ramirez .10 .30
17 Lance Berkman .10 .30
18 Javy Lopez .10 .30
19 Adam LaRoche .10 .30
20 Jorge Posada .20 .50
21 Sean Casey .10 .30
22 Mark Prior .20 .50
23 Phil Nevin .10 .30
24 Manny Ramirez .20 .50
25 Andruw Jones .20 .50
26 Matt Lawton .10 .30
27 Vladimir Guerrero .30 .75
28 Austin Kearns .10 .30
29 John Smoltz .20 .50
30 Ken Griffey Jr. .50 1.25
31 Mike Piazza .30 .75
32 Jason Jennings .10 .30
33 Jason Varitek .30 .75
34 David Ortiz .30 .75
35 Mike Mussina .20 .50
36 Joe Nathan .10 .30
37 Kenny Rogers .10 .30
38 Carlos Zambrano .10 .30
39 Eric Byrnes .10 .30
40 Clint Barmes .10 .30
41 Danny Kolb .10 .30
42 Mariano Rivera .30 .75
43 Joey Gathright .10 .30
44 Adam Dunn .10 .30
45 Carlos Lee .10 .30
46 Yhency Brazoban .10 .30
47 Roy Oswalt .10 .30
48 Torii Hunter .10 .30
49 Scott Podsednik .10 .30
50 Jason Hammel RC .20 .50
51 Ichiro Suzuki .60 1.50
52 C.C. Sabathia .10 .30
53 Bobby Abreu .10 .30
54 Jon Garland .10 .30
55 Brandon Webb .10 .30
56 Mark Buehrle .10 .30
57 Johan Santana .30 .75
58 Mike Sweeney .10 .30
59 Tadahito Iguchi RC .75 2.00
60 Edgar Renteria .10 .30
61 Aaron Rowand .10 .30
62 Craig Wilson .10 .30
63 J.D. Drew .10 .30
64 Bobby Crosby .10 .30
65 Justin Morneau .10 .30
66 Scott Rolen .20 .50
67 Jose Vidro .10 .30
68 Carlos Beltran .10 .30
69 Jeff Weaver .10 .30
70 Jason Schmidt .10 .30
71 Brad Wilkerson .10 .30
72 Yuniesky Betancourt RC .75 2.00
73 Octavio Dotel .10 .30
74 Mike Cameron .10 .30
75 Barry Zito .10 .30
76 Woody Williams .10 .30
77 Russ Rohlicek RC .20 .50
78 Mark Kotsay .10 .30
79 Jeff Suppan .10 .30
80 Eric Gagne .10 .30
81 Tim Salmon .20 .50
82 Troy Glaus .10 .30
83 Kevin Mench .10 .30
84 Ivan Rodriguez .20 .50
85 Sean Burroughs .10 .30
86 Dallas McPherson .10 .30
87 Jamie Moyer .10 .30
88 Orlando Cabrera .10 .30
89 Wladimir Balentien RC .40 1.00
90 Phil Humber RC .40 1.00
91 Francisco Cordero .10 .30
92 Danny Graves .10 .30
93 Bucky Jacobsen .10 .30
94 Cliff Lee .10 .30
95 Oliver Perez .10 .30
96 Jake Peavy .10 .30
97 Doug Mientkiewicz .10 .30
98 Brad Radke .10 .30
99 Jeremy Reed .10 .30
100 Garret Anderson .10 .30
101 Rafael Furcal .10 .30
102 Jack Wilson .10 .30
103 Bernie Williams .20 .50
104 Josh Beckett .10 .30
105 Albert Pujols .60 1.50
106 Ubaldo Jimenez RC .60 1.50
107 Richard Hidalgo .10 .30
108 Luke Scott RC .75 2.00
109 Hideo Nomo .30 .75
110 Vernon Wells .10 .30
111 Richie Sexson .10 .30
112 Chad Cordero .10 .30
113 Alex Rodriguez .50 1.25
114 Paul Konerko .10 .30
115 Carlos Guillen .10 .30
116 Francisco Rodriguez .10 .30
117 Johnny Damon .20 .50
118 David Wright .50 1.25
119 Lyle Overbay .10 .30
120 Brian Roberts .10 .30
121 Sammy Sosa .30 .75
122 Roger Clemens .50 1.25
123 Rickie Weeks .10 .30
124 Larry Bigbie .10 .30
125 Rafael Palmeiro .20 .50
126 Jason Giambi .10 .30
127 Hideki Matsui .50 1.25
128 Brad Lidge .10 .30
129 Jeremy Affeldt .10 .30
130 Mike MacDougal .10 .30
131 Troy Percival .10 .30
132 Matt Morris .10 .30
133 Dave Gassner RC .20 .50
134 Kerry Wood .10 .30
135 Dontrelle Willis .10 .30
136 Michael Young .10 .30
137 Andy Pettitte .20 .50
138 Kris Benson .10 .30
139 Miguel Negron RC .30 .75
140 Rich Harden .10 .30
141 Bret Boone .10 .30
142 Danny Rueckel RC .20 .50
143 Jeff Niemann RC .40 1.00
144 Randy Messenger RC .20 .50
145 Pedro Martinez .20 .50
146 Kazuhisa Ishii .10 .30
147 Carlos Delgado .10 .30
148 Tom Glavine .20 .50
149 Russ Ortiz .10 .30
150 Gavin Floyd .10 .30
151 Randy Johnson .30 .75
152 Prince Fielder RC 1.50 4.00
153 Nomar Garciaparra .30 .75
154 Pat Burrell .10 .30
155 Melvin Mora .10 .30
156 Jose Reyes .10 .30
157 Trot Nixon .10 .30
158 B.J. Upton .10 .30
159 Jody Gerut .10 .30
160 Juan Pierre .10 .30
161 Miguel Tejada .10 .30
162 Barry Larkin .20 .50
163 Carl Crawford .10 .30
164 Ben Sheets .10 .30
165 Tim Hudson .10 .30
166 Darin Erstad .10 .30
167 Todd Helton .20 .50
168 Luis Gonzalez .10 .30
169 Mark Mulder .10 .30
170 David Dellucci .10 .30
171 Marcus Giles .10 .30
172 Shannon Stewart .10 .30
173 Zack Greinke .10 .30
174 Miguel Cabrera .20 .50
175 Nick Johnson .10 .30
176 Derrek Lee .20 .50
177 Jim Thome .20 .50
178 Ken Harvey .10 .30
179 Ambiorix Concepcion RC .20 .50
180 Roy Halladay .10 .30
181 Larry Walker .20 .50
182 Greg Maddux .50 1.25
183 Frank Thomas .30 .75
184 Travis Hafner .10 .30
185 Matt Holliday .15 .40
186 Victor Martinez .10 .30
187 Jason Isringhausen .10 .30
188 Bill Mueller .10 .30
189 Dewon Brazelton .10 .30
190 Adrian Beltre .10 .30
191 Tim Wakefield .10 .30
192 Alexis Rios .10 .30
193 Alfonso Soriano .10 .30
194 Fernando Vina .10 .30
195 Armando Benitez .10 .30
196 Bartolo Colon .10 .30
197 A.J. Burnett .10 .30
198 Milton Bradley .10 .30
199 Brad Penny .10 .30
200 Rocco Baldelli .10 .30
201 Curt Schilling .20 .50
202 Ryan Wagner .10 .30
203 Preston Wilson .10 .30
204 Akinori Otsuka .10 .30
205 Bill McCarthy RC .20 .50
206 Edgardo Alfonzo .10 .30
207 Mike Lieberthal .10 .30
208 Shea Hillenbrand .10 .30
209 Tom Gordon .10 .30
210 Kip Wells .10 .30
211 Frank Catalanotto .10 .30
212 Casey Kotchman .10 .30
213 Justin Verlander RC 1.50 4.00
214 Brandon Inge .10 .30
215 Terrmel Sledge .10 .30
216 Gary Sheffield .10 .30
217 Steve Finley .10 .30
218 Kenny Lofton .10 .30
219 Chris Carpenter .10 .30
220 Dan Haren .10 .30
221 Brett Myers .10 .30
222 Joe Mauer .30 .75
223 David Wells .10 .30
224 Brian Giles .10 .30
225 Moises Alou .10 .30
226 Casey Rogowski RC .30 .75
227 Chase Utley .20 .50
228 Corey Koskie .10 .30
229 Derek Lowe .10 .30
230 Erick Threets RC .20 .50
231 Grady Sizemore .20 .50
232 Jason Lane .10 .30
233 Jeremy Bonderman .10 .30
234 Livan Hernandez .10 .30
235 Ryan Klesko .10 .30
236 Sidney Ponson .10 .30
237 Jimmy Rollins .10 .30
238 Eric Milton .10 .30
239 Shingo Takatsu .10 .30
240 Scott Kazmir .10 .30
241 Shawn Green .10 .30
242 Nick Swisher .10 .30
243 Shawn Chacon .10 .30
244 Javier Vazquez .10 .30
245 Mark Loretta .10 .30
246 Dmitri Young .10 .30
247 Charles Johnson .10 .30
248 Magglio Ordonez .10 .30
249 Sean Thompson RC .20 .50
250 Jared Gothreaux RC .20 .50
251 Kevin Millwood .10 .30
252 Mike Lowell .10 .30
253 Cristian Guzman .10 .30
254 Nate McLouth RC .30 .75
255 Delmon Young .20 .50
256 Jeromy Burnitz .10 .30
257 Garrett Atkins .10 .30
258 Junior Spivey .10 .30
259 Morgan Ensberg .10 .30
260 Chone Figgins .10 .30
261 Hayden Penn RC .40 1.00
262 Jason Bay .10 .30
263 Jose Cruz Jr. .10 .30
264 Khalil Greene .20 .50
265 Ray Durham .10 .30
266 Juan Gonzalez .10 .30
267 Jeff Kent .10 .30
268 Dioner Navarro .10 .30
269 Rodrigo Lopez .10 .30
270 Geoff Jenkins .10 .30
271 Jermaine Dye .10 .30
272 Orlando Hudson .10 .30
273 Jose Lima .10 .30
274 Jeff Francis .10 .30
275 Luis Matos .10 .30
276 Jason Kendall .10 .30
277 Mike Hampton .10 .30
278 Al Kaline RET .40 1.00
279 Bert Blyleven RET .20 .50
280 Bill Madlock RET .20 .50
281 Cal Ripken RET 1.50 4.00
282 Dale Murphy RET .30 .75
283 Gary Carter RET .20 .50
284 George Brett RET .75 2.00
285 Harmon Killebrew RET .40 1.00
286 Harold Baines RET .20 .50
287 John Kruk RET .30 .75
288 Keith Hernandez RET .20 .50
289 Willie Mays RET .75 2.00
290 Matt Williams RET .30 .75
291 Nolan Ryan RET 1.00 2.50
292 Paul Molitor RET .20 .50
293 Reggie Jackson RET .30 .75
294 Rickey Henderson RET .40 1.00
295 Ron Cey RET .20 .50
296 Ryne Sandberg RET .75 2.00
297 Ted Williams RET .75 2.00
298 Tom Seaver RET .30 .75

299 Tony Gwynn RET .50 1.25
300 Babe Ruth RET SP 10.00 20.00

2005 Throwback Threads Blue Century Proof

*BLUE 1-277: 3X TO 8X BASIC
*BLUE 1-277: 2X TO 5X BASIC RC
*BLUE 278-300: 2.5X TO 6X BASIC
OVERALL INSERT ODDS 1:2
STATED PRINT RUN 150 SERIAL #'d SETS
300 Babe Ruth RET 5.00 12.00

2005 Throwback Threads Gold Century Proof

*GOLD 1-277: 3X TO 8X BASIC
*GOLD 1-277: 2X TO 5X BASIC RC
*GOLD 278-300: 2.5X TO 6X BASIC
OVERALL INSERT ODDS 1:2
STATED PRINT RUN 100 SERIAL #'d SETS
300 Babe Ruth RET 5.00 12.00

2005 Throwback Threads Green Century Proof

*GREEN 1-277: 3X TO 8X BASIC
*GREEN 1-277: 2X TO 5X BASIC RC
*GREEN 278-300: 2.5X TO 6X BASIC
RANDOM INSERTS IN BLASTER PACKS
300 Babe Ruth RET 5.00 12.00

2005 Throwback Threads Platinum Blue Century Proof

OVERALL INSERT ODDS 1:2
STATED PRINT RUN 10 SERIAL #'d SETS
NO PRICING DUE TO SCARCITY

2005 Throwback Threads Material Bat

*1-277 p/r 150-250: .4X TO 1X JSYp/r150-250
*1-277 p/r 150-250: .3X TO .8X JSY p/r 75-100
*1-277 p/r 150-250: .25X TO .6X JSY p/r 40-50
*1-277 p/r 150-250: .2X TO .5X JSY p/r 20-35
*1-277 p/r 100: .3X TO .8X JSY p/r 40-50
*1-277 p/r 50: .6X TO 1.5X JSY p/r 150-250
*1-277 p/r 50: .5X TO 1.2X JSY p/r 75-100
*1-277 p/r 20-35: .75X TO 2X JSY p/r 150-250
*1-277 p/r 20-35: .4X TO 1X JSY p/r 20-35
*1-277 p/r 20-35: .3X TO .8X JSY p/r 15
*1-277 p/r 15: 1X TO 2.5X JSY p/r 150-250
*278-300 p/r 150-250: .25X TO .6X JSY p/r 50
*278-300 p/r 50: .4X TO 1X JSYp/r 50
*278-300 p/r 25: .5X TO 1.2X JSYp/r 50
*278-300 p/r 25: .4X TO 1X JSYp/r 25
OVERALL AU-GU ODDS 1:8
PRINT RUNS B/WN 5-250 COPIES PER
NO PRICING ON QTY OF 10 OR LESS
4 Angel Berroa/250 1.50 4.00
14 Paul Lo Duca/250 1.50 4.00
26 Matt Lawton/250 1.50 4.00
33 Jason Varitek/50 5.00 12.00
55 Brandon Webb/250 1.50 4.00
63 J.D. Drew/250 2.50 6.00
68 Carlos Beltran/250 2.50 6.00
81 Tim Salmon/250 4.00 10.00
82 Troy Glaus/250 2.50 6.00
88 Orlando Cabrera/15 4.00 10.00
107 Richard Hidalgo/250 1.50 4.00
111 Richie Sexson/100 2.00 5.00
121 Sammy Sosa/50 5.00 12.00
123 Rickie Weeks/25 3.00 8.00
153 Nomar Garciaparra/150 3.00 8.00
160 Juan Pierre/250 1.50 4.00
165 Tim Hudson/250 2.50 6.00
169 Mark Mulder/35 3.00 8.00
175 Nick Johnson/250 1.50 4.00
192 Alexis Rios/50 2.50 6.00
206 Edgardo Alfonzo/250 1.50 4.00
215 Terrmel Sledge/250 1.50 4.00
218 Kenny Lofton/150 1.50 4.00
225 Moises Alou/250 1.50 4.00
241 Shawn Green/250 1.50 4.00
247 Charles Johnson/250 1.50 4.00
248 Magglio Ordonez/250 1.50 4.00
255 Delmon Young/250 2.50 6.00
265 Ray Durham/200 1.50 4.00
266 Juan Gonzalez/250 1.50 4.00
267 Jeff Kent/250 1.50 4.00
280 Bill Madlock RET/100 2.50 6.00
288 Keith Hernandez RET/25 4.00 10.00
300 Babe Ruth RET/25 125.00 200.00

2005 Throwback Threads Material Combo

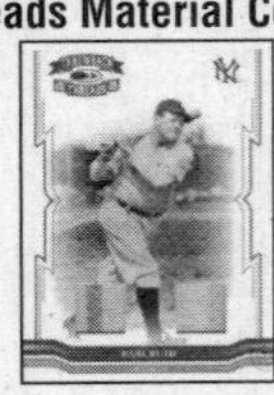

*1-277 p/r 85-100: .6X TO 1.5X JSYp/r150-250
*1-277 p/r 85-100: .5X TO 1.2X JSY p/r 75-100
*1-277 p/r 85-100: .4X TO 1X JSY p/r 40-50
*1-277 p/r 40-65: .75X TO 2X JSY p/r 150-250
*1-277 p/r 40-65: .6X TO 1.5X JSY p/r 75-100
*1-277 p/r 40-65: .4X TO 1X JSY p/r 20-35
*1-277 p/r 40-65: .3X TO .8X JSY p/r 15
*1-277 p/r 25-30: 1X TO 2.5X JSY p/r 150-250
*1-277 p/r 25-30: .75X TO 2X JSY p/r 75-100
*1-277 p/r 25-30: .6X TO 1.5X JSY p/r 40-50
*1-277 p/r 25-30: .5X TO 1.2X JSY p/r 20-35
*1-277 p/r 15: 1.25X TO 3X JSY p/r 150-250
*278-300 p/r 50: .5X TO 1.2X JSY p/r 50
*278-300 p/r 25: .6X TO 1.5X JSY p/r 50
*278-300 p/r 25: .5X TO 1.2X JSY p/r 25
OVERALL AU-GU ODDS 1:8
PRINT RUNS B/WN 10-100 COPIES PER
NO PRICING ON QTY OF 10
55 B.Webb Bat-Pants/100 2.50 6.00
85 Sean Burroughs Bat-Jsy/15 5.00 12.00
160 Juan Pierre Bat-Fld Glv/95 2.50 6.00
183 Frank Thomas Hat-Jsy/25 8.00 20.00
218 K.Lofton Bat-Fld Glv/100 2.50 6.00
288 K.Hern RET Bat-Jsy/25 5.00 12.00
300 Babe Ruth RET Bat-Jsy/25 250.00 400.00

2005 Throwback Threads Material Combo Prime

*1-277 p/r 20-25: 1.25X TO 3X JSYp/r150-250
*1-277 p/r 20-25: 1X TO 2.5X JSY p/r 75-100
*1-277 p/r 20-25: .75X TO 2X JSY p/r 40-50
*1-277 p/r 20-25: .6X TO 1.5X JSY p/r 20-35
*1-277 p/r 20-25: .5X TO 1.2X JSY p/r 15
*1-277 p/r 15: 1.5X TO 4X JSY p/r 150-250
*1-277 p/r 15: 1X TO 2.5X JSY p/r 40-50
*278-300 p/r 25: .75X TO 2X JSY p/r 50
*278-300 p/r 25: .6X TO 1.5X JSY p/r 25
OVERALL AU-GU ODDS 1:8
PRINT RUNS B/WN 5-40 COPIES PER
NO PRICING ON QTY OF 10 OR LESS
4 Angel Berroa Bat-Jsy/25 5.00 12.00
81 Tim Salmon Bat-Jsy/25 8.00 20.00
183 Frank Thomas Hat-Jsy/15 12.50 30.00
266 Juan Gonzalez Bat-Jsy/40 4.00 10.00
288 K.Hern RET Bat-Jsy/25 6.00 15.00

2005 Throwback Threads Material Jersey

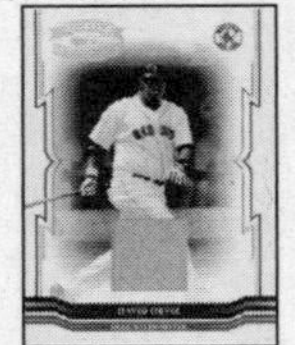

OVERALL AU-GU ODDS 1:8
PRINT RUNS B/WN 5-250 COPIES PER
NO PRICING ON QTY OF 10 OR LESS
1 Luis Castillo/45 2.50 6.00
3 Eric Chavez/250 1.50 4.00
5 Jeff Bagwell/250 2.50 6.00
6 J.T. Snow/250 1.50 4.00
7 Craig Biggio/50 4.00 10.00
9 Hank Blalock/25 3.00 8.00
10 Chipper Jones/250 3.00 8.00
11 Jacque Jones/250 1.50 4.00
12 Mark Teixeira/150 2.50 6.00
15 Jim Edmonds/250 1.50 4.00
16 Aramis Ramirez/250 1.50 4.00
17 Lance Berkman/250 1.50 4.00
18 Javy Lopez/250 1.50 4.00
20 Jorge Posada/250 2.50 6.00
21 Sean Casey/250 1.50 4.00
22 Mark Prior/50 4.00 10.00
23 Phil Nevin/50 2.50 6.00
24 Manny Ramirez/250 2.50 6.00
25 Andruw Jones/250 2.50 6.00
27 Vladimir Guerrero/250 3.00 8.00
28 Austin Kearns/250 1.50 4.00
29 John Smoltz/250 2.50 6.00
31 Mike Piazza/250 3.00 8.00
32 Jason Jennings/250 1.50 4.00
34 David Ortiz/250 2.50 6.00
35 Mike Mussina/250 2.50 6.00
38 Carlos Zambrano/250 1.50 4.00
42 Mariano Rivera/50 5.00 12.00
43 Joey Gathright/100 2.00 5.00
44 Adam Dunn/250 1.50 4.00
47 Roy Oswalt/250 1.50 4.00
49 Torii Hunter/100 2.00 5.00
52 C.C. Sabathia/250 1.50 4.00
53 Bobby Abreu/250 1.50 4.00
56 Mark Buehrle/250 1.50 4.00
57 Johan Santana/250 3.00 8.00
58 Mike Sweeney/75 2.00 5.00
62 Craig Wilson/250 1.50 4.00
64 Bobby Crosby/100 2.00 5.00
66 Scott Rolen/250 2.50 6.00
67 Jose Vidro/75 2.00 5.00
74 Mike Cameron/250 1.50 4.00
75 Barry Zito/250 1.50 4.00
83 Kevin Mench/250 1.50 4.00
84 Ivan Rodriguez/250 2.50 6.00
87 Jamie Moyer/50 2.50 6.00
91 Francisco Cordero/250 1.50 4.00
94 Cliff Lee/250 1.50 4.00
98 Brad Radke/250 1.50 4.00
100 Garret Anderson/50 2.50 6.00
101 Rafael Furcal/100 2.00 5.00
102 Jack Wilson/15 4.00 10.00
103 Bernie Williams/250 2.50 6.00
104 Josh Beckett/25 3.00 8.00
105 Albert Pujols/250 6.00 15.00
109 Hideo Nomo/250 3.00 8.00
110 Vernon Wells/250 1.50 4.00
114 Paul Konerko/250 1.50 4.00
116 Francisco Rodriguez/250 1.50 4.00
117 Johnny Damon/250 2.50 6.00
118 David Wright/250 4.00 10.00
119 Lyle Overbay/250 1.50 4.00
120 Brian Roberts/100 2.00 5.00
122 Roger Clemens/100 5.00 12.00
124 Larry Bigbie/200 1.50 4.00
125 Rafael Palmeiro/250 2.50 6.00
126 Jason Giambi/250 1.50 4.00
127 Higeki Matsui/250 6.00 15.00
132 Matt Morris/20 3.00 8.00
134 Kerry Wood/250 1.50 4.00
135 Dontrelle Willis/250 1.50 4.00
136 Michael Young/250 1.50 4.00
137 Andy Pettitte/250 2.50 6.00
140 Rich Harden/5
141 Bret Boone/250 1.50 4.00
146 Kazuhisa Ishii/250 1.50 4.00
147 Carlos Delgado/250 1.50 4.00
148 Tom Glavine/250 2.50 6.00
154 Pat Burrell/250 1.50 4.00
155 Melvin Mora/250 1.50 4.00
156 Jose Reyes/200 1.50 4.00
157 Trot Nixon/250 1.50 4.00
158 B.J. Upton/250 1.50 4.00
159 Jody Gerut/100 2.00 5.00
161 Miguel Tejada/35 3.00 8.00
162 Barry Larkin/40 4.00 10.00
163 Carl Crawford/40 2.50 6.00
164 Ben Sheets/250 1.50 4.00
166 Darin Erstad/25 3.00 8.00
167 Todd Helton/150 2.50 6.00
168 Luis Gonzalez/250 1.50 4.00
170 David Dellucci/150 1.50 4.00
171 Marcus Giles/15 4.00 10.00
172 Shannon Stewart/250 1.50 4.00
174 Miguel Cabrera/100 3.00 8.00
176 Derrek Lee/250 2.50 6.00
177 Jim Thome/250 2.50 6.00
178 Ken Harvey/150 1.50 4.00
180 Roy Halladay/250 1.50 4.00
182 Greg Maddux/250 4.00 10.00
184 Travis Hafner/5
186 Victor Martinez/250 1.50 4.00
189 Dewon Brazelton/250 1.50 4.00
190 Adrian Beltre/250 1.50 4.00
193 Alfonso Soriano/250 1.50 4.00
197 A.J. Burnett/250 1.50 4.00
200 Rocco Baldelli/250 1.50 4.00
201 Curt Schilling/250 2.50 6.00
202 Ryan Wagner/250 1.50 4.00
203 Preston Wilson/250 1.50 4.00
211 Frank Catalanotto/250 1.50 4.00
212 Casey Kotchman/250 1.50 4.00
214 Brandon Inge/250 1.50 4.00
221 Brett Myers/50 2.50 6.00
224 Brian Giles/20 3.00 8.00
232 Jason Lane/95 2.00 5.00
233 Jeremy Bonderman/250 1.50 4.00
234 Livan Hernandez/250 1.50 4.00
235 Ryan Klesko/250 1.50 4.00
237 Jimmy Rollins/35 3.00 8.00
252 Mike Lowell/250 1.50 4.00
257 Garrett Atkins/250 1.50 4.00
258 Junior Spivey/250 1.50 4.00
259 Morgan Ensberg/150 1.50 4.00
260 Chone Figgins/250 1.50 4.00
262 Jason Bay/250 1.50 4.00
269 Rodrigo Lopez/250 1.50 4.00
270 Geoff Jenkins/250 1.50 4.00
272 Orlando Hudson/20 3.00 8.00
275 Luis Matos/250 1.50 4.00
279 Bert Blyleven RET/50 3.00 8.00
281 Cal Ripken RET/250 15.00 40.00
282 Dale Murphy RET/25 6.00 15.00
283 Gary Carter RET/50 3.00 8.00
284 George Brett RET/50 8.00 20.00
285 Harmon Killebrew RET/25 8.00 20.00
286 Harold Baines RET/50 3.00 8.00
287 John Kruk RET/50 5.00 12.00
288 Keith Hernandez RET/10
289 Willie Mays RET Pants/25 20.00 50.00
290 Matt Williams RET/50 5.00 12.00
291 Nolan Ryan RET/50 10.00 25.00
292 Paul Molitor RET/50 3.00 8.00
293 Reggie Jackson RET/25 6.00 15.00
294 Rickey Henderson RET/50 6.00 15.00
295 Ron Cey RET/50 3.00 8.00
296 Ryne Sandberg RET/50 8.00 20.00
297 Ted Williams RET/25 30.00 60.00
298 Tom Seaver RET/25 6.00 15.00
299 Tony Gwynn RET/50 6.00 15.00
300 Babe Ruth RET/25 200.00 300.00

2005 Throwback Threads Material Jersey Prime

*1-277 p/r 75-100: .75X TO 2X JSYp/r150-250
*1-277 p/r 75-100: .6X TO 1.5X JSY p/r 75-100
*1-277 p/r 75-100: .5X TO 1.2X JSY p/r 40-50
*1-277 p/r 75-100: .4X TO 1X JSY p/r 20-35
*1-277 p/r 75-100: .3X TO .8X JSY p/r 15
*1-277 p/r 40-50: 1X TO 2.5X JSY p/r 150-250
*1-277 p/r 40-50: .75X TO 2X JSY p/r 75-100
*1-277 p/r 40-50: .6X TO 1.5X JSY p/r 40-50
*1-277 p/r 40-50: .5X TO 1.2X JSY p/r 20-35
*1-277 p/r 20-35: 1.25X TO 3X JSYp/r150-250
*1-277 p/r 20-35: 1X TO 2.5X JSY p/r 75-100
*1-277 p/r 20-35: .75X TO 2X JSY p/r 40-50
*278-300 p/r 100: .4X TO 1X JSY p/r 25
*278-300 p/r 50: .6X TO 1.5X JSY p/r 50
*278-300 p/r 25: .75X TO 2X JSY p/r 50
*278-300 p/r 25: .6X TO 1.5X JSY p/r 25
OVERALL AU-GU ODDS 1:8
PRINT RUNS B/WN 10-100 COPIES PER
NO PRICING ON QTY OF 10
4 Angel Berroa/50 4.00 10.00
39 Eric Byrnes/100 3.00 8.00
55 Brandon Webb/25 5.00 12.00
81 Tim Salmon/30 8.00 20.00
85 Sean Burroughs/100 3.00 8.00
140 Rich Harden/40 4.00 10.00
183 Frank Thomas/100 6.00 15.00
184 Travis Hafner/35 5.00 12.00
194 Fernando Vina/100 3.00 8.00
266 Juan Gonzalez/50 4.00 10.00
288 Keith Hernandez RET/100 4.00 10.00

2005 Throwback Threads Signature Marks

OVERALL AU-GU ODDS 1:8
PRINT RUNS B/WN 5-1000 COPIES PER
NO PRICING ON QTY OF 10 OR LESS
3 Eric Chavez/10
4 Angel Berroa/25 6.00 15.00
7 Craig Biggio/5
10 Chipper Jones/5
11 Jacque Jones/15 12.50 30.00
13 Omar Vizquel/15 20.00 50.00
15 Jim Edmonds/5
19 Adam LaRoche/50 5.00 12.00
21 Sean Casey/15 12.50 30.00
22 Mark Prior/5
28 Austin Kearns/15 8.00 20.00
36 Joe Nathan/25 10.00 25.00
38 Carlos Zambrano/25 15.00 40.00
39 Eric Byrnes/50 5.00 12.00
41 Danny Kolb/25 6.00 15.00
44 Adam Dunn/5
45 Carlos Lee/25 10.00 25.00
47 Roy Oswalt/15 12.50 30.00
48 Torii Hunter/15 12.50 30.00
49 Scott Podsednik/20 15.00 40.00
52 C.C. Sabathia/25 10.00 25.00
56 Mark Buehrle/25 15.00 40.00
60 Edgar Renteria/10
62 Craig Wilson/50 5.00 12.00
64 Bobby Crosby/100 6.00 15.00
66 Scott Rolen/10
67 Jose Vidro/25 6.00 15.00
73 Octavio Dotel/25 6.00 15.00
75 Barry Zito/5
77 Russ Rohlicek/250 3.00 8.00
81 Tim Salmon/50 12.50 30.00
85 Sean Burroughs/25 6.00 15.00
87 Jamie Moyer/25 10.00 25.00
88 Orlando Cabrera/25 10.00 25.00
90 Phil Humber/50 10.00 25.00
91 Francisco Cordero/50 5.00 12.00
92 Danny Graves/25 6.00 15.00
93 Bucky Jacobsen/64 5.00 12.00
94 Cliff Lee/50 5.00 12.00
96 Jake Peavy/25 15.00 40.00
100 Garret Anderson/15 12.50 30.00
101 Rafael Furcal/25 10.00 25.00
102 Jack Wilson/100 6.00 15.00
104 Josh Beckett/5
108 Luke Scott/250 12.50 30.00
110 Vernon Wells/25 10.00 25.00
112 Chad Cordero/25 10.00 25.00
114 Paul Konerko/25 15.00 40.00
116 Francisco Rodriguez/25 10.00 25.00
118 David Wright/25 40.00 80.00
119 Lyle Overbay/25 6.00 15.00
120 Brian Roberts/100 6.00 15.00
123 Rickie Weeks/15 12.50 30.00
124 Larry Bigbie/75 4.00 10.00
129 Jeremy Affeldt/50 5.00 12.00
131 Troy Percival/25 10.00 25.00
133 Dave Gassner/1000 3.00 8.00
134 Kerry Wood/5
135 Dontrelle Willis/5
136 Michael Young/25 10.00 25.00
139 Miguel Negron/250 4.00 10.00
140 Rich Harden/50 8.00 20.00
142 Danny Rueckel/250 3.00 8.00
144 Randy Messenger/500 3.00 8.00
149 Russ Ortiz/25 6.00 15.00
155 Melvin Mora/10
157 Trot Nixon/25 10.00 25.00
158 B.J. Upton/25 10.00 25.00
159 Jody Gerut/25 6.00 15.00
162 Barry Larkin/10
164 Ben Sheets/15 12.50 30.00
165 Tim Hudson/10
170 David Dellucci/50 8.00 20.00
172 Shannon Stewart/25 10.00 25.00
174 Miguel Cabrera/15 20.00 50.00
175 Nick Johnson/25 10.00 25.00
176 Derrek Lee/25 15.00 40.00
178 Ken Harvey/50 5.00 12.00
179 Ambiorix Concepcion/500 3.00 8.00
180 Roy Halladay/10
183 Frank Thomas/5
184 Travis Hafner/50 8.00 20.00
189 Dewon Brazelton/66 4.00 10.00
190 Adrian Beltre/5
192 Alexis Rios/25 10.00 25.00
193 Alfonso Soriano/5
198 Milton Bradley/100 6.00 15.00
199 Brad Penny/25 6.00 15.00
202 Ryan Wagner/25 6.00 15.00
204 Akinori Otsuka/25 10.00 25.00
207 Mike Lieberthal/25 10.00 25.00
208 Shea Hillenbrand/25 10.00 25.00
209 Tom Gordon/25 6.00 15.00
212 Casey Kotchman/100 6.00 15.00
213 Justin Verlander/50 30.00 60.00
217 Steve Finley/15 12.50 30.00
220 Dan Haren/25 10.00 25.00
226 Casey Rogowski/250 4.00 10.00
230 Erick Threets/500 3.00 8.00
232 Jason Lane/25 10.00 25.00
233 Jeremy Bonderman/50 8.00 20.00
234 Livan Hernandez/25 10.00 25.00
239 Shingo Takatsu/25 10.00 25.00
240 Scott Kazmir/5
245 Mark Loretta/25 6.00 15.00
248 Magglio Ordonez/15 12.50 30.00
250 Jared Gothreaux/1000 3.00 8.00
254 Nate McLouth/1000 6.00 15.00
255 Delmon Young/10
258 Junior Spivey/25 6.00 15.00
259 Morgan Ensberg/25 10.00 25.00
260 Chone Figgins/50 5.00 12.00
262 Jason Bay/186 6.00 15.00
266 Juan Gonzalez/15 12.50 30.00
268 Dioner Navarro/75 4.00 10.00
269 Rodrigo Lopez/5
271 Jermaine Dye/25 10.00 25.00
272 Orlando Hudson/100 4.00 10.00
275 Luis Matos/50 5.00 12.00
278 Al Kaline RET/15 30.00 60.00
279 Bert Blyleven RET/25 10.00 25.00
280 Bill Madlock RET/50 8.00 20.00
281 Cal Ripken RET/25 100.00 175.00
282 Dale Murphy RET/25 15.00 40.00
283 Gary Carter RET/10
284 George Brett RET/5
285 Harmon Killebrew RET/15 30.00 60.00
286 Harold Baines RET/25 10.00 25.00
288 Keith Hernandez RET/25 10.00 25.00
290 Matt Williams RET/25 15.00 40.00
291 Nolan Ryan RET/10
292 Paul Molitor RET/10
293 Reggie Jackson RET/10
295 Ron Cey RET/15 12.50 30.00
296 Ryne Sandberg RET/10
298 Tom Seaver RET/5
299 Tony Gwynn RET/10

2005 Throwback Threads Century Stars

*SPECTRUM: 1X TO 2.5X BASIC
SPECTRUM PRINT RUN 100 #'d SETS
OVERALL INSERT ODDS 1:2
1 Bobby Doerr .60 1.50
2 Derek Jeter 2.00 5.00
3 Harmon Killebrew 1.00 2.50
4 Paul Molitor .60 1.50
5 Brooks Robinson 1.00 2.50
6 Steve Garvey .60 1.50
7 Ivan Rodriguez 1.00 2.50
8 Carl Yastrzemski 1.50 4.00
9 Nomar Garciaparra 1.00 2.50
10 Miguel Tejada .60 1.50
11 Edgar Martinez 1.00 2.50
12 Kevin Brown .60 1.50
13 Alex Rodriguez 1.50 4.00
14 Carlton Fisk 1.00 2.50
15 Craig Biggio 1.00 2.50
16 Dwight Gooden .60 1.50
17 Jim Palmer .60 1.50
18 Ken Griffey Jr. 1.50 4.00
19 Bob Feller .60 1.50
20 Don Sutton .60 1.50
21 Al Kaline 1.00 2.50
22 Roger Clemens 1.50 4.00
23 Kirk Gibson .60 1.50
24 Willie Mays 2.00 5.00
25 Frank Robinson .60 1.50
26 Randy Johnson 1.00 2.50
27 Catfish Hunter .60 1.50
28 Austin Kearns .60 1.50
29 John Smoltz 1.00 2.50
30 Nolan Ryan 2.50 6.00
31 Duke Snider 1.00 2.50
32 Bernie Williams 1.00 2.50
33 David Wells .60 1.50
34 Bo Jackson 1.00 2.50
35 Mike Mussina 1.00 2.50
36 Gaylord Perry .60 1.50
37 Andre Dawson .60 1.50
38 Curt Schilling 1.00 2.50
39 Darryl Strawberry .60 1.50
40 Willie McCovey 1.00 2.50
41 Tom Seaver 1.00 2.50
42 Mariano Rivera 1.00 2.50
43 Dennis Eckersley .60 1.50
44 David Cone .60 1.50
45 Bret Boone .60 1.50
46 Will Clark 1.00 2.50
47 Jack Morris .60 1.50
48 Ichiro Suzuki 2.00 5.00
49 Alan Trammell .60 1.50
50 Cal Ripken 4.00 10.00

2005 Throwback Threads Century Stars Material

PRINT RUNS B/WN 20-50 COPIES PER
PRIME PRINT RUN 5 SERIAL #'d SETS
NO PRIME PRICING DUE TO SCARCITY
OVERALL AU-GU ODDS 1:8
1 Bobby Doerr Pants/50 3.00 8.00
3 Harmon Killebrew Jsy/50 6.00 15.00
4 Paul Molitor Jsy/50 3.00 8.00
5 Brooks Robinson Bat/50 5.00 12.00
6 Steve Garvey Jsy/50 3.00 8.00
7 Ivan Rodriguez Jsy/50 4.00 10.00
8 Carl Yastrzemski Jsy/50 6.00 15.00
10 Miguel Tejada Jsy/50 2.50 6.00
11 Edgar Martinez Jsy/50 5.00 12.00
12 Kevin Brown Jsy/50 2.50 6.00
14 Carlton Fisk Jsy/50 5.00 12.00
15 Craig Biggio Jsy/50 4.00 10.00
16 Dwight Gooden Jsy/50 3.00 8.00
17 Jim Palmer Jsy/50 3.00 8.00
19 Bob Feller Pants/20 4.00 10.00
20 Don Sutton Jsy/50 3.00 8.00
21 Al Kaline Bat/50 6.00 15.00
22 Roger Clemens Jsy/50 6.00 15.00
23 Kirk Gibson Jsy/50 3.00 8.00
24 Willie Mays Jsy/20 20.00 50.00
25 Frank Robinson Bat/50 3.00 8.00
26 Randy Johnson Jsy/50 5.00 12.00
27 Catfish Hunter Jsy/20 4.00 10.00
28 Austin Kearns Jsy/50 2.50 6.00
29 John Smoltz Jsy/50 4.00 10.00
30 Nolan Ryan Jkt/50 10.00 25.00
31 Duke Snider Pants/20 6.00 15.00
32 Bernie Williams Jsy/50 4.00 10.00
33 David Wells Jsy/50 2.50 6.00
34 Bo Jackson Jsy/50 6.00 15.00
35 Mike Mussina Jsy/50 4.00 10.00
36 Gaylord Perry Jsy/50 3.00 8.00
37 Andre Dawson Jsy/50 3.00 8.00
38 Curt Schilling Jsy/50 4.00 10.00
39 Darryl Strawberry Jsy/50 3.00 8.00
40 Willie McCovey Jsy/50 5.00 12.00
41 Tom Seaver Jsy/20 6.00 15.00
42 Mariano Rivera Jsy/50 5.00 12.00
43 Dennis Eckersley Jsy/50 3.00 8.00
44 David Cone Jsy/50 3.00 8.00
45 Bret Boone Jsy/50 2.50 6.00
46 Will Clark Jsy/20 6.00 15.00
47 Jack Morris Jsy/50 3.00 8.00
49 Alan Trammell Jsy/50 3.00 8.00
50 Cal Ripken Jsy/50 15.00 40.00

2005 Throwback Threads Century Stars Signature Material

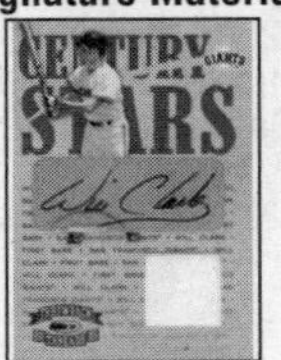

STATED PRINT RUN 10 SERIAL #'d SETS
PRIME PRINT RUN 5 SERIAL #'d SETS
OVERALL AU-GU ODDS 1:8
NO PRICING DUE TO SCARCITY

2005 Throwback Threads Dynasty

*SPECTRUM: 1X TO 2.5X BASIC
SPECTRUM PRINT RUN 100 #'d SETS
OVERALL INSERT ODDS 1:2
1 Reggie Jackson 1.00 2.50
Catfish Hunter
Sparky Lyle
2 Cal Ripken 4.00 10.00
Jim Palmer
Eddie Murray
3 Dwight Gooden .60 1.50

Gary Carter
Darryl Strawberry
4 Rickey Henderson 1.00 2.50
Dennis Eckersley
Jose Canseco
5 Chipper Jones 1.50 4.00
Greg Maddux
David Justice
6 Roger Clemens 1.50 4.00
Alfonso Soriano
Bernie Williams
7 Randy Johnson 1.00 2.50
Curt Schilling
Matt Williams
8 Troy Glaus .60 1.50
Garret Anderson
Francisco Rodriguez
9 Josh Beckett 1.00 2.50
Miguel Cabrera
Mike Lowell
10 Curt Schilling 1.00 2.50
Manny Ramirez
Jason Varitek

2005 Throwback Threads Dynasty Material

PRINT RUNS B/WN 20-50 COPIES PER
PRIME PRINT RUN 5 SERIAL #'d SETS
NO PRIME PRICING DUE TO SCARCITY
OVERALL AU-GU ODDS 1:8
1 Reggie Jackson Pants 8.00 20.00
Catfish Hunter Pants
Sparky Lyle Pants/50
2 Cal Ripken Jsy 20.00 50.00
Jim Palmer Jsy
Eddie Murray Jsy/50
3 Dwight Gooden Jsy 6.00 15.00
Gary Carter Jsy
Darryl Strawberry Pants/20
4 Rickey Henderson Jsy 20.00 50.00
Dennis Eckersley Pants
Jose Canseco Jsy/50
5 Chipper Jones Jsy 12.50 30.00
Greg Maddux Jsy
David Justice Jsy/50
6 Roger Clemens Jsy 12.50 30.00
Alfonso Soriano Jsy
Bernie Williams Jsy/50
7 Randy Johnson Jsy 10.00 25.00
Curt Schilling Jsy
Matt Williams Jsy/50
8 Troy Glaus Jsy 5.00 12.00
Garret Anderson Jsy
Francisco Rodriguez Jsy/50
9 Josh Beckett Jsy 6.00 15.00
Miguel Cabrera Jsy
Mike Lowell Jsy/20
10 Curt Schilling Jsy 15.00 40.00
Manny Ramirez Jsy
Jason Varitek Jsy/50

2005 Throwback Threads Generations

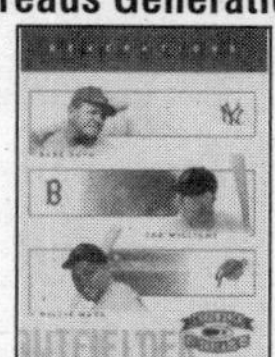

*SPECTRUM: 1X TO 2.5X BASIC
SPECTRUM PRINT RUN 100 #'d SETS
OVERALL INSERT ODDS 1:2
1 Duke Snider 1.00 2.50
Reggie Jackson
Sammy Sosa
2 Rod Carew 1.00 2.50
John Kruk
Eric Chavez
3 Bo Jackson 1.00 2.50
Deion Sanders
Brian Jordan
4 George Brett 2.00 5.00
Tony Gwynn
Todd Helton
5 Babe Ruth 2.00 5.00
Ted Williams
Willie Mays
6 Rickey Henderson 2.00 5.00
Lenny Dykstra
Ichiro Suzuki
7 Keith Hernandez 2.00 5.00
Don Mattingly
Casey Kotchman
8 Wade Boggs 1.00 2.50
Mark Grace
Hank Blalock
9 Gary Carter 1.00 2.50
Ivan Rodriguez
Victor Martinez
10 Gaylord Perry 1.50 4.00
Jack Morris
Greg Maddux
11 Joe Morgan 2.00 5.00
Ryne Sandberg
Alfonso Soriano
12 Juan Marichal 1.00 2.50
Luis Tiant
Pedro Martinez
13 Stan Musial 1.50 4.00
Carl Yastrzemski
Lance Berkman
14 Johnny Bench 1.00 2.50
Carlton Fisk
Mike Piazza
15 Harmon Killebrew 4.00 10.00
Cal Ripken
Albert Pujols
16 Frank Robinson .60 1.50
Andre Dawson
Gary Sheffield
17 Bob Feller 1.50 4.00
Roger Clemens
Kerry Wood
18 Steve Carlton 1.00 2.50
Tom Glavine
Barry Zito
19 Eddie Murray 1.00 2.50
Rafael Palmeiro
Mark Teixeira
20 Brooks Robinson 2.00 5.00
Mike Schmidt
Scott Rolen
21 Luis Aparicio 1.00 2.50
Omar Vizquel
Rafael Furcal
22 Don Sutton .60 1.50
David Cone
Roy Oswalt
23 Fred Lynn 1.00 2.50
Dale Murphy
Jim Edmonds
24 Ozzie Smith 1.50 4.00
Barry Larkin
B.J. Upton
25 Bob Gibson 2.50 6.00
Nolan Ryan
Mark Prior

2005 Throwback Threads Generations Material

PRINT RUNS B/WN 20-50 COPIES PER
PRIME PRINT RUN 10 SERIAL #'d SETS
NO PRIME PRICING DUE TO SCARCITY
OVERALL AU-GU ODDS 1:8
1 Duke Snider Pants 15.00 40.00
Reggie Jackson Jsy
Sammy Sosa Jsy/20
2 Rod Carew Jsy 8.00 20.00
John Kruk Jsy
Eric Chavez Jsy/50
3 Bo Jackson Jsy 12.50 30.00
Deion Sanders Jsy
Brian Jordan Jsy/50
4 George Brett Jsy 12.50 30.00
Tony Gwynn Jsy
Todd Helton Jsy/50
5 Babe Ruth Jsy 300.00 500.00
Ted Williams Jsy
Willie Mays Jsy/20
7 Keith Hernandez Jsy 15.00 40.00
Don Mattingly Pants
Casey Kotchman Jsy/20
8 Wade Boggs Jsy 8.00 20.00
Mark Grace Jsy
Hank Blalock Jsy/50
9 Gary Carter Jsy 8.00 20.00
Ivan Rodriguez Jsy
Victor Martinez Jsy/50
10 Gaylord Perry Jsy 12.50 30.00
Jack Morris Jsy
Greg Maddux Jsy/50
11 Joe Morgan Jsy 12.50 30.00
Ryne Sandberg Jsy
Alfonso Soriano Jsy/50
12 Juan Marichal Pants 8.00 20.00
Luis Tiant Pants
Pedro Martinez Jsy/50
13 Stan Musial Pants 20.00 50.00
Carl Yastrzemski Pants
Lance Berkman Jsy/20
14 Johnny Bench Pants 10.00 25.00
Carlton Fisk Jsy
Mike Piazza Jsy/50
15 Harmon Killebrew Jsy 30.00 60.00
Cal Ripken Jsy
Albert Pujols Jsy/50
16 Frank Robinson Bat 6.00 15.00
Andre Dawson Jsy
Gary Sheffield Jsy/20
17 Bob Feller Pants 15.00 40.00
Roger Clemens Jsy
Kerry Wood Jsy/20
18 Steve Carlton Jsy 8.00 20.00
Tom Glavine Jsy
Barry Zito Jsy/50
19 Eddie Murray Jsy 10.00 25.00
Rafael Palmeiro Jsy
Mark Teixeira Jsy/50
20 Brooks Robinson Jsy 15.00 40.00
Mike Schmidt Jsy
Scott Rolen Jsy/20
21 Luis Aparicio Jsy 10.00 25.00
Omar Vizquel Jsy
Rafael Furcal Jsy/20
22 Don Sutton Jsy 6.00 15.00
David Cone Jsy
Roy Oswalt Jsy/20
23 Fred Lynn Jsy 8.00 20.00
Dale Murphy Jsy
Jim Edmonds Jsy/50
24 Ozzie Smith Jsy 12.50 30.00
Barry Larkin Jsy
B.J. Upton Bat/20
25 Bob Gibson Jsy 20.00 50.00
Nolan Ryan Jsy
Mark Prior Jsy/50

2005 Throwback Threads Player Timelines

*SPECTRUM: 1X TO 2.5X BASIC
SPECTRUM PRINT RUN 100 #'d SETS
OVERALL INSERT ODDS 1:2
1 D.Murphy Braves-Phils 1.00 2.50
2 G.Maddux Braves-Cubs 1.50 4.00
3 T.Glavine Braves-Mets 1.00 2.50
4 David Ortiz Twins-Sox 1.00 2.50
5 Bo Jackson Royals-Sox 1.00 2.50
6 Lyle Overbay D'backs-Brew .60 1.50
7 Tommy John Yanks-Angels .60 1.50
8 Shawn Green Jays-Dgr .60 1.50
9 Aramis Ramirez Pirates-Cubs .60 1.50
10 Javy Lopez Braves-O's .60 1.50
11 Vladimir Guerrero Expos-Angels 1.00 2.50
12 Travis Hafner Rgr-Indians .60 1.50
13 Junior Spivey D'backs-Brew .60 1.50
14 Alfonso Soriano Yanks-Rgr .60 1.50
15 Andre Dawson Expos-Cubs-Sox .60 1.50
16 Sammy Sosa Sox-Cubs 1.00 2.50
17 Andy Pettitte Yanks-Astros 1.00 2.50
18 Jim Edmonds Angels-Cards .60 1.50
19 Willie McCovey Giants-Padres 1.00 2.50
20 Scott Rolen Phils-Cards 1.00 2.50
21 Jermaine Dye Royals-A's .60 1.50
22 Pedro Martinez Dgr-Expos-Sox 1.00 2.50
23 Don Sutton Dgr-Astros-Angels .60 1.50
24 Randy Johnson Expos-M's-Astros 1.00 2.50
25 Nolan Ryan Mets-Angels-Astros 2.50 6.00
26 Dennis Eckersley Sox-A's-Cards .60 1.50
27 Reggie Jackson A's-Yanks-Angels 1.00 2.50
28 Deion Sanders Yanks-Braves-Reds 1.00 2.50
29 Curt Schilling Phils-D'backs-Sox .60 1.50
30 Rickey Henderson Yanks-Padres-Dgr 1.00 2.50
31 Mike Piazza Dgr-M's-Mets 1.00 2.50
32 Gary Carter Expos-Mets-Dgr .60 1.50
33 Roberto Alomar O's-Indians-Mets 1.00 2.50
34 Hideo Nomo Dgr-Mets-Sox 1.00 2.50
35 Andres Galarraga Braves-Rgr-Giants .60 1.50
36 Juan Gonzalez Rgr-Indians-Royals .60 1.50
37 Roger Clemens Sox-Yanks-Astros 1.50 4.00
38 Jeff Kent Jays-Giants-Astros .60 1.50
39 Steve Carlton Phils-Sox-Giants .60 1.50
40 Wade Boggs Sox-Yanks-Rays 1.00 2.50

2005 Throwback Threads Player Timelines Material

OVERALL AU-GU ODDS 1:8
PRINT RUNS B/WN 25-250 COPIES PER
1 D.Murphy Braves-Phils/50 6.00 15.00
2 G.Maddux Braves-Cubs/100 5.00 12.00
3 T.Glavine Braves-Mets/50 5.00 12.00
4 David Ortiz Twins-Sox/250 3.00 8.00
5 Bo Jackson Royals-Sox/100 6.00 15.00
6 Lyle Overbay D'backs-Brew/250 2.00 5.00
7 Tommy John Yanks Pants-Angels/250 2.50 6.00
8 Shawn Green Jays-Dgr/100 2.50 6.00
9 Aramis Ramirez Pirates-Cubs/250 2.00 5.00
10 Javy Lopez Braves-O's/100 2.50 6.00
11 Vladimir Guerrero Expos-Angels/25 8.00 20.00
12 Travis Hafner Rgr-Indians/25 4.00 10.00
13 Junior Spivey D'backs-Brew/250 2.00 5.00
14 Alfonso Soriano Yanks-Rgr/100 2.50 6.00
16 Sammy Sosa Sox-Cubs/250 4.00 10.00
17 Andy Pettitte Yanks-Astros/100 4.00 10.00
18 Jim Edmonds Angels-Cards/100 2.50 6.00
19 Willie McCovey 6.00 15.00
Giants Pants-Padres/50
20 Scott Rolen Phils-Cards/50 5.00 12.00
21 Jermaine Dye Royals-A's/100 2.50 6.00
22 Pedro Martinez 6.00 15.00
Dodgers-Expos-Red Sox/50
23 Don Sutton Dgr-Astros-Angels/25 6.00 15.00
24 Randy Johnson Expos-M's-Astros/50 8.00 20.00
25 Nolan Ryan 20.00 50.00
Mets-Angels Jacket-Astros/50
27 Reggie Jackson 8.00 20.00
A's-Yanks Pants-Angels/50
28 Deion Sanders Yanks-Braves-Reds/25 10.00 25.00
29 Curt Schilling Phils-D'backs-Sox/50 4.00 10.00
30 Rickey Henderson 8.00 20.00
Yanks Pants-Padres Pants-Dodgers/100
31 Mike Piazza Dgr-M's-Mets/50 8.00 20.00
32 Gary Carter 5.00 12.00
Expos-Mets-Dgr Chest Prot/50
33 Roberto Alomar O's-Indians-Mets/250 5.00 12.00
34 Hideo Nomo Dgr-Mets-Sox/50 8.00 20.00
35 Andres Galarraga 3.00 8.00
Braves-Rangers-Giants/250
36 Juan Gonzalez Rgr-Indians-Royals/25 5.00 12.00
37 Roger Clemens Sox-Yanks-Astros/25 15.00 40.00
38 Jeff Kent Jays-Giants-Astros/50 4.00 10.00

2005 Throwback Threads Player Timelines Signature Material

PRINT RUNS B/WN 5-50 COPIES PER
NO PRICING ON QTY OF 10 OR LESS
PRIME PRINT RUNS B/WN 5-10 COPIES PER
NO PRIME PRICING DUE TO SCARCITY
OVERALL AU-GU ODDS 1:8
1 D.Murphy Braves-Phils/50 15.00 40.00
5 Bo Jackson Royals-Sox/10
6 Lyle Overbay D'backs-Brew/50 6.00 15.00
7 Tommy John Yanks Pants-Angels/50 10.00 25.00
8 Shawn Green Jays-Dgr/10
12 Travis Hafner Rgr-Indians/25 12.50 30.00
13 Junior Spivey D'backs-Brew/50 6.00 15.00
14 Alfonso Soriano Yanks-Rgr/10
15 Andre Dawson 12.50 30.00
Expos-Cubs-White Sox/25
18 Jim Edmonds Angels-Cards/10
19 Willie McCovey Giants Pants-Padres/10
20 Scott Rolen Phils-Cards/10
21 Jermaine Dye Royals-A's/50 10.00 25.00
22 Pedro Martinez Dgr-Expos-Sox/5
23 Don Sutton Dgr-Astros-Angels/25 12.50 30.00
25 Nolan Ryan Mets-Angels Jkt-Astros/10
26 Dennis Eckersley Sox-A's-Cards/10
27 Reggie Jackson A's-Yanks Pants-Angels/10
28 Deion Sanders Yanks-Braves-Reds/5
29 Curt Schilling Phils-D'backs-Sox/5
30 Rickey Henderson Yanks Pants-Padres Pants-Dgr/5
32 Gary Carter 10.00 25.00
Expos-Mets-Dodgers Chest Prot/50
33 Roberto Alomar O's-Indians-Mets/10
36 Juan Gonzalez Rgr-Indians-Royals/25 12.50 30.00
37 Roger Clemens Sox-Yanks-Astros/5
40 Wade Boggs Sox-Yanks-Rays/15 30.00 60.00

2005 Throwback Threads Polo Grounds 85 HIT Long Fly

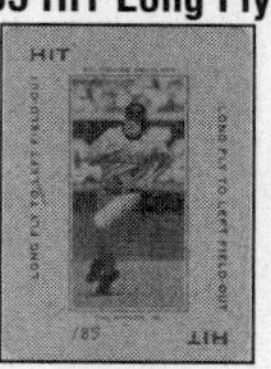

STATED PRINT RUN 85 SERIAL #'d SETS
*PARALLEL #'d OF 50-75: .4X TO 1X
*PARALLEL #'d OF 40-45: .5X TO 1.2X
*PARALLEL #'d OF 30-35: .6X TO 1.5X
*PARALLEL #'d OF 20-25: .75X TO 2X
*PARALLEL #'d OF 15: 1X TO 2.5X
PARALLELS #'d FROM 5-75 COPIES PER
NO PRICING ON QTY OF 5
OVERALL INSERT ODDS 1:2
1 Ken Griffey Jr. 2.50 6.00
2 Roger Clemens 3.00 8.00
3 Barry Zito 1.25 3.00
4 Alex Rodriguez 2.50 6.00
5 Melvin Mora 1.25 3.00
6 Kevin Brown 1.25 3.00
7 Chipper Jones 1.50 4.00
8 Scott Kazmir 1.25 3.00
9 Kip Wells 1.25 3.00
10 Khalil Greene 1.50 4.00
11 Kevin Millwood 1.25 3.00
12 Kerry Wood 1.25 3.00
13 Mark Kotsay 1.25 3.00
14 Jeff Bagwell 1.50 4.00
15 Hank Blalock 1.25 3.00
16 Scott Rolen 1.50 4.00
17 Lance Berkman 1.25 3.00
18 Mike Mussina 1.50 4.00
19 Jim Edmonds 1.25 3.00
20 Jorge Posada 1.50 4.00
21 Curt Schilling 1.50 4.00
22 Vernon Wells 1.25 3.00
23 Pedro Martinez 1.50 4.00
24 Jeremy Reed 1.25 3.00
25 Hideki Matsui 2.50 6.00
26 Steve Finley 1.25 3.00
27 Gavin Floyd 1.25 3.00
28 Darin Erstad 1.25 3.00
29 Bernie Williams 1.50 4.00
30 Mark Mulder 1.25 3.00
31 Rafael Palmeiro 1.50 4.00
32 Andruw Jones 1.50 4.00
33 Roy Halladay 1.25 3.00
34 Dontrelle Willis 1.25 3.00
35 Bret Boone 1.25 3.00
36 Andy Pettitte 1.50 4.00
37 Vladimir Guerrero 1.50 4.00
38 Randy Johnson 1.50 4.00
39 Michael Young 1.25 3.00
40 Frank Thomas 1.50 4.00
41 Todd Helton 1.50 4.00
42 Johan Santana 1.50 4.00
43 Mark Teixeira 1.50 4.00
44 Justin Morneau 1.25 3.00
45 Brad Radke 1.25 3.00
46 Dallas McPherson 1.25 3.00
47 Tim Hudson 1.25 3.00
48 Carl Crawford 1.25 3.00
49 Eric Gagne 1.25 3.00
50 Mark Prior 1.50 4.00
51 Tom Glavine 1.50 4.00
52 Craig Biggio 1.50 4.00
53 John Smoltz 1.50 4.00
54 Manny Ramirez 1.50 4.00
55 Ivan Rodriguez 1.50 4.00
56 Gary Sheffield 1.25 3.00
57 Josh Beckett 1.25 3.00
58 Miguel Tejada 1.25 3.00
59 Bobby Abreu 1.25 3.00
60 Ichiro Suzuki 3.00 8.00
61 Sammy Sosa 1.50 4.00
62 Garret Anderson 1.25 3.00
63 Sean Casey 1.25 3.00
64 Troy Glaus 1.25 3.00
65 Larry Walker 1.50 4.00
66 Alfonso Soriano 1.25 3.00
67 Luis Gonzalez 1.25 3.00
68 Eric Chavez 1.25 3.00
69 Adrian Beltre 1.25 3.00
70 Miguel Cabrera 1.50 4.00
71 Carlos Beltran 1.25 3.00
72 Jim Thome 1.50 4.00
73 David Ortiz 1.50 4.00
74 Adam Dunn 1.25 3.00
75 Jacque Jones 1.25 3.00
76 Shawn Green 1.25 3.00
77 Victor Martinez 1.25 3.00
78 Torii Hunter 1.25 3.00
79 Carlos Lee 1.25 3.00
80 C.C. Sabathia 1.25 3.00
81 Joe Mauer 1.50 4.00
82 Kris Benson 1.25 3.00
83 Zack Greinke 1.25 3.00
84 Greg Maddux 2.50 6.00
85 David Wright 2.50 6.00
86 Mike Piazza 1.50 4.00
87 Johnny Damon 1.50 4.00
88 Derek Jeter 3.00 8.00
89 B.J. Upton 1.25 3.00
90 Albert Pujols 3.00 8.00
91 Cal Ripken 6.00 15.00
92 Nolan Ryan 4.00 10.00
93 George Brett 3.00 8.00
94 Don Mattingly 3.00 8.00
95 Ryne Sandberg 3.00 8.00
96 Rickey Henderson 1.50 4.00
97 Robin Yount 1.50 4.00
98 Mike Schmidt 3.00 8.00
99 Tony Gwynn 2.00 5.00
100 Willie Mays 3.00 8.00

2005 Throwback Threads Throwback Collection

*SPECTRUM: 1X TO 2.5X BASIC
SPECTRUM PRINT RUN 100 #'d SETS
OVERALL INSERT ODDS 1:2
1 Billy Martin 1.00 2.50
2 Tony Gwynn 1.25 3.00
3 Babe Ruth 2.00 5.00
4 Angel Berroa .60 1.50
5 Jeff Bagwell 1.00 2.50
6 Tony Oliva .60 1.50
7 Ivan Rodriguez 1.00 2.50
8 Gary Carter .60 1.50
9 Ted Williams 2.00 5.00
10 Chipper Jones 1.00 2.50
11 Al Oliver .60 1.50
12 Roberto Alomar 1.00 2.50
13 Omar Vizquel 1.00 2.50
14 Ernie Banks 1.00 2.50
15 Carlos Beltran .60 1.50
16 Garret Anderson .60 1.50
17 Mark Grace 1.00 2.50
18 Jason Giambi .60 1.50
19 Dave Righetti .60 1.50
20 Mike Schmidt 2.00 5.00
21 Roger Clemens 1.50 4.00
22 Juan Gonzalez .60 1.50
23 Carlos Delgado .60 1.50
24 Manny Ramirez 1.00 2.50
25 Jim Thome .60 1.50
26 Wade Boggs 1.00 2.50
27 Luis Tiant .60 1.50
28 Kerry Wood .60 1.50
29 Rod Carew 1.00 2.50
30 Dwight Evans 1.00 2.50
31 Mike Piazza 1.00 2.50
32 Billy Williams .60 1.50
33 Larry Walker 1.00 2.50
34 Nolan Ryan 2.50 6.00
35 Edgar Renteria .60 1.50
36 Greg Maddux 1.50 4.00
37 Gaylord Perry .60 1.50
38 Curt Schilling .60 1.50
39 Dave Parker .60 1.50
40 Andruw Jones 1.00 2.50
41 Orlando Cepeda .60 1.50
42 Fergie Jenkins .60 1.50
43 Kirby Puckett 1.00 2.50
44 Reggie Jackson 1.00 2.50
45 Bob Gibson 1.00 2.50
46 Rickey Henderson 1.00 2.50
47 Lee Smith .60 1.50
48 Lou Brock 1.00 2.50
49 Fred Lynn .60 1.50
50 Lance Berkman .60 1.50
51 Shawn Green .60 1.50
52 Hoyt Wilhelm .60 1.50
53 Sammy Sosa 1.00 2.50
54 Tim Hudson .60 1.50
55 Matt Williams 1.00 2.50
56 Marty Marion .60 1.50
57 Eric Chavez .60 1.50
58 Rafael Palmeiro 1.00 2.50
59 Randy Johnson 1.00 2.50
60 David Ortiz 1.00 2.50
61 Hank Blalock .60 1.50
62 Jim Rice .60 1.50
63 Mark Mulder .60 1.50
64 Kazuo Matsui .60 1.50
65 Pedro Martinez 1.00 2.50
66 Sean Casey .60 1.50
67 Carlos Lee .60 1.50
68 Stan Musial 1.50 4.00
69 Fred McGriff 1.00 2.50
70 Darryl Strawberry .60 1.50
71 Tommy John .60 1.50
72 Hideo Nomo 1.00 2.50
73 Johnny Bench 1.00 2.50
74 Cal Ripken 4.00 10.00
75 Harold Baines .60 1.50

2005 Throwback Threads Throwback Collection Material

OVERALL AU-GU ODDS 1:8
PRINT RUNS B/WN 5-500 COPIES PER
NO PRICING ON QTY OF 5
1 Billy Martin Pants/250 3.00 8.00
2 Tony Gwynn Jsy/250 4.00 10.00
3 Babe Ruth Pants/20 175.00 300.00
4 Angel Berroa Pants/100 2.00 5.00
5 Jeff Bagwell Jsy/250 2.50 6.00
6 Tony Oliva Jsy/250 2.00 5.00
7 Ivan Rodriguez Jsy/500 2.50 6.00
8 Gary Carter Pants/250 2.00 5.00
9 Ted Williams Jsy/20 30.00 60.00
10 Chipper Jones Jsy/250 3.00 8.00
11 Al Oliver Jsy/250 2.00 5.00
12 Roberto Alomar Jsy/500 3.00 8.00
13 Omar Vizquel Jsy/500 2.50 6.00
14 Ernie Banks Jsy/20 10.00 25.00
15 Carlos Beltran Jsy/100 2.00 5.00
16 Garret Anderson Jsy/50 2.50 6.00
17 Mark Grace Jsy/250 3.00 8.00
18 Jason Giambi Jsy/500 1.50 4.00
19 Dave Righetti Jsy/250 2.00 5.00
20 Mike Schmidt Jsy/20 10.00 25.00
21 Roger Clemens Jsy/250 4.00 10.00
22 Juan Gonzalez Jsy/150 1.50 4.00
23 Carlos Delgado Jsy/150 1.50 4.00
24 Manny Ramirez Jsy/50 4.00 10.00
25 Jim Thome Jsy/500 2.50 6.00
26 Wade Boggs Jsy/250 3.00 8.00
27 Luis Tiant Pants/500 2.00 5.00
28 Kerry Wood Jsy/50 2.50 6.00
29 Rod Carew Jkt/250 3.00 8.00
30 Dwight Evans Jsy/50 5.00 12.00
31 Mike Piazza Jsy/250 3.00 8.00
32 Billy Williams Jsy/100 2.50 6.00
33 Larry Walker Jsy/500 2.50 6.00
34 Nolan Ryan Pants/100 8.00 20.00
35 Edgar Renteria Jsy/500 1.50 4.00
36 Greg Maddux Jsy/375 4.00 10.00
37 Gaylord Perry Jsy/250 2.00 5.00
38 Curt Schilling Jsy/500 1.50 4.00
39 Dave Parker Jsy/50 3.00 8.00
40 Andruw Jones Jsy/500 2.50 6.00
41 Orlando Cepeda Pants/250 2.00 5.00
42 Fergie Jenkins Jsy/250 2.00 5.00
43 Kirby Puckett Jsy/400 4.00 10.00
44 Reggie Jackson Jsy/250 3.00 8.00
45 Bob Gibson Jsy/100 4.00 10.00
46 Rickey Henderson Jsy/500 4.00 10.00
47 Lee Smith Jsy/250 2.00 5.00
49 Fred Lynn Jsy/250 2.00 5.00
50 Lance Berkman Jsy/500 1.50 4.00
51 Shawn Green Jsy/500 1.50 4.00
52 Hoyt Wilhelm Jsy/250 2.00 5.00
53 Sammy Sosa Jsy/500 3.00 8.00
54 Tim Hudson Jsy/500 1.50 4.00
55 Matt Williams Jsy/250 3.00 8.00
56 Marty Marion Jsy/5
57 Eric Chavez Jsy/500 1.50 4.00
58 Rafael Palmeiro Jsy/500 2.50 6.00
59 Randy Johnson Jsy/250 3.00 8.00
60 David Ortiz Jsy/500 2.50 6.00
61 Hank Blalock Jsy/50 2.50 6.00
62 Jim Rice Pants/250 2.00 5.00
63 Mark Mulder Jsy/100 2.00 5.00
64 Kazuo Matsui Jsy/500 1.50 4.00
65 Pedro Martinez Jsy/250 2.50 6.00
66 Sean Casey Jsy/500 1.50 4.00
67 Carlos Lee Jsy/500 1.50 4.00
68 Stan Musial Pants/100 8.00 20.00
69 Fred McGriff Jsy/500 3.00 8.00
70 Darryl Strawberry Jsy/250 2.00 5.00
71 Tommy John Jsy/250 2.00 5.00
72 Hideo Nomo Jsy/500 3.00 8.00
73 Johnny Bench Pants/100 5.00 12.00
74 Cal Ripken Jsy/250 10.00 25.00
75 Harold Baines Jsy/250 2.00 5.00

2005 Throwback Threads Throwback Collection Material Prime

*PRIME p/r 25: 1.25X TO 3X MTL p/r 150+
*PRIME p/r 25: 1X TO 2.5X MTL p/r 100
*PRIME p/r 25: .75X TO 2X MTL p/r 50
*PRIME p/r 25: .6X TO 1.5X MTL p/r 20
OVERALL AU-GU ODDS 1:8
PRINT RUNS B/WN 5-25 COPIES PER
NO PRICING ON QTY OF 5
48 Lou Brock Jsy/25 10.00 25.00

2005 Throwback Threads Throwback Collection Material Combo

*COMBO p/r 100: .6X TO 1.5X MTL p/r 150+
*COMBO p/r 100: .5X TO 1.2X MTL p/r 100
*COMBO p/r 50: .75X TO 2X MTL p/r 150+
*COMBO p/r 50: .5X TO 1.2X MTL p/r 50
*COMBO p/r 20-25: .75X TO 2X MTL p/r 100
*COMBO p/r 20-25: .6X TO 1.5X MTL p/r 50
*COMBO p/r 20-25: .5X TO 1.2X MTL p/r 20
OVERALL AU-GU ODDS 1:8
PRINT RUNS B/WN 5-100 COPIES PER
NO PRICING ON QTY OF 10 OR LESS
3 Babe Ruth Bat-Pants/20 250.00 400.00

2005 Throwback Threads Throwback Collection Material Combo Prime

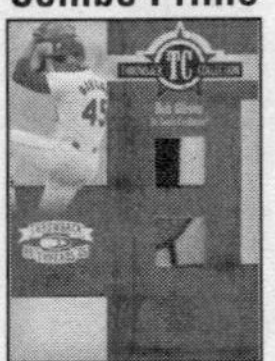

*COM.PRIMEp/r25: 1.25X TO 3X MTLp/r150+
*COM.PRIME p/r 25: 1X TO 2.5X MTL p/r 100
*COM.PRIME p/r 25: .75X TO 2X MTL p/r 50
OVERALL AU-GU ODDS 1:8
PRINT RUNS B/WN 5-25 COPIES PER
NO PRICING ON QTY OF 5
48 Lou Brock Bat-Jsy/25 10.00 25.00

2005 Throwback Threads Throwback Collection Signature Material

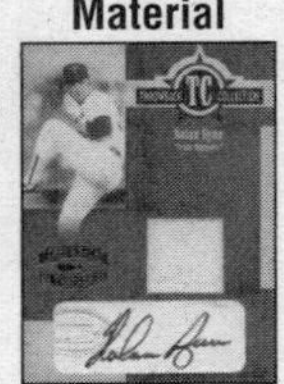

OVERALL AU-GU ODDS 1:8
PRINT RUNS B/WN 5-50 COPIES PER
NO PRICING ON QTY OF 10 OR LESS
2 Tony Gwynn Jsy/50 20.00 50.00
4 Angel Berroa Pants/50 6.00 15.00
5 Jeff Bagwell Jsy/20 30.00 60.00
6 Tony Oliva Jsy/50 10.00 25.00
8 Gary Carter Pants/50 10.00 25.00
10 Chipper Jones Jsy/20 30.00 60.00
12 Roberto Alomar Jsy/50 15.00 40.00
13 Omar Vizquel Jsy/50 15.00 40.00
14 Ernie Banks Jsy/20 30.00 60.00
15 Carlos Beltran Jsy/50 10.00 25.00
16 Garret Anderson Jsy/20 12.50 30.00
17 Mark Grace Jsy/50 15.00 40.00
19 Dave Righetti Jsy/50 10.00 25.00
20 Mike Schmidt Jsy/5
21 Roger Clemens Jsy/5
24 Manny Ramirez Jsy/5
26 Wade Boggs Jsy/50 15.00 40.00
27 Luis Tiant Pants/50 10.00 25.00
28 Kerry Wood Jsy/20 20.00 50.00
29 Rod Carew Jkt/50 15.00 40.00
30 Dwight Evans Jsy/25 20.00 50.00
32 Billy Williams Jsy/50 10.00 25.00
34 Nolan Ryan Pants/20 50.00 100.00
35 Edgar Renteria Jsy/50 10.00 25.00
37 Gaylord Perry Jsy/50 10.00 25.00
38 Curt Schilling Jsy/5
39 Dave Parker Jsy/50 10.00 25.00
41 Orlando Cepeda Pants/25 12.50 30.00
42 Fergie Jenkins Jsy/10 10.00 25.00
43 Kirby Puckett Jsy/10
44 Reggie Jackson Jsy/25 30.00 60.00
45 Bob Gibson Jsy/25 20.00 50.00
46 Rickey Henderson Jsy/5
49 Fred Lynn Jsy/50 10.00 25.00
51 Shawn Green Jsy/5
54 Tim Hudson Jsy/25 12.50 30.00
55 Matt Williams Jsy/50 15.00 40.00
56 Marty Marion Jsy/20 12.50 30.00
57 Eric Chavez Jsy/50 10.00 25.00
60 David Ortiz Jsy/5
61 Hank Blalock Jsy/5
62 Jim Rice Pants/50 10.00 25.00
63 Mark Mulder Jsy/50 10.00 25.00
65 Pedro Martinez Jsy/5
66 Sean Casey Jsy/50 10.00 25.00
67 Carlos Lee Jsy/50 10.00 25.00
68 Stan Musial Pants/25 40.00 80.00
70 Darryl Strawberry Jsy/50 10.00 25.00
71 Tommy John Jsy/50 10.00 25.00
72 Hideo Nomo Jsy/5
73 Johnny Bench Pants/25 30.00 60.00
74 Cal Ripken Jsy/10
75 Harold Baines Jsy/50 10.00 25.00

2005 Throwback Threads Throwback Collection Signature Material Prime

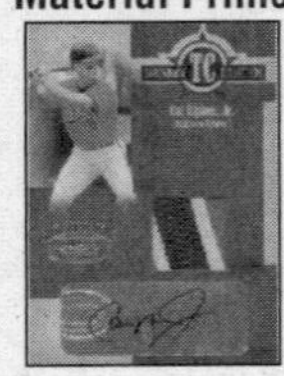

*PRIME p/r 25: .6X TO 1.5X SIG.MTL p/r 50
*PRIME p/r 25: .5X TO 1.2X SIG.MTL p/r 20-25
OVERALL AU-GU ODDS 1:8
PRINT RUNS B/WN 5-25 COPIES PER
NO PRICING ON QTY OF 10 OR LESS
20 Mike Schmidt Jsy/25 50.00 100.00
48 Lou Brock Jsy/25 30.00 60.00

2005 Throwback Threads Throwback Collection Signature Material Combo

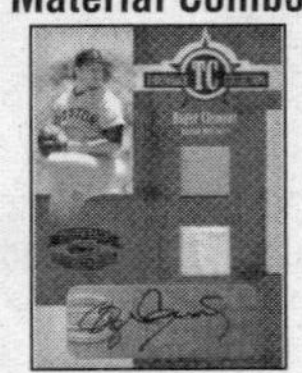

*COMBOp/r20-25: .5X TO 1.2X SIG.MTLp/r50
*COMBOp/r20-25: .4X TO 1X SIG.MTLp/r20-25
*COMBO p/r 15: .6X TO 1.5X SIG.MTL p/r 50
PRINT RUNS B/WN 5-25 COPIES PER
NO PRICING ON QTY OF 10 OR LESS
PRIME PRINT RUN B/WN 5-10 COPIES PER
NO PRIME PRICING DUE TO SCARCITY
OVERALL AU-GU ODDS 1:8

2003 Timeless Treasures

This 100 card standard-size set was released in July, 2003. These cards were issued in four card tins with an $100 SRP which came one group of cards to a tin and 15 tins to a case. Please note that these cards are sequenced in alphabetical order by the player's first name.

STATED PRINT RUN 900 SERIAL #'d SETS
PRODUCED BY DONRUSS/PLAYOFF
1 Adam Dunn 1.50 4.00
2 Al Kaline 2.00 5.00
3 Alan Trammell 1.50 4.00
4 Albert Pujols 3.00 8.00
5 Alex Rodriguez 2.50 6.00
6 Alfonso Soriano 1.50 4.00
7 Andre Dawson 1.50 4.00
8 Andruw Jones 1.50 4.00
9 Austin Kearns 1.50 4.00
10 Babe Ruth 4.00 10.00
11 Barry Bonds 4.00 10.00
12 Barry Larkin 1.50 4.00
13 Barry Zito 1.50 4.00
14 Bernie Williams 1.50 4.00
15 Bo Jackson 2.00 5.00
16 Brooks Robinson 1.50 4.00
17 Cal Ripken 5.00 12.00
18 Carlton Fisk 1.50 4.00
19 Chipper Jones 2.00 5.00
20 Curt Schilling 1.50 4.00
21 Dale Murphy 1.50 4.00
22 Derek Jeter 4.00 10.00
23 Don Mattingly 3.00 8.00
24 Duke Snider 1.50 4.00
25 Eddie Mathews 2.00 5.00
26 Frank Robinson 1.50 4.00
27 Frank Thomas 2.00 5.00
28 Garret Anderson 1.50 4.00
29 Gary Carter 1.50 4.00
30 George Brett 3.00 8.00
31 Greg Maddux 2.50 6.00
32 Harmon Killebrew 2.00 5.00
33 Hideki Matsui RC 4.00 10.00
34 Hideo Nomo 2.00 5.00
35 Ichiro Suzuki 3.00 8.00
36 Ivan Rodriguez 1.50 4.00
37 Jackie Robinson 2.00 5.00
38 Jason Giambi 1.50 4.00
39 Jeff Bagwell 1.50 4.00
40 Jim Edmonds 1.50 4.00
41 Jim Palmer 1.50 4.00
42 Jim Thome 1.50 4.00
43 Joe Morgan 1.50 4.00
44 Jorge Posada 1.50 4.00
45 Jose Contreras RC 2.00 5.00
46 Juan Gonzalez 1.50 4.00
47 Kazuhisa Ishii 1.50 4.00
48 Ken Griffey Jr. 2.50 6.00
49 Kerry Wood 1.50 4.00
50 Kirby Puckett 2.00 5.00
51 Lance Berkman 1.50 4.00
52 Larry Walker 1.50 4.00
53 Lou Brock 1.50 4.00
54 Lou Gehrig 2.50 6.00
55 Magglio Ordonez 1.50 4.00
56 Mark Prior 1.50 4.00
57 Miguel Tejada 1.50 4.00
58 Mike Mussina 1.50 4.00
59 Mike Piazza 2.50 6.00
60 Mike Schmidt 3.00 8.00
61 Nolan Ryan 4.00 10.00
62 Nomar Garciaparra 2.50 6.00
63 Ozzie Smith 2.50 6.00
64 Pat Burrell 1.50 4.00
65 Pedro Martinez 1.50 4.00
66 Pee Wee Reese 1.50 4.00
67 Phil Rizzuto 1.50 4.00
68 Rafael Palmeiro 1.50 4.00
69 Randy Johnson 2.00 5.00
70 Reggie Jackson 1.50 4.00
71 Richie Ashburn 1.50 4.00
72 Rickey Henderson 2.00 5.00
73 Roberto Alomar 1.50 4.00
74 Roberto Clemente 3.00 8.00
75 Robin Yount 2.00 5.00
76 Rod Carew 1.50 4.00
77 Roger Clemens 3.00 8.00
78 Rogers Hornsby 2.00 5.00
79 Roy Oswalt 1.50 4.00
80 Ryan Klesko 1.50 4.00
81 Ryne Sandberg 3.00 8.00
82 Sammy Sosa 2.00 5.00
83 Scott Rolen 1.50 4.00
84 Shawn Green 1.50 4.00
85 Stan Musial 2.50 6.00
86 Steve Carlton 1.50 4.00
87 Thurman Munson 2.00 5.00
88 Todd Helton 1.50 4.00
89 Tom Glavine 1.50 4.00
90 Tom Seaver 1.50 4.00
91 Tony Gwynn 2.00 5.00
92 Tony Perez 1.50 4.00
93 Torii Hunter 1.50 4.00
94 Troy Glaus 1.50 4.00
95 Ty Cobb 2.50 6.00
96 Vernon Wells 1.50 4.00
97 Vladimir Guerrero 2.00 5.00
98 Warren Spahn 1.50 4.00
99 Willie McCovey 1.50 4.00
100 Yogi Berra 2.00 5.00

2003 Timeless Treasures Gold

RANDOM INSERTS IN PACKS
STATED PRINT RUN 10 SERIAL #'d SETS
NO PRICING DUE TO SCARCITY

2003 Timeless Treasures Platinum

RANDOM INSERTS IN PACKS
STATED PRINT RUN 1 SERIAL #'d SETS
NO PRICING DUE TO SCARCITY

2003 Timeless Treasures Silver

*ACTIVE STARS: 1.25X TO 3X BASIC
*RETIRED POST-WAR STARS: 1.5X TO 4X
*RETIRED PRE-WAR STARS: 1X TO 2.5X
*ROOKIES: 1X TO 2.5X BASIC
RANDOM INSERTS IN PACKS
STATED PRINT RUN 50 SERIAL #'d SETS
33 Hideki Matsui 10.00 25.00

2003 Timeless Treasures Award

RANDOM INSERTS IN PACKS
PRINT RUNS B/WN 50-100 COPIES PER CARD
1 Ivan Rodriguez Bat/100 8.00 20.00

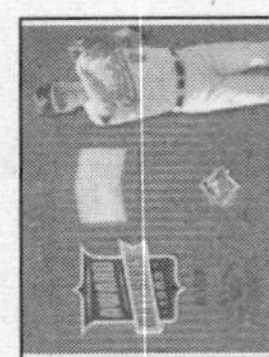

2 Mike Schmidt Bat-Jsy/50 75.00 150.00
3 Roberto Clemente Bat/50 60.00 120.00
4 Roger Clemens Jsy/50 30.00 60.00
5 Randy Johnson Jsy/100 8.00 20.00
6 Pedro Martinez Jsy/100 8.00 20.00
7 Ivan Rodriguez Chest/100 8.00 20.00
8 Jeff Bagwell Pants/100 8.00 20.00
9 Frank Thomas Jsy/100 8.00 20.00
10 Cal Ripken Bat/75 50.00 100.00
11 Tom Seaver Jsy/50 15.00 40.00

2003 Timeless Treasures Award Autographs

RANDOM INSERTS IN PACKS
PRINT RUNS B/WN 5-15 COPIES PER CARD
NO PRICING DUE TO SCARCITY
2 Mike Schmidt Bat-Jsy/15
4 Roger Clemens Jsy/5
5 Randy Johnson Jsy/5
6 Pedro Martinez Jsy/5
8 Jeff Bagwell Pants/5
9 Frank Thomas Jsy/5
10 Cal Ripken Bat/15
11 Tom Seaver Jsy/10

2003 Timeless Treasures Award MLB Logos

RANDOM INSERTS IN PACKS
STATED PRINT RUN 1 SERIAL #'d SET
NO PRICING DUE TO SCARCITY
5 Randy Johnson
6 Pedro Martinez

2003 Timeless Treasures Award Prime

RANDOM INSERTS IN PACKS
PRINT RUNS B/WN 15-50 COPIES PER CARD
NO PRICING ON QTY OF 30 OR LESS
2 Mike Schmidt Bat-Jsy/25
4 Roger Clemens Jsy/30
5 Randy Johnson Jsy/30
6 Pedro Martinez Jsy/50 20.00 50.00
9 Frank Thomas Jsy/50 30.00 60.00
11 Tom Seaver Jsy/15

2003 Timeless Treasures Award Prime Autographs

RANDOM INSERTS IN PACKS
STATED PRINT RUN 1 SERIAL #'d SET
NO PRICING DUE TO SCARCITY
2 Mike Schmidt Bat-Jsy
4 Roger Clemens Jsy
5 Randy Johnson Jsy
6 Pedro Martinez Jsy
9 Frank Thomas Jsy
11 Tom Seaver Jsy

2003 Timeless Treasures Classic Combos

RANDOM INSERTS IN PACKS
STATED PRINT RUN 100 SERIAL #'d SETS
1 Jason Giambi Hat-Jsy 8.00 20.00
2 Adrian Beltre Hat-Shoes 8.00 20.00
3 Alex Rodriguez Bat-Jsy 15.00 40.00
4 Alfonso Soriano Bat-Jsy 8.00 20.00
5 Andruw Jones Fld Glv-Jsy 10.00 25.00
6 Andre Dawson ST Bat-Jsy 8.00 20.00
7 Barry Larkin Bat-Jsy 10.00 25.00

8 Barry Zito Fld Glv-Jsy 8.00 20.00
9 Cal Ripken Bat-Jsy 50.00 100.00
10 Chipper Jones Bat-Jsy 10.00 25.00
11 Don Mattingly Bat-Jsy 40.00 80.00
12 Eric Chavez Bat-Jsy 8.00 20.00
13 Frank Thomas Bat-Jsy 10.00 25.00
14 Greg Maddux Bat-Jsy 15.00 40.00
15 Ivan Rodriguez Fld Glv-Jsy 10.00 25.00
16 Jeff Bagwell Bat-Jsy 10.00 25.00
17 Jim Thome Bat-Jsy 10.00 25.00
18 Juan Gonzalez Bat-Jsy 8.00 20.00
19 Kazuhisa Ishii Bat-Jsy 8.00 20.00
20 Kerry Wood Jsy-Shoes 8.00 20.00
21 Lance Berkman Fld Glv-Jsy 8.00 20.00
22 Magglio Ordonez Bat-Jsy 8.00 20.00
23 Manny Ramirez Bat-Jsy 10.00 25.00
24 Miguel Tejada Hat-Jsy 8.00 20.00
25 Mike Piazza Bat-Jsy 15.00 40.00
26 Nomar Garciaparra Bat-Jsy 20.00 50.00
27 Pedro Martinez Bat-Jsy 10.00 25.00
28 Randy Johnson Bat-Jsy 10.00 25.00
29 Rickey Henderson Bat-Jsy 10.00 25.00
30 Ryne Sandberg Bat-Jsy 40.00 80.00
31 Sammy Sosa Bat-Jsy 10.00 25.00
32 Shawn Green Bat-Jsy 8.00 20.00
33 Todd Helton Bat-Jsy 10.00 25.00
34 Tony Gwynn Bat-Jsy 20.00 50.00
35 Vladimir Guerrero Bat-Jsy 10.00 25.00

2003 Timeless Treasures Classic Combos Autographs

RANDOM INSERTS IN PACKS
PRINT RUNS B/WN 5-50 COPIES PER CARD
NO PRICING ON QTY OF 25 OR LESS
3 Alex Rodriguez Bat-Jsy/15
4 Alfonso Soriano Bat-Jsy/5
5 Andruw Jones Fld Glv-Jsy/10
6 Andre Dawson Bat-ST Jsy/50 30.00 60.00
7 Barry Larkin Bat-Jsy/5
8 Barry Zito Fld Glv-Jsy/25
9 Cal Ripken Bat-Jsy/25
10 Chipper Jones Bat-Jsy/5
11 Don Mattingly Bat-Jsy/25
12 Eric Chavez Bat-Jsy/15
13 Frank Thomas Bat-Jsy/5
14 Greg Maddux Bat-Jsy/25
17 Jim Thome Bat-Jsy/10
19 Kazuhisa Ishii Bat-Jsy/25
20 Kerry Wood Jsy-Shoes/15
21 Lance Berkman Fld Glv-Jsy/15
22 Magglio Ordonez Bat-Jsy/25
24 Miguel Tejada Hat-Jsy/15
27 Pedro Martinez Bat-Jsy/10
28 Randy Johnson Bat-Jsy/10
29 Rickey Henderson Bat-Jsy/10
30 Ryne Sandberg Bat-Jsy/50 100.00 200.00
32 Shawn Green Bat-Jsy/25
33 Todd Helton Bat-Jsy/15
34 Tony Gwynn Bat-Jsy/25
35 Vladimir Guerrero Bat-Jsy/50 50.00 100.00

2003 Timeless Treasures Classic Prime Combos

RANDOM INSERTS IN PACKS
STATED PRINT RUN 25 SERIAL #'d SETS
NO PRICING DUE TO SCARCITY

2003 Timeless Treasures Classic Prime Combos Autographs

RANDOM INSERTS IN PACKS
STATED PRINT RUN 1 SERIAL #'d SET
NO PRICING DUE TO SCARCITY
3 Alex Rodriguez Bat-Jsy
4 Alfonso Soriano Bat-Jsy
5 Andruw Jones Fld Glv-Jsy
6 Andre Dawson Bat-ST Jsy
7 Barry Larkin Bat-Jsy
8 Barry Zito Hat-Jsy
9 Cal Ripken Bat-Jsy
10 Chipper Jones Bat-Jsy
11 Don Mattingly Bat-Jsy
12 Eric Chavez Bat-Jsy
13 Frank Thomas Bat-Jsy
14 Greg Maddux Bat-Jsy
17 Jim Thome Bat-Jsy
19 Kazuhisa Ishii Bat-Jsy
20 Kerry Wood Jsy-Shoes
21 Lance Berkman Fld Glv-Jsy
22 Magglio Ordonez Bat-Jsy
24 Miguel Tejada Hat-Jsy
27 Pedro Martinez Bat-Jsy
28 Randy Johnson Bat-Jsy
29 Rickey Henderson Bat-Jsy
30 Ryne Sandberg Bat-Jsy
32 Shawn Green Bat-Jsy
33 Todd Helton Bat-Jsy
34 Tony Gwynn Bat-Jsy
35 Vladimir Guerrero Bat-Jsy

2003 Timeless Treasures Game Day

RANDOM INSERTS IN PACKS
BAT-HAT-JSY PRINT RUN 100 #'d SETS
BALL PRINT RUN 20 SERIAL #'d SETS
NO BALL PRICING DUE TO SCARCITY
1 Tony Gwynn Bat 15.00 40.00
2 Magglio Ordonez Hat 6.00 15.00
3 George Brett Bat 30.00 60.00
4 Rickey Henderson Jsy 8.00 20.00
5 Billy Williams Bat 6.00 15.00
6 Frank Thomas Bat 8.00 20.00
7 Tony Gwynn Jsy 15.00 40.00
8 Billy Williams Ball/20
9 Frank Robinson Ball/20
10 Ryne Sandberg Bat 30.00 60.00
11 Miguel Tejada Jsy 6.00 15.00

2003 Timeless Treasures Game Day Autographs

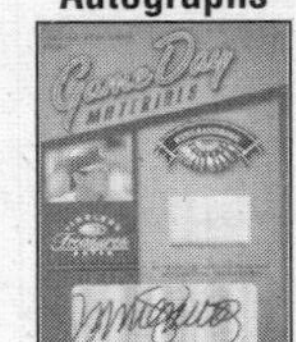

RANDOM INSERTS IN PACKS
PRINT RUNS B/WN 1-25 COPIES PER CARD
NO PRICING DUE TO SCARCITY
1 Tony Gwynn Bat/10
2 Magglio Ordonez Hat/10
3 George Brett Bat/15
4 Rickey Henderson Jsy/5
5 Billy Williams Bat/25
6 Frank Thomas Bat/1
7 Tony Gwynn Jsy/10
8 Billy Williams Ball/5
9 Frank Robinson Ball/5
10 Ryne Sandberg Bat/25
11 Miguel Tejada Jsy/25

2003 Timeless Treasures Game Day Prime

RANDOM INSERTS IN PACKS
PRINT RUNS B/WN 5-75 COPIES PER CARD
NO PRICING ON QTY OF 25 OR LESS
2 Magglio Ordonez Hat/5
4 Rickey Henderson Jsy/75 20.00 50.00
7 Tony Gwynn Jsy/75 40.00 80.00
11 Miguel Tejada Jsy/75 12.50 30.00

2003 Timeless Treasures Game Day Prime Autographs

RANDOM INSERTS IN PACKS
STATED PRINT RUN 1 SERIAL #'d SET
NO PRICING DUE TO SCARCITY
2 Magglio Ordonez Hat
4 Rickey Henderson Jsy
7 Tony Gwynn Jsy
11 Miguel Tejada Jsy

2003 Timeless Treasures HOF Combos

RANDOM INSERTS IN PACKS
PRINT RUNS B/WN 25-100 COPIES PER CARD
NO PRICING ON QTY 25 OR LESS
1 Al Kaline Bat-Jsy/50 40.00 80.00
2 Babe Ruth Bat-Jsy/25
3 Eddie Mathews Bat-Jsy/50 30.00 60.00
4 Kirby Puckett Bat-Hat/75 20.00 50.00
5 Lou Gehrig Bat-Jsy/25
6 Mike Schmidt Bat-Jsy/100 40.00 80.00
7 Nolan Ryan Fld Glv-Jsy/50 75.00 150.00
8 Phil Rizzuto Bat-Jsy/50 30.00 60.00
9 Reggie Jackson Hat-Jsy/25
10 Roberto Clemente Hat-Jsy/25
11 Rod Carew Bat-Jsy/100 20.00 50.00
12 Stan Musial Bat-Jsy/25
13 Ty Cobb Bat-Pants/25
14 George Brett Bat-Hat/50 75.00 150.00
15 Carlton Fisk Bat-Jsy/100 20.00 50.00

2003 Timeless Treasures HOF Combos Autographs

RANDOM INSERTS IN PACKS
PRINT RUNS B/WN 1-25 COPIES PER CARD
NO PRICING DUE TO SCARCITY
1 Al Kaline Bat-Jsy/25
4 Kirby Puckett Bat-Hat/25
6 Mike Schmidt Bat-Jsy/15
7 Nolan Ryan Fld Glv-Jsy/25
8 Phil Rizzuto Bat-Jsy/25
9 Reggie Jackson Hat-Jsy/1
11 Rod Carew Bat-Jsy/10
12 Stan Musial Bat-Jsy/25
14 George Brett Bat-Hat/15
15 Carlton Fisk Bat-Jsy/25

2003 Timeless Treasures HOF Cuts

RANDOM INSERTS IN PACKS
STATED PRINT RUN 1 SERIAL #'d SET
NO PRICING DUE TO SCARCITY
1 Ty Cobb
2 Babe Ruth
3 Jackie Robinson
4 Pee Wee Reese

2003 Timeless Treasures HOF Induction Year Combos

RANDOM INSERTS IN PACKS
STATED PRINT RUN 25 SERIAL #'d SETS
NO PRICING DUE TO SCARCITY
1 Ty Cobb Bat
Babe Ruth Bat
2 Mel Ott Bat
Jimmie Foxx Bat
3 Yogi Berra Jsy
Early Wynn Jsy
4 Roberto Clemente Jsy
Warren Spahn Jsy
5 Al Kaline Jsy
Duke Snider Jsy
6 Lou Brock Jsy
Enos Slaughter Jsy
7 Jim Palmer Jsy
Joe Morgan Jsy
8 Steve Carlton Jsy
Phil Rizzuto Jsy
9 Mike Schmidt Bat
Richie Ashburn Bat
10 George Brett Jsy
Robin Yount Jsy

2003 Timeless Treasures HOF Induction Year Combos Autographs

RANDOM INSERTS IN PACKS
STATED PRINT RUN 5 SERIAL #'d SETS
NO PRICING DUE TO SCARCITY
5 Al Kaline Jsy
Duke Snider Jsy
7 Jim Palmer Jsy
Joe Morgan Jsy
8 Steve Carlton Jsy
Phil Rizzuto Jsy
10 George Brett Jsy
Robin Yount Jsy

2003 Timeless Treasures HOF Letters

RANDOM INSERTS IN PACKS
PRINT RUNS B/WN 5-25 COPIES PER CARD
NO PRICING DUE TO SCARCITY
28 Brooks Robinson/5
32 Joe Morgan/5
33 Lou Brock/10
35 Mike Schmidt/25
36 Nolan Ryan Angels/15
37 Nolan Ryan Astros/15
38 Nolan Ryan Rangers/15
41 Reggie Jackson/15
44 Rod Carew/20
46 Tom Seaver/25
47 Steve Carlton/15

2003 Timeless Treasures HOF Letters Autographs

RANDOM INSERTS IN PACKS
STATED PRINT RUN 1 SERIAL #'d SET
NO PRICING DUE TO SCARCITY
28 Brooks Robinson
32 Joe Morgan
33 Lou Brock
35 Mike Schmidt
36 Nolan Ryan Angels
37 Nolan Ryan Astros
38 Nolan Ryan Rangers
41 Reggie Jackson
44 Rod Carew
46 Tom Seaver
47 Steve Carlton

2003 Timeless Treasures HOF Logos

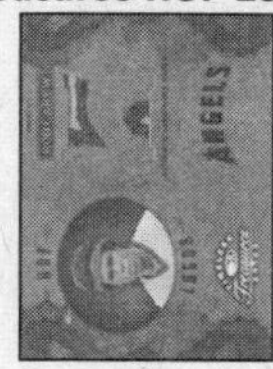

RANDOM INSERTS IN PACKS
PRINT RUNS B/WN 1-35 COPIES PER CARD
NO PRICING ON QTY OF 25 OR LESS
25 Al Kaline/5
27 Bobby Doerr/15
28 Brooks Robinson/10
29 Eddie Mathews/35 40.00 80.00
32 Joe Morgan/5
33 Lou Brock/10
35 Mike Schmidt/25
36 Nolan Ryan Angels/35 75.00 150.00
37 Nolan Ryan Astros/35 75.00 150.00
38 Nolan Ryan Rangers/25
39 Phil Rizzuto/5
41 Reggie Jackson/15
42 Roberto Clemente/15
43 Robin Yount/35 40.00 80.00
44 Rod Carew/35 30.00 60.00
45 Stan Musial/1
49 Pee Wee Reese/15
50 Jackie Robinson/5

2003 Timeless Treasures HOF Logos Autographs

RANDOM INSERTS IN PACKS
STATED PRINT RUN 1 SERIAL #'d SET
NO PRICING DUE TO SCARCITY
25 Al Kaline
27 Bobby Doerr
28 Brooks Robinson

32 Joe Morgan
33 Lou Brock
35 Mike Schmidt
36 Nolan Ryan Angels
37 Nolan Ryan Astros
38 Nolan Ryan Rangers
39 Phil Rizzuto
40 Reggie Jackson Yanks
41 Reggie Jackson A's
43 Robin Yount
44 Rod Carew
45 Stan Musial

2003 Timeless Treasures HOF Materials

RANDOM INSERTS IN PACKS
PRINT RUNS B/WN 25-100 COPIES PER CARD
NO PRICING ON QTY OF 25 OR LESS
1 Al Kaline Bat/100 15.00 40.00
2 Babe Ruth Bat/75 125.00 250.00
3 Carlton Fisk Bat/100 10.00 25.00
4 Eddie Mathews Bat/100 15.00 40.00
5 Gary Carter Bat/100 8.00 20.00
6 George Brett Bat/100 20.00 50.00
7 Harmon Killebrew Bat/100 15.00 40.00
8 Joe Morgan Bat/100 8.00 20.00
9 Kirby Puckett Bat/100 10.00 25.00
10 Lou Gehrig Bat/100 100.00 200.00
11 Luis Aparicio Bat/100 8.00 20.00
12 Mike Schmidt Bat/100 20.00 50.00
13 Ozzie Smith Bat/100 15.00 40.00
14 Phil Rizzuto Bat/100 10.00 25.00
15 Reggie Jackson Bat/100 10.00 25.00
16 Richie Ashburn Bat/100 10.00 25.00
17 Roberto Clemente Bat/100 50.00 100.00
18 Robin Yount Bat/100 10.00 25.00
19 Rod Carew Bat/100 10.00 25.00
20 Rogers Hornsby Bat/100 30.00 60.00
21 Stan Musial Bat/100 20.00 50.00
22 Ty Cobb Bat/100 100.00 200.00
23 Willie McCovey Bat/100 8.00 20.00
24 Yogi Berra Bat/100 10.00 25.00
25 Al Kaline Jsy/100 15.00 40.00
26 Babe Ruth Jsy/50 250.00 400.00
27 Bobby Doerr Jsy/100 8.00 20.00
28 Brooks Robinson Jsy/100 10.00 25.00
29 Eddie Mathews Jsy/100 15.00 40.00
30 Harmon Killebrew Jsy/100 15.00 40.00
31 Ty Cobb Pants/50 100.00 200.00
32 Joe Morgan Jsy/100 8.00 20.00
33 Lou Brock Jsy/100 10.00 25.00
34 Lou Gehrig Jsy/50 150.00 300.00
35 Mike Schmidt Jsy/100 20.00 50.00
36 Nolan Ryan Angels Jsy/100 40.00 80.00
37 Nolan Ryan Astros Jsy/100 30.00 60.00
38 Nolan Ryan Rangers Jsy/100 40.00 80.00
39 Phil Rizzuto Jsy/100 10.00 25.00
40 Reggie Jackson Yanks Jsy/25
41 Reggie Jackson A's Jsy/100 10.00 25.00
42 Roberto Clemente Jsy/50 75.00 150.00
43 Robin Yount Jsy/100 10.00 25.00
44 Rod Carew Jsy/100 10.00 25.00
45 Stan Musial Jsy/100 30.00 60.00
46 Tom Seaver Jsy/100 10.00 25.00
47 Steve Carlton Jsy/100 8.00 20.00
48 Carlton Fisk Jsy/100 10.00 25.00
49 Pee Wee Reese Jsy/100 10.00 25.00
50 Jackie Robinson Jsy/50 50.00 100.00

2003 Timeless Treasures HOF Materials Autographs

RANDOM INSERTS IN PACKS
PRINT RUNS B/WN 5-50 COPIES PER CARD
NO PRICING ON QTY OF 25 OR LESS
1 Al Kaline Bat/15
3 Carlton Fisk Bat/15
5 Gary Carter Bat/25
6 George Brett Bat/25
7 Harmon Killebrew Bat/25
8 Joe Morgan Bat/15
9 Kirby Puckett Bat/25
11 Luis Aparicio Bat/25
12 Mike Schmidt Bat/15
13 Ozzie Smith Bat/10
14 Phil Rizzuto Bat/15
15 Reggie Jackson Bat/10
18 Robin Yount Bat/15
19 Rod Carew Bat/10
21 Stan Musial Bat/25
23 Willie McCovey Bat/25
24 Yogi Berra Bat/15
25 Al Kaline Jsy/25
27 Bobby Doerr Jsy/25
28 Brooks Robinson Jsy/25
30 Harmon Killebrew Jsy/50 50.00 100.00
32 Joe Morgan Jsy/25
33 Lou Brock Jsy/50 40.00 80.00
35 Mike Schmidt Jsy/25
36 Nolan Ryan Angels Jsy/25
37 Nolan Ryan Astros Jsy/25
38 Nolan Ryan Rangers Jsy/25
39 Phil Rizzuto Jsy/25
40 Reggie Jackson Yanks Jsy/5
41 Reggie Jackson A's Jsy/15
43 Robin Yount Jsy/25
44 Rod Carew Jsy/15
45 Stan Musial Jsy/50 60.00 120.00
46 Tom Seaver Jsy/25
47 Steve Carlton Jsy/25
48 Carlton Fisk Jsy/25

2003 Timeless Treasures HOF Numbers

RANDOM INSERTS IN PACKS
PRINT RUNS B/WN 5-50 COPIES PER CARD
NO PRICING ON QTY OF 30 OR LESS
26 Babe Ruth/5
28 Brooks Robinson/5
29 Eddie Mathews/35 40.00 80.00
33 Lou Brock/25
34 Lou Gehrig/5
35 Mike Schmidt/50 50.00 100.00
36 Nolan Ryan Angels/35 100.00 200.00
37 Nolan Ryan Astros/25
38 Nolan Ryan Rangers/5
39 Phil Rizzuto/10
41 Reggie Jackson/25
42 Roberto Clemente/15
43 Robin Yount/35 40.00 80.00
44 Rod Carew/25
45 Stan Musial/10
46 Tom Seaver/35 30.00 60.00
47 Steve Carlton/40 20.00 50.00
48 Carlton Fisk/35 30.00 60.00
49 Pee Wee Reese/10
50 Jackie Robinson/5

2003 Timeless Treasures HOF Numbers Autographs

RANDOM INSERTS IN PACKS
STATED PRINT RUN 1 SERIAL #'d SET
NO PRICING DUE TO SCARCITY
25 Al Kaline
28 Brooks Robinson
32 Joe Morgan
33 Lou Brock
35 Mike Schmidt
36 Nolan Ryan Angels
37 Nolan Ryan Astros
38 Nolan Ryan Rangers
39 Phil Rizzuto
41 Reggie Jackson
43 Robin Yount
44 Rod Carew
45 Stan Musial
46 Tom Seaver
47 Steve Carlton
48 Carlton Fisk

2003 Timeless Treasures HOF Prime Combos

RANDOM INSERTS IN PACKS
PRINT RUNS B/WN 5-25 COPIES PER CARD
NO PRICING DUE TO SCARCITY
1 Al Kaline Bat-Jsy/5
2 Babe Ruth Bat-Jsy/5
3 Eddie Mathews Bat-Jsy/25
4 Kirby Puckett Bat-Hat/15
6 Mike Schmidt Bat-Jsy/25
7 Nolan Ryan Fld Glv-Jsy/15
8 Phil Rizzuto Bat-Jsy/5
10 Roberto Clemente Hat-Jsy/5
11 Rod Carew Bat-Jsy/5
14 George Brett Bat-Hat/10
15 Carlton Fisk Bat-Jsy/5

2003 Timeless Treasures HOF Prime Combos Autographs

RANDOM INSERTS IN PACKS
STATED PRINT RUN 1 SERIAL #'d SET
NO PRICING DUE TO SCARCITY
1 Al Kaline Bat-Jsy
4 Kirby Puckett Bat-Hat
6 Mike Schmidt Bat-Jsy
7 Nolan Ryan Fld Glv-Jsy
8 Phil Rizzuto Bat-Jsy
9 Reggie Jackson Hat-Jsy
11 Rod Carew Bat-Jsy
14 George Brett Bat-Hat
15 Carlton Fisk Bat-Jsy

2003 Timeless Treasures Home Run

RANDOM INSERTS IN PACKS
BAT-JSY PRINT RUN 100 SERIAL #'d SETS
BALL PRINT RUN 20 SERIAL #'d SETS
NO BALL PRICING DUE TO SCARCITY
1 Harmon Killebrew HR 570 Bat 15.00 40.00
2 Harmon Killebrew HR 565 Bat 15.00 40.00
3 Jose Canseco HR 311 Bat 15.00 40.00
4 Magglio Ordonez 00 HR 17 Bat 6.00 15.00
5 Rafael Palmeiro HR 425 Bat 8.00 20.00
6 Rafael Palmeiro HR 440 Bat 8.00 20.00
7 Rafael Palmeiro HR 448 Jsy 8.00 20.00
8 Alex Rodriguez 00 HR 36 Bat 10.00 25.00
9 Alex Rodriguez 00 HR 37 Bat 10.00 25.00
10 Alex Rodriguez 00 HR 33 Bat 10.00 25.00
11 Alex Rodriguez 98 HR 23 Ball/20
12 Adam Dunn 00 HR 9 Jsy 6.00 15.00

2003 Timeless Treasures Home Run Autographs

RANDOM INSERTS IN PACKS
PRINT RUNS B/WN 1-25 COPIES PER CARD
NO PRICING DUE TO SCARCITY
1 Harmon Killebrew HR 570 Bat/25
2 Harmon Killebrew HR 565 Bat/25
3 Jose Canseco HR 311 Bat/25
4 Magglio Ordonez 00 HR 17 Bat/15
5 Rafael Palmeiro HR 425 Bat/1
6 Rafael Palmeiro HR 440 Bat/1
7 Rafael Palmeiro HR 448 Jsy/1
8 Alex Rodriguez 00 HR 36 Bat/15
9 Alex Rodriguez 00 HR 37 Bat/15
10 Alex Rodriguez 00 HR 33 Bat/15
11 Alex Rodriguez 98 HR 23 Ball/5
12 Adam Dunn 00 HR 9 Jsy/25

2003 Timeless Treasures Home Run MLB Logos

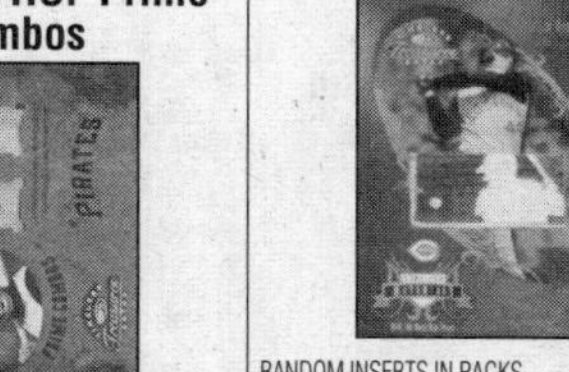

RANDOM INSERTS IN PACKS
STATED PRINT RUN 1 SERIAL #'d SET
NO PRICING DUE TO SCARCITY
7 Rafael Palmeiro HR 448
12 Adam Dunn 00 HR 9

2003 Timeless Treasures Material Ink

COMMON CARD p/r 75-100 15.00 40.00
COMMON CARD p/r 50 30.00 60.00
RANDOM INSERTS IN PACKS
PRINT RUNS B/WN 25-100 COPIES PER CARD
NO PRICING ON QTY OF 25 OR LESS

1 Adam Dunn/50 40.00 80.00
2 Alan Trammell/100 15.00 40.00
3 Alex Rodriguez White Jsy/25
4 Alex Rodriguez Blue Jsy/25
5 Andre Dawson/100 15.00 40.00
6 Barry Zito/50 40.00 80.00
7 Bo Jackson/100 50.00 100.00
8 Bob Feller/25
9 Bobby Doerr/50 30.00 60.00
10 Brooks Robinson/50
11 Cal Ripken No Sleeve/50 150.00 300.00
12 Cal Ripken Black Sleeve/50 150.00 300.00
13 Cal Ripken Throwing/25
14 Dale Murphy/50 40.00 80.00
15 Dave Parker/75 15.00 40.00
16 David Cone/100 15.00 40.00
17 Don Mattingly/100 75.00 150.00
18 Duke Snider/25
19 Edgar Martinez/50 40.00 80.00
20 Gary Carter/100 15.00 40.00
21 Harmon Killebrew/75 50.00 100.00
22 Jim Edmonds/25
23 Jim Thome/50 40.00 80.00
24 Joe Carter/100 15.00 40.00
25 Jose Canseco/50 40.00 80.00
26 Jose Vidro/100 15.00 40.00
27 Kazuhisa Ishii/100 15.00 40.00
28 Kerry Wood/50 40.00 80.00
29 Lance Berkman/50 40.00 80.00
30 Mark Mulder/25
31 Mark Prior/50 20.00 50.00
32 Mike Schmidt/50 75.00 150.00
33 Nick Johnson/100 15.00 40.00
34 Nolan Ryan Astros/25
35 Nolan Ryan Rangers/25
36 Nolan Ryan Angels/25
37 Paul LoDuca/100 15.00 40.00
38 Paul Molitor/50 30.00 60.00
39 Randy Johnson/25
40 Reggie Jackson/25
41 Roberto Alomar Mets/50 40.00 80.00
42 Roberto Alomar Indians/100 30.00 60.00
43 Robin Yount/50 75.00 150.00
44 Rod Carew/25
45 Roger Clemens Yanks/25
46 Roger Clemens Sox/25
47 Ryan Klesko/75 15.00 40.00
48 Ryne Sandberg/25
50 Shawn Green/25
51 Stan Musial/25
52 Steve Carlton Giants/100 15.00 40.00
53 Steve Carlton Sox/100 15.00 40.00
54 Todd Helton/50 40.00 80.00
55 Tom Seaver/50 40.00 80.00
56 Tony Gwynn/25
57 Torii Hunter/100 15.00 40.00
58 Vladimir Guerrero/100 30.00 60.00
59 Will Clark/50 60.00 120.00

2003 Timeless Treasures Milestone

RANDOM INSERTS IN PACKS
JSY PRINT RUN 100 SERIAL #'d SETS
BALL PRINT RUN 24 SERIAL #'d SETS
NO BALL PRICING DUE TO SCARCITY
1 Cal Ripken Ball/24
2 Willie McCovey Ball/24
3 R.Henderson Padres Jsy/100 10.00 25.00
4 Gaylord Perry Jsy/100 8.00 20.00
5 R.Henderson A's Jsy/100 10.00 25.00

2003 Timeless Treasures Milestone Autographs

RANDOM INSERTS IN PACKS
STATED PRINT RUN 1 SERIAL #'d SET
NO PRICING DUE TO SCARCITY
1 Cal Ripken Ball
2 Willie McCovey Ball
3 Rickey Henderson Padres Jsy
5 Rickey Henderson A's Jsy

2003 Timeless Treasures MLB Logo Ink

RANDOM INSERTS IN PACKS
STATED PRINT RUN 1 SERIAL #'d SET
NO PRICING DUE TO SCARCITY
3 Alex Rodriguez White Jsy
4 Alex Rodriguez Blue Jsy

6 Barry Zito
13 Cal Ripken Throwing
19 Edgar Martinez
22 Jim Edmonds
23 Jim Thome
26 Jose Vidro
27 Kazuhisa Ishii
28 Kerry Wood
29 Lance Berkman
30 Mark Mulder
31 Mark Prior
33 Nick Johnson
37 Paul LoDuca
39 Randy Johnson
42 Roberto Alomar Indians
45 Roger Clemens Yanks
47 Ryan Klesko
50 Shawn Green
54 Todd Helton
57 Torii Hunter

2003 Timeless Treasures Past and Present

RANDOM INSERTS IN PACKS
STATED PRINT RUN 100 SERIAL #'d SETS
1 Alex Rodriguez 15.00 40.00
2 Hideo Nomo 10.00 25.00
3 Jason Giambi 8.00 20.00
4 Juan Gonzalez 8.00 20.00
5 Mike Piazza 15.00 40.00
6 Pedro Martinez 10.00 25.00
7 Randy Johnson 10.00 25.00
8 Rickey Henderson 10.00 25.00
9 Roberto Alomar 10.00 25.00
10 Roger Clemens 15.00 40.00
11 Sammy Sosa 10.00 25.00

2003 Timeless Treasures Past and Present Autographs

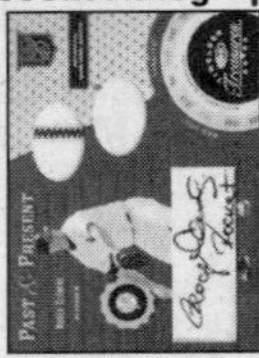

RANDOM INSERTS IN PACKS
PRINT RUNS B/WN 5-25 COPIES PER CARD
NO PRICING DUE TO SCARCITY
1 Alex Rodriguez/25
6 Pedro Martinez/5
7 Randy Johnson/5
8 Rickey Henderson/10
9 Roberto Alomar/25
10 Roger Clemens/15

2003 Timeless Treasures Past and Present Letters

RANDOM INSERTS IN PACKS
PRINT RUNS B/WN 25-75 COPIES PER CARD
NO PRICING ON QTY OF 25 OR LESS
1 Alex Rodriguez/75 40.00 80.00
2 Hideo Nomo/25
4 Juan Gonzalez/50 15.00 40.00
6 Pedro Martinez/75 15.00 40.00
7 Randy Johnson/75 20.00 50.00
9 Roberto Alomar/25

2003 Timeless Treasures Past and Present Letters Autographs

RANDOM INSERTS IN PACKS
STATED PRINT RUN 1 SERIAL #'d SET
NO PRICING DUE TO SCARCITY
1 Alex Rodriguez
7 Randy Johnson
9 Roberto Alomar

2003 Timeless Treasures Past and Present Logos

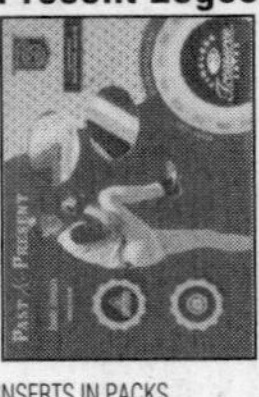

RANDOM INSERTS IN PACKS
PRINT RUNS B/WN 5-75 COPIES PER CARD
NO PRICING ON QTY OF 25 OR LESS
1 Alex Rodriguez/60 40.00 80.00
2 Hideo Nomo/25
3 Jason Giambi/75 12.50 30.00
4 Juan Gonzalez/25
5 Mike Piazza/50 40.00 80.00
7 Randy Johnson/5
8 Rickey Henderson/25
10 Roger Clemens/35 50.00 100.00
11 Sammy Sosa/25

2003 Timeless Treasures Past and Present Logos Autographs

RANDOM INSERTS IN PACKS
STATED PRINT RUN 1 SERIAL #'d SET
NO PRICING DUE TO SCARCITY
1 Alex Rodriguez
7 Randy Johnson
8 Rickey Henderson
10 Roger Clemens

2003 Timeless Treasures Past and Present Numbers

RANDOM INSERTS IN PACKS
PRINT RUNS B/WN 5-75 COPIES PER CARD
NO PRICING ON QTY OF 25 OR LESS
1 Alex Rodriguez/35 50.00 100.00
2 Hideo Nomo/25
3 Jason Giambi/75 12.50 30.00
4 Juan Gonzalez/25
5 Mike Piazza/5
6 Pedro Martinez/50 20.00 50.00
7 Randy Johnson/50 30.00 60.00
8 Rickey Henderson /25
11 Sammy Sosa/25

2003 Timeless Treasures Past and Present Numbers Autographs

RANDOM INSERTS IN PACKS
STATED PRINT RUN 1 SERIAL #'d SET
NO PRICING DUE TO SCARCITY
1 Alex Rodriguez
6 Pedro Martinez
7 Randy Johnson
8 Rickey Henderson

2003 Timeless Treasures Past and Present Patches

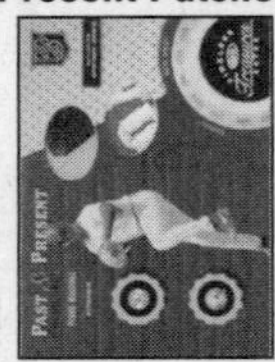

RANDOM INSERTS IN PACKS
PRINT RUNS B/WN 5-20 COPIES PER CARD
NO PRICING DUE TO SCARCITY
1 Alex Rodriguez/10
5 Mike Piazza/15
6 Pedro Martinez/5
8 Rickey Henderson/5
9 Roberto Alomar/20

2003 Timeless Treasures Past and Present Patches Autographs

RANDOM INSERTS IN PACKS
STATED PRINT RUN 1 SERIAL #'d SET
NO PRICING DUE TO SCARCITY
1 Alex Rodriguez
6 Pedro Martinez
8 Rickey Henderson
9 Roberto Alomar

2003 Timeless Treasures Post Season

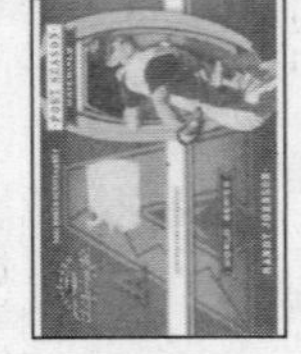

RANDOM INSERTS IN PACKS
PRINT RUNS B/WN 25-100 COPIES PER CARD
NO PRICING ON QTY OF 25 OR LESS
1 Ozzie Smith Jsy/100 15.00 40.00
2 Tom Glavine Jsy/50 15.00 40.00
3 Bernie Williams Bat/100 8.00 20.00
4 Roger Clemens Jsy/100 15.00 40.00
5 Babe Ruth Ball/25
6 Christy Mathewson Seat/100 20.00 50.00
7 Derek Jeter Ball/25
8 Alfonso Soriano Ball/25
9 Randy Johnson NLCS Ball/25
10 Ichiro Suzuki Ball/25
11 Curt Schilling Ball/25
12 Randy Johnson WS Ball/25

2003 Timeless Treasures Post Season Autographs

RANDOM INSERTS IN PACKS
PRINT RUNS B/WN 5-15 COPIES PER CARD
NO PRICING DUE TO SCARCITY
1 Ozzie Smith Jsy/15
3 Bernie Williams Bat/5
4 Roger Clemens Jsy/10
8 Alfonso Soriano Ball/5
9 Randy Johnson NLCS Ball/5
12 Randy Johnson WS Ball/5

2003 Timeless Treasures Post Season Prime

RANDOM INSERTS IN PACKS
PRINT RUNS B/WN 5-75 COPIES PER CARD
NO PRICING ON QTY OF 25 OR LESS
1 Ozzie Smith Jsy/75 30.00 60.00
2 Tom Glavine Jsy/25
4 Roger Clemens Jsy/15
7 Derek Jeter Ball/5
8 Alfonso Soriano Ball/5
9 Randy Johnson NLCS Ball/5
10 Ichiro Suzuki Ball/5
11 Curt Schilling Ball/5
12 Randy Johnson WS Ball/5

2003 Timeless Treasures Post Season Prime Autographs

RANDOM INSERTS IN PACKS
STATED PRINT RUN 1 SERIAL #'d SET
NO PRICING DUE TO SCARCITY
1 Ozzie Smith Jsy
2 Tom Glavine Jsy
4 Roger Clemens Jsy
8 Alfonso Soriano Ball
9 Randy Johnson NLCS Ball
12 Randy Johnson WS Ball

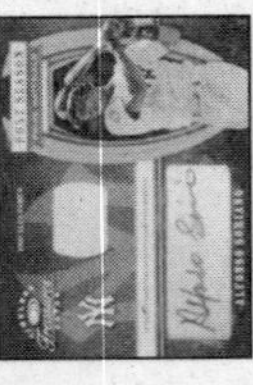

2003 Timeless Treasures Prime Ink

RANDOM INSERTS IN PACKS
PRINT RUNS B/WN 5-50 COPIES PER CARD
NO PRICING ON QTY OF 25 OR LESS
1 Adam Dunn/10
2 Alan Trammell/50 15.00 40.00
3 Alex Rodriguez White Jsy/10
4 Alex Rodriguez Blue Jsy/5
5 Andre Dawson/25
6 Barry Zito/10
7 Bo Jackson/50 100.00 200.00
8 Bob Feller/5
10 Brooks Robinson/10
11 Cal Ripken No Sleeve/25
12 Cal Ripken Black Sleeve/25
13 Cal Ripken Throwing/5
14 Dale Murphy/15
15 Dave Parker/15
16 David Cone/25
19 Edgar Martinez/10
20 Gary Carter/50 15.00 40.00
21 Harmon Killebrew/15
22 Jim Edmonds/5
23 Jim Thome/10
24 Joe Carter/50 15.00 40.00
25 Jose Canseco/15
26 Jose Vidro/25
27 Kazuhisa Ishii/50 15.00 40.00
28 Kerry Wood/10
29 Lance Berkman/10
30 Mark Mulder/5
31 Mark Prior/10
32 Mike Schmidt/10
33 Nick Johnson/50 15.00 40.00
34 Nolan Ryan Astros/5
37 Paul LoDuca/25
38 Paul Molitor/10
39 Randy Johnson/5
40 Reggie Jackson/5
41 Roberto Alomar Mets/10
42 Roberto Alomar Indians/25
43 Robin Yount/10
44 Rod Carew/5
45 Roger Clemens Yanks/5
46 Roger Clemens Sox/5
47 Ryan Klesko/25
48 Ryne Sandberg/5
50 Shawn Green/5
52 Steve Carlton Giants/50 15.00 40.00
53 Steve Carlton Sox/50 15.00 40.00
54 Todd Helton/10
56 Tony Gwynn/10
57 Torii Hunter/50 15.00 40.00
58 Vladimir Guerrero/50 30.00 60.00
59 Will Clark/25

2003 Timeless Treasures Rookie Year

COMMON ACTIVE p/r 100 4.00 10.00
COMMON RETIRED p/r 100 6.00 15.00
PRINT RUNS B/WN 50-100 COPIES PER CARD
*PARALLEL p/r 75-100: .4X TO 1X BASIC RY
*PARALLEL p/r 61-68: .5X TO 1.2X BASIC RY
*PARALLEL p/r 42-47: .6X TO 1.5X BASIC RY
PARALLEL PRINT B/WN 42-100 COPIES PER
RANDOM INSERTS IN PACKS
1 Cal Ripken Bat/100 40.00 80.00
2 Mike Schmidt Bat/50 30.00 60.00
3 Rafael Palmeiro Bat/100 6.00 15.00
4 Nomar Garciaparra Jsy/100 15.00 40.00
5 Sean Casey Jsy/100 4.00 10.00
6 Stan Musial Jsy/100 20.00 50.00
7 Yogi Berra Jsy/100 15.00 40.00
8 Bernie Williams Bat/100 6.00 15.00
9 Ivan Rodriguez Jsy/100 6.00 15.00
10 J.D. Drew Jsy/100 4.00 10.00
11 Scott Rolen Jsy/100 6.00 15.00
12 Vladimir Guerrero Jsy/100 6.00 15.00
13 Johnny Bench Bat/100 10.00 25.00
14 Ivan Rodriguez Bat/100 6.00 15.00
15 Andruw Jones Jsy/100 6.00 15.00
16 Andruw Jones Bat/100 6.00 15.00
17 Fred Lynn Jsy/100 6.00 15.00
18 Jeff Kent Jsy/100 4.00 10.00
19 Gary Sheffield Jsy/100 4.00 10.00
20 Ron Santo Bat/100 10.00 25.00
21 Juan Gonzalez Jsy/100 4.00 10.00
22 Alfonso Soriano Jsy/100 4.00 10.00
23 Ryan Klesko Jsy/100 4.00 10.00
24 Adam Dunn Btg Glv/100 4.00 10.00
25 Hideo Nomo Jsy/100 6.00 15.00
26 Mark Prior Jsy/100 6.00 15.00
27 Pat Burrell Bat/50 10.00 25.00
28 Magglio Ordonez Bat/100 4.00 10.00
29 Kirby Puckett Bat/100 15.00 40.00
30 Albert Pujols Jsy/100 15.00 40.00
31 Albert Pujols Bat/100 15.00 40.00

2003 Timeless Treasures Rookie Year Autographs

RANDOM INSERTS IN PACKS
PRINT RUNS B/WN 10-25 COPIES PER CARD
NO PRICING DUE TO SCARCITY
1 Cal Ripken Bat/25
2 Mike Schmidt Bat/25
6 Stan Musial Jsy/25
7 Yogi Berra Jsy/15
8 Bernie Williams Bat/25
12 Vladimir Guerrero Jsy/25
13 Johnny Bench Bat/25
15 Andruw Jones Jsy/10
16 Andruw Jones Bat/10
17 Fred Lynn Jsy/25
19 Gary Sheffield Jsy/10
20 Ron Santo Bat/25
22 Alfonso Soriano Jsy/10
23 Ryan Klesko Jsy/25
24 Adam Dunn Btg Glv/10
26 Mark Prior Jsy/25
27 Pat Burrell Bat/10
28 Magglio Ordonez Bat/25
29 Kirby Puckett Bat/15

2003 Timeless Treasures Rookie Year Combos

RANDOM INSERTS IN PACKS
PRINT RUNS B/WN 25-50 COPIES PER CARD
NO PRICJNG ON QTY OF 25 OR LESS
1 Alfonso Soriano Btg Glv-Hat/25
2 Adam Dunn Hat-Shoes/25
3 Andruw Jones Bat-Jsy/50 15.00 40.00
4 Ivan Rodriguez Bat-Jsy/50 15.00 40.00
5 Hank Blalock Bat-ST Jsy/25
6 Mark Prior Hat-Jsy/50 15.00 40.00
7 Albert Pujols Bat-Jsy/50 50.00 100.00

2003 Timeless Treasures Rookie Year Combos Autographs

RANDOM INSERTS IN PACKS
STATED PRINT RUN 1 SERIAL #'d SET
NO PRICING DUE TO SCARCITY
1 Alfonso Soriano Btg Glv-Hat
2 Adam Dunn Hat-Shoes
3 Andruw Jones Bat-Jsy
5 Hank Blalock Bat-ST Jsy
6 Mark Prior Hat-Jsy

2003 Timeless Treasures Rookie Year Letters

RANDOM INSERTS IN PACKS
PRINT RUNS B/WN 15-35 COPIES PER CARD
NO PRICING ON QTY OF 25 OR LESS
4 Nomar Garciaparra/35 30.00 60.00
5 Sean Casey/25
9 Ivan Rodriguez/35 20.00 50.00
10 J.D. Drew/15
11 Scott Rolen/15
12 Vladimir Guerrero/35 20.00 50.00
15 Andruw Jones/25
18 Jeff Kent/15
23 Ryan Klesko/15
25 Hideo Nomo/25
30 Albert Pujols/25

2003 Timeless Treasures Rookie Year Letters Autographs

RANDOM INSERTS IN PACKS
STATED PRINT RUN 1 SERIAL #'d SET
NO PRICING DUE TO SCARCITY
11 Scott Rolen
12 Vladimir Guerrero
15 Andruw Jones
19 Gary Sheffield
23 Ryan Klesko
26 Mark Prior

2003 Timeless Treasures Rookie Year Logos

RANDOM INSERTS IN PACKS
PRINT RUNS B/WN 10-50 COPIES PER CARD
NO PRICING ON QTY OF 25 OR LESS
4 Nomar Garciaparra/15
5 Sean Casey/50 15.00 40.00
6 Stan Musial/15
7 Yogi Berra/10
9 Ivan Rodriguez/10
10 J.D. Drew/50 15.00 40.00
11 Scott Rolen/50 20.00 50.00
12 Vladimir Guerrero/50 20.00 50.00
15 Andruw Jones/50 20.00 50.00
17 Fred Lynn/25
18 Jeff Kent/50 15.00 40.00
19 Gary Sheffield/50 15.00 40.00
21 Juan Gonzalez/25
22 Alfonso Soriano/20
23 Ryan Klesko/50 15.00 40.00
25 Hideo Nomo/25
26 Mark Prior/25
30 Albert Pujols/50 50.00 100.00

2003 Timeless Treasures Rookie Year Logos Autographs

RANDOM INSERTS IN PACKS
STATED PRINT RUN 1 SERIAL #'d SET
NO PRICING DUE TO SCARCITY
6 Stan Musial
7 Yogi Berra
11 Scott Rolen
12 Vladimir Guerrero
15 Andruw Jones
17 Fred Lynn
19 Gary Sheffield
22 Alfonso Soriano
23 Ryan Klesko
26 Mark Prior

2003 Timeless Treasures Rookie Year Numbers

RANDOM INSERTS IN PACKS
PRINT RUNS B/WN 15-50 COPIES PER CARD
NO PRICING ON QTY OF 30 OR LESS
5 Sean Casey/30
6 Stan Musial/15
7 Yogi Berra/15
9 Ivan Rodriguez/15
10 J.D. Drew/25
11 Scott Rolen/30
12 Vladimir Guerrero/50 15.00 40.00
15 Andruw Jones/50 15.00 40.00
17 Fred Lynn/30
18 Jeff Kent/25
19 Gary Sheffield/25
21 Juan Gonzalez/30
22 Alfonso Soriano/35 10.00 25.00
23 Ryan Klesko/35 10.00 25.00
25 Hideo Nomo/25
26 Mark Prior/35 15.00 40.00
30 Albert Pujols/25

2003 Timeless Treasures Rookie Year Numbers Autographs

RANDOM INSERTS IN PACKS
STATED PRINT RUN 1 SERIAL #'d SET
NO PRICING DUE TO SCARCITY
6 Stan Musial
7 Yogi Berra
12 Vladimir Guerrero
15 Andruw Jones
17 Fred Lynn
19 Gary Sheffield
22 Alfonso Soriano
23 Ryan Klesko
26 Mark Prior

2003 Timeless Treasures Rookie Year Parallel

*PARALLEL p/r 75-99: .4X TO 1X BASIC RYM
*PARALLEL p/r 61-68: .5X TO 1.2X BASIC RYM
*PARALLEL p/r 42-47: .4X TO 1X BASIC RYM
RANDOM INSERTS IN PACKS
PRINT RUNS B/WN 42-99 COPIES PER CARD
1 Cal Ripken Bat/82 30.00 80.00
3 Rafael Palmeiro Bat/86 6.00 15.00
5 Sean Casey Jsy/97 4.00 10.00
6 Stan Musial Jsy/42 30.00 80.00
7 Yogi Berra Jsy/47 25.00 60.00
8 Bernie Williams Bat/91 6.00 15.00
9 Ivan Rodriguez Jsy/91 6.00 15.00
10 J.D. Drew Jsy/99 4.00 10.00
11 Scott Rolen Jsy/96 6.00 15.00
12 Vladimir Guerrero Jsy/97 8.00 20.00
13 Johnny Bench Bat/68 10.00 25.00
14 Ivan Rodriguez Bat/91 6.00 15.00
15 Andruw Jones Jsy/96 6.00 15.00
16 Andruw Jones Bat/96 6.00 15.00
17 Fred Lynn Jsy/75 6.00 15.00
18 Jeff Kent Jsy/92 4.00 10.00
19 Gary Sheffield Jsy/89 4.00 10.00
20 Ron Santo Bat/61 12.50 30.00
21 Juan Gonzalez Jsy/89 4.00 10.00
23 Ryan Klesko Jsy/92 4.00 10.00
25 Hideo Nomo Jsy/95 6.00 15.00
27 Pat Burrell Bat/99 10.00 25.00
28 Magglio Ordonez Bat/98 4.00 10.00
29 Kirby Puckett Bat/84 15.00 40.00

2003 Timeless Treasures Rookie Year Patches

RANDOM INSERTS IN PACKS
PRINT RUNS B/WN 10-15 COPIES PER CARD
NO PRICING DUE TO SCARCITY
5 Sean Casey/15
11 Scott Rolen/10
12 Vladimir Guerrero/15
22 Alfonso Soriano/10
26 Mark Prior/10

2003 Timeless Treasures Rookie Year Patches Autographs

RANDOM INSERTS IN PACKS
STATED PRINT RUN 1 SERIAL #'d SET
NO PRICING DUE TO SCARCITY
12 Vladimir Guerrero
22 Alfonso Soriano
23 Ryan Klesko
26 Mark Prior

2004 Timeless Treasures

This 100 card set was released in May, 2004. This set was issed in four card packs with an $100 SRP and which came one pack to a box and 15 boxes to a case.
COMPLETE SET (100) 125.00 250.00
STATED PRINT RUN 999 SERIAL #'d SETS
1 Albert Pujols 3.00 8.00
2 Garret Anderson 1.50 4.00
3 Randy Johnson 1.50 4.00
4 Alex Rodriguez Yanks 2.00 5.00
5 Manny Ramirez 1.50 4.00
6 Mark Prior 1.50 4.00
7 Roberto Alomar 1.50 4.00
8 Barry Larkin 1.50 4.00
9 Todd Helton 1.50 4.00
10 Ivan Rodriguez 1.50 4.00
11 Jacque Jones 1.50 4.00
12 Jeff Kent 1.50 4.00
13 Mike Sweeney 1.50 4.00
14 Shawn Green 1.50 4.00
15 Richie Sexson 1.50 4.00
16 Mike Piazza 2.00 5.00
17 Vladimir Guerrero 3.00 8.00
18 Mike Mussina 1.50 4.00
19 Barry Zito 1.50 4.00
20 Don Mattingly 3.00 8.00
21 Ichiro Suzuki 3.00 8.00
22 Rocco Baldelli 1.50 4.00
23 Rafael Palmeiro 1.50 4.00
24 Carlos Delgado 1.50 4.00
25 Roger Clemens 2.00 5.00
26 Luis Gonzalez 1.50 4.00
27 Gary Sheffield 1.50 4.00
28 Jay Gibbons 1.50 4.00
29 Nomar Garciaparra 1.50 4.00
30 Aramis Ramirez 1.50 4.00
31 Frank Thomas 1.50 4.00
32 Ryan Wagner 1.50 4.00
33 Preston Wilson 1.50 4.00
34 Hideki Matsui 2.50 6.00
35 Roy Oswalt 1.50 4.00
36 Angel Berroa 1.50 4.00
37 Kazuhisa Ishii 1.50 4.00
38 Scott Podsednik 1.50 4.00
39 Torii Hunter 1.50 4.00
40 Tom Glavine 1.50 4.00
41 Jason Giambi 1.50 4.00
42 Eric Chavez 1.50 4.00
43 Jim Thome 1.50 4.00
44 Tony Gwynn 1.50 4.00
45 Edgar Martinez 1.50 4.00
46 Jim Edmonds 1.50 4.00
47 Delmon Young 1.50 4.00
48 Hank Blalock 1.50 4.00
49 Vernon Wells 1.50 4.00
50 Curt Schilling 1.50 4.00
51 Chipper Jones 1.50 4.00
52 Cal Ripken 4.00 10.00
53 Jason Varitek 1.50 4.00
54 Kerry Wood 1.50 4.00
55 Magglio Ordonez 1.50 4.00
56 Adam Dunn 1.50 4.00
57 Jay Payton 1.50 4.00
58 Josh Beckett 1.50 4.00
59 Jeff Bagwell 1.50 4.00
60 Carlos Beltran 1.50 4.00
61 Hideo Nomo 1.50 4.00
62 Rickie Weeks 1.50 4.00
63 Alfonso Soriano 1.50 4.00
64 Miguel Tejada 1.50 4.00
65 Bret Boone 1.50 4.00
66 Scott Rolen 1.50 4.00
67 Aubrey Huff 1.50 4.00
68 Juan Gonzalez 1.50 4.00
69 Roy Halladay 1.50 4.00
70 Brandon Webb 1.50 4.00
71 Andruw Jones 1.50 4.00
72 Pedro Martinez 1.50 4.00
73 Carlos Lee 1.50 4.00
74 Lance Berkman 1.50 4.00
75 Paul LoDuca 1.50 4.00
76 Jorge Posada 1.50 4.00
77 Tim Hudson 1.50 4.00
78 Stan Musial 2.00 5.00
79 Mark Teixeira 1.50 4.00
80 Trot Nixon 1.50 4.00
81 Fred McGriff 1.50 4.00
82 Nick Johnson 1.50 4.00
83 Nolan Ryan 3.00 8.00
84 Ken Griffey Jr. 2.00 5.00
85 Mariano Rivera 1.50 4.00
86 Mark Mulder 1.50 4.00
87 Bob Gibson 1.50 4.00
88 Dale Murphy UER 1.50 4.00
89 Bernie Williams 1.50 4.00
90 Carl Yastrzemski 2.00 5.00
91 Sammy Sosa 1.50 4.00
92 Miguel Cabrera 1.50 4.00
93 Craig Biggio 1.50 4.00
94 George Brett 3.00 8.00
95 Rickey Henderson 1.50 4.00
96 Derek Jeter 3.00 8.00
97 Greg Maddux 2.00 5.00
98 Bob Abreu 1.50 4.00
99 Troy Glaus 1.50 4.00
100 Dontrelle Willis 1.50 4.00

2004 Timeless Treasures Bronze

*BRONZE ACTIVE: .75X TO 2X BASIC
*BRONZE RETIRED: 1X TO 2.5X BASIC
RANDOM INSERTS IN PACKS
STATED PRINT RUN 100 SERIAL #'d SETS

2004 Timeless Treasures Gold

RANDOM INSERTS IN PACKS
STATED PRINT RUN 10 SERIAL #'d SETS
NO PRICING DUE TO SCARCITY

2004 Timeless Treasures Platinum

RANDOM INSERTS IN PACKS
STATED PRINT RUN 1 SERIAL #'d SET
NO PRICING DUE TO SCARCITY

2004 Timeless Treasures Silver

*SILVER ACTIVE: 2X TO 5X BASIC
*SILVER RETIRED: 2X TO 5X BASIC
RANDOM INSERTS IN PACKS
STATED PRINT RUN 25 SERIAL #'d SETS

2004 Timeless Treasures Signature Bronze

RANDOM INSERTS IN PACKS
PRINT RUNS B/WN 1-73 COPIES PER
NO PRICING ON QTY OF 11 OR LESS
1 Albert Pujols/25 150.00 250.00
2 Garret Anderson/16 15.00 40.00
3 Randy Johnson/1
4 Alex Rodriguez/25 100.00 200.00
5 Manny Ramirez/24 30.00 60.00
6 Mark Prior/50 12.50 30.00
7 Roberto Alomar/10
8 Barry Larkin/25 20.00 50.00
9 Todd Helton/17 30.00 60.00
10 Ivan Rodriguez/10
11 Jacque Jones/1
13 Mike Sweeney/5
14 Shawn Green/15 30.00 60.00
15 Richie Sexson/11
16 Mike Piazza/10
17 Vladimir Guerrero/50 20.00 50.00
18 Mike Mussina/1
19 Barry Zito/10
20 Don Mattingly/50 40.00 80.00
22 Rocco Baldelli/10
23 Rafael Palmeiro/25 30.00 60.00
25 Roger Clemens/1
27 Gary Sheffield/50 12.50 30.00
28 Jay Gibbons/10
30 Aramis Ramirez/10
31 Frank Thomas/1
32 Ryan Wagner/1
35 Roy Oswalt/5
36 Angel Berroa/10
37 Kazuhisa Ishii/17 15.00 40.00
38 Scott Podsednik/1
39 Torii Hunter/5
40 Tom Glavine/25 20.00 50.00
42 Eric Chavez/25 12.50 30.00
44 Tony Gwynn/50 30.00 60.00
45 Edgar Martinez/10
46 Jim Edmonds/15 30.00 60.00
47 Delmon Young/73 10.00 25.00
48 Hank Blalock/10
49 Vernon Wells/25 12.50 30.00
50 Curt Schilling/38 30.00 60.00
51 Chipper Jones/10
52 Cal Ripken/8
53 Jason Varitek/33 30.00 60.00
55 Magglio Ordonez/5
56 Adam Dunn/25 20.00 50.00
57 Jay Payton/1
58 Josh Beckett/21 20.00 50.00
59 Jeff Bagwell/25 30.00 60.00
60 Carlos Beltran/15 15.00 40.00
61 Hideo Nomo/10
62 Rickie Weeks/10
67 Aubrey Huff/10
68 Juan Gonzalez/25 12.50 30.00
70 Brandon Webb/10
71 Andruw Jones/25 20.00 50.00
72 Pedro Martinez/1
73 Carlos Lee/10
74 Lance Berkman/5
75 Paul LoDuca/10
76 Jorge Posada/25 20.00 50.00
77 Tim Hudson/15 30.00 60.00
78 Stan Musial/50 30.00 60.00
79 Mark Teixeira/23 20.00 50.00
80 Trot Nixon/10
81 Fred McGriff/10
82 Nick Johnson/10
83 Nolan Ryan/50 60.00 120.00
85 Mariano Rivera/10
86 Mark Mulder/5
87 Bob Gibson/25 20.00 50.00
88 Dale Murphy UER/50 12.50 30.00
90 Carl Yastrzemski/25 40.00 80.00
91 Sammy Sosa/50 50.00 100.00
92 Miguel Cabrera/24 20.00 50.00
93 Craig Biggio/10
94 George Brett/25 75.00 150.00
95 Rickey Henderson/25 60.00 120.00
97 Greg Maddux/31 60.00 120.00
98 Bob Abreu/10
99 Troy Glaus/10
100 Dontrelle Willis/35 15.00 40.00

2004 Timeless Treasures Signature Gold

RANDOM INSERTS IN PACKS
PRINT RUNS B/WN 1-11 COPIES PER
NO PRICING DUE TO SCARCITY

2004 Timeless Treasures Signature Platinum

RANDOM INSERTS IN PACKS
STATED PRINT RUN 1 SERIAL #'d SET
NO PRICING DUE TO SCARCITY

2004 Timeless Treasures Signature Silver

RANDOM INSERTS IN PACKS
PRINT RUNS B/WN 1-34 COPIES PER
NO PRICING ON QTY OF 13 OR LESS
6 Mark Prior/22 15.00 40.00
17 Vladimir Guerrero/27 30.00 60.00
20 Don Mattingly/23 60.00 120.00
27 Gary Sheffield/25 20.00 50.00
44 Tony Gwynn/19 50.00 100.00
47 Delmon Young/25 20.00 50.00
68 Juan Gonzalez/22
76 Jorge Posada/20 20.00 50.00
78 Stan Musial/25 40.00 80.00
83 Nolan Ryan/34 75.00 150.00
88 Dale Murphy UER/25 20.00 50.00
91 Sammy Sosa/21 50.00 100.00

2004 Timeless Treasures Award Materials

PRINT RUNS B/WN 9-99 COPIES PER
NO PRICING ON QTY OF 9 OR LESS
*NBR p/r 45-51: .5X TO 1.2X BASIC p/r 97
*NBR p/r 45-51: .4X TO 1X BASIC p/r 68
*NBR p/r 45-51: .3X TO .8X BASIC p/r 25
*NBR p/r 33-35: .6X TO 1.5X BASIC p/r 88-94
*NBR p/r 20-22: .75X TO 2X BASIC p/r 80-81
*NBR p/r 20-22: .6X TO 1.5X BASIC p/r 50
*NBR p/r 19: .75X TO 2X BASIC p/r 75
*NBR p/r 19: .4X TO 1X BASIC p/r 19
NUMBER PRINT RUNS B/WN 3-51 PER
NO NUMBER PRICING ON QTY 14 OR LESS
*PRIME p/r 25: 1X TO 2.5X BASIC p/r 78-97
*PRIME p/r 25: 1X TO 2.5X BASIC p/r 50-68
*PRIME p/r 25: .75X TO 2X BASIC p/r 25
PRIME PRINT RUNS B/WN 1-25 COPIES PER
NO PRIME PRICING ON QTY OF 10 OR LESS
RANDOM INSERTS IN PACKS
1 Jimmie Foxx Bat/9
2 Stan Musial Jsy/43 15.00 40.00
3 Lou Boudreau Jsy/19 8.00 20.00
4 Roger Maris Pants/61 20.00 50.00
5 Roger Maris Bat/61 20.00 50.00
6 Roberto Clemente Bat/66 30.00 60.00
7 Bob Gibson 68 CY Jsy/68 6.00 15.00
8 Bob Gibson 68 MVP Jsy/68 6.00 15.00
9 Tom Seaver Jsy/19 10.00 25.00
10 Fred Lynn Jsy/75 4.00 10.00
11 Jim Rice Jsy/78 4.00 10.00
12 M.Schmidt 80 MVP Jsy/80 8.00 20.00
13 M.Schmidt 80 MVP Pants/80 8.00 20.00
14 M.Schmidt 80 MVP Stir/80 8.00 20.00
15 M.Schmidt 81 MVP Jsy/81 8.00 20.00
16 M.Schmidt 81 MVP Bat/81 8.00 20.00
17 Dale Murphy Jsy/82 6.00 15.00
18 M.Schmidt 86 MVP Hat/19 20.00 50.00
19 M.Schmidt 86 MVP Shoe/19 20.00 50.00
20 M.Schmidt 86 MVP Bat/86 8.00 20.00
21 M.Schmidt 86 MVP Stir/19 20.00 50.00
22 Jose Canseco Jsy/88 6.00 15.00
23 F.Thomas 93 MVP Bat/93 6.00 15.00
24 F.Thomas 93 MVP Jsy/93 6.00 15.00
25 Jeff Bagwell Pants/94 6.00 15.00
26 F.Thomas 94 MVP Jsy/94 6.00 15.00
27 F.Thomas 94 MVP Pants/94 6.00 15.00
28 Jeff Bagwell Bat/94 6.00 15.00
29 Pedro Martinez 97 CY Jsy/97 6.00 15.00
30 Ivan Rodriguez Bat/99 6.00 15.00
31 R.Johnson 00 CY Jsy/25 8.00 20.00
32 P.Martinez 00 CY Jsy/25 8.00 20.00
33 Roger Clemens Jsy/50 10.00 25.00
34 R.Johnson 02 CY Jsy/25 8.00 20.00
35 Miguel Tejada Jsy/25 6.00 15.00

2004 Timeless Treasures Award Materials Signature

PRINT RUNS B/WN 1-78 COPIES PER
NO PRICING ON QTY OF 9 OR LESS
*NBR p/r 19: .75X TO 2X BASIC p/r 75
NUMBER PRINT RUNS B/WN 1-19 PER
NO NUMBER PRICES ON QTY OF 14 OR LESS
PRIME PRINT RUNS B/WN 1-14 COPIES PER
NO PRIME PRICING DUE TO SCARCITY
RANDOM INSERTS IN PACKS
2 Stan Musial Jsy/9
7 Bob Gibson 68 CY Jsy/19 30.00 60.00
8 Bob Gibson 68 MVP Jsy/19 30.00 60.00
9 Tom Seaver Jsy/9
10 Fred Lynn Jsy/75 8.00 20.00
11 Jim Rice Jsy/78 10.00 25.00
17 Dale Murphy Jsy/9
22 Jose Canseco Jsy/9
23 F.Thomas 93 MVP Bat/9
24 F.Thomas 93 MVP Jsy/9
25 Jeff Bagwell Pants/9
26 F.Thomas 94 MVP Jsy/9
27 F.Thomas 94 MVP Pants/9
28 Jeff Bagwell Bat/9
29 Pedro Martinez 97 CY Jsy/1
30 Ivan Rodriguez Bat/9
31 Randy Johnson 00 CY Jsy/9
32 Pedro Martinez 00 CY Jsy/1
33 Roger Clemens Jsy/9
34 Randy Johnson 02 CY Jsy/9

2004 Timeless Treasures Award Materials Combos

PRINT RUNS B/WN 25-50 COPIES PER
*PRIME: .6X TO 1.5X BASIC p/r 25
PRIME PRINT RUN 19 SERIAL #'d SETS
RANDOM INSERTS IN PACKS
4 Roger Maris Bat-Pants/25 40.00 80.00
12 M.Schmidt 80M Jsy-Pant/25 20.00 50.00
13 M.Schmidt 80M Pant-Stir/50 15.00 40.00
14 M.Schmidt 80M Jsy-Stir/50 15.00 40.00
15 M.Schmidt 81M Bat-Jsy/25 20.00 50.00
16 M.Schmidt 81M Bat-Stir/50 15.00 40.00
18 M.Schmidt 86M Hat-Shoe/50 15.00 40.00
19 M.Schmidt 86M Hat-Bat/50 15.00 40.00
20 M.Schmidt 86M Hat-Stir/50 15.00 40.00
21 M.Schmidt 86M Bat-Shoe/50 15.00 40.00
23 F.Thomas 93M Bat-Jsy/25 12.50 30.00
25 Jeff Bagwell Bat-Jsy/25 12.50 30.00
26 F.Thomas 94M Bat-Jsy/25 12.50 30.00
35 Miguel Tejada Bat-Jsy/25 8.00 20.00

2004 Timeless Treasures Award Materials Combos Signature

STATED PRINT RUN 5 SERIAL #'d SETS
PRIME PRINT RUN 5 SERIAL #'d SETS
RANDOM INSERTS IN PACKS
NO PRICING DUE TO SCARCITY
23 F.Thomas 93 MVP Bat-Jsy
25 Jeff Bagwell Bat-Jsy
26 F.Thomas 94 MVP Bat-Jsy

2004 Timeless Treasures Game Day Materials

RANDOM INSERTS IN PACKS
PRINT RUNS B/WN 8-99 COPIES PER
NO PRICING ON QTY OF 9 OR LESS
1 Nellie Fox Bat/58 30.00 60.00
2 Frank Robinson Bat/61 6.00 15.00
3 George Brett Bat/77 10.00 25.00
4 George Brett Hat/82 15.00 40.00
5 Nolan Ryan Hat/19 60.00 120.00
6 Cal Ripken Hat/85 30.00 60.00
7 Rod Carew Hat/19 12.50 30.00
8 Ryne Sandberg Bat/91 10.00 25.00
9 Kirby Puckett Bat/92 6.00 15.00
10 Frank Thomas Bat/93 6.00 15.00
11 George Brett Ball/9
12 Tony Gwynn Pants/99 6.00 15.00
13 Vladimir Guerrero Bat/99 6.00 15.00
14 Tony Gwynn Hat/99 12.50 30.00
15 Magglio Ordonez Hat/15 10.00 25.00
16 Rickey Henderson Bat/50 6.00 15.00
17 Cal Ripken Ball/8

2004 Timeless Treasures Game Day Materials Signature

RANDOM INSERTS IN PACKS
PRINT RUNS B/WN 8-25 COPIES PER
NO PRICING ON QTY OF 10 OR LESS
2 Frank Robinson Bat/25 30.00 60.00
3 George Brett Bat/10
4 George Brett Hat/10
5 Nolan Ryan Hat/10
6 Cal Ripken Hat/8
7 Rod Carew Hat/10
8 Ryne Sandberg Bat/10
9 Kirby Puckett Bat/10
10 Frank Thomas Bat/10
11 George Brett Ball/5
12 Tony Gwynn Pants/10
13 Vladimir Guerrero Bat/10
14 Tony Gwynn Hat/10
15 Magglio Ordonez Hat/25 20.00 50.00
16 Rickey Henderson Bat/10
17 Cal Ripken Ball/8

2004 Timeless Treasures HOF Materials Signature

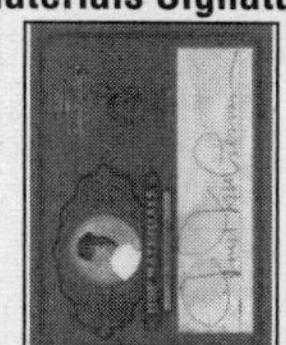

RANDOM INSERTS IN PACKS
PRINT RUNS B/WN 1-34 COPIES PER
NO PRICING ON QTY OF 11 OR LESS
1 Al Kaline/25 30.00 60.00
2 Babe Ruth/1
3 Bob Feller/25 15.00 40.00
4 Bobby Doerr/1
5 Brooks Robinson/25 20.00 50.00
6 Carl Yastrzemski/8
7 Carlton Fisk/27 20.00 50.00
8 Dave Winfield/5
9 Duke Snider/25 20.00 50.00
10 Eddie Murray/5
11 Ernie Banks/25 30.00 60.00
12 Fergie Jenkins/31 15.00 40.00
13 Frank Robinson/20 20.00 50.00
14 Hal Newhouser/5
15 Hoyt Wilhelm/25 20.00 50.00
17 Jim Palmer/22 15.00 40.00
18 Joe Morgan/8
19 Johnny Bench/5
20 Juan Marichal/27 15.00 40.00
21 Kirby Puckett/34 50.00 100.00
22 Lou Brock/20 20.00 50.00

23 Lou Gehrig/1
24 Luis Aparicio/11
26 Orlando Cepeda/30 15.00 40.00
27 Pee Wee Reese/5
28 Phil Rizzuto/25 20.00 50.00
29 Red Schoendienst/25 15.00 40.00
32 Paul Molitor/25 15.00 40.00
34 Warren Spahn/21 30.00 60.00
35 Willie McCovey/25 20.00 50.00

2004 Timeless Treasures HOF Materials Barrel

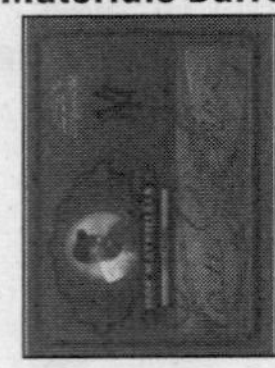

RANDOM INSERTS IN PACKS
STATED PRINT RUN 1 SERIAL #'d SET
NO PRICING DUE TO SCARCITY
1 Al Kaline
2 Babe Ruth
4 Bobby Doerr
5 Brooks Robinson
6 Carl Yastrzemski
7 Carlton Fisk
8 Dave Winfield
9 Duke Snider
10 Eddie Murray
11 Ernie Banks
13 Frank Robinson
18 Joe Morgan
19 Johnny Bench
21 Kirby Puckett
22 Lou Brock
23 Lou Gehrig
24 Luis Aparicio
25 Mel Ott
26 Orlando Cepeda
27 Pee Wee Reese
28 Phil Rizzuto
29 Red Schoendienst
30 Roberto Clemente
31 Roy Campanella
32 Paul Molitor
33 Ty Cobb
36 Willie Stargell

2004 Timeless Treasures HOF Materials Bat

RANDOM INSERTS IN PACKS
PRINT RUNS B/WN 5-50 COPIES PER
NO PRICING ON QTY OF 5 OR LESS
1 Al Kaline/25 15.00 40.00
2 Babe Ruth/50 100.00 200.00
4 Bobby Doerr/25 6.00 15.00
5 Brooks Robinson/25 10.00 25.00
6 Carl Yastrzemski/25 15.00 40.00
7 Carlton Fisk/25 10.00 25.00
8 Dave Winfield/25 8.00 20.00
9 Duke Snider/5
10 Eddie Murray/25 15.00 40.00
11 Ernie Banks/25 15.00 40.00
13 Frank Robinson/25 10.00 25.00
18 Joe Morgan/25 8.00 20.00
19 Johnny Bench/25 15.00 40.00
21 Kirby Puckett/25 15.00 40.00
22 Lou Brock/25 10.00 25.00
23 Lou Gehrig/50 75.00 150.00
24 Luis Aparicio/25 6.00 15.00
25 Mel Ott/25 20.00 50.00
26 Orlando Cepeda/25 8.00 20.00
27 Pee Wee Reese/25 10.00 25.00
28 Phil Rizzuto/25 10.00 25.00
29 Red Schoendienst/25 8.00 20.00
30 Roberto Clemente/25 40.00 80.00
31 Roy Campanella/25 15.00 40.00
32 Paul Molitor/25 8.00 20.00
33 Ty Cobb/25 60.00 120.00
35 Willie McCovey/25 8.00 20.00
36 Willie Stargell/25 10.00 25.00

2004 Timeless Treasures HOF Materials Bat Signature

RANDOM INSERTS IN PACKS
PRINT RUNS B/WN 10-50 COPIES PER
NO PRICING ON QTY OF 10 OR LESS
1 Al Kaline/50 20.00 50.00
4 Bobby Doerr/50 10.00 25.00
5 Brooks Robinson/50 15.00 40.00
6 Carl Yastrzemski/10
7 Carlton Fisk/10
8 Dave Winfield/10
9 Duke Snider/10
10 Eddie Murray/10
11 Ernie Banks/25 40.00 80.00
13 Frank Robinson/50 15.00 40.00
18 Joe Morgan/25 15.00 40.00
19 Johnny Bench/25 40.00 80.00
21 Kirby Puckett/10
22 Lou Brock/50 15.00 40.00
24 Luis Aparicio/50 10.00 25.00
26 Orlando Cepeda/50 12.50 30.00
28 Phil Rizzuto/50 15.00 40.00
29 Red Schoendienst/50 12.50 30.00
32 Paul Molitor/25 15.00 40.00
35 Willie McCovey/10

2004 Timeless Treasures HOF Materials Jersey

PRINT RUNS B/WN 5-50 COPIES PER
NO PRICING ON QTY OF 10 OR LESS
PRIME PRINT RUNS B/WN 1-10 COPIES PER
NO PRIME PRICING DUE TO SCARCITY
RANDOM INSERTS IN PACKS
1 Al Kaline/6
2 Babe Ruth/25 300.00 500.00
3 Bob Feller/50 6.00 15.00
4 Bobby Doerr/25 6.00 15.00
5 Brooks Robinson/50 8.00 20.00
6 Carl Yastrzemski/50 12.50 30.00
7 Carlton Fisk/50 8.00 20.00
8 Dave Winfield/50 6.00 15.00
9 Duke Snider/10
10 Eddie Murray/25 15.00 40.00
11 Ernie Banks/10
13 Frank Robinson/25 10.00 25.00
14 Hal Newhouser/50 6.00 15.00
15 Hoyt Wilhelm/50 6.00 15.00
16 Jackie Robinson/10
17 Jim Palmer/50 6.00 15.00
18 Joe Morgan/50 6.00 15.00
20 Juan Marichal/50 6.00 15.00
21 Kirby Puckett/50 10.00 25.00
22 Lou Brock/25 10.00 25.00
23 Lou Gehrig/25 100.00 200.00
24 Luis Aparicio/25 6.00 15.00
25 Mel Ott/25 20.00 50.00
26 Orlando Cepeda/5
27 Pee Wee Reese/50 8.00 20.00
28 Phil Rizzuto/50 8.00 20.00
29 Red Schoendienst/25
30 Roberto Clemente/50 40.00 80.00
32 Paul Molitor/50 6.00 15.00
34 Warren Spahn/50 10.00 25.00
35 Willie McCovey/50 6.00 15.00
36 Willie Stargell/50 8.00 20.00

2004 Timeless Treasures HOF Materials Jersey Number

*NUMBER p/r 44: .4X TO 1X BASIC p/r 50
*NUMBER p/r 27-34: .5X TO 1.2X BASIC p/r 50
*NUMBER p/r 27-34: .4X TO 1X BASIC p/r 25
*NUMBER p/r 20-22: .6X TO 1.5X BASIC p/r 50
*NUMBER p/r 20-22: .4X TO 1X BASIC p/r 25
*NUMBER p/r 16-19: .6X TO 1.5X BASIC p/r 50
RANDOM INSERTS IN PACKS
PRINT RUNS B/WN 1-44 COPIES PER
NO PRICING ON QTY OF 14 OR LESS
3 Bob Feller/19 10.00 25.00
16 Jackie Robinson/42 30.00 60.00

2004 Timeless Treasures HOF Materials Jersey Signature

PRINT RUNS B/WN 5-50 COPIES PER
NO PRICING ON QTY OF 10 OR LESS
PRIME PRINT RUNS B/WN 1-10 COPIES PER
NO PRIME PRICING DUE TO SCARCITY
RANDOM INSERTS IN PACKS
1 Al Kaline/25 30.00 60.00
3 Bob Feller/10
4 Bobby Doerr/50 10.00 25.00
5 Brooks Robinson/25 20.00 50.00
6 Carl Yastrzemski/10
7 Carlton Fisk/10
8 Dave Winfield/10
10 Eddie Murray/10
11 Ernie Banks/10
13 Frank Robinson/50 15.00 40.00
15 Hoyt Wilhelm/25 20.00 50.00
17 Jim Palmer/50 12.50 30.00
18 Joe Morgan/25 15.00 40.00
19 Johnny Bench/5
20 Juan Marichal/50 12.50 30.00
21 Kirby Puckett/10
22 Lou Brock/50 15.00 40.00
24 Luis Aparicio/50 10.00 25.00
26 Orlando Cepeda/25 15.00 40.00
28 Phil Rizzuto/50 15.00 40.00
29 Red Schoendienst/50 12.50 30.00
32 Paul Molitor/50 12.50 30.00
34 Warren Spahn/25 40.00 80.00
35 Willie McCovey/10

2004 Timeless Treasures HOF Materials Jersey Signature Number

*NUMBER p/r 25: .5X TO 1.2X BASIC p/r 50
*NUMBER p/r 25: .4X TO 1X BASIC p/r 25
RANDOM INSERTS IN PACKS
PRINT RUNS B/WN 10-25 COPIES PER
NO PRICING ON QTY OF 10 OR LESS
12 Fergie Jenkins Pants/25 15.00 40.00

2004 Timeless Treasures HOF Materials Pants

RANDOM INSERTS IN PACKS
PRINT RUNS B/WN 25-50 COPIES PER
1 Al Kaline/25 15.00 40.00
2 Babe Ruth/50 100.00 200.00
12 Fergie Jenkins/25 8.00 20.00
23 Lou Gehrig/50 75.00 150.00
24 Luis Aparicio/25 6.00 15.00
25 Mel Ott/25 20.00 50.00
31 Roy Campanella/25 15.00 40.00
33 Ty Cobb/25 60.00 120.00

2004 Timeless Treasures HOF Materials Pants Signature

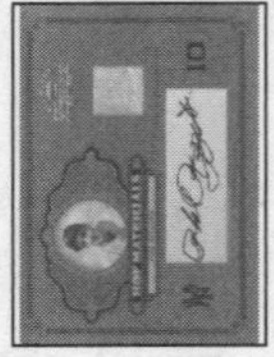

RANDOM INSERTS IN PACKS
STATED PRINT RUN 25 SERIAL #'d SETS
1 Al Kaline 30.00 60.00
12 Fergie Jenkins 15.00 40.00
24 Luis Aparicio 12.50 30.00
28 Phil Rizzuto 20.00 50.00

2004 Timeless Treasures HOF Materials Combos Bat-Jersey

PRINT RUNS B/WN 1-50 COPIES PER
PRIME PRINT RUNS B/WN 1-5 COPIES PER
NO PRIME PRICING DUE TO SCARCITY
RANDOM INSERTS IN PACKS
1 Al Kaline/25 20.00 50.00
2 Babe Ruth/25 300.00 500.00
4 Bobby Doerr/25 8.00 20.00
5 Brooks Robinson/50 10.00 25.00
6 Carl Yastrzemski/50 15.00 40.00
7 Carlton Fisk/50 10.00 25.00
8 Dave Winfield/50 8.00 20.00
10 Eddie Murray/50 15.00 40.00
11 Ernie Banks/10
13 Frank Robinson/50 10.00 25.00
18 Joe Morgan/50 8.00 20.00
19 Johnny Bench/1
21 Kirby Puckett/50 15.00 40.00
22 Lou Brock/50 10.00 25.00
23 Lou Gehrig/25 175.00 300.00
24 Luis Aparicio/25 8.00 20.00
25 Mel Ott/25 40.00 80.00
26 Orlando Cepeda/5
27 Pee Wee Reese/50 10.00 25.00
28 Phil Rizzuto/50 10.00 25.00
29 Red Schoendienst/25 10.00 25.00
30 Roberto Clemente/50 75.00 150.00
32 Paul Molitor/50 8.00 20.00
35 Willie McCovey/50 8.00 20.00
36 Willie Stargell/50 10.00 25.00

2004 Timeless Treasures HOF Materials Combos Bat-Jersey Signature

PRINT RUNS B/WN 1-25 COPIES PER
NO PRICING ON QTY OF 10 OR LESS
PRIME PRINT RUNS B/WN 1-5 COPIES PER
NO PRIME PRICING DUE TO SCARCITY
RANDOM INSERTS IN PACKS
1 Al Kaline/5
4 Bobby Doerr/25 15.00 40.00
5 Brooks Robinson/25 30.00 60.00
6 Carl Yastrzemski/10
7 Carlton Fisk/10
8 Dave Winfield/10
10 Eddie Murray/10
11 Ernie Banks/25 60.00 120.00
13 Frank Robinson/25 30.00 60.00
18 Joe Morgan/25 20.00 50.00
19 Johnny Bench/1
21 Kirby Puckett/10
22 Lou Brock/25 30.00 60.00
24 Luis Aparicio/25 15.00 40.00
26 Orlando Cepeda/10
28 Phil Rizzuto/10
29 Red Schoendienst/25 20.00 50.00
32 Paul Molitor/25 20.00 50.00
35 Willie McCovey/10

2004 Timeless Treasures HOF Materials Combos Bat-Pants

RANDOM INSERTS IN PACKS
STATED PRINT RUN 25 SERIAL #'d SETS
1 Al Kaline/25 20.00 50.00
2 Babe Ruth/25 250.00 400.00
12 F.Jenkins Fld Glv-Pants/25 10.00 25.00
23 Lou Gehrig/25 150.00 250.00
24 Luis Aparicio/25 8.00 20.00
25 Mel Ott/25 40.00 80.00
31 Roy Campanella/25 30.00 60.00
33 Ty Cobb/25 150.00 250.00

2004 Timeless Treasures HOF Materials Combos Bat-Pants Signature

RANDOM INSERTS IN PACKS
STATED PRINT RUN 25 SERIAL #'d SETS
1 Al Kaline/25 50.00 100.00
12 F.Jenkins Fld Glv-Pants/25 20.00 50.00
24 Luis Aparicio/25 15.00 40.00

2004 Timeless Treasures HOF Materials Combos Jersey-Pants

PRINT RUNS B/WN 10-25 COPIES PER
NO PRICING ON QTY OF 10 OR LESS
PRIME PRINT RUNS B/WN 1-5 COPIES PER
NO PRIME PRICING DUE TO SCARCITY
RANDOM INSERTS IN PACKS
1 Al Kaline/10

2 Babe Ruth/25 300.00 500.00
16 J.Robinson Jacket-Jsy/10
23 Lou Gehrig/25 175.00 300.00
24 Luis Aparicio/25 8.00 20.00
25 Mel Ott/10

2004 Timeless Treasures HOF Materials Combos Jersey-Pants Signature

PRINT RUNS B/WN 5-25 COPIES PER
PRIME PRINT RUNS B/WN 1-5 COPIES PER
NO PRIME PRICING DUE TO SCARCITY
RANDOM INSERTS IN PACKS
1 Al Kaline/5
24 Luis Aparicio/25 15.00 40.00

2004 Timeless Treasures Home Away Gamers

PRINT RUNS B/WN 5-100 COPIES PER
NO PRICING ON QTY OF 10 OR LESS
PRIME PRINT RUNS B/WN 3-5 COPIES PER
NO PRIME PRICING DUE TO SCARCITY
1 Babe Ruth Jsy-Jsy/25 500.00 800.00
2 Yogi Berra Jsy-Jsy/8
3 Wade Boggs Jsy-Jsy/50 10.00 25.00
4 Tony Gwynn Jsy-Jsy/50 15.00 40.00
5 Steve Carlton Jsy-Jsy/50 8.00 20.00
6 Stan Musial Jsy-Jsy/10
7 Ryne Sandberg Jsy-Jsy/50 20.00 50.00
8 Rod Carew Jsy-Jsy/50 10.00 25.00
9 R.Henderson Jsy-Jsy/50 15.00 40.00
10 Brooks Robinson Jsy-Jsy/5
11 Ted Williams Jsy-Jsy/100 60.00 120.00
12 Ozzie Smith Jsy-Jsy/50 15.00 40.00
13 Mike Schmidt Jsy-Jsy/50 15.00 40.00
14 Harmon Killebrew Jsy-Jsy/50 15.00 40.00
15 George Brett Jsy-Jsy/100 15.00 40.00
16 Don Mattingly Jsy-Jsy/50 20.00 50.00
17 Dale Murphy Jsy-Jsy/50 10.00 25.00
18 Cal Ripken Jsy-Jsy/100 30.00 60.00
19 Lou Gehrig Jsy-Jsy/50 175.00 300.00
20 Nolan Ryan Jsy-Jsy/100 20.00 50.00

2004 Timeless Treasures Home Away Gamers Signature

RANDOM INSERTS IN PACKS
PRINT RUNS B/WN 1-25 COPIES PER
NO PRICING ON QTY OF 10 OR LESS
1 Babe Ruth Jsy-Jsy/1
2 Yogi Berra Jsy-Jsy/5
3 Wade Boggs Jsy-Jsy/10
4 Tony Gwynn Jsy-Jsy/10
5 Steve Carlton Jsy-Jsy/25 20.00 50.00
6 Stan Musial Jsy-Jsy/10
7 Ryne Sandberg Jsy-Jsy/10
8 Rod Carew Jsy-Jsy/10
9 R.Henderson Jsy-Jsy/10
10 Brooks Robinson Jsy-Jsy/5
11 Ted Williams Jsy-Jsy/1
12 Ozzie Smith Jsy-Jsy/10
13 Mike Schmidt Jsy-Jsy/20 75.00 150.00
14 H.Killebrew Jsy-Jsy/25 50.00 100.00
15 George Brett Jsy-Jsy/10
16 Don Mattingly Jsy-Jsy/25 100.00 200.00
17 Dale Murphy Jsy-Jsy/25 30.00 60.00
18 Cal Ripken Jsy-Jsy/10
19 Lou Gehrig Jsy-Jsy/1
20 Nolan Ryan Jsy-Jsy/10

2004 Timeless Treasures Home Away Gamers Combos

PRINT RUNS B/WN 5-100 COPIES PER
NO PRICING ON QTY OF 8 OR LESS
PRIME PRINT RUNS B/WN 3-10 COPIES PER
NO PRIME PRICING DUE TO SCARCITY
1 Babe Ruth/25 700.00 1000.00
2 Yogi Berra/8
3 Wade Boggs/50 15.00 40.00
4 Tony Gwynn/50 30.00 60.00
5 Steve Carlton/50 15.00 40.00
6 Stan Musial/25 60.00 120.00
7 Ryne Sandberg/50 30.00 60.00
8 Rod Carew/50 15.00 40.00
9 Rickey Henderson/50 20.00 50.00
10 Brooks Robinson/5
11 Ted Williams/100 75.00 150.00
12 Ozzie Smith/50 20.00 50.00
13 Mike Schmidt/50 30.00 60.00
14 Harmon Killebrew/25 30.00 60.00
15 George Brett/100 30.00 60.00
16 Don Mattingly/50 40.00 80.00
17 Dale Murphy/50 15.00 40.00
18 Cal Ripken/100 40.00 80.00
19 Lou Gehrig/25 350.00 600.00
20 Nolan Ryan/100 40.00 80.00

2004 Timeless Treasures Home Away Gamers Combos Signature

PRINT RUNS B/WN 1-5 COPIES PER
PRIME PRINT RUN 1 SERIAL #'d SET
RANDOM INSERTS IN PACKS
NO PRICING DUE TO SCARCITY
1 Babe Ruth/1
2 Yogi Berra/5
3 Wade Boggs/5
4 Tony Gwynn/5
5 Steve Carlton/5
6 Stan Musial/5
7 Ryne Sandberg/5
8 Rod Carew/5
9 Rickey Henderson/5
10 Brooks Robinson/5
11 Ted Williams/5
12 Ozzie Smith/5
13 Mike Schmidt/5
14 Harmon Killebrew/5
15 George Brett/5
16 Don Mattingly/5
17 Dale Murphy/5
18 Cal Ripken/5
19 Lou Gehrig/1
20 Nolan Ryan/5

2004 Timeless Treasures Home Run Materials

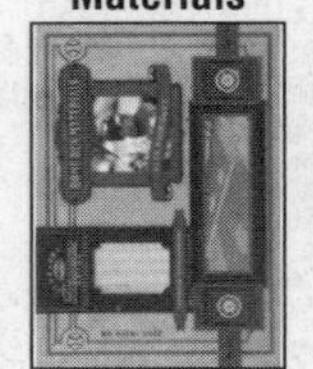

RANDOM INSERTS IN PACKS
PRINT RUNS B/WN 12-100 COPIES PER
NO PRICING ON QTY OF 12 OR LESS
1 Roger Maris Bat/61 20.00 50.00
2 Ron Santo Ball/12
3 H.Killebrew HR 570 Bat/75 10.00 25.00
4 H.Killebrew HR 565 Bat/75 10.00 25.00
5 Jose Canseco Bat/96 6.00 15.00
6 Alex Rodriguez Bat/100 6.00 15.00
7 Sammy Sosa Jsy/100 6.00 15.00
8 Rafael Palmeiro Jsy/25 8.00 20.00
9 Ivan Rodriguez Jsy/25 8.00 20.00

2004 Timeless Treasures Home Run Materials Signature

RANDOM INSERTS IN PACKS
PRINT RUNS B/WN 9-19 COPIES PER
NO PRICING ON QTY OF 12 OR LESS
2 Ron Santo Ball/12
3 H.Killebrew HR 570 Bat/19 40.00 80.00
4 H.Killebrew HR 565 Bat/19 40.00 80.00
5 Jose Canseco Bat/9
6 Alex Rodriguez Bat/9
7 Sammy Sosa Jsy/9

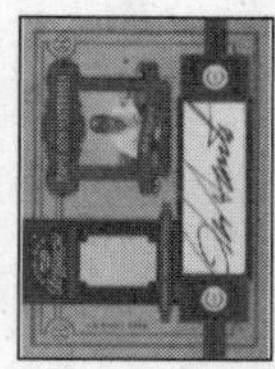

8 Rafael Palmeiro Jsy/9
9 Ivan Rodriguez Jsy/9

2004 Timeless Treasures Material Ink Bat

RANDOM INSERTS IN PACKS
PRINT RUNS B/WN 1-50 COPIES PER
NO PRICING ON QTY OF 10 OR LESS
1 Adam Dunn/25 20.00 50.00
2 Alan Trammell/25 15.00 40.00
3 Alex Rodriguez/10
4 Andre Dawson/25 15.00 40.00
5 Bo Jackson/25 50.00 100.00
6 Cal Ripken/8
7 Dale Murphy/25 20.00 50.00
8 Darryl Strawberry/10
9 Dave Parker/10
10 Deion Sanders/5
12 Don Mattingly/50 50.00 100.00
13 Dontrelle Willis/10
14 Hideo Nomo/1
15 Ivan Rodriguez/7
16 Joe Carter/10
17 Jose Canseco/10
19 Mark Grace/10
20 Mark Prior/25 15.00 40.00
21 Mark Teixeira/10
23 Mike Piazza/1
24 Paul Molitor/10
25 Paul O'Neill/25 30.00 60.00
26 Rocco Baldelli/10
29 Ron Santo/50 20.00 50.00
30 Ryne Sandberg/25 60.00 120.00
31 Ernie Banks/10
32 Tony Gwynn/25 50.00 100.00
33 Vladimir Guerrero/10
34 Will Clark/25 20.00 50.00

2004 Timeless Treasures Material Ink Jersey

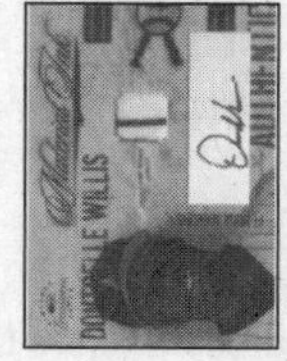

PRINT RUNS B/WN 10-100 COPIES PER
NO PRICING ON QTY OF 10 OR LESS
*PRIME p/r 25: .75X TO 2X BASIC p/r 100
*PRIME p/r 25: .6X TO 1.5X BASIC p/r 50
PRIME PRINT RUNS B/WN 1-25 COPIES PER
NO PRIME PRICING ON QTY OF 10 OR LESS
RANDOM INSERTS IN PACKS
1 Adam Dunn/25 20.00 50.00
2 Alan Trammell/100 10.00 25.00
3 Alex Rodriguez/10
4 Andre Dawson/100 10.00 25.00
5 Bo Jackson/25 50.00 100.00
6 Cal Ripken/10
7 Dale Murphy/50 15.00 40.00
8 Darryl Strawberry/100 10.00 25.00
9 Dave Parker/25 15.00 40.00
10 Deion Sanders/10
11 Doc Gooden/100 10.00 25.00
12 Don Mattingly/50 50.00 100.00
13 Dontrelle Willis/25 20.00 50.00
14 Hideo Nomo/1
15 Ivan Rodriguez/25 40.00 80.00
16 Joe Carter/25 15.00 40.00
17 Jose Canseco/25 20.00 50.00
18 Kerry Wood/15 60.00 120.00
19 Mark Grace/10
20 Mark Prior/50 12.50 30.00
21 Mark Teixeira/25 20.00 50.00
22 Marty Marion/25 12.50 30.00
23 Mike Piazza/1
24 Paul Molitor/10
26 Rocco Baldelli/25 15.00 40.00
27 Roger Clemens Yanks/5
28 Roger Clemens Sox/5
30 Ryne Sandberg/50 40.00 80.00
31 Ernie Banks/50 30.00 60.00
32 Tony Gwynn/10
33 Vladimir Guerrero/25 40.00 80.00
34 Will Clark/50 15.00 40.00

2004 Timeless Treasures Material Ink Jersey Number

*NUMBER p/r 100: .4X TO 1X BASIC p/r 100
*NUMBER p/r 50: .4X TO 1X BASIC p/r 50

*NUMBER p/r 25: .5X TO 1.2X BASIC p/r 50
*NUMBER p/r 25: .4X TO 1X BASIC p/r 25
RANDOM INSERTS IN PACKS
PRINT RUNS B/WN 1-100 COPIES PER
NO PRICING ON QTY OF 10 OR LESS
10 Deion Sanders/24 40.00 80.00
19 Mark Grace/25 20.00 50.00
32 Tony Gwynn/25

2004 Timeless Treasures Material Ink Combos

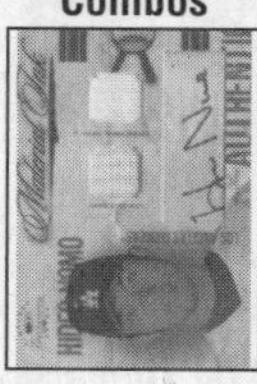

PRINT RUNS B/WN 1-50 COPIES PER
NO PRICING ON QTY OF 10 OR LESS
PRIME PRINT RUNS B/WN 1-10 COPIES PER
NO PRIME PRICING DUE TO SCARCITY
RANDOM INSERTS IN PACKS
1 Adam Dunn Bat-Jsy/25 30.00 60.00
2 Alan Trammell Bat-Jsy/25 20.00 50.00
3 Alex Rodriguez Bat-Jsy/3
4 Andre Dawson Bat-Jsy/25 20.00 50.00
5 Bo Jackson Bat-Jsy/25 60.00 120.00
6 Cal Ripken Bat-Jsy/8
7 Dale Murphy Bat-Jsy/25 30.00 60.00
8 Darryl Strawberry Bat-Jsy/10
9 Dave Parker Bat-Jsy/10
10 Deion Sanders Bat-Jsy/10
12 Don Mattingly Bat-Jsy/25 100.00 200.00
13 Dontrelle Willis Bat-Jsy/10
14 Hideo Nomo Bat-Jsy/1
15 Ivan Rodriguez Bat-Jsy/10
16 Joe Carter Bat-Jsy/10
17 Jose Canseco Bat-Jsy/25 30.00 60.00
19 Mark Grace Bat-Jsy/10
20 Mark Prior Bat-Jsy/10
21 Mark Teixeira Bat-Jsy/10
23 Mike Piazza Bat-Jsy/1
24 Paul Molitor Bat-Jsy/5
26 Rocco Baldelli Bat-Jsy/10
30 Ryne Sandberg Bat-Jsy/25 75.00 150.00
31 Ernie Banks Bat-Jsy/5
32 Tony Gwynn Bat-Jsy/25 60.00 120.00
33 Vladimir Guerrero Bat-Jsy/10
34 Will Clark Bat-Jsy/50 20.00 50.00

2004 Timeless Treasures Milestone Materials

PRINT RUNS B/WN 16-100 COPIES PER
*NBR p/r 35-36: .5X TO 1.2X BASIC p/r 80-82
*NBR p/r 24: .6X TO 1.5X BASIC p/r 100
NUMBER PRINT RUNS B/WN 9-36 PER
NO NUMBER PRICING ON QTY 9 OR LESS
*PRIME p/r 25: 1X TO 2.5X BASIC p/r 80-100
PRIME PRINT RUN 25 SERIAL #'d SETS
RANDOM INSERTS IN PACKS
2 Roger Maris Pants/61 20.00 50.00
3 R.Henderson A's Jsy/80 6.00 15.00
4 Gaylord Perry Jsy/82 4.00 10.00
5 Cal Ripken Ball/16
6 R.Henderson Padres Jsy/100 6.00 15.00

2004 Timeless Treasures Milestone Materials Signature

PRINT RUNS B/WN 5-82 COPIES PER
NO PRICING ON QTY OF 8 OR LESS
*NBR p/r 82: .4X TO 1X BASIC p/r 82
NUMBER PRINT RUNS B/WN 5-82 PER
NO NUMBER PRICING ON QTY 5 OR LESS
*PRIME p/r 19: .75X TO 2X BASIC p/r 82
PRIME PRINT RUNS B/WN 5-19 COPIES PER
NO PRIME PRICING ON QTY OF 5 OR LESS
RANDOM INSERTS IN PACKS
3 R.Henderson A's Jsy/5
4 Gaylord Perry Jsy/82 10.00 25.00
5 Cal Ripken Ball/8
6 R.Henderson Padres Jsy/5

2004 Timeless Treasures No-Hitters Quad Signature

RANDOM INSERTS IN PACKS
STATED PRINT RUN 1 SERIAL #'d SET
NO PRICING DUE TO SCARCITY
1 Cy Young Sox
Nolan Ryan Angels
Hideo Nomo Sox
Jim Bunning Tigers
2 Cy Young Sox
Nolan Ryan Rgr
Hideo Nomo Sox
Jim Bunning Tigers
3 Cy Young Spiders
Nolan Ryan Astros
Hideo Nomo Dodgers
Jim Bunning Phils

2004 Timeless Treasures Rookie Year Materials

PRINT RUNS B/WN 5-100 COPIES PER
NO PRICING ON QTY OF 5 OR LESS
PRIME PRINT RUNS B/WN 5-10 COPIES PER
NO PRIME PRICING DUE TO SCARCITY
RANDOM INSERTS IN PACKS
1 Stan Musial Jsy/19 20.00 50.00
2 Yogi Berra Stripe Jsy/19 20.00 50.00
3 Yogi Berra Grey Jsy/47 10.00 25.00
4 Whitey Ford Jsy/50 10.00 25.00
5 Catfish Hunter Jsy/65 6.00 15.00
6 Johnny Bench Bat/68 6.00 15.00
7 Mike Schmidt Bat/72 8.00 20.00
8 Gary Carter Jsy/74 4.00 10.00
9 Robin Yount Jsy/74 6.00 15.00
11 Cal Ripken Bat/81 20.00 50.00
12 Kirby Puckett Bat/84 6.00 15.00
13 Roger Clemens Jsy/84 8.00 20.00
15 Gary Sheffield Jsy/89 4.00 10.00
16 Juan Gonzalez Jsy/89 4.00 10.00
17 Randy Johnson Jsy/89 6.00 15.00
18 Ivan Rodriguez Jsy/91 6.00 15.00
20 Pedro Martinez Jsy/92 6.00 15.00
21 Mike Piazza Jsy/93 6.00 15.00
22 Hideo Nomo Jsy/95 6.00 15.00
23 Hideo Nomo Pants/95 6.00 15.00
24 Alex Rodriguez Jsy/95 6.00 15.00
25 Scott Rolen Jsy/96 6.00 15.00
27 Andruw Jones Jsy/96 6.00 15.00
28 Nomar Garciaparra Jsy/97 6.00 15.00
29 Vladimir Guerrero Jsy/97 6.00 15.00
31 Alfonso Soriano Jsy/100 4.00 10.00
32 Albert Pujols White Jsy/100 8.00 20.00
33 Albert Pujols Grey Jsy/100 8.00 20.00
34 Albert Pujols Bat/100 8.00 20.00
35 Albert Pujols Hat/5
36 Mark Prior Blue Jsy/100 6.00 15.00
37 Mark Prior Grey Jsy/100 6.00 15.00
38 Dontrelle Willis Jsy/35 10.00 25.00
39 Rocco Baldelli Jsy/15

2004 Timeless Treasures Rookie Year Materials Number

*NBR p/r 42-51: .5X TO 1.2X BASIC p/r 89-92
*NBR p/r 27-35: .6X TO 1.5X BASIC p/r 93-100
*NBR p/r 27-35: .5X TO 1.2X BASIC p/r 65
*NBR p/r 27-35: .4X TO 1X BASIC p/r 35
*NBR p/r 21-25: .75X TO 2X BASIC p/r 84-100
*NBR p/r 16-19: .75X TO 2X BASIC p/r 74-96
*NBR p/r 16-19: .6X TO 1.5X BASIC p/r 50
RANDOM INSERTS IN PACKS
PRINT RUNS B/WN 3-51 COPIES PER
NO PRICING ON QTY OF 11 OR LESS
10 Fred Lynn Jsy/19 8.00 20.00
25 Garret Anderson Jsy/16 8.00 20.00

2004 Timeless Treasures Rookie Year Materials Signature

PRINT RUNS B/WN 1-97 COPIES PER
NO PRICING ON QTY OF 11 OR LESS
*PRIME p/r 35: .5X TO 1.2X BASIC p/r 35
*PRIME p/r 25: .75X TO 2X BASIC p/r 95-97
*PRIME p/r 22: .5X TO 1.2X BASIC p/r 22
*PRIME p/r 16: .5X TO 1.2X BASIC p/r 19
PRIME PRINT RUNS B/WN 1-35 COPIES PER
NO PRIME PRICING ON QTY OF 11 OR LESS
RANDOM INSERTS IN PACKS
1 Stan Musial Jsy/9
2 Yogi Berra Stripe Jsy/9
3 Yogi Berra Grey Jsy/19 50.00 100.00
4 Whitey Ford Jsy/19 50.00 100.00
6 Johnny Bench Bat/9
7 Mike Schmidt Bat/9
8 Gary Carter Jsy/19 20.00 50.00
9 Robin Yount Jsy/9
10 Fred Lynn Jsy/75 8.00 20.00
11 Cal Ripken Bat/9
12 Kirby Puckett Bat/9
13 Roger Clemens Jsy/9
14 Lenny Dykstra Fld Glv/85 10.00 25.00
15 Gary Sheffield Jsy/11
16 Juan Gonzalez Jsy/19 20.00 50.00
17 Randy Johnson Jsy/9
18 Ivan Rodriguez Jsy/9
20 Pedro Martinez Jsy/1
21 Mike Piazza Jsy/1
22 Hideo Nomo Jsy/1
23 Hideo Nomo Pants/1
24 Alex Rodriguez Jsy/9
25 Garret Anderson Jsy/95 10.00 25.00
26 Scott Rolen Jsy/1
27 Andruw Jones Jsy/9
29 Vladimir Guerrero Jsy/9
30 Shannon Stewart Jsy/97 8.00 20.00
32 Albert Pujols White Jsy/5
33 Albert Pujols Grey Jsy/5
34 Albert Pujols Bat/5
35 Albert Pujols Hat/5
36 Mark Prior Blue Jsy/22 15.00 40.00
37 Mark Prior Grey Jsy/22 15.00 40.00
38 Dontrelle Willis Jsy/35 20.00 50.00
39 Rocco Baldelli Jsy/19 20.00 50.00

2004 Timeless Treasures Rookie Year Materials Signature Number

*NBR p/r 35: .4X TO 1X BASIC p/r 35
*NBR p/r 22: .4X TO 1X BASIC p/r 22
*NBR p/r 16-19: .75X TO 2X BASIC p/r 75-95
*NBR p/r 16-19: .4X TO 1X BASIC p/r 19
RANDOM INSERTS IN PACKS
PRINT RUNS B/WN 1-35 COPIES PER
NO PRICING ON QTY OF 11 OR LESS
26 Scott Rolen Jsy/17 30.00 60.00

2004 Timeless Treasures Rookie Year Materials Combos

PRINT RUNS B/WN 5-35 COPIES PER
NO PRICING ON QTY OF 8 OR LESS
*PRIME: .5X TO 1.2X BASIC
PRIME PRINT RUNS B/WN 1-35 COPIES PER
NO PRIME PRICING ON QTY OF 5 OR LESS
RANDOM INSERTS IN PACKS
2 Yogi Berra Jsy-Jsy/8
22 Hideo Nomo Jsy-Pants/16 15.00 40.00
32 Albert Pujols Jsy-Jsy/5
33 Albert Pujols Bat-Jsy/5
34 Albert Pujols Bat-Jsy/5
35 Albert Pujols Bat-Hat/5
36 Mark Prior Jsy-Jsy/22 12.50 30.00
38 Dontrelle Willis Jsy-Jsy/35 10.00 25.00
39 Rocco Baldelli Jsy-Jsy/5

2004 Timeless Treasures Rookie Year Materials Combos Signature

PRINT RUNS B/WN 1-35 COPIES PER
NO PRICING ON QTY OF 8 OR LESS
*PRIME: .5X TO 1.2X BASIC
PRIME PRINT RUNS B/WN 1-35 COPIES PER
NO PRIME PRICING ON QTY OF 5 OR LESS
RANDOM INSERTS IN PACKS
2 Yogi Berra Jsy-Jsy/8
22 Hideo Nomo Jsy-Pants/1
32 Albert Pujols Jsy-Jsy/5
33 Albert Pujols Bat-Jsy/5
34 Albert Pujols Bat-Jsy/5
35 Albert Pujols Bat-Hat/5
36 Mark Prior Jsy-Jsy/22 15.00 40.00
38 Dontrelle Willis Jsy-Jsy/35 20.00 50.00
39 Rocco Baldelli Jsy-Jsy/5

2004 Timeless Treasures Rookie Year Materials Dual

STATED PRINT RUN 25 SERIAL #'d SETS
PRIME PRINT RUN 10 SERIAL #'d SETS
NO PRIME PRICING DUE TO SCARCITY
RANDOM INSERTS IN PACKS
40 Roger Clemens Jsy 30.00 60.00
Nomar Garciaparra Jsy
41 Pedro Martinez Jsy 20.00 50.00
Mike Piazza Jsy
42 Mike Piazza Jsy 20.00 50.00
Hideo Nomo Jsy
43 Pedro Martinez Jsy 12.50 30.00
Hideo Nomo Jsy
44 Yogi Berra Jsy 40.00 80.00
Whitey Ford Jsy
45 Mike Schmidt Bat 30.00 60.00
Scott Rolen Jsy
47 Juan Gonzalez Jsy 12.50 30.00
Ivan Rodriguez Jsy

2004 Timeless Treasures Rookie Year Materials Dual Signature

RANDOM INSERTS IN PACKS
STATED PRINT RUN 5 SERIAL #'d SETS
NO PRICING DUE TO SCARCITY
41 Pedro Martinez Jsy
Mike Piazza Jsy
42 Mike Piazza Jsy
Hideo Nomo Jsy
43 Pedro Martinez Jsy
Hideo Nomo Jsy
44 Yogi Berra Jsy
Whitey Ford Jsy
46 Stan Musial Jsy
Albert Pujols Jsy
47 Juan Gonzalez Jsy
Ivan Rodriguez Jsy

2004 Timeless Treasures Statistical Champions

PRINT RUNS B/WN 3-100 COPIES PER
NO PRICING ON QTY OF 9 OR LESS
*NBR p/r 38-51: .4X TO 1X BASIC p/r 68
*NBR p/r 38-51: .4X TO 1X BASIC p/r 19-25
*NBR p/r 26-34: .6X TO 1.5X BASIC p/r 86-100
*NBR p/r 20-25: .75X TO 2X BASIC p/r 88-100
*NBR p/r 20-25: .4X TO 1X BASIC p/r 25
*NBR p/r 21: .3X TO .8X BASIC p/r 19
*NBR p/r 17-19: .5X TO 1.2X BASIC p/r 25
NUMBER PRINT RUNS B/WN 1-51 PER
NO NUMBER PRICES ON QTY 9 OR LESS
PRIME PRINT RUNS B/WN 5-10 COPIES PER
NO PRIME PRICING DUE TO SCARCITY
RANDOM INSERTS IN PACKS
1 Jimmie Foxx Bat/9
2 Stan Musial 43 BA Jsy/19 20.00 50.00
3 Ralph Kiner Bat/49 6.00 15.00
4 Stan Musial 57 BA Jsy/57 15.00 40.00
5 Ted Williams Jsy/25 60.00 120.00
6 Warren Spahn Jsy/25 15.00 40.00
7 Eddie Mathews Jsy/19 20.00 50.00
8 Roger Maris 61 HR Bat/61 20.00 50.00
9 Roger Maris 61 HR Pants/61 20.00 50.00
10 Roger Maris 61 RBI Bat/61 20.00 50.00
11 R.Maris 61 RBI Pants/61 20.00 50.00
12 Roberto Clemente Jsy/19 60.00 120.00
13 Frank Robinson Bat/66 6.00 15.00
14 Bob Gibson 68 ERA Jsy/68 6.00 15.00
15 Bob Gibson 68 K Jsy/68 6.00 15.00
16 Tom Seaver Jsy/19 12.50 30.00
17 Harmon Killebrew Jsy/3
18 Harmon Killebrew Pants/71 10.00 25.00
19 Mike Schmidt Jsy/74 8.00 20.00
20 Reggie Jackson Jsy/19 12.50 30.00
21 Phil Niekro Jsy/5
22 Rod Carew Hat/78 6.00 15.00
23 Jim Rice 78 HR Jsy/78 4.00 10.00
24 Jim Rice 78 RBI Jsy/78 4.00 10.00
25 Reggie Jackson Hat/80 6.00 15.00
26 Dale Murphy 82 RBI Jsy/82 6.00 15.00
27 Steve Carlton Jsy/83 4.00 10.00
28 Dale Murphy 85 HR Jsy/85 6.00 15.00
29 Wade Boggs 86 BA Jsy/86 6.00 15.00
30 Wade Boggs 87 BA Jsy/87 6.00 15.00
31 Will Clark Jsy/88 6.00 15.00
32 Nolan Ryan 89 K Jsy/89 10.00 25.00
33 Nolan Ryan 90 K Jsy/90 10.00 25.00
34 Nolan Ryan 90 K Pants/90 10.00 25.00
35 Ryne Sandberg Jsy/90 10.00 25.00
36 Roger Clemens 90 K Jsy/90 8.00 20.00
37 George Brett Jsy/90 10.00 25.00
38 R.Clemens 92 ERA Jsy/100 8.00 20.00
39 R.Clemens 96 K Jsy/100 8.00 20.00
40 Tony Gwynn Jsy/25 20.00 50.00
41 P.Martinez Expos Jsy/25 8.00 20.00
42 Greg Maddux Jsy/100 6.00 15.00
43 Juan Gonzalez Pants/25 6.00 15.00
44 Manny Ramirez Bat/25 8.00 20.00
45 N.G'parra 99 BA Jsy/100 6.00 15.00
46 N.Garciaparra 99 BA Bat/5
47 N.G'parra 00 BA Jsy/100 6.00 15.00
48 Todd Helton 00 BA Jsy/25 8.00 20.00
49 Todd Helton 00 RBI Jsy/25 8.00 20.00
50 Troy Glaus Jsy/25 6.00 15.00
51 Randy Johnson 00 K Jsy/25 8.00 20.00
52 Tom Glavine Jsy/25 8.00 20.00
53 Sammy Sosa 00 HR Jsy/100 6.00 15.00
54 A.Rodriguez 01 HR Bat/100 6.00 15.00
55 Curt Schilling Jsy/25 6.00 15.00
56 Pedro Martinez 99 K Jsy/25 8.00 20.00
57 A.Rodriguez 01 HR Jsy/100 6.00 15.00
58 Mark Mulder Jsy/25 6.00 15.00
59 S.Sosa 01 RBI Jsy/100 6.00 15.00
60 Manny Ramirez Jsy/25 8.00 20.00
61 Lance Berkman Jsy/25 6.00 15.00
62 Randy Johnson 02 W Jsy/25 8.00 20.00
63 A.Rodriguez 02 HR Jsy/100 6.00 15.00
64 A.Rodriguez 02 RBI Jsy/100 6.00 15.00
65 A.Rodriguez 02 HR Bat/100 6.00 15.00
66 A.Rodriguez 02 RBI Bat/100 6.00 15.00
67 Pedro Martinez 02 K Jsy/25 8.00 20.00
68 P.Martinez 02 ERA Jsy/25 8.00 20.00
69 Sammy Sosa 02 HR Jsy/100 6.00 15.00
70 Jim Thome Jsy/25 8.00 20.00
71 A.Rodriguez 03 HR Bat/100 6.00 15.00
72 Albert Pujols Bat/100 8.00 20.00
73 A.Rodriguez 03 HR Jsy/100 6.00 15.00
74 Albert Pujols Jsy/100 8.00 20.00

2004 Timeless Treasures Statistical Champions Signature

PRINT RUNS B/WN 1-88 COPIES PER
NO PRICING ON QTY OF 10 OR LESS
*NBR p/r 47: .3X TO .8X BASIC p/r 20
*NBR p/r 32-34: .4X TO 1X BASIC p/r 19-25
*NBR p/r 22: 1.25X TO 3X BASIC p/r 88
*NBR p/r 20-25: .4X TO 1X BASIC p/r 20-25
*NBR p/r 19: .4X TO 1X BASIC p/r 19
*NBR p/r 17-19: .5X TO 1.2X BASIC p/r 20-25
NUMBER PRINT RUNS B/WN 1-47 PER
NO NUMBER PRICING ON QTY 14 OR LESS
PRIME PRINT RUNS B/WN 1-10 COPIES PER
NO PRIME PRICING DUE TO SCARCITY
RANDOM INSERTS IN PACKS
2 Stan Musial 43 BA Jsy/10
3 Ralph Kiner Bat/49 20.00 50.00
4 Stan Musial 57 BA Jsy/10
6 Warren Spahn Jsy/25 40.00 80.00
13 Frank Robinson Bat/66 15.00 40.00
14 Bob Gibson 68 ERA Jsy/25 20.00 50.00
15 Bob Gibson 68 K Jsy/25 20.00 50.00
16 Tom Seaver Jsy/10
17 Harmon Killebrew Jsy/71 20.00 50.00
18 Harmon Killebrew Pants/71 20.00 50.00
19 Mike Schmidt Jsy/25 60.00 120.00
20 Reggie Jackson Jsy/25 40.00 80.00
21 Phil Niekro Jsy/50 15.00 40.00
22 Rod Carew Hat/25 20.00 50.00
23 Jim Rice 78 HR Jsy/78 10.00 25.00
24 Jim Rice 78 RBI Jsy/78 10.00 25.00
25 Reggie Jackson Hat/25 40.00 80.00
26 Dale Murphy 82 RBI Jsy/25 20.00 50.00

27 Steve Carlton Jsy/25 15.00 40.00
28 Dale Murphy 85 HR Jsy/25 20.00 50.00
29 Wade Boggs 86 BA Jsy/25 20.00 50.00
30 Wade Boggs 87 BA Jsy/25 20.00 50.00
31 Will Clark Jsy/88 12.50 30.00
32 Nolan Ryan 89 K Jsy/25 75.00 150.00
33 Nolan Ryan 90 K Jsy/25 75.00 150.00
34 Nolan Ryan 90 K Pants/25 75.00 150.00
35 Ryne Sandberg Jsy/25 60.00 120.00
36 Roger Clemens 90 K Jsy/5
37 George Brett Jsy/10
38 R.Clemens 92 ERA Jsy/5
39 Roger Clemens 96 K Jsy/5
40 Tony Gwynn Jsy/25 50.00 100.00
41 Pedro Martinez Expos Jsy/1
42 Greg Maddux Jsy/10
43 Juan Gonzalez Pants/19 20.00 50.00
44 Manny Ramirez Bat/10
48 Todd Helton 00 BA Jsy/10
49 Todd Helton 00 RBI Jsy/10
50 Troy Glaus Jsy/25 20.00 50.00
51 Randy Johnson 00 K Jsy/10
52 Tom Glavine Jsy/20 20.00 50.00
53 Sammy Sosa 00 HR Jsy/25 30.00 60.00
54 A.Rodriguez 01 HR Bat/10
55 Curt Schilling Jsy/25 30.00 60.00
56 Pedro Martinez 99 K Jsy/1
57 A.Rodriguez 01 HR Jsy/10
58 Mark Mulder Jsy/25 15.00 40.00
59 S.Sosa 01 RBI Jsy/25 30.00 60.00
60 Manny Ramirez Jsy/10
61 Lance Berkman Jsy/20 20.00 50.00
62 Randy Johnson 02 W Jsy/9
63 A.Rodriguez 02 HR Jsy/10
64 A.Rodriguez 02 RBI Jsy/10
65 A.Rodriguez 02 HR Bat/10
66 A.Rodriguez 02 RBI Bat/10
67 Pedro Martinez 02 K Jsy/1
68 Pedro Martinez 02 ERA Jsy/1
69 S.Sosa 02 HR Jsy/25 30.00 60.00
71 A.Rodriguez 03 HR Bat/10
72 Albert Pujols Bat/10
73 A.Rodriguez 03 HR Jsy/10
74 Albert Pujols Jsy/10

2004 Timeless Treasures World Series Materials

PRINT RUNS B/WN 2-100 COPIES PER
NO PRICING ON QTY OF 8 OR LESS
*PRIME p/r 19-20: 1.25X TO 3X p/r 87-100
PRIME PRINT RUNS B/WN 1-20 COPIES PER
NO PRIME PRICING ON QTY OF 1
RANDOM INSERTS IN PACKS
1 Frank Robinson Bat/61 6.00 15.00
2 Ozzie Smith Jsy/87 8.00 20.00
3 Rickey Henderson Bat/93 6.00 15.00
4 Tom Glavine Jsy/96 6.00 15.00
5 Roger Clemens Jsy/100 8.00 20.00
6 Bob Gibson G1 Ball/6
7 Bob Gibson G4 Ball/3
8 Bob Gibson G7 Ball/7
9 Lou Brock Ball/2
10 Roger Maris Ball/2
11 Carl Yastrzemski Ball/2
12 Bob Gibson
Lou Brock
Roger Maris Ball/2
13 Bob Gibson
Lou Brock
Roger Maris
Carl Yastrzemski Ball/8
14 Bob Gibson G1 Ball/5

2004 Timeless Treasures World Series Materials Signature

1-11 PRINT RUNS B/WN 2-19 COPIES PER
CARD 14 PRINT RUN 5 SERIAL #'d COPIES
NO CARD 14 PRICING DUE TO SCARCITY
PRIME PRINT RUNS B/WN 9-10 COPIES PER
NO PRIME PRICING DUE TO SCARCITY
RANDOM INSERTS IN PACKS
1 Frank Robinson Bat/19 30.00 60.00
2 Ozzie Smith Jsy/9
3 Rickey Henderson Bat/9
4 Tom Glavine Jsy/19 30.00 60.00
5 Roger Clemens Jsy/9
6 Bob Gibson G1 Ball/5
7 Bob Gibson G4 Ball/2
8 Bob Gibson G7 Ball/7
9 Lou Brock Ball/2
11 Carl Yastrzemski Ball/2
14 Bob Gibson G1 Ball/5

2005 Timeless Treasures

This 100-card set was released in April, 2005. The set was issued in four-card tins with an $100 SRP which came 15 to a case.

STATED PRINT RUN 799 SERIAL #'d SETS
1 David Ortiz 1.50 4.00
2 Derek Jeter 3.00 8.00
3 Edgar Renteria 1.25 3.00
4 Paul Molitor 1.25 3.00
5 Jeff Bagwell 1.50 4.00
6 Melvin Mora 1.25 3.00
7 Bobby Crosby 1.25 3.00
8 Cal Ripken 5.00 12.00
9 Hank Blalock 1.25 3.00
10 Hideo Nomo Rays 1.50 4.00
11 Gary Sheffield 1.25 3.00
12 Alfonso Soriano 1.25 3.00
13 Carl Crawford 1.25 3.00
14 Paul Konerko 1.25 3.00
15 Jim Edmonds 1.25 3.00
16 Garret Anderson 1.25 3.00
17 Lance Berkman 1.25 3.00
18 Javy Lopez 1.25 3.00
19 Tony Gwynn 1.50 4.00
20 Mark Mulder 1.25 3.00
21 Sammy Sosa 1.50 4.00
22 Roger Clemens Yanks 2.00 5.00
23 Mark Teixeira 1.50 4.00
24 Miguel Cabrera 1.50 4.00
25 Jim Thome 1.50 4.00
26 Mike Piazza Dgr 1.50 4.00
27 Vladimir Guerrero 1.50 4.00
28 Austin Kearns 1.25 3.00
29 Rod Carew 1.25 3.00
30 Ken Griffey Jr. 2.00 5.00
31 Mike Piazza Mets 1.50 4.00
32 David Wright 2.00 5.00
33 Jason Varitek 1.50 4.00
34 Kerry Wood 1.25 3.00
35 Frank Thomas 1.50 4.00
36 Mark Prior 1.50 4.00
37 Mike Mussina O's 1.50 4.00
38 Curt Schilling Phils 1.25 3.00
39 Greg Maddux Cubs 2.00 5.00
40 Miguel Tejada 1.25 3.00
41 Tom Seaver 1.25 3.00
42 Mariano Rivera 1.50 4.00
43 Jason Giambi 1.25 3.00
44 Roy Oswalt 1.25 3.00
45 Pedro Martinez 1.50 4.00
46 Jeff Niemann RC 2.00 5.00
47 Tom Glavine 1.50 4.00
48 Torii Hunter 1.25 3.00
49 Scott Rolen 1.50 4.00
50 Curt Schilling Sox 1.50 4.00
51 Randy Johnson 1.50 4.00
52 C.C. Sabathia 1.25 3.00
53 Rafael Palmeiro O's 1.50 4.00
54 Jake Peavy 1.50 4.00
55 Hideki Matsui 2.50 6.00
56 Ichiro Suzuki 3.00 8.00
57 Johan Santana 1.50 4.00
58 Todd Helton 1.50 4.00
59 Justin Verlander RC 3.00 8.00
60 Kazuo Matsui 1.25 3.00
61 Rafael Palmeiro Rgr 1.50 4.00
62 Sean Casey 1.25 3.00
63 Nolan Ryan 3.00 8.00
64 Magglio Ordonez 1.25 3.00
65 Craig Biggio 1.50 4.00
66 Vernon Wells 1.25 3.00
67 Manny Ramirez 1.50 4.00
68 Aramis Ramirez 1.25 3.00
69 Omar Vizquel 1.50 4.00
70 Eric Gagne 1.25 3.00
71 Troy Glaus 1.25 3.00
72 Carlton Fisk 1.50 4.00
73 Victor Martinez 1.25 3.00
74 Adrian Beltre 1.25 3.00
75 Barry Zito 1.25 3.00
76 Josh Beckett 1.25 3.00
77 Michael Young 1.25 3.00
78 Eric Chavez 1.25 3.00
79 Hideo Nomo Sox 1.50 4.00
80 Andruw Jones 1.50 4.00
81 Ivan Rodriguez 1.50 4.00
82 Don Mattingly 2.50 6.00
83 Larry Walker 1.50 4.00
84 Phil Humber RC 2.00 5.00
85 Juan Gonzalez 1.25 3.00
86 Tim Hudson 1.25 3.00
87 Alex Rodriguez 2.00 5.00
88 Greg Maddux Braves 2.00 5.00
89 J.D. Drew 1.25 3.00
90 Shawn Green 1.25 3.00
91 Roger Clemens Astros 2.00 5.00
92 Nomar Garciaparra 1.50 4.00
93 Andy Pettitte 1.50 4.00
94 Khalil Greene 1.50 4.00
95 Mike Schmidt 2.50 6.00
96 Carlos Beltran 1.25 3.00
97 Mike Mussina Yanks 1.25 3.00
98 Ben Sheets 1.25 3.00
99 Chipper Jones 1.50 4.00
100 Albert Pujols 3.00 8.00

2005 Timeless Treasures Bronze

*BRONZE: .75X TO 2X BASIC ACTIVE
*BRONZE: .75X TO 2X BASIC RETIRED
*BRONZE: .75X TO 2X BASIC RC's
RANDOM INSERTS IN PACKS
STATED PRINT RUN 100 SERIAL #'d SETS

2005 Timeless Treasures Gold

*GOLD: 2X TO 5X BASIC ACTIVE
*GOLD: 2X TO 5X BASIC RETIRED
RANDOM INSERTS IN PACKS
STATED PRINT RUN 25 SERIAL #'d SETS
NO RC YR PRICING DUE TO SCARCITY

2005 Timeless Treasures Platinum

RANDOM INSERTS IN PACKS
STATED PRINT RUN 1 SERIAL #'d SET
NO PRICING DUE TO SCARCITY

2005 Timeless Treasures Silver

*SILVER: 1.25X TO 3X BASIC ACTIVE
*SILVER: 1.25X TO 3X BASIC RETIRED
*SILVER: 1X TO 2.5X BASIC RC's
RANDOM INSERTS IN PACKS
STATED PRINT RUN 50 SERIAL #'d SETS

2005 Timeless Treasures HOF Silver

STATED PRINT RUN 500 SERIAL #'d SETS
*GOLD: 1.5X TO 4X BASIC
GOLD PRINT RUN 25 SERIAL #'d SETS
PLATINUM PRINT RUN 1 SERIAL #'d SET
NO PLATINUM PRICING DUE TO SCARCITY
RANDOM INSERTS IN PACKS
1 Pee Wee Reese 2.00 5.00
2 Red Schoendienst 1.50 4.00
3 Harmon Killebrew 2.00 5.00
4 Hack Wilson 2.00 5.00
5 Brooks Robinson 2.00 5.00
6 Stan Musial 2.50 6.00
7 Al Simmons 1.50 4.00
8 Carl Yastrzemski 2.50 6.00
9 Ted Williams 3.00 8.00
10 Phil Rizzuto 2.00 5.00
11 Luis Aparicio 1.50 4.00
12 Bobby Doerr 1.50 4.00
13 Bob Lemon 1.50 4.00
14 Ernie Banks 2.00 5.00
15 Ralph Kiner 1.50 4.00
16 Whitey Ford 2.00 5.00
17 Duke Snider 2.00 5.00
18 Willie McCovey 2.00 5.00
19 Bob Feller 2.00 5.00
20 Mike Schmidt 3.00 8.00
21 Roberto Clemente 5.00 12.00
22 Jim Palmer 1.50 4.00
23 Enos Slaughter 1.50 4.00
24 Willie Mays 3.00 8.00
25 Willie Stargell 2.00 5.00
26 Frank Robinson 1.50 4.00
27 Carl Hubbell 1.50 4.00
28 Reggie Jackson 2.00 5.00
29 Warren Spahn 2.00 5.00
30 Orlando Cepeda 1.50 4.00
31 Hoyt Wilhelm 1.50 4.00
32 Sandy Koufax 10.00 25.00
33 Hal Newhouser 1.50 4.00
34 Nolan Ryan 4.00 10.00
35 George Brett 3.00 8.00
36 Bill Dickey 1.50 4.00
37 Catfish Hunter 2.00 5.00
38 Frankie Frisch 1.50 4.00
39 Nellie Fox 2.00 5.00
40 Lou Boudreau 1.50 4.00
41 Hank Greenberg 2.00 5.00
42 Burleigh Grimes 1.50 4.00
43 Johnny Bench 2.00 5.00
44 Hank Aaron 3.00 8.00
45 Joe Cronin 1.50 4.00
46 Fergie Jenkins 1.50 4.00
47 Luke Appling 1.50 4.00
48 Yogi Berra 2.00 5.00
49 Early Wynn 1.50 4.00
50 Al Kaline 2.00 5.00

2005 Timeless Treasures Signature Bronze

OVERALL AU-GU'S ONE PER PACK
PRINT RUNS B/WN 10-100 COPIES PER
NO PRICING ON QTY OF 10
3 Edgar Renteria/50 8.00 20.00
4 Paul Molitor/100 6.00 15.00
5 Jeff Bagwell/10
6 Melvin Mora/10
7 Bobby Crosby/25 10.00 25.00
8 Cal Ripken/25 125.00 200.00
9 Hank Blalock/50 8.00 20.00
10 Hideo Nomo Rays/10
11 Gary Sheffield/50 12.50 30.00
12 Alfonso Soriano/50 8.00 20.00
14 Paul Konerko/50 12.50 30.00
15 Jim Edmonds/50 12.50 30.00
16 Garret Anderson/50 8.00 20.00
19 Tony Gwynn/100 20.00 50.00
20 Mark Mulder/100 10.00 25.00
22 Roger Clemens Yanks/10
23 Mark Teixeira/50 12.50 30.00
24 Miguel Cabrera/50 12.50 30.00
28 Austin Kearns/50 5.00 12.00
29 Rod Carew/100 10.00 25.00
32 David Wright/25 40.00 80.00
34 Kerry Wood/50 12.50 30.00
36 Mark Prior/100 10.00 25.00
38 Curt Schilling Phils/10
41 Tom Seaver/100 20.00 50.00
44 Roy Oswalt/25 10.00 25.00
45 Pedro Martinez/10
46 Jeff Niemann/100 8.00 20.00
48 Torii Hunter/50 8.00 20.00
49 Scott Rolen/50 12.50 30.00
50 Curt Schilling Sox/10
51 Randy Johnson/10
52 C.C. Sabathia/25 10.00 25.00
53 Rafael Palmeiro O's/25 30.00 60.00
54 Jake Peavy/10
57 Johan Santana/50 15.00 40.00
59 Justin Verlander/100 20.00 50.00
61 Rafael Palmeiro Rgr/25 30.00 60.00
62 Sean Casey/25 10.00 25.00
63 Nolan Ryan/100 50.00 100.00
64 Magglio Ordonez/50 8.00 20.00
65 Craig Biggio/50 12.50 30.00
66 Vernon Wells/25 10.00 25.00
67 Manny Ramirez/25 30.00 60.00
68 Aramis Ramirez/10
69 Omar Vizquel/50 20.00 50.00
72 Carlton Fisk/100 10.00 25.00
73 Victor Martinez/50 8.00 20.00
74 Adrian Beltre/50 8.00 20.00
75 Barry Zito/50 8.00 20.00
76 Josh Beckett/25 15.00 40.00
77 Michael Young/50 8.00 20.00
78 Eric Chavez/50 8.00 20.00
79 Hideo Nomo Sox/10
82 Don Mattingly/100 30.00 60.00
84 Phil Humber/100 8.00 20.00
85 Juan Gonzalez/50 8.00 20.00
86 Tim Hudson Braves/50 12.50 30.00
90 Shawn Green/25 15.00 40.00
91 Roger Clemens Astros/10
95 Mike Schmidt/100 30.00 60.00
98 Ben Sheets/25 10.00 25.00
99 Chipper Jones/25 50.00 100.00
100 Albert Pujols/10

2005 Timeless Treasures Signature Gold

*GOLD p/r 25: .6X TO 1.5X BRZ p/r 100
OVERALL AU-GU'S ONE PER PACK
PRINT RUNS B/WN 3-25 COPIES PER
NO PRICING ON QTY OF 10 OR LESS
NO RC YR PRICING ON QTY OF 25

2005 Timeless Treasures Signature Platinum

OVERALL AU-GU'S ONE PER PACK
STATED PRINT RUN 1 SERIAL #'d SET
NO PRICING DUE TO SCARCITY

2005 Timeless Treasures Signature Silver

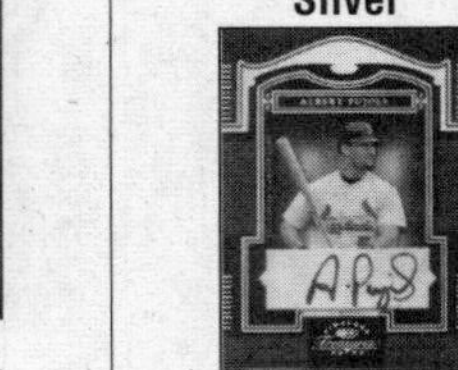

*SILV p/r 50: .5X TO 1.2X BRZ p/r 100
*SILV p/r 50: .5X TO 1.2X BRZ RC YR p/r 100
*SILV p/r 25: .5X TO 1.2X BRZ p/r 50
OVERALL AU-GU'S ONE PER PACK
PRINT RUNS B/WN 5-50 COPIES PER
NO PRICING ON QTY OF 10 OR LESS

2005 Timeless Treasures Award Materials Number

*NBR p/r 20-29: .6X TO 1.5X YR p/r 72-99
*NBR p/r 16-19: .75X TO 2X YR p/r 72-99
*NBR p/r 16-19: .5X TO 1.2X YR p/r 20
OVERALL AU-GU'S ONE PER PACK
PRINT RUNS B/WN 1-29 COPIES PER
NO PRICING ON QTY OF 12 OR LESS

2005 Timeless Treasures Award Materials Year

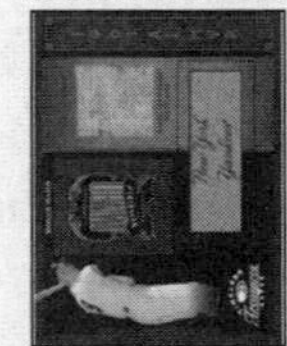

OVERALL AU-GU'S ONE PER PACK
PRINT RUNS B/WN 1-99 COPIES PER
NO PRICING ON QTY OF 5 OR LESS
1 Lou Boudreau Jsy/48 8.00 20.00
2 Roger Maris Pants/61 15.00 40.00
3 Maury Wills Jsy/5
4 Roberto Clemente Jsy/1
6 Johnny Bench Jsy/72 6.00 15.00
7 Tom Seaver Jsy/1
8 Fred Lynn Jsy/5
9 Jim Palmer Pants/76 4.00 10.00
10 Rod Carew Jsy/77 6.00 15.00
11 Jim Rice Jsy/5
12 Mike Schmidt Jsy/81 8.00 20.00
13 Robin Yount Jsy/89 6.00 15.00
14 Dale Murphy Jsy/83 6.00 15.00
15 Roger Clemens Jsy/86 6.00 15.00
16 Cal Ripken Jsy/91 12.50 30.00
17 Tom Glavine Jsy/91 4.00 10.00
18 Frank Thomas Jsy/94 4.00 10.00
19 Jeff Bagwell Pants/94 4.00 10.00
20 Randy Johnson Jsy/95 4.00 10.00
21 Pedro Martinez Jsy/97 4.00 10.00
22 Ivan Rodriguez Jsy/99 4.00 10.00
23 Jason Giambi Jsy/20 5.00 12.00
24 Jeff Kent Jsy/5
25 Miguel Tejada Jsy/20 5.00 12.00

2005 Timeless Treasures Award Materials Signature Year

PRINT RUNS B/WN 1-25 COPIES PER
NO PRICING ON QTY OF 5 OR LESS
SIG NBR PRINT RUN B/WN 1-5 COPIES PER
NO SIG NBR PRICING DUE TO SCARCITY
SIG PRIME PRINT B/WN 1-5 COPIES PER
NO SIG PRIME PRICING DUE TO SCARCITY
OVERALL AU-GU'S ONE PER PACK
3 Maury Wills Jsy/5
6 Johnny Bench Jsy/25 30.00 60.00
7 Tom Seaver Jsy/5
8 Fred Lynn Jsy/5
9 Jim Palmer Pants/25 12.50 30.00
10 Rod Carew Jsy/25 20.00 50.00
11 Jim Rice Jsy/5
12 Mike Schmidt Jsy/25 40.00 80.00
13 Robin Yount Jsy/5
14 Dale Murphy Jsy/25 20.00 50.00
15 Roger Clemens Jsy/5
16 Cal Ripken Jsy/5
18 Frank Thomas Jsy/1
19 Jeff Bagwell Pants/5
20 Randy Johnson Jsy/5
21 Pedro Martinez Jsy/5

2005 Timeless Treasures Game Day Materials

OVERALL AU-GU'S ONE PER PACK
PRINT RUNS B/WN 5-100 COPIES PER
NO PRICING ON QTY OF 10 OR LESS
1 Rod Carew Hat/25 10.00 25.00
2 Kirby Puckett Bat/100 6.00 15.00
3 George Brett Ball/10
4 Cal Ripken Bat/5
5 Nellie Fox Bat/25 60.00 120.00
6 Vladimir Guerrero Fld Glv/25 6.00 15.00
7 Tony Gwynn Jsy/100 6.00 15.00
8 Rickey Henderson Bat/100 6.00 15.00
9 David Ortiz Hat/100 4.00 10.00
10 Carlos Beltran Jsy/50 4.00 10.00

2005 Timeless Treasures Game Day Materials Signatures

OVERALL AU-GU'S ONE PER PACK
PRINT RUNS B/WN 3-25 COPIES PER
NO PRICING ON QTY OF 10 OR LESS
1 Rod Carew Hat/10
2 Kirby Puckett Bat/10
3 George Brett Ball/4
4 Cal Ripken Ball/3
6 Vladimir Guerrero Fld Glv/5
7 Tony Gwynn Jsy/25 30.00 60.00
8 Rickey Henderson Bat/10
9 David Ortiz Hat/10

2005 Timeless Treasures Gamers NY

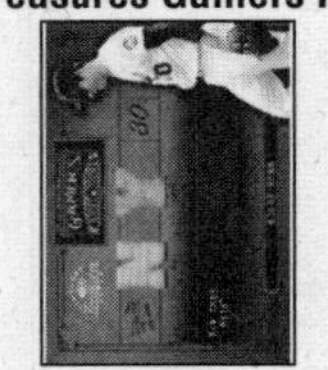

OVERALL AU-GU'S ONE PER PACK
STATED PRINT RUN 25 SERIAL #'d SETS
1 Jim Thorpe Jsy-Jsy/25 175.00 300.00
2 Willie Mays Jsy-Pants/25 50.00 100.00
3 Nolan Ryan Bat-Jsy/25 40.00 80.00

2005 Timeless Treasures Gamers NY Signatures

OVERALL AU-GU'S ONE PER PACK
STATED PRINT RUN 25 SERIAL #'d SETS
2 Willie Mays Jsy-Pants/25 175.00 300.00
3 Nolan Ryan Bat-Jsy/25 125.00 200.00

2005 Timeless Treasures HOF Cuts

OVERALL AU-GU'S ONE PER PACK
PRINT RUNS B/WN 1-10 COPIES PER
NO PRICING DUE TO SCARCITY

1 Pee Wee Reese/10
2 Red Schoendienst/1
5 Brooks Robinson/2
6 Stan Musial/1
7 Al Simmons/2
9 Ted Williams/1
10 Phil Rizzuto/1
12 Bobby Doerr/1
13 Bob Lemon/2
15 Ralph Kiner/10
16 Whitey Ford/1
17 Duke Snider/1
21 Roberto Clemente/1
22 Jim Palmer/1
23 Enos Slaughter/10
25 Willie Stargell/10
27 Carl Hubbell/10
28 Reggie Jackson/1
29 Warren Spahn/1
31 Hoyt Wilhelm/10
33 Hal Newhouser/10
36 Bill Dickey/3
37 Catfish Hunter/10
40 Lou Boudreau/10
41 Hank Greenberg/2
42 Burleigh Grimes/10
44 Hank Aaron/1
45 Joe Cronin/1
46 Fergie Jenkins/1
47 Luke Appling/2
48 Yogi Berra/1
49 Early Wynn/5
50 Al Kaline/1

2005 Timeless Treasures HOF Cuts Materials

OVERALL AU-GU'S ONE PER PACK
PRINT RUNS B/WN 1-10 COPIES PER
NO PRICING DUE TO SCARCITY
5 Brooks Robinson Jsy/1
10 Phil Rizzuto Pants/1
12 Bobby Doerr Pants/1
15 Ralph Kiner Bat/10
16 Whitey Ford Jsy/1
22 Jim Palmer Jsy/1
31 Hoyt Wilhelm Jsy/10
44 Hank Aaron Jsy/1
48 Yogi Berra Jsy/1

2005 Timeless Treasures HOF Materials Barrel

OVERALL AU-GU'S ONE PER PACK
STATED PRINT RUN 1 SERIAL #'d SET
NO PRICING DUE TO SCARCITY
3 Harmon Killebrew
4 Hack Wilson
5 Brooks Robinson
6 Stan Musial
8 Carl Yastrzemski
9 Ted Williams
11 Luis Aparicio
12 Bobby Doerr
14 Ernie Banks
20 Mike Schmidt
21 Roberto Clemente
24 Willie Mays
25 Willie Stargell
26 Frank Robinson
28 Reggie Jackson
34 Nolan Ryan
35 George Brett
39 Nellie Fox
43 Johnny Bench
44 Hank Aaron

2005 Timeless Treasures HOF Materials Bat

*BAT p/r 50: .5X TO 1.2X JSY p/r 100
*BAT p/r 50: .4X TO 1X JSY p/r 50
*BAT p/r 50: .3X TO .8X JSY p/r 25
*BAT p/r 25: .6X TO 1.5X JSY p/r 100
*BAT p/r 25: .5X TO 1.2X JSY p/r 50
OVERALL AU-GU'S ONE PER PACK
PRINT RUNS B/WN 5-50 COPIES PER

NO PRICING ON QTY OF 5
1 Pee Wee Reese/25 10.00 25.00
4 Hack Wilson/50 40.00 80.00
9 Ted Williams/50 20.00 50.00
11 Luis Aparicio/25 6.00 15.00
12 Bobby Doerr/25 6.00 15.00
15 Ralph Kiner/25 10.00 25.00
21 Roberto Clemente/50 40.00 80.00
26 Frank Robinson/50 5.00 12.00
30 Orlando Cepeda/50 5.00 12.00
39 Nellie Fox/50 40.00 80.00
50 Al Kaline/50 8.00 20.00

2005 Timeless Treasures HOF Materials Combos

*COMBO p/r 25: .75X TO 2X JSY p/r 100
*COMBO p/r 25: .6X TO 1.5X JSY p/r 50
*COMBO p/r 25: .5X TO 1.2X JSY p/r 25
PRINT RUNS B/WN 1-25 COPIES PER
NO PRICING ON QTY OF 10 OR LESS
PRIME PRINT RUNS B/WN 1-5 COPIES PER
NO PRIME PRICING DUE TO SCARCITY
OVERALL AU-GU'S ONE PER PACK
9 Ted Williams Bat-Jsy/25 50.00 100.00
24 Willie Mays Bat-Jsy/25 50.00 100.00

2005 Timeless Treasures HOF Materials Jersey

PRINT RUNS B/WN 1-100 COPIES PER
NO PRICING ON QTY OF 5 OR LESS
PRIME PRINT RUN B/WN 1-5 COPIES PER
NO PRIME PRICING DUE TO SCARCITY
OVERALL AU-GU'S ONE PER PACK
1 Pee Wee Reese/5
2 Red Schoendienst/5
3 Harmon Killebrew/100 6.00 15.00
5 Brooks Robinson/50 8.00 20.00
6 Stan Musial/100 12.50 30.00
8 Carl Yastrzemski/100 8.00 20.00
9 Ted Williams/100 30.00 60.00
11 Luis Aparicio/5
12 Bobby Doerr/5
14 Ernie Banks/100 6.00 15.00
16 Whitey Ford/100 6.00 15.00
17 Duke Snider/25 10.00 25.00
18 Willie McCovey/25 10.00 25.00
20 Mike Schmidt/50 10.00 25.00
21 Roberto Clemente/1
22 Jim Palmer/25 6.00 15.00
23 Enos Slaughter/50 8.00 20.00
24 Willie Mays/100 20.00 50.00
25 Willie Stargell/50 8.00 20.00
26 Frank Robinson/1
28 Reggie Jackson/25 10.00 25.00
29 Warren Spahn/25 10.00 25.00
31 Hoyt Wilhelm/50 5.00 12.00
32 Sandy Koufax/25 75.00 150.00
33 Hal Newhouser/50 5.00 12.00
34 Nolan Ryan/50 12.50 30.00
35 George Brett/50 10.00 25.00
37 Catfish Hunter/25 10.00 25.00
38 Frankie Frisch Jkt/50 10.00 25.00
40 Lou Boudreau/25 10.00 25.00
43 Johnny Bench/50 8.00 20.00
44 Hank Aaron/100 15.00 40.00
45 Joe Cronin/50 8.00 20.00
48 Yogi Berra/1
49 Early Wynn/50 8.00 20.00

2005 Timeless Treasures HOF Materials Jersey Number

*NBR p/r 44: .5X TO 1.2X JSY p/r 100
*NBR p/r 44: .3X TO .8X JSY p/r 25
*NBR p/r 20-34: .6X TO 1.5X JSY p/r 100
*NBR p/r 20-34: .5X TO 1.2X JSY p/r 50
*NBR p/r 20-34: .4X TO 1X JSY p/r 25
*NBR p/r 16: .75X TO 2X JSY p/r 100
*NBR p/r 16: .6X TO 1.5X JSY p/r 50
OVERALL AU-GU'S ONE PER PACK
PRINT RUNS B/WN 1-44 COPIES PER
NO PRICING ON QTY OF 14 OR LESS
32 Sandy Koufax/32 75.00 150.00

2005 Timeless Treasures HOF Materials Pants

*PANTS p/r 50: .5X TO 1.2X JSY p/r 100
*PANTS p/r 50: .4X TO 1X JSY p/r 50
*PANTS p/r 50: .3X TO .8X JSY p/r 25
*PANTS p/r 25: .4X TO 1X JSY p/r 25
OVERALL AU-GU'S ONE PER PACK
PRINT RUNS B/WN 1-50 COPIES PER
NO PRICING ON QTY OF 11 OR LESS
12 Bobby Doerr/50 5.00 12.00
19 Bob Feller/25 10.00 25.00
30 Orlando Cepeda/50 5.00 12.00
42 Burleigh Grimes/50 30.00 60.00
46 Fergie Jenkins/50 5.00 12.00

2005 Timeless Treasures HOF Materials Signature Bat

*BAT p/r 25: .4X TO 1X JSY p/r 25
OVERALL AU-GU'S ONE PER PACK
PRINT RUNS B/WN 1-25 COPIES PER
NO PRICING ON QTY OF 5 OR LESS
11 Luis Aparicio/25 12.50 30.00
12 Bobby Doerr/25 12.50 30.00
15 Ralph Kiner/25 20.00 50.00
24 Willie Mays/25 150.00 250.00
26 Frank Robinson/25 20.00 50.00
30 Orlando Cepeda/25 12.50 30.00
50 Al Kaline/25 30.00 60.00

2005 Timeless Treasures HOF Materials Signature Combos

*COMBO p/r 25: .5X TO 1.2X JSY p/r 25
PRINT RUNS B/WN 1-25 COPIES PER
NO PRICING ON QTY OF 10 OR LESS
PRIME PRINT RUNS B/WN 1-5 COPIES PER
NO PRIME PRICING DUE TO SCARCITY
OVERALL AU-GU'S ONE PER PACK
6 Stan Musial Bat-Jsy/25 60.00 120.00
12 Bobby Doerr Bat-Pants/25 15.00 40.00
24 Willie Mays Bat-Jsy/25 175.00 300.00
30 O.Cepeda Bat-Pants/25 15.00 40.00

2005 Timeless Treasures HOF Materials Signature Hat

OVERALL AU-GU'S ONE PER PACK
PRINT RUNS B/WN 1-10 COPIES PER
NO PRICING DUE TO SCARCITY

2005 Timeless Treasures HOF Materials Signature Jersey

PRINT RUNS B/WN 1-25 COPIES PER
NO PRICING ON QTY OF 5 OR LESS
PRIME PRINT RUN B/WN 1-5 COPIES PER
NO PRIME PRICING DUE TO SCARCITY
OVERALL AU-GU'S ONE PER PACK
1 Pee Wee Reese/1
2 Red Schoendienst/5
3 Harmon Killebrew/25 30.00 60.00
5 Brooks Robinson/25 30.00 60.00
6 Stan Musial/25 40.00 80.00
8 Carl Yastrzemski/5
9 Ted Williams/1
11 Luis Aparicio/5
12 Bobby Doerr/5
14 Ernie Banks/5
16 Whitey Ford/5
17 Duke Snider/25 20.00 50.00
18 Willie McCovey/25 20.00 50.00
20 Mike Schmidt/25 40.00 80.00
22 Jim Palmer/25 12.50 30.00
23 Enos Slaughter/1
24 Willie Mays/25 150.00 250.00
25 Willie Stargell/1
26 Frank Robinson/1
28 Reggie Jackson/5
31 Hoyt Wilhelm/5
32 Sandy Koufax/5
33 Hal Newhouser/1
34 Nolan Ryan/25 60.00 120.00
35 George Brett/5
37 Catfish Hunter/1
40 Lou Boudreau/1
43 Johnny Bench/25 30.00 60.00
44 Hank Aaron/5
45 Joe Cronin/1
49 Early Wynn/1

2005 Timeless Treasures HOF Materials Signature Jersey Number

*NBR p/r 44: .3X TO .8X JSY p/r 25
*NBR p/r 20-34: .4X TO 1X JSY p/r 25
OVERALL AU-GU'S ONE PER PACK
PRINT RUNS B/WN 1-44 COPIES PER
NO PRICING ON QTY OF 11 OR LESS
16 Whitey Ford/16 30.00 60.00
24 Willie Mays/24 150.00 250.00

2005 Timeless Treasures HOF Materials Signature Pants

*PANTS p/r 25: .4X TO 1X JSY p/r 25
OVERALL AU-GU'S ONE PER PACK
PRINT RUNS B/WN 1-50 COPIES PER
NO PRICING ON QTY OF 11 OR LESS
12 Bobby Doerr/50 10.00 25.00
19 Bob Feller/25 20.00 50.00
24 Willie Mays/25 150.00 250.00
30 Orlando Cepeda/25 12.50 30.00
46 Fergie Jenkins/25 12.50 30.00

2005 Timeless Treasures Home Road Gamers Duos

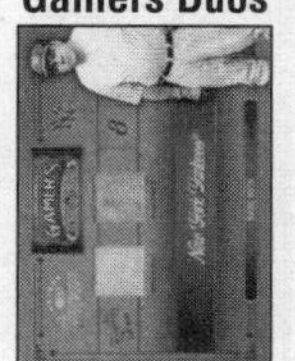

PRINT RUNS B/WN 1-100 COPIES PER
NO PRICING ON QTY OF 5 OR LESS
PRIME PRINT RUNS B/WN 1-10 COPIES PER
NO PRIME PRICING DUE TO SCARCITY
OVERALL AU-GU'S ONE PER PACK
1 Randy Johnson Jsy-Jsy/5
2 Carlton Fisk Jsy-Jsy/5
3 Babe Ruth Jsy-Jsy/25 300.00 500.00
4 Paul Molitor Jsy-Pants/100 5.00 12.00
5 George Brett Jsy-Jsy/5
6 Stan Musial Jsy-Jsy/1
7 Ivan Rodriguez Jsy-Jsy/100 5.00 12.00
8 Yogi Berra Jsy-Jsy/5
9 Ted Williams Jsy-Jsy/25 50.00 100.00
10 Andre Dawson Jsy-Jsy/25 8.00 20.00
11 Darryl Strawberry Jsy-Jsy/25 8.00 20.00
12 Alfonso Soriano Jsy-Jsy/1
13 Manny Ramirez Jsy-Jsy/5
14 Ernie Banks Jsy-Jsy/25 12.50 30.00
15 Jim Edmonds Jsy-Jsy/25 6.00 15.00
16 Bo Jackson Jsy-Jsy/25 12.50 30.00
17 Mark Grace Jsy-Jsy/100 8.00 20.00
18 Albert Pujols Jsy-Jsy/100 10.00 25.00
19 Tony Gwynn Jsy-Jsy/100 8.00 20.00
20 Cal Ripken Jsy-Jsy/100 20.00 50.00
21 Chipper Jones Jsy-Jsy/50 6.00 15.00
22 Roger Clemens Jsy-Jsy/10
23 Don Mattingly Jsy-Jsy/100 10.00 25.00
24 Willie Mays Jsy-Jsy/25 50.00 100.00
25 Tony Oliva Jsy-Jsy/50 6.00 15.00
26 Brooks Robinson Jsy-Jsy/1
27 Vladimir Guerrero Jsy-Jsy/5
28 Reggie Jackson Jsy-Jsy/100 8.00 20.00
29 Rod Carew Jsy-Jsy/100 8.00 20.00
30 Harmon Killebrew Jsy-Jsy/25 12.50 30.00
31 Dave Winfield Jsy-Pants/1
32 N.Ryan Astros Jsy-Jsy/100 12.50 30.00
33 Eddie Murray Jsy-Pants/100 8.00 20.00
34 Nolan Ryan Rgr Jsy-Jsy/10
35 R.Henderson Jsy-Jsy/100 8.00 20.00
36 Jim Rice Jsy-Jsy/50 6.00 15.00
37 Hoyt Wilhelm Jsy-Jsy/50 6.00 15.00
38 Curt Schilling Jsy-Jsy/100 5.00 12.00
39 Dave Parker Jsy-Jsy/5
40 F.Jenkins Pants-Pants/5
41 Tom Seaver Jsy-Jsy/1
42 Greg Maddux Jsy-Jsy/100 8.00 20.00
43 Dennis Eckersley Jsy-Jsy/50 6.00 15.00
44 W.McCovey Jsy-Pants/100 8.00 20.00
45 Willie Stargell Jsy-Jsy/50 10.00 25.00
46 Mike Mussina Jsy-Pants/50 10.00 25.00
47 Gary Carter Jsy-Jsy/50 10.00 25.00
48 Dale Murphy Jsy-Jsy/50 10.00 25.00
49 Mike Piazza Jsy-Jsy/50 6.00 15.00
50 Jim Palmer Jsy-Pants/100 5.00 12.00

2005 Timeless Treasures Home Road Gamers Trios

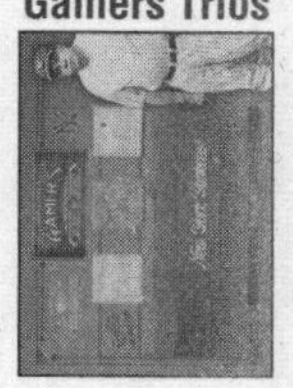

*TRIO p/r 100: .6X TO 1.5X DUO p/r 100
*TRIO p/r 50: .75X TO 2X DUO p/r 100
*TRIO p/r 50: .6X TO 1.5X DUO p/r 50
*TRIO p/r 25: .75X TO 2X DUO p/r 50
*TRIO p/r 25: .6X TO 1.5X DUO p/r 25
PRINT RUNS B/WN 1-100 COPIES PER
NO PRICING ON QTY OF 10 OR LESS
PRIME PRINT RUNS B/WN 1-10 COPIES PER
NO PRIME PRICING DUE TO SCARCITY
OVERALL AU-GU'S ONE PER PACK
3 Babe Ruth Bat-Jsy-Jsy/25 450.00 750.00
9 Ted Williams Bat-Jsy-Jsy/25 75.00 150.00
24 Willie Mays Bat-Jsy-Jsy/25 60.00 120.00

2005 Timeless Treasures Home Road Gamers Signature Duos

OVERALL AU-GU'S ONE PER PACK
PRINT RUNS B/WN 1-25 COPIES PER
NO PRICING ON QTY OF 10 OR LESS
1 Randy Johnson Jsy-Jsy/1
2 Carlton Fisk Jsy/5
4 Paul Molitor Jsy-Pants/25 15.00 40.00
5 George Brett Jsy-Jsy/5
6 Stan Musial Jsy-Jsy/1
8 Yogi Berra Jsy-Jsy/5
9 Ted Williams Jsy-Jsy/1
10 Andre Dawson Jsy-Jsy/10
11 Darryl Strawberry Jsy-Jsy/25 15.00 40.00
12 Alfonso Soriano Jsy-Jsy/1
13 Manny Ramirez Jsy-Jsy/1
14 Ernie Banks Jsy-Jsy/5
15 Jim Edmonds Jsy-Jsy/10
16 Bo Jackson Jsy-Jsy/10
17 Mark Grace Jsy-Jsy/25 30.00 60.00
18 Albert Pujols Jsy-Jsy/5
19 Tony Gwynn Jsy-Jsy/25 40.00 80.00
20 Cal Ripken Jsy-Jsy/10
21 Chipper Jones Jsy-Jsy/10
22 Roger Clemens Jsy-Jsy/1
23 Don Mattingly Jsy-Jsy/25 50.00 100.00
24 Willie Mays Jsy-Jsy/10
25 Tony Oliva Jsy-Jsy/25 15.00 40.00
26 Brooks Robinson Jsy-Jsy/1
27 Vladimir Guerrero Jsy-Jsy/1
28 Reggie Jackson Jsy-Jsy/10
29 Rod Carew Jsy-Jsy/25 30.00 60.00
30 Harmon Killebrew Jsy-Jsy/25 40.00 80.00
31 Dave Winfield Jsy-Pants/1
32 Nolan Ryan Astros Jsy-Jsy/10
34 Nolan Ryan Rgr Jsy-Jsy/10
35 Rickey Henderson Jsy-Jsy/5
36 Jim Rice Jsy-Jsy/25 15.00 40.00
37 Hoyt Wilhelm Jsy-Jsy/10
38 Curt Schilling Jsy-Jsy/5
39 Dave Parker Jsy-Jsy/5
40 F.Jenkins Pants-Pants/5
41 Tom Seaver Jsy-Jsy/1
42 Greg Maddux Jsy-Jsy/5
43 Dennis Eckersley Jsy-Jsy/25 15.00 40.00
44 W.McCovey Jsy-Pants/25 30.00 60.00
45 Willie Stargell Jsy-Jsy/1
46 Mike Mussina Jsy-Pants/5
47 Gary Carter Jsy-Jsy/25 15.00 40.00
48 Dale Murphy Jsy-Jsy/25 30.00 60.00
49 Mike Piazza Jsy-Jsy/1
50 Jim Palmer Jsy-Pants/25 15.00 40.00

2005 Timeless Treasures Home Road Gamers Signature Trios

*SIG TRIOS: .5X TO 1.2X SIG DUOS
PRINT RUNS B/WN 1-25 COPIES PER
NO PRICING ON QTY OF 10 OR LESS
PRIME PRINT RUN B/WN 1-5 COPIES PER
NO PRIME PRICING DUE TO SCARCITY
OVERALL AU-GU'S ONE PER PACK

2005 Timeless Treasures Home Run Materials

OVERALL AU-GU'S ONE PER PACK
PRINT RUNS B/WN 1-100 COPIES PER
NO PRICING ON QTY OF 10 OR LESS
1 Ernie Banks Bat/60 8.00 20.00
2 Roger Maris Bat/61 15.00 40.00
3 Ron Santo Ball/1
4 Johnny Bench Pants/71 6.00 15.00
5 Harmon Killebrew Bat/75 6.00 15.00
6 Jose Canseco Bat/25 10.00 25.00
7 Cal Ripken Ball/10
8 Sammy Sosa Jsy/100 4.00 10.00
9 Jim Thome Jsy/50 5.00 12.00
10 Rafael Palmeiro Jsy/50 5.00 12.00

2005 Timeless Treasures Home Run Materials Signature

OVERALL AU-GU'S ONE PER PACK
PRINT RUNS B/WN 1-25 COPIES PER
NO PRICING ON QTY OF 10 OR LESS
1 Ernie Banks Bat/25 40.00 80.00
3 Ron Santo Ball/5
4 Johnny Bench Pants/25 40.00 80.00
5 Harmon Killebrew Bat/25 40.00 80.00
6 Jose Canseco Bat/3
7 Cal Ripken Ball/5
8 Sammy Sosa Jsy/5
10 Rafael Palmeiro Jsy/10

2005 Timeless Treasures Material Ink Bat

OVERALL AU-GU'S ONE PER PACK
PRINT RUNS B/WN 1-10 COPIES PER
NO PRICING DUE TO SCARCITY

2005 Timeless Treasures Material Ink Combos

*COMBO p/r 25: .6X TO 1.5X JSY p/r 50
*COMBO p/r 25: .5X TO 1.2X JSY p/r 25
PRINT RUNS B/WN 1-25 COPIES PER
NO PRICING ON QTY OF 10 OR LESS

PRIME PRINT RUNS B/WN 1-5 COPIES PER
NO PRIME PRICING DUE TO SCARCITY
OVERALL AU-GU'S ONE PER PACK
37 Miguel Cabrera Bat-Jsy/25 30.00 60.00

2005 Timeless Treasures Material Ink Jersey

PRINT RUNS B/WN 1-50 COPIES PER
NO PRICING ON QTY OF 10 OR LESS
1 Ozzie Smith/5
2 Fred Lynn/50 10.00 25.00
3 Dale Murphy/50 15.00 40.00
4 Paul Molitor/50 10.00 25.00
5 Alan Trammell/50 10.00 25.00
6 Marty Marion/5
7 Deion Sanders/5
8 Gary Carter/50 10.00 25.00
9 Hideo Nomo/1
10 Andre Dawson/50 10.00 25.00
11 Luis Aparicio/50 10.00 25.00
12 Eric Chavez/10
13 Dave Concepcion/5
14 Darryl Strawberry/50 10.00 25.00
15 Carlos Beltran/10
16 Garret Anderson/10
17 Lance Berkman/1
18 Kirk Gibson/50 10.00 25.00
19 Robin Yount/5
20 Don Sutton/25 12.50 30.00
21 Josh Beckett/5
22 Mark Prior/10
23 Don Mattingly Jkt/25 40.00 80.00
24 Tony Perez/50 10.00 25.00
25 Rafael Palmeiro/5
26 Billy Williams/5
27 Carlton Fisk/25 20.00 50.00
28 Jim Edmonds/5
29 Fred McGriff/25 20.00 50.00
30 John Kruk/25 40.00 80.00
31 Fergie Jenkins Hat/5
32 Dwight Evans/50 15.00 40.00
33 Gary Sheffield/25 20.00 50.00
34 Bo Jackson/25 50.00 100.00
35 Mike Mussina/5
36 Gaylord Perry/50 10.00 25.00
37 Miguel Cabrera/5
38 Curt Schilling/5
39 Dave Parker/25 12.50 30.00
40 Mark Teixeira/10
41 Rickey Henderson/5
42 Harmon Killebrew/50 20.00 50.00
43 Dennis Eckersley/25 12.50 30.00
44 Willie McCovey/25 20.00 50.00
45 Willie Mays/10
46 Luis Tiant/50 10.00 25.00
47 Dontrelle Willis/10
48 Mark Grace/25 20.00 50.00
49 Joe Morgan/10
50 Cal Ripken/10

2005 Timeless Treasures Material Ink Jersey Number

*NBR p/r 36-44: .4X TO 1X JSY p/r 50
*NBR p/r 36-44: .3X TO .8X JSY p/r 25
*NBR p/r 20-29: .5X TO 1.2X JSY p/r 50
*NBR p/r 20-29: .4X TO 1X JSY p/r 25
*NBR p/r 15-19: .6X TO 1.5X JSY p/r 50
*NBR p/r 15-19: .5X TO 1.2X JSY p/r 25
OVERALL AU-GU'S ONE PER PACK
PRINT RUNS B/WN 1-44 COPIES PER
NO PRICING ON QTY OF 11 OR LESS
22 Mark Prior/22 15.00 40.00
28 Jim Edmonds/15 30.00 60.00
40 Mark Teixeira/23 20.00 50.00

2005 Timeless Treasures Milestone Materials Number

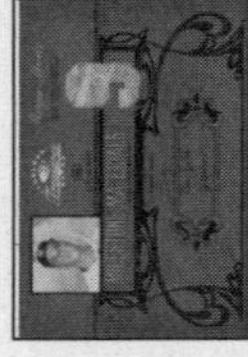

*NBR p/r 21-31: .4X TO 1X JSY p/r 25
*NBR p/r 19: .5X TO 1.2X JSY p/r 25
OVERALL AU-GU'S ONE PER PACK
PRINT RUNS B/WN 1-31 COPIES PER
NO PRICING ON QTY OF 12 OR LESS

2005 Timeless Treasures Milestone Materials Year

PRINT RUNS B/WN 10-25 COPIES PER
NO PRICING ON QTY OF 10
PRIME PRINT RUNS B/WN 1-10 COPIES PER
NO PRIME PRICING DUE TO SCARCITY
OVERALL AU-GU'S ONE PER PACK
1 Roger Maris Pants/25 20.00 50.00
2 Nolan Ryan Jsy/25 15.00 40.00
4 Rollie Fingers Jsy/10
5 Steve Garvey Jsy/25 6.00 15.00
6 Wade Boggs Jsy/25 10.00 25.00
7 Tony Gwynn Jsy/25 10.00 25.00
8 Sammy Sosa Jsy/25 6.00 15.00
9 Randy Johnson Jsy/25 6.00 15.00
10 Greg Maddux Jsy/25 10.00 25.00

2005 Timeless Treasures Milestone Materials Signature Year

PRINT RUNS B/WN 1-25 COPIES PER
NO PRICING ON QTY OF 10 OR LESS
NBR PRINT RUNS B/WN 1-10 COPIES PER
NO NBR PRICING DUE TO SCARCITY
PRIME PRINT RUNS B/WN 1-10 COPIES PER
NO PRIME PRICING DUE TO SCARCITY
OVERALL AU-GU'S ONE PER PACK
2 Nolan Ryan Jsy/25 60.00 120.00
4 Rollie Fingers Jsy/10
5 Steve Garvey Jsy/25 12.50 30.00
6 Wade Boggs Jsy/10
7 Tony Gwynn Jsy/25 30.00 60.00
8 Sammy Sosa Jsy/1
9 Randy Johnson Jsy/5
10 Greg Maddux Jsy/1

2005 Timeless Treasures No-Hitters

OVERALL AU-GU'S ONE PER PACK
PRINT RUNS B/WN 3-25 COPIES PER
NO PRICING ON QTY OF 10 OR LESS
1 Randy Johnson D'backs
Nolan Ryan Astros
Hideo Nomo Dodgers
Jim Bunning Phillies/5
2 Randy Johnson Mariners
Nolan Ryan Angels
Hideo Nomo Red Sox
Jim Bunning Tigers/5
3 Dave Righetti
Dwight Gooden
David Cone
Jim Abbott/10
4 Bob Feller
Sandy Koufax
Tom Seaver/5
5 Warren Spahn
Hoyt Wilhelm
Vida Blue/3
6 Jack Morris
Nolan Ryan
Dave Stewart/10
7 Dennis Eckersley 20.00 50.00
Bert Blyleven/25
8 Juan Marichal 20.00 50.00
Gaylord Perry/25
9 Jim Palmer 30.00 60.00
Bob Gibson/25
10 Catfish Hunter
Bob Lemon/5

2005 Timeless Treasures Rookie Year Materials Number

*NBR p/r 41-44: .5X TO 1.2X YR p/r 100
*NBR p/r 41-44: .3X TO .8X YR p/r 25
*NBR p/r 20-34: .6X TO 1.5X YR p/r 100
*NBR p/r 20-34: .4X TO 1X YR p/r 25
*NBR p/r 15-19: .75X TO 2X YR p/r 100
*NBR p/r 15-19: .5X TO 1.2X YR p/r 25
OVERALL AU-GU'S ONE PER PACK
PRINT RUNS B/WN 1-44 COPIES PER
NO PRICING ON QTY OF 11 OR LESS
5 Whitey Ford Jsy/16 12.50 30.00

8 Jim Palmer Hat/22 6.00 15.00
16 Kirk Gibson Hat/23 6.00 15.00
31 Garret Anderson Jsy/16 8.00 20.00

2005 Timeless Treasures Rookie Year Materials Year

PRINT RUNS B/WN 1-100 COPIES PER
NO PRICING ON QTY OF 5 OR LESS
PRIME PRINT RUN 5 SERIAL #'d SETS
NO PRIME PRICING DUE TO SCARCITY
OVERALL AU-GU'S ONE PER PACK
1 Rod Carew Jsy/100 6.00 15.00
2 Stan Musial Jsy/1
3 Yogi Berra Jsy/1
4 Duke Snider Jsy/100 6.00 15.00
5 Whitey Ford Jsy/5
6 Juan Marichal Jsy/100 4.00 10.00
7 Catfish Hunter Jsy/1
8 Jim Palmer Hat/5
10 Dave Parker Jsy/1
11 Gary Carter Jsy/100 4.00 10.00
12 Robin Yount Jsy/100 6.00 15.00
13 Keith Hernandez Jsy/25 6.00 15.00
14 Eddie Murray Jsy/1
15 Ozzie Smith Jsy/25 10.00 25.00
16 Kirk Gibson Hat/5
17 Dave Righetti Jsy/25 6.00 15.00
18 Roger Clemens Jsy/100 6.00 15.00
19 Greg Maddux Jsy/25 10.00 25.00
20 David Cone Jsy/100 4.00 10.00
21 Gary Sheffield Jsy/100 3.00 8.00
22 Randy Johnson Jsy/100 4.00 10.00
23 Deion Sanders Jsy/100 6.00 15.00
24 Dwight Gooden Jsy/25 6.00 15.00
25 Ivan Rodriguez Jsy/100 4.00 10.00
26 Jeff Bagwell Pants/100 4.00 10.00
27 Pedro Martinez Jsy/100 4.00 10.00
28 Mike Piazza Jsy/100 4.00 10.00
29 Chipper Jones Jsy/100 4.00 10.00
30 Hideo Nomo Jsy/100 6.00 15.00
31 Garret Anderson Jsy/5
32 Scott Rolen Jsy/100 4.00 10.00
33 Andruw Jones Jsy/100 4.00 10.00
34 Vladimir Guerrero Jsy/100 4.00 10.00
35 Sean Casey Jsy/25 5.00 12.00
36 Paul Lo Duca Jsy/25 5.00 12.00
37 Kerry Wood Jsy/100 3.00 8.00
38 Magglio Ordonez Jsy/25 5.00 12.00
39 Vernon Wells Jsy/25 5.00 12.00
40 Mark Mulder Jsy/100 3.00 8.00
41 Lance Berkman Jsy/100 3.00 8.00
42 Alfonso Soriano Jsy/100 3.00 8.00
43 Albert Pujols Jsy/100 8.00 20.00
44 Ben Sheets Jsy/25 5.00 12.00
45 Roy Oswalt Jsy/25 5.00 12.00
46 Mark Prior Jsy/100 4.00 10.00
47 Mark Teixeira Jsy/100 4.00 10.00
48 Miguel Cabrera Jsy/100 4.00 10.00
49 Travis Hafner Jsy/25 5.00 12.00
50 Victor Martinez Jsy/25 5.00 12.00

2005 Timeless Treasures Rookie Year Materials Signature Number

*NBR p/r 20-30: .4X TO 1X YR p/r 25
*NBR p/r 15-19: .5X TO 1.2X YR p/r 25
OVERALL AU-GU'S ONE PER PACK
PRINT RUNS B/WN 1-30 COPIES PER
NO PRICING ON QTY OF 10 OR LESS

2005 Timeless Treasures Rookie Year Materials Signature Year

PRINT RUNS B/WN 1-25 COPIES PER
NO PRICING ON QTY OF 5 OR LESS
PRIME PRINT RUNS B/WN 1-5 COPIES PER
NO PRIME PRINT RUNS DUE TO SCARCITY
OVERALL AU-GU'S ONE PER PACK
1 Rod Carew Jsy/25 20.00 50.00
2 Stan Musial Jsy/1
3 Yogi Berra Jsy/1
4 Duke Snider Jsy/25 20.00 50.00
5 Whitey Ford Jsy/5

6 Juan Marichal Jsy/25 12.50 30.00
8 Jim Palmer Hat/5
10 Dave Parker Jsy/5
11 Gary Carter Jsy/25 12.50 30.00
12 Robin Yount Jsy/25 30.00 60.00
13 Keith Hernandez Jsy/25 12.50 30.00
15 Ozzie Smith Jsy/25 30.00 60.00
16 Kirk Gibson Hat/5
17 Dave Righetti Jsy/25 12.50 30.00
18 Roger Clemens Jsy/5
19 Greg Maddux Jsy/1
20 David Cone Jsy/25 12.50 30.00
21 Gary Sheffield Jsy/25 20.00 50.00
22 Randy Johnson Jsy/5
23 Deion Sanders Jsy/5
24 Dwight Gooden Jsy/25 12.50 30.00
26 Jeff Bagwell Pants/1
27 Pedro Martinez Jsy/5
28 Mike Piazza Jsy/1
29 Chipper Jones Jsy/5
30 Hideo Nomo Jsy/5
31 Garret Anderson Jsy/5
32 Scott Rolen Jsy/25 20.00 50.00
34 Vladimir Guerrero Jsy/1
35 Sean Casey Jsy/25 12.50 30.00
36 Paul Lo Duca Jsy/25 12.50 30.00
37 Kerry Wood Jsy/5
38 Magglio Ordonez Jsy/25 12.50 30.00
39 Vernon Wells Jsy/25 12.50 30.00
40 Mark Mulder Jsy/25 12.50 30.00
41 Lance Berkman Jsy/1
42 Alfonso Soriano Jsy/25 12.50 30.00
43 Albert Pujols Jsy/5
44 Ben Sheets Jsy/25 12.50 30.00
45 Roy Oswalt Jsy/1
46 Mark Prior Jsy/25 15.00 40.00
47 Mark Teixeira Jsy/25 20.00 50.00
48 Miguel Cabrera Jsy/25 20.00 50.00
49 Travis Hafner Jsy/25 12.50 30.00
50 Victor Martinez Jsy/25 12.50 30.00

2005 Timeless Treasures Salutations Signature

It appears some (and possibly most or all of) Don Mattingly's cards were signed without any salutation added on.
OVERALL AU-GU'S ONE PER PACK
PRINT RUNS B/WN 1-24 COPIES PER
NO PRICING ON QTY OF 10 OR LESS
1 Al Kaline/24 40.00 80.00
2 Babe Ruth/1
3 Bob Gibson/24 30.00 60.00
4 Cal Ripken/10
5 Dale Murphy/24 30.00 60.00
6 Don Mattingly/24 40.00 80.00
7 Duke Snider/24 30.00 60.00
8 George Brett/10
9 Harmon Killebrew/24 40.00 80.00
10 Jim Palmer/24 20.00 50.00
11 Johnny Bench/24 40.00 80.00
12 Maury Wills/24 20.00 50.00
13 Dennis Eckersley/24 20.00 50.00
14 Mike Schmidt/6
15 Nolan Ryan/10
16 Robin Yount/10
17 Roger Maris/1
18 Stan Musial/10
19 Steve Carlton/24 20.00 50.00
20 Tony Gwynn/24 40.00 80.00
21 Whitey Ford/16 40.00 80.00
22 Carl Yastrzemski/10
23 Reggie Jackson/10
24 Rod Carew/24 30.00 60.00
25 Paul Molitor/24 20.00 50.00
26 Will Clark/24 30.00 60.00
27 Willie Mays/24

2005 Timeless Treasures Statistical Champions Materials Number

*NBR p/r 38-47: .5X TO 1.2X YR p/r 100
*NBR p/r 38-47: .3X TO .8X YR p/r 25
*NBR p/r 20-35: .6X TO 1.5X YR p/r 100
*NBR p/r 20-35: .4X TO 1X YR p/r 25
*NBR p/r 17-19: .75X TO 2X YR p/r 100
OVERALL AU-GU'S ONE PER PACK
PRINT RUNS B/WN 1-47 COPIES PER
NO PRICING ON QTY OF 11 OR LESS
32 Sandy Koufax Jsy/32 75.00 150.00

2005 Timeless Treasures Statistical Champions Materials Year

PRINT RUNS B/WN 1-100 COPIES PER
NO PRICING ON QTY OF 5 OR LESS
PRIME PRINT RUNS B/WN 1-5 COPIES PER
NO PRIME PRICING DUE TO SCARCITY
OVERALL AU-GU'S ONE PER PACK
1 Nolan Ryan Rgr Jsy/100 10.00 25.00
2 Lee Smith Jsy/25 6.00 15.00
3 Harmon Killebrew Jsy/100 6.00 15.00
4 Kerry Wood Jsy/100 3.00 8.00
5 Albert Pujols Jsy/100 8.00 20.00
6 C.Schill D'backs Jsy/100 4.00 10.00
7 Joe Cronin Pants/100 6.00 15.00
8 Cal Ripken Jsy/100 12.50 30.00
9 Barry Zito Jsy/100 3.00 8.00
10 Miguel Tejada Jsy/100 3.00 8.00
11 Edgar Martinez Jsy/25 6.00 15.00
13 Steve Carlton Jsy/5
14 Andre Dawson Jsy/25 6.00 15.00
15 George Foster Jsy/5
16 Dwight Gooden Jsy/5
17 Todd Helton Jsy/100 4.00 10.00
18 Darryl Strawberry Jsy/5
19 Tony Gwynn Jsy/100 6.00 15.00
20 Mark Mulder Jsy/100 3.00 8.00
21 Roger Clemens Jsy/100 6.00 15.00
22 Will Clark Jsy/25 10.00 25.00
23 Don Mattingly Jsy/100 8.00 20.00
24 Manny Ramirez Jsy/25 6.00 15.00
25 Billy Williams Jsy/100 4.00 10.00
26 Wade Boggs Jsy/100 6.00 15.00
27 Kevin Brown Jsy/25 5.00 12.00
28 George Brett Jsy/100 8.00 20.00
29 Adrian Beltre Jsy/25 5.00 12.00
30 Lance Berkman Jsy/100 3.00 8.00
31 Sammy Sosa Jsy/100 4.00 10.00
32 Sandy Koufax Jsy/25 75.00 150.00
33 Jose Canseco Jsy/25 10.00 25.00
34 Kirby Puckett Jsy/100 6.00 15.00
35 Rickey Henderson Jsy/100 6.00 15.00
36 Juan Gonzalez Jsy/100 3.00 8.00
37 Orel Hershiser Jsy/1
38 Curt Schilling Sox Jsy/100 4.00 10.00
39 Don Sutton Jsy/100 4.00 10.00
40 Johan Santana Jsy/100 4.00 10.00
41 Nolan Ryan Astros Jsy/100 10.00 25.00
42 Mariano Rivera Jsy/25 6.00 15.00
43 Lou Brock Jsy/100 6.00 15.00
44 Roy Oswalt Jsy/25 5.00 12.00
45 Dale Murphy Jsy/100 6.00 15.00

2005 Timeless Treasures Statistical Champions Materials Signature Number

*NBR p/r 20-34: .5X TO 1.2X p/r YR p/r 50
*NBR p/r 20-34: .4X TO 1X p/r YR p/r 25
*NBR p/r 19: .6X TO 1.5X p/r YR p/r 50
*NBR p/r 19: .5X TO 1.2X p/r YR p/r 25
OVERALL AU-GU'S ONE PER PACK
PRINT RUNS B/WN 1-34 COPIES PER
NO PRICING ON QTY OF 11 OR LESS

2005 Timeless Treasures Statistical Champions Materials Signature Year

PRINT RUNS B/WN 1-50 COPIES PER
NO PRICING ON QTY OF 5 OR LESS
PRIME PRINT RUNS B/WN 1-5 COPIES PER
NO PRIME PRICING DUE TO SCARCITY
OVERALL AU-GU'S ONE PER PACK
1 Nolan Ryan Rgr Jsy/50 50.00 100.00
2 Lee Smith Jsy/5
3 Harmon Killebrew Jsy/50 20.00 50.00
4 Kerry Wood Jsy/25 20.00 50.00
5 Albert Pujols Jsy/5
6 Curt Schilling D'backs Jsy/5
8 Cal Ripken Jsy/25 125.00 200.00
9 Barry Zito Jsy/25 12.50 30.00
11 Edgar Martinez Jsy/25 30.00 60.00
13 Steve Carlton Jsy/5
14 Andre Dawson Jsy/25 12.50 30.00
15 George Foster Jsy/5
16 Dwight Gooden Jsy/5
17 Todd Helton Jsy/1
18 Darryl Strawberry Jsy/5
19 Tony Gwynn Jsy/50 20.00 50.00
20 Mark Mulder Jsy/25 12.50 30.00
21 Roger Clemens Jsy/5
22 Will Clark Jsy/25 20.00 50.00
23 Don Mattingly Jsy/50 30.00 60.00
24 Manny Ramirez Jsy/5
25 Billy Williams Jsy/5
26 Wade Boggs Jsy/25 20.00 50.00
28 George Brett Jsy/5
29 Adrian Beltre Jsy/25 12.50 30.00
30 Lance Berkman Jsy/1
31 Sammy Sosa Jsy/1
32 Sandy Koufax Jsy/5
33 Jose Canseco Jsy/25 30.00 60.00
34 Kirby Puckett Jsy/5
35 Rickey Henderson Jsy/5
36 Juan Gonzalez Jsy/25 12.50 30.00
37 Orel Hershiser Jsy/5
38 Curt Schilling Sox Jsy/5
39 Don Sutton Jsy/25 12.50 30.00
40 Johan Santana Jsy/25 20.00 50.00
41 Nolan Ryan Astros Jsy/50 50.00 100.00
43 Lou Brock Jsy/50 15.00 40.00
44 Roy Oswalt Jsy/1
45 Dale Murphy Jsy/50 15.00 40.00

2005 Timeless Treasures World Series Materials

OVERALL AU-GU'S ONE PER PACK
PRINT RUNS B/WN 1-100 COPIES PER
NO PRICING ON QTY OF 10 OR LESS
1 Frank Robinson Bat/100 4.00 10.00
2 Bob Gibson Ball/10
3 Carl Yastrzemski Bat/100 8.00 20.00
4 Jack Morris Jsy/50 5.00 12.00
5 Wade Boggs Bat/100 6.00 15.00
6 Ozzie Smith Jsy/1
7 Rickey Henderson Jsy/10
8 Andruw Jones Jsy/100 4.00 10.00
9 Tom Glavine Jsy/1
10 Darryl Strawberry Jsy/25 6.00 15.00

2005 Timeless Treasures World Series Materials Signature

PRINT RUNS B/WN 1-25 COPIES PER
NO PRICING ON QTY OF 10 OR LESS
PRIME PRINT RUNS B/WN 1-10 COPIES PER
NO PRIME PRICING DUE TO SCARCITY
OVERALL AU-GU'S ONE PER PACK
1 Frank Robinson Bat/25 20.00 50.00
2 Bob Gibson Ball/1
3 Carl Yastrzemski Bat/10
4 Jack Morris Jsy/25 12.50 30.00
5 Wade Boggs Bat/25 20.00 50.00
6 Ozzie Smith Jsy/1
7 Rickey Henderson Jsy/5
9 Tom Glavine Jsy/1
10 Darryl Strawberry Jsy/25 12.50 30.00

1951 Topps Blue Backs

The cards in this 52-card set measure approximately 2" by 2 5/8". The 1951 Topps series of blue-backed baseball cards could be used to play a baseball game by shuffling the cards and drawing them from a pile. These cards (packaged two adjoined in a penny pack) were marketed with a piece of caramel candy, which often melted or was squashed in such a way as to damage the card and wrapper (despite the fact that a paper shield was inserted between candy and card). Blue Backs are more difficult to obtain than the similarly styled Red Backs. The set is denoted on the cards as "Set B" and the Red Back set is correspondingly Set A. The only notable Rookie Card in the set is Billy Pierce.
COMPLETE SET (52) 1000.00 1700.00
WRAPPER (1-CENT) 150.00 200.00
1 Eddie Yost 35.00 60.00
2 Hank Majeski 15.00 30.00

3 Richie Ashburn 125.00 200.00
4 Del Ennis 15.00 30.00
5 Johnny Pesky 15.00 30.00
6 Red Schoendienst 60.00 100.00
7 Gerry Staley RC 15.00 30.00
8 Dick Sisler 15.00 30.00
9 Johnny Sain 30.00 50.00
10 Joe Page 30.00 50.00
11 Johnny Groth 15.00 30.00
12 Sam Jethroe 20.00 40.00
13 Mickey Vernon 15.00 30.00
14 George Munger 15.00 30.00
15 Eddie Joost 15.00 30.00
16 Murry Dickson 15.00 30.00
17 Roy Smalley 15.00 30.00
18 Ned Garver 15.00 30.00
19 Phil Masi 15.00 30.00
20 Ralph Branca 30.00 50.00
21 Billy Johnson 15.00 30.00
22 Bob Kuzava 15.00 30.00
23 Dizzy Trout 20.00 40.00
24 Sherman Lollar 15.00 30.00
25 Sam Mele 15.00 30.00
26 Chico Carrasquel RC 20.00 40.00
27 Andy Pafko 15.00 30.00
28 Harry Brecheen 15.00 30.00
29 Granville Hamner 15.00 30.00
30 Enos Slaughter 60.00 100.00
31 Lou Brissie 15.00 30.00
32 Bob Elliott 20.00 40.00
33 Don Lenhardt RC 15.00 30.00
34 Earl Torgeson 15.00 30.00
35 Tommy Byrne RC 15.00 30.00
36 Cliff Fannin 15.00 30.00
37 Bobby Doerr 60.00 100.00
38 Irv Noren 15.00 30.00
39 Ed Lopat 30.00 50.00
40 Vic Wertz 15.00 30.00
41 Johnny Schmitz 15.00 30.00
42 Bruce Edwards 15.00 30.00
43 Willie Jones 15.00 30.00
44 Johnny Wyrostek 15.00 30.00
45 Billy Pierce RC 30.00 50.00
46 Gerry Priddy 15.00 30.00
47 Herman Wehmeier 15.00 30.00
48 Billy Cox 20.00 40.00
49 Hank Sauer 20.00 40.00
50 Johnny Mize 60.00 100.00
51 Eddie Waitkus 20.00 40.00
52 Sam Chapman 30.00 50.00

1951 Topps Red Backs

The cards in this 52-card set measure approximately 2" by 2 5/8". The 1951 Topps Red Back set is identical in style to the Blue Back set of the same year. The cards have rounded corners and were designed to be used as a baseball game. Zernial, number 36, is listed with either the White Sox or Athletics, and Holmes, number 52, with either the Braves or Hartford. The set is denoted on the cards as "Set A" and the Blue Back set is correspondingly Set B. The cards were packaged as two connected cards along with a piece of caramel in a penny pack. There were 120 penny packs in a box. The most notable Rookie Card in the set is Monte Irvin.

COMPLETE SET (54) 500.00 800.00
WRAPPER (1-CENT) 4.00 5.00
1 Yogi Berra 75.00 125.00
2 Sid Gordon 5.00 10.00
3 Ferris Fain 6.00 12.00
4 Vern Stephens 6.00 12.00
5 Phil Rizzuto 35.00 60.00
6 Allie Reynolds 10.00 20.00
7 Howie Pollet 5.00 10.00
8 Early Wynn 12.50 25.00
9 Roy Sievers 7.50 15.00
10 Mel Parnell 6.00 12.00
11 Gene Hermanski 6.00 12.00
12 Jim Hegan 6.00 12.00
13 Dale Mitchell 6.00 12.00
14 Wayne Terwilliger 5.00 10.00
15 Ralph Kiner 12.50 25.00
16 Preacher Roe 7.50 15.00
17 Gus Bell RC 7.50 15.00
18 Jerry Coleman 7.50 15.00
19 Dick Kokos 5.00 10.00
20 Dom DiMaggio 10.00 20.00
21 Larry Jansen 6.00 12.00
22 Bob Feller 35.00 60.00
23 Ray Boone RC 7.50 15.00
24 Hank Bauer 10.00 20.00
25 Cliff Chambers 5.00 10.00
26 Luke Easter RC 7.50 15.00
27 Wally Westlake 6.00 12.00
28 Elmer Valo 5.00 10.00
29 Bob Kennedy RC 6.00 12.00
30 Warren Spahn 35.00 60.00
31 Gil Hodges 30.00 50.00
32 Henry Thompson 6.00 12.00
33 William Werle 5.00 10.00
34 Grady Hatton 5.00 10.00
35 Al Rosen 7.50 15.00
36A Gus Zernial 20.00 40.00
(Chicago)
36B Gus Zernial 10.00 20.00
(Philadelphia)
37 Wes Westrum RC 6.00 12.00
38 Duke Snider 35.00 60.00
39 Ted Kluszewski 12.50 25.00
40 Mike Garcia 7.50 15.00
41 Whitey Lockman 6.00 12.00
42 Ray Scarborough 5.00 10.00
43 Maurice McDermott 5.00 10.00
44 Sid Hudson 5.00 10.00
45 Andy Seminick 6.00 12.00
46 Billy Goodman 6.00 12.00
47 Tommy Glaviano RC 5.00 10.00
48 Eddie Stanky 6.00 12.00
49 Al Zarilla 5.00 10.00
50 Monte Irvin RC 20.00 40.00
51 Eddie Robinson 5.00 10.00
52A Tommy Holmes 20.00 40.00
(Boston)
52B Tommy Holmes 12.50 25.00
(Hartford)

1951 Topps Connie Mack's All-Stars

The cards in this 11-card set measure approximately 2 1/16" by 5 1/4". The series of die-cut cards which comprise the set entitled Connie Mack All-Stars was one of Topps' most distinctive and fragile card designs. Printed on thin cardboard, these elegant cards were protected in the wrapper by panels of accompanying Red Backs, but once removed were easily damaged (after all, they were intended to be folded and used as toy figures). Cards without tops have a value less than one-half of that listed below. The cards are unnumbered and are listed below in alphabetical order.

COMPLETE SET (11) 4200.00 7000.00
WRAPPER (1-CENT) 300.00 350.00
1 Grover C. Alexander 250.00 400.00
2 Mickey Cochrane 175.00 300.00
3 Eddie Collins 90.00 150.00
4 Jimmy Collins 90.00 150.00
5 Lou Gehrig 1200.00 2000.00
6 Walter Johnson 450.00 700.00
7 Connie Mack 175.00 300.00
8 Christy Mathewson 300.00 500.00
9 Babe Ruth 1500.00 2500.00
10 Tris Speaker 150.00 250.00
11 Honus Wagner 250.00 400.00

1951 Topps Major League All-Stars

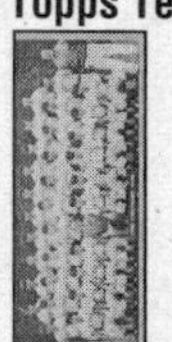

The cards in this 11-card set measure approximately 2 1/16" by 5 1/4". The 1951 Topps Current All-Star series is probably the rarest of all legitimate, nationally issued, post war baseball issues. The set price listed below does not include the prices for the cards of Konstanty, Roberts and Stanky, which likely never were released to the public in gum packs. These three cards (SP in the checklist below) were probably obtained directly from the company and exist in extremely limited numbers. As with the Connie Mack set, cards without the die-cut background are worth half of the value listed below. The cards are unnumbered and are listed below in alphabetical order. These cards were issued in two card packs (one being a Current AS the other being a Topps Team card).

COMPLETE SET (8) 2700.00 4500.00
WRAPPER (1-CENT) 400.00 500.00
1 Yogi Berra 1000.00 1500.00
2 Larry Doby 250.00 400.00
3 Walt Dropo 150.00 250.00
4 Hoot Evers 150.00 250.00
5 George Kell 350.00 600.00
6 Ralph Kiner 450.00 750.00
7 Jim Konstanty SP 7500.00 12500.00
8 Bob Lemon 350.00 600.00
9 Phil Rizzuto 500.00 800.00
10 Robin Roberts SP 9000.00 15000.00
11 Eddie Stanky SP 7500.00 12500.00

1951 Topps Teams

The cards in this nine-card set measure approximately 2 1/16" by 5 1/4". These unnumbered team cards issued by Topps in 1951 carry black and white photographs framed by a yellow border. These cards were issued in the same five-cent wrapper as the Connie Mack and Current All Stars. They have been assigned reference numbers in the checklist alphabetically by team city and name. They are found with or without "1950" printed in the name panel before the team name. Although the dated variations are slightly more difficult to find, there is usually no difference in value.

COMPLETE SET (9) 1500.00 3000.00
1 Boston Red Sox 250.00 500.00
2 Brooklyn Dodgers 250.00 500.00
3 Chicago White Sox 150.00 300.00
4 Cincinnati Reds 150.00 300.00
5 New York Giants 200.00 400.00
6 Philadelphia Athletics 150.00 300.00
7 Philadelphia Phillies 150.00 300.00
8 St. Louis Cardinals 250.00 500.00
9 Washington Senators 150.00 300.00

1952 Topps

The cards in this 407-card set measure approximately 2 5/8" by 3 3/4". The 1952 Topps set is Topps' first truly major set. Card numbers 1 to 80 were issued with red or black backs, both of which are less plentiful than card numbers 81 to 250. In fact, the first series is considered the most difficult with respect to finding perfect condition cards. Card number 48 (Joe Page) and number 49 (Johnny Sain) can be found with each other's write-up on their back. However, many dealers today believe that all cards numbered 1-250 were produced in the same quantities. Card numbers 251 to 310 are somewhat scarce and numbers 311 to 407 are quite scarce. Cards 281-300 were single printed compared to the other cards in the next to last series. Cards 311-313 were double printed on the last high number printing sheet. The key card in the set is Mickey Mantle, number 311, which was Mickey's first of many Topps cards. A minor variation on cards from 311 through 313 is that they exist with the stitching on the number circle in the back pointing right or left. There seems to be no print run difference between the two versions. Card number 307, Frank Campos, can be found in a scarce version with one red star and one black star next to the words "Topps Baseball" on the back. In the early 1980's, Topps issued a standard-size reprint set of the 52 Topps set. These cards were issued only as a factory set. Five people portrayed in the regular set: Billy Loes (number 20), Dom DiMaggio (number 22), Saul Rogovin (number 159), Solly Hemus (number 196) and Tommy Holmes (number 289) are not in the reprint set. Although rarely seen, salesman sample panels of three cards containing the fronts of regular cards with ad information on the back do exist.

COMP.MASTER SET (487) 40000.00 80000.00
COMPLETE SET (407) 40000.00 65000.00
COMMON CARD (1-80) 35.00 60.00
COMMON CARD (81-250) 20.00 40.00
COMMON (251-310) 30.00 50.00
COMMON (311-407) 150.00 250.00
WRAPPER (1-cent) 200.00 250.00
WRAPPER (5-cent) 75.00 100.00
1 Andy Pafko 3000.00 5000.00
1A Andy Pafko Black 1800.00 3000.00
2 Pete Runnels RC 150.00 250.00
2A Pete Runnels Black 150.00 250.00
3 Hank Thompson 40.00 70.00
3A Hank Thompson Black 40.00 70.00
4 Don Lenhardt 35.00 60.00
4A Don Lenhardt Black 35.00 60.00
5 Larry Jansen 40.00 70.00
5A Larry Jansen Black 40.00 70.00
6 Grady Hatton 35.00 60.00
6A Grady Hatton Black 35.00 60.00
7 Wayne Terwilliger 35.00 60.00
7A W. Terwilliger Black 35.00 60.00
8 Fred Marsh RC 35.00 60.00
8A Fred Marsh Black 35.00 60.00
9 Robert Hogue RC 35.00 60.00
9A Robert Hogue Black 35.00 60.00
10 Al Rosen 40.00 70.00
10A Al Rosen Black 40.00 70.00
11 Phil Rizzuto 250.00 400.00
11A Phil Rizzuto Black 200.00 350.00
12 Monty Basgall RC 35.00 60.00
12A Monty Basgall Black 35.00 60.00
13 Johnny Wyrostek 35.00 60.00
13A J. Wyrostek Black 35.00 60.00
14 Bob Elliott 40.00 70.00
14A Bob Elliott Black 40.00 70.00
15 Johnny Pesky 40.00 70.00
15A Johnny Pesky Black 40.00 70.00
16 Gene Hermanski 35.00 60.00
16A G. Hermanski Black 35.00 60.00
17 Jim Hegan 40.00 70.00
17A Jim Hegan Black 40.00 70.00
18 Merrill Combs RC 35.00 60.00
18A Merrill Combs Black 35.00 60.00
19 Johnny Bucha RC 35.00 60.00
19A Johnny Bucha Black 35.00 60.00
20 Billy Loes SP RC 90.00 150.00
20A Billy Loes Black 90.00 150.00
21 Ferris Fain 40.00 70.00
21A Ferris Fain Black 40.00 70.00
22 Dom DiMaggio 75.00 125.00
22A Dom DiMaggio Black 60.00 100.00
23 Billy Goodman 40.00 70.00
23A Billy Goodman Black 40.00 70.00
24 Luke Easter 50.00 80.00
24A Luke Easter Black 50.00 80.00
25 Johnny Groth 35.00 60.00
25A Johnny Groth Black 35.00 60.00
26 Monte Irvin 90.00 150.00
26A Monte Irvin Black 90.00 150.00
27 Sam Jethroe 40.00 70.00
27A Sam Jethroe Black 40.00 70.00
28 Jerry Priddy 35.00 60.00
28A Jerry Priddy Black 35.00 60.00
29 Ted Kluszewski 75.00 125.00
29A Ted Kluszewski Black 75.00 125.00
30 Mel Parnell 40.00 70.00
30A Mel Parnell Black 40.00 70.00
31 Gus Zernial 50.00 80.00
Posed with six baseballs
31A Gus Zernial Black 50.00 80.00
Posed with six baseballs
32 Eddie Robinson 35.00 60.00
32A Eddie Robinson Black 35.00 60.00
33 Warren Spahn 175.00 300.00
33A Warren Spahn Black 175.00 300.00
34 Elmer Valo 35.00 60.00
34A Elmer Valo Black 35.00 60.00
35 Hank Sauer 40.00 70.00
35A Hank Sauer Black 40.00 70.00
36 Gil Hodges 175.00 300.00
36A Gil Hodges Black 175.00 300.00
37 Duke Snider 300.00 500.00
37A Duke Snider Black 300.00 500.00
38 Wally Westlake 35.00 60.00
38A Wally Westlake Black 35.00 60.00
39 Dizzy Trout 40.00 70.00
39A Dizzy Trout Black 40.00 70.00
40 Irv Noren 40.00 70.00
40A Irv Noren Black 40.00 70.00
41 Bob Wellman RC 35.00 60.00
41A Bob Wellman Black 35.00 60.00
42 Lou Kretlow RC 35.00 60.00
42A Lou Kretlow Black 35.00 60.00
43 Ray Scarborough 35.00 60.00
43A R. Scarborough Black 35.00 60.00
44 Con Dempsey RC 35.00 60.00
44A Con Dempsey Black 35.00 60.00
45 Eddie Joost 35.00 60.00
45A Eddie Joost Black 35.00 60.00
46 Gordon Goldsberry RC 35.00 60.00
46A Gordon Goldsberry Black 35.00 60.00
47 Willie Jones 40.00 70.00
47A Willie Jones Black 40.00 70.00
48A Joe Page ERR 250.00 400.00
Bio for Sain
Black Back
48B Joe Page COR 75.00 125.00
Black Back
48C Joe Page COR 75.00 125.00
Red Back
49A John Sain ERR 250.00 400.00
Bio for Page
Black Back
49B John Sain COR 75.00 125.00
Black Back
49C John Sain COR 75.00 125.00
Red Back
50 Marv Rickert RC 35.00 60.00
50A Marv Rickert Black 35.00 60.00
51 Jim Russell 35.00 60.00
51A Jim Russell Black 35.00 60.00
52 Don Mueller 40.00 70.00
52A Don Mueller Black 40.00 70.00
53 Chris Van Cuyk RC 35.00 60.00
53A Chris Van Cuyk Black 35.00 60.00
54 Leo Kiely RC 35.00 60.00
54A Leo Kiely Black 35.00 60.00
55 Ray Boone 50.00 80.00
55A Ray Boone Black 50.00 80.00
56 Tommy Glaviano 35.00 60.00
56A T. Glaviano Black 35.00 60.00
57 Ed Lopat 60.00 100.00
57A Ed Lopat Black 60.00 100.00
58 Bob Mahoney RC 35.00 60.00
58A Bob Mahoney Black 35.00 60.00
59 Robin Roberts 100.00 175.00
59A Robin Roberts Black 100.00 175.00
60 Sid Hudson 35.00 60.00
60A Sid Hudson Black 35.00 60.00
61 Tookie Gilbert 35.00 60.00
61A Tookie Gilbert Black 35.00 60.00
62 Chuck Stobbs RC 35.00 60.00
62A Chuck Stobbs Black 35.00 60.00
63 Howie Pollet 35.00 60.00
63A Howie Pollet Black 35.00 60.00
64 Roy Sievers 40.00 70.00
64A Roy Sievers Black 40.00 70.00
65 Enos Slaughter 100.00 175.00
65A Enos Slaughter Black 100.00 175.00
66 Preacher Roe 60.00 100.00
66A Preacher Roe Black 60.00 100.00
67 Allie Reynolds 75.00 125.00
67A Allie Reynolds Black 75.00 125.00
68 Cliff Chambers 35.00 60.00
68A Cliff Chambers Black 35.00 60.00
69 Virgil Stallcup 35.00 60.00
69A Virgil Stallcup Black 35.00 60.00
70 Al Zarilla 35.00 60.00
70A Al Zarilla Black 35.00 60.00
71 Tom Upton RC 35.00 60.00
71A Tom Upton Black 35.00 60.00
72 Karl Olson RC 35.00 60.00
72A Karl Olson Black 35.00 60.00
73 Bill Werle 35.00 60.00
73A Bill Werle Black 35.00 60.00
74 Andy Hansen RC 35.00 60.00
74A Andy Hansen Black 35.00 60.00
75 Wes Westrum 40.00 70.00
75A Wes Westrum Black 40.00 70.00
76 Eddie Stanky 40.00 70.00
76A Eddie Stanky Black 40.00 70.00
77 Bob Kennedy 40.00 70.00
77A Bob Kennedy Black 40.00 70.00
78 Ellis Kinder 35.00 60.00
78A Ellis Kinder Black 35.00 60.00
79 Gerry Staley 35.00 60.00
79A Gerry Staley Black 35.00 60.00
80 Herman Wehmeier 50.00 80.00
80A H. Wehmeier Black 50.00 80.00
81 Vernon Law 50.00 80.00
82 Duane Pillette 20.00 40.00
83 Billy Johnson 20.00 40.00
84 Vern Stephens 30.00 50.00
85 Bob Kuzava 30.00 50.00
86 Ted Gray 20.00 40.00
87 Dale Coogan 20.00 40.00
88 Bob Feller 150.00 250.00
89 Johnny Lipon 20.00 40.00
90 Mickey Grasso 20.00 40.00
91 Red Schoendienst 90.00 150.00
92 Dale Mitchell 30.00 50.00
93 Al Sima RC 20.00 40.00
94 Sam Mele 20.00 40.00
95 Ken Holcombe 20.00 40.00
96 Willard Marshall 20.00 40.00
97 Earl Torgeson 20.00 40.00
98 Billy Pierce 30.00 50.00
99 Gene Woodling 35.00 60.00
100 Del Rice 20.00 40.00
101 Max Lanier 20.00 40.00
102 Bill Kennedy 20.00 40.00
103 Cliff Mapes 20.00 40.00
104 Don Kolloway 20.00 40.00
105 Johnny Pramesa 20.00 40.00
106 Mickey Vernon 35.00 60.00
107 Connie Ryan 20.00 40.00
108 Jim Konstanty 35.00 60.00
109 Ted Wilks 20.00 40.00
110 Dutch Leonard 20.00 40.00
111 Peanuts Lowrey 20.00 40.00
112 Hank Majeski 20.00 40.00
113 Dick Sisler 30.00 50.00
114 Willard Ramsdell 20.00 40.00
115 George Munger 20.00 40.00
116 Carl Scheib 20.00 40.00
117 Sherm Lollar 30.00 50.00
118 Ken Raffensberger 20.00 40.00
119 Mickey McDermott 20.00 40.00
120 Bob Chakales RC 20.00 40.00
121 Gus Niarhos 20.00 40.00
122 Jackie Jensen 50.00 80.00
123 Eddie Yost 30.00 50.00
124 Monte Kennedy 20.00 40.00
125 Bill Rigney 20.00 40.00
126 Fred Hutchinson 30.00 50.00
127 Paul Minner RC 20.00 40.00
128 Don Bollweg RC 20.00 40.00
129 Johnny Mize 90.00 150.00
130 Sheldon Jones 20.00 40.00
131 Morrie Martin RC 20.00 40.00
132 Clyde Kluttz RC 20.00 40.00
133 Al Widmar 20.00 40.00
134 Joe Tipton 20.00 40.00
135 Dixie Howell 20.00 40.00
136 Johnny Schmitz 20.00 40.00
137 Roy McMillan RC 30.00 50.00
138 Bill MacDonald 20.00 40.00
139 Ken Wood 20.00 40.00
140 Johnny Antonelli 35.00 60.00
141 Clint Hartung 20.00 40.00
142 Harry Perkowski RC 20.00 40.00
143 Les Moss 20.00 40.00
144 Ed Blake RC 20.00 40.00
145 Joe Haynes 20.00 40.00
146 Frank House RC 20.00 40.00
147 Bob Young RC 20.00 40.00
148 Johnny Klippstein 20.00 40.00
149 Dick Kryhoski 20.00 40.00
150 Ted Beard 20.00 40.00
151 Wally Post RC 30.00 50.00
152 Al Evans 20.00 40.00
153 Bob Rush 20.00 40.00
154 Joe Muir RC 20.00 40.00
155 Frank Overmire 20.00 40.00
156 Frank Hiller RC 20.00 40.00
157 Bob Usher 20.00 40.00
158 Eddie Waitkus 20.00 40.00
159 Saul Rogovin RC 20.00 40.00
160 Owen Friend 20.00 40.00
161 Bud Byerly RC 20.00 40.00
162 Del Crandall 30.00 50.00
163 Stan Rojek 20.00 40.00
164 Walt Dubiel 20.00 40.00
165 Eddie Kazak 20.00 40.00
166 Paul LaPalme RC 20.00 40.00
167 Bill Howerton 20.00 40.00
168 Charlie Silvera RC 35.00 60.00
169 Howie Judson 20.00 40.00
170 Gus Bell 30.00 50.00
171 Ed Erautt RC 20.00 40.00
172 Eddie Miksis 20.00 40.00
173 Roy Smalley 20.00 40.00
174 Clarence Marshall RC 35.00 60.00
175 Billy Martin RC 300.00 500.00
176 Hank Edwards 20.00 40.00
177 Bill Wight 20.00 40.00
178 Cass Michaels 20.00 40.00
179 Frank Smith RC 20.00 40.00
180 Charlie Maxwell RC 30.00 50.00
181 Bob Swift 20.00 40.00
182 Billy Hitchcock 20.00 40.00
183 Erv Dusak 20.00 40.00
184 Bob Ramazzotti 20.00 40.00
185 Bill Nicholson 30.00 50.00
186 Walt Masterson 20.00 40.00
187 Bob Miller 20.00 40.00
188 Clarence Podbielan RC 20.00 40.00
189 Pete Reiser 35.00 60.00
190 Don Johnson RC 20.00 40.00
191 Yogi Berra 500.00 800.00
192 Myron Ginsberg RC 20.00 40.00
193 Harry Simpson RC 30.00 50.00
194 Joe Hatton 20.00 40.00
195 Minnie Minoso RC 90.00 150.00
196 Solly Hemus RC 35.00 60.00
197 George Strickland RC 20.00 40.00
198 Phil Haugstad RC 20.00 40.00
199 George Zuverink RC 20.00 40.00
200 Ralph Houk RC 50.00 80.00
201 Alex Kellner 20.00 40.00
202 Joe Collins RC 35.00 60.00
203 Curt Simmons 35.00 60.00
204 Ron Northey 20.00 40.00
205 Clyde King 35.00 60.00
206 Joe Ostrowski RC 20.00 40.00
207 Mickey Harris 20.00 40.00
208 Martin Stuart RC 20.00 40.00
209 Howie Fox 20.00 40.00
210 Dick Fowler 20.00 40.00
211 Ray Coleman 20.00 40.00
212 Ned Garver 20.00 40.00
213 Nippy Jones 20.00 40.00
214 Johnny Hopp 30.00 50.00
215 Hank Bauer 60.00 100.00
216 Richie Ashburn 150.00 250.00
217 Snuffy Stirnweiss 30.00 50.00
218 Clyde McCullough 20.00 40.00
219 Bobby Shantz 35.00 60.00
220 Joe Presko RC 20.00 40.00
221 Granny Hamner 20.00 40.00
222 Hoot Evers 20.00 40.00
223 Del Ennis 30.00 50.00
224 Bruce Edwards 20.00 40.00
225 Frank Baumholtz 20.00 40.00
226 Dave Philley 20.00 40.00
227 Joe Garagiola 50.00 80.00
228 Al Brazle 20.00 40.00
229 Gene Bearden UER 20.00 40.00
(Misspelled Beardon)
230 Matt Batts 20.00 40.00
231 Sam Zoldak 20.00 40.00
232 Billy Cox 30.00 50.00
233 Bob Friend RC 50.00 80.00
234 Steve Souchock RC 20.00 40.00
235 Walt Dropo 20.00 40.00
236 Ed Fitzgerald 20.00 40.00
237 Jerry Coleman 35.00 60.00
238 Art Houtteman 20.00 40.00
239 Rocky Bridges RC 30.00 50.00
240 Jack Phillips RC 20.00 40.00
241 Tommy Byrne 20.00 40.00
242 Tom Poholsky RC 20.00 40.00
243 Larry Doby 50.00 80.00
244 Vic Wertz 20.00 40.00
245 Sherry Robertson 20.00 40.00
246 George Kell 50.00 80.00
247 Randy Gumpert 20.00 40.00
248 Frank Shea 20.00 40.00
249 Bobby Adams 20.00 40.00
250 Carl Erskine 60.00 100.00
251 Chico Carrasquel 30.00 50.00
252 Vern Bickford 30.00 50.00
253 Johnny Berardino 60.00 100.00
254 Joe Dobson 30.00 50.00
255 Clyde Vollmer 30.00 50.00
256 Pete Suder 30.00 50.00
257 Bobby Avila 35.00 60.00
258 Steve Gromek 35.00 60.00
259 Bob Addis RC 30.00 50.00
260 Pete Castiglione 30.00 50.00
261 Willie Mays 2000.00 3000.00
262 Virgil Trucks 35.00 60.00
263 Harry Brecheen 35.00 60.00
264 Roy Hartsfield 30.00 50.00
265 Chuck Diering 30.00 50.00
266 Murry Dickson 30.00 50.00
267 Sid Gordon 35.00 60.00
268 Bob Lemon 90.00 150.00
269 Willard Nixon 30.00 50.00
270 Lou Brissie 30.00 50.00
271 Jim Delsing 35.00 60.00
272 Mike Garcia 50.00 80.00
273 Erv Palica 30.00 50.00
274 Ralph Branca 75.00 125.00
275 Pat Mullin 30.00 50.00
276 Jim Wilson RC 30.00 50.00
277 Early Wynn 100.00 175.00
278 Allie Clark 30.00 50.00
279 Eddie Stewart 30.00 50.00
280 Cloyd Boyer 50.00 80.00
281 Tommy Brown SP 50.00 80.00
282 Birdie Tebbetts SP 50.00 80.00
283 Phil Masi SP 35.00 60.00
284 Hank Arft SP 35.00 60.00
285 Cliff Fannin SP 35.00 60.00
286 Joe DeMaestri SP RC 35.00 60.00
287 Steve Bilko SP 35.00 60.00
288 Chet Nichols SP RC 50.00 80.00
289 Tommy Holmes SP 60.00 100.00
290 Joe Astroth SP 35.00 60.00
291 Gil Coan SP 35.00 60.00
292 Floyd Baker SP 35.00 60.00
293 Sibby Sisti SP 35.00 60.00
294 Walker Cooper SP 35.00 60.00
295 Phil Cavarretta SP 50.00 80.00
296 Red Rolfe MG SP 35.00 60.00
297 Andy Seminick SP 35.00 60.00
298 Bob Ross SP RC 35.00 60.00
299 Ray Murray SP RC 50.00 80.00
300 Barney McCosky SP 50.00 80.00
301 Bob Porterfield 30.00 50.00
302 Max Surkont RC 30.00 50.00
303 Harry Dorish 30.00 50.00
304 Sam Dente 30.00 50.00
305 Paul Richards MG 35.00 60.00
306 Lou Sleater RC 30.00 50.00
307 Frank Campos RC 30.00 50.00
Two red stars on back in copyright line
307A Frank Campos RC
One red/one black star on back in copyright line
308 Luis Aloma 30.00 50.00
309 Jim Busby 35.00 60.00
310 George Metkovich 60.00 100.00
311 Mickey Mantle DP 18000.00 30000.00
Rough marquee along top edge on front,
Last E on facsimile autograph curls upward
Stitching on back number circle points left
311B Mickey Mantle DP 18000.00 30000.00
Clean marquee along top edge on front,
Last E on facsimile autograph stops at bottom
Stitching on back number circle points right
312 Jackie Robinson DP 1500.00 2500.00
Stitching on back number circle points left,
Seven stars and white circle on left side of marquee
312B Jackie Robinson DP 1500.00 2500.00
Stitching on back number circle points right
Seven stars only on left side of marquee
313 Bobby Thomson DP 200.00 350.00
Stitching on back number circle points left
Marquee is clean along top and right edges
313B Bobby Thomson DP 200.00 350.00
Stitching on back number circle points right
Marquee is rough along top and right edges
314 Roy Campanella 1500.00 2500.00
315 Leo Durocher MG 350.00 600.00
316 Dave Williams RC 175.00 300.00
317 Conrado Marrero 175.00 300.00
318 Harold Gregg RC 175.00 300.00
319 Rube Walker RC 150.00 250.00
320 John Rutherford RC 175.00 300.00
321 Joe Black RC 350.00 500.00
322 Randy Jackson RC 175.00 300.00
323 Bubba Church 150.00 250.00
324 Warren Hacker 150.00 250.00
325 Bill Serena 175.00 300.00
326 George Shuba RC 350.00 500.00
327 Al Wilson RC 150.00 250.00
328 Bob Borkowski RC 175.00 300.00
329 Ike Delock RC 175.00 300.00
330 Turk Lown RC 175.00 300.00
331 Tom Morgan RC 175.00 300.00
332 Tony Bartirome RC 175.00 300.00
333 Pee Wee Reese 1000.00 1800.00
334 Wilmer Mizell RC 175.00 300.00
335 Ted Lepcio RC 150.00 250.00
336 Dave Koslo 150.00 250.00
337 Jim Hearn 175.00 300.00
338 Sal Yvars RC 175.00 300.00
339 Russ Meyer 175.00 300.00
340 Bob Hooper 175.00 300.00
341 Hal Jeffcoat 175.00 300.00
342 Clem Labine RC 350.00 500.00
343 Dick Gernert RC 150.00 250.00
344 Ewell Blackwell 175.00 300.00
345 Sammy White RC 150.00 250.00
346 George Spencer RC 150.00 250.00
347 Joe Adcock 250.00 400.00

348 Robert Kelly RC 150.00 250.00
349 Bob Cain 175.00 300.00
350 Cal Abrams 175.00 300.00
351 Alvin Dark 175.00 300.00
352 Karl Drews 175.00 300.00
353 Bobby Del Greco RC 175.00 300.00
354 Fred Hatfield RC 175.00 300.00
355 Bobby Morgan 175.00 300.00
356 Toby Atwell RC 175.00 300.00
357 Smoky Burgess 175.00 300.00
358 John Kucab RC 175.00 300.00
359 Dee Fondy RC 150.00 250.00
360 George Crowe RC 175.00 300.00
361 Bill Posedel CO 150.00 250.00
362 Ken Heintzelman 175.00 300.00
363 Dick Rozek RC 175.00 300.00
364 Clyde Sukeforth CO RC 175.00 300.00
365 Cookie Lavagetto CO 250.00 400.00
366 Dave Madison RC 150.00 250.00
367 Ben Thorpe RC 175.00 300.00
368 Ed Wright RC 175.00 300.00
369 Dick Groat RC 350.00 500.00
370 Billy Hoeft RC 175.00 300.00
371 Bobby Hofman 150.00 250.00
372 Gil McDougald RC 300.00 500.00
373 Jim Turner CO RC 250.00 400.00
374 Al Benton RC 150.00 250.00
375 John Merson RC 150.00 250.00
376 Faye Throneberry RC 150.00 250.00
377 Chuck Dressen MG 250.00 400.00
378 Leroy Fusselman RC 175.00 300.00
379 Joe Rossi RC 150.00 250.00
380 Clem Koshorek RC 150.00 250.00
381 Milton Stock CO RC 150.00 250.00
382 Sam Jones RC 200.00 350.00
383 Del Wilber RC 150.00 250.00
384 Frank Crosetti CO 300.00 500.00
385 H.Franks CO RC 150.00 250.00
386 Ed Yuhas RC 175.00 300.00
387 Billy Meyer MG 150.00 250.00
388 Bob Chipman 150.00 250.00
389 Ben Wade RC 175.00 300.00
390 Rocky Nelson RC 175.00 300.00
391 Ben Chapman UER CO 150.00 250.00
Photo actually
Sam Chapman
392 Hoyt Wilhelm RC 600.00 1000.00
393 Ebba St.Claire RC 175.00 300.00
394 Billy Herman CO 350.00 600.00
395 Jake Pitler CO 175.00 300.00
396 Dick Williams RC 300.00 500.00
397 Forrest Main RC 150.00 250.00
398 Hal Rice 150.00 250.00
399 Jim Fridley RC 150.00 250.00
400 Bill Dickey CO 1000.00 1800.00
401 Bob Schultz RC 175.00 300.00
402 Earl Harrist RC 175.00 300.00
403 Bill Miller RC 175.00 300.00
404 Dick Brodowski RC 175.00 300.00
405 Eddie Pellagrini 175.00 300.00
406 Joe Nuxhall RC 250.00 400.00
407 Eddie Mathews RC 6000.00 10000.00

1953 Topps

The cards in this 274-card set measure 2 5/8" by 3 3/4". Card number 69, Dick Brodowski, features the first known drawing of a player during a night game. Although the last card is numbered 280, there are only 274 cards in the set since numbers 253, 261, 267, 268, 271, and 275 were never issued. The 1953 Topps series contains line drawings of players in full color. The name and team panel at the card base is easily damaged, making it very difficult to complete a mint set. The high number series, 221 to 280, was produced in shorter supply late in the year and hence is more difficult to complete than the lower numbers. The key cards in the set are Mickey Mantle (82) and Willie Mays (244). The key Rookie Cards in this set are Roy Face, Jim Gilliam, and Johnny Podres, all from the last series. There are a number of double-printed cards (actually not double but 50 percent more of each of these numbers were printed compared to the other cards in the series) indicated by DP in the checklist below. There were five players (10 Smoky Burgess, 44 Ellis Kinder, 61 Early Wynn, 72 Fred Hutchinson, and 81 Joe Black) held out of the first run of 1-85 (but printed in with numbers 86-165), who are each marked by SP in the checklist below. In addition, there are five numbers which were printed with the more plentiful series 166-220; these cards (94, 107, 131, 145, and 156) are also indicated by DP in the checklist below. All these aforementioned cards from 86 through 165 and the five short prints come with the biographical information on the back in either white or black lettering. These seem to be printed in equal quantities and no price differential is given for either variety. The cards were issued in one-card penny packs or six-card nickel packs. The nickel packs were issued 24 to a box. There were some three-card advertising panels produced by Topps; the players include Johnny Mize/Clem Koshorek/Toby Atwell; Jim Hearn/Johnny Groth/Sherman Lollar and Mickey Mantle/Johnny Wyrostek/

COMPLETE SET (274) 9000.00 15000.00
COMMON CARD (1-165) 15.00 30.00
COMMON DP (1-165) 7.50 15.00
COMMON (166-220) 12.50 25.00
COMMON (221-280) 50.00 100.00
NOT ISSUED (253/261/267)
NOT ISSUED (268/271/275)
WRAP.(1-CENT, DATED) 150.00 200.00
WRAP.(1-CENT, UNDATED) 250.00 300.00
WRAP.(5-CENT, DATED) 300.00 400.00
WRAP.(5-CENT, UNDATED) 275.00 350.00
1 Jackie Robinson DP 500.00 800.00
2 Luke Easter DP 10.00 20.00
3 George Crowe 25.00 40.00
4 Ben Wade 15.00 30.00
5 Joe Dobson 15.00 30.00
6 Sam Jones 25.00 40.00
7 Bob Borkowski DP 7.50 15.00
8 Clem Koshorek DP 7.50 15.00
9 Joe Collins 35.00 60.00
10 Smoky Burgess SP 50.00 80.00
11 Sal Yvars 15.00 30.00
12 Howie Judson DP 7.50 15.00
13 Conrado Marrero DP 7.50 15.00
14 Clem Labine DP 10.00 20.00
15 Bobo Newsom DP RC 10.00 20.00
16 Peanuts Lowrey DP 7.50 15.00
17 Billy Hitchcock 15.00 30.00
18 Ted Lepcio DP 7.50 15.00
19 Mel Parnell DP 10.00 20.00
20 Hank Thompson 25.00 40.00
21 Billy Johnson 15.00 30.00
22 Howie Fox 15.00 30.00
23 Toby Atwell DP 7.50 15.00
24 Ferris Fain 25.00 40.00
25 Ray Boone 25.00 40.00
26 Dale Mitchell DP 10.00 20.00
27 Roy Campanella DP 175.00 300.00
28 Eddie Pellagrini 15.00 30.00
29 Hal Jeffcoat 15.00 30.00
30 Willard Nixon 15.00 30.00
31 Ewell Blackwell 35.00 60.00
32 Clyde Vollmer 15.00 30.00
33 Bob Kennedy DP 7.50 15.00
34 George Shuba 25.00 40.00
35 Irv Noren DP 7.50 15.00
36 Johnny Groth DP 7.50 15.00
37 Eddie Mathews DP 150.00 250.00
38 Jim Hearn DP 7.50 15.00
39 Eddie Miksis 15.00 30.00
40 John Lipon 15.00 30.00
41 Enos Slaughter 50.00 80.00
42 Gus Zernial DP 10.00 20.00
43 Gil McDougald 35.00 60.00
44 Ellis Kinder SP 35.00 60.00
45 Grady Hatton DP 7.50 15.00
46 Johnny Klippstein DP 7.50 15.00
47 Bubba Church DP 7.50 15.00
48 Bob Del Greco DP 7.50 15.00
49 Faye Throneberry DP 7.50 15.00
50 Chuck Dressen MG DP 10.00 20.00
51 Frank Campos DP 7.50 15.00
52 Ted Gray DP 7.50 15.00
53 Sherm Lollar DP 10.00 20.00
54 Bob Feller DP 90.00 150.00
55 Maurice McDermott DP 7.50 15.00
56 Gerry Staley DP 7.50 15.00
57 Carl Scheib 15.00 30.00
58 George Metkovich 15.00 30.00
59 Karl Drews DP 7.50 15.00
60 Cloyd Boyer DP 7.50 15.00
61 Early Wynn SP 75.00 125.00
62 Monte Irvin DP 25.00 40.00
63 Gus Niarhos DP 7.50 15.00
64 Dave Philley 15.00 30.00
65 Earl Harrist 15.00 30.00
66 Minnie Minoso 35.00 60.00
67 Roy Sievers DP 10.00 20.00
68 Del Rice 15.00 30.00
69 Dick Brodowski 15.00 30.00
70 Ed Yuhas 15.00 30.00
71 Tony Bartirome 15.00 30.00
72 F.Hutchinson MG SP 35.00 60.00
73 Eddie Robinson 15.00 30.00
74 Joe Rossi 15.00 30.00
75 Mike Garcia 25.00 40.00
76 Pee Wee Reese 100.00 175.00
77 Johnny Mize DP 50.00 80.00
78 Red Schoendienst 50.00 80.00
79 Johnny Wyrostek 15.00 30.00
80 Jim Hegan 25.00 40.00
81 Joe Black SP 50.00 80.00
82 Mickey Mantle 2000.00 3000.00
83 Howie Pollet 15.00 30.00
84 Bob Hooper DP 7.50 15.00
85 Bobby Morgan DP 7.50 15.00
86 Billy Martin 75.00 125.00
87 Ed Lopat 35.00 60.00
88 Willie Jones DP 7.50 15.00
89 Chuck Stobbs DP 7.50 15.00
90 Hank Edwards DP 7.50 15.00
91 Ebba St.Claire DP 7.50 15.00
92 Paul Minner DP 7.50 15.00
93 Hal Rice DP 7.50 15.00
94 Bill Kennedy DP 7.50 15.00
95 Willard Marshall DP 7.50 15.00
96 Virgil Trucks 25.00 40.00
97 Don Kolloway DP 7.50 15.00
98 Cal Abrams DP 7.50 15.00
99 Dave Madison 15.00 30.00
100 Bill Miller 15.00 30.00
101 Ted Wilks 15.00 30.00
102 Connie Ryan DP 7.50 15.00
103 Joe Astroth DP 7.50 15.00
104 Yogi Berra 250.00 400.00
105 Joe Nuxhall DP 10.00 20.00
106 Johnny Antonelli 25.00 40.00
107 Danny O'Connell DP 7.50 15.00
108 Bob Porterfield DP 7.50 15.00
109 Alvin Dark 35.00 60.00
110 Herman Wehmeier DP 7.50 15.00
111 Hank Sauer DP 7.50 15.00
112 Ned Garver DP 7.50 15.00
113 Jerry Priddy 15.00 30.00
114 Phil Rizzuto 150.00 250.00
115 George Spencer 15.00 30.00
116 Frank Smith DP 7.50 15.00
117 Sid Gordon DP 7.50 15.00
118 Gus Bell DP 10.00 20.00
119 Johnny Sain SP 35.00 60.00
120 Davey Williams 25.00 40.00
121 Walt Dropo 25.00 40.00
122 Elmer Valo 15.00 30.00
123 Tommy Byrne DP 7.50 15.00
124 Sibby Sisti DP 7.50 15.00
125 Dick Williams DP 10.00 20.00
126 Bill Connelly DP RC 7.50 15.00
127 Clint Courtney DP RC 7.50 15.00
128 Wilmer Mizell DP 10.00 20.00
(Inconsistent design,
logo on front with
black birds)
129 Keith Thomas RC 15.00 30.00
130 Turk Lown DP 7.50 15.00
131 Harry Byrd DP RC 7.50 15.00
132 Tom Morgan 15.00 30.00
133 Gil Coan 15.00 30.00
134 Rube Walker 25.00 40.00
135 Al Rosen DP 10.00 20.00
136 Ken Heintzelman DP 7.50 15.00
137 John Rutherford DP 7.50 15.00
138 George Kell 50.00 80.00
139 Sammy White 15.00 30.00
140 Tommy Glaviano 15.00 30.00
141 Allie Reynolds DP 7.50 15.00
142 Vic Wertz 25.00 40.00
143 Billy Pierce 35.00 60.00
144 Bob Schultz DP 7.50 15.00
145 Harry Dorish DP 7.50 15.00
146 Granny Hamner 15.00 30.00
147 Warren Spahn 100.00 175.00
148 Mickey Grasso 15.00 30.00
149 Dom DiMaggio DP 7.50 15.00
150 Harry Simpson DP 7.50 15.00
151 Hoyt Wilhelm 60.00 100.00
152 Bob Adams DP 7.50 15.00
153 Andy Seminick DP 7.50 15.00
154 Dick Groat 25.00 40.00
155 Dutch Leonard 15.00 30.00
156 Jim Rivera DP RC 10.00 20.00
157 Bob Addis DP 7.50 15.00
158 Johnny Logan RC 25.00 40.00
159 Wayne Terwilliger DP 7.50 15.00
160 Bob Young 15.00 30.00
161 Vern Bickford DP 7.50 15.00
162 Ted Kluszewski 35.00 60.00
163 Fred Hatfield DP 7.50 15.00
164 Frank Shea DP 7.50 15.00
165 Billy Hoeft 15.00 30.00
166 Billy Hunter RC 12.50 25.00
167 Art Schult RC 12.50 25.00
168 Willard Schmidt RC 12.50 25.00
169 Dizzy Trout 15.00 30.00
170 Bill Werle 12.50 25.00
171 Bill Glynn RC 12.50 25.00
172 Rip Repulski RC 12.50 25.00
173 Preston Ward 12.50 25.00
174 Billy Loes 15.00 30.00
175 Ron Kline RC 12.50 25.00
176 Don Hoak RC 25.00 40.00
177 Jim Dyck RC 12.50 25.00
178 Jim Waugh RC 12.50 25.00
179 Gene Hermanski 12.50 25.00
180 Virgil Stallcup 12.50 25.00
181 Al Zarilla 12.50 25.00
182 Bobby Hofman 12.50 25.00
183 Stu Miller RC 25.00 40.00
184 Hal Brown RC 12.50 25.00
185 Jim Pendleton RC 12.50 25.00
186 Charlie Bishop RC 12.50 25.00
187 Jim Fridley 12.50 25.00
188 Andy Carey RC 25.00 40.00
189 Ray Jablonski RC 12.50 25.00
190 Dixie Walker CO 15.00 30.00
191 Ralph Kiner 50.00 80.00
192 Wally Westlake 12.50 25.00
193 Mike Clark RC 12.50 25.00
194 Eddie Kazak 12.50 25.00
195 Ed McGhee RC 12.50 25.00
196 Bob Keegan RC 12.50 25.00
197 Del Crandall 25.00 40.00
198 Forrest Main 12.50 25.00
199 Marion Fricano RC 12.50 25.00
200 Gordon Goldsberry 12.50 25.00
201 Paul LaPalme 12.50 25.00
202 Carl Sawatski RC 12.50 25.00
203 Cliff Fannin 12.50 25.00
204 Dick Bokelman RC 12.50 25.00
205 Vern Benson RC 12.50 25.00
206 Ed Bailey RC 15.00 30.00
207 Whitey Ford 175.00 300.00
208 Jim Wilson 12.50 25.00
209 Jim Greengrass RC 12.50 25.00
210 Bob Cerv RC 25.00 40.00
211 J.W. Porter RC 12.50 25.00
212 Jack Dittmer RC 12.50 25.00
213 Ray Scarborough 12.50 25.00
214 Bill Bruton RC 25.00 40.00
215 Gene Conley RC 15.00 30.00
216 Jim Hughes RC 12.50 25.00
217 Murray Wall RC 12.50 25.00
218 Les Fusselman 12.50 25.00
219 Pete Runnels UER 15.00 30.00
(Photo actually
Don Johnson)
220 Satchel Paige UER 350.00 600.00
(Misspelled Satchell
on card front)
221 Bob Milliken RC 50.00 100.00
222 Vic Janowicz DP RC 25.00 50.00
223 Johnny O'Brien DP RC 25.00 50.00
224 Lou Sleater DP 25.00 50.00
225 Bobby Shantz 75.00 125.00
226 Ed Erautt 50.00 100.00
227 Morrie Martin 50.00 100.00
228 Hal Newhouser 90.00 150.00
229 Rocky Krsnich RC 50.00 100.00
230 Johnny Lindell DP 25.00 50.00
231 Solly Hemus DP 25.00 50.00
232 Dick Kokos 50.00 100.00
233 Al Aber RC 50.00 100.00
234 Ray Murray DP 25.00 50.00
235 John Hetki DP RC 25.00 50.00
236 Harry Perkowski DP 25.00 50.00
237 Bud Podbielan DP 25.00 50.00
238 Cal Hogue DP RC 25.00 50.00
239 Jim Delsing 50.00 100.00
240 Fred Marsh 50.00 100.00
241 Al Sima DP 25.00 50.00
242 Charlie Silvera 75.00 125.00
243 Carlos Bernier DP RC 25.00 50.00
244 Willie Mays 1500.00 2500.00
245 Bill Norman CO 50.00 100.00
246 Roy Face DP RC 50.00 80.00
247 Mike Sandlock DP RC 25.00 50.00
248 Gene Stephens DP RC 25.00 50.00
249 Eddie O'Brien RC 50.00 100.00
250 Bob Wilson RC 50.00 100.00
251 Sid Hudson 50.00 100.00
252 Hank Foiles RC 50.00 100.00
253 Does not exist
254 Preacher Roe DP 50.00 80.00
255 Dixie Howell 50.00 100.00
256 Les Peden RC 50.00 100.00
257 Bob Boyd RC 50.00 100.00
258 Jim Gilliam RC 250.00 400.00
259 Roy McMillan DP 25.00 50.00
260 Sam Calderone RC 50.00 100.00
261 Does not exist
262 Bob Oldis RC 50.00 100.00
263 Johnny Podres RC 175.00 300.00
264 Gene Woodling DP 30.00 60.00
265 Jackie Jensen 75.00 125.00
266 Bob Cain 50.00 100.00
267 Does not exist
268 Does not exist
269 Duane Pillette 50.00 100.00
270 Vern Stephens 75.00 125.00
271 Does not exist
272 Bill Antonello RC 50.00 100.00
273 Harvey Haddix RC 90.00 150.00
274 John Riddle CO 50.00 100.00
275 Does not exist
276 Ken Raffensberger 50.00 100.00
277 Don Lund RC 50.00 100.00
278 Willie Miranda RC 50.00 100.00
279 Joe Coleman DP 25.00 50.00
280 Milt Bolling RC 200.00 350.00

1954 Topps

The cards in this 250-card set measure approximately 2 5/8" by 3 3/4". Each of the cards in the 1954 Topps set contains a large "head" shot of the player in color plus a smaller full-length photo in black and white set against a color background. The cards were issued in one-card penny packs or five-card nickel packs. Fifteen-card cello packs have also been seen. The penny packs came 120 to a box while the nickel packs came 24 to a box. The nickel boxes had a drawing of Ted Williams along with his name printed on the box to indicate that Williams was part of this product. This set contains the Rookie Cards of Hank Aaron, Ernie Banks, and Al Kaline and two separate cards of Ted Williams (number 1 and number 250). Conspicuous by its absence is Mickey Mantle who apparently was the exclusive property of Bowman during 1954 (and 1955). The first two issues of Sports Illustrated magazine contained "card" inserts on regular paper stock. The first issue showed actual cards in the set in color, while the second issue showed some created cards of New York Yankees players in black and white, including Mickey Mantle. There was also a Canadian printing of the first 50 cards. These cards can be easily discerned as they have "grey" backs rather than the white backs of the American printed cards. To celebrate this set as the first Topps set to feature Ted Williams, his visage is also featured on the five cent box. The Canadian cards came four cards to a pack and 36 packs to a box and cost five cents when issued.

COMPLETE SET (250) 5000.00 8000.00
COMMON (1-50/76-250) 7.50 15.00
COMMON CARD (51-75) 12.50 25.00
WRAP.(1-CENT, DATED) 150.00 200.00
WRAP.(1-CENT, UNDATED) 100.00 150.00
WRAP.(5-CENT, DATED) 250.00 300.00
WRAP.(5-CENT, UNDATED) 200.00 250.00
1 Ted Williams 500.00 800.00
2 Gus Zernial 12.50 25.00
3 Monte Irvin 25.00 50.00
4 Hank Sauer 12.50 25.00
5 Ed Lopat 12.50 25.00
6 Pete Runnels 12.50 25.00
7 Ted Kluszewski 25.00 50.00
8 Bob Young 7.50 15.00
9 Harvey Haddix 12.50 25.00
10 Jackie Robinson 250.00 400.00
11 Paul Leslie Smith RC 7.50 15.00
12 Del Crandall 12.50 25.00
13 Billy Martin 60.00 100.00
14 Preacher Roe UER 12.50 25.00
February is misspelled
15 Al Rosen 12.50 25.00
16 Vic Janowicz 12.50 25.00
17 Phil Rizzuto 75.00 125.00
18 Walt Dropo 12.50 25.00
19 Johnny Lipon 7.50 15.00
Orioles Team Name on Front
White Sox team on Back
Wearing a Red Sox cap
20 Warren Spahn 75.00 125.00
21 Bobby Shantz 12.50 25.00
22 Jim Greengrass 7.50 15.00
23 Luke Easter 12.50 25.00
24 Granny Hamner 7.50 15.00
25 Harvey Kuenn RC 20.00 40.00
26 Ray Jablonski 7.50 15.00
27 Ferris Fain 12.50 25.00
28 Paul Minner 7.50 15.00
29 Jim Hegan 12.50 25.00
30 Eddie Mathews 60.00 100.00
31 Johnny Klippstein 7.50 15.00
32 Duke Snider 125.00 200.00
33 Johnny Schmitz 7.50 15.00
34 Jim Rivera 7.50 15.00
35 Junior Gilliam 25.00 50.00
36 Hoyt Wilhelm 25.00 50.00
37 Whitey Ford 125.00 200.00
38 Eddie Stanky MG 12.50 25.00
39 Sherm Lollar 12.50 25.00
40 Mel Parnell 12.50 25.00
41 Willie Jones 7.50 15.00
42 Don Mueller 12.50 25.00
43 Dick Groat 12.50 25.00
44 Ned Garver 7.50 15.00
45 Richie Ashburn 50.00 80.00
46 Ken Raffensberger 7.50 15.00
47 Ellis Kinder 7.50 15.00
48 Billy Hunter 12.50 25.00
49 Ray Murray 7.50 15.00
50 Yogi Berra 175.00 300.00
51 Johnny Lindell 12.50 25.00
52 Vic Power RC 15.00 30.00
53 Jack Dittmer 12.50 25.00
54 Vern Stephens 15.00 30.00
55 Phil Cavarretta MG 15.00 30.00
56 Willie Miranda 12.50 25.00
57 Luis Aloma 12.50 25.00
58 Bob Wilson 12.50 25.00
59 Gene Conley 15.00 30.00
60 Frank Baumholtz 12.50 25.00
61 Bob Cain 12.50 25.00
62 Eddie Robinson 12.50 25.00
63 Johnny Pesky 15.00 30.00
64 Hank Thompson 12.50 25.00
65 Bob Swift CO 12.50 25.00
66 Ted Lepcio 12.50 25.00
67 Jim Willis RC 12.50 25.00
68 Sam Calderone 12.50 25.00
69 Bud Podbielan 12.50 25.00
70 Larry Doby 30.00 60.00
71 Frank Smith 12.50 25.00
72 Preston Ward 12.50 25.00
73 Wayne Terwilliger 12.50 25.00
74 Bill Taylor RC 12.50 25.00
75 Fred Haney MG RC 12.50 25.00
76 Bob Scheffing CO 7.50 15.00
77 Ray Boone 12.50 25.00
78 Ted Kazanski RC 7.50 15.00
79 Andy Pafko 12.50 25.00
80 Jackie Jensen 12.50 25.00
81 Dave Hoskins RC 7.50 15.00
82 Milt Bolling 7.50 15.00
83 Joe Collins 12.50 25.00
84 Dick Cole RC 7.50 15.00
85 Bob Turley RC 20.00 40.00
86 Billy Herman CO 12.50 25.00
87 Roy Face 12.50 25.00
88 Matt Batts 7.50 15.00
89 Howie Pollet 7.50 15.00
90 Willie Mays 500.00 800.00
91 Bob Oldis 7.50 15.00
92 Wally Westlake 7.50 15.00
93 Sid Hudson 7.50 15.00
94 Ernie Banks RC 900.00 1500.00
95 Hal Rice 7.50 15.00
96 Charlie Silvera 12.50 25.00
97 Jerald Hal Lane RC 7.50 15.00
98 Joe Black 20.00 40.00
99 Bobby Hofman 7.50 15.00
100 Bob Keegan 7.50 15.00
101 Gene Woodling 12.50 25.00
102 Gil Hodges 50.00 80.00
103 Jim Lemon RC 7.50 15.00
104 Mike Sandlock 7.50 15.00
105 Andy Carey 12.50 25.00
106 Dick Kokos 7.50 15.00
107 Duane Pillette 7.50 15.00
108 Thornton Kipper RC 7.50 15.00
109 Bill Bruton 12.50 25.00
110 Harry Dorish 7.50 15.00
111 Jim Delsing 7.50 15.00
112 Bill Renna RC 7.50 15.00
113 Bob Boyd 7.50 15.00
114 Dean Stone RC 7.50 15.00
115 Rip Repulski 7.50 15.00
116 Steve Bilko 7.50 15.00
117 Solly Hemus 7.50 15.00
118 Carl Scheib 7.50 15.00
119 Johnny Antonelli 12.50 25.00
120 Roy McMillan 12.50 25.00
121 Clem Labine 12.50 25.00
122 Johnny Logan 12.50 25.00
123 Bobby Adams 7.50 15.00
124 Marion Fricano 7.50 15.00
125 Harry Perkowski 7.50 15.00
126 Ben Wade 7.50 15.00
127 Steve O'Neill MG 7.50 15.00
128 Hank Aaron RC 1000.00 1800.00
129 Forrest Jacobs RC 7.50 15.00
130 Hank Bauer 12.50 25.00
131 Reno Bertoia RC 12.50 25.00
132 Tommy Lasorda RC 150.00 250.00
133 Del Baker CO 7.50 15.00
134 Cal Hogue 7.50 15.00
135 Joe Presko 7.50 15.00
136 Connie Ryan 7.50 15.00
137 Wally Moon RC 20.00 40.00
138 Bob Borkowski 7.50 15.00
139 The O'Briens 25.00 50.00
Johnny O'Brien
Eddie O'Brien
140 Tom Wright 7.50 15.00
141 Joey Jay RC 12.50 25.00
142 Tom Poholsky 7.50 15.00
143 Rollie Hemsley CO 7.50 15.00
144 Bill Werle 7.50 15.00
145 Elmer Valo 7.50 15.00
146 Don Johnson 7.50 15.00
147 Johnny Riddle CO 7.50 15.00
148 Bob Trice RC 7.50 15.00
149 Al Robertson 7.50 15.00
150 Dick Kryhoski 7.50 15.00
151 Alex Grammas RC 7.50 15.00
152 Michael Blyzka RC 7.50 15.00
153 Al Walker 12.50 25.00
154 Mike Fornieles RC 7.50 15.00
155 Bob Kennedy 12.50 25.00
156 Joe Coleman 12.50 25.00
157 Don Lenhardt 12.50 25.00
158 Peanuts Lowrey 7.50 15.00
159 Dave Philley 7.50 15.00
160 Ralph Kress CO 7.50 15.00
161 John Hetki 7.50 15.00
162 Herman Wehmeier 7.50 15.00
163 Frank House 7.50 15.00
164 Stu Miller 7.50 15.00
165 Jim Pendleton 7.50 15.00
166 Johnny Podres 20.00 40.00
167 Don Lund 7.50 15.00
168 Morrie Martin 12.50 25.00
169 Jim Hughes 20.00 40.00
170 Dusty Rhodes RC 12.50 25.00
171 Leo Kiely 7.50 15.00
172 Harold Brown RC 7.50 15.00
173 Jack Harshman RC 7.50 15.00
174 Tom Qualters RC 7.50 15.00
175 Frank Leja RC 12.50 25.00
176 Robert Keely CO 7.50 15.00
177 Bob Milliken 7.50 15.00
178 Bill Glynn UER 7.50 15.00
Spelled Gylnn on the front
179 Gair Allie RC 7.50 15.00
180 Wes Westrum 12.50 25.00
181 Mel Roach RC 7.50 15.00
182 Chuck Harmon RC 7.50 15.00
183 Earle Combs CO 12.50 25.00
184 Ed Bailey 7.50 15.00
185 Chuck Stobbs 7.50 15.00
186 Karl Olson 7.50 15.00
187 Heinie Manush CO 12.50 25.00
188 Dave Jolly RC 7.50 15.00
189 Bob Ross 7.50 15.00
190 Ray Herbert RC 7.50 15.00
191 John Schofield RC 12.50 25.00
192 Ellis Deal CO 7.50 15.00
193 Johnny Hopp CO 12.50 25.00
194 Bill Sarni RC 7.50 15.00
195 Billy Consolo RC 7.50 15.00
196 Stan Jok RC 7.50 15.00
197 Lynwood Rowe CO 12.50 25.00
(Schoolboy)
198 Carl Sawatski 7.50 15.00
199 Glenn (Rocky) Nelson 7.50 15.00
200 Larry Jansen 12.50 25.00
201 Al Kaline RC 400.00 700.00
202 Bob Purkey RC 12.50 25.00
203 Harry Brecheen CO 12.50 25.00
204 Angel Scull RC 7.50 15.00
205 Johnny Sain 20.00 40.00
206 Ray Crone RC 7.50 15.00
207 Tom Oliver CO RC 7.50 15.00
208 Grady Hatton 7.50 15.00
209 Chuck Thompson RC 7.50 15.00
210 Bob Buhl RC 12.50 25.00
211 Don Hoak 12.50 25.00
212 Bob Micelotta RC 7.50 15.00
213 Johnny Fitzpatrick CO RC 7.50 15.00
214 Arnie Portocarrero RC 7.50 15.00
215 Ed McGhee 12.50 25.00
216 Al Sima 7.50 15.00
217 Paul Schreiber CO RC 7.50 15.00
218 Fred Marsh 7.50 15.00
219 Chuck Kress RC 7.50 15.00
220 Ruben Gomez RC 12.50 25.00
221 Dick Brodowski 7.50 15.00
222 Bill Wilson RC 7.50 15.00
223 Joe Haynes CO 7.50 15.00
224 Dick Weik RC 7.50 15.00
225 Don Liddle RC 7.50 15.00
226 Jehosie Heard RC 12.50 25.00
227 Buster Mills CO RC 7.50 15.00
228 Gene Hermanski 7.50 15.00
229 Bob Talbot RC 7.50 15.00
230 Bob Kuzava 12.50 25.00
231 Roy Smalley 7.50 15.00
232 Lou Limmer RC 7.50 15.00
233 Augie Galan CO 7.50 15.00
234 Jerry Lynch RC 7.50 15.00
235 Vern Law 12.50 25.00
236 Paul Penson RC 7.50 15.00
237 Mike Ryba CO RC 7.50 15.00
238 Al Aber 7.50 15.00
239 Bill Skowron RC 60.00 100.00
240 Sam Mele 12.50 25.00
241 Robert Miller RC 7.50 15.00
242 Curt Roberts RC 7.50 15.00
243 Ray Blades CO RC 7.50 15.00
244 Leroy Wheat RC 7.50 15.00
245 Roy Sievers 12.50 25.00
246 Howie Fox 7.50 15.00
247 Ed Mayo CO 7.50 15.00
248 Al Smith RC 12.50 25.00
249 Wilmer Mizell 12.50 25.00
250 Ted Williams 500.00 1000.00

1955 Topps

The cards in this 206-card set measure approximately 2 5/8" by 3 3/4". Both the large "head" shot and the smaller full-length photos used on each card of the 1955 Topps set are in color. The card fronts were designed horizontally for the first time in Topps' history. The first card features Dusty Rhodes, hitting star and MVP in the New York Giants' 1954 World Series sweep over the Cleveland Indians. A "high" series, 161 to 210, is more difficult to find than cards 1 to 160. Numbers 175, 186, 203, and 209 were never issued. To fill in for the four cards not issued in the high number series, Topps double printed four players, those appearing on cards 170, 172, 184, and 188. Cards were issued in one-card penny packs or six-card nickel packs (which came 36 packs to a box) and 15-card cello packs (rarely seen). Although rarely seen, there exist salesman sample panels of three cards containing the fronts of regular cards with ad information for the 1955 Topps regular and the 1955 Topps Doubleheaders on the back. One panel depicts (from top to bottom) Danny Schell, Jake Thies, and Howie Pollet. Another Panel consists of Jackie Robinson, Bill Taylor and Curt Roberts. The key Rookie Cards in this set are Ken Boyer, Roberto Clemente, Harmon Killebrew, and Sandy Koufax. The Frank Sullivan card has a very noticable print dot which appears on some of the cards but not all of the cards. We are not listing that card as a variation at this point, but we will continue to monitor information about that card.

COMPLETE SET (206) 5000.00 8000.00
COMMON CARD (1-150) 6.00 12.00
COMMON (151-160) 10.00 20.00
COMMON (161-210) 15.00 30.00
NOT ISSUED (175/186/203/209)
WRAP.(1-CENT, DATED) 100.00 150.00
WRAP.(1-CENT, UNDATED) 40.00 50.00
WRAP.(5-CENT, DATED) 100.00 150.00
WRAP.(5-CENT, UNDATED) 75.00 100.00
1 Dusty Rhodes 75.00 125.00
2 Ted Williams 400.00 700.00

3 Art Fowler RC 7.50 15.00
4 Al Kaline 90.00 150.00
5 Jim Gilliam 20.00 40.00
6 Stan Hack MG RC 12.50 25.00
7 Jim Hegan 7.50 15.00
8 Harold Smith RC 6.00 12.00
9 Robert Miller 6.00 12.00
10 Bob Keegan 6.00 12.00
11 Ferris Fain 7.50 15.00
12 Vernon (Jake) Thies RC 6.00 12.00
13 Fred Marsh 6.00 12.00
14 Jim Finigan RC 6.00 12.00
15 Jim Pendleton 6.00 12.00
16 Roy Sievers 7.50 15.00
17 Bobby Hofman 6.00 12.00
18 Russ Kemmerer RC 6.00 12.00
19 Billy Herman CO 7.50 15.00
20 Andy Carey 7.50 15.00
21 Alex Grammas 6.00 12.00
22 Bill Skowron 20.00 40.00
23 Jack Parks RC 6.00 12.00
24 Hal Newhouser 20.00 40.00
25 Johnny Podres 12.50 25.00
26 Dick Groat 7.50 15.00
27 Billy Gardner RC 7.50 15.00
28 Ernie Banks 125.00 200.00
29 Herman Wehmeier 6.00 12.00
30 Vic Power 7.50 15.00
31 Warren Spahn 60.00 100.00
32 Warren McGhee RC 6.00 12.00
33 Tom Qualters 6.00 12.00
34 Wayne Terwilliger 6.00 12.00
35 Dave Jolly 6.00 12.00
36 Leo Kiely 6.00 12.00
37 Joe Cunningham RC 7.50 15.00
38 Bob Turley 7.50 15.00
39 Bill Glynn 6.00 12.00
40 Don Hoak 7.50 15.00
41 Chuck Stobbs 6.00 12.00
42 John (Windy) McCall RC 6.00 12.00
43 Harvey Haddix 7.50 15.00
44 Harold Valentine RC 6.00 12.00
45 Hank Sauer 7.50 15.00
46 Ted Kazanski 6.00 12.00
47 Hank Aaron 250.00 400.00
48 Bob Kennedy 7.50 15.00
49 J.W. Porter 6.00 12.00
50 Jackie Robinson 300.00 500.00
51 Jim Hughes 7.50 15.00
52 Bill Tremel RC 6.00 12.00
53 Bill Taylor 6.00 12.00
54 Lou Limmer 6.00 12.00
55 Rip Repulski 6.00 12.00
56 Ray Jablonski 6.00 12.00
57 Billy O'Dell RC 6.00 12.00
58 Jim Rivera 6.00 12.00
59 Gair Allie 6.00 12.00
60 Dean Stone 6.00 12.00
61 Forrest Jacobs 6.00 12.00
62 Thornton Kipper 6.00 12.00
63 Joe Collins 7.50 15.00
64 Gus Triandos RC 7.50 15.00
65 Ray Boone 7.50 15.00
66 Ron Jackson RC 6.00 12.00
67 Wally Moon 7.50 15.00
68 Jim Davis RC 6.00 12.00
69 Ed Bailey 7.50 15.00
70 Al Rosen 7.50 15.00
71 Ruben Gomez 6.00 12.00
72 Karl Olson 6.00 12.00
73 Jack Shepard RC 6.00 12.00
74 Bob Borkowski 6.00 12.00
75 Sandy Amoros RC 20.00 40.00
76 Howie Pollet 6.00 12.00
77 Arnie Portocarrero 6.00 12.00
78 Gordon Jones RC 6.00 12.00
79 Clyde (Danny) Schell RC 6.00 12.00
80 Bob Grim RC 7.50 15.00
81 Gene Conley 7.50 15.00
82 Chuck Harmon 6.00 12.00
83 Tom Brewer RC 6.00 12.00
84 Camilo Pascual RC 7.50 15.00
85 Don Mossi RC 12.50 25.00
86 Bill Wilson 6.00 12.00
87 Frank House 6.00 12.00
88 Bob Skinner RC 7.50 15.00
89 Joe Frazier RC 7.50 15.00
90 Karl Spooner RC 7.50 15.00
91 Milt Bolling 6.00 12.00
92 Don Zimmer RC 12.50 25.00
93 Steve Bilko 6.00 12.00
94 Reno Bertoia 6.00 12.00
95 Preston Ward 6.00 12.00
96 Chuck Bishop 6.00 12.00
97 Carlos Paula RC 6.00 12.00
98 John Riddle CO 6.00 12.00
99 Frank Leja 6.00 12.00
100 Monte Irvin 20.00 40.00
101 Johnny Gray RC 6.00 12.00
102 Wally Westlake 6.00 12.00
103 Chuck White RC 6.00 12.00
104 Jack Harshman 6.00 12.00
105 Chuck Diering 6.00 12.00
106 Frank Sullivan RC 6.00 12.00
107 Curt Roberts 6.00 12.00
108 Rube Walker 7.50 15.00
109 Ed Lopat 7.50 15.00
110 Gus Zernial 7.50 15.00
111 Bob Milliken 7.50 15.00
112 Nelson King RC 6.00 12.00
113 Harry Brecheen CO 7.50 15.00
114 Louis Ortiz RC 6.00 12.00
115 Ellis Kinder 6.00 12.00
116 Tom Hurd RC 6.00 12.00
117 Mel Roach 6.00 12.00
118 Bob Purkey 6.00 12.00
119 Bob Lennon RC 6.00 12.00
120 Ted Kluszewski 50.00 80.00
121 Bill Renna 6.00 12.00
122 Carl Sawatski 6.00 12.00
123 Sandy Koufax RC 700.00 1200.00
124 Harmon Killebrew RC 150.00 250.00
125 Ken Boyer RC 50.00 80.00
126 Dick Hall RC 6.00 12.00
127 Dale Long RC 7.50 15.00
128 Ted Lepcio 6.00 12.00
129 Elvin Tappe 7.50 15.00
130 Mayo Smith MG RC 6.00 12.00
131 Grady Hatton 6.00 12.00
132 Bob Trice 6.00 12.00
133 Dave Hoskins 6.00 12.00
134 Joey Jay 7.50 15.00
135 Johnny O'Brien 7.50 15.00
136 Veston (Bunky) Stewart RC 6.00 12.00
137 Harry Elliott RC 6.00 12.00
138 Ray Herbert 6.00 12.00
139 Steve Kraly RC 6.00 12.00
140 Mel Parnell 7.50 15.00
141 Tom Wright 6.00 12.00
142 Jerry Lynch 7.50 15.00
143 John Schofield 7.50 15.00
144 Joe Amalfitano RC 6.00 12.00
145 Elmer Valo 6.00 12.00
146 Dick Donovan RC 6.00 12.00
147 Hugh Pepper RC 6.00 12.00
148 Hector Brown 6.00 12.00
149 Ray Crone 6.00 12.00
150 Mike Higgins MG 6.00 12.00
151 Ralph Kress CO 10.00 20.00
152 Harry Agganis RC 60.00 100.00
153 Bud Podbielan 12.50 25.00
154 Willie Miranda 10.00 20.00
155 Eddie Mathews 125.00 200.00
156 Joe Black 30.00 50.00
157 Robert Miller 10.00 20.00
158 Tommy Carroll RC 12.50 25.00
159 Johnny Schmitz 10.00 20.00
160 Ray Narleski RC 10.00 20.00
161 Chuck Tanner RC 20.00 40.00
162 Joe Coleman 15.00 30.00
163 Faye Throneberry 15.00 30.00
164 Roberto Clemente RC 1400.00 2200.00
165 Don Johnson 15.00 30.00
166 Hank Bauer 50.00 80.00
167 Tom Casagrande RC 15.00 30.00
168 Duane Pillette 15.00 30.00
169 Bob Oldis 20.00 40.00
170 Jim Pearce DP RC 7.50 15.00
171 Dick Brodowski 15.00 30.00
172 Frank Baumholtz DP 7.50 15.00
173 Bob Kline RC 15.00 30.00
174 Rudy Minarcin RC 15.00 30.00
175 Does not exist
176 Norm Zauchin RC 15.00 30.00
177 Al Robertson 15.00 30.00
178 Bobby Adams 15.00 30.00
179 Jim Bolger RC 15.00 30.00
180 Clem Labine 30.00 60.00
181 Roy McMillan 20.00 40.00
182 Humberto Robinson RC 15.00 30.00
183 Anthony Jacobs RC 15.00 30.00
184 Harry Perkowski DP 7.50 15.00
185 Don Ferrarese RC 15.00 30.00
186 Does not exist
187 Gil Hodges 100.00 175.00
188 Charlie Silvera DP 7.50 15.00
189 Phil Rizzuto 100.00 175.00
190 Gene Woodling 20.00 40.00
191 Eddie Stanky MG 20.00 40.00
192 Jim Delsing 20.00 40.00
193 Johnny Sain 30.00 60.00
194 Willie Mays 350.00 600.00
195 Ed Roebuck RC 30.00 60.00
196 Gale Wade RC 15.00 30.00
197 Al Smith 30.00 60.00
198 Yogi Berra 175.00 300.00
199 Bert Hamric RC 20.00 40.00
200 Jackie Jensen 30.00 60.00
201 Sherman Lollar 20.00 40.00
202 Jim Owens RC 15.00 30.00
203 Does not exist
204 Frank Smith 15.00 30.00
205 Gene Freese RC 20.00 40.00
206 Pete Daley RC 15.00 30.00
207 Billy Consolo 15.00 30.00
208 Ray Moore RC 20.00 40.00
209 Does not exist
210 Duke Snider 350.00 600.00

1955 Topps Double Header

The cards in this 66-card set measure approximately 2 1/16" by 4 7/8". Borrowing a design from the T201 Mecca series, Topps issued a 132-player "Double Header" set in a separate wrapper in 1955. Each player is numbered in the biographical section on the reverse. When open, with perforated flap up, one player is revealed; when the flap is lowered, or closed, the player design on top incorporates a portion of the inside player artwork. When the cards are placed side by side, a continuous ballpark background is formed. Some cards have been found without perforations, and all players pictured appear in the low series of the 1955 regular issue. The cards were issued in one-card penny packs which came 120 packs to a box with a piece of bubble gum.

COMPLETE SET (66) 2500.00 4000.00
WRAPPER (1-CENT) 150.00 200.00
1 Al Rosen and 2 Chuck Diering 30.00 50.00
3 Monte Irvin and 4 Russ Kemmerer 35.00 60.00
5 Ted Kazanski and 6 Gordon Jones 25.00 40.00
7 Bill Taylor and 8 Billy O'Dell 25.00 40.00
9 J.W. Porter and 10 Thornton Kipper 25.00 40.00
11 Curt Roberts and 12 Arnie Portocarrero 25.00 40.00
13 Wally Westlake and 14 Frank House 30.00 50.00
15 Rube Walker and 16 Lou Limmer 30.00 50.00
17 Dean Stone and 18 Charlie White 25.00 40.00
19 Karl Spooner and 20 Jim Hughes 30.00 50.00
21 Bill Skowron and 22 Frank Sullivan 35.00 60.00
23 Jack Shepard and 24 Stan Hack MG 25.00 40.00
25 Jackie Robinson and 26 Don Hoak 150.00 250.00
27 Dusty Rhodes and 28 Jim Davis 30.00 50.00
29 Vic Power and 30 Ed Bailey 25.00 40.00
31 Howie Pollet and 32 Ernie Banks 125.00 200.00
33 Jim Pendleton and 34 Gene Conley 25.00 40.00
35 Karl Olson and 36 Andy Carey 25.00 40.00
37 Wally Moon and 38 Joe Cunningham 30.00 50.00
39 Freddie Marsh and 40 Vernon Thies 25.00 40.00
41 Eddie Lopat and 42 Harvey Haddix 35.00 60.00
43 Leo Kiely and 44 Chuck Stobbs 25.00 40.00
45 Al Kaline and 46 Harold Valentine 125.00 200.00
47 Forrest Jacobs and 48 Johnny Gray 25.00 40.00
49 Ron Jackson and 50 Jim Finigan 25.00 40.00
51 Ray Jablonski and 52 Bob Keegan 25.00 40.00
53 Billy Herman CO and 54 Sandy Amoros 50.00 80.00
55 Chuck Harmon and 56 Bob Skinner 25.00 40.00
57 Dick Hall and 58 Bob Grim 25.00 40.00
59 Billy Glynn and 60 Bob Miller 30.00 50.00
61 Billy Gardner and 62 John Hetki 25.00 40.00
63 Bob Borkowski and 64 Bob Turley 25.00 40.00
65 Joe Collins and 66 Jack Harshman 25.00 40.00
67 Jim Hegan and 68 Jack Parks 25.00 40.00
69 Ted Williams and 70 Mayo Smith MG 250.00 400.00
71 Gair Allie and 72 Grady Hatton 25.00 40.00
73 Jerry Lynch and 74 Harry Brecheen CO 25.00 40.00
75 Tom Wright and 76 Vernon Stewart 25.00 40.00
77 Dave Hoskins and 78 Warren McGhee 25.00 40.00
79 Roy Sievers and 80 Art Fowler 30.00 50.00
81 Danny Schell and 82 Gus Triandos 25.00 40.00
83 Joe Frazier and 84 Don Mossi 25.00 40.00
85 Elmer Valo and 86 Hector Brown 25.00 40.00
87 Bob Kennedy and 88 Windy McCall 30.00 50.00
89 Ruben Gomez and 90 Jim Rivera 25.00 40.00
91 Louis Ortiz and 92 Milt Bolling 25.00 40.00
93 Carl Sawatski and 94 El Tappe 25.00 40.00
95 Dave Jolly and 96 Bobby Hofman 25.00 40.00
97 Preston Ward and 98 Don Zimmer 35.00 60.00
99 Bill Renna and 100 Dick Groat 30.00 50.00
101 Bill Wilson and 102 Bill Tremel 25.00 40.00
103 Hank Sauer and 104 Camilo Pascual 30.00 50.00
105 Hank Aaron and 106 Ray Herbert 300.00 500.00
107 Alex Grammas and 108 Tom Qualters 25.00 40.00
109 Hal Newhouser and 110 Chuck Bishop 35.00 60.00
111 Harmon Killebrew and 112 John Podres 125.00 200.00
113 Ray Boone and 114 Bob Purkey 25.00 40.00
115 Dale Long and 116 Ferris Fain 30.00 50.00
117 Steve Bilko and 118 Bob Milliken 25.00 40.00
119 Mel Parnell and 120 Tom Hurd 30.00 50.00
121 Ted Kluszewski and 122 Jim Owens 50.00 80.00
123 Gus Zernial and 124 Bob Trice 25.00 40.00
125 Rip Repulski and 126 Ted Lepcio 25.00 40.00
127 Warren Spahn and 128 Tom Brewer 90.00 150.00
129 Jim Gilliam and 130 Ellis Kinder 50.00 80.00
131 Herm Wehmeier and 132 Wayne Terwilliger 25.00 40.00

1956 Topps

The cards in this 340-card set measure approximately 2 5/8" by 3 3/4". Following up with another horizontally oriented card in 1956, Topps improved the format by layering the color "head" shot onto an actual action sequence involving the player. Cards 1 to 180 come with either white or gray backs: in the 1 to 100 sequence, gray backs are less common (worth about 10 percent more) and in the 101 to 180 sequence, white backs are less common (worth 30 percent more). The team cards, used for the first time in a regular set by Topps, are found dated 1955, or undated, with the team name appearing on either side. The dated team cards in the first series were not printed on the gray stock. The two unnumbered checklist cards are highly prized (must be unmarked to qualify as excellent or mint). The complete set price below does not include the unnumbered checklist cards or any of the variations. The set was issued in one-card penny packs or six-card nickel packs. The six card nickel packs came 24 to a box with 24 boxes in a case while the once cent packs came 120 to a box. Both types of packs included a piece of bubble gum. Promotional three card strips were issued for this set. Among those strips were one featuring Johnny O'Brien/Harvey Haddix and Frank House. The key Rookie Cards in this set are Walt Alston, Luis Aparicio, and Roger Craig. There are ten double-printed cards in the first series as evidenced by the discovery of an uncut sheet of 110 cards (10 by 11); these DP's are listed below.

COMPLETE SET (340) 5000.00 8000.00
COMMON CARD (1-100) 5.00 10.00
COMMON (101-180) 6.00 12.00
COMMON (261-340) 6.00 12.00
COMMON (181-260) 7.50 15.00
WRAPPER (1-CENT) 200.00 250.00
WRAP.(1-CENT, REPEAT) 75.00 100.00
WRAPPER (5-CENT) 150.00 200.00
1 Will Harridge PRES 75.00 125.00
2 Warren Giles PRES DP 30.00 50.00
3 Elmer Valo 7.50 15.00
4 Carlos Paula 7.50 15.00
5 Ted Williams 300.00 500.00
6 Ray Boone 15.00 25.00
7 Ron Negray RC 5.00 10.00
8 Walter Alston MG RC 25.00 40.00
9 Ruben Gomez DP 5.00 10.00
10 Warren Spahn 70.00 120.00
11A Chicago Cubs TC (Centered) 15.00 30.00
11B Chicago Cubs TC (Dated 1955) 50.00 80.00
11C Chicago Cubs TC (Name at far left) 15.00 30.00
12 Andy Carey 7.50 15.00
13 Roy Face 7.50 15.00
14 Ken Boyer DP 7.50 15.00
15 Ernie Banks DP 60.00 100.00
16 Hector Lopez RC 7.50 15.00
17 Gene Conley 7.50 15.00
18 Dick Donovan 5.00 10.00
19 Chuck Diering DP 5.00 10.00
20 Al Kaline 75.00 125.00
21 Joe Collins DP 7.50 15.00
22 Jim Finigan 5.00 10.00
23 Fred Marsh 5.00 10.00
24 Dick Groat 7.50 15.00
25 Ted Kluszewski 50.00 80.00
25A Ted Kluszewski GB
26 Grady Hatton 5.00 10.00
27 Nelson Burbrink DP RC 5.00 10.00
28 Bobby Hofman 5.00 10.00
29 Jack Harshman 5.00 10.00
30 Jackie Robinson DP 150.00 250.00
31 Hank Aaron UER DP (Small photo actually Willie Mays) 200.00 350.00
32 Frank House 5.00 10.00
33 Roberto Clemente 250.00 400.00
34 Tom Brewer DP 5.00 10.00
35 Al Rosen 7.50 15.00
36 Rudy Minarcin 7.50 15.00
37 Alex Grammas 7.50 15.00
38 Bob Kennedy 7.50 15.00
39 Don Mossi 7.50 15.00
40 Bob Turley 7.50 15.00
41 Hank Sauer 7.50 15.00
42 Sandy Amoros 15.00 25.00
43 Ray Moore 5.00 10.00
44 Windy McCall 5.00 10.00
45 Gus Zernial 5.00 10.00
46 Gene Freese DP 5.00 10.00
47 Art Fowler 5.00 10.00
48 Jim Hegan 7.50 15.00
49 Pedro Ramos RC 5.00 10.00
50 Dusty Rhodes DP 7.50 15.00
51 Ernie Oravetz RC 5.00 10.00
52 Bob Grim DP 7.50 15.00
53 Arnie Portocarrero 5.00 10.00
54 Bob Keegan 5.00 10.00
55 Wally Moon 7.50 15.00
56 Dale Long 7.50 15.00
57 Duke Maas RC 5.00 10.00
58 Ed Roebuck 15.00 25.00
59 Jose Santiago RC 5.00 10.00
60 Mayo Smith MG DP 5.00 10.00
61 Bill Skowron 15.00 25.00
62 Hal Smith 7.50 15.00
63 Roger Craig RC 25.00 40.00
64 Luis Arroyo RC 5.00 10.00
65 Johnny O'Brien 7.50 15.00
66 Bob Speake DP RC 5.00 10.00
67 Vic Power 7.50 15.00
68 Chuck Stobbs 5.00 10.00
69 Chuck Tanner 7.50 15.00
70 Jim Rivera 5.00 10.00
71 Frank Sullivan 5.00 10.00
72A Philadelphia Phillies TC (Centered) 15.00 30.00
72B Philadelphia Phillies TC (Dated 1955) 50.00 80.00
72C Philadelphia Phillies TC (Name at far left) DP 15.00 30.00
73 Wayne Terwilliger 5.00 10.00
74 Jim King RC 5.00 10.00
75 Roy Sievers DP 7.50 15.00
76 Ray Crone 5.00 10.00
77 Harvey Haddix 7.50 15.00
78 Herman Wehmeier 5.00 10.00
79 Sandy Koufax 200.00 350.00
80 Gus Triandos DP 5.00 10.00
81 Wally Westlake 5.00 10.00
82 Bill Renna DP 5.00 10.00
83 Karl Spooner 7.50 15.00
84 Babe Birrer RC 5.00 10.00
85A Cleveland Indians TC (Centered) 15.00 30.00
85B Cleveland Indians TC (Dated 1955) 50.00 80.00
85C Cleveland Indians TC (Name at far left) 15.00 30.00
86 Ray Jablonski DP 5.00 10.00
87 Dean Stone 5.00 10.00
88 Johnny Kucks RC 7.50 15.00
89 Norm Zauchin 5.00 10.00
90A Cincinnati Redleg TC (Centered) 15.00 30.00
90B Cincinnati Reds TC (Dated 1955) 50.00 80.00
90C Cincinnati Reds TC (Name at far left) 15.00 30.00
91 Gail Harris RC 5.00 10.00
92 Bob (Red) Wilson 5.00 10.00
93 George Susce 5.00 10.00
94 Ron Kline 5.00 10.00
95A Milwaukee Braves TC (Centered) 20.00 40.00
95B Milwaukee Braves TC (Dated 1955) 50.00 80.00
95C Milwaukee Braves TC (Name at far left) 20.00 40.00
96 Bill Tremel 5.00 10.00
97 Jerry Lynch 7.50 15.00
98 Camilo Pascual 7.50 15.00
99 Don Zimmer 15.00 25.00
100A Baltimore Orioles TC (Centered) 20.00 40.00
100B Baltimore Orioles TC (Dated 1955) 50.00 80.00
100C Baltimore Orioles TC (Name at far left) 20.00 40.00
101 Roy Campanella 90.00 150.00
102 Jim Davis 6.00 12.00
103 Willie Miranda 6.00 12.00
104 Bob Lennon 6.00 12.00
105 Al Smith 6.00 12.00
106 Joe Astroth 6.00 12.00
107 Eddie Mathews 60.00 100.00
108 Laurin Pepper 6.00 12.00
109 Enos Slaughter 25.00 40.00
110 Yogi Berra 100.00 175.00
111 Boston Red Sox TC 20.00 40.00
112 Dee Fondy 6.00 12.00
113 Phil Rizzuto 90.00 150.00
114 Jim Owens 7.50 15.00
115 Jackie Jensen 7.50 15.00
116 Eddie O'Brien 6.00 12.00
117 Virgil Trucks 6.00 12.00
118 Nellie Fox 50.00 80.00
119 Larry Jackson RC 7.50 15.00
120 Richie Ashburn 35.00 60.00
121 Pittsburgh Pirates TC 20.00 40.00
122 Willard Nixon 6.00 12.00
123 Roy McMillan 7.50 15.00
124 Don Kaiser 6.00 12.00
125 Minnie Minoso 25.00 40.00
126 Jim Brady RC 6.00 12.00
127 Willie Jones 7.50 15.00
128 Eddie Yost 7.50 15.00
129 Jake Martin RC 6.00 12.00
130 Willie Mays 175.00 300.00
131 Bob Roselli RC 6.00 12.00
132 Bobby Avila 6.00 12.00
133 Ray Narleski 6.00 12.00
134 St. Louis Cardinals TC 20.00 40.00
135 Mickey Mantle 900.00 1500.00
136 Johnny Logan 7.50 15.00
137 Al Silvera RC 6.00 12.00
138 Johnny Antonelli 7.50 15.00
139 Tommy Carroll 7.50 15.00
140 Herb Score RC 35.00 60.00
141 Joe Frazier 6.00 12.00
142 Gene Baker 6.00 12.00
143 Jim Piersall 7.50 15.00
144 Leroy Powell RC 6.00 12.00
145 Gil Hodges 35.00 60.00
146 Washington Nationals TC 20.00 40.00
147 Earl Torgeson 6.00 12.00
148 Alvin Dark 7.50 15.00
149 Dixie Howell 6.00 12.00
150 Duke Snider 75.00 125.00
151 Spook Jacobs 7.50 15.00
152 Billy Hoeft 7.50 15.00
153 Frank Thomas 7.50 15.00
154 Dave Pope 6.00 12.00
155 Harvey Kuenn 7.50 15.00
156 Wes Westrum 7.50 15.00
157 Dick Brodowski 6.00 12.00
158 Wally Post 6.00 12.00
159 Clint Courtney 6.00 12.00
160 Billy Pierce 7.50 15.00
161 Joe DeMaestri 6.00 12.00
162 Dave (Gus) Bell 7.50 15.00
163 Gene Woodling 7.50 15.00
164 Harmon Killebrew 60.00 100.00
165 Red Schoendienst 25.00 40.00
166 Brooklyn Dodgers TC 125.00 200.00
167 Harry Dorish 6.00 12.00
168 Sammy White 6.00 12.00
169 Bob Nelson RC 6.00 12.00
170 Bill Virdon 7.50 15.00
171 Jim Wilson 6.00 12.00
172 Frank Torre RC 7.50 15.00
173 Johnny Podres 15.00 25.00
174 Glen Gorbous RC 6.00 12.00
175 Del Crandall 7.50 15.00
176 Alex Kellner 6.00 12.00
177 Hank Bauer 15.00 25.00
178 Joe Black 7.50 15.00
179 Harry Chiti 6.00 12.00
180 Robin Roberts 30.00 50.00
181 Billy Martin 75.00 125.00
182 Paul Minner 7.50 15.00
183 Stan Lopata 10.00 20.00
184 Don Bessent RC 10.00 20.00
185 Bill Bruton 10.00 20.00
186 Ron Jackson 7.50 15.00
187 Early Wynn 30.00 50.00
188 Chicago White Sox TC 30.00 50.00
189 Ned Garver 7.50 15.00
190 Carl Furillo 18.00 30.00
191 Frank Lary 10.00 20.00
192 Smoky Burgess 10.00 20.00
193 Wilmer Mizell 10.00 20.00
194 Monte Irvin 18.00 30.00
195 George Kell 18.00 30.00
196 Tom Poholsky 7.50 15.00
197 Granny Hamner 7.50 15.00
198 Ed Fitzgerald 7.50 15.00
199 Hank Thompson 10.00 20.00
200 Bob Feller 75.00 125.00
201 Rip Repulski 7.50 15.00
202 Jim Hearn 7.50 15.00
203 Bill Tuttle 7.50 15.00
204 Art Swanson RC 7.50 15.00
205 Whitey Lockman 10.00 20.00
206 Erv Palica 7.50 15.00
207 Jim Small RC 7.50 15.00
208 Elston Howard 35.00 60.00
209 Max Surkont 7.50 15.00
210 Mike Garcia 10.00 20.00
211 Murry Dickson 7.50 15.00
212 Johnny Temple 7.50 15.00
213 Detroit Tigers TC 35.00 60.00
214 Bob Rush 7.50 15.00
215 Tommy Byrne 10.00 20.00
216 Jerry Schoonmaker RC 7.50 15.00
217 Billy Klaus 7.50 15.00
218 Joe Nuxhall UER (Misspelled Nuxall) 10.00 20.00
219 Lew Burdette 10.00 20.00
220 Del Ennis 10.00 20.00
221 Bob Friend 10.00 20.00
222 Dave Philley 7.50 15.00
223 Randy Jackson 7.50 15.00
224 Bud Podbielan 7.50 15.00
225 Gil McDougald 30.00 50.00
226 New York Giants TC 50.00 80.00
227 Russ Meyer 7.50 15.00
228 Mickey Vernon 10.00 20.00
229 Harry Brecheen CO 10.00 20.00
230 Chico Carrasquel 7.50 15.00
231 Bob Hale RC 7.50 15.00
232 Toby Atwell 7.50 15.00
233 Carl Erskine 18.00 30.00
234 Pete Runnels 7.50 15.00
235 Don Newcombe 30.00 50.00
236 Kansas City Athletics TC 20.00 40.00
237 Jose Valdivielso RC 7.50 15.00
238 Walt Dropo 10.00 20.00
239 Harry Simpson 7.50 15.00
240 Whitey Ford 75.00 125.00
241 Don Mueller UER (6-inch Tall) 10.00 20.00
242 Hershell Freeman 7.50 15.00
243 Sherm Lollar 10.00 20.00
244 Bob Buhl 18.00 30.00
245 Billy Goodman 10.00 20.00
246 Tom Gorman 7.50 15.00
247 Bill Sarni 7.50 15.00
248 Bob Porterfield 7.50 15.00
249 Johnny Klippstein 7.50 15.00
250 Larry Doby 18.00 30.00
251 New York Yankees TC UER Larsen misspelled as Larson on front) 150.00 250.00
252 Vern Law 10.00 20.00
253 Irv Noren 18.00 30.00
254 George Crowe 7.50 15.00
255 Bob Lemon 30.00 50.00
256 Tom Hurd 7.50 15.00
257 Bobby Thomson 18.00 30.00
258 Art Ditmar 7.50 15.00
259 Sam Jones 10.00 20.00
260 Pee Wee Reese 90.00 150.00
261 Bobby Shantz 7.50 15.00
262 Howie Pollet 6.00 12.00
263 Bob Miller 6.00 12.00
264 Ray Monzant RC 6.00 12.00
265 Sandy Consuegra 6.00 12.00
266 Don Ferrarese 6.00 12.00
267 Bob Nieman 6.00 12.00
268 Dale Mitchell 7.50 15.00
269 Jack Meyer RC 6.00 12.00
270 Billy Loes 7.50 15.00
271 Foster Castleman RC 6.00 12.00
272 Danny O'Connell 6.00 12.00
273 Walker Cooper 6.00 12.00
274 Frank Baumholtz 6.00 12.00
275 Jim Greengrass 6.00 12.00
276 George Zuverink 6.00 12.00
277 Daryl Spencer 6.00 12.00
278 Chet Nichols 6.00 12.00
279 Johnny Groth 6.00 12.00
280 Jim Gilliam 25.00 40.00
281 Art Houtteman 6.00 12.00
282 Warren Hacker 6.00 12.00
283 Hal Smith RC UER 7.50 15.00
Wrong Facsimile Autograph, belongs to Hal W. Smith
284 Ike Delock 6.00 12.00
285 Eddie Miksis 6.00 12.00
286 Bill Wight 6.00 12.00
287 Bobby Adams 6.00 12.00
288 Bob Cerv 25.00 40.00
289 Hal Jeffcoat 6.00 12.00
290 Curt Simmons 7.50 15.00
291 Frank Kellert RC 6.00 12.00
292 Luis Aparicio RC 90.00 150.00
293 Stu Miller 15.00 25.00
294 Ernie Johnson 7.50 15.00
295 Clem Labine 7.50 15.00
296 Andy Seminick 6.00 12.00
297 Bob Skinner 7.50 15.00
298 Johnny Schmitz 6.00 12.00
299 Charlie Neal 25.00 40.00
300 Vic Wertz 7.50 15.00
301 Marv Grissom 6.00 12.00
302 Eddie Robinson 6.00 12.00
303 Jim Dyck 6.00 12.00
304 Frank Malzone 7.50 15.00
305 Brooks Lawrence 6.00 12.00
306 Curt Roberts 6.00 12.00
307 Hoyt Wilhelm 25.00 40.00
308 Chuck Harmon 6.00 12.00
309 Don Blasingame RC 7.50 15.00
310 Steve Gromek 6.00 12.00
311 Hal Naragon 6.00 12.00
312 Andy Pafko 7.50 15.00
313 Gene Stephens 6.00 12.00
314 Hobie Landrith 6.00 12.00
315 Milt Bolling 6.00 12.00

316 Jerry Coleman 7.50 15.00
317 Al Aber 6.00 12.00
318 Fred Hatfield 6.00 12.00
319 Jack Crimian RC 6.00 12.00
320 Joe Adcock 7.50 15.00
321 Jim Konstanty 7.50 15.00
322 Karl Olson 6.00 12.00
323 Willard Schmidt 6.00 12.00
324 Rocky Bridges 7.50 15.00
325 Don Liddle 6.00 12.00
326 Connie Johnson RC 6.00 12.00
327 Bob Wiesler RC 6.00 12.00
328 Preston Ward 6.00 12.00
329 Lou Berberet RC 6.00 12.00
330 Jim Busby 7.50 15.00
331 Dick Hall 6.00 12.00
332 Don Larsen 35.00 60.00
333 Rube Walker 6.00 12.00
334 Bob Miller 7.50 15.00
335 Don Hoak 7.50 15.00
336 Ellis Kinder 6.00 12.00
337 Bobby Morgan 6.00 12.00
338 Jim Delsing 6.00 12.00
339 Rance Pless RC 6.00 12.00
340 Mickey McDermott 35.00 60.00
CL1 Checklist 1/3 175.00 300.00
CL2 Checklist 2/4 175.00 300.00

1957 Topps

The cards in this 407-card set measure 2 1/2" by 3 1/2". In 1957, Topps returned to the vertical obverse, adopted what we now call the standard card size, and used a large, uncluttered color photo for the first time since 1952. Cards in the series 265 to 352 and the unnumbered checklist cards are scarcer than other cards in the set. However within this scarce series (265-352) there are 22 cards which were printed in double the quantity of the other cards in the series; these 22 double prints are indicated by DP in the checklist below. The first star combination cards, cards 400 and 407, are quite popular with collectors. They feature the big stars of the previous season's World Series teams, the Dodgers (Furillo, Hodges, Campanella, and Snider) and Yankees (Berra and Mantle). The complete set price below does not include the unnumbered checklist cards. Confirmed packaging includes one-cent penny packs and six-card nickel packs. Cello packs are definately known to exist and some collectors remember buying rack packs of 57's as well. The key Rookie Cards in this set are Jim Bunning, Rocky Colavito, Don Drysdale, Whitey Herzog, Tony Kubek, Bill Mazeroski, Bobby Richardson, Brooks Robinson, and Frank Robinson.

COMPLETE SET (407) 7000.00 10000.00
COMMON CARD (1-88) 5.00 10.00
COMMON CARD (89-176) 4.00 8.00
COMMON (177-264) 4.00 8.00
COMMON (265-352) 10.00 20.00
COMMON (353-407) 4.00 8.00
COMMON DP (265-352) 6.00 12.00
WRAPPER (1-CENT) 250.00 300.00
WRAPPER (5-CENT) 150.00 200.00
1 Ted Williams 350.00 600.00
2 Yogi Berra 125.00 200.00
3 Dale Long 10.00 20.00
4 Johnny Logan 10.00 20.00
5 Sal Maglie 10.00 20.00
6 Hector Lopez 7.50 15.00
7 Luis Aparicio 15.00 30.00
8 Don Mossi 7.50 15.00
9 Johnny Temple 7.50 15.00
10 Willie Mays 250.00 400.00
11 George Zuverink 5.00 10.00
12 Dick Groat 10.00 20.00
13 Wally Burnette RC 5.00 10.00
14 Bob Nieman 5.00 10.00
15 Robin Roberts 15.00 30.00
16 Walt Moryn 5.00 10.00
17 Billy Gardner 5.00 10.00
18 Don Drysdale RC 150.00 250.00
19 Bob Wilson 5.00 10.00
20 Hank Aaron UER 175.00 300.00
(Reverse negative photo on front)
21 Frank Sullivan 5.00 10.00
22 Jerry Snyder UER 5.00 10.00
Photo actually Ed Fitzgerald
23 Sherm Lollar 7.50 15.00
24 Bill Mazeroski RC 50.00 80.00
25 Whitey Ford 100.00 175.00
26 Bob Boyd 5.00 10.00
27 Ted Kazanski 5.00 10.00
28 Gene Conley 7.50 15.00
29 Whitey Herzog RC 15.00 30.00
30 Pee Wee Reese 50.00 80.00
31 Ron Northey 5.00 10.00
32 Hershell Freeman 5.00 10.00
33 Jim Small 5.00 10.00
34 Tom Sturdivant RC 7.50 15.00
35 Frank Robinson RC 175.00 300.00
36 Bob Grim 5.00 10.00
37 Frank Torre 7.50 15.00
38 Nellie Fox 30.00 50.00
39 Al Worthington RC 5.00 10.00
40 Early Wynn 15.00 30.00
41 Hal W. Smith 5.00 10.00
42 Dee Fondy 5.00 10.00
43 Connie Johnson 5.00 10.00
44 Joe DeMaestri 5.00 10.00
45 Carl Furillo 15.00 30.00
46 Robert J. Miller 5.00 10.00
47 Don Blasingame 5.00 10.00
48 Bill Bruton 7.50 15.00
49 Daryl Spencer 5.00 10.00
50 Herb Score 15.00 30.00
51 Clint Courtney 5.00 10.00
52 Lee Walls 5.00 10.00
53 Clem Labine 10.00 20.00
54 Elmer Valo 5.00 10.00
55 Ernie Banks 75.00 125.00
56 Dave Sisler RC 5.00 10.00
57 Jim Lemon 7.50 15.00
58 Ruben Gomez 5.00 10.00
59 Dick Williams 7.50 15.00
60 Billy Hoeft 7.50 15.00
61 Dusty Rhodes 7.50 15.00
62 Billy Martin 35.00 60.00
63 Ike Delock 5.00 10.00
64 Pete Runnels 7.50 15.00
65 Wally Moon 7.50 15.00
66 Brooks Lawrence 5.00 10.00
67 Chico Carrasquel 5.00 10.00
68 Ray Crone 5.00 10.00
69 Roy McMillan 7.50 15.00
70 Richie Ashburn 30.00 50.00
71 Murry Dickson 5.00 10.00
72 Bill Tuttle 5.00 10.00
73 George Crowe 5.00 10.00
74 Vito Valentinetti RC 5.00 10.00
75 Jimmy Piersall 7.50 15.00
76 Roberto Clemente 175.00 300.00
77 Paul Foytack RC 5.00 10.00
78 Vic Wertz 7.50 15.00
79 Lindy McDaniel RC 7.50 15.00
80 Gil Hodges 30.00 50.00
81 Herman Wehmeier 5.00 10.00
82 Elston Howard 15.00 30.00
83 Lou Skizas RC 5.00 10.00
84 Moe Drabowsky RC 7.50 15.00
85 Larry Doby 15.00 30.00
86 Bill Sarni 5.00 10.00
87 Tom Gorman 5.00 10.00
88 Harvey Kuenn 7.50 15.00
89 Roy Sievers 7.50 15.00
90 Warren Spahn 50.00 80.00
91 Mack Burk RC 4.00 8.00
92 Mickey Vernon 7.50 15.00
93 Hal Jeffcoat 4.00 8.00
94 Bobby Del Greco 4.00 8.00
95 Mickey Mantle 700.00 1200.00
96 Hank Aguirre RC 4.00 8.00
97 New York Yankees TC 60.00 100.00
98 Alvin Dark 7.50 15.00
99 Bob Keegan 4.00 8.00
100 Warren Giles PRES 7.50 15.00
Will Harridge PRES
101 Chuck Stobbs 4.00 8.00
102 Ray Boone 7.50 15.00
103 Joe Nuxhall 7.50 15.00
104 Hank Foiles 4.00 8.00
105 Johnny Antonelli 7.50 15.00
106 Ray Moore 4.00 8.00
107 Jim Rivera 4.00 8.00
108 Tommy Byrne 7.50 15.00
109 Hank Thompson 4.00 8.00
110 Bill Virdon 7.50 15.00
111 Hal R. Smith 4.00 8.00
112 Tom Brewer 4.00 8.00
113 Wilmer Mizell 7.50 15.00
114 Milwaukee Braves TC 10.00 20.00
115 Jim Gilliam 7.50 15.00
116 Mike Fornieles 4.00 8.00
117 Joe Adcock 10.00 20.00
118 Bob Porterfield 4.00 8.00
119 Stan Lopata 4.00 8.00
120 Bob Lemon 15.00 30.00
121 Clete Boyer RC 15.00 30.00
122 Ken Boyer 10.00 20.00
123 Steve Ridzik 4.00 8.00
124 Dave Philley 4.00 8.00
125 Al Kaline 60.00 100.00
126 Bob Wiesler 4.00 8.00
127 Bob Buhl 7.50 15.00
128 Ed Bailey 7.50 15.00
129 Saul Rogovin 4.00 8.00
130 Don Newcombe 10.00 20.00
131 Milt Bolling 4.00 8.00
132 Art Ditmar 7.50 15.00
133 Del Crandall 7.50 15.00
134 Don Kaiser 4.00 8.00
135 Bill Skowron 10.00 20.00
136 Jim Hegan 7.50 15.00
137 Bob Rush 4.00 8.00
138 Minnie Minoso 10.00 20.00
139 Lou Kretlow 4.00 8.00
140 Frank Thomas 7.50 15.00
141 Al Aber 4.00 8.00
142 Charley Thompson 4.00 8.00
143 Andy Pafko 7.50 15.00
144 Ray Narleski 4.00 8.00
145 Al Smith 4.00 8.00
146 Don Ferrarese 4.00 8.00
147 Al Walker 4.00 8.00
148 Don Mueller 7.50 15.00
149 Bob Kennedy 7.50 15.00
150 Bob Friend 7.50 15.00
151 Willie Miranda 4.00 8.00
152 Jack Harshman 4.00 8.00
153 Karl Olson 4.00 8.00
154 Red Schoendienst 15.00 30.00
155 Jim Brosnan 7.50 15.00
156 Gus Triandos 7.50 15.00
157 Wally Post 7.50 15.00
158 Curt Simmons 7.50 15.00
159 Solly Drake RC 4.00 8.00
160 Billy Pierce 7.50 15.00
161 Pittsburgh Pirates TC 7.50 15.00
162 Jack Meyer 4.00 8.00
163 Sammy White 4.00 8.00
164 Tommy Carroll 4.00 8.00
165 Ted Kluszewski 60.00 100.00
166 Roy Face 7.50 15.00
167 Vic Power 7.50 15.00
168 Frank Lary 7.50 15.00
169 Herb Plews RC 4.00 8.00
170 Duke Snider 75.00 125.00
171 Boston Red Sox TC 7.50 15.00
172 Gene Woodling 7.50 15.00
173 Roger Craig 7.50 15.00
174 Willie Jones 4.00 8.00
175 Don Larsen 15.00 30.00
176A Gene Baker ERR 200.00 350.00
(Misspelled Bakep on card back)
176B Gene Baker COR 7.50 15.00
177 Eddie Yost 7.50 15.00
178 Don Bessent 4.00 8.00
179 Ernie Oravetz 4.00 8.00
180 Gus Bell 7.50 15.00
181 Dick Donovan 4.00 8.00
182 Hobie Landrith 4.00 8.00
183 Chicago Cubs TC 7.50 15.00
184 Tito Francona RC 4.00 8.00
185 Johnny Kucks 7.50 15.00
186 Jim King 7.50 15.00
187 Virgil Trucks 7.50 15.00
188 Felix Mantilla RC 7.50 15.00
189 Willard Nixon 4.00 8.00
190 Randy Jackson 4.00 8.00
191 Joe Margoneri RC 4.00 8.00
192 Jerry Coleman 7.50 15.00
193 Del Rice 4.00 8.00
194 Hal Brown 4.00 8.00
195 Bobby Avila 4.00 8.00
196 Larry Jackson 7.50 15.00
197 Hank Sauer 7.50 15.00
198 Detroit Tigers TC 7.50 15.00
199 Vern Law 7.50 15.00
200 Gil McDougald 7.50 15.00
201 Sandy Amoros 7.50 15.00
202 Dick Gernert 4.00 8.00
203 Hoyt Wilhelm 15.00 30.00
204 Kansas City Athletics TC 7.50 15.00
205 Charlie Maxwell 7.50 15.00
206 Willard Schmidt 4.00 8.00
207 Gordon (Billy) Hunter 4.00 8.00
208 Lou Burdette 7.50 15.00
209 Bob Skinner 7.50 15.00
210 Roy Campanella 90.00 150.00
211 Camilo Pascual 7.50 15.00
212 Rocky Colavito RC 75.00 125.00
213 Les Moss 4.00 8.00
214 Philadelphia Phillies TC 7.50 15.00
215 Enos Slaughter 15.00 30.00
216 Marv Grissom 4.00 8.00
217 Gene Stephens 4.00 8.00
218 Ray Jablonski 4.00 8.00
219 Tom Acker RC 4.00 8.00
220 Jackie Jensen 10.00 20.00
221 Dixie Howell 4.00 8.00
222 Alex Grammas 4.00 8.00
223 Frank House 4.00 8.00
224 Marv Blaylock 4.00 8.00
225 Harry Simpson 4.00 8.00
226 Preston Ward 4.00 8.00
227 Gerry Staley 4.00 8.00
228 Smoky Burgess UER 7.50 15.00
(Misspelled Smokey on card back)
229 George Susce 4.00 8.00
230 George Kell 15.00 30.00
231 Solly Hemus 4.00 8.00
232 Whitey Lockman 7.50 15.00
233 Art Fowler 4.00 8.00
234 Dick Cole 4.00 8.00
235 Tom Poholsky 4.00 8.00
236 Joe Ginsberg 4.00 8.00
237 Foster Castleman 4.00 8.00
238 Eddie Robinson 4.00 8.00
239 Tom Morgan 4.00 8.00
240 Hank Bauer 7.50 15.00
241 Joe Lonnett RC 4.00 8.00
242 Charlie Neal 7.50 15.00
243 St. Louis Cardinals TC 7.50 15.00
244 Billy Loes 7.50 15.00
245 Rip Repulski 4.00 8.00
246 Jose Valdivielso 4.00 8.00
247 Turk Lown 4.00 8.00
248 Jim Finigan 4.00 8.00
249 Dave Pope 4.00 8.00
250 Eddie Mathews 30.00 50.00
251 Baltimore Orioles TC 7.50 15.00
252 Carl Erskine 7.50 15.00
253 Gus Zernial 7.50 15.00
254 Ron Negray 4.00 8.00
255 Charlie Silvera 7.50 15.00
256 Ron Kline 4.00 8.00
257 Walt Dropo 4.00 8.00
258 Steve Gromek 4.00 8.00
259 Eddie O'Brien 4.00 8.00
260 Del Ennis 7.50 15.00
261 Bob Chakales 4.00 8.00
262 Bobby Thomson 7.50 15.00
263 George Strickland 4.00 8.00
264 Bob Turley 7.50 15.00
265 Harvey Haddix DP 6.00 12.00
266 Ken Kuhn DP RC 6.00 12.00
267 Danny Kravitz RC 10.00 20.00
268 Jack Collum 10.00 20.00
269 Bob Cerv 15.00 30.00
270 Washington Senators TC 35.00 60.00
271 Danny O'Connell DP 6.00 12.00
272 Bobby Shantz 15.00 30.00
273 Jim Davis 10.00 20.00
274 Don Hoak 7.50 15.00
275 Cleveland Indians TC 35.00 60.00
UER Text on back credits Tribe with winning AL title in '28. The Yankees won that year.)
276 Jim Pyburn RC 10.00 20.00
277 Johnny Podres DP 20.00 40.00
278 Fred Hatfield DP 6.00 12.00
279 Bob Thurman RC 10.00 20.00
280 Alex Kellner 10.00 20.00
281 Gail Harris 10.00 20.00
282 Jack Dittmer DP 6.00 12.00
283 Wes Covington DP RC 6.00 12.00
284 Don Zimmer 20.00 40.00
285 Ned Garver 10.00 20.00
286 Bobby Richardson RC 75.00 125.00
287 Sam Jones 10.00 20.00
288 Ted Lepcio 10.00 20.00
289 Jim Bolger DP 6.00 12.00
290 Andy Carey DP 20.00 40.00
291 Windy McCall 10.00 20.00
292 Billy Klaus 10.00 20.00
293 Ted Abernathy RC 10.00 20.00
294 Rocky Bridges DP 6.00 12.00
295 Joe Collins DP 20.00 40.00
296 Johnny Klippstein 10.00 20.00
297 Jack Crimian 10.00 20.00
298 Irv Noren DP 6.00 12.00
299 Chuck Harmon 10.00 20.00
300 Mike Garcia 15.00 30.00
301 Sammy Esposito DP RC 10.00 20.00
302 Sandy Koufax DP 200.00 350.00
303 Billy Goodman 15.00 30.00
304 Joe Cunningham 15.00 30.00
305 Chico Fernandez 10.00 20.00
306 Darrell Johnson DP RC 6.00 12.00
307 Jack D. Phillips DP 6.00 12.00
308 Dick Hall 10.00 20.00
309 Jim Busby DP 6.00 12.00
310 Max Surkont DP 6.00 12.00
311 Al Pilarcik DP RC 6.00 12.00
312 Tony Kubek DP RC 60.00 100.00
313 Mel Parnell 7.50 15.00
314 Ed Bouchee DP RC 6.00 12.00
315 Lou Berberet DP 6.00 12.00
316 Billy O'Dell 10.00 20.00
317 New York Giants TC 50.00 80.00
318 Mickey McDermott 10.00 20.00
319 Gino Cimoli RC 10.00 20.00
320 Neil Chrisley RC 10.00 20.00
321 John (Red) Murff RC 10.00 20.00
322 Cincinnati Reds TC 50.00 80.00
323 Wes Westrum 15.00 30.00
324 Brooklyn Dodgers TC 90.00 150.00
325 Frank Bolling 10.00 20.00
326 Pedro Ramos 10.00 20.00
327 Jim Pendleton 10.00 20.00
328 Brooks Robinson RC 250.00 400.00
329 Chicago White Sox TC 35.00 60.00
330 Jim Wilson 10.00 20.00
331 Ray Katt 10.00 20.00
332 Bob Bowman RC 10.00 20.00
333 Ernie Johnson 10.00 20.00
334 Jerry Schoonmaker 10.00 20.00
335 Granny Hamner 10.00 20.00
336 Haywood Sullivan RC 20.00 40.00
337 Rene Valdes RC 10.00 20.00
338 Jim Bunning RC 90.00 150.00
339 Bob Speake 10.00 20.00
340 Bill Wight 10.00 20.00
341 Don Gross RC 10.00 20.00
342 Gene Mauch 15.00 30.00
343 Taylor Phillips RC 7.50 15.00
344 Paul LaPalme 10.00 20.00
345 Paul Smith 10.00 20.00
346 Dick Littlefield 10.00 20.00
347 Hal Naragon 10.00 20.00
348 Jim Hearn 10.00 20.00
349 Nellie King 10.00 20.00
350 Eddie Miksis 10.00 20.00
351 Dave Hillman RC 10.00 20.00
352 Ellis Kinder 10.00 20.00
353 Cal Neeman RC 4.00 8.00
354 Rip Coleman RC 4.00 8.00
355 Frank Malzone 7.50 15.00
356 Faye Throneberry 4.00 8.00
357 Earl Torgeson 4.00 8.00
358 Jerry Lynch 7.50 15.00
359 Tom Cheney RC 4.00 8.00
360 Johnny Groth 4.00 8.00
361 Curt Barclay RC 4.00 8.00
362 Roman Mejias RC 7.50 15.00
363 Eddie Kasko RC 4.00 8.00
364 Cal McLish RC 7.50 15.00
365 Ozzie Virgil RC 4.00 8.00
366 Ken Lehman 4.00 8.00
367 Ed Fitzgerald 4.00 8.00
368 Bob Purkey 4.00 8.00
369 Milt Graff RC 4.00 8.00
370 Warren Hacker 4.00 8.00
371 Bob Lennon 4.00 8.00
372 Norm Zauchin 4.00 8.00
373 Pete Whisenant RC 4.00 8.00
374 Don Cardwell RC 4.00 8.00
375 Jim Landis RC 7.50 15.00
376 Don Elston RC 4.00 8.00
377 Andre Rodgers RC 4.00 8.00
378 Elmer Singleton 4.00 8.00
379 Don Lee RC 4.00 8.00
380 Walker Cooper 4.00 8.00
381 Dean Stone 4.00 8.00
382 Jim Brideweser 4.00 8.00
383 Juan Pizarro RC 4.00 8.00
384 Bobby G. Smith RC 4.00 8.00
385 Art Houtteman 4.00 8.00
386 Lyle Luttrell RC 4.00 8.00
387 Jack Sanford RC 7.50 15.00
388 Pete Daley 4.00 8.00
389 Dave Jolly 4.00 8.00
390 Reno Bertoia 4.00 8.00
391 Ralph Terry RC 7.50 15.00
392 Chuck Tanner 7.50 15.00
393 Raul Sanchez RC 4.00 8.00
394 Luis Arroyo 7.50 15.00
395 Bubba Phillips 4.00 8.00
396 Casey Wise RC 4.00 8.00
397 Roy Smalley 4.00 8.00
398 Al Cicotte RC 7.50 15.00
399 Billy Consolo 4.00 8.00
400 Dodgers Sluggers 150.00 250.00
Carl Furillo
Gil Hodges
Roy Campanella
Duke Snider
401 Earl Battey RC 7.50 15.00
402 Jim Pisoni RC 4.00 8.00
403 Dick Hyde RC 4.00 8.00
404 Harry Anderson RC 4.00 8.00
405 Duke Maas 4.00 8.00
406 Bob Hale 4.00 8.00
407 Yankees Power Hitters 350.00 600.00
Mickey Mantle
Yogi Berra
CC1 Contest Card 60.00 100.00
Saturday, May 4th
Boston Red Sox
vs. Cleveland Indians
Cincinnati Redlegs
vs. New York Giants
CC2 Contest Card 60.00 100.00
Saturday, May 25th
Detroit Tigers
vs. Kansas City Athletics
Pittsburgh Pirates
vs. Philadelphia Phillies
CC3 Contest Card 75.00 125.00
Saturday, June 22nd
Brooklyn Dodgers
vs. St. Louis Cardinals
Chicago White Sox
vs. New York Yankees
CC4 Contest Card 75.00 125.00
Saturday, July 19th
Milwaukee Braves
vs. New York Giants
Baltimore Orioles
vs. Kansas City Athletics
NNO Checklist 1/2 150.00 250.00
Bazooka Back
NNO Checklist 1/2 150.00 250.00
Blony Back
NNO Checklist 2/3 250.00 400.00
Bazooka Back
NNO Checklist 2/3 250.00 400.00
Blony Back
NNO Checklist 3/4 500.00 800.00
(Bazooka Back
NNO Checklist 3/4 350.00 600.00
Blony Back
NNO Checklist 4/5 600.00 1000.00
Bazooka Back
NNO Checklist 4/5 500.00 800.00
Blony Back
NNO Lucky Penny Charm 60.00 100.00
and Key Chain
offer card

1958 Topps

This is a 494-card standard-size set. Card number 145, which was supposedly to be Ed Bouchee, was not issued. The 1958 Topps set contains the first Sport Magazine All-Star Selection series (475-495) and expanded use of combination cards. For the first time team cards carried series checklists on back (Milwaukee, Detroit, Baltimore, and Cincinnati are also found with players listed alphabetically). In the first series some cards were issued with yellow name (YN) or team (YT) lettering, as opposed to the common white lettering. They are explicity noted below. Cards were issued in one-card penny packs or six-card nickel packs. In the last series, All-Star cards of Stan Musial and Mickey Mantle were triple printed; the cards they replaced (443, 446, 450, and 462) on the printing sheet were hence printed in shorter supply than other cards in the last series and are marked with an SP in the list below. The All-Star card of Musial marked his first appearence on a Topps card. Technically the New York Giants team card (19) is an error as the Giants had already moved to San Francisco. The key Rookie Cards in this set are Orlando Cepeda, Curt Flood, Roger Maris, and Vada Pinson. These cards were issued in varying formats, including one cent packs which were issued 120 to a box.

COMP. MASTER (534) 8000.00 12000.00
COMPLETE SET (494) 4000.00 6000.00
COMMON CARD (1-110) 6.00 12.00
COMMON (111-495) 4.00 8.00
WRAPPER (1-CENT) 75.00 100.00
WRAPPER (5-CENT) 100.00 125.00
1 Ted Williams 350.00 600.00
2A Bob Lemon 15.00 30.00
2B Bob Lemon YT 35.00 60.00
3 Alex Kellner 6.00 12.00
4 Hank Foiles 6.00 12.00
5 Willie Mays 175.00 300.00
6 George Zuverink 6.00 12.00
7 Dale Long 7.50 15.00
8A Eddie Kasko 6.00 12.00
8B Eddie Kasko YN 20.00 40.00
9 Hank Bauer 10.00 20.00
10 Lou Burdette 10.00 20.00
11A Jim Rivera 6.00 12.00
11B Jim Rivera YT 20.00 40.00
12 George Crowe 6.00 12.00
13A Billy Hoeft 6.00 12.00
13B Billy Hoeft YN 20.00 40.00
14 Rip Repulski 6.00 12.00
15 Jim Lemon 7.50 15.00
16 Charlie Neal 7.50 15.00
17 Felix Mantilla 6.00 12.00
18 Frank Sullivan 6.00 12.00
19 San Francisco Giants TC 20.00 40.00
20A Gil McDougald 10.00 20.00
20B Gil McDougald YN 35.00 60.00
21 Curt Barclay 6.00 12.00
22 Hal Naragon 6.00 12.00
23A Bill Tuttle 6.00 12.00
23B Bill Tuttle YN 20.00 40.00
24A Hobie Landrith 6.00 12.00
24B Hobie Landrith YN 20.00 40.00
25 Don Drysdale 60.00 100.00
26 Ron Jackson 6.00 12.00
27 Bud Freeman 6.00 12.00
28 Jim Busby 6.00 12.00
29 Ted Lepcio 6.00 12.00
30A Hank Aaron 125.00 200.00
30B Hank Aaron YN 350.00 600.00
31 Tex Clevenger RC 6.00 12.00
32A J.W. Porter 6.00 12.00
32B J.W. Porter YN 20.00 40.00
33A Cal Neeman 6.00 12.00
33B Cal Neeman YT 20.00 40.00
34 Bob Thurman 6.00 12.00
35A Don Mossi 7.50 15.00
35B Don Mossi YT 20.00 40.00
36 Ted Kazanski 6.00 12.00
37 Mike McCormick RC 7.50 15.00
UER Photo actually
Ray Monzant
38 Dick Gernert 6.00 12.00
39 Bob Martyn RC 6.00 12.00
40 George Kell 15.00 30.00
41 Dave Hillman 6.00 12.00
42 John Roseboro RC 15.00 30.00
43 Sal Maglie 7.50 15.00
44 Washington Senators TC 10.00 20.00
45 Dick Groat 7.50 15.00
46A Lou Sleater 6.00 12.00
46B Lou Sleater YN 20.00 40.00
47 Roger Maris RC 300.00 500.00
48 Chuck Harmon 6.00 12.00
49 Smoky Burgess 7.50 15.00
50A Billy Pierce 7.50 15.00
50B Billy Pierce YT 20.00 40.00
51 Del Rice 6.00 12.00
52A Roberto Clemente 175.00 300.00
52B Roberto Clemente YT 300.00 500.00
53A Morrie Martin 6.00 12.00
53B Morrie Martin YN 20.00 40.00
54 Norm Siebern RC 10.00 20.00
55 Chico Carrasquel 6.00 12.00
56 Bill Fischer RC 6.00 12.00
57A Tim Thompson 6.00 12.00
57B Tim Thompson YN 20.00 40.00
58A Art Schult 6.00 12.00
58B Art Schult YT 20.00 40.00
59 Dave Sisler 6.00 12.00
60A Del Ennis 7.50 15.00
60B Del Ennis YN 20.00 40.00
61A Darrell Johnson 6.00 12.00
61B Darrell Johnson YN 20.00 40.00
62 Joe DeMaestri 6.00 12.00
63 Joe Nuxhall 7.50 15.00
64 Joe Lonnett 6.00 12.00
65A Von McDaniel RC 6.00 12.00
65B Von McDaniel YN 20.00 40.00
66 Lee Walls 6.00 12.00
67 Joe Ginsberg 6.00 12.00
68 Daryl Spencer 6.00 12.00
69 Wally Burnette 6.00 12.00
70A Al Kaline 60.00 100.00
70B Al Kaline YN 150.00 250.00
71 Los Angeles Dodgers TC 35.00 60.00
72 Bud Byerly UER 6.00 12.00
Photo is Hal Griggs
73 Pete Daley 6.00 12.00
74 Roy Face 7.50 15.00
75 Gus Bell 7.50 15.00
76A Dick Farrell RC 6.00 12.00
76B Dick Farrell YT 20.00 40.00
77A Don Zimmer 7.50 15.00
77B Don Zimmer YT 20.00 40.00
78A Ernie Johnson 7.50 15.00
78B Ernie Johnson YN 20.00 40.00
79A Dick Williams 7.50 15.00
79B Dick Williams YT 20.00 40.00
80 Dick Drott RC 6.00 12.00
81A Steve Boros RC 6.00 12.00
81B Steve Boros YT 20.00 40.00
82 Ron Kline 6.00 12.00
83 Bob Hazle RC 6.00 12.00
84 Billy O'Dell 6.00 12.00
85A Luis Aparicio 15.00 30.00
85B Luis Aparicio YT 50.00 80.00
86 Valmy Thomas RC 6.00 12.00
87 Johnny Kucks 6.00 12.00
88 Duke Snider 50.00 80.00
89 Billy Klaus 6.00 12.00
90 Robin Roberts 15.00 30.00
91 Chuck Tanner 7.50 15.00
92A Clint Courtney 6.00 12.00
92B Clint Courtney YN 20.00 40.00
93 Sandy Amoros 7.50 15.00
94 Bob Skinner 7.50 15.00
95 Frank Bolling 6.00 12.00
96 Joe Durham RC 6.00 12.00
97A Larry Jackson 6.00 12.00
97B Larry Jackson YN 20.00 40.00
98A Billy Hunter 6.00 12.00
98B Billy Hunter YN 20.00 40.00
99 Bobby Adams 6.00 12.00
100A Early Wynn 15.00 30.00
100B Early Wynn YT 50.00 80.00
101A Bobby Richardson 15.00 30.00
101B B.Richardson YN 35.00 60.00
102 George Strickland 6.00 12.00
103 Jerry Lynch 7.50 15.00
104 Jim Pendleton 6.00 12.00
105 Billy Gardner 6.00 12.00
106 Dick Schofield 7.50 15.00
107 Ossie Virgil 6.00 12.00
108A Jim Landis 6.00 12.00
108B Jim Landis YT 20.00 40.00
109 Herb Plews 6.00 12.00
110 Johnny Logan 7.50 15.00
111 Stu Miller 5.00 10.00
112 Gus Zernial 5.00 10.00
113 Jerry Walker RC 4.00 8.00
114 Irv Noren 5.00 10.00
115 Jim Bunning 15.00 30.00
116 Dave Philley 4.00 8.00
117 Frank Torre 5.00 10.00
118 Harvey Haddix 5.00 10.00
119 Harry Chiti 4.00 8.00
120 Johnny Podres 5.00 10.00
121 Eddie Miksis 4.00 8.00
122 Walt Moryn 4.00 8.00
123 Dick Tomanek RC 4.00 8.00
124 Bobby Usher 4.00 8.00
125 Alvin Dark 5.00 10.00
126 Stan Palys RC 4.00 8.00
127 Tom Sturdivant 5.00 10.00
128 Willie Kirkland RC 4.00 8.00
129 Jim Derrington RC 4.00 8.00
130 Jackie Jensen 5.00 10.00
131 Bob Henrich RC 4.00 8.00
132 Vern Law 5.00 10.00
133 Russ Nixon RC 4.00 8.00
134 Philadelphia Phillies TC 7.50 15.00
135 Mike (Moe)Drabowsky 5.00 10.00
136 Jim Finigan 4.00 8.00
137 Russ Kemmerer 4.00 8.00
138 Earl Torgeson 4.00 8.00
139 George Brunet RC 4.00 8.00
140 Wes Covington 5.00 10.00
141 Ken Lehman 4.00 8.00
142 Enos Slaughter 12.50 25.00
143 Billy Muffett RC 4.00 8.00
144 Bobby Morgan 4.00 8.00
145 Never issued
146 Dick Gray RC 4.00 8.00
147 Don McMahon RC 4.00 8.00
148 Billy Consolo 4.00 8.00
149 Tom Acker 4.00 8.00
150 Mickey Mantle 600.00 1000.00
151 Buddy Pritchard RC 4.00 8.00
152 Johnny Antonelli 5.00 10.00
153 Les Moss 4.00 8.00
154 Harry Byrd 4.00 8.00
155 Hector Lopez 5.00 10.00
156 Dick Hyde 4.00 8.00
157 Dee Fondy 4.00 8.00

1957 Topps

158 Cleveland Indians TC 7.50 15.00
159 Taylor Phillips 4.00 8.00
160 Don Hoak 5.00 10.00
161 Don Larsen 7.50 15.00
162 Gil Hodges 20.00 40.00
163 Jim Wilson 4.00 8.00
164 Bob Taylor RC 4.00 8.00
165 Bob Nieman 4.00 8.00
166 Danny O'Connell 4.00 8.00
167 Frank Baumann RC 4.00 8.00
168 Joe Cunningham 4.00 8.00
169 Ralph Terry 5.00 10.00
170 Vic Wertz 5.00 10.00
171 Harry Anderson 4.00 8.00
172 Don Gross 4.00 8.00
173 Eddie Yost 4.00 8.00
174 Kansas City Athletics TC 7.50 15.00
175 Marv Throneberry RC 7.50 15.00
176 Bob Buhl 5.00 10.00
177 Al Smith 4.00 8.00
178 Ted Kluszewski 12.50 25.00
179 Willie Miranda 4.00 8.00
180 Lindy McDaniel 5.00 10.00
181 Willie Jones 4.00 8.00
182 Joe Caffie RC 4.00 8.00
183 Dave Jolly 4.00 8.00
184 Elvin Tappe 4.00 8.00
185 Ray Boone 5.00 10.00
186 Jack Meyer 4.00 8.00
187 Sandy Koufax 150.00 250.00
188 Milt Bolling UER 4.00 8.00
(Photo actually
Lou Berberet)
189 George Susce 4.00 8.00
190 Red Schoendienst 12.50 25.00
191 Art Ceccarelli RC 4.00 8.00
192 Milt Graff 4.00 8.00
193 Jerry Lumpe RC 4.00 8.00
194 Roger Craig 5.00 10.00
195 Whitey Lockman 5.00 10.00
196 Mike Garcia 5.00 10.00
197 Haywood Sullivan 5.00 10.00
198 Bill Virdon 5.00 10.00
199 Don Blasingame 4.00 8.00
200 Bob Keegan 4.00 8.00
201 Jim Bolger 4.00 8.00
202 Woody Held RC 4.00 8.00
203 Al Walker 4.00 8.00
204 Leo Kiely 4.00 8.00
205 Johnny Temple 5.00 10.00
206 Bob Shaw RC 4.00 8.00
207 Solly Hemus 4.00 8.00
208 Cal McLish 4.00 8.00
209 Bob Anderson RC 4.00 8.00
210 Wally Moon 5.00 10.00
211 Pete Burnside RC 4.00 8.00
212 Bubba Phillips 4.00 8.00
213 Red Wilson 4.00 8.00
214 Willard Schmidt 4.00 8.00
215 Jim Gilliam 7.50 15.00
216 St. Louis Cardinals TC 7.50 15.00
217 Jack Harshman 4.00 8.00
218 Dick Rand RC 4.00 8.00
219 Camilo Pascual 5.00 10.00
220 Tom Brewer 4.00 8.00
221 Jerry Kindall RC 4.00 8.00
222 Bud Daley RC 4.00 8.00
223 Andy Pafko 5.00 10.00
224 Bob Grim 5.00 10.00
225 Billy Goodman 5.00 10.00
226 Bob Smith RC 4.00 8.00
227 Gene Stephens 4.00 8.00
228 Duke Maas 4.00 8.00
229 Frank Zupo RC 4.00 8.00
230 Richie Ashburn 20.00 40.00
231 Lloyd Merritt RC 4.00 8.00
232 Reno Bertoia 4.00 8.00
233 Mickey Vernon 5.00 10.00
234 Carl Sawatski 4.00 8.00
235 Tom Gorman 4.00 8.00
236 Ed Fitzgerald 4.00 8.00
237 Bill Wight 4.00 8.00
238 Bill Mazeroski 15.00 30.00
239 Chuck Stobbs 4.00 8.00
240 Bill Skowron 12.50 25.00
241 Dick Littlefield 4.00 8.00
242 Johnny Klippstein 4.00 8.00
243 Larry Raines RC 4.00 8.00
244 Don Demeter RC 4.00 8.00
245 Frank Lary 5.00 10.00
246 New York Yankees TC 60.00 100.00
247 Casey Wise 4.00 8.00
248 Herman Wehmeier 4.00 8.00
249 Ray Moore 4.00 8.00
250 Roy Sievers 5.00 10.00
251 Warren Hacker 4.00 8.00
252 Bob Trowbridge RC 4.00 8.00
253 Don Mueller 5.00 10.00
254 Alex Grammas 4.00 8.00
255 Bob Turley 5.00 10.00
256 Chicago White Sox TC 7.50 15.00
257 Hal Smith 4.00 8.00
258 Carl Erskine 7.50 15.00
259 Al Pilarcik 4.00 8.00
260 Frank Malzone 5.00 10.00
261 Turk Lown 4.00 8.00
262 Johnny Groth 4.00 8.00
263 Eddie Bressoud RC 5.00 10.00
264 Jack Sanford 5.00 10.00
265 Pete Runnels 5.00 10.00
266 Connie Johnson 4.00 8.00
267 Sherm Lollar 5.00 10.00
268 Granny Hamner 4.00 8.00
269 Paul Smith 4.00 8.00
270 Warren Spahn 35.00 60.00
271 Billy Martin 20.00 40.00
272 Ray Crone 4.00 8.00
273 Hal Smith 4.00 8.00
274 Rocky Bridges 4.00 8.00
275 Elston Howard 7.50 15.00
276 Bobby Avila 4.00 8.00
277 Virgil Trucks 5.00 10.00
278 Mack Burk 4.00 8.00
279 Bob Boyd 4.00 8.00
280 Jim Piersall 5.00 10.00
281 Sammy Taylor RC 4.00 8.00
282 Paul Foytack 4.00 8.00
283 Ray Shearer RC 4.00 8.00
284 Ray Katt 4.00 8.00
285 Frank Robinson 60.00 100.00
286 Gino Cimoli 4.00 8.00
287 Sam Jones 5.00 10.00
288 Harmon Killebrew 60.00 100.00
289 Series Hurling Rivals 5.00 10.00
Lou Burdette
Bobby Shantz
290 Dick Donovan 4.00 8.00
291 Don Landrum RC 4.00 8.00
292 Ned Garver 4.00 8.00
293 Gene Freese 4.00 8.00
294 Hal Jeffcoat 4.00 8.00
295 Minnie Minoso 12.50 25.00
296 Ryne Duren RC 7.50 15.00
297 Don Buddin RC 4.00 8.00
298 Jim Hearn 4.00 8.00
299 Harry Simpson 4.00 8.00
300 League Presidents 7.50 15.00
Will Harridge
Warren Giles
301 Randy Jackson 4.00 8.00
302 Mike Baxes RC 4.00 8.00
303 Neil Chrisley 4.00 8.00
304 Tigers Big Bats 12.50 25.00
Harvey Kuenn
Al Kaline
305 Clem Labine 5.00 10.00
306 Whammy Douglas RC 4.00 8.00
307 Brooks Robinson 60.00 100.00
308 Paul Giel 5.00 10.00
309 Gail Harris 4.00 8.00
310 Ernie Banks 60.00 100.00
311 Bob Purkey 4.00 8.00
312 Boston Red Sox TC 7.50 15.00
313 Bob Rush 4.00 8.00
314 Dodgers Boss and Power 30.00 50.00
Duke Snider
Walt Alston MG
315 Bob Friend 5.00 10.00
316 Tito Francona 5.00 10.00
317 Albie Pearson RC 5.00 10.00
318 Frank House 4.00 8.00
319 Lou Skizas 4.00 8.00
320 Whitey Ford 35.00 60.00
321 Sluggers Supreme 60.00 100.00
Ted Kluszewski
Ted Williams
322 Harding Peterson RC 5.00 10.00
323 Elmer Valo 4.00 8.00
324 Hoyt Wilhelm 12.50 25.00
325 Joe Adcock 5.00 10.00
326 Bob Miller 4.00 8.00
327 Chicago Cubs TC 7.50 15.00
328 Ike Delock 4.00 8.00
329 Bob Cerv 5.00 10.00
330 Ed Bailey 5.00 10.00
331 Pedro Ramos 4.00 8.00
332 Jim King 4.00 8.00
333 Andy Carey 5.00 10.00
334 Mound Aces 5.00 10.00
Bob Friend
Billy Pierce
335 Ruben Gomez 4.00 8.00
336 Bert Hamric 4.00 8.00
337 Hank Aguirre 4.00 8.00
338 Walt Dropo 5.00 10.00
339 Fred Hatfield 4.00 8.00
340 Don Newcombe 7.50 15.00
341 Pittsburgh Pirates TC 7.50 15.00
342 Jim Brosnan 5.00 10.00
343 Orlando Cepeda RC 60.00 100.00
344 Bob Porterfield 4.00 8.00
345 Jim Hegan 5.00 10.00
346 Steve Bilko 4.00 8.00
347 Don Rudolph RC 4.00 8.00
348 Chico Fernandez 4.00 8.00
349 Murry Dickson 4.00 8.00
350 Ken Boyer 12.50 25.00
351 Braves Fence Busters 20.00 40.00
Del Crandall
Eddie Mathews
Hank Aaron
Joe Adcock
352 Herb Score 7.50 15.00
353 Stan Lopata 4.00 8.00
354 Art Ditmar 5.00 10.00
355 Bill Bruton 5.00 10.00
356 Bob Malkmus RC 4.00 8.00
357 Danny McDevitt RC 4.00 8.00
358 Gene Baker 4.00 8.00
359 Billy Loes 5.00 10.00
360 Roy McMillan 5.00 10.00
361 Mike Fornieles 4.00 8.00
362 Ray Jablonski 4.00 8.00
363 Don Elston 4.00 8.00
364 Earl Battey 4.00 8.00
365 Tom Morgan 4.00 8.00
366 Gene Green RC 4.00 8.00
367 Jack Urban RC 4.00 8.00
368 Rocky Colavito 30.00 50.00
369 Ralph Lumenti RC 4.00 8.00
370 Yogi Berra 60.00 100.00
371 Marty Keough RC 4.00 8.00
372 Don Cardwell 4.00 8.00
373 Joe Pignatano RC 4.00 8.00
374 Brooks Lawrence 4.00 8.00
375 Pee Wee Reese 50.00 80.00
376 Charley Rabe RC 4.00 8.00
377A Milwaukee Braves TC 7.50 15.00
Alphabetical
377B Milwaukee Braves TC 60.00 100.00
Numerical
378 Hank Sauer 5.00 10.00
379 Ray Herbert 4.00 8.00
380 Charlie Maxwell 5.00 10.00
381 Hal Brown 4.00 8.00
382 Al Cicotte 4.00 8.00
383 Lou Berberet 4.00 8.00
384 John Goryl RC 4.00 8.00
385 Wilmer Mizell 5.00 10.00
386 Birds Young Sluggers 7.50 15.00
Ed Bailey
Birdie Tebbetts MG
Frank Robinson
387 Wally Post 5.00 10.00
388 Billy Moran RC 4.00 8.00
389 Bill Taylor 4.00 8.00
390 Del Crandall 5.00 10.00
391 Dave Melton RC 4.00 8.00
392 Bennie Daniels RC 4.00 8.00
393 Tony Kubek 15.00 30.00
394 Jim Grant RC 4.00 8.00
395 Willard Nixon 4.00 8.00
396 Dutch Dotterer RC 4.00 8.00
397A Detroit Tigers TC 7.50 15.00
Alphabetical
397B Detroit Tigers TC 60.00 100.00
Numerical
398 Gene Woodling 5.00 10.00
399 Marv Grissom 4.00 8.00
400 Nellie Fox 20.00 40.00
401 Don Bessent 4.00 8.00
402 Bobby Gene Smith 4.00 8.00
403 Steve Korcheck RC 4.00 8.00
404 Curt Simmons 5.00 10.00
405 Ken Aspromonte RC 4.00 8.00
406 Vic Power 5.00 10.00
407 Carlton Willey RC 5.00 10.00
408A Baltimore Orioles TC 7.50 15.00
Alphabetical
408B Baltimore Orioles TC 60.00 100.00
Numerical
409 Frank Thomas 5.00 10.00
410 Murray Wall 4.00 8.00
411 Tony Taylor RC 5.00 10.00
412 Gerry Staley 4.00 8.00
413 Jim Davenport RC 4.00 8.00
414 Sammy White 4.00 8.00
415 Bob Bowman 4.00 8.00
416 Foster Castleman 4.00 8.00
417 Carl Furillo 7.50 15.00
418 World Series Batting Foes 250.00 400.00
Mickey Mantle
Hank Aaron
419 Bobby Shantz 5.00 10.00
420 Vada Pinson RC 20.00 40.00
421 Dixie Howell 4.00 8.00
422 Norm Zauchin 4.00 8.00
423 Phil Clark RC 4.00 8.00
424 Larry Doby UER 12.50 25.00
Spelled Lary on the back
425 Sammy Esposito 4.00 8.00
426 Johnny O'Brien 5.00 10.00
427 Al Worthington 4.00 8.00
428A Cincinnati Reds TC 7.50 15.00
Alphabetical
428B Cincinnati Reds TC 60.00 100.00
Numerical
429 Gus Triandos 5.00 10.00
430 Bobby Thomson 5.00 10.00
431 Gene Conley 5.00 10.00
432 John Powers RC 4.00 8.00
433A Pancho Herrera COR RC 5.00 10.00
433B Pancho Herrera ERR 350.00 600.00
(most or all of the last A
missing from player's name on front)
434 Harvey Kuenn 5.00 10.00
435 Ed Roebuck 5.00 10.00
436 Rival Fence Busters 60.00 100.00
Willie Mays
Duke Snider
437 Bob Speake 4.00 8.00
438 Whitey Herzog 5.00 10.00
439 Ray Narleski 4.00 8.00
440 Eddie Mathews 50.00 80.00
441 Jim Marshall RC 5.00 10.00
442 Phil Paine RC 4.00 8.00
443 Billy Harrell SP RC 10.00 20.00
444 Danny Kravitz 4.00 8.00
445 Bob Smith RC 4.00 8.00
446 Carroll Hardy SP RC 10.00 20.00
447 Ray Monzant 4.00 8.00
448 Charlie Lau RC 5.00 10.00
449 Gene Fodge RC 4.00 8.00
450 Preston Ward SP 10.00 20.00
451 Joe Taylor RC 4.00 8.00
452 Roman Mejias 4.00 8.00
453 Tom Qualters 4.00 8.00
454 Harry Hanebrink RC 4.00 8.00
455 Hal Griggs RC 4.00 8.00
456 Dick Brown RC 4.00 8.00
457 Milt Pappas RC 5.00 10.00
458 Julio Becquer RC 4.00 8.00
459 Ron Blackburn RC 4.00 8.00
460 Chuck Essegian RC 4.00 8.00
461 Ed Mayer RC 4.00 8.00
462 Gary Geiger SP RC 10.00 20.00
463 Vito Valentinetti 4.00 8.00
464 Curt Flood RC 15.00 30.00
465 Arnie Portocarrero 4.00 8.00
466 Pete Whisenant 4.00 8.00
467 Glen Hobbie RC 4.00 8.00
468 Bob Schmidt RC 4.00 8.00
469 Don Ferrarese 4.00 8.00
470 R.C. Stevens RC 4.00 8.00
471 Lenny Green RC 4.00 8.00
472 Joey Jay 5.00 10.00
473 Bill Renna 4.00 8.00
474 Roman Semproch RC 4.00 8.00
475 All-Star Managers 12.50 25.00
Fred Haney
Casey Stengel
476 Stan Musial AS TP 30.00 50.00
477 Bill Skowron AS 5.00 10.00
478 Johnny Temple AS UER 4.00 8.00
Card says record vs American League
Temple was NL AS
479 Nellie Fox AS 7.50 15.00
480 Eddie Mathews AS 15.00 30.00
481 Frank Malzone AS 4.00 8.00
482 Ernie Banks AS 20.00 40.00
483 Luis Aparicio AS 7.50 15.00
484 Frank Robinson AS 20.00 40.00
485 Ted Williams AS 90.00 150.00
486 Willie Mays AS 35.00 60.00
487 Mickey Mantle AS TP 125.00 200.00
488 Hank Aaron AS 35.00 60.00
489 Jackie Jensen AS 5.00 10.00
490 Ed Bailey AS 4.00 8.00
491 Sherm Lollar AS 4.00 8.00
492 Bob Friend AS 4.00 8.00
493 Bob Turley AS 5.00 10.00
494 Warren Spahn AS 12.50 25.00
495 Herb Score AS 7.50 15.00
NNO Contest Cards 20.00 40.00
NNO Felt Emblem Insert

1959 Topps

The cards in this 572-card set measure 2 1/2" by 3 1/2". The 1959 Topps set contains bust pictures of the players in a colored circle. Card numbers 551 to 572 are Sporting News All-Star Selections. High numbers 507 to 572 have the card number in a black

background on the reverse rather than a green background as in the lower numbers. The high numbers are more difficult to obtain. Several cards in the 300s exist with or without an extra traded or option line on the back of the card. Cards 199 to 286 exist with either white or gray backs. There is no price differential for either colored back. Cards 461 to 470 contain "Highlights" while cards 116 to 146 give an alphabetically ordered listing of "Rookie Prospects." These Rookie Prospects (RP) were Topps' first organized inclusion of untested "Rookie" cards. Card 440 features Lew Burdette erroneously posing as a left-handed pitcher. Cards were issued in one-card penny packs or six-card nickel packs. There were some three-card advertising panels produced by Topps; the players included are from the first series. Panels which had Ted Kluszewski's card back on the back included Don McMahon/Red Wilson/Bob Boyd; Joe Pignatano/Sam Jones/Jack Urban also with Kluszewski's card back on back. Strips with Nellie Fox on the back included Billy Hunter/Chuck Stobbs/Carl Sawatski; Vito Valentinetti/Ken Lehman/Ed Bouchee; Mel Roach/Brooks Lawrence/Warren Spahn. Other panels include Harvey Kuenn/Alex Grammas/Bob Cerv; and Bob Cerv/Jim Bolger/Mickey Mantle. When separated, these advertising cards are distinguished by the non-standard card back, i.e., part of an advertisement for the 1959 Topps set instead of the typical statistics and biographical information about the player pictured. The key Rookie Cards in this set are Felipe Alou, Sparky Anderson (called George on the card), Norm Cash, Bob Gibson, and Bill White.

COMPLETE SET (572) 5000.00 8000.00
COMMON CARD (1-110) 3.00 6.00
COMMON (111-506) 2.00 4.00
COMMON (507-572) 7.50 15.00
WRAPPER (1-CENT) 100.00 125.00
WRAPPER (5-CENT) 75.00 100.00
1 Ford Frick COMM 35.00 60.00
2 Eddie Yost 4.00 8.00
3 Don McMahon 4.00 8.00
4 Albie Pearson 4.00 8.00
5 Dick Donovan 4.00 8.00
6 Alex Grammas 3.00 6.00
7 Al Pilarcik 3.00 6.00
8 Philadelphia Phillies CL 50.00 80.00
9 Paul Giel 4.00 8.00
10 Mickey Mantle 600.00 1000.00
11 Billy Hunter 4.00 8.00
12 Vern Law 4.00 8.00
13 Dick Gernert 3.00 6.00
14 Pete Whisenant 3.00 6.00
15 Dick Drott 3.00 6.00
16 Joe Pignatano 3.00 6.00
17 Danny's All-Stars 4.00 8.00
Frank Thomas
Danny Murtaugh MG
Ted Kluszewski
18 Jack Urban 3.00 6.00
19 Eddie Bressoud 3.00 6.00
20 Duke Snider 35.00 60.00
21 Connie Johnson 3.00 6.00
22 Al Smith 3.00 6.00
23 Murry Dickson 4.00 8.00
24 Red Wilson 3.00 6.00
25 Don Hoak 4.00 8.00
26 Chuck Stobbs 3.00 6.00
27 Andy Pafko 4.00 8.00
28 Al Worthington 3.00 6.00
29 Jim Bolger 3.00 6.00
30 Nellie Fox 15.00 30.00
31 Ken Lehman 3.00 6.00
32 Don Buddin 3.00 6.00
33 Ed Fitzgerald 3.00 6.00
34 Pitchers Beware 10.00 20.00
Al Kaline
Charley Maxwell
35 Ted Kluszewski 6.00 12.00
36 Hank Aguirre 3.00 6.00
37 Gene Green 3.00 6.00
38 Morrie Martin 3.00 6.00
39 Ed Bouchee 3.00 6.00
40A Warren Spahn ERR 50.00 80.00
(Born 1931)
40B Warren Spahn ERR 60.00 100.00
(Born 1931, but three
is partially obscured)
40C Warren Spahn COR 35.00 60.00
(Born 1921)
41 Bob Martyn 3.00 6.00
42 Murray Wall 3.00 6.00
43 Steve Bilko 3.00 6.00
44 Vito Valentinetti 3.00 6.00
45 Andy Carey 4.00 8.00
46 Bill R. Henry 3.00 6.00
47 Jim Finigan 3.00 6.00
48 Baltimore Orioles CL 12.50 25.00
49 Bill Hall RC 3.00 6.00
50 Willie Mays 100.00 175.00
51 Rip Coleman 3.00 6.00
52 Coot Veal RC 3.00 6.00
53 Stan Williams RC 4.00 8.00
54 Mel Roach 3.00 6.00
55 Tom Brewer 3.00 6.00
56 Carl Sawatski 3.00 6.00
57 Al Cicotte 3.00 6.00
58 Eddie Miksis 3.00 6.00
59 Irv Noren 4.00 8.00
60 Bob Turley 4.00 8.00
61 Dick Brown 3.00 6.00
62 Tony Taylor 4.00 8.00
63 Jim Hearn 3.00 6.00
64 Joe DeMaestri 3.00 6.00
65 Frank Torre 4.00 8.00
66 Joe Ginsberg 3.00 6.00
67 Brooks Lawrence 3.00 6.00
68 Dick Schofield 4.00 8.00
69 San Francisco Giants CL 12.50 25.00
70 Harvey Kuenn 4.00 8.00
71 Don Bessent 3.00 6.00
72 Bill Renna 3.00 6.00
73 Ron Jackson 4.00 8.00
74 Directing the Power 4.00 8.00
Jim Lemon
Cookie Lavagetto MG
Roy Sievers
75 Sam Jones 4.00 8.00
76 Bobby Richardson 10.00 20.00
77 John Goryl 3.00 6.00
78 Pedro Ramos 3.00 6.00
79 Harry Chiti 3.00 6.00
80 Minnie Minoso 6.00 12.00
81 Hal Jeffcoat 3.00 6.00
82 Bob Boyd 3.00 6.00
83 Bob Smith 3.00 6.00
84 Reno Bertoia 3.00 6.00
85 Harry Anderson 3.00 6.00
86 Bob Keegan 4.00 8.00
87 Danny O'Connell 3.00 6.00
88 Herb Score 6.00 12.00
89 Billy Gardner 3.00 6.00
90 Bill Skowron 6.00 12.00
91 Herb Moford RC 3.00 6.00
92 Dave Philley 3.00 6.00
93 Julio Becquer 3.00 6.00
94 Chicago White Sox CL 20.00 40.00
95 Carl Willey 3.00 6.00
96 Lou Berberet 3.00 6.00
97 Jerry Lynch 4.00 8.00
98 Arnie Portocarrero 3.00 6.00
99 Ted Kazanski 3.00 6.00
100 Bob Cerv 4.00 8.00
101 Alex Kellner 3.00 6.00
102 Felipe Alou RC 15.00 30.00
103 Billy Goodman 4.00 8.00
104 Del Rice 4.00 8.00
105 Lee Walls 3.00 6.00
106 Hal Woodeshick RC 3.00 6.00
107 Norm Larker RC 4.00 8.00
108 Zack Monroe RC 4.00 8.00
109 Bob Schmidt 3.00 6.00
110 George Witt RC 4.00 8.00
111 Cincinnati Redlegs CL 7.50 15.00
112 Billy Consolo 2.00 4.00
113 Taylor Phillips 2.00 4.00
114 Earl Battey 4.00 8.00
115 Mickey Vernon 4.00 8.00
116 Bob Allison RS RC 6.00 12.00
117 John Blanchard RS RC 6.00 12.00
118 John Buzhardt RS RC 2.50 5.00
119 Johnny Callison RS RC 6.00 12.00
120 Chuck Coles RS RC 2.50 5.00
121 Bob Conley RS RC 2.50 5.00
122 Bennie Daniels RS 2.50 5.00
123 Don Dillard RS RC 2.50 5.00
124 Dan Dobbek RS RC 2.50 5.00
125 Ron Fairly RS RC 6.00 12.00
126 Eddie Haas RS RC 2.50 5.00
127 Kent Hadley RS RC 2.50 5.00
128 Bob Hartman RS RC 2.50 5.00
129 Frank Herrera RS 2.50 5.00
130 Lou Jackson RS RC 2.50 5.00
131 Deron Johnson RS RC 6.00 12.00
132 Don Lee RS 2.50 5.00
133 Bob Lillis RS RC 2.50 5.00
134 Jim McDaniel RS RC 2.50 5.00
135 Gene Oliver RS RC 2.50 5.00
136 Jim O'Toole RS RC 2.50 5.00
137 Dick Ricketts RS RC 2.50 5.00
138 John Romano RS RC 2.50 5.00
139 Ed Sadowski RS RC 2.50 5.00
140 Charlie Secrest RS RC 2.50 5.00
141 Joe Shipley RS RC 2.50 5.00
142 Dick Stigman RS RC 2.50 5.00
143 Willie Tasby RS RC 2.50 5.00
144 Jerry Walker RS 2.50 5.00
145 Dom Zanni RS RC 2.50 5.00
146 Jerry Zimmerman RS RC 2.50 5.00
147 Cubs Clubbers 15.00 30.00
Dale Long
Ernie Banks
Walt Moryn
148 Mike McCormick 4.00 8.00
149 Jim Bunning 10.00 20.00
150 Stan Musial 60.00 120.00
151 Bob Malkmus 2.00 4.00
152 Johnny Klippstein 2.00 4.00
153 Jim Marshall 2.00 4.00
154 Ray Herbert 2.00 4.00
155 Enos Slaughter 10.00 20.00
156 Ace Hurlers 6.00 12.00
Billy Pierce
Robin Roberts
157 Felix Mantilla 2.00 4.00
158 Walt Dropo 2.00 4.00
159 Bob Shaw 4.00 8.00
160 Dick Groat 4.00 8.00
161 Frank Baumann 2.00 4.00
162 Bobby G. Smith 2.00 4.00
163 Sandy Koufax 90.00 150.00
164 Johnny Groth 2.00 4.00
165 Bill Bruton 2.00 4.00
166 Destruction Crew 15.00 30.00
Minnie Minoso
Rocky Colavito UER
(Misspelled Colovito
on card back)
Larry Doby
167 Duke Maas 2.00 4.00
168 Carroll Hardy 2.00 4.00
169 Ted Abernathy 2.00 4.00
170 Gene Woodling 4.00 8.00
171 Willard Schmidt 2.00 4.00
172 Kansas City Athletics CL 7.50 15.00
173 Bill Monbouquette RC 4.00 8.00
174 Jim Pendleton 2.00 4.00
175 Dick Farrell 4.00 8.00
176 Preston Ward 2.00 4.00
177 John Briggs RC 2.00 4.00
178 Ruben Amaro RC 6.00 12.00
179 Don Rudolph 2.00 4.00
180 Yogi Berra 50.00 80.00
181 Bob Porterfield 2.00 4.00
182 Milt Graff 2.00 4.00
183 Stu Miller 4.00 8.00
184 Harvey Haddix 4.00 8.00
185 Jim Busby 2.00 4.00
186 Mudcat Grant 4.00 8.00
187 Bubba Phillips 4.00 8.00
188 Juan Pizarro 2.00 4.00
189 Neil Chrisley 2.00 4.00
190 Bill Virdon 4.00 8.00
191 Russ Kemmerer 2.00 4.00
192 Charlie Beamon RC 2.00 4.00
193 Sammy Taylor 2.00 4.00
194 Jim Brosnan 4.00 8.00
195 Rip Repulski 2.00 4.00
196 Billy Moran 2.00 4.00
197 Ray Semproch 2.00 4.00
198 Jim Davenport 4.00 8.00
199 Leo Kiely 2.00 4.00
200 Warren Giles NL PRES 4.00 8.00
201 Tom Acker 2.00 4.00
202 Roger Maris 75.00 125.00
203 Ossie Virgil 2.00 4.00
204 Casey Wise 2.00 4.00
205 Don Larsen 4.00 8.00
206 Carl Furillo 6.00 12.00
207 George Strickland 2.00 4.00
208 Willie Jones 2.00 4.00
209 Lenny Green 2.00 4.00
210 Ed Bailey 2.00 4.00
211 Bob Blaylock RC 2.00 4.00
212 Fence Busters 50.00 80.00
Hank Aaron
Eddie Mathews
213 Jim Rivera 4.00 8.00
214 Marcelino Solis RC 2.00 4.00
215 Jim Lemon 4.00 8.00
216 Andre Rodgers 2.00 4.00
217 Carl Erskine 6.00 12.00
218 Roman Mejias 2.00 4.00
219 George Zuverink 2.00 4.00
220 Frank Malzone 4.00 8.00
221 Bob Bowman 2.00 4.00
222 Bobby Shantz 4.00 8.00
223 St. Louis Cardinals CL 7.50 15.00
224 Claude Osteen RC 4.00 8.00
225 Johnny Logan 4.00 8.00
226 Art Ceccarelli 2.00 4.00
227 Hal W. Smith 2.00 4.00
228 Don Gross 2.00 4.00
229 Vic Power 4.00 8.00
230 Bill Fischer 2.00 4.00
231 Ellis Burton RC 2.00 4.00
232 Eddie Kasko 2.00 4.00
233 Paul Foytack 2.00 4.00
234 Chuck Tanner 4.00 8.00
235 Valmy Thomas 2.00 4.00
236 Ted Bowsfield RC 2.00 4.00
237 Run Preventers 6.00 12.00
Gil McDougald
Bob Turley
Bobby Richardson
238 Gene Baker 2.00 4.00
239 Bob Trowbridge 2.00 4.00
240 Hank Bauer 6.00 12.00
241 Billy Muffett 2.00 4.00
242 Ron Samford RC 2.00 4.00
243 Marv Grissom 2.00 4.00
244 Ted Gray 2.00 4.00
245 Ned Garver 2.00 4.00
246 J.W. Porter 2.00 4.00
247 Don Ferrarese 2.00 4.00
248 Boston Red Sox CL 7.50 15.00
249 Bobby Adams 2.00 4.00
250 Billy O'Dell 2.00 4.00
251 Clete Boyer 6.00 12.00
252 Ray Boone 4.00 8.00
253 Seth Morehead RC 2.00 4.00
254 Zeke Bella RC 2.00 4.00
255 Del Ennis 4.00 8.00
256 Jerry Davie RC 2.00 4.00
257 Leon Wagner RC 4.00 8.00
258 Fred Kipp RC 2.00 4.00
259 Jim Pisoni 2.00 4.00
260 Early Wynn UER 10.00 20.00
1957 Cleevland
261 Gene Stephens 2.00 4.00
262 Hitters Foes 6.00 12.00
Johnny Podres
Clem Labine
Don Drysdale
263 Bud Daley 2.00 4.00
264 Chico Carrasquel 2.00 4.00
265 Ron Kline 2.00 4.00
266 Woody Held 2.00 4.00
267 John Romonosky RC 2.00 4.00
268 Tito Francona 4.00 8.00
269 Jack Meyer 2.00 4.00
270 Gil Hodges 15.00 30.00
271 Orlando Pena RC 2.00 4.00
272 Jerry Lumpe 2.00 4.00
273 Joey Jay 4.00 8.00
274 Jerry Kindall 4.00 8.00
275 Jack Sanford 4.00 8.00
276 Pete Daley 2.00 4.00
277 Turk Lown 4.00 8.00
278 Chuck Essegian 2.00 4.00
279 Ernie Johnson 2.00 4.00
280 Frank Bolling 2.00 4.00
281 Walt Craddock RC 2.00 4.00
282 R.C. Stevens 2.00 4.00
283 Russ Heman RC 2.00 4.00
284 Steve Korcheck 2.00 4.00
285 Joe Cunningham 2.00 4.00
286 Dean Stone 2.00 4.00
287 Don Zimmer 6.00 12.00
288 Dutch Dotterer 2.00 4.00
289 Johnny Kucks 4.00 8.00
290 Wes Covington 2.00 4.00
291 Pitching Partners 2.00 4.00
Pedro Ramos
Camilo Pascual
292 Dick Williams 4.00 8.00
293 Ray Moore 2.00 4.00
294 Hank Foiles 2.00 4.00
295 Billy Martin 15.00 30.00
296 Ernie Broglio RC 2.00 4.00
297 Jackie Brandt RC 2.00 4.00
298 Tex Clevenger 2.00 4.00
299 Billy Klaus 2.00 4.00
300 Richie Ashburn 15.00 30.00
301 Earl Averill Jr. RC 2.00 4.00
302 Don Mossi 4.00 8.00
303 Marty Keough 2.00 4.00
304 Chicago Cubs CL 7.50 15.00

Card	Low	High
305 Curt Raydon RC	2.00	4.00
306 Jim Gilliam	4.00	8.00
307 Curt Barclay	2.00	4.00
308 Norm Siebern	2.00	4.00
309 Sal Maglie	4.00	8.00
310 Luis Aparicio	10.00	20.00
311 Norm Zauchin	2.00	4.00
312 Don Newcombe	4.00	8.00
313 Frank House	2.00	4.00
314 Don Cardwell	2.00	4.00
315 Joe Adcock	4.00	8.00
316A Ralph Lumenti UER	2.00	4.00
(Option)		
(Photo actually		
Camilo Pascual)		
316B Ralph Lumenti UER	50.00	80.00
(No option)		
(Photo actually		
Camilo Pascual)		
317 NL Hitting Kings	50.00	80.00
Willie Mays		
Richie Ashburn		
318 Rocky Bridges	2.00	4.00
319 Dave Hillman	2.00	4.00
320 Bob Skinner	4.00	8.00
321A Bob Giallombardo RC	4.00	8.00
(With Option line)		
321B Bob Giallombardo ERR	50.00	80.00
(No option)		
322A Harry Hanebrink	4.00	8.00
(Traded)		
322B Harry Hanebrink	50.00	80.00
(No trade)		
323 Frank Sullivan	2.00	4.00
324 Don Demeter	2.00	4.00
325 Ken Boyer	6.00	12.00
326 Marv Throneberry	4.00	8.00
327 Gary Bell RC	2.00	4.00
328 Lou Skizas	2.00	4.00
329 Detroit Tigers CL	7.50	15.00
330 Gus Triandos	4.00	8.00
331 Steve Boros	2.00	4.00
332 Ray Monzant	2.00	4.00
333 Harry Simpson	2.00	4.00
334 Glen Hobbie	2.00	4.00
335 Johnny Temple	4.00	8.00
336A Billy Loes	4.00	8.00
(With traded line)		
336B Billy Loes	50.00	80.00
(No trade)		
337 George Crowe	2.00	4.00
338 Sparky Anderson RC	35.00	60.00
339 Roy Face	4.00	8.00
340 Roy Sievers	4.00	8.00
341 Tom Qualters	2.00	4.00
342 Ray Jablonski	2.00	4.00
343 Billy Hoeft	2.00	4.00
344 Russ Nixon	2.00	4.00
345 Gil McDougald	6.00	12.00
346 Batter Bafflers	2.00	4.00
Dave Sisler		
Tom Brewer		
347 Bob Buhl	2.00	4.00
348 Ted Lepcio	2.00	4.00
349 Hoyt Wilhelm	10.00	20.00
350 Ernie Banks	50.00	80.00
351 Earl Torgeson	2.00	4.00
352 Robin Roberts	10.00	20.00
353 Curt Flood	4.00	8.00
354 Pete Burnside	2.00	4.00
355 Jimmy Piersall	4.00	8.00
356 Bob Mabe RC	2.00	4.00
357 Dick Stuart RC	4.00	8.00
358 Ralph Terry	4.00	8.00
359 Bill White RC	10.00	20.00
360 Al Kaline	35.00	60.00
361 Willard Nixon	2.00	4.00
362A Dolan Nichols RC	2.00	4.00
(With option line)		
362B Dolan Nichols	50.00	80.00
(No option)		
363 Bobby Avila	2.00	4.00
364 Danny McDevitt	2.00	4.00
365 Gus Bell	4.00	8.00
366 Humberto Robinson	2.00	4.00
367 Cal Neeman	2.00	4.00
368 Don Mueller	4.00	8.00
369 Dick Tomanek	2.00	4.00
370 Pete Runnels	4.00	8.00
371 Dick Brodowski	2.00	4.00
372 Jim Hegan	4.00	8.00
373 Herb Plews	2.00	4.00
374 Art Ditmar	4.00	8.00
375 Bob Nieman	2.00	4.00
376 Hal Naragon	2.00	4.00
377 John Antonelli	4.00	8.00
378 Gail Harris	2.00	4.00
379 Bob Miller	2.00	4.00
380 Hank Aaron	90.00	150.00
381 Mike Baxes	2.00	4.00
382 Curt Simmons	4.00	8.00
383 Words of Wisdom	6.00	12.00
Don Larsen		
Casey Stengel MG		
384 Dave Sisler	2.00	4.00
385 Sherm Lollar	4.00	8.00
386 Jim Delsing	2.00	4.00
387 Don Drysdale	30.00	50.00
388 Bob Will RC	2.00	4.00
389 Joe Nuxhall	4.00	8.00
390 Orlando Cepeda	10.00	20.00
391 Milt Pappas	4.00	8.00
392 Whitey Herzog	4.00	8.00
393 Frank Lary	4.00	8.00
394 Randy Jackson	2.00	4.00
395 Elston Howard	6.00	12.00
396 Bob Rush	2.00	4.00
397 Washington Senators CL	7.50	15.00
398 Wally Post	4.00	8.00
399 Larry Jackson	2.00	4.00
400 Jackie Jensen	4.00	8.00
401 Ron Blackburn	2.00	4.00
402 Hector Lopez	4.00	8.00
403 Clem Labine	4.00	8.00
404 Hank Sauer	4.00	8.00
405 Roy McMillan	4.00	8.00
406 Solly Drake	2.00	4.00
407 Moe Drabowsky	4.00	8.00
408 Keystone Combo	20.00	40.00
Nellie Fox		
Luis Aparicio		
409 Gus Zernial	4.00	8.00
410 Billy Pierce	4.00	8.00
411 Whitey Lockman	4.00	8.00
412 Stan Lopata	2.00	4.00
413 Camilo Pascual UER	4.00	8.00
(Listed as Camillo		
on front and Pasqual		
on back)		
414 Dale Long	4.00	8.00
415 Bill Mazeroski	6.00	12.00
416 Haywood Sullivan	4.00	8.00
417 Virgil Trucks	4.00	8.00
418 Gino Cimoli	2.00	4.00
419 Milwaukee Braves CL	7.50	15.00
420 Rocky Colavito	15.00	30.00
421 Herman Wehmeier	2.00	4.00
422 Hobie Landrith	2.00	4.00
423 Bob Grim	4.00	8.00
424 Ken Aspromonte	2.00	4.00
425 Del Crandall	4.00	8.00
426 Gerry Staley	4.00	8.00
427 Charlie Neal	4.00	8.00
428 Buc Hill Aces	2.00	4.00
Ron Kline		
Bob Friend		
Vernon Law		
Roy Face		
429 Bobby Thomson	4.00	8.00
430 Whitey Ford	35.00	60.00
431 Whammy Douglas	2.00	4.00
432 Smoky Burgess	4.00	8.00
433 Billy Harrell	2.00	4.00
434 Hal Griggs	2.00	4.00
435 Frank Robinson	30.00	50.00
436 Granny Hamner	2.00	4.00
437 Ike Delock	2.00	4.00
438 Sammy Esposito	2.00	4.00
439 Brooks Robinson	30.00	50.00
440 Lou Burdette	4.00	8.00
(Posing as if		
lefthanded)		
441 John Roseboro	4.00	8.00
442 Ray Narleski	2.00	4.00
443 Daryl Spencer	2.00	4.00
444 Ron Hansen RC	4.00	8.00
445 Cal McLish	2.00	4.00
446 Rocky Nelson	2.00	4.00
447 Bob Anderson	2.00	4.00
448 Vada Pinson UER	6.00	12.00
(Born: 8/8/38		
should be 8/11/38)		
449 Tom Gorman	2.00	4.00
450 Eddie Mathews	20.00	40.00
451 Jimmy Constable RC	2.00	4.00
452 Chico Fernandez	2.00	4.00
453 Les Moss	2.00	4.00
454 Phil Clark	2.00	4.00
455 Larry Doby	6.00	12.00
456 Jerry Casale RC	2.00	4.00
457 Los Angeles Dodgers CL	15.00	30.00
458 Gordon Jones	2.00	4.00
459 Bill Tuttle	2.00	4.00
460 Bob Friend	4.00	8.00
461 Mickey Mantle BT	75.00	125.00
42nd Homer		
462 Rocky Colavito BT	6.00	12.00
Great Catch		
463 Al Kaline BT	15.00	30.00
Bat Champ		
464 Willie Mays BT	20.00	40.00
Catch		
465 Roy Sievers BT	4.00	8.00
Homer Mark		
466 Billy Pierce BT	4.00	8.00
AS Starter		
467 Hank Aaron BT	20.00	40.00
WS Homer		
468 Duke Snider BT	10.00	20.00
LA Victory		
469 Ernie Banks BT	10.00	20.00
MVP Award		
470 Stan Musial BT	15.00	30.00
3000 Hits		
471 Tom Sturdivant	2.00	4.00
472 Gene Freese	2.00	4.00
473 Mike Fornieles	2.00	4.00
474 Moe Thacker RC	2.00	4.00
475 Jack Harshman	2.00	4.00
476 Cleveland Indians CL	7.50	15.00
477 Barry Latman RC	2.00	4.00
478 Roberto Clemente UER	100.00	175.00
The words the best run together		
479 Lindy McDaniel	4.00	8.00
480 Red Schoendienst	6.00	12.00
481 Charlie Maxwell	4.00	8.00
482 Russ Meyer	2.00	4.00
483 Clint Courtney	2.00	4.00
484 Willie Kirkland	2.00	4.00
485 Ryne Duren	4.00	8.00
486 Sammy White	2.00	4.00
487 Hal Brown	2.00	4.00
488 Walt Moryn	2.00	4.00
489 John Powers	2.00	4.00
490 Frank Thomas	4.00	8.00
491 Don Blasingame	2.00	4.00
492 Gene Conley	4.00	8.00
493 Jim Landis	4.00	8.00
494 Don Pavletich RC	2.00	4.00
495 Johnny Podres	6.00	12.00
496 W.Terwilliger UER	2.00	4.00
Athlftics on front		
497 Hal R. Smith	2.00	4.00
498 Dick Hyde	2.00	4.00
499 Johnny O'Brien	4.00	8.00
500 Vic Wertz	4.00	8.00
501 Bob Tiefenauer RC	2.00	4.00
502 Alvin Dark	4.00	8.00
503 Jim Owens	2.00	4.00
504 Ossie Alvarez RC	2.00	4.00
505 Tony Kubek	6.00	12.00
506 Bob Purkey	2.00	4.00
507 Bob Hale	7.50	15.00
508 Art Fowler	7.50	15.00
509 Norm Cash RC	50.00	80.00
510 New York Yankees CL	75.00	125.00
511 George Susce	7.50	15.00
512 George Altman RC	7.50	15.00
513 Tommy Carroll	7.50	15.00
514 Bob Gibson RC	175.00	300.00
515 Harmon Killebrew	75.00	125.00
516 Mike Garcia	10.00	20.00
517 Joe Koppe RC	7.50	15.00
518 Mike Cueller UER RC	18.00	30.00
Sic, Cuellar		
519 Infield Power	10.00	20.00
Pete Runnels		
Dick Gernert		
Frank Malzone		
520 Don Elston	7.50	15.00
521 Gary Geiger	7.50	15.00
522 Gene Snyder RC	7.50	15.00
523 Harry Bright RC	7.50	15.00
524 Larry Osborne RC	7.50	15.00
525 Jim Coates RC	10.00	20.00
526 Bob Speake	7.50	15.00
527 Solly Hemus	7.50	15.00
528 Pittsburgh Pirates CL	50.00	80.00
529 G.Bamberger RC	10.00	20.00
530 Wally Moon	10.00	20.00
531 Ray Webster RC	7.50	15.00
532 Mark Freeman RC	7.50	15.00
533 Darrell Johnson	10.00	20.00
534 Faye Throneberry	7.50	15.00
535 Ruben Gomez	7.50	15.00
536 Danny Kravitz	7.50	15.00
537 Rudolph Arias RC	7.50	15.00
538 Chick King	7.50	15.00
539 Gary Blaylock RC	7.50	15.00
540 Willie Miranda	7.50	15.00
541 Bob Thurman	7.50	15.00
542 Jim Perry RC	18.00	30.00
543 Corsair Trio	75.00	125.00
Bob Skinner		
Bill Virdon		
Roberto Clemente		
544 Lee Tate RC	7.50	15.00
545 Tom Morgan	7.50	15.00
546 Al Schroll	7.50	15.00
547 Jim Baxes RC	7.50	15.00
548 Elmer Singleton	7.50	15.00
549 Howie Nunn RC	7.50	15.00
550 Roy Campanella	90.00	150.00
(Symbol of Courage)		
551 Fred Haney AS MG	7.50	15.00
552 Casey Stengel AS MG	18.00	30.00
553 Orlando Cepeda AS	18.00	30.00
554 Bill Skowron AS	10.00	20.00
555 Bill Mazeroski AS	18.00	30.00
556 Nellie Fox AS	20.00	40.00
557 Ken Boyer AS	18.00	30.00
558 Frank Malzone AS	7.50	15.00
559 Ernie Banks AS	35.00	60.00
560 Luis Aparicio AS	25.00	40.00
561 Hank Aaron AS	75.00	125.00
562 Al Kaline AS	35.00	60.00
563 Willie Mays AS	75.00	125.00
564 Mickey Mantle AS	175.00	300.00
565 Wes Covington AS	10.00	20.00
566 Roy Sievers AS	7.50	15.00
567 Del Crandall AS	7.50	15.00
568 Gus Triandos AS	7.50	15.00
569 Bob Friend AS	7.50	15.00
570 Bob Turley AS	7.50	15.00
571 Warren Spahn AS	30.00	50.00
572 Billy Pierce AS	25.00	40.00

1960 Topps

The cards in this 572-card set measure 2 1/2" by 3 1/2". The 1960 Topps set is the first Topps standard size issue to use a horizontally oriented front. World Series cards appeared for the first time (385 to 391), and there is a Rookie Prospect (RP) series (117-148), the most famous of which is Carl Yastrzemski, and a Sport Magazine All-Star Selection (AS) series (553-572). There are 16 manager cards listed alphabetically from 212 through 227. The 1959 Topps All-Rookie team is featured on cards 316-325. This was the first time the Topps All-Rookie team was ever selected and the only time that all of the cards were placed together in a subset. The coaching staff of each team was also afforded their own card in a 16-card subset (455-470). There is no price differential for either color back. The high series (507-572) were printed on a more limited basis than the rest of the set. The team cards have series checklists on the reverse. Cards were issued in one-card penny packs, six-card nickel packs (which came 24 to a box), 10 cent cello packs (which came 36 packs to a box) and 36-card rack packs which cost 29 cents . Three card ad-sheets have been seen. One such sheet features Wayne Terwilliger, Kent Hadley and Faye Throneberry on the front with Gene Woodling and an Ad on the back. Another sheet featured Hank Foiles/Hobie Landrith and Hal Smith on the front. The key Rookie Cards in this set are Jim Kaat, Willie McCovey and Carl Yastrzemski. Recently, a Kent Hadley was discovered with a Kansas City A's logo on the front, while this card was rumoured to exist for years, this is the first known spotting of the card. According the published reports at the time, seven copies of the Hadley card, along with the Gino Cimoli and the Faye Throneberry cards were produced. Each series of this set had different card backs. Cards numbered 1-110 had cream colored white back, cards numbered 111-198 had grey backs, cards numbered 119-286 had cream colored white backs, cards numbered 287-

Card	Low	High
COMPLETE SET (572)	2500.00	5000.00
COMMON CARD (1-440)	1.50	4.00
COMMON (441-506)	3.00	8.00
COMMON (507-572)	6.00	15.00
WRAPPER (1-CENT)	500.00	1000.00
WRAP. (1-CENT REPEAT)	250.00	500.00
WRAPPER (5-CENT)	15.00	40.00
1 Early Wynn	15.00	40.00
2 Roman Mejias	1.50	4.00
3 Joe Adcock	2.50	6.00
4 Bob Purkey	1.50	4.00
5 Wally Moon	2.50	6.00
6 Lou Berberet	1.50	4.00
7 Master and Mentor	10.00	25.00
Willie Mays		
Bill Rigney MG		
8 Bud Daley	1.50	4.00
9 Faye Throneberry	1.50	4.00
9A Faye Throneberry		
Yankees logo on Card		
10 Ernie Banks	20.00	50.00
11 Norm Siebern	1.50	4.00
12 Milt Pappas	2.50	6.00
13 Wally Post	2.50	6.00
14 Jim Grant	2.50	6.00
15 Pete Runnels	2.50	6.00
16 Ernie Broglio	2.50	6.00
17 Johnny Callison	2.50	6.00
18 Los Angeles Dodgers CL	20.00	50.00
19 Felix Mantilla	1.50	4.00
20 Roy Face	2.50	6.00
21 Dutch Dotterer	1.50	4.00
22 Rocky Bridges	1.50	4.00
23 Eddie Fisher RC	1.50	4.00
24 Dick Gray	1.50	4.00
25 Roy Sievers	2.50	6.00
26 Wayne Terwilliger	1.50	4.00
27 Dick Drott	1.50	4.00
28 Brooks Robinson	20.00	50.00
29 Clem Labine	2.50	6.00
30 Tito Francona	1.50	4.00
31 Sammy Esposito	1.50	4.00
32 Sophomore Stalwarts	1.50	4.00
Jim O'Toole		
Vada Pinson		
33 Tom Morgan	1.50	4.00
34 Sparky Anderson	6.00	15.00
35 Whitey Ford	20.00	50.00
36 Russ Nixon	1.50	4.00
37 Bill Bruton	1.50	4.00
38 Jerry Casale	1.50	4.00
39 Earl Averill Jr.	1.50	4.00
40 Joe Cunningham	1.50	4.00
41 Barry Latman	1.50	4.00
42 Hobie Landrith	1.50	4.00
43 Washington Senators CL	4.00	10.00
44 Bobby Locke RC	1.50	4.00
45 Roy McMillan	2.50	6.00
46 Jack Fisher RC	1.50	4.00
47 Don Zimmer	2.50	6.00
48 Hal W. Smith	1.50	4.00
49 Curt Raydon	1.50	4.00
50 Al Kaline	20.00	50.00
51 Jim Coates	2.50	6.00
52 Dave Philley	1.50	4.00
53 Jackie Brandt	1.50	4.00
54 Mike Fornieles	1.50	4.00
55 Bill Mazeroski	6.00	15.00
56 Steve Korcheck	1.50	4.00
57 Win Savers	1.50	4.00
Turk Lown		
Gerry Staley		
58 Gino Cimoli	1.50	4.00
58A Gino Cimoli		
Cardinals Team Logo		
Final Date on Back is July 24		
59 Juan Pizarro	1.50	4.00
60 Gus Triandos	2.50	6.00
61 Eddie Kasko	1.50	4.00
62 Roger Craig	2.50	6.00
63 George Strickland	1.50	4.00
64 Jack Meyer	1.50	4.00
65 Elston Howard	2.50	6.00
66 Bob Trowbridge	1.50	4.00
67 Jose Pagan RC	1.50	4.00
68 Dave Hillman	1.50	4.00
69 Billy Goodman	2.50	6.00
70 Lew Burdette UER	2.50	6.00
Card spelled as Lou on front and back		
71 Marty Keough	1.50	4.00
72 Detroit Tigers CL	10.00	25.00
73 Bob Gibson	20.00	50.00
74 Walt Moryn	1.50	4.00
75 Vic Power	2.50	6.00
76 Bill Fischer	1.50	4.00
77 Hank Foiles	1.50	4.00
78 Bob Grim	1.50	4.00
79 Walt Dropo	1.50	4.00
80 Johnny Antonelli	2.50	6.00
81 Russ Snyder RC	1.50	4.00
82 Ruben Gomez	1.50	4.00
83 Tony Kubek	6.00	15.00
84 Hal R. Smith	1.50	4.00
85 Frank Lary	2.50	6.00
86 Dick Gernert	1.50	4.00
87 John Romonosky	1.50	4.00
88 John Roseboro	2.50	6.00
89 Hal Brown	1.50	4.00
90 Bobby Avila	1.50	4.00
91 Bennie Daniels	1.50	4.00
92 Whitey Herzog	2.50	6.00
93 Art Schult	1.50	4.00
94 Leo Kiely	1.50	4.00
95 Frank Thomas	2.50	6.00
96 Ralph Terry	2.50	6.00
97 Ted Lepcio	1.50	4.00
98 Gordon Jones	1.50	4.00
99 Lenny Green	1.50	4.00
100 Nellie Fox	8.00	20.00
101 Bob Miller RC	1.50	4.00
102 Kent Hadley	1.50	4.00
102A Kent Hadley		
Athletics Team Logo		
103 Dick Farrell	2.50	6.00
104 Dick Schofield	2.50	6.00
105 Larry Sherry RC	2.50	6.00
106 Billy Gardner	1.50	4.00
107 Carlton Willey	1.50	4.00
108 Pete Daley	1.50	4.00
109 Clete Boyer	6.00	15.00
110 Cal McLish	1.50	4.00
111 Vic Wertz	2.50	6.00
112 Jack Harshman	1.50	4.00
113 Bob Skinner	1.50	4.00
114 Ken Aspromonte	1.50	4.00
115 Fork and Knuckler	2.50	6.00
Roy Face		
Hoyt Wilhelm		
116 Jim Rivera	1.50	4.00
117 Tom Borland RS	1.50	4.00
118 Bob Bruce RS RC	1.50	4.00
119 Chico Cardenas RS RC	2.50	6.00
120 Duke Carmel RS RC	1.50	4.00
121 Camilo Carreon RS RC	1.50	4.00
122 Don Dillard RS	1.50	4.00
123 Dan Dobbek RS	1.50	4.00
124 Jim Donohue RS RC	1.50	4.00
125 Dick Ellsworth RS RC	2.50	6.00
126 Chuck Estrada RS RC	1.50	4.00
127 Ron Hansen RS	2.50	6.00
128 Bill Harris RS RC	1.50	4.00
129 Bob Hartman RS	1.50	4.00
130 Frank Herrera RS	1.50	4.00
131 Ed Hobaugh RS RC	1.50	4.00
132 Frank Howard RS RC	10.00	25.00
133 Manuel Javier RS RC	2.50	6.00
(Sic, Julian)		
134 Deron Johnson RS	2.50	6.00
135 Ken Johnson RS RC	1.50	4.00
136 Jim Kaat RS RC	15.00	40.00
137 Lou Klimchock RS RC	1.50	4.00
138 Art Mahaffey RS RC	2.50	6.00
139 Carl Mathias RS RC	1.50	4.00
140 Julio Navarro RS RC	1.50	4.00
141 Jim Proctor RS RC	1.50	4.00
142 Bill Short RS RC	1.50	4.00
143 Al Spangler RS RC	1.50	4.00
144 Al Stieglitz RS RC	1.50	4.00
145 Jim Umbricht RS RC	1.50	4.00
146 Ted Wieand RS RC	1.50	4.00
147 Bob Will RS	1.50	4.00
148 Carl Yastrzemski RS RC	100.00	200.00
149 Bob Nieman	1.50	4.00
150 Billy Pierce	2.50	6.00
151 San Francisco Giants CL	4.00	10.00
152 Gail Harris	1.50	4.00
153 Bobby Thomson	2.50	6.00
154 Jim Davenport	2.50	6.00
155 Charlie Neal	2.50	6.00
156 Art Ceccarelli	1.50	4.00
157 Rocky Nelson	2.50	6.00
158 Wes Covington	2.50	6.00
159 Jim Piersall	2.50	6.00
160 Rival All-Stars	60.00	120.00
Mickey Mantle		
Ken Boyer		
161 Ray Narleski	1.50	4.00
162 Sammy Taylor	1.50	4.00
163 Hector Lopez	2.50	6.00
164 Cincinnati Reds CL	4.00	10.00
165 Jack Sanford	2.50	6.00
166 Chuck Essegian	1.50	4.00
167 Valmy Thomas	1.50	4.00
168 Alex Grammas	1.50	4.00
169 Jake Striker RC	1.50	4.00
170 Del Crandall	2.50	6.00
171 Johnny Groth	1.50	4.00
172 Willie Kirkland	1.50	4.00
173 Billy Martin	8.00	20.00
174 Cleveland Indians CL	4.00	10.00
175 Pedro Ramos	1.50	4.00
176 Vada Pinson	2.50	6.00
177 Johnny Kucks	1.50	4.00
178 Woody Held	1.50	4.00
179 Rip Coleman	1.50	4.00
180 Harry Simpson	1.50	4.00
181 Billy Loes	2.50	6.00
182 Glen Hobbie	1.50	4.00
183 Eli Grba RC	1.50	4.00
184 Gary Geiger	1.50	4.00
185 Jim Owens	1.50	4.00
186 Dave Sisler	1.50	4.00
187 Jay Hook RC	1.50	4.00
188 Dick Williams	2.50	6.00
189 Don McMahon	1.50	4.00
190 Gene Woodling	2.50	6.00
191 Johnny Klippstein	1.50	4.00
192 Danny O'Connell	1.50	4.00
193 Dick Hyde	1.50	4.00
194 Bobby Gene Smith	1.50	4.00
195 Lindy McDaniel	2.50	6.00
196 Andy Carey	2.50	6.00
197 Ron Kline	1.50	4.00
198 Jerry Lynch	2.50	6.00
199 Dick Donovan	2.50	6.00
200 Willie Mays	60.00	120.00
201 Larry Osborne	1.50	4.00
202 Fred Kipp	1.50	4.00
203 Sammy White	1.50	4.00
204 Ryne Duren	2.50	6.00
205 Johnny Logan	2.50	6.00
206 Claude Osteen	2.50	6.00
207 Bob Boyd	1.50	4.00
208 Chicago White Sox CL	4.00	10.00
209 Ron Blackburn	1.50	4.00
210 Harmon Killebrew	15.00	40.00
211 Taylor Phillips	1.50	4.00
212 Walter Alston MG	4.00	10.00
213 Chuck Dressen MG	2.50	6.00
214 Jimmy Dykes MG	2.50	6.00
215 Bob Elliott MG	2.50	6.00
216 Joe Gordon MG	2.50	6.00
217 Charlie Grimm MG	2.50	6.00
218 Solly Hemus MG	1.50	4.00
219 Fred Hutchinson MG	2.50	6.00
220 Billy Jurges MG	1.50	4.00
221 Cookie Lavagetto MG	1.50	4.00
222 Al Lopez MG	4.00	10.00
223 Danny Murtaugh MG	2.50	6.00
224 Paul Richards MG	2.50	6.00
225 Bill Rigney MG	1.50	4.00
226 Eddie Sawyer MG	1.50	4.00
227 Casey Stengel MG	6.00	15.00
228 Ernie Johnson	2.50	6.00
229 Joe M. Morgan RC	1.50.	4.00
230 Mound Magicians	4.00	10.00
Lou Burdette		
Warren Spahn		
Bob Buhl		
231 Hal Naragon	1.50	4.00
232 Jim Busby	1.50	4.00
233 Don Elston	1.50	4.00
234 Don Demeter	1.50	4.00
235 Gus Bell	2.50	6.00
236 Dick Ricketts	1.50	4.00
237 Elmer Valo	1.50	4.00
238 Danny Kravitz	1.50	4.00
239 Joe Shipley	1.50	4.00
240 Luis Aparicio	6.00	15.00
241 Albie Pearson	2.50	6.00
242 St. Louis Cardinals CL	4.00	10.00
243 Bubba Phillips	1.50	4.00
244 Hal Griggs	1.50	4.00
245 Eddie Yost	2.50	6.00
246 Lee Maye RC	2.50	6.00
247 Gil McDougald	4.00	10.00
248 Del Rice	1.50	4.00
249 Earl Wilson RC	2.50	6.00
250 Stan Musial	50.00	100.00
251 Bob Malkmus	1.50	4.00
252 Ray Herbert	1.50	4.00
253 Eddie Bressoud	1.50	4.00
254 Arnie Portocarrero	1.50	4.00
255 Jim Gilliam	2.50	6.00
256 Dick Brown	1.50	4.00
257 Gordy Coleman RC	1.50	4.00
258 Dick Groat	2.50	6.00
259 George Altman	1.50	4.00
260 Power Plus	6.00	15.00
Rocky Colavito		
Tito Francona		
261 Pete Burnside	1.50	4.00
262 Hank Bauer	2.50	6.00
263 Darrell Johnson	1.50	4.00
264 Robin Roberts	6.00	15.00
265 Rip Repulski	1.50	4.00
266 Joey Jay	2.50	6.00
267 Jim Marshall	1.50	4.00
268 Al Worthington	1.50	4.00
269 Gene Green	1.50	4.00
270 Bob Turley	2.50	6.00
271 Julio Becquer	1.50	4.00
272 Fred Green RC	2.50	6.00
273 Neil Chrisley	1.50	4.00
274 Tom Acker	1.50	4.00
275 Curt Flood	2.50	6.00
276 Ken McBride RC	1.50	4.00
277 Harry Bright	1.50	4.00
278 Stan Williams	2.50	6.00
279 Chuck Tanner	2.50	6.00
280 Frank Sullivan	1.50	4.00
281 Ray Boone	2.50	6.00
282 Joe Nuxhall	2.50	6.00
283 John Blanchard	2.50	6.00
284 Don Gross	1.50	4.00
285 Harry Anderson	1.50	4.00
286 Ray Semproch	1.50	4.00
287 Felipe Alou	2.50	6.00
288 Bob Mabe	1.50	4.00
289 Willie Jones	1.50	4.00
290 Jerry Lumpe	1.50	4.00
291 Bob Keegan	1.50	4.00
292 Dodger Backstops	2.50	6.00
Joe Pignatano		
John Roseboro		
293 Gene Conley	2.50	6.00
294 Tony Taylor	2.50	6.00
295 Gil Hodges	10.00	25.00
296 Nelson Chittum RC	1.50	4.00
297 Reno Bertoia	1.50	4.00
298 George Witt	1.50	4.00
299 Earl Torgeson	1.50	4.00
300 Hank Aaron	60.00	120.00
301 Jerry Davie	1.50	4.00
302 Philadelphia Phillies CL	4.00	10.00
303 Billy O'Dell	1.50	4.00
304 Joe Ginsberg	1.50	4.00
305 Richie Ashburn	8.00	20.00
306 Frank Baumann	1.50	4.00
307 Gene Oliver	1.50	4.00
308 Dick Hall	1.50	4.00
309 Bob Hale	1.50	4.00
310 Frank Malzone	2.50	6.00
311 Raul Sanchez	1.50	4.00
312 Charley Lau	2.50	6.00
313 Turk Lown	1.50	4.00
314 Chico Fernandez	1.50	4.00
315 Bobby Shantz	4.00	10.00
316 Willie McCovey ASR RC	60.00	120.00
317 Pumpsie Green ASR	2.50	6.00
318 Jim Baxes ASR	2.50	6.00
319 Joe Koppe ASR	2.50	6.00
320 Bob Allison ASR	2.50	6.00
321 Ron Fairly ASR	2.50	6.00
322 Willie Tasby ASR	2.50	6.00
323 John Romano ASR	2.50	6.00
324 Jim Perry ASR	2.50	6.00
325 Jim O'Toole ASR	2.50	6.00
326 Roberto Clemente	100.00	200.00
327 Ray Sadecki RC	1.50	4.00
328 Earl Battey	1.50	4.00
329 Zack Monroe	1.50	4.00
330 Harvey Kuenn	2.50	6.00
331 Henry Mason RC	1.50	4.00
332 New York Yankees CL	40.00	80.00
333 Danny McDevitt	1.50	4.00
334 Ted Abernathy	1.50	4.00
335 Red Schoendienst	6.00	15.00
336 Ike Delock	1.50	4.00
337 Cal Neeman	1.50	4.00
338 Ray Monzant	1.50	4.00
339 Harry Chiti	1.50	4.00
340 Harvey Haddix	2.50	6.00
341 Carroll Hardy	1.50	4.00
342 Casey Wise	1.50	4.00
343 Sandy Koufax	60.00	120.00
344 Clint Courtney	1.50	4.00
345 Don Newcombe	2.50	6.00
346 J.C. Martin UER RC	2.50	6.00
(Face actually		
Gary Peters)		
347 Ed Bouchee	1.50	4.00
348 Barry Shetrone RC	1.50	4.00
349 Moe Drabowsky	2.50	6.00
350 Mickey Mantle	300.00	600.00
351 Don Nottebart RC	1.50	4.00
352 Cincy Clouters	4.00	10.00
Gus Bell		
Frank Robinson		
Jerry Lynch		
353 Don Larsen	2.50	6.00
354 Bob Lillis	1.50	4.00
355 Bill White	2.50	6.00
356 Joe Amalfitano	1.50	4.00
357 Al Schroll	1.50	4.00
358 Joe DeMaestri	1.50	4.00
359 Buddy Gilbert RC	1.50	4.00
360 Herb Score	2.50	6.00
361 Bob Oldis	2.50	6.00
362 Russ Kemmerer	1.50	4.00
363 Gene Stephens	1.50	4.00
364 Paul Foytack	1.50	4.00
365 Minnie Minoso	4.00	10.00

366 Dallas Green RC 4.00 10.00
367 Bill Tuttle 1.50 4.00
368 Daryl Spencer 1.50 4.00
369 Billy Hoeft 1.50 4.00
370 Bill Skowron 4.00 10.00
371 Bud Byerly 1.50 4.00
372 Frank House 1.50 4.00
373 Don Hoak 2.50 6.00
374 Bob Buhl 2.50 6.00
375 Dale Long 4.00 10.00
376 John Briggs 1.50 4.00
377 Roger Maris 50.00 100.00
378 Stu Miller 2.50 6.00
379 Red Wilson 1.50 4.00
380 Bob Shaw 1.50 4.00
381 Milwaukee Braves CL 4.00 10.00
382 Ted Bowsfield 1.50 4.00
383 Leon Wagner 1.50 4.00
384 Don Cardwell 1.50 4.00
385 World Series Game 1 3.00 8.00
Charlie Neal
Steals Second
386 World Series Game 2 3.00 8.00
Charlie Neal
Belts Second Homer
387 World Series Game 3 3.00 8.00
Carl Furillo
Breaks Game
388 World Series Game 4 4.00 10.00
Gil Hodges
Winning Homer
389 World Series Game 5 4.00 10.00
Aparicio Steals Base
w/Maury Wills
390 World Series Game 6 3.00 8.00
Scrambling After Ball
391 World Series Summary 3.00 8.00
The Champs Celebrate
392 Tex Clevenger 1.50 4.00
393 Smoky Burgess 2.50 6.00
394 Norm Larker 2.50 6.00
395 Hoyt Wilhelm 6.00 15.00
396 Steve Bilko 1.50 4.00
397 Don Blasingame 1.50 4.00
398 Mike Cuellar 2.50 6.00
399 Young Hill Stars 2.50 6.00
Milt Pappas
Jack Fisher
Jerry Walker
400 Rocky Colavito 8.00 20.00
401 Bob Duliba RC 1.50 4.00
402 Dick Stuart 6.00 15.00
403 Ed Sadowski 1.50 4.00
404 Bob Rush 1.50 4.00
405 Bobby Richardson 6.00 15.00
406 Billy Klaus 1.50 4.00
407 Gary Peters RC UER 2.50 6.00
(Face actually
J.C. Martin)
408 Carl Furillo 4.00 10.00
409 Ron Samford 1.50 4.00
410 Sam Jones 2.50 6.00
411 Ed Bailey 1.50 4.00
412 Bob Anderson 1.50 4.00
413 Kansas City Athletics CL 4.00 10.00
414 Don Williams RC 1.50 4.00
415 Bob Cerv 1.50 4.00
416 Humberto Robinson 1.50 4.00
417 Chuck Cottier RC 1.50 4.00
418 Don Mossi 2.50 6.00
419 George Crowe 1.50 4.00
420 Eddie Mathews 15.00 40.00
421 Duke Maas 1.50 4.00
422 John Powers 1.50 4.00
423 Ed Fitzgerald 1.50 4.00
424 Pete Whisenant 1.50 4.00
425 Johnny Podres 2.50 6.00
426 Ron Jackson 1.50 4.00
427 Al Grunwald RC 1.50 4.00
428 Al Smith 1.50 4.00
429 American League Kings 4.00 10.00
Nellie Fox
Harvey Kuenn
430 Art Ditmar 1.50 4.00
431 Andre Rodgers 1.50 4.00
432 Chuck Stobbs 1.50 4.00
433 Irv Noren 1.50 4.00
434 Brooks Lawrence 2.50 6.00
435 Gene Freese 1.50 4.00
436 Marv Throneberry 2.50 6.00
437 Bob Friend 2.50 6.00
438 Jim Coker RC 1.50 4.00
439 Tom Brewer 1.50 4.00
440 Jim Lemon 2.50 6.00
441 Gary Bell 4.00 10.00
442 Joe Pignatano 3.00 8.00
443 Charlie Maxwell 3.00 8.00
444 Jerry Kindall 3.00 8.00
445 Warren Spahn 20.00 50.00
446 Ellis Burton 3.00 8.00
447 Ray Moore 3.00 8.00
448 Jim Gentile RC 6.00 15.00
449 Jim Brosnan 3.00 8.00
450 Orlando Cepeda 10.00 25.00
451 Curt Simmons 3.00 8.00
452 Ray Webster 3.00 8.00
453 Vern Law 10.00 25.00
454 Hal Woodeshick 3.00 8.00
455 Baltimore Coaches 3.00 8.00
Eddie Robinson
Harry Brecheen
Luman Harris
456 Red Sox Coaches 4.00 10.00
Rudy York
Billy Herman
Sal Maglie
Del Baker
457 Cubs Coaches 3.00 8.00
Charlie Root
Lou Klein
Elvin Tappe
458 White Sox Coaches 3.00 8.00
Johnny Cooney
Don Gutteridge
Tony Cuccinello
Ray Berres
459 Reds Coaches 3.00 8.00
Reggie Otero
Cot Deal
Wally Moses
460 Indians Coaches 6.00 15.00
Mel Harder
Jo Jo White
Bob Lemon
Ralph (Red) Kress
461 Tigers Coaches 4.00 10.00
Tom Ferrick
Luke Appling
Billy Hitchcock
462 Athletics Coaches 3.00 8.00
Fred Fitzsimmons
Don Heffner
Walker Cooper
463 Dodgers Coaches 3.00 8.00
Bobby Bragan
Pete Reiser
Joe Becker
Greg Mulleavy
464 Braves Coaches 3.00 8.00
Bob Scheffing
Whitlow Wyatt
Andy Pafko
George Myatt
465 Yankees Coaches 10.00 25.00
Bill Dickey
Ralph Houk
Frank Crosetti
Ed Lopat
466 Phillies Coaches 3.00 8.00
Ken Silvestri
Dick Carter
Andy Cohen
467 Pirates Coaches 3.00 8.00
Mickey Vernon
Frank Oceak
Sam Narron
Bill Burwell
468 Cardinals Coaches 3.00 8.00
Johnny Keane
Howie Pollet
Ray Katt
Harry Walker
469 Giants Coaches 3.00 8.00
Wes Westrum
Salty Parker
Bill Posedel
470 Senators Coaches 3.00 8.00
Bob Swift
Ellis Clary
Sam Mele
471 Ned Garver 3.00 8.00
472 Alvin Dark 3.00 8.00
473 Al Cicotte 3.00 8.00
474 Haywood Sullivan 3.00 8.00
475 Don Drysdale 15.00 40.00
476 Lou Johnson RC 3.00 8.00
477 Don Ferrarese 3.00 8.00
478 Frank Torre 3.00 8.00
479 Georges Maranda RC 3.00 8.00
480 Yogi Berra 40.00 80.00
481 Wes Stock RC 3.00 8.00
482 Frank Bolling 3.00 8.00
483 Camilo Pascual 3.00 8.00
484 Pittsburgh Pirates CL 15.00 40.00
485 Ken Boyer 6.00 15.00
486 Bobby Del Greco 3.00 8.00
487 Tom Sturdivant 3.00 8.00
488 Norm Cash 10.00 25.00
Shown with Indians Cap but listed as a Tiger
489 Steve Ridzik 3.00 8.00
490 Frank Robinson 20.00 50.00
491 Mel Roach 3.00 8.00
492 Larry Jackson 3.00 8.00
493 Duke Snider 20.00 50.00
494 Baltimore Orioles CL 10.00 25.00
495 Sherm Lollar 3.00 8.00
496 Bill Virdon 4.00 10.00
497 John Tsitouris 3.00 8.00
498 Al Pilarcik 3.00 8.00
499 Johnny James RC 4.00 10.00
500 Johnny Temple 3.00 8.00
501 Bob Schmidt 3.00 8.00
502 Jim Bunning 10.00 25.00
503 Don Lee 3.00 8.00
504 Seth Morehead 3.00 8.00
505 Ted Kluszewski 10.00 25.00
506 Lee Walls 3.00 8.00
507 Dick Stigman 6.00 15.00
508 Billy Consolo 6.00 15.00
509 Tommy Davis RC 10.00 25.00
510 Gerry Staley 6.00 15.00
511 Ken Walters RC 6.00 15.00
512 Joe Gibbon RC 6.00 15.00
513 Chicago Cubs CL 12.50 30.00
514 Steve Barber RC 6.00 15.00
515 Stan Lopata 6.00 15.00
516 Marty Kutyna RC 6.00 15.00
517 Charlie James RC 10.00 25.00
518 Tony Gonzalez RC 6.00 15.00
519 Ed Roebuck 6.00 15.00
520 Don Buddin 6.00 15.00
521 Mike Lee RC 6.00 15.00
522 Ken Hunt RC 12.50 30.00
523 Clay Dalrymple RC 6.00 15.00
524 Bill Henry 6.00 15.00
525 Marv Breeding RC 6.00 15.00
526 Paul Giel 10.00 25.00
527 Jose Valdivielso 10.00 25.00
528 Ben Johnson RC 6.00 15.00
529 Norm Sherry RC 8.00 20.00
530 Mike McCormick 6.00 15.00
531 Sandy Amoros 8.00 20.00
532 Mike Garcia 8.00 20.00
533 Lu Clinton RC 6.00 15.00
534 Ken MacKenzie RC 6.00 15.00
535 Whitey Lockman 6.00 15.00
536 Wynn Hawkins RC 6.00 15.00
537 Boston Red Sox CL 12.50 30.00
538 Frank Barnes RC 6.00 15.00
539 Gene Baker 6.00 15.00
540 Jerry Walker 6.00 15.00
541 Tony Curry RC 6.00 15.00
542 Ken Hamlin RC 6.00 15.00
543 Elio Chacon RC 6.00 15.00
544 Bill Monbouquette 8.00 20.00
545 Carl Sawatski 6.00 15.00
546 Hank Aguirre 6.00 15.00
547 Bob Aspromonte RC 8.00 20.00
548 Don Mincher RC 6.00 15.00
549 John Buzhardt 6.00 15.00
550 Jim Landis 6.00 15.00
551 Ed Rakow RC 6.00 15.00
552 Walt Bond RC 6.00 15.00
553 Bill Skowron AS 8.00 20.00
554 Willie McCovey AS 15.00 40.00
555 Nellie Fox AS 12.50 30.00
556 Charlie Neal AS 6.00 15.00
557 Frank Malzone AS 6.00 15.00
558 Eddie Mathews AS 15.00 40.00
559 Luis Aparicio AS 12.50 30.00
560 Ernie Banks AS 30.00 60.00
561 Al Kaline AS 30.00 60.00
562 Joe Cunningham AS 6.00 15.00
563 Mickey Mantle AS 125.00 250.00
564 Willie Mays AS 50.00 100.00
565 Roger Maris AS 50.00 100.00
566 Hank Aaron AS 50.00 100.00
567 Sherm Lollar AS 6.00 15.00
568 Del Crandall AS 6.00 15.00
569 Camilo Pascual AS 6.00 15.00
570 Don Drysdale AS 15.00 40.00
571 Billy Pierce AS 6.00 15.00
572 Johnny Antonelli AS 12.50 30.00
NNO Iron-on team transfer 2.00 5.00

1961 Topps

The cards in this 587-card set measure 2 1/2" by 3 1/2". In 1961, Topps returned to the vertical obverse format. Introduced for the first time were "League Leaders" (41-50) and separate, numbered checklist cards. Two number 463s exist: the Braves team card carrying that number was meant to be number 426. There are three versions of the second series checklist card number 98; the variations are distinguished by the color of the "CHECKLIST" headline on the front of the card, the color of the printing of the card number on the bottom of the reverse, and the presence of the copyright notice running vertically on the card back. There are two groups of managers (131-139/219-226) as well as separate subsets of World Series cards (306-313), Baseball Thrills (401-410), MVP's of the 1950's (AL 471-478/NL 479-486) and Sporting News All-Stars (566-589). The usual last series scarcity (523-589) exists. Some collectors believe that 61 high numbers are the toughest of all the Topps hi series numbers. The set actually totals 587 cards since numbers 587 and 588 were never issued. These card advertising promos have been seen: Dan Dobbek/Russ Nixon/60 NL Pitching Leaders on the front along with an ad and Roger Maris on the back.Other strips feature Jack Kralick/Dick Stigman/Joe Christopher; Ed Roebuck/Bob Schmidt/Zoilo Versalles; Lindy (McDaniel) Shows Larry (Jackson)/John Blanchard/Johnny Kucks. Cards were issued in one-card penny packs, five-card nickel packs, 10 cent cello packs (which came 36 to a box) and 36-card rack packs which cost 29 cents. The one card packs came 120 to a box. The key Rookie Cards in this set are Juan Marichal, Ron Santo and Billy Williams.

COMPLETE SET (587) 3500.00 7000.00
COMMON CARD (1-370) 1.25 3.00
COMMON (371-446) 1.50 4.00
COMMON (447-522) 3.00 8.00
COMMON (523-589) 12.50 30.00
NOT ISSUED (587/588)
WRAPPER (1-CENT) 100.00 200.00
WRAP.(1-CENT, REPEAT) 50.00 100.00
WRAPPER (5-CENT) 15.00 40.00
1 Dick Groat 12.50 30.00
2 Roger Maris 125.00 250.00
3 John Buzhardt 1.25 3.00
4 Lenny Green 1.25 3.00
5 John Romano 1.25 3.00
6 Ed Roebuck 1.25 3.00
7 Chicago White Sox TC 3.00 8.00
8 Dick Williams UER 2.50 6.00
Blurb states career high in RBI, however his career high in RBI was in 1959
9 Bob Purkey 1.25 3.00
10 Brooks Robinson 20.00 50.00
11 Curt Simmons 2.50 6.00
12 Moe Thacker 1.25 3.00
13 Chuck Cottier 1.25 3.00
14 Don Mossi 2.50 6.00
15 Willie Kirkland 1.25 3.00
16 Billy Muffett 1.25 3.00
17 Checklist 1 4.00 10.00
18 Jim Grant 2.50 6.00
19 Clete Boyer 3.00 8.00
20 Robin Roberts 6.00 15.00
21 Zorro Versalles 3.00 8.00
UER RC
First name should
be Zoilo
22 Clem Labine 2.50 6.00
23 Don Demeter 1.25 3.00
24 Ken Johnson 2.50 6.00
25 Reds Heavy Artillery 3.00 8.00
Vada Pinson
Gus Bell
Frank Robinson
26 Wes Stock 1.25 3.00
27 Jerry Kindall 1.25 3.00
28 Hector Lopez 2.50 6.00
29 Don Nottebart 1.25 3.00
30 Nellie Fox 6.00 15.00
31 Bob Schmidt 1.25 3.00
32 Ray Sadecki 1.25 3.00
33 Gary Geiger 1.25 3.00
34 Wynn Hawkins 1.25 3.00
35 Ron Santo RC 15.00 40.00
36 Jack Kralick RC 1.25 3.00
37 Charley Maxwell 2.50 6.00
38 Bob Lillis 1.25 3.00
39 Leo Posada RC 1.25 3.00
40 Bob Turley 2.50 6.00
41 NL Batting Leaders 15.00 40.00
Dick Groat
Norm Larker
Willie Mays
Roberto Clemente
42 AL Batting Leaders 3.00 8.00
Pete Runnels
Al Smith
Minnie Minoso
Bill Skowron
43 NL Home Run Leaders 12.50 30.00
Ernie Banks
Hank Aaron
Ed Mathews
Ken Boyer
44 AL Home Run Leaders 40.00 80.00
Mickey Mantle
Roger Maris
Jim Lemon
Rocky Colavito
45 NL ERA Leaders 3.00 8.00
Mike McCormick
Ernie Broglio
Don Drysdale
Bob Friend
Stan Williams
46 AL ERA Leaders 3.00 8.00
Frank Baumann
Jim Bunning
Art Ditmar
Hal Brown
47 NL Pitching Leaders 3.00 8.00
Ernie Broglio
Warren Spahn
Vern Law
Lou Burdette
48 AL Pitching Leaders 3.00 8.00
Chuck Estrada
Jim Perry UER
(Listed as an Oriole)
Bud Daley
Art Ditmar
Frank Lary
Milt Pappas
49 NL Strikeout Leaders 8.00 20.00
Don Drysdale
Sandy Koufax
Sam Jones
Ernie Broglio
50 AL Strikeout Leaders 3.00 8.00
Jim Bunning
Pedro Ramos
Early Wynn
Frank Lary
51 Detroit Tigers TC 3.00 8.00
52 George Crowe 1.25 3.00
53 Russ Nixon 1.50 3.00
54 Earl Francis RC 1.25 3.00
55 Jim Davenport 2.50 6.00
56 Russ Kemmerer 1.25 3.00
57 Marv Throneberry 2.50 6.00
58 Joe Schaffernoth RC 1.25 3.00
59 Jim Woods 1.25 3.00
60 Woody Held 1.25 3.00
61 Ron Piche RC 1.25 3.00
62 Al Pilarcik 1.25 3.00
63 Jim Kaat 3.00 8.00
64 Alex Grammas 1.25 3.00
65 Ted Kluszewski 3.00 8.00
66 Bill Henry 1.25 3.00
67 Ossie Virgil 1.25 3.00
68 Deron Johnson 2.50 6.00
69 Earl Wilson 2.50 6.00
70 Bill Virdon 2.50 6.00
71 Jerry Adair 1.25 3.00
72 Stu Miller 2.50 6.00
73 Al Spangler 1.25 3.00
74 Joe Pignatano 1.25 3.00
75 Lindy Shows Larry 2.50 6.00
Lindy McDaniel
Larry Jackson
76 Harry Anderson 1.25 3.00
77 Dick Stigman 1.25 3.00
78 Lee Walls 2.50 6.00
79 Joe Ginsberg 1.25 3.00
80 Harmon Killebrew 8.00 20.00
81 Tracy Stallard RC 1.25 3.00
82 Joe Christopher RC 1.25 3.00
83 Bob Bruce 1.25 3.00
84 Lee Maye 1.25 3.00
85 Jerry Walker 1.25 3.00
86 Los Angeles Dodgers TC 3.00 8.00
87 Joe Amalfitano 1.25 3.00
88 Richie Ashburn 6.00 15.00
89 Billy Martin 6.00 15.00
90 Gerry Staley 1.25 3.00
91 Walt Moryn 1.25 3.00
92 Hal Naragon 1.25 3.00
93 Tony Gonzalez 1.25 3.00
94 Johnny Kucks 1.25 3.00
95 Norm Cash 3.00 8.00
96 Billy O'Dell 1.25 3.00
97 Jerry Lynch 2.50 6.00
98A Checklist 2 4.00 10.00
(Red Checklist
98 black on white)
98B Checklist 2 4.00 10.00
(Yellow Checklist
98 black on white)
98C Checklist 2 4.00 10.00
(Yellow Checklist
98 white on black
no copyright)
99 Don Buddin UER 1.25 3.00
(66 HR's)
100 Harvey Haddix 2.50 6.00
101 Bubba Phillips 1.25 3.00
102 Gene Stephens 1.25 3.00
103 Ruben Amaro 1.25 3.00
104 John Blanchard 3.00 8.00
105 Carl Willey 1.25 3.00
106 Whitey Herzog 2.50 6.00
107 Seth Morehead 1.25 3.00
108 Dan Dobbek 1.25 3.00
109 Johnny Podres 3.00 8.00
110 Vada Pinson 3.00 8.00
111 Jack Meyer 1.25 3.00
112 Chico Fernandez 1.25 3.00
113 Mike Fornieles 1.25 3.00
114 Hobie Landrith 1.25 3.00
115 Johnny Antonelli 2.50 6.00
116 Joe DeMaestri 1.25 3.00
117 Dale Long 2.50 6.00
118 Chris Cannizzaro RC 1.25 3.00
119 A's Big Armor 2.50 6.00
Norm Siebern
Hank Bauer
Jerry Lumpe
120 Eddie Mathews 12.50 30.00
121 Eli Grba 2.50 6.00
122 Chicago Cubs TC 3.00 8.00
123 Billy Gardner 1.25 3.00
124 J.C. Martin 1.25 3.00
125 Steve Barber 1.25 3.00
126 Dick Stuart 2.50 6.00
127 Ron Kline 1.25 3.00
128 Rip Repulski 1.25 3.00
129 Ed Hobaugh 1.25 3.00
130 Norm Larker 1.25 3.00
131 Paul Richards MG 2.50 6.00
132 Al Lopez MG 3.00 8.00
133 Ralph Houk MG 2.50 6.00
134 Mickey Vernon MG 2.50 6.00
135 Fred Hutchinson MG 2.50 6.00
136 Walter Alston MG 3.00 8.00
137 Chuck Dressen MG 2.50 6.00
138 Danny Murtaugh MG 2.50 6.00
139 Solly Hemus MG 2.50 6.00
140 Gus Triandos 2.50 6.00
141 Billy Williams RC 30.00 60.00
142 Luis Arroyo 2.50 6.00
143 Russ Snyder 1.25 3.00
144 Jim Coker 1.25 3.00
145 Bob Buhl 2.50 6.00
146 Marty Keough 1.25 3.00
147 Ed Rakow 1.25 3.00
148 Julian Javier 2.50 6.00
149 Bob Oldis 1.25 3.00
150 Willie Mays 50.00 100.00
151 Jim Donohue 1.25 3.00
152 Earl Torgeson 1.25 3.00
153 Don Lee 1.25 3.00
154 Bobby Del Greco 1.25 3.00
155 Johnny Temple 2.50 6.00
156 Ken Hunt 2.50 6.00
157 Cal McLish 1.25 3.00
158 Pete Daley 1.25 3.00
159 Baltimore Orioles TC 3.00 8.00
160 Whitey Ford UER 20.00 50.00
Incorrectly listed
as 5'0 tall
161 Sherman Jones UER RC 1.25 3.00
(Photo actually
Eddie Fisher)
162 Jay Hook 1.25 3.00
163 Ed Sadowski 1.25 3.00
164 Felix Mantilla 1.25 3.00
165 Gino Cimoli 1.25 3.00
166 Danny Kravitz 1.25 3.00
167 San Francisco Giants TC 3.00 8.00
168 Tommy Davis 3.00 8.00
169 Don Elston 1.25 3.00
170 Al Smith 1.25 3.00
171 Paul Foytack 1.25 3.00
172 Don Dillard 1.25 3.00
173 Beantown Bombers 2.50 6.00
Frank Malzone
Vic Wertz
Jackie Jensen
174 Ray Semproch 1.25 3.00
175 Gene Freese 1.25 3.00
176 Ken Aspromonte 1.25 3.00
177 Don Larsen 2.50 6.00
178 Bob Nieman 1.25 3.00
179 Joe Koppe 1.25 3.00
180 Bobby Richardson 5.00 12.00
181 Fred Green 1.25 3.00
182 Dave Nicholson RC 1.25 3.00
183 Andre Rodgers 1.25 3.00
184 Steve Bilko 2.50 6.00
185 Herb Score 2.50 6.00
186 Elmer Valo 2.50 6.00
187 Billy Klaus 1.25 3.00
188 Jim Marshall 1.25 3.00
189A Checklist 3 4.00 10.00
(Copyright symbol
almost adjacent to
263 Ken Hamlin)
189B Checklist 3 4.00 10.00
(Copyright symbol
adjacent to
264 Glen Hobbie)
190 Stan Williams 2.50 6.00
191 Mike de la Hoz RC 1.25 3.00
192 Dick Brown 1.25 3.00
193 Gene Conley 2.50 6.00
194 Gordy Coleman 2.50 6.00
195 Jerry Casale 1.25 3.00
196 Ed Bouchee 1.25 3.00
197 Dick Hall 1.25 3.00
198 Carl Sawatski 1.25 3.00
199 Bob Boyd 1.25 3.00
200 Warren Spahn 15.00 40.00
201 Pete Whisenant 1.25 3.00
202 Al Neiger RC 1.25 3.00
203 Eddie Bressoud 1.25 3.00
204 Bob Skinner 2.50 6.00
205 Billy Pierce 2.50 6.00
206 Gene Green 1.25 3.00
207 Dodger Southpaws 12.50 30.00
Sandy Koufax
Johnny Podres
208 Larry Osborne 1.25 3.00
209 Ken McBride 1.25 3.00
210 Pete Runnels 2.50 6.00
211 Bob Gibson 15.00 40.00
212 Haywood Sullivan 2.50 6.00
213 Bill Stafford RC 1.25 3.00
214 Danny Murphy RC 2.50 6.00
215 Gus Bell 2.50 6.00
216 Ted Bowsfield 1.25 3.00
217 Mel Roach 1.25 3.00
218 Hal Brown 1.25 3.00
219 Gene Mauch MG 2.50 6.00
220 Alvin Dark MG 2.50 6.00
221 Mike Higgins MG 1.25 3.00
222 Jimmy Dykes MG 2.50 6.00
223 Bob Scheffing MG 1.25 3.00
224 Joe Gordon MG 2.50 6.00
225 Bill Rigney MG 2.50 6.00
226 Cookie Lavagetto MG 2.50 6.00
227 Juan Pizarro 1.25 3.00
228 New York Yankees TC 30.00 60.00
229 Rudy Hernandez RC 1.25 3.00
230 Don Hoak 2.50 6.00
231 Dick Drott 1.25 3.00
232 Bill White 2.50 6.00
233 Joey Jay 2.50 6.00
234 Ted Lepcio 1.25 3.00
235 Camilo Pascual 2.50 6.00
236 Don Gile RC 1.25 3.00
237 Billy Loes 2.50 6.00
238 Jim Gilliam 2.50 6.00
239 Dave Sisler 1.25 3.00
240 Ron Hansen 1.25 3.00
241 Al Cicotte 1.25 3.00
242 Hal Smith 1.25 3.00
243 Frank Lary 2.50 6.00
244 Chico Cardenas 2.50 6.00
245 Joe Adcock 2.50 6.00
246 Bob Davis RC 1.25 3.00
247 Billy Goodman 2.50 6.00
248 Ed Keegan RC 1.25 3.00
249 Cincinnati Reds TC 3.00 8.00
250 Buc Hill Aces 2.50 6.00
Vern Law
Roy Face
251 Bill Bruton 1.25 3.00
252 Bill Short 1.25 3.00
253 Sammy Taylor 1.25 3.00
254 Ted Sadowski RC 2.50 6.00
255 Vic Power 2.50 6.00
256 Billy Hoeft 1.25 3.00
257 Carroll Hardy 1.25 3.00
258 Jack Sanford 2.50 6.00
259 John Schaive RC 1.25 3.00
260 Don Drysdale 12.50 30.00
261 Charlie Lau 2.50 6.00
262 Tony Curry 1.25 3.00
263 Ken Hamlin 1.25 3.00
264 Glen Hobbie 1.25 3.00
265 Tony Kubek 5.00 12.00
266 Lindy McDaniel 2.50 6.00
267 Norm Siebern 1.25 3.00
268 Ike Delock 1.25 3.00
269 Harry Chiti 1.25 3.00
270 Bob Friend 2.50 6.00
271 Jim Landis 1.25 3.00
272 Tom Morgan 1.25 3.00
273A Checklist 4 6.00 15.00
(Copyright symbol
adjacent to
336 Don Mincher)
273B Checklist 4 4.00 10.00
(Copyright symbol
adjacent to
339 Gene Baker)
274 Gary Bell 1.25 3.00
275 Gene Woodling 2.50 6.00
276 Ray Rippelmeyer RC 1.25 3.00
277 Hank Foiles 1.25 3.00
278 Don McMahon 1.25 3.00
279 Jose Pagan 1.25 3.00
280 Frank Howard 3.00 8.00
281 Frank Sullivan 1.25 3.00
282 Faye Throneberry 1.25 3.00
283 Bob Anderson 1.25 3.00
284 Dick Gernert 1.25 3.00
285 Sherm Lollar 2.50 6.00
286 George Witt 1.25 3.00
287 Carl Yastrzemski 20.00 50.00
288 Albie Pearson 2.50 6.00
289 Ray Moore 1.25 3.00
290 Stan Musial 50.00 100.00
291 Tex Clevenger 1.25 3.00
292 Jim Baumer RC 1.25 3.00
293 Tom Sturdivant 1.25 3.00
294 Don Blasingame 1.25 3.00
295 Milt Pappas 2.50 6.00
296 Wes Covington 2.50 6.00
297 Kansas City Athletics TC 3.00 8.00
298 Jim Golden RC 1.25 3.00
299 Clay Dalrymple 1.25 3.00
300 Mickey Mantle 300.00 600.00
301 Chet Nichols 1.25 3.00
302 Al Heist RC 1.25 3.00
303 Gary Peters 2.50 6.00
304 Rocky Nelson 1.25 3.00
305 Mike McCormick 2.50 6.00
306 World Series Game 1 4.00 10.00
Bill Virdon
307 World Series Game 2 40.00 80.00
Mickey Mantle
308 World Series Game 3 5.00 12.00
Bobby Richardson
309 World Series Game 4 4.00 10.00
Gino Cimoli
310 World Series Game 5 4.00 10.00
Roy Face
311 World Series Game 6 6.00 15.00
Whitey Ford
312 World Series Game 7 8.00 20.00
Bill Mazeroski
313 World Series Summary 6.00 15.00
Winners Celebrate
314 Bob Miller 1.25 3.00
315 Earl Battey 2.50 6.00
316 Bobby Gene Smith 1.25 3.00
317 Jim Brewer RC 1.25 3.00
318 Danny O'Connell 1.25 3.00
319 Valmy Thomas 1.25 3.00
320 Lou Burdette 2.50 6.00
321 Marv Breeding 1.25 3.00
322 Bill Kunkel RC 2.50 6.00
323 Sammy Esposito 1.25 3.00
324 Hank Aguirre 1.25 3.00
325 Wally Moon 2.50 6.00
326 Dave Hillman 1.25 3.00
327 Matty Alou RC 5.00 12.00
328 Jim O'Toole 2.50 6.00
329 Julio Becquer 1.25 3.00
330 Rocky Colavito 8.00 20.00
331 Ned Garver 1.25 3.00
332 Dutch Dotterer UER 1.25 3.00
(Photo actually
Tommy Dotterer
Dutch's brother)
333 Fritz Brickell RC 1.25 3.00
334 Walt Bond 1.25 3.00
335 Frank Bolling 1.25 3.00
336 Don Mincher 2.50 6.00
337 Al's Aces 3.00 8.00
Early Wynn
Al Lopez

Herb Score
338 Don Landrum 1.25 3.00
339 Gene Baker 1.25 3.00
340 Vic Wertz 2.50 6.00
341 Jim Owens 1.25 3.00
342 Clint Courtney 1.25 3.00
343 Earl Robinson RC 1.25 3.00
344 Sandy Koufax 50.00 100.00
345 Jimmy Piersall 3.00 8.00
346 Howie Nunn 1.25 3.00
347 St. Louis Cardinals TC 3.00 8.00
348 Steve Boros 1.25 3.00
349 Danny McDevitt 1.25 3.00
350 Ernie Banks 15.00 40.00
351 Jim King 1.25 3.00
352 Bob Shaw 1.25 3.00
353 Howie Bedell RC 1.25 3.00
354 Billy Harrell 2.50 6.00
355 Bob Allison 3.00 8.00
356 Ryne Duren 1.25 3.00
357 Daryl Spencer 1.25 3.00
358 Earl Averill Jr. 2.50 6.00
359 Dallas Green 1.25 3.00
360 Frank Robinson 15.00 40.00
361A Checklist 5 6.00 15.00
(No ad on back)
361B Checklist 5 6.00 15.00
(Special Feature
ad on back)
362 Frank Funk RC 1.25 3.00
363 John Roseboro 2.50 6.00
364 Moe Drabowsky 2.50 6.00
365 Jerry Lumpe 1.25 3.00
366 Eddie Fisher 1.25 3.00
367 Jim Rivera 1.25 3.00
368 Bennie Daniels 1.25 3.00
369 Dave Philley 1.25 3.00
370 Roy Face 2.50 6.00
371 Bill Skowron SP 20.00 50.00
372 Bob Hendley RC 1.50 4.00
373 Boston Red Sox TC 3.00 8.00
374 Paul Giel 1.50 4.00
375 Ken Boyer 5.00 12.00
376 Mike Roarke RC 2.50 6.00
377 Ruben Gomez 1.50 4.00
378 Wally Post 2.50 6.00
379 Bobby Shantz 1.50 4.00
380 Minnie Minoso 3.00 8.00
381 Dave Wickersham RC 1.50 4.00
382 Frank Thomas 2.50 6.00
383 Frisco First Liners 2.50 6.00
Mike McCormick
Jack Sanford
Billy O'Dell
384 Chuck Essegian 1.50 4.00
385 Jim Perry 2.50 6.00
386 Joe Hicks 1.50 4.00
387 Duke Maas 1.50 4.00
388 Roberto Clemente 60.00 120.00
389 Ralph Terry 2.50 6.00
390 Del Crandall 3.00 8.00
391 Winston Brown RC 1.50 4.00
392 Reno Bertoia 1.50 4.00
393 Batter Bafflers 1.50 4.00
Don Cardwell
Glen Hobbie
394 Ken Walters 1.50 4.00
395 Chuck Estrada 2.50 6.00
396 Bob Aspromonte 1.50 4.00
397 Hal Woodeshick 1.50 4.00
398 Hank Bauer 2.50 6.00
399 Cliff Cook RC 1.50 4.00
400 Vern Law 2.50 6.00
401 Babe Ruth 60th HR 30.00 60.00
402 Don Larsen Perfect SP 10.00 25.00
403 26 Inning Tie 3.00 8.00
Joe OeschgerL
Leon Cadore
404 Rogers Hornsby .424 5.00 12.00
405 Lou Gehrig Streak 40.00 80.00
406 Mickey Mantle 565 HR 50.00 100.00
407 Jack Chesbro Wins 41 3.00 8.00
408 Christy Mathewson K's SP 8.00 20.00
409 Walter Johnson Shutout 5.00 12.00
410 Harvey Haddix 12 Perfect 3.00 8.00
411 Tony Taylor 2.50 6.00
412 Larry Sherry 2.50 6.00
413 Eddie Yost 2.50 6.00
414 Dick Donovan 2.50 6.00
415 Hank Aaron 60.00 120.00
416 Dick Howser RC 3.00 8.00
417 Juan Marichal SP RC 50.00 100.00
418 Ed Bailey 2.50 6.00
419 Tom Borland 1.50 4.00
420 Ernie Broglio 2.50 6.00
421 Ty Cline SP RC 8.00 20.00
422 Bud Daley 1.50 4.00
423 Charlie Neal SP 8.00 20.00
424 Turk Lown 1.50 4.00
425 Yogi Berra 40.00 80.00
426 Milwaukee Braves TC 5.00 12.00
(Back numbered 463)
427 Dick Ellsworth 2.50 6.00
428 Ray Barker SP RC 8.00 20.00
429 Al Kaline 20.00 50.00
430 Bill Mazeroski SP 20.00 50.00
431 Chuck Stobbs 1.50 4.00
432 Coot Veal 2.50 6.00
433 Art Mahaffey 1.50 4.00
434 Tom Brewer 1.50 4.00
435 Orlando Cepeda UER 5.00 12.00
(San Francis on
card front)
436 Jim Maloney SP RC 8.00 20.00
437A Checklist 6 6.00 15.00
440 Louis Aparicio
437B Checklist 6 6.00 15.00
440 Luis Aparicio
438 Curt Flood 3.00 8.00
439 Phil Regan RC 2.50 6.00
440 Luis Aparicio 5.00 12.00
441 Dick Bertell RC 1.50 4.00
442 Gordon Jones 1.50 4.00
443 Duke Snider 20.00 50.00
444 Joe Nuxhall 2.50 6.00
445 Frank Malzone 2.50 6.00
446 Bob Taylor 1.50 4.00
447 Harry Bright 3.00 8.00
448 Del Rice 6.00 15.00
449 Bob Bolin RC 3.00 8.00
450 Jim Lemon 3.00 8.00
451 Power for Ernie 3.00 8.00
Daryl Spencer
Bill White
Ernie Broglio
452 Bob Allen RC 3.00 8.00
453 Dick Schofield 3.00 8.00
454 Pumpsie Green 3.00 8.00
455 Early Wynn 6.00 15.00
456 Hal Bevan 3.00 8.00
457 Johnny James 3.00 8.00
(Listed as Angel,
but wearing Yankee
uniform and cap)
458 Willie Tasby 3.00 8.00
459 Terry Fox RC 4.00 10.00
460 Gil Hodges 10.00 25.00
461 Smoky Burgess 6.00 15.00
462 Lou Klimchock 3.00 8.00
463 Jack Fisher 3.00 8.00
(See also 426)
464 Lee Thomas RC 4.00 10.00
(Pictured with Yankee
cap but listed as
Los Angeles Angel)
465 Roy McMillan 6.00 15.00
466 Ron Moeller RC 3.00 8.00
467 Cleveland Indians TC 5.00 12.00
468 John Callison 4.00 10.00
469 Ralph Lumenti 3.00 8.00
470 Roy Sievers 4.00 10.00
471 Phil Rizzuto MVP 10.00 25.00
472 Yogi Berra MVP 20.00 50.00
473 Bob Shantz MVP 3.00 8.00
474 Al Rosen MVP 4.00 10.00
475 Mickey Mantle MVP 100.00 200.00
476 Jackie Jensen MVP 4.00 10.00
477 Nellie Fox MVP 6.00 15.00
478 Roger Maris MVP 30.00 60.00
479 Jim Konstanty MVP 3.00 8.00
480 Roy Campanella MVP 15.00 40.00
481 Hank Sauer MVP 3.00 8.00
482 Willie Mays MVP 20.00 50.00
483 Don Newcombe MVP 4.00 10.00
484 Hank Aaron MVP 20.00 50.00
485 Ernie Banks MVP 15.00 40.00
486 Dick Groat MVP 4.00 10.00
487 Gene Oliver 3.00 8.00
488 Joe McClain RC 4.00 10.00
489 Walt Dropo 3.00 8.00
490 Jim Bunning 10.00 25.00
491 Philadelphia Phillies TC 5.00 12.00
492A Ron Fairly 4.00 10.00
Area below bottom stitch of baseball is white
492B Ron Fairly 8.00 20.00
Area below bottom stitch of baseball is green
493 Don Zimmer UER 4.00 10.00
(Brooklyn A.L.)
494 Tom Cheney 6.00 15.00
495 Elston Howard 4.00 10.00
496 Ken MacKenzie 3.00 8.00
497 Willie Jones 3.00 8.00
498 Ray Herbert 3.00 8.00
499 Chuck Schilling RC 3.00 8.00
500 Harvey Kuenn 4.00 10.00
501 John DeMerit RC 3.00 8.00
502 Choo Choo Coleman RC 4.00 10.00
503 Tito Francona 3.00 8.00
504 Billy Consolo 3.00 8.00
505 Red Schoendienst 6.00 15.00
506 Willie Davis RC 6.00 15.00
507 Pete Burnside 3.00 8.00
508 Rocky Bridges 3.00 8.00
509 Camilo Carreon 3.00 8.00
510 Art Ditmar 3.00 8.00
511 Joe M. Morgan 3.00 8.00
512 Bob Will 3.00 8.00
513 Jim Brosnan 3.00 8.00
514 Jake Wood RC 3.00 8.00
515 Jackie Brandt 3.00 8.00
516 Checklist 7 6.00 15.00
517 Willie McCovey 15.00 40.00
518 Andy Carey 3.00 8.00
519 Jim Pagliaroni RC 3.00 8.00
520 Joe Cunningham 3.00 8.00
521 Brother Battery 3.00 8.00
Norm Sherry
Larry Sherry
522 Dick Farrell UER 6.00 15.00
(Phillies cap but
listed on Dodgers)
523 Joe Gibbon 12.50 30.00
524 Johnny Logan 12.50 30.00
525 Ron Perranoski RC 30.00 60.00
526 R.C. Stevens 12.50 30.00
527 Gene Leek RC 12.50 30.00
528 Pedro Ramos 12.50 30.00
529 Bob Roselli 12.50 30.00
530 Bob Malkmus 12.50 30.00
531 Jim Coates 20.00 50.00
532 Bob Hale 12.50 30.00
533 Jack Curtis RC 12.50 30.00
534 Eddie Kasko 15.00 40.00
535 Larry Jackson 12.50 30.00
536 Bill Tuttle 12.50 30.00
537 Bobby Locke 12.50 30.00
538 Chuck Hiller RC 12.50 30.00
539 Johnny Klippstein 12.50 30.00
540 Jackie Jensen 15.00 40.00
541 Roland Sheldon RC 20.00 50.00
542 Minnesota Twins TC 30.00 60.00
543 Roger Craig 15.00 40.00
544 George Thomas RC 20.00 50.00
545 Hoyt Wilhelm 30.00 60.00
546 Marty Kutyna 12.50 30.00
547 Leon Wagner 12.50 30.00
548 Ted Wills 12.50 30.00
549 Hal R. Smith 12.50 30.00
550 Frank Baumann 12.50 30.00
551 George Altman 15.00 40.00
552 Jim Archer RC 12.50 30.00
553 Bill Fischer 12.50 30.00
554 Pittsburgh Pirates TC 40.00 80.00
555 Sam Jones 12.50 30.00
556 Ken R. Hunt RC 12.50 30.00
557 Jose Valdivielso 12.50 30.00
558 Don Ferrarese 12.50 30.00
559 Jim Gentile 30.00 60.00
560 Barry Latman 15.00 40.00
561 Charley James 12.50 30.00
562 Bill Monbouquette 12.50 30.00
563 Bob Cerv 30.00 60.00
564 Don Cardwell 12.50 30.00
565 Felipe Alou 20.00 50.00
566 Paul Richards AS MG 12.50 30.00
567 Danny Murtaugh AS MG 12.50 30.00
568 Bill Skowron AS 20.00 50.00
569 Frank Herrera AS 15.00 40.00
570 Nellie Fox AS 30.00 60.00
571 Bill Mazeroski AS 30.00 60.00
572 Brooks Robinson AS 40.00 80.00
573 Ken Boyer AS 20.00 50.00
574 Luis Aparicio AS 30.00 60.00
575 Ernie Banks AS 40.00 80.00
576 Roger Maris AS 100.00 200.00
577 Hank Aaron AS 75.00 150.00
578 Mickey Mantle AS 250.00 500.00
579 Willie Mays AS 75.00 150.00
580 Al Kaline AS 40.00 80.00
581 Frank Robinson AS 40.00 80.00
582 Earl Battey AS 12.50 30.00
583 Del Crandall AS 12.50 30.00
584 Jim Perry AS 12.50 30.00
585 Bob Friend AS 12.50 30.00
586 Whitey Ford AS 50.00 100.00
589 Warren Spahn AS 50.00 100.00

1962 Topps

The cards in this 598-card set measure 2 1/2" by 3 1/2". The 1962 Topps set contains a mini-series spotlighting Babe Ruth (135-144). Other subsets in the set include League Leaders (51-60), World Series cards (232-237), In Action cards (311-319), NL All Stars (390-399), AL All Stars (466-475), and Rookie Prospects (591-598). The All-Star selections were again provided by Sport Magazine, as in 1958 and 1960. The second series had two distinct printings which are distinguishable by numerous color and pose variations. Those cards with a distinctive "green tint" are valued at a slight premuim as they are basically the result of a flawed printing process occuring early in the second series run. Card number 139 exists as A: Babe Ruth Special card, B: Hal Reniff with arms over head, or C: Hal Reniff in the same pose as card number 159. In addition, two poses exist for these cards: 129, 132, 134, 147, 174, 176, and 190. The high number series, 523 to 598, is somewhat more difficult to obtain than other cards in the set. Within the last series (523-598) there are 43 cards which were printed in lesser quantities; these are marked SP in the checklist below. In particular, the Rookie Parade subset (591-598) of this last series is even more difficult. This was the first year Topps produced multi-player Rookie Cards. The set price listed does not include the pose variations (see checklist below for individual values). A three card ad sheet has been seen. The players on the front include AL HR leaders, Barney Schultz and Carl Sawatski, while the back features an ad and a Roger Maris card. Cards were issued in one-card penny packs as well as five-card nickel packs. The five card packs came 24 to a box. The key Rookie Cards in this set are Lou Brock, Tim McCarver, Gaylord Perry, and Bob Uecker.

COMP. MASTER (688) 5000.00 10000.00
COMPLETE SET (598) 4000.00 8000.00
COMMON CARD (1-370) 2.00 5.00
COMMON (371-446) 2.50 6.00
COMMON (447-522) 5.00 12.00
COMMON (523-598) 8.00 20.00
WRAPPER (1-CENT) 50.00 100.00
WRAPPER (5-CENT) 12.50 30.00
1 Roger Maris 250.00 500.00
2 Jim Brosnan 2.00 5.00
3 Pete Runnels 2.00 5.00
4 John DeMerit 3.00 8.00
5 Sandy Koufax UER 75.00 150.00
Struck ou 18
6 Marv Breeding 2.00 5.00
7 Frank Thomas 4.00 10.00
8 Ray Herbert 2.00 5.00
9 Jim Davenport 3.00 8.00
10 Roberto Clemente 100.00 200.00
11 Tom Morgan 2.00 5.00
12 Harry Craft MG 3.00 8.00
13 Dick Howser 3.00 8.00
14 Bill White 3.00 8.00
15 Dick Donovan 2.00 5.00
16 Darrell Johnson 2.00 5.00
17 Johnny Callison 3.00 8.00
18 Managers Dream 100.00 200.00
Mickey Mantle
Willie Mays
19 Ray Washburn RC 2.00 5.00
20 Rocky Colavito 6.00 15.00
21 Jim Kaat 3.00 8.00
22A Checklist 1 ERR 5.00 12.00
(121-176 on back)
22B Checklist 1 COR 5.00 12.00
33-88 on back)
23 Norm Larker 2.00 5.00
24 Detroit Tigers TC 4.00 10.00
25 Ernie Banks 20.00 50.00
26 Chris Cannizzaro 3.00 8.00
27 Chuck Cottier 2.00 5.00
28 Minnie Minoso 4.00 10.00
29 Casey Stengel MG 8.00 20.00
30 Eddie Mathews 15.00 40.00
31 Tom Tresh RC 6.00 15.00
32 John Roseboro 3.00 8.00
33 Don Larsen 3.00 8.00
34 Johnny Temple 3.00 8.00
35 Don Schwall RC 4.00 10.00
36 Don Leppert RC 2.00 5.00
37 Tribe Hill Trio 2.00 5.00
Barry Latman
Dick Stigman
Jim Perry
38 Gene Stephens 2.00 5.00
39 Joe Koppe 2.00 5.00
40 Orlando Cepeda 6.00 15.00
41 Cliff Cook 2.00 5.00
42 Jim King 2.00 5.00
43 Los Angeles Dodgers TC 4.00 10.00
44 Don Taussig RC 2.00 5.00
45 Brooks Robinson 20.00 50.00
46 Jack Baldschun RC 2.00 5.00
47 Bob Will 2.00 5.00
48 Ralph Terry 3.00 8.00
49 Hal Jones RC 2.00 5.00
50 Stan Musial 50.00 100.00
51 AL Batting Leaders 3.00 8.00
Norm Cash
Jim Piersall
Al Kaline
Elston Howard
52 NL Batting Leaders 8.00 20.00
Roberto Clemente
Vada Pinson
Ken Boyer
Wally Moon
53 AL Home Run Leaders 50.00 100.00
Roger Maris
Mickey Mantle
Jim Gentile
Harmon Killebrew
54 NL Home Run Leaders 8.00 20.00
Orlando Cepeda
Willie Mays
Frank Robinson
55 AL ERA Leaders 3.00 8.00
Dick Donovan
Bill Stafford
Don Mossi
Milt Pappas
56 NL ERA Leaders 3.00 8.00
Warren Spahn
Jim O'Toole
Curt Simmons
Mike McCormick
57 AL Win Leaders 3.00 8.00
Whitey Ford
Frank Lary
Steve Barber
Jim Bunning
58 NL Win Leaders 3.00 8.00
Warren Spahn
Joe Jay
Jim O'Toole
59 AL Strikout Leaders 3.00 8.00
Camilo Pascual
Whitey Ford
Jim Bunning
Juan Pizzaro
60 NL Strikeout Leaders 8.00 20.00
Sandy Koufax
Stan Williams
Don Drysdale
Jim O'Toole
61 St. Louis Cardinals TC 4.00 10.00
62 Steve Boros 2.00 5.00
63 Tony Cloninger RC 3.00 8.00
64 Russ Snyder 2.00 5.00
65 Bobby Richardson 4.00 10.00
66 Cuno Barragan RC 3.00 8.00
67 Harvey Haddix 3.00 8.00
68 Ken Hunt 2.00 5.00
69 Phil Ortega RC 2.00 5.00
70 Harmon Killebrew 10.00 25.00
71 Dick LeMay RC 2.00 5.00
72 Bob's Pupils 2.00 5.00
Steve Boros
Bob Scheffing MG
Jake Wood
73 Nellie Fox 8.00 20.00
74 Bob Lillis 3.00 8.00
75 Milt Pappas 3.00 8.00
76 Howie Bedell 2.00 5.00
77 Tony Taylor 3.00 8.00
78 Gene Green 2.00 5.00
79 Ed Hobaugh 2.00 5.00
80 Vada Pinson 3.00 8.00
81 Jim Pagliaroni 2.00 5.00
82 Deron Johnson 3.00 8.00
83 Larry Jackson 2.00 5.00
84 Lenny Green 2.00 5.00
85 Gil Hodges 8.00 20.00
86 Donn Clendenon RC 3.00 8.00
87 Mike Roarke 2.00 5.00
88 Ralph Houk MG 3.00 8.00
(Berra in background)
89 Barney Schultz RC 2.00 5.00
90 Jimmy Piersall 3.00 8.00
91 J.C. Martin 2.00 5.00
92 Sam Jones 2.00 5.00
93 John Blanchard 3.00 8.00
94 Jay Hook 3.00 8.00
95 Don Hoak 3.00 8.00
96 Eli Grba 2.00 5.00
97 Tito Francona 2.00 5.00
98 Checklist 2 5.00 12.00
99 John (Boog) Powell RC 12.50 30.00
100 Warren Spahn 15.00 40.00
101 Carroll Hardy 2.00 5.00
102 Al Schroll 2.00 5.00
103 Don Blasingame 2.00 5.00
104 Ted Savage RC 2.00 5.00
105 Don Mossi 3.00 8.00
106 Carl Sawatski 2.00 5.00
107 Mike McCormick 3.00 8.00
108 Willie Davis 3.00 8.00
109 Bob Shaw 2.00 5.00
110 Bill Skowron 3.00 8.00
110A Bill Skowron 3.00 8.00
Green Tint
111 Dallas Green 3.00 8.00
111A Dallas Green 3.00 8.00
Green Tint
112 Hank Foiles 2.00 5.00
112A Hank Foiles 2.00 5.00
Green Tint
113 Chicago White Sox TC 4.00 10.00
113A Chicago White Sox TC 4.00 10.00
Green Tint
114 Howie Koplitz RC 2.00 5.00
114A Howie Koplitz 2.00 5.00
Green Tint
115 Bob Skinner 3.00 8.00
115A Bob Skinner 3.00 8.00
Green Tint
116 Herb Score 3.00 8.00
116A Herb Score 3.00 8.00
Green Tint
117 Gary Geiger 3.00 8.00
117A Gary Geiger 3.00 8.00
Green Tint
118 Julian Javier 3.00 8.00
118A Julian Javier 3.00 8.00
Green Tint
119 Danny Murphy 2.00 5.00
119A Danny Murphy 2.00 5.00
Green Tint
120 Bob Purkey 2.00 5.00
120A Bob Purkey 2.00 5.00
Green Tint
121 Billy Hitchcock MG 2.00 5.00
121A Billy Hitchcock 2.00 5.00
Green Tint
122 Norm Bass RC 2.00 5.00
122A Norm Bass 2.00 5.00
Green Tint
123 Mike de la Hoz 2.00 5.00
123A Mike de la Hoz 2.00 5.00
Green Tint
124 Bill Pleis RC 2.00 5.00
124A Bill Pleis 2.00 5.00
Green Tint
125 Gene Woodling 3.00 8.00
125A Gene Woodling 3.00 8.00
Green Tint
126 Al Cicotte 2.00 5.00
126A Al Cicotte 2.00 5.00
Green Tint
127 Pride of A's 2.00 5.00
Norm Siebern
Hank Bauer MG
Jerry Lumpe
127A Pride of A's 2.00 5.00
Norm Siebern
Hank Bauer MG
Jerry Lumpe
Green Tint
128 Art Fowler 2.00 5.00
128A Art Fowler 2.00 5.00
Green Tint
129A Lee Walls 2.00 5.00
Pinstriped Jersey
129B Lee Walls 12.50 30.00
Plain Jersey
130 Frank Bolling 2.00 5.00
130A Frank Bolling 2.00 5.00
Green Tint
131 Pete Richert RC 2.00 5.00
131A Pete Richert 2.00 5.00
Green Tint
132A Los Angeles Angels TC 4.00 10.00
(w/o Photo)
132B Los Angeles Angels TC 12.50 30.00
(With Photo)
133 Felipe Alou 3.00 8.00
133A Felipe Alou 3.00 8.00
Green Tint
134A Billy Hoeft 2.00 5.00
Blue Sky
134B Billy Hoeft 12.50 30.00
Green Sky
135 Babe Ruth Special 1 8.00 20.00
Babe as a Boy
135A Babe Ruth Special 1 8.00 20.00
Babe as a Boy
Green Tint
136 Babe Ruth Special 2 8.00 20.00
Babe Joins Yanks
Pictured Owner with Jacob Ruppert
136A Babe Ruth Special 2 8.00 20.00
Babe Joins Yanks
Pictured Owner with Jacob Ruppert
GReen Tint
137 Babe Ruth Special 3 8.00 20.00
Babe with Mgr. Huggins
137A Babe Ruth Special 3 8.00 20.00
Babe with Mgr. Huggins
Green Tint
138 Babe Ruth Special 4 8.00 20.00
The Famous Slugger
138A Babe Ruth Special 4 8.00 20.00
The Famous Slugger
Green Tint
139A1 Babe Ruth Special 5 12.50 30.00
Babe Hits 60 (Pole)
139B Hal Reniff Portrait 6.00 15.00
139C Hal Reniff Pitching 30.00 60.00
140 Babe Ruth Special 6 30.00 60.00
Gehrig and Ruth
140A Babe Ruth Special 6 30.00 60.00
Gehrig and Ruth
Green Tint
141 Babe Ruth Special 7 8.00 20.00
Twilight Years
141A Babe Ruth Special 7 8.00 20.00
Twilight Years
Green Tint
142 Babe Ruth Special 8 8.00 20.00
Coaching the Dodgers
142A Babe Ruth Special 8 8.00 20.00
Coaching the Dodgers
Green Tint
143 Babe Ruth Special 9 8.00 20.00
Greatest Sports Hero
143A Babe Ruth Special 9 8.00 20.00
Greatest Sports Hero
Green Tint
144 Babe Ruth Special 10 8.00 20.00
Farewell Speech
144A Babe Ruth Special 10 8.00 20.00
Farewell Speech
Green Tint
145 Barry Latman 2.00 5.00
145A Barry Latman 2.00 5.00
Green Tint
146 Don Demeter 2.00 5.00
146A Don Demeter 2.00 5.00
Green Tint
147A Bill Kunkel Portrait 2.00 5.00
147B Bill Kunkel Pitching 12.50 30.00
148 Wally Post 2.00 5.00
148A Wally Post 2.00 5.00
Green Tint
149 Bob Duliba 2.00 5.00
149A Bob Duliba 2.00 5.00
Green Tint
150 Al Kaline 20.00 50.00
150A Al Kaline 20.00 50.00
Green Tint
151 Johnny Klippstein 2.00 5.00
151A Johnny Klippstein 2.00 5.00
Green Tint
152 Mickey Vernon MG 3.00 8.00
152A Mickey Vernon MG 3.00 8.00
Green Tint
153 Pumpsie Green 2.50 6.00
153A Pumpsie Green 2.50 6.00
Green Tint
154 Lee Thomas 2.50 6.00
154A Lee Thomas 2.50 6.00
Green Tint
155 Stu Miller 2.50 6.00
155A Stu Miller 2.50 6.00
Green Tint
156 Merritt Ranew RC 2.00 5.00
156A Merritt Ranew 2.00 5.00
Green Tint
157 Wes Covington 3.00 8.00
157A Wes Covington 3.00 8.00
Green Tint
158 Milwaukee Braves TC 4.00 10.00
158A Milwaukee Braves TC 6.00 15.00
Green Tint
159 Hal Reniff RC 3.00 8.00
160 Dick Stuart 3.00 8.00
160A Dick Stuart 3.00 8.00
Green Tint
161 Frank Baumann 2.00 5.00
161A Frank Baumann 2.00 5.00
Green Tint
162 Sammy Drake RC 2.00 5.00
162A Sammy Drake 2.00 5.00
Green Tint
163 Hot Corner Guard 3.00 8.00
Billy Gardner
Cletis Boyer
163A Hot Corner Guard 3.00 8.00
Billy Gardner
Cletis Boyer
Green Tint
164 Hal Naragon 2.00 5.00
164A Hal Naragon 2.00 5.00
Green Tint
165 Jackie Brandt 2.00 5.00
165A Jackie Brandt 2.00 5.00
Green Tint
166 Don Lee 2.00 5.00
166A Don Lee 2.00 5.00
Green Tint
167 Tim McCarver RC 12.50 30.00
167A Tim McCarver 12.50 30.00
Green Tint
168 Leo Posada 2.00 5.00
168A Leo Posada 2.00 5.00
Green Tint
169 Bob Cerv 4.00 10.00
169A Bob Cerv 4.00 10.00
Green Tint
170 Ron Santo 6.00 15.00
170A Ron Santo 6.00 15.00
Green Tint
171 Dave Sisler 2.00 5.00
171A Dave Sisler 2.00 5.00
Green Tint
172 Fred Hutchinson MG 3.00 8.00
172A Fred Hutchinson MG 3.00 8.00
Green Tint
173 Chico Fernandez 2.00 5.00
173A Chico Fernandez 2.00 5.00
Green Tint
174A Carl Willey w/o Cap 2.00 5.00
174B Carl Willey w/Cap 12.50 30.00
175 Frank Howard 4.00 10.00
175A Frank Howard 4.00 10.00
Green Tint
176A Eddie Yost Portrait 2.00 5.00
176B Eddie Yost Batting 12.50 30.00
177 Bobby Shantz 3.00 8.00
177A Bobby Shantz 3.00 8.00
Green Tint
178 Camilo Carreon 2.00 5.00
178A Camilo Carreon 2.00 5.00
Green Tint
179 Tom Sturdivant 2.00 5.00
179A Tom Sturdivant 2.00 5.00
Green Tint
180 Bob Allison 4.00 10.00
180A Bob Allison 4.00 10.00
Green Tint
181 Paul Brown RC 2.00 5.00
181A Paul Brown 2.00 5.00
Green Tint
182 Bob Nieman 2.00 5.00
182A Bob Nieman 2.00 5.00
Green Tint
183 Roger Craig 3.00 8.00
183A Roger Craig 3.00 8.00
Green Tint
184 Haywood Sullivan 3.00 8.00
184A Haywood Sullivan 3.00 8.00
Green Tint
185 Roland Sheldon 4.00 10.00
185A Roland Sheldon 4.00 10.00
Green Tint
186 Mack Jones RC 2.00 5.00
186A Mack Jones 2.00 5.00
Green Tint
187 Gene Conley 2.00 5.00
187A Gene Conley 2.00 5.00
Green Tint
188 Chuck Hiller 2.00 5.00
188A Chuck Hiller 2.00 5.00
Green Tint
189 Dick Hall 2.00 5.00
189A Dick Hall 2.00 5.00
Green Tint
190A Wally Moon No Cap 3.00 8.00
190B Wally Moon With Cap 12.50 30.00
191 Jim Brewer 2.00 5.00
191A Jim Brewer 2.00 5.00
Green Tint
192A Checklist 3 w/o Comma 5.00 12.00
192B Checklist 3 w/Comma 6.00 15.00
193 Eddie Kasko 2.00 5.00
193A Eddie Kasko 2.00 5.00
Green Tint
194 Dean Chance RC 3.00 8.00

194A Dean Chance 3.00 8.00
Green Tint
195 Joe Cunningham 2.00 5.00
195A Joe Cunningham 2.00 5.00
Green Tint
196 Terry Fox 2.00 5.00
196A Terry Fox 2.00 5.00
Green Tint
197 Daryl Spencer 2.00 5.00
198 Johnny Keane MG 2.00 5.00
199 Gaylord Perry RC 40.00 80.00
200 Mickey Mantle 300.00 600.00
201 Ike Delock 2.00 5.00
202 Carl Warwick RC 2.00 5.00
203 Jack Fisher 2.00 5.00
204 Johnny Weekly RC 2.00 5.00
205 Gene Freese 2.00 5.00
206 Washington Senators TC 4.00 10.00
207 Pete Burnside 2.00 5.00
208 Billy Martin 8.00 20.00
209 Jim Fregosi RC 6.00 15.00
210 Roy Face 3.00 8.00
211 Midway Masters 2.00 5.00
Frank Bolling
Roy McMillan
212 Jim Owens 2.00 5.00
213 Richie Ashburn 8.00 20.00
214 Dom Zanni 2.00 5.00
215 Woody Held 2.00 5.00
216 Ron Kline 2.00 5.00
217 Walter Alston MG 4.00 10.00
218 Joe Torre RC 15.00 40.00
219 Al Downing RC 3.00 8.00
220 Roy Sievers 3.00 8.00
221 Bill Short 2.00 5.00
222 Jerry Zimmerman 2.00 5.00
223 Alex Grammas 2.00 5.00
224 Don Rudolph 2.00 5.00
225 Frank Malzone 3.00 8.00
226 San Francisco Giants TC 4.00 10.00
227 Bob Tiefenauer 2.00 5.00
228 Dale Long 4.00 10.00
229 Jesus McFarlane RC 2.00 5.00
230 Camilo Pascual 3.00 8.00
231 Ernie Bowman RC 2.00 5.00
232 World Series Game 1 4.00 10.00
Yanks Win Opener
233 World Series Game 2 4.00 10.00
Joey Jay
234 World Series Game 3 10.00 25.00
Roger Maris
235 World Series Game 4 6.00 15.00
Whitey Ford
236 World Series Game 5 4.00 10.00
Yanks Crush Reds
237 World Series Summary 4.00 10.00
Yanks Celebrate
238 Norm Sherry 2.00 5.00
239 Cecil Butler RC 2.00 5.00
240 George Altman 2.00 5.00
241 Johnny Kucks 2.00 5.00
242 Mel McGaha MG RC 2.00 5.00
243 Robin Roberts 6.00 15.00
244 Don Gile 2.00 5.00
245 Ron Hansen 2.00 5.00
246 Art Ditmar 2.00 5.00
247 Joe Pignatano 2.00 5.00
248 Bob Aspromonte 3.00 8.00
249 Ed Keegan 2.00 5.00
250 Norm Cash 4.00 10.00
251 New York Yankees TC 20.00 50.00
252 Earl Francis 2.00 5.00
253 Harry Chiti CO 2.00 5.00
254 Gordon Windhorn RC 2.00 5.00
255 Juan Pizarro 2.00 5.00
256 Elio Chacon 3.00 8.00
257 Jack Spring RC 2.00 5.00
258 Marty Keough 2.00 5.00
259 Lou Klimchock 2.00 5.00
260 Billy Pierce 3.00 8.00
261 George Alusik RC 2.00 5.00
262 Bob Schmidt 2.00 5.00
263 The Right Pitch 2.00 5.00
Bob Purkey
Jim Turner CO
Joe Jay
264 Dick Ellsworth 3.00 8.00
265 Joe Adcock 3.00 8.00
266 John Anderson RC 2.00 5.00
267 Dan Dobbek 2.00 5.00
268 Ken McBride 2.00 5.00
269 Bob Oldis 2.00 5.00
270 Dick Groat 3.00 8.00
271 Ray Rippelmeyer 2.00 5.00
272 Earl Robinson 2.00 5.00
273 Gary Bell 2.00 5.00
274 Sammy Taylor 2.00 5.00
275 Norm Siebern 2.00 5.00
276 Hal Kolstad RC 2.00 5.00
277 Checklist 4 6.00 15.00
278 Ken Johnson 3.00 8.00
279 Hobie Landrith UER 3.00 8.00
(Wrong birthdate)
280 Johnny Podres 3.00 8.00
281 Jake Gibbs RC 4.00 10.00
282 Dave Hillman 2.00 5.00
283 Charlie Smith RC 2.00 5.00
284 Ruben Amaro 2.00 5.00
285 Curt Simmons 3.00 8.00
286 Al Lopez MG 4.00 10.00
287 George Witt 2.00 5.00
288 Billy Williams 12.50 30.00
289 Mike Krsnich RC 2.00 5.00
290 Jim Gentile 3.00 8.00
291 Hal Stowe RC 2.00 5.00
292 Jerry Kindall 2.00 5.00
293 Bob Miller 3.00 8.00
294 Philadelphia Phillies TC 4.00 10.00
295 Vern Law 3.00 8.00
296 Ken Hamlin 2.00 5.00
297 Ron Perranoski 3.00 8.00
298 Bill Tuttle 2.00 5.00
299 Don Wert RC 2.00 5.00
300 Willie Mays 125.00 250.00
301 Galen Cisco RC 2.00 5.00
302 Johnny Edwards RC 2.00 5.00
303 Frank Torre 3.00 8.00
304 Dick Farrell 3.00 8.00
305 Jerry Lumpe 2.00 5.00
306 Redbird Rippers 2.00 5.00
Lindy McDaniel
Larry Jackson
307 Jim Grant 3.00 8.00
308 Neil Chrisley 3.00 8.00
309 Moe Morhardt RC 2.00 5.00
310 Whitey Ford 20.00 50.00
311 Tony Kubek IA 3.00 8.00
312 Warren Spahn IA 6.00 15.00
313 Roger Maris IA 40.00 80.00
314 Rocky Colavito IA 3.00 8.00
315 Whitey Ford IA 6.00 15.00
316 Harmon Killebrew IA 6.00 15.00
317 Stan Musial IA 8.00 20.00
318 Mickey Mantle IA 75.00 150.00
319 Mike McCormick IA 2.00 5.00
320 Hank Aaron 75.00 150.00
321 Lee Stange RC 2.00 5.00
322 Alvin Dark MG 3.00 8.00
323 Don Landrum 2.00 5.00
324 Joe McClain 2.00 5.00
325 Luis Aparicio 6.00 15.00
326 Tom Parsons RC 2.00 5.00
327 Ozzie Virgil 2.00 5.00
328 Ken Walters 2.00 5.00
329 Bob Bolin 2.00 5.00
330 John Romano 2.00 5.00
331 Moe Drabowsky 3.00 8.00
332 Don Buddin 2.00 5.00
333 Frank Cipriani RC 2.00 5.00
334 Boston Red Sox TC 4.00 10.00
335 Bill Bruton 2.00 5.00
336 Billy Muffett 2.00 5.00
337 Jim Marshall 3.00 8.00
338 Billy Gardner 2.00 5.00
339 Jose Valdivielso 2.00 5.00
340 Don Drysdale 20.00 50.00
341 Mike Hershberger RC 2.00 5.00
342 Ed Rakow 2.00 5.00
343 Albie Pearson 3.00 8.00
344 Ed Bauta RC 2.00 5.00
345 Chuck Schilling 2.00 5.00
346 Jack Kralick 2.00 5.00
347 Chuck Hinton RC 2.00 5.00
348 Larry Burright RC 3.00 8.00
349 Paul Foytack 2.00 5.00
350 Frank Robinson 20.00 50.00
351 Braves Backstops 3.00 8.00
Joe Torre
Del Crandall
352 Frank Sullivan 2.00 5.00
353 Bill Mazeroski 6.00 15.00
354 Roman Mejias 3.00 8.00
355 Steve Barber 2.00 5.00
356 Tom Haller RC 2.00 5.00
357 Jerry Walker 2.00 5.00
358 Tommy Davis 3.00 8.00
359 Bobby Locke 2.00 5.00
360 Yogi Berra 40.00 80.00
361 Bob Hendley 2.00 5.00
362 Ty Cline 2.00 5.00
363 Bob Roselli 2.00 5.00
364 Ken Hunt 2.00 5.00
365 Charlie Neal 3.00 8.00
366 Phil Regan 3.00 8.00
367 Checklist 5 6.00 15.00
368 Bob Tillman RC 2.00 5.00
369 Ted Bowsfield 2.00 5.00
370 Ken Boyer 4.00 10.00
371 Earl Battey 2.50 6.00
372 Jack Curtis 2.50 6.00
373 Al Heist 2.50 6.00
374 Gene Mauch MG 4.00 10.00
375 Ron Fairly 4.00 10.00
376 Bud Daley 3.00 8.00
377 John Orsino RC 2.50 6.00
378 Bennie Daniels 2.50 6.00
379 Chuck Essegian 2.50 6.00
380 Lou Burdette 4.00 10.00
381 Chico Cardenas 4.00 10.00
382 Dick Williams 3.00 8.00
383 Ray Sadecki 2.50 6.00
384 Kansas City Athletics TC 4.00 10.00
385 Early Wynn 6.00 15.00
386 Don Mincher 3.00 8.00
387 Lou Brock RC 60.00 120.00
388 Ryne Duren 3.00 8.00
389 Smoky Burgess 4.00 10.00
390 Orlando Cepeda AS 4.00 10.00
391 Bill Mazeroski AS 4.00 10.00
392 Ken Boyer AS UER 3.00 8.00
Batting Average mistakenly listed as .392
393 Roy McMillan AS 2.50 6.00
394 Hank Aaron AS 20.00 50.00
395 Willie Mays AS 20.00 50.00
396 Frank Robinson AS 6.00 15.00
397 John Roseboro AS 2.50 6.00
398 Don Drysdale AS 6.00 15.00
399 Warren Spahn AS 6.00 15.00
400 Elston Howard 4.00 10.00
401 AL and NL Homer Kings 30.00 60.00
Roger Maris
Orlando Cepeda
402 Gino Cimoli 2.50 6.00
403 Chet Nichols 2.50 6.00
404 Tim Harkness RC 2.50 6.00
405 Jim Perry 3.00 8.00
406 Bob Taylor 2.50 6.00
407 Hank Aguirre 2.50 6.00
408 Gus Bell 3.00 8.00
409 Pittsburgh Pirates TC 4.00 10.00
410 Al Smith 2.50 6.00
411 Danny O'Connell 2.50 6.00
412 Charlie James 2.50 6.00
413 Matty Alou 4.00 10.00
414 Joe Gaines RC 2.50 6.00
415 Bill Virdon 4.00 10.00
416 Bob Scheffing MG 2.50 6.00
417 Joe Azcue RC 2.50 6.00
418 Andy Carey 2.50 6.00
419 Bob Bruce 3.00 8.00
420 Gus Triandos 3.00 8.00
421 Ken MacKenzie 3.00 8.00
422 Steve Bilko 2.50 6.00
423 Rival League Relief Aces 4.00 10.00
Roy Face
Hoyt Wilhelm
424 Al McBean RC 2.50 6.00
425 Carl Yastrzemski 60.00 120.00
426 Bob Farley RC 2.50 6.00
427 Jake Wood 2.50 6.00
428 Joe Hicks 2.50 6.00
429 Billy O'Dell 2.50 6.00
430 Tony Kubek 6.00 15.00
431 Bob (Buck) Rodgers RC 3.00 8.00
432 Jim Pendleton 2.50 6.00
433 Jim Archer 2.50 6.00
434 Clay Dalrymple 2.50 6.00
435 Larry Sherry 3.00 8.00
436 Felix Mantilla 3.00 8.00
437 Ray Moore 2.50 6.00
438 Dick Brown 2.50 6.00
439 Jerry Buchek RC 2.50 6.00
440 Joey Jay 2.50 6.00
441 Checklist 6 6.00 15.00
442 Wes Stock 2.50 6.00
443 Del Crandall 3.00 8.00
444 Ted Wills 2.50 6.00
445 Vic Power 3.00 8.00
446 Don Elston 2.50 6.00
447 Willie Kirkland 5.00 12.00
448 Joe Gibbon 5.00 12.00
449 Jerry Adair 5.00 12.00
450 Jim O'Toole 6.00 15.00
451 Jose Tartabull RC 6.00 15.00
452 Earl Averill Jr. 5.00 12.00
453 Cal McLish 5.00 12.00
454 Floyd Robinson RC 5.00 12.00
455 Luis Arroyo 6.00 15.00
456 Joe Amalfitano 6.00 15.00
457 Lou Clinton 5.00 12.00
458A Bob Buhl M on Cap 6.00 15.00
458B Bob Buhl Plain Cap 20.00 50.00
459 Ed Bailey 5.00 12.00
460 Jim Bunning 8.00 20.00
461 Ken Hubbs RC 12.50 30.00
462A Willie Tasby W on Cap 5.00 12.00
462B Willie Tasby Plain Cap 20.00 50.00
463 Hank Bauer MG 6.00 15.00
464 Al Jackson RC 5.00 12.00
465 Cincinnati Reds TC 8.00 20.00
466 Norm Cash AS 6.00 15.00
467 Chuck Schilling AS 5.00 12.00
468 Brooks Robinson AS 10.00 25.00
469 Luis Aparicio AS 6.00 15.00
470 Al Kaline AS 10.00 25.00
471 Mickey Mantle AS 100.00 200.00
472 Rocky Colavito AS 6.00 15.00
473 Elston Howard AS 6.00 15.00
474 Frank Lary AS 5.00 12.00
475 Whitey Ford AS 8.00 20.00
476 Baltimore Orioles TC 8.00 20.00
477 Andre Rodgers 5.00 12.00
478 Don Zimmer 8.00 20.00
479 Joel Horlen RC 5.00 12.00
480 Harvey Kuenn 6.00 15.00
481 Vic Wertz 6.00 15.00
482 Sam Mele MG 5.00 12.00
483 Don McMahon 5.00 12.00
484 Dick Schofield 5.00 12.00
485 Pedro Ramos 5.00 12.00
486 Jim Gilliam 6.00 15.00
487 Jerry Lynch 5.00 12.00
488 Hal Brown 5.00 12.00
489 Julio Gotay RC 5.00 12.00
490 Clete Boyer UER 6.00 15.00
Reversed Negative
491 Leon Wagner 5.00 12.00
492 Hal W. Smith 6.00 15.00
493 Danny McDevitt 5.00 12.00
494 Sammy White 5.00 12.00
495 Don Cardwell 5.00 12.00
496 Wayne Causey RC 5.00 12.00
497 Ed Bouchee 6.00 15.00
498 Jim Donohue 5.00 12.00
499 Zoilo Versalles 6.00 15.00
500 Duke Snider 30.00 60.00
501 Claude Osteen 6.00 15.00
502 Hector Lopez 6.00 15.00
503 Danny Murtaugh MG 6.00 15.00
504 Eddie Bressoud 6.00 15.00
505 Juan Marichal 15.00 40.00
506 Charlie Maxwell 6.00 15.00
507 Ernie Broglio 6.00 15.00
508 Gordy Coleman 6.00 15.00
509 Dave Giusti RC 6.00 15.00
510 Jim Lemon 5.00 12.00
511 Bubba Phillips 5.00 12.00
512 Mike Fornieles 5.00 12.00
513 Whitey Herzog 6.00 15.00
514 Sherm Lollar 6.00 15.00
515 Stan Williams 6.00 15.00
516A Checklist 7 6.00 15.00
White Boxes
516B Checklist 7 6.00 15.00
Yellow Boxes
517 Dave Wickersham 5.00 12.00
518 Lee Maye 5.00 12.00
519 Bob Johnson RC 5.00 12.00
520 Bob Friend 6.00 15.00
521 Jacke Davis UER RC 5.00 12.00
(Listed as OF on
front and P on back)
522 Lindy McDaniel 6.00 15.00
523 Russ Nixon SP 12.50 30.00
524 Howie Nunn SP 12.50 30.00
525 George Thomas 8.00 20.00
526 Hal Woodeshick SP 12.50 30.00
527 Dick McAuliffe RC 12.50 30.00
528 Turk Lown 8.00 20.00
529 John Schaive SP 12.50 30.00
530 Bob Gibson SP 60.00 120.00
531 Bobby G. Smith 8.00 20.00
532 Dick Stigman 8.00 20.00
533 Charley Lau SP 12.50 30.00
534 Tony Gonzalez SP 12.50 30.00
535 Ed Roebuck 8.00 20.00
536 Dick Gernert 8.00 20.00
537 Cleveland Indians TC 20.00 50.00
538 Jack Sanford 8.00 20.00
539 Billy Moran 8.00 20.00
540 Jim Landis SP 12.50 30.00
541 Don Nottebart SP 12.50 30.00
542 Dave Philley 8.00 20.00
543 Bob Allen SP 12.50 30.00
544 Willie McCovey SP 60.00 120.00
545 Hoyt Wilhelm SP 20.00 50.00
546 Moe Thacker SP 8.00 20.00
547 Don Ferrarese 8.00 20.00
548 Bobby Del Greco 8.00 20.00
549 Bill Rigney MG SP 12.50 30.00
550 Art Mahaffey SP 12.50 30.00
551 Harry Bright 8.00 20.00
552 Chicago Cubs TC SP 20.00 50.00
553 Jim Coates 12.50 30.00
554 Bubba Morton SP RC 12.50 30.00
555 John Buzhardt SP 12.50 30.00
556 Al Spangler 8.00 20.00
557 Bob Anderson SP 12.50 30.00
558 John Goryl 8.00 20.00
559 Mike Higgins MG 8.00 20.00
560 Chuck Estrada SP 12.50 30.00
561 Gene Oliver SP 12.50 30.00
562 Bill Henry 8.00 20.00
563 Ken Aspromonte 8.00 20.00
564 Bob Grim 8.00 20.00
565 Jose Pagan 8.00 20.00
566 Marty Kutyna SP 12.50 30.00
567 Tracy Stallard SP 12.50 30.00
568 Jim Golden 8.00 20.00
569 Ed Sadowski SP 12.50 30.00
570 Bill Stafford SP 12.50 30.00
571 Billy Klaus SP 12.50 30.00
572 Bob G. Miller SP 12.50 30.00
573 Johnny Logan 8.00 20.00
574 Dean Stone 8.00 20.00
575 Red Schoendienst SP 20.00 50.00
576 Russ Kemmerer SP 12.50 30.00
577 Dave Nicholson SP 12.50 30.00
578 Jim Duffalo RC 8.00 20.00
579 Jim Schaffer SP RC 12.50 30.00
580 Bill Monbouquette 8.00 20.00
581 Mel Roach 8.00 20.00
582 Ron Piche 8.00 20.00
583 Larry Osborne 8.00 20.00
584 Minnesota Twins TC SP 30.00 60.00
585 Glen Hobbie SP 12.50 30.00
586 Sammy Esposito SP 12.50 30.00
587 Frank Funk SP 12.50 30.00
588 Birdie Tebbetts MG 8.00 20.00
589 Bob Turley 12.50 30.00
590 Curt Flood 12.50 30.00
591 Rookie Parade 40.00 80.00
Sam McDowell RC
Ron Taylor RC
Ron Nischwitz RC
Art Quirk RC
Dick Radatz RC SP
592 Rookie Parade 40.00 80.00
Dan Pfister RC
Bo Belinsky RC
Dave Stenhouse RCe
Jim Bouton RC
Joe Bonikowski RC SP
593 Rookie Parade 20.00 50.00
Jack Lamabe RC
Craig Anderson RC
Jack Hamilton RC
Bob Moorhead RC
Bob Veale RC SP
594 Rookie Parade 40.00 80.00
Doc Edwards RC
Ken Retzer RC
Bob Uecker RC
Doug Camilli RC
Don Pavletich SP
595 Rookie Parade 20.00 50.00
Bob Sadowski RC
Felix Torres RC
Marlan Coughtry RC
Ed Charles RC SP
596 Rookie Parade 40.00 80.00
Bernie Allen RC
Joe Pepitone RC
Phil Linz RC
Rich Rollins RC SP
597 Rookie Parade 20.00 50.00
Jim McKnight RC
Rod Kanehl RC
Amado Samuel RC
Denis Menke RC SP
598 Rookie Parade 40.00 80.00
Al Luplow RC
Manny Jimenez RC
Howie Goss RC
Jim Hickman RC
Ed Olivares RC SP

1963 Topps

The cards in this 576-card set measure 2 1/2" by 3 1/2". The sharp color photographs of the 1963 set are a vivid contrast to the drab pictures of 1962. In addition to the "League Leaders" series (1-10) and World Series cards (142-148), the seventh and last series of cards (523-576) contains seven rookie cards (each depicting four players). Cards were issued, among other ways, in one-card penny packs and five-card nickel packs. There were some three-card advertising panels produced by Topps; the players included are from the first series; one panel shows Hoyt Wilhelm, Don Lock, and Bob Duliba on the front with a Stan Musial ad/endorsement on one of the backs. Key Rookie Cards in this set are Bill Freehan, Tony Oliva, Pete Rose, Willie Stargell and Rusty Staub.

COMPLETE SET (576) 3000.00 6000.00
COMMON CARD (1-196) 1.50 4.00
COMMON (197-283) 2.00 5.00
COMMON (284-370) 2.00 5.00
COMMON (371-446) 2.00 5.00
COMMON (447-522) 10.00 25.00
COMMON (523-576) 6.00 15.00
WRAPPER (1-CENT) 15.00 40.00
WRAPPER (5-CENT) 12.50 30.00
1 NL Batting Leaders 15.00 40.00
Tommy Davis
Frank Robinson
Stan Musial
Hank Aaron
Bill White
2 AL Batting Leaders 20.00 50.00
Pete Runnels
Mickey Mantle
Floyd Robinson
Norm Siebern
Chuck Hinton
3 NL Home Run Leaders 15.00 40.00
Willie Mays
Hank Aaron
Frank Robinson
Orlando Cepeda
Ernie Banks
4 AL Home Run Leaders 8.00 20.00
Harmon Killebrew
Norm Cash
Rocky Colavito
Roger Maris
Jim Gentile
Leon Wagner
5 NL ERA Leaders 10.00 25.00
Sandy Koufax
Bob Shaw
Bob Purkey
Bob Gibson
Don Drysdale
6 AL ERA Leaders 4.00 10.00
Hank Aguirre
Robin Roberts
Whitey Ford
Eddie Fisher
Dean Chance
7 NL Pitching Leaders 4.00 10.00
Don Drysdale
Jack Sanford
Bob Purkey
Billy O'Dell
Art Mahaffey
Joe Jay
8 AL Pitching Leaders 3.00 8.00
Ralph Terry
Dick Donovan
Ray Herbert
Jim Bunning
Camilo Pascual
9 NL Strikeout Leaders 12.50 30.00
Don Drysdale
Sandy Koufax
Bob Gibson
Billy O'Dell
Dick Farrell
10 AL Strikeout Leaders 3.00 8.00
Camilo Pascual
Jim Bunning
Ralph Terry
Juan Pizarro
Jim Kaat
11 Lee Walls 1.50 4.00
12 Steve Barber 1.50 4.00
13 Philadelphia Phillies TC 3.00 8.00
14 Pedro Ramos 1.50 4.00
15 Ken Hubbs UER 4.00 10.00
(No position listed
on front of card)
16 Al Smith 1.50 4.00
17 Ryne Duren 3.00 8.00
18 Buc Blasters 40.00 80.00
Smoky Burgess
Dick Stuart
Bob Clemente
Bob Skinner
19 Pete Burnside 1.50 4.00
20 Tony Kubek 4.00 10.00
21 Marty Keough 1.50 4.00
22 Curt Simmons 3.00 8.00
23 Ed Lopat MG 3.00 8.00
24 Bob Bruce 1.50 4.00
25 Al Kaline 20.00 50.00
26 Ray Moore 1.50 4.00
27 Choo Choo Coleman 3.00 8.00
28 Mike Fornieles 1.50 4.00
29A Rookie Stars 1962 4.00 10.00
Sammy Ellis
Ray Culp
John Boozer
Jesse Gonder
29B Rookie Stars 1963 1.50 4.00
Sammy Ellis RC
Ray Culp
John Boozer RC
Jesse Gonder RC
30 Harvey Kuenn 3.00 8.00
31 Cal Koonce RC 1.50 4.00
32 Tony Gonzalez 1.50 4.00
33 Bo Belinsky 3.00 8.00
34 Dick Schofield 1.50 4.00
35 John Buzhardt 1.50 4.00
36 Jerry Kindall 1.50 4.00
37 Jerry Lynch 1.50 4.00
38 Bud Daley 3.00 8.00
39 Los Angeles Angels TC 3.00 8.00
40 Vic Power 3.00 8.00
41 Charley Lau 3.00 8.00
42 Stan Williams 3.00 8.00
(Listed as a Yankee, but wearing an LA cap)
43 Veteran Masters 3.00 8.00
Casey Stengel
Gene Woodling
44 Terry Fox 1.50 4.00
45 Bob Aspromonte 1.50 4.00
46 Tommie Aaron RC 1.50 4.00
47 Don Lock RC 1.50 4.00
48 Birdie Tebbetts MG 3.00 8.00
49 Dal Maxvill RC 3.00 8.00
50 Billy Pierce 3.00 8.00
51 George Alusik 1.50 4.00
52 Chuck Schilling 1.50 4.00
53 Joe Moeller RC 1.50 4.00
54A Rookie Stars 1962 6.00 15.00
Nelson Mathews
Harry Fanok
Jack Cullen
Dave DeBusschere RC
54B Rookie Stars 1963 3.00 8.00
Nelson Mathews RC
Harry Fanok RC
Jack Cullen RC
Dave DeBusschere RC
55 Bill Virdon 3.00 8.00
56 Dennis Bennett RC 1.50 4.00
57 Billy Moran 1.50 4.00
58 Bob Will 1.50 4.00
59 Craig Anderson 1.50 4.00
60 Elston Howard 3.00 8.00
61 Ernie Bowman 1.50 4.00
62 Bob Hendley 1.50 4.00
63 Cincinnati Reds TC 3.00 8.00
64 Dick McAuliffe 3.00 8.00
65 Jackie Brandt 1.50 4.00
66 Mike Joyce RC 1.50 4.00
67 Ed Charles 1.50 4.00
68 Friendly Foes 10.00 25.00
Duke Snider
Gil Hodges
69 Bud Zipfel RC 1.50 4.00
70 Jim O'Toole 3.00 8.00
71 Bobby Wine RC 3.00 8.00
72 Johnny Romano 1.50 4.00
73 Bobby Bragan MG RC 3.00 8.00
74 Denny Lemaster RC 1.50 4.00
75 Bob Allison 3.00 8.00
76 Earl Wilson 3.00 8.00
77 Al Spangler 1.50 4.00
78 Marv Throneberry 3.00 8.00
79 Checklist 1 5.00 12.00
80 Jim Gilliam 3.00 8.00
81 Jim Schaffer 1.50 4.00
82 Ed Rakow 1.50 4.00
83 Charley James 1.50 4.00
84 Ron Kline 1.50 4.00
85 Tom Haller 3.00 8.00
86 Charley Maxwell 3.00 8.00
87 Bob Veale 3.00 8.00
88 Ron Hansen 1.50 4.00
89 Dick Stigman 1.50 4.00
90 Gordy Coleman 3.00 8.00
91 Dallas Green 3.00 8.00
92 Hector Lopez 3.00 8.00
93 Galen Cisco 1.50 4.00
94 Bob Schmidt 1.50 4.00
95 Larry Jackson 1.50 4.00
96 Lou Clinton 1.50 4.00
97 Bob Duliba 1.50 4.00
98 George Thomas 1.50 4.00
99 Jim Umbricht 1.50 4.00
100 Joe Cunningham 1.50 4.00
101 Joe Gibbon 1.50 4.00
102A Checklist 2 Red/Yellow 5.00 12.00
102B Checklist 2 White/Red 5.00 12.00
103 Chuck Essegian 1.50 4.00
104 Lew Krausse RC 1.50 4.00
105 Ron Fairly 3.00 8.00
106 Bobby Bolin 3.00 8.00
107 Jim Hickman 3.00 8.00
108 Hoyt Wilhelm 4.00 10.00
109 Lee Maye 1.50 4.00
110 Rich Rollins 3.00 8.00
111 Al Jackson 1.50 4.00
112 Dick Brown 1.50 4.00
113 Don Landrum UER 1.50 4.00
(Photo actually
Ron Santo)
114 Dan Osinski RC 1.50 4.00
115 Carl Yastrzemski 15.00 40.00
116 Jim Brosnan 1.50 4.00
117 Jacke Davis 1.50 4.00
118 Sherm Lollar 1.50 4.00
119 Bob Lillis 1.50 4.00
120 Roger Maris 40.00 80.00
121 Jim Hannan RC 1.50 4.00
122 Julio Gotay 1.50 4.00
123 Frank Howard 3.00 8.00
124 Dick Howser 1.50 4.00
125 Robin Roberts 6.00 15.00
126 Bob Uecker 6.00 15.00
127 Bill Tuttle 1.50 4.00
128 Matty Alou 3.00 8.00
129 Gary Bell 1.50 4.00
130 Dick Groat 3.00 8.00
131 Washington Senators TC 3.00 8.00
132 Jack Hamilton 1.50 4.00
133 Gene Freese 1.50 4.00
134 Bob Scheffing MG 1.50 4.00
135 Richie Ashburn 8.00 20.00
136 Ike Delock 1.50 4.00
137 Mack Jones 1.50 4.00
138 Pride of NL 40.00 80.00
Willie Mays
Stan Musial
139 Earl Averill Jr. 1.50 4.00
140 Frank Lary 3.00 8.00
141 Manny Mota RC 3.00 8.00
142 World Series Game 1 4.00 10.00
Whitey Ford
143 World Series Game 2 3.00 8.00
Jack Sanford
144 World Series Game 3 6.00 15.00
Roger Maris
145 World Series Game 4 3.00 8.00
Chuck Hiller
146 World Series Game 5 3.00 8.00
Tom Tresh
147 World Series Game 6 3.00 8.00
Billy Pierce
148 World Series Game 7 3.00 8.00
Yanks Celebrate
Ralph Terry
149 Marv Breeding 1.50 4.00
150 Johnny Podres 3.00 8.00
151 Pittsburgh Pirates TC 3.00 8.00
152 Ron Nischwitz 1.50 4.00
153 Hal Smith 1.50 4.00
154 Walter Alston MG 3.00 8.00
155 Bill Stafford 1.50 4.00
156 Roy McMillan 3.00 8.00
157 Diego Segui RC 3.00 8.00
158 Rookie Stars 3.00 8.00
Rogelio Alvares RC
Dave Roberts RC
Tommy Harper RC
Bob Saverine RC
159 Jim Pagliaroni 1.50 4.00
160 Juan Pizarro 1.50 4.00
161 Frank Torre 3.00 8.00
162 Minnesota Twins TC 3.00 8.00
163 Don Larsen 3.00 8.00
164 Bubba Morton 1.50 4.00
165 Jim Kaat 3.00 8.00
166 Johnny Keane MG 1.50 4.00
167 Jim Fregosi 3.00 8.00
168 Russ Nixon 1.50 4.00
169 Rookie Stars 10.00 25.00
Dick Egan RC
Julio Navarro

Tommie Sisk RC
Gaylord Perry
170 Joe Adcock 3.00 8.00
171 Steve Hamilton RC 1.50 4.00
172 Gene Oliver 1.50 4.00
173 Bomber's Best 75.00 150.00
Tom Tresh
Mickey Mantle
Bobby Richardson
174 Larry Burright 1.50 4.00
175 Bob Buhl 3.00 8.00
176 Jim King 1.50 4.00
177 Bubba Phillips 1.50 4.00
178 Johnny Edwards 1.50 4.00
179 Ron Piche 1.50 4.00
180 Bill Skowron 3.00 8.00
181 Sammy Esposito 1.50 4.00
182 Albie Pearson 3.00 8.00
183 Joe Pepitone 3.00 8.00
184 Vern Law 3.00 8.00
185 Chuck Hiller 1.50 4.00
186 Jerry Zimmerman 1.50 4.00
187 Willie Kirkland 1.50 4.00
188 Eddie Bressoud 1.50 4.00
189 Dave Giusti 3.00 8.00
190 Minnie Minoso 3.00 8.00
191 Checklist 3 5.00 12.00
192 Clay Dalrymple 1.50 4.00
193 Andre Rodgers 1.50 4.00
194 Joe Nuxhall 3.00 8.00
195 Manny Jimenez 1.50 4.00
196 Doug Camilli 1.50 4.00
197 Roger Craig 3.00 8.00
198 Lenny Green 2.00 5.00
199 Joe Amalfitano 2.00 5.00
200 Mickey Mantle 300.00 600.00
201 Cecil Butler 2.00 5.00
202 Boston Red Sox TC 3.00 8.00
203 Chico Cardenas 3.00 8.00
204 Don Nottebart 2.00 5.00
205 Luis Aparicio 6.00 15.00
206 Ray Washburn 2.00 5.00
207 Ken Hunt 2.00 5.00
208 Rookie Stars 2.00 5.00
Ron Herbel RC
John Miller RC
Wally Wolf RC
Ron Taylor
209 Hobie Landrith 2.00 5.00
210 Sandy Koufax 75.00 150.00
211 Fred Whitfield RC 2.00 5.00
212 Glen Hobbie 2.00 5.00
213 Billy Hitchcock MG 2.00 5.00
214 Orlando Pena 2.00 5.00
215 Bob Skinner 3.00 8.00
216 Gene Conley 3.00 8.00
217 Joe Christopher 2.00 5.00
218 Tiger Twirlers 3.00 8.00
Frank Lary
Don Mossi
Jim Bunning
219 Chuck Cottier 2.00 5.00
220 Camilo Pascual 3.00 8.00
221 Cookie Rojas RC 3.00 8.00
222 Chicago Cubs TC 3.00 8.00
223 Eddie Fisher 2.00 5.00
224 Mike Roarke 2.00 5.00
225 Joey Jay 2.00 5.00
226 Julian Javier 3.00 8.00
227 Jim Grant 3.00 8.00
228 Rookie Stars 20.00 50.00
Max Alvis RC
Bob Bailey RC
Tony Oliva RC
(Listed as Pedro)
Ed Kranepool RC
229 Willie Davis 3.00 8.00
230 Pete Runnels 3.00 8.00
231 Eli Grba UER 2.00 5.00
(Large photo is
Ryne Duren)
232 Frank Malzone 3.00 8.00
233 Casey Stengel MG 8.00 20.00
234 Dave Nicholson 2.00 5.00
235 Billy O'Dell 2.00 5.00
236 Bill Bryan RC 2.00 5.00
237 Jim Coates 3.00 8.00
238 Lou Johnson 2.00 5.00
239 Harvey Haddix 3.00 8.00
240 Rocky Colavito 6.00 15.00
241 Billy Smith RC 2.00 5.00
242 Power Plus 30.00 60.00
Ernie Banks
Hank Aaron
243 Don Leppert 2.00 5.00
244 John Tsitouris 2.00 5.00
245 Gil Hodges 8.00 20.00
246 Lee Stange 2.00 5.00
247 New York Yankees TC 20.00 50.00
248 Tito Francona 2.00 5.00
249 Leo Burke RC 2.00 5.00
250 Stan Musial 50.00 100.00
251 Jack Lamabe 2.00 5.00
252 Ron Santo 4.00 10.00
253 Rookie Stars 2.00 5.00
Len Gabrielson RC
Pete Jernigan RC
John Wojcik RC
Deacon Jones RC
254 Mike Hershberger 2.00 5.00
255 Bob Shaw 2.00 5.00
256 Jerry Lumpe 2.00 5.00
257 Hank Aguirre 2.00 5.00
258 Alvin Dark MG 3.00 8.00
259 Johnny Logan 3.00 8.00
260 Jim Gentile 3.00 8.00
261 Bob Miller 2.00 5.00
262 Ellis Burton 2.00 5.00
263 Dave Stenhouse 2.00 5.00
264 Phil Linz 2.00 5.00
265 Vada Pinson 3.00 8.00
266 Bob Allen 2.00 5.00
267 Carl Sawatski 2.00 5.00
268 Don Demeter 2.00 5.00
269 Don Mincher 2.00 5.00
270 Felipe Alou 3.00 8.00
271 Dean Stone 2.00 5.00
272 Danny Murphy 2.00 5.00
273 Sammy Taylor 2.00 5.00
274 Checklist 4 5.00 12.00
275 Eddie Mathews 12.50 30.00
276 Barry Shetrone 2.00 5.00
277 Dick Farrell 2.00 5.00
278 Chico Fernandez 2.00 5.00
279 Wally Moon 3.00 8.00
280 Bob (Buck) Rodgers 2.00 5.00
281 Tom Sturdivant 2.00 5.00
282 Bobby Del Greco 2.00 5.00
283 Roy Sievers 3.00 8.00
284 Dave Sisler 2.00 5.00
285 Dick Stuart 3.00 8.00
286 Stu Miller 3.00 8.00
287 Dick Bertell 2.00 5.00
288 Chicago White Sox TC 4.00 10.00
289 Hal Brown 2.00 5.00
290 Bill White 3.00 8.00
291 Don Rudolph 2.00 5.00
292 Pumpsie Green 3.00 8.00
293 Bill Pleis 2.00 5.00
294 Bill Rigney MG 2.00 5.00
295 Ed Roebuck 2.00 5.00
296 Doc Edwards 2.00 5.00
297 Jim Golden 2.00 5.00
298 Don Dillard 2.00 5.00
299 Rookie Stars 3.00 8.00
Dave Morehead RC
Bob Dustal RC
Tom Butters RC
Dan Schneider RC
300 Willie Mays 75.00 150.00
301 Bill Fischer 2.00 5.00
302 Whitey Herzog 3.00 8.00
303 Earl Francis 2.00 5.00
304 Harry Bright 2.00 5.00
305 Don Hoak 2.00 5.00
306 Star Receivers 4.00 10.00
Earl Battey
Elston Howard
307 Chet Nichols 2.00 5.00
308 Camilo Carreon 2.00 5.00
309 Jim Brewer 2.00 5.00
310 Tommy Davis 3.00 8.00
311 Joe McClain 2.00 5.00
312 Houston Colts TC 10.00 25.00
313 Ernie Broglio 2.00 5.00
314 John Goryl 2.00 5.00
315 Ralph Terry 3.00 8.00
316 Norm Sherry 3.00 8.00
317 Sam McDowell 3.00 8.00
318 Gene Mauch MG 3.00 8.00
319 Joe Gaines 2.00 5.00
320 Warren Spahn 30.00 60.00
321 Gino Cimoli 2.00 5.00
322 Bob Turley 3.00 8.00
323 Bill Mazeroski 6.00 15.00
324 Rookie Stars 3.00 8.00
George Williams RC
Pete Ward RC
Phil Roof RC
Vic Davalillo RC
325 Jack Sanford 2.00 5.00
326 Hank Foiles 2.00 5.00
327 Paul Foytack 2.00 5.00
328 Dick Williams 3.00 8.00
329 Lindy McDaniel 3.00 8.00
330 Chuck Hinton 2.00 5.00
331 Series Foes 3.00 8.00
Bill Stafford
Bill Pierce
332 Joel Horlen 3.00 8.00
333 Carl Warwick 2.00 5.00
334 Wynn Hawkins 2.00 5.00
335 Leon Wagner 2.00 5.00
336 Ed Bauta 2.00 5.00
337 Los Angeles Dodgers TC 10.00 25.00
338 Russ Kemmerer 2.00 5.00
339 Ted Bowsfield 2.00 5.00
340 Yogi Berra P/CO 50.00 100.00
341 Jack Baldschun 2.00 5.00
342 Gene Woodling 3.00 8.00
343 Johnny Pesky MG 3.00 8.00
344 Don Schwall 2.00 5.00
345 Brooks Robinson 30.00 60.00
346 Billy Hoeft 2.00 5.00
347 Joe Torre 6.00 15.00
348 Vic Wertz 3.00 8.00
349 Zoilo Versalles 3.00 8.00
350 Bob Purkey 2.00 5.00
351 Al Luplow 2.00 5.00
352 Ken Johnson 2.00 5.00
353 Billy Williams 12.50 30.00
354 Dom Zanni 2.00 5.00
355 Dean Chance 3.00 8.00
356 John Schaive 2.00 5.00
357 George Altman 2.00 5.00
358 Milt Pappas 3.00 8.00
359 Haywood Sullivan 3.00 8.00
360 Don Drysdale 30.00 60.00
361 Clete Boyer 4.00 10.00
362 Checklist 5 5.00 12.00
363 Dick Radatz 3.00 8.00
364 Howie Goss 2.00 5.00
365 Jim Bunning 8.00 20.00
366 Tony Taylor 3.00 8.00
367 Tony Cloninger 2.00 5.00
368 Ed Bailey 2.00 5.00
369 Jim Lemon 2.00 5.00
370 Dick Donovan 2.00 5.00
371 Rod Kanehl 3.00 8.00
372 Don Lee 2.00 5.00
373 Jim Campbell RC 2.00 5.00
374 Claude Osteen 3.00 8.00
375 Ken Boyer 6.00 15.00
376 John Wyatt RC 2.00 5.00
377 Baltimore Orioles TC 4.00 10.00
378 Bill Henry 2.00 5.00
379 Bob Anderson 2.00 5.00
380 Ernie Banks UER 50.00 100.00
(Back has career Major
and Minor, but he
never played in Minors)
381 Frank Baumann 2.00 5.00
382 Ralph Houk MG 4.00 10.00
383 Pete Richert 2.00 5.00
384 Bob Tillman 2.00 5.00
385 Art Mahaffey 2.00 5.00
386 Rookie Stars 2.00 5.00
Ed Kirkpatrick RC
John Bateman RC
Larry Bearnarth RC
Garry Roggenburk RC
387 Al McBean 2.00 5.00
388 Jim Davenport 3.00 8.00
389 Frank Sullivan 2.00 5.00
390 Hank Aaron 100.00 200.00
391 Bill Dailey RC 2.00 5.00
392 Tribe Thumpers 2.00 5.00
Johnny Romano
Tito Francona
393 Ken MacKenzie 3.00 8.00
394 Tim McCarver 6.00 15.00
395 Don McMahon 2.00 5.00
396 Joe Koppe 3.00 8.00
397 Kansas City Athletics TC 4.00 10.00
398 Boog Powell 10.00 25.00
399 Dick Ellsworth 2.00 5.00
400 Frank Robinson 30.00 60.00
401 Jim Bouton 6.00 15.00
402 Mickey Vernon MG 3.00 8.00
403 Ron Perranoski 3.00 8.00
404 Bob Oldis 2.00 5.00
405 Floyd Robinson 2.00 5.00
406 Howie Koplitz 2.00 5.00
407 Rookie Stars 3.00 8.00
Frank Kostro RC
Chico Ruiz RC
Larry Elliot RC
Dick Simpson RC
408 Billy Gardner 2.00 5.00
409 Roy Face 3.00 8.00
410 Earl Battey 2.00 5.00
411 Jim Constable 2.00 5.00
412 Dodgers Big Three 20.00 50.00
Johnny Podres
Don Drysdale
Sandy Koufax
413 Jerry Walker 2.00 5.00
414 Ty Cline 2.00 5.00
415 Bob Gibson 30.00 60.00
416 Alex Grammas 2.00 5.00
417 San Francisco Giants TC 4.00 10.00
418 John Orsino 2.00 5.00
419 Tracy Stallard 2.00 5.00
420 Bobby Richardson 6.00 15.00
421 Tom Morgan 2.00 5.00
422 Fred Hutchinson MG 3.00 8.00
423 Ed Hobaugh 2.00 5.00
424 Charlie Smith 2.00 5.00
425 Smoky Burgess 3.00 8.00
426 Barry Latman 2.00 5.00
427 Bernie Allen 2.00 5.00
428 Carl Boles RC 2.00 5.00
429 Lou Burdette 3.00 8.00
430 Norm Siebern 2.00 5.00
431A Checklist 6 White/Red 5.00 12.00
431B Checklist 6 Black/Orange 12.50 30.00
432 Roman Mejias 2.00 5.00
433 Denis Menke 2.00 5.00
434 John Callison 3.00 8.00
435 Woody Held 2.00 5.00
436 Tim Harkness 3.00 8.00
437 Bill Bruton 2.00 5.00
438 Wes Stock 2.00 5.00
439 Don Zimmer 3.00 8.00
440 Juan Marichal 12.50 30.00
441 Lee Thomas 3.00 8.00
442 J.C. Hartman RC 2.00 5.00
443 Jimmy Piersall 3.00 8.00
444 Jim Maloney 3.00 8.00
445 Norm Cash 4.00 10.00
446 Whitey Ford 30.00 60.00
447 Felix Mantilla 10.00 25.00
448 Jack Kralick 10.00 25.00
449 Jose Tartabull 10.00 25.00
450 Bob Friend 12.50 30.00
451 Cleveland Indians TC 15.00 40.00
452 Barney Schultz 10.00 25.00
453 Jake Wood 10.00 25.00
454A Art Fowler 10.00 25.00
(Card number on
white background)
454B Art Fowler 12.50 30.00
(Card number on
orange background)
455 Ruben Amaro 10.00 25.00
456 Jim Coker 10.00 25.00
457 Tex Clevenger 10.00 25.00
458 Al Lopez MG 12.50 30.00
459 Dick LeMay 10.00 25.00
460 Del Crandall 12.50 30.00
461 Norm Bass 10.00 25.00
462 Wally Post 10.00 25.00
463 Joe Schaffernoth 10.00 25.00
464 Ken Aspromonte 10.00 25.00
465 Chuck Estrada 10.00 25.00
466 Rookie Stars 30.00 60.00
Nate Oliver RC
Tony Martinez RC
Bill Freehan RC
Jerry Robinson RC SP
467 Phil Ortega 10.00 25.00
468 Carroll Hardy 12.50 30.00
469 Jay Hook 12.50 30.00
470 Tom Tresh SP 30.00 60.00
471 Ken Retzer 10.00 25.00
472 Lou Brock 40.00 80.00
473 New York Mets TC 50.00 100.00
474 Jack Fisher 10.00 25.00
475 Gus Triandos 12.50 30.00
476 Frank Funk 10.00 25.00
477 Donn Clendenon 12.50 30.00
478 Paul Brown 10.00 25.00
479 Ed Brinkman RC 10.00 25.00
480 Bill Monbouquette 10.00 25.00
481 Bob Taylor 10.00 25.00
482 Felix Torres 10.00 25.00
483 Jim Owens UER 10.00 25.00
(Stat column for Wins
has an R instead)
484 Dale Long SP 12.50 30.00
485 Jim Landis 10.00 25.00
486 Ray Sadecki 10.00 25.00
487 John Roseboro 12.50 30.00
488 Jerry Adair 10.00 25.00
489 Paul Toth RC 10.00 25.00
490 Willie McCovey 50.00 100.00
491 Harry Craft MG 10.00 25.00
492 Dave Wickersham 10.00 25.00
493 Walt Bond 10.00 25.00
494 Phil Regan 10.00 25.00
495 Frank Thomas SP 12.50 30.00
496 Rookie Stars 12.50 30.00
Steve Dalkowski RC
Fred Newman RC
Jack Smith RC
Carl Bouldin RC
497 Bennie Daniels 10.00 25.00
498 Eddie Kasko 10.00 25.00
499 J.C. Martin 10.00 25.00
500 Harmon Killebrew SP 75.00 150.00
501 Joe Azcue 10.00 25.00
502 Daryl Spencer 10.00 25.00
503 Milwaukee Braves TC 15.00 40.00
504 Bob Johnson 10.00 25.00
505 Curt Flood 15.00 40.00
506 Gene Green 10.00 25.00
507 Roland Sheldon 12.50 30.00
508 Ted Savage 10.00 25.00
509A Checklist 7 Centered 12.50 30.00
509B Checklist 7 Right 12.50 30.00
510 Ken McBride 10.00 25.00
511 Charlie Neal 12.50 30.00
512 Cal McLish 10.00 25.00
513 Gary Geiger 10.00 25.00
514 Larry Osborne 10.00 25.00
515 Don Elston 10.00 25.00
516 Purnell Goldy RC 10.00 25.00
517 Hal Woodeshick 10.00 25.00
518 Don Blasingame 10.00 25.00
519 Claude Raymond RC 10.00 25.00
520 Orlando Cepeda 15.00 40.00
521 Dan Pfister 10.00 25.00
522 Rookie Stars 12.50 30.00
Mel Nelson RC
Gary Peters
Jim Roland RC
Art Quirk
523 Bill Kunkel 6.00 15.00
524 St. Louis Cardinals TC 12.50 30.00
525 Nellie Fox 20.00 50.00
526 Dick Hall 6.00 15.00
527 Ed Sadowski 6.00 15.00
528 Carl Willey 6.00 15.00
529 Wes Covington 6.00 15.00
530 Don Mossi 8.00 20.00
531 Sam Mele MG 6.00 15.00
532 Steve Boros 6.00 15.00
533 Bobby Shantz 8.00 20.00
534 Ken Walters 6.00 15.00
535 Jim Perry 8.00 20.00
536 Norm Larker 6.00 15.00
537 Rookie Stars 500.00 1000.00
Pedro Gonzalez RC
Ken McMullen RC
Al Weis RC
Pete Rose RC
538 George Brunet 6.00 15.00
539 Wayne Causey 6.00 15.00
540 Roberto Clemente 125.00 250.00
541 Ron Moeller 6.00 15.00
542 Lou Klimchock 6.00 15.00
543 Russ Snyder 6.00 15.00
544 Rookie Stars 20.00 50.00
Duke Carmel
Bill Haas RC
Rusty Staub RC
Dick Phillips RC
545 Jose Pagan 6.00 15.00
546 Hal Reniff 8.00 20.00
547 Gus Bell 6.00 15.00
548 Tom Satriano RC 6.00 15.00
549 Rookie Stars 6.00 15.00
Marcelino Lopez RC
Pete Lovrich RC
Paul Ratliff RC
Elmo Plaskett RC
550 Duke Snider 40.00 80.00
551 Billy Klaus 6.00 15.00
552 Detroit Tigers TC 20.00 50.00
553 Rookie Stars 60.00 120.00
Brock Davis RC
Jim Gosger RC
Willie Stargell RC
John Herrnstein RC
554 Hank Fischer RC 6.00 15.00
555 John Blanchard 8.00 20.00
556 Al Worthington 6.00 15.00
557 Cuno Barragan 6.00 15.00
558 Rookie Stars 8.00 20.00
Bill Faul RC
Ron Hunt RC
Al Moran RC
Bob Lipski RC
559 Danny Murtaugh MG 6.00 15.00
560 Ray Herbert 6.00 15.00
561 Mike De La Hoz 6.00 15.00
562 Rookie Stars 12.50 30.00
Randy Cardinal RC
Dave McNally RC
Ken Rowe RC
Don Rowe RC
563 Mike McCormick 6.00 15.00
564 George Banks RC 6.00 15.00
565 Larry Sherry 6.00 15.00
566 Cliff Cook 6.00 15.00
567 Jim Duffalo 6.00 15.00
568 Bob Sadowski 6.00 15.00
569 Luis Arroyo 8.00 20.00
570 Frank Bolling 6.00 15.00
571 Johnny Klippstein 6.00 15.00
572 Jack Spring 6.00 15.00
573 Coot Veal 6.00 15.00
574 Hal Kolstad 6.00 15.00
575 Don Cardwell 6.00 15.00
576 Johnny Temple 12.50 30.00

1964 Topps

The cards in this 587-card set measure 2 1/2" by 3 1/2". Players in the 1964 Topps baseball series were easy to sort by team due to the giant block lettering found at the top of each card. The name and position of the player are found underneath the picture, and the card is numbered in a ball design on the orange-colored back. The usual last series scarcity holds for this set (523 to 587). Subsets within this set include League Leaders (1-12) and World Series cards (136-140). Among other vehicles, cards were issued in one-card penny packs as well as five-card nickel packs. There were some three-card advertising panels produced by Topps; the players included are from the first series; Panels with Mickey Mantle card backs include Walt Alston/Bill Henry/Vada Pinson; Carl Willey/White Sox Rookies/Bob Friend; and Jimmie Hall/Ernie Broglio/A.L. ERA Leaders on the front with a Mickey Mantle card back on one of the backs. The key Rookie Cards in this set are Richie Allen, Tony Conigliaro, Tommy John, Tony LaRussa, Phil Niekro and Lou Piniella.

COMPLETE SET (587) 2750.00 3500.00
COMMON CARD (1-196) 1.25 3.00
COMMON (197-370) 1.50 4.00
COMMON (371-522) 3.00 8.00
COMMON (523-587) 6.00 15.00
WRAPPER (1-CENT) 50.00 100.00
WRAP. (1-CENT, REPEAT) 60.00 120.00
WRAPPER (5-CENT) 12.50 30.00
WRAP.(5-CENT, COIN) 15.00 40.00
1 NL ERA Leaders 12.50 30.00
Sandy Koufax
Dick Ellsworth
Bob Friend
2 AL ERA Leaders 3.00 8.00
Gary Peters
Juan Pizarro
Camilo Pascual
3 NL Pitching Leaders 8.00 20.00
Sandy Koufax
Juan Marichal
Warren Spahn
Jim Maloney
4 AL Pitching Leaders 3.00 8.00
Whitey Ford
Camilo Pascual
Jim Bouton
5 NL Strikeout Leaders 6.00 15.00
Sandy Koufax
Jim Maloney
Don Drysdale
6 AL Strikeout Leaders 3.00 8.00
Camilo Pascual
Jim Bunning
Dick Stigman
7 NL Batting Leaders 8.00 20.00
Tommy Davis
Roberto Clemente
Dick Groat
Hank Aaron
8 AL Batting Leaders 6.00 15.00
Carl Yastrzemski
Al Kaline
Rich Rollins
9 NL Home Run Leaders 12.50 30.00
Hank Aaron
Willie McCovey
Willie Mays
Orlando Cepeda
10 AL Home Run Leaders 3.00 8.00
Harmon Killebrew
Dick Stuart
Bob Allison
11 NL RBI Leaders 6.00 15.00
Hank Aaron
Ken Boyer
Bill White
12 AL RBI Leaders 3.00 8.00
Dick Stuart
Al Kaline
Harmon Killebrew
13 Hoyt Wilhelm 5.00 12.00
14 Rookie Stars 1.25 3.00
Dick Nen RC
Nick Willhite RC
15 Zoilo Versalles 2.50 6.00
16 John Boozer 1.25 3.00
17 Willie Kirkland 1.25 3.00
18 Billy O'Dell 1.25 3.00
19 Don Wert 1.25 3.00
20 Bob Friend 2.50 6.00
21 Yogi Berra MG 15.00 40.00
22 Jerry Adair 1.25 3.00
23 Chris Zachary RC 1.25 3.00
24 Carl Sawatski 1.25 3.00
25 Bill Monbouquette 1.25 3.00
26 Gino Cimoli 1.25 3.00
27 New York Mets TC 3.00 8.00
28 Claude Osteen 2.50 6.00
29 Lou Brock 15.00 40.00
30 Ron Perranoski 2.50 6.00
31 Dave Nicholson 1.25 3.00
32 Dean Chance 2.50 6.00
33 Rookie Stars 2.50 6.00
Sammy Ellis
Mel Queen
34 Jim Perry 2.50 6.00
35 Eddie Mathews 8.00 20.00
36 Hal Reniff 1.25 3.00
37 Smoky Burgess 2.50 6.00
38 Jim Wynn RC 3.00 8.00
39 Hank Aguirre 1.25 3.00
40 Dick Groat 2.50 6.00
41 Friendly Foes 3.00 8.00
Willie McCovey
Leon Wagner
42 Moe Drabowsky 2.50 6.00
43 Roy Sievers 2.50 6.00
44 Duke Carmel 1.25 3.00
45 Milt Pappas 2.50 6.00
46 Ed Brinkman 1.25 3.00
47 Rookie Stars 2.50 6.00
Jesus Alou RC
Ron Herbel
48 Bob Perry RC 1.25 3.00
49 Bill Henry 1.25 3.00
50 Mickey Mantle 250.00 500.00
51 Pete Richert 1.25 3.00
52 Chuck Hinton 1.25 3.00
53 Denis Menke 1.25 3.00
54 Sam Mele MG 1.25 3.00
55 Ernie Banks 15.00 40.00
56 Hal Brown 1.25 3.00
57 Tim Harkness 2.50 6.00
58 Don Demeter 2.50 6.00
59 Ernie Broglio 1.25 3.00
60 Frank Malzone 2.50 6.00
61 Angel Backstops 2.50 6.00
Bob Rodgers
Ed Sadowski
62 Ted Savage 1.25 3.00
63 John Orsino 1.25 3.00
64 Ted Abernathy 1.25 3.00
65 Felipe Alou 2.50 6.00
66 Eddie Fisher 1.25 3.00
67 Detroit Tigers TC 2.50 6.00
68 Willie Davis 2.50 6.00
69 Clete Boyer 2.50 6.00
70 Joe Torre 3.00 8.00
71 Jack Spring 1.25 3.00
72 Chico Cardenas 2.50 6.00
73 Jimmie Hall RC 3.00 8.00
74 Rookie Stars 1.25 3.00
Bob Priddy RC
Tom Butters
75 Wayne Causey 1.25 3.00
76 Checklist 1 4.00 10.00
77 Jerry Walker 1.25 3.00
78 Merritt Ranew 1.25 3.00
79 Bob Heffner RC 1.25 3.00
80 Vada Pinson 3.00 8.00
81 All-Star Vets 5.00 12.00
Nellie Fox
Harmon Killebrew
82 Jim Davenport 2.50 6.00
83 Gus Triandos 2.50 6.00
84 Carl Willey 1.25 3.00
85 Pete Ward 1.25 3.00
86 Al Downing 2.50 6.00
87 St. Louis Cardinals TC 2.50 6.00
88 John Roseboro 2.50 6.00
89 Boog Powell 2.50 6.00
90 Earl Battey 1.25 3.00
91 Bob Bailey 2.50 6.00
92 Steve Ridzik 1.25 3.00
93 Gary Geiger 1.25 3.00
94 Rookie Stars 1.25 3.00
Jim Britton RC
Larry Maxie RC
95 George Altman 1.25 3.00
96 Bob Buhl 2.50 6.00
97 Jim Fregosi 2.50 6.00
98 Bill Bruton 1.25 3.00
99 Al Stanek RC 1.25 3.00
100 Elston Howard 2.50 6.00
101 Walt Alston MG 3.00 8.00
102 Checklist 2 4.00 10.00
103 Curt Flood 2.50 6.00
104 Art Mahaffey 2.50 6.00
105 Woody Held 1.25 3.00
106 Joe Nuxhall 2.50 6.00
107 Rookie Stars 1.25 3.00
Bruce Howard RC
Frank Kreutzer RC
108 John Wyatt 1.25 3.00
109 Rusty Staub 2.50 6.00
110 Albie Pearson 2.50 6.00
111 Don Elston 1.25 3.00
112 Bob Tillman 1.25 3.00
113 Grover Powell RC 2.50 6.00
114 Don Lock 1.25 3.00
115 Frank Bolling 1.25 3.00
116 Rookie Stars 5.00 12.00
Jay Ward RC
Tony Oliva
117 Earl Francis 1.25 3.00
118 John Blanchard 2.50 6.00
119 Gary Kolb RC 1.25 3.00
120 Don Drysdale 8.00 20.00
121 Pete Runnels 2.50 6.00
122 Don McMahon 1.25 3.00
123 Jose Pagan 1.25 3.00
124 Orlando Pena 1.25 3.00
125 Pete Rose UER 125.00 250.00
Born in 1942
126 Russ Snyder 1.25 3.00
127 Rookie Stars 1.25 3.00
Aubrey Gatewood RC
Dick Simpson
128 Mickey Lolich RC 8.00 20.00
129 Amado Samuel 1.25 3.00
130 Gary Peters 2.50 6.00
131 Steve Boros 1.25 3.00
132 Milwaukee Braves TC 2.50 6.00
133 Jim Grant 2.50 6.00
134 Don Zimmer 2.50 6.00
135 Johnny Callison 2.50 6.00
136 World Series Game 1 8.00 20.00
Sandy Koufax
137 World Series Game 2 3.00 8.00
Willie Davis
138 World Series Game 3 3.00 8.00
Ron Fairly
139 World Series Game 4 3.00 8.00
Frank Howard
140 World Series Summary 3.00 8.00
Dodgers Celebrate
141 Danny Murtaugh MG 2.50 6.00
142 John Bateman 1.25 3.00
143 Bubba Phillips 1.25 3.00
144 Al Worthington 1.25 3.00
145 Norm Siebern 1.25 3.00
146 Rookie Stars 12.50 30.00
Tommy John RC
Bob Chance RC
147 Ray Sadecki 1.25 3.00
148 J.C. Martin 1.25 3.00
149 Paul Foytack 1.25 3.00
150 Willie Mays 60.00 120.00
151 Kansas City Athletics TC 2.50 6.00
152 Denny Lemaster 1.25 3.00
153 Dick Williams 2.50 6.00
154 Dick Tracewski RC 2.50 6.00
155 Duke Snider 12.50 30.00
156 Bill Dailey 1.25 3.00
157 Gene Mauch MG 2.50 6.00
158 Ken Johnson 1.25 3.00
159 Charlie Dees RC 1.25 3.00
160 Ken Boyer 2.50 6.00
161 Dave McNally 2.50 6.00
162 Hitting Area 2.50 6.00
Dick Sisler CO
Vada Pinson
163 Donn Clendenon 2.50 6.00

Card	Low	High
164 Bud Daley	1.25	3.00
165 Jerry Lumpe	1.25	3.00
166 Marty Keough	1.25	3.00
167 Rookie Stars	12.50	30.00
Mike Brumley RC		
Lou Piniella RC		
168 Al Weis	1.25	3.00
169 Del Crandall	2.50	6.00
170 Dick Radatz	2.50	6.00
171 Ty Cline	1.25	3.00
172 Cleveland Indians TC	2.50	6.00
173 Ryne Duren	2.50	6.00
174 Doc Edwards	1.25	3.00
175 Billy Williams	5.00	12.00
176 Tracy Stallard	1.25	3.00
177 Harmon Killebrew	8.00	20.00
178 Hank Bauer MG	2.50	6.00
179 Carl Warwick	1.25	3.00
180 Tommy Davis	2.50	6.00
181 Dave Wickersham	1.25	3.00
182 Sox Sockers	6.00	15.00
Carl Yastrzemski		
Chuck Schilling		
183 Ron Taylor	1.25	3.00
184 Al Luplow	1.25	3.00
185 Jim O'Toole	2.50	6.00
186 Roman Mejias	1.25	3.00
187 Ed Roebuck	1.25	3.00
188 Checklist 3	4.00	10.00
189 Bob Hendley	1.25	3.00
190 Bobby Richardson	3.00	8.00
191 Clay Dalrymple	2.50	6.00
192 Rookie Stars	1.25	3.00
John Boccabella RC		
Billy Cowan RC		
193 Jerry Lynch	1.25	3.00
194 John Goryl	1.25	3.00
195 Floyd Robinson	1.25	3.00
196 Jim Gentile	1.25	3.00
197 Frank Lary	2.50	6.00
198 Len Gabrielson	1.50	4.00
199 Joe Azcue	1.50	4.00
200 Sandy Koufax	60.00	120.00
201 Rookie Stars	2.50	6.00
Sam Bowens RC		
Wally Bunker RC		
202 Galen Cisco	2.50	6.00
203 John Kennedy RC	2.50	6.00
204 Matty Alou	2.50	6.00
205 Nellie Fox	5.00	12.00
206 Steve Hamilton	2.50	6.00
207 Fred Hutchinson MG	2.50	6.00
208 Wes Covington	2.50	6.00
209 Bob Allen	1.50	4.00
210 Carl Yastrzemski	15.00	40.00
211 Jim Coker	1.50	4.00
212 Pete Lovrich	1.50	4.00
213 Los Angeles Angels TC	2.50	6.00
214 Ken McMullen	2.50	6.00
215 Ray Herbert	1.50	4.00
216 Mike de la Hoz	1.50	4.00
217 Jim King	1.50	4.00
218 Hank Fischer	1.50	4.00
219 Young Aces	2.50	6.00
Al Downing		
Jim Bouton		
220 Dick Ellsworth	2.50	6.00
221 Bob Saverine	1.50	4.00
222 Billy Pierce	2.50	6.00
223 George Banks	1.50	4.00
224 Tommie Sisk	1.50	4.00
225 Roger Maris	30.00	60.00
226 Rookie Stars	2.50	6.00
Jerry Grote RC		
Larry Yellen RC		
227 Barry Latman	1.50	4.00
228 Felix Mantilla	1.50	4.00
229 Charley Lau	2.50	6.00
230 Brooks Robinson	15.00	40.00
231 Dick Calmus RC	1.50	4.00
232 Al Lopez MG	3.00	8.00
233 Hal Smith	1.50	4.00
234 Gary Bell	1.50	4.00
235 Ron Hunt	1.50	4.00
236 Bill Faul	1.50	4.00
237 Chicago Cubs TC	2.50	6.00
238 Roy McMillan	2.50	6.00
239 Herm Starrette RC	1.50	4.00
240 Bill White	2.50	6.00
241 Jim Owens	1.50	4.00
242 Harvey Kuenn	2.50	6.00
243 Rookie Stars	12.50	30.00
Richie Allen RC		
John Herrnstein		
244 Tony LaRussa RC	12.50	30.00
245 Dick Stigman	1.50	4.00
246 Manny Mota	2.50	6.00
247 Dave DeBusschere	2.50	6.00
248 Johnny Pesky MG	2.50	6.00
249 Doug Camilli	1.50	4.00
250 Al Kaline	15.00	40.00
251 Choo Choo Coleman	2.50	6.00
252 Ken Aspromonte	1.50	4.00
253 Wally Post	2.50	6.00
254 Don Hoak	2.50	6.00
255 Lee Thomas	2.50	6.00
256 Johnny Weekly	1.50	4.00
257 San Francisco Giants TC	2.50	6.00
258 Garry Roggenburk	1.50	4.00
259 Harry Bright	1.50	4.00
260 Frank Robinson	15.00	40.00
261 Jim Hannan	1.50	4.00
262 Rookie Stars	3.00	8.00
Mike Shannon RC		
Harry Fanok		
263 Chuck Estrada	1.50	4.00
264 Jim Landis	1.50	4.00
265 Jim Bunning	5.00	12.00
266 Gene Freese	1.50	4.00
267 Wilbur Wood RC	2.50	6.00
268 Bill's Got It	2.50	6.00
Danny Murtaugh MG		
Bill Virdon		
269 Ellis Burton	1.50	4.00
270 Rich Rollins	2.50	6.00
271 Bob Sadowski	1.50	4.00
272 Jake Wood	1.50	4.00
273 Mel Nelson	1.50	4.00
274 Checklist 4	4.00	10.00
275 John Tsitouris	1.50	4.00
276 Jose Tartabull	2.50	6.00
277 Ken Retzer	1.50	4.00
278 Bobby Shantz	2.50	6.00
279 Joe Koppe	1.50	4.00
280 Juan Marichal	6.00	15.00
281 Rookie Stars	2.50	6.00
Jake Gibbs		
Tom Metcalf RC		
282 Bob Bruce	1.50	4.00
283 Tom McCraw RC	1.50	4.00
284 Dick Schofield	1.50	4.00
285 Robin Roberts	6.00	15.00
286 Don Landrum	1.50	4.00
287 Rookie Stars	20.00	50.00
Tony Conigliaro RC		
Bill Spanswick RC		
288 Al Moran	1.50	4.00
289 Frank Funk	1.50	4.00
290 Bob Allison	2.50	6.00
291 Phil Ortega	1.50	4.00
292 Mike Roarke	1.50	4.00
293 Philadelphia Phillies TC	2.50	6.00
294 Ken L. Hunt	1.50	4.00
295 Roger Craig	2.50	6.00
296 Ed Kirkpatrick	1.50	4.00
297 Ken MacKenzie	1.50	4.00
298 Harry Craft MG	1.50	4.00
299 Bill Stafford	1.50	4.00
300 Hank Aaron	50.00	100.00
301 Larry Brown RC	1.50	4.00
302 Dan Pfister	1.50	4.00
303 Jim Campbell	1.50	4.00
304 Bob Johnson	1.50	4.00
305 Jack Lamabe	1.50	4.00
306 Giant Gunners	15.00	40.00
Willie Mays		
Orlando Cepeda		
307 Joe Gibbon	1.50	4.00
308 Gene Stephens	1.50	4.00
309 Paul Toth	1.50	4.00
310 Jim Gilliam	2.50	6.00
311 Tom W. Brown RC	2.50	6.00
312 Rookie Stars	1.50	4.00
Fritz Fisher RC		
Fred Gladding RC		
313 Chuck Hiller	1.50	4.00
314 Jerry Buchek	1.50	4.00
315 Bo Belinsky	2.50	6.00
316 Gene Oliver	1.50	4.00
317 Al Smith	1.50	4.00
318 Minnesota Twins TC	2.50	6.00
319 Paul Brown	1.50	4.00
320 Rocky Colavito	5.00	12.00
321 Bob Lillis	1.50	4.00
322 George Brunet	1.50	4.00
323 John Buzhardt	1.50	4.00
324 Casey Stengel MG	6.00	15.00
325 Hector Lopez	2.50	6.00
326 Ron Brand RC	1.50	4.00
327 Don Blasingame	1.50	4.00
328 Bob Shaw	1.50	4.00
329 Russ Nixon	1.50	4.00
330 Tommy Harper	2.50	6.00
331 AL Bombers	75.00	150.00
Roger Maris		
Norm Cash		
Mickey Mantle		
Al Kaline		
332 Ray Washburn	1.50	4.00
333 Billy Moran	1.50	4.00
334 Lew Krausse	1.50	4.00
335 Don Mossi	2.50	6.00
336 Andre Rodgers	1.50	4.00
337 Rookie Stars	2.50	6.00
Al Ferrara RC		
Jeff Torborg RC		
338 Jack Kralick	1.50	4.00
339 Walt Bond	1.50	4.00
340 Joe Cunningham	1.50	4.00
341 Jim Roland	1.50	4.00
342 Willie Stargell	12.50	30.00
343 Washington Senators TC	2.50	6.00
344 Phil Linz	2.50	6.00
345 Frank Thomas	3.00	8.00
346 Joey Jay	1.50	4.00
347 Bobby Wine	2.50	6.00
348 Ed Lopat MG	2.50	6.00
349 Art Fowler	1.50	4.00
350 Willie McCovey	10.00	25.00
351 Dan Schneider	1.50	4.00
352 Eddie Bressoud	1.50	4.00
353 Wally Moon	2.50	6.00
354 Dave Giusti	1.50	4.00
355 Vic Power	2.50	6.00
356 Rookie Stars	2.50	6.00
Bill McCool RC		
Chico Ruiz		
357 Charley James	1.50	4.00
358 Ron Kline	1.50	4.00
359 Jim Schaffer	1.50	4.00
360 Joe Pepitone	5.00	12.00
361 Jay Hook	1.50	4.00
362 Checklist 5	4.00	10.00
363 Dick McAuliffe	2.50	6.00
364 Joe Gaines	1.50	4.00
365 Cal McLish	2.50	6.00
366 Nelson Mathews	1.50	4.00
367 Fred Whitfield	1.50	4.00
368 Rookie Stars	2.50	6.00
Fritz Ackley RC		
Don Buford RC		
369 Jerry Zimmerman	1.50	4.00
370 Hal Woodeshick	1.50	4.00
371 Frank Howard	3.00	8.00
372 Howie Koplitz	3.00	8.00
373 Pittsburgh Pirates TC	5.00	12.00
374 Bobby Bolin	3.00	8.00
375 Ron Santo	4.00	10.00
376 Dave Morehead	3.00	8.00
377 Bob Skinner	3.00	8.00
378 Rookie Stars	4.00	10.00
Woody Woodward RC		
Jack Smith		
379 Tony Gonzalez	3.00	8.00
380 Whitey Ford	15.00	40.00
381 Bob Taylor	3.00	8.00
382 Wes Stock	3.00	8.00
383 Bill Rigney MG	3.00	8.00
384 Ron Hansen	3.00	8.00
385 Curt Simmons	4.00	10.00
386 Lenny Green	3.00	8.00
387 Terry Fox	3.00	8.00
388 Rookie Stars	4.00	10.00
John O'Donoghue RC		
George Williams		
389 Jim Umbricht	4.00	10.00
390 Orlando Cepeda	10.00	25.00
391 Sam McDowell	4.00	10.00
392 Jim Pagliaroni	3.00	8.00
393 Casey Teaches	6.00	15.00
Casey Stengel MG		
Ed Kranepool		
394 Bob Miller	3.00	8.00
395 Tom Tresh	4.00	10.00
396 Dennis Bennett	3.00	8.00
397 Chuck Cottier	3.00	8.00
398 Rookie Stars	4.00	10.00
Bill Haas		
Dick Smith		
399 Jackie Brandt	3.00	8.00
400 Warren Spahn	15.00	40.00
401 Charlie Maxwell	3.00	8.00
402 Tom Sturdivant	3.00	8.00
403 Cincinnati Reds TC	5.00	12.00
404 Tony Martinez	3.00	8.00
405 Ken McBride	3.00	8.00
406 Al Spangler	3.00	8.00
407 Bill Freehan	4.00	10.00
408 Rookie Stars	3.00	8.00
Jim Stewart RC		
Fred Burdette RC		
409 Bill Fischer	3.00	8.00
410 Dick Stuart	4.00	10.00
411 Lee Walls	3.00	8.00
412 Ray Culp	4.00	10.00
413 Johnny Keane MG	3.00	8.00
414 Jack Sanford	3.00	8.00
415 Tony Kubek	6.00	15.00
416 Lee Maye	3.00	8.00
417 Don Cardwell	3.00	8.00
418 Rookie Stars	4.00	10.00
Darold Knowles RC		
Buster Narum RC		
419 Ken Harrelson RC	6.00	15.00
420 Jim Maloney	4.00	10.00
421 Camilo Carreon	3.00	8.00
422 Jack Fisher	3.00	8.00
423 Tops in NL	60.00	120.00
Hank Aaron		
Willie Mays		
424 Dick Bertell	3.00	8.00
425 Norm Cash	4.00	10.00
426 Bob Rodgers	3.00	8.00
427 Don Rudolph	3.00	8.00
428 Rookie Stars	3.00	8.00
Archie Skeen RC		
Pete Smith RC		
429 Tim McCarver	4.00	10.00
430 Juan Pizarro	3.00	8.00
431 George Alusik	3.00	8.00
432 Ruben Amaro	4.00	10.00
433 New York Yankees TC	15.00	40.00
434 Don Nottebart	3.00	8.00
435 Vic Davalillo	3.00	8.00
436 Charlie Neal	4.00	10.00
437 Ed Bailey	3.00	8.00
438 Checklist 6	6.00	15.00
439 Harvey Haddix	4.00	10.00
440 R.Clemente UER	100.00	200.00
1960 Pittsburgh		
441 Bob Duliba	3.00	8.00
442 Pumpsie Green	4.00	10.00
443 Chuck Dressen MG	4.00	10.00
444 Larry Jackson	3.00	8.00
445 Bill Skowron	4.00	10.00
446 Julian Javier	6.00	15.00
447 Ted Bowsfield	3.00	8.00
448 Cookie Rojas	4.00	10.00
449 Deron Johnson	4.00	10.00
450 Steve Barber	3.00	8.00
451 Joe Amalfitano	3.00	8.00
452 Rookie Stars	4.00	10.00
Gil Garrido RC		
Jim Ray Hart RC		
453 Frank Baumann	3.00	8.00
454 Tommie Aaron	4.00	10.00
455 Bernie Allen	3.00	8.00
456 Rookie Stars	4.00	10.00
Wes Parker RC		
John Werhas RC		
457 Jesse Gonder	3.00	8.00
458 Ralph Terry	4.00	10.00
459 Rookie Stars	3.00	8.00
Pete Charton RC		
Dalton Jones RC		
460 Bob Gibson	15.00	40.00
461 George Thomas	3.00	8.00
462 Birdie Tebbetts MG	3.00	8.00
463 Don Leppert	3.00	8.00
464 Dallas Green	6.00	15.00
465 Mike Hershberger	3.00	8.00
466 Rookie Stars	4.00	10.00
Dick Green RC		
Aurelio Monteagudo RC		
467 Bob Aspromonte	3.00	8.00
468 Gaylord Perry	15.00	40.00
469 Rookie Stars	4.00	10.00
Fred Norman RC		
Sterling Slaughter RC		
470 Jim Bouton	4.00	10.00
471 Gates Brown RC	4.00	10.00
472 Vern Law	4.00	10.00
473 Baltimore Orioles TC	5.00	12.00
474 Larry Sherry	4.00	10.00
475 Ed Charles	3.00	8.00
476 Rookie Stars	6.00	15.00
Rico Carty RC		
Dick Kelley RC		
477 Mike Joyce	3.00	8.00
478 Dick Howser	4.00	10.00
479 Rookie Stars	3.00	8.00
Dave Bakenhaster RC		
Johnny Lewis RC		
480 Bob Purkey	3.00	8.00
481 Chuck Schilling	3.00	8.00
482 Rookie Stars	4.00	10.00
John Briggs RC		
Danny Cater RC		
483 Fred Valentine RC	3.00	8.00
484 Bill Pleis	3.00	8.00
485 Tom Haller	3.00	8.00
486 Bob Kennedy MG	3.00	8.00
487 Mike McCormick	4.00	10.00
488 Rookie Stars	6.00	15.00
Pete Mikkelsen RC		
Bob Meyer RC		
489 Julio Navarro	3.00	8.00
490 Ron Fairly	4.00	10.00
491 Ed Rakow	3.00	8.00
492 Rookie Stars	3.00	8.00
Jim Beauchamp RC		
Mike White RC		
493 Don Lee	3.00	8.00
494 Al Jackson	3.00	8.00
495 Bill Virdon	4.00	10.00
496 Chicago White Sox TC	5.00	12.00
497 Jeoff Long RC	3.00	8.00
498 Dave Stenhouse	3.00	8.00
499 Rookie Stars	3.00	8.00
Chico Salmon RC		
Gordon Seyfried RC		
500 Camilo Pascual	4.00	10.00
501 Bob Veale	4.00	10.00
502 Rookie Stars	3.00	8.00
Bobby Knoop RC		
Bob Lee RC		
503 Earl Wilson	3.00	8.00
504 Claude Raymond	3.00	8.00
505 Stan Williams	3.00	8.00
506 Bobby Bragan MG	3.00	8.00
507 Johnny Edwards	3.00	8.00
508 Diego Segui	3.00	8.00
509 Rookie Stars	4.00	10.00
Gene Alley RC		
Orlando McFarlane RC		
510 Lindy McDaniel	4.00	10.00
511 Lou Jackson	4.00	10.00
512 Rookie Stars	6.00	15.00
Willie Horton RC		
Joe Sparma RC		
513 Don Larsen	4.00	10.00
514 Jim Hickman	4.00	10.00
515 Johnny Romano	3.00	8.00
516 Rookie Stars	3.00	8.00
Jerry Arrigo RC		
Dwight Siebler RC		
517A Checklist 7 ERR	10.00	25.00
(Incorrect numbering		
sequence on back)		
517B Checklist 7 COR	6.00	15.00
(Correct numbering		
on back)		
518 Carl Bouldin	3.00	8.00
519 Charlie Smith	3.00	8.00
520 Jack Baldschun	4.00	10.00
521 Tom Satriano	3.00	8.00
522 Bob Tiefenauer	3.00	8.00
523 Lou Burdette UER	8.00	20.00
(Pitching lefty)		
524 Rookie Stars	6.00	15.00
Jim Dickson RC		
Bobby Klaus RC		
525 Al McBean	6.00	15.00
526 Lou Clinton	6.00	15.00
527 Larry Bearnarth	6.00	15.00
528 Rookie Stars	8.00	20.00
Dave Duncan RC		
Tommie Reynolds RC		
529 Alvin Dark MG	8.00	20.00
530 Leon Wagner	6.00	15.00
531 Los Angeles Dodgers TC	10.00	25.00
532 Rookie Stars	6.00	15.00
Bud Bloomfield UER RC		
(Photo is Jay Ward)		
Joe Nossek RC		
533 Johnny Klippstein	6.00	15.00
534 Gus Bell	6.00	15.00
535 Phil Regan	6.00	15.00
536 Rookie Stars	6.00	15.00
Larry Elliot		
John Stephenson RC		
537 Dan Osinski	6.00	15.00
538 Minnie Minoso	8.00	20.00
539 Roy Face	8.00	20.00
540 Luis Aparicio	15.00	40.00
541 Rookie Stars	40.00	80.00
Phil Roof		
Phil Niekro RC		
542 Don Mincher	6.00	15.00
543 Bob Uecker	15.00	40.00
544 Rookie Stars	6.00	15.00
Steve Hertz RC		
Joe Hoerner RC		
545 Max Alvis	6.00	15.00
546 Joe Christopher	6.00	15.00
547 Gil Hodges MG	12.50	30.00
548 Rookie Stars	8.00	20.00
Wayne Schurr RC		
Paul Speckenbach RC		
549 Joe Moeller	6.00	15.00
550 Ken Hubbs	15.00	40.00
In Memoriam		
551 Billy Hoeft	6.00	15.00
552 Rookie Stars	6.00	15.00
Tom Kelley RC		
Sonny Siebert RC		
553 Jim Brewer	6.00	15.00
554 Hank Foiles	6.00	15.00
555 Lee Stange	6.00	15.00
556 Rookie Stars	6.00	15.00
Steve Dillon RC		
Ron Locke RC		
557 Leo Burke	6.00	15.00
558 Don Schwall	6.00	15.00
559 Dick Phillips	6.00	15.00
560 Dick Farrell	6.00	15.00
561 Rookie Stars	8.00	20.00
Dave Bennett UER RC		
(19 ... is 18)		
Rick Wise RC		
562 Pedro Ramos	6.00	15.00
563 Dal Maxvill	8.00	20.00
564 Rookie Stars	8.00	20.00
Joe McCabe RC		
Jerry McNertney RC		
565 Stu Miller	6.00	15.00
566 Ed Kranepool	6.00	15.00
567 Jim Kaat	8.00	20.00
568 Rookie Stars	6.00	15.00
Phil Gagliano RC		
Cap Peterson RC		
569 Fred Newman	6.00	15.00
570 Bill Mazeroski	15.00	40.00
571 Gene Conley	6.00	15.00
572 Rookie Stars	6.00	15.00
Dave Gray RC		
Dick Egan		
573 Jim Duffalo	6.00	15.00
574 Manny Jimenez	6.00	15.00
575 Tony Cloninger	6.00	15.00
576 Rookie Stars	6.00	15.00
Jerry Hinsley RC		
Bill Wakefield RC		
577 Gordy Coleman	6.00	15.00
578 Glen Hobbie	6.00	15.00
579 Boston Red Sox TC	10.00	25.00
580 Johnny Podres	8.00	20.00
581 Rookie Stars	8.00	20.00
Pedro Gonzalez		
Archie Moore RC		
582 Rod Kanehl	8.00	20.00
583 Tito Francona	6.00	15.00
584 Joel Horlen	6.00	15.00
585 Tony Taylor	8.00	20.00
586 Jimmy Piersall	8.00	20.00
587 Bennie Daniels	8.00	20.00

1964 Topps Giants

The cards in this 60-card set measure approximately 3 1/8" by 5 1/4". The 1964 Topps Giants are postcard size cards containing color player photographs. They are numbered on the backs, which also contain biographical information presented in a newspaper format. These "giant size" cards were distributed in both cellophane and waxed gum packs apart from the Topps regular issue of 1964. The gum packs contain three cards. The Cards 3, 28, 42, 45, 47, 51 and 60 are more difficult to find and are indicated by SP in the checklist below.

Card	Low	High
COMPLETE SET (60)	150.00	300.00
COMMON CARD (1-60)	.60	1.50
COMMON SP'S	4.00	10.00
WRAPPER (5-CENT)	15.00	40.00
1 Gary Peters	.75	2.00
2 Ken Johnson	.60	1.50
3 Sandy Koufax SP	15.00	40.00
4 Bob Bailey	.60	1.50
5 Milt Pappas	.75	2.00
6 Ron Hunt	.60	1.50
7 Whitey Ford	2.00	5.00
8 Roy McMillan	.60	1.50
9 Rocky Colavito	2.00	5.00
10 Jim Bunning	1.25	3.00
11 Roberto Clemente	12.50	30.00
12 Al Kaline	2.00	5.00
13 Nellie Fox	2.00	5.00
14 Tony Gonzalez	.60	1.50
15 Jim Gentile	.75	2.00
16 Dean Chance	.75	2.00
17 Dick Ellsworth	.75	2.00
18 Jim Fregosi	.75	2.00
19 Dick Groat	.75	2.00
20 Chuck Hinton	.60	1.50
21 Elston Howard	.75	2.00
22 Dick Farrell	.60	1.50
23 Albie Pearson	.60	1.50
24 Frank Howard	.75	2.00
25 Mickey Mantle	20.00	50.00
26 Joe Torre	2.00	5.00
27 Eddie Brinkman	.60	1.50
28 Bob Friend SP	4.00	10.00
29 Frank Robinson	2.00	5.00
30 Bill Freehan	.75	2.00
31 Warren Spahn	2.00	5.00
32 Camilo Pascual	.75	2.00
33 Pete Ward	.60	1.50
34 Jim Maloney	.75	2.00
35 Dave Wickersham	.60	1.50
36 Johnny Callison	.75	2.00
37 Juan Marichal	1.25	3.00
38 Harmon Killebrew	2.00	5.00
39 Luis Aparicio	1.25	3.00
40 Dick Radatz	.60	1.50
41 Bob Gibson	2.00	5.00
42 Dick Stuart SP	4.00	10.00
43 Tommy Davis	.75	2.00
44 Tony Oliva	1.25	3.00
45 Wayne Causey SP	4.00	10.00
46 Max Alvis	.60	1.50
47 Galen Cisco SP	4.00	10.00
48 Carl Yastrzemski	2.00	5.00
49 Hank Aaron	4.00	10.00
50 Brooks Robinson	2.00	5.00
51 Willie Mays SP	20.00	50.00
52 Billy Williams	1.25	3.00
53 Juan Pizarro	.60	1.50
54 Leon Wagner	.60	1.50
55 Orlando Cepeda	1.25	3.00
56 Vada Pinson	.75	2.00
57 Ken Boyer	1.25	3.00
58 Ron Santo	1.25	3.00
59 John Romano	.60	1.50
60 Bill Skowron SP	6.00	15.00

1964 Topps Stand-Ups

In 1964 Topps produced a die-cut "Stand-Up" card design for the first time since their Connie Mack and Current All Stars of 1951. These cards were issued in both one cent and five cent packs. The cards have full-length, color player photos set against a green and yellow background. Of the 77 cards in the set, 22 were single printed and these are marked in the checklist below with an SP. These unnumbered cards are standard-size (2 1/2" by 3 1/2"), blank backed, and have been numbered here for reference in alphabetical order of players. Interestingly there were four different wrapper designs used for this set. All the design variations are valued at the same price.

Card	Low	High
COMPLETE SET (77)	2500.00	4000.00
COMMON CARD (1-77)	4.00	10.00
COMMON CARD SP	15.00	40.00
WRAPPER (1-CENT)	75.00	150.00
WRAPPER (5-CENT)	175.00	350.00
1 Hank Aaron	100.00	200.00
2 Hank Aguirre	5.00	12.00
3 George Altman	8.00	20.00
4 Max Alvis	5.00	12.00
5 Bob Aspromonte	5.00	12.00
6 Jack Baldschun SP	20.00	50.00
7 Ernie Banks	50.00	100.00
8 Steve Barber	5.00	12.00
9 Earl Battey	5.00	12.00
10 Ken Boyer	10.00	25.00
11 Ernie Broglio	5.00	12.00
12 John Callison	8.00	20.00
13 Norm Cash SP	40.00	80.00
14 Wayne Causey	5.00	12.00
15 Orlando Cepeda	10.00	25.00
16 Ed Charles	8.00	20.00
17 Roberto Clemente	125.00	250.00
18 Donn Clendenon SP	20.00	50.00
19 Rocky Colavito	15.00	40.00
20 Ray Culp SP	30.00	60.00
21 Tommy Davis	8.00	20.00
22 Don Drysdale SP	75.00	150.00
23 Dick Ellsworth	5.00	12.00
24 Dick Farrell	5.00	12.00
25 Jim Fregosi	8.00	20.00
26 Bob Friend	5.00	12.00
27 Jim Gentile	8.00	20.00
28 Jesse Gonder SP	20.00	50.00
29 Tony Gonzalez SP	20.00	50.00
30 Dick Groat	10.00	25.00
31 Woody Held	5.00	12.00
32 Chuck Hinton	5.00	12.00
33 Elston Howard	10.00	25.00
34 Frank Howard SP	40.00	80.00
35 Ron Hunt	8.00	20.00
36 Al Jackson	5.00	12.00
37 Ken Johnson	5.00	12.00
38 Al Kaline	50.00	100.00
39 Harmon Killebrew	50.00	100.00
40 Sandy Koufax	100.00	200.00
41 Don Lock SP	20.00	50.00
42 Jerry Lumpe SP	20.00	50.00
43 Jim Maloney	8.00	20.00
44 Frank Malzone	5.00	12.00
45 Mickey Mantle	300.00	600.00
46 Juan Marichal SP	60.00	120.00
47 Eddie Mathews SP	75.00	150.00
48 Willie Mays	150.00	300.00
49 Bill Mazeroski	15.00	40.00
50 Ken McBride	5.00	12.00
51 Willie McCovey SP	60.00	120.00
52 Claude Osteen	8.00	20.00
53 Jim O'Toole	5.00	12.00
54 Camilo Pascual	5.00	12.00
55 Albie Pearson SP	30.00	60.00
56 Gary Peters	5.00	12.00
57 Vada Pinson	8.00	20.00
58 Juan Pizarro	5.00	12.00
59 Boog Powell	10.00	25.00
60 Bobby Richardson	10.00	25.00
61 Brooks Robinson	50.00	100.00
62 Floyd Robinson	5.00	12.00
63 Frank Robinson	50.00	100.00
64 Ed Roebuck SP	20.00	50.00
65 Rich Rollins	5.00	12.00
66 John Romano	5.00	12.00
67 Ron Santo SP	40.00	80.00
68 Norm Siebern	5.00	12.00
69 Warren Spahn SP	75.00	150.00
70 Dick Stuart SP	30.00	60.00
71 Lee Thomas	5.00	12.00
72 Joe Torre	10.00	25.00
73 Pete Ward	5.00	12.00
74 Bill White SP	30.00	60.00
75 Billy Williams SP	60.00	120.00
76 Hal Woodeshick SP	20.00	50.00
77 Carl Yastrzemski SP	250.00	500.00

1965 Topps

The cards in this 598-card set measure 2 1/2" by 3 1/2". The cards comprising the 1965 Topps set have team names located within a distinctive pennant design below the picture. The cards have blue borders on the reverse and were issued by series. Within this last series (523-598) there are 44 cards that were printed in lesser quantities than the other cards in that series; these shorter-printed cards are marked by SP in the checklist below. Featured subsets within this set include League Leaders (1-12) and World Series cards (132-139). This was the last year Topps issued one-card penny packs. Card were also issued in five-card nickel packs. The key Rookie Cards in this set are Steve Carlton, Jim "Catfish" Hunter, Joe Morgan, Mansori Murakami and Tony Perez.

Card	Low	High
COMPLETE SET (598)	2500.00	5000.00
COMMON CARD (1-196)	.75	2.00
COMMON (197-283)	1.00	2.50
COMMON (284-370)	1.50	4.00
COMMON (371-598)	3.00	8.00

WRAPPER (1-CENT) 60.00 120.00
WRAPPER (5-CENT) 50.00 100.00
1 AL Batting Leaders 8.00 20.00
Tony Oliva
Elston Howard
Brooks Robinson
2 NL Batting Leaders 10.00 25.00
Roberto Clemente
Hank Aaron
Rico Carty
3 AL Home Run Leaders 20.00 50.00
Harmon Killebrew
Mickey Mantle
Boog Powell
4 NL Home Run Leaders 6.00 15.00
Willie Mays
Billy Williams
Jim Ray Hart
Orlando Cepeda
Johnny Callison
5 AL RBI Leaders 15.00 40.00
Brooks Robinson
Harmon Killebrew
Mickey Mantle
Dick Stuart
6 NL RBI Leaders 5.00 12.00
Ken Boyer
Willie Mays
Ron Santo
7 AL ERA Leaders 2.00 5.00
Dean Chance
Joel Horlen
8 NL ERA Leaders 8.00 20.00
Sandy Koufax
Don Drysdale
9 AL Pitching Leaders 2.00 5.00
Dean Chance
Gary Peters
Dave Wickersham
Juan Pizarro
Wally Bunker
10 NL Pitching Leaders 2.00 5.00
Larry Jackson
Ray Sadecki
Juan Marichal
11 AL Strikeout Leaders 2.00 5.00
Al Downing
Dean Chance
Camilo Pascual
12 NL Strikeout Leaders 4.00 10.00
Bob Veale
Don Drysdale
Bob Gibson
13 Pedro Ramos 1.50 4.00
14 Len Gabrielson .75 2.00
15 Robin Roberts 4.00 10.00
16 Rookie Stars 30.00 60.00
Joe Morgan RC
Sonny Jackson RC DP
17 Johnny Romano .75 2.00
18 Bill McCool .75 2.00
19 Gates Brown 1.50 4.00
20 Jim Bunning 4.00 10.00
21 Don Blasingame .75 2.00
22 Charlie Smith .75 2.00
23 Bob Tiefenauer .75 2.00
24 Minnesota Twins TC 2.50 6.00
25 Al McBean .75 2.00
26 Bobby Knoop .75 2.00
27 Dick Bertell .75 2.00
28 Barney Schultz .75 2.00
29 Felix Mantilla .75 2.00
30 Jim Bouton 2.50 6.00
31 Mike White .75 2.00
32 Herman Franks MG .75 2.00
33 Jackie Brandt .75 2.00
34 Cal Koonce .75 2.00
35 Ed Charles .75 2.00
36 Bobby Wine .75 2.00
37 Fred Gladding .75 2.00
38 Jim King .75 2.00
39 Gerry Arrigo .75 2.00
40 Frank Howard 2.50 6.00
41 Rookie Stars .75 2.00
Bruce Howard
Marv Staehle RC
42 Earl Wilson 1.50 4.00
43 Mike Shannon 1.50 4.00
(Name in red, other
Cardinals in yellow)
44 Wade Blasingame RC .75 2.00
45 Roy McMillan 1.50 4.00
46 Bob Lee .75 2.00
47 Tommy Harper 1.50 4.00
48 Claude Raymond 1.50 4.00
49 Rookie Stars 1.50 4.00
Curt Blefary RC
John Miller
50 Juan Marichal 4.00 10.00
51 Bill Bryan .75 2.00
52 Ed Roebuck .75 2.00
53 Dick McAuliffe 1.50 4.00
54 Joe Gibbon .75 2.00
55 Tony Conigliaro 6.00 15.00
56 Ron Kline .75 2.00
57 St. Louis Cardinals TC 2.50 6.00
58 Fred Talbot RC .75 2.00
59 Nate Oliver .75 2.00
60 Jim O'Toole 1.50 4.00
61 Chris Cannizzaro .75 2.00
62 Jim Kaat UER DP 2.50 6.00
(Misspelled Katt)
63 Ty Cline .75 2.00
64 Lou Burdette 1.50 4.00
65 Tony Kubek 4.00 10.00
66 Bill Rigney MG .75 2.00
67 Harvey Haddix 1.50 4.00
68 Del Crandall 1.50 4.00
69 Bill Virdon 1.50 4.00
70 Bill Skowron 2.50 6.00
71 John O'Donoghue .75 2.00
72 Tony Gonzalez .75 2.00
73 Dennis Ribant RC .75 2.00
74 Rookie Stars 4.00 10.00
Rico Petrocelli RC
Jerry Stephenson RC
75 Deron Johnson 1.50 4.00
76 Sam McDowell 2.50 6.00
77 Doug Camilli .75 2.00
78 Dal Maxvill .75 2.00
79A Checklist 1 4.00 10.00
(61 Cannizzaro)
79B Checklist 1 4.00 10.00
(61 C.Cannizzaro)
80 Turk Farrell .75 2.00
81 Don Buford 1.50 4.00
82 Rookie Stars 2.50 6.00
Santos Alomar RC
John Braun RC
83 George Thomas .75 2.00
84 Ron Herbel .75 2.00
85 Willie Smith RC .75 2.00
86 Buster Narum .75 2.00
87 Nelson Mathews .75 2.00
88 Jack Lamabe .75 2.00
89 Mike Hershberger .75 2.00
90 Rich Rollins 1.50 4.00
91 Chicago Cubs TC 2.50 6.00
92 Dick Howser 1.50 4.00
93 Jack Fisher .75 2.00
94 Charlie Lau 1.50 4.00
95 Bill Mazeroski DP 2.50 6.00
96 Sonny Siebert 1.50 4.00
97 Pedro Gonzalez .75 2.00
98 Bob Miller .75 2.00
99 Gil Hodges MG 2.50 6.00
100 Ken Boyer 4.00 10.00
101 Fred Newman .75 2.00
102 Steve Boros .75 2.00
103 Harvey Kuenn 1.50 4.00
104 Checklist 2 4.00 10.00
105 Chico Salmon .75 2.00
106 Gene Oliver .75 2.00
107 Rookie Stars 1.50 4.00
Pat Corrales RC
Costen Shockley RC
108 Don Mincher .75 2.00
109 Walt Bond .75 2.00
110 Ron Santo 2.50 6.00
111 Lee Thomas 1.50 4.00
112 Derrell Griffith RC .75 2.00
113 Steve Barber .75 2.00
114 Jim Hickman 1.50 4.00
115 Bobby Richardson 4.00 10.00
116 Rookie Stars 1.50 4.00
Dave Dowling RC
Bob Tolan RC
117 Wes Stock .75 2.00
118 Hal Lanier RC 1.50 4.00
119 John Kennedy .75 2.00
120 Frank Robinson 15.00 40.00
121 Gene Alley 1.50 4.00
122 Bill Pleis .75 2.00
123 Frank Thomas 1.50 4.00
124 Tom Satriano .75 2.00
125 Juan Pizarro .75 2.00
126 Los Angeles Dodgers TC 2.50 6.00
127 Frank Lary .75 2.00
128 Vic Davalillo .75 2.00
129 Bennie Daniels .75 2.00
130 Al Kaline 15.00 40.00
131 Johnny Keane MG .75 2.00
132 World Series Game 1 4.00 10.00
Cards Take Opener
133 World Series Game 2 2.50 6.00
Mel Stottlemyre
134 World Series Game 3 40.00 80.00
Mickey Mantle
135 World Series Game 4 4.00 10.00
Ken Boyer
136 World Series Game 5 2.50 6.00
Tim McCarver
137 World Series Game 6 2.50 6.00
Jim Bouton
138 World Series Game 7 5.00 12.00
Bob Gibson
139 World Series Summary 2.50 6.00
Cards Celebrate
140 Dean Chance 1.50 4.00
141 Charlie James .75 2.00
142 Bill Monbouquette .75 2.00
143 Rookie Stars .75 2.00
John Gelnar RC
Jerry May RC
144 Ed Kranepool 1.50 4.00
145 Luis Tiant RC 4.00 10.00
146 Ron Hansen .75 2.00
147 Dennis Bennett .75 2.00
148 Willie Kirkland .75 2.00
149 Wayne Schurr .75 2.00
150 Brooks Robinson 15.00 40.00
151 Kansas City Athletics TC 2.50 6.00
152 Phil Ortega .75 2.00
153 Norm Cash 2.50 6.00
154 Bob Humphreys RC .75 2.00
155 Roger Maris 30.00 60.00
156 Bob Sadowski .75 2.00
157 Zoilo Versalles 1.50 4.00
158 Dick Sisler .75 2.00
159 Jim Duffalo .75 2.00
160 R.Clemente UER 100.00 200.00
1960 Pittsburfh
161 Frank Baumann .75 2.00
162 Russ Nixon .75 2.00
163 Johnny Briggs .75 2.00
164 Al Spangler .75 2.00
165 Dick Ellsworth .75 2.00
166 Rookie Stars 1.50 4.00
George Culver RC
Tommie Agee RC
167 Bill Wakefield .75 2.00
168 Dick Green .75 2.00
169 Dave Vineyard RC .75 2.00
170 Hank Aaron 75.00 150.00
171 Jim Roland .75 2.00
172 Jimmy Piersall 2.50 6.00
173 Detroit Tigers TC 2.50 6.00
174 Joey Jay .75 2.00
175 Bob Aspromonte .75 2.00
176 Willie McCovey 8.00 20.00
177 Pete Mikkelsen .75 2.00
178 Dalton Jones .75 2.00
179 Hal Woodeshick .75 2.00
180 Bob Allison 1.50 4.00
181 Rookie Stars .75 2.00
Don Loun RC
Joe McCabe
182 Mike de la Hoz .75 2.00
183 Dave Nicholson .75 2.00
184 John Boozer .75 2.00
185 Max Alvis .75 2.00
186 Billy Cowan .75 2.00
187 Casey Stengel MG 6.00 15.00
188 Sam Bowens .75 2.00
189 Checklist 3 4.00 10.00
190 Bill White 2.50 6.00
191 Phil Regan 1.50 4.00
192 Jim Coker .75 2.00
193 Gaylord Perry 6.00 15.00
194 Rookie Stars .75 2.00
Bill Kelso RC
Rick Reichardt RC
195 Bob Veale 1.50 4.00
196 Ron Fairly 1.50 4.00
197 Diego Segui 1.00 2.50
198 Smoky Burgess 1.50 4.00
199 Bob Heffner 1.00 2.50
200 Joe Torre 2.50 6.00
201 Rookie Stars 1.50 4.00
Sandy Valdespino RC
Cesar Tovar RC
202 Leo Burke 1.00 2.50
203 Dallas Green 1.50 4.00
204 Russ Snyder 1.00 2.50
205 Warren Spahn 12.50 30.00
206 Willie Horton 1.50 4.00
207 Pete Rose 100.00 200.00
208 Tommy John 2.50 6.00
209 Pittsburgh Pirates TC 2.50 6.00
210 Jim Fregosi 1.50 4.00
211 Steve Ridzik 1.00 2.50
212 Ron Brand 1.00 2.50
213 Jim Davenport 1.00 2.50
214 Bob Purkey 1.00 2.50
215 Pete Ward 1.00 2.50
216 Al Worthington 1.00 2.50
217 Walter Alston MG 2.50 6.00
218 Dick Schofield 1.00 2.50
219 Bob Meyer 1.00 2.50
220 Billy Williams 4.00 10.00
221 John Tsitouris 1.00 2.50
222 Bob Tillman 1.00 2.50
223 Dan Osinski 1.00 2.50
224 Bob Chance 1.00 2.50
225 Bo Belinsky 1.50 4.00
226 Rookie Stars 2.50 6.00
Elvio Jimenez RC
Jake Gibbs
227 Bobby Klaus 1.00 2.50
228 Jack Sanford 1.00 2.50
229 Lou Clinton 1.00 2.50
230 Ray Sadecki 1.00 2.50
231 Jerry Adair 1.00 2.50
232 Steve Blass RC 1.50 4.00
233 Don Zimmer 1.50 4.00
234 Chicago White Sox TC 2.50 6.00
235 Chuck Hinton 1.00 2.50
236 Denny McLain RC 10.00 25.00
237 Bernie Allen 1.00 2.50
238 Joe Moeller 1.00 2.50
239 Doc Edwards 1.00 2.50
240 Bob Bruce 1.00 2.50
241 Mack Jones 1.00 2.50
242 George Brunet 1.00 2.50
243 Rookie Stars 1.50 4.00
Ted Davidson RC
Tommy Helms RC
244 Lindy McDaniel 1.50 4.00
245 Joe Pepitone 2.50 6.00
246 Tom Butters 1.50 4.00
247 Wally Moon 1.50 4.00
248 Gus Triandos 1.50 4.00
249 Dave McNally 1.50 4.00
250 Willie Mays 75.00 150.00
251 Billy Herman MG 1.50 4.00
252 Pete Richert 1.00 2.50
253 Danny Cater 1.00 2.50
254 Roland Sheldon 1.00 2.50
255 Camilo Pascual 1.50 4.00
256 Tito Francona 1.00 2.50
257 Jim Wynn 1.50 4.00
258 Larry Bearnarth 1.00 2.50
259 Rookie Stars 2.50 6.00
Jim Northrup RC
Ray Oyler RC
260 Don Drysdale 8.00 20.00
261 Duke Carmel 1.00 2.50
262 Bud Daley 1.00 2.50
263 Marty Keough 1.00 2.50
264 Bob Buhl 1.00 2.50
265 Jim Pagliaroni 1.00 2.50
266 Bert Campaneris RC 4.00 10.00
267 Washington Senators TC 2.50 6.00
268 Ken McBride 1.00 2.50
269 Frank Bolling 1.00 2.50
270 Milt Pappas 1.50 4.00
271 Don Wert 1.50 4.00
272 Chuck Schilling 1.00 2.50
273 Checklist 4 4.00 10.00
274 Lum Harris MG RC 1.00 2.50
275 Dick Groat 2.50 6.00
276 Hoyt Wilhelm 4.00 10.00
277 Johnny Lewis 1.00 2.50
278 Ken Retzer 1.00 2.50
279 Dick Tracewski 1.00 2.50
280 Dick Stuart 1.50 4.00
281 Bill Stafford 1.00 2.50
282 Rookie Stars 15.00 40.00
Dick Estelle RC
Masanori Murakami RC
283 Fred Whitfield 1.00 2.50
284 Nick Willhite 1.50 4.00
285 Ron Hunt 1.50 4.00
286 Rookie Stars 1.50 4.00
Jim Dickson
Aurelio Monteagudo
287 Gary Kolb 1.50 4.00
288 Jack Hamilton 1.50 4.00
289 Gordy Coleman 2.50 6.00
290 Wally Bunker 2.50 6.00
291 Jerry Lynch 1.50 4.00
292 Larry Yellen 1.50 4.00
293 Los Angeles Angels TC 2.50 6.00
294 Tim McCarver 4.00 10.00
295 Dick Radatz 2.50 6.00
296 Tony Taylor 2.50 6.00
297 Dave DeBusschere 4.00 10.00
298 Jim Stewart 1.50 4.00
299 Jerry Zimmerman 1.50 4.00
300 Sandy Koufax 50.00 100.00
301 Birdie Tebbetts MG 2.50 6.00
302 Al Stanek 1.50 4.00
303 John Orsino 1.50 4.00
304 Dave Stenhouse 1.50 4.00
305 Rico Carty 2.50 6.00
306 Bubba Phillips 1.50 4.00
307 Barry Latman 1.50 4.00
308 Rookie Stars 2.50 6.00
Cleon Jones RC
Tom Parsons
309 Steve Hamilton 2.50 6.00
310 Johnny Callison 2.50 6.00
311 Orlando Pena 1.50 4.00
312 Joe Nuxhall 1.50 4.00
313 Jim Schaffer 1.50 4.00
314 Sterling Slaughter 1.50 4.00
315 Frank Malzone 2.50 6.00
316 Cincinnati Reds TC 2.50 6.00
317 Don McMahon 1.50 4.00
318 Matty Alou 2.50 6.00
319 Ken McMullen 1.50 4.00
320 Bob Gibson 20.00 50.00
321 Rusty Staub 4.00 10.00
322 Rick Wise 2.50 6.00
323 Hank Bauer MG 2.50 6.00
324 Bobby Locke 1.50 4.00
325 Donn Clendenon 2.50 6.00
326 Dwight Siebler 1.50 4.00
327 Denis Menke 1.50 4.00
328 Eddie Fisher 1.50 4.00
329 Hawk Taylor RC 1.50 4.00
330 Whitey Ford 15.00 40.00
331 Rookie Stars 2.50 6.00
Al Ferrara
John Purdin RC
332 Ted Abernathy 1.50 4.00
333 Tom Reynolds 1.50 4.00
334 Vic Roznovsky RC 1.50 4.00
335 Mickey Lolich 2.50 6.00
336 Woody Held 1.50 4.00
337 Mike Cuellar 2.50 6.00
338 Philadelphia Phillies TC 2.50 6.00
339 Ryne Duren 2.50 6.00
340 Tony Oliva 8.00 20.00
341 Bob Bolin 1.50 4.00
342 Bob Rodgers 2.50 6.00
343 Mike McCormick 2.50 6.00
344 Wes Parker 2.50 6.00
345 Floyd Robinson 1.50 4.00
346 Bobby Bragan MG 1.50 4.00
347 Roy Face 2.50 6.00
348 George Banks 1.50 4.00
349 Larry Miller RC 1.50 4.00
350 Mickey Mantle 300.00 600.00
351 Jim Perry 2.50 6.00
352 Alex Johnson RC 2.50 6.00
353 Jerry Lumpe 1.50 4.00
354 Rookie Stars 1.50 4.00
Billy Ott RC
Jack Warner RC
355 Vada Pinson 4.00 10.00
356 Bill Spanswick 1.50 4.00
357 Carl Warwick 1.50 4.00
358 Albie Pearson 2.50 6.00
359 Ken Johnson 1.50 4.00
360 Orlando Cepeda 6.00 15.00
361 Checklist 5 5.00 12.00
362 Don Schwall 1.50 4.00
363 Bob Johnson 1.50 4.00
364 Galen Cisco 1.50 4.00
365 Jim Gentile 2.50 6.00
366 Dan Schneider 1.50 4.00
367 Leon Wagner 1.50 4.00
368 Rookie Stars 2.50 6.00
Ken Berry RC
Joel Gibson RC
369 Phil Linz 2.50 6.00
370 Tommy Davis 2.50 6.00
371 Frank Kreutzer 3.00 8.00
372 Clay Dalrymple 3.00 8.00
373 Curt Simmons 3.00 8.00
374 Rookie Stars 3.00 8.00
Jose Cardenal RC
Dick Simpson
375 Dave Wickersham 3.00 8.00
376 Jim Landis 3.00 8.00
377 Willie Stargell 10.00 25.00
378 Chuck Estrada 3.00 8.00
379 San Francisco Giants TC 3.00 8.00
380 Rocky Colavito 10.00 25.00
381 Al Jackson 3.00 8.00
382 J.C. Martin 3.00 8.00
383 Felipe Alou 6.00 15.00
384 Johnny Klippstein 3.00 8.00
385 Carl Yastrzemski 30.00 60.00
386 Rookie Stars 3.00 8.00
Paul Jaeckel RC
Fred Norman
387 Johnny Podres 6.00 15.00
388 John Blanchard 6.00 15.00
389 Don Larsen 6.00 15.00
390 Bill Freehan 6.00 15.00
391 Mel McGaha MG 3.00 8.00
392 Bob Friend 6.00 15.00
393 Ed Kirkpatrick 3.00 8.00
394 Jim Hannan 3.00 8.00
395 Jim Ray Hart 3.00 8.00
396 Frank Bertaina RC 3.00 8.00
397 Jerry Buchek 3.00 8.00
398 Rookie Stars 6.00 15.00
Dan Neville RC
Art Shamsky RC
399 Ray Herbert 3.00 8.00
400 Harmon Killebrew 20.00 50.00
401 Carl Willey 3.00 8.00
402 Joe Amalfitano 3.00 8.00
403 Boston Red Sox TC 3.00 8.00
404 Stan Williams 3.00 8.00
(Listed as Indian
but Yankee cap)
405 John Roseboro 8.00 20.00
406 Ralph Terry 6.00 15.00
407 Lee Maye 3.00 8.00
408 Larry Sherry 3.00 8.00
409 Rookie Stars 6.00 15.00
Jim Beauchamp
Larry Dierker RC
410 Luis Aparicio 10.00 25.00
411 Roger Craig 6.00 15.00
412 Bob Bailey 3.00 8.00
413 Hal Reniff 3.00 8.00
414 Al Lopez MG 6.00 15.00
415 Curt Flood 6.00 15.00
416 Jim Brewer 3.00 8.00
417 Ed Brinkman 3.00 8.00
418 Johnny Edwards 3.00 8.00
419 Ruben Amaro 3.00 8.00
420 Larry Jackson 3.00 8.00
421 Rookie Stars 3.00 8.00
Gary Dotter RC
Jay Ward
422 Aubrey Gatewood 3.00 8.00
423 Jesse Gonder 3.00 8.00
424 Gary Bell 3.00 8.00
425 Wayne Causey 3.00 8.00
426 Milwaukee Braves TC 3.00 8.00
427 Bob Saverine 3.00 8.00
428 Bob Shaw 3.00 8.00
429 Don Demeter 3.00 8.00
430 Gary Peters 3.00 8.00
431 Rookie Stars 6.00 15.00
Nelson Briles RC
Wayne Spiezio RC
432 Jim Grant 6.00 15.00
433 John Bateman 3.00 8.00
434 Dave Morehead 3.00 8.00
435 Willie Davis 6.00 15.00
436 Don Elston 3.00 8.00
437 Chico Cardenas 6.00 15.00
438 Harry Walker MG 3.00 8.00
439 Moe Drabowsky 6.00 15.00
440 Tom Tresh 6.00 15.00
441 Denny Lemaster 3.00 8.00
442 Vic Power 3.00 8.00
443 Checklist 6 5.00 12.00
444 Bob Hendley 3.00 8.00
445 Don Lock 3.00 8.00
446 Art Mahaffey 3.00 8.00
447 Julian Javier 6.00 15.00
448 Lee Stange 3.00 8.00
449 Rookie Stars 6.00 15.00
Jerry Hinsley
Gary Kroll RC
450 Elston Howard 6.00 15.00
451 Jim Owens 3.00 8.00
452 Gary Geiger 3.00 8.00
453 Rookie Stars 6.00 15.00
Willie Crawford RC
John Werhas
454 Ed Rakow 3.00 8.00
455 Norm Siebern 3.00 8.00
456 Bill Henry 3.00 8.00
457 Bob Kennedy MG 6.00 15.00
458 John Buzhardt 3.00 8.00
459 Frank Kostro 3.00 8.00
460 Richie Allen 15.00 40.00
461 Rookie Stars 20.00 50.00
Clay Carroll RC
Phil Niekro
462 Lew Krausse UER 3.00 8.00
(Photo actually
Pete Lovrich)
463 Manny Mota 6.00 15.00
464 Ron Piche 3.00 8.00
465 Tom Haller 6.00 15.00
466 Rookie Stars 3.00 8.00
Pete Craig RC
Dick Nen
467 Ray Washburn 3.00 8.00
468 Larry Brown 3.00 8.00
469 Don Nottebart 3.00 8.00
470 Yogi Berra P/CO 20.00 50.00
471 Billy Hoeft 3.00 8.00
472 Don Pavletich UER 3.00 8.00
Listed as a pitcher
473 Rookie Stars 6.00 15.00
Paul Blair RC
Davey Johnson RC
474 Cookie Rojas 6.00 15.00
475 Clete Boyer 6.00 15.00
476 Billy O'Dell 3.00 8.00
477 Rookie Stars 100.00 200.00
Fritz Ackley
Steve Carlton RC
478 Wilbur Wood 6.00 15.00
479 Ken Harrelson 6.00 15.00
480 Joel Horlen 3.00 8.00
481 Cleveland Indians TC 4.00 10.00
482 Bob Priddy 3.00 8.00
483 George Smith RC 3.00 8.00
484 Ron Perranoski 8.00 20.00
485 Nellie Fox P/CO 10.00 25.00
486 Rookie Stars 3.00 8.00
Tom Egan RC
Pat Rogan RC
487 Woody Woodward 6.00 15.00
488 Ted Wills 3.00 8.00
489 Gene Mauch MG 6.00 15.00
490 Earl Battey 3.00 8.00
491 Tracy Stallard 3.00 8.00
492 Gene Freese 3.00 8.00
493 Rookie Stars 3.00 8.00
Bill Roman RC
Bruce Brubaker RC
494 Jay Ritchie RC 3.00 8.00
495 Joe Christopher 3.00 8.00
496 Joe Cunningham 3.00 8.00
497 Rookie Stars 6.00 15.00
Ken Henderson RC
Jack Hiatt RC
498 Gene Stephens 3.00 8.00
499 Stu Miller 6.00 15.00
500 Eddie Mathews 15.00 40.00
501 Rookie Stars 3.00 8.00
Ralph Gagliano RC
Jim Rittwage RC
502 Don Cardwell 3.00 8.00
503 Phil Gagliano 3.00 8.00
504 Jerry Grote 6.00 15.00
505 Ray Culp 3.00 8.00
506 Sam Mele MG 3.00 8.00
507 Sammy Ellis 3.00 8.00
508 Checklist 7 5.00 12.00
509 Rookie Stars 3.00 8.00
Bob Guindon RC
Gerry Vezendy RC
510 Ernie Banks 40.00 80.00
511 Ron Locke 3.00 8.00
512 Cap Peterson 3.00 8.00
513 New York Yankees TC 15.00 40.00
514 Joe Azcue 3.00 8.00
515 Vern Law 6.00 15.00
516 Al Weis 3.00 8.00
517 Rookie Stars 6.00 15.00
Paul Schaal RC
Jack Warner
518 Ken Rowe 3.00 8.00
519 Bob Uecker UER 12.50 30.00
(Posing as a left-
handed batter)
520 Tony Cloninger 3.00 8.00
521 Rookie Stars 3.00 8.00
Dave Bennett
Morrie Stevens RC
522 Hank Aguirre 3.00 8.00
523 Mike Brumley SP 5.00 12.00
524 Dave Giusti SP 5.00 12.00
525 Eddie Bressoud 3.00 8.00
526 Rookie Stars 40.00 80.00
Rene Lachemann RC
Johnny Odom RC
Jim Hunter RC
(UER Tim on back)
Skip Lockwood RC SP
527 Jeff Torborg SP 5.00 12.00
528 George Altman 3.00 8.00
529 Jerry Fosnow SP RC 5.00 12.00
530 Jim Maloney 6.00 15.00
531 Chuck Hiller 3.00 8.00
532 Hector Lopez 6.00 15.00
533 Rookie Stars 10.00 25.00
Dan Napoleon RC
Ron Swoboda RC
Tug McGraw RC
Jim Bethke RC SP
534 John Herrnstein 3.00 8.00
535 Jack Kralick SP 5.00 12.00
536 Andre Rodgers SP 5.00 12.00
537 Rookie Stars 3.00 8.00
Marcelino Lopez
Phil Roof
Rudy May RC
538 Chuck Dressen MG SP 5.00 12.00
539 Herm Starrette 3.00 8.00
540 Lou Brock SP 20.00 50.00
541 Rookie Stars 3.00 8.00
Greg Bollo RC
Bob Locker RC
542 Lou Klimchock 3.00 8.00
543 Ed Connolly SP RC 5.00 12.00
544 Howie Reed RC 3.00 8.00
545 Jesus Alou SP 6.00 15.00
546 Rookie Stars 3.00 8.00
Bill Davis RC
Mike Hedlund RC
Ray Barker
Floyd Weaver RC
547 Jake Wood SP 5.00 12.00
548 Dick Stigman 3.00 8.00
549 Rookie Stars 8.00 20.00
Roberto Pena RC
Glenn Beckert RC
550 Mel Stottlemyre SP RC 12.50 30.00
551 New York Mets TC SP 12.50 30.00
552 Julio Gotay 3.00 8.00
553 Rookie Stars 3.00 8.00
Dan Coombs RC
Gene Ratliff RC
Jack McClure RC
554 Chico Ruiz SP 5.00 12.00
555 Jack Baldschun SP 5.00 12.00
556 Red Schoendienst MG SP 10.00 25.00
557 Jose Santiago RC 3.00 8.00
558 Tommie Sisk 3.00 8.00
559 Ed Bailey SP 5.00 12.00
560 Boog Powell SP 10.00 25.00
561 Rookie Stars 6.00 15.00
Dennis Daboll RC
Mike Kekich RC
Hector Valle RC
Jim Lefebvre RC
562 Billy Moran 3.00 8.00
563 Julio Navarro 3.00 8.00
564 Mel Nelson 3.00 8.00
565 Ernie Broglio SP 5.00 12.00
566 Rookie Stars 5.00 12.00
Gil Blanco RC
Ross Moschitto RC
Art Lopez RC SP
567 Tommie Aaron 3.00 8.00
568 Ron Taylor SP 5.00 12.00
569 Gino Cimoli SP 5.00 12.00
570 Claude Osteen SP 6.00 15.00
571 Ossie Virgil SP 5.00 12.00
572 Baltimore Orioles TC SP 10.00 25.00
573 Rookie Stars 10.00 25.00
Jim Lonborg RC
Gerry Moses RC
Bill Schlesinger RC
Mike Ryan RC SP
574 Roy Sievers 6.00 15.00
575 Jose Pagan 3.00 8.00
576 Terry Fox SP 5.00 12.00
577 Rookie Stars 5.00 12.00
Darold Knowles
Don Buschhorn RC
Richie Scheinblum RC SP
578 Camilo Carreon SP 5.00 12.00
579 Dick Smith SP 5.00 12.00
580 Jimmie Hall SP 5.00 12.00
581 Rookie Stars 40.00 80.00
Tony Perez RC
Dave Ricketts RC
Kevin Collins RC SP
582 Bob Schmidt SP 5.00 12.00
583 Wes Covington SP 5.00 12.00
584 Harry Bright 6.00 15.00
585 Hank Fischer 3.00 8.00
586 Tom McCraw SP UER 5.00 12.00
Name is spelled McGraw on the back
587 Joe Sparma 3.00 8.00
588 Lenny Green 3.00 8.00
589 Rookie Stars 5.00 12.00
Frank Linzy RC
Bob Schroder RC SP
590 John Wyatt 3.00 8.00
591 Bob Skinner SP 5.00 12.00
592 Frank Bork SP RC 5.00 12.00
593 Rookie Stars 5.00 12.00
Jackie Moore RC
John Sullivan RC SP
594 Joe Gaines 3.00 8.00
595 Don Lee 3.00 8.00
596 Don Landrum SP 5.00 12.00
597 Rookie Stars 3.00 8.00
Joe Nossek

1966 Topps

John Sevcik RC
Dick Reese RC
598 Al Downing SP 10.00 25.00

1966 Topps

The cards in this 598-card set measure 2 1/2" by 3 1/2". There are the same number of cards as in the 1965 set. Once again, the seventh series cards (523 to 598) are considered more difficult to obtain than the cards of any other series in the set. Within this last series there are 43 cards that were printed in lesser quantities than the other cards in that series; these shorter-printed cards are marked by SP in the checklist below. Among other ways, cards were issued in five-card nickel wax packs, 12-card dime cello packs which came 36 packs to a box and 12 boxes to a case. These cards were also issued in 36-card rack packs which cost 29 cents. These rack packs were issued 48 to a case. The only featured subset within this set is League Leaders (215-226). Noteworthy Rookie Cards in the set include Jim Palmer (126), Ferguson Jenkins (254), and Don Sutton (288). Jim Palmer is described in the bio (on his card back) as a left-hander.

COMPLETE SET (598) 2500.00 4000.00
COMMON CARD (1-109) .60 1.50
COMMON (110-283) .75 2.00
COMMON (284-370) 1.25 3.00
COMMON (371-446) 2.00 5.00
COMMON (447-522) 4.00 10.00
COMMON (523-598) 6.00 15.00
COMMON SP (523-598) 12.50 30.00
WRAPPER (5-CENT) 10.00 25.00
1 Willie Mays 125.00 250.00
2 Ted Abernathy .60 1.50
3 Sam Mele MG .60 1.50
4 Ray Culp .60 1.50
5 Jim Fregosi .75 2.00
6 Chuck Schilling .60 1.50
7 Tracy Stallard .60 1.50
8 Floyd Robinson .60 1.50
9 Clete Boyer .75 2.00
10 Tony Cloninger .60 1.50
11 Rookie Stars .60 1.50
Brant Alyea RC
Pete Craig
12 John Tsitouris .60 1.50
13 Lou Johnson .75 2.00
14 Norm Siebern .60 1.50
15 Vern Law .75 2.00
16 Larry Brown .60 1.50
17 John Stephenson .60 1.50
18 Roland Sheldon .60 1.50
19 San Francisco Giants TC 2.00 5.00
20 Willie Horton .75 2.00
21 Don Nottebart .60 1.50
22 Joe Nossek .60 1.50
23 Jack Sanford .60 1.50
24 Don Kessinger RC 1.50 4.00
25 Pete Ward .60 1.50
26 Ray Sadecki .60 1.50
27 Rookie Stars .60 1.50
Darold Knowles
Andy Etchebarren RC
28 Phil Niekro 8.00 20.00
29 Mike Brumley .60 1.50
30 Pete Rose DP UER 50.00 100.00
1963 Hit total is wrong
31 Jack Cullen .75 2.00
32 Adolfo Phillips RC .60 1.50
33 Jim Pagliaroni .60 1.50
34 Checklist 1 3.00 8.00
35 Ron Swoboda 1.50 4.00
36 Jim Hunter DP 8.00 20.00
UER Stats say 1963 and 1964 should be 1964 and 1965
37 Billy Herman MG .75 2.00
38 Ron Nischwitz .60 1.50
39 Ken Henderson .60 1.50
40 Jim Grant .60 1.50
41 Don LeJohn RC .60 1.50
42 Aubrey Gatewood .60 1.50
43A Don Landrum .75 2.00
(Dark button on pants showing)
43B Don Landrum 8.00 20.00
(Button on pants partially airbrushed)
43C Don Landrum .75 2.00
(Button on pants not showing)
44 Rookie Stars .60 1.50
Bill Davis
Tom Kelley
45 Jim Gentile .75 2.00
46 Howie Koplitz .60 1.50
47 J.C. Martin .60 1.50
48 Paul Blair .75 2.00
49 Woody Woodward .75 2.00
50 Mickey Mantle DP 175.00 350.00
51 Gordon Richardson RC .60 1.50
52 Power Plus 1.50 4.00
Wes Covington
Johnny Callison
53 Bob Duliba .60 1.50
54 Jose Pagan .60 1.50
55 Ken Harrelson .75 2.00
56 Sandy Valdespino .60 1.50
57 Jim Lefebvre .75 2.00
58 Dave Wickersham .60 1.50
59 Cincinnati Reds TC 2.00 5.00
60 Curt Flood 1.50 4.00
61 Bob Bolin .60 1.50
62A Merritt Ranew .75 2.00
(With sold line)
62B Merritt Ranew 12.50 30.00
(Without sold line)
63 Jim Stewart .60 1.50
64 Bob Bruce .60 1.50
65 Leon Wagner .60 1.50
66 Al Weis .60 1.50
67 Rookie Stars 1.50 4.00
Cleon Jones
Dick Selma RC
68 Hal Reniff .60 1.50
69 Ken Hamlin .60 1.50
70 Carl Yastrzemski 12.50 30.00
71 Frank Carpin RC .60 1.50
72 Tony Perez 10.00 25.00
73 Jerry Zimmerman .60 1.50
74 Don Mossi .75 2.00
75 Tommy Davis .75 2.00
76 Red Schoendienst MG 1.50 4.00
77 John Orsino .60 1.50
78 Frank Linzy .60 1.50
79 Joe Pepitone 1.50 4.00
80 Richie Allen 2.50 6.00
81 Ray Oyler .60 1.50
82 Bob Hendley .60 1.50
83 Albie Pearson .75 2.00
84 Rookie Stars .60 1.50
Jim Beauchamp
Dick Kelley
85 Eddie Fisher .60 1.50
86 John Bateman .60 1.50
87 Dan Napoleon .60 1.50
88 Fred Whitfield .60 1.50
89 Ted Davidson .60 1.50
90 Luis Aparicio 3.00 8.00
91A Bob Uecker TR 4.00 10.00
91B Bob Uecker NTR 15.00 40.00
92 New York Yankees TC 6.00 15.00
93 Jim Lonborg DP .75 2.00
94 Matty Alou .75 2.00
95 Pete Richert .60 1.50
96 Felipe Alou 1.50 4.00
97 Jim Merritt RC .60 1.50
98 Don Demeter .60 1.50
99 Buc Belters 2.50 6.00
Willie Stargell
Donn Clendenon
100 Sandy Koufax 50.00 100.00
101A Checklist 2 6.00 15.00
(115 W. Spahn) ERR
101B Checklist 2 4.00 10.00
(115 Bill Henry) COR
102 Ed Kirkpatrick .60 1.50
103A Dick Groat TR .75 2.00
103B Dick Groat NTR 15.00 40.00
104A Alex Johnson TR .75 2.00
104B Alex Johnson NTR 12.50 30.00
105 Milt Pappas .75 2.00
106 Rusty Staub 1.50 4.00
107 Rookie Stars .60 1.50
Larry Stahl RC
Ron Tompkins RC
108 Bobby Klaus .60 1.50
109 Ralph Terry .75 2.00
110 Ernie Banks 12.50 30.00
111 Gary Peters .75 2.00
112 Manny Mota 1.50 4.00
113 Hank Aguirre .75 2.00
114 Jim Gosger .75 2.00
115 Bill Henry .75 2.00
116 Walter Alston MG 2.50 6.00
117 Jake Gibbs .75 2.00
118 Mike McCormick .75 2.00
119 Art Shamsky .75 2.00
120 Harmon Killebrew 6.00 15.00
121 Ray Herbert .75 2.00
122 Joe Gaines .75 2.00
123 Rookie Stars .75 2.00
Frank Bork
Jerry May
124 Tug McGraw 1.50 4.00
125 Lou Brock 8.00 20.00
126 Jim Palmer RC 50.00 100.00
UER Described as lefthander on card back
127 Ken Berry .75 2.00
128 Jim Landis .75 2.00
129 Jack Kralick .75 2.00
130 Joe Torre 2.50 6.00
131 California Angels TC 2.00 5.00
132 Orlando Cepeda 3.00 8.00
133 Don McMahon .75 2.00
134 Wes Parker 1.50 4.00
135 Dave Morehead .75 2.00
136 Woody Held .75 2.00
137 Pat Corrales .75 2.00
138 Roger Repoz RC .75 2.00
139 Rookie Stars .75 2.00
Byron Browne RC
Don Young RC
140 Jim Maloney 1.50 4.00
141 Tom McCraw .75 2.00
142 Don Dennis RC .75 2.00
143 Jose Tartabull 1.50 4.00
144 Don Schwall .75 2.00
145 Bill Freehan 1.50 4.00
146 George Altman .75 2.00
147 Lum Harris MG .75 2.00
148 Bob Johnson .75 2.00
149 Dick Nen .75 2.00
150 Rocky Colavito 3.00 8.00
151 Gary Wagner RC .75 2.00
152 Frank Malzone 1.50 4.00
153 Rico Carty 1.50 4.00
154 Chuck Hiller .75 2.00
155 Marcelino Lopez .75 2.00
156 DP Combo .75 2.00
Dick Schofield
Hal Lanier
157 Rene Lachemann .75 2.00
158 Jim Brewer .75 2.00
159 Chico Ruiz .75 2.00
160 Whitey Ford 12.50 30.00
161 Jerry Lumpe .75 2.00
162 Lee Maye .75 2.00
163 Tito Francona .75 2.00
164 Rookie Stars 1.50 4.00
Tommie Agee
Marv Staehle
165 Don Lock .75 2.00
166 Chris Krug RC .75 2.00
167 Boog Powell 2.50 6.00
168 Dan Osinski .75 2.00
169 Duke Sims RC .75 2.00
170 Cookie Rojas 1.50 4.00
171 Nick Willhite .75 2.00
172 New York Mets TC 2.00 5.00
173 Al Spangler .75 2.00
174 Ron Taylor .75 2.00
175 Bert Campaneris 1.50 4.00
176 Jim Davenport .75 2.00
177 Hector Lopez .75 2.00
178 Bob Tillman .75 2.00
179 Rookie Stars 1.50 4.00
Dennis Aust RC
Bob Tolan
180 Vada Pinson 1.50 4.00
181 Al Worthington .75 2.00
182 Jerry Lynch .75 2.00
183A Checklist 3 3.00 8.00
(Large print on front)
183B Checklist 3 3.00 8.00
(Small print on front)
184 Denis Menke .75 2.00
185 Bob Buhl 1.50 4.00
186 Ruben Amaro .75 2.00
187 Chuck Dressen MG 1.50 4.00
188 Al Luplow .75 2.00
189 John Roseboro 1.50 4.00
190 Jimmie Hall .75 2.00
191 Darrell Sutherland RC .75 2.00
192 Vic Power 1.50 4.00
193 Dave McNally 1.50 4.00
194 Washington Senators TC 2.00 5.00
195 Joe Morgan 6.00 15.00
196 Don Pavletich .75 2.00
197 Sonny Siebert .75 2.00
198 Mickey Stanley RC 2.50 6.00
199 ChiSox Clubbers 1.50 4.00
Bill Skowron
Johnny Romano
Floyd Robinson
200 Eddie Mathews 6.00 15.00
201 Jim Dickson .75 2.00
202 Clay Dalrymple .75 2.00
203 Jose Santiago .75 2.00
204 Chicago Cubs TC 2.00 5.00
205 Tom Tresh 1.50 4.00
206 Al Jackson .75 2.00
207 Frank Quilici RC .75 2.00
208 Bob Miller .75 2.00
209 Rookie Stars 1.50 4.00
Fritz Fisher
John Hiller RC
210 Bill Mazeroski 3.00 8.00
211 Frank Kreutzer .75 2.00
212 Ed Kranepool 1.50 4.00
213 Fred Newman .75 2.00
214 Tommy Harper 1.50 4.00
215 NL Batting Leaders 20.00 50.00
Bob Clemente
Hank Aaron
Willie Mays
216 AL Batting Leaders 2.00 5.00
Tony Oliva
Carl Yastrzemski
Vic Davalillo
217 NL Home Run Leaders 8.00 20.00
Willie Mays
Willie McCovey
Billy Williams
218 AL Home Run Leaders 2.00 5.00
Tony Conigliaro
Norm Cash
Willie Horton
219 NL RBI Leaders 5.00 12.00
Deron Johnson
Frank Robinson
Willie Mays
220 AL RBI Leaders 2.00 5.00
Rocky Colavito
Willie Horton
Tony Oliva
221 NL ERA Leaders 5.00 12.00
Sandy Koufax
Juan Marichal
Vern Law
222 AL ERA Leaders 2.00 5.00
Sam McDowell
Eddie Fisher
Sonny Siebert
223 NL Pitching Leaders 5.00 12.00
Sandy Koufax
Tony Cloninger
Don Drysdale
224 AL Pitching Leaders 2.00 5.00
Jim Grant
Mel Stottlemyre
Jim Kaat
225 NL Strikeout Leaders 5.00 12.00
Sandy Koufax
Bob Veale
Bob Gibson
226 AL Strikeout Leaders 2.00 5.00
Sam McDowell
Mickey Lolich
Dennis McLain
Sonny Siebert
227 Russ Nixon .75 2.00
228 Larry Dierker 1.50 4.00
229 Hank Bauer MG 1.50 4.00
230 Johnny Callison 1.50 4.00
231 Floyd Weaver .75 2.00
232 Glenn Beckert 1.50 4.00
233 Dom Zanni .75 2.00
234 Rookie Stars 3.00 8.00
Rich Beck RC
Roy White RC
235 Don Cardwell .75 2.00
236 Mike Hershberger .75 2.00
237 Billy O'Dell .75 2.00
238 Los Angeles Dodgers TC 2.00 5.00
239 Orlando Pena .75 2.00
240 Earl Battey .75 2.00
241 Dennis Ribant .75 2.00
242 Jesus Alou .75 2.00
243 Nelson Briles 1.50 4.00
244 Rookie Stars .75 2.00
Chuck Harrison RC
Sonny Jackson
245 John Buzhardt .75 2.00
246 Ed Bailey .75 2.00
247 Carl Warwick .75 2.00
248 Pete Mikkelsen .75 2.00
249 Bill Rigney MG .75 2.00
250 Sammy Ellis .75 2.00
251 Ed Brinkman .75 2.00
252 Denny Lemaster .75 2.00
253 Don Wert .75 2.00
254 Rookie Stars 30.00 60.00
Fergie Jenkins RC
Bill Sorrell RC
255 Willie Stargell 8.00 20.00
256 Lew Krausse .75 2.00
257 Jeff Torborg 1.50 4.00
258 Dave Giusti .75 2.00
259 Boston Red Sox TC 2.00 5.00
260 Bob Shaw .75 2.00
261 Ron Hansen .75 2.00
262 Jack Hamilton .75 2.00
263 Tom Egan .75 2.00
264 Rookie Stars .75 2.00
Andy Kosco RC
Ted Uhlaender RC
265 Stu Miller 1.50 4.00
266 Pedro Gonzalez UER .75 2.00
(Misspelled Gonzales on card back)
267 Joe Sparma .75 2.00
268 John Blanchard .75 2.00
269 Don Heffner MG .75 2.00
270 Claude Osteen 1.50 4.00
271 Hal Lanier .75 2.00
272 Jack Baldschun .75 2.00
273 Astro Aces 1.50 4.00
Bob Aspromonte
Rusty Staub
274 Buster Narum .75 2.00
275 Tim McCarver 1.50 4.00
276 Jim Bouton 1.50 4.00
277 George Thomas .75 2.00
278 Cal Koonce .75 2.00
279A Checklist 4 3.00 8.00
(Player's cap black)
279B Checklist 4 3.00 8.00
(Player's cap red)
280 Bobby Knoop .75 2.00
281 Bruce Howard .75 2.00
282 Johnny Lewis .75 2.00
283 Jim Perry 1.50 4.00
284 Bobby Wine 1.25 3.00
285 Luis Tiant 2.00 5.00
286 Gary Geiger 1.25 3.00
287 Jack Aker RC 1.25 3.00
288 Rookie Stars 30.00 60.00
Bill Singer RC
Don Sutton RC
289 Larry Sherry 1.25 3.00
290 Ron Santo 2.00 5.00
291 Moe Drabowsky 2.00 5.00
292 Jim Coker 1.25 3.00
293 Mike Shannon 2.00 5.00
294 Steve Ridzik 1.25 3.00
295 Jim Ray Hart 2.00 5.00
296 Johnny Keane MG 2.00 5.00
297 Jim Owens 1.25 3.00
298 Rico Petrocelli 2.00 5.00
299 Lou Burdette 2.00 5.00
300 Bob Clemente 75.00 150.00
301 Greg Bollo 1.25 3.00
302 Ernie Bowman 1.25 3.00
303 Cleveland Indians TC 2.00 5.00
304 John Herrnstein 1.25 3.00
305 Camilo Pascual 2.00 5.00
306 Ty Cline 1.25 3.00
307 Clay Carroll 2.00 5.00
308 Tom Haller 2.00 5.00
309 Diego Segui 1.25 3.00
310 Frank Robinson 15.00 40.00
311 Rookie Stars 2.00 5.00
Tommy Helms
Dick Simpson
312 Bob Saverine 1.25 3.00
313 Chris Zachary 1.25 3.00
314 Hector Valle 1.25 3.00
315 Norm Cash 2.00 5.00
316 Jack Fisher 1.25 3.00
317 Dalton Jones 1.25 3.00
318 Harry Walker MG 1.25 3.00
319 Gene Freese 1.25 3.00
320 Bob Gibson 10.00 25.00
321 Rick Reichardt 1.25 3.00
322 Bill Faul 1.25 3.00
323 Ray Barker 1.25 3.00
324 John Boozer UER 1.25 3.00
1965 Record is incorrect
325 Vic Davalillo 1.25 3.00
326 Atlanta Braves TC 2.00 5.00
327 Bernie Allen 1.25 3.00
328 Jerry Grote 2.00 5.00
329 Pete Charton 1.25 3.00
330 Ron Fairly 2.00 5.00
331 Ron Herbel 1.25 3.00
332 Bill Bryan 1.25 3.00
333 Rookie Stars 1.25 3.00
Joe Coleman RC
Jim French RC
334 Marty Keough 1.25 3.00
335 Juan Pizarro 1.25 3.00
336 Gene Alley 2.00 5.00
337 Fred Gladding 1.25 3.00
338 Dal Maxvill 1.25 3.00
339 Del Crandall 2.00 5.00
340 Dean Chance 2.00 5.00
341 Wes Westrum MG 2.00 5.00
342 Bob Humphreys 1.25 3.00
343 Joe Christopher 1.25 3.00
344 Steve Blass 2.00 5.00
345 Bob Allison 2.00 5.00
346 Mike de la Hoz 1.25 3.00
347 Phil Regan 2.00 5.00
348 Baltimore Orioles TC 3.00 8.00
349 Cap Peterson 1.25 3.00
350 Mel Stottlemyre 3.00 8.00
351 Fred Valentine 1.25 3.00
352 Bob Aspromonte 1.25 3.00
353 Al McBean 1.25 3.00
354 Smoky Burgess 2.00 5.00
355 Wade Blasingame 1.25 3.00
356 Rookie Stars 1.25 3.00
Owen Johnson RC
Ken Sanders RC
357 Gerry Arrigo 1.25 3.00
358 Charlie Smith 1.25 3.00
359 Johnny Briggs 1.25 3.00
360 Ron Hunt 1.25 3.00
361 Tom Satriano 1.25 3.00
362 Gates Brown 2.00 5.00
363 Checklist 5 4.00 10.00
364 Nate Oliver 1.25 3.00
365 Roger Maris UER 20.00 50.00
Wrong birth year listed on card
366 Wayne Causey 1.25 3.00
367 Mel Nelson 1.25 3.00
368 Charlie Lau 2.00 5.00
369 Jim King 1.25 3.00
370 Chico Cardenas 1.25 3.00
371 Lee Stange 2.00 5.00
372 Harvey Kuenn 3.00 8.00
373 Rookie Stars 3.00 8.00
Jack Hiatt
Dick Estelle
374 Bob Locker 2.00 5.00
375 Donn Clendenon 3.00 8.00
376 Paul Schaal 2.00 5.00
377 Turk Farrell 2.00 5.00
378 Dick Tracewski 2.00 5.00
379 St. Louis Cardinals TC 4.00 10.00
380 Tony Conigliaro 4.00 10.00
381 Hank Fischer 2.00 5.00
382 Phil Roof 2.00 5.00
383 Jackie Brandt 2.00 5.00
384 Al Downing 3.00 8.00
385 Ken Boyer 4.00 10.00
386 Gil Hodges MG 3.00 8.00
387 Howie Reed 2.00 5.00
388 Don Mincher 2.00 5.00
389 Jim O'Toole 3.00 8.00
390 Brooks Robinson 20.00 50.00
391 Chuck Hinton 2.00 5.00
392 Rookie Stars 3.00 8.00
Bill Hands RC
Randy Hundley RC
393 George Brunet 2.00 5.00
394 Ron Brand 2.00 5.00
395 Len Gabrielson 2.00 5.00
396 Jerry Stephenson 2.00 5.00
397 Bill White 3.00 8.00
398 Danny Cater 2.00 5.00
399 Ray Washburn 2.00 5.00
400 Zoilo Versalles 3.00 8.00
401 Ken McMullen 2.00 5.00
402 Jim Hickman 2.00 5.00
403 Fred Talbot 2.00 5.00
404 Pittsburgh Pirates TC 4.00 10.00
405 Elston Howard 3.00 8.00
406 Joey Jay 2.00 5.00
407 John Kennedy 2.00 5.00
408 Lee Thomas 3.00 8.00
409 Billy Hoeft 2.00 5.00
410 Al Kaline 15.00 40.00
411 Gene Mauch MG 2.00 5.00
412 Sam Bowens 2.00 5.00
413 Johnny Romano 2.00 5.00
414 Dan Coombs 2.00 5.00
415 Max Alvis 2.00 5.00
416 Phil Ortega 2.00 5.00
417 Rookie Stars 2.00 5.00
Jim McGlothlin RC
Ed Sukla RC
418 Phil Gagliano 2.00 5.00
419 Mike Ryan 2.00 5.00
420 Juan Marichal 6.00 15.00
421 Roy McMillan 3.00 8.00
422 Ed Charles 2.00 5.00
423 Ernie Broglio 2.00 5.00
424 Rookie Stars 4.00 10.00
Lee May RC
Darrell Osteen RC
425 Bob Veale 3.00 8.00
426 Chicago White Sox TC 4.00 10.00
427 John Miller 2.00 5.00
428 Sandy Alomar 2.00 5.00
429 Bill Monbouquette 2.00 5.00
430 Don Drysdale 8.00 20.00
431 Walt Bond 2.00 5.00
432 Bob Heffner 2.00 5.00
433 Alvin Dark MG 3.00 8.00
434 Willie Kirkland 2.00 5.00
435 Jim Bunning 6.00 15.00
436 Julian Javier 3.00 8.00
437 Al Stanek 2.00 5.00
438 Willie Smith 2.00 5.00
439 Pedro Ramos 2.00 5.00
440 Deron Johnson 3.00 8.00
441 Tommie Sisk 2.00 5.00
442 Rookie Stars 2.00 5.00
Ed Barnowski RC
Eddie Watt RC
443 Bill Wakefield 1.25 3.00
444 Checklist 6 4.00 10.00
445 Jim Kaat 4.00 10.00
446 Mack Jones 2.00 5.00
447 Dick Ellsworth UER 6.00 15.00
(Photo actually Ken Hubbs)
448 Eddie Stanky MG 4.00 10.00
449 Joe Moeller 4.00 10.00
450 Tony Oliva 6.00 15.00
451 Barry Latman 4.00 10.00
452 Joe Azcue 4.00 10.00
453 Ron Kline 4.00 10.00
454 Jerry Buchek 4.00 10.00
455 Mickey Lolich 6.00 15.00
456 Rookie Stars 4.00 10.00
Darrell Brandon RC
Joe Foy RC
457 Joe Gibbon 4.00 10.00
458 Manny Jiminez 4.00 10.00
459 Bill McCool 4.00 10.00
460 Curt Blefary 4.00 10.00
461 Roy Face 6.00 15.00
462 Bob Rodgers 4.00 10.00
463 Philadelphia Phillies TC 6.00 15.00
464 Larry Bearnarth 4.00 10.00
465 Don Buford 4.00 10.00
466 Ken Johnson 4.00 10.00
467 Vic Roznovsky 4.00 10.00
468 Johnny Podres 6.00 15.00
469 Rookie Stars 12.50 30.00
Bobby Murcer RC
Dooley Womack RC
470 Sam McDowell 6.00 15.00
471 Bob Skinner 4.00 10.00
472 Terry Fox 4.00 10.00
473 Rich Rollins 4.00 10.00
474 Dick Schofield 4.00 10.00
475 Dick Radatz 4.00 10.00
476 Bobby Bragan MG 4.00 10.00
477 Steve Barber 4.00 10.00
478 Tony Gonzalez 4.00 10.00
479 Jim Hannan 4.00 10.00
480 Dick Stuart 4.00 10.00
481 Bob Lee 4.00 10.00
482 Rookie Stars 4.00 10.00
John Boccabella
Dave Dowling
483 Joe Nuxhall 4.00 10.00
484 Wes Covington 4.00 10.00
485 Bob Bailey 4.00 10.00
486 Tommy John 6.00 15.00
487 Al Ferrara 4.00 10.00
488 George Banks 4.00 10.00
489 Curt Simmons 4.00 10.00
490 Bobby Richardson 10.00 25.00
491 Dennis Bennett 4.00 10.00
492 Kansas City Athletics TC 6.00 15.00
493 Johnny Klippstein 4.00 10.00
494 Gordy Coleman 4.00 10.00
495 Dick McAuliffe 6.00 15.00
496 Lindy McDaniel 4.00 10.00
497 Chris Cannizzaro 4.00 10.00
498 Rookie Stars 4.00 10.00
Luke Walker RC
Woody Fryman RC
499 Wally Bunker 4.00 10.00
500 Hank Aaron 60.00 120.00
501 John O'Donoghue 4.00 10.00
502 Lenny Green UER 4.00 10.00
Born: aJn. 6, 1933
503 Steve Hamilton 6.00 15.00
504 Grady Hatton MG 4.00 10.00
505 Jose Cardenal 4.00 10.00
506 Bo Belinsky 6.00 15.00
507 Johnny Edwards 4.00 10.00
508 Steve Hargan RC 6.00 15.00
509 Jake Wood 4.00 10.00
510 Hoyt Wilhelm 10.00 25.00
511 Rookie Stars 4.00 10.00
Bob Barton RC
Tito Fuentes RC
512 Dick Stigman 4.00 10.00
513 Camilo Carreon 4.00 10.00
514 Hal Woodeshick 4.00 10.00
515 Frank Howard 6.00 15.00
516 Eddie Bressoud 4.00 10.00
517A Checklist 7 6.00 15.00
529 White Sox Rookies
544 Cardinals Rookies
517B Checklist 7 6.00 15.00
529 W. Sox Rookies
544 Cards Rookies
518 Rookie Stars 4.00 10.00
Herb Hippauf RC
Arnie Umbach RC
519 Bob Friend 6.00 15.00
520 Jim Wynn 6.00 15.00
521 John Wyatt 4.00 10.00
522 Phil Linz 4.00 10.00
523 Bob Sadowski 4.00 10.00
524 Rookie Stars 12.50 30.00
Ollie Brown RC
Don Mason RC SP
525 Gary Bell SP 12.50 30.00
526 Minnesota Twins TC SP 50.00 100.00
527 Julio Navarro 6.00 15.00
528 Jesse Gonder SP 12.50 30.00
529 Rookie Stars 6.00 15.00
Lee Elia RC
Dennis Higgins RC
Bill Voss RC
530 Robin Roberts 20.00 50.00
531 Joe Cunningham 6.00 15.00
532 A.Monteagudo SP 12.50 30.00
533 Jerry Adair SP 12.50 30.00
534 Rookie Stars 6.00 15.00
Dave Eilers RC
Rob Gardner RC
535 Willie Davis SP 15.00 40.00
536 Dick Egan 6.00 15.00
537 Herman Franks MG 6.00 15.00
538 Bob Allen SP 12.50 30.00
539 Rookie Stars 10.00 25.00
Bill Heath RC
Carroll Sembera RC
540 Denny McLain SP 30.00 60.00
541 Gene Oliver SP 12.50 30.00
542 George Smith 6.00 15.00
543 Roger Craig SP 12.50 30.00
544 Rookie Stars 12.50 30.00
Joe Hoerner
George Kernek RC
Jimy Williams RC SP
(UER Misspelled Jimmy on card)
545 Dick Green SP 12.50 30.00
546 Dwight Siebler 10.00 25.00
547 Horace Clarke SP RC 15.00 40.00
548 Gary Kroll SP 12.50 30.00
549 Rookie Stars 6.00 15.00
Al Closter RC
Casey Cox RC
550 Willie McCovey SP 50.00 100.00
551 Bob Purkey SP 12.50 30.00
552 B.Tebbetts MG SP 12.50 30.00
553 Rookie Stars 6.00 15.00
Pat Garrett RC
Jackie Warner
554 Jim Northrup SP 12.50 30.00
555 Ron Perranoski SP 12.50 30.00
556 Mel Queen SP 12.50 30.00
557 Felix Mantilla SP 12.50 30.00
558 Rookie Stars 8.00 20.00
Guido Grilli RC
Pete Magrini RC
George Scott RC
559 Roberto Pena SP 12.50 30.00
560 Joel Horlen 6.00 15.00
561 Choo Choo Coleman SP 12.50 30.00
562 Russ Snyder 10.00 25.00
563 Rookie Stars 6.00 15.00
Pete Cimino RC
Cesar Tovar RC
564 Bob Chance SP 12.50 30.00
565 Jimmy Piersall SP 15.00 40.00

566 Mike Cuellar SP 12.50 30.00
567 Dick Howser SP 15.00 40.00
568 Rookie Stars 6.00 15.00
Paul Lindblad RC
Ron Stone RC
569 Orlando McFarlane SP 12.50 30.00
570 Art Mahaffey SP 12.50 30.00
571 Dave Roberts SP 12.50 30.00
572 Bob Priddy 6.00 15.00
573 Derrell Griffith 6.00 15.00
574 Rookie Stars 6.00 15.00
Bill Hepler RC
Bill Murphy RC
575 Earl Wilson 6.00 15.00
576 Dave Nicholson SP 12.50 30.00
577 Jack Lamabe SP 12.50 30.00
578 Chi Chi Olivo SP RC 12.50 30.00
579 Rookie Stars 8.00 20.00
Frank Bertaina
Gene Brabender RC
Dave Johnson
580 Billy Williams SP 30.00 60.00
581 Tony Martinez 6.00 15.00
582 Garry Roggenburk 6.00 15.00
583 Detroit Tigers TC SP 60.00 120.00
UER Text on back states Tigers finished third in 1965 instead of fourth
584 Rookie Stars 6.00 15.00
Frank Fernandez RC
Fritz Peterson RC
585 Tony Taylor 10.00 25.00
586 Claude Raymond SP 12.50 30.00
587 Dick Bertell 6.00 15.00
588 Rookie Stars 6.00 15.00
Chuck Dobson RC
Ken Suarez RC
589 Lou Klimchock SP 12.50 30.00
590 Bill Skowron SP 15.00 40.00
591 Rookie Stars 15.00 40.00
Bart Shirley RC
Grant Jackson RC SP
592 Andre Rodgers 6.00 15.00
593 Doug Camilli SP 12.50 30.00
594 Chico Salmon 6.00 15.00
595 Larry Jackson 6.00 15.00
596 Rookie Stars 12.50 30.00
Nate Colbert RC
Greg Sims RC SP
597 John Sullivan 6.00 15.00
598 Gaylord Perry SP 100.00 200.00

1967 Topps

The cards in this 609-card set measure 2 1/2" by 3 1/2". The 1967 Topps series is considered by some collectors to be one of the company's finest accomplishments in baseball card production. Excellent color photographs are combined with easy-to-read backs. Cards 458 to 533 are slightly harder to find than numbers 1 to 457, and the inevitable high series (534 to 609) exists. Each checklist card features a small circular picture of a popular player included in that series. Printing discrepancies resulted in some high series cards being in shorter supply. The checklist below identifies (by DP) 22 double-printed high numbers; of the 76 cards in the last series, 54 cards were short printed and the other 22 cards are much more plentiful. Featured subsets within this set include World Series cards (151-155) and League Leaders (233-244). A limited number of "proof" Roger Maris cards were produced. These cards are blank backed and Maris is listed as a New York Yankee on it. Some Bob Bolin cards: (number 252) have a white smear in between his names. Another tough variation that has been recently discovered involves card number 58 Paul Schaal. The tough version has a green bat above his name. The key Rookie Cards in the set are high number cards of Rod Carew and Tom Seaver. Confirmed methods of selling these cards include five-card nickel wax packs. Although rarely seen, there exists a salesman's sample panel of three cards that pictures Earl Battey, Manny Mota, and Gene Brabender with ad information on the back about the "new" Topps cards.

COMPLETE SET (609) 2500.00 5000.00
COMMON CARD (1-109) .60 1.50
COMMON (110-283) .75 2.00
COMMON (284-370) 1.00 2.50
COMMON (371-457) 1.50 4.00
COMMON (458-533) 2.50 6.00
COMMON (534-609) 6.00 15.00
COMMON DP (534-609) 3.00 8.00
WRAPPER (5-CENT) 10.00 25.00
1 The Champs 10.00 25.00
Frank Robinson
Hank Bauer MG
Brooks Robinson DP
2 Jack Hamilton .60 1.50
3 Duke Sims .60 1.50
4 Hal Lanier .60 1.50
5 Whitey Ford UER 8.00 20.00
(1953 listed as 1933 in stats on back)
6 Dick Simpson .60 1.50
7 Don McMahon .60 1.50
8 Chuck Harrison .60 1.50
9 Ron Hansen .60 1.50
10 Matty Alou 1.50 4.00
11 Barry Moore RC .60 1.50
12 Rookie Stars 1.50 4.00
Jim Campanis RC
Bill Singer
13 Joe Sparma .60 1.50
14 Phil Linz 1.50 4.00
15 Earl Battey .60 1.50
16 Bill Hands .60 1.50
17 Jim Gosger .60 1.50
18 Gene Oliver .60 1.50
19 Jim McGlothlin .60 1.50
20 Orlando Cepeda 3.00 8.00
21 Dave Bristol MG RC .60 1.50
22 Gene Brabender .60 1.50
23 Larry Elliot .60 1.50
24 Bob Allen .60 1.50
25 Elston Howard 1.50 4.00
26A Bob Priddy NTR 12.50 30.00
26B Bob Priddy TR 1.50 4.00
27 Bob Saverine .60 1.50
28 Barry Latman .60 1.50
29 Tom McCraw .60 1.50
30 Al Kaline DP 8.00 20.00
31 Jim Brewer .60 1.50
32 Bob Bailey 1.50 4.00
33 Rookie Stars 2.50 6.00
Sal Bando RC
Randy Schwartz RC
34 Pete Cimino .60 1.50
35 Rico Carty 1.50 4.00
36 Bob Tillman .60 1.50
37 Rick Wise 1.50 4.00
38 Bob Johnson .60 1.50
39 Curt Simmons 1.50 4.00
40 Rick Reichardt .60 1.50
41 Joe Hoerner .60 1.50
42 New York Mets TC 4.00 10.00
43 Chico Salmon .60 1.50
44 Joe Nuxhall 1.50 4.00
45 Roger Maris 20.00 50.00
45A Roger Maris 900.00 1500.00
Yankees listed as team
Blank Back
46 Lindy McDaniel 1.50 4.00
47 Ken McMullen .60 1.50
48 Bill Freehan 1.50 4.00
49 Roy Face 1.50 4.00
50 Tony Oliva 2.50 6.00
51 Rookie Stars .60 1.50
Dave Adlesh RC
Wes Bales RC
52 Dennis Higgins .60 1.50
53 Clay Dalrymple .60 1.50
54 Dick Green .60 1.50
55 Don Drysdale 6.00 15.00
56 Jose Tartabull 1.50 4.00
57 Pat Jarvis RC 1.50 4.00
58A Paul Schaal 8.00 20.00
Green Bat
58B Paul Schaal .60 1.50
Normal Colored Bat
59 Ralph Terry 1.50 4.00
60 Luis Aparicio 3.00 8.00
61 Gordy Coleman .60 1.50
62 Frank Robinson CL1 3.00 8.00
63 Cards Clubbers 3.00 8.00
Lou Brock
Curt Flood
64 Fred Valentine .60 1.50
65 Tom Haller 1.50 4.00
66 Manny Mota 1.50 4.00
67 Ken Berry .60 1.50
68 Bob Buhl 1.50 4.00
69 Vic Davalillo .60 1.50
70 Ron Santo 2.50 6.00
71 Camilo Pascual 1.50 4.00
72 Rookie Stars .60 1.50
George Korince RC
(UER Photo is James Murray Brown)
John (Tom) Matchick RC
73 Rusty Staub 2.50 6.00
74 Wes Stock .60 1.50
75 George Scott 1.50 4.00
76 Jim Barbieri RC .60 1.50
77 Dooley Womack 1.50 4.00
78 Pat Corrales .60 1.50
79 Bubba Morton .60 1.50
80 Jim Maloney 1.50 4.00
81 Eddie Stanky MG 1.50 4.00
82 Steve Barber .60 1.50
83 Ollie Brown .60 1.50
84 Tommie Sisk .60 1.50
85 Johnny Callison 1.50 4.00
86A Mike McCormick NTR 12.50 30.00
(Senators on front and Senators on back)
86B Mike McCormick TR 1.50 4.00
(Traded line at end of bio; Senators on front, but Giants on back)
87 George Altman .60 1.50
88 Mickey Lolich 1.50 4.00
89 Felix Millan RC 1.50 4.00
90 Jim Nash RC .60 1.50
91 Johnny Lewis .60 1.50
92 Ray Washburn .60 1.50
93 Rookie Stars 1.50 4.00
Stan Bahnsen RC
Bobby Murcer
94 Ron Fairly 1.50 4.00
95 Sonny Siebert .60 1.50
96 Art Shamsky .60 1.50
97 Mike Cuellar 1.50 4.00
98 Rich Rollins .60 1.50
99 Lee Stange .60 1.50
100 Frank Robinson DP 6.00 15.00
101 Ken Johnson .60 1.50
102 Philadelphia Phillies TC 1.50 4.00
103A Mickey Mantle CL2 DP 8.00 20.00
170 is D.McAuliffe
104 Minnie Rojas RC .60 1.50
105 Ken Boyer 2.50 6.00
106 Randy Hundley 1.50 4.00
107 Joel Horlen .60 1.50
108 Alex Johnson 1.50 4.00
109 Tribe Thumpers 2.50 6.00
Rocky Colavito
Leon Wagner
110 Jack Aker 1.50 4.00
111 John Kennedy .75 2.00
112 Dave Wickersham .75 2.00
113 Dave Nicholson .75 2.00
114 Jack Baldschun .75 2.00
115 Paul Casanova RC .75 2.00
116 Herman Franks MG .75 2.00
117 Darrell Brandon .75 2.00
118 Bernie Allen .75 2.00
119 Wade Blasingame .75 2.00
120 Floyd Robinson .75 2.00
121 Eddie Bressoud .75 2.00
122 George Brunet .75 2.00
123 Rookie Stars 1.50 4.00
Jim Price RC
Luke Walker
124 Jim Stewart .75 2.00
125 Moe Drabowsky 1.50 4.00
126 Tony Taylor .75 2.00
127 John O'Donoghue .75 2.00
128 Ed Spiezio RC .75 2.00
129 Phil Roof .75 2.00
130 Phil Regan 1.50 4.00
131 New York Yankees TC 4.00 10.00
132 Ozzie Virgil .75 2.00
133 Ron Kline .75 2.00
134 Gates Brown 2.50 6.00
135 Deron Johnson 1.50 4.00
136 Carroll Sembera .75 2.00
137 Rookie Stars .75 2.00
Ron Clark RC
Jim Ollum
138 Dick Kelley .75 2.00
139 Dalton Jones 1.50 4.00
140 Willie Stargell 8.00 20.00
141 John Miller .75 2.00
142 Jackie Brandt .75 2.00
143 Sox Sockers .75 2.00
Pete Ward
Don Buford
144 Bill Hepler .75 2.00
145 Larry Brown .75 2.00
146 Steve Carlton 20.00 50.00
147 Tom Egan .75 2.00
148 Adolfo Phillips .75 2.00
149 Joe Moeller .75 2.00
150 Mickey Mantle 175.00 350.00
151 World Series Game 1 2.00 5.00
Moe Drabowsky
152 World Series Game 2 3.00 8.00
Jim Palmer
153 World Series Game 3 2.00 5.00
Paul Blair
154 World Series Game 4 2.00 5.00
Robinson/McNally
155 World Series Summary 2.00 5.00
Winners Celebrate
156 Ron Herbel .75 2.00
157 Danny Cater .75 2.00
158 Jimmie Coker .75 2.00
159 Bruce Howard .75 2.00
160 Willie Davis 1.50 4.00
161 Dick Williams MG 1.50 4.00
162 Billy O'Dell .75 2.00
163 Vic Roznovsky .75 2.00
164 Dwight Siebler UER .75 2.00
(Last line of stats shows 1960 Minnesota)
165 Cleon Jones 1.50 4.00
166 Eddie Mathews 6.00 15.00
167 Rookie Stars .75 2.00
Joe Coleman RC
Tim Cullen RC
168 Ray Culp .75 2.00
169 Horace Clarke 1.50 4.00
170 Dick McAuliffe 1.50 4.00
171 Cal Koonce .75 2.00
172 Bill Heath .75 2.00
173 St. Louis Cardinals TC 1.50 4.00
174 Dick Radatz 1.50 4.00
175 Bobby Knoop .75 2.00
176 Sammy Ellis .75 2.00
177 Tito Fuentes .60 1.50
178 John Buzhardt .75 2.00
179 Rookie Stars 1.50 4.00
Charles Vaughan RC
Cecil Upshaw RC
180 Curt Blefary .75 2.00
181 Terry Fox .75 2.00
182 Ed Charles .75 2.00
183 Jim Pagliaroni .75 2.00
184 George Thomas .75 2.00
185 Ken Holtzman RC 1.50 4.00
186 Mets Maulers 1.50 4.00
Ed Kranepool
Ron Swoboda
187 Pedro Ramos .75 2.00
188 Ken Harrelson .75 2.00
189 Chuck Hinton .75 2.00
190 Turk Farrell .75 2.00
191A Willie Mays CL3 4.00 10.00
214 Tom Kelley
191B Willie Mays CL3 5.00 12.00
214 Dick Kelley
192 Fred Gladding .75 2.00
193 Jose Cardenal 1.50 4.00
194 Bob Allison 1.50 4.00
195 Al Jackson .75 2.00
196 Johnny Romano .75 2.00
197 Ron Perranoski 1.50 4.00
198 Chuck Hiller .75 2.00
199 Billy Hitchcock MG .75 2.00
200 Willie Mays UER 50.00 100.00
('63 Sna Francisco on card back stats)
201 Hal Reniff 1.50 4.00
202 Johnny Edwards .75 2.00
203 Al McBean .75 2.00
204 Rookie Stars 2.50 6.00
Mike Epstein RC
Tom Phoebus RC
205 Dick Groat 1.50 4.00
206 Dennis Bennett .75 2.00
207 John Orsino .75 2.00
208 Jack Lamabe .75 2.00
209 Joe Nossek .75 2.00
210 Bob Gibson 8.00 20.00
211 Minnesota Twins TC 1.50 4.00
212 Chris Zachary .75 2.00
213 Jay Johnstone RC 1.50 4.00
214 Dick Kelley .75 2.00
215 Ernie Banks 8.00 20.00
216 Bengal Belters 3.00 8.00
Norm Cash
Al Kaline
217 Rob Gardner .75 2.00
218 Wes Parker 1.50 4.00
219 Clay Carroll 1.50 4.00
220 Jim Ray Hart 1.50 4.00
221 Woody Fryman 1.50 4.00
222 Rookie Stars 1.50 4.00
Darrell Osteen
Lee May
223 Mike Ryan 1.50 4.00
224 Walt Bond .75 2.00
225 Mel Stottlemyre 2.50 6.00
226 Julian Javier 1.50 4.00
227 Paul Lindblad .75 2.00
228 Gil Hodges MG 2.50 6.00
229 Larry Jackson .75 2.00
230 Boog Powell 2.50 6.00
231 John Bateman .75 2.00
232 Don Buford .75 2.00
233 AL ERA Leaders 1.50 4.00
Gary Peters
Joel Horlen
Steve Hargan
234 NL ERA Leaders 6.00 15.00
Sandy Koufax
Mike Cuellar
Juan Marichal
235 AL Pitching Leaders 2.50 6.00
Jim Kaat
Denny McLain
Earl Wilson
236 NL Pitching Leaders 10.00 25.00
Sandy Koufax
Juan Marichal
Bob Gibson
Gaylord Perry
237 AL Strikeout Leaders 2.50 6.00
Sam McDowell
Jim Kaat
Earl Wilson
238 NL Strikeout Leaders 5.00 12.00
Sandy Koufax
Jim Bunning
Bob Veale
239 AL Batting Leaders 4.00 10.00
Frank Robinson
Tony Oliva
Al Kaline
240 NL Batting Leaders 2.50 6.00
Matty Alou
Felipe Alou
Rico Carty
241 AL RBI Leaders 4.00 10.00
Frank Robinson
Harmon Killebrew
Boog Powell
242 NL RBI Leaders 10.00 25.00
Hank Aaron
Bob Clemente
Richie Allen
243 AL Home Run Leaders 4.00 10.00
Frank Robinson
Harmon Killebrew
Boog Powell
244 NL Home Run Leaders 8.00 20.00
Hank Aaron
Richie Allen
Willie Mays
245 Curt Flood 2.50 6.00
246 Jim Perry 1.50 4.00
247 Jerry Lumpe .75 2.00
248 Gene Mauch MG 1.50 4.00
249 Nick Willhite .75 2.00
250 Hank Aaron UER 40.00 80.00
(Second 1961 in stats should be 1962)
251 Woody Held .75 2.00
252 Bob Bolin .75 2.00
253 Rookie Stars .75 2.00
Bill Davis
Gus Gil RC
254 Milt Pappas 1.50 4.00
(No facsimile autograph on card front)
255 Frank Howard 1.50 4.00
256 Bob Hendley .75 2.00
257 Charlie Smith .75 2.00
258 Lee Maye .75 2.00
259 Don Dennis .75 2.00
260 Jim Lefebvre 1.50 4.00
261 John Wyatt .75 2.00
262 Kansas City Athletics TC 1.50 4.00
263 Hank Aguirre .75 2.00
264 Ron Swoboda 1.50 4.00
265 Lou Burdette 1.50 4.00
266 Pitt Power 1.50 4.00
Willie Stargell
Donn Clendenon
267 Don Schwall .75 2.00
268 Johnny Briggs .75 2.00
269 Don Nottebart .75 2.00
270 Zoilo Versalles .75 2.00
271 Eddie Watt .75 2.00
272 Rookie Stars 1.50 4.00
Bill Connors RC
Dave Dowling
273 Dick Lines RC .75 2.00
274 Bob Aspromonte .75 2.00
275 Fred Whitfield .75 2.00
276 Bruce Brubaker .75 2.00
277 Steve Whitaker RC 2.50 6.00
278 Jim Kaat CL4 3.00 8.00
279 Frank Linzy .75 2.00
280 Tony Conigliaro 3.00 8.00
281 Bob Rodgers .75 2.00
282 John Odom .75 2.00
283 Gene Alley 1.50 4.00
284 Johnny Podres 1.50 4.00
285 Lou Brock 8.00 20.00
286 Wayne Causey 1.00 2.50
287 Rookie Stars 1.00 2.50
Greg Goossen RC
Bart Shirley
288 Denny Lemaster 1.00 2.50
289 Tom Tresh 2.00 5.00
290 Bill White 2.00 5.00
291 Jim Hannan 1.00 2.50
292 Don Pavletich 1.00 2.50
293 Ed Kirkpatrick 1.00 2.50
294 Walter Alston MG 3.00 8.00
295 Sam McDowell 2.00 5.00
296 Glenn Beckert 2.00 5.00
297 Dave Morehead 2.00 5.00
298 Ron Davis RC 1.00 2.50
299 Norm Siebern 1.00 2.50
300 Jim Kaat 2.00 5.00
301 Jesse Gonder 1.00 2.50
302 Baltimore Orioles TC 3.00 8.00
303 Gil Blanco 1.00 2.50
304 Phil Gagliano 1.00 2.50
305 Earl Wilson 2.00 5.00
306 Bud Harrelson RC 2.00 5.00
307 Jim Beauchamp 1.00 2.50
308 Al Downing 2.00 5.00
309 Hurlers Beware 2.00 5.00
Johnny Callison
Richie Allen
310 Gary Peters 1.00 2.50
311 Ed Brinkman 1.00 2.50
312 Don Mincher 1.00 2.50
313 Bob Lee 1.00 2.50
314 Rookie Stars 3.00 8.00
Mike Andrews RC
Reggie Smith RC
315 Billy Williams 6.00 15.00
316 Jack Kralick 1.00 2.50
317 Cesar Tovar 1.00 2.50
318 Dave Giusti 1.00 2.50
319 Paul Blair 2.00 5.00
320 Gaylord Perry 6.00 15.00
321 Mayo Smith MG 1.00 2.50
322 Jose Pagan 1.00 2.50
323 Mike Hershberger 1.00 2.50
324 Hal Woodeshick 1.00 2.50
325 Chico Cardenas 2.00 5.00
326 Bob Uecker 4.00 10.00
327 California Angels TC 3.00 8.00
328 Clete Boyer UER 2.00 5.00
(Stats only go up through 1965)
329 Charlie Lau 2.00 5.00
330 Claude Osteen 2.00 5.00
331 Joe Foy 2.00 5.00
332 Jesus Alou 1.00 2.50
333 Fergie Jenkins 8.00 20.00
334 Twin Terrors 4.00 10.00
Bob Allison
Harmon Killebrew
335 Bob Veale 2.00 5.00
336 Joe Azcue 1.00 2.50
337 Joe Morgan 6.00 15.00
338 Bob Locker 1.00 2.50
339 Chico Ruiz 1.00 2.50
340 Joe Pepitone 3.00 8.00
341 Rookie Stars 1.00 2.50
Dick Dietz RC
Bill Sorrell
342 Hank Fischer 1.00 2.50
343 Tom Satriano 1.00 2.50
344 Ossie Chavarria RC 1.00 2.50
345 Stu Miller 2.00 5.00
346 Jim Hickman 1.00 2.50
347 Grady Hatton MG 1.00 2.50
348 Tug McGraw 2.00 5.00
349 Bob Chance 1.00 2.50
350 Joe Torre 3.00 8.00
351 Vern Law 2.00 5.00
352 Ray Oyler 1.00 2.50
353 Bill McCool 1.00 2.50
354 Chicago Cubs TC 3.00 8.00
355 Carl Yastrzemski 30.00 60.00
356 Larry Jaster RC 1.00 2.50
357 Bill Skowron 2.00 5.00
358 Ruben Amaro 1.00 2.50
359 Dick Ellsworth 1.00 2.50
360 Leon Wagner 1.00 2.50
361 Roberto Clemente CL5 6.00 15.00
362 Darold Knowles 1.00 2.50
363 Davey Johnson 2.00 5.00
364 Claude Raymond 1.00 2.50
365 John Roseboro 2.00 5.00
366 Andy Kosco 1.00 2.50
367 Rookie Stars 1.00 2.50
Bill Kelso
Don Wallace RC
368 Jack Hiatt 1.00 2.50
369 Jim Hunter 6.00 15.00
370 Tommy Davis 2.00 5.00
371 Jim Lonborg 3.00 8.00
372 Mike de la Hoz 1.50 4.00
373 Rookie Stars 1.50 4.00
Duane Josephson RC
Fred Klages RC DP
374A Mel Queen ERR 8.00 20.00
(Incomplete stat line on back)
374B Mel Queen COR DP 1.50 4.00
(Complete stat line on back)
375 Jake Gibbs 3.00 8.00
376 Don Lock DP 1.50 4.00
377 Luis Tiant 3.00 8.00
378 Detroit Tigers TC 3.00 8.00
(UER Willie Horton with 262 RBI's in 1966)
379 Jerry May DP 1.50 4.00
380 Dean Chance DP 1.50 4.00
381 Dick Schofield DP 1.50 4.00
382 Dave McNally 3.00 8.00
383 Ken Henderson DP 1.50 4.00
384 Rookie Stars 1.50 4.00
Jim Cosman RC
Dick Hughes RC
385 Jim Fregosi 3.00 8.00
(Batting wrong)
386 Dick Selma DP 1.50 4.00
387 Cap Peterson DP 1.50 4.00
388 Arnold Earley DP 1.50 4.00
389 Alvin Dark MG DP 3.00 8.00
390 Jim Wynn DP 3.00 8.00
391 Wilbur Wood DP 3.00 8.00
392 Tommy Harper DP 3.00 8.00
393 Jim Bouton DP 3.00 8.00
394 Jake Wood DP 1.50 4.00
395 Chris Short RC 3.00 8.00
396 Atlanta Aces 1.50 4.00
Denis Menke
Tony Cloninger
397 Willie Smith DP 1.50 4.00
398 Jeff Torborg 3.00 8.00
399 Al Worthington DP 1.50 4.00
400 Bob Clemente DP 60.00 120.00
401 Jim Coates 1.50 4.00
402A Rookie Stars 8.00 20.00
Grant Jackson
Billy Wilson
Incomplete stat line
402B Rookie Stars 3.00 8.00
Grant Jackson
Billy Wilson RC DP
403 Dick Nen 1.50 4.00
404 Nelson Briles 3.00 8.00
405 Russ Snyder 1.50 4.00
406 Lee Elia DP 1.50 4.00
407 Cincinnati Reds TC 3.00 8.00
408 Jim Northrup DP 3.00 8.00
409 Ray Sadecki 1.50 4.00
410 Lou Johnson DP 1.50 4.00
411 Dick Howser DP 1.50 4.00
412 Rookie Stars 3.00 8.00
Norm Miller RC
Doug Rader RC
413 Jerry Grote 1.50 4.00
414 Casey Cox 1.50 4.00
415 Sonny Jackson 1.50 4.00
416 Roger Repoz 1.50 4.00
417A Bob Bruce ERR 12.50 30.00
(RBAVES on back)
417B Bob Bruce COR DP 1.50 4.00
418 Sam Mele MG 1.50 4.00
419 Don Kessinger DP 4.00 8.00
420 Denny McLain 5.00 12.00
421 Dal Maxvill DP 1.50 4.00
422 Hoyt Wilhelm 6.00 15.00
423 Fence Busters 10.00 25.00
Willie Mays
Willie McCovey DP
424 Pedro Gonzalez 1.50 4.00
425 Pete Mikkelsen 1.50 4.00
426 Lou Clinton 1.50 4.00
427A Ruben Gomez ERR 8.00 20.00
Incomplete stat line on back
427B R.Gomez COR DP 1.50 4.00
Complete stat line on back
428 Rookie Stars 3.00 8.00
Tom Hutton RC
Gene Michael RCDP
429 Garry Roggenburk DP 1.50 4.00
430 Pete Rose 50.00 100.00
431 Ted Uhlaender 1.50 4.00
432 Jimmie Hall DP 1.50 4.00
433 Al Luplow DP 1.50 4.00
434 Eddie Fisher DP 1.50 4.00
435 Mack Jones DP 1.50 4.00
436 Pete Ward 1.50 4.00
437 Washington Senators TC 3.00 8.00
438 Chuck Dobson 1.50 4.00
439 Byron Browne 1.50 4.00
440 Steve Hargan 1.50 4.00
441 Jim Davenport 1.50 4.00
442 Rookie Stars 3.00 8.00
Bill Robinson RC
Joe Verbanic RC DP
443 Tito Francona DP 1.50 4.00
444 George Smith 1.50 4.00
445 Don Sutton 10.00 25.00
446 Russ Nixon DP 1.50 4.00
447A Bo Belinsky ERR DP 1.50 4.00
(Incomplete stat line on back)
447B Bo Belinsky COR 3.00 8.00
(Complete stat line on back)
448 Harry Walker MG DP 1.50 4.00
449 Orlando Pena 1.50 4.00
450 Richie Allen 3.00 8.00
451 Fred Newman DP 1.50 4.00
452 Ed Kranepool 3.00 8.00
453 A.Monteagudo DP 1.50 4.00
454A Juan Marichal CL6 DP 5.00 12.00
Missing left ear
454B Juan Marichal CL6 5.00 12.00
left ear showing
455 Tommie Agee 3.00 8.00
456 Phil Niekro UER 6.00 15.00
(ERA incorrect as .288)
457 Andy Etchebarren DP 3.00 8.00
458 Lee Thomas 2.50 6.00
459 Rookie Stars 2.50 6.00
Dick Bosman RC
Pete Craig
460 Harmon Killebrew 30.00 60.00
461 Bob Miller 5.00 12.00
462 Bob Barton 2.50 6.00
463 Hill Aces 5.00 12.00
Sam McDowell
Sonny Siebert
464 Dan Coombs 2.50 6.00
465 Willie Horton 5.00 12.00
466 Bobby Wine 2.50 6.00
467 Jim O'Toole 2.50 6.00
468 Ralph Houk MG 2.50 6.00
469 Len Gabrielson 2.50 6.00
470 Bob Shaw 2.50 6.00
471 Rene Lachemann 2.50 6.00
472 Rookie Stars 2.50 6.00
John Gelnar
George Spriggs RC
473 Jose Santiago 2.50 6.00
474 Bob Tolan 2.50 6.00
475 Jim Palmer 40.00 80.00
476 Tony Perez SP 30.00 60.00
477 Atlanta Braves TC 6.00 15.00
478 Bob Humphreys 2.50 6.00
479 Gary Bell 2.50 6.00
480 Willie McCovey 15.00 40.00
481 Leo Durocher MG 8.00 20.00
482 Bill Monbouquette 2.50 6.00
483 Jim Landis 2.50 6.00
484 Jerry Adair 2.50 6.00
485 Tim McCarver 10.00 25.00
486 Rookie Stars 2.50 6.00
Rich Reese RC
Bill Whitby RC
487 Tommie Reynolds 2.50 6.00
488 Gerry Arrigo 2.50 6.00
489 Doug Clemens RC 2.50 6.00
490 Tony Cloninger 2.50 6.00
491 Sam Bowens 2.50 6.00
492 Pittsburgh Pirates TC 6.00 15.00
493 Phil Ortega 2.50 6.00
494 Bill Rigney MG 2.50 6.00
495 Fritz Peterson 2.50 6.00
496 Orlando McFarlane 2.50 6.00
497 Ron Campbell RC 2.50 6.00
498 Larry Dierker 5.00 12.00
499 Rookie Stars 2.50 6.00

George Culver
Jose Vidal RC
500 Juan Marichal 10.00 25.00
501 Jerry Zimmerman 2.50 6.00
502 Derrell Griffith 2.50 6.00
503 Los Angeles Dodgers TC 8.00 20.00
504 Orlando Martinez RC 2.50 6.00
505 Tommy Helms 5.00 12.00
506 Smoky Burgess 2.50 6.00
507 Rookie Stars 2.50 6.00
Ed Barnowski
Larry Haney RC
508 Dick Hall 2.50 6.00
509 Jim King 2.50 6.00
510 Bill Mazeroski 10.00 25.00
511 Don Wert 2.50 6.00
512 Red Schoendienst MG 10.00 25.00
513 Marcelino Lopez 2.50 6.00
514 John Werhas 2.50 6.00
515 Bert Campaneris 5.00 12.00
516 San Francisco Giants TC 6.00 15.00
517 Fred Talbot 5.00 12.00
518 Denis Menke 2.50 6.00
519 Ted Davidson 2.50 6.00
520 Max Alvis 2.50 6.00
521 Bird Bombers 5.00 12.00
Boog Powell
Curt Blefary
522 John Stephenson 2.50 6.00
523 Jim Merritt 2.50 6.00
524 Felix Mantilla 2.50 6.00
525 Ron Hunt 2.50 6.00
526 Rookie Stars 2.50 6.00
Pat Dobson RC
George Korince RC
(See 67T card 72 ERR)
527 Dennis Ribant 2.50 6.00
528 Rico Petrocelli 8.00 20.00
529 Gary Wagner 2.50 6.00
530 Felipe Alou 5.00 12.00
531 Brooks Robinson CL7 DP 6.00 15.00
532 Jim Hicks RC 2.50 6.00
533 Jack Fisher 2.50 6.00
534 Hank Bauer MG DP 3.00 8.00
535 Donn Clendenon 10.00 25.00
536 Rookie Stars 20.00 50.00
Joe Niekro RC
Paul Popovich RC
537 Chuck Estrada DP 3.00 8.00
538 J.C. Martin 6.00 15.00
539 Dick Egan DP 3.00 8.00
540 Norm Cash 20.00 50.00
541 Joe Gibbon 6.00 15.00
542 Rookie Stars 6.00 15.00
Rick Monday RC
Tony Pierce RC DP
543 Dan Schneider 6.00 15.00
544 Cleveland Indians TC 12.50 30.00
545 Jim Grant 10.00 25.00
546 Woody Woodward 10.00 25.00
547 Rookie Stars 3.00 8.00
Russ Gibson RC
Bill Rohr RC DP
548 Tony Gonzalez DP 3.00 8.00
549 Jack Sanford 6.00 15.00
550 Vada Pinson DP 4.00 10.00
551 Doug Camilli DP 3.00 8.00
552 Ted Savage 10.00 25.00
553 Rookie Stars 15.00 40.00
Mike Hegan RC
Thad Tillotson
554 Andre Rodgers DP 3.00 8.00
555 Don Cardwell 10.00 25.00
556 Al Weis DP 3.00 8.00
557 Al Ferrara 10.00 25.00
558 Rookie Stars 20.00 50.00
Mark Belanger RC
Bill Dillman RC
559 Dick Tracewski DP 3.00 8.00
560 Jim Bunning 30.00 60.00
561 Sandy Alomar 15.00 40.00
562 Steve Blass DP 3.00 8.00
563 Joe Adcock 15.00 40.00
564 Rookie Stars 3.00 8.00
Alonzo Harris RC
Aaron Pointer RC DP
565 Lew Krausse 10.00 25.00
566 Gary Geiger DP 3.00 8.00
567 Steve Hamilton 15.00 40.00
568 John Sullivan 15.00 40.00
569 Rookie Stars 150.00 300.00
Rod Carew RC
Hank Allen RC DP
570 Maury Wills 40.00 80.00
571 Larry Sherry 10.00 25.00
572 Don Demeter 10.00 25.00
573 Chicago White Sox TC 12.50 30.00
574 Jerry Buchek 10.00 25.00
575 Dave Boswell RC 6.00 15.00
576 Rookie Stars 15.00 40.00
Ramon Hernandez RC
Norm Gigon RC
577 Bill Short 6.00 15.00
578 John Boccabella 6.00 15.00
579 Bill Henry 6.00 15.00
580 Rocky Colavito 75.00 150.00
581 Rookie Stars 300.00 600.00
Bill Denehy RC
Tom Seaver RC
582 Jim Owens DP 3.00 8.00
583 Ray Barker 15.00 40.00
584 Jimmy Piersall 15.00 40.00
585 Wally Bunker 10.00 25.00
586 Manny Jimenez 6.00 15.00
587 Rookie Stars 15.00 40.00
Don Shaw RC
Gary Sutherland RC
588 Johnny Klippstein DP 3.00 8.00
589 Dave Ricketts DP 3.00 8.00
590 Pete Richert 6.00 15.00
591 Ty Cline 10.00 25.00
592 Rookie Stars 10.00 25.00
Jim Shellenback RC
Ron Willis RC
593 Wes Westrum MG 20.00 50.00
594 Dan Osinski 15.00 40.00
595 Cookie Rojas 10.00 25.00
596 Galen Cisco DP 3.00 8.00
597 Ted Abernathy 6.00 15.00
598 Rookie Stars 10.00 25.00
Walt Williams RC
Ed Stroud RC
599 Bob Duliba DP 3.00 8.00
600 Brooks Robinson 125.00 250.00
601 Bill Bryan DP 3.00 8.00
602 Juan Pizarro 15.00 40.00
603 Rookie Stars 10.00 25.00
Tim Talton RC
Ramon Webster RC
604 Boston Red Sox TC 60.00 120.00
605 Mike Shannon 20.00 50.00
606 Ron Taylor 10.00 25.00
607 Mickey Stanley 20.00 50.00
608 Rookie Stars 3.00 8.00
Rich Nye RC
John Upham RC DP
609 Tommy John 40.00 80.00

1968 Topps

The cards in this 598-card set measure 2 1/2" by 3 1/2". The 1968 Topps set includes Sporting News All-Star Selections as card numbers 361 to 380. Other subsets in the set include League Leaders (1-12) and World Series cards (151-158). The front of each checklist card features a picture of a popular player inside a circle. Higher numbers 458 to 598 are slightly more difficult to obtain. The first series looks different from the other series, as it has a lighter, wider mesh background on the card front. The later series all had a much darker, finer mesh pattern. Among other fashions, cards were issued in five-card nickel packs. Those five cent packs were issued 24 packs to a box. Thirty-six card rack packs with an SRP of 29 cents were also issued. The key Rookie Cards in the set are Johnny Bench and Nolan Ryan. Lastly, some cards were also issued along with the "Win-A-Card" board game from Milton Bradley that included cards from the 1965 Topps Hot Rods and 1967 Topps football card sets. This version of these cards is somewhat difficult to distinguish, but are often found with a slight touch of the 1967 football set white border on the front top or bottom edge as well as a brighter yellow card back instead of the darker yellow or gold color. The known cards from this product include card numbers 16, 20, 34, 45, 108, and 149.

COMPLETE SET (598) 1500.00 3000.00
COMMON CARD (1-457) .75 2.00
COMMON (458-598) 1.50 4.00
WRAPPER (5-CENT) 10.00 25.00
1 NL Batting Leaders 12.50 30.00
Roberto Clemente
Tony Gonzalez
Matty Alou
2 AL Batting Leaders 6.00 15.00
Carl Yastrzemski
Frank Robinson
Al Kaline
3 NL RBI Leaders 8.00 20.00
Orlando Cepeda
Roberto Clemente
Hank Aaron
4 AL RBI Leaders 6.00 15.00
Carl Yastrzemski
Harmon Killebrew
Frank Robinson
5 NL Home Run Leaders 3.00 8.00
Hank Aaron
Jim Wynn
Ron Santo
Willie McCovey
6 AL Home Run Leaders 3.00 8.00
Carl Yastrzemski
Harmon Killebrew
Frank Howard
7 NL ERA Leaders 1.50 4.00
Phil Niekro
Jim Bunning
Chris Short
8 AL ERA Leaders 1.50 4.00
Joel Horlen
Gary Peters
Sonny Siebert
9 NL Pitching Leaders 1.50 4.00
Mike McCormick
Ferguson Jenkins
Jim Bunning
Claude Osteen
10A AL Pitching Leaders 1.50 4.00
Jim Lonborg ERR
(Misspelled Lonberg
on card back)
Earl Wilson
Dean Chance
10B AL Pitching Leaders 1.50 4.00
Jim Lonborg COR
Earl Wilson
Dean Chance
11 NL Strikeout Leaders 2.50 6.00
Jim Bunning
Ferguson Jenkins
Gaylord Perry
12 AL Strikeout Leaders 1.50 4.00
Jim Lonborg UER
(Misspelled Longberg
on card back)
Sam McDowell
Dean Chance
13 Chuck Hartenstein RC .75 2.00
14 Jerry McNertney .75 2.00
15 Ron Hunt .75 2.00
16 Rookie Stars 2.50 6.00
Lou Piniella
Richie Scheinblum
17 Dick Hall .75 2.00
18 Mike Hershberger .75 2.00
19 Juan Pizarro .75 2.00
20 Brooks Robinson 10.00 25.00
21 Ron Davis .75 2.00
22 Pat Dobson 1.50 4.00
23 Chico Cardenas 1.50 4.00
24 Bobby Locke .75 2.00
25 Julian Javier 1.50 4.00
26 Darrell Brandon .75 2.00
27 Gil Hodges MG 3.00 8.00
28 Ted Uhlaender .75 2.00
29 Joe Verbanic .75 2.00
30 Joe Torre 2.50 6.00
31 Ed Stroud .75 2.00
32 Joe Gibbon .75 2.00
33 Pete Ward .75 2.00
34 Al Ferrara .75 2.00
35 Steve Hargan .75 2.00
36 Rookie Stars 1.50 4.00
Bob Moose RC
Bob Robertson RC
37 Billy Williams 3.00 8.00
38 Tony Pierce .75 2.00
39 Cookie Rojas .75 2.00
40 Denny McLain 3.00 8.00
41 Julio Gotay .75 2.00
42 Larry Haney .75 2.00
43 Gary Bell .75 2.00
44 Frank Kostro .75 2.00
45 Tom Seaver 20.00 50.00
46 Dave Ricketts .75 2.00
47 Ralph Houk MG 1.50 4.00
48 Ted Davidson .75 2.00
49A Eddie Brinkman .75 2.00
(White team name)
49B Eddie Brinkman 20.00 50.00
(Yellow team name)
50 Willie Mays 30.00 60.00
51 Bob Locker .75 2.00
52 Hawk Taylor .75 2.00
53 Gene Alley 1.50 4.00
54 Stan Williams .75 2.00
55 Felipe Alou 1.50 4.00
56 Rookie Stars .75 2.00
Dave Leonhard RC
Dave May RC
57 Dan Schneider .75 2.00
58 Eddie Mathews 6.00 15.00
59 Don Lock .75 2.00
60 Ken Holtzman 1.50 4.00
61 Reggie Smith 1.50 4.00
62 Chuck Dobson .75 2.00
63 Dick Kenworthy RC .75 2.00
64 Jim Merritt .75 2.00
65 John Roseboro 1.50 4.00
66A Casey Cox .75 2.00
(White team name)
66B Casey Cox 50.00 100.00
(Yellow team name)
67 Checklist 1 2.50 6.00
Jim Kaat
68 Ron Willis .75 2.00
69 Tom Tresh 1.50 4.00
70 Bob Veale 1.50 4.00
71 Vern Fuller RC .75 2.00
72 Tommy John 2.50 6.00
73 Jim Ray Hart 1.50 4.00
74 Milt Pappas 1.50 4.00
75 Don Mincher .75 2.00
76 Rookie Stars 1.50 4.00
Jim Britton
Ron Reed RC
77 Don Wilson RC 1.50 4.00
78 Jim Northrup 2.50 6.00
79 Ted Kubiak RC .75 2.00
80 Rod Carew 20.00 50.00
81 Larry Jackson .75 2.00
82 Sam Bowens .75 2.00
83 John Stephenson .75 2.00
84 Bob Tolan .75 2.00
85 Gaylord Perry 3.00 8.00
86 Willie Stargell 3.00 8.00
87 Dick Williams MG 1.50 4.00
88 Phil Regan 1.50 4.00
89 Jake Gibbs 1.50 4.00
90 Vada Pinson 1.50 4.00
91 Jim Ollom RC .75 2.00
92 Ed Kranepool 1.50 4.00
93 Tony Cloninger .75 2.00
94 Lee Maye .75 2.00
95 Bob Aspromonte .75 2.00
96 Rookie Stars .75 2.00
Frank Coggins RC
Dick Nold
97 Tom Phoebus .75 2.00
98 Gary Sutherland .75 2.00
99 Rocky Colavito 3.00 8.00
100 Bob Gibson 10.00 25.00
101 Glenn Beckert 1.50 4.00
102 Jose Cardenal 1.50 4.00
103 Don Sutton 3.00 8.00
104 Dick Dietz .75 2.00
105 Al Downing 1.50 4.00
106 Dalton Jones .75 2.00
107A Checklist 2 2.50 6.00
Juan Marichal
(Tan wide mesh)
107B Checklist 2 2.50 6.00
Juan Marichal
(Brown fine mesh)
108 Don Pavletich .75 2.00
109 Bert Campaneris 1.50 4.00
110 Hank Aaron 30.00 60.00
111 Rich Reese .75 2.00
112 Woody Fryman .75 2.00
113 Rookie Stars 1.50 4.00
Tom Matchick
Daryl Patterson RC
114 Ron Swoboda 1.50 4.00
115 Sam McDowell 1.50 4.00
116 Ken McMullen .75 2.00
117 Larry Jaster .75 2.00
118 Mark Belanger 1.50 4.00
119 Ted Savage .75 2.00
120 Mel Stottlemyre 1.50 4.00
121 Jimmie Hall .75 2.00
122 Gene Mauch MG 1.50 4.00
123 Jose Santiago .75 2.00
124 Nate Oliver .75 2.00
125 Joel Horlen .75 2.00
126 Bobby Etheridge RC .75 2.00
127 Paul Lindblad .75 2.00
128 Rookie Stars .75 2.00
Tom Dukes RC
Alonzo Harris
129 Mickey Stanley 2.50 6.00
130 Tony Perez 3.00 8.00
131 Frank Bertaina .75 2.00
132 Bud Harrelson 1.50 4.00
133 Fred Whitfield .75 2.00
134 Pat Jarvis .75 2.00
135 Paul Blair 1.50 4.00
136 Randy Hundley 1.50 4.00
137 Minnesota Twins TC 1.50 4.00
138 Ruben Amaro .75 2.00
139 Chris Short .75 2.00
140 Tony Conigliaro 3.00 8.00
141 Dal Maxvill .75 2.00
142 Rookie Stars .75 2.00
Buddy Bradford RC
Bill Voss
143 Pete Cimino .75 2.00
144 Joe Morgan 5.00 12.00
145 Don Drysdale 5.00 12.00
146 Sal Bando 1.50 4.00
147 Frank Linzy .75 2.00
148 Dave Bristol MG .75 2.00
149 Bob Saverine .75 2.00
150 Roberto Clemente 40.00 80.00
151 World Series Game 1 4.00 10.00
Lou Brock
152 World Series Game 2 4.00 10.00
Carl Yastrzemski
153 World Series Game 3 2.00 5.00
Nelson Briles
154 World Series Game 4 4.00 10.00
Bob Gibson
155 World Series Game 5 2.00 5.00
Jim Lonborg
156 World Series Game 6 2.00 5.00
Rico Petrocelli
157 World Series Game 7 2.00 5.00
St. Louis wins it
Red Schoendienst, Bob Gibson and Bobby Tolan among those visible
158 WS Summary 2.00 5.00
Cardinals Celebrate
Tim McCarver and Joe Schultz very visible in photo
159 Don Kessinger 1.50 4.00
160 Earl Wilson 1.50 4.00
161 Norm Miller .75 2.00
162 Rookie Stars 1.50 4.00
Hal Gilson RC
Mike Torrez RC
163 Gene Brabender .75 2.00
164 Ramon Webster .75 2.00
165 Tony Oliva 2.50 6.00
166 Claude Raymond .75 2.00
167 Elston Howard 2.50 6.00
168 Los Angeles Dodgers TC 1.50 4.00
169 Bob Bolin .75 2.00
170 Jim Fregosi 1.50 4.00
171 Don Nottebart .75 2.00
172 Walt Williams .75 2.00
173 John Boozer .75 2.00
174 Bob Tillman .75 2.00
175 Maury Wills 2.50 6.00
176 Bob Allen .75 2.00
177 Rookie Stars 250.00 500.00
Jerry Koosman RC
Nolan Ryan RC
UER Sensational
is spelled incorrectly
178 Don Wert 1.50 4.00
179 Bill Stoneman RC .75 2.00
180 Curt Flood 2.50 6.00
181 Jerry Zimmerman .75 2.00
182 Dave Giusti .75 2.00
183 Bob Kennedy MG 1.50 4.00
184 Lou Johnson .75 2.00
185 Tom Haller .75 2.00
186 Eddie Watt .75 2.00
187 Sonny Jackson .75 2.00
188 Cap Peterson .75 2.00
189 Bill Landis RC .75 2.00
190 Bill White 1.50 4.00
191 Dan Frisella RC .75 2.00
192A Checklist 3 3.00 8.00
Carl Yastrzemski
(Special Baseball
192B Checklist 3 3.00 8.00
Carl Yastrzemski
(Special Baseball
Playing Card Game
193 Jack Hamilton .75 2.00
194 Don Buford .75 2.00
195 Joe Pepitone 1.50 4.00
196 Gary Nolan RC 1.50 4.00
197 Larry Brown .75 2.00
198 Roy Face 1.50 4.00
199 Rookie Stars .75 2.00
Roberto Rodriguez RC
Darrell Osteen
200 Orlando Cepeda 3.00 8.00
201 Mike Marshall RC 1.50 4.00
202 Adolfo Phillips .75 2.00
203 Dick Kelley .75 2.00
204 Andy Etchebarren .75 2.00
205 Juan Marichal 3.00 8.00
206 Cal Ermer MG RC .75 2.00
207 Carroll Sembera .75 2.00
208 Willie Davis 1.50 4.00
209 Tim Cullen .75 2.00
210 Gary Peters .75 2.00
211 J.C. Martin .75 2.00
212 Dave Morehead .75 2.00
213 Chico Ruiz .75 2.00
214 Rookie Stars 1.50 4.00
Stan Bahnsen
Frank Fernandez
215 Jim Bunning 3.00 8.00
216 Bubba Morton .75 2.00
217 Dick Farrell .75 2.00
218 Ken Suarez .75 2.00
219 Rob Gardner .75 2.00
220 Harmon Killebrew 6.00 15.00
221 Atlanta Braves TC 1.50 4.00
222 Jim Hardin RC .75 2.00
223 Ollie Brown .75 2.00
224 Jack Aker .75 2.00
225 Richie Allen 2.50 6.00
226 Jimmie Price .75 2.00
227 Joe Hoerner .75 2.00
228 Rookie Stars 1.50 4.00
Jack Billingham RC
Jim Fairey RC
229 Fred Klages .75 2.00
230 Pete Rose 30.00 60.00
231 Dave Baldwin RC .75 2.00
232 Denis Menke .75 2.00
233 George Scott 1.50 4.00
234 Bill Monbouquette .75 2.00
235 Ron Santo 3.00 8.00
236 Tug McGraw 2.50 6.00
237 Alvin Dark MG 1.50 4.00
238 Tom Satriano .75 2.00
239 Bill Henry .75 2.00
240 Al Kaline 15.00 40.00
241 Felix Millan .75 2.00
242 Moe Drabowsky 1.50 4.00
243 Rich Rollins .75 2.00
244 John Donaldson RC .75 2.00
245 Tony Gonzalez .75 2.00
246 Fritz Peterson 1.50 4.00
247 Rookie Stars 60.00 120.00
Johnny Bench RC
Ron Tompkins UER (the is Misspelled in First Line)
248 Fred Valentine .75 2.00
249 Bill Singer .75 2.00
250 Carl Yastrzemski 12.50 30.00
251 Manny Sanguillen RC 2.50 6.00
252 California Angels TC 1.50 4.00
253 Dick Hughes .75 2.00
254 Cleon Jones 1.50 4.00
255 Dean Chance 1.50 4.00
256 Norm Cash 2.50 6.00
257 Phil Niekro 3.00 8.00
258 Rookie Stars .75 2.00
Jose Arcia RC
Bill Schlesinger
259 Ken Boyer 2.50 6.00
260 Jim Wynn 1.50 4.00
261 Dave Duncan 1.50 4.00
262 Rick Wise 1.50 4.00
263 Horace Clarke 1.50 4.00
264 Ted Abernathy .75 2.00
265 Tommy Davis 1.50 4.00
266 Paul Popovich .75 2.00
267 Herman Franks MG .75 2.00
268 Bob Humphreys .75 2.00
269 Bob Tiefenauer .75 2.00
270 Matty Alou 1.50 4.00
271 Bobby Knoop .75 2.00
272 Ray Culp .75 2.00
273 Dave Johnson 1.50 4.00
274 Mike Cuellar 1.50 4.00
275 Tim McCarver 2.50 6.00
276 Jim Roland .75 2.00
277 Jerry Buchek .75 2.00
278 Checklist 4 2.50 6.00
Orlando Cepeda
279 Bill Hands .75 2.00
280 Mickey Mantle 175.00 350.00
281 Jim Campanis .75 2.00
282 Rick Monday 1.50 4.00
283 Mel Queen .75 2.00
284 Johnny Briggs .75 2.00
285 Dick McAuliffe 2.50 6.00
286 Cecil Upshaw .75 2.00
287 Rookie Stars .75 2.00
Mickey Abarbanel RC
Cisco Carlos RC
288 Dave Wickersham .75 2.00
289 Woody Held .75 2.00
290 Willie McCovey 5.00 12.00
291 Dick Lines .75 2.00
292 Art Shamsky .75 2.00
293 Bruce Howard .75 2.00
294 Red Schoendienst MG 2.50 6.00
295 Sonny Siebert .75 2.00
296 Byron Browne .75 2.00
297 Russ Gibson .75 2.00
298 Jim Brewer .75 2.00
299 Gene Michael 1.50 4.00
300 Rusty Staub 1.50 4.00
301 Rookie Stars .75 2.00
George Mitterwald RC
Rick Renick RC
302 Gerry Arrigo .75 2.00
303 Dick Green 1.50 4.00
304 Sandy Valdespino .75 2.00
305 Minnie Rojas .75 2.00
306 Mike Ryan .75 2.00
307 John Hiller 1.50 4.00
308 Pittsburgh Pirates TC 1.50 4.00
309 Ken Henderson .75 2.00
310 Luis Aparicio 3.00 8.00
311 Jack Lamabe .75 2.00
312 Curt Blefary .75 2.00
313 Al Weis .75 2.00
314 Rookie Stars .75 2.00
Bill Rohr
George Spriggs
315 Zoilo Versalles .75 2.00
316 Steve Barber .75 2.00
317 Ron Brand .75 2.00
318 Chico Salmon .75 2.00
319 George Culver .75 2.00
320 Frank Howard 1.50 4.00
321 Leo Durocher MG 2.50 6.00
322 Dave Boswell .75 2.00
323 Deron Johnson 1.50 4.00
324 Jim Nash .75 2.00
325 Manny Mota 1.50 4.00
326 Dennis Ribant .75 2.00
327 Tony Taylor 1.50 4.00
328 Rookie Stars .75 2.00
Chuck Vinson RC
Jim Weaver RC
329 Duane Josephson .75 2.00
330 Roger Maris 20.00 50.00
331 Dan Osinski .75 2.00
332 Doug Rader 1.50 4.00
333 Ron Herbel .75 2.00
334 Baltimore Orioles TC 1.50 4.00
335 Bob Allison 1.50 4.00
336 John Purdin .75 2.00
337 Bill Robinson 1.50 4.00
338 Bob Johnson .75 2.00
339 Rich Nye .75 2.00
340 Max Alvis .75 2.00
341 Jim Lemon MG .75 2.00
342 Ken Johnson .75 2.00
343 Jim Gosger .75 2.00
344 Donn Clendenon 1.50 4.00
345 Bob Hendley .75 2.00
346 Jerry Adair .75 2.00
347 George Brunet .75 2.00
348 Rookie Stars .75 2.00
Larry Colton RC
Dick Thoenen RC
349 Ed Spiezio 1.50 4.00
350 Hoyt Wilhelm 3.00 8.00
351 Bob Barton .75 2.00
352 Jackie Hernandez RC .75 2.00
353 Mack Jones .75 2.00
354 Pete Richert .75 2.00
355 Ernie Banks 10.00 25.00
356A Checklist 5 2.50 6.00
Ken Holtzman
(Head centered
within circle
356B Checklist 5 2.50 6.00
Ken Holtzman
Head shifted right
within circle
357 Len Gabrielson .75 2.00
358 Mike Epstein .75 2.00
359 Joe Moeller .75 2.00
360 Willie Horton 2.50 6.00
361 Harmon Killebrew AS 3.00 8.00
362 Orlando Cepeda AS 2.50 6.00
363 Rod Carew AS 3.00 8.00
364 Joe Morgan AS 3.00 8.00
365 Brooks Robinson AS 3.00 8.00
366 Ron Santo AS 2.50 6.00
367 Jim Fregosi AS 1.50 4.00
368 Gene Alley AS 1.50 4.00
369 Carl Yastrzemski AS 4.00 10.00
370 Hank Aaron AS 8.00 20.00
371 Tony Oliva AS 2.50 6.00
372 Lou Brock AS 3.00 8.00
373 Frank Robinson AS 3.00 8.00
374 Bob Clemente AS 12.50 30.00
375 Bill Freehan AS 1.50 4.00
376 Tim McCarver AS 1.50 4.00
377 Joel Horlen AS 1.50 4.00
378 Bob Gibson AS 3.00 8.00
379 Gary Peters AS 1.50 4.00
380 Ken Holtzman AS 1.50 4.00
381 Boog Powell 1.50 4.00
382 Ramon Hernandez .75 2.00
383 Steve Whitaker .75 2.00
384 Rookie Stars 2.50 6.00
Bill Henry
Hal McRae RC
385 Jim Hunter 4.00 10.00
386 Greg Goossen .75 2.00
387 Joe Foy .75 2.00
388 Ray Washburn .75 2.00
389 Jay Johnstone 1.50 4.00
390 Bill Mazeroski 3.00 8.00
391 Bob Priddy .75 2.00
392 Grady Hatton MG .75 2.00
393 Jim Perry 1.50 4.00
394 Tommie Aaron 2.50 6.00
395 Camilo Pascual 1.50 4.00
396 Bobby Wine .75 2.00
397 Vic Davalillo .75 2.00
398 Jim Grant .75 2.00
399 Ray Oyler 1.50 4.00
400A Mike McCormick 1.50 4.00
(Yellow letters)
400B Mike McCormick 75.00 150.00
(Team name in
white letters)
401 Mets Team 1.50 4.00
402 Mike Hegan 1.50 4.00
403 John Buzhardt .75 2.00
404 Floyd Robinson .75 2.00
405 Tommy Helms 1.50 4.00
406 Dick Ellsworth .75 2.00
407 Gary Kolb .75 2.00
408 Steve Carlton 12.50 30.00
409 Rookie Stars .75 2.00
Frank Peters RC
Ron Stone
410 Ferguson Jenkins 4.00 10.00
411 Ron Hansen .75 2.00
412 Clay Carroll 1.50 4.00
413 Tom McCraw .75 2.00
414 Mickey Lolich 3.00 8.00
415 Johnny Callison 1.50 4.00
416 Bill Rigney MG .75 2.00
417 Willie Crawford .75 2.00
418 Eddie Fisher .75 2.00
419 Jack Hiatt .75 2.00
420 Cesar Tovar .75 2.00
421 Ron Taylor .75 2.00
422 Rene Lachemann .75 2.00
423 Fred Gladding .75 2.00
424 Chicago White Sox TC 1.50 4.00
425 Jim Maloney 1.50 4.00
426 Hank Allen .75 2.00
427 Dick Calmus .75 2.00
428 Vic Roznovsky .75 2.00
429 Tommie Sisk .75 2.00
430 Rico Petrocelli 1.50 4.00
431 Dooley Womack .75 2.00
432 Rookie Stars .75 2.00
Bill Davis
Jose Vidal
433 Bob Rodgers .75 2.00
434 Ricardo Joseph RC .75 2.00
435 Ron Perranoski 1.50 4.00
436 Hal Lanier .75 2.00
437 Don Cardwell .75 2.00
438 Lee Thomas 1.50 4.00
439 Lum Harris MG .75 2.00
440 Claude Osteen 1.50 4.00
441 Alex Johnson 1.50 4.00
442 Dick Bosman .75 2.00
443 Joe Azcue .75 2.00
444 Jack Fisher .75 2.00
445 Mike Shannon 1.50 4.00
446 Ron Kline .75 2.00
447 Rookie Stars 1.50 4.00
George Korince
Fred Lasher RC
448 Gary Wagner .75 2.00
449 Gene Oliver .75 2.00
450 Jim Kaat 2.50 6.00
451 Al Spangler .75 2.00
452 Jesus Alou .75 2.00
453 Sammy Ellis .75 2.00

454A Checklist 6 3.00 8.00
Frank Robinson
(Cap complete
within circle
454B Checklist 6 3.00 8.00
Frank Robinson CL
Cap partially within circle
455 Rico Carty 1.50 4.00
456 John O'Donoghue .75 2.00
457 Jim Lefebvre 1.50 4.00
458 Lew Krausse 2.50 6.00
459 Dick Simpson 1.50 4.00
460 Jim Lonborg 2.50 6.00
461 Chuck Hiller 1.50 4.00
462 Barry Moore 1.50 4.00
463 Jim Schaffer 1.50 4.00
464 Don McMahon 1.50 4.00
465 Tommie Agee 4.00 10.00
466 Bill Dillman 1.50 4.00
467 Dick Howser 4.00 10.00
468 Larry Sherry 1.50 4.00
469 Ty Cline 1.50 4.00
470 Bill Freehan 4.00 10.00
471 Orlando Pena 1.50 4.00
472 Walter Alston MG 2.50 6.00
473 Al Worthington 1.50 4.00
474 Paul Schaal 1.50 4.00
475 Joe Niekro 2.50 6.00
476 Woody Woodward 1.50 4.00
477 Philadelphia Phillies TC 3.00 8.00
478 Dave McNally 2.50 6.00
479 Phil Gagliano 2.50 6.00
480 Manager's Dream 40.00 80.00
Tony Oliva
Chico Cardenas
Bob Clemente
481 John Wyatt 1.50 4.00
482 Jose Pagan 1.50 4.00
483 Darold Knowles 1.50 4.00
484 Phil Roof 1.50 4.00
485 Ken Berry 2.50 6.00
486 Cal Koonce 1.50 4.00
487 Lee May 4.00 10.00
488 Dick Tracewski 2.50 6.00
489 Wally Bunker 1.50 4.00
490 Super Stars 75.00 150.00
Harmon Killebrew
Willie Mays
Mickey Mantle
491 Denny Lemaster 1.50 4.00
492 Jeff Torborg 2.50 6.00
493 Jim McGlothlin 1.50 4.00
494 Ray Sadecki 1.50 4.00
495 Leon Wagner 1.50 4.00
496 Steve Hamilton 2.50 6.00
497 St. Louis Cardinals TC 3.00 8.00
498 Bill Bryan 2.50 6.00
499 Steve Blass 2.50 6.00
500 Frank Robinson 12.50 30.00
501 John Odom 2.50 6.00
502 Mike Andrews 1.50 4.00
503 Al Jackson 2.50 6.00
504 Russ Snyder 1.50 4.00
505 Joe Sparma 4.00 10.00
506 Clarence Jones RC 1.50 4.00
507 Wade Blasingame 1.50 4.00
508 Duke Sims 1.50 4.00
509 Dennis Higgins 1.50 4.00
510 Ron Fairly 4.00 10.00
511 Bill Kelso 1.50 4.00
512 Grant Jackson 1.50 4.00
513 Hank Bauer MG 2.50 6.00
514 Al McBean 1.50 4.00
515 Russ Nixon 1.50 4.00
516 Pete Mikkelsen 1.50 4.00
517 Diego Segui 2.50 6.00
518A Checklist 7 ERR 5.00 12.00
(539 AL Rookies)
(Clete Boyer)
518B Checklist 7 COR 5.00 12.00
(539 ML Rookies)
(Clete Boyer)
519 Jerry Stephenson 1.50 4.00
520 Lou Brock 10.00 25.00
521 Don Shaw 1.50 4.00
522 Wayne Causey 1.50 4.00
523 John Tsitouris 1.50 4.00
524 Andy Kosco 2.50 6.00
525 Jim Davenport 1.50 4.00
526 Bill Denehy 1.50 4.00
527 Tito Francona 1.50 4.00
528 Detroit Tigers TC 30.00 60.00
529 Bruce Von Hoff RC 1.50 4.00
530 Bird Belters 15.00 40.00
Brooks Robinson
Frank Robinson
531 Chuck Hinton 1.50 4.00
532 Luis Tiant 2.50 6.00
533 Wes Parker 2.50 6.00
534 Bob Miller 2.50 6.00
535 Danny Cater 2.50 6.00
536 Bill Short 1.50 4.00
537 Norm Siebern 2.50 6.00
538 Manny Jimenez 2.50 6.00
539 Rookie Stars 1.50 4.00
Jim Ray RC
Mike Ferraro RC
540 Nelson Briles 2.50 6.00
541 Sandy Alomar 2.50 6.00
542 John Boccabella 1.50 4.00
543 Bob Lee 1.50 4.00
544 Mayo Smith MG 5.00 12.00
545 Lindy McDaniel 2.50 6.00
546 Roy White 2.50 6.00
547 Dan Coombs 1.50 4.00
548 Bernie Allen 1.50 4.00
549 Rookie Stars 1.50 4.00
Curt Motton RC
Roger Nelson RC
550 Clete Boyer 2.50 6.00
551 Darrell Sutherland 1.50 4.00
552 Ed Kirkpatrick 1.50 4.00
553 Hank Aguirre 1.50 4.00
554 Oakland Athletics TC 4.00 10.00
555 Jose Tartabull 2.50 6.00
556 Dick Selma 1.50 4.00
557 Frank Quilici 2.50 6.00
558 Johnny Edwards 1.50 4.00
559 Rookie Stars 1.50 4.00
Carl Taylor RC
Luke Walker
560 Paul Casanova 1.50 4.00
561 Lee Elia 1.50 4.00
562 Jim Bouton 2.50 6.00
563 Ed Charles 1.50 4.00
564 Eddie Stanky MG 2.50 6.00
565 Larry Dierker 2.50 6.00
566 Ken Harrelson 2.50 6.00
567 Clay Dalrymple 1.50 4.00
568 Willie Smith 1.50 4.00
569 Rookie Stars 1.50 4.00
Ivan Murrell RC
Les Rohr RC
570 Rick Reichardt 1.50 4.00
571 Tony LaRussa 5.00 12.00
572 Don Bosch RC 1.50 4.00
573 Joe Coleman 1.50 4.00
574 Cincinnati Reds TC 4.00 10.00
575 Jim Palmer 15.00 40.00
576 Dave Adlesh 1.50 4.00
577 Fred Talbot 1.50 4.00
578 Orlando Martinez 1.50 4.00
579 Rookie Stars 4.00 10.00
Larry Hisle RC
Mike Lum RC
580 Bob Bailey 1.50 4.00
581 Garry Roggenburk 1.50 4.00
582 Jerry Grote 4.00 10.00
583 Gates Brown 4.00 10.00
584 Larry Shepard MG RC 1.50 4.00
585 Wilbur Wood 2.50 6.00
586 Jim Pagliaroni 2.50 6.00
587 Roger Repoz 1.50 4.00
588 Dick Schofield 1.50 4.00
589 Rookie Stars 1.50 4.00
Ron Clark
Moe Ogier RC
590 Tommy Harper 2.50 6.00
591 Dick Nen 1.50 4.00
592 John Bateman 1.50 4.00
593 Lee Stange 1.50 4.00
594 Phil Linz 2.50 6.00
595 Phil Ortega 1.50 4.00
596 Charlie Smith 1.50 4.00
597 Bill McCool 1.50 4.00
598 Jerry May 2.50 6.00

1969 Topps

The cards in this 664-card set measure 2 1/2" by 3 1/2". The 1969 Topps set includes Sporting News All-Star Selections as card numbers 416 to 435. Other popular subsets within this set include League Leaders (1-12) and World Series cards (162-169). The fifth series contains several variations; the more difficult variety consists of cards with the player's first name, last name, and/or position in white letters instead of lettering in some other color. These are designated in the checklist below by WL (white letters). Each checklist card features a different popular player's picture inside a circle on the front of the checklist card. Two different team identifications of Clay Dalrymple and Donn Clendenon exist, as indicated in the checklist. The key Rookie Cards in this set are Rollie Fingers, Reggie Jackson, and Graig Nettles. This was the last year that Topps issued multi-player special star cards, ending a 13-year tradition, which they had begun in 1957. There were cropping differences in checklist cards 57, 214, and 412, due to their each being printed with two different series. The differences are difficult to explain and have not been greatly sought by collectors; hence they are not listed explicitly in the list below. The All-Star cards 426-435, when turned over and placed together, form a puzzle back of Pete Rose. This would turn out to be the final year that Topps issued cards in five-card nickel wax packs. Cards were also issued in thirty-six card rack packs which were sold for 29 cents.

COMP. MASTER (695) 2500.00 5000.00
COMPLETE SET (664) 1500.00 3000.00
COMMON (1-218/328-512) .60 1.50
COMMON (219-327) 1.00 2.50
COMMON (513-588) .75 2.00
COMMON (589-664) 1.25 3.00
WRAPPER (5-CENT) 8.00 20.00
1 AL Batting Leaders 6.00 15.00
Carl Yastrzemski
Danny Cater
Tony Oliva
2 NL Batting Leaders 3.00 8.00
Pete Rose
Matty Alou
Felipe Alou
3 AL RBI Leaders 1.50 4.00
Ken Harrelson
Frank Howard
Jim Northrup
4 NL RBI Leaders 2.50 6.00
Willie McCovey
Ron Santo
Billy Williams
5 AL Home Run Leaders 1.50 4.00
Frank Howard
Willie Horton
Ken Harrelson
6 NL Home Run Leaders 2.50 6.00
Willie McCovey
Richie Allen
Ernie Banks
7 AL ERA Leaders 1.50 4.00
Luis Tiant
Sam McDowell
Dave McNally
8 NL ERA Leaders 2.50 6.00
Bob Gibson
Bobby Bolin
Bob Veale
9 AL Pitching Leaders 1.50 4.00
Denny McLain
Dave McNally
Luis Tiant
Mel Stottlemyre
10 NL Pitching Leaders 3.00 8.00
Juan Marichal
Bob Gibson
Fergie Jenkins
11 AL Strikeout Leaders 1.50 4.00
Sam McDowell
Denny McLain
Luis Tiant
12 NL Strikeout Leaders 1.50 4.00
Bob Gibson
Fergie Jenkins
Bill Singer
13 Mickey Stanley 1.00 2.50
14 Al McBean .60 1.50
15 Boog Powell 1.50 4.00
16 Rookie Stars .60 1.50
Cesar Gutierrez RC
Rich Robertson RC
17 Mike Marshall 1.00 2.50
18 Dick Schofield .60 1.50
19 Ken Suarez .60 1.50
20 Ernie Banks 8.00 20.00
21 Jose Santiago .60 1.50
22 Jesus Alou 1.00 2.50
23 Lew Krausse .60 1.50
24 Walt Alston MG 1.50 4.00
25 Roy White 1.00 2.50
26 Clay Carroll 1.00 2.50
27 Bernie Allen .60 1.50
28 Mike Ryan .60 1.50
29 Dave Morehead .60 1.50
30 Bob Allison 1.00 2.50
31 Rookie Stars 1.00 2.50
Gary Gentry RC
Amos Otis RC
32 Sammy Ellis .60 1.50
33 Wayne Causey .60 1.50
34 Gary Peters .60 1.50
35 Joe Morgan 4.00 10.00
36 Luke Walker .60 1.50
37 Curt Motton .60 1.50
38 Zoilo Versalles 1.00 2.50
39 Dick Hughes .60 1.50
40 Mayo Smith MG .60 1.50
41 Bob Barton .60 1.50
42 Tommy Harper 1.00 2.50
43 Joe Niekro 1.00 2.50
44 Danny Cater .60 1.50
45 Maury Wills 1.00 2.50
46 Fritz Peterson 1.00 2.50
47A Paul Popovich 1.00 2.50
No helmet emblem, thick airbrushing
47B Paul Popovich 1.00 2.50
No helmet emblem, light airbrushing
47C Paul Popovich 10.00 25.00
(C emblem on helmet)
48 Brant Alyea .60 1.50
49A Rookie Stars 10.00 25.00
Steve Jones
E. Rodriquez ERR
49B Rookie Stars .60 1.50
Steve Jones RC
Ellie Rodriguez RC COR
50 Roberto Clemente 30.00 60.00
UER Bats Right listed twice
51 Woody Fryman 1.00 2.50
52 Mike Andrews .60 1.50
53 Sonny Jackson .60 1.50
54 Cisco Carlos .60 1.50
55 Jerry Grote 1.00 2.50
56 Rich Reese .60 1.50
57 Checklist 1 2.50 6.00
Denny McLain
58 Fred Gladding .60 1.50
59 Jay Johnstone 1.00 2.50
60 Nelson Briles 1.00 2.50
61 Jimmie Hall .60 1.50
62 Chico Salmon .60 1.50
63 Jim Hickman 1.00 2.50
64 Bill Monbouquette .60 1.50
65 Willie Davis 1.00 2.50
66 Rookie Stars .60 1.50
Mike Adamson RC
Merv Rettenmund RC
67 Bill Stoneman 1.00 2.50
68 Dave Duncan 1.00 2.50
69 Steve Hamilton 1.00 2.50
70 Tommy Helms 1.00 2.50
71 Steve Whitaker 1.00 2.50
72 Ron Taylor .60 1.50
73 Johnny Briggs .60 1.50
74 Preston Gomez MG RC .60 1.50
75 Luis Aparicio 2.50 6.00
76 Norm Miller .60 1.50
77A Ron Perranoski 1.00 2.50
(No emblem on cap)
77B Ron Perranoski 10.00 25.00
(LA on cap)
78 Tom Satriano .60 1.50
79 Milt Pappas 1.00 2.50
80 Norm Cash 1.00 2.50
81 Mel Queen .60 1.50
82 Rookie Stars 3.00 8.00
Rich Hebner RC
Al Oliver RC
83 Mike Ferraro 1.00 2.50
84 Bob Humphreys .60 1.50
85 Lou Brock 8.00 20.00
86 Pete Richert .60 1.50
87 Horace Clarke 1.00 2.50
88 Rich Nye .60 1.50
89 Russ Gibson .60 1.50
90 Jerry Koosman 1.00 2.50
91 Alvin Dark MG 1.00 2.50
92 Jack Billingham 1.00 2.50
93 Joe Foy 1.00 2.50
94 Hank Aguirre .60 1.50
95 Johnny Bench 20.00 50.00
96 Denny Lemaster .60 1.50
97 Buddy Bradford .60 1.50
98 Dave Giusti .60 1.50
99A Rookie Stars 6.00 15.00
Danny Morris RC
Graig Nettles RC
(No loop)
99B Rookie Stars 6.00 15.00
Danny Morris
Graig Nettles
(Errant loop in
upper left corner
of obverse)
100 Hank Aaron 20.00 50.00
101 Daryl Patterson .60 1.50
102 Jim Davenport .60 1.50
103 Roger Repoz .60 1.50
104 Steve Blass .60 1.50
105 Rick Monday 1.00 2.50
106 Jim Hannan .60 1.50
107A Checklist 2 ERR 2.50 6.00
Bob Gibson
161 Jim Purdin
107B Checklist 2 COR 3.00 8.00
Bob Gibson
161 John Purdin
108 Tony Taylor 1.00 2.50
109 Jim Lonborg 1.00 2.50
110 Mike Shannon 1.00 2.50
111 John Morris RC .60 1.50
112 J.C. Martin 1.00 2.50
113 Dave May .60 1.50
114 Rookie Stars 1.00 2.50
Alan Closter
John Cumberland RC
115 Bill Hands .60 1.50
116 Chuck Harrison .60 1.50
117 Jim Fairey 1.00 2.50
118 Stan Williams .60 1.50
119 Doug Rader 1.00 2.50
120 Pete Rose 20.00 50.00
121 Joe Grzenda RC .60 1.50
122 Ron Fairly 1.00 2.50
123 Wilbur Wood 1.00 2.50
124 Hank Bauer MG 1.00 2.50
125 Ray Sadecki .60 1.50
126 Dick Tracewski .60 1.50
127 Kevin Collins 1.00 2.50
128 Tommie Aaron 1.00 2.50
129 Bill McCool .60 1.50
130 Carl Yastrzemski 8.00 20.00
131 Chris Cannizzaro .60 1.50
132 Dave Baldwin .60 1.50
133 Johnny Callison 1.00 2.50
134 Jim Weaver .60 1.50
135 Tommy Davis 1.00 2.50
136 Rookie Stars .60 1.50
Steve Huntz RC
Mike Torrez
137 Wally Bunker .60 1.50
138 John Bateman .60 1.50
139 Andy Kosco .60 1.50
140 Jim Lefebvre 1.00 2.50
141 Bill Dillman .60 1.50
142 Woody Woodward .60 1.50
143 Joe Nossek .60 1.50
144 Bob Hendley 1.00 2.50
145 Max Alvis .60 1.50
146 Jim Perry 1.00 2.50
147 Leo Durocher MG 1.50 4.00
148 Lee Stange .60 1.50
149 Ollie Brown 1.00 2.50
150 Denny McLain 1.50 4.00
151A Clay Dalrymple .60 1.50
Portrait, Orioles
151B Clay Dalrymple 6.00 15.00
Catching, Phillies
152 Tommie Sisk .60 1.50
153 Ed Brinkman .60 1.50
154 Jim Britton .60 1.50
155 Pete Ward .60 1.50
156 Rookie Stars .60 1.50
Hal Gilson
Leon McFadden RC
157 Bob Rodgers 1.00 2.50
158 Joe Gibbon .60 1.50
159 Jerry Adair .60 1.50
160 Vada Pinson 1.00 2.50
161 John Purdin .60 1.50
162 World Series Game 1 3.00 8.00
Bob Gibson
163 World Series Game 2 2.50 6.00
Willie Horton
164 World Series Game 3 5.00 12.00
Tim McCarver
w/Maris
165 World Series Game 4 3.00 8.00
Lou Brock
166 World Series Game 5 3.00 8.00
Al Kaline
167 World Series Game 6 2.50 6.00
Jim Northrup
168 World Series Game 7 3.00 8.00
Mickey Lolich
Bob Gibson
169 World Series Summary 2.50 6.00
Tigers Celebrate
Dick McAuliffe
Denny McLain
Willie Horton
170 Frank Howard 1.00 2.50
171 Glenn Beckert 1.00 2.50
172 Jerry Stephenson .60 1.50
173 Rookie Stars .60 1.50
Bob Christian RC
Gerry Nyman RC
174 Grant Jackson .60 1.50
175 Jim Bunning 2.50 6.00
176 Joe Azcue .60 1.50
177 Ron Reed .60 1.50
178 Ray Oyler 1.00 2.50
179 Don Pavletich .60 1.50
180 Willie Horton 1.00 2.50
181 Mel Nelson .60 1.50
182 Bill Rigney MG .60 1.50
183 Don Shaw 1.00 2.50
184 Roberto Pena .60 1.50
185 Tom Phoebus .60 1.50
186 Johnny Edwards .60 1.50
187 Leon Wagner .60 1.50
188 Rick Wise 1.00 2.50
189 Rookie Stars .60 1.50
Joe Lahoud RC
John Thibodeau RC
190 Willie Mays 40.00 80.00
191 Lindy McDaniel 1.00 2.50
192 Jose Pagan .60 1.50
193 Don Cardwell 1.00 2.50
194 Ted Uhlaender .60 1.50
195 John Odom .60 1.50
196 Lum Harris MG .60 1.50
197 Dick Selma .60 1.50
198 Willie Smith .60 1.50
199 Jim French .60 1.50
200 Bob Gibson 5.00 12.00
201 Russ Snyder .60 1.50
202 Don Wilson 1.00 2.50
203 Dave Johnson 1.00 2.50
204 Jack Hiatt .60 1.50
205 Rick Reichardt .60 1.50
206 Rookie Stars 1.00 2.50
Larry Hisle
Barry Lersch RC
207 Roy Face 1.00 2.50
208A Donn Clendenon 1.00 2.50
Houston
208B Donn Clendenon 6.00 15.00
Expos
209 Larry Haney UER .60 1.50
(Reverse negative)
210 Felix Millan .60 1.50
211 Galen Cisco .60 1.50
212 Tom Tresh 1.00 2.50
213 Gerry Arrigo .60 1.50
214 Checklist 3 2.50 6.00
With 69T deckle CL
on back (no player)
215 Rico Petrocelli 1.00 2.50
216 Don Sutton 2.50 6.00
217 John Donaldson .60 1.50
218 John Roseboro 1.00 2.50
219 Freddie Patek RC 1.50 4.00
220 Sam McDowell 1.50 4.00
221 Art Shamsky 1.50 4.00
222 Duane Josephson 1.00 2.50
223 Tom Dukes 1.50 4.00
224 Rookie Stars 1.00 2.50
Bill Harrelson RC
Steve Kealey RC
225 Don Kessinger 1.50 4.00
226 Bruce Howard 1.00 2.50
227 Frank Johnson RC 1.00 2.50
228 Dave Leonhard 1.00 2.50
229 Don Lock 1.00 2.50
230 Rusty Staub UER 1.50 4.00
For 1966 stats, Houston spelled Huoston
231 Pat Dobson 1.50 4.00
232 Dave Ricketts 1.00 2.50
233 Steve Barber 1.50 4.00
234 Dave Bristol MG 1.00 2.50
235 Jim Hunter 4.00 10.00
236 Manny Mota 1.50 4.00
237 Bobby Cox RC 4.00 10.00
238 Ken Johnson 1.00 2.50
239 Bob Taylor 1.50 4.00
240 Ken Harrelson 1.50 4.00
241 Jim Brewer 1.00 2.50
242 Frank Kostro 1.00 2.50
243 Ron Kline 1.00 2.50
244 Rookie Stars 1.50 4.00
Ray Fosse RC
George Woodson RC
245 Ed Charles 1.50 4.00
246 Joe Coleman 1.00 2.50
247 Gene Oliver 1.00 2.50
248 Bob Priddy 1.00 2.50
249 Ed Spiezio 1.50 4.00
250 Frank Robinson 8.00 20.00
251 Ron Herbel 1.00 2.50
252 Chuck Cottier 1.00 2.50
253 Jerry Johnson RC 1.00 2.50
254 Joe Schultz MG RC 1.00 2.50
255 Steve Carlton 12.50 30.00
256 Gates Brown 1.50 4.00
257 Jim Ray 1.00 2.50
258 Jackie Hernandez 1.50 4.00
259 Bill Short 1.00 2.50
260 Reggie Jackson RC 150.00 300.00
261 Bob Johnson 1.00 2.50
262 Mike Kekich 1.50 4.00
263 Jerry May 1.00 2.50
264 Bill Landis 1.00 2.50
265 Chico Cardenas 1.50 4.00
266 Rookie Stars 1.50 4.00
Tom Hutton
Alan Foster RC
267 Vicente Romo RC 1.00 2.50
268 Al Spangler 1.00 2.50
269 Al Weis 1.50 4.00
270 Mickey Lolich 1.50 4.00
271 Larry Stahl 1.50 4.00
272 Ed Stroud 1.00 2.50
273 Ron Willis 1.00 2.50
274 Clyde King MG 1.00 2.50
275 Vic Davalillo 1.00 2.50
276 Gary Wagner 1.00 2.50
277 Elrod Hendricks RC 1.00 2.50
278 Gary Geiger UER 1.00 2.50
(Batting wrong)
279 Roger Nelson 1.50 4.00
280 Alex Johnson 1.50 4.00
281 Ted Kubiak 1.00 2.50
282 Pat Jarvis 1.00 2.50
283 Sandy Alomar 1.50 4.00
284 Rookie Stars 1.50 4.00
Jerry Robertson RC
Mike Wegener RC
285 Don Mincher 1.50 4.00
286 Dock Ellis RC 1.50 4.00
287 Jose Tartabull 1.50 4.00
288 Ken Holtzman 1.50 4.00
289 Bart Shirley 1.00 2.50
290 Jim Kaat 1.50 4.00
291 Vern Fuller 1.00 2.50
292 Al Downing 1.50 4.00
293 Dick Dietz 1.00 2.50
294 Jim Lemon MG 1.00 2.50
295 Tony Perez 5.00 12.00
296 Andy Messersmith RC 1.50 4.00
297 Deron Johnson 1.00 2.50
298 Dave Nicholson 1.50 4.00
299 Mark Belanger 1.50 4.00
300 Felipe Alou 1.50 4.00
301 Darrell Brandon 1.50 4.00
302 Jim Pagliaroni 1.00 2.50
303 Cal Koonce 1.50 4.00
304 Rookie Stars 2.50 6.00
Bill Davis
Clarence Gaston RC
305 Dick McAuliffe 1.50 4.00
306 Jim Grant 1.50 4.00
307 Gary Kolb 1.00 2.50
308 Wade Blasingame 1.00 2.50
309 Walt Williams 1.00 2.50
310 Tom Haller 1.00 2.50
311 Sparky Lyle RC 4.00 10.00
312 Lee Elia 1.00 2.50
313 Bill Robinson 1.50 4.00
314 Checklist 4 2.50 6.00
Don Drysdale
315 Eddie Fisher 1.00 2.50
316 Hal Lanier 1.00 2.50
317 Bruce Look RC 1.00 2.50
318 Jack Fisher 1.00 2.50
319 Ken McMullen UER 1.00 2.50
(Headings on back
are for a pitcher)
320 Dal Maxvill 1.00 2.50
321 Jim McAndrew RC 1.50 4.00
322 Jose Vidal 1.50 4.00
323 Larry Miller 1.00 2.50
324 Rookie Stars 1.50 4.00
Les Cain RC
Dave Campbell RC
325 Jose Cardenal 1.50 4.00
326 Gary Sutherland 1.50 4.00
327 Willie Crawford 1.00 2.50
328 Joel Horlen .60 1.50
329 Rick Joseph .60 1.50
330 Tony Conigliaro 1.50 4.00
331 Rookie Stars 1.00 2.50
Gil Garrido
Tom House RC
332 Fred Talbot .60 1.50
333 Ivan Murrell .60 1.50
334 Phil Roof .60 1.50
335 Bill Mazeroski 2.50 6.00
336 Jim Roland .60 1.50
337 Marty Martinez RC .60 1.50
338 Del Unser RC .60 1.50
339 Rookie Stars .60 1.50
Steve Mingori RC
Jose Pena RC
340 Dave McNally 1.00 2.50
341 Dave Adlesh .60 1.50
342 Bubba Morton .60 1.50
343 Dan Frisella .60 1.50
344 Tom Matchick .60 1.50
345 Frank Linzy .60 1.50
346 Wayne Comer RC .60 1.50
347 Randy Hundley 1.00 2.50
348 Steve Hargan .60 1.50
349 Dick Williams MG 1.00 2.50
350 Richie Allen 1.50 4.00
351 Carroll Sembera .60 1.50
352 Paul Schaal 1.00 2.50
353 Jeff Torborg 1.00 2.50
354 Nate Oliver .60 1.50
355 Phil Niekro 2.50 6.00
356 Frank Quilici .60 1.50
357 Carl Taylor .60 1.50
358 Rookie Stars .60 1.50
George Lauzerique RC
Roberto Rodriquez
359 Dick Kelley .60 1.50
360 Jim Wynn 1.00 2.50
361 Gary Holman RC .60 1.50
362 Jim Maloney 1.00 2.50
363 Russ Nixon .60 1.50
364 Tommie Agee 1.50 4.00
365 Jim Fregosi 1.00 2.50
366 Bo Belinsky 1.00 2.50
367 Lou Johnson 1.00 2.50
368 Vic Roznovsky .60 1.50
369 Bob Skinner MG 1.00 2.50
370 Juan Marichal 3.00 8.00
371 Sal Bando 1.00 2.50
372 Adolfo Phillips .60 1.50
373 Fred Lasher .60 1.50
374 Bob Tillman .60 1.50
375 Harmon Killebrew 6.00 15.00
376 Rookie Stars .60 1.50
Mike Fiore RC
Jim Rooker RC
377 Gary Bell 1.00 2.50
378 Jose Herrera RC .60 1.50
379 Ken Boyer 1.00 2.50
380 Stan Bahnsen 1.00 2.50
381 Ed Kranepool 1.00 2.50
382 Pat Corrales 1.00 2.50
383 Casey Cox .60 1.50
384 Larry Shepard MG .60 1.50
385 Orlando Cepeda 2.50 6.00
386 Jim McGlothlin .60 1.50
387 Bobby Klaus .60 1.50
388 Tom McCraw .60 1.50
389 Dan Coombs .60 1.50
390 Bill Freehan 1.00 2.50
391 Ray Culp .60 1.50
392 Bob Burda RC .60 1.50
393 Gene Brabender 1.00 2.50
394 Rookie Stars 2.50 6.00
Lou Piniella
Marv Staehle
395 Chris Short .60 1.50
396 Jim Campanis .60 1.50
397 Chuck Dobson .60 1.50
398 Tito Francona .60 1.50
399 Bob Bailey 1.00 2.50
400 Don Drysdale 6.00 15.00
401 Jake Gibbs 1.00 2.50
402 Ken Boswell RC 1.00 2.50
403 Bob Miller .60 1.50
404 Rookie Stars 1.00 2.50
Vic LaRose RC
Gary Ross RC
405 Lee May 1.00 2.50
406 Phil Ortega .60 1.50
407 Tom Egan .60 1.50
408 Nate Colbert .60 1.50
409 Bob Moose .60 1.50
410 Al Kaline 10.00 25.00
411 Larry Dierker 1.00 2.50
412 Checklist 5 6.00 15.00
Mickey Mantle DP
413 Roland Sheldon 1.00 2.50
414 Duke Sims .60 1.50
415 Ray Washburn .60 1.50
416 Willie McCovey AS 3.00 8.00
417 Ken Harrelson AS 1.25 3.00
418 Tommy Helms AS 1.25 3.00

419 Rod Carew AS 4.00 10.00
420 Ron Santo AS 1.50 4.00
421 Brooks Robinson AS 3.00 8.00
422 Don Kessinger AS 1.25 3.00
423 Bert Campaneris AS 1.50 4.00
424 Pete Rose AS 6.00 15.00
425 Carl Yastrzemski AS 4.00 10.00
426 Curt Flood AS 1.50 4.00
427 Tony Oliva AS 1.50 4.00
428 Lou Brock AS 2.50 6.00
429 Willie Horton AS 1.25 3.00
430 Johnny Bench AS 4.00 10.00
431 Bill Freehan AS 1.50 4.00
432 Bob Gibson AS 2.50 6.00
433 Denny McLain AS 1.25 3.00
434 Jerry Koosman AS 1.25 3.00
435 Sam McDowell AS 1.00 2.50
436 Gene Alley 1.00 2.50
437 Luis Alcaraz RC .60 1.50
438 Gary Waslewski RC .60 1.50
439 Rookie Stars .60 1.50
Ed Herrmann RC
Dan Lazar RC
440A Willie McCovey 6.00 15.00
440B Willie McCovey WL 50.00 100.00
(McCovey white)
441A Dennis Higgins .60 1.50
441B Dennis Higgins WL 10.00 25.00
(Higgins white)
442 Ty Cline .60 1.50
443 Don Wert .60 1.50
444A Joe Moeller .60 1.50
444B Joe Moeller WL 10.00 25.00
(Moeller white)
445 Bobby Knoop .60 1.50
446 Claude Raymond .60 1.50
447A Ralph Houk MG 1.00 2.50
447B Ralph Houk MG WL 10.00 25.00
(Houk white)
448 Bob Tolan 1.00 2.50
449 Paul Lindblad .60 1.50
450 Billy Williams 3.00 8.00
451A Rich Rollins 1.00 2.50
451B Rich Rollins WL 10.00 25.00
(Rich and 3B white)
452A Al Ferrara .60 1.50
452B Al Ferrara WL 10.00 25.00
(Al and OF white)
453 Mike Cuellar 1.00 2.50
454A Rookie Stars 1.00 2.50
Larry Colton
Don Money RC
454B Rookie Stars 10.00 25.00
Larry Colton
Don Money
(Names in white) WL
455 Sonny Siebert .60 1.50
456 Bud Harrelson 1.00 2.50
457 Dalton Jones .60 1.50
458 Curt Blefary .60 1.50
459 Dave Boswell .60 1.50
460 Joe Torre 1.50 4.00
461A Mike Epstein .60 1.50
461B Mike Epstein WL 10.00 25.00
(Epstein white)
462 R.Schoendienst MG 1.00 2.50
463 Dennis Ribant .60 1.50
464A Dave Marshall RC .60 1.50
464B Dave Marshall WL 10.00 25.00
(Marshall white)
465 Tommy John 1.50 4.00
466 John Boccabella 1.00 2.50
467 Tommie Reynolds .60 1.50
468A Rookie Stars .60 1.50
Bruce Dal Canton RC
Bob Robertson
468B Rookie Stars 10.00 25.00
Bruce Dal Canton
Bob Robertson
(Names in white) WL
469 Chico Ruiz .60 1.50
470A Mel Stottlemyre 1.00 2.50
470B Mel Stottlemyre WL 12.50 30.00
(Stottlemyre white)
471A Ted Savage .60 1.50
471B Ted Savage WL 10.00 25.00
(Savage white)
472 Jim Price .60 1.50
473A Jose Arcia .60 1.50
473B Jose Arcia WL 10.00 25.00
(Jose and 2B white)
474 Tom Murphy RC .60 1.50
475 Tim McCarver 1.50 4.00
476A Rookie Stars 1.00 2.50
Ken Brett RC
Gerry Moses
476B Rookie Stars 12.50 30.00
Ken Brett
Gerry Moses
(Names in white) WL
477 Jeff James RC .60 1.50
478 Don Buford .60 1.50
479 Richie Scheinblum .60 1.50
480 Tom Seaver 40.00 80.00
481 Bill Melton RC 1.00 2.50
482A Jim Gosger .60 1.50
482B Jim Gosger WL 10.00 25.00
(Jim and OF white)
483 Ted Abernathy .60 1.50
484 Joe Gordon MG 1.00 2.50
485A Gaylord Perry 4.00 10.00
485B Gaylord Perry WL 40.00 80.00
(Perry white)
486A Paul Casanova .60 1.50
486B Paul Casanova WL 10.00 25.00
(Casanova white)
487 Denis Menke .60 1.50
488 Joe Sparma .60 1.50
489 Clete Boyer 1.00 2.50
490 Matty Alou 1.00 2.50
491A Rookie Stars .60 1.50
Jerry Crider RC
George Mitterwald
491B Rookie Stars 10.00 25.00
Jerry Crider
George Mitterwald
(Names in white) WL
492 Tony Cloninger .60 1.50
493A Wes Parker 1.00 2.50
493B Wes Parker WL 10.00 25.00
(Parker white)
494 Ken Berry .60 1.50
495 Bert Campaneris 1.00 2.50
496 Larry Jaster .60 1.50
497 Julian Javier 1.00 2.50
498 Juan Pizarro 1.00 2.50
499 Rookie Stars .60 1.50
Don Bryant RC
Steve Shea RC
500A Mickey Mantle UER 175.00 350.00
(No Topps copy-
right on card back)
500B Mickey Mantle WL 1000.00 2000.00
(Mantle in white;
no Topps copyright
on card back) UER
501A Tony Gonzalez 1.00 2.50
501B Tony Gonzalez WL 10.00 25.00
(Tony and OF white)
502 Minnie Rojas .60 1.50
503 Larry Brown .60 1.50
504 Checklist 6 3.00 8.00
Brooks Robinson
505A Bobby Bolin .60 1.50
505B Bobby Bolin WL 10.00 25.00
(Bolin white)
506 Paul Blair 1.00 2.50
507 Cookie Rojas 1.00 2.50
508 Moe Drabowsky 1.00 2.50
509 Manny Sanguillen 1.00 2.50
510 Rod Carew 15.00 40.00
511A Diego Segui 1.00 2.50
511B Diego Segui WL 10.00 25.00
(Diego and P white)
512 Cleon Jones 1.00 2.50
513 Camilo Pascual 1.25 3.00
514 Mike Lum .75 2.00
515 Dick Green .75 2.00
516 Earl Weaver MG RC 8.00 20.00
517 Mike McCormick 1.25 3.00
518 Fred Whitfield .75 2.00
519 Rookie Stars .75 2.00
Jerry Kenney RC
Len Boehmer RC
520 Bob Veale 1.25 3.00
521 George Thomas .75 2.00
522 Joe Hoerner .75 2.00
523 Bob Chance .75 2.00
524 Rookie Stars 1.25 3.00
Jose Laboy RC
Floyd Wicker RC
525 Earl Wilson 1.25 3.00
526 Hector Torres RC 1.25 3.00
527 Al Lopez MG 2.00 5.00
528 Claude Osteen 1.25 3.00
529 Ed Kirkpatrick 1.25 3.00
530 Cesar Tovar .75 2.00
531 Dick Farrell .75 2.00
532 Bird Hill Aces 1.25 3.00
Tom Phoebus
Jim Hardin
Dave McNally
Mike Cuellar
533 Nolan Ryan 100.00 200.00
534 Jerry McNertney 1.25 3.00
535 Phil Regan 1.25 3.00
536 Rookie Stars .75 2.00
Danny Breeden RC
Dave Roberts RC
537 Mike Paul RC .75 2.00
538 Charlie Smith .75 2.00
539 Ted Shows How 5.00 12.00
Mike Epstein
Ted Williams MG
540 Curt Flood 1.25 3.00
541 Joe Verbanic .75 2.00
542 Bob Aspromonte .75 2.00
543 Fred Newman .75 2.00
544 Rookie Stars .75 2.00
Mike Kilkenny RC
Ron Woods RC
545 Willie Stargell 5.00 12.00
546 Jim Nash .75 2.00
547 Billy Martin MG 2.00 5.00
548 Bob Locker .75 2.00
549 Ron Brand .75 2.00
550 Brooks Robinson 12.50 30.00
551 Wayne Granger RC .75 2.00
552 Rookie Stars 1.25 3.00
Ted Sizemore RC
Bill Sudakis RC
553 Ron Davis .75 2.00
554 Frank Bertaina .75 2.00
555 Jim Ray Hart 1.25 3.00
556 A's Stars 1.25 3.00
Sal Bando
Bert Campaneris
Danny Cater
557 Frank Fernandez .75 2.00
558 Tom Burgmeier RC 1.25 3.00
559 Rookie Stars .75 2.00
Joe Hague RC
Jim Hicks
560 Luis Tiant 1.25 3.00
561 Ron Clark .75 2.00
562 Bob Watson RC 3.00 8.00
563 Marty Pattin RC 1.25 3.00
564 Gil Hodges MG 4.00 10.00
565 Hoyt Wilhelm 3.00 8.00
566 Ron Hansen .75 2.00
567 Rookie Stars .75 2.00
Elvio Jimenez
Jim Shellenback
568 Cecil Upshaw .75 2.00
569 Billy Harris .60 1.50
570 Ron Santo 3.00 8.00
571 Cap Peterson .75 2.00
572 Giants Heroes 6.00 15.00
Willie McCovey
Juan Marichal
573 Jim Palmer 12.50 30.00
574 George Scott 1.25 3.00
575 Bill Singer 1.25 3.00
576 Rookie Stars .75 2.00
Ron Stone
Bill Wilson
577 Mike Hegan 1.25 3.00
578 Don Bosch .75 2.00
579 Dave Nelson RC .75 2.00
580 Jim Northrup 1.25 3.00
581 Gary Nolan 1.25 3.00
582A Checklist 7 2.50 6.00
Tony Oliva
White circle on back
582B Checklist 7 3.00 8.00
Tony Oliva
Red circle on back
583 Clyde Wright RC .75 2.00
584 Don Mason .75 2.00
585 Ron Swoboda 1.25 3.00
586 Tim Cullen .75 2.00
587 Joe Rudi RC 3.00 8.00
588 Bill White 1.25 3.00
589 Joe Pepitone 2.00 5.00
590 Rico Carty 2.00 5.00
591 Mike Hedlund 1.25 3.00
592 Rookie Stars 2.00 5.00
Rafael Robles RC
Al Santorini RC
593 Don Nottebart 1.25 3.00
594 Dooley Womack 1.25 3.00
595 Lee Maye 1.25 3.00
596 Chuck Hartenstein 1.25 3.00
597 Rookie Stars 15.00 40.00
Bob Floyd RC
Larry Burchart RC
Rollie Fingers RC
598 Ruben Amaro 1.25 3.00
599 John Boozer 1.25 3.00
600 Tony Oliva 3.00 8.00
601 Tug McGraw 3.00 8.00
602 Rookie Stars 2.00 5.00
Alec Distaso RC
Don Young
Jim Qualls RC
603 Joe Keough RC 1.25 3.00
604 Bobby Etheridge 1.25 3.00
605 Dick Ellsworth 1.25 3.00
606 Gene Mauch MG 2.00 5.00
607 Dick Bosman 1.25 3.00
608 Dick Simpson 1.25 3.00
609 Phil Gagliano 1.25 3.00
610 Jim Hardin 1.25 3.00
611 Rookie Stars 2.00 5.00
Bob Didier RC
Walt Hriniak RC
Gary Neibauer RC
612 Jack Aker 2.00 5.00
613 Jim Beauchamp 1.25 3.00
614 Rookie Stars 1.25 3.00
Tom Griffin RC
Skip Guinn RC
615 Len Gabrielson 1.25 3.00
616 Don McMahon 1.25 3.00
617 Jesse Gonder 1.25 3.00
618 Ramon Webster 1.25 3.00
619 Rookie Stars 2.00 5.00
Bill Butler RC
Pat Kelly RC
Juan Rios RC
620 Dean Chance 2.00 5.00
621 Bill Voss 1.25 3.00
622 Dan Osinski 1.25 3.00
623 Hank Allen 1.25 3.00
624 Rookie Stars 2.00 5.00
Darrel Chaney RC
Duffy Dyer RC
Terry Harmon RC
625 Mack Jones UER 2.00 5.00
(Batting wrong)
626 Gene Michael 2.00 5.00
627 George Stone RC 1.25 3.00
628 Rookie Stars 2.00 5.00
Bill Conigliaro RC
Syd O'Brien RC
Fred Wenz RC
629 Jack Hamilton 1.25 3.00
630 Bobby Bonds RC 12.50 30.00
631 John Kennedy 2.00 5.00
632 Jon Warden RC 1.25 3.00
633 Harry Walker MG 1.25 3.00
634 Andy Etchebarren 1.25 3.00
635 George Culver 1.25 3.00
636 Woody Held 1.25 3.00
637 Rookie Stars 2.00 5.00
Jerry DaVanon RC
Frank Reberger RC
Clay Kirby RC
638 Ed Sprague RC 1.25 3.00
639 Barry Moore 1.25 3.00
640 Ferguson Jenkins 8.00 20.00
641 Rookie Stars 2.00 5.00
Bobby Darwin RC
John Miller
Tommy Dean RC
642 John Hiller 1.25 3.00
643 Billy Cowan 1.25 3.00
644 Chuck Hinton 1.25 3.00
645 George Brunet 1.25 3.00
646 Rookie Stars 2.00 5.00
Dan McGinn RC
Carl Morton RC
647 Dave Wickersham 1.25 3.00
648 Bobby Wine 2.00 5.00
649 Al Jackson 1.25 3.00
650 Ted Williams MG 8.00 20.00
651 Gus Gil 2.00 5.00
652 Eddie Watt 1.25 3.00
653 Aurelio Rodriguez RC 2.00 5.00
UER Photo is
Angels batboy Leonard Garcia
654 Rookie Stars 2.00 5.00
Carlos May RC
Don Secrist RC
Rich Morales RC
655 Mike Hershberger 1.25 3.00
656 Dan Schneider 1.25 3.00
657 Bobby Murcer 3.00 8.00
658 Rookie Stars 1.25 3.00
Tom Hall RC
Bill Burbach RC
Jim Miles RC
659 Johnny Podres 2.00 5.00
660 Reggie Smith 2.00 5.00
661 Jim Merritt 1.25 3.00
662 Rookie Stars 2.00 5.00
Dick Drago RC
George Spriggs
Bob Oliver RC
663 Dick Radatz 2.00 5.00
664 Ron Hunt 2.00 5.00

1970 Topps

The cards in this 720-card set measure 2 1/2" by 3 1/2". The Topps set for 1970 has color photos surrounded by white frame lines and gray borders. The backs have a blue biographical section and a yellow record section. All-Star selections are featured on cards 450 to 469. Other topical subsets within this set include League Leaders (61-72), Playoffs cards (195-202), and World Series cards (305-310). There are graduations of scarcity, terminating in the high series (634-720), which are outlined in the value summary. Cards were issued in ten-card dime packs as well as thirty-three card cello packs which sold for a quarter and were encased in a small Topps box, and in 54-card rack packs which sold for 39 cents. The key Rookie Card in this set is Thurman Munson.

COMPLETE SET (720) 1000.00 2000.00
COMMON CARD (1-132) .30 .75
COMMON (133-372) .40 1.00
COMMON CARD (373-459) .60 1.50
COMMON (460-546) .75 2.00
COMMON (547-633) 1.50 4.00
COMMON (634-720) 4.00 10.00
WRAPPER (10-CENT) 8.00 20.00
1 New York Mets TC 12.50 30.00
2 Diego Segui .40 1.00
3 Darrel Chaney .30 .75
4 Tom Egan .30 .75
5 Wes Parker .40 1.00
6 Grant Jackson .30 .75
7 Rookie Stars .30 .75
Gary Boyd RC
Russ Nagelson RC
8 Jose Martinez RC .30 .75
9 Checklist 1 5.00 12.00
10 Carl Yastrzemski 8.00 20.00
11 Nate Colbert .30 .75
12 John Hiller .30 .75
13 Jack Hiatt .30 .75
14 Hank Allen .30 .75
15 Larry Dierker .30 .75
16 Charlie Metro MG RC .30 .75
17 Hoyt Wilhelm 1.50 4.00
18 Carlos May .40 1.00
19 John Boccabella .30 .75
20 Dave McNally .40 1.00
21 Rookie Stars 1.50 4.00
Vida Blue RC
Gene Tenace RC
22 Ray Washburn .30 .75
23 Bill Robinson .40 1.00
24 Dick Selma .30 .75
25 Cesar Tovar .30 .75
26 Tug McGraw .75 2.00
27 Chuck Hinton .30 .75
28 Billy Wilson .30 .75
29 Sandy Alomar .40 1.00
30 Matty Alou .40 1.00
31 Marty Pattin .40 1.00
32 Harry Walker MG .30 .75
33 Don Wert .30 .75
34 Willie Crawford .30 .75
35 Joel Horlen .30 .75
36 Rookie Stars .40 1.00
Danny Breeden
Bernie Carbo RC
37 Dick Drago .30 .75
38 Mack Jones .30 .75
39 Mike Nagy RC .30 .75
40 Rich Allen .75 2.00
41 George Lauzerique .30 .75
42 Tito Fuentes .30 .75
43 Jack Aker .30 .75
44 Roberto Pena .30 .75
45 Dave Johnson .40 1.00
46 Ken Rudolph RC .30 .75
47 Bob Miller .30 .75
48 Gil Garrido .30 .75
49 Tim Cullen .30 .75
50 Tommie Agee .40 1.00
51 Bob Christian .30 .75
52 Bruce Dal Canton .30 .75
53 John Kennedy .30 .75
54 Jeff Torborg .40 1.00
55 John Odom .30 .75
56 Rookie Stars .30 .75
Joe Lis RC
Scott Reid RC
57 Pat Kelly .30 .75
58 Dave Marshall .30 .75
59 Dick Ellsworth .30 .75
60 Jim Wynn .40 1.00
61 NL Batting Leaders 5.00 12.00
Pete Rose
Bob Clemente
Cleon Jones
62 AL Batting Leaders .75 2.00
Rod Carew
Reggie Smith
Tony Oliva
63 NL RBI Leaders .75 2.00
Willie McCovey
Ron Santo
Tony Perez
64 AL RBI Leaders 1.50 4.00
Harmon Killebrew
Boog Powell
Reggie Jackson
65 NL Home Run Leaders 1.50 4.00
Willie McCovey
Hank Aaron
Lee May
66 AL Home Run Leaders 1.50 4.00
Harmon Killebrew
Frank Howard
Reggie Jackson
67 NL ERA Leaders 1.50 4.00
Juan Marichal
Steve Carlton
Bob Gibson
68 AL ERA Leaders .40 1.00
Dick Bosman
Jim Palmer
Mike Cuellar
69 NL Pitching Leaders 1.50 4.00
Tom Seaver
Phil Niekro
Fergie Jenkins
Juan Marichal
70 AL Pitching Leaders .40 1.00
Dennis McLain
Mike Cuellar
Dave Boswell
Dave McNally
Jim Perry
Mel Stottlemyre
71 NL Strikeout Leaders .75 2.00
Fergie Jenkins
Bob Gibson
Bill Singer
72 AL Strikeout Leaders .40 1.00
Sam McDowell
Mickey Lolich
Andy Messersmith
73 Wayne Granger .30 .75
74 Rookie Stars .30 .75
Greg Washburn RC
Wally Wolf
75 Jim Kaat .40 1.00
76 Carl Taylor UER .30 .75
Collecting is spelled incorrectly in the cartoon
77 Frank Linzy .30 .75
78 Joe Lahoud .30 .75
79 Clay Kirby .30 .75
80 Don Kessinger .40 1.00
81 Dave May .30 .75
82 Frank Fernandez .30 .75
83 Don Cardwell .30 .75
84 Paul Casanova .30 .75
85 Max Alvis .30 .75
86 Lum Harris MG .30 .75
87 Steve Renko RC .30 .75
88 Rookie Stars .40 1.00
Miguel Fuentes RC
Dick Baney RC
89 Juan Rios .30 .75
90 Tim McCarver .40 1.00
91 Rich Morales .30 .75
92 George Culver .30 .75
93 Rick Renick .30 .75
94 Freddie Patek .40 1.00
95 Earl Wilson .40 1.00
96 Rookie Stars .40 1.00
Leron Lee RC
Jerry Reuss RC
97 Joe Moeller .30 .75
98 Gates Brown .40 1.00
99 Bobby Pfeil RC .30 .75
100 Mel Stottlemyre .40 1.00
101 Bobby Floyd .30 .75
102 Joe Rudi .40 1.00
103 Frank Reberger .30 .75
104 Gerry Moses .30 .75
105 Tony Gonzalez .30 .75
106 Darold Knowles .30 .75
107 Bobby Etheridge .30 .75
108 Tom Burgmeier .30 .75
109 Rookie Stars .30 .75
Garry Jestadt RC
Carl Morton
110 Bob Moose .30 .75
111 Mike Hegan .40 1.00
112 Dave Nelson .30 .75
113 Jim Ray .30 .75
114 Gene Michael .40 1.00
115 Alex Johnson .40 1.00
116 Sparky Lyle .40 1.00
117 Don Young .30 .75
118 George Mitterwald .30 .75
119 Chuck Taylor RC .30 .75
120 Sal Bando .40 1.00
121 Rookie Stars .30 .75
Fred Beene RC
Terry Crowley RC
122 George Stone .30 .75
123 Don Gutteridge MG RC .30 .75
124 Larry Jaster .30 .75
125 Deron Johnson .30 .75
126 Marty Martinez .30 .75
127 Joe Coleman .30 .75
128A Checklist 2 ERR 2.50 6.00
(226 R Perranoski)
128B Checklist 2 COR 2.50 6.00
(226 R. Perranoski)
129 Jimmie Price .30 .75
130 Ollie Brown .30 .75
131 Rookie Stars .30 .75
Ray Lamb RC
Bob Stinson RC
132 Jim McGlothlin .30 .75
133 Clay Carroll .40 1.00
134 Danny Walton RC .40 1.00
135 Dick Dietz .40 1.00
136 Steve Hargan .40 1.00
137 Art Shamsky .40 1.00
138 Joe Foy .40 1.00
139 Rich Nye .40 1.00
140 Reggie Jackson 20.00 50.00
141 Rookie Stars .60 1.50
Dave Cash RC
Johnny Jeter RC
142 Fritz Peterson .40 1.00
143 Phil Gagliano .40 1.00
144 Ray Culp .40 1.00
145 Rico Carty .60 1.50
146 Danny Murphy .40 1.00
147 Angel Hermoso RC .40 1.00
148 Earl Weaver MG 1.25 3.00
149 Billy Champion RC .40 1.00
150 Harmon Killebrew 3.00 8.00
151 Dave Roberts .40 1.00
152 Ike Brown RC .40 1.00
153 Gary Gentry .40 1.00
154 Rookie Stars .40 1.00
Jim Miles
Jan Dukes RC
155 Denis Menke .40 1.00
156 Eddie Fisher .40 1.00
157 Manny Mota .60 1.50
158 Jerry McNertney .60 1.50
159 Tommy Helms .60 1.50
160 Phil Niekro 2.00 5.00
161 Richie Scheinblum .40 1.00
162 Jerry Johnson .40 1.00
163 Syd O'Brien .40 1.00
164 Ty Cline .40 1.00
165 Ed Kirkpatrick .40 1.00
166 Al Oliver 1.25 3.00
167 Bill Burbach .40 1.00
168 Dave Watkins RC .40 1.00
169 Tom Hall .40 1.00
170 Billy Williams 2.00 5.00
171 Jim Nash .40 1.00
172 Rookie Stars .60 1.50
Garry Hill RC
Ralph Garr RC
173 Jim Hicks .40 1.00
174 Ted Sizemore .60 1.50
175 Dick Bosman .40 1.00
176 Jim Ray Hart .60 1.50
177 Jim Northrup .60 1.50
178 Denny Lemaster .40 1.00
179 Ivan Murrell .40 1.00
180 Tommy John .60 1.50
181 Sparky Anderson MG 2.00 5.00
182 Dick Hall .40 1.00
183 Jerry Grote .60 1.50
184 Ray Fosse .60 1.50
185 Don Mincher .60 1.50
186 Rick Joseph .40 1.00
187 Mike Hedlund .40 1.00
188 Manny Sanguillen .60 1.50
189 Rookie Stars 50.00 100.00
Thurman Munson RC
Dave McDonald RC
190 Joe Torre 1.25 3.00
191 Vicente Romo .40 1.00
192 Jim Qualls .40 1.00
193 Mike Wegener .40 1.00
194 Chuck Manuel RC .40 1.00
195 NL Playoff Game 1 6.00 15.00
Tom Seaver
196 NL Playoff Game 2 .75 2.00
Ken Boswell
197 NL Playoff Game 3 12.50 30.00
Nolan Ryan
198 NL Playoff Summary 6.00 15.00
Mets Celebrate
(w/Nolan Ryan
199 AL Playoff Game 1 .75 2.00
Mike Cuellar
200 AL Playoff Game 2 1.25 3.00
Boog Powell
Scoring over George Mitterwald
201 AL Playoff Game 3 .75 2.00
Boog Powell
Andy Etchebarren
202 AL Playoff Summary .75 2.00
Orioles Celebrate
203 Rudy May .40 1.00
204 Len Gabrielson .40 1.00
205 Bert Campaneris .60 1.50
206 Clete Boyer .60 1.50
207 Rookie Stars .40 1.00
Norman McRae RC
Bob Reed RC
208 Fred Gladding .40 1.00
209 Ken Suarez .40 1.00
210 Juan Marichal 2.00 5.00
211 Ted Williams MG UER 6.00 15.00
Throwing information on back incorrect
212 Al Santorini .40 1.00
213 Andy Etchebarren .40 1.00
214 Ken Boswell .40 1.00
215 Reggie Smith .60 1.50
216 Chuck Hartenstein .40 1.00
217 Ron Hansen .40 1.00
218 Ron Stone .40 1.00
219 Jerry Kenney .40 1.00
220 Steve Carlton 6.00 15.00
221 Ron Brand .40 1.00
222 Jim Rooker .40 1.00
223 Nate Oliver .40 1.00
224 Steve Barber .60 1.50
225 Lee May .60 1.50
226 Ron Perranoski .40 1.00
227 Rookie Stars .60 1.50
John Mayberry RC
Bob Watkins RC
228 Aurelio Rodriguez .40 1.00
229 Rich Robertson .40 1.00
230 Brooks Robinson 6.00 15.00
231 Luis Tiant .60 1.50
232 Bob Didier .40 1.00
233 Lew Krausse .40 1.00
234 Tommy Dean .40 1.00
235 Mike Epstein .40 1.00
236 Bob Veale .40 1.00
237 Russ Gibson .40 1.00
238 Jose Laboy .40 1.00
239 Ken Berry .40 1.00
240 Ferguson Jenkins 2.00 5.00
241 Rookie Stars .40 1.00
Al Fitzmorris RC
Scott Northey RC
242 Walter Alston MG 1.25 3.00
243 Joe Sparma .40 1.00
244A Checklist 3 2.50 6.00
(Red bat on front)
244B Checklist 3 2.50 6.00
(Brown bat on front)
245 Leo Cardenas .40 1.00
246 Jim McAndrew .40 1.00
247 Lou Klimchock .40 1.00
248 Jesus Alou .40 1.00
249 Bob Locker .40 1.00
250 Willie McCovey UER 4.00 10.00
(1963 San Francisci)
251 Dick Schofield .40 1.00
252 Lowell Palmer RC .40 1.00
253 Ron Woods .40 1.00
254 Camilo Pascual .40 1.00
255 Jim Spencer RC .40 1.00
256 Vic Davalillo .40 1.00
257 Dennis Higgins .40 1.00
258 Paul Popovich .40 1.00
259 Tommie Reynolds .40 1.00
260 Claude Osteen .40 1.00

261 Curt Motton	.40	1.00
262 Rookie Stars	.40	1.00
Jerry Morales RC		
Jim Williams RC		
263 Duane Josephson	.40	1.00
264 Rich Hebner	.40	1.00
265 Randy Hundley	.40	1.00
266 Wally Bunker	.40	1.00
267 Rookie Stars	.40	1.00
Herman Hill RC		
Paul Ratliff		
268 Claude Raymond	.40	1.00
269 Cesar Gutierrez	.40	1.00
270 Chris Short	.40	1.00
271 Greg Goossen	.60	1.50
272 Hector Torres	.40	1.00
273 Ralph Houk MG	.60	1.50
274 Gerry Arrigo	.40	1.00
275 Duke Sims	.40	1.00
276 Ron Hunt	.40	1.00
277 Paul Doyle RC	.40	1.00
278 Tommie Aaron	.40	1.00
279 Bill Lee RC	.60	1.50
280 Donn Clendenon	.60	1.50
281 Casey Cox	.40	1.00
282 Steve Huntz	.40	1.00
283 Angel Bravo RC	.40	1.00
284 Jack Baldschun	.40	1.00
285 Paul Blair	.60	1.50
286 Rookie Stars	2.00	5.00
Jack Jenkins RC		
Bill Buckner RC		
287 Fred Talbot	.40	1.00
288 Larry Hisle	.60	1.50
289 Gene Brabender	.40	1.00
290 Rod Carew	6.00	15.00
291 Leo Durocher MG	1.25	3.00
292 Eddie Leon RC	.40	1.00
293 Bob Bailey	.60	1.50
294 Jose Azcue	.40	1.00
295 Cecil Upshaw	.40	1.00
296 Woody Woodward	.40	1.00
297 Curt Blefary	.40	1.00
298 Ken Henderson	.40	1.00
299 Buddy Bradford	.40	1.00
300 Tom Seaver	12.50	30.00
301 Chico Salmon	.40	1.00
302 Jeff James	.40	1.00
303 Brant Alyea	.40	1.00
304 Bill Russell RC	2.00	5.00
305 World Series Game 1	1.50	4.00
Don Buford		
306 World Series Game 2	1.50	4.00
Donn Clendenon		
307 World Series Game 3	1.50	4.00
Tommie Agee		
308 World Series Game 4	1.50	4.00
J.C. Martin		
309 World Series Game 5	1.50	4.00
Jerry Koosman		
310 World Series Summary	2.00	5.00
Mets Whoop it Up		
311 Dick Green	.40	1.00
312 Mike Torrez	.40	1.00
313 Mayo Smith MG	.40	1.00
314 Bill McCool	.40	1.00
315 Luis Aparicio	2.00	5.00
316 Skip Guinn	.40	1.00
317 Rookie Stars	.60	1.50
Billy Conigliaro		
Luis Alvarado RC		
318 Willie Smith	.40	1.00
319 Clay Dalrymple	.40	1.00
320 Jim Maloney	.60	1.50
321 Lou Piniella	.60	1.50
322 Luke Walker	.40	1.00
323 Wayne Comer	.40	1.00
324 Tony Taylor	.60	1.50
325 Dave Boswell	.40	1.00
326 Bill Voss	.40	1.00
327 Hal King RC	.40	1.00
328 George Brunet	.40	1.00
329 Chris Cannizzaro	.40	1.00
330 Lou Brock	4.00	10.00
331 Chuck Dobson	.40	1.00
332 Bobby Wine	.40	1.00
333 Bobby Murcer	.60	1.50
334 Phil Regan	.40	1.00
335 Bill Freehan	.60	1.50
336 Del Unser	.40	1.00
337 Mike McCormick	.60	1.50
338 Paul Schaal	.40	1.00
339 Johnny Edwards	.40	1.00
340 Tony Conigliaro	1.25	3.00
341 Bill Sudakis	.40	1.00
342 Wilbur Wood	.60	1.50
343A Checklist 4	2.50	6.00
(Red bat on front)		
343B Checklist 4	2.50	6.00
(Brown bat on front)		
344 Marcelino Lopez	.40	1.00
345 Al Ferrara	.40	1.00
346 Red Schoendienst MG	.60	1.50
347 Russ Snyder	.40	1.00
348 Rookie Stars	.60	1.50
Mike Jorgensen RC		
Jesse Hudson RC		
349 Steve Hamilton	.40	1.00
350 Roberto Clemente	30.00	60.00
351 Tom Murphy	.40	1.00
352 Bob Barton	.40	1.00
353 Stan Williams	.40	1.00
354 Amos Otis	.60	1.50
355 Doug Rader	.40	1.00
356 Fred Lasher	.40	1.00
357 Bob Burda	.40	1.00
358 Pedro Borbon RC	.60	1.50
359 Phil Roof	.40	1.00
360 Curt Flood	.60	1.50
361 Ray Jarvis	.40	1.00
362 Joe Hague	.40	1.00
363 Tom Shopay RC	.40	1.00
364 Dan McGinn	.40	1.00
365 Zoilo Versalles	.40	1.00
366 Barry Moore	.40	1.00
367 Mike Lum	.40	1.00
368 Ed Herrmann	.40	1.00
369 Alan Foster	.40	1.00
370 Tommy Harper	.60	1.50
371 Rod Gaspar RC	.40	1.00
372 Dave Giusti	.40	1.00
373 Roy White	.75	2.00
374 Tommie Sisk	.60	1.50
375 Johnny Callison	.75	2.00
376 Lefty Phillips MG RC	.60	1.50
377 Bill Butler	.60	1.50
378 Jim Davenport	.60	1.50
379 Tom Tischinski RC	.60	1.50
380 Tony Perez	2.50	6.00
381 Rookie Stars	.60	1.50
Bobby Brooks RC		
Mike Olivo RC		
382 Jack DiLauro RC	.60	1.50
383 Mickey Stanley	.75	2.00
384 Gary Neibauer	.60	1.50
385 George Scott	.75	2.00
386 Bill Dillman	.60	1.50
387 Baltimore Orioles TC	1.25	3.00
388 Byron Browne	.60	1.50
389 Jim Shellenback	.60	1.50
390 Willie Davis	.75	2.00
391 Larry Brown	.60	1.50
392 Walt Hriniak	.75	2.00
393 John Gelnar	.60	1.50
394 Gil Hodges MG	1.50	4.00
395 Walt Williams	.60	1.50
396 Steve Blass	.75	2.00
397 Roger Repoz	.60	1.50
398 Bill Stoneman	.60	1.50
399 New York Yankees TC	1.25	3.00
400 Denny McLain	1.50	4.00
401 Rookie Stars	.60	1.50
John Harrell RC		
Bernie Williams RC		
402 Ellie Rodriguez	.60	1.50
403 Jim Bunning	2.50	6.00
404 Rich Reese	.60	1.50
405 Bill Hands	.60	1.50
406 Mike Andrews	.60	1.50
407 Bob Watson	.75	2.00
408 Paul Lindblad	.60	1.50
409 Bob Tolan	.60	1.50
410 Boog Powell	1.50	4.00
411 Los Angeles Dodgers TC	1.25	3.00
412 Larry Burchart	.60	1.50
413 Sonny Jackson	.60	1.50
414 Paul Edmondson RC	.60	1.50
415 Julian Javier	.75	2.00
416 Joe Verbanic	.60	1.50
417 John Bateman	.60	1.50
418 John Donaldson	.60	1.50
419 Ron Taylor	.60	1.50
420 Ken McMullen	.75	2.00
421 Pat Dobson	.75	2.00
422 Kansas City Royals TC	1.25	3.00
423 Jerry May	.60	1.50
424 Mike Kilkenny	.60	1.50
(Inconsistent design		
card number in		
white circle)		
425 Bobby Bonds	2.50	6.00
426 Bill Rigney MG	.60	1.50
427 Fred Norman	.60	1.50
428 Don Buford	.60	1.50
429 Rookie Stars	.60	1.50
Randy Bobb RC		
Jim Cosman		
430 Andy Messersmith	.75	2.00
431 Ron Swoboda	.75	2.00
432A Checklist 5	2.50	6.00
(Baseball in		
yellow letters)		
432B Checklist 5	2.50	6.00
(Baseball in		
white letters)		
433 Ron Bryant RC	.60	1.50
434 Felipe Alou	.75	2.00
435 Nelson Briles	.75	2.00
436 Philadelphia Phillies TC	1.25	3.00
437 Danny Cater	.60	1.50
438 Pat Jarvis	.60	1.50
439 Lee Maye	.60	1.50
440 Bill Mazeroski	2.50	6.00
441 John O'Donoghue	.60	1.50
442 Gene Mauch MG	.75	2.00
443 Al Jackson	.60	1.50
444 Rookie Stars	.60	1.50
Billy Farmer RC		
John Matias RC		
445 Vada Pinson	.75	2.00
446 Billy Grabarkewitz RC	.60	1.50
447 Lee Stange	.60	1.50
448 Houston Astros TC	1.25	3.00
449 Jim Palmer	5.00	12.00
450 Willie McCovey AS	2.50	6.00
451 Boog Powell AS	1.50	4.00
452 Felix Millan AS	.75	2.00
453 Rod Carew AS	2.50	6.00
454 Ron Santo AS	1.50	4.00
455 Brooks Robinson AS	2.50	6.00
456 Don Kessinger AS	.75	2.00
457 Rico Petrocelli AS	1.50	4.00
458 Pete Rose AS	6.00	15.00
459 Reggie Jackson AS	5.00	12.00
460 Matty Alou AS	1.25	3.00
461 Carl Yastrzemski AS	4.00	10.00
462 Hank Aaron AS	6.00	15.00
463 Frank Robinson AS	3.00	8.00
464 Johnny Bench AS	6.00	15.00
465 Bill Freehan AS	1.25	3.00
466 Juan Marichal AS	2.00	5.00
467 Denny McLain AS	1.25	3.00
468 Jerry Koosman AS	1.25	3.00
469 Sam McDowell AS	1.25	3.00
470 Willie Stargell	4.00	10.00
471 Chris Zachary	.75	2.00
472 Atlanta Braves TC	1.50	4.00
473 Don Bryant	.75	2.00
474 Dick Kelley	.75	2.00
475 Dick McAuliffe	1.25	3.00
476 Don Shaw	.75	2.00
477 Rookie Stars	.75	2.00
Al Severinsen RC		
Roger Freed RC		
478 Bobby Heise RC	.75	2.00
479 Dick Woodson RC	.75	2.00
480 Glenn Beckert	1.25	3.00
481 Jose Tartabull	.75	2.00
482 Tom Hilgendorf RC	.75	2.00
483 Gail Hopkins RC	.75	2.00
484 Gary Nolan	1.25	3.00
485 Jay Johnstone	1.25	3.00
486 Terry Harmon	.75	2.00
487 Cisco Carlos	.75	2.00
488 J.C. Martin	.75	2.00
489 Eddie Kasko MG	.75	2.00
490 Bill Singer	1.25	3.00
491 Graig Nettles	2.00	5.00
492 Rookie Stars	.75	2.00
Keith Lampard RC		
Scipio Spinks RC		
493 Lindy McDaniel	1.25	3.00
494 Larry Stahl	.75	2.00
495 Dave Morehead	.75	2.00
496 Steve Whitaker	.75	2.00
497 Eddie Watt	.75	2.00
498 Al Weis	.75	2.00
499 Skip Lockwood	1.25	3.00
500 Hank Aaron	20.00	50.00
501 Chicago White Sox TC	1.50	4.00
502 Rollie Fingers	4.00	10.00
503 Dal Maxvill	.75	2.00
504 Don Pavletich	.75	2.00
505 Ken Holtzman	1.25	3.00
506 Ed Stroud	.75	2.00
507 Pat Corrales	.75	2.00
508 Joe Niekro	1.25	3.00
509 Montreal Expos TC	1.50	4.00
510 Tony Oliva	2.00	5.00
511 Joe Hoerner	.75	2.00
512 Billy Harris	.75	2.00
513 Preston Gomez MG	.75	2.00
514 Steve Hovley RC	.75	2.00
515 Don Wilson	1.25	3.00
516 Rookie Stars	.75	2.00
John Ellis RC		
Jim Lyttle RC		
517 Joe Gibbon	.75	2.00
518 Bill Melton	.75	2.00
519 Don McMahon	.75	2.00
520 Willie Horton	1.25	3.00
521 Cal Koonce	.75	2.00
522 California Angels TC	1.50	4.00
523 Jose Pena	.75	2.00
524 Alvin Dark MG	1.25	3.00
525 Jerry Adair	.75	2.00
526 Ron Herbel	.75	2.00
527 Don Bosch	.75	2.00
528 Elrod Hendricks	.75	2.00
529 Bob Aspromonte	.75	2.00
530 Bob Gibson	6.00	15.00
531 Ron Clark	.75	2.00
532 Danny Murtaugh MG	1.25	3.00
533 Buzz Stephen RC	.75	2.00
534 Minnesota Twins TC	1.50	4.00
535 Andy Kosco	.75	2.00
536 Mike Kekich	.75	2.00
537 Joe Morgan	4.00	10.00
538 Bob Humphreys	.75	2.00
539 Rookie Stars	3.00	8.00
Denny Doyle RC		
Larry Bowa RC		
540 Gary Peters	.75	2.00
541 Bill Heath	.75	2.00
542A Checklist 6	2.50	6.00
Brown Bat on Front		
543 Clyde Wright	.75	2.00
544 Cincinnati Reds TC	1.50	4.00
545 Ken Harrelson	.75	2.00
546 Ron Reed	.75	2.00
547 Rick Monday	2.50	6.00
548 Howie Reed	1.50	4.00
549 St. Louis Cardinals TC	2.50	6.00
550 Frank Howard	2.50	6.00
551 Dock Ellis	2.50	6.00
552 Rookie Stars	1.50	4.00
Don O'Riley RC		
Dennis Paepke RC		
Fred Rico RC		
553 Jim Lefebvre	2.50	6.00
554 Tom Timmermann RC	1.50	4.00
555 Orlando Cepeda	5.00	12.00
556 Dave Bristol MG	2.50	6.00
557 Ed Kranepool	2.50	6.00
558 Vern Fuller	1.50	4.00
559 Tommy Davis	2.50	6.00
560 Gaylord Perry	5.00	12.00
561 Tom McCraw	1.50	4.00
562 Ted Abernathy	1.50	4.00
563 Boston Red Sox TC	2.50	6.00
564 Johnny Briggs	1.50	4.00
565 Jim Hunter	5.00	12.00
566 Gene Alley	2.50	6.00
567 Bob Oliver	1.50	4.00
568 Stan Bahnsen	2.50	6.00
569 Cookie Rojas	2.50	6.00
570 Jim Fregosi	2.50	6.00
White Chevy Pick-Up in Background		
571 Jim Brewer	1.50	4.00
572 Frank Quilici	1.50	4.00
573 Rookie Stars	1.50	4.00
Mike Corkins RC		
Rafael Robles		
Ron Slocum RC		
574 Bobby Bolin	2.50	6.00
575 Cleon Jones	2.50	6.00
576 Milt Pappas	2.50	6.00
577 Bernie Allen	1.50	4.00
578 Tom Griffin	1.50	4.00
579 Detroit Tigers TC	2.50	6.00
580 Pete Rose	30.00	60.00
581 Tom Satriano	1.50	4.00
582 Mike Paul	1.50	4.00
583 Hal Lanier	1.50	4.00
584 Al Downing	2.50	6.00
585 Rusty Staub	3.00	8.00
586 Rickey Clark RC	1.50	4.00
587 Jose Arcia	1.50	4.00
588A Checklist 7 ERR	3.00	8.00
(666 Adolfo)		
588B Checklist 7 COR	2.50	6.00
(666 Adolpho)		
589 Joe Keough	1.50	4.00
590 Mike Cuellar	2.50	6.00
591 Mike Ryan UER	1.50	4.00
(Pitching Record		
header on card back)		
592 Daryl Patterson	1.50	4.00
593 Chicago Cubs TC	3.00	8.00
594 Jake Gibbs	1.50	4.00
595 Maury Wills	3.00	8.00
596 Mike Hershberger	2.50	6.00
597 Sonny Siebert	1.50	4.00
598 Joe Pepitone	2.50	6.00
599 Rookie Stars	1.50	4.00
Dick Stelmaszek RC		
Gene Martin RC		
Dick Such RC		
600 Willie Mays	40.00	80.00
601 Pete Richert	1.50	4.00
602 Ted Savage	1.50	4.00
603 Ray Oyler	1.50	4.00
604 Clarence Gaston	2.50	6.00
605 Rick Wise	2.50	6.00
606 Chico Ruiz	1.50	4.00
607 Gary Waslewski	1.50	4.00
608 Pittsburgh Pirates TC	2.50	6.00
609 Buck Martinez RC	2.50	6.00
(Inconsistent design		
card number in		
white circle)		
610 Jerry Koosman	3.00	8.00
611 Norm Cash	2.50	6.00
612 Jim Hickman	2.50	6.00
613 Dave Baldwin	2.50	6.00
614 Mike Shannon	2.50	6.00
615 Mark Belanger	2.50	6.00
616 Jim Merritt	1.50	4.00
617 Jim French	1.50	4.00
618 Billy Wynne RC	1.50	4.00
619 Norm Miller	1.50	4.00
620 Jim Perry	2.50	6.00
621 Rookie Stars	5.00	12.00
Mike McQueen RC		
Darrell Evans RC		
Rick Kester RC		
622 Don Sutton	5.00	12.00
623 Horace Clarke	2.50	6.00
624 Clyde King MG	1.50	4.00
625 Dean Chance	1.50	4.00
626 Dave Ricketts	1.50	4.00
627 Gary Wagner	1.50	4.00
628 Wayne Garrett RC	1.50	4.00
629 Merv Rettenmund	1.50	4.00
630 Ernie Banks	20.00	50.00
631 Oakland Athletics TC	2.50	6.00
632 Gary Sutherland	1.50	4.00
633 Roger Nelson	1.50	4.00
634 Bud Harrelson	6.00	15.00
635 Bob Allison	6.00	15.00
636 Jim Stewart	4.00	10.00
637 Cleveland Indians TC	5.00	12.00
638 Frank Bertaina	4.00	10.00
639 Dave Campbell	6.00	15.00
640 Al Kaline	20.00	50.00
641 Al McBean	4.00	10.00
642 Rookie Stars	4.00	10.00
Greg Garrett RC		
Gordon Lund RC		
Jarvis Tatum RC		
643 Jose Pagan	4.00	10.00
644 Gerry Nyman	4.00	10.00
645 Don Money	6.00	15.00
646 Jim Britton	4.00	10.00
647 Tom Matchick	4.00	10.00
648 Larry Haney	4.00	10.00
649 Jimmie Hall	4.00	10.00
650 Sam McDowell	6.00	15.00
651 Jim Gosger	4.00	10.00
652 Rich Rollins	6.00	15.00
653 Moe Drabowsky	4.00	10.00
654 Rookie Stars	6.00	15.00
Oscar Gamble RC		
Boots Day RC		
Angel Mangual RC		
655 John Roseboro	6.00	15.00
656 Jim Hardin	4.00	10.00
657 San Diego Padres TC	5.00	12.00
658 Ken Tatum RC	4.00	10.00
659 Pete Ward	4.00	10.00
660 Johnny Bench	40.00	80.00
661 Jerry Robertson	4.00	10.00
662 Frank Lucchesi MG RC	4.00	10.00
663 Tito Francona	4.00	10.00
664 Bob Robertson	4.00	10.00
665 Jim Lonborg	6.00	15.00
666 Adolpho Phillips	4.00	10.00
667 Bob Meyer	6.00	15.00
668 Bob Tillman	4.00	10.00
669 Rookie Stars	4.00	10.00
Bart Johnson RC		
Dan Lazar		
Mickey Scott RC		
670 Ron Santo	6.00	15.00
671 Jim Campanis	4.00	10.00
672 Leon McFadden	4.00	10.00
673 Ted Uhlaender	4.00	10.00
674 Dave Leonhard	4.00	10.00
675 Jose Cardenal	6.00	15.00
676 Washington Senators TC	5.00	12.00
677 Woodie Fryman	4.00	10.00
678 Dave Duncan	6.00	15.00
679 Ray Sadecki	4.00	10.00
680 Rico Petrocelli	6.00	15.00
681 Bob Garibaldi RC	4.00	10.00
682 Dalton Jones	4.00	10.00
683 Rookie Stars	6.00	15.00
Vern Geishert RC		
Hal McRae		
Wayne Simpson RC		
684 Jack Fisher	4.00	10.00
685 Tom Haller	4.00	10.00
686 Jackie Hernandez	4.00	10.00
687 Bob Priddy	4.00	10.00
688 Ted Kubiak	6.00	15.00
689 Frank Tepedino RC	6.00	15.00
690 Ron Fairly	6.00	15.00
691 Joe Grzenda	4.00	10.00
692 Duffy Dyer	4.00	10.00
693 Bob Johnson	4.00	10.00
694 Gary Ross	4.00	10.00
695 Bobby Knoop	4.00	10.00
696 San Francisco Giants TC	5.00	12.00
697 Jim Hannan	4.00	10.00
698 Tom Tresh	6.00	15.00
699 Hank Aguirre	4.00	10.00
700 Frank Robinson	20.00	50.00
701 Jack Billingham	4.00	10.00
702 Rookie Stars	4.00	10.00
Bob Johnson		
Ron Klimkowski RC		
Bill Zepp RC		
703 Lou Marone RC	4.00	10.00
704 Frank Baker RC	4.00	10.00
705 Tony Cloninger UER	4.00	10.00
(Batter headings		
on card back)		
706 John McNamara MG RC	4.00	10.00
707 Kevin Collins	4.00	10.00
708 Jose Santiago	4.00	10.00
709 Mike Fiore	4.00	10.00
710 Felix Millan	4.00	10.00
711 Ed Brinkman	4.00	10.00
712 Nolan Ryan	100.00	200.00
713 Seattle Pilots TC	10.00	25.00
714 Al Spangler	4.00	10.00
715 Mickey Lolich	6.00	15.00
716 Rookie Stars	6.00	15.00
Sal Campisi RC		
Reggie Cleveland RC		
Santiago Guzman RC		
717 Tom Phoebus	4.00	10.00
718 Ed Spiezio	4.00	10.00
719 Jim Roland	4.00	10.00
720 Rick Reichardt	6.00	15.00

1971 Topps

The cards in this 752-card set measure 2 1/2" by 3 1/2". The 1971 Topps set is a challenge to complete in strict mint condition because the black obverse border is easily scratched and damaged. An unusual feature of this set is that the player is also pictured in black and white on the back of the card. Featured subsets within this set include League Leaders (61-72), Playoffs cards (195-202), and World Series cards (327-332). Cards 524-643 and the last series (644-752) are somewhat scarce. The last series was printed in two sheets of 132. On the printing sheets 44 cards were printed in 50 percent greater quantity than the other 66 cards. These 66 (slightly) shorter-printed numbers are identified in the checklist below by SP. The key Rookie Cards in this set are the multi-player Rookie Card of Dusty Baker and Don Baylor and the individual cards of Bert Blyleven, Dave Concepcion, Steve Garvey, and Ted Simmons. The Jim Northrup and Jim Nash cards have been seen with our without printing "blotches" on the card. There is still debate on whether those two cards are just printing issues or legitimate variations. Among the ways these cards were issued were in 54-card rack packs which retailed for 39 cents.

COMPLETE SET (752)	1250.00	2500.00
COMMON CARD (1-393)	.60	1.50
COMMON (394-523)	1.00	2.50
COMMON (524-643)	1.50	4.00
COMMON (644-752)	3.00	8.00
COMMON SP (644-752)	5.00	12.00
WRAPPER (10-CENT)	6.00	15.00
1 Baltimore Orioles TC	8.00	20.00
2 Dock Ellis	.60	1.50
3 Dick McAuliffe	.75	2.00
4 Vic Davalillo	.60	1.50
5 Thurman Munson	60.00	120.00
6 Ed Spiezio	.60	1.50
7 Jim Holt RC	.60	1.50
8 Mike McQueen	.60	1.50
9 George Scott	.75	2.00
10 Claude Osteen	.75	2.00
11 Elliott Maddox RC	.60	1.50
12 Johnny Callison	.75	2.00
13 Rookie Stars	.60	1.50
Charlie Brinkman RC		
Dick Moloney RC		
14 Dave Concepcion RC	6.00	15.00
15 Andy Messersmith	.75	2.00
16 Ken Singleton RC	1.50	4.00
17 Billy Sorrell	.60	1.50
18 Norm Miller	.60	1.50
19 Skip Pitlock RC	.60	1.50
20 Reggie Jackson	20.00	50.00
21 Dan McGinn	.60	1.50
22 Phil Roof	.60	1.50
23 Oscar Gamble	.60	1.50
24 Rich Hand RC	.60	1.50
25 Clarence Gaston	.75	2.00
26 Bert Blyleven RC	8.00	20.00
27 Rookie Stars	.60	1.50
Fred Cambria RC		
Gene Clines RC		
28 Ron Klimkowski	.60	1.50
29 Don Buford	.60	1.50
30 Phil Niekro	2.50	6.00
31 Eddie Kasko MG	.60	1.50
32 Jerry DaVanon	.60	1.50
33 Del Unser	.60	1.50
34 Sandy Vance RC	.60	1.50
35 Lou Piniella	.75	2.00
36 Dean Chance	.75	2.00
37 Rich McKinney RC	.60	1.50
38 Jim Colborn RC	.60	1.50
39 Rookie Stars	.75	2.00
Lerrin LaGrow RC		
Gene Lamont RC		
40 Lee May	.75	2.00
41 Rick Austin RC	.60	1.50
42 Boots Day	.60	1.50
43 Steve Kealey	.60	1.50
44 Johnny Edwards	.60	1.50
45 Jim Hunter	2.50	6.00
46 Dave Campbell	.75	2.00
47 Johnny Jeter	.60	1.50
48 Dave Baldwin	.60	1.50
49 Don Money	.60	1.50
50 Willie McCovey	4.00	10.00
51 Steve Kline RC	.60	1.50
52 Rookie Stars	.60	1.50
Oscar Brown RC		
Earl Williams RC		
53 Paul Blair	.75	2.00
54 Checklist 1	4.00	10.00
55 Steve Carlton	8.00	20.00
56 Duane Josephson	.60	1.50
57 Von Joshua RC	.60	1.50
58 Bill Lee	.75	2.00
59 Gene Mauch MG	.75	2.00
60 Dick Bosman	.60	1.50
61 AL Batting Leaders	1.50	4.00
Alex Johnson		
Carl Yastrzemski		
Tony Oliva		
62 NL Batting Leaders	.75	2.00
Rico Carty		
Joe Torre		
Manny Sanguillen		
63 AL RBI Leaders	1.50	4.00
Frank Howard		
Tony Conigliaro		
Boog Powell		
64 NL RBI Leaders	2.50	6.00
Johnny Bench		
Tony Perez		
Billy Williams		
65 AL Home Run Leaders	1.50	4.00
Frank Howard		
Harmon Killebrew		
Carl Yastrzemski		
66 NL Home Run Leaders	2.50	6.00
Johnny Bench		
Billy Williams		
Tony Perez		
67 AL ERA Leaders	1.50	4.00
Diego Segui		
Jim Palmer		
Clyde Wright		
68 NL ERA Leaders	1.50	4.00
Tom Seaver		
Wayne Simpson		
Luke Walker		
69 AL Pitching Leaders	.75	2.00
Mike Cuellar		
Dave McNally		
Jim Perry		
70 NL Pitching Leaders	2.50	6.00
Bob Gibson		
Gaylord Perry		
Fergie Jenkins		
71 AL Strikeout Leaders	.75	2.00
Sam McDowell		
Mickey Lolich		
Bob Johnson		
72 NL Strikeout Leaders	2.50	6.00
Tom Seaver		
Bob Gibson		
Fergie Jenkins		
73 George Brunet	.60	1.50
74 Rookie Stars	.60	1.50
Pete Hamm RC		
Jim Nettles RC		
75 Gary Nolan	.75	2.00
76 Ted Savage	.60	1.50
77 Mike Compton RC	.60	1.50
78 Jim Spencer	.60	1.50
79 Wade Blasingame	.60	1.50
80 Bill Melton	.60	1.50
81 Felix Millan	.60	1.50
82 Casey Cox	.60	1.50
83 Rookie Stars	.75	2.00
Tim Foli RC		
Randy Bobb		
84 Marcel Lachemann RC	.60	1.50
85 Billy Grabarkewitz	.60	1.50
86 Mike Kilkenny	.60	1.50
87 Jack Heidemann RC	.60	1.50
88 Hal King	.60	1.50
89 Ken Brett	.60	1.50
90 Joe Pepitone	.75	2.00
91 Bob Lemon MG	.75	2.00
92 Fred Wenz	.60	1.50
93 Rookie Stars	.60	1.50
Norm McRae		
Denny Riddleberger		
94 Don Hahn RC	.60	1.50
95 Luis Tiant	.75	2.00
96 Joe Hague	.60	1.50
97 Floyd Wicker	.60	1.50
98 Joe Decker RC	.60	1.50
99 Mark Belanger	.75	2.00
100 Pete Rose	40.00	80.00
101 Les Cain	.60	1.50
102 Rookie Stars	.75	2.00
Ken Forsch RC		
Larry Howard RC		
103 Rich Severson RC	.60	1.50
104 Dan Frisella	.60	1.50
105 Tony Conigliaro	.75	2.00
106 Tom Dukes	.60	1.50
107 Roy Foster RC	.60	1.50
108 John Cumberland	.60	1.50
109 Steve Hovley	.60	1.50
110 Bill Mazeroski	2.50	6.00
111 Rookie Stars	.60	1.50
Loyd Colson RC		
Bobby Mitchell RC		
112 Manny Mota	.75	2.00
113 Jerry Crider	.60	1.50
114 Billy Conigliaro	.75	2.00
115 Donn Clendenon	.75	2.00
116 Ken Sanders	.60	1.50
117 Ted Simmons RC	3.00	8.00
118 Cookie Rojas	.75	2.00
119 Frank Lucchesi MG	.75	2.00
120 Willie Horton	.75	2.00
121 Rookie Stars	.60	1.50
Jim Dunegan RC		
Roe Skidmore RC		
122 Eddie Watt	.60	1.50
123A Checklist 2	4.00	10.00
(Card number		
at bottom right)		
123B Checklist 2	4.00	10.00
(Card number		
centered)		
124 Don Gullett RC	.75	2.00
125 Ray Fosse	.60	1.50
126 Danny Coombs	.60	1.50
127 Danny Thompson RC	.75	2.00
128 Frank Johnson	.60	1.50
129 Aurelio Monteagudo	.60	1.50
130 Denis Menke	.60	1.50
131 Curt Blefary	.60	1.50
132 Jose Laboy	.60	1.50

133 Mickey Lolich .75 2.00
134 Jose Arcia .60 1.50
135 Rick Monday .75 2.00
136 Duffy Dyer .60 1.50
137 Marcelino Lopez .60 1.50
138 Rookie Stars .75 2.00
Joe Lis
Willie Montanez RC
139 Paul Casanova .60 1.50
140 Gaylord Perry 2.50 6.00
141 Frank Quilici .60 1.50
142 Mack Jones .60 1.50
143 Steve Blass .75 2.00
144 Jackie Hernandez .60 1.50
145 Bill Singer .75 2.00
146 Ralph Houk MG .75 2.00
147 Bob Priddy .60 1.50
148 John Mayberry .75 2.00
149 Mike Hershberger .60 1.50
150 Sam McDowell .75 2.00
151 Tommy Davis .75 2.00
152 Rookie Stars .60 1.50
Lloyd Allen RC
Winston Llenas RC
153 Gary Ross .60 1.50
154 Cesar Gutierrez .60 1.50
155 Ken Henderson .60 1.50
156 Bart Johnson .60 1.50
157 Bob Bailey .75 2.00
158 Jerry Reuss .75 2.00
159 Jarvis Tatum .60 1.50
160 Tom Seaver 12.50 30.00
161 Coin Checklist 4.00 10.00
162 Jack Billingham .60 1.50
163 Buck Martinez .75 2.00
164 Rookie Stars .75 2.00
Frank Duffy RC
Milt Wilcox RC
165 Cesar Tovar .60 1.50
166 Joe Hoerner .60 1.50
167 Tom Grieve RC .75 2.00
168 Bruce Dal Canton .60 1.50
169 Ed Herrmann .60 1.50
170 Mike Cuellar .75 2.00
171 Bobby Wine .60 1.50
172 Duke Sims .60 1.50
173 Gil Garrido .60 1.50
174 Dave LaRoche RC .60 1.50
175 Jim Hickman .60 1.50
176 Rookie Stars .75 2.00
Bob Montgomery RC
Doug Griffin RC
177 Hal McRae .75 2.00
178 Dave Duncan .75 2.00
179 Mike Corkins .60 1.50
180 Al Kaline UER 8.00 20.00
(Home instead
of Birth)
181 Hal Lanier .60 1.50
182 Al Downing .75 2.00
183 Gil Hodges MG 1.50 4.00
184 Stan Bahnsen .60 1.50
185 Julian Javier .60 1.50
186 Bob Spence RC .60 1.50
187 Ted Abernathy .60 1.50
188 Rookie Stars 2.50 6.00
Bob Valentine RC
Mike Strahler RC
189 George Mitterwald .60 1.50
190 Bob Tolan .60 1.50
191 Mike Andrews .60 1.50
192 Billy Wilson .60 1.50
193 Bob Grich RC 1.50 4.00
194 Mike Lum .60 1.50
195 AL Playoff Game 1 .75 2.00
Boog Powell
196 AL Playoff Game 2 .75 2.00
Dave McNally
197 AL Playoff Game 3 1.50 4.00
Jim Palmer
198 AL Playoff Summary .75 2.00
Orioles Celebrate
199 NL Playoff Game 1 .75 2.00
Ty Cline
200 NL Playoff Game 2 .75 2.00
Bobby Tolan
201 NL Playoff Game 3 .75 2.00
Ty Cline
202 NL Playoff Summary .75 2.00
Reds Celebrate
203 Larry Gura RC .75 2.00
204 Rookie Stars .60 1.50
Bernie Smith RC
George Kopacz RC
205 Gerry Moses .60 1.50
206 Checklist 3 4.00 10.00
207 Alan Foster .60 1.50
208 Billy Martin MG 1.50 4.00
209 Steve Renko .60 1.50
210 Rod Carew 6.00 15.00
211 Phil Hennigan RC .60 1.50
212 Rich Hebner .75 2.00
213 Frank Baker RC .60 1.50
214 Al Ferrara .60 1.50
215 Diego Segui .60 1.50
216 Rookie Stars .60 1.50
Reggie Cleveland
Luis Melendez RC
217 Ed Stroud .60 1.50
218 Tony Cloninger .60 1.50
219 Elrod Hendricks .60 1.50
220 Ron Santo 1.50 4.00
221 Dave Morehead .60 1.50
222 Bob Watson .75 2.00
223 Cecil Upshaw .60 1.50
224 Alan Gallagher RC .60 1.50
225 Gary Peters .60 1.50
226 Bill Russell .75 2.00
227 Floyd Weaver .60 1.50
228 Wayne Garrett .60 1.50
229 Jim Hannan .60 1.50
230 Willie Stargell 6.00 15.00
231 Rookie Stars .75 2.00
Vince Colbert RC
John Lowenstein RC
232 John Strohmayer RC .60 1.50
233 Larry Bowa .75 2.00
234 Jim Lyttle .60 1.50
235 Nate Colbert .60 1.50
236 Bob Humphreys .60 1.50
237 Cesar Cedeno RC .75 2.00
238 Chuck Dobson .60 1.50
239 Red Schoendienst MG .75 2.00
240 Clyde Wright .60 1.50
241 Dave Nelson .60 1.50
242 Jim Ray .60 1.50
243 Carlos May .60 1.50
244 Bob Tillman .60 1.50
245 Jim Kaat .75 2.00
246 Tony Taylor .60 1.50
247 Rookie Stars .75 2.00
Jerry Cram RC
Paul Splittorff RC
248 Hoyt Wilhelm 2.50 6.00
249 Chico Salmon .60 1.50
250 Johnny Bench 20.00 50.00
251 Frank Reberger .60 1.50
252 Eddie Leon .60 1.50
253 Bill Sudakis .60 1.50
254 Cal Koonce .60 1.50
255 Bob Robertson .75 2.00
256 Tony Gonzalez .60 1.50
257 Nelson Briles .75 2.00
258 Dick Green .60 1.50
259 Dave Marshall .60 1.50
260 Tommy Harper .75 2.00
261 Darold Knowles .60 1.50
262 Rookie Stars .60 1.50
Jim Williams
Dave Robinson RC
263 John Ellis .60 1.50
264 Joe Morgan 3.00 8.00
265 Jim Northrup .75 2.00
266 Bill Stoneman .60 1.50
267 Rich Morales .60 1.50
268 Philadelphia Phillies TC 1.50 4.00
269 Gail Hopkins .60 1.50
270 Rico Carty .75 2.00
271 Bill Zepp .60 1.50
272 Tommy Helms .75 2.00
273 Pete Richert .60 1.50
274 Ron Slocum .60 1.50
275 Vada Pinson .75 2.00
276 Rookie Stars 3.00 8.00
Mike Davison RC
George Foster RC
277 Gary Waslewski .60 1.50
278 Jerry Grote .75 2.00
279 Lefty Phillips MG .60 1.50
280 Ferguson Jenkins 2.50 6.00
281 Danny Walton .60 1.50
282 Jose Pagan .60 1.50
283 Dick Such .60 1.50
284 Jim Gosger .60 1.50
285 Sal Bando .75 2.00
286 Jerry McNertney .60 1.50
287 Mike Fiore .60 1.50
288 Joe Moeller .60 1.50
289 Chicago White Sox TC 1.50 4.00
290 Tony Oliva 1.50 4.00
291 George Culver .60 1.50
292 Jay Johnstone .75 2.00
293 Pat Corrales .75 2.00
294 Steve Dunning RC .60 1.50
295 Bobby Bonds 1.50 4.00
296 Tom Timmermann .60 1.50
297 Johnny Briggs .60 1.50
298 Jim Nelson RC .60 1.50
299 Ed Kirkpatrick .60 1.50
300 Brooks Robinson 8.00 20.00
301 Earl Wilson .60 1.50
302 Phil Gagliano .60 1.50
303 Lindy McDaniel .75 2.00
304 Ron Brand .60 1.50
305 Reggie Smith .75 2.00
306 Jim Nash .60 1.50
307 Don Wert .60 1.50
308 St. Louis Cardinals TC 1.50 4.00
309 Dick Ellsworth .60 1.50
310 Tommie Agee .75 2.00
311 Lee Stange .60 1.50
312 Harry Walker MG .60 1.50
313 Tom Hall .60 1.50
314 Jeff Torborg .75 2.00
315 Ron Fairly .75 2.00
316 Fred Scherman RC .60 1.50
317 Rookie Stars .60 1.50
Jim Driscoll RC
Angel Mangual
318 Rudy May .60 1.50
319 Ty Cline .60 1.50
320 Dave McNally .75 2.00
321 Tom Matchick .60 1.50
322 Jim Beauchamp .60 1.50
323 Billy Champion .60 1.50
324 Graig Nettles .75 2.00
325 Juan Marichal 3.00 8.00
326 Richie Scheinblum .60 1.50
327 World Series Game 1 .75 2.00
Boog Powell
328 World Series Game 2 .75 2.00
Don Buford
329 World Series Game 3 1.50 4.00
Frank Robinson
330 World Series Game 4 .75 2.00
Reds Stay Alive
331 World Series Game 5 2.50 6.00
Brooks Robinson
332 World Series Summary .75 2.00
Orioles Celebrate
333 Clay Kirby .60 1.50
334 Roberto Pena .60 1.50
335 Jerry Koosman .75 2.00
336 Detroit Tigers TC 1.50 4.00
337 Jesus Alou .60 1.50
338 Gene Tenace .75 2.00
339 Wayne Simpson .60 1.50
340 Rico Petrocelli .75 2.00
341 Steve Garvey RC 12.50 40.00
342 Frank Tepedino .75 2.00
343 Rookie Stars .75 2.00
Ed Acosta RC
Milt May RC
344 Ellie Rodriguez .60 1.50
345 Joel Horlen .60 1.50
346 Lum Harris MG .60 1.50
347 Ted Uhlaender .60 1.50
348 Fred Norman .60 1.50
349 Rich Reese .60 1.50
350 Billy Williams 2.50 6.00
351 Jim Shellenback .60 1.50
352 Denny Doyle .60 1.50
353 Carl Taylor .60 1.50
354 Don McMahon .60 1.50
355 Bud Harrelson 1.50 4.00
(Nolan Ryan in photo)
356 Bob Locker .60 1.50
357 Cincinnati Reds TC 1.50 4.00
358 Danny Cater .60 1.50
359 Ron Reed .60 1.50
360 Jim Fregosi .75 2.00
361 Don Sutton 2.50 6.00
362 Rookie Stars .60 1.50
Mike Adamson
Roger Freed
363 Mike Nagy .60 1.50
364 Tommy Dean .60 1.50
365 Bob Johnson .60 1.50
366 Ron Stone .60 1.50
367 Dalton Jones .60 1.50
368 Bob Veale .75 2.00
369 Checklist 4 4.00 10.00
370 Joe Torre 1.50 4.00
371 Jack Hiatt .60 1.50
372 Lew Krausse .60 1.50
373 Tom McCraw .60 1.50
374 Clete Boyer .75 2.00
375 Steve Hargan .60 1.50
376 Rookie Stars .60 1.50
Clyde Mashore RC
Ernie McAnally RC
377 Greg Garrett .60 1.50
378 Tito Fuentes .60 1.50
379 Wayne Granger .60 1.50
380 Ted Williams MG 5.00 12.00
381 Fred Gladding .60 1.50
382 Jake Gibbs .60 1.50
383 Rod Gaspar .60 1.50
384 Rollie Fingers 2.50 6.00
385 Maury Wills 1.50 4.00
386 Boston Red Sox TC .75 2.00
387 Ron Herbel .60 1.50
388 Al Oliver 1.50 4.00
389 Ed Brinkman .60 1.50
390 Glenn Beckert .75 2.00
391 Rookie Stars .75 2.00
Steve Brye RC
Cotton Nash RC
392 Grant Jackson .60 1.50
393 Merv Rettenmund .75 2.00
394 Clay Carroll 1.00 2.50
395 Roy White 1.50 4.00
396 Dick Schofield 1.00 2.50
397 Alvin Dark MG 1.50 4.00
398 Howie Reed 1.00 2.50
399 Jim French 1.00 2.50
400 Hank Aaron 30.00 60.00
401 Tom Murphy 1.00 2.50
402 Los Angeles Dodgers TC 2.50 6.00
403 Joe Coleman 1.00 2.50
404 Rookie Stars 1.00 2.50
Buddy Harris RC
Roger Metzger RC
405 Leo Cardenas 1.00 2.50
406 Ray Sadecki 1.00 2.50
407 Joe Rudi 1.50 4.00
408 Rafael Robles 1.00 2.50
409 Don Pavletich 1.00 2.50
410 Ken Holtzman 1.50 4.00
411 George Spriggs 1.00 2.50
412 Jerry Johnson 1.00 2.50
413 Pat Kelly 1.00 2.50
414 Woodie Fryman 1.00 2.50
415 Mike Hegan 1.00 2.50
416 Gene Alley 1.00 2.50
417 Dick Hall 1.00 2.50
418 Adolfo Phillips 1.00 2.50
419 Ron Hansen 1.00 2.50
420 Jim Merritt 1.00 2.50
421 John Stephenson 1.00 2.50
422 Frank Bertaina 1.00 2.50
423 Rookie Stars 1.00 2.50
Dennis Saunders RC
Tim Marting RC
424 Roberto Rodriquez 1.00 2.50
425 Doug Rader 1.50 4.00
426 Chris Cannizzaro 1.00 2.50
427 Bernie Allen 1.00 2.50
428 Jim McAndrew 1.00 2.50
429 Chuck Hinton 1.00 2.50
430 Wes Parker 1.50 4.00
431 Tom Burgmeier 1.00 2.50
432 Bob Didier 1.00 2.50
433 Skip Lockwood 1.00 2.50
434 Gary Sutherland 1.00 2.50
435 Jose Cardenal 1.50 4.00
436 Wilbur Wood 1.50 4.00
437 Danny Murtaugh MG 1.50 4.00
438 Mike McCormick 1.50 4.00
439 Rookie Stars 2.50 6.00
Greg Luzinski RC
Scott Reid
440 Bert Campaneris 1.50 4.00
441 Milt Pappas 1.50 4.00
442 California Angels TC 1.50 4.00
443 Rich Robertson 1.00 2.50
444 Jimmie Price 1.00 2.50
445 Art Shamsky 1.00 2.50
446 Bobby Bolin 1.00 2.50
447 Cesar Geronimo RC 1.50 4.00
448 Dave Roberts 1.00 2.50
449 Brant Alyea 1.00 2.50
450 Bob Gibson 6.00 15.00
451 Joe Keough 1.00 2.50
452 John Boccabella 1.00 2.50
453 Terry Crowley 1.00 2.50
454 Mike Paul 1.00 2.50
455 Don Kessinger 1.50 4.00
456 Bob Meyer 1.00 2.50
457 Willie Smith 1.00 2.50
458 Rookie Stars 1.00 2.50
Ron Lolich RC
Dave Lemonds RC
459 Jim Lefebvre 1.00 2.50
460 Fritz Peterson 1.00 2.50
461 Jim Ray Hart 1.00 2.50
462 Washington Senators TC 2.50 6.00
463 Tom Kelley 1.00 2.50
464 Aurelio Rodriguez 1.00 2.50
465 Tim McCarver 2.50 6.00
466 Ken Berry 1.00 2.50
467 Al Santorini 1.00 2.50
468 Frank Fernandez 1.00 2.50
469 Bob Aspromonte 1.00 2.50
470 Bob Oliver 1.00 2.50
471 Tom Griffin 1.00 2.50
472 Ken Rudolph 1.00 2.50
473 Gary Wagner 1.00 2.50
474 Jim Fairey 1.00 2.50
475 Ron Perranoski 1.00 2.50
476 Dal Maxvill 1.00 2.50
477 Earl Weaver MG 2.50 6.00
478 Bernie Carbo 1.00 2.50
479 Dennis Higgins 1.00 2.50
480 Manny Sanguillen 1.50 4.00
481 Daryl Patterson 1.00 2.50
482 San Diego Padres TC 2.50 6.00
483 Gene Michael 1.00 2.50
484 Don Wilson 1.00 2.50
485 Ken McMullen 1.00 2.50
486 Steve Huntz 1.00 2.50
487 Paul Schaal 1.00 2.50
488 Jerry Stephenson 1.00 2.50
489 Luis Alvarado 1.00 2.50
490 Deron Johnson 1.00 2.50
491 Jim Hardin 1.00 2.50
492 Ken Boswell 1.00 2.50
493 Dave May 1.00 2.50
494 Rookie Stars 1.50 4.00
Ralph Garr
Rick Kester
495 Felipe Alou 1.50 4.00
496 Woody Woodward 1.00 2.50
497 Horacio Pina RC 1.00 2.50
498 John Kennedy 1.00 2.50
499 Checklist 5 4.00 10.00
500 Jim Perry 1.50 4.00
501 Andy Etchebarren 1.00 2.50
502 Chicago Cubs TC 2.50 6.00
503 Gates Brown 1.50 4.00
504 Ken Wright RC 1.00 2.50
505 Ollie Brown 1.00 2.50
506 Bobby Knoop 1.00 2.50
507 George Stone 1.00 2.50
508 Roger Repoz 1.00 2.50
509 Jim Grant 1.00 2.50
510 Ken Harrelson 1.50 4.00
511 Chris Short 1.50 4.00
(Pete Rose leading off second)
512 Rookie Stars 1.00 2.50
Dick Mills RC
Mike Garman RC
513 Nolan Ryan 75.00 150.00
514 Ron Woods 1.00 2.50
515 Carl Morton 1.00 2.50
516 Ted Kubiak 1.00 2.50
517 Charlie Fox MG RC 1.00 2.50
518 Joe Grzenda 1.00 2.50
519 Willie Crawford 1.00 2.50
520 Tommy John 2.50 6.00
521 Leron Lee 1.00 2.50
522 Minnesota Twins TC 2.50 6.00
523 John Odom 1.00 2.50
524 Mickey Stanley 2.50 6.00
525 Ernie Banks 20.00 50.00
526 Ray Jarvis 1.50 4.00
527 Cleon Jones 2.50 6.00
528 Wally Bunker 1.50 4.00
529 Rookie Stars 2.50 6.00
Enzo Hernandez RC
Bill Buckner
Marty Perez RC
530 Carl Yastrzemski 12.50 30.00
531 Mike Torrez 1.50 4.00
532 Bill Rigney MG 1.50 4.00
533 Mike Ryan 1.50 4.00
534 Luke Walker 1.50 4.00
535 Curt Flood 2.50 6.00
536 Claude Raymond 1.50 4.00
537 Tom Egan 1.50 4.00
538 Angel Bravo 1.50 4.00
539 Larry Brown 1.50 4.00
540 Larry Dierker 2.50 6.00
541 Bob Burda 1.50 4.00
542 Bob Miller 1.50 4.00
543 New York Yankees TC 4.00 10.00
544 Vida Blue 2.50 6.00
545 Dick Dietz 1.50 4.00
546 John Matias 1.50 4.00
547 Pat Dobson 2.50 6.00
548 Don Mason 1.50 4.00
549 Jim Brewer 2.50 6.00
550 Harmon Killebrew 10.00 25.00
551 Frank Linzy 1.50 4.00
552 Buddy Bradford 1.50 4.00
553 Kevin Collins 1.50 4.00
554 Lowell Palmer 1.50 4.00
555 Walt Williams 1.50 4.00
556 Jim McGlothlin 1.50 4.00
557 Tom Satriano 1.50 4.00
558 Hector Torres 1.50 4.00
559 Rookie Stars 1.50 4.00
Terry Cox RC
Bill Gogolewski RC
Gary Jones RC
560 Rusty Staub 2.50 6.00
561 Syd O'Brien 1.50 4.00
562 Dave Giusti 1.50 4.00
563 San Francisco Giants TC 3.00 8.00
564 Al Fitzmorris 1.50 4.00
565 Jim Wynn 2.50 6.00
566 Tim Cullen 1.50 4.00
567 Walt Alston MG 3.00 8.00
568 Sal Campisi 1.50 4.00
569 Ivan Murrell 1.50 4.00
570 Jim Palmer 12.50 30.00
571 Ted Sizemore 1.50 4.00
572 Jerry Kenney 1.50 4.00
573 Ed Kranepool 2.50 6.00
574 Jim Bunning 3.00 8.00
575 Bill Freehan 2.50 6.00
576 Rookie Stars 1.50 4.00
Adrian Garrett RC
Brock Davis
Garry Jestadt
577 Jim Lonborg 2.50 6.00
578 Ron Hunt 1.50 4.00
579 Marty Pattin 1.50 4.00
580 Tony Perez 8.00 20.00
581 Roger Nelson 1.50 4.00
582 Dave Cash 2.50 6.00
583 Ron Cook RC 1.50 4.00
584 Cleveland Indians TC 3.00 8.00
585 Willie Davis 2.50 6.00
586 Dick Woodson 1.50 4.00
587 Sonny Jackson 1.50 4.00
588 Tom Bradley RC 1.50 4.00
589 Bob Barton 1.50 4.00
590 Alex Johnson 2.50 6.00
591 Jackie Brown RC 1.50 4.00
592 Randy Hundley 2.50 6.00
593 Jack Aker 1.50 4.00
594 Rookie Stars 2.50 6.00
Bob Chlupsa RC
Bob Stinson
Al Hrabosky RC
595 Dave Johnson 2.50 6.00
596 Mike Jorgensen 1.50 4.00
597 Ken Suarez 1.50 4.00
598 Rick Wise 2.50 6.00
599 Norm Cash 2.50 6.00
600 Willie Mays 50.00 100.00
601 Ken Tatum 1.50 4.00
602 Marty Martinez 1.50 4.00
603 Pittsburgh Pirates TC 3.00 8.00
604 John Gelnar 1.50 4.00
605 Orlando Cepeda 3.00 8.00
606 Chuck Taylor 1.50 4.00
607 Paul Ratliff 1.50 4.00
608 Mike Wegener 1.50 4.00
609 Leo Durocher MG 3.00 8.00
610 Amos Otis 2.50 6.00
611 Tom Phoebus 1.50 4.00
612 Rookie Stars 1.50 4.00
Lou Camilli RC
Ted Ford RC
Steve Mingori
613 Pedro Borbon 1.50 4.00
614 Billy Cowan 1.50 4.00
615 Mel Stottlemyre 2.50 6.00
616 Larry Hisle 2.50 6.00
617 Clay Dalrymple 1.50 4.00
618 Tug McGraw 2.50 6.00
619A Checklist 6 ERR 4.00 10.00
(No copyright)
619B Checklist 6 COR 2.50 6.00
(Copyright on back)
620 Frank Howard 2.50 6.00
621 Ron Bryant 1.50 4.00
622 Joe Lahoud 1.50 4.00
623 Pat Jarvis 1.50 4.00
624 Oakland Athletics TC 3.00 8.00
625 Lou Brock 12.50 30.00
626 Freddie Patek 2.50 6.00
627 Steve Hamilton 1.50 4.00
628 John Bateman 1.50 4.00
629 John Hiller 2.50 6.00
630 Roberto Clemente 75.00 150.00
631 Eddie Fisher 1.50 4.00
632 Darrel Chaney 1.50 4.00
633 Rookie Stars 1.50 4.00
Bobby Brooks
Pete Koegel RC
Scott Northey
634 Phil Regan 1.50 4.00
635 Bobby Murcer 2.50 6.00
636 Denny Lemaster 1.50 4.00
637 Dave Bristol MG 1.50 4.00
638 Stan Williams 1.50 4.00
639 Tom Haller 1.50 4.00
640 Frank Robinson 12.50 40.00
641 New York Mets TC 6.00 15.00
642 Jim Roland 1.50 4.00
643 Rick Reichardt 1.50 4.00
644 Jim Stewart SP 5.00 12.00
645 Jim Maloney SP 6.00 15.00
646 Bobby Floyd SP 5.00 12.00
647 Juan Pizarro 3.00 8.00
648 Rookie Stars 10.00 25.00
Rich Folkers RC
Ted Martinez RC
John Matlack RC SP
649 Sparky Lyle SP 6.00 15.00
650 Rich Allen SP 12.50 30.00
651 Jerry Robertson SP 5.00 12.00
652 Atlanta Braves TC 5.00 12.00
653 Russ Snyder SP 5.00 12.00
654 Don Shaw SP 5.00 12.00
655 Mike Epstein SP 5.00 12.00
656 Gerry Nyman SP 5.00 12.00
657 Jose Azcue 3.00 8.00
658 Paul Lindblad SP 5.00 12.00
659 Byron Browne SP 5.00 12.00
660 Ray Culp 3.00 8.00
661 Chuck Tanner MG SP 6.00 15.00
662 Mike Hedlund SP 5.00 12.00
663 Marv Staehle 3.00 8.00
664 Rookie Stars 5.00 12.00
Archie Reynolds RC
Bob Reynolds RC
Ken Reynolds RC SP
665 Ron Swoboda SP 6.00 15.00
666 Gene Brabender SP 5.00 12.00
667 Pete Ward 3.00 8.00
668 Gary Neibauer 3.00 8.00
669 Ike Brown SP 5.00 12.00
670 Bill Hands 3.00 8.00
671 Bill Voss SP 5.00 12.00
672 Ed Crosby SP RC 5.00 12.00
673 Gerry Janeski SP RC 5.00 12.00
674 Montreal Expos TC 5.00 12.00
675 Dave Boswell 3.00 8.00
676 Tommie Reynolds 3.00 8.00
677 Jack DiLauro SP 5.00 12.00
678 George Thomas 3.00 8.00
679 Don O'Riley 3.00 8.00
680 Don Mincher SP 5.00 12.00
681 Bill Butler 3.00 8.00
682 Terry Harmon 3.00 8.00
683 Bill Burbach SP 5.00 12.00
684 Curt Motton 3.00 8.00
685 Moe Drabowsky 3.00 8.00
686 Chico Ruiz SP 5.00 12.00
687 Ron Taylor SP 5.00 12.00
688 Sparky Anderson MG SP 12.50 30.00
689 Frank Baker 3.00 8.00
690 Bob Moose 3.00 8.00
691 Bobby Heise 3.00 8.00
692 Rookie Stars 5.00 12.00
Hal Haydel RC
Rogelio Moret RC
Wayne Twitchell RC SP
693 Jose Pena SP 5.00 12.00
694 Rick Renick SP 5.00 12.00
695 Joe Niekro 5.00 12.00
696 Jerry Morales 3.00 8.00
697 Rickey Clark SP 5.00 12.00
698 Milwaukee Brewers TC SP 8.00 20.00
699 Jim Britton 3.00 8.00
700 Boog Powell SP 10.00 25.00
701 Bob Garibaldi 3.00 8.00
702 Milt Ramirez RC 3.00 8.00
703 Mike Kekich 3.00 8.00
704 J.C. Martin SP 5.00 12.00
705 Dick Selma SP 5.00 12.00
706 Joe Foy SP 5.00 12.00
707 Fred Lasher 3.00 8.00
708 Russ Nagelson SP 5.00 12.00
709 Rookie Stars 40.00 80.00
Dusty Baker RC
Don Baylor RC
Tom Paciorek RC SP
710 Sonny Siebert 3.00 8.00
711 Larry Stahl SP 5.00 12.00
712 Jose Martinez 3.00 8.00
713 Mike Marshall SP 6.00 15.00
714 Dick Williams MG SP 6.00 15.00
715 Horace Clarke SP 6.00 15.00
716 Dave Leonhard 3.00 8.00
717 Tommie Aaron SP 5.00 12.00
718 Billy Wynne 3.00 8.00
719 Jerry May SP 5.00 12.00
720 Matty Alou 5.00 12.00
721 John Morris 3.00 8.00
722 Houston Astros TC SP 8.00 20.00
723 Vicente Romo SP 5.00 12.00
724 Tom Tischinski SP 5.00 12.00
725 Gary Gentry SP 5.00 12.00
726 Paul Popovich 3.00 8.00
727 Ray Lamb SP 5.00 12.00
728 Rookie Stars 3.00 8.00
Wayne Redmond RC
Keith Lampard
Bernie Williams
729 Dick Billings RC 3.00 8.00
730 Jim Rooker 3.00 8.00
731 Jim Qualls SP 5.00 12.00
732 Bob Reed 3.00 8.00
733 Lee Maye SP 5.00 12.00
734 Rob Gardner SP 5.00 12.00
735 Mike Shannon SP 6.00 15.00
736 Mel Queen SP 5.00 12.00
737 Preston Gomez MG SP 5.00 12.00
738 Russ Gibson SP 5.00 12.00
739 Barry Lersch SP 5.00 12.00
740 Luis Aparicio UER SP 12.50 30.00
(Led AL in steals
from 1965 to 1964,
should be 1956 to 1964)
741 Skip Guinn 3.00 8.00
742 Kansas City Royals TC 5.00 12.00
743 John O'Donoghue SP 5.00 12.00
744 Chuck Manuel SP 5.00 12.00
745 Sandy Alomar SP 5.00 12.00
746 Andy Kosco 3.00 8.00
747 Rookie Stars 3.00 8.00
Al Severinsen
Scipio Spinks
Balor Moore RC
748 John Purdin SP 5.00 12.00
749 Ken Szotkiewicz RC 3.00 8.00
750 Denny McLain SP 10.00 25.00
751 Al Weis SP 6.00 15.00
752 Dick Drago 5.00 12.00

1972 Topps

The cards in this 787-card set measure 2 1/2" by 3 1/2". The 1972 Topps set contained the most cards ever for a Topps set to that point in time. Features appearing for the first time were "Boyhood Photos" (341-348/491-498), Awards and Trophy cards (621-626), "In Action" (distributed throughout the set), and "Traded Cards" (751-757). Other subsets included League Leaders (85-96), Playoffs cards (221-222), and World Series cards (223-230). The curved lines of the color picture are a departure from the rectangular designs of other years. There is a series of intermediate scarcity (526-656) and the usual high numbers (657-787). The backs of cards 692, 694, 696, 700, 706 and 710 form a picture back of Tom Seaver. The backs of cards 698, 702, 704, 708, 712, 714 form a picture back of Tony Oliva. As in previous years, cards were issued in a variety of ways including ten-card wax packs which cost a dime, 28-card cello packs which cost a quarter and 54-card rack packs which cost 39 cents. The 10 cents wax packs were issued 24 packs to a box while the cello packs were also issued 24 packs to a box. Rookie Cards in this set include Ron Cey and Carlton Fisk.

COMPLETE SET (787) 750.00 1500.00
COMMON CARD (1-132) .25 .60
COMMON (133-263) .40 1.00
COMMON (264-394) .50 1.25
COMMON (395-525) .60 1.50
COMMON (526-656) 1.50 4.00
COMMON (657-787) 5.00 12.00
WRAPPER (10-CENT) 6.00 15.00
1 Pittsburgh Pirates TC 3.00 8.00
2 Ray Culp .25 .60
3 Bob Tolan .25 .60
4 Checklist 1-132 2.50 6.00
5 John Bateman .25 .60
6 Fred Scherman .25 .60
7 Enzo Hernandez .25 .60
8 Ron Swoboda .50 1.25
9 Stan Williams .25 .60
10 Amos Otis .50 1.25
11 Bobby Valentine .50 1.25
12 Jose Cardenal .25 .60
13 Joe Grzenda .25 .60
14 Rookie Stars .25 .60

Pete Koegel
Mike Anderson RC
Wayne Twitchell
15 Walt Williams .25 .60
16 Mike Jorgensen .25 .60
17 Dave Duncan .50 1.25
18A Juan Pizarro .25 .60
(Yellow underline
C and S of Cubs)
18B Juan Pizarro 2.00 5.00
(Green underline
C and S of Cubs)
19 Billy Cowan .25 .60
20 Don Wilson .25 .60
21 Atlanta Braves TC .60 1.50
22 Rob Gardner .25 .60
23 Ted Kubiak .25 .60
24 Ted Ford .25 .60
25 Bill Singer .25 .60
26 Andy Etchebarren .25 .60
27 Bob Johnson .25 .60
28 Rookie Stars .25 .60
Bob Gebhard RC
Steve Brye
Hal Haydel
29A Bill Bonham RC .25 .60
(Yellow underline
C and S of Cubs)
29B Bill Bonham 2.00 5.00
(Green underline
C and S of Cubs)
30 Rico Petrocelli .50 1.25
31 Cleon Jones .50 1.25
32 Cleon Jones IA .25 .60
33 Billy Martin MG 1.50 4.00
34 Billy Martin IA 1.00 2.50
35 Jerry Johnson .25 .60
36 Jerry Johnson IA .25 .60
37 Carl Yastrzemski 4.00 10.00
38 Carl Yastrzemski IA 3.00 8.00
39 Bob Barton .25 .60
40 Bob Barton IA .25 .60
41 Tommy Davis .50 1.25
42 Tommy Davis IA .25 .60
43 Rick Wise .50 1.25
44 Rick Wise IA .25 .60
45A Glenn Beckert .50 1.25
(Yellow underline
C and S of Cubs)
45B Glenn Beckert 2.00 5.00
(Green underline
C and S of Cubs)
46 Glenn Beckert IA .25 .60
47 John Ellis .25 .60
48 John Ellis IA .25 .60
49 Willie Mays 12.50 40.00
50 Willie Mays IA 8.00 20.00
51 Harmon Killebrew 3.00 8.00
52 Harmon Killebrew IA 1.50 4.00
53 Bud Harrelson .50 1.25
54 Bud Harrelson IA .25 .60
55 Clyde Wright .25 .60
56 Rich Chiles RC .25 .60
57 Bob Oliver .25 .60
58 Ernie McAnally .25 .60
59 Fred Stanley RC .25 .60
60 Manny Sanguillen .50 1.25
61 Rookie Stars .50 1.25
Burt Hooton RC
Gene Hiser RC
Earl Stephenson RC
62 Angel Mangual .25 .60
63 Duke Sims .25 .60
64 Pete Broberg RC .25 .60
65 Cesar Cedeno .50 1.25
66 Ray Corbin RC .25 .60
67 Red Schoendienst MG 1.00 2.50
68 Jim York RC .25 .60
69 Roger Freed .25 .60
70 Mike Cuellar .50 1.25
71 California Angels TC .60 1.50
72 Bruce Kison RC .25 .60
73 Steve Huntz .25 .60
74 Cecil Upshaw .25 .60
75 Bert Campaneris .50 1.25
76 Don Carrithers RC .25 .60
77 Ron Theobald RC .25 .60
78 Steve Arlin RC .25 .60
79 Rookie Stars 20.00 50.00
Mike Garman
Cecil Cooper RC
Carlton Fisk RC
80 Tony Perez 1.50 4.00
81 Mike Hedlund .25 .60
82 Ron Woods .25 .60
83 Dalton Jones .25 .60
84 Vince Colbert .25 .60
85 NL Batting Leaders 1.00 2.50
Joe Torre
Ralph Garr
Glenn Beckert
86 AL Batting Leaders 1.00 2.50
Tony Oliva
Bobby Murcer
Merv Rettenmund
87 NL RBI Leaders 1.50 4.00
Joe Torre
Willie Stargell
Hank Aaron
88 AL RBI Leaders 1.50 4.00
Harmon Killebrew
Frank Robinson
Reggie Smith
89 NL Home Run Leaders 1.00 2.50
Willie Stargell
Hank Aaron
Lee May
90 AL Home Run Leaders 1.00 2.50
Bill Melton
Norm Cash
Reggie Jackson
91 NL ERA Leaders 1.00 2.50
Tom Seaver
Dave Roberts UER
(Photo actually
Danny Coombs)
Don Wilson
92 AL ERA Leaders 1.00 2.50
Vida Blue
Wilbur Wood
Jim Palmer
93 NL Pitching Leaders 1.50 4.00
Fergie Jenkins
Steve Carlton
Al Downing
Tom Seaver
94 AL Pitching Leaders 1.00 2.50
Mickey Lolich
Vida Blue
Wilbur Wood
95 NL Strikeout Leaders 1.50 4.00
Tom Seaver
Fergie Jenkins
Bill Stoneman
96 AL Strikeout Leaders 1.00 2.50
Mickey Lolich
Vida Blue
Joe Coleman
97 Tom Kelley .25 .60
98 Chuck Tanner MG .50 1.25
99 Ross Grimsley RC .25 .60
100 Frank Robinson 3.00 8.00
101 Rookie Stars 1.00 2.50
Bill Greif RC
J.R. Richard RC
Ray Busse RC
102 Lloyd Allen .25 .60
103 Checklist 133-263 2.50 6.00
104 Toby Harrah RC .50 1.25
105 Gary Gentry .25 .60
106 Milwaukee Brewers TC .60 1.50
107 Jose Cruz RC .50 1.25
108 Gary Waslewski .25 .60
109 Jerry May .25 .60
110 Ron Hunt .25 .60
111 Jim Grant .25 .60
112 Greg Luzinski .50 1.25
113 Rogelio Moret .25 .60
114 Bill Buckner .50 1.25
115 Jim Fregosi .50 1.25
116 Ed Farmer RC .25 .60
117A Cleo James RC .25 .60
(Yellow underline
C and S of Cubs)
117B Cleo James 2.00 5.00
(Green underline
C and S of Cubs)
118 Skip Lockwood .25 .60
119 Marty Perez .25 .60
120 Bill Freehan .50 1.25
121 Ed Sprague .25 .60
122 Larry Biittner RC .25 .60
123 Ed Acosta .25 .60
124 Rookie Stars .25 .60
Alan Closter
Rusty Torres RC
Roger Hambright RC
125 Dave Cash .50 1.25
126 Bart Johnson .25 .60
127 Duffy Dyer .25 .60
128 Eddie Watt .25 .60
129 Charlie Fox MG .25 .60
130 Bob Gibson 3.00 8.00
131 Jim Nettles .25 .60
132 Joe Morgan 2.50 6.00
133 Joe Keough .40 1.00
134 Carl Morton .40 1.00
135 Vada Pinson .75 2.00
136 Darrel Chaney .40 1.00
137 Dick Williams MG .75 2.00
138 Mike Kekich .40 1.00
139 Tim McCarver .75 2.00
140 Pat Dobson .75 2.00
141 Rookie Stars .75 2.00
Buzz Capra RC
Lee Stanton RC
Jon Matlack
142 Chris Chambliss RC 1.50 4.00
143 Garry Jestadt .40 1.00
144 Marty Pattin .40 1.00
145 Don Kessinger .75 2.00
146 Steve Kealey .40 1.00
147 Dave Kingman RC 2.50 6.00
148 Dick Billings .40 1.00
149 Gary Neibauer .40 1.00
150 Norm Cash .75 2.00
151 Jim Brewer .40 1.00
152 Gene Clines .40 1.00
153 Rick Auerbach RC .40 1.00
154 Ted Simmons 1.50 4.00
155 Larry Dierker .40 1.00
156 Minnesota Twins TC .75 2.00
157 Don Gullett .40 1.00
158 Jerry Kenney .40 1.00
159 John Boccabella .40 1.00
160 Andy Messersmith .75 2.00
161 Brock Davis .40 1.00
162 Rookie Stars .75 2.00
Jerry Bell RC
Darrell Porter RC
Bob Reynolds UER
(Porter and Bell
photos switched)
163 Tug McGraw 1.50 4.00
164 Tug McGraw IA .75 2.00
165 Chris Speier RC .75 2.00
166 Chris Speier IA .40 1.00
167 Deron Johnson .40 1.00
168 Deron Johnson IA .40 1.00
169 Vida Blue 1.50 4.00
170 Vida Blue IA .75 2.00
171 Darrell Evans 1.50 4.00
172 Darrell Evans IA .75 2.00
173 Clay Kirby .40 1.00
174 Clay Kirby IA .40 1.00
175 Tom Haller .40 1.00
176 Tom Haller IA .40 1.00
177 Paul Schaal .40 1.00
178 Paul Schaal IA .40 1.00
179 Dock Ellis .40 1.00
180 Dock Ellis IA .40 1.00
181 Ed Kranepool .75 2.00
182 Ed Kranepool IA .40 1.00
183 Bill Melton .40 1.00
184 Bill Melton IA .40 1.00
185 Ron Bryant .40 1.00
186 Ron Bryant IA .40 1.00
187 Gates Brown .40 1.00
188 Frank Lucchesi MG .40 1.00
189 Gene Tenace .75 2.00
190 Dave Giusti .40 1.00
191 Jeff Burroughs RC 1.50 4.00
192 Chicago Cubs TC .75 2.00
193 Kurt Bevacqua RC .40 1.00
194 Fred Norman .40 1.00
195 Orlando Cepeda 2.50 6.00
196 Mel Queen .40 1.00
197 Johnny Briggs .40 1.00
198 Rookie Stars 2.50 6.00
Charlie Hough RC
Bob O'Brien RC
Mike Strahler
199 Mike Fiore .40 1.00
200 Lou Brock 3.00 8.00
201 Phil Roof .40 1.00
202 Scipio Spinks .40 1.00
203 Ron Blomberg RC .40 1.00
204 Tommy Helms .40 1.00
205 Dick Drago .40 1.00
206 Dal Maxvill .40 1.00
207 Tom Egan .40 1.00
208 Milt Pappas .75 2.00
209 Joe Rudi .75 2.00
210 Denny McLain .75 2.00
211 Gary Sutherland .40 1.00
212 Grant Jackson .40 1.00
213 Rookie Stars .40 1.00
Billy Parker RC
Art Kusnyer RC
Tom Silverio RC
214 Mike McQueen .40 1.00
215 Alex Johnson .75 2.00
216 Joe Niekro .75 2.00
217 Roger Metzger .40 1.00
218 Eddie Kasko MG .40 1.00
219 Rennie Stennett RC .75 2.00
220 Jim Perry .75 2.00
221 NL Playoffs .75 2.00
Bucs Champs
222 AL Playoffs 1.50 4.00
Orioles Champs
Brooks Robinson
223 World Series Game 1 .75 2.00
Dave McNally
224 World Series Game 2 .75 2.00
Dave Johnson
Mark Belanger
225 World Series Game 3 .75 2.00
Manny Sanguillen
226 World Series Game 4 3.00 8.00
Roberto Clemente
227 World Series Game 5 .75 2.00
Nellie Briles
228 World Series Game 6 .75 2.00
Frank Robinson
Manny Sanguillen
229 World Series Game 7 .75 2.00
Steve Blass
230 World Series Summary .75 2.00
Pirates Celebrate
231 Casey Cox .40 1.00
232 Rookie Stars .40 1.00
Chris Arnold RC
Jim Barr RC
Dave Rader RC
233 Jay Johnstone .75 2.00
234 Ron Taylor .40 1.00
235 Merv Rettenmund .40 1.00
236 Jim McGlothlin .40 1.00
237 New York Yankees TC .75 2.00
238 Leron Lee .40 1.00
239 Tom Timmermann .40 1.00
240 Rich Allen .75 2.00
241 Rollie Fingers 2.50 6.00
242 Don Mincher .40 1.00
243 Frank Linzy .40 1.00
244 Steve Braun RC .40 1.00
245 Tommie Agee .75 2.00
246 Tom Burgmeier .40 1.00
247 Milt May .40 1.00
248 Tom Bradley .40 1.00
249 Harry Walker MG .40 1.00
250 Boog Powell .75 2.00
251 Checklist 264-394 2.50 6.00
252 Ken Reynolds .40 1.00
253 Sandy Alomar .75 2.00
254 Boots Day .40 1.00
255 Jim Lonborg .75 2.00
256 George Foster .75 2.00
257 Rookie Stars .40 1.00
Jim Foor RC
Tim Hosley RC
Paul Jata RC
258 Randy Hundley .40 1.00
259 Sparky Lyle .75 2.00
260 Ralph Garr .75 2.00
261 Steve Mingori .40 1.00
262 San Diego Padres TC .75 2.00
263 Felipe Alou .75 2.00
264 Tommy John .75 2.00
265 Wes Parker .75 2.00
266 Bobby Bolin .50 1.25
267 Dave Concepcion 1.50 4.00
268 Rookie Stars .50 1.25
Dwain Anderson RC
Chris Floethe RC
269 Don Hahn .50 1.25
270 Jim Palmer 3.00 8.00
271 Ken Rudolph .50 1.25
272 Mickey Rivers RC .75 2.00
273 Bobby Floyd .50 1.25
274 Al Severinsen .50 1.25
275 Cesar Tovar .50 1.25
276 Gene Mauch MG .75 2.00
277 Elliott Maddox .50 1.25
278 Dennis Higgins .50 1.25
279 Larry Brown .50 1.25
280 Willie McCovey 2.50 6.00
281 Bill Parsons RC .50 1.25
282 Houston Astros TC .75 2.00
283 Darrell Brandon .50 1.25
284 Ike Brown .50 1.25
285 Gaylord Perry 2.50 6.00
286 Gene Alley .50 1.25
287 Jim Hardin .50 1.25
288 Johnny Jeter .50 1.25
289 Syd O'Brien .50 1.25
290 Sonny Siebert .50 1.25
291 Hal McRae .75 2.00
292 Hal McRae IA .50 1.25
293 Dan Frisella .50 1.25
294 Dan Frisella IA .50 1.25
295 Dick Dietz .50 1.25
296 Dick Dietz IA .50 1.25
297 Claude Osteen .75 2.00
298 Claude Osteen IA .50 1.25
299 Hank Aaron 12.50 40.00
300 Hank Aaron IA 8.00 20.00
301 George Mitterwald .50 1.25
302 George Mitterwald IA .50 1.25
303 Joe Pepitone .75 2.00
304 Joe Pepitone IA .50 1.25
305 Ken Boswell .50 1.25
306 Ken Boswell IA .50 1.25
307 Steve Renko .50 1.25
308 Steve Renko IA .50 1.25
309 Roberto Clemente 20.00 50.00
310 Roberto Clemente IA 10.00 25.00
311 Clay Carroll .50 1.25
312 Clay Carroll IA .50 1.25
313 Luis Aparicio 2.50 6.00
314 Luis Aparicio IA .75 2.00
315 Paul Splittorff .50 1.25
316 Rookie Stars .75 2.00
Jim Bibby RC
Jorge Roque RC
Santiago Guzman
317 Rich Hand .50 1.25
318 Sonny Jackson .50 1.25
319 Aurelio Rodriguez .50 1.25
320 Steve Blass .75 2.00
321 Joe Lahoud .50 1.25
322 Jose Pena .50 1.25
323 Earl Weaver MG 1.50 4.00
324 Mike Ryan .50 1.25
325 Mel Stottlemyre .75 2.00
326 Pat Kelly .50 1.25
327 Steve Stone RC .75 2.00
328 Boston Red Sox TC .75 2.00
329 Roy Foster .50 1.25
330 Jim Hunter 2.50 6.00
331 Stan Swanson RC .50 1.25
332 Buck Martinez .50 1.25
333 Steve Barber .50 1.25
334 Rookie Stars .50 1.25
Bill Fahey RC
Jim Mason RC
Tom Ragland RC
335 Bill Hands .50 1.25
336 Marty Martinez .50 1.25
337 Mike Kilkenny .50 1.25
338 Bob Grich .75 2.00
339 Ron Cook .50 1.25
340 Roy White .75 2.00
341 Joe Torre KP .50 1.25
342 Wilbur Wood KP .50 1.25
343 Willie Stargell KP .75 2.00
344 Dave McNally KP .50 1.25
345 Rick Wise KP .50 1.25
346 Jim Fregosi KP .50 1.25
347 Tom Seaver KP 1.50 4.00
348 Sal Bando KP .50 1.25
349 Al Fitzmorris .50 1.25
350 Frank Howard .75 2.00
351 Rookie Stars .75 2.00
Tom House
Rick Kester
Jimmy Britton
352 Dave LaRoche .50 1.25
353 Art Shamsky .50 1.25
354 Tom Murphy .50 1.25
355 Bob Watson .75 2.00
356 Gerry Moses .50 1.25
357 Woody Fryman .50 1.25
358 Sparky Anderson MG 1.50 4.00
359 Don Pavletich .50 1.25
360 Dave Roberts .50 1.25
361 Mike Andrews .50 1.25
362 New York Mets TC .75 2.00
363 Ron Klimkowski .50 1.25
364 Johnny Callison .75 2.00
365 Dick Bosman .75 2.00
366 Jimmy Rosario RC .50 1.25
367 Ron Perranoski .50 1.25
368 Danny Thompson .50 1.25
369 Jim Lefebvre .75 2.00
370 Don Buford .50 1.25
371 Denny Lemaster .50 1.25
372 Rookie Stars .50 1.25
Lance Clemons RC
Monty Montgomery RC
373 John Mayberry .75 2.00
374 Jack Heidemann .50 1.25
375 Reggie Cleveland .50 1.25
376 Andy Kosco .50 1.25
377 Terry Harmon .50 1.25
378 Checklist 395-525 2.50 6.00
379 Ken Berry .50 1.25
380 Earl Williams .50 1.25
381 Chicago White Sox TC .75 2.00
382 Joe Gibbon .50 1.25
383 Brant Alyea .50 1.25
384 Dave Campbell .75 2.00
385 Mickey Stanley .75 2.00
386 Jim Colborn .50 1.25
387 Horace Clarke .75 2.00
388 Charlie Williams RC .50 1.25
389 Bill Rigney MG .50 1.25
390 Willie Davis .75 2.00
391 Ken Sanders .50 1.25
392 Rookie Stars .75 2.00
Fred Cambria
Richie Zisk RC
393 Curt Motton .50 1.25
394 Ken Forsch .75 2.00
395 Matty Alou .75 2.00
396 Paul Lindblad .60 1.50
397 Philadelphia Phillies TC .75 2.00
398 Larry Hisle .75 2.00
399 Milt Wilcox .75 2.00
400 Tony Oliva 1.50 4.00
401 Jim Nash .60 1.50
402 Bobby Heise .60 1.50
403 John Cumberland .60 1.50
404 Jeff Torborg .75 2.00
405 Ron Fairly .75 2.00
406 George Hendrick RC .75 2.00
407 Chuck Taylor .60 1.50
408 Jim Northrup .75 2.00
409 Frank Baker .60 1.50
410 Ferguson Jenkins 2.50 6.00
411 Bob Montgomery .60 1.50
412 Dick Kelley .60 1.50
413 Rookie Stars .60 1.50
Don Eddy RC
Dave Lemonds
414 Bob Miller .60 1.50
415 Cookie Rojas .75 2.00
416 Johnny Edwards .60 1.50
417 Tom Hall .60 1.50
418 Tom Shopay .60 1.50
419 Jim Spencer .60 1.50
420 Steve Carlton 8.00 20.00
421 Ellie Rodriguez .60 1.50
422 Ray Lamb .60 1.50
423 Oscar Gamble .75 2.00
424 Bill Gogolewski .60 1.50
425 Ken Singleton .75 2.00
426 Ken Singleton IA .60 1.50
427 Tito Fuentes .60 1.50
428 Tito Fuentes IA .60 1.50
429 Bob Robertson .60 1.50
430 Bob Robertson IA .60 1.50
431 Clarence Gaston .75 2.00
432 Clarence Gaston IA .75 2.00
433 Johnny Bench 10.00 25.00
434 Johnny Bench IA 6.00 15.00
435 Reggie Jackson 12.50 30.00
436 Reggie Jackson IA 5.00 12.00
437 Maury Wills .75 2.00
438 Maury Wills IA .75 2.00
439 Billy Williams 2.50 6.00
440 Billy Williams IA 1.50 4.00
441 Thurman Munson 6.00 15.00
442 Thurman Munson IA 3.00 8.00
443 Ken Henderson .60 1.50
444 Ken Henderson IA .60 1.50
445 Tom Seaver 12.50 30.00
446 Tom Seaver IA 6.00 15.00
447 Willie Stargell 3.00 8.00
448 Willie Stargell IA 1.50 4.00
449 Bob Lemon MG .75 2.00
450 Mickey Lolich .75 2.00
451 Tony LaRussa 1.50 4.00
452 Ed Herrmann .60 1.50
453 Barry Lersch .60 1.50
454 Oakland Athletics TC .75 2.00
455 Tommy Harper .75 2.00
456 Mark Belanger .75 2.00
457 Rookie Stars .60 1.50
Darcy Fast RC
Derrel Thomas RC
Mike Ivie RC
458 Aurelio Monteagudo .60 1.50
459 Rick Renick .60 1.50
460 Al Downing .60 1.50
461 Tim Cullen .60 1.50
462 Rickey Clark .60 1.50
463 Bernie Carbo .60 1.50
464 Jim Roland .60 1.50
465 Gil Hodges MG 1.50 4.00
466 Norm Miller .60 1.50
467 Steve Kline .60 1.50
468 Richie Scheinblum .60 1.50
469 Ron Herbel .60 1.50
470 Ray Fosse .60 1.50
471 Luke Walker .60 1.50
472 Phil Gagliano .60 1.50
473 Dan McGinn .60 1.50
474 Rookie Stars 6.00 15.00
Don Baylor
Roric Harrison RC
Johnny Oates RC
475 Gary Nolan .75 2.00
476 Lee Richard RC .60 1.50
477 Tom Phoebus .60 1.50
478 Checklist 526-656 2.50 6.00
479 Don Shaw .60 1.50
480 Lee May .75 2.00
481 Billy Conigliaro .75 2.00
482 Joe Hoerner .60 1.50
483 Ken Suarez .60 1.50
484 Lum Harris MG .60 1.50
485 Phil Regan .75 2.00
486 John Lowenstein .60 1.50
487 Detroit Tigers TC .75 2.00
488 Mike Nagy .60 1.50
489 Rookie Stars .60 1.50
Terry Humphrey RC
Keith Lampard
490 Dave McNally .75 2.00
491 Lou Piniella KP .75 2.00
492 Mel Stottlemyre KP .75 2.00
493 Bob Bailey KP .75 2.00
494 Willie Horton KP .75 2.00
495 Bill Melton KP .75 2.00
496 Bud Harrelson KP .75 2.00
497 Jim Perry KP .75 2.00
498 Brooks Robinson KP 1.50 4.00
499 Vicente Romo .60 1.50
500 Joe Torre 1.50 4.00
501 Pete Hamm .60 1.50
502 Jackie Hernandez .60 1.50
503 Gary Peters .60 1.50
504 Ed Spiezio .60 1.50
505 Mike Marshall .75 2.00
506 Rookie Stars .60 1.50
Terry Ley RC
Jim Moyer RC
Dick Tidrow RC
507 Fred Gladding .60 1.50
508 Elrod Hendricks .60 1.50
509 Don McMahon .60 1.50
510 Ted Williams MG 5.00 12.00
511 Tony Taylor .75 2.00
512 Paul Popovich .60 1.50
513 Lindy McDaniel .75 2.00
514 Ted Sizemore .60 1.50
515 Bert Blyleven 1.50 4.00
516 Oscar Brown .60 1.50
517 Ken Brett .60 1.50
518 Wayne Garrett .60 1.50
519 Ted Abernathy .60 1.50
520 Larry Bowa .75 2.00
521 Alan Foster .60 1.50
522 Los Angeles Dodgers TC .75 2.00
523 Chuck Dobson .60 1.50
524 Rookie Stars .60 1.50
Ed Armbrister RC
Mel Behney RC
525 Carlos May .75 2.00
526 Bob Bailey 2.50 6.00
527 Dave Leonhard 1.50 4.00
528 Ron Stone 1.50 4.00
529 Dave Nelson 2.50 6.00
530 Don Sutton 5.00 12.00
531 Freddie Patek 2.50 6.00
532 Fred Kendall RC 1.50 4.00
533 Ralph Houk MG 2.50 6.00
534 Jim Hickman 2.50 6.00
535 Ed Brinkman 1.50 4.00
536 Doug Rader 2.50 6.00
537 Bob Locker 1.50 4.00
538 Charlie Sands RC 1.50 4.00
539 Terry Forster RC 2.50 6.00
540 Felix Millan 1.50 4.00
541 Roger Repoz 1.50 4.00
542 Jack Billingham 1.50 4.00
543 Duane Josephson 1.50 4.00
544 Ted Martinez 1.50 4.00
545 Wayne Granger 1.50 4.00
546 Joe Hague 1.50 4.00
547 Cleveland Indians TC 3.00 8.00
548 Frank Reberger 1.50 4.00
549 Dave May 1.50 4.00
550 Brooks Robinson 10.00 25.00
551 Ollie Brown 1.50 4.00
552 Ollie Brown IA 1.50 4.00
553 Wilbur Wood 2.50 6.00
554 Wilbur Wood IA 1.50 4.00
555 Ron Santo 3.00 8.00
556 Ron Santo IA 2.50 6.00
557 John Odom 1.50 4.00
558 John Odom IA 1.50 4.00
559 Pete Rose 20.00 50.00
560 Pete Rose IA 10.00 25.00
561 Leo Cardenas 1.50 4.00
562 Leo Cardenas IA 1.50 4.00
563 Ray Sadecki 1.50 4.00
564 Ray Sadecki IA 1.50 4.00
565 Reggie Smith 2.50 6.00
566 Reggie Smith IA 1.50 4.00
567 Juan Marichal 5.00 12.00
568 Juan Marichal IA 2.50 6.00
569 Ed Kirkpatrick 1.50 4.00
570 Ed Kirkpatrick IA 1.50 4.00
571 Nate Colbert 1.50 4.00
572 Nate Colbert IA 1.50 4.00
573 Fritz Peterson 1.50 4.00
574 Fritz Peterson IA 1.50 4.00
575 Al Oliver 3.00 8.00
576 Leo Durocher MG 2.50 6.00
577 Mike Paul 2.50 6.00
578 Billy Grabarkewitz 1.50 4.00
579 Doyle Alexander RC 2.50 6.00
580 Lou Piniella 2.50 6.00
581 Wade Blasingame 1.50 4.00
582 Montreal Expos TC 3.00 8.00
583 Darold Knowles 1.50 4.00
584 Jerry McNertney 1.50 4.00
585 George Scott 2.50 6.00
586 Denis Menke 1.50 4.00
587 Billy Wilson 1.50 4.00
588 Jim Holt 1.50 4.00
589 Hal Lanier 1.50 4.00
590 Graig Nettles 3.00 8.00
591 Paul Casanova 1.50 4.00
592 Lew Krausse 1.50 4.00
593 Rich Morales 1.50 4.00
594 Jim Beauchamp 1.50 4.00
595 Nolan Ryan 50.00 100.00
596 Manny Mota 2.50 6.00
597 Jim Magnuson RC 1.50 4.00
598 Hal King 2.50 6.00
599 Billy Champion 1.50 4.00
600 Al Kaline 10.00 25.00
601 George Stone 1.50 4.00
602 Dave Bristol MG 1.50 4.00
603 Jim Ray 1.50 4.00
604A Checklist 657-787 5.00 12.00
(Copyright on back
bottom right)
604B Checklist 657-787 5.00 12.00
(Copyright on back
bottom left)
605 Nelson Briles 2.50 6.00
606 Luis Melendez 1.50 4.00
607 Frank Duffy 1.50 4.00
608 Mike Corkins 1.50 4.00
609 Tom Grieve 2.50 6.00
610 Bill Stoneman 2.50 6.00
611 Rich Reese 1.50 4.00
612 Joe Decker 1.50 4.00
613 Mike Ferraro 1.50 4.00
614 Ted Uhlaender 1.50 4.00
615 Steve Hargan 1.50 4.00
616 Joe Ferguson RC 2.50 6.00
617 Kansas City Royals TC 3.00 8.00
618 Rich Robertson 1.50 4.00
619 Rich McKinney 1.50 4.00
620 Phil Niekro 5.00 12.00
621 Comm. Award 3.00 8.00
622 MVP Award 3.00 8.00
623 Cy Young Award 3.00 8.00
624 Minor League Player 3.00 8.00
of the Year Award
625 Rookie of the Year 3.00 8.00
626 Babe Ruth Award 3.00 8.00
627 Moe Drabowsky 1.50 4.00
628 Terry Crowley 1.50 4.00
629 Paul Doyle 1.50 4.00
630 Rich Hebner 2.50 6.00
631 John Strohmayer 1.50 4.00
632 Mike Hegan 1.50 4.00
633 Jack Hiatt 1.50 4.00
634 Dick Woodson 1.50 4.00
635 Don Money 2.50 6.00
636 Bill Lee 2.50 6.00
637 Preston Gomez MG 1.50 4.00
638 Ken Wright 1.50 4.00
639 J.C. Martin 1.50 4.00
640 Joe Coleman 1.50 4.00
641 Mike Lum 1.50 4.00
642 Dennis Riddleberger RC 1.50 4.00
643 Russ Gibson 1.50 4.00
644 Bernie Allen 1.50 4.00
645 Jim Maloney 2.50 6.00
646 Chico Salmon 1.50 4.00
647 Bob Moose 1.50 4.00
648 Jim Lyttle 1.50 4.00
649 Pete Richert 1.50 4.00
650 Sal Bando 2.50 6.00
651 Cincinnati Reds TC 3.00 8.00
652 Marcelino Lopez 1.50 4.00
653 Jim Fairey 1.50 4.00
654 Horacio Pina 2.50 6.00

655 Jerry Grote 1.50 4.00
656 Rudy May 1.50 4.00
657 Bobby Wine 5.00 12.00
658 Steve Dunning 5.00 12.00
659 Bob Aspromonte 5.00 12.00
660 Paul Blair 6.00 15.00
661 Bill Virdon MG 5.00 12.00
662 Stan Bahnsen 5.00 12.00
663 Fran Healy RC 6.00 15.00
664 Bobby Knoop 5.00 12.00
665 Chris Short 5.00 12.00
666 Hector Torres 5.00 12.00
667 Ray Newman RC 5.00 12.00
668 Texas Rangers TC 12.50 30.00
669 Willie Crawford 5.00 12.00
670 Ken Holtzman 6.00 15.00
671 Donn Clendenon 6.00 15.00
672 Archie Reynolds 5.00 12.00
673 Dave Marshall 5.00 12.00
674 John Kennedy 5.00 12.00
675 Pat Jarvis 5.00 12.00
676 Danny Cater 5.00 12.00
677 Ivan Murrell 5.00 12.00
678 Steve Luebber RC 5.00 12.00
679 Rookie Stars 5.00 12.00
Bob Fenwick RC
Bob Stinson
680 Dave Johnson 6.00 15.00
681 Bobby Pfeil 5.00 12.00
682 Mike McCormick 6.00 15.00
683 Steve Hovley 5.00 12.00
684 Hal Breeden RC 5.00 12.00
685 Joel Horlen 5.00 12.00
686 Steve Garvey 12.50 40.00
687 Del Unser 5.00 12.00
688 St. Louis Cardinals TC 8.00 20.00
689 Eddie Fisher 5.00 12.00
690 Willie Montanez 6.00 15.00
691 Curt Blefary 5.00 12.00
692 Curt Blefary IA 5.00 12.00
693 Alan Gallagher 5.00 12.00
694 Alan Gallagher IA 5.00 12.00
695 Rod Carew 20.00 50.00
696 Rod Carew IA 12.50 30.00
697 Jerry Koosman 6.00 15.00
698 Jerry Koosman IA 6.00 15.00
699 Bobby Murcer 6.00 15.00
700 Bobby Murcer IA 6.00 15.00
701 Jose Pagan 5.00 12.00
702 Jose Pagan IA 5.00 12.00
703 Doug Griffin 5.00 12.00
704 Doug Griffin IA 5.00 12.00
705 Pat Corrales 6.00 15.00
706 Pat Corrales IA 6.00 15.00
707 Tim Foli 5.00 12.00
708 Tim Foli IA 5.00 12.00
709 Jim Kaat 6.00 15.00
710 Jim Kaat IA 6.00 15.00
711 Bobby Bonds 8.00 20.00
712 Bobby Bonds IA 6.00 15.00
713 Gene Michael 8.00 20.00
714 Gene Michael IA 6.00 15.00
715 Mike Epstein 5.00 12.00
716 Jesus Alou 5.00 12.00
717 Bruce Dal Canton 5.00 12.00
718 Del Rice MG 5.00 12.00
719 Cesar Geronimo 5.00 12.00
720 Sam McDowell 6.00 15.00
721 Eddie Leon 5.00 12.00
722 Bill Sudakis 5.00 12.00
723 Al Santorini 5.00 12.00
724 Rookie Stars 5.00 12.00
John Curtis RC
Rich Hinton RC
Mickey Scott
725 Dick McAuliffe 6.00 15.00
726 Dick Selma 5.00 12.00
727 Jose Laboy 5.00 12.00
728 Gail Hopkins 5.00 12.00
729 Bob Veale 6.00 15.00
730 Rick Monday 6.00 15.00
731 Baltimore Orioles TC 8.00 20.00
732 George Culver 5.00 12.00
733 Jim Ray Hart 6.00 15.00
734 Bob Burda 5.00 12.00
735 Diego Segui 5.00 12.00
736 Bill Russell 6.00 15.00
737 Len Randle RC 6.00 15.00
738 Jim Merritt 5.00 12.00
739 Don Mason 5.00 12.00
740 Rico Carty 6.00 15.00
741 Rookie Stars 6.00 15.00
Tom Hutton
John Milner RC
Rick Miller RC
742 Jim Rooker 5.00 12.00
743 Cesar Gutierrez 5.00 12.00
744 Jim Slaton RC 5.00 12.00
745 Julian Javier 6.00 15.00
746 Lowell Palmer 5.00 12.00
747 Jim Stewart 5.00 12.00
748 Phil Hennigan 5.00 12.00
749 Walter Alston MG 8.00 20.00
750 Willie Horton 6.00 15.00
751 Steve Carlton TR 12.50 40.00
752 Joe Morgan TR 12.50 40.00
753 Denny McLain TR 8.00 20.00
754 Frank Robinson TR 12.50 40.00
755 Jim Fregosi TR 6.00 15.00
756 Rick Wise TR 6.00 15.00
757 Jose Cardenal TR 6.00 15.00
758 Gil Garrido 5.00 12.00
759 Chris Cannizzaro 5.00 12.00
760 Bill Mazeroski 10.00 25.00
761 Rookie Stars 10.00 25.00
Ben Oglivie RC
Ron Cey RC
Bernie Williams
762 Wayne Simpson 5.00 12.00
763 Ron Hansen 5.00 12.00
764 Dusty Baker 8.00 20.00
765 Ken McMullen 5.00 12.00
766 Steve Hamilton 5.00 12.00
767 Tom McCraw 6.00 15.00
768 Denny Doyle 5.00 12.00
769 Jack Aker 5.00 12.00
770 Jim Wynn 6.00 15.00
771 San Francisco Giants TC 8.00 20.00
772 Ken Tatum 5.00 12.00
773 Ron Brand 5.00 12.00
774 Luis Alvarado 5.00 12.00
775 Jerry Reuss 6.00 15.00
776 Bill Voss 5.00 12.00
777 Hoyt Wilhelm 10.00 25.00
778 Rookie Stars 8.00 20.00
Vic Albury RC
Rick Dempsey RC
Jim Strickland RC
779 Tony Cloninger 5.00 12.00
780 Dick Green 5.00 12.00
781 Jim McAndrew 5.00 12.00
782 Larry Stahl 5.00 12.00
783 Les Cain 5.00 12.00
784 Ken Aspromonte 5.00 12.00
785 Vic Davalillo 5.00 12.00
786 Chuck Brinkman 5.00 12.00
787 Ron Reed 6.00 15.00

1973 Topps

The cards in this 660-card set measure 2 1/2" by 3 1/2". The 1973 Topps set marked the last year in which Topps marketed baseball cards in consecutive series. The last series (529-660) is more difficult to obtain. In some parts of the country, however, all five series were distributed together. Beginning in 1974, all Topps cards were printed at the same time, thus eliminating the "high number" factor. The set features team leader cards with small individual pictures of the coaching staff members and a larger picture of the manager. The "background" variations below with respect to these leader cards are subtle and are best understood after a side-by-side comparison of the two varieties. An "All-Time Leaders" series (471-478) appeared for the first time in this set. Kid Pictures appeared again for the second year in a row (341-346). Other topical subsets within the set included League Leaders (61-68), Playoffs cards (201-202), World Series cards (203-210), and Rookie Prospects (601-616). For the fourth and final time, cards were issued in ten-card dime packs which were issued 24 packs to a box, in addition, these cards were also released in 54-card rack packs which cost 39 cents upon release. The key Rookie Cards in this set are all in the Rookie Prospect series: Bob Boone, Dwight Evans, and Mike Schmidt.

COMPLETE SET (660) 350.00 700.00
COMMON CARD (1-264) .20 .50
COMMON (265-396) .30 .75
COMMON (397-528) .50 1.25
COMMON (529-660) 1.25 3.00
WRAP. (10-CENT, BAT) 6.00 15.00
WRAPPER (10-CENT) 6.00 15.00
1 Babe Ruth 714 12.50 40.00
Hank Aaron 673
Willie Mays 654
All-Time Home Run Leaders
2 Rich Hebner .60 1.50
3 Jim Lonborg .60 1.50
4 John Milner .20 .50
5 Ed Brinkman .20 .50
6 Mac Scarce RC .20 .50
7 Texas Rangers TC .75 2.00
8 Tom Hall .20 .50
9 Johnny Oates .60 1.50
10 Don Sutton 1.50 4.00
11 Chris Chambliss UER .60 1.50
His Home town is spelled incorrectly
12A Don Zimmer MG 1.25 3.00
Dave Garcia CO
Johnny Podres CO
Bob Skinner CO
Whitey Wietelmann CO
(Podres no right ear)
12B Don Zimmer MG .30 .75
Dave Garcia CO
Johnny Podres CO
Bob Skinner CO
Whitey Wietelmann CO
(Podres has right ear)
13 George Hendrick .60 1.50
14 Sonny Siebert .20 .50
15 Ralph Garr .60 1.50
16 Steve Braun .20 .50
17 Fred Gladding .20 .50
18 Leroy Stanton .20 .50
19 Tim Foli .20 .50
20 Stan Bahnsen .20 .50
21 Randy Hundley .60 1.50
22 Ted Abernathy .20 .50
23 Dave Kingman .60 1.50
24 Al Santorini .20 .50
25 Roy White .60 1.50
26 Pittsburgh Pirates TC .75 2.00
27 Bill Gogolewski .20 .50
28 Hal McRae .60 1.50
29 Tony Taylor .60 1.50
30 Tug McGraw .60 1.50
31 Buddy Bell RC 1.00 2.50
32 Fred Norman .20 .50
33 Jim Breazeale RC .20 .50
34 Pat Dobson .20 .50
35 Willie Davis .60 1.50
36 Steve Barber .20 .50
37 Bill Robinson .60 1.50
38 Mike Epstein .20 .50
39 Dave Roberts .20 .50
40 Reggie Smith .60 1.50
41 Tom Walker RC .20 .50
42 Mike Andrews .20 .50
43 Randy Moffitt RC .20 .50
44 Rick Monday .60 1.50
45 Ellie Rodriguez UER .20 .50
(Photo is either John Felske or Paul Ratliff
46 Lindy McDaniel .60 1.50
47 Luis Melendez .20 .50
48 Paul Splittorff .20 .50
49A Frank Quilici MG 1.25 3.00
Vern Morgan CO
Bob Rodgers CO
Ralph Rowe CO
Al Worthington CO
(Solid backgrounds)
49B Frank Quilici MG .30 .75
Vern Morgan CO
Bob Rodgers CO
Ralph Rowe CO
Al Worthington CO
(Natural backgrounds)
50 Roberto Clemente 12.50 40.00
51 Chuck Seelbach RC .20 .50
52 Denis Menke .20 .50
53 Steve Dunning .20 .50
54 Checklist 1-132 1.25 3.00
55 Jon Matlack .60 1.50
56 Merv Rettenmund .20 .50
57 Derrel Thomas .20 .50
58 Mike Paul .20 .50
59 Steve Yeager RC .60 1.50
60 Ken Holtzman .60 1.50
61 Batting Leaders 1.00 2.50
Billy Williams
Rod Carew
62 Home Run Leaders 1.00 2.50
Johnny Bench
Dick Allen
63 RBI Leaders 1.00 2.50
Johnny Bench
Dick Allen
64 Stolen Base Leaders .60 1.50
Lou Brock
Bert Campaneris
65 ERA Leaders .60 1.50
Steve Carlton
Luis Tiant
66 Victory Leaders .60 1.50
Steve Carlton
Gaylord Perry
Wilbur Wood
67 Strikeout Leaders 10.00 25.00
Steve Carlton
Nolan Ryan
68 Leading Firemen .60 1.50
Clay Carroll
Sparky Lyle
69 Phil Gagliano .20 .50
70 Milt Pappas .60 1.50
71 Johnny Briggs .20 .50
72 Ron Reed .20 .50
73 Ed Herrmann .20 .50
74 Billy Champion .20 .50
75 Vada Pinson .60 1.50
76 Doug Rader .20 .50
77 Mike Torrez .60 1.50
78 Richie Scheinblum .20 .50
79 Jim Willoughby RC .20 .50
80 Tony Oliva UER 1.00 2.50
(Minnseota on front)
81A Whitey Lockman MG .60 1.50
Hank Aguirre CO
Ernie Banks CO
Larry Jansen CO
Pete Reiser CO
(Solid backgrounds)
81B Whitey Lockman MG .60 1.50
Hank Aguirre CO
Ernie Banks CO
Larry Jansen CO
Pete Reiser CO
(Natural backgrounds)
82 Fritz Peterson .20 .50
83 Leron Lee .20 .50
84 Rollie Fingers 1.50 4.00
85 Ted Simmons .60 1.50
86 Tom McCraw .20 .50
87 Ken Boswell .20 .50
88 Mickey Stanley .60 1.50
89 Jack Billingham .20 .50
90 Brooks Robinson 3.00 8.00
91 Los Angeles Dodgers TC .75 2.00
92 Jerry Bell .20 .50
93 Jesus Alou .20 .50
94 Dick Billings .20 .50
95 Steve Blass .60 1.50
96 Doug Griffin .20 .50
97 Willie Montanez .60 1.50
98 Dick Woodson .20 .50
99 Carl Taylor .20 .50
100 Hank Aaron 12.50 40.00
101 Ken Henderson .20 .50
102 Rudy May .20 .50
103 Celerino Sanchez RC .20 .50
104 Reggie Cleveland .20 .50
105 Carlos May .20 .50
106 Terry Humphrey .20 .50
107 Phil Hennigan .20 .50
108 Bill Russell .60 1.50
109 Doyle Alexander .60 1.50
110 Bob Watson .60 1.50
111 Dave Nelson .20 .50
112 Gary Ross .20 .50
113 Jerry Grote .60 1.50
114 Lynn McGlothen RC .20 .50
115 Ron Santo .60 1.50
116A Ralph Houk MG 1.25 3.00
Jim Hegan CO
Elston Howard CO
Dick Howser CO
Jim Turner CO
(Solid backgrounds)
116B Ralph Houk MG .30 .75
Jim Hegan CO
Elston Howard CO
Dick Howser CO
Jim Turner CO
(Natural backgrounds)
117 Ramon Hernandez .20 .50
118 John Mayberry .60 1.50
119 Larry Bowa .60 1.50
120 Joe Coleman .20 .50
121 Dave Rader .20 .50
122 Jim Strickland .20 .50
123 Sandy Alomar .60 1.50
124 Jim Hardin .20 .50
125 Ron Fairly .60 1.50
126 Jim Brewer .20 .50
127 Milwaukee Brewers TC .75 2.00
128 Ted Sizemore .20 .50
129 Terry Forster .60 1.50
130 Pete Rose 12.50 30.00
131A Eddie Kasko MG 1.25 3.00
Doug Camilli CO
Don Lenhardt CO
Eddie Popowski CO
(No right ear)
Lee Stange CO
131B Eddie Kasko MG .60 1.50
Doug Camilli CO
Don Lenhardt CO
Eddie Popowski CO
(Right ear showing)
Lee Stange CO
132 Matty Alou .60 1.50
133 Dave Roberts RC .20 .50
134 Milt Wilcox .20 .50
135 Lee May UER .60 1.50
(Career average .000)
136A Earl Weaver MG .60 1.50
George Bamberger CO
Jim Frey CO
Billy Hunter CO
George Staller CO
(Orange background)
136B Earl Weaver MG 1.25 3.00
George Bamberger CO
Jim Frey CO
Billy Hunter CO
George Staller CO
(Dark Pale background)
137 Jim Beauchamp .20 .50
138 Horacio Pina .20 .50
139 Carmen Fanzone RC .20 .50
140 Lou Piniella 1.00 2.50
141 Bruce Kison .20 .50
142 Thurman Munson 3.00 8.00
143 John Curtis .20 .50
144 Marty Perez .20 .50
145 Bobby Bonds 1.00 2.50
146 Woodie Fryman .20 .50
147 Mike Anderson .20 .50
148 Dave Goltz .20 .50
149 Ron Hunt .20 .50
150 Wilbur Wood .60 1.50
151 Wes Parker .60 1.50
152 Dave May .20 .50
153 Al Hrabosky .60 1.50
154 Jeff Torborg .60 1.50
155 Sal Bando .60 1.50
156 Cesar Geronimo .20 .50
157 Denny Riddleberger .20 .50
158 Houston Astros TC .75 2.00
159 Clarence Gaston .60 1.50
160 Jim Palmer 2.50 6.00
161 Ted Martinez .20 .50
162 Pete Broberg .20 .50
163 Vic Davalillo .20 .50
164 Monty Montgomery .20 .50
165 Luis Aparicio 1.50 4.00
166 Terry Harmon .20 .50
167 Steve Stone .60 1.50
168 Jim Northrup .60 1.50
169 Ron Schueler RC .60 1.50
170 Harmon Killebrew 2.00 5.00
171 Bernie Carbo .20 .50
172 Steve Kline .20 .50
173 Hal Breeden .20 .50
174 Goose Gossage RC 2.50 6.00
175 Frank Robinson 2.50 6.00
176 Chuck Taylor .20 .50
177 Bill Plummer RC .20 .50
178 Don Rose RC .20 .50
179A Dick Williams MG 1.50 4.00
Jerry Adair CO
Vern Hoscheit CO
Irv Noren CO
Wes Stock CO
(Hoscheit left ear
showing)
179B Dick Williams MG .60 1.50
Jerry Adair CO
Vern Hoscheit CO
Irv Noren CO
Wes Stock CO
(Hoscheit left ear
not showing)
180 Ferguson Jenkins 1.50 4.00
181 Jack Brohamer RC .20 .50
182 Mike Caldwell RC .60 1.50
183 Don Buford .20 .50
184 Jerry Koosman .60 1.50
185 Jim Wynn .60 1.50
186 Bill Fahey .20 .50
187 Luke Walker .20 .50
188 Cookie Rojas .60 1.50
189 Greg Luzinski 1.00 2.50
190 Bob Gibson 3.00 8.00
191 Detroit Tigers TC 1.00 2.50
192 Pat Jarvis .20 .50
193 Carlton Fisk 4.00 10.00
194 Jorge Orta RC .20 .50
195 Clay Carroll .20 .50
196 Ken McMullen .20 .50
197 Ed Goodson RC .20 .50
198 Horace Clarke .20 .50
199 Bert Blyleven 1.00 2.50
200 Billy Williams 1.50 4.00
201 AL Playoffs .60 1.50
George Hendrick
202 NL Playoff .60 1.50
George Foster
203 World Series Game 1 .60 1.50
Gene Tenace
204 World Series Game 2 .60 1.50
A's Two Straight
205 World Series Game 3 1.00 2.50
Tony Perez
206 World Series Game 4 .60 1.50
Gene Tenace
207 World Series Game 5 .60 1.50
Blue Moon Odom
208 World Series Game 6 2.00 5.00
Johnny Bench
209 World Series Game 7 .60 1.50
Bert Campaneris
210 World Series Summary .20 .50
World Champions
A's Win
211 Balor Moore .20 .50
212 Joe Lahoud .20 .50
213 Steve Garvey 2.00 5.00
214 Dave Hamilton RC .20 .50
215 Dusty Baker 1.00 2.50
216 Toby Harrah .60 1.50
217 Don Wilson .20 .50
218 Aurelio Rodriguez .20 .50
219 St. Louis Cardinals TC 1.00 2.50
220 Nolan Ryan 20.00 50.00
221 Fred Kendall .20 .50
222 Rob Gardner .20 .50
223 Bud Harrelson .60 1.50
224 Bill Lee .60 1.50
225 Al Oliver .60 1.50
226 Ray Fosse .20 .50
227 Wayne Twitchell .20 .50
228 Bobby Darwin .20 .50
229 Roric Harrison .20 .50
230 Joe Morgan 2.50 6.00
231 Bill Parsons .20 .50
232 Ken Singleton .60 1.50
233 Ed Kirkpatrick .20 .50
234 Bill North RC .20 .50
235 Jim Hunter 1.50 4.00
236 Tito Fuentes .20 .50
237A Eddie Mathews MG .60 1.50
Lew Burdette CO
Jim Busby CO
Roy Hartsfield CO
Ken Silvestri CO
(Burdette right ear
showing)
237B Eddie Mathews MG 1.25 3.00
Lew Burdette CO
Jim Busby CO
Roy Hartsfield CO
Ken Silvestri CO
(Burdette right ear
not showing)
238 Tony Muser RC .20 .50
239 Pete Richert .20 .50
240 Bobby Murcer .60 1.50
241 Dwain Anderson .20 .50
242 George Culver .20 .50
243 California Angels TC 1.00 2.50
244 Ed Acosta .20 .50
245 Carl Yastrzemski 4.00 10.00
246 Ken Sanders .20 .50
247 Del Unser .20 .50
248 Jerry Johnson .20 .50
249 Larry Biittner .20 .50
250 Manny Sanguillen .60 1.50
251 Roger Nelson .20 .50
252A Charlie Fox MG 1.50 4.00
Joe Amalfitano CO
Andy Gilbert CO
Don McMahon CO
John McNamara CO
(Orange background)
252B Charlie Fox MG .60 1.50
Joe Amalfitano CO
Andy Gilbert CO
Don McMahon CO
John McNamara CO
(Dark Pale background)
253 Mark Belanger .60 1.50
254 Bill Stoneman .20 .50
255 Reggie Jackson 6.00 15.00
256 Chris Zachary .20 .50
257A Yogi Berra MG 1.25 3.00
Roy McMillan CO
Joe Pignatano CO
Rube Walker CO
Eddie Yost CO
(Orange background)
257B Yogi Berra MG 2.00 5.00
Roy McMillan CO
Joe Pignatano CO
Rube Walker CO
Eddie Yost CO
(Dark Pale Orange background)
258 Tommy John .60 1.50
259 Jim Holt .20 .50
260 Gary Nolan .60 1.50
261 Pat Kelly .20 .50
262 Jack Aker .20 .50
263 George Scott .60 1.50
264 Checklist 133-264 1.25 3.00
265 Gene Michael .60 1.50
266 Mike Lum .30 .75
267 Lloyd Allen .30 .75
268 Jerry Morales .30 .75
269 Tim McCarver .60 1.50
270 Luis Tiant .60 1.50
271 Tom Hutton .30 .75
272 Ed Farmer .30 .75
273 Chris Speier .30 .75
274 Darold Knowles .30 .75
275 Tony Perez 1.50 4.00
276 Joe Lovitto RC .30 .75
277 Bob Miller .30 .75
278 Baltimore Orioles TC .60 1.50
279 Mike Strahler .30 .75
280 Al Kaline 3.00 8.00
281 Mike Jorgensen .30 .75
282 Steve Hovley .30 .75
283 Ray Sadecki .30 .75
284 Glenn Borgmann RC .30 .75
285 Don Kessinger .60 1.50
286 Frank Linzy .30 .75
287 Eddie Leon .30 .75
288 Gary Gentry .30 .75
289 Bob Oliver .30 .75
290 Cesar Cedeno .60 1.50
291 Rogelio Moret .30 .75
292 Jose Cruz .60 1.50
293 Bernie Allen .30 .75
294 Steve Arlin .30 .75
295 Bert Campaneris .60 1.50
296 Sparky Anderson MG 1.00 2.50
Alex Grammas CO
Ted Kluszewski CO
George Scherger CO
Larry Shepard CO
297 Walt Williams .30 .75
298 Ron Bryant .30 .75
299 Ted Ford .30 .75
300 Steve Carlton 4.00 10.00
301 Billy Grabarkewitz .30 .75
302 Terry Crowley .30 .75
303 Nelson Briles .30 .75
304 Duke Sims .30 .75
305 Willie Mays 12.50 40.00
306 Tom Burgmeier .30 .75
307 Boots Day .30 .75
308 Skip Lockwood .30 .75
309 Paul Popovich .30 .75
310 Dick Allen .60 1.50
311 Joe Decker .30 .75
312 Oscar Brown .30 .75
313 Jim Ray .30 .75
314 Ron Swoboda .60 1.50
315 John Odom .30 .75
316 San Diego Padres TC .60 1.50
317 Danny Cater .30 .75
318 Jim McGlothlin .30 .75
319 Jim Spencer .30 .75
320 Lou Brock 3.00 8.00
321 Rich Hinton .30 .75
322 Garry Maddox RC .60 1.50
323 Billy Martin MG .60 1.50
Art Fowler CO
Charlie Silvera CO
Dick Tracewski CO
Joe Schultz CO UER
Schult's name not printed on card
324 Al Downing .30 .75
325 Boog Powell .60 1.50
326 Darrell Brandon .30 .75
327 John Lowenstein .30 .75
328 Bill Bonham .30 .75
329 Ed Kranepool .60 1.50
330 Rod Carew 3.00 8.00
331 Carl Morton .30 .75
332 John Felske RC .30 .75
333 Gene Clines .30 .75
334 Freddie Patek .30 .75
335 Bob Tolan .30 .75
336 Tom Bradley .30 .75
337 Dave Duncan .60 1.50
338 Checklist 265-396 1.25 3.00
339 Dick Tidrow .30 .75
340 Nate Colbert .30 .75
341 Jim Palmer KP 1.00 2.50
342 Sam McDowell KP .30 .75
343 Bobby Murcer KP .30 .75
344 Jim Hunter KP 1.00 2.50
345 Chris Speier KP .30 .75
346 Gaylord Perry KP .60 1.50
347 Kansas City Royals TC .60 1.50
348 Rennie Stennett .30 .75
349 Dick McAuliffe .30 .75
350 Tom Seaver 5.00 12.00
351 Jimmy Stewart .30 .75
352 Don Stanhouse RC .30 .75
353 Steve Brye .30 .75
354 Billy Parker .30 .75
355 Mike Marshall .60 1.50
356 Chuck Tanner MG 1.50 4.00
Joe Lonnett CO
Jim Mahoney CO
Al Monchak CO
Johnny Sain CO
357 Ross Grimsley .30 .75
358 Jim Nettles .30 .75
359 Cecil Upshaw .30 .75
360 Joe Rudi UER .60 1.50
(Photo actually
Gene Tenace)
361 Fran Healy .30 .75
362 Eddie Watt .30 .75
363 Jackie Hernandez .30 .75
364 Rick Wise .30 .75
365 Rico Petrocelli .60 1.50
366 Brock Davis .30 .75
367 Burt Hooton .60 1.50
368 Bill Buckner .60 1.50
369 Lerrin LaGrow .30 .75
370 Willie Stargell 2.00 5.00
371 Mike Kekich .30 .75
372 Oscar Gamble .30 .75
373 Clyde Wright .30 .75
374 Darrell Evans .60 1.50
375 Larry Dierker .60 1.50
376 Frank Duffy .30 .75
377 Gene Mauch MG 1.50 4.00
Dave Bristol CO
Larry Doby CO
Cal McLish CO
Jerry Zimmerman CO
378 Len Randle .30 .75
379 Cy Acosta RC .30 .75
380 Johnny Bench 5.00 12.00
381 Vicente Romo .30 .75
382 Mike Hegan .30 .75
383 Diego Segui .30 .75
384 Don Baylor 1.50 4.00
385 Jim Perry .60 1.50
386 Don Money .60 1.50
387 Jim Barr .30 .75
388 Ben Oglivie .60 1.50
389 New York Mets TC 1.50 4.00
390 Mickey Lolich .60 1.50
391 Lee Lacy RC .60 1.50
392 Dick Drago .30 .75
393 Jose Cardenal .30 .75
394 Sparky Lyle .60 1.50
395 Roger Metzger .30 .75
396 Grant Jackson .30 .75
397 Dave Cash .50 1.25
398 Rich Hand .50 1.25
399 George Foster .75 2.00
400 Gaylord Perry 2.00 5.00
401 Clyde Mashore .50 1.25
402 Jack Hiatt .50 1.25
403 Sonny Jackson .50 1.25
404 Chuck Brinkman .50 1.25
405 Cesar Tovar .50 1.25
406 Paul Lindblad .50 1.25
407 Felix Millan .50 1.25
408 Jim Colborn .50 1.25
409 Ivan Murrell .50 1.25
410 Willie McCovey 2.50 6.00
(Bench behind plate)
411 Ray Corbin .50 1.25
412 Manny Mota .75 2.00
413 Tom Timmermann .50 1.25
414 Ken Rudolph .50 1.25
415 Marty Pattin .50 1.25
416 Paul Schaal .50 1.25
417 Scipio Spinks .50 1.25
418 Bob Grich .75 2.00
419 Casey Cox .50 1.25
420 Tommie Agee .50 1.25

421A Bobby Winkles MG RC .60 1.50
Tom Morgan CO
Salty Parker CO
Jimmie Reese CO
John Roseboro CO
(Orange background)
421B Bobby Winkles MG 1.25 3.00
Tom Morgan CO
Salty Parker CO
Jimmie Reese CO
John Roseboro CO
(Dark Pale background)
422 Bob Robertson .50 1.25
423 Johnny Jeter .50 1.25
424 Denny Doyle .50 1.25
425 Alex Johnson .50 1.25
426 Dave LaRoche .50 1.25
427 Rick Auerbach .50 1.25
428 Wayne Simpson .50 1.25
429 Jim Fairey .50 1.25
430 Vida Blue .75 2.00
431 Gerry Moses .50 1.25
432 Dan Frisella .50 1.25
433 Willie Horton .75 2.00
434 San Francisco Giants TC 1.25 3.00
435 Rico Carty .75 2.00
436 Jim McAndrew .50 1.25
437 John Kennedy .50 1.25
438 Enzo Hernandez .50 1.25
439 Eddie Fisher .50 1.25
440 Glenn Beckert .50 1.25
441 Gail Hopkins .50 1.25
442 Dick Dietz .50 1.25
443 Danny Thompson .50 1.25
444 Ken Brett .50 1.25
445 Ken Berry .50 1.25
446 Jerry Reuss .75 2.00
447 Joe Hague .50 1.25
448 John Hiller .50 1.25
449A Ken Aspromonte MG 1.50 4.00
Rocky Colavito CO
Joe Lutz CO
Warren Spahn CO
(Spahn's right
ear pointed)
449B Ken Aspromonte MG 1.50 4.00
Rocky Colavito CO
Joe Lutz CO
Warren Spahn CO
(Spahn's right
ear round)
450 Joe Torre 1.25 3.00
451 John Vukovich RC .50 1.25
452 Paul Casanova .50 1.25
453 Checklist 397-528 1.25 3.00
454 Tom Haller .50 1.25
455 Bill Melton .50 1.25
456 Dick Green .50 1.25
457 John Strohmayer .50 1.25
458 Jim Mason .50 1.25
459 Jimmy Howarth RC .50 1.25
460 Bill Freehan .75 2.00
461 Mike Corkins .50 1.25
462 Ron Blomberg .50 1.25
463 Ken Tatum .50 1.25
464 Chicago Cubs TC 1.25 3.00
465 Dave Giusti .50 1.25
466 Jose Arcia .50 1.25
467 Mike Ryan .50 1.25
468 Tom Griffin .50 1.25
469 Dan Monzon RC .50 1.25
470 Mike Cuellar .75 2.00
471 Ty Cobb 4.00 10.00
All-Time Hit Leader
472 Lou Gehrig 6.00 15.00
All-Time Grand Slam Leader
473 Hank Aaron 4.00 10.00
All-Time Total Base Leader
474 Babe Ruth 8.00 20.00
All-Time RBI Leader
475 Ty Cobb 3.00 8.00
All-Time Batting Leader
476 Walter Johnson 1.25 3.00
All-Time Shutout Leader
477 Cy Young 1.25 3.00
All-Time Victory Leader
478 Walter Johnson 1.25 3.00
All-Time Strikeout Leader
479 Hal Lanier .50 1.25
480 Juan Marichal 2.00 5.00
481 Chicago White Sox TC 1.25 3.00
482 Rick Reuschel RC 1.25 3.00
483 Dal Maxvill .50 1.25
484 Ernie McAnally .50 1.25
485 Norm Cash .75 2.00
486A Danny Ozark MG RC .60 1.50
Carroll Beringer CO
Billy DeMars CO
Ray Rippelmeyer CO
Bobby Wine CO
(Orange background)
486B Danny Ozark MG 1.25 3.00
Carroll Beringer CO
Billy DeMars CO
Ray Rippelmeyer CO
Bobby Wine CO
(Dark Pale background)
487 Bruce Dal Canton .50 1.25
488 Dave Campbell .75 2.00
489 Jeff Burroughs .75 2.00
490 Claude Osteen .75 2.00
491 Bob Montgomery .50 1.25
492 Pedro Borbon .50 1.25
493 Duffy Dyer .50 1.25
494 Rich Morales .50 1.25
495 Tommy Helms .50 1.25
496 Ray Lamb .50 1.25
497A Red Schoendienst MG .75 2.00
Vern Benson CO
George Kissell CO
Barney Schultz CO
(Orange background)
497B Red Schoendienst MG 1.25 3.00
Vern Benson CO
George Kissell CO
Barney Schultz CO
(Dark Pale background)
498 Graig Nettles 1.25 3.00
499 Bob Moose .50 1.25
500 Oakland Athletics TC 1.25 3.00
501 Larry Gura .50 1.25
502 Bobby Valentine 1.25 3.00
503 Phil Niekro 2.00 5.00
504 Earl Williams .50 1.25
505 Bob Bailey .50 1.25
506 Bart Johnson .50 1.25
507 Darrel Chaney .50 1.25
508 Gates Brown .50 1.25
509 Jim Nash .50 1.25
510 Amos Otis .75 2.00
511 Sam McDowell .75 2.00
512 Dalton Jones .50 1.25
513 Dave Marshall .50 1.25
514 Jerry Kenney .50 1.25
515 Andy Messersmith .75 2.00
516 Danny Walton .50 1.25
517A Bill Virdon MG .60 1.50
Don Leppert CO
Bill Mazeroski CO
Dave Ricketts CO
Mel Wright CO
(Mazeroski has
no right ear)
517B Bill Virdon MG 1.25 3.00
Don Leppert CO
Bill Mazeroski CO
Dave Ricketts CO
Mel Wright CO
(Mazeroski has
right ear)
518 Bob Veale .50 1.25
519 Johnny Edwards .50 1.25
520 Mel Stottlemyre .75 2.00
521 Atlanta Braves TC 1.25 3.00
522 Leo Cardenas .50 1.25
523 Wayne Granger .50 1.25
524 Gene Tenace .75 2.00
525 Jim Fregosi .75 2.00
526 Ollie Brown .50 1.25
527 Dan McGinn .50 1.25
528 Paul Blair .50 1.25
529 Milt May 1.25 3.00
530 Jim Kaat 2.00 5.00
531 Ron Woods 1.25 3.00
532 Steve Mingori 1.25 3.00
533 Larry Stahl 1.25 3.00
534 Dave Lemonds 1.25 3.00
535 Johnny Callison 2.00 5.00
536 Philadelphia Phillies TC 2.50 6.00
537 Bill Slayback RC 1.25 3.00
538 Jim Ray Hart 2.00 5.00
539 Tom Murphy 1.25 3.00
540 Cleon Jones 2.00 5.00
541 Bob Bolin 1.25 3.00
542 Pat Corrales 2.00 5.00
543 Alan Foster 1.25 3.00
544 Von Joshua 1.25 3.00
545 Orlando Cepeda 3.00 8.00
546 Jim York 1.25 3.00
547 Bobby Heise 1.25 3.00
548 Don Durham RC 1.25 3.00
549 Whitey Herzog MG 2.00 5.00
Chuck Estrada CO
Chuck Hiller CO
Jackie Moore CO
550 Dave Johnson 2.00 5.00
551 Mike Kilkenny 1.25 3.00
552 J.C. Martin 1.25 3.00
553 Mickey Scott 1.25 3.00
554 Dave Concepcion 2.00 5.00
555 Bill Hands 1.25 3.00
556 New York Yankees TC 3.00 8.00
557 Bernie Williams 1.25 3.00
558 Jerry May 1.25 3.00
559 Barry Lersch 1.25 3.00
560 Frank Howard 2.00 5.00
561 Jim Geddes RC 1.25 3.00
562 Wayne Garrett 1.25 3.00
563 Larry Haney 1.25 3.00
564 Mike Thompson RC 1.25 3.00
565 Jim Hickman 1.25 3.00
566 Lew Krausse 1.25 3.00
567 Bob Fenwick 1.25 3.00
568 Ray Newman 1.25 3.00
569 Walt Alston MG 3.00 8.00
Red Adams CO
Monty Basgall CO
Jim Gilliam CO
Tom Lasorda CO
570 Bill Singer 2.00 5.00
571 Rusty Torres 1.25 3.00
572 Gary Sutherland 1.25 3.00
573 Fred Beene 1.25 3.00
574 Bob Didier 1.25 3.00
575 Dock Ellis 1.25 3.00
576 Montreal Expos TC 2.50 6.00
577 Eric Soderholm RC 1.25 3.00
578 Ken Wright 1.25 3.00
579 Tom Grieve 2.00 5.00
580 Joe Pepitone 2.00 5.00
581 Steve Kealey 1.25 3.00
582 Darrell Porter 2.00 5.00
583 Bill Greif 1.25 3.00
584 Chris Arnold 1.25 3.00
585 Joe Niekro 2.00 5.00
586 Bill Sudakis 1.25 3.00
587 Rich McKinney 1.25 3.00
588 Checklist 529-660 8.00 20.00
589 Ken Forsch 1.25 3.00
590 Deron Johnson 1.25 3.00
591 Mike Hedlund 1.25 3.00
592 John Boccabella 1.25 3.00
593 Jack McKeon MG RC 1.50 4.00
Galen Cisco CO
Harry Dunlop CO
Charlie Lau CO
594 Vic Harris RC 1.25 3.00
595 Don Gullett 2.00 5.00
596 Boston Red Sox TC 2.50 6.00
597 Mickey Rivers 2.00 5.00
598 Phil Roof 1.25 3.00
599 Ed Crosby 1.25 3.00
600 Dave McNally 2.00 5.00
601 Rookie Catchers 2.00 5.00
Sergio Robles RC
George Pena RC
Rick Stelmaszek
602 Rookie Pitchers 2.00 5.00
Mel Behney
Ralph Garcia RC
Doug Rau RC
603 Rookie Third Basemen 2.00 5.00
Terry Hughes RC
Bill McNulty RC
Ken Reitz RC
604 Rookie Pitchers 2.00 5.00
Jesse Jefferson RC
Dennis O'Toole RC
Bob Strampe RC
605 Rookie First Baseman 2.00 5.00
Enos Cabell RC
Pat Bourque RC
Gonzalo Marquez RC
606 Rookie Outfielders 2.00 5.00
Gary Matthews RC
Tom Paciorek
Jorge Roque
607 Rookie Shortstops 2.00 5.00
Pepe Frias RC
Ray Busse
Mario Guerrero RC
608 Rookie Pitchers 2.00 5.00
Steve Busby RC
Dick Colpaert RC
George Medich RC
609 Rookie Second Basemen 2.00 5.00
Larvell Blanks RC
Pedro Garcia RC
Dave Lopes RC
610 Rookie Pitchers 2.00 5.00
Jimmy Freeman
Charlie Hough
Hank Webb RC
611 Rookie Outfielders 2.00 5.00
Rich Coggins RC
Jim Wohlford RC
Richie Zisk
612 Rookie Pitchers 2.00 5.00
Steve Lawson RC
Bob Reynolds
Brent Strom RC
613 Rookie Catchers 6.00 15.00
Bob Boone RC
Skip Jutze RC
Mike Ivie
614 Rookie Outfielders 8.00 20.00
Al Bumbry RC
Dwight Evans RC
Charlie Spikes RC
615 Rookie Third Basemen 75.00 150.00
Ron Cey
John Hilton RC
Mike Schmidt RC
616 Rookie Pitchers 2.00 5.00
Norm Angelini RC
Steve Blateric
Mike Garman
617 Rich Chiles 1.25 3.00
618 Andy Etchebarren 1.25 3.00
619 Billy Wilson 1.25 3.00
620 Tommy Harper 2.00 5.00
621 Joe Ferguson 2.00 5.00
622 Larry Hisle 2.00 5.00
623 Steve Renko 1.25 3.00
624 Leo Durocher MG 2.00 5.00
Preston Gomez CO
Grady Hatton CO
Hub Kittle CO
Jim Owens CO
625 Angel Mangual 1.25 3.00
626 Bob Barton 1.25 3.00
627 Luis Alvarado 1.25 3.00
628 Jim Slaton 1.25 3.00
629 Cleveland Indians TC 2.50 6.00
630 Denny McLain 3.00 8.00
631 Tom Matchick 1.25 3.00
632 Dick Selma 1.25 3.00
633 Ike Brown 1.25 3.00
634 Alan Closter 1.25 3.00
635 Gene Alley 2.00 5.00
636 Rickey Clark 1.25 3.00
637 Norm Miller 1.25 3.00
638 Ken Reynolds 1.25 3.00
639 Willie Crawford 1.25 3.00
640 Dick Bosman 1.25 3.00
641 Cincinnati Reds TC 2.50 6.00
642 Jose Laboy 1.25 3.00
643 Al Fitzmorris 1.25 3.00
644 Jack Heidemann 1.25 3.00
645 Bob Locker 1.25 3.00
646 Del Crandall MG 1.50 4.00
Harvey Kuenn CO
Joe Nossek CO
Bob Shaw CO
Jim Walton CO
647 George Stone 1.25 3.00
648 Tom Egan 1.25 3.00
649 Rich Folkers 1.25 3.00
650 Felipe Alou 2.00 5.00
651 Don Carrithers 1.25 3.00
652 Ted Kubiak 1.25 3.00
653 Joe Hoerner 1.25 3.00
654 Minnesota Twins TC 2.50 6.00
655 Clay Kirby 1.25 3.00
656 John Ellis 1.25 3.00
657 Bob Johnson 1.25 3.00
658 Elliott Maddox 1.25 3.00
659 Jose Pagan 1.25 3.00
660 Fred Scherman 2.00 5.00

1974 Topps

The cards in this 660-card set measure 2 1/2" by 3 1/2". This year marked the first time Topps issued all the cards of its baseball set at the same time rather than in series. Among other methods, cards were issued in eight-card fifteen-cent wax packs and 42 card rack packs. The ten cent packs were issued 36 to a box. For the first time, factory sets were issued through the JC Penny's catalog. Sales were probably disappointing for it would be several years before factory sets were issued again. Some interesting variations were created by the rumored move of the San Diego Padres to Washington. Fifteen cards (13 players, the team card, and the rookie card (599) of the Padres were printed either as "San Diego" (SD) or "Washington." The latter are the scarcer variety and are denoted in the checklist below by WAS. Each team's manager and his coaches again have a combined card with small pictures of each coach below the larger photo of the team's manager. The first six cards in the set (1-6) feature Hank Aaron and his illustrious career. Other topical subsets included in the set are League Leaders (201-208), All-Star selections (331-339), Playoffs cards (470-471), World Series cards (472-479), and Rookie Prospects (596-608). The card backs for the All-Stars (331-339) have no statistics, but form a picture puzzle of Bobby Bonds, the 1973 All-Star Game MVP. The key Rookie Cards in this set are Ken Griffey Sr., Dave Parker and Dave Winfield.

COMPLETE SET (660) 200.00 400.00
COMP.FACT.SET (660) 300.00 600.00
WRAPPERS (10-CENTS) 4.00 10.00
1 Hank Aaron 715 20.00 50.00
2 Hank Aaron 54-57 3.00 8.00
3 Hank Aaron 58-61 3.00 8.00
4 Hank Aaron 62-65 3.00 8.00
5 Hank Aaron 66-69 3.00 8.00
6 Hank Aaron 70-73 3.00 8.00
7 Jim Hunter 1.50 4.00
8 George Theodore RC .20 .50
9 Mickey Lolich .40 1.00
10 Johnny Bench 6.00 15.00
11 Jim Bibby .20 .50
12 Dave May .20 .50
13 Tom Hilgendorf .20 .50
14 Paul Popovich .20 .50
15 Joe Torre .75 2.00
16 Baltimore Orioles TC .40 1.00
17 Doug Bird RC .20 .50
18 Gary Thomasson RC .20 .50
19 Gerry Moses .20 .50
20 Nolan Ryan 12.50 40.00
21 Bob Gallagher RC .20 .50
22 Cy Acosta .20 .50
23 Craig Robinson RC .20 .50
24 John Hiller .40 1.00
25 Ken Singleton .40 1.00
26 Bill Campbell RC .20 .50
27 George Scott .40 1.00
28 Manny Sanguillen .40 1.00
29 Phil Niekro 1.25 3.00
30 Bobby Bonds .75 2.00
31 Preston Gomez MG .40 1.00
Roger Craig CO
Hub Kittle CO
Grady Hatton CO
Bob Lillis CO
32A Johnny Grubb SD RC .40 1.00
32B Johnny Grubb WASH 1.50 4.00
33 Don Newhauser RC .20 .50
34 Andy Kosco .20 .50
35 Gaylord Perry 1.25 3.00
36 St. Louis Cardinals TC .40 1.00
37 Dave Sells RC .20 .50
38 Don Kessinger .40 1.00
39 Ken Suarez .20 .50
40 Jim Palmer 3.00 8.00
41 Bobby Floyd .20 .50
42 Claude Osteen .40 1.00
43 Jim Wynn .40 1.00
44 Mel Stottlemyre .40 1.00
45 Dave Johnson .40 1.00
46 Pat Kelly .20 .50
47 Dick Ruthven RC .20 .50
48 Dick Sharon RC .20 .50
49 Steve Renko .20 .50
50 Rod Carew 3.00 8.00
51 Bobby Heise .20 .50
52 Al Oliver .40 1.00
53A Fred Kendall SD .40 1.00
53B Fred Kendall WASH 1.50 4.00
54 Elias Sosa RC .20 .50
55 Frank Robinson 3.00 8.00
56 New York Mets TC .40 1.00
57 Darold Knowles .20 .50
58 Charlie Spikes .20 .50
59 Ross Grimsley .20 .50
60 Lou Brock 2.50 6.00
61 Luis Aparicio 1.25 3.00
62 Bob Locker .20 .50
63 Bill Sudakis .20 .50
64 Doug Rau .20 .50
65 Amos Otis .40 1.00
66 Sparky Lyle .40 1.00
67 Tommy Helms .20 .50
68 Grant Jackson .20 .50
69 Del Unser .20 .50
70 Dick Allen .75 2.00
71 Dan Frisella .20 .50
72 Aurelio Rodriguez .20 .50
73 Mike Marshall .75 2.00
74 Minnesota Twins TC .40 1.00
75 Jim Colborn .20 .50
76 Mickey Rivers .40 1.00
77A Rich Troedson SD RC .40 1.00
77B Rich Troedson WASH 1.50 4.00
78 Charlie Fox MG .40 1.00
John McNamara CO
Joe Amalfitano CO
Andy Gilbert CO
Don McMahon CO
79 Gene Tenace .40 1.00
80 Tom Seaver 5.00 12.00
81 Frank Duffy .20 .50
82 Dave Giusti .20 .50
83 Orlando Cepeda 1.25 3.00
84 Rick Wise .20 .50
85 Joe Morgan 3.00 8.00
86 Joe Ferguson .40 1.00
87 Fergie Jenkins 1.25 3.00
88 Freddie Patek .40 1.00
89 Jackie Brown .20 .50
90 Bobby Murcer .40 1.00
91 Ken Forsch .20 .50
92 Paul Blair .40 1.00
93 Rod Gilbreath RC .20 .50
94 Detroit Tigers TC .40 1.00
95 Steve Carlton 3.00 8.00
96 Jerry Hairston RC .20 .50
97 Bob Bailey .20 .50
98 Bert Blyleven .75 2.00
99 Del Crandall MG .40 1.00
Harvey Kuenn CO
Joe Nossek CO
Jim Walton CO
Al Widmar CO
100 Willie Stargell 2.50 6.00
101 Bobby Valentine .40 1.00
102A Bill Greif SD .40 1.00
102B Bill Greif WASH 1.50 4.00
103 Sal Bando .40 1.00
104 Ron Bryant .20 .50
105 Carlton Fisk 5.00 12.00
106 Harry Parker RC .20 .50
107 Alex Johnson .20 .50
108 Al Hrabosky .40 1.00
109 Bob Grich .40 1.00
110 Billy Williams 1.25 3.00
111 Clay Carroll .20 .50
112 Dave Lopes .75 2.00
113 Dick Drago .20 .50
114 California Angels TC .40 1.00
115 Willie Horton .40 1.00
116 Jerry Reuss .40 1.00
117 Ron Blomberg .20 .50
118 Bill Lee .40 1.00
119 Danny Ozark MG .40 1.00
Ray Ripplemeyer CO
Bobby Wine CO
Carroll Beringer CO
Billy DeMars CO
120 Wilbur Wood .20 .50
121 Larry Lintz RC .20 .50
122 Jim Holt .20 .50
123 Nelson Briles .40 1.00
124 Bobby Coluccio RC .20 .50
125A Nate Colbert SD .40 1.00
125B Nate Colbert WASH 1.50 4.00
126 Checklist 1-132 1.25 3.00
127 Tom Paciorek .40 1.00
128 John Ellis .20 .50
129 Chris Speier .20 .50
130 Reggie Jackson 6.00 15.00
131 Bob Boone .75 2.00
132 Felix Millan .20 .50
133 David Clyde RC .40 1.00
134 Denis Menke .20 .50
135 Roy White .40 1.00
136 Rick Reuschel .40 1.00
137 Al Bumbry .40 1.00
138 Eddie Brinkman .20 .50
139 Aurelio Monteagudo .20 .50
140 Darrell Evans .75 2.00
141 Pat Bourque .20 .50
142 Pedro Garcia .20 .50
143 Dick Woodson .20 .50
144 Walter Alston MG 1.25 3.00
Tom Lasorda CO
Jim Gilliam CO
Red Adams CO
Monty Basgall CO
145 Dock Ellis .20 .50
146 Ron Fairly .40 1.00
147 Bart Johnson .20 .50
148A Dave Hilton SD .40 1.00
148B Dave Hilton WASH 1.50 4.00
149 Mac Scarce .20 .50
150 John Mayberry .40 1.00
151 Diego Segui .20 .50
152 Oscar Gamble .40 1.00
153 Jon Matlack .40 1.00
154 Houston Astros TC .40 1.00
155 Bert Campaneris .40 1.00
156 Randy Moffitt .20 .50
157 Vic Harris .20 .50
158 Jack Billingham .20 .50
159 Jim Ray Hart .20 .50
160 Brooks Robinson 3.00 8.00
161 Ray Burris RC .40 1.00
(UER Card number is
printed sideways)
162 Bill Freehan .40 1.00
163 Ken Berry .20 .50
164 Tom House .20 .50
165 Willie Davis .40 1.00
166 Jack McKeon MG .40 1.00
Charlie Lau CO
Harry Dunlop CO
Galen Cisco CO
167 Luis Tiant .75 2.00
168 Danny Thompson .20 .50
169 Steve Rogers RC .75 2.00
170 Bill Melton .20 .50
171 Eduardo Rodriguez RC .20 .50
172 Gene Clines .20 .50
173A Randy Jones SD RC .75 2.00
173B Randy Jones WASH 2.00 5.00
174 Bill Robinson .40 1.00
175 Reggie Cleveland .20 .50
176 John Lowenstein .20 .50
177 Dave Roberts .20 .50
178 Garry Maddox .40 1.00
179 Yogi Berra MG 2.00 5.00
Rube Walker CO
Eddie Yost CO
Roy McMillan CO
Joe Pignatano CO
180 Ken Holtzman .40 1.00
181 Cesar Geronimo .20 .50
182 Lindy McDaniel .40 1.00
183 Johnny Oates .40 1.00
184 Texas Rangers TC .40 1.00
185 Jose Cardenal .20 .50
186 Fred Scherman .20 .50
187 Don Baylor .75 2.00
188 Rudy Meoli RC .20 .50
189 Jim Brewer .20 .50
190 Tony Oliva .75 2.00
191 Al Fitzmorris .20 .50
192 Mario Guerrero .20 .50
193 Tom Walker .20 .50
194 Darrell Porter .40 1.00
195 Carlos May .20 .50
196 Jim Fregosi .40 1.00
197A Vicente Romo SD .40 1.00
197B V.Romo WASH 1.50 4.00
198 Dave Cash .20 .50
199 Mike Kekich .20 .50
200 Cesar Cedeno .40 1.00
201 Batting Leaders 2.50 6.00
Rod Carew
Pete Rose
202 Home Run Leaders 2.00 5.00
Reggie Jackson
Willie Stargell
203 RBI Leaders 2.00 5.00
Reggie Jackson
Willie Stargell
204 Stolen Base Leaders .75 2.00
Tommy Harper
Lou Brock
205 Victory Leaders .40 1.00
Wilbur Wood
Ron Bryant
206 ERA Leaders 2.00 5.00
Jim Palmer
Tom Seaver
207 Strikeout Leaders 5.00 12.00
Nolan Ryan
Tom Seaver
208 Leading Firemen .40 1.00
John Hiller
Mike Marshall
209 Ted Sizemore .20 .50
210 Bill Singer .20 .50
211 Chicago Cubs TC .40 1.00
212 Rollie Fingers 1.25 3.00
213 Dave Rader .20 .50
214 Billy Grabarkewitz .20 .50
215 Al Kaline UER 4.00 10.00
(No copyright on back)
216 Ray Sadecki .20 .50
217 Tim Foli .20 .50
218 Johnny Briggs .20 .50
219 Doug Griffin .20 .50
220 Don Sutton 1.25 3.00
221 Chuck Tanner MG .40 1.00
Jim Mahoney CO
Alex Monchak CO
Johnny Sain CO
Joe Lonnett CO
222 Ramon Hernandez .20 .50
223 Jeff Burroughs .75 2.00
224 Roger Metzger .20 .50
225 Paul Splittorff .20 .50
226A San Diego Padres TC SD .75 2.00
226B San Diego Padres TC 3.00 8.00
Washington Variation
227 Mike Lum .20 .50
228 Ted Kubiak .20 .50
229 Fritz Peterson .20 .50
230 Tony Perez 1.50 4.00
231 Dick Tidrow .20 .50
232 Steve Brye .20 .50
233 Jim Barr .20 .50
234 John Milner .20 .50
235 Dave McNally .40 1.00
236 Red Schoendienst MG 1.25 3.00
Barney Schultz CO
George Kissell CO
Johnny Lewis CO
Vern Benson CO
237 Ken Brett .20 .50
238 Fran Healy .20 .50
(Munson sliding
in background)
239 Bill Russell .40 1.00
240 Joe Coleman .20 .50
241A Glenn Beckert SD .40 1.00
241B Glenn Beckert WASH 1.50 4.00
242 Bill Gogolewski .20 .50
243 Bob Oliver .20 .50
244 Carl Morton .20 .50
245 Cleon Jones .20 .50
246 Oakland Athletics TC .75 2.00
247 Rick Miller .20 .50
248 Tom Hall .20 .50
249 George Mitterwald .20 .50
250A Willie McCovey SD 3.00 8.00
250B W.McCovey WASH 10.00 25.00
251 Graig Nettles .75 2.00
252 Dave Parker RC 4.00 10.00
253 John Boccabella .20 .50
254 Stan Bahnsen .20 .50
255 Larry Bowa .40 1.00
256 Tom Griffin .20 .50
257 Buddy Bell .75 2.00
258 Jerry Morales .20 .50
259 Bob Reynolds .20 .50
260 Ted Simmons .75 2.00
261 Jerry Bell .20 .50
262 Ed Kirkpatrick .20 .50
263 Checklist 133-264 1.25 3.00
264 Joe Rudi .40 1.00
265 Tug McGraw .75 2.00
266 Jim Northrup .40 1.00
267 Andy Messersmith .40 1.00
268 Tom Grieve .40 1.00
269 Bob Johnson .20 .50
270 Ron Santo .75 2.00
271 Bill Hands .20 .50
272 Paul Casanova .20 .50
273 Checklist 265-396 1.25 3.00
274 Fred Beene .20 .50
275 Ron Hunt .20 .50
276 Bobby Winkles MG .40 1.00
John Roseboro CO
Tom Morgan CO
Jimmie Reese CO
Salty Parker CO
277 Gary Nolan .40 1.00
278 Cookie Rojas .40 1.00
279 Jim Crawford RC .20 .50
280 Carl Yastrzemski 5.00 12.00
281 San Francisco Giants TC .40 1.00
282 Doyle Alexander .40 1.00
283 Mike Schmidt 8.00 20.00
284 Dave Duncan .40 1.00
285 Reggie Smith .40 1.00
286 Tony Muser .20 .50
287 Clay Kirby .20 .50
288 Gorman Thomas RC .75 2.00
289 Rick Auerbach .20 .50
290 Vida Blue .40 1.00
291 Don Hahn .20 .50
292 Chuck Seelbach .20 .50
293 Milt May .20 .50
294 Steve Foucault RC .20 .50
295 Rick Monday .40 1.00

296 Ray Corbin .20 .50
297 Hal Breeden .20 .50
298 Roric Harrison .20 .50
299 Gene Michael .20 .50
300 Pete Rose 10.00 25.00
301 Bob Montgomery .20 .50
302 Rudy May .20 .50
303 George Hendrick .40 1.00
304 Don Wilson .20 .50
305 Tito Fuentes .20 .50
306 Earl Weaver MG 1.25 3.00
Jim Frey CO
George Bamberger CO
Billy Hunter CO
George Staller CO
307 Luis Melendez .20 .50
308 Bruce Dal Canton .20 .50
309A Dave Roberts SD .40 1.00
309B Dave Roberts WASH 2.50 6.00
310 Terry Forster .40 1.00
311 Jerry Grote .40 1.00
312 Deron Johnson .20 .50
313 Barry Lersch .20 .50
314 Milwaukee Brewers TC .40 1.00
315 Ron Cey .75 2.00
316 Jim Perry .40 1.00
317 Richie Zisk .40 1.00
318 Jim Merritt .20 .50
319 Randy Hundley .20 .50
320 Dusty Baker .75 2.00
321 Steve Braun .20 .50
322 Ernie McAnally .20 .50
323 Richie Scheinblum .20 .50
324 Steve Kline .20 .50
325 Tommy Harper .40 1.00
326 Sparky Anderson MG 1.25 3.00
Larry Shepard CO
George Scherger CO
Alex Grammas CO
Ted Kluszewski CO
327 Tom Timmermann .20 .50
328 Skip Jutze .20 .50
329 Mark Belanger .40 1.00
330 Juan Marichal 2.00 5.00
331 Carlton Fisk 2.00 5.00
Johnny Bench AS
332 Dick Allen 3.00 8.00
Hank Aaron AS
333 Rod Carew 1.50 4.00
Joe Morgan AS
334 Brooks Robinson .75 2.00
Ron Santo AS
335 Bert Campaneris .40 1.00
Chris Speier AS
336 Bobby Murcer 2.00 5.00
Pete Rose AS
337 Amos Otis .40 1.00
Cesar Cedeno AS
338 Reggie Jackson 2.00 5.00
Billy Williams AS
339 Jim Hunter 1.25 3.00
Rick Wise AS
340 Thurman Munson 3.00 8.00
341 Dan Driessen RC .40 1.00
342 Jim Lonborg .40 1.00
343 Kansas City Royals TC .40 1.00
344 Mike Caldwell .20 .50
345 Bill North .20 .50
346 Ron Reed .20 .50
347 Sandy Alomar .40 1.00
348 Pete Richert .20 .50
349 John Vukovich .20 .50
350 Bob Gibson 3.00 8.00
351 Dwight Evans 1.25 3.00
352 Bill Stoneman .20 .50
353 Rich Coggins .20 .50
354 Whitey Lockman MG .40 1.00
J.C. Martin CO
Hank Aguirre CO
Al Spangler CO
Jim Marshall CO
355 Dave Nelson .20 .50
356 Jerry Koosman .40 1.00
357 Buddy Bradford .20 .50
358 Dal Maxvill .20 .50
359 Brent Strom .20 .50
360 Greg Luzinski .75 2.00
361 Don Carrithers .20 .50
362 Hal King .20 .50
363 New York Yankees TC .75 2.00
364A Cito Gaston SD .75 2.00
364B Cito Gaston WASH 3.00 8.00
365 Steve Busby .40 1.00
366 Larry Hisle .40 1.00
367 Norm Cash .75 2.00
368 Manny Mota .40 1.00
369 Paul Lindblad .20 .50
370 Bob Watson .40 1.00
371 Jim Slaton .20 .50
372 Ken Reitz .20 .50
373 John Curtis .20 .50
374 Marty Perez .20 .50
375 Earl Williams .20 .50
376 Jorge Orta .20 .50
377 Ron Woods .20 .50
378 Burt Hooton .40 1.00
379 Billy Martin MG .75 2.00
Frank Lucchesi CO
Art Fowler CO
Charlie Silvera CO
Jackie Moore CO
380 Bud Harrelson .40 1.00
381 Charlie Sands .20 .50
382 Bob Moose .20 .50
383 Philadelphia Phillies TC .40 1.00
384 Chris Chambliss .40 1.00
385 Don Gullett .40 1.00
386 Gary Matthews .75 2.00
387A Rich Morales SD .40 1.00
387B Rich Morales WASH 2.50 6.00
388 Phil Roof .20 .50
389 Gates Brown .20 .50
390 Lou Piniella .75 2.00
391 Billy Champion .20 .50
392 Dick Green .20 .50
393 Orlando Pena .20 .50
394 Ken Henderson .20 .50
395 Doug Rader .20 .50
396 Tommy Davis .40 1.00
397 George Stone .20 .50
398 Duke Sims .20 .50
399 Mike Paul .20 .50
400 Harmon Killebrew 2.50 6.00
401 Elliott Maddox .20 .50
402 Jim Rooker .20 .50
403 Darrell Johnson MG .40 1.00
Eddie Popowski CO
Lee Stange CO
Don Zimmer CO
Don Bryant CO
404 Jim Howarth .20 .50
405 Ellie Rodriguez .20 .50
406 Steve Arlin .20 .50
407 Jim Wohlford .20 .50
408 Charlie Hough .40 1.00
409 Ike Brown .20 .50
410 Pedro Borbon .20 .50
411 Frank Baker .20 .50
412 Chuck Taylor .20 .50
413 Don Money .40 1.00
414 Checklist 397-528 1.25 3.00
415 Gary Gentry .20 .50
416 Chicago White Sox TC .40 1.00
417 Rich Folkers .20 .50
418 Walt Williams .20 .50
419 Wayne Twitchell .20 .50
420 Ray Fosse .20 .50
421 Dan Fife RC .20 .50
422 Gonzalo Marquez .20 .50
423 Fred Stanley .20 .50
424 Jim Beauchamp .20 .50
425 Pete Broberg .20 .50
426 Rennie Stennett .20 .50
427 Bobby Bolin .20 .50
428 Gary Sutherland .20 .50
429 Dick Lange RC .20 .50
430 Matty Alou .40 1.00
431 Gene Garber RC .40 1.00
432 Chris Arnold .20 .50
433 Lerrin LaGrow .20 .50
434 Ken McMullen .20 .50
435 Dave Concepcion .75 2.00
436 Don Hood RC .20 .50
437 Jim Lyttle .20 .50
438 Ed Herrmann .20 .50
439 Norm Miller .20 .50
440 Jim Kaat .75 2.00
441 Tom Ragland .20 .50
442 Alan Foster .20 .50
443 Tom Hutton .20 .50
444 Vic Davalillo .20 .50
445 George Medich .20 .50
446 Len Randle .20 .50
447 Frank Quilici MG .40 1.00
Ralph Rowe CO
Bob Rodgers CO
Vern Morgan CO
448 Ron Hodges RC .20 .50
449 Tom McCraw .20 .50
450 Rich Hebner .40 1.00
451 Tommy John .75 2.00
452 Gene Hiser .20 .50
453 Balor Moore .20 .50
454 Kurt Bevacqua .20 .50
455 Tom Bradley .20 .50
456 Dave Winfield RC 20.00 50.00
457 Chuck Goggin RC .20 .50
458 Jim Ray .20 .50
459 Cincinnati Reds TC .75 2.00
460 Boog Powell .75 2.00
461 John Odom .20 .50
462 Luis Alvarado .20 .50
463 Pat Dobson .20 .50
464 Jose Cruz .75 2.00
465 Dick Bosman .20 .50
466 Dick Billings .20 .50
467 Winston Llenas .20 .50
468 Pepe Frias .20 .50
469 Joe Decker .20 .50
470 AL Playoffs 2.00 5.00
Reggie Jackson
471 NL Playoffs .40 1.00
Jon Matlack
472 World Series Game 1 .40 1.00
Darold Knowles
473 World Series Game 2 3.00 8.00
Willie Mays
474 World Series Game 3 .40 1.00
Bert Campaneris
475 World Series Game 4 .40 1.00
Rusty Staub
476 World Series Game 5 .40 1.00
Cleon Jones
477 World Series Game 6 2.00 5.00
Reggie Jackson
478 World Series Game 7 .40 1.00
Bert Campaneris
479 World Series Summary .40 1.00
A's Celebrate
480 Willie Crawford .20 .50
481 Jerry Terrell RC .20 .50
482 Bob Didier .20 .50
483 Atlanta Braves TC .40 1.00
484 Carmen Fanzone .20 .50
485 Felipe Alou .75 2.00
486 Steve Stone .40 1.00
487 Ted Martinez .20 .50
488 Andy Etchebarren .20 .50
489 Danny Murtaugh MG .40 1.00
Don Osborn CO
Don Leppert CO
Bill Mazeroski CO
Bob Skinner CO
490 Vada Pinson .75 2.00
491 Roger Nelson .20 .50
492 Mike Rogodzinski RC .20 .50
493 Joe Hoerner .20 .50
494 Ed Goodson .20 .50
495 Dick McAuliffe .40 1.00
496 Tom Murphy .20 .50
497 Bobby Mitchell .20 .50
498 Pat Corrales .20 .50
499 Rusty Torres .20 .50
500 Lee May .40 1.00
501 Eddie Leon .20 .50
502 Dave LaRoche .20 .50
503 Eric Soderholm .20 .50
504 Joe Niekro .40 1.00
505 Bill Buckner .40 1.00
506 Ed Farmer .20 .50
507 Larry Stahl .20 .50
508 Montreal Expos TC .40 1.00
509 Jesse Jefferson .20 .50
510 Wayne Garrett .20 .50
511 Toby Harrah .40 1.00
512 Joe Lahoud .20 .50
513 Jim Campanis .20 .50
514 Paul Schaal .20 .50
515 Willie Montanez .20 .50
516 Horacio Pina .20 .50
517 Mike Hegan .20 .50
518 Derrel Thomas .20 .50
519 Bill Sharp RC .20 .50
520 Tim McCarver .75 2.00
521 Ken Aspromonte MG .40 1.00
Clay Bryant CO
Tony Pacheco CO
522 J.R. Richard .75 2.00
523 Cecil Cooper .75 2.00
524 Bill Plummer .20 .50
525 Clyde Wright .20 .50
526 Frank Tepedino .40 1.00
527 Bobby Darwin .20 .50
528 Bill Bonham .20 .50
529 Horace Clarke .40 1.00
530 Mickey Stanley .40 1.00
531 Gene Mauch MG .40 1.00
Dave Bristol CO
Cal McLish CO
Larry Doby CO
Jerry Zimmerman CO
532 Skip Lockwood .20 .50
533 Mike Phillips RC .20 .50
534 Eddie Watt .20 .50
535 Bob Tolan .20 .50
536 Duffy Dyer .20 .50
537 Steve Mingori .20 .50
538 Cesar Tovar .20 .50
539 Lloyd Allen .20 .50
540 Bob Robertson .20 .50
541 Cleveland Indians TC .40 1.00
542 Goose Gossage .75 2.00
543 Danny Cater .20 .50
544 Ron Schueler .20 .50
545 Billy Conigliaro .40 1.00
546 Mike Corkins .20 .50
547 Glenn Borgmann .20 .50
548 Sonny Siebert .20 .50
549 Mike Jorgensen .20 .50
550 Sam McDowell .40 1.00
551 Von Joshua .20 .50
552 Denny Doyle .20 .50
553 Jim Willoughby .20 .50
554 Tim Johnson RC .20 .50
555 Woodie Fryman .20 .50
556 Dave Campbell .40 1.00
557 Jim McGlothlin .20 .50
558 Bill Fahey .20 .50
559 Darrel Chaney .20 .50
560 Mike Cuellar .40 1.00
561 Ed Kranepool .40 1.00
562 Jack Aker .20 .50
563 Hal McRae .40 1.00
564 Mike Ryan .20 .50
565 Milt Wilcox .20 .50
566 Jackie Hernandez .20 .50
567 Boston Red Sox TC .40 1.00
568 Mike Torrez .40 1.00
569 Rick Dempsey .40 1.00
570 Ralph Garr .40 1.00
571 Rich Hand .20 .50
572 Enzo Hernandez .20 .50
573 Mike Adams RC .20 .50
574 Bill Parsons .20 .50
575 Steve Garvey 1.25 3.00
576 Scipio Spinks .20 .50
577 Mike Sadek RC .20 .50
578 Ralph Houk MG .40 1.00
579 Cecil Upshaw .20 .50
580 Jim Spencer .20 .50
581 Fred Norman .20 .50
582 Bucky Dent RC 2.00 5.00
583 Marty Pattin .20 .50
584 Ken Rudolph .20 .50
585 Merv Rettenmund .20 .50
586 Jack Brohamer .20 .50
587 Larry Christenson RC .20 .50
588 Hal Lanier .20 .50
589 Boots Day .20 .50
590 Roger Moret .20 .50
591 Sonny Jackson .20 .50
592 Ed Bane RC .20 .50
593 Steve Yeager .40 1.00
594 Leroy Stanton .20 .50
595 Steve Blass .40 1.00
596 Rookie Pitchers .20 .50
Wayne Garland RC
Fred Holdsworth RC
Mark Littell RC
Dick Pole RC
597 Rookie Infielders .40 1.00
Dave Chalk RC
John Gamble RC
Pete MacKanin RC
Manny Trillo RC
598 Rookie Outfielders 5.00 12.00
Dave Augustine RC
Ken Griffey RC
Steve Ontiveros RC
Jim Tyrone RC
599A Rookie Pitchers .75 2.00
Ron Diorio RC
Dave Freisleben RC
Frank Riccelli RC
Greg Shanahan RC (Washington)
599B Rookie Pitchers 6.00 15.00
Ron Diorio
Dave Freisleben
Frank Riccelli
Greg Shanahan (San Diego - in Large Print)
599C Rookie Pitchers 2.50 6.00
Ron Diorio
Dave Freisleben
Frank Riccelli
Greg Shanahan (San Diego - in Small Print)
600 Rookie Infielders 2.00 5.00
Ron Cash RC
Jim Cox RC
Bill Madlock RC
Reggie Sanders RC
601 Rookie Outfielders 1.25 3.00
Ed Armbrister
Rich Bladt RC
Brian Downing RC
Bake McBride RC
602 Rookie Pitchers .40 1.00
Glen Abbott RC
Rick Henninger RC
Craig Swan RC
Dan Vossler RC
603 Rookie Catchers .40 1.00
Barry Foote RC
Tom Lundstedt RC
Charlie Moore RC
Sergio Robles
604 Rookie Infielders 2.00 5.00
Terry Hughes
John Knox RC
Andre Thornton RC
Frank White RC
605 Rookie Pitchers 1.50 4.00
Vic Albury
Ken Frailing RC
Kevin Kobel RC
Frank Tanana RC
606 Rookie Outfielders .40 1.00
Jim Fuller RC
Wilbur Howard RC
Tommy Smith RC
Otto Velez RC
607 Rookie Shortstops .40 1.00
Leo Foster RC
Tom Heintzelman RC
Dave Rosello RC
Frank Taveras RC
608A Rookie Pitchers .75 2.00
Bob Apodaco ERR (Apodaca)
Dick Baney
John D'Acquisto
Mike Wallace
608B Rookie Pitchers .40 1.00
Bob Apodaca COR RC
Dick Baney
John D'Acquisto RC
Mike Wallace RC
609 Rico Petrocelli .40 1.00
610 Dave Kingman .75 2.00
611 Rich Stelmaszek .20 .50
612 Luke Walker .20 .50
613 Dan Monzon .20 .50
614 Adrian Devine RC .20 .50
615 Johnny Jeter UER .20 .50
(Misspelled Johnnie
on card back)
616 Larry Gura .20 .50
617 Ted Ford .20 .50
618 Jim Mason .20 .50
619 Mike Anderson .20 .50
620 Al Downing .20 .50
621 Bernie Carbo .20 .50
622 Phil Gagliano .20 .50
623 Celerino Sanchez .20 .50
624 Bob Miller .20 .50
625 Ollie Brown .20 .50
626 Pittsburgh Pirates TC .40 1.00
627 Carl Taylor .20 .50
628 Ivan Murrell .20 .50
629 Rusty Staub .75 2.00
630 Tommie Agee .40 1.00
631 Steve Barber .20 .50
632 George Culver .20 .50
633 Dave Hamilton .20 .50
634 Eddie Mathews MG 1.25 3.00
Herm Starrette CO
Connie Ryan CO
Jim Busby CO
Ken Silvestri CO
635 Johnny Edwards .20 .50
636 Dave Goltz .20 .50
637 Checklist 529-660 1.25 3.00
638 Ken Sanders .20 .50
639 Joe Lovitto .20 .50
640 Milt Pappas .40 1.00
641 Chuck Brinkman .20 .50
642 Terry Harmon .20 .50
643 Los Angeles Dodgers TC .40 1.00
644 Wayne Granger .20 .50
645 Ken Boswell .20 .50
646 George Foster .75 2.00
647 Juan Beniquez RC .20 .50
648 Terry Crowley .20 .50
649 Fernando Gonzalez RC .20 .50
650 Mike Epstein .20 .50
651 Leron Lee .20 .50
652 Gail Hopkins .20 .50
653 Bob Stinson .20 .50
654A Jesus Alou ERR 1.50 4.00
(No Position)
654B Jesus Alou COR .40 1.00
(Outfield)
655 Mike Tyson RC .20 .50
656 Adrian Garrett .20 .50
657 Jim Shellenback .20 .50
658 Lee Lacy .20 .50
659 Joe Lis .20 .50
660 Larry Dierker .75 2.00

1974 Topps Traded

The cards in this 44-card set measure 2 1/2" by 3 1/2". The 1974 Topps Traded set contains 43 player cards and one unnumbered checklist card. The fronts have the word "traded" in block letters and the backs are designed in newspaper style. Card numbers are the same as in the regular set except they are followed by a "T." No known scarcities exist for this set. The cards were inserted in all packs toward the end of the production run. They were produced in large enough quantity that they are no scarcer than the regular Topps cards.

COMPLETE SET (44) 8.00 20.00
23T Craig Robinson .20 .50
42T Claude Osteen .30 .75
43T Jim Wynn .30 .75
51T Bobby Heise .20 .50
59T Ross Grimsley .20 .50
62T Bob Locker .20 .50
63T Bill Sudakis .20 .50
73T Mike Marshall .30 .75
123T Nelson Briles .30 .75
139T Aurelio Monteagudo .20 .50
151T Diego Segui .20 .50
165T Willie Davis .30 .75
175T Reggie Cleveland .20 .50
182T Lindy McDaniel .30 .75
186T Fred Scherman .20 .50
249T George Mitterwald .20 .50
262T Ed Kirkpatrick .20 .50
269T Bob Johnson .20 .50
270T Ron Santo .40 1.00
313T Barry Lersch .20 .50
319T Randy Hundley .30 .75
330T Juan Marichal .75 2.00
348T Pete Richert .20 .50
373T John Curtis .20 .50
390T Lou Piniella .40 1.00
428T Gary Sutherland .20 .50
454T Kurt Bevacqua .20 .50
458T Jim Ray .20 .50
485T Felipe Alou .40 1.00
486T Steve Stone .30 .75
496T Tom Murphy .20 .50
516T Horacio Pina .20 .50
534T Eddie Watt .20 .50
538T Cesar Tovar .20 .50
544T Ron Schueler .20 .50
579T Cecil Upshaw .20 .50
585T Merv Rettenmund .20 .50
612T Luke Walker .20 .50
616T Larry Gura .30 .75
618T Jim Mason .20 .50
630T Tommie Agee .30 .75
648T Terry Crowley .20 .50
649T Fernando Gonzalez .20 .50
NNO Traded Checklist .60 1.50

1975 Topps

The 1975 Topps set consists of 660 standard size cards. The design was radically different in appearance from sets of the preceding years. The most prominent change was the use of a two-color frame surrounding the picture area rather than a single, subdued color. A facsimile autograph appears on the picture, and the backs are printed in red and green on gray. Cards were released in ten-card wax packs, 18-card cello packs with a 25 cent SRP and were packaged 24 to a box and 15 boxes to a case, as well as in 42-card rack packs which cost 49 cents upon release. The cello packs were issued 24 to a box. Cards 189-212 depict the MVP's of both leagues from 1951 through 1974. The first seven cards (1-7) feature players (listed in alphabetical order) breaking records or achieving milestones during the previous season. Cards 306-313 picture league leaders in various statistical categories. Cards 459-466 depict the results of post-season action. Team cards feature a checklist back for players on that team and show a small inset photo of the manager on the front. The following players' regular issue cards are explicitly denoted as All-Stars, 1, 50, 80, 140, 170, 180, 260, 320, 350, 390, 400, 420, 440, 470, 530, 570, and 600. This set is quite popular with collectors, at least in part due to the fact that the Rookie Cards of George Brett, Gary Carter, Keith Hernandez, Fred Lynn, Jim Rice and Robin Yount are all in the set.

COMPLETE SET (660) 300.00 600.00
WRAPPER (15-CENT) 3.00 8.00
1 Hank Aaron HL 12.50 30.00
Sets Homer Mark
2 Lou Brock HL 1.25 3.00
118 Stolen Bases
3 Bob Gibson HL 1.25 3.00
3000th Strikeout
4 Al Kaline HL 2.50 6.00
3000 Hit Club
5 Nolan Ryan HL 6.00 15.00
Fans 300 for
3rd Year in a Row
6 Mike Marshall HL .40 1.00
Hurls 106 Games
7 Steve Busby HL 3.00 8.00
Dick Bosman
Nolan Ryan
8 Rogelio Moret .20 .50
9 Frank Tepedino .40 1.00
10 Willie Davis .40 1.00
11 Bill Melton .20 .50
12 David Clyde .20 .50
13 Gene Locklear RC .40 1.00
14 Milt Wilcox .20 .50
15 Jose Cardenal .40 1.00
16 Frank Tanana .75 2.00
17 Dave Concepcion .75 2.00
18 Detroit Tigers CL .75 2.00
Ralph Houk MG
19 Jerry Koosman .40 1.00
20 Thurman Munson 3.00 8.00
21 Rollie Fingers 1.25 3.00
22 Dave Cash .20 .50
23 Bill Russell .40 1.00
24 Al Fitzmorris .20 .50
25 Lee May .40 1.00
26 Dave McNally .40 1.00
27 Ken Reitz .20 .50
28 Tom Murphy .20 .50
29 Dave Parker 1.25 3.00
30 Bert Blyleven .75 2.00
31 Dave Rader .20 .50
32 Reggie Cleveland .20 .50
33 Dusty Baker .75 2.00
34 Steve Renko .20 .50
35 Ron Santo .40 1.00
36 Joe Lovitto .20 .50
37 Dave Freisleben .20 .50
38 Buddy Bell .75 2.00
39 Andre Thornton .40 1.00
40 Bill Singer .20 .50
41 Cesar Geronimo .40 1.00
42 Joe Coleman .20 .50
43 Cleon Jones .40 1.00
44 Pat Dobson .20 .50
45 Joe Rudi .40 1.00
46 Philadelphia Phillies CL .75 2.00
Danny Ozark MG UER
Terry Harmon listed as 339
instead of 399
47 Tommy John .75 2.00
48 Freddie Patek .40 1.00
49 Larry Dierker .40 1.00
50 Brooks Robinson 3.00 8.00
51 Bob Forsch RC .40 1.00
52 Darrell Porter .40 1.00
53 Dave Giusti .20 .50
54 Eric Soderholm .20 .50
55 Bobby Bonds .75 2.00
56 Rick Wise .40 1.00
57 Dave Johnson .40 1.00
58 Chuck Taylor .20 .50
59 Ken Henderson .20 .50
60 Fergie Jenkins 1.25 3.00
61 Dave Winfield 6.00 15.00
62 Fritz Peterson .20 .50
63 Steve Swisher RC .20 .50
64 Dave Chalk .20 .50
65 Don Gullett .40 1.00
66 Willie Horton .40 1.00
67 Tug McGraw .40 1.00
68 Ron Blomberg .20 .50
69 John Odom .20 .50
70 Mike Schmidt 8.00 20.00
71 Charlie Hough .40 1.00
72 Kansas City Royals CL .75 2.00
Jack McKeon MG
73 J.R. Richard .40 1.00
74 Mark Belanger .40 1.00
75 Ted Simmons .75 2.00
76 Ed Sprague .20 .50
77 Richie Zisk .40 1.00
78 Ray Corbin .20 .50
79 Gary Matthews .40 1.00
80 Carlton Fisk 3.00 8.00
81 Ron Reed .20 .50
82 Pat Kelly .20 .50
83 Jim Merritt .20 .50
84 Enzo Hernandez .20 .50
85 Bill Bonham .20 .50
86 Joe Lis .20 .50
87 George Foster .75 2.00
88 Tom Egan .20 .50
89 Jim Ray .20 .50
90 Rusty Staub .75 2.00
91 Dick Green .20 .50
92 Cecil Upshaw .20 .50
93 Dave Lopes .75 2.00
94 Jim Lonborg .40 1.00
95 John Mayberry .40 1.00
96 Mike Cosgrove RC .20 .50
97 Earl Williams .20 .50
98 Rich Folkers .20 .50
99 Mike Hegan .20 .50
100 Willie Stargell 1.50 4.00
101 Montreal Expos CL .75 2.00
Gene Mauch MG
102 Joe Decker .20 .50
103 Rick Miller .20 .50
104 Bill Madlock .75 2.00
105 Buzz Capra .20 .50
106 Mike Hargrove RC 1.25 3.00
UER Gastonia At-Bats are wrong
107 Jim Barr .20 .50
108 Tom Hall .20 .50
109 George Hendrick .40 1.00
110 Wilbur Wood .20 .50
111 Wayne Garrett .20 .50
112 Larry Hardy RC .20 .50
113 Elliott Maddox .20 .50
114 Dick Lange .20 .50
115 Joe Ferguson .20 .50
116 Lerrin LaGrow .20 .50
117 Baltimore Orioles CL 1.25 3.00
Earl Weaver MG
118 Mike Anderson .20 .50
119 Tommy Helms .20 .50
120 Steve Busby UER .40 1.00
(Photo actually
Fran Healy)
121 Bill North .20 .50
122 Al Hrabosky .40 1.00
123 Johnny Briggs .20 .50
124 Jerry Reuss .40 1.00
125 Ken Singleton .40 1.00
126 Checklist 1-132 1.25 3.00
127 Glenn Borgmann .20 .50
128 Bill Lee .40 1.00
129 Rick Monday .40 1.00
130 Phil Niekro 1.25 3.00
131 Toby Harrah .40 1.00
132 Randy Moffitt .20 .50
133 Dan Driessen .40 1.00
134 Ron Hodges .20 .50
135 Charlie Spikes .20 .50
136 Jim Mason .20 .50
137 Terry Forster .40 1.00
138 Del Unser .20 .50
139 Horacio Pina .20 .50
140 Steve Garvey 1.25 3.00
141 Mickey Stanley .40 1.00
142 Bob Reynolds .20 .50
143 Cliff Johnson RC .40 1.00
144 Jim Wohlford .20 .50
145 Ken Holtzman .40 1.00
146 San Diego Padres CL .75 2.00
John McNamara MG
147 Pedro Garcia .20 .50
148 Jim Rooker .20 .50
149 Tim Foli .20 .50
150 Bob Gibson 2.50 6.00
151 Steve Brye .20 .50

152 Mario Guerrero .20 .50
153 Rick Reuschel .40 1.00
154 Mike Lum .20 .50
155 Jim Bibby .20 .50
156 Dave Kingman .75 2.00
157 Pedro Borbon .40 1.00
158 Jerry Grote .20 .50
159 Steve Arlin .20 .50
160 Graig Nettles .75 2.00
161 Stan Bahnsen .20 .50
162 Willie Montanez .20 .50
163 Jim Brewer .20 .50
164 Mickey Rivers .40 1.00
165 Doug Rader .40 1.00
166 Woodie Fryman .20 .50
167 Rich Coggins .20 .50
168 Bill Greif .20 .50
169 Cookie Rojas .20 .50
170 Bert Campaneris .40 1.00
171 Ed Kirkpatrick .20 .50
172 Boston Red Sox CL 1.25 3.00
Darrell Johnson MG
173 Steve Rogers .40 1.00
174 Bake McBride .40 1.00
175 Don Money .40 1.00
176 Burt Hooton .40 1.00
177 Vic Correll RC .20 .50
178 Cesar Tovar .20 .50
179 Tom Bradley .20 .50
180 Joe Morgan 2.50 6.00
181 Fred Beene .20 .50
182 Don Hahn .20 .50
183 Mel Stottlemyre .40 1.00
184 Jorge Orta .20 .50
185 Steve Carlton 3.00 8.00
186 Willie Crawford .20 .50
187 Denny Doyle .20 .50
188 Tom Griffin .20 .50
189 Yogi Berra 1.50 4.00
Roy Campanella MVP
Campanella card never issued
190 Bobby Shantz .75 2.00
Hank Sauer MVP
191 Al Rosen .75 2.00
Roy Campanella MVP
192 Yogi Berra 1.50 4.00
Willie Mays MVP
193 Yogi Berra 1.25 3.00
Roy Campanella MVP
Campanella card never issued
he is pictured with LA cap
194 Mickey Mantle 4.00 10.00
Don Newcombe MVP
195 Mickey Mantle 5.00 12.00
Hank Aaron MVP
196 Jackie Jensen 1.25 3.00
Ernie Banks MVP
197 Nellie Fox .75 2.00
Ernie Banks MVP
198 Roger Maris .75 2.00
Dick Groat MVP
199 Roger Maris 1.25 3.00
Frank Robinson MVP
200 Mickey Mantle 4.00 10.00
Maury Wills MVP
(Wills card never issued)
201 Elston Howard .75 2.00
Sandy Koufax MVP
202 Brooks Robinson .40 1.00
Ken Boyer MVP
203 Zoilo Versalles .75 2.00
Willie Mays MVP
204 Frank Robinson 2.50 6.00
Bob Clemente MVP
205 Carl Yastrzemski .75 2.00
Orlando Cepeda MVP
206 Denny McLain UER .75 2.00
Bob Gibson MVP
On the back McLain is spelled McClain
207 Harmon Killebrew .40 1.00
Willie McCovey MVP
208 Boog Powell .75 2.00
Johnny Bench MVP
209 Vida Blue .75 2.00
Joe Torre MVP
210 Rich Allen .75 2.00
Johnny Bench MVP
211 Reggie Jackson 2.00 5.00
Pete Rose MVP
212 Jeff Burroughs .75 2.00
Steve Garvey MVP
213 Oscar Gamble .40 1.00
214 Harry Parker .20 .50
215 Bobby Valentine .40 1.00
216 San Francisco Giants CL .75 2.00
Wes Westrum MG
217 Lou Piniella .75 2.00
218 Jerry Johnson .20 .50
219 Ed Herrmann .20 .50
220 Don Sutton 1.25 3.00
221 Aurelio Rodriguez .20 .50
222 Dan Spillner RC .20 .50
223 Robin Yount RC 20.00 50.00
224 Ramon Hernandez .20 .50
225 Bob Grich .40 1.00
226 Bill Campbell .20 .50
227 Bob Watson .40 1.00
228 George Brett RC 40.00 80.00
229 Barry Foote .20 .50
230 Jim Hunter 1.50 4.00
231 Mike Tyson .20 .50
232 Diego Segui .20 .50
233 Billy Grabarkewitz .20 .50
234 Tom Grieve .40 1.00
235 Jack Billingham .40 1.00
236 California Angels CL .75 2.00
Dick Williams MG
237 Carl Morton .40 1.00
238 Dave Duncan .40 1.00
239 George Stone .20 .50
240 Garry Maddox .40 1.00
241 Dick Tidrow .20 .50
242 Jay Johnstone .40 1.00
243 Jim Kaat .75 2.00
244 Bill Buckner .40 1.00
245 Mickey Lolich .75 2.00
246 St. Louis Cardinals CL .75 2.00
Red Schoendienst MG
247 Enos Cabell .20 .50
248 Randy Jones .75 2.00
249 Danny Thompson .20 .50
250 Ken Brett .20 .50
251 Fran Healy .20 .50
252 Fred Scherman .20 .50
253 Jesus Alou .20 .50
254 Mike Torrez .40 1.00
255 Dwight Evans .75 2.00
256 Billy Champion .20 .50
257 Checklist: 133-264 1.25 3.00
258 Dave LaRoche .20 .50
259 Len Randle .20 .50
260 Johnny Bench 6.00 15.00
261 Andy Hassler RC .20 .50
262 Rowland Office RC .20 .50
263 Jim Perry .40 1.00
264 John Milner .20 .50
265 Ron Bryant .20 .50
266 Sandy Alomar .40 1.00
267 Dick Ruthven .20 .50
268 Hal McRae .40 1.00
269 Doug Rau .20 .50
270 Ron Fairly .40 1.00
271 Gerry Moses .20 .50
272 Lynn McGlothen .20 .50
273 Steve Braun .20 .50
274 Vicente Romo .20 .50
275 Paul Blair .40 1.00
276 Chicago White Sox CL .75 2.00
Chuck Tanner MG
277 Frank Taveras .20 .50
278 Paul Lindblad .20 .50
279 Milt May .20 .50
280 Carl Yastrzemski 5.00 12.00
281 Jim Slaton .20 .50
282 Jerry Morales .20 .50
283 Steve Foucault .20 .50
284 Ken Griffey 1.50 4.00
285 Ellie Rodriguez .20 .50
286 Mike Jorgensen .20 .50
287 Roric Harrison .20 .50
288 Bruce Ellingsen RC .20 .50
289 Ken Rudolph .20 .50
290 Jon Matlack .20 .50
291 Bill Sudakis .20 .50
292 Ron Schueler .20 .50
293 Dick Sharon .20 .50
294 Geoff Zahn RC .20 .50
295 Vada Pinson .75 2.00
296 Alan Foster .20 .50
297 Craig Kusick RC .20 .50
298 Johnny Grubb .20 .50
299 Bucky Dent .75 2.00
300 Reggie Jackson 6.00 15.00
301 Dave Roberts .20 .50
302 Rick Burleson RC .40 1.00
303 Grant Jackson .20 .50
304 Pittsburgh Pirates CL .75 2.00
Danny Murtaugh MG
305 Jim Colborn .20 .50
306 Batting Leaders .75 2.00
Rod Carew
Ralph Garr
307 Home Run Leaders 1.50 4.00
Dick Allen
Mike Schmidt
308 RBI Leaders .75 2.00
Jeff Burroughs
Johnny Bench
309 Stolen Base Leaders .75 2.00
Bill North
Lou Brock
310 Victory Leaders .75 2.00
Jim Hunter
Fergie Jenkins
Andy Messersmith
Phil Niekro
311 ERA Leaders .75 2.00
Jim Hunter
Buzz Capra
312 Strikeout Leaders 5.00 12.00
Nolan Ryan
Steve Carlton
313 Leading Firemen .40 1.00
Terry Forster
Mike Marshall
314 Buck Martinez .20 .50
315 Don Kessinger .40 1.00
316 Jackie Brown .20 .50
317 Joe Lahoud .20 .50
318 Ernie McAnally .20 .50
319 Johnny Oates .40 1.00
320 Pete Rose 12.50 30.00
321 Rudy May .20 .50
322 Ed Goodson .20 .50
323 Fred Holdsworth .20 .50
324 Ed Kranepool .40 1.00
325 Tony Oliva .75 2.00
326 Wayne Twitchell .20 .50
327 Jerry Hairston .20 .50
328 Sonny Siebert .20 .50
329 Ted Kubiak .20 .50
330 Mike Marshall .40 1.00
331 Cleveland Indians CL .75 2.00
Frank Robinson MG
332 Fred Kendall .20 .50
333 Dick Drago .20 .50
334 Greg Gross RC .20 .50
335 Jim Palmer 2.50 6.00
336 Rennie Stennett .20 .50
337 Kevin Kobel .20 .50
338 Rich Stelmaszek .20 .50
339 Jim Fregosi .40 1.00
340 Paul Splittorff .20 .50
341 Hal Breeden .20 .50
342 Leroy Stanton .20 .50
343 Danny Frisella .20 .50
344 Ben Oglivie .40 1.00
345 Clay Carroll .40 1.00
346 Bobby Darwin .20 .50
347 Mike Caldwell .20 .50
348 Tony Muser .20 .50
349 Ray Sadecki .20 .50
350 Bobby Murcer .40 1.00
351 Bob Boone .75 2.00
352 Darold Knowles .20 .50
353 Luis Melendez .20 .50
354 Dick Bosman .20 .50
355 Chris Cannizzaro .20 .50
356 Rico Petrocelli .40 1.00
357 Ken Forsch UER .20 .50
Forsch is misspelled in blurb
358 Al Bumbry .40 1.00
359 Paul Popovich .20 .50
360 George Scott .40 1.00
361 Los Angeles Dodgers CL .75 2.00
Walter Alston MG
362 Steve Hargan .20 .50
363 Carmen Fanzone .20 .50
364 Doug Bird .20 .50
365 Bob Bailey .20 .50
366 Ken Sanders .20 .50
367 Craig Robinson .20 .50
368 Vic Albury .20 .50
369 Merv Rettenmund .20 .50
370 Tom Seaver 5.00 12.00
371 Gates Brown .20 .50
372 John D'Acquisto .20 .50
373 Bill Sharp .20 .50
374 Eddie Watt .20 .50
375 Roy White .40 1.00
376 Steve Yeager .40 1.00
377 Tom Hilgendorf .20 .50
378 Derrel Thomas .20 .50
379 Bernie Carbo .20 .50
380 Sal Bando .40 1.00
381 John Curtis .20 .50
382 Don Baylor .75 2.00
383 Jim York .20 .50
384 Milwaukee Brewers CL .75 2.00
Del Crandall MG
385 Dock Ellis .20 .50
386 Checklist: 265-396 UER 1.25 3.00
Dick Sharon's name is misspelled
387 Jim Spencer .20 .50
388 Steve Stone .40 1.00
389 Tony Solaita RC .20 .50
390 Ron Cey .75 2.00
391 Don DeMola RC .20 .50
392 Bruce Bochte RC .40 1.00
393 Gary Gentry .20 .50
394 Larvell Blanks .20 .50
395 Bud Harrelson .40 1.00
396 Fred Norman .40 1.00
397 Bill Freehan .40 1.00
398 Elias Sosa .20 .50
399 Terry Harmon .20 .50
400 Dick Allen .75 2.00
401 Mike Wallace .20 .50
402 Bob Tolan .20 .50
403 Tom Buskey RC .20 .50
404 Ted Sizemore .20 .50
405 John Montague RC .20 .50
406 Bob Gallagher .20 .50
407 Herb Washington RC .75 2.00
408 Clyde Wright UER .20 .50
Listed with wrong 1974 team
409 Bob Robertson .20 .50
410 Mike Cueller UER .40 1.00
Sic, Cuellar
411 George Mitterwald .20 .50
412 Bill Hands .20 .50
413 Marty Pattin .20 .50
414 Manny Mota .40 1.00
415 John Hiller .40 1.00
416 Larry Lintz .20 .50
417 Skip Lockwood .20 .50
418 Leo Foster .20 .50
419 Dave Goltz .20 .50
420 Larry Bowa .75 2.00
421 New York Mets CL 1.25 3.00
Yogi Berra MG
422 Brian Downing .40 1.00
423 Clay Kirby .20 .50
424 John Lowenstein .20 .50
425 Tito Fuentes .20 .50
426 George Medich .20 .50
427 Clarence Gaston .40 1.00
428 Dave Hamilton .20 .50
429 Jim Dwyer RC .20 .50
430 Luis Tiant .75 2.00
431 Rod Gilbreath .20 .50
432 Ken Berry .20 .50
433 Larry Demery RC .20 .50
434 Bob Locker .20 .50
435 Dave Nelson .20 .50
436 Ken Frailing .20 .50
437 Al Cowens RC .40 1.00
438 Don Carrithers .20 .50
439 Ed Brinkman .20 .50
440 Andy Messersmith .40 1.00
441 Bobby Heise .20 .50
442 Maximino Leon RC .20 .50
443 Minnesota Twins CL .75 2.00
Frank Quilici MG
444 Gene Garber .40 1.00
445 Felix Millan .20 .50
446 Bart Johnson .20 .50
447 Terry Crowley .20 .50
448 Frank Duffy .20 .50
449 Charlie Williams .20 .50
450 Willie McCovey 2.50 6.00
451 Rick Dempsey .40 1.00
452 Angel Mangual .20 .50
453 Claude Osteen .40 1.00
454 Doug Griffin .20 .50
455 Don Wilson .20 .50
456 Bob Coluccio .20 .50
457 Mario Mendoza RC .20 .50
458 Ross Grimsley .20 .50
459 1974 AL Championships .40 1.00
Brooks Robinson
A's 2nd Baseman
460 1974 NL Championships .75 2.00
Steve Garvey
Frank Taveras
461 World Series Game 1 2.00 5.00
Reggie Jackson
462 World Series Game 2 .40 1.00
Walter Alston
Joe Ferguson
463 World Series Game 3 .75 2.00
Rollie Fingers
464 World Series Game 4 .40 1.00
A's Batter
465 World Series Game 5 .40 1.00
Joe Rudi
466 World Series Summary .75 2.00
A's Do it Again
467 Ed Halicki RC .20 .50
468 Bobby Mitchell .20 .50
469 Tom Dettore RC .20 .50
470 Jeff Burroughs .40 1.00
471 Bob Stinson .20 .50
472 Bruce Dal Canton .20 .50
473 Ken McMullen .20 .50
474 Luke Walker .20 .50
475 Darrell Evans .40 1.00
476 Ed Figueroa RC .20 .50
477 Tom Hutton .20 .50
478 Tom Burgmeier .20 .50
479 Ken Boswell .20 .50
480 Carlos May .20 .50
481 Will McEnaney RC .40 1.00
482 Tom McCraw .20 .50
483 Steve Ontiveros .20 .50
484 Glenn Beckert .40 1.00
485 Sparky Lyle .40 1.00
486 Ray Fosse .20 .50
487 Houston Astros CL .75 2.00
Preston Gomez MG
488 Bill Travers RC .20 .50
489 Cecil Cooper .75 2.00
490 Reggie Smith .40 1.00
491 Doyle Alexander .40 1.00
492 Rich Hebner .40 1.00
493 Don Stanhouse .20 .50
494 Pete LaCock RC .20 .50
495 Nelson Briles .40 1.00
496 Pepe Frias .20 .50
497 Jim Nettles .20 .50
498 Al Downing .20 .50
499 Marty Perez .20 .50
500 Nolan Ryan 20.00 50.00
501 Bill Robinson .40 1.00
502 Pat Bourque .20 .50
503 Fred Stanley .20 .50
504 Buddy Bradford .20 .50
505 Chris Speier .20 .50
506 Leron Lee .20 .50
507 Tom Carroll RC .20 .50
508 Bob Hansen RC .20 .50
509 Dave Hilton .20 .50
510 Vida Blue .40 1.00
511 Texas Rangers CL .75 2.00
Billy Martin MG
512 Larry Milbourne RC .20 .50
513 Dick Pole .20 .50
514 Jose Cruz .75 2.00
515 Manny Sanguillen .40 1.00
516 Don Hood .20 .50
517 Checklist: 397-528 1.25 3.00
518 Leo Cardenas .20 .50
519 Jim Todd RC .20 .50
520 Amos Otis .40 1.00
521 Dennis Blair RC .20 .50
522 Gary Sutherland .20 .50
523 Tom Paciorek .40 1.00
524 John Doherty RC .20 .50
525 Tom House .20 .50
526 Larry Hisle .40 1.00
527 Mac Scarce .20 .50
528 Eddie Leon .20 .50
529 Gary Thomasson .20 .50
530 Gaylord Perry 1.25 3.00
531 Cincinnati Reds CL 2.00 5.00
Sparky Anderson MG
532 Gorman Thomas .40 1.00
533 Rudy Meoli .20 .50
534 Alex Johnson .20 .50
535 Gene Tenace .40 1.00
536 Bob Moose .20 .50
537 Tommy Harper .40 1.00
538 Duffy Dyer .20 .50
539 Jesse Jefferson .20 .50
540 Lou Brock 2.50 6.00
541 Roger Metzger .20 .50
542 Pete Broberg .20 .50
543 Larry Biittner .20 .50
544 Steve Mingori .20 .50
545 Billy Williams 1.25 3.00
546 John Knox .20 .50
547 Von Joshua .20 .50
548 Charlie Sands .20 .50
549 Bill Butler .20 .50
550 Ralph Garr .40 1.00
551 Larry Christenson .20 .50
552 Jack Brohamer .20 .50
553 John Boccabella .20 .50
554 Goose Gossage .75 2.00
555 Al Oliver .40 1.00
556 Tim Johnson .20 .50
557 Larry Gura .20 .50
558 Dave Roberts .20 .50
559 Bob Montgomery .20 .50
560 Tony Perez 1.50 4.00
561 Oakland Athletics CL .75 2.00
Alvin Dark MG
562 Gary Nolan .40 1.00
563 Wilbur Howard .20 .50
564 Tommy Davis .40 1.00
565 Joe Torre .75 2.00
566 Ray Burris .20 .50
567 Jim Sundberg RC .75 2.00
568 Dale Murray RC .20 .50
569 Frank White .40 1.00
570 Jim Wynn .40 1.00
571 Dave Lemanczyk RC .20 .50
572 Roger Nelson .20 .50
573 Orlando Pena .20 .50
574 Tony Taylor .20 .50
575 Gene Clines .20 .50
576 Phil Roof .20 .50
577 John Morris .20 .50
578 Dave Tomlin RC .20 .50
579 Skip Pitlock .20 .50
580 Frank Robinson 2.50 6.00
581 Darrel Chaney .20 .50
582 Eduardo Rodriguez .20 .50
583 Andy Etchebarren .20 .50
584 Mike Garman .20 .50
585 Chris Chambliss .40 1.00
586 Tim McCarver .75 2.00
587 Chris Ward RC .20 .50
588 Rick Auerbach .20 .50
589 Atlanta Braves CL .75 2.00
Clyde King MG
590 Cesar Cedeno .40 1.00
591 Glenn Abbott .20 .50
592 Balor Moore .20 .50
593 Gene Lamont .20 .50
594 Jim Fuller .20 .50
595 Joe Niekro .40 1.00
596 Ollie Brown .20 .50
597 Winston Llenas .20 .50
598 Bruce Kison .20 .50
599 Nate Colbert .20 .50
600 Rod Carew 3.00 8.00
601 Juan Beniquez .20 .50
602 John Vukovich .20 .50
603 Lew Krausse .20 .50
604 Oscar Zamora RC .20 .50
605 John Ellis .20 .50
606 Bruce Miller RC .20 .50
607 Jim Holt .20 .50
608 Gene Michael .20 .50
609 Elrod Hendricks .20 .50
610 Ron Hunt .20 .50
611 New York Yankees CL .75 2.00
Bill Virdon MG
612 Terry Hughes .20 .50
613 Bill Parsons .20 .50
614 Rookie Pitchers .40 1.00
Jack Kucek RC
Dyar Miller RC
Vern Ruhle RC
Paul Siebert RC
615 Rookie Pitchers .75 2.00
Pat Darcy RC
Dennis Leonard RC
Tom Underwood RC
Hank Webb
616 Rookie Outfielders 6.00 15.00
Dave Augustine
Pepe Mangual RC
Jim Rice RC
John Scott RC
617 Rookie Infielders .75 2.00
Mike Cubbage RC
Doug DeCinces RC
Reggie Sanders
Manny Trillo
618 Rookie Pitchers .40 1.00
Jamie Easterly RC
Tom Johnson RC
Scott McGregor RC
Rick Rhoden RC
619 Rookie Outfielders .40 1.00
Benny Ayala RC
Nyls Nyman RC
Tommy Smith
Jerry Turner RC
620 Rookie Catchers and Outfielders 6.00 15.00
Gary Carter RC
Marc Hill RC
Danny Meyer RC
Leon Roberts RC
621 Rookie Pitchers .75 2.00
John Denny RC
Rawly Eastwick RC
Jim Kern RC
Juan Veintidos RC
622 Rookie Outfielders 3.00 8.00
Ed Armbrister RC
Fred Lynn RC
Tom Poquette RC
Terry Whitfield RC
(UER Listed as Ney York)
623 Rookie Infielders 4.00 10.00
Phil Garner RC
Keith Hernandez RC
(UER Sic, bats right)
Bob Sheldon RC
Tom Veryzer RC
624 Rookie Pitchers .40 1.00
Doug Konieczny RC
Gary Lavelle RC
Jim Otten RC
Eddie Solomon RC
625 Boog Powell .75 2.00
626 Larry Haney UER .20 .50
Photo actually
Dave Duncan
627 Tom Walker .20 .50
628 Ron LeFlore RC .40 1.00
629 Joe Hoerner .20 .50
630 Greg Luzinski .75 2.00
631 Lee Lacy .20 .50
632 Morris Nettles RC .20 .50
633 Paul Casanova .20 .50
634 Cy Acosta .20 .50
635 Chuck Dobson .20 .50
636 Charlie Moore .20 .50
637 Ted Martinez .20 .50
638 Chicago Cubs CL .75 2.00
Jim Marshall MG
639 Steve Kline .20 .50
640 Harmon Killebrew 2.50 6.00
641 Jim Northrup .40 1.00
642 Mike Phillips .20 .50
643 Brent Strom .20 .50
644 Bill Fahey .20 .50
645 Danny Cater .20 .50
646 Checklist: 529-660 1.25 3.00
647 Cl. Washington RC .75 2.00
648 Dave Pagan RC .20 .50
649 Jack Heidemann .20 .50
650 Dave May .20 .50
651 John Morlan RC .20 .50
652 Lindy McDaniel .40 1.00
653 Lee Richard UER .20 .50
(Listed as Richards
on card front)
654 Jerry Terrell .20 .50
655 Rico Carty .40 1.00
656 Bill Plummer .20 .50
657 Bob Oliver .20 .50
658 Vic Harris .20 .50
659 Bob Apodaca .20 .50
660 Hank Aaron 12.50 30.00

1975 Topps Mini

This set is a parallel to the regular 1975 Topps set. Each card measures 2 1/4" by 3 1/8" and the set was regionally issued. Michigan and California were among the two areas to receive this issue. These cards were also sporadically distributed in other areas as collectors have recalled getting them in their local areas other than those mentioned above. The cards are currently valued the same as the regular 75 Topps cards and have proven not to have remained as popular as the regular 1975 issue. These cards were issued in 10 card packs which cost 15 cents on issue and were packed 36 to a box.

COMPLETE SET (660) 300.00 600.00
*MINI STARS: .75X TO 1.5X BASIC CARDS
*MINI RC'S: .5X TO 1X BASIC ROOKIE CARDS

1976 Topps

The 1976 Topps set of 660 standard-size cards is known for its sharp color photographs and interesting presentation of subjects. Cards were issued in ten-card wax packs which cost 15 cents upon release, 42-card rack packs as well as cello packs and other options. Team cards feature a checklist back for players on that team and show a small inset photo of the manager on the front. A "Father and Son" series (66-70) spotlights five Major Leaguers whose fathers also made the "Big Show." Other subseries include "All Time All Stars" (341-350), "Record Breakers" from the previous season (1-6), League Leaders (191-205), Post-season cards (461-462), and Rookie Prospects (589-599). The following players' regular issue cards are explicitly denoted as All-Stars, 10, 48, 60, 140, 150, 165, 169, 240, 300, 370, 380, 395, 400, 420, 475, 500, 580, and 650. The key Rookie Cards in this set are Dennis Eckersley, Ron Guidry, and Willie Randolph. We've heard recent reports that this set was also issued in seven-card wax packs which cost a dime. Confirmation of that information would be appreciated.

COMPLETE SET (660) 125.00 250.00
1 Hank Aaron RB 6.00 15.00
2 Bobby Bonds RB .60 1.50
3 Mickey Lolich RB .30 .75
4 Dave Lopes RB .30 .75
5 Tom Seaver RB 2.00 5.00
6 Rennie Stennett RB .30 .75
7 Jim Umbarger RC .15 .40
8 Tito Fuentes .15 .40
9 Paul Lindblad .15 .40
10 Lou Brock 2.00 5.00
11 Jim Hughes .15 .40
12 Richie Zisk .30 .75
13 John Wockenfuss RC .15 .40
14 Gene Garber .30 .75
15 George Scott .30 .75
16 Bob Apodaca .15 .40
17 New York Yankees CL .60 1.50
Billy Martin MG
18 Dale Murray .15 .40
19 George Brett 12.50 30.00
20 Bob Watson .30 .75
21 Dave LaRoche .15 .40
22 Bill Russell .30 .75
23 Brian Downing .15 .40
24 Cesar Geronimo .30 .75
25 Mike Torrez .30 .75
26 Andre Thornton .30 .75
27 Ed Figueroa .15 .40
28 Dusty Baker .60 1.50
29 Rick Burleson .30 .75
30 John Montefusco RC .30 .75
31 Len Randle .15 .40
32 Danny Frisella .15 .40
33 Bill North .15 .40
34 Mike Garman .15 .40
35 Tony Oliva .60 1.50
36 Frank Taveras .15 .40
37 John Hiller .30 .75
38 Garry Maddox .30 .75
39 Pete Broberg .15 .40
40 Dave Kingman .60 1.50
41 Tippy Martinez RC .30 .75
42 Barry Foote .15 .40
43 Paul Splittorff .15 .40
44 Doug Rader .30 .75
45 Boog Powell .60 1.50
46 Los Angeles Dodgers CL .60 1.50
Walter Alston MG
47 Jesse Jefferson .15 .40
48 Dave Concepcion .60 1.50
49 Dave Duncan .30 .75
50 Fred Lynn .60 1.50
51 Ray Burris .15 .40
52 Dave Chalk .15 .40
53 Mike Beard RC .15 .40
54 Dave Rader .15 .40
55 Gaylord Perry 1.00 2.50
56 Bob Tolan .15 .40
57 Phil Garner .30 .75
58 Ron Reed .15 .40
59 Larry Hisle .30 .75
60 Jerry Reuss .30 .75
61 Ron LeFlore .30 .75
62 Johnny Oates .30 .75
63 Bobby Darwin .15 .40
64 Jerry Koosman .30 .75
65 Chris Chambliss .30 .75
66 Gus Bell FS .30 .75
Buddy Bell
67 Ray Boone FS .30 .75
Bob Boone
68 Joe Coleman FS .15 .40
Joe Coleman Jr.
69 Jim Hegan FS .15 .40
Mike Hegan
70 Roy Smalley FS .30 .75
Roy Smalley Jr.
71 Steve Rogers .30 .75
72 Hal McRae .30 .75
73 Baltimore Orioles CL .60 1.50
Earl Weaver MG
74 Oscar Gamble .30 .75
75 Larry Dierker .30 .75
76 Willie Crawford .15 .40
77 Pedro Borbon .30 .75
78 Cecil Cooper .30 .75
79 Jerry Morales .15 .40
80 Jim Kaat .60 1.50

81 Darrell Evans .30 .75
82 Von Joshua .15 .40
83 Jim Spencer .15 .40
84 Brent Strom .15 .40
85 Mickey Rivers .30 .75
86 Mike Tyson .15 .40
87 Tom Burgmeier .15 .40
88 Duffy Dyer .15 .40
89 Vern Ruhle .15 .40
90 Sal Bando .30 .75
91 Tom Hutton .15 .40
92 Eduardo Rodriguez .15 .40
93 Mike Phillips .15 .40
94 Jim Dwyer .15 .40
95 Brooks Robinson 2.50 6.00
96 Doug Bird .15 .40
97 Wilbur Howard .15 .40
98 Dennis Eckersley RC 12.50 30.00
99 Lee Lacy .15 .40
100 Jim Hunter 1.25 3.00
101 Pete LaCock .15 .40
102 Jim Willoughby .15 .40
103 Biff Pocoroba RC .15 .40
104 Cincinnati Reds CL 1.00 2.50
Sparky Anderson MG
105 Gary Lavelle .15 .40
106 Tom Grieve .30 .75
107 Dave Roberts .15 .40
108 Don Kirkwood RC .15 .40
109 Larry Lintz .15 .40
110 Carlos May .15 .40
111 Danny Thompson .15 .40
112 Kent Tekulve RC .60 1.50
113 Gary Sutherland .15 .40
114 Jay Johnstone .30 .75
115 Ken Holtzman .30 .75
116 Charlie Moore .15 .40
117 Mike Jorgensen .15 .40
118 Boston Red Sox CL .60 1.50
Darrell Johnson MG
119 Checklist 1-132 .60 1.50
120 Rusty Staub .30 .75
121 Tony Solaita .15 .40
122 Mike Cosgrove .15 .40
123 Walt Williams .15 .40
124 Doug Rau .15 .40
125 Don Baylor .60 1.50
126 Tom Dettore .15 .40
127 Larvell Blanks .15 .40
128 Ken Griffey Sr. 1.00 2.50
129 Andy Etchebarren .15 .40
130 Luis Tiant .60 1.50
131 Bill Stein RC .15 .40
132 Don Hood .15 .40
133 Gary Matthews .30 .75
134 Mike Ivie .15 .40
135 Bake McBride .30 .75
136 Dave Goltz .15 .40
137 Bill Robinson .30 .75
138 Lerrin LaGrow .15 .40
139 Gorman Thomas .30 .75
140 Vida Blue .30 .75
141 Larry Parrish RC .60 1.50
142 Dick Drago .15 .40
143 Jerry Grote .15 .40
144 Al Fitzmorris .15 .40
145 Larry Bowa .30 .75
146 George Medich .15 .40
147 Houston Astros CL .60 1.50
Bill Virdon MG
148 Stan Thomas RC .15 .40
149 Tommy Davis .30 .75
150 Steve Garvey 1.00 2.50
151 Bill Bonham .15 .40
152 Leroy Stanton .15 .40
153 Buzz Capra .15 .40
154 Bucky Dent .30 .75
155 Jack Billingham .30 .75
156 Rico Carty .30 .75
157 Mike Caldwell .15 .40
158 Ken Reitz .15 .40
159 Jerry Terrell .15 .40
160 Dave Winfield 4.00 10.00
161 Bruce Kison .15 .40
162 Jack Pierce RC .15 .40
163 Jim Slaton .15 .40
164 Pepe Mangual .15 .40
165 Gene Tenace .30 .75
166 Skip Lockwood .15 .40
167 Freddie Patek .30 .75
168 Tom Hilgendorf .15 .40
169 Graig Nettles .60 1.50
170 Rick Wise .15 .40
171 Greg Gross .15 .40
172 Texas Rangers CL .60 1.50
Frank Lucchesi MG
173 Steve Swisher .15 .40
174 Charlie Hough .30 .75
175 Ken Singleton .30 .75
176 Dick Lange .15 .40
177 Marty Perez .15 .40
178 Tom Buskey .15 .40
179 George Foster .60 1.50
180 Goose Gossage .60 1.50
181 Willie Montanez .15 .40
182 Harry Rasmussen .15 .40
183 Steve Braun .15 .40
184 Bill Greif .15 .40
185 Dave Parker .60 1.50
186 Tom Walker .15 .40
187 Pedro Garcia .15 .40
188 Fred Scherman .15 .40
189 Claudell Washington .30 .75
190 Jon Matlack .15 .40
191 NL Batting Leaders .30 .75
Bill Madlock
Ted Simmons
Manny Sanguillen
192 AL Batting Leaders 1.00 2.50
Rod Carew
Fred Lynn
Thurman Munson
193 NL Home Run Leaders 1.25 3.00
Mike Schmidt
Dave Kingman
Greg Luzinski
194 AL Home Run Leaders 1.25 3.00
Reggie Jackson
George Scott
John Mayberry
195 NL RBI Leaders .60 1.50
Greg Luzinski
Johnny Bench
Tony Perez
196 AL RBI Leaders .30 .75
George Scott
John Mayberry
Fred Lynn
197 NL Stolen Base Leaders .60 1.50
Dave Lopes
Joe Morgan
Lou Brock
198 AL Stolen Base Leaders .30 .75
Mickey Rivers
Claudell Washington
Amos Otis
199 NL Victory Leaders 1.00 2.50
Tom Seaver
Randy Jones
Andy Messersmith
200 AL Victory Leaders .60 1.50
Jim Hunter
Jim Palmer
Vida Blue
201 NL ERA Leaders .60 1.50
Randy Jones
Andy Messersmith
Tom Seaver
202 AL ERA Leaders 1.25 3.00
Jim Palmer
Jim Hunter
Dennis Eckersley
203 NL Strikeout Leaders 1.00 2.50
Tom Seaver
John Montefusco
Andy Messersmith
204 AL Strikeout Leaders .30 .75
Frank Tanana
Bert Blyleven
Gaylord Perry
205 NL/AL Leading Firemen .30 .75
Al Hrabosky
Rich Gossage
206 Manny Trillo .15 .40
207 Andy Hassler .15 .40
208 Mike Lum .15 .40
209 Alan Ashby RC .15 .40
210 Lee May .30 .75
211 Clay Carroll .30 .75
212 Pat Kelly .15 .40
213 Dave Heaverlo RC .15 .40
214 Eric Soderholm .15 .40
215 Reggie Smith .30 .75
216 Montreal Expos CL .60 1.50
Karl Kuehl MG
217 Dave Freisleben .15 .40
218 John Knox .15 .40
219 Tom Murphy .15 .40
220 Manny Sanguillen .30 .75
221 Jim Todd .15 .40
222 Wayne Garrett .15 .40
223 Ollie Brown .15 .40
224 Jim York .15 .40
225 Roy White .30 .75
226 Jim Sundberg .30 .75
227 Oscar Zamora .15 .40
228 John Hale RC .15 .40
229 Jerry Remy RC .15 .40
230 Carl Yastrzemski 4.00 10.00
231 Tom House .15 .40
232 Frank Duffy .15 .40
233 Grant Jackson .15 .40
234 Mike Sadek .15 .40
235 Bert Blyleven .60 1.50
236 Kansas City Royals CL .60 1.50
Whitey Herzog MG
237 Dave Hamilton .15 .40
238 Larry Biittner .15 .40
239 John Curtis .15 .40
240 Pete Rose 10.00 25.00
241 Hector Torres .15 .40
242 Dan Meyer .15 .40
243 Jim Rooker .15 .40
244 Bill Sharp .15 .40
245 Felix Millan .15 .40
246 Cesar Tovar .15 .40
247 Terry Harmon .15 .40
248 Dick Tidrow .15 .40
249 Cliff Johnson .30 .75
250 Fergie Jenkins 1.00 2.50
251 Rick Monday .30 .75
252 Tim Nordbrook RC .15 .40
253 Bill Buckner .30 .75
254 Rudy Meoli .15 .40
255 Fritz Peterson .15 .40
256 Rowland Office .15 .40
257 Ross Grimsley .15 .40
258 Nyls Nyman .15 .40
259 Darrel Chaney .15 .40
260 Steve Busby .15 .40
261 Gary Thomasson .15 .40
262 Checklist 133-264 .60 1.50
263 Lyman Bostock RC .60 1.50
264 Steve Renko .15 .40
265 Willie Davis .30 .75
266 Alan Foster .15 .40
267 Aurelio Rodriguez .15 .40
268 Del Unser .15 .40
269 Rick Austin .15 .40
270 Willie Stargell 1.25 3.00
271 Jim Lonborg .30 .75
272 Rick Dempsey .30 .75
273 Joe Niekro .30 .75
274 Tommy Harper .30 .75
275 Rick Manning RC .15 .40
276 Mickey Scott .15 .40
277 Chicago Cubs CL .60 1.50
Jim Marshall MG
278 Bernie Carbo .15 .40
279 Roy Howell RC .15 .40
280 Burt Hooton .30 .75
281 Dave May .15 .40
282 Dan Osborn RC .15 .40
283 Merv Rettenmund .15 .40
284 Steve Ontiveros .15 .40
285 Mike Cuellar .30 .75
286 Jim Wohlford .15 .40
287 Pete Mackanin .15 .40
288 Bill Campbell .15 .40
289 Enzo Hernandez .15 .40
290 Ted Simmons .30 .75
291 Ken Sanders .15 .40
292 Leon Roberts .15 .40
293 Bill Castro RC .15 .40
294 Ed Kirkpatrick .15 .40
295 Dave Cash .15 .40
296 Pat Dobson .15 .40
297 Roger Metzger .15 .40
298 Dick Bosman .15 .40
299 Champ Summers RC .15 .40
300 Johnny Bench 5.00 12.00
301 Jackie Brown .15 .40
302 Rick Miller .15 .40
303 Steve Foucault .15 .40
304 California Angels CL .60 1.50
Dick Williams MG
305 Andy Messersmith .30 .75
306 Rod Gilbreath .15 .40
307 Al Bumbry .30 .75
308 Jim Barr .15 .40
309 Bill Melton .15 .40
310 Randy Jones .30 .75
311 Cookie Rojas .15 .40
312 Don Carrithers .15 .40
313 Dan Ford RC .15 .40
314 Ed Kranepool .15 .40
315 Al Hrabosky .30 .75
316 Robin Yount 6.00 15.00
317 John Candelaria RC .60 1.50
318 Bob Boone .60 1.50
319 Larry Gura .15 .40
320 Willie Horton .30 .75
321 Jose Cruz .60 1.50
322 Glenn Abbott .15 .40
323 Rob Sperring RC .15 .40
324 Jim Bibby .15 .40
325 Tony Perez 1.25 3.00
326 Dick Pole .15 .40
327 Dave Moates RC .15 .40
328 Carl Morton .15 .40
329 Joe Ferguson .15 .40
330 Nolan Ryan 10.00 25.00
331 San Diego Padres CL .60 1.50
John McNamara MG
332 Charlie Williams .15 .40
333 Bob Coluccio .15 .40
334 Dennis Leonard .30 .75
335 Bob Grich .30 .75
336 Vic Albury .15 .40
337 Bud Harrelson .30 .75
338 Bob Bailey .15 .40
339 John Denny .30 .75
340 Jim Rice 1.50 4.00
341 Lou Gehrig ATG 5.00 12.00
342 Rogers Hornsby ATG 1.25 3.00
343 Pie Traynor ATG .60 1.50
344 Honus Wagner ATG 2.00 5.00
345 Babe Ruth ATG 6.00 15.00
346 Ty Cobb ATG 5.00 12.00
347 Ted Williams ATG 5.00 12.00
348 Mickey Cochrane ATG .60 1.50
349 Walter Johnson ATG 2.00 5.00
350 Lefty Grove ATG .60 1.50
351 Randy Hundley .30 .75
352 Dave Giusti .15 .40
353 Sixto Lezcano RC .30 .75
354 Ron Blomberg .15 .40
355 Steve Carlton 2.50 6.00
356 Ted Martinez .15 .40
357 Ken Forsch .15 .40
358 Buddy Bell .30 .75
359 Rick Reuschel .30 .75
360 Jeff Burroughs .30 .75
361 Detroit Tigers CL .60 1.50
Ralph Houk MG
362 Will McEnaney .30 .75
363 Dave Collins RC .30 .75
364 Elias Sosa .15 .40
365 Carlton Fisk 2.50 6.00
366 Bobby Valentine .30 .75
367 Bruce Miller .15 .40
368 Wilbur Wood .15 .40
369 Frank White .30 .75
370 Ron Cey .30 .75
371 Elrod Hendricks .15 .40
372 Rick Baldwin RC .15 .40
373 Johnny Briggs .15 .40
374 Dan Warthen RC .15 .40
375 Ron Fairly .30 .75
376 Rich Hebner .30 .75
377 Mike Hegan .15 .40
378 Steve Stone .30 .75
379 Ken Boswell .15 .40
380 Bobby Bonds .60 1.50
381 Denny Doyle .15 .40
382 Matt Alexander RC .15 .40
383 John Ellis .15 .40
384 Philadelphia Phillies CL .60 1.50
Danny Ozark MG
385 Mickey Lolich .30 .75
386 Ed Goodson .15 .40
387 Mike Miley RC .15 .40
388 Stan Perzanowski RC .15 .40
389 Glenn Adams RC .15 .40
390 Don Gullett .30 .75
391 Jerry Hairston .15 .40
392 Checklist 265-396 .60 1.50
393 Paul Mitchell RC .15 .40
394 Fran Healy .15 .40
395 Jim Wynn .30 .75
396 Bill Lee .15 .40
397 Tim Foli .15 .40
398 Dave Tomlin .15 .40
399 Luis Melendez .15 .40
400 Rod Carew 2.50 6.00
401 Ken Brett .15 .40
402 Don Money .30 .75
403 Geoff Zahn .15 .40
404 Enos Cabell .15 .40
405 Rollie Fingers 1.00 2.50
406 Ed Herrmann .15 .40
407 Tom Underwood .15 .40
408 Charlie Spikes .15 .40
409 Dave Lemanczyk .15 .40
410 Ralph Garr .30 .75
411 Bill Singer .15 .40
412 Toby Harrah .30 .75
413 Pete Varney RC .15 .40
414 Wayne Garland .15 .40
415 Vada Pinson .60 1.50
416 Tommy John .60 1.50
417 Gene Clines .15 .40
418 Jose Morales RC .15 .40
419 Reggie Cleveland .15 .40
420 Joe Morgan 2.00 5.00
421 Oakland Athletics CL .60 1.50
(No Manager on front
422 Johnny Grubb .15 .40
423 Ed Halicki .15 .40
424 Phil Roof .15 .40
425 Rennie Stennett .15 .40
426 Bob Forsch .15 .40
427 Kurt Bevacqua .15 .40
428 Jim Crawford .15 .40
429 Fred Stanley .15 .40
430 Jose Cardenal .30 .75
431 Dick Ruthven .15 .40
432 Tom Veryzer .15 .40
433 Rick Waits RC .15 .40
434 Morris Nettles .15 .40
435 Phil Niekro 1.00 2.50
436 Bill Fahey .15 .40
437 Terry Forster .15 .40
438 Doug DeCinces .30 .75
439 Rick Rhoden .30 .75
440 John Mayberry .15 .40
441 Gary Carter 1.50 4.00
442 Hank Webb .15 .40
443 San Francisco Giants CL .60 1.50
(No Manager on front
444 Gary Nolan .30 .75
445 Rico Petrocelli .30 .75
446 Larry Haney .15 .40
447 Gene Locklear .30 .75
448 Tom Johnson .15 .40
449 Bob Robertson .15 .40
450 Jim Palmer 2.00 5.00
451 Buddy Bradford .15 .40
452 Tom Hausman RC .15 .40
453 Lou Piniella .60 1.50
454 Tom Griffin .15 .40
455 Dick Allen .60 1.50
456 Joe Coleman .15 .40
457 Ed Crosby .15 .40
458 Earl Williams .15 .40
459 Jim Brewer .15 .40
460 Cesar Cedeno .30 .75
461 NL and AL Championships .30 .75
Bench/Gullett/Perez
Luis Tiant
462 1975 World Series .30 .75
Reds Champs
463 Steve Hargan .15 .40
464 Ken Henderson .15 .40
465 Mike Marshall .30 .75
466 Bob Stinson .15 .40
467 Woodie Fryman .15 .40
468 Jesus Alou .15 .40
469 Rawly Eastwick .30 .75
470 Bobby Murcer .30 .75
471 Jim Burton .15 .40
472 Bob Davis RC .15 .40
473 Paul Blair .30 .75
474 Ray Corbin .15 .40
475 Joe Rudi .30 .75
476 Bob Moose .15 .40
477 Cleveland Indians CL .60 1.50
Frank Robinson MG
478 Lynn McGlothen .15 .40
479 Bobby Mitchell .15 .40
480 Mike Schmidt 6.00 15.00
481 Rudy May .15 .40
482 Tim Hosley .15 .40
483 Mickey Stanley .15 .40
484 Eric Raich RC .15 .40
485 Mike Hargrove .30 .75
486 Bruce Dal Canton .15 .40
487 Leron Lee .15 .40
488 Claude Osteen .30 .75
489 Skip Jutze .15 .40
490 Frank Tanana .30 .75
491 Terry Crowley .15 .40
492 Marty Pattin .15 .40
493 Derrel Thomas .15 .40
494 Craig Swan .30 .75
495 Nate Colbert .15 .40
496 Juan Beniquez .15 .40
497 Joe McIntosh RC .15 .40
498 Glenn Borgmann .15 .40
499 Mario Guerrero .15 .40
500 Reggie Jackson 5.00 12.00
501 Billy Champion .15 .40
502 Tim McCarver .60 1.50
503 Elliott Maddox .15 .40
504 Pittsburgh Pirates CL .60 1.50
Danny Murtaugh MG
505 Mark Belanger .30 .75
506 George Mitterwald .15 .40
507 Ray Bare RC .15 .40
508 Duane Kuiper RC .15 .40
509 Bill Hands .15 .40
510 Amos Otis .30 .75
511 Jamie Easterley .15 .40
512 Ellie Rodriguez .15 .40
513 Bart Johnson .15 .40
514 Dan Driessen .30 .75
515 Steve Yeager .30 .75
516 Wayne Granger .15 .40
517 John Milner .15 .40
518 Doug Flynn RC .15 .40
519 Steve Brye .15 .40
520 Willie McCovey 2.00 5.00
521 Jim Colborn .15 .40
522 Ted Sizemore .15 .40
523 Bob Montgomery .15 .40
524 Pete Falcone RC .15 .40
525 Billy Williams 1.00 2.50
526 Checklist 397-528 .60 1.50
527 Mike Anderson .15 .40
528 Dock Ellis .15 .40
529 Deron Johnson .15 .40
530 Don Sutton 1.00 2.50
531 New York Mets CL .60 1.50
Joe Frazier MG
532 Milt May .15 .40
533 Lee Richard .15 .40
534 Stan Bahnsen .15 .40
535 Dave Nelson .15 .40
536 Mike Thompson .15 .40
537 Tony Muser .15 .40
538 Pat Darcy .15 .40
539 John Balaz RC .15 .40
540 Bill Freehan .30 .75
541 Steve Mingori .15 .40
542 Keith Hernandez .30 .75
543 Wayne Twitchell .15 .40
544 Pepe Frias .15 .40
545 Sparky Lyle .30 .75
546 Dave Rosello .15 .40
547 Roric Harrison .15 .40
548 Manny Mota .30 .75
549 Randy Tate RC .15 .40
550 Hank Aaron 10.00 25.00
551 Jerry DaVanon .15 .40
552 Terry Humphrey .15 .40
553 Randy Moffitt .15 .40
554 Ray Fosse .15 .40
555 Dyar Miller .15 .40
556 Minnesota Twins CL .60 1.50
Gene Mauch MG
557 Dan Spillner .15 .40
558 Clarence Gaston .30 .75
559 Clyde Wright .15 .40
560 Jorge Orta .15 .40
561 Tom Carroll .15 .40
562 Adrian Garrett .15 .40
563 Larry Demery .15 .40
564 Kurt Bevacqua .60 1.50
Bubble Gum Champ
565 Tug McGraw .30 .75
566 Ken McMullen .15 .40
567 George Stone .15 .40
568 Rob Andrews RC .15 .40
569 Nelson Briles .30 .75
570 George Hendrick .30 .75
571 Don DeMola .15 .40
572 Rich Coggins .15 .40
573 Bill Travers .15 .40
574 Don Kessinger .30 .75
575 Dwight Evans .60 1.50
576 Maximino Leon .15 .40
577 Marc Hill .15 .40
578 Ted Kubiak .15 .40
579 Clay Kirby .15 .40
580 Bert Campaneris .30 .75
581 St. Louis Cardinals CL .60 1.50
Red Schoendienst MG
582 Mike Kekich .15 .40
583 Tommy Helms .15 .40
584 Stan Wall RC .15 .40
585 Joe Torre .60 1.50
586 Ron Schueler .15 .40
587 Leo Cardenas .15 .40
588 Kevin Kobel .15 .40
589 Rookie Pitchers .60 1.50
Santo Alcala RC
Mike Flanagan RC
Joe Pactwa RC
Pablo Torrealba RC
590 Rookie Outfielders .30 .75
Henry Cruz RC
Chet Lemon RC
Ellis Valentine RC
Terry Whitfield
591 Rookie Pitchers .30 .75
Steve Grilli RC
Craig Mitchell RC
Jose Sosa RC
George Throop RC
592 Rookie Infielders 2.00 5.00
Willie Randolph RC
Dave McKay RC
Jerry Royster RC
Roy Staiger RC
593 Rookie Pitchers .30 .75
Larry Anderson RC
Ken Crosby RC
Mark Littell
Butch Metzger RC
594 Rookie Catchers and Outfielders .30 .75
Andy Merchant RC
Ed Ott RC
Royle Stillman RC
Jerry White RC
595 Rookie Pitchers .30 .75
Art DeFillipis RC
Randy Lerch RC
Sid Monge RC
Steve Barr RC
596 Rookie Infielders .30 .75
Craig Reynolds RC
Lamar Johnson RC
Johnnie LeMaster RC
Jerry Manuel RC
597 Rookie Pitchers .30 .75
Don Aase RC
Jack Kucek
Frank LaCorte RC
Mike Pazik RC
598 Rookie Outfielders .30 .75
Hector Cruz RC
Jamie Quirk RC
Jerry Turner
Joe Wallis RC
599 Rookie Pitchers 3.00 8.00
Rob Dressler RC
Ron Guidry RC
Bob McClure RC
Pat Zachry RC
600 Tom Seaver 4.00 10.00
601 Ken Rudolph .15 .40
602 Doug Konieczny .15 .40
603 Jim Holt .15 .40
604 Joe Lovitto .15 .40
605 Al Downing .15 .40
606 Milwaukee Brewers CL .60 1.50
Alex Grammas MG
607 Rich Hinton .15 .40
608 Vic Correll .15 .40
609 Fred Norman .15 .40
610 Greg Luzinski .60 1.50
611 Rich Folkers .15 .40
612 Joe Lahoud .15 .40
613 Tim Johnson .15 .40
614 Fernando Arroyo RC .15 .40
615 Mike Cubbage .15 .40
616 Buck Martinez .15 .40
617 Darold Knowles .15 .40
618 Jack Brohamer .15 .40
619 Bill Butler .15 .40
620 Al Oliver .30 .75
621 Tom Hall .15 .40
622 Rick Auerbach .15 .40
623 Bob Allietta RC .15 .40
624 Tony Taylor .15 .40
625 J.R. Richard .30 .75
626 Bob Sheldon .15 .40
627 Bill Plummer .15 .40
628 John D'Acquisto .15 .40
629 Sandy Alomar .30 .75
630 Chris Speier .15 .40
631 Atlanta Braves CL .60 1.50
Dave Bristol MG
632 Rogelio Moret .15 .40
633 John Stearns RC .30 .75
634 Larry Christenson .15 .40
635 Jim Fregosi .30 .75
636 Joe Decker .15 .40
637 Bruce Bochte .15 .40
638 Doyle Alexander .30 .75
639 Fred Kendall .15 .40
640 Bill Madlock .60 1.50
641 Tom Paciorek .30 .75
642 Dennis Blair .15 .40
643 Checklist 529-660 .60 1.50
644 Tom Bradley .15 .40
645 Darrell Porter .30 .75
646 John Lowenstein .15 .40
647 Ramon Hernandez .15 .40
648 Al Cowens .30 .75
649 Dave Roberts .15 .40
650 Thurman Munson 2.50 6.00
651 John Odom .15 .40
652 Ed Armbrister .15 .40
653 Mike Norris RC .30 .75
654 Doug Griffin .15 .40
655 Mike Vail RC .15 .40
656 Chicago White Sox CL .60 1.50
Chuck Tanner MG
657 Roy Smalley RC .30 .75
658 Jerry Johnson .15 .40
659 Ben Oglivie .30 .75
660 Dave Lopes .60 1.50

1976 Topps Traded

The cards in this 44-card set measure 2 1/2" by 3 1/2". The 1976 Topps Traded set contains 43 players and one unnumbered checklist card. The individuals pictured were traded after the Topps regular set was printed. A "Sports Extra" heading design is found on each picture and is also used to introduce the biographical section of the reverse. Each card is numbered according to the player's regular 1976 card with the addition of "T" to indicate his new status. As in 1974, the cards were inserted in all packs toward the end of the production run. According to published reports at the time, they were not released until April, 1976. Because they were produced in large quantities, they are no scarcer than the basic cards. Reports at the time indicated that a dealer could make approximately 35 sets from a vending case. The vending cases included both regular and traded cards.

COMPLETE SET (44) 12.50 30.00
27T Ed Figueroa .15 .40
28T Dusty Baker .60 1.50
44T Doug Rader .30 .75
58T Ron Reed .15 .40
74T Oscar Gamble .60 1.50
80T Jim Kaat .60 1.50
83T Jim Spencer .15 .40
85T Mickey Rivers .30 .75
99T Lee Lacy .15 .40
120T Rusty Staub .30 .75
127T Larvell Blanks .15 .40
146T George Medich .15 .40
158T Ken Reitz .15 .40
208T Mike Lum .15 .40
211T Clay Carroll .15 .40
231T Tom House .15 .40
250T Fergie Jenkins 1.25 3.00
259T Darrel Chaney .15 .40
292T Leon Roberts .15 .40
296T Pat Dobson .15 .40
309T Bill Melton .15 .40
338T Bob Bailey .15 .40
380T Bobby Bonds .60 1.50
383T John Ellis .15 .40
385T Mickey Lolich .30 .75
401T Ken Brett .15 .40
410T Ralph Garr .15 .40
411T Bill Singer .15 .40
428T Jim Crawford .15 .40
434T Morris Nettles .15 .40
464T Ken Henderson .15 .40
497T Joe McIntosh .15 .40
524T Pete Falcone .15 .40
527T Mike Anderson .15 .40
528T Dock Ellis .15 .40
532T Milt May .15 .40
554T Ray Fosse .15 .40
579T Clay Kirby .15 .40
583T Tommy Helms .15 .40
592T Willie Randolph 2.00 5.00
618T Jack Brohamer .15 .40
632T Rogelio Moret .15 .40
649T Dave Roberts .15 .40
NNO Traded Checklist .75 2.00

1977 Topps

In 1977 for the fifth consecutive year, Topps produced a 660-card standard-size baseball set. Among other fashions, this set was released in 10-card wax packs as well as thirty-nine card rack packs. The player's name, team affiliation, and his position are compactly arranged over the picture area and a facsimile autograph appears on the photo. Team cards feature a checklist of that team's players in the set and a small picture of the manager on the front of the card. Appearing for the first time are the series "Brothers" (631-634) and "Turn Back

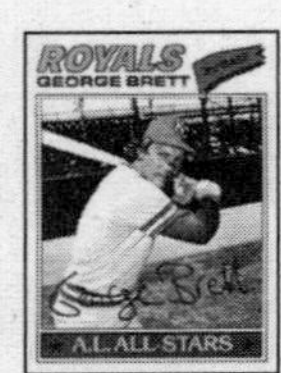

the Clock" (433-437). Other subseries in the set are League Leaders (1-8), Record Breakers (231-234), Playoffs cards (276-277), World Series cards (411-413), and Rookie Prospects (472-479/487-494). The following players' regular issue cards are explicitly denoted as All-Stars, 30, 70, 100, 120, 170, 210, 240, 265, 301, 347, 400, 420, 450, 500, 521, 550, 560, and 580. The key Rookie Cards in the set are Jack Clark, Andre Dawson, Mark "The Bird" Fidrych, Dennis Martinez and Dale Murphy. Cards numbered 23 or lower, that feature Yankees and do not follow the numbering checklisted below, are not necessarily error cards. Those cards were issued in the NY area and distributed by Burger King. There was an aluminum version of the Dale Murphy rookie card number 476 produced (legally) in the early '80s; proceeds from the sales originally priced at 10.00) of this "card" went to the Huntington's Disease Foundation.

COMPLETE SET (660) 125.00 250.00
1 Batting Leaders 3.00 8.00
George Brett
Bill Madlock
2 Home Run Leaders 1.00 2.50
Graig Nettles
Mike Schmidt
3 RBI Leaders .60 1.50
Lee May
George Foster
4 Stolen Base Leaders .30 .75
Bill North
Dave Lopes
5 Victory Leaders .60 1.50
Jim Palmer
Randy Jones
6 Strikeout Leaders 6.00 15.00
Nolan Ryan
Tom Seaver
7 ERA Leaders .30 .75
Mark Fidrych
John Denny
8 Leading Firemen .30 .75
Bill Campbell
Rawly Eastwick
9 Doug Rader .12 .30
10 Reggie Jackson 4.00 10.00
11 Rob Dressler .12 .30
12 Larry Haney .12 .30
13 Luis Gomez RC .12 .30
14 Tommy Smith .12 .30
15 Don Gullett .30 .75
16 Bob Jones RC .12 .30
17 Steve Stone .30 .75
18 Cleveland Indians CL .60 1.50
Frank Robinson MG
19 John D'Acquisto .12 .30
20 Graig Nettles .60 1.50
21 Ken Forsch .12 .30
22 Bill Freehan .30 .75
23 Dan Driessen .12 .30
24 Carl Morton .12 .30
25 Dwight Evans .60 1.50
26 Ray Sadecki .12 .30
27 Bill Buckner .30 .75
28 Woodie Fryman .12 .30
29 Bucky Dent .30 .75
30 Greg Luzinski .60 1.50
31 Jim Todd .12 .30
32 Checklist 1-132 .60 1.50
33 Wayne Garland .12 .30
34 California Angels CL .60 1.50
Norm Sherry MG
35 Rennie Stennett .12 .30
36 John Ellis .12 .30
37 Steve Hargan .12 .30
38 Craig Kusick .12 .30
39 Tom Griffin .12 .30
40 Bobby Murcer .30 .75
41 Jim Kern .12 .30
42 Jose Cruz .30 .75
43 Ray Bare .12 .30
44 Bud Harrelson .30 .75
45 Rawly Eastwick .12 .30
46 Buck Martinez .12 .30
47 Lynn McGlothen .12 .30
48 Tom Paciorek .30 .75
49 Grant Jackson .12 .30
50 Ron Cey .30 .75
51 Milwaukee Brewers CL .60 1.50
Alex Grammas MG
52 Ellis Valentine .12 .30
53 Paul Mitchell .12 .30
54 Sandy Alomar .30 .75
55 Jeff Burroughs .30 .75
56 Rudy May .12 .30
57 Marc Hill .12 .30
58 Chet Lemon .30 .75
59 Larry Christenson .12 .30
60 Jim Rice 1.00 2.50
61 Manny Sanguillen .30 .75
62 Eric Raich .12 .30
63 Tito Fuentes .12 .30
64 Larry Biittner .12 .30
65 Skip Lockwood .12 .30
66 Roy Smalley .30 .75
67 Joaquin Andujar RC .30 .75
68 Bruce Bochte .12 .30
69 Jim Crawford .12 .30
70 Johnny Bench 4.00 10.00
71 Dock Ellis .12 .30
72 Mike Anderson .12 .30
73 Charlie Williams .12 .30
74 Oakland Athletics CL .60 1.50
Jack McKeon MG
75 Dennis Leonard .30 .75
76 Tim Foli .12 .30
77 Dyar Miller .12 .30
78 Bob Davis .12 .30
79 Don Money .30 .75
80 Andy Messersmith .30 .75
81 Juan Beniquez .12 .30
82 Jim Rooker .12 .30
83 Kevin Bell RC .12 .30
84 Ollie Brown .12 .30
85 Duane Kuiper .12 .30
86 Pat Zachry .12 .30
87 Glenn Borgmann .12 .30
88 Stan Wall .12 .30
89 Butch Hobson RC .30 .75
90 Cesar Cedeno .30 .75
91 John Verhoeven RC .12 .30
92 Dave Rosello .12 .30
93 Tom Poquette .12 .30
94 Craig Swan .12 .30
95 Keith Hernandez .30 .75
96 Lou Piniella .30 .75
97 Dave Heaverlo .12 .30
98 Milt May .12 .30
99 Tom Hausman .12 .30
100 Joe Morgan 1.50 4.00
101 Dick Bosman .12 .30
102 Jose Morales .12 .30
103 Mike Bacsik RC .12 .30
104 Omar Moreno RC .30 .75
105 Steve Yeager .30 .75
106 Mike Flanagan .30 .75
107 Bill Melton .12 .30
108 Alan Foster .12 .30
109 Jorge Orta .12 .30
110 Steve Carlton 2.00 5.00
111 Rico Petrocelli .30 .75
112 Bill Greif .12 .30
113 Blue Jays Leaders .60 1.50
Roy Hartsfield MG
Don Leppert CO
Bob Miller CO
Jackie Moore CO
Harry Warner CO
114 Bruce Dal Canton .12 .30
115 Rick Manning .12 .30
116 Joe Niekro .30 .75
117 Frank White .30 .75
118 Rick Jones RC .12 .30
119 John Stearns .12 .30
120 Rod Carew 2.00 5.00
121 Gary Nolan .12 .30
122 Ben Oglivie .30 .75
123 Fred Stanley .12 .30
124 George Mitterwald .12 .30
125 Bill Travers .12 .30
126 Rod Gilbreath .12 .30
127 Ron Fairly .30 .75
128 Tommy John .60 1.50
129 Mike Sadek .12 .30
130 Al Oliver .30 .75
131 Orlando Ramirez RC .12 .30
132 Chip Lang RC .12 .30
133 Ralph Garr .30 .75
134 San Diego Padres CL .60 1.50
John McNamara MG
135 Mark Belanger .30 .75
136 Jerry Mumphrey RC .30 .75
137 Jeff Terpko RC .12 .30
138 Bob Stinson .12 .30
139 Fred Norman .12 .30
140 Mike Schmidt 5.00 12.00
141 Mark Littell .12 .30
142 Steve Dillard RC .12 .30
143 Ed Herrmann .12 .30
144 Bruce Sutter RC 6.00 15.00
145 Tom Veryzer .12 .30
146 Dusty Baker .60 1.50
147 Jackie Brown .12 .30
148 Fran Healy .12 .30
149 Mike Cubbage .12 .30
150 Tom Seaver 3.00 8.00
151 Johnny LeMaster .12 .30
152 Gaylord Perry 1.00 2.50
153 Ron Jackson RC .12 .30
154 Dave Giusti .12 .30
155 Joe Rudi .30 .75
156 Pete Mackanin .12 .30
157 Ken Brett .12 .30
158 Ted Kubiak .12 .30
159 Bernie Carbo .12 .30
160 Will McEnaney .12 .30
161 Garry Templeton RC .60 1.50
162 Mike Cuellar .30 .75
163 Dave Hilton .12 .30
164 Tug McGraw .30 .75
165 Jim Wynn .30 .75
166 Bill Campbell .12 .30
167 Rich Hebner .30 .75
168 Charlie Spikes .12 .30
169 Darold Knowles .12 .30
170 Thurman Munson 2.00 5.00
171 Ken Sanders .12 .30
172 John Milner .12 .30
173 Chuck Scrivener RC .12 .30
174 Nelson Briles .30 .75
175 Butch Wynegar RC .30 .75
176 Bob Robertson .12 .30
177 Bart Johnson .12 .30
178 Bombo Rivera RC .12 .30
179 Paul Hartzell RC .12 .30
180 Dave Lopes .30 .75
181 Ken McMullen .12 .30
182 Dan Spillner .12 .30
183 St. Louis Cardinals CL .60 1.50
Vern Rapp MG
184 Bo McLaughlin RC .12 .30
185 Sixto Lezcano .12 .30
186 Doug Flynn .12 .30
187 Dick Pole .12 .30
188 Bob Tolan .12 .30
189 Rick Dempsey .30 .75
190 Ray Burris .12 .30
191 Doug Griffin .12 .30
192 Clarence Gaston .30 .75
193 Larry Gura .12 .30
194 Gary Matthews .30 .75
195 Ed Figueroa .12 .30
196 Len Randle .12 .30
197 Ed Ott .12 .30
198 Wilbur Wood .12 .30
199 Pepe Frias .12 .30
200 Frank Tanana .30 .75
201 Ed Kranepool .12 .30
202 Tom Johnson .12 .30
203 Ed Armbrister .12 .30
204 Jeff Newman RC .12 .30
205 Pete Falcone .12 .30
206 Boog Powell .60 1.50
207 Glenn Abbott .12 .30
208 Checklist 133-264 .60 1.50
209 Rob Andrews .12 .30
210 Fred Lynn .30 .75
211 San Francisco Giants CL .60 1.50
Joe Altobelli MG
212 Jim Mason .12 .30
213 Maximino Leon .12 .30
214 Darrell Porter .30 .75
215 Butch Metzger .12 .30
216 Doug DeCinces .30 .75
217 Tom Underwood .12 .30
218 John Wathan RC .30 .75
219 Joe Coleman .12 .30
220 Chris Chambliss .30 .75
221 Bob Bailey .12 .30
222 Francisco Barrios RC .12 .30
223 Earl Williams .12 .30
224 Rusty Torres .12 .30
225 Bob Apodaca .12 .30
226 Leroy Stanton .30 .75
227 Joe Sambito RC .12 .30
228 Minnesota Twins CL .60 1.50
Gene Mauch MG
229 Don Kessinger .30 .75
230 Vida Blue .30 .75
231 George Brett RB 3.00 8.00
232 Minnie Minoso RB .30 .75
233 Jose Morales RB .12 .30
234 Nolan Ryan RB 6.00 15.00
235 Cecil Cooper .30 .75
236 Tom Buskey .12 .30
237 Gene Clines .12 .30
238 Tippy Martinez .12 .30
239 Bill Plummer .12 .30
240 Ron LeFlore .30 .75
241 Dave Tomlin .12 .30
242 Ken Henderson .12 .30
243 Ron Reed .12 .30
244 John Mayberry .30 .75
(Cartoon mentions
T206 Wagner)
245 Rick Rhoden .30 .75
246 Mike Vail .12 .30
247 Chris Knapp RC .12 .30
248 Wilbur Howard .12 .30
249 Pete Redfern RC .12 .30
250 Bill Madlock .30 .75
251 Tony Muser .12 .30
252 Dale Murray .12 .30
253 John Hale .12 .30
254 Doyle Alexander .12 .30
255 George Scott .30 .75
256 Joe Hoerner .12 .30
257 Mike Miley .12 .30
258 Luis Tiant .30 .75
259 New York Mets CL .60 1.50
Joe Frazier MG
260 J.R. Richard .30 .75
261 Phil Garner .30 .75
262 Al Cowens .30 .75
263 Mike Marshall .30 .75
264 Tom Hutton .12 .30
265 Mark Fidrych RC 1.25 3.00
266 Derrel Thomas .12 .30
267 Ray Fosse .12 .30
268 Rick Sawyer RC .12 .30
269 Joe Lis .12 .30
270 Dave Parker .60 1.50
271 Terry Forster .12 .30
272 Lee Lacy .12 .30
273 Eric Soderholm .12 .30
274 Don Stanhouse .12 .30
275 Mike Hargrove .30 .75
276 AL Championship .60 1.50
Chris Chambliss
277 NL Championship 2.00 5.00
Pete Rose
278 Danny Frisella .12 .30
279 Joe Wallis .12 .30
280 Jim Hunter 1.00 2.50
281 Roy Staiger .12 .30
282 Sid Monge .12 .30
283 Jerry DaVanon .12 .30
284 Mike Norris .12 .30
285 Brooks Robinson 2.00 5.00
286 Johnny Grubb .12 .30
287 Cincinnati Reds CL .60 1.50
Sparky Anderson MG
288 Bob Montgomery .12 .30
289 Gene Garber .30 .75
290 Amos Otis .30 .75
291 Jason Thompson RC .30 .75
292 Rogelio Moret .12 .30
293 Jack Brohamer .12 .30
294 George Medich .12 .30
295 Gary Carter 1.00 2.50
296 Don Hood .12 .30
297 Ken Reitz .12 .30
298 Charlie Hough .30 .75
299 Otto Velez .30 .75
300 Jerry Koosman .30 .75
301 Toby Harrah .30 .75
302 Mike Garman .12 .30
303 Gene Tenace .30 .75
304 Jim Hughes .12 .30
305 Mickey Rivers .30 .75
306 Rick Waits .12 .30
307 Gary Sutherland .12 .30
308 Gene Pentz RC .12 .30
309 Boston Red Sox CL .60 1.50
Don Zimmer MG
310 Larry Bowa .30 .75
311 Vern Ruhle .12 .30
312 Rob Belloir RC .12 .30
313 Paul Blair .30 .75
314 Steve Mingori .12 .30
315 Dave Chalk .12 .30
316 Steve Rogers .30 .75
317 Kurt Bevacqua .12 .30
318 Duffy Dyer .12 .30
319 Goose Gossage .60 1.50
320 Ken Griffey Sr. .60 1.50
321 Dave Goltz .12 .30
322 Bill Russell .30 .75
323 Larry Lintz .12 .30
324 John Curtis .12 .30
325 Mike Ivie .12 .30
326 Jesse Jefferson .12 .30
327 Houston Astros CL .60 1.50
Bill Virdon MG
328 Tommy Boggs RC .12 .30
329 Ron Hodges .12 .30
330 George Hendrick .30 .75
331 Jim Colborn .12 .30
332 Elliott Maddox .12 .30
333 Paul Reuschel RC .12 .30
334 Bill Stein .12 .30
335 Bill Robinson .30 .75
336 Denny Doyle .12 .30
337 Ron Schueler .12 .30
338 Dave Duncan .30 .75
339 Adrian Devine .12 .30
340 Hal McRae .30 .75
341 Joe Kerrigan RC .12 .30
342 Jerry Remy .12 .30
343 Ed Halicki .12 .30
344 Brian Downing .30 .75
345 Reggie Smith .30 .75
346 Bill Singer .12 .30
347 George Foster .60 1.50
348 Brent Strom .12 .30
349 Jim Holt .12 .30
350 Larry Dierker .30 .75
351 Jim Sundberg .30 .75
352 Mike Phillips .12 .30
353 Stan Thomas .12 .30
354 Pittsburgh Pirates CL .60 1.50
Chuck Tanner MG
355 Lou Brock 1.50 4.00
356 Checklist 265-396 .60 1.50
357 Tim McCarver .60 1.50
358 Tom House .12 .30
359 Willie Randolph .60 1.50
360 Rick Monday .30 .75
361 Eduardo Rodriguez .12 .30
362 Tommy Davis .30 .75
363 Dave Roberts .12 .30
364 Vic Correll .12 .30
365 Mike Torrez .30 .75
366 Ted Sizemore .12 .30
367 Dave Hamilton .12 .30
368 Mike Jorgensen .12 .30
369 Terry Humphrey .12 .30
370 John Montefusco .12 .30
371 Kansas City Royals CL .60 1.50
Whitey Herzog MG
372 Rich Folkers .12 .30
373 Bert Campaneris .30 .75
374 Kent Tekulve .30 .75
375 Larry Hisle .30 .75
376 Nino Espinosa RC .12 .30
377 Dave McKay .12 .30
378 Jim Umbarger .12 .30
379 Larry Cox RC .12 .30
380 Lee May .30 .75
381 Bob Forsch .12 .30
382 Charlie Moore .12 .30
383 Stan Bahnsen .12 .30
384 Darrel Chaney .12 .30
385 Dave LaRoche .12 .30
386 Manny Mota .30 .75
387 New York Yankees CL 1.00 2.50
Billy Martin MG
388 Terry Harmon .12 .30
389 Ken Kravec RC .12 .30
390 Dave Winfield 2.50 6.00
391 Dan Warthen .12 .30
392 Phil Roof .12 .30
393 John Lowenstein .12 .30
394 Bill Laxton RC .12 .30
395 Manny Trillo .12 .30
396 Tom Murphy .12 .30
397 Larry Herndon RC .30 .75
398 Tom Burgmeier .12 .30
399 Bruce Boisclair RC .12 .30
400 Steve Garvey 1.00 2.50
401 Mickey Scott .12 .30
402 Tommy Helms .12 .30
403 Tom Grieve .30 .75
404 Eric Rasmussen RC .12 .30
405 Claudell Washington .30 .75
406 Tim Johnson .12 .30
407 Dave Freisleben .12 .30
408 Cesar Tovar .12 .30
409 Pete Broberg .12 .30
410 Willie Montanez .12 .30
411 World Series 1.00 2.50
Joe Morgan
Johnny Bench
412 World Series 1.00 2.50
Johnny Bench
413 World Series .30 .75
Cincy Wins
414 Tommy Harper .30 .75
415 Jay Johnstone .30 .75
416 Chuck Hartenstein .12 .30
417 Wayne Garrett .12 .30
418 Chicago White Sox CL .60 1.50
Bob Lemon MG
419 Steve Swisher .12 .30
420 Rusty Staub .60 1.50
421 Doug Rau .12 .30
422 Freddie Patek .30 .75
423 Gary Lavelle .12 .30
424 Steve Brye .12 .30
425 Joe Torre .60 1.50
426 Dick Drago .12 .30
427 Dave Rader .12 .30
428 Texas Rangers CL .60 1.50
Frank Lucchesi
429 Ken Boswell .12 .30
430 Fergie Jenkins 1.00 2.50
431 Dave Collins UER .30 .75
(Photo actually
Bobby Jones)
432 Buzz Capra .12 .30
433 Nate Colbert TBC .12 .30
434 Carl Yastrzemski TBC .60 1.50
435 Maury Wills TBC .12 .30
436 Bob Keegan TBC .12 .30
437 Ralph Kiner TBC .60 1.50
438 Marty Perez .12 .30
439 Gorman Thomas .12 .30
440 Jon Matlack .12 .30
441 Larvell Blanks .12 .30
442 Atlanta Braves CL .60 1.50
Dave Bristol MG
443 Lamar Johnson .12 .30
444 Wayne Twitchell .12 .30
445 Ken Singleton .30 .75
446 Bill Bonham .12 .30
447 Jerry Turner .12 .30
448 Ellie Rodriguez .12 .30
449 Al Fitzmorris .12 .30
450 Pete Rose 8.00 20.00
451 Checklist 397-528 .60 1.50
452 Mike Caldwell .12 .30
453 Pedro Garcia .12 .30
454 Andy Etchebarren .12 .30
455 Rick Wise .12 .30
456 Leon Roberts .12 .30
457 Steve Luebber .12 .30
458 Leo Foster .12 .30
459 Steve Foucault .12 .30
460 Willie Stargell 1.00 2.50
461 Dick Tidrow .12 .30
462 Don Baylor .60 1.50
463 Jamie Quirk .12 .30
464 Randy Moffitt .12 .30
465 Rico Carty .30 .75
466 Fred Holdsworth .12 .30
467 Philadelphia Phillies CL .60 1.50
Danny Ozark MG
468 Ramon Hernandez .12 .30
469 Pat Kelly .12 .30
470 Ted Simmons .30 .75
471 Del Unser .12 .30
472 Rookie Pitchers .12 .30
Don Aase
Bob McClure
Gil Patterson RC
Dave Wehrmeister RC
UER Sheldon Gill pictured
instead of Gil Patterson
473 Rookie Outfielders 8.00 20.00
Andre Dawson RC
Gene Richards RC
John Scott
Denny Walling RC
474 Rookie Shortstops .30 .75
Bob Bailor RC
Kiko Garcia RC
Craig Reynolds
Alex Taveras RC
475 Rookie Pitchers .30 .75
Chris Batton RC
Rick Camp RC
Scott McGregor
Manny Sarmiento RC
476 Rookie Catchers 6.00 15.00
Gary Alexander RC
Rick Cerone RC
Dale Murphy RC
Kevin Pasley RC
477 Rookie Infielders .30 .75
Doug Ault RC
Rich Dauer RC
Orlando Gonzalez RC
Phil Mankowski RC
478 Rookie Pitchers .30 .75
Jim Gideon RC
Leon Hooten RC
Dave Johnson RC
Mark Lemongello RC
479 Rookie Outfielders .30 .75
Brian Asselstine RC
Wayne Gross RC
Sam Mejias RC
Alvis Woods RC
480 Carl Yastrzemski 3.00 8.00
481 Roger Metzger .12 .30
482 Tony Solaita .12 .30
483 Richie Zisk .12 .30
484 Burt Hooton .30 .75
485 Roy White .30 .75
486 Ed Bane .12 .30
487 Rookie Pitchers .30 .75
Larry Anderson
Ed Glynn RC
Joe Henderson RC
Greg Terlecky RC
488 Rookie Outfielders 1.25 3.00
Jack Clark RC
Ruppert Jones RC
Lee Mazzilli RC
Dan Thomas RC
489 Rookie Pitchers .30 .75
Len Barker RC
Randy Lerch
Greg Minton RC
Mike Overy RC
490 Rookie Shortstops .30 .75
Billy Almon RC
Mickey Klutts RC
Tommy McMillan RC
Mark Wagner RC
491 Rookie Pitchers 1.25 3.00
Mike Dupree RC
Dennis Martinez RC
Craig Mitchell
Bob Sykes RC
492 Rookie Outfielders .30 .75
Tony Armas RC
Steve Kemp RC
Carlos Lopez RC
Gary Woods RC
493 Rookie Pitchers .30 .75
Mike Krukow RC
Jim Otten
Gary Wheelock RC
Mike Willis RC
494 Rookie Infielders .60 1.50
Juan Bernhardt RC
Mike Champion RC
Jim Gantner RC
Bump Wills RC
495 Al Hrabosky .30 .75
496 Gary Thomasson .12 .30
497 Clay Carroll .12 .30
498 Sal Bando .30 .75
499 Pablo Torrealba .12 .30
500 Dave Kingman .60 1.50
501 Jim Bibby .12 .30
502 Randy Hundley .12 .30
503 Bill Lee .12 .30
504 Los Angeles Dodgers CL .60 1.50
Tom Lasorda MG
505 Oscar Gamble .30 .75
506 Steve Grilli .12 .30
507 Mike Hegan .12 .30
508 Dave Pagan .12 .30
509 Cookie Rojas .30 .75
510 John Candelaria .30 .75
511 Bill Fahey .12 .30
512 Jack Billingham .12 .30
513 Jerry Terrell .12 .30
514 Cliff Johnson .12 .30
515 Chris Speier .12 .30
516 Bake McBride .30 .75
517 Pete Vuckovich RC .30 .75
518 Chicago Cubs CL .60 1.50
Herman Franks MG
519 Don Kirkwood .12 .30
520 Garry Maddox .12 .30
521 Bob Grich .30 .75
Only card in set with no date of birth
522 Enzo Hernandez .12 .30
523 Rollie Fingers 1.00 2.50
524 Rowland Office .12 .30
525 Dennis Eckersley 2.00 5.00
526 Larry Parrish .30 .75
527 Dan Meyer .30 .75
528 Bill Castro .12 .30
529 Jim Essian RC .12 .30
530 Rick Reuschel .30 .75
531 Lyman Bostock .30 .75
532 Jim Willoughby .12 .30
533 Mickey Stanley .12 .30
534 Paul Splittorff .12 .30
535 Cesar Geronimo .12 .30
536 Vic Albury .12 .30
537 Dave Roberts .12 .30
538 Frank Taveras .12 .30
539 Mike Wallace .12 .30
540 Bob Watson .30 .75
541 John Denny .30 .75
542 Frank Duffy .12 .30
543 Ron Blomberg .12 .30
544 Gary Ross .10 .30
545 Bob Boone .30 .75
546 Baltimore Orioles CL .60 1.50
Earl Weaver MG
547 Willie McCovey 1.50 4.00
548 Joel Youngblood RC .12 .30
549 Jerry Royster .12 .30
550 Randy Jones .12 .30
551 Bill North .12 .30
552 Pepe Mangual .12 .30
553 Jack Heidemann .12 .30
554 Bruce Kimm RC .12 .30
555 Dan Ford .12 .30
556 Doug Bird .12 .30
557 Jerry White .12 .30
558 Elias Sosa .12 .30
559 Alan Bannister RC .12 .30
560 Dave Concepcion .60 1.50
561 Pete LaCock .12 .30
562 Checklist 529-660 .60 1.50
563 Bruce Kison .12 .30
564 Alan Ashby .12 .30
565 Mickey Lolich .30 .75
566 Rick Miller .12 .30
567 Enos Cabell .12 .30
568 Carlos May .12 .30
569 Jim Lonborg .30 .75
570 Bobby Bonds .60 1.50
571 Darrell Evans .30 .75
572 Ross Grimsley .12 .30
573 Joe Ferguson .12 .30
574 Aurelio Rodriguez .12 .30
575 Dick Ruthven .12 .30
576 Fred Kendall .12 .30
577 Jerry Augustine RC .12 .30
578 Bob Randall RC .12 .30
579 Don Carrithers .12 .30
580 George Brett 6.00 15.00
581 Pedro Borbon .12 .30
582 Ed Kirkpatrick .12 .30
583 Paul Lindblad .12 .30
584 Ed Goodson .12 .30
585 Rick Burleson .30 .75
586 Steve Renko .12 .30
587 Rick Baldwin .12 .30
588 Dave Moates .12 .30
589 Mike Cosgrove .12 .30
590 Buddy Bell .30 .75
591 Chris Arnold .12 .30
592 Dan Briggs RC .12 .30
593 Dennis Blair .12 .30
594 Biff Pocoroba .12 .30
595 John Hiller .12 .30
596 Jerry Martin RC .12 .30
597 Mariners Leaders CL .60 1.50
Darrell Johnson MG
Don Bryant CO
Jim Busby CO
Vada Pinson CO
Wes Stock CO
598 Sparky Lyle .30 .75
599 Mike Tyson .12 .30
600 Jim Palmer 1.50 4.00
601 Mike Lum .12 .30
602 Andy Hassler .12 .30
603 Willie Davis .30 .75
604 Jim Slaton .12 .30
605 Felix Millan .12 .30
606 Steve Braun .12 .30
607 Larry Demery .12 .30
608 Roy Howell .12 .30
609 Jim Barr .12 .30
610 Jose Cardenal .30 .75
611 Dave Lemanczyk .12 .30
612 Barry Foote .12 .30
613 Reggie Cleveland .12 .30
614 Greg Gross .12 .30
615 Phil Niekro 1.00 2.50
616 Tommy Sandt RC .12 .30
617 Bobby Darwin .12 .30
618 Pat Dobson .12 .30
619 Johnny Oates .30 .75
620 Don Sutton 1.00 2.50
621 Detroit Tigers CL .60 1.50
Ralph Houk MG
622 Jim Wohlford .12 .30
623 Jack Kucek .12 .30
624 Hector Cruz .12 .30
625 Ken Holtzman .30 .75
626 Al Bumbry .30 .75

Card	Low	High
627 Bob Myrick RC	.12	.30
628 Mario Guerrero	.12	.30
629 Bobby Valentine	.30	.75
630 Bert Blyleven	.60	1.50
631 Brothers	2.50	6.00
George Brett		
Ken Brett		
632 Brothers	.30	.75
Bob Forsch		
Ken Forsch		
633 Brothers	.30	.75
Lee May		
Carlos May		
634 Brothers	.30	.75
Paul Reuschel		
Rick Reuschel UER		
(Photos switched)		
635 Robin Yount	3.00	8.00
636 Santo Alcala	.12	.30
637 Alex Johnson	.12	.30
638 Jim Kaat	.60	1.50
639 Jerry Morales	.12	.30
640 Carlton Fisk	2.00	5.00
641 Dan Larson RC	.12	.30
642 Willie Crawford	.12	.30
643 Mike Pazik	.12	.30
644 Matt Alexander	.12	.30
645 Jerry Reuss	.30	.75
646 Andres Mora RC	.12	.30
647 Montreal Expos CL	.60	1.50
Dick Williams MG		
648 Jim Spencer	.12	.30
649 Dave Cash	.12	.30
650 Nolan Ryan	12.50	30.00
651 Von Joshua	.12	.30
652 Tom Walker	.12	.30
653 Diego Segui	.30	.75
654 Ron Pruitt RC	.12	.30
655 Tony Perez	1.00	2.50
656 Ron Guidry	.60	1.50
657 Mick Kelleher RC	.12	.30
658 Marty Pattin	.12	.30
659 Merv Rettenmund	.12	.30
660 Willie Horton	.60	1.50

1978 Topps

The cards in this 726-card set measure 2 1/2" by 3 1/2". As in previous years, this set was issued in many different ways: some of them include 14-card wax packs, 30-card supermarket packs which came 48 to a case and had an SRP of 20 cents and 39-card rack packs. The 1978 Topps set experienced an increase in number of cards from the previous five regular issue sets of 660. Card numbers 1 through 7 feature Record Breakers (RB) of the 1977 season. Other subsets within this set include League Leaders (201-208), Post-season cards (411-413), and Rookie Prospects (701-711). The key Rookie Cards in this set are the multi-player Rookie Card of Paul Molitor and Alan Trammell, Jack Morris, Eddie Murray, Lance Parrish, and Lou Whitaker. Many of the Molitor/Trammell cards are found with black printing smudges. The manager cards in the set feature a "then and now" format on the card front showing the manager as he looked during his playing days. While no scarcities exist, 66 of the cards are more abundant in supply, as they were "double printed." These 66 double-printed cards are noted in the checklist by DP. Team cards again feature a checklist of that team's players in the set on the back. Cards numbered 23 or lower, that feature Astros, Rangers, Tigers, or Yankees and do not follow the numbering checklisted below, are not necessarily error cards. They are undoubtedly Burger King cards, separate sets with their own pricing and mass distribution. The Bump Wills card has been seen with either no black mark or a major black mark on the front of the card. We will continue to investigate this card and see whether or not it should be considered a variation.

Card	Low	High
COMPLETE SET (726)	100.00	200.00
COMMON CARD (1-726)	.10	.25
COMMON CARD DP	.08	.20
1 Lou Brock RB	1.25	3.00
2 Sparky Lyle RB	.25	.60
3 Willie McCovey RB	1.00	2.50
4 Brooks Robinson RB	.50	1.25
5 Pete Rose RB	3.00	8.00
6 Nolan Ryan RB	6.00	15.00
7 Reggie Jackson RB	1.50	4.00
8 Mike Sadek	.10	.25
9 Doug DeCinces	.25	.60
10 Phil Niekro	1.00	2.50
11 Rick Manning	.10	.25
12 Don Aase	.10	.25
13 Art Howe RC	.25	.60
14 Lerrin LaGrow	.10	.25
15 Tony Perez DP	.50	1.25
16 Roy White	.25	.60
17 Mike Krukow	.10	.25
18 Bob Grich	.25	.60
19 Darrell Porter	.25	.60
20 Pete Rose DP	5.00	12.00
21 Steve Kemp	.10	.25
22 Charlie Hough	.25	.60
23 Bump Wills	.10	.25
24 Don Money DP	.08	.20
25 Jon Matlack	.10	.25
26 Rich Hebner	.25	.60
27 Geoff Zahn	.10	.25
28 Ed Ott	.10	.25
29 Bob Lacey RC	.10	.25
30 George Hendrick	.25	.60
31 Glenn Abbott	.10	.25
32 Garry Templeton	.25	.60
33 Dave Lemanczyk	.10	.25
34 Willie McCovey	1.25	3.00
35 Sparky Lyle	.25	.60
36 Eddie Murray RC	20.00	50.00
37 Rick Waits	.10	.25
38 Willie Montanez	.10	.25
39 Floyd Bannister RC	.10	.25
40 Carl Yastrzemski	2.50	6.00
41 Burt Hooton	.25	.60
42 Jorge Orta	.10	.25
43 Bill Atkinson RC	.10	.25
44 Toby Harrah	.25	.60
45 Mark Fidrych	1.00	2.50
46 Al Cowens	.25	.60
47 Jack Billingham	.10	.25
48 Don Baylor	.50	1.25
49 Ed Kranepool	.25	.60
50 Rick Reuschel	.25	.60
51 Charlie Moore DP	.08	.20
52 Jim Lonborg	.25	.60
53 Phil Garner DP	.10	.25
54 Tom Johnson	.10	.25
55 Mitchell Page RC	.10	.25
56 Randy Jones	.10	.25
57 Dan Meyer	.10	.25
58 Bob Forsch	.10	.25
59 Otto Velez	.10	.25
60 Thurman Munson	1.50	4.00
61 Larvell Blanks	.10	.25
62 Jim Barr	.10	.25
63 Don Zimmer MG	.25	.60
64 Gene Pentz	.10	.25
65 Ken Singleton	.25	.60
66 Chicago White Sox CL	.50	1.25
67 Claudell Washington	.25	.60
68 Steve Foucault DP	.08	.20
69 Mike Vail	.10	.25
70 Goose Gossage	.50	1.25
71 Terry Humphrey	.10	.25
72 Andre Dawson	1.50	4.00
73 Andy Hassler	.10	.25
74 Checklist 1-121	.50	1.25
75 Dick Ruthven	.10	.25
76 Steve Ontiveros	.10	.25
77 Ed Kirkpatrick	.10	.25
78 Pablo Torrealba	.10	.25
79 Darrell Johnson MG DP	.08	.20
80 Ken Griffey Sr.	.50	1.25
81 Pete Redfern	.10	.25
82 San Francisco Giants CL	.50	1.25
83 Bob Montgomery	.10	.25
84 Kent Tekulve	.25	.60
85 Ron Fairly	.25	.60
86 Dave Tomlin	.10	.25
87 John Lowenstein	.10	.25
88 Mike Phillips	.10	.25
89 Ken Clay RC	.10	.25
90 Larry Bowa	.50	1.25
91 Oscar Zamora	.10	.25
92 Adrian Devine	.10	.25
93 Bobby Cox DP	.08	.20
94 Chuck Scrivener	.10	.25
95 Jamie Quirk	.10	.25
96 Baltimore Orioles CL	.50	1.25
97 Stan Bahnsen	.10	.25
98 Jim Essian	.25	.60
99 Willie Hernandez RC	.50	1.25
100 George Brett	6.00	15.00
101 Sid Monge	.10	.25
102 Matt Alexander	.10	.25
103 Tom Murphy	.10	.25
104 Lee Lacy	.10	.25
105 Reggie Cleveland	.10	.25
106 Bill Plummer	.10	.25
107 Ed Halicki	.10	.25
108 Von Joshua	.10	.25
109 Joe Torre MG	.25	.60
110 Richie Zisk	.10	.25
111 Mike Tyson	.10	.25
112 Houston Astros CL	.50	1.25
113 Don Carrithers	.10	.25
114 Paul Blair	.25	.60
115 Gary Nolan	.10	.25
116 Tucker Ashford RC	.10	.25
117 John Montague	.10	.25
118 Terry Harmon	.10	.25
119 Dennis Martinez	1.00	2.50
120 Gary Carter	1.00	2.50
121 Alvis Woods	.10	.25
122 Dennis Eckersley	1.25	3.00
123 Manny Trillo	.10	.25
124 Dave Rozema RC	.10	.25
125 George Scott	.25	.60
126 Paul Moskau RC	.10	.25
127 Chet Lemon	.25	.60
128 Bill Russell	.25	.60
129 Jim Colborn	.10	.25
130 Jeff Burroughs	.25	.60
131 Bert Blyleven	.50	1.25
132 Enos Cabell	.10	.25
133 Jerry Augustine	.10	.25
134 Steve Henderson RC	.10	.25
135 Ron Guidry DP	.50	1.25
136 Ted Sizemore	.10	.25
137 Craig Kusick	.10	.25
138 Larry Demery	.10	.25
139 Wayne Gross	.10	.25
140 Rollie Fingers	1.00	2.50
141 Ruppert Jones	.10	.25
142 John Montefusco	.10	.25
143 Keith Hernandez	.25	.60
144 Jesse Jefferson	.10	.25
145 Rick Monday	.25	.60
146 Doyle Alexander	.25	.60
147 Lee Mazzilli	.10	.25
148 Andre Thornton	.25	.60
149 Dale Murray	.10	.25
150 Bobby Bonds	.50	1.25
151 Milt Wilcox	.10	.25
152 Ivan DeJesus RC	.10	.25
153 Steve Stone	.25	.60
154 Cecil Cooper DP	.10	.25
155 Butch Hobson	.10	.25
156 Andy Messersmith	.25	.60
157 Pete LaCock DP	.08	.20
158 Joaquin Andujar	.25	.60
159 Lou Piniella	.25	.60
160 Jim Palmer	1.25	3.00
161 Bob Boone	.50	1.25
162 Paul Thormodsgard RC	.10	.25
163 Bill North	.10	.25
164 Bob Owchinko RC	.10	.25
165 Rennie Stennett	.10	.25
166 Carlos Lopez	.10	.25
167 Tim Foli	.10	.25
168 Reggie Smith	.25	.60
169 Jerry Johnson	.10	.25
170 Lou Brock	1.25	3.00
171 Pat Zachry	.10	.25
172 Mike Hargrove	.25	.60
173 Robin Yount UER	2.00	5.00
(Played for Newark		
in 1973, not 1971)		
174 Wayne Garland	.10	.25
175 Jerry Morales	.10	.25
176 Milt May	.10	.25
177 Gene Garber DP	.10	.25
178 Dave Chalk	.10	.25
179 Dick Tidrow	.10	.25
180 Dave Concepcion	.50	1.25
181 Ken Forsch	.10	.25
182 Jim Spencer	.10	.25
183 Doug Bird	.10	.25
184 Checklist 122-242	.50	1.25
185 Ellis Valentine	.10	.25
186 Bob Stanley DP RC	.08	.20
187 Jerry Royster DP	.08	.20
188 Al Bumbry	.25	.60
189 Tom Lasorda MG DP	1.00	2.50
190 John Candelaria	.25	.60
191 Rodney Scott RC	.10	.25
192 San Diego Padres CL	.50	1.25
193 Rich Chiles	.10	.25
194 Derrel Thomas	.10	.25
195 Larry Dierker	.25	.60
196 Bob Bailor	.10	.25
197 Nino Espinosa	.10	.25
198 Ron Pruitt	.10	.25
199 Craig Reynolds	.10	.25
200 Reggie Jackson	3.00	8.00
201 Batting Leaders	.50	1.25
Dave Parker		
Rod Carew		
202 Home Run Leaders DP	.25	.60
George Foster		
Jim Rice		
203 RBI Leaders	.25	.60
George Foster		
Larry Hisle		
204 Stolen Base Leaders DP	.10	.25
Frank Taveras		
Freddie Patek		
205 Victory Leaders	1.00	2.50
Steve Carlton		
Dave Goltz		
Dennis Leonard		
Jim Palmer		
206 Strikeout Leaders DP	2.50	6.00
Phil Niekro		
Nolan Ryan		
207 ERA Leaders DP	.25	.60
John Candelaria		
Frank Tanana		
208 Leading Firemen	.50	1.25
Rollie Fingers		
Bill Campbell		
209 Dock Ellis	.10	.25
210 Jose Cardenal	.10	.25
211 Earl Weaver MG DP	.50	1.25
212 Mike Caldwell	.10	.25
213 Alan Bannister	.10	.25
214 California Angels CL	.50	1.25
215 Darrell Evans	.25	.60
216 Mike Paxton RC	.10	.25
217 Rod Gilbreath	.10	.25
218 Marty Pattin	.10	.25
219 Mike Cubbage	.10	.25
220 Pedro Borbon	.10	.25
221 Chris Speier	.10	.25
222 Jerry Martin	.10	.25
223 Bruce Kison	.10	.25
224 Jerry Tabb RC	.10	.25
225 Don Gullett DP	.10	.25
226 Joe Ferguson	.10	.25
227 Al Fitzmorris	.10	.25
228 Manny Mota DP	.10	.25
229 Leo Foster	.10	.25
230 Al Hrabosky	.25	.60
231 Wayne Nordhagen RC	.10	.25
232 Mickey Stanley	.10	.25
233 Dick Pole	.10	.25
234 Herman Franks MG	.10	.25
235 Tim McCarver	.25	.60
236 Terry Whitfield	.10	.25
237 Rich Dauer	.10	.25
238 Juan Beniquez	.10	.25
239 Dyar Miller	.10	.25
240 Gene Tenace	.25	.60
241 Pete Vuckovich	.25	.60
242 Barry Bonnell DP RC	.08	.20
243 Bob McClure	.10	.25
244 Montreal Expos CL DP	.25	.60
245 Rick Burleson	.25	.60
246 Dan Driessen	.10	.25
247 Larry Christenson	.10	.25
248 Frank White DP	.25	.60
249 Dave Goltz DP	.08	.20
250 Graig Nettles DP	.25	.60
251 Don Kirkwood	.10	.25
252 Steve Swisher DP	.08	.20
253 Jim Kern	.10	.25
254 Dave Collins	.25	.60
255 Jerry Reuss	.25	.60
256 Joe Altobelli MG RC	.10	.25
257 Hector Cruz	.10	.25
258 John Hiller	.10	.25
259 Los Angeles Dodgers CL	.50	1.25
260 Bert Campaneris	.25	.60
261 Tim Hosley	.10	.25
262 Rudy May	.10	.25
263 Danny Walton	.10	.25
264 Jamie Easterly	.10	.25
265 Sal Bando DP	.25	.60
266 Bob Shirley RC	.10	.25
267 Doug Ault	.10	.25
268 Gil Flores RC	.10	.25
269 Wayne Twitchell	.10	.25
270 Carlton Fisk	1.50	4.00
271 Randy Lerch DP	.08	.20
272 Royle Stillman	.10	.25
273 Fred Norman	.10	.25
274 Freddie Patek	.25	.60
275 Dan Ford	.10	.25
276 Bill Bonham DP	.08	.20
277 Bruce Boisclair	.10	.25
278 Enrique Romo RC	.10	.25
279 Bill Virdon MG	.10	.25
280 Buddy Bell	.25	.60
281 Eric Rasmussen DP	.08	.20
282 New York Yankees CL	1.00	2.50
283 Omar Moreno	.10	.25
284 Randy Moffitt	.10	.25
285 Steve Yeager DP	.25	.60
286 Ben Oglivie	.25	.60
287 Kiko Garcia	.10	.25
288 Dave Hamilton	.10	.25
289 Checklist 243-363	.50	1.25
290 Willie Horton	.25	.60
291 Gary Ross	.10	.25
292 Gene Richards	.10	.25
293 Mike Willis	.10	.25
294 Larry Parrish	.25	.60
295 Bill Lee	.10	.25
296 Biff Pocoroba	.10	.25
297 Warren Brusstar DP RC	.08	.20
298 Tony Armas	.25	.60
299 Whitey Herzog MG	.25	.60
300 Joe Morgan	1.25	3.00
301 Buddy Schultz RC	.10	.25
302 Chicago Cubs CL	.50	1.25
303 Sam Hinds RC	.10	.25
304 John Milner	.10	.25
305 Rico Carty	.25	.60
306 Joe Niekro	.25	.60
307 Glenn Borgmann	.10	.25
308 Jim Rooker	.10	.25
309 Cliff Johnson	.10	.25
310 Don Sutton	1.00	2.50
311 Jose Baez DP RC	.08	.20
312 Greg Minton	.10	.25
313 Andy Etchebarren	.10	.25
314 Paul Lindblad	.10	.25
315 Mark Belanger	.25	.60
316 Henry Cruz DP	.08	.20
317 Dave Johnson	.10	.25
318 Tom Griffin	.10	.25
319 Alan Ashby	.10	.25
320 Fred Lynn	.25	.60
321 Santo Alcala	.10	.25
322 Tom Paciorek	.25	.60
323 Jim Fregosi DP	.10	.25
324 Vern Rapp MG RC	.10	.25
325 Bruce Sutter	1.25	3.00
326 Mike Lum DP	.08	.20
327 Rick Langford DP RC	.08	.20
328 Milwaukee Brewers CL	.50	1.25
329 John Verhoeven	.10	.25
330 Bob Watson	.25	.60
331 Mark Littell	.10	.25
332 Duane Kuiper	.10	.25
333 Jim Todd	.10	.25
334 John Stearns	.10	.25
335 Bucky Dent	.25	.60
336 Steve Busby	.10	.25
337 Tom Grieve	.25	.60
338 Dave Heaverlo	.10	.25
339 Mario Guerrero	.10	.25
340 Bake McBride	.25	.60
341 Mike Flanagan	.25	.60
342 Aurelio Rodriguez	.10	.25
343 John Wathan DP	.08	.20
344 Sam Ewing RC	.10	.25
345 Luis Tiant	.25	.60
346 Larry Biittner	.10	.25
347 Terry Forster	.10	.25
348 Del Unser	.10	.25
349 Rick Camp DP	.08	.20
350 Steve Garvey	1.00	2.50
351 Jeff Torborg	.25	.60
352 Tony Scott RC	.10	.25
353 Doug Bair RC	.10	.25
354 Cesar Geronimo	.10	.25
355 Bill Travers	.10	.25
356 New York Mets CL	.50	1.25
357 Tom Poquette	.10	.25
358 Mark Lemongello	.10	.25
359 Marc Hill	.10	.25
360 Mike Schmidt	4.00	10.00
361 Chris Knapp	.10	.25
362 Dave May	.10	.25
363 Bob Randall	.10	.25
364 Jerry Turner	.10	.25
365 Ed Figueroa	.10	.25
366 Larry Milbourne DP	.08	.20
367 Rick Dempsey	.25	.60
368 Balor Moore	.10	.25
369 Tim Nordbrook	.10	.25
370 Rusty Staub	.50	1.25
371 Ray Burris	.10	.25
372 Brian Asselstine	.10	.25
373 Jim Willoughby	.10	.25
374 Jose Morales	.10	.25
375 Tommy John	.50	1.25
376 Jim Wohlford	.10	.25
377 Manny Sarmiento	.10	.25
378 Bobby Winkles MG	.10	.25
379 Skip Lockwood	.10	.25
380 Ted Simmons	.25	.60
381 Philadelphia Phillies CL	.50	1.25
382 Joe Lahoud	.10	.25
383 Mario Mendoza	.10	.25
384 Jack Clark	.50	1.25
385 Tito Fuentes	.10	.25
386 Bob Gorinski RC	.10	.25
387 Ken Holtzman	.25	.60
388 Bill Fahey DP	.08	.20
389 Julio Gonzalez RC	.10	.25
390 Oscar Gamble	.25	.60
391 Larry Haney	.10	.25
392 Billy Almon	.10	.25
393 Tippy Martinez	.25	.60
394 Roy Howell DP	.08	.20
395 Jim Hughes	.10	.25
396 Bob Stinson DP	.08	.20
397 Greg Gross	.10	.25
398 Don Hood	.10	.25
399 Pete Mackanin	.10	.25
400 Nolan Ryan	10.00	25.00
401 Sparky Anderson MG	.25	.60
402 Dave Campbell	.10	.25
403 Bud Harrelson	.25	.60
404 Detroit Tigers CL	.50	1.25
405 Rawly Eastwick	.10	.25
406 Mike Jorgensen	.10	.25
407 Odell Jones RC	.10	.25
408 Joe Zdeb RC	.10	.25
409 Ron Schueler	.10	.25
410 Bill Madlock	.25	.60
411 AL Championships	.25	.60
Mickey Rivers		
412 NL Championships	.25	.60
Davey Lopes		
413 World Series	1.50	4.00
Reggie Jackson		
414 Darold Knowles DP	.08	.20
415 Ray Fosse	.10	.25
416 Jack Brohamer	.10	.25
417 Mike Garman DP	.08	.20
418 Tony Muser	.10	.25
419 Jerry Garvin RC	.10	.25
420 Greg Luzinski	.50	1.25
421 Junior Moore RC	.10	.25
422 Steve Braun	.10	.25
423 Dave Rosello	.10	.25
424 Boston Red Sox CL	.50	1.25
425 Steve Rogers DP	.10	.25
426 Fred Kendall	.10	.25
427 Mario Soto RC	.25	.60
428 Joel Youngblood	.10	.25
429 Mike Barlow RC	.10	.25
430 Al Oliver	.25	.60
431 Butch Metzger	.10	.25
432 Terry Bulling RC	.10	.25
433 Fernando Gonzalez	.10	.25
434 Mike Norris	.10	.25
435 Checklist 364-484	.50	1.25
436 Vic Harris DP	.08	.20
437 Bo McLaughlin	.10	.25
438 John Ellis	.10	.25
439 Ken Kravec	.10	.25
440 Dave Lopes	.25	.60
441 Larry Gura	.10	.25
442 Elliott Maddox	.10	.25
443 Darrel Chaney	.10	.25
444 Roy Hartsfield MG	.10	.25
445 Mike Ivie	.10	.25
446 Tug McGraw	.25	.60
447 Leroy Stanton	.10	.25
448 Bill Castro	.10	.25
449 Tim Blackwell DP RC	.08	.20
450 Tom Seaver	2.50	6.00
451 Minnesota Twins CL	.50	1.25
452 Jerry Mumphrey	.10	.25
453 Doug Flynn	.10	.25
454 Dave LaRoche	.10	.25
455 Bill Robinson	.25	.60
456 Vern Ruhle	.10	.25
457 Bob Bailey	.10	.25
458 Jeff Newman	.10	.25
459 Charlie Spikes	.10	.25
460 Jim Hunter	1.00	2.50
461 Rob Andrews DP	.08	.20
462 Rogelio Moret	.10	.25
463 Kevin Bell	.10	.25
464 Jerry Grote	.10	.25
465 Hal McRae	.25	.60
466 Dennis Blair	.10	.25
467 Alvin Dark MG	.25	.60
468 Warren Cromartie RC	.25	.60
469 Rick Cerone	.25	.60
470 J.R. Richard	.25	.60
471 Roy Smalley	.25	.60
472 Ron Reed	.10	.25
473 Bill Buckner	.25	.60
474 Jim Slaton	.10	.25
475 Gary Matthews	.25	.60
476 Bill Stein	.10	.25
477 Doug Capilla RC	.10	.25
478 Jerry Remy	.10	.25
479 St. Louis Cardinals CL	.50	1.25
480 Ron LeFlore	.25	.60
481 Jackson Todd RC	.10	.25
482 Rick Miller	.10	.25
483 Ken Macha RC	.10	.25
484 Jim Norris RC	.10	.25
485 Chris Chambliss	.25	.60
486 John Curtis	.10	.25
487 Jim Tyrone	.10	.25
488 Dan Spillner	.10	.25
489 Rudy Meoli	.10	.25
490 Amos Otis	.25	.60
491 Scott McGregor	.25	.60
492 Jim Sundberg	.25	.60
493 Steve Renko	.10	.25
494 Chuck Tanner MG	.25	.60
495 Dave Cash	.10	.25
496 Jim Clancy DP RC	.08	.20
497 Glenn Adams	.10	.25
498 Joe Sambito	.10	.25
499 Seattle Mariners CL	.50	1.25
500 George Foster	.50	1.25
501 Dave Roberts	.10	.25
502 Pat Rockett RC	.10	.25
503 Ike Hampton RC	.10	.25
504 Roger Freed	.10	.25
505 Felix Millan	.10	.25
506 Ron Blomberg	.10	.25
507 Willie Crawford	.10	.25
508 Johnny Oates	.25	.60
509 Brent Strom	.10	.25
510 Willie Stargell	1.00	2.50
511 Frank Duffy	.10	.25
512 Larry Herndon	.10	.25
513 Barry Foote	.10	.25
514 Rob Sperring	.10	.25
515 Tim Corcoran RC	.10	.25
516 Gary Beare RC	.10	.25
517 Andres Mora	.10	.25
518 Tommy Boggs DP	.08	.20
519 Brian Downing	.25	.60
520 Larry Hisle	.10	.25
521 Steve Staggs RC	.10	.25
522 Dick Williams MG	.25	.60
523 Donnie Moore RC	.10	.25
524 Bernie Carbo	.10	.25
525 Jerry Terrell	.10	.25
526 Cincinnati Reds CL	.50	1.25
527 Vic Correll	.10	.25
528 Rob Picciolo RC	.10	.25
529 Paul Hartzell	.10	.25
530 Dave Winfield	1.50	4.00
531 Tom Underwood	.10	.25
532 Skip Jutze	.10	.25
533 Sandy Alomar	.25	.60
534 Wilbur Howard	.10	.25
535 Checklist 485-605	.50	1.25
536 Roric Harrison	.10	.25
537 Bruce Bochte	.10	.25
538 Johnny LeMaster	.10	.25
539 Vic Davalillo DP	.08	.20
540 Steve Carlton	1.50	4.00
541 Larry Cox	.10	.25
542 Tim Johnson	.10	.25
543 Larry Harlow DP RC	.08	.20
544 Len Randle DP	.08	.20
545 Bill Campbell	.10	.25
546 Ted Martinez	.10	.25
547 John Scott	.10	.25
548 Billy Hunter MG DP	.08	.20
549 Joe Kerrigan	.10	.25
550 John Mayberry	.25	.60
551 Atlanta Braves CL	.50	1.25
552 Francisco Barrios	.10	.25
553 Terry Puhl RC	.25	.60
554 Joe Coleman	.10	.25
555 Butch Wynegar	.10	.25
556 Ed Armbrister	.10	.25
557 Tony Solaita	.10	.25
558 Paul Mitchell	.10	.25
559 Phil Mankowski	.10	.25
560 Dave Parker	.50	1.25
561 Charlie Williams	.10	.25
562 Glenn Burke RC	.10	.25
563 Dave Rader	.10	.25
564 Mick Kelleher	.10	.25
565 Jerry Koosman	.25	.60
566 Merv Rettenmund	.10	.25
567 Dick Drago	.10	.25
568 Tom Hutton	.10	.25
569 Lary Sorensen RC	.10	.25
570 Dave Kingman	.50	1.25
571 Buck Martinez	.10	.25
572 Rick Wise	.10	.25
573 Luis Gomez	.10	.25
574 Bob Lemon MG	.50	1.25
575 Pat Dobson	.10	.25
576 Sam Mejias	.10	.25
577 Oakland Athletics CL	.50	1.25
578 Buzz Capra	.10	.25
579 Rance Mulliniks RC	.10	.25
580 Rod Carew	1.50	4.00
581 Lynn McGlothen	.10	.25
582 Fran Healy	.10	.25
583 George Medich	.10	.25
584 John Hale	.10	.25
585 Woodie Fryman DP	.08	.20
586 Ed Goodson	.10	.25
587 John Urrea RC	.10	.25
588 Jim Mason	.10	.25
589 Bob Knepper RC	.10	.25
590 Bobby Murcer	.25	.60
591 George Zeber RC	.10	.25
592 Bob Apodaca	.10	.25
593 Dave Skaggs RC	.10	.25
594 Dave Freisleben	.10	.25
595 Sixto Lezcano	.10	.25
596 Gary Wheelock	.10	.25
597 Steve Dillard	.10	.25
598 Eddie Solomon	.10	.25
599 Gary Woods	.10	.25
600 Frank Tanana	.25	.60
601 Gene Mauch MG	.25	.60
602 Eric Soderholm	.10	.25
603 Will McEnaney	.10	.25
604 Earl Williams	.10	.25
605 Rick Rhoden	.25	.60
606 Pittsburgh Pirates CL	.50	1.25
607 Fernando Arroyo	.10	.25
608 Johnny Grubb	.10	.25
609 John Denny	.10	.25
610 Garry Maddox	.25	.60
611 Pat Scanlon RC	.10	.25
612 Ken Henderson	.10	.25
613 Marty Perez	.10	.25
614 Joe Wallis	.10	.25
615 Clay Carroll	.10	.25
616 Pat Kelly	.10	.25
617 Joe Nolan RC	.10	.25
618 Tommy Helms	.10	.25
619 Thad Bosley DP RC	.08	.20
620 Willie Randolph	.50	1.25
621 Craig Swan DP	.08	.20
622 Champ Summers	.10	.25
623 Eduardo Rodriguez	.10	.25
624 Gary Alexander DP	.08	.20
625 Jose Cruz	.25	.60
626 Toronto Blue Jays CL DP	.50	1.25
627 David Johnson	.10	.25
628 Ralph Garr	.25	.60
629 Don Stanhouse	.10	.25
630 Ron Cey	.50	1.25
631 Danny Ozark MG	.10	.25
632 Rowland Office	.10	.25
633 Tom Veryzer	.10	.25
634 Len Barker	.10	.25
635 Joe Rudi	.25	.60
636 Jim Bibby	.10	.25
637 Duffy Dyer	.10	.25
638 Paul Splittorff	.10	.25
639 Gene Clines	.10	.25
640 Lee May DP	.10	.25
641 Doug Rau	.10	.25
642 Denny Doyle	.10	.25
643 Tom House	.10	.25
644 Jim Dwyer	.10	.25
645 Mike Torrez	.25	.60
646 Rick Auerbach DP	.08	.20
647 Steve Dunning	.10	.25
648 Gary Thomasson	.10	.25
649 Moose Haas RC	.10	.25
650 Cesar Cedeno	.25	.60
651 Doug Rader	.10	.25
652 Checklist 606-726	.50	1.25
653 Ron Hodges DP	.08	.20
654 Pepe Frias	.10	.25
655 Lyman Bostock	.25	.60
656 Dave Garcia MG RC	.10	.25
657 Bombo Rivera	.10	.25
658 Manny Sanguillen	.25	.60
659 Texas Rangers CL	.50	1.25
660 Jason Thompson	.25	.60
661 Grant Jackson	.10	.25
662 Paul Dade RC	.10	.25
663 Paul Reuschel	.10	.25
664 Fred Stanley	.10	.25
665 Dennis Leonard	.25	.60
666 Billy Smith RC	.10	.25

667 Jeff Byrd RC .10 .25
668 Dusty Baker .50 1.25
669 Pete Falcone .10 .25
670 Jim Rice .50 1.25
671 Gary Lavelle .10 .25
672 Don Kessinger .25 .60
673 Steve Brye .10 .25
674 Ray Knight RC 1.00 2.50
675 Jay Johnstone .25 .60
676 Bob Myrick .10 .25
677 Ed Herrmann .10 .25
678 Tom Burgmeier .10 .25
679 Wayne Garrett .10 .25
680 Vida Blue .25 .60
681 Rob Belloir .10 .25
682 Ken Brett .10 .25
683 Mike Champion .10 .25
684 Ralph Houk MG .25 .60
685 Frank Taveras .10 .25
686 Gaylord Perry 1.00 2.50
687 Julio Cruz RC .10 .25
688 George Mitterwald .10 .25
689 Cleveland Indians CL .50 1.25
690 Mickey Rivers .25 .60
691 Ross Grimsley .10 .25
692 Ken Reitz .10 .25
693 Lamar Johnson .10 .25
694 Elias Sosa .10 .25
695 Dwight Evans .50 1.25
696 Steve Mingori .10 .25
697 Roger Metzger .10 .25
698 Juan Bernhardt .10 .25
699 Jackie Brown .10 .25
700 Johnny Bench 3.00 8.00
701 Rookie Pitchers .25 .60
Tom Hume RC
Larry Landreth RC
Steve McCatty RC
Bruce Taylor
702 Rookie Catchers .25 .60
Bill Nahorodny RC
Kevin Pasley
Rick Sweet RC
Don Werner RC
703 Rookie Pitchers 2.00 5.00
Larry Andersen RC
Tim Jones RC
Mickey Mahler RC
Jack Morris RC DP
704 Rookie 2nd Basemen 3.00 8.00
Garth Iorg RC
Dave Oliver RC
Sam Perlozzo RC
Lou Whitaker RC
705 Rookie Outfielders .50 1.25
Dave Bergman RC
Miguel Dilone RC
Clint Hurdle RC
Willie Norwood RC
706 Rookie 1st Basemen .25 .60
Wayne Cage RC
Ted Cox RC
Pat Putnam RC
Dave Revering RC
707 Rookie Shortstops 20.00 50.00
Mickey Klutts
Paul Molitor RC
Alan Trammell RC
U.L. Washington RC
708 Rookie Catchers 1.50 4.00
Bo Diaz RC
Dale Murphy
Lance Parrish RC
Ernie Whitt RC
709 Rookie Pitchers .25 .60
Steve Burke RC
Matt Keough RC
Lance Rautzhan RC
Dan Schatzeder RC
710 Rookie Outfielders .50 1.25
Dell Alston RC
Rick Bosetti RC
Mike Easler RC
Keith Smith RC
711 Rookie Pitchers .10 .25
Cardell Campe RCr
Dennis Lamp RC
Craig Mitchell
Roy Thomas RC DP
712 Bobby Valentine .25 .60
713 Bob Davis .10 .25
714 Mike Anderson .10 .25
715 Jim Kaat .50 1.25
716 Clarence Gaston .25 .60
717 Nelson Briles .10 .25
718 Ron Jackson .10 .25
719 Randy Elliott RC .10 .25
720 Fergie Jenkins 1.00 2.50
721 Billy Martin MG .50 1.25
722 Pete Broberg .10 .25
723 John Wockenfuss .10 .25
724 Kansas City Royals CL .50 1.25
725 Kurt Bevacqua .10 .25
726 Wilbur Wood .50 1.25

1979 Topps

The cards in this 726-card set measure 2 1/2" by 3 1/2". Topps continued with the same number of cards as in 1978. As in previous years, this set was released in many different formats, among them are 12-card wax packs and 39-card rack packs which cost 59 cents upon release. Those rack packs came 24 packs to a box and three boxes to a case. Various series spotlight League Leaders (1-8), "Season and Career Record Holders" (411-418), "Record Breakers" (201-206), and one "Prospects" card for each team (701-726). Team cards feature a checklist on back of that team's players in the set and a small picture of the manager on the front of the card. There are 66 cards that were double printed and these are noted in the checklist by the abbreviation DP. Bump Wills (369) was initially depicted in a Ranger uniform but with a Blue Jays affiliation; later printings correctly labeled him with Texas. The set price includes either Wills card. The key Rookie Cards in this set are Pedro Guerrero, Carney Lansford, Ozzie Smith, Bob Welch and Willie Wilson. Cards numbered 23 or lower, which feature Phillies or Yankees and do not follow the numbering checklisted below, are not necessarily error cards. They are undoubtedly Burger King cards, separate sets for each team with their own pricing and mass distribution.

COMPLETE SET (726) 100.00 200.00
COMMON CARD (1-726) .10 .25
COMMON CARD DP .08 .20
1 Batting Leaders 1.00 2.50
Rod Carew
Dave Parker
2 Home Run Leaders .60 1.50
Jim Rice
George Foster
3 RBI Leaders .60 1.50
Jim Rice
George Foster
4 Stolen Base Leaders .30 .75
Ron LeFlore
Omar Moreno
5 Victory Leaders .30 .75
Ron Guidry
Gaylord Perry
6 Strikeout Leaders 2.00 5.00
Nolan Ryan
J.R. Richard
7 ERA Leaders .30 .75
Ron Guidry
Craig Swan
8 Leading Firemen .60 1.50
Rich Gossage
Rollie Fingers
9 Dave Campbell .10 .25
10 Lee May .30 .75
11 Marc Hill .10 .25
12 Dick Drago .10 .25
13 Paul Dade .10 .25
14 Rafael Landestoy RC .10 .25
15 Ross Grimsley .10 .25
16 Fred Stanley .10 .25
17 Donnie Moore .10 .25
18 Tony Solaita .10 .25
19 Larry Gura DP .08 .20
20 Joe Morgan DP 1.00 2.50
21 Kevin Kobel .10 .25
22 Mike Jorgensen .10 .25
23 Terry Forster .10 .25
24 Paul Molitor 4.00 10.00
25 Steve Carlton 1.25 3.00
26 Jamie Quirk .10 .25
27 Dave Goltz .10 .25
28 Steve Brye .10 .25
29 Rick Langford .10 .25
30 Dave Winfield 1.50 4.00
31 Tom House DP .08 .20
32 Jerry Mumphrey .10 .25
33 Dave Rozema .10 .25
34 Rob Andrews .10 .25
35 Ed Figueroa .10 .25
36 Alan Ashby .10 .25
37 Joe Kerrigan DP .08 .20
38 Bernie Carbo .10 .25
39 Dale Murphy 1.25 3.00
40 Dennis Eckersley 1.00 2.50
41 Minnesota Twins CL .60 1.50
Gene Mauch MG
42 Ron Blomberg .10 .25
43 Wayne Twitchell .10 .25
44 Kurt Bevacqua .10 .25
45 Al Hrabosky .30 .75
46 Ron Hodges .10 .25
47 Fred Norman .10 .25
48 Merv Rettenmund .10 .25
49 Vern Ruhle .10 .25
50 Steve Garvey DP .60 1.50
51 Ray Fosse DP .08 .20
52 Randy Lerch .10 .25
53 Mick Kelleher .10 .25
54 Dell Alston DP .08 .20
55 Willie Stargell 1.00 2.50
56 John Hale .10 .25
57 Eric Rasmussen .10 .25
58 Bob Randall DP .08 .20
59 John Denny DP .10 .25
60 Mickey Rivers .30 .75
61 Bo Diaz .10 .25
62 Randy Moffitt .10 .25
63 Jack Brohamer .10 .25
64 Tom Underwood .10 .25
65 Mark Belanger .30 .75
66 Detroit Tigers CL .60 1.50
Les Moss MG
67 Jim Mason DP .08 .20
68 Joe Niekro DP .10 .25
69 Elliott Maddox .10 .25
70 John Candelaria .30 .75
71 Brian Downing .30 .75
72 Steve Mingori .10 .25
73 Ken Henderson .10 .25
74 Shane Rawley RC .10 .25
75 Steve Yeager .30 .75
76 Warren Cromartie .30 .75
77 Dan Briggs DP .08 .20
78 Elias Sosa .10 .25
79 Ted Cox .10 .25
80 Jason Thompson .30 .75
81 Roger Erickson RC .10 .25
82 New York Mets CL .60 1.50
Joe Torre MG
83 Fred Kendall .10 .25
84 Greg Minton .10 .25
85 Gary Matthews .30 .75
86 Rodney Scott .10 .25
87 Pete Falcone .10 .25
88 Bob Molinaro RC .10 .25
89 Dick Tidrow .10 .25
90 Bob Boone .60 1.50
91 Terry Crowley .10 .25
92 Jim Bibby .10 .25
93 Phil Mankowski .10 .25
94 Len Barker .10 .25
95 Robin Yount 2.00 5.00
96 Cleveland Indians CL .60 1.50
Jeff Torborg
97 Sam Mejias .10 .25
98 Ray Burris .10 .25
99 John Wathan .30 .75
100 Tom Seaver DP 1.50 4.00
101 Roy Howell .10 .25
102 Mike Anderson .10 .25
103 Jim Todd .10 .25
104 Johnny Oates DP .10 .25
105 Rick Camp DP .08 .20
106 Frank Duffy .10 .25
107 Jesus Alou DP .08 .20
108 Eduardo Rodriguez .10 .25
109 Joel Youngblood .10 .25
110 Vida Blue .30 .75
111 Roger Freed .10 .25
112 Phillies Team .60 1.50
Danny Ozark MG
113 Pete Redfern .10 .25
114 Cliff Johnson .10 .25
115 Nolan Ryan 8.00 20.00
116 Ozzie Smith RC 30.00 60.00
117 Grant Jackson .10 .25
118 Bud Harrelson .30 .75
119 Don Stanhouse .10 .25
120 Jim Sundberg .30 .75
121 Checklist 1-121 DP .30 .75
122 Mike Paxton .10 .25
123 Lou Whitaker 1.00 2.50
124 Dan Schatzeder .10 .25
125 Rick Burleson .10 .25
126 Doug Bair .10 .25
127 Thad Bosley .10 .25
128 Ted Martinez .10 .25
129 Marty Pattin DP .08 .20
130 Bob Watson DP .10 .25
131 Jim Clancy .10 .25
132 Rowland Office .10 .25
133 Bill Castro .10 .25
134 Alan Bannister .10 .25
135 Bobby Murcer .30 .75
136 Jim Kaat .30 .75
137 Larry Wolfe DP RC .08 .20
138 Mark Lee RC .10 .25
139 Luis Pujols RC .10 .25
140 Don Gullett .30 .75
141 Tom Paciorek .30 .75
142 Charlie Williams .10 .25
143 Tony Scott .10 .25
144 Sandy Alomar .10 .25
145 Rick Rhoden .10 .25
146 Duane Kuiper .10 .25
147 Dave Hamilton .10 .25
148 Bruce Boisclair .10 .25
149 Manny Sarmiento .10 .25
150 Wayne Cage .10 .25
151 John Hiller .10 .25
152 Rick Cerone .10 .25
153 Dennis Lamp .10 .25
154 Jim Gantner DP .10 .25
155 Dwight Evans .60 1.50
156 Buddy Solomon RC .10 .25
157 U.L. Washington UER .10 .25
(Sic, bats left,
should be right)
158 Joe Sambito .10 .25
159 Roy White .30 .75
160 Mike Flanagan .60 1.50
161 Barry Foote .10 .25
162 Tom Johnson .10 .25
163 Glenn Burke .10 .25
164 Mickey Lolich .30 .75
165 Frank Taveras .10 .25
166 Leon Roberts .10 .25
167 Roger Metzger DP .08 .20
168 Dave Freisleben .10 .25
169 Bill Nahorodny .10 .25
170 Don Sutton 1.00 2.50
171 Gene Clines .10 .25
172 Mike Bruhert RC .10 .25
173 John Lowenstein .10 .25
174 Rick Auerbach .10 .25
175 George Hendrick .60 1.50
176 Aurelio Rodriguez .10 .25
177 Ron Reed .10 .25
178 Alvis Woods .10 .25
179 Jim Beattie DP RC .08 .20
180 Larry Hisle .10 .25
181 Mike Garman .10 .25
182 Tim Johnson .10 .25
183 Paul Splittorff .10 .25
184 Darrel Chaney .10 .25
185 Mike Torrez .30 .75
186 Eric Soderholm .10 .25
187 Mark Lemongello .10 .25
188 Pat Kelly .10 .25
189 Eddie Whitson RC .10 .25
190 Ron Cey .30 .75
191 Mike Norris .30 .75
192 St. Louis Cardinals CL .60 1.50
Ken Boyer MG
193 Glenn Adams .10 .25
194 Randy Jones .10 .25
195 Bill Madlock .30 .75
196 Steve Kemp DP .10 .25
197 Bob Apodaca .10 .25
198 Johnny Grubb .10 .25
199 Larry Milbourne .10 .25
200 Johnny Bench DP 2.00 5.00
201 Mike Edwards RB .10 .25
202 Ron Guidry RB .30 .75
203 J.R. Richard RB .10 .25
204 Pete Rose RB 2.00 5.00
205 John Stearns RB .10 .25
206 Sammy Stewart RB .10 .25
207 Dave Lemanczyk .10 .25
208 Clarence Gaston .10 .25
209 Reggie Cleveland .10 .25
210 Larry Bowa .30 .75
211 Denny Martinez 1.00 2.50
212 Carney Lansford RC .60 1.50
213 Bill Travers .10 .25
214 Boston Red Sox CL .60 1.50
Don Zimmer MG
215 Willie McCovey 1.00 2.50
216 Wilbur Wood .10 .25
217 Steve Dillard .10 .25
218 Dennis Leonard .30 .75
219 Roy Smalley .30 .75
220 Cesar Geronimo .10 .25
221 Jesse Jefferson .10 .25
222 Bob Beall RC .10 .25
223 Kent Tekulve .30 .75
224 Dave Revering .10 .25
225 Goose Gossage .60 1.50
226 Ron Pruitt .10 .25
227 Steve Stone .30 .75
228 Vic Davalillo .10 .25
229 Doug Flynn .10 .25
230 Bob Forsch .10 .25
231 John Wockenfuss .10 .25
232 Jimmy Sexton RC .10 .25
233 Paul Mitchell .10 .25
234 Toby Harrah .30 .75
235 Steve Rogers .10 .25
236 Jim Dwyer .10 .25
237 Billy Smith .10 .25
238 Balor Moore .10 .25
239 Willie Horton .30 .75
240 Rick Reuschel .30 .75
241 Checklist 122-242 DP .30 .75
242 Pablo Torrealba .10 .25
243 Buck Martinez DP .08 .20
244 Pittsburgh Pirates CL .60 1.50
Chuck Tanner MG
245 Jeff Burroughs .30 .75
246 Darrell Jackson RC .10 .25
247 Tucker Ashford DP .08 .20
248 Pete LaCock .10 .25
249 Paul Thormodsgard .10 .25
250 Willie Randolph .30 .75
251 Jack Morris 1.00 2.50
252 Bob Stinson .10 .25
253 Rick Wise .10 .25
254 Luis Gomez .10 .25
255 Tommy John .60 1.50
256 Mike Sadek .10 .25
257 Adrian Devine .10 .25
258 Mike Phillips .10 .25
259 Cincinnati Reds CL .60 1.50
Sparky Anderson MG
260 Richie Zisk .10 .25
261 Mario Guerrero .10 .25
262 Nelson Briles .10 .25
263 Oscar Gamble .30 .75
264 Don Robinson RC .10 .25
265 Don Money .10 .25
266 Jim Willoughby .10 .25
267 Joe Rudi .30 .75
268 Julio Gonzalez .10 .25
269 Woodie Fryman .10 .25
270 Butch Hobson .30 .75
271 Rawly Eastwick .10 .25
272 Tim Corcoran .10 .25
273 Jerry Terrell .10 .25
274 Willie Norwood .10 .25
275 Junior Moore .10 .25
276 Jim Colborn .10 .25
277 Tom Grieve .30 .75
278 Andy Messersmith .30 .75
279 Jerry Grote DP .08 .20
280 Andre Thornton .30 .75
281 Vic Correll DP .08 .20
282 Toronto Blue Jays CL .30 .75
Roy Hartsfield MG
283 Ken Kravec .10 .25
284 Johnnie LeMaster .10 .25
285 Bobby Bonds .60 1.50
286 Duffy Dyer .10 .25
287 Andres Mora .10 .25
288 Milt Wilcox .10 .25
289 Jose Cruz .60 1.50
290 Dave Lopes .30 .75
291 Tom Griffin .10 .25
292 Don Reynolds RC .10 .25
293 Jerry Garvin .10 .25
294 Pepe Frias .10 .25
295 Mitchell Page .10 .25
296 Preston Hanna RC .10 .25
297 Ted Sizemore .10 .25
298 Rich Gale RC .10 .25
299 Steve Ontiveros .10 .25
300 Rod Carew 1.25 3.00
301 Tom Hume .10 .25
302 Atlanta Braves CL .60 1.50
Bobby Cox MG
303 Lary Sorensen DP .08 .20
304 Steve Swisher .10 .25
305 Willie Montanez .10 .25
306 Floyd Bannister .10 .25
307 Larvell Blanks .10 .25
308 Bert Blyleven .60 1.50
309 Ralph Garr .30 .75
310 Thurman Munson 1.25 3.00
311 Gary Lavelle .10 .25
312 Bob Robertson .10 .25
313 Dyar Miller .10 .25
314 Larry Harlow .10 .25
315 Jon Matlack .10 .25
316 Milt May .10 .25
317 Jose Cardenal .30 .75
318 Bob Welch RC 1.00 2.50
319 Wayne Garrett .10 .25
320 Carl Yastrzemski 2.00 5.00
321 Gaylord Perry 1.00 2.50
322 Danny Goodwin RC .10 .25
323 Lynn McGlothen .10 .25
324 Mike Tyson .10 .25
325 Cecil Cooper .30 .75
326 Pedro Borbon .10 .25
327 Art Howe DP .10 .25
328 Oakland Athletics CL .60 1.50
Jack McKeon MG
329 Joe Coleman .10 .25
330 George Brett 4.00 10.00
331 Mickey Mahler .10 .25
332 Gary Alexander .10 .25
333 Chet Lemon .30 .75
334 Craig Swan .10 .25
335 Chris Chambliss .30 .75
336 Bobby Thompson RC .10 .25
337 John Montague .10 .25
338 Vic Harris .10 .25
339 Ron Jackson .10 .25
340 Jim Palmer 1.00 2.50
341 Willie Upshaw RC .30 .75
342 Dave Roberts .10 .25
343 Ed Glynn .10 .25
344 Jerry Royster .10 .25
345 Tug McGraw .30 .75
346 Bill Buckner .30 .75
347 Doug Rau .10 .25
348 Andre Dawson 1.25 3.00
349 Jim Wright RC .10 .25
350 Garry Templeton .30 .75
351 Wayne Nordhagen DP .08 .20
352 Steve Renko .10 .25
353 Checklist 243-363 .60 1.50
354 Bill Bonham .10 .25
355 Lee Mazzilli .10 .25
356 San Francisco Giants CL .60 1.50
Joe Altobelli MG
357 Jerry Augustine .10 .25
358 Alan Trammell 1.25 3.00
359 Dan Spillner DP .08 .20
360 Amos Otis .30 .75
361 Tom Dixon RC .10 .25
362 Mike Cubbage .10 .25
363 Craig Skok RC .10 .25
364 Gene Richards .10 .25
365 Sparky Lyle .30 .75
366 Juan Bernhardt .10 .25
367 Dave Skaggs .10 .25
368 Don Aase .10 .25
369A Bump Wills ERR 1.25 3.00
(Blue Jays)
369B Bump Wills COR 1.25 3.00
(Rangers)
370 Dave Kingman .60 1.50
371 Jeff Holly RC .10 .25
372 Lamar Johnson .10 .25
373 Lance Rautzhan .10 .25
374 Ed Herrmann .10 .25
375 Bill Campbell .10 .25
376 Gorman Thomas .30 .75
377 Paul Moskau .10 .25
378 Rob Picciolo DP .08 .20
379 Dale Murray .10 .25
380 John Mayberry .30 .75
381 Houston Astros CL .60 1.50
Bill Virdon MG
382 Jerry Martin .10 .25
383 Phil Garner .30 .75
384 Tommy Boggs .10 .25
385 Dan Ford .10 .25
386 Francisco Barrios .10 .25
387 Gary Thomasson .10 .25
388 Jack Billingham .10 .25
389 Joe Zdeb .10 .25
390 Rollie Fingers 1.00 2.50
391 Al Oliver .30 .75
392 Doug Ault .10 .25
393 Scott McGregor .30 .75
394 Randy Stein RC .10 .25
395 Dave Cash .10 .25
396 Bill Plummer .10 .25
397 Sergio Ferrer RC .10 .25
398 Ivan DeJesus .10 .25
399 David Clyde .10 .25
400 Jim Rice .60 1.50
401 Ray Knight .30 .75
402 Paul Hartzell .10 .25
403 Tim Foli .10 .25
404 Chicago White Sox CL .60 1.50
Don Kessinger MG
405 Butch Wynegar DP .08 .20
406 Joe Wallis DP .08 .20
407 Pete Vuckovich .30 .75
408 Charlie Moore DP .08 .20
409 Willie Wilson RC .60 1.50
410 Darrell Evans .60 1.50
411 George Sisler ATL 1.00 2.50
Ty Cobb
412 Hack Wilson ATL 1.00 2.50
Hank Aaron
413 Roger Maris ATL 1.50 4.00
Hank Aaron
414 Rogers Hornsby ATL 1.00 2.50
Ty Cobb
415 Lou Brock ATL .60 1.50
Lou Brock
416 Jack Chesbro ATL .30 .75
Cy Young
417 Nolan Ryan ATL DP 2.00 5.00
Walter Johnson
418 Dutch Leonard ATL DP .10 .25
Walter Johnson
419 Dick Ruthven .10 .25
420 Ken Griffey Sr. .30 .75
421 Doug DeCinces .30 .75
422 Ruppert Jones .10 .25
423 Bob Montgomery .10 .25
424 California Angels CL .60 1.50
Jim Fregosi MG
425 Rick Manning .10 .25
426 Chris Speier .10 .25
427 Andy Replogle RC .10 .25
428 Bobby Valentine .30 .75
429 John Urrea DP .08 .20
430 Dave Parker .30 .75
431 Glenn Borgmann .10 .25
432 Dave Heaverlo .10 .25
433 Larry Biittner .10 .25
434 Ken Clay .10 .25
435 Gene Tenace .30 .75
436 Hector Cruz .10 .25
437 Rick Williams RC .10 .25
438 Horace Speed RC .10 .25
439 Frank White .30 .75
440 Rusty Staub .60 1.50
441 Lee Lacy .10 .25
442 Doyle Alexander .10 .25
443 Bruce Bochte .10 .25
444 Aurelio Lopez RC .10 .25
445 Steve Henderson .10 .25
446 Jim Lonborg .30 .75
447 Manny Sanguillen .30 .75
448 Moose Haas .10 .25
449 Bombo Rivera .10 .25
450 Dave Concepcion .60 1.50
451 Kansas City Royals CL .60 1.50
Whitey Herzog MG
452 Jerry Morales .10 .25
453 Chris Knapp .10 .25
454 Len Randle .10 .25
455 Bill Lee DP .08 .20
456 Chuck Baker RC .10 .25
457 Bruce Sutter 1.00 2.50
458 Jim Essian .10 .25
459 Sid Monge .10 .25
460 Graig Nettles .60 1.50
461 Jim Barr DP .08 .20
462 Otto Velez .10 .25
463 Steve Comer RC .10 .25
464 Joe Nolan .10 .25
465 Reggie Smith .30 .75
466 Mark Littell .10 .25
467 Don Kessinger DP .10 .25
468 Stan Bahnsen DP .08 .20
469 Lance Parrish .60 1.50
470 Garry Maddox DP .10 .25
471 Joaquin Andujar .30 .75
472 Craig Kusick .10 .25
473 Dave Roberts .10 .25
474 Dick Davis RC .10 .25
475 Dan Driessen .10 .25
476 Tom Poquette .10 .25
477 Bob Grich .30 .75
478 Juan Beniquez .10 .25
479 San Diego Padres CL .60 1.50
Roger Craig MG
480 Fred Lynn .30 .75
481 Skip Lockwood .10 .25
482 Craig Reynolds .10 .25
483 Checklist 364-484 DP .30 .75
484 Rick Waits .10 .25
485 Bucky Dent .30 .75
486 Bob Knepper .10 .25
487 Miguel Dilone .10 .25
488 Bob Owchinko .10 .25
489 Larry Cox UER .10 .25
(Photo actually
Dave Rader)
490 Al Cowens .30 .75
491 Tippy Martinez .10 .25
492 Bob Bailor .10 .25
493 Larry Christenson .10 .25
494 Jerry White .10 .25
495 Tony Perez 1.00 2.50
496 Barry Bonnell DP .08 .20
497 Glenn Abbott .10 .25
498 Rich Chiles .10 .25
499 Texas Rangers CL .60 1.50
Pat Corrales MG
500 Ron Guidry .30 .75
501 Junior Kennedy RC .10 .25
502 Steve Braun .10 .25
503 Terry Humphrey .10 .25
504 Larry McWilliams RC .10 .25
505 Ed Kranepool .10 .25
506 John D'Acquisto .10 .25
507 Tony Armas .30 .75
508 Charlie Hough .30 .75
509 Mario Mendoza UER .10 .25
(Career BA .278,
should say .204)
510 Ted Simmons .60 1.50
511 Paul Reuschel DP .08 .20
512 Jack Clark .30 .75
513 Dave Johnson .30 .75
514 Mike Proly RC .10 .25
515 Enos Cabell .10 .25
516 Champ Summers DP .08 .20
517 Al Bumbry .30 .75
518 Jim Umbarger .10 .25
519 Ben Oglivie .30 .75
520 Gary Carter .60 1.50
521 Sam Ewing .10 .25
522 Ken Holtzman .30 .75
523 John Milner .10 .25
524 Tom Burgmeier .10 .25
525 Freddie Patek .10 .25
526 Los Angeles Dodgers CL .60 1.50
Tom Lasorda MG
527 Lerrin LaGrow .10 .25
528 Wayne Gross DP .08 .20
529 Brian Asselstine .10 .25
530 Frank Tanana .30 .75
531 Fernando Gonzalez .10 .25
532 Buddy Schultz .10 .25
533 Leroy Stanton .10 .25
534 Ken Forsch .10 .25
535 Ellis Valentine .10 .25
536 Jerry Reuss .30 .75
537 Tom Veryzer .10 .25
538 Mike Ivie DP .08 .20
539 John Ellis .10 .25
540 Greg Luzinski .30 .75
541 Jim Slaton .10 .25
542 Rick Bosetti .10 .25
543 Kiko Garcia .10 .25
544 Fergie Jenkins 1.00 2.50
545 John Stearns .10 .25
546 Bill Russell .30 .75
547 Clint Hurdle .10 .25
548 Enrique Romo .10 .25
549 Bob Bailey .10 .25
550 Sal Bando .30 .75
551 Chicago Cubs CL .60 1.50
Herman Franks MG
552 Jose Morales .10 .25
553 Denny Walling .10 .25
554 Matt Keough .10 .25
555 Biff Pocoroba .10 .25
556 Mike Lum .10 .25
557 Ken Brett .10 .25
558 Jay Johnstone .30 .75
559 Greg Pryor RC .10 .25
560 John Montefusco .10 .25
561 Ed Ott .10 .25
562 Dusty Baker .60 1.50
563 Roy Thomas .10 .25
564 Jerry Turner .10 .25
565 Rico Carty .30 .75
566 Nino Espinosa .10 .25
567 Richie Hebner .30 .75
568 Carlos Lopez .10 .25
569 Bob Sykes .10 .25
570 Cesar Cedeno .30 .75
571 Darrell Porter .30 .75
572 Rod Gilbreath .10 .25
573 Jim Kern .10 .25
574 Claudell Washington .30 .75
575 Luis Tiant .30 .75
576 Mike Parrott RC .10 .25
577 Milwaukee Brewers CL .60 1.50
George Bamberger MG
578 Pete Broberg .10 .25
579 Greg Gross .10 .25
580 Ron Fairly .30 .75

581 Darold Knowles .10 .25
582 Paul Blair .30 .75
583 Julio Cruz .10 .25
584 Jim Rooker .10 .25
585 Hal McRae .60 1.50
586 Bob Horner RC .60 1.50
587 Ken Reitz .10 .25
588 Tom Murphy .10 .25
589 Terry Whitfield .10 .25
590 J.R. Richard .30 .75
591 Mike Hargrove .30 .75
592 Mike Krukow .10 .25
593 Rick Dempsey .30 .75
594 Bob Shirley .10 .25
595 Phil Niekro 1.00 2.50
596 Jim Wohlford .10 .25
597 Bob Stanley .10 .25
598 Mark Wagner .10 .25
599 Jim Spencer .10 .25
600 George Foster .30 .75
601 Dave LaRoche .10 .25
602 Checklist 485-605 .60 1.50
603 Rudy May .10 .25
604 Jeff Newman .10 .25
605 Rick Monday DP .10 .25
606 Montreal Expos CL .60 1.50
Dick Williams MG
607 Omar Moreno .10 .25
608 Dave McKay .10 .25
609 Silvio Martinez RC .10 .25
610 Mike Schmidt 3.00 8.00
611 Jim Norris .10 .25
612 Rick Honeycutt RC .30 .75
613 Mike Edwards RC .10 .25
614 Willie Hernandez .30 .75
615 Ken Singleton .30 .75
616 Billy Almon .10 .25
617 Terry Puhl .10 .25
618 Jerry Remy .10 .25
619 Ken Landreaux RC .30 .75
620 Bert Campaneris .30 .75
621 Pat Zachry .10 .25
622 Dave Collins .30 .75
623 Bob McClure .10 .25
624 Larry Herndon .10 .25
625 Mark Fidrych 1.00 2.50
626 New York Yankees CL .60 1.50
Bob Lemon MG
627 Gary Serum RC .10 .25
628 Del Unser .10 .25
629 Gene Garber .30 .75
630 Bake McBride .30 .75
631 Jorge Orta .10 .25
632 Don Kirkwood .10 .25
633 Rob Wilfong DP RC .08 .20
634 Paul Lindblad .10 .25
635 Don Baylor .60 1.50
636 Wayne Garland .10 .25
637 Bill Robinson .30 .75
638 Al Fitzmorris .10 .25
639 Manny Trillo .10 .25
640 Eddie Murray 5.00 12.00
641 Bobby Castillo RC .10 .25
642 Wilbur Howard DP .08 .20
643 Tom Hausman .10 .25
644 Manny Mota .30 .75
645 George Scott DP .10 .25
646 Rick Sweet .10 .25
647 Bob Lacey .10 .25
648 Lou Piniella .30 .75
649 John Curtis .10 .25
650 Pete Rose 5.00 12.00
651 Mike Caldwell .10 .25
652 Stan Papi RC .10 .25
653 Warren Brusstar DP .08 .20
654 Rick Miller .10 .25
655 Jerry Koosman .30 .75
656 Hosken Powell RC .10 .25
657 George Medich .10 .25
658 Taylor Duncan RC .10 .25
659 Seattle Mariners CL .60 1.50
Darrell Johnson MG
660 Ron LeFlore DP .10 .25
661 Bruce Kison .10 .25
662 Kevin Bell .10 .25
663 Mike Vail .10 .25
664 Doug Bird .10 .25
665 Lou Brock 1.00 2.50
666 Rich Dauer .10 .25
667 Don Hood .10 .25
668 Bill North .10 .25
669 Checklist 606-726 .60 1.50
670 Jim Hunter DP .60 1.50
671 Joe Ferguson DP .08 .20
672 Ed Halicki .10 .25
673 Tom Hutton .10 .25
674 Dave Tomlin .10 .25
675 Tim McCarver .60 1.50
676 Johnny Sutton RC .10 .25
677 Larry Parrish .30 .75
678 Geoff Zahn .10 .25
679 Derrel Thomas .10 .25
680 Carlton Fisk 1.25 3.00
681 John Henry Johnson RC .10 .25
682 Dave Chalk .10 .25
683 Dan Meyer DP .08 .20
684 Jamie Easterly DP .08 .20
685 Sixto Lezcano .10 .25
686 Ron Schueler DP .08 .20
687 Rennie Stennett .10 .25
688 Mike Willis .10 .25
689 Baltimore Orioles CL .60 1.50
Earl Weaver MG
690 Buddy Bell DP .10 .25
691 Dock Ellis DP .08 .20
692 Mickey Stanley .10 .25
693 Dave Rader .10 .25
694 Burt Hooton .30 .75
695 Keith Hernandez .30 .75
696 Andy Hassler .10 .25
697 Dave Bergman .10 .25
698 Bill Stein .10 .25
699 Hal Dues RC .10 .25
700 Reggie Jackson DP 2.00 5.00
701 Mark Corey RC .30 .75
John Flinn RC
Sammy Stewart RC
702 Joel Finch RC .30 .75
Garry Hancock RC
Allen Ripley RC
703 Jim Anderson RC .30 .75
Dave Frost RC
Bob Slater RC
704 Ross Baumgarten RC .30 .75
Mike Colbern RC
Mike Squires RC
705 Alfredo Griffin RC .60 1.50
Tim Norrid RC
Dave Oliver
706 Dave Stegman RC .30 .75
Dave Tobik RC
Kip Young RC
707 Randy Bass RC .60 1.50
Jim Gaudet RC
Randy McGilberry RC
708 Kevin Bass RC .60 1.50
Eddie Romero RC
Ned Yost RC
709 Sam Perlozzo .30 .75
Rick Sofield RC
Kevin Stanfield RC
710 Brian Doyle RC .30 .75
Mike Heath RC
Dave Rajsich RC
711 Dwayne Murphy RC .60 1.50
Bruce Robinson RC
Alan Wirth RC
712 Bud Anderson RC .30 .75
Greg Biercevicz RC
Byron McLaughlin RC
713 Danny Darwin RC .60 1.50
Pat Putnam
Billy Sample RC
714 Victor Cruz RC .30 .75
Pat Kelly
Ernie Whitt
715 Bruce Benedict RC .60 1.50
Glenn Hubbard RC
Larry Whisenton RC
716 Dave Geisel RC .30 .75
Karl Pagel RC
Scot Thompson RC
717 Mike LaCoss RC .30 .75
Ron Oester RC
Harry Spilman RC
718 Bruce Bochy RC .30 .75
Mike Fischlin RC
Don Pisker RC
719 Pedro Guerrero RC .60 1.50
Rudy Law RC
Joe Simpson RC
720 Jerry Fry RC .60 1.50
Jerry Pirtle RC
Scott Sanderson RC
721 Juan Berenguer RC .30 .75
Dwight Bernard RC
Dan Norman RC
722 Jim Morrison RC .60 1.50
Lonnie Smith RC
Jim Wright RC
723 Dale Berra RC .30 .75
Eugenio Cotes RC
Ben Wiltbank RC
724 Tom Bruno RC .60 1.50
George Frazier RC
Terry Kennedy RC
725 Jim Beswick RC .30 .75
Steve Mura RC
Broderick Perkins RC
726 Greg Johnston RC .30 .75
Joe Strain RC
John Tamargo RC

1980 Topps

The cards in this 726-card set measure the standard size. In 1980 Topps released another set of the same size and number of cards as the previous two years. Distribution for these cards included 15-card wax packs as well as 42-card rack packs. The 15-card wax packs had an 25 cent SRP and came 36 packs to a box and 20 boxes to a case. A special experiment in 1980 was the issuance of a 28-card cello pack with a 59 cent SRP which had a three-pack of gum at the bottom so no cards would be damaged. As with those sets, Topps again produced 66 double-printed cards in the set; they are noted by DP in the checklist below. The player's name appears over the picture and his position and team are found in pennant design. Every card carries a facsimile autograph. Team cards feature a team checklist of players in the set on the back and the manager's name on the front. Cards 1-6 show Highlights (HL) of the 1979 season, cards 201-207 are League Leaders, and cards 661-686 feature American and National League rookie "Future Stars," one card for each team showing three young prospects. The key Rookie Card in this set is Rickey Henderson; other Rookie Cards included in this set are Dan Quisenberry, Dave Stieb and Rick Sutcliffe.

COMPLETE SET (726) 70.00 120.00
COMMON CARD (1-726) .08 .25
COMMON DP .08 .25
1 Lou Brock HL 1.00 2.50
Carl Yastrzemski
2 Willie McCovey HL .30 .75
3 Manny Mota HL .08 .25
4 Pete Rose HL 1.25 3.00
5 Garry Templeton HL .08 .25
6 Del Unser HL .08 .25
7 Mike Lum .08 .25
8 Craig Swan .08 .25
9 Steve Braun .08 .25
10 Dennis Martinez .30 .75
11 Jimmy Sexton .08 .25
12 John Curtis DP .08 .25
13 Ron Pruitt .08 .25
14 Dave Cash .30 .75
15 Bill Campbell .08 .25
16 Jerry Narron RC .08 .25
17 Bruce Sutter .60 1.50
18 Ron Jackson .08 .25
19 Balor Moore .08 .25
20 Dan Ford .08 .25
21 Manny Sarmiento .08 .25
22 Pat Putnam .08 .25
23 Derrel Thomas .08 .25
24 Jim Slaton .08 .25
25 Lee Mazzilli .30 .75
26 Marty Pattin .08 .25
27 Del Unser .08 .25
28 Bruce Kison .08 .25
29 Mark Wagner .08 .25
30 Vida Blue .30 .75
31 Jay Johnstone .08 .25
32 Julio Cruz DP .08 .25
33 Tony Scott .08 .25
34 Jeff Newman DP .08 .25
35 Luis Tiant .30 .75
36 Rusty Torres .08 .25
37 Kiko Garcia .08 .25
38 Dan Spillner DP .08 .25
39 Rowland Office .08 .25
40 Carlton Fisk 1.00 2.50
41 Texas Rangers CL .30 .75
Pat Corrales MG
42 David Palmer RC .08 .25
43 Bombo Rivera .08 .25
44 Bill Fahey .08 .25
45 Frank White .30 .75
46 Rico Carty .30 .75
47 Bill Bonham DP .08 .25
48 Rick Miller .08 .25
49 Mario Guerrero .08 .25
50 J.R. Richard .30 .75
51 Joe Ferguson DP .08 .25
52 Warren Brusstar .08 .25
53 Ben Oglivie .30 .75
54 Dennis Lamp .08 .25
55 Bill Madlock .30 .75
56 Bobby Valentine .30 .75
57 Pete Vuckovich .08 .25
58 Doug Flynn .08 .25
59 Eddy Putman RC .08 .25
60 Bucky Dent .30 .75
61 Gary Serum .08 .25
62 Mike Ivie .08 .25
63 Bob Stanley .08 .25
64 Joe Nolan .08 .25
65 Al Bumbry .30 .75
66 Kansas City Royals CL .30 .75
Jim Frey MG
67 Doyle Alexander .08 .25
68 Larry Harlow .08 .25
69 Rick Williams .08 .25
70 Gary Carter .60 1.50
71 John Milner DP .08 .25
72 Fred Howard DP RC .08 .25
73 Dave Collins .08 .25
74 Sid Monge .08 .25
75 Bill Russell .30 .75
76 John Stearns .08 .25
77 Dave Stieb RC .60 1.50
78 Ruppert Jones .08 .25
79 Bob Owchinko .08 .25
80 Ron LeFlore .30 .75
81 Ted Sizemore .08 .25
82 Houston Astros CL .30 .75
Bill Virdon MG
83 Steve Trout RC .08 .25
84 Gary Lavelle .08 .25
85 Ted Simmons .30 .75
86 Dave Hamilton .08 .25
87 Pepe Frias .08 .25
88 Ken Landreaux .08 .25
89 Don Hood .08 .25
90 Manny Trillo .30 .75
91 Rick Dempsey .30 .75
92 Rick Rhoden .08 .25
93 Dave Roberts DP .08 .25
94 Neil Allen RC .08 .25
95 Cecil Cooper .30 .75
96 Oakland Athletics CL .30 .75
Jim Marshall MG
97 Bill Lee .30 .75
98 Jerry Terrell .08 .25
99 Victor Cruz .08 .25
100 Johnny Bench 1.25 3.00
101 Aurelio Lopez .08 .25
102 Rich Dauer .08 .25
103 Bill Caudill RC .08 .25
104 Manny Mota .30 .75
105 Frank Tanana .30 .75
106 Jeff Leonard RC .60 1.50
107 Francisco Barrios .08 .25
108 Bob Horner .30 .75
109 Bill Travers .08 .25
110 Fred Lynn DP .20 .50
111 Bob Knepper .08 .25
112 Chicago White Sox CL .30 .75
Tony LaRussa MG
113 Geoff Zahn .08 .25
114 Juan Beniquez .08 .25
115 Sparky Lyle .30 .75
116 Larry Cox .08 .25
117 Dock Ellis .30 .75
118 Phil Garner .30 .75
119 Sammy Stewart .08 .25
120 Greg Luzinski .30 .75
121 Checklist 1-121 .30 .75
122 Dave Rosello DP .08 .25
123 Lynn Jones RC .08 .25
124 Dave Lemanczyk .08 .25
125 Tony Perez .30 .75
126 Dave Tomlin .08 .25
127 Gary Thomasson .08 .25
128 Tom Burgmeier .08 .25
129 Craig Reynolds .08 .25
130 Amos Otis .30 .75
131 Paul Mitchell .08 .25
132 Biff Pocoroba .08 .25
133 Jerry Turner .08 .25
134 Matt Keough .08 .25
135 Bill Buckner .30 .75
136 Dick Ruthven .08 .25
137 John Castino RC .08 .25
138 Ross Baumgarten .08 .25
139 Dane Iorg RC .08 .25
140 Rich Gossage .30 .75
141 Gary Alexander .08 .25
142 Phil Huffman RC .08 .25
143 Bruce Bochte DP .08 .25
144 Steve Comer .08 .25
145 Darrell Evans .30 .75
146 Bob Welch .30 .75
147 Terry Puhl .08 .25
148 Manny Sanguillen .30 .75
149 Tom Hume .08 .25
150 Jason Thompson .08 .25
151 Tom Hausman DP .08 .25
152 John Fulgham RC .08 .25
153 Tim Blackwell .08 .25
154 Lary Sorensen .08 .25
155 Jerry Remy .08 .25
156 Tony Brizzolara RC .08 .25
157 Willie Wilson DP .20 .50
158 Rob Picciolo DP .08 .25
159 Ken Clay .08 .25
160 Eddie Murray 2.00 5.00
161 Larry Christenson .08 .25
162 Bob Randall .08 .25
163 Steve Swisher .08 .25
164 Greg Pryor .08 .25
165 Omar Moreno .08 .25
166 Glenn Abbott .08 .25
167 Jack Clark .30 .75
168 Rick Waits .08 .25
169 Luis Gomez .08 .25
170 Burt Hooton .30 .75
171 Fernando Gonzalez .08 .25
172 Ron Hodges .08 .25
173 John Henry Johnson .08 .25
174 Ray Knight .30 .75
175 Rick Reuschel .30 .75
176 Champ Summers .08 .25
177 Dave Heaverlo .08 .25
178 Tim McCarver .30 .75
179 Ron Davis RC .08 .25
180 Warren Cromartie .08 .25
181 Moose Haas .08 .25
182 Ken Reitz .08 .25
183 Jim Anderson DP .08 .25
184 Steve Renko DP .08 .25
185 Hal McRae .30 .75
186 Junior Moore .08 .25
187 Alan Ashby .08 .25
188 Terry Crowley .08 .25
189 Kevin Kobel .08 .25
190 Buddy Bell .30 .75
191 Ted Martinez .08 .25
192 Atlanta Braves CL .30 .75
Bobby Cox MG
193 Dave Goltz .08 .25
194 Mike Easler .08 .25
195 John Montefusco .30 .75
196 Lance Parrish .30 .75
197 Byron McLaughlin .08 .25
198 Dell Alston DP .08 .25
199 Mike LaCoss .08 .25
200 Jim Rice .30 .75
201 Batting Leaders .30 .75
Keith Hernandez
Fred Lynn
202 Home Run Leaders .60 1.50
Dave Kingman
Gorman Thomas
203 RBI Leaders .60 1.50
Dave Winfield
Don Baylor
204 Stolen Base Leaders .30 .75
Omar Moreno
Willie Wilson
205 Victory Leaders .30 .75
Joe Niekro
Phil Niekro
Mike Flanagan
206 Strikeout Leaders 2.00 5.00
J.R. Richard
Nolan Ryan
207 ERA Leaders .30 .75
J.R. Richard
Ron Guidry
208 Wayne Cage .08 .25
209 Von Joshua .08 .25
210 Steve Carlton .60 1.50
211 Dave Skaggs DP .08 .25
212 Dave Roberts .08 .25
213 Mike Jorgensen DP .08 .25
214 California Angels CL .30 .75
Jim Fregosi MG
215 Sixto Lezcano .08 .25
216 Phil Mankowski .08 .25
217 Ed Halicki .08 .25
218 Jose Morales .08 .25
219 Steve Mingori .08 .25
220 Dave Concepcion .30 .75
221 Joe Cannon RC .08 .25
222 Ron Hassey RC .08 .25
223 Bob Sykes .08 .25
224 Willie Montanez .08 .25
225 Lou Piniella .30 .75
226 Bill Stein .08 .25
227 Len Barker .08 .25
228 Johnny Oates .30 .75
229 Jim Bibby .08 .25
230 Dave Winfield .60 1.50
231 Steve McCatty .08 .25
232 Alan Trammell .60 1.50
233 LaRue Washington RC .08 .25
234 Vern Ruhle .08 .25
235 Andre Dawson .60 1.50
236 Marc Hill .08 .25
237 Scott McGregor .30 .75
238 Rob Wilfong .08 .25
239 Don Aase .08 .25
240 Dave Kingman .30 .75
241 Checklist 122-242 .30 .75
242 Lamar Johnson .08 .25
243 Jerry Augustine .08 .25
244 St. Louis Cardinals CL .30 .75
Ken Boyer MG
245 Phil Niekro .30 .75
246 Tim Foli DP .08 .25
247 Frank Riccelli .08 .25
248 Jamie Quirk .08 .25
249 Jim Clancy .08 .25
250 Jim Kaat .30 .75
251 Kip Young .08 .25
252 Ted Cox .08 .25
253 John Montague .08 .25
254 Paul Dade DP .08 .25
255 Dusty Baker DP .20 .50
256 Roger Erickson .08 .25
257 Larry Herndon .08 .25
258 Paul Moskau .08 .25
259 New York Mets CL .60 1.50
Joe Torre MG
260 Al Oliver .30 .75
261 Dave Chalk .08 .25
262 Benny Ayala .08 .25
263 Dave LaRoche DP .08 .25
264 Bill Robinson .08 .25
265 Robin Yount 1.25 3.00
266 Bernie Carbo .08 .25
267 Dan Schatzeder .08 .25
268 Rafael Landestoy .08 .25
269 Dave Tobik .08 .25
270 Mike Schmidt DP 1.25 3.00
271 Dick Drago DP .08 .25
272 Ralph Garr .30 .75
273 Eduardo Rodriguez .08 .25
274 Dale Murphy 1.00 2.50
275 Jerry Koosman .30 .75
276 Tom Veryzer .08 .25
277 Rick Bosetti .08 .25
278 Jim Spencer .08 .25
279 Rob Andrews .08 .25
280 Gaylord Perry .30 .75
281 Paul Blair .30 .75
282 Seattle Mariners CL .30 .75
Darrell Johnson MG
283 John Ellis .08 .25
284 Larry Murray DP RC .08 .25
285 Don Baylor .30 .75
286 Darold Knowles DP .08 .25
287 John Lowenstein .08 .25
288 Dave Rozema .08 .25
289 Bruce Bochy .08 .25
290 Steve Garvey .60 1.50
291 Randy Scarberry RC .08 .25
292 Dale Berra .08 .25
293 Elias Sosa .08 .25
294 Charlie Spikes .08 .25
295 Larry Gura .08 .25
296 Dave Rader .08 .25
297 Tim Johnson .08 .25
298 Ken Holtzman .30 .75
299 Steve Henderson .08 .25
300 Ron Guidry .30 .75
301 Mike Edwards .08 .25
302 Los Angeles Dodgers CL .60 1.50
Tom Lasorda MG
303 Bill Castro .08 .25
304 Butch Wynegar .08 .25
305 Randy Jones .30 .75
306 Denny Walling .08 .25
307 Rick Honeycutt .08 .25
308 Mike Hargrove .30 .75
309 Larry McWilliams .08 .25
310 Dave Parker .30 .75
311 Roger Metzger .08 .25
312 Mike Barlow .08 .25
313 Johnny Grubb .08 .25
314 Tim Stoddard RC .08 .25
315 Steve Kemp .30 .75
316 Bob Lacey .08 .25
317 Mike Anderson DP .08 .25
318 Jerry Reuss .30 .75
319 Chris Speier .08 .25
320 Dennis Eckersley .60 1.50
321 Keith Hernandez .30 .75
322 Claudell Washington .08 .25
323 Mick Kelleher .08 .25
324 Tom Underwood .08 .25
325 Dan Driessen .08 .25
326 Bo McLaughlin .08 .25
327 Ray Fosse DP .20 .50
328 Minnesota Twins CL .30 .75
Gene Mauch MG
329 Bert Roberge RC .08 .25
330 Al Cowens .30 .75
331 Richie Hebner .08 .25
332 Enrique Romo .08 .25
333 Jim Norris DP .08 .25
334 Jim Beattie .08 .25
335 Willie McCovey .60 1.50
336 George Medich .08 .25
337 Carney Lansford .30 .75
338 John Wockenfuss .08 .25
339 John D'Acquisto .08 .25
340 Ken Singleton .30 .75
341 Jim Essian .08 .25
342 Odell Jones .08 .25
343 Mike Vail .08 .25
344 Randy Lerch .08 .25
345 Larry Parrish .30 .75
346 Buddy Solomon .08 .25
347 Harry Chappas RC .08 .25
348 Checklist 243-363 .30 .75
349 Jack Brohamer .08 .25
350 George Hendrick .30 .75
351 Bob Davis .08 .25
352 Dan Briggs .08 .25
353 Andy Hassler .08 .25
354 Rick Auerbach .08 .25
355 Gary Matthews .30 .75
356 San Diego Padres CL .30 .75
Jerry Coleman MG
357 Bob McClure .08 .25
358 Lou Whitaker .30 .75
359 Randy Moffitt .08 .25
360 Darrell Porter DP .20 .50
361 Wayne Garland .08 .25
362 Danny Goodwin .08 .25
363 Wayne Gross .08 .25
364 Ray Burris .08 .25
365 Bobby Murcer .30 .75
366 Rob Dressler .08 .25
367 Billy Smith .08 .25
368 Willie Aikens RC .08 .25
369 Jim Kern .08 .25
370 Cesar Cedeno .30 .75
371 Jack Morris .30 .75
372 Joel Youngblood .08 .25
373 Dan Petry DP RC .30 .75
374 Jim Gantner .30 .75
375 Ross Grimsley .08 .25
376 Gary Allenson RC .08 .25
377 Junior Kennedy .08 .25
378 Jerry Mumphrey .08 .25
379 Kevin Bell .08 .25
380 Garry Maddox .30 .75
381 Chicago Cubs CL .30 .75
Preston Gomez MG
382 Dave Freisleben .08 .25
383 Ed Ott .08 .25
384 Joey McLaughlin RC .08 .25
385 Enos Cabell .08 .25
386 Darrell Jackson .08 .25
387A Fred Stanley .75 2.00
Yellow Name on Front
387B Fred Stanley .08 .25
(Red name on front)
388 Mike Paxton .08 .25
389 Pete LaCock .08 .25
390 Fergie Jenkins .30 .75
391 Tony Armas DP .20 .50
392 Milt Wilcox .08 .25
393 Ozzie Smith 4.00 10.00
394 Reggie Cleveland .08 .25
395 Ellis Valentine .08 .25
396 Dan Meyer .08 .25
397 Roy Thomas DP .08 .25
398 Barry Foote .08 .25
399 Mike Proly DP .08 .25
400 George Foster .30 .75
401 Pete Falcone .08 .25
402 Merv Rettenmund .08 .25
403 Pete Redfern DP .08 .25
404 Baltimore Orioles CL .30 .75
Earl Weaver MG
405 Dwight Evans .60 1.50
406 Paul Molitor 1.50 4.00
407 Tony Solaita .08 .25
408 Bill North .08 .25
409 Paul Splittorff .08 .25
410 Bobby Bonds .30 .75
411 Frank LaCorte .08 .25
412 Thad Bosley .08 .25
413 Allen Ripley .08 .25
414 George Scott .30 .75
415 Bill Atkinson .08 .25
416 Tom Brookens RC .08 .25
417 Craig Chamberlain DP RC .08 .25
418 Roger Freed DP .08 .25
419 Vic Correll .08 .25
420 Butch Hobson .08 .25
421 Doug Bird .08 .25
422 Larry Milbourne .08 .25
423 Dave Frost .08 .25
424 New York Yankees CL .30 .75
Dick Howser MG
424A New York Yankees CL
Billy Martin MG
Card is believed to be a Pre-Production issue
425 Mark Belanger .30 .75
426 Grant Jackson .08 .25
427 Tom Hutton DP .08 .25
428 Pat Zachry .08 .25
429 Duane Kuiper .08 .25
430 Larry Hisle DP .08 .25
431 Mike Krukow .08 .25
432 Willie Norwood .08 .25
433 Rich Gale .08 .25
434 Johnnie LeMaster .08 .25
435 Don Gullett .30 .75
436 Billy Almon .08 .25
437 Joe Niekro .30 .75
438 Dave Revering .08 .25
439 Mike Phillips .08 .25
440 Don Sutton .30 .75
441 Eric Soderholm .08 .25
442 Jorge Orta .08 .25
443 Mike Parrott .08 .25
444 Alvis Woods .08 .25
445 Mark Fidrych .30 .75
446 Duffy Dyer .08 .25
447 Nino Espinosa .08 .25
448 Jim Wohlford .08 .25
449 Doug Bair .08 .25
450 George Brett 3.00 8.00
451 Cleveland Indians CL .30 .75
Dave Garcia MG
452 Steve Dillard .08 .25
453 Mike Bacsik .08 .25
454 Tom Donohue RC .08 .25
455 Mike Torrez .30 .75
456 Frank Taveras .08 .25
457 Bert Blyleven .30 .75
458 Billy Sample .08 .25
459 Mickey Lolich DP .20 .50
460 Willie Randolph .30 .75
461 Dwayne Murphy .08 .25
462 Mike Sadek DP .08 .25
463 Jerry Royster .08 .25
464 John Denny .30 .75
465 Rick Monday .30 .75
466 Mike Squires .08 .25
467 Jesse Jefferson .08 .25
468 Aurelio Rodriguez .08 .25
469 Randy Niemann DP RC .08 .25
470 Bob Boone .30 .75
471 Hosken Powell DP .08 .25
472 Willie Hernandez .30 .75
473 Bump Wills .08 .25
474 Steve Busby .30 .75
475 Cesar Geronimo .30 .75
476 Bob Shirley .08 .25
477 Buck Martinez .08 .25
478 Gil Flores .08 .25
479 Montreal Expos CL .30 .75
Dick Williams MG
480 Bob Watson .30 .75
481 Tom Paciorek .30 .75
482 Rickey Henderson RC 30.00 60.00
UER 7 steals at
Modesto should be Fresno
483 Bo Diaz .08 .25
484 Checklist 364-484 .30 .75
485 Mickey Rivers .30 .75
486 Mike Tyson DP .08 .25
487 Wayne Nordhagen .08 .25
488 Roy Howell .08 .25
489 Preston Hanna DP .08 .25
490 Lee May .30 .75
491 Steve Mura DP .08 .25
492 Todd Cruz RC .08 .25
493 Jerry Martin .08 .25
494 Craig Minetto RC .08 .25
495 Bake McBride .30 .75
496 Silvio Martinez .08 .25
497 Jim Mason .08 .25
498 Danny Darwin .30 .75

499 San Francisco Giants CL .30 .75
Dave Bristol MG
500 Tom Seaver 1.25 3.00
501 Rennie Stennett .08 .25
502 Rich Wortham DP RC .08 .25
503 Mike Cubbage .08 .25
504 Gene Garber .08 .25
505 Bert Campaneris .30 .75
506 Tom Buskey .08 .25
507 Leon Roberts .08 .25
508 U.L. Washington .08 .25
509 Ed Glynn .08 .25
510 Ron Cey .30 .75
511 Eric Wilkins RC .08 .25
512 Jose Cardenal .08 .25
513 Tom Dixon DP .08 .25
514 Steve Ontiveros .08 .25
515 Mike Caldwell UER .08 .25
1979 loss total reads
96 instead of 6
516 Hector Cruz .08 .25
517 Don Stanhouse .08 .25
518 Nelson Norman RC .08 .25
519 Steve Nicosia RC .08 .25
520 Steve Rogers .30 .75
521 Ken Brett .08 .25
522 Jim Morrison .08 .25
523 Ken Henderson .08 .25
524 Jim Wright DP .08 .25
525 Clint Hurdle .08 .25
526 Philadelphia Phillies CL .30 .75
Dallas Green MG
527 Doug Rau DP .08 .25
528 Adrian Devine .08 .25
529 Jim Barr .08 .25
530 Jim Sundberg DP .20 .50
531 Eric Rasmussen .08 .25
532 Willie Horton .30 .75
533 Checklist 485-605 .30 .75
534 Andre Thornton .30 .75
535 Bob Forsch .08 .25
536 Lee Lacy .08 .25
537 Alex Trevino RC .08 .25
538 Joe Strain .08 .25
539 Rudy May .08 .25
540 Pete Rose 3.00 8.00
541 Miguel Dilone .08 .25
542 Joe Coleman .08 .25
543 Pat Kelly .08 .25
544 Rick Sutcliffe RC .60 1.50
545 Jeff Burroughs .30 .75
546 Rick Langford .08 .25
547 John Wathan .08 .25
548 Dave Rajsich .08 .25
549 Larry Wolfe .08 .25
550 Ken Griffey Sr. .30 .75
551 Pittsburgh Pirates CL .30 .75
Chuck Tanner MG
552 Bill Nahorodny .08 .25
553 Dick Davis .08 .25
554 Art Howe .30 .75
555 Ed Figueroa .08 .25
556 Joe Rudi .30 .75
557 Mark Lee .08 .25
558 Alfredo Griffin .08 .25
559 Dale Murray .08 .25
560 Dave Lopes .30 .75
561 Eddie Whitson .08 .25
562 Joe Wallis .08 .25
563 Will McEnaney .08 .25
564 Rick Manning .08 .25
565 Dennis Leonard .08 .25
566 Bud Harrelson .30 .75
567 Skip Lockwood .08 .25
568 Gary Roenicke RC .08 .25
569 Terry Kennedy .08 .25
570 Roy Smalley .30 .75
571 Joe Sambito .08 .25
572 Jerry Morales DP .08 .25
573 Kent Tekulve .30 .75
574 Scot Thompson .08 .25
575 Ken Kravec .08 .25
576 Jim Dwyer .08 .25
577 Toronto Blue Jays CL .30 .75
Bobby Mattick MG
578 Scott Sanderson .08 .25
579 Charlie Moore .08 .25
580 Nolan Ryan 6.00 15.00
581 Bob Bailor .08 .25
582 Brian Doyle .08 .25
583 Bob Stinson .08 .25
584 Kurt Bevacqua .08 .25
585 Al Hrabosky .30 .75
586 Mitchell Page .08 .25
587 Garry Templeton .30 .75
588 Greg Minton .08 .25
589 Chet Lemon .30 .75
590 Jim Palmer .60 1.50
591 Rick Cerone .08 .25
592 Jon Matlack .30 .75
593 Jesus Alou .08 .25
594 Dick Tidrow .08 .25
595 Don Money .08 .25
596 Rick Matula RC .08 .25
597 Tom Poquette .08 .25
598 Fred Kendall DP .08 .25
599 Mike Norris .08 .25
600 Reggie Jackson 1.25 3.00
601 Buddy Schultz .08 .25
602 Brian Downing .30 .75
603 Jack Billingham DP .08 .25
604 Glenn Adams .08 .25
605 Terry Forster .30 .75
606 Cincinnati Reds CL .30 .75
John McNamara MG
607 Woodie Fryman .08 .25
608 Alan Bannister .08 .25
609 Ron Reed .08 .25
610 Willie Stargell .60 1.50
611 Jerry Garvin DP .08 .25
612 Cliff Johnson .08 .25
613 Randy Stein .08 .25
614 John Hiller .08 .25
615 Doug DeCinces .30 .75
616 Gene Richards .08 .25
617 Joaquin Andujar .30 .75
618 Bob Montgomery DP .08 .25
619 Sergio Ferrer .08 .25
620 Richie Zisk .30 .75
621 Bob Grich .30 .75
622 Mario Soto .30 .75
623 Gorman Thomas .30 .75
624 Lerrin LaGrow .08 .25
625 Chris Chambliss .30 .75
626 Detroit Tigers CL .30 .75
Sparky Anderson MG
627 Pedro Borbon .08 .25
628 Doug Capilla .08 .25
629 Jim Todd .08 .25
630 Larry Bowa .30 .75
631 Mark Littell .08 .25
632 Barry Bonnell .08 .25
633 Bob Apodaca .08 .25
634 Glenn Borgmann DP .08 .25
635 John Candelaria .30 .75
636 Toby Harrah .30 .75
637 Joe Simpson .08 .25
638 Mark Clear RC .08 .25
639 Larry Biittner .08 .25
640 Mike Flanagan .30 .75
641 Ed Kranepool .30 .75
642 Ken Forsch DP .08 .25
643 John Mayberry .30 .75
644 Charlie Hough .30 .75
645 Rick Burleson .30 .75
646 Checklist 606-726 .30 .75
647 Milt May .08 .25
648 Roy White .30 .75
649 Tom Griffin .08 .25
650 Joe Morgan .60 1.50
651 Rollie Fingers .30 .75
652 Mario Mendoza .08 .25
653 Stan Bahnsen .08 .25
654 Bruce Boisclair DP .08 .25
655 Tug McGraw .30 .75
656 Larvell Blanks .08 .25
657 Dave Edwards RC .08 .25
658 Chris Knapp .08 .25
659 Milwaukee Brewers CL .30 .75
George Bamberger MG
660 Rusty Staub .30 .75
661 Mark Corey .08 .25
Dave Ford
Wayne Krenchicki RC
662 Joel Finch .08 .25
Mike O'Berry RC
Chuck Rainey RC
663 Ralph Botting RC .30 .75
Bob Clark RC
Dickie Thon RC
664 Mike Colbern .08 .25
Guy Hoffman RC
Dewey Robinson RC
665 Larry Andersen .08 .25
Bobby Cuellar RC
Sandy Wihtol RC
666 Mike Chris RC .08 .25
Al Greene RC
Bruce Robbins RC
667 Renie Martin RC .30 .75
Bill Paschall RC
Dan Quisenberry RC
668 Danny Boitano RC .08 .25
Willie Mueller RC
Lenn Sakata RC
669 Dan Graham RC .30 .75
Rick Sofield
Gary Ward RC
670 Bobby Brown RC .08 .25
Brad Gulden RC
Darryl Jones RC
671 Derek Bryant RC .30 .75
Brian Kingman RC
Mike Morgan RC
672 Charlie Beamon RC .08 .25
Rodney Craig RC
Rafael Vasquez RC
673 Brian Allard RC .08 .25
Jerry Don Gleaton RC
Greg Mahlberg RC
674 Butch Edge RC .08 .25
Pat Kelly
Ted Wilborn RC
675 Bruce Benedict .08 .25
Larry Bradford RC
Eddie Miller
676 Dave Geisel .08 .25
Steve Macko RC
Karl Pagel
677 Art DeFreites RC .08 .25
Frank Pastore RC
Harry Spilman
678 Reggie Baldwin RC .08 .25
Alan Knicely RC
Pete Ladd RC
679 Joe Beckwith RC .30 .75
Mickey Hatcher RC
Dave Patterson RC
680 Tony Bernazard RC .08 .25
Randy Miller RC
John Tamargo
681 Dan Norman .60 1.50
Jesse Orosco RC
Mike Scott RC
682 Ramon Aviles RC .08 .25
Dickie Noles RC
Kevin Saucier RC
683 Dorian Boyland RC .08 .25
Alberto Lois RC
Harry Saferight RC
684 George Frazier .30 .75
Tom Herr RC
Dan O'Brien RC
685 Tim Flannery RC .08 .25
Brian Greer RC
Jim Wilhelm RC
686 Greg Johnston .08 .25
Dennis Littlejohn RC
Phil Nastu RC
687 Mike Heath DP .08 .25
688 Steve Stone .30 .75
689 Boston Red Sox CL .30 .75
Don Zimmer MG
690 Tommy John .30 .75
691 Ivan DeJesus .08 .25
692 Rawly Eastwick DP .20 .50
693 Craig Kusick .08 .25
694 Jim Rooker .08 .25
695 Reggie Smith .30 .75
696 Julio Gonzalez .08 .25
697 David Clyde .08 .25
698 Oscar Gamble .30 .75
699 Floyd Bannister .08 .25
700 Rod Carew DP .30 .75
701 Ken Oberkfell RC .08 .25
702 Ed Farmer .08 .25
703 Otto Velez .08 .25
704 Gene Tenace .30 .75
705 Freddie Patek .30 .75
706 Tippy Martinez .08 .25
707 Elliott Maddox .30 .75
708 Bob Tolan .08 .25
709 Pat Underwood RC .08 .25
710 Graig Nettles .30 .75
711 Bob Galasso RC .08 .25
712 Rodney Scott .08 .25
713 Terry Whitfield .08 .25
714 Fred Norman .08 .25
715 Sal Bando .30 .75
716 Lynn McGlothen .08 .25
717 Mickey Klutts DP .08 .25
718 Greg Gross .08 .25
719 Don Robinson .30 .75
720 Carl Yastrzemski DP .75 2.00
721 Paul Hartzell .08 .25
722 Jose Cruz .30 .75
723 Shane Rawley .08 .25
724 Jerry White .08 .25
725 Rick Wise .08 .25
726 Steve Yeager .30 .75

1981 Topps

The cards in this 726-card set measure the standard size. This set was issued primarily in 15-card wax packs and 50-card rack packs. League Leaders (1-8), Record Breakers (201-208), and Post-season cards (401-404) are the topical subsets. The team cards are all grouped together (661-686) and feature team checklist backs and a very small photo of the team's manager in the upper right corner of the obverse. The obverses carry the player's position and team in a baseball cap design, and the company name is printed in a small baseball. The backs are red and gray. The 66 double-printed cards are noted in the checklist by DP. Notable Rookie Cards in the set include Harold Baines, Kirk Gibson, Tim Raines, Jeff Reardon, and Fernando Valenzuela. During 1981, a promotion existed where collectors could order complete set in sheet form from Topps for $24.

COMPLETE SET (726) 30.00 60.00
COMMON CARD (1-726) .05 .15
COMMON CARD DP .05 .15
1 George Brett 1.25 3.00
Bill Buckner LL
2 Reggie Jackson .60 1.50
Ben Oglivie
Mike Schmidt LL
3 Cecil Cooper .60 1.50
Mike Schmidt LL
4 Rickey Henderson 1.25 3.00
Ron LeFlore LL
5 Steve Stone .15 .40
Steve Carlton LL
6 Len Barker .15 .40
Steve Carlton LL
7 Rudy May .15 .40
Don Sutton LL
8 Dan Quisenberry .15 .40
Rollie Fingers
Tom Hume LL
9 Pete LaCock DP .05 .15
10 Mike Flanagan .05 .15
11 Jim Wohlford DP .05 .15
12 Mark Clear .05 .15
13 Joe Charboneau RC .60 1.50
14 John Tudor RC .60 1.50
15 Larry Parrish .05 .15
16 Ron Davis .05 .15
17 Cliff Johnson .05 .15
18 Glenn Adams .05 .15
19 Jim Clancy .05 .15
20 Jeff Burroughs .15 .40
21 Ron Oester .05 .15
22 Danny Darwin .05 .15
23 Alex Trevino .05 .15
24 Don Stanhouse .05 .15
25 Sixto Lezcano .05 .15
26 U.L. Washington .05 .15
27 Champ Summers DP .05 .15
28 Enrique Romo .05 .15
29 Gene Tenace .15 .40
30 Jack Clark .15 .40
31 Checklist 1-121 DP .08 .25
32 Ken Oberkfell .05 .15
33 Rick Honeycutt .05 .15
34 Aurelio Rodriguez .05 .15
35 Mitchell Page .05 .15
36 Ed Farmer .05 .15
37 Gary Roenicke .05 .15
38 Win Remmerswaal RC .05 .15
39 Tom Veryzer .05 .15
40 Tug McGraw .15 .40
41 Bob Bacock RC .08 .25
John Butcher RC
Jerry Don Gleaton
42 Jerry White DP .05 .15
43 Jose Morales .05 .15
44 Larry McWilliams .05 .15
45 Enos Cabell .05 .15
46 Rick Bosetti .05 .15
47 Ken Brett .05 .15
48 Dave Skaggs .05 .15
49 Bob Shirley .05 .15
50 Dave Lopes .15 .40
51 Bill Robinson DP .05 .15
52 Hector Cruz .05 .15
53 Kevin Saucier .05 .15
54 Ivan DeJesus .05 .15
55 Mike Norris .05 .15
56 Buck Martinez .05 .15
57 Dave Roberts .05 .15
58 Joel Youngblood .05 .15
59 Dan Petry .05 .15
60 Willie Randolph .15 .40
61 Butch Wynegar .05 .15
62 Joe Pettini RC .05 .15
63 Steve Renko DP .05 .15
64 Brian Asselstine .05 .15
65 Scott McGregor .05 .15
66 Manny Castillo RC .08 .25
Tim Ireland RC
Mike Jones RC
67 Ken Kravec .05 .15
68 Matt Alexander DP .05 .15
69 Ed Halicki .05 .15
70 Al Oliver DP .08 .25
71 Hal Dues .05 .15
72 Barry Evans DP RC .05 .15
73 Doug Bair .05 .15
74 Mike Hargrove .05 .15
75 Reggie Smith .15 .40
76 Mario Mendoza .05 .15
77 Mike Barlow .05 .15
78 Steve Dillard .05 .15
79 Bruce Robbins .05 .15
80 Rusty Staub .15 .40
81 Dave Stapleton RC .05 .15
82 Danny Heep RC .08 .25
Alan Knicely
Bobby Sprowl RC
83 Mike Proly .05 .15
84 Johnnie LeMaster .05 .15
85 Mike Caldwell .05 .15
86 Wayne Gross .05 .15
87 Rick Camp .05 .15
88 Joe Lefebvre RC .05 .15
89 Darrell Jackson .05 .15
90 Bake McBride .15 .40
91 Tim Stoddard DP .05 .15
92 Mike Easler .05 .15
93 Ed Glynn DP .05 .15
94 Harry Spilman DP .05 .15
95 Jim Sundberg .15 .40
96 Dave Beard RC .08 .25
Ernie Camacho RC
Pat Dempsey RC
97 Chris Speier .05 .15
98 Clint Hurdle .05 .15
99 Eric Wilkins .05 .15
100 Rod Carew .30 .75
101 Benny Ayala .05 .15
102 Dave Tobik .05 .15
103 Jerry Martin .05 .15
104 Terry Forster .15 .40
105 Jose Cruz .15 .40
106 Don Money .05 .15
107 Rich Wortham .05 .15
108 Bruce Benedict .05 .15
109 Mike Scott .15 .40
110 Carl Yastrzemski 1.00 2.50
111 Greg Minton .05 .15
112 Rusty Kuntz RC .08 .25
Fran Mullins RC
Leo Sutherland RC
113 Mike Phillips .05 .15
114 Tom Underwood .05 .15
115 Roy Smalley .15 .40
116 Joe Simpson .05 .15
117 Pete Falcone .05 .15
118 Kurt Bevacqua .05 .15
119 Tippy Martinez .05 .15
120 Larry Bowa .15 .40
121 Larry Harlow .05 .15
122 John Denny .05 .15
123 Al Cowens .05 .15
124 Jerry Garvin .05 .15
125 Andre Dawson .30 .75
126 Charlie Leibrandt RC .30 .75
127 Rudy Law .05 .15
128 Gary Allenson DP .05 .15
129 Art Howe .05 .15
130 Larry Gura .05 .15
131 Keith Moreland RC .05 .15
132 Tommy Boggs .05 .15
133 Jeff Cox RC .05 .15
134 Steve Mura .05 .15
135 Gorman Thomas .15 .40
136 Doug Capilla .05 .15
137 Hosken Powell .05 .15
138 Rich Dotson DP RC .05 .15
139 Oscar Gamble .05 .15
140 Bob Forsch .05 .15
141 Miguel Dilone .05 .15
142 Jackson Todd .05 .15
143 Dan Meyer .05 .15
144 Allen Ripley .05 .15
145 Mickey Rivers .05 .15
146 Bobby Castillo .05 .15
147 Dale Berra .05 .15
148 Randy Niemann .05 .15
149 Joe Nolan RC .05 .15
150 Mark Fidrych .15 .40
151 Claudell Washington .05 .15
152 John Urrea .05 .15
153 Tom Poquette .05 .15
154 Rick Langford .05 .15
155 Chris Chambliss .15 .40
156 Bob McClure .05 .15
157 John Wathan .05 .15
158 Fergie Jenkins .15 .40
159 Brian Doyle .05 .15
160 Garry Maddox .05 .15
161 Dan Graham .05 .15
162 Doug Corbett RC .05 .15
163 Billy Almon RC .05 .15
164 LaMarr Hoyt RC .30 .75
165 Tony Scott .05 .15
166 Floyd Bannister .05 .15
167 Terry Whitfield .05 .15
168 Don Robinson DP .05 .15
169 John Mayberry .05 .15
170 Ross Grimsley .05 .15
171 Gene Richards .05 .15
172 Gary Woods .05 .15
173 Bump Wills .05 .15
174 Doug Rau .05 .15
175 Dave Collins .05 .15
176 Mike Krukow RC .05 .15
177 Rick Peters RC .05 .15
178 Jim Essian DP .05 .15
179 Rudy May .05 .15
180 Pete Rose 2.00 5.00
181 Elias Sosa .05 .15
182 Bob Grich .15 .40
183 Dick Davis DP .05 .15
184 Jim Dwyer .05 .15
185 Dennis Leonard .05 .15
186 Wayne Nordhagen .05 .15
187 Mike Parrott .05 .15
188 Doug DeCinces .05 .15
189 Craig Swan .05 .15
190 Cesar Cedeno .15 .40
191 Rick Sutcliffe .15 .40
192 Terry Harper RC .08 .25
Ed Miller RC
Rafael Ramirez RC
193 Pete Vuckovich .05 .15
194 Rod Scurry RC .05 .15
195 Rich Murray RC .05 .15
196 Duffy Dyer .05 .15
197 Jim Kern .05 .15
198 Jerry Dybzinski RC .05 .15
199 Chuck Rainey .05 .15
200 George Foster .15 .40
201 Johnny Bench RB .30 .75
202 Steve Carlton RB .15 .40
203 Bill Gullickson RB .05 .15
204 Ron LeFlore RB .15 .40
Rodney Scott
205 Pete Rose RB .60 1.50
206 Mike Schmidt RB .60 1.50
207 Ozzie Smith RB .75 2.00
208 Willie Wilson RB .05 .15
209 Dickie Thon DP .05 .15
210 Jim Palmer .30 .75
211 Derrel Thomas .05 .15
212 Steve Nicosia .05 .15
213 Al Holland RC .05 .15
214 Ralph Botting .08 .25
Jim Dorsey RC
John Harris RC
215 Larry Hisle .05 .15
216 John Henry Johnson .05 .15
217 Rich Hebner .05 .15
218 Paul Splittorff .05 .15
219 Ken Landreaux .05 .15
220 Tom Seaver .60 1.50
221 Bob Davis .05 .15
222 Jorge Orta .05 .15
223 Roy Lee Jackson RC .05 .15
224 Pat Zachry .05 .15
225 Ruppert Jones .05 .15
226 Manny Sanguillen DP .08 .25
227 Fred Martinez RC .05 .15
228 Tom Paciorek .05 .15
229 Rollie Fingers .15 .40
230 George Hendrick .15 .40
231 Joe Beckwith .05 .15
232 Mickey Klutts .05 .15
233 Skip Lockwood .05 .15
234 Lou Whitaker .30 .75
235 Scott Sanderson .05 .15
236 Mike Ivie .05 .15
237 Charlie Moore .05 .15
238 Willie Hernandez .05 .15
239 Rick Miller DP .05 .15
240 Nolan Ryan 3.00 8.00
241 Checklist 122-242 DP .08 .25
242 Chet Lemon .15 .40
243 Sal Butera RC .05 .15
244 Tito Landrum RC .08 .25
Al Olmsted RC
Andy Rincon RC
245 Ed Figueroa .05 .15
246 Ed Ott DP .05 .15
247 Glenn Hubbard DP .05 .15
248 Joey McLaughlin .05 .15
249 Larry Cox .05 .15
250 Ron Guidry .15 .40
251 Tom Brookens .05 .15
252 Victor Cruz .05 .15
253 Dave Bergman .05 .15
254 Ozzie Smith 2.00 5.00
255 Mark Littell .05 .15
256 Bombo Rivera .05 .15
257 Rennie Stennett .05 .15
258 Joe Price RC .05 .15
259 Juan Berenguer 2.00 5.00
Hubie Brooks RC
Mookie Wilson RC
260 Ron Cey .15 .40
261 Rickey Henderson 4.00 10.00
262 Sammy Stewart .05 .15
263 Brian Downing .15 .40
264 Jim Norris .05 .15
265 John Candelaria .15 .40
266 Tom Herr .05 .15
267 Stan Bahnsen .05 .15
268 Jerry Royster .05 .15
269 Ken Forsch .05 .15
270 Greg Luzinski .15 .40
271 Bill Castro .05 .15
272 Bruce Kimm .05 .15
273 Stan Papi .05 .15
274 Craig Chamberlain .05 .15
275 Dwight Evans .30 .75
276 Dan Spillner .05 .15
277 Alfredo Griffin .05 .15
278 Rick Sofield .05 .15
279 Bob Knepper .05 .15
280 Ken Griffey .15 .40
281 Fred Stanley .05 .15
282 Rick Anderson RC .08 .25
Greg Biercevicz
Rodney Craig
283 Billy Sample .05 .15
284 Brian Kingman .05 .15
285 Jerry Turner .05 .15
286 Dave Frost .05 .15
287 Lenn Sakata .05 .15
288 Bob Clark .05 .15
289 Mickey Hatcher .05 .15
290 Bob Boone DP .08 .25
291 Aurelio Lopez .05 .15
292 Mike Squires .05 .15
293 Charlie Lea RC .05 .15
294 Mike Tyson DP .05 .15
295 Hal McRae .15 .40
296 Bill Nahorodny DP .05 .15
297 Bob Bailor .05 .15
298 Buddy Solomon .05 .15
299 Elliott Maddox .05 .15
300 Paul Molitor .60 1.50
301 Matt Keough .05 .15
302 Jack Perconte RC 3.00 8.00
Mike Scioscia RC
Fernando Valenzuela RC
303 Johnny Oates .15 .40
304 John Castino .05 .15
305 Ken Clay .05 .15
306 Juan Beniquez DP .05 .15
307 Gene Garber .05 .15
308 Rick Manning .05 .15
309 Luis Salazar RC .30 .75
310 Vida Blue DP .08 .25
311 Freddie Patek .05 .15
312 Rick Rhoden .05 .15
313 Luis Pujols .05 .15
314 Rich Dauer .05 .15
315 Kirk Gibson RC 3.00 8.00
316 Craig Minetto .05 .15
317 Lonnie Smith .15 .40
318 Steve Yeager .15 .40
319 Rowland Office .05 .15
320 Tom Burgmeier .05 .15
321 Leon Durham RC .30 .75
322 Neil Allen .05 .15
323 Jim Morrison DP .05 .15
324 Mike Willis .05 .15
325 Ray Knight .15 .40
326 Biff Pocoroba .05 .15
327 Moose Haas .05 .15
328 Dave Engle RC .08 .25
Greg Johnston
Gary Ward
329 Joaquin Andujar .15 .40
330 Frank White .15 .40
331 Dennis Lamp .05 .15
332 Lee Lacy DP .05 .15
333 Sid Monge .05 .15
334 Dane Iorg .05 .15
335 Rick Cerone .05 .15
336 Eddie Whitson .05 .15
337 Lynn Jones .05 .15
338 Checklist 243-363 .15 .40
339 John Ellis .05 .15
340 Bruce Kison .05 .15
341 Dwayne Murphy .05 .15
342 Eric Rasmussen DP .05 .15
343 Frank Taveras .05 .15
344 Byron McLaughlin .05 .15
345 Warren Cromartie .05 .15
346 Larry Christenson DP .05 .15
347 Harold Baines RC 1.25 3.00
348 Bob Sykes .05 .15
349 Glenn Hoffman RC .05 .15
350 J.R. Richard .15 .40
351 Otto Velez .05 .15
352 Dick Tidrow DP .05 .15
353 Terry Kennedy .05 .15
354 Mario Soto .15 .40
355 Bob Horner .15 .40
356 George Stablein RC .08 .25
Craig Stimac RC
Tom Tellmann RC
357 Jim Slaton .05 .15
358 Mark Wagner .05 .15
359 Tom Hausman .05 .15
360 Willie Wilson .15 .40
361 Joe Strain .05 .15
362 Bo Diaz .05 .15
363 Geoff Zahn .05 .15
364 Mike Davis RC .08 .25
365 Graig Nettles DP .08 .25
366 Mike Ramsey RC .08 .25
367 Dennis Martinez .15 .40
368 Leon Roberts .05 .15
369 Frank Tanana .15 .40
370 Dave Winfield .30 .75
371 Charlie Hough .15 .40
372 Jay Johnstone .05 .15
373 Pat Underwood .05 .15
374 Tommy Hutton .05 .15
375 Dave Concepcion .15 .40
376 Ron Reed .05 .15
377 Jerry Morales .05 .15
378 Dave Rader .05 .15
379 Lary Sorensen .05 .15
380 Willie Stargell .30 .75
381 Carlos Lezcano RC .08 .25
Steve Macko
Randy Martz RC
382 Paul Mirabella RC .05 .15
383 Eric Soderholm DP .05 .15
384 Mike Sadek .05 .15
385 Joe Sambito .05 .15
386 Dave Edwards .05 .15
387 Phil Niekro .15 .40
388 Andre Thornton .15 .40
389 Marty Pattin .05 .15
390 Cesar Geronimo .05 .15
391 Dave Lemanczyk DP .05 .15
392 Lance Parrish .15 .40
393 Broderick Perkins .05 .15
394 Woodie Fryman .05 .15
395 Scot Thompson .05 .15
396 Bill Campbell .05 .15
397 Julio Cruz .05 .15
398 Ross Baumgarten .05 .15
399 Mike Boddicker RC .30 .75
Mark Corey
Floyd Rayford RC
400 Reggie Jackson .60 1.50
401 George Brett ALCS 1.00 2.50
402 NL Champs .30 .75
Phillies squeak
past Astros
(Phillies celebrating)
403 Larry Bowa WS .30 .75
404 Tug McGraw WS .30 .75
405 Nino Espinosa .05 .15
406 Dickie Noles .05 .15
407 Ernie Whitt .05 .15
408 Fernando Arroyo .05 .15
409 Larry Herndon .05 .15
410 Bert Campaneris .15 .40
411 Terry Puhl .05 .15
412 Britt Burns RC .05 .15
413 Tony Bernazard .05 .15
414 John Pacella DP RC .05 .15
415 Ben Oglivie .15 .40

416 Gary Alexander .05 .15
417 Dan Schatzeder .05 .15
418 Bobby Brown .05 .15
419 Tom Hume .05 .15
420 Keith Hernandez .15 .40
421 Bob Stanley .05 .15
422 Dan Ford .05 .15
423 Shane Rawley .05 .15
424 Tim Lollar RC .08 .25
Bruce Robinson
Dennis Werth RC
425 Al Bumbry .05 .15
426 Warren Brusstar .05 .15
427 John D'Acquisto .05 .15
428 John Stearns .05 .15
429 Mick Kelleher .05 .15
430 Jim Bibby .05 .15
431 Dave Roberts .05 .15
432 Len Barker .15 .40
433 Rance Mulliniks .05 .15
434 Roger Erickson .05 .15
435 Jim Spencer .05 .15
436 Gary Lucas RC .05 .15
437 Mike Heath DP .05 .15
438 John Montefusco .05 .15
439 Denny Walling .05 .15
440 Jerry Reuss .05 .15
441 Ken Reitz .05 .15
442 Ron Pruitt .05 .15
443 Jim Beattie DP .05 .15
444 Garth Iorg .05 .15
445 Ellis Valentine .05 .15
446 Checklist 364-484 .15 .40
447 Junior Kennedy DP .05 .15
448 Tim Corcoran .05 .15
449 Paul Mitchell .05 .15
450 Dave Kingman DP .08 .25
451 Chris Bando RC .08 .25
Tom Brennan RC
Sandy Wihtol
452 Renie Martin .05 .15
453 Rob Wilfong DP .05 .15
454 Andy Hassler .05 .15
455 Rick Burleson .05 .15
456 Jeff Reardon RC .60 1.50
457 Mike Lum .05 .15
458 Randy Jones .15 .40
459 Greg Gross .05 .15
460 Rich Gossage .15 .40
461 Dave McKay RC .05 .15
462 Jack Brohamer .05 .15
463 Milt May .05 .15
464 Adrian Devine .05 .15
465 Bill Russell .15 .40
466 Bob Molinaro .05 .15
467 Dave Stieb .15 .40
468 John Wockenfuss .05 .15
469 Jeff Leonard .15 .40
470 Manny Trillo .05 .15
471 Mike Vail .05 .15
472 Dyar Miller DP .05 .15
473 Jose Cardenal .05 .15
474 Mike LaCoss .05 .15
475 Buddy Bell .15 .40
476 Jerry Koosman .15 .40
477 Luis Gomez .05 .15
478 Juan Eichelberger RC .05 .15
479 Tim Raines RC 1.50 4.00
Roberto Ramos RC
Bobby Pate RC
480 Carlton Fisk .30 .75
481 Bob Lacey DP .05 .15
482 Jim Gantner .05 .15
483 Mike Griffin RC .08 .25
484 Max Venable DP RC .05 .15
485 Garry Templeton .15 .40
486 Marc Hill .05 .15
487 Dewey Robinson .05 .15
488 Damaso Garcia RC .05 .15
489 John Littlefield RC .05 .15
Photo on card believed to be Mark Riggins
490 Eddie Murray 1.00 2.50
491 Gordy Pladson RC .05 .15
492 Barry Foote .05 .15
493 Dan Quisenberry .05 .15
494 Bob Walk RC .30 .75
495 Dusty Baker .15 .40
496 Paul Dade .05 .15
497 Fred Norman .05 .15
498 Pat Putnam .05 .15
499 Frank Pastore .05 .15
500 Jim Rice .15 .40
501 Tim Foli DP .05 .15
502 Chris Bourjos RC .08 .25
Al Hargesheimer RC
Mike Rowland RC
503 Steve McCatty .05 .15
504 Dale Murphy .30 .75
505 Jason Thompson .05 .15
506 Phil Huffman .05 .15
507 Jamie Quirk .05 .15
508 Rob Dressler .05 .15
509 Pete Mackanin .05 .15
510 Lee Mazzilli .15 .40
511 Wayne Garland .05 .15
512 Gary Thomasson .05 .15
513 Frank LaCorte .05 .15
514 George Riley RC .05 .15
515 Robin Yount 1.00 2.50
516 Doug Bird .05 .15
517 Richie Zisk .05 .15
518 Grant Jackson .05 .15
519 John Tamargo DP .05 .15
520 Steve Stone .05 .15
521 Sam Mejias .05 .15
522 Mike Colbern .05 .15
523 John Fulgham .05 .15
524 Willie Aikens .05 .15
525 Mike Torrez .05 .15
526 Marty Bystrom RC .08 .25
Jay Loviglio RC
Jim Wright
527 Danny Goodwin .05 .15
528 Gary Matthews .15 .40
529 Dave LaRoche .05 .15
530 Steve Garvey .30 .75
531 John Curtis .05 .15
532 Bill Stein .05 .15
533 Jesus Figueroa RC .05 .15
534 Dave Smith RC .30 .75
535 Omar Moreno .05 .15
536 Bob Owchinko DP .05 .15
537 Ron Hodges .05 .15
538 Tom Griffin .05 .15
539 Rodney Scott .05 .15
540 Mike Schmidt DP .75 2.00
541 Steve Swisher .05 .15
542 Larry Bradford DP .05 .15
543 Terry Crowley .05 .15
544 Rich Gale .05 .15
545 Johnny Grubb .05 .15
546 Paul Moskau .05 .15
547 Mario Guerrero .05 .15
548 Dave Goltz .05 .15
549 Jerry Remy .05 .15
550 Tommy John .15 .40
551 Vance Law RC .30 .75
Tony Pena RC
Pascual Perez RC
552 Steve Trout .05 .15
553 Tim Blackwell .05 .15
554 Bert Blyleven UER .15 .40
(1 is missing from
1980 on card back)
555 Cecil Cooper .15 .40
556 Jerry Mumphrey .05 .15
557 Chris Knapp .05 .15
558 Barry Bonnell .05 .15
559 Willie Montanez .05 .15
560 Joe Morgan .30 .75
561 Dennis Littlejohn .05 .15
562 Checklist 485-605 .15 .40
563 Jim Kaat .15 .40
564 Ron Hassey DP .05 .15
565 Burt Hooton .05 .15
566 Del Unser .05 .15
567 Mark Bomback RC .05 .15
568 Dave Revering .05 .15
569 Al Williams DP RC .05 .15
570 Ken Singleton .15 .40
571 Todd Cruz .05 .15
572 Jack Morris .30 .75
573 Phil Garner .15 .40
574 Bill Caudill .05 .15
575 Tony Perez .30 .75
576 Reggie Cleveland .05 .15
577 Luis Leal RC .08 .25
Brian Milner RC
Ken Schrom RC
578 Bill Gullickson RC .30 .75
579 Tim Flannery .05 .15
580 Don Baylor .15 .40
581 Roy Howell .05 .15
582 Gaylord Perry .15 .40
583 Larry Milbourne .05 .15
584 Randy Lerch .05 .15
585 Amos Otis .15 .40
586 Silvio Martinez .05 .15
587 Jeff Newman .05 .15
588 Gary Lavelle .05 .15
589 Lamar Johnson .05 .15
590 Bruce Sutter .30 .75
591 John Lowenstein .05 .15
592 Steve Comer .05 .15
593 Steve Kemp .05 .15
594 Preston Hanna DP .05 .15
595 Butch Hobson .05 .15
596 Jerry Augustine .05 .15
597 Rafael Landestoy .05 .15
598 George Vukovich DP RC .05 .15
599 Dennis Kinney RC .05 .15
600 Johnny Bench .60 1.50
601 Don Aase .05 .15
602 Bobby Murcer .15 .40
603 John Verhoeven .05 .15
604 Rob Picciolo .05 .15
605 Don Sutton .15 .40
606 Bruce Berenyi RC .08 .25
Geoff Combe RC
Paul Householder RC DP
607 David Palmer .05 .15
608 Greg Pryor .05 .15
609 Lynn McGlothen .05 .15
610 Darrell Porter .05 .15
611 Rick Matula DP .05 .15
612 Duane Kuiper .05 .15
613 Jim Anderson .05 .15
614 Dave Rozema .05 .15
615 Rick Dempsey .05 .15
616 Rick Wise .05 .15
617 Craig Reynolds .05 .15
618 John Milner .05 .15
619 Steve Henderson .05 .15
620 Dennis Eckersley .30 .75
621 Tom Donohue .05 .15
622 Randy Moffitt .05 .15
623 Sal Bando .15 .40
624 Bob Welch .15 .40
625 Bill Buckner .15 .40
626 Dave Steffen RC .08 .25
Jerry Ujdur RC
Roger Weaver RC
627 Luis Tiant .15 .40
628 Vic Correll .05 .15
629 Tony Armas .15 .40
630 Steve Carlton .30 .75
631 Ron Jackson .05 .15
632 Alan Bannister .05 .15
633 Bill Lee .15 .40
634 Doug Flynn .05 .15
635 Bobby Bonds .15 .40
636 Al Hrabosky .15 .40
637 Jerry Narron .05 .15
638 Checklist 606-726 .15 .40
639 Carney Lansford .15 .40
640 Dave Parker .15 .40
641 Mark Belanger .05 .15
642 Vern Ruhle .05 .15
643 Lloyd Moseby RC .30 .75
644 Ramon Aviles DP .05 .15
645 Rick Reuschel .15 .40
646 Marvis Foley RC .05 .15
647 Dick Drago .05 .15
648 Darrell Evans .15 .40
649 Manny Sarmiento .05 .15
650 Bucky Dent .15 .40
651 Pedro Guerrero .15 .40
652 John Montague .05 .15
653 Bill Fahey .05 .15
654 Ray Burris .05 .15
655 Dan Driessen .05 .15
656 Jon Matlack .05 .15
657 Mike Cubbage DP .05 .15
658 Milt Wilcox .05 .15
659 John Flinn .30 .75
Ed Romero
Ned Yost
660 Gary Carter .30 .75
661 Orioles Team CL .15 .40
Earl Weaver MG
662 Red Sox Team CL .15 .40
Ralph Houk MG
663 Angels Team CL .15 .40
Jim Fregosi MG
664 White Sox CL .15 .40
Tony LaRussa MG
665 Indians Team CL .15 .40
Dave Garcia MG
666 Tigers Team CL .15 .40
Sparky Anderson MG
667 Royals Team CL .15 .40
Jim Frey MG
668 Brewers Team CL .15 .40
Bob Rodgers MG
669 Twins Team CL. .15 .40
John Goryl MG
670 Yankees Team CL .15 .40
Gene Michael MG
671 A's Team CL .30 .75
Billy Martin MG
672 Mariners Team CL .15 .40
Maury Wills MG
673 Rangers Team CL .15 .40
Don Zimmer MG
674 Blue Jays Team CL .15 .40
Bobby Mattick MG
675 Braves Team CL .15 .40
Bobby Cox MG
676 Cubs Team CL .15 .40
Joe Amalfitano MG
677 Reds Team CL .15 .40
John McNamara MG
678 Astros Team CL .15 .40
Bill Virdon MG
679 Dodgers Team CL .30 .75
Tom Lasorda MG
680 Expos Team CL .15 .40
Dick Williams MG
681 Mets Team CL .30 .75
Joe Torre MG
682 Phillies Team CL .15 .40
Dallas Green MG
683 Pirates Team CL .15 .40
Chuck Tanner MG
684 Cardinals Team CL .15 .40
Whitey Herzog MG
685 Padres Team CL .15 .40
Frank Howard MG
686 Giants Team CL .15 .40
Dave Bristol MG
687 Jeff Jones RC .05 .15
688 Kiko Garcia .05 .15
689 Bruce Hurst RC .30 .75
Keith MacWhorter RC
Reid Nichols RC
690 Bob Watson .05 .15
691 Dick Ruthven .05 .15
692 Lenny Randle .05 .15
693 Steve Howe RC .08 .25
694 Bud Harrelson DP .08 .25
695 Kent Tekulve .05 .15
696 Alan Ashby .05 .15
697 Rick Waits .05 .15
698 Mike Jorgensen .05 .15
699 Glenn Abbott .05 .15
700 George Brett 1.50 4.00
701 Joe Rudi .15 .40
702 George Medich .05 .15
703 Alvis Woods .05 .15
704 Bill Travers DP .05 .15
705 Ted Simmons .15 .40
706 Dave Ford .05 .15
707 Dave Cash .05 .15
708 Doyle Alexander .05 .15
709 Alan Trammell DP .20 .50
710 Ron LeFlore DP .08 .25
711 Joe Ferguson .05 .15
712 Bill Bonham .05 .15
713 Bill North .05 .15
714 Pete Redfern .05 .15
715 Bill Madlock .15 .40
716 Glenn Borgmann .05 .15
717 Jim Barr DP .05 .15
718 Larry Biittner .05 .15
719 Sparky Lyle .15 .40
720 Fred Lynn .15 .40
721 Toby Harrah .15 .40
722 Joe Niekro .15 .40
723 Bruce Bochte .15 .40
724 Lou Piniella .15 .40
725 Steve Rogers .15 .40
726 Rick Monday .15 .40

1981 Topps Traded

For the first time since 1976, Topps issued a 132-card factory boxed "traded" set in 1981, issued exclusively through hobby dealers. This set was sequentially numbered, alphabetically, from 727 to 858 and carries the same design as the regular issue 1981 Topps set. There are no key Rookie Cards in this set although Hubie Brooks, Tim Raines, Jeff Reardon, and Fernando Valenzuela are depicted in their rookie year for cards. The key extended Rookie Card in the set is Danny Ainge. According to reports at the time, dealers were required to order a minimum of two cases, which cost them $4.50 per set.

COMP.FACT.SET (132) 10.00 25.00
727 Danny Ainge XRC 2.00 5.00
728 Doyle Alexander .08 .25
729 Gary Alexander .08 .25
730 Bill Almon .08 .25
731 Joaquin Andujar .40 1.00
732 Bob Bailor .08 .25
733 Juan Beniquez .08 .25
734 Dave Bergman .08 .25
735 Tony Bernazard .08 .25
736 Larry Biittner .08 .25
737 Doug Bird .08 .25
738 Bert Blyleven .40 1.00
739 Mark Bomback .08 .25
740 Bobby Bonds .40 1.00
741 Rick Bosetti .08 .25
742 Hubie Brooks .75 2.00
743 Rick Burleson .08 .25
744 Ray Burris .08 .25
745 Jeff Burroughs .40 1.00
746 Enos Cabell .08 .25
747 Ken Clay .08 .25
748 Mark Clear .08 .25
749 Larry Cox .08 .25
750 Hector Cruz .08 .25
751 Victor Cruz .08 .25
752 Mike Cubbage .08 .25
753 Dick Davis .08 .25
754 Brian Doyle .08 .25
755 Dick Drago .08 .25
756 Leon Durham .40 1.00
757 Jim Dwyer .08 .25
758 Dave Edwards UER .08 .25
No birthdate on card
759 Jim Essian .08 .25
760 Bill Fahey .08 .25
761 Rollie Fingers .40 1.00
762 Carlton Fisk .75 2.00
763 Barry Foote .08 .25
764 Ken Forsch .08 .25
765 Kiko Garcia .08 .25
766 Cesar Geronimo .08 .25
767 Gary Gray XRC .08 .25
768 Mickey Hatcher .08 .25
769 Steve Henderson .08 .25
770 Marc Hill .08 .25
771 Butch Hobson .08 .25
772 Rick Honeycutt .08 .25
773 Roy Howell .08 .25
774 Mike Ivie .08 .25
775 Roy Lee Jackson .08 .25
776 Cliff Johnson .08 .25
777 Randy Jones .40 1.00
778 Ruppert Jones .08 .25
779 Mick Kelleher .08 .25
780 Terry Kennedy .08 .25
781 Dave Kingman .40 1.00
782 Bob Knepper .08 .25
783 Ken Kravec .08 .25
784 Bob Lacey .08 .25
785 Dennis Lamp .08 .25
786 Rafael Landestoy .08 .25
787 Ken Landreaux .08 .25
788 Carney Lansford .40 1.00
789 Dave LaRoche .08 .25
790 Joe Lefebvre .08 .25
791 Ron LeFlore .40 1.00
792 Randy Lerch .08 .25
793 Sixto Lezcano .08 .25
794 John Littlefield .08 .25
795 Mike Lum .08 .25
796 Greg Luzinski .40 1.00
797 Fred Lynn .40 1.00
798 Jerry Martin .08 .25
799 Buck Martinez .08 .25
800 Gary Matthews .40 1.00
801 Mario Mendoza .08 .25
802 Larry Milbourne .08 .25
803 Rick Miller .08 .25
804 John Montefusco .08 .25
805 Jerry Morales .08 .25
806 Jose Morales .08 .25
807 Joe Morgan .75 2.00
808 Jerry Mumphrey .08 .25
809 Gene Nelson XRC .08 .25
810 Ed Ott .08 .25
811 Bob Owchinko .08 .25
812 Gaylord Perry .40 1.00
813 Mike Phillips .08 .25
814 Darrell Porter .08 .25
815 Mike Proly .08 .25
816 Tim Raines 2.00 5.00
817 Lenny Randle .08 .25
818 Doug Rau .08 .25
819 Jeff Reardon .75 2.00
820 Ken Reitz .08 .25
821 Steve Renko .08 .25
822 Rick Reuschel .40 1.00
823 Dave Revering .08 .25
824 Dave Roberts .08 .25
825 Leon Roberts .08 .25
826 Joe Rudi .40 1.00
827 Kevin Saucier .08 .25
828 Tony Scott .08 .25
829 Bob Shirley .08 .25
830 Ted Simmons .40 1.00
831 Lary Sorensen .08 .25
832 Jim Spencer .08 .25
833 Harry Spilman .08 .25
834 Fred Stanley .08 .25
835 Rusty Staub .40 1.00
836 Bill Stein .08 .25
837 Joe Strain .08 .25
838 Bruce Sutter .75 2.00
839 Don Sutton .40 1.00
840 Steve Swisher .08 .25
841 Frank Tanana .40 1.00
842 Gene Tenace .40 1.00
843 Jason Thompson .08 .25
844 Dickie Thon .08 .25
845 Bill Travers .08 .25
846 Tom Underwood .08 .25
847 John Urrea .08 .25
848 Mike Vail .08 .25
849 Ellis Valentine .08 .25
850 Fernando Valenzuela 4.00 10.00
851 Pete Vuckovich .08 .25
852 Mark Wagner .08 .25
853 Bob Walk .40 1.00
854 Claudell Washington .08 .25
855 Dave Winfield .75 2.00
856 Geoff Zahn .08 .25
857 Richie Zisk .08 .25
858 Checklist 727-858 .08 .25

1982 Topps

The cards in this 792-card set measure the standard size. Cards were primarily distributed in 15-card wax packs and 51-card rack packs. The 1982 baseball series was the first of the largest sets Topps issued at one printing. The 66-card increase from the previous year's total eliminated the "double print" practice, that had occurred in every regular issue since 1978. Cards 1-6 depict Highlights of the strike-shortened 1981 season, cards 161-168 picture League Leaders, and there are subsets of AL (547-557) and NL (337-347) All-Stars (AS). The abbreviation "SA" in the checklist is given for the 40 "Super Action" cards introduced in this set. The team cards are actually Team Leader (TL) cards picturing the batting average and ERA leader for that team with a checklist back. All 26 of these cards were available from Topps on a perforated sheet through an offer on wax pack wrappers. Notable Rookie Cards include Brett Butler, Chili Davis, Cal Ripken Jr., Lee Smith, and Dave Stewart. Be careful when purchasing blank-back Cal Ripken Jr. Rookie Cards. Those cards are extremely likely to be counterfeit.

COMPLETE SET (792) 40.00 80.00
1 Steve Carlton HL .10 .30
2 Ron Davis HL .05 .15
3 Tim Raines HL .10 .30
4 Pete Rose HL .25 .60
5 Nolan Ryan HL 1.25 3.00
6 Fernando Valenzuela HL .25 .60
7 Scott Sanderson .05 .15
8 Rich Dauer .05 .15
9 Ron Guidry .10 .30
10 Ron Guidry SA .05 .15
11 Gary Alexander .05 .15
12 Moose Haas .05 .15
13 Lamar Johnson .05 .15
14 Steve Howe .05 .15
15 Ellis Valentine .05 .15
16 Steve Comer .05 .15
17 Darrell Evans .10 .30
18 Fernando Arroyo .05 .15
19 Ernie Whitt .05 .15
20 Garry Maddox .05 .15
21 Bob Bonner RC 15.00 40.00
Cal Ripken RC
Jeff Schneider RC
Birthdate for Jeff Scheider is wrong
22 Jim Beattie .05 .15
23 Willie Hernandez .05 .15
24 Dave Frost .05 .15
25 Jerry Remy .05 .15
26 Jorge Orta .05 .15
27 Tom Herr .05 .15
28 John Urrea .05 .15
29 Dwayne Murphy .05 .15
30 Tom Seaver .50 1.25
31 Tom Seaver SA .10 .30
32 Gene Garber .05 .15
33 Jerry Morales .05 .15
34 Joe Sambito .05 .15
35 Willie Aikens .05 .15
36 Al Oliver .25 .60
Doc Medich TL
37 Dan Graham .05 .15
38 Charlie Lea .05 .15
39 Lou Whitaker .10 .30
40 Dave Parker .10 .30
41 Dave Parker SA .05 .15
42 Rick Sofield .05 .15
43 Mike Cubbage .05 .15
44 Britt Burns .05 .15
45 Rick Cerone .05 .15
46 Jerry Augustine .05 .15
47 Jeff Leonard .05 .15
48 Bobby Castillo .05 .15
49 Alvis Woods .05 .15
50 Buddy Bell .10 .30
51 Jay Howell RC .30 .75
Carlos Lezcano
Ty Waller RC
52 Larry Andersen .05 .15
53 Greg Gross .05 .15
54 Ron Hassey .05 .15
55 Rick Burleson .05 .15
56 Mark Littell .05 .15
57 Craig Reynolds .05 .15
58 John D'Acquisto .05 .15
59 Rich Gedman .30 .75
60 Tony Armas .10 .30
61 Tommy Boggs .05 .15
62 Mike Tyson .05 .15
63 Mario Soto .10 .30
64 Lynn Jones .05 .15
65 Terry Kennedy .05 .15
66 Art Howe .75 2.00
Nolan Ryan TL
67 Rich Gale .05 .15
68 Roy Howell .05 .15
69 Al Williams .05 .15
70 Tim Raines .25 .60
71 Roy Lee Jackson .05 .15
72 Rick Auerbach .05 .15
73 Buddy Solomon .05 .15
74 Bob Clark .05 .15
75 Tommy John .10 .30
76 Greg Pryor .05 .15
77 Miguel Dilone .05 .15
78 George Medich .05 .15
79 Bob Bailor .05 .15
80 Jim Palmer .10 .30
81 Jim Palmer SA .05 .15
82 Bob Welch .10 .30
83 Steve Balboni RC .30 .75
Andy McGaffigan RC
Andre Robertson RC
84 Rennie Stennett .05 .15
85 Lynn McGlothen .05 .15
86 Dane Iorg .05 .15
87 Matt Keough .05 .15
88 Biff Pocoroba .05 .15
89 Steve Henderson .05 .15
90 Nolan Ryan 2.50 6.00
91 Carney Lansford .10 .30
92 Brad Havens .05 .15
93 Larry Hisle .05 .15
94 Andy Hassler .05 .15
95 Ozzie Smith 1.00 2.50
96 George Brett .50 1.25
Larry Gura TL
97 Paul Moskau .05 .15
98 Terry Bulling .05 .15
99 Barry Bonnell .05 .15
100 Mike Schmidt 1.25 3.00
101 Mike Schmidt SA .50 1.25
102 Dan Briggs .05 .15
103 Bob Lacey .05 .15
104 Rance Mulliniks .05 .15
105 Kirk Gibson .50 1.25
106 Enrique Romo .05 .15
107 Wayne Krenchicki .05 .15
108 Bob Sykes .05 .15
109 Dave Revering .05 .15
110 Carlton Fisk .25 .60
111 Carlton Fisk SA .10 .30
112 Billy Sample .05 .15
113 Steve McCatty .05 .15
114 Ken Landreaux .05 .15
115 Gaylord Perry .10 .30
116 Jim Wohlford .05 .15
117 Rawly Eastwick .10 .30
118 Terry Francona RC 2.00 5.00
Brad Mills RC
Bryn Smith RC
119 Joe Pittman .05 .15
120 Gary Lucas .05 .15
121 Ed Lynch .05 .15
122 Jamie Easterly UER .05 .15
(Photo actually
Reggie Cleveland)
123 Danny Goodwin .05 .15
124 Reid Nichols .05 .15
125 Danny Ainge .10 .30
126 Claudell Washington .25 .60
Rick Mahler TL
127 Lonnie Smith .05 .15
128 Frank Pastore .05 .15
129 Checklist 1-132 .10 .30
130 Julio Cruz .05 .15
131 Stan Bahnsen .05 .15
132 Lee May .05 .15
133 Pat Underwood .05 .15
134 Dan Ford .05 .15
135 Andy Rincon .05 .15
136 Lenn Sakata .05 .15
137 George Cappuzzello .05 .15
138 Tony Pena .10 .30
139 Jeff Jones .05 .15
140 Ron LeFlore .10 .30
141 Chris Bando .30 .75
Tom Brennan
Von Hayes RC
142 Dave LaRoche .05 .15
143 Mookie Wilson .10 .30
144 Fred Breining .05 .15
145 Bob Horner .10 .30
146 Mike Griffin .05 .15
147 Denny Walling .05 .15
148 Mickey Klutts .05 .15
149 Pat Putnam .05 .15
150 Ted Simmons .10 .30
151 Dave Edwards .05 .15
152 Ramon Aviles .05 .15
153 Roger Erickson .05 .15
154 Dennis Werth .05 .15
155 Otto Velez .05 .15
156 Rickey Henderson .50 1.25
Steve McCatty TL
157 Steve Crawford .05 .15
158 Brian Downing .10 .30
159 Larry Biittner .05 .15
160 Luis Tiant .10 .30
161 Bill Madlock .10 .30
Carney Lansford LL
162 Mike Schmidt .50 1.25
Tony Armas
Dwight Evans
Bobby Grich
Eddie Murray LL
163 Mike Schmidt .50 1.25
Eddie Murray LL
164 Tim Raines .50 1.25
Rickey Henderson LL
165 Tom Seaver .10 .30
Denny Martinez
Steve McCatty
Jack Morris
Pete Vuckovich LL
166 Fernando Valenzuela .10 .30
Len Barker LL
167 Nolan Ryan .75 2.00
Steve McCatty LL
168 Bruce Sutter .10 .30
Rollie Fingers LL
169 Charlie Leibrandt .05 .15
170 Jim Bibby .05 .15
171 Bob Brenly RC .60 1.50
Chili Davis RC
Bob Tufts RC
172 Bill Gullickson .05 .15
173 Jamie Quirk .05 .15
174 Dave Ford .05 .15
175 Jerry Mumphrey .05 .15
176 Dewey Robinson .05 .15
177 John Ellis .05 .15
178 Dyar Miller .05 .15
179 Steve Garvey .10 .30
180 Steve Garvey SA .05 .15
181 Silvio Martinez .05 .15
182 Larry Herndon .05 .15
183 Mike Proly .05 .15
184 Mick Kelleher .05 .15
185 Phil Niekro .10 .30
186 Keith Hernandez .10 .30

Bob Forsch TL
187 Jeff Newman .05 .15
188 Randy Martz .05 .15
189 Glenn Hoffman .05 .15
190 J.R. Richard .10 .30
191 Tim Wallach RC .60 1.50
192 Broderick Perkins .05 .15
193 Darrell Jackson .05 .15
194 Mike Vail .05 .15
195 Paul Molitor .10 .30
196 Willie Upshaw .30 .75
197 Shane Rawley .05 .15
198 Chris Speier .05 .15
199 Don Aase .05 .15
200 George Brett 1.25 3.00
201 George Brett SA .60 1.50
202 Rick Manning .05 .15
203 Jesse Barfield RC .60 1.50
Brian Milner
Boomer Wells RC
204 Gary Roenicke .05 .15
205 Neil Allen .05 .15
206 Tony Bernazard .05 .15
207 Rod Scurry .05 .15
208 Bobby Murcer .10 .30
209 Gary Lavelle .05 .15
210 Keith Hernandez .10 .30
211 Dan Petry .05 .15
212 Mario Mendoza .05 .15
213 Dave Stewart RC 1.00 2.50
214 Brian Asselstine .05 .15
215 Mike Krukow .05 .15
216 Chet Lemon .25 .60
Dennis Lamp TL
217 Bo McLaughlin .05 .15
218 Dave Roberts .05 .15
219 John Curtis .05 .15
220 Manny Trillo .05 .15
221 Jim Slaton .05 .15
222 Butch Wynegar .05 .15
223 Lloyd Moseby .05 .15
224 Bruce Bochte .05 .15
225 Mike Torrez .05 .15
226 Checklist 133-264 .25 .60
227 Ray Burris .05 .15
228 Sam Mejias .05 .15
229 Geoff Zahn .05 .15
230 Willie Wilson .10 .30
231 Mark Davis RC .30 .75
Bob Dernier RC
Ozzie Virgil RC
232 Terry Crowley .05 .15
233 Duane Kuiper .05 .15
234 Ron Hodges .05 .15
235 Mike Easler .05 .15
236 John Martin RC .08 .25
237 Rusty Kuntz .05 .15
238 Kevin Saucier .05 .15
239 Jon Matlack .05 .15
240 Bucky Dent .10 .30
241 Bucky Dent SA .05 .15
242 Milt May .05 .15
243 Bob Owchinko .05 .15
244 Rufino Linares .05 .15
245 Ken Reitz .05 .15
246 Hubie Brooks .25 .60
Mike Scott TL
247 Pedro Guerrero .10 .30
248 Frank LaCorte .05 .15
249 Tim Flannery .05 .15
250 Tug McGraw .10 .30
251 Fred Lynn .10 .30
252 Fred Lynn SA .05 .15
253 Chuck Baker .05 .15
254 Jorge Bell RC .60 1.50
255 Tony Perez .25 .60
256 Tony Perez SA .10 .30
257 Larry Harlow .05 .15
258 Bo Diaz .05 .15
259 Rodney Scott .05 .15
260 Bruce Sutter .25 .60
261 Howard Bailey RC .05 .15
Marty Castillo RC
Dave Rucker RC
(UER Rucker photo
is Roger Weaver)
262 Doug Bair .05 .15
263 Victor Cruz .05 .15
264 Dan Quisenberry .05 .15
265 Al Bumbry .05 .15
266 Rick Leach .05 .15
267 Kurt Bevacqua .05 .15
268 Rickey Keeton .05 .15
269 Jim Essian .05 .15
270 Rusty Staub .10 .30
271 Larry Bradford .05 .15
272 Bump Wills .05 .15
273 Doug Bird .05 .15
274 Bob Ojeda RC .30 .75
275 Bob Watson .05 .15
276 Rod Carew .25 .60
Ken Forsch TL
277 Terry Puhl .05 .15
278 John Littlefield .05 .15
279 Bill Russell .10 .30
280 Ben Oglivie .10 .30
281 John Verhoeven .05 .15
282 Ken Macha .05 .15
283 Brian Allard .05 .15
284 Bobby Grich .10 .30
285 Sparky Lyle .10 .30
286 Bill Fahey .05 .15
287 Alan Bannister .05 .15
288 Garry Templeton .10 .30
289 Bob Stanley .05 .15
290 Ken Singleton .10 .30
291 Vance Law .10 .30
Bob Long
Johnny Ray RC
292 David Palmer .05 .15
293 Rob Picciolo .05 .15
294 Mike LaCoss .05 .15
295 Jason Thompson .05 .15
296 Bob Walk .05 .15
297 Clint Hurdle .05 .15
298 Danny Darwin .05 .15
299 Steve Trout .05 .15
300 Reggie Jackson .25 .60
301 Reggie Jackson SA .10 .30
302 Doug Flynn .05 .15
303 Bill Caudill .05 .15
304 Johnnie LeMaster .05 .15
305 Don Sutton .10 .30
306 Don Sutton SA .05 .15
307 Randy Bass .30 .75
308 Charlie Moore .05 .15
309 Pete Redfern .05 .15
310 Mike Hargrove .05 .15
311 Dusty Baker .10 .30
Burt Hooton TL
312 Lenny Randle .05 .15
313 John Harris .05 .15
314 Buck Martinez .05 .15
315 Burt Hooton .05 .15
316 Steve Braun .05 .15
317 Dick Ruthven .05 .15
318 Mike Heath .05 .15
319 Dave Rozema .05 .15
320 Chris Chambliss .10 .30
321 Chris Chambliss SA .05 .15
322 Garry Hancock .05 .15
323 Bill Lee .10 .30
324 Steve Dillard .05 .15
325 Jose Cruz .10 .30
326 Pete Falcone .05 .15
327 Joe Nolan .05 .15
328 Ed Farmer .05 .15
329 U.L. Washington .05 .15
330 Rick Wise .05 .15
331 Benny Ayala .05 .15
332 Don Robinson .05 .15
333 Frank DiPino RC .05 .15
Marshall Edwards RC
Chuck Porter RC
334 Aurelio Rodriguez .05 .15
335 Jim Sundberg .10 .30
336 Tom Paciorek .25 .60
Glenn Abbott TL
337 Pete Rose AS .25 .60
338 Dave Lopes AS .05 .15
339 Mike Schmidt AS .50 1.25
340 Dave Concepcion AS .05 .15
341 Andre Dawson AS .05 .15
342A George Foster AS w/Auto .10 .30
342B George Foster AS .50 1.25
(W/o autograph)
343 Dave Parker AS .05 .15
344 Gary Carter AS .05 .15
345 F. Valenzuela AS .25 .60
346 Tom Seaver AS ERR .10 .30
('t ed')
346B Tom Seaver AS COR .10 .30
347 Bruce Sutter AS .05 .15
348 Derrel Thomas .05 .15
349 George Frazier .05 .15
350 Thad Bosley .05 .15
351 Scott Brown RC .05 .15
Geoff Combe
Paul Householder
352 Dick Davis .05 .15
353 Jack O'Connor .05 .15
354 Roberto Ramos .05 .15
355 Dwight Evans .25 .60
356 Denny Lewallyn .05 .15
357 Butch Hobson .05 .15
358 Mike Parrott .05 .15
359 Jim Dwyer .05 .15
360 Len Barker .05 .15
361 Rafael Landestoy .05 .15
362 Jim Wright UER .05 .15
(Wrong Jim Wright
pictured)
363 Bob Molinaro .05 .15
364 Doyle Alexander .05 .15
365 Bill Madlock .10 .30
366 Luis Salazar .25 .60
Juan Eichelberger TL
367 Jim Kaat .10 .30
368 Alex Trevino .05 .15
369 Champ Summers .05 .15
370 Mike Norris .05 .15
371 Jerry Don Gleaton .05 .15
372 Luis Gomez .05 .15
373 Gene Nelson .05 .15
374 Tim Blackwell .05 .15
375 Dusty Baker .10 .30
376 Chris Welsh .05 .15
377 Kiko Garcia .05 .15
378 Mike Caldwell .05 .15
379 Rob Wilfong .05 .15
380 Dave Stieb .10 .30
381 Bruce Hurst .05 .15
Dave Schmidt RC
Julio Valdez RC
382 Joe Simpson .05 .15
383A Pascual Perez ERR 15.00 40.00
(No position
on front)
383B Pascual Perez COR .10 .30
384 Keith Moreland .05 .15
385 Ken Forsch .05 .15
386 Jerry White .05 .15
387 Tom Veryzer .05 .15
388 Joe Rudi .10 .30
389 George Vukovich .05 .15
390 Eddie Murray .50 1.25
391 Dave Tobik .05 .15
392 Rick Bosetti .05 .15
393 Al Hrabosky .05 .15
394 Checklist 265-396 .25 .60
395 Omar Moreno .05 .15
396 John Castino .25 .60
Fernando Arroyo TL
397 Ken Brett .05 .15
398 Mike Squires .05 .15
399 Pat Zachry .05 .15
400 Johnny Bench .50 1.25
401 Johnny Bench SA .25 .60
402 Bill Stein .05 .15
403 Jim Tracy .10 .30
404 Dickie Thon .05 .15
405 Rick Reuschel .10 .30
406 Al Holland .05 .15
407 Danny Boone .05 .15
408 Ed Romero .05 .15
409 Don Cooper .05 .15
410 Ron Cey .10 .30
411 Ron Cey SA .05 .15
412 Luis Leal .05 .15
413 Dan Meyer .05 .15
414 Elias Sosa .05 .15
415 Don Baylor .10 .30
416 Marty Bystrom .05 .15
417 Pat Kelly .05 .15
418 John Butcher .05 .15
Bobby Johnson RC
Dave Schmidt RC
419 Steve Stone .05 .15
420 George Hendrick .10 .30
421 Mark Clear .05 .15
422 Cliff Johnson .05 .15
423 Stan Papi .05 .15
424 Bruce Benedict .05 .15
425 John Candelaria .05 .15
426 Eddie Murray .25 .60
Sammy Stewart
427 Ron Oester .05 .15
428 LaMarr Hoyt .05 .15
429 John Wathan .05 .15
430 Vida Blue .10 .30
431 Vida Blue SA .05 .15
432 Mike Scott .10 .30
433 Alan Ashby .05 .15
434 Joe Lefebvre .05 .15
435 Robin Yount .75 2.00
436 Joe Strain .05 .15
437 Juan Berenguer .05 .15
438 Pete Mackanin .05 .15
439 Dave Righetti RC 1.00 2.50
440 Jeff Burroughs .05 .15
441 Danny Heep .05 .15
Billy Smith RC
Bobby Sprowl
442 Bruce Kison .05 .15
443 Mark Wagner .05 .15
444 Terry Forster .10 .30
445 Larry Parrish .05 .15
446 Wayne Garland .05 .15
447 Darrell Porter .05 .15
448 Darrell Porter SA .05 .15
449 Luis Aguayo .05 .15
450 Jack Morris .10 .30
451 Ed Miller .05 .15
452 Lee Smith RC 1.25 3.00
453 Art Howe .05 .15
454 Rick Langford .05 .15
455 Tom Burgmeier .05 .15
456 Bill Buckner .10 .30
Randy Martz TL
457 Tim Stoddard .05 .15
458 Willie Montanez .05 .15
459 Bruce Berenyi .05 .15
460 Jack Clark .10 .30
461 Rich Dotson .05 .15
462 Dave Chalk .05 .15
463 Jim Kern .05 .15
464 Juan Bonilla RC .08 .25
465 Lee Mazzilli .10 .30
466 Randy Lerch .05 .15
467 Mickey Hatcher .05 .15
468 Floyd Bannister .05 .15
469 Ed Ott .05 .15
470 John Mayberry .05 .15
471 Atlee Hammaker RC .05 .15
Mike Jones
Darryl Motley RC
472 Oscar Gamble .05 .15
473 Mike Stanton .05 .15
474 Ken Oberkfell .05 .15
475 Alan Trammell .10 .30
476 Brian Kingman .05 .15
477 Steve Yeager .10 .30
478 Ray Searage .05 .15
479 Rowland Office .05 .15
480 Steve Carlton .25 .60
481 Steve Carlton SA .10 .30
482 Glenn Hubbard .05 .15
483 Gary Woods .05 .15
484 Ivan DeJesus .05 .15
485 Kent Tekulve .05 .15
486 Jerry Mumphrey .10 .30
Tommy John TL
487 Bob McClure .05 .15
488 Ron Jackson .05 .15
489 Rick Dempsey .05 .15
490 Dennis Eckersley .25 .60
491 Checklist 397-528 .25 .60
492 Joe Price .05 .15
493 Chet Lemon .10 .30
494 Hubie Brooks .05 .15
495 Dennis Leonard .05 .15
496 Johnny Grubb .05 .15
497 Jim Anderson .05 .15
498 Dave Bergman .05 .15
499 Paul Mirabella .05 .15
500 Rod Carew .25 .60
501 Rod Carew SA .10 .30
502 Steve Bedrosian RC UER .60 1.50
Photo actually Larry Owen)
Brett Butler RC
Larry Owen
503 Julio Gonzalez .05 .15
504 Rick Peters .05 .15
505 Graig Nettles .10 .30
506 Graig Nettles SA .05 .15
507 Terry Harper .05 .15
508 Jody Davis .05 .15
509 Harry Spilman .05 .15
510 Fernando Valenzuela .50 1.25
511 Ruppert Jones .05 .15
512 Jerry Dybzinski .05 .15
513 Rick Rhoden .05 .15
514 Joe Ferguson .05 .15
515 Larry Bowa .10 .30
516 Larry Bowa SA .05 .15
517 Mark Brouhard .05 .15
518 Garth Iorg .05 .15
519 Glenn Adams .05 .15
520 Mike Flanagan .05 .15
521 Bill Almon .05 .15
522 Chuck Rainey .05 .15
523 Gary Gray .05 .15
524 Tom Hausman .05 .15
525 Ray Knight .10 .30
526 Warren Cromartie .25 .60
Bill Gullickson TL
527 John Henry Johnson .05 .15
528 Matt Alexander .05 .15
529 Allen Ripley .05 .15
530 Dickie Noles .05 .15
531 Rich Bordi RC .05 .15
Mark Budaska RC
Kelvin Moore RC
532 Toby Harrah .10 .30
533 Joaquin Andujar .10 .30
534 Dave McKay .05 .15
535 Lance Parrish .10 .30
536 Rafael Ramirez .05 .15
537 Doug Capilla .05 .15
538 Lou Piniella .10 .30
539 Vern Ruhle .05 .15
540 Andre Dawson .10 .30
541 Barry Evans .05 .15
542 Ned Yost .05 .15
543 Bill Robinson .05 .15
544 Larry Christenson .05 .15
545 Reggie Smith .10 .30
546 Reggie Smith SA .05 .15
547 Rod Carew AS .10 .30
548 Willie Randolph AS .05 .15
549 George Brett AS .60 1.50
550 Bucky Dent AS .05 .15
551 Reggie Jackson AS .10 .30
552 Ken Singleton AS .05 .15
553 Dave Winfield AS .05 .15
554 Carlton Fisk AS .10 .30
555 Scott McGregor AS .05 .15
556 Jack Morris AS .05 .15
557 Rich Gossage AS .05 .15
558 John Tudor .10 .30
559 Mike Hargrove .10 .30
Bert Blyleven TL
560 Doug Corbett .05 .15
561 Glenn Brummer RC .05 .15
Luis DeLeon RC
Gene Roof RC
562 Mike O'Berry .05 .15
563 Ross Baumgarten .05 .15
564 Doug DeCinces .05 .15
565 Jackson Todd .05 .15
566 Mike Jorgensen .05 .15
567 Bob Babcock .05 .15
568 Joe Pettini .05 .15
569 Willie Randolph .10 .30
570 Willie Randolph SA .05 .15
571 Glenn Abbott .05 .15
572 Juan Beniquez .05 .15
573 Rick Waits .05 .15
574 Mike Ramsey .05 .15
575 Al Cowens .05 .15
576 Milt May .25 .60
Vida Blue TL
577 Rick Monday .10 .30
578 Shooty Babitt .05 .15
579 Rick Mahler .05 .15
580 Bobby Bonds .10 .30
581 Ron Reed .05 .15
582 Luis Pujols .05 .15
583 Tippy Martinez .05 .15
584 Hosken Powell .05 .15
585 Rollie Fingers .10 .30
586 Rollie Fingers SA .05 .15
587 Tim Lollar .05 .15
588 Dale Berra .05 .15
589 Dave Stapleton .05 .15
590 Al Oliver .10 .30
591 Al Oliver SA .05 .15
592 Craig Swan .05 .15
593 Billy Smith .05 .15
594 Renie Martin .05 .15
595 Dave Collins .05 .15
596 Damaso Garcia .05 .15
597 Wayne Nordhagen .05 .15
598 Bob Galasso .05 .15
599 Jay Loviglio .05 .15
Reggie Patterson RC
Leo Sutherland
600 Dave Winfield .10 .30
601 Sid Monge .05 .15
602 Freddie Patek .05 .15
603 Rich Hebner .05 .15
604 Orlando Sanchez .05 .15
605 Steve Rogers .10 .30
606 John Mayberry .10 .30
Dave Stieb TL
607 Leon Durham .05 .15
608 Jerry Royster .05 .15
609 Rick Sutcliffe .10 .30
610 Rickey Henderson 1.50 4.00
611 Joe Niekro .05 .15
612 Gary Ward .05 .15
613 Jim Gantner .05 .15
614 Juan Eichelberger .05 .15
615 Bob Boone .10 .30
616 Bob Boone SA .05 .15
617 Scott McGregor .05 .15
618 Tim Foli .05 .15
619 Bill Campbell .05 .15
620 Ken Griffey .10 .30
621 Ken Griffey SA .05 .15
622 Dennis Lamp .05 .15
623 Ron Gardenhire RC .30 .75
Terry Leach RC
Tim Leary RC
624 Fergie Jenkins .10 .30
625 Hal McRae .10 .30
626 Randy Jones .05 .15
627 Enos Cabell .05 .15
628 Bill Travers .05 .15
629 John Wockenfuss .05 .15
630 Joe Charboneau .10 .30
631 Gene Tenace .10 .30
632 Bryan Clark RC .08 .25
633 Mitchell Page .05 .15
634 Checklist 529-660 .25 .60
635 Ron Davis .05 .15
636 Pete Rose .50 1.25
Steve Carlton TL
637 Rick Camp .05 .15
638 John Milner .05 .15
639 Ken Kravec .05 .15
640 Cesar Cedeno .10 .30
641 Steve Mura .05 .15
642 Mike Scioscia .10 .30
643 Pete Vuckovich .05 .15
644 John Castino .05 .15
645 Frank White .10 .30
646 Frank White SA .05 .15
647 Warren Brusstar .05 .15
648 Jose Morales .05 .15
649 Ken Clay .05 .15
650 Carl Yastrzemski .75 2.00
651 Carl Yastrzemski SA .50 1.25
652 Steve Nicosia .05 .15
653 Tom Brunansky RC .60 1.50
Luis Sanchez RC
Daryl Sconiers RC
654 Jim Morrison .05 .15
655 Joel Youngblood .05 .15
656 Eddie Whitson .05 .15
657 Tom Poquette .05 .15
658 Tito Landrum .05 .15
659 Fred Martinez .05 .15
660 Dave Concepcion .10 .30
661 Dave Concepcion SA .05 .15
662 Luis Salazar .05 .15
663 Hector Cruz .05 .15
664 Dan Spillner .05 .15
665 Jim Clancy .05 .15
666 Steve Kemp .25 .60
Dan Petry TL
667 Jeff Reardon .10 .30
668 Dale Murphy .25 .60
669 Larry Milbourne .05 .15
670 Steve Kemp .05 .15
671 Mike Davis .05 .15
672 Bob Knepper .05 .15
673 Keith Drumwright .05 .15
674 Dave Goltz .05 .15
675 Cecil Cooper .10 .30
676 Sal Butera .05 .15
677 Alfredo Griffin .05 .15
678 Tom Paciorek .05 .15
679 Sammy Stewart .05 .15
680 Gary Matthews .10 .30
681 Mike Marshall RC .60 1.50
Ron Roenicke RC
Steve Sax RC
682 Jesse Jefferson .05 .15
683 Phil Garner .10 .30
684 Harold Baines .10 .30
685 Bert Blyleven .10 .30
686 Gary Allenson .05 .15
687 Greg Minton .05 .15
688 Leon Roberts .05 .15
689 Larry Sorensen .05 .15
690 Dave Kingman .10 .30
691 Dan Schatzeder .05 .15
692 Wayne Gross .05 .15
693 Cesar Geronimo .05 .15
694 Dave Wehrmeister .05 .15
695 Warren Cromartie .05 .15
696 Bill Madlock .25 .60
Eddie Solomon TL
697 John Montefusco .05 .15
698 Tony Scott .05 .15
699 Dick Tidrow .05 .15
700 George Foster .10 .30
701 George Foster SA .05 .15
702 Steve Renko .05 .15
703 Cecil Cooper .25 .60
Pete Vuckovich TL
704 Mickey Rivers .05 .15
705 Mickey Rivers SA .05 .15
706 Barry Foote .05 .15
707 Mark Bomback .05 .15
708 Gene Richards .05 .15
709 Don Money .05 .15
710 Jerry Reuss .05 .15
711 Dave Edler .30 .75
Dave Henderson RC
Reggie Walton RC
712 Dennis Martinez .10 .30
713 Del Unser .05 .15
714 Jerry Koosman .10 .30
715 Willie Stargell .25 .60
716 Willie Stargell SA .10 .30
717 Rick Miller .05 .15
718 Charlie Hough .10 .30
719 Jerry Narron .05 .15
720 Greg Luzinski .10 .30
721 Greg Luzinski SA .05 .15
722 Jerry Martin .05 .15
723 Junior Kennedy .05 .15
724 Dave Rosello .05 .15
725 Amos Otis .10 .30
726 Amos Otis SA .05 .15
727 Sixto Lezcano .05 .15
728 Aurelio Lopez .05 .15
729 Jim Spencer .05 .15
730 Gary Carter .10 .30
731 Mike Armstrong .05 .15
Doug Gwosdz RC
Fred Kuhaulua
732 Mike Lum .05 .15
733 Larry McWilliams .05 .15
734 Mike Ivie .05 .15
735 Rudy May .05 .15
736 Jerry Turner .05 .15
737 Reggie Cleveland .05 .15
738 Dave Engle .05 .15
739 Joey McLaughlin .05 .15
740 Dave Lopes .10 .30
741 Dave Lopes SA .05 .15
742 Dick Drago .05 .15
743 John Stearns .05 .15
744 Mike Witt .30 .75
745 Bake McBride .10 .30
746 Andre Thornton .05 .15
747 John Lowenstein .05 .15
748 Marc Hill .05 .15
749 Bob Shirley .05 .15
750 Jim Rice .10 .30
751 Rick Honeycutt .05 .15
752 Lee Lacy .05 .15
753 Tom Brookens .05 .15
754 Joe Morgan .10 .30
755 Joe Morgan SA .05 .15
756 Ken Griffey .10 .30
Tom Seaver TL
757 Tom Underwood .05 .15
758 Claudell Washington .05 .15
759 Paul Splittorff .05 .15
760 Bill Buckner .10 .30
761 Dave Smith .05 .15
762 Mike Phillips .05 .15
763 Tom Hume .05 .15
764 Steve Swisher .05 .15
765 Gorman Thomas .10 .30
766 Lenny Faedo RC .60 1.50
Kent Hrbek RC
Tim Laudner RC
767 Roy Smalley .05 .15
768 Jerry Garvin .05 .15
769 Richie Zisk .05 .15
770 Rich Gossage .10 .30
771 Rich Gossage SA .05 .15
772 Bert Campaneris .10 .30
773 John Denny .05 .15
774 Jay Johnstone .05 .15
775 Bob Forsch .05 .15
776 Mark Belanger .05 .15
777 Tom Griffin .05 .15
778 Kevin Hickey RC .08 .25
779 Grant Jackson .05 .15
780 Pete Rose 1.50 4.00
781 Pete Rose SA .50 1.25
782 Frank Taveras .05 .15
783 Greg Harris RC .08 .25
784 Milt Wilcox .05 .15
785 Dan Driessen .05 .15
786 Carney Lansford .25 .60
Mike Torrez TL
787 Fred Stanley .05 .15
788 Woodie Fryman .05 .15
789 Checklist 661-792 .25 .60
790 Larry Gura .05 .15
791 Bobby Brown .05 .15
792 Frank Tanana .10 .30

1982 Topps Traded

The cards in this 132-card set measure the standard size. These sets were shipped to hobby dealers in 100-ct cases. The 1982 Topps Traded or extended series is distinguished by a "T" printed after the number (located on the reverse). This was the first time Topps began a tradition of newly numbering (and alphabetizing) their traded series from 1T to 132T. All 131 player photos used in the set are completely new. Of this total, 112 individuals are seen in the uniform of their new team, 11 youngsters have been elevated to single card status from multi-player "Future Stars" cards, and eight more are entirely new to the 1982 Topps lineup. The backs are almost completely red in color with black print. There are no key Rookie Cards in this set. Although the Cal Ripken card is this set's most valuable card, it is not his Rookie Card since he had already been included in the 1982 regular set, albeit on a multi-player card.

COMP.FACT.SET (132) 100.00 175.00
1T Doyle Alexander .20 .50
2T Jesse Barfield 1.25 3.00
3T Ross Baumgarten .20 .50
4T Steve Bedrosian .60 1.50
5T Mark Belanger .20 .50
6T Kurt Bevacqua .20 .50
7T Tim Blackwell .20 .50
8T Vida Blue .40 1.00
9T Bob Boone .40 1.00
10T Larry Bowa .40 1.00
11T Dan Briggs .20 .50
12T Bobby Brown .20 .50
13T Tom Brunansky 1.25 3.00
14T Jeff Burroughs .20 .50
15T Enos Cabell .20 .50
16T Bill Campbell .20 .50
17T Bobby Castillo .20 .50
18T Bill Caudill .20 .50
19T Cesar Cedeno .40 1.00
20T Dave Collins .20 .50
21T Doug Corbett .20 .50
22T Al Cowens .20 .50
23T Chili Davis 1.25 3.00
24T Dick Davis .20 .50
25T Ron Davis .20 .50
26T Doug DeCinces .20 .50
27T Ivan DeJesus .20 .50
28T Bob Dernier .20 .50
29T Bo Diaz .20 .50
30T Roger Erickson .20 .50
31T Jim Essian .20 .50
32T Ed Farmer .20 .50
33T Doug Flynn .20 .50
34T Tim Foli .20 .50
35T Dan Ford .20 .50
36T George Foster .40 1.00
37T Dave Frost .20 .50
38T Rich Gale .20 .50
39T Ron Gardenhire .60 1.50
40T Ken Griffey .40 1.00
41T Greg Harris .20 .50
42T Von Hayes .60 1.50
43T Larry Herndon .20 .50
44T Kent Hrbek 1.25 3.00
45T Mike Ivie .20 .50
46T Grant Jackson .20 .50
47T Reggie Jackson .75 2.00
48T Ron Jackson .20 .50
49T Fergie Jenkins .40 1.00
50T Lamar Johnson .20 .50
51T Randy Johnson .20 .50
52T Jay Johnstone .20 .50
53T Mick Kelleher .20 .50
54T Steve Kemp .20 .50
55T Junior Kennedy .20 .50
56T Jim Kern .20 .50
57T Ray Knight .40 1.00
58T Wayne Krenchicki .20 .50
59T Mike Krukow .20 .50
60T Duane Kuiper .20 .50
61T Mike LaCoss .20 .50
62T Chet Lemon .40 1.00
63T Sixto Lezcano .20 .50
64T Dave Lopes .40 1.00
65T Jerry Martin .20 .50
66T Renie Martin .20 .50
67T John Mayberry .20 .50
68T Lee Mazzilli .40 1.00
69T Bake McBride .40 1.00
70T Dan Meyer .20 .50
71T Larry Milbourne .20 .50

72T Eddie Milner .20 .50
73T Sid Monge .20 .50
74T John Montefusco .20 .50
75T Jose Morales .20 .50
76T Keith Moreland .20 .50
77T Jim Morrison .20 .50
78T Rance Mulliniks .20 .50
79T Steve Mura .20 .50
80T Gene Nelson .20 .50
81T Joe Nolan .20 .50
82T Dickie Noles .20 .50
83T Al Oliver .40 1.00
84T Jorge Orta .20 .50
85T Tom Paciorek .20 .50
86T Larry Parrish .20 .50
87T Jack Perconte .20 .50
88T Gaylord Perry .40 1.00
89T Rob Picciolo .20 .50
90T Joe Pittman .20 .50
91T Hosken Powell .20 .50
92T Mike Proly .20 .50
93T Greg Pryor .20 .50
94T Charlie Puleo .20 .50
95T Shane Rawley .20 .50
96T Johnny Ray .60 1.50
97T Dave Revering .20 .50
98T Cal Ripken 90.00 150.00
99T Allen Ripley .20 .50
100T Bill Robinson .20 .50
101T Aurelio Rodriguez .20 .50
102T Joe Rudi .40 1.00
103T Steve Sax 1.25 3.00
104T Dan Schatzeder .20 .50
105T Bob Shirley .20 .50
106T Eric Show XRC .60 1.50
107T Roy Smalley .20 .50
108T Lonnie Smith .20 .50
109T Ozzie Smith 6.00 15.00
110T Reggie Smith .40 1.00
111T Lary Sorensen .20 .50
112T Elias Sosa .20 .50
113T Mike Stanton .20 .50
114T Steve Stroughter .20 .50
115T Champ Summers .20 .50
116T Rick Sutcliffe .40 1.00
117T Frank Tanana .40 1.00
118T Frank Taveras .20 .50
119T Garry Templeton .40 1.00
120T Alex Trevino .20 .50
121T Jerry Turner .20 .50
122T Ed VandeBerg .20 .50
123T Tom Veryzer .20 .50
124T Ron Washington .20 .50
125T Bob Watson .20 .50
126T Dennis Werth .20 .50
127T Eddie Whitson .20 .50
128T Rob Wilfong .20 .50
129T Bump Wills .20 .50
130T Gary Woods .20 .50
131T Butch Wynegar .20 .50
132T Checklist: 1-132 .20 .50

1983 Topps

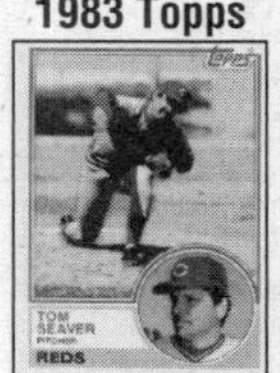

The cards in this 792-card set measure the standard size. Cards were primarily issued in 15-card wax packs and 51-card rack packs. The wax packs had 15 cards in each pack with an 30 cent SRP and were packed 36 packs to a box and 20 boxes to a case. Each player card front features a large action shot with a small cameo portrait at bottom right. There are special series for AL and NL All Stars (386-407), League Leaders (701-708), and Record Breakers (1-6). In addition, there are 34 "Super Veteran" (SV) cards and six numbered checklist cards. The Super Veteran cards are oriented horizontally and show two pictures of the featured player, a recent picture and a picture showing the player as a rookie. The team cards are actually Team Leader (TL) cards picturing the batting and pitching leader for that team with a checklist back. Notable Rookie Cards include Wade Boggs, Tony Gwynn and Ryne Sandberg. In each wax pack a game card was included which included prizes all the way up to a trip and tickets to the World Series. Card prizes possible from these cards included the 1983 Topps League Leaders sheet as well as with enough run accumulation, ordering of a part of the 1983 Topps Mail-Away glossy set. The factory sets were available in JC Penney's Christmas Catalog for $15.99.

COMPLETE SET (792) 40.00 80.00
1 Tony Armas RB .10 .30
2 Rickey Henderson RB .50 1.25
3 Greg Minton RB .05 .15
4 Lance Parrish RB .05 .15
5 Manny Trillo RB .05 .15
6 John Wathan RB .05 .15
7 Gene Richards .05 .15
8 Steve Balboni .05 .15
9 Joey McLaughlin .05 .15
10 Gorman Thomas .10 .30
11 Billy Gardner MG .05 .15
12 Paul Mirabella .05 .15
13 Larry Herndon .05 .15
14 Frank LaCorte .05 .15
15 Ron Cey .10 .30
16 George Vukovich .05 .15
17 Kent Tekulve .05 .15
18 Kent Tekulve SV .05 .15
19 Oscar Gamble .05 .15
20 Carlton Fisk .25 .60
21 Eddie Murray .25 .60
Jim Palmer TL
22 Randy Martz .05 .15
23 Mike Heath .05 .15
24 Steve Mura .05 .15
25 Hal McRae .10 .30
26 Jerry Royster .05 .15
27 Doug Corbett .05 .15
28 Bruce Bochte .05 .15
29 Randy Jones .05 .15
30 Jim Rice .10 .30
31 Bill Gullickson .05 .15
32 Dave Bergman .05 .15
33 Jack O'Connor .05 .15
34 Paul Householder .05 .15
35 Rollie Fingers .10 .30
36 Rollie Fingers SV .05 .15
37 Darrell Johnson MG .05 .15
38 Tim Flannery .05 .15
39 Terry Puhl .05 .15
40 Fernando Valenzuela .10 .30
41 Jerry Turner .05 .15
42 Dale Murray .05 .15
43 Bob Dernier .05 .15
44 Don Robinson .05 .15
45 John Mayberry .05 .15
46 Richard Dotson .05 .15
47 Dave McKay .05 .15
48 Lary Sorensen .05 .15
49 Willie McGee RC 1.00 2.50
50 Bob Horner UER .10 .30
('82 RBI total 7)
51 Leon Durham .05 .15
Fergie Jenkins TL
52 Onix Concepcion .05 .15
53 Mike Witt .05 .15
54 Jim Maler .05 .15
55 Mookie Wilson .10 .30
56 Chuck Rainey .05 .15
57 Tim Blackwell .05 .15
58 Al Holland .05 .15
59 Benny Ayala .05 .15
60 Johnny Bench .50 1.25
61 Johnny Bench SV .25 .60
62 Bob McClure .05 .15
63 Rick Monday .10 .30
64 Bill Stein .05 .15
65 Jack Morris .10 .30
66 Bob Lillis MG .05 .15
67 Sal Butera .05 .15
68 Eric Show RC .30 .75
69 Lee Lacy .05 .15
70 Steve Carlton .25 .60
71 Steve Carlton SV .10 .30
72 Tom Paciorek .05 .15
73 Allen Ripley .05 .15
74 Julio Gonzalez .05 .15
75 Amos Otis .10 .30
76 Rick Mahler .05 .15
77 Hosken Powell .05 .15
78 Bill Caudill .05 .15
79 Mick Kelleher .05 .15
80 George Foster .10 .30
81 Jerry Mumphrey .10 .30
Dave Righetti TL
82 Bruce Hurst .05 .15
83 Ryne Sandberg RC 8.00 20.00
84 Milt May .05 .15
85 Ken Singleton .10 .30
86 Tom Hume .05 .15
87 Joe Rudi .10 .30
88 Jim Gantner .05 .15
89 Leon Roberts .05 .15
90 Jerry Reuss .05 .15
91 Larry Milbourne .05 .15
92 Mike LaCoss .05 .15
93 John Castino .05 .15
94 Dave Edwards .05 .15
95 Alan Trammell .10 .30
96 Dick Howser MG .05 .15
97 Ross Baumgarten .05 .15
98 Vance Law .05 .15
99 Dickie Noles .05 .15
100 Pete Rose 1.50 4.00
101 Pete Rose SV .50 1.25
102 Dave Beard .05 .15
103 Darrell Porter .05 .15
104 Bob Walk .05 .15
105 Don Baylor .10 .30
106 Gene Nelson .05 .15
107 Mike Jorgensen .05 .15
108 Glenn Hoffman .05 .15
109 Luis Leal .05 .15
110 Ken Griffey .10 .30
111 Al Oliver .10 .30
Steve Rogers TL
112 Bob Shirley .05 .15
113 Ron Roenicke .05 .15
114 Jim Slaton .05 .15
115 Chili Davis .10 .30
116 Dave Schmidt .05 .15
117 Alan Knicely .05 .15
118 Chris Welsh .05 .15
119 Tom Brookens .05 .15
120 Len Barker .05 .15
121 Mickey Hatcher .05 .15
122 Jimmy Smith .05 .15
123 George Frazier .05 .15
124 Marc Hill .05 .15
125 Leon Durham .05 .15
126 Joe Torre MG .10 .30
127 Preston Hanna .05 .15
128 Mike Ramsey .05 .15
129 Checklist: 1-132 .05 .15
130 Dave Stieb .10 .30
131 Ed Ott .05 .15
132 Todd Cruz .05 .15
133 Jim Barr .05 .15
134 Hubie Brooks .05 .15
135 Dwight Evans .25 .60
136 Willie Aikens .05 .15
137 Woodie Fryman .05 .15
138 Rick Dempsey .05 .15
139 Bruce Berenyi .05 .15
140 Willie Randolph .10 .30
141 Toby Harrah .10 .30
Rick Sutcliffe TL
142 Mike Caldwell .05 .15
143 Joe Pettini .05 .15
144 Mark Wagner .05 .15
145 Don Sutton .10 .30
146 Don Sutton SV .05 .15
147 Rick Leach .05 .15
148 Dave Roberts .05 .15
149 Johnny Ray .05 .15
150 Bruce Sutter .25 .60
151 Bruce Sutter SV .10 .30
152 Jay Johnstone .05 .15
153 Jerry Koosman .10 .30
154 Johnnie LeMaster .05 .15
155 Dan Quisenberry .05 .15
156 Billy Martin MG .25 .60
157 Steve Bedrosian .05 .15
158 Rob Wilfong .05 .15
159 Mike Stanton .05 .15
160 Dave Kingman .10 .30
161 Dave Kingman SV .05 .15
162 Mark Clear .05 .15
163 Cal Ripken 4.00 10.00
164 David Palmer .05 .15
165 Dan Driessen .05 .15
166 John Pacella .05 .15
167 Mark Brouhard .05 .15
168 Juan Eichelberger .05 .15
169 Doug Flynn .05 .15
170 Steve Howe .05 .15
171 Joe Morgan .10 .30
Bill Laskey TL
172 Vern Ruhle .05 .15
173 Jim Morrison .05 .15
174 Jerry Ujdur .05 .15
175 Bo Diaz .05 .15
176 Dave Righetti .10 .30
177 Harold Baines .10 .30
178 Luis Tiant .10 .30
179 Luis Tiant SV .05 .15
180 Rickey Henderson 1.00 2.50
181 Terry Felton .05 .15
182 Mike Fischlin .05 .15
183 Ed VandeBerg .05 .15
184 Bob Clark .05 .15
185 Tim Lollar .05 .15
186 Whitey Herzog MG .10 .30
187 Terry Leach .05 .15
188 Rick Miller .05 .15
189 Dan Schatzeder .05 .15
190 Cecil Cooper .10 .30
191 Joe Price .05 .15
192 Floyd Rayford .05 .15
193 Harry Spilman .05 .15
194 Cesar Geronimo .05 .15
195 Bob Stoddard .05 .15
196 Bill Fahey .05 .15
197 Jim Eisenreich RC .30 .75
198 Kiko Garcia .05 .15
199 Marty Bystrom .05 .15
200 Rod Carew .25 .60
201 Rod Carew SV .10 .30
202 Damaso Garcia .10 .30
Dave Stieb TL
203 Mike Morgan .05 .15
204 Junior Kennedy .05 .15
205 Dave Parker .10 .30
206 Ken Oberkfell .05 .15
207 Rick Camp .05 .15
208 Dan Meyer .05 .15
209 Mike Moore RC .30 .75
210 Jack Clark .10 .30
211 John Denny .05 .15
212 John Stearns .05 .15
213 Tom Burgmeier .05 .15
214 Jerry White .05 .15
215 Mario Soto .10 .30
216 Tony LaRussa MG .10 .30
217 Tim Stoddard .05 .15
218 Roy Howell .05 .15
219 Mike Armstrong .05 .15
220 Dusty Baker .10 .30
221 Joe Niekro .05 .15
222 Damaso Garcia .05 .15
223 John Montefusco .05 .15
224 Mickey Rivers .05 .15
225 Enos Cabell .05 .15
226 Enrique Romo .05 .15
227 Chris Bando .05 .15
228 Joaquin Andujar .10 .30
229 Bo Diaz .05 .15
Steve Carlton TL
230 Fergie Jenkins .10 .30
231 Fergie Jenkins SV .05 .15
232 Tom Brunansky .10 .30
233 Wayne Gross .05 .15
234 Larry Andersen .05 .15
235 Claudell Washington .05 .15
236 Steve Renko .05 .15
237 Dan Norman .05 .15
238 Bud Black RC .30 .75
239 Dave Stapleton .05 .15
240 Rich Gossage .10 .30
241 Rich Gossage SV .05 .15
242 Joe Nolan .05 .15
243 Duane Walker .05 .15
244 Dwight Bernard .05 .15
245 Steve Sax .05 .15
246 G.Bamberger MG .05 .15
247 Dave Smith .05 .15
248 Bake McBride .10 .30
249 Checklist: 133-264 .10 .30
250 Bill Buckner .10 .30
251 Alan Wiggins .05 .15
252 Luis Aguayo .05 .15
253 Larry McWilliams .05 .15
254 Rick Cerone .05 .15
255 Gene Garber .05 .15
256 Gene Garber SV .05 .15
257 Jesse Barfield .10 .30
258 Manny Castillo .05 .15
259 Jeff Jones .05 .15
260 Steve Kemp .05 .15
261 Larry Herndon .10 .30
Dan Petry TL
262 Ron Jackson .05 .15
263 Renie Martin .05 .15
264 Jamie Quirk .05 .15
265 Joel Youngblood .05 .15
266 Paul Boris .05 .15
267 Terry Francona .05 .15
268 Storm Davis RC .30 .75
269 Ron Oester .05 .15
270 Dennis Eckersley .25 .60
271 Ed Romero .05 .15
272 Frank Tanana .10 .30
273 Mark Belanger .05 .15
274 Terry Kennedy .05 .15
275 Ray Knight .10 .30
276 Gene Mauch MG .05 .15
277 Rance Mulliniks .05 .15
278 Kevin Hickey .05 .15
279 Greg Gross .05 .15
280 Bert Blyleven .10 .30
281 Andre Robertson .05 .15
282 Reggie Smith .50 1.25
(Ryne Sandberg
ducking back)
283 Reggie Smith SV .05 .15
284 Jeff Lahti .05 .15
285 Lance Parrish .10 .30
286 Rick Langford .05 .15
287 Bobby Brown .05 .15
288 Joe Cowley .05 .15
289 Jerry Dybzinski .05 .15
290 Jeff Reardon .10 .30
291 Bill Madlock .10 .30
John Candelaria TL
292 Craig Swan .05 .15
293 Glenn Gulliver .05 .15
294 Dave Engle .05 .15
295 Jerry Remy .05 .15
296 Greg Harris .05 .15
297 Ned Yost .05 .15
298 Floyd Chiffer .05 .15
299 George Wright RC .30 .75
300 Mike Schmidt 1.25 3.00
301 Mike Schmidt SV .50 1.25
302 Ernie Whitt .05 .15
303 Miguel Dilone .05 .15
304 Dave Rucker .05 .15
305 Larry Bowa .10 .30
306 Tom Lasorda MG .25 .60
307 Lou Piniella .10 .30
308 Jesus Vega .05 .15
309 Jeff Leonard .05 .15
310 Greg Luzinski .10 .30
311 Glenn Brummer .05 .15
312 Brian Kingman .05 .15
313 Gary Gray .05 .15
314 Ken Dayley .05 .15
315 Rick Burleson .05 .15
316 Paul Splittorff .05 .15
317 Gary Rajsich .05 .15
318 John Tudor .10 .30
319 Lenn Sakata .05 .15
320 Steve Rogers .10 .30
321 Robin Yount .50 1.25
Pete Vuckovich TL
322 Dave Van Gorder .05 .15
323 Luis DeLeon .05 .15
324 Mike Marshall .10 .30
325 Von Hayes .05 .15
326 Garth Iorg .05 .15
327 Bobby Castillo .05 .15
328 Craig Reynolds .05 .15
329 Randy Niemann .05 .15
330 Buddy Bell .10 .30
331 Mike Krukow .05 .15
332 Glenn Wilson .30 .75
333 Dave LaRoche .05 .15
334 Dave LaRoche SV .05 .15
335 Steve Henderson .05 .15
336 Rene Lachemann MG .05 .15
337 Tito Landrum .05 .15
338 Bob Owchinko .05 .15
339 Terry Harper .05 .15
340 Larry Gura .05 .15
341 Doug DeCinces .05 .15
342 Atlee Hammaker .05 .15
343 Bob Bailor .05 .15
344 Roger LaFrancois .05 .15
345 Jim Clancy .05 .15
346 Joe Pittman .05 .15
347 Sammy Stewart .05 .15
348 Alan Bannister .05 .15
349 Checklist: 265-396 .10 .30
350 Robin Yount .75 2.00
351 Cesar Cedeno .10 .30
Mario Soto TL
352 Mike Scioscia .10 .30
353 Steve Comer .05 .15
354 Randy Johnson .05 .15
355 Jim Bibby .05 .15
356 Gary Woods .05 .15
357 Len Matuszek .05 .15
358 Jerry Garvin .05 .15
359 Dave Collins .05 .15
360 Nolan Ryan 2.50 6.00
361 Nolan Ryan SV 1.25 3.00
362 Bill Almon .05 .15
363 John Stuper .05 .15
364 Brett Butler .10 .30
365 Dave Lopes .10 .30
366 Dick Williams MG .05 .15
367 Bud Anderson .05 .15
368 Richie Zisk .05 .15
369 Jesse Orosco .05 .15
370 Gary Carter .10 .30
371 Mike Richardt .05 .15
372 Terry Crowley .05 .15
373 Kevin Saucier .05 .15
374 Wayne Krenchicki .05 .15
375 Pete Vuckovich .05 .15
376 Ken Landreaux .05 .15
377 Lee May .05 .15
378 Lee May SV .05 .15
379 Guy Sularz .05 .15
380 Ron Davis .05 .15
381 Jim Rice .10 .30
Bob Stanley TL
382 Bob Knepper .05 .15
383 Ozzie Virgil .05 .15
384 Dave Dravecky RC .60 1.50
385 Mike Easler .05 .15
386 Rod Carew AS .10 .30
387 Bob Grich AS .05 .15
388 George Brett AS .60 1.50
389 Robin Yount AS .50 1.25
390 Reggie Jackson AS .10 .30
391 Rickey Henderson AS .50 1.25
392 Fred Lynn AS .05 .15
393 Carlton Fisk AS .10 .30
394 Pete Vuckovich AS .05 .15
395 Larry Gura AS .05 .15
396 Dan Quisenberry AS .05 .15
397 Pete Rose AS .25 .60
398 Manny Trillo AS .05 .15
399 Mike Schmidt AS .50 1.25
400 Dave Concepcion AS .05 .15
401 Dale Murphy AS .10 .30
402 Andre Dawson AS .05 .15
403 Tim Raines AS .05 .15
404 Gary Carter AS .05 .15
405 Steve Rogers AS .05 .15
406 Steve Carlton AS .10 .30
407 Bruce Sutter AS .10 .30
408 Rudy May .05 .15
409 Marvis Foley .05 .15
410 Phil Niekro .10 .30
411 Phil Niekro SV .05 .15
412 Buddy Bell .10 .30
Charlie Hough TL
413 Matt Keough .05 .15
414 Julio Cruz .05 .15
415 Bob Forsch .05 .15
416 Joe Ferguson .05 .15
417 Tom Hausman .05 .15
418 Greg Pryor .05 .15
419 Steve Crawford .05 .15
420 Al Oliver .10 .30
421 Al Oliver SV .05 .15
422 George Cappuzzello .05 .15
423 Tom Lawless .05 .15
424 Jerry Augustine .05 .15
425 Pedro Guerrero .10 .30
426 Earl Weaver MG .10 .30
427 Roy Lee Jackson .05 .15
428 Champ Summers .05 .15
429 Eddie Whitson .05 .15
430 Kirk Gibson .10 .30
431 Gary Gaetti RC .60 1.50
432 Porfirio Altamirano .05 .15
433 Dale Berra .05 .15
434 Dennis Lamp .05 .15
435 Tony Armas .10 .30
436 Bill Campbell .05 .15
437 Rick Sweet .05 .15
438 Dave LaPoint .05 .15
439 Rafael Ramirez .05 .15
440 Ron Guidry .10 .30
441 Ray Knight .10 .30
Joe Niekro TL
442 Brian Downing .10 .30
443 Don Hood .05 .15
444 Wally Backman .05 .15
445 Mike Flanagan .05 .15
446 Reid Nichols .05 .15
447 Bryn Smith .05 .15
448 Darrell Evans .10 .30
449 Eddie Milner .05 .15
450 Ted Simmons .10 .30
451 Ted Simmons SV .05 .15
452 Lloyd Moseby .05 .15
453 Lamar Johnson .05 .15
454 Bob Welch .10 .30
455 Sixto Lezcano .05 .15
456 Lee Elia MG .05 .15
457 Milt Wilcox .05 .15
458 Ron Washington .05 .15
459 Ed Farmer .05 .15
460 Roy Smalley .05 .15
461 Steve Trout .05 .15
462 Steve Nicosia .05 .15
463 Gaylord Perry .10 .30
464 Gaylord Perry SV .05 .15
465 Lonnie Smith .05 .15
466 Tom Underwood .05 .15
467 Rufino Linares .05 .15
468 Dave Goltz .05 .15
469 Ron Gardenhire .05 .15
470 Greg Minton .05 .15
471 Willie Wilson .10 .30
Vida Blue TL
472 Gary Allenson .05 .15
473 John Lowenstein .05 .15
474 Ray Burris .05 .15
475 Cesar Cedeno .10 .30
476 Rob Picciolo .05 .15
477 Tom Niedenfuer .05 .15
478 Phil Garner .10 .30
479 Charlie Hough .10 .30
480 Toby Harrah .10 .30
481 Scot Thompson .05 .15
482 Tony Gwynn UER RC 10.00 25.00
No Topps logo under
card number on back
483 Lynn Jones .05 .15
484 Dick Ruthven .05 .15
485 Omar Moreno .05 .15
486 Clyde King MG .05 .15
487 Jerry Hairston .05 .15
488 Alfredo Griffin .05 .15
489 Tom Herr .10 .30
490 Jim Palmer .10 .30
491 Jim Palmer SV .05 .15
492 Paul Serna .05 .15
493 Steve McCatty .05 .15
494 Bob Brenly .05 .15
495 Warren Cromartie .05 .15
496 Tom Veryzer .05 .15
497 Rick Sutcliffe .05 .15
498 Wade Boggs RC 6.00 15.00
499 Jeff Little .05 .15
500 Reggie Jackson .25 .60
501 Reggie Jackson SV .10 .30
502 Dale Murphy .25 .60
Phil Niekro TL
503 Moose Haas .05 .15
504 Don Werner .05 .15
505 Garry Templeton .10 .30
506 Jim Gott RC .30 .75
507 Tony Scott .05 .15
508 Tom Filer .05 .15
509 Lou Whitaker .10 .30
510 Tug McGraw .10 .30
511 Tug McGraw SV .05 .15
512 Doyle Alexander .05 .15
513 Fred Stanley .05 .15
514 Rudy Law .05 .15
515 Gene Tenace .10 .30
516 Bill Virdon MG .05 .15
517 Gary Ward .05 .15
518 Bill Laskey .05 .15
519 Terry Bulling .05 .15
520 Fred Lynn .10 .30
521 Bruce Benedict .05 .15
522 Pat Zachry .05 .15
523 Carney Lansford .10 .30
524 Tom Brennan .05 .15
525 Frank White .10 .30
526 Checklist: 397-528 .10 .30
527 Larry Biittner .05 .15
528 Jamie Easterly .05 .15
529 Tim Laudner .05 .15
530 Eddie Murray .50 1.25
531 Rickey Henderson .50 1.25
Rick Langford TL
532 Dave Stewart .10 .30
533 Luis Salazar .05 .15
534 John Butcher .05 .15
535 Manny Trillo .05 .15
536 John Wockenfuss .05 .15
537 Rod Scurry .05 .15
538 Danny Heep .05 .15
539 Roger Erickson .05 .15
540 Ozzie Smith .75 2.00
541 Britt Burns .05 .15
542 Jody Davis .05 .15
543 Alan Fowlkes .05 .15
544 Larry Whisenton .05 .15
545 Floyd Bannister .05 .15
546 Dave Garcia MG .05 .15
547 Geoff Zahn .05 .15
548 Brian Giles .05 .15
549 Charlie Puleo .05 .15
550 Carl Yastrzemski .75 2.00
551 Carl Yastrzemski SV .50 1.25
552 Tim Wallach .10 .30
553 Dennis Martinez .10 .30
554 Mike Vail .05 .15
555 Steve Yeager .10 .30
556 Willie Upshaw .05 .15
557 Rick Honeycutt .05 .15
558 Dickie Thon .05 .15
559 Pete Redfern .05 .15
560 Ron LeFlore .10 .30
561 Lonnie Smith .10 .30
Joaquin Andujar TL
562 Dave Rozema .05 .15
563 Juan Bonilla .05 .15
564 Sid Monge .05 .15
565 Bucky Dent .10 .30
566 Manny Sarmiento .05 .15
567 Joe Simpson .05 .15
568 Willie Hernandez .05 .15
569 Jack Perconte .05 .15
570 Vida Blue .10 .30
571 Mickey Klutts .05 .15
572 Bob Watson .05 .15
573 Andy Hassler .05 .15
574 Glenn Adams .05 .15
575 Neil Allen .05 .15
576 Frank Robinson MG .25 .60
577 Luis Aponte .05 .15
578 David Green RC .30 .75
579 Rich Dauer .05 .15
580 Tom Seaver .50 1.25
581 Tom Seaver SV .10 .30
582 Marshall Edwards .05 .15
583 Terry Forster .10 .30
584 Dave Hostetler .05 .15
585 Jose Cruz .10 .30
586 Frank Viola RC 1.00 2.50
587 Ivan DeJesus .05 .15
588 Pat Underwood .05 .15
589 Alvis Woods .05 .15
590 Tony Pena .05 .15
591 Greg Luzinski .10 .30
LaMarr Hoyt TL
592 Shane Rawley .05 .15
593 Broderick Perkins .05 .15
594 Eric Rasmussen .05 .15
595 Tim Raines .10 .30
596 Randy Johnson .05 .15
597 Mike Proly .05 .15
598 Dwayne Murphy .05 .15
599 Don Aase .05 .15
600 George Brett 1.25 3.00
601 Ed Lynch .05 .15
602 Rich Gedman .05 .15
603 Joe Morgan .10 .30
604 Joe Morgan SV .05 .15
605 Gary Roenicke .05 .15
606 Bobby Cox MG .10 .30
607 Charlie Leibrandt .05 .15
608 Don Money .05 .15
609 Danny Darwin .05 .15
610 Steve Garvey .10 .30
611 Bert Roberge .05 .15
612 Steve Swisher .05 .15
613 Mike Ivie .05 .15
614 Ed Glynn .05 .15
615 Garry Maddox .05 .15
616 Bill Nahorodny .05 .15
617 Butch Wynegar .05 .15
618 LaMarr Hoyt .05 .15
619 Keith Moreland .05 .15
620 Mike Norris .05 .15
621 Mookie Wilson .10 .30
Craig Swan TL
622 Dave Edler .05 .15
623 Luis Sanchez .05 .15
624 Glenn Hubbard .05 .15
625 Ken Forsch .05 .15
626 Jerry Martin .05 .15
627 Doug Bair .05 .15
628 Julio Valdez .05 .15
629 Charlie Lea .05 .15
630 Paul Molitor .10 .30
631 Tippy Martinez .05 .15
632 Alex Trevino .05 .15
633 Vicente Romo .05 .15
634 Max Venable .05 .15
635 Graig Nettles .10 .30
636 Graig Nettles SV .05 .15
637 Pat Corrales MG .05 .15
638 Dan Petry .05 .15
639 Art Howe .05 .15
640 Andre Thornton .05 .15
641 Billy Sample .05 .15
642 Checklist: 529-660 .10 .30
643 Bump Wills .05 .15
644 Joe Lefebvre .05 .15
645 Bill Madlock .10 .30
646 Jim Essian .05 .15
647 Bobby Mitchell .05 .15
648 Jeff Burroughs .05 .15
649 Tommy Boggs .05 .15
650 George Hendrick .10 .30
651 Rod Carew .10 .30
Mike Witt TL
652 Butch Hobson .05 .15
653 Ellis Valentine .05 .15
654 Bob Ojeda .05 .15

655 Al Bumbry	.05	.15
656 Dave Frost	.05	.15
657 Mike Gates	.05	.15
658 Frank Pastore	.05	.15
659 Charlie Moore	.05	.15
660 Mike Hargrove	.05	.15
661 Bill Russell	.10	.30
662 Joe Sambito	.05	.15
663 Tom O'Malley	.05	.15
664 Bob Molinaro	.05	.15
665 Jim Sundberg	.10	.30
666 Sparky Anderson MG	.10	.30
667 Dick Davis	.05	.15
668 Larry Christenson	.05	.15
669 Mike Squires	.05	.15
670 Jerry Mumphrey	.05	.15
671 Lenny Faedo	.05	.15
672 Jim Kaat	.10	.30
673 Jim Kaat SV	.05	.15
674 Kurt Bevacqua	.05	.15
675 Jim Beattie	.05	.15
676 Biff Pocoroba	.05	.15
677 Dave Revering	.05	.15
678 Juan Beniquez	.05	.15
679 Mike Scott	.10	.30
680 Andre Dawson	.10	.30
681 Pedro Guerrero	.10	.30
Fernando Valenzuela TL		
682 Bob Stanley	.05	.15
683 Dan Ford	.05	.15
684 Rafael Landestoy	.05	.15
685 Lee Mazzilli	.10	.30
686 Randy Lerch	.05	.15
687 U.L. Washington	.05	.15
688 Jim Wohlford	.05	.15
689 Ron Hassey	.05	.15
690 Kent Hrbek	.10	.30
691 Dave Tobik	.05	.15
692 Denny Walling	.05	.15
693 Sparky Lyle	.10	.30
694 Sparky Lyle SV	.05	.15
695 Ruppert Jones	.05	.15
696 Chuck Tanner MG	.05	.15
697 Barry Foote	.05	.15
698 Tony Bernazard	.05	.15
699 Lee Smith	.25	.60
700 Keith Hernandez	.10	.30
701 Willie Wilson	.10	.30
Al Oliver LL		
702 Reggie Jackson	.10	.30
Gorman Thomas		
Dave Kingman LL		
703 Hal McRae	.25	.60
Dale Murphy		
Al Oliver LL		
704 Rickey Henderson	.50	1.25
Tim Raines LL		
705 LaMarr Hoyt	.10	.30
Steve Carlton LL		
706 Floyd Bannister	.10	.30
Steve Carlton LL		
707 Rick Sutcliffe	.10	.30
Steve Rogers LL		
708 Dan Quisenberry	.10	.30
Bruce Sutter LL		
709 Jimmy Sexton	.05	.15
710 Willie Wilson	.10	.30
711 Bruce Bochte	.10	.30
Jim Beattie TL		
712 Bruce Kison	.05	.15
713 Ron Hodges	.05	.15
714 Wayne Nordhagen	.05	.15
715 Tony Perez	.25	.60
716 Tony Perez SV	.10	.30
717 Scott Sanderson	.05	.15
718 Jim Dwyer	.05	.15
719 Rich Gale	.05	.15
720 Dave Concepcion	.10	.30
721 John Martin	.05	.15
722 Jorge Orta	.05	.15
723 Randy Moffitt	.05	.15
724 Johnny Grubb	.05	.15
725 Dan Spillner	.05	.15
726 Harvey Kuenn MG	.05	.15
727 Chet Lemon	.10	.30
728 Ron Reed	.05	.15
729 Jerry Morales	.05	.15
730 Jason Thompson	.05	.15
731 Al Williams	.05	.15
732 Dave Henderson	.05	.15
733 Buck Martinez	.05	.15
734 Steve Braun	.05	.15
735 Tommy John	.10	.30
736 Tommy John SV	.05	.15
737 Mitchell Page	.05	.15
738 Tim Foli	.05	.15
739 Rick Ownbey	.05	.15
740 Rusty Staub	.10	.30
741 Rusty Staub SV	.05	.15
742 Terry Kennedy	.10	.30
Tim Lollar		
743 Mike Torrez	.05	.15
744 Brad Mills	.05	.15
745 Scott McGregor	.05	.15
746 John Wathan	.05	.15
747 Fred Breining	.05	.15
748 Derrel Thomas	.05	.15
749 Jon Matlack	.05	.15
750 Ben Oglivie	.10	.30
751 Brad Havens	.05	.15
752 Luis Pujols	.05	.15
753 Elias Sosa	.05	.15
754 Bill Robinson	.05	.15
755 John Candelaria	.05	.15
756 Russ Nixon MG	.05	.15
757 Rick Manning	.05	.15
758 Aurelio Rodriguez	.05	.15
759 Doug Bird	.05	.15
760 Dale Murphy	.25	.60
761 Gary Lucas	.05	.15
762 Cliff Johnson	.05	.15
763 Al Cowens	.05	.15
764 Pete Falcone	.05	.15
765 Bob Boone	.10	.30
766 Barry Bonnell	.05	.15
767 Duane Kuiper	.05	.15
768 Chris Speier	.05	.15
769 Checklist: 661-792	.10	.30
770 Dave Winfield	.10	.30
771 Kent Hrbek	.10	.30
Bobby Castillo TL		
772 Jim Kern	.05	.15
773 Larry Hisle	.05	.15
774 Alan Ashby	.05	.15
775 Burt Hooton	.05	.15
776 Larry Parrish	.05	.15
777 John Curtis	.05	.15
778 Rich Hebner	.05	.15
779 Rick Waits	.05	.15
780 Gary Matthews	.10	.30
781 Rick Rhoden	.05	.15
782 Bobby Murcer	.10	.30
783 Bobby Murcer SV	.05	.15
784 Jeff Newman	.05	.15
785 Dennis Leonard	.05	.15
786 Ralph Houk MG	.05	.15
787 Dick Tidrow	.05	.15
788 Dane Iorg	.05	.15
789 Bryan Clark	.05	.15
790 Bob Grich	.10	.30
791 Gary Lavelle	.05	.15
792 Chris Chambliss	.10	.30
XX Game Insert Card	.02	.10

1983 Topps Traded

For the third year in a row, Topps issued a 132-card standard-size Traded (or extended) set featuring some of the year's top rookies and players who had changed teams during the year. The cards were available through hobby dealers only in factory set form and were printed in Ireland by the Topps affiliate in that country. The set is numbered alphabetically by player. The Darryl Strawberry card number 108 can be found with either one or two asterisks (in the lower left corner of the reverse). There is no difference in value for either version. The key (extended) Rookie Cards in this set include Julio Franco, Tony Phillips and Darryl Strawberry.

COMP.FACT.SET (132)	15.00	40.00
1T Neil Allen	.08	.25
2T Bill Almon	.08	.25
3T Joe Altobelli MG	.08	.25
4T Tony Armas	.40	1.00
5T Doug Bair	.08	.25
6T Steve Baker	.08	.25
7T Floyd Bannister	.08	.25
8T Don Baylor	.40	1.00
9T Tony Bernazard	.08	.25
10T Larry Biittner	.08	.25
11T Dann Bilardello	.08	.25
12T Doug Bird	.08	.25
13T Steve Boros MG	.08	.25
14T Greg Brock	.08	.25
15T Mike C. Brown	.08	.25
16T Tom Burgmeier	.08	.25
17T Randy Bush	.08	.25
18T Bert Campaneris	.40	1.00
19T Ron Cey	.40	1.00
20T Chris Codiroli	.08	.25
21T Dave Collins	.08	.25
22T Terry Crowley	.08	.25
23T Julio Cruz	.08	.25
24T Mike Davis	.08	.25
25T Frank DiPino	.08	.25
26T Bill Doran XRC	.40	1.00
27T Jerry Dybzinski	.08	.25
28T Jamie Easterly	.08	.25
29T Juan Eichelberger	.08	.25
30T Jim Essian	.08	.25
31T Pete Falcone	.08	.25
32T Mike Ferraro MG	.08	.25
33T Terry Forster	.40	1.00
34T Julio Franco XRC	3.00	8.00
35T Rich Gale	.08	.25
36T Kiko Garcia	.08	.25
37T Steve Garvey	.40	1.00
38T Johnny Grubb	.08	.25
39T Mel Hall XRC	.40	1.00
40T Von Hayes	.08	.25
41T Danny Heep	.08	.25
42T Steve Henderson	.08	.25
43T Keith Hernandez	.40	1.00
44T Leo Hernandez	.08	.25
45T Willie Hernandez	.08	.25
46T Al Holland	.08	.25
47T Frank Howard MG	.40	1.00
48T Bobby Johnson	.08	.25
49T Cliff Johnson	.08	.25
50T Odell Jones	.08	.25
51T Mike Jorgensen	.08	.25
52T Bob Kearney	.08	.25
53T Steve Kemp	.08	.25
54T Matt Keough	.08	.25
55T Ron Kittle XRC	.75	2.00
56T Mickey Klutts	.08	.25
57T Alan Knicely	.08	.25
58T Mike Krukow	.08	.25
59T Rafael Landestoy	.08	.25
60T Carney Lansford	.40	1.00
61T Joe Lefebvre	.08	.25
62T Bryan Little	.08	.25
63T Aurelio Lopez	.08	.25
64T Mike Madden	.08	.25
65T Rick Manning	.08	.25
66T Billy Martin MG	.75	2.00
67T Lee Mazzilli	.40	1.00
68T Andy McGaffigan	.08	.25
69T Craig McMurtry	.08	.25
70T John McNamara MG	.08	.25
71T Orlando Mercado	.08	.25
72T Larry Milbourne	.08	.25
73T Randy Moffitt	.08	.25
74T Sid Monge	.08	.25
75T Jose Morales	.08	.25
76T Omar Moreno	.08	.25
77T Joe Morgan	.40	1.00
78T Mike Morgan	.08	.25
79T Dale Murray	.08	.25
80T Jeff Newman	.08	.25
81T Pete O'Brien XRC	.40	1.00
82T Jorge Orta	.08	.25
83T Alejandro Pena XRC	.75	2.00
84T Pascual Perez	.08	.25
85T Tony Perez	.75	2.00
86T Broderick Perkins	.08	.25
87T Tony Phillips XRC	.75	2.00
88T Charlie Puleo	.08	.25
89T Pat Putnam	.08	.25
90T Jamie Quirk	.08	.25
91T Doug Rader MG	.08	.25
92T Chuck Rainey	.08	.25
93T Bobby Ramos	.08	.25
94T Gary Redus XRC	.40	1.00
95T Steve Renko	.08	.25
96T Leon Roberts	.08	.25
97T Aurelio Rodriguez	.08	.25
98T Dick Ruthven	.08	.25
99T Daryl Sconiers	.08	.25
100T Mike Scott	.40	1.00
101T Tom Seaver	.75	2.00
102T John Shelby	.08	.25
103T Bob Shirley	.08	.25
104T Joe Simpson	.08	.25
105T Doug Sisk	.08	.25
106T Mike Smithson	.08	.25
107T Elias Sosa	.08	.25
108T D.Strawberry XRC	5.00	12.00
109T Tom Tellmann	.08	.25
110T Gene Tenace	.40	1.00
111T Gorman Thomas	.40	1.00
112T Dick Tidrow	.08	.25
113T Dave Tobik	.08	.25
114T Wayne Tolleson	.08	.25
115T Mike Torrez	.08	.25
116T Manny Trillo	.08	.25
117T Steve Trout	.08	.25
118T Lee Tunnell	.08	.25
119T Mike Vail	.08	.25
120T Ellis Valentine	.08	.25
121T Tom Veryzer	.08	.25
122T George Vukovich	.08	.25
123T Rick Waits	.08	.25
124T Greg Walker	.40	1.00
125T Chris Welsh	.08	.25
126T Len Whitehouse	.08	.25
127T Eddie Whitson	.08	.25
128T Jim Wohlford	.08	.25
129T Matt Young XRC	.40	1.00
130T Joel Youngblood	.08	.25
131T Pat Zachry	.08	.25
132T Checklist 1T-132T	.08	.25

1984 Topps

The cards in this 792-card set measure the standard size. Cards were primarily distributed in 15-card wax packs and 54-card rack packs. For the second year in a row, Topps utilized a dual picture on the front of the card. A portrait is shown in a square insert and an action shot is featured in the main photo. Card numbers 1-6 feature 1983 Highlights (HL), cards 131-138 depict League Leaders, card numbers 386-407 feature All-Stars, and card numbers 701-718 feature active Major League career leaders in various statistical categories. Each team leader (TL) card features the team's leading hitter and pitcher pictured on the front with a team checklist back. There are six numerical checklist cards in the set. The player cards feature team logos in the upper right corner of the reverse. The key Rookie Cards in this set are Don Mattingly and Darryl Strawberry. Topps tested a special send-in offer in Michigan and a few other states whereby collectors could obtain direct from Topps ten cards of their choice. Needless to say most people ordered the key (most valuable) players necessitating the printing of a special sheet to keep up with the demand. The special sheet had five cards of Darryl Strawberry, three cards of Don Mattingly, etc. The test was apparently a failure in Topps' eyes as they have never tried it again.

COMPLETE SET (792)	20.00	50.00
1 Steve Carlton HL	.08	.25
2 Rickey Henderson HL	.25	.60
3 Dan Quisenberry HL	.05	.15
4 Nolan Ryan HL	.40	1.00
Steve Carlton		
Gaylord Perry		
5 Dave Righetti HL	.08	.25
Bob Forsch		
Mike Warren		
6 Johnny Bench HL	.15	.40
Gaylord Perry		
Carl Yastrzemski		
7 Gary Lucas	.05	.15
8 Don Mattingly RC	6.00	15.00
9 Jim Gott	.05	.15
10 Robin Yount	.40	1.00
11 Kent Hrbek	.08	.25
Ken Schrom TL		
12 Billy Sample	.05	.15
13 Scott Holman	.05	.15
14 Tom Brookens	.08	.25
15 Burt Hooton	.05	.15
16 Omar Moreno	.05	.15
17 John Denny	.05	.15
18 Dale Berra	.05	.15
19 Ray Fontenot	.05	.15
20 Greg Luzinski	.08	.25
21 Joe Altobelli MG	.05	.15
22 Bryan Clark	.05	.15
23 Keith Moreland	.05	.15
24 John Martin	.05	.15
25 Glenn Hubbard	.05	.15
26 Bud Black	.05	.15
27 Daryl Sconiers	.05	.15
28 Frank Viola	.15	.40
29 Danny Heep	.05	.15
30 Wade Boggs	.60	1.50
31 Andy McGaffigan	.05	.15
32 Bobby Ramos	.05	.15
33 Tom Burgmeier	.05	.15
34 Eddie Milner	.05	.15
35 Don Sutton	.08	.25
36 Denny Walling	.05	.15
37 Buddy Bell	.08	.25
Rick Honeycutt TL		
38 Luis DeLeon	.05	.15
39 Garth Iorg	.05	.15
40 Dusty Baker	.08	.25
41 Tony Bernazard	.05	.15
42 Johnny Grubb	.05	.15
43 Ron Reed	.05	.15
44 Jim Morrison	.05	.15
45 Jerry Mumphrey	.05	.15
46 Ray Smith	.05	.15
47 Rudy Law	.05	.15
48 Julio Franco	.08	.25
49 John Stuper	.05	.15
50 Chris Chambliss	.08	.25
51 Jim Frey MG	.05	.15
52 Paul Splittorff	.05	.15
53 Juan Beniquez	.05	.15
54 Jesse Orosco	.05	.15
55 Dave Concepcion	.08	.25
56 Gary Allenson	.05	.15
57 Dan Schatzeder	.05	.15
58 Max Venable	.05	.15
59 Sammy Stewart	.05	.15
60 Paul Molitor UER	.08	.25
('83 stats .272, 613,		
167; should be .270,		
608, 164)		
61 Chris Codiroli	.05	.15
62 Dave Hostetler	.05	.15
63 Ed VandeBerg	.05	.15
64 Mike Scioscia	.08	.25
65 Kirk Gibson	.25	.60
66 Jose Cruz	.40	1.00
Nolan Ryan TL		
67 Gary Ward	.05	.15
68 Luis Salazar	.05	.15
69 Rod Scurry	.05	.15
70 Gary Matthews	.08	.25
71 Leo Hernandez	.05	.15
72 Mike Squires	.05	.15
73 Jody Davis	.05	.15
74 Jerry Martin	.05	.15
75 Bob Forsch	.05	.15
76 Alfredo Griffin	.05	.15
77 Brett Butler	.08	.25
78 Mike Torrez	.05	.15
79 Rob Wilfong	.05	.15
80 Steve Rogers	.08	.25
81 Billy Martin MG	.15	.40
82 Doug Bird	.05	.15
83 Richie Zisk	.05	.15
84 Lenny Faedo	.05	.15
85 Atlee Hammaker	.05	.15
86 John Shelby	.05	.15
87 Frank Pastore	.05	.15
88 Rob Picciolo	.05	.15
89 Mike Smithson	.05	.15
90 Pedro Guerrero	.08	.25
91 Dan Spillner	.05	.15
92 Lloyd Moseby	.05	.15
93 Bob Knepper	.05	.15
94 Mario Ramirez	.05	.15
95 Aurelio Lopez	.08	.25
96 Hal McRae	.08	.25
Larry Gura TL		
97 LaMarr Hoyt	.05	.15
98 Steve Nicosia	.05	.15
99 Craig Lefferts RC	.05	.15
100 Reggie Jackson	.15	.40
101 Porfirio Altamirano	.05	.15
102 Ken Oberkfell	.05	.15
103 Dwayne Murphy	.05	.15
104 Ken Dayley	.05	.15
105 Tony Armas	.08	.25
106 Tim Stoddard	.05	.15
107 Ned Yost	.05	.15
108 Randy Moffitt	.05	.15
109 Brad Wellman	.05	.15
110 Ron Guidry	.08	.25
111 Bill Virdon MG	.05	.15
112 Tom Niedenfuer	.05	.15
113 Kelly Paris	.05	.15
114 Checklist 1-132	.08	.25
115 Andre Thornton	.05	.15
116 George Bjorkman	.05	.15
117 Tom Veryzer	.05	.15
118 Charlie Hough	.08	.25
119 John Wockenfuss	.05	.15
120 Keith Hernandez	.08	.25
121 Pat Sheridan	.05	.15
122 Cecilio Guante	.05	.15
123 Butch Wynegar	.05	.15
124 Damaso Garcia	.05	.15
125 Britt Burns	.05	.15
126 Dale Murphy	.15	.40
Craig McMurtry TL		
127 Mike Madden	.05	.15
128 Rick Manning	.05	.15
129 Bill Laskey	.05	.15
130 Ozzie Smith	.40	1.00
131 Bill Madlock	.25	.60
Wade Boggs LL		
132 Mike Schmidt	.25	.60
Jim Rice LL		
133 Dale Murphy	.15	.40
Cecil Cooper		
Jim Rice LL		
134 Tim Raines	.25	.60
Rickey Henderson LL		
135 John Denny	.25	.60
LaMarr Hoyt LL		
136 Steve Carlton	.08	.25
Jack Morris LL		
137 Atlee Hammaker	.08	.25
Rick Honeycutt LL		
138 Al Holland	.08	.25
Dan Quisenberry LL		
139 Bert Campaneris	.08	.25
140 Storm Davis	.05	.15
141 Pat Corrales MG	.05	.15
142 Rich Gale	.05	.15
143 Jose Morales	.05	.15
144 Brian Harper RC	.15	.40
145 Gary Lavelle	.05	.15
146 Ed Romero	.05	.15
147 Dan Petry	.08	.25
148 Joe Lefebvre	.05	.15
149 Jon Matlack	.05	.15
150 Dale Murphy	.15	.40
151 Steve Trout	.05	.15
152 Glenn Brummer	.05	.15
153 Dick Tidrow	.05	.15
154 Dave Henderson	.08	.25
155 Frank White	.08	.25
156 Rickey Henderson	.25	.60
Tim Conroy TL		
157 Gary Gaetti	.15	.40
158 John Curtis	.05	.15
159 Darryl Cias	.05	.15
160 Mario Soto	.08	.25
161 Junior Ortiz	.05	.15
162 Bob Ojeda	.05	.15
163 Lorenzo Gray	.05	.15
164 Scott Sanderson	.05	.15
165 Ken Singleton	.08	.25
166 Jamie Nelson	.05	.15
167 Marshall Edwards	.05	.15
168 Juan Bonilla	.05	.15
169 Larry Parrish	.05	.15
170 Jerry Reuss	.05	.15
171 Frank Robinson MG	.15	.40
172 Frank DiPino	.05	.15
173 Marvell Wynne	.15	.40
174 Juan Berenguer	.05	.15
175 Graig Nettles	.08	.25
176 Lee Smith	.08	.25
177 Jerry Hairston	.05	.15
178 Bill Krueger RC	.05	.15
179 Buck Martinez	.05	.15
180 Manny Trillo	.05	.15
181 Roy Thomas	.05	.15
182 Darryl Strawberry RC	1.25	3.00
183 Al Williams	.05	.15
184 Mike O'Berry	.05	.15
185 Sixto Lezcano	.05	.15
186 Lonnie Smith	.08	.25
John Stuper TL		
187 Luis Aponte	.05	.15
188 Bryan Little	.05	.15
189 Tim Conroy	.05	.15
190 Ben Oglivie	.08	.25
191 Mike Boddicker	.05	.15
192 Nick Esasky	.05	.15
193 Darrell Brown	.05	.15
194 Domingo Ramos	.05	.15
195 Jack Morris	.08	.25
196 Don Slaught	.08	.25
197 Garry Hancock	.05	.15
198 Bill Doran RC	.15	.40
199 Willie Hernandez	.05	.15
200 Andre Dawson	.08	.25
201 Bruce Kison	.05	.15
202 Bobby Cox MG	.08	.25
203 Matt Keough	.05	.15
204 Bobby Meacham	.05	.15
205 Greg Minton	.05	.15
206 Andy Van Slyke RC	.60	1.50
207 Donnie Moore	.05	.15
208 Jose Oquendo RC	.15	.40
209 Manny Sarmiento	.05	.15
210 Joe Morgan	.08	.25
211 Rick Sweet	.05	.15
212 Broderick Perkins	.05	.15
213 Bruce Hurst	.05	.15
214 Paul Householder	.05	.15
215 Tippy Martinez	.05	.15
216 Carlton Fisk	.08	.25
Richard Dotson TL		
217 Alan Ashby	.05	.15
218 Rick Waits	.05	.15
219 Joe Simpson	.05	.15
220 Fernando Valenzuela	.08	.25
221 Cliff Johnson	.05	.15
222 Rick Honeycutt	.05	.15
223 Wayne Krenchicki	.05	.15
224 Sid Monge	.05	.15
225 Lee Mazzilli	.08	.25
226 Juan Eichelberger	.05	.15
227 Steve Braun	.05	.15
228 John Rabb	.05	.15
229 Paul Owens MG	.05	.15
230 Rickey Henderson	.40	1.00
231 Gary Woods	.05	.15
232 Tim Wallach	.05	.15
233 Checklist 133-264	.08	.25
234 Rafael Ramirez	.05	.15
235 Matt Young RC	.15	.40
236 Ellis Valentine	.05	.15
237 John Castino	.05	.15
238 Reid Nichols	.05	.15
239 Jay Howell	.05	.15
240 Eddie Murray	.25	.60
241 Bill Almon	.05	.15
242 Alex Trevino	.05	.15
243 Pete Ladd	.05	.15
244 Candy Maldonado	.05	.15
245 Rick Sutcliffe	.08	.25
246 Mookie Wilson	.08	.25
Tom Seaver TL		
247 Onix Concepcion	.05	.15
248 Bill Dawley	.05	.15
249 Jay Johnstone	.05	.15
250 Bill Madlock	.08	.25
251 Tony Gwynn	1.00	2.50
252 Larry Christenson	.05	.15
253 Jim Wohlford	.05	.15
254 Shane Rawley	.05	.15
255 Bruce Benedict	.05	.15
256 Dave Geisel	.05	.15
257 Julio Cruz	.05	.15
258 Luis Sanchez	.05	.15
259 Sparky Anderson MG	.08	.25
260 Scott McGregor	.05	.15
261 Bobby Brown	.05	.15
262 Tom Candiotti RC	.30	.75
263 Jack Fimple	.05	.15
264 Doug Frobel RC	.05	.15
265 Donnie Hill	.05	.15
266 Steve Lubratich	.05	.15
267 Carmelo Martinez	.05	.15
268 Jack O'Connor	.05	.15
269 Aurelio Rodriguez	.05	.15
270 Jeff Russell RC	.15	.40
271 Moose Haas	.05	.15
272 Rick Dempsey	.05	.15
273 Charlie Puleo	.05	.15
274 Rick Monday	.08	.25
275 Len Matuszek	.05	.15
276 Rod Carew	.08	.25
Geoff Zahn TL		
277 Eddie Whitson	.05	.15
278 Jorge Bell	.08	.25
279 Ivan DeJesus	.05	.15
280 Floyd Bannister	.05	.15
281 Larry Milbourne	.05	.15
282 Jim Barr	.05	.15
283 Larry Biittner	.05	.15
284 Howard Bailey	.05	.15
285 Darrell Porter	.05	.15
286 Lary Sorensen	.05	.15
287 Warren Cromartie	.05	.15
288 Jim Beattie	.05	.15
289 Randy Johnson	.05	.15
290 Dave Dravecky	.05	.15
291 Chuck Tanner MG	.05	.15
292 Tony Scott	.05	.15
293 Ed Lynch	.05	.15
294 U.L. Washington	.05	.15
295 Mike Flanagan	.05	.15
296 Jeff Newman	.05	.15
297 Bruce Berenyi	.05	.15
298 Jim Gantner	.05	.15
299 John Butcher	.05	.15
300 Pete Rose	.75	2.00
301 Frank LaCorte	.05	.15
302 Barry Bonnell	.05	.15
303 Marty Castillo	.05	.15
304 Warren Brusstar	.05	.15
305 Roy Smalley	.05	.15
306 Pedro Guerrero	.08	.25
Bob Welch TL		
307 Bobby Mitchell	.05	.15
308 Ron Hassey	.05	.15
309 Tony Phillips RC	.30	.75
310 Willie McGee	.08	.25
311 Jerry Koosman	.08	.25
312 Jorge Orta	.05	.15
313 Mike Jorgensen	.05	.15
314 Orlando Mercado	.05	.15
315 Bobby Grich	.08	.25
316 Mark Bradley	.05	.15
317 Greg Pryor	.05	.15
318 Bill Gullickson	.05	.15
319 Al Bumbry	.05	.15
320 Bob Stanley	.05	.15
321 Harvey Kuenn MG	.05	.15
322 Ken Schrom	.05	.15
323 Alan Knicely	.05	.15
324 Alejandro Pena RC	.30	.75
325 Darrell Evans	.08	.25
326 Bob Kearney	.05	.15
327 Ruppert Jones	.05	.15
328 Vern Ruhle	.05	.15
329 Pat Tabler	.05	.15
330 John Candelaria	.05	.15
331 Bucky Dent	.08	.25
332 Kevin Gross RC	.15	.40
333 Larry Herndon	.08	.25
334 Chuck Rainey	.05	.15
335 Don Baylor	.08	.25
336 Pat Putnam	.08	.25
Matt Young TL		
337 Kevin Hagen	.05	.15
338 Mike Warren	.05	.15
339 Roy Lee Jackson	.05	.15
340 Hal McRae	.08	.25
341 Dave Tobik	.05	.15
342 Tim Foli	.05	.15
343 Mark Davis	.05	.15
344 Rick Miller	.05	.15
345 Kent Hrbek	.08	.25
346 Kurt Bevacqua	.05	.15
347 Allan Ramirez	.05	.15
348 Toby Harrah	.08	.25
349 Bob L. Gibson RC	.05	.15
350 George Foster	.08	.25
351 Russ Nixon MG	.05	.15
352 Dave Stewart	.08	.25
353 Jim Anderson	.05	.15
354 Jeff Burroughs	.05	.15
355 Jason Thompson	.05	.15
356 Glenn Abbott	.05	.15
357 Ron Cey	.08	.25
358 Bob Dernier	.05	.15
359 Jim Acker	.05	.15
360 Willie Randolph	.08	.25
361 Dave Smith	.05	.15
362 David Green	.05	.15
363 Tim Laudner	.05	.15
364 Scott Fletcher	.05	.15
365 Steve Bedrosian	.05	.15
366 Terry Kennedy	.08	.25
Dave Dravecky TL		
367 Jamie Easterly	.05	.15
368 Hubie Brooks	.05	.15
369 Steve McCatty	.05	.15
370 Tim Raines	.08	.25
371 Dave Gumpert	.05	.15
372 Gary Roenicke	.05	.15
373 Bill Scherrer	.05	.15
374 Don Money	.05	.15
375 Dennis Leonard	.05	.15
376 Dave Anderson RC	.05	.15
377 Danny Darwin	.05	.15
378 Bob Brenly	.05	.15
379 Checklist 265-396	.08	.25
380 Steve Garvey	.08	.25
381 Ralph Houk MG	.05	.15
382 Chris Nyman	.05	.15
383 Terry Puhl	.05	.15
384 Lee Tunnell	.05	.15
385 Tony Perez	.15	.40
386 George Hendrick AS	.05	.15
387 Johnny Ray AS	.05	.15
388 Mike Schmidt AS	.25	.60
389 Ozzie Smith AS	.25	.60
390 Tim Raines AS	.05	.15
391 Dale Murphy AS	.08	.25
392 Andre Dawson AS	.05	.15
393 Gary Carter AS	.05	.15
394 Steve Rogers AS	.05	.15
395 Steve Carlton AS	.08	.25
396 Jesse Orosco AS	.05	.15

397 Eddie Murray AS .15 .40
398 Lou Whitaker AS .05 .15
399 George Brett AS .25 .60
400 Cal Ripken AS .75 2.00
401 Jim Rice AS .05 .15
402 Dave Winfield AS .05 .15
403 Lloyd Moseby AS .05 .15
404 Ted Simmons AS .05 .15
405 LaMarr Hoyt AS .05 .15
406 Ron Guidry AS .05 .15
407 Dan Quisenberry AS .05 .15
408 Lou Piniella .08 .25
409 Juan Agosto .05 .15
410 Claudell Washington .05 .15
411 Houston Jimenez .05 .15
412 Doug Rader MG .05 .15
413 Spike Owen RC .15 .40
414 Mitchell Page .05 .15
415 Tommy John .08 .25
416 Dane Iorg .05 .15
417 Mike Armstrong .05 .15
418 Ron Hodges .05 .15
419 John Henry Johnson .05 .15
420 Cecil Cooper .08 .25
421 Charlie Lea .05 .15
422 Jose Cruz .08 .25
423 Mike Morgan .05 .15
424 Dann Bilardello .05 .15
425 Steve Howe .05 .15
426 Cal Ripken .60 1.50
Mike Boddicker TL
427 Rick Leach .05 .15
428 Fred Breining .05 .15
429 Randy Bush .05 .15
430 Rusty Staub .08 .25
431 Chris Bando .05 .15
432 Charles Hudson .05 .15
433 Rich Hebner .05 .15
434 Harold Baines .08 .25
435 Neil Allen .05 .15
436 Rick Peters .05 .15
437 Mike Proly .05 .15
438 Biff Pocoroba .05 .15
439 Bob Stoddard .05 .15
440 Steve Kemp .05 .15
441 Bob Lillis MG .05 .15
442 Byron McLaughlin .05 .15
443 Benny Ayala .05 .15
444 Steve Renko .05 .15
445 Jerry Remy .05 .15
446 Luis Pujols .05 .15
447 Tom Brunansky .05 .15
448 Ben Hayes .05 .15
449 Joe Pettini .05 .15
450 Gary Carter .08 .25
451 Bob Jones .05 .15
452 Chuck Porter .05 .15
453 Willie Upshaw .05 .15
454 Joe Beckwith .05 .15
455 Terry Kennedy .05 .15
456 Keith Moreland .05 .15
Fergie Jenkins TL
457 Dave Rozema .05 .15
458 Kiko Garcia .05 .15
459 Kevin Hickey .05 .15
460 Dave Winfield .08 .25
461 Jim Maler .05 .15
462 Lee Lacy .05 .15
463 Dave Engle .05 .15
464 Jeff A. Jones .05 .15
465 Mookie Wilson .08 .25
466 Gene Garber .05 .15
467 Mike Ramsey .05 .15
468 Geoff Zahn .05 .15
469 Tom O'Malley .05 .15
470 Nolan Ryan 1.25 3.00
471 Dick Howser MG .05 .15
472 Mike G. Brown RC .05 .15
473 Jim Dwyer .05 .15
474 Greg Bargar .05 .15
475 Gary Redus RC .15 .40
476 Tom Tellmann .05 .15
477 Rafael Landestoy .05 .15
478 Alan Bannister .05 .15
479 Frank Tanana .08 .25
480 Ron Kittle .05 .15
481 Mark Thurmond .05 .15
482 Enos Cabell .05 .15
483 Fergie Jenkins .08 .25
484 Ozzie Virgil .05 .15
485 Rick Rhoden .05 .15
486 Don Baylor .08 .25
Ron Guidry TL
487 Ricky Adams .05 .15
488 Jesse Barfield .08 .25
489 Dave Von Ohlen .05 .15
490 Cal Ripken 1.50 4.00
491 Bobby Castillo .05 .15
492 Tucker Ashford .05 .15
493 Mike Norris .05 .15
494 Chili Davis .08 .25
495 Rollie Fingers .08 .25
496 Terry Francona .08 .25
497 Bud Anderson .05 .15
498 Rich Gedman .05 .15
499 Mike Witt .05 .15
500 George Brett .60 1.50
501 Steve Henderson .05 .15
502 Joe Torre MG .08 .25
503 Elias Sosa .05 .15
504 Mickey Rivers .05 .15
505 Pete Vuckovich .05 .15
506 Ernie Whitt .05 .15
507 Mike LaCoss .05 .15
508 Mel Hall .08 .25
509 Brad Havens .05 .15
510 Alan Trammell .08 .25
511 Marty Bystrom .05 .15
512 Oscar Gamble .05 .15
513 Dave Beard .05 .15
514 Floyd Rayford .05 .15
515 Gorman Thomas .08 .25
516 Al Oliver .08 .25
Charlie Lea TL
517 John Moses .05 .15
518 Greg Walker .15 .40
519 Ron Davis .05 .15
520 Bob Boone .08 .25
521 Pete Falcone .05 .15
522 Dave Bergman .05 .15
523 Glenn Hoffman .05 .15
524 Carlos Diaz .05 .15
525 Willie Wilson .08 .25
526 Ron Oester .05 .15
527 Checklist 397-528 .08 .25
528 Mark Brouhard .05 .15
529 Keith Atherton .05 .15
530 Dan Ford .05 .15
531 Steve Boros MG .05 .15
532 Eric Show .05 .15
533 Ken Landreaux .05 .15
534 Pete O'Brien RC .15 .40
535 Bo Diaz .05 .15
536 Doug Bair .05 .15
537 Johnny Ray .05 .15
538 Kevin Bass .05 .15
539 George Frazier .05 .15
540 George Hendrick .08 .25
541 Dennis Lamp .05 .15
542 Duane Kuiper .05 .15
543 Craig McMurtry .05 .15
544 Cesar Geronimo .05 .15
545 Bill Buckner .08 .25
546 Mike Hargrove .08 .25
Lary Sorensen TL
547 Mike Moore .05 .15
548 Ron Jackson .05 .15
549 Walt Terrell .05 .15
550 Jim Rice .08 .25
551 Scott Ullger .05 .15
552 Ray Burris .05 .15
553 Joe Nolan .05 .15
554 Ted Power .05 .15
555 Greg Brock .05 .15
556 Joey McLaughlin .05 .15
557 Wayne Tolleson .05 .15
558 Mike Davis .05 .15
559 Mike Scott .08 .25
560 Carlton Fisk .15 .40
561 Whitey Herzog MG .08 .25
562 Manny Castillo .05 .15
563 Glenn Wilson .08 .25
564 Al Holland .05 .15
565 Leon Durham .05 .15
566 Jim Bibby .05 .15
567 Mike Heath .05 .15
568 Pete Filson .05 .15
569 Bake McBride .08 .25
570 Dan Quisenberry .05 .15
571 Bruce Bochy .05 .15
572 Jerry Royster .05 .15
573 Dave Kingman .08 .25
574 Brian Downing .08 .25
575 Jim Clancy .05 .15
576 Jeff Leonard .08 .25
Atlee Hammaker TL
577 Mark Clear .05 .15
578 Lenn Sakata .05 .15
579 Bob James .05 .15
580 Lonnie Smith .05 .15
581 Jose DeLeon RC .15 .40
582 Bob McClure .05 .15
583 Derrel Thomas .05 .15
584 Dave Schmidt .05 .15
585 Dan Driessen .05 .15
586 Joe Niekro .05 .15
587 Von Hayes .05 .15
588 Milt Wilcox .05 .15
589 Mike Easler .05 .15
590 Dave Stieb .08 .25
591 Tony LaRussa MG .08 .25
592 Andre Robertson .05 .15
593 Jeff Lahti .05 .15
594 Gene Richards .05 .15
595 Jeff Reardon .08 .25
596 Ryne Sandberg 1.00 2.50
597 Rick Camp .05 .15
598 Rusty Kuntz .05 .15
599 Doug Sisk .05 .15
600 Rod Carew .15 .40
601 John Tudor .08 .25
602 John Wathan .05 .15
603 Renie Martin .05 .15
604 John Lowenstein .05 .15
605 Mike Caldwell .05 .15
606 Lloyd Moseby .08 .25
Dave Stieb TL
607 Tom Hume .05 .15
608 Bobby Johnson .05 .15
609 Dan Meyer .05 .15
610 Steve Sax .05 .15
611 Chet Lemon .08 .25
612 Harry Spilman .05 .15
613 Greg Gross .05 .15
614 Len Barker .05 .15
615 Garry Templeton .08 .25
616 Don Robinson .05 .15
617 Rick Cerone .05 .15
618 Dickie Noles .05 .15
619 Jerry Dybzinski .05 .15
620 Al Oliver .08 .25
621 Frank Howard MG .08 .25
622 Al Cowens .05 .15
623 Ron Washington .05 .15
624 Terry Harper .05 .15
625 Larry Gura .05 .15
626 Bob Clark .05 .15
627 Dave LaPoint .05 .15
628 Ed Jurak .05 .15
629 Rick Langford .05 .15
630 Ted Simmons .08 .25
631 Dennis Martinez .08 .25
632 Tom Foley .05 .15
633 Mike Krukow .05 .15
634 Mike Marshall .05 .15
635 Dave Righetti .08 .25
636 Pat Putnam .05 .15
637 Gary Matthews .08 .25
John Denny TL
638 George Vukovich .05 .15
639 Rick Lysander .05 .15
640 Lance Parrish .15 .40
641 Mike Richardt .05 .15
642 Tom Underwood .05 .15
643 Mike C. Brown .05 .15
644 Tim Lollar .05 .15
645 Tony Pena .05 .15
646 Checklist 529-660 .08 .25
647 Ron Roenicke .05 .15
648 Len Whitehouse .05 .15
649 Tom Herr .05 .15
650 Phil Niekro .08 .25
651 John McNamara MG .05 .15
652 Rudy May .05 .15
653 Dave Stapleton .05 .15
654 Bob Bailor .05 .15
655 Amos Otis .08 .25
656 Bryn Smith .05 .15
657 Thad Bosley .05 .15
658 Jerry Augustine .05 .15
659 Duane Walker .05 .15
660 Ray Knight .08 .25
661 Steve Yeager .08 .25
662 Tom Brennan .05 .15
663 Johnnie LeMaster .05 .15
664 Dave Stegman .05 .15
665 Buddy Bell .08 .25
666 Lou Whitaker .08 .25
Jack Morris TL
667 Vance Law .05 .15
668 Larry McWilliams .05 .15
669 Dave Lopes .08 .25
670 Rich Gossage .08 .25
671 Jamie Quirk .05 .15
672 Ricky Nelson .05 .15
673 Mike Walters .05 .15
674 Tim Flannery .05 .15
675 Pascual Perez .05 .15
676 Brian Giles .05 .15
677 Doyle Alexander .05 .15
678 Chris Speier .05 .15
679 Art Howe .05 .15
680 Fred Lynn .08 .25
681 Tom Lasorda MG .15 .40
682 Dan Morogiello .05 .15
683 Marty Barrett RC .15 .40
684 Bob Shirley .05 .15
685 Willie Aikens .05 .15
686 Joe Price .05 .15
687 Roy Howell .05 .15
688 George Wright .05 .15
689 Mike Fischlin .05 .15
690 Jack Clark .08 .25
691 Steve Lake .05 .15
692 Dickie Thon .05 .15
693 Alan Wiggins .05 .15
694 Mike Stanton .05 .15
695 Lou Whitaker .08 .25
696 Bill Madlock .08 .25
Rick Rhoden TL
697 Dale Murray .05 .15
698 Marc Hill .05 .15
699 Dave Rucker .05 .15
700 Mike Schmidt .60 1.50
701 Bill Madlock .25 .60
Pete Rose
Dave Parker LL
702 Pete Rose .25 .60
Rusty Staub
Tony Perez LL
703 Mike Schmidt .25 .60
Tony Perez
Dave Kingman LL
704 Tony Perez .08 .25
Rusty Staub
Al Oliver LL
705 Joe Morgan .15 .40
Cesar Cedeno
Larry Bowa LL
706 Steve Carlton .08 .25
Fergie Jenkins
Tom Seaver LL
707 Steve Carlton .60 1.50
Nolan Ryan
Tom Seaver LL
708 Tom Seaver .08 .25
Steve Carlton
Steve Rogers LL
709 Bruce Sutter .08 .25
Tug McGraw
Gene Garber LL
710 Rod Carew .15 .40
George Brett
Cecil Cooper LL
711 Rod Carew .08 .25
Bert Campaneris
Reggie Jackson LL
712 Reggie Jackson .08 .25
Graig Nettles
Greg Luzinski LL
713 Reggie Jackson .08 .25
Ted Simmons
Graig Nettles LL
714 Bert Campaneris .08 .25
Dave Lopes
Omar Moreno LL
715 Jim Palmer .08 .25
Don Sutton
Tommy John LL
716 Don Sutton .15 .40
Bert Blyleven
Jerry Koosman LL
717 Jim Palmer .08 .25
Rollie Fingers
Ron Guidry LL
718 Rollie Fingers .08 .25
Rich Gossage
Dan Quisenberry LL
719 Andy Hassler .05 .15
720 Dwight Evans .15 .40
721 Del Crandall MG .05 .15
722 Bob Welch .08 .25
723 Rich Dauer .05 .15
724 Eric Rasmussen .05 .15
725 Cesar Cedeno .05 .15
726 Ted Simmons .08 .25
Moose Haas TL
727 Joel Youngblood .05 .15
728 Tug McGraw .08 .25
729 Gene Tenace .08 .25
730 Bruce Sutter .15 .40
731 Lynn Jones .05 .15
732 Terry Crowley .05 .15
733 Dave Collins .05 .15
734 Odell Jones .05 .15
735 Rick Burleson .05 .15
736 Dick Ruthven .05 .15
737 Jim Essian .05 .15
738 Bill Schroeder .08 .25
739 Bob Watson .05 .15
740 Tom Seaver .25 .60
741 Wayne Gross .05 .15
742 Dick Williams MG .05 .15
743 Don Hood .05 .15
744 Jamie Allen .05 .15
745 Dennis Eckersley .15 .40
746 Mickey Hatcher .05 .15
747 Pat Zachry .05 .15
748 Jeff Leonard .05 .15
749 Doug Flynn .05 .15
750 Jim Palmer .08 .25
751 Charlie Moore .05 .15
752 Phil Garner .08 .25
753 Doug Gwosdz .05 .15
754 Kent Tekulve .05 .15
755 Garry Maddox .05 .15
756 Ron Oester .08 .25
Mario Soto TL
757 Larry Bowa .08 .25
758 Bill Stein .05 .15
759 Richard Dotson .05 .15
760 Bob Horner .08 .25
761 John Montefusco .05 .15
762 Rance Mulliniks .05 .15
763 Craig Swan .05 .15
764 Mike Hargrove .05 .15
765 Ken Forsch .05 .15
766 Mike Vail .05 .15
767 Carney Lansford .08 .25
768 Champ Summers .05 .15
769 Bill Caudill .05 .15
770 Ken Griffey .08 .25
771 Billy Gardner MG .05 .15
772 Jim Slaton .05 .15
773 Todd Cruz .05 .15
774 Tom Gorman .05 .15
775 Dave Parker .08 .25
776 Craig Reynolds .05 .15
777 Tom Paciorek .05 .15
778 Andy Hawkins .05 .15
779 Jim Sundberg .08 .25
780 Steve Carlton .15 .40
781 Checklist 661-792 .08 .25
782 Steve Balboni .05 .15
783 Luis Leal .05 .15
784 Leon Roberts .05 .15
785 Joaquin Andujar .08 .25
786 Wade Boggs .15 .40
Bob Ojeda TL
787 Bill Campbell .05 .15
788 Milt May .05 .15
789 Bert Blyleven .08 .25
790 Doug DeCinces .05 .15
791 Terry Forster .08 .25
792 Bill Russell .08 .25

1984 Topps Glossy All-Stars

The cards in this 22-card set measure the standard size. Unlike the 1983 Topps Glossy set which was not distributed with its regular baseball cards, the 1984 Topps Glossy set was distributed as inserts in Topps Rak-Paks. The set features the nine American and National League All-Stars who started in the 1983 All Star game in Chicago. The managers and team captains (Yastrzemski and Bench) complete the set. The cards are numbered on the back and are ordered by position within league (AL: 1-11 and NL: 12-22).

COMPLETE SET (22) 2.00 5.00
1 Harvey Kuenn MG .01 .05
2 Rod Carew .20 .50
3 Manny Trillo .01 .05
4 George Brett .40 1.00
5 Robin Yount .20 .50
6 Jim Rice .02 .10
7 Fred Lynn .02 .10
8 Dave Winfield .20 .50
9 Ted Simmons .02 .10
10 Dave Stieb .01 .05
11 Carl Yastrzemski CAPT .20 .50
12 Whitey Herzog MG .01 .05
13 Al Oliver .02 .10
14 Steve Sax .02 .10
15 Mike Schmidt .30 .75
16 Ozzie Smith .40 1.00
17 Tim Raines .05 .15
18 Andre Dawson .08 .25
19 Dale Murphy .08 .25
20 Gary Carter .15 .40
21 Mario Soto .01 .05
22 Johnny Bench CAPT .20 .50

1984 Topps Glossy Send-Ins

The cards in this 40-card set measure the standard size. Similar to last year's glossy set, this set was issued as a bonus prize to Topps All-Star Baseball Game cards found in wax packs. Twenty-five bonus runs from the game cards were necessary to obtain a five card subset of the series. There were eight different subsets of five cards. The cards are numbered and the set contains 20 stars from each league.

COMPLETE SET (40) 4.80 12.00
1 Pete Rose .50 1.25
2 Lance Parrish .07 .20
3 Steve Rogers .02 .10
4 Eddie Murray .40 1.00
5 Johnny Ray .02 .10
6 Rickey Henderson .75 2.00
7 Atlee Hammaker .02 .10
8 Wade Boggs .60 1.50
9 Gary Carter .50 1.25
10 Jack Morris .07 .20
11 Darrell Evans .07 .20
12 George Brett 1.00 2.50
13 Bob Horner .02 .10
14 Ron Guidry .07 .20
15 Nolan Ryan 2.00 5.00
16 Dave Winfield .40 1.00
17 Ozzie Smith .75 2.00
18 Ted Simmons .07 .20
19 Bill Madlock .02 .10
20 Tony Armas .02 .10
21 Al Oliver .07 .20
22 Jim Rice .07 .20
23 George Hendrick .02 .10
24 Dave Stieb .02 .10
25 Pedro Guerrero .02 .10
26 Rod Carew .40 1.00
27 Steve Carlton .40 1.00
28 Dave Righetti .07 .20
29 Darryl Strawberry .20 .50
30 Lou Whitaker .07 .20
31 Dale Murphy .10 .30
32 LaMarr Hoyt .02 .10
33 Jesse Orosco .07 .20
34 Cecil Cooper .07 .20
35 Andre Dawson .20 .50
36 Robin Yount .50 1.25
37 Tim Raines .10 .30
38 Dan Quisenberry .02 .10
39 Mike Schmidt .75 2.00
40 Carlton Fisk .60 1.50

1984 Topps Traded

In what was now standard procedure, Topps issued its standard-size Traded (or extended) set for the fourth year in a row. Several of 1984's top rookies not contained in the regular set are pictured in the Traded set. Extended Rookie Cards in this set include Dwight Gooden, Jimmy Key, Mark Langston, Jose Rijo, and Bret Saberhagen. Again this year, the Topps affiliate in Ireland printed the cards, and the cards were available through hobby channels only in factory set form. The set numbering is in alphabetical order by player's name. The 132-card sets were shipped to dealers in 100-ct set cases. A few cards have been seen with a "grey" logo for Topps, these cards draw a significant multiplier of the regular Topps Traded cards, but are not yet known in sufficient quantity to price in our checklist.

COMP.FACT.SET (132) 15.00 30.00
1T Willie Aikens .15 .40
2T Luis Aponte .15 .40
3T Mike Armstrong .15 .40
4T Bob Bailor .15 .40
5T Dusty Baker .25 .60
6T Steve Balboni .15 .40
7T Alan Bannister .15 .40
8T Dave Beard .15 .40
9T Joe Beckwith .15 .40
10T Bruce Berenyi .15 .40
11T Dave Bergman .15 .40
12T Tony Bernazard .15 .40
13T Yogi Berra MG .60 1.50
14T Barry Bonnell .15 .40
15T Phil Bradley .40 1.00
16T Fred Breining .15 .40
17T Bill Buckner .25 .60
18T Ray Burris .15 .40
19T John Butcher .15 .40
20T Brett Butler .25 .60
21T Enos Cabell .15 .40
22T Bill Campbell .15 .40
23T Bill Caudill .15 .40
24T Bob Clark .15 .40
25T Bryan Clark .15 .40
26T Jaime Cocanower .15 .40
27T Ron Darling XRC .75 2.00
28T Alvin Davis XRC .40 1.00
29T Ken Dayley .15 .40
30T Jeff Dedmon .15 .40
31T Bob Dernier .15 .40
32T Carlos Diaz .15 .40
33T Mike Easler .15 .40
34T Dennis Eckersley .40 1.00
35T Jim Essian .15 .40
36T Darrell Evans .25 .60
37T Mike Fitzgerald .15 .40
38T Tim Foli .15 .40
39T George Frazier .15 .40
40T Rich Gale .15 .40
41T Barbaro Garbey .15 .40
42T Dwight Gooden XRC 4.00 10.00
43T Rich Gossage .25 .60
44T Wayne Gross .15 .40
45T Mark Gubicza XRC .40 1.00
46T Jackie Gutierrez .15 .40
47T Mel Hall .25 .60
48T Toby Harrah .25 .60
49T Ron Hassey .15 .40
50T Rich Hebner .15 .40
51T Willie Hernandez .15 .40
52T Ricky Horton .15 .40
53T Art Howe .15 .40
54T Dane Iorg .15 .40
55T Brook Jacoby .40 1.00
56T Mike Jeffcoat XRC .20 .50
57T Dave Johnson MG .15 .40
58T Lynn Jones .15 .40
59T Ruppert Jones .15 .40
60T Mike Jorgensen .15 .40
61T Bob Kearney .15 .40
62T Jimmy Key XRC .75 2.00
63T Dave Kingman .25 .60
64T Jerry Koosman .25 .60
65T Wayne Krenchicki .15 .40
66T Rusty Kuntz .15 .40
67T Rene Lachemann MG .15 .40
68T Frank LaCorte .15 .40
69T Dennis Lamp .15 .40
70T Mark Langston XRC .75 2.00
71T Rick Leach .15 .40
72T Craig Lefferts .20 .50
73T Gary Lucas .15 .40
74T Jerry Martin .15 .40
75T Carmelo Martinez .15 .40
76T Mike Mason XRC .20 .50
77T Gary Matthews .25 .60
78T Andy McGaffigan .15 .40
79T Larry Milbourne .15 .40
80T Sid Monge .15 .40
81T Jackie Moore MG .15 .40
82T Joe Morgan .25 .60
83T Graig Nettles .25 .60
84T Phil Niekro .25 .60
85T Ken Oberkfell .15 .40
86T Mike O'Berry .15 .40
87T Al Oliver .25 .60
88T Jorge Orta .15 .40
89T Amos Otis .25 .60
90T Dave Parker .25 .60
91T Tony Perez .40 1.00
92T Gerald Perry .40 1.00
93T Gary Pettis .15 .40
94T Rob Picciolo .15 .40
95T Vern Rapp MG .15 .40
96T Floyd Rayford .15 .40
97T Randy Ready XRC .40 1.00
98T Ron Reed .15 .40
99T Gene Richards .15 .40
100T Jose Rijo XRC .75 2.00
101T Jeff D. Robinson .15 .40
102T Ron Romanick .15 .40
103T Pete Rose 2.00 5.00
104T Bret Saberhagen XRC 1.50 4.00
105T Juan Samuel XRC .75 2.00
106T Scott Sanderson .15 .40
107T Dick Schofield XRC .40 1.00
108T Tom Seaver .60 1.50
109T Jim Slaton .15 .40
110T Mike Smithson .15 .40
111T Lary Sorensen .15 .40
112T Tim Stoddard .15 .40
113T Champ Summers .15 .40
114T Jim Sundberg .25 .60
115T Rick Sutcliffe .25 .60
116T Craig Swan .15 .40
117T Tim Teufel XRC .40 1.00
118T Derrel Thomas .15 .40
119T Gorman Thomas .25 .60
120T Alex Trevino .15 .40
121T Manny Trillo .15 .40
122T John Tudor .25 .60
123T Tom Underwood .15 .40
124T Mike Vail .15 .40
125T Tom Waddell .15 .40
126T Gary Ward .15 .40
127T Curtis Wilkerson .15 .40
128T Frank Williams .15 .40
129T Glenn Wilson .25 .60
130T John Wockenfuss .15 .40
131T Ned Yost .15 .40
132T Checklist 1T-132T .15 .40

1984 Topps Traded Tiffany

This 132-card standard-size set was issued by Topps as a premium parallel to their regular issue. This set was printed in the Topps Ireland factory and are differentiated from the regular cards by their glossy sheen and clean backs. These sets were only available through the Topps hobby distribution system. Topps issued these sets only if a dealer ordered the regular Tiffany sets, therefore approximately 10,000 of these sets were produced as well.

COMP.FACT.SET (132) 30.00 60.00
*STARS: .6X TO 1.5X BASIC CARDS
*ROOKIES: 1X TO 2.5X BASIC CARDS

1985 Topps

The 1985 Topps set contains 792 standard-size full-color cards. Cards were primarily distributed in 15-card wax packs, 51-card rack packs and factory (usually available through retail catalogs) sets. The wax packs were issued with an 35 cent SRP and were packaged 36 packs to a box and 20 boxes to a case. Manager cards feature the team checklist on the reverse. Full color card fronts feature both the Topps and team logos along with the team name, player's name, and his position. The first ten cards

(1-10) are Record Breakers, cards 131-143 are Father and Sons, and cards 701 to 722 portray All-Star selections. Cards 271-282 represent "First Draft Picks" still active in professional baseball and cards 389-404 feature selected members of the 1984 U.S. Olympic Baseball Team. Rookie Cards include Roger Clemens, Eric Davis, Shawon Dunston, Dwight Gooden, Orel Hershiser, Jimmy Key, Mark Langston, Mark McGwire, Terry Pendleton, Kirby Puckett and Bret Saberhagen.

COMPLETE SET (792) 40.00 80.00
COMP.FACT.SET (792) 100.00 175.00
1 Carlton Fisk RB .08 .25
2 Steve Garvey RB .05 .15
3 Dwight Gooden RB .25 .60
4 Cliff Johnson RB .05 .15
5 Joe Morgan RB .05 .15
6 Pete Rose RB .15 .40
7 Nolan Ryan RB .60 1.50
8 Juan Samuel RB .05 .15
9 Bruce Sutter RB .05 .15
10 Don Sutton RB .05 .15
11 Ralph Houk MG .05 .15
12 Dave Lopes .08 .25
13 Tim Lollar .05 .15
14 Chris Bando .05 .15
15 Jerry Koosman .08 .25
16 Bobby Meacham .05 .15
17 Mike Scott .08 .25
18 Mickey Hatcher .05 .15
19 George Frazier .05 .15
20 Chet Lemon .08 .25
21 Lee Tunnell .05 .15
22 Duane Kuiper .05 .15
23 Bret Saberhagen RC .40 1.00
24 Jesse Barfield .08 .25
25 Steve Bedrosian .05 .15
26 Roy Smalley .05 .15
27 Bruce Berenyi .05 .15
28 Dann Bilardello .05 .15
29 Odell Jones .05 .15
30 Cal Ripken 1.00 2.50
31 Terry Whitfield .05 .15
32 Chuck Porter .05 .15
33 Tito Landrum .05 .15
34 Ed Nunez .05 .15
35 Graig Nettles .08 .25
36 Fred Breining .05 .15
37 Reid Nichols .05 .15
38 Jackie Moore MG .05 .15
39 John Wockenfuss .05 .15
40 Phil Niekro .08 .25
41 Mike Fischlin .05 .15
42 Luis Sanchez .05 .15
43 Andre David .05 .15
44 Dickie Thon .05 .15
45 Greg Minton .05 .15
46 Gary Woods .05 .15
47 Dave Rozema .05 .15
48 Tony Fernandez .08 .25
49 Butch Davis .05 .15
50 John Candelaria .05 .15
51 Bob Watson .05 .15
52 Jerry Dybzinski .05 .15
53 Tom Gorman .05 .15
54 Cesar Cedeno .08 .25
55 Frank Tanana .08 .25
56 Jim Dwyer .05 .15
57 Pat Zachry .05 .15
58 Orlando Mercado .05 .15
59 Rick Waits .05 .15
60 George Hendrick .08 .25
61 Curt Kaufman .05 .15
62 Mike Ramsey .05 .15
63 Steve McCatty .05 .15
64 Mark Bailey .05 .15
65 Bill Buckner .08 .25
66 Dick Williams MG .05 .15
67 Rafael Santana .05 .15
68 Von Hayes .05 .15
69 Jim Winn .05 .15
70 Don Baylor .08 .25
71 Tim Laudner .05 .15
72 Rick Sutcliffe .08 .25
73 Rusty Kuntz .05 .15
74 Mike Krukow .05 .15
75 Willie Upshaw .05 .15
76 Alan Bannister .05 .15
77 Joe Beckwith .05 .15
78 Scott Fletcher .05 .15
79 Rick Mahler .05 .15
80 Keith Hernandez .08 .25
81 Lenn Sakata .05 .15
82 Joe Price .05 .15
83 Charlie Moore .05 .15
84 Spike Owen .05 .15
85 Mike Marshall .05 .15
86 Don Aase .05 .15
87 David Green .05 .15
88 Bryn Smith .05 .15
89 Jackie Gutierrez .05 .15
90 Rich Gossage .08 .25
91 Jeff Burroughs .05 .15
92 Paul Owens MG .05 .15
93 Don Schulze .05 .15
94 Toby Harrah .08 .25
95 Jose Cruz .08 .25
96 Johnny Ray .05 .15
97 Pete Filson .05 .15
98 Steve Lake .05 .15
99 Milt Wilcox .05 .15
100 George Brett .60 1.50
101 Jim Acker .05 .15
102 Tommy Dunbar .05 .15
103 Randy Lerch .05 .15
104 Mike Fitzgerald .05 .15
105 Ron Kittle .05 .15
106 Pascual Perez .05 .15
107 Tom Foley .05 .15
108 Darnell Coles .05 .15
109 Gary Roenicke .05 .15
110 Alejandro Pena .05 .15
111 Doug DeCinces .05 .15
112 Tom Tellmann .05 .15
113 Tom Herr .05 .15
114 Bob James .05 .15
115 Rickey Henderson .30 .75
116 Dennis Boyd .05 .15
117 Greg Gross .05 .15
118 Eric Show .05 .15
119 Pat Corrales MG .05 .15
120 Steve Kemp .05 .15
121 Checklist: 1-132 .05 .15
122 Tom Brunansky .05 .15
123 Dave Smith .05 .15
124 Rich Hebner .05 .15
125 Kent Tekulve .05 .15
126 Ruppert Jones .05 .15
127 Mark Gubicza RC* .15 .40
128 Ernie Whitt .05 .15
129 Gene Garber .05 .15
130 Al Oliver .08 .25
131 Buddy Bell FS .08 .25
Gus Bell
132 Dale Berra FS .25 .60
Yogi Berra
133 Bob Boone FS .05 .15
Ray Boone
134 Terry Francona FS .08 .25
Tito Francona
135 Terry Kennedy FS .05 .15
Bob Kennedy
136 Jeff Kunkel FS .05 .15
Bill Kunkel
137 Vance Law FS .08 .25
Vern Law
138 Dick Schofield FS .05 .15
Dick Schofield
139 Joel Skinner FS .05 .15
Bob Skinner
140 Roy Smalley Jr. FS .05 .15
Roy Smalley
141 Mike Stenhouse FS .05 .15
Dave Stenhouse
142 Steve Trout FS .05 .15
Dizzy Trout
143 Ozzie Virgil FS .05 .15
Ossie Virgil
144 Ron Gardenhire .05 .15
145 Alvin Davis RC* .15 .40
146 Gary Redus .05 .15
147 Bill Swaggerty .05 .15
148 Steve Yeager .08 .25
149 Dickie Noles .05 .15
150 Jim Rice .08 .25
151 Moose Haas .05 .15
152 Steve Braun .05 .15
153 Frank LaCorte .05 .15
154 Angel Salazar .05 .15
155 Yogi Berra MG .25 .60
156 Craig Reynolds .05 .15
157 Tug McGraw .08 .25
158 Pat Tabler .05 .15
159 Carlos Diaz .05 .15
160 Lance Parrish .08 .25
161 Ken Schrom .05 .15
162 Benny Distefano .05 .15
163 Dennis Eckersley .15 .40
164 Jorge Orta .05 .15
165 Dusty Baker .08 .25
166 Keith Atherton .05 .15
167 Rufino Linares .05 .15
168 Garth Iorg .05 .15
169 Dan Spillner .05 .15
170 George Foster .08 .25
171 Bill Stein .05 .15
172 Jack Perconte .05 .15
173 Mike Young .05 .15
174 Rick Honeycutt .05 .15
175 Dave Parker .08 .25
176 Bill Schroeder .05 .15
177 Dave Von Ohlen .05 .15
178 Miguel Dilone .05 .15
179 Tommy John .08 .25
180 Dave Winfield .08 .25
181 Roger Clemens RC 8.00 20.00
182 Tim Flannery .05 .15
183 Larry McWilliams .05 .15
184 Carmen Castillo .05 .15
185 Al Holland .05 .15
186 Bob Lillis MG .05 .15
187 Mike Walters .05 .15
188 Greg Pryor .05 .15
189 Warren Brusstar .05 .15
190 Rusty Staub .08 .25
191 Steve Nicosia .05 .15
192 Howard Johnson .08 .25
193 Jimmy Key RC .30 .75
194 Dave Stegman .05 .15
195 Glenn Hubbard .05 .15
196 Pete O'Brien .05 .15
197 Mike Warren .05 .15
198 Eddie Milner .05 .15
199 Dennis Martinez .08 .25
200 Reggie Jackson .15 .40
201 Burt Hooton .05 .15
202 Gorman Thomas .08 .25
203 Bob McClure .05 .15
204 Art Howe .05 .15
205 Steve Rogers .08 .25
206 Phil Garner .08 .25
207 Mark Clear .05 .15
208 Champ Summers .05 .15
209 Bill Campbell .05 .15
210 Gary Matthews .08 .25
211 Clay Christiansen .05 .15
212 George Vukovich .05 .15
213 Billy Gardner MG .05 .15
214 John Tudor .08 .25
215 Bob Brenly .05 .15
216 Jerry Don Gleaton .05 .15
217 Leon Roberts .05 .15
218 Doyle Alexander .05 .15
219 Gerald Perry .05 .15
220 Fred Lynn .08 .25
221 Ron Reed .05 .15
222 Hubie Brooks .05 .15
223 Tom Hume .05 .15
224 Al Cowens .05 .15
225 Mike Boddicker .05 .15
226 Juan Beniquez .05 .15
227 Danny Darwin .05 .15
228 Dion James .05 .15
229 Dave LaPoint .05 .15
230 Gary Carter .08 .25
231 Dwayne Murphy .05 .15
232 Dave Beard .05 .15
233 Ed Jurak .05 .15
234 Jerry Narron .05 .15
235 Garry Maddox .05 .15
236 Mark Thurmond .05 .15
237 Julio Franco .08 .25
238 Jose Rijo RC .30 .75
239 Tim Teufel .05 .15
240 Dave Stieb .08 .25
241 Jim Frey MG .05 .15
242 Greg Harris .05 .15
243 Barbaro Garbey .05 .15
244 Mike Jones .05 .15
245 Chili Davis .08 .25
246 Mike Norris .05 .15
247 Wayne Tolleson .05 .15
248 Terry Forster .08 .25
249 Harold Baines .08 .25
250 Jesse Orosco .05 .15
251 Brad Gulden .05 .15
252 Dan Ford .05 .15
253 Sid Bream RC .15 .40
254 Pete Vuckovich .05 .15
255 Lonnie Smith .05 .15
256 Mike Stanton .05 .15
257 Bryan Little UER .05 .15
Name spelled Brian on front
258 Mike C. Brown .05 .15
259 Gary Allenson .05 .15
260 Dave Righetti .08 .25
261 Checklist: 133-264 .05 .15
262 Greg Booker .05 .15
263 Mel Hall .05 .15
264 Joe Sambito .05 .15
265 Juan Samuel .05 .15
266 Frank Viola .08 .25
267 Henry Cotto RC .05 .15
268 Chuck Tanner MG .05 .15
269 Doug Baker .05 .15
270 Dan Quisenberry .05 .15
271 Tim Foli FDP .05 .15
272 Jeff Burroughs FDP .05 .15
273 Bill Almon FDP .05 .15
274 F.Bannister FDP76 .05 .15
275 Harold Baines FDP77 .05 .15
276 Bob Horner FDP .05 .15
277 Al Chambers FDP .05 .15
278 Darryl Strawberry .15 .40
FDP80
279 Mike Moore FDP .05 .15
280 S.Dunston FDP82 RC .30 .75
281 T.Belcher RC FDP83 .15 .40
282 Shawn Abner FDP RC .05 .15
283 Fran Mullins .05 .15
284 Marty Bystrom .05 .15
285 Dan Driessen .05 .15
286 Rudy Law .05 .15
287 Walt Terrell .05 .15
288 Jeff Kunkel .05 .15
289 Tom Underwood .05 .15
290 Cecil Cooper .08 .25
291 Bob Welch .08 .25
292 Brad Komminsk .05 .15
293 Curt Young .05 .15
294 Tom Nieto .05 .15
295 Joe Niekro .05 .15
296 Ricky Nelson .05 .15
297 Gary Lucas .05 .15
298 Marty Barrett .05 .15
299 Andy Hawkins .05 .15
300 Rod Carew .15 .40
301 John Montefusco .05 .15
302 Tim Corcoran .05 .15
303 Mike Jeffcoat .05 .15
304 Gary Gaetti .08 .25
305 Dale Berra .05 .15
306 Rick Reuschel .08 .25
307 Sparky Anderson MG .08 .25
308 John Wathan .05 .15
309 Mike Witt .05 .15
310 Manny Trillo .05 .15
311 Jim Gott .05 .15
312 Marc Hill .05 .15
313 Dave Schmidt .05 .15
314 Ron Oester .05 .15
315 Doug Sisk .05 .15
316 John Lowenstein .05 .15
317 Jack Lazorko .05 .15
318 Ted Simmons .08 .25
319 Jeff Jones .05 .15
320 Dale Murphy .15 .40
321 Ricky Horton .05 .15
322 Dave Stapleton .05 .15
323 Andy McGaffigan .05 .15
324 Bruce Bochy .05 .15
325 John Denny .05 .15
326 Kevin Bass .05 .15
327 Brook Jacoby .05 .15
328 Bob Shirley .05 .15
329 Ron Washington .05 .15
330 Leon Durham .05 .15
331 Bill Laskey .05 .15
332 Brian Harper .05 .15
333 Willie Hernandez .05 .15
334 Dick Howser MG .05 .15
335 Bruce Benedict .05 .15
336 Rance Mulliniks .05 .15
337 Billy Sample .05 .15
338 Britt Burns .05 .15
339 Danny Heep .05 .15
340 Robin Yount .40 1.00
341 Floyd Rayford .05 .15
342 Ted Power .05 .15
343 Bill Russell .08 .25
344 Dave Henderson .05 .15
345 Charlie Lea .05 .15
346 Terry Pendleton RC .30 .75
347 Rick Langford .05 .15
348 Bob Boone .08 .25
349 Domingo Ramos .05 .15
350 Wade Boggs .25 .60
351 Juan Agosto .05 .15
352 Joe Morgan .08 .25
353 Julio Solano .05 .15
354 Andre Robertson .05 .15
355 Bert Blyleven .08 .25
356 Dave Meier .05 .15
357 Rich Bordi .05 .15
358 Tony Pena .05 .15
359 Pat Sheridan .05 .15
360 Steve Carlton .08 .25
361 Alfredo Griffin .05 .15
362 Craig McMurtry .05 .15
363 Ron Hodges .05 .15
364 Richard Dotson .05 .15
365 Danny Ozark MG .05 .15
366 Todd Cruz .05 .15
367 Keefe Cato .05 .15
368 Dave Bergman .05 .15
369 R.J. Reynolds .05 .15
370 Bruce Sutter .08 .25
371 Mickey Rivers .05 .15
372 Roy Howell .05 .15
373 Mike Moore .05 .15
374 Brian Downing .08 .25
375 Jeff Reardon .08 .25
376 Jeff Newman .05 .15
377 Checklist: 265-396 .05 .15
378 Alan Wiggins .05 .15
379 Charles Hudson .05 .15
380 Ken Griffey .08 .25
381 Roy Smith .05 .15
382 Denny Walling .05 .15
383 Rick Lysander .05 .15
384 Jody Davis .05 .15
385 Jose DeLeon .05 .15
386 Dan Gladden RC .15 .40
387 Buddy Biancalana .05 .15
388 Bert Roberge .05 .15
389 Rod Dedeaux OLY CO RC .08 .25
390 Sid Akins OLY RC .05 .15
391 Flavio Alfaro OLY RC .05 .15
392 Don August OLY RC .05 .15
393 S.Bankhead RC OLY .05 .15
394 Bob Caffrey OLY RC .05 .15
395 Mike Dunne OLY RC .05 .15
396 Gary Green OLY RC .05 .15
397 John Hoover OLY RC .05 .15
398 Shane Mack RC OLY .15 .40
399 John Marzano OLY RC .05 .15
400 O.McDowell RC OLY .15 .40
401 Mark McGwire OLY RC 12.50 30.00
402 Pat Pacillo OLY RC .05 .15
403 Cory Snyder OLY RC .30 .75
404 Billy Swift OLY RC .15 .40
405 Tom Veryzer .05 .15
406 Len Whitehouse .05 .15
407 Bobby Ramos .05 .15
408 Sid Monge .05 .15
409 Brad Wellman .05 .15
410 Bob Horner .08 .25
411 Bobby Cox MG .08 .25
412 Bud Black .05 .15
413 Vance Law .05 .15
414 Gary Ward .05 .15
415 Ron Darling UER .08 .25
(No trivia answer)
416 Wayne Gross .05 .15
417 John Franco RC .30 .75
418 Ken Landreaux .05 .15
419 Mike Caldwell .05 .15
420 Andre Dawson .08 .25
421 Dave Rucker .05 .15
422 Carney Lansford .08 .25
423 Barry Bonnell .05 .15
424 Al Nipper .05 .15
425 Mike Hargrove .05 .15
426 Vern Ruhle .05 .15
427 Mario Ramirez .05 .15
428 Larry Andersen .05 .15
429 Rick Cerone .05 .15
430 Ron Davis .05 .15
431 U.L. Washington .05 .15
432 Thad Bosley .05 .15
433 Jim Morrison .05 .15
434 Gene Richards .05 .15
435 Dan Petry .05 .15
436 Willie Aikens .05 .15
437 Al Jones .05 .15
438 Joe Torre MG .08 .25
439 Junior Ortiz .05 .15
440 Fernando Valenzuela .08 .25
441 Duane Walker .05 .15
442 Ken Forsch .05 .15
443 George Wright .05 .15
444 Tony Phillips .05 .15
445 Tippy Martinez .05 .15
446 Jim Sundberg .08 .25
447 Jeff Lahti .05 .15
448 Derrel Thomas .05 .15
449 Phil Bradley .15 .40
450 Steve Garvey .08 .25
451 Bruce Hurst .05 .15
452 John Castino .05 .15
453 Tom Waddell .05 .15
454 Glenn Wilson .05 .15
455 Bob Knepper .05 .15
456 Tim Foli .05 .15
457 Cecilio Guante .05 .15
458 Randy Johnson .05 .15
459 Charlie Leibrandt .05 .15
460 Ryne Sandberg .50 1.25
461 Marty Castillo .05 .15
462 Gary Lavelle .05 .15
463 Dave Collins .05 .15
464 Mike Mason RC .05 .15
465 Bob Grich .08 .25
466 Tony LaRussa MG .08 .25
467 Ed Lynch .05 .15
468 Wayne Krenchicki .05 .15
469 Sammy Stewart .05 .15
470 Steve Sax .05 .15
471 Pete Ladd .05 .15
472 Jim Essian .05 .15
473 Tim Wallach .05 .15
474 Kurt Kepshire .05 .15
475 Andre Thornton .05 .15
476 Jeff Stone RC .05 .15
477 Bob Ojeda .05 .15
478 Kurt Bevacqua .05 .15
479 Mike Madden .05 .15
480 Lou Whitaker .08 .25
481 Dale Murray .05 .15
482 Harry Spilman .05 .15
483 Mike Smithson .05 .15
484 Larry Bowa .08 .25
485 Matt Young .05 .15
486 Steve Balboni .05 .15
487 Frank Williams .05 .15
488 Joel Skinner .05 .15
489 Bryan Clark .05 .15
490 Jason Thompson .05 .15
491 Rick Camp .05 .15
492 Dave Johnson MG .05 .15
493 Orel Hershiser RC .75 2.00
494 Rich Dauer .05 .15
495 Mario Soto .08 .25
496 Donnie Scott .05 .15
497 Gary Pettis UER .05 .15
(Photo actually
Gary's little
brother Lynn)
498 Ed Romero .05 .15
499 Danny Cox .05 .15
500 Mike Schmidt .60 1.50
501 Dan Schatzeder .05 .15
502 Rick Miller .05 .15
503 Tim Conroy .05 .15
504 Jerry Willard .05 .15
505 Jim Beattie .05 .15
506 Franklin Stubbs .05 .15
507 Ray Fontenot .05 .15
508 John Shelby .05 .15
509 Milt May .05 .15
510 Kent Hrbek .08 .25
511 Lee Smith .08 .25
512 Tom Brookens .05 .15
513 Lynn Jones .05 .15
514 Jeff Cornell .05 .15
515 Dave Concepcion .08 .25
516 Roy Lee Jackson .05 .15
517 Jerry Martin .05 .15
518 Chris Chambliss .08 .25
519 Doug Rader MG .05 .15
520 LaMarr Hoyt .05 .15
521 Rick Dempsey .05 .15
522 Paul Molitor .08 .25
523 Candy Maldonado .05 .15
524 Rob Wilfong .05 .15
525 Darrell Porter .05 .15
526 David Palmer .05 .15
527 Checklist: 397-528 .05 .15
528 Bill Krueger .05 .15
529 Rich Gedman .05 .15
530 Dave Dravecky .05 .15
531 Joe Lefebvre .05 .15
532 Frank DiPino .05 .15
533 Tony Bernazard .05 .15
534 Brian Dayett .05 .15
535 Pat Putnam .05 .15
536 Kirby Puckett RC 5.00 12.00
537 Don Robinson .05 .15
538 Keith Moreland .05 .15
539 Aurelio Lopez .05 .15
540 Claudell Washington .05 .15
541 Mark Davis .05 .15
542 Don Slaught .05 .15
543 Mike Squires .05 .15
544 Bruce Kison .05 .15
545 Lloyd Moseby .05 .15
546 Brent Gaff .05 .15
547 Pete Rose MG .15 .40
548 Larry Parrish .05 .15
549 Mike Scioscia .08 .25
550 Scott McGregor .05 .15
551 Andy Van Slyke .15 .40
552 Chris Codiroli .05 .15
553 Bob Clark .05 .15
554 Doug Flynn .05 .15
555 Bob Stanley .05 .15
556 Sixto Lezcano .05 .15
557 Len Barker .05 .15
558 Carmelo Martinez .05 .15
559 Jay Howell .05 .15
560 Bill Madlock .08 .25
561 Darryl Motley .05 .15
562 Houston Jimenez .05 .15
563 Dick Ruthven .05 .15
564 Alan Ashby .05 .15
565 Kirk Gibson .08 .25
566 Ed VandeBerg .05 .15
567 Joel Youngblood .05 .15
568 Cliff Johnson .05 .15
569 Ken Oberkfell .05 .15
570 Darryl Strawberry .25 .60
571 Charlie Hough .08 .25
572 Tom Paciorek .05 .15
573 Jay Tibbs .05 .15
574 Joe Altobelli MG .05 .15
575 Pedro Guerrero .08 .25
576 Jaime Cocanower .05 .15
577 Chris Speier .05 .15
578 Terry Francona .08 .25
579 Ron Romanick .05 .15
580 Dwight Evans .15 .40
581 Mark Wagner .05 .15
582 Ken Phelps .05 .15
583 Bobby Brown .05 .15
584 Kevin Gross .05 .15
585 Butch Wynegar .05 .15
586 Bill Scherrer .05 .15
587 Doug Frobel .05 .15
588 Bobby Castillo .05 .15
589 Bob Dernier .05 .15
590 Ray Knight .08 .25
591 Larry Herndon .05 .15
592 Jeff D. Robinson .05 .15
593 Rick Leach .05 .15
594 Curt Wilkerson .05 .15
595 Larry Gura .05 .15
596 Jerry Hairston .05 .15
597 Brad Lesley .05 .15
598 Jose Oquendo .05 .15
599 Storm Davis .05 .15
600 Pete Rose .60 1.50
601 Tom Lasorda MG .15 .40
602 Jeff Dedmon .05 .15
603 Rick Manning .05 .15
604 Daryl Sconiers .05 .15
605 Ozzie Smith .40 1.00
606 Rich Gale .05 .15
607 Bill Almon .05 .15
608 Craig Lefferts .05 .15
609 Broderick Perkins .05 .15
610 Jack Morris .08 .25
611 Ozzie Virgil .05 .15
612 Mike Armstrong .05 .15
613 Terry Puhl .05 .15
614 Al Williams .05 .15
615 Marvell Wynne .05 .15
616 Scott Sanderson .05 .15
617 Willie Wilson .08 .25
618 Pete Falcone .05 .15
619 Jeff Leonard .05 .15
620 Dwight Gooden RC .75 2.00
621 Marvis Foley .05 .15
622 Luis Leal .05 .15
623 Greg Walker .05 .15
624 Benny Ayala .05 .15
625 Mark Langston RC .30 .75
626 German Rivera .05 .15
627 Eric Davis RC .75 2.00
628 Rene Lachemann MG .05 .15
629 Dick Schofield .05 .15
630 Tim Raines .08 .25
631 Bob Forsch .05 .15
632 Bruce Bochte .05 .15
633 Glenn Hoffman .05 .15
634 Bill Dawley .05 .15
635 Terry Kennedy .05 .15
636 Shane Rawley .05 .15
637 Brett Butler .08 .25
638 Mike Pagliarulo .05 .15
639 Ed Hodge .05 .15
640 Steve Henderson .05 .15
641 Rod Scurry .05 .15
642 Dave Owen .05 .15
643 Johnny Grubb .05 .15
644 Mark Huismann .05 .15
645 Damaso Garcia .05 .15
646 Scot Thompson .05 .15
647 Rafael Ramirez .05 .15
648 Bob Jones .05 .15
649 Sid Fernandez .08 .25
650 Greg Luzinski .08 .25
651 Jeff Russell .05 .15
652 Joe Nolan .05 .15
653 Mark Brouhard .05 .15
654 Dave Anderson .05 .15
655 Joaquin Andujar .08 .25
656 Chuck Cottier MG .05 .15
657 Jim Slaton .05 .15
658 Mike Stenhouse .05 .15
659 Checklist: 529-660 .05 .15
660 Tony Gwynn .50 1.25
661 Steve Crawford .05 .15
662 Mike Heath .05 .15
663 Luis Aguayo .05 .15
664 Steve Farr RC .15 .40
665 Don Mattingly 1.00 2.50
666 Mike LaCoss .05 .15
667 Dave Engle .05 .15
668 Steve Trout .05 .15
669 Lee Lacy .05 .15
670 Tom Seaver .15 .40
671 Dane Iorg .05 .15
672 Juan Berenguer .05 .15
673 Buck Martinez .05 .15
674 Atlee Hammaker .05 .15
675 Tony Perez .15 .40
676 Albert Hall .05 .15
677 Wally Backman .05 .15
678 Joey McLaughlin .05 .15
679 Bob Kearney .05 .15
680 Jerry Reuss .05 .15
681 Ben Oglivie .08 .25
682 Doug Corbett .05 .15
683 Whitey Herzog MG .08 .25
684 Bill Doran .05 .15
685 Bill Caudill .05 .15
686 Mike Easler .05 .15
687 Bill Gullickson .05 .15
688 Len Matuszek .05 .15
689 Luis DeLeon .05 .15
690 Alan Trammell .08 .25
691 Dennis Rasmussen .05 .15
692 Randy Bush .05 .15
693 Tim Stoddard .05 .15
694 Joe Carter .25 .60
695 Rick Rhoden .05 .15
696 John Rabb .05 .15
697 Onix Concepcion .05 .15
698 Jorge Bell .08 .25
699 Donnie Moore .05 .15
700 Eddie Murray .25 .60
701 Eddie Murray AS .15 .40
702 Damaso Garcia AS .05 .15
703 George Brett AS .25 .60
704 Cal Ripken AS .60 1.50
705 Dave Winfield AS .05 .15
706 Rickey Henderson AS .15 .40
707 Tony Armas AS .05 .15
708 Lance Parrish AS .05 .15
709 Mike Boddicker AS .05 .15
710 Frank Viola AS .05 .15
711 Dan Quisenberry AS .05 .15
712 Keith Hernandez AS .05 .15
713 Ryne Sandberg AS .25 .60
714 Mike Schmidt AS .25 .60
715 Ozzie Smith AS .25 .60
716 Dale Murphy AS .08 .25
717 Tony Gwynn AS .40 1.00
718 Jeff Leonard AS .05 .15
719 Gary Carter AS .05 .15
720 Rick Sutcliffe AS .05 .15
721 Bob Knepper AS .05 .15
722 Bruce Sutter AS .05 .15
723 Dave Stewart .08 .25
724 Oscar Gamble .05 .15
725 Floyd Bannister .05 .15
726 Al Bumbry .05 .15
727 Frank Pastore .05 .15
728 Bob Bailor .05 .15
729 Don Sutton .08 .25
730 Dave Kingman .08 .25
731 Neil Allen .05 .15
732 John McNamara MG .05 .15
733 Tony Scott .05 .15
734 John Henry Johnson .05 .15
735 Garry Templeton .08 .25
736 Jerry Mumphrey .05 .15
737 Bo Diaz .05 .15
738 Omar Moreno .05 .15
739 Ernie Camacho .05 .15
740 Jack Clark .08 .25
741 John Butcher .05 .15
742 Ron Hassey .05 .15
743 Frank White .08 .25
744 Doug Bair .05 .15
745 Buddy Bell .08 .25
746 Jim Clancy .05 .15
747 Alex Trevino .05 .15
748 Lee Mazzilli .08 .25
749 Julio Cruz .05 .15
750 Rollie Fingers .08 .25
751 Kelvin Chapman .05 .15
752 Bob Owchinko .05 .15
753 Greg Brock .05 .15
754 Larry Milbourne .05 .15

755 Ken Singleton .08 .25
756 Rob Picciolo .05 .15
757 Willie McGee .08 .25
758 Ray Burris .05 .15
759 Jim Fanning MG .05 .15
760 Nolan Ryan 1.25 3.00
761 Jerry Remy .05 .15
762 Eddie Whitson .05 .15
763 Kiko Garcia .05 .15
764 Jamie Easterly .05 .15
765 Willie Randolph .08 .25
766 Paul Mirabella .05 .15
767 Darrell Brown .05 .15
768 Ron Cey .08 .25
769 Joe Cowley .05 .15
770 Carlton Fisk .15 .40
771 Geoff Zahn .05 .15
772 Johnnie LeMaster .05 .15
773 Hal McRae .08 .25
774 Dennis Lamp .05 .15
775 Mookie Wilson .08 .25
776 Jerry Royster .05 .15
777 Ned Yost .05 .15
778 Mike Davis .05 .15
779 Nick Esasky .05 .15
780 Mike Flanagan .05 .15
781 Jim Gantner .05 .15
782 Tom Niedenfuer .05 .15
783 Mike Jorgensen .05 .15
784 Checklist: 661-792 .05 .15
785 Tony Armas .08 .25
786 Enos Cabell .05 .15
787 Jim Wohlford .05 .15
788 Steve Comer .05 .15
789 Luis Salazar .05 .15
790 Ron Guidry .08 .25
791 Ivan DeJesus .05 .15
792 Darrell Evans .08 .25

1985 Topps Tiffany

For the second year, Topps issued a special glossy set through their hobby dealers. This set is a direct parallel to the regular Topps issue. These 792 cards are differentiated from the regular issue by their glossy fronts and very clear backs. These sets were only available through Topps' hobby dealers. According to original reports in 1985, only 5,000 of these sets were produced.

COMP.FACT.SET (792) 350.00 600.00
*STARS: 3X TO 8X BASIC CARDS
*ROOKIES: 2.5X TO 6X BASIC CARDS

1985 Topps Glossy All-Stars

The cards in this 22-card set the standard size. Similar in design, both front and back, to last year's Glossy set, this edition features the managers, starting nine players and honorary captains of the National and American League teams in the 1984 All-Star game. The set is numbered on the reverse with players essentially ordered by position within league, NL: 1-11 and AL: 12-22.

COMPLETE SET (22) 2.00 5.00
1 Paul Owens MG .01 .05
2 Steve Garvey .05 .15
3 Ryne Sandberg .40 1.00
4 Mike Schmidt .30 .75
5 Ozzie Smith .40 1.00
6 Tony Gwynn .50 1.25
7 Dale Murphy .07 .20
8 Darryl Strawberry .02 .10
9 Gary Carter .20 .50
10 Charlie Lea .01 .05
11 Willie McCovey CAPT .02 .10
12 Joe Altobelli MG .01 .05
13 Rod Carew .20 .50
14 Lou Whitaker .02 .10
15 George Brett .40 1.00
16 Cal Ripken .75 2.00
17 Dave Winfield .20 .50
18 Chet Lemon .01 .05
19 Reggie Jackson .20 .50
20 Lance Parrish .01 .05
21 Dave Stieb .01 .05
22 Hank Greenberg CAPT .02 .10

1985 Topps Traded

In its now standard procedure, Topps issued its standard-size Traded (or extended) set for the fifth year in a row. In addition to the typical factory set hobby distribution, Topps tested the limited issuance of these Traded cards in wax packs. Card design is identical to the regular-issue 1985 Topps set except for whiter card stock and T-suffixed numbering on back. The set numbering is in alphabetical order by player's name. The key extended Rookie Cards in this set include Vince Coleman, Ozzie Guillen, and Mickey Tettleton.

COMP.FACT.SET (132) 3.00 8.00
1T Don Aase .05 .15
2T Bill Almon .05 .15
3T Benny Ayala .05 .15
4T Dusty Baker .15 .40
5T George Bamberger MG .05 .15
6T Dale Berra .05 .15
7T Rich Bordi .05 .15
8T Daryl Boston XRC .08 .25
9T Hubie Brooks .05 .15
10T Chris Brown XRC .08 .25
11T Tom Browning XRC .20 .50
12T Al Bumbry .05 .15
13T Ray Burris .05 .15
14T Jeff Burroughs .05 .15
15T Bill Campbell .05 .15
16T Don Carman .05 .15
17T Gary Carter .15 .40
18T Bobby Castillo .05 .15
19T Bill Caudill .05 .15
20T Rick Cerone .05 .15
21T Bryan Clark .05 .15
22T Jack Clark .15 .40
23T Pat Clements .05 .15
24T Vince Coleman XRC .40 1.00
25T Dave Collins .05 .15
26T Danny Darwin .05 .15
27T Jim Davenport MG .05 .15
28T Jerry Davis .05 .15
29T Brian Dayett .05 .15
30T Ivan DeJesus .05 .15
31T Ken Dixon .05 .15
32T Mariano Duncan XRC .20 .50
33T John Felske MG .05 .15
34T Mike Fitzgerald .05 .15
35T Ray Fontenot .05 .15
36T Greg Gagne XRC .20 .50
37T Oscar Gamble .05 .15
38T Scott Garrelts .05 .15
39T Bob L. Gibson .05 .15
40T Jim Gott .05 .15
41T David Green .05 .15
42T Alfredo Griffin .05 .15
43T Ozzie Guillen XRC 2.00 5.00
44T Eddie Haas MG .05 .15
45T Terry Harper .05 .15
46T Toby Harrah .15 .40
47T Greg Harris .05 .15
48T Ron Hassey .05 .15
49T Rickey Henderson 1.00 2.50
50T Steve Henderson .05 .15
51T George Hendrick .15 .40
52T Joe Hesketh .05 .15
53T Teddy Higuera XRC .20 .50
54T Donnie Hill .05 .15
55T Al Holland .05 .15
56T Burt Hooton .05 .15
57T Jay Howell .05 .15
58T Ken Howell .05 .15
59T LaMarr Hoyt .05 .15
60T Tim Hulett XRC .08 .25
61T Bob James .05 .15
62T Steve Jeltz XRC .08 .25
63T Cliff Johnson .05 .15
64T Howard Johnson .15 .40
65T Ruppert Jones .05 .15
66T Steve Kemp .05 .15
67T Bruce Kison .05 .15
68T Alan Knicely .05 .15
69T Mike LaCoss .05 .15
70T Lee Lacy .05 .15
71T Dave LaPoint .05 .15
72T Gary Lavelle .05 .15
73T Vance Law .05 .15
74T Johnnie LeMaster .05 .15
75T Sixto Lezcano .05 .15
76T Tim Lollar .05 .15
77T Fred Lynn .15 .40
78T Billy Martin MG .30 .75
79T Ron Mathis .05 .15
80T Len Matuszek .05 .15
81T Gene Mauch MG .05 .15
82T Oddibe McDowell .20 .50
83T Roger McDowell XRC .20 .50
84T John McNamara MG .05 .15
85T Donnie Moore .05 .15
86T Gene Nelson .05 .15
87T Steve Nicosia .05 .15
88T Al Oliver .15 .40
89T Joe Orsulak XRC .20 .50
90T Rob Picciolo .05 .15
91T Chris Pittaro .05 .15
92T Jim Presley .20 .50
93T Rick Reuschel .15 .40
94T Bert Roberge .05 .15
95T Bob Rodgers MG .05 .15
96T Jerry Royster .05 .15
97T Dave Rozema .05 .15
98T Dave Rucker .05 .15
99T Vern Ruhle .05 .15
100T Paul Runge XRC .08 .25
101T Mark Salas .05 .15
102T Luis Salazar .05 .15
103T Joe Sambito .05 .15
104T Rick Schu .05 .15
105T Donnie Scott .05 .15
106T Larry Sheets XRC .08 .25
107T Don Slaught .05 .15
108T Roy Smalley .05 .15
109T Lonnie Smith .05 .15
110T Nate Snell UER .05 .15
(Headings on back
for a batter)
111T Chris Speier .05 .15
112T Mike Stenhouse .05 .15
113T Tim Stoddard .05 .15
114T Jim Sundberg .15 .40
115T Bruce Sutter .15 .40
116T Don Sutton .15 .40
117T Kent Tekulve .05 .15
118T Tom Tellmann .05 .15
119T Walt Terrell .05 .15
120T M.Tettleton XRC .20 .50
121T Derrel Thomas .05 .15
122T Rich Thompson .05 .15
123T Alex Trevino .05 .15
124T John Tudor .15 .40
125T Jose Uribe .05 .15
126T Bobby Valentine MG .15 .40
127T Dave Von Ohlen .05 .15
128T U.L. Washington .05 .15
129T Earl Weaver MG .15 .40
130T Eddie Whitson .05 .15
131T Herm Winningham .05 .15
132T Checklist 1-132 .05 .15

1985 Topps Traded Tiffany

Just as in 1984, Topps issued an glossy update set. The 132-card standard-size set is a parallel to the Topps update issue. These sets were issued to the hobby through Topps dealer network and were printed in Ireland. Again -- similar to the regular Tiffany issue -- it is believed that 5,000 of these sets were produced.

COMP.FACT.SET (132) 20.00 50.00
*STARS: 1.5X TO 4X BASIC CARDS
*ROOKIES: 1.5X TO 4X BASIC CARDS

1986 Topps

This set consists of 792 standard-size cards. Cards were primarily distributed in 15-card wax packs, 48-card rack packs and factors sets. This was also the first year Topps offered a factory set to hobby dealers. Standard card fronts feature a black and white split border framing a color photo with team name on top and player name on bottom. Subsets include Pete Rose tribute (1-7), Record Breakers (201-207), Turn Back the Clock (401-405), All-Stars (701-722) and Team Leaders (seeded throughout the set). Manager cards feature the team checklist on the reverse. There are two uncorrected errors involving misnumbered cards; see card numbers 51, 57, 141, and 171 in the checklist below. The key Rookie Cards in this set are Darren Daulton, Len Dykstra, Cecil Fielder, and Mickey Tettleton.

COMPLETE SET (792) 10.00 25.00
COMP.X-MAS.SET (792) 75.00 150.00
1 Pete Rose .75 2.00
2 Pete Rose 63-66 .08 .25
3 Pete Rose 67-70 .08 .25
4 Pete Rose 71-74 .08 .25
5 Pete Rose 75-78 .08 .25
6 Pete Rose 79-82 .08 .25
7 Pete Rose 83-85 .08 .25
8 Dwayne Murphy .02 .10
9 Roy Smith .02 .10
10 Tony Gwynn .25 .60
11 Bob Ojeda .02 .10
12 Jose Uribe .02 .10
13 Bob Kearney .02 .10
14 Julio Cruz .02 .10
15 Eddie Whitson .02 .10
16 Rick Schu .02 .10
17 Mike Stenhouse .02 .10
18 Brent Gaff .02 .10
19 Rich Hebner .02 .10
20 Lou Whitaker .05 .15
21 George Bamberger MG .02 .10
22 Duane Walker .02 .10
23 Manny Lee RC .02 .10
24 Len Barker .02 .10
25 Willie Wilson .05 .15
26 Frank DiPino .02 .10
27 Ray Knight .05 .15
28 Eric Davis .15 .40
29 Tony Phillips .02 .10
30 Eddie Murray .15 .40
31 Jamie Easterly .02 .10
32 Steve Yeager .05 .15
33 Jeff Lahti .02 .10
34 Ken Phelps .02 .10
35 Jeff Reardon .05 .15
36 Lance Parrish TL .05 .15
37 Mark Thurmond .02 .10
38 Glenn Hoffman .02 .10
39 Dave Rucker .02 .10
40 Ken Griffey .05 .15
41 Brad Wellman .02 .10
42 Geoff Zahn .02 .10
43 Dave Engle .02 .10
44 Lance McCullers .02 .10
45 Damaso Garcia .02 .10
46 Billy Hatcher .02 .10
47 Juan Berenguer .02 .10
48 Bill Almon .02 .10
49 Rick Manning .02 .10
50 Dan Quisenberry .02 .10
51 Bobby Wine MG ERR .02 .10
Number of card on
back is actually 57)
52 Chris Welsh .02 .10
53 Len Dykstra RC .30 .75
54 John Franco .05 .15
55 Fred Lynn .05 .15
56 Tom Niedenfuer .02 .10
57 Bill Doran .02 .10
(See also 51)
58 Bill Krueger .02 .10
59 Andre Thornton .02 .10
60 Dwight Evans .08 .25
61 Karl Best .02 .10
62 Bob Boone .05 .15
63 Ron Roenicke .02 .10
64 Floyd Bannister .02 .10
65 Dan Driessen .02 .10
66 Bob Forsch TL .02 .10
67 Carmelo Martinez .02 .10
68 Ed Lynch .02 .10
69 Luis Aguayo .02 .10
70 Dave Winfield .05 .15
71 Ken Schrom .02 .10
72 Shawon Dunston .05 .15
73 Randy O'Neal .02 .10
74 Rance Mulliniks .02 .10
75 Jose DeLeon .02 .10
76 Dion James .02 .10
77 Charlie Leibrandt .02 .10
78 Bruce Benedict .02 .10
79 Dave Schmidt .02 .10
80 Darryl Strawberry .08 .25
81 Gene Mauch MG .02 .10
82 Tippy Martinez .02 .10
83 Phil Garner .05 .15
84 Curt Young .02 .10
85 Tony Perez .05 .15
(Eric Davis also
shown on card)
86 Tom Waddell .02 .10
87 Candy Maldonado .02 .10
88 Tom Nieto .02 .10
89 Randy St.Claire .02 .10
90 Garry Templeton .05 .15
91 Steve Crawford .02 .10
92 Al Cowens .02 .10
93 Scot Thompson .02 .10
94 Rich Bordi .02 .10
95 Ozzie Virgil .02 .10
96 Jim Clancy TL .02 .10
97 Gary Gaetti .05 .15
98 Dick Ruthven .02 .10
99 Buddy Biancalana .02 .10
100 Nolan Ryan .75 2.00
101 Dave Bergman .02 .10
102 Joe Orsulak RC .08 .25
103 Luis Salazar .02 .10
104 Sid Fernandez .02 .10
105 Gary Ward .02 .10
106 Ray Burris .02 .10
107 Rafael Ramirez .02 .10
108 Ted Power .02 .10
109 Len Matuszek .02 .10
110 Scott McGregor .02 .10
111 Roger Craig MG .05 .15
112 Bill Campbell .02 .10
113 U.L. Washington .02 .10
114 Mike C. Brown .02 .10
115 Jay Howell .02 .10
116 Brook Jacoby .02 .10
117 Bruce Kison .02 .10
118 Jerry Royster .02 .10
119 Barry Bonnell .02 .10
120 Steve Carlton .05 .15
121 Nelson Simmons .02 .10
122 Pete Filson .02 .10
123 Greg Walker .02 .10
124 Luis Sanchez .02 .10
125 Dave Lopes .05 .15
126 Mookie Wilson TL .02 .10
127 Jack Howell .02 .10
128 John Wathan .02 .10
129 Jeff Dedmon .02 .10
130 Alan Trammell .05 .15
131 Checklist: 1-132 .05 .15
132 Razor Shines .02 .10
133 Andy McGaffigan .02 .10
134 Carney Lansford .02 .10
135 Joe Niekro .02 .10
136 Mike Hargrove .02 .10
137 Charlie Moore .02 .10
138 Mark Davis .02 .10
139 Daryl Boston .02 .10
140 John Candelaria .02 .10
141 Chuck Cottier MG .02 .10
See also 171
142 Bob Jones .02 .10
143 Dave Van Gorder .02 .10
144 Doug Sisk .02 .10
145 Pedro Guerrero .05 .15
146 Jack Perconte .02 .10
147 Larry Sheets .02 .10
148 Mike Heath .02 .10
149 Brett Butler .05 .15
150 Joaquin Andujar .05 .15
151 Dave Stapleton .02 .10
152 Mike Morgan .02 .10
153 Ricky Adams .02 .10
154 Bert Roberge .02 .10
155 Bobby Grich .05 .15
156 Richard Dotson TL .02 .10
157 Ron Hassey .02 .10
158 Derrel Thomas .02 .10
159 Orel Hershiser UER .15 .40
(82 Alburquerque)
160 Chet Lemon .05 .15
161 Lee Tunnell .02 .10
162 Greg Gagne .05 .15
163 Pete Ladd .02 .10
164 Steve Balboni .02 .10
165 Mike Davis .02 .10
166 Dickie Thon .02 .10
167 Zane Smith .02 .10
168 Jeff Burroughs .02 .10
169 George Wright .02 .10
170 Gary Carter .05 .15
171 Bob Rodgers MG ERR .02 .10
Number of card on
back actually 141)
172 Jerry Reed .02 .10
173 Wayne Gross .02 .10
174 Brian Snyder .02 .10
175 Steve Sax .02 .10
176 Jay Tibbs .02 .10
177 Joel Youngblood .02 .10
178 Ivan DeJesus .02 .10
179 Stu Cliburn .02 .10
180 Don Mattingly .50 1.25
181 Al Nipper .02 .10
182 Bobby Brown .02 .10
183 Larry Andersen .02 .10
184 Tim Laudner .02 .10
185 Rollie Fingers .05 .15
186 Jose Cruz TL .02 .10
187 Scott Fletcher .02 .10
188 Bob Dernier .02 .10
189 Mike Mason .02 .10
190 George Hendrick .05 .15
191 Wally Backman .02 .10
192 Milt Wilcox .02 .10
193 Daryl Sconiers .02 .10
194 Craig McMurtry .02 .10
195 Dave Concepcion .05 .15
196 Doyle Alexander .02 .10
197 Enos Cabell .02 .10
198 Ken Dixon .02 .10
199 Dick Howser MG .02 .10
200 Mike Schmidt .40 1.00
201 Vince Coleman RB .05 .15
202 Dwight Gooden RB .08 .25
203 Keith Hernandez RB .02 .10
204 Phil Niekro RB .05 .15
205 Tony Perez RB .05 .15
206 Pete Rose RB .15 .40
207 F. Valenzuela RB .02 .10
208 Ramon Romero .02 .10
209 Randy Ready .02 .10
210 Calvin Schiraldi .02 .10
211 Ed Wojna .02 .10
212 Chris Speier .02 .10
213 Bob Shirley .02 .10
214 Randy Bush .02 .10
215 Frank White .05 .15
216 Dwayne Murphy TL .02 .10
217 Bill Scherrer .02 .10
218 Randy Hunt .02 .10
219 Dennis Lamp .02 .10
220 Bob Horner .05 .15
221 Dave Henderson .02 .10
222 Craig Gerber .02 .10
223 Atlee Hammaker .02 .10
224 Cesar Cedeno .05 .15
225 Ron Darling .05 .15
226 Lee Lacy .02 .10
227 Al Jones .02 .10
228 Tom Lawless .02 .10
229 Bill Gullickson .02 .10
230 Terry Kennedy .02 .10
231 Jim Frey MG .02 .10
232 Rick Rhoden .02 .10
233 Steve Lyons .02 .10
234 Doug Corbett .02 .10
235 Butch Wynegar .02 .10
236 Frank Eufemia .02 .10
237 Ted Simmons .05 .15
238 Larry Parrish .02 .10
239 Joel Skinner .02 .10
240 Tommy John .05 .15
241 Tony Fernandez .02 .10
242 Rich Thompson .02 .10
243 Johnny Grubb .02 .10
244 Craig Lefferts .02 .10
245 Jim Sundberg .05 .15
246 Steve Carlton TL .05 .15
247 Terry Harper .02 .10
248 Spike Owen .02 .10
249 Rob Deer .02 .10
250 Dwight Gooden .15 .40
251 Rich Dauer .02 .10
252 Bobby Castillo .02 .10
253 Dann Bilardello .02 .10
254 Ozzie Guillen RC .60 1.50
255 Tony Armas .05 .15
256 Kurt Kepshire .02 .10
257 Doug DeCinces .02 .10
258 Tim Burke .02 .10
259 Dan Pasqua .02 .10
260 Tony Pena .02 .10
261 Bobby Valentine MG .05 .15
262 Mario Ramirez .02 .10
263 Checklist: 133-264 .05 .15
264 Darren Daulton RC .20 .50
265 Ron Davis .02 .10
266 Keith Moreland .02 .10
267 Paul Molitor .05 .15
268 Mike Scott .05 .15
269 Dane Iorg .02 .10
270 Jack Morris .05 .15
271 Dave Collins .02 .10
272 Tim Tolman .02 .10
273 Jerry Willard .02 .10
274 Ron Gardenhire .02 .10
275 Charlie Hough .05 .15
276 Willie Randolph TL .05 .15
277 Jaime Cocanower .02 .10
278 Sixto Lezcano .02 .10
279 Al Pardo .02 .10
280 Tim Raines .05 .15
281 Steve Mura .02 .10
282 Jerry Mumphrey .02 .10
283 Mike Fischlin .02 .10
284 Brian Dayett .02 .10
285 Buddy Bell .05 .15
286 Luis DeLeon .02 .10
287 John Christensen .02 .10
288 Don Aase .02 .10
289 Johnnie LeMaster .02 .10
290 Carlton Fisk .08 .25
291 Tom Lasorda MG .08 .25
292 Chuck Porter .02 .10
293 Chris Chambliss .05 .15
294 Danny Cox .02 .10
295 Kirk Gibson .05 .15
296 Geno Petralli .02 .10
297 Tim Lollar .02 .10
298 Craig Reynolds .02 .10
299 Bryn Smith .02 .10
300 George Brett .40 1.00
301 Dennis Rasmussen .02 .10
302 Greg Gross .02 .10
303 Curt Wardle .02 .10
304 Mike Gallego RC .02 .10
305 Phil Bradley .02 .10
306 Terry Kennedy TL .02 .10
307 Dave Sax .02 .10
308 Ray Fontenot .02 .10
309 John Shelby .02 .10
310 Greg Minton .02 .10
311 Dick Schofield .02 .10
312 Tom Filer .02 .10
313 Joe DeSa .02 .10
314 Frank Pastore .02 .10
315 Mookie Wilson .05 .15
316 Sammy Khalifa .02 .10
317 Ed Romero .02 .10
318 Terry Whitfield .02 .10
319 Rick Camp .02 .10
320 Jim Rice .05 .15
321 Earl Weaver MG .05 .15
322 Bob Forsch .02 .10
323 Jerry Davis .02 .10
324 Dan Schatzeder .02 .10
325 Juan Beniquez .02 .10
326 Kent Tekulve .02 .10
327 Mike Pagliarulo .02 .10
328 Pete O'Brien .02 .10
329 Kirby Puckett .40 1.00
330 Rick Sutcliffe .05 .15
331 Alan Ashby .02 .10
332 Darryl Motley .02 .10
333 Tom Henke .05 .15
334 Ken Oberkfell .02 .10
335 Don Sutton .05 .15
336 Andre Thornton TL .05 .15
337 Darnell Coles .02 .10
338 Jorge Bell .05 .15
339 Bruce Berenyi .02 .10
340 Cal Ripken .60 1.50
341 Frank Williams .02 .10
342 Gary Redus .02 .10
343 Carlos Diaz .02 .10
344 Jim Wohlford .02 .10
345 Donnie Moore .02 .10
346 Bryan Little .02 .10
347 Teddy Higuera RC .08 .25
348 Cliff Johnson .02 .10
349 Mark Clear .02 .10
350 Jack Clark .05 .15
351 Chuck Tanner MG .02 .10
352 Harry Spilman .02 .10
353 Keith Atherton .02 .10
354 Tony Bernazard .02 .10
355 Lee Smith .05 .15
356 Mickey Hatcher .02 .10
357 Ed VandeBerg .02 .10
358 Rick Dempsey .02 .10
359 Mike LaCoss .02 .10
360 Lloyd Moseby .02 .10
361 Shane Rawley .02 .10
362 Tom Paciorek .02 .10
363 Terry Forster .05 .15
364 Reid Nichols .02 .10
365 Mike Flanagan .02 .10
366 Dave Concepcion TL .05 .15
367 Aurelio Lopez .02 .10
368 Greg Brock .02 .10
369 Al Holland .02 .10
370 Vince Coleman RC .20 .50
371 Bill Stein .02 .10
372 Ben Oglivie .05 .15
373 Urbano Lugo .02 .10
374 Terry Francona .05 .15
375 Rich Gedman .02 .10
376 Bill Dawley .02 .10
377 Joe Carter .05 .15
378 Bruce Bochte .02 .10
379 Bobby Meacham .02 .10
380 LaMarr Hoyt .02 .10
381 Ray Miller MG .02 .10
382 Ivan Calderon RC .08 .25
383 Chris Brown RC .02 .10
384 Steve Trout .02 .10
385 Cecil Cooper .05 .15
386 Cecil Fielder RC .40 1.00
387 Steve Kemp .02 .10
388 Dickie Noles .02 .10
389 Glenn Davis .02 .10
390 Tom Seaver .08 .25
391 Julio Franco .05 .15
392 John Russell .02 .10
393 Chris Pittaro .02 .10
394 Checklist: 265-396 .05 .15
395 Scott Garrelts .02 .10
396 Dwight Evans TL .08 .25
397 Steve Buechele RC .08 .25
398 Earnie Riles .02 .10
399 Bill Swift .02 .10
400 Rod Carew .08 .25
401 Fernando Valenzuela .02 .10
TBC '81
402 Tom Seaver TBC '76 .05 .15
403 Willie Mays TBC '71 .15 .40
404 Frank Robinson .05 .15
TBC '66
405 Roger Maris TBC '61 .15 .40
406 Scott Sanderson .02 .10
407 Sal Butera .02 .10
408 Dave Smith .02 .10
409 Paul Runge RC .02 .10
410 Dave Kingman .05 .15
411 Sparky Anderson MG .05 .15
412 Jim Clancy .02 .10
413 Tim Flannery .02 .10
414 Tom Gorman .02 .10
415 Hal McRae .05 .15
416 Dennis Martinez .05 .15
417 R.J. Reynolds .02 .10
418 Alan Knicely .02 .10
419 Frank Wills .02 .10
420 Von Hayes .02 .10
421 David Palmer .02 .10
422 Mike Jorgensen .02 .10
423 Dan Spillner .02 .10
424 Rick Miller .02 .10
425 Larry McWilliams .02 .10
426 Charlie Moore TL .02 .10
427 Joe Cowley .02 .10
428 Max Venable .02 .10
429 Greg Booker .02 .10
430 Kent Hrbek .05 .15
431 George Frazier .02 .10
432 Mark Bailey .02 .10
433 Chris Codiroli .02 .10
434 Curt Wilkerson .02 .10
435 Bill Caudill .02 .10
436 Doug Flynn .02 .10
437 Rick Mahler .02 .10
438 Clint Hurdle .02 .10
439 Rick Honeycutt .02 .10

440 Alvin Davis .02 .10
441 Whitey Herzog MG .08 .25
442 Ron Robinson .02 .10
443 Bill Buckner .05 .15
444 Alex Trevino .02 .10
445 Bert Blyleven .05 .15
446 Lenn Sakata .02 .10
447 Jerry Don Gleaton .02 .10
448 Herm Winningham .02 .10
449 Rod Scurry .02 .10
450 Graig Nettles .05 .15
451 Mark Brown .02 .10
452 Bob Clark .02 .10
453 Steve Jeltz .02 .10
454 Burt Hooton .02 .10
455 Willie Randolph .05 .15
456 Dale Murphy TL .08 .25
457 Mickey Tettleton RC .08 .25
458 Kevin Bass .02 .10
459 Luis Leal .02 .10
460 Leon Durham .02 .10
461 Walt Terrell .02 .10
462 Domingo Ramos .02 .10
463 Jim Gott .02 .10
464 Ruppert Jones .02 .10
465 Jesse Orosco .02 .10
466 Tom Foley .02 .10
467 Bob James .02 .10
468 Mike Scioscia .05 .15
469 Storm Davis .02 .10
470 Bill Madlock .05 .15
471 Bobby Cox MG .05 .15
472 Joe Hesketh .02 .10
473 Mark Brouhard .02 .10
474 John Tudor .05 .15
475 Juan Samuel .02 .10
476 Ron Mathis .02 .10
477 Mike Easler .02 .10
478 Andy Hawkins .02 .10
479 Bob Melvin .02 .10
480 Oddibe McDowell .02 .10
481 Scott Bradley .02 .10
482 Rick Lysander .02 .10
483 George Vukovich .02 .10
484 Donnie Hill .02 .10
485 Gary Matthews .05 .15
486 Bobby Grich TL .05 .15
487 Bret Saberhagen .05 .15
488 Lou Thornton .02 .10
489 Jim Winn .02 .10
490 Jeff Leonard .02 .10
491 Pascual Perez .02 .10
492 Kelvin Chapman .02 .10
493 Gene Nelson .02 .10
494 Gary Roenicke .02 .10
495 Mark Langston .05 .15
496 Jay Johnstone .02 .10
497 John Stuper .02 .10
498 Tito Landrum .02 .10
499 Bob L. Gibson .02 .10
500 Rickey Henderson .15 .40
501 Dave Johnson MG .02 .10
502 Glen Cook .02 .10
503 Mike Fitzgerald .02 .10
504 Denny Walling .02 .10
505 Jerry Koosman .05 .15
506 Bill Russell .05 .15
507 Steve Ontiveros RC .02 .10
508 Alan Wiggins .02 .10
509 Ernie Camacho .02 .10
510 Wade Boggs .08 .25
511 Ed Nunez .02 .10
512 Thad Bosley .02 .10
513 Ron Washington .02 .10
514 Mike Jones .02 .10
515 Darrell Evans .05 .15
516 Greg Minton TL .02 .10
517 Milt Thompson RC .08 .25
518 Buck Martinez .02 .10
519 Danny Darwin .02 .10
520 Keith Hernandez .05 .15
521 Nate Snell .02 .10
522 Bob Bailor .02 .10
523 Joe Price .02 .10
524 Darrell Miller .02 .10
525 Marvell Wynne .02 .10
526 Charlie Lea .02 .10
527 Checklist: 397-528 .05 .15
528 Terry Pendleton .05 .15
529 Marc Sullivan .02 .10
530 Rich Gossage .05 .15
531 Tony LaRussa MG .05 .15
532 Don Carman .02 .10
533 Billy Sample .02 .10
534 Jeff Calhoun .02 .10
535 Toby Harrah .05 .15
536 Jose Rijo .05 .15
537 Mark Salas .02 .10
538 Dennis Eckersley .08 .25
539 Glenn Hubbard .02 .10
540 Dan Petry .02 .10
541 Jorge Orta .02 .10
542 Don Schulze .02 .10
543 Jerry Narron .02 .10
544 Eddie Milner .02 .10
545 Jimmy Key .05 .15
546 Dave Henderson TL .02 .10
547 Roger McDowell RC .08 .25
548 Mike Young .02 .10
549 Bob Welch .05 .15
550 Tom Herr .02 .10
551 Dave LaPoint .02 .10
552 Marc Hill .02 .10
553 Jim Morrison .02 .10
554 Paul Householder .02 .10
555 Hubie Brooks .02 .10
556 John Denny .02 .10
557 Gerald Perry .02 .10
558 Tim Stoddard .02 .10
559 Tommy Dunbar .02 .10
560 Dave Righetti .05 .15
561 Bob Lillis MG .02 .10
562 Joe Beckwith .02 .10
563 Alejandro Sanchez .02 .10
564 Warren Brusstar .02 .10
565 Tom Brunansky .02 .10
566 Alfredo Griffin .02 .10
567 Jeff Barkley .02 .10
568 Donnie Scott .02 .10
569 Jim Acker .02 .10
570 Rusty Staub .05 .15
571 Mike Jeffcoat .02 .10
572 Paul Zuvella .02 .10
573 Tom Hume .02 .10
574 Ron Kittle .02 .10
575 Mike Boddicker .02 .10
576 Andre Dawson TL .02 .10
577 Jerry Reuss .02 .10
578 Lee Mazzilli .05 .15
579 Jim Slaton .02 .10
580 Willie McGee .05 .15
581 Bruce Hurst .02 .10
582 Jim Gantner .02 .10
583 Al Bumbry .02 .10
584 Brian Fisher RC .02 .10
585 Garry Maddox .02 .10
586 Greg Harris .02 .10
587 Rafael Santana .02 .10
588 Steve Lake .02 .10
589 Sid Bream .02 .10
590 Bob Knepper .02 .10
591 Jackie Moore MG .02 .10
592 Frank Tanana .05 .15
593 Jesse Barfield .05 .15
594 Chris Bando .02 .10
595 Dave Parker .05 .15
596 Onix Concepcion .02 .10
597 Sammy Stewart .02 .10
598 Jim Presley .02 .10
599 Rick Aguilera RC .08 .25
600 Dale Murphy .08 .25
601 Gary Lucas .02 .10
602 Mariano Duncan RC .08 .25
603 Bill Laskey .02 .10
604 Gary Pettis .02 .10
605 Dennis Boyd .02 .10
606 Hal McRae TL .05 .15
607 Ken Dayley .02 .10
608 Bruce Bochy .02 .10
609 Barbaro Garbey .02 .10
610 Ron Guidry .05 .15
611 Gary Woods .02 .10
612 Richard Dotson .02 .10
613 Roy Smalley .02 .10
614 Rick Waits .02 .10
615 Johnny Ray .02 .10
616 Glenn Brummer .02 .10
617 Lonnie Smith .02 .10
618 Jim Pankovits .02 .10
619 Danny Heep .02 .10
620 Bruce Sutter .05 .15
621 John Felske MG .02 .10
622 Gary Lavelle .02 .10
623 Floyd Rayford .02 .10
624 Steve McCatty .02 .10
625 Bob Brenly .02 .10
626 Roy Thomas .02 .10
627 Ron Oester .02 .10
628 Kirk McCaskill RC .08 .25
629 Mitch Webster .02 .10
630 Fernando Valenzuela .05 .15
631 Steve Braun .02 .10
632 Dave Von Ohlen .02 .10
633 Jackie Gutierrez .02 .10
634 Roy Lee Jackson .02 .10
635 Jason Thompson .02 .10
636 Lee Smith TL .05 .15
637 Rudy Law .02 .10
638 John Butcher .02 .10
639 Bo Diaz .02 .10
640 Jose Cruz .05 .15
641 Wayne Tolleson .02 .10
642 Ray Searage .02 .10
643 Tom Brookens .02 .10
644 Mark Gubicza .02 .10
645 Dusty Baker .05 .15
646 Mike Moore .02 .10
647 Mel Hall .02 .10
648 Steve Bedrosian .02 .10
649 Ronn Reynolds .02 .10
650 Dave Stieb .05 .15
651 Billy Martin MG .08 .25
652 Tom Browning .02 .10
653 Jim Dwyer .02 .10
654 Ken Howell .02 .10
655 Manny Trillo .02 .10
656 Brian Harper .02 .10
657 Juan Agosto .02 .10
658 Rob Wilfong .02 .10
659 Checklist: 529-660 .05 .15
660 Steve Garvey .05 .15
661 Roger Clemens 1.50 4.00
662 Bill Schroeder .02 .10
663 Neil Allen .02 .10
664 Tim Corcoran .02 .10
665 Alejandro Pena .02 .10
666 Charlie Hough TL .05 .15
667 Tim Teufel .02 .10
668 Cecilio Guante .02 .10
669 Ron Cey .05 .15
670 Willie Hernandez .02 .10
671 Lynn Jones .02 .10
672 Rob Picciolo .02 .10
673 Ernie Whitt .02 .10
674 Pat Tabler .02 .10
675 Claudell Washington .02 .10
676 Matt Young .02 .10
677 Nick Esasky .02 .10
678 Dan Gladden .02 .10
679 Britt Burns .02 .10
680 George Foster .05 .15
681 Dick Williams MG .02 .10
682 Junior Ortiz .02 .10
683 Andy Van Slyke .08 .25
684 Bob McClure .02 .10
685 Tim Wallach .02 .10
686 Jeff Stone .02 .10
687 Mike Trujillo .02 .10
688 Larry Herndon .02 .10
689 Dave Stewart .05 .15
690 Ryne Sandberg UER .30 .75
(No Topps logo
on front)
691 Mike Madden .02 .10
692 Dale Berra .02 .10
693 Tom Tellmann .02 .10
694 Garth Iorg .02 .10
695 Mike Smithson .02 .10
696 Bill Russell TL .05 .15
697 Bud Black .02 .10
698 Brad Komminsk .02 .10
699 Pat Corrales MG .02 .10
700 Reggie Jackson .08 .25
701 Keith Hernandez AS .02 .10
702 Tom Herr AS .02 .10
703 Tim Wallach AS .02 .10
704 Ozzie Smith AS .15 .40
705 Dale Murphy AS .05 .15
706 Pedro Guerrero AS .02 .10
707 Willie McGee AS .02 .10
708 Gary Carter AS .02 .10
709 Dwight Gooden AS .08 .25
710 John Tudor AS .02 .10
711 Jeff Reardon AS .02 .10
712 Don Mattingly AS .25 .60
713 Damaso Garcia AS .02 .10
714 George Brett AS .15 .40
715 Cal Ripken AS .15 .40
716 Rickey Henderson AS .08 .25
717 Dave Winfield AS .02 .10
718 George Bell AS .02 .10
719 Carlton Fisk AS .05 .15
720 Bret Saberhagen AS .02 .10
721 Ron Guidry AS .02 .10
722 Dan Quisenberry AS .02 .10
723 Marty Bystrom .02 .10
724 Tim Hulett .02 .10
725 Mario Soto .05 .15
726 Rick Dempsey TL .05 .15
727 David Green .02 .10
728 Mike Marshall .02 .10
729 Jim Beattie .02 .10
730 Ozzie Smith .25 .60
731 Don Robinson .02 .10
732 Floyd Youmans .02 .10
733 Ron Romanick .02 .10
734 Marty Barrett .02 .10
735 Dave Dravecky .02 .10
736 Glenn Wilson .02 .10
737 Pete Vuckovich .02 .10
738 Andre Robertson .02 .10
739 Dave Rozema .02 .10
740 Lance Parrish .05 .15
741 Pete Rose MG .15 .40
742 Frank Viola .05 .15
743 Pat Sheridan .02 .10
744 Lary Sorensen .02 .10
745 Willie Upshaw .02 .10
746 Denny Gonzalez .02 .10
747 Rick Cerone .02 .10
748 Steve Henderson .02 .10
749 Ed Jurak .02 .10
750 Gorman Thomas .05 .15
751 Howard Johnson .05 .15
752 Mike Krukow .02 .10
753 Dan Ford .02 .10
754 Pat Clements .02 .10
755 Harold Baines .05 .15
756 Rick Rhoden TL .05 .15
757 Darrell Porter .02 .10
758 Dave Anderson .02 .10
759 Moose Haas .02 .10
760 Andre Dawson .05 .15
761 Don Slaught .02 .10
762 Eric Show .02 .10
763 Terry Puhl .02 .10
764 Kevin Gross .02 .10
765 Don Baylor .05 .15
766 Rick Langford .02 .10
767 Jody Davis .02 .10
768 Vern Ruhle .02 .10
769 Harold Reynolds RC .30 .75
770 Vida Blue .05 .15
771 John McNamara MG .02 .10
772 Brian Downing .05 .15
773 Greg Pryor .02 .10
774 Terry Leach .02 .10
775 Al Oliver .05 .15
776 Gene Garber .02 .10
777 Wayne Krenchicki .02 .10
778 Jerry Hairston .02 .10
779 Rick Reuschel .05 .15
780 Robin Yount .25 .60
781 Joe Nolan .02 .10
782 Ken Landreaux .02 .10
783 Ricky Horton .02 .10
784 Alan Bannister .02 .10
785 Bob Stanley .02 .10
786 Mickey Hatcher TL .02 .10
787 Vance Law .02 .10
788 Marty Castillo .02 .10
789 Kurt Bevacqua .02 .10
790 Phil Niekro .05 .15
791 Checklist: 661-792 .05 .15
792 Charles Hudson .02 .10

1986 Topps Tiffany

These 792 cards form a parallel to the regular Topps set. These cards, available only through the Topps dealer network were issued in factory sealed boxes. Each case contained six sets. These cards have a "glossy" front and a very clear back. These cards were printed in the Topps Ireland plant. Reports within the hobby indicate that it is believed that 5,000 of these sets were produced.

COMP.FACT.SET (792) 75.00 150.00
*STARS: 5X TO 12X BASIC CARDS
*ROOKIES: 5X TO 12X BASIC CARDS

1986 Topps Glossy All-Stars

This 22-card standard-size set was distributed as an insert, one card per rak pack. The players featured are the starting lineups of the 1985 All-Star Game played in Minnesota. The cards are very colorful and have a high gloss finish.

COMPLETE SET (22) 2.00 5.00

1 Sparky Anderson MG .01 .05
2 Eddie Murray .20 .50
3 Lou Whitaker .02 .10
4 George Brett .40 1.00
5 Cal Ripken .75 2.00
6 Jim Rice .02 .10
7 Rickey Henderson .20 .50
8 Dave Winfield .20 .50
9 Carlton Fisk .15 .40
10 Jack Morris .02 .10
11 AL Team Photo .01 .05
12 Dick Williams MG .01 .05
13 Steve Garvey .02 .10
14 Tom Herr .01 .05
15 Graig Nettles .02 .10
16 Ozzie Smith .40 1.00
17 Tony Gwynn .40 1.00
18 Dale Murphy .07 .20
19 Darryl Strawberry .02 .10
20 Terry Kennedy .01 .05
21 LaMarr Hoyt .01 .05
22 NL Team Photo .01 .05

1986 Topps Traded

This 132-card standard-size Traded set was distributed in factory set form, which were packed 100 to a case, in a red and white box through hobby dealers. The cards are identical in style to regular-issue 1986 Topps cards except for whiter stock and t-suffixed numbering. The key extended Rookie Cards in this set are Barry Bonds, Bobby Bonilla, Jose Canseco, Will Clark, Andres Galarraga, Bo Jackson, Wally Joyner, John Kruk, and Kevin Mitchell.

COMP.FACT.SET (132) 15.00 40.00
1T Andy Allanson XRC .02 .10
2T Neil Allen .02 .10
3T Joaquin Andujar .05 .15
4T Paul Assenmacher .15 .40
5T Scott Bailes .02 .10
6T Don Baylor .05 .15
7T Steve Bedrosian .02 .10
8T Juan Beniquez .02 .10
9T Juan Berenguer .02 .10
10T Mike Bielecki .02 .10
11T Barry Bonds XRC 6.00 15.00
12T Bobby Bonilla XRC .30 .75
13T Juan Bonilla .02 .10
14T Rich Bordi .02 .10
15T Steve Boros MG .02 .10
16T Rick Burleson .02 .10
17T Bill Campbell .02 .10
18T Tom Candiotti .02 .10
19T John Cangelosi .02 .10
20T Jose Canseco XRC 1.50 4.00
21T Carmen Castillo .02 .10
22T Rick Cerone .02 .10
23T John Cerutti .02 .10
24T Will Clark XRC .60 1.50
25T Mark Clear .02 .10
26T Darnell Coles .02 .10
27T Dave Collins .02 .10
28T Tim Conroy .02 .10
29T Joe Cowley .02 .10
30T Joel Davis .02 .10
31T Rob Deer .02 .10
32T John Denny .02 .10
33T Mike Easler .02 .10
34T Mark Eichhorn .02 .10
35T Steve Farr .02 .10
36T Scott Fletcher .02 .10
37T Terry Forster .05 .15
38T Terry Francona .05 .15
39T Jim Fregosi MG .02 .10
40T Andres Galarraga XRC .40 1.00
41T Ken Griffey .05 .15
42T Bill Gullickson .02 .10
43T Jose Guzman XRC .02 .10
44T Moose Haas .02 .10
45T Billy Hatcher .02 .10
46T Mike Heath .02 .10
47T Tom Hume .02 .10
48T Pete Incaviglia XRC .15 .40
49T Dane Iorg .02 .10
50T Bo Jackson XRC 2.00 5.00
51T Wally Joyner XRC .30 .75
52T Charlie Kerfeld .02 .10
53T Eric King .02 .10
54T Bob Kipper .02 .10
55T Wayne Krenchicki .02 .10
56T John Kruk XRC .40 1.00
57T Mike LaCoss .02 .10
58T Pete Ladd .02 .10
59T Mike Laga .02 .10
60T Hal Lanier MG .02 .10
61T Dave LaPoint .02 .10
62T Rudy Law .02 .10
63T Rick Leach .02 .10
64T Tim Leary .02 .10
65T Dennis Leonard .02 .10
66T Jim Leyland MG XRC .20 .50
67T Steve Lyons .02 .10
68T Mickey Mahler .02 .10
69T Candy Maldonado .02 .10
70T Roger Mason XRC .02 .10
71T Bob McClure .02 .10
72T Andy McGaffigan .02 .10
73T Gene Michael MG .02 .10
74T Kevin Mitchell XRC .30 .75
75T Omar Moreno .02 .10
76T Jerry Mumphrey .02 .10
77T Phil Niekro .05 .15
78T Randy Niemann .02 .10
79T Juan Nieves .02 .10
80T Otis Nixon XRC .30 .75
81T Bob Ojeda .02 .10
82T Jose Oquendo .02 .10
83T Tom Paciorek .02 .10
84T David Palmer .02 .10
85T Frank Pastore .02 .10
86T Lou Piniella MG .05 .15
87T Dan Plesac .15 .40
88T Darrell Porter .02 .10
89T Rey Quinones .02 .10
90T Gary Redus .02 .10
91T Bip Roberts XRC .15 .40
92T Billy Joe Robidoux XRC .02 .10
93T Jeff D. Robinson .02 .10
94T Gary Roenicke .02 .10
95T Ed Romero .02 .10
96T Angel Salazar .02 .10
97T Joe Sambito .02 .10
98T Billy Sample .02 .10
99T Dave Schmidt .02 .10
100T Ken Schrom .02 .10
101T Tom Seaver .08 .25
102T Ted Simmons .05 .15
103T Sammy Stewart .02 .10
104T Kurt Stillwell .02 .10
105T Franklin Stubbs .02 .10
106T Dale Sveum .02 .10
107T Chuck Tanner MG .02 .10
108T Danny Tartabull .05 .15
109T Tim Teufel .02 .10
110T Bob Tewksbury XRC .15 .40
111T Andres Thomas .02 .10
112T Milt Thompson .15 .40
113T R.Thompson XRC .15 .40
114T Jay Tibbs .02 .10
115T Wayne Tolleson .02 .10
116T Alex Trevino .02 .10
117T Manny Trillo .02 .10
118T Ed VandeBerg .02 .10
119T Ozzie Virgil .02 .10
120T Bob Walk .02 .10
121T Gene Walter .02 .10
122T Claudell Washington .02 .10
123T Bill Wegman XRC .02 .10
124T Dick Williams MG .02 .10
125T Mitch Williams XRC .15 .40
126T Bobby Witt XRC .15 .40
127T Todd Worrell XRC .15 .40
128T George Wright .02 .10
129T Ricky Wright .02 .10
130T Steve Yeager .05 .15
131T Paul Zuvella .02 .10
132T Checklist 1T-132T .02 .10

1986 Topps Traded Tiffany

For the third consecutive season, Topps issued a Tiffany Update issue to go with their regular issue. These 132 cards feature the same players as in the regular set but have a "glossy" front and very clear back. These cards, released through Topps hobby dealers, were sent out only if the dealer ordered the regular Tiffany set. These cards were printed in Topps' Ireland plant. Again, similar to the regular set, it is believed that 5,000 of these sets were produced.

COMP.FACT.SET (132) 300.00 500.00
*STARS: 5X TO 12X BASIC CARDS
*ROOKIES: 4X TO 10X BASIC CARDS
FACTORY SET PRICE IS FOR SEALED SETS
OPENED SETS SELL FOR 50-60% OF SEALED

1987 Topps

This set consists of 792 standard-size cards. Cards were primarily issued in 17-card wax packs, 50-card rack packs and factory sets. Card fronts feature wood grain borders encasing a color photo (reminiscent of Topps' classic 1962 baseball set). Subsets include Record Breakers (1-7), Turn Back the Clock (311-315), All-Star selections (595-616) and Team Leaders (scattered throughout the set). The manager cards contain a team checklist on back. The key Rookie Cards in this set are Barry Bonds, Bobby Bonilla, Will Clark, Bo Jackson, Wally Joyner, John Kruk, Barry Larkin, Rafael Palmeiro, Ruben Sierra, and Devon White.

COMPLETE SET (792) 10.00 25.00
COMP.FACT.SET (792) 15.00 40.00
COMP.HOBBY SET (792) 15.00 40.00
COMP.X-MAS.SET (792) 15.00 40.00
1 Roger Clemens RB .40 1.00
2 Jim Deshaies RB .01 .05
3 Dwight Evans RB .05 .15
4 Davey Lopes RB .01 .05
5 Dave Righetti RB .01 .05
6 Ruben Sierra RB .08 .25
7 Todd Worrell RB .01 .05
8 Terry Pendleton .02 .10
9 Jay Tibbs .01 .05
10 Cecil Cooper .02 .10
11 Indians Team .01 .05
(Mound conference)
12 Jeff Sellers .01 .05
13 Nick Esasky .01 .05
14 Dave Stewart .02 .10
15 Claudell Washington .01 .05
16 Pat Clements .01 .05
17 Pete O'Brien .01 .05
18 Dick Howser MG .01 .05
19 Matt Young .01 .05
20 Gary Carter .02 .10
21 Mark Davis .01 .05
22 Doug DeCinces .01 .05
23 Lee Smith .02 .10
24 Tony Walker .01 .05
25 Bert Blyleven .02 .10
26 Greg Brock .01 .05
27 Joe Cowley .01 .05
28 Rick Dempsey .01 .05
29 Jimmy Key .02 .10
30 Tim Raines .02 .10
31 Braves Team .01 .05
(Glenn Hubbard and
Rafael Ramirez)
32 Tim Leary .01 .05
33 Andy Van Slyke .05 .15
34 Jose Rijo .02 .10
35 Sid Bream .01 .05
36 Eric King .01 .05
37 Marvell Wynne .01 .05
38 Dennis Leonard .01 .05
39 Marty Barrett .01 .05
40 Dave Righetti .02 .10
41 Bo Diaz .01 .05
42 Gary Redus .01 .05
43 Gene Michael MG .01 .05
44 Greg Harris .01 .05
45 Jim Presley .01 .05
46 Dan Gladden .01 .05
47 Dennis Powell .01 .05
48 Wally Backman .01 .05
49 Terry Harper .01 .05
50 Dave Smith .01 .05
51 Mel Hall .01 .05
52 Keith Atherton .01 .05
53 Ruppert Jones .01 .05
54 Bill Dawley .01 .05
55 Tim Wallach .01 .05
56 Brewers Team .02 .10
(Mound conference)
57 Scott Nielsen .01 .05
58 Thad Bosley .01 .05
59 Ken Dayley .01 .05
60 Tony Pena .01 .05
61 Bobby Thigpen RC .08 .25
62 Bobby Meacham .01 .05
63 Fred Toliver .01 .05
64 Harry Spilman .01 .05
65 Tom Browning .01 .05
66 Marc Sullivan .01 .05
67 Bill Swift .01 .05
68 Tony LaRussa MG .02 .10
69 Lonnie Smith .01 .05
70 Charlie Hough .02 .10
71 Mike Aldrete .01 .05
72 Walt Terrell .01 .05
73 Dave Anderson .01 .05
74 Dan Pasqua .01 .05
75 Ron Darling .02 .10
76 Rafael Ramirez .01 .05
77 Bryan Oelkers .01 .05
78 Tom Foley .01 .05
79 Juan Nieves .01 .05
80 Wally Joyner RC .15 .40
81 Padres Team .01 .05
(Andy Hawkins and
Terry Kennedy)
82 Rob Murphy .01 .05
83 Mike Davis .01 .05
84 Steve Lake .01 .05
85 Kevin Bass .01 .05
86 Nate Snell .01 .05
87 Mark Salas .01 .05
88 Ed Wojna .01 .05
89 Ozzie Guillen .05 .15
90 Dave Stieb .02 .10
91 Harold Reynolds .02 .10
92A Urbano Lugo .05 .15
ERR (no trademark)
92B Urbano Lugo COR .01 .05
93 Jim Leyland MG/TC RC .08 .25
94 Calvin Schiraldi .01 .05
95 Oddibe McDowell .01 .05
96 Frank Williams .01 .05
97 Glenn Wilson .01 .05
98 Bill Scherrer .01 .05
99 Darryl Motley .01 .05
(Now with Braves
on card front)
100 Steve Garvey .02 .10
101 Carl Willis RC .02 .10
102 Paul Zuvella .01 .05
103 Rick Aguilera .01 .05
104 Billy Sample .01 .05
105 Floyd Youmans .01 .05
106 Blue Jays Team .01 .05
(George Bell and
Jesse Barfield)
107 John Butcher .01 .05
108 Jim Gantner UER .01 .05
(Brewers logo
reversed)
109 R.J. Reynolds .01 .05
110 John Tudor .02 .10
111 Alfredo Griffin .01 .05
112 Alan Ashby .01 .05
113 Neil Allen .01 .05
114 Billy Beane .02 .10
115 Donnie Moore .01 .05
116 Bill Russell .02 .10
117 Jim Beattie .01 .05
118 Bobby Valentine MG .02 .10
119 Ron Robinson .01 .05
120 Eddie Murray .08 .25
121 Kevin Romine .01 .05
122 Jim Clancy .01 .05
123 John Kruk RC .20 .50
124 Ray Fontenot .01 .05
125 Bob Brenly .01 .05
126 Mike Loynd RC .02 .10
127 Vance Law .01 .05
128 Checklist 1-132 .01 .05
129 Rick Cerone .01 .05
130 Dwight Gooden .05 .15
131 Pirates Team .01 .05
(Sid Bream and

Tony Pena)
132 Paul Assenmacher .08 .25
133 Jose Oquendo .01 .05
134 Rich Yett .01 .05
135 Mike Easler .01 .05
136 Ron Romanick .01 .05
137 Jerry Willard .01 .05
138 Roy Lee Jackson .01 .05
139 Devon White RC .15 .40
140 Bret Saberhagen .02 .10
141 Herm Winningham .01 .05
142 Rick Sutcliffe .02 .10
143 Steve Boros MG .01 .05
144 Mike Scioscia .02 .10
145 Charlie Kerfeld .01 .05
146 Tracy Jones .01 .05
147 Randy Niemann .01 .05
148 Dave Collins .01 .05
149 Ray Searage .01 .05
150 Wade Boggs .05 .15
151 Mike LaCoss .01 .05
152 Toby Harrah .02 .10
153 Duane Ward RC .08 .25
154 Tom O'Malley .01 .05
155 Eddie Whitson .01 .05
156 Mariners Team .01 .05
(Mound conference)
157 Danny Darwin .01 .05
158 Tim Teufel .01 .05
159 Ed Olwine .01 .05
160 Julio Franco .02 .10
161 Steve Ontiveros .01 .05
162 Mike LaValliere RC .08 .25
163 Kevin Gross .01 .05
164 Sammy Khalifa .01 .05
165 Jeff Reardon .02 .10
166 Bob Boone .02 .10
167 Jim Deshaies RC .02 .10
168 Lou Piniella MG .02 .10
169 Ron Washington .01 .05
170 Bo Jackson RC 1.25 3.00
171 Chuck Cary .01 .05
172 Ron Oester .01 .05
173 Alex Trevino .01 .05
174 Henry Cotto .01 .05
175 Bob Stanley .01 .05
176 Steve Buechele .01 .05
177 Keith Moreland .01 .05
178 Cecil Fielder .02 .10
179 Bill Wegman .01 .05
180 Chris Brown .01 .05
181 Cardinals Team .01 .05
(Mound conference)
182 Lee Lacy .01 .05
183 Andy Hawkins .01 .05
184 Bobby Bonilla RC .15 .40
185 Roger McDowell .01 .05
186 Bruce Benedict .01 .05
187 Mark Huismann .01 .05
188 Tony Phillips .01 .05
189 Joe Hesketh .01 .05
190 Jim Sundberg .02 .10
191 Charles Hudson .01 .05
192 Cory Snyder .01 .05
193 Roger Craig MG .02 .10
194 Kirk McCaskill .01 .05
195 Mike Pagliarulo .01 .05
196 Randy O'Neal UER .01 .05
(Wrong ML career
W-L totals)
197 Mark Bailey .01 .05
198 Lee Mazzilli .02 .10
199 Mariano Duncan .01 .05
200 Pete Rose .25 .60
201 John Cangelosi .01 .05
202 Ricky Wright .01 .05
203 Mike Kingery RC .02 .10
204 Sammy Stewart .01 .05
205 Graig Nettles .02 .10
206 Twins Team .01 .05
(Frank Viola and
Tim Laudner)
207 George Frazier .01 .05
208 John Shelby .01 .05
209 Rick Schu .01 .05
210 Lloyd Moseby .01 .05
211 John Morris .01 .05
212 Mike Fitzgerald .01 .05
213 Randy Myers RC .15 .40
214 Omar Moreno .01 .05
215 Mark Langston .01 .05
216 B.J. Surhoff RC .15 .40
217 Chris Codiroli .01 .05
218 Sparky Anderson MG .02 .10
219 Cecilio Guante .01 .05
220 Joe Carter .02 .10
221 Vern Ruhle .01 .05
222 Denny Walling .01 .05
223 Charlie Leibrandt .01 .05
224 Wayne Tolleson .01 .05
225 Mike Smithson .01 .05
226 Max Venable .01 .05
227 Jamie Moyer RC .20 .50
228 Curt Wilkerson .01 .05
229 Mike Birkbeck .02 .10
230 Don Baylor .02 .10
231 Giants Team .01 .05
(Bob Brenly and
Jim Gott)
232 Reggie Williams .01 .05
233 Russ Morman .01 .05
234 Pat Sheridan .01 .05
235 Alvin Davis .01 .05
236 Tommy John .02 .10
237 Jim Morrison .01 .05
238 Bill Krueger .01 .05
239 Juan Espino .01 .05
240 Steve Balboni .01 .05
241 Danny Heep .01 .05
242 Rick Mahler .01 .05
243 Whitey Herzog MG .02 .10
244 Dickie Noles .01 .05
245 Willie Upshaw .01 .05
246 Jim Dwyer .01 .05
247 Jeff Reed .01 .05
248 Gene Walter .01 .05
249 Jim Pankovits .01 .05
250 Teddy Higuera .01 .05
251 Rob Wilfong .01 .05
252 Dennis Martinez .02 .10
253 Eddie Milner .01 .05
254 Bob Tewksbury RC .08 .25
255 Juan Samuel .01 .05
256 Royals Team .05 .15
(George Brett and
Frank White)
257 Bob Forsch .01 .05
258 Steve Yeager .02 .10
259 Mike Greenwell RC .08 .25
260 Vida Blue .02 .10
261 Ruben Sierra RC .20 .50
262 Jim Winn .01 .05
263 Stan Javier .01 .05
264 Checklist 133-264 .01 .05
265 Darrell Evans .02 .10
266 Jeff Hamilton .01 .05
267 Howard Johnson .02 .10
268 Pat Corrales MG .01 .05
269 Cliff Speck .01 .05
270 Jody Davis .01 .05
271 Mike G. Brown .01 .05
272 Andres Galarraga .02 .10
273 Gene Nelson .01 .05
274 Jeff Hearron UER .01 .05
(Duplicate 1986
stat line on back)
275 LaMarr Hoyt .01 .05
276 Jackie Gutierrez .01 .05
277 Juan Agosto .01 .05
278 Gary Pettis .01 .05
279 Dan Plesac .01 .05
280 Jeff Leonard .01 .05
281 Reds Team .08 .25
Pete Rose, Bo Diaz
and Bill Gullickson
282 Jeff Calhoun .01 .05
283 Doug Drabek RC .15 .40
284 John Moses .01 .05
285 Dennis Boyd .01 .05
286 Mike Woodard .01 .05
287 Dave Von Ohlen .01 .05
288 Tito Landrum .01 .05
289 Bob Kipper .01 .05
290 Leon Durham .01 .05
291 Mitch Williams RC .08 .25
292 Franklin Stubbs .01 .05
293 Bob Rodgers MG .01 .05
294 Steve Jeltz .01 .05
295 Len Dykstra .02 .10
296 Andres Thomas .01 .05
297 Don Schulze .01 .05
298 Larry Herndon .01 .05
299 Joel Davis .01 .05
300 Reggie Jackson .05 .15
301 Luis Aquino UER .01 .05
(No trademark
never corrected)
302 Bill Schroeder .01 .05
303 Juan Berenguer .01 .05
304 Phil Garner .02 .10
305 John Franco .02 .10
306 Red Sox Team .02 .10
(Tom Seaver,
John McNamara MG,
and Rich Gedman)
307 Lee Guetterman .01 .05
308 Don Slaught .01 .05
309 Mike Young .01 .05
310 Frank Viola .02 .10
311 Rickey Henderson .05 .15
TBC '82
312 Reggie Jackson .02 .10
TBC '77
313 Roberto Clemente .08 .25
TBC '72
314 Carl Yastrzemski UER .08 .25
TBC '67 (Sic, 112
RBI's on back)
315 Maury Wills TBC '62 .02 .10
316 Brian Fisher .01 .05
317 Clint Hurdle .01 .05
318 Jim Fregosi MG .01 .05
319 Greg Swindell RC .08 .25
320 Barry Bonds RC 4.00 10.00
321 Mike Laga .01 .05
322 Chris Bando .01 .05
323 Al Newman RC .01 .05
324 David Palmer .01 .05
325 Garry Templeton .02 .10
326 Mark Gubicza .01 .05
327 Dale Sveum .01 .05
328 Bob Welch .02 .10
329 Ron Roenicke .01 .05
330 Mike Scott .02 .10
331 Mets Team .02 .10
(Gary Carter and
Darryl Strawberry)
332 Joe Price .01 .05
333 Ken Phelps .01 .05
334 Ed Correa .01 .05
335 Candy Maldonado .01 .05
336 Allan Anderson RC .01 .05
337 Darrell Miller .01 .05
338 Tim Conroy .01 .05
339 Donnie Hill .01 .05
340 Roger Clemens .60 1.50
341 Mike C. Brown .01 .05
342 Bob James .01 .05
343 Hal Lanier MG .01 .05
344A Joe Niekro .01 .05
(Copyright inside
righthand border)
344B Joe Niekro .01 .05
(Copyright outside
righthand border)
345 Andre Dawson .02 .10
346 Shawon Dunston .01 .05
347 Mickey Brantley .01 .05
348 Carmelo Martinez .01 .05
349 Storm Davis .01 .05
350 Keith Hernandez .02 .10
351 Gene Garber .01 .05
352 Mike Felder .01 .05
353 Ernie Camacho .01 .05
354 Jamie Quirk .01 .05
355 Don Carman .01 .05
356 White Sox Team .01 .05
(Mound conference)
357 Steve Fireovid .01 .05
358 Sal Butera .01 .05
359 Doug Corbett .01 .05
360 Pedro Guerrero .02 .10
361 Mark Thurmond .01 .05
362 Luis Quinones .01 .05
363 Jose Guzman .01 .05
364 Randy Bush .01 .05
365 Rick Rhoden .01 .05
366 Mark McGwire 1.50 4.00
367 Jeff Lahti .01 .05
368 John McNamara MG .01 .05
369 Brian Dayett .01 .05
370 Fred Lynn .02 .10
371 Mark Eichhorn .01 .05
372 Jerry Mumphrey .01 .05
373 Jeff Dedmon .01 .05
374 Glenn Hoffman .01 .05
375 Ron Guidry .02 .10
376 Scott Bradley .01 .05
377 John Henry Johnson .01 .05
378 Rafael Santana .01 .05
379 John Russell .01 .05
380 Rich Gossage .02 .10
381 Expos Team .01 .05
(Mound conference)
382 Rudy Law .01 .05
383 Ron Davis .01 .05
384 Johnny Grubb .01 .05
385 Orel Hershiser .05 .15
386 Dickie Thon .01 .05
387 T.R. Bryden .01 .05
388 Geno Petralli .01 .05
389 Jeff D. Robinson .01 .05
390 Gary Matthews .02 .10
391 Jay Howell .01 .05
392 Checklist 265-396 .01 .05
393 Pete Rose MG .05 .15
394 Mike Bielecki .01 .05
395 Damaso Garcia .01 .05
396 Tim Lollar .01 .05
397 Greg Walker .01 .05
398 Brad Havens .01 .05
399 Curt Ford .01 .05
400 George Brett .25 .60
401 Billy Joe Robidoux .01 .05
402 Mike Trujillo .01 .05
403 Jerry Royster .01 .05
404 Doug Sisk .01 .05
405 Brook Jacoby .01 .05
406 Yankees Team .20 .50
(Rickey Henderson and
Don Mattingly)
407 Jim Acker .01 .05
408 John Mizerock .01 .05
409 Milt Thompson .01 .05
410 Fernando Valenzuela .02 .10
411 Darnell Coles .01 .05
412 Eric Davis .05 .15
413 Moose Haas .01 .05
414 Joe Orsulak .01 .05
415 Bobby Witt RC .08 .25
416 Tom Nieto .01 .05
417 Pat Perry .01 .05
418 Dick Williams MG .01 .05
419 Mark Portugal RC .08 .25
420 Will Clark RC .40 1.00
421 Jose DeLeon .01 .05
422 Jack Howell .01 .05
423 Jaime Cocanower .01 .05
424 Chris Speier .01 .05
425 Tom Seaver UER .05 .15
Earned Runs amount is wrong
For 86 Red Sox and Career
Also the ERA is wrong for 86 and career
426 Floyd Rayford .01 .05
427 Edwin Nunez .01 .05
428 Bruce Bochy .01 .05
429 Tim Pyznarski .01 .05
430 Mike Schmidt .20 .50
431 Dodgers Team .01 .05
(Mound conference)
432 Jim Slaton .01 .05
433 Ed Hearn RC .01 .05
434 Mike Fischlin .01 .05
435 Bruce Sutter .02 .10
436 Andy Allanson RC .01 .05
437 Ted Power .01 .05
438 Kelly Downs RC .02 .10
439 Karl Best .01 .05
440 Willie McGee .02 .10
441 Dave Leiper .01 .05
442 Mitch Webster .01 .05
443 John Felske MG .01 .05
444 Jeff Russell .01 .05
445 Dave Lopes .02 .10
446 Chuck Finley RC .15 .40
447 Bill Almon .01 .05
448 Chris Bosio RC .08 .25
449 Pat Dodson .02 .10
450 Kirby Puckett .20 .50
451 Joe Sambito .01 .05
452 Dave Henderson .01 .05
453 Scott Terry RC .02 .10
454 Luis Salazar .01 .05
455 Mike Boddicker .01 .05
456 A's Team .01 .05
(Mound conference)
457 Len Matuszek .01 .05
458 Kelly Gruber .01 .05
459 Dennis Eckersley .05 .15
460 Darryl Strawberry .02 .10
461 Craig McMurtry .01 .05
462 Scott Fletcher .01 .05
463 Tom Candiotti .01 .05
464 Butch Wynegar .01 .05
465 Todd Worrell .01 .05
466 Kal Daniels .01 .05
467 Randy St.Claire .01 .05
468 G.Bamberger MG .01 .05
469 Mike Diaz .01 .05
470 Dave Dravecky .01 .05
471 Ronn Reynolds .01 .05
472 Bill Doran .02 .10
473 Steve Farr .01 .05
474 Jerry Narron .01 .05
475 Scott Garrelts .01 .05
476 Danny Tartabull .01 .05
477 Ken Howell .01 .05
478 Tim Laudner .01 .05
479 Bob Sebra .01 .05
480 Jim Rice .02 .10
481 Phillies Team .01 .05
(Glenn Wilson
Juan Samuel and
Von Hayes)
482 Daryl Boston .01 .05
483 Dwight Lowry .01 .05
484 Jim Traber .01 .05
485 Tony Fernandez .01 .05
486 Otis Nixon .01 .05
487 Dave Gumpert .01 .05
488 Ray Knight .02 .10
489 Bill Gullickson .01 .05
490 Dale Murphy .05 .15
491 Ron Karkovice RC .08 .25
492 Mike Heath .01 .05
493 Tom Lasorda MG .05 .15
494 Barry Jones .01 .05
495 Gorman Thomas .02 .10
496 Bruce Bochte .01 .05
497 Dale Mohorcic .01 .05
498 Bob Kearney .01 .05
499 Bruce Ruffin RC .02 .10
500 Don Mattingly .25 .60
501 Craig Lefferts .01 .05
502 Dick Schofield .01 .05
503 Larry Andersen .01 .05
504 Mickey Hatcher .01 .05
505 Bryn Smith .01 .05
506 Orioles Team .01 .05
(Mound conference)
507 Dave L. Stapleton .01 .05
508 Scott Bankhead .01 .05
509 Enos Cabell .01 .05
510 Tom Henke .01 .05
511 Steve Lyons .01 .05
512 Dave Magadan RC .08 .25
513 Carmen Castillo .01 .05
514 Orlando Mercado .01 .05
515 Willie Hernandez .01 .05
516 Ted Simmons .02 .10
517 Mario Soto .02 .10
518 Gene Mauch MG .01 .05
519 Curt Young .01 .05
520 Jack Clark .02 .10
521 Rick Reuschel .02 .10
522 Checklist 397-528 .01 .05
523 Earnie Riles .01 .05
524 Bob Shirley .01 .05
525 Phil Bradley .01 .05
526 Roger Mason .01 .05
527 Jim Wohlford .01 .05
528 Ken Dixon .01 .05
529 Alvaro Espinoza RC .02 .10
530 Tony Gwynn .10 .30
531 Astros Team .02 .10
(Yogi Berra conference)
532 Jeff Stone .01 .05
533 Angel Salazar .01 .05
534 Scott Sanderson .01 .05
535 Tony Armas .02 .10
536 Terry Mulholland RC .08 .25
537 Rance Mulliniks .01 .05
538 Tom Niedenfuer .01 .05
539 Reid Nichols .01 .05
540 Terry Kennedy .01 .05
541 Rafael Belliard RC .08 .25
542 Ricky Horton .01 .05
543 Dave Johnson MG .01 .05
544 Zane Smith .01 .05
545 Buddy Bell .02 .10
546 Mike Morgan .01 .05
547 Rob Deer .01 .05
548 Bill Mooneyham .01 .05
549 Bob Melvin .01 .05
550 Pete Incaviglia RC .08 .25
551 Frank Wills .01 .05
552 Larry Sheets .01 .05
553 Mike Maddux RC .01 .05
554 Buddy Biancalana .01 .05
555 Dennis Rasmussen .01 .05
556 Angels Team .01 .05
(Rene Lachemann CO,
Mike Witt, and
Bob Boone)
557 John Cerutti .01 .05
558 Greg Gagne .01 .05
559 Lance McCullers .01 .05
560 Glenn Davis .01 .05
561 Rey Quinones .01 .05
562 Bryan Clutterbuck .01 .05
563 John Stefero .01 .05
564 Larry McWilliams .01 .05
565 Dusty Baker .02 .10
566 Tim Hulett .01 .05
567 Greg Mathews .01 .05
568 Earl Weaver MG .02 .10
569 Wade Rowdon .01 .05
570 Sid Fernandez .01 .05
571 Ozzie Virgil .01 .05
572 Pete Ladd .01 .05
573 Hal McRae .02 .10
574 Manny Lee .01 .05
575 Pat Tabler .01 .05
576 Frank Pastore .01 .05
577 Dann Bilardello .01 .05
578 Billy Hatcher .01 .05
579 Rick Burleson .01 .05
580 Mike Krukow .01 .05
581 Cubs Team .01 .05
(Ron Cey and
Steve Trout)
582 Bruce Berenyi .01 .05
583 Junior Ortiz .01 .05
584 Ron Kittle .01 .05
585 Scott Bailes .01 .05
586 Ben Oglivie .02 .10
587 Eric Plunk .01 .05
588 Wallace Johnson .01 .05
589 Steve Crawford .01 .05
590 Vince Coleman .01 .05
591 Spike Owen .01 .05
592 Chris Welsh .01 .05
593 Chuck Tanner MG .01 .05
594 Rick Anderson .01 .05
595 Keith Hernandez AS .01 .05
596 Steve Sax AS .01 .05
597 Mike Schmidt AS .08 .25
598 Ozzie Smith AS .08 .25
599 Tony Gwynn AS .05 .15
600 Dave Parker AS .01 .05
601 Darryl Strawberry AS .01 .05
602 Gary Carter AS .01 .05
603A D.Gooden AS .02 .10
ERR no trademark
603B D.Gooden AS COR .02 .10
604 Fernando Valenzuela AS .01 .05
605 Todd Worrell AS .01 .05
606 Don Mattingly AS COR .10 .30
606A Don Mattingly AS .40 1.00
ERR (no trademark)
607 Tony Bernazard AS .01 .05
608 Wade Boggs AS .02 .10
609 Cal Ripken AS .08 .25
610 Jim Rice AS .01 .05
611 Kirby Puckett AS .08 .25
612 George Bell AS .01 .05
613 Lance Parrish AS UER .01 .05
(Pitcher heading
on back)
614 Roger Clemens AS .40 1.00
615 Teddy Higuera AS .01 .05
616 Dave Righetti AS .01 .05
617 Al Nipper .01 .05
618 Tom Kelly MG .01 .05
619 Jerry Reed .01 .05
620 Jose Canseco .40 1.00
621 Danny Cox .01 .05
622 Glenn Braggs RC .02 .10
623 Kurt Stillwell .01 .05
624 Tim Burke .01 .05
625 Mookie Wilson .02 .10
626 Joel Skinner .01 .05
627 Ken Oberkfell .01 .05
628 Bob Walk .01 .05
629 Larry Parrish .01 .05
630 John Candelaria .01 .05
631 Tigers Team .01 .05
(Mound conference)
632 Rob Woodward .01 .05
633 Jose Uribe .01 .05
634 Rafael Palmeiro RC .60 1.50
635 Ken Schrom .01 .05
636 Darren Daulton .02 .10
637 Bip Roberts RC .08 .25
638 Rich Bordi .01 .05
639 Gerald Perry .01 .05
640 Mark Clear .01 .05
641 Domingo Ramos .01 .05
642 Al Pulido .01 .05
643 Ron Shepherd .01 .05
644 John Denny .01 .05
645 Dwight Evans .05 .15
646 Mike Mason .01 .05
647 Tom Lawless .01 .05
648 Barry Larkin RC .40 1.00
649 Mickey Tettleton .01 .05
650 Hubie Brooks .01 .05
651 Benny Distefano .01 .05
652 Terry Forster .02 .10
653 Kevin Mitchell RC .15 .40
654 Checklist 529-660 .02 .10
655 Jesse Barfield .02 .10
656 Rangers Team .01 .05
(Bobby Valentine MG
and Ricky Wright)
657 Tom Waddell .01 .05
658 Robby Thompson RC .08 .25
659 Aurelio Lopez .01 .05
660 Bob Horner .02 .10
661 Lou Whitaker .02 .10
662 Frank DiPino .01 .05
663 Cliff Johnson .01 .05
664 Mike Marshall .01 .05
665 Rod Scurry .01 .05
666 Von Hayes .01 .05
667 Ron Hassey .01 .05
668 Juan Bonilla .01 .05
669 Bud Black .01 .05
670 Jose Cruz .02 .10
671A Ray Soff ERR .01 .05
(No D* before
copyright line)
671B Ray Soff COR .01 .05
(D* before
copyright line)
672 Chili Davis .02 .10
673 Don Sutton .02 .10
674 Bill Campbell .01 .05
675 Ed Romero .01 .05
676 Charlie Moore .01 .05
677 Bob Grich .02 .10
678 Carney Lansford .02 .10
679 Kent Hrbek .02 .10
680 Ryne Sandberg .15 .40
681 George Bell .02 .10
682 Jerry Reuss .01 .05
683 Gary Roenicke .01 .05
684 Kent Tekulve .01 .05
685 Jerry Hairston .01 .05
686 Doyle Alexander .01 .05
687 Alan Trammell .02 .10
688 Juan Beniquez .01 .05
689 Darrell Porter .01 .05
690 Dane Iorg .01 .05
691 Dave Parker .02 .10
692 Frank White .02 .10
693 Terry Puhl .01 .05
694 Phil Niekro .02 .10
695 Chico Walker .01 .05
696 Gary Lucas .01 .05
697 Ed Lynch .01 .05
698 Ernie Whitt .01 .05
699 Ken Landreaux .01 .05
700 Dave Bergman .01 .05
701 Willie Randolph .02 .10
702 Greg Gross .01 .05
703 Dave Schmidt .01 .05
704 Jesse Orosco .01 .05
705 Bruce Hurst .01 .05
706 Rick Manning .01 .05
707 Bob McClure .01 .05
708 Scott McGregor .01 .05
709 Dave Kingman .02 .10
710 Gary Gaetti .02 .10
711 Ken Griffey .02 .10
712 Don Robinson .01 .05
713 Tom Brookens .01 .05
714 Dan Quisenberry .01 .05
715 Bob Dernier .01 .05
716 Rick Leach .01 .05
717 Ed VandeBerg .01 .05
718 Steve Carlton .02 .10
719 Tom Hume .01 .05
720 Richard Dotson .01 .05
721 Tom Herr .01 .05
722 Bob Knepper .01 .05
723 Brett Butler .02 .10
724 Greg Minton .01 .05
725 George Hendrick .02 .10
726 Frank Tanana .02 .10
727 Mike Moore .01 .05
728 Tippy Martinez .01 .05
729 Tom Paciorek .01 .05
730 Eric Show .01 .05
731 Dave Concepcion .02 .10
732 Manny Trillo .01 .05
733 Bill Caudill .01 .05
734 Bill Madlock .02 .10
735 Rickey Henderson .08 .25
736 Steve Bedrosian .01 .05
737 Floyd Bannister .01 .05
738 Jorge Orta .01 .05
739 Chet Lemon .02 .10
740 Rich Gedman .01 .05
741 Paul Molitor .02 .10
742 Andy McGaffigan .01 .05
743 Dwayne Murphy .01 .05
744 Roy Smalley .01 .05
745 Glenn Hubbard .01 .05
746 Bob Ojeda .01 .05
747 Johnny Ray .01 .05
748 Mike Flanagan .01 .05
749 Ozzie Smith .15 .40
750 Steve Trout .01 .05
751 Garth Iorg .01 .05
752 Dan Petry .01 .05
753 Rick Honeycutt .01 .05
754 Dave LaPoint .01 .05
755 Luis Aguayo .01 .05
756 Carlton Fisk .05 .15
757 Nolan Ryan .40 1.00
758 Tony Bernazard .01 .05
759 Joel Youngblood .01 .05
760 Mike Witt .01 .05
761 Greg Pryor .01 .05
762 Gary Ward .01 .05
763 Tim Flannery .01 .05
764 Bill Buckner .02 .10
765 Kirk Gibson .02 .10
766 Don Aase .01 .05
767 Ron Cey .02 .10
768 Dennis Lamp .01 .05
769 Steve Sax .01 .05
770 Dave Winfield .02 .10
771 Shane Rawley .01 .05
772 Harold Baines .02 .10
773 Robin Yount .15 .40
774 Wayne Krenchicki .01 .05
775 Joaquin Andujar .02 .10
776 Tom Brunansky .01 .05
777 Chris Chambliss .02 .10
778 Jack Morris .02 .10
779 Craig Reynolds .01 .05
780 Andre Thornton .01 .05
781 Atlee Hammaker .01 .05
782 Brian Downing .02 .10
783 Willie Wilson .02 .10
784 Cal Ripken .30 .75
785 Terry Francona .02 .10
786 Jimy Williams MG .01 .05
787 Alejandro Pena .01 .05
788 Tim Stoddard .01 .05
789 Dan Schatzeder .01 .05
790 Julio Cruz .01 .05
791 Lance Parrish .02 .10
792 Checklist 661-792 .01 .05

1987 Topps Tiffany

These 792 standard-size cards were a parallel to the regular Topps issue. These cards feature "glossy" fronts and easy to read backs. These cards are in the same style as the regular Topps issue. This set was printed in Ireland and was issued only in factory set form. Unlike previous years, a significantly higher amount of these cards were produced. Therefore, the values of these cards are a much lower multiplier to the regular cards than previous years. It is believed that as many as 30,000 of these sets were produced. This increase was probably in response to increased dealer interest.

COMP.FACT.SET (792) 60.00 120.00
*STARS: 2.5X TO 6X BASIC CARDS
*ROOKIES: 2.5X TO 6X BASIC CARDS

1987 Topps Glossy All-Stars

This set of 22 glossy cards was inserted one per rack pack. Players selected for the set are the starting players (plus manager and two pitchers) in the 1986 All-Star Game in Houston. Cards measure the standard size and the backs feature red and blue printing on a white card stock.

COMPLETE SET (22) 2.00 5.00
1 Whitey Herzog MG .02 .10
2 Keith Hernandez .02 .10
3 Ryne Sandberg .40 1.00
4 Mike Schmidt .20 .50
5 Ozzie Smith .40 1.00

6 Tony Gwynn .40 1.00
7 Dale Murphy .07 .20
8 Darryl Strawberry .02 .10
9 Gary Carter .20 .50
10 Dwight Gooden .05 .15
11 Fernando Valenzuela .02 .10
12 Dick Howser MG .01 .05
13 Wally Joyner .02 .10
14 Lou Whitaker .02 .10
15 Wade Boggs .20 .50
16 Cal Ripken .75 2.00
17 Dave Winfield .20 .50
18 Rickey Henderson .25 .60
19 Kirby Puckett .30 .75
20 Lance Parrish .02 .10
21 Roger Clemens .40 1.00
22 Teddy Higuera .01 .05

1987 Topps Rookies

Inserted in each supermarket jumbo pack is a card from this series of 22 of 1986's best rookies as determined by Topps. Jumbo packs consisted of 100 (regular issue 1987 Topps baseball) cards with a stick of gum plus the insert "Rookie" card. The card fronts are in full color and measure the standard size. The card backs are printed in red and blue on white card stock and are numbered at the bottom essentially by alphabetical order.

COMPLETE SET (22) 6.00 12.00
1 Andy Allanson .08 .25
2 John Cangelosi .08 .25
3 Jose Canseco .75 2.00
4 Will Clark 1.00 2.50
5 Mark Eichhorn .08 .25
6 Pete Incaviglia .20 .50
7 Wally Joyner .30 .75
8 Eric King .08 .25
9 Dave Magadan .20 .50
10 John Morris .08 .25
11 Juan Nieves .08 .25
12 Rafael Palmeiro 2.00 5.00
13 Billy Joe Robidoux .08 .25
14 Bruce Ruffin .08 .25
15 Ruben Sierra .40 1.00
16 Cory Snyder .08 .25
17 Kurt Stillwell .08 .25
18 Dale Sveum .08 .25
19 Danny Tartabull .08 .25
20 Andres Thomas .08 .25
21 Robby Thompson .20 .50
22 Todd Worrell .20 .50

1987 Topps Traded

This 132-card standard-size Traded set was distributed exclusively in factory set form in a special green and white box through hobby dealers. The card fronts are identical in style to the Topps regular issue except for whiter stock and t-suffixed numbering on back. The cards are ordered alphabetically by player's last name. The key extended Rookie Cards in this set are Ellis Burks, David Cone, Greg Maddux, Fred McGriff and Matt Williams.

COMP.FACT.SET (132) 3.00 8.00
1T Bill Almon .01 .05
2T Scott Bankhead .01 .05
3T Eric Bell .02 .10
4T Juan Beniquez .01 .05
5T Juan Berenguer .01 .05
6T Greg Booker .01 .05
7T Thad Bosley .01 .05
8T Larry Bowa MG .02 .10
9T Greg Brock .01 .05
10T Bob Brower .01 .05
11T Jerry Browne .02 .10
12T Ralph Bryant .01 .05
13T DeWayne Buice .01 .05
14T Ellis Burks XRC .20 .50
15T Ivan Calderon .01 .05
16T Jeff Calhoun .01 .05
17T Casey Candaele .01 .05
18T John Cangelosi .01 .05
19T Steve Carlton .02 .10
20T Juan Castillo .02 .10
21T Rick Cerone .01 .05
22T Ron Cey .02 .10
23T John Christensen .01 .05
24T David Cone XRC .30 .75
25T Chuck Crim .01 .05
26T Storm Davis .01 .05
27T Andre Dawson .02 .10
28T Rick Dempsey .01 .05
29T Doug Drabek .20 .50
30T Mike Dunne .01 .05
31T Dennis Eckersley .05 .15
32T Lee Elia MG .01 .05
33T Brian Fisher .01 .05
34T Terry Francona .02 .10
35T Willie Fraser .02 .10
36T Billy Gardner MG .01 .05
37T Ken Gerhart .01 .05
38T Dan Gladden .01 .05
39T Jim Gott .01 .05
40T Cecilio Guante .01 .05
41T Albert Hall .01 .05
42T Terry Harper .01 .05
43T Mickey Hatcher .01 .05
44T Brad Havens .01 .05
45T Neal Heaton .01 .05
46T Mike Henneman XRC .08 .25
47T Donnie Hill .01 .05
48T Guy Hoffman .01 .05
49T Brian Holton .01 .05
50T Charles Hudson .01 .05
51T Danny Jackson .01 .05
52T Reggie Jackson .05 .15
53T Chris James XRC .02 .10
54T Dion James .01 .05
55T Stan Jefferson .01 .05
56T Joe Johnson .01 .05
57T Terry Kennedy .01 .05
58T Mike Kingery .02 .10
59T Ray Knight .02 .10
60T Gene Larkin XRC .08 .25
61T Mike LaValliere .08 .25
62T Jack Lazorko .01 .05
63T Terry Leach .01 .05
64T Tim Leary .01 .05
65T Jim Lindeman .02 .10
66T Steve Lombardozzi .01 .05
67T Bill Long .01 .05
68T Barry Lyons .01 .05
69T Shane Mack .01 .05
70T Greg Maddux XRC 2.00 5.00
71T Bill Madlock .02 .10
72T Joe Magrane XRC .02 .10
73T Dave Martinez XRC .08 .25
74T Fred McGriff .25 .60
75T Mark McLemore .02 .10
76T Kevin McReynolds .01 .05
77T Dave Meads .01 .05
78T Eddie Milner .01 .05
79T Greg Minton .01 .05
80T John Mitchell XRC .02 .10
81T Kevin Mitchell .05 .15
82T Charlie Moore .01 .05
83T Jeff Musselman .01 .05
84T Gene Nelson .01 .05
85T Graig Nettles .02 .10
86T Al Newman .01 .05
87T Reid Nichols .01 .05
88T Tom Niedenfuer .01 .05
89T Joe Niekro .01 .05
90T Tom Nieto .01 .05
91T Matt Nokes XRC .08 .25
92T Dickie Noles .01 .05
93T Pat Pacillo .01 .05
94T Lance Parrish .02 .10
95T Tony Pena .01 .05
96T Luis Polonia XRC .08 .25
97T Randy Ready .01 .05
98T Jeff Reardon .02 .10
99T Gary Redus .01 .05
100T Jeff Reed .01 .05
101T Rick Rhoden .01 .05
102T Cal Ripken Sr. MG .01 .05
103T Wally Ritchie .01 .05
104T Jeff M. Robinson .01 .05
105T Gary Roenicke .01 .05
106T Jerry Royster .01 .05
107T Mark Salas .01 .05
108T Luis Salazar .01 .05
109T Benny Santiago .02 .10
110T Dave Schmidt .01 .05
111T Kevin Seitzer XRC .08 .25
112T John Shelby .01 .05
113T Steve Shields .01 .05
114T John Smiley XRC .08 .25
115T Chris Speier .01 .05
116T Mike Stanley XRC .08 .25
117T Terry Steinbach XRC .20 .50
118T Les Straker .01 .05
119T Jim Sundberg .02 .10
120T Danny Tartabull .01 .05
121T Tom Trebelhorn MG .01 .05
122T Dave Valle XRC .02 .10
123T Ed VandeBerg .01 .05
124T Andy Van Slyke .05 .15
125T Gary Ward .01 .05
126T Alan Wiggins .01 .05
127T Bill Wilkinson .01 .05
128T Frank Williams .01 .05
129T Matt Williams XRC .40 1.00
130T Jim Winn .01 .05
131T Matt Young .01 .05
132T Checklist 1T-132T .01 .05

1987 Topps Traded Tiffany

Since the update Tiffany cards were issued in the same quantities as the regular cards, again these cards are not valued as high as a multiplier as the previous years. These 132 standard-size cards parallel the regular cards but have glossy fronts and easy to read backs. These cards were issued in factory set form only. These sets, believed to be issued in the range of 30,000, are among the easiest of the Tiffany sets to find in the secondary market.

COMP.FACT.SET (132) 15.00 40.00
*STARS: 2X TO 5X BASIC CARDS
*ROOKIES: 2X TO 5X BASIC CARDS

1988 Topps

This set consists of 792 standard-size cards. The cards were primarily issued in 15-card wax packs, 42-card rack packs and factory sets. Card fronts feature white borders encasing a color photo with team name running across the top and player name diagonally across the bottom. Subsets include

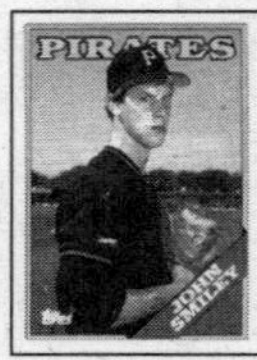

Record Breakers (1-7), All-Stars (386-407), Turn Back the Clock (661-665), and Team Leaders (scattered throughout the set). The manager cards contain a team checklist on back. The key Rookie Cards in this set are Ellis Burks, Ken Caminiti, Tom Glavine, and Matt Williams.

COMPLETE SET (792) 6.00 15.00
COMP.FACT.SET (792) 6.00 15.00
COMP.X-MAS.SET (792) 15.00 40.00
1 Vince Coleman RB .01 .05
2 Don Mattingly RB .10 .30
3 Mark McGwire RB .30 .75
Rookie Homer Record
(No white spot)
3A Mark McGwire RB .30 .75
Rookie Homer Record
(White spot behind
left foot)
4 Eddie Murray RB .05 .15
Switch Home Runs,
Two Straight Games
(No caption on front)
4A Eddie Murray RB .20 .50
Switch Home Runs,
Two Straight Games
(Caption in box
on card front)
5 Phil Niekro .02 .10
Joe Niekro RB
6 Nolan Ryan RB .15 .40
7 Benito Santiago RB .01 .05
8 Kevin Elster .01 .05
9 Andy Hawkins .01 .05
10 Ryne Sandberg .15 .40
11 Mike Young .01 .05
12 Bill Schroeder .01 .05
13 Andres Thomas .01 .05
14 Sparky Anderson MG .02 .10
15 Chili Davis .02 .10
16 Kirk McCaskill .01 .05
17 Ron Oester .01 .05
18A Al Leiter ERR .20 .50
(Photo actually
Steve George,
right ear visible)
18B Al Leiter RC .20 .50
(COR Left ear visible)
19 Mark Davidson .01 .05
20 Kevin Gross .01 .05
21 Wade Boggs .02 .10
Spike Owen TL
22 Greg Swindell .01 .05
23 Ken Landreaux .01 .05
24 Jim Deshaies .01 .05
25 Andres Galarraga .02 .10
26 Mitch Williams .01 .05
27 R.J. Reynolds .01 .05
28 Jose Nunez .01 .05
29 Angel Salazar .01 .05
30 Sid Fernandez .01 .05
31 Bruce Bochy .01 .05
32 Mike Morgan .01 .05
33 Rob Deer .01 .05
34 Ricky Horton .01 .05
35 Harold Baines .02 .10
36 Jamie Moyer .02 .10
37 Ed Romero .01 .05
38 Jeff Calhoun .01 .05
39 Gerald Perry .01 .05
40 Orel Hershiser .02 .10
41 Bob Melvin .01 .05
42 Bill Landrum .01 .05
43 Dick Schofield .01 .05
44 Lou Piniella MG .02 .10
45 Kent Hrbek .02 .10
46 Darnell Coles .01 .05
47 Joaquin Andujar .02 .10
48 Alan Ashby .01 .05
49 Dave Clark .01 .05
50 Hubie Brooks .01 .05
51 Eddie Murray .15 .40
Cal Ripken TL
52 Don Robinson .01 .05
53 Curt Wilkerson .01 .05
54 Jim Clancy .01 .05
55 Phil Bradley .01 .05
56 Ed Hearn .01 .05
57 Tim Crews RC .08 .25
58 Dave Magadan .01 .05
59 Danny Cox .01 .05
60 Rickey Henderson .07 .20
61 Mark Knudson .01 .05
62 Jeff Hamilton .01 .05
63 Jimmy Jones .01 .05
64 Ken Caminiti RC .75 2.00
65 Leon Durham .01 .05
66 Shane Rawley .01 .05
67 Ken Oberkfell .01 .05
68 Dave Dravecky .01 .05
69 Mike Hart .01 .05
70 Roger Clemens .40 1.00
71 Gary Pettis .01 .05
72 Dennis Eckersley .05 .15
73 Randy Bush .01 .05
74 Tom Lasorda MG .05 .15
75 Joe Carter .02 .10
76 Dennis Martinez .02 .10
77 Tom O'Malley .01 .05
78 Dan Petry .01 .05
79 Ernie Whitt .01 .05
80 Mark Langston .01 .05
81 Ron Robinson .01 .05
John Franco TL
82 Darrel Akerfelds .01 .05
83 Jose Oquendo .01 .05
84 Cecilio Guante .01 .05
85 Howard Johnson .02 .10
86 Ron Karkovice .01 .05
87 Mike Mason .01 .05
88 Earnie Riles .01 .05
89 Gary Thurman .01 .05
90 Dale Murphy .05 .15
91 Joey Cora RC .08 .25
92 Len Matuszek .01 .05
93 Bob Sebra .01 .05
94 Chuck Jackson .01 .05
95 Lance Parrish .02 .10
96 Todd Benzinger RC .08 .25
97 Scott Garrelts .01 .05
98 Rene Gonzales RC .02 .10
99 Chuck Finley .02 .10
100 Jack Clark .02 .10
101 Allan Anderson .01 .05
102 Barry Larkin .05 .15
103 Curt Young .01 .05
104 Dick Williams MG .01 .05
105 Jesse Orosco .01 .05
106 Jim Walewander .01 .05
107 Scott Bailes .01 .05
108 Steve Lyons .01 .05
109 Joel Skinner .01 .05
110 Teddy Higuera .01 .05
111 Hubie Brooks .01 .05
Vance Law TL
112 Les Lancaster .01 .05
113 Kelly Gruber .01 .05
114 Jeff Russell .01 .05
115 Johnny Ray .01 .05
116 Jerry Don Gleaton .01 .05
117 James Steels .01 .05
118 Bob Welch .02 .10
119 Robbie Wine .01 .05
120 Kirby Puckett .07 .20
121 Checklist 1-132 .01 .05
122 Tony Bernazard .01 .05
123 Tom Candiotti .01 .05
124 Ray Knight .02 .10
125 Bruce Hurst .01 .05
126 Steve Jeltz .01 .05
127 Jim Gott .01 .05
128 Johnny Grubb .01 .05
129 Greg Minton .01 .05
130 Buddy Bell .02 .10
131 Don Schulze .01 .05
132 Donnie Hill .01 .05
133 Greg Mathews .01 .05
134 Chuck Tanner MG .01 .05
135 Dennis Rasmussen .01 .05
136 Brian Dayett .01 .05
137 Chris Bosio .01 .05
138 Mitch Webster .01 .05
139 Jerry Browne .01 .05
140 Jesse Barfield .02 .10
141 George Brett .07 .20
Bret Saberhagen TL
142 Andy Van Slyke .05 .15
143 Mickey Tettleton .01 .05
144 Don Gordon .01 .05
145 Bill Madlock .02 .10
146 Donell Nixon .01 .05
147 Bill Buckner .02 .10
148 Carmelo Martinez .01 .05
149 Ken Howell .01 .05
150 Eric Davis .02 .10
151 Bob Knepper .01 .05
152 Jody Reed RC .08 .25
153 John Habyan .01 .05
154 Jeff Stone .01 .05
155 Bruce Sutter .02 .10
156 Gary Matthews .02 .10
157 Atlee Hammaker .01 .05
158 Tim Hulett .01 .05
159 Brad Arnsberg .01 .05
160 Willie McGee .02 .10
161 Bryn Smith .01 .05
162 Mark McLemore .01 .05
163 Dale Mohorcic .01 .05
164 Dave Johnson MG .01 .05
165 Robin Yount .10 .30
166 Rick Rodriquez .01 .05
167 Rance Mulliniks .01 .05
168 Barry Jones .01 .05
169 Ross Jones .01 .05
170 Rich Gossage .02 .10
171 Shawon Dunston .01 .05
Manny Trillo TL
172 Lloyd McClendon RC .08 .25
173 Eric Plunk .01 .05
174 Phil Garner .02 .10
175 Kevin Bass .01 .05
176 Jeff Reed .01 .05
177 Frank Tanana .02 .10
178 Dwayne Henry .01 .05
179 Charlie Puleo .01 .05
180 Terry Kennedy .01 .05
181 David Cone .02 .10
182 Ken Phelps .01 .05
183 Tom Lawless .01 .05
184 Ivan Calderon .01 .05
185 Rick Rhoden .01 .05
186 Rafael Palmeiro .15 .40
187 Steve Kiefer .01 .05
188 John Russell .01 .05
189 Wes Gardner .01 .05
190 Candy Maldonado .01 .05
191 John Cerutti .01 .05
192 Devon White .02 .10
193 Brian Fisher .01 .05
194 Tom Kelly MG .01 .05
195 Dan Quisenberry .01 .05
196 Dave Engle .01 .05
197 Lance McCullers .01 .05
198 Franklin Stubbs .01 .05
199 Dave Meads .01 .05
200 Wade Boggs .05 .15
201 Bobby Valentine MG .01 .05
Pete O'Brien
Pete Incaviglia
Steve Buechele TL
202 Glenn Hoffman .01 .05
203 Fred Toliver .01 .05
204 Paul O'Neill .05 .15
205 Nelson Liriano .01 .05
206 Domingo Ramos .01 .05
207 John Mitchell RC .02 .10
208 Steve Lake .01 .05
209 Richard Dotson .01 .05
210 Willie Randolph .02 .10
211 Frank DiPino .01 .05
212 Greg Brock .01 .05
213 Albert Hall .01 .05
214 Dave Schmidt .01 .05
215 Von Hayes .01 .05
216 Jerry Reuss .01 .05
217 Harry Spilman .01 .05
218 Dan Schatzeder .01 .05
219 Mike Stanley .01 .05
220 Tom Henke .01 .05
221 Rafael Belliard .01 .05
222 Steve Farr .01 .05
223 Stan Jefferson .01 .05
224 Tom Trebelhorn MG .01 .05
225 Mike Scioscia .02 .10
226 Dave Lopes .02 .10
227 Ed Correa .01 .05
228 Wallace Johnson .01 .05
229 Jeff Musselman .01 .05
230 Pat Tabler .01 .05
231 Barry Bonds .40 1.00
Bobby Bonilla TL
232 Bob James .01 .05
233 Rafael Santana .01 .05
234 Ken Dayley .01 .05
235 Gary Ward .01 .05
236 Ted Power .01 .05
237 Mike Heath .01 .05
238 Luis Polonia RC .08 .25
239 Roy Smalley .01 .05
240 Lee Smith .02 .10
241 Damaso Garcia .01 .05
242 Tom Niedenfuer .01 .05
243 Mark Ryal .01 .05
244 Jeff D. Robinson .01 .05
245 Rich Gedman .01 .05
246 Mike Campbell .01 .05
247 Thad Bosley .01 .05
248 Storm Davis .01 .05
249 Mike Marshall .01 .05
250 Nolan Ryan .40 1.00
251 Tom Foley .01 .05
252 Bob Brower .01 .05
253 Checklist 133-264 .01 .05
254 Lee Elia MG .01 .05
255 Mookie Wilson .02 .10
256 Ken Schrom .01 .05
257 Jerry Royster .01 .05
258 Ed Nunez .01 .05
259 Ron Kittle .01 .05
260 Vince Coleman .01 .05
261 Giants TL .01 .05
(Five players)
262 Drew Hall .01 .05
263 Glenn Braggs .01 .05
264 Les Straker .01 .05
265 Bo Diaz .01 .05
266 Paul Assenmacher .01 .05
267 Billy Bean RC .02 .10
268 Bruce Ruffin .01 .05
269 Ellis Burks RC .15 .40
270 Mike Witt .01 .05
271 Ken Gerhart .01 .05
272 Steve Ontiveros .01 .05
273 Garth Iorg .01 .05
274 Junior Ortiz .01 .05
275 Kevin Seitzer .01 .05
276 Luis Salazar .01 .05
277 Alejandro Pena .01 .05
278 Jose Cruz .02 .10
279 Randy St.Claire .01 .05
280 Pete Incaviglia .01 .05
281 Jerry Hairston .01 .05
282 Pat Perry .01 .05
283 Phil Lombardi .01 .05
284 Larry Bowa MG .02 .10
285 Jim Presley .01 .05
286 Chuck Crim .01 .05
287 Manny Trillo .01 .05
288 Pat Pacillo .01 .05
289 Dave Bergman .01 .05
290 Tony Fernandez .01 .05
291 Billy Hatcher .01 .05
Kevin Bass TL
292 Carney Lansford .02 .10
293 Doug Jones RC .08 .25
294 Al Pedrique .01 .05
295 Bert Blyleven .02 .10
296 Floyd Rayford .01 .05
297 Zane Smith .01 .05
298 Milt Thompson .01 .05
299 Steve Crawford .01 .05
300 Don Mattingly .25 .60
301 Bud Black .01 .05
302 Jose Uribe .01 .05
303 Eric Show .01 .05
304 George Hendrick .02 .10
305 Steve Sax .01 .05
306 Billy Hatcher .01 .05
307 Mike Trujillo .01 .05
308 Lee Mazzilli .02 .10
309 Bill Long .01 .05
310 Tom Herr .01 .05
311 Scott Sanderson .01 .05
312 Joey Meyer .01 .05
313 Bob McClure .01 .05
314 Jimy Williams MG .01 .05
315 Dave Parker .02 .10
316 Jose Rijo .02 .10
317 Tom Nieto .01 .05
318 Mel Hall .01 .05
319 Mike Loynd .01 .05
320 Alan Trammell .02 .10
321 Harold Baines .02 .10
Carlton Fisk TL
322 Vicente Palacios .01 .05
323 Rick Leach .01 .05
324 Danny Jackson .01 .05
325 Glenn Hubbard .01 .05
326 Al Nipper .01 .05
327 Larry Sheets .01 .05
328 Greg Cadaret .01 .05
329 Chris Speier .01 .05
330 Eddie Whitson .01 .05
331 Brian Downing .02 .10
332 Jerry Reed .01 .05
333 Wally Backman .01 .05
334 Dave LaPoint .01 .05
335 Claudell Washington .01 .05
336 Ed Lynch .01 .05
337 Jim Gantner .01 .05
338 Brian Holton UER .01 .05
1987 ERA .389,
should be 3.89
339 Kurt Stillwell .01 .05
340 Jack Morris .02 .10
341 Carmen Castillo .01 .05
342 Larry Andersen .01 .05
343 Greg Gagne .01 .05
344 Tony LaRussa MG .02 .10
345 Scott Fletcher .01 .05
346 Vance Law .01 .05
347 Joe Johnson .01 .05
348 Jim Eisenreich .01 .05
349 Bob Walk .01 .05
350 Will Clark .07 .20
351 Red Schoendienst CO .02 .10
Tony Pena TL
352 Bill Ripken RC .01 .05
353 Ed Olwine .01 .05
354 Marc Sullivan .01 .05
355 Roger McDowell .01 .05
356 Luis Aguayo .01 .05
357 Floyd Bannister .01 .05
358 Rey Quinones .01 .05
359 Tim Stoddard .01 .05
360 Tony Gwynn .10 .30
361 Greg Maddux .40 1.00
362 Juan Castillo .01 .05
363 Willie Fraser .01 .05
364 Nick Esasky .01 .05
365 Floyd Youmans .01 .05
366 Chet Lemon .02 .10
367 Tim Leary .01 .05
368 Gerald Young .01 .05
369 Greg Harris .01 .05
370 Jose Canseco .20 .50
371 Joe Hesketh .01 .05
372 Matt Williams RC .30 .75
373 Checklist 265-396 .01 .05
374 Doc Edwards MG .01 .05
375 Tom Brunansky .01 .05
376 Bill Wilkinson .01 .05
377 Sam Horn RC .02 .10
378 Todd Frohwirth .01 .05
379 Rafael Ramirez .01 .05
380 Joe Magrane RC .01 .05
381 Wally Joyner .02 .10
Jack Howell TL
382 Keith A. Miller RC .08 .25
383 Eric Bell .01 .05
384 Neil Allen .01 .05
385 Carlton Fisk .05 .15
386 Don Mattingly AS .10 .30
387 Willie Randolph AS .01 .05
388 Wade Boggs AS .02 .10
389 Alan Trammell AS .01 .05
390 George Bell AS .01 .05
391 Kirby Puckett AS .05 .15
392 Dave Winfield AS .01 .05
393 Matt Nokes AS .01 .05
394 Roger Clemens AS .20 .50
395 Jimmy Key AS .01 .05
396 Tom Henke AS .01 .05
397 Jack Clark AS .01 .05
398 Juan Samuel AS .01 .05
399 Tim Wallach AS .01 .05
400 Ozzie Smith AS .07 .20
401 Andre Dawson AS .01 .05
402 Tony Gwynn AS .05 .15
403 Tim Raines AS .01 .05
404 Benny Santiago AS .01 .05
405 Dwight Gooden AS .01 .05
406 Shane Rawley AS .01 .05
407 Steve Bedrosian AS .01 .05
408 Dion James .01 .05
409 Joel McKeon .01 .05
410 Tony Pena .01 .05
411 Wayne Tolleson .01 .05
412 Randy Myers .02 .10
413 John Christensen .01 .05
414 John McNamara MG .01 .05
415 Don Carman .01 .05
416 Keith Moreland .01 .05
417 Mark Ciardi .01 .05
418 Joel Youngblood .01 .05
419 Scott McGregor .01 .05
420 Wally Joyner .02 .10
421 Ed VandeBerg .01 .05
422 Dave Concepcion .02 .10
423 John Smiley RC .08 .25
424 Dwayne Murphy .01 .05
425 Jeff Reardon .02 .10
426 Randy Ready .01 .05
427 Paul Kilgus .01 .05
428 John Shelby .01 .05
429 Alan Trammell .02 .10
Kirk Gibson TL
430 Glenn Davis .01 .05
431 Casey Candaele .01 .05
432 Mike Moore .01 .05
433 Bill Pecota RC .01 .05
434 Rick Aguilera .01 .05
435 Mike Pagliarulo .01 .05
436 Mike Bielecki .01 .05
437 Fred Manrique .01 .05
438 Rob Ducey .01 .05
439 Dave Martinez .01 .05
440 Steve Bedrosian .01 .05
441 Rick Manning .01 .05
442 Tom Bolton .01 .05
443 Ken Griffey .02 .10
444 C.Ripken Sr. MG UER .01 .05
two copyrights
445 Mike Krukow .01 .05
446 Doug DeCinces .01 .05
(Now with Cardinals
on card front)
447 Jeff Montgomery RC .08 .25
448 Mike Davis .01 .05
449 Jeff M. Robinson .01 .05
450 Barry Bonds .75 2.00
451 Keith Atherton .01 .05
452 Willie Wilson .02 .10
453 Dennis Powell .01 .05
454 Marvell Wynne .01 .05
455 Shawn Hillegas .01 .05
456 Dave Anderson .01 .05
457 Terry Leach .01 .05
458 Ron Hassey .01 .05
459 Dave Winfield .01 .05
Willie Randolph TL

460 Ozzie Smith .10 .30
461 Danny Darwin .01 .05
462 Don Slaught .01 .05
463 Fred McGriff .07 .20
464 Jay Tibbs .01 .05
465 Paul Molitor .02 .10
466 Jerry Mumphrey .01 .05
467 Don Aase .01 .05
468 Darren Daulton .02 .10
469 Jeff Dedmon .01 .05
470 Dwight Evans .05 .15
471 Donnie Moore .01 .05
472 Robby Thompson .01 .05
473 Joe Niekro .01 .05
474 Tom Brookens .01 .05
475 Pete Rose MG .20 .50
476 Dave Stewart .02 .10
477 Jamie Quirk .01 .05
478 Sid Bream .01 .05
479 Brett Butler .02 .10
480 Dwight Gooden .02 .10
481 Mariano Duncan .01 .05
482 Mark Davis .01 .05
483 Rod Booker .01 .05
484 Pat Clements .01 .05
485 Harold Reynolds .02 .10
486 Pat Keedy .01 .05
487 Jim Pankovits .01 .05
488 Andy McGaffigan .01 .05
489 Pedro Guerrero .01 .05
Fernando Valenzuela TL
490 Larry Parrish .01 .05
491 B.J. Surhoff .02 .10
492 Doyle Alexander .01 .05
493 Mike Greenwell .01 .05
494 Wally Ritchie .01 .05
495 Eddie Murray .07 .20
496 Guy Hoffman .01 .05
497 Kevin Mitchell .02 .10
498 Bob Boone .02 .10
499 Eric King .01 .05
500 Andre Dawson .02 .10
501 Tim Birtsas .01 .05
502 Dan Gladden .01 .05
503 Junior Noboa .01 .05
504 Bob Rodgers MG .01 .05
505 Willie Upshaw .01 .05
506 John Cangelosi .01 .05
507 Mark Gubicza .01 .05
508 Tim Teufel .01 .05
509 Bill Dawley .01 .05
510 Dave Winfield .02 .10
511 Joel Davis .01 .05
512 Alex Trevino .01 .05
513 Tim Flannery .01 .05
514 Pat Sheridan .01 .05
515 Juan Nieves .01 .05
516 Jim Sundberg .02 .10
517 Ron Robinson .01 .05
518 Greg Gross .01 .05
519 Harold Reynolds .01 .05
Phil Bradley TL
520 Dave Smith .01 .05
521 Jim Dwyer .01 .05
522 Bob Patterson .01 .05
523 Gary Roenicke .01 .05
524 Gary Lucas .01 .05
525 Marty Barrett .01 .05
526 Juan Berenguer .01 .05
527 Steve Henderson .01 .05
528A Checklist 397-528 .05 .15
ERR (455 S. Carlton)
528B Checklist 397-528 .02 .10
COR (455 S. Hillegas)
529 Tim Burke .01 .05
530 Gary Carter .02 .10
531 Rich Yett .01 .05
532 Mike Kingery .01 .05
533 John Farrell RC .02 .10
534 John Wathan MG .01 .05
535 Ron Guidry .02 .10
536 John Morris .01 .05
537 Steve Buechele .01 .05
538 Bill Wegman .01 .05
539 Mike LaValliere .01 .05
540 Bret Saberhagen .02 .10
541 Juan Beniquez .01 .05
542 Paul Noce .01 .05
543 Kent Tekulve .01 .05
544 Jim Traber .01 .05
545 Don Baylor .02 .10
546 John Candelaria .01 .05
547 Felix Fermin .01 .05
548 Shane Mack .01 .05
549 Albert Hall .02 .10
Dale Murphy
Ken Griffey
Dion James TL
550 Pedro Guerrero .02 .10
551 Terry Steinbach .02 .10
552 Mark Thurmond .01 .05
553 Tracy Jones .01 .05
554 Mike Smithson .01 .05
555 Brook Jacoby .01 .05
556 Stan Clarke .01 .05
557 Craig Reynolds .01 .05
558 Bob Ojeda .01 .05
559 Ken Williams RC .01 .05
560 Tim Wallach .01 .05
561 Rick Cerone .01 .05
562 Jim Lindeman .01 .05
563 Jose Guzman .01 .05
564 Frank Lucchesi MG .01 .05
565 Lloyd Moseby .01 .05
566 Charlie O'Brien .01 .05
567 Mike Diaz .01 .05
568 Chris Brown .01 .05
569 Charlie Leibrandt .01 .05
570 Jeffrey Leonard .01 .05
571 Mark Williamson .01 .05
572 Chris James .01 .05
573 Bob Stanley .01 .05
574 Graig Nettles .02 .10
575 Don Sutton .02 .10
576 Tommy Hinzo .01 .05
577 Tom Browning .01 .05
578 Gary Gaetti .02 .10
579 Gary Carter .01 .05
Kevin McReynolds TL
580 Mark McGwire .60 1.50
581 Tito Landrum .01 .05
582 Mike Henneman RC .08 .25
583 Dave Valle .01 .05
584 Steve Trout .01 .05
585 Ozzie Guillen .02 .10
586 Bob Forsch .01 .05
587 Terry Puhl .01 .05
588 Jeff Parrett .01 .05
589 Geno Petralli .01 .05
590 George Bell .02 .10
591 Doug Drabek .01 .05
592 Dale Sveum .01 .05
593 Bob Tewksbury .01 .05
594 Bobby Valentine MG .02 .10
595 Frank White .02 .10
596 John Kruk .02 .10
597 Gene Garber .01 .05
598 Lee Lacy .01 .05
599 Calvin Schiraldi .01 .05
600 Mike Schmidt .20 .50
601 Jack Lazorko .01 .05
602 Mike Aldrete .01 .05
603 Rob Murphy .01 .05
604 Chris Bando .01 .05
605 Kirk Gibson .07 .20
606 Moose Haas .01 .05
607 Mickey Hatcher .01 .05
608 Charlie Kerfeld .01 .05
609 Gary Gaetti .02 .10
Kent Hrbek TL
610 Keith Hernandez .02 .10
611 Tommy John .02 .10
612 Curt Ford .01 .05
613 Bobby Thigpen .01 .05
614 Herm Winningham .01 .05
615 Jody Davis .01 .05
616 Jay Aldrich .01 .05
617 Oddibe McDowell .01 .05
618 Cecil Fielder .02 .10
619 Mike Dunne .01 .05
Inconsistent design,
black name on front
620 Cory Snyder .01 .05
621 Gene Nelson .01 .05
622 Kal Daniels .01 .05
623 Mike Flanagan .01 .05
624 Jim Leyland MG .02 .10
625 Frank Viola .01 .05
626 Glenn Wilson .01 .05
627 Joe Boever .01 .05
628 Dave Henderson .01 .05
629 Kelly Downs .01 .05
630 Darrell Evans .02 .10
631 Jack Howell .01 .05
632 Steve Shields .01 .05
633 Barry Lyons .01 .05
634 Jose DeLeon .01 .05
635 Terry Pendleton .02 .10
636 Charles Hudson .01 .05
637 Jay Bell RC .15 .40
638 Steve Balboni .01 .05
639 Glenn Braggs .01 .05
Tony Muser CO TL
640 Garry Templeton .02 .10
(Inconsistent design,
green border)
641 Rick Honeycutt .01 .05
642 Bob Dernier .01 .05
643 Rocky Childress .01 .05
644 Terry McGriff .01 .05
645 Matt Nokes RC .08 .25
646 Checklist 529-660 .01 .05
647 Pascual Perez .01 .05
648 Al Newman .01 .05
649 DeWayne Buice .01 .05
650 Cal Ripken .30 .75
651 Mike Jackson RC .08 .25
652 Bruce Benedict .01 .05
653 Jeff Sellers .01 .05
654 Roger Craig MG .02 .10
655 Len Dykstra .02 .10
656 Lee Guetterman .01 .05
657 Gary Redus .01 .05
658 Tim Conroy .01 .05
(Inconsistent design,
name in white)
659 Bobby Meacham .01 .05
660 Rick Reuschel .02 .10
661 Nolan Ryan TBC '83 .20 .50
662 Jim Rice TBC .01 .05
663 Ron Blomberg TBC .01 .05
664 Bob Gibson TBC '68 .08 .25
665 Stan Musial TBC '63 .07 .20
666 Mario Soto .01 .05
667 Luis Quinones .01 .05
668 Walt Terrell .01 .05
669 Lance Parrish .01 .05
Mike Ryan CO TL
670 Dan Plesac .01 .05
671 Tim Laudner .01 .05
672 John Davis .01 .05
673 Tony Phillips .01 .05
674 Mike Fitzgerald .01 .05
675 Jim Rice .02 .10
676 Ken Dixon .01 .05
677 Eddie Milner .01 .05
678 Jim Acker .01 .05
679 Darrell Miller .01 .05
680 Charlie Hough .02 .10
681 Bobby Bonilla .02 .10
682 Jimmy Key .02 .10
683 Julio Franco .02 .10
684 Hal Lanier MG .01 .05
685 Ron Darling .02 .10
686 Terry Francona .02 .10
687 Mickey Brantley .01 .05
688 Jim Winn .01 .05
689 Tom Pagnozzi RC .02 .10
690 Jay Howell .01 .05
691 Dan Pasqua .01 .05
692 Mike Birkbeck .01 .05
693 Benito Santiago .02 .10
694 Eric Nolte .01 .05
695 Shawon Dunston .01 .05
696 Duane Ward .01 .05
697 Steve Lombardozzi .01 .05
698 Brad Havens .01 .05
699 Benito Santiago .02 .10
Tony Gwynn TL
700 George Brett .20 .50
701 Sammy Stewart .01 .05
702 Mike Gallego .01 .05
703 Bob Brenly .01 .05
704 Dennis Boyd .01 .05
705 Juan Samuel .01 .05
706 Rick Mahler .01 .05
707 Fred Lynn .02 .10
708 Gus Polidor .01 .05
709 George Frazier .01 .05
710 Darryl Strawberry .02 .10
711 Bill Gullickson .01 .05
712 John Moses .01 .05
713 Willie Hernandez .01 .05
714 Jim Fregosi MG .01 .05
715 Todd Worrell .01 .05
716 Lenn Sakata .01 .05
717 Jay Baller .01 .05
718 Mike Felder .01 .05
719 Denny Walling .01 .05
720 Tim Raines .02 .10
721 Pete O'Brien .01 .05
722 Manny Lee .01 .05
723 Bob Kipper .01 .05
724 Danny Tartabull .01 .05
725 Mike Boddicker .01 .05
726 Alfredo Griffin .01 .05
727 Greg Booker .01 .05
728 Andy Allanson .01 .05
729 George Bell .02 .10
Fred McGriff TL
730 John Franco .02 .10
731 Rick Schu .01 .05
732 David Palmer .01 .05
733 Spike Owen .01 .05
734 Craig Lefferts .01 .05
735 Kevin McReynolds .01 .05
736 Matt Young .01 .05
737 Butch Wynegar .01 .05
738 Scott Bankhead .01 .05
739 Daryl Boston .01 .05
740 Rick Sutcliffe .02 .10
741 Mike Easler .01 .05
742 Mark Clear .01 .05
743 Larry Herndon .01 .05
744 Whitey Herzog MG .02 .10
745 Bill Doran .01 .05
746 Gene Larkin RC .08 .25
747 Bobby Witt .01 .05
748 Reid Nichols .01 .05
749 Mark Eichhorn .01 .05
750 Bo Jackson .07 .20
751 Jim Morrison .01 .05
752 Mark Grant .01 .05
753 Danny Heep .01 .05
754 Mike LaCoss .01 .05
755 Ozzie Virgil .01 .05
756 Mike Maddux .01 .05
757 John Marzano .01 .05
758 Eddie Williams RC .02 .10
759 Mark McGwire .40 1.00
Jose Canseco TL UER
(two copyrights)
760 Mike Scott .02 .10
761 Tony Armas .02 .10
762 Scott Bradley .01 .05
763 Doug Sisk .01 .05
764 Greg Walker .01 .05
765 Neal Heaton .01 .05
766 Henry Cotto .01 .05
767 Jose Lind RC .08 .25
768 Dickie Noles .01 .05
(Now with Tigers
on card front)
769 Cecil Cooper .02 .10
770 Lou Whitaker .02 .10
771 Ruben Sierra .02 .10
772 Sal Butera .01 .05
773 Frank Williams .01 .05
774 Gene Mauch MG .01 .05
775 Dave Stieb .02 .10
776 Checklist 661-792 .01 .05
777 Lonnie Smith .01 .05
778A Keith Comstock ERR .75 2.00
(White Padres)
778B Keith Comstock COR .01 .05
(Blue Padres)
779 Tom Glavine RC 1.00 2.50
780 Fernando Valenzuela .02 .10
781 Keith Hughes .01 .05
782 Jeff Ballard .01 .05
783 Ron Roenicke .01 .05
784 Joe Sambito .01 .05
785 Alvin Davis .01 .05
786 Joe Price .01 .05
Inconsistent design,
orange team name
787 Bill Almon .01 .05
788 Ray Searage .01 .05
789 Joe Carter .01 .05
Cory Snyder TL
790 Dave Righetti .02 .10
791 Ted Simmons .02 .10
792 John Tudor .02 .10

1988 Topps Tiffany

This was the fifth year that Topps issued a "Tiffany" set. These 792 standard-size cards parallel the regular Topps cards. These cards were issued in factory set form only, produced in Topps Irish facility, and only available through Topps hobby dealers. These cards were again produced in relatively large quantities and the multiplier value is reduced compared to pre-1987 levels. It is believed that as many as 25,000 of these sets were produced.

COMP.FACT.SET (792) 40.00 80.00
*STARS: 4X TO 10X BASIC CARDS
*ROOKIES: 3X TO 8X BASIC CARDS

1988 Topps Glossy All-Stars

This set of 22 glossy cards was inserted one per rack pack. Players selected for the set are the starting players (plus manager and honorary captain) in the 1987 All-Star Game in Oakland. Cards measure the standard size and the backs feature red and blue printing on a white card stock.

COMPLETE SET (22) 1.60 4.00
1 John McNamara MG .01 .05
2 Don Mattingly .40 1.00
3 Willie Randolph .02 .10
4 Wade Boggs .20 .50
5 Cal Ripken .75 2.00
6 George Bell .01 .05
7 Rickey Henderson .30 .75
8 Dave Winfield .15 .40
9 Terry Kennedy .01 .05
10 Bret Saberhagen .02 .10
11 Jim Hunter CAPT .08 .25
12 Dave Johnson MG .02 .10
13 Jack Clark .02 .10
14 Ryne Sandberg .40 1.00
15 Mike Schmidt .20 .50
16 Ozzie Smith .40 1.00
17 Eric Davis .02 .10
18 Andre Dawson .07 .20
19 Darryl Strawberry .02 .10
20 Gary Carter .15 .40
21 Mike Scott .01 .05
22 Billy Williams CAPT .08 .25

1988 Topps Rookies

Inserted in each supermarket jumbo pack is a card from this series of 22 of 1987's best rookies as determined by Topps. Jumbo packs consisted of 100 (regular issue 1988 Topps baseball) cards with a stick of gum plus the insert "Rookie" card. The card fronts are in full color and measure the standard size. The card backs are printed in red and blue on white card stock and are numbered at the bottom.

COMPLETE SET (22) 12.50 25.00
1 Bill Ripken .08 .25
2 Ellis Burks .40 1.00
3 Mike Greenwell .08 .25
4 DeWayne Buice .08 .25
5 Devon White .20 .50
6 Fred Manrique .08 .25
7 Mike Henneman .20 .50
8 Matt Nokes .08 .25
9 Kevin Seitzer .20 .50
10 B.J. Surhoff .20 .50
11 Casey Candaele .08 .25
12 Randy Myers .30 .75
13 Mark McGwire 6.00 15.00
14 Luis Polonia .08 .25
15 Terry Steinbach .20 .50
16 Mike Dunne .08 .25
17 Al Pedrique .08 .25
18 Benito Santiago .20 .50
19 Kelly Downs .08 .25
20 Joe Magrane .08 .25
21 Jerry Browne .08 .25
22 Jeff Musselman .08 .25

1988 Topps Traded

This standard-size 132-card Traded set was distributed exclusively in factory set form in blue and white taped boxes through hobby dealers. The cards are identical in style to the Topps regular issue except for whiter stock and t-suffixed numbering on back. Cards are ordered alphabetically by player's last name. This set generated additional interest upon release due to the inclusion of members of the 1988 U.S. Olympic baseball team. These Olympians are indicated in the checklist below by OLY. The key extended Rookie Cards in this set are Jim Abbott, Roberto Alomar, Brady Anderson, Andy Benes, Jay Buhner, Ron Gant, Mark Grace, Tino Martinez, Charles Nagy, Robin Ventura and Walt Weiss.

COMP.FACT.SET (132) 3.00 8.00
1T Jim Abbott OLY XRC .75 2.00
2T Juan Agosto .02 .10
3T Luis Alicea XRC .20 .50
4T Roberto Alomar XRC .75 2.00
5T Brady Anderson XRC .30 .75
6T Jack Armstrong XRC .20 .50
7T Don August .02 .10
8T Floyd Bannister .02 .10
9T Bret Barberie OLY XRC .08 .25
10T Jose Bautista XRC .08 .25
11T Don Baylor .07 .20
12T Tim Belcher .02 .10
13T Buddy Bell .07 .20
14T Andy Benes OLY XRC .30 .75
15T Damon Berryhill XRC .20 .50
16T Bud Black .02 .10
17T Pat Borders XRC .20 .50
18T Phil Bradley .02 .10
19T Jeff Branson OLY XRC .20 .50
20T Tom Brunansky .02 .10
21T Jay Buhner XRC .40 1.00
22T Brett Butler .07 .20
23T Jim Campanis OLY XRC .02 .10
24T Sil Campusano .02 .10
25T John Candelaria .02 .10
26T Jose Cecena .02 .10
27T Rick Cerone .02 .10
28T Jack Clark .07 .20
29T Kevin Coffman .02 .10
30T Pat Combs OLY XRC .08 .25
31T Henry Cotto .02 .10
32T Chili Davis .07 .20
33T Mike Davis .02 .10
34T Jose DeLeon .02 .10
35T Richard Dotson .02 .10
36T Cecil Espy XRC .02 .10
37T Tom Filer .02 .10
38T Mike Fiore OLY .02 .10
39T Ron Gant XRC .30 .75
40T Kirk Gibson .20 .50
41T Rich Gossage .07 .20
42T Mark Grace XRC .75 2.00
43T Alfredo Griffin .02 .10
44T Ty Griffin OLY .02 .10
45T Bryan Harvey XRC .20 .50
46T Ron Hassey .02 .10
47T Ray Hayward .02 .10
48T Dave Henderson .02 .10
49T Tom Herr .02 .10
50T Bob Horner .07 .20
51T Ricky Horton .02 .10
52T Jay Howell .02 .10
53T Glenn Hubbard .02 .10
54T Jeff Innis .02 .10
55T Danny Jackson .02 .10
56T Darrin Jackson XRC .08 .25
57T Roberto Kelly XRC .20 .50
58T Ron Kittle .02 .10
59T Ray Knight .07 .20
60T Vance Law .02 .10
61T Jeffrey Leonard .02 .10
62T Mike Macfarlane XRC .20 .50
63T Scotti Madison .02 .10
64T Kirt Manwaring .02 .10
65T M.Marquess OLY CO .02 .10
66T Tino Martinez OLY XRC 1.25 3.00
67T Billy Masse OLY XRC .08 .25
68T Jack McDowell XRC .30 .75
69T Jack McKeon MG .07 .20
70T Larry McWilliams .02 .10
71T Mickey Morandini OLY XRC .20 .50
72T Keith Moreland .02 .10
73T Mike Morgan .02 .10
74T Charles Nagy OLY XRC .20 .50
75T Al Nipper .02 .10
76T Russ Nixon MG .02 .10
77T Jesse Orosco .02 .10
78T Joe Orsulak .02 .10
79T Dave Palmer .02 .10
80T Mark Parent .02 .10
81T Dave Parker .07 .20
82T Dan Pasqua .02 .10
83T Melido Perez XRC .20 .50
84T Steve Peters .02 .10
85T Dan Petry .02 .10
86T Gary Pettis .02 .10
87T Jeff Pico .02 .10
88T Jim Poole OLY XRC .08 .25
89T Ted Power .02 .10
90T Rafael Ramirez .02 .10
91T Dennis Rasmussen .02 .10
92T Jose Rijo .07 .20
93T Ernie Riles .02 .10
94T Luis Rivera .02 .10
95T Doug Robbins OLY XRC .08 .25
96T Frank Robinson MG .10 .30
97T Cookie Rojas MG .02 .10
98T Chris Sabo XRC .30 .75
99T Mark Salas .02 .10
100T Luis Salazar .02 .10
101T Rafael Santana .02 .10
102T Nelson Santovenia .02 .10
103T Mackey Sasser XRC .20 .50
104T Calvin Schiraldi .02 .10
105T Mike Schooler .02 .10
106T Scott Servais OLY XRC .20 .50
107T Dave Silvestri OLY XRC .08 .25
108T Don Slaught .02 .10
109T Jeff Slusarski OLY XRC .08 .25
110T Lee Smith .07 .20
111T Pete Smith XRC .08 .25
112T Jim Snyder MG .02 .10
113T Ed Sprague OLY XRC .20 .50
114T Pete Stanicek .02 .10
115T Kurt Stillwell .02 .10
116T Todd Stottlemyre XRC .20 .50
117T Bill Swift .02 .10
118T Pat Tabler .02 .10
119T Scott Terry .02 .10
120T Mickey Tettleton .02 .10
121T Dickie Thon .02 .10
122T Jeff Treadway XRC .20 .50
123T Willie Upshaw .02 .10
124T Robin Ventura OLY XRC .60 1.50
125T Ron Washington .02 .10
126T Walt Weiss XRC .30 .75
127T Bob Welch .07 .20
128T David Wells XRC .60 1.50
129T Glenn Wilson .02 .10
130T Ted Wood OLY XRC .08 .25
131T Don Zimmer MG .07 .20
132T Checklist 1T-132T .02 .10

1988 Topps Traded Tiffany

As a bonus for those dealers who ordered the regular Tiffany sets, they received an equivalent number of Tiffany update sets. These 132 standard-size cards parallel the regular traded issue. Again issued in the Topps Irish facility, these cards feature glossy fronts and easy to read backs. These sets were only issued in complete factory form.

COMP.FACT.SET (132) 15.00 40.00
*STARS: 1.5X TO 4X BASIC CARDS
*ROOKIES: 2.5X TO 6X BASIC CARDS
66T Tino Martinez OLY 4.00 10.00

1989 Topps

This set consists of 792 standard-size cards. Cards were primarily issued in 15-card wax packs, 42-card rack packs and factory sets. Subsets in the set include Record Breakers (1-7), Turn Back the Clock (661-665), All-Star selections (386-407) and First Draft Picks, Future Stars and Team Leaders (all scattered throughout the set). The manager cards contain a team checklist on back. The key Rookie Cards in this set are Jim Abbott, Sandy Alomar Jr., Brady Anderson, Steve Avery, Andy Benes, Dante Bichette, Craig Biggio, Randy Johnson, Ramon Martinez, Gary Sheffield, John Smoltz, and Robin Ventura.

COMPLETE SET (792) 8.00 20.00
COMP.FACT.SET (792) 10.00 25.00
COMP.X-MAS.SET (792) 10.00 25.00
FS SUBSET VARIATIONS EXIST
FS PHOTOS ARE PLACED HIGHER/LOWER
1 George Bell RB .01 .05
Slams 3 HR on
Opening Day
2 Wade Boggs RB .02 .10
3 Gary Carter RB .01 .05
Sets Record for
Career Putouts
4 Andre Dawson RB .01 .05
Logs Double Figures
in HR and SB
5 Orel Hershiser RB .01 .05
Pitches 59
Scoreless Innings
6 Doug Jones RB UER .01 .05
Earns His 15th
Straight Save

Photo actually Chris Codiroli
7 Kevin McReynolds RB .01 .05
Steals 21 Without
Being Caught
8 Dave Eiland .01 .05
9 Tim Teufel .01 .05
10 Andre Dawson .02 .10
11 Bruce Sutter .02 .10
12 Dale Sveum .01 .05
13 Doug Sisk .01 .05
14 Tom Kelly MG .01 .05
15 Robby Thompson .01 .05
16 Ron Robinson .01 .05
17 Brian Downing .02 .10
18 Rick Rhoden .01 .05
19 Greg Gagne .01 .05
20 Steve Bedrosian .01 .05
21 Greg Walker TL .01 .05
22 Tim Crews .01 .05
23 Mike Fitzgerald .01 .05
24 Larry Andersen .01 .05
25 Frank White .02 .10
26 Dale Mohorcic .01 .05
27A Orestes Destrade .02 .10
(F* next to copyright) RC
27B Orestes Destrade .02 .10
(E*F* next to
copyright) VAR
28 Mike Moore .01 .05
29 Kelly Gruber .01 .05
30 Dwight Gooden .02 .10
31 Terry Francona .02 .10
32 Dennis Rasmussen .01 .05
33 B.J. Surhoff .02 .10
34 Ken Williams .01 .05
35 John Tudor UER .02 .10
(With Red Sox in '84,should be Pirates)
36 Mitch Webster .01 .05
37 Bob Stanley .01 .05
38 Paul Runge .01 .05
39 Mike Maddux .01 .05
40 Steve Sax .01 .05
41 Terry Mulholland .01 .05
42 Jim Eppard .01 .05
43 Guillermo Hernandez .01 .05
44 Jim Snyder MG .01 .05
45 Kal Daniels .01 .05
46 Mark Portugal .01 .05
47 Carney Lansford .02 .10
48 Tim Burke .01 .05
49 Craig Biggio RC 1.25 3.00
50 George Bell .02 .10
51 Mark McLemore TL .01 .05

52 Bob Brenly .01 .05
53 Ruben Sierra .02 .10
54 Steve Trout .01 .05
55 Julio Franco .02 .10
56 Pat Tabler .01 .05
57 Alejandro Pena .01 .05
58 Lee Mazzilli .02 .10
59 Mark Davis .01 .05
60 Tom Brunansky .01 .05
61 Neil Allen .01 .05
62 Alfredo Griffin .01 .05
63 Mark Clear .01 .05
64 Alex Trevino .01 .05
65 Rick Reuschel .02 .10
66 Manny Trillo .01 .05
67 Dave Palmer .01 .05
68 Darrell Miller .01 .05
69 Jeff Ballard .01 .05
70 Mark McGwire .40 1.00
71 Mike Boddicker .01 .05
72 John Moses .01 .05
73 Pascual Perez .01 .05
74 Nick Leyva MG .01 .05
75 Tom Henke .01 .05
76 Terry Blocker .01 .05
77 Doyle Alexander .01 .05
78 Jim Sundberg .02 .10
79 Scott Bankhead .01 .05
80 Cory Snyder .01 .05
81 Tim Raines TL .01 .05
82 Dave Leiper .01 .05
83 Jeff Blauser .01 .05
84 Bill Bene FDP .01 .05
85 Kevin McReynolds .01 .05
86 Al Nipper .01 .05
87 Larry Owen .01 .05
88 Darryl Hamilton RC .08 .25
89 Dave LaPoint .01 .05
90 Vince Coleman UER .01 .05
(Wrong birth year)
91 Floyd Youmans .01 .05
92 Jeff Kunkel .01 .05
93 Ken Howell .01 .05
94 Chris Speier .01 .05
95 Gerald Young .01 .05
96 Rick Cerone .01 .05
97 Greg Mathews .01 .05
98 Larry Sheets .01 .05
99 Sherman Corbett .01 .05
100 Mike Schmidt .20 .50
101 Les Straker .01 .05
102 Mike Gallego .01 .05
103 Tim Birtsas .01 .05
104 Dallas Green MG .01 .05
105 Ron Darling .02 .10
106 Willie Upshaw .01 .05
107 Jose DeLeon .01 .05
108 Fred Manrique .01 .05
109 Hipolito Pena .01 .05
110 Paul Molitor .02 .10
111 Eric Davis TL .01 .05
112 Jim Presley .01 .05
113 Lloyd Moseby .01 .05
114 Bob Kipper .01 .05
115 Jody Davis .01 .05
116 Jeff Montgomery .01 .05
117 Dave Anderson .01 .05
118 Checklist 1-132 .01 .05
119 Terry Puhl .01 .05
120 Frank Viola .02 .10
121 Garry Templeton .02 .10
122 Lance Johnson .01 .05
123 Spike Owen .01 .05
124 Jim Traber .01 .05
125 Mike Krukow .01 .05
126 Sid Bream .01 .05
127 Walt Terrell .01 .05
128 Milt Thompson .01 .05
129 Terry Clark .01 .05
130 Gerald Perry .01 .05
131 Dave Otto .01 .05
132 Curt Ford .01 .05
133 Bill Long .01 .05
134 Don Zimmer MG .02 .10
135 Jose Rijo .02 .10
136 Joey Meyer .01 .05
137 Geno Petralli .01 .05
138 Wallace Johnson .01 .05
139 Mike Flanagan .01 .05
140 Shawon Dunston .01 .05
141 Brook Jacoby TL .01 .05
142 Mike Diaz .01 .05
143 Mike Campbell .01 .05
144 Jay Bell .02 .10
145 Dave Stewart .02 .10
146 Gary Pettis .01 .05
147 DeWayne Buice .01 .05
148 Bill Pecota .01 .05
149 Doug Dascenzo .01 .05
150 Fernando Valenzuela .02 .10
151 Terry McGriff .01 .05
152 Mark Thurmond .01 .05
153 Jim Pankovits .01 .05
154 Don Carman .01 .05
155 Marty Barrett .01 .05
156 Dave Gallagher .01 .05
157 Tom Glavine .08 .25
158 Mike Aldrete .01 .05
159 Pat Clements .01 .05
160 Jeffrey Leonard .01 .05
161 G. Olson RC FDP UER .08 .25
Born Scribner, NE, should be Omaha, NE
162 John Davis .01 .05
163 Bob Forsch .01 .05
164 Hal Lanier MG .01 .05
165 Mike Dunne .01 .05
166 Doug Jennings .01 .05
167 Steve Searcy FS .01 .05
168 Willie Wilson .02 .10
169 Mike Jackson .01 .05
170 Tony Fernandez .01 .05
171 Andres Thomas TL .01 .05
172 Frank Williams .01 .05
173 Mel Hall .01 .05
174 Todd Burns .01 .05
175 John Shelby .01 .05
176 Jeff Parrett .01 .05
177 Monty Fariss FDP .01 .05
178 Mark Grant .01 .05
179 Ozzie Virgil .01 .05
180 Mike Scott .02 .10
181 Craig Worthington .01 .05
182 Bob McClure .01 .05
183 Oddibe McDowell .01 .05
184 John Costello .01 .05
185 Claudell Washington .01 .05
186 Pat Perry .01 .05
187 Darren Daulton .02 .10
188 Dennis Lamp .01 .05
189 Kevin Mitchell .02 .10
190 Mike Witt .01 .05
191 Sil Campusano .01 .05
192 Paul Mirabella .01 .05
193 Sparky Anderson MG .02 .10
UER (553 Salazer)
194 Greg W. Harris RC .02 .10
195 Ozzie Guillen .02 .10
196 Denny Walling .01 .05
197 Neal Heaton .01 .05
198 Danny Heep .01 .05
199 Mike Schooler RC .02 .10
200 George Brett .25 .60
201 Kelly Gruber TL .01 .05
202 Brad Moore .01 .05
203 Rob Ducey .01 .05
204 Brad Havens .01 .05
205 Dwight Evans .05 .15
206 Roberto Alomar .08 .25
207 Terry Leach .01 .05
208 Tom Pagnozzi .01 .05
209 Jeff Bittiger .01 .05
210 Dale Murphy .05 .15
211 Mike Pagliarulo .01 .05
212 Scott Sanderson .01 .05
213 Rene Gonzales .01 .05
214 Charlie O'Brien .01 .05
215 Kevin Gross .01 .05
216 Jack Howell .01 .05
217 Joe Price .01 .05
218 Mike LaValliere .01 .05
219 Jim Clancy .01 .05
220 Gary Gaetti .02 .10
221 Cecil Espy .01 .05
222 Mark Lewis FDP RC .08 .25
223 Jay Buhner .02 .10
224 Tony LaRussa MG .02 .10
225 Ramon Martinez RC .08 .25
226 Bill Doran .01 .05
227 John Farrell .01 .05
228 Nelson Santovenia .01 .05
229 Jimmy Key .02 .10
230 Ozzie Smith .15 .40
231 Roberto Alomar TL .08 .25
(Gary Carter at plate)
232 Ricky Horton .01 .05
233 Gregg Jefferies FS .08 .25
234 Tom Browning .01 .05
235 John Kruk .02 .10
236 Charles Hudson .01 .05
237 Glenn Hubbard .01 .05
238 Eric King .01 .05
239 Tim Laudner .01 .05
240 Greg Maddux .20 .50
241 Brett Butler .02 .10
242 Ed VandeBerg .01 .05
243 Bob Boone .02 .10
244 Jim Acker .01 .05
245 Jim Rice .02 .10
246 Rey Quinones .01 .05
247 Shawn Hillegas .01 .05
248 Tony Phillips .01 .05
249 Tim Leary .01 .05
250 Cal Ripken .30 .75
251 John Dopson .01 .05
252 Billy Hatcher .01 .05
253 Jose Alvarez RC .02 .10
254 Tom Lasorda MG .05 .15
255 Ron Guidry .02 .10
256 Benny Santiago .02 .10
257 Rick Aguilera .01 .05
258 Checklist 133-264 .01 .05
259 Larry McWilliams .01 .05
260 Dave Winfield .02 .10
261 Tom Brunansky .01 .05
Luis Alicea TL
262 Jeff Pico .01 .05
263 Mike Felder .01 .05
264 Rob Dibble RC .15 .40
265 Kent Hrbek .02 .10
266 Luis Aquino .01 .05
267 Jeff M. Robinson .01 .05
268 Keith Miller RC .08 .25
269 Tom Bolton .01 .05
270 Wally Joyner .02 .10
271 Jay Tibbs .01 .05
272 Ron Hassey .01 .05
273 Jose Lind .01 .05
274 Mark Eichhorn .01 .05
275 Danny Tartabull UER .01 .05
(Born San Juan, PR should be Miami, FL)
276 Paul Kilgus .01 .05
277 Mike Davis .01 .05
278 Andy McGaffigan .01 .05
279 Scott Bradley .01 .05
280 Bob Knepper .01 .05
281 Gary Redus .01 .05
282 Cris Carpenter RC .02 .10
283 Andy Allanson .01 .05
284 Jim Leyland MG .02 .10
285 John Candelaria .01 .05
286 Darrin Jackson .02 .10
287 Juan Nieves .01 .05
288 Pat Sheridan .01 .05
289 Ernie Whitt .01 .05
290 John Franco .02 .10
291 Darryl Strawberry .01 .05
Keith Hernandez
Kevin McReynolds TL
292 Jim Corsi .01 .05
293 Glenn Wilson .01 .05
294 Juan Berenguer .01 .05
295 Scott Fletcher .01 .05
296 Ron Gant .02 .10
297 Oswald Peraza .01 .05
298 Chris James .01 .05
299 Steve Ellsworth .01 .05
300 Darryl Strawberry .02 .10
301 Charlie Leibrandt .01 .05
302 Gary Ward .01 .05
303 Felix Fermin .01 .05
304 Joel Youngblood .01 .05
305 Dave Smith .01 .05
306 Tracy Woodson .01 .05
307 Lance McCullers .01 .05
308 Ron Karkovice .01 .05
309 Mario Diaz .01 .05
310 Rafael Palmeiro .08 .25
311 Chris Bosio .02 .10
312 Tom Lawless .01 .05
313 Dennis Martinez .02 .10
314 Bobby Valentine MG .02 .10
315 Greg Swindell .01 .05
316 Walt Weiss .01 .05
317 Jack Armstrong RC .08 .25
318 Gene Larkin .01 .05
319 Greg Booker .01 .05
320 Lou Whitaker .02 .10
321 Jody Reed TL .01 .05
322 John Smiley .01 .05
323 Gary Thurman .01 .05
324 Bob Milacki .01 .05
325 Jesse Barfield .02 .10
326 Dennis Boyd .01 .05
327 Mark Lemke RC .15 .40
328 Rick Honeycutt .01 .05
329 Bob Melvin .01 .05
330 Eric Davis .02 .10
331 Curt Wilkerson .01 .05
332 Tony Armas .02 .10
333 Bob Ojeda .01 .05
334 Steve Lyons .01 .05
335 Dave Righetti .02 .10
336 Steve Balboni .01 .05
337 Calvin Schiraldi .01 .05
338 Jim Adduci .01 .05
339 Scott Bailes .01 .05
340 Kirk Gibson .02 .10
341 Jim Deshaies .01 .05
342 Tom Brookens .01 .05
343 Gary Sheffield FS RC .60 1.50
344 Tom Trebelhorn MG .01 .05
345 Charlie Hough .02 .10
346 Rex Hudler .01 .05
347 John Cerutti .01 .05
348 Ed Hearn .01 .05
349 Ron Jones .02 .10
350 Andy Van Slyke .05 .15
351 Bob Melvin .01 .05
Bill Fahey CO TL
352 Rick Schu .01 .05
353 Marvell Wynne .01 .05
354 Larry Parrish .01 .05
355 Mark Langston .01 .05
356 Kevin Elster .01 .05
357 Jerry Reuss .01 .05
358 Ricky Jordan RC .08 .25
359 Tommy John .02 .10
360 Ryne Sandberg .15 .40
361 Kelly Downs .01 .05
362 Jack Lazorko .01 .05
363 Rich Yett .01 .05
364 Rob Deer .01 .05
365 Mike Henneman .01 .05
366 Herm Winningham .01 .05
367 Johnny Paredes .01 .05
368 Brian Holton .01 .05
369 Ken Caminiti .05 .15
370 Dennis Eckersley .05 .15
371 Manny Lee .01 .05
372 Craig Lefferts .01 .05
373 Tracy Jones .01 .05
374 John Wathan MG .01 .05
375 Terry Pendleton .02 .10
376 Steve Lombardozzi .01 .05
377 Mike Smithson .01 .05
378 Checklist 265-396 .01 .05
379 Tim Flannery .01 .05
380 Rickey Henderson .08 .25
381 Larry Sheets TL .01 .05
382 John Smoltz RC .60 1.50
383 Howard Johnson .02 .10
384 Mark Salas .01 .05
385 Von Hayes .01 .05
386 Andres Galarraga AS .01 .05
387 Ryne Sandberg AS .08 .25
388 Bobby Bonilla AS .01 .05
389 Ozzie Smith AS .08 .25
390 Darryl Strawberry AS .01 .05
391 Andre Dawson AS .01 .05
392 Andy Van Slyke AS .02 .10
393 Gary Carter AS .01 .05
394 Orel Hershiser AS .01 .05
395 Danny Jackson AS .01 .05
396 Kirk Gibson AS .02 .10
397 Don Mattingly AS .10 .30
398 Julio Franco AS .01 .05
399 Wade Boggs AS .02 .10
400 Alan Trammell AS .01 .05
401 Jose Canseco AS .05 .15
402 Mike Greenwell AS .01 .05
403 Kirby Puckett AS .05 .15
404 Bob Boone AS .01 .05
405 Roger Clemens AS .20 .50
406 Frank Viola AS .01 .05
407 Dave Winfield AS .01 .05
408 Greg Walker .01 .05
409 Ken Dayley .01 .05
410 Jack Clark .02 .10
411 Mitch Williams .01 .05
412 Barry Lyons .01 .05
413 Mike Kingery .01 .05
414 Jim Fregosi MG .01 .05
415 Rich Gossage .02 .10
416 Fred Lynn .02 .10
417 Mike LaCoss .01 .05
418 Bob Dernier .01 .05
419 Tom Filer .01 .05
420 Joe Carter .02 .10
421 Kirk McCaskill .01 .05
422 Bo Diaz .01 .05
423 Brian Fisher .01 .05
424 Luis Polonia UER .01 .05
(Wrong birthdate)
425 Jay Howell .01 .05
426 Dan Gladden .01 .05
427 Eric Show .01 .05
428 Craig Reynolds .01 .05
429 Greg Gagne TL .01 .05
430 Mark Gubicza .01 .05
431 Luis Rivera .01 .05
432 Chad Kreuter RC .08 .25
433 Albert Hall .01 .05
434 Ken Patterson .01 .05
435 Len Dykstra .02 .10
436 Bobby Meacham .01 .05
437 Andy Benes FDP RC .15 .40
438 Greg Gross .01 .05
439 Frank DiPino .01 .05
440 Bobby Bonilla .02 .10
441 Jerry Reed .01 .05
442 Jose Oquendo .01 .05
443 Rod Nichols .01 .05
444 Moose Stubing MG .01 .05
445 Matt Nokes .01 .05
446 Rob Murphy .01 .05
447 Donell Nixon .01 .05
448 Eric Plunk .01 .05
449 Carmelo Martinez .01 .05
450 Roger Clemens .40 1.00
451 Mark Davidson .01 .05
452 Israel Sanchez .01 .05
453 Tom Prince .01 .05
454 Paul Assenmacher .01 .05
455 Johnny Ray .01 .05
456 Tim Belcher .01 .05
457 Mackey Sasser .01 .05
458 Donn Pall .01 .05
459 Dave Valle TL .01 .05
460 Dave Stieb .02 .10
461 Buddy Bell .02 .10
462 Jose Guzman .01 .05
463 Steve Lake .01 .05
464 Bryn Smith .01 .05
465 Mark Grace .08 .25
466 Chuck Crim .01 .05
467 Jim Walewander .01 .05
468 Henry Cotto .01 .05
469 Jose Bautista RC .02 .10
470 Lance Parrish .02 .10
471 Steve Curry .01 .05
472 Brian Harper .01 .05
473 Don Robinson .01 .05
474 Bob Rodgers MG .01 .05
475 Dave Parker .02 .10
476 Jon Perlman .01 .05
477 Dick Schofield .01 .05
478 Doug Drabek .01 .05
479 Mike Macfarlane RC .08 .25
480 Keith Hernandez .02 .10
481 Chris Brown .01 .05
482 Steve Peters .01 .05
483 Mickey Hatcher .01 .05
484 Steve Shields .01 .05
485 Hubie Brooks .01 .05
486 Jack McDowell .02 .10
487 Scott Lusader .01 .05
488 Kevin Coffman .01 .05
Now with Cubs
489 Mike Schmidt TL .05 .15
490 Chris Sabo RC .15 .40
491 Mike Birkbeck .01 .05
492 Alan Ashby .01 .05
493 Todd Benzinger .01 .05
494 Shane Rawley .01 .05
495 Candy Maldonado .01 .05
496 Dwayne Henry .01 .05
497 Pete Stanicek .01 .05
498 Dave Valle .01 .05
499 Don Heinkel .01 .05
500 Jose Canseco .08 .25
501 Vance Law .01 .05
502 Duane Ward .01 .05
503 Al Newman .01 .05
504 Bob Walk .01 .05
505 Pete Rose MG .20 .50
506 Kirt Manwaring .01 .05
507 Steve Farr .01 .05
508 Wally Backman .01 .05
509 Bud Black .01 .05
510 Bob Horner .02 .10
511 Richard Dotson .01 .05
512 Donnie Hill .01 .05
513 Jesse Orosco .01 .05
514 Chet Lemon .02 .10
515 Barry Larkin .05 .15
516 Eddie Whitson .01 .05
517 Greg Brock .01 .05
518 Bruce Ruffin .01 .05
519 Willie Randolph TL .01 .05
520 Rick Sutcliffe .02 .10
521 Mickey Tettleton .01 .05
522 Randy Kramer .01 .05
523 Andres Thomas .01 .05
524 Checklist 397-528 .01 .05
525 Chili Davis .02 .10
526 Wes Gardner .01 .05
527 Dave Henderson .01 .05
528 Luis Medina .01 .05
(Lower left front has white triangle)
529 Tom Foley .01 .05
530 Nolan Ryan .40 1.00
531 Dave Hengel .01 .05
532 Jerry Browne .01 .05
533 Andy Hawkins .01 .05
534 Doc Edwards MG .01 .05
535 Todd Worrell UER .01 .05
(4 wins in '88, should be 5)
536 Joel Skinner .01 .05
537 Pete Smith .01 .05
538 Juan Castillo .01 .05
539 Barry Jones .01 .05
540 Bo Jackson .08 .25
541 Cecil Fielder .02 .10
542 Todd Frohwirth .01 .05
543 Damon Berryhill .01 .05
544 Jeff Sellers .01 .05
545 Mookie Wilson .02 .10
546 Mark Williamson .01 .05
547 Mark McLemore .01 .05
548 Bobby Witt .01 .05
549 Jamie Moyer TL .01 .05
550 Orel Hershiser .02 .10
551 Randy Ready .01 .05
552 Greg Cadaret .01 .05
553 Luis Salazar .01 .05
554 Nick Esasky .01 .05
555 Bert Blyleven .02 .10
556 Bruce Fields .01 .05
557 Keith A. Miller .01 .05
558 Dan Pasqua .01 .05
559 Juan Agosto .01 .05
560 Tim Raines .02 .10
561 Luis Aguayo .01 .05
562 Danny Cox .01 .05
563 Bill Schroeder .01 .05
564 Russ Nixon MG .01 .05
565 Jeff Russell .01 .05
566 Al Pedrique .01 .05
567 David Wells UER .02 .10
(Complete Pitching Recor)
568 Mickey Brantley .01 .05
569 German Jimenez .01 .05
570 Tony Gwynn UER .10 .30
('88 average should be italicized as league leader)
571 Billy Ripken .01 .05
572 Atlee Hammaker .01 .05
573 Jim Abbott FDP RC .40 1.00
574 Dave Clark .01 .05
575 Juan Samuel .01 .05
576 Greg Minton .01 .05
577 Randy Bush .01 .05
578 John Morris .01 .05
579 Glenn Davis TL .01 .05
580 Harold Reynolds .02 .10
581 Gene Nelson .01 .05
582 Mike Marshall .01 .05
583 Paul Gibson .01 .05
584 Randy Velarde UER .01 .05
(Signed 1935, should be 1985)
585 Harold Baines .02 .10
586 Joe Boever .01 .05
587 Mike Stanley .01 .05
588 Luis Alicea RC .08 .25
589 Dave Meads .01 .05
590 Andres Galarraga .02 .10
591 Jeff Musselman .01 .05
592 John Cangelosi .01 .05
593 Drew Hall .01 .05
594 Jimy Williams MG .01 .05
595 Teddy Higuera .01 .05
596 Kurt Stillwell .01 .05
597 Terry Taylor RC .02 .10
598 Ken Gerhart .01 .05
599 Tom Candiotti .01 .05
600 Wade Boggs .05 .15
601 Dave Dravecky .01 .05
602 Devon White .02 .10
603 Frank Tanana .02 .10
604 Paul O'Neill .05 .15
605A Bob Welch ERR 4.00 10.00
(Missing line on back Complete M.L. Pitching Record
605B Bob Welch COR .02 .10
606 Rick Dempsey .01 .05
607 Willie Ansley FDP RC .02 .10
608 Phil Bradley .01 .05
609 Frank Tanana .01 .05
Alan Trammell
Mike Heath TL
610 Randy Myers .02 .10
611 Don Slaught .01 .05
612 Dan Quisenberry .01 .05
613 Gary Varsho .01 .05
614 Joe Hesketh .01 .05
615 Robin Yount .15 .40
616 Steve Rosenberg .01 .05
617 Mark Parent .01 .05
618 Rance Mulliniks .01 .05
619 Checklist 529-660 .01 .05
620 Barry Bonds .60 1.50
621 Rick Mahler .01 .05
622 Stan Javier .01 .05
623 Fred Toliver .01 .05
624 Jack McKeon MG .02 .10
625 Eddie Murray .08 .25
626 Jeff Reed .01 .05
627 Greg A. Harris .01 .05
628 Matt Williams .08 .25
629 Pete O'Brien .01 .05
630 Mike Greenwell .01 .05
631 Dave Bergman .01 .05
632 Bryan Harvey RC .08 .25
633 Daryl Boston .01 .05
634 Marvin Freeman .01 .05
635 Willie Randolph .02 .10
636 Bill Wilkinson .01 .05
637 Carmen Castillo .01 .05
638 Floyd Bannister .01 .05
639 Walt Weiss TL .01 .05
640 Willie McGee .02 .10
641 Curt Young .01 .05
642 Angel Salazar .01 .05
643 Louie Meadows .01 .05
644 Lloyd McClendon .01 .05
645 Jack Morris .02 .10
646 Kevin Bass .01 .05
647 Randy Johnson RC .75 2.00
648 Sandy Alomar FS RC .15 .40
649 Stu Cliburn .01 .05
650 Kirby Puckett .08 .25
651 Tom Niedenfuer .01 .05
652 Rich Gedman .01 .05
653 Tommy Barrett .01 .05
654 Whitey Herzog MG .02 .10
655 Dave Magadan .01 .05
656 Ivan Calderon .01 .05
657 Joe Magrane .01 .05
658 R.J. Reynolds .01 .05
659 Al Leiter .08 .25
660 Will Clark .05 .15
661 D.Gooden TBC84 .01 .05
662 Lou Brock TBC79 .02 .10
663 Hank Aaron TBC74 .08 .25
664 Gil Hodges TBC 69 .02 .10
665A Tony Oliva TBC64
ERR (fabricated card is enlarged version of Oliva's 64T card; Topps copyright missing)
665B Tony Oliva TBC 64 .02 .10
COR (fabricated card)
666 Randy St.Claire .01 .05
667 Dwayne Murphy .01 .05
668 Mike Bielecki .01 .05
669 Orel Hershiser .02 .10
Mike Scioscia TL
670 Kevin Seitzer .01 .05
671 Jim Gantner .01 .05
672 Allan Anderson .01 .05
673 Don Baylor .02 .10
674 Otis Nixon .01 .05
675 Bruce Hurst .01 .05
676 Ernie Riles .01 .05
677 Dave Schmidt .01 .05
678 Dion James .01 .05
679 Willie Fraser .01 .05
680 Gary Carter .02 .10
681 Jeff D. Robinson .01 .05
682 Rick Leach .01 .05
683 Jose Cecena .01 .05
684 Dave Johnson MG .01 .05
685 Jeff Treadway .01 .05
686 Scott Terry .01 .05
687 Alvin Davis .01 .05
688 Zane Smith .01 .05
689A Stan Jefferson 4.00 10.00
(Pink triangle on front bottom left)
689B Stan Jefferson .01 .05
(Violet triangle on front bottom left)
690 Doug Jones .01 .05
691 Roberto Kelly UER .01 .05
(83 Oneonita)
692 Steve Ontiveros .01 .05
693 Pat Borders RC .08 .25
694 Les Lancaster .01 .05
695 Carlton Fisk .05 .15
696 Don August .01 .05
697A Franklin Stubbs ERR 4.00 10.00
(Team name on front in white)
697B Franklin Stubbs .01 .05
(Team name on front in gray)
698 Keith Atherton .01 .05
699 Al Pedrique TL .01 .05
Tony Gwynn sliding
700 Don Mattingly .25 .60
701 Storm Davis .01 .05
702 Jamie Quirk .01 .05
703 Scott Garrelts .01 .05
704 Carlos Quintana RC .02 .10
705 Terry Kennedy .01 .05
706 Pete Incaviglia .01 .05
707 Steve Jeltz .01 .05
708 Chuck Finley .02 .10
709 Tom Herr .01 .05
710 David Cone .02 .10
711 Candy Sierra .01 .05
712 Bill Swift .01 .05
713 Ty Griffin FDP .01 .05
714 Joe Morgan MG .02 .10
715 Tony Pena .01 .05
716 Wayne Tolleson .01 .05
717 Jamie Moyer .02 .10
718 Glenn Braggs .01 .05
719 Danny Darwin .01 .05
720 Tim Wallach .01 .05
721 Ron Tingley .01 .05
722 Todd Stottlemyre .01 .05
723 Rafael Belliard .01 .05
724 Jerry Don Gleaton .01 .05
725 Terry Steinbach .02 .10
726 Dickie Thon .01 .05
727 Joe Orsulak .01 .05
728 Charlie Puleo .01 .05
729 Steve Buechele TL .01 .05
(Inconsistent design, team name on front surrounded by black, should be white)
730 Danny Jackson .01 .05
731 Mike Young .01 .05
732 Steve Buechele .01 .05
733 Randy Bockus .01 .05
734 Jody Reed .01 .05
735 Roger McDowell .01 .05
736 Jeff Hamilton .01 .05
737 Norm Charlton RC .08 .25
738 Darnell Coles .01 .05
739 Brook Jacoby .01 .05
740 Dan Plesac .01 .05
741 Ken Phelps .01 .05
742 Mike Harkey FS RC .02 .10
743 Mike Heath .01 .05
744 Roger Craig MG .02 .10
745 Fred McGriff .05 .15
746 G.Gonzalez UER .01 .05
Wrong birthdate
747 Wil Tejada .01 .05
748 Jimmy Jones .01 .05
749 Rafael Ramirez .01 .05
750 Bret Saberhagen .02 .10
751 Ken Oberkfell .01 .05
752 Jim Gott .01 .05
753 Jose Uribe .01 .05
754 Bob Brower .01 .05
755 Mike Scioscia .02 .10
756 Scott Medvin .01 .05
757 Brady Anderson RC .15 .40
758 Gene Walter .01 .05
759 Rob Deer TL .02 .10
760 Lee Smith .02 .10
761 Dante Bichette RC .15 .40
762 Bobby Thigpen .01 .05
763 Dave Martinez .01 .05
764 Robin Ventura FDP RC .30 .75
765 Glenn Davis .01 .05
766 Cecilio Guante .01 .05
767 Mike Capel .01 .05
768 Bill Wegman .01 .05
769 Junior Ortiz .01 .05
770 Alan Trammell .02 .10
771 Ron Kittle .01 .05
772 Ron Oester .01 .05
773 Keith Moreland .01 .05
774 Frank Robinson MG .05 .15
775 Jeff Reardon .02 .10
776 Nelson Liriano .01 .05
777 Ted Power .01 .05
778 Bruce Benedict .01 .05
779 Craig McMurtry .01 .05
780 Pedro Guerrero .02 .10
781 Greg Briley .02 .10
782 Checklist 661-792 .01 .05

783 Trevor Wilson RC .02 .10
784 Steve Avery FDP RC .08 .25
785 Ellis Burks .02 .10
786 Melido Perez .01 .05
787 Dave West RC .02 .10
788 Mike Morgan .01 .05
789 Bo Jackson TL .08 .25
790 Sid Fernandez .01 .05
791 Jim Lindeman .01 .05
792 Rafael Santana .01 .05

1989 Topps Tiffany

Again, Topps issed a standard-size "Glossy" parallel to their regular set. These cards, printed in the Topps Irish facility, have 792 standard-size cards and were issued in complete set form only. These cards have a "shiny" front as well as an easy to read back. These cards were issued only through Topps hobby dealers. With the "glut" of the previous two years Tiffany sets in the marketplace, it seems that approximately 15,000 of these sets were produced in 1989.

COMP.FACT.SET (792) 60.00 120.00
*STARS: 5X TO 12X BASIC CARDS
*ROOKIES: 5X TO 12X BASIC CARDS

1989 Topps Glossy All-Stars

These glossy cards were inserted with Topps rack packs and honor the starting line-ups, managers, and honorary captains of the 1988 National and American League All-Star teams. The standard size cards are very similar in design to what Topps has used since 1984. The backs are printed in red and blue on white card stock.

COMPLETE SET (22) 1.20 3.00
1 Tom Kelly MG .01 .05
2 Mark McGwire .30 .75
3 Paul Molitor .15 .40
4 Wade Boggs .10 .30
5 Cal Ripken .60 1.50
6 Jose Canseco .08 .25
7 Rickey Henderson .25 .60
8 Dave Winfield .15 .40
9 Terry Steinbach .01 .05
10 Frank Viola .01 .05
11 Bobby Doerr CAPT .08 .25
12 Whitey Herzog MG .01 .05
13 Will Clark .07 .20
14 Ryne Sandberg .20 .50
15 Bobby Bonilla .02 .10
16 Ozzie Smith .20 .50
17 Vince Coleman .01 .05
18 Andre Dawson .07 .20
19 Darryl Strawberry .02 .10
20 Gary Carter .15 .40
21 Dwight Gooden .02 .10
22 Willie Stargell CAPT .08 .25

1989 Topps Rookies

Inserted in each supermarket jumbo pack is a card from this series of 22 of 1988's best rookies as determined by Topps. Jumbo packs consisted of 100 (regular issue 1989 Topps baseball) cards with a stick of gum plus the insert "Rookie" card. The card fronts are in full color and measure the standard size. The card backs are printed in red and blue on white card stock and are numbered at the bottom. The order of the set is alphabetical by player's name.

COMPLETE SET (22) 6.00 12.00
1 Roberto Alomar 1.00 2.50
2 Brady Anderson .30 .75
3 Tim Belcher .08 .25
4 Damon Berryhill .08 .25
5 Jay Buhner .40 1.00
6 Kevin Elster .08 .25
7 Cecil Espy .08 .25
8 Dave Gallagher .08 .25
9 Ron Gant .40 1.00
10 Paul Gibson .08 .25
11 Mark Grace .75 2.00
12 Darrin Jackson .08 .25
13 Gregg Jefferies .20 .50
14 Ricky Jordan .08 .25
15 Al Leiter .40 1.00
16 Melido Perez .08 .25
17 Chris Sabo .08 .25
18 Nelson Santovenia .08 .25
19 Mackey Sasser .08 .25
20 Gary Sheffield 1.25 3.00
21 Walt Weiss .08 .25
22 David Wells .75 2.00

1989 Topps Traded

The 1989 Topps Traded set contains 132 standard-size cards. The cards were distributed exclusively in factory set form in red and white taped boxes through hobby dealers. The cards are identical to the 1989 Topps regular issue cards except for whiter stock and t-suffixed numbering on back. Rookie Cards in this set include Ken Griffey Jr., Kenny Rogers, Deion Sanders and Omar Vizquel.

COMP.FACT.SET (132) 4.00 10.00
1T Don Aase .01 .05
2T Jim Abbott .20 .50
3T Kent Anderson .01 .05
4T Keith Atherton .01 .05
5T Wally Backman .01 .05
6T Steve Balboni .01 .05
7T Jesse Barfield .02 .10
8T Steve Bedrosian .01 .05
9T Todd Benzinger .01 .05
10T Geronimo Berroa .01 .05
11T Bert Blyleven .02 .10
12T Bob Boone .02 .10
13T Phil Bradley .01 .05
14T Jeff Brantley RC .08 .25
15T Kevin Brown .08 .25
16T Jerry Browne .01 .05
17T Chuck Cary .01 .05
18T Carmen Castillo .01 .05
19T Jim Clancy .01 .05
20T Jack Clark .02 .10
21T Bryan Clutterbuck .01 .05
22T Jody Davis .01 .05
23T Mike Devereaux .01 .05
24T Frank DiPino .01 .05
25T Benny Distefano .01 .05
26T John Dopson .01 .05
27T Len Dykstra .02 .10
28T Jim Eisenreich .01 .05
29T Nick Esasky .01 .05
30T Alvaro Espinoza .01 .05
31T Darrell Evans UER .02 .10
(Stat headings on back are for a pitcher)
32T Junior Felix RC .02 .10
33T Felix Fermin .01 .05
34T Julio Franco .02 .10
35T Terry Francona .02 .10
36T Cito Gaston MG .01 .05
37T Bob Geren UER RC .01 .05
38T Tom Gordon RC .20 .50
39T Tommy Gregg .01 .05
40T Ken Griffey Sr. .02 .10
41T Ken Griffey Jr. RC 3.00 8.00
42T Kevin Gross .01 .05
43T Lee Guetterman .01 .05
44T Mel Hall .01 .05
45T Erik Hanson RC .08 .25
46T Gene Harris RC .02 .10
47T Andy Hawkins .01 .05
48T Rickey Henderson .08 .25
49T Tom Herr .01 .05
50T Ken Hill RC .08 .25
51T Brian Holman RC .02 .10
52T Brian Holton .01 .05
53T Art Howe MG .01 .05
54T Ken Howell .01 .05
55T Bruce Hurst .01 .05
56T Chris James .01 .05
57T Randy Johnson .60 1.50
58T Jimmy Jones .01 .05
59T Terry Kennedy .01 .05
60T Paul Kilgus .01 .05
61T Eric King .01 .05
62T Ron Kittle .01 .05
63T John Kruk .02 .10
64T Randy Kutcher .01 .05
65T Steve Lake .01 .05
66T Mark Langston .01 .05
67T Dave LaPoint .01 .05
68T Rick Leach .01 .05
69T Terry Leach .01 .05
70T Jim Lefebvre MG .01 .05
71T Al Leiter .08 .25
72T Jeffrey Leonard .01 .05
73T Derek Lilliquist RC .02 .10
74T Rick Mahler .01 .05
75T Tom McCarthy .01 .05
76T Lloyd McClendon .01 .05
77T Lance McCullers .01 .05
78T Oddibe McDowell .01 .05
79T Roger McDowell .01 .05
80T Larry McWilliams .01 .05
81T Randy Milligan .01 .05
82T Mike Moore .01 .05
83T Keith Moreland .01 .05
84T Mike Morgan .01 .05
85T Jamie Moyer .02 .10
86T Rob Murphy .01 .05
87T Eddie Murray .08 .25
88T Pete O'Brien .01 .05
89T Gregg Olson .08 .25
90T Steve Ontiveros .01 .05
91T Jesse Orosco .01 .05
92T Spike Owen .01 .05
93T Rafael Palmeiro .08 .25
94T Clay Parker .01 .05
95T Jeff Parrett .01 .05
96T Lance Parrish .02 .10
97T Dennis Powell .01 .05
98T Rey Quinones .01 .05
99T Doug Rader MG .01 .05
100T Willie Randolph .02 .10
101T Shane Rawley .01 .05
102T Randy Ready .01 .05
103T Bip Roberts .01 .05
104T Kenny Rogers RC .75 2.00
105T Ed Romero .01 .05
106T Nolan Ryan .60 1.50
107T Luis Salazar .01 .05
108T Juan Samuel .01 .05
109T Alex Sanchez RC .01 .05
110T Deion Sanders RC .60 1.50
111T Steve Sax .01 .05
112T Rick Schu .01 .05
113T Dwight Smith RC .08 .25
114T Lonnie Smith .01 .05
115T Billy Spiers RC .08 .25
116T Kent Tekulve .01 .05
117T Walt Terrell .01 .05
118T Milt Thompson .01 .05
119T Dickie Thon .01 .05
120T Jeff Torborg MG .01 .05
121T Jeff Treadway .01 .05
122T Omar Vizquel RC .40 1.00
123T Jerome Walton RC .08 .25
124T Gary Ward .01 .05
125T Claudell Washington .01 .05
126T Curt Wilkerson .01 .05
127T Eddie Williams .01 .05
128T Frank Williams .01 .05
129T Ken Williams .01 .05
130T Mitch Williams .01 .05
131T Steve Wilson RC .02 .10
132T Checklist 1T-132T .01 .05

1989 Topps Traded Tiffany

For each set of regular Tiffany cards ordered, dealers received an update set. These 132 standard-size cards update the regular Topps issue. Again, these cards feature "glossy" fronts as well as easy to read backs. This set was issued only in complete form from the company. Again, the Topps Ireland printing facility produced these cards. Again, approximately 15,000 of these sets were produced.

COMP.FACT.SET (132) 60.00 120.00
*STARS: 4X TO 10X BASIC CARDS
*ROOKIES: 4X TO 10X BASIC CARDS

1990 Topps

The 1990 Topps set contains 792 standard-size cards. Cards were issued primarily in wax packs, rack packs and hobby and retail Christmas factory sets. Card fronts feature various colored borders with the player's name at the bottom and team name at top. Subsets include All-Stars (385-407), Turn Back the Clock (661-665) and Draft Picks (scattered throughout the set). The key Rookie Cards in this set are Juan Gonzalez, Marquis Grissom, Sammy Sosa, Frank Thomas, Larry Walker and Bernie Williams. The Thomas card (414A) was printed without his name on front creating a scarce variation. The card is rarely seen and, for a newer issue, has experienced unprecedented growth as far as value. Be careful when purchasing this card as counterfeits have been produced. A very few cards of President George Bush made their ways into packs. While these cards were supposed to have never been issued, a few collectors did receive these cards when opening packs.

COMPLETE SET (792) 8.00 20.00
COMP.FACT.SET (792) 10.00 25.00
COMP.X-MAS.SET (792) 15.00 40.00
1 Nolan Ryan .40 1.00
2 Nolan Ryan Mets .20 .50
3 Nolan Ryan Angels .20 .50
4 Nolan Ryan Astros .20 .50
5 N.Ryan Rangers UER .20 .50
(Says Texas Stadium rather than Arlington Stadium)
6 Vince Coleman RB .01 .05
7 Rickey Henderson RB .05 .15
8 Cal Ripken RB .08 .25
9 Eric Plunk .01 .05
10 Barry Larkin .05 .15
11 Paul Gibson .01 .05
12 Joe Girardi .05 .15
13 Mark Williamson .01 .05
14 Mike Fetters RC .08 .25
15 Teddy Higuera .01 .05
16 Kent Anderson .01 .05
17 Kelly Downs .01 .05
18 Carlos Quintana .01 .05
19 Al Newman .01 .05
20 Mark Gubicza .01 .05
21 Jeff Torborg MG .01 .05
22 Bruce Ruffin .01 .05
23 Randy Velarde .01 .05
24 Joe Hesketh .01 .05
25 Willie Randolph .02 .10
26 Don Slaught .01 .05
27 Rick Leach .01 .05
28 Duane Ward .01 .05
29 John Cangelosi .01 .05
30 David Cone .02 .10
31 Henry Cotto .01 .05
32 John Farrell .01 .05
33 Greg Walker .01 .05
34 Tony Fossas RC .01 .05
35 Benito Santiago .02 .10
36 John Costello .01 .05
37 Domingo Ramos .01 .05
38 Wes Gardner .01 .05
39 Curt Ford .01 .05
40 Jay Howell .01 .05
41 Matt Williams .02 .10
42 Jeff M. Robinson .01 .05
43 Dante Bichette .02 .10
44 Roger Salkeld FDP RC .02 .10
45 Dave Parker UER .02 .10
(Born in Jackson, not Calhoun)
46 Rob Dibble .02 .10
47 Brian Harper .01 .05
48 Zane Smith .01 .05
49 Tom Lawless .01 .05
50 Glenn Davis .01 .05
51 Doug Rader MG .01 .05
52 Jack Daugherty RC .01 .05
53 Mike LaCoss .01 .05
54 Joel Skinner .01 .05
55 Darrell Evans UER .02 .10
(HR total should be 414, not 424)
56 Franklin Stubbs .01 .05
57 Greg Vaughn .01 .05
58 Keith Miller .01 .05
59 Ted Power .01 .05
60 George Brett .25 .60
61 Deion Sanders .08 .25
62 Ramon Martinez .01 .05
63 Mike Pagliarulo .01 .05
64 Danny Darwin .01 .05
65 Devon White .02 .10
66 Greg Litton .01 .05
67 Scott Sanderson .01 .05
68 Dave Henderson .01 .05
69 Todd Frohwirth .01 .05
70 Mike Greenwell .01 .05
71 Allan Anderson .01 .05
72 Jeff Huson RC .02 .10
73 Bob Milacki .01 .05
74 Jeff Jackson FDP RC .02 .10
75 Doug Jones .01 .05
76 Dave Valle .01 .05
77 Dave Bergman .01 .05
78 Mike Flanagan .01 .05
79 Ron Kittle .01 .05
80 Jeff Russell .01 .05
81 Bob Rodgers MG .01 .05
82 Scott Terry .01 .05
83 Hensley Meulens .01 .05
84 Ray Searage .01 .05
85 Juan Samuel .01 .05
86 Paul Kilgus .01 .05
87 Rick Luecken RC .01 .05
88 Glenn Braggs .01 .05
89 Clint Zavaras RC .01 .05
90 Jack Clark .02 .10
91 Steve Frey RC .01 .05
92 Mike Stanley .01 .05
93 Shawn Hillegas .01 .05
94 Herm Winningham .01 .05
95 Todd Worrell .01 .05
96 Jody Reed .01 .05
97 Curt Schilling .40 1.00
98 Jose Gonzalez .01 .05
99 Rich Monteleone .01 .05
100 Will Clark .05 .15
101 Shane Rawley .01 .05
102 Stan Javier .01 .05
103 Marvin Freeman .01 .05
104 Bob Knepper .01 .05
105 Randy Myers .02 .10
106 Charlie O'Brien .01 .05
107 Fred Lynn .01 .05
108 Rod Nichols .01 .05
109 Roberto Kelly .01 .05
110 Tommy Helms MG .01 .05
111 Ed Whited RC .01 .05
112 Glenn Wilson .01 .05
113 Manny Lee .01 .05
114 Mike Bielecki .01 .05
115 Tony Pena .01 .05
116 Floyd Bannister .01 .05
117 Mike Sharperson .01 .05
118 Erik Hanson .01 .05
119 Billy Hatcher .01 .05
120 John Franco .01 .05
121 Robin Ventura .08 .25
122 Shawn Abner .01 .05
123 Rich Gedman .01 .05
124 Dave Dravecky .02 .10
125 Kent Hrbek .02 .10
126 Randy Kramer .01 .05
127 Mike Devereaux .01 .05
128 Checklist 1 .01 .05
129 Ron Jones .01 .05
130 Bert Blyleven .02 .10
131 Matt Nokes .01 .05
132 Lance Blankenship .01 .05
133 Ricky Horton .01 .05
134 Earl Cunningham FDP RC .02 .10
135 Dave Magadan .01 .05
136 Kevin Brown .02 .10
137 Marty Pevey RC .01 .05
138 Al Leiter .08 .25
139 Greg Brock .01 .05
140 Andre Dawson .02 .10
141 John Hart MG RC .01 .05
142 Jeff Wetherby RC .01 .05
143 Rafael Belliard .01 .05
144 Bud Black .01 .05
145 Terry Steinbach .01 .05
146 Rob Richie RC .01 .05
147 Chuck Finley .02 .10
148 Edgar Martinez .05 .15
149 Steve Farr .01 .05
150 Kirk Gibson .02 .10
151 Rick Mahler .01 .05
152 Lonnie Smith .01 .05
153 Randy Milligan .01 .05
154 Mike Maddux .01 .05
155 Ellis Burks .05 .15
156 Ken Patterson .01 .05
157 Craig Biggio .08 .25
158 Craig Lefferts .01 .05
159 Mike Felder .01 .05
160 Dave Righetti .01 .05
161 Harold Reynolds .02 .10
162 Todd Zeile .02 .10
163 Phil Bradley .01 .05
164 Jeff Juden FDP RC .02 .10
165 Walt Weiss .01 .05
166 Bobby Witt .01 .05
167 Kevin Appier .02 .10
168 Jose Lind .01 .05
169 Richard Dotson .01 .05
170 George Bell .01 .05
171 Russ Nixon MG .01 .05
172 Tom Lampkin .01 .05
173 Tim Belcher .01 .05
174 Jeff Kunkel .01 .05
175 Mike Moore .01 .05
176 Luis Quinones .01 .05
177 Mike Henneman .01 .05
178 Chris James .01 .05
179 Brian Holton .01 .05
180 Tim Raines .02 .10
181 Juan Agosto .01 .05
182 Mookie Wilson .02 .10
183 Steve Lake .01 .05
184 Danny Cox .01 .05
185 Ruben Sierra .02 .10
186 Dave LaPoint .01 .05
187 Rick Wrona .01 .05
188 Mike Smithson .01 .05
189 Dick Schofield .01 .05
190 Rick Reuschel .01 .05
191 Pat Borders .01 .05
192 Don August .01 .05
193 Andy Benes .02 .10
194 Glenallen Hill .01 .05
195 Tim Burke .01 .05
196 Gerald Young .01 .05
197 Doug Drabek .01 .05
198 Mike Marshall .01 .05
199 Sergio Valdez RC .01 .05
200 Don Mattingly .25 .60
201 Cito Gaston MG .01 .05
202 Mike Macfarlane .01 .05
203 Mike Roesler RC .01 .05
204 Bob Dernier .01 .05
205 Mark Davis .01 .05
206 Nick Esasky .01 .05
207 Bob Ojeda .01 .05
208 Brook Jacoby .01 .05
209 Greg Mathews .01 .05
210 Ryne Sandberg .15 .40
211 John Cerutti .01 .05
212 Joe Orsulak .01 .05
213 Scott Bankhead .01 .05
214 Terry Francona .02 .10
215 Kirk McCaskill .01 .05
216 Ricky Jordan .01 .05
217 Don Robinson .01 .05
218 Wally Backman .01 .05
219 Donn Pall .01 .05
220 Barry Bonds .40 1.00
221 Gary Mielke RC .01 .05
222 Kurt Stillwell UER .01 .05
(Graduate misspelled as gradute)
223 Tommy Gregg .01 .05
224 Delino DeShields RC .08 .25
225 Jim Deshaies .01 .05
226 Mickey Hatcher .01 .05
227 Kevin Tapani RC .08 .25
228 Dave Martinez .01 .05
229 David Wells .02 .10
230 Keith Hernandez .02 .10
231 Jack McKeon MG .01 .05
232 Darnell Coles .01 .05
233 Ken Hill .02 .10
234 Mariano Duncan .01 .05
235 Jeff Reardon .02 .10
236 Hal Morris .01 .05
237 Kevin Ritz RC .01 .05
238 Felix Jose .01 .05
239 Eric Show .01 .05
240 Mark Grace .05 .15
241 Mike Krukow .01 .05
242 Fred Manrique .01 .05
243 Barry Jones .01 .05
244 Bill Schroeder .01 .05
245 Roger Clemens .40 1.00
246 Jim Eisenreich .01 .05
247 Jerry Reed .01 .05
248 Dave Anderson .01 .05
249 Mike (Texas) Smith RC .01 .05
250 Jose Canseco .05 .15
251 Jeff Blauser .01 .05
252 Otis Nixon .01 .05
253 Mark Portugal .01 .05
254 Francisco Cabrera .01 .05
255 Bobby Thigpen .01 .05
256 Marvell Wynne .01 .05
257 Jose DeLeon .01 .05
258 Barry Lyons .01 .05
259 Lance McCullers .01 .05
260 Eric Davis .02 .10
261 Whitey Herzog MG .02 .10
262 Checklist 2 .01 .05
263 Mel Stottlemyre Jr. .01 .05
264 Bryan Clutterbuck .01 .05
265 Pete O'Brien .01 .05
266 German Gonzalez .01 .05
267 Mark Davidson .01 .05
268 Rob Murphy .01 .05
269 Dickie Thon .01 .05
270 Dave Stewart .02 .10
271 Chet Lemon .01 .05
272 Bryan Harvey .01 .05
273 Bobby Bonilla .02 .10
274 Mauro Gozzo RC .01 .05
275 Mickey Tettleton .01 .05
276 Gary Thurman .01 .05
277 Lenny Harris .01 .05
278 Pascual Perez .01 .05
279 Steve Buechele .01 .05
280 Lou Whitaker .02 .10
281 Kevin Bass .01 .05
282 Derek Lilliquist .01 .05
283 Joey Belle .08 .25
284 Mark Gardner RC .02 .10
285 Willie McGee .02 .10
286 Lee Guetterman .01 .05
287 Vance Law .01 .05
288 Greg Briley .01 .05
289 Norm Charlton .01 .05
290 Robin Yount .15 .40
291 Dave Johnson MG .02 .10
292 Jim Gott .01 .05
293 Mike Gallego .01 .05
294 Craig McMurtry .01 .05
295 Fred McGriff .08 .25
296 Jeff Ballard .01 .05
297 Tommy Herr .01 .05
298 Dan Gladden .01 .05
299 Adam Peterson .01 .05
300 Bo Jackson .08 .25
301 Don Aase .01 .05
302 Marcus Lawton RC .01 .05
303 Rick Cerone .01 .05
304 Marty Clary .01 .05
305 Eddie Murray .08 .25
306 Tom Niedenfuer .01 .05
307 Bip Roberts .01 .05
308 Jose Guzman .01 .05
309 Eric Yelding RC .01 .05
310 Steve Bedrosian .01 .05
311 Dwight Smith .01 .05
312 Dan Quisenberry .01 .05
313 Gus Polidor .01 .05
314 Donald Harris FDP RC .01 .05
315 Bruce Hurst .01 .05
316 Carney Lansford .02 .10
317 Mark Guthrie RC .01 .05
318 Wallace Johnson .01 .05
319 Dion James .01 .05
320 Dave Stieb .02 .10
321 Joe Morgan MG .01 .05
322 Junior Ortiz .01 .05
323 Willie Wilson .01 .05
324 Pete Harnisch .01 .05
325 Robby Thompson .01 .05
326 Tom McCarthy .01 .05
327 Ken Williams .01 .05
328 Curt Young .01 .05
329 Oddibe McDowell .01 .05
330 Ron Darling .01 .05
331 Juan Gonzalez RC .40 1.00
332 Paul O'Neill .05 .15
333 Bill Wegman .01 .05
334 Johnny Ray .01 .05
335 Andy Hawkins .01 .05
336 Ken Griffey Jr. .30 .75
337 Lloyd McClendon .01 .05
338 Dennis Lamp .01 .05
339 Dave Clark .01 .05
340 Fernando Valenzuela .02 .10
341 Tom Foley .01 .05
342 Alex Trevino .01 .05
343 Frank Tanana .01 .05
344 George Canale RC .01 .05
345 Harold Baines .02 .10
346 Jim Presley .01 .05
347 Junior Felix .01 .05
348 Gary Wayne .01 .05
349 Steve Finley .02 .10
350 Bret Saberhagen .02 .10
351 Roger Craig MG .01 .05
352 Bryn Smith .01 .05
353 Sandy Alomar Jr. .02 .10
(Not listed as Jr. on card front)
354 Stan Belinda RC .02 .10
355 Marty Barrett .01 .05
356 Randy Ready .01 .05
357 Dave West .01 .05
358 Andres Thomas .01 .05
359 Jimmy Jones .01 .05
360 Paul Molitor .02 .10
361 Randy McCament RC .01 .05
362 Damon Berryhill .01 .05
363 Dan Petry .01 .05
364 Rolando Roomes .01 .05
365 Ozzie Guillen .02 .10
366 Mike Heath .01 .05
367 Mike Morgan .01 .05
368 Bill Doran .01 .05
369 Todd Burns .01 .05
370 Tim Wallach .01 .05
371 Jimmy Key .02 .10
372 Terry Kennedy .01 .05
373 Alvin Davis .01 .05
374 Steve Cummings RC .01 .05
375 Dwight Evans .05 .15
376 Checklist 3 UER .01 .05
(Higuera misalphabetized in Brewer list)
377 Mickey Weston RC .01 .05
378 Luis Salazar .01 .05
379 Steve Rosenberg .01 .05
380 Dave Winfield .02 .10
381 Frank Robinson MG .05 .15
382 Jeff Musselman .01 .05
383 John Morris .01 .05
384 Pat Combs .01 .05
385 Fred McGriff AS .02 .10
386 Julio Franco AS .01 .05
387 Wade Boggs AS .02 .10
388 Cal Ripken AS .15 .40
389 Robin Yount AS .08 .25
390 Ruben Sierra AS .01 .05
391 Kirby Puckett AS .05 .15
392 Carlton Fisk AS .02 .10
393 Bret Saberhagen AS .01 .05
394 Jeff Ballard AS .01 .05
395 Jeff Russell AS .01 .05
396 A.Bartlett Giamatti COMM MEM .08 .25
397 Will Clark AS .02 .10
398 Ryne Sandberg AS .08 .25
399 Howard Johnson AS .01 .05
400 Ozzie Smith AS .08 .25
401 Kevin Mitchell AS .01 .05
402 Eric Davis AS .01 .05
403 Tony Gwynn AS .05 .15
404 Craig Biggio AS .08 .25
405 Mike Scott AS .01 .05
406 Joe Magrane AS .01 .05
407 Mark Davis AS .01 .05
408 Trevor Wilson .01 .05
409 Tom Brunansky .01 .05
410 Joe Boever .01 .05
411 Ken Phelps .01 .05
412 Jamie Moyer .02 .10
413 Brian DuBois RC .01 .05
414A Frank Thomas FDP 400.00 700.00
ERR (Name missing on card front)
414B Frank Thomas FDP RC .75 2.00
415 Shawon Dunston .01 .05
416 Dave Wayne Johnson RC .01 .05
417 Jim Gantner .01 .05
418 Tom Browning .01 .05
419 Beau Allred RC .01 .05
420 Carlton Fisk .05 .15
421 Greg Minton .01 .05
422 Pat Sheridan .01 .05
423 Fred Toliver .01 .05
424 Jerry Reuss .01 .05
425 Bill Landrum .01 .05
426 Jeff Hamilton UER .01 .05
(Stats say he fanned 197 times in 1987, but he only had 147 at bats)
427 Carmen Castillo .01 .05
428 Steve Davis RC .01 .05
429 Tom Kelly MG .01 .05

430 Pete Incaviglia .01 .05
431 Randy Johnson .20 .50
432 Damaso Garcia .01 .05
433 Steve Olin RC .08 .25
434 Mark Carreon .01 .05
435 Kevin Seitzer .01 .05
436 Mel Hall .01 .05
437 Les Lancaster .01 .05
438 Greg Myers .01 .05
439 Jeff Parrett .01 .05
440 Alan Trammell .02 .10
441 Bob Kipper .01 .05
442 Jerry Browne .01 .05
443 Cris Carpenter .01 .05
444 Kyle Abbott FDP RC .01 .05
445 Danny Jackson .01 .05
446 Dan Pasqua .01 .05
447 Atlee Hammaker .01 .05
448 Greg Gagne .01 .05
449 Dennis Rasmussen .01 .05
450 Rickey Henderson .08 .25
451 Mark Lemke .01 .05
452 Luis DeLosSantos .01 .05
453 Jody Davis .01 .05
454 Jeff King .01 .05
455 Jeffrey Leonard .01 .05
456 Chris Gwynn .01 .05
457 Gregg Jefferies .02 .10
458 Bob McClure .01 .05
459 Jim Lefebvre MG .01 .05
460 Mike Scott .01 .05
461 Carlos Martinez .01 .05
462 Denny Walling .01 .05
463 Drew Hall .01 .05
464 Jerome Walton .01 .05
465 Kevin Gross .01 .05
466 Rance Mulliniks .01 .05
467 Juan Nieves .01 .05
468 Bill Ripken .01 .05
469 John Kruk .02 .10
470 Frank Viola .01 .05
471 Mike Brumley .01 .05
472 Jose Uribe .01 .05
473 Joe Price .01 .05
474 Rich Thompson .01 .05
475 Bob Welch .01 .05
476 Brad Komminsk .01 .05
477 Willie Fraser .01 .05
478 Mike LaValliere .01 .05
479 Frank White .02 .10
480 Sid Fernandez .01 .05
481 Garry Templeton .01 .05
482 Steve Carter .01 .05
483 Alejandro Pena .01 .05
484 Mike Fitzgerald .01 .05
485 John Candelaria .01 .05
486 Jeff Treadway .01 .05
487 Steve Searcy .01 .05
488 Ken Oberkfell .01 .05
489 Nick Leyva MG .01 .05
490 Dan Plesac .01 .05
491 Dave Cochrane RC .01 .05
492 Ron Oester .01 .05
493 Jason Grimsley RC .02 .10
494 Terry Puhl .01 .05
495 Lee Smith .02 .10
496 Cecil Espy UER .01 .05
('88 stats have 3 SB's, should be 33)
497 Dave Schmidt .01 .05
498 Rick Schu .01 .05
499 Bill Long .01 .05
500 Kevin Mitchell .01 .05
501 Matt Young .01 .05
502 Mitch Webster .01 .05
503 Randy St.Claire .01 .05
504 Tom O'Malley .01 .05
505 Kelly Gruber .01 .05
506 Tom Glavine .05 .15
507 Gary Redus .01 .05
508 Terry Leach .01 .05
509 Tom Pagnozzi .01 .05
510 Dwight Gooden .02 .10
511 Clay Parker .01 .05
512 Gary Pettis .01 .05
513 Mark Eichhorn .01 .05
514 Andy Allanson .01 .05
515 Len Dykstra .02 .10
516 Tim Leary .01 .05
517 Roberto Alomar .05 .15
518 Bill Krueger .01 .05
519 Bucky Dent MG .01 .05
520 Mitch Williams .01 .05
521 Craig Worthington .01 .05
522 Mike Dunne .01 .05
523 Jay Bell .02 .10
524 Daryl Boston .01 .05
525 Wally Joyner .02 .10
526 Checklist 4 .01 .05
527 Ron Hassey .01 .05
528 Kevin Wickander UER .01 .05
(Monthly scoreboard strikeout total was 2.2, that was his innings pitched total)
529 Greg A. Harris .01 .05
530 Mark Langston .01 .05
531 Ken Caminiti .02 .10
532 Cecilio Guante .01 .05
533 Tim Jones .01 .05
534 Louie Meadows .01 .05
535 John Smoltz .08 .25
536 Bob Geren .01 .05
537 Mark Grant .01 .05
538 Bill Spiers UER .01 .05
(Photo actually George Canale)
539 Neal Heaton .01 .05
540 Danny Tartabull .01 .05
541 Pat Perry .01 .05
542 Darren Daulton .02 .10
543 Nelson Liriano .01 .05
544 Dennis Boyd .01 .05
545 Kevin McReynolds .01 .05
546 Kevin Hickey .01 .05
547 Jack Howell .01 .05
548 Pat Clements .01 .05
549 Don Zimmer MG .01 .05
550 Julio Franco .02 .10
551 Tim Crews .01 .05
552 Mike (Miss.) Smith RC .01 .05
553 Scott Scudder UER .01 .05
(Cedar Rap1ds)
554 Jay Buhner .02 .10
555 Jack Morris .02 .10
556 Gene Larkin .01 .05
557 Jeff Innis RC .01 .05
558 Rafael Ramirez .01 .05
559 Andy McGaffigan .01 .05
560 Steve Sax .01 .05
561 Ken Dayley .01 .05
562 Chad Kreuter .01 .05
563 Alex Sanchez .01 .05
564 Tyler Houston FDP RC .08 .25
565 Scott Fletcher .01 .05
566 Mark Knudson .01 .05
567 Ron Gant .02 .10
568 John Smiley .01 .05
569 Ivan Calderon .01 .05
570 Cal Ripken .30 .75
571 Brett Butler .02 .10
572 Greg W. Harris .01 .05
573 Danny Heep .01 .05
574 Bill Swift .01 .05
575 Lance Parrish .01 .05
576 Mike Dyer RC .01 .05
577 Charlie Hayes .01 .05
578 Joe Magrane .01 .05
579 Art Howe MG .01 .05
580 Joe Carter .02 .10
581 Ken Griffey Sr. .02 .10
582 Rick Honeycutt .01 .05
583 Bruce Benedict .01 .05
584 Phil Stephenson .01 .05
585 Kal Daniels .01 .05
586 Edwin Nunez .01 .05
587 Lance Johnson .01 .05
588 Rick Rhoden .01 .05
589 Mike Aldrete .01 .05
590 Ozzie Smith .15 .40
591 Todd Stottlemyre .02 .10
592 R.J. Reynolds .01 .05
593 Scott Bradley .01 .05
594 Luis Sojo RC .01 .05
595 Greg Swindell .01 .05
596 Jose DeJesus .01 .05
597 Chris Bosio .01 .05
598 Brady Anderson .02 .10
599 Frank Williams .01 .05
600 Darryl Strawberry .02 .10
601 Luis Rivera .01 .05
602 Scott Garrelts .01 .05
603 Tony Armas .01 .05
604 Ron Robinson .01 .05
605 Mike Scioscia .01 .05
606 Storm Davis .01 .05
607 Steve Jeltz .01 .05
608 Eric Anthony RC .02 .10
609 Sparky Anderson MG .02 .10
610 Pedro Guerrero .01 .05
611 Walt Terrell .01 .05
612 Dave Gallagher .01 .05
613 Jeff Pico .01 .05
614 Nelson Santovenia .01 .05
615 Rob Deer .01 .05
616 Brian Holman .01 .05
617 Geronimo Berroa .01 .05
618 Ed Whitson .01 .05
619 Rob Ducey .01 .05
620 Tony Castillo .01 .05
621 Melido Perez .01 .05
622 Sid Bream .01 .05
623 Jim Corsi .01 .05
624 Darrin Jackson .01 .05
625 Roger McDowell .01 .05
626 Bob Melvin .01 .05
627 Jose Rijo .01 .05
628 Candy Maldonado .01 .05
629 Eric Hetzel .01 .05
630 Gary Gaetti .02 .10
631 John Wetteland .08 .25
632 Scott Lusader .01 .05
633 Dennis Cook .01 .05
634 Luis Polonia .01 .05
635 Brian Downing .01 .05
636 Jesse Orosco .01 .05
637 Craig Reynolds .01 .05
638 Jeff Montgomery .02 .10
639 Tony LaRussa MG .02 .10
640 Rick Sutcliffe .02 .10
641 Doug Strange RC .01 .05
642 Jack Armstrong .01 .05
643 Alfredo Griffin .01 .05
644 Paul Assenmacher .01 .05
645 Jose Oquendo .01 .05
646 Checklist 5 .01 .05
647 Rex Hudler .01 .05
648 Jim Clancy .01 .05
649 Dan Murphy RC .02 .10
650 Mike Witt .01 .05
651 Rafael Santana .01 .05
652 Mike Boddicker .01 .05
653 John Moses .01 .05
654 Paul Coleman FDP RC .02 .10
655 Gregg Olson .02 .10
656 Mackey Sasser .01 .05
657 Terry Mulholland .01 .05
658 Donell Nixon .01 .05
659 Greg Cadaret .01 .05
660 Vince Coleman .01 .05
661 Dick Howser TBC'85 .01 .05
UER (Seaver's 300th on 7/11/85, should be 8/4/85)
662 Mike Schmidt TBC'80 .08 .25
663 Fred Lynn TBC'75 .01 .05
664 Johnny Bench TBC'70 .05 .15
665 Sandy Koufax TBC'65 .20 .50
666 Brian Fisher .01 .05
667 Curt Wilkerson .01 .05
668 Joe Oliver .01 .05
669 Tom Lasorda MG .08 .25
670 Dennis Eckersley .02 .10
671 Bob Boone .02 .10
672 Roy Smith .01 .05
673 Joey Meyer .01 .05
674 Spike Owen .01 .05
675 Jim Abbott .05 .15
676 Randy Kutcher .01 .05
677 Jay Tibbs .01 .05
678 Kirt Manwaring UER .01 .05
('88 Phoenix stats repeated)
679 Gary Ward .01 .05
680 Howard Johnson .01 .05
681 Mike Schooler .01 .05
682 Dann Bilardello .01 .05
683 Kenny Rogers .02 .10
684 Julio Machado RC .01 .05
685 Tony Fernandez .01 .05
686 Carmelo Martinez .01 .05
687 Tim Birtsas .01 .05
688 Milt Thompson .01 .05
689 Rich Yett .01 .05
690 Mark McGwire .25 .60
691 Chuck Cary .01 .05
692 Sammy Sosa RC 1.00 2.50
693 Calvin Schiraldi .01 .05
694 Mike Stanton RC .08 .25
695 Tom Henke .01 .05
696 B.J. Surhoff .02 .10
697 Mike Davis .01 .05
698 Omar Vizquel .08 .25
699 Jim Leyland MG .01 .05
700 Kirby Puckett .08 .25
701 Bernie Williams RC .60 1.50
702 Tony Phillips .01 .05
703 Jeff Brantley .01 .05
704 Chip Hale RC .01 .05
705 Claudell Washington .01 .05
706 Geno Petralli .01 .05
707 Luis Aquino .01 .05
708 Larry Sheets .01 .05
709 Juan Berenguer .01 .05
710 Von Hayes .01 .05
711 Rick Aguilera .02 .10
712 Todd Benzinger .01 .05
713 Tim Drummond RC .01 .05
714 Marquis Grissom RC .15 .40
715 Greg Maddux .15 .40
716 Steve Balboni .01 .05
717 Ron Karkovice .01 .05
718 Gary Sheffield .08 .25
719 Wally Whitehurst .01 .05
720 Andres Galarraga .02 .10
721 Lee Mazzilli .01 .05
722 Felix Fermin .01 .05
723 Jeff D. Robinson .01 .05
724 Juan Bell .01 .05
725 Terry Pendleton .02 .10
726 Gene Nelson .01 .05
727 Pat Tabler .01 .05
728 Jim Acker .01 .05
729 Bobby Valentine MG .01 .05
730 Tony Gwynn .10 .30
731 Don Carman .01 .05
732 Ernest Riles .01 .05
733 John Dopson .01 .05
734 Kevin Elster .01 .05
735 Charlie Hough .02 .10
736 Rick Dempsey .01 .05
737 Chris Sabo .01 .05
738 Gene Harris .01 .05
739 Dale Sveum .01 .05
740 Jesse Barfield .01 .05
741 Steve Wilson .01 .05
742 Ernie Whitt .01 .05
743 Tom Candiotti .01 .05
744 Kelly Mann RC .01 .05
745 Hubie Brooks .01 .05
746 Dave Smith .01 .05
747 Randy Bush .01 .05
748 Doyle Alexander .01 .05
749 Mark Parent UER .01 .05
('87 BA .80, should be .080)
750 Dale Murphy .05 .15
751 Steve Lyons .01 .05
752 Tom Gordon .02 .10
753 Chris Speier .01 .05
754 Bob Walk .01 .05
755 Rafael Palmeiro .05 .15
756 Ken Howell .01 .05
757 Larry Walker RC .40 1.00
758 Mark Thurmond .01 .05
759 Tom Trebelhorn MG .01 .05
760 Wade Boggs .05 .15
761 Mike Jackson .01 .05
762 Doug Dascenzo .01 .05
763 Dennis Martinez .02 .10
764 Tim Teufel .01 .05
765 Chili Davis .02 .10
766 Brian Meyer .01 .05
767 Tracy Jones .01 .05
768 Chuck Crim .01 .05
769 Greg Hibbard RC .02 .10
770 Cory Snyder .01 .05
771 Pete Smith .01 .05
772 Jeff Reed .01 .05
773 Dave Leiper .01 .05
774 Ben McDonald RC .08 .25
775 Andy Van Slyke .05 .15
776 Charlie Leibrandt .01 .05
777 Tim Laudner .01 .05
778 Mike Jeffcoat .01 .05
779 Lloyd Moseby .01 .05
780 Orel Hershiser .02 .10
781 Mario Diaz .01 .05
782 Jose Alvarez .01 .05
783 Checklist 6 .01 .05
784 Scott Bailes .01 .05
785 Jim Rice .02 .10
786 Eric King .01 .05
787 Rene Gonzales .01 .05
788 Frank DiPino .01 .05
789 John Wathan MG .01 .05
790 Gary Carter .02 .10
791 Alvaro Espinoza .01 .05
792 Gerald Perry .01 .05
NNO George Bush PRES

1990 Topps Tiffany

For the seventh year, Topps issued through its hobby dealer network a special "Tiffany" set. These sets which parallel the regular cards consist of 792 standard-size cards. These cards were only issued in complete set form. Since the number of cards produced is similar to the 1989 issue, it is believed that approximately 15,000 of these sets were produced.

COMP.FACT.SET (792) 100.00 200.00

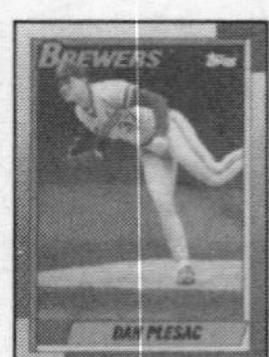

*STARS: 6X TO 15X BASIC CARDS
*ROOKIES: 4X TO 10X BASIC CARDS
414 Frank Thomas FDP 8.00 20.00

1990 Topps Batting Leaders

The 1990 Topps Batting Leaders set contains 22 standard-size cards. The front borders are emerald green, and the backs are white, blue and evergreen. This set, like the 1989 set of the same name, depicts the 22 major leaguers with the highest lifetime batting averages (minimum 765 games). The card numbers correspond to the player's rank in terms of career batting average. Many of the photos are the same as those from the 1989 set. The cards were distributed one per special 100-card Topps blister pack available only at K-Mart stores and were produced by Topps. The K-Mart logo does not appear anywhere on the cards themselves, although there is a Topps logo on the front and back of each card.

COMPLETE SET (22) 40.00 100.00
1 Wade Boggs 4.00 10.00
2 Tony Gwynn 8.00 20.00
3 Kirby Puckett 6.00 15.00
4 Don Mattingly 8.00 20.00
5 George Brett 8.00 20.00
6 Pedro Guerrero .20 .50
7 Tim Raines .40 1.00
8 Paul Molitor 3.00 8.00
9 Jim Rice .40 1.00
10 Keith Hernandez .40 1.00
11 Julio Franco .40 1.00
12 Carney Lansford .40 1.00
13 Dave Parker .40 1.00
14 Willie McGee .40 1.00
15 Robin Yount 3.00 8.00
16 Tony Fernandez .40 1.00
17 Eddie Murray 3.00 8.00
18 Johnny Ray .20 .50
19 Lonnie Smith .20 .50
20 Phil Bradley .20 .50
21 Rickey Henderson 5.00 12.00
22 Kent Hrbek .40 1.00

1990 Topps Glossy All-Stars

The 1990 Topps Glossy All-Star set contains 22 standard-size glossy cards. The front and back borders are white, and other design elements are red, blue and yellow. This set is almost identical to previous year sets of the same name. One card was included in each 1990 Topps rack pack. The players selected for the set were the starters, managers, and honorary captains in the previous year's All-Star Game.

COMPLETE SET (22) 1.20 3.00
1 Tom Lasorda MG .07 .20
2 Will Clark .07 .20
3 Ryne Sandberg .20 .50
4 Howard Johnson .01 .05
5 Ozzie Smith .25 .60
6 Kevin Mitchell .01 .05
7 Eric Davis .02 .10
8 Tony Gwynn .30 .75
9 Benito Santiago .02 .10
10 Rick Reuschel .01 .05
11 Don Drysdale CAPT .08 .25
12 Tony LaRussa MG .01 .05
13 Mark McGwire .30 .75
14 Julio Franco .02 .10
15 Wade Boggs .15 .40
16 Cal Ripken .60 1.50
17 Bo Jackson .08 .25
18 Kirby Puckett .15 .40
19 Ruben Sierra .02 .10
20 Terry Steinbach .01 .05
21 Dave Stewart .02 .10
22 Carl Yastrzemski CAPT .10 .30

1990 Topps Glossy Send-Ins

The 1990 Topps Glossy 60 set was issued as a mailaway by Topps for the eighth straight year. This standard-size, 60-card set features two young players among every ten players as Topps again broke down these cards into six series of ten cards each.

COMPLETE SET (60) 4.80 12.00
1 Ryne Sandberg .60 1.50
2 Nolan Ryan 2.00 5.00
3 Glenn Davis .02 .10
4 Dave Stewart .07 .20
5 Barry Larkin .15 .40
6 Carney Lansford .07 .20
7 Darryl Strawberry .07 .20
8 Steve Sax .02 .10
9 Carlos Martinez .02 .10
10 Gary Sheffield .30 .75
11 Don Mattingly 1.00 2.50
12 Mark Grace .40 1.00
13 Bret Saberhagen .07 .20
14 Mike Scott .02 .10
15 Robin Yount .20 .50
16 Ozzie Smith .60 1.50
17 Jeff Ballard .02 .10
18 Rick Reuschel .02 .10
19 Greg Briley .02 .10
20 Ken Griffey Jr. 1.00 2.50
21 Kevin Mitchell .02 .10
22 Wade Boggs .30 .75
23 Dwight Gooden .07 .20
24 George Bell .02 .10
25 Eric Davis .07 .20
26 Ruben Sierra .07 .20
27 Roberto Alomar .30 .75
28 Gary Gaetti .07 .20
29 Gregg Olson .02 .10
30 Tom Gordon .10 .30
31 Jose Canseco .30 .75
32 Pedro Guerrero .02 .10
33 Joe Carter .07 .20
34 Mike Scioscia .07 .20
35 Julio Franco .07 .20
36 Joe Magrane .02 .10
37 Rickey Henderson .40 1.00
38 Tim Raines .07 .20
39 Jerome Walton .02 .10
40 Bob Geren .02 .10
41 Andre Dawson .15 .40
42 Mark McGwire 1.00 2.50
43 Howard Johnson .02 .10
44 Bo Jackson .20 .50
45 Shawon Dunston .02 .10
46 Carlton Fisk .20 .50
47 Mitch Williams .02 .10
48 Kirby Puckett .40 1.00
49 Craig Worthington .02 .10
50 Jim Abbott .20 .50
51 Cal Ripken 2.00 5.00
52 Will Clark .15 .40
53 Dennis Eckersley .20 .50
54 Craig Biggio .10 .30
55 Fred McGriff .15 .40
56 Tony Gwynn .75 2.00
57 Mickey Tettleton .07 .20
58 Mark Davis .02 .10
59 Omar Vizquel .15 .40
60 Gregg Jefferies .02 .10

1990 Topps Rookies

The 1990 Topps Jumbo Rookies set contains 33 standard-size glossy cards. The front and back borders are white, and other design elements are red, blue and yellow. This set is almost identical to previous year sets of the same name except that it contains 33 cards rather than only 22. One card was included in each 1990 Topps "jumbo" pack. The cards are numbered in alphabetical order. Sets of these cards were issued and stamped with various colors so Topps could test for colors of foil stamping.

COMPLETE SET (33) 12.50 25.00
1 Jim Abbott .30 .75
2 Albert Belle .40 1.00
3 Andy Benes .20 .50
4 Greg Briley .08 .25
5 Kevin Brown .20 .50
6 Mark Carreon .08 .25
7 Mike Devereaux .08 .25
8 Junior Felix .08 .25
9 Bob Geren .08 .25
10 Tom Gordon .08 .25
11 Ken Griffey Jr. 2.00 5.00
12 Pete Harnisch .08 .25
13 Greg W. Harris .08 .25
14 Greg Hibbard .08 .25
15 Ken Hill .08 .25
16 Gregg Jefferies .08 .25
17 Jeff King .08 .25
18 Derek Lilliquist .08 .25
19 Carlos Martinez .08 .25
20 Ramon Martinez .08 .25
21 Bob Milacki .08 .25
22 Gregg Olson .08 .25
23 Donn Pall .08 .25
24 Kenny Rogers .20 .50
25 Gary Sheffield .40 1.00
26 Dwight Smith .08 .25
27 Billy Spiers .08 .25
28 Omar Vizquel .40 1.00
29 Jerome Walton .08 .25
30 Dave West .08 .25
31 John Wetteland .20 .50
32 Steve Wilson .08 .25
33 Craig Worthington .08 .25

1990 Topps Traded

The 1990 Topps Traded Set was the tenth consecutive year Topps issued a 132-card standard-size set at the end of the year. For the first time, Topps not only issued the set in factory set form but also distributed (on a significant basis) the set via seven-card wax packs. Unlike the factory set cards (which feature the whiter paper stock typical of the previous years Traded sets), the wax pack cards feature gray paper stock. Gray and white stock cards are equally valued. This set was arranged alphabetically by player and includes a mix of traded players and rookies for whom Topps did not include a card in the regular set. The key Rookie Cards in this set are Travis Fryman, Todd Hundley and Dave Justice.

COMPLETE SET (132) 1.25 3.00
COMP.FACT.SET (132) 1.25 3.00
1T Darrel Akerfelds .01 .05
2T Sandy Alomar Jr. .02 .10
3T Brad Arnsberg .01 .05
4T Steve Avery .01 .05
5T Wally Backman .01 .05
6T Carlos Baerga RC .08 .25
7T Kevin Bass .01 .05
8T Willie Blair RC .02 .10
9T Mike Blowers RC .08 .25
10T Shawn Boskie RC .02 .10
11T Daryl Boston .01 .05
12T Dennis Boyd .01 .05
13T Glenn Braggs .01 .05
14T Hubie Brooks .01 .05
15T Tom Brunansky .01 .05
16T John Burkett .01 .05
17T Casey Candaele .01 .05
18T John Candelaria .01 .05
19T Gary Carter .02 .10
20T Joe Carter .02 .10
21T Rick Cerone .01 .05
22T Scott Coolbaugh RC .01 .05
23T Bobby Cox MG .02 .10
24T Mark Davis .01 .05
25T Storm Davis .01 .05
26T Edgar Diaz RC .01 .05
27T Wayne Edwards RC .01 .05
28T Mark Eichhorn .01 .05
29T Scott Erickson RC .08 .25
30T Nick Esasky .01 .05
31T Cecil Fielder .02 .10
32T John Franco .02 .10
33T Travis Fryman RC .15 .40
34T Bill Gullickson .01 .05
35T Darryl Hamilton .01 .05
36T Mike Harkey .01 .05
37T Bud Harrelson MG .01 .05
38T Billy Hatcher .01 .05
39T Keith Hernandez .02 .10
40T Joe Hesketh .01 .05
41T Dave Hollins RC .08 .25
42T Sam Horn .01 .05
43T Steve Howard RC .01 .05
44T Todd Hundley RC .08 .25
45T Jeff Huson .01 .05
46T Chris James .01 .05
47T Stan Javier .01 .05
48T Dave Justice RC .20 .50
49T Jeff Kaiser .01 .05
50T Dana Kiecker RC .01 .05
51T Joe Klink RC .01 .05
52T Brent Knackert RC .02 .10
53T Brad Komminsk .01 .05
54T Mark Langston .01 .05
55T Tim Layana RC .01 .05
56T Rick Leach .01 .05
57T Terry Leach .01 .05
58T Tim Leary .01 .05
59T Craig Lefferts .01 .05
60T Charlie Leibrandt .01 .05
61T Jim Leyritz RC .08 .25
62T Fred Lynn .01 .05
63T Kevin Maas RC .08 .25
64T Shane Mack .01 .05
65T Candy Maldonado .01 .05
66T Fred Manrique .01 .05
67T Mike Marshall .01 .05
68T Carmelo Martinez .01 .05
69T John Marzano .01 .05
70T Ben McDonald .01 .05
71T Jack McDowell .01 .05
72T John McNamara MG .01 .05
73T Orlando Mercado .01 .05
74T Stump Merrill MG RC .01 .05
75T Alan Mills RC .02 .10
76T Hal Morris .01 .05
77T Lloyd Moseby .01 .05
78T Randy Myers .02 .10
79T Tim Naehring RC .02 .10
80T Junior Noboa .01 .05
81T Matt Nokes .01 .05
82T Pete O'Brien .01 .05
83T John Olerud RC .20 .50
84T Greg Olson (C) RC .02 .10
85T Junior Ortiz .01 .05
86T Dave Parker .02 .10
87T Rick Parker RC .01 .05
88T Bob Patterson .01 .05
89T Alejandro Pena .01 .05
90T Tony Pena .01 .05
91T Pascual Perez .01 .05
92T Gerald Perry .01 .05
93T Dan Petry .01 .05
94T Gary Pettis .01 .05

95T Tony Phillips .01 .05
96T Lou Piniella MG .02 .10
97T Luis Polonia .01 .05
98T Jim Presley .01 .05
99T Scott Radinsky RC .02 .10
100T Willie Randolph .02 .10
101T Jeff Reardon .02 .10
102T Greg Riddoch MG RC .01 .05
103T Jeff Robinson .01 .05
104T Ron Robinson .01 .05
105T Kevin Romine .01 .05
106T Scott Ruskin RC .01 .05
107T John Russell .01 .05
108T Bill Sampen RC .01 .05
109T Juan Samuel .01 .05
110T Scott Sanderson .01 .05
111T Jack Savage .01 .05
112T Dave Schmidt .01 .05
113T R.Schoendienst MG .08 .25
114T Terry Shumpert RC .01 .05
115T Matt Sinatro .01 .05
116T Don Slaught .01 .05
117T Bryn Smith .01 .05
118T Lee Smith .02 .10
119T Paul Sorrento RC .08 .25
120T Franklin Stubbs UER .01 .05
('84 says '99 and has the same stats as '89, '83 stats are missing)
121T Russ Swan RC .02 .10
122T Bob Tewksbury .01 .05
123T Wayne Tolleson .01 .05
124T John Tudor .01 .05
125T Randy Veres .01 .05
126T Hector Villanueva RC .02 .10
127T Mitch Webster .01 .05
128T Ernie Whitt .01 .05
129T Frank Wills .01 .05
130T Dave Winfield .02 .10
131T Matt Young .01 .05
132T Checklist 1T-132T .01 .05

1990 Topps Traded Tiffany

Again, one of these sets were issued for each regular Tiffany set produced. These 132 standard-size cards parallel the regular Traded issue and feature Glossy fronts and clearer backs. These cards were issued in complete set form only and were distributed through Topps hobby network. Similar to the regular Topps Tiffany set, it is believed that 15,000 of these sets were produced.

COMP.FACT.SET (132) 12.50 30.00
*STARS: 6X TO 15X BASIC CARDS
*ROOKIES: 6X TO 15X BASIC CARDS

1990 Topps Debut '89

The 1990 Topps Major League Debut Set is a 152-card, standard-size set arranged in alphabetical order by player's name. Each card front features the date of the player's first major league appearance. Strangely enough, even though the set commemorates the 1989 Major League debuts, the set was not issued until the 1990 season had almost begun. Key cards in this set include Joey (Albert) Belle, Juan Gonzalez, Ken Griffey, Jr., David Justice, Deion Sanders and Sammy Sosa (pictured as a member of the Texas Rangers). These sets were issued 50 to a case.

COMP.FACT.SET (152) 6.00 15.00
1 Jim Abbott .20 .50
2 Beau Allred .05 .15
3 Wilson Alvarez .08 .25
4 Kent Anderson .05 .15
5 Eric Anthony .05 .15
6 Kevin Appier .08 .25
7 Larry Arndt .05 .15
8 John Barfield .05 .15
9 Billy Bates .05 .15
10 Kevin Batiste .05 .15
11 Blaine Beatty .05 .15
12 Stan Belinda .05 .15
13 Juan Bell .05 .15
14 Joey Belle .30 .75
(Now known as Albert)
15 Andy Benes .08 .25
16 Mike Benjamin .05 .15
17 Geronimo Berroa .05 .15
18 Mike Blowers .08 .25
19 Brian Brady .05 .15
20 Francisco Cabrera .05 .15
21 George Canale .05 .15
22 Jose Cano .05 .15
23 Steve Carter .05 .15
24 Pat Combs .05 .15
25 Scott Coolbaugh .05 .15
26 Steve Cummings .05 .15
27 Pete Dalena .05 .15
28 Jeff Datz .05 .15
29 Bobby Davidson .05 .15
30 Drew Denson .05 .15
31 Gary DiSarcina .08 .25
32 Brian DuBois .05 .15
33 Mike Dyer .05 .15
34 Wayne Edwards .05 .15
35 Junior Felix .05 .15
36 Mike Fetters .05 .15
37 Steve Finley .08 .25
38 Darrin Fletcher .08 .25
39 LaVel Freeman .05 .15
40 Steve Frey .05 .15
41 Mark Gardner .05 .15
42 Joe Girardi .08 .25
43 Juan Gonzalez 1.00 2.50
44 Goose Gozzo .05 .15
45 Tommy Greene .05 .15
46 Ken Griffey Jr. 2.00 5.00
47 Jason Grimsley .05 .15
48 Marquis Grissom .30 .75
49 Mark Guthrie .05 .15
50 Chip Hale .05 .15
51 Jack Hardy .05 .15
52 Gene Harris .05 .15
53 Mike Hartley .05 .15
54 Scott Hemond .05 .15
55 Xavier Hernandez .05 .15
56 Eric Hetzel .05 .15
57 Greg Hibbard .05 .15
58 Mark Higgins .05 .15
59 Glenallen Hill .05 .15
60 Chris Hoiles .08 .25
61 Shawn Holman .05 .15
62 Dann Howitt .05 .15
63 Mike Huff .05 .15
64 Terry Jorgensen .05 .15
65 David Justice .40 1.00
66 Jeff King .05 .15
67 Matt Kinzer RC .05 .15
68 Joe Kraemer .05 .15
69 Marcus Lawton .05 .15
70 Derek Lilliquist .05 .15
71 Scott Little .05 .15
72 Greg Litton .05 .15
73 Rick Luecken .05 .15
74 Julio Machado .05 .15
75 Tom Magrann .05 .15
76 Kelly Mann .05 .15
77 Randy McCament .05 .15
78 Ben McDonald .05 .15
79 Chuck McElroy .05 .15
80 Jeff McKnight .05 .15
81 Kent Mercker .05 .15
82 Matt Merullo .05 .15
83 Hensley Meulens .05 .15
84 Kevin Mmahat .05 .15
85 Mike Munoz .05 .15
86 Dan Murphy .05 .15
87 Jaime Navarro .05 .15
88 Randy Nosek .05 .15
89 John Olerud .40 1.00
90 Steve Olin .08 .25
91 Joe Oliver .05 .15
92 Francisco Oliveras .05 .15
93 Gregg Olson .08 .25
94 John Orton .05 .15
95 Dean Palmer .20 .50
96 Ramon Pena .05 .15
97 Jeff Peterek .05 .15
98 Marty Pevey .05 .15
99 Rusty Richards .05 .15
100 Jeff Richardson .05 .15
101 Rob Richie .05 .15
102 Kevin Ritz .05 .15
103 Rosario Rodriguez .05 .15
104 Mike Roesler .05 .15
105 Kenny Rogers .08 .25
106 Bobby Rose .05 .15
107 Alex Sanchez .05 .15
108 Deion Sanders .30 .75
109 Jeff Schaefer .05 .15
110 Jeff Schulz .05 .15
111 Mike Schwabe .05 .15
112 Dick Scott .05 .15
113 Scott Scudder .05 .15
114 Rudy Seanez .05 .15
115 Joe Skalski .05 .15
116 Dwight Smith .05 .15
117 Greg Smith .05 .15
118 Mike Smith .05 .15
119 Paul Sorrento .08 .25
120 Sammy Sosa 1.50 4.00
121 Billy Spiers .05 .15
122 Mike Stanton .05 .15
123 Phil Stephenson .05 .15
124 Doug Strange .05 .15
125 Russ Swan .05 .15
126 Kevin Tapani .08 .25
127 Stu Tate .05 .15
128 Greg Vaughn .05 .15
129 Robin Ventura .30 .75
130 Randy Veres .05 .15
131 Jose Vizcaino .08 .25
132 Omar Vizquel .30 .75
133 Larry Walker 1.00 2.50
134 Jerome Walton .05 .15
135 Gary Wayne .05 .15
136 Lenny Webster .05 .15
137 Mickey Weston .05 .15
138 Jeff Wetherby .05 .15
139 John Wetteland .20 .50
140 Ed Whited .05 .15
141 Wally Whitehurst .05 .15
142 Kevin Wickander .05 .15
143 Dean Wilkins .05 .15
144 Dana Williams .05 .15
145 Paul Wilmet .05 .15
146 Craig Wilson .05 .15
147 Matt Winters .05 .15
148 Eric Yelding .05 .15
149 Clint Zavaras .05 .15
150 Todd Zeile .20 .50
151 Checklist Card .05 .15
152 Checklist Card .05 .15

1991 Topps

This set marks Topps tenth consecutive year of issuing a 792-card standard-size set. Cards were primarily issued in wax packs, rack packs and factory sets. The fronts feature a full color player photo with a white border. Topps also commemorated their fortieth anniversary by including a "Topps 40" logo on the front and back of each card. Virtually all of the cards have been

discovered without the 40th logo on the back. Subsets include Record Breakers (2-8) and All-Stars (386-407). In addition, First Draft Picks and Future Stars subset cards are scattered throughout the set. The key Rookie Cards include Chipper Jones and Brian McRae. As a special promotion Topps inserted (randomly) into their wax packs one of every previous card they ever issued.

COMPLETE SET (792) 8.00 20.00
COMP.FACT.SET (792) 10.00 25.00
1 Nolan Ryan .60 1.50
2 George Brett RB .10 .30
3 Carlton Fisk RB .02 .10
4 Kevin Maas RB .01 .05
5 Cal Ripken RB .15 .40
6 Nolan Ryan RB .20 .50
7 Ryne Sandberg RB .08 .25
8 Bobby Thigpen RB .01 .05
9 Darrin Fletcher .01 .05
10 Gregg Olson .01 .05
11 Roberto Kelly .01 .05
12 Paul Assenmacher .01 .05
13 Mariano Duncan .01 .05
14 Dennis Lamp .01 .05
15 Von Hayes .01 .05
16 Mike Heath .01 .05
17 Jeff Brantley .01 .05
18 Nelson Liriano .01 .05
19 Jeff D. Robinson .01 .05
20 Pedro Guerrero .02 .10
21 Joe Morgan MG .01 .05
22 Storm Davis .01 .05
23 Jim Gantner .01 .05
24 Dave Martinez .01 .05
25 Tim Belcher .01 .05
26 Luis Sojo UER .01 .05
(Born in Barquisimento, not Carquis)
27 Bobby Witt .01 .05
28 Alvaro Espinoza .01 .05
29 Bob Walk .01 .05
30 Gregg Jefferies .01 .05
31 Colby Ward RC .01 .05
32 Mike Simms RC .01 .05
33 Barry Jones .01 .05
34 Atlee Hammaker .01 .05
35 Greg Maddux .15 .40
36 Donnie Hill .01 .05
37 Tom Bolton .01 .05
38 Scott Bradley .01 .05
39 Jim Neidlinger RC .01 .05
40 Kevin Mitchell .01 .05
41 Ken Dayley .01 .05
42 Chris Hoiles .01 .05
43 Roger McDowell .01 .05
44 Mike Felder .01 .05
45 Chris Sabo .01 .05
46 Tim Drummond .01 .05
47 Brook Jacoby .01 .05
48 Dennis Boyd .01 .05
49A Pat Borders ERR .08 .25
(40 steals at Kinston in '86)
49B Pat Borders COR .01 .05
(0 steals at Kinston in '86)
50 Bob Welch .01 .05
51 Art Howe MG .01 .05
52 Francisco Oliveras .01 .05
53 Mike Sharperson UER .01 .05
(Born in 1961, not 1960)
54 Gary Mielke .01 .05
55 Jeffrey Leonard .01 .05
56 Jeff Parrett .01 .05
57 Jack Howell .01 .05
58 Mel Stottlemyre Jr. .01 .05
59 Eric Yelding .01 .05
60 Frank Viola .02 .10
61 Stan Javier .01 .05
62 Lee Guetterman .01 .05
63 Milt Thompson .01 .05
64 Tom Herr .01 .05
65 Bruce Hurst .01 .05
66 Terry Kennedy .01 .05
67 Rick Honeycutt .01 .05
68 Gary Sheffield .02 .10
69 Steve Wilson .01 .05
70 Ellis Burks .02 .10
71 Jim Acker .01 .05
72 Junior Ortiz .01 .05
73 Craig Worthington .01 .05
74 Shane Andrews RC .08 .25
75 Jack Morris .02 .10
76 Jerry Browne .01 .05
77 Drew Hall .01 .05
78 Geno Petralli .01 .05
79 Frank Thomas .08 .25
80A Fernando Valenzuela .15 .40
ERR (104 earned runs in '90 tied for league lead)
80B Fernando Valenzuela .02 .10
COR (104 earned runs in '90 led league, 20 CG's in 1986 now italicized)
81 Cito Gaston MG .01 .05
82 Tom Glavine .05 .15
83 Daryl Boston .01 .05
84 Bob McClure .01 .05
85 Jesse Barfield .01 .05
86 Les Lancaster .01 .05
87 Tracy Jones .01 .05
88 Bob Tewksbury .01 .05
89 Darren Daulton .02 .10
90 Danny Tartabull .01 .05
91 Greg Colbrunn RC .08 .25
92 Danny Jackson .01 .05
93 Ivan Calderon .01 .05
94 John Dopson .01 .05
95 Paul Molitor .02 .10
96 Trevor Wilson .01 .05
97A Brady Anderson ERR .15 .40
(September, 2 RBI and 3 hits, should be 3 RBI and 14 hits
97B Brady Anderson COR .02 .10
98 Sergio Valdez .01 .05
99 Chris Gwynn .01 .05
100 Don Mattingly COR .25 .60
(101 hits in 1990)
100A Don Mattingly ERR .75 2.00
(10 hits in 1990)
101 Rob Ducey .01 .05
102 Gene Larkin .01 .05
103 Tim Costo RC .01 .05
104 Don Robinson .01 .05
105 Kevin McReynolds .01 .05
106 Ed Nunez .01 .05
107 Luis Polonia .01 .05
108 Matt Young .01 .05
109 Greg Riddoch MG .01 .05
110 Tom Henke .01 .05
111 Andres Thomas .01 .05
112 Frank DiPino .01 .05
113 Carl Everett RC .20 .50
114 Lance Dickson RC .02 .10
115 Hubie Brooks .01 .05
116 Mark Davis .01 .05
117 Dion James .01 .05
118 Tom Edens RC .01 .05
119 Carl Nichols .01 .05
120 Joe Carter .02 .10
121 Eric King .01 .05
122 Paul O'Neill .05 .15
123 Greg A. Harris .01 .05
124 Randy Bush .01 .05
125 Steve Bedrosian .01 .05
126 Bernard Gilkey .01 .05
127 Joe Price .01 .05
128 Travis Fryman .02 .10
(Front has SS back has SS-3B)
129 Mark Eichhorn .01 .05
130 Ozzie Smith .15 .40
131A Checklist 1 ERR .08 .25
727 Phil Bradley
131B Checklist 1 COR .01 .05
717 Phil Bradley
132 Jamie Quirk .01 .05
133 Greg Briley .01 .05
134 Kevin Elster .01 .05
135 Jerome Walton .01 .05
136 Dave Schmidt .01 .05
137 Randy Ready .01 .05
138 Jamie Moyer .02 .10
139 Jeff Treadway .01 .05
140 Fred McGriff .05 .15
141 Nick Leyva MG .01 .05
142 Curt Wilkerson .01 .05
143 John Smiley .01 .05
144 Dave Henderson .01 .05
145 Lou Whitaker .02 .10
146 Dan Plesac .01 .05
147 Carlos Baerga .01 .05
148 Rey Palacios .01 .05
149 Al Osuna UER RC .02 .10
(Shown throwing right, but bio says lefty)
150 Cal Ripken .30 .75
151 Tom Browning .01 .05
152 Mickey Hatcher .01 .05
153 Bryan Harvey .01 .05
154 Jay Buhner .02 .10
155A Dwight Evans ERR .20 .50
(Led league with 162 games in '82)
155B Dwight Evans COR .05 .15
(Tied for lead with 162 games in '82)
156 Carlos Martinez .01 .05
157 John Smoltz .05 .15
158 Jose Uribe .01 .05
159 Joe Boever .01 .05
160 Vince Coleman UER .01 .05
(Wrong birth year, born 9/22/60)
161 Tim Leary .01 .05
162 Ozzie Canseco .01 .05
163 Dave Johnson .01 .05
164 Edgar Diaz .01 .05
165 Sandy Alomar Jr. .01 .05
166 Harold Baines .02 .10
167A R.Tomlin ERR .08 .25
Harriburg
167B R.Tomlin RC COR .02 .10
Harrisburg
168 John Olerud .02 .10
169 Luis Aquino .01 .05
170 Carlton Fisk .05 .15
171 Tony LaRussa MG .02 .10
172 Pete Incaviglia .01 .05
173 Jason Grimsley .01 .05
174 Ken Caminiti .02 .10
175 Jack Armstrong .01 .05
176 John Orton .01 .05
177 Reggie Harris .01 .05
178 Dave Valle .01 .05
179 Pete Harnisch .01 .05
180 Tony Gwynn .10 .30
181 Duane Ward .01 .05
182 Junior Noboa .01 .05
183 Clay Parker .01 .05
184 Gary Green .01 .05
185 Joe Magrane .01 .05
186 Rod Booker .01 .05
187 Greg Cadaret .01 .05
188 Damon Berryhill .01 .05
189 Daryl Irvine RC .01 .05
190 Matt Williams .02 .10
191 Willie Blair .01 .05
192 Rob Deer .01 .05
193 Felix Fermin .01 .05
194 Xavier Hernandez .01 .05
195 Wally Joyner .02 .10
196 Jim Vatcher RC .01 .05
197 Chris Nabholz .01 .05
198 R.J. Reynolds .01 .05
199 Mike Hartley .01 .05
200 Darryl Strawberry .02 .10
201 Tom Kelly MG .01 .05
202 Jim Leyritz .01 .05
203 Gene Harris .01 .05
204 Herm Winningham .01 .05
205 Mike Perez RC .02 .10
206 Carlos Quintana .01 .05
207 Gary Wayne .01 .05
208 Willie Wilson .01 .05
209 Ken Howell .01 .05
210 Lance Parrish .02 .10
211 Brian Barnes RC .01 .05
212 Steve Finley .02 .10
213 Frank Wills .01 .05
214 Joe Girardi .01 .05
215 Dave Smith .01 .05
216 Greg Gagne .01 .05
217 Chris Bosio .01 .05
218 Rick Parker .01 .05
219 Jack McDowell .01 .05
220 Tim Wallach .01 .05
221 Don Slaught .01 .05
222 Brian McRae RC .08 .25
223 Allan Anderson .01 .05
224 Juan Gonzalez .08 .25
225 Randy Johnson .10 .30
226 Alfredo Griffin .01 .05
227 Steve Avery UER .01 .05
(Pitched 13 games for Durham in 1989, not 2)
228 Rex Hudler .01 .05
229 Rance Mulliniks .01 .05
230 Sid Fernandez .01 .05
231 Doug Rader MG .01 .05
232 Jose DeJesus .01 .05
233 Al Leiter .02 .10
234 Scott Erickson .01 .05
235 Dave Parker .02 .10
236A Frank Tanana ERR .08 .25
(Tied for lead with 269 K's in '75)
236B Frank Tanana COR .01 .05
(Led league with 269 K's in '75)
237 Rick Cerone .01 .05
238 Mike Dunne .01 .05
239 Darren Lewis .01 .05
240 Mike Scott .01 .05
241 Dave Clark UER .01 .05
(Career totals 19 HR and 5 3B, should be 22 and 3)
242 Mike LaCoss .01 .05
243 Lance Johnson .01 .05
244 Mike Jeffcoat .01 .05
245 Kal Daniels .01 .05
246 Kevin Wickander .01 .05
247 Jody Reed .01 .05
248 Tom Gordon .01 .05
249 Bob Melvin .01 .05
250 Dennis Eckersley .02 .10
251 Mark Lemke .01 .05
252 Mel Rojas .01 .05
253 Garry Templeton .01 .05
254 Shawn Boskie .01 .05
255 Brian Downing .01 .05
256 Greg Hibbard .01 .05
257 Tom O'Malley .01 .05
258 Chris Hammond .01 .05
259 Hensley Meulens .01 .05
260 Harold Reynolds .02 .10
261 Bud Harrelson MG .01 .05
262 Tim Jones .01 .05
263 Checklist 2 .01 .05
264 Dave Hollins .01 .05
265 Mark Gubicza .01 .05
266 Carmelo Castillo .01 .05
267 Mark Knudson .01 .05
268 Tom Brookens .01 .05
269 Joe Hesketh .01 .05
270 Mark McGwire COR .30 .75
(1987 Slugging Pctg. listed as .618)
270A Mark McGwire ERR .75 2.00
(1987 Slugging Pctg. listed as 618)
271 Omar Olivares RC .02 .10
272 Jeff King .01 .05
273 Johnny Ray .01 .05
274 Ken Williams .01 .05
275 Alan Trammell .02 .10
276 Bill Swift .01 .05
277 Scott Coolbaugh .01 .05
278 Alex Fernandez UER .01 .05
(No '90 White Sox stats)
279A Jose Gonzalez ERR .08 .25
(Photo actually Billy Bean)
279B Jose Gonzalez COR .01 .05
280 Bret Saberhagen .02 .10
281 Larry Sheets .01 .05
282 Don Carman .01 .05
283 Marquis Grissom .02 .10
284 Billy Spiers .01 .05
285 Jim Abbott .05 .15
286 Ken Oberkfell .01 .05
287 Mark Grant .01 .05
288 Derrick May .01 .05
289 Tim Birtsas .01 .05
290 Steve Sax .01 .05
291 John Wathan MG .01 .05
292 Bud Black .01 .05
293 Jay Bell .02 .10
294 Mike Moore .01 .05
295 Rafael Palmeiro .05 .15
296 Mark Williamson .01 .05
297 Manny Lee .01 .05
298 Omar Vizquel .05 .15
299 Scott Radinsky .01 .05
300 Kirby Puckett .08 .25
301 Steve Farr .01 .05
302 Tim Teufel .01 .05
303 Mike Boddicker .01 .05
304 Kevin Reimer .01 .05
305 Mike Scioscia .01 .05
306A Lonnie Smith ERR .15 .40
(136 games in '90)
306B Lonnie Smith COR .01 .05
(135 games in '90)
307 Andy Benes .01 .05
308 Tom Pagnozzi .01 .05
309 Norm Charlton .01 .05
310 Gary Carter .02 .10
311 Jeff Pico .01 .05
312 Charlie Hayes .01 .05
313 Ron Robinson .01 .05
314 Gary Pettis .01 .05
315 Roberto Alomar .05 .15
316 Gene Nelson .01 .05
317 Mike Fitzgerald .01 .05
318 Rick Aguilera .02 .10
319 Jeff McKnight .01 .05
320 Tony Fernandez .01 .05
321 Bob Rodgers MG .01 .05
322 Terry Shumpert .01 .05
323 Cory Snyder .01 .05
324A Ron Kittle ERR .15 .40
(Set another standard ...)
324B Ron Kittle COR .01 .05
(Tied another standard ...)
325 Brett Butler .02 .10
326 Ken Patterson .01 .05
327 Ron Hassey .01 .05
328 Walt Terrell .01 .05
329 Dave Justice UER .02 .10
(Drafted third round on card, should say fourth pick)
330 Dwight Gooden .02 .10
331 Eric Anthony .01 .05
332 Kenny Rogers .02 .10
333 C.Jones FDP RC 1.50 4.00
334 Todd Benzinger .01 .05
335 Mitch Williams .01 .05
336 Matt Nokes .01 .05
337A Keith Comstock ERR .08 .25
(Cubs logo on front)
337B Keith Comstock COR .01 .05
(Mariners logo on front)
338 Luis Rivera .01 .05
339 Larry Walker .08 .25
340 Ramon Martinez .01 .05
341 John Moses .01 .05
342 Mickey Morandini .01 .05
343 Jose Oquendo .01 .05
344 Jeff Russell .01 .05
345 Len Dykstra .02 .10
346 Jesse Orosco .01 .05
347 Greg Vaughn .01 .05
348 Todd Stottlemyre .01 .05
349 Dave Gallagher .01 .05
350 Glenn Davis .01 .05
351 Joe Torre MG .02 .10
352 Frank White .02 .10
353 Tony Castillo .01 .05
354 Sid Bream .01 .05
355 Chili Davis .02 .10
356 Mike Marshall .01 .05
357 Jack Savage .01 .05
358 Mark Parent .01 .05
359 Chuck Cary .01 .05
360 Tim Raines .02 .10
361 Scott Garrelts .01 .05
362 Hector Villenueva .01 .05
363 Rick Mahler .01 .05
364 Dan Pasqua .01 .05
365 Mike Schooler .01 .05
366A Checklist 3 ERR .08 .25
19 Carl Nichols
366B Checklist 3 COR .01 .05
119 Carl Nichols
367 Dave Walsh RC .01 .05
368 Felix Jose .01 .05
369 Steve Searcy .01 .05
370 Kelly Gruber .01 .05
371 Jeff Montgomery .01 .05
372 Spike Owen .01 .05
373 Darrin Jackson .01 .05
374 Larry Casian RC .01 .05
375 Tony Pena .01 .05
376 Mike Harkey .01 .05
377 Rene Gonzales .01 .05
378A Wilson Alvarez ERR .08 .25
('89 Port Charlotte and '90 Birmingham stat lines omitted)
378B Wilson Alvarez COR .01 .05
Text still says 143 K's in 1988, whereas stats say 134
379 Randy Velarde .01 .05
380 Willie McGee .02 .10
381 Jim Leyland MG .01 .05
382 Mackey Sasser .01 .05
383 Pete Smith .01 .05
384 Gerald Perry .01 .05
385 Mickey Tettleton .01 .05
386 Cecil Fielder AS .01 .05
387 Julio Franco AS .01 .05
388 Kelly Gruber AS .01 .05
389 Alan Trammell AS .02 .10
390 Jose Canseco AS .02 .10
391 Rickey Henderson AS .05 .15
392 Ken Griffey Jr. AS .15 .40
393 Carlton Fisk AS .02 .10
394 Bob Welch AS .01 .05
395 Chuck Finley AS .01 .05
396 Bobby Thigpen AS .01 .05
397 Eddie Murray AS .05 .15
398 Ryne Sandberg AS .08 .25
399 Matt Williams AS .01 .05
400 Barry Larkin AS .02 .10
401 Barry Bonds AS .20 .50
402 Darryl Strawbery AS .01 .05
403 Bobby Bonilla AS .01 .05
404 Mike Scioscia AS .01 .05
405 Doug Drabek AS .01 .05
406 Frank Viola AS .01 .05
407 John Franco AS .01 .05
408 Earnest Riles .01 .05
409 Mike Stanley .01 .05
410 Dave Righetti .02 .10
411 Lance Blankenship .01 .05
412 Dave Bergman .01 .05
413 Terry Mulholland .01 .05
414 Sammy Sosa .08 .25
415 Rick Sutcliffe .02 .10
416 Randy Milligan .01 .05
417 Bill Krueger .01 .05

418 Nick Esasky .01 .05
419 Jeff Reed .01 .05
420 Bobby Thigpen .01 .05
421 Alex Cole .01 .05
422 Rick Reuschel .01 .05
423 Rafael Ramirez UER .01 .05
(Born 1959, not 1958)
424 Calvin Schiraldi .01 .05
425 Andy Van Slyke .05 .15
426 Joe Grahe RC .02 .10
427 Rick Dempsey .01 .05
428 John Barfield .01 .05
429 Stump Merrill MG .01 .05
430 Gary Gaetti .02 .10
431 Paul Gibson .01 .05
432 Delino DeShields .02 .10
433 Pat Tabler .01 .05
434 Julio Machado .01 .05
435 Kevin Maas .01 .05
436 Scott Bankhead .01 .05
437 Doug Dascenzo .01 .05
438 Vicente Palacios .01 .05
439 Dickie Thon .01 .05
440 George Bell .01 .05
441 Zane Smith .01 .05
442 Charlie O'Brien .01 .05
443 Jeff Innis .01 .05
444 Glenn Braggs .01 .05
445 Greg Swindell .01 .05
446 Craig Grebeck .01 .05
447 John Burkett .01 .05
448 Craig Lefferts .01 .05
449 Juan Berenguer .01 .05
450 Wade Boggs .05 .15
451 Neal Heaton .01 .05
452 Bill Schroeder .01 .05
453 Lenny Harris .01 .05
454A Kevin Appier ERR .15 .40
('90 Omaha stat
line omitted)
454B Kevin Appier COR .02 .10
455 Walt Weiss .01 .05
456 Charlie Leibrandt .01 .05
457 Todd Hundley .01 .05
458 Brian Holman .01 .05
459 T.Trebelhorn MG UER .01 .05
Pitching and batting
columns switched
460 Dave Stieb .01 .05
461 Robin Ventura .02 .10
462 Steve Frey .01 .05
463 Dwight Smith .01 .05
464 Steve Buechele .01 .05
465 Ken Griffey Sr. .02 .10
466 Charles Nagy .01 .05
467 Dennis Cook .01 .05
468 Tim Hulett .01 .05
469 Chet Lemon .01 .05
470 Howard Johnson .01 .05
471 Mike Lieberthal RC .15 .40
472 Kirt Manwaring .01 .05
473 Curt Young .01 .05
474 Phil Plantier RC .02 .10
475 Ted Higuera .01 .05
476 Glenn Wilson .01 .05
477 Mike Fetters .01 .05
478 Kurt Stillwell .01 .05
479 Bob Patterson UER .01 .05
(Has a decimal point
between 7 and 9)
480 Dave Magadan .01 .05
481 Eddie Whitson .01 .05
482 Tino Martinez .08 .25
483 Mike Aldrete .01 .05
484 Dave LaPoint .01 .05
485 Terry Pendleton .02 .10
486 Tommy Greene .01 .05
487 Rafael Belliard .01 .05
488 Jeff Manto .01 .05
489 Bobby Valentine MG .01 .05
490 Kirk Gibson .02 .10
491 Kurt Miller RC .01 .05
492 Ernie Whitt .01 .05
493 Jose Rijo .01 .05
494 Chris James .01 .05
495 Charlie Hough .02 .10
496 Marty Barrett .01 .05
497 Ben McDonald .01 .05
498 Mark Salas .01 .05
499 Melido Perez .01 .05
500 Will Clark .05 .15
501 Mike Bielecki .01 .05
502 Carney Lansford .02 .10
503 Roy Smith .01 .05
504 Julio Valera .01 .05
505 Chuck Finley .02 .10
506 Darnell Coles .01 .05
507 Steve Jeltz .01 .05
508 Mike York RC .01 .05
509 Glenallen Hill .01 .05
510 John Franco .02 .10
511 Steve Balboni .01 .05
512 Jose Mesa .01 .05
513 Jerald Clark .01 .05
514 Mike Stanton .01 .05
515 Alvin Davis .01 .05
516 Karl Rhodes .01 .05
517 Joe Oliver .01 .05
518 Cris Carpenter .01 .05
519 Sparky Anderson MG .02 .10
520 Mark Grace .05 .15
521 Joe Orsulak .01 .05
522 Stan Belinda .01 .05
523 Rodney McCray RC .01 .05
524 Darrel Akerfelds .01 .05
525 Willie Randolph .02 .10
526A Moises Alou ERR .15 .40
(37 runs in 2 games
for '90 Pirates)
526B Moises Alou COR .02 .10
(0 runs in 2 games
for '90 Pirates)
527A Checklist 4 ERR .08 .25
105 Keith Miller
719 Kevin McReynolds
527B Checklist 4 COR .01 .05
105 Kevin McReynolds
719 Keith Miller
528 Dennis Martinez .02 .10
529 Marc Newfield RC .02 .10
530 Roger Clemens .30 .75
531 Dave Rohde .01 .05
532 Kirk McCaskill .01 .05
533 Oddibe McDowell .01 .05
534 Mike Jackson .01 .05
535 Ruben Sierra UER .02 .10
(Back reads 100 Runs
amd 100 RBI's)
536 Mike Witt .01 .05
537 Jose Lind .01 .05
538 Bip Roberts .01 .05
539 Scott Terry .01 .05
540 George Brett .25 .60
541 Domingo Ramos .01 .05
542 Rob Murphy .01 .05
543 Junior Felix .01 .05
544 Alejandro Pena .01 .05
545 Dale Murphy .05 .15
546 Jeff Ballard .01 .05
547 Mike Pagliarulo .01 .05
548 Jaime Navarro .01 .05
549 John McNamara MG .01 .05
550 Eric Davis .02 .10
551 Bob Kipper .01 .05
552 Jeff Hamilton .01 .05
553 Joe Klink .01 .05
554 Brian Harper .01 .05
555 Turner Ward RC .02 .10
556 Gary Ward .01 .05
557 Wally Whitehurst .01 .05
558 Otis Nixon .01 .05
559 Adam Peterson .01 .05
560 Greg Smith .01 .05
561 Tim McIntosh .01 .05
562 Jeff Kunkel .01 .05
563 Brent Knackert .01 .05
564 Dante Bichette .02 .10
565 Craig Biggio .05 .15
566 Craig Wilson RC .01 .05
567 Dwayne Henry .01 .05
568 Ron Karkovice .01 .05
569 Curt Schilling .08 .25
570 Barry Bonds .40 1.00
571 Pat Combs .01 .05
572 Dave Anderson .01 .05
573 Rich Rodriguez UER RC .01 .05
(Stats say drafted 4th,
but bio says 9th round)
574 John Marzano .01 .05
575 Robin Yount .15 .40
576 Jeff Kaiser .01 .05
577 Bill Doran .01 .05
578 Dave West .01 .05
579 Roger Craig MG .01 .05
580 Dave Stewart .02 .10
581 Luis Quinones .01 .05
582 Marty Clary .01 .05
583 Tony Phillips .01 .05
584 Kevin Brown .02 .10
585 Pete O'Brien .01 .05
586 Fred Lynn .01 .05
587 Jose Offerman UER .01 .05
(Text says he signed
7/24/86, but bio
says 1988)
588 Mark Whiten .01 .05
589 Scott Ruskin .01 .05
590 Eddie Murray .08 .25
591 Ken Hill .01 .05
592 B.J. Surhoff .02 .10
593A Mike Walker ERR .08 .25
('90 Canton-Akron
stat line omitted)
593B Mike Walker COR .01 .05
594 Rich Garces RC .02 .10
595 Bill Landrum .01 .05
596 Ronnie Walden RC .02 .10
597 Jerry Don Gleaton .01 .05
598 Sam Horn .01 .05
599A Greg Myers ERR .08 .25
('90 Syracuse
stat line omitted)
599B Greg Myers COR .01 .05
600 Bo Jackson .08 .25
601 Bob Ojeda .01 .05
602 Casey Candaele .01 .05
603A W.Chamberlain RC ERR .15 .40
Photo actually
Louie Meadows
603B Wes Chamberlain COR RC .02 .10
604 Billy Hatcher .01 .05
605 Jeff Reardon .02 .10
606 Jim Gott .01 .05
607 Edgar Martinez .05 .15
608 Todd Burns .01 .05
609 Jeff Torborg MG .01 .05
610 Andres Galarraga .02 .10
611 Dave Eiland .01 .05
612 Steve Lyons .01 .05
613 Eric Show .01 .05
614 Luis Salazar .01 .05
615 Bert Blyleven .02 .10
616 Todd Zeile .01 .05
617 Bill Wegman .01 .05
618 Sil Campusano .01 .05
619 David Wells .02 .10
620 Ozzie Guillen .02 .10
621 Ted Power .01 .05
622 Jack Daugherty .01 .05
623 Jeff Blauser .01 .05
624 Tom Candiotti .01 .05
625 Terry Steinbach .01 .05
626 Gerald Young .01 .05
627 Tim Layana .01 .05
628 Greg Litton .01 .05
629 Wes Gardner .01 .05
630 Dave Winfield .02 .10
631 Mike Morgan .01 .05
632 Lloyd Moseby .01 .05
633 Kevin Tapani .01 .05
634 Henry Cotto .01 .05
635 Andy Hawkins .01 .05
636 Geronimo Pena .01 .05
637 Bruce Ruffin .01 .05
638 Mike Macfarlane .01 .05
639 Frank Robinson MG .05 .15
640 Andre Dawson .02 .10
641 Mike Henneman .01 .05
642 Hal Morris .01 .05
643 Jim Presley .01 .05
644 Chuck Crim .01 .05
645 Juan Samuel .01 .05
646 Andujar Cedeno .01 .05
647 Mark Portugal .01 .05
648 Lee Stevens .01 .05
649 Bill Sampen .01 .05
650 Jack Clark .02 .10
651 Alan Mills .01 .05
652 Kevin Romine .01 .05
653 Anthony Telford RC .01 .05
654 Paul Sorrento .01 .05
655 Erik Hanson .01 .05
656A Checklist 5 ERR .08 .25
348 Vicente Palacios
381 Jose Lind
537 Mike LaValliere
665 Jim Leyland
656B Checklist 5 ERR .08 .25
433 Vicente Palacios
(Palacios should be 438)
537 Jose Lind
665 Mike LaValliere
381 Jim Leyland
656C Checklist 5 COR .01 .05
438 Vicente Palacios
537 Jose Lind
665 Mike LaValliere
381 Jim Leyland
657 Mike Kingery .01 .05
658 Scott Aldred .01 .05
659 Oscar Azocar .01 .05
660 Lee Smith .02 .10
661 Steve Lake .01 .05
662 Ron Dibble .02 .10
663 Greg Brock .01 .05
664 John Farrell .01 .05
665 Mike LaValliere .01 .05
666 Danny Darwin .01 .05
667 Kent Anderson .01 .05
668 Bill Long .01 .05
669 Lou Piniella MG .02 .10
670 Rickey Henderson .08 .25
671 Andy McGaffigan .01 .05
672 Shane Mack .01 .05
673 Greg Olson UER .01 .05
(6 RBI in '88 at Tidewater
and 2 RBI in '87,
should be 48 and 15)
674A Kevin Gross ERR .08 .25
(89 BB with Phillies
in '88 tied for
league lead)
674B Kevin Gross COR .01 .05
(89 BB with Phillies
in '88 led league)
675 Tom Brunansky .01 .05
676 Scott Chiamparino .01 .05
677 Billy Ripken .01 .05
678 Mark Davidson .01 .05
679 Bill Bathe .01 .05
680 David Cone .02 .10
681 Jeff Schaefer .01 .05
682 Ray Lankford .02 .10
683 Derek Lilliquist .01 .05
684 Milt Cuyler .01 .05
685 Doug Drabek .01 .05
686 Mike Gallego .01 .05
687A John Cerutti ERR .08 .25
(4.46 ERA in '90)
687B John Cerutti COR .01 .05
(4.76 ERA in '90)
688 Rosario Rodriguez RC .01 .05
689 John Kruk .02 .10
690 Orel Hershiser .02 .10
691 Mike Blowers .01 .05
692A Efrain Valdez ERR .08 .25
(Born 6/11/66)
692B Efrain Valdez COR RC .01 .05
(Born 7/11/66 and two
lines of text added)
693 Francisco Cabrera .01 .05
694 Randy Veres .01 .05
695 Kevin Seitzer .01 .05
696 Steve Olin .01 .05
697 Shawn Abner .01 .05
698 Mark Guthrie .01 .05
699 Jim Lefebvre MG .01 .05
700 Jose Canseco .05 .15
701 Pascual Perez .01 .05
702 Tim Naehring .01 .05
703 Juan Agosto .01 .05
704 Devon White .02 .10
705 Robby Thompson .01 .05
706A Brad Arnsberg ERR .08 .25
(68.2 IP in '90)
706B Brad Arnsberg COR .01 .05
(62.2 IP in '90)
707 Jim Eisenreich .01 .05
708 John Mitchell .01 .05
709 Matt Sinatro .01 .05
710 Kent Hrbek .02 .10
711 Jose DeLeon .01 .05
712 Ricky Jordan .01 .05
713 Scott Scudder .01 .05
714 Marvell Wynne .01 .05
715 Tim Burke .01 .05
716 Bob Geren .01 .05
717 Phil Bradley .01 .05
718 Steve Crawford .01 .05
719 Keith Miller .01 .05
720 Cecil Fielder .02 .10
721 Mark Lee RC .01 .05
722 Wally Backman .01 .05
723 Candy Maldonado .01 .05
724 David Segui .01 .05
725 Ron Gant .02 .10
726 Phil Stephenson .01 .05
727 Mookie Wilson .02 .10
728 Scott Sanderson .01 .05
729 Don Zimmer MG .02 .10
730 Barry Larkin .05 .15
731 Jeff Gray RC .01 .05
732 Franklin Stubbs .01 .05
733 Kelly Downs .01 .05
734 John Russell .01 .05
735 Ron Darling .01 .05
736 Dick Schofield .01 .05
737 Tim Crews .01 .05
738 Mel Hall .01 .05
739 Russ Swan .01 .05
740 Ryne Sandberg .15 .40
741 Jimmy Key .02 .10
742 Tommy Gregg .01 .05
743 Bryn Smith .01 .05
744 Nelson Santovenia .01 .05
745 Doug Jones .01 .05
746 John Shelby .01 .05
747 Tony Fossas .01 .05
748 Al Newman .01 .05
749 Greg W. Harris .01 .05
750 Bobby Bonilla .02 .10
751 Wayne Edwards .01 .05
752 Kevin Bass .01 .05
753 Paul Marak UER RC .01 .05
(Stats say drafted in
Jan. but bio says May)
754 Bill Pecota .01 .05
755 Mark Langston .01 .05
756 Jeff Huson .01 .05
757 Mark Gardner .01 .05
758 Mike Devereaux .01 .05
759 Bobby Cox MG .01 .05
760 Benny Santiago .02 .10
761 Larry Andersen .01 .05
762 Mitch Webster .01 .05
763 Dana Kiecker .01 .05
764 Mark Carreon .01 .05
765 Shawon Dunston .01 .05
766 Jeff Robinson .01 .05
767 Dan Wilson RC .08 .25
768 Don Pall .01 .05
769 Tim Sherrill .01 .05
770 Jay Howell .01 .05
771 Gary Redus UER .01 .05
(Born in Tanner,
should say Athens)
772 Kent Mercker UER .01 .05
(Born in Indianapolis,
should say Dublin, Ohio)
773 Tom Foley .01 .05
774 Dennis Rasmussen .01 .05
775 Julio Franco .02 .10
776 Brent Mayne .01 .05
777 John Candelaria .01 .05
778 Dan Gladden .01 .05
779 Carmelo Martinez .01 .05
780A Randy Myers ERR .15 .40
(15 career losses)
780B Randy Myers COR .01 .05
(19 career losses)
781 Darryl Hamilton .01 .05
782 Jim Deshaies .01 .05
783 Joel Skinner .01 .05
784 Willie Fraser .01 .05
785 Scott Fletcher .01 .05
786 Eric Plunk .01 .05
787 Checklist 6 .01 .05
788 Bob Milacki .01 .05
789 Tom Lasorda MG .08 .25
790 Ken Griffey Jr. .30 .75
791 Mike Benjamin .01 .05
792 Mike Greenwell .01 .05

1991 Topps Desert Shield

These 792 standard-size cards are parallel to the regular Topps issue. These cards were issued in special packs available only to servicepeople serving in the Desert Shield (later to be Desert Storm) campaign. The cards are differentiated by a "Desert Shield" logo in the upper right corner. There were many different types of forgeries created for these cards so some caution is urged in purchasing any expensive cards from the set.

*STARS: 40X TO 100X BASIC CARDS
*ROOKIES: 15X TO 40X BASIC CARDS
333 Chipper Jones FDP 100.00 200.00

1991 Topps Tiffany

This 792 standard-size set proved to be the final time Topps issued their Tiffany sets. These cards again parallel the regular issue and have "glossy" fronts and easy to read backs. These cards were issued in complete set form only. Since a limited amount of these sets were produced, the multiplier is one of the highest for any of these Topps sets. While no production number is guessed at for these sets, it is perceived in the hobby to be among the shortest printed Tiffany sets.

COMP.FACT.SET (792) 100.00 200.00
*STARS: 12.5X TO 30X BASIC CARDS
*ROOKIES: 6X TO 15X BASIC CARDS

1991 Topps Rookies

This set contains 33 standard-size cards and were distributed at a rate of one per retail jumbo pack. The front and back borders are white and other design elements are red, blue, and yellow. This set is identical to the previous year's set. Topps also commemorated its 40th anniversary by including a "Topps 40" logo on the front. The cards are unnumbered and checklisted below in alphabetical order.

COMPLETE SET (33) 10.00 20.00
1 Sandy Alomar .20 .50

2 Kevin Appier .20 .50
3 Steve Avery .08 .25
4 Carlos Baerga .20 .50
5 John Burkett .08 .25
6 Alex Cole .08 .25
7 Pat Combs .08 .25
8 Delino DeShields .20 .50
9 Travis Fryman .20 .50
10 Marquis Grissom .40 1.00
11 Mike Harkey .08 .25
12 Glenallen Hill .08 .25
13 Jeff Huson .08 .25
14 Felix Jose .08 .25
15 Dave Justice .60 1.50
16 Jim Leyritz .08 .25
17 Kevin Maas .08 .25
18 Ben McDonald .08 .25
19 Kent Mercker .08 .25
20 Hal Morris .08 .25
21 Chris Nabholz .08 .25
22 Tim Naehring .08 .25
23 Jose Offerman .08 .25
24 John Olerud .75 2.00
25 Scott Radinsky .08 .25
26 Scott Ruskin .08 .25
27 Kevin Tapani .08 .25
28 Frank Thomas 3.00 8.00
29 Randy Tomlin .08 .25
30 Greg Vaughn .20 .50
31 Robin Ventura .40 1.00
32 Larry Walker .60 1.50
33 Todd Zeile .20 .50

1991 Topps Traded

The 1991 Topps Traded set contains 132 standard-size cards. The cards were issued primarily in factory set form through hobby dealers but were also made available on a limited basis in wax packs. The cards in the wax packs (gray backs) and collated factory sets (white backs) are from different card stock. Both versions are valued equally. The card design is identical to the regular issue 1991 Topps cards except for the whiter stock (for factory set cards) and T-suffixed numbering. The set is numbered in alphabetical order. The set includes a Team U.S.A. subset, featuring 25 of America's top collegiate players. The key Rookie Cards in this set are Jeff Bagwell, Jason Giambi, Luis Gonzalez, Charles Johnson and Ivan Rodriguez.

COMPLETE SET (132) 4.00 10.00
COMP.FACT.SET (132) 4.00 10.00
1T Juan Agosto .01 .05
2T Roberto Alomar .05 .15
3T Wally Backman .01 .05
4T Jeff Bagwell RC .60 1.50
5T Skeeter Barnes .01 .05
6T Steve Bedrosian .01 .05
7T Derek Bell .02 .10
8T George Bell .01 .05
9T Rafael Belliard .01 .05
10T Dante Bichette .02 .10
11T Bud Black .01 .05
12T Mike Boddicker .01 .05
13T Sid Bream .01 .05
14T Hubie Brooks .01 .05
15T Brett Butler .02 .10
16T Ivan Calderon .01 .05
17T John Candelaria .01 .05
18T Tom Candiotti .01 .05
19T Gary Carter .02 .10
20T Joe Carter .02 .10
21T Rick Cerone .01 .05
22T Jack Clark .02 .10
23T Vince Coleman .01 .05
24T Scott Coolbaugh .01 .05
25T Danny Cox .01 .05
26T Danny Darwin .01 .05
27T Chili Davis .02 .10
28T Glenn Davis .01 .05
29T Steve Decker RC .01 .05
30T Rob Deer .01 .05
31T Rich DeLucia RC .01 .05
32T John Dettmer USA RC .08 .25
33T Brian Downing .01 .05
34T D.Dreifort USA RC .08 .25
35T K.Dressendorfer RC .01 .05
36T Jim Essian MG .01 .05
37T Dwight Evans .05 .15
38T Steve Farr .01 .05
39T Jeff Fassero RC .08 .25
40T Junior Felix .01 .05
41T Tony Fernandez .01 .05
42T Steve Finley .02 .10
43T Jim Fregosi MG .01 .05
44T Gary Gaetti .02 .10
45T Jason Giambi USA RC 2.00 5.00
46T Kirk Gibson .02 .10
47T Leo Gomez .01 .05
48T Luis Gonzalez RC .20 .50
49T Jeff Granger USA RC .08 .25
50T Todd Greene USA RC .20 .50
51T J.Hammonds USA RC .20 .50
52T Mike Hargrove MG .01 .05
53T Pete Harnisch .01 .05
54T R.Helling USA UER RC .20 .50
Misspelled Hellings on card back)
55T Glenallen Hill .01 .05
56T Charlie Hough .02 .10
57T Pete Incaviglia .01 .05
58T Bo Jackson .08 .25
59T Danny Jackson .01 .05
60T Reggie Jefferson .01 .05
61T C.Johnson USA RC .30 .75
62T Jeff Johnson RC .01 .05
63T Todd Johnson USA RC .08 .25
64T Barry Jones .01 .05
65T Chris Jones RC .02 .10
66T Scott Kamieniecki RC .02 .10
67T Pat Kelly RC .02 .10
68T Darryl Kile .02 .10
69T Chuck Knoblauch .02 .10
70T Bill Krueger .01 .05
71T Scott Leius .01 .05
72T Donnie Leshnock USA RC .08 .25
73T Mark Lewis .01 .05
74T Candy Maldonado .01 .05
75T Jason McDonald USA RC .08 .25
76T Willie McGee .02 .10
77T Fred McGriff .05 .15
78T Billy McMillon USA RC .08 .25
79T Hal McRae MG .02 .10
80T Dan Melendez USA RC .08 .25
81T Orlando Merced RC .02 .10
82T Jack Morris .02 .10
83T Phil Nevin USA RC .30 .75
84T Otis Nixon .01 .05
85T Johnny Oates MG .01 .05
86T Bob Ojeda .01 .05
87T Mike Pagliarulo .01 .05
88T Dean Palmer .02 .10
89T Dave Parker .02 .10
90T Terry Pendleton .02 .10
91T Tony Phillips (P) USA RC .08 .25
92T Doug Platt RC .01 .05
93T Ron Polk USA CO .08 .25
94T Tim Raines .02 .10
95T Willie Randolph .02 .10
96T Dave Righetti .02 .10
97T Ernie Riles .01 .05
98T Chris Roberts USA RC .08 .25
99T Jeff D. Robinson .01 .05
100T Jeff M. Robinson .01 .05
101T Ivan Rodriguez RC 1.25 3.00
102T Steve Rodriguez USA RC .08 .25
103T Tom Runnells MG .01 .05
104T Scott Sanderson .01 .05
105T Bob Scanlan RC .01 .05
106T Pete Schourek RC .02 .10
107T Gary Scott RC .01 .05
108T Paul Shuey USA RC .20 .50
109T Doug Simons RC .01 .05
110T Dave Smith .01 .05
111T Cory Snyder .01 .05
112T Luis Sojo .01 .05
113T Kennie Steenstra USA RC .08 .25
114T Darryl Strawberry .02 .10
115T Franklin Stubbs .01 .05
116T Todd Taylor USA RC .08 .25
117T Wade Taylor RC .01 .05
118T Garry Templeton .01 .05
119T Mickey Tettleton .01 .05
120T Tim Teufel .01 .05
121T Mike Timlin RC .08 .25
122T David Tuttle USA RC .08 .25
123T Mo Vaughn .02 .10
124T Jeff Ware USA RC .08 .25
125T Devon White .02 .10
126T Mark Whiten .01 .05
127T Mitch Williams .01 .05
128T Craig Wilson USA RC .08 .25
129T Willie Wilson .01 .05
130T Chris Wimmer USA RC .08 .25
131T Ivan Zweig USA RC .08 .25
132T Checklist 1T-132T .01 .05

1991 Topps Traded Tiffany

In the final Tiffany relase, this 132-card standard-size set was released as a parallel issue to the regular Topps Traded issue. These cards were released in very limited quantities and the multiplier for these cards is higher than many previous Tiffany issues. These cards were issued in complete factory set form only. The set is considered to be among the shortest print of the Tiffany run and these cards are rarely seen in the secondary market.

COMP.FACT.SET (132) 90.00 150.00
*STARS: 12.5X TO 30X BASIC CARDS
*ROOKIES: 10X TO 25X BASIC CARDS
*USA ROOKIES: 6X TO 15X BASIC CARDS

1991 Topps Debut '90

The 1991 Topps Major League Debut Set contains 171 standard-size cards. Although the checklist card is arranged chronologically in order of first major league appearance in 1990, the player cards are arranged alphabetically by the player's last name. Carlos Baerga and Frank Thomas are among the more prominent players featured in this set.

COMP. FACT SET (171) 10.00 20.00
1 Paul Abbott .05 .15
2 Steve Adkins .05 .15
3 Scott Aldred .05 .15
4 Gerald Alexander .05 .15
5 Moises Alou .30 .75
6 Steve Avery .05 .15
7 Oscar Azocar .05 .15
8 Carlos Baerga .05 .15
9 Kevin Baez .05 .15

10 Jeff Baldwin .05 .15
11 Brian Barnes .05 .15
12 Kevin Bearse .05 .15
13 Kevin Belcher .05 .15
14 Mike Bell .05 .15
15 Sean Berry .30 .75
16 Joe Bitker .05 .15
17 Willie Blair .05 .15
18 Brian Bohanon .05 .15
19 Mike Bordick .30 .75
20 Shawn Boskie .05 .15
21 Rod Brewer .05 .15
22 Kevin D. Brown .05 .15
23 Dave Burba .30 .75
24 Jim Campbell .05 .15
25 Ozzie Canseco .05 .15
26 Chuck Carr .05 .15
27 Larry Casian .05 .15
28 Andujar Cedeno .05 .15
29 Wes Chamberlain .05 .15
30 Scott Chiamparino .05 .15
31 Steve Chitren .05 .15
32 Pete Coachman .05 .15
33 Alex Cole .05 .15
34 Jeff Conine .30 .75
35 Scott Cooper .05 .15
36 Milt Cuyler .05 .15
37 Steve Decker .05 .15
38 Rich DeLucia .05 .15
39 Delino DeShields .30 .75
40 Mark Dewey .05 .15
41 Carlos Diaz .05 .15
42 Lance Dickson .05 .15
43 Narciso Elvira .05 .15
44 Luis Encarnacion .05 .15
45 Scott Erickson .05 .15
46 Paul Faries .05 .15
47 Howard Farmer .05 .15
48 Alex Fernandez .05 .15
49 Travis Fryman .30 .75
50 Rich Garces .05 .15
51 Carlos Garcia .05 .15
52 Mike Gardiner .05 .15
53 Bernard Gilkey .05 .15
54 Tom Gilles .05 .15
55 Jerry Goff .05 .15
56 Leo Gomez .05 .15
57 Luis Gonzalez 1.25 3.00
58 Joe Grahe .05 .15
59 Craig Grebeck .05 .15
60 Kip Gross .05 .15
61 Eric Gunderson .05 .15
62 Chris Hammond .05 .15
63 Dave Hansen .05 .15
64 Reggie Harris .05 .15
65 Bill Haselman .05 .15
66 Randy Hennis .05 .15
67 Carlos Hernandez .05 .15
68 Howard Hilton .05 .15
69 Dave Hollins .05 .15
70 Darren Holmes .30 .75
71 John Hoover .05 .15
72 Steve Howard .05 .15
73 Thomas Howard .05 .15
74 Todd Hundley .05 .15
75 Daryl Irvine .05 .15
76 Chris Jelic .05 .15
77 Dana Kiecker .05 .15
78 Brent Knackert .05 .15
79 Jimmy Kremers .05 .15
80 Jerry Kutzler .05 .15
81 Ray Lankford .30 .75
82 Tim Layana .05 .15
83 Terry Lee .05 .15
84 Mark Leiter .05 .15
85 Scott Leius .05 .15
86 Mark Leonard .05 .15
87 Darren Lewis .05 .15
88 Scott Lewis .05 .15
89 Jim Leyritz .05 .15
90 Dave Liddell .05 .15
91 Luis Lopez .05 .15
92 Kevin Maas .05 .15
93 Bob MacDonald .05 .15
94 Carlos Maldonado .05 .15
95 Chuck Malone .05 .15
96 Ramon Manon .05 .15
97 Jeff Manto .05 .15
98 Paul Marak .05 .15
99 Tino Martinez 1.25 3.00
100 Derrick May .05 .15
101 Brent Mayne .05 .15
102 Paul McClellan .05 .15
103 Rodney McCray .05 .15
104 Tim McIntosh .05 .15
105 Brian McRae .30 .75
106 Jose Melendez .05 .15
107 Orlando Merced .05 .15
108 Alan Mills .05 .15
109 Gino Minutelli .05 .15
110 Mickey Morandini .05 .15
111 Pedro Munoz .05 .15
112 Chris Nabholz .05 .15
113 Tim Naehring .05 .15
114 Charles Nagy .05 .15
115 Jim Neidlinger .05 .15
116 Rafael Novoa .05 .15
117 Jose Offerman .05 .15
118 Omar Olivares .30 .75
119 Javier Ortiz .05 .15
120 Al Osuna .05 .15
121 Rick Parker .05 .15
122 Dave Pavlas .05 .15
123 Geronimo Pena .05 .15
124 Mike Perez .05 .15
125 Phil Plantier .05 .15
126 Jim Poole .05 .15
127 Tom Quinlan .05 .15
128 Scott Radinsky .05 .15
129 Darren Reed .05 .15
130 Karl Rhodes .05 .15
131 Jeff Richardson .05 .15
132 Rich Rodriguez .05 .15
133 Dave Rohde .05 .15
134 Mel Rojas .05 .15
135 Vic Rosario .05 .15
136 Rich Rowland .05 .15
137 Scott Ruskin .05 .15
138 Bill Sampen .05 .15
139 Andres Santana .05 .15
140 David Segui .05 .15
141 Jeff Shaw .05 .15
142 Tim Sherrill .05 .15
143 Terry Shumpert .05 .15
144 Mike Simms .05 .15
145 Daryl Smith .05 .15
146 Luis Sojo .05 .15
147 Steve Springer .05 .15
148 Ray Stephens .05 .15
149 Lee Stevens .05 .15
150 Mel Stottlemyre Jr. .05 .15
151 Glenn Sutko .05 .15
152 Anthony Telford .05 .15
153 Frank Thomas 2.00 5.00
154 Randy Tomlin .05 .15
155 Brian Traxler .05 .15
156 Efrain Valdez .05 .15
157 Rafael Valdez .05 .15
158 Julio Valera .05 .15
159 Jim Vatcher .05 .15
160 Hector Villanueva .05 .15
161 Hector Wagner .05 .15
162 Dave Walsh .05 .15
163 Steve Wapnick .05 .15
164 Colby Ward .05 .15
165 Turner Ward .30 .75
166 Terry Wells .05 .15
167 Mark Whiten .05 .15
168 Mike York .05 .15
169 Cliff Young .05 .15
170 Checklist Card .05 .15
171 Checklist Card .05 .15

1991 Topps Glossy All-Stars

These 22 glossy standard-size cards were inserted one per Topps rack packs and honor the starting lineup, managers and honorary captains of the 1990 National and American League All-Star teams. This would be the final year that this insert set was issued and the design is similar to what Topps produced each year since 1984.

COMPLETE SET (22) 4.00 10.00
1 Tony LaRussa MG .07 .20
2 Mark McGwire .60 1.50
3 Steve Sax .02 .10
4 Wade Boggs .20 .50
5 Cal Ripken Jr 1.25 3.00
6 Rickey Henderson .30 .75
7 Ken Griffey, Jr. .60 1.50
8 Jose Canseco .20 .50
9 Sandy Alomar Jr. .07 .20
10 Bob Welch .02 .10
11 Al Lopez CAPT .20 .50
12 Roger Craig MG .02 .10
13 Will Clark .20 .50
14 Ryne Sandberg .30 .75
15 Chris Sabo .02 .10
16 Ozzie Smith .40 1.00
17 Kevin Mitchell .02 .10
18 Len Dykstra .07 .20
19 Andre Dawson .20 .50
20 Mike Scioscia .07 .20
21 Jack Armstrong .02 .10
22 Juan Marichal CAPT .20 .50

1992 Topps

The 1992 Topps set contains 792 standard-size cards. Cards were distributed in plastic wrap packs, jumbo packs, rack packs and factory sets. The fronts have either posed or action color player photos on a white card face. Different color stripes frame the pictures, and the player's name and team name appear in two short color stripes respectively at the bottom. Special subsets included are Record Breakers (2-5), Prospects (58, 126, 179, 473, 551, 591, 618, 656, 676), and All-Stars (386-407). The key Rookie Cards in this set are Shawn Green and Manny Ramirez.

COMPLETE SET (792) 10.00 25.00
COMP.FACT.SET (802) 10.00 25.00
COMP.HOLIDAY (811) 15.00 40.00
1 Nolan Ryan .40 1.00
2 Ricky Henderson RB .05 .15
Most career SB's
(Some cards have print marks that show 1.991 on the front)
3 Jeff Reardon RB .01 .05
4 Nolan Ryan RB .20 .50
5 Dave Winfield RB .01 .05
6 Brien Taylor RC .08 .25
7 Jim Olander .01 .05
8 Bryan Hickerson RC .02 .10
9 Jon Farrell RC .02 .10
10 Wade Boggs .05 .15
11 Jack McDowell .01 .05
12 Luis Gonzalez .02 .10
13 Mike Scioscia .01 .05
14 Wes Chamberlain .01 .05
15 Dennis Martinez .02 .10
16 Jeff Montgomery .01 .05
17 Randy Milligan .01 .05
18 Greg Cadaret .01 .05
19 Jamie Quirk .01 .05
20 Bip Roberts .01 .05
21 Buck Rodgers MG .01 .05
22 Bill Wegman .01 .05
23 Chuck Knoblauch .02 .10
24 Randy Myers .01 .05
25 Ron Gant .02 .10
26 Mike Bielecki .01 .05
27 Juan Gonzalez .05 .15
28 Mike Schooler .01 .05
29 Mickey Tettleton .01 .05
30 John Kruk .02 .10
31 Bryn Smith .01 .05
32 Chris Nabholz .01 .05
33 Carlos Baerga .01 .05
34 Jeff Juden .01 .05
35 Dave Righetti .02 .10
36 Scott Ruffcorn RC .02 .10
37 Luis Polonia .01 .05
38 Tom Candiotti .01 .05
39 Greg Olson .01 .05
40 Cal Ripken .75 2.00
41 Craig Lefferts .01 .05
42 Mike Macfarlane .01 .05
43 Jose Lind .01 .05
44 Rick Aguilera .02 .10
45 Gary Carter .02 .10
46 Steve Farr .01 .05
47 Rex Hudler .01 .05
48 Scott Scudder .01 .05
49 Damon Berryhill .01 .05
50 Ken Griffey Jr. .15 .40
51 Tom Runnells MG .01 .05
52 Juan Bell .01 .05
53 Tommy Gregg .01 .05
54 David Wells .02 .10
55 Rafael Palmeiro .05 .15
56 Charlie O'Brien .01 .05
57 Donn Pall .01 .05
58 Brad Ausmus RC .60 1.50
Jim Campanis Jr.
Dave Nilsson
Doug Robbins
59 Mo Vaughn .02 .10
60 Tony Fernandez .01 .05
61 Paul O'Neill .05 .15
62 Gene Nelson .01 .05
63 Randy Ready .01 .05
64 Bob Kipper .01 .05
65 Willie McGee .02 .10
66 Scott Stahoviak RC .02 .10
67 Luis Salazar .01 .05
68 Marvin Freeman .01 .05
69 Kenny Lofton .05 .15
70 Gary Gaetti .02 .10
71 Erik Hanson .01 .05
72 Eddie Zosky .01 .05
73 Brian Barnes .01 .05
74 Scott Leius .01 .05
75 Bret Saberhagen .02 .10
76 Mike Gallego .01 .05
77 Jack Armstrong .01 .05
78 Ivan Rodriguez .08 .25
79 Jesse Orosco .01 .05
80 David Justice .02 .10
81 Ced Landrum .01 .05
82 Doug Simons .01 .05
83 Tommy Greene .01 .05
84 Leo Gomez .01 .05
85 Jose DeLeon .01 .05
86 Steve Finley .02 .10
87 Bob MacDonald .01 .05
88 Darrin Jackson .01 .05
89 Neal Heaton .01 .05
90 Robin Yount .15 .40
91 Jeff Reed .01 .05
92 Lenny Harris .01 .05
93 Reggie Jefferson .01 .05
94 Sammy Sosa .08 .25
95 Scott Bailes .01 .05
96 Tom McKinnon RC .02 .10
97 Luis Rivera .01 .05
98 Mike Harkey .01 .05
99 Jeff Treadway .01 .05
100 Jose Canseco .05 .15
101 Omar Vizquel .05 .15
102 Scott Kamieniecki .01 .05
103 Ricky Jordan .01 .05
104 Jeff Ballard .01 .05
105 Felix Jose .01 .05
106 Mike Boddicker .01 .05
107 Dan Pasqua .01 .05
108 Mike Timlin .01 .05
109 Roger Craig MG .01 .05
110 Ryne Sandberg .15 .40
111 Mark Carreon .01 .05
112 Oscar Azocar .01 .05
113 Mike Greenwell .01 .05
114 Mark Portugal .01 .05
115 Terry Pendleton .02 .10
116 Willie Randolph .02 .10
117 Scott Terry .01 .05
118 Chili Davis .02 .10
119 Mark Gardner .01 .05
120 Alan Trammell .02 .10
121 Derek Bell .02 .10
122 Gary Varsho .01 .05
123 Bob Ojeda .01 .05
124 Shawn Livsey RC .02 .10
125 Chris Hoiles .01 .05
126 Ryan Klesko .08 .25
John Jaha RC
Rico Brogna
Dave Staton
127 Carlos Quintana .01 .05
128 Kurt Stillwell .01 .05
129 Melido Perez .01 .05
130 Alvin Davis .01 .05
131 Checklist 1-132 .01 .05
132 Eric Show .01 .05
133 Rance Mulliniks .01 .05
134 Darryl Kile .02 .10
135 Von Hayes .01 .05
136 Bill Doran .01 .05
137 Jeff D. Robinson .01 .05
138 Monty Fariss .01 .05
139 Jeff Innis .01 .05
140 Mark Grace UER .05 .15
Home Calie., should be Calif.
141 Jim Leyland MG UER .02 .10
(No closed parenthesis after East in 1991)
142 Todd Van Poppel .01 .05
143 Paul Gibson .01 .05
144 Bill Swift .01 .05
145 Danny Tartabull .01 .05
146 Al Newman .01 .05
147 Cris Carpenter .01 .05
148 Anthony Young .01 .05
149 Brian Bohanon .01 .05
150 Roger Clemens UER .20 .50
(League leading ERA in 1990 not italicized)
151 Jeff Hamilton .01 .05
152 Charlie Leibrandt .01 .05
153 Ron Karkovice .01 .05
154 Hensley Meulens .01 .05
155 Scott Bankhead .01 .05
156 Manny Ramirez RC 2.00 5.00
157 Keith Miller .01 .05
158 Todd Frohwirth .01 .05
159 Darrin Fletcher .01 .05
160 Bobby Bonilla .02 .10
161 Casey Candaele .01 .05
162 Paul Faries .01 .05
163 Dana Kiecker .01 .05
164 Shane Mack .01 .05
165 Mark Langston .01 .05
166 Geronimo Pena .01 .05
167 Andy Allanson .01 .05
168 Dwight Smith .01 .05
169 Chuck Crim .01 .05
170 Alex Cole .01 .05
171 Bill Plummer MG .01 .05
172 Juan Berenguer .01 .05
173 Brian Downing .01 .05
174 Steve Frey .01 .05
175 Orel Hershiser .02 .10
176 Ramon Garcia .01 .05
177 Dan Gladden .01 .05
178 Jim Acker .01 .05
179 Bobby DeJardin .01 .05
Cesar Bernhardt
Armando Moreno
Andy Stankiewicz
180 Kevin Mitchell .01 .05
181 Hector Villanueva .01 .05
182 Jeff Reardon .02 .10
183 Brent Mayne .01 .05
184 Jimmy Jones .01 .05
185 Benito Santiago .02 .10
186 Cliff Floyd RC .30 .75
187 Ernie Riles .01 .05
188 Jose Guzman .01 .05
189 Junior Felix .01 .05
190 Glenn Davis .01 .05
191 Charlie Hough .02 .10
192 Dave Fleming .01 .05
193 Omar Olivares .01 .05
194 Eric Karros .02 .10
195 David Cone .02 .10
196 Frank Castillo .01 .05
197 Glenn Braggs .01 .05
198 Scott Aldred .01 .05
199 Jeff Blauser .01 .05
200 Len Dykstra .02 .10
201 Buck Showalter MG RC .08 .25
202 Rick Honeycutt .01 .05
203 Greg Myers .01 .05
204 Trevor Wilson .01 .05
205 Jay Howell .01 .05
206 Luis Sojo .01 .05
207 Jack Clark .02 .10
208 Julio Machado .01 .05
209 Lloyd McClendon .01 .05
210 Ozzie Guillen .02 .10
211 Jeremy Hernandez RC .02 .10
212 Randy Velarde .01 .05
213 Les Lancaster .01 .05
214 Andy Mota .01 .05
215 Rich Gossage .02 .10
216 Brent Gates RC .02 .10
217 Brian Harper .01 .05
218 Mike Flanagan .01 .05
219 Jerry Browne .01 .05
220 Jose Rijo .01 .05
221 Skeeter Barnes .01 .05
222 Jaime Navarro .01 .05
223 Mel Hall .01 .05
224 Bret Barberie .01 .05
225 Roberto Alomar .05 .15
226 Pete Smith .01 .05
227 Daryl Boston .01 .05
228 Eddie Whitson .01 .05
229 Shawn Boskie .01 .05
230 Dick Schofield .01 .05
231 Brian Drahman .01 .05
232 John Smiley .01 .05
233 Mitch Webster .01 .05
234 Terry Steinbach .01 .05
235 Jack Morris .02 .10
236 Bill Pecota .01 .05
237 Jose Hernandez RC .08 .25
238 Greg Litton .01 .05
239 Brian Holman .01 .05
240 Andres Galarraga .02 .10
241 Gerald Young .01 .05
242 Mike Mussina .08 .25
243 Alvaro Espinoza .01 .05
244 Darren Daulton .02 .10
245 John Smoltz .05 .15
246 Jason Pruitt RC .02 .10
247 Chuck Finley .02 .10
248 Jim Gantner .01 .05
249 Tony Fossas .01 .05
250 Ken Griffey Sr. .02 .10
251 Kevin Elster .01 .05
252 Dennis Rasmussen .01 .05
253 Terry Kennedy .01 .05
254 Ryan Bowen .01 .05
255 Robin Ventura .02 .10
256 Mike Aldrete .01 .05
257 Jeff Russell .01 .05
258 Jim Lindeman .01 .05
259 Ron Darling .01 .05
260 Devon White .02 .10
261 Tom Lasorda MG .02 .10
262 Terry Lee .01 .05
263 Bob Patterson .01 .05
264 Checklist 133-264 .01 .05
265 Teddy Higuera .01 .05
266 Roberto Kelly .01 .05
267 Steve Bedrosian .01 .05
268 Brady Anderson .02 .10
269 Ruben Amaro .01 .05
270 Tony Gwynn .10 .30
271 Tracy Jones .01 .05
272 Jerry Don Gleaton .01 .05
273 Craig Grebeck .01 .05
274 Bob Scanlan .01 .05
275 Todd Zeile .01 .05
276 Shawn Green RC .40 1.00
277 Scott Chiamparino .01 .05
278 Darryl Hamilton .01 .05
279 Jim Clancy .01 .05
280 Carlos Martinez .01 .05
281 Kevin Appier .02 .10
282 John Wehner .01 .05
283 Reggie Sanders .02 .10
284 Gene Larkin .01 .05
285 Bob Welch .01 .05
286 Gilberto Reyes .01 .05
287 Pete Schourek .01 .05
288 Andujar Cedeno .01 .05
289 Mike Morgan .01 .05
290 Bo Jackson .08 .25
291 Phil Garner MG .02 .10
292 Ray Lankford .02 .10
293 Mike Henneman .01 .05
294 Dave Valle .01 .05
295 Alonzo Powell .01 .05
296 Tom Brunansky .01 .05
297 Kevin Brown .02 .10
298 Kelly Gruber .01 .05
299 Charles Nagy .01 .05
300 Don Mattingly .25 .60
301 Kirk McCaskill .01 .05
302 Joey Cora .01 .05
303 Dan Plesac .01 .05
304 Joe Oliver .01 .05
305 Tom Glavine .05 .15
306 Al Shirley RC .02 .10
307 Bruce Ruffin .01 .05
308 Craig Shipley .01 .05
309 Dave Martinez .01 .05
310 Jose Mesa .01 .05
311 Henry Cotto .01 .05
312 Mike LaValliere .01 .05
313 Kevin Tapani .01 .05
314 Jeff Huson .01 .05
315 Juan Samuel .01 .05
316 Curt Schilling .05 .15
317 Mike Bordick .01 .05
318 Steve Howe .01 .05
319 Tony Phillips .01 .05
320 George Bell .01 .05
321 Lou Piniella MG .02 .10
322 Tim Burke .01 .05
323 Milt Thompson .01 .05
324 Danny Darwin .01 .05
325 Joe Orsulak .01 .05
326 Eric King .01 .05
327 Jay Buhner .02 .10
328 Joel Johnston .01 .05
329 Franklin Stubbs .01 .05
330 Will Clark .05 .15
331 Steve Lake .01 .05
332 Chris Jones .01 .05
333 Pat Tabler .01 .05
334 Kevin Gross .01 .05
335 Dave Henderson .01 .05
336 Greg Anthony RC .02 .10
337 Alejandro Pena .01 .05
338 Shawn Abner .01 .05
339 Tom Browning .01 .05
340 Otis Nixon .01 .05
341 Bob Geren .01 .05
342 Tim Spehr .01 .05
343 John Vander Wal .01 .05
344 Jack Daugherty .01 .05
345 Zane Smith .01 .05
346 Rheal Cormier .01 .05
347 Kent Hrbek .02 .10
348 Rick Wilkins .01 .05
349 Steve Lyons .01 .05
350 Gregg Olson .01 .05
351 Greg Riddoch MG .01 .05
352 Ed Nunez .01 .05
353 Braulio Castillo .01 .05
354 Dave Bergman .01 .05
355 Warren Newson .01 .05
356 Luis Quinones .01 .05
357 Mike Witt .01 .05
358 Ted Wood .01 .05
359 Mike Moore .01 .05
360 Lance Parrish .02 .10
361 Barry Jones .01 .05
362 Javier Ortiz .01 .05
363 John Candelaria .01 .05
364 Glenallen Hill .01 .05
365 Duane Ward .01 .05
366 Checklist 265-396 .01 .05
367 Rafael Belliard .01 .05
368 Bill Krueger .01 .05
369 Steve Whitaker RC .02 .10
370 Shawon Dunston .01 .05
371 Dante Bichette .02 .10
372 Kip Gross .01 .05
373 Don Robinson .01 .05
374 Bernie Williams .05 .15
375 Bert Blyleven .02 .10
376 Chris Donnels .01 .05
377 Bob Zupcic RC .02 .10
378 Joel Skinner .01 .05
379 Steve Chitren .01 .05
380 Barry Bonds .40 1.00
381 Sparky Anderson MG .02 .10
382 Sid Fernandez .01 .05
383 Dave Hollins .01 .05
384 Mark Lee .01 .05
385 Tim Wallach .01 .05
386 Will Clark AS .02 .10
387 Ryne Sandberg AS .08 .25
388 Howard Johnson AS .01 .05
389 Barry Larkin AS .02 .10
390 Barry Bonds AS .20 .50
391 Ron Gant AS .01 .05
392 Bobby Bonilla AS .01 .05
393 Craig Biggio AS .02 .10
394 Dennis Martinez AS .01 .05
395 Tom Glavine AS .02 .10
396 Lee Smith AS .01 .05
397 Cecil Fielder AS .01 .05
398 Julio Franco AS .01 .05
399 Wade Boggs AS .02 .10
400 Cal Ripken AS .15 .40
401 Jose Canseco AS .05 .15
402 Joe Carter AS .01 .05
403 Ruben Sierra AS .01 .05
404 Matt Nokes AS .01 .05
405 Roger Clemens AS .08 .25
406 Jim Abbott AS .02 .10
407 Bryan Harvey AS .01 .05
408 Bob Milacki .01 .05
409 Geno Petralli .01 .05
410 Dave Stewart .02 .10
411 Mike Jackson .01 .05
412 Luis Aquino .01 .05
413 Tim Teufel .01 .05
414 Jeff Ware .01 .05
415 Jim Deshaies .01 .05
416 Ellis Burks .02 .10
417 Allan Anderson .01 .05
418 Alfredo Griffin .01 .05
419 Wally Whitehurst .01 .05
420 Sandy Alomar Jr. .01 .05
421 Juan Agosto .01 .05
422 Sam Horn .01 .05
423 Jeff Fassero .01 .05
424 Paul McClellan .01 .05
425 Cecil Fielder .02 .10
426 Tim Raines .02 .10
427 Eddie Taubensee RC .08 .25
428 Dennis Boyd .01 .05
429 Tony LaRussa MG .02 .10
430 Steve Sax .01 .05
431 Tom Gordon .01 .05
432 Billy Hatcher .01 .05
433 Cal Eldred .01 .05
434 Wally Backman .01 .05
435 Mark Eichhorn .01 .05
436 Mookie Wilson .02 .10
437 Scott Servais .01 .05
438 Mike Maddux .01 .05
439 Chico Walker .01 .05
440 Doug Drabek .01 .05
441 Rob Deer .01 .05
442 Dave West .01 .05
443 Spike Owen .01 .05
444 Tyrone Hill RC .02 .10
445 Matt Williams .02 .10
446 Mark Lewis .01 .05
447 David Segui .01 .05
448 Tom Pagnozzi .01 .05
449 Jeff Johnson .01 .05
450 Mark McGwire .25 .60
451 Tom Henke .01 .05
452 Wilson Alvarez .01 .05
453 Gary Redus .01 .05
454 Darren Holmes .01 .05
455 Pete O'Brien .01 .05
456 Pat Combs .01 .05
457 Hubie Brooks .01 .05
458 Frank Tanana .01 .05
459 Tom Kelly MG .01 .05
460 Andre Dawson .02 .10
461 Doug Jones .01 .05
462 Rich Rodriguez .01 .05
463 Mike Simms .01 .05
464 Mike Jeffcoat .01 .05
465 Barry Larkin .05 .15
466 Stan Belinda .01 .05
467 Lonnie Smith .01 .05
468 Greg Harris .01 .05
469 Jim Eisenreich .01 .05
470 Pedro Guerrero .02 .10
471 Jose DeJesus .01 .05
472 Rich Rowland RC .02 .10
473 Frank Bolick .01 .05
Craig Paquette
Tom Redington
Paul Russo UER
(Line around top border)
474 Mike Rossiter RC .02 .10
475 Robby Thompson .01 .05
476 Randy Bush .01 .05
477 Greg Hibbard .01 .05
478 Dale Sveum .01 .05
479 Chito Martinez .01 .05
480 Scott Sanderson .01 .05
481 Tino Martinez .05 .15
482 Jimmy Key .02 .10
483 Terry Shumpert .01 .05
484 Mike Hartley .01 .05
485 Chris Sabo .01 .05
486 Bob Walk .01 .05
487 John Cerutti .01 .05
488 Scott Cooper .01 .05
489 Bobby Cox MG .02 .10
490 Julio Franco .02 .10
491 Jeff Brantley .01 .05
492 Mike Devereaux .01 .05
493 Jose Offerman .01 .05
494 Gary Thurman .01 .05
495 Carney Lansford .02 .10
496 Joe Grahe .01 .05
497 Andy Ashby .01 .05
498 Gerald Perry .01 .05
499 Dave Otto .01 .05
500 Vince Coleman .01 .05
501 Rob Mallicoat .01 .05
502 Greg Briley .01 .05
503 Pascual Perez .01 .05
504 Aaron Sele RC .08 .25
505 Bobby Thigpen .01 .05
506 Todd Benzinger .01 .05
507 Candy Maldonado .01 .05
508 Bill Gullickson .01 .05
509 Doug Dascenzo .01 .05
510 Frank Viola .02 .10
511 Kenny Rogers .02 .10
512 Mike Heath .01 .05
513 Kevin Bass .01 .05
514 Kim Batiste .01 .05
515 Delino DeShields .01 .05
516 Ed Sprague .01 .05
517 Jim Gott .01 .05
518 Jose Melendez .01 .05
519 Hal McRae MG .02 .10
520 Jeff Bagwell .08 .25
521 Joe Hesketh .01 .05
522 Milt Cuyler .01 .05
523 Shawn Hillegas .01 .05

524 Don Slaught .01 .05
525 Randy Johnson .08 .25
526 Doug Platt .01 .05
527 Checklist 397-528 .01 .05
528 Steve Foster .01 .05
529 Joe Girardi .01 .05
530 Jim Abbott .05 .15
531 Larry Walker .05 .15
532 Mike Huff .01 .05
533 Mackey Sasser .01 .05
534 Benji Gil RC .08 .25
535 Dave Stieb .01 .05
536 Willie Wilson .01 .05
537 Mark Leiter .01 .05
538 Jose Uribe .01 .05
539 Thomas Howard .01 .05
540 Ben McDonald .01 .05
541 Jose Tolentino .01 .05
542 Keith Mitchell .01 .05
543 Jerome Walton .01 .05
544 Cliff Brantley .01 .05
545 Andy Van Slyke .05 .15
546 Paul Sorrento .01 .05
547 Herm Winningham .01 .05
548 Mark Guthrie .01 .05
549 Joe Torre MG .02 .10
550 Darryl Strawberry .02 .10
551 Wilfredo Cordero .08 .25
Chipper Jones
Manny Alexander
Alex Arias UER
(No line around
top border)
552 Dave Gallagher .01 .05
553 Edgar Martinez .05 .15
554 Donald Harris .01 .05
555 Frank Thomas .08 .25
556 Storm Davis .01 .05
557 Dickie Thon .01 .05
558 Scott Garrelts .01 .05
559 Steve Olin .01 .05
560 Rickey Henderson .08 .25
561 Jose Vizcaino .01 .05
562 Wade Taylor .01 .05
563 Pat Borders .01 .05
564 Jimmy Gonzalez RC .02 .10
565 Lee Smith .02 .10
566 Bill Sampen .01 .05
567 Dean Palmer .02 .10
568 Bryan Harvey .01 .05
569 Tony Pena .01 .05
570 Lou Whitaker .02 .10
571 Randy Tomlin .01 .05
572 Greg Vaughn .01 .05
573 Kelly Downs .01 .05
574 Steve Avery UER .01 .05
(Should be 13 games
for Durham in 1989)
575 Kirby Puckett .08 .25
576 Heathcliff Slocumb .01 .05
577 Kevin Seitzer .01 .05
578 Lee Guetterman .01 .05
579 Johnny Oates MG .01 .05
580 Greg Maddux .15 .40
581 Stan Javier .01 .05
582 Vicente Palacios .01 .05
583 Mel Rojas .01 .05
584 Wayne Rosenthal RC .02 .10
585 Lenny Webster .01 .05
586 Rod Nichols .01 .05
587 Mickey Morandini .01 .05
588 Russ Swan .01 .05
589 Mariano Duncan .01 .05
590 Howard Johnson .01 .05
591 Jeromy Burnitz .02 .10
Jacob Brumfield
Alan Cockrell
D.J. Dozier
592 Denny Neagle .02 .10
593 Steve Decker .01 .05
594 Brian Barber RC .02 .10
595 Bruce Hurst .01 .05
596 Kent Mercker .01 .05
597 Mike Magnante RC .02 .10
598 Jody Reed .01 .05
599 Steve Searcy .01 .05
600 Paul Molitor .02 .10
601 Dave Smith .01 .05
602 Mike Fetters .01 .05
603 Luis Mercedes .01 .05
604 Chris Gwynn .01 .05
605 Scott Erickson .01 .05
606 Brook Jacoby .01 .05
607 Todd Stottlemyre .01 .05
608 Scott Bradley .01 .05
609 Mike Hargrove MG .02 .10
610 Eric Davis .02 .10
611 Brian Hunter .01 .05
612 Pat Kelly .01 .05
613 Pedro Munoz .01 .05
614 Al Osuna .01 .05
615 Matt Merullo .01 .05
616 Larry Andersen .01 .05
617 Junior Ortiz .01 .05
618 Cesar Hernandez .01 .05
Steve Hosey
Jeff McNeely
Dan Peltier
619 Danny Jackson .01 .05
620 George Brett .25 .60
621 Dan Gakeler .01 .05
622 Steve Buechele .01 .05
623 Bob Tewksbury .01 .05
624 Shawn Estes RC .08 .25
625 Kevin McReynolds .01 .05
626 Chris Haney .01 .05
627 Mike Sharperson .01 .05
628 Mark Williamson .01 .05
629 Wally Joyner .02 .10
630 Carlton Fisk .05 .15
631 Armando Reynoso RC .08 .25
632 Felix Fermin .01 .05
633 Mitch Williams .01 .05
634 Manuel Lee .01 .05
635 Harold Baines .02 .10
636 Greg Harris .01 .05
637 Orlando Merced .01 .05
638 Chris Bosio .01 .05
639 Wayne Housie .01 .05
640 Xavier Hernandez .01 .05
641 David Howard .01 .05
642 Tim Crews .01 .05
643 Rick Cerone .01 .05
644 Terry Leach .01 .05
645 Deion Sanders .05 .15
646 Craig Wilson .01 .05
647 Marquis Grissom .02 .10
648 Scott Fletcher .01 .05
649 Norm Charlton .01 .05
650 Jesse Barfield .01 .05
651 Joe Slusarski .01 .05
652 Bobby Rose .01 .05
653 Dennis Lamp .01 .05
654 Allen Watson RC .02 .10
655 Brett Butler .02 .10
656 Rudy Pemberton .02 .10
Henry Rodriguez
Lee Tinsley RC
Gerald Williams
657 Dave Johnson .01 .05
658 Checklist 529-660 .01 .05
659 Brian McRae .01 .05
660 Fred McGriff .05 .15
661 Bill Landrum .01 .05
662 Juan Guzman .01 .05
663 Greg Gagne .01 .05
664 Ken Hill .01 .05
665 Dave Haas .01 .05
666 Tom Foley .01 .05
667 Roberto Hernandez .01 .05
668 Dwayne Henry .01 .05
669 Jim Fregosi MG .01 .05
670 Harold Reynolds .02 .10
671 Mark Whiten .01 .05
672 Eric Plunk .01 .05
673 Todd Hundley .01 .05
674 Mo Sanford .01 .05
675 Bobby Witt .01 .05
676 Sam Militello .08 .25
Pat Mahomes RC
Turk Wendell
Roger Salkeld
677 John Marzano .01 .05
678 Joe Klink .01 .05
679 Pete Incaviglia .01 .05
680 Dale Murphy .05 .15
681 Rene Gonzales .01 .05
682 Andy Benes .01 .05
683 Jim Poole .01 .05
684 Trever Miller RC .02 .10
685 Scott Livingstone .01 .05
686 Rich DeLucia .01 .05
687 Harvey Pulliam .01 .05
688 Tim Belcher .01 .05
689 Mark Lemke .01 .05
690 John Franco .02 .10
691 Walt Weiss .01 .05
692 Scott Ruskin .01 .05
693 Jeff King .01 .05
694 Mike Gardiner .01 .05
695 Gary Sheffield .02 .10
696 Joe Boever .01 .05
697 Mike Felder .01 .05
698 John Habyan .01 .05
699 Cito Gaston MG .01 .05
700 Ruben Sierra .02 .10
701 Scott Radinsky .01 .05
702 Lee Stevens .01 .05
703 Mark Wohlers .01 .05
704 Curt Young .01 .05
705 Dwight Evans .05 .15
706 Rob Murphy .01 .05
707 Gregg Jefferies .01 .05
708 Tom Bolton .01 .05
709 Chris James .01 .05
710 Kevin Maas .01 .05
711 Ricky Bones .01 .05
712 Curt Wilkerson .01 .05
713 Roger McDowell .01 .05
714 Pokey Reese RC .08 .25
715 Craig Biggio .05 .15
716 Kirk Dressendorfer .01 .05
717 Ken Dayley .01 .05
718 B.J. Surhoff .02 .10
719 Terry Mulholland .01 .05
720 Kirk Gibson .02 .10
721 Mike Pagliarulo .01 .05
722 Walt Terrell .01 .05
723 Jose Oquendo .01 .05
724 Kevin Morton .01 .05
725 Dwight Gooden .02 .10
726 Kirt Manwaring .01 .05
727 Chuck McElroy .01 .05
728 Dave Burba .01 .05
729 Art Howe MG .01 .05
730 Ramon Martinez .01 .05
731 Donnie Hill .01 .05
732 Nelson Santovenia .01 .05
733 Bob Melvin .01 .05
734 Scott Hatteberg RC .08 .25
735 Greg Swindell .01 .05
736 Lance Johnson .01 .05
737 Kevin Reimer .01 .05
738 Dennis Eckersley .02 .10
739 Rob Ducey .01 .05
740 Ken Caminiti .02 .10
741 Mark Gubicza .01 .05
742 Bill Spiers .01 .05
743 Darren Lewis .01 .05
744 Chris Hammond .01 .05
745 Dave Magadan .01 .05
746 Bernard Gilkey .01 .05
747 Willie Banks .01 .05
748 Matt Nokes .01 .05
749 Jerald Clark .01 .05
750 Travis Fryman .02 .10
751 Steve Wilson .01 .05
752 Billy Ripken .01 .05
753 Paul Assenmacher .01 .05
754 Charlie Hayes .01 .05
755 Alex Fernandez .01 .05
756 Gary Pettis .01 .05
757 Rob Dibble .02 .10
758 Tim Naehring .01 .05
759 Jeff Torborg MG .01 .05
760 Ozzie Smith .15 .40
761 Mike Fitzgerald .01 .05
762 John Burkett .01 .05
763 Kyle Abbott .01 .05
764 Tyler Green RC .02 .10
765 Pete Harnisch .01 .05
766 Mark Davis .01 .05
767 Kal Daniels .01 .05
768 Jim Thome .08 .25
769 Jack Howell .01 .05
770 Sid Bream .01 .05
771 Arthur Rhodes .01 .05
772 Garry Templeton UER .01 .05
(Stat heading in for pitchers)
773 Hal Morris .01 .05
774 Bud Black .01 .05
775 Ivan Calderon .01 .05
776 Doug Henry RC .02 .10
777 John Olerud .02 .10
778 Tim Leary .01 .05
779 Jay Bell .02 .10
780 Eddie Murray .08 .25
781 Paul Abbott .01 .05
782 Phil Plantier .01 .05
783 Joe Magrane .01 .05
784 Ken Patterson .01 .05
785 Albert Belle .02 .10
786 Royce Clayton .01 .05
787 Checklist 661-792 .01 .05
788 Mike Stanton .01 .05
789 Bobby Valentine MG .01 .05
790 Joe Carter .02 .10
791 Danny Cox .01 .05
792 Dave Winfield .02 .10

1992 Topps Gold

Topps produced a 792-card Topps Gold factory set packaged in a foil display box. Only this factory set contained an additional card of Brien Taylor, numbered 793 and hand signed by him. The production run was 12,000 sets. The Topps Gold cards were also available in regular series packs. According to Topps, on average collectors would find one Topps Gold card in every 36 wax packs, one in every 18 cello packs, one in every 12 rak packs, five per Vending box, one in every six jumbo packs, and ten per regular factory set. The checklist cards in the regular set were replaced with six individual Rookie player cards (131, 264, 366, 527, 658, 787) in the gold set. There were a number of uncorrected errors in the Gold set. Steve Finley (86) has gold band indicating he is Mark Davidson of the Astros. Andujar Cedeno (288) is listed as a member of the New York Yankees. Mike Huff (532) is listed as a member of the Boston Red Sox. Barry Larkin (465) is listed as a member of the Houston Astros but is correctly listed as a member of the Cincinnati Reds on his Gold Winners cards. Typically the individual cards are sold at a multiple of the player's respective value in the regular set.

COMPLETE SET (792) 30.00 80.00
COMP.FACT.SET (793) 30.00 80.00
*STARS: 6X TO 15X BASIC CARDS
*ROOKIES: 4X TO 10X BASIC CARDS
131 Terry Mathews .30 .75
264 Rod Beck .30 .75
366 Tony Perezchica .30 .75
527 Terry McDaniel .30 .75
658 John Ramos .30 .75
787 Brian Williams .30 .75
793 Brien Taylor AU/12000 6.00 15.00

1992 Topps Gold Winners

The 1992 Topps baseball card packs featured "Match-the-Stats" game cards in which the consumer could save "Runs". For 2.00 and every 100 Runs saved in this game, the consumer could receive through a mail-in offer ten Topps Gold cards. These particular Topps Gold cards carry the word "Winner" in gold foil on the card front. The checklist cards in the regular set were replaced with six individual Rookie player cards (131, 264, 366, 527, 658, 787) in the gold set. Typically the individual cards are sold at a multiple of the player's respective value in the regular set. The Gold winner promotion was very popular and the cards are in noticably larger supply than the basic Gold parallels. It did not hurt the supply of Winner cards collectors could hold their cards up to the light to see which were the correct answers. Later printing of 1992 game cards were fixed so collectors could not cheat to get the answers.

COMPLETE SET (792) 20.00 40.00
*STARS: 1.25X TO 3X BASIC CARDS
*ROOKIES: 1.25X TO 3X BASIC CARDS
131 Terry Mathews .05 .15
264 Rod Beck .05 .15
366 Tony Perezchica .05 .15
527 Terry McDaniel .05 .15
658 John Ramos .05 .15
787 Brian Williams .05 .15

1992 Topps Traded

The 1992 Topps Traded set comprises 132 standard-size cards. The set was distributed exclusively in factory set form through hobby dealers. As in past editions, the set focuses on promising rookies, new managers, and players who changed teams. The set also includes a Team U.S.A. subset, featuring 25 of America's top college players and the Team U.S.A. coach. Card design is identical to the regular issue 1992 Topps cards except for the T-suffixed numbering. The cards are arranged in alphabetical order by player's last name. The key Rookie Cards in this set are Nomar Garciaparra, Brian Jordan and Jason Varitek.

COMP.FACT.SET (132) 20.00 50.00
1T Willie Adams USA RC .08 .25
2T Jeff Alkire USA RC .08 .25
3T Felipe Alou MG .07 .20
4T Moises Alou .07 .20
5T Ruben Amaro .02 .10
6T Jack Armstrong .02 .10
7T Scott Bankhead .02 .10
8T Tim Belcher .02 .10
9T George Bell .02 .10
10T Freddie Benavides .02 .10
11T Todd Benzinger .02 .10
12T Joe Boever .02 .10
13T Ricky Bones .02 .10
14T Bobby Bonilla .07 .20
15T Hubie Brooks .02 .10
16T Jerry Browne .02 .10
17T Jim Bullinger .02 .10
18T Dave Burba .02 .10
19T Kevin Campbell .02 .10
20T Tom Candiotti .02 .10
21T Mark Carreon .02 .10
22T Gary Carter .07 .20
23T Archi Cianfrocco RC .02 .10
24T Phil Clark .02 .10
25T Chad Curtis RC .15 .40
26T Eric Davis .07 .20
27T Tim Davis USA RC .08 .25
28T Gary DiSarcina .02 .10
29T Darren Dreifort USA .02 .10
30T Mariano Duncan .02 .10
31T Mike Fitzgerald .02 .10
32T John Flaherty .02 .10
33T Darrin Fletcher .02 .10
34T Scott Fletcher .02 .10
35T Ron Fraser USA CO RC .08 .25
36T Andres Galarraga .07 .20
37T Dave Gallagher .02 .10
38T Mike Gallego .02 .10
39T Nomar Garciaparra USA RC 8.00 20.00
40T Jason Giambi USA .40 1.00
41T Danny Gladden .02 .10
42T Rene Gonzales .02 .10
43T Jeff Granger USA .02 .10
44T Rick Greene USA RC .08 .25
45T J.Hammonds USA .07 .20
46T Charlie Hayes .02 .10
47T Von Hayes .02 .10
48T Rick Helling USA .02 .10
49T Butch Henry RC .02 .10
50T Carlos Hernandez .02 .10
51T Ken Hill .02 .10
52T Butch Hobson .02 .10
53T Vince Horsman .02 .10
54T Pete Incaviglia .02 .10
55T Gregg Jefferies .02 .10
56T Charles Johnson USA .07 .20
57T Doug Jones .02 .10
58T Brian Jordan RC .30 .75
59T Wally Joyner .07 .20
60T D.Kirkreit USA RC .08 .25
61T Bill Krueger .02 .10
62T Gene Lamont MG .02 .10
63T Jim Lefebvre MG .02 .10
64T Danny Leon .02 .10
65T Pat Listach RC .15 .40
66T Kenny Lofton .10 .30
67T Dave Martinez .02 .10
68T Derrick May .02 .10
69T Kirk McCaskill .02 .10
70T Chad McConnell USA RC .08 .25
71T Kevin McReynolds .02 .10
72T Rusty Meacham .02 .10
73T Keith Miller .02 .10
74T Kevin Mitchell .02 .10
75T Jason Moler USA RC .08 .25
76T Mike Morgan .02 .10
77T Jack Morris .07 .20
78T Calvin Murray USA RC .30 .75
79T Eddie Murray .20 .50
80T Randy Myers .07 .20
81T Denny Neagle .07 .20
82T Phil Nevin USA .07 .20
83T Dave Nilsson .02 .10
84T Junior Ortiz .02 .10
85T Donovan Osborne .02 .10
86T Bill Pecota .02 .10
87T Melido Perez .02 .10
88T Mike Perez .02 .10
89T Hipolito Pichardo RC .02 .10
90T Willie Randolph .07 .20
91T Darren Reed .02 .10
92T Bip Roberts .02 .10
93T Chris Roberts USA .02 .10
94T Steve Rodriguez USA .02 .10
95T Bruce Ruffin .02 .10
96T Scott Ruskin .02 .10
97T Bret Saberhagen .07 .20
98T Rey Sanchez RC .15 .40
99T Steve Sax .02 .10
100T Curt Schilling .10 .30
101T Dick Schofield .02 .10
102T Gary Scott .02 .10
103T Kevin Seitzer .02 .10
104T Frank Seminara RC .02 .10
105T Gary Sheffield .07 .20
106T John Smiley .02 .10
107T Cory Snyder .02 .10
108T Paul Sorrento .02 .10
109T Sammy Sosa .60 1.50
110T Matt Stairs RC .20 .50
111T Andy Stankiewicz .02 .10
112T Kurt Stillwell .02 .10
113T Rick Sutcliffe .07 .20
114T Bill Swift .02 .10
115T Jeff Tackett .02 .10
116T Danny Tartabull .02 .10
117T Eddie Taubensee .07 .20
118T Dickie Thon .02 .10
119T Michael Tucker USA RC .30 .75
120T Scooter Tucker .02 .10
121T Marc Valdes USA RC .08 .25
122T Julio Valera .02 .10
123T Jason Varitek USA RC 5.00 12.00
124T Ron Villone USA RC .08 .25
125T Frank Viola .07 .20
126T B.J. Wallace USA RC .08 .25
127T Dan Walters .02 .10
128T Craig Wilson USA .02 .10
129T Chris Wimmer USA .02 .10
130T Dave Winfield .07 .20
131T Herm Winningham .02 .10
132T Checklist 1T-132T .02 .10

1992 Topps Traded Gold

This 132 card standard-size set parallels the regular 1992 Topps Traded set. It was only issued through the Topps dealer network. Six thousand of these sets were produced and the only player difference is that Kerry Woodson replaces the checklist card

COMP.FACT.SET (132) 50.00 100.00
*GOLD STARS: 1.5X TO 4X BASIC CARDS
*GOLD RC's: .75X TO 2X BASIC CARDS

1992 Topps Debut '91

The 1991 Topps Debut '91 set contains 194 standard-size cards. The fronts feature a mix of either posed or action glossy color player photos, framed with two color border stripes on a white card face. Future MVP's Jeff Bagwell, Ivan Rodriguez and Mo Vaughn along with Vinny Castilla and Mike Mussina are among the featured players in the set.

COMP.FACT.SET (194) 6.00 15.00
1 Kyle Abbott .08 .25
2 Dana Allison .08 .25
3 Rich Amaral .08 .25
4 Ruben Amaro .08 .25
5 Andy Ashby .08 .25
6 Jim Austin .08 .25
7 Jeff Bagwell .75 2.00
8 Jeff Banister .08 .25
9 Willie Banks .08 .25
10 Bret Barberie .08 .25
11 Kim Batiste .08 .25
12 Chris Beasley .08 .25
13 Rod Beck .20 .50
14 Derek Bell .20 .50
15 Esteban Beltre .08 .25
16 Freddie Benavides .08 .25
17 Ricky Bones .08 .25
18 Denis Boucher .08 .25
19 Ryan Bowen .08 .25
20 Cliff Brantley .08 .25
21 John Briscoe .08 .25
22 Scott Brosius .75 2.00
23 Terry Bross .08 .25
24 Jarvis Brown .08 .25
25 Scott Bullett .08 .25
26 Kevin Campbell .08 .25
27 Amalio Carreno .08 .25
28 Matias Carrillo .08 .25
29 Jeff Carter .08 .25
30 Vinny Castilla 1.25 3.00
31 Braulio Castillo .08 .25
32 Frank Castillo .08 .25
33 Darrin Chapin .08 .25
34 Mike Christopher .08 .25
35 Mark Clark .20 .50
36 Royce Clayton .08 .25
37 Stu Cole .08 .25
38 Gary Cooper .08 .25
39 Archie Corbin .08 .25
40 Rheal Cormier .08 .25
41 Chris Cron .08 .25
42 Mike Dalton .08 .25
43 Mark Davis .08 .25
44 Francisco de la Rosa .08 .25
45 Chris Donnels .08 .25
46 Brian Drahman .08 .25
47 Tom Drees .08 .25
48 Kirk Dressendorfer .08 .25
49 Bruce Egloff .08 .25
50 Cal Eldred .08 .25
51 Jose Escobar .08 .25
52 Tony Eusebio .20 .50
53 Hector Fajardo .08 .25
54 Monty Fariss .08 .25
55 Jeff Fassero .08 .25
56 Dave Fleming .08 .25
57 Kevin Flora .08 .25
58 Steve Foster .08 .25
59 Dan Gakeler .08 .25
60 Ramon Garcia .08 .25
61 Chris Gardner .08 .25
62 Jeff Gardner .08 .25
63 Chris George .08 .25
64 Ray Giannelli .08 .25
65 Tom Goodwin .08 .25
66 Mark Grater .08 .25
67 Johnny Guzman .08 .25
68 Juan Guzman .08 .25
69 Dave Haas .08 .25
70 Chris Haney .08 .25
71 Shawn Hare .08 .25
72 Donald Harris .08 .25
73 Doug Henry .08 .25
74 Pat Hentgen .08 .25
75 Gil Heredia .20 .50
76 Jeremy Hernandez .08 .25
77 Jose Hernandez .20 .50
78 Roberto Hernandez .08 .25
79 Bryan Hickerson .08 .25
80 Milt Hill .08 .25
81 Vince Horsman .08 .25
82 Wayne Housie .08 .25
83 Chris Howard .08 .25
84 David Howard .08 .25
85 Mike Humphreys .08 .25
86 Brian Hunter .08 .25
87 Jim Hunter .08 .25
88 Mike Ignasiak .08 .25
89 Reggie Jefferson .08 .25
90 Jeff Johnson .08 .25
91 Joel Johnston .08 .25
92 Calvin Jones .08 .25
93 Chris Jones .08 .25
94 Stacy Jones .08 .25
95 Jeff Juden .08 .25
96 Scott Kamieniecki .08 .25
97 Eric Karros .20 .50
98 Pat Kelly .08 .25
99 John Kiely .08 .25
100 Darryl Kile .20 .50
101 Wayne Kirby .08 .25
102 Garland Kiser .08 .25
103 Chuck Knoblauch .20 .50
104 Randy Knorr .08 .25
105 Tom Kramer .08 .25
106 Ced Landrum .08 .25
107 Patrick Lennon .08 .25
108 Jim Lewis .08 .25
109 Mark Lewis .08 .25
110 Doug Lindsey .08 .25
111 Scott Livingstone .08 .25
112 Kenny Lofton .40 1.00
113 Ever Magallanes .08 .25
114 Mike Magnante .08 .25
115 Barry Manuel .08 .25
116 Josias Manzanillo .08 .25
117 Chito Martinez .08 .25
118 Terry Mathews .08 .25
119 Rob Maurer .08 .25
120 Tim Mauser .08 .25
121 Terry McDaniel .08 .25
122 Rusty Meacham .08 .25
123 Luis Mercedes .08 .25
124 Paul Miller .08 .25
125 Keith Mitchell .08 .25
126 Bobby Moore .08 .25
127 Kevin Morton .08 .25
128 Andy Mota .08 .25
129 Jose Mota .08 .25
130 Mike Mussina .75 2.00
131 Jeff Mutis .08 .25
132 Denny Neagle .20 .50
133 Warren Newson .08 .25
134 Jim Olander .08 .25
135 Erik Pappas .08 .25
136 Jorge Pedre .08 .25
137 Yorkis Perez .08 .25
138 Mark Petkovsek .08 .25
139 Doug Piatt .08 .25
140 Jeff Plympton .08 .25
141 Harvey Pulliam .08 .25
142 John Ramos .08 .25
143 Mike Remlinger .08 .25
144 Laddie Renfroe .08 .25
145 Armando Reynoso .20 .50
146 Arthur Rhodes .08 .25
147 Pat Rice .08 .25
148 Nikco Riesgo .08 .25
149 Carlos Rodriguez .08 .25
150 Ivan Rodriguez .75 2.00
151 Wayne Rosenthal .08 .25
152 Rico Rossy .08 .25
153 Stan Royer .08 .25
154 Rey Sanchez .20 .50
155 Reggie Sanders .20 .50
156 Mo Sanford .08 .25
157 Bob Scanlan .08 .25
158 Pete Schourek .08 .25
159 Gary Scott .08 .25
160 Tim Scott .08 .25
161 Tony Scruggs .08 .25
162 Scott Servais .08 .25
163 Doug Simons .08 .25
164 Heathcliff Slocumb .08 .25
165 Joe Slusarski .08 .25
166 Tim Spehr .08 .25
167 Ed Sprague .08 .25
168 Jeff Tackett .08 .25
169 Eddie Taubensee .20 .50
170 Wade Taylor .08 .25
171 Jim Thome .75 2.00
172 Mike Timlin .08 .25
173 Jose Tolentino .08 .25
174 John Vander Wal .08 .25
175 Todd Van Poppel .08 .25
176 Mo Vaughn .20 .50
177 Dave Wainhouse .08 .25
178 Don Wakamatsu .08 .25
179 Bruce Walton .08 .25
180 Kevin Ward .08 .25
181 Dave Weathers .08 .25
182 Eric Wedge .08 .25
183 John Wehner .08 .25
184 Rick Wilkins .08 .25
185 Bernie Williams .40 1.00
186 Brian Williams .08 .25
187 Ron Witmeyer .08 .25
188 Mark Wohlers .08 .25
189 Ted Wood .08 .25
190 Anthony Young .08 .25

191 Eddie Zosky .08 .25
192 Bob Zupcic .08 .25
193 Checklist 1 .08 .25
194 Checklist 2 .08 .25

1993 Topps

The 1993 Topps baseball set consists of two series, respectively, of 396 and 429 standard-size cards. A Topps Gold card was inserted in every 15-card pack. In addition, hobby and retail factory sets were produced. The fronts feature color action player photos with white borders. The player's name appears in a stripe at the bottom of the picture, and this stripe and two short diagonal stripes at the bottom corners of the picture are team color-coded. The backs are colorful and carry a color head shot, biography, complete statistical information, with a career highlight if space permitted. Cards 401-411 comprise an All-Star subset. Rookie Cards in this set include Jim Edmonds, Derek Jeter and Jason Kendall.

COMPLETE SET (825) 20.00 50.00
COMP.HOBBY SET (847) 30.00 60.00
COMP.RETAIL SET (838) 20.00 50.00
COMP. SERIES 1 (396) 10.00 25.00
COMP.SERIES 2 (429) 10.00 25.00
1 Robin Yount .30 .75
2 Barry Bonds .60 1.50
3 Ryne Sandberg .30 .75
4 Roger Clemens .40 1.00
5 Tony Gwynn .25 .60
6 Jeff Tackett .02 .10
7 Pete Incaviglia .02 .10
8 Mark Wohlers .02 .10
9 Kent Hrbek .07 .20
10 Will Clark .10 .30
11 Eric Karros .07 .20
12 Lee Smith .07 .20
13 Esteban Beltre .02 .10
14 Greg Briley .02 .10
15 Marquis Grissom .07 .20
16 Dan Plesac .02 .10
17 Dave Hollins .02 .10
18 Terry Steinbach .02 .10
19 Ed Nunez .02 .10
20 Tim Salmon .10 .30
21 Luis Salazar .02 .10
22 Jim Eisenreich .02 .10
23 Todd Stottlemyre .02 .10
24 Tim Naehring .02 .10
25 John Franco .07 .20
26 Skeeter Barnes .02 .10
27 Carlos Garcia .02 .10
28 Joe Orsulak .02 .10
29 Dwayne Henry .02 .10
30 Fred McGriff .10 .30
31 Derek Lilliquist .02 .10
32 Don Mattingly .50 1.25
33 B.J. Wallace .02 .10
34 Juan Gonzalez .07 .20
35 John Smoltz .10 .30
36 Scott Servais .02 .10
37 Lenny Webster .02 .10
38 Chris James .02 .10
39 Roger McDowell .02 .10
40 Ozzie Smith .30 .75
41 Alex Fernandez .02 .10
42 Spike Owen .02 .10
43 Ruben Amaro .02 .10
44 Kevin Seitzer .02 .10
45 Dave Fleming .02 .10
46 Eric Fox .02 .10
47 Bob Scanlan .02 .10
48 Bert Blyleven .07 .20
49 Brian McRae .02 .10
50 Roberto Alomar .10 .30
51 Mo Vaughn .07 .20
52 Bobby Bonilla .07 .20
53 Frank Tanana .02 .10
54 Mike LaValliere .02 .10
55 Mark McLemore .02 .10
56 Chad Mottola RC .02 .10
57 Norm Charlton .02 .10
58 Jose Melendez .02 .10
59 Carlos Martinez .02 .10
60 Roberto Kelly .02 .10
61 Gene Larkin .02 .10
62 Rafael Belliard .02 .10
63 Al Osuna .02 .10
64 Scott Chiamparino .02 .10
65 Brett Butler .07 .20
66 John Burkett .02 .10
67 Felix Jose .02 .10
68 Omar Vizquel .10 .30
69 John Vander Wal .02 .10
70 Roberto Hernandez .02 .10
71 Ricky Bones .02 .10
72 Jeff Grotewold .02 .10
73 Mike Moore .02 .10
74 Steve Buechele .02 .10
75 Juan Guzman .02 .10
76 Kevin Appier .07 .20
77 Junior Felix .02 .10
78 Greg W. Harris .02 .10
79 Dick Schofield .02 .10
80 Cecil Fielder .07 .20
81 Lloyd McClendon .02 .10
82 David Segui .02 .10
83 Reggie Sanders .07 .20
84 Kurt Stillwell .02 .10
85 Sandy Alomar Jr. .02 .10
86 John Habyan .02 .10
87 Kevin Reimer .02 .10
88 Mike Stanton .02 .10
89 Eric Anthony .02 .10
90 Scott Erickson .02 .10
91 Craig Colbert .02 .10
92 Tom Pagnozzi .02 .10
93 Pedro Astacio .02 .10
94 Lance Johnson .02 .10
95 Larry Walker .07 .20
96 Russ Swan .02 .10
97 Scott Fletcher .02 .10
98 Derek Jeter RC 5.00 12.00
99 Mike Williams .02 .10
100 Mark McGwire .50 1.25
101 Jim Bullinger .02 .10
102 Brian Hunter .02 .10
103 Jody Reed .02 .10
104 Mike Butcher .02 .10
105 Gregg Jefferies .02 .10
106 Howard Johnson .02 .10
107 John Kiely .02 .10
108 Jose Lind .02 .10
109 Sam Horn .02 .10
110 Barry Larkin .10 .30
111 Bruce Hurst .02 .10
112 Brian Barnes .02 .10
113 Thomas Howard .02 .10
114 Mel Hall .02 .10
115 Robby Thompson .02 .10
116 Mark Lemke .02 .10
117 Eddie Taubensee .02 .10
118 David Hulse RC .02 .10
119 Pedro Munoz .02 .10
120 Ramon Martinez .02 .10
121 Todd Worrell .02 .10
122 Joey Cora .02 .10
123 Moises Alou .07 .20
124 Franklin Stubbs .02 .10
125 Pete O'Brien .02 .10
126 Bob Ayrault .02 .10
127 Carney Lansford .07 .20
128 Kal Daniels .02 .10
129 Joe Grahe .02 .10
130 Jeff Montgomery .02 .10
131 Dave Winfield .07 .20
132 Preston Wilson RC .30 .75
133 Steve Wilson .02 .10
134 Lee Guetterman .02 .10
135 Mickey Tettleton .02 .10
136 Jeff King .02 .10
137 Alan Mills .02 .10
138 Joe Oliver .02 .10
139 Gary Gaetti .07 .20
140 Gary Sheffield .07 .20
141 Dennis Cook .02 .10
142 Charlie Hayes .02 .10
143 Jeff Huson .02 .10
144 Kent Mercker .02 .10
145 Eric Young .02 .10
146 Scott Leius .02 .10
147 Bryan Hickerson .02 .10
148 Steve Finley .07 .20
149 Rheal Cormier .02 .10
150 Frank Thomas UER .20 .50
(Categories leading league are italicized but not printed in red)
151 Archi Cianfrocco .02 .10
152 Rich DeLucia .02 .10
153 Greg Vaughn .02 .10
154 Wes Chamberlain .02 .10
155 Dennis Eckersley .07 .20
156 Sammy Sosa .20 .50
157 Gary DiSarcina .02 .10
158 Kevin Koslofski .02 .10
159 Doug Linton .02 .10
160 Lou Whitaker .07 .20
161 Chad McConnell .02 .10
162 Joe Hesketh .02 .10
163 Tim Wakefield .20 .50
164 Leo Gomez .02 .10
165 Jose Rijo .02 .10
166 Tim Scott .02 .10
167 Steve Olin UER .02 .10
(Born 10/4/65 should say 10/10/65)
168 Kevin Maas .02 .10
169 Kenny Rogers .07 .20
170 David Justice .07 .20
171 Doug Jones .02 .10
172 Jeff Reboulet .02 .10
173 Andres Galarraga .07 .20
174 Randy Velarde .02 .10
175 Kirk McCaskill .02 .10
176 Darren Lewis .02 .10
177 Lenny Harris .02 .10
178 Jeff Fassero .02 .10
179 Ken Griffey Jr. .30 .75
180 Darren Daulton .07 .20
181 John Jaha .02 .10
182 Ron Darling .02 .10
183 Greg Maddux .30 .75
184 Damion Easley .02 .10
185 Jack Morris .07 .20
186 Mike Magnante .02 .10
187 John Dopson .02 .10
188 Sid Fernandez .02 .10
189 Tony Phillips .02 .10
190 Doug Drabek .02 .10
191 Sean Lowe RC .02 .10
192 Bob Milacki .02 .10
193 Steve Foster .02 .10
194 Jerald Clark .02 .10
195 Pete Harnisch .02 .10
196 Pat Kelly .02 .10
197 Jeff Frye .02 .10
198 Alejandro Pena .02 .10
199 Junior Ortiz .02 .10
200 Kirby Puckett .20 .50
201 Jose Uribe .02 .10
202 Mike Scioscia .02 .10
203 Bernard Gilkey .02 .10
204 Dan Pasqua .02 .10
205 Gary Carter .07 .20
206 Henry Cotto .02 .10
207 Paul Molitor .07 .20
208 Mike Hartley .02 .10
209 Jeff Parrett .02 .10
210 Mark Langston .02 .10
211 Doug Dascenzo .02 .10
212 Rick Reed .02 .10
213 Candy Maldonado .02 .10
214 Danny Darwin .02 .10
215 Pat Howell .02 .10
216 Mark Leiter .02 .10
217 Kevin Mitchell .02 .10
218 Ben McDonald .02 .10
219 Bip Roberts .02 .10
220 Benny Santiago .07 .20
221 Carlos Baerga .02 .10
222 Bernie Williams .10 .30
223 Roger Pavlik .02 .10
224 Sid Bream .02 .10
225 Matt Williams .07 .20
226 Willie Banks .02 .10
227 Jeff Bagwell .10 .30
228 Tom Goodwin .02 .10
229 Mike Perez .02 .10
230 Carlton Fisk .10 .30
231 John Wetteland .07 .20
232 Tino Martinez .10 .30
233 Rick Greene .02 .10
234 Tim McIntosh .02 .10
235 Mitch Williams .02 .10
236 Kevin Campbell .02 .10
237 Jose Vizcaino .02 .10
238 Chris Donnels .02 .10
239 Mike Boddicker .02 .10
240 John Olerud .07 .20
241 Mike Gardiner .02 .10
242 Charlie O'Brien .02 .10
243 Rob Deer .02 .10
244 Denny Neagle .07 .20
245 Chris Sabo .02 .10
246 Gregg Olson .02 .10
247 Frank Seminara UER .02 .10
(Acquired 12/3/98)
248 Scott Scudder .02 .10
249 Tim Burke .02 .10
250 Chuck Knoblauch .07 .20
251 Mike Bielecki .02 .10
252 Xavier Hernandez .02 .10
253 Jose Guzman .02 .10
254 Cory Snyder .02 .10
255 Orel Hershiser .07 .20
256 Wil Cordero .02 .10
257 Luis Alicea .02 .10
258 Mike Schooler .02 .10
259 Craig Grebeck .02 .10
260 Duane Ward .02 .10
261 Bill Wegman .02 .10
262 Mickey Morandini .02 .10
263 Vince Horsman .02 .10
264 Paul Sorrento .02 .10
265 Andre Dawson .07 .20
266 Rene Gonzales .02 .10
267 Keith Miller .02 .10
268 Derek Bell .02 .10
269 Todd Steverson RC .02 .10
270 Frank Viola .07 .20
271 Wally Whitehurst .02 .10
272 Kurt Knudsen .02 .10
273 Dan Walters .02 .10
274 Rick Sutcliffe .07 .20
275 Andy Van Slyke .10 .30
276 Paul O'Neill .10 .30
277 Mark Whiten .02 .10
278 Chris Nabholz .02 .10
279 Todd Burns .02 .10
280 Tom Glavine .10 .30
281 Butch Henry .02 .10
282 Shane Mack .02 .10
283 Mike Jackson .02 .10
284 Henry Rodriguez .02 .10
285 Bob Tewksbury .02 .10
286 Ron Karkovice .02 .10
287 Mike Gallego .02 .10
288 Dave Cochrane .02 .10
289 Jesse Orosco .02 .10
290 Dave Stewart .07 .20
291 Tommy Greene .02 .10
292 Rey Sanchez .02 .10
293 Rob Ducey .02 .10
294 Brent Mayne .02 .10
295 Dave Stieb .02 .10
296 Luis Rivera .02 .10
297 Jeff Innis .02 .10
298 Scott Livingstone .02 .10
299 Bob Patterson .02 .10
300 Cal Ripken .60 1.50
301 Cesar Hernandez .02 .10
302 Randy Myers .02 .10
303 Brook Jacoby .02 .10
304 Melido Perez .02 .10
305 Rafael Palmeiro .10 .30
306 Damon Berryhill .02 .10
307 Dan Serafini RC .02 .10
308 Darryl Kile .07 .20
309 J.T. Bruett .02 .10
310 Dave Righetti .07 .20
311 Jay Howell .02 .10
312 Geronimo Pena .02 .10
313 Greg Hibbard .02 .10
314 Mark Gardner .02 .10
315 Edgar Martinez .10 .30
316 Dave Nilsson .02 .10
317 Kyle Abbott .02 .10
318 Willie Wilson .02 .10
319 Paul Assenmacher .02 .10
320 Tim Fortugno .02 .10
321 Rusty Meacham .02 .10
322 Pat Borders .02 .10
323 Mike Greenwell .02 .10
324 Willie Randolph .07 .20
325 Bill Gullickson .02 .10
326 Gary Varsho .02 .10
327 Tim Hulett .02 .10
328 Scott Ruskin .02 .10
329 Mike Maddux .02 .10
330 Danny Tartabull .02 .10
331 Kenny Lofton .07 .20
332 Geno Petralli .02 .10
333 Otis Nixon .02 .10
334 Jason Kendall RC .40 1.00
335 Mark Portugal .02 .10
336 Mike Pagliarulo .02 .10
337 Kirt Manwaring .02 .10
338 Bob Ojeda .02 .10
339 Mark Clark .02 .10
340 John Kruk .07 .20
341 Mel Rojas .02 .10
342 Erik Hanson .02 .10
343 Doug Henry .02 .10
344 Jack McDowell .02 .10
345 Harold Baines .07 .20
346 Chuck McElroy .02 .10
347 Luis Sojo .02 .10
348 Andy Stankiewicz .02 .10
349 Hipolito Pichardo .02 .10
350 Joe Carter .07 .20
351 Ellis Burks .07 .20
352 Pete Schourek .02 .10
353 Buddy Groom .02 .10
354 Jay Bell .07 .20
355 Brady Anderson .07 .20
356 Freddie Benavides .02 .10
357 Phil Stephenson .02 .10
358 Kevin Wickander .02 .10
359 Mike Stanley .02 .10
360 Ivan Rodriguez .10 .30
361 Scott Bankhead .02 .10
362 Luis Gonzalez .07 .20
363 John Smiley .02 .10
364 Trevor Wilson .02 .10
365 Tom Candiotti .02 .10
366 Craig Wilson .02 .10
367 Steve Sax .02 .10
368 Delino DeShields .02 .10
369 Jaime Navarro .02 .10
370 Dave Valle .02 .10
371 Mariano Duncan .02 .10
372 Rod Nichols .02 .10
373 Mike Morgan .02 .10
374 Julio Valera .02 .10
375 Wally Joyner .07 .20
376 Tom Henke .02 .10
377 Herm Winningham .02 .10
378 Orlando Merced .02 .10
379 Mike Munoz .02 .10
380 Todd Hundley .02 .10
381 Mike Flanagan .02 .10
382 Tim Belcher .02 .10
383 Jerry Browne .02 .10
384 Mike Benjamin .02 .10
385 Jim Leyritz .02 .10
386 Ray Lankford .07 .20
387 Devon White .07 .20
388 Jeremy Hernandez .02 .10
389 Brian Harper .02 .10
390 Wade Boggs .10 .30
391 Derrick May .02 .10
392 Travis Fryman .07 .20
393 Ron Gant .07 .20
394 Checklist 1-132 .02 .10
395 CL 133-264 UER .02 .10
Eckerlsey
396 Checklist 265-396 .02 .10
397 George Brett .50 1.25
398 Bobby Witt .02 .10
399 Daryl Boston .02 .10
400 Bo Jackson .20 .50
401 Fred McGriff .10 .30
Frank Thomas AS
402 Ryne Sandberg .20 .50
Carlos Baerga AS
403 Gary Sheffield .07 .20
Edgar Martinez AS
404 Barry Larkin .07 .20
Travis Fryman AS
405 Andy Van Slyke .20 .50
Ken Griffey Jr. AS
406 Larry Walker .10 .30
Kirby Puckett AS
407 Barry Bonds .30 .75
Joe Carter AS
408 Darren Daulton .07 .20
Brian Harper AS
409 Greg Maddux .20 .50
Roger Clemens AS
410 Tom Glavine .07 .20
Dave Fleming AS
411 Lee Smith .07 .20
Dennis Eckersley AS
412 Jamie McAndrew .02 .10
413 Pete Smith .02 .10
414 Juan Guerrero .02 .10
415 Todd Frohwirth .02 .10
416 Randy Tomlin .02 .10
417 B.J. Surhoff .07 .20
418 Jim Gott .02 .10
419 Mark Thompson RC .02 .10
420 Kevin Tapani .02 .10
421 Curt Schilling .07 .20
422 J.T. Snow RC .20 .50
423 Ryan Klesko .07 .20
Ivan Cruz
Bubba Smith
Larry Sutton RC
424 John Valentin .02 .10
425 Joe Girardi .02 .10
426 Nigel Wilson .02 .10
427 Bob MacDonald .02 .10
428 Todd Zeile .02 .10
429 Milt Cuyler .02 .10
430 Eddie Murray .20 .50
431 Rich Amaral .02 .10
432 Pete Young .02 .10
433 Roger Bailey RC .02 .10
Tom Schmidt
434 Jack Armstrong .02 .10
435 Willie McGee .07 .20
436 Greg W. Harris .02 .10
437 Chris Hammond .02 .10
438 Ritchie Moody RC .02 .10
439 Bryan Harvey .02 .10
440 Ruben Sierra .07 .20
441 Don Lemon .02 .10
Todd Pridy RC
442 Kevin McReynolds .02 .10
443 Terry Leach .02 .10
444 David Nied .02 .10
445 Dale Murphy .10 .30
446 Luis Mercedes .02 .10
447 Keith Shepherd RC .02 .10
448 Ken Caminiti .07 .20
449 Jim Austin .02 .10
450 Darryl Strawberry .07 .20
451 Ramon Caraballo .08 .25
Jon Shave RC
Brent Gates
Quinton McCracken
452 Bob Wickman .02 .10
453 Victor Cole .02 .10
454 John Johnstone RC .02 .10
455 Chili Davis .07 .20
456 Scott Taylor .02 .10
457 Tracy Woodson .02 .10
458 David Wells .07 .20
459 Derek Wallace RC .02 .10
460 Randy Johnson .20 .50
461 Steve Reed RC .02 .10
462 Felix Fermin .02 .10
463 Scott Aldred .02 .10
464 Greg Colbrunn .02 .10
465 Tony Fernandez .02 .10
466 Mike Felder .02 .10
467 Lee Stevens .02 .10
468 Matt Whiteside RC .02 .10
469 Dave Hansen .02 .10
470 Rob Dibble .07 .20
471 Dave Gallagher .02 .10
472 Chris Gwynn .02 .10
473 Dave Henderson .02 .10
474 Ozzie Guillen .07 .20
475 Jeff Reardon .07 .20
476 Mark Voisard .02 .10
Will Scalzitti RC
477 Jimmy Jones .02 .10
478 Greg Cadaret .02 .10
479 Todd Pratt RC .02 .10
480 Pat Listach .02 .10
481 Ryan Luzinski RC .02 .10
482 Darren Reed .02 .10
483 Brian Griffiths RC .02 .10
484 John Wehner .02 .10
485 Glenn Davis .02 .10
486 Eric Wedge RC .02 .10
487 Jesse Hollins .02 .10
488 Manuel Lee .02 .10
489 Scott Fredrickson RC .02 .10
490 Omar Olivares .02 .10
491 Shawn Hare .02 .10
492 Tom Lampkin .02 .10
493 Jeff Nelson .02 .10
494 Kevin Young .02 .10
Adell Davenport
Eduardo Perez
Lou Lucca RC
495 Ken Hill .02 .10
496 Reggie Jefferson .02 .10
497 Matt Petersen .02 .10
Willie Brown RC
498 Bud Black .02 .10
499 Chuck Crim .02 .10
500 Jose Canseco .10 .30
501 Johnny Oates MG .07 .20
Bobby Cox MG
502 Butch Hobson MG .02 .10
Jim Lefebvre MG
503 Buck Rodgers MG .07 .20
Tony Perez MG
504 Gene Lamont MG .07 .20
Don Baylor MG
505 Mike Hargrove MG .07 .20
Rene Lachemann MG
506 Sparky Anderson MG .07 .20
Art Howe MG
507 Hal McRae MG .07 .20
Tom Lasorda MG
508 Phil Garner MG .07 .20
Felipe Alou MG
509 Tom Kelly MG .02 .10
Jeff Torborg MG
510 Buck Showalter MG .07 .20
Jim Fregosi MG
511 Tony LaRussa MG .07 .20
Jim Leyland MG
512 Lou Piniella MG .07 .20
Joe Torre MG
513 Kevin Kennedy MG .02 .10
Jim Riggleman MG
514 Cito Gaston MG .07 .20
Dusty Baker MG
515 Greg Swindell .02 .10
516 Alex Arias .02 .10
517 Bill Pecota .02 .10
518 Benji Grigsby RC UER .02 .10
(Misspelled Bengi on card front)
519 David Howard .02 .10
520 Charlie Hough .07 .20
521 Kevin Flora .02 .10
522 Shane Reynolds .02 .10
523 Doug Bochtler RC .02 .10
524 Chris Hoiles .02 .10
525 Scott Sanderson .02 .10
526 Mike Sharperson .02 .10
527 Mike Fetters .02 .10
528 Paul Quantrill .02 .10
529 Dave Silvestri .20 .50
Chipper Jones
Benji Gil
Jeff Patzke
530 Sterling Hitchcock RC .08 .25
531 Joe Millette .02 .10
532 Tom Brunansky .02 .10
533 Frank Castillo .02 .10
534 Randy Knorr .02 .10
535 Jose Oquendo .02 .10
536 Dave Haas .02 .10
537 Jason Hutchins RC .02 .10
Ryan Turner
538 Jimmy Baron RC .02 .10
539 Kerry Woodson .02 .10
540 Ivan Calderon .02 .10
541 Denis Boucher .02 .10
542 Royce Clayton .02 .10
543 Reggie Williams .02 .10
544 Steve Decker .02 .10
545 Dean Palmer .07 .20
546 Hal Morris .02 .10
547 Ryan Thompson .02 .10
548 Lance Blankenship .02 .10
549 Hensley Meulens .02 .10
550 Scott Radinsky .02 .10
551 Eric Young .02 .10
552 Jeff Blauser .02 .10
553 Andujar Cedeno .02 .10
554 Arthur Rhodes .02 .10
555 Terry Mulholland .02 .10
556 Darryl Hamilton .02 .10
557 Pedro Martinez .40 1.00
558 Ryan Whitman RC .02 .10
Mark Skeels
559 Jamie Arnold RC .02 .10
560 Zane Smith .02 .10
561 Matt Nokes .02 .10
562 Bob Zupcic .02 .10
563 Shawn Boskie .02 .10
564 Mike Timlin .02 .10
565 Jerald Clark .02 .10
566 Rod Brewer .02 .10
567 Mark Carreon .02 .10
568 Andy Benes .02 .10
569 Shawn Barton RC .02 .10
570 Tim Wallach .02 .10
571 Dave Mlicki .02 .10
572 Trevor Hoffman .20 .50
573 John Patterson .02 .10
574 De Shawn Warren RC .02 .10
575 Monty Fariss .02 .10
576 Darrell Sherman .07 .20
Damon Buford
Cliff Floyd
Michael Moore
577 Tim Costo .02 .10
578 Dave Magadan .02 .10
579 Neil Garrett .02 .10
Jason Bates RC
580 Walt Weiss .02 .10
581 Chris Haney .02 .10
582 Shawn Abner .02 .10
583 Marvin Freeman .02 .10
584 Casey Candaele .02 .10
585 Ricky Jordan .02 .10
586 Jeff Tabaka RC .02 .10
587 Manny Alexander .02 .10
588 Mike Trombley .02 .10
589 Carlos Hernandez .02 .10
590 Cal Eldred .02 .10
591 Alex Cole .02 .10
592 Phil Plantier .02 .10
593 Brett Merriman RC .02 .10
594 Jerry Nielsen .02 .10
595 Shawon Dunston .02 .10
596 Jimmy Key .07 .20
597 Gerald Perry .02 .10
598 Rico Brogna .02 .10
599 Clemente Nunez .02 .10
Daniel Robinson
600 Bret Saberhagen .07 .20
601 Craig Shipley .02 .10
602 Henry Mercedes .02 .10
603 Jim Thome .10 .30
604 Rod Beck .02 .10
605 Chuck Finley .07 .20
606 Jayhawk Owens RC .02 .10
607 Dan Smith .02 .10
608 Bill Doran .02 .10
609 Lance Parrish .07 .20
610 Dennis Martinez .07 .20
611 Tom Gordon .02 .10
612 Byron Mathews RC .02 .10
613 Joel Adamson RC .02 .10
614 Brian Williams .02 .10
615 Steve Avery .02 .10
616 Matt Mieske .02 .10
Tracy Sanders
Midre Cummings RC
Ryan Freeburg
617 Craig Lefferts .02 .10
618 Tony Pena .02 .10
619 Billy Spiers .02 .10
620 Todd Benzinger .02 .10
621 Mike Kotarski .02 .10
Greg Boyd RC
622 Ben Rivera .02 .10
623 Al Martin .02 .10
624 Sam Militello UER .02 .10
(Profile says drafted in 1988, bio says drafted in 1990)
625 Rick Aguilera .02 .10
626 Dan Gladden .02 .10
627 Andres Berumen RC .02 .10
628 Kelly Gruber .02 .10
629 Cris Carpenter .02 .10
630 Mark Grace .10 .30
631 Jeff Brantley .02 .10
632 Chris Widger RC .08 .25
633 Three Russians UER .02 .10
Rudolf Razjigaev
Eugneyi Puchkov
Ilya Bogatyrev
Bogatyrev is a shortstop, card has pitching header
634 Mo Sanford .02 .10
635 Albert Belle .07 .20
636 Tim Teufel .02 .10
637 Greg Myers .02 .10
638 Brian Bohanon .02 .10
639 Mike Bordick .02 .10
640 Dwight Gooden .07 .20
641 Pat Leahy .02 .10
Gavin Baugh RC
642 Milt Hill .02 .10
643 Luis Aquino .02 .10
644 Dante Bichette .07 .20
645 Bobby Thigpen .02 .10
646 Rich Scheid RC .02 .10
647 Brian Sackinsky RC .02 .10
648 Ryan Hawblitzel .02 .10
649 Tom Marsh .02 .10
650 Terry Pendleton .07 .20
651 Rafael Bournigal .02 .10
652 Dave West .02 .10
653 Steve Hosey .02 .10
654 Gerald Williams .02 .10
655 Scott Cooper .02 .10
656 Gary Scott .02 .10
657 Mike Harkey .02 .10
658 Jeromy Burnitz .07 .20
Melvin Nieves
Rich Becker
Shon Walker RC
659 Ed Sprague .02 .10
660 Alan Trammell .07 .20
661 Garvin Alston RC .02 .10
Michael Case
662 Donovan Osborne .02 .10
663 Jeff Gardner .02 .10
664 Calvin Jones .02 .10
665 Darrin Fletcher .02 .10
666 Glenallen Hill .02 .10
667 Jim Rosenbohm RC .02 .10
668 Scott Lewis .02 .10
669 Kip Yaughn RC .02 .10
670 Julio Franco .07 .20
671 Dave Martinez .02 .10
672 Kevin Bass .02 .10

673 Todd Van Poppel .02 .10
674 Mark Gubicza .02 .10
675 Tim Raines .07 .20
676 Rudy Seanez .02 .10
677 Charlie Leibrandt .02 .10
678 Randy Milligan .02 .10
679 Kim Batiste .02 .10
680 Craig Biggio .10 .30
681 Darren Holmes .02 .10
682 John Candelaria .02 .10
683 Jerry Stafford .02 .10
Eddie Christian RC
684 Pat Mahomes .02 .10
685 Bob Walk .02 .10
686 Russ Springer .02 .10
687 Tony Sheffield RC .02 .10
688 Dwight Smith .02 .10
689 Eddie Zosky .02 .10
690 Bien Figueroa .02 .10
691 Jim Tatum RC .02 .10
692 Chad Kreuter .02 .10
693 Rich Rodriguez .02 .10
694 Shane Turner .02 .10
695 Kent Bottenfield .02 .10
696 Jose Mesa .02 .10
697 Darrell Whitmore RC .02 .10
698 Ted Wood .02 .10
699 Chad Curtis .02 .10
700 Nolan Ryan .75 2.00
701 Mike Piazza 1.50 4.00
Brook Fordyce
Carlos Delgado
Donnie Leshnock
702 Tim Pugh RC .02 .10
703 Jeff Kent .20 .50
704 Jon Goodrich .02 .10
Danny Figueroa RC
705 Bob Welch .02 .10
706 S.Clinkscales RC .02 .10
707 Donn Pall .02 .10
708 Greg Olson .02 .10
709 Jeff Juden .02 .10
710 Mike Mussina .10 .30
711 Scott Chiamparino .02 .10
712 Stan Javier .02 .10
713 John Doherty .02 .10
714 Kevin Gross .02 .10
715 Greg Gagne .02 .10
716 Steve Cooke .02 .10
717 Steve Farr .02 .10
718 Jay Buhner .07 .20
719 Butch Henry .02 .10
720 David Cone .07 .20
721 Rick Wilkins .02 .10
722 Chuck Carr .02 .10
723 Kenny Felder RC .02 .10
724 Guillermo Velasquez .02 .10
725 Billy Hatcher .02 .10
726 Mike Veneziale RC .02 .10
Ken Kendrena
727 Jonathan Hurst .02 .10
728 Steve Frey .02 .10
729 Mark Leonard .02 .10
730 Charles Nagy .02 .10
731 Donald Harris .02 .10
732 Travis Buckley RC .02 .10
733 Tom Browning .02 .10
734 Anthony Young .02 .10
735 Steve Shifflett .02 .10
736 Jeff Russell .02 .10
737 Wilson Alvarez .02 .10
738 Lance Painter RC .02 .10
739 Dave Weathers .02 .10
740 Len Dykstra .07 .20
741 Mike Devereaux .02 .10
742 Rene Arocha .08 .25
Alan Embree
Brien Taylor
Tim Crabtree
743 Dave Landaker RC .02 .10
744 Chris George .02 .10
745 Eric Davis .07 .20
746 Mark Strittmatter .02 .10
Lamarr Rogers RC
747 Carl Willis .02 .10
748 Stan Belinda .02 .10
749 Scott Kamieniecki .02 .10
750 Rickey Henderson .20 .50
751 Eric Hillman .02 .10
752 Pat Hentgen .02 .10
753 Jim Corsi .02 .10
754 Brian Jordan .07 .20
755 Bill Swift .02 .10
756 Mike Henneman .02 .10
757 Harold Reynolds .07 .20
758 Sean Berry .02 .10
759 Charlie Hayes .02 .10
760 Luis Polonia .02 .10
761 Darrin Jackson .02 .10
762 Mark Lewis .02 .10
763 Rob Maurer .02 .10
764 Willie Greene .02 .10
765 Vince Coleman .02 .10
766 Todd Revenig .02 .10
767 Rich Ireland RC .02 .10
768 Mike Macfarlane .02 .10
769 Francisco Cabrera .02 .10
770 Robin Ventura .07 .20
771 Kevin Ritz .02 .10
772 Chito Martinez .02 .10
773 Cliff Brantley .02 .10
774 Curt Leskanic RC .08 .25
775 Chris Bosio .02 .10
776 Jose Offerman .02 .10
777 Mark Guthrie .02 .10
778 Don Slaught .02 .10
779 Rich Monteleone .02 .10
780 Jim Abbott .10 .30
781 Jack Clark .07 .20
782 Reynol Mendoza .02 .10
Dan Roman RC
783 Heathcliff Slocumb .02 .10
784 Jeff Branson .02 .10
785 Kevin Brown .07 .20
786 Mike Christopher .02 .10
Ken Ryan
Aaron Taylor
Gus Gandarillas RC
787 Mike Matthews RC .02 .10
788 Mackey Sasser .02 .10
789 Jeff Conine UER .07 .20
No inclusion of 1990 RBI stats in career total
790 George Bell .02 .10
791 Pat Rapp .02 .10
792 Joe Boever .02 .10
793 Jim Poole .02 .10
794 Andy Ashby .02 .10
795 Deion Sanders .10 .30
796 Scott Brosius .07 .20
797 Brad Pennington .02 .10
798 Greg Blosser .02 .10
799 Jim Edmonds RC .75 2.00
800 Shawn Jeter .02 .10
801 Jesse Levis .02 .10
802 Phil Clark UER .02 .10
(Word a is missing in sentence beginning with In 1992 ...)
803 Ed Pierce RC .02 .10
804 Jose Valentin RC .08 .25
805 Terry Jorgensen .02 .10
806 Mark Hutton .02 .10
807 Troy Neel .02 .10
808 Bret Boone .07 .20
809 Cris Colon .02 .10
810 Domingo Martinez RC .02 .10
811 Javier Lopez .10 .30
812 Matt Walbeck RC .02 .10
813 Dan Wilson .07 .20
814 Scooter Tucker .02 .10
815 Billy Ashley .02 .10
816 Tim Laker RC .02 .10
817 Bobby Jones .07 .20
818 Brad Brink .02 .10
819 William Pennyfeather .02 .10
820 Stan Royer .02 .10
821 Doug Brocail .02 .10
822 Kevin Rogers .02 .10
823 Checklist 397-540 .02 .10
824 Checklist 541-691 .02 .10
825 Checklist 692-825 .02 .10

1993 Topps Gold

Several insertion schemes were devised for these 825 standard-size cards. Gold cards were inserted one per wax pack, three per rack pack, five per jumbo pack, and ten per factory set. The cards are identical to the regular-issue 1993 Topps baseball cards except that the gold-foil Topps Gold logo appears in an upper corner, and the team color-coded stripe at the bottom of the front, which carried the player's name, has been replaced with an embossed gold-foil stripe. The checklist cards (394-396, 823-825) have been replaced by player cards.

*STARS: 1X TO 2.5X BASIC CARDS
*ROOKIES: 1.25X TO 3X BASIC CARDS
394 Bernardo Brito .08 .25
395 Jim McNamara .08 .25
396 Rich Sauveur .08 .25
823 Keith Brown .08 .25
824 Russ McGinnis .08 .25
825 Mike Walker UER .08 .25
(Card has 1993 Mariner stats, should be 1992)

1993 Topps Inaugural Marlins

These 825-card standard-size sets were issued by Topps to commemorate the debut seasons of the Colorado Rockies and Florida Marlins. Gold foil Marlins or Rockies logos distinguish these from regular issue cards. These cards were only issued in factory set form. 5,000 Rockies sets and 4,000 Marlins sets were initially printed, but each team had the option of receiving a maximum of 10,000 sets. The Rockies sets were distributed through the four team-owned stores and at Mile High Stadium. The Marlins sets were distributed through FMI and Joe Robbie Stadium.

COMP.FACT.SET (825) 40.00 100.00
*STARS: 2.5X TO 6X BASIC CARDS
*ROOKIES: 2.5X TO 6X BASIC CARDS

1993 Topps Inaugural Rockies

Similar to the Marlins set. This was a 1993 set with the Rockies logo imprinted on the card. They were only issued in factory set form. They were distributed through four Rockie owned stores and at Mile High Stadium. They are valued slightly less than the Marlins card as 1,000 more sets of Rockies were produced

COMP.FACT.SET (825) 40.00 100.00
*STARS: 2.5X TO 6X BASIC CARDS
*ROOKIES: 2.5X TO 6X BASIC CARDS

1993 Topps Black Gold

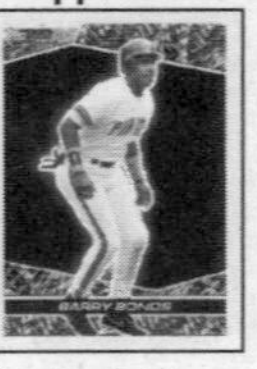

Topps Black Gold cards 1-22 were randomly inserted in series I packs while card numbers 23-44 were featured in series II packs. They were also inserted three per factory set. In the packs, the cards were inserted one evrery 72 hobby or retail packs; one every 12 jumbo packs and one every 24 rack packs. Hobbyists could obtain the set by collecting individual random insert cards or receive 11, 22, or 44 Black Gold cards by mail when they sent in special "You've Just Won" cards, which were randomly inserted in packs. Series I packs featured three different "You've Just Won" cards, entitling the holder to receive Group A (cards 1-11), Group B (cards 12-22), or Groups A and B (Cards 1-22). In a similar fashion, four "You've Just Won" cards were inserted in series II packs and entitled the holder to receive Group C (23-33), Group D (34-44), Groups C and D (23-44), or Groups A-D (1-44). By returning the "You've Just Won" card with 1.50 for postage and handling, the collector received not only the Black Gold cards won but also a special "You've Just Won" card and a congratulatory letter informing the collector that his/her name has been entered into a drawing for one of 500 uncut sheets of all 44 Topps Black Gold cards in a leatherette frame. These standard-size cards feature different color player photos than either the 1993 Topps regular issue or the Topps Gold issue. The player pictures are cut out and superimposed on a black gloss background. Inside white borders, gold refractory foil edges the top and bottom of the card face. On a black-and-gray pinstripe pattern inside white borders, the horizontal backs have a a second cut out player photo and a player profile on a blue panel. The player's name appears in gold foil lettering on a blue-and-gray geometric shape. The first 22 cards are National Leaguers while the second 22 cards are American Leaguers. Winner cards C and D were both originally produced erroneously and later corrected; the error versions show the players from Winner A and B on the respective fronts of Winner cards Cand D. There is no value difference in the variations at this time. The winner cards were redeemable until January 31, 1994.

COMPLETE SET (44) 4.00 10.00
COMPLETE SERIES 1 (22) 1.50 4.00
COMPLETE SERIES 2 (22) 2.50 6.00
1 Barry Bonds 1.00 2.50
2 Will Clark .20 .50
3 Darren Daulton .10 .30
4 Andre Dawson .10 .30
5 Delino DeShields .05 .15
6 Tom Glavine .20 .50
7 Marquis Grissom .10 .30
8 Tony Gwynn .40 1.00
9 Eric Karros .10 .30
10 Ray Lankford .10 .30
11 Barry Larkin .20 .50
12 Greg Maddux .50 1.25
13 Fred McGriff .20 .50
14 Joe Oliver .05 .15
15 Terry Pendleton .10 .30
16 Bip Roberts .05 .15
17 Ryne Sandberg .50 1.25
18 Gary Sheffield .10 .30
19 Lee Smith .10 .30
20 Ozzie Smith .50 1.25
21 Andy Van Slyke .20 .50
22 Larry Walker .10 .30
23 Roberto Alomar .20 .50
24 Brady Anderson .10 .30
25 Carlos Baerga .05 .15
26 Joe Carter .10 .30
27 Roger Clemens .60 1.50
28 Mike Devereaux .05 .15
29 Dennis Eckersley .10 .30
30 Cecil Fielder .10 .30
31 Travis Fryman .10 .30
32 Juan Gonzalez UER .10 .30
(No copyright or licensing on card)
33 Ken Griffey Jr. .50 1.25
34 Brian Harper .05 .15
35 Pat Listach .05 .15
36 Kenny Lofton .10 .30
37 Edgar Martinez .20 .50
38 Jack McDowell .05 .15
39 Mark McGwire .75 2.00
40 Kirby Puckett .30 .75
41 Mickey Tettleton .05 .15
42 Frank Thomas UER .30 .75
(No copyright or licensing on card)
43 Robin Ventura .10 .30
44 Dave Winfield .10 .30

1993 Topps Traded

This 132-card standard-size set focuses on promising rookies, new managers, free agents, and players who changed teams. The set also includes 22 members of Team USA. The set has the same design on the front as the regular 1993 Topps issue. The backs are also the same design and carry a head shot, biography, stats, and career highlights. Rookie Cards in this set include Todd Helton.

COMP.FACT.SET (132) 10.00 25.00
1T Barry Bonds .60 1.50
2T Rich Renteria .02 .10

3T Aaron Sele .02 .10
4T C.Loewer USA RC .08 .25
5T Erik Pappas .02 .10
6T Greg McMichael RC .08 .25
7T Freddie Benavides .02 .10
8T Kirk Gibson .07 .20
9T Tony Fernandez .02 .10
10T Jay Gainer RC .08 .25
11T Orestes Destrade .02 .10
12T A.J. Hinch USA RC .20 .50
13T Bobby Munoz .02 .10
14T Tom Henke .02 .10
15T Rob Butler .02 .10
16T Gary Wayne .02 .10
17T David McCarty .02 .10
18T Walt Weiss .02 .10
19T Todd Helton USA RC 4.00 10.00
20T Mark Whiten .02 .10
21T Ricky Gutierrez .02 .10
22T D.Hermanson USA RC .40 1.00
23T Sherman Obando RC .08 .25
24T Mike Piazza 1.25 3.00
25T Jeff Russell .02 .10
26T Jason Bere .02 .10
27T Jack Voigt RC .08 .25
28T Chris Bosio .02 .10
29T Phil Hiatt .02 .10
30T M.Beaumont USA RC .08 .25
31T Andres Galarraga .07 .20
32T Greg Swindell .02 .10
33T Vinny Castilla .20 .50
34T P.Clougherty RC USA .08 .25
35T Greg Briley .02 .10
36T Dallas Green MG .02 .10
Davey Johnson MG
37T Tyler Green .02 .10
38T Craig Paquette .02 .10
39T Danny Sheaffer RC .08 .25
40T Jim Converse RC .08 .25
41T Terry Harvey USA RC .08 .25
42T Phil Plantier .02 .10
43T Doug Saunders RC .08 .25
44T Benny Santiago .07 .20
45T Dante Powell USA RC .08 .25
46T Jeff Parrett .02 .10
47T Wade Boggs .10 .30
48T Paul Molitor .07 .20
49T Turk Wendell .02 .10
50T David Wells .07 .20
51T Gary Sheffield .07 .20
52T Kevin Young .07 .20
53T Nelson Liriano .02 .10
54T Greg Maddux .30 .75
55T Derek Bell .02 .10
56T Matt Turner RC .08 .25
57T C.Nelson RC USA .08 .25
58T Mike Hampton .07 .20
59T Troy O'Leary RC .20 .50
60T Benji Gil .02 .10
61T Mitch Lyden RC .08 .25
62T J.T. Snow .10 .30
63T Damon Buford .02 .10
64T Gene Harris .02 .10
65T Randy Myers .02 .10
66T Felix Jose .02 .10
67T Todd Dunn USA RC .08 .25
68T Jimmy Key .07 .20
69T Pedro Castellano .02 .10
70T Mark Merila USA RC .08 .25
71T Rich Rodriguez .02 .10
72T Matt Mieske .02 .10
73T Pete Incaviglia .02 .10
74T Carl Everett .07 .20
75T Jim Abbott .10 .30
76T Luis Aquino .02 .10
77T Rene Arocha .07 .20
78T Jon Shave .02 .10
79T Todd Walker USA RC .40 1.00
80T Jack Armstrong .02 .10
81T Jeff Richardson .02 .10
82T Blas Minor .02 .10
83T Dave Winfield .07 .20
84T Paul O'Neill .10 .30
85T Steve Reich USA RC .08 .25
86T Chris Hammond .02 .10
87T Hilly Hathaway RC .08 .25
88T Fred McGriff .10 .30
89T Dave Telgheder RC .08 .25
90T Richie Lewis RC .08 .25
91T Brent Gates .02 .10
92T Andre Dawson .07 .20
93T Andy Barkett USA RC .08 .25
94T Doug Drabek .02 .10
95T Joe Klink .02 .10
96T Willie Blair .02 .10
97T D.Graves USA RC .20 .50
98T Pat Meares RC .20 .50
99T Mike Lansing RC .20 .50
100T Marcos Armas RC .08 .25
101T D.Grass RC USA .08 .25
102T Chris Jones .02 .10
103T Ken Ryan RC .08 .25
104T Ellis Burks .07 .20
105T Roberto Kelly .02 .10
106T Dave Magadan .02 .10
107T Paul Wilson USA RC .20 .50
108T Rob Natal .02 .10
109T Paul Wagner .02 .10
110T Jeromy Burnitz .07 .20
111T Monty Fariss .02 .10
112T Kevin Mitchell .02 .10
113T Scott Pose RC .08 .25
114T Dave Stewart .07 .20
115T R.Johnson USA RC .08 .25
116T Armando Reynoso .02 .10
117T Geronimo Berroa .02 .10
118T Woody Williams RC .40 1.00
119T Tim Bogar RC .08 .25
120T Bob Scafa USA RC .08 .25
121T Henry Cotto .02 .10
122T Gregg Jefferies .02 .10
123T Norm Charlton .02 .10
124T B.Wagner USA RC .08 .25
125T David Cone .07 .20
126T Daryl Boston .02 .10
127T Tim Wallach .02 .10
128T Mike Martin USA RC .08 .25
129T John Cummings RC .08 .25
130T Ryan Bowen .02 .10
131T John Powell USA RC .08 .25
132T Checklist 1-132 .02 .10

1994 Topps

These 792 standard-size cards were issued in two series of 396. Two types of factory sets were also issued. One features the 792 basic cards, ten Topps Gold, three Black Gold and three Finest Pre-Production cards for a total of 808. The other factory set (Bakers Dozen) includes the 792 basic cards, ten Topps Gold, three Black Gold, nine 1995 Topps Pre-Production cards and a sample pack of three special Topps cards for a total of 817. The standard cards feature glossy color player photos with white borders on the fronts. The player's name is in white cursive lettering at the bottom left, with the team name and player's position printed on a team color-coded bar. There is an inner multicolored border along the left side that extends obliquely across the bottom. The horizontal backs carry an action shot of the player with biography, statistics and highlights. Subsets include Draft Picks (201-210/739-762), All-Stars (384-394) and Stat Twins (601-609). Rookie Cards include Billy Wagner.

COMPLETE SET (792) 20.00 50.00
COMP.FACT.SET (808) 40.00 80.00
COMP.BAKER SET (817) 40.00 80.00
COMP. SERIES 1 (396) 10.00 25.00
COMP. SERIES 2 (396) 10.00 25.00
1 Mike Piazza .40 1.00
2 Bernie Williams .10 .30
3 Kevin Rogers .02 .10
4 Paul Carey .02 .10
5 Ozzie Guillen .07 .20
6 Derrick May .02 .10
7 Jose Mesa .02 .10
8 Todd Hundley .02 .10
9 Chris Haney .02 .10
10 John Olerud .07 .20
11 Andujar Cedeno .02 .10
12 John Smiley .02 .10
13 Phil Plantier .02 .10
14 Willie Banks .02 .10
15 Jay Bell .07 .20
16 Doug Henry .02 .10
17 Lance Blankenship .02 .10
18 Greg W. Harris .02 .10
19 Scott Livingstone .02 .10
20 Bryan Harvey .02 .10
21 Wil Cordero .02 .10
22 Roger Pavlik .02 .10
23 Mark Lemke .02 .10
24 Jeff Nelson .02 .10
25 Todd Zeile .02 .10
26 Billy Hatcher .02 .10
27 Joe Magrane .02 .10
28 Tony Longmire .02 .10
29 Omar Daal .02 .10
30 Kirt Manwaring .02 .10
31 Melido Perez .02 .10
32 Tim Hulett .02 .10
33 Jeff Schwarz .02 .10
34 Nolan Ryan .75 2.00
35 Jose Guzman .02 .10
36 Felix Fermin .02 .10
37 Jeff Innis .02 .10
38 Brett Mayne .02 .10
39 Huck Flener RC .02 .10
40 Jeff Bagwell .10 .30
41 Kevin Wickander .02 .10
42 Ricky Gutierrez .02 .10
43 Pat Mahomes .02 .10
44 Jeff King .02 .10
45 Cal Eldred .02 .10
46 Craig Paquette .02 .10
47 Richie Lewis .02 .10
48 Tony Phillips .02 .10
49 Armando Reynoso .02 .10
50 Moises Alou .07 .20
51 Manuel Lee .02 .10
52 Otis Nixon .02 .10
53 Billy Ashley .02 .10
54 Mark Whiten .02 .10
55 Jeff Russell .02 .10
56 Chad Curtis .02 .10
57 Kevin Stocker .02 .10
58 Mike Jackson .02 .10
59 Matt Nokes .02 .10
60 Chris Bosio .02 .10
61 Damon Buford .02 .10
62 Tim Belcher .02 .10
63 Glenallen Hill .02 .10
64 Bill Wertz .02 .10
65 Eddie Murray .20 .50
66 Tom Gordon .02 .10
67 Alex Gonzalez .02 .10
68 Eddie Taubensee .02 .10
69 Jacob Brumfield .02 .10
70 Andy Benes .02 .10
71 Rich Becker .02 .10
72 Steve Cooke .02 .10
73 Billy Spiers .02 .10
74 Scott Brosius .07 .20
75 Alan Trammell .07 .20
76 Luis Aquino .02 .10
77 Jerald Clark .02 .10
78 Mel Rojas .02 .10
79 Billy Masse .02 .10
Stanton Cameron
Tim Clark
Craig McClure RC
80 Jose Canseco .10 .30
81 Greg McMichael .02 .10
82 Brian Turang RC .02 .10
83 Tom Urbani .02 .10
84 Garret Anderson .20 .50
85 Tony Pena .02 .10
86 Ricky Jordan .02 .10
87 Jim Gott .02 .10
88 Pat Kelly .02 .10
89 Bud Black .02 .10
90 Robin Ventura .07 .20
91 Rick Sutcliffe .07 .20
92 Jose Bautista .02 .10
93 Bob Ojeda .02 .10
94 Phil Hiatt .02 .10
95 Tim Pugh .02 .10
96 Randy Knorr .02 .10
97 Todd Jones .02 .10
98 Ryan Thompson .02 .10
99 Tim Mauser .02 .10
100 Kirby Puckett .20 .50
101 Mark Dewey .02 .10
102 B.J. Surhoff .07 .20
103 Sterling Hitchcock .02 .10
104 Alex Arias .02 .10
105 David Wells .07 .20
106 Daryl Boston .02 .10
107 Mike Stanton .02 .10
108 Gary Redus .02 .10
109 Delino DeShields .02 .10
110 Lee Smith .07 .20
111 Greg Litton .02 .10
112 Frankie Rodriguez .02 .10
113 Russ Springer .02 .10
114 Mitch Williams .02 .10
115 Eric Karros .07 .20
116 Jeff Brantley .02 .10
117 Jack Voigt .02 .10
118 Jason Bere .02 .10
119 Kevin Roberson .02 .10
120 Jimmy Key .07 .20
121 Reggie Jefferson .02 .10
122 Jeromy Burnitz .07 .20
123 Billy Brewer .02 .10
124 Willie Canate .02 .10
125 Greg Swindell .02 .10
126 Hal Morris .02 .10
127 Brad Ausmus .10 .30
128 George Tsamis .02 .10
129 Denny Neagle .07 .20
130 Pat Listach .02 .10
131 Steve Karsay .02 .10
132 Bret Barberie .02 .10
133 Mark Leiter .02 .10
134 Greg Colbrunn .02 .10
135 David Nied .02 .10
136 Dean Palmer .07 .20
137 Steve Avery .02 .10
138 Bill Haselman .02 .10
139 Tripp Cromer .02 .10
140 Frank Viola .07 .20
141 Rene Gonzales .02 .10
142 Curt Schilling .07 .20
143 Tim Wallach .02 .10
144 Bobby Munoz .02 .10
145 Brady Anderson .07 .20
146 Rod Beck .02 .10
147 Mike LaValliere .02 .10
148 Greg Hibbard .02 .10
149 Kenny Lofton .07 .20
150 Dwight Gooden .07 .20
151 Greg Gagne .02 .10
152 Ray McDavid .02 .10
153 Chris Donnels .02 .10
154 Dan Wilson .02 .10
155 Todd Stottlemyre .02 .10
156 David McCarty .02 .10
157 Paul Wagner .02 .10
158 Orlando Miller .60 1.50
Brandon Wilson
Derek Jeter
Mike Neal
159 Mike Fetters .02 .10
160 Scott Lydy .02 .10
161 Darrell Whitmore .02 .10
162 Bob MacDonald .02 .10
163 Vinny Castilla .07 .20
164 Denis Boucher .02 .10
165 Ivan Rodriguez .10 .30
166 Ron Gant .07 .20
167 Tim Davis .02 .10
168 Steve Dixon .02 .10
169 Scott Fletcher .02 .10
170 Terry Mulholland .02 .10
171 Greg Myers .02 .10
172 Brett Butler .07 .20
173 Bob Wickman .02 .10
174 Dave Martinez .02 .10
175 Fernando Valenzuela .07 .20
176 Craig Grebeck .02 .10
177 Shawn Boskie .02 .10
178 Albie Lopez .02 .10
179 Butch Huskey .02 .10
180 George Brett .50 1.25
181 Juan Guzman .02 .10
182 Eric Anthony .02 .10
183 Rob Dibble .07 .20
184 Craig Shipley .02 .10
185 Kevin Tapani .02 .10
186 Marcus Moore .02 .10
187 Graeme Lloyd .02 .10
188 Mike Bordick .02 .10
189 Chris Hammond .02 .10
190 Cecil Fielder .07 .20
191 Curt Leskanic .02 .10
192 Lou Frazier .02 .10
193 Steve Dreyer RC .02 .10
194 Javier Lopez .07 .20
195 Edgar Martinez .10 .30
196 Allen Watson .02 .10
197 John Flaherty .02 .10
198 Kurt Stillwell .02 .10
199 Danny Jackson .02 .10
200 Cal Ripken .60 1.50
201 Mike Bell FDP RC .02 .10
202 Alan Benes FDP RC .08 .25

Card	Low	High
203 Matt Farner FDP RC	.02	.10
204 Jeff Granger	.02	.10
205 B.Kieschnick FDP RC	.02	.10
206 Jeremy Lee FDP RC	.02	.10
207 C.Peterson FDP RC	.02	.10
208 Alan Rice FDP RC	.02	.10
209 Billy Wagner FDP RC	.60	1.50
210 Kelly Wunsch FDP RC	.08	.25
211 Tom Candiotti	.02	.10
212 Domingo Jean	.02	.10
213 John Burkett	.02	.10
214 George Bell	.02	.10
215 Dan Plesac	.02	.10
216 Manny Ramirez	.20	.50
217 Mike Maddux	.02	.10
218 Kevin McReynolds	.02	.10
219 Pat Borders	.02	.10
220 Doug Drabek	.02	.10
221 Larry Luebbers RC	.02	.10
222 Trevor Hoffman	.10	.30
223 Pat Meares	.02	.10
224 Danny Miceli	.02	.10
225 Greg Vaughn	.02	.10
226 Scott Hemond	.02	.10
227 Pat Rapp	.02	.10
228 Kirk Gibson	.07	.20
229 Lance Painter	.02	.10
230 Larry Walker	.07	.20
231 Benji Gil	.02	.10
232 Mark Wohlers	.02	.10
233 Rich Amaral	.02	.10
234 Eric Pappas	.02	.10
235 Scott Cooper	.02	.10
236 Mike Butcher	.02	.10
237 Curtis Pride RC	.20	.50
Shawn Green		
Mark Sweeney RC		
Eddie Davis RC		
238 Kim Batiste	.02	.10
239 Paul Assenmacher	.02	.10
240 Will Clark	.10	.30
241 Jose Offerman	.02	.10
242 Todd Frohwirth	.02	.10
243 Tim Raines	.07	.20
244 Rick Wilkins	.02	.10
245 Bret Saberhagen	.07	.20
246 Thomas Howard	.02	.10
247 Stan Belinda	.02	.10
248 Rickey Henderson	.20	.50
249 Brian Williams	.02	.10
250 Barry Larkin	.10	.30
251 Jose Valentin	.02	.10
252 Lenny Webster	.02	.10
253 Blas Minor	.02	.10
254 Tim Teufel	.02	.10
255 Bobby Witt	.02	.10
256 Walt Weiss	.02	.10
257 Chad Kreuter	.02	.10
258 Roberto Mejia	.02	.10
259 Cliff Floyd	.07	.20
260 Julio Franco	.07	.20
261 Rafael Belliard	.02	.10
262 Marc Newfield	.02	.10
263 Gerald Perry	.02	.10
264 Ken Ryan	.02	.10
265 Chili Davis	.07	.20
266 Dave West	.02	.10
267 Royce Clayton	.02	.10
268 Pedro Martinez	.20	.50
269 Mark Hutton	.02	.10
270 Frank Thomas	.20	.50
271 Brad Pennington	.02	.10
272 Mike Harkey	.02	.10
273 Sandy Alomar Jr.	.02	.10
274 Dave Gallagher	.02	.10
275 Wally Joyner	.07	.20
276 Ricky Trlicek	.02	.10
277 Al Osuna	.02	.10
278 Pokey Reese	.02	.10
279 Kevin Higgins	.02	.10
280 Rick Aguilera	.02	.10
281 Orlando Merced	.02	.10
282 Mike Mohler	.02	.10
283 John Jaha	.02	.10
284 Robb Nen	.07	.20
285 Travis Fryman	.07	.20
286 Mark Thompson	.02	.10
287 Mike Lansing	.02	.10
288 Craig Lefferts	.02	.10
289 Damon Berryhill	.02	.10
290 Randy Johnson	.20	.50
291 Jeff Reed	.02	.10
292 Danny Darwin	.02	.10
293 J.T. Snow	.07	.20
294 Tyler Green	.02	.10
295 Chris Hoiles	.02	.10
296 Roger McDowell	.02	.10
297 Spike Owen	.02	.10
298 Salomon Torres	.02	.10
299 Wilson Alvarez	.02	.10
300 Ryne Sandberg	.30	.75
301 Derek Lilliquist	.02	.10
302 Howard Johnson	.02	.10
303 Greg Cadaret	.02	.10
304 Pat Hentgen	.02	.10
305 Craig Biggio	.10	.30
306 Scott Service	.02	.10
307 Melvin Nieves	.02	.10
308 Mike Trombley	.02	.10
309 Carlos Garcia	.02	.10
310 Robin Yount UER (listed with 111 triples in 1988; should be 11)	.30	.75
311 Marcos Armas	.02	.10
312 Rich Rodriguez	.02	.10
313 Justin Thompson	.02	.10
314 Danny Sheaffer	.02	.10
315 Ken Hill	.02	.10
316 Chad Ogea	.02	.10
Duff Brumley		
Terrell Wade RC		
Chris Michalak		
317 Cris Carpenter	.02	.10
318 Jeff Blauser	.02	.10
319 Ted Power	.02	.10
320 Ozzie Smith	.30	.75
321 John Dopson	.02	.10
322 Chris Turner	.02	.10
323 Pete Incaviglia	.02	.10
324 Alan Mills	.02	.10
325 Jody Reed	.02	.10
326 Rich Monteleone	.02	.10
327 Mark Carreon	.02	.10
328 Donn Pall	.02	.10
329 Matt Walbeck	.02	.10
330 Charles Nagy	.02	.10
331 Jeff McKnight	.02	.10
332 Jose Lind	.02	.10
333 Mike Timlin	.02	.10
334 Doug Jones	.02	.10
335 Kevin Mitchell	.02	.10
336 Luis Lopez	.02	.10
337 Shane Mack	.02	.10
338 Randy Tomlin	.02	.10
339 Matt Mieske	.02	.10
340 Mark McGwire	.50	1.25
341 Nigel Wilson	.02	.10
342 Danny Gladden	.02	.10
343 Mo Sanford	.02	.10
344 Sean Berry	.02	.10
345 Kevin Brown	.07	.20
346 Greg Olson	.02	.10
347 Dave Magadan	.02	.10
348 Rene Arocha	.02	.10
349 Carlos Quintana	.02	.10
350 Jim Abbott	.10	.30
351 Gary DiSarcina	.02	.10
352 Ben Rivera	.02	.10
353 Carlos Hernandez	.02	.10
354 Darren Lewis	.02	.10
355 Harold Reynolds	.07	.20
356 Scott Ruffcorn	.02	.10
357 Mark Gubicza	.02	.10
358 Paul Sorrento	.02	.10
359 Anthony Young	.02	.10
360 Mark Grace	.10	.30
361 Rob Butler	.02	.10
362 Kevin Bass	.02	.10
363 Eric Helfand	.02	.10
364 Derek Bell	.02	.10
365 Scott Erickson	.02	.10
366 Al Martin	.02	.10
367 Ricky Bones	.02	.10
368 Jeff Branson	.02	.10
369 Luis Ortiz	.20	.50
David Bell RC		
Jason Giambi		
George Arias		
370 Benito Santiago (See also 379)	.07	.20
371 John Doherty	.02	.10
372 Joe Girardi	.02	.10
373 Tim Scott	.02	.10
374 Marvin Freeman	.02	.10
375 Deion Sanders	.10	.30
376 Roger Salkeld	.02	.10
377 Bernard Gilkey	.02	.10
378 Tony Fossas	.02	.10
379 Mark McLemore UER (Card number is 370)	.02	.10
380 Darren Daulton	.07	.20
381 Chuck Finley	.07	.20
382 Mitch Webster	.02	.10
383 Gerald Williams	.02	.10
384 Frank Thomas AS	.10	.30
Fred McGriff AS		
385 Roberto Alomar AS	.07	.20
Robby Thompson AS		
386 Wade Boggs AS	.07	.20
Matt Williams AS		
387 Cal Ripken AS	.20	.50
Jeff Blauser AS		
388 Ken Griffey Jr. AS	.20	.50
Len Dykstra AS		
389 Juan Gonzalez AS	.07	.20
David Justice AS		
390 George Belle AS	.30	.75
Barry Bonds AS		
391 Mike Stanley AS	.20	.50
Mike Piazza AS		
392 Jack McDowell AS	.10	.30
Greg Maddux AS		
393 Jimmy Key AS	.07	.20
Tom Glavine AS		
394 Jeff Montgomery AS	.02	.10
Randy Myers AS		
395 Checklist 1-198	.02	.10
396 Checklist 199-396	.02	.10
397 Tim Salmon	.10	.30
398 Todd Benzinger	.02	.10
399 Frank Castillo	.02	.10
400 Ken Griffey Jr.	.30	.75
401 John Kruk	.07	.20
402 Dave Telgheder	.02	.10
403 Gary Gaetti	.07	.20
404 Jim Edmonds	.20	.50
405 Don Slaught	.02	.10
406 Jose Oquendo	.02	.10
407 Bruce Ruffin	.02	.10
408 Phil Clark	.02	.10
409 Joe Klink	.02	.10
410 Lou Whitaker	.07	.20
411 Kevin Seltzer	.02	.10
412 Darrin Fletcher	.02	.10
413 Kenny Rogers	.07	.20
414 Bill Pecota	.02	.10
415 Dave Fleming	.02	.10
416 Luis Alicea	.02	.10
417 Paul Quantrill	.02	.10
418 Damion Easley	.02	.10
419 Wes Chamberlain	.02	.10
420 Harold Baines	.07	.20
421 Scott Radinsky	.02	.10
422 Rey Sanchez	.02	.10
423 Junior Ortiz	.02	.10
424 Jeff Kent	.10	.30
425 Brian McRae	.02	.10
426 Ed Sprague	.02	.10
427 Tom Edens	.02	.10
428 Willie Greene	.02	.10
429 Bryan Hickerson	.02	.10
430 Dave Winfield	.07	.20
431 Pedro Astacio	.02	.10
432 Mike Gallego	.02	.10
433 Dave Burba	.02	.10
434 Bob Walk	.02	.10
435 Darryl Hamilton	.02	.10
436 Vince Horsman	.02	.10
437 Bob Natal	.02	.10
438 Mike Henneman	.02	.10
439 Willie Blair	.02	.10
440 Dennis Martinez	.07	.20
441 Dan Peltier	.02	.10
442 Tony Tarasco	.02	.10
443 John Cummings	.02	.10
444 Geronimo Pena	.02	.10
445 Aaron Sele	.02	.10
446 Stan Javier	.02	.10
447 Mike Williams	.02	.10
448 Greg Pirkl	.02	.10
Roberto Petagine		
D.J.Boston		
Shawn Wooten RC		
449 Jim Poole	.02	.10
450 Carlos Baerga	.02	.10
451 Bob Scanlan	.02	.10
452 Lance Johnson	.02	.10
453 Eric Hillman	.02	.10
454 Keith Miller	.02	.10
455 Dave Stewart	.07	.20
456 Pete Harnisch	.02	.10
457 Roberto Kelly	.02	.10
458 Tim Worrell	.02	.10
459 Pedro Munoz	.02	.10
460 Orel Hershiser	.07	.20
461 Randy Velarde	.02	.10
462 Trevor Wilson	.02	.10
463 Jerry Goff	.02	.10
464 Bill Wegman	.02	.10
465 Dennis Eckersley	.07	.20
466 Jeff Conine	.07	.20
467 Joe Boever	.02	.10
468 Dante Bichette	.07	.20
469 Jeff Shaw	.02	.10
470 Rafael Palmeiro	.10	.30
471 Phil Leftwich RC	.02	.10
472 Jay Buhner	.07	.20
473 Bob Tewksbury	.02	.10
474 Tim Naehring	.02	.10
475 Tom Glavine	.10	.30
476 Dave Hollins	.02	.10
477 Arthur Rhodes	.02	.10
478 Joey Cora	.02	.10
479 Mike Morgan	.02	.10
480 Albert Belle	.07	.20
481 John Franco	.07	.20
482 Hipolito Pichardo	.02	.10
483 Duane Ward	.02	.10
484 Luis Gonzalez	.07	.20
485 Joe Oliver	.02	.10
486 Wally Whitehurst	.02	.10
487 Mike Benjamin	.02	.10
488 Eric Davis	.07	.20
489 Scott Kamieniecki	.02	.10
490 Kent Hrbek	.07	.20
491 John Hope RC	.02	.10
492 Jesse Orosco	.02	.10
493 Troy Neel	.02	.10
494 Ryan Bowen	.02	.10
495 Mickey Tettleton	.02	.10
496 Chris Jones	.02	.10
497 John Wetteland	.07	.20
498 David Hulse	.02	.10
499 Greg Maddux	.30	.75
500 Bo Jackson	.20	.50
501 Donovan Osborne	.02	.10
502 Mike Greenwell	.02	.10
503 Steve Frey	.02	.10
504 Jim Eisenreich	.02	.10
505 Robby Thompson	.02	.10
506 Leo Gomez	.02	.10
507 Dave Staton	.02	.10
508 Wayne Kirby	.02	.10
509 Tim Bogar	.02	.10
510 David Cone	.07	.20
511 Devon White	.07	.20
512 Xavier Hernandez	.02	.10
513 Tim Costo	.02	.10
514 Gene Harris	.02	.10
515 Jack McDowell	.02	.10
516 Kevin Gross	.02	.10
517 Scott Leius	.02	.10
518 Lloyd McClendon	.02	.10
519 Alex Diaz RC	.02	.10
520 Wade Boggs	.10	.30
521 Bob Welch	.02	.10
522 Henry Cotto	.02	.10
523 Mike Moore	.02	.10
524 Tim Laker	.02	.10
525 Andres Galarraga	.07	.20
526 Jamie Moyer	.07	.20
527 Norberto Martin	.02	.10
Ruben Santana		
Jason Hardtke		
Chris Sexton RC		
528 Sid Bream	.02	.10
529 Erik Hanson	.02	.10
530 Ray Lankford	.07	.20
531 Rob Deer	.02	.10
532 Rod Correia	.02	.10
533 Roger Mason	.02	.10
534 Mike Devereaux	.02	.10
535 Jeff Montgomery	.02	.10
536 Dwight Smith	.02	.10
537 Jeremy Hernandez	.02	.10
538 Ellis Burks	.07	.20
539 Bobby Jones	.02	.10
540 Paul Molitor	.07	.20
541 Jeff Juden	.02	.10
542 Chris Sabo	.02	.10
543 Larry Casian	.02	.10
544 Jeff Gardner	.02	.10
545 Ramon Martinez	.02	.10
546 Paul O'Neill	.10	.30
547 Steve Hosey	.02	.10
548 Dave Nilsson	.02	.10
549 Ron Darling	.02	.10
550 Matt Williams	.07	.20
551 Jack Armstrong	.02	.10
552 Bill Krueger	.02	.10
553 Freddie Benavides	.02	.10
554 Jeff Fassero	.02	.10
555 Chuck Knoblauch	.07	.20
556 Guillermo Velasquez	.02	.10
557 Joel Johnston	.02	.10
558 Tom Lampkin	.02	.10
559 Todd Van Poppel	.02	.10
560 Gary Sheffield	.07	.20
561 Skeeter Barnes	.02	.10
562 Darren Holmes	.02	.10
563 John Vander Wal	.02	.10
564 Mike Ignasiak	.02	.10
565 Fred McGriff	.10	.30
566 Luis Polonia	.02	.10
567 Mike Perez	.02	.10
568 John Valentin	.02	.10
569 Mike Felder	.02	.10
570 Tommy Greene	.02	.10
571 David Segui	.02	.10
572 Roberto Hernandez	.02	.10
573 Steve Wilson	.02	.10
574 Willie McGee	.07	.20
575 Randy Myers	.02	.10
576 Darrin Jackson	.02	.10
577 Eric Plunk	.02	.10
578 Mike Macfarlane	.02	.10
579 Doug Brocail	.02	.10
580 Steve Finley	.07	.20
581 John Roper	.02	.10
582 Danny Cox	.02	.10
583 Chip Hale	.02	.10
584 Scott Bullett	.02	.10
585 Kevin Reimer	.02	.10
586 Brent Gates	.02	.10
587 Matt Turner	.02	.10
588 Rich Rowland	.02	.10
589 Kent Bottenfield	.02	.10
590 Marquis Grissom	.07	.20
591 Doug Strange	.02	.10
592 Jay Howell	.02	.10
593 Omar Vizquel	.10	.30
594 Rheal Cormier	.02	.10
595 Andre Dawson	.07	.20
596 Hilly Hathaway	.02	.10
597 Todd Pratt	.02	.10
598 Mike Mussina	.10	.30
599 Alex Fernandez	.02	.10
600 Don Mattingly	.50	1.25
601 Frank Thomas MOG	.10	.30
602 Ryne Sandberg MOG	.20	.50
603 Wade Boggs MOG	.07	.20
604 Cal Ripken MOG	.30	.75
605 Barry Bonds MOG	.30	.75
606 Ken Griffey Jr. MOG	.20	.50
607 Kirby Puckett MOG	.10	.30
608 Darren Daulton MOG	.02	.10
609 Paul Molitor MOG	.02	.10
610 Terry Steinbach	.02	.10
611 Todd Worrell	.02	.10
612 Jim Thome	.10	.30
613 Chuck McElroy	.02	.10
614 John Habyan	.02	.10
615 Sid Fernandez	.02	.10
616 Eddie Zambrano	.02	.10
Glenn Murray		
Chad Mottola		
Jermaine Allensworth RC		
617 Steve Bedrosian	.02	.10
618 Rob Ducey	.02	.10
619 Tom Browning	.02	.10
620 Tony Gwynn	.25	.60
621 Carl Willis	.02	.10
622 Kevin Young	.02	.10
623 Rafael Novoa	.02	.10
624 Jerry Browne	.02	.10
625 Charlie Hough	.07	.20
626 Chris Gomez	.02	.10
627 Steve Reed	.02	.10
628 Kirk Rueter	.02	.10
629 Matt Whiteside	.02	.10
630 David Justice	.07	.20
631 Brad Holman	.02	.10
632 Brian Jordan	.07	.20
633 Scott Bankhead	.02	.10
634 Torey Lovullo	.02	.10
635 Len Dykstra	.07	.20
636 Ben McDonald	.02	.10
637 Steve Howe	.02	.10
638 Jose Vizcaino	.02	.10
639 Bill Swift	.02	.10
640 Darryl Strawberry	.07	.20
641 Steve Farr	.02	.10
642 Tom Kramer	.02	.10
643 Joe Orsulak	.02	.10
644 Tom Henke	.02	.10
645 Joe Carter	.07	.20
646 Ken Caminiti	.07	.20
647 Reggie Sanders	.07	.20
648 Andy Ashby	.02	.10
649 Derek Parks	.02	.10
650 Andy Van Slyke	.10	.30
651 Juan Bell	.02	.10
652 Roger Smithberg	.02	.10
653 Chuck Carr	.02	.10
654 Bill Gullickson	.02	.10
655 Charlie Hayes	.02	.10
656 Chris Nabholz	.02	.10
657 Karl Rhodes	.02	.10
658 Pete Smith	.02	.10
659 Bret Boone	.07	.20
660 Gregg Jefferies	.02	.10
661 Bob Zupcic	.02	.10
662 Steve Sax	.02	.10
663 Mariano Duncan	.02	.10
664 Jeff Tackett	.02	.10
665 Mark Langston	.02	.10
666 Steve Buechele	.02	.10
667 Candy Maldonado	.02	.10
668 Woody Williams	.07	.20
669 Tim Wakefield	.10	.30
670 Danny Tartabull	.02	.10
671 Charlie O'Brien	.02	.10
672 Felix Jose	.02	.10
673 Bobby Ayala	.02	.10
674 Scott Servais	.02	.10
675 Roberto Alomar	.10	.30
676 Pedro A.Martinez RC	.02	.10
677 Eddie Guardado	.07	.20
678 Mark Lewis	.02	.10
679 Jaime Navarro	.02	.10
680 Ruben Sierra	.07	.20
681 Rick Renteria	.02	.10
682 Storm Davis	.02	.10
683 Cory Snyder	.02	.10
684 Ron Karkovice	.02	.10
685 Juan Gonzalez	.07	.20
686 Chris Howard	.10	.30
Carlos Delgado		
Jason Kendall		
Paul Bako		
687 John Smoltz	.10	.30
688 Brian Dorsett	.02	.10
689 Omar Olivares	.02	.10
690 Mo Vaughn	.07	.20
691 Joe Grahe	.02	.10
692 Mickey Morandini	.02	.10
693 Tino Martinez	.10	.30
694 Brian Barnes	.02	.10
695 Mike Stanley	.02	.10
696 Mark Clark	.02	.10
697 Dave Hansen	.02	.10
698 Willie Wilson	.02	.10
699 Pete Schourek	.02	.10
700 Barry Bonds	.60	1.50
701 Kevin Appier	.07	.20
702 Tony Fernandez	.02	.10
703 Darryl Kile	.07	.20
704 Archi Cianfrocco	.02	.10
705 Jose Rijo	.02	.10
706 Brian Harper	.02	.10
707 Zane Smith	.02	.10
708 Dave Henderson	.02	.10
709 Angel Miranda UER (no Topps logo on back)	.02	.10
710 Orestes Destrade	.02	.10
711 Greg Gohr	.02	.10
712 Eric Young	.02	.10
713 Todd Williams	.02	.10
Ron Watson		
Kirk Bullinger		
Mike Welch		
714 Tim Spehr	.02	.10
715 Hank Aaron 715 HR	.20	.50
716 Nate Minchey	.02	.10
717 Mike Blowers	.02	.10
718 Kent Mercker	.02	.10
719 Tom Pagnozzi	.02	.10
720 Roger Clemens	.40	1.00
721 Eduardo Perez	.02	.10
722 Milt Thompson	.02	.10
723 Gregg Olson	.02	.10
724 Kirk McCaskill	.02	.10
725 Sammy Sosa	.20	.50
726 Alvaro Espinoza	.02	.10
727 Henry Rodriguez	.02	.10
728 Jim Leyritz	.02	.10
729 Steve Scarsone	.02	.10
730 Bobby Bonilla	.07	.20
731 Chris Gwynn	.02	.10
732 Al Leiter	.07	.20
733 Bip Roberts	.02	.10
734 Mark Portugal	.02	.10
735 Terry Pendleton	.07	.20
736 Dave Valle	.02	.10
737 Paul Kilgus	.02	.10
738 Greg A. Harris	.02	.10
739 Jon Ratliff DP RC	.02	.10
740 Kirk Presley DP RC	.02	.10
741 Josue Estrada DP RC	.02	.10
742 Wayne Gomes DP RC	.02	.10
743 Pat Watkins DP RC	.02	.10
744 Jamey Wright DP RC	.08	.25
745 Jay Powell DP RC	.02	.10
746 Ryan McGuire DP RC	.02	.10
747 Marc Barcelo DP RC	.02	.10
748 Sloan Smith DP RC	.02	.10
749 John Wasdin DP RC	.02	.10
750 Marc Vlades DP	.02	.10
751 Dan Ehler DP RC	.02	.10
752 Andre King DP RC	.02	.10
753 Greg Keagle DP RC	.02	.10
754 Jason Myers DP RC	.02	.10
755 Dax Winslett DP RC	.02	.10
756 Casey Whitten DP RC	.02	.10
757 Tony Fuduric DP RC	.02	.10
758 Greg Norton DP RC	.08	.25
759 Jeff D'Amico DP RC	.02	.10
760 Ryan Hancock DP RC	.02	.10
761 David Cooper DP RC	.02	.10
762 Kevin Orie DP RC	.02	.10
763 John O'Donoghue	.02	.10
Mike Oquist		
764 Cory Bailey RC	.02	.10
Scott Hatteberg		
765 Mark Holzemer	.02	.10
Paul Swingle RC		
766 James Baldwin	.02	.10
Rod Bolton		
767 Jerry Di Poto	.08	.25
Julian Tavarez RC		
768 Danny Bautista	.02	.10
Sean Bergman		
769 Bob Hamelin	.02	.10
Joe Vitiello		
770 Mark Kiefer	.02	.10
Troy O'Leary		
771 Denny Hocking	.02	.10
Oscar Munoz RC		
772 Russ Davis	.02	.10
Brien Taylor		
773 Kyle Abbott	.08	.25
Miguel Jimenez		
774 Kevin King	.02	.10
Eric Plantenberg RC		
775 Jon Shave	.02	.10
Desi Wilson		
776 Domingo Cedeno	.02	.10
Paul Spoljaric		
777 Chipper Jones	.20	.50
Ryan Klesko		
778 Steve Trachsel	.02	.10
Turk Wendell		
779 Johnny Ruffin	.02	.10
Jerry Spradlin RC		
780 Jason Bates	.02	.10
John Burke		
781 Carl Everett	.07	.20
Dave Weathers		
782 Gary Mota	.02	.10
James Mouton		
783 Raul Mondesi	.07	.20
Ben Van Ryn		
784 Gabe White	.07	.20
Rondell White		
785 Brook Fordyce	.07	.20
Bill Pulsipher		
786 Kevin Foster RC	.02	.10
Gene Schall		
787 Rich Aude RC	.02	.10
Midre Cummings		
788 Brian Barber	.02	.10
Rich Batchelor		
789 Brian Johnson RC	.02	.10
Scott Sanders		
790 Ricky Faneyte	.02	.10
J.R. Phillips		
791 Checklist 3	.02	.10
792 Checklist 4	.02	.10

1994 Topps Gold

The 1994 Topps Gold set is parallel to the basic issue. They were inserted one per wax or mini pack, two per mini jumbo, three per rack pack, four per jumbo, five per jumbo rack and ten per factory set. The only difference between the Gold issue and the basic cards is gold foil on the player's name and the Topps logo. As in previous Gold Sets, player cards (cards 395-96 and 791-92) replace the Checklist cards.

*STARS: 1.5X to 4X BASIC CARDS
*ROOKIES: 1.25X to 3X BASIC CARDS

Card	Low	High
395 Bill Brennan	.15	.40
396 Jeff Bronkey	.15	.40
791 Mike Cook	.15	.40
792 Dan Pasqua	.15	.40

1994 Topps Spanish

Issued in complete factory set form only, these 792 standard-size cards parallel the regular Topps issue. These cards have the same front photos but are billingual. The factory set also contains the Topps Spanish Legends 10-card set. That set which is entitled "Topps Legends" features retired Latin players.

*STARS: 3X to 6X BASIC CARDS

Card	Low	High
L1 Felipe Alou	.30	.75
L2 Ruben Amaro	.08	.25
L3 Luis Aparicio	.40	1.00
L4 Rod Carew	.40	1.00
L5 Chico Carrasquel	.20	.50
L6 Orlando Cepeda	.40	1.00
L7 Juan Marichal	.40	1.00
L8 Minnie Minoso	.30	.75
L9 Cookie Rojas	.08	.25
L10 Luis Tiant	.20	.50

1994 Topps Black Gold

Randomly inserted one in every 72 packs, this 44-card standard-size set was issued in two series of 22. Cards were also issued three per 1994 Topps factory set. Collectors had a chance, through redemption cards to receive all or part of the set. There are seven Winner redemption cards for a total 51 cards associated with this set. The set is considered complete with the 44 player cards. Card fronts feature color player action photos. The player's name at bottom and the team name at top are screened in gold foil. The backs contain a player photo and statistical rankings. The winner cards were redeemable until January 31, 1995

Card	Low	High
COMPLETE SET (44)	10.00	25.00
COMPLETE SERIES 1 (22)	6.00	15.00
COMPLETE SERIES 2 (22)	4.00	10.00
1 Roberto Alomar	.25	.60
2 Carlos Baerga	.07	.20
3 Albert Belle	.15	.40
4 Joe Carter	.15	.40
5 Cecil Fielder	.15	.40
6 Travis Fryman	.15	.40
7 Juan Gonzalez	.15	.40
8 Ken Griffey Jr.	.60	1.50
9 Chris Hoiles	.07	.20
10 Randy Johnson	.40	1.00
11 Kenny Lofton	.15	.40
12 Jack McDowell	.07	.20
13 Paul Molitor	.15	.40
14 Jeff Montgomery	.07	.20
15 John Olerud	.15	.40
16 Rafael Palmeiro	.25	.60
17 Kirby Puckett	.40	1.00
18 Cal Ripken	1.25	3.00
19 Tim Salmon	.25	.60
20 Mike Stanley	.07	.20
21 Frank Thomas	.40	1.00
22 Robin Ventura	.15	.40
23 Jeff Bagwell	.25	.60
24 Jay Bell	.15	.40
25 Craig Biggio	.25	.60
26 Jeff Blauser	.07	.20
27 Barry Bonds	1.25	3.00
28 Darren Daulton	.15	.40
29 Len Dykstra	.15	.40
30 Andres Galarraga	.15	.40
31 Ron Gant	.15	.40
32 Tom Glavine	.25	.60

Card	Low	High
33 Mark Grace	.25	.60
34 Marquis Grissom	.15	.40
35 Gregg Jefferies	.07	.20
36 David Justice	.15	.40
37 John Kruk	.15	.40
38 Greg Maddux	.60	1.50
39 Fred McGriff	.25	.60
40 Randy Myers	.07	.20
41 Mike Piazza	.75	2.00
42 Sammy Sosa	.40	1.00
43 Robby Thompson	.07	.20
44 Matt Williams	.15	.40
A Winner A 1-11	.07	.20
B Winner B 12-22	.07	.20
C Winner C 23-33	.07	.20
D Winner D 34-44	.07	.20
AB Winner AB 1-22	.07	.20
CD Winner CD 23-44	.07	.20
ABCD Winner ABCD 1-44	.07	.20

1994 Topps Traded

This set consists of 132 standard-size cards featuring traded players in their new uniforms, rookies and draft choices. Factory sets consisted of 140 cards including a set of eight Topps Finest cards. Card fronts feature a player photo with the player's name, team and position at the bottom. The horizontal backs have a player photo to the left with complete career statistics and highlights. Rookie Cards include Rusty Greer, Ben Grieve, Paul Konerko Terrence Long and Chan Ho Park.

Card	Low	High
COMP.FACT.SET (140)	20.00	40.00
1T Paul Wilson	.02	.10
2T Bill Taylor RC	.40	1.00
3T Dan Wilson	.02	.10
4T Mark Smith	.02	.10
5T Toby Borland RC	.08	.25
6T Dave Clark	.02	.10
7T Dennis Martinez	.07	.20
8T Dave Gallagher	.02	.10
9T Josias Manzanillo	.02	.10
10T Brian Anderson RC	.40	1.00
11T Damon Berryhill	.02	.10
12T Alex Cole	.02	.10
13T Jacob Shumate RC	.08	.25
14T Oddibe McDowell	.02	.10
15T Willie Banks	.02	.10
16T Jerry Browne	.02	.10
17T Donnie Elliott	.02	.10
18T Ellis Burks	.07	.20
19T Chuck McElroy	.02	.10
20T Luis Polonia	.02	.10
21T Brian Harper	.02	.10
22T Mark Portugal	.02	.10
23T Dave Henderson	.02	.10
24T Mark Acre RC	.08	.25
25T Julio Franco	.07	.20
26T Darren Hall RC	.08	.25
27T Eric Anthony	.02	.10
28T Sid Fernandez	.02	.10
29T Rusty Greer RC	.60	1.50
30T Riccardo Ingram RC	.08	.25
31T Gabe White	.02	.10
32T Tim Belcher	.02	.10
33T Terrence Long RC	.40	1.00
34T Mark Dalesandro RC	.08	.25
35T Mike Kelly	.02	.10
36T Jack Morris	.07	.20
37T Jeff Brantley	.02	.10
38T Larry Barnes RC	.08	.25
39T Brian R. Hunter	.02	.10
40T Otis Nixon	.02	.10
41T Bret Wagner	.02	.10
42T Pedro Martinez TR	.20	.50
Delino Deshields		
43T Heathcliff Slocumb	.02	.10
44T Ben Grieve RC	.40	1.00
45T John Hudek RC	.08	.25
46T Shawon Dunston	.02	.10
47T Greg Colbrunn	.02	.10
48T Joey Hamilton	.02	.10
49T Marvin Freeman	.02	.10
50T Terry Mulholland	.02	.10
51T Keith Mitchell	.02	.10
52T Dwight Smith	.02	.10
53T Shawn Boskie	.02	.10
54T Kevin Witt RC	.40	1.00
55T Ron Gant	.07	.20
56T Trenidad Hubbard RC	4.00	10.00
Jason Schmidt RC		
Larry Sutton		
Stephen Larkin RC		
57T Jody Reed	.02	.10
58T Rick Helling	.02	.10
59T John Powell	.02	.10
60T Eddie Murray	.20	.50
61T Joe Hall RC	.08	.25
62T Jorge Fabregas	.02	.10
63T Mike Mordecai RC	.08	.25
64T Ed Vosberg	.02	.10
65T Rickey Henderson	.20	.50
66T Tim Grieve RC	.08	.25
67T Jon Lieber	.07	.20
68T Chris Howard	.02	.10
69T Matt Walbeck	.02	.10
70T Chan Ho Park RC	.60	1.50
71T Bryan Eversgerd RC	.08	.25
72T John Dettmer	.02	.10
73T Erik Hanson	.02	.10
74T Mike Thurman RC	.08	.25
75T Bobby Ayala	.02	.10
76T Rafael Palmeiro	.10	.30
77T Bret Boone	.07	.20
78T Paul Shuey	.07	.20
79T Kevin Foster RC	.08	.25
80T Dave Magadan	.02	.10
81T Bip Roberts	.02	.10
82T Howard Johnson	.02	.10
83T Xavier Hernandez	.02	.10
84T Ross Powell RC	.08	.25
85T Doug Million RC	.08	.25
86T Geronimo Berroa	.02	.10
87T Mark Farris RC	.08	.25
88T Butch Henry	.02	.10
89T Junior Felix	.02	.10
90T Bo Jackson	.20	.50
91T Hector Carrasco	.02	.10
92T Charlie O'Brien	.02	.10
93T Omar Vizquel	.10	.30
94T David Segui	.02	.10
95T Dustin Hermanson	.02	.10
96T Gar Finnvold RC	.08	.25
97T Dave Stevens	.02	.10
98T Corey Pointer RC	.08	.25
99T Felix Fermin	.02	.10
100T Lee Smith	.07	.20
101T Reid Ryan RC	.40	1.00
102T Bobby Munoz	.02	.10
103T Deion Sanders TR	.10	.30
Roberto Kelly		
104T Turner Ward	.02	.10
105T W.VanLandingham RC	.08	.25
106T Vince Coleman	.02	.10
107T Stan Javier	.02	.10
108T Darrin Jackson	.02	.10
109T C.J. Nitkowski RC	.08	.25
110T Anthony Young	.02	.10
111T Kurt Miller	.02	.10
112T Paul Konerko RC	6.00	15.00
113T Walt Weiss	.02	.10
114T Daryl Boston	.02	.10
115T Will Clark	.10	.30
116T Matt Smith RC	.08	.25
117T Mark Leiter	.02	.10
118T Gregg Olson	.02	.10
119T Tony Pena	.02	.10
120T Jose Vizcaino	.02	.10
121T Rick White RC	.08	.25
122T Rich Rowland	.02	.10
123T Jeff Reboulet	.02	.10
124T Greg Hibbard	.02	.10
125T Chris Sabo	.02	.10
126T Doug Jones	.02	.10
127T Tony Fernandez	.02	.10
128T Carlos Reyes RC	.08	.25
129T Kevin L.Brown RC	.40	1.00
130T Ryne Sandberg	.50	1.25
Farewell		
131T Ryne Sandberg	.50	1.25
Farewell		
132T Checklist 1-132	.02	.10

1994 Topps Traded Finest Inserts

Each Topps Traded factory set contained a complete eight card set of Finest Inserts. These cards are numbered separately and designed differently from the base cards. Each Finest Insert features a action shot of a player set against purple chrome background. The set highlights the top performers midway through the 1994 season, detailing their performances through July. The cards are numbered on back "X of 8".

Card	Low	High
COMPLETE SET (8)	2.00	5.00
1 Greg Maddux	.30	.75
2 Mike Piazza	.40	1.00
3 Matt Williams	.07	.20
4 Raul Mondesi	.07	.20
5 Ken Griffey Jr.	.30	.75
6 Kenny Lofton	.07	.20
7 Frank Thomas	.20	.50
8 Manny Ramirez	.20	.50

1994 Topps Superstar Samplers

Sold only in retail outlets, each 1994 Topps Baker's Dozen factory set included a cello-wrapped three-card sampler of a MLB player. Each player is represented by a Bowman, a Finest, and a Stadium Club card. These cards are identical to their regular issue counterparts except for a special "Topps Superstar Sampler" emblem on their backs. The prices listed below are for all three cards; the Finest card represents 50 percent of the value, while the Bowman or Stadium Club card are worth 25 percent each of the value. We have sequenced each player in alphabetical order.

Card	Low	High
COMPLETE SET (135)	400.00	1000.00
COMMON BAG (1-45)	2.40	6.00
1 Roberto Alomar	8.00	20.00
2 Carlos Baerga	2.50	6.00
3 Jeff Bagwell	12.50	30.00
4 Albert Belle	4.00	10.00
5 Barry Bonds	20.00	50.00
6 Bobby Bonilla	4.00	10.00
7 Jose Canseco	12.50	30.00
8 Joe Carter	4.00	10.00
9 Will Clark	8.00	20.00
10 Roger Clemens	20.00	50.00
11 Darren Daulton	4.00	10.00
12 Len Dykstra	2.50	6.00
13 Cecil Fielder	4.00	10.00
14 Cliff Floyd	6.00	15.00
15 Andres Galarraga	8.00	20.00
16 Tom Glavine	10.00	25.00
17 Juan Gonzalez	8.00	20.00
18 Mark Grace	6.00	15.00
19 Ken Griffey Jr.	20.00	50.00
20 Marquis Grissom	4.00	10.00
21 Tony Gwynn	20.00	50.00
22 Gregg Jefferies	2.50	6.00
23 Randy Johnson	15.00	40.00
24 David Justice	8.00	20.00
25 Barry Larkin	8.00	20.00
26 Greg Maddux	25.00	60.00
27 Don Mattingly	20.00	50.00
28 Jack McDowell	2.50	6.00
29 Fred McGriff	6.00	15.00
30 Paul Molitor	10.00	25.00
31 Raul Mondesi	4.00	10.00
32 John Olerud	4.00	10.00
33 Rafael Palmeiro	10.00	25.00
34 Mike Piazza	20.00	50.00
35 Kirby Puckett	12.50	30.00
36 Manny Ramirez	12.50	30.00
37 Cal Ripken	40.00	100.00
38 Tim Salmon	4.00	10.00
39 Ryne Sandberg	15.00	40.00
40 Gary Sheffield	12.50	30.00
41 Frank Thomas	12.50	30.00
42 Andy Van Slyke	2.50	6.00
43 Mo Vaughn	4.00	10.00
44 Larry Walker	10.00	25.00
45 Matt Williams	6.00	15.00

1995 Topps

These 660 standard-size cards feature color action player photos with white borders on the fronts. This set was released in two series. The first series contained 396 cards while the second series had 264 cards. Cards were distributed in 11-card packs (SRP $1.29), jumbo packs and factory sets. One "Own The Game" instant winner card has been inserted in every 120 packs. Rookie cards in this set include Rey Ordonez. Due to the 1994 baseball strike, it was publicly announced that production for this set was the lowest print run since 1966.

Card	Low	High
COMPLETE SET (660)	50.00	80.00
COMP.HOBBY SET (677)	60.00	120.00
COMP.RETAIL SET (677)	60.00	120.00
COMP.SERIES 1 (396)	25.00	40.00
COMP.SERIES 2 (264)	25.00	40.00
1 Frank Thomas	.30	.75
2 Mickey Morandini	.05	.15
3 Babe Ruth 100th B-Day	.75	2.00
4 Scott Cooper	.05	.15
5 David Cone	.10	.30
6 Jacob Shumate	.05	.15
7 Trevor Hoffman	.10	.30
8 Shane Mack	.05	.15
9 Delino DeShields	.05	.15
10 Matt Williams	.10	.30
11 Sammy Sosa	.30	.75
12 Gary DiSarcina	.05	.15
13 Kenny Rogers	.10	.30
14 Jose Vizcaino	.05	.15
15 Lou Whitaker	.10	.30
16 Ron Darling	.05	.15
17 Dave Nilsson	.05	.15
18 Chris Hammond	.05	.15
19 Sid Bream	.05	.15
20 Denny Martinez	.10	.30
21 Orlando Merced	.05	.15
22 John Wetteland	.10	.30
23 Mike Devereaux	.05	.15
24 Rene Arocha	.05	.15
25 Jay Buhner	.10	.30
26 Darren Holmes	.05	.15
27 Hal Morris	.05	.15
28 Brian Buchanan RC	.05	.15
29 Keith Miller	.05	.15
30 Paul Molitor	.10	.30
31 Dave West	.05	.15
32 Tony Tarasco	.05	.15
33 Scott Sanders	.05	.15
34 Eddie Zambrano	.05	.15
35 Ricky Bones	.05	.15
36 John Valentin	.05	.15
37 Kevin Tapani	.05	.15
38 Tim Wallach	.05	.15
39 Darren Lewis	.05	.15
40 Travis Fryman	.10	.30
41 Mark Leiter	.05	.15
42 Jose Bautista	.05	.15
43 Pete Smith	.05	.15
44 Bret Barberie	.05	.15
45 Dennis Eckersley	.10	.30
46 Ken Hill	.05	.15
47 Chad Ogea	.05	.15
48 Pete Harnisch	.05	.15
49 James Baldwin	.05	.15
50 Mike Mussina	.20	.50
51 Al Martin	.05	.15
52 Mark Thompson	.05	.15
53 Matt Smith	.05	.15
54 Joey Hamilton	.05	.15
55 Edgar Martinez	.20	.50
56 John Smiley	.05	.15
57 Rey Sanchez	.05	.15
58 Mike Timlin	.05	.15
59 Ricky Bottalico	.05	.15
60 Jim Abbott	.20	.50
61 Mike Kelly	.05	.15
62 Brian Jordan	.10	.30
63 Ken Ryan	.05	.15
64 Matt Mieske	.05	.15
65 Rick Aguilera	.05	.15
66 Ismael Valdes	.05	.15
67 Royce Clayton	.05	.15
68 Junior Felix	.05	.15
69 Harold Reynolds	.10	.30
70 Juan Gonzalez	.10	.30
71 Kelly Stinnett	.05	.15
72 Carlos Reyes	.05	.15
73 Dave Weathers	.05	.15
74 Mel Rojas	.05	.15
75 Doug Drabek	.05	.15
76 Charles Nagy	.05	.15
77 Tim Raines	.10	.30
78 Midre Cummings	.05	.15
79 Gene Schall	.05	.15
Scott Talanoa		
Harold Williams		
Ray Brown RC		
80 Rafael Palmeiro	.20	.50
81 Charlie Hayes	.05	.15
82 Ray Lankford	.10	.30
83 Tim Davis	.05	.15
84 C.J. Nitkowski	.05	.15
85 Andy Ashby	.05	.15
86 Gerald Williams	.05	.15
87 Terry Shumpert	.05	.15
88 Heathcliff Slocumb	.05	.15
89 Domingo Cedeno	.05	.15
90 Mark Grace	.20	.50
91 Brad Woodall RC	.05	.15
92 Gar Finnvold	.05	.15
93 Jaime Navarro	.05	.15
94 Carlos Hernandez	.05	.15
95 Mark Langston	.05	.15
96 Chuck Carr	.05	.15
97 Mike Gardiner	.05	.15
98 Dave McCarty	.05	.15
99 Cris Carpenter	.05	.15
100 Barry Bonds	.75	2.00
101 David Segui	.05	.15
102 Scott Brosius	.10	.30
103 Mariano Duncan	.05	.15
104 Kenny Lofton	.10	.30
105 Ken Caminiti	.10	.30
106 Darrin Jackson	.05	.15
107 Jim Poole	.05	.15
108 Wil Cordero	.05	.15
109 Danny Miceli	.05	.15
110 Walt Weiss	.05	.15
111 Tom Pagnozzi	.05	.15
112 Terrence Long	.05	.15
113 Bret Boone	.10	.30
114 Daryl Boston	.05	.15
115 Wally Joyner	.10	.30
116 Rob Butler	.05	.15
117 Rafael Belliard	.05	.15
118 Luis Lopez	.05	.15
119 Tony Fossas	.05	.15
120 Len Dykstra	.10	.30
121 Mike Morgan	.05	.15
122 Denny Hocking	.05	.15
123 Kevin Gross	.05	.15
124 Todd Benzinger	.05	.15
125 John Doherty	.05	.15
126 Eduardo Perez	.05	.15
127 Dan Smith	.05	.15
128 Joe Orsulak	.05	.15
129 Brent Gates	.05	.15
130 Jeff Conine	.10	.30
131 Doug Henry	.05	.15
132 Paul Sorrento	.05	.15
133 Mike Hampton	.10	.30
134 Tim Spehr	.05	.15
135 Julio Franco	.10	.30
136 Mike Dyer	.05	.15
137 Chris Sabo	.05	.15
138 Rheal Cormier	.05	.15
139 Paul Konerko	.40	1.00
140 Dante Bichette	.10	.30
141 Chuck McElroy	.05	.15
142 Mike Stanley	.05	.15
143 Bob Hamelin	.05	.15
144 Tommy Greene	.05	.15
145 John Smoltz	.20	.50
146 Ed Sprague	.05	.15
147 Ray McDavid	.05	.15
148 Otis Nixon	.05	.15
149 Turk Wendell	.05	.15
150 Chris James	.05	.15
151 Derek Parks	.05	.15
152 Jose Offerman	.05	.15
153 Tony Clark	.05	.15
154 Chad Curtis	.05	.15
155 Mark Portugal	.05	.15
156 Bill Pulsipher	.05	.15
157 Troy Neel	.05	.15
158 Dave Winfield	.10	.30
159 Bill Wegman	.05	.15
160 Benito Santiago	.10	.30
161 Jose Mesa	.05	.15
162 Luis Gonzalez	.10	.30
163 Alex Fernandez	.05	.15
164 Freddie Benavides	.05	.15
165 Ben McDonald	.05	.15
166 Blas Minor	.05	.15
167 Bret Wagner	.05	.15
168 Mac Suzuki	.05	.15
169 Roberto Mejia	.05	.15
170 Wade Boggs	.20	.50
171 Pokey Reese	.05	.15
172 Hipolito Pichardo	.05	.15
173 Kim Batiste	.05	.15
174 Darren Hall	.05	.15
175 Tom Glavine	.20	.50
176 Phil Plantier	.05	.15
177 Chris Howard	.05	.15
178 Karl Rhodes	.05	.15
179 LaTroy Hawkins	.05	.15
180 Raul Mondesi	.10	.30
181 Jeff Reed	.05	.15
182 Milt Cuyler	.05	.15
183 Jim Edmonds	.20	.50
184 Hector Fajardo	.05	.15
185 Jeff Kent	.10	.30
186 Wilson Alvarez	.05	.15
187 Geronimo Berroa	.05	.15
188 Billy Spiers	.05	.15
189 Derek Lilliquist	.05	.15
190 Craig Biggio	.20	.50
191 Roberto Hernandez	.05	.15
192 Bob Natal	.05	.15
193 Bobby Ayala	.05	.15
194 Travis Miller RC	.05	.15
195 Bob Tewksbury	.05	.15
196 Rondell White	.10	.30
197 Steve Cooke	.05	.15
198 Jeff Branson	.05	.15
199 Derek Jeter	.75	2.00
200 Tim Salmon	.20	.50
201 Steve Frey	.05	.15
202 Kent Mercker	.05	.15
203 Randy Johnson	.30	.75
204 Todd Worrell	.05	.15
205 Mo Vaughn	.10	.30
206 Howard Johnson	.05	.15
207 John Wasdin	.05	.15
208 Eddie Williams	.05	.15
209 Tim Belcher	.05	.15
210 Jeff Montgomery	.05	.15
211 Kirt Manwaring	.05	.15
212 Ben Grieve	.05	.15
213 Pat Hentgen	.05	.15
214 Shawon Dunston	.05	.15
215 Mike Greenwell	.05	.15
216 Alex Diaz	.05	.15
217 Pat Mahomes	.05	.15
218 Dave Hansen	.05	.15
219 Kevin Rogers	.05	.15
220 Cecil Fielder	.10	.30
221 Andrew Lorraine	.05	.15
222 Jack Armstrong	.05	.15
223 Todd Hundley	.05	.15
224 Mark Acre	.05	.15
225 Darrell Whitmore	.05	.15
226 Randy Milligan	.05	.15
227 Wayne Kirby	.05	.15
228 Darryl Kile	.10	.30
229 Bob Zupcic	.05	.15
230 Jay Bell	.10	.30
231 Dustin Hermanson	.05	.15
232 Harold Baines	.10	.30
233 Alan Benes	.05	.15
234 Felix Fermin	.05	.15
235 Ellis Burks	.10	.30
236 Jeff Brantley	.05	.15
237 Brian Hunter	.05	.15
Jose Malave		
Karim Garcia RC		
Shane Pullen		
238 Matt Nokes	.05	.15
239 Ben Rivera	.05	.15
240 Joe Carter	.10	.30
241 Jeff Granger	.05	.15
242 Terry Pendleton	.10	.30
243 Melvin Nieves	.05	.15
244 Frankie Rodriguez	.05	.15
245 Darryl Hamilton	.05	.15
246 Brooks Kieschnick	.05	.15
247 Todd Hollandsworth	.05	.15
248 Joe Rosselli	.05	.15
249 Bill Gullickson	.05	.15
250 Chuck Knoblauch	.10	.30
251 Kurt Miller	.05	.15
252 Bobby Jones	.05	.15
253 Lance Blankenship	.05	.15
254 Matt Whiteside	.05	.15
255 Darrin Fletcher	.05	.15
256 Eric Plunk	.05	.15
257 Shane Reynolds	.05	.15
258 Norberto Martin	.05	.15
259 Mike Thurman	.05	.15
260 Andy Van Slyke	.20	.50
261 Dwight Smith	.05	.15
262 Allen Watson	.05	.15
263 Dan Wilson	.05	.15
264 Brent Mayne	.05	.15
265 Bip Roberts	.05	.15
266 Sterling Hitchcock	.05	.15
267 Alex Gonzalez	.05	.15
268 Greg Harris	.05	.15
269 Ricky Jordan	.05	.15
270 Johnny Ruffin	.05	.15
271 Mike Stanton	.05	.15
272 Rich Rowland	.05	.15
273 Steve Trachsel	.05	.15
274 Pedro Munoz	.05	.15
275 Ramon Martinez	.05	.15
276 Dave Henderson	.05	.15
277 Chris Gomez	.05	.15
278 Joe Grahe	.05	.15
279 Rusty Greer	.10	.30
280 John Franco	.10	.30
281 Mike Bordick	.05	.15
282 Jeff D'Amico	.05	.15
283 Dave Magadan	.05	.15
284 Tony Pena	.05	.15
285 Greg Swindell	.05	.15
286 Doug Million	.05	.15
287 Gabe White	.05	.15
288 Trey Beamon	.05	.15
289 Arthur Rhodes	.05	.15
290 Juan Guzman	.05	.15
291 Jose Oquendo	.05	.15
292 Willie Blair	.05	.15
293 Eddie Taubensee	.05	.15
294 Steve Howe	.05	.15
295 Greg Maddux	.50	1.25
296 Mike Macfarlane	.05	.15
297 Curt Schilling	.10	.30
298 Phil Clark	.05	.15
299 Woody Williams	.05	.15
300 Jose Canseco	.20	.50
301 Aaron Sele	.05	.15
302 Carl Willis	.05	.15
303 Steve Buechele	.05	.15
304 Dave Burba	.05	.15
305 Orel Hershiser	.10	.30
306 Damion Easley	.05	.15
307 Mike Henneman	.05	.15
308 Josias Manzanillo	.05	.15
309 Kevin Seitzer	.05	.15
310 Ruben Sierra	.10	.30
311 Bryan Harvey	.05	.15
312 Jim Thome	.20	.50
313 Ramon Castro RC	.15	.40
314 Lance Johnson	.05	.15
315 Marquis Grissom	.10	.30
316 Terrell Wade	.05	.15
Juan Acevedo		
Matt Arrandale		
Eddie Priest RC		
317 Paul Wagner	.05	.15
318 Jamie Moyer	.10	.30
319 Todd Zeile	.05	.15
320 Chris Bosio	.05	.15
321 Steve Reed	.05	.15
322 Erik Hanson	.05	.15
323 Luis Polonia	.05	.15
324 Ryan Klesko	.10	.30
325 Kevin Appier	.10	.30
326 Jim Eisenreich	.05	.15
327 Randy Knorr	.05	.15
328 Craig Shipley	.05	.15
329 Tim Naehring	.05	.15
330 Randy Myers	.05	.15
331 Alex Cole	.05	.15
332 Jim Gott	.05	.15
333 Mike Jackson	.05	.15
334 John Flaherty	.05	.15
335 Chili Davis	.10	.30
336 Benji Gil	.05	.15
337 Jason Jacome	.05	.15
338 Stan Javier	.05	.15
339 Mike Fetters	.05	.15
340 Rich Renteria	.05	.15
341 Kevin Witt	.05	.15
342 Scott Servais	.05	.15
343 Craig Grebeck	.05	.15
344 Kirk Rueter	.05	.15
345 Don Slaught	.05	.15
346 Armando Benitez	.05	.15
347 Ozzie Smith	.50	1.25
348 Mike Blowers	.05	.15
349 Armando Reynoso	.05	.15
350 Barry Larkin	.20	.50
351 Mike Williams	.05	.15
352 Scott Kamieniecki	.05	.15
353 Gary Gaetti	.10	.30
354 Todd Stottlemyre	.05	.15
355 Fred McGriff	.20	.50
356 Tim Mauser	.05	.15
357 Chris Gwynn	.05	.15
358 Frank Castillo	.05	.15
359 Jeff Reboulet	.05	.15
360 Roger Clemens	.60	1.50
361 Mark Carreon	.05	.15
362 Chad Kreuter	.05	.15
363 Mark Farris	.05	.15
364 Bob Welch	.05	.15
365 Dean Palmer	.10	.30
366 Jeromy Burnitz	.10	.30
367 B.J. Surhoff	.10	.30
368 Mike Butcher	.05	.15
369 Brad Clontz	.05	.15
Steve Phoenix		
Scott Gentile		
Bucky Buckles RC		
370 Eddie Murray	.30	.75
371 Orlando Miller	.05	.15
372 Ron Karkovice	.05	.15
373 Richie Lewis	.05	.15
374 Lenny Webster	.05	.15
375 Jeff Tackett	.05	.15
376 Tom Urbani	.05	.15
377 Tino Martinez	.20	.50
378 Mark Dewey	.05	.15
379 Charles O'Brien	.05	.15
380 Terry Mulholland	.05	.15
381 Thomas Howard	.05	.15
382 Chris Haney	.05	.15
383 Billy Hatcher	.05	.15
384 Jeff Bagwell AS	.20	.50
Frank Thomas AS		
385 Bret Boone AS	.10	.30
Carlos Baerga AS		
386 Matt Williams AS	.10	.30
Wade Boggs AS		
387 Wil Cordero AS	.30	.75
Cal Ripken AS		
388 Barry Bonds AS	.40	1.00
Ken Griffey AS		
389 Tony Gwynn AS	.10	.30
Albert Belle AS		
390 Dante Bichette AS	.20	.50
Kirby Puckett AS		
391 Mike Piazza AS	.30	.75
Mike Stanley AS		
392 Greg Maddux AS	.30	.75
David Cone AS		
393 Danny Jackson AS	.05	.15
Jimmy Key AS		
394 John Franco AS	.05	.15
Lee Smith AS		
395 Checklist 1-198	.05	.15
396 Checklist 199-396	.05	.15
397 Ken Griffey Jr.	.50	1.25
398 Rick Heiserman RC	.05	.15
399 Don Mattingly	.75	2.00
400 Henry Rodriguez	.05	.15
401 Lenny Harris	.05	.15
402 Ryan Thompson	.05	.15
403 Darren Oliver	.05	.15
404 Omar Vizquel	.20	.50
405 Jeff Bagwell	.20	.50
406 Doug Webb RC	.05	.15
407 Todd Van Poppel	.05	.15
408 Leo Gomez	.05	.15
409 Mark Whiten	.05	.15
410 Pedro A.Martinez	.05	.15
411 Reggie Sanders	.10	.30
412 Kevin Foster	.05	.15
413 Danny Tartabull	.05	.15
414 Jeff Blauser	.05	.15
415 Mike Magnante	.05	.15
416 Tom Candiotti	.05	.15
417 Rod Beck	.05	.15
418 Jody Reed	.05	.15
419 Vince Coleman	.05	.15
420 Danny Jackson	.05	.15
421 Ryan Nye RC	.05	.15
422 Larry Walker	.10	.30
423 Russ Johnson DP	.05	.15
424 Pat Borders	.05	.15
425 Lee Smith	.10	.30
426 Paul O'Neill	.20	.50
427 Devon White	.10	.30
428 Jim Bullinger	.05	.15
429 Greg Hansell	.05	.15
Brian Sackinsky		
Carey Paige		
Rob Welch RC		
430 Steve Avery	.05	.15
431 Tony Gwynn	.40	1.00

432 Pat Meares .05 .15
433 Bill Swift .05 .15
434 David Wells .10 .30
435 John Briscoe .05 .15
436 Roger Pavlik .05 .15
437 Jayson Peterson RC .05 .15
438 Roberto Alomar .20 .50
439 Billy Brewer .05 .15
440 Gary Sheffield .10 .30
441 Lou Frazier .05 .15
442 Terry Steinbach .05 .15
443 Jay Payton RC .30 .75
444 Jason Bere .05 .15
445 Denny Neagle .10 .30
446 Andres Galarraga .10 .30
447 Hector Carrasco .05 .15
448 Bill Risley .05 .15
449 Andy Benes .05 .15
450 Jim Leyritz .05 .15
451 Jose Oliva .05 .15
452 Greg Vaughn .05 .15
453 Rich Monteleone .05 .15
454 Tony Eusebio .05 .15
455 Chuck Finley .10 .30
456 Kevin Brown .10 .30
457 Joe Boever .05 .15
458 Bobby Munoz .05 .15
459 Bret Saberhagen .10 .30
460 Kurt Abbott .05 .15
461 Bobby Witt .05 .15
462 Cliff Floyd .10 .30
463 Mark Clark .05 .15
464 Andujar Cedeno .05 .15
465 Marvin Freeman .05 .15
466 Mike Piazza .50 1.25
467 Willie Greene .05 .15
468 Pat Kelly .05 .15
469 Carlos Delgado .10 .30
470 Willie Banks .05 .15
471 Matt Walbeck .05 .15
472 Mark McGwire .75 2.00
473 M.Christensen RC .05 .15
474 Alan Trammell .10 .30
475 Tom Gordon .05 .15
476 Greg Colbrunn .05 .15
477 Darren Daulton .10 .30
478 Albie Lopez .05 .15
479 Robin Ventura .10 .30
480 Eddie Perez RC .15 .40
Jason Kendall
Einar Diaz
Bret Hemphill
481 Bryan Eversgerd .05 .15
482 Dave Fleming .05 .15
483 Scott Livingstone .05 .15
484 Pete Schourek .05 .15
485 Bernie Williams .20 .50
486 Mark Lemke .05 .15
487 Eric Karros .10 .30
488 Scott Ruffcorn .05 .15
489 Billy Ashley .05 .15
490 Rico Brogna .05 .15
491 John Burkett .05 .15
492 Cade Gaspar RC .05 .15
493 Jorge Fabregas .05 .15
494 Greg Gagne .05 .15
495 Doug Jones .05 .15
496 Troy O'Leary .05 .15
497 Pat Rapp .05 .15
498 Butch Henry .05 .15
499 John Olerud .10 .30
500 John Hudek .05 .15
501 Jeff King .05 .15
502 Bobby Bonilla .10 .30
503 Albert Belle .10 .30
504 Rick Wilkins .05 .15
505 John Jaha .05 .15
506 Nigel Wilson .05 .15
507 Sid Fernandez .05 .15
508 Deion Sanders .20 .50
509 Gil Heredia .05 .15
510 Scott Elarton RC .15 .40
511 Melido Perez .05 .15
512 Greg McMichael .05 .15
513 Rusty Meacham .05 .15
514 Shawn Green .10 .30
515 Carlos Garcia .05 .15
516 Dave Stevens .05 .15
517 Eric Young .05 .15
518 Omar Daal .05 .15
519 Kirk Gibson .10 .30
520 Spike Owen .05 .15
521 Jacob Cruz RC .10 .30
522 Sandy Alomar Jr. .05 .15
523 Steve Bedrosian .05 .15
524 Ricky Gutierrez .05 .15
525 Dave Veres .05 .15
526 Gregg Jefferies .05 .15
527 Jose Valentin .05 .15
528 Robb Nen .10 .30
529 Jose Rijo .05 .15
530 Sean Berry .05 .15
531 Mike Gallego .05 .15
532 Roberto Kelly .05 .15
533 Kevin Stocker .05 .15
534 Kirby Puckett .30 .75
535 Chipper Jones .30 .75
536 Russ Davis .05 .15
537 Jon Lieber .05 .15
538 Trey Moore RC .05 .15
539 Joe Girardi .05 .15
540 Quilvio Veras .05 .15
Arquimedez Pozo
Miguel Cairo RC
Jason Camilli
541 Tony Phillips .05 .15
542 Brian Anderson .05 .15
543 Ivan Rodriguez .20 .50
544 Jeff Cirillo .05 .15
545 Joey Cora .05 .15
546 Chris Hoiles .05 .15
547 Bernard Gilkey .05 .15
548 Mike Lansing .05 .15
549 Jimmy Key .10 .30
550 Mark Wohlers .05 .15
551 Chris Clemons RC .05 .15
552 Vinny Castilla .10 .30
553 Mark Guthrie .05 .15
554 Mike Lieberthal .10 .30
555 Tommy Davis RC .05 .15
556 Robby Thompson .05 .15
557 Danny Bautista .05 .15
558 Will Clark .20 .50
559 Rickey Henderson .30 .75
560 Todd Jones .05 .15
561 Jack McDowell .05 .15
562 Carlos Rodriguez .05 .15
563 Mark Eichhorn .05 .15
564 Jeff Nelson .05 .15
565 Eric Anthony .05 .15
566 Randy Velarde .05 .15
567 Javier Lopez .10 .30
568 Kevin Mitchell .05 .15
569 Steve Karsay .05 .15
570 Brian Meadows RC .05 .15
571 Rey Ordonez RC .30 .75
Mike Metcalfe
Kevin Orie
Ray Holbert
572 John Kruk .10 .30
573 Scott Leius .05 .15
574 John Patterson .05 .15
575 Kevin Brown .10 .30
576 Mike Moore .05 .15
577 Manny Ramirez .20 .50
578 Jose Lind .05 .15
579 Derrick May .05 .15
580 Cal Eldred .05 .15
581 David Bell .30 .75
Joel Chelmis
Lino Diaz
Aaron Boone RC
582 J.T. Snow .10 .30
583 Luis Sojo .05 .15
584 Moises Alou .10 .30
585 Dave Clark .05 .15
586 Dave Hollins .05 .15
587 Nomar Garciaparra .75 2.00
588 Cal Ripken 1.00 2.50
589 Pedro Astacio .05 .15
590 J.R. Phillips .05 .15
591 Jeff Frye .05 .15
592 Bo Jackson .30 .75
593 Steve Ontiveros .05 .15
594 David Nied .05 .15
595 Brad Ausmus .10 .30
596 Carlos Baerga .05 .15
597 James Mouton .05 .15
598 Ozzie Guillen .10 .30
599 Ozzie Timmons .30 .75
Curtis Goodwin
Johnny Damon
Jeff Abbott RC
600 Yorkis Perez .05 .15
601 Rich Rodriguez .05 .15
602 Mark McLemore .05 .15
603 Jeff Fassero .05 .15
604 John Roper .05 .15
605 Mark Johnson RC .15 .40
606 Wes Chamberlain .05 .15
607 Felix Jose .05 .15
608 Tony Longmire .05 .15
609 Duane Ward .05 .15
610 Brett Butler .10 .30
611 W.VanLandingham .05 .15
612 Mickey Tettleton .05 .15
613 Brady Anderson .10 .30
614 Reggie Jefferson .05 .15
615 Mike Kingery .05 .15
616 Derek Bell .05 .15
617 Scott Erickson .05 .15
618 Bob Wickman .05 .15
619 Phil Leftwich .05 .15
620 David Justice .10 .30
621 Paul Wilson .05 .15
622 Pedro Martinez .20 .50
623 Terry Mathews .05 .15
624 Brian McRae .05 .15
625 Bruce Ruffin .05 .15
626 Steve Finley .10 .30
627 Ron Gant .10 .30
628 Rafael Bournigal .05 .15
629 Darryl Strawberry .10 .30
630 Luis Alicea .05 .15
631 Mark Smith .05 .15
Scott Klingenbeck
632 Cory Bailey .05 .15
Scott Hatteberg
633 Todd Greene .10 .30
Troy Percival
634 Rod Bolton .05 .15
Olmedo Saenz
635 Steve Kline .05 .15
Herb Perry
636 Sean Bergman .05 .15
Shannon Penn
637 Joe Randa .10 .30
Joe Vitiello
638 Jose Mercedes .05 .15
Duane Singleton
639 Marc Barcelo .05 .15
Marty Cordova
640 Andy Pettitte .10 .30
Ruben Rivera
641 Willie Adams .05 .15
Scott Spiezio
642 Eddy Diaz RC .05 .15
Desi Relaford
643 Terrell Lowery .05 .15
Jon Shave
644 Angel Martinez .05 .15
Paul Spoljaric
645 Tony Graffanino .05 .15
Damon Hollins
646 Darron Cox .05 .15
Doug Glanville
647 Tim Belk .05 .15
Pat Watkins
648 Rod Pedraza .05 .15
Phil Schneider
649 Vic Darensbourg .05 .15
Marc Valdes
650 Rick Huisman .05 .15
Roberto Petagine
651 Roger Cedeno .05 .15
Ron Coomer RC
652 Shane Andrews .15 .40
Carlos Perez RC
653 Jason Isringhausen .10 .30
Chris Roberts
654 Wayne Gomes .05 .15
Kevin Jordan
655 Esteban Loiaza .05 .15
Steve Pegues
656 Terry Bradshaw .05 .15
John Frascatore
657 Andres Berumen .05 .15
Bryce Florie
658 Dan Carlson .05 .15
Keith Williams
659 Checklist .05 .15
660 Checklist .05 .15

1995 Topps Cyberstats

The 396-card Cyberstats insert set was issued one per pack and three per jumbo pack. Each 1995 Topps series had 198 Cyberstat cards. The idea was to present prorated statistics for the 1994 strike shortened season. The photos on front are the same as the basic issue. The difference is that the photo is given a glossy or metallic finish. The backs contain yearly and career statistics, including the prorated 1994 numbers.

COMPLETE SET (396) 25.00 60.00
COMP.SERIES 1 (198) 10.00 25.00
COMP.SERIES 2 (198) 15.00 40.00
*STARS: 1X TO 2.5X BASIC CARDS

1995 Topps Cyber Season in Review

This seven-card set was distributed exclusively in 1995 Topps hobby factory sets. It continues the Cyberstats insert theme used in the regular issue product, which presented "what if" statistics to fill in the strike-shortened 1994 season. The Season in Review cards commemorate projected accomplishments including Barry Bonds' 61 home runs and Kenny Lofton's World Series MVP.

COMPLETE SET (7) 4.00 10.00
1 Barry Bonds 1.50 4.00
2 Jose Canseco .75 2.00
3 Juan Gonzalez .60 1.50
4 Fred McGriff .40 1.00
5 Carlos Baerga .20 .50
6 Ryan Klesko .40 1.00
7 Kenny Lofton .30 .75

1995 Topps Finest Inserts

This 15-card standard-size set was inserted one every 36 Topps series two packs. This set featured the top 15 players in total bases from the 1994 season. The fronts feature a player photo, with his team identification and name on the bottom of the card. The horizontal backs feature another player photo along with a breakdown of how many of each type of hit each player got on the way to their season total. The set is sequenced in order of how they finished in the majors for the 1994 season.

COMPLETE SET (15) 25.00 60.00
1 Jeff Bagwell 1.25 3.00
2 Albert Belle .75 2.00
3 Ken Griffey Jr. 3.00 8.00
4 Frank Thomas 2.00 5.00
5 Matt Williams .75 2.00
6 Dante Bichette .75 2.00
7 Barry Bonds 5.00 12.00
8 Moises Alou .75 2.00
9 Andres Galarraga .75 2.00
10 Kenny Lofton .75 2.00
11 Rafael Palmeiro 1.25 3.00
12 Tony Gwynn 2.50 6.00
13 Kirby Puckett 2.00 5.00
14 Jose Canseco 1.25 3.00
15 Jeff Conine .75 2.00

1995 Topps League Leaders

Randomly inserted in jumbo packs at a rate of one in three and retail packs at a rate of one in six, this 50-card standard-size set showcases those that were among league leaders in various categories. Card fronts feature a player photo with a black background. The player's name appears in gold foil at the bottom and the category with which he led the league or was among the leaders is in yellow letters up the right side. The backs contain various graphs and where the player placed among the leaders.

COMPLETE SET (50) 20.00 50.00

COMPLETE SERIES 1 (25) 8.00 20.00
COMPLETE SERIES 2 (25) 12.50 30.00
LL1 Albert Belle .25 .60
LL2 Kevin Mitchell .10 .30
LL3 Wade Boggs .40 1.00
LL4 Tony Gwynn .75 2.00
LL5 Moises Alou .25 .60
LL6 Andres Galarraga .25 .60
LL7 Matt Williams .25 .60
LL8 Barry Bonds 1.50 4.00
LL9 Frank Thomas .60 1.50
LL10 Jose Canseco .40 1.00
LL11 Jeff Bagwell .40 1.00
LL12 Kirby Puckett .60 1.50
LL13 Julio Franco .25 .60
LL14 Albert Belle .25 .60
LL15 Fred McGriff .40 1.00
LL16 Kenny Lofton .25 .60
LL17 Otis Nixon .10 .30
LL18 Brady Anderson .25 .60
LL19 Deion Sanders .40 1.00
LL20 Chuck Carr .10 .30
LL21 Pat Hentgen .10 .30
LL22 Andy Benes .10 .30
LL23 Roger Clemens 1.25 3.00
LL24 Greg Maddux 1.00 2.50
LL25 Pedro Martinez .10 .30
LL26 Paul O'Neill .40 1.00
LL27 Jeff Bagwell .40 1.00
LL28 Frank Thomas .60 1.50
LL29 Hal Morris .10 .30
LL30 Kenny Lofton .25 .60
LL31 Ken Griffey Jr. 1.00 2.50
LL32 Jeff Bagwell .40 1.00
LL33 Albert Belle .25 .60
LL34 Fred McGriff .40 1.00
LL35 Cecil Fielder .25 .60
LL36 Matt Williams .25 .60
LL37 Joe Carter .25 .60
LL38 Dante Bichette .25 .60
LL39 Frank Thomas .60 1.50
LL40 Mike Piazza 1.00 2.50
LL41 Craig Biggio .40 1.00
LL42 Vince Coleman .10 .30
LL43 Marquis Grissom .25 .60
LL44 Chuck Knoblauch .25 .60
LL45 Darren Lewis .10 .30
LL46 Randy Johnson .60 1.50
LL47 Jose Rijo .10 .30
LL48 Chuck Finley .25 .60
LL49 Bret Saberhagen .25 .60
LL50 Kevin Appier .25 .60

1995 Topps Opening Day

This 10-card standard-size set was inserted into all retail factory sets. The borderless fronts feature the player's photo set against a prismatic star background and the player's name on the bottom. In the lower right, the player's opening day highlight is mentioned and there is an "Opening Day" verbiage and logo in the upper right. The horizontal back has a player photo, description of the player's opening day as well as a line score for the player.

COMPLETE SET (10) 10.00 25.00
1 Kevin Appier .20 .50
2 Dante Bichette .40 1.00
3 Ken Griffey Jr. 6.00 15.00
4 Todd Hundley .40 1.00
5 John Jaha .20 .50
6 Fred McGriff .60 1.50
7 Raul Mondesi .40 1.00
8 Manny Ramirez 2.50 6.00
9 Danny Tartabull .20 .50
10 Devon White .40 1.00

1995 Topps Traded

This set contains 165 standard-size cards and was sold in 11-card packs for $1.29. The set features rookies, draft picks and players who had been traded. The fronts contain a photo with a white border. The backs have a player picture in a scoreboard and his statistics and information. Subsets featured are: At the Break (1T-10T) and All-Stars (156T-164T). Rookie Cards in this set include Michael Barrett, Carlos Beltran, Ben Davis, Hideo Nomo and Richie Sexson.

COMPLETE SET (165) 15.00 40.00
1T Frank Thomas ATB .25 .60
2T Ken Griffey Jr. ATB .40 1.00
3T Barry Bonds ATB .50 1.25
4T Albert Belle ATB .15 .40
5T Cal Ripken ATB .60 1.50
6T Mike Piazza ATB .40 1.00
7T Tony Gwynn ATB .25 .60
8T Jeff Bagwell ATB .15 .40
9T Mo Vaughn ATB .07 .20
10T Matt Williams ATB .07 .20
11T Ray Durham .15 .40
12T Juan LeBron RC 2.50 6.00
Card pictures Carlos Beltran
13T Shawn Green .15 .40
14T Kevin Gross .07 .20
15T Jon Nunnally .07 .20
16T Brian Maxcy RC .08 .25
17T Mark Kiefer .07 .20
18T Carlos Beltran UER RC 6.00 15.00
Card pictures Juan LeBron
19T Mike Mimbs RC .08 .25
20T Larry Walker .15 .40
21T Chad Curtis .07 .20
22T Jeff Barry .07 .20
23T Joe Oliver .07 .20
24T Tomas Perez RC .08 .25
25T Michael Barrett RC .40 1.00
26T Brian McRae .07 .20
27T Derek Bell .07 .20
28T Ray Durham .15 .40
29T Todd Williams .07 .20
30T Ryan Jaroncyk RC .08 .25
31T Todd Steverson .07 .20
32T Mike Devereaux .07 .20
33T Rheal Cormier .07 .20
34T Benny Santiago .15 .40
35T Bobby Higginson RC .40 1.00
36T Jack McDowell .07 .20
37T Mike Macfarlane .07 .20
38T Tony McKnight RC .08 .25
39T Brian Hunter .07 .20
40T Hideo Nomo RC 1.50 4.00
41T Brett Butler .15 .40
42T Donovan Osborne .07 .20
43T Scott Karl .07 .20
44T Tony Phillips .07 .20
45T Marty Cordova .07 .20
46T Dave Mlicki .07 .20
47T Bronson Arroyo RC 2.50 6.00
48T John Burkett .07 .20
49T J.D. Smart RC .08 .25
50T Mickey Tettleton .07 .20
51T Todd Stottlemyre .07 .20
52T Mike Perez .07 .20
53T Terry Mulholland .07 .20
54T Edgardo Alfonzo .07 .20
55T Zane Smith .07 .20
56T Jacob Brumfield .07 .20
57T Andujar Cedeno .07 .20
58T Jose Parra .07 .20
59T Manny Alexander .07 .20
60T Tony Tarasco .07 .20
61T Orel Hershiser .15 .40
62T Tim Scott .07 .20
63T Felix Rodriguez RC .08 .25
64T Ken Hill .07 .20
65T Marquis Grissom .15 .40
66T Lee Smith .15 .40
67T Jason Bates .07 .20
68T Felipe Lira .07 .20
69T Alex Hernandez RC .08 .25
70T Tony Fernandez .07 .20
71T Scott Radinsky .07 .20
72T Jose Canseco .25 .60
73T Mark Grudzielanek RC .40 1.00
74T Ben Davis RC .08 .25
75T Jim Abbott .25 .60
76T Roger Bailey .07 .20
77T Gregg Jefferies .07 .20
78T Erik Hanson .07 .20
79T Brad Radke RC .40 1.00
80T Jaime Navarro .07 .20
81T John Wetteland .15 .40
82T Chad Fonville RC .08 .25
83T John Mabry .07 .20
84T Glenallen Hill .07 .20
85T Ken Caminiti .15 .40
86T Tom Goodwin .07 .20
87T Darren Bragg .07 .20
88T Pat Ahearne .08 .25
Gary Rath
Larry Wimberly
Robbie Bell RC
89T Jeff Russell .07 .20
90T Dave Gallagher .07 .20
91T Steve Finley .15 .40
92T Vaughn Eshelman .07 .20
93T Kevin Jarvis .07 .20
94T Mark Gubicza .07 .20
95T Tim Wakefield .15 .40
96T Bob Tewksbury .07 .20
97T Sid Roberson RC .08 .25
98T Tom Henke .07 .20
99T Michael Tucker .07 .20
100T Jason Bates .07 .20
101T Otis Nixon .07 .20
102T Mark Whiten .07 .20
103T Dilson Torres RC .08 .25
104T Melvin Bunch RC .08 .25
105T Terry Pendleton .15 .40
106T Corey Jenkins RC .08 .25
107T Glenn Dishman RC .08 .25
Rob Grable
108T Reggie Taylor RC .08 .25
109T Curtis Goodwin .07 .20
110T David Cone .15 .40
111T Antonio Osuna .07 .20
112T Paul Shuey .07 .20
113T Doug Jones .07 .20
114T Mark McLemore .07 .20
115T Kevin Ritz .07 .20
116T John Kruk .15 .40
117T Trevor Wilson .07 .20
118T Jerald Clark .07 .20
119T Julian Tavarez .07 .20
120T Tim Pugh .07 .20
121T Todd Zeile .07 .20
122T Mark Sweeney UER 1.50 4.00
George Arias
Richie Sexson RC
Brian Schneider
123T Bobby Witt .07 .20
124T Hideo Nomo .60 1.50
125T Joey Cora .07 .20
126T Jim Scharrer RC .08 .25
127T Paul Quantrill .07 .20
128T Chipper Jones ROY .25 .60
129T Kenny James RC .08 .25
130T Lyle Mouton .50 1.25
Mariano Rivera
131T Tyler Green .07 .20
132T Brad Clontz .07 .20
133T Jon Nunnally .07 .20
134T Dave Magadan .07 .20
135T Al Leiter .15 .40
136T Bret Barberie .07 .20
137T Bill Swift .07 .20
138T Scott Cooper .07 .20
139T Roberto Kelly .07 .20
140T Charlie Hayes .07 .20
141T Pete Harnisch .07 .20
142T Rich Amaral .07 .20
143T Rudy Seanez .07 .20
144T Pat Listach .07 .20
145T Quilvio Veras .07 .20
146T Jose Olmeda RC .08 .25
147T Roberto Petagine .07 .20
148T Kevin Brown .15 .40
149T Phil Plantier .07 .20
150T Carlos Perez .15 .40
151T Pat Borders .07 .20
152T Tyler Green .07 .20
153T Stan Belinda .07 .20
154T Dave Stewart .15 .40
155T Andre Dawson .15 .40
156T Frank Thomas AS .25 .60
Fred McGriff UER
(McGriff's team shown as Blue Jays)
157T Carlos Baerga AS .15 .40
Craig Biggio
158T Wade Boggs AS .15 .40
Matt Williams
159T Cal Ripken AS .40 1.00
Ozzie Smith
160T Ken Griffey Jr. AS .40 1.00
Tony Gwynn
161T Albert Belle AS .50 1.25
Barry Bonds
162T Kirby Puckett .25 .60
Len Dykstra
163T Ivan Rodriguez AS .40 1.00
Mike Piazza
164T Randy Johnson AS .60 1.50
Hideo Nomo
165T Checklist .07 .20

1995 Topps Traded Proofs

Little is known about these cards, the one sample we have has a photo of Shawn Green used on his 1995 Topps Traded card but the back is the one used in the regular 1995 Topps set. There may be more cards so all additional information is appreciated.

NNO Shawn Green 4.00 10.00

1995 Topps Traded Power Boosters

This 10-card standard-size set was inserted in packs at a rate of one in 36. The set is comprised of parallel cards for the first 10 cards of the regular Topps Traded set which was the "At the Break" subset. The cards are done on extra-thick stock. The fronts have an action photo on a "Power Boosted" background, which is similar to diffraction technology, with the words "at the break" on the left side. The backs have a head shot and player information including his mid-season statistics for 1995 and previous years.

COMPLETE SET (10) 30.00 80.00
1 Frank Thomas 4.00 10.00
2 Ken Griffey Jr. 6.00 15.00
3 Barry Bonds 8.00 20.00
4 Albert Belle 2.50 6.00
5 Cal Ripken 10.00 25.00
6 Mike Piazza 6.00 15.00
7 Tony Gwynn 4.00 10.00
8 Jeff Bagwell 2.50 6.00
9 Mo Vaughn 1.25 3.00
10 Matt Williams 1.25 3.00

1995 Topps Legends of the '60s Medallions

These 12 bronze medallions feature some of the best players of the 60's, duplicating the regular issue Topps cards from various years. This was a special offering for Topps Stadium Club members. One medallion was issued each month; the issue price was $39.95 per card.

COMPLETE SET (12) 200.00 500.00
1 Willie Mays 20.00 50.00
2 Hank Aaron 20.00 50.00
3 Bob Gibson 15.00 40.00
4 Don Drysdale 15.00 40.00
5 Frank Robinson 15.00 40.00
6 Carl Yastrzemski 15.00 40.00
7 Willie McCovey 15.00 40.00
8 Roberto Clemente 20.00 50.00
9 Juan Marichal 15.00 40.00
10 Brooks Robinson 15.00 40.00
11 Harmon Killebrew 15.00 40.00
12 Billy Williams 15.00 40.00

1996 Topps

This set consists of 440 standard-size cards. These cards were issued in 12-card foil packs with a

suggested retail price of $1.29. The fronts feature full-color photos surrounded by a white background. Information on the backs includes a player photo, season and career stats and text. First series subsets include Star Power (1-6, 8-12), Draft Picks (13-26), AAA Stars (101-104), and Future Stars (210-219). A special Mickey Mantle card was issued as card number 7 (his uniform number) and became the last card to be issued as card number 7 in the Topps brand set. Rookie Cards in this set include Sean Casey, Geoff Jenkins and Daryle Ward.

COMPLETE SET (440) 15.00 40.00
COMP.HOBBY SET (449) 15.00 40.00
COMP.CEREAL SET (444) 25.00 50.00
COMP.SERIES 1 (220) 8.00 20.00
COMP.SERIES 2 (220) 8.00 20.00
COMMON CARD (1-440) .07 .20
COMMON RC .08 .25
1 Tony Gwynn STP .10 .30
2 Mike Piazza STP .20 .50
3 Greg Maddux STP .20 .50
4 Jeff Bagwell STP .07 .20
5 Larry Walker STP .07 .20
6 Barry Larkin STP .07 .20
7 Mickey Mantle 1.50 4.00
8 Tom Glavine STP UER .07 .20
Won 21 games in June 95
9 Craig Biggio STP .07 .20
10 Barry Bonds STP .30 .75
11 H.Slocumb STP .07 .20
12 Matt Williams STP .07 .20
13 Todd Helton .40 1.00
14 Mark Redman .08 .25
15 Michael Barrett .08 .25
16 Ben Davis .08 .25
17 Juan LeBron .08 .25
18 Tony McKnight .08 .25
19 Ryan Jaroncyk .08 .25
20 Corey Jenkins .08 .25
21 Jim Scharrer .08 .25
22 Mark Bellhorn RC .40 1.00
23 Jarrod Washburn RC .30 .75
24 Geoff Jenkins RC .30 .75
25 Sean Casey RC 1.50 4.00
26 Brett Tomko RC .15 .40
27 Tony Fernandez .07 .20
28 Rich Becker .07 .20
29 Andujar Cedeno .07 .20
30 Paul Molitor .07 .20
31 Brent Gates .07 .20
32 Glenallen Hill .07 .20
33 Mike Macfarlane .07 .20
34 Manny Alexander .07 .20
35 Todd Zeile .07 .20
36 Joe Girardi .07 .20
37 Tony Tarasco .07 .20
38 Tim Belcher .07 .20
39 Tom Goodwin .07 .20
40 Orel Hershiser .07 .20
41 Tripp Cromer .07 .20
42 Sean Bergman .07 .20
43 Troy Percival .07 .20
44 Kevin Stocker .07 .20
45 Albert Belle .07 .20
46 Tony Eusebio .07 .20
47 Sid Roberson .07 .20
48 Todd Hollandsworth .07 .20
49 Mark Wohlers .07 .20
50 Kirby Puckett .20 .50
51 Darren Holmes .07 .20
52 Ron Karkovice .07 .20
53 Al Martin .07 .20
54 Pat Rapp .07 .20
55 Mark Grace .10 .30
56 Greg Gagne .07 .20
57 Stan Javier .07 .20
58 Scott Sanders .07 .20
59 J.T. Snow .07 .20
60 David Justice .07 .20
61 Royce Clayton .07 .20
62 Kevin Foster .07 .20
63 Tim Naehring .07 .20
64 Orlando Miller .07 .20
65 Mike Mussina .10 .30
66 Jim Eisenreich .07 .20
67 Felix Fermin .07 .20
68 Bernie Williams .10 .30
69 Robb Nen .07 .20
70 Ron Gant .07 .20
71 Felipe Lira .07 .20
72 Jacob Brumfield .07 .20
73 John Mabry .07 .20
74 Mark Carreon .07 .20
75 Carlos Baerga .07 .20
76 Jim Dougherty .07 .20
77 Ryan Thompson .07 .20
78 Scott Leius .07 .20
79 Roger Pavlik .07 .20
80 Gary Sheffield .07 .20
81 Julian Tavarez .07 .20
82 Andy Ashby .07 .20
83 Mark Lemke .07 .20
84 Omar Vizquel .10 .30
85 Darren Daulton .07 .20
86 Mike Lansing .07 .20
87 Rusty Greer .07 .20
88 Dave Stevens .07 .20
89 Jose Offerman .07 .20
90 Tom Henke .07 .20
91 Troy O'Leary .07 .20
92 Michael Tucker .07 .20
93 Marvin Freeman .07 .20
94 Alex Diaz .07 .20
95 John Wetteland .07 .20
96 Cal Ripken 2131 .75 2.00
97 Mike Mimbs .07 .20
98 Bobby Higginson .07 .20
99 Edgardo Alfonzo .07 .20
100 Frank Thomas .20 .50
101 Steve Gibralter .20 .50
Bob Abreu
102 Brian Givens .08 .25
T.J. Mathews
103 Chris Pritchett .08 .25
Trenidad Hubbard
104 Eric Owens .08 .25
Butch Huskey
105 Doug Drabek .07 .20
106 Tomas Perez .07 .20
107 Mark Leiter .07 .20
108 Joe Oliver .07 .20
109 Tony Castillo .07 .20
110 Checklist (1-110) .07 .20
111 Kevin Seitzer .07 .20
112 Pete Schourek .07 .20
113 Sean Berry .07 .20
114 Todd Stottlemyre .07 .20
115 Joe Carter .07 .20
116 Jeff King .07 .20
117 Dan Wilson .07 .20
118 Kurt Abbott .07 .20
119 Lyle Mouton .07 .20
120 Jose Rijo .07 .20
121 Curtis Goodwin .07 .20
122 Jose Valentin .07 .20
123 Ellis Burks .07 .20
124 David Cone .07 .20
125 Eddie Murray .20 .50
126 Brian Jordan .07 .20
127 Darrin Fletcher .07 .20
128 Curt Schilling .07 .20
129 Ozzie Guillen .07 .20
130 Kenny Rogers .07 .20
131 Tom Pagnozzi .07 .20
132 Garret Anderson .07 .20
133 Bobby Jones .07 .20
134 Chris Gomez .07 .20
135 Mike Stanley .07 .20
136 Hideo Nomo .20 .50
137 Jon Nunnally .07 .20
138 Tim Wakefield .07 .20
139 Steve Finley .07 .20
140 Ivan Rodriguez .10 .30
141 Quilvio Veras .07 .20
142 Mike Fetters .07 .20
143 Mike Greenwell .07 .20
144 Bill Pulsipher .07 .20
145 Mark McGwire .50 1.25
146 Frank Castillo .07 .20
147 Greg Vaughn .07 .20
148 Pat Hentgen .07 .20
149 Walt Weiss .07 .20
150 Randy Johnson .20 .50
151 David Segui .07 .20
152 Benji Gil .07 .20
153 Tom Candiotti .07 .20
154 Geronimo Berroa .07 .20
155 John Franco .07 .20
156 Jay Bell .07 .20
157 Mark Gubicza .07 .20
158 Hal Morris .07 .20
159 Wilson Alvarez .07 .20
160 Derek Bell .07 .20
161 Ricky Bottalico .07 .20
162 Bret Boone .07 .20
163 Brad Radke .07 .20
164 John Valentin .07 .20
165 Steve Avery .07 .20
166 Mark McLemore .07 .20
167 Danny Jackson .07 .20
168 Tino Martinez .10 .30
169 Shane Reynolds .07 .20
170 Terry Pendleton .07 .20
171 Jim Edmonds .07 .20
172 Esteban Loaiza .07 .20
173 Ray Durham .07 .20
174 Carlos Perez .07 .20
175 Raul Mondesi .07 .20
176 Steve Ontiveros .07 .20
177 Chipper Jones .20 .50
178 Otis Nixon .07 .20
179 John Burkett .07 .20
180 Gregg Jefferies .07 .20
181 Denny Martinez .07 .20
182 Ken Caminiti .07 .20
183 Doug Jones .07 .20
184 Brian McRae .07 .20
185 Don Mattingly .50 1.25
186 Mel Rojas .07 .20
187 Marty Cordova .07 .20
188 Vinny Castilla .07 .20
189 John Smoltz .10 .30
190 Travis Fryman .07 .20
191 Chris Hoiles .07 .20
192 Chuck Finley .07 .20
193 Ryan Klesko .10 .30
194 Alex Fernandez .07 .20
195 Dante Bichette .07 .20
196 Eric Karros .07 .20
197 Roger Clemens .40 1.00
198 Randy Myers .07 .20
199 Tony Phillips .07 .20
200 Cal Ripken .60 1.50
201 Rod Beck .07 .20
202 Chad Curtis .07 .20
203 Jack McDowell .07 .20
204 Gary Gaetti .07 .20
205 Ken Griffey Jr. .30 .75
206 Ramon Martinez .07 .20
207 Jeff Kent .07 .20
208 Brad Ausmus .07 .20
209 Devon White .07 .20
210 Jason Giambi .07 .20
211 Nomar Garciaparra .30 .75
212 Billy Wagner .07 .20
213 Todd Greene .07 .20
214 Paul Wilson .07 .20
215 Johnny Damon .10 .30
216 Alan Benes .07 .20
217 Karim Garcia .07 .20
218 Dustin Hermanson .07 .20
219 Derek Jeter .50 1.25
220 Checklist (111-220) .07 .20
221 Kirby Puckett STP .10 .30
222 Cal Ripken STP .30 .75
223 Albert Belle STP .07 .20
224 Randy Johnson STP .10 .30
225 Wade Boggs STP .07 .20
226 Carlos Baerga STP .07 .20
227 Ivan Rodriguez STP .07 .20
228 Mike Mussina STP .07 .20
229 Frank Thomas STP .10 .30
230 Ken Griffey Jr. STP .20 .50
231 Jose Mesa STP .07 .20
232 Matt Morris RC .60 1.50
233 Craig Wilson RC .30 .75
234 Alvie Shepherd .08 .25
235 Randy Winn RC .30 .75
236 David Yocum RC .08 .25
237 Jason Brester RC .08 .25
238 Shane Monahan RC .08 .25
239 Brian McNichol RC .08 .25
240 Reggie Taylor .08 .25
241 Garrett Long .08 .25
242 Jonathan Johnson .08 .25
243 Jeff Liefer RC .08 .25
244 Brian Powell .08 .25
245 Brian Buchanan RC .08 .25
246 Mike Piazza .30 .75
247 Edgar Martinez .10 .30
248 Chuck Knoblauch .07 .20
249 Andres Galarraga .07 .20
250 Tony Gwynn .25 .60
251 Lee Smith .07 .20
252 Sammy Sosa .20 .50
253 Jim Thome .10 .30
254 Frank Rodriguez .07 .20
255 Charlie Hayes .07 .20
256 Bernard Gilkey .07 .20
257 John Smiley .07 .20
258 Brady Anderson .07 .20
259 Rico Brogna .07 .20
260 Kirt Manwaring .07 .20
261 Len Dykstra .07 .20
262 Tom Glavine .10 .30
263 Vince Coleman .07 .20
264 John Olerud .07 .20
265 Orlando Merced .07 .20
266 Kent Mercker .07 .20
267 Terry Steinbach .07 .20
268 Brian L. Hunter .07 .20
269 Jeff Fassero .07 .20
270 Jay Buhner .07 .20
271 Jeff Brantley .07 .20
272 Tim Raines .07 .20
273 Jimmy Key .07 .20
274 Mo Vaughn .07 .20
275 Andre Dawson .07 .20
276 Jose Mesa .07 .20
277 Brett Butler .07 .20
278 Luis Gonzalez .07 .20
279 Steve Sparks .07 .20
280 Chili Davis .07 .20
281 Carl Everett .07 .20
282 Jeff Cirillo .07 .20
283 Thomas Howard .07 .20
284 Paul O'Neill .10 .30
285 Pat Meares .07 .20
286 Mickey Tettleton .07 .20
287 Rey Sanchez .07 .20
288 Bip Roberts .07 .20
289 Roberto Alomar .10 .30
290 Ruben Sierra .07 .20
291 John Flaherty .07 .20
292 Bret Saberhagen .07 .20
293 Barry Larkin .10 .30
294 Sandy Alomar Jr. .07 .20
295 Ed Sprague .07 .20
296 Gary DiSarcina .07 .20
297 Marquis Grissom .07 .20
298 John Frascatore .07 .20
299 Will Clark .10 .30
300 Barry Bonds .60 1.50
301 Ozzie Smith UER .30 .75
Padres is listed as Padre
302 Dave Nilsson .07 .20
303 Pedro Martinez .10 .30
304 Joey Cora .07 .20
305 Rick Aguilera .07 .20
306 Craig Biggio .10 .30
307 Jose Vizcaino .07 .20
308 Jeff Montgomery .07 .20
309 Moises Alou .07 .20
310 Robin Ventura .07 .20
311 David Wells .07 .20
312 Delino DeShields .07 .20
313 Trevor Hoffman .07 .20
314 Andy Benes .07 .20
315 Deion Sanders .10 .30
316 Jim Bullinger .07 .20
317 John Jaha .07 .20
318 Greg Maddux .30 .75
319 Tim Salmon .10 .30
320 Ben McDonald .07 .20
321 Sandy Martinez .07 .20
322 Dan Miceli .07 .20
323 Wade Boggs .10 .30
324 Ismael Valdes .07 .20
325 Juan Gonzalez .07 .20
326 Charles Nagy .07 .20
327 Ray Lankford .07 .20
328 Mark Portugal .07 .20
329 Bobby Bonilla .07 .20
330 Reggie Sanders .07 .20
331 Jamie Brewington RC .08 .25
332 Aaron Sele .07 .20
333 Pete Harnisch .07 .20
334 Cliff Floyd .07 .20
335 Cal Eldred .07 .20
336 Jason Bates .07 .20
337 Tony Clark .07 .20
338 Jose Herrera .07 .20
339 Alex Ochoa .07 .20
340 Mark Loretta .07 .20
341 Donne Wall .07 .20
342 Jason Kendall .07 .20
343 Shannon Stewart .07 .20
344 Brooks Kieschnick .07 .20
345 Chris Snopek .07 .20
346 Ruben Rivera .07 .20
347 Jeff Suppan .07 .20
348 Phil Nevin .07 .20
349 John Wasdin .07 .20
350 Jay Payton .07 .20
351 Tim Crabtree .07 .20
352 Rick Krivda .07 .20
353 Bob Wolcott .07 .20
354 Jimmy Haynes .07 .20
355 Herb Perry .07 .20
356 Ryne Sandberg .30 .75
357 Harold Baines .07 .20
358 Chad Ogea .07 .20
359 Lee Tinsley .07 .20
360 Matt Williams .07 .20
361 Randy Velarde .07 .20
362 Jose Canseco .10 .30
363 Larry Walker .07 .20
364 Kevin Appier .07 .20
365 Darryl Hamilton .07 .20
366 Jose Lima .07 .20
367 Javy Lopez .07 .20
368 Dennis Eckersley .07 .20
369 Jason Isringhausen .07 .20
370 Mickey Morandini .07 .20
371 Scott Cooper .07 .20
372 Jim Abbott .10 .30
373 Paul Sorrento .07 .20
374 Chris Hammond .07 .20
375 Lance Johnson .07 .20
376 Kevin Brown .07 .20
377 Luis Alicea .07 .20
378 Andy Pettitte .10 .30
379 Dean Palmer .07 .20
380 Jeff Bagwell .10 .30
381 Jaime Navarro .07 .20
382 Rondell White .07 .20
383 Erik Hanson .07 .20
384 Pedro Munoz .07 .20
385 Heathcliff Slocumb .07 .20
386 Wally Joyner .07 .20
387 Bob Tewksbury .07 .20
388 David Bell .07 .20
389 Fred McGriff .10 .30
390 Mike Henneman .07 .20
391 Robby Thompson .07 .20
392 Norm Charlton .07 .20
393 Cecil Fielder .07 .20
394 Benito Santiago .07 .20
395 Rafael Palmeiro .10 .30
396 Ricky Bones .07 .20
397 Rickey Henderson .20 .50
398 C.J. Nitkowski .07 .20
399 Shawon Dunston .07 .20
400 Manny Ramirez .10 .30
401 Bill Swift .07 .20
402 Chad Fonville .07 .20
403 Joey Hamilton .07 .20
404 Alex Gonzalez .07 .20
405 Roberto Hernandez .07 .20
406 Jeff Blauser .07 .20
407 LaTroy Hawkins .07 .20
408 Greg Colbrunn .07 .20
409 Todd Hundley .07 .20
410 Glenn Dishman .07 .20
411 Joe Vitiello .07 .20
412 Todd Worrell .07 .20
413 Wil Cordero .07 .20
414 Ken Hill .07 .20
415 Carlos Garcia .07 .20
416 Bryan Rekar .07 .20
417 Shawn Green .07 .20
418 Tyler Green .07 .20
419 Mike Blowers .07 .20
420 Kenny Lofton .07 .20
421 Denny Neagle .07 .20
422 Jeff Conine .07 .20
423 Mark Langston .07 .20
424 Steve Cox .30 .75
Jesse Ibarra
Derrek Lee
Ron Wright RC
425 Jim Bonnici .40 1.00
Billy Owens
Richie Sexson
Daryle Ward RC
426 Kevin Jordan .08 .25
Bobby Morris
Desi Relaford
Adam Riggs RC
427 Tim Harkrider .08 .25
Rey Ordonez
Neifi Perez
Enrique Wilson
428 Bartolo Colon .20 .50
Doug Million
Rafael Orellano
Ray Ricken
429 Jeff D'Amico .08 .25
Marty Janzen RC
Gary Rath
Clint Sodowsky
430 Matt Drews .08 .25
Rich Hunter RC
Matt Ruebel
Bret Wagner
431 Jaime Bluma .08 .25
David Coggin
Steve Montgomery
Brandon Reed RC
432 Mike Figga .60 1.50
Raul Ibanez
Paul Konerko
Julio Mosquera
433 Brian Barber .07 .20
Marc Kroon
Marc Valdes
Don Wengert
434 George Arias .20 .50
Chris Haas RC
Scott Rolen
Scott Spiezio
435 Brian Banks 1.00 2.50
Vladimir Guerrero
Andrew Jones
Billy McMillon
436 Roger Cedeno .15 .40
Derrick Gibson
Ben Grieve
Shane Spencer RC
437 Anton French .08 .25
Demond Smith
DaRond Stovall RC
Keith Williams
438 Michael Coleman RC .08 .25
Jacob Cruz
Richard Hidalgo
Charles Peterson
439 Trey Beamon .07 .20
Yamil Benitez
Jermaine Dye
Angel Echevarria
440 Checklist .07 .20
F7 M.Mantle Last Day 2.00 5.00
NNO Mickey Mantle TRIB 1.25 3.00
Promotes the Mantle Foundation
Black and White Photo

1996 Topps Classic Confrontations

These cards were inserted at a rate of one in every five-card Series one retail pack sold at Walmart. The first ten cards showcase hitters, while the last five cards feature pitchers. Inside white borders, the fronts show player cutouts on a brownish rock background featuring a shadow image of the player. The player's name is gold foil stamped across the bottom. The horizontal backs of the hitters' cards are aqua and present headshots and statistics. The backs of the pitchers cards are purple and present the same information.

COMPLETE SET (15) 2.50 6.00
CC1 Ken Griffey Jr. .25 .60
CC2 Cal Ripken .50 1.25
CC3 Edgar Martinez .08 .25
CC4 Kirby Puckett .15 .40
CC5 Frank Thomas .15 .40
CC6 Barry Bonds .50 1.25
CC7 Reggie Sanders .05 .15
CC8 Andres Galarraga .05 .15
CC9 Tony Gwynn .20 .50
CC10 Mike Piazza .25 .60
CC11 Randy Johnson .15 .40
CC12 Mike Mussina .08 .25
CC13 Roger Clemens .30 .75
CC14 Tom Glavine .08 .25
CC15 Greg Maddux .25 .60

1996 Topps Mantle

Randomly inserted in Series one packs at a rate of one in nine hobby packs, one in six retail packs and one in two jumbo packs; these cards are reprints of the original Mickey Mantle cards issued from 1951 through 1969. The fronts look the same except for a commemorative stamp, while the backs clearly state that they are "Mickey Mantle Commemorative" cards and have a 1996 copyright date. These cards honor Yankee great Mickey Mantle, who passed away in August 1995 after a gallant battle against cancer. Based on evidence from an uncut sheet auctioned off at the 1996 Kit Young Hawaii Trade Show, some collectors/dealers believe that cards 15 through 19 were slightly shorter printed in relation to the other 14 cards.

COMPLETE SET (19) 60.00 120.00
COMMON MANTLE (3-14) 3.00 8.00
COM.MANTLE SP (15-19) 4.00 10.00
SER.1 ODDS 1:9 HOB, 1:6 RET, 1:2 JUM
FOUR PER CEREAL FACT.SET
CARDS 15-19 SHORTPRINTED BY 20%
1 Mickey Mantle 10.00 25.00
1951 Bowman
2 Mickey Mantle 10.00 25.00
1952 Topps

1996 Topps Mantle Finest

Randomly inserted in Series two packs at a rate of one in 18 and one in 12 ANCO, this 19-card set is a reprint of the regular insert set using Finest technology. Each card front is covered with the exclusive Topps Finest Protector to guarantee its brilliant uncirculated condition.

COMPLETE SET (19) 60.00 120.00
COMMON MANTLE (1-14) 3.00 8.00
COM.MANTLE SP (15-19) 4.00 10.00
1 Mickey Mantle 6.00 15.00
1951 Bowman
2 Mickey Mantle 6.00 15.00
1952 Topps
3 Mickey Mantle 3.00 8.00
1953 Topps

1996 Topps Masters of the Game

Cards from this 20-card standard-size set were randomly inserted into first-series hobby packs at a rate of one in 18. In addition, every factory set contained two Masters of the Game cards. The cards

are numbered with a "MG" prefix in the lower left corner.

COMPLETE SET (20) 12.50 30.00
1 Dennis Eckersley .40 1.00
2 Denny Martinez .40 1.00
3 Eddie Murray 1.00 2.50
4 Paul Molitor .40 1.00
5 Ozzie Smith 1.50 4.00
6 Rickey Henderson 1.00 2.50
7 Tim Raines .40 1.00
8 Lee Smith .40 1.00
9 Cal Ripken 3.00 8.00
10 Chili Davis .40 1.00
11 Wade Boggs .60 1.50
12 Tony Gwynn 1.25 3.00
13 Don Mattingly 2.50 6.00
14 Bret Saberhagen .40 1.00
15 Kirby Puckett 1.00 2.50
16 Joe Carter .40 1.00
17 Roger Clemens 2.00 5.00
18 Barry Bonds 3.00 8.00
19 Greg Maddux 1.50 4.00
20 Frank Thomas 1.00 2.50

1996 Topps Mystery Finest

Randomly inserted in first-series packs at a rate of one in 36 hobby and retail packs and one in eight jumbo packs, this 26-card standard-size set features a bit of a mystery. The fronts have opaque coating that must be removed before the player can be identified. After the opaque coating is removed, the fronts feature a player photo surrounded by silver borders. The backs feature a choice of players along with a corresponding mystery finest trivia fact. Some of these cards were also issued with refractor fronts.

COMPLETE SET (26) 50.00 120.00
*REF: 1.25X TO 3X BASIC MYSTERY FINEST
REF.SER.1 ODDS 1:216 HOB/RET, 1:36 JUM
M1 Hideo Nomo 2.00 5.00
M2 Greg Maddux 3.00 8.00
M3 Randy Johnson 2.00 5.00
M4 Chipper Jones 2.00 5.00
M5 Marty Cordova .75 2.00
M6 Garret Anderson .75 2.00
M7 Cal Ripken 6.00 15.00
M8 Kirby Puckett 2.00 5.00
M9 Tony Gwynn 2.50 6.00
M10 Manny Ramirez 1.25 3.00
M11 Jim Edmonds .75 2.00
M12 Mike Piazza 3.00 8.00
M13 Barry Bonds 6.00 15.00
M14 Raul Mondesi .75 2.00
M15 Sammy Sosa 2.00 5.00
M16 Ken Griffey Jr. 3.00 8.00
M17 Albert Belle .75 2.00
M18 Dante Bichette .75 2.00
M19 Mo Vaughn .75 2.00
M20 Jeff Bagwell 1.25 3.00
M21 Frank Thomas 2.00 5.00
M22 Hideo Nomo 2.00 5.00
M23 Cal Ripken 6.00 15.00
M24 Mike Piazza 3.00 8.00
M25 Ken Griffey Jr. 3.00 8.00
M26 Frank Thomas 2.00 5.00

1996 Topps Power Boosters

Randomly inserted into packs, these cards are a metallic version of 25 of the first 26 cards from the basic Topps set. Card numbers 1-6 and 8-12 were issued at a rate of one every 36 first series retail packs, while numbers 13-26 were issued in hobby packs at a rate of one in 36. Inserted in place of two basic cards, they are printed on 28 point stock and the fronts have prismatic foil printing. Card number 7, which is Mickey Mantle in the regular set, was not issued in a Power Booster form. A first year card of Sean Casey highlights this set.

COMP. STAR POWER SET (11) 25.00 50.00
COMMON (1-6/8-12) .75 2.00
COMP. DRAFT PICKS SET (14) 1.25 3.00
COMMON (12-26) .75 2.00
1 Tony Gwynn 2.50 6.00
2 Mike Piazza 3.00 8.00
3 Greg Maddux 3.00 8.00
4 Jeff Bagwell 1.25 3.00
5 Larry Walker .75 2.00
6 Barry Larkin 1.25 3.00

8 Tom Glavine	1.25	3.00
9 Craig Biggio	1.25	3.00
10 Barry Bonds	6.00	15.00
11 Heathcliff Slocumb	.75	2.00
12 Matt Williams	.75	2.00
13 Todd Helton	3.00	8.00
14 Mark Redman	.75	2.00
15 Michael Barrett	.75	2.00
16 Ben Davis	.75	2.00
17 Juan LeBron	.75	2.00
18 Tony McKnight	.75	2.00
19 Ryan Jaroncyk	.75	2.00
20 Corey Jenkins	.75	2.00
21 Jim Scharrer	.75	2.00
22 Mark Bellhorn	4.00	10.00
23 Jarrod Washburn	3.00	8.00
24 Geoff Jenkins	3.00	8.00
25 Sean Casey	6.00	15.00
26 Brett Tomko	2.00	5.00

1996 Topps Profiles

Randomly inserted into Series one and two packs at a rate of one in 12 hobby and retail packs, one in six jumbo packs and one in eight ANCO packs;, this 20-card standard-size set features 10 players from each league. One card from the first series and two from the second series were also included in all Topps factory sets. Topps spokesmen Kirby Puckett (AL) and Tony Gwynn (NL) give opinions on players within their league. The fronts feature a player photo set against a silver-foil background. The playerâ ™s name is on the bottom. A photo of either Gwynn or Puckett as well as the words "Profiles by ..." is on the right. The backs feature a player photo, some career data as well as Gwynn's or Puckett's opinion about the featured player. The cards are numbered with either an "AL or NL" prefix on the back depending on the playerâ ™s league. The cards are sequenced in alphabetical order within league.

COMPLETE SET (40)	15.00	40.00
COMPLETE SERIES 1 (20)	12.50	30.00
COMPLETE SERIES 2 (20)	4.00	10.00
AL1 Roberto Alomar	.30	.75
AL2 Carlos Baerga	.20	.50
AL3 Albert Belle	.20	.50
AL4 Cecil Fielder	.20	.50
AL5 Ken Griffey Jr.	.75	2.00
AL6 Randy Johnson	.50	1.25
AL7 Paul O'Neill	.30	.75
AL8 Cal Ripken	1.50	4.00
AL9 Frank Thomas	.50	1.25
AL10 Mo Vaughn	.20	.50
AL11 Jay Buhner	.20	.50
AL12 Marty Cordova	.20	.50
AL13 Jim Edmonds	.20	.50
AL14 Juan Gonzalez	.20	.50
AL15 Kenny Lofton	.20	.50
AL16 Edgar Martinez	.30	.75
AL17 Don Mattingly	1.25	3.00
AL18 Mark McGwire	1.25	3.00
AL19 Rafael Palmeiro	.30	.75
AL20 Tim Salmon	.30	.75
NL1 Jeff Bagwell	.30	.75
NL2 Derek Bell	.20	.50
NL3 Barry Bonds	1.50	4.00
NL4 Greg Maddux	.75	2.00
NL5 Fred McGriff	.30	.75
NL6 Raul Mondesi	.20	.50
NL7 Mike Piazza	.75	2.00
NL8 Reggie Sanders	.20	.50
NL9 Sammy Sosa	.50	1.25
NL10 Larry Walker	.20	.50
NL11 Dante Bichette	.20	.50
NL12 Andres Galarraga	.20	.50
NL13 Ron Gant	.20	.50
NL14 Tom Glavine	.30	.75
NL15 Chipper Jones	.50	1.25
NL16 David Justice	.20	.50
NL17 Barry Larkin	.30	.75
NL18 Hideo Nomo	.50	1.25
NL19 Gary Sheffield	.20	.50
NL20 Matt Williams	.20	.50

1996 Topps Road Warriors

This 20-card set was inserted only into Series two WalMart packs at a rate of one per pack and featured leading hitters of the majors. The set is sequenced in alphabetical order.

COMPLETE SET (20)	5.00	12.00
RW1 Derek Bell	.15	.40
RW2 Albert Belle	.15	.40
RW3 Craig Biggio	.25	.60
RW4 Barry Bonds	1.25	3.00
RW5 Jay Buhner	.15	.40
RW6 Jim Edmonds	.15	.40
RW7 Gary Gaetti	.15	.40
RW8 Ron Gant	.15	.40
RW9 Edgar Martinez	.25	.60
RW10 Tino Martinez	.25	.60
RW11 Mark McGwire	1.00	2.50
RW12 Mike Piazza	.60	1.50
RW13 Manny Ramirez	.25	.60
RW14 Tim Salmon	.25	.60
RW15 Reggie Sanders	.15	.40
RW16 Frank Thomas	.40	1.00
RW17 John Valentin	.15	.40
RW18 Mo Vaughn	.15	.40
RW19 Robin Ventura	.15	.40
RW20 Matt Williams	.15	.40

1996 Topps Wrecking Crew

Randomly inserted in Series two hobby packs at a rate of one in 18, this 15-card set honors some of the hottest home run producers in the League. One card from this set was also inserted into Topps Hobby Factory sets. The cards feature color action player photos with foil stamping.

COMPLETE SET (15)	25.00	60.00
WC1 Jeff Bagwell	1.25	3.00
WC2 Albert Belle	.75	2.00
WC3 Barry Bonds	6.00	15.00
WC4 Jose Canseco	1.25	3.00
WC5 Joe Carter	.75	2.00
WC6 Cecil Fielder	.75	2.00
WC7 Ron Gant	.75	2.00
WC8 Juan Gonzalez	.75	2.00
WC9 Ken Griffey Jr	3.00	8.00
WC10 Fred McGriff	1.25	3.00
WC11 Mark McGwire	5.00	12.00
WC12 Mike Piazza	3.00	8.00
WC13 Frank Thomas	2.00	5.00
WC14 Mo Vaughn	.75	2.00
WC15 Matt Williams	.75	2.00

1997 Topps

This 495-card set was primarily distributed in first and second series 11-card packs with a suggested retail price of $1.29. In addition, eight-card retail packs, 40-card jumbo packs and 504-card factory sets (containing the complete 495-card set plus a random selection of eight insert cards and one hermetically sealed Willie Mays or Mickey Mantle Reprint insert) were made available. The card fronts feature a color action player photo with a gloss coating and a spot matte finish on the outside border with gold foil stamping. The backs carry another player photo, player information and statistics. The set includes the following subsets: Season Highlights (100-104, 462-466), Prospects (200-207, 487-494), the first ever expansion team cards of the Arizona Diamondbacks (249-251,468-469 and the Tampa Bay Devil Rays (252-253, 470-472) and Draft Picks (269-274, 477-483). Card 42 is a special Jackie Robinson tribute card commemorating the 50th anniversary of his contribution to baseball history and numbered for his Dodgers uniform number. Card number 7 does not exist because it was retired in honor of Mickey Mantle. Card number 84 does not exist because Mike Fetters' card was incorrectly numbered 61. Card number 277 does not exist because Chipper Jones' card was incorrectly numbered 276. Rookie Cards include Kris Benson and Eric Chavez. The Derek Jeter autograph card found at the end of our checklist was seeded one every 576 second series packs.

COMPLETE SET (495)	40.00	80.00
COMP SERIES 1 (275)	20.00	40.00
COMP.SERIES 2 (220)	20.00	40.00
1 Barry Bonds	.60	1.50
2 Tom Pagnozzi	.07	.20
3 Terrell Wade	.07	.20
4 Jose Valentin	.07	.20
5 Mark Clark	.07	.20
6 Brady Anderson	.07	.20
8 Wade Boggs	.10	.30
9 Scott Stahoviak	.07	.20
10 Andres Galarraga	.07	.20
11 Steve Avery	.07	.20
12 Rusty Greer	.07	.20
13 Derek Jeter	.50	1.25
14 Ricky Bottalico	.07	.20
15 Andy Ashby	.07	.20
16 Paul Shuey	.07	.20
17 F.P. Santangelo	.07	.20
18 Royce Clayton	.07	.20
19 Mike Mohler	.07	.20
20 Mike Piazza	.30	.75
21 Jaime Navarro	.07	.20
22 Billy Wagner	.07	.20
23 Mike Timlin	.07	.20
24 Garret Anderson	.07	.20
25 Ben McDonald	.07	.20
26 Mel Rojas	.07	.20
27 John Burkett	.07	.20
28 Jeff King	.07	.20
29 Reggie Jefferson	.07	.20
30 Kevin Appier	.07	.20
31 Felipe Lira	.07	.20
32 Kevin Tapani	.07	.20
33 Mark Portugal	.07	.20
34 Carlos Garcia	.07	.20
35 Joey Cora	.07	.20
36 David Segui	.07	.20
37 Mark Grace	.10	.30
38 Erik Hanson	.07	.20
39 Jeff D'Amico	.07	.20
40 Jay Buhner	.07	.20
41 B.J. Surhoff	.07	.20
42 Jackie Robinson TRIB	.20	.50
43 Roger Pavlik	.07	.20
44 Hal Morris	.07	.20
45 Mariano Duncan	.07	.20
46 Harold Baines	.07	.20
47 Jorge Fabregas	.07	.20
48 Jose Herrera	.07	.20
49 Jeff Cirillo	.07	.20
50 Tom Glavine	.10	.30
51 Pedro Astacio	.07	.20
52 Mark Gardner	.07	.20
53 Arthur Rhodes	.07	.20
54 Troy O'Leary	.07	.20
55 Bip Roberts	.07	.20
56 Mike Lieberthal	.07	.20
57 Shane Andrews	.07	.20
58 Scott Karl	.07	.20
59 Gary DiSarcina	.07	.20
60 Andy Pettitte	.10	.30
61 Kevin Elster	.07	.20
61B Mike Fetters UER	.07	.20
Card was intended as number 84		
62 Mark McGwire	.50	1.25
63 Dan Wilson	.07	.20
64 Mickey Morandini	.07	.20
65 Chuck Knoblauch	.07	.20
66 Tim Wakefield	.07	.20
67 Raul Mondesi	.07	.20
68 Todd Jones	.07	.20
69 Albert Belle	.07	.20
70 Trevor Hoffman	.07	.20
71 Eric Young	.07	.20
72 Robert Perez	.07	.20
73 Butch Huskey	.07	.20
74 Brian McRae	.07	.20
75 Jim Edmonds	.07	.20
76 Mike Henneman	.07	.20
77 Frank Rodriguez	.07	.20
78 Danny Tartabull	.07	.20
79 Robb Nen	.07	.20
80 Reggie Sanders	.07	.20
81 Ron Karkovice	.07	.20
82 Benito Santiago	.07	.20
83 Mike Lansing	.07	.20
85 Craig Biggio	.10	.30
86 Mike Bordick	.07	.20
87 Ray Lankford	.07	.20
88 Charles Nagy	.07	.20
89 Paul Wilson	.07	.20
90 John Wetteland	.07	.20
91 Tom Candiotti	.07	.20
92 Carlos Delgado	.07	.20
93 Derek Bell	.07	.20
94 Mark Lemke	.07	.20
95 Edgar Martinez	.10	.30
96 Rickey Henderson	.20	.50
97 Greg Myers	.07	.20
98 Jim Leyritz	.07	.20
99 Mark Johnson	.07	.20
100 Dwight Gooden HL	.07	.20
101 Al Leiter HL	.07	.20
102 John Mabry HL	.07	.20
103 Alex Ochoa HL	.07	.20
104 Mike Piazza HL	.20	.50
105 Jim Thome	.10	.30
106 Ricky Otero	.07	.20
107 Jamey Wright	.07	.20
108 Frank Thomas	.20	.50
109 Jody Reed	.07	.20
110 Orel Hershiser	.07	.20
111 Terry Steinbach	.07	.20
112 Mark Loretta	.07	.20
113 Turk Wendell	.07	.20
114 Marvin Benard	.07	.20
115 Kevin Brown	.07	.20
116 Robert Person	.07	.20
117 Joey Hamilton	.07	.20
118 Francisco Cordova	.07	.20
119 John Smiley	.07	.20
120 Travis Fryman	.07	.20
121 Jimmy Key	.07	.20
122 Tom Goodwin	.07	.20
123 Mike Greenwell	.07	.20
124 Juan Gonzalez	.07	.20
125 Pete Harnisch	.07	.20
126 Roger Cedeno	.07	.20
127 Ron Gant	.07	.20
128 Mark Langston	.07	.20
129 Tim Crabtree	.07	.20
130 Greg Maddux	.30	.75
131 W.VanLandingham	.07	.20
132 Wally Joyner	.07	.20
133 Randy Myers	.07	.20
134 John Valentin	.07	.20
135 Bret Boone	.07	.20
136 Bruce Ruffin	.07	.20
137 Chris Snopek	.07	.20
138 Paul Molitor	.07	.20
139 Mark McLemore	.07	.20
140 Rafael Palmeiro	.10	.30
141 Herb Perry	.07	.20
142 Luis Gonzalez	.07	.20
143 Doug Drabek	.07	.20
144 Ken Ryan	.07	.20
145 Todd Hundley	.07	.20
146 Ellis Burks	.07	.20
147 Ozzie Guillen	.07	.20
148 Rich Becker	.07	.20
149 Sterling Hitchcock	.07	.20
150 Bernie Williams	.10	.30
151 Mike Stanley	.07	.20
152 Roberto Alomar	.10	.30
153 Jose Mesa	.07	.20
154 Steve Trachsel	.07	.20
155 Alex Gonzalez	.07	.20
156 Troy Percival	.07	.20
157 John Smoltz	.10	.30
158 Pedro Martinez	.10	.30
159 Jeff Conine	.07	.20
160 Bernard Gilkey	.07	.20
161 Jim Eisenreich	.07	.20
162 Mickey Tettleton	.07	.20
163 Justin Thompson	.07	.20
164 Jose Offerman	.07	.20
165 Tony Phillips	.07	.20
166 Ismael Valdes	.07	.20
167 Ryne Sandberg UER	.30	.75
Card has him with 252 homers in 1996		
168 Matt Mieske	.07	.20
169 Geronimo Berroa	.07	.20
170 Otis Nixon	.07	.20
171 John Mabry	.07	.20
172 Shawon Dunston	.07	.20
173 Omar Vizquel	.10	.30
174 Chris Hoiles	.07	.20
175 Dwight Gooden	.07	.20
176 Wilson Alvarez	.07	.20
177 Todd Hollandsworth	.07	.20
178 Roger Salkeld	.07	.20
179 Rey Sanchez	.07	.20
180 Rey Ordonez	.07	.20
181 Denny Martinez	.07	.20
182 Ramon Martinez	.07	.20
183 Dave Nilsson	.07	.20
184 Marquis Grissom	.07	.20
185 Randy Velarde	.07	.20
186 Ron Coomer	.07	.20
187 Tino Martinez	.10	.30
188 Jeff Brantley	.07	.20
189 Steve Finley	.07	.20
190 Andy Benes	.07	.20
191 Terry Adams	.07	.20
192 Mike Blowers	.07	.20
193 Russ Davis	.07	.20
194 Darryl Hamilton	.07	.20
195 Jason Kendall	.07	.20
196 Johnny Damon	.10	.30
197 Dave Martinez	.07	.20
198 Mike Macfarlane	.07	.20
199 Norm Charlton	.07	.20
200 Doug Million RC	.08	.25
Damian Moss		
Bobby Rodgers		
201 Geoff Jenkins	.07	.20
Raul Ibanez		
Mike Cameron		
202 Sean Casey	.10	.30
Jim Bonnici		
Dmitri Young		
203 Jed Hansen	.07	.20
Homer Bush		
Felipe Crespo		
204 Kevin Orie	.07	.20
Gabe Alvarez		
Aaron Boone		
205 Ben Davis	.07	.20
Kevin Brown		
Bobby Estalella		
206 Billy McMillon RC	.15	.40
Bubba Trammell		
Dante Powell		
207 Jarrod Washburn	.07	.20
Marc Wilkins RC		
Glendon Rusch		
208 Brian Hunter	.07	.20
209 Jason Giambi	.07	.20
210 Henry Rodriguez	.07	.20
211 Edgar Renteria	.07	.20
212 Edgardo Alfonzo	.07	.20
213 Fernando Vina	.07	.20
214 Shawn Green	.07	.20
215 Ray Durham	.07	.20
216 Joe Randa	.07	.20
217 Armando Reynoso	.07	.20
218 Eric Davis	.07	.20
219 Bob Tewksbury	.07	.20
220 Jacob Cruz	.07	.20
221 Glenallen Hill	.07	.20
222 Gary Gaetti	.07	.20
223 Donne Wall	.07	.20
224 Brad Clontz	.07	.20
225 Marty Janzen	.07	.20
226 Todd Worrell	.07	.20
227 John Franco	.07	.20
228 David Wells	.07	.20
229 Gregg Jefferies	.07	.20
230 Tim Naehring	.07	.20
231 Thomas Howard	.07	.20
232 Roberto Hernandez	.07	.20
233 Kevin Ritz	.07	.20
234 Julian Tavarez	.07	.20
235 Ken Hill	.07	.20
236 Greg Gagne	.07	.20
237 Bobby Chouinard	.07	.20
238 Joe Carter	.07	.20
239 Jermaine Dye	.07	.20
240 Antonio Osuna	.07	.20
241 Julio Franco	.07	.20
242 Mike Grace	.07	.20
243 Aaron Sele	.07	.20
244 David Justice	.07	.20
245 Sandy Alomar Jr.	.07	.20
246 Jose Canseco	.10	.30
247 Paul O'Neill	.10	.30
248 Sean Berry	.07	.20
249 Nick Bierbrodt	.08	.25
Kevin Sweeney RC		
250 Larry Rodriguez RC	.08	.25
Vladimir Nunez RC		
251 Ron Hartman	.08	.25
David Hayman RC		
252 Alex Sanchez	.15	.40
Matthew Quatraro RC		
253 Ronni Seberino RC	.08	.25
Pablo Ortega RC		
254 Rex Hudler	.07	.20
255 Orlando Miller	.07	.20
256 Mariano Rivera	.20	.50
257 Brad Radke	.07	.20
258 Bobby Higginson	.07	.20
259 Jay Bell	.07	.20
260 Mark Grudzielanek	.07	.20
261 Lance Johnson	.07	.20
262 Ken Caminiti	.07	.20
263 J.T. Snow	.07	.20
264 Gary Sheffield	.07	.20
265 Darrin Fletcher	.07	.20
266 Eric Owens	.07	.20
267 Luis Castillo	.07	.20
268 Scott Rolen	.10	.30
269 Todd Noel	.08	.25
John Oliver RC		
270 Robert Stratton RC	.15	.40
Corey Lee RC		
271 Gil Meche RC	.40	1.00
Matt Halloran RC		
272 Eric Milton RC	.15	.40
Dee Brown RC		
273 Josh Garrett	.15	.40
Chris Reitsma RC		
274 A.J.Zapp RC	.20	.50
Jason Marquis		
275 Checklist	.07	.20
276 Checklist	.07	.20
277 Chipper Jones UER	.20	.50
incorrectly numbered 276		
278 Orlando Merced	.07	.20
279 Ariel Prieto	.07	.20
280 Al Leiter	.07	.20
281 Pat Meares	.07	.20
282 Darryl Strawberry	.07	.20
283 Jamie Moyer	.07	.20
284 Scott Servais	.07	.20
285 Delino DeShields	.07	.20
286 Danny Graves	.07	.20
287 Gerald Williams	.07	.20
288 Todd Greene	.07	.20
289 Rico Brogna	.07	.20
290 Derrick Gibson	.07	.20
291 Joe Girardi	.07	.20
292 Darren Lewis	.07	.20
293 Nomar Garciaparra	.30	.75
294 Greg Colbrunn	.07	.20
295 Jeff Bagwell	.10	.30
296 Brent Gates	.07	.20
297 Jose Vizcaino	.07	.20
298 Alex Ochoa	.07	.20
299 Sid Fernandez	.07	.20
300 Ken Griffey Jr.	.30	.75
301 Chris Gomez	.07	.20
302 Wendell Magee	.07	.20
303 Darren Oliver	.07	.20
304 Mel Nieves	.07	.20
305 Sammy Sosa	.20	.50
306 George Arias	.07	.20
307 Jack McDowell	.07	.20
308 Stan Javier	.07	.20
309 Kimera Bartee	.07	.20
310 James Baldwin	.07	.20
311 Rocky Coppinger	.07	.20
312 Keith Lockhart	.07	.20
313 C.J. Nitkowski	.07	.20
314 Allen Watson	.07	.20
315 Darryl Kile	.07	.20
316 Amaury Telemaco	.07	.20
317 Jason Isringhausen	.07	.20
318 Manny Ramirez	.10	.30
319 Terry Pendleton	.07	.20
320 Tim Salmon	.10	.30
321 Eric Karros	.07	.20
322 Mark Whiten	.07	.20
323 Rick Krivda	.07	.20
324 Brett Butler	.07	.20
325 Randy Johnson	.20	.50
326 Eddie Taubensee	.07	.20
327 Mark Leiter	.07	.20
328 Kevin Gross	.07	.20
329 Ernie Young	.07	.20
330 Pat Hentgen	.07	.20
331 Rondell White	.07	.20
332 Bobby Witt	.07	.20
333 Eddie Murray	.20	.50
334 Tim Raines	.07	.20
335 Jeff Fassero	.07	.20
336 Chuck Finley	.07	.20
337 Willie Adams	.07	.20
338 Chan Ho Park	.07	.20
339 Jay Powell	.07	.20
340 Ivan Rodriguez	.10	.30
341 Jermaine Allensworth	.07	.20
342 Jay Payton	.07	.20
343 T.J. Mathews	.07	.20
344 Tony Batista	.07	.20
345 Ed Sprague	.07	.20
346 Jeff Kent	.07	.20
347 Scott Erickson	.07	.20
348 Jeff Suppan	.07	.20
349 Pete Schourek	.07	.20
350 Kenny Lofton	.07	.20
351 Alan Benes	.07	.20
352 Fred McGriff	.10	.30
353 Charlie O'Brien	.07	.20
354 Darren Bragg	.07	.20
355 Alex Fernandez	.07	.20
356 Al Martin	.07	.20
357 Bob Wells	.07	.20
358 Chad Mottola	.07	.20
359 Devon White	.07	.20
360 David Cone	.07	.20
361 Bobby Jones	.07	.20
362 Scott Sanders	.07	.20
363 Karim Garcia	.07	.20
364 Kirt Manwaring	.07	.20
365 Chili Davis	.07	.20
366 Mike Hampton	.07	.20
367 Chad Ogea	.07	.20
368 Curt Schilling	.07	.20
369 Phil Nevin	.07	.20
370 Roger Clemens	.40	1.00
371 Willie Greene	.07	.20
372 Kenny Rogers	.07	.20
373 Jose Rijo	.07	.20
374 Bobby Bonilla	.07	.20
375 Mike Mussina	.10	.30
376 Curtis Pride	.07	.20
377 Todd Walker	.07	.20
378 Jason Bere	.07	.20
379 Heathcliff Slocumb	.07	.20
380 Dante Bichette	.07	.20
381 Carlos Baerga	.07	.20
382 Livan Hernandez	.07	.20
383 Jason Schmidt	.07	.20
384 Kevin Stocker	.07	.20
385 Matt Williams	.07	.20
386 Bartolo Colon	.07	.20
387 Will Clark	.10	.30
388 Dennis Eckersley	.07	.20
389 Brooks Kieschnick	.07	.20
390 Ryan Klesko	.07	.20
391 Mark Carreon	.07	.20
392 Tim Worrell	.07	.20
393 Dean Palmer	.07	.20
394 Wil Cordero	.07	.20
395 Javy Lopez	.07	.20
396 Rich Aurilia	.07	.20
397 Greg Vaughn	.07	.20
398 Vinny Castilla	.07	.20
399 Jeff Montgomery	.07	.20
400 Cal Ripken	.60	1.50
401 Walt Weiss	.07	.20
402 Brad Ausmus	.07	.20
403 Ruben Rivera	.07	.20
404 Mark Wohlers	.07	.20
405 Rick Aguilera	.07	.20
406 Tony Clark	.07	.20
407 Lyle Mouton	.07	.20
408 Bill Pulsipher	.07	.20
409 Jose Rosado	.07	.20
410 Tony Gwynn	.25	.60
411 Cecil Fielder	.07	.20
412 John Flaherty	.07	.20
413 Lenny Dykstra	.07	.20
414 Ugueth Urbina	.07	.20
415 Brian Jordan	.07	.20
416 Bob Abreu	.10	.30
417 Craig Paquette	.07	.20
418 Sandy Martinez	.07	.20
419 Jeff Blauser	.07	.20
420 Barry Larkin	.10	.30
421 Kevin Seitzer	.07	.20
422 Tim Belcher	.07	.20
423 Paul Sorrento	.07	.20
424 Cal Eldred	.07	.20
425 Robin Ventura	.07	.20
426 John Olerud	.07	.20
427 Bob Wolcott	.07	.20
428 Matt Lawton	.07	.20
429 Rod Beck	.07	.20
430 Shane Reynolds	.07	.20
431 Mike James	.07	.20
432 Steve Wojciechowski	.07	.20
433 Vladimir Guerrero	.20	.50
434 Dustin Hermanson	.07	.20
435 Marty Cordova	.07	.20
436 Marc Newfield	.07	.20
437 Todd Stottlemyre	.07	.20
438 Jeffrey Hammonds	.07	.20
439 Dave Stevens	.07	.20
440 Hideo Nomo	.20	.50
441 Mark Thompson	.07	.20
442 Mark Lewis	.07	.20
443 Quinton McCracken	.07	.20
444 Cliff Floyd	.07	.20
445 Denny Neagle	.07	.20
446 John Jaha	.07	.20
447 Mike Sweeney	.07	.20
448 John Wasdin	.07	.20
449 Chad Curtis	.07	.20
450 Mo Vaughn	.07	.20
451 Donovan Osborne	.07	.20
452 Ruben Sierra	.07	.20
453 Michael Tucker	.07	.20
454 Kurt Abbott	.07	.20
455 Andruw Jones UER	.10	.30
Birthdate is incorrectly listed as 1-22-67, should be 1-22-77		
456 Shannon Stewart	.07	.20
457 Scott Brosius	.07	.20
458 Juan Guzman	.07	.20
459 Ron Villone	.07	.20
460 Moises Alou	.07	.20
461 Larry Walker	.07	.20
462 Eddie Murray SH	.10	.30
463 Paul Molitor SH	.07	.20
464 Hideo Nomo SH	.07	.20
465 Barry Bonds SH	.30	.75
466 Todd Hundley SH	.07	.20
467 Rheal Cormier	.07	.20
468 Jason Conti RC	.08	.25
Jhensy Sandoval		
469 Rod Barajas	.60	1.50
Jackie Rexrode RC		
470 Cedric Bowers RC	.08	.25
Jared Sandberg RC		
471 Chei Gunner RC	.08	.25
Paul Wilder		
472 Mike Decelle	.08	.25
Marcus McCain RC		
473 Todd Zeile	.07	.20
474 Neifi Perez	.07	.20
475 Jeromy Burnitz	.07	.20
476 Trey Beamon	.07	.20
477 Braden Looper RC	.30	.75
John Patterson		
478 Danny Peoples	.20	.50
Jake Westbrook RC		
479 Eric Chavez	.75	2.00
Adam Eaton RC		
480 Joe Lawrence RC	.08	.25
Pete Tucci		
481 Kris Benson	.20	.50
Billy Koch RC		
482 John Nicholson	.08	.25
Andy Prater RC		
483 Mark Johnson RC	.30	.75
Mark Kotsay		
484 Armando Benitez	.07	.20
485 Mike Matheny	.07	.20
486 Jeff Reed	.07	.20
487 Mark Bellhorn	.07	.20
Russ Johnson		
Enrique Wilson		
488 Ben Grieve	.07	.20
Richard Hidalgo		
Scott Morgan RC		
489 Paul Konerko	.10	.30
Derrek Lee UER		
spelled Derek on back		
Ron Wright		
490 Wes Helms RC	.50	1.25
Bill Mueller		
Brad Seitzer		
491 Jeff Abbott	.07	.20
Shane Monahan		
Edgard Velazquez		
492 Jimmy Anderson RC	.08	.25
Ron Blazier		
Gerald Witasick		
493 Darin Blood	.07	.20
Heath Murray		
Carl Pavano		
494 Nelson Figueroa RC	.08	.25
Mark Redman		
Mike Villano		
495 Checklist	.07	.20
496 Checklist	.07	.20
NNO Derek Jeter AU	75.00	150.00

1997 Topps All-Stars

Randomly inserted in Series one hobby and retail packs at a rate of one in 18 and one in every six jumbo packs, this 22-card set printed on rainbow foilboard features the top 11 players from each league and from each position as voted by the Topps Sports Department. The fronts carry a photo of a "first team" all-star player while the backs carry a different photo of that player alongside the "second team" and "third team" selections. Only the "first team" players are checklisted listed below.

COMPLETE SET (22)	10.00	25.00
AS1 Ivan Rodriguez	.40	1.00
AS2 Todd Hundley	.25	.60
AS3 Frank Thomas	.60	1.50
AS4 Andres Galarraga	.25	.60
AS5 Chuck Knoblauch	.25	.60
AS6 Eric Young	.25	.60
AS7 Jim Thome	.40	1.00
AS8 Chipper Jones	.60	1.50
AS9 Cal Ripken	2.00	5.00
AS10 Barry Larkin	.40	1.00
AS11 Albert Belle	.25	.60
AS12 Barry Bonds	2.00	5.00
AS13 Ken Griffey Jr.	1.00	2.50
AS14 Ellis Burks	.25	.60
AS15 Juan Gonzalez	.25	.60
AS16 Gary Sheffield	.25	.60
AS17 Andy Pettitte	.40	1.00
AS18 Tom Glavine	.40	1.00
AS19 Pat Hentgen	.25	.60
AS20 John Smoltz	.40	1.00
AS21 Roberto Hernandez	.25	.60
AS22 Mark Wohlers	.25	.60

1997 Topps Awesome Impact

Randomly inserted in second series 11-card retail packs at a rate of 1:18, cards from this 20-card set feature a selection of top young stars and prospects. Each card front features a color player action shot cut out against a silver prismatic background.

COMPLETE SET (20)	40.00	100.00
AI1 Jaime Bluma	1.25	3.00
AI2 Tony Clark	1.25	3.00
AI3 Jermaine Dye	1.25	3.00
AI4 Nomar Garciaparra	5.00	12.00
AI5 Vladimir Guerrero	3.00	8.00
AI6 Todd Hollandsworth	1.25	3.00
AI7 Derek Jeter	8.00	20.00
AI8 Andruw Jones	2.00	5.00
AI9 Chipper Jones	3.00	8.00
AI10 Jason Kendall	1.25	3.00
AI11 Brooks Kieschnick	1.25	3.00
AI12 Alex Ochoa	1.25	3.00
AI13 Rey Ordonez	1.25	3.00
AI14 Neifi Perez	1.25	3.00
AI15 Edgar Renteria	1.25	3.00
AI16 Mariano Rivera	3.00	8.00
AI17 Ruben Rivera	1.25	3.00
AI18 Scott Rolen	2.00	5.00
AI19 Billy Wagner	1.25	3.00
AI20 Todd Walker	1.25	3.00

1997 Topps Hobby Masters

Randomly inserted in first and second series hobby packs at a rate of one in 36, cards from this 10-card set honor twenty players picked by hobby dealers from across the country as their all-time favorites. Cards 1-10 were issued in first series packs and 11-20 in second series. Printed on 28-point diffraction foilboard, one card replaces two regular cards when inserted in packs. The fronts feature borderless color player photos on a background of the player's profile. The backs carry player information.

COMPLETE SET (20)	30.00	80.00
COMPLETE SERIES 1 (10)	15.00	40.00
COMPLETE SERIES 2 (10)	15.00	40.00
HM1 Ken Griffey Jr.	2.50	6.00
HM2 Cal Ripken	5.00	12.00
HM3 Greg Maddux	2.50	6.00
HM4 Albert Belle	.60	1.50
HM5 Tony Gwynn	2.00	5.00
HM6 Jeff Bagwell	1.00	2.50
HM7 Randy Johnson	1.50	4.00
HM8 Raul Mondesi	.60	1.50
HM9 Juan Gonzalez	.60	1.50
HM10 Kenny Lofton	.60	1.50
HM11 Frank Thomas	1.50	4.00
HM12 Mike Piazza	2.50	6.00
HM13 Chipper Jones	1.50	4.00
HM14 Brady Anderson	.60	1.50
HM15 Ken Caminiti	.60	1.50
HM16 Barry Bonds	5.00	12.00
HM17 Mo Vaughn	.60	1.50
HM18 Derek Jeter	4.00	10.00
HM19 Sammy Sosa	1.50	4.00
HM20 Andres Galarraga	.60	1.50

1997 Topps Inter-League Finest

Randomly inserted in Series one hobby and retail packs at a rate of one in 36 and jumbo packs at a rate of one in 10; this 14-card set features top individual match-ups from inter-league rivalries. One player from each major league team is represented on each side of this double-sided set with a color photo and is covered with the patented Finest clear protector.

COMPLETE SET (14)	25.00	60.00
*REF.: 1X TO 2.5X BASIC INTER-LG		
REF.SER.1 ODDS 1:216 HOB/RET, 1:56 JUM		
ILM1 Mark McGwire Barry Bonds	4.00	10.00
ILM2 Tim Salmon Mike Piazza	2.50	6.00
ILM3 Ken Griffey Jr. Dante Bichette	2.50	6.00
ILM4 Juan Gonzalez Tony Gwynn	2.00	5.00
ILM5 Frank Thomas Sammy Sosa	1.50	4.00
ILM6 Albert Belle Barry Larkin	.60	1.50
ILM7 Johnny Damon Brian Jordan	.60	1.50
ILM8 Paul Molitor Jeff King	.60	1.50
ILM9 John Jaha Jeff Bagwell	1.00	2.50
ILM10 Bernie Williams Todd Hundley	1.00	2.50
ILM11 Joe Carter Henry Rodriguez	.60	1.50
ILM12 Cal Ripken Gregg Jefferies	5.00	12.00
ILM13 Mo Vaughn Chipper Jones	1.50	4.00
ILM14 Travis Fryman Gary Sheffield	.60	1.50

1997 Topps Mantle

Randomly inserted at the rate of one in 12 Series one hobby/retail packs and one every three jumbo packs, this 16-card set features authentic reprints of Topps Mickey Mantle cards that were not reprinted last year. Each card is stamped with the commemorative gold foil logo.

COMPLETE SET (16)	50.00	100.00
COMMON (21-36)	3.00	8.00
COMMON FINEST (21-36)	3.00	8.00
FINEST SER.2 1:24 HOB/RET, 1:6 JUM		
COMMON REF. (21-36)	12.50	30.00
REF.SER.2 1:216 HOB/RET,1:60 JUM		

1997 Topps Mays

Randomly inserted at the rate of one in eight first series hobby/retail packs and one every two jumbo packs; cards from this 27-card set feature reprints of both the Topps and Bowman vintage Mays cards . Each card front is highlighted by a special commemorative gold foil stamp. Randomly inserted in first series hobby packs only (at the rate of one in 2,400) are personally signed cards. A special 4 1/4" by 5 3/4" jumbo reprint of the 1952 Topps Willie Mays card was made available exclusively in special series one Wal-Mart boxes. Each box (shaped much like a cereal box) contained ten eight-card retail packs and the aforementioned jumbo card and retailed for $10.

COMPLETE SET (27)	50.00	100.00
COMMON MAYS (3-27)	1.50	4.00
COMMON FINEST (1-27)	1.50	4.00
*'51-'52 FINEST: .4X TO 1X BASIC MAYS REPRINTS		
FINEST SER.2 1:20 HOB/RET,1:4 JUM		
COMMON REF. (1-27)	4.00	10.00
*'51-'52 REF: 1X TO 2.5X BASIC MAYS REPRINTS		
REF.SER.2 1:180 HOB/RET,1:48 JUM		
1 Willie Mays 1951 Bowman	3.00	8.00
2 Willie Mays 1952 Topps	2.50	6.00
J261 W.Mays 1952 Jumbo	3.00	8.00

1997 Topps Mays Autographs

Acording to Topps, Mays signed about 65 each of the following cards: 51B, 52T, 53T, 55B, 55T, 57T, 58T, 60T, 60T AS, 61T, 61T AS, 63T, 64T, 65T, 66T, 69T, 70T, 72T, 73T. The cards all have a "Certified Topps Autograph" stamp on them.

COMMON CARD (1953-1958)	100.00	200.00
COMMON CARD (1960-1973)	100.00	200.00
1 Willie Mays 1951 Bowman	100.00	200.00
2 Willie Mays 1952 Topps	100.00	200.00

1997 Topps Season's Best

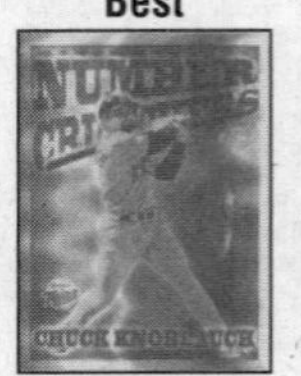

This 25-card set was randomly inserted into Topps Series two packs at a rate of one every six hobby/retail packs and one per jumbo pack; this set features five top players from each of the following five statistical categories: Leading Looters (top base stealers), Bleacher Reachers (top home run hitters), Hill Toppers (most wins), Number Crunchers (most RBI's), Kings of Swings (top slugging percentages). The fronts display color player photos printed on prismatic illusion foilboard. The backs carry another player photo and statistics.

COMPLETE SET (25)	10.00	25.00
SB1 Tony Gwynn	1.00	2.50
SB2 Frank Thomas	.75	2.00
SB3 Ellis Burks	.30	.75
SB4 Paul Molitor	.30	.75
SB5 Chuck Knoblauch	.30	.75
SB6 Mark McGwire	2.00	5.00
SB7 Brady Anderson	.30	.75
SB8 Ken Griffey Jr.	1.25	3.00
SB9 Albert Belle	.30	.75
SB10 Andres Galarraga	.30	.75
SB11 Andres Galarraga	.30	.75
SB12 Albert Belle	.30	.75
SB13 Juan Gonzalez	.30	.75
SB14 Mo Vaughn	.30	.75
SB15 Rafael Palmeiro	.50	1.25
SB16 John Smoltz	.50	1.25
SB17 Andy Pettitte	.50	1.25
SB18 Pat Hentgen	.30	.75
SB19 Mike Mussina	.50	1.25
SB20 Andy Benes	.30	.75
SB21 Kenny Lofton	.30	.75
SB22 Tom Goodwin	.30	.75
SB23 Otis Nixon	.30	.75
SB24 Eric Young	.30	.75
SB25 Lance Johnson	.30	.75

1997 Topps Sweet Strokes

This 15-card retail only set was randomly inserted in series one retail packs at a rate of one in 12. Printed on Rainbow foilboard, the set features color photos of some of Baseball's top hitters.

COMPLETE SET (15)	15.00	40.00
SS1 Roberto Alomar	.60	1.50
SS2 Jeff Bagwell	.60	1.50
SS3 Albert Belle	.40	1.00
SS4 Barry Bonds	3.00	8.00
SS5 Mark Grace	.60	1.50
SS6 Ken Griffey Jr.	1.50	4.00
SS7 Tony Gwynn	1.25	3.00
SS8 Chipper Jones	1.00	2.50
SS9 Edgar Martinez	.60	1.50
SS10 Mark McGwire	2.50	6.00
SS11 Rafael Palmeiro	.60	1.50
SS12 Mike Piazza	1.50	4.00
SS13 Gary Sheffield	.40	1.00
SS14 Frank Thomas	1.00	2.50
SS15 Mo Vaughn	.40	1.00

1997 Topps Team Timber

Randomly inserted into all second series hobby/retail packs at a rate of 1:36 and second series Hobby Collector (jumbo) packs at a rate of 1:8, cards from this 16-card set highlight a selection of baseball's top sluggers. Each card features a simulated wood-grain stock, but the fronts are UV-coated, making the cards bow noticeably.

COMPLETE SET (16)	15.00	40.00
TT1 Ken Griffey Jr.	1.50	4.00
TT2 Ken Caminiti	.40	1.00
TT3 Bernie Williams	.60	1.50
TT4 Jeff Bagwell	.60	1.50
TT5 Frank Thomas	1.00	2.50
TT6 Andres Galarraga	.40	1.00
TT7 Barry Bonds	3.00	8.00
TT8 Rafael Palmeiro	.60	1.50
TT9 Brady Anderson	.40	1.00
TT10 Juan Gonzalez	.40	1.00
TT11 Mo Vaughn	.40	1.00
TT12 Mark McGwire	2.50	6.00
TT13 Gary Sheffield	.40	1.00
TT14 Albert Belle	.40	1.00
TT15 Chipper Jones	1.00	2.50
TT16 Mike Piazza	1.50	4.00

1997 Topps 22k Gold

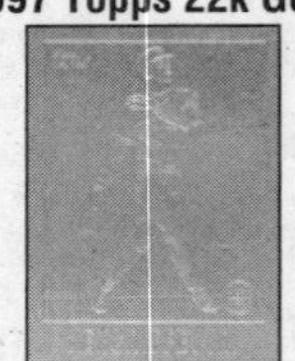

This one-card set is an embossed 22 karat gold foil replica of the 1997 Topps regular Ken Griffey Jr. card. Only a limited number of this set were produced and are serially numbered. Each card is packed in a protective display holder.

1 Ken Griffey Jr.	12.50	30.00

1998 Topps

This 503-card set was distributed in two separate series: 282 cards in first series and 221 cards in second series. 11-card packs carried a suggested retail price of $1.29. Cards were also distributed in Home Team Advantage jumbo packs and hobby, retail and Christmas factory sets. Card fronts feature color action player photos printed on 16 pt. stock with player information and career statistics on the back. Card number 7 was permanently retired in 1996 to honor Mickey Mantle. Series one contains the following subsets: Draft Picks (245-249), Prospects (250-259), Season Highlights (265-269), Interleague (270-274) Checklists (275-276) and World Series (277-283). Series two contains Season Highlights (474-478), Interleague (479-483), Prospects (484-495/498-501) and Checklists (502-503). Rookie Cards of note include Ryan Anderson, Michael Cuddyer, Jack Cust and Troy Glaus. This set also features Topps long-awaited first regular-issue Alex Rodriguez card (504). The superstar shortstop was left out of all Topps sets for the first four years of his career due to a problem between Topps and Rodriguez's agent Scott Boras. Finally, as part of an agreement with the Baseball Hall of Fame, Topps produced commemorative admission tickets featuring Roberto Clemente memorabilia from the Hall in the form of a Topps card. These were the standard admission tickets for the shrine, and were also included one per case in 1998 Topps series two baseball.

COMPLETE SET (503)	40.00	80.00
COMP.HOBBY SET (511)	60.00	120.00
COMP.RETAIL SET (511)	60.00	120.00
COMP.SERIES 1 (282)	20.00	40.00
COMP.SERIES 2 (221)	20.00	40.00
1 Tony Gwynn	.25	.60
2 Larry Walker	.07	.20
3 Billy Wagner	.07	.20
4 Denny Neagle	.07	.20
5 Vladimir Guerrero	.20	.50
6 Kevin Brown	.10	.30
8 Mariano Rivera	.20	.50
9 Tony Clark	.07	.20
10 Deion Sanders	.10	.30
11 Francisco Cordova	.07	.20
12 Matt Williams	.07	.20
13 Carlos Baerga	.07	.20
14 Mo Vaughn	.07	.20
15 Bobby Witt	.07	.20
16 Matt Stairs	.07	.20
17 Chan Ho Park	.07	.20
18 Mike Bordick	.07	.20
19 Michael Tucker	.07	.20
20 Frank Thomas	.20	.50
21 Roberto Clemente	.40	1.00
22 Dmitri Young	.07	.20
23 Steve Trachsel	.07	.20
24 Jeff Kent	.07	.20
25 Scott Rolen	.10	.30
26 John Thomson	.07	.20
27 Joe Vitiello	.07	.20
28 Eddie Guardado	.07	.20
29 Charlie Hayes	.07	.20
30 Juan Gonzalez	.07	.20
31 Garret Anderson	.07	.20
32 John Jaha	.07	.20
33 Omar Vizquel	.10	.30
34 Brian Hunter	.07	.20
35 Jeff Bagwell	.10	.30
36 Mark Lemke	.07	.20
37 Doug Glanville	.07	.20
38 Dan Wilson	.07	.20
39 Steve Cooke	.07	.20
40 Chili Davis	.07	.20
41 Mike Cameron	.07	.20
42 F.P. Santangelo	.07	.20
43 Brad Ausmus	.07	.20
44 Gary DiSarcina	.07	.20
45 Pat Hentgen	.07	.20
46 Wilton Guerrero	.07	.20
47 Devon White	.07	.20
48 Danny Patterson	.07	.20
49 Pat Meares	.07	.20
50 Rafael Palmeiro	.10	.30
51 Mark Gardner	.07	.20
52 Jeff Blauser	.07	.20
53 Dave Hollins	.07	.20
54 Carlos Garcia	.07	.20
55 Ben McDonald	.07	.20
56 John Mabry	.07	.20
57 Trevor Hoffman	.07	.20
58 Tony Fernandez	.07	.20
59 Rich Loiselle	.07	.20
60 Mark Leiter	.07	.20
61 Pat Kelly	.07	.20
62 John Flaherty	.07	.20
63 Roger Bailey	.07	.20
64 Tom Gordon	.07	.20
65 Ryan Klesko	.07	.20
66 Darryl Hamilton	.07	.20
67 Jim Eisenreich	.07	.20
68 Butch Huskey	.07	.20
69 Mark Grudzielanek	.07	.20
70 Marquis Grissom	.07	.20
71 Mark McLemore	.07	.20
72 Gary Gaetti	.07	.20
73 Greg Gagne	.07	.20
74 Lyle Mouton	.07	.20
75 Jim Edmonds	.07	.20
76 Shawn Green	.07	.20
77 Greg Vaughn	.07	.20
78 Terry Adams	.07	.20
79 Kevin Polcovich	.07	.20
80 Troy O'Leary	.07	.20
81 Jeff Shaw	.07	.20
82 Rich Becker	.07	.20
83 David Wells	.07	.20
84 Steve Karsay	.07	.20
85 Charles Nagy	.07	.20
86 B.J. Surhoff	.07	.20
87 Jamey Wright	.07	.20
88 James Baldwin	.07	.20
89 Edgardo Alfonzo	.07	.20
90 Jay Buhner	.07	.20
91 Brady Anderson	.07	.20
92 Scott Servais	.07	.20
93 Edgar Renteria	.07	.20
94 Mike Lieberthal	.07	.20
95 Rick Aguilera	.07	.20
96 Walt Weiss	.07	.20
97 Deivi Cruz	.07	.20
98 Kurt Abbott	.07	.20
99 Henry Rodriguez	.07	.20
100 Mike Piazza	.30	.75
101 Bill Taylor	.07	.20
102 Todd Zeile	.07	.20
103 Rey Ordonez	.07	.20
104 Willie Greene	.07	.20
105 Tony Womack	.07	.20
106 Mike Sweeney	.07	.20
107 Jeffrey Hammonds	.07	.20
108 Kevin Orie	.07	.20
109 Alex Gonzalez	.07	.20
110 Jose Canseco	.10	.30
111 Paul Sorrento	.07	.20
112 Joey Hamilton	.07	.20
113 Brad Radke	.07	.20
114 Steve Avery	.07	.20
115 Esteban Loaiza	.07	.20
116 Stan Javier	.07	.20
117 Chris Gomez	.07	.20
118 Royce Clayton	.07	.20
119 Orlando Merced	.07	.20
120 Kevin Appier	.07	.20
121 Mel Nieves	.07	.20
122 Joe Girardi	.07	.20
123 Rico Brogna	.07	.20
124 Kent Mercker	.07	.20
125 Manny Ramirez	.10	.30
126 Jeromy Burnitz	.07	.20
127 Kevin Foster	.07	.20
128 Matt Morris	.07	.20
129 Jason Dickson	.07	.20
130 Tom Glavine	.10	.30
131 Wally Joyner	.07	.20
132 Rick Reed	.07	.20
133 Todd Jones	.07	.20
134 Dave Martinez	.07	.20
135 Sandy Alomar Jr.	.07	.20
136 Mike Lansing	.07	.20
137 Sean Berry	.07	.20
138 Doug Jones	.07	.20
139 Todd Stottlemyre	.07	.20
140 Jay Bell	.07	.20
141 Jaime Navarro	.07	.20
142 Chris Hoiles	.07	.20
143 Joey Cora	.07	.20
144 Scott Spiezio	.07	.20
145 Joe Carter	.07	.20
146 Jose Guillen	.07	.20
147 Damion Easley	.07	.20
148 Lee Stevens	.07	.20
149 Alex Fernandez	.07	.20
150 Randy Johnson	.20	.50
151 J.T. Snow	.07	.20
152 Chuck Finley	.07	.20
153 Bernard Gilkey	.07	.20
154 David Segui	.07	.20
155 Dante Bichette	.07	.20
156 Kevin Stocker	.07	.20
157 Carl Everett	.07	.20
158 Jose Valentin	.07	.20
159 Pokey Reese	.07	.20
160 Derek Jeter	.50	1.25
161 Roger Pavlik	.07	.20
162 Mark Wohlers	.07	.20
163 Ricky Bottalico	.07	.20
164 Ozzie Guillen	.07	.20
165 Mike Mussina	.10	.30
166 Gary Sheffield	.07	.20
167 Hideo Nomo	.20	.50
168 Mark Grace	.10	.30
169 Aaron Sele	.07	.20
170 Darryl Kile	.07	.20
171 Shawn Estes	.07	.20
172 Vinny Castilla	.07	.20
173 Ron Coomer	.07	.20
174 Jose Rosado	.07	.20
175 Kenny Lofton	.07	.20
176 Jason Giambi	.07	.20
177 Hal Morris	.07	.20
178 Darren Bragg	.07	.20
179 Orel Hershiser	.07	.20
180 Ray Lankford	.07	.20
181 Hideki Irabu	.07	.20
182 Kevin Young	.07	.20
183 Javy Lopez	.07	.20
184 Jeff Montgomery	.07	.20
185 Mike Holtz	.07	.20
186 George Williams	.07	.20
187 Cal Eldred	.07	.20
188 Tom Candiotti	.07	.20
189 Glenallen Hill	.07	.20
190 Brian Giles	.07	.20
191 Dave Mlicki	.07	.20
192 Garrett Stephenson	.07	.20
193 Jeff Frye	.07	.20
194 Joe Oliver	.07	.20
195 Bob Hamelin	.07	.20
196 Luis Sojo	.07	.20
197 LaTroy Hawkins	.07	.20
198 Kevin Elster	.07	.20
199 Jeff Reed	.07	.20
200 Dennis Eckersley	.07	.20
201 Bill Mueller	.07	.20
202 Russ Davis	.07	.20
203 Armando Benitez	.07	.20
204 Quilvio Veras	.07	.20
205 Tim Naehring	.07	.20
206 Quinton McCracken	.07	.20
207 Raul Casanova	.07	.20
208 Matt Lawton	.07	.20
209 Luis Alicea	.07	.20
210 Luis Gonzalez	.07	.20
211 Allen Watson	.07	.20
212 Gerald Williams	.07	.20
213 David Bell	.07	.20
214 Todd Hollandsworth	.07	.20
215 Wade Boggs	.10	.30
216 Jose Mesa	.07	.20
217 Jamie Moyer	.07	.20
218 Darren Daulton	.07	.20
219 Mickey Morandini	.07	.20
220 Rusty Greer	.07	.20
221 Jim Bullinger	.07	.20
222 Jose Offerman	.07	.20
223 Matt Karchner	.07	.20
224 Woody Williams	.07	.20
225 Mark Loretta	.07	.20
226 Mike Hampton	.07	.20
227 Willie Adams	.07	.20
228 Scott Hatteberg	.07	.20
229 Rich Amaral	.07	.20
230 Terry Steinbach	.07	.20
231 Glendon Rusch	.07	.20
232 Bret Boone	.07	.20
233 Robert Person	.07	.20
234 Jose Hernandez	.07	.20
235 Doug Drabek	.07	.20
236 Jason McDonald	.07	.20
237 Chris Widger	.07	.20
238 Tom Martin	.07	.20
239 Dave Burba	.07	.20
240 Pete Rose Jr.	.07	.20
241 Bobby Ayala	.07	.20
242 Tim Wakefield	.07	.20
243 Dennis Springer	.07	.20
244 Tim Belcher	.07	.20
245 Jon Garland Geoff Goetz	.10	.30
246 Glenn Davis Lance Berkman	.10	.30
247 Vernon Wells Aaron Akin	.10	.30
248 Adam Kennedy Jason Romano	.07	.20
249 Jason Dellaero Troy Cameron	.07	.20
250 Alex Sanchez Jared Sandberg	.07	.20
251 Pablo Ortega James Manias	.07	.20
252 Jason Conti RC Mike Stoner	.07	.20
253 John Patterson Larry Rodriguez	.07	.20
254 Adrian Beltre Ryan Minor RC Aaron Boone	.10	.30
255 Ben Grieve Brian Buchanan Dermal Brown	.07	.20
256 Kerrry Wood Carl Pavano Gil Meche	.10	.30
257 David Ortiz Daryle Ward Richie Sexson	1.00	2.50
258 Randy Winn Juan Encarnacion Andrew Vessel	.07	.20
259 Kris Benson Travis Smith Courtney Duncan RC	.07	.20
260 Chad Hermansen Brent Butler Warren Morris RC	.07	.20
261 Ben Davis Eli Marrero Ramon Hernandez	.07	.20
262 Eric Chavez Russell Branyan Russ Johnson	.10	.30
263 Todd Dunwoody RC John Barnes	.07	.20

Ryan Jackson
264 Matt Clement .10 .30
Roy Halladay
Brian Fuentes RC
265 Randy Johnson SH .10 .30
266 Kevin Brown SH .07 .20
267 Ricardo Rincon SH .07 .20
Francisco Cordova
268 N.Garciaparra SH .20 .50
269 Tino Martinez SH .07 .20
270 Chuck Knoblauch IL .07 .20
271 Pedro Martinez IL .10 .30
272 Denny Neagle IL .07 .20
273 Juan Gonzalez IL .07 .20
274 Andres Galarraga IL .07 .20
275 Checklist .07 .20
276 Checklist .07 .20
277 Moises Alou WS .07 .20
278 Sandy Alomar Jr. WS .07 .20
279 Gary Sheffield WS .07 .20
280 Matt Williams WS .07 .20
281 Livan Hernandez WS .07 .20
282 Chad Ogea WS .07 .20
283 Marlins Champs .07 .20
284 Tino Martinez .10 .30
285 Roberto Alomar .10 .30
286 Jeff King .07 .20
287 Brian Jordan .07 .20
288 Darin Erstad .07 .20
289 Ken Caminiti .07 .20
290 Jim Thome .10 .30
291 Paul Molitor .07 .20
292 Ivan Rodriguez .10 .30
293 Bernie Williams .10 .30
294 Todd Hundley .07 .20
295 Andres Galarraga .07 .20
296 Greg Maddux .30 .75
297 Edgar Martinez .10 .30
298 Ron Gant .07 .20
299 Derek Bell .07 .20
300 Roger Clemens .40 1.00
301 Rondell White .07 .20
302 Barry Larkin .10 .30
303 Robin Ventura .07 .20
304 Jason Kendall .07 .20
305 Chipper Jones .20 .50
306 John Franco .07 .20
307 Sammy Sosa .20 .50
308 Troy Percival .07 .20
309 Chuck Knoblauch .07 .20
310 Ellis Burks .07 .20
311 Al Martin .07 .20
312 Tim Salmon .10 .30
313 Moises Alou .07 .20
314 Lance Johnson .07 .20
315 Justin Thompson .07 .20
316 Will Clark .10 .30
317 Barry Bonds .60 1.50
318 Craig Biggio .10 .30
319 John Smoltz .10 .30
320 Cal Ripken .60 1.50
321 Ken Griffey Jr. .30 .75
322 Paul O'Neill .10 .30
323 Todd Helton .10 .30
324 John Olerud .07 .20
325 Mark McGwire .50 1.25
326 Jose Cruz Jr. .07 .20
327 Jeff Cirillo .07 .20
328 Dean Palmer .07 .20
329 John Wetteland .07 .20
330 Steve Finley .07 .20
331 Albert Belle .07 .20
332 Curt Schilling .07 .20
333 Raul Mondesi .07 .20
334 Andruw Jones .10 .30
335 Nomar Garciaparra .30 .75
336 David Justice .07 .20
337 Andy Pettitte .10 .30
338 Pedro Martinez .10 .30
339 Travis Miller .07 .20
340 Chris Stynes .07 .20
341 Gregg Jefferies .07 .20
342 Jeff Fassero .07 .20
343 Craig Counsell .07 .20
344 Wilson Alvarez .07 .20
345 Bip Roberts .07 .20
346 Kelvim Escobar .07 .20
347 Mark Bellhorn .07 .20
348 Cory Lidle RC .60 1.50
349 Fred McGriff .10 .30
350 Chuck Carr .07 .20
351 Bob Abreu .07 .20
352 Juan Guzman .07 .20
353 Fernando Vina .07 .20
354 Andy Benes .07 .20
355 Dave Nilsson .07 .20
356 Bobby Bonilla .07 .20
357 Ismael Valdes .07 .20
358 Carlos Perez .07 .20
359 Kirk Rueter .07 .20
360 Bartolo Colon .07 .20
361 Mel Rojas .07 .20
362 Johnny Damon .10 .30
363 Geronimo Berroa .07 .20
364 Reggie Sanders .07 .20
365 Jermaine Allensworth .07 .20
366 Orlando Cabrera .07 .20
367 Jorge Fabregas .07 .20
368 Scott Stahoviak .07 .20
369 Ken Cloude .07 .20
370 Donovan Osborne .07 .20
371 Roger Cedeno .07 .20
372 Neifi Perez .07 .20
373 Chris Holt .07 .20
374 Cecil Fielder .07 .20
375 Marty Cordova .07 .20
376 Tom Goodwin .07 .20
377 Jeff Suppan .07 .20
378 Jeff Brantley .07 .20
379 Mark Langston .07 .20
380 Shane Reynolds .07 .20
381 Mike Fetters .07 .20
382 Todd Greene .07 .20
383 Ray Durham .07 .20
384 Carlos Delgado .07 .20
385 Jeff D'Amico .07 .20
386 Brian McRae .07 .20
387 Alan Benes .07 .20
388 Heathcliff Slocumb .07 .20
389 Eric Young .07 .20
390 Travis Fryman .07 .20
391 David Cone .07 .20
392 Otis Nixon .07 .20
393 Jeremi Gonzalez .07 .20
394 Jeff Juden .07 .20
395 Jose Vizcaino .07 .20
396 Ugueth Urbina .07 .20
397 Ramon Martinez .07 .20
398 Robb Nen .07 .20
399 Harold Baines .07 .20
400 Delino DeShields .07 .20
401 John Burkett .07 .20
402 Sterling Hitchcock .07 .20
403 Mark Clark .07 .20
404 Terrell Wade .07 .20
405 Scott Brosius .07 .20
406 Chad Curtis .07 .20
407 Brian Johnson .07 .20
408 Roberto Kelly .07 .20
409 Dave Dellucci RC .15 .40
410 Michael Tucker .07 .20
411 Mark Kotsay .07 .20
412 Mark Lewis .07 .20
413 Ryan McGuire .07 .20
414 Shawon Dunston .07 .20
415 Brad Rigby .07 .20
416 Scott Erickson .07 .20
417 Bobby Jones .07 .20
418 Darren Oliver .07 .20
419 John Smiley .07 .20
420 T.J. Mathews .07 .20
421 Dustin Hermanson .07 .20
422 Mike Timlin .07 .20
423 Willie Blair .07 .20
424 Manny Alexander .07 .20
425 Bob Tewksbury .07 .20
426 Pete Schourek .07 .20
427 Reggie Jefferson .07 .20
428 Ed Sprague .07 .20
429 Jeff Conine .07 .20
430 Roberto Hernandez .07 .20
431 Tom Pagnozzi .07 .20
432 Jaret Wright .07 .20
433 Livan Hernandez .07 .20
434 Andy Ashby .07 .20
435 Todd Dunn .07 .20
436 Bobby Higginson .07 .20
437 Rod Beck .07 .20
438 Jim Leyritz .07 .20
439 Matt Williams .07 .20
440 Brett Tomko .07 .20
441 Joe Randa .07 .20
442 Chris Carpenter .07 .20
443 Dennis Reyes .07 .20
444 Al Leiter .07 .20
445 Jason Schmidt .07 .20
446 Ken Hill .07 .20
447 Shannon Stewart .07 .20
448 Enrique Wilson .07 .20
449 Fernando Tatis .07 .20
450 Jimmy Key .07 .20
451 Darrin Fletcher .07 .20
452 John Valentin .07 .20
453 Kevin Tapani .07 .20
454 Eric Karros .07 .20
455 Jay Bell .07 .20
456 Walt Weiss .07 .20
457 Devon White .07 .20
458 Carl Pavano .07 .20
459 Mike Lansing .07 .20
460 John Flaherty .07 .20
461 Richard Hidalgo .07 .20
462 Quinton McCracken .07 .20
463 Karim Garcia .07 .20
464 Miguel Cairo .07 .20
465 Edwin Diaz .07 .20
466 Bobby Smith .07 .20
467 Yamil Benitez .07 .20
468 Rich Butler .07 .20
469 Ben Ford RC .07 .20
470 Bubba Trammell .07 .20
471 Brent Brede .07 .20
472 Brooks Kieschnick .07 .20
473 Carlos Castillo .07 .20
474 Brad Radke SH .07 .20
475 Roger Clemens SH .20 .50
476 Curt Schilling SH .07 .20
477 John Olerud SH .07 .20
478 Mark McGwire SH .25 .60
479 Mike Piazza .20 .50
Ken Griffey Jr. IL
480 Jeff Bagwell .10 .30
Frank Thomas IL
481 Chipper Jones .10 .30
Nomar Garciaparra IL
482 Larry Walker .07 .20
Juan Gonzalez IL
483 Gary Sheffield .07 .20
Tino Martinez IL
484 Derrick Gibson .07 .20
Michael Coleman
Norm Hutchins
485 Braden Looper .07 .20
Cliff Politte
Brian Rose
486 Eric Milton .07 .20
Jason Marquis
Corey Lee
487 A.J.Hinch .10 .30
Mark Osborne
Robert Fick RC
488 Aramis Ramirez .10 .30
Alex Gonzalez
Sean Casey
489 Donnie Bridges .07 .20
Tim Drew RC
490 Ntema Ndungidi RC .07 .20
Darnell McDonald
491 Ryan Anderson RC .07 .20
Mark Mangum
492 J.J.Davis .50 1.25
Troy Glaus RC
493 Jayson Werth RC .07 .20
Dan Reichert
494 John Curtice RC .30 .75
Michael Cuddyer RC
495 Jack Cust RC .20 .50
Jason Standridge
496 Brian Anderson .07 .20
497 Tony Saunders .07 .20
498 Vladimir Nunez .07 .20
Jhensy Sandoval
499 Brad Penny .10 .30
Nick Bierbrodt
500 Dustin Carr .07 .20
Luis Cruz RC
501 Cedric Bowers .07 .20
Marcus McCain
502 Checklist .07 .20
503 Checklist .07 .20
504 Alex Rodriguez .75 2.00

1998 Topps Minted in Cooperstown

Randomly inserted in first and second series packs at the rate of one in eight, this 503 card set is a parallel version of the base set. The set is distinguished by the special "Minted in Cooperstown" logo stamped on each card. Similar to the regular set, card number 7 does not exist.

*STARS: 5X TO 12X BASIC CARDS
*ROOKIES: 6X TO 15X BASIC CARDS

1998 Topps Inaugural Devil Rays

This 503 card set was issued by Topps only in factory set form. Just as for the teams which began play in 1993, special sets with a Devil Rays logo was issued. The sets were sold only through retail outlets. These sets apparently did not sell well enough at the stadium and were later closed out to one of the home shopping networks. The logo is in gold foil and is in the middle of the card.

COMP.FACT.SET (503) 60.00 120.00
*STARS: 1.5X TO 4X BASIC CARDS
*ROOKIES: 2.5X TO 6X BASIC CARDS

1998 Topps Inaugural Diamondbacks

Similar to the Devil Rays set, Topps issued a factory set with the Diamond Backs logo to honor the first season the Arizona Diamondbacks played. The sets were issued in factory form and were only available through the Diamondback retail outlet.

COMP.FACT.SET (503) 60.00 120.00
*STARS: 1.5X TO 4X BASIC CARDS
*ROOKIES: 2.5X TO 6X BASIC CARDS

1998 Topps Baby Boomers

Randomly inserted in retail packs only at the rate of one in 36, this 15-card set features color photos of young players who have already made their mark in the game dispite less than three years in the majors.

COMPLETE SET (15) 20.00 50.00
BB1 Derek Jeter 5.00 12.00
BB2 Scott Rolen 1.25 3.00
BB3 Nomar Garciaparra 3.00 8.00
BB4 Jose Cruz Jr. .75 2.00
BB5 Darin Erstad .75 2.00
BB6 Todd Helton 1.25 3.00
BB7 Tony Clark .75 2.00
BB8 Jose Guillen .75 2.00
BB9 Andruw Jones 1.25 3.00
BB10 Vladimir Guerrero 2.00 5.00
BB11 Mark Kotsay .75 2.00
BB12 Todd Greene .75 2.00
BB13 Andy Pettitte 1.25 3.00
BB14 Justin Thompson .75 2.00
BB15 Alan Benes .75 2.00

1998 Topps Clemente

Randomly inserted in first and second series packs at the rate of one in 18, cards from this 19-card set honor the memory of Roberto Clemente on the 25th anniversay of his untimely death with conventional reprints of his Topps cards. All odd numbered cards were seeded in first series packs. All even numbered cards were seeded in second series packs.

COMPLETE SET (19) 60.00 120.00
COMPLETE SERIES 1 (10) 30.00 60.00
COMPLETE SERIES 2 (9) 30.00 60.00
COMMON CARD (2-19) 3.00 8.00
1 Roberto Clemente 1955 6.00 15.00

1998 Topps Clemente Memorabilia Madness

As a major promotion for 1998 Topps series one, Topps created 46 different Roberto Clemente exchange cards for a total of 854 prizes. All 46 prizes (including the quantity available of each prize) is detailed explicitly in the listings below. The quantity is noted immediately after the prize. All 854 exchange cards looked identical to each other on front and almost identical to each other on back. Card fronts feature a blue, purple and white dot matrix head shot of Clemente surrounded by burgundy borders. Card backs featured extensive guidelines and rules for the exchange program. The only difference for each card were the few sentences on back detailing which specific prize each of the 46 different cards could be exchanged for. Lucky collectors that got their hands on these scarce exchange cards had until August 31st, 1998 to redeem their prizes. Odds for pulling one of these cards was approximately 1:3,708 hobby packs and approximately 1:1,020 hobby collector packs. Prices for almost all of these exchange cards have been excluded due to scarcity and lack of market information.

COMMON CARD (1-46) 50.00 80.00
NNO Wild Card .40 1.00

1998 Topps Clemente Sealed

Each 1998 Topps hobby factory set contained one of 19 different hermetically sealed Roberto Clemente reprint cards. The actual cards are identical to standard Clemente reprints available in 1998 Topps packs. The difference in these special cards is the clear plastic seal entirely encasing the card. Each seal is stamped with a gold foil logo on the card back stating "Factory Topps Seal 1998".

*SEALED: .4X TO 1X BASIC CLEMENTE

1998 Topps Clemente Tins

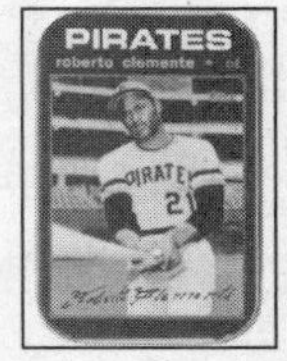

This four-tin set features reproductions of four different Roberto Clemente Topps cards printed on commemorative tins with a suggested retail price of $4.99. The tops of the tins feature color reprints of the card fronts with the backs carrying reproductions of the card backs. The cards highlighted are from the years 1955, 1956, 1965, and 1971. Inside each of these tins is a hermetically-sealed commemorative reprint of one of Clemente's 19 original Topps baseball cards dating from 1955 through 1973.

COMMON TIN (1-4) 2.00 5.00

1998 Topps Clemente Tribute

Randomly inserted in packs at the rate of one in 12, this five-card set honors the memory of Roberto Clemente on the 25th anniversay of his untimely death and features color photos printed on mirror foilboard on newly designed cards.

COMPLETE SET (5) 3.00 8.00
COMMON (RC1-RC5) .75 2.00

1998 Topps Clout Nine

Randomly inserted in Topps Series two packs at the rate of one in 72, this nine-card set features color photos of the top players statiscally at each of the nine playing positions.

COMPLETE SET (9) 15.00 40.00
C1 Edgar Martinez 1.50 4.00
C2 Mike Piazza 4.00 10.00
C3 Frank Thomas 2.50 6.00

C4 Craig Biggio 1.50 4.00
C5 Vinny Castilla 1.00 2.50
C6 Jeff Blauser 1.00 2.50
C7 Barry Bonds 8.00 20.00
C8 Ken Griffey Jr. 4.00 10.00
C9 Larry Walker 1.00 2.50

1998 Topps Etch-A-Sketch

Randomly inserted in Topps Series one packs at the rate of one in 36, this nine-card set features drawings by artist George Vlosich III of some of baseball's hottest superstars using an Etch A Sketch as a canvas.

COMPLETE SET (9) 12.50 30.00
ES1 Albert Belle .50 1.25
ES2 Barry Bonds 4.00 10.00
ES3 Ken Griffey Jr. 2.00 5.00
ES4 Greg Maddux 2.00 5.00
ES5 Hideo Nomo 1.25 3.00
ES6 Mike Piazza 2.00 5.00
ES7 Cal Ripken 4.00 10.00
ES8 Frank Thomas 1.25 3.00
ES9 Mo Vaughn .50 1.25

1998 Topps Flashback

Randomly inserted in Topps Series one packs at the rate of one in 72, these two-sided cards of top players feature photographs of how they looked "then" as rookies on one side and how they look "now" as stars on the other.

COMPLETE SET (10) 30.00 80.00
FB1 Barry Bonds 10.00 25.00
FB2 Ken Griffey Jr. 5.00 12.00
FB3 Paul Molitor 1.25 3.00
FB4 Randy Johnson 3.00 8.00
FB5 Cal Ripken 10.00 25.00
FB6 Tony Gwynn 4.00 10.00
FB7 Kenny Lofton 1.25 3.00
FB8 Gary Sheffield 1.25 3.00
FB9 Deion Sanders 2.00 5.00
FB10 Brady Anderson 1.25 3.00

1998 Topps Focal Points

Randomly inserted in Topps Series two hobby packs only at the rate of one in 36, this 15-card set features color photos of current superstars with a special focus on the skills that have put them at the top.

COMPLETE SET (15) 30.00 80.00
FP1 Juan Gonzalez .75 2.00
FP2 Nomar Garciaparra 3.00 8.00
FP3 Jose Cruz Jr. .75 2.00
FP4 Cal Ripken 6.00 15.00
FP5 Ken Griffey Jr. 3.00 8.00
FP6 Ivan Rodriguez 1.25 3.00
FP7 Larry Walker .75 2.00
FP8 Barry Bonds 6.00 15.00
FP9 Roger Clemens 4.00 10.00
FP10 Frank Thomas 2.00 5.00
FP11 Chuck Knoblauch .75 2.00
FP12 Mike Piazza 3.00 8.00
FP13 Greg Maddux 3.00 8.00
FP14 Vladimir Guerrero 2.00 5.00
FP15 Andruw Jones 1.25 3.00

1998 Topps HallBound

Randomly inserted in Topps Series one hobby packs only at the rate of one in 36, this 15-card set features color photos of top stars who are bound for the Hall of Fame printed on foil mirrorboard cards.

COMPLETE SET (15) 30.00 80.00
HB1 Paul Molitor .75 2.00
HB2 Tony Gwynn 2.50 6.00
HB3 Wade Boggs 1.25 3.00
HB4 Roger Clemens 4.00 10.00

HB5 Dennis Eckersley .75 2.00
HB6 Cal Ripken 6.00 15.00
HB7 Greg Maddux 3.00 8.00
HB8 Rickey Henderson 1.25 3.00
HB9 Ken Griffey Jr. 3.00 8.00
HB10 Frank Thomas 2.00 5.00
HB11 Mark McGwire 5.00 12.00
HB12 Barry Bonds 6.00 15.00
HB13 Mike Piazza 3.00 8.00
HB14 Juan Gonzalez .75 2.00
HB15 Randy Johnson 2.00 5.00

1998 Topps Milestones

Randomly inserted in Topps Series two retail packs only at the rate of one in 36, this ten-card set features color photos of players with the ability to set new records in the sport.

COMPLETE SET (10) 20.00 50.00
MS1 Barry Bonds 5.00 12.00
MS2 Roger Clemens 3.00 8.00
MS3 Dennis Eckersley .60 1.50
MS4 Juan Gonzalez .60 1.50
MS5 Ken Griffey Jr. 2.50 6.00
MS6 Tony Gwynn 2.00 5.00
MS7 Greg Maddux 2.50 6.00
MS8 Mark McGwire 4.00 10.00
MS9 Cal Ripken 5.00 12.00
MS10 Frank Thomas 1.50 4.00

1998 Topps Mystery Finest

Randomly inserted in first series packs at the rate of one in 36, this 20-card set features color action player photos which showcase five of the 1997 season's most intriguing inter-league matchups.

COMPLETE SET (20) 30.00 80.00
*REFRACTOR: 1X TO 2.5X BASIC MYS.FIN.
REFRACTOR SER.1 STATED ODDS: 1:144
ILM1 Chipper Jones 2.00 5.00
ILM2 Cal Ripken 6.00 15.00
ILM3 Greg Maddux 3.00 8.00
ILM4 Rafael Palmeiro 1.25 3.00
ILM5 Todd Hundley .75 2.00
ILM6 Derek Jeter 5.00 12.00
ILM7 John Olerud .75 2.00
ILM8 Tino Martinez 1.25 3.00
ILM9 Larry Walker .75 2.00
ILM10 Ken Griffey Jr. 3.00 8.00
ILM11 Andres Galarraga .75 2.00
ILM12 Randy Johnson 2.00 5.00
ILM13 Mike Piazza 3.00 8.00
ILM14 Jim Edmonds .75 2.00
ILM15 Eric Karros .75 2.00
ILM16 Tim Salmon 1.25 3.00
ILM17 Sammy Sosa 2.00 5.00
ILM18 Frank Thomas 2.00 5.00
ILM19 Mark Grace 1.25 3.00
ILM20 Albert Belle .75 2.00

1998 Topps Mystery Finest Bordered

Randomly inserted in Topps Series two packs at the rate of one in 36, this 20-card set features bordered color player photos of current hot players.

COMPLETE SET (20) 40.00 100.00
*BORDERED REF: .75X TO 2X BORDERED
BORDERED REF.SER.2 ODDS 1:108
*BORDERLESS: .6X TO 1.5X BORDERED
BORDERLESS SER.2 ODDS 1:72
*BORDERLESS REF: 1.25X TO 3X BORDERED
BORDERLESS REF.SER.2 ODDS 1:288
M1 Nomar Garciaparra 3.00 8.00
M2 Chipper Jones 2.00 5.00
M3 Scott Rolen 1.25 3.00
M4 Albert Belle .75 2.00
M5 Mo Vaughn .75 2.00

M6 Jose Cruz Jr.	.75	2.00
M7 Mark McGwire	5.00	12.00
M8 Derek Jeter	5.00	12.00
M9 Tony Gwynn	2.50	6.00
M10 Frank Thomas	2.00	5.00
M11 Tino Martinez	1.25	3.00
M12 Greg Maddux	3.00	8.00
M13 Juan Gonzalez	.75	2.00
M14 Larry Walker	.75	2.00
M15 Mike Piazza	3.00	8.00
M16 Cal Ripken	6.00	15.00
M17 Jeff Bagwell	1.25	3.00
M18 Andruw Jones	1.25	3.00
M19 Barry Bonds	6.00	15.00
M20 Ken Griffey Jr.	3.00	8.00

1998 Topps Rookie Class

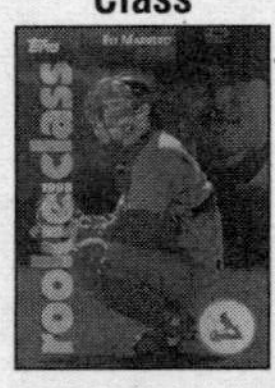

Randomly inserted in Topps Series two packs at the rate of one in 12, this 10-card set features color photos of top young stars with less than one year's playing time in the Majors. The backs carry player information.

COMPLETE SET (10)	2.50	6.00
R1 Travis Lee	.30	.75
R2 Richard Hidalgo	.30	.75
R3 Todd Helton	.50	1.25
R4 Paul Konerko	.30	.75
R5 Mark Kotsay	.30	.75
R6 Derrek Lee	.30	.75
R7 Eli Marrero	.30	.75
R8 Fernando Tatis	.30	.75
R9 Juan Encarnacion	.30	.75
R10 Ben Grieve	.30	.75

1998 Topps Fruit Roll-Ups

This eight-card set measures approximately 1 1/2" by 2" and were found on boxes of specially marked 38-pack Betty Crocker Fruit Roll-ups. The fronts of these perforated cards feature color action player photos with a thin red border. The backs are blank. The cards are unnumbered and checklisted below in alphabetical order.

COMPLETE SET (8)	8.00	20.00
1 Tony Gwynn	1.00	2.50
2 Derek Jeter	2.00	5.00
3 Kenny Lofton	.20	.50
4 Mark McGwire	1.00	2.50
5 Mike Piazza	1.25	3.00
6 Cal Ripken	2.00	5.00
7 Ivan Rodriguez	.50	1.25
8 Frank Thomas	.50	1.25

1999 Topps

The 1999 Topps set consisted of 462 standard-size cards. Each 11 card pack carried a suggested retail price of $1.29 per pack. Cards were also distributed in 40-card Home Team advantage jumbo packs, hobby, retail and Christmas factory sets. The Mark McGwire number 220 card was issued in 70 different varieties to honor his record setting season. The Sammy Sosa number 461 card was issued in 66 different varieties to honor his 1998 season. Basic sets are considered complete with any one of the 70 McGwire and 66 Sosa variations. A.J. Burnett, Pat Burrell, and Alex Escobar are the most notable Rookie Cards in the set. Card number 7 was not issued as Topps continues to honor the memory of Mickey Mantle. The Christmas factory set contains one Nolan Ryan finest reprint card as an added bonus, while the hobby and retail factory sets just contained the regular sets in a factory box.

COMPLETE SET (462)	30.00	80.00
COMP.HOBBY SET (462)	40.00	80.00
COMP.X-MAS SET (463)	40.00	80.00
COMP. SERIES 1 (241)	15.00	40.00
COMP. SERIES 2 (221)	15.00	40.00
COMP.MAC HR SET (70)	250.00	500.00
COMP.SOSA HR SET (66)	100.00	250.00
1 Roger Clemens	.40	1.00
2 Andres Galarraga	.07	.20
3 Scott Brosius	.07	.20
4 John Flaherty	.07	.20
5 Jim Leyritz	.07	.20
6 Ray Durham	.07	.20
8 Jose Vizcaino	.07	.20
9 Will Clark	.10	.30
10 David Wells	.07	.20
11 Jose Guillen	.07	.20
12 Scott Hatteberg	.07	.20
13 Edgardo Alfonzo	.07	.20
14 Mike Bordick	.07	.20
15 Manny Ramirez	.10	.30
16 Greg Maddux	.30	.75
17 David Segui	.07	.20
18 Darryl Strawberry	.07	.20
19 Brad Radke	.07	.20
20 Kerry Wood	.07	.20
21 Matt Anderson	.07	.20
22 Derrek Lee	.10	.30
23 Mickey Morandini	.07	.20
24 Paul Konerko	.07	.20
25 Travis Lee	.07	.20
26 Ken Hill	.07	.20
27 Kenny Rogers	.07	.20
28 Paul Sorrento	.07	.20
29 Quilvio Veras	.07	.20
30 Todd Walker	.07	.20
31 Ryan Jackson	.07	.20
32 John Olerud	.07	.20
33 Doug Glanville	.07	.20
34 Nolan Ryan	.75	2.00
35 Ray Lankford	.07	.20
36 Mark Loretta	.07	.20
37 Jason Dickson	.07	.20
38 Sean Bergman	.07	.20
39 Quinton McCracken	.07	.20
40 Bartolo Colon	.07	.20
41 Brady Anderson	.07	.20
42 Chris Stynes	.07	.20
43 Jorge Posada	.10	.30
44 Justin Thompson	.07	.20
45 Johnny Damon	.10	.30
46 Armando Benitez	.07	.20
47 Brant Brown	.07	.20
48 Charlie Hayes	.07	.20
49 Darren Dreifort	.07	.20
50 Juan Gonzalez	.07	.20
51 Chuck Knoblauch	.07	.20
52 Todd Helton	.10	.30
53 Rick Reed	.07	.20
54 Chris Gomez	.07	.20
55 Gary Sheffield	.07	.20
56 Rod Beck	.07	.20
57 Rey Sanchez	.07	.20
58 Garret Anderson	.07	.20
59 Jimmy Haynes	.07	.20
60 Steve Woodard	.07	.20
61 Rondell White	.07	.20
62 Vladimir Guerrero	.20	.50
63 Eric Karros	.07	.20
64 Russ Davis	.07	.20
65 Mo Vaughn	.07	.20
66 Sammy Sosa	.20	.50
67 Troy Percival	.07	.20
68 Kenny Lofton	.07	.20
69 Bill Taylor	.07	.20
70 Mark McGwire	.50	1.25
71 Roger Cedeno	.07	.20
72 Javy Lopez	.07	.20
73 Damion Easley	.07	.20
74 Andy Pettitte	.10	.30
75 Tony Gwynn	.25	.60
76 Ricardo Rincon	.07	.20
77 F.P. Santangelo	.07	.20
78 Jay Bell	.07	.20
79 Scott Servais	.07	.20
80 Jose Canseco	.10	.30
81 Roberto Hernandez	.07	.20
82 Todd Dunwoody	.07	.20
83 John Wetteland	.07	.20
84 Mike Caruso	.07	.20
85 Derek Jeter	.50	1.25
86 Aaron Sele	.07	.20
87 Jose Lima	.07	.20
88 Ryan Christenson	.07	.20
89 Jeff Cirillo	.07	.20
90 Jose Hernandez	.07	.20
91 Mark Kotsay	.07	.20
92 Darren Bragg	.07	.20
93 Albert Belle	.07	.20
94 Matt Lawton	.07	.20
95 Pedro Martinez	.10	.30
96 Greg Vaughn	.07	.20
97 Neifi Perez	.07	.20
98 Gerald Williams	.07	.20
99 Derek Bell	.07	.20
100 Ken Griffey Jr.	.30	.75
101 David Cone	.07	.20
102 Brian Johnson	.07	.20
103 Dean Palmer	.07	.20
104 Javier Valentin	.07	.20
105 Trevor Hoffman	.07	.20
106 Butch Huskey	.07	.20
107 Dave Martinez	.07	.20
108 Billy Wagner	.07	.20
109 Shawn Green	.07	.20
110 Ben Grieve	.07	.20
111 Tom Goodwin	.07	.20
112 Jaret Wright	.07	.20
113 Aramis Ramirez	.07	.20
114 Dmitri Young	.07	.20
115 Hideki Irabu	.07	.20
116 Roberto Kelly	.07	.20
117 Jeff Fassero	.07	.20
118 Mark Clark UER	.07	.20
1997 and Career Victory totals are wrong		
119 Jason McDonald	.07	.20
120 Matt Williams	.07	.20
121 Dave Burba	.07	.20
122 Bret Saberhagen	.07	.20
123 Deivi Cruz	.07	.20
124 Chad Curtis	.07	.20
125 Scott Rolen	.10	.30
126 Lee Stevens	.07	.20
127 J.T. Snow	.07	.20
128 Rusty Greer	.07	.20
129 Brian Meadows	.07	.20
130 Jim Edmonds	.07	.20
131 Ron Gant	.07	.20
132 A.J. Hinch UER	.07	.20
Photo is a reverse negative		
133 Shannon Stewart	.07	.20
134 Brad Fullmer	.07	.20
135 Cal Eldred	.07	.20
136 Matt Walbeck	.07	.20
137 Carl Everett	.07	.20
138 Walt Weiss	.07	.20
139 Fred McGriff	.10	.30
140 Darin Erstad	.07	.20
141 Dave Nilsson	.07	.20
142 Eric Young	.07	.20
143 Dan Wilson	.07	.20
144 Jeff Reed	.07	.20
145 Brett Tomko	.07	.20
146 Terry Steinbach	.07	.20
147 Seth Greisinger	.07	.20
148 Pat Meares	.07	.20
149 Livan Hernandez	.07	.20
150 Jeff Bagwell	.10	.30
151 Bob Wickman	.07	.20
152 Omar Vizquel	.10	.30
153 Eric Davis	.07	.20
154 Larry Sutton	.07	.20
155 Magglio Ordonez	.07	.20
156 Eric Milton	.07	.20
157 Darren Lewis	.07	.20
158 Rick Aguilera	.07	.20
159 Mike Lieberthal	.07	.20
160 Robb Nen	.07	.20
161 Brian Giles	.07	.20
162 Jeff Brantley	.07	.20
163 Gary DiSarcina	.07	.20
164 John Valentin	.07	.20
165 David Dellucci	.07	.20
166 Chan Ho Park	.07	.20
167 Masato Yoshii	.07	.20
168 Jason Schmidt	.07	.20
169 LaTroy Hawkins	.07	.20
170 Bret Boone	.07	.20
171 Jerry DiPoto	.07	.20
172 Mariano Rivera	.20	.50
173 Mike Cameron	.07	.20
174 Scott Erickson	.07	.20
175 Charles Johnson	.07	.20
176 Bobby Jones	.07	.20
177 Francisco Cordova	.07	.20
178 Todd Jones	.07	.20
179 Jeff Montgomery	.07	.20
180 Mike Mussina	.10	.30
181 Bob Abreu	.07	.20
182 Ismael Valdes	.07	.20
183 Andy Fox	.07	.20
184 Woody Williams	.07	.20
185 Denny Neagle	.07	.20
186 Jose Valentin	.07	.20
187 Darrin Fletcher	.07	.20
188 Gabe Alvarez	.07	.20
189 Eddie Taubensee	.07	.20
190 Edgar Martinez	.10	.30
191 Jason Kendall	.07	.20
192 Darryl Kile	.07	.20
193 Jeff King	.07	.20
194 Rey Ordonez	.07	.20
195 Andruw Jones	.10	.30
196 Tony Fernandez	.07	.20
197 Jamey Wright	.07	.20
198 B.J. Surhoff	.07	.20
199 Vinny Castilla	.07	.20
200 David Wells HL	.07	.20
201 Mark McGwire HL	.25	.60
202 Sammy Sosa HL	.10	.30
203 Roger Clemens HL	.20	.50
204 Kerry Wood HL	.07	.20
205 Lance Berkman	.15	.40
Mike Frank		
Gabe Kapler		
206 Alex Escobar RC	.15	.40
Ricky Ledee		
Mike Stoner		
207 Peter Bergeron RC	.08	.25
Jeremy Giambi		
George Lombard		
208 Michael Barrett	.08	.25
Ben Davis		
Robert Fick		
209 Pat Cline	.08	.25
Ramon Hernandez		
Jayson Werth		
210 Bruce Chen	.08	.25
Chris Enochs		
Ryan Anderson		
211 Mike Lincoln	.08	.25
Octavio Dotel		
Brad Penny		
212 Chuck Abbott RC	.08	.25
Brent Butler		
Danny Klassen		
213 Chris C.Jones	.08	.25
Jeff Urban RC		
214 Arturo McDowell RC	.08	.25
Tony Torcato		
215 Josh McKinley RC	.08	.25
Jason Tyner		
216 Matt Burch	.08	.25
Seth Etheron RC		
UER back Etherton		
217 Mamon Tucker RC	.08	.25
Rick Elder		
218 J.M.Gold	.08	.25
Ryan Mills RC		
219 Adam Brown	.08	.25
Choo Freeman RC		
220A Mark McGwire HR 1	15.00	40.00
220B Mark McGwire HR 2	6.00	15.00
220C Mark McGwire HR 3	6.00	15.00
220D Mark McGwire HR 4	6.00	15.00
220E Mark McGwire HR 5	6.00	15.00
220F Mark McGwire HR 6	6.00	15.00
220G Mark McGwire HR 7	6.00	15.00
220H Mark McGwire HR 8	6.00	15.00
220I Mark McGwire HR 9	6.00	15.00
220J M.McGwire HR 10	6.00	15.00
220K M.McGwire HR 11	6.00	15.00
220L M.McGwire HR 12	6.00	15.00
220M M.McGwire HR 13	6.00	15.00
220N M.McGwire HR 14	6.00	15.00
220O M.McGwire HR 15	6.00	15.00
220P M.McGwire HR 16	6.00	15.00
220Q M.McGwire HR 17	6.00	15.00
220R M.McGwire HR 18	6.00	15.00
220S M.McGwire HR 19	6.00	15.00
220T M.McGwire HR 20	6.00	15.00
220U M.McGwire HR 21	6.00	15.00
220V M.McGwire HR 22	6.00	15.00
220W M.McGwire HR 23	6.00	15.00
220X M.McGwire HR 24	6.00	15.00
220Y M.McGwire HR 25	6.00	15.00
220Z M.McGwire HR 26	6.00	15.00
220AA M.McGwire HR 27	6.00	15.00
220AB M.McGwire HR 28	6.00	15.00
220AC M.McGwire HR 29	6.00	15.00
220AD M.McGwire HR 30	6.00	15.00
220AE M.McGwire HR 31	6.00	15.00
220AF M.McGwire HR 32	6.00	15.00
220AG M.McGwire HR 33	6.00	15.00
220AH M.McGwire HR 34	6.00	15.00
220AI M.McGwire HR 35	6.00	15.00
220AJ M.McGwire HR 36	6.00	15.00
220AK M.McGwire HR 37	6.00	15.00
220AL M.McGwire HR 38	6.00	15.00
220AM M.McGwire HR 39	6.00	15.00
220AN M.McGwire HR 40	6.00	15.00
220AO M.McGwire HR 41	6.00	15.00
220AP M.McGwire HR 42	6.00	15.00
220AQ M.McGwire HR 43	6.00	15.00
220AR M.McGwire HR 44	6.00	15.00
220AS M.McGwire HR 45	6.00	15.00
220AT M.McGwire HR 46	6.00	15.00
220AU M.McGwire HR 47	6.00	15.00
220AV M.McGwire HR 48	6.00	15.00
220AW M.McGwire HR 49	6.00	15.00
220AX M.McGwire HR 50	6.00	15.00
220AY M.McGwire HR 51	6.00	15.00
220AZ M.McGwire HR 52	6.00	15.00
220BB M.McGwire HR 53	6.00	15.00
220CC M.McGwire HR 54	6.00	15.00
220DD M.McGwire HR 55	6.00	15.00
220EE M.McGwire HR 56	6.00	15.00
220FF M.McGwire HR 57	6.00	15.00
220GG M.McGwire HR 58	6.00	15.00
220HH M.McGwire HR 59	6.00	15.00
220II M.McGwire HR 60	6.00	15.00
220JJ M.McGwire HR 61	12.50	30.00
220KK M.McGwire HR 62	15.00	40.00
220LL M.McGwire HR 63	6.00	15.00
220MM M.McGwire HR 64	6.00	15.00
220NN M.McGwire HR 65	6.00	15.00
220OO M.McGwire HR 66	6.00	15.00
220PP M.McGwire HR 67	6.00	15.00
220QQ M.McGwire HR 68	6.00	15.00
220RR M.McGwire HR 69	6.00	15.00
220SS M.McGwire HR 70	50.00	100.00
221 Larry Walker LL	.07	.20
222 Bernie Williams LL	.07	.20
223 Mark McGwire LL	.25	.60
224 Ken Griffey Jr. LL	.20	.50
225 Sammy Sosa LL	.10	.30
226 Juan Gonzalez LL	.07	.20
227 Dante Bichette LL	.07	.20
228 Alex Rodriguez LL	.20	.50
229 Sammy Sosa LL	.10	.30
230 Derek Jeter LL	.25	.60
231 Greg Maddux LL	.20	.50
232 Roger Clemens LL	.20	.50
233 Ricky Ledee WS	.07	.20
234 Chuck Knoblauch WS	.07	.20
235 Bernie Williams WS	.07	.20
236 Tino Martinez WS	.07	.20
237 Orl. Hernandez WS	.07	.20
238 Scott Brosius WS	.07	.20
239 Andy Pettitte WS	.07	.20
240 Mariano Rivera WS	.10	.30
241 Checklist 1	.07	.20
242 Checklist 2	.07	.20
243 Tom Glavine	.10	.30
244 Andy Benes	.07	.20
245 Sandy Alomar Jr.	.07	.20
246 Wilton Guerrero	.07	.20
247 Alex Gonzalez	.07	.20
248 Roberto Alomar	.10	.30
249 Ruben Rivera	.07	.20
250 Eric Chavez	.07	.20
251 Ellis Burks	.07	.20
252 Richie Sexson	.07	.20
253 Steve Finley	.07	.20
254 Dwight Gooden	.07	.20
255 Dustin Hermanson	.07	.20
256 Kirk Rueter	.07	.20
257 Steve Trachsel	.07	.20
258 Gregg Jefferies	.07	.20
259 Matt Stairs	.07	.20
260 Shane Reynolds	.07	.20
261 Gregg Olson	.07	.20
262 Kevin Tapani	.07	.20
263 Matt Morris	.07	.20
264 Carl Pavano	.07	.20
265 Nomar Garciaparra	.30	.75
266 Kevin Young	.07	.20
267 Rick Helling	.07	.20
268 Matt Franco	.07	.20
269 Brian McRae	.07	.20
270 Cal Ripken	.60	1.50
271 Jeff Abbott	.07	.20
272 Tony Batista	.07	.20
273 Bill Simas	.07	.20
274 Brian Hunter	.07	.20
275 John Franco	.07	.20
276 Devon White	.07	.20
277 Rickey Henderson	.20	.50
278 Chuck Finley	.07	.20
279 Mike Blowers	.07	.20
280 Mark Grace	.10	.30
281 Randy Winn	.07	.20
282 Bobby Bonilla	.07	.20
283 David Justice	.07	.20
284 Shane Monahan	.07	.20
285 Kevin Brown	.10	.30
286 Todd Zeile	.07	.20
287 Al Martin	.07	.20
288 Troy O'Leary	.07	.20
289 Darryl Hamilton	.07	.20
290 Tino Martinez	.10	.30
291 David Ortiz	.20	.50
292 Tony Clark	.07	.20
293 Ryan Minor	.07	.20
294 Mark Leiter	.07	.20
295 Wally Joyner	.07	.20
296 Cliff Floyd	.07	.20
297 Shawn Estes	.07	.20
298 Pat Hentgen	.07	.20
299 Scott Elarton	.07	.20
300 Alex Rodriguez	.30	.75
301 Ozzie Guillen	.07	.20
302 Hideo Nomo	.20	.50
303 Ryan McGuire	.07	.20
304 Brad Ausmus	.07	.20
305 Alex Gonzalez	.07	.20
306 Brian Jordan	.07	.20
307 John Jaha	.07	.20
308 Mark Grudzielanek	.07	.20
309 Juan Guzman	.07	.20
310 Tony Womack	.07	.20
311 Dennis Reyes	.07	.20
312 Marty Cordova	.07	.20
313 Ramiro Mendoza	.07	.20
314 Robin Ventura	.07	.20
315 Rafael Palmeiro	.10	.30
316 Ramon Martinez	.07	.20
317 Pedro Astacio	.07	.20
318 Dave Hollins	.07	.20
319 Tom Candiotti	.07	.20
320 Al Leiter	.07	.20
321 Rico Brogna	.07	.20
322 Reggie Jefferson	.07	.20
323 Bernard Gilkey	.07	.20
324 Jason Giambi	.07	.20
325 Craig Biggio	.10	.30
326 Troy Glaus	.10	.30
327 Delino DeShields	.07	.20
328 Fernando Vina	.07	.20
329 John Smoltz	.10	.30
330 Jeff Kent	.07	.20
331 Roy Halladay	.07	.20
332 Andy Ashby	.07	.20
333 Tim Wakefield	.07	.20
334 Roger Clemens	.40	1.00
335 Bernie Williams	.10	.30
336 Desi Relaford	.07	.20
337 John Burkett	.07	.20
338 Mike Hampton	.07	.20
339 Royce Clayton	.07	.20
340 Mike Piazza	.30	.75
341 Jeremi Gonzalez	.07	.20
342 Mike Lansing	.07	.20
343 Jamie Moyer	.07	.20
344 Ron Coomer	.07	.20
345 Barry Larkin	.10	.30
346 Fernando Tatis	.07	.20
347 Chili Davis	.07	.20
348 Bobby Higginson	.07	.20
349 Hal Morris	.07	.20
350 Larry Walker	.07	.20
351 Carlos Guillen	.07	.20
352 Miguel Tejada	.07	.20
353 Travis Fryman	.07	.20
354 Jarrod Washburn	.07	.20
355 Chipper Jones	.20	.50
356 Todd Stottlemyre	.07	.20
357 Henry Rodriguez	.07	.20
358 Eli Marrero	.07	.20
359 Alan Benes	.07	.20
360 Tim Salmon	.10	.30
361 Luis Gonzalez	.07	.20
362 Scott Spiezio	.07	.20
363 Chris Carpenter	.07	.20
364 Bobby Howry	.07	.20
365 Raul Mondesi	.07	.20
366 Ugueth Urbina	.07	.20
367 Tom Evans	.07	.20
368 Kerry Ligtenberg RC	.08	.25
369 Adrian Beltre	.07	.20
370 Ryan Klesko	.07	.20
371 Wilson Alvarez	.07	.20
372 John Thomson	.07	.20
373 Tony Saunders	.07	.20
374 Dave Mlicki	.07	.20
375 Ken Caminiti	.07	.20
376 Jay Buhner	.07	.20
377 Bill Mueller	.07	.20
378 Jeff Blauser	.07	.20
379 Edgar Renteria	.07	.20
380 Jim Thome	.10	.30
381 Joey Hamilton	.07	.20
382 Calvin Pickering	.07	.20
383 Marquis Grissom	.07	.20
384 Omar Daal	.07	.20
385 Curt Schilling	.07	.20
386 Jose Cruz Jr.	.07	.20
387 Chris Widger	.07	.20
388 Pete Harnisch	.07	.20
389 Charles Nagy	.07	.20
390 Tom Gordon	.07	.20
391 Bobby Smith	.07	.20
392 Derrick Gibson	.07	.20
393 Jeff Conine	.07	.20
394 Carlos Perez	.07	.20
395 Barry Bonds	.60	1.50
396 Mark McLemore	.07	.20
397 Juan Encarnacion	.07	.20
398 Wade Boggs	.10	.30
399 Ivan Rodriguez	.10	.30
400 Moises Alou	.07	.20
401 Jeromy Burnitz	.07	.20
402 Sean Casey	.07	.20
403 Jose Offerman	.07	.20
404 Joe Fontenot	.07	.20
405 Kevin Millwood	.07	.20
406 Lance Johnson	.07	.20
407 Richard Hidalgo	.07	.20
408 Mike Jackson	.07	.20
409 Brian Anderson	.07	.20
410 Jeff Shaw	.07	.20
411 Preston Wilson	.07	.20
412 Todd Hundley	.07	.20
413 Jim Parque	.07	.20
414 Justin Baughman	.07	.20
415 Dante Bichette	.07	.20
416 Paul O'Neill	.10	.30
417 Miguel Cairo	.07	.20
418 Randy Johnson	.20	.50
419 Jesus Sanchez	.07	.20
420 Carlos Delgado	.07	.20
421 Ricky Ledee	.07	.20
422 Orlando Hernandez	.07	.20
423 Frank Thomas	.20	.50
424 Pokey Reese	.07	.20
425 Carlos Lee	.15	.40
Mike Lowell		
Kit Pellow RC		
426 Michael Cuddyer	.08	.25
Mark DeRosa		
Jerry Hairston Jr.		
427 Marlon Anderson	.15	.40
Ron Belliard		
Orlando Cabrera		
428 Micah Bowie	.08	.25
Phil Norton RC		
Randy Wolf		
429 Jack Cressend RC	.15	.40
Jason Rakers		
John Rocker		
430 Ruben Mateo	.08	.25
Scott Morgan		
Mike Zywica RC		
431 Jason LaRue	.08	.25
Matt LeCroy		
Mitch Meluskey		
432 Gabe Kapler	.15	.40
Armando Rios		
Fernando Seguignol		
433 Adam Kennedy	.08	.25
Mickey Lopez RC		
Jackie Rexrode		
434 Jose Fernandez RC	.08	.25
Jeff Liefer		
Chris Truby		
435 Corey Koskie	.20	.50
Doug Mientkiewicz RC		
Damon Minor		
436 Roosevelt Brown RC	.08	.25
Dernell Stenson		
Vernon Wells		
437 A.J. Burnett RC	.30	.75
Billy Koch		
John Nicholson		
438 Matt Belisle	.08	.25
Matt Roney RC		
439 Austin Kearns	.60	1.50
Chris George RC		
440 Nate Bump RC	.08	.25
Nate Cornejo		
441 Brad Lidge	.60	1.50
Mike Nannini RC		
442 Matt Holliday	1.50	4.00
Jeff Winchester RC		
443 Adam Everett	.20	.50
Chip Ambres RC		
444 Pat Burrell	.60	1.50
Eric Valent RC		
445 Roger Clemens SK	.20	.50
446 Kerry Wood SK	.07	.20
447 Curt Schilling SK	.07	.20
448 Randy Johnson SK	.10	.30
449 Pedro Martinez SK	.10	.30
450 Jeff Bagwell AT	.20	.50
Andres Galarraga		
Mark McGwire		
451 John Olerud AT	.07	.20
Jim Thome		
Tino Martinez		
452 Alex Rodriguez AT	.25	.60
Nomar Garciaparra		
Derek Jeter		
453 Vinny Castilla AT	.10	.30
Chipper Jones		
Scott Rolen		
454 Sammy Sosa AT	.20	.50
Ken Griffey Jr.		
Juan Gonzalez		
455 Barry Bonds AT	.30	.75
Manny Ramirez		
Larry Walker		
456 Frank Thomas AT	.20	.50
Tim Salmon		
David Justice		
457 Travis Lee AT	.07	.20
Todd Helton		
Ben Grieve		
458 Vladimir Guerrero AT	.07	.20
Greg Vaughn		
Bernie Williams		
459 Mike Piazza AT	.20	.50
Ivan Rodriguez		
Jason Kendall		
460 Roger Clemens AT	.20	.50
Kerry Wood		
Greg Maddux		
461A Sammy Sosa HR 1	6.00	15.00
461B Sammy Sosa HR 2	2.50	6.00
461C Sammy Sosa HR 3	2.50	6.00
461D Sammy Sosa HR 4	2.50	6.00
461E Sammy Sosa HR 5	2.50	6.00
461F Sammy Sosa HR 6	2.50	6.00
461G Sammy Sosa HR 7	2.50	6.00
461H Sammy Sosa HR 8	2.50	6.00
461I Sammy Sosa HR 9	2.50	6.00
461J Sammy Sosa HR 10	2.50	6.00
461K Sammy Sosa HR 11	2.50	6.00
461L Sammy Sosa HR 12	2.50	6.00
461M Sammy Sosa HR 13	2.50	6.00
461N Sammy Sosa HR 14	2.50	6.00
461O Sammy Sosa HR 15	2.50	6.00
461P Sammy Sosa HR 16	2.50	6.00
461Q Sammy Sosa HR 17	2.50	6.00
461R Sammy Sosa HR 18	2.50	6.00
461S Sammy Sosa HR 19	2.50	6.00
461T Sammy Sosa HR 20	2.50	6.00
461U Sammy Sosa HR 21	2.50	6.00
461V Sammy Sosa HR 22	2.50	6.00
461W Sammy Sosa HR 23	2.50	6.00
461X Sammy Sosa HR 24	2.50	6.00
461Y Sammy Sosa HR 25	2.50	6.00
461Z Sammy Sosa HR 26	2.50	6.00
461AA S.Sosa HR 27	2.50	6.00
461AB S.Sosa HR 28	2.50	6.00
461AC S.Sosa HR 29	2.50	6.00
461AD S.Sosa HR 30	2.50	6.00
461AE S.Sosa HR 31	2.50	6.00
461AF S.Sosa HR 32	2.50	6.00
461AG S.Sosa HR 33	2.50	6.00
461AH S.Sosa HR 34	2.50	6.00
461AI S.Sosa HR 35	2.50	6.00
461AJ S.Sosa HR 36	2.50	6.00
461AK S.Sosa HR 37	2.50	6.00
461AL S.Sosa HR 38	2.50	6.00
461AM S.Sosa HR 39	2.50	6.00
461AN S.Sosa HR 40	2.50	6.00
461AO S.Sosa HR 41	2.50	6.00
461AP S.Sosa HR 42	2.50	6.00
461AR S.Sosa HR 43	2.50	6.00
461AS S.Sosa HR 44	2.50	6.00
461AT S.Sosa HR 45	2.50	6.00
461AU S.Sosa HR 46	2.50	6.00
461AV S.Sosa HR 47	2.50	6.00
461AW S.Sosa HR 48	2.50	6.00
461AX S.Sosa HR 49	2.50	6.00
461AY S.Sosa HR 50	2.50	6.00
461AZ S.Sosa HR 51	2.50	6.00
461BB S.Sosa HR 52	2.50	6.00
461CC S.Sosa HR 53	2.50	6.00
461DD S.Sosa HR 54	2.50	6.00
461EE S.Sosa HR 55	2.50	6.00

461FF S.Sosa HR 56	2.50	6.00
461GG S.Sosa HR 57	2.50	6.00
461HH S.Sosa HR 58	2.50	6.00
461II S.Sosa HR 59	2.50	6.00
461JJ S.Sosa HR 60	2.50	6.00
461KK S.Sosa HR 61	6.00	15.00
461LL S.Sosa HR 62	8.00	20.00
461MM S.Sosa HR 63	3.00	8.00
461NN S.Sosa HR 64	3.00	8.00
461OO S.Sosa HR 65	3.00	8.00
461PP S.Sosa HR 66	10.00	25.00
462 Checklist	.07	.20
463 Checklist	.07	.20

1999 Topps MVP Promotion

This is a partial parallel to the regular Topps set. Draft pick and Prospect cards were not included in series one but were included in series two. The front of the card features the same photo as the basic issue card but is adorned with a bold gold foil MVP Promotion logo. The back features contest guidelines for the Topps MVP Promotion. If the featured player was awarded player of the week status (as determined by Topps) his card was then redeemable at season's end for a special set of all the weekly winners. Only 100 of each MVP Promotion card was produced. Stated odds were as follows: series 1 hobby packs 1:515, series 1 Home Team Advantage packs 1:142 and series 2 hobby packs 1:504, Series 2 Home Team Advantage 1:139 and series 2 retail 1:504. The exchange deadline to redeem winning cards was December 31st, 1999. Winning prize cards were mailed out between February 15th, 2000 and April 30th, 2000. The winning cards were the following numbers (which correspond to the regular Topps set): 35, 52, 70, 96, 101, 125, 127, 139, 159, 198, 248, 265, 290, 292, 300, 315, 340, 346, 350, 352, 355, 360, 365, 416, and 418. Since Topps destroyed these Winner exchange cards once they received them, they're in noticeably shorter supply than other cards from this set. Despite this fact, no noticeable premiums in secondary trading levels have been detected for these cards.

*STARS: 20X TO 50X BASIC CARDS
*ROOKIES: 8X TO 20X BASIC CARDS

35 Ray Lankford W	4.00	10.00
52 Todd Helton W	6.00	15.00
70 Mark McGwire W	25.00	60.00
96 Greg Vaughn W	4.00	10.00
101 David Cone W	4.00	10.00
125 Scott Rolen W	6.00	15.00
127 J.T. Snow W	4.00	10.00
139 Fred McGriff W	6.00	15.00
159 Mike Lieberthal W	4.00	10.00
198 B.J. Surhoff W	4.00	10.00
248 Roberto Alomar W	6.00	15.00
265 Nomar Garciaparra W	15.00	40.00
290 Tino Martinez W	6.00	15.00
292 Tony Clark W	4.00	10.00
300 Alex Rodriguez W	15.00	40.00
315 Rafael Palmeiro W	6.00	15.00
340 Mike Piazza W	15.00	40.00
346 Fernando Tatis W	4.00	10.00
350 Larry Walker W	4.00	10.00
352 Miguel Tejada W	4.00	10.00
355 Chipper Jones W	10.00	25.00
360 Tim Salmon W	6.00	15.00
365 Raul Mondesi W	4.00	10.00
416 Paul O'Neill W	6.00	15.00
418 Randy Johnson W	10.00	25.00

1999 Topps MVP Promotion Exchange

This 25-card set was available only to those lucky collectors who obtained one of the twenty-five winning player cards from the 1999 Topps MVP Promotion parallel set. Each week, throughout the 1999 season, Topps named a new Player of the Week, and that player's Topps MVP Promotion parallel card was made redeemable for this 25-card set. The deadline to exchange the winning cards was December 31st, 1999. The exchange cards shipped out in mid-February, 2000.

COMP.FACT.SET (25)	20.00	50.00
MVP1 Raul Mondesi	.60	1.50
MVP2 Tim Salmon	1.00	2.50
MVP3 Fernando Tatis	.60	1.50
MVP4 Larry Walker	.60	1.50
MVP5 Fred McGriff	1.00	2.50
MVP6 Nomar Garciaparra	2.50	6.00
MVP7 Rafael Palmeiro	1.00	2.50
MVP8 Randy Johnson	1.50	4.00
MVP9 Mike Lieberthal	.60	1.50
MVP10 B.J. Surhoff	.60	1.50
MVP11 Todd Helton	1.00	2.50
MVP12 Tino Martinez	1.00	2.50
MVP13 Scott Rolen	1.00	2.50
MVP14 Mike Piazza	2.50	6.00
MVP15 David Cone	.60	1.50
MVP16 Tony Clark	.60	1.50
MVP17 Roberto Alomar	1.00	2.50
MVP18 Miguel Tejada	.60	1.50
MVP19 Alex Rodriguez	2.50	6.00
MVP20 J.T. Snow	.60	1.50
MVP21 Ray Lankford	.60	1.50
MVP22 Greg Vaughn	.60	1.50
MVP23 Paul O'Neill	1.00	2.50
MVP24 Chipper Jones	1.50	4.00
MVP25 Mark McGwire	4.00	10.00

1999 Topps Oversize

Inserted one per Home Team Advantage and one per Hobby box, these cards feature sixteen of the leading players in an oversize version. The photos are the same as the regular Topps cards. We have numbered the cards with A and B prefixes to denote series one versus series two distribution, although Topps decided to number each series 1 through 8.

COMPLETE SERIES 1 (8)	6.00	15.00
COMPLETE SERIES 2 (8)	6.00	15.00

1999 Topps All-Matrix

This 30-card insert set consists of three thematic subsets (Club 40 are numbers 1-13, '99 Rookie Rush are number's 14-23 and Club K are numbers 24-30). All 30-cards feature silver foil dot-matrix technology. Cards were seeded exclusively into series 2 packs as follows: 1:18 hobby, 1:18 retail and 1:5 Home Team Advantage.

COMPLETE SET (30)	40.00	80.00
AM1 Mark McGwire	4.00	10.00
AM2 Sammy Sosa	1.50	4.00
AM3 Ken Griffey Jr.	2.50	6.00
AM4 Greg Vaughn	.60	1.50
AM5 Albert Belle	.60	1.50
AM6 Vinny Castilla	.60	1.50
AM7 Jose Canseco	1.00	2.50
AM8 Juan Gonzalez	.60	1.50
AM9 Manny Ramirez	1.00	2.50
AM10 Andres Galarraga	.60	1.50
AM11 Rafael Palmeiro	1.00	2.50
AM12 Alex Rodriguez	2.50	6.00
AM13 Mo Vaughn	.60	1.50
AM14 Eric Chavez	.60	1.50
AM15 Gabe Kapler	1.25	3.00
AM16 Calvin Pickering	.60	1.50
AM17 Ruben Mateo	.75	2.00
AM18 Roy Halladay	.60	1.50
AM19 Jeremy Giambi	.60	1.50
AM20 Alex Gonzalez	.60	1.50
AM21 Ron Belliard	1.25	3.00
AM22 Marlon Anderson	1.25	3.00
AM23 Carlos Lee	1.25	3.00
AM24 Kerry Wood	.60	1.50
AM25 Roger Clemens	3.00	8.00
AM26 Curt Schilling	.60	1.50
AM27 Kevin Brown	1.00	2.50
AM28 Randy Johnson	1.50	4.00
AM29 Pedro Martinez	1.00	2.50
AM30 Orlando Hernandez	.60	1.50

1999 Topps All-Topps Mystery Finest

Randomly inserted in Topps Series two packs at the the rate of one in 36, this 33-card set features 11 three-player positional parallels of the All-Topps subset printed using Finest technology. All three players are printed on the back, but the collector has to peel off the opaque protector to reveal who is on the front.

COMPLETE SET (33)	125.00	250.00
*REFRACTORS: 1X TO 2.5X BASIC ATMF		
SER.2 REF.ODDS 1:144 HOB/RET, 1:32 HTA		
M1 Jeff Bagwell	2.00	5.00
M2 Andres Galarraga	1.25	3.00
M3 Mark McGwire	8.00	20.00
M4 John Olerud	1.25	3.00
M5 Jim Thome	2.00	5.00
M6 Tino Martinez	2.00	5.00
M7 Alex Rodriguez	5.00	12.00
M8 Nomar Garciaparra	5.00	12.00
M9 Derek Jeter	8.00	20.00
M10 Vinny Castilla	1.25	3.00
M11 Chipper Jones	3.00	8.00
M12 Scott Rolen	2.00	5.00
M13 Sammy Sosa	3.00	8.00
M14 Ken Griffey Jr.	5.00	12.00
M15 Juan Gonzalez	1.25	3.00
M16 Barry Bonds	10.00	25.00
M17 Manny Ramirez	2.00	5.00
M18 Larry Walker	1.25	3.00
M19 Frank Thomas	3.00	8.00
M20 Tim Salmon	2.00	5.00
M21 Dave Justice	1.25	3.00
M22 Travis Lee	1.25	3.00
M23 Todd Helton	2.00	5.00
M24 Ben Grieve	1.25	3.00
M25 Vladimir Guerrero	3.00	8.00
M26 Greg Vaughn	1.25	3.00
M27 Bernie Williams	2.00	5.00
M28 Mike Piazza	5.00	12.00
M29 Ivan Rodriguez	2.00	5.00
M30 Jason Kendall	1.25	3.00
M31 Roger Clemens	6.00	15.00
M32 Kerry Wood	1.25	3.00
M33 Greg Maddux	5.00	12.00

1999 Topps Autographs

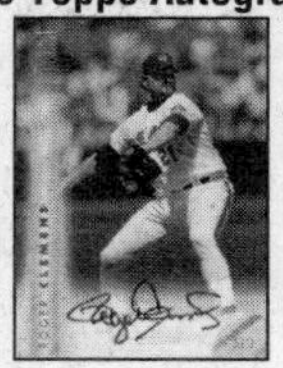

Inserted one in every 532 first series hobby packs, one in every 146 first series Home Team Advantage packs,d one in every 501 second series hobby packs and one in every 138 second series Home Team Advantage packs, these cards feature an assortment of young and old players affixing their signature to these cards. Cards A1-A8 were distributed exclusively in first series packs and cards A9-A16 were distributed exclusively in second series packs. The fronts feature a player photo with the authentic autograph on the bottom.

A1 Roger Clemens	30.00	60.00
A2 Chipper Jones	20.00	50.00
A3 Scott Rolen	10.00	25.00
A4 Alex Rodriguez	60.00	120.00
A5 Andres Galarraga	6.00	15.00
A6 Rondell White	6.00	15.00
A7 Ben Grieve	4.00	10.00
A8 Troy Glaus	10.00	25.00
A9 Moises Alou	6.00	15.00
A10 Barry Bonds	100.00	175.00
A11 Vladimir Guerrero	15.00	40.00
A12 Andruw Jones	6.00	15.00
A13 Darin Erstad	6.00	15.00
A14 Shawn Green	6.00	15.00
A15 Eric Chavez	6.00	15.00
A16 Pat Burrell	10.00	25.00

1999 Topps Hall of Fame Collection

This 10 card set features Hall of Famers with photos of the plaques and a silhouetted photo. These cards were inserted one every 12 hobby packs and one every three HTA packs.

COMPLETE SET (10)	10.00	20.00
HOF1 Mike Schmidt	1.50	4.00
HOF2 Brooks Robinson	.75	2.00
HOF3 Stan Musial	1.25	3.00
HOF4 Willie McCovey	.75	2.00
HOF5 Eddie Mathews	.75	2.00
HOF6 Reggie Jackson	.75	2.00
HOF7 Ernie Banks	.75	2.00
HOF8 Whitey Ford	.75	2.00
HOF9 Bob Feller	.75	2.00
HOF10 Yogi Berra	.75	2.00

1999 Topps Lords of the Diamond

This die-cut insert set was inserted one every 18 hobby packs and one every five HTA packs. The words "Lords of the Diamond" are printed on the top while the players name is at the bottom. The middle of the card has the players photo.

COMPLETE SET (15)	25.00	50.00
LD1 Ken Griffey Jr.	1.50	4.00
LD2 Chipper Jones	1.00	2.50
LD3 Sammy Sosa	1.00	2.50
LD4 Frank Thomas	1.00	2.50
LD5 Mark McGwire	2.50	6.00
LD6 Jeff Bagwell	.60	1.50
LD7 Alex Rodriguez	1.50	4.00
LD8 Juan Gonzalez	.40	1.00
LD9 Barry Bonds	3.00	8.00
LD10 Nomar Garciaparra	1.50	4.00
LD11 Darin Erstad	.40	1.00
LD12 Tony Gwynn	1.25	3.00
LD13 Andres Galarraga	.40	1.00
LD14 Mike Piazza	1.50	4.00
LD15 Greg Maddux	1.50	4.00

1999 Topps New Breed

Fifteen of the young stars of the game are featured in this insert set. The cards were seeded into the 99 Topps packs at a rate of one every 18 hobby packs and one every five HTA packs.

COMPLETE SET (15)	12.50	25.00
NB1 Darin Erstad	.30	.75
NB2 Brad Fullmer	.30	.75
NB3 Kerry Wood	.30	.75
NB4 Nomar Garciaparra	1.25	3.00
NB5 Travis Lee	.30	.75
NB6 Scott Rolen	.50	1.25
NB7 Todd Helton	.50	1.25
NB8 Vladimir Guerrero	.75	2.00
NB9 Derek Jeter	2.00	5.00
NB10 Alex Rodriguez	1.25	3.00
NB11 Ben Grieve	.30	.75
NB12 Andruw Jones	.50	1.25
NB13 Paul Konerko	.30	.75
NB14 Aramis Ramirez	.30	.75
NB15 Adrian Beltre	.30	.75

1999 Topps Picture Perfect

This 10 card insert set was inserted one every eight hobby packs and one every two HTA packs. These cards all contain a minor, very difficult to determine mistake and part of the charm is to figure out what the error is in the card.

COMPLETE SET (10)	7.50	15.00
P1 Ken Griffey Jr.	.60	1.50
P2 Kerry Wood	.15	.40
P3 Pedro Martinez	.25	.60
P4 Mark McGwire	1.00	2.50
P5 Greg Maddux	.60	1.50
P6 Sammy Sosa	.40	1.00
P7 Greg Vaughn	.15	.40
P8 Juan Gonzalez	.15	.40
P9 Jeff Bagwell	.25	.60
P10 Derek Jeter	1.00	2.50

1999 Topps Power Brokers

This 20 card set features leading baseball players. They were inserted at a seeded rate of one every 36 hobby/retail packs and one every eight HTA packs.

COMPLETE SET (20)	60.00	120.00
*REFRACTORS: 1X TO 2.5X BASIC BROKERS		
SER.1 REF.ODDS 1:144 HOB/RET, 1:32 HTA		
PB1 Mark McGwire	5.00	12.00
PB2 Andres Galarraga	.75	2.00
PB3 Ken Griffey Jr.	3.00	8.00
PB4 Sammy Sosa	2.00	5.00
PB5 Juan Gonzalez	.75	2.00
PB6 Alex Rodriguez	3.00	8.00
PB7 Frank Thomas	2.00	5.00
PB8 Jeff Bagwell	1.25	3.00
PB9 Vinny Castilla	.75	2.00
PB10 Mike Piazza	3.00	8.00
PB11 Greg Vaughn	.75	2.00
PB12 Barry Bonds	6.00	15.00
PB13 Mo Vaughn	.75	2.00
PB14 Jim Thome	1.25	3.00
PB15 Larry Walker	.75	2.00
PB16 Chipper Jones	2.00	5.00
PB17 Nomar Garciaparra	3.00	8.00
PB18 Manny Ramirez	1.25	3.00
PB19 Roger Clemens	4.00	10.00
PB20 Kerry Wood	.75	2.00

1999 Topps Record Numbers

Randomly inserted in Series two hobby and retail packs at the rate of one in eight and HTA packs at a rate of one in two, this 10-card set features action color photos of record-setting players with silver foil highlights.

COMPLETE SET (10)	7.50	15.00
RN1 Mark McGwire	1.00	2.50
RN2 Mike Piazza	.60	1.50
RN3 Curt Schilling	.15	.40
RN4 Ken Griffey Jr.	.60	1.50
RN5 Sammy Sosa	.40	1.00
RN6 Nomar Garciaparra	.60	1.50
RN7 Kerry Wood	.15	.40
RN8 Roger Clemens	.75	2.00
RN9 Cal Ripken	1.25	3.00
RN10 Mark McGwire	1.00	2.50

1999 Topps Record Numbers Gold

Randomly seeded in series two packs, these scarce gold-foiled cards parallel the more common "silver-foiled" Record Numbers inserts. The print run for each card was based upon the statistic specified on the card. Erroneous stated odds for these Gold cards were unfortunately printed on all series two wrappers. According to sources at Topps the correct pack odds are as follows: RN1 1:151,320 hob, 1:38,016 HTA, 1:138,567 ret, RN2 1:28,317 hob, 1:7,797 HTA, 1:28,340 ret, RN3 1:32,134 hob, 1:8,848 HTA, 1:32,160 ret, RN4 1:29,288 hob, 1:8,064 HTA, 1:29,312 ret, RN5 1:907,920 hob, 1:133,056 HTA, 1:1,524,420 ret, RN6 1:605,280 hob, 1:88,704 HTA, 1:1,016,280 ret, RN7 1:907,920 hob, 1:133,056 HTA, 1:1,524,420 ret, RN8 1:907,920 hob, 1:133,056 HTA, 1:1,524,420 ret, RN9 1:3891 hob, 1:1069 HTA, 1:3888 ret, RN10 1:63,312 hob, 1:17,741 HTA, 1:63,510 ret. No pricing is available for cards with print runs of 30 or less.

RN1 Mark McGwire/70	50.00	100.00
RN2 Mike Piazza/362	6.00	15.00
RN3 Curt Schilling/319	3.00	8.00
RN4 Ken Griffey Jr./350	8.00	20.00
RN5 Sammy Sosa/20		
RN6 N.Garciaparra/30		
RN7 Kerry Wood/20		
RN8 Roger Clemens/20		
RN9 Cal Ripken/2632	6.00	15.00
RN10 Mark McGwire/162	15.00	40.00

1999 Topps Ryan

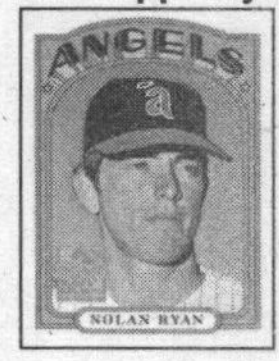

These cards reflect the Nolan Ryan Reprints of earlier Topps cards featuring the pitcher known for "Texas Heat". These cards are replicas of Ryan's cards and have a commemorative sticker placed on them as well. The cards were seeded one every 18 hobby/retail packs and one every five HTA packs. Odd-numbered cards (i.e. 1, 3, 5 etc.) were distributed in first series packs and even numbered cards were distributed in second series packs.

COMPLETE SET (27)	30.00	80.00
COMPLETE SERIES 1 (14)	15.00	40.00
COMPLETE SERIES 2 (13)	15.00	40.00
COMMON CARD (1-27)	2.00	5.00
1 Nolan Ryan 1968 UER	4.00	10.00

All the Ryan Rookie parallels in this set have the word sensational misspelled

1999 Topps Ryan Autographs

Nolan Ryan signed a selection of all 27 cards for this reprint set. The autographed cards were issued one every 4,250 series one hobby packs, one in every 5,007 series two hobby packs and one in every 1,176 series one HTA packs.

COMMON CARD (1-13)	125.00	200.00
COMMON CARD (14-27)	100.00	200.00
1 Nolan Ryan 1968	300.00	500.00

1999 Topps Traded

This set contains 121 cards and was distributed as factory boxed sets only. The fronts feature color action player photo. The backs carry player information. Rookie Cards include Sean Burroughs, Josh Hamilton, Corey Patterson and Alfonso Soriano.

COMP.FACT.SET (122)	20.00	50.00
COMPLETE SET (121)	12.50	30.00
T1 Seth Etherton	.07	.20
T2 Mark Harriger RC	.08	.25
T3 Matt Wise RC	.08	.25
T4 Carlos E. Hernandez RC	.15	.40
T5 Julio Lugo RC	.30	.75
T6 Mike Nannini	.07	.20
T7 Justin Bowles RC	.08	.25
T8 Mark Mulder RC	.60	1.50
T9 Roberto Vaz RC	.08	.25
T10 Felipe Lopez RC	.60	1.50
T11 Matt Belisle	.20	.50
T12 Micah Bowie	.07	.20
T13 Ruben Quevedo RC	.08	.25
T14 Jose Garcia RC	.08	.25
T15 David Kelton RC	.08	.25
T16 Phil Norton	.07	.20
T17 Corey Patterson RC	.40	1.00
T18 Ron Walker RC	.08	.25
T19 Paul Hoover RC	.08	.25
T20 Ryan Rupe RC	.08	.25
T21 J.D. Closser RC	.15	.40
T22 Rob Ryan RC	.08	.25
T23 Steve Colyer RC	.08	.25
T24 Bubba Crosby RC	.25	.60
T25 Luke Prokopec RC	.08	.25
T26 Matt Blank RC	.08	.25
T27 Josh McKinley	.07	.20
T28 Nate Bump	.07	.20
T29 G.Chiaramonte RC	.08	.25
T30 Arturo McDowell	.07	.20
T31 Tony Torcato	.07	.20
T32 Dave Roberts RC	.25	.60
T33 C.C. Sabathia RC	.75	2.00
T34 Sean Spencer RC	.08	.25
T35 Chip Ambres	.07	.20
T36 A.J. Burnett	.40	1.00
T37 Mo Bruce RC	.08	.25
T38 Jason Tyner	.07	.20
T39 Mamon Tucker	.07	.20
T40 Sean Burroughs RC	.25	.60
T41 Kevin Eberwein RC	.08	.25
T42 Junior Herndon RC	.08	.25
T43 Bryan Wolff RC	.08	.25
T44 Pat Burrell	.50	1.25
T45 Eric Valent	.07	.20
T46 Carlos Pena RC	.20	.50
T47 Mike Zywica	.07	.20
T48 Adam Everett	.10	.30
T49 Juan Pena RC	.15	.40
T50 Adam Dunn RC	1.50	4.00
T51 Austin Kearns	.50	1.25
T52 Jacobo Sequea RC	.08	.25
T53 Choo Freeman	.07	.20
T54 Jeff Winchester	.07	.20
T55 Matt Burch	.07	.20
T56 Chris George	.07	.20
T57 Scott Mullen RC	.08	.25
T58 Kit Pellow	.07	.20
T59 Mark Quinn RC	.08	.25
T60 Nate Cornejo	.08	.25
T61 Ryan Mills	.07	.20
T62 Kevin Beirne RC	.08	.25
T63 Kip Wells RC	.15	.40
T64 Juan Rivera RC	.40	1.00
T65 Alfonso Soriano RC	2.00	5.00
T66 Josh Hamilton RC	3.00	8.00
T67 Josh Girdley RC	.08	.25
T68 Kyle Snyder RC	.08	.25
T69 Mike Paradis RC	.08	.25
T70 Jason Jennings RC	.25	.60
T71 David Walling RC	.08	.25
T72 Omar Ortiz RC	.08	.25
T73 Jay Gehrke RC	.15	.40
T74 Casey Burns RC	.15	.40
T75 Carl Crawford RC	1.50	4.00
T76 Reggie Sanders	.07	.20
T77 Will Clark	.10	.30
T78 David Wells	.07	.20
T79 Paul Konerko	.07	.20
T80 Armando Benitez	.07	.20
T81 Brant Brown	.07	.20
T82 Mo Vaughn	.07	.20
T83 Jose Canseco	.10	.30
T84 Albert Belle	.07	.20
T85 Dean Palmer	.07	.20
T86 Greg Vaughn	.07	.20
T87 Mark Clark	.07	.20
T88 Pat Meares	.07	.20
T89 Eric Davis	.07	.20
T90 Brian Giles	.07	.20
T91 Jeff Brantley	.07	.20
T92 Bret Boone	.07	.20
T93 Ron Gant	.07	.20
T94 Mike Cameron	.07	.20
T95 Charles Johnson	.07	.20
T96 Denny Neagle	.07	.20
T97 Brian Hunter	.07	.20
T98 Jose Hernandez	.07	.20
T99 Rick Aguilera	.07	.20
T100 Tony Batista	.07	.20
T101 Roger Cedeno	.07	.20
T102 C.Gubanich RC	.08	.25
T103 Tim Belcher	.07	.20
T104 Bruce Aven	.07	.20
T105 Brian Daubach RC	.15	.40
T106 Ed Sprague	.07	.20
T107 Michael Tucker	.07	.20
T108 Homer Bush	.07	.20
T109 Armando Reynoso	.07	.20
T110 Brook Fordyce	.07	.20
T111 Matt Mantei	.07	.20
T112 Dave Mlicki	.07	.20
T113 Kenny Rogers	.07	.20
T114 Livan Hernandez	.07	.20
T115 Butch Huskey	.07	.20
T116 David Segui	.07	.20
T117 Darryl Hamilton	.07	.20
T118 Terry Mulholland	.07	.20
T119 Randy Velarde	.07	.20

T120 Bill Taylor	.07	.20
T121 Kevin Appier	.07	.20

1999 Topps Traded Autographs

Inserted one per factory box set, this 75-card set features autographed parallel version of the first 75 cards of the basic 1999 Topps Traded set. The card fronts have a light faded image on the base to accentuate the signature.

COMPLETE SET (75)	400.00	800.00
T1 Seth Etherton	2.00	5.00
T2 Mark Harriger	4.00	10.00
T3 Matt Wise	4.00	10.00
T4 Carlos E. Hernandez	4.00	10.00
T5 Julio Lugo	8.00	20.00
T6 Mike Nannini	2.00	5.00
T7 Justin Bowles	4.00	10.00
T8 Mark Mulder	12.50	30.00
T9 Roberto Vaz	4.00	10.00
T10 Felipe Lopez	15.00	40.00
T11 Matt Belisle	2.00	5.00
T12 Micah Bowie	2.00	5.00
T13 Ruben Quevedo	2.00	5.00
T14 Jose Garcia	4.00	10.00
T15 David Kelton	2.00	5.00
T16 Phil Norton	4.00	10.00
T17 Corey Patterson	12.50	30.00
T18 Ron Walker	2.00	5.00
T19 Paul Hoover	4.00	10.00
T20 Ryan Rupe	2.00	5.00
T21 J.D. Closser	4.00	10.00
T22 Rob Ryan	2.00	5.00
T23 Steve Colyer	2.00	5.00
T24 Bubba Crosby	6.00	15.00
T25 Luke Prokopec	2.00	5.00
T26 Matt Blank	4.00	10.00
T27 Josh McKinley	2.00	5.00
T28 Nate Bump	4.00	10.00
T29 G.Chiaramonte	2.00	5.00
T30 Arturo McDowell	2.00	5.00
T31 Tony Torcato	2.00	5.00
T32 Dave Roberts	6.00	15.00
T33 C.C. Sabathia	75.00	150.00
T34 Sean Spencer	2.00	5.00
T35 Chip Ambres	2.00	5.00
T36 A.J. Burnett	30.00	60.00
T37 Mo Bruce	2.00	5.00
T38 Jason Tyner	2.00	5.00
T39 Mamon Tucker	2.00	5.00
T40 Sean Burroughs	6.00	15.00
T41 Kevin Eberwein	2.00	5.00
T42 Junior Herndon	2.00	5.00
T43 Bryan Wolff	4.00	10.00
T44 Pat Burrell	15.00	40.00
T45 Eric Valent	4.00	10.00
T46 Carlos Pena	20.00	50.00
T47 Mike Zywica	4.00	10.00
T48 Adam Everett	6.00	15.00
T49 Juan Pena	4.00	10.00
T50 Adam Dunn	40.00	80.00
T51 Austin Kearns	12.50	30.00
T52 Jacobo Sequea	2.00	5.00
T53 Choo Freeman	4.00	10.00
T54 Jeff Winchester	2.00	5.00
T55 Matt Burch	4.00	10.00
T56 Chris George	2.00	5.00
T57 Scott Mullen	2.00	5.00
T58 Kit Pellow	2.00	5.00
T59 Mark Quinn	2.00	5.00
T60 Nate Cornejo	2.00	5.00
T61 Ryan Mills	2.00	5.00
T62 Kevin Beirne	2.00	5.00
T63 Kip Wells	4.00	10.00
T64 Juan Rivera	10.00	25.00
T65 Alfonso Soriano	60.00	120.00
T66 Josh Hamilton	100.00	175.00
T67 Josh Girdley	2.00	5.00
T68 Kyle Snyder	2.00	5.00
T69 Mike Paradis	2.00	5.00
T70 Jason Jennings	8.00	20.00
T71 David Walling	2.00	5.00
T72 Omar Ortiz	4.00	10.00
T73 Jay Gehrke	4.00	10.00
T74 Casey Burns	4.00	10.00
T75 Carl Crawford	20.00	50.00

2000 Topps Pre-Production

This three card set was issued in a sealed cello pack to dealers and hobby media several weeks prior to the products release. The cards have a "PP" prefix so they can be differentiated from the regular cards.

COMPLETE SET (3)	1.20	3.00
PP1 Brady Anderson	.40	1.00
PP2 Jason Kendall	.40	1.00
PP3 Ryan Klesko	.40	1.00

2000 Topps

This 478 card set was issued in two separate series. The first series (containing cards 1-239) was released in December, 1999. The second series

(containing cards 240-479) was released in April, 2000. The cards were issued in various formats including an eleven card hobby or retail pack with an SRP of $1.29 and a 40 card HomeTeam Advantage jumbo pack. Cards 1-200 and 240-440 are individual player cards with subsets as follows: Prospects (201-208/441-448), Draft Picks (209-220/449-455), Season Highlights (217-221/456-460), Post Season Highlights (222-228), 20th Century's Best (229-235/468-474), Magic Moments (236-240/475-479) and League Leaders (461-467). After the success Topps had with the multiple versions of Mark McGwire 220 and Sammy Sosa 461 in 1999, they made five versions each of the Magic Moments cards this year. Each Magic Moment variation featured different gold foil text on front commemorating a specific achievement in the featured player's career. Please note, that basic hand-collected sets are considered complete with the inclusion of any one of each of these Magic Moment cards. A reprint of the 1985 Mark McGwire Rookie Card was inserted one every 36 hobby and retail first series packs and one every eight HTA first series packs. Card number 7 was not issued as Topps continues to honor the memory of Mickey Mantle who wore that number during his career. Players with notable Rookie Cards in this set include Ben Sheets and Barry Zito.

COMPLETE SET (478)	20.00	50.00
COMP.HOBBY SET (478)	30.00	60.00
COMP. SERIES 1 (239)	10.00	25.00
COMP. SERIES 2 (240)	10.00	25.00
MCGWIRE MM SET (5)	5.00	12.00
AARON MM SET (5)	4.00	10.00
RIPKEN MM SET (5)	6.00	15.00
BOGGS MM SET (5)	1.25	3.00
GWYNN MM SET (5)	2.50	6.00
GRIFFEY MM SET (5)	3.00	8.00
BONDS MM SET (5)	5.00	12.00
SOSA MM SET (5)	3.00	8.00
JETER MM SET (5)	5.00	12.00
A.ROD MM SET (5)	3.00	8.00
1 Mark McGwire	.50	1.25
2 Tony Gwynn	.25	.60
3 Wade Boggs	.10	.30
4 Cal Ripken	.60	1.50
5 Matt Williams	.07	.20
6 Jay Buhner	.07	.20
8 Jeff Conine	.07	.20
9 Todd Greene	.07	.20
10 Mike Lieberthal	.07	.20
11 Steve Avery	.07	.20
12 Bret Saberhagen	.07	.20
13 Magglio Ordonez	.07	.20
14 Brad Radke	.07	.20
15 Derek Jeter	.50	1.25
16 Javy Lopez	.07	.20
17 Russ Davis	.07	.20
18 Armando Benitez	.07	.20
19 B.J. Surhoff	.07	.20
20 Darryl Kile	.07	.20
21 Mark Lewis	.07	.20
22 Mike Williams	.07	.20
23 Mark McLemore	.07	.20
24 Sterling Hitchcock	.07	.20
25 Darin Erstad	.07	.20
26 Ricky Gutierrez	.07	.20
27 John Jaha	.07	.20
28 Homer Bush	.07	.20
29 Darrin Fletcher	.07	.20
30 Mark Grace	.10	.30
31 Fred McGriff	.10	.30
32 Omar Daal	.07	.20
33 Eric Karros	.07	.20
34 Orlando Cabrera	.07	.20
35 J.T. Snow	.07	.20
36 Luis Castillo	.07	.20
37 Rey Ordonez	.07	.20
38 Bob Abreu	.07	.20
39 Warren Morris	.07	.20
40 Juan Gonzalez	.07	.20
41 Mike Lansing	.07	.20
42 Chili Davis	.07	.20
43 Dean Palmer	.07	.20
44 Hank Aaron	.30	.75
45 Jeff Bagwell	.10	.30
46 Jose Valentin	.07	.20
47 Shannon Stewart	.07	.20
48 Kent Bottenfield	.07	.20
49 Jeff Shaw	.07	.20
50 Sammy Sosa	.20	.50
51 Randy Johnson	.20	.50
52 Benny Agbayani	.07	.20
53 Dante Bichette	.07	.20
54 Pete Harnisch	.07	.20
55 Frank Thomas	.20	.50
56 Jorge Posada	.10	.30
57 Todd Walker	.07	.20
58 Juan Encarnacion	.07	.20
59 Mike Sweeney	.07	.20
60 Pedro Martinez	.10	.30
61 Lee Stevens	.07	.20
62 Brian Giles	.07	.20
63 Chad Ogea	.07	.20
64 Ivan Rodriguez	.10	.30
65 Roger Cedeno	.07	.20
66 David Justice	.07	.20
67 Steve Trachsel	.07	.20
68 Eli Marrero	.07	.20
69 Dave Nilsson	.07	.20
70 Ken Caminiti	.07	.20
71 Tim Raines	.07	.20
72 Brian Jordan	.07	.20
73 Jeff Blauser	.07	.20
74 Bernard Gilkey	.07	.20
75 John Flaherty	.07	.20
76 Brent Mayne	.07	.20
77 Jose Vidro	.07	.20
78 David Bell	.07	.20
79 Bruce Aven	.07	.20
80 John Olerud	.07	.20
81 Pokey Reese	.07	.20
82 Woody Williams	.07	.20
83 Ed Sprague	.07	.20
84 Joe Girardi	.07	.20
85 Barry Larkin	.10	.30
86 Mike Caruso	.07	.20
87 Bobby Higginson	.07	.20
88 Roberto Kelly	.07	.20
89 Edgar Martinez	.10	.30
90 Mark Kotsay	.07	.20
91 Paul Sorrento	.07	.20
92 Eric Young	.07	.20
93 Carlos Delgado	.07	.20
94 Troy Glaus	.07	.20
95 Ben Grieve	.07	.20
96 Jose Lima	.07	.20
97 Garret Anderson	.07	.20
98 Luis Gonzalez	.07	.20
99 Carl Pavano	.07	.20
100 Alex Rodriguez	.30	.75
101 Preston Wilson	.07	.20
102 Ron Gant	.07	.20
103 Brady Anderson	.07	.20
104 Rickey Henderson	.20	.50
105 Gary Sheffield	.07	.20
106 Mickey Morandini	.07	.20
107 Jim Edmonds	.07	.20
108 Kris Benson	.07	.20
109 Adrian Beltre	.07	.20
110 Alex Fernandez	.07	.20
111 Dan Wilson	.07	.20
112 Mark Clark	.07	.20
113 Greg Vaughn	.07	.20
114 Neifi Perez	.07	.20
115 Paul O'Neill	.10	.30
116 Jermaine Dye	.07	.20
117 Todd Jones	.07	.20
118 Terry Steinbach	.07	.20
119 Greg Norton	.07	.20
120 Curt Schilling	.07	.20
121 Todd Zeile	.07	.20
122 Edgardo Alfonzo	.07	.20
123 Ryan McGuire	.07	.20
124 Rich Aurilia	.07	.20
125 John Smoltz	.10	.30
126 Bob Wickman	.07	.20
127 Richard Hidalgo	.07	.20
128 Chuck Finley	.07	.20
129 Billy Wagner	.07	.20
130 Todd Hundley	.07	.20
131 Dwight Gooden	.07	.20
132 Russ Ortiz	.07	.20
133 Mike Lowell	.07	.20
134 Reggie Sanders	.07	.20
135 John Valentin	.07	.20
136 Brad Ausmus	.07	.20
137 Chad Kreuter	.07	.20
138 David Cone	.07	.20
139 Brook Fordyce	.07	.20
140 Roberto Alomar	.10	.30
141 Charles Nagy	.07	.20
142 Brian Hunter	.07	.20
143 Mike Mussina	.10	.30
144 Robin Ventura	.10	.30
145 Kevin Brown	.10	.30
146 Pat Hentgen	.07	.20
147 Ryan Klesko	.07	.20
148 Derek Bell	.07	.20
149 Andy Sheets	.07	.20
150 Larry Walker	.07	.20
151 Scott Williamson	.07	.20
152 Jose Offerman	.07	.20
153 Doug Mientkiewicz	.07	.20
154 John Snyder RC	.15	.40
155 Sandy Alomar Jr.	.07	.20
156 Joe Nathan	.07	.20
157 Lance Johnson	.07	.20
158 Odalis Perez	.07	.20
159 Hideo Nomo	.20	.50
160 Steve Finley	.07	.20
161 Dave Martinez	.07	.20
162 Matt Walbeck	.07	.20
163 Bill Spiers	.07	.20
164 Fernando Tatis	.07	.20
165 Kenny Lofton	.07	.20
166 Paul Byrd	.07	.20
167 Aaron Sele	.07	.20
168 Eddie Taubensee	.07	.20
169 Reggie Jefferson	.07	.20
170 Roger Clemens	.40	1.00
171 Francisco Cordova	.07	.20
172 Mike Bordick	.07	.20
173 Wally Joyner	.07	.20
174 Marvin Benard	.07	.20
175 Jason Kendall	.07	.20
176 Mike Stanley	.07	.20
177 Chad Allen	.07	.20
178 Carlos Beltran	.07	.20
179 Deivi Cruz	.07	.20
180 Chipper Jones	.20	.50
181 Vladimir Guerrero	.20	.50
182 Dave Burba	.07	.20
183 Tom Goodwin	.07	.20
184 Brian Daubach	.07	.20
185 Jay Bell	.07	.20
186 Roy Halladay	.07	.20
187 Miguel Tejada	.07	.20
188 Armando Rios	.07	.20
189 Fernando Vina	.07	.20
190 Eric Davis	.07	.20
191 Henry Rodriguez	.07	.20
192 Joe McEwing	.07	.20
193 Jeff Kent	.07	.20
194 Mike Jackson	.07	.20
195 Mike Morgan	.07	.20
196 Jeff Montgomery	.07	.20
197 Jeff Zimmerman	.07	.20
198 Tony Fernandez	.07	.20
199 Jason Giambi	.07	.20
200 Jose Canseco	.10	.30
201 Alex Gonzalez	.07	.20
202 Jack Cust	.15	.40
Mike Colangelo		
Dee Brown		
203 Felipe Lopez	.20	.50
Alfonso Soriano		
Pablo Ozuna		
204 Erubiel Durazo	.15	.40
Pat Burrell		
Nick Johnson		
205 John Sneed RC	.15	.40
Kip Wells		
Matt Blank		
206 Josh Kalinowski	.15	.40
Michael Tejera		
Chris Mears RC		
207 Roosevelt Brown	.15	.40
Corey Patterson		
Lance Berkman		
208 Kit Pellow	.15	.40
Kevin Barker		
Russ Branyan		
209 B.J. Garbe	.20	.50
Larry Bigbie RC		
210 Eric Munson	.15	.40
Bobby Bradley RC		
211 Josh Girdley	.15	.40
Kyle Snyder		
212 Chance Caple RC	.15	.40
Jason Jennings		
213 Ryan Christianson	.40	1.00
Brett Myers RC		
214 Jason Stumm	.15	.40
Rob Purvis RC		
215 David Walling	.15	.40
Mike Paradis		
216 Omar Ortiz	.15	.40
Jay Gehrke		
217 David Cone HL	.07	.20
218 Jose Jimenez HL	.07	.20
219 Chris Singleton HL	.07	.20
220 Fernando Tatis HL	.07	.20
221 Todd Helton HL	.07	.20
222 Kevin Millwood DIV	.07	.20
223 Todd Pratt DIV	.07	.20
224 Orl.Hernandez DIV	.07	.20
225 Pedro Martinez DIV	.10	.30
226 Tom Glavine LCS	.07	.20
227 Bernie Williams LCS	.07	.20
228 Mariano Rivera WS	.10	.30
229 Tony Gwynn 20CB	.25	.60
230 Wade Boggs 20CB	.10	.30
231 Lance Johnson CB	.07	.20
232 Mark McGwire 20CB	.50	1.25
233 R.Henderson 20CB	.20	.50
234 R.Henderson 20CB	.20	.50
235 Roger Clemens 20CB	.40	1.00
236A M.McGwire MM	.75	2.00
1st HR		
236B M.McGwire MM	.75	2.00
1987 ROY		
236C M.McGwire MM	.75	2.00
62nd HR		
236D M.McGwire MM	.75	2.00
70th HR		
236E M.McGwire MM	.75	2.00
500th HR		
237A H.Aaron MM	.75	2.00
1st Career HR		
237B H.Aaron MM	.75	2.00
1957 MVP		
237C H.Aaron MM	.75	2.00
3000th Hit		
237D H.Aaron MM	.75	2.00
715th HR		
237E H.Aaron MM	.75	2.00
755th HR		
238A C.Ripken MM	1.50	4.00
1982 ROY		
238B C.Ripken MM	1.50	4.00
1991 MVP		
238C C.Ripken MM	1.50	4.00
2131 Game		
238D C.Ripken MM	1.50	4.00
Streak Ends		
238E C.Ripken MM	1.50	4.00
400th HR		
239A W.Boggs MM	.30	.75
1983 Batting		
239B W.Boggs MM	.30	.75
1988 Batting		
239C W.Boggs MM	.30	.75
2000th Hit		
239D W.Boggs MM	.30	.75
1996 Champs		
239E W.Boggs MM	.30	.75
3000th Hit		
240A T.Gwynn MM	.60	1.50
1984 Batting		
240B T.Gwynn MM	.60	1.50
1984 NLCS		
240C T.Gwynn MM	.60	1.50
1995 Batting		
240D T.Gwynn MM	.60	1.50
1998 NLCS		
240E T.Gwynn MM	.60	1.50
3000th Hit		
241 Tom Glavine	.10	.30
242 David Wells	.07	.20
243 Kevin Appier	.07	.20
244 Troy Percival	.07	.20
245 Ray Lankford	.07	.20
246 Marquis Grissom	.07	.20
247 Randy Winn	.07	.20
248 Miguel Batista	.07	.20
249 Darren Dreifort	.07	.20
250 Barry Bonds	.60	1.50
251 Harold Baines	.07	.20
252 Cliff Floyd	.07	.20
253 Freddy Garcia	.07	.20
254 Kenny Rogers	.07	.20
255 Ben Davis	.07	.20
256 Charles Johnson	.07	.20
257 Bubba Trammell	.07	.20
258 Desi Relaford	.07	.20
259 Al Martin	.07	.20
260 Andy Pettitte	.10	.30
261 Carlos Lee	.07	.20
262 Matt Lawton	.07	.20
263 Andy Fox	.07	.20
264 Chan Ho Park	.07	.20
265 Billy Koch	.07	.20
266 Dave Roberts	.07	.20
267 Carl Everett	.07	.20
268 Orel Hershiser	.07	.20
269 Trot Nixon	.07	.20
270 Rusty Greer	.07	.20
271 Will Clark	.10	.30
272 Quilvio Veras	.07	.20
273 Rico Brogna	.07	.20
274 Devon White	.07	.20
275 Tim Hudson	.07	.20
276 Mike Hampton	.07	.20
277 Miguel Cairo	.07	.20
278 Darren Oliver	.07	.20
279 Jeff Cirillo	.07	.20
280 Al Leiter	.07	.20
281 Shane Andrews	.07	.20
282 Carlos Febles	.07	.20
283 Pedro Astacio	.07	.20
284 Juan Guzman	.07	.20
285 Orlando Hernandez	.07	.20
286 Paul Konerko	.07	.20
287 Tony Clark	.07	.20
288 Aaron Boone	.07	.20
289 Ismael Valdes	.07	.20
290 Moises Alou	.07	.20
291 Kevin Tapani	.07	.20
292 John Franco	.07	.20
293 Todd Zeile	.07	.20
294 Jason Schmidt	.07	.20
295 Johnny Damon	.10	.30
296 Scott Brosius	.07	.20
297 Travis Fryman	.07	.20
298 Jose Vizcaino	.07	.20
299 Eric Chavez	.07	.20
300 Mike Piazza	.30	.75
301 Matt Clement	.07	.20
302 Cristian Guzman	.07	.20
303 C.J. Nitkowski	.07	.20
304 Michael Tucker	.07	.20
305 Brett Tomko	.07	.20
306 Mike Lansing	.07	.20
307 Eric Owens	.07	.20
308 Livan Hernandez	.07	.20
309 Rondell White	.07	.20
310 Todd Stottlemyre	.07	.20
311 Chris Carpenter	.07	.20
312 Ken Hill	.07	.20
313 Mark Loretta	.07	.20
314 John Rocker	.07	.20
315 Richie Sexson	.07	.20
316 Ruben Mateo	.07	.20
317 Joe Randa	.07	.20
318 Mike Sirotka	.07	.20
319 Jose Rosado	.07	.20
320 Matt Mantei	.07	.20
321 Kevin Millwood	.07	.20
322 Gary DiSarcina	.07	.20
323 Dustin Hermanson	.07	.20
324 Mike Stanton	.07	.20
325 Kirk Rueter	.07	.20
326 Damian Miller RC	.15	.40
327 Doug Glanville	.07	.20
328 Scott Rolen	.10	.30
329 Ray Durham	.07	.20
330 Butch Huskey	.07	.20
331 Mariano Rivera	.20	.50
332 Darren Lewis	.07	.20
333 Mike Timlin	.07	.20
334 Mark Grudzielanek	.07	.20
335 Mike Cameron	.07	.20
336 Kelvim Escobar	.07	.20
337 Bret Boone	.07	.20
338 Mo Vaughn	.07	.20
339 Craig Biggio	.10	.30
340 Michael Barrett	.07	.20
341 Marlon Anderson	.07	.20
342 Bobby Jones	.07	.20
343 John Halama	.07	.20
344 Todd Ritchie	.07	.20
345 Chuck Knoblauch	.07	.20
346 Rick Reed	.07	.20
347 Kelly Stinnett	.07	.20
348 Tim Salmon	.10	.30
349 A.J. Hinch	.07	.20
350 Jose Cruz Jr.	.07	.20
351 Roberto Hernandez	.07	.20
352 Edgar Renteria	.07	.20
353 Jose Hernandez	.07	.20
354 Brad Fullmer	.07	.20
355 Trevor Hoffman	.07	.20
356 Troy O'Leary	.07	.20
357 Justin Thompson	.07	.20
358 Kevin Young	.07	.20
359 Hideki Irabu	.07	.20
360 Jim Thome	.10	.30
361 Steve Karsay	.07	.20
362 Octavio Dotel	.07	.20
363 Omar Vizquel	.10	.30
364 Raul Mondesi	.07	.20
365 Shane Reynolds	.07	.20
366 Bartolo Colon	.07	.20
367 Chris Widger	.07	.20
368 Gabe Kapler	.07	.20
369 Bill Simas	.07	.20
370 Tino Martinez	.10	.30
371 John Thomson	.07	.20
372 Delino DeShields	.07	.20
373 Carlos Perez	.07	.20
374 Eddie Perez	.07	.20
375 Jeromy Burnitz	.07	.20
376 Jimmy Haynes	.07	.20
377 Travis Lee	.07	.20
378 Darryl Hamilton	.07	.20
379 Jamie Moyer	.07	.20
380 Alex Gonzalez	.07	.20
381 John Wetteland	.07	.20
382 Vinny Castilla	.07	.20
383 Jeff Suppan	.07	.20
384 Jim Leyritz	.07	.20
385 Robb Nen	.07	.20
386 Wilson Alvarez	.07	.20
387 Andres Galarraga	.07	.20
388 Mike Remlinger	.07	.20
389 Geoff Jenkins	.07	.20
390 Matt Stairs	.07	.20
391 Bill Mueller	.07	.20
392 Mike Lowell	.07	.20
393 Andy Ashby	.07	.20
394 Ruben Rivera	.07	.20
395 Todd Helton	.10	.30
396 Bernie Williams	.10	.30
397 Royce Clayton	.07	.20
398 Manny Ramirez	.10	.30
399 Kerry Wood	.07	.20
400 Ken Griffey Jr.	.30	.75
401 Enrique Wilson	.07	.20
402 Joey Hamilton	.07	.20
403 Shawn Estes	.07	.20
404 Ugueth Urbina	.07	.20
405 Albert Belle	.07	.20
406 Rick Helling	.07	.20
407 Steve Parris	.07	.20
408 Eric Milton	.07	.20
409 Dave Mlicki	.07	.20
410 Shawn Green	.07	.20
411 Jaret Wright	.07	.20
412 Tony Womack	.07	.20
413 Vernon Wells	.07	.20
414 Ron Belliard	.07	.20
415 Ellis Burks	.07	.20
416 Scott Erickson	.07	.20
417 Rafael Palmeiro	.10	.30
418 Damion Easley	.07	.20
419 Jamey Wright	.07	.20
420 Corey Koskie	.07	.20
421 Bobby Howry	.07	.20
422 Ricky Ledee	.07	.20
423 Dmitri Young	.07	.20
424 Sidney Ponson	.07	.20
425 Greg Maddux	.30	.75
426 Jose Guillen	.07	.20
427 Jon Lieber	.07	.20
428 Andy Benes	.07	.20
429 Randy Velarde	.07	.20
430 Sean Casey	.07	.20
431 Torii Hunter	.07	.20
432 Ryan Rupe	.07	.20
433 David Segui	.07	.20
434 Todd Pratt	.07	.20
435 Nomar Garciaparra	.30	.75
436 Denny Neagle	.07	.20
437 Ron Coomer	.07	.20
438 Chris Singleton	.07	.20
439 Tony Batista	.07	.20
440 Andruw Jones	.10	.30
441 Aubrey Huff	.07	.20
Sean Burroughs		
Adam Piatt		
442 Rafael Furcal	.15	.40
Travis Dawkins		
Jason Dellaero		
443 Mike Lamb RC	.40	1.00
Joe Crede		
Wilton Veras		
444 Julio Zuleta RC	.15	.40
Jorge Toca		
Dernell Stenson		
445 Garry Maddox Jr. RC	.15	.40
Gary Matthews Jr.		
Tim Raines Jr.		
446 Mark Mulder	.15	.40
C.C. Sabathia		
Matt Riley		
447 Scott Downs RC	.15	.40
Chris George		
Matt Belisle		
448 Doug Mirabelli	.15	.40
Ben Petrick		
Jayson Werth		
449 Josh Hamilton	.20	.50
Corey Myers RC		
450 Ben Christensen RC	.15	.40
Richard Stahl RC		
451 Ben Sheets RC	1.00	2.50
Barry Zito		
452 Kurt Ainsworth	.15	.40
Ty Howington RC		
453 Vince Faison RC	.15	.40
Rick Asadoorian		
454 Keith Reed RC	.15	.40
Jeff Heaverlo		
455 Mike MacDougal	.15	.40
Brad Baker RC		
456 Mark McGwire SH	.25	.60
457 Cal Ripken SH	.30	.75
458 Wade Boggs SH	.07	.20
459 Tony Gwynn SH	.10	.30
460 Jesse Orosco SH	.07	.20
461 Larry Walker	.10	.30
Nomar Garciaparra LL		
462 Ken Griffey Jr.	.20	.50
Mark McGwire LL		
463 Manny Ramirez	.20	.50
Mark McGwire LL		
464 Pedro Martinez	.10	.30
Randy Johnson LL		
465 Pedro Martinez	.10	.30
Randy Johnson LL		
466 Derek Jeter	.20	.50
Luis Gonzalez LL		
467 Larry Walker	.10	.30
Manny Ramirez LL		
468 Tony Gwynn 20CB	.25	.60
469 Mark McGwire 20CB	.50	1.25
470 Frank Thomas 20CB	.10	.30
471 Harold Baines 20CB	.07	.20
472 Roger Clemens 20CB	.40	1.00
473 John Franco 20CB	.07	.20
474 John Franco 20CB	.07	.20
475A K.Griffey Jr. MM	.75	2.00
350th HR		
475B K.Griffey Jr. MM	.75	2.00
1997 MVP		
475C K.Griffey Jr. MM	.75	2.00
HR Dad		
475D K.Griffey Jr. MM	.75	2.00
1992 AS MVP		
475E K.Griffey Jr. MM	.75	2.00
50 HR 1997		
476A B.Bonds MM	1.25	3.00
400HR/400SB		
476B B.Bonds MM	1.25	3.00
40HR/40SB		
476C B.Bonds MM	1.25	3.00
1993 MVP		
476D B.Bonds MM	1.25	3.00
1990 MVP		
476E B.Bonds MM	1.25	3.00
1992 MVP		
477A S.Sosa MM	.75	2.00
20 HR June		
477B S.Sosa MM	.75	2.00
66 HR 1998		
477C S.Sosa MM	.75	2.00
60 HR 1999		
477D S.Sosa MM	.75	2.00
1998 MVP		
477E S.Sosa MM HR's	.75	2.00

Card	Low	High
61/62		
478A D.Jeter MM 1996 ROY	1.25	3.00
478B D.Jeter MM Wins 1999 WS	1.25	3.00
478C D.Jeter MM Wins 1998 WS	1.25	3.00
478D D.Jeter MM Wins 1996 WS	1.25	3.00
478E D.Jeter MM 17 GM Hit Streak	1.25	3.00
479A A.Rodriguez MM 40HR/40SB	.75	2.00
479B A.Rodriguez MM 100th HR	.75	2.00
479C A.Rodriguez MM 1996 POY	.75	2.00
479D A.Rodriguez MM Wins 1 Million	.75	2.00
479E A.Rodriguez MM 1996 Batting Leader	.75	2.00
NNO M. McGwire 85 Reprint	2.00	5.00

2000 Topps 20th Century Best Sequential

Inserted into first series hobby packs at an overall rate of one in 869 and one in 239 HTA packs, and into series two hobby packs at one in 362 and one in 100 HTA packs, these cards parallel the Century's Best subset within the base 2000 Topps set (cards 229-235/468-474). These insert cards, unlike the regular cards, feature "CB" prefixed numbering on back and have dramatic sparkling foil-coated fronts. Each card is sequentially numbered to the featured players highlighted career statistic.

Card	Low	High
CB1 T.Gwynn AVG/339	15.00	40.00
CB2 W.Boggs 2B/578	8.00	20.00
CB3 L.Johnson 3B/117	10.00	25.00
CB4 M.McGwire HR/522	20.00	50.00
CB5 Rickey Henderson SB/1334	6.00	15.00
CB6 Rickey Henderson RUN/2103	6.00	15.00
CB7 R.Clemens WIN/247	30.00	60.00
CB8 Tony Gwynn HIT/3067	6.00	15.00
CB9 Mark McGwire SLG/587	20.00	50.00
CB10 Frank Thomas OBP/440	12.50	30.00
CB11 Harold Baines RBI/1583	3.00	8.00
CB12 Roger Clemens K's/3316	10.00	25.00
CB13 John Franco ERA/264	5.00	12.00
CB14 John Franco SV/416	5.00	12.00

2000 Topps Home Team Advantage

These cards were distributed exclusively in a 479-card factory set. Each set contained the 478-card base issue 2000 Topps set plus one Hank Aaron Chrome Reprint card. All of the base cards within Home Team Advantage factory sets were stamped with a special "HTA" gold foil logo on the card front. Oddly, cards 222-228 (Divisional Playoffs), 229-235 (20th Century's Best), 236-240 (Magic Moments), 461-467 (League Leaders) and 468-474 (20th Century Best) did NOT feature the gold-foil HTA tag. Thus, those cards are identical to basic issue Topps cards and are not included within our checklist for this set (though they are included within the complete factory set).

Card	Low	High
COMP.FACT.SET (479)	40.00	80.00
*HTA: .75X TO 2X BASIC CARDS		

2000 Topps MVP Promotion

Inserted one in every 510 first series hobby and retail packs and one in every 140 first series HTA packs, this set is an almost complete parallel of the regular Topps set. The cards in the first series parallel cards number 1 through 201 and second series parallels cards 241-440. Card numbers 7 and 44 were never produced for this set. Each MVP Promotion parallel card has a prominent gold foil MVP logo on the front and contest rules and guidelines on back. Only 100 of each of these cards were printed and a new winner was announced each week throughout the 2000 season as Topps selected their top player of the week. Winning cards could be redeemed for a complete set of exchnage cards featuring every weekly winning player. Winning cards were verified through either calling 1-888-Go-Topps or checking on the Topps web site prior to the deadline. The exchange deadline for these cards was December 31st, 2000. The winning cards were the following numbers (in correspondence with the basic issue 2000 Topps card): 13, 15, 45, 50, 53, 55, 60, 72, 87, 90, 93, 107, 109, 116, 148, 165, 180, 199, 250, 271, 350, 395, 398, 403 and 427. Since Topps destroyed these Winner exchange cards once they received them, they're in noticeably shorter supply than other cards from this set. Despite this fact, no noticeable premiums in secondary trading levels have been detected for these cards.

Card	Low	High
*STARS: 30X TO 60X BASIC CARDS		
13 Magglio Ordonez W	6.00	12.00
15 Derek Jeter W	40.00	80.00
45 Jeff Bagwell W	10.00	20.00
50 Sammy Sosa W	15.00	30.00
53 Dante Bichette W	6.00	12.00
55 Frank Thomas W	15.00	30.00
60 Pedro Martinez W	10.00	20.00
72 Brian Jordan W	6.00	12.00
87 Bobby Higginson W	6.00	12.00
90 Mark Kotsay W	6.00	12.00
93 Carlos Delgado W	6.00	12.00
107 Jim Edmonds W	6.00	12.00
109 Adrian Beltre W	6.00	12.00
116 Jermaine Dye W	6.00	12.00
148 Derek Bell W	6.00	12.00
165 Kenny Lofton W	6.00	12.00
180 Chipper Jones W	15.00	30.00
199 Jason Giambi W	6.00	12.00
250 Barry Bonds W	50.00	100.00
271 Will Clark W	10.00	20.00
350 Jose Cruz Jr. W	6.00	12.00
395 Todd Helton W	10.00	20.00
398 Manny Ramirez W	10.00	20.00
403 Shawn Estes W	6.00	12.00
427 Jon Lieber W	6.00	12.00

2000 Topps MVP Promotion Exchange

This 25-card set was available only to those lucky collectors who obtained one of the twenty-five winning player cards from the 2000 Topps MVP Promotion parallel set. Each week, throughout the 2000 season, Topps named a new Player of the Week, and that player's Topps MVP Promotion parallel card was made redeemable for this 25-card set. The deadline to exchange the winning cards was 12/31/00.

Card	Low	High
COMPLETE SET (25)	20.00	50.00
MVP1 Pedro Martinez	1.00	2.50
MVP2 Jim Edmonds	.60	1.50
MVP3 Derek Bell	.60	1.50
MVP4 Jermaine Dye	.60	1.50
MVP5 Jose Cruz Jr.	.60	1.50
MVP6 Todd Helton	1.00	2.50
MVP7 Brian Jordan	.60	1.50
MVP8 Shawn Estes	.60	1.50
MVP9 Dante Bichette	.60	1.50
MVP10 Carlos Delgado	.60	1.50
MVP11 Bobby Higginson	.60	1.50
MVP12 Mark Kotsay	.60	1.50
MVP13 Magglio Ordonez	.60	1.50
MVP14 Jon Lieber	.60	1.50
MVP15 Frank Thomas	1.50	4.00
MVP16 Manny Ramirez	1.00	2.50
MVP17 Sammy Sosa	1.50	4.00
MVP18 Will Clark	1.00	2.50
MVP19 Jeff Bagwell	1.00	2.50
MVP20 Derek Jeter	4.00	10.00
MVP21 Adrian Beltre	.60	1.50
MVP22 Kenny Lofton	.60	1.50
MVP23 Barry Bonds	4.00	10.00
MVP24 Jason Giambi	.60	1.50
MVP25 Chipper Jones	1.50	4.00

2000 Topps Oversize

Each 2000 Topps hobby and Home Team Advantage box has one of these cards as a chiptopper. A chiptopper is a card that lies on top of the packs within the sealed box. These cards are exact parallels of their corresponding base issue card except, of course, for their larger size (3" by 5") and 1-8 numbering on back. Please note, for checklisting purposes, we've added "A" and "B" prefixes to each card number to signify which cards were seeded in first versus second series packs.

Card	Low	High
COMPLETE SERIES 1 (8)	8.00	20.00
COMPLETE SERIES 2 (8)	6.00	15.00
A1 Mark McGwire	1.25	3.00
A2 Hank Aaron	.75	2.00
A3 Derek Jeter	1.25	3.00
A4 Sammy Sosa	.50	1.25
A5 Alex Rodriguez	.75	2.00
A6 Chipper Jones	.50	1.25
A7 Cal Ripken	1.50	4.00
A8 Pedro Martinez	.30	.75
B1 Barry Bonds	1.50	4.00
B2 Orlando Hernandez	.20	.50
B3 Mike Piazza	.75	2.00
B4 Manny Ramirez	.30	.75
B5 Ken Griffey Jr.	.75	2.00
B6 Rafael Palmeiro	.30	.75
B7 Greg Maddux	.75	2.00
B8 Nomar Garciaparra	.75	2.00

2000 Topps 21st Century

Inserted one every 18 first series hobby and retail packs and one every five first series HTA packs, these 10 cards feature players who are among those expected to be among the best players in the first part of the 21st century.

Card	Low	High
COMPLETE SET (10)	4.00	10.00
C1 Ben Grieve	.15	.40
C2 Alex Gonzalez	.15	.40
C3 Derek Jeter	1.00	2.50
C4 Sean Casey	.15	.40
C5 Nomar Garciaparra	.60	1.50
C6 Alex Rodriguez	.60	1.50
C7 Scott Rolen	.25	.60
C8 Andruw Jones	.25	.60
C9 Vladimir Guerrero	.40	1.00
C10 Todd Helton	.25	.60

2000 Topps Aaron

For their year 2000 product, Topps chose to reprint cards of All-Time Home Run King, Hank Aaron. The cards were inserted one every 18 hobby and retail pack and one every five HTA packs in both first and second series. The even year cards were released in the first series and the odd year cards were issued in the second series. Each card can be easily detected from the original cards issued from the 1950-70s by the large gold foil logo on front and the glossy card stock.

Card	Low	High
COMMON CARD (1-23)	2.00	5.00
1 Hank Aaron 1954	4.00	10.00

2000 Topps Aaron Autographs

Due to the fact that Topps could not obtain actual signed Hank Aaron cards prior to pack out for first series in December, 2000 - Topps inserted into first series packs at a rate of one in 4361 hobby and retail and 1 in 1199 first series HTA packs exchange cards of which were redeemable (prior to the May 31st, 2000 deadline) for a signed Hank Aaron Reprint card. The 12 exchange cards distributed in series one were redeemable exclusively for specific even year Reprint cards. The 11 odd year Autographs were obtained by Topps well in time for the second series release in April, 2000 and thus those actual autographed cards were seeded directly into the series two packs.

Card	Low	High
COMMON CARD (2-23)	200.00	400.00
1 Hank Aaron 1954	300.00	500.00

2000 Topps Aaron Chrome

Issued one every 72 Hobby or Retail packs and one every 16 HTA packs for both first and second series, these cards parallel the Aaron reprint set. They are issued using the Chrome treatment Topps uses on many of their products. In this set, the odd year cards were issued in the first series and the even year cards in the second series.

Card	Low	High
COMMON CARD (1-23)	4.00	10.00
*CHROME REF: 1X TO 2.5X CHROME		
CH.REF.ODDS 1:288 HOB/RET, 1:76 HTA		
1 Hank Aaron 1954	6.00	15.00

2000 Topps All-Star Rookie Team

Randomly inserted into packs at one in 36 HOB/RET packs and one in eight HTA packs, this 10-card insert set features players that had break-through seasons their first year. Card backs carry a "RT" prefix.

Card	Low	High
COMPLETE SET (10)	10.00	25.00
RT1 Mark McGwire	2.00	5.00
RT2 Chuck Knoblauch	.30	.75
RT3 Chipper Jones	.75	2.00
RT4 Cal Ripken	2.50	6.00
RT5 Manny Ramirez	.50	1.25
RT6 Jose Canseco	.50	1.25
RT7 Ken Griffey Jr.	1.25	3.00
RT8 Mike Piazza	1.25	3.00
RT9 Dwight Gooden	.30	.75
RT10 Billy Wagner UER Les Cain's name is spelled Less	.30	.75

2000 Topps All-Topps

Inserted one every 12 first series hobby and retail packs and one every three first series HTA packs, this set features 10 star National Leaguers, 10 star American Leaguers, and a comparision to Hall of Famers at their respective position. Each card is printed on silver foil-board with select metalization. The National League players were issued in series one, while the American League players were issued in series two.

Card	Low	High
COMPLETE SET (20)	10.00	20.00
COMPLETE N.L.(10)	4.00	10.00
COMPLETE A.L. (10)	4.00	10.00
AT1 Greg Maddux	.60	1.50
AT2 Mike Piazza	.60	1.50
AT3 Mark McGwire	1.00	2.50
AT4 Craig Biggio	.25	.60
AT5 Chipper Jones	.40	1.00
AT6 Barry Larkin	.25	.60
AT7 Barry Bonds	1.25	3.00
AT8 Andruw Jones	.25	.60
AT9 Sammy Sosa	.40	1.00
AT10 Larry Walker	.15	.40
AT11 Pedro Martinez	.25	.60
AT12 Ivan Rodriguez	.25	.60
AT13 Rafael Palmeiro	.25	.60
AT14 Roberto Alomar	.25	.60
AT15 Cal Ripken	1.25	3.00
AT16 Derek Jeter	1.00	2.50
AT17 Albert Belle	.15	.40
AT18 Ken Griffey Jr.	.60	1.50
AT19 Manny Ramirez	.25	.60
AT20 Jose Canseco	.25	.60

2000 Topps Autographs

Inserted at various level of difficulty, these players signed autographs for the 2000 Topps product. Group A players were inserted one every 7589 first series hobby and retail packs and one every 2087 first series HTA packs. Group A players were issued at a rate of one in every 5840 second series hobby and retail packs, and one every 1607 HTA packs. Group B players were inserted one every 4553 first series hobby and retail packs and one every 1252 first series HTA packs. Group B players were inserted at a rate of one every 2337 second series hobby and retail packs, and one every 643 HTA packs. Group C players were inserted one every 1518 first series hobby and retail packs and one every 417 first series HTA packs. Group C players were inserted one every 1169 second series hobby and retail packs, and one in every 321 HTA packs. Group D players were inserted one every 911 first series hobby and retails packs and one every 250 first series HTA packs. Group D players were inserted one in every 701 second series hobby and retail packs, and one in every 193 HTA packs. Group E autographs were issued one every 1138 first series hobby and retail packs and one every 313 first series HTA packs. Group E players were inserted one in every 1754 second series hobby and retail packs, and one in every 482 HTA packs. Originally intended to be a straight numerical run of TA1-TA15 for series one, cards TA 4 (Sean Casey) and TA 15 (Carlos Beltran) were dropped and replaced with TA 20 (Vladimir Guerrero) and TA 27 (Mike Sweeney).

Card	Low	High
TA1 Alex Rodriguez A	60.00	120.00
TA2 Tony Gwynn A	30.00	60.00
TA3 Vinny Castilla B	10.00	25.00
TA4 Sean Casey B	10.00	25.00
TA5 Shawn Green C	15.00	40.00
TA6 Rey Ordonez C	6.00	15.00
TA7 Matt Lawton C	6.00	15.00
TA8 Tony Womack C	6.00	15.00
TA9 Gabe Kapler D	10.00	25.00
TA10 Pat Burrell D	10.00	25.00
TA11 Preston Wilson D	10.00	25.00
TA12 Troy Glaus D	15.00	40.00
TA13 Carlos Beltran D	10.00	25.00
TA14 Josh Girdley E	6.00	15.00
TA15 B.J. Garbe E	6.00	15.00
TA16 Derek Jeter A	75.00	150.00
TA17 Cal Ripken A	100.00	200.00
TA18 Ivan Rodriguez B	20.00	50.00
TA19 Rafael Palmeiro B	30.00	60.00
TA20 Vladimir Guerrero B	20.00	50.00
TA21 Raul Mondesi C	10.00	25.00
TA22 Scott Rolen C	15.00	40.00
TA23 Billy Wagner C	15.00	40.00
TA24 Fernando Tatis C	6.00	15.00
TA25 Ruben Mateo D	6.00	15.00
TA26 Carlos Febles D	6.00	15.00
TA27 Mike Sweeney D	10.00	25.00
TA28 Alex Gonzalez D	6.00	15.00
TA29 Miguel Tejada D	15.00	40.00
TA30 Josh Hamilton E	50.00	100.00

2000 Topps Combos

Randomly inserted into packs at one in 18 hobby and retail packs, and one in every five HTA packs, this 10-card insert set showcases player groupings unified by a common theme, such as Home Run Kings, and features artist renderings of each player reminiscent of Topps' classic 1959 set. Card backs carry a "TC" prefix.

Card	Low	High
COMPLETE SET (10)	12.50	25.00
TC1 Roberto Alomar / Manny Ramirez / Kenny Lofton / Jim Thome	.60	1.50
TC2 Tom Glavine / Greg Maddux / John Smoltz	1.25	3.00
TC3 Derek Jeter / Bernie Williams / Tino Martinez	1.50	4.00
TC4 Ivan Rodriguez / Mike Piazza	1.00	2.50
TC5 Nomar Garciaparra / Alex Rodriguez / Derek Jeter	1.00	2.50
TC6 Sammy Sosa / Mark McGwire	.60	1.50
TC7 Pedro Martinez / Randy Johnson	.60	1.50
TC8 Barry Bonds / Ken Griffey Jr.	1.50	4.00
TC9 Chipper Jones / Ivan Rodriguez	.60	1.50
TC10 Cal Ripken / Tony Gwynn / Wade Boggs	.60	1.50

2000 Topps Hands of Gold

Inserted on every 18 first series hobby and retail packs and one every five first series HTA packs, this seven card set features players who have won at least five Gold Gloves. Each card is foil-stamped, die-cut and specially embossed.

Card	Low	High
COMPLETE SET (7)	3.00	8.00
HG1 Barry Bonds	1.25	3.00
HG2 Ivan Rodriguez	.25	.60
HG3 Ken Griffey Jr.	.60	1.50
HG4 Roberto Alomar	.25	.60
HG5 Tony Gwynn	.50	1.25
HG6 Omar Vizquel	.25	.60
HG7 Greg Maddux	.60	1.50

2000 Topps Own the Game

Randomly inserted into series two hobby and retail packs at a rate one in every 12, and one in every three series two HTA packs, this 30-card insert set features the top statistical leaders in major league baseball. Card backs carry an "OTG" prefix.

Card	Low	High
COMPLETE SET (30)	20.00	50.00
OTG1 Derek Jeter	2.00	5.00
OTG2 B.J. Surhoff	.30	.75
OTG3 Luis Gonzalez	.30	.75
OTG4 Manny Ramirez	.50	1.25
OTG5 Rafael Palmeiro	.50	1.25
OTG6 Mark McGwire	2.00	5.00
OTG7 Mark McGwire	2.00	5.00
OTG8 Sammy Sosa	.75	2.00
OTG9 Ken Griffey Jr.	1.25	3.00
OTG10 Larry Walker	.30	.75
OTG11 Nomar Garciaparra	1.25	3.00
OTG12 Derek Jeter	2.00	5.00
OTG13 Larry Walker	.30	.75
OTG14 Mark McGwire	2.00	5.00
OTG15 Manny Ramirez	.50	1.25
OTG16 Pedro Martinez	.50	1.25
OTG17 Randy Johnson	.75	2.00
OTG18 Kevin Millwood	.30	.75
OTG19 Randy Johnson	.75	2.00
OTG20 Pedro Martinez	.50	1.25
OTG21 Kevin Brown	.50	1.25
OTG22 Chipper Jones	.75	2.00
OTG23 Ivan Rodriguez	.50	1.25
OTG24 Mariano Rivera	.75	2.00
OTG25 Scott Williamson	.30	.75
OTG26 Carlos Beltran	.30	.75
OTG27 Randy Johnson	.75	2.00
OTG28 Pedro Martinez	.50	1.25
OTG29 Sammy Sosa	.75	2.00
OTG30 Manny Ramirez	.50	1.25

2000 Topps Perennial All-Stars

This set is inserted into first series hobby and retail packs at a rate of one in 18 and first series HTA packs at a rate of one every five packs. These 10 cards feature players who consistently achieve All-Star recognition.

Card	Low	High
COMPLETE SET (10)	8.00	20.00
PA1 Ken Griffey Jr.	.60	1.50
PA2 Derek Jeter	1.00	2.50
PA3 Sammy Sosa	.40	1.00
PA4 Cal Ripken	1.25	3.00
PA5 Mike Piazza	.60	1.50
PA6 Nomar Garciaparra	.60	1.50
PA7 Jeff Bagwell	.25	.60
PA8 Barry Bonds	1.25	3.00
PA9 Alex Rodriguez	.60	1.50
PA10 Mark McGwire	1.00	2.50

2000 Topps Power Players

Inserted into hobby and retail first series packs at a rate of one in eight and first series HTA packs at a rate one every other pack, this set features 20 of the best sluggers in baseball.

Card	Low	High
COMPLETE SET (20)	10.00	25.00
P1 Juan Gonzalez	.15	.40
P2 Ken Griffey Jr.	.60	1.50
P3 Mark McGwire	1.00	2.50
P4 Nomar Garciaparra	.60	1.50
P5 Barry Bonds	1.25	3.00
P6 Mo Vaughn	.15	.40
P7 Larry Walker	.15	.40
P8 Alex Rodriguez	.60	1.50
P9 Jose Canseco	.25	.60
P10 Jeff Bagwell	.25	.60
P11 Manny Ramirez	.25	.60
P12 Albert Belle	.15	.40
P13 Frank Thomas	.40	1.00
P14 Mike Piazza	.60	1.50
P15 Chipper Jones	.40	1.00
P16 Sammy Sosa	.40	1.00
P17 Vladimir Guerrero	.40	1.00
P18 Scott Rolen	.25	.60
P19 Raul Mondesi	.15	.40
P20 Derek Jeter	1.00	2.50

2000 Topps Stadium Autograph Relics

Exclusively inserted into first series HTA jumbo packs at a rate of one in 165 first series packs, and one in every 135 second series HTA packs, these cards feature a piece of a major league stadium (mostly infield bases) as well as as a photo and an autograph of the featured superstar who played there. Among the venerable ballparks included in this set are Wrigley Field, Fenway Park and Yankee Stadium.

Card	Low	High
SR1 Don Mattingly	75.00	150.00
SR2 Carl Yastrzemski	60.00	120.00
SR3 Ernie Banks	50.00	100.00
SR4 Johnny Bench	50.00	100.00
SR5 Willie Mays	125.00	200.00
SR6 Mike Schmidt	60.00	120.00
SR7 Lou Brock	40.00	80.00
SR8 Al Kaline	50.00	100.00
SR9 Paul Molitor	20.00	50.00
SR10 Eddie Mathews	60.00	120.00

2000 Topps Limited

These parallel cards were issued exclusively in factory set form (an attractive black box with a glossy teal overlay) and offered collectors the chance to get an upgraded premium version of the basic 2000 Topps. Each factory set contained a total of 619 cards including the complete 478 card basic Topps set plus the following insert sets: 21st Century Topps, Aaron Reprints, All-Star Rookie Team, All-Topps, Combos, Hands of Gold, Own the Game, Perennial All-Stars, Power Players and the

Mark McGwire 1985 Reprint. Collectors received only one of five different variations of the Magic Moments subset cards (236-240/475-479) per factory set. Each card has thick gloss and features a "Limited Edition" gold foil stamp on front. Stated print run was originally 6000 serial numbered sets but actual production turned out to be 4,000 sets (with only 800 copies of each of the Magic Moments variation subset cards). Each factory box is serial numbered x/4000 but the individual cards are not numbered in any way. The sets were distributed in late September, 2000.

COMP.FACT.SET (619) 60.00 150.00
COMPLETE SET (478) 50.00 100.00
*STARS: 1.5X TO 4X BASIC CARDS
*ROOKIES: 1.5X TO 4X BASIC CARDS
*MAGIC MOMENTS: .75X TO 2X BASIC MM

2000 Topps Limited 21st Century

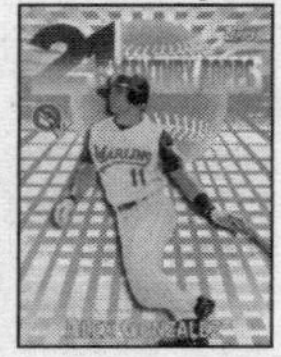

These inserts were seeded at one complete set per sealed Topps Limited factory set. This is a complete parallel of the 21st Century insert that is found in 2000 Topps, and can be easily distinguished by the thicker card stock, glossy finish, and the words "Limited Edition" stamped in gold lettering on each card. Please note that only 4000 sets were produced.

COMPLETE SET (10) 10.00 25.00
*LIMITED: 1X TO 2.5X TOPPS 21ST CENT.

2000 Topps Limited Aaron

These inserts were seeded at one complete set per sealed Topps Limited factory set. This is a complete parallel of the Aaron insert that is found in 2000 Topps, and can be easily distinguished by the thicker card stock, glossy finish, and the words "Limited Edition" stamped in gold lettering on each card. Please note that only 4000 sets were produced.

COMPLETE SET (23) 50.00 100.00
*LIMITED: .3X TO .8X TOPPS AARON
1 Hank Aaron 1954 4.00 10.00

2000 Topps Limited All-Star Rookie Team

These inserts were seeded at one complete set per sealed Topps Limited factory set. This is a complete parallel of the All-Star Rookie Team insert that is found in 2000 Topps, and can be easily distinguished by the thicker card stock, glossy finish, and the words "Limited Edition" stamped in gold lettering on each card. Please note that only 4000 sets were produced.

COMPLETE SET (10) 12.50 30.00
*LIMITED: .5X TO 1.2X TOPPS AS ROOK.

2000 Topps Limited All-Topps

These inserts were seeded at one complete set per sealed Topps Limited factory set. This is a complete parallel of the All-Topps insert that is found in 2000 Topps, and can be easily distinguished by the thicker card stock, glossy finish, and the words "Limited Edition" stamped in gold lettering on each card. Please note that only 4000 sets were produced.

COMPLETE SET (20) 15.00 40.00
*LIMITED: 1X TO 2.5X TOPPS ALL-TOPPS

2000 Topps Limited Combos

These inserts were seeded at one complete set per sealed Topps Limited factory set. This is a complete parallel of the Combos insert that is found in 2000 Topps, and can be easily distinguished by the thicker card stock, glossy finish, and the words "Limited Edition" stamped in gold lettering on each card. Please note that only 4000 sets were produced.

COMPLETE SET (10) 20.00 50.00
*LIMITED: .75X TO 2X TOPPS COMBOS

2000 Topps Limited Hands of Gold

These inserts were seeded at one complete set per sealed Topps Limited factory set. This is a complete parallel of the Hands of Gold insert that is found in 2000 Topps, and can be easily distinguished by the thicker card stock, glossy finish, and the words "Limited Edition" stamped in gold lettering on each card. Please note that only 4000 sets were produced.

COMPLETE SET (7) 6.00 15.00
*LIMITED: 1X TO 2.5X TOPPS HANDS

2000 Topps Limited Own the Game

These inserts were seeded at one complete set per sealed Topps Limited factory set. This is a complete parallel of the Own the Game insert that is found in 2000 Topps, and can be easily distinguished by the thicker card stock, glossy finish, and the words "Limited Edition" stamped in gold lettering on each card. Please note that only 4000 sets were produced.

COMPLETE SET (30) 25.00 60.00
*LIMITED: .5X TO 1.2X TOPPS OTG

2000 Topps Limited Perennial All-Stars

These inserts were seeded at one complete set per sealed Topps Limited factory set. This is a complete parallel of the Perennial All-Stars insert that is found in 2000 Topps, and can be easily distinguished by the thicker card stock, glossy finish, and the words "Limited Edition" stamped in gold lettering on each card. Please note that only 4000 sets were produced.

COMPLETE SET (10) 15.00 40.00
*LIMITED: 1X TO 2.5X TOPPS PER.AS

2000 Topps Limited Power Players

These inserts were seeded at one complete set per sealed Topps Limited factory set. This is a complete parallel of the Power Players insert that is found in 2000 Topps, and can be easily distinguished by the thicker card stock, glossy finish, and the words "Limited Edition" stamped in gold lettering on each card. Please note that only 4000 sets were produced.

COMPLETE SET (20) 20.00 50.00
*LIMITED: 1X TO 2.5X TOPPS POWER

2000 Topps Traded

The 2000 Topps Traded sets were released in October, 2000 and featured a 135-card base set, and one additional autograph card. The set carried a suggested retail price of $29.99. Please note that each card in the base set carried a "T" prefix before the card number. Topps announced that due to the unavailability of certain players previously scheduled to sign autographs, Topps will include a small quantity of autographed cards from the 2000 Topps Baseball Rookies/Traded set into its 2000 Bowman Baseball Draft Picks and Prospects set. Notable Rookie Cards include Cristian Guerrero and J.R. House.

COMP.FACT.SET (136) 25.00 40.00
COMPLETE SET (135) 15.00 30.00
FACT.SET PRICE IS FOR SEALED SETS
T1 Mike MacDougal .10 .30
T2 Andy Tracy RC .10 .30
T3 Brandon Phillips RC .40 1.00
T4 Brandon Inge RC .75 2.00
T5 Robbie Morrison RC .10 .30
T6 Josh Pressley RC .10 .30
T7 Todd Moser RC .10 .30
T8 Rob Purvis .10 .30
T9 Chance Caple .07 .20
T10 Ben Sheets .40 1.00
T11 Russ Jacobson RC .10 .30
T12 Brian Cole RC .10 .30
T13 Brad Baker .07 .20
T14 Alex Cintron RC .10 .30
T15 Lyle Overbay RC .30 .75
T16 Mike Edwards RC .10 .30
T17 Sean McGowan RC .10 .30
T18 Jose Molina .07 .20
T19 Marcos Castillo RC .10 .30
T20 Josue Espada RC .10 .30
T21 Alex Gordon RC .10 .30
T22 Rob Pugmire RC .10 .30
T23 Jason Stumm .07 .20
T24 Ty Howington .07 .20
T25 Brett Myers .25 .60
T26 Maicer Izturis RC .10 .30
T27 John McDonald .07 .20
T28 W.Rodriguez RC .10 .30
T29 Carlos Zambrano RC 2.00 5.00
T30 Alejandro Diaz RC .10 .30
T31 Geraldo Guzman RC .10 .30
T32 J.R. House RC .10 .30
T33 Elvin Nina RC .10 .30
T34 Juan Pierre RC .25 .60
T35 Ben Johnson RC .50 1.25
T36 Jeff Bailey RC .10 .30
T37 Miguel Olivo RC .20 .50
T38 F.Rodriguez RC .75 2.00
T39 Tony Pena Jr. RC .10 .30
T40 Miguel Cabrera RC 5.00 12.00
T41 Asdrubal Oropeza RC .10 .30
T42 Junior Zamora RC .10 .30
T43 Jovanny Cedeno RC .10 .30
T44 John Sneed .10 .30
T45 Josh Kalinowski .10 .30
T46 Mike Young RC 1.50 4.00
T47 Rico Washington RC .10 .30
T48 Chad Durbin RC .10 .30
T49 Junior Brignac RC .10 .30
T50 Carlos Hernandez RC .10 .30
T51 Cesar Izturis RC .20 .50
T52 Oscar Salazar RC .10 .30
T53 Pat Strange RC .10 .30
T54 Rick Asadoorian .10 .30
T55 Keith Reed .07 .20
T56 Leo Estrella RC .10 .30
T57 Wascar Serrano RC .10 .30
T58 Richard Gomez RC .10 .30
T59 Ramon Santiago RC .10 .30
T60 Jovanny Sosa RC .10 .30
T61 Aaron Rowand RC .50 1.25
T62 Junior Guerrero RC .10 .30
T63 Luis Terrero RC .10 .30
T64 Brian Sanches RC .10 .30
T65 Scott Sobkowiak RC .10 .30
T66 Gary Majewski RC .10 .30
T67 Barry Zito .50 1.25
T68 Ryan Christianson .07 .20
T69 Cristian Guerrero RC .10 .30
T70 T.De La Rosa RC .10 .30
T71 Andrew Beinbrink RC .10 .30
T72 Ryan Knox RC .10 .30
T73 Alex Graman RC .10 .30
T74 Juan Guzman RC .10 .30
T75 Ruben Salazar RC .10 .30
T76 Luis Matos RC .10 .30
T77 Tony Mota RC .10 .30
T78 Doug Davis .10 .30
T79 Ben Christensen .07 .20
T80 Mike Lamb .20 .50
T81 Adrian Gonzalez RC 1.00 2.50
T82 Mike Stodolka RC .10 .30
T83 Adam Johnson RC .10 .30
T84 Matt Wheatland RC .10 .30
T85 Corey Smith RC .10 .30
T86 Rocco Baldelli RC .50 1.25
T87 Keith Bucktrot RC .10 .30
T88 Adam Wainwright RC .40 1.00
T89 Scott Thorman RC .30 .75
T90 Tripper Johnson RC .10 .30
T91 Jim Edmonds Cards .10 .30
T92 Masato Yoshii .07 .20
T93 Adam Kennedy .07 .20
T94 Darryl Kile .10 .30
T95 Mark McLemore .07 .20
T96 Ricky Gutierrez .07 .20
T97 Juan Gonzalez .10 .30
T98 Melvin Mora .10 .30
T99 Dante Bichette .10 .30
T100 Lee Stevens .07 .20
T101 Roger Cedeno .07 .20
T102 John Olerud .10 .30
T103 Eric Young .07 .20
T104 Mickey Morandini .07 .20
T105 Travis Lee .07 .20
T106 Greg Vaughn .07 .20
T107 Todd Zeile .10 .30
T108 Chuck Finley .10 .30
T109 Ismael Valdes .07 .20
T110 Reggie Sanders .10 .30
T111 Pat Hentgen .07 .20
T112 Ryan Klesko .10 .30
T113 Derek Bell .07 .20
T114 Hideo Nomo .30 .75
T115 Aaron Sele .07 .20
T116 Fernando Vina .07 .20
T117 Wally Joyner .10 .30
T118 Brian Hunter .07 .20
T119 Joe Girardi .07 .20
T120 Omar Daal .07 .20
T121 Brook Fordyce .07 .20
T122 Jose Valentin .07 .20
T123 Curt Schilling .10 .30
T124 B.J. Surhoff .10 .30
T125 Henry Rodriguez .07 .20
T126 Mike Bordick .07 .20
T127 David Justice .10 .30
T128 Charles Johnson .10 .30
T129 Will Clark .20 .50
T130 Dwight Gooden .10 .30
T131 David Segui .07 .20
T132 Denny Neagle .10 .30
T133 Jose Canseco .20 .50
T134 Bruce Chen .07 .20
T135 Jason Bere .07 .20

2000 Topps Traded Autographs

Randomly inserted into 2000 Topps Traded sets at a rate of one per sealed factory set, this 80-card set features autographed cards of some of the Major League's most talented prospects. Card backs carry a "TTA" prefix.

TTA1 Mike MacDougal 4.00 10.00
TTA2 Andy Tracy 2.00 5.00
TTA3 Brandon Phillips 12.50 30.00
TTA4 Brandon Inge 12.50 30.00
TTA5 Robbie Morrison 2.00 5.00
TTA6 Josh Pressley 2.00 5.00
TTA7 Todd Moser 2.00 5.00
TTA8 Rob Purvis 4.00 10.00
TTA9 Chance Caple 2.00 5.00
TTA10 Ben Sheets 15.00 40.00
TTA11 Russ Jacobson 2.00 5.00
TTA12 Brian Cole 2.00 5.00
TTA13 Brad Baker 2.00 5.00
TTA14 Alex Cintron 4.00 10.00
TTA15 Lyle Overbay 10.00 25.00
TTA16 Mike Edwards 2.00 5.00
TTA17 Sean McGowan 2.00 5.00
TTA18 Jose Molina 2.00 5.00
TTA19 Marcos Castillo 2.00 5.00
TTA20 Josue Espada 2.00 5.00
TTA21 Alex Gordon 2.00 5.00
TTA22 Rob Pugmire 2.00 5.00
TTA23 Jason Stumm 2.00 5.00
TTA24 Ty Howington 2.00 5.00
TTA25 Brett Myers 10.00 25.00
TTA26 Maicer Izturis 4.00 10.00
TTA27 John McDonald 2.00 5.00
TTA28 Wilfredo Rodriguez 2.00 5.00
TTA29 Carlos Zambrano 100.00 175.00
TTA30 Alejandro Diaz 2.00 5.00
TTA31 Geraldo Guzman 2.00 5.00
TTA32 J.R. House 2.00 5.00
TTA33 Elvin Nina 2.00 5.00
TTA34 Juan Pierre 15.00 40.00
TTA35 Ben Johnson 10.00 25.00
TTA36 Jeff Bailey 2.00 5.00
TTA37 Miguel Olivo 6.00 15.00
TTA38 F.Rodriguez 30.00 60.00
TTA39 Tony Pena Jr. 2.00 5.00
TTA40 Miguel Cabrera 400.00 600.00
TTA41 Asdrubal Oropeza 2.00 5.00
TTA42 Junior Zamora 2.00 5.00
TTA43 Jovanny Cedeno 2.00 5.00
TTA44 John Sneed 2.00 5.00
TTA45 Josh Kalinowski 4.00 10.00
TTA46 Mike Young 100.00 150.00
TTA47 Rico Washington 2.00 5.00
TTA48 Chad Durbin 2.00 5.00
TTA49 Junior Brignac 2.00 5.00
TTA50 Carlos Hernandez 4.00 10.00
TTA51 Cesar Izturis 6.00 15.00
TTA52 Oscar Salazar 2.00 5.00
TTA53 Pat Strange 2.00 5.00
TTA54 Rick Asadoorian 4.00 10.00
TTA55 Keith Reed 2.00 5.00
TTA56 Leo Estrella 2.00 5.00
TTA57 Wascar Serrano 2.00 5.00
TTA58 Richard Gomez 2.00 5.00
TTA59 Ramon Santiago 2.00 5.00
TTA60 Jovanny Sosa 2.00 5.00
TTA61 Aaron Rowand 20.00 50.00
TTA62 Junior Guerrero 2.00 5.00
TTA63 Luis Terrero 4.00 10.00
TTA64 Brian Sanches 2.00 5.00
TTA65 Scott Sobkowiak 2.00 5.00
TTA66 Gary Majewski 4.00 10.00
TTA67 Barry Zito 15.00 40.00
TTA68 Ryan Christianson 2.00 5.00
TTA69 Cristian Guerrero 2.00 5.00
TTA70 Tomas De La Rosa 2.00 5.00
TTA71 Andrew Beinbrink 4.00 10.00
TTA72 Ryan Knox 2.00 5.00
TTA73 Alex Graman 2.00 5.00
TTA74 Juan Guzman 2.00 5.00
TTA75 Ruben Salazar 2.00 5.00
TTA76 Luis Matos 4.00 10.00
TTA77 Tony Mota 2.00 5.00
TTA78 Doug Davis 6.00 15.00
TTA79 Ben Christensen 2.00 5.00
TTA80 Mike Lamb 6.00 15.00

2001 Topps

The 2001 Topps set featured 790 cards and was issued over two series. The set looks to bring back some of the heritage that Topps established in the past by bringing back Manager cards, dual-player prospect cards, and the 2000 season highlight cards. Notable Rookie Cards include Hee Seop Choi. Please note that some cards have been discovered with nothing printed on front but blank white except for the players name and 50th Topps anniversary logo printed in Gold. Factory sets include five special cards inserted specifically in those sets. Card number 7 was not issued as Topps continued to honor the memory of Mickey Mantle.

COMPLETE SET (790) 40.00 80.00
COMP.FACT.BLUE SET (795) 60.00 120.00
COMP.SERIES 1 (405) 20.00 40.00
COMP. SERIES 2 (385) 20.00 40.00
COMMON (1-6/8-791) .07 .20
COMMON (352-376/727-751) .08 .25
1 Cal Ripken .60 1.50
2 Chipper Jones .20 .50
3 Roger Cedeno .07 .20
4 Garret Anderson .07 .20
5 Robin Ventura .07 .20
6 Daryle Ward .07 .20
7 Does Not Exist
8 Craig Paquette .07 .20
9 Phil Nevin .07 .20
10 Jermaine Dye .07 .20
11 Chris Singleton .07 .20
12 Mike Stanton .07 .20
13 Brian Hunter .07 .20
14 Mike Redmond .07 .20
15 Jim Thome .10 .30
16 Brian Jordan .07 .20
17 Joe Girardi .07 .20
18 Steve Woodard .07 .20
19 Dustin Hermanson .07 .20
20 Shawn Green .07 .20
21 Todd Stottlemyre .07 .20
22 Dan Wilson .07 .20
23 Todd Pratt .07 .20
24 Derek Lowe .07 .20
25 Juan Gonzalez .07 .20
26 Clay Bellinger .07 .20
27 Jeff Fassero .07 .20
28 Pat Meares .07 .20
29 Eddie Taubensee .07 .20
30 Paul O'Neill .10 .30
31 Jeffrey Hammonds .07 .20
32 Pokey Reese .07 .20
33 Mike Mussina .10 .30
34 Rico Brogna .07 .20
35 Jay Buhner .07 .20
36 Steve Cox .07 .20
37 Quilvio Veras .07 .20
38 Marquis Grissom .07 .20
39 Shigetoshi Hasegawa .07 .20
40 Shane Reynolds .07 .20
41 Adam Piatt .07 .20
42 Luis Polonia .07 .20
43 Brook Fordyce .07 .20
44 Preston Wilson .07 .20
45 Ellis Burks .07 .20
46 Armando Rios .07 .20
47 Chuck Finley .07 .20
48 Dan Plesac .07 .20
49 Shannon Stewart .07 .20
50 Mark McGwire .50 1.25
51 Mark Loretta .07 .20
52 Gerald Williams .07 .20
53 Eric Young .07 .20
54 Peter Bergeron .07 .20
55 Dave Hansen .07 .20
56 Arthur Rhodes .07 .20
57 Bobby Jones .07 .20
58 Matt Clement .07 .20
59 Mike Benjamin .07 .20
60 Pedro Martinez .10 .30
61 Jose Canseco .10 .30
62 Matt Anderson .07 .20
63 Torii Hunter .07 .20
64 Carlos Lee UER .07 .20
1999 Charlotte Games Played are wrong
65 David Cone .07 .20
66 Rey Sanchez .07 .20
67 Eric Chavez .07 .20
68 Rick Helling .07 .20
69 Manny Alexander .07 .20
70 John Franco .07 .20
71 Mike Bordick .07 .20
72 Andres Galarraga .07 .20
73 Jose Cruz Jr. .07 .20
74 Mike Matheny .07 .20
75 Randy Johnson .20 .50
76 Richie Sexson .07 .20
77 Vladimir Nunez .07 .20
78 Harold Baines .07 .20
79 Aaron Boone .07 .20
80 Darin Erstad .07 .20
81 Alex Gonzalez .07 .20
82 Gil Heredia .07 .20
83 Shane Andrews .07 .20
84 Todd Hundley .07 .20
85 Bill Mueller .07 .20
86 Mark McLemore .07 .20
87 Scott Spiezio .07 .20
88 Kevin McGlinchy .07 .20
89 Bubba Trammell .07 .20
90 Manny Ramirez .10 .30
91 Mike Lamb .07 .20
92 Scott Karl .07 .20
93 Brian Buchanan .07 .20
94 Chris Turner .07 .20
95 Mike Sweeney .07 .20
96 John Wetteland .07 .20
97 Rob Bell .07 .20
98 Pat Rapp .07 .20
99 John Burkett .07 .20
100 Derek Jeter .50 1.25
101 J.D. Drew .07 .20
102 Jose Offerman .07 .20
103 Rick Reed .07 .20
104 Will Clark .10 .30
105 Rickey Henderson .20 .50
106 Dave Berg .07 .20
107 Kirk Rueter .07 .20
108 Lee Stevens .07 .20
109 Jay Bell .07 .20
110 Fred McGriff .10 .30
111 Julio Zuleta .07 .20
112 Brian Anderson .07 .20
113 Orlando Cabrera .07 .20
114 Alex Fernandez .07 .20
115 Derek Bell .07 .20
116 Eric Owens .07 .20
117 Brian Bohanon .07 .20
118 Dennys Reyes .07 .20
119 Mike Stanley .07 .20
120 Jorge Posada .10 .30
121 Rich Becker .07 .20
122 Paul Konerko .07 .20
123 Mike Remlinger .07 .20
124 Travis Lee .07 .20
125 Ken Caminiti .07 .20
126 Kevin Barker .07 .20
127 Paul Quantrill .07 .20
128 Ozzie Guillen .07 .20
129 Kevin Tapani .07 .20
130 Mark Johnson .07 .20
131 Randy Wolf .07 .20
132 Michael Tucker .07 .20
133 Darren Lewis .07 .20
134 Joe Randa .07 .20
135 Jeff Cirillo .07 .20
136 David Ortiz .20 .50
137 Herb Perry .07 .20
138 Jeff Nelson .07 .20
139 Chris Stynes .07 .20
140 Johnny Damon .10 .30
141 Jeff Reboulet .07 .20
142 Jason Schmidt .07 .20
143 Charles Johnson .07 .20
144 Pat Burrell .07 .20
145 Gary Sheffield .07 .20
146 Tom Glavine .10 .30
147 Jason Isringhausen .07 .20
148 Chris Carpenter .07 .20
149 Jeff Suppan .07 .20
150 Ivan Rodriguez .10 .30
151 Luis Sojo .07 .20
152 Ron Villone .07 .20
153 Mike Sirotka .07 .20
154 Chuck Knoblauch .07 .20
155 Jason Kendall .07 .20
156 Dennis Cook .07 .20
157 Bobby Estalella .07 .20
158 Jose Guillen .07 .20
159 Thomas Howard .07 .20
160 Carlos Delgado .07 .20
161 Benji Gil .07 .20
162 Tim Bogar .07 .20
163 Kevin Elster .07 .20
164 Einar Diaz .07 .20
165 Andy Benes .07 .20
166 Adrian Beltre .07 .20
167 David Bell .07 .20
168 Turk Wendell .07 .20
169 Pete Harnisch .07 .20
170 Roger Clemens .40 1.00
171 Scott Williamson .07 .20
172 Kevin Jordan .07 .20
173 Brad Penny .07 .20
174 John Flaherty .07 .20
175 Troy Glaus .07 .20
176 Kevin Appier .07 .20
177 Walt Weiss .07 .20
178 Tyler Houston .07 .20
179 Michael Barrett .07 .20
180 Mike Hampton .07 .20
181 Francisco Cordova .07 .20
182 Mike Jackson .07 .20
183 David Segui .07 .20
184 Carlos Febles .07 .20
185 Roy Halladay .07 .20
186 Seth Etherton .07 .20
187 Charlie Hayes .07 .20
188 Fernando Tatis .07 .20
189 Steve Trachsel .07 .20
190 Livan Hernandez .07 .20
191 Joe Oliver .07 .20
192 Stan Javier .07 .20
193 B.J. Surhoff .07 .20
194 Rob Ducey .07 .20
195 Barry Larkin .10 .30
196 Danny Patterson .07 .20
197 Bobby Howry .07 .20
198 Dmitri Young .07 .20
199 Brian Hunter .07 .20
200 Alex Rodriguez .30 .75
201 Hideo Nomo .20 .50
202 Luis Alicea .07 .20
203 Warren Morris .07 .20

204 Antonio Alfonseca .07 .20
205 Edgardo Alfonzo .07 .20
206 Mark Grudzielanek .07 .20
207 Fernando Vina .07 .20
208 Willie Greene .07 .20
209 Homer Bush .07 .20
210 Jason Giambi .07 .20
211 Mike Morgan .07 .20
212 Steve Karsay .07 .20
213 Matt Lawton .07 .20
214 Wendell Magee Jr. .07 .20
215 Rusty Greer .07 .20
216 Keith Lockhart .07 .20
217 Billy Koch .07 .20
218 Todd Hollandsworth .07 .20
219 Raul Ibanez .07 .20
220 Tony Gwynn .25 .60
221 Carl Everett .07 .20
222 Hector Carrasco .07 .20
223 Jose Valentin .07 .20
224 Deivi Cruz .07 .20
225 Bret Boone .07 .20
226 Kurt Abbott .07 .20
227 Melvin Mora .07 .20
228 Danny Graves .07 .20
229 Jose Jimenez .07 .20
230 James Baldwin .07 .20
231 C.J. Nitkowski .07 .20
232 Jeff Zimmerman .07 .20
233 Mike Lowell .07 .20
234 Hideki Irabu .07 .20
235 Greg Vaughn .07 .20
236 Omar Daal .07 .20
237 Darren Dreifort .07 .20
238 Gil Meche .07 .20
239 Damian Jackson .07 .20
240 Frank Thomas .20 .50
241 Travis Miller .07 .20
242 Jeff Frye .07 .20
243 Dave Magadan .07 .20
244 Luis Castillo .07 .20
245 Bartolo Colon .07 .20
246 Steve Kline .07 .20
247 Shawon Dunston .07 .20
248 Rick Aguilera .07 .20
249 Omar Olivares .07 .20
250 Craig Biggio .10 .30
251 Scott Schoeneweis .07 .20
252 Dave Veres .07 .20
253 Ramon Martinez .07 .20
254 Jose Vidro .07 .20
255 Todd Helton .10 .30
256 Greg Norton .07 .20
257 Jacque Jones .07 .20
258 Jason Grimsley .07 .20
259 Dan Reichert .07 .20
260 Robb Nen .07 .20
261 Mark Clark .07 .20
262 Scott Hatteberg .07 .20
263 Doug Brocail .07 .20
264 Mark Johnson .07 .20
265 Eric Davis .07 .20
266 Terry Shumpert .07 .20
267 Kevin Millar .07 .20
268 Ismael Valdes .07 .20
269 Richard Hidalgo .07 .20
270 Randy Velarde .07 .20
271 Bengie Molina .07 .20
272 Tony Womack .07 .20
273 Enrique Wilson .07 .20
274 Jeff Brantley .07 .20
275 Rick Ankiel .07 .20
276 Terry Mulholland .07 .20
277 Ron Belliard .07 .20
278 Terrence Long .07 .20
279 Alberto Castillo .07 .20
280 Royce Clayton .07 .20
281 Joe McEwing .07 .20
282 Jason McDonald .07 .20
283 Ricky Bottalico .07 .20
284 Keith Foulke .07 .20
285 Brad Radke .07 .20
286 Gabe Kapler .07 .20
287 Pedro Astacio .07 .20
288 Armando Reynoso .07 .20
289 Darryl Kile .07 .20
290 Reggie Sanders .07 .20
291 Esteban Yan .07 .20
292 Joe Nathan .07 .20
293 Jay Payton .07 .20
294 Francisco Cordero .07 .20
295 Gregg Jefferies .07 .20
296 LaTroy Hawkins .07 .20
297 Jeff Tam RC .15 .40
298 Jacob Cruz .07 .20
299 Chris Holt .07 .20
300 Vladimir Guerrero .20 .50
301 Marvin Benard .07 .20
302 Alex Ramirez .07 .20
303 Mike Williams .07 .20
304 Sean Bergman .07 .20
305 Juan Encarnacion .07 .20
306 Russ Davis .07 .20
307 Hanley Frias .07 .20
308 Ramon Hernandez .07 .20
309 Matt Walbeck .07 .20
310 Bill Spiers .07 .20
311 Bob Wickman .07 .20
312 Sandy Alomar Jr. .07 .20
313 Eddie Guardado .07 .20
314 Shane Halter .07 .20
315 Geoff Jenkins .07 .20
316 Brian Meadows .07 .20
317 Damian Miller .07 .20
318 Darrin Fletcher .07 .20
319 Rafael Furcal .07 .20
320 Mark Grace .10 .30
321 Mark Mulder .07 .20
322 Joe Torre MG .10 .30
323 Bobby Cox MG .07 .20
324 Mike Scioscia MG .07 .20
325 Mike Hargrove MG .07 .20
326 Jimy Williams MG .07 .20
327 Jerry Manuel MG .07 .20
328 Buck Showalter MG .07 .20
329 Charlie Manuel MG .07 .20
330 Don Baylor MG .07 .20
331 Phil Garner MG .07 .20
332 Jack McKeon MG .07 .20
333 Tony Muser MG .07 .20
334 Buddy Bell MG .07 .20
335 Tom Kelly MG .07 .20
336 John Boles MG .07 .20
337 Art Howe MG .07 .20
338 Larry Dierker MG .07 .20
339 Lou Piniella MG .07 .20
340 Davey Johnson MG .07 .20
341 Larry Rothschild MG .07 .20
342 Davey Lopes MG .07 .20
343 Johnny Oates MG .07 .20
344 Felipe Alou MG .07 .20
345 Jim Fregosi MG .07 .20
346 Bobby Valentine MG .07 .20
347 Terry Francona MG .07 .20
348 Gene Lamont MG .07 .20
349 Tony LaRussa MG .07 .20
350 Bruce Bochy MG .07 .20
351 Dusty Baker MG .07 .20
352 Adrian Gonzalez .08 .25
Adam Johnson
353 Matt Wheatland .08 .25
Bryan Digby
354 Tripper Johnson .08 .25
Scott Thorman
355 Phil Dumatrait .08 .25
Adam Wainwright
356 Scott Heard .08 .25
David Parrish RC
357 Rocco Baldelli .15 .40
Mark Folsom RC
358 Dominic Rich RC .08 .25
Aaron Herr
359 Mike Stodolka .08 .25
Sean Burnett
360 Derek Thompson .08 .25
Corey Smith
361 Danny Borrell RC .08 .25
Jason Bourgeois RC
362 Chin-Feng Chen .20 .50
Corey Patterson
Josh Hamilton
363 Ryan Anderson .20 .50
Barry Zito
C.C. Sabathia
364 Scott Sobkowiak .20 .50
David Walling
Ben Sheets
365 Ty Howington .08 .25
Josh Kalinowski
Josh Girdley
366 Hee Seop Choi RC .20 .50
Aaron McNeal
Jason Hart
367 Bobby Bradley .15 .40
Kurt Ainsworth
Chin-Hui Tsao
368 Mike Glendenning .08 .25
Kenny Kelly
Juan Silvestre
369 J.R. House .08 .25
Ramon Castro
Ben Davis
370 Chance Caple .15 .40
Rafael Soriano RC
Pasqual Coco
371 Travis Hafner RC 1.50 4.00
Eric Munson
Bucky Jacobsen
372 Jason Conti .08 .25
Chris Wakeland
Brian Cole
373 Scott Seabol .30 .75
Aubrey Huff
Joe Crede
374 Adam Everett .08 .25
Jose Ortiz
Keith Ginter
375 Carlos Hernandez .08 .25
Geraldo Guzman
Adam Eaton
376 Bobby Kielty .15 .40
Milton Bradley
Juan Rivera
377 Mark McGwire GM .25 .60
378 Don Larsen GM .07 .20
379 Bobby Thomson GM .07 .20
380 Bill Mazeroski GM .07 .20
381 Reggie Jackson GM .10 .30
382 Kirk Gibson GM .07 .20
383 Roger Maris GM .10 .30
384 Cal Ripken GM .30 .75
385 Hank Aaron GM .20 .50
386 Joe Carter GM .07 .20
387 Cal Ripken SH .60 1.50
388 Randy Johnson SH .10 .30
389 Ken Griffey Jr. SH .30 .75
390 Troy Glaus SH .07 .20
391 Kazuhiro Sasaki SH .07 .20
392 Sammy Sosa LL .10 .30
Troy Glaus
393 Todd Helton LL .07 .20
Edgar Martinez
394 Todd Helton LL .20 .50
Nomar Garciaparra
395 Barry Bonds LL .30 .75
Jason Giambi
396 Todd Helton LL .07 .20
Manny Ramirez
397 Todd Helton LL .07 .20
Darin Erstad
398 Kevin Brown LL .10 .30
Pedro Martinez
399 Randy Johnson LL .10 .30
Pedro Martinez
400 Will Clark HL .10 .30
401 New York Mets HL .20 .50
402 New York Yankees HL .30 .75
403 Seattle Mariners HL .07 .20
404 Mike Hampton HL .07 .20
405 New York Yankees HL .40 1.00
406 N.Y. Yankees Champs .75 2.00
407 Jeff Bagwell .10 .30
408 Brant Brown .07 .20
409 Brad Fullmer .07 .20
410 Dean Palmer .07 .20
411 Greg Zaun .07 .20
412 Jose Vizcaino .07 .20
413 Jeff Abbott .07 .20
414 Travis Fryman .07 .20
415 Mike Cameron .07 .20
416 Matt Mantei .07 .20
417 Alan Benes .07 .20
418 Mickey Morandini .07 .20
419 Troy Percival .07 .20
420 Eddie Perez .07 .20
421 Vernon Wells .07 .20
422 Ricky Gutierrez .07 .20
423 Carlos Hernandez .07 .20
424 Chan Ho Park .07 .20
425 Armando Benitez .07 .20
426 Sidney Ponson .07 .20
427 Adrian Brown .07 .20
428 Ruben Mateo .07 .20
429 Alex Ochoa .07 .20
430 Jose Rosado .07 .20
431 Masato Yoshii .07 .20
432 Corey Koskie .07 .20
433 Andy Pettitte .10 .30
434 Brian Daubach .07 .20
435 Sterling Hitchcock .07 .20
436 Timo Perez .07 .20
437 Shawn Estes .07 .20
438 Tony Armas Jr. .07 .20
439 Danny Bautista .07 .20
440 Randy Winn .07 .20
441 Wilson Alvarez .07 .20
442 Rondell White .07 .20
443 Jeromy Burnitz .07 .20
444 Kelvim Escobar .07 .20
445 Paul Bako .07 .20
446 Javier Vazquez .07 .20
447 Eric Gagne .07 .20
448 Kenny Lofton .07 .20
449 Mark Kotsay .07 .20
450 Jamie Moyer .07 .20
451 Delino DeShields .07 .20
452 Rey Ordonez .07 .20
453 Russ Ortiz .07 .20
454 Dave Burba .07 .20
455 Eric Karros .07 .20
456 Felix Martinez .07 .20
457 Tony Batista .07 .20
458 Bobby Higginson .07 .20
459 Jeff D'Amico .07 .20
460 Shane Spencer .07 .20
461 Brent Mayne .07 .20
462 Glendon Rusch .07 .20
463 Chris Gomez .07 .20
464 Jeff Shaw .07 .20
465 Damon Buford .07 .20
466 Mike DiFelice .07 .20
467 Jimmy Haynes .07 .20
468 Billy Wagner .07 .20
469 A.J. Hinch .07 .20
470 Gary DiSarcina .07 .20
471 Tom Lampkin .07 .20
472 Adam Eaton .07 .20
473 Brian Giles .07 .20
474 John Thomson .07 .20
475 Cal Eldred .07 .20
476 Ramiro Mendoza .07 .20
477 Scott Sullivan .07 .20
478 Scott Rolen .10 .30
479 Todd Ritchie .07 .20
480 Pablo Ozuna .07 .20
481 Carl Pavano .07 .20
482 Matt Morris .07 .20
483 Matt Stairs .07 .20
484 Tim Belcher .07 .20
485 Lance Berkman .07 .20
486 Brian Meadows .07 .20
487 Bob Abreu .07 .20
488 John VanderWal .07 .20
489 Donnie Sadler .07 .20
490 Damion Easley .07 .20
491 David Justice .07 .20
492 Ray Durham .07 .20
493 Todd Zeile .07 .20
494 Desi Relaford .07 .20
495 Cliff Floyd .07 .20
496 Scott Downs .07 .20
497 Barry Bonds .50 1.25
498 Jeff D'Amico .07 .20
499 Octavio Dotel .07 .20
500 Kent Mercker .07 .20
501 Craig Grebeck .07 .20
502 Roberto Hernandez .07 .20
503 Matt Williams .07 .20
504 Bruce Aven .07 .20
505 Brett Tomko .07 .20
506 Kris Benson .07 .20
507 Neifi Perez .07 .20
508 Alfonso Soriano .10 .30
509 Keith Osik .07 .20
510 Matt Franco .07 .20
511 Steve Finley .07 .20
512 Olmedo Saenz .07 .20
513 Esteban Loaiza .07 .20
514 Adam Kennedy .07 .20
515 Scott Elarton .07 .20
516 Moises Alou .07 .20
517 Bryan Rekar .07 .20
518 Darryl Hamilton .07 .20
519 Osvaldo Fernandez .07 .20
520 Kip Wells .07 .20
521 Bernie Williams .10 .30
522 Mike Darr .07 .20
523 Marlon Anderson .07 .20
524 Derrek Lee .10 .30
525 Ugueth Urbina .07 .20
526 Vinny Castilla .07 .20
527 David Wells .07 .20
528 Jason Marquis .07 .20
529 Orlando Palmeiro .07 .20
530 Carlos Perez .07 .20
531 J.T. Snow .07 .20
532 Al Leiter .07 .20
533 Jimmy Anderson .07 .20
534 Brett Laxton .07 .20
535 Butch Huskey .07 .20
536 Orlando Hernandez .07 .20
537 Magglio Ordonez .07 .20
538 Willie Blair .07 .20
539 Kevin Sefcik .07 .20
540 Chad Curtis .07 .20
541 John Halama .07 .20
542 Andy Fox .07 .20
543 Juan Guzman .07 .20
544 Frank Menechino RC .07 .20
545 Raul Mondesi .07 .20
546 Tim Salmon .10 .30
547 Ryan Rupe .07 .20
548 Jeff Reed .07 .20
549 Mike Mordecai .07 .20
550 Jeff Kent .07 .20
551 Wiki Gonzalez .07 .20
552 Kenny Rogers .07 .20
553 Kevin Young .07 .20
554 Brian Johnson .07 .20
555 Tom Goodwin .07 .20
556 Tony Clark UER .07 .20
games, 208 At-Bats
557 Mac Suzuki .07 .20
558 Brian Moehler .07 .20
559 Jim Parque .07 .20
560 Mariano Rivera .20 .50
561 Trot Nixon .07 .20
562 Mike Mussina .10 .30
563 Nelson Figueroa .07 .20
564 Alex Gonzalez .07 .20
565 Benny Agbayani .07 .20
566 Ed Sprague .07 .20
567 Scott Erickson .07 .20
568 Abraham Nunez .07 .20
569 Jerry DiPoto .07 .20
570 Sean Casey .07 .20
571 Wilton Veras .07 .20
572 Joe Mays .07 .20
573 Bill Simas .07 .20
574 Doug Glanville .07 .20
575 Scott Sauerbeck .07 .20
576 Ben Davis .07 .20
577 Jesus Sanchez .07 .20
578 Ricardo Rincon .07 .20
579 John Olerud .07 .20
580 Curt Schilling .07 .20
581 Alex Cora .07 .20
582 Pat Hentgen .07 .20
583 Javy Lopez .07 .20
584 Ben Grieve .07 .20
585 Frank Castillo .07 .20
586 Kevin Stocker .07 .20
587 Mark Sweeney .07 .20
588 Ray Lankford .07 .20
589 Turner Ward .07 .20
590 Felipe Crespo .07 .20
591 Omar Vizquel .10 .30
592 Mike Lieberthal .07 .20
593 Ken Griffey Jr. .30 .75
594 Troy O'Leary .07 .20
595 Dave Mlicki .07 .20
596 Manny Ramirez Sox .10 .30
597 Mike Lansing .07 .20
598 Rich Aurilia .07 .20
599 Russell Branyan .07 .20
600 Russ Johnson .07 .20
601 Greg Colbrunn .07 .20
602 Andruw Jones .10 .30
603 Henry Blanco .07 .20
604 Jarrod Washburn .07 .20
605 Tony Eusebio .07 .20
606 Aaron Sele .07 .20
607 Charles Nagy .07 .20
608 Ryan Klesko .07 .20
609 Dante Bichette .07 .20
610 Bill Haselman .07 .20
611 Jerry Spradlin .07 .20
612 A. Rodriguez Rangers .30 .75
613 Jose Silva .07 .20
614 Darren Oliver .07 .20
615 Pat Mahomes .07 .20
616 Roberto Alomar .10 .30
617 Edgar Renteria .07 .20
618 Jon Lieber .07 .20
619 John Rocker .07 .20
620 Miguel Tejada .07 .20
621 Mo Vaughn .07 .20
622 Jose Lima .07 .20
623 Kerry Wood .07 .20
624 Mike Timlin .07 .20
625 Wil Cordero .07 .20
626 Albert Belle .07 .20
627 Bobby Jones .07 .20
628 Doug Mirabelli .07 .20
629 Jason Tyner .07 .20
630 Andy Ashby .07 .20
631 Jose Hernandez .07 .20
632 Devon White .07 .20
633 Ruben Rivera .07 .20
634 Steve Parris .07 .20
635 David McCarty .07 .20
636 Jose Canseco .10 .30
637 Todd Walker .07 .20
638 Stan Spencer .07 .20
639 Wayne Gomes .07 .20
640 Freddy Garcia .07 .20
641 Jeremy Giambi .07 .20
642 Luis Lopez .07 .20
643 John Smoltz .10 .30
644 Kelly Stinnett .07 .20
645 Kevin Brown .07 .20
646 Wilton Guerrero .07 .20
647 Al Martin .07 .20
648 Woody Williams .07 .20
649 Brian Rose .07 .20
650 Rafael Palmeiro .10 .30
651 Pete Schourek .07 .20
652 Kevin Jarvis .07 .20
653 Mark Redman .07 .20
654 Ricky Ledee .07 .20
655 Larry Walker .07 .20
656 Paul Byrd .07 .20
657 Jason Bere .07 .20
658 Rick White .07 .20
659 Calvin Murray .07 .20
660 Greg Maddux .30 .75
661 Ron Gant .07 .20
662 Eli Marrero .07 .20
663 Graeme Lloyd .07 .20
664 Trevor Hoffman .07 .20
665 Nomar Garciaparra .30 .75
666 Glenallen Hill .07 .20
667 Matt LeCroy .07 .20
668 Justin Thompson .07 .20
669 Brady Anderson .07 .20
670 Miguel Batista .07 .20
671 Erubiel Durazo .07 .20
672 Kevin Millwood .07 .20
673 Mitch Meluskey .07 .20
674 Luis Gonzalez .07 .20
675 Edgar Martinez .10 .30
676 Robert Person .07 .20
677 Benito Santiago .07 .20
678 Todd Jones .07 .20
679 Tino Martinez .10 .30
680 Carlos Beltran .07 .20
681 Gabe White .07 .20
682 Bret Saberhagen .07 .20
683 Jeff Conine .07 .20
684 Jaret Wright .07 .20
685 Bernard Gilkey .07 .20
686 Garrett Stephenson .07 .20
687 Jamey Wright .07 .20
688 Sammy Sosa .20 .50
689 John Jaha .07 .20
690 Ramon Martinez .07 .20
691 Robert Fick .07 .20
692 Eric Milton .07 .20
693 Denny Neagle .07 .20
694 Ron Coomer .07 .20
695 John Valentin .07 .20
696 Placido Polanco .07 .20
697 Tim Hudson .07 .20
698 Marty Cordova .07 .20
699 Chad Kreuter .07 .20
700 Frank Catalanotto .07 .20
701 Tim Wakefield .07 .20
702 Jim Edmonds .07 .20
703 Michael Tucker .07 .20
704 Cristian Guzman .07 .20
705 Joey Hamilton .07 .20
706 Mike Piazza .30 .75
707 Dave Martinez .07 .20
708 Mike Hampton .07 .20
709 Bobby Bonilla .07 .20
710 Juan Pierre .07 .20
711 John Parrish .07 .20
712 Kory DeHaan .07 .20
713 Brian Tollberg .07 .20
714 Chris Truby .07 .20
715 Emil Brown .07 .20
716 Ryan Dempster .07 .20
717 Rich Garces .07 .20
718 Mike Myers .07 .20
719 Luis Ordaz .07 .20
720 Kazuhiro Sasaki .07 .20
721 Mark Quinn .07 .20
722 Ramon Ortiz .07 .20
723 Kerry Ligtenberg .07 .20
724 Rolando Arrojo .07 .20
725 Tsuyoshi Shinjo RC .20 .50
726 Ichiro Suzuki RC 5.00 12.00
727 Roy Oswalt .30 .75
Pat Strange
Jon Rauch
728 Phil Wilson RC 1.40 4.00
Jake Peavy RC
Darwin Cubillan RC UER
Sic, Peavey
729 Steve Smyth RC .08 .25
Mike Bynum
Nathan Haynes
730 Michael Cuddyer .08 .25
Joe Lawrence
Choo Freeman
731 Carlos Pena .08 .25
Larry Barnes
DeWayne Wise
732 Travis Dawkins .08 .25
Erick Almonte
Felipe Lopez
733 Alex Escobar .08 .25
Eric Valent
Brad Wilkerson
734 Toby Hall .08 .25
Rod Barajas
Jeff Goldbach
735 Jason Romano .15 .40
Marcus Giles
Pablo Ozuna
736 Dee Brown .08 .25
Jack Cust
Vernon Wells
737 David Espinosa .08 .25
Luis Montanez RC
738 Anthony Pluta RC .08 .25
Justin Wayne RC
739 Josh Axelson RC .08 .25
Carmen Cali RC
740 Shaun Boyd RC .08 .25
Chris Morris RC
741 Tommy Arko RC .08 .25
Dan Moylan RC
742 Luis Cotto RC .08 .25
Luis Escobar
743 Brandon Mims RC .08 .25
Blake Williams RC
744 Chris Russ RC .08 .25
Bryan Edwards
745 Joe Torres .08 .25
Ben Diggins
746 Hugh Quattlebaum RC 1.25 3.00
Edwin Encarnacion RC
747 Brian Bass RC .08 .25
Odannis Ayala RC
748 Jason Kaanoi .08 .25
Michael Matthews RC UER
name misspelled Mathews
749 Stuart McFarland RC .08 .25
Adam Sterrett RC
750 David Krynzel .60 1.50
Grady Sizemore
751 Keith Bucktrot .08 .25
Dane Sardinha
752 Anaheim Angels TC .07 .20
753 Ariz. Diamondbacks TC .07 .20
754 Atlanta Braves TC .07 .20
755 Baltimore Orioles TC .07 .20
756 Boston Red Sox TC .07 .20
757 Chicago Cubs TC .07 .20
758 Chicago White Sox TC .07 .20
759 Cincinnati Reds TC .07 .20
760 Cleveland Indians TC .07 .20
761 Colorado Rockies TC .07 .20
762 Detroit Tigers TC .07 .20
763 Florida Marlins TC .07 .20
764 Houston Astros TC .07 .20
765 K.C. Royals TC .07 .20
766 L.A. Dodgers TC .07 .20
767 Milw. Brewers TC .07 .20
768 Minnesota Twins TC .07 .20
769 Montreal Expos TC .07 .20
770 New York Mets TC .07 .20
771 New York Yankees TC .40 1.00
772 Oakland Athletics TC .07 .20
773 Phil. Phillies TC .07 .20
774 Pittsburgh Pirates TC .07 .20
775 San Diego Padres TC .07 .20
776 San Francisco Giants TC .07 .20
777 Seattle Mariners TC .07 .20
778 St. Louis Cardinals TC .07 .20
779 T.B. Devil Rays TC .07 .20
780 Texas Rangers TC .07 .20
781 Toronto Blue Jays TC .07 .20
782 Bucky Dent GM .07 .20
783 Jackie Robinson GM .20 .50
784 Roberto Clemente GM .25 .60
785 Nolan Ryan GM .30 .75
786 Kerry Wood GM .07 .20
787 Rickey Henderson GM .07 .20
788 Lou Brock GM .10 .30
789 David Wells GM .07 .20
790 Andruw Jones GM .07 .20
791 Carlton Fisk GM .07 .20
TK Bo Jackson 60.00 120.00
Deion Sanders Bat
NNO Bobby Thomson 30.00 60.00
Ralph Branca
1991 Bowman Autograph

2001 Topps Employee

Topps created as a special bonus for their employees, a "parallel" factory set of the 2001 Topps set with a special employee logo embossed on the card. It is believed approximately 150 of these sets were produced.

*STARS: 6X TO 15X BASIC CARDS
CARD NO.7 DOES NOT EXIST
726 Ichiro Suzuki 60.00 150.00

2001 Topps Gold

Randomly inserted into first series packs at a rate of 1:17 Hobby/Retail and 1:4 HTA and second series packs at a rate of 1:14 Hobby/Retail and 1:3 HTA, this 790-card set is a complete parallel of the 2001 Topps base set. These cards were produced with a special gold-foil border on front and were individually serial numbered to 2001 on back. Please note that card number 7 does not exist.

*STARS: 10X TO 25X BASIC CARDS
*PROSPECTS 352-376/725/751: 4X TO 10X
*ROOKIES 352-376/725-751: 4X TO 10X

2001 Topps Home Team Advantage

This factory-sealed 790-card set was issued exclusively to Topps network of Home Team Advantage baseball card shops. The sets were packaged in attractive gold foil boxes and each card features a distinctive "HTA" foil stamp on front.

COMP.HTA.GOLD SET (790) 60.00 120.00
*HTA: .75X TO 2X BASIC CARDS

2001 Topps Limited

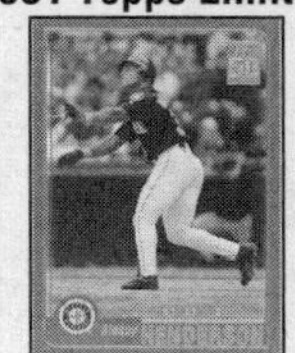

These attractive cards parallel the basic 2001 Topps set. The product was distributed exclusively in factory set format. Each set contained the 790-card basic set plus five Topps Archives Reserve Future Rookie Reprints chrome inserts wrapped together in a plastic cello pack. The sets were distributed through hobby dealers in attractive wood boxes and carried a suggested retail price of $173. Each Topps Limited card was printed on 20 pt. stock paper featuring glossy fronts and backs and a "Limited Edition" gold foil logo on front. Though the cards lack individual serial-numbering, Topps announced production at 3,805 sets. Each set states that total on the bottom of the wooden box.

COMP.FACT.SET (790) 60.00 150.00
*STARS: 1.5X TO 4X BASIC CARDS
*ROOKIES: 1.5X TO 4X BASIC CARDS

2001 Topps A Look Ahead

Randomly inserted into packs at 1:25 Hobby/Retail and 1:5 HTA, this 10-card insert takes a look a players that are on their way to Cooperstown. Card backs carry a "LA" prefix.

COMPLETE SET (10) 12.50 30.00
LA1 Vladimir Guerrero 1.00 2.50
LA2 Derek Jeter 2.50 6.00
LA3 Todd Helton .60 1.50

LA4 Alex Rodriguez	1.50	4.00
LA5 Ken Griffey Jr.	1.50	4.00
LA6 Nomar Garciaparra	1.50	4.00
LA7 Chipper Jones	1.00	2.50
LA8 Ivan Rodriguez	.60	1.50
LA9 Pedro Martinez	.60	1.50
LA10 Rick Ankiel	.40	1.00

2001 Topps A Tradition Continues

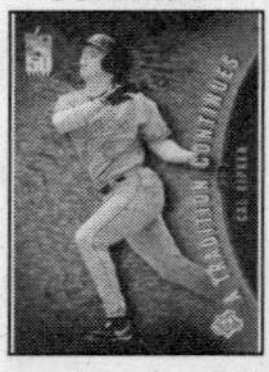

Randomly inserted into packs at 1:17 Hobby/Retail and 1:5 HTA, this 30-card insert features players that look to carry the tradition of Major League Baseball well into the 21st century. Card backs carry a "TRC" prefix.

COMPLETE SET (30)	50.00	100.00
TRC1 Chipper Jones	1.25	3.00
TRC2 Cal Ripken	4.00	10.00
TRC3 Mike Piazza	2.00	5.00
TRC4 Ken Griffey Jr.	2.00	5.00
TRC5 Randy Johnson	1.25	3.00
TRC6 Derek Jeter	3.00	8.00
TRC7 Scott Rolen	.75	2.00
TRC8 Nomar Garciaparra	2.00	5.00
TRC9 Roberto Alomar	.75	2.00
TRC10 Greg Maddux	2.00	5.00
TRC11 Ivan Rodriguez	.75	2.00
TRC12 Jeff Bagwell	.75	2.00
TRC13 Alex Rodriguez	2.00	5.00
TRC14 Pedro Martinez	.75	2.00
TRC15 Sammy Sosa	1.25	3.00
TRC16 Jim Edmonds	.50	1.25
TRC17 Mo Vaughn	.50	1.25
TRC18 Barry Bonds	3.00	8.00
TRC19 Larry Walker	.50	1.25
TRC20 Mark McGwire	3.00	8.00
TRC21 Vladimir Guerrero	1.25	3.00
TRC22 Andruw Jones	.75	2.00
TRC23 Todd Helton	.75	2.00
TRC24 Kevin Brown	.50	1.25
TRC25 Tony Gwynn	1.50	4.00
TRC26 Manny Ramirez	.75	2.00
TRC27 Roger Clemens	2.50	6.00
TRC28 Frank Thomas	1.25	3.00
TRC29 Shawn Green	.50	1.25
TRC30 Jim Thome	.75	2.00

2001 Topps Base Hit Autograph Relics

Inserted in series two packs at a rate of one in 1,1462 hobby or retail packs and one in 325 HTA packs, these 28 cards features managers along with a game-used base piece and an autograph.

BH1 Mike Scioscia	40.00	80.00
BH2 Larry Dierker	20.00	50.00
BH3 Art Howe	40.00	80.00
BH4 Jim Fregosi	20.00	50.00
BH5 Bobby Cox	50.00	100.00
BH6 Davey Lopes	20.00	50.00
BH7 Tony LaRussa	40.00	80.00
BH8 Don Baylor	40.00	80.00
BH9 Larry Rothschild	20.00	50.00
BH10 Buck Showalter	20.00	50.00
BH11 Davey Johnson	20.00	50.00
BH12 Felipe Alou	40.00	80.00
BH13 Charlie Manuel	30.00	60.00
BH14 Lou Piniella	40.00	80.00
BH15 John Boles	20.00	50.00
BH16 Bobby Valentine	40.00	80.00
BH17 Mike Hargrove	40.00	80.00
BH18 Bruce Bochy	20.00	50.00
BH19 Terry Francona	100.00	200.00
BH20 Gene Lamont	20.00	50.00
BH21 Johnny Oates	50.00	100.00
BH22 Jimy Williams	20.00	50.00
BH23 Jack McKeon	40.00	80.00
BH24 Buddy Bell	40.00	80.00
BH25 Tony Muser	20.00	50.00
BH26 Phil Garner	40.00	80.00
BH27 Tom Kelly	20.00	50.00
BH28 Jerry Manuel	20.00	50.00

2001 Topps Before There Was Topps

Issued in series two packs at a rate of one in 25 hobby/retail packs and one in five HTA packs; these 10 cards feature superstars who concluded their career before Topps started their dominance of the card market.

COMPLETE SET (10)	15.00	40.00
BT1 Lou Gehrig	2.50	6.00
BT2 Babe Ruth	4.00	10.00
BT3 Cy Young	1.25	3.00
BT4 Walter Johnson	1.25	3.00
BT5 Ty Cobb	2.00	5.00
BT6 Rogers Hornsby	1.25	3.00
BT7 Honus Wagner	1.25	3.00
BT8 Christy Mathewson	1.25	3.00
BT9 Grover Alexander	1.25	3.00
BT10 Joe DiMaggio	2.50	6.00

2001 Topps Combos

Randomly inserted into packs at a rate of 1:12 Hobby/Retail and 1:4 HTA, this 20-card insert set pairs up players that have put up similar statistics throughout their carrers. Card backs carry a "TC" prefix. Instead of having photographs, these cards feature drawings of the featured players.

COMPLETE SET (20)	25.00	60.00
COMPLETE SERIES 1 (10)	12.50	30.00
COMPLETE SERIES 2 (10)	12.50	30.00
TC1 Derek Jeter	2.00	5.00
Yogi Berra		
Whitey Ford		
Don Mattingly		
Reggie Jackson		
TC2 Chipper Jones	.60	1.50
Mike Schmidt		
TC3 Brooks Robinson	1.50	4.00
Cal Ripken		
TC4 Bob Gibson	.60	1.50
Pedro Martinez		
TC5 Ivan Rodriguez	.60	1.50
Johnny Bench		
TC6 Ernie Banks	1.00	2.50
Alex Rodriguez		
TC7 Joe Morgan	.60	1.50
Ken Griffey Jr.		
Barry Larkin		
Johnny Bench		
TC8 Vladmir Guerrero	.60	1.50
Roberto Clemente		
TC9 Ken Griffey Jr.	.75	2.00
Hank Aaron		
TC10 Casey Stengel MG	.60	1.50
Joe Torre MG		
TC11 Kevin Brown	1.25	3.00
Sandy Koufax		
Don Drysdale UER		
Card states the Dodgers swept the 1965 World Series		
They won the Series in 7 games		
TC12 Mark McGwire	1.50	4.00
Sammy Sosa		
Roger Maris		
Babe Ruth		
TC13 Ted Williams	1.25	3.00
Carl Yastrzemski		
Nomar Garciaparra		
TC14 Greg Maddux	1.00	2.50
Roger Clemens		
Cy Young		
TC15 Tony Gwynn	1.25	3.00
Ted Williams		
TC16 Cal Ripken	2.00	5.00
Lou Gehrig		
TC17 Sandy Koufax	2.00	5.00
Randy Johnson		
Warren Spahn		
Steve Carlton		
TC18 Mike Piazza	.75	2.00
Josh Gibson		
TC19 Barry Bonds	1.50	4.00
Willie Mays		
TC20 Jackie Robinson	.60	1.50
Larry Doby		

2001 Topps Golden Anniversary

Randomly inserted into packs at 1:10 Hobby/Retail and 1:1 HTA, this 50-card insert celibrates Topp's 50th Anniversary by taking a look at some of the all-time greats. Card backs carry a "GA" prefix.

COMPLETE SET (50)	40.00	80.00
GA1 Hank Aaron	2.00	5.00
GA2 Ernie Banks	1.00	2.50
GA3 Mike Schmidt	2.00	5.00
GA4 Willie Mays	2.00	5.00
GA5 Johnny Bench	1.00	2.50
GA6 Tom Seaver	.60	1.50
GA7 Frank Robinson	.60	1.50
GA8 Sandy Koufax	3.00	8.00
GA9 Bob Gibson	.60	1.50
GA10 Ted Williams	2.00	5.00
GA11 Cal Ripken	3.00	8.00
GA12 Tony Gwynn	1.25	3.00
GA13 Mark McGwire	2.50	6.00
GA14 Ken Griffey Jr.	1.50	4.00
GA15 Greg Maddux	1.50	4.00
GA16 Roger Clemens	2.00	5.00
GA17 Barry Bonds	2.50	6.00
GA18 Rickey Henderson	1.00	2.50
GA19 Mike Piazza	1.50	4.00
GA20 Jose Canseco	.60	1.50
GA21 Derek Jeter	2.50	6.00
GA22 N.Garciaparra UER	1.50	4.00
Card has incorrect bat and throw information		
Garciaparra bats and throws righthanded		
GA23 Alex Rodriguez	1.50	4.00
GA24 Sammy Sosa	1.00	2.50
GA25 Ivan Rodriguez	.60	1.50
GA26 Vladimir Guerrero	1.00	2.50
GA27 Chipper Jones	1.00	2.50
GA28 Jeff Bagwell	.60	1.50
GA29 Pedro Martinez	.60	1.50
GA30 Randy Johnson	1.00	2.50
GA31 Pat Burrell	.40	1.00
GA32 Josh Hamilton	.75	2.00
GA33 Ryan Anderson	.40	1.00
GA34 Corey Patterson	.40	1.00
GA35 Eric Munson	.40	1.00
GA36 Sean Burroughs	.40	1.00
GA37 C.C. Sabathia	.40	1.00
GA38 Chin-Feng Chen	.40	1.00
GA39 Barry Zito	.60	1.50
GA40 Adrian Gonzalez	.40	1.00
GA41 Mark McGwire	2.50	6.00
GA42 Nomar Garciaparra	1.50	4.00
GA43 Todd Helton	.60	1.50
GA44 Matt Williams	.40	1.00
GA45 Troy Glaus	.40	1.00
GA46 Geoff Jenkins	.40	1.00
GA47 Frank Thomas	1.00	2.50
GA48 Mo Vaughn	.40	1.00
GA49 Barry Larkin	.60	1.50
GA50 J.D. Drew	.40	1.00

2001 Topps Golden Anniversary Autographs

Randomly inserted into packs, this 98-card insert features authentic autographs of both modern day and former greats. Card backs carry a "GAA" prefix followed by the players initials. Please note that the Andy Pafko, Lou Brock, Rafael Furcal and Todd Zeile cards all packed out in series one packs as exchange cards with a redemption deadline of November 30th, 2001. In addition, Carlos Silva, Eddy Furniss, Phil Merrell and Carlos Silva packed out as exchange cards in series two packs with a redemption deadline of April 30th, 2003.

SER.1 GROUP A 1:22866 H/R, 1:5056 HTA
SER.2 GROUP A ODDS 1: 10,583 H/R, 1:2,355 HTA
SER.1 GROUP B 1:3054 H/R, 1:678 HTA
SER.2 GROUP B ODDS 1:11,781 H/R, 1:2,612 HTA
SER.1 GROUP C 1:1431 H/R, 1:318 HTA
SER.2 GROUP C 1:4236 H/R, 1:942 HTA
SER.1 GROUP D ODDS 1:18339 H/R, 1:4095 HTA
SER.2 GROUP D 1:981 H/R, 1:218 HTA
SER.1 GROUP E ODDS 1:13737 H/R, 1:3,056 HTA
SER.2 GROUP E 1:14157 H/R, 1:3139 HTA
SER.1 GROUP F 1:11015 H/R, 1:2438 HTA
SER.2 GROUP F 1:3532 H/R, 1:785 HTA
SER.1 GROUP G 1:625 H/R, 1:139 HTA
SER.2 GROUP G 1:3532 H/R, 1:785 HTA
SER.2 GROUP H 1:2,037 H/R, 1:452 HTA
SER.2 GROUP I 1:481 H/R, 1:107 HTA

GAAAG A.Gonzalez G	10.00	25.00
GAAAH Aaron Herr I2	4.00	10.00
GAAAJ A. Johnson G1-I2	4.00	10.00
GAAAO Augie Ojeda B2	75.00	150.00
GAAAP Andy Pafko C1	15.00	40.00
GAABB Barry Bonds B2	150.00	250.00
GAABE Brian Esposito I2	4.00	10.00
GAABG Bob Gibson C2	30.00	60.00
GAABK Bobby Kielty I2	4.00	10.00
GAABO Ben Oglivie D2	4.00	10.00
GAABR B.Robinson B	30.00	60.00
GAABT Brian Tollberg I2	4.00	10.00
GAACC Chris Clapinski I2	4.00	10.00
GAACD Chad Durbin I2	4.00	10.00
GAACE Carl Erskine D2	6.00	15.00
GAACJ Chipper Jones B1	60.00	120.00
GAACL Colby Lewis I2	4.00	10.00
GAACR Chris Richard I2	4.00	10.00
GAACS Carlos Silva I2	4.00	10.00
GAACY C. Yastrzemski C2	60.00	120.00
GAADA Dick Allen C1	20.00	50.00
GAADA Denny Abreu I2	4.00	10.00
GAADG Dick Groat D2	10.00	25.00
GAADT D. Thompson I2	4.00	10.00
GAAEB Ernie Banks B1	50.00	100.00
GAAEB Eric Byrnes I2	10.00	25.00
GAAEF Eddy Furniss I2	4.00	10.00
GAAEM Eric Munson G2	4.00	10.00
GAAER E. Ramirez I2	4.00	10.00
GAAGB George Bell D2	4.00	10.00
GAAGG G. Guzman I2	4.00	10.00
GAAGM G. Matthews Jr. D2	4.00	10.00
GAAGS G. Sizemore I2	40.00	80.00
GAAGT G.Templeton C	6.00	15.00
GAAHA Hank Aaron B1	250.00	350.00
GAAJB Johnny Bench C2	50.00	100.00
GAAJC Jorge Cantu I2	6.00	15.00
GAAJL John Lackey I2	10.00	25.00
GAAJM J. Marquis G1	6.00	15.00
GAAJR Joe Rudi C1	6.00	15.00
GAAJR Juan Rincon I2	4.00	10.00
GAAJS Juan Salas I2	4.00	10.00
GAAJV Jose Vidro F1	4.00	10.00
GAAJW Justin Wayne H2	4.00	10.00
GAAKG Kevin Gregg B2	6.00	15.00
GAAKH Ken Holtzman D2	4.00	10.00
GAAKT Kent Tekulve D2	4.00	10.00
GAALB Lou Brock B1	30.00	60.00
GAALM L. Montanez H2	10.00	25.00
GAALR Luis Rivas I2	4.00	10.00
GAAMB M. Bradley G2	6.00	15.00
GAAMC Mike Cuellar C1	6.00	15.00
GAAMG M. Glendenning I2	4.00	10.00
GAAML Matt Lawton F2	4.00	10.00
GAAML Mike Lamb G1	4.00	10.00
GAAMO M.Ordonez B	20.00	50.00
GAAMS Mike Schmidt B1	60.00	120.00
GAAMS Mike Sweeney F2	6.00	15.00
GAAMS Mike Stodolka I2	4.00	10.00
GAAMW M.Wheatland G	4.00	10.00
GAAMW M. Wenner I2	4.00	10.00
GAANG Nick Green I2	4.00	10.00
GAANJ Neil Jenkins I2	4.00	10.00
GAANR Nolan Ryan A2	200.00	400.00
GAAPB Pat Burrell G1	6.00	15.00
GAAPM Phil Merrell I2	4.00	10.00
GAARA Rick Ankiel D1	10.00	25.00
GAARB R. Baldelli G1-I2	10.00	25.00
GAARC Rod Carew B1	30.00	60.00
GAARF Rafael Furcal G1	6.00	15.00
GAARJ R. Jackson A2	125.00	200.00
GAARS Ron Swoboda C1	10.00	25.00
GAASH Scott Heard G1	4.00	10.00
GAASK Sandy Koufax A1	800.00	950.00
GAASM Stan Musial A2	175.00	300.00
GAASR Scott Rolen F2	10.00	25.00
GAAST Scott Thorman I2	4.00	10.00
GAATA Tony Alvarez I2	4.00	10.00
GAATH Todd Helton B2	40.00	80.00
GAATJ T. Johnson I2	4.00	10.00
GAATS Tom Seaver A2	100.00	175.00
GAAVL Vernon Law C1	6.00	15.00
GAAWD Willie Davis D2	4.00	10.00
GAAWF Whitey Ford C2	40.00	80.00
GAAWH W.Hernandez C	6.00	15.00
GAAWM Willie Mays A1	350.00	450.00
GAAWW Wilbur Wood D2	4.00	10.00
GAAYB Yogi Berra B1	40.00	80.00
GAAYH Yamid Haad I2	4.00	10.00
GAAYT Y. Torrealba I2	15.00	40.00
GAACCS Corey Smith I2	4.00	10.00
GAAGHB George Brett A2	175.00	300.00
GAAJDD J.D. Drew E2	10.00	25.00
GAAMAB Mike Bynum I2	4.00	10.00
GAAMFL M. Lockwood I2	4.00	10.00
GAAMJS M. Stodolka G1	4.00	10.00
GAAMJW M. Wheatland I2	4.00	10.00
GAATDLR T. De la Rosa I2	4.00	10.00

2001 Topps Hit Parade Bat Relics

Issued in retail packs at odds of one in 2,607 these six cards feature players who have achieved major career milestones along with a piece of memorabilia.

HP1 Reggie Jackson	40.00	80.00
HP2 Dave Winfield	40.00	80.00
HP3 Eddie Murray	40.00	80.00
HP4 Rickey Henderson	40.00	80.00
HP5 Robin Yount	40.00	80.00
HP6 Carl Yastrzemski	50.00	100.00

2001 Topps King of Kings Relics

Randomly inserted into packs at 1:2056 Hobby/Retail and 1:457 HTA, this four-card insert features game-used memorabilia from Nolan Ryan, Rickey Henderson, and Hank Aaron. Please note that a special fourth card containing game-used memorabila of all three were inserted into HTA packs at 1:8903. Card backs carry a "KKG" prefix.

KKR1 Hank Aaron	40.00	80.00
KKR2 Nolan Ryan	40.00	80.00
KKR3 Rickey Henderson	15.00	40.00
KKR4 Mark McGwire B	50.00	100.00
KKR5 Bob Gibson A	15.00	40.00
KKR6 Nolan Ryan B	40.00	80.00
KKGE Hank Aaron	175.00	300.00
Nolan Ryan		
Rickey Henderson		
KKLE2 Mark Mcgwire	300.00	500.00
Bob Gibson		
Nolan Ryan		

2001 Topps Noteworthy

Inserted in hobby/retail packs at a rate of one in eight and HTA packs at a rate of one per pack; this 50-card set feature a mix of active and retired players who achieved significant feats during their career.

COMPLETE SET (50)	40.00	80.00
TN1 Mark McGwire	1.50	4.00
TN2 Derek Jeter	1.50	4.00
TN3 Sammy Sosa	.60	1.50
TN4 Todd Helton	.40	1.00
TN5 Alex Rodriguez	1.00	2.50
TN6 Chipper Jones	.60	1.50
TN7 Barry Bonds	1.50	4.00
TN8 Ken Griffey Jr.	1.00	2.50
TN9 Nomar Garciaparra	1.00	2.50
TN10 Frank Thomas	.60	1.50
TN11 Randy Johnson	.60	1.50
TN12 Cal Ripken	2.00	5.00
TN13 Mike Piazza	1.00	2.50
TN14 Ivan Rodriguez	.40	1.00
TN15 Jeff Bagwell	.40	1.00
TN16 Vladimir Guerrero	.60	1.50
TN17 Greg Maddux	1.00	2.50
TN18 Tony Gwynn	.75	2.00
TN19 Larry Walker	.40	1.00
TN20 Juan Gonzalez	.40	1.00
TN21 Scott Rolen	.40	1.00
TN22 Jason Giambi	.40	1.00
TN23 Jeff Kent	.40	1.00
TN24 Pat Burrell	.40	1.00
TN25 Pedro Martinez	.40	1.00
TN26 Willie Mays	1.50	4.00
TN27 Whitey Ford	.40	1.00
TN28 Jackie Robinson	.60	1.50
TN29 Ted Williams UER	1.50	4.00
Card has wrong year for his last at-bat		
TN30 Babe Ruth	3.00	8.00
TN31 Warren Spahn	.40	1.00
TN32 Nolan Ryan	2.50	6.00
TN33 Yogi Berra	.60	1.50
TN34 Mike Schmidt	1.50	4.00
TN35 Steve Carlton	.40	1.00
TN36 Brooks Robinson	.40	1.00
TN37 Bob Gibson	.40	1.00
TN38 Reggie Jackson	.40	1.00
TN39 Johnny Bench	.60	1.50
TN40 Ernie Banks	.60	1.50
TN41 Eddie Mathews	.60	1.50
TN42 Don Mattingly	1.50	4.00
TN43 Duke Snider	.40	1.00
TN44 Hank Aaron	1.50	4.00
TN45 Roberto Clemente	2.00	5.00
TN46 Harmon Killebrew	.60	1.50
TN47 Frank Robinson	.40	1.00
TN48 Stan Musial	1.25	3.00
TN49 Lou Brock	.40	1.00
TN50 Joe Morgan	.40	1.00

2001 Topps Originals Relics

Randomly inserted into packs at different rates depening which series these cards were inserted in, this ten-card insert set features game-used jersey cards of players like Roberto Clemente and Carl Yastrzemski. Please note that the Willie Mays card is actually a game-used jacket.

SER.1 STATED ODDS 1:1172 H/R, 1:260 HTA
SER.2 STATED ODDS 1:1023 H/R, 1:227 HTA

1 Roberto Clemente 55	50.00	100.00
2 Carl Yastrzemski 60	15.00	40.00
3 Mike Schmidt 73	15.00	40.00
4 Wade Boggs 83	10.00	25.00
5 Chipper Jones 91	10.00	25.00
6 Willie Mays 52	20.00	50.00
7 Lou Brock 62	10.00	25.00
8 Dave Parker 74	6.00	15.00
9 Barry Bonds 86	20.00	50.00
10 Alex Rodriguez 98	10.00	25.00

2001 Topps Team Topps Legends Autographs

These signed cards were inserted into various 2001-2003 Topps products. As these cards were inserted into different products and some were exchange cards. Most players in this set were featured on reprinted versions of their classic Topps "rookie" and "final" cards. The checklist was originally comprised of cards TT1-TT50 (with each player having an R and F suffix (i.e. Willie Mays is featured on TT1F with his 1973 card and TT1R with his 1952 card). In late 2002 and throughout 2003, additional players were added to the set with checklist numbering outside of the TT1-TT50 schematic. The numbering for these late additions was based on player's initials (i.e. Lou Brock's card is TT-LB) and only reprints of their rookie-year cards were produced.

RANDOM INSERTS IN 01-03 TOPPS BRANDS
TOPPS AMER.PIE EXCH.DEADLINE 11/01/03
TOPPS GALLERY EXCH.DEADLINE 06/30/03
02 TOPPS EXCH.DEADLINE 12/01/03

TT1F Willie Mays 73	100.00	200.00
T'02-TA'02/A		
TT1R Willie Mays 52	125.00	200.00
AP		
TT2F Hank Aaron 76		
TT3F Stan Musial 63		
TT3R Stan Musial 58 AS	30.00	60.00
TT6F Whitey Ford 67	20.00	50.00
TT/A-T10'02		
TT6R Whitey Ford 53	30.00	60.00
T'02/F-TA'02/B		
TT7R Nolan Ryan 68	125.00	200.00
T206'02/A-TA'02/A		
TT8F Carl Yastrzemski 83	20.00	50.00
TT8R Carl Yastrzemski 60	60.00	120.00
AP-T'02/A-TA'02/B-T10'02		
TT9R Brooks Robinson 57	30.00	60.00
TT10F Frank Robinson 75	10.00	25.00
BH5-TH'02/2		
TT10R Frank Robinson 57	20.00	50.00
GL-T'02/A-TA'02/B		
TT11R Tom Seaver 67	125.00	200.00
TA'02/A		
TT12R Duke Snider 52	40.00	80.00
TT13F Warren Spahn 65	15.00	40.00
BH1-TT-T'02/B-TA'02/B		
TT13R Warren Spahn 52	30.00	60.00
AP-BB/A-TT/C		
TT14F Johnny Bench 83	30.00	60.00
TT14R Johnny Bench 68	60.00	120.00
AP		
TT15R Reggie Jackson 69	60.00	120.00
AP-TA'02/A		
TT16R Al Kaline 54	30.00	60.00
TT17F Willie McCovey 80		
TT18F Bob Gibson 75	10.00	25.00
AP'02		
TT18R Bob Gibson 59	20.00	50.00
AP-BB/A-T'02/A		
TT19R Mike Schmidt 73	60.00	120.00
TT20F Harmon Killebrew 75		
TT20R Harmon Killebrew 55	30.00	60.00
TT21R Bob Feller 52 BH2	10.00	25.00
TT23F Gil McDougald 60	6.00	15.00
GL-TA'02/B		
TT23R Gil McDougald 52	6.00	15.00
BB/B		
TT24F Jimmy Piersall 67		
TT24R Jimmy Piersall 56		
TT25F Luis Tiant 83	6.00	15.00
GL EXCH		
TT25R Luis Tiant 65	6.00	15.00
AP-BB/B-'02 TA/B		
TT26F Minnie Minoso 64		
TT27F Andy Pafko 59	6.00	15.00
GL		
TT27R Andy Pafko 52	10.00	25.00
BB/B-BH/3-GL		
TT28F Herb Score 62	6.00	15.00
BB/B-GL-TT/B		
TT28R Herb Score 56	6.00	15.00
BB/B-TA'02/B		
TT29F Bill Skowron 67	6.00	15.00
TT29R Bill Skowron 54	6.00	15.00
AP-BB/A-T206'02/C		
TT30F Maury Wills 72		
TT31F Clete Boyer 71	6.00	15.00
TA'02/B		
TT31R Clete Boyer 57	6.00	15.00
AP-BB/B		
TT32F Hank Bauer 61		
TT33F Vida Blue 87	6.00	15.00
T'02/C/TR		
TT33R Vida Blue 70	6.00	15.00
AP-T206'02/B-TH'02/4		
TT34R Don Larsen 56	10.00	25.00
TT35F Joe Pepitone 73	6.00	15.00
TT/A		
TT35R Joe Pepitone 62	10.00	25.00
AP		
TT36F Enos Slaughter 59	10.00	25.00
BH4-TT/A		
TT36R Enos Slaughter 52	15.00	40.00
TAR'02		
TT37F Tug McGraw 85	10.00	25.00
BB/B		
TT37R Tug McGraw 65	15.00	40.00
AP-BB/B-TT/B		
TT38R Fergie Jenkins 66	6.00	15.00
TT40R Gaylord Perry 62	6.00	15.00
TT43F Bobby Thomson 60	6.00	15.00
TT-TH'02/3		
TT43R Bobby Thomson 52	6.00	15.00
AP-TT/D-T'02/B-T10'02		
TT46F Robin Roberts 66 T'02/E	10.00	25.00
TT46R Robin Roberts 52	15.00	40.00
TT47F Frank Howard 73	6.00	15.00
TT/A-TH'02/1		
TT47R Frank Howard 60	6.00	15.00
AP-T'02/D-TA'02/B		
TT48F Bobby Richardson 66	6.00	15.00
TT/A-T'02/B-T10'02		
TT48R Bobby Richardson 57	10.00	25.00
AP-BB/B		
TT49R Tony Kubek 57	50.00	100.00
AP-TA/B		
TT50F Mickey Lolich 80	6.00	15.00
TT/A		
TT50R Mickey Lolich 64	6.00	15.00
AP-T'02/C-TA'02/B-TH'02/1		
TT51RF Ralph Branca 52	6.00	15.00
TT/D-T'02/E		
TTGC Gary Carter 75	6.00	15.00
TTGG Goose Gossage 73	10.00	25.00
TAR'02		
TTGN Craig Nettles 69	6.00	15.00
2 'TAR		
TTJB Jim Bunning 65	10.00	25.00
TTJM Joe Morgan 65	15.00	40.00
TTJP Jim Palmer 66	15.00	40.00
TAR '02		
TTJS Johnny Sain 52	10.00	25.00
TTLA Luis Aparicio 56	10.00	25.00
TTLB Lou Brock 62	20.00	50.00

TTPB Paul Blair 65 4.00 10.00
TTRY Robin Yount 75 40.00 80.00
TTVL Vern Law 52 6.00 15.00

2001 Topps Through the Years Reprints

Randomly inserted into packs at 1:8 Hobby/Retail and 1:1 HTA, this 50-card set takes a look at some of the best players to every make it onto a Topps trading card.

COMPLETE SET (50) 60.00 120.00
1 Yogi Berra '57 1.25 3.00
2 Roy Campanella '56 1.25 3.00
3 Willie Mays '53 2.00 5.00
4 Andy Pafko '52 1.25 3.00
5 Jackie Robinson '52 1.25 3.00
6 Stan Musial '59 1.50 4.00
7 Duke Snider '56 1.25 3.00
8 Warren Spahn '56 1.25 3.00
9 Ted Williams '54 UER 3.00 8.00
Williams is spelled William
Also wrong birthdate
10 Eddie Mathews '55 1.25 3.00
11 Willie McCovey '60 1.25 3.00
12 Frank Robinson '69 1.25 3.00
13 Ernie Banks '66 1.25 3.00
14 Hank Aaron '65 2.00 5.00
15 Sandy Koufax '61 2.50 6.00
16 Bob Gibson '68 1.25 3.00
17 Harmon Killebrew '67 1.25 3.00
18 Whitey Ford '64 1.25 3.00
19 Roberto Clemente '63 3.00 8.00
20 Juan Marichal '62 1.25 3.00
21 Johnny Bench '70 1.25 3.00
22 Willie Stargell '73 1.25 3.00
23 Joe Morgan '74 1.25 3.00
24 Carl Yastrzemski '71 1.50 4.00
25 Reggie Jackson '76 1.25 3.00
26 Tom Seaver '78 1.25 3.00
27 Steve Carlton '77 1.25 3.00
28 Jim Palmer 79 1.25 3.00
29 Rod Carew '72 1.25 3.00
30 George Brett '75 3.00 8.00
31 Roger Clemens '85 2.50 6.00
32 Don Mattingly '84 3.00 8.00
33 Ryne Sandberg '89 2.00 5.00
34 Mike Schmidt '81 2.00 5.00
35 Cal Ripken '82 4.00 10.00
36 Tony Gwynn '83 1.50 4.00
37 Ozzie Smith '87 2.00 5.00
38 Wade Boggs '88 1.25 3.00
39 Nolan Ryan '80 2.50 6.00
40 Robin Yount '86 1.25 3.00
41 Mark McGwire '99 2.50 6.00
42 Ken Griffey Jr. '92 1.50 4.00
43 Sammy Sosa '90 1.25 3.00
44 Alex Rodriguez '98 1.50 4.00
45 Barry Bonds '94 2.50 6.00
46 Mike Piazza '95 1.50 4.00
47 Chipper Jones '91 1.25 3.00
48 Greg Maddux '96 1.50 4.00
49 Nomar Garciaparra '97 1.50 4.00
50 Derek Jeter '93 3.00 8.00

2001 Topps What Could Have Been

Inserted at a rate of one in 25 hobby/retail packs or one in five HTA packs, these 10 cards feature stars of the Negro leagues who never got to play in the majors while they were at their peak.

COMPLETE SET (10) 10.00 25.00
WCB1 Josh Gibson 2.00 5.00
WCB2 Satchel Paige 1.25 3.00
WCB3 Buck Leonard .75 2.00
WCB4 James Bell 1.25 3.00
WCB5 Rube Foster 1.25 3.00
WCB6 Martin DiHigo .75 2.00
WCB7 William Johnson .75 2.00
WCB8 Mule Suttles .75 2.00
WCB9 Ray Dandridge .75 2.00
WCB10 John Lloyd .75 2.00

2001 Topps Traded

The 2001 Topps Traded product was released in October 2001, and features a 265-card base set. The 2001 Topps Traded and the 2001 Topps Chrome Traded were combined and sold together. Each pack contained eight 2001 Topps Traded and two 2001 Topps Chrome Traded cards for a total of ten cards in each pack. The 265-card set is broken down as follows: 99 cards highlighting player deals made during the 2000 off-season and 2001 season; 60 future stars who have never appeared alone on a Topps card; 55 rookies who make their premiere on a Topps card; six managers (T145-T150) who've either switched teams or were newly hired for the 2001 season and 45 traded repints (T100 through T144) of rookie cards featured in past Topps Traded sets. The packs carried a 3.00 per pack SRP and came 24 packs to a box.

COMPLETE SET (265) 100.00 175.00
COMMON (T1-T99/T145-T265) .15 .40
COMMON (100-144) .40 1.00
T1 Sandy Alomar Jr. .15 .40
T2 Kevin Appier .20 .50
T3 Brad Ausmus .20 .50
T4 Derek Bell .15 .40
T5 Bret Boone .20 .50
T6 Rico Brogna .15 .40
T7 Ellis Burks .20 .50
T8 Ken Caminiti .20 .50
T9 Roger Cedeno .15 .40
T10 Royce Clayton .15 .40
T11 Enrique Wilson .15 .40
T12 Rheal Cormier .15 .40
T13 Eric Davis .20 .50
T14 Shawon Dunston .15 .40
T15 Andres Galarraga .20 .50
T16 Tom Gordon .15 .40
T17 Mark Grace .30 .75
T18 Jeffrey Hammonds .15 .40
T19 Dustin Hermanson .15 .40
T20 Quinton McCracken .15 .40
T21 Todd Hundley .15 .40
T22 Charles Johnson .20 .50
T23 Marquis Grissom .20 .50
T24 Jose Mesa .15 .40
T25 Brian Boehringer .15 .40
T26 John Rocker .20 .50
T27 Jeff Frye .15 .40
T28 Reggie Sanders .20 .50
T29 David Segui .15 .40
T30 Mike Sirotka .15 .40
T31 Fernando Tatis .15 .40
T32 Steve Trachsel .15 .40
T33 Ismael Valdes .15 .40
T34 Randy Velarde .15 .40
T35 Ryan Kohlmeier .15 .40
T36 Mike Bordick .20 .50
T37 Kent Bottenfield .15 .40
T38 Pat Rapp .15 .40
T39 Jeff Nelson .15 .40
T40 Ricky Bottalico .15 .40
T41 Luke Prokopec .15 .40
T42 Hideo Nomo .50 1.25
T43 Bill Mueller .20 .50
T44 Roberto Kelly .15 .40
T45 Chris Holt .15 .40
T46 Mike Jackson .15 .40
T47 Devon White .20 .50
T48 Gerald Williams .15 .40
T49 Eddie Taubensee .15 .40
T50 Brian Hunter UER .15 .40
Brian R Hunter pictured
Brian L Hunter stats
T51 Nelson Cruz .15 .40
T52 Jeff Fassero .15 .40
T53 Bubba Trammell .15 .40
T54 Bo Porter .15 .40
T55 Greg Norton .15 .40
T56 Benito Santiago .20 .50
T57 Ruben Rivera .15 .40
T58 Dee Brown .15 .40
T59 Jose Canseco UER .30 .75
2000 strikeout totals are wrong
T60 Chris Michalak .15 .40
T61 Tim Worrell .15 .40
T62 Matt Clement .20 .50
T63 Bill Pulsipher .15 .40
T64 Troy Brohawn RC .15 .40
T65 Mark Kotsay .20 .50
T66 Jimmy Rollins .20 .50
T67 Shea Hillenbrand .20 .50
T68 Ted Lilly .15 .40
T69 Jermaine Dye .20 .50
T70 Jerry Hairston Jr. .15 .40
T71 John Mabry .15 .40
T72 Kurt Abbott .15 .40
T73 Eric Owens .15 .40
T74 Jeff Brantley .15 .40
T75 Roy Oswalt .50 1.25
T76 Doug Mientkiewicz .20 .50
T77 Rickey Henderson .50 1.25
T78 Jason Grimsley .15 .40
T79 Christian Parker RC .15 .40
T80 Donne Wall .15 .40
T81 Alex Arias .15 .40
T82 Willis Roberts .15 .40
T83 Ryan Minor .15 .40
T84 Jason LaRue .15 .40
T85 Ruben Sierra .20 .50
T86 Johnny Damon .30 .75
T87 Juan Gonzalez .20 .50
T88 C.C. Sabathia .20 .50
T89 Tony Batista .15 .40
T90 Jay Witasick .15 .40
T91 Brent Abernathy .15 .40
T92 Paul LoDuca .20 .50
T93 Wes Helms .15 .40
T94 Mark Wohlers .15 .40
T95 Rob Bell .15 .40
T96 Tim Redding .15 .40
T97 Bud Smith RC .15 .40
T98 Adam Dunn .30 .75
T99 Ichiro Suzuki 6.00 15.00
Albert Pujols ROY
T100 Carlton Fisk 81 .50 1.25
T101 Tim Raines 81 .40 1.00
T102 Juan Marichal 74 .40 1.00
T103 Dave Winfield 81 .40 1.00
T104 Reggie Jackson 82 .50 1.25
T105 Cal Ripken 82 2.50 6.00
T106 Ozzie Smith 82 1.25 3.00
T107 Tom Seaver 83 .50 1.25
T108 Lou Piniella 74 .40 1.00
T109 Dwight Gooden 84 .40 1.00
T110 Bret Saberhagen 84 .40 1.00
T111 Gary Carter 85 .40 1.00
T112 Jack Clark 85 .40 1.00
T113 R. Henderson 85 .75 2.00
T114 Barry Bonds 86 2.00 5.00
T115 Bobby Bonilla 86 .40 1.00
T116 Jose Canseco 86 .50 1.25
T117 Will Clark 86 .50 1.25
T118 Andres Galarraga 86 .40 1.00
T119 Bo Jackson 86 .75 2.00
T120 Wally Joyner 86 .40 1.00
T121 Ellis Burks 87 .40 1.00
T122 David Cone 87 .40 1.00
T123 Greg Maddux 87 1.25 3.00
T124 Willie Randolph 76 .40 1.00
T125 Dennis Eckersley 87 .40 1.00
T126 Matt Williams 87 .40 1.00
T127 Joe Morgan 81 .40 1.00
T128 Fred McGriff 87 .50 1.25
T129 Roberto Alomar 88 .50 1.25
T130 Lee Smith 88 .40 1.00
T131 David Wells 88 .40 1.00
T132 Ken Griffey Jr. 89 1.25 3.00
T133 Deion Sanders 89 .50 1.25
T134 Nolan Ryan 89 1.50 4.00
T135 David Justice 90 .40 1.00
T136 Joe Carter 91 .40 1.00
T137 Jack Morris 92 .40 1.00
T138 Mike Piazza 93 1.25 3.00
T139 Barry Bonds 93 2.00 5.00
T140 Terrence Long 94 .40 1.00
T141 Ben Grieve 94 .40 1.00
T142 Richie Sexson 95 .40 1.00
George Arias
Mark Sweeney
Brian Schneider
T143 Sean Burroughs 99 .40 1.00
T144 Alfonso Soriano 99 .50 1.25
T145 Bob Boone MG .20 .50
T146 Larry Bowa MG .20 .50
T147 Bob Brenly MG .15 .40
T148 Buck Martinez MG .15 .40
T149 L. McClendon MG .15 .40
T150 Jim Tracy MG .15 .40
T151 Jared Abruzzo RC .15 .40
T152 Kurt Ainsworth .15 .40
T153 Willie Bloomquist .20 .50
T154 Ben Broussard .15 .40
T155 Bobby Bradley .15 .40
T156 Mike Bynum .15 .40
T157 A.J. Hinch .15 .40
T158 Ryan Christianson .15 .40
T159 Carlos Silva .15 .40
T160 Joe Crede .50 1.25
T161 Jack Cust .15 .40
T162 Ben Diggins .15 .40
T163 Phil Dumatrait .15 .40
T164 Alex Escobar .15 .40
T165 Miguel Olivo .15 .40
T166 Chris George .15 .40
T167 Marcus Giles .20 .50
T168 Keith Ginter .15 .40
T169 Josh Girdley .15 .40
T170 Tony Alvarez .15 .40
T171 Scott Seabol .15 .40
T172 Josh Hamilton .30 .75
T173 Jason Hart .15 .40
T174 Israel Alcantara .15 .40
T175 Jake Peavy .75 2.00
T176 Stubby Clapp RC .15 .40
T177 D'Angelo Jimenez .15 .40
T178 Nick Johnson .20 .50
T179 Ben Johnson .20 .50
T180 Larry Bigbie .15 .40
T181 Allen Levrault .15 .40
T182 Felipe Lopez .20 .50
T183 Sean Burnett .15 .40
T184 Nick Neugebauer .15 .40
T185 Austin Kearns .20 .50
T186 Corey Patterson .15 .40
T187 Carlos Pena .15 .40
T188 R. Rodriguez RC .15 .40
T189 Juan Rivera .15 .40
T190 Grant Roberts .15 .40
T191 Adam Pettyjohn RC .15 .40
T192 Jared Sandberg .15 .40
T193 Xavier Nady .15 .40
T194 Dane Sardinha .15 .40
T195 Shawn Sonnier .15 .40
T196 Rafael Soriano .15 .40
T197 Brian Specht RC .15 .40
T198 Aaron Myette .15 .40
T199 Juan Uribe RC .20 .50
T200 Jayson Werth .15 .40
T201 Brad Wilkerson .15 .40
T202 Horacio Estrada .15 .40
T203 Joel Pineiro .20 .50
T204 Matt LeCroy .15 .40
T205 Michael Coleman .15 .40
T206 Ben Sheets .30 .75
T207 Eric Byrnes .15 .40
T208 Sean Burroughs .15 .40
T209 Ken Harvey .15 .40
T210 Travis Hafner 1.50 4.00
T211 Erick Almonte .15 .40
T212 Jason Belcher RC .15 .40
T213 Wilson Betemit RC .60 1.50
T214 Hank Blalock RC 1.00 2.50
T215 Danny Borrell .15 .40
T216 John Buck RC .20 .50
T217 Freddie Bynum RC .15 .40
T218 Noel Devarez RC .15 .40
T219 Juan Diaz RC .15 .40
T220 Felix Diaz RC .15 .40
T221 Josh Fogg RC .15 .40
T222 Matt Ford RC .15 .40
T223 Scott Heard .15 .40
T224 Ben Hendrickson RC .15 .40
T225 Cody Ross RC .15 .40
T226 A. Hernandez RC .15 .40
T227 Alfredo Amezaga RC .15 .40
T228 Bob Keppel RC .15 .40
T229 Ryan Madson RC .30 .75
T230 Octavio Martinez RC .15 .40
T231 Hee Seop Choi .20 .50
T232 Thomas Mitchell .15 .40
T233 Luis Montanez .15 .40
T234 Andy Morales RC .15 .40
T235 Justin Morneau RC 2.50 6.00
T236 Toe Nash RC .15 .40
T237 V. Pascucci RC .15 .40
T238 Roy Smith RC .15 .40
T239 Antonio Perez RC .20 .50
T240 Chad Petty RC .15 .40
T241 Steve Smyth .15 .40
T242 Jose Reyes RC 6.00 15.00
T243 Eric Reynolds RC .15 .40
T244 Dominic Rich .15 .40
T245 J. Richardson RC .15 .40
T246 Ed Rogers RC .15 .40
T247 Albert Pujols RC 15.00 40.00
T248 Esix Snead RC .15 .40
T249 Luis Torres RC .15 .40
T250 Matt White RC .15 .40
T251 Blake Williams .15 .40
T252 Chris Russ .15 .40
T253 Joe Kennedy RC .20 .50
T254 Jeff Randazzo RC .15 .40
T255 Beau Hale RC .15 .40
T256 Brad Hennessey RC .50 1.25
T257 Jake Gautreau RC .15 .40
T258 Jeff Mathis RC .20 .50
T259 Aaron Heilman RC .20 .50
T260 B. Sardinha RC .15 .40
T261 Irvin Guzman RC 1.50 4.00
T262 Gabe Gross RC .20 .50
T263 J.D. Martin RC .15 .40
T264 Chris Smith RC .15 .40
T265 Kenny Baugh RC .15 .40

2001 Topps Traded Gold

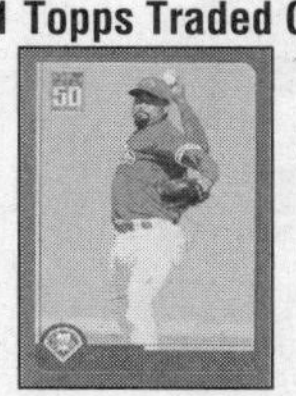

This set is a parallel to the 2001 Topps Traded set. Inserted into the 2001 Topps Traded at a rate of one in three, these cards are serial numbered to 2001 have have a gold foil border.

*STARS: 4X TO 10X BASIC CARDS
*REPRINTS: 1.5X TO 4X BASIC
*ROOKIES: 1X TO 2.5X BASIC
T242 Jose Reyes 20.00 50.00

2001 Topps Traded Autographs

Inserted at a rate of one in 626, these cards share the same design as the 2001 Topps Golden Anniversary Autographs. The only difference is the front bottom of the card reads "Golden Anniversary Traded Star". The cards carry a 'TTA' prefix.

TTAJD Johnny Damon 15.00 40.00
TTAMM Mike Mussina 12.50 30.00

2001 Topps Traded Dual Jersey Relics

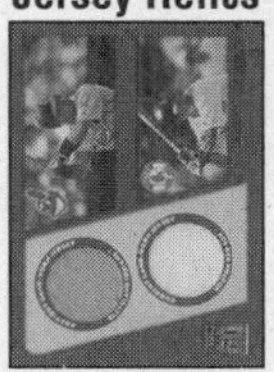

Inserted at a rate of one in 376, these cards highlight a player who has switched teams and feature a swatch of game-used jersey from both his former and current teams. The cards carry a 'TRR' prefix. Ben Grieve packed out as an exchange card.

TTRBG Ben Grieve 6.00 15.00
TTRDH D. Hermanson 6.00 15.00
TTRFT Fernando Tatis 6.00 15.00
TTRMR Manny Ramirez Sox 8.00 20.00

2001 Topps Traded Farewell Dual Bat Relic

Inserted at a rate of one in 4693, this card features bat pieces from both Cal Ripken and Tony Gwynn and is a farewell tribute to both players. The card carries a 'FR' prefix.

FRRG Cal Ripken 60.00 120.00
Tony Gwynn

2001 Topps Traded Hall of Fame Bat Relic

Inserted at a rate of one in 2796, this card features bat pieces from both Kirby Puckett and Dave Winfield and commemorates their entrance in Cooperstown. The card carries a 'HFR' prefix.

HFRPW Kirby Puckett 20.00 50.00
Dave Winfield

2001 Topps Traded Relics

Inserted at a rate of one in 29, this 33-card set features game used bats or jersey swatches for players who have switched teams this season. All jersey swatches represent each player's new team. The cards carry a 'TTR' prefix. An exchange card for a Matt Stairs Jersey card was packed out.

AG A. Galarraga Bat 4.00 10.00
BB1 Bobby Bonilla Bat 4.00 10.00
BB2 Bret Boone Jsy 4.00 10.00
BM Bill Mueller Jsy 6.00 15.00
CJ C. Johnson Jsy 4.00 10.00
DB Derek Bell Bat 4.00 10.00
DN Denny Neagle Jsy 4.00 10.00
DW David Wells Jsy 4.00 10.00
ED Eric Davis Bat 4.00 10.00
EW E. Wilson Bat 4.00 10.00
FM Fred McGriff Bat 6.00 15.00
GW G. Williams Bat 4.00 10.00
HR Hideo Nomo Jsy 20.00 50.00
JC Jose Canseco Bat 6.00 15.00
JD J. Dye Bat SP 4.00 10.00
JD1 J. Damon Bat 6.00 15.00
JD2 Johnny Damon Jsy 6.00 15.00
JG Juan Gonzalez Bat 4.00 10.00
JH J. Hammonds Jsy 4.00 10.00
KC Ken Caminiti Bat 4.00 10.00
KS K. Stinnett Bat SP 4.00 10.00
MG1 Mark Grace Bat 6.00 15.00
MG2 M. Grissom Bat 4.00 10.00
MH M. Hampton Jsy 4.00 10.00
MS M. Stairs Jsy EXCH 4.00 10.00
NP Neifi Perez Bat 4.00 10.00
RB Rico Brogna Jsy 4.00 10.00
RG Ron Gant Bat 4.00 10.00
ROC R. Cedeno Jsy 4.00 10.00
RS Ruben Sierra Bat 4.00 10.00
RSC R. Clayton Bat 4.00 10.00
SA S. Alomar Jr. Bat 4.00 10.00
TH Todd Hundley Jsy 4.00 10.00
TR Tim Raines Jsy 4.00 10.00

2001 Topps Traded Rookie Relics

Inserted at a rate of one in 91, this 18-card set features bat pieces or jersey swatches for rookies. The cards carry a 'TRR' prefix. An exchange card for the Ed Rogers Bat card was seeded into packs.

TRRAB Angel Berroa Jsy 4.00 10.00
TRRAP A. Pujols Bat SP 100.00 175.00
TRRBO Bill Ortega Jsy 3.00 8.00
TRRER E.Rogers Bat SP EXCH 4.00 10.00
TRRHC H. Cota Jsy 3.00 8.00
TRRJL Jason Lane Jsy 3.00 8.00
TRRJS Jae Seo Jsy 3.00 8.00
TRRJS Jamal Strong Jsy 3.00 8.00
TRRJV Jose Valverde Jsy 3.00 8.00
TRRJY Jason Young Jsy 3.00 8.00
TRRNC Nate Cornejo Jsy 3.00 8.00
TRRNN N. Neugebauer Jsy 3.00 8.00
TRRPF P. Feliz Jsy SP 3.00 8.00
TRRRS Richard Stahl Jsy 3.00 8.00
TRRSB S. Burroughs Jsy 3.00 8.00
TRRTS T. Shinjo Bat SP 4.00 10.00
TRRWB W. Betemit Bat 4.00 10.00
TRRWR Wilkin Ruan Jsy 3.00 8.00

2001 Topps Traded Who Would Have Thought

Inserted at a rate of one in eight, this 20-card set portrays players who fans thought would never be traded. The cards carry a 'WWHT' prefix.

COMPLETE SET (20) 15.00 40.00
WWHT1 Nolan Ryan 2.50 6.00
WWHT2 Ozzie Smith 1.50 4.00
WWHT3 Tom Seaver .60 1.50
WWHT4 Steve Carlton .60 1.50
WWHT5 Reggie Jackson .60 1.50
WWHT6 Frank Robinson .60 1.50
WWHT7 Keith Hernandez .60 1.50
WWHT8 Andre Dawson .60 1.50
WWHT9 Lou Brock .60 1.50
WWHT10 D. Eckersley .60 1.50
WWHT11 Dave Winfield .60 1.50
WWHT12 Rod Carew .60 1.50
WWHT13 Willie Randolph .60 1.50
WWHT14 Dwight Gooden .60 1.50
WWHT15 Carlton Fisk .60 1.50
WWHT16 Dale Murphy .60 1.50
WWHT17 Paul Molitor .60 1.50
WWHT18 Gary Carter .60 1.50
WWHT19 Wade Boggs .60 1.50
WWHT20 Willie Mays 2.00 5.00

2002 Topps

The complete set of 2002 Topps consists of 718 cards issued in two separate series. The first series of 364 cards was distributed in November, 2001 and the second series of 354 cards followed up in April, 2002. Please note, the first series is numbered 1-365, but card number seven does not exist (the number was "retired" in 1996 by Topps to honor Mickey Mantle). Similar to the 1999 McGwire and Sosa home run cards, Barry Bonds is featured on card number 365 with 73 different versions to commemorate each of the homers he smashed during the 2001 season. The first series set is considered complete with any "one" of these variations. The cards were issued either in 10 card hobby/retail packs with an SRP of $1.29 or 37 card HTA packs with an SRP of $5 per pack. The hobby packs were issued 36 to a box and 12 boxes to a case. The HTA packs were issued 12 to a box and eight to a case. Cards numbered 277-305 feature managers; cards numbered 307-325/671-690 feature leading prospects; cards numbered 326-331/691-695 feature 2001 draft picks; cards numbered 332-336 feature leading highlights of the 2001 season; cards numbered 337-348 feature league leaders; cards numbered 349-356 feature the eight teams which made the playoffs; cards numbered 357-364 feature major league baseball's stirring tribute to the events of September 11, 2001; cards 641-670 feature Team Cards; 696-713 are Gold Glove subsets, 714-715 are Cy Young subsets, 716-717 are MVP subsets and 718-719 are Rookie of the Year subsets. Notable Rookie Cards include Joe Mauer and Kazhuisa Ishii. Also, Topps repurchased more than 21,000 actual vintage Topps cards and randomly seeded them into packs as follows - Ser.1 Home Team Advantage 1:169, ser.1 retail 1:tbd, ser.2 hobby 1:431, ser.2 Home Team Advantage 1:113 and ser.2 retail 1:331. Brown-boxed hobby factory sets were issued in May, 2002 containing the full 718-card basic set and five Topps Archives Reprints inserts. Green-boxed retail factory sets were issued in late August, 2002 containing the full 718-card basic set and cards 1-5 of a 10-card Draft Picks set. There has been a recently discovered variation of card 160 in which there is a correct back picture for Albert Pujols (#160). While Topps has confirmed this variation, it is unknown what percent of the print run has the correct back photo.

COMPLETE SET (718) 30.00 80.00
COMP.FACT.BROWN SET (723) 40.00 80.00
COMP.FACT.GREEN SET (723) 40.00 80.00
COMP. SERIES 1 (365) 15.00 40.00
COMPLETE SERIES 2 (354) 15.00 40.00
COMMON CARD (1-6/8-719) .07 .20
COMMON (307-331) .20 .50
COMMON CARD (332-364) .20 .50
1 Pedro Martinez .10 .30
2 Mike Stanton .07 .20
3 Brad Penny .07 .20
4 Mike Matheny .07 .20
5 Johnny Damon .10 .30
6 Bret Boone .07 .20
7 Does Not Exist
8 Chris Truby .07 .20
9 B.J. Surhoff .07 .20
10 Mike Hampton .07 .20
11 Juan Pierre .07 .20
12 Mark Buehrle .07 .20
13 Bob Abreu .07 .20
14 David Cone .07 .20
15 Aaron Sele UER .07 .20
Card lists him as being born in New Mexico
He was born in Minnesota
16 Fernando Tatis .07 .20
17 Bobby Jones .07 .20
18 Rick Helling .07 .20
19 Dmitri Young .07 .20
20 Mike Mussina UER .10 .30
Career win total is wrong
21 Mike Sweeney .07 .20
22 Cristian Guzman .07 .20
23 Ryan Kohlmeier .07 .20
24 Adam Kennedy .07 .20
25 Larry Walker .07 .20
26 Eric Davis UER .07 .20
2000 Stolen Base totals are wrong
27 Jason Tyner .07 .20
28 Eric Young .07 .20
29 Jason Marquis .07 .20
30 Luis Gonzalez .07 .20
31 Kevin Tapani .07 .20
32 Orlando Cabrera .07 .20
33 Marty Cordova UER .07 .20
Career homer total, 1003

34 Brad Ausmus .07 .20
35 Livan Hernandez .07 .20
36 Alex Gonzalez .07 .20
37 Edgar Renteria .07 .20
38 Bengie Molina .07 .20
39 Frank Menechino .07 .20
40 Rafael Palmeiro .10 .30
41 Brad Fullmer .07 .20
42 Julio Zuleta .07 .20
43 Darren Dreifort .07 .20
44 Trot Nixon .07 .20
45 Trevor Hoffman .07 .20
46 Vladimir Nunez .07 .20
47 Mark Kotsay .07 .20
48 Kenny Rogers .07 .20
49 Ben Petrick .07 .20
50 Jeff Bagwell .10 .30
51 Juan Encarnacion .07 .20
52 Ramiro Mendoza .07 .20
53 Brian Meadows .07 .20
54 Chad Curtis .07 .20
55 Aramis Ramirez .07 .20
56 Mark McLemore .07 .20
57 Dante Bichette .07 .20
58 Scott Schoeneweis .07 .20
59 Jose Cruz Jr. .07 .20
60 Roger Clemens .40 1.00
61 Jose Guillen .07 .20
62 Darren Oliver .07 .20
63 Chris Reitsma .07 .20
64 Jeff Abbott .07 .20
65 Robin Ventura .07 .20
66 Denny Neagle .07 .20
67 Al Martin .07 .20
68 Benito Santiago .07 .20
69 Roy Oswalt .07 .20
70 Juan Gonzalez .07 .20
71 Garret Anderson .07 .20
72 Bobby Bonilla .07 .20
73 Danny Bautista .07 .20
74 J.T. Snow .07 .20
75 Derek Jeter .50 1.25
76 John Olerud .07 .20
77 Kevin Appier .07 .20
78 Phil Nevin .07 .20
79 Sean Casey .07 .20
80 Troy Glaus .07 .20
81 Joe Randa .07 .20
82 Jose Valentin .07 .20
83 Ricky Bottalico .07 .20
84 Todd Zeile .07 .20
85 Barry Larkin .10 .30
86 Bob Wickman .07 .20
87 Jeff Shaw .07 .20
88 Greg Vaughn .07 .20
89 Fernando Vina .07 .20
90 Mark Mulder .07 .20
91 Paul Bako .07 .20
92 Aaron Boone .07 .20
93 Esteban Loaiza .07 .20
94 Richie Sexson .07 .20
95 Alfonso Soriano .07 .20
96 Tony Womack .07 .20
97 Paul Shuey .07 .20
98 Melvin Mora .07 .20
99 Tony Gwynn .25 .60
100 Vladimir Guerrero .20 .50
101 Keith Osik .07 .20
102 Bud Smith .07 .20
103 Scott Williamson .07 .20
104 Daryle Ward .07 .20
105 Doug Mientkiewicz .07 .20
106 Stan Javier .07 .20
107 Russ Ortiz .07 .20
108 Wade Miller .07 .20
109 Luke Prokopec .07 .20
110 Andruw Jones UER .10 .30
Career SB total, 1442
111 Ron Coomer .07 .20
112 Dan Wilson UER .07 .20
Career SB total, 1245
113 Luis Castillo .07 .20
114 Derek Bell .07 .20
115 Gary Sheffield .07 .20
116 Ruben Rivera .07 .20
117 Paul O'Neill .10 .30
118 Craig Paquette .07 .20
119 Kelvin Escobar .07 .20
120 Brad Radke .07 .20
121 Jorge Fabregas .07 .20
122 Randy Winn .07 .20
123 Tom Goodwin .07 .20
124 Jaret Wright .07 .20
125 Manny Ramirez .10 .30
126 Al Leiter .07 .20
127 Ben Davis .07 .20
128 Frank Catalanotto .07 .20
129 Jose Cabrera .07 .20
130 Magglio Ordonez .07 .20
131 Jose Macias .07 .20
132 Ted Lilly .07 .20
133 Chris Holt .07 .20
134 Eric Milton .07 .20
135 Shannon Stewart .07 .20
136 Omar Olivares .07 .20
137 David Segui .07 .20
138 Jeff Nelson .07 .20
139 Matt Williams .07 .20
140 Ellis Burks .07 .20
141 Jason Bere .07 .20
142 Jimmy Haynes .07 .20
143 Ramon Hernandez .07 .20
144 Craig Counsell UER .07 .20
Card pictures Greg Colbrunn
Some vital stats are wrong as well
145 John Smoltz .10 .30
146 Homer Bush .07 .20
147 Quilvio Veras .07 .20
148 Esteban Yan .07 .20
149 Ramon Ortiz .07 .20
150 Carlos Delgado .07 .20
151 Lee Stevens .07 .20
152 Wil Cordero .07 .20
153 Mike Bordick .07 .20
154 John Flaherty .07 .20
155 Omar Daal .07 .20
156 Todd Ritchie .07 .20
157 Carl Everett .07 .20
158 Scott Sullivan .07 .20
159 Deivi Cruz .07 .20
160 Albert Pujols UER .40 1.00
Placido Polanco pictured on back
160A Albert Pujols COR
Pujols correctly pictured on back
161 Royce Clayton .07 .20
162 Jeff Suppan .07 .20
163 C.C. Sabathia .07 .20
164 Jimmy Rollins .07 .20
165 Rickey Henderson .20 .50
166 Rey Ordonez .07 .20
167 Shawn Estes .07 .20
168 Reggie Sanders .07 .20
169 Jon Lieber .07 .20
170 Armando Benitez .07 .20
171 Mike Remlinger .07 .20
172 Billy Wagner .07 .20
173 Troy Percival .07 .20
174 Devon White .07 .20
175 Ivan Rodriguez .10 .30
176 Dustin Hermanson .07 .20
177 Brian Anderson .07 .20
178 Graeme Lloyd .07 .20
179 Russel Branyan .07 .20
180 Bobby Higginson .07 .20
181 Alex Gonzalez .07 .20
182 John Franco .07 .20
183 Sidney Ponson .07 .20
184 Jose Mesa .07 .20
185 Todd Hollandsworth .07 .20
186 Kevin Young .07 .20
187 Tim Wakefield .07 .20
188 Craig Biggio .10 .30
189 Jason Isringhausen .07 .20
190 Mark Quinn .07 .20
191 Glendon Rusch .07 .20
192 Damian Miller .07 .20
193 Sandy Alomar Jr. .07 .20
194 Scott Brosius .07 .20
195 Dave Martinez .07 .20
196 Danny Graves .07 .20
197 Shea Hillenbrand .07 .20
198 Jimmy Anderson .07 .20
199 Travis Lee .07 .20
200 Randy Johnson .20 .50
201 Carlos Beltran .07 .20
202 Jerry Hairston .07 .20
203 Jesus Sanchez .07 .20
204 Eddie Taubensee .07 .20
205 David Wells .07 .20
206 Russ Davis .07 .20
207 Michael Barrett .07 .20
208 Marquis Grissom .07 .20
209 Byung-Hyun Kim .07 .20
210 Hideo Nomo .20 .50
211 Ryan Rupe .07 .20
212 Ricky Gutierrez .07 .20
213 Darryl Kile .07 .20
214 Rico Brogna .07 .20
215 Terrence Long .07 .20
216 Mike Jackson .07 .20
217 Jamey Wright .07 .20
218 Adrian Beltre .07 .20
219 Benny Agbayani .07 .20
220 Chuck Knoblauch .07 .20
221 Randy Wolf .07 .20
222 Andy Ashby .07 .20
223 Corey Koskie .07 .20
224 Roger Cedeno .07 .20
225 Ichiro Suzuki .40 1.00
226 Keith Foulke .07 .20
227 Ryan Minor .07 .20
228 Shawon Dunston .07 .20
229 Alex Cora .07 .20
230 Jeromy Burnitz .07 .20
231 Mark Grace .10 .30
232 Aubrey Huff .07 .20
233 Jeffrey Hammonds .07 .20
234 Olmedo Saenz .07 .20
235 Brian Jordan .07 .20
236 Jeremy Giambi .07 .20
237 Joe Girardi .07 .20
238 Eric Gagne .07 .20
239 Masato Yoshii .07 .20
240 Greg Maddux .30 .75
241 Bryan Rekar .07 .20
242 Ray Durham .07 .20
243 Torii Hunter .07 .20
244 Derrek Lee .10 .30
245 Jim Edmonds .07 .20
246 Einar Diaz .07 .20
247 Brian Bohanon .07 .20
248 Ron Belliard .07 .20
249 Mike Lowell .07 .20
250 Sammy Sosa .20 .50
251 Richard Hidalgo .07 .20
252 Bartolo Colon .07 .20
253 Jorge Posada .10 .30
254 LaTroy Hawkins .07 .20
255 Paul LoDuca .07 .20
256 Carlos Febles .07 .20
257 Nelson Cruz .07 .20
258 Edgardo Alfonzo .07 .20
259 Joey Hamilton .07 .20
260 Cliff Floyd .07 .20
261 Wes Helms .07 .20
262 Jay Bell .07 .20
263 Mike Cameron .07 .20
264 Paul Konerko .07 .20
265 Jeff Kent .07 .20
266 Robert Fick .07 .20
267 Allen Levrault .07 .20
268 Placido Polanco .07 .20
269 Marlon Anderson .07 .20
270 Mariano Rivera .20 .50
271 Chan Ho Park .07 .20
272 Jose Vizcaino .07 .20
273 Jeff D'Amico .07 .20
274 Mark Gardner .07 .20
275 Travis Fryman .07 .20
276 Darren Lewis .07 .20
277 Bruce Bochy MG .07 .20
278 Jerry Manuel MG .07 .20
279 Bob Brenly MG .07 .20
280 Don Baylor MG .07 .20
281 Davey Lopes MG .07 .20
282 Jerry Narron MG .07 .20
283 Tony Muser MG .07 .20
284 Hal McRae MG .07 .20
285 Bobby Cox MG .07 .20
286 Larry Dierker MG .07 .20
287 Phil Garner MG .07 .20
288 Joe Kerrigan MG .07 .20
289 Bobby Valentine MG .07 .20
290 Dusty Baker MG .07 .20
291 Lloyd McClendon MG .07 .20
292 Mike Scioscia MG .07 .20
293 Buck Martinez MG .07 .20
294 Larry Bowa MG .07 .20
295 Tony LaRussa MG .07 .20
296 Jeff Torborg MG .07 .20
297 Tom Kelly MG .07 .20
298 Mike Hargrove MG .07 .20
299 Art Howe MG .07 .20
300 Lou Piniella MG .07 .20
301 Charlie Manuel MG .07 .20
302 Buddy Bell MG .07 .20
303 Tony Perez MG .07 .20
304 Bob Boone MG .07 .20
305 Joe Torre MG .10 .30
306 Jim Tracy MG .07 .20
307 Jason Lane PROS .20 .50
308 Chris George PROS .20 .50
309 Hank Blalock PROS UER .40 1.00
Bio has him throwing lefty
310 Joe Borchard PROS .20 .50
311 Marlon Byrd PROS .20 .50
312 R. Cabrera PROS RC .20 .50
313 F. Sanchez PROS RC .75 2.00
314 S. Wiggins PROS RC .20 .50
315 J. Maule PROS RC .20 .50
316 D. Cesar PROS RC .20 .50
317 Boof Bonser PROS .20 .50
318 J. Tolentino PROS RC .20 .50
319 Earl Snyder PROS RC .20 .50
320 T. Wade PROS RC .20 .50
321 N. Calzado PROS RC .20 .50
322 Eric Glaser PROS RC .20 .50
323 C. Kuzmic PROS RC .20 .50
324 Nic Jackson PROS RC .20 .50
325 Mike Rivera PROS .20 .50
326 Jason Bay PROS RC 1.50 4.00
327 Chris Smith DP .20 .50
328 Jake Gautreau DP .20 .50
329 Gabe Gross DP .20 .50
330 Kenny Baugh DP .20 .50
331 J.D. Martin DP .20 .50
332 Barry Bonds HL .50 1.25
500th Homer
333 Rickey Henderson HL .20 .50
Sets record for career walks
334 Bud Smith HL .20 .50
335 R. Henderson HL 3000 .20 .50
336 Barry Bonds HL .50 1.25
73 homers in a season
337 Ichiro Suzuki .20 .50
Jason Giambi
Roberto Alomar LL
338 Alex Rodriguez .20 .50
Ichiro Suzuki
Bret Boone LL
339 Alex Rodriguez .20 .50
Jim Thome
Rafael Palmeiro LL
340 Bret Boone .20 .50
Juan Gonzalez
Alex Rodriguez LL
341 Freddy Garcia .20 .50
Mike Mussina
Joe Mays LL
342 Hideo Nomo .20 .50
Mike Mussina
Roger Clemens LL
343 Larry Walker .20 .50
Todd Helton
Moises Alou
Lance Berkman LL
344 Sammy Sosa .30 .75
Todd Helton
Barry Bonds LL
345 Barry Bonds .30 .75
Sammy Sosa
Luis Gonzalez LL
346 Sammy Sosa .20 .50
Todd Helton
Luis Gonzalez LL
347 Randy Johnson .20 .50
Curt Schilling
John Burkett LL
348 Randy Johnson .20 .50
Curt Schilling
Chan Ho Park LL
349 Seattle Mariners PB .20 .50
350 Oakland Athletics PB .20 .50
351 New York Yankees PB .20 .50
352 Cleveland Indians PB .20 .50
353 Ariz. Diamondbacks PB .20 .50
354 Atlanta Braves PB .20 .50
355 St. Louis Cardinals PB .20 .50
356 Houston Astros PB .20 .50
357 Ariz.Diamondbacks .20 .50
Colorado Rockies UWS
358 Mike Piazza UWS .20 .50
359 Braves-Phillies UWS .20 .50
360 Curt Schilling UWS .20 .50
361 Roger Clemens .20 .50
Lee Mazzilli UWS
362 Sammy Sosa UWS .10 .30
363 Tom Lampkin .20 .50
Ichiro Suzuki
Bret Boone UWS
364 Barry Bonds .30 .75
Jeff Bagwell UWS
365 Barry Bonds HR 1 6.00 15.00
365 Barry Bonds HR 2 4.00 10.00
365 Barry Bonds HR 3 4.00 10.00
365 Barry Bonds HR 4 4.00 10.00
365 Barry Bonds HR 5 4.00 10.00
365 Barry Bonds HR 6 4.00 10.00
365 Barry Bonds HR 7 4.00 10.00
365 Barry Bonds HR 8 4.00 10.00
365 Barry Bonds HR 9 4.00 10.00
365 Barry Bonds HR 10 4.00 10.00
365 Barry Bonds HR 11 4.00 10.00
365 Barry Bonds HR 12 4.00 10.00
365 Barry Bonds HR 13 4.00 10.00
365 Barry Bonds HR 14 4.00 10.00
365 Barry Bonds HR 15 4.00 10.00
365 Barry Bonds HR 16 4.00 10.00
365 Barry Bonds HR 17 4.00 10.00
365 Barry Bonds HR 18 4.00 10.00
365 Barry Bonds HR 19 4.00 10.00
365 Barry Bonds HR 20 4.00 10.00
365 Barry Bonds HR 21 4.00 10.00
365 Barry Bonds HR 22 4.00 10.00
365 Barry Bonds HR 23 4.00 10.00
365 Barry Bonds HR 24 4.00 10.00
365 Barry Bonds HR 25 4.00 10.00
365 Barry Bonds HR 26 4.00 10.00
365 Barry Bonds HR 27 4.00 10.00
365 Barry Bonds HR 28 4.00 10.00
365 Barry Bonds HR 29 4.00 10.00
365 Barry Bonds HR 30 4.00 10.00
365 Barry Bonds HR 31 4.00 10.00
365 Barry Bonds HR 32 UER 4.00 10.00
No pitcher is listed on this card
365 Barry Bonds HR 33 4.00 10.00
365 Barry Bonds HR 34 4.00 10.00
365 Barry Bonds HR 35 4.00 10.00
365 Barry Bonds HR 36 4.00 10.00
365 Barry Bonds HR 37 4.00 10.00
365 Barry Bonds HR 38 4.00 10.00
365 Barry Bonds HR 39 4.00 10.00
365 Barry Bonds HR 40 4.00 10.00
365 Barry Bonds HR 41 4.00 10.00
365 Barry Bonds HR 42 4.00 10.00
365 Barry Bonds HR 43 4.00 10.00
365 Barry Bonds HR 44 4.00 10.00
365 Barry Bonds HR 45 4.00 10.00
365 Barry Bonds HR 46 4.00 10.00
365 Barry Bonds HR 47 4.00 10.00
365 Barry Bonds HR 48 4.00 10.00
365 Barry Bonds HR 49 4.00 10.00
365 Barry Bonds HR 50 4.00 10.00
365 Barry Bonds HR 51 4.00 10.00
365 Barry Bonds HR 52 4.00 10.00
365 Barry Bonds HR 53 4.00 10.00
365 Barry Bonds HR 54 4.00 10.00
365 Barry Bonds HR 55 4.00 10.00
365 Barry Bonds HR 56 4.00 10.00
365 Barry Bonds HR 57 4.00 10.00
365 Barry Bonds HR 58 4.00 10.00
365 Barry Bonds HR 59 4.00 10.00
365 Barry Bonds HR 60 4.00 10.00
365 Barry Bonds HR 61 6.00 15.00
365 Barry Bonds HR 62 4.00 10.00
365 Barry Bonds HR 63 4.00 10.00
365 Barry Bonds HR 64 4.00 10.00
365 Barry Bonds HR 65 4.00 10.00
365 Barry Bonds HR 66 4.00 10.00
365 Barry Bonds HR 67 4.00 10.00
365 Barry Bonds HR 68 4.00 10.00
365 Barry Bonds HR 69 4.00 10.00
365 Barry Bonds HR 70 6.00 15.00
365 Barry Bonds HR 71 4.00 10.00
365 Barry Bonds HR 72 4.00 10.00
365 Barry Bonds HR 73 20.00 50.00
366 Pat Meares .07 .20
367 Mike Lieberthal .07 .20
368 Larry Bigbie .07 .20
369 Ron Gant .07 .20
370 Moises Alou .07 .20
371 Chad Kreuter .07 .20
372 Willis Roberts .07 .20
373 Toby Hall .07 .20
374 Miguel Batista .07 .20
375 John Burkett .07 .20
376 Cory Lidle .07 .20
377 Nick Neugebauer .07 .20
378 Jay Payton .07 .20
379 Steve Karsay .07 .20
380 Eric Chavez .07 .20
381 Kelly Stinnett .07 .20
382 Jarrod Washburn .07 .20
383 Rick White .07 .20
384 Jeff Conine .07 .20
385 Fred McGriff .10 .30
386 Marvin Benard .07 .20
387 Joe Crede .07 .20
388 Dennis Cook .07 .20
389 Rick Reed .07 .20
390 Tom Glavine .10 .30
391 Rondell White .07 .20
392 Matt Morris .07 .20
393 Pat Rapp .07 .20
394 Robert Person .07 .20
395 Omar Vizquel .10 .30
396 Jeff Cirillo .07 .20
397 Dave Mlicki .07 .20
398 Jose Ortiz .07 .20
399 Ryan Dempster .07 .20
400 Curt Schilling .07 .20
401 Peter Bergeron .07 .20
402 Kyle Lohse .07 .20
403 Craig Wilson UER .07 .20
Homer totals are wrong
404 David Justice .07 .20
405 Darin Erstad .07 .20
406 Jose Mercedes .07 .20
407 Carl Pavano .07 .20
408 Albie Lopez .07 .20
409 Alex Ochoa .07 .20
410 Chipper Jones .20 .50
411 Tyler Houston .07 .20
412 Dean Palmer .07 .20
413 Damian Jackson .07 .20
414 Josh Towers .07 .20
415 Rafael Furcal .07 .20
416 Mike Morgan .07 .20
417 Herb Perry .07 .20
418 Mike Sirotka .07 .20
419 Mark Wohlers .07 .20
420 Nomar Garciaparra .30 .75
421 Felipe Lopez .07 .20
422 Joe McEwing .07 .20
423 Jacque Jones .07 .20
424 Julio Franco .07 .20
425 Frank Thomas .20 .50
426 So Taguchi RC .30 .75
427 Kazuhisa Ishii RC .20 .50
428 D'Angelo Jimenez .07 .20
429 Chris Stynes .07 .20
430 Kerry Wood .07 .20
431 Chris Singleton .07 .20
432 Erubiel Durazo .07 .20
433 Matt Lawton .07 .20
434 Bill Mueller .07 .20
435 Jose Canseco .10 .30
436 Ben Grieve .07 .20
437 Terry Mulholland .07 .20
438 David Bell .07 .20
439 A.J. Pierzynski .07 .20
440 Adam Dunn .07 .20
441 Jon Garland .07 .20
442 Jeff Fassero .07 .20
443 Julio Lugo .07 .20
444 Carlos Guillen .07 .20
445 Orlando Hernandez .07 .20
446 Mark Loretta UER .07 .20
Photo is Curtis Leskanic
447 Scott Spiezio .07 .20
448 Kevin Millwood .07 .20
449 Jamie Moyer .07 .20
450 Todd Helton .10 .30
451 Todd Walker .07 .20
452 Jose Lima .07 .20
453 Brook Fordyce .07 .20
454 Aaron Rowand .07 .20
455 Barry Zito .07 .20
456 Eric Owens .07 .20
457 Charles Nagy .07 .20
458 Raul Ibanez .07 .20
459 Joe Mays .07 .20
460 Jim Thome .10 .30
461 Adam Eaton .07 .20
462 Felix Martinez .07 .20
463 Vernon Wells .07 .20
464 Donnie Sadler .07 .20
465 Tony Clark .07 .20
466 Jose Hernandez .07 .20
467 Ramon Martinez .07 .20
468 Rusty Greer .07 .20
469 Rod Barajas .07 .20
470 Lance Berkman .07 .20
471 Brady Anderson .07 .20
472 Pedro Astacio .07 .20
473 Shane Halter .07 .20
474 Bret Prinz .07 .20
475 Edgar Martinez .10 .30
476 Steve Trachsel .07 .20
477 Gary Matthews Jr. .07 .20
478 Ismael Valdes .07 .20
479 Juan Uribe .07 .20
480 Shawn Green .07 .20
481 Kirk Rueter .07 .20
482 Damion Easley .07 .20
483 Chris Carpenter .07 .20
484 Kris Benson .07 .20
485 Antonio Alfonseca .07 .20
486 Kyle Farnsworth .07 .20
487 Brandon Lyon .07 .20
488 Hideki Irabu .07 .20
489 David Ortiz .20 .50
490 Mike Piazza .30 .75
491 Derek Lowe .07 .20
492 Chris Gomez .07 .20
493 Mark Johnson .07 .20
494 John Rocker .07 .20
495 Eric Karros .07 .20
496 Bill Haselman .07 .20
497 Dave Veres .07 .20
498 Pete Harnisch .07 .20
499 Tomokazu Ohka .07 .20
500 Barry Bonds .50 1.25
501 David Dellucci .07 .20
502 Wendell Magee .07 .20
503 Tom Gordon .07 .20
504 Javier Vazquez .07 .20
505 Ben Sheets .07 .20
506 Wilton Guerrero .07 .20
507 John Halama .07 .20
508 Mark Redman .07 .20
509 Jack Wilson .07 .20
510 Bernie Williams .10 .30
511 Miguel Cairo .07 .20
512 Denny Hocking .07 .20
513 Tony Batista .07 .20
514 Mark Grudzielanek .07 .20
515 Jose Vidro .07 .20
516 Sterling Hitchcock .07 .20
517 Billy Koch .07 .20
518 Matt Clement .07 .20
519 Bruce Chen .07 .20
520 Roberto Alomar .10 .30
521 Orlando Palmeiro .07 .20
522 Steve Finley .07 .20
523 Danny Patterson .07 .20
524 Terry Adams .07 .20
525 Tino Martinez .10 .30
526 Tony Armas Jr. .07 .20
527 Geoff Jenkins .07 .20
528 Kerry Robinson .07 .20
529 Corey Patterson .07 .20
530 Brian Giles .07 .20
531 Jose Jimenez .07 .20
532 Joe Kennedy .07 .20
533 Armando Rios .07 .20
534 Osvaldo Fernandez .07 .20
535 Ruben Sierra .07 .20
536 Octavio Dotel .07 .20
537 Luis Sojo .07 .20
538 Brent Butler .07 .20
539 Pablo Ozuna UER .07 .20
Games played for Portland is wrong for 2002
540 Freddy Garcia .07 .20
541 Chad Durbin .07 .20
542 Orlando Merced .07 .20
543 Michael Tucker .07 .20
544 Roberto Hernandez .07 .20
545 Pat Burrell .07 .20
546 A.J. Burnett .07 .20
547 Bubba Trammell .07 .20
548 Scott Elarton .07 .20
549 Mike Darr .07 .20
550 Ken Griffey Jr. .30 .75
551 Ugueth Urbina .07 .20
552 Todd Jones .07 .20
553 Delino Deshields .07 .20
554 Adam Piatt .07 .20
555 Jason Kendall .07 .20
556 Hector Ortiz .07 .20
557 Turk Wendell .07 .20
558 Rob Bell .07 .20
559 Sun Woo Kim .07 .20
560 Raul Mondesi .07 .20
561 Brent Abernathy .07 .20
562 Seth Etherton .07 .20
563 Shawn Wooten .07 .20
564 Jay Buhner .07 .20
565 Andres Galarraga .07 .20
566 Shane Reynolds .07 .20
567 Rod Beck .07 .20
568 Dee Brown .07 .20
569 Pedro Feliz .07 .20
570 Ryan Klesko .07 .20
571 John Vander Wal UER .07 .20
Home Run Total in 1999 was 64
572 Nick Bierbrodt .07 .20
573 Joe Nathan .07 .20
574 James Baldwin .07 .20
575 J.D. Drew .07 .20
576 Greg Colbrunn .07 .20
577 Doug Glanville .07 .20
578 Brandon Duckworth .07 .20
579 Shawn Chacon .07 .20
580 Rich Aurilia .07 .20
581 Chuck Finley .07 .20
582 Abraham Nunez .07 .20
583 Kenny Lofton .07 .20
584 Brian Daubach .07 .20
585 Miguel Tejada .07 .20
586 Nate Cornejo .07 .20
587 Kazuhiro Sasaki .07 .20
588 Chris Richard .07 .20
589 Armando Reynoso .07 .20
590 Tim Hudson .07 .20
591 Neifi Perez .07 .20
592 Steve Cox .07 .20
593 Henry Blanco .07 .20
594 Ricky Ledee .07 .20
595 Tim Salmon .10 .30
596 Luis Rivas .07 .20
597 Jeff Zimmerman .07 .20
598 Matt Stairs .07 .20
599 Preston Wilson .07 .20
600 Mark McGwire .50 1.25
601 Timo Perez UER .07 .20
Biographical Information is that of Aaron Rowand's
602 Matt Anderson .07 .20
603 Todd Hundley .07 .20
604 Rick Ankiel .07 .20
605 Tsuyoshi Shinjo .07 .20
606 Woody Williams .07 .20
607 Jason LaRue .07 .20
608 Carlos Lee .07 .20
609 Russ Johnson .07 .20
610 Scott Rolen .10 .30
611 Brent Mayne .07 .20
612 Darrin Fletcher .07 .20
613 Ray Lankford .07 .20
614 Troy O'Leary .07 .20
615 Javier Lopez .07 .20
616 Randy Velarde .07 .20
617 Vinny Castilla .07 .20
618 Milton Bradley .07 .20
619 Ruben Mateo .07 .20
620 Jason Giambi Yankees .07 .20
621 Andy Benes .07 .20
622 Joe Mauer RC 4.00 10.00
623 Andy Pettitte .10 .30
624 Jose Offerman .07 .20
625 Mo Vaughn .07 .20
626 Steve Sparks .07 .20
627 Mike Matthews .07 .20
628 Robb Nen .07 .20
629 Kip Wells .07 .20
630 Kevin Brown .07 .20
631 Arthur Rhodes .07 .20
632 Gabe Kapler .07 .20
633 Jermaine Dye .07 .20
634 Josh Beckett .07 .20
635 Pokey Reese .07 .20
636 Benji Gil .07 .20
637 Marcus Giles .07 .20
638 Julian Tavarez .07 .20
639 Jason Schmidt .07 .20
640 Alex Rodriguez .30 .75
641 Anaheim Angels TC .07 .20
642 Arizona Diamondbacks TC .10 .30
643 Atlanta Braves TC .07 .20
644 Baltimore Orioles TC .07 .20
645 Boston Red Sox TC .07 .20
646 Chicago Cubs TC .07 .20
647 Chicago White Sox TC .07 .20
648 Cincinnati Reds TC .07 .20
649 Cleveland Indians TC .07 .20
650 Colorado Rockies TC .07 .20
651 Detroit Tigers TC .07 .20
652 Florida Marlins TC .07 .20
653 Houston Astros TC .07 .20
654 Kansas City Royals TC .07 .20
655 Los Angeles Dodgers TC .07 .20
656 Milwaukee Brewers TC .07 .20
657 Minnesota Twins TC .07 .20
658 Montreal Expos TC .07 .20
659 New York Mets TC .07 .20
660 New York Yankees TC .20 .50
661 Oakland Athletics TC .07 .20
662 Philadelphia Phillies TC .07 .20
663 Pittsburgh Pirates TC .07 .20
664 San Diego Padres TC .07 .20
665 San Francisco Giants TC .07 .20
666 Seattle Mariners TC .10 .30
667 St. Louis Cardinals TC .07 .20
668 T.B. Devil Rays TC .07 .20
669 Texas Rangers TC .07 .20
670 Toronto Blue Jays TC .07 .20
671 Juan Cruz PROS .20 .50
672 Kevin Cash PROS RC .20 .50
673 Jimmy Gobble PROS RC .20 .50
674 Mike Hill PROS RC .20 .50
675 T.Buchholz PROS RC .20 .50
676 Bill Hall PROS .20 .50
677 B.Roneberg PROS RC .20 .50
678 R.Huffman PROS RC .20 .50
679 Chris Tritle PROS RC .20 .50
680 Nate Espy PROS RC .20 .50
681 Nick Alvarez PROS RC .20 .50
682 Jason Botts PROS RC .20 .50
683 Ryan Gripp PROS RC .20 .50
684 Dan Phillips PROS RC .20 .50
685 Pablo Arias PROS RC .20 .50
686 J.Rodriguez PROS RC .20 .50
687 Rich Harden PROS RC 1.25 3.00
688 Neal Frendling PROS RC .20 .50
689 Rich Thompson PROS RC .20 .50
690 G.Montalbano PROS RC .20 .50
691 Len Dinardo DP RC .20 .50
692 Ryan Raburn DP RC .20 .50
693 Josh Barfield DP RC 1.00 2.50
694 David Bacani DP RC .20 .50
695 Dan Johnson DP RC .40 1.00
696 Mike Mussina GG .07 .20
697 Ivan Rodriguez GG .10 .30
698 Doug Mientkiewicz GG .07 .20
699 Roberto Alomar GG .07 .20

700 Eric Chavez GG .07 .20
701 Omar Vizquel GG .07 .20
702 Mike Cameron GG .07 .20
703 Torii Hunter GG .07 .20
704 Ichiro Suzuki GG .20 .50
705 Greg Maddux GG .20 .50
706 Brad Ausmus GG .07 .20
707 Todd Helton GG .07 .20
708 Fernando Vina GG .07 .20
709 Scott Rolen GG .07 .20
710 Orlando Cabrera GG .07 .20
711 Andruw Jones GG .07 .20
712 Jim Edmonds GG .07 .20
713 Larry Walker GG .07 .20
714 Roger Clemens CY .20 .50
715 Randy Johnson CY .10 .30
716 Ichiro Suzuki MVP .20 .50
717 Barry Bonds MVP .30 .75
718 Ichiro Suzuki ROY .20 .50
719 Albert Pujols ROY .20 .50

2002 Topps Gold

Inserted one per 19 first series hobby packs, one per 15 first series retail packs, one per 5 first series HTA packs, one per 12 second series hobby packs, one per 9 second series retail packs and one per three second series HTA packs, this set parallels cards 1-330 and 366-695 of the 2002 Topps set. Each card features bold, gold-foil borders on front and 2002 serial-numbered sets were produced.

*GOLD 1-306/366-670: 8X TO 20X BASIC
*GOLD 307-330/671-695: 1.5X TO 4X BASIC
*GOLD 426-427: 1.5X TO 4X BASIC
622 Joe Mauer 10.00 25.00

2002 Topps Home Team Advantage

This is a parallel to the Topps set. Each of these cards, which were available only in the blue factory sets have the words "Home Team Advantage" stamped on them.

COMP.FACT.SET (718) 40.00 80.00
*HTA: .75X TO 2X BASIC
*BONDS HR 70: .2X TO .5X BASIC HR 70

2002 Topps Limited

This 790 card factory set was issued in October, 2002. It had a SRP of $150 and parallels the regular Topps set except for the reprinting of all 73 Barry Bonds 365 cards. These cards can be differentiated from the regular cards by their "glossy" finish on the front. Though the cards are not serial-numbered, Topps announced that 1,950 sets were issued.

COMP.FACT.SET (790) 60.00 150.00
*LTD STARS: 1.5X TO 4X BASIC CARDS
*307-331/426-427/622/671-695: 1.5X TO 4X
*BONDS HR: .2X TO .5X BASIC BONDS HR
622 Joe Mauer 15.00 40.00

2002 Topps 1952 Reprints

Inserted at a rate of one in 25 hobby, one in five HTA packs and one in 16 retail packs, these nineteen reprint cards feature players who participated in the 1952 World Series which was won by the New York Yankees.

COMPLETE SET (19) 20.00 50.00
COMPLETE SERIES 1 (9) 10.00 25.00
COMPLETE SERIES 2 (10) 10.00 25.00
52R1 Roy Campanella 2.00 5.00
52R2 Duke Snider 1.50 4.00
52R3 Carl Erskine 1.50 4.00
52R4 Andy Pafko 1.50 4.00
52R5 Johnny Mize 1.50 4.00
52R6 Billy Martin 1.50 4.00
52R7 Phil Rizzuto 2.00 5.00
52R8 Gil McDougald 1.50 4.00
52R9 Allie Reynolds 1.50 4.00
52R10 Jackie Robinson 2.00 5.00
52R11 Preacher Roe 1.50 4.00
52R12 Gil Hodges 2.00 5.00
52R13 Billy Cox 1.50 4.00
52R14 Yogi Berra 2.00 5.00
52R15 Gene Woodling 1.50 4.00
52R16 Johnny Sain 1.50 4.00
52R17 Ralph Houk 1.50 4.00
52R18 Joe Collins 1.50 4.00
52R19 Hank Bauer 1.50 4.00

2002 Topps 1952 Reprints Autographs

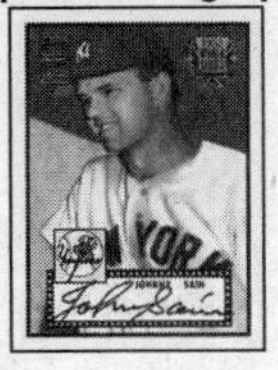

Inserted in series one packs at a rate of one in 10,268 hobby packs, one in 2826 HTA packs and one in 8,005 retail packs and series two packs at a rate of 1:7524 hobby, one in 1985 HTA packs and one in 5839 retail packs these eleven cards feature signed copies of the 1952 reprints. Phil Rizzuto did not return his cards in time for inclusion in this product and those cards could be redeemed until December 1st, 2003. Due to scarcity, no pricing is provided for these cards. These cards were released in different series and we have notated that information next to the player's name in our checklist.

APA Andy Pafko S1 75.00 150.00
CEA Carl Erskine S1 50.00 100.00
DSA Duke Snider S1 75.00 150.00
GMA Gil McDougald S1 50.00 100.00
HBA Hank Bauer S2
JBA Joe Black S1 50.00 100.00
JSA Johnny Sain S2
PRA Preacher Roe S2
PRA Phil Rizzuto S1 75.00 150.00
RHA Ralph Houk S2
YBA Yogi Berra S2

2002 Topps 1952 World Series Highlights

Inserted in first and second series packs at a rate of one in 25 hobby, one in five HTA and one in 16 retail packs, these eleven cards feature highlights of the 1952 World Series. Next to the card, we have notated whether they were released in the first or second series.

COMPLETE SET (7) 4.00 10.00
COMPLETE SERIES 1 (3) 1.50 4.00
COMPLETE SERIES 2 (4) 2.50 6.00
52WS1 Dodgers Line Up 1 .75 2.00
52WS2 Billy Martin's Homer 2 .75 2.00
52WS3 Dodgers Celebrate 1 .75 2.00
52WS4 Yanks Slip Dodgers 2 .75 2.00
52WS5 Carl Erskine 1 .75 2.00
52WS6 Casey Stengel MG .75 2.00
Allie Reynolds 2
52WS7 Allie Reynolds .75 2.00
Relieves Ed Lopat 2

2002 Topps 5-Card Stud Aces Relics

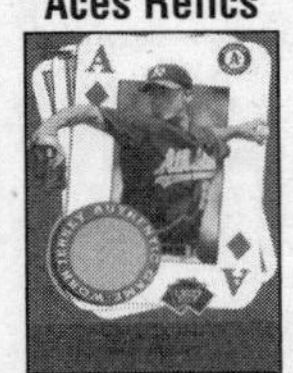

Inserted into second series packs at a rate of one in 1180 hobby, one in 293 HTA and one in 966 retail, these five cards feature some of the best pitchers in baseball along with a game jersey swatch "relic".

5AGM Greg Maddux Jsy 30.00 60.00
5AMH Mike Hampton Jsy 10.00 25.00
5AMM Mark Mulder Jsy 10.00 25.00
5APM Pedro Martinez Jsy 15.00 40.00
5ARJ Randy Johnson Jsy 15.00 40.00

2002 Topps 5-Card Stud Deuces are Wild Relics

Inserted into second series packs at an overall rate of one in 1962 hobby, one in 487 HTA and one in 1609 retail, these five cards feature memorabilia game bat and game jersey relics from two of the stars from the same team. These cards were issued in different odds depending on which series they were from and we have notated which group next to the card in the checklist.

SER.2 A ODDS 1:3078 H, 1:796 HTA, 1:2422 R
SER.2 B ODDS 1:5410 H, 1:1254 HTA, 1:4827 R
5DBG Bret Boone Jsy 15.00 40.00
Freddy Garcia Jsy A
5DBK Barry Bonds Jsy 40.00 80.00
Jeff Kent Jsy A
5DJG Randy Johnson Jsy 30.00 60.00
Luis Gonzalez Bat B
5DTA Jim Thome Jsy 30.00 60.00
Roberto Alomar Bat B
5DWH Larry Walker Bat 30.00 60.00
Todd Helton Bat B

2002 Topps 5-Card Stud Jack of All Trades Relics

Inserted into second series packs at an overall rate of one in 1350 Hobby packs, one in 333 HTA packs and one on 1119 retail packs, these five cards feature some of the best five-tool players in the field along with a game-used memorabilia relic from their career. These cards were issued at different odds depending on the player and we have notated that information in our checklist.

5JAJ Andruw Jones A 15.00 40.00
5JBB Barry Bonds Uni A 30.00 60.00
5JBW Bernie Williams Uni A 15.00 40.00
5JIR Ivan Rodriguez A 15.00 40.00
5JRO Roberto Alomar B 30.00 60.00

2002 Topps 5-Card Stud Kings of the Clubhouse Relics

Inserted into packs at an overall rate of one in 1449 hobby packs, one in 334 HTA packs and one in 1119 retail packs, these five cards feature some of the most effective and highly driven clubhouse leaders along with a game-used memorabilia relic from their career. Depending on the player, these cards were issued in two groups and we have notated that information in our checklist.

SER.2 A ODDS 1:1570 H, 1:358 HTA, 1:1211 R
SER.2B ODDS 1:18883 H,1:4943 HTA,1:14736 R
5KEM Edgar Martinez Jsy A 15.00 40.00
5KPO Paul O'Neill B 30.00 60.00
5KRJ Randy Johnson Jsy A 15.00 40.00
5KTG Tom Glavine Uni A 15.00 40.00
5KTH Todd Helton A 15.00 40.00

2002 Topps 5-Card Stud Three of a Kind Relics

Inserted into packs at an overall rate of one in 2039 Hobby packs, one in 524 HTA packs and one in retail 1609 packs, these five cards feature memorabilia relics from three stars from the same team. Depending on the team, these cards were issued as part of two groups, and we have notated that information next to the card in our checklist

SER.2 A ODDS 1:3078 H, 1:796 HTA, 1:2422 R
SER.2 B ODDS 1:6043 H, 1:1532 HTA, 1:4827 R
5TBDB A.J. Burnett Uni 30.00 60.00
Ryan Dempster Uni
Josh Beckett Uni A
5TFBJ Rafael Furcal 40.00 80.00
Wilson Betemit
Andruw Jones B
5TLOC Carlos Lee 40.00 80.00
Magglio Ordonez
Jose Canseco B
5TPSW Jorge Posada 40.00 80.00
Alfonso Soriano
Bernie Williams B
5TSPA Tsuyoshi Shinjo Uni 40.00 80.00
Mike Piazza Uni
Edgardo Alfonzo Uni A

2002 Topps All-World Team

Inserted into second series packs at a rate of one in 12 packs and one in 4 HTA packs, these 25 cards feature an international mix of upper-echelon stars. These cards are extremely thick as well.

COMPLETE SET (25) 30.00 60.00
AW1 Ichiro Suzuki 1.50 4.00
AW2 Barry Bonds 2.00 5.00
AW3 Pedro Martinez .60 1.50
AW4 Juan Gonzalez .60 1.50
AW5 Larry Walker .60 1.50
AW6 Sammy Sosa .75 2.00
AW7 Mariano Rivera .75 2.00
AW8 Vladimir Guerrero .75 2.00
AW9 Alex Rodriguez 1.25 3.00
AW10 Albert Pujols 1.50 4.00
AW11 Luis Gonzalez .60 1.50
AW12 Ken Griffey Jr. 1.25 3.00
AW13 Kazuhiro Sasaki .60 1.50
AW14 Bob Abreu .60 1.50
AW15 Todd Helton .60 1.50
AW16 Nomar Garciaparra 1.25 3.00
AW17 Miguel Tejada .60 1.50
AW18 Roger Clemens 1.50 4.00
AW19 Mike Piazza 1.25 3.00
AW20 Carlos Delgado .60 1.50
AW21 Derek Jeter 2.00 5.00
AW22 Hideo Nomo .75 2.00
AW23 Randy Johnson .75 2.00
AW24 Ivan Rodriguez .60 1.50
AW25 Chan Ho Park .60 1.50

2002 Topps Autographs

Inserted at varying odds, these 40 cards feature authentic autographs. Alex Rodriguez, Barry Bonds and Xavier Nady did not return their cards in time for series one packout, thus exchange cards were seeded into packs. Those cards could be redeemed until December 1st, 2003. First series cards have a numerical card number on back (i.e. TA-1) and series two cards have card numbering based on player's initials (i.e. TA-AB).

SER.1 A 1:15,402 H, 1:4256 HTA, 1:12,008 R
SER.2 A 1:10,071 H, 1:2404, 1:7702 R
SER.1 B 1:49,599 H, 1:12,312 HTA, 1:46,944 R
SER.2 B 1:1867 H, 1:487 HTA, 1:1449 R
SER.1 C 1:4104 H, 1:1130 HTA, 1:3238 R
SER.2 C 1:10,071 H, 1:2646 HTA, 1:7702 R
SER.1 D 1:9853 H, 1:2714 HTA, 1:7284 R
SER.2 D 1:1885 H, 1:496 HTA, 1:1449 R
SER.1 E 1:4104 H, 1:1130 HTA, 1:3238 R
SER.2 E 1:5023 H, 1:1323 HTA, 1:3851 R
SER.2 F 1:985 H, 1:271 HTA, 1:776 R
SER.2 F 1:940 H, 1:247 HTA, 1:725 R
SER.2 G 1:3017 H, 1:794 HTA, 1:2327 R
NO A1 PRICING DUE TO SCARCITY
TA1 Carlos Delgado B1 15.00 40.00
TA2 Ivan Rodriguez A1
TA3 Miguel Tejada C1 12.50 30.00
TA4 Geoff Jenkins E1 6.00 15.00
TA5 Johnny Damon A1
TA6 Tim Hudson C1 15.00 40.00
TA7 Terrence Long E1 4.00 10.00
TA8 Gabe Kapler C1 10.00 25.00
TA9 Magglio Ordonez C1 10.00 25.00
TA10 Barry Bonds A1
TA11 Pat Burrell C1 10.00 25.00
TA12 Mike Mussina A1
TA13 Eric Valent F1 4.00 10.00
TA14 Xavier Nady F1 4.00 10.00
TA15 Cristian Guerrero F1 4.00 10.00
TA16 Ben Sheets F1 10.00 25.00
TA17 Corey Patterson C1 6.00 15.00
TA18 Carlos Pena F1 4.00 10.00
TA19 Alex Rodriguez 75.00 150.00
D1/A2 EXCH
TAAB Adrian Beltre B2 12.50 30.00
TAAE Alex Escobar F2 4.00 10.00
TABG Brian Giles B2 12.50 30.00
TABW Brad Wilkerson G2 4.00 10.00
TABGR Ben Grieve B2 8.00 20.00
TACF Cliff Floyd C2 10.00 25.00
TACG Cristian Guzman B2 8.00 20.00
TAJD Jermaine Dye D2 10.00 25.00
TAJH Josh Hamilton E2 20.00 50.00
TAJO Jose Ortiz D2 6.00 15.00
TAJR Jimmy Rollins D2 12.50 30.00
TAJW Justin Wayne D2 6.00 15.00
TAKG Keith Ginter F2 4.00 10.00
TAMS Mike Sweeney B2 12.50 30.00
TANJ Nick Johnson F2 6.00 15.00
TARF Rafael Furcal B2 12.50 30.00
TARK Ryan Klesko B2 12.50 30.00
TARO Roy Oswalt F2 8.00 20.00
TARP Rafael Palmeiro A2 40.00 80.00
TARS Richie Sexson B2 12.50 30.00
TATG Troy Glaus A2 20.00 50.00

2002 Topps Coaches Collection Relics

Inserted at overall odds of one in 236 retail packs, these 26 cards feature memorabilia from either a coach or a manager currently involved in major league baseball. The Billy Williams jersey card was not available when these cards were packed and that card could be redeemed until April 30th, 2004.

SER.2 BAT ODDS 1:404 RETAIL
SER.2 UNIFORM ODDS 1:565 RETAIL
OVERALL SER.2 ODDS 1:236 RETAIL
CCAH Art Howe Bat 10.00 25.00
CCAT Alan Trammell Bat 15.00 40.00
CCBB Bruce Bochy Bat 10.00 25.00
CCBM Buck Martinez Bat 10.00 25.00
CCBV Bobby Valentine Bat 15.00 40.00
CCBW Billy Williams Jsy 15.00 40.00
CCBBE Buddy Bell Bat 15.00 40.00
CCBBR Bob Brenly Bat 15.00 40.00
CCDB Dusty Baker Bat 15.00 40.00
CCDL Davey Lopes Bat 15.00 40.00
CCDBA Don Baylor Bat 15.00 40.00
CCEH Elrod Hendricks Bat 10.00 25.00
CCEM Eddie Murray Bat 30.00 60.00
CCFW Frank White Bat 15.00 40.00
CCHM Hal McRae Jsy 4.00 10.00
CCJT Joe Torre Jsy 6.00 15.00
CCKG Ken Griffey Sr. Jsy 4.00 10.00
CCLB Larry Bowa Bat 15.00 40.00
CCLP Lance Parrish Bat 15.00 40.00
CCMH Mike Hargrove Bat 15.00 40.00
CCMS Mike Scioscia Bat 15.00 40.00
CCMW Mookie Wilson Bat 15.00 40.00
CCPG Phil Garner Bat 15.00 40.00
CCPM Paul Molitor Bat 15.00 40.00
CCTP Tony Perez Jsy 4.00 10.00
CCWR Willie Randolph Bat 15.00 40.00

2002 Topps Draft Picks

This 10-card set was distributed in two separate cello-wrapped five-card packets. Cards 1-5 were distributed in late August, 2002 as a bonus in green-boxed 2002 Topps retail factory sets. Cards 6-10 were distributed in November, 2002 within 2002 Topps Holiday factory sets. The cards are designed in the same manner as the Draft Picks and Prospects subsets from the basic 2002 Topps set and feature a selection of players chosen in the 2002 MLB Draft.

COMPLETE SET (10) 15.00 40.00
COMP.SERIES 1 SET (5) 6.00 15.00
COMP.SERIES 2 SET (5) 10.00 25.00
1 Scott Moore 2.00 5.00
2 Val Majewski 1.50 4.00
3 Brian Slocum 1.50 4.00
4 Chris Gruler 1.50 4.00
5 Mark Schramek 1.50 4.00
6 Joe Saunders 3.00 8.00
7 Jeff Francis 3.00 8.00
8 Royce Ring 1.50 4.00
9 Greg Miller 1.50 4.00
10 Brandon Weeden 1.50 4.00

2002 Topps East Meets West

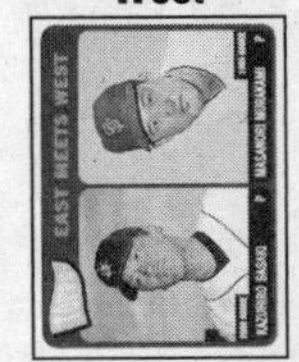

Issued at a rate of one in 24, these eight cards feature Masanori Murakami along with eight other Japanese players who have also played in the major leagues.

COMPLETE SET (8) 6.00 15.00
EWHI Hideki Irabu .75 2.00
Masanori Murakami
EWHN Hideo Nomo .75 2.00
Masanori Murakami
EWKS Kazuhiro Sasaki .75 2.00
Masanori Murakami
EWMS Mac Suzuki .75 2.00
Masanori Murakami
EWMY Masato Yoshii .75 2.00
Masanori Murakami
EWSH S. Hasagawa .75 2.00
Masanori Murakami
EWTO Tomo Ohka .75 2.00
Masanori Murakami
EWTS Tsuyoshi Shinjo .75 2.00
Masanori Murakami

2002 Topps East Meets West Relics

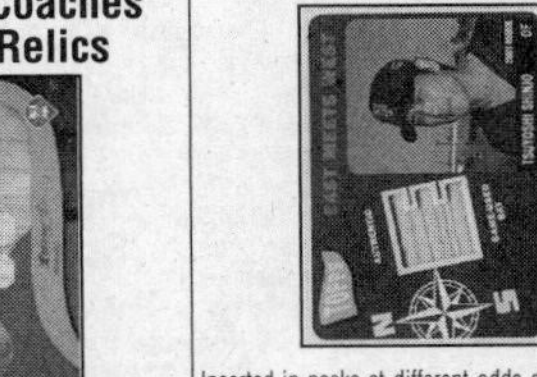

Inserted in packs at different odds depending on whether it is a bat or jersey card, these three cards feature game-used relics from Japanese born players.

SR1 BAT 1:12296 H,1:3380 HTA,1:9606 R
SER.1 JSY 1:3419 H, 1:939 HTA, 1:2685 R
EWRHN Hideo Nomo Jsy 20.00 50.00
EWRKS K. Sasaki Jsy 10.00 25.00
EWRTS T. Shinjo Bat 10.00 25.00

2002 Topps Ebbets Field Seat Relics

Inserted at a rate of one in 9,116 hobby packs, one in 2516 HTA packs and one in 7,222 retail packs, these nine cards feature not only the player but a slice of a seat used at Brooklyn's Ebbets Field.

EFRAP Andy Pafko 75.00 150.00
EFRBC Billy Cox 200.00 300.00
EFRCF Carl Furillo 75.00 150.00
EFRDS Duke Snider 150.00 250.00
EFRGH Gil Hodges 150.00 250.00
EFRJB Joe Black 75.00 150.00
EFRJR Jackie Robinson 200.00 300.00
EFRRC Roy Campanella 200.00 300.00
EFRPWR Pee Wee Reese 200.00 300.00

2002 Topps Ebbets Field/Yankee Stadium Seat Dual Relics

Featuring a slice of a seat from both Ebbets Field and from Yankee Stadium, these cards feature a selection of leading players from the 1952 World Series paired up with actual pieces of stadium seats taken from the historic Ebbets Field and Yankee Stadium ballparks. The Snider/Berra card was inserted at a rate of one in 86,070 series one hobby packs and the Rizzuto/Pafko card was inserted ata rate of one in 59,511 series two hobby packs. Only 52 copies of each card were produced. Both cards were intended to be hand-numbered (i.e. 1/52, 2/52 etc.) but due to production errors only the Snider/Berra card packed out as such.

RP Phil Rizzuto
Andy Pafko
SB Duke Snider
Yogi Berra

2002 Topps Ebbets Field/Yankee Stadium Seat Dual Relics Autographs

Inserted into first series packs at stated odds of one in 15,670 HTA packs and second series packs at a rate of one in 11,908 HTA packs, these cards feature a stadium seat along with an autograph of both featured players on these cards. Each card was issued to 25 serial numbered sets and due to market scarcity, no pricing is provided. The Rizzuto/Pafko card from series two was seeded into packs as an exchange card with a deadline of April 30th, 2004.

RP Phil Rizzuto
Andy Pafko 2
SB Duke Snider
Yogi Berra 1

2002 Topps Hall of Fame Vintage BuyBacks AutoProofs

In one of the most ambitious efforts put forth by a manufacturer in hobby history, Topps went into the secondary market and bought more than 3,500 vintage Topps cards (including an amazing selection from the 1950's and 1960's) featuring almost two dozen Hall of Famers (including stars such as Nolan Ryan, Yogi Berra and Carl Yastrzemski) for this far-reaching AutoProofs promotion. In most cases, 100 count lots of each vintage card were used (a staggering figure considering the scarcity of many of the 1950's and 1960's cards) with a few of the more common cards from the early 1980's tallying 200 or 300 count lots. After repurchase, each card was signed by the featured athlete, serial-numbered to a specific amount (exact print runs provided in our checklist) and affixed with a Topps hologram of authenticity on back. The cards were distributed across many 2002 Topps products - starting off with 2002 Topps series one baseball in November, 2001. Odds for finding these cards in packs is as follows: series 1 - 1:2341 hobby and 1:1841 retail; series 2 - 1:2341 hobby, 1:1841 retail.

OC2 Orl Cepeda 82 KM/200	10.00	25.00
SC7 S.Carlton 84 LL V/100	10.00	25.00
SC8 Steve Carlton 85/200	10.00	25.00
BR17 B.Robinson 82 KM/200	15.00	40.00
EW10 Earl Weaver 87/100	10.00	25.00
FJ33 F.Jenkins 84/100	10.00	25.00
GP26 G.Perry 82/100	10.00	25.00
GP29 G.Perry 83/100	10.00	25.00
GP30 G.Perry 83 SV/200	10.00	25.00
RF15 R.Fingers 81/300	10.00	25.00
RF16 R.Fingers 81 LL/100	10.00	25.00
RF18 R.Fingers 82/100	10.00	25.00
RF19 Rollie Fingers 82 IA/200	10.00	25.00
RF21 Rollie Fingers 82 KM/300	10.00	25.00
RF22 Rollie Fingers 83/200	10.00	25.00
RF24 Rollie Fingers 84/200	10.00	25.00
RF27 R.Fingers 85/300	10.00	25.00
RF28 Rollie Fingers 86/100	10.00	25.00
SC10 Steve Carlton 87/200	10.00	25.00

2002 Topps Hobby Masters

Inserted at a rate of one in 25 hobby and one in 16 retail packs, these 20 cards feature some of the leading players in the game.

COMPLETE SET (20)	30.00	80.00
HM1 Mark McGwire	3.00	8.00
HM2 Derek Jeter	3.00	8.00
HM3 Chipper Jones	1.25	3.00
HM4 Roger Clemens	2.50	6.00
HM5 Vladimir Guerrero	1.25	3.00
HM6 Ichiro Suzuki	2.50	6.00
HM7 Todd Helton	1.25	3.00
HM8 Alex Rodriguez	2.00	5.00
HM9 Albert Pujols	2.50	6.00
HM10 Sammy Sosa	1.25	3.00
HM11 Ken Griffey Jr.	2.00	5.00
HM12 Randy Johnson	1.25	3.00
HM13 Nomar Garciaparra	2.00	5.00
HM14 Ivan Rodriguez	1.25	3.00
HM15 Manny Ramirez	1.25	3.00
HM16 Barry Bonds	3.00	8.00
HM17 Mike Piazza	2.00	5.00
HM18 Pedro Martinez	1.25	3.00
HM19 Jeff Bagwell	1.25	3.00
HM20 Luis Gonzalez	1.25	3.00

2002 Topps Like Father Like Son Relics

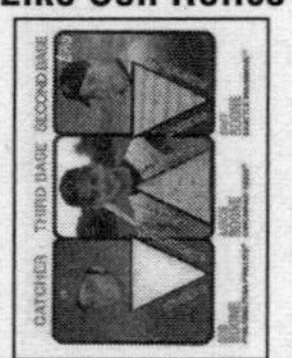

These combination memorabilia cards feature famous baseball families with two generations of fathers and sons. The card designs are each based upon the original Topps design of the father's rookie card season (aka The Boone Family card features a 1973 Topps style to honor the year Bob Boone had his Rookie Card issued). The cards were seeded exclusively into retail packs at a rate of 1:1304.

FSAL Sandy Alomar Sr. Bat Sandy Alomar Jr. Bat Roberto Alomar Bat	40.00	80.00
FSBE Yogi Berra Jsy Dale Berra Jsy	40.00	80.00
FSBON Bobby Bonds Uni Barry Bonds Uni	40.00	80.00
FSBOO Bob Boone Jsy Aaron Boone Jsy Bret Boone Bat	40.00	80.00
FSCR Jose Cruz Sr. Jose Cruz Jr.	40.00	80.00

2002 Topps Own the Game

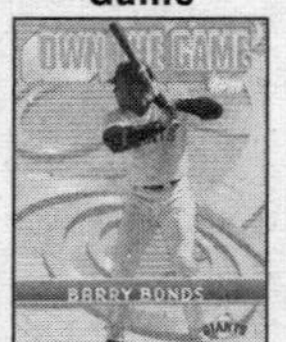

Issued at a rate of one in 12 hobby packs and one in eight retail packs, these 30 cards feature players who are among the league leaders for their position.

COMPLETE SET (30)	15.00	40.00
OG1 Moises Alou	.40	1.00
OG2 Roberto Alomar	.60	1.50
OG3 Luis Gonzalez	.40	1.00
OG4 Bret Boone	.40	1.00
OG5 Barry Bonds	2.50	6.00
OG6 Jim Thome	.60	1.50
OG7 Jimmy Rollins	.40	1.00
OG8 Cristian Guzman	.40	1.00
OG9 Lance Berkman	.40	1.00
OG10 Mike Sweeney	.40	1.00
OG11 Rich Aurilia	.40	1.00
OG12 Ichiro Suzuki	2.00	5.00
OG13 Luis Gonzalez	.40	1.00
OG14 Ichiro Suzuki	2.00	5.00
OG15 Jimmy Rollins	.40	1.00
OG16 Roger Cedeno	.40	1.00
OG17 Barry Bonds	2.50	6.00
OG18 Jim Thome	.60	1.50
OG19 Curt Schilling	.40	1.00
OG20 Roger Clemens	2.00	5.00
OG21 Curt Schilling	.40	1.00
OG22 Brad Radke	.40	1.00
OG23 Greg Maddux	1.50	4.00
OG24 Mark Mulder	.40	1.00
OG25 Jeff Shaw	.40	1.00
OG26 Mariano Rivera	1.00	2.50
OG27 Randy Johnson	1.00	2.50
OG28 Pedro Martinez	.60	1.50
OG29 John Burkett	.40	1.00
OG30 Tim Hudson	.40	1.00

2002 Topps Prime Cuts Autograph Relics

Inserted into first series packs at a rate of one in 88,678 hobby and one in 24,624 HTA and second series packs at one in 8927 hobby and one in 2360 HTA packs, these eight cards feature both a memorabilia relic from the player's career as well as their autograph. Cards from series one were issued to a stated print run of 60 serial numbered sets while cards from series two were issued to a stated print run of 50 serial numbered sets. We have notated next to the players name which series the card was issued in.

NO PRICING DUE TO SCARCITY
PCAAE Alex Escobar S2
PCABB Barry Bonds S1
PCAJH Josh Hamilton S2
PCANJ Nick Johnson S2
PCATH Toby Hall S2
PCAWB Wilson Betemit S2
PCAXN Xavier Nady S2
PCACPE Carlos Pena S2

2002 Topps Prime Cuts Barrel Relics

Inserted in second series packs at a rate of one in 7824 hobby packs and one in 2063 HTA packs, these eight cards feature a piece from the selected player bat barrel. These cards were issued to a stated print run of 50 serial numbered sets.

NO PRICING DUE TO SCARCITY
PCAAD Adam Dunn
PCAAG Alexis Gomez
PCAAR Aaron Rowand
PCACP Corey Patterson
PCAJC Joe Crede
PCAMG Marcus Giles
PCARS Ruben Salazar
PCASB Sean Burroughs

2002 Topps Prime Cuts Pine Tar Relics

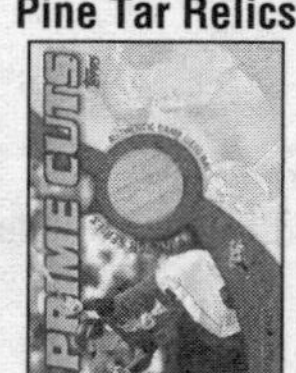

Inserted in packs at stated odds of one in 4,420 hobby packs and one in 1214 HTA packs for first series packs and one in 1043 hobby and one in 275 HTA packs for second series packs, these 20 cards feature pieces from the pine tar section of the player's bat. We have notated which series the player was issued in next to his name in our checklist. These cards have a stated print run of 200 serial numbered sets.

PCPAD Adam Dunn 2	20.00	50.00
PCPAE Alex Escobar 2	20.00	50.00
PCPAG Alexis Gomez 2	20.00	50.00
PCPAP Albert Pujols 1	40.00	80.00
PCPAR Aaron Rowand 2	20.00	50.00
PCPBB Barry Bonds 1	40.00	80.00
PCPCP Corey Patterson 2	20.00	50.00
PCPJC Joe Crede 2	20.00	50.00
PCPJH Josh Hamilton 2	50.00	100.00
PCPLG Luis Gonzalez 1	20.00	50.00
PCPMG Marcus Giles 2	20.00	50.00
PCPNJ Nick Johnson 2	20.00	50.00
PCPRS Ruben Salazar 2	20.00	50.00
PCPSB Sean Burroughs 2	20.00	50.00
PCPTG Tony Gwynn 1	30.00	60.00
PCPTH Todd Helton 1	30.00	60.00
PCPTH Toby Hall 2	20.00	50.00
PCPWB Wilson Betemit 2	20.00	50.00
PCPXN Xavier Nady 2	20.00	50.00
PCPCPE Carlos Pena 2	20.00	50.00

2002 Topps Prime Cuts Trademark Relics

Issued in first series packs at a rate of one in 8,868 hobby and one in 2428 HTA packs and second series packs at a rate of one in 2087 hobby and one in 549 HTA packs, these cards feature a slice of bat taken from the trademark section of a game used bat. Only 100 serial numbered copies of each card were produced. First and second series distribution information is detailed after the player's name in our set checklist.

PCTAD Adam Dunn 2	30.00	60.00
PCTAE Alex Escobar 2	30.00	60.00
PCTAG Alexis Gomez 2	30.00	60.00
PCTAP Albert Pujols 1	60.00	120.00
PCTAR Aaron Rowand 2	30.00	60.00
PCTBB Barry Bonds 1	60.00	120.00
PCTCP Corey Patterson 2	30.00	60.00
PCTJC Joe Crede 2	30.00	60.00
PCTJH Josh Hamilton 2	60.00	120.00
PCTLG Luis Gonzalez 1	30.00	60.00
PCTMG Marcus Giles 2	30.00	60.00
PCTNJ Nick Johnson 2	30.00	60.00
PCTRS Ruben Salazar 2	30.00	60.00
PCTSB Sean Burroughs 2	30.00	60.00
PCTTG Tony Gwynn 1	50.00	100.00
PCTTH Todd Helton 1	40.00	80.00
PCTTH Toby Hall 2	30.00	60.00
PCTWB Wilson Betemit 2	30.00	60.00
PCTXN Xavier Nady 2	30.00	60.00
PCTCPE Carlos Pena 2	30.00	60.00

2002 Topps Ring Masters

Issued at a rate of one in 25 hobby packs and one in 16 retail packs, these 10 cards feature players who have earned World Series rings in their career.

COMPLETE SET (10)	10.00	25.00
RM1 Derek Jeter	2.00	5.00
RM2 Mark McGwire	2.00	5.00
RM3 Mariano Rivera	.75	2.00
RM4 Gary Sheffield	.60	1.50
RM5 Al Leiter	.60	1.50
RM6 Chipper Jones	.75	2.00
RM7 Roger Clemens	1.50	4.00
RM8 Greg Maddux	1.25	3.00
RM9 Roberto Alomar	.60	1.50
RM10 Paul O'Neill	.60	1.50

2002 Topps Summer School Battery Mates Relics

Issued at a rate of one in 4,4401 hobby packs and one in 3,477 retail packs, these two cards feature a pitcher and catcher from the same team.

BMLP Al Leiter Mike Piazza	15.00	40.00
BMML Greg Maddux Javy Lopez	15.00	40.00

2002 Topps Summer School Heart of the Order Relics

Issued at an overall rate of one in 4,247 hobby packs and one in 3,325 retail packs, these four cards feature relics from three key players from a team's lineup.

SER.1 A 1:8,220 H, 1:2253 HTA, 1:6452 R
SER.1 B 1:8,778 H, 1:2411 HTA, 1:6862 R

HTOARB Bob Abreu Scott Rolen Pat Burrell A	40.00	80.00
HTOKBA Jeff Kent Barry Bonds Rich Aurilia A	50.00	100.00
HTOOWM Paul O'Neill Bernie Williams Tino Martinez A	40.00	80.00
HTOTGA Jim Thome Juan Gonzalez Roberto Alomar B	40.00	80.00

2002 Topps Summer School Hit and Run Relics

Issued at an overall rate of one in 4,241 hobby packs and one in 3,325 HTA packs, these three cards feature relics from some of the leading young stars in baseball.

SER.1 A 1:24591 H, 1:6760 HTA, 1:19649 R
SER.1 B 1:12296 H, 1:3380 HTA, 1:9606 R
SER.1 C 1:8788 H, 1:2411 HTA, 1:6862 R

HRRDE Darin Erstad Bat B {UER Name spelled Darrin on front	6.00	15.00
HRRJD J.Damon Bat A	10.00	25.00
HRRRF R.Furcal Jsy C	6.00	15.00

2002 Topps Summer School Turn Two Relics

Issued at a rate of one in 4,401 hobby packs and one in 3,477 retail packs, these two cards feature relics from two of the best double play combination in baseball's history.

TTRTW Alan Trammell Lou Whitaker	20.00	50.00
TTRVA Omar Vizquel Roberto Alomar	20.00	50.00

2002 Topps Summer School Two Bagger Relics

Issued at an overall rate of one in 3,733 hobby packs and one in 2,941 retail packs, these three cards feature game-used relics from leading hitters in the game.

SER.1 A 1:4401 H, 1:1210 HTA, 1:3477 R
SER.1 B 1:24591 H,1:6760 HTA,1:19649 R

2BSR Scott Rolen Jsy A	10.00	25.00
2BTG Tony Gwynn Bat B	15.00	40.00
2BTH Todd Helton Jsy A	10.00	25.00

2002 Topps Yankee Stadium Seat Relics

Inserted into second series packs at a stated rate of one in 579 Hobby, one in 1472 HTA and one in 4313 Retail, these nine cards feature retired Yankee greats along with a piece of a seat used in the originaly Yankee Stadium.

YSRAR Allie Reynolds	75.00	150.00
YSRBM Billy Martin	150.00	250.00
YSRGM Gil McDougald	75.00	150.00
YSRGW Gene Woodling	75.00	150.00
YSRHB Hank Bauer	100.00	200.00
YSRJC Joe Collins	75.00	150.00
YSRJM Johnny Mize	75.00	150.00
YSRPR Phil Rizzuto	150.00	250.00
YSRYB Yogi Berra	150.00	250.00

2002 Topps Traded

This 275 card set was released in October, 2002. These cards were issued in 10 card hobby packs which were issued 24 packs to a box and 12 boxes to a case with an SRP of $3 per pack. In addition,

this product was also issued in 35 count HTA packs. Cards numbered 1 to 100 were issued one per pack. Cards from previous traded sets were repurchased by Topps and were issued at a stated rate of one in 24 Hobby and Retail Packs and one in 10 HTA packs. However, there is no way of being able to identify that these cards are anything but original cards as no marking or stamping is on these cards.

COMPLETE SET (275)	100.00	200.00
COMMON CARD (T1-T110)	.75	2.00
COMMON CARD (T111-T275)	.15	.40
T1 Jeff Weaver	.75	2.00
T2 Jay Powell	.75	2.00
T3 Alex Gonzalez	.75	2.00
T4 Jason Isringhausen	.75	2.00
T5 Tyler Houston	.75	2.00
T6 Ben Broussard	.75	2.00
T7 Chuck Knoblauch	.75	2.00
T8 Brian L. Hunter	.75	2.00
T9 Dustan Mohr	.75	2.00
T10 Eric Hinske	.75	2.00
T11 Roger Cedeno	.75	2.00
T12 Eddie Perez	.75	2.00
T13 Jeromy Burnitz	.75	2.00
T14 Bartolo Colon	.75	2.00
T15 Rick Helling	.75	2.00
T16 Dan Plesac	.75	2.00
T17 Scott Strickland	.75	2.00
T18 Antonio Alfonseca	.75	2.00
T19 Ricky Gutierrez	.75	2.00
T20 John Valentin	.75	2.00
T21 Raul Mondesi	.75	2.00
T22 Ben Davis	.75	2.00
T23 Nelson Figueroa	.75	2.00
T24 Earl Snyder	.75	2.00
T25 Robin Ventura	.75	2.00
T26 Jimmy Haynes	.75	2.00
T27 Kenny Kelly	.75	2.00
T28 Morgan Ensberg	.40	1.00
T29 Reggie Sanders	.75	2.00
T30 Shigetoshi Hasegawa	.75	2.00
T31 Mike Timlin	.75	2.00
T32 Russell Branyan	.75	2.00
T33 Alan Embree	.75	2.00
T34 D'Angelo Jimenez	.75	2.00
T35 Kent Mercker	.75	2.00
T36 Jesse Orosco	.75	2.00
T37 Gregg Zaun	.75	2.00
T38 Reggie Taylor	.75	2.00
T39 Andres Galarraga	.75	2.00
T40 Chris Truby	.75	2.00
T41 Bruce Chen	.75	2.00
T42 Darren Lewis	.75	2.00
T43 Ryan Kohlmeier	.75	2.00
T44 John McDonald	.75	2.00
T45 Omar Daal	.75	2.00
T46 Matt Clement	.75	2.00
T47 Glendon Rusch	.75	2.00
T48 Chan Ho Park	.75	2.00
T49 Benny Agbayani	.75	2.00
T50 Juan Gonzalez	.75	2.00
T51 Carlos Baerga	.75	2.00
T52 Tim Raines	.75	2.00
T53 Kevin Appier	.75	2.00
T54 Marty Cordova	.75	2.00
T55 Jeff D'Amico	.75	2.00
T56 Dmitri Young	.75	2.00
T57 Roosevelt Brown	.75	2.00
T58 Dustin Hermanson	.75	2.00
T59 Jose Rijo	.75	2.00
T60 Todd Ritchie	.75	2.00
T61 Lee Stevens	.75	2.00
T62 Placido Polanco	.75	2.00
T63 Eric Young	.75	2.00
T64 Chuck Finley	.75	2.00
T65 Dicky Gonzalez	.75	2.00
T66 Jose Macias	.75	2.00
T67 Gabe Kapler	.75	2.00
T68 Sandy Alomar Jr.	.75	2.00
T69 Henry Blanco	.75	2.00
T70 Julian Tavarez	.75	2.00
T71 Paul Bako	.75	2.00
T72 Scott Rolen	1.25	3.00
T73 Brian Jordan	.75	2.00
T74 Rickey Henderson	1.50	4.00
T75 Kevin Mench	.75	2.00
T76 Hideo Nomo	1.50	4.00
T77 Jeremy Giambi	.75	2.00
T78 Brad Fullmer	.75	2.00
T79 Carl Everett	.75	2.00
T80 David Wells	.75	2.00
T81 Aaron Sele	.75	2.00
T82 Todd Hollandsworth	.75	2.00
T83 Vicente Padilla	.75	2.00
T84 Kenny Lofton	.75	2.00
T85 Corky Miller	.75	2.00
T86 Josh Fogg	.75	2.00
T87 Cliff Floyd	.75	2.00
T88 Craig Paquette	.75	2.00
T89 Jay Payton	.75	2.00
T90 Carlos Pena	.75	2.00
T91 Juan Encarnacion	.75	2.00
T92 Rey Sanchez	.75	2.00
T93 Ryan Dempster	.75	2.00
T94 Mario Encarnacion	.75	2.00
T95 Jorge Julio	.75	2.00
T96 John Mabry	.75	2.00
T97 Todd Zeile	.75	2.00
T98 Johnny Damon Sox	1.25	3.00
T99 Deivi Cruz	.75	2.00
T100 Gary Sheffield	.75	2.00
T101 Ted Lilly	.75	2.00
T102 Todd Van Poppel	.75	2.00
T103 Shawn Estes	.75	2.00
T104 Cesar Izturis	.75	2.00
T105 Ron Coomer	.75	2.00
T106 Grady Little MG RC	.75	2.00
T107 Jimy Williams MG	.75	2.00
T108 Tony Pena MG	.75	2.00
T109 Frank Robinson MG	1.25	3.00
T110 Ron Gardenhire MG	.75	2.00
T111 Dennis Tankersley	.15	.40
T112 Alejandro Cadena RC	.15	.40
T113 Justin Reid RC	.15	.40
T114 Nate Field RC	.15	.40
T115 Rene Reyes RC	.15	.40
T116 Nelson Castro RC	.15	.40
T117 Miguel Olivo	.15	.40
T118 David Espinosa	.15	.40
T119 Chris Bootcheck RC	.15	.40
T120 Rob Henkel RC	.15	.40
T121 Steve Bechler RC	.15	.40
T122 Mark Outlaw RC	.15	.40
T123 Henry Pichardo RC	.15	.40
T124 Michael Floyd RC	.15	.40
T125 Richard Lane RC	.15	.40
T126 Pete Zamora RC	.15	.40
T127 Javier Colina	.15	.40
T128 Greg Sain RC	.15	.40
T129 Ronnie Merrill	.15	.40
T130 Gavin Floyd RC	.40	1.00
T131 Josh Bonifay RC	.15	.40
T132 Tommy Marx RC	.15	.40
T133 Gary Cates Jr. RC	.15	.40
T134 Neal Cotts RC	.40	1.00
T135 Angel Berroa	.15	.40
T136 Elio Serrano RC	.15	.40
T137 J.J. Putz RC	.20	.50
T138 Ruben Gotay RC	.20	.50
T139 Eddie Rogers	.15	.40
T140 Wily Mo Pena	.15	.40
T141 Tyler Yates RC	.15	.40
T142 Colin Young RC	.15	.40
T143 Chance Caple	.15	.40
T144 Ben Howard RC	.15	.40
T145 Ryan Bukvich RC	.15	.40
T146 Cliff Bartosh RC	.15	.40
T147 Brandon Claussen	.15	.40
T148 Cristian Guerrero	.15	.40
T149 Derrick Lewis	.15	.40
T150 Eric Miller RC	.15	.40
T151 Justin Huber RC	.30	.75
T152 Adrian Gonzalez	.15	.40
T153 Brian West RC	.15	.40
T154 Chris Baker RC	.15	.40
T155 Drew Henson	.15	.40
T156 Scott Hairston RC	.20	.50
T157 Jason Simontacchi RC	.15	.40
T158 Jason Arnold RC	.15	.40
T159 Brandon Phillips	.15	.40
T160 Adam Roller RC	.15	.40
T161 Scotty Layfield RC	.15	.40
T162 Freddie Money RC	.15	.40
T163 Noochie Varner RC	.15	.40
T164 Terrance Hill RC	.15	.40
T165 Jeremy Hill RC	.15	.40
T166 Carlos Cabrera RC	.15	.40
T167 Jose Morban RC	.15	.40
T168 Kevin Frederick RC	.15	.40
T169 Mark Teixeira	.60	1.50
T170 Brian Rogers	.15	.40
T171 Anastacio Martinez RC	.15	.40
T172 Bobby Jenks RC	.60	1.50
T173 David Gil RC	.15	.40
T174 Andres Torres	.15	.40
T175 James Barrett RC	.15	.40
T176 Jimmy Journell	.15	.40
T177 Brett Kay RC	.15	.40
T178 Jason Young RC	.15	.40
T179 Mark Hamilton RC	.15	.40
T180 Jose Bautista RC	.40	1.00
T181 Blake McGinley RC	.15	.40
T182 Ryan Mottl RC	.15	.40
T183 Jeff Austin RC	.15	.40
T184 Xavier Nady	.15	.40
T185 Kyle Kane RC	.15	.40
T186 Travis Foley RC	.15	.40
T187 Nathan Kaup RC	.15	.40
T188 Eric Cyr	.15	.40
T189 Josh Cisneros RC	.15	.40
T190 Brad Nelson RC	.15	.40
T191 Clint Weibl RC	.15	.40
T192 Ron Calloway RC	.15	.40
T193 Jung Bong	.15	.40
T194 Rolando Viera RC	.15	.40
T195 Jason Bulger RC	.15	.40
T196 Chone Figgins RC	.60	1.50
T197 Jimmy Alvarez RC	.15	.40
T198 Joel Crump RC	.15	.40
T199 Ryan Doumit RC	.25	.60
T200 Demetrius Heath RC	.15	.40
T201 John Ennis RC	.15	.40
T202 Doug Sessions RC	.15	.40
T203 Clinton Hosford RC	.15	.40
T204 Chris Narveson RC	.15	.40
T205 Ross Peeples RC	.15	.40
T206 Alex Requena RC	.15	.40
T207 Matt Erickson RC	.15	.40
T208 Brian Forystek RC	.15	.40
T209 Dewon Brazelton	.15	.40
T210 Nathan Haynes	.15	.40
T211 Jack Cust	.15	.40
T212 Jesse Foppert RC	.20	.50
T213 Jesus Cota RC	.15	.40
T214 Juan M. Gonzalez RC	.15	.40
T215 Tim Kalita RC	.15	.40
T216 Manny Delcarmen RC	.20	.50
T217 Jim Kavourias RC	.15	.40
T218 C.J. Wilson RC	.15	.40
T219 Edwin Yan RC	.15	.40
T220 Andy Van Hekken	.15	.40
T221 Michael Cuddyer	.15	.40
T222 Jeff Verplancke RC	.15	.40
T223 Mike Wilson RC	.15	.40
T224 Corwin Malone RC	.15	.40
T225 Chris Snelling RC	.25	.60
T226 Joe Rogers RC	.15	.40
T227 Jason Bay	1.50	4.00
T228 Ezequiel Astacio RC	.15	.40
T229 Joey Hammond RC	.15	.40
T230 Chris Duffy RC	.20	.50
T231 Mark Prior	.60	1.50
T232 Hansel Izquierdo RC	.15	.40
T233 Franklyn German RC	.15	.40
T234 Alexis Gomez	.15	.40
T235 Jorge Padilla RC	.15	.40
T236 Ryan Snare RC	.15	.40
T237 Deivis Santos	.15	.40

T238 Taggert Bozied RC .20 .50
T239 Mike Peeples RC .15 .40
T240 Ronald Acuna RC .15 .40
T241 Koyie Hill .15 .40
T242 Garrett Guzman RC .15 .40
T243 Ryan Church RC .40 1.00
T244 Tony Fontana RC .15 .40
T245 Keto Anderson RC .15 .40
T246 Brad Bouras RC .15 .40
T247 Jason Dubois RC .20 .50
T248 Angel Guzman RC .30 .75
T249 Joel Hanrahan RC .15 .40
T250 Joe Jiannetti RC .15 .40
T251 Sean Pierce RC .15 .40
T252 Jake Mauer RC .15 .40
T253 Marshall McDougall RC .15 .40
T254 Edwin Almonte RC .15 .40
T255 Shawn Riggans RC .15 .40
T256 Steven Shell RC .15 .40
T257 Kevin Hooper RC .15 .40
T258 Michael Frick RC .15 .40
T259 Travis Chapman RC .15 .40
T260 Tim Hummel RC .15 .40
T261 Adam Morrissey RC .15 .40
T262 Dontrelle Willis RC 2.00 5.00
T263 Justin Sherrod RC .15 .40
T264 Gerald Smiley RC .15 .40
T265 Tony Miller RC .15 .40
T266 Nolan Ryan WW 1.00 2.50
T267 Reggie Jackson WW .25 .60
T268 Steve Garvey WW .15 .40
T269 Wade Boggs WW .25 .60
T270 Sammy Sosa WW .40 1.00
T271 Curt Schilling WW .15 .40
T272 Mark Grace WW .25 .60
T273 Jason Giambi WW .15 .40
T274 Ken Griffey Jr. WW .60 1.50
T275 Roberto Alomar WW .25 .60

2002 Topps Traded Gold

Inserted at a stated rate of one in three hobby and retail and one per HTA pack, this is a paralle of the 2002 Topps Traded set. Each card has "gold" borders and were issued to a stated print run of 2002 serial numbered sets.

*GOLD 1-110: .6X TO 1.5X BASIC
*GOLD 111-275: 2.5X TO 6X BASIC
*GOLD RC'S 111-275: 1.5X TO 4X BASIC RC'S
T262 Dontrelle Willis 5.00 12.00

2002 Topps Traded Farewell Relic

Inserted at a stated rate of one in 590 Hobby, one in 169 HTA and in 595 Retail packs, this one card set features one-time MVP Jose Canseco along with a game-used bat piece from his career. Canseco had announced his retirement during the 2002 season in an failed attempt to return to the majors.

FWJC Jose Canseco Bat 6.00 15.00

2002 Topps Traded Hall of Fame Relic

Inserted at a stated rate of one in 1533 Hobby Packs, one in 439 HTA packs and one in 1574 Retail packs, this one card set features Ozzie Smith along with a game-used bat piece from his career. Ozzie Smith was inducted into the HOF in 2002.

HOFOS Ozzie Smith Bat 12.50 30.00

2002 Topps Traded Signature Moves

Inserted at overall odds of one in 91 Hobby or Retail packs and one in 26 HTA packs, these 26 cards feature a mix of basically prospects along with a couple of stars who moved to new teams for 2002 and signed these cards for inclusion in the Topps Traded set. Since there were nine different insertion odds for these cards we have notated both the insertion odds for each group along with which group the player belong to.

A ODDS 1:15,292 H, 1:4288 HTA, 1:22,032 R
B ODDS 1:3846 H, 1:1105 HTA, 1:3840 R
C ODDS 1:6147 H, 1:1778 HTA, 1:6418 R
D ODDS 1:1917 H, 1:548 HTA, 1:1953 R
E ODDS 1:341 H, 1:97 HTA, 1:342 R
F ODDS 1:2247 H, 1:645 HTA, 1:2261 R
G ODDS 1:568 H, 1:162 HTA, 1:571 R
GROUP H ODDS 1:256 H/R, 1:73 HTA
I ODDS 1:1023 H, 1:293 HTA, 1:1025 R
OVERALL ODDS 1:91 HOB/RET, 1:26 HTA
AC Antoine Cameron D 4.00 10.00
AM Andy Morales H 3.00 8.00
BB Boof Bonser E 4.00 10.00
BC Brandon Claussen E 4.00 10.00
CS Chris Smith G 3.00 8.00
CU Chase Utley E 60.00 120.00
CW Corwin Malone H 3.00 8.00
DT Dennis Tankersley F 4.00 10.00
FJ Forrest Johnson E 4.00 10.00
JD Johnny Damon Sox B 15.00 40.00
JD Jeff DaVanon I 3.00 8.00
JM Jake Mauer G 4.00 10.00
JM Justin Morneau H 10.00 25.00
JP Juan Pena E 4.00 10.00
JS Juan Silvestre D 4.00 10.00
JW Justin Wayne E 4.00 10.00
KI Kazuhisa Ishii A 15.00 40.00
MC Matt Cooper E 4.00 10.00
MO Moises Alou B 6.00 15.00
MT Marcus Thames G 3.00 8.00
RA Roberto Alomar C 10.00 25.00
RH Ryan Hannaman E 4.00 10.00
RM Ramon Moreta H 4.00 10.00
TB Tony Blanco E 4.00 10.00
TL Todd Linden H 4.00 10.00
VD Victor Diaz H 4.00 10.00

2002 Topps Traded Tools of the Trade Dual Relics

Inserted at overall odds of one in 539 Hobby, one in 155 HTA and one in 542 Retail packs, these three cards feature two game-used relics from the featured players. As these cards were issued in different insertion ratios, we have notated that information as to the player's specific group next to their name in our checklist.

A ODDS 1:3407 H, 1:972 HTA, 1:3672 R
B ODDS 1:639 H, 1:183 HTA, 1:642 R
DTRRCP Chan Ho Park Jsy-Jsy B 6.00 15.00
DTRRHN Hideo Nomo Jsy-Jsy A 15.00 40.00
DTRRMO Moises Alou Jsy-Jsy B 6.00 15.00

2002 Topps Traded Tools of the Trade Relics

Inserted at overall odds for bats of one in 34 Hobby and Retail and one in 10 HTA and for jerseys at one in 426 Hobby, one in 122 HTA and one in 427 retail, these 35 cards feature players who switched teams for the 2002 season along with a game-used memorabilia piece. We have notated in our checklist what type of memorabilia piece on each player's card. In addition, since the bat cards were inserted at three different odds, we have notated that information as to the card's group next to their name in our checklist.

BAT A 1:1203 H, 1:344 HTA, 1:1224 R
BAT B 1:1807 H, 1:517 HTA, 1:1836 R
BAT C 1:35 H/R, 1:10 HTA
AB Roberto Alomar Bat C 4.00 10.00
AG Andres Galarraga Bat C 3.00 8.00
BF Brad Fullmer Bat C 3.00 8.00
BJ Brian Jordan Bat C 3.00 8.00
CE Carl Everett Bat C 3.00 8.00
CK Chuck Knoblauch Bat C 3.00 8.00
CP Carlos Pena Bat A 4.00 10.00
DB David Bell Bat C 3.00 8.00
DJ Dave Justice Bat C 3.00 8.00
EY Eric Young Bat C 3.00 8.00
GS Gary Sheffield Bat C 3.00 8.00
HB Rickey Henderson Bat C 4.00 10.00
JBU Jeromy Burnitz Bat C 3.00 8.00
JCI Jeff Cirillo Bat B 3.00 8.00
JDB Johnny Damon Sox Bat C 4.00 10.00
JG Juan Gonzalez Jsy 3.00 8.00
JP Josh Phelps Jsy 3.00 8.00
JV John Vander Wal Bat C 3.00 8.00
KL Kenny Lofton Bat C 3.00 8.00
MA Moises Alou Bat C 3.00 8.00
MLB Matt Lawton Bat C 3.00 8.00
MT Michael Tucker Bat C 3.00 8.00
MVB Mo Vaughn Bat C 3.00 8.00
MVJ Mo Vaughn Jsy 3.00 8.00
PP Placido Polanco Bat A 4.00 10.00
RS Reggie Sanders Bat C 3.00 8.00
RV Robin Ventura Bat C 3.00 8.00
RW Rondell White Bat C 3.00 8.00
SI Ruben Sierra Bat C 3.00 8.00
SR Scott Rolen Bat A 10.00 25.00
TC Tony Clark Bat C 3.00 8.00
TM Tino Martinez Bat C 4.00 10.00
TR Tim Raines Bat C 3.00 8.00
TS Tsuyoshi Shinjo Bat C 3.00 8.00
VC Vinny Castilla Bat C 3.00 8.00

2003 Topps

The first series of 366 cards was released in November, 2002. The second series of 354 cards were released in April, 2003. The set was issued either in 10 card hobby packs or 36 card HTA packs. The regular packs were issued 36 packs to a box and 12 boxes to a case with an SRP of $1.59. The HTA packs were issued 12 packs to a box and eight boxes to a case with an SRP of $5 per pack. The following subsets were issued in the first series: 262 through 291 basically featured current managers, cards numbered 292 through 321 featured players in their first year on a Topps card, cards numbered 322 through 331 featured two players who were expected to be major rookies during the 2003 season, cards numbered 332 through 336 honored players who achieved major feats during 2002, cards numbered 337 through 352 featured league leaders, cards 354 and 355 had post season highlights and cards 356 through 367 honored the best players in the American League. Second series subsets included Team Checklists (630-659); Draft Picks (660-674); Prospects (675-684); Award Winners (685-708) All-Stars (709-719) and World Series (720-721). As has been Topps tradition since 1997, there was no card number 7 issued in honor of the memory of Mickey Mantle.

COMPLETE SET (720) 40.00 80.00
COMPLETE SERIES 1 (366) 20.00 40.00
COMPLETE SERIES 2 (354) 20.00 40.00
COMMON CARD (1-6/8-721) .07 .20
COMMON (292-331/660-684) .20 .50
1 Alex Rodriguez .30 .75
2 Dan Wilson .07 .20
3 Jimmy Rollins .07 .20
4 Jermaine Dye .07 .20
5 Steve Karsay .07 .20
6 Timo Perez .07 .20
8 Jose Vidro .07 .20
9 Eddie Guardado .07 .20
10 Mark Prior .10 .30
11 Curt Schilling .07 .20
12 Dennis Cook .07 .20
13 Andruw Jones .10 .30
14 David Segui .07 .20
15 Trot Nixon .07 .20
16 Kerry Wood .07 .20
17 Magglio Ordonez .07 .20
18 Jason LaRue .07 .20
19 Danys Baez .07 .20
20 Todd Helton .10 .30
21 Denny Neagle .07 .20
22 Dave Mlicki .07 .20
23 Roberto Hernandez .07 .20
24 Odalis Perez .07 .20
25 Nick Neugebauer .07 .20
26 David Ortiz .20 .50
27 Andres Galarraga .07 .20
28 Edgardo Alfonzo .07 .20
29 Chad Bradford .07 .20
30 Jason Giambi .07 .20
31 Brian Giles .07 .20
32 Deivi Cruz .07 .20
33 Robb Nen .07 .20
34 Jeff Nelson .07 .20
35 Edgar Renteria .07 .20
36 Aubrey Huff .07 .20
37 Brandon Duckworth .07 .20
38 Juan Gonzalez .07 .20
39 Sidney Ponson .07 .20
40 Eric Hinske .07 .20
41 Kevin Appier .07 .20
42 Danny Bautista .07 .20
43 Javier Lopez .07 .20
44 Jeff Conine .07 .20
45 Carlos Baerga .07 .20
46 Ugueth Urbina .07 .20
47 Mark Buehrle .07 .20
48 Aaron Boone .07 .20
49 Jason Simontacchi .07 .20
50 Sammy Sosa .20 .50
51 Jose Jimenez .07 .20
52 Bobby Higginson .07 .20
53 Luis Castillo .07 .20
54 Orlando Merced .07 .20
55 Brian Jordan .07 .20
56 Eric Young .07 .20
57 Bobby Kielty .07 .20
58 Luis Rivas .07 .20
59 Brad Wilkerson .07 .20
60 Roberto Alomar .10 .30
61 Roger Clemens .40 1.00
62 Scott Hatteberg .07 .20
63 Andy Ashby .07 .20
64 Mike Williams .07 .20
65 Ron Gant .07 .20
66 Benito Santiago .07 .20
67 Bret Boone .07 .20
68 Matt Morris .07 .20
69 Troy Glaus .07 .20
70 Austin Kearns .07 .20
71 Jim Thome .10 .30
72 Rickey Henderson .20 .50
73 Luis Gonzalez .07 .20
74 Brad Fullmer .07 .20
75 Herbert Perry .07 .20
76 Randy Wolf .07 .20
77 Miguel Tejada .07 .20
78 Jimmy Anderson .07 .20
79 Ramon Martinez .07 .20
80 Ivan Rodriguez .10 .30
81 John Flaherty .07 .20
82 Shannon Stewart .07 .20
83 Orlando Palmeiro .07 .20
84 Rafael Furcal .07 .20
85 Kenny Rogers .07 .20
86 Terry Adams .07 .20
87 Mo Vaughn .07 .20
88 Jose Cruz Jr. .07 .20
89 Mike Matheny .07 .20
90 Alfonso Soriano .07 .20
91 Orlando Cabrera .07 .20
92 Jeffrey Hammonds .07 .20
93 Hideo Nomo .20 .50
94 Carlos Febles .07 .20
95 Billy Wagner .07 .20
96 Alex Gonzalez .07 .20
97 Todd Zeile .07 .20
98 Omar Vizquel .10 .30
99 Jose Rijo .07 .20
100 Ichiro Suzuki .40 1.00
101 Steve Cox .07 .20
102 Hideki Irabu .07 .20
103 Roy Halladay .07 .20
104 David Eckstein .07 .20
105 Greg Maddux .30 .75
106 Jay Gibbons .07 .20
107 Travis Driskill .07 .20
108 Fred McGriff .10 .30
109 Frank Thomas .20 .50
110 Shawn Green .07 .20
111 Ruben Quevedo .07 .20
112 Jacque Jones .07 .20
113 Tomo Ohka .07 .20
114 Joe McEwing .07 .20
115 Ramiro Mendoza .07 .20
116 Mark Mulder .07 .20
117 Mike Lieberthal .07 .20
118 Jack Wilson .07 .20
119 Randall Simon .07 .20
120 Bernie Williams .10 .30
121 Marvin Benard .07 .20
122 Jamie Moyer .07 .20
123 Andy Benes .07 .20
124 Tino Martinez .10 .30
125 Esteban Yan .07 .20
126 Juan Uribe .07 .20
127 Jason Isringhausen .07 .20
128 Chris Carpenter .07 .20
129 Mike Cameron .07 .20
130 Gary Sheffield .07 .20
131 Geronimo Gil .07 .20
132 Brian Daubach .07 .20
133 Corey Patterson .07 .20
134 Aaron Rowand .07 .20
135 Chris Reitsma .07 .20
136 Bob Wickman .07 .20
137 Cesar Izturis .07 .20
138 Jason Jennings .07 .20
139 Brandon Inge .07 .20
140 Larry Walker .07 .20
141 Ramon Santiago .07 .20
142 Vladimir Nunez .07 .20
143 Jose Vizcaino .07 .20
144 Mark Quinn .07 .20
145 Michael Tucker .07 .20
146 Darren Dreifort .07 .20
147 Ben Sheets .07 .20
148 Corey Koskie .07 .20
149 Tony Armas Jr. .07 .20
150 Kazuhisa Ishii .07 .20
151 Al Leiter .07 .20
152 Steve Trachsel .07 .20
153 Mike Stanton .07 .20
154 David Justice .07 .20
155 Marlon Anderson .07 .20
156 Jason Kendall .07 .20
157 Brian Lawrence .07 .20
158 J.T. Snow .07 .20
159 Edgar Martinez .10 .30
160 Pat Burrell .07 .20
161 Kerry Robinson .07 .20
162 Greg Vaughn .07 .20
163 Carl Everett .07 .20
164 Vernon Wells .07 .20
165 Jose Mesa .07 .20
166 Troy Percival .07 .20
167 Erubiel Durazo .07 .20
168 Jason Marquis .07 .20
169 Jerry Hairston Jr. .07 .20
170 Vladimir Guerrero .20 .50
171 Byung-Hyun Kim .07 .20
172 Marcus Giles .07 .20
173 Johnny Damon .10 .30
174 Jon Lieber .07 .20
175 Terrence Long .07 .20
176 Sean Casey .07 .20
177 Adam Dunn .07 .20
178 Juan Pierre .07 .20
179 Wendell Magee .07 .20
180 Barry Zito .07 .20
181 Aramis Ramirez .07 .20
182 Pokey Reese .07 .20
183 Jeff Kent .07 .20
184 Russ Ortiz .07 .20
185 Ruben Sierra .07 .20
186 Brent Abernathy .07 .20
187 Ismael Valdes UER .07 .20
Card does not include 2002 Rangers stats
188 Tom Wilson .07 .20
189 Craig Counsell .07 .20
190 Mike Mussina .10 .30
191 Ramon Hernandez .07 .20
192 Adam Kennedy .07 .20
193 Tony Womack .07 .20
194 Wes Helms .07 .20
195 Tony Batista .07 .20
196 Rolando Arrojo .07 .20
197 Kyle Farnsworth .07 .20
198 Gary Bennett .07 .20
199 Scott Sullivan .07 .20
200 Albert Pujols .40 1.00
201 Kirk Rueter .07 .20
202 Phil Nevin .07 .20
203 Kip Wells .07 .20
204 Ron Coomer .07 .20
205 Jeromy Burnitz .07 .20
206 Kyle Lohse .07 .20
207 Mike DeJean .07 .20
208 Paul Lo Duca .07 .20
209 Carlos Beltran .07 .20
210 Roy Oswalt .07 .20
211 Mike Lowell .07 .20
212 Robert Fick .07 .20
213 Todd Jones .07 .20
214 C.C. Sabathia .07 .20
215 Danny Graves .07 .20
216 Todd Hundley .07 .20
217 Tim Wakefield .07 .20
218 Derek Lowe .07 .20
219 Kevin Millwood .07 .20
220 Jorge Posada .10 .30
221 Bobby J. Jones .07 .20
222 Carlos Guillen .07 .20
223 Fernando Vina .07 .20
224 Ryan Rupe .07 .20
225 Kelvim Escobar .07 .20
226 Ramon Ortiz .07 .20
227 Junior Spivey .07 .20
228 Juan Cruz .07 .20
229 Melvin Mora .07 .20
230 Lance Berkman .07 .20
231 Brent Butler .07 .20
232 Shane Halter .07 .20
233 Derrek Lee .10 .30
234 Matt Lawton .07 .20
235 Chuck Knoblauch .07 .20
236 Eric Gagne .07 .20
237 Alex Sanchez .07 .20
238 Denny Hocking .07 .20
239 Eric Milton .07 .20
240 Rey Ordonez .07 .20
241 Orlando Hernandez .07 .20
242 Robert Person .07 .20
243 Sean Burroughs .07 .20
244 Jeff Cirillo .07 .20
245 Mike Lamb .07 .20
246 Jose Valentin .07 .20
247 Ellis Burks .07 .20
248 Shawn Chacon .07 .20
249 Josh Beckett .07 .20
250 Nomar Garciaparra .30 .75
251 Craig Biggio .10 .30
252 Joe Randa .07 .20
253 Mark Grudzielanek .07 .20
254 Glendon Rusch .07 .20
255 Michael Barrett .07 .20
256 Omar Daal .07 .20
257 Elmer Dessens .07 .20
258 Wade Miller .07 .20
259 Adrian Beltre .07 .20
260 Vicente Padilla .07 .20
261 Kazuhiro Sasaki .07 .20
262 Mike Scioscia MG .07 .20
263 Bobby Cox MG .07 .20
264 Mike Hargrove MG .07 .20
265 Grady Little MG RC .07 .20
266 Alex Gonzalez UER .07 .20
2002 stats are listed as all zero's
267 Jerry Manuel MG .07 .20
268 Bob Boone MG .07 .20
269 Joel Skinner MG .07 .20
270 Clint Hurdle MG .07 .20
271 Miguel Batista UER .07 .20
All 2002 Stats are 0's
272 Bob Brenly MG .07 .20
273 Jeff Torborg MG .07 .20
274 Jimy Williams MG UER .07 .20
Career managerial record is wrong
275 Tony Pena MG .07 .20
276 Jim Tracy MG .07 .20
277 Jerry Royster MG .07 .20
278 Ron Gardenhire MG .07 .20
279 Frank Robinson MG .10 .30
280 John Halama .07 .20
281 Joe Torre MG .10 .30
282 Art Howe MG .07 .20
283 Larry Bowa MG .07 .20
284 Lloyd McClendon MG .07 .20
285 Bruce Bochy MG .07 .20
286 Dusty Baker MG .07 .20
287 Lou Piniella MG .07 .20
288 Tony LaRussa MG .07 .20
289 Todd Walker .07 .20
290 Jerry Narron MG .07 .20
291 Carlos Tosca MG .07 .20
292 Chris Duncan FY RC 2.00 5.00
293 Franklin Gutierrez FY RC .40 1.00
294 Adam LaRoche FY .20 .50
295 Manuel Ramirez FY RC .20 .50
296 Il Kim FY RC .20 .50
297 Wayne Lydon FY RC .20 .50
298 Daryl Clark FY RC .20 .50
299 Sean Pierce FY .20 .50
300 Andy Marte FY RC 1.25 3.00
301 Matthew Peterson FY RC .20 .50
302 Gonzalo Lopez FY RC .20 .50
303 Bernie Castro FY RC .20 .50
304 Cliff Lee FY .20 .50
305 Jason Perry FY RC .20 .50
306 Jaime Bubela FY RC .20 .50
307 Alexis Rios FY .40 1.00
308 Brendan Harris FY RC .20 .50
309 R.Nivar-Martinez FY RC .20 .50
310 Terry Tiffee FY RC .20 .50
311 Kevin Youkilis FY RC .75 2.00
312 Ruddy Lugo FY RC .20 .50
313 C.J. Wilson FY .20 .50
314 Mike McNutt FY RC .20 .50
315 Jeff Clark FY RC .20 .50
316 Mark Malaska FY RC .20 .50
317 Doug Waechter FY RC .20 .50
318 Derell McCall FY RC .20 .50
319 Scott Tyler FY RC .20 .50
320 Craig Brazell FY RC .20 .50
321 Walter Young FY .20 .50
322 Marlon Byrd .20 .50
Jorge Padilla FS
323 Chris Snelling .20 .50
Shin-Soo Choo FS
324 Hank Blalock .20 .50
Mark Teixeira FS
325 Josh Hamilton .40 1.00
Carl Crawford FS
326 Orlando Hudson .20 .50
Josh Phelps FS
327 Jack Cust .20 .50
Rene Reyes FS
328 Angel Berroa .20 .50
Alexis Gomez FS
329 Michael Cuddyer .20 .50
Michael Restovich FS
330 Juan Rivera .20 .50
Marcus Thames FS
331 Brandon Puffer .20 .50
Jung Bong FS
332 Mike Cameron SH .07 .20
333 Shawn Green SH .07 .20
334 Oakland A's SH .07 .20
335 Jason Giambi SH .07 .20
336 Derek Lowe SH .07 .20
337 Manny Ramirez .10 .30
Mike Sweeney
Bernie Williams LL
338 Alfonso Soriano .07 .20
Alex Rodriguez
Derek Jeter LL
339 Alex Rodriguez .10 .30
Jim Thome
Rafael Palmeiro LL
340 Alex Rodriguez .20 .50
Magglio Ordonez
Miguel Tejada LL
341 Pedro Martinez .07 .20
Derek Lowe
Barry Zito LL
342 Pedro Martinez .10 .30
Roger Clemens
Mike Mussina LL
343 Larry Walker .20 .50
Vladimir Guerrero
Todd Helton LL
344 Sammy Sosa .20 .50
Albert Pujols
Shawn Green LL
345 Sammy Sosa .20 .50
Lance Berkman
Shawn Green LL
346 Lance Berkman .07 .20
Albert Pujols
Pat Burrell LL
347 Randy Johnson .10 .30
Greg Maddux
Tom Glavine LL
348 Randy Johnson .10 .30
Curt Schilling
Kerry Wood LL
349 Francisco Rodriguez .07 .20
Darin Erstad
Tim Salmon
AL Division Series
350 Minnesota Twins .10 .30
St Louis Cardinals
AL and NL Division Series
351 Anaheim Angels .10 .30
San Francisco Giants
AL and NL Division Series
352 Jim Edmonds .10 .30
Scott Rolen
NL Division Series
353 Adam Kennedy ALCS .07 .20
354 J.T. Snow WS .10 .30
355 David Bell NLCS .10 .30
356 Jason Giambi AS .07 .20
357 Alfonso Soriano AS .07 .20
358 Alex Rodriguez AS .20 .50
359 Eric Chavez AS .07 .20
360 Torii Hunter AS .07 .20
361 Bernie Williams AS .07 .20
362 Garret Anderson AS .07 .20
363 Jorge Posada AS .07 .20
364 Derek Lowe AS .07 .20
365 Barry Zito AS .07 .20
366 Manny Ramirez AS .10 .30
367 Mike Scioscia AS .07 .20
368 Francisco Rodriguez .07 .20
369 Chris Hammond .07 .20
370 Chipper Jones .20 .50
371 Chris Singleton .07 .20
372 Cliff Floyd .07 .20
373 Bobby Hill .07 .20
374 Antonio Osuna .07 .20
375 Barry Larkin .10 .30
376 Charles Nagy .07 .20
377 Denny Stark .07 .20
378 Dean Palmer .07 .20
379 Eric Owens .07 .20
380 Randy Johnson .20 .50
381 Jeff Suppan .07 .20
382 Eric Karros .07 .20
383 Luis Vizcaino .07 .20
384 Johan Santana .30 .75
385 Javier Vazquez .07 .20
386 John Thomson .07 .20
387 Nick Johnson .07 .20
388 Mark Ellis .07 .20
389 Doug Glanville .07 .20
390 Ken Griffey Jr. .30 .75
391 Bubba Trammell .07 .20
392 Livan Hernandez .07 .20
393 Desi Relaford .07 .20
394 Eli Marrero .07 .20
395 Jared Sandberg .07 .20
396 Barry Bonds .50 1.25
397 Esteban Loaiza .07 .20
398 Aaron Sele .07 .20
399 Geoff Blum .07 .20
400 Derek Jeter .50 1.25
401 Eric Byrnes .07 .20
402 Mike Timlin .07 .20
403 Mark Kotsay .07 .20
404 Rich Aurilia .07 .20
405 Joel Pineiro .07 .20
406 Chuck Finley .07 .20
407 Bengie Molina .07 .20
408 Steve Finley .07 .20
409 Julio Franco .07 .20
410 Marty Cordova .07 .20
411 Shea Hillenbrand .07 .20
412 Mark Bellhorn .07 .20
413 Jon Garland .07 .20
414 Reggie Taylor .07 .20
415 Milton Bradley .07 .20
416 Carlos Pena .07 .20
417 Andy Fox .07 .20
418 Brad Ausmus .07 .20
419 Brent Mayne .07 .20
420 Paul Quantrill .07 .20
421 Carlos Delgado .07 .20
422 Kevin Mench .07 .20

423 Joe Kennedy .07 .20
424 Mike Crudale .07 .20
425 Mark McLemore .07 .20
426 Bill Mueller .07 .20
427 Rob Mackowiak .07 .20
428 Ricky Ledee .07 .20
429 Ted Lilly .07 .20
430 Sterling Hitchcock .07 .20
431 Scott Strickland .07 .20
432 Damion Easley .07 .20
433 Torii Hunter .07 .20
434 Brad Radke .07 .20
435 Geoff Jenkins .07 .20
436 Paul Byrd .07 .20
437 Morgan Ensberg .07 .20
438 Mike Maroth .07 .20
439 Mike Hampton .07 .20
440 Adam Hyzdu .07 .20
441 Vance Wilson .07 .20
442 Todd Ritchie .07 .20
443 Tom Gordon .07 .20
444 John Burkett .07 .20
445 Rodrigo Lopez .07 .20
446 Tim Spooneybarger .07 .20
447 Quinton Mccracken .07 .20
448 Tim Salmon .10 .30
449 Jarrod Washburn .07 .20
450 Pedro Martinez .10 .30
451 Dustan Mohr .07 .20
452 Julio Lugo .07 .20
453 Scott Stewart .07 .20
454 Armando Benitez .07 .20
455 Raul Mondesi .07 .20
456 Robin Ventura .07 .20
457 Bobby Abreu .07 .20
458 Josh Fogg .07 .20
459 Ryan Klesko .07 .20
460 Tsuyoshi Shinjo .07 .20
461 Jim Edmonds .07 .20
462 Cliff Politte .07 .20
463 Chan Ho Park .07 .20
464 John Mabry .07 .20
465 Woody Williams .07 .20
466 Jason Michaels .07 .20
467 Scott Schoeneweis .07 .20
468 Brian Anderson .07 .20
469 Brett Tomko .07 .20
470 Scott Erickson .07 .20
471 Kevin Millar Sox .07 .20
472 Danny Wright .07 .20
473 Jason Schmidt .07 .20
474 Scott Williamson .07 .20
475 Einar Diaz .07 .20
476 Jay Payton .07 .20
477 Juan Acevedo .07 .20
478 Ben Grieve .07 .20
479 Raul Ibanez .07 .20
480 Richie Sexson .07 .20
481 Rick Reed .07 .20
482 Pedro Astacio .07 .20
483 Adam Piatt .07 .20
484 Bud Smith .07 .20
485 Tomas Perez .07 .20
486 Adam Eaton .07 .20
487 Rafael Palmeiro .10 .30
488 Jason Tyner .07 .20
489 Scott Rolen .10 .30
490 Randy Winn .07 .20
491 Ryan Jensen .07 .20
492 Trevor Hoffman .07 .20
493 Craig Wilson .07 .20
494 Jeremy Giambi .07 .20
495 Daryle Ward .07 .20
496 Shane Spencer .07 .20
497 Andy Pettitte .10 .30
498 John Franco .07 .20
499 Felipe Lopez .07 .20
500 Mike Piazza .30 .75
501 Cristian Guzman .07 .20
502 Jose Hernandez .07 .20
503 Octavio Dotel .07 .20
504 Brad Penny .07 .20
505 Dave Veres .07 .20
506 Ryan Dempster .07 .20
507 Joe Crede .07 .20
508 Chad Hermansen .07 .20
509 Gary Matthews Jr. .07 .20
510 Matt Franco .07 .20
511 Ben Weber .07 .20
512 Dave Berg .07 .20
513 Michael Young .10 .30
514 Frank Catalanotto .07 .20
515 Darin Erstad .07 .20
516 Matt Williams .07 .20
517 B.J. Surhoff .07 .20
518 Kerry Ligtenberg .07 .20
519 Mike Bordick .07 .20
520 Arthur Rhodes .07 .20
521 Joe Girardi .07 .20
522 D'Angelo Jimenez .07 .20
523 Paul Konerko .07 .20
524 Jose Macias .07 .20
525 Joe Mays .07 .20
526 Marquis Grissom .07 .20
527 Neifi Perez .07 .20
528 Preston Wilson .07 .20
529 Jeff Weaver .07 .20
530 Eric Chavez .07 .20
531 Placido Polanco .07 .20
532 Matt Mantei .07 .20
533 James Baldwin .07 .20
534 Toby Hall .07 .20
535 Brendan Donnelly .07 .20
536 Benji Gil .07 .20
537 Damian Moss .07 .20
538 Jorge Julio .07 .20
539 Matt Clement .07 .20
540 Brian Moehler .07 .20
541 Lee Stevens .07 .20
542 Jimmy Haynes .07 .20
543 Terry Mulholland .07 .20
544 Dave Roberts .07 .20
545 J.C. Romero .07 .20
546 Bartolo Colon .07 .20
547 Roger Cedeno .07 .20
548 Mariano Rivera .20 .50
549 Billy Koch .07 .20
550 Manny Ramirez .10 .30
551 Travis Lee .07 .20
552 Oliver Perez .07 .20
553 Tim Worrell .07 .20
554 Rafael Soriano .07 .20
555 Damian Miller .07 .20
556 John Smoltz .10 .30
557 Willis Roberts .07 .20
558 Tim Hudson .07 .20
559 Moises Alou .07 .20
560 Gary Glover .07 .20
561 Corky Miller .07 .20
562 Ben Broussard .07 .20
563 Gabe Kapler .07 .20
564 Chris Woodward .07 .20
565 Paul Wilson .07 .20
566 Todd Hollandsworth .07 .20
567 So Taguchi .07 .20
568 John Olerud .07 .20
569 Reggie Sanders .07 .20
570 Jake Peavy .07 .20
571 Kris Benson .07 .20
572 Todd Pratt .07 .20
573 Ray Durham .07 .20
574 Boomer Wells .07 .20
575 Chris Widger .07 .20
576 Shawn Wooten .07 .20
577 Tom Glavine .10 .30
578 Antonio Alfonseca .07 .20
579 Keith Foulke .07 .20
580 Shawn Estes .07 .20
581 Mark Grace .10 .30
582 Dmitri Young .07 .20
583 A.J. Burnett .07 .20
584 Richard Hidalgo .07 .20
585 Mike Sweeney .07 .20
586 Alex Cora .07 .20
587 Matt Stairs .07 .20
588 Doug Mientkiewicz .07 .20
589 Fernando Tatis .07 .20
590 David Weathers .07 .20
591 Cory Lidle .07 .20
592 Dan Plesac .07 .20
593 Jeff Bagwell .10 .30
594 Steve Sparks .07 .20
595 Sandy Alomar Jr. .07 .20
596 John Lackey .07 .20
597 Rick Helling .07 .20
598 Mark DeRosa .07 .20
599 Carlos Lee .07 .20
600 Garret Anderson .07 .20
601 Vinny Castilla .07 .20
602 Ryan Drese .07 .20
603 LaTroy Hawkins .07 .20
604 David Bell .07 .20
605 Freddy Garcia .07 .20
606 Miguel Cairo .07 .20
607 Scott Spiezio .07 .20
608 Mike Remlinger .07 .20
609 Tony Graffanino .07 .20
610 Russell Branyan .07 .20
611 Chris Magruder .07 .20
612 Jose Contreras RC .40 1.00
613 Carl Pavano .07 .20
614 Kevin Brown .07 .20
615 Tyler Houston .07 .20
616 A.J. Pierzynski .07 .20
617 Tony Fiore .07 .20
618 Peter Bergeron .07 .20
619 Rondell White .07 .20
620 Brett Myers .07 .20
621 Kevin Young .07 .20
622 Kenny Lofton .07 .20
623 Ben Davis .07 .20
624 J.D. Drew .07 .20
625 Chris Gomez .07 .20
626 Karim Garcia .07 .20
627 Ricky Gutierrez .07 .20
628 Mark Redman .07 .20
629 Juan Encarnacion .07 .20
630 Anaheim Angels TC .10 .30
631 Ariz.Diamondbacks TC .07 .20
632 Atlanta Braves TC .07 .20
633 Baltimore Orioles TC .07 .20
634 Boston Red Sox TC .07 .20
635 Chicago Cubs TC .07 .20
636 Chicago White Sox TC .07 .20
637 Cincinnati Reds TC .07 .20
638 Cleveland Indians TC .07 .20
639 Colorado Rockies TC .07 .20
640 Detroit Tigers TC .07 .20
641 Florida Marlins TC .07 .20
642 Houston Astros TC .07 .20
643 Kansas City Royals TC .07 .20
644 Los Angeles Dodgers TC .07 .20
645 Milwaukee Brewers TC .07 .20
646 Minnesota Twins TC .07 .20
647 Montreal Expos TC .07 .20
648 New York Mets TC .07 .20
649 New York Yankees TC .10 .30
650 Oakland Athletics TC .07 .20
651 Philadelphia Phillies TC .07 .20
652 Pittsburgh Pirates TC .07 .20
653 San Diego Padres TC .07 .20
654 San Francisco Giants TC .07 .20
655 Seattle Mariners TC .07 .20
656 St. Louis Cardinals TC .07 .20
657 T.B. Devil Rays TC .07 .20
658 Texas Rangers TC .07 .20
659 Toronto Blue Jays TC .07 .20
660 Bryan Bullington DP RC .20 .50
661 Jeremy Guthrie DP .20 .50
662 Joey Gomes DP RC .20 .50
663 E.Bastida-Martinez DP RC .20 .50
664 Brian Wright DP RC .20 .50
665 B.J. Upton DP .30 .75
666 Jeff Francis DP .20 .50
667 Drew Meyer DP .20 .50
668 Jeremy Hermida DP .30 .75
669 Khalil Greene DP .30 .75
670 Darrell Rasner DP RC .20 .50
671 Cole Hamels DP .75 2.00
672 James Loney DP .25 .60
673 Sergio Santos DP .20 .50
674 Jason Pridie DP .20 .50
675 Brandon Phillips .20 .50
Victor Martinez
676 Hee Seop Choi .20 .50
Nic Jackson
677 Dontrelle Willis .30 .75
Jason Stokes
678 Chad Tracy .20 .50
Lyle Overbay
679 Joe Borchard .20 .50
Corwin Malone
680 Joe Mauer .30 .75
Justin Morneau
681 Drew Henson .20 .50
Brandon Claussen
682 Chase Utley .30 .75
Gavin Floyd
683 Taggert Bozied .20 .50
Xavier Nady
684 Aaron Heilman .20 .50
Jose Reyes
685 Kenny Rogers AW .07 .20
686 Bengie Molina AW .07 .20
687 John Olerud AW .07 .20
688 Bret Boone AW .07 .20
689 Eric Chavez AW .07 .20
690 Alex Rodriguez AW .20 .50
691 Darin Erstad AW .07 .20
692 Ichiro Suzuki AW .20 .50
693 Torii Hunter AW .07 .20
694 Greg Maddux AW .20 .50
695 Brad Ausmus AW .07 .20
696 Todd Helton AW .07 .20
697 Fernando Vina AW .07 .20
698 Scott Rolen AW .07 .20
699 Edgar Renteria AW .07 .20
700 Andruw Jones AW .07 .20
701 Larry Walker AW .07 .20
702 Jim Edmonds AW .07 .20
703 Barry Zito AW .07 .20
704 Randy Johnson AW .10 .30
705 Miguel Tejada AW .07 .20
706 Barry Bonds AW .30 .75
707 Eric Hinske AW .07 .20
708 Jason Jennings AW .07 .20
709 Todd Helton AS .07 .20
710 Jeff Kent AS .07 .20
711 Edgar Renteria AS .07 .20
712 Scott Rolen AS .07 .20
713 Barry Bonds AS .30 .75
714 Sammy Sosa AS .10 .30
715 Vladimir Guerrero AS .10 .30
716 Mike Piazza AS .20 .50
717 Curt Schilling AS .07 .20
718 Randy Johnson AS .10 .30
719 Bobby Cox AS .07 .20
720 Anaheim Angels WS .10 .30
721 Anaheim Angels WS .20 .50

2003 Topps Black

Inserted at a stated rate of one in 16 HTA series one packs and one in 10 HTA series 2 packs, this is a partial parallel to the Topps set. Only cards numbered from 1 through 331 were printed (though card number 7 does not exist, thus 330 cards comprise the series one set). However, the second series was issued in complete parallel form. These cards were issued to a stated print run of 52 serial numbered sets.

COM 1-291/368-659/685-721 10.00 25.00
SEMIS 1-291/368-659/685-721 15.00 30.00
UNL 1-291/368-659/685-721 20.00 40.00
COM. 292-331/660-684 10.00 25.00
UNL 292-331/660-684 15.00 30.00
COM. 292-331/612/660-684 10.00 25.00
SEMIS 292-331/612/660-684 15.00 30.00
UNL 92-331/612/660-684 20.00 40.00
292 Chris Duncan FY 30.00 60.00
300 Andy Marte FY 20.00 50.00

2003 Topps Box Bottoms

These cards were issued as a four-card sheet on the bottom of first and second series Home Team Advantage boxes. The sheets were not perforated, but did include dotted lines between each card indicating where the cards should be cut if they were to be separated. The cards are identical parallels to the basic issue 2003 Topps cards (including the same checklist numbers on the card backs). The key difference is the readily noticeable plain cardboard stock used for these Box Bottom parallels as averse to the high gloss card stock used for the basic issue cards.

*BOX BOTTOM CARDS: 1X TO 2.5X BASIC
1 Alex Rodriguez 1 .75 2.00
10 Mark Prior 4 .30 .75
11 Curt Schilling 1 .20 .50
20 Todd Helton 1 .30 .75
50 Sammy Sosa 2 .50 1.25
73 Luis Gonzalez 1 .20 .50
77 Miguel Tejada 4 .20 .50
80 Ivan Rodriguez 4 .30 .75
90 Alfonso Soriano 2 .20 .50
150 Kazuhisa Ishii 2 .20 .50
160 Pat Burrell 4 .20 .50
177 Adam Dunn 3 .20 .50
180 Barry Zito 3 .20 .50
200 Albert Pujols 2 1.00 2.50
230 Lance Berkman 3 .20 .50
250 Nomar Garciaparra 3 .75 2.00
368 Francisco Rodriguez 5 .20 .50
370 Chipper Jones 8 .50 1.25
380 Randy Johnson 8 .50 1.25
387 Nick Johnson 7 .20 .50
390 Ken Griffey Jr. 6 .75 2.00
396 Barry Bonds 5 1.25 3.00
433 Torii Hunter 5 .20 .50
450 Pedro Martinez 6 .30 .75
489 Scott Rolen 8 .30 .75
500 Mike Piazza 6 .75 2.00
530 Eric Chavez 6 .20 .50
550 Manny Ramirez 7 .30 .75
558 Tim Hudson 7 .20 .50
585 Mike Sweeney 8 .20 .50
593 Jeff Bagwell 5 .30 .75
600 Garret Anderson 7 .20 .50

2003 Topps Gold

Inserted at a stated rate of one in 16 first series hobby packs and one in five first series HTA packs, this is a partial parallel to the first series set. For the first series, nly cards numbered from 1 through 331 were printed. The second series was issued in its totality for this parallel. The second series cards were also issued at a stated rate of one in seven hobby packs, one in two HTA packs and one in five retail packs. All gold cards were issued to a stated print run of 2003 serial numbered sets.

*GOLD 1-291/368-659/685-721: 6X TO 15X
*GOLD: 292-331/660-684: 3X TO 8X
*GOLD RC's: 292-331/612/660-684: 3X TO 8X

2003 Topps Home Team Advantage

COMP.FACT.SET (720) 40.00 80.00
*HTA: .75X TO 2X BASIC
DISTRIBUTED IN FACTORY SET FORM
CARD 7 DOES NOT EXIST

2003 Topps All-Stars

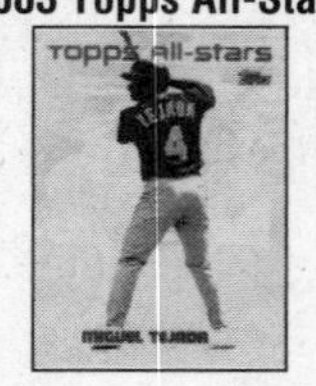

Issued at a stated rate of one in 15 second series hobby packs and one in five second series HTA packs, this 20 card set features most of the leading players in baseball.

COMPLETE SET (20) 20.00 50.00
1 Alfonso Soriano .75 2.00
2 Barry Bonds 2.50 6.00
3 Ichiro Suzuki 2.00 5.00
4 Alex Rodriguez 1.50 4.00
5 Miguel Tejada .75 2.00
6 Nomar Garciaparra 1.50 4.00
7 Jason Giambi .75 2.00
8 Manny Ramirez .75 2.00
9 Derek Jeter 2.50 6.00
10 Garret Anderson .75 2.00
11 Barry Zito .75 2.00
12 Sammy Sosa 1.00 2.50
13 Adam Dunn .75 2.00
14 Vladimir Guerrero 1.00 2.50
15 Mike Piazza 1.50 4.00
16 Shawn Green .75 2.00
17 Luis Gonzalez .75 2.00
18 Todd Helton .75 2.00
19 Torii Hunter .75 2.00
20 Curt Schilling .75 2.00

2003 Topps Autographs

Issued at varying stated odds, these 38 cards feature a mix of prospect and starts who signed cards for inclusion in the 2003 Topps product. The following players did not return their cards in time for inclusion in series 1 packs and these cards could be redeemed until November 30, 2004: Darin Erstad and Scott Rolen.

GROUP A1 SER.1 1:8910 H, 1: 2533 HTA
GROUP B1 SER.1 1:24,710 H, 1:7037 HTA
GROUP C1 SER.1 1:11,097 H, 1:3167 HTA
GROUP D1 SER.1 1:20,144 H, 1:5758 HTA
GROUP E1 SER.1 1:11,730 H, 1:3333 HTA
GROUP F1 SER.1 1:2209 H, 1:395 HTA
GROUP G1 SER.1 1:3471 H, 1:460 HTA
GROUP A2 1:31,408 H, 1:8808 HTA, 1:26,208 R
GROUP B2 1:5188 H, 1:1460 HTA, 1:4368 R
GROUP C2 1:864 H, 1:232 HTA, 1:708 R
GROUP D2 1:790 H, 1:214 HTA, 1:647 R
AJ Andruw Jones A1 40.00 80.00
AK1 Austin Kearns F1 4.00 10.00
AK2 Austin Kearns C2 4.00 10.00
AP Albert Pujols B2 150.00 250.00
AS Alfonso Soriano A1 30.00 60.00
BH Brad Hawpe D2 8.00 20.00
BS Ben Sheets E1 6.00 15.00
BU B.J. Upton D2 15.00 40.00
BZ Barry Zito C2 15.00 40.00
CE Clint Everts D2 4.00 10.00
CF Cliff Floyd C2 10.00 25.00
DE Darin Erstad B1 10.00 25.00
DW Dontrelle Willis D2 20.00 50.00
EC Eric Chavez A1 15.00 40.00
EH Eric Hinske C2 6.00 15.00
EM Eric Milton C1 6.00 15.00
HB Hank Blalock F1 6.00 15.00
JB Josh Beckett C2 20.00 50.00
JDM J.D. Martin G1 4.00 10.00
JL Jason Lane G1 6.00 15.00
JM Joe Mauer F1 15.00 40.00
JPH Josh Phelps C2 6.00 15.00
JV Jose Vidro C2 6.00 15.00
LB Lance Berkman A2 30.00 60.00
MB Mark Buehrle C1 15.00 40.00
MO Magglio Ordonez B2 10.00 25.00
MP Mark Prior F1 10.00 25.00
MTE Mark Teixeira F1 10.00 25.00
MTH Marcus Thames G1 4.00 10.00
MT1 Miguel Tejada A1 30.00 60.00
MT2 Miguel Tejada C2 15.00 40.00
NN Nick Neugebauer D1 6.00 15.00
OH Orlando Hudson G1 4.00 10.00
PK Paul Konerko C2 15.00 40.00
PL1 Paul Lo Duca F1 6.00 15.00
PL2 Paul Lo Duca C2 10.00 25.00
SR Scott Rolen A1 30.00 60.00
TH Torii Hunter C2 10.00 25.00

2003 Topps Blue Backs

Issued in the style of the 1951 Topps Blue Back set, these 40 cards were inserted into first series packs at a stated rate of one in 12 hobby packs and one in four HTA packs.

BB1 Albert Pujols 1.50 4.00
BB2 Ichiro Suzuki 1.50 4.00
BB3 Sammy Sosa .75 2.00
BB4 Kazuhisa Ishii .75 2.00
BB5 Alex Rodriguez 1.25 3.00
BB6 Derek Jeter 2.00 5.00
BB7 Vladimir Guerrero .75 2.00
BB8 Ken Griffey Jr. 1.25 3.00
BB9 Jason Giambi .75 2.00
BB10 Todd Helton .75 2.00
BB11 Mike Piazza 1.25 3.00
BB12 Nomar Garciaparra 1.25 3.00
BB13 Chipper Jones .75 2.00
BB14 Ivan Rodriguez .75 2.00
BB15 Luis Gonzalez .75 2.00
BB16 Pat Burrell .75 2.00
BB17 Mark Prior .75 2.00
BB18 Adam Dunn .75 2.00
BB19 Jeff Bagwell .75 2.00
BB20 Austin Kearns .75 2.00
BB21 Alfonso Soriano .75 2.00
BB22 Jim Thome .75 2.00
BB23 Bernie Williams .75 2.00
BB24 Pedro Martinez .75 2.00
BB25 Lance Berkman .75 2.00
BB26 Randy Johnson .75 2.00
BB27 Rafael Palmeiro .75 2.00
BB28 Richie Sexson .75 2.00
BB29 Troy Glaus .75 2.00
BB30 Shawn Green .75 2.00
BB31 Larry Walker .75 2.00
BB32 Eric Hinske .75 2.00
BB33 Andruw Jones .75 2.00
BB34 Barry Bonds 2.00 5.00
BB35 Curt Schilling .75 2.00
BB36 Greg Maddux 1.25 3.00
BB37 Jimmy Rollins .75 2.00
BB38 Eric Chavez .75 2.00
BB39 Scott Rolen .75 2.00
BB40 Mike Sweeney .75 2.00

2003 Topps Blue Chips Autographs

SEEDED IN VARIOUS 03-06 TOPPS BRANDS
AH Aubrey Huff 6.00 15.00
BC Bobby Crosby 6.00 15.00
BEP Brandon Phillips 4.00 10.00
BF Ben Fritz 4.00 10.00
BS Brian Slocum 4.00 10.00
CCE Clint Everts 4.00 10.00
CH Cole Hamels 40.00 80.00
CN Clint Nageotte 4.00 10.00
CT Chad Tracy 4.00 10.00
JG Jay Gibbons 4.00 10.00
JHA J.J. Hardy 8.00 20.00
JHU Justin Huber 4.00 10.00
JR Jeremy Reed 4.00 10.00
JRB Jason Bay 6.00 15.00
KH Kris Honel 4.00 10.00
MB Milton Bradley 4.00 10.00
OH Orlando Hudson 4.00 10.00
RN Ramon Nivar 4.00 10.00
VM Val Majewski 4.00 10.00
ZG Zack Greinke 6.00 15.00

2003 Topps Draft Picks

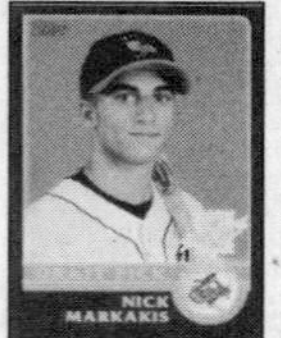

COMPLETE SERIES 1 (5) 30.00 60.00
COMPLETE SERIES 2 (5) 20.00 40.00
1-5 ISSUED IN RETAIL SETS
6-10 DISTRIBUTED IN HOLIDAY SETS
1 Brandon Wood 6.00 15.00
2 Ryan Wagner 1.25 3.00
3 Sean Rodriguez 3.00 8.00
4 Chris Lubanski 3.00 8.00
5 Chad Billingsley 6.00 15.00
6 Javi Herrera 1.50 4.00
7 Brian McFall 1.25 3.00
8 Nick Markakis 6.00 15.00
9 Adam Miller 5.00 12.00
10 Daric Barton 5.00 12.00

2003 Topps Farewell to Riverfront Stadium Relics

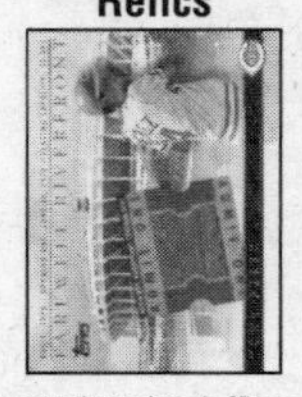

Issued at a stated rate of one in 37 second series HTA packs, this 10 card set featured leading current and retired Cincinnati Reds players since 1970 as well as a piece of Riverfront Stadium.

AD Adam Dunn 10.00 25.00
AK Austin Kearns 10.00 25.00
BL Barry Larkin 10.00 25.00
DC Dave Concepcion 10.00 25.00
JB Johnny Bench 15.00 40.00
JM Joe Morgan 10.00 25.00
KG Ken Griffey Jr. 10.00 25.00
PO Paul O'Neill 10.00 25.00
TP Tony Perez 10.00 25.00
TS Tom Seaver 10.00 25.00

2003 Topps First Year Player Bonus

Issued as five card bonus "packs" these 10 cards featured players in their first year on a Topps card. Cards number 1 through 5 were issued in a sealed clear cello pack within the "red" hobby factory sets while cards number 6-10 were issued in the "blue" Sears/JC Penney factory sets.

1 Ismael Castro
2 Branden Florence
3 Michael Garciaparra 2.00 5.00
4 Pete LaForest 2.00 5.00
5 Hanley Ramirez 6.00 15.00
6 Rajai Davis
7 Gary Schneidmiller
8 Corey Shafer
9 Thomari Story-Harden
10 Bryan Grace

2003 Topps Flashback

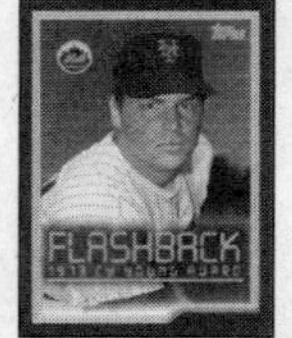

This set, featuring basically retired players, was inserted at a stated rate of one in 12 HTA first series packs. Only Mike Piazza and Randy Johnson were active at the time this set was issued.

AR Al Rosen 2.00 5.00
BM Bill Madlock 2.00 5.00
CY Carl Yastrzemski 5.00 12.00
DM Dale Murphy 2.00 5.00
EM Eddie Mathews 2.50 6.00
GB George Brett 5.00 12.00
HK Harmon Killebrew 2.50 6.00
JP Jim Palmer 2.00 5.00
LD Lenny Dykstra 2.00 5.00
MP Mike Piazza 4.00 10.00
NR Nolan Ryan 6.00 15.00
RJ Randy Johnson 2.50 6.00
RR Robin Roberts 2.00 5.00
TS Tom Seaver 2.00 5.00
WS Warren Spahn 2.00 5.00

2003 Topps Hit Parade

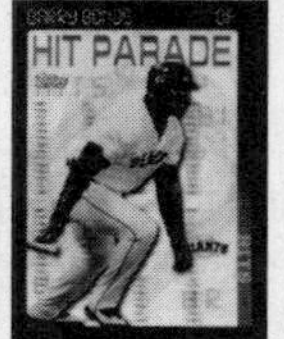

Issued at a stated rate of one in 15 hobby packs, one in 5 HTA packs and one in 10 retail packs, this 30 card set feature active players in the top 10 of home runs, runs batted in or hits.

COMPLETE SET (30) 30.00 60.00
1 Barry Bonds 2.00 5.00
2 Sammy Sosa .75 2.00
3 Rafael Palmeiro .75 2.00
4 Fred McGriff .75 2.00
5 Ken Griffey Jr. 1.25 3.00
6 Juan Gonzalez .75 2.00
7 Andres Galarraga .75 2.00
8 Jeff Bagwell .75 2.00

9 Frank Thomas .75 2.00
10 Matt Williams .75 2.00
11 Barry Bonds 2.00 5.00
12 Rafael Palmeiro .75 2.00
13 Fred McGriff .75 2.00
14 Andres Galarraga .75 2.00
15 Ken Griffey Jr. 1.25 3.00
16 Sammy Sosa .75 2.00
17 Jeff Bagwell .75 2.00
18 Juan Gonzalez .75 2.00
19 Frank Thomas .75 2.00
20 Matt Williams .75 2.00
21 Rickey Henderson .75 2.00
22 Rafael Palmeiro .75 2.00
23 Roberto Alomar .75 2.00
24 Barry Bonds 2.00 5.00
25 Mark Grace .75 2.00
26 Fred McGriff .75 2.00
27 Julio Franco .75 2.00
28 Craig Biggio .75 2.00
29 Andres Galarraga .75 2.00
30 Barry Larkin .75 2.00

2003 Topps Hobby Masters

Inserted into first series packs at stated odds of one in 18 Hobby packs and one in six HTA packs, these 20 cards feature some of the most popular players in the hobby.

COMPLETE SET (20) 15.00 40.00
HM1 Ichiro Suzuki 1.50 4.00
HM2 Kazuhisa Ishii .75 2.00
HM3 Derek Jeter 2.00 5.00
HM4 Sammy Sosa .75 2.00
HM5 Alex Rodriguez 1.25 3.00
HM6 Mike Piazza 1.25 3.00
HM7 Chipper Jones .75 2.00
HM8 Vladimir Guerrero .75 2.00
HM9 Nomar Garciaparra 1.25 3.00
HM10 Todd Helton .75 2.00
HM11 Jason Giambi .75 2.00
HM12 Ken Griffey Jr. 1.25 3.00
HM13 Albert Pujols 1.50 4.00
HM14 Ivan Rodriguez .75 2.00
HM15 Mark Prior .75 2.00
HM16 Adam Dunn .75 2.00
HM17 Randy Johnson .75 2.00
HM18 Barry Bonds 2.00 5.00
HM19 Alfonso Soriano .75 2.00
HM20 Pat Burrell .75 2.00

2003 Topps Own the Game

Inserted into first series packs at stated odds of one in 12 hobby and one in four HTA, these 30 cards feature players who put up big numbers during the 2002 season.

OG1 Ichiro Suzuki 1.50 4.00
OG2 Todd Helton .75 2.00
OG3 Larry Walker .75 2.00
OG4 Mike Sweeney .75 2.00
OG5 Sammy Sosa .75 2.00
OG6 Lance Berkman .75 2.00
OG7 Alex Rodriguez 1.25 3.00
OG8 Jim Thome .75 2.00
OG9 Shawn Green .75 2.00
OG10 Nomar Garciaparra 1.25 3.00
OG11 Miguel Tejada .75 2.00
OG12 Jason Giambi .75 2.00
OG13 Magglio Ordonez .75 2.00
OG14 Manny Ramirez .75 2.00
OG15 Alfonso Soriano .75 2.00
OG16 Johnny Damon .75 2.00
OG17 Derek Jeter 2.00 5.00
OG18 Albert Pujols 1.50 4.00
OG19 Luis Castillo .75 2.00
OG20 Barry Bonds 2.00 5.00
OG21 Garret Anderson .75 2.00
OG22 Jimmy Rollins .75 2.00
OG23 Curt Schilling .75 2.00
OG24 Barry Zito .75 2.00
OG25 Randy Johnson .75 2.00
OG26 Tom Glavine .75 2.00
OG27 Roger Clemens 1.50 4.00
OG28 Pedro Martinez .75 2.00
OG29 Derek Lowe .75 2.00
OG30 John Smoltz .75 2.00

2003 Topps Prime Cuts Relics

Inserted into first series packs at a stated rate of one in 37,066 hobby packs and one in 5067 HTA packs and second series packs at a rate of one in 116,208 hobby, one in 1480 HTA and one in 4368 retail packs, these 31 cards featured game-used bat pieces taken from the barrel of the bat. Each of these cards were issued to a stated print run of 50 serial numbered sets.

AD1 Adam Dunn 1 50.00 100.00
AD2 Adam Dunn 2 50.00 100.00
AP Albert Pujols 1 125.00 200.00

AR1 Alex Rodriguez 1 75.00 150.00
AR2 Alex Rodriguez 2 75.00 150.00
AS Alfonso Soriano 2 50.00 100.00
BBO Barry Bonds 2 125.00 200.00
BW Bernie Williams 1 60.00 120.00
CD Carlos Delgado 2 50.00 100.00
EC Eric Chavez 2 50.00 100.00
EM Edgar Martinez 2 60.00 120.00
FT Frank Thomas 1 60.00 120.00
HB Hank Blalock 2 60.00 120.00
IR Ivan Rodriguez 1 60.00 120.00
JG Juan Gonzalez 1 50.00 100.00
JP Jorge Posada 2 60.00 120.00
LB Lance Berkman 1 90.00 150.00
LG Luis Gonzalez 2 50.00 100.00
MP Mark Prior 2 60.00 120.00
MP Mike Piazza 1 60.00 120.00
MV Mo Vaughn 1 50.00 100.00
NG1 Nomar Garciaparra 1 60.00 120.00
NG2 Nomar Garciaparra 2 60.00 120.00
RA1 Roberto Alomar 1 60.00 120.00
RA2 Roberto Alomar 2 60.00 120.00
RH Rickey Henderson 2 60.00 120.00
RJ Randy Johnson 2 60.00 120.00
RP Rafael Palmeiro 2 60.00 120.00
TG Tony Gwynn 2 60.00 120.00
TH Todd Helton 1 60.00 120.00
TM Tino Martinez 2 60.00 120.00

2003 Topps Prime Cuts Autograph Relics

Inserted into first series packs at stated odds of one in 27,661 hobby and one in 7,917 HTA packs or second series packs at stated odds of one in 232,416 hobb packs, one in 8808 HTA packs or one in 28,598 retail packs, these ten cards feature players who signed the relics cut from the barrel of the bat they used in a game. These cards were issued to a stated print run of 50 serial numbered sets.

AJ Andruw Jones 1 125.00 200.00
AP Albert Pujols 2
CJ Chipper Jones 1 125.00 200.00
DE Darin Erstad 1
EC Eric Chavez 1 90.00 150.00
LB Lance Berkman 2 125.00 200.00
MO Magglio Ordonez 2 100.00 175.00
MT Miguel Tejada 1 125.00 200.00
RP Rafael Palmeiro 1
SR Scott Rolen 1

2003 Topps Prime Cuts Pine Tar Relics

Inserted into first series packs at a stated rate of one in 9266 hobby packs and one in 1267 HTA packs and second series packs at a rate of one in 4288 hobby, one in 587 HTA and one in 928 retail, these 42 cards featured game-used bat pieces taken from the handle of the bat. Each of these cards were issued to a stated print run of 200 serial numbered sets.

AD1 Adam Dunn 1 30.00 60.00
AD2 Adam Dunn 2 30.00 60.00
AJ Andruw Jones 1 40.00 80.00
AP1 Albert Pujols 1 60.00 120.00
AP2 Albert Pujols 2 60.00 120.00
AR1 Alex Rodriguez 1 50.00 100.00
AR2 Alex Rodriguez 2 50.00 100.00
AS1 Alfonso Soriano 1 30.00 60.00
AS2 Alfonso Soriano 2 30.00 60.00
BBO Barry Bonds 2 60.00 120.00
BW Bernie Williams 1 40.00 80.00
CD Carlos Delgado 2 30.00 60.00
CJ Chipper Jones 1 40.00 80.00
DE Darin Erstad 1 30.00 60.00
EC1 Eric Chavez 1 30.00 60.00
EC2 Eric Chavez 2 30.00 60.00
EM Edgar Martinez 2 40.00 80.00
FT Frank Thomas 1 40.00 80.00
HB Hank Blalock 2 30.00 60.00
IR Ivan Rodriguez 1 40.00 80.00
JG Juan Gonzalez 1 30.00 60.00
JP Jorge Posada 2 40.00 80.00
LB1 Lance Berkman 1 30.00 60.00
LB2 Lance Berkman 2 30.00 60.00
LG Luis Gonzalez 2 30.00 60.00
MO Magglio Ordonez 2 30.00 60.00
MP Mark Prior 2 40.00 80.00
MP Mike Piazza 1 40.00 80.00
MT Miguel Tejada 1 30.00 60.00
MV Mo Vaughn 1 30.00 60.00
NG1 Nomar Garciaparra 1 40.00 80.00
NG2 Nomar Garciaparra 2 40.00 80.00
RA1 Roberto Alomar 1 40.00 80.00
RA2 Roberto Alomar 2 40.00 80.00
RH Rickey Henderson 2 40.00 80.00
RJ Randy Johnson 2 40.00 80.00
RP1 Rafael Palmeiro 1 40.00 80.00
RP2 Rafael Palmeiro 2 40.00 80.00
SR Scott Rolen 1 40.00 80.00
TG Tony Gwynn 2 40.00 80.00
TH Todd Helton 1 40.00 80.00
TM Tino Martinez 2 40.00 80.00

2003 Topps Prime Cuts Trademark Relics

Inserted into first series packs at a stated rate of one in 18,533 hobby packs and one in 2533 HTA packs or second series packs at a rate of one in 12,912 hobby, one in 881 HTA or one in 1857 retail; these 42 cards featured game-used bat pieces taken from the middle of the bat. Each of these cards were issued to a stated print run of 100 serial numbered sets.

AD1 Adam Dunn 1 40.00 80.00
AD2 Adam Dunn 2 40.00 80.00
AJ Andruw Jones 1 50.00 100.00
AP1 Albert Pujols 1 75.00 150.00
AP2 Albert Pujols 2 75.00 150.00
AR1 Alex Rodriguez 1 60.00 120.00
AR2 Alex Rodriguez 2 60.00 120.00
AS1 Alfonso Soriano 1 50.00 100.00
AS2 Alfonso Soriano 2 50.00 100.00
BBO Barry Bonds 2 75.00 150.00
BW Bernie Williams 1 50.00 100.00
CD Carlos Delgado 2 40.00 80.00
CJ Chipper Jones 1 50.00 100.00
DE Darin Erstad 1 40.00 80.00
EC1 Eric Chavez 1 40.00 80.00
EC2 Eric Chavez 2 40.00 80.00
EM Edgar Martinez 2 50.00 100.00
FT Frank Thomas 1 50.00 100.00
HB Hank Blalock 2 40.00 80.00
IR Ivan Rodriguez 1 50.00 100.00
JG Juan Gonzalez 1 40.00 80.00
JP Jorge Posada 2 50.00 100.00
LB1 Lance Berkman 1 40.00 80.00
LB2 Lance Berkman 2 40.00 80.00
LG Luis Gonzalez 2 40.00 80.00
MO Magglio Ordonez 2 40.00 80.00
MP Mark Prior 2 50.00 100.00
MP Mike Piazza 1 50.00 100.00
MT Miguel Tejada 1 40.00 80.00
MV Mo Vaughn 1 40.00 80.00
NG1 Nomar Garciaparra 1 50.00 100.00
NG2 Nomar Garciaparra 2 50.00 100.00
RA1 Roberto Alomar 1 50.00 100.00
RA2 Roberto Alomar 2 50.00 100.00
RH Rickey Henderson 2 50.00 100.00
RJ Randy Johnson 2 50.00 100.00
RP1 Rafael Palmeiro 1 50.00 100.00
RP2 Rafael Palmeiro 2 50.00 100.00
SR Scott Rolen 1 50.00 100.00
TG Tony Gwynn 2 50.00 100.00
TH Todd Helton 1 50.00 100.00
TM Tino Martinez 2 50.00 100.00

2003 Topps Record Breakers

Inserted into packs at a stated rate of one in six hobby, one in two HTA and one in four retail, these 101 cards feature a mix of active and retired players who hold some sort of season, team, league or major league record.

COMPLETE SET (100) 60.00 120.00
COMPLETE SERIES 1 (50) 30.00 60.00
COMPLETE SERIES 2 (50) 30.00 60.00
AG Andres Galarraga 1 .60 1.50
AR1 Alex Rodriguez 1 1.00 2.50
AR2 Alex Rodriguez 2 1.00 2.50
BB1 Barry Bonds 1 1.50 4.00
BB2 Barry Bonds 2 1.50 4.00
BF Bob Feller 2 .60 1.50
BG Bob Gibson 1 .60 1.50
CB Craig Biggio 2 .60 1.50
CD1 Carlos Delgado 1 .60 1.50
CD2 Carlos Delgado 2 .60 1.50
CF Cliff Floyd 1 .60 1.50
CJ Chipper Jones 1 .60 1.50
CK Chuck Klein 1 .60 1.50
CS Curt Schilling 1 .60 1.50
DE Darin Erstad 2 .60 1.50
DG Dwight Gooden 2 .60 1.50
DM Don Mattingly 1 1.50 4.00
EM Edgar Martinez 2 .60 1.50
EM Eddie Mathews 1 .75 2.00
FJ Fergie Jenkins 1 .60 1.50
FM Fred McGriff 1 .60 1.50
FR1 Frank Robinson 1 .75 2.00
FR2 Frank Robinson 2 .75 2.00
FT Frank Thomas 2 .60 1.50
GA Garret Anderson 2 .60 1.50
GB1 George Brett 1 1.50 4.00
GB2 George Brett 2 1.50 4.00
GF1 George Foster 1 .60 1.50
GF2 George Foster 2 .60 1.50
GM Greg Maddux 2 1.00 2.50
GS Gary Sheffield 1 .60 1.50
HG Hank Greenberg 1 .75 2.00
HK Harmon Killebrew 1 .75 2.00
HW Hack Wilson 1 .75 2.00
IS Ichiro Suzuki 2 1.25 3.00
JB1 Jeff Bagwell 1 .60 1.50
JB2 Jeff Bagwell 2 .60 1.50
JD Johnny Damon 2 .60 1.50
JG Jason Giambi 1 .60 1.50
JK Jeff Kent 2 .60 1.50
JME Jose Mesa 2 .60 1.50
JM1 Juan Marichal 1 .60 1.50
JM2 Juan Marichal 2 .60 1.50
JO John Olerud 1 .60 1.50
JP Jim Palmer 2 .60 1.50
JR Jim Rice 2 .60 1.50
JS John Smoltz 2 .60 1.50
JT Jim Thome 2 .60 1.50
KG1 Ken Griffey Jr. 1 1.00 2.50
KG2 Ken Griffey Jr. 2 1.00 2.50
LA Luis Aparicio 2 .60 1.50
LBR1 Lou Brock 1 .75 2.00
LBR2 Lou Brock 2 .75 2.00
LB1 Lance Berkman 1 .60 1.50
LB2 Lance Berkman 2 .60 1.50
LC Luis Castillo 1 .60 1.50
LD Lenny Dykstra 2 .60 1.50
LG1 Luis Gonzalez 1 .60 1.50
LG2 Luis Gonzalez 2 .60 1.50
LW Larry Walker 2 .60 1.50
MP Mike Piazza 1 1.00 2.50
MR Manny Ramirez 2 .60 1.50
MS Mike Sweeney 1 .60 1.50
MSC Mike Schmidt 1 1.50 4.00
NG Nomar Garciaparra 2 1.00 2.50
NR Nolan Ryan 1 2.00 5.00
PM Pedro Martinez 1 .60 1.50
PM Paul Molitor 2 .60 1.50
PW Preston Wilson 1 .60 1.50
RA Roberto Alomar 2 .60 1.50
RC Roger Clemens 1 1.25 3.00
RCA Rod Carew 1 .75 2.00
RG Ron Guidry 1 .60 1.50
RH1 Rickey Henderson 1 .60 1.50
RH2 Rickey Henderson 2 .60 1.50
RJ1 Randy Johnson 1 .60 1.50
RJ2 Randy Johnson 2 .60 1.50
RP Rafael Palmeiro 1 .60 1.50
RS1 Richie Sexson 1 .60 1.50
RS2 Richie Sexson 2 .60 1.50
RY1 Robin Yount 1 .75 2.00
RY2 Robin Yount 2 .75 2.00
SG1 Shawn Green 1 .60 1.50
SG2 Shawn Green 2 .60 1.50
SS1 Sammy Sosa 1 .60 1.50
SS2 Sammy Sosa 2 .60 1.50
TG Troy Glaus 1 .60 1.50
TG1 Tony Gwynn 1 1.00 2.50
TG2 Tony Gwynn 2 1.00 2.50
TH1 Todd Helton 1 .60 1.50
TH2 Todd Helton 2 .60 1.50
TK Ted Kluszewski 2 .75 2.00
TR Tim Raines 2 .60 1.50
TS1 Tom Seaver 1 .75 2.00
TS2 Tom Seaver 2 .75 2.00
VG1 Vladimir Guerrero 1 .60 1.50
VG2 Vladimir Guerrero 2 .60 1.50
WB Wade Boggs 2 .75 2.00
WM Willie Mays 2 2.00 5.00
WS Willie Stargell 2 .75 2.00

2003 Topps Record Breakers Autographs

This 19 card set partially parallels the Record Breaker insert set. Most of the cards, except for Luis Gonzalez, were inserted into first series packs at a stated rate of one in 6941 hobby packs and one in 1178 HTA packs. The second series cards were issued at a stated rate of one in 2218 hobby, one in 634 HTA and one in 1850 retail packs.

GROUP A1 SER.1 1:6941 H, 1:1178 HTA
GROUP B1 SER.1 1:34,320 H, 1:9744 HTA
GRP 2 SER.2 1:2218 H, 1:634 HTA, 1:1850 R
CF Cliff Floyd A1 15.00 40.00
CJ Chipper Jones A1 50.00 100.00
DM Don Mattingly 2 60.00 120.00
FJ Fergie Jenkins A1 15.00 40.00
GF George Foster 2 15.00 40.00
HK Harmon Killebrew A1 40.00 80.00
JM Juan Marichal 2 30.00 60.00
LA Luis Aparicio 2 15.00 40.00
LB Lance Berkman 2 20.00 50.00
LBR Lou Brock 2 30.00 60.00
LG Luis Gonzalez B1 15.00 40.00
MS Mike Schmidt A1 60.00 120.00
RP Rafael Palmeiro A1 40.00 80.00
RS Richie Sexson A1 15.00 40.00
RY Robin Yount A1 40.00 80.00
SG Shawn Green A1 30.00 60.00
SW Mike Sweeney A1 15.00 40.00
TG Troy Glaus A1
WM Willie Mays 2 100.00 175.00

2003 Topps Record Breakers Relics

This 40 card set partially parallels the Record Breaker insert set. These cards, depending on the group they belonged to, were inserted into first and second series packs at different rates and we have

noted all that information in our headers.

BAT A1 SER.1 ODDS 1:13,528 H, 1:4872 HTA
BAT B1 SER.1 ODDS 1:9058 H, 1:1689 HTA
BAT C1 SER.1 ODDS 1:743 H, 1:90 HTA
UNI A1 SER.1 ODDS 1:6178 H, 1:700 HTA
UNI B1 SER.1 ODDS 1:355 H, 1:51 HTA
BAT 2 SER.2 ODDS 1:191 H, 1:59 HTA
UNI A2 SER.2 ODDS 1:5235, 1:400 HTA
UNI B2 SER.2 ODDS 1:418, 1:176 HTA
UNI C2 SER.2 ODDS 1:1151, 1:87 HTA
AR1 Alex Rodriguez Uni B1 6.00 15.00
AR2 Alex Rodriguez Uni B2 6.00 15.00
CD1 Carlos Delgado Uni B1 4.00 10.00
CD2 Carlos Delgado Uni B2 4.00 10.00
CJ Chipper Jones Uni B1 6.00 15.00
DE Darin Erstad Uni A2 4.00 10.00
DG Dwight Gooden Uni B2 4.00 10.00
DM Don Mattingly Bat C1 10.00 25.00
EM Edgar Martinez Bat 2 6.00 15.00
FR1 Frank Robinson Bat C1 6.00 15.00
FR2 Frank Robinson Bat 2 6.00 15.00
FT Frank Thomas Bat 2 6.00 15.00
GB1 George Brett Bat C1 10.00 25.00
GB2 George Brett Bat 2 10.00 25.00
HG Hank Greenberg Bat B1 15.00 40.00
HW Hack Wilson Bat A1 30.00 60.00
JB Jeff Bagwell Uni B1 6.00 15.00
JR Jim Rice Uni B2 4.00 10.00
LBE Lance Berkman Bat C1 4.00 10.00
LC Luis Castillo Bat C1 4.00 10.00
LG Luis Gonzalez Bat 2 4.00 10.00
LGO Luis Gonzalez Uni B1 4.00 10.00
MP Mike Piazza Bat C1 10.00 25.00
MS Mike Sweeney Bat C1 4.00 10.00
NR Nolan Ryan Uni A1 20.00 50.00
NRA Nolan Ryan Uni C2 15.00 40.00
PM Pedro Martinez Uni B1 6.00 15.00
RH Rickey Henderson Bat C1 6.00 15.00
RHO Rogers Hornsby Bat 2 15.00 40.00
RS Richie Sexson Uni C2 4.00 10.00
RY1 Robin Yount Uni B1 6.00 15.00
RY2 Robin Yount Bat 2 6.00 15.00
SG Shawn Green Uni B1 4.00 10.00
TG Tony Gwynn 2B Bat 2 6.00 15.00
TG2 Tony Gwynn Avg Bat 2 6.00 15.00
TH1 Todd Helton Uni B1 6.00 15.00
TH2 Todd Helton Uni B2 6.00 15.00
TK Ted Kluszewski Bat 2 6.00 15.00
TR Tim Raines Bat 2 4.00 10.00
WB Wade Boggs Bat 2 6.00 15.00

2003 Topps Record Breakers Nolan Ryan

Inserted at a stated rate of one in two HTA packs, this seven card set features all-time strikeout king Nolan Ryan. Each of these cards commemorate one of his record setting seven no-hitters.

COMPLETE SET (7) 30.00 60.00
COMMON CARD (NR1-NR7) 4.00 10.00

2003 Topps Record Breakers Nolan Ryan Autographs

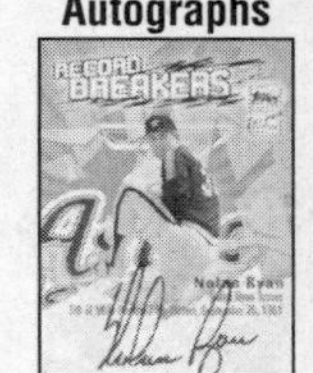

Inserted at a stated rate of one in 1894 HTA packs, this three card set honors Nolan Ryan and the teams he tossed no-hitters for.

COMMON CARD 125.00 200.00

2003 Topps Red Backs

Inserted in second series packs at a stated rate of one in 12 hobby and one in eight retail; this 40-card set features leading players in the style of the 1951 Topps Red Back set.

COMPLETE SET (40) 50.00 100.00
1 Nomar Garciaparra 1.50 4.00
2 Ichiro Suzuki 2.00 5.00
3 Alex Rodriguez 1.50 4.00
4 Sammy Sosa 1.00 2.50
5 Barry Bonds 2.50 6.00
6 Vladimir Guerrero 1.00 2.50
7 Derek Jeter 2.50 6.00
8 Miguel Tejada .75 2.00
9 Alfonso Soriano .75 2.00
10 Manny Ramirez .75 2.00
11 Adam Dunn .75 2.00
12 Jason Giambi .75 2.00
13 Mike Piazza 1.50 4.00
14 Scott Rolen .75 2.00
15 Shawn Green .75 2.00
16 Randy Johnson 1.00 2.50
17 Todd Helton .75 2.00
18 Garret Anderson .75 2.00
19 Curt Schilling .75 2.00
20 Albert Pujols 2.00 5.00
21 Chipper Jones 1.00 2.50
22 Luis Gonzalez .75 2.00
23 Mark Prior .75 2.00
24 Jim Thome .75 2.00
25 Ivan Rodriguez .75 2.00
26 Torii Hunter .75 2.00
27 Lance Berkman .75 2.00
28 Troy Glaus .75 2.00
29 Andruw Jones .75 2.00
30 Barry Zito .75 2.00
31 Jeff Bagwell .75 2.00
32 Magglio Ordonez .75 2.00
33 Pat Burrell .75 2.00
34 Mike Sweeney .75 2.00
35 Rafael Palmeiro .75 2.00
36 Larry Walker .75 2.00
37 Carlos Delgado .75 2.00
38 Brian Giles .75 2.00
39 Pedro Martinez .75 2.00
40 Greg Maddux 1.50 4.00

2003 Topps Turn Back the Clock Autographs

This five card set was inserted at a stated rate of one in 134 HTA packs except for Bill Madlock who signed fewer cards and his card was inserted at a stated rate of one in 268 HTA packs.

GROUP A SER.1 ODDS 1:134 HTA
GROUP B SER.1 ODDS 1:268 HTA
BM Bill Madlock B 6.00 15.00
DM Dale Murphy A 10.00 25.00
HK Harmon Killebrew A
JP Jim Palmer A 8.00 20.00
LD Lenny Dykstra A 8.00 20.00

2003 Topps Traded

This 275 card-set was released in October, 2003. The set was issued in 10 card packs with an $3 SRP which came 24 packs to a box and 12 boxes to a case. Cards numbered 1 through 115 feature veterans who were traded while cards 116 through 120 feature managers. Cards numbered 121 through 165 featured prospects and cards 166 through 275 feature Rookie Cards. All of these cards were issued with a "T" prefix.

COMPLETE SET (275) 20.00 50.00
COMMON CARD (T1-T120) .07 .20
COMMON CARD (121-165) .15 .40
T1 Juan Pierre .07 .20
T2 Mark Grudzielanek .07 .20
T3 Tanyon Sturtze .07 .20
T4 Greg Vaughn .07 .20
T5 Greg Myers .07 .20
T6 Randall Simon .07 .20
T7 Todd Hundley .07 .20
T8 Marlon Anderson .07 .20
T9 Jeff Reboulet .07 .20
T10 Alex Sanchez .07 .20
T11 Mike Rivera .07 .20
T12 Todd Walker .07 .20
T13 Ray King .07 .20
T14 Shawn Estes .07 .20
T15 Gary Matthews Jr. .07 .20
T16 Jaret Wright .07 .20
T17 Edgardo Alfonzo .07 .20
T18 Omar Daal .07 .20
T19 Ryan Rupe .07 .20
T20 Tony Clark .07 .20
T21 Jeff Suppan .07 .20
T22 Mike Stanton .07 .20
T23 Ramon Martinez .07 .20
T24 Armando Rios .07 .20
T25 Johnny Estrada .07 .20
T26 Joe Girardi .07 .20
T27 Ivan Rodriguez .10 .30
T28 Robert Fick .07 .20
T29 Rick White .07 .20
T30 Robert Person .07 .20
T31 Alan Benes .07 .20
T32 Chris Carpenter .07 .20
T33 Chris Widger .07 .20
T34 Travis Hafner .07 .20
T35 Mike Venafro .07 .20
T36 Jon Lieber .07 .20

T37 Orlando Hernandez .07 .20
T38 Aaron Myette .07 .20
T39 Paul Bako .07 .20
T40 Erubiel Durazo .07 .20
T41 Mark Guthrie .07 .20
T42 Steve Avery .07 .20
T43 Damian Jackson .07 .20
T44 Rey Ordonez .07 .20
T45 John Flaherty .07 .20
T46 Byung-Hyun Kim .07 .20
T47 Tom Goodwin .07 .20
T48 Elmer Dessens .07 .20
T49 Al Martin .07 .20
T50 Gene Kingsale .07 .20
T51 Lenny Harris .07 .20
T52 David Ortiz Sox .20 .50
T53 Jose Lima .07 .20
T54 Mike Difelice .07 .20
T55 Jose Hernandez .07 .20
T56 Todd Zeile .07 .20
T57 Roberto Hernandez .07 .20
T58 Albie Lopez .07 .20
T59 Roberto Alomar .10 .30
T60 Russ Ortiz .07 .20
T61 Brian Daubach .07 .20
T62 Carl Everett .07 .20
T63 Jeromy Burnitz .07 .20
T64 Mark Bellhorn .07 .20
T65 Ruben Sierra .07 .20
T66 Mike Fetters .07 .20
T67 Armando Benitez .07 .20
T68 Deivi Cruz .07 .20
T69 Jose Cruz Jr. .07 .20
T70 Jeremy Fikac .07 .20
T71 Jeff Kent .07 .20
T72 Andres Galarraga .07 .20
T73 Rickey Henderson .20 .50
T74 Royce Clayton .07 .20
T75 Troy O'Leary .07 .20
T76 Ron Coomer .07 .20
T77 Greg Colbrunn .07 .20
T78 Wes Helms .07 .20
T79 Kevin Millwood .07 .20
T80 Damion Easley .07 .20
T81 Bobby Kielty .07 .20
T82 Keith Osik .07 .20
T83 Ramiro Mendoza .07 .20
T84 Shea Hillenbrand .07 .20
T85 Shannon Stewart .07 .20
T86 Eddie Perez .07 .20
T87 Ugueth Urbina .07 .20
T88 Orlando Palmeiro .07 .20
T89 Graeme Lloyd .07 .20
T90 John Vander Wal .07 .20
T91 Gary Bennett .07 .20
T92 Shane Reynolds .07 .20
T93 Steve Parris .07 .20
T94 Julio Lugo .07 .20
T95 John Halama .07 .20
T96 Carlos Baerga .07 .20
T97 Jim Parque .07 .20
T98 Mike Williams .07 .20
T99 Fred McGriff .10 .30
T100 Kenny Rogers .07 .20
T101 Matt Herges .07 .20
T102 Jay Bell .07 .20
T103 Esteban Yan .07 .20
T104 Eric Owens .07 .20
T105 Aaron Fultz .07 .20
T106 Rey Sanchez .07 .20
T107 Jim Thome .10 .30
T108 Aaron Boone .07 .20
T109 Raul Mondesi .07 .20
T110 Kenny Lofton .07 .20
T111 Jose Guillen .07 .20
T112 Aramis Ramirez .07 .20
T113 Sidney Ponson .07 .20
T114 Scott Williamson .07 .20
T115 Robin Ventura .07 .20
T116 Dusty Baker MG .07 .20
T117 Felipe Alou MG .07 .20
T118 Buck Showalter MG .07 .20
T119 Jack McKeon MG .07 .20
T120 Art Howe MG .07 .20
T121 Bobby Crosby PROS .15 .40
T122 Adrian Gonzalez PROS .15 .40
T123 Kevin Cash PROS .15 .40
T124 Shin-Soo Choo PROS .15 .40
T125 Chin-Feng Chen PROS .40 1.00
T126 Miguel Cabrera PROS .40 1.00
T127 Jason Young PROS .15 .40
T128 Alex Herrera PROS .15 .40
T129 Jason Dubois PROS .15 .40
T130 Jeff Mathis PROS .15 .40
T131 Casey Kotchman PROS .15 .40
T132 Ed Rogers PROS .15 .40
T133 Wilson Betemit PROS .15 .40
T134 Jim Kavourias PROS .15 .40
T135 Taylor Buchholz PROS .15 .40
T136 Adam LaRoche PROS .15 .40
T137 D.McPherson PROS .15 .40
T138 Jesus Cota PROS .15 .40
T139 Clint Nageotte PROS .15 .40
T140 Boof Bonser PROS .15 .40
T141 Walter Young PROS .15 .40
T142 Joe Crede PROS .15 .40
T143 Denny Bautista PROS .15 .40
T144 Victor Diaz PROS .15 .40
T145 Chris Narveson PROS .15 .40
T146 Gabe Gross PROS .15 .40
T147 Jimmy Journell PROS .15 .40
T148 Rafael Soriano PROS .15 .40
T149 Jerome Williams PROS .15 .40
T150 Aaron Cook PROS .15 .40
T151 An. Martinez PROS .15 .40
T152 Scott Hairston PROS .15 .40
T153 John Buck PROS .15 .40
T154 Ryan Ludwick PROS .15 .40
T155 Chris Bootcheck PROS .15 .40
T156 John Rheinecker PROS .15 .40
T157 Jason Lane PROS .15 .40
T158 Shelley Duncan PROS .75 2.00
T159 Adam Wainwright PROS .15 .40
T160 Jason Arnold PROS .15 .40
T161 Jonny Gomes PROS .25 .60
T162 James Loney PROS .20 .50
T163 Mike Fontenot PROS .15 .40
T164 Khalil Greene PROS .40 1.00
T165 Sean Burnett PROS .15 .40
T166 David Martinez FY RC .15 .40
T167 Felix Pie FY RC 1.50 4.00
T168 Joe Valentine FY RC .15 .40
T169 Brandon Webb FY RC 1.25 3.00
T170 Matt Diaz FY RC .30 .75
T171 Lew Ford FY RC .20 .50
T172 Jeremy Griffiths FY RC .15 .40
T173 Matt Hensley FY RC .15 .40
T174 Charlie Manning FY RC .15 .40
T175 Elizardo Ramirez FY RC .20 .50
T176 Greg Aquino FY RC .15 .40
T177 Felix Sanchez FY RC .15 .40
T178 Kelly Shoppach FY RC .30 .75
T179 Bubba Nelson FY RC .20 .50
T180 Mike OâKeefe FY RC .15 .40
T181 Hanley Ramirez FY RC 2.00 5.00
T182 T.Wellemeyer FY RC .15 .40
T183 Dustin Moseley FY RC .15 .40
T184 Eric Crozier FY RC .20 .50
T185 Ryan Shealy FY RC 1.00 2.50
T186 Jer. Bonderman FY RC 1.25 3.00
T187 T.Story-Harden FY RC .15 .40
T188 Dusty Brown FY RC .15 .40
T189 Rob Hammock FY RC .15 .40
T190 Jorge Piedra FY RC .20 .50
T191 Chris De La Cruz FY RC .15 .40
T192 Eli Whiteside FY RC .15 .40
T193 Jason Kubel FY RC .40 1.00
T194 Jon Schuerholz FY RC .15 .40
T195 St. Randolph FY RC .15 .40
T196 Andy Sisco FY RC .15 .40
T197 Sean Smith FY RC .20 .50
T198 Jon-Mark Sprowl FY RC .15 .40
T199 Matt Kata FY RC .15 .40
T200 Robinson Cano FY RC 3.00 8.00
T201 Nook Logan FY RC .20 .50
T202 Ben Francisco FY RC .15 .40
T203 Arnie Munoz FY RC .15 .40
T204 Ozzie Chavez FY RC .15 .40
T205 Eric Riggs FY RC .20 .50
T206 Beau Kemp FY RC .15 .40
T207 Travis Wong FY RC .20 .50
T208 Dustin Yount FY RC .20 .50
T209 Brian McCann FY RC 2.50 6.00
T210 Wilton Reynolds FY RC .20 .50
T211 Matt Bruback FY RC .15 .40
T212 Andrew Brown FY RC .20 .50
T213 Edgar Gonzalez FY RC .15 .40
T214 Eider Torres FY RC .15 .40
T215 Aquilino Lopez FY RC .15 .40
T216 Bobby Basham FY RC .15 .40
T217 Tim Olson FY RC .15 .40
T218 Nathan Panther FY RC .15 .40
T219 Bryan Grace FY RC .15 .40
T220 Dusty Gomon FY RC .20 .50
T221 Wil Ledezma FY RC .15 .40
T222 Josh Willingham FY RC .40 1.00
T223 David Cash FY RC .15 .40
T224 Oscar Villarreal FY RC .15 .40
T225 Jeff Duncan FY RC .15 .40
T226 Kade Johnson FY RC .15 .40
T227 L.Steidlmayer FY RC .15 .40
T228 Brandon Watson FY RC .15 .40
T229 Jose Morales FY RC .15 .40
T230 Mike Gallo FY RC .15 .40
T231 Tyler Adamczyk FY RC .15 .40
T232 Adam Stern FY RC .15 .40
T233 Brennan King FY RC .15 .40
T234 Dan Haren FY RC .30 .75
T235 Mi. Hernandez FY RC .15 .40
T236 Ben Fritz FY RC .15 .40
T237 Clay Hensley FY RC .15 .40
T238 Tyler Johnson FY RC .15 .40
T239 Pete LaForest FY RC .15 .40
T240 Tyler Martin FY RC .15 .40
T241 J.D. Durbin FY RC .15 .40
T242 Shane Victorino FY RC .40 1.00
T243 Rajai Davis FY RC .15 .40
T244 Ismael Castro FY RC .15 .40
T245 C.Wang FY RC 2.50 6.00
T246 Travis Ishikawa FY RC .30 .75
T247 Corey Shafer FY RC .15 .40
T248 G.Schneidmiller FY RC .15 .40
T249 Dave Pember FY RC .15 .40
T250 Keith Stamler FY RC .15 .40
T251 Tyson Graham FY RC .15 .40
T252 Ryan Cameron FY RC .15 .40
T253 E.Eckenstahler FY .15 .40
T254 Ma. Peterson FY RC .15 .40
T255 D. McGowan FY RC .20 .50
T256 Pr. Redman FY RC .15 .40
T257 Haj Turay FY RC .15 .40
T258 Carlos Guzman FY RC .20 .50
T259 Matt DeMarco FY RC .15 .40
T260 Derek Michaelis FY RC .15 .40
T261 Brian Burgamy FY RC .15 .40
T262 Jay Sitzman FY RC .15 .40
T263 Chris Fallon FY RC .15 .40
T264 Mike Adams FY RC .15 .40
T265 Clint Barmes FY RC .40 1.00
T266 Eric Reed FY RC .15 .40
T267 Willie Eyre FY RC .15 .40
T268 Carlos Duran FY RC .15 .40
T269 Nick Trzesniak FY RC .15 .40
T270 Ferdin Tejeda FY RC .15 .40
T271 Mi. Garciaparra FY RC .15 .40
T272 Michael Hinckley FY RC .20 .50
T273 Br. Florence FY RC .15 .40
T274 Trent Oeltjen FY RC .20 .50
T275 Mike Neu FY RC .15 .40

2003 Topps Traded Gold

*GOLD 1-120: 5X TO 12X BASIC
*GOLD 121-165: 2.5X TO 6X BASIC
*GOLD 166-275: 1.5X TO 4X BASIC
STATED ODDS 1:2 HOB/RET, 1:1 HTA
STATED PRINT RUN 2003 SERIAL #'d SETS
T245 Chien-Ming Wang FY 12.50 30.00

2003 Topps Traded Future Phenoms Relics

GROUP A ODDS 1:2330 HOB/RET, 1:669 HTA
GROUP B ODDS 1:505 HOB/RET, 1:144 HTA
GROUP C ODDS 1:101 HOB/RET, 1:29 HTA
BP Brandon Phillips Bat B 3.00 8.00
CC Chin-Feng Chen Jsy C 10.00 25.00
CDC Carl Crawford Bat C 3.00 8.00
CS Chris Snelling Bat C 3.00 8.00
HB Hank Blalock Bat C 3.00 8.00
JM Justin Morneau Bat C 3.00 8.00
JT Joe Thurston Jsy C 3.00 8.00
MB Marlon Byrd Bat C 3.00 8.00
MR Michael Restovich Bat B 3.00 8.00
MT Mark Teixeira Bat B 4.00 10.00
RB Rocco Baldelli Bat B 3.00 8.00
TAH Trey Hodges Jsy C 3.00 8.00
TH Travis Hafner Bat C 3.00 8.00
WB Wilson Betemit Bat C 3.00 8.00
WPB Willie Bloomquist Bat A 6.00 15.00

2003 Topps Traded Hall of Fame Relics

STATED ODDS 1:1009 HOB/RET, 1:289 HTA
EM Eddie Murray Bat 10.00 25.00
GC Gary Carter Uni 6.00 15.00

2003 Topps Traded Hall of Fame Dual Relic

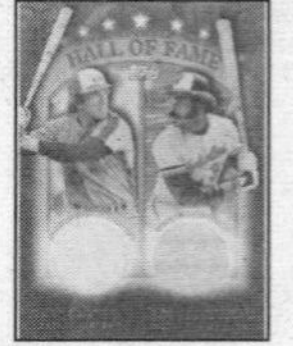

STATED ODDS 1:2015 HOB/RET, 1:578 HTA
CM Gary Carter Uni 12.50 30.00
Eddie Murray Bat

2003 Topps Traded Signature Moves Autographs

GROUP A ODDS 1:280 HOB/RET, 1:80 HTA
GROUP B ODDS 1:114 HOB/RET, 1:33 HTA
BC Bartolo Colon A 6.00 15.00
BU B.J. Upton B 12.50 30.00
CF Cliff Floyd A 6.00 15.00
DB David Bell A 6.00 15.00
EA Erick Almonte B 4.00 10.00
ER Elizardo Ramirez B 4.00 10.00
FP Felix Pie B 35.00 60.00
IR Robert Fick A 4.00 10.00
JB Joe Borchard B 4.00 10.00
JC Jose Cruz Jr. A 4.00 10.00
JF Jesse Foppert B 4.00 10.00
JG Joey Gomes B 4.00 10.00
JJC Jack Cust A 4.00 10.00
JL James Loney B 10.00 25.00
JR Jose Reyes B 6.00 15.00
JS Jason Stokes A 4.00 10.00
KG Khalil Greene A 10.00 25.00
MT Mark Teixeira A 10.00 25.00
VM Victor Martinez B 10.00 25.00
WY Walter Young B 4.00 10.00

2003 Topps Traded Transactions Bat Relics

GROUP A ODDS 1:168 HOB/RET, 1:48 HTA
GROUP B ODDS 1:78 HOB/RET, 1:22 HTA
AG Andres Galarraga A 3.00 8.00
CF Cliff Floyd B 3.00 8.00
DB David Bell B 3.00 8.00
EA Edgardo Alfonzo B 3.00 8.00
ED Erubiel Durazo B 3.00 8.00
EK Eric Karros B 3.00 8.00
FL Felipe Lopez A 3.00 8.00
FM Fred McGriff B 4.00 10.00
JC Jose Cruz Jr. B 3.00 8.00
JG Jeremy Giambi A 3.00 8.00
JK Jeff Kent B 3.00 8.00
JP Juan Pierre B 3.00 8.00
JT Jim Thome A 4.00 10.00
KL Kenny Lofton A 4.00 10.00
KM Kevin Millar Sox B 4.00 10.00
PW Preston Wilson A 3.00 8.00
RD Ray Durham A 3.00 8.00
RF Robert Fick A 3.00 8.00
RO Rey Ordonez B 3.00 8.00
RS Ruben Sierra A 3.00 8.00
RW Rondell White B 3.00 8.00
SH Tsuyoshi Shinjo B 3.00 8.00
SS Shane Spencer A 3.00 8.00
TG Tom Glavine A 4.00 10.00
TZ Todd Zeile A 3.00 8.00

2003 Topps Traded Transactions Dual Relics

STATED ODDS 1:421 HOB/RET, 1:120 HTA
IR Ivan Rodriguez Marlins-Rgr 8.00 20.00
JT Jim Thome Phils-Indians 8.00 20.00
KM Kevin Millwood Phils-Braves 6.00 15.00

2004 Topps

This 366-card standard-size first series was released in November, 2003. In addition, a 366-card second series was released in April, 2004. The cards were issued in 10-card hobby or retail packs with an $1.59 SRP which came 36 packs to a box and 12 boxes to a case. In addition, these cards were also issued in 35-card HTA packs with an $5 SRP which came 12 packs to a box and eight boxes to a case. Please note that insert cards were issued in different rates in retail packs as they were in hobby packs. In addition, to continuing honoring the memory of Mickey Mantle, there was no card number 7 issued in this set. Both cards numbered 267 and 274 are numbered as 267 and thus no card number 274 exists. Please note the following subsets were issued: Managers (268-295); First Year Cards (297-326); Future Stars (327-331); Highlights (332-336); League Leaders (337-348); Post-Season Play (349-355); American League All-Stars (356-367). The second series had the following subsets: Team Card (638-667), Draft Picks (668-687), Prospects (688-692), Combo Cards (693-695), Gold Gloves (696-713), Award Winners (714-718), National League All-Stars (719-729) and World Series Highlights (730-733).

COMP.HOBBY SET (737) 40.00 80.00
COMP.HOLIDAY SET (742) 40.00 80.00
COMP.RETAIL SET (737) 40.00 80.00
COMP.ASTROS SET (737) 40.00 80.00
COMP.CUBS SET (737) 40.00 80.00
COMP.RED SOX SET (737) 40.00 80.00
COMP.YANKEES SET (737) 40.00 80.00
COMPLETE SET (732) 30.00 80.00
COMPLETE SERIES 1 (366) 15.00 40.00
COMPLETE SERIES 2 (366) 15.00 40.00
COMMON CARD (1-6/8-732) .07 .20
COMMON (297-326/668-687) .20 .50
COMMON (327-331/688-692) .20 .50
1 Jim Thome .10 .30
2 Reggie Sanders .07 .20
3 Mark Kotsay .07 .20
4 Edgardo Alfonzo .07 .20
5 Ben Davis .07 .20
6 Mike Matheny .07 .20
8 Marlon Anderson .07 .20
9 Chan Ho Park .07 .20
10 Ichiro Suzuki .40 1.00
11 Kevin Millwood .07 .20
12 Bengie Molina .07 .20
13 Tom Glavine .10 .30
14 Junior Spivey .07 .20
15 Marcus Giles .07 .20
16 David Segui .07 .20
17 Kevin Millar .07 .20
18 Corey Patterson .07 .20
19 Aaron Rowand .07 .20
20 Derek Jeter .40 1.00
21 Jason LaRue .07 .20
22 Chris Hammond .07 .20
23 Jay Payton .07 .20
24 Bobby Higginson .07 .20
25 Lance Berkman .07 .20
26 Juan Pierre .07 .20
27 Brent Mayne .07 .20
28 Fred McGriff .10 .30
29 Richie Sexson .07 .20
30 Tim Hudson .07 .20
31 Mike Piazza .30 .75
32 Brad Radke .07 .20
33 Jeff Weaver .07 .20
34 Ramon Hernandez .07 .20
35 David Bell .07 .20
36 Craig Wilson .07 .20
37 Jake Peavy .07 .20
38 Tim Worrell .07 .20
39 Gil Meche .07 .20
40 Albert Pujols .40 1.00
41 Michael Young .07 .20
42 Josh Phelps .07 .20
43 Brendan Donnelly .07 .20
44 Steve Finley .07 .20
45 John Smoltz .10 .30
46 Jay Gibbons .07 .20
47 Trot Nixon .07 .20
48 Carl Pavano .07 .20
49 Frank Thomas .20 .50
50 Mark Prior .10 .30
51 Danny Graves .07 .20
52 Milton Bradley UER .07 .20
53 Jose Jimenez .07 .20
54 Shane Halter .07 .20
55 Mike Lowell .07 .20
56 Geoff Blum .07 .20
57 Michael Tucker UER .07 .20
Dee Brown pictured
58 Paul Lo Duca .07 .20
59 Vicente Padilla .07 .20
60 Jacque Jones .07 .20
61 Fernando Tatis .07 .20
62 Ty Wigginton .07 .20
63 Pedro Astacio .07 .20
64 Andy Pettitte .10 .30
65 Terrence Long .07 .20
66 Cliff Floyd .07 .20
67 Mariano Rivera .20 .50
68 Carlos Silva .07 .20
69 Marlon Byrd .07 .20
70 Mark Mulder .07 .20
71 Kerry Ligtenberg .07 .20
72 Carlos Guillen .07 .20
73 Fernando Vina .07 .20
74 Lance Carter .07 .20
75 Hank Blalock .07 .20
76 Jimmy Rollins .07 .20
77 Francisco Rodriguez .07 .20
78 Javy Lopez .07 .20
79 Jerry Hairston Jr. .07 .20
80 Andruw Jones .10 .30
81 Rodrigo Lopez .07 .20
82 Johnny Damon .10 .30
83 Hee Seop Choi .07 .20
84 Miguel Olivo .07 .20
85 Jon Garland .07 .20
86 Matt Lawton .07 .20
87 Juan Uribe .07 .20
88 Steve Sparks .07 .20
89 Tim Spooneybarger .07 .20
90 Jose Vidro .07 .20
91 Luis Rivas .07 .20
92 Hideo Nomo .20 .50
93 Javier Vazquez .07 .20
94 Al Leiter .07 .20
95 Darren Dreifort .07 .20
96 Alex Cintron .07 .20
97 Zach Day .07 .20
98 Jorge Posada .10 .30
99 John Halama .07 .20
100 Alex Rodriguez .30 .75
101 Orlando Palmeiro .07 .20
102 Dave Berg .07 .20
103 Brad Fullmer .07 .20
104 Mike Hampton .07 .20
105 Willis Roberts .07 .20
106 Ramiro Mendoza .07 .20
107 Juan Cruz .07 .20
108 Esteban Loaiza .07 .20
109 Russell Branyan .07 .20
110 Todd Helton .10 .30
111 Braden Looper .07 .20
112 Octavio Dotel .07 .20
113 Mike MacDougal .07 .20
114 Cesar Izturis .07 .20
115 Johan Santana .20 .50
116 Jose Contreras .07 .20
117 Placido Polanco .07 .20
118 Jason Phillips .07 .20
119 Adam Eaton .07 .20
120 Vernon Wells .07 .20
121 Ben Grieve .07 .20
122 Randy Winn .07 .20
123 Ismael Valdes .07 .20
124 Eric Owens .07 .20
125 Curt Schilling .07 .20
126 Russ Ortiz .07 .20
127 Mark Buehrle .07 .20
128 Danys Baez .07 .20
129 Dmitri Young .07 .20
130 Kazuhisa Ishii .07 .20
131 A.J. Pierzynski .07 .20
132 Michael Barrett .07 .20
133 Joe McEwing .07 .20
134 Alex Cora .07 .20
135 Tom Wilson .07 .20
136 Carlos Zambrano .07 .20
137 Brett Tomko .07 .20
138 Shigetoshi Hasegawa .07 .20
139 Jarrod Washburn .07 .20
140 Greg Maddux .30 .75
141 Craig Counsell .07 .20
142 Reggie Taylor .07 .20
143 Omar Vizquel .10 .30
144 Alex Gonzalez .07 .20
145 Billy Wagner .07 .20
146 Brian Jordan .07 .20
147 Wes Helms .07 .20
148 Kyle Lohse .07 .20
149 Timo Perez .07 .20
150 Jason Giambi .07 .20
151 Erubiel Durazo .07 .20
152 Mike Lieberthal .07 .20
153 Jason Kendall .07 .20
154 Xavier Nady .07 .20
155 Kirk Rueter .07 .20
156 Mike Cameron .07 .20
157 Miguel Cairo .07 .20
158 Woody Williams .07 .20
159 Toby Hall .07 .20
160 Bernie Williams .10 .30
161 Darin Erstad .07 .20
162 Matt Mantei .07 .20
163 Geronimo Gil .07 .20
164 Bill Mueller .07 .20
165 Damian Miller .07 .20
166 Tony Graffanino .07 .20
167 Sean Casey .07 .20
168 Brandon Phillips .07 .20
169 Mike Remlinger .07 .20
170 Adam Dunn .07 .20
171 Carlos Lee .07 .20
172 Juan Encarnacion .07 .20
173 Angel Berroa .07 .20
174 Desi Relaford .07 .20
175 Paul Quantrill .07 .20
176 Ben Sheets .07 .20
177 Eddie Guardado .07 .20
178 Rocky Biddle .07 .20
179 Mike Stanton .07 .20
180 Eric Chavez .07 .20
181 Jason Michaels .07 .20
182 Terry Adams .07 .20
183 Kip Wells .07 .20
184 Brian Lawrence .07 .20
185 Bret Boone .07 .20
186 Tino Martinez .10 .30
187 Aubrey Huff .07 .20
188 Kevin Mench .07 .20
189 Tim Salmon .10 .30
190 Carlos Delgado .07 .20
191 John Lackey .07 .20
192 Oscar Villarreal .07 .20
193 Luis Matos .07 .20
194 Derek Lowe .07 .20
195 Mark Grudzielanek .07 .20
196 Tom Gordon .07 .20
197 Matt Clement .07 .20
198 Byung-Hyun Kim .07 .20
199 Brandon Inge .07 .20
200 Nomar Garciaparra .30 .75
201 Antonio Osuna .07 .20
202 Jose Mesa .07 .20
203 Bo Hart .07 .20
204 Jack Wilson .07 .20
205 Ray Durham .07 .20
206 Freddy Garcia .07 .20
207 J.D. Drew .07 .20
208 Einar Diaz .07 .20
209 Roy Halladay .07 .20
210 David Eckstein UER .07 .20
Adam Kennedy pictured
211 Jason Marquis .07 .20
212 Jorge Julio .07 .20
213 Tim Wakefield .07 .20
214 Moises Alou .07 .20
215 Bartolo Colon .07 .20
216 Jimmy Haynes .07 .20
217 Preston Wilson .07 .20
218 Luis Castillo .07 .20
219 Richard Hidalgo .07 .20
220 Manny Ramirez .10 .30
221 Mike Mussina .10 .30
222 Randy Wolf .07 .20
223 Kris Benson .07 .20
224 Ryan Klesko .07 .20
225 Rich Aurilia .07 .20
226 Kelvim Escobar .07 .20
227 Francisco Cordero .07 .20
228 Kazuhiro Sasaki .07 .20
229 Danny Bautista .07 .20
230 Rafael Furcal .07 .20
231 Travis Driskill .07 .20
232 Kyle Farnsworth .07 .20
233 Jose Valentin .07 .20
234 Felipe Lopez .07 .20
235 C.C. Sabathia .07 .20
236 Brad Penny .07 .20
237 Brad Ausmus .07 .20
238 Raul Ibanez .07 .20
239 Adrian Beltre .07 .20
240 Rocco Baldelli .07 .20
241 Orlando Hudson .07 .20
242 Dave Roberts .07 .20
243 Doug Mientkiewicz .07 .20
244 Brad Wilkerson .07 .20
245 Scott Strickland .07 .20
246 Ryan Franklin .07 .20
247 Chad Bradford .07 .20
248 Gary Bennett .07 .20
249 Jose Cruz Jr. .07 .20
250 Jeff Kent .07 .20
251 Josh Beckett .07 .20
252 Ramon Ortiz .07 .20
253 Miguel Batista .07 .20
254 Jung Bong .07 .20
255 Deivi Cruz .07 .20
256 Alex Gonzalez .07 .20
257 Shawn Chacon .07 .20
258 Runelvys Hernandez .07 .20
259 Joe Mays .07 .20
260 Eric Gagne .07 .20
261 Dustan Mohr UER .07 .20
1998 Kinston stats are wrong
262 Tomokazu Ohka .07 .20
263 Eric Byrnes .07 .20
264 Frank Catalanotto .07 .20
265 Cristian Guzman .07 .20
266 Orlando Cabrera .07 .20
267A Juan Castro .07 .20
267B M.Scioscia MG UER 274 .07 .20
268 Bob Brenly MG .07 .20
269 Bobby Cox MG .07 .20
270 Mike Hargrove MG .07 .20
271 Grady Little MG .07 .20
272 Dusty Baker MG .07 .20
273 Jerry Manuel MG .07 .20
275 Eric Wedge MG .07 .20
276 Clint Hurdle MG .07 .20
277 Alan Trammell MG .07 .20
278 Jack McKeon MG .07 .20
279 Jimy Williams MG .07 .20
280 Tony Pena MG .07 .20
281 Jim Tracy MG .07 .20
282 Ned Yost MG .07 .20
283 Ron Gardenhire MG .07 .20
284 Frank Robinson MG .07 .20
285 Art Howe MG .07 .20
286 Joe Torre MG .10 .30
287 Ken Macha MG .07 .20

288 Larry Bowa MG .07 .20
289 Lloyd McClendon MG .07 .20
290 Bruce Bochy MG .07 .20
291 Felipe Alou MG .07 .20
292 Bob Melvin MG .07 .20
293 Tony LaRussa MG .07 .20
294 Lou Piniella MG .07 .20
295 Buck Showalter MG .07 .20
296 Carlos Tosca MG .07 .20
297 Anthony Acevedo FY RC .20 .50
298 Anthony Lerew FY RC .30 .75
299 Blake Hawksworth FY RC .20 .50
300 Brayan Pena FY RC .20 .50
301 Casey Myers FY RC .20 .50
302 Craig Ansman FY RC .20 .50
303 David Murphy FY RC .30 .75
304 Dave Crouthers FY RC .20 .50
305 Dioner Navarro FY RC .30 .75
306 Donald Levinski FY RC .20 .50
307 Jesse Roman FY RC .20 .50
308 Sung Jung FY RC .20 .50
309 Jon Knott FY RC .20 .50
310 Josh Labandeira FY RC .20 .50
311 Kenny Perez FY RC .20 .50
312 Khalid Ballouli FY RC .20 .50
313 Kyle Davies FY RC 1.00 2.50
314 Marcus McBeth FY RC .20 .50
315 Matt Creighton FY RC .20 .50
316 Chris O'Riordan FY RC .20 .50
317 Mike Gosling FY RC .20 .50
318 Nic Ungs FY RC .20 .50
319 Omar Falcon FY RC .20 .50
320 Rodney Choy Foo FY RC .20 .50
321 Tim Frend FY RC .20 .50
322 Todd Self FY RC .20 .50
323 Tydus Meadows FY RC .20 .50
324 Yadier Molina FY RC .75 2.00
325 Zach Duke FY RC .75 2.00
326 Zach Miner FY RC .50 1.25
327 Bernie Castro .20 .50
Khalil Greene FS
328 Ryan Madson .20 .50
Elizardo Ramirez FS
329 Rich Harden .20 .50
Bobby Crosby FS
330 Zack Greinke .20 .50
Jimmy Gobble FS
331 Bobby Jenks .20 .50
Casey Kotchman FS
332 Sammy Sosa HL .10 .30
333 Kevin Millwood HL .07 .20
334 Rafael Palmeiro HL .07 .20
335 Roger Clemens HL .20 .50
336 Eric Gagne HL .07 .20
337 Bill Mueller .10 .30
Manny Ramirez
Derek Jeter
AL Batting Avg LL
338 Vernon Wells .20 .50
Ichiro Suzuki
Michael Young
AL Hits LL
339 Alex Rodriguez .20 .50
Frank Thomas
Carlos Delgado
AL Home Runs LL
340 Carlos Delgado .20 .50
Alex Rodriguez
Bret Boone
AL RBI's LL
341 Pedro Martinez .10 .30
Tim Hudson
Esteban Loaiza
AL ERA LL
342 Esteban Loaiza .10 .30
Pedro Martinez
Roy Halladay
AL Strikeouts LL
343 Albert Pujols .20 .50
Todd Helton
Edgar Renteria
NL Batting Avg LL
344 Albert Pujols .20 .50
Todd Helton
Juan Pierre
NL Hits LL
345 Jim Thome .07 .20
Richie Sexson
Javy Lopez
NL Home Runs LL
346 Preston Wilson .07 .20
Gary Sheffield
Jim Thome
NL RBI's LL
347 Jason Schmidt .10 .30
Kevin Brown
Mark Prior
NL ERA LL
348 Kerry Wood .10 .30
Mark Prior
Javier Vazquez
NL Strikeouts LL
349 Roger Clemens .20 .50
David Wells ALDS
350 Kerry Wood .10 .30
Mark Prior NLDS
351 Josh Beckett .20 .50
Miguel Cabrera
Ivan Rodriguez NLCS
352 Jason Giambi .20 .50
Mariano Rivera
Aaron Boone ALCS
353 Derek Lowe .20 .50
Ivan Rodriguez AL/NLDS
354 Pedro Martinez .20 .50
Jorge Posada
Roger Clemens ALCS
355 Juan Pierre WS .07 .20
356 Carlos Delgado AS .07 .20
357 Bret Boone AS .07 .20
358 Alex Rodriguez AS .20 .50
359 Bill Mueller AS .07 .20
360 Vernon Wells AS .07 .20
361 Garret Anderson AS .07 .20
362 Magglio Ordonez AS .07 .20
363 Jorge Posada AS .07 .20
364 Roy Halladay AS .07 .20
365 Andy Pettitte AS .07 .20
366 Frank Thomas AS .10 .30
367 Jody Gerut AS .07 .20
368 Sammy Sosa .20 .50
369 Joe Crede .07 .20
370 Gary Sheffield .07 .20
371 Coco Crisp .07 .20
372 Torii Hunter .07 .20
373 Derrek Lee .10 .30
374 Adam Everett .07 .20
375 Miguel Tejada .07 .20
376 Jeremy Affeldt .07 .20
377 Robin Ventura .07 .20
378 Scott Podsednik .07 .20
379 Matthew LeCroy .07 .20
380 Vladimir Guerrero .20 .50
381 Tike Redman .07 .20
382 Jeff Nelson .07 .20
383 Cliff Lee .07 .20
384 Bobby Abreu .07 .20
385 Josh Fogg .07 .20
386 Trevor Hoffman .07 .20
387 Jesse Foppert .07 .20
388 Edgar Martinez .10 .30
389 Edgar Renteria .07 .20
390 Chipper Jones .20 .50
391 Eric Munson .07 .20
392 Dewon Brazelton .07 .20
393 John Thomson .07 .20
394 Chris Woodward .07 .20
395 Adam LaRoche .07 .20
396 Elmer Dessens .07 .20
397 Johnny Estrada .07 .20
398 Damian Moss .07 .20
399 Gabe Kapler .07 .20
400 Dontrelle Willis .10 .30
401 Troy Glaus .07 .20
402 Raul Mondesi .07 .20
403 Shane Reynolds .07 .20
404 Kurt Ainsworth .07 .20
405 Pedro Martinez .10 .30
406 Eric Karros .07 .20
407 Billy Koch .07 .20
408 Scott Schoeneweis .07 .20
409 Paul Wilson .07 .20
410 Mike Sweeney .07 .20
411 Jason Bay .07 .20
412 Mark Redman .07 .20
413 Jason Jennings .07 .20
414 Rondell White .07 .20
415 Todd Hundley .07 .20
416 Shannon Stewart .07 .20
417 Jae Weong Seo .07 .20
418 Livan Hernandez .07 .20
419 Mark Ellis .07 .20
420 Pat Burrell .07 .20
421 Mark Loretta .07 .20
422 Robb Nen .07 .20
423 Joel Pineiro .07 .20
424 Jason Simontacchi .07 .20
425 Sterling Hitchcock .07 .20
426 Rey Ordonez .07 .20
427 Greg Myers .07 .20
428 Shane Spencer .07 .20
429 Carlos Baerga .07 .20
430 Garret Anderson .07 .20
431 Horacio Ramirez .07 .20
432 Brian Roberts .07 .20
433 Damian Jackson .07 .20
434 Doug Glanville .07 .20
435 Brian Daubach .07 .20
436 Alex Escobar .07 .20
437 Alex Sanchez .07 .20
438 Jeff Bagwell .10 .30
439 Darrell May .07 .20
440 Shawn Green .07 .20
441 Geoff Jenkins .07 .20
442 Endy Chavez .07 .20
443 Nick Johnson .07 .20
444 Jose Guillen .07 .20
445 Tomas Perez .07 .20
446 Phil Nevin .07 .20
447 Jason Schmidt .07 .20
448 Julio Mateo .07 .20
449 So Taguchi .07 .20
450 Randy Johnson .20 .50
451 Paul Byrd .07 .20
452 Chone Figgins .07 .20
453 Larry Bigbie .07 .20
454 Scott Williamson .07 .20
455 Ramon Martinez .07 .20
456 Roberto Alomar .10 .30
457 Ryan Dempster .07 .20
458 Ryan Ludwick .07 .20
459 Ramon Santiago .07 .20
460 Jeff Conine .07 .20
461 Brad Lidge .07 .20
462 Ken Harvey .07 .20
463 Guillermo Mota .07 .20
464 Rick Reed .07 .20
465 Joey Eischen .07 .20
466 Wade Miller .07 .20
467 Steve Karsay .07 .20
468 Chase Utley .10 .30
469 Matt Stairs .07 .20
470 Yorvit Torrealba .07 .20
471 Joe Kennedy .07 .20
472 Reed Johnson .07 .20
473 Victor Zambrano .07 .20
474 Jeff Davanon .07 .20
475 Luis Gonzalez .07 .20
476 Eli Marrero .07 .20
477 Ray King .07 .20
478 Jack Cust .07 .20
479 Omar Daal .07 .20
480 Todd Walker .07 .20
481 Shawn Estes .07 .20
482 Chris Reitsma .07 .20
483 Jake Westbrook .07 .20
484 Jeremy Bonderman .07 .20
485 A.J. Burnett .07 .20
486 Roy Oswalt .07 .20
487 Kevin Brown .07 .20
488 Eric Milton .07 .20
489 Claudio Vargas .07 .20
490 Roger Cedeno .07 .20
491 David Wells .07 .20
492 Scott Hatteberg .07 .20
493 Ricky Ledee .07 .20
494 Eric Young .07 .20
495 Armando Benitez .07 .20
496 Dan Haren .07 .20
497 Carl Crawford .07 .20
498 Laynce Nix .07 .20
499 Eric Hinske .07 .20
500 Ivan Rodriguez .10 .30
501 Scot Shields .07 .20
502 Brandon Webb .07 .20
503 Mark DeRosa .07 .20
504 Jhonny Peralta .07 .20
505 Adam Kennedy .07 .20
506 Tony Batista .07 .20
507 Jeff Suppan .07 .20
508 Kenny Lofton .07 .20
509 Scott Sullivan .07 .20
510 Ken Griffey Jr. .30 .75
511 Billy Traber .07 .20
512 Larry Walker .07 .20
513 Mike Maroth .07 .20
514 Todd Hollandsworth .07 .20
515 Kirk Saarloos .07 .20
516 Carlos Beltran .07 .20
517 Juan Rivera .07 .20
518 Roger Clemens .40 1.00
519 Karim Garcia .07 .20
520 Jose Reyes .07 .20
521 Brandon Duckworth .07 .20
522 Brian Giles .07 .20
523 J.T. Snow .07 .20
524 Jamie Moyer .07 .20
525 Jason Isringhausen .07 .20
526 Julio Lugo .07 .20
527 Mark Teixeira .10 .30
528 Cory Lidle .07 .20
529 Lyle Overbay .07 .20
530 Troy Percival .07 .20
531 Robby Hammock .07 .20
532 Robert Fick .07 .20
533 Jason Johnson .07 .20
534 Brandon Lyon .07 .20
535 Antonio Alfonseca .07 .20
536 Tom Goodwin .07 .20
537 Paul Konerko .07 .20
538 D'Angelo Jimenez .07 .20
539 Ben Broussard .07 .20
540 Magglio Ordonez .07 .20
541 Ellis Burks .07 .20
542 Carlos Pena .07 .20
543 Chad Fox .07 .20
544 Jeriome Robertson .07 .20
545 Travis Hafner .07 .20
546 Joe Randa .07 .20
547 Wil Cordero .07 .20
548 Brady Clark .07 .20
549 Ruben Sierra .07 .20
550 Barry Zito .07 .20
551 Brett Myers .07 .20
552 Oliver Perez .07 .20
553 Trey Hodges .07 .20
554 Benito Santiago .07 .20
555 David Ross .07 .20
556 Ramon Vazquez .07 .20
557 Joe Nathan .07 .20
558 Dan Wilson .07 .20
559 Joe Mauer .20 .50
560 Jim Edmonds .07 .20
561 Shawn Wooten .07 .20
562 Matt Kata .07 .20
563 Vinny Castilla .07 .20
564 Marty Cordova .07 .20
565 Aramis Ramirez .07 .20
566 Carl Everett .07 .20
567 Ryan Freel .07 .20
568 Jason Davis .07 .20
569 Mark Bellhorn Sox .07 .20
570 Craig Monroe .07 .20
571 Roberto Hernandez .07 .20
572 Tim Redding .07 .20
573 Kevin Appier .07 .20
574 Jeromy Burnitz .07 .20
575 Miguel Cabrera .10 .30
576 Ramon Nivar .07 .20
577 Casey Blake .07 .20
578 Aaron Boone .07 .20
579 Jermaine Dye .07 .20
580 Jeremie Williams .07 .20
581 John Olerud .07 .20
582 Scott Rolen .10 .30
583 Bobby Kielty .07 .20
584 Travis Lee .07 .20
585 Jeff Cirillo .07 .20
586 Scott Spiezio .07 .20
587 Stephen Randolph .07 .20
588 Melvin Mora .07 .20
589 Mike Timlin .07 .20
590 Kerry Wood .07 .20
591 Tony Womack .07 .20
592 Jody Gerut .07 .20
593 Franklyn German .07 .20
594 Morgan Ensberg .07 .20
595 Odalis Perez .07 .20
596 Michael Cuddyer .07 .20
597 Jon Lieber .07 .20
598 Mike Williams .07 .20
599 Jose Hernandez .07 .20
600 Alfonso Soriano .07 .20
601 Marquis Grissom .07 .20
602 Matt Morris .07 .20
603 Damian Rolls .07 .20
604 Juan Gonzalez .07 .20
605 Aquilino Lopez .07 .20
606 Jose Valverde .07 .20
607 Kenny Rogers .07 .20
608 Joe Borowski .07 .20
609 Josh Bard .07 .20
610 Austin Kearns .07 .20
611 Chin-Hui Tsao .07 .20
612 Wil Ledezma .07 .20
613 Aaron Guiel .07 .20
614 LaTroy Hawkins .07 .20
615 Tony Armas Jr. .07 .20
616 Steve Trachsel .07 .20
617 Ted Lilly .07 .20
618 Todd Pratt .07 .20
619 Sean Burroughs .07 .20
620 Rafael Palmeiro .10 .30
621 Jeremi Gonzalez .07 .20
622 Quinton McCracken .07 .20
623 David Ortiz .20 .50
624 Randall Simon .07 .20
625 Wily Mo Pena .07 .20
626 Nate Cornejo .07 .20
627 Brian Anderson .07 .20
628 Corey Koskie .07 .20
629 Keith Foulke Sox .07 .20
630 Rheal Cormier .07 .20
631 Sidney Ponson .07 .20
632 Gary Matthews Jr. .07 .20
633 Herbert Perry .07 .20
634 Shea Hillenbrand .07 .20
635 Craig Biggio .10 .30
636 Barry Larkin .10 .30
637 Arthur Rhodes .07 .20
638 Anaheim Angels TC .07 .20
639 Arizona Diamondbacks TC .07 .20
640 Atlanta Braves TC .07 .20
641 Baltimore Orioles TC .07 .20
642 Boston Red Sox TC .10 .30
643 Chicago Cubs TC .07 .20
644 Chicago White Sox TC .07 .20
645 Cincinnati Reds TC .07 .20
646 Cleveland Indians TC .07 .20
647 Colorado Rockies TC .07 .20
648 Detroit Tigers TC .07 .20
649 Florida Marlins TC .07 .20
650 Houston Astros TC .07 .20
651 Kansas City Royals TC .07 .20
652 Los Angeles Dodgers TC .07 .20
653 Milwaukee Brewers TC .07 .20
654 Minnesota Twins TC .07 .20
655 Montreal Expos TC .07 .20
656 New York Mets TC .07 .20
657 New York Yankees TC .20 .50
658 Oakland Athletics TC .07 .20
659 Philadelphia Phillies TC .07 .20
660 Pittsburgh Pirates TC .07 .20
661 San Diego Padres TC .07 .20
662 San Francisco Giants TC .07 .20
663 Seattle Mariners TC .07 .20
664 St. Louis Cardinals TC .07 .20
665 Tampa Bay Devil Rays TC .07 .20
666 Texas Rangers TC .07 .20
667 Toronto Blue Jays TC .07 .20
668 Kyle Sleeth DP RC .20 .50
669 Bradley Sullivan DP RC .20 .50
670 Carlos Quentin DP RC 1.00 2.50
671 Conor Jackson DP RC 1.25 3.00
672 Jeffrey Allison DP RC .20 .50
673 Matthew Moses DP RC .40 1.00
674 Tim Stauffer DP RC .30 .75
675 Estee Harris DP RC .20 .50
676 David Aardsma DP RC .20 .50
677 Omar Quintanilla DP RC .20 .50
678 Aaron Hill DP .20 .50
679 Tony Richie DP RC .20 .50
680 Lastings Milledge DP RC 1.50 4.00
681 Brad Snyder DP RC .40 1.00
682 Jason Hirsh DP RC .60 1.50
683 Logan Kensing DP RC .20 .50
684 Chris Lubanski DP .20 .50
685 Ryan Harvey DP .20 .50
686 Ryan Wagner DP .20 .50
687 Rickie Weeks DP .20 .50
688 Grady Sizemore .20 .50
Jeremy Guthrie
689 Edwin Jackson .20 .50
Greg Miller
690 Jeremy Reed .20 .50
Neal Cotts
691 Adam Loewen .20 .50
Nick Markakis
692 B.J. Upton .20 .50
Delmon Young
693 Kings of New York .60 1.50
Alex Rodriguez
Derek Jeter
694 Fan Favorites .40 1.00
Ichiro Suzuki
Albert Pujols
695 South Philly Sluggers .40 1.00
Jim Thome
Mike Schmidt
696 Mike Mussina GG .07 .20
697 Bengie Molina GG .07 .20
698 John Olerud GG .07 .20
699 Bret Boone GG .07 .20
700 Eric Chavez GG .07 .20
701 Alex Rodriguez GG .20 .50
702 Mike Cameron GG UER .07 .20
Pictures Randy Winn
703 Ichiro Suzuki GG .20 .50
704 Torii Hunter GG .07 .20
705 Mike Hampton GG .07 .20
706 Mike Matheny GG .07 .20
707 Derrek Lee GG .07 .20
708 Luis Castillo GG .07 .20
709 Scott Rolen GG .07 .20
710 Edgar Renteria GG .07 .20
711 Andruw Jones GG .07 .20
712 Jose Cruz Jr. GG .07 .20
713 Jim Edmonds GG .07 .20
714 Roy Halladay CY .07 .20
715 Eric Gagne CY .07 .20
716 Alex Rodriguez MVP .20 .50
717 Angel Berroa ROY .07 .20
718 Dontrelle Willis ROY .07 .20
719 Todd Helton AS .07 .20
720 Marcus Giles AS .07 .20
721 Edgar Renteria AS .07 .20
722 Scott Rolen AS .07 .20
723 Albert Pujols AS .20 .50
724 Gary Sheffield AS .07 .20
725 Javy Lopez AS .07 .20
726 Eric Gagne AS .07 .20
727 Randy Wolf AS .07 .20
728 Bobby Cox AS .07 .20
729 Scott Podsednik AS .07 .20
730 Alex Gonzalez WS .10 .30
731 Brad Penny WS .10 .30
732 Josh Beckett .10 .30
Ivan Rodriguez
Alex Gonzalez WS
733 Josh Beckett WS MVP .10 .30

2004 Topps Black

COM. (1-6/8-331/368-695) 10.00 25.00
SEMIS 1-296/368-667/693-695 15.00 30.00
UNL 1-296/368-667/693-695 20.00 40.00
COM. 297-326/668-687 10.00 25.00
UNL 297-326/668-687 15.00 30.00
COM. 327-331/688-692 10.00 25.00
SEMIS 327-331/688-692 15.00 30.00
UNL 327-331/688-692 20.00 40.00
SERIES 1 ODDS 1:13 HTA
SERIES 2 ODDS 1:12 HTA
STATED PRINT RUN 53 SERIAL #'d SETS

CARDS 7 AND 274 DO NOT EXIST
SCIOSCIA AND J.CASTRO NUMBERED 267
671 Conor Jackson DP 50.00 100.00
680 Lastings Milledge DP 40.00 80.00

2004 Topps Box Bottoms

The player list in our checklist has the player's name as well as what sheet his card is located on. Sheets 1-4 were issued on the bottom of first series HTA boxes and sheets 5-8 on second series.

*BOX BOTTOM CARDS: 1X TO 2.5X BASIC
ONE 4-CARD SHEET PER HTA BOX

2004 Topps Gold

*GOLD 1-296/368-: 6X TO 15X
*GOLD 297-326/668-687: 2X TO 5X
*GOLD 327-331/688-692: 2X TO 5X
SERIES 1 ODDS 1:11 HOB, 1:3 HTA, 1:10 RET
SERIES 2 ODDS 1:8 HOB, 1:2 HTA, 1:8 RET
STATED PRINT RUN 2004 SERIAL #'d SETS
CARDS 7 AND 274 DO NOT EXIST
SCIOSCIA AND J.CASTRO NUMBERED 267

2004 Topps All-Star Patch Relics

SER.2 ODDS 1:7698 H, 1:2208 HTA, 1:7819 R
STATED PRINT RUN 15 SETS
CARDS ARE NOT SERIAL-NUMBERED
PRINT RUN INFO PROVIDED BY TOPPS
NO PRICING DUE TO SCARCITY
AB Aaron Boone
AJ Andruw Jones
AP Albert Pujols
AR Alex Rodriguez
BB Bret Boone
BD Brendan Donnelly
BW Billy Wagner
CD Carlos Delgado
CE Carl Everett
EG Eddie Guardado
EGA Eric Gagne
EL Esteban Loaiza
EM Edgar Martinez
ER Edgar Renteria
GA Garret Anderson
HB Hank Blalock
JE Jim Edmonds
JG Jason Giambi
JL Javy Lopez
JM Jamie Moyer
JP Jorge Posada
JS Jason Schmidt
JV Jose Vidro
KF Keith Foulke
KW Kerry Wood
ML Mike Lowell
MM Mark Mulder
MMO Melvin Mora
NG Nomar Garciaparra
PL Paul Lo Duca
PW Preston Wilson
RF Rafael Furcal
RH Ramon Hernandez
RO Russ Ortiz
RS Richie Sexson
RW Randy Wolf
RWH Rondell White
SH Shigetoshi Hasegawa
SR Scott Rolen
TG Troy Glaus
TH Todd Helton
VW Vernon Wells
WW Woody Williams

2004 Topps 1st Edition

*1ST ED 1-296: 1.25X TO 3X BASIC
*1ST ED 297-RC'S: X TO X BASIC
*1ST ED 327-331/688-: 1.25X TO 3X BASIC
DISTRIBUTED IN 1ST EDITION BOXES
CARDS 7 AND 274 DO NOT EXIST
SCIOSCIA AND J.CASTRO NUMBERED 267

2004 Topps All-Star Stitches Jersey Relics

SERIES 1 ODDS 1:137 HOB/RET, 1:39 HTA
AB Aaron Boone 4.00 10.00
AJ Andruw Jones 4.00 10.00
AR Alex Rodriguez 6.00 15.00
BD Brendan Donnelly 4.00 10.00
BW Billy Wagner 4.00 10.00
CE Carl Everett 4.00 10.00
EG Eddie Guardado 4.00 10.00
EGA Eric Gagne 4.00 10.00
EL Esteban Loaiza 4.00 10.00
EM Edgar Martinez 4.00 10.00
ER Edgar Renteria 4.00 10.00
HB Hank Blalock 4.00 10.00
JL Javy Lopez 4.00 10.00
JM Jamie Moyer 4.00 10.00
JP Jorge Posada 4.00 10.00
JS Jason Schmidt 4.00 10.00
JV Jose Vidro 4.00 10.00
KF Keith Foulke 4.00 10.00
KW Kerry Wood 4.00 10.00
ML Mike Lowell 4.00 10.00
MM Mark Mulder 4.00 10.00
MMO Melvin Mora 4.00 10.00
NG Nomar Garciaparra 6.00 15.00
PL Paul Lo Duca 4.00 10.00
PW Preston Wilson 4.00 10.00
RF Rafael Furcal 4.00 10.00
RH Ramon Hernandez 4.00 10.00
RO Russ Ortiz 4.00 10.00
RW Randy Wolf 4.00 10.00
RWH Rondell White 4.00 10.00
SH Shigetoshi Hasegawa 4.00 10.00
SR Scott Rolen 4.00 10.00
TG Troy Glaus 4.00 10.00
TH Todd Helton 4.00 10.00
VW Vernon Wells 4.00 10.00
WW Woody Williams 4.00 10.00

2004 Topps All-Stars

COMPLETE SET (20) 15.00 40.00
SERIES 2 ODDS 1:16 H, 1:4 HTA
TAS1 Jason Giambi .75 2.00
TAS2 Ichiro Suzuki 1.50 4.00
TAS3 Alex Rodriguez 1.25 3.00
TAS4 Albert Pujols 1.50 4.00
TAS5 Alfonso Soriano .75 2.00
TAS6 Nomar Garciaparra 1.25 3.00
TAS7 Andruw Jones .75 2.00
TAS8 Carlos Delgado .75 2.00
TAS9 Gary Sheffield .75 2.00
TAS10 Jorge Posada .75 2.00
TAS11 Magglio Ordonez .75 2.00
TAS12 Kerry Wood .75 2.00
TAS13 Garret Anderson .75 2.00
TAS14 Bret Boone .75 2.00
TAS15 Hank Blalock .75 2.00
TAS16 Mike Lowell .75 2.00
TAS17 Todd Helton .75 2.00
TAS18 Vernon Wells .75 2.00
TAS19 Roger Clemens 1.50 4.00
TAS20 Scott Rolen .75 2.00

2004 Topps American Treasures Presidential Signatures

Randomly inserted into packs, this set features a "cut" signature from each of the United State Presidents. Each of these cards feature the cut signature against a United States flag background while the back features an informational blurb about that president.

SER.1 ODDS 1:175,770 HOBBY, 1:52,080 HTA
SER.1 ODDS 1:138,240 RETAIL
STATED PRINT RUN 1 SERIAL #'d SET
NO PRICING DUE TO SCARCITY

AJ Andrew Jackson
AJO Andrew Johnson
AL Abraham Lincoln
BC Bill Clinton
BH Benjamin Harrison
CA Chester A. Arthur
CC Calvin Coolidge
DE Dwight D. Eisenhower
FP Franklin Pierce
FR Franklin D. Roosevelt
GB George W. Bush
GC Grover Cleveland
GF Gerald Ford
GHB George H.W. Bush
GW George Washington
HH Herbert Hoover
HT Harry S. Truman
JA John Adams
JB James Buchanan
JC Jimmy Carter
JG James Garfield
JK John F. Kennedy
JM James Madison
JMO James Monroe
JP James K. Polk
JQA John Quincy Adams
JT John Tyler
LJ Lyndon B. Johnson
MF Millard Fillmore
MV Martin Van Buren
RH Rutherford B. Hayes
RN Richard Nixon
RR Ronald Reagan
TJ Thomas Jefferson
TR Theodore Roosevelt
UG Ulysses S. Grant
WH Warren Harding
WHH William H. Harrison
WM William McKinley
WT William Howard Taft
WW Woodrow Wilson
ZT Zachary Taylor

2004 Topps American Treasures Presidential Signatures Dual

This card is similar to the basic American Treasures Presidential Cut Signatures but feature two signatures from George H. Bush and his son George W. Bush. Only one copy of this card was produced and it was seeded exclusively into first series Home Team Advantage packs.

SERIES 1 ODDS 1:208,320 HTA
STATED PRINT RUN 1 SERIAL #'d CARD
NO PRICING DUE TO SCARCITY
GB2 George H.W. Bush
George W. Bush

2004 Topps American Treasures Signatures

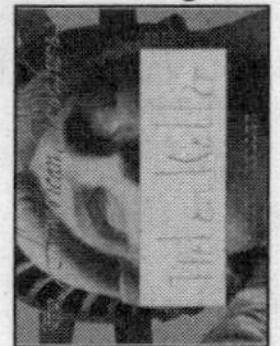

Building on the popularity and interest the first series Presidential Autographs gave this product, Topps issed 17 signed cards of famed Americans past and present as very tough inserts (one in 658,152 hobby, one in 98,256 HTA and one in 1,156,384 retail packs). Each of these cards were issued to a stated print run of one serial numbered set.

SER.2 ODDS 1:658,152 HOBBY, 1:98,256 HTA
SER.2 ODDS 1:156,384 RETAIL
STATED PRINT RUN 1 SERIAL #'d SET
NO PRICING DUE TO SCARCITY

AB Alexander Graham Bell
ABU Aaron Burr
AE Albert Einstein
CL Charles Lindbergh
DM Douglas MacArthur
DW Daniel Webster
GP George S. Patton
HK Helen Keller
JS Jonas Salk
MT Mark Twain
NA Neil Armstrong
OW Orville Wright
PH Patrick Henry
RK Robert F. Kennedy
TE Thomas A. Edison
WD Walt Disney
WH William Randolph Hearst

2004 Topps American Treasures Signatures Dual

This card which was issued at a stated rate of one in 1,196,512 HTA packs feature signatures of Mark Twain/Samuel Clemens. Samuel Clemens, who wrote under the pseudonym of Mark Twain, signed items both ways during his lifetime and Topps found one type of each signature to put on this card. This card was issued to a stated print run of one serial numbered set.

SERIES 2 STATED ODDS 1:196,512 HTA
STATED PRINT RUN 1 SERIAL #'d CARD
NO PRICING DUE TO SCARCITY
MT Mark Twain
Samuel Clemens

2004 Topps Autographs

Please note Josh Beckett, Mike Lowell, Mark Prior, Ivan Rodriguez and Scott Rolen did not return their cards in time for inclusion into packs and the exchange date for these cards were November 30th, 2005 for Series one exchange cards and April 30th, 2006 for Series two exchange cards. Cards issued in first series packs carry a "1" and cards from series 2 carry a "2" after their group seeding notes within our checklist.

SER.1 B 1:7362 H, 1:1911 HTA, 1:7472 R
SER.1 C 1:10,900 H, 1:2741 HTA, 1:11,059 R
SER.1 D 1:1053 H, 1:273 HTA, 1:1055 R
SER.1 E 1:6278 H, 1:1640 HTA, 1:6284 R
SER.1 F 1:1229 H, 1:318 HTA, 1:1229 R
SER.1 G 1:2340 H, 1:668 HTA, 1:1881 R
SER.1 H 1:1167 H, 1:351 HTA, 1:1229 R
SER.2 A 1:10,530 H, 1:2848 HTA, 1:9774 R
SER.2 B 1:1504 H, 1:391 HTA, 1:1422 R
SER.2 C 1:1319 H, 1:333 HTA, 1:1303 R

Card	Low	High
AB Aaron Boone B2	15.00	40.00
AH Aubrey Huff B2	6.00	15.00
AK Austin Kearns B1	6.00	15.00
BB Bobby Brownlie C2	10.00	25.00
BS Benito Santiago D1	10.00	25.00
BU B.J. Upton F1	10.00	25.00
CF Cliff Floyd D1	6.00	15.00
DM Dustin McGowan C2	4.00	10.00
DW Dontrelle Willis B2	10.00	25.00
EH Eric Hinske H1	4.00	10.00
ER Elizardo Ramirez H1	4.00	10.00
GA Garret Anderson B2	10.00	25.00
HB Hank Blalock D1	6.00	15.00
IR Ivan Rodriguez B2	10.00	25.00
JB Josh Beckett B1	12.50	30.00
JG Jay Gibbons A1	6.00	15.00
JP1 Josh Phelps G1	4.00	10.00
JP2 Jorge Posada B2	10.00	25.00
JV Jose Vidro F1	4.00	10.00
KG Khalil Greene H1	10.00	25.00
LB Lance Berkman A2	12.50	30.00
MC Miguel Cabrera C2	10.00	25.00
ML Mike Lowell F1	6.00	15.00
MO Magglio Ordonez F1	6.00	15.00
MP Mark Prior D1	10.00	25.00
MS Mike Sweeney D1	6.00	15.00
MT Mark Teixeira D1	10.00	25.00
PK Paul Konerko G1	10.00	25.00
PL Paul Lo Duca E1	6.00	15.00
SP Scott Podsednik B2	10.00	25.00
SR Scott Rolen A2 EXCH	12.50	30.00
TH Torii Hunter C1	6.00	15.00
VM Victor Martinez D1	6.00	15.00
ZG Zack Greinke C2	6.00	15.00

2004 Topps Derby Digs Jersey Relics

SERIES 1 ODDS 1:585 H, 1:167 HTA, 1:586 R

Card	Low	High
AP Albert Pujols	10.00	25.00
BB Bret Boone	4.00	10.00
CD Carlos Delgado	4.00	10.00
GA Garret Anderson	4.00	10.00
JE Jim Edmonds	4.00	10.00
JG Jason Giambi	4.00	10.00
RS Richie Sexson	4.00	10.00

2004 Topps Draft Pick Bonus

Card	Low	High
COMPLETE SET (10)	20.00	50.00
COMP.RETAIL SET (5)	8.00	20.00
COMP.HOLIDAY SET (10)	12.50	30.00

1-5 ISSUED IN BLUE RETAIL FACT.SET
6-15 ISSUED IN GREEN HOLIDAY FACT.SET

Card	Low	High
1 Josh Johnson	2.00	5.00
2 Donny Lucy	1.50	4.00
3 Greg Golson	3.00	8.00
4 K.C. Herren	2.00	5.00
5 Jeff Marquez	2.00	5.00
6 Mark Rogers	3.00	8.00
7 Eric Hurley	3.00	8.00
8 Gio Gonzalez	3.00	8.00
9 Thomas Diamond	3.00	8.00
10 Matt Bush	3.00	8.00
11 Kyle Waldrop	3.00	8.00
12 Neil Walker	3.00	8.00
13 Mike Ferris	2.00	5.00
14 Ray Liotta	3.00	8.00
15 Philip Hughes	6.00	15.00

2004 Topps Fall Classic Covers

Card	Low	High
COMPLETE SET (99)	120.00	240.00
COMPLETE SERIES 1 (48)	60.00	120.00
COMPLETE SERIES 2 (51)	60.00	120.00
COMMON CARD	1.50	4.00

SERIES 1 ODDS 1:12 HOB/RET, 1:4 HTA
SERIES 2 ODDS 1:12 HOB/RET, 1:5 HTA
EVEN YEARS DISTRIBUTED IN SERIES 1
ODD YEARS DISTRIBUTED IN SERIES 2

2004 Topps First Year Player Bonus

Card	Low	High
COMPLETE SERIES 1 (5)	7.50	15.00
COMPLETE SERIES 2 (5)	7.50	15.00

1-5 ISSUED IN BROWN HOBBY FACT.SETS
6-10 ISSUED IN JC PENNEY FACT.SETS

Card	Low	High
1 Travis Blackley	1.50	4.00
2 Rudy Guillen	2.00	5.00
3 Ervin Santana	2.00	5.00
4 Wanell Severino	1.50	4.00
5 Kevin Kouzmanoff	3.00	8.00
6 Alberto Callaspo	2.00	5.00
7 Bobby Brownlie	1.50	4.00
8 Travis Hanson	2.00	5.00
9 Joaquin Arias	2.00	5.00
10 Merkin Valdez	2.00	5.00

2004 Topps Hit Parade

Card	Low	High
COMPLETE SET (30)	15.00	40.00

SERIES 2 ODDS 1:7 HOB, 1:2 HTA, 1:9 RET

Card	Low	High
HP1 Sammy Sosa HR	.75	2.00
HP2 Rafael Palmeiro HR	.75	2.00
HP3 Fred McGriff HR	.75	2.00
HP4 Ken Griffey Jr. HR	1.25	3.00
HP5 Juan Gonzalez HR	.75	2.00
HP6 Frank Thomas HR	.75	2.00
HP7 Andres Galarraga HR	.75	2.00
HP8 Jim Thome HR	.75	2.00
HP9 Jeff Bagwell HR	.75	2.00
HP10 Gary Sheffield HR	.75	2.00
HP11 Rafael Palmeiro RBI	.75	2.00
HP12 Sammy Sosa RBI	.75	2.00
HP13 Fred McGriff RBI	.75	2.00
HP14 Andres Galarraga RBI	.75	2.00
HP15 Juan Gonzalez RBI	.75	2.00
HP16 Frank Thomas RBI	.75	2.00
HP17 Jeff Bagwell RBI	.75	2.00
HP18 Ken Griffey Jr. RBI	1.25	3.00
HP19 Ruben Sierra RBI	.75	2.00
HP20 Gary Sheffield RBI	.75	2.00
HP21 Rafael Palmeiro Hits	.75	2.00
HP22 Roberto Alomar Hits Card number in Blue	.75	2.00
HP22A Roberto Alomar Hits Card number in White	.75	2.00
HP23 Julio Franco Hits	.75	2.00
HP24 Andres Galarraga Hits	.75	2.00
HP25 Fred McGriff Hits	.75	2.00
HP26 Craig Biggio Hits	.75	2.00
HP27 Barry Larkin Hits	.75	2.00
HP28 Steve Finley Hits	.75	2.00
HP29 B.J. Surhoff Hits	.75	2.00
HP30 Jeff Bagwell Hits	.75	2.00

2004 Topps Hobby Masters

Card	Low	High
COMPLETE SET (20)	15.00	40.00

SERIES 1 ODDS 1:12 HOBBY, 1:4 HTA

Card	Low	High
1 Albert Pujols	1.50	4.00
2 Mark Prior	.75	2.00
3 Alex Rodriguez	1.25	3.00
4 Nomar Garciaparra	1.25	3.00
5 Barry Bonds	2.00	5.00
6 Sammy Sosa	.75	2.00
7 Alfonso Soriano	.75	2.00
8 Ichiro Suzuki	1.50	4.00
9 Derek Jeter	1.50	4.00
10 Jim Thome	.75	2.00
11 Jason Giambi	.75	2.00
12 Mike Piazza	1.25	3.00
13 Barry Zito	.75	2.00
14 Randy Johnson	.75	2.00
15 Adam Dunn	.75	2.00
16 Vladimir Guerrero	.75	2.00
17 Gary Sheffield	.75	2.00
18 Carlos Delgado	.75	2.00
19 Chipper Jones	.75	2.00
20 Dontrelle Willis	.75	2.00

2004 Topps Own the Game

Card	Low	High
COMPLETE SET (30)	30.00	60.00

SERIES 1 ODDS 1:18 HOB/RET, 1:6 HTA

Card	Low	High
1 Jim Thome	.75	2.00
2 Albert Pujols	1.50	4.00
3 Alex Rodriguez	1.25	3.00
4 Barry Bonds	2.00	5.00
5 Ichiro Suzuki	1.50	4.00
6 Derek Jeter	1.50	4.00
7 Nomar Garciaparra	1.25	3.00
8 Alfonso Soriano	.75	2.00
9 Gary Sheffield	.75	2.00
10 Jason Giambi	.75	2.00
11 Todd Helton	.75	2.00
12 Garret Anderson	.75	2.00
13 Carlos Delgado	.75	2.00
14 Manny Ramirez	.75	2.00
15 Richie Sexson	.75	2.00
16 Vernon Wells	.75	2.00
17 Preston Wilson	.75	2.00
18 Frank Thomas	.75	2.00
19 Shawn Green	.75	2.00
20 Rafael Furcal	.75	2.00
21 Juan Pierre	.75	2.00
22 Javy Lopez	.75	2.00
23 Edgar Renteria	.75	2.00
24 Mark Prior	.75	2.00
25 Pedro Martinez	.75	2.00
26 Kerry Wood	.75	2.00
27 Curt Schilling	.75	2.00
28 Roy Halladay	.75	2.00
29 Eric Gagne	.75	2.00
30 Brandon Webb	.75	2.00

2004 Topps Presidential First Pitch Seat Relics

SERIES 2 ODDS 1:592 H, 1:169 HTA, 1:592 R

Card	Low	High
BC Bill Clinton	20.00	50.00
CC Calvin Coolidge	10.00	25.00
DE Dwight Eisenhower	10.00	25.00
FR Franklin D. Roosevelt	15.00	40.00
GB George W. Bush	20.00	50.00
GF Gerald Ford	15.00	40.00
HH Herbert Hoover	10.00	25.00
HT Harry Truman	10.00	25.00
JK John F. Kennedy	20.00	50.00
LJ Lyndon B. Johnson	10.00	25.00
RN Richard Nixon	20.00	50.00
RR Ronald Reagan	30.00	60.00
WH Warren Harding	10.00	25.00
WT William Taft	10.00	25.00
WW Woodrow Wilson	10.00	25.00
GHB George H.W. Bush	15.00	40.00

2004 Topps Presidential Pastime

Card	Low	High
COMPLETE SET (42)	50.00	100.00

SERIES 2 ODDS 1:6 HOB, 1:2 HTA, 1:6 RET

Card	Low	High
PP1 George Washington	2.00	5.00
PP2 John Adams	1.25	3.00
PP3 Thomas Jefferson	2.00	5.00
PP4 James Madison	1.25	3.00
PP5 James Monroe	1.25	3.00
PP6 John Quincy Adams	1.25	3.00
PP7 Andrew Jackson	1.25	3.00
PP8 Martin Van Buren	1.25	3.00
PP9 William Harrison	1.25	3.00
PP10 John Tyler	1.25	3.00
PP11 James Polk	1.25	3.00
PP12 Zachary Taylor	1.25	3.00
PP13 Millard Fillmore	1.25	3.00
PP14 Franklin Pierce	1.25	3.00
PP15 James Buchanan	1.25	3.00
PP16 Abraham Lincoln	2.00	5.00
PP17 Andrew Johnson	1.25	3.00
PP18 Ulysses S. Grant	1.50	4.00
PP19 Rutherford B. Hayes	1.25	3.00
PP20 James Garfield	1.25	3.00
PP21 Chester Arthur	1.25	3.00
PP22 Grover Cleveland	1.25	3.00
PP23 Benjamin Harrison	1.25	3.00
PP24 William McKinley	1.25	3.00
PP25 Theodore Roosevelt	1.50	4.00
PP26 William Taft	1.25	3.00
PP27 Woodrow Wilson	1.25	3.00
PP28 Warren Harding	1.25	3.00
PP29 Calvin Coolidge	1.25	3.00
PP30 Herbert Hoover	1.25	3.00
PP31 Franklin D. Roosevelt	1.50	4.00
PP32 Harry Truman	1.25	3.00
PP33 Dwight Eisenhower	1.25	3.00
PP34 John F. Kennedy	1.50	4.00
PP35 Lyndon B. Johnson	1.25	3.00
PP36 Richard Nixon	1.50	4.00
PP37 Gerald Ford	1.50	4.00
PP38 Jimmy Carter	1.25	3.00
PP39 Ronald Reagan	4.00	10.00
PP40 George H.W. Bush	1.50	4.00
PP41 Bill Clinton	2.00	5.00
PP42 George W. Bush	2.00	5.00

2004 Topps Team Set Prospect Bonus

Card	Low	High
COMP.ASTROS SET (5)	7.50	15.00
COMP.CUBS SET (5)	7.50	15.00
COMP.RED SOX SET (5)	7.50	15.00
COMP.YANKEES SET (5)	7.50	15.00

A1-A5 ISSUED IN ASTROS FACTORY SET
C1-C5 ISSUED IN CUBS FACTORY SET
R1-R5 ISSUED IN RED SOX FACTORY SET
Y1-Y5 ISSUED IN YANKEES FACTORY SET

Card	Low	High
A1 Brooks Conrad	1.50	4.00
A2 Hector Gimenez	1.50	4.00
A3 Kevin Davidson	1.50	4.00
A4 Chris Burke	1.50	4.00
A5 John Buck	1.50	4.00
C1 Bobby Brownlie	1.50	4.00
C2 Felix Pie	2.00	5.00
C3 Jon Connolly	2.00	5.00
C4 David Kelton	1.50	4.00
C5 Ricky Nolasco	2.50	6.00
R1 David Murphy	2.00	5.00
R2 Kevin Youkilis	1.50	4.00
R3 Juan Cedeno	1.50	4.00
R4 Matt Murton	1.50	4.00
R5 Kenny Perez	1.50	4.00
Y1 Rudy Guillen	2.00	5.00
Y2 David Parrish	1.50	4.00
Y3 Brad Halsey	2.00	5.00
Y4 Hector Made	2.00	5.00
Y5 Robinson Cano	2.00	5.00

2004 Topps Series Seats Relics

SERIES 2 ODDS 1:316 HOB/RET, 1:89 HTA

Card	Low	High
AK Al Kaline	10.00	25.00
BF Bob Feller	6.00	15.00
BM Bill Mazeroski	10.00	25.00
BP Boog Powell	6.00	15.00
BR Brooks Robinson	6.00	15.00
FR Frank Robinson	6.00	15.00
HK Harmon Killebrew	10.00	25.00
JP Jim Palmer	6.00	15.00
LA Luis Aparicio	6.00	15.00
LP Lou Piniella	6.00	15.00
PM Paul Molitor	6.00	15.00
RJ Reggie Jackson	6.00	15.00
RY Robin Yount	10.00	25.00
WM Willie Mays	15.00	40.00
WS Warren Spahn	10.00	25.00

2004 Topps Series Stitches Relics

SER.2 GROUP A 1:829 H, 1:236 HTA, 1:832 R
SER.2 GROUP B 1:980 H, 1:280 HTA, 1:984 R
SER.2 GROUP C 1:686 H, 1:196 HTA, 1:686 R

Card	Low	High
AS Alfonso Soriano Bat B	6.00	15.00
CJ Chipper Jones Jsy C	6.00	15.00
DG Dwight Gooden Jsy A	4.00	10.00
DJ David Justice Bat B	6.00	15.00
FR Frank Robinson Bat A	6.00	15.00
GB George Brett Bat A	15.00	40.00
GC Gary Carter Jkt C	4.00	10.00
HK Harmon Killebrew Bat A	15.00	40.00
JB Johnny Bench Bat A	10.00	25.00
JBE Josh Beckett Jsy C	4.00	10.00
JC Joe Carter Bat B	6.00	15.00
JCA Jose Canseco Bat C	10.00	25.00
KG Kirk Gibson Bat B	6.00	15.00
KP Kirby Puckett Bat B	10.00	25.00
LD Lenny Dykstra Bat A	6.00	15.00
MS Mike Schmidt Uni A	15.00	40.00
PO Paul O'Neill Bat A	10.00	25.00
RC Roger Clemens Uni C	8.00	20.00
RJ Randy Johnson Jsy A	6.00	15.00
RJA Reggie Jackson Bat B	10.00	25.00
RY Robin Yount Uni A	6.00	15.00
SG Steve Garvey Bat B	6.00	15.00
TS Tom Seaver Uni A	6.00	15.00
WM Willie Mays Bat A	20.00	50.00

2004 Topps Legends Autographs

ISSUED IN VARIOUS 03-05 TOPPS BRANDS
SER.1 ODDS 1:1399 H, 1:421 HTA, 1:1494 R
SER.2 ODDS 1:766 H, 1:216 HTA, 1:802 R
01 APARICIO/CARTER AU'S DIST.IN 04 PACKS
SEE 01 TOPPS FOR APARICIO/CARTER

Card	Low	High
AD Andre Dawson	6.00	15.00
BC Bert Campaneris	6.00	15.00
BP Boog Powell	6.00	15.00
CE Carl Erskine	6.00	15.00
DE Dwight Evans	10.00	25.00
DJ Davey Johnson	4.00	10.00
JP Jim Piersall	6.00	15.00
JP Johnny Podres	6.00	15.00
JR Joe Rudi	6.00	15.00
LB Lou Brock		
LD Lenny Dykstra		
NR Nolan Ryan	125.00	200.00
SA Sparky Anderson	6.00	15.00
SG Steve Garvey	6.00	15.00
WM Willie Mays	125.00	200.00

2004 Topps World Series Highlights

Card	Low	High
COMPLETE SET (30)	30.00	80.00
COMPLETE SERIES 1 (15)	15.00	40.00
COMPLETE SERIES 2 (15)	15.00	40.00

SERIES 1 ODDS 1:18 HOB/RET, 1:6 HTA
SERIES 2 ODDS 1:18 HOB/RET, 1:7 HTA

Card	Low	High
AJ Andruw Jones 2	1.25	3.00
AK Al Kaline 2	1.25	3.00
BM Bill Mazeroski 1	1.25	3.00
BR Brooks Robinson 1	1.25	3.00
BT Bobby Thomson 2	.75	2.00
CF Carlton Fisk 1	1.25	3.00
CY Carl Yastrzemski 1	1.50	4.00
DB Dusty Baker 2	.75	2.00
DJ David Justice 2	.75	2.00
DL Don Larsen 1	.75	2.00
DS Duke Snider 2	1.25	3.00
FR Frank Robinson 2	.75	2.00
JB Johnny Bench 2	1.25	3.00
JC Joe Carter 2	.75	2.00
JCA Jose Canseco 2	1.25	3.00
JP1 Jim Palmer 1	.75	2.00
JP2 Johnny Podres 2	.75	2.00
KG Kirk Gibson 1	.75	2.00
KP Kirby Puckett 1	1.25	3.00
LB Lou Brock 1	1.25	3.00
LG Luis Gonzalez 2	.75	2.00
MS Mike Schmidt 1	2.00	5.00
OS Ozzie Smith 2	1.50	4.00
RJ Reggie Jackson 1	1.25	3.00
RY Robin Yount 1	1.25	3.00
SM Stan Musial 1	1.50	4.00
TS Tom Seaver 1	1.25	3.00
WF Whitey Ford 2	1.25	3.00
WM1 Willie Mays 1	2.00	5.00
WM2 Willie McCovey 2	.75	2.00

2004 Topps World Series Highlights Autographs

SERIES 1 ODDS 1:74 HTA
SERIES 2 ODDS 1:69 HTA

AK Al Kaline 2 15.00 40.00
BM Bill Mazeroski 1 15.00 40.00
BR Brooks Robinson 1 15.00 40.00
BT Bobby Thomson 2 10.00 25.00
CF Carlton Fisk 1 40.00 80.00
DB Dusty Baker 2 10.00 25.00
DJ David Justice 2 10.00 25.00
DL Don Larsen 1 10.00 25.00
DS Duke Snider 2 15.00 40.00
HK Harmon Killebrew 1 15.00 40.00
JB Johnny Bench 2 30.00 60.00
JP1 Jim Palmer 1 10.00 25.00
JP2 Johnny Podres 2 10.00 25.00
KG Kirk Gibson 1 10.00 25.00
LB Lou Brock 1 15.00 40.00
MS Mike Schmidt 1 30.00 60.00
RJ Reggie Jackson 2 30.00 60.00
RY Robin Yount 1 15.00 40.00
SM Stan Musial 2 40.00 80.00
WF Whitey Ford 2 15.00 40.00

2004 Topps Traded

This 220-card set was released in October, 2004. The set was issued in 11-card hobby and retail packs (including one puzzle piece) which had an $3 SRP and which came 24 packs to a box and 12 boxes to a case. Cards numbered 1-65 feature players who were traded, while cards numbered 66 through 70 feature managers who took over teams after the basic set was issued and cards 71 through 90 are high draft picks, cards numbered 91 through 110 are prospect cards and cards numbered 111-220 feature Rookie Cards. Please note, an additional card (#T221) featuring Barry Bonds was distributed by Topps directly to hobby shop accounts enrolled in the Home Team Advantage program in early January, 2005. Collectors could obtain the card by purchasing a pack of 2005 Topps series 1 baseball. The program was limited to one card per customer.

COMPLETE SET (220) 20.00 50.00
COMMON CARD (1-70) .07 .20
COMMON CARD (71-90) .20 .50
COMMON CARD (91-110) .15 .40
COMMON CARD (111-220) .15 .40
BONDS AVAIL VIA HTA SHOP EXCHANGE
PLATE ODDS 1:1151 H, 1:1173 R, 1:327 HTA
PLATE PRINT RUN 1 SET PER COLOR
BLACK-CYAN-MAGENTA-YELLOW ISSUED
NO PLATE PRICING DUE TO SCARCITY
T1 Pokey Reese .07 .20
T2 Tony Womack .07 .20
T3 Richard Hidalgo .07 .20
T4 Juan Uribe .07 .20
T5 J.D. Drew .07 .20
T6 Alex Gonzalez .07 .20
T7 Carlos Guillen .07 .20
T8 Doug Mientkiewicz .07 .20
T9 Fernando Vina .07 .20
T10 Milton Bradley .07 .20
T11 Kelvim Escobar .07 .20
T12 Ben Grieve .07 .20
T13 Brian Jordan .07 .20
T14 A.J. Pierzynski .07 .20
T15 Billy Wagner .07 .20
T16 Terrence Long .07 .20
T17 Carlos Beltran .07 .20
T18 Carl Everett .07 .20
T19 Reggie Sanders .07 .20
T20 Javy Lopez .07 .20
T21 Jay Payton .07 .20
T22 Octavio Dotel .07 .20
T23 Eddie Guardado .07 .20
T24 Andy Pettitte .10 .30
T25 Richie Sexson .07 .20
T26 Ronnie Belliard .07 .20
T27 Michael Tucker .07 .20
T28 Brad Fullmer .07 .20
T29 Freddy Garcia .07 .20
T30 Bartolo Colon .07 .20
T31 Larry Walker Cards .10 .30
T32 Mark Kotsay .07 .20
T33 Jason Marquis .07 .20
T34 Dustan Mohr .07 .20
T35 Javier Vazquez .07 .20
T36 Nomar Garciaparra .30 .75
T37 Tino Martinez .10 .30
T38 Hee Seop Choi .07 .20
T39 Damian Miller .07 .20
T40 Jose Lima .07 .20
T41 Ty Wigginton .07 .20
T42 Raul Ibanez .07 .20
T43 Danys Baez .07 .20
T44 Tony Clark .07 .20
T45 Greg Maddux .30 .75
T46 Victor Zambrano .07 .20
T47 Orlando Cabrera Sox .07 .20
T48 Jose Cruz Jr. .07 .20
T49 Kris Benson .07 .20
T50 Alex Rodriguez .40 1.00
T51 Steve Finley .07 .20
T52 Ramon Hernandez .07 .20
T53 Esteban Loaiza .07 .20
T54 Ugueth Urbina .07 .20
T55 Jeff Weaver .07 .20
T56 Flash Gordon .07 .20
T57 Jose Contreras .07 .20
T58 Paul Lo Duca .07 .20
T59 Junior Spivey .07 .20
T60 Curt Schilling .10 .30
T61 Brad Penny .07 .20
T62 Braden Looper .07 .20
T63 Miguel Cairo .07 .20
T64 Juan Encarnacion .07 .20
T65 Miguel Batista .07 .20
T66 Terry Francona MG .07 .20
T67 Lee Mazzilli MG .07 .20
T68 Al Pedrique MG .07 .20
T69 Ozzie Guillen MG .20 .50
T70 Phil Garner MG .07 .20
T71 Matt Bush DP RC .60 1.50
T72 Homer Bailey DP RC 1.25 3.00
T73 Greg Golson DP RC .60 1.50
T74 Kyle Waldrop DP RC .50 1.25
T75 Richie Robnett DP RC .50 1.25
T76 Jay Rainville DP RC .60 1.50
T77 Bill Bray DP RC .20 .50
T78 Philip Hughes DP RC 3.00 8.00
T79 Scott Elbert DP RC .50 1.25
T80 Josh Fields DP RC .75 2.00
T81 Justin Orenduff DP RC .30 .75
T82 Dan Putnam DP RC .30 .75
T83 Chris Nelson DP RC .75 2.00
T84 Blake DeWitt DP RC .75 2.00
T85 J.P. Howell DP RC .50 1.25
T86 Huston Street DP RC .75 2.00
T87 Kurt Suzuki DP RC .50 1.25
T88 Erick San Pedro DP RC .20 .50
T89 Matt Tuiasosopo DP RC .75 2.00
T90 Matt Macri DP RC .40 1.00
T91 Chad Tracy PROS .15 .40
T92 Scott Hairston PROS .15 .40
T93 Jonny Gomes PROS .15 .40
T94 Chin-Feng Chen PROS .15 .40
T95 Chien-Ming Wang PROS .30 .75
T96 Dustin McGowan PROS .15 .40
T97 Chris Burke PROS .15 .40
T98 Denny Bautista PROS .15 .40
T99 Preston Larrison PROS .15 .40
T100 Kevin Youkilis PROS .15 .40
T101 John Maine PROS .15 .40
T102 Guillermo Quiroz PROS .15 .40
T103 Dave Krynzel PROS .15 .40
T104 David Kelton PROS .15 .40
T105 Edwin Encarnacion PROS .15 .40
T106 Chad Gaudin PROS .15 .40
T107 Sergio Mitre PROS .15 .40
T108 Laynce Nix PROS .15 .40
T109 David Parrish PROS .15 .40
T110 Brandon Claussen PROS .15 .40
T111 Frank Francisco FY RC .15 .40
T112 Brian Dallimore FY RC .15 .40
T113 Jim Crowell FY RC .20 .50
T114 Andres Blanco FY RC .15 .40
T115 Eduardo Villacis FY RC .15 .40
T116 Kazuhito Tadano FY RC .20 .50
T117 Aarom Baldiris FY RC .20 .50
T118 Justin Germano FY RC .15 .40
T119 Joey Gathright FY RC .50 1.25
T120 Franklyn Gracesqui FY RC .15 .40
T121 Chin-Lung Hu FY RC .50 1.25
T122 Scott Olsen FY RC .60 1.50
T123 Tyler Davidson FY RC .20 .50
T124 Fausto Carmona FY RC .60 1.50
T125 Tim Hutting FY RC .15 .40
T126 Ryan Meaux FY RC .15 .40
T127 Jon Connolly FY RC .40 1.00
T128 Hector Made FY RC .30 .75
T129 Jamie Brown FY RC .15 .40
T130 Paul McAnulty FY RC .30 .75
T131 Chris Saenz FY RC .15 .40
T132 Marland Williams FY RC .20 .50
T133 Mike Huggins FY RC .15 .40
T134 Jesse Crain FY RC .30 .75
T135 Chad Bentz FY RC .15 .40
T136 Kazuo Matsui FY RC .30 .75
T137 Paul Maholm FY RC .50 1.25
T138 Brock Jacobsen FY RC .15 .40
T139 Casey Daigle FY RC .15 .40
T140 Nyjer Morgan FY RC .15 .40
T141 Tom Mastny FY RC .15 .40
T142 Kody Kirkland FY RC .20 .50
T143 Jose Capellan FY RC .20 .50
T144 Felix Hernandez FY RC 3.00 8.00
T145 Shawn Hill FY RC .15 .40
T146 Danny Gonzalez FY RC .15 .40
T147 Scott Dohmann FY RC .15 .40
T148 Tommy Murphy FY RC .15 .40
T149 Akinori Otsuka FY RC .15 .40
T150 Miguel Perez FY RC .15 .40
T151 Mike Rouse FY RC .15 .40
T152 Ramon Ramirez FY RC .15 .40
T153 Luke Hughes FY RC .15 .40
T154 Howie Kendrick FY RC 4.00 10.00
T155 Ryan Budde FY RC .15 .40
T156 Charlie Zink FY RC .15 .40
T157 Warner Madrigal FY RC .30 .75
T158 Jason Szominski FY RC .15 .40
T159 Chad Chop FY RC .15 .40
T160 Shingo Takatsu FY RC .30 .75
T161 Matt Lemanczyk FY RC .15 .40
T162 Wardell Starling FY RC .15 .40
T163 Nick Gorneault FY RC .20 .50
T164 Scott Proctor FY RC .20 .50
T165 Brooks Conrad FY RC .20 .50
T166 Hector Gimenez FY RC .15 .40
T167 Kevin Howard FY RC .20 .50
T168 Vince Perkins FY RC .20 .50
T169 Brock Peterson FY RC .20 .50
T170 Chris Shelton FY RC .50 1.25
T171 Erick Aybar FY RC .30 .75
T172 Paul Bacot FY RC .20 .50
T173 Matt Capps FY RC .15 .40
T174 Kory Casto FY RC .20 .50
T175 Juan Cedeno FY RC .15 .40
T176 Vito Chiaravalloti FY RC .15 .40
T177 Alec Zumwalt FY RC .15 .40
T178 J.J. Furmaniak FY RC .30 .75
T179 Lee Gwaltney FY RC .15 .40
T180 Donald Kelly FY RC .15 .40
T181 Benji DeQuin FY RC .15 .40
T182 Brant Colamarino FY RC .30 .75
T183 Juan Gutierrez FY RC .15 .40
T184 Carl Loadenthal FY RC .20 .50
T185 Ricky Nolasco FY RC .60 1.50
T186 Jeff Salazar FY RC .40 1.00
T187 Rob Tejeda FY RC .30 .75
T188 Alex Romero FY RC .15 .40
T189 Yoann Torrealba FY RC .15 .40
T190 Carlos Sosa FY RC .15 .40
T191 Tim Bittner FY RC .15 .40
T192 Chris Aguila FY RC .15 .40
T193 Jason Frasor FY RC .15 .40
T194 Reid Gorecki FY RC .15 .40
T195 Dustin Nippert FY RC .20 .50
T196 Javier Guzman FY RC .20 .50
T197 Harvey Garcia FY RC .15 .40
T198 Ivan Ochoa FY RC .15 .40
T199 David Wallace FY RC .20 .50
T200 Joel Zumaya FY RC 1.50 4.00
T201 Casey Kopitzke FY RC .15 .40
T202 Lincoln Holdzkom FY RC .15 .40
T203 Chad Santos FY RC .15 .40
T204 Brian Pilkington FY RC .15 .40
T205 Terry Jones FY RC .20 .50
T206 Jerome Gamble FY RC .15 .40
T207 Brad Eldred FY RC .20 .50
T208 David Pauley FY RC .60 1.50
T209 Kevin Davidson FY RC .15 .40
T210 Damaso Espino FY RC .15 .40
T211 Tom Farmer FY RC .15 .40
T212 Michael Mooney FY RC .15 .40
T213 James Tomlin FY RC .15 .40
T214 Greg Thissen FY RC .15 .40
T215 Calvin Hayes FY RC .20 .50
T216 Fernando Cortez FY RC .15 .40
T217 Sergio Silva FY RC .15 .40
T218 Jon de Vries FY RC .15 .40
T219 Don Sutton FY RC .40 1.00
T220 Leo Nunez FY RC .15 .40
T221 Barry Bonds HTA EXCH 3.00 8.00

2004 Topps Traded Blue

ODDS 1:4574 H, 1:4925 R, 1:1238 HTA
STATED PRINT RUN 1 SERIAL #'d SET
NO PRICING DUE TO SCARCITY

2004 Topps Traded Gold

*GOLD 1-70: 5X TO 12X BASIC
*GOLD 71-90: 1X TO 2.5X BASIC
*GOLD 91-110: 2.5X TO 6X BASIC
*GOLD 111-220: 1.5X TO 4X BASIC
STATED ODDS 1:2 HOB/RET, 1:1 HTA
STATED PRINT RUN 2004 SERIAL #'d SETS

2004 Topps Traded Future Phenoms Relics

GROUP A ODDS 1:184 H/R, 1:53 HTA
GROUP B ODDS 1:65 H/R, 1:27 HTA
AG Adrian Gonzalez Bat A 3.00 8.00
BC Bobby Crosby Bat A 4.00 10.00
BU B.J. Upton Bat A 6.00 15.00
DN Dioner Navarro Bat B 3.00 8.00
DY Delmon Young Bat A 6.00 15.00
ED Eric Duncan Bat B 2.00 5.00
EJ Edwin Jackson Jsy B 2.00 5.00
JH J.J. Hardy Bat B 6.00 15.00
JM Justin Morneau Bat A 4.00 10.00
JW Jayson Werth Bat A 6.00 15.00
KC Kevin Cash Bat B 2.00 5.00
KM Kazuo Matsui Bat A 4.00 10.00
LM Lastings Milledge Bat B 4.00 10.00
MM Mark Malaska Jsy A 3.00 8.00
NG Nick Green Bat A 3.00 8.00
RN Ramon Nivar Bat A 3.00 8.00
VM Victor Martinez Bat A 4.00 10.00

2004 Topps Traded Hall of Fame Relics

A ODDS 1:3388 H, 1:3518 R, 1:966 HTA
B ODDS 1:1011 H, 1:1026 R, 1:289 HTA
DE Dennis Eckersley Jsy B 6.00 15.00
PM Paul Molitor Bat A 6.00 15.00

2004 Topps Traded Hall of Fame Dual Relic

ODDS 1:3388 H, 1:3518 R, 1:966 HTA
ME Paul Molitor Bat 10.00 25.00
Dennis Eckersley Jsy

2004 Topps Traded Puzzle

COMPLETE PUZZLE (110) 25.00 50.00
COMMON PIECE (1-110) .20 .50
ONE PER PACK

2004 Topps Traded Signature Cuts

STATED ODDS 1:91,472 HOB, 1:39,600 HTA
STATED PRINT RUN 1 SERIAL #'d SET
NO PRICING DUE TO SCARCITY
BR Babe Ruth
CH Catfish Hunter
JM Johnny Mize
RM Roger Maris
WS Warren Spahn

2004 Topps Traded Signature Moves

A ODDS 1:675 H, 1:684 R, 1:193 HTA
B ODDS 1:169 H/R, 1:48 HTA
EXCHANGE DEADLINE 12/31/06
AR Alex Rodriguez A 125.00 200.00
AW Adam Wainwright B 4.00 10.00
EM Eli Marrero B 4.00 10.00
FV Fernando Vina B 4.00 10.00
IR Ivan Rodriguez A EXCH 15.00 40.00
JV Javier Vazquez A 6.00 15.00
MB Milton Bradley B 6.00 15.00
MK Mark Kotsay B 6.00 15.00
MN Mike Neu B 4.00 10.00

2004 Topps Traded Transactions Relics

STATED ODDS 1:106 H, 1:107 R, 1:30 HTA
AP Andy Pettitte Bat 4.00 10.00
AR Alex Rodriguez Yanks Jsy 10.00 25.00
BJ Brian Jordan Bat 3.00 8.00
CE Carl Everett Bat 3.00 8.00
GS Gary Sheffield Bat 4.00 10.00
HC Hee Seop Choi Bat 3.00 8.00
IR Ivan Rodriguez Bat 4.00 10.00
JB Jeromy Burnitz Bat 3.00 8.00
JG Juan Gonzalez Bat 3.00 8.00
JL Javy Lopez Bat 3.00 8.00
KL Kenny Lofton Bat 3.00 8.00
KM Kazuo Matsui Bat 3.00 8.00
MT Miguel Tejada Bat 3.00 8.00
RA Roberto Alomar Bat 4.00 10.00
RC Roger Clemens Bat 6.00 15.00
RLS Richie Sexson Bat 3.00 8.00
RP Rafael Palmeiro Bat 4.00 10.00
RS Reggie Sanders Bat 3.00 8.00
RW Rondell White Bat 3.00 8.00
VG Vladimir Guerrero Bat 4.00 10.00

2004 Topps Traded Transactions Dual Relics

STATED ODDS 1:562 H, 1:563 R, 1:160 HTA
AR Alex Rodriguez Rgr-Yanks 10.00 25.00
CS Curt Schilling D'backs-Sox 6.00 15.00
RP Rafael Palmeiro O's-Rgr 6.00 15.00

2004 Topps McGruff

Inserted one per Topps of the Class Packs (which also included 3 Opening Day cards) these six cards feature noted anti-crime cartoon character McGruff along with a major leaguer.

COMPLETE SET 2.00 5.00
1 Ichiro Suzuki .20 .50
McGruff
Bullying

2 Albert Pujols .40 1.00
McGruff
Hearing Threats
3 Nomar Garciaparra .20 .50
McGruff
Home Safety
4 Derek Jeter .75 2.00
McGruff
Internet Safety
5 Sammy Sosa .30 .75
McGruff
Solving Problems
6 Carlos Delgado .15 .40
McGruff
Volunteerism

2005 Topps

This 367-card first series was released in November, 2004 while the 366 card second series was issued in April. The set was issued in 10-card hobby/retail packs with a $2 SRP which came 36 packs to a box and 12 boxes to a case. These cards were also issued in 35-card HTA packs with a $5 SRP which came 20 packs to a box and two boxes to a case. Please note that card number 7 was not issued. In addition, the following subsets were issued in the first series: Managers (267-296); First year cards (297-326); Prospects (327-331); Season Highlights (332-336); League Leaders (337-348); Post-Season (349-355); AL All-Stars (356-367). In addition, card number 368, which was not on the original checklist, honored the Boston Red Sox World Championship. Subsets in the second series included Team Cards (638-667); First Year players (668-687); Multi player prospect cards (688-694); Award Winners (695-718); NL All-Stars (719-730) and World Series Cards (731-734).

COMP.HOBBY SET (737) 40.00 80.00
COMP.HOLIDAY SET (742) 40.00 80.00
COMP.CUBS SET (737) 40.00 80.00
COMP.GIANTS SET (737) 40.00 80.00
COMP.NATIONALS SET (737) 40.00 80.00
COMP.RED SOX SET (737) 40.00 80.00
COMP.TIGERS SET (737) 40.00 80.00
COMP.YANKEES SET (737) 40.00 80.00
COMPLETE SET (732) 40.00 80.00
COMPLETE SERIES 1 (366) 20.00 40.00
COMPLETE SERIES 2 (366) 20.00 40.00
COMMON (1-6/8-296) .07 .20
COMMON (297-326/668-687) .20 .50
COMMON CARD 327- .20 .50
COM (349-355/368/731-734) .40 1.00
CARD NUMBER 7 DOES NOT EXIST
OVERALL PLATE SER.1 ODDS 1:154 HTA
OVERALL PLATE SER.2 ODDS 1:112 HTA
PLATE PRINT RUN 1 SET PER COLOR
BLACK-CYAN-MAGENTA-YELLOW ISSUED
NO PLATE PRICING DUE TO SCARCITY
1 Alex Rodriguez .40 1.00
2 Placido Polanco .07 .20
3 Torii Hunter .07 .20
4 Lyle Overbay .07 .20
5 Johnny Damon .10 .30
6 Johnny Estrada .07 .20
8 Francisco Rodriguez .07 .20
9 Jason LaRue .07 .20
10 Sammy Sosa .20 .50
11 Randy Wolf .07 .20
12 Jason Bay .07 .20
13 Tom Glavine .10 .30
14 Michael Tucker .07 .20
15 Brian Giles .07 .20
16 Dan Wilson .07 .20
17 Jim Edmonds .07 .20
18 Danys Baez .07 .20
19 Roy Halladay .07 .20
20 Hank Blalock .07 .20
21 Darin Erstad .07 .20
22 Robby Hammock .07 .20
23 Mike Hampton .07 .20
24 Mark Bellhorn .07 .20
25 Jim Thome .10 .30
26 Scott Schoeneweis .07 .20
27 Jody Gerut .07 .20
28 Vinny Castilla .07 .20
29 Luis Castillo .07 .20
30 Ivan Rodriguez .10 .30
31 Craig Biggio .10 .30
32 Joe Randa .07 .20
33 Adrian Beltre .07 .20
34 Scott Podsednik .07 .20
35 Cliff Floyd .07 .20
36 Livan Hernandez .07 .20
37 Eric Byrnes .07 .20
38 Gabe Kapler .07 .20
39 Jack Wilson .07 .20
40 Gary Sheffield .07 .20
41 Chan Ho Park .07 .20
42 Carl Crawford .07 .20
43 Miguel Batista .07 .20
44 David Bell .07 .20
45 Jeff DaVanon .07 .20
46 Brandon Webb .07 .20
47 Bronson Arroyo .07 .20
48 Melvin Mora .07 .20
49 David Ortiz .20 .50
50 Andruw Jones .10 .30
51 Chone Figgins .07 .20
52 Danny Graves .07 .20
53 Preston Wilson .07 .20
54 Jeremy Bonderman .07 .20
55 Chad Fox .07 .20
56 Dan Miceli .07 .20
57 Jimmy Gobble .07 .20
58 Darren Dreifort .07 .20
59 Matt LeCroy .07 .20
60 Jose Vidro .07 .20
61 Al Leiter .07 .20
62 Javier Vazquez .07 .20
63 Erubiel Durazo .07 .20
64 Doug Glanville .07 .20
65 Scot Shields .07 .20
66 Edgardo Alfonzo .07 .20
67 Ryan Franklin .07 .20
68 Francisco Cordero .07 .20
69 Brett Myers .07 .20
70 Curt Schilling .10 .30
71 Matt Kata .07 .20
72 Mark DeRosa .07 .20
73 Rodrigo Lopez .07 .20
74 Tim Wakefield .10 .30
75 Frank Thomas .20 .50
76 Jimmy Rollins .07 .20
77 Barry Zito .07 .20
78 Hideo Nomo .20 .50
79 Brad Wilkerson .07 .20
80 Adam Dunn .07 .20
81 Billy Traber .07 .20
82 Fernando Vina .07 .20
83 Nate Robertson .07 .20
84 Brad Ausmus .07 .20
85 Mike Sweeney .07 .20
86 Kip Wells .07 .20
87 Chris Reitsma .07 .20
88 Zach Day .07 .20
89 Tony Clark .07 .20
90 Bret Boone .07 .20
91 Mark Loretta .07 .20
92 Jerome Williams .07 .20
93 Randy Winn .07 .20
94 Marlon Anderson .07 .20
95 Aubrey Huff .07 .20
96 Kevin Mench .07 .20
97 Frank Catalanotto .07 .20
98 Flash Gordon .07 .20
99 Scott Hatteberg .07 .20
100 Albert Pujols .40 1.00
101 Jose/Bengie Molina .20 .50
102 Oscar Villarreal .07 .20
103 Jay Gibbons .07 .20
104 Byung-Hyun Kim .07 .20
105 Joe Borowski .07 .20
106 Mark Grudzielanek .07 .20
107 Mark Buehrle .07 .20
108 Paul Wilson .07 .20
109 Ronnie Belliard .07 .20
110 Reggie Sanders .07 .20
111 Tim Redding .07 .20
112 Brian Lawrence .07 .20
113 Darrell May .07 .20
114 Jose Hernandez .07 .20
115 Ben Sheets .07 .20
116 Johan Santana .20 .50
117 Billy Wagner .07 .20
118 Mariano Rivera .20 .50
119 Steve Trachsel .07 .20
120 Akinori Otsuka .07 .20
121 Bobby Kielty .07 .20
122 Orlando Hernandez .07 .20
123 Raul Ibanez .07 .20
124 Mike Matheny .07 .20
125 Vernon Wells .07 .20
126 Jason Isringhausen .07 .20
127 Jose Guillen .07 .20
128 Danny Bautista .07 .20
129 Marcus Giles .07 .20
130 Javy Lopez .07 .20
131 Kevin Millar .07 .20
132 Kyle Farnsworth .07 .20
133 Carl Pavano .07 .20
134 D'Angelo Jimenez .07 .20
135 Casey Blake .07 .20
136 Matt Holliday .08 .25
137 Bobby Higginson .07 .20
138 Nate Field .07 .20
139 Alex Gonzalez .07 .20
140 Jeff Kent .07 .20
141 Aaron Guiel .07 .20
142 Shawn Green .07 .20
143 Bill Hall .07 .20
144 Shannon Stewart .07 .20
145 Juan Rivera .07 .20
146 Coco Crisp .07 .20
147 Mike Mussina .10 .30
148 Eric Chavez .07 .20
149 Jon Lieber .07 .20
150 Vladimir Guerrero .20 .50
151 Alex Cintron .07 .20
152 Horacio Ramirez .07 .20
153 Sidney Ponson .07 .20
154 Trot Nixon .10 .30
155 Greg Maddux .30 .75
156 Edgar Renteria .07 .20
157 Ryan Freel .07 .20
158 Matt Lawton .07 .20
159 Shawn Chacon .07 .20
160 Josh Beckett .07 .20
161 Ken Harvey .07 .20
162 Juan Cruz .07 .20
163 Juan Encarnacion .07 .20
164 Wes Helms .07 .20
165 Brad Radke .07 .20
166 Claudio Vargas .07 .20
167 Mike Cameron .07 .20
168 Billy Koch .07 .20
169 Bobby Crosby .07 .20
170 Mike Lieberthal .07 .20
171 Rob Mackowiak .07 .20
172 Sean Burroughs .07 .20
173 J.T. Snow Jr. .07 .20
174 Paul Konerko .07 .20
175 Luis Gonzalez .07 .20
176 John Lackey .07 .20
177 Antonio Alfonseca .07 .20
178 Brian Roberts .07 .20

179 Bill Mueller .07 .20
180 Carlos Lee .07 .20
181 Corey Patterson .07 .20
182 Sean Casey .07 .20
183 Cliff Lee .07 .20
184 Jason Jennings .07 .20
185 Dmitri Young .07 .20
186 Juan Uribe .07 .20
187 Andy Pettitte .10 .30
188 Juan Gonzalez .07 .20
189 Pokey Reese .07 .20
190 Jason Phillips .07 .20
191 Rocky Biddle .07 .20
192 Lew Ford .07 .20
193 Mark Mulder .07 .20
194 Bobby Abreu .07 .20
195 Jason Kendall .07 .20
196 Terrence Long .07 .20
197 A.J. Pierzynski .07 .20
198 Eddie Guardado .07 .20
199 So Taguchi .07 .20
200 Jason Giambi .07 .20
201 Tony Batista .07 .20
202 Kyle Lohse .07 .20
203 Trevor Hoffman .07 .20
204 Tike Redman .07 .20
205 Matt Herges .07 .20
206 Gil Meche .07 .20
207 Chris Carpenter .07 .20
208 Ben Broussard .07 .20
209 Eric Young .07 .20
210 Doug Waechter .07 .20
211 Jarrod Washburn .07 .20
212 Chad Tracy .07 .20
213 John Smoltz .10 .30
214 Jorge Julio .07 .20
215 Todd Walker .07 .20
216 Shingo Takatsu .07 .20
217 Jose Acevedo .07 .20
218 David Riske .07 .20
219 Shawn Estes .07 .20
220 Lance Berkman .07 .20
221 Carlos Guillen .07 .20
222 Jeremy Affeldt .07 .20
223 Cesar Izturis .07 .20
224 Scott Sullivan .07 .20
225 Kazuo Matsui .07 .20
226 Josh Fogg .07 .20
227 Jason Schmidt .07 .20
228 Jason Marquis .07 .20
229 Scott Spiezio .07 .20
230 Miguel Tejada .07 .20
231 Bartolo Colon .07 .20
232 Jose Valverde .07 .20
233 Derrek Lee .10 .30
234 Scott Williamson .07 .20
235 Joe Crede .07 .20
236 John Thomson .07 .20
237 Mike MacDougal .07 .20
238 Eric Gagne .07 .20
239 Alex Sanchez .07 .20
240 Miguel Cabrera .10 .30
241 Luis Rivas .07 .20
242 Adam Everett .07 .20
243 Jason Johnson .07 .20
244 Travis Hafner .07 .20
245 Jose Valentin .07 .20
246 Stephen Randolph .07 .20
247 Rafael Furcal .07 .20
248 Adam Kennedy .07 .20
249 Luis Matos .07 .20
250 Mark Prior .10 .30
251 Angel Berroa .07 .20
252 Phil Nevin .07 .20
253 Oliver Perez .07 .20
254 Orlando Hudson .07 .20
255 Braden Looper .07 .20
256 Khalil Greene .10 .30
257 Tim Worrell .07 .20
258 Carlos Zambrano .07 .20
259 Odalis Perez .07 .20
260 Gerald Laird .07 .20
261 Jose Cruz Jr. .07 .20
262 Michael Barrett .07 .20
263 Michael Young UER .07 .20
Rod Barajas pictured sliding
264 Toby Hall .07 .20
265 Woody Williams .07 .20
266 Rich Harden .07 .20
267 Mike Scioscia MG .07 .20
268 Al Pedrique MG .07 .20
269 Bobby Cox MG .07 .20
270 Lee Mazzilli MG .07 .20
271 Terry Francona MG .10 .30
272 Dusty Baker MG .07 .20
273 Ozzie Guillen MG .20 .50
274 Dave Miley MG .07 .20
275 Eric Wedge MG .07 .20
276 Clint Hurdle MG .07 .20
277 Alan Trammell MG .07 .20
278 Jack McKeon MG .07 .20
279 Phil Garner MG .07 .20
280 Tony Pena MG .07 .20
281 Jim Tracy MG .07 .20
282 Ned Yost MG .07 .20
283 Ron Gardenhire MG .07 .20
284 Frank Robinson MG .07 .20
285 Art Howe MG .07 .20
286 Joe Torre MG .10 .30
287 Ken Macha MG .07 .20
288 Larry Bowa MG .07 .20
289 Lloyd McClendon MG .07 .20
290 Bruce Bochy MG .07 .20
291 Felipe Alou MG .07 .20
292 Bob Melvin MG .07 .20
293 Tony LaRussa MG .07 .20
294 Lou Piniella MG .07 .20
295 Buck Showalter MG .07 .20
296 John Gibbons MG .07 .20
297 Steve Doetsch FY RC .30 .75
298 Melky Cabrera FY RC .75 2.00
299 Luis Ramirez FY RC .20 .50
300 Chris Seddon FY RC .20 .50
301 Nate Schierholtz FY .30 .75
302 Ian Kinsler FY RC 1.00 2.50
303 Brandon Moss FY RC .60 1.50
304 Chadd Blasko FY RC .30 .75
305 Jeremy West FY RC .30 .75
306 Sean Marshall FY RC .60 1.50
307 Matt DeSalvo FY RC .30 .75
308 Ryan Sweeney FY RC .40 1.00
309 Matthew Lindstrom FY RC .20 .50
310 Ryan Goleski FY RC .30 .75
311 Brett Harper FY RC .30 .75
312 Chris Roberson FY RC .20 .50
313 Andre Ethier FY RC 2.00 5.00
314 Chris Denorfia FY RC .40 1.00
315 Ian Bladergroen FY RC .30 .75
316 Darren Fenster FY RC .20 .50
317 Kevin West FY RC .20 .50
318 Chaz Lytle FY RC .30 .75
319 James Jurries FY RC .30 .75
320 Matt Rogelstad FY RC .20 .50
321 Wade Robinson FY RC .20 .50
322 Jake Dittler FY .20 .50
323 Brian Stavisky FY RC .20 .50
324 Kole Strayhorn FY RC .20 .50
325 Jose Vaquedano FY RC .20 .50
326 Elvys Quezada FY RC .20 .50
327 John Maine .20 .50
Val Majewski FS
328 Rickie Weeks .20 .50
J.J. Hardy FS
329 Gabe Gross .20 .50
Guillermo Quiroz FS
330 David Wright 1.25 3.00
Craig Brazell FS
331 Dallas McPherson .20 .50
Jeff Mathis FS
332 Randy Johnson SH .10 .30
333 Randy Johnson SH .10 .30
334 Ichiro Suzuki SH .20 .50
335 Ken Griffey Jr. SH .20 .50
336 Greg Maddux SH .20 .50
337 Ichiro Suzuki .20 .50
Melvin Mora
Vladimir Guerrero LL
338 Ichiro Suzuki .20 .50
Michael Young
Vladimir Guerrero LL
339 Manny Ramirez .10 .30
Paul Konerko
David Ortiz LL
340 Miguel Tejada .10 .30
David Ortiz
Manny Ramirez LL
341 Johan Santana .10 .30
Curt Schilling
Jake Westbrook LL
342 Johan Santana .10 .30
Pedro Martinez
Curt Schilling LL
343 Todd Helton .07 .20
Mark Loretta
Adrian Beltre LL
344 Juan Pierre .07 .20
Mark Loretta
Jack Wilson LL
345 Adrian Beltre .20 .50
Adam Dunn
Albert Pujols LL
346 Vinny Castilla .20 .50
Scott Rolen
Albert Pujols LL
347 Jake Peavy .10 .30
Randy Johnson
Ben Sheets LL
348 Randy Johnson .10 .30
Ben Sheets
Jason Schmidt LL
349 Alex Rodriguez .40 1.00
Ruben Sierra ALDS
350 Larry Walker .40 1.00
Albert Pujols NLDS
351 Curt Schilling .40 1.00
David Ortiz ALDS
352 Curt Schilling WS2 .40 1.00
353 Sox Celebration .40 1.00
David Ortiz
Curt Schilling ALCS
354 Cards Celebration .40 1.00
Albert Pujols
Jim Edmonds NLCS
355 Mark Bellhorn WS1 .40 1.00
356 Paul Konerko AS .07 .20
357 Alfonso Soriano AS .07 .20
358 Miguel Tejada AS .07 .20
359 Melvin Mora AS .07 .20
360 Vladimir Guerrero AS .10 .30
361 Ichiro Suzuki AS .20 .50
362 Manny Ramirez AS .10 .30
363 Ivan Rodriguez AS .07 .20
364 Johan Santana AS .10 .30
365 Paul Konerko AS .07 .20
366 David Ortiz AS .10 .30
367 Bobby Crosby AS .07 .20
368 Sox Celebration .60 1.50
Manny Ramirez
Derek Lowe WS4
369 Garret Anderson .07 .20
370 Randy Johnson .20 .50
371 Charles Thomas .07 .20
372 Rafael Palmeiro .10 .30
373 Kevin Youkilis .07 .20
374 Freddy Garcia .07 .20
375 Magglio Ordonez .07 .20
376 Aaron Harang .07 .20
377 Grady Sizemore .10 .30
378 Chin-Hui Tsao .07 .20
379 Eric Munson .07 .20
380 Juan Pierre .07 .20
381 Brad Lidge .07 .20
382 Brian Anderson .07 .20
383 Alex Cora .07 .20
384 Brady Clark .07 .20
385 Todd Helton .10 .30
386 Chad Cordero .07 .20
387 Kris Benson .07 .20
388 Brad Halsey .07 .20
389 Jermaine Dye .07 .20
390 Manny Ramirez .10 .30
391 Daryle Ward .07 .20
392 Adam Eaton .07 .20
393 Brett Tomko .07 .20
394 Bucky Jacobsen .07 .20
395 Dontrelle Willis .07 .20
396 B.J. Upton .07 .20
397 Rocco Baldelli .07 .20
398 Ted Lilly .07 .20
399 Ryan Drese .07 .20
400 Ichiro Suzuki .40 1.00
401 Brendan Donnelly .07 .20
402 Brandon Lyon .07 .20
403 Nick Green .07 .20
404 Jerry Hairston Jr. .07 .20
405 Mike Lowell .07 .20
406 Kerry Wood .07 .20
407 Carl Everett .07 .20
408 Hideki Matsui .30 .75
409 Omar Vizquel .10 .30
410 Joe Kennedy .07 .20
411 Carlos Pena .07 .20
412 Armando Benitez .07 .20
413 Carlos Beltran .07 .20
414 Kevin Appier .07 .20
415 Jeff Weaver .07 .20
416 Chad Moeller .07 .20
417 Joe Mays .07 .20
418 Terrmel Sledge .07 .20
419 Richard Hidalgo .07 .20
420 Kenny Lofton .07 .20
421 Justin Duchscherer .07 .20
422 Eric Milton .07 .20
423 Jose Mesa .07 .20
424 Ramon Hernandez .07 .20
425 Jose Reyes .07 .20
426 Joel Pineiro .07 .20
427 Matt Morris .07 .20
428 John Halama .07 .20
429 Gary Matthews Jr. .07 .20
430 Ryan Madson .07 .20
431 Mark Kotsay .07 .20
432 Carlos Delgado .07 .20
433 Casey Kotchman .07 .20
434 Greg Aquino .07 .20
435 Eli Marrero .07 .20
436 David Newhan .07 .20
437 Mike Timlin .07 .20
438 LaTroy Hawkins .07 .20
439 Jose Contreras .07 .20
440 Ken Griffey Jr. .30 .75
441 C.C. Sabathia .07 .20
442 Brandon Inge .07 .20
443 Pete Munro .07 .20
444 John Buck .07 .20
445 Hee Seop Choi .07 .20
446 Chris Capuano .07 .20
447 Jesse Crain .07 .20
448 Geoff Jenkins .07 .20
449 Brian Schneider .07 .20
450 Mike Piazza .20 .50
451 Jorge Posada .10 .30
452 Nick Swisher .07 .20
453 Kevin Millwood .07 .20
454 Mike Gonzalez .07 .20
455 Jake Peavy .07 .20
456 Dustin Hermanson .07 .20
457 Jeremy Reed .07 .20
458 Julian Tavarez .07 .20
459 Geoff Blum .07 .20
460 Alfonso Soriano .07 .20
461 Alexis Rios .07 .20
462 David Eckstein .07 .20
463 Shea Hillenbrand .07 .20
464 Russ Ortiz .07 .20
465 Kurt Ainsworth .07 .20
466 Orlando Cabrera .07 .20
467 Carlos Silva .07 .20
468 Ross Gload .07 .20
469 Josh Phelps .07 .20
470 Marquis Grissom .07 .20
471 Mike Maroth .07 .20
472 Guillermo Mota .07 .20
473 Chris Burke .07 .20
474 David DeJesus .07 .20
475 Jose Lima .07 .20
476 Cristian Guzman .07 .20
477 Nick Johnson .07 .20
478 Victor Zambrano .07 .20
479 Rod Barajas .07 .20
480 Damian Miller .07 .20
481 Chase Utley .10 .30
482 Todd Pratt .07 .20
483 Sean Burnett .07 .20
484 Boomer Wells .07 .20
485 Dustan Mohr .07 .20
486 Bobby Madritsch .07 .20
487 Ray King .07 .20
488 Reed Johnson .07 .20
489 R.A. Dickey .07 .20
490 Scott Kazmir .07 .20
491 Tony Womack .07 .20
492 Tomas Perez .07 .20
493 Esteban Loaiza .07 .20
494 Tomo Ohka .07 .20
495 Mike Lamb .07 .20
496 Ramon Ortiz .07 .20
497 Richie Sexson .07 .20
498 J.D. Drew .07 .20
499 David Segui .07 .20
500 Barry Bonds .75 2.00
501 Aramis Ramirez .07 .20
502 Wily Mo Pena .07 .20
503 Jeromy Burnitz .07 .20
504 Craig Monroe .07 .20
505 Nomar Garciaparra .20 .50
506 Brandon Backe .07 .20
507 Marcus Thames .07 .20
508 Derek Lowe .07 .20
509 Doug Davis .07 .20
510 Joe Mauer .20 .50
511 Endy Chavez .07 .20
512 Bernie Williams .10 .30
513 Mark Redman .07 .20
514 Jason Michaels .07 .20
515 Craig Wilson .07 .20
516 Ryan Klesko .07 .20
517 Ray Durham .07 .20
518 Jose Lopez .07 .20
519 Jeff Suppan .07 .20
520 Julio Lugo .07 .20
521 Mike Wood .07 .20
522 David Bush .07 .20
523 Juan Rincon .07 .20
524 Paul Quantrill .07 .20
525 Marlon Byrd .07 .20
526 Roy Oswalt .07 .20
527 Rondell White .07 .20
528 Troy Glaus .07 .20
529 Scott Hairston .07 .20
530 Chipper Jones .20 .50
531 Daniel Cabrera .07 .20
532 Doug Mientkiewicz .07 .20
533 Glendon Rusch .07 .20
534 Jon Garland .07 .20
535 Austin Kearns .07 .20
536 Jake Westbrook .07 .20
537 Aaron Miles .07 .20
538 Omar Infante .07 .20
539 Paul Lo Duca .07 .20
540 Morgan Ensberg .07 .20
541 Tony Graffanino .07 .20
542 Milton Bradley .07 .20
543 Keith Ginter .07 .20
544 Justin Morneau .07 .20
545 Tony Armas Jr. .07 .20
546 Mike Stanton .07 .20
547 Kevin Brown .07 .20
548 Marco Scutaro .07 .20
549 Tim Hudson .07 .20
550 Pat Burrell .07 .20
551 Ty Wigginton .07 .20
552 Jeff Cirillo .07 .20
553 Jim Brower .07 .20
554 Jamie Moyer .07 .20
555 Larry Walker .10 .30
556 Dewon Brazelton .07 .20
557 Brian Jordan .07 .20
558 Josh Towers .07 .20
559 Shigetoshi Hasegawa .07 .20
560 Octavio Dotel .07 .20
561 Travis Lee .07 .20
562 Michael Cuddyer .07 .20
563 Junior Spivey .07 .20
564 Zack Greinke .07 .20
565 Roger Clemens .30 .75
566 Chris Shelton .10 .30
567 Ugueth Urbina .07 .20
568 Rafael Betancourt .07 .20
569 Willie Harris .07 .20
570 Todd Hollandsworth .07 .20
571 Keith Foulke .07 .20
572 Larry Bigbie .07 .20
573 Paul Byrd .07 .20
574 Troy Percival .07 .20
575 Pedro Martinez .10 .30
576 Matt Clement .07 .20
577 Ryan Wagner .07 .20
578 Jeff Francis .07 .20
579 Jeff Conine .07 .20
580 Wade Miller .07 .20
581 Matt Stairs .07 .20
582 Gavin Floyd .07 .20
583 Kazuhisa Ishii .07 .20
584 Victor Santos .07 .20
585 Jacque Jones .07 .20
586 Sunny Kim .07 .20
587 Dan Kolb .07 .20
588 Cory Lidle .07 .20
589 Jose Castillo .07 .20
590 Alex Gonzalez .07 .20
591 Kirk Rueter .07 .20
592 Jolbert Cabrera .07 .20
593 Erik Bedard .07 .20
594 Ben Grieve .07 .20
595 Ricky Ledee .07 .20
596 Mark Hendrickson .07 .20
597 Laynce Nix .07 .20
598 Jason Frasor .07 .20
599 Kevin Gregg .07 .20
600 Derek Jeter .40 1.00
601 Luis Terrero .07 .20
602 Jaret Wright .07 .20
603 Edwin Jackson .07 .20
604 Dave Roberts .07 .20
605 Moises Alou .07 .20
606 Aaron Rowand .07 .20
607 Kazuhito Tadano .07 .20
608 Luis A. Gonzalez .07 .20
609 A.J. Burnett .07 .20
610 Jeff Bagwell .10 .30
611 Brad Penny .07 .20
612 Craig Counsell .07 .20
613 Corey Koskie .07 .20
614 Mark Ellis .07 .20
615 Felix Rodriguez .07 .20
616 Jay Payton .07 .20
617 Hector Luna .07 .20
618 Miguel Olivo .07 .20
619 Rob Bell .07 .20
620 Scott Rolen .10 .30
621 Ricardo Rodriguez .07 .20
622 Eric Hinske .07 .20
623 Tim Salmon .10 .30
624 Adam LaRoche .07 .20
625 B.J. Ryan .07 .20
626 Roberto Alomar .10 .30
627 Steve Finley .07 .20
628 Joe Nathan .07 .20
629 Scott Linebrink .07 .20
630 Vicente Padilla .07 .20
631 Raul Mondesi .07 .20
632 Yadier Molina .07 .20
633 Tino Martinez .10 .30
634 Mark Teixeira .10 .30
635 Kelvim Escobar .07 .20
636 Pedro Feliz .07 .20
637 Rich Aurilia .07 .20
638 Los Angeles Angels TC .07 .20
639 Arizona Diamondbacks TC .07 .20
640 Atlanta Braves TC .10 .30
641 Baltimore Orioles TC .07 .20
642 Boston Red Sox TC .20 .50
643 Chicago Cubs TC .10 .30
644 Chicago White Sox TC .07 .20
645 Cincinnati Reds TC .07 .20
646 Cleveland Indians TC .07 .20
647 Colorado Rockies TC .07 .20
648 Detroit Tigers TC .07 .20
649 Florida Marlins TC .07 .20
650 Houston Astros TC .07 .20
651 Kansas City Royals TC .07 .20
652 Los Angeles Dodgers TC .07 .20
653 Milwaukee Brewers TC .07 .20
654 Minnesota Twins TC .07 .20
655 Montreal Expos TC .07 .20
656 New York Mets TC .07 .20
657 New York Yankees TC .20 .50
658 Oakland Athletics TC .07 .20
659 Philadelphia Phillies TC .07 .20
660 Pittsburgh Pirates TC .07 .20
661 San Diego Padres TC .07 .20
662 San Francisco Giants TC .07 .20
663 Seattle Mariners TC .07 .20
664 St. Louis Cardinals TC .10 .30
665 Tampa Bay Devil Rays TC .07 .20
666 Texas Rangers TC .07 .20
667 Toronto Blue Jays TC .07 .20
668 Billy Butler FY RC 1.50 4.00
669 Wes Swackhamer FY RC .20 .50
670 Matt Campbell FY RC .20 .50
671 Ryan Webb FY .20 .50
672 Glen Perkins FY RC .30 .75
673 Michael Rogers FY RC .20 .50
674 Kevin Melillo FY RC .30 .75
675 Erik Cordier FY RC .20 .50
676 Landon Powell FY RC .30 .75
677 Justin Verlander FY RC 1.50 4.00
678 Eric Nielsen FY RC .20 .50
679 Alexander Smit FY RC .20 .50
680 Ryan Garko FY RC .60 1.50
681 Bobby Livingston FY RC .20 .50
682 Jeff Niemann FY RC .30 .75
683 Wladimir Balentien FY RC .30 .75
684 Chip Cannon FY RC .30 .75
685 Yorman Bazardo FY RC .20 .50
686 Mike Bourn FY RC .30 .75
687 Andy LaRoche FY RC 1.25 3.00
688 Felix Hernandez .20 .50
Justin Leone
689 Ryan Howard 2.00 5.00
Cole Hamels
690 Matt Cain .40 1.00
Merkin Valdez
691 Andy Marte .75 2.00
Jeff Francoeur UER
Francoeur's stat line says pitching instead of hitting
692 Chad Billingsley .20 .50
Joel Guzman
693 Jerry Hairston Jr. .07 .20
Scott Hairston
694 Miguel Tejada .10 .30
Lance Berkman
695 Kenny Rogers GG .07 .20
696 Ivan Rodriguez GG .07 .20
697 Darin Erstad GG .07 .20
698 Bret Boone GG .07 .20
699 Eric Chavez GG .07 .20
700 Derek Jeter GG .20 .50
701 Vernon Wells GG .07 .20
702 Ichiro Suzuki GG .20 .50
703 Torii Hunter GG .07 .20
704 Greg Maddux GG .20 .50
705 Mike Matheny GG .07 .20
706 Todd Helton GG .07 .20
707 Luis Castillo GG .07 .20
708 Scott Rolen GG .07 .20
709 Cesar Izturis GG .07 .20
710 Jim Edmonds GG .07 .20
711 Andruw Jones GG .07 .20
712 Steve Finley GG .07 .20
713 Johan Santana CY .10 .30
714 Roger Clemens CY .20 .50
715 Vladimir Guerrero MVP .10 .30
716 Barry Bonds MVP .40 1.00
717 Bobby Crosby ROY .07 .20
718 Jason Bay ROY .07 .20
719 Albert Pujols AS .20 .50
720 Mark Loretta AS .07 .20
721 Edgar Renteria AS .07 .20
722 Scott Rolen AS .07 .20
723 J.D. Drew AS .07 .20
724 Jim Edmonds AS .07 .20
725 Johnny Estrada AS .07 .20
726 Jason Schmidt AS .07 .20
727 Chris Carpenter AS .07 .20
728 Eric Gagne AS .07 .20
729 Jason Bay AS .07 .20
730 Bobby Cox MG AS .07 .20
731 David Ortiz .40 1.00
Mark Bellhorn WS1
732 Curt Schilling WS2 .40 1.00
733 Manny Ramirez .40 1.00
Pedro Martinez WS3
734 Red Sox Win .60 1.50
Johnny Damon
Derek Lowe WS4

2005 Topps 1st Edition

*1st ED 1-296/332-348/356-367: 1.25X TO 3X
*1st ED 369-667/693-69: 1.25X TO 3X
*1st ED 297-326/668-687: .6X TO 1.5X
*1st ED 327-331/688-692: .6X TO 1.5X
*1st ED 349-355/368/731-734: 1.25X TO 3X
ISSUED IN SER.1 & 2 1ST EDITION BOXES
CARD NUMBER 7 DOES NOT EXIST

2005 Topps Black

COMMON (1-6/8-331/369-734) 10.00 25.00
UNL 1-6/8-331/396-734 15.00 30.00
COMMON 297-326/668-687 10.00 25.00
UNL 297-326/668-687 15.00 30.00
COMMON 327-331/688-692 10.00 25.00
SEMIS 327-331/688-692 15.00 30.00
UNL 327-331/688-692 20.00 40.00
COMMON 731-734 20.00 40.00
SERIES 1 ODDS 1:13 HTA
SERIES 2 ODDS 1:9 HTA
STATED PRINT RUN 54 SERIAL #'d SETS
CARD NUMBER 7 DOES NOT EXIST
1 Alex Rodriguez 40.00 80.00
100 Albert Pujols 40.00 80.00
155 Greg Maddux 30.00 60.00
298 Melky Cabrera FY 25.00 50.00
302 Ian Kinsler FY 25.00 50.00
303 Brandon Moss FY 25.00 50.00
306 Sean Marshall FY 20.00 40.00
313 Andre Ethier FY 50.00 100.00
330 David Wright 25.00 50.00
Craig Brazell FS
400 Ichiro Suzuki 40.00 80.00
408 Hideki Matsui 30.00 60.00
440 Ken Griffey Jr. 30.00 60.00
500 Barry Bonds 125.00 200.00
565 Roger Clemens 30.00 60.00
566 Chris Shelton 20.00 40.00
600 Derek Jeter 50.00 100.00
668 Billy Butler FY 40.00 80.00
677 Justin Verlander FY 40.00 80.00
680 Ryan Garko FY 20.00 40.00
687 Andy LaRoche FY 30.00 60.00
688 Felix Hernandez 25.00 50.00
Justin Leone
689 Ryan Howard 50.00 100.00
Cole Hamels
691 Andy Marte 20.00 40.00
Jeff Francoeur
716 Barry Bonds MVP 75.00 150.00
734 Red Sox Win 25.00 50.00
Johnny Damon
Derek Lowe WS4

2005 Topps Box Bottoms

A.Rod/Vlad/Sosa/Shef 1.50 4.00
Thome/Giambi/Blal/Dunn 1.50 4.00
Pujols/I.Rod/Teja/Cabrera 1.50 4.00
Kaz/Takatsu/Otsuka/Nomo 1.50 4.00
Bonds/Piazza/Chipper/Wood 1.50 4.00
Soriano/Kotsay/Helton/Oswalt 1.50 4.00
Willis/Mauer/Manny/Nomar 1.50 4.00
Peavy/Garret/Rolen/Burrell 1.50 4.00
*BOX BOTTOM CARDS: 1X TO 2.5X BASIC
ONE 4-CARD SHEET PER HTA BOX

2005 Topps Gold

*1st ED 1-296/332-348
*GOLD 297-326/668-687: 2X TO 5X
*GOLD 327-331/688-692: 2X TO 5X
*GOLD 731-734: 3X TO 8X
SERIES 1 ODDS 1:8 HOB, 1:3 HTA, 1:10 RET
SERIES 2 ODDS 1:5 HOB, 1:2 HTA, 1:6 RET
STATED PRINT RUN 2005 SERIAL #'d SETS
CARD NUMBER 7 DOES NOT EXIST
313 Andre Ethier FY 6.00 15.00
330 David Wright 4.00 10.00
Craig Brazell FS
500 Barry Bonds 8.00 20.00
668 Billy Butler FY 6.00 15.00
677 Justin Verlander FY 6.00 15.00
689 Ryan Howard 6.00 15.00
Cole Hamels

2005 Topps 1955 World Series Cut Signature

SER.2 ODDS 1:297,056 H, 1:77,616 HTA
SER.2 ODDS 1:171,072 R
STATED PRINT RUN 1 SERIAL #'d SET
NO PRICING DUE TO SCARCITY
BB Bob Borkowski
BL Billy Loes
BR Bobby Richardson
BS Bill Skowron
BT Bob Turley
CE Carl Erskine
CL Clem Labine
DL Don Larsen
DN Don Newcombe
DS Duke Snider
ER Ed Roebuck
GM Gil McDougald
GS George Shuba
HB Hank Bauer
JB Joe Black
JG Jim Gilliam
JH Jim Hughes
JP Johnny Podres
RM Russ Meyer
WF Whitey Ford
YB Yogi Berra

2005 Topps 1955 World Series Dual Cut Signatures

SER.2 ODDS 1:51,744 HTA
STATED PRINT RUN 1 SERIAL #'d SET
NO PRICING DUE TO SCARCITY
AB Walt Alston
Yogi Berra

NF Don Newcombe
(Whitey Ford
SB Duke Snider
(Yogi Berra

2005 Topps 1955 World Series Dual Match-Ups Autographs

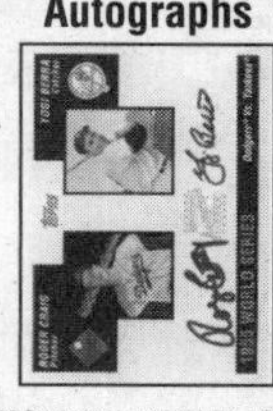

SER.2 ODDS 1:9002 H, 1:2587 HTA, 1:9004 R
STATED PRINT RUN 50 SERIAL #'d SETS
SER.2 EXCH.DEADLINE 04/30/07
NO PRICING DUE TO SCARCITY
CB Roger Craig
Yogi Berra
EL Carl Erskine
Don Larsen
LL Don Larsen
Clem Labine
NB Don Newcombe
Hank Bauer
NF Don Newcombe
Whitey Ford
PS Johnny Podres
Bill Skowron
PT Johnny Podres
(Bob Turley
SB Duke Snider
Yogi Berra
ZR Don Zimmer
Phil Rizzuto EXCH

2005 Topps A-Rod Spokesman

COMPLETE SET (4) 4.00 10.00
SER.2 ODDS 1:24 HOB, 1:8 HTA, 1:24 RET
1 Alex Rodriguez 1994 1.25 3.00
2 Alex Rodriguez 1995 1.25 3.00
3 Alex Rodriguez 1996 1.25 3.00
4 Alex Rodriguez 1997 1.25 3.00

2005 Topps A-Rod Spokesman Autographed Jersey Relics

SER.2 ODDS 1:89,117 H, 1:22,176 HTA
SER.2 ODDS 1:85,536 R
STATED PRINT RUN 13 SERIAL #'d SETS
NO PRICING DUE TO SCARCITY
EXCHANGE DEADLINE 04/30/07
1 Alex Rodriguez 1994 EXCH
2 Alex Rodriguez 1995 EXCH
3 Alex Rodriguez 1996 EXCH
4 Alex Rodriguez 1997 EXCH

2005 Topps A-Rod Spokesman Autographs

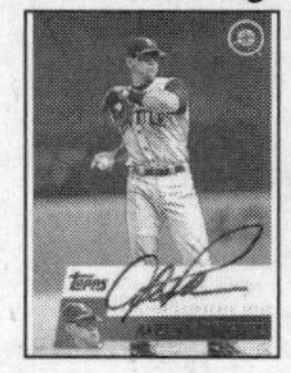

SER.2 ODDS 1:22,279 H, 1:6749 HTA
SER.2 ODDS 1:24,439 R
PRINT RUNS B/WN 1-200 COPIES PER
NO PRICING ON QTY OF 25 OR LESS
1 Alex Rodriguez 1994/1
2 Alex Rodriguez 1995/25
3 Alex Rodriguez 1996/100 150.00 250.00
4 Alex Rodriguez 1997/200 125.00 200.00

2005 Topps A-Rod Spokesman Jersey Relics

SER.2 ODDS 1:3550 H, 1:1015 HTA, 1:3564 R
PRINT RUNS B/WN 1-800 COPIES PER
NO PRICING ON QTY OF 1
1 Alex Rodriguez 1994/1
2 Alex Rodriguez 1995/50 30.00 60.00
3 Alex Rodriguez 1996/300 8.00 20.00
4 Alex Rodriguez 1997/800 6.00 15.00

2005 Topps All-Star Patches Relics

SER.2 ODDS 1:3495 H, 1:1001 HTA, 1:3491 R
STATED PRINT RUN 25 SERIAL #'d SETS
NO PRICING DUE TO SCARCITY

2005 Topps All-Star Stitches Relics

SERIES 1 ODDS 1:96 H, 1:27 HTA, 1:80 R
AP Albert Pujols 8.00 20.00
AS Alfonso Soriano 4.00 10.00
BA Bobby Abreu 4.00 10.00
BL Barry Larkin 4.00 10.00
BS Ben Sheets 4.00 10.00
CB Carlos Beltran 4.00 10.00
CC Carl Crawford 4.00 10.00
CP Carl Pavano 4.00 10.00
CS C.C. Sabathia 4.00 10.00
CZ Carlos Zambrano 4.00 10.00
DK Danny Kolb 4.00 10.00
DO David Ortiz 4.00 10.00
EL Esteban Loaiza 4.00 10.00
ER Edgar Renteria 4.00 10.00
FG Tom Gordon 4.00 10.00
FR Francisco Rodriguez 4.00 10.00
GS Gary Sheffield 4.00 10.00
HB Hank Blalock 4.00 10.00
IR Ivan Rodriguez 4.00 10.00
JE Johnny Estrada 4.00 10.00
JG Jason Giambi 4.00 10.00
JK Jeff Kent 4.00 10.00
JN Joe Nathan 4.00 10.00
JT Jim Thome 4.00 10.00
JW Jack Wilson 4.00 10.00
KH Ken Harvey 4.00 10.00
LB Lance Berkman 4.00 10.00
MA Moises Alou 4.00 10.00
MC Miguel Cabrera 4.00 10.00
ML Mike Lowell 4.00 10.00
MLA Matt Lawton 4.00 10.00
MLO Mark Loretta 4.00 10.00
MM Mark Mulder 4.00 10.00
MP Mike Piazza 4.00 10.00
MR Manny Ramirez 4.00 10.00
MRI Mariano Rivera 4.00 10.00
MT Miguel Tejada 4.00 10.00
MY Michael Young 4.00 10.00
PL Paul Lo Duca 4.00 10.00
RB Ronnie Belliard 4.00 10.00
SR Scott Rolen 4.00 10.00
SS Sammy Sosa 4.00 10.00
TG Tom Glavine 4.00 10.00
TH Todd Helton 4.00 10.00
TL Ted Lilly 4.00 10.00
VG Vladimir Guerrero 4.00 10.00
VM Victor Martinez 4.00 10.00

2005 Topps All-Stars

COMPLETE SET (15) 10.00 25.00
SER.2 ODDS 1:9 HOBBY, 1:3 HTA
1 Todd Helton .75 2.00
2 Albert Pujols 1.50 4.00
3 Vladimir Guerrero .75 2.00
4 Ichiro Suzuki 1.50 4.00
5 Randy Johnson .75 2.00
6 Manny Ramirez .75 2.00
7 Sammy Sosa .75 2.00
8 Alfonso Soriano .60 1.50
9 Jim Thome .75 2.00
10 Barry Bonds 2.00 5.00
11 Roger Clemens 1.25 3.00
12 Mike Piazza .75 2.00
13 Derek Jeter 1.50 4.00
14 Alex Rodriguez 1.25 3.00
15 Carlos Beltran .60 1.50

2005 Topps Autographs

Carlos Beltran and Zack Greinke did not return their cards in time to be included within first series packs, thus exchange cards with a deadline redemption date of November 30th, 2006 were placed into packs in their place.

SER.1 A 1:2683 H, 1:767 HTA, 1:2238 R
SER.1 B 1:3950 H, 1:1129 HTA, 1:3300 R
SER.1 C 1:305 H, 1:87 HTA, 1:254 R

SER.1 D 1:2913 H, 1:833 HTA, 1:2432 R
SER.2 A 1:178,234H,1:51,744HTA,1:171,072R
SER.2 B 1:89,117 H, 1:22,176 HTA, 1:85,536 R
SER.2 C 1:2751 H, 1:780 HTA, 1:2715 R
SER.2 D 1:1367 H, 1:390 HTA, 1:1369 R
SER.2 E 1:2039 H, 1:586 HTA, 1:2061 R
SER.2 F 1:285 H, 1:129 HTA, 1:301 R
SER.2 GROUP A PRINT RUN 25 COPIES
SER.2 GROUP B PRINT RUN 50 COPIES
SER.2 GROUP A-B ARE NOT SERIAL #'d
PRINT RUN INFO PROVIDED BY TOPPS
SER.1 EXCH.DEADLINE 11/30/06
SER.2 EXCH.DEADLINE 04/30/07
NO GROUP A2 PRICING DUE TO SCARCITY
AR Alex Rodriguez A1 125.00 200.00
AR2 Alex Rodriguez B2/50 * 150.00 250.00
ARI Alexis Rios C1 4.00 10.00
BB Billy Butler E2 20.00 50.00
BBO Barry Bonds A2/25 *
CB Carlos Beltran A1 EXCH 10.00 25.00
CB2 Carlos Beltran C2 EXCH 10.00 25.00
CC Carl Crawford D2 10.00 25.00
CK Casey Kotchman C1 4.00 10.00
CT Chad Tracy C1 4.00 10.00
CW Craig Wilson D2 6.00 15.00
DD David DeJesus C1 4.00 10.00
DM Dallas McPherson D1 4.00 10.00
DW David Wright C1 30.00 60.00
EC Eric Chavez A1 10.00 25.00
EC2 Eric Chavez C2 10.00 25.00
ECO Erik Cordier F2 4.00 10.00
EG Eric Gagne C2 15.00 40.00
FH Felix Hernandez D2 20.00 40.00
GP Glen Perkins F2 6.00 15.00
IR Ivan Rodriguez C2 30.00 60.00
JB Jason Bay D2 10.00 25.00
JC Jose Capellan B1 4.00 10.00
JM Justin Morneau C1 4.00 10.00
JMA John Maine C1 15.00 40.00
JS Johan Santana C2 15.00 40.00
JSM Jeff Mathis C1 4.00 10.00
LP Landon Powell F2 6.00 15.00
MB Milton Bradley F2 10.00 25.00
MC Miguel Cabrera C1 10.00 25.00
MCA Matt Campbell F2 4.00 10.00
MH Matt Holliday C1 12.50 30.00
ML Mark Loretta D2 6.00 15.00
MR Michael Rogers F2 4.00 10.00
SK Scott Kazmir C2 10.00 25.00
TH Torii Hunter A1 10.00 25.00
TS Termel Sledge E2 4.00 10.00
VW Vernon Wells A1 10.00 25.00
ZG Zack Greinke C1 4.00 10.00

2005 Topps Barry Bonds Chase to 715

COMMON CARD 15.00 40.00
SER.2 ODDS 1:2539 H, 1:722 HTA, 1:2516 R
STATED PRINT RUN 1 SERIAL #'d SET

2005 Topps Barry Bonds Home Run History

COMP.SERIES 3 (48) 20.00 50.00
COMP.06 UPDATE (26) 10.00 25.00
COMP.07 UPDATE (22) 20.00 50.00
COMMON CARD (1-754) 1.25 3.00
COMMON HR 1 15.00 40.00
COMMON HR 100/200/300/400 6.00 15.00
COMMON HR 500/600 6.00 15.00
COMMON HR 661/700 3.00 8.00
COMMON HR 755/756 2.00 5.00
05 SER.2 ODDS 1:4 H, 1:1 HTA, 1:4 R
05 UPDATE ODDS 1:4 H, 1:1 HTA, 1:4 R
06 SER.1 ODDS 1:4 HOB, 1:4 MINI, 1:4 RET
06 SER.1 ODDS 1:2 RACK
06 UPDATE ODDS 1:6 HOB,1:6 RET
07 UPDATE ODDS 1:12 HOBBY
05 SER.2 EXCH ODDS 1:178,234 HOB
05 SER.2 EXCH ODDS 1:51,744 HTA
05 SER.2 EXCH ODDS 1:171,072 RET
07 UPDATE ODDS 1:12 H,1:3 HTA,1:12 R
EXCH CARD PRINT RUN 25 COPIES
EXCH.CARD PRINT RUN INFO FROM TOPPS
NO EXCH CARD PRICING DUE TO SCARCITY
1-330 ISSUED IN 05 SERIES 2 PACKS
331-660 ISSUED IN 05 UPDATE PACKS
661-708 ISSUED IN 06 SERIES 1 PACKS
709-734 ISSUED IN 06 UPDATE PACKS
735-575 ISSUED IN 07 UPDATE PACKS
1/100/200/300/400/500/600 ARE GOLD FOIL
661/700/755/766 ARE SILVER FOIL
NNO Series 2 Set Exch.Card/25 *

2005 Topps Barry Bonds MVP

SER.2 ODDS 1:2613 H, 1:743 HTA, 1:2592 R
PRINT RUNS B/WN 25-500 COPIES PER
NO PRICING ON QTY OF 25
1 Barry Bonds 1990/25
2 Barry Bonds 1992/50
3 Barry Bonds 1993/100 15.00 40.00
4 Barry Bonds 2001/200 12.50 30.00
5 Barry Bonds 2002/300 12.50 30.00
6 Barry Bonds 2003/400 10.00 25.00
7 Barry Bonds 2004/500 10.00 25.00

2005 Topps Barry Bonds MVP Autographed Jersey Relics

SER.2 ODDS 1:22,176 HTA
STATED PRINT RUN 1 SERIAL #'d SET
NO PRICING DUE TO SCARCITY
EXCHANGE DEADLINE 11/30/07
1 Barry Bonds 1990 EXCH
2 Barry Bonds 1992 EXCH
3 Barry Bonds 1993 EXCH
4 Barry Bonds 2001 EXCH
5 Barry Bonds 2002 EXCH
6 Barry Bonds 2003 EXCH
7 Barry Bonds 2004 EXCH

2005 Topps Barry Bonds MVP Autographs

SER.2 ODDS 1:222,792 H, 1:51,744 HTA
SER.2 ODDS 1:171,072 R
PRINT RUNS B/WN 1-7 COPIES PER
NO PRICING DUE TO SCARCITY
1 Barry Bonds 1990/1
2 Barry Bonds 1992/2
3 Barry Bonds 1993/3
4 Barry Bonds 2001/4
5 Barry Bonds 2002/5
6 Barry Bonds 2003/6
7 Barry Bonds 2004/7

2005 Topps Barry Bonds MVP Jersey Relics

SER.2 ODDS 1:2613 H, 1:743 HTA, 1:2592 R
PRINT RUNS B/WN 25-500 COPIES PER
NO PRICING ON QTY OF 25
1 Barry Bonds 1990/25
2 Barry Bonds 1992/50
3 Barry Bonds 1993/100 50.00 100.00
4 Barry Bonds 2001/200 30.00 60.00
5 Barry Bonds 2002/300 20.00 50.00
6 Barry Bonds 2003/400 15.00 40.00
7 Barry Bonds 2004/500 12.50 30.00

2005 Topps Celebrity Threads Jersey Relics

SERIES 1 ODDS 1:562 H, 1:161 HTA, 1:468 R
RELICS ARE FROM CELEBRITY AS EVENT
CC Cesar Cedeno 4.00 10.00
CF Cecil Fielder 6.00 15.00
DW Dave Winfield 4.00 10.00
GG Goose Gossage 4.00 10.00
HR Harold Reynolds 4.00 10.00
MS Mike Scott 4.00 10.00
OS Ozzie Smith 8.00 20.00
RF Rollie Fingers 4.00 10.00

2005 Topps Dem Bums

COMPLETE SET (21) 20.00 50.00
SERIES 1 ODDS 1:12 H, 1:4 HTA, 1:12 R
BB Bob Borkowski 1.25 3.00
CE Carl Erskine 1.25 3.00
CF Carl Furillo 1.25 3.00
CL Clem Labine 1.25 3.00
DH Don Hoak 1.25 3.00
DN Don Newcombe 1.25 3.00
DS Duke Snider 2.00 5.00
DZ Don Zimmer 1.25 3.00
ER Ed Roebuck 1.25 3.00
GS George Shuba 1.25 3.00
JB Joe Black 1.25 3.00
JG Jim Gilliam 1.25 3.00
JH Jim Hughes 1.25 3.00
JP Johnny Podres 1.25 3.00
JR Jackie Robinson 2.00 5.00
KS Karl Spooner 1.25 3.00
RC Roy Campanella 2.00 5.00
RCR Roger Craig 1.25 3.00
RM Russ Meyer 1.25 3.00
RW Rube Walker 1.25 3.00
WA Walter Alston 1.25 3.00

2005 Topps Dem Bums Autographs

SERIES 1 ODDS 1:150 HTA
SERIES 2 ODDS 1:182 HTA
SER.2 EXCH.DEADLINE 04/30/07
CE Carl Erskine 15.00 40.00
CL Clem Labine 15.00 40.00
DN Don Newcombe 20.00 50.00
DS Duke Snider 20.00 50.00
DZ Don Zimmer 20.00 50.00
ER Ed Roebuck 20.00 50.00
GS George Shuba EXCH 20.00 50.00
JP Johnny Podres 15.00 40.00
RC Roger Craig 15.00 40.00

2005 Topps Dem Bums Cut Signatures

SER.1 ODDS 1:347,438 H, 1:71,104 HTA
SER.1 ODDS 1:436,320 R
STATED PRINT RUN 1 SERIAL #'d SET
NO PRICING DUE TO SCARCITY
BB Bob Borkowski
CE Carl Erskine
CF Carl Furillo
CL Clem Labine
DN Don Newcombe
DS Duke Snider
DZ Don Zimmer
ER Ed Roebuck
JB Joe Black
JG Jim Gilliam
RM Russ Meyer
SA Sandy Amoros

2005 Topps Derby Digs Ball Relics

SER.2 ODDS 1:63,655 H, 1:17,248 HTA
SER.2 ODDS 1:57,024 R
STATED PRINT RUN 10 SERIAL #'d SETS
NO PRICING DUE TO SCARCITY
DO David Ortiz
HB Hank Blalock
JT Jim Thome
LB Lance Berkman
MT Miguel Tejada
RP Rafael Palmeiro
SS Sammy Sosa

2005 Topps Derby Digs Jersey Relics

SER.1 ODDS 1:11,208 HOBBY, 1:3232 HTA
SER.1 ODDS 1:9630 RETAIL
STATED PRINT RUN 100 SERIAL #'d SETS
DO David Ortiz 15.00 40.00
HB Hank Blalock 10.00 25.00
JT Jim Thome 15.00 40.00
LB Lance Berkman 10.00 25.00
MT Miguel Tejada 10.00 25.00
SS Sammy Sosa 15.00 40.00

2005 Topps Factory Set Draft Picks Bonus

COMPLETE SET (5) 10.00 20.00
ONE SET PER FACTORY SET
1 Beau Jones 2.00 5.00
2 Cliff Pennington 1.50 4.00
3 Chris Volstad 2.00 5.00
4 Ricky Romero 2.00 5.00
5 Jay Bruce 30.00 60.00

2005 Topps Factory Set First Year Draft Bonus

COMPLETE SET (10) 15.00 30.00
ONE SET PER GREEN HOLIDAY FACT.SET
1 Nick Webber 1.50 4.00
2 Aaron Thompson 2.00 5.00
3 Matt Garza 4.00 10.00
4 Tyler Greene 2.00 5.00
5 Ryan Braun 12.50 30.00
6 C.J. Henry 2.00 5.00
7 Ryan Zimmerman 8.00 20.00
8 John Mayberry Jr. 2.00 5.00
9 Cesar Carrillo 2.00 5.00
10 Mark McCormick 1.50 4.00

2005 Topps Factory Set First Year Player Bonus

COMPLETE SERIES 1 (5) 7.50 15.00
1-5 ISSUED IN RED HOBBY SETS
1 Bill McCarthy 1.50 4.00
2 John Hudgins 1.50 4.00
3 Kyle Nichols 2.00 5.00
4 Thomas Pauly 1.50 4.00
5 Philip Humber 2.00 5.00

2005 Topps Factory Set Team Bonus

Issued five per selected Topps factory sets, these cards feature leading prospects from seven-different organizations.

COMP.CUBS SET (5) 7.50 15.00
COMP.GIANTS SET (5) 7.50 15.00
COMP.NATIONALS SET (5) 7.50 15.00
COMP.RED SOX SET (5) 7.50 15.00
COMP.TIGERS SET (5) 7.50 15.00
COMP.YANKEES SET (5) 7.50 15.00
C1-C5 ISSUED IN CUBS FACTORY SET
G1-G5 ISSUED IN GIANTS FACTORY SET
N1-N5 ISSUED IN NATIONALS FACTORY SET
R1-R5 ISSUED IN RED SOX FACTORY SET
T1-T5 ISSUED IN TIGERS FACTORY SET
Y1-Y5 ISSUED IN YANKEES FACTORY SET
C1 Casey McGehee 1.50 4.00
C2 Andy Santana 1.50 4.00
C3 Buck Coats 1.50 4.00
C4 Kevin Collins 1.50 4.00
C5 Brandon Sing 1.50 4.00
G1 Pat Misch 1.50 4.00
G2 J.B. Thurmond 1.50 4.00
G3 Billy Sadler 1.50 4.00
G4 Jonathan Sanchez 2.00 5.00
G5 Fred Lewis 1.50 4.00
N1 Daryl Thompson 1.50 4.00
N2 Ender Chavez 1.50 4.00
N3 Ryan Church 1.50 4.00
N4 Brendan Harris 1.50 4.00
N5 Darrell Rasner 1.50 4.00
R1 Stefan Bailie 1.50 4.00
R2 Willy Mota 1.50 4.00
R3 Matt Van Der Bosch 1.50 4.00
R4 Mike Garber 1.50 4.00
R5 Dustin Pedroia 1.50 4.00
T1 Eulogio de la Cruz 1.50 4.00
T2 Humberto Sanchez 4.00 10.00

T3 Danny Zell 1.50 4.00
T4 Kyle Sleeth 1.50 4.00
T5 Curtis Granderson 1.50 4.00
Y1 T.J. Beam 1.50 4.00
Y2 Ben Jones 1.50 4.00
Y3 Robinson Cano 4.00 10.00
Y4 Steven White 1.50 4.00
Y5 Philip Hughes 1.50 4.00

2005 Topps Grudge Match

COMPLETE SET (10) 8.00 20.00
SERIES 1 ODDS 1:24 H, 1:8 HTA, 1:18 R
1 Jorge Posada .75 2.00
Pedro Martinez
2 Mike Piazza 1.00 2.50
Roger Clemens
3 Mariano Rivera .75 2.00
Luis Gonzalez
4 Jim Edmonds .75 2.00
Carlos Zambrano
5 Aaron Boone .75 2.00
Tim Wakefield
6 Manny Ramirez 1.00 2.50
Roger Clemens
7 Michael Tucker .75 2.00
Eric Gagne
8 Ivan Rodriguez .75 2.00
J.T. Snow
9 Alex Rodriguez 1.25 3.00
Bronson Arroyo
10 Corky Miller .75 2.00
Sammy Sosa

2005 Topps Hit Parade

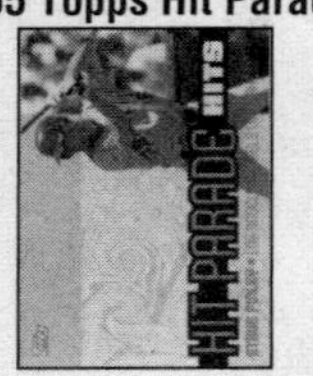

COMPLETE SET (30) 30.00 60.00
SER.2 ODDS 1:12 H, 1:4 HTA, 1:12 R
HR1 Barry Bonds HR 2.00 5.00
HR2 Sammy Sosa HR .75 2.00
HR3 Rafael Palmeiro HR .75 2.00
HR4 Ken Griffey Jr. HR 1.25 3.00
HR5 Jeff Bagwell HR .75 2.00
HR6 Frank Thomas HR .75 2.00
HR7 Juan Gonzalez HR .75 2.00
HR8 Jim Thome HR .75 2.00
HR9 Gary Sheffield HR .75 2.00
HR10 Manny Ramirez HR .75 2.00
HIT1 Rafael Palmeiro HIT .75 2.00
HIT2 Barry Bonds HIT 2.00 5.00
HIT3 Roberto Alomar HIT .75 2.00
HIT4 Craig Biggio HIT .75 2.00
HIT5 Julio Franco HIT .75 2.00
HIT6 Steve Finley HIT .75 2.00
HIT7 Jeff Bagwell HIT .75 2.00
HIT8 B.J. Surhoff HIT .75 2.00
HIT9 Marquis Grissom HIT .75 2.00
HIT10 Sammy Sosa HIT .75 2.00
RBI1 Barry Bonds RBI 2.00 5.00
RBI2 Rafael Palmeiro RBI .75 2.00
RBI3 Sammy Sosa RBI .75 2.00
RBI4 Jeff Bagwell RBI .75 2.00
RBI5 Ken Griffey Jr. RBI 1.25 3.00
RBI6 Frank Thomas RBI .75 2.00
RBI7 Juan Gonzalez RBI .75 2.00
RBI8 Gary Sheffield RBI .75 2.00
RBI9 Ruben Sierra RBI .75 2.00
RBI10 Manny Ramirez RBI .75 2.00

2005 Topps Hobby Masters

COMPLETE SET (20) 15.00 40.00
SERIES 1 ODDS 1:18 HOBBY, 1:6 HTA
1 Alex Rodriguez 1.25 3.00
2 Sammy Sosa .75 2.00
3 Ichiro Suzuki 1.50 4.00
4 Albert Pujols 1.50 4.00
5 Derek Jeter 1.50 4.00
6 Jim Thome .75 2.00
7 Vladimir Guerrero .75 2.00
8 Nomar Garciaparra .75 2.00
9 Mike Piazza .75 2.00
10 Jason Giambi .75 2.00
11 Ivan Rodriguez .75 2.00
12 Alfonso Soriano .75 2.00
13 Dontrelle Willis .75 2.00
14 Chipper Jones .75 2.00
15 Mark Prior .75 2.00
16 Todd Helton .75 2.00
17 Randy Johnson .75 2.00
18 Hank Blalock .75 2.00
19 Ken Griffey Jr. 1.25 3.00
20 Roger Clemens 1.25 3.00

2005 Topps Midsummer Covers Ball Relics

SER.1 ODDS 1:46,325 H, 1:3333 HTA
SER.2 ODDS 1:17,474 H, 1:3610 HTA
STATED PRINT RUN 10 SERIAL #'d SETS
NO PRICING DUE TO SCARCITY
AP Albert Pujols S1
AP2 Albert Pujols S2
AR Alex Rodriguez S1
AR2 Alex Rodriguez S2
AS Alfonso Soriano S1
AS2 Alfonso Soriano S2
CB Carlos Beltran S2
IR Ivan Rodriguez S1
IR2 Ivan Rodriguez S2
JG Jason Giambi S1
JT Jim Thome S1
JT2 Jim Thome S2
MP Mike Piazza S2
RC Roger Clemens S1
RC2 Roger Clemens S2
RJ Randy Johnson S1
RJ2 Randy Johnson S2
SS Sammy Sosa S1
VG Vladimir Guerrero S1
VG2 Vladimir Guerrero S2

2005 Topps On Deck Circle Relics

SER.2 ODDS 1:1493 H, 1:425 HTA, 1:1488 R
STATED PRINT RUN 275 SETS
CARDS ARE NOT SERIAL-NUMBERED
PRINT RUN INFO PROVIDED BY TOPPS
AP Albert Pujols 15.00 40.00
AR Alex Rodriguez 15.00 40.00
AS Alfonso Soriano 4.00 10.00
CB Carlos Beltran 4.00 10.00
HB Hank Blalock 4.00 10.00
IR Ivan Rodriguez 6.00 15.00
JT Jim Thome 6.00 15.00
SR Scott Rolen 6.00 15.00
SS Sammy Sosa 6.00 15.00
TH Todd Helton 6.00 15.00

2005 Topps Own the Game

COMPLETE SET (30) 20.00 50.00
SERIES 1 ODDS 1:12 H, 1:4 HTA, 1:12 R
1 Ichiro Suzuki 1.50 4.00
2 Todd Helton .75 2.00
3 Adrian Beltre .75 2.00
4 Albert Pujols 1.50 4.00
5 Adam Dunn .75 2.00
6 Jim Thome .75 2.00
7 Miguel Tejada .75 2.00
8 David Ortiz .75 2.00
9 Manny Ramirez .75 2.00
10 Scott Rolen .75 2.00
11 Gary Sheffield .75 2.00
12 Vladimir Guerrero .75 2.00
13 Jim Edmonds .75 2.00
14 Ivan Rodriguez .75 2.00
15 Lance Berkman .75 2.00
16 Michael Young .75 2.00
17 Juan Pierre .75 2.00
18 Craig Biggio .75 2.00
19 Johnny Damon .75 2.00
20 Jimmy Rollins .75 2.00
21 Scott Podsednik .75 2.00
22 Bobby Abreu .75 2.00
23 Lyle Overbay .75 2.00
24 Carl Crawford .75 2.00
25 Mark Loretta .75 2.00
26 Vinny Castilla .75 2.00
27 Curt Schilling .75 2.00
28 Johan Santana .75 2.00
29 Randy Johnson .75 2.00
30 Pedro Martinez .75 2.00

2005 Topps Power Brokers Cut Signatures

SER.2 ODDS 1:99,019H,1:22,176R,1:85,536R
STATED PRINT RUN 1 SERIAL #'d SET
NO PRICING DUE TO SCARCITY

2005 Topps Spokesman Jersey Relic

SER.1 ODDS 1:5627 H, 1:1604 HTA, 1:4692 R
RELIC IS EVENT WORN
AR Alex Rodriguez 20.00 50.00

2005 Topps Team Topps Autographs

These cards were issued in some late season 2005 Topps products.

BOWMAN DRAFT ODDS 1:697 H
TOP.UP.ODDS 1:5374H,1:1537 HTA,1:5347R
BH Ben Hendrickson BD 4.00 10.00
JK Josh Kroeger BD 4.00 10.00
KS Kurt Suzuki TU 4.00 10.00

2005 Topps Touch Em All Base Relics

SER.1 ODDS 1:13,493 H, 1:3878 HTA
SER.1 ODDS 1:11,440 R
SER.2 ODDS 1:8329 H, 1:2352 HTA
SER.2 ODDS 1:8146 R
STATED PRINT RUN 50 SERIAL #'d SETS
NO PRICING DUE TO SCARCITY
AP Albert Pujols S1
AP2 Albert Pujols S2
AR Alex Rodriguez S1
AR2 Alex Rodriguez S2
AS Alfonso Soriano S1
AS2 Alfonso Soriano S2
CB Carlos Beltran S1
CB2 Carlos Beltran S2
DO David Ortiz S2
IR Ivan Rodriguez S1
IR2 Ivan Rodriguez S2
JG Jason Giambi S1
JT Jim Thome S1
JT2 Jim Thome S2
MR Manny Ramirez S2
SR Scott Rolen S1
SS Sammy Sosa S1
SS2 Sammy Sosa S2
VG Vladimir Guerrero S1
VG2 Vladimir Guerrero S2

2005 Topps World Champions Red Sox Relics

SER.2 A ODDS 1:649 H, 1:185 HTA, 1:648 R
SER.2 B ODDS 1:311 H, 1:89 HTA, 1:310 R
BM Bill Mueller Bat A 6.00 15.00
BM2 Bill Mueller Jsy B 6.00 15.00
CS Curt Schilling Jsy B 6.00 15.00
DL Derek Lowe Jsy B 6.00 15.00
DMI Doug Mientkiewicz Bat B 6.00 15.00
DO David Ortiz Bat B 6.00 15.00
DO2 David Ortiz Jsy B 6.00 15.00
DR Dave Roberts Bat A 6.00 15.00
JD Johnny Damon Bat A 6.00 15.00
JD2 Johnny Damon Jsy B 6.00 15.00
KM Kevin Millar Bat B 6.00 15.00
KY Kevin Youkilis Bat A 4.00 10.00
MR Manny Ramirez Bat A 6.00 15.00
MR2 Manny Ramirez Home Jsy B 6.00 15.00
MR3 Manny Ramirez Road Jsy B 6.00 15.00
OC Orlando Cabrera Bat A 6.00 15.00
OC2 Orlando Cabrera Jsy B 6.00 15.00
PM Pedro Martinez Uni A 6.00 15.00
PR Pokey Reese Bat B 4.00 10.00
TN Trot Nixon Bat A 6.00 15.00

2005 Topps World Treasures Cut Signatures

SER.1 ODDS 1:135,475 HOB, 1:42,662 HTA
SER.1 ODDS 1:109,080 RETAIL
STATED PRINT RUN 1 SERIAL #'d SET
NO PRICING DUE TO SCARCITY

2005 Topps World Treasures Dual Signatures

SERIES 1 ODDS 1:213,312 HTA
STATED PRINT RUN 1 SERIAL #'d SET
NO PRICING DUE TO SCARCITY
BC George W. Bush
Dick Cheney
BK George W. Bush
John Kerry
CE Dick Cheney
John Edwards
KE John Kerry
John Edwards

2005 Topps Update

This 330-card set was released in November, 2005. The set was issued in 10-card packs with a $1.50 SRP which came 36 packs to a box and eight boxes to a case. It is also important to note that a factory set consisting of just the base set (no inserts) was also included in the sealed hobby cases. The basic set consists of cards 1-84 featuring either players who were traded/signed as free agents after the original 2005 Topps set was released. Cards numbered 85-89 feature managers with new teams. Cards numbered 90-110 feature prospects, who previously had cards, who made an impact in baseball in 2005. Cards numbered 111 through 115 feature players who set records in 2005. Cards numbered 116 through 134 feature post-season highlights. Cards numbered 135 through 146 feature 2005 league leaders. Cards numbered 147 through 194 feature a mix of award winners and 2005 All-Stars. Cards numbered 195 through 202 feature players who were in the 2005 All-Star Home Run Derby. Cards numbered 203 through 220 feature players with tremendous futures. Cards numbered 221 through 310 feature Rookie Cards of players who had not been on Topps cards previously. Cards 311 through 330 feature some of the leading players selected in the 2005 amateur draft.

COMPLETE SET (330) 15.00 40.00
COMP.FACT.SET (330) 25.00 40.00
COMMON CARD (1-330) .07 .20
COM (90-110/203-220) .20 .50
COMMON (116-134) .20 .50
COM (14/66/221-310) .20 .50
COMMON (311-330) .20 .50
PLATE ODDS 1:2009 H, 1:582 HTA, 1:2009 R
PLATE PRINT RUN 1 SET PER COLOR
BLACK-CYAN-MAGENTA-YELLOW ISSUED
NO PLATE PRICING DUE TO SCARCITY
1 Sammy Sosa .20 .50
2 Jeff Francoeur .60 1.50
3 Tony Clark .07 .20
4 Michael Tucker .07 .20
5 Mike Matheny .07 .20
6 Eric Young .07 .20
7 Jose Valentin .07 .20
8 Matt Lawton .07 .20
9 Juan Rivera .07 .20
10 Shawn Green .07 .20
11 Aaron Boone .07 .20
12 Woody Williams .07 .20
13 Brad Wilkerson .07 .20
14 Anthony Reyes RC .40 1.00
15 Russ Adams .07 .20
16 Gustavo Chacin .07 .20
17 Michael Restovich .07 .20
18 Humberto Quintero .07 .20
19 Matt Ginter .07 .20
20 Scott Podsednik .07 .20
21 Byung-Hyun Kim .07 .20
22 Orlando Hernandez .07 .20
23 Mark Grudzielanek .07 .20
24 Jody Gerut .07 .20
25 Adrian Beltre .07 .20
26 Scott Schoeneweis .07 .20
27 Marlon Anderson .07 .20
28 Jason Vargas .07 .20
29 Claudio Vargas .07 .20
30 Jason Kendall .07 .20
31 Aaron Small .07 .20
32 Juan Cruz .07 .20
33 Placido Polanco .07 .20
34 Jorge Sosa .07 .20
35 John Olerud .07 .20
36 Ryan Langerhans .07 .20
37 Randy Winn .07 .20
38 Zach Duke .10 .30
39 Garrett Atkins .07 .20
40 Al Leiter .07 .20
41 Shawn Chacon .07 .20
42 Mark DeRosa .07 .20
43 Miguel Ojeda .07 .20
44 A.J. Pierzynski .07 .20
45 Carlos Lee .07 .20
46 LaTroy Hawkins .07 .20
47 Nick Green .07 .20
48 Shawn Estes .07 .20
49 Eli Marrero .07 .20
50 Jeff Kent .07 .20
51 Joe Randa .07 .20
52 Jose Hernandez .07 .20
53 Joe Blanton .07 .20
54 Huston Street .10 .30
55 Marlon Byrd .07 .20
56 Alex Sanchez .07 .20
57 Livan Hernandez .07 .20
58 Chris Young .07 .20
59 Brad Eldred .07 .20
60 Terrence Long .07 .20
61 Phil Nevin .07 .20
62 Kyle Farnsworth .07 .20
63 Jon Lieber .07 .20
64 Antonio Alfonseca .07 .20
65 Tony Graffanino .07 .20
66 Tadahito Iguchi RC .60 1.50
67 Brad Thompson .07 .20
68 Jose Vidro .07 .20
69 Jason Phillips .07 .20
70 Carl Pavano .07 .20
71 Pokey Reese .07 .20
72 Jerome Williams .07 .20
73 Kazuhisa Ishii .07 .20
74 Zach Day .07 .20
75 Edgar Renteria .07 .20
76 Mike Myers .07 .20
77 Jeff Cirillo .07 .20
78 Endy Chavez .07 .20
79 Jose Guillen .07 .20
80 Ugueth Urbina .07 .20
81 Vinny Castilla .07 .20
82 Javier Vazquez .07 .20
83 Willy Taveras .07 .20
84 Mark Mulder .07 .20
85 Mike Hargrove MG .07 .20
86 Buddy Bell MG .07 .20
87 Charlie Manuel MG .07 .20
88 Willie Randolph MG .07 .20
89 Bob Melvin MG .07 .20
90 Chris Lambert PROS .20 .50
91 Homer Bailey PROS .20 .50
92 Ervin Santana PROS .20 .50
93 Bill Bray PROS .20 .50
94 Thomas Diamond PROS .20 .50
95 Trevor Plouffe PROS .20 .50
96 James Houser PROS .20 .50
97 Jake Stevens PROS .20 .50
98 Anthony Whittington PROS .20 .50
99 Philip Hughes PROS .20 .50
100 Greg Golson PROS .20 .50
101 Paul Maholm PROS .20 .50
102 Carlos Quentin PROS .20 .50
103 Dan Johnson PROS .20 .50
104 Mark Rogers PROS .20 .50
105 Neil Walker PROS .20 .50
106 Omar Quintanilla PROS .20 .50
107 Blake DeWitt PROS .20 .50
108 Taylor Tankersley PROS .20 .50
109 David Murphy PROS .20 .50
110 Felix Hernandez PROS .40 1.00
111 Craig Biggio HL .07 .20
112 Greg Maddux HL .20 .50
113 Bobby Abreu HL .07 .20
114 Alex Rodriguez HL .20 .50
115 Trevor Hoffman HL .07 .20
116 A.J. Pierzynski .20 .50
Tadahito Iguchi ALDS
117 Reggie Sanders NLDS .20 .50
118 Bengie Molina .20 .50
Ervin Santana ALDS
119 Chris Burke .20 .50
Lance Berkman
Adam LaRoche NLDS
120 Garret Anderson ALCS .20 .50
121 A.J. Pierzynski ALCS .20 .50
122 Paul Konerko ALCS .20 .50
123 Joe Crede ALCS .20 .50
124 Mark Buehrle .20 .50
Jon Garland ALCS
125 Freddy Garcia .20 .50
Jose Contreras ALCS
126 Reggie Sanders NLCS .20 .50
127 Roy Oswalt NLCS .20 .50
128 Roger Clemens NLCS .40 1.00
129 Albert Pujols NLCS .40 1.00
130 Roy Oswalt NLCS .20 .50
131 Joe Crede .30 .75
Bobby Jenks WS
132 Paul Konerko .30 .75
Scott Podsednik WS
133 Geoff Blum WS .20 .50
134 White Sox Sweep WS .40 1.00
135 Alex Rodriguez .20 .50
David Ortiz
Manny Ramirez AL HR
136 Michael Young .10 .30
Alex Rodriguez
Vladimir Guerrero AL BA
137 David Ortiz .10 .30
Mark Teixeira
Manny Ramirez AL RBI
138 Bartolo Colon .07 .20
Jon Garland
Cliff Lee AL Wins
139 Kevin Millwood .10 .30
Johan Santana
Mark Buehrle AL ERA
140 Johan Santana .10 .30
Randy Johnson
John Lackey AL K's
141 Andruw Jones .20 .50
Derrek Lee
Albert Pujols NL HR
142 Derrek Lee .20 .50
Albert Pujols
Miguel Cabrera NL BA
143 Andruw Jones .20 .50
Albert Pujols
Pat Burrell NL RBI
144 Dontrelle Willis .07 .20
Chris Carpenter
Roy Oswalt NL Wins
145 Roger Clemens .20 .50
Andy Pettitte
Dontrelle Willis NL ERA
146 Jake Peavy .07 .20
Chris Carpenter
Pedro Martinez NL K's
147 Mark Teixeira AS .07 .20
148 Brian Roberts AS .07 .20
149 Michael Young AS .07 .20
150 Alex Rodriguez AS .20 .50
151 Johnny Damon AS .07 .20
152 Vladimir Guerrero AS .10 .30
153 Manny Ramirez AS .07 .20
154 David Ortiz AS .10 .30
155 Mariano Rivera AS .10 .30
156 Joe Nathan AS .07 .20
157 Albert Pujols AS .20 .50
158 Jeff Kent AS .07 .20
159 Felipe Lopez AS .07 .20
160 Morgan Ensberg AS .07 .20
161 Miguel Cabrera AS .07 .20
162 Ken Griffey Jr. AS .20 .50
163 Andruw Jones AS .07 .20
164 Paul Lo Duca AS .07 .20
165 Chad Cordero AS .07 .20
166 Ken Griffey Jr. Comeback .20 .50
167 Jason Giambi Comeback .07 .20
168 Willy Taveras ROY .07 .20
169 Huston Street ROY .07 .20
170 Chris Carpenter AS .07 .20
171 Bartolo Colon AS .07 .20
172 Bobby Cox AS MG .07 .20
173 Ozzie Guillen AS MG .20 .50
174 Andruw Jones POY .07 .20
175 Johnny Damon AS .07 .20
176 Alex Rodriguez AS .20 .50
177 David Ortiz AS .10 .30
178 Manny Ramirez AS .07 .20
179 Miguel Tejada AS .07 .20
180 Vladimir Guerrero AS .10 .30
181 Mark Teixeira AS .07 .20
182 Ivan Rodriguez AS .07 .20
183 Brian Roberts AS .07 .20
184 Mark Buehrle AS .07 .20
185 Bobby Abreu AS .07 .20
186 Carlos Beltran AS .07 .20
187 Albert Pujols AS .20 .50
188 Derrek Lee AS .07 .20
189 Jim Edmonds AS .07 .20
190 Aramis Ramirez AS .07 .20
191 Mike Piazza AS .10 .30
192 Jeff Kent AS .07 .20
193 David Eckstein AS .07 .20
194 Chris Carpenter AS .07 .20
195 Bobby Abreu HR .07 .20
196 Ivan Rodriguez HR .07 .20
197 Carlos Lee HR .07 .20
198 David Ortiz HR .10 .30
199 Hee-Seop Choi HR .07 .20
200 Andruw Jones HR .07 .20
201 Mark Teixeira HR .07 .20
202 Jason Bay HR .07 .20
203 Hanley Ramirez FUT .20 .50
204 Shin-Soo Choo FUT .20 .50
205 Justin Huber FUT .20 .50
206 Nelson Cruz FUT RC .50 1.25
207 Edwin Encarnacion FUT .20 .50
208 Miguel Montero FUT RC .50 1.25
209 William Bergolla FUT .20 .50
210 Luis Montanez FUT .20 .50
211 Francisco Liriano FUT .60 1.50
212 Kevin Thompson FUT .20 .50
213 B.J. Upton FUT .20 .50
214 Conor Jackson FUT .20 .50
215 Delmon Young FUT .20 .50
216 Andy LaRoche FUT .40 1.00
217 Ryan Garko FUT .50 1.25
218 Josh Barfield FUT .20 .50
219 Chris B.Young FUT .20 .50
220 Justin Verlander FUT .60 1.50
221 Drew Anderson FY RC .20 .50
222 Luis Hernandez FY RC .20 .50
223 Jim Burt FY RC .20 .50
224 Mike Morse FY RC .20 .50
225 Elliot Johnson FY RC .20 .50
226 C.J. Smith FY RC .20 .50
227 Casey McGehee FY RC .20 .50
228 Brian Miller FY RC .20 .50
229 Chris Vines FY RC .20 .50
230 D.J. Houlton FY RC .20 .50
231 Chuck Tiffany FY RC .40 1.00
232 Humberto Sanchez FY RC .75 2.00
233 Baltazar Lopez FY RC .20 .50
234 Russ Martin FY RC 1.00 2.50
235 Dana Eveland FY RC .20 .50
236 Johan Silva FY RC .20 .50
237 Adam Harben FY RC .30 .75
238 Brian Bannister FY RC .40 1.00
239 Adam Boeve FY RC .20 .50
240 Thomas Oldham FY RC .20 .50
241 Cody Haerther FY RC .20 .50
242 Dan Santin FY RC .20 .50
243 Daniel Haigwood FY RC .30 .75
244 Craig Tatum FY RC .20 .50
245 Martin Prado FY RC .20 .50
246 Errol Simonitsch FY RC .30 .75
247 Lorenzo Scott FY RC .20 .50
248 Hayden Penn FY RC .30 .75
249 Heath Totten FY RC .20 .50
250 Nick Masset FY RC .20 .50
251 Pedro Lopez FY RC .20 .50
252 Ben Harrison FY .20 .50
253 Mike Spidale FY RC .20 .50
254 Jeremy Harts FY RC .20 .50
255 Danny Zell FY RC .20 .50
256 Kevin Collins FY RC .20 .50
257 Tony Arnerich FY RC .20 .50
258 Matt Albers FY RC .50 1.25
259 Ricky Barrett FY RC .20 .50
260 Hernan Iribarren FY RC .30 .75

261 Sean Tracey FY RC .20 .50
262 Jerry Owens FY RC .30 .75
263 Steve Nelson FY RC .20 .50
264 Brandon McCarthy FY RC .40 1.00
265 David Shepard FY RC .20 .50
266 Steven Bondurant FY RC .20 .50
267 Billy Sadler FY RC .20 .50
268 Ryan Feierabend FY RC .20 .50
269 Stuart Pomeranz FY RC .20 .50
270 Shaun Marcum FY .20 .50
271 Erik Schindewolf FY RC .20 .50
272 Stefan Bailie FY RC .20 .50
273 Mike Esposito FY RC UER .20 .50
Photo is Darwinson Salazar
274 Buck Coats FY RC .20 .50
275 Andy Sides FY RC .20 .50
276 Micah Schnurstein FY RC .20 .50
277 Jesse Gutierrez FY RC .20 .50
278 Jake Postlewait FY RC .20 .50
279 Willy Mota FY RC .20 .50
280 Ryan Speier FY RC .20 .50
281 Frank Mata FY RC .20 .50
282 Jair Jurrjens FY RC .60 1.50
283 Nick Touchstone FY RC .20 .50
284 Matthew Kemp FY RC 1.25 3.00
285 Vinny Rottino FY RC .20 .50
286 J.B. Thurmond FY RC .20 .50
287 Kelvin Pichardo FY RC .20 .50
288 Scott Mitchinson FY RC .20 .50
289 Darwinson Salazar FY RC .20 .50
290 George Kottaras FY RC .30 .75
291 Kenny Durost FY RC .20 .50
292 Jonathan Sanchez FY RC .50 1.25
293 Brandon Moorhead FY RC .20 .50
294 Kennard Bibbs FY RC .20 .50
295 David Gassner FY RC .20 .50
296 Micah Furtado FY RC .20 .50
297 Ismael Ramirez FY RC .20 .50
298 Carlos Gonzalez FY RC 1.00 1.50
299 Brandon Sing FY RC .30 .75
300 Jason Motte FY RC .20 .50
301 Chuck James FY RC .50 1.25
302 Andy Santana FY RC .20 .50
303 Manny Parra FY RC .15 .40
304 Chris B.Young FY RC .50 1.25
305 Juan Senreiso FY RC .20 .50
306 Franklin Morales FY RC .30 .75
307 Jared Gothreaux FY RC .20 .50
308 Jayce Tingler FY RC .20 .50
309 Matt Brown FY RC .20 .50
310 Frank Diaz FY RC .20 .50
311 Stephen Drew DP RC 1.50 4.00
312 Jered Weaver DP RC 1.50 4.00
313 Ryan Braun DP RC 5.00 12.00
314 John Mayberry Jr. DP RC .40 1.00
315 Aaron Thompson DP RC .30 .75
316 Cesar Carrillo DP RC .40 1.00
317 Jacoby Ellsbury DP RC 6.00 15.00
318 Matt Garza DP RC 1.00 2.50
319 Cliff Pennington DP RC .30 .75
320 Colby Rasmus DP RC 2.50 6.00
321 Chris Volstad DP RC .40 1.00
322 Ricky Romero DP RC .30 .75
323 Ryan Zimmerman DP RC 2.00 5.00
324 C.J. Henry DP RC .60 1.50
325 Jay Bruce DP RC 5.00 12.00
326 Beau Jones DP RC .40 1.00
327 Mark McCormick DP RC .30 .75
328 Eli Iorg DP RC .30 .75
329 Andrew McCutchen DP RC .75 2.00
330 Mike Costanzo DP RC .50 1.25

2005 Topps Update Blue

ODDS 1:8035 H, 1:2341 HTA, 1:8035 R
STATED PRINT RUN 1 SERIAL #'d SET
NO PRICING DUE TO SCARCITY

2005 Topps Update Box Bottoms

*BOX BOTTOM: 1X TO 2.5X BASIC
*BOX BOTTOM: .6X TO 1.5X BASIC RC
ONE FOUR-CARD SHEET PER HTA BOX
CL: 1/10/20/22/25/45/50/57/70/84/110
CL: 224/264/311-313

2005 Topps Update Gold

*GOLD 1-89: 6X TO 15X BASIC
*GOLD 90-110: 2X TO 5X BASIC
*GOLD 111-115/135-202: 6X TO 15X BASIC
*GOLD: 116-134: 3X TO 8X BASIC
*GOLD: 203-220: 2X TO 5X BASIC
*GOLD 14/66/221-310: 2X TO 5X BASIC
*GOLD 311-330: 2X TO 5X BASIC
STATED ODDS 1:4 H, 1:1 HTA, 1:4 R
STATED PRINT RUN 2005 SERIAL #'d SETS
2 Jeff Francoeur 5.00 12.00
325 Jay Bruce DP 12.50 30.00

2005 Topps Update All-Star Patches

STATED ODDS 1:910 H, 1:268 HTA, 1:910 R
PRINT RUNS B/WN 20-70 COPIES PER

NO PRICING ON QTY OF 25 OR LESS
AJ Andruw Jones/70 12.50 30.00
AP Albert Pujols/35 30.00 60.00
AR Alex Rodriguez/50 15.00 40.00
ARA Aramis Ramirez/60 10.00 25.00
BA Bobby Abreu/65 10.00 25.00
BC Bartolo Colon/60 10.00 25.00
BL Brad Lidge/65 10.00 25.00
BR Brian Roberts/25
BW Billy Wagner/50 10.00 25.00
CB Carlos Beltran/60 10.00 25.00
CC Chris Carpenter/70 10.00 25.00
CCO Chad Cordero/65 6.00 15.00
CL Carlos Lee/65 10.00 25.00
DE David Eckstein/65 12.50 30.00
DL Derrek Lee/65 12.50 30.00
DO David Ortiz/70 12.50 30.00
DW Dontrelle Willis/60 10.00 25.00
FL Felipe Lopez/35 8.00 20.00
GS Gary Sheffield/50 10.00 25.00
IR Ivan Rodriguez/25
IS Ichiro Suzuki/50 20.00 50.00
JB Jason Bay/50 10.00 25.00
JD Johnny Damon/60 12.50 30.00
JE Jim Edmonds/50 10.00 25.00
JG Jon Garland/70 12.50 30.00
JI Jason Isringhausen/65 10.00 25.00
JK Jeff Kent/65 10.00 25.00
JN Joe Nathan/65 6.00 15.00
JP Jake Peavy/60 10.00 25.00
JS Johan Santana/60 12.50 30.00
JSM John Smoltz/65 12.50 30.00
KR Kenny Rogers/50 6.00 15.00
LC Luis Castillo/20
LG Luis Gonzalez/70 10.00 25.00
LH Livan Hernandez/50 10.00 25.00
MA Moises Alou/65 6.00 15.00
MB Mark Buehrle/60 10.00 25.00
MC Miguel Cabrera/70 12.50 30.00
MCL Matt Clement/70 10.00 25.00
ME Morgan Ensberg/60 10.00 25.00
MM Melvin Mora/30 12.50 30.00
MP Mike Piazza/50 15.00 40.00
MR Manny Ramirez/65 12.50 30.00
MRI Mariano Rivera/65 15.00 40.00
MT Miguel Tejada/60 10.00 25.00
MTE Mark Teixeira/60 12.50 30.00
MY Michael Young/50 10.00 25.00
PK Paul Konerko/70 10.00 25.00
RO Roy Oswalt/60 10.00 25.00
SP Scott Podsednik/65 10.00 25.00

2005 Topps Update All-Star Stitches

GROUP A ODDS 1:131 H, 1:81 HTA, 1:127 R
GROUP B ODDS 1:91 H, 1:45 HTA, 1:91 R
GROUP C ODDS 1:100 H, 1:41 HTA, 1:100 R
GROUP D ODDS 1:109 H, 1:34 HTA, 1:109 R
GROUP E ODDS 1:98 H, 1:29 HTA, 1:98 R
GROUP F ODDS 1:272 H, 1:89 HTA, 1:272 R
AJ Andruw Jones C 4.00 10.00
AP Albert Pujols E 8.00 20.00
AR Alex Rodriguez D 6.00 15.00
ARA Aramis Ramirez E 3.00 8.00
BA Bobby Abreu B 3.00 8.00
BC Bartolo Colon D 3.00 8.00
BL Brad Lidge D 3.00 8.00
BR Brian Roberts C 3.00 8.00
BW Billy Wagner C 3.00 8.00
CB Carlos Beltran D 3.00 8.00
CC Chris Carpenter E 4.00 10.00
CCO Chad Cordero D 3.00 8.00
CL Carlos Lee E 3.00 8.00
DE David Eckstein B 6.00 15.00
DL Derrek Lee F 4.00 10.00
DO David Ortiz E 4.00 10.00
DW Dontrelle Willis F 3.00 8.00
FL Felipe Lopez B 3.00 8.00
GS Gary Sheffield D 3.00 8.00
IR Ivan Rodriguez A 4.00 10.00
IS Ichiro Suzuki A 8.00 20.00
JB Jason Bay C 3.00 8.00
JD Johnny Damon B 4.00 10.00
JE Jim Edmonds A 3.00 8.00
JG Jon Garland E 4.00 10.00
JI Jason Isringhausen E 3.00 8.00
JK Jeff Kent C 3.00 8.00
JN Joe Nathan D 3.00 8.00
JP Jake Peavy D 3.00 8.00
JS Johan Santana C 4.00 10.00
JSM John Smoltz D 4.00 10.00
KR Kenny Rogers A 3.00 8.00
LC Luis Castillo B 3.00 8.00
LG Luis Gonzalez C 3.00 8.00
LH Livan Hernandez F 3.00 8.00
MA Moises Alou C 3.00 8.00
MB Mark Buehrle B 3.00 8.00
MC Miguel Cabrera E 4.00 10.00
MCL Matt Clement B 3.00 8.00
ME Morgan Ensberg B 3.00 8.00
MM Melvin Mora B 3.00 8.00
MP Mike Piazza E 4.00 10.00
MR Manny Ramirez E 4.00 10.00
MRI Mariano Rivera B 4.00 10.00
MT Miguel Tejada B 3.00 8.00
MTE Mark Teixeira C 4.00 10.00
MY Michael Young A 3.00 8.00
PK Paul Konerko A 3.00 8.00
RO Roy Oswalt A 3.00 8.00
SP Scott Podsednik A 6.00 15.00

2005 Topps Update Barry Bonds Home Run History

SEE 05 TOPPS BONDS HRH FOR PRICING

2005 Topps Update Derby Digs Jersey Relics

STATED ODDS 1:3320 H,1:637 HTA,1:3320 R
STATED PRINT RUN 100 SERIAL #'d SETS
AJ Andruw Jones 10.00 25.00
BA Bobby Abreu 10.00 25.00
CL Carlos Lee 6.00 15.00
DO David Ortiz 10.00 25.00
IR Ivan Rodriguez 10.00 25.00
JB Jason Bay 6.00 15.00
MT Mark Teixeira 10.00 25.00

2005 Topps Update Hall of Fame Bat Relics

A ODDS 1:6406 H, 1:2012 HTA, 1:6406 R
B ODDS 1:1860 H, 1:548 HTA, 1:1860 R
RS Ryne Sandberg B 8.00 20.00
WB Wade Boggs A 6.00 15.00

2005 Topps Update Hall of Fame Dual Bat Relic

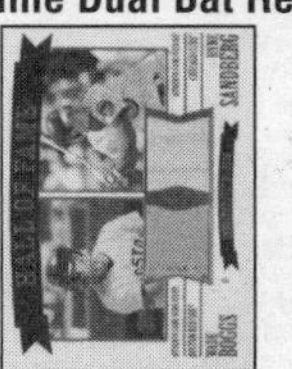

ODDS 1:13,392 H, 1:3815 HTA, 1:13,392 R
STATED PRINT RUN 200 SERIAL #'d CARDS
BS Wade Boggs 12.50 30.00
Ryne Sandberg

2005 Topps Update Legendary Sacks Relics

STATED ODDS 1:965 H, 1:281 HTA, 1:965 R
STATED PRINT RUN 300 SERIAL #'d SETS
CARDS FEATURE CELEBRITY JSY SWATCH
AD Andre Dawson 6.00 15.00
BJ Bo Jackson 10.00 25.00
DW Dave Winfield 6.00 15.00
HR Harold Reynolds 6.00 15.00
JA Jim Abbott 6.00 15.00
LW Lou Whitaker 6.00 15.00
MF Mark Fidrych 10.00 25.00
OS Ozzie Smith 10.00 25.00
RF Rollie Fingers 6.00 15.00

2005 Topps Update Midsummer Covers Ball Relics

STATED ODDS 1:524 H, 1:512 HTA
STATED PRINT RUN 150 SERIAL #'d SETS

AP Albert Pujols 20.00 50.00
AR Alex Rodriguez 15.00 40.00
BR Brian Roberts 10.00 25.00
CB Carlos Beltran 10.00 25.00
DL Derrek Lee 15.00 40.00
DW Dontrelle Willis 10.00 25.00
IS Ichiro Suzuki 30.00 60.00
MT Miguel Tejada 10.00 25.00
RC Roger Clemens 15.00 40.00
VG Vladimir Guerrero 15.00 40.00

2005 Topps Update Signature Moves

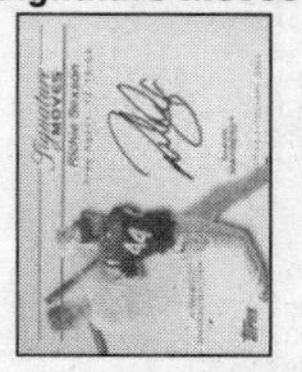

A ODDS 1:317,088H,1:103,008HTA,1:40,176R
B ODDS 1:126,836 H,1:51,504 HTA,1:40,176 R
C ODDS 1:1220 H, 1:339 HTA, 1:1220 R
D ODDS 1:1128 H, 1:323 HTA, 1:1128 R
E ODDS 1:916 H, 1:262 HTA, 1:916 R
GROUP A PRINT RUN 15 #'d CARDS
GROUP B PRINT RUN 25 #'d CARDS
GROUP C PRINT RUN 275 #'d SETS
GROUP D PRINT RUN 475 #'d SETS
NO GROUP A-B PRICING DUE TO SCARCITY
RED ODDS 1:6676 H, 1:1908 HTA, 1:6676 R
RED FOIL PRINT RUN 25 SERIAL #'d SETS
NO RED FOIL PRICING DUE TO SCARCITY
BB Barry Bonds A/15
BL Bobby Livingston D/475 6.00 15.00
BS Benito Santiago E 8.00 20.00
CJS C.J. Smith D/475 6.00 15.00
GK George Kottaras D/475 8.00 20.00
GP Glen Perkins C/275 8.00 20.00
HS Humberto Sanchez E 10.00 25.00
JP Jake Postlewait C/275 6.00 15.00
JV Justin Verlander C/275 15.00 40.00
KI Kazuhisa Ishii C/275 10.00 25.00
MA Matt Albers D/475 6.00 15.00
MM Mark Mulder C/275 10.00 25.00
PM Pedro Martinez B/25
RS Richie Sexson C/275 10.00 25.00
TC Travis Chick D/475 6.00 15.00
TG Troy Glaus C/275 10.00 25.00
TH Tim Hudson C/275 10.00 25.00
TW Tony Womack E 8.00 20.00

2005 Topps Update Touch Em All Base Relics

STATED ODDS 1:238 H, 1:77 HTA, 1:238 R
STATED PRINT RUN 1000 SERIAL #'d SETS
AP Albert Pujols 10.00 25.00
AR Alex Rodriguez 8.00 20.00
DL Derrek Lee 6.00 15.00
DO David Ortiz 6.00 15.00
GS Gary Sheffield 4.00 10.00
IR Ivan Rodriguez 6.00 15.00
IS Ichiro Suzuki 10.00 25.00
MR Manny Ramirez 6.00 15.00
MT Miguel Tejada 4.00 10.00
VG Vladimir Guerrero 6.00 15.00

2005 Topps Update Washington Nationals Inaugural Lineup

COMPLETE SET (10) 6.00 15.00
STATED ODDS 1:10 H, 1:4 HTA, 1:10 R
BS Brian Schneider .75 2.00
BW Brad Wilkerson .75 2.00
CG Cristian Guzman .75 2.00
JG Jose Guillen .75 2.00
JV Jose Vidro .75 2.00
LH Livan Hernandez .75 2.00
NJ Nick Johnson .75 2.00
TS Termel Sledge .75 2.00
VC Vinny Castilla .75 2.00
TEAM Team Photo .75 2.00

2005 Topps Update Washington Nationals Inaugural Lineup Ball Relics

These exceedingly scarce cards (only five serial #'d sets issued) each feature a swatch of leather material derived from a ball actually used at the first home game played for the 2005 season of the Washington Nationals. The checklist features the eight position players in the starting lineup in addition to Opening Day starting pitcher Livan Hernandez. Finally, a tenth card featuring a photo of the entire starting lineup standing on the base line as they're being introduced rounds out the 10-card set.

ODDS 1:49,104 H, 1:14,715 HTA, 1:40,176 R
STATED PRINT RUN 5 SERIAL #'d SETS
NO PRICING DUE TO SCARCITY
BS Brian Schneider
BW Brad Wilkerson
CG Cristian Guzman
JG Jose Guillen
JV Jose Vidro
LH Livan Hernandez
NJ Nick Johnson
TS Termel Sledge
VC Vinny Castilla
TEAM Team Photo

2005 Topps 1955 National

Each collector who purchased a VIP ticket for the 2005 Sports Collectors National Convention in Chicago received this four-card set of 1955 stars who were not issued in the original set. The card numbers assigned matched those numbers not used in the original 1955 Topps set and the card size matches the original 1955 measurements.

COMPLETE SET (4)
175 Stan Musial 6.00 15.00
186 Whitey Ford 5.00 12.00
203 Bob Feller 4.00 10.00
209 Herb Score 1.25 3.00

2005 Topps XXL Cubs

ONE 4-CARD SET PER PACK
1 Derrek Lee 1.00 2.50
2 Mark Prior 1.00 2.50
3 Nomar Garciaparra 1.25 3.00
4 Greg Maddux 1.50 4.00

2005 Topps XXL Red Sox

COMPLETE SET (4)
ONE 4-CARD SET PER PACK
1 David Ortiz 1.25 3.00
2 Manny Ramirez 1.25 3.00
3 Johnny Damon 1.25 3.00
4 Curt Schilling 1.25 3.00

2005 Topps XXL Yankees

COMPLETE SET (4)
ONE 4-CARD SET PER PACK
1 Alex Rodriguez 1.25 3.00
2 Derek Jeter 1.50 4.00
3 Hideki Matsui 1.00 2.50
4 Randy Johnson .75 2.00

2006 Topps Pre-Production

This three-card set was released to hobby dealers and media in January, 2006 to preview the upcoming 2006 Topps Series I product.

COMPLETE SET (3) .75 2.00
3-CARD SETS MAILED TO HOBBY DEALERS
PP1 Ichiro Suzuki .40 1.00
PP2 Alex Rodriguez .40 1.00
PP3 Albert Pujols .40 1.00

2006 Topps

This 659-card set was issued over two series. The first series was released in February, 2006 and the second series was released in June, 2006. The cards were issued in a myriad of forms including 10-card hobby packs with an $1.59 SRP which came 36 packs to a box and 10 boxes to a case. Retail packs consisted of 12-card packs with an $1.99 SRP and those cards came 24 packs to a box and 20 boxes to a case. There were also rack packs which had 18 cards and a $2.99 SRP and those packs came 24 packs to a box and three boxes to a case. There were also special packs issued for Target and Walmart. Card number 297, Alex Gordon, was pulled from circulation almost immediately, although a few copies in various forms of production were located in packs. In addition, Pete Mackanin and John Koronka cards were changed for the factory sets. This product has many sub sets including Award Winners (243-265); Managers/Team Cards (266-295, 586-615); Rookies (296-330), 616-645), Team Stars (326-330). Assorted Multi-Player Cards (646-660). A few Alay Soler cards were inserted into series two packs unannounced and those cards are very scarce.

COMP.HOBBY SET (664) 50.00 80.00
COMP.HOLIDAY SET (659) 50.00 80.00
COMP.CARDINALS SET (664) 50.00 80.00
COMP.CUBS SET (664) 50.00 80.00
COMP.PIRATES SET (664) 50.00 80.00
COMP.RED SOX SET (664) 50.00 80.00
COMP.YANKEES SET (664) 50.00 80.00
COMPLETE SET (659) 30.00 80.00
COMPLETE SERIES 1 (329) 15.00 40.00
COMPLETE SERIES 2 (330) 15.00 40.00
COMMON CARD (1-660) .07 .20
COMP.SER.1 SET EXCLUDES CARD 297
CARD 297 NOT INTENDED FOR RELEASE
CARDS 287b AND 312b ISSUED IN FACT.SET
2 TICKETS EXCH.CARD RANDOM IN PACKS
OVERALL PLATE SER.1 ODDS 1:246 HTA
OVERALL PLATE SER.2 ODDS 1:193 HTA
PLATE PRINT RUN 1 SET PER COLOR
BLACK-CYAN-MAGENTA-YELLOW ISSUED
NO PLATE PRICING DUE TO SCARCITY
1 Alex Rodriguez .30 .75
2 Jose Valentin .07 .20
3 Garrett Atkins .07 .20
4 Scott Hatteberg .07 .20
5 Carl Crawford .07 .20
6 Armando Benitez .07 .20
7 Mickey Mantle UER 3.00 8.00
High single home run season credited to wrong year
Length of longest homer in cartoon is also wrong
8 Mike Morse .07 .20
9 Damian Miller .07 .20
10 Clint Barmes .07 .20
11 Michael Barrett .07 .20
12 Coco Crisp .07 .20
13 Tadahito Iguchi .07 .20
14 Chris Snyder .07 .20
15 Brian Roberts .07 .20
16 David Wright .30 .75
17 Victor Santos .07 .20
18 Trevor Hoffman .07 .20
19 Jeremy Reed .07 .20
20 Bobby Abreu .07 .20
21 Lance Berkman .07 .20
22 Zach Day .07 .20
23 Jonny Gomes .07 .20
24 Jason Marquis .07 .20
25 Chipper Jones .20 .50
26 Scott Hairston .07 .20
27 Ryan Dempster .07 .20
28 Brandon Inge .07 .20
29 Aaron Harang .07 .20
30 Jon Garland .07 .20
31 Pokey Reese .07 .20
32 Mike MacDougal .07 .20
33 Mike Lieberthal .07 .20
34 Cesar Izturis .07 .20
35 Brad Wilkerson .07 .20
36 Jeff Suppan .07 .20

37 Adam Everett .07 .20
38 Bengie Molina .07 .20
39 Rickie Weeks .07 .20
40 Jorge Posada .10 .30
41 Rheal Cormier .07 .20
42 Reed Johnson .07 .20
43 Laynce Nix .07 .20
44 Carl Everett .07 .20
45 Greg Maddux .30 .75
46 Jeff Francis .07 .20
47 Felipe Lopez .07 .20
48 Dan Johnson .07 .20
49 Humberto Cota .07 .20
50 Manny Ramirez .10 .30
51 Juan Uribe .07 .20
52 Jaret Wright .07 .20
53 Tomo Ohka .07 .20
54 Mike Matheny .07 .20
55 Joe Mauer .20 .50
56 Jarrod Washburn .07 .20
57 Randy Winn .07 .20
58 Pedro Feliz .07 .20
59 Kenny Rogers .07 .20
60 Rocco Baldelli .07 .20
61 Eric Hinske .07 .20
62 Damaso Marte .07 .20
Front lists him as a Pirate, back says White Sox
63 Desi Relaford .07 .20
64 Juan Encarnacion .07 .20
65 Nomar Garciaparra .20 .50
66 Shawn Estes .07 .20
67 Brian Jordan .07 .20
68 Steve Kline .07 .20
69 Braden Looper .07 .20
70 Carlos Lee .07 .20
71 Tom Glavine .10 .30
72 Craig Biggio .10 .30
73 Steve Finley .07 .20
74 David Newhan .07 .20
75 Eric Gagne .07 .20
76 Tony Graffanino .07 .20
77 Dallas McPherson .07 .20
78 Nick Punto .07 .20
79 Mark Kotsay .07 .20
80 Kerry Wood .07 .20
81 Kyle Farnsworth .07 .20
82 Huston Street .07 .20
83 Endy Chavez .07 .20
84 So Taguchi .07 .20
85 Hank Blalock .07 .20
86 Brad Radke .07 .20
87 Chien-Ming Wang .30 .75
88 B.J. Surhoff .07 .20
89 Glendon Rusch .07 .20
90 Mark Buehrle .07 .20
91 Rafael Betancourt .07 .20
92 Lance Cormier .07 .20
93 Alex Gonzalez .07 .20
94 Matt Stairs .07 .20
95 Andy Pettitte .10 .30
96 Jesse Crain .07 .20
97 Kenny Lofton .07 .20
98 Geoff Blum .07 .20
99 Mark Redman .07 .20
100 Barry Bonds .40 1.00
101 Chad Orvella .07 .20
102 Xavier Nady .07 .20
103 Junior Spivey UER .07 .20
Card forgets to credit the 2nd Washington Senators term from 1961-71
104 Bernie Williams .10 .30
105 Victor Martinez .07 .20
106 Nook Logan .07 .20
107 Mark Teahen .07 .20
108 Mike Lamb .07 .20
109 Jayson Werth .07 .20
110 Mariano Rivera .20 .50
111 Erubiel Durazo .07 .20
112 Ryan Vogelsong .07 .20
113 Bobby Madritsch .07 .20
114 Travis Lee .07 .20
115 Adam Dunn .07 .20
116 David Riske .07 .20
117 Troy Percival .07 .20
118 Chad Tracy .07 .20
119 Andy Marte .07 .20
120 Edgar Renteria .07 .20
121 Jason Giambi .07 .20
122 Justin Morneau .07 .20
123 J.T. Snow .07 .20
124 Danys Baez .07 .20
125 Carlos Delgado .07 .20
126 John Buck .07 .20
127 Shannon Stewart .07 .20
128 Mike Cameron .07 .20
129 Joe McEwing .07 .20
130 Richie Sexson .07 .20
131 Rod Barajas .07 .20
132 Russ Adams .07 .20
133 J.D. Closser .07 .20
134 Ramon Ortiz .07 .20
135 Josh Beckett .07 .20
136 Ryan Freel .07 .20
137 Victor Zambrano .07 .20
138 Ronnie Belliard .07 .20
139 Jason Michaels .07 .20
140 Brian Giles .07 .20
141 Randy Wolf .07 .20
142 Robinson Cano .10 .30
143 Joe Blanton .07 .20
144 Esteban Loaiza .07 .20
145 Troy Glaus .07 .20
146 Matt Clement .07 .20
147 Geoff Jenkins .07 .20
148 John Thomson .07 .20
149 A.J. Pierzynski .07 .20
150 Pedro Martinez .10 .30
151 Roger Clemens .40 1.00
152 Jack Wilson .07 .20
153 Ray King .07 .20
154 Ryan Church .07 .20
155 Paul Lo Duca .07 .20
156 Dan Wheeler .07 .20
157 Carlos Zambrano .07 .20
158 Mike Timlin .07 .20
159 Brandon Claussen UER .07 .20
Cincinnati is misspelled in cartoon
160 Travis Hafner .07 .20
161 Chris Shelton .07 .20
162 Rafael Furcal .07 .20
163 Tom Gordon .07 .20
Listed as a Yankee but in a Phillies uniform
164 Noah Lowry .07 .20
165 Larry Walker .10 .30
166 Dave Roberts .07 .20
167 Scott Schoeneweis .07 .20
168 Julian Tavarez .07 .20
169 Jhonny Peralta .07 .20
170 Vernon Wells .07 .20
171 Jorge Cantu .07 .20
172 Todd Greene .07 .20
173 Willy Taveras .07 .20
174 Corey Patterson .07 .20
175 Ivan Rodriguez .10 .30
176 Bobby Kielty .07 .20
177 Jose Reyes .07 .20
178 Barry Zito .07 .20
179 Deivi Cruz .07 .20
180 Mark Teixeira .10 .30
181 Chone Figgins .07 .20
182 Aaron Rowand .07 .20
183 Tim Wakefield .07 .20
184 Mike Maroth .07 .20
185 Johnny Damon .10 .30
186 Vicente Padilla .07 .20
187 Ryan Klesko .07 .20
188 Gary Matthews .07 .20
189 Jose Mesa .07 .20
190 Nick Johnson .07 .20
191 Freddy Garcia .07 .20
192 Larry Bigbie UER .07 .20
Photo is Brian Roberts
193 Chris Ray .07 .20
194 Torii Hunter .07 .20
195 Mike Sweeney .07 .20
196 Brad Penny .07 .20
197 Jason Frasor .07 .20
198 Kevin Mench .07 .20
199 Adam Kennedy .07 .20
200 Albert Pujols .40 1.00
201 Jody Gerut .07 .20
202 Luis Gonzalez UER .07 .20
The wrong Luis Gonzalez's career stats are posted
203 Zack Greinke .07 .20
204 Miguel Cairo .07 .20
205 Jimmy Rollins .07 .20
206 Edgardo Alfonzo .07 .20
207 Billy Wagner .07 .20
208 B.J. Ryan .07 .20
209 Orlando Hudson .07 .20
210 Preston Wilson .07 .20
211 Melvin Mora .07 .20
212 Bill Mueller .07 .20
213 Javy Lopez .07 .20
214 Wilson Betemit .07 .20
215 Garret Anderson .07 .20
216 Russell Branyan .07 .20
217 Jeff Weaver .07 .20
218 Doug Mientkiewicz UER .07 .20
Final out of 2004 WS incorrectly described
219 Mark Ellis .07 .20
220 Jason Bay .07 .20
221 Adam LaRoche .07 .20
222 C.C. Sabathia .07 .20
223 Humberto Quintero .07 .20
224 Bartolo Colon .07 .20
225 Ichiro Suzuki UER .30 .75
Career Stats are all incorrect
226 Brett Tomko .07 .20
227 Corey Koskie .07 .20
228 David Eckstein .07 .20
229 Cristian Guzman .07 .20
230 Jeff Kent UER .07 .20
Credited with 1312 RBI's in 2005
231 Chris Capuano .07 .20
232 Rodrigo Lopez .07 .20
233 Jason Phillips .07 .20
234 Luis Rivas .07 .20
235 Cliff Floyd .07 .20
236 Gil Meche .07 .20
237 Adam Eaton .07 .20
238 Matt Morris .07 .20
239 Kyle Davies .07 .20
240 David Wells .07 .20
241 John Smoltz .10 .30
242 Felix Hernandez .20 .50
243 Kenny Rogers GG .07 .20
244 Mark Teixeira GG .07 .20
245 Orlando Hudson GG .07 .20
246 Derek Jeter GG .20 .50
247 Eric Chavez GG .07 .20
248 Torii Hunter GG .07 .20
249 Vernon Wells GG .07 .20
250 Ichiro Suzuki GG .20 .50
251 Greg Maddux GG .20 .50
252 Mike Matheny GG .07 .20
253 Derrek Lee GG .07 .20
254 Luis Castillo GG .07 .20
255 Omar Vizquel GG .07 .20
256 Mike Lowell GG .07 .20
257 Andruw Jones GG .07 .20
258 Jim Edmonds GG .07 .20
259 Bobby Abreu GG .07 .20
260 Bartolo Colon CY UER .07 .20
2005 record does not match between the front and the back
261 Chris Carpenter CY .07 .20
262 Alex Rodriguez MVP .20 .50
263 Albert Pujols MVP .20 .50
264 Huston Street ROY .07 .20
265 Ryan Howard ROY .15 .40
266 Bob Melvin MG .07 .20
267 Bobby Cox MG .07 .20
268 Baltimore Orioles TC .07 .20
269 Boston Red Sox TC .20 .50
270 Chicago White Sox TC .20 .50
271 Dusty Baker MG .07 .20
272 Jerry Narron MG .07 .20
273 Cleveland Indians TC .07 .20
274 Clint Hurdle MG .07 .20
275 Detroit Tigers TC .07 .20
276 Jack McKeon MG .07 .20
277 Phil Garner MG .07 .20
278 Kansas City Royals TC UER .07 .20
The stadium is pictured but not the team
279 Jim Tracy MG .07 .20
280 Los Angeles Angels TC .07 .20
281 Milwaukee Brewers TC .07 .20
282 Minnesota Twins TC .07 .20
283 Willie Randolph MG .07 .20
284 New York Yankees TC .20 .50
285 Oakland Athletics TC .07 .20
286 Charlie Manuel MG .07 .20
287a Pete Mackanin MG ERR .07 .20
Lloyd McClendon is pictured
287b Pete Mackanin MG COR .07 .20
288 Bruce Bochy MG .07 .20
289 Felipe Alou MG .07 .20
290 Seattle Mariners TC .07 .20
291 Tony LaRussa MG .07 .20
292 Tampa Bay Devil Rays TC .07 .20
293 Texas Rangers TC .07 .20
294 Toronto Blue Jays TC .07 .20
295 Frank Robinson MG .10 .30
296 Anderson Hernandez (RC) .20 .50
297A Alex Gordon (RC) Full 300.00 600.00
297B Alex Gordon Cut Out 60.00 120.00
297C Alex Gordon Blank Gold 30.00 60.00
297D Alex Gordon Blank Silver
298 Jason Botts (RC) .20 .50
299 Jeff Mathis (RC) .20 .50
300 Ryan Garko (RC) .20 .50
301 Charlton Jimerson (RC) .20 .50
302 Chris Denorfia (RC) .20 .50
303 Anthony Reyes (RC) .20 .50
304 Bryan Bullington (RC) .20 .50
305 Chuck James (RC) .20 .50
306 Danny Sandoval RC .20 .50
307 Walter Young (RC) .20 .50
308 Fausto Carmona (RC) .20 .50
309 Francisco Liriano (RC) .75 2.00
310 Hong-Chih Kuo (RC) .40 1.00
311 Joe Saunders (RC) .20 .50
312a John Koronka (RC) .20 .50
Pictured in Cubs uniform
312b John Koronka (RC) .20 .50
Pictured in Rangers uniform
313 Robert Andino RC .20 .50
314 Shaun Marcum (RC) .20 .50
315 Tom Gorzelanny (RC) .20 .50
316 Craig Breslow RC .20 .50
317 Chris DeMaria RC .20 .50
Front lists him as a Brewer, Back has him as a Royal
318 Brayan Pena (RC) .20 .50
319 Rich Hill (RC) .20 .50
320 Rick Short (RC) .20 .50
321 C.J. Wilson (RC) .20 .50
322 Marshall McDougall (RC) .20 .50
323 Darrell Rasner (RC) .20 .50
324 Brandon Watson (RC) .20 .50
325 Paul McAnulty (RC) .20 .50
326 Derek Jeter .40 1.00
Alex Rodriguez TS
327 Miguel Tejada .07 .20
Melvin Mora TS
328 Marcus Giles .10 .30
Chipper Jones TS
329 Manny Ramirez .20 .50
David Ortiz TS
330 Michael Barrett .20 .50
Greg Maddux TS
331 Matt Holliday .08 .25
332 Orlando Cabrera .07 .20
333 Ryan Langerhans .07 .20
334 Lew Ford .07 .20
335 Mark Prior .10 .30
336 Ted Lilly .07 .20
337 Michael Young .07 .20
338 Livan Hernandez .07 .20
339 Yadier Molina .07 .20
340 Eric Chavez .07 .20
341 Miguel Batista .07 .20
342 Bruce Chen .07 .20
343 Sean Casey .07 .20
344 Doug Davis .07 .20
345 Andruw Jones .10 .30
346 Hideki Matsui .20 .50
347 Joe Randa .07 .20
348 Reggie Sanders .07 .20
349 Jason Jennings .07 .20
350 Joe Nathan .07 .20
351 Jose Lopez .07 .20
352 John Lackey .07 .20
353 Claudio Vargas .07 .20
354 Grady Sizemore .10 .30
355 Jon Papelbon (RC) .75 2.00
356 Luis Matos .07 .20
357 Orlando Hernandez .07 .20
358 Jamie Moyer .07 .20
359 Chase Utley .20 .50
360 Moises Alou .07 .20
361 Chad Cordero .07 .20
362 Brian McCann .07 .20
363 Jermaine Dye .07 .20
364 Ryan Madson .07 .20
365 Aramis Ramirez .07 .20
366 Matt Treanor .07 .20
367 Ray Durham .07 .20
368 Khalil Greene .10 .30
369 Mike Hampton .07 .20
370 Mike Mussina .10 .30
371 Brad Hawpe .07 .20
372 Marlon Byrd .07 .20
373 Woody Williams .07 .20
374 Victor Diaz .07 .20
375 Brady Clark .07 .20
376 Luis Gonzalez .07 .20
377 Raul Ibanez .07 .20
378 Tony Clark .07 .20
379 Shawn Chacon .07 .20
380 Marcus Giles .07 .20
381 Odalis Perez .07 .20
382 Steve Trachsel .07 .20
383 Russ Ortiz .07 .20
384 Toby Hall .07 .20
385 Bill Hall .07 .20
386 Luke Hudson .07 .20
387 Ken Griffey Jr. .30 .75
388 Tim Hudson .07 .20
389 Brian Moehler .07 .20
390 Jake Peavy .07 .20
391 Casey Blake .07 .20
392 Sidney Ponson .07 .20
393 Brian Schneider .07 .20
394 J.J. Hardy .07 .20
395 Austin Kearns .07 .20
396 Pat Burrell .07 .20
397 Jason Vargas .07 .20
398 Ryan Howard .30 .75
399 Joe Crede .07 .20
400 Vladimir Guerrero .20 .50
401 Roy Halladay .07 .20
402 David Dellucci .07 .20
403 Brandon Webb .07 .20
404 Marlon Anderson .07 .20
405 Miguel Tejada .07 .20
406 Ryan Doumit .07 .20
407 Kevin Youkilis .07 .20
408 Jon Lieber .07 .20
409 Edwin Encarnacion .07 .20
410 Miguel Cabrera .10 .30
411 A.J. Burnett .07 .20
412 David Bell .07 .20
413 Gregg Zaun .07 .20
414 Lance Niekro .07 .20
415 Shawn Green .07 .20
416 Roberto Hernandez .07 .20
417 Jay Gibbons .07 .20
418 Johnny Estrada .07 .20
419 Omar Vizquel .10 .30
420 Gary Sheffield .07 .20
421 Brad Halsey .07 .20
422 Aaron Cook .07 .20
423 David Ortiz .20 .50
424 Tony Womack .07 .20
425 Joe Kennedy .07 .20
426 Dustin McGowan .07 .20
427 Carl Pavano .07 .20
428 Nick Green .07 .20
429 Francisco Cordero .07 .20
430 Octavio Dotel .07 .20
431 Julio Franco .07 .20
432 Brett Myers .07 .20
433 Casey Kotchman .07 .20
434 Frank Catalanotto .07 .20
435 Paul Konerko .07 .20
436 Keith Foulke .07 .20
437 Juan Rivera .07 .20
438 Todd Pratt .07 .20
439 Ben Broussard .07 .20
440 Scott Kazmir .10 .30
441 Rich Aurilia .07 .20
442 Craig Monroe .07 .20
443 Danny Kolb .07 .20
444 Curtis Granderson .07 .20
445 Jeff Francoeur .20 .50
446 Dustin Hermanson .07 .20
447 Jacque Jones .07 .20
448 Bobby Crosby .07 .20
449 Jason LaRue .07 .20
450 Derrek Lee .07 .20
451 Curt Schilling .10 .30
452 Jake Westbrook .07 .20
453 Daniel Cabrera .07 .20
454 Bobby Jenks .07 .20
455 Dontrelle Willis .07 .20
456 Brad Lidge .07 .20
457 Shea Hillenbrand .07 .20
458 Luis Castillo .07 .20
459 Mark Hendrickson .07 .20
460 Randy Johnson .20 .50
461 Placido Polanco .07 .20
462 Aaron Boone .07 .20
463 Todd Walker .07 .20
464 Nick Swisher .07 .20
465 Joel Pineiro .07 .20
466 Jay Payton .07 .20
467 Cliff Lee .07 .20
468 Johan Santana .10 .30
469 Josh Willingham .07 .20
470 Jeremy Bonderman .07 .20
471 Runelvys Hernandez .07 .20
472 Duaner Sanchez .07 .20
473 Jason Lane .07 .20
474 Trot Nixon .07 .20
475 Ramon Hernandez .07 .20
476 Mike Lowell .07 .20
477 Chan Ho Park .07 .20
478 Doug Waechter .07 .20
479 Carlos Silva .07 .20
480 Jose Contreras .07 .20
481 Vinny Castilla .07 .20
482 Chris Reitsma .07 .20
483 Jose Guillen .07 .20
484 Aaron Hill .07 .20
485 Kevin Millwood .07 .20
486 Wily Mo Pena .07 .20
487 Rich Harden .07 .20
488 Chris Carpenter .07 .20
489 Jason Bartlett .07 .20
490 Magglio Ordonez .07 .20
491 John Rodriguez .07 .20
492 Bob Wickman .07 .20
493 Eddie Guardado .07 .20
494 Kip Wells .07 .20
495 Adrian Beltre .07 .20
496 Jose Capellan (RC) .20 .50
497 Scott Podsednik .07 .20
498 Brad Thompson .07 .20
499 Aaron Heilman .07 .20
500 Derek Jeter .50 1.25
501 Emil Brown .07 .20
502 Morgan Ensberg .07 .20
503 Nate Bump .07 .20
504 Phil Nevin .07 .20
505 Jason Schmidt .07 .20
506 Michael Cuddyer .07 .20
507 John Patterson .07 .20
508 Danny Haren .07 .20
509 Freddy Sanchez .07 .20
510 J.D. Drew .07 .20
511 Dmitri Young .07 .20
512 Eric Milton .07 .20
513 Ervin Santana .07 .20
514 Mark Loretta .07 .20
515 Mark Grudzielanek .07 .20
516 Derrick Turnbow .07 .20
517 Denny Bautista .07 .20
518 Lyle Overbay .07 .20
519 Julio Lugo .07 .20
520 Carlos Beltran .07 .20
521 Jose Cruz Jr. .07 .20
522 Jason Isringhausen .07 .20
523 Bronson Arroyo .07 .20
524 Ben Sheets .07 .20
525 Zach Duke .07 .20
526 Ryan Wagner .07 .20
527 Jose Vidro .07 .20
528 Doug Mirabelli .07 .20
529 Kris Benson .07 .20
530 Carlos Guillen .07 .20
531 Juan Pierre .07 .20
532 Scot Shields .07 .20
533 Scott Hatteberg .07 .20
534 Tim Stauffer .07 .20
535 Jim Edmonds .10 .30
536 Scot Eyre .07 .20
537 Ben Johnson .07 .20
538 Mark Mulder .07 .20
539 Juan Rincon .07 .20
540 Gustavo Chacin .07 .20
541 Oliver Perez .07 .20
542 Chris Young .07 .20
543 Edinson Volquez .07 .20
544 Mark Bellhorn .07 .20
545 Kelvim Escobar .07 .20
546 Andy Sisco .07 .20
547 Derek Lowe .07 .20
548 Sean Burroughs .07 .20
549 Erik Bedard .07 .20
550 Alfonso Soriano .07 .20
551 Matt Murton .07 .20
552 Eric Byrnes .07 .20
553 Chris Duffy .07 .20
554 Kazuo Matsui .07 .20
555 Scott Rolen .10 .30
556 Rob Mackowiak .07 .20
557 Chris Burke .07 .20
558 Jeromy Burnitz .07 .20
559 Jerry Hairston Jr. .07 .20
560 Jim Thome .10 .30
561 Miguel Olivo .07 .20
562 Jose Castillo .07 .20
563 Brad Ausmus .07 .20
564 Yorvit Torrealba .07 .20
565 David DeJesus .07 .20
566 Paul Byrd .07 .20
567 Brandon Backe .07 .20
568 Aubrey Huff .07 .20
569 Mike Jacobs .07 .20
570 Todd Helton .10 .30
571 Angel Berroa .07 .20
572 Todd Jones .07 .20
573 Jeff Bagwell .10 .30
574 Darin Erstad .07 .20
575 Roy Oswalt .07 .20
576 Rondell White .07 .20
577 Alex Rios .07 .20
578 Wes Helms .07 .20
579 Javier Vazquez .07 .20
580 Frank Thomas .20 .50
581 Brian Fuentes .07 .20
582 Francisco Rodriguez .07 .20
583 Craig Counsell .07 .20
584 Jorge Sosa .07 .20
585 Mike Piazza .20 .50
586 Mike Scioscia MG .07 .20
587 Joe Torre MG .10 .30
588 Ken Macha MG .07 .20
589 John Gibbons MG .07 .20
590 Joe Maddon MG .07 .20
591 Eric Wedge MG .07 .20
592 Mike Hargrove MG .07 .20
593 Sam Perlozzo MG .07 .20
594 Buck Showalter MG .07 .20
595 Terry Francona MG .07 .20
596 Buddy Bell MG .07 .20
597 Jim Leyland MG .07 .20
598 Ron Gardenhire MG .07 .20
599 Ozzie Guillen MG .07 .20
600 Ned Yost MG .07 .20
601 Atlanta Braves TC .10 .30
602 Philadelphia Phillies TC .07 .20
603 New York Mets TC .07 .20
604 Washington Nationals TC .07 .20
605 Florida Marlins TC .07 .20
606 Houston Astros TC .07 .20
607 Chicago Cubs TC .10 .30
608 St. Louis Cardinals TC .10 .30
609 Pittsburgh Pirates TC .07 .20
610 Cincinnati Reds TC .07 .20
611 Colorado Rockies TC .07 .20
612 Los Angeles Dodgers TC .07 .20
613 San Francisco Giants TC .07 .20
614 San Diego Padres TC .07 .20
615 Arizona Diamondbacks TC .07 .20
616 Kenji Johjima RC .75 2.00
617 Ryan Zimmerman (RC) 1.00 2.50
618 Craig Hansen RC .60 1.50
619 Joey Devine RC .20 .50
620 Hanley Ramirez (RC) .25 .60
621 Scott Olsen (RC) .20 .50
622 Jason Bergmann RC .20 .50
623 Geovany Soto (RC) .20 .50
624 J.J. Furmaniak (RC) .20 .50
625 Jeremy Accardo RC .20 .50
626 Mark Woodyard (RC) .20 .50
627 Matt Capps (RC) .20 .50
628 Tim Corcoran RC .20 .50
629 Ryan Jorgensen RC .20 .50
630 Ronny Paulino (RC) .20 .50
631 Dan Uggla (RC) .40 1.00
632 Ian Kinsler (RC) .25 .60
633 Josh Barfield (RC) .20 .50
634 Reggie Abercrombie (RC) .20 .50
635 Joel Zumaya (RC) .50 1.25
636 Matt Cain (RC) .30 .75
637 Conor Jackson (RC) .30 .75
638 Brian Anderson (RC) .20 .50
639 Prince Fielder (RC) .60 1.50
640 Jeremy Hermida (RC) .30 .75
641 Justin Verlander (RC) .60 1.50
642 Brian Bannister (RC) .20 .50
643 Willie Eyre (RC) .20 .50
644 Ricky Nolasco (RC) .20 .50
645 Paul Maholm (RC) .20 .50
646 Johnny Damon .10 .30
Jason Giambi
647 Rondell White .07 .20
Lew Ford UER
Michael Cuddyer is pictured
648 Orlando Hernandez .07 .20
Orlando Hudson
649 Adam Dunn .30 .75
Ken Griffey Jr.
650 Pat Burrell .07 .20
Mike Lieberthal
651 Jose Reyes .07 .20
Kaz Matsui
652 Hank Blalock .07 .20
Michael Young
653 Prince Fielder .30 .75
Rickie Weeks
654 Travis Lee .07 .20
Rocco Baldelli
655 Derrek Lee .07 .20
Aramis Ramirez
656 Grady Sizemore .10 .30
Aaron Boone
657 Luis Gonzalez .07 .20
Shawn Green
Koyie Hill
658 Ivan Rodriguez .10 .30
Carlos Guillen
659 Alex Rodriguez .30 .75
Gary Sheffield
660 Ervin Santana .07 .20
Francisco Rodriguez
RC1 Alay Soler 30.00 60.00
NNO 2 Tickets EXCH 8.00 20.00

2006 Topps Black

COMMON CARD (1-660) 10.00 25.00
SEMISTARS 15.00 30.00
UNLISTED STARS 20.00 40.00
SERIES 1 ODDS 1:18 HTA
SERIES 2 ODDS 1:14 HTA
STATED PRINT RUN 55 SERIAL #'d SETS
CARD 297 DOES NOT EXIST
1 Alex Rodriguez 50.00 100.00
7 Mickey Mantle 125.00 200.00
16 David Wright 30.00 60.00
45 Greg Maddux 40.00 80.00
87 Chien-Ming Wang 30.00 60.00
100 Barry Bonds 50.00 100.00
110 Mariano Rivera 30.00 60.00
151 Roger Clemens 60.00 120.00
200 Albert Pujols 60.00 120.00
225 Ichiro Suzuki 50.00 100.00
246 Derek Jeter GG 40.00 80.00
250 Ichiro Suzuki GG 25.00 50.00
262 Alex Rodriguez MVP 25.00 50.00
263 Albert Pujols MVP 30.00 60.00
309 Francisco Liriano 25.00 50.00
326 Derek Jeter 40.00 80.00
Alex Rodriguez TS
355 Jon Papelbon 25.00 50.00
387 Ken Griffey Jr. 40.00 80.00
398 Ryan Howard 30.00 60.00
500 Derek Jeter 75.00 150.00
616 Kenji Johjima 25.00 50.00
617 Ryan Zimmerman 30.00 60.00
618 Craig Hansen 15.00 40.00
631 Dan Uggla 25.00 50.00

2006 Topps Box Bottoms

ONE 4-CARD SHEET PER HTA BOX
1 Alex Rodriguez .75 2.00
16 David Wright .50 1.25
20 Bobby Abreu .20 .50
25 Chipper Jones .50 1.25
50 Manny Ramirez .30 .75
70 Carlos Lee .20 .50
90 Mark Buehrle .20 .50
100 Barry Bonds 1.50 4.00
115 Adam Dunn .20 .50
125 Carlos Delgado .20 .50
150 Pedro Martinez .30 .75
151 Roger Clemens 1.00 2.50
180 Mark Teixeira .30 .75
194 Torii Hunter .20 .50
200 Albert Pujols 1.00 2.50
225 Ichiro Suzuki .75 2.00
337 Michael Young .20 .50
345 Andruw Jones .30 .75
357 Orlando Hernandez .20 .50
390 Jake Peavy .20 .50
405 Miguel Tejada .20 .50
423 David Ortiz .50 1.25
450 Derrek Lee .20 .50
468 Johan Santana .30 .75
550 Alfonso Soriano .30 .75
560 Jim Thome .30 .75
570 Todd Helton .30 .75
599 Ozzie Guillen MG .20 .50
616 Kenji Johjima 1.25 3.00
637 Conor Jackson .30 .75
639 Prince Fielder .50 1.25
659 Alex Rodriguez .75 2.00
Gary Sheffield

2006 Topps Gold

*GOLD 1-295/326-615/646-660: 6X TO 15X
*GOLD 296-325/616-645: 2.5X TO 6X
SER.1 ODDS 1:15 HOB, 1:4 HTA, 1:26 MINI
SER.1 ODDS 1:8 RACK, 1:14 RET
SER.2 ODDS 1:11 HOB, 1:4 HTA, 1:21 MINI
SER.2 ODDS 1:6 RACK, 1:11 RET
STATED PRINT RUN 2006 SERIAL #'d SETS
CARD 297 DOES NOT EXIST
1 Alex Rodriguez 3.00 8.00
7 Mickey Mantle 10.00 25.00
45 Greg Maddux 3.00 8.00
100 Barry Bonds 4.00 10.00
151 Roger Clemens 4.00 10.00
200 Albert Pujols 4.00 10.00

225 Ichiro Suzuki 3.00 8.00
326 Derek Jeter 3.00 8.00
Alex Rodriguez TS
355 Jon Papelbon 6.00 15.00
500 Derek Jeter 5.00 12.00

2006 Topps Platinum

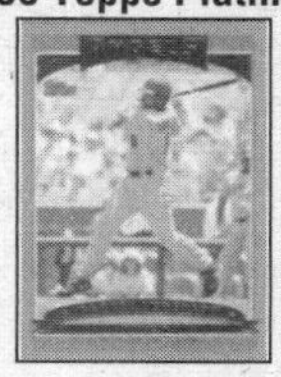

SER.1 ODDS 1:29,000 HOBBY, 1:9,930 HTA
SER.1 ODDS 1:52,000 MINI, 1:15,000 RACK
SER.1 ODDS 1:27,000 RETAIL
SER.2 ODDS 1:23,500 HOBBY, 1:14,000 HTA
SER.2 ODDS 1:35,000 MINI, 1:12,000 RACK
SER.2 ODDS 1:26,000 RETAIL
STATED PRINT RUN 1 SERIAL #'d SET
NO PRICING DUE TO SCARCITY
CARD 297 DOES NOT EXIST

2006 Topps 2K All-Stars

SER.1 ODDS 1:18 H, 1:18 HTA, 1:18 MINI
SER.1 ODDS 1:6 RACK, 1:18 RETAIL
1-6 ISSUED IN 2K ALL-STAR GAMES
7-11 ISSUED IN SER.1 TOPPS PACKS
1 Derek Jeter
2 Andruw Jones
3 Miguel Cabrera
4 Derrek Lee
5 Mariano Rivera
6 Ivan Rodriguez
7 Vladimir Guerrero .75 2.00
8 Albert Pujols 1.50 4.00
9 Alex Rodriguez 1.25 3.00
10 Alfonso Soriano .60 1.50
11 Dontrelle Willis .60 1.50

2006 Topps 2K All-Stars Autograph

RANDOM INSERT IN 06 2K ALL-STAR GAME
STATED PRINT RUN 100 COPIES
AJ Andruw Jones

2006 Topps Autographs

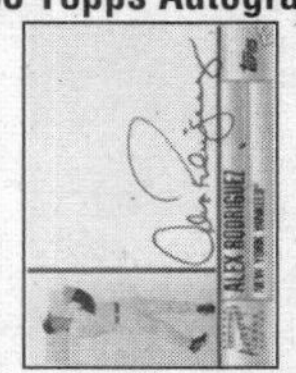

SER.1 A 1:681,120 HOBBY, 1:152,750 HTA
SER.1 A 1:220,032 RACK
SER.1 B 1:14500 H,1:2932 HTA,1:26,900 MINI
SER.1 B 1:7124 RACK, 1:11,500 RETAIL
SER.1 C 1:17400 H,1:4966 HTA, 1:28,622 MINI
SER.1 C 1:8400 RACK, 1:14,000 RET
SER.1 D 1:42,570 H, 1:11,841 HTA
SER.1 D 1:70,000 MINI, 1:20,000 RACK
SER.1 D 1:33,000 RETAIL
SER.1 E 1:3451 H, 1:980 HTA, 1:5800 MINI
SER.1 E 1:1650 RACK, 1:2900 RET
SER.1 F 1:2090 H, 1:560 HTA, 1:3480 MINI
SER.1 F 1:995 RACK, 1:1750 RETAIL
SER.1 G 1:3481 H, 1:944 HTA, 1:5800 MINI
SER.1 G 1:1660 RACK, 1:2900 RETAIL
SER.1 H 1:430 H, 1:121 HTA, 1:725 MINI
SER.1 H 1:207 RACK, 1:363 RETAIL
OVERALL SER.1 AU-GU ODDS 1:137 H/R
OVERALL SER.1 AU-GU ODDS 1:47 HTA
GROUP A PRINT RUN 10 #'d CARDS
GROUP B PRINT RUN 100 #'d SETS
GROUP C PRINT RUN 200 #'d SETS
GROUP D PRINT RUN 250 #'d CARDS
NO GROUP A PRICING DUE TO SCARCITY
B.LIVINGSTON ISSUED IN SER.2 PACKS
EXCHANGE DEADLINE 02/28/08
AG Alex Gordon H 50.00 100.00
AL Anthony Lerew H 4.00 10.00
AR Alex Rodriguez B/100 400.00 600.00
ARE Anthony Reyes H 10.00 25.00
BB Barry Bonds A/10
BC Brian Cashman B/100 125.00 200.00
BL Bobby Livingston F2 4.00 10.00
BW Brad Wilkerson E 6.00 15.00
CB Craig Breslow H 4.00 10.00
CG Carlos Guillen E 6.00 15.00
CJ Chuck James G 15.00 40.00
CR Cal Ripken B/100 EXCH 150.00 250.00
DD Doug DeVore H 4.00 10.00
DO David Ortiz B/100 90.00 150.00
DR Darrell Rasner H 4.00 10.00
DW Dave Winfield B/100 90.00 150.00
EC Eric Chavez C/200 40.00 80.00
FC Fausto Carmona H 8.00 20.00
FL Francisco Liriano H 30.00 60.00
GN Graig Nettles E 10.00 25.00
GS Gary Sheffield C/200 20.00 50.00
HR Horacio Ramirez F 4.00 10.00
JB Jason Botts H 4.00 10.00
JJ Josh Johnson H 6.00 15.00
JM Jeff Mathis F 4.00 10.00
LC Lance Cormier E 6.00 15.00
LH Livan Hernandez F 6.00 15.00
MB Milton Bradley C/200 15.00 40.00
MY Michael Young E 10.00 25.00
NC Nelson Cruz G 6.00 15.00
RG Ryan Garko F 6.00 15.00
RH Rich Hill H 12.50 30.00
RO Roy Oswalt F 10.00 25.00
RS Ryne Sandberg B/100 90.00 150.00
SO Scott Olsen H 4.00 10.00
TE Theo Epstein B/100 EXCH 90.00 150.00
TS Terrmel Sledge E 6.00 15.00
WB Wade Boggs D/250 40.00 80.00

2006 Topps Autographs Green

SER.2 A 1:160,000 HOBBY, 1:48,000 HTA
SER.2 A 1:350,000 MINI, 1:90,000 RACK
SER.2 A 1:150,000 RETAIL
SER.2 B 1:70,000 HOBBY, 1:12,000 HTA
SER.2 B 1:125,000 MINI, 1:33,000 RACK
SER.2 B 1:80,000 RETAIL
SER.2 C 1:4060 H, 1:1150 HTA, 1:6800 MINI
SER.2 C 1:1400 R, 1:1940 RACK
SER.2 D 1:4750 H, 1:1000 HTA, 1:6500 MINI
SER.2 D 1:4750 R, 1:2000 RACK
SER.2 E 1:2030 H, 1:575 HTA, 1:3390 MINI
SER.2 E 1:2025 R, 1:966 RACK
SER.2 F 1:510 H, 1:190 HTA, 1:1125 MINI
SER.2 F 1:506 R, 1:325 RACK
GROUP A PRINT RUN 50 CARDS
GROUP B PRINT RUN 120 CARDS
GROUP C PRINT RUN 250 SETS
A-C ARE NOT SERIAL-NUMBERED
A-C PRINT RUNS PROVIDED BY TOPPS
NO GROUP A PRICING DUE TO SCARCITY
EXCHANGE DEADLINE 06/30/08
AJ Andruw Jones C/250 * 30.00 60.00
AR Alex Rodriguez A/50 *
BB Barry Bonds B/120 * 350.00 500.00
BC Brandon Claussen F 4.00 10.00
BM Brandon McCarthy E 6.00 15.00
BR Brian Roberts C/250 * 30.00 60.00
CB Clint Barmes E 6.00 15.00
CO Chad Orvella F 4.00 10.00
CV Claudio Vargas F 4.00 10.00
DD Doug Drabek C/250 * 10.00 25.00
DJ Dan Johnson D 6.00 15.00
DL Derrek Lee C/250 * EXCH 30.00 60.00
DS Darryl Strawberry C/250 * 20.00 50.00
DSN Duke Snider C/250 * 40.00 80.00
GA Garrett Atkins D 6.00 15.00
GC Gary Carter C/250 * 15.00 40.00
JB Jose Bautista F 4.00 10.00
JF Jeff Francis D 6.00 15.00
JP Jonathan Papelbon F 15.00 40.00
RC Robinson Cano E 15.00 40.00
RZ Ryan Zimmerman E 20.00 50.00
SK Scott Kazmir D 10.00 25.00
WP Wily Mo Pena C/250 * 15.00 40.00

2006 Topps Barry Bonds Chase to 715

COMMON CARD 20.00 50.00
SER.1 ODDS 1:4800 HOBBY, 1:5400 HTA
SER.1 ODDS 1:10,900 MINI, 1:3076 RACK
SER.1 ODDS 1:5,300 RETAIL
STATED PRINT RUN 1 SERIAL #'d SET

2006 Topps Barry Bonds Home Run History

SEE 05 TOPPS BONDS HRH FOR PRICING

2006 Topps United States Constitution

COMPLETE SET (42) 30.00 60.00
SER.2 ODDS 1:8 HOBBY, 1:2 HTA, 1:16 MINI
SER.2 ODDS 1:8 RETAIL, 1:4 RACK
AB Abraham Baldwin .75 2.00
AH Alexander Hamilton .75 2.00
BF Benjamin Franklin 1.25 3.00
CP Charles Pinckney .75 2.00
DB David Brearly .75 2.00
DC Daniel Carroll .75 2.00
DJ Daniel of St. Thomas Jenifer .75 2.00
GB Gunning Bedford Jr. .75 2.00
GC George Clymer .75 2.00
GM Gouverneur Morris .75 2.00
GR George Read .75 2.00
GW George Washington 1.25 3.00
HW Hugh Williamson .75 2.00
JB John Blair .75 2.00
JD Jonathan Dayton .75 2.00
JI Jared Ingersoll .75 2.00
JL John Langdon .75 2.00
JM James Madison .75 2.00
JR John Rutledge .75 2.00
JW James Wilson .75 2.00
NG Nicholas Gilman .75 2.00
PB Pierce Butler .75 2.00
RB Richard Bassett .75 2.00
RK Rufus King .75 2.00
RM Robert Morris .75 2.00
RS Roger Sherman .75 2.00
TF Thomas Fitzsimons .75 2.00
TM Thomas Mifflin .75 2.00
WB William Blount .75 2.00
WF William Few .75 2.00
WJ William Samuel Johnson .75 2.00
WL William Livingston .75 2.00
WP William Paterson .75 2.00
CCP Charles Cotesworth Pinckney .75 2.00
JBR Jacob Broom .75 2.00
JDI John Dickinson .75 2.00
JMC James McHenry .75 2.00
NGO Nathaniel Gorham .75 2.00
RDS Richard Dobbs Spaight .75 2.00
HDR1 Header Card 1 .75 2.00
HDR2 Header Card 2 .75 2.00
HDR3 Header Card 3 .75 2.00

2006 Topps United States Constitution Cut Signatures

SER.2 ODDS 1:300,000 HOBBY
SER.2 ODDS 1:80,000 HTA
SER.2 ODDS 1:450,000 MINI
SER.2 ODDS 1:150,000 RETAIL
STATED PRINT RUN 1 SET
NO PRICING DUE TO SCARCITY
AB Abraham Baldwin
AH Alexander Hamilton
BF Benjamin Franklin
CP Charles Pinckney
DB David Brearly
DC Daniel Carroll
DJ Daniel of St. Thomas Jenifer
GC George Clymer
GR George Read
GW George Washington
JB John Blair
JD Jonathan Dayton
JI Jared Ingersoll
JL John Langdon
JM James Madison
JW James Wilson
NG Nicholas Gilman
PB Pierce Butler
RM Robert Morris
RS Roger Sherman
TF Thomas Fitzsimons
TM Thomas Mifflin
WF William Few
WJ William Samuel Johnson
WL William Livingston
CCP Charles Cotesworth Pinckney
JBR Jacob Broom
JDI John Dickinson
JMC James McHenry
NGO Nathaniel Gorham
RDS Richard Dobbs Spaight

2006 Topps Declaration of Independence

COMPLETE SET (56) 70.00 120.00
SER.1 ODDS 1:8 HOBBY, 1:4 HTA, 1:12 MINI
SER.1 ODDS 1:4 RACK, 1:6 RETAIL
AC Abraham Clark 1.25 3.00
AM Arthur Middleton 1.25 3.00
BF Benjamin Franklin 2.00 5.00
BG Button Gwinnett 1.25 3.00
BH Benjamin Harrison 1.25 3.00
BR Benjamin Rush 1.25 3.00
CB Carter Braxton 1.25 3.00
CC Charles Carroll 1.25 3.00
CR Caesar Rodney 1.25 3.00
EG Elbridge Gerry 1.25 3.00
ER Edward Rutledge 1.25 3.00
FH Francis Hopkinson 1.25 3.00
FL Francis Lewis 1.25 3.00
FLL Francis Lightfoot Lee 1.25 3.00
GC George Clymer 1.25 3.00
GR George Ross 1.25 3.00
GRE George Read 1.25 3.00
GT George Taylor 1.25 3.00
GW George Walton 1.25 3.00
GWY George Wythe 1.25 3.00
JA John Adams 1.25 3.00
JB Josiah Bartlett 1.25 3.00
JH John Hancock 2.00 5.00
JHA John Hart 1.25 3.00
JHE Joseph Hewes 1.25 3.00
JM John Morton 1.25 3.00
JP John Penn 1.25 3.00
JS James Smith 1.25 3.00
JW James Wilson 1.25 3.00
JWI John Witherspoon 1.25 3.00
LH Lyman Hall 1.25 3.00
LM Lewis Morris 1.25 3.00
MT Matthew Thornton 1.25 3.00
OW Oliver Wolcott 1.25 3.00
PL Philip Livingston 1.25 3.00
RHL Richard Henry Lee 1.25 3.00
RM Robert Morris 1.25 3.00
RS Roger Sherman 1.25 3.00
RST Richard Stockton 1.25 3.00
RTP Robert Treat Paine 1.25 3.00
SA Samuel Adams 2.00 5.00
SC Samuel Chase 1.25 3.00
SH Stephen Hopkins 1.25 3.00
SHU Samuel Huntington 1.25 3.00
TH Thomas Heyward Jr. 1.25 3.00
TJ Thomas Jefferson 2.00 5.00
TL Thomas Lynch Jr. 1.25 3.00
TM Thomas McKean 1.25 3.00
TN Thomas Nelson Jr. 1.25 3.00
TS Thomas Stone 1.25 3.00
WE William Ellery 1.25 3.00
WF William Floyd 1.25 3.00
WH William Hooper 1.25 3.00
WP William Paca 1.25 3.00
WW William Whipple 1.25 3.00
WWI William Williams 1.25 3.00

2006 Topps Declaration of Independence Cut Signatures

SER.1 ODDS 1:255,375 HOBBY
SER.1 ODDS 1:102,624 HTA
SER.1 ODDS 1:320,576 MINI
SER.1 ODDS 1:145,104 RETAIL
STATED PRINT RUN 1 SERIAL #'d SET
NO PRICING DUE TO SCARCITY

2006 Topps Factory Set Rookie Bonus

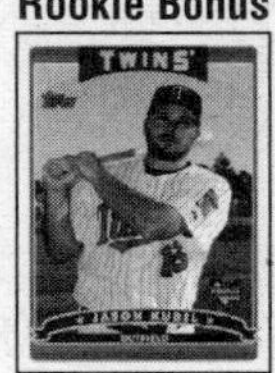

COMP.RETAIL SET (5) 7.50 15.00
COMP.HOBBY SET (5) 7.50 15.00
COMP.HOLIDAY SET (10) 10.00 25.00
1-5 ISSUED IN RETAIL FACTORY SETS
6-10 ISSUED IN HOBBY FACTORY SETS
11-20 ISSUED IN HOLIDAY FACTORY SETS
1 Nick Markakis 2.00 5.00
2 Kelly Shoppach 1.50 4.00
3 Jordan Tata 1.50 4.00
4 Ruddy Lugo 1.50 4.00
5 Josh Wilson 1.50 4.00
6 Fernando Nieve 1.50 4.00
7 Sendy Rleal 1.50 4.00
8 Jason Kubel 1.50 4.00
9 James Loney 2.00 5.00
10 Fabio Castro 1.50 4.00
11 Jonathan Broxton 1.50 4.00
12 Eliezer Alfonzo 1.50 4.00
13 Jason Hirsh 1.50 4.00
14 Rajai Davis 1.50 4.00
15 Henry Owens 2.00 5.00
16 Kevin Frandsen 1.50 4.00
17 Matt Garza 1.50 4.00
18 Chris Duncan 1.50 4.00
19 Chris Coste 1.50 4.00
20 Jeff Karstens 2.00 5.00

2006 Topps Factory Set Team Bonus

COMP.CARDINALS SET (5) 7.50 15.00
COMP.CUBS SET (5) 7.50 15.00
COMP.PIRATES SET (5) 7.50 15.00
COMP.RED SOX SET (5) 12.50 25.00
COMP.YANKEES SET (5) 10.00 20.00
BRS1-5 ISSUED IN RED SOX FACTORY SET
CC1-5 ISSUED IN CUBS FACTORY SET
NYY1-5 ISSUED IN YANKEES FACTORY SET
PP1-5 ISSUED IN PIRATES FACTORY SET
SLC1-5 ISSUED IN CARDINALS FACTORY SET
BRS1 Jonathan Papelbon 4.00 10.00
BRS2 Manny Ramirez 2.00 5.00
BRS3 David Ortiz 2.00 5.00
BRS4 Josh Beckett 1.50 4.00
BRS5 Curt Schilling 2.00 5.00
CC1 Sean Marshall 1.50 4.00
CC2 Freddie Bynum 1.50 4.00
CC3 Derrek Lee 2.00 5.00
CC4 Juan Pierre 1.50 4.00
CC5 Carlos Zambrano 1.50 4.00
NYY1 Wil Nieves 1.50 4.00
NYY2 Alex Rodriguez 3.00 8.00
NYY3 Derek Jeter 4.00 10.00
NYY4 Mariano Rivera 2.00 5.00
NYY5 Randy Johnson 2.00 5.00
PP1 Matt Capps 1.50 4.00
PP2 Paul Maholm 1.50 4.00
PP3 Nate McLouth 1.50 4.00
PP4 John Van Benschoten 1.50 4.00
PP5 Jason Bay 1.50 4.00
SLC1 Adam Wainwright 1.50 4.00
SLC2 Skip Schumaker 1.50 4.00
SLC3 Albert Pujols 4.00 10.00
SLC4 Jim Edmonds 1.50 4.00
SLC5 Scott Rolen 2.00 5.00

2006 Topps Hit Parade

COMPLETE SET (30) 35.00 60.00
SER.2 ODDS 1:18 H, 1:6 HTA, 1:27 MINI
SER.2 ODDS 1:18 R, 1:9 RACK
HR1 Barry Bonds HR 3.00 8.00
HR2 Ken Griffey Jr HR 2.50 6.00
HR3 Jeff Bagwell HR 1.00 2.50
HR4 Gary Sheffield HR .60 1.50
HR5 Frank Thomas HR 1.50 4.00
HR6 Manny Ramirez HR 1.00 2.50
HR7 Jim Thome HR 1.00 2.50
HR8 Alex Rodriguez HR 2.50 6.00
HR9 Mike Piazza HR 1.50 4.00
HIT1 Craig Biggio HIT 1.00 2.50
HIT2 Barry Bonds HIT 3.00 8.00
HIT3 Julio Franco HIT .60 1.50
HIT4 Steve Finley HIT .60 1.50
HIT5 Gary Sheffield HIT .60 1.50
HIT6 Jeff Bagwell HIT 1.00 2.50
HIT7 Ken Griffey Jr HIT 2.50 6.00
HIT8 Omar Vizquel HIT 1.00 2.50
HIT9 Marquis Grissom HIT .60 1.50
HR10 Carlos Delgado HR .60 1.50
RBI1 Barry Bonds RBI 3.00 8.00
RBI2 Ken Griffey Jr RBI 2.50 6.00
RBI3 Jeff Bagwell RBI 1.00 2.50
RBI4 Gary Sheffield RBI .60 1.50
RBI5 Frank Thomas RBI 1.50 4.00
RBI6 Manny Ramirez RBI 1.00 2.50
RBI7 Ruben Sierra RBI .60 1.50
RBI8 Jeff Kent RBI .60 1.50
RBI9 Luis Gonzalez RBI .60 1.50
HIT10 Bernie Williams HIT 1.00 2.50
RBI10 Alex Rodriguez RBI 2.50 6.00

2006 Topps Hobby Masters

COMPLETE SET (20) 15.00 40.00
SER.1 ODDS 1:18 HOBBY, 1:6 HTA
HM1 Derrek Lee .75 2.00
HM2 Albert Pujols 2.00 5.00
HM3 Nomar Garciaparra 1.00 2.50
HM4 Alfonso Soriano .75 2.00
HM5 Derek Jeter 2.00 5.00
HM6 Miguel Tejada .75 2.00
HM7 Alex Rodriguez 1.50 4.00
HM8 Jim Edmonds UER .75 2.00
Back Photo is Andruw Jones
HM9 Mark Prior .75 2.00
HM10 Roger Clemens 2.00 5.00
HM11 Randy Johnson 1.00 2.50
HM12 Manny Ramirez .75 2.00
HM13 Curt Schilling .75 2.00
HM14 Vladimir Guerrero 1.00 2.50
HM15 Barry Bonds 2.00 5.00
HM16 Ichiro Suzuki 1.50 4.00
HM17 Pedro Martinez .75 2.00
HM18 Carlos Beltran .75 2.00
HM19 David Ortiz 1.00 2.50
HM20 Andruw Jones .75 2.00

2006 Topps Home Run Derby Contest

SER.2 ODDS 1:48,000 H, 1:14,000 HTA
SER.2 ODDS 1:23,500 MINI, 1:12,000 R
SER.2 ODDS 1:7700 RACK
STATED PRINT RUN 10 SERIAL #'d SETS
NO PRICING DUE TO SCARCITY
AB Adrian Beltre
AD Adam Dunn
AJ Andruw Jones
AP Albert Pujols
AR Alex Rodriguez
ARA Aramis Ramirez
AS Alfonso Soriano
BA Bobby Abreu
BB Barry Bonds
BG Brian Giles
CB Carlos Beltran
CD Carlos Delgado
CJ Chipper Jones
CL Carlos Lee
DL Derrek Lee
DO David Ortiz
DW David Wright
EC Eric Chavez
GS Gary Sheffield
HB Hank Blalock
HM Hideki Matsui
IR Ivan Rodriguez
JB Jason Bay
JC Jorge Cantu
JE Jim Edmonds
JG Jason Giambi
JM Justin Morneau
JT Jim Thome
KG Ken Griffey Jr.
LB Lance Berkman
MA Moises Alou
MC Miguel Cabrera
ME Morgan Ensberg
MO Magglio Ordonez
MR Manny Ramirez
MT Mark Teixeira
MTE Miguel Tejada
PB Pat Burrell
PF Prince Fielder
PK Paul Konerko
RH Ryan Howard
RS Richie Sexson
SG Shawn Green
SR Scott Rolen
TG Troy Glaus
TH Todd Helton
THA Travis Hafner
VC Vinny Castilla
VW Vernon Wells
WP Wily Mo Pena

2006 Topps Mantle Collection

COMPLETE SET (10) 60.00 120.00
SER.1 ODDS 1:36 HOB, 1:36 HTA, 1:36 MINI
SER.1 ODDS 1:12 RACK, 1:36 RETAIL
BLACK SER.1 ODDS 1:4,665 HTA
BLACK PRINT RUN 7 SERIAL #'d SETS
NO BLACK PRICING DUE TO SCARCITY
*GOLD p/r 477-977: 1.25X TO 3X BASIC
*GOLD p/r 277-377: 1.5X TO 4X BASIC
*GOLD p/r 177: 2X TO 5X BASIC
*GOLD p/r 77: 4X TO 10X BASIC
GOLD SER.1 ODDS 1:1500 HOB, 1:2332 HTA
GOLD SER.1 ODDS 1:3376 MINI, 1:970 RACK
GOLD SER.1 ODDS 1:1500 RETAIL
GOLD PRINT RUNS B/WN 77-977 PER
1996 Mickey Mantle 96 6.00 15.00
1997 Mickey Mantle 97 6.00 15.00
1998 Mickey Mantle 98 6.00 15.00
1999 Mickey Mantle 99 6.00 15.00
2000 Mickey Mantle 00 6.00 15.00
2001 Mickey Mantle 01 6.00 15.00
2002 Mickey Mantle 02 6.00 15.00
2003 Mickey Mantle 03 6.00 15.00
2004 Mickey Mantle 04 6.00 15.00
2005 Mickey Mantle 05 6.00 15.00

2006 Topps Mantle Collection Bat Relics

SER.1 ODDS 1:4540 HOBBY, 1:8552 HTA
SER.1 ODDS 1:14,000 MINI, 1:6500 RETAIL
PRINT RUNS B/WN 77-167 COPIES PER
BLACK SER.1 ODDS 1:4,665 HTA
BLACK PRINT RUN 7 SERIAL #'d SETS
NO BLACK PRICING DUE TO SCARCITY
1996 Mickey Mantle 96/77 125.00 200.00
1997 Mickey Mantle 97/87 125.00 200.00
1998 Mickey Mantle 98/97 125.00 200.00
1999 Mickey Mantle 99/107 100.00 175.00
2000 Mickey Mantle 00/117 100.00 175.00
2001 Mickey Mantle 01/127 100.00 175.00
2002 Mickey Mantle 02/137 100.00 175.00
2003 Mickey Mantle 03/147 100.00 175.00
2004 Mickey Mantle 04/157 100.00 175.00
2005 Mickey Mantle 05/167 100.00 175.00

2006 Topps Mantle Home Run History

COMPLETE SET (301) 500.00 900.00
COMP.06 SERIES 1-2 SET (1-101) 60.00 120.00
COMP.06 UPDATE (102-201) 60.00 120.00
COMP.07 SERIES 1 SET (202-301) 75.00 150.00
COMP.07 SERIES 2 SET (302-401) 125.00 250.00
COMP.07 UPDATE (402-501) 125.00 250.00
COMP.08 TOPPS (502-536) 20.00 50.00
COMMON CARD (1-301) .40 1.00
COMMON CARD (202-301) 1.00 2.50
COMMON CARD (302-536) .75 2.00
SER.1 ODDS 1:4 HOBBY, 1:4 HTA, 1:4 MINI
SER.1 ODDS 1:2 RACK, 1:4 RETAIL
SER.2 ODDS 1:4 HOBBY, 1:1 HTA, 1:8 MINI
SER.2 ODDS 1:2 RACK, 1:4 RETAIL
UPDATE ODDS 1:4 HOB,1:4 RET
07 SER.1 ODDS 1:9 H, 1:2 HTA, 1:9 K-MART
07 SER.1 ODDS 1:9 RACK, 1:9 TARGET
07 SER.1 ODDS 1:9 WAL-MART
07 SER.2 ODDS 1:9 HOBBY
07 UPDATE ODDS 1:9 HOB, 1:9 RET
08 SER.1 ODDS 1:9 HOB, 1:9 RET
CARD 1 ISSUED IN SERIES 1 PACKS
CARDS 2-101 ISSUED IN SERIES 2 PACKS
CARDS 102-201 ISSUED IN UPDATE PACKS
CARDS 202-301 ISSUED IN 07 SERIES 1
CARDS 302-401 ISSUED IN 07 SERIES 2
CARDS 402-501 ISSUED IN 07 UPDATE
CARDS 502-537 ISSUED IN 08 SERIES 1

2006 Topps Mantle Home Run History Bat Relics

COMMON CARD (R1-R536) 50.00 100.00
SER.1 ODDS 1:681,120 H, 1:102,624 HTA
SER.2 ODDS 1:6250 H, 1:16,000 HTA
SER.2 ODDS 1:21,000 MINI, 1:1575 R
UPD ODDS 1:5100 H,1:1859 HTA,1:5800 R
07 SER.1 ODDS 1:14,618 H, 1:494 HTA
07 SER.1 ODDS 1:32,000 K-MART
07 SER.1 ODDS 1:16,225 RACK
07 SER.1 ODDS 1:32,00 WAL-MART
07 SER.2 ODDS 1:12,106 HOBBY, 1:693 HTA
07 UPD. ODDS 1:5,550 HOBBY
07 UPD. ODDS 1:1,475 HTA
07 UPD. ODDS 1:5,550 RETAIL
08 SER.1 ODDS 1:29,331 H,1:1492 HTA
08 SER.1 ODDS 1:207,000 RETAIL
1 ISSUED IN SERIES 1 PACKS
2-101 ISSUED IN SERIES 2 PACKS
102-201 ISSUED IN UPDATE PACKS
202-301 ISSUED IN 07 SERIES 1 PACKS
302-401 ISSUED IN 07 SERIES 2 PACKS
402-501 ISSUED IN 07 UPDATE
502-536 ISSUED IN 08 SERIES 1
STATED PRINT RUN 7 SERIAL #'d SETS

2006 Topps Mantle Home Run History Cut Signature

SER.1 ODDS 1:308,872 HTA
STATED PRINT RUN 1 SERIAL #'d CARD
NO PRICING DUE TO SCARCITY
CS1 Mickey Mantle

2006 Topps Opening Day Team vs. Team

COMPLETE SET (15) 6.00 15.00
SER.2 ODDS 1:12 HOBBY, 1:3 HTA, 1:24 MINI
SER.2 ODDS 1:6 RACK, 1:12 RETAIL
AM Houston Astros vs. Marlins .60 1.50
AY Oakland Athletics vs. Yankees .60 1.50
BP Milwaukee Brewers vs. Pirates .60 1.50
DB Los Angeles Dodgers vs. Braves .60 1.50
JT Toronto Blue Jays vs. Twins .60 1.50
MA Seattle Mariners vs. Angels .60 1.50
MN New York Mets vs. Nationals .60 1.50
OD Baltimore Orioles vs. Devil Rays .60 1.50
PC Philadelphia Phillies vs. Cardinals .60 1.50
PG San Diego Padres vs. Giants .60 1.50
RC Cincinnati Reds vs. Cubs .60 1.50
RD Colorado Rockies vs. Diamondbacks .60 1.50
RR Texas Rangers vs. Red Sox .60 1.50
RT Kansas City Royals vs. Tigers .60 1.50
WI Chicago White Sox vs. Indians .60 1.50

2006 Topps Opening Day Team vs. Team Relics

SER.2 A ODDS 1:8800 H, 1:22,000 HTA
SER.2 A ODDS 1:25,000 MINI, 1:2100 R
SER.2 B ODDS 1:810 H, 1:2850 HTA
SER.2 B ODDS 1:3075 MINI, 1:1200 R
GROUP A PRINT RUN 50 SERIAL #'d SETS
NO GROUP A PRICING DUE TO SCARCITY
EXCHANGE DEADLINE 06/30/08
AM Houston Astros Ball A EXCH
AY Oakland Athletics Base B 6.00 15.00
BP Milwaukee Brewers Ball A
DB Los Angeles Dodgers Ball A
JT Toronto Blue Jays Ball A EXCH
MA Seattle Mariners Ball A EXCH
MN New York Mets Ball A EXCH
OD Baltimore Orioles Base B 6.00 15.00
PC Philadelphia Phillies Ball A EXCH
PG San Diego Padres Ball A
RC Cincinnati Reds Ball A EXCH
RD Colorado Rockies Base B 6.00 15.00
RR Texas Rangers Ball A EXCH
RT Kansas City Royals Base B 10.00 25.00
WI Chicago White Sox Ball A

2006 Topps Own the Game

COMPLETE SET (30) 20.00 50.00
SER.1 ODDS 1:12 HOB, 1:4 HTA, 1:12 MINI
SER.1 ODDS 1:6 RACK, 1:8 RETAIL
OG1 Derrek Lee .75 2.00
OG2 Michael Young .75 2.00
OG3 Albert Pujols 2.00 5.00
OG4 Roger Clemens 2.00 5.00
OG5 Andy Pettitte .75 2.00
OG6 Dontrelle Willis .75 2.00
OG7 Michael Young .75 2.00
OG8 Ichiro Suzuki 1.50 4.00
OG9 Derek Jeter 2.00 5.00
OG10 Andruw Jones .75 2.00
OG11 Alex Rodriguez 1.50 4.00
OG12 David Ortiz 1.00 2.50
OG13 David Ortiz 1.00 2.50
OG14 Manny Ramirez .75 2.00
OG15 Mark Teixeira UER .75 2.00
Name is spelled Teixiera
OG16 Albert Pujols 2.00 5.00
OG17 Alex Rodriguez 1.50 4.00
OG18 Derek Jeter 2.00 5.00
OG19 Chad Cordero .75 2.00
OG20 Francisco Rodriguez .75 2.00
OG21 Mariano Rivera 1.00 2.50
OG22 Chone Figgins .75 2.00
OG23 Jose Reyes .75 2.00
OG24 Scott Podsednik .75 2.00
OG25 Jake Peavy .75 2.00
OG26 Johan Santana 1.00 2.50
OG27 Pedro Martinez .75 2.00
OG28 Dontrelle Willis .75 2.00
OG29 Chris Carpenter .75 2.00
OG30 Bartolo Colon .75 2.00

2006 Topps Rookie of the Week

COMPLETE SET (25) 15.00 40.00
COMMON CARD (1-13) .75 2.00
ISSUED ONE PER WEEK VIA HTA SHOPS
1 Mickey Mantle 52 4.00 10.00
2 Barry Bonds 87 1.50 4.00
3 Roger Clemens 85 1.50 4.00
4 Ernie Banks 54 .75 2.00
5 Nolan Ryan 68 2.00 5.00
The spelling mistake on the word sensational was finally corrected
6 Albert Pujols 01 1.50 4.00
7 Roberto Clemente 55 2.50 6.00
8 Frank Robinson 57 .75 2.00
9 Brooks Robinson 57 .75 2.00
10 Harmon Killebrew 55 .75 2.00
11 Reggie Jackson 69 .75 2.00
12 George Brett 75 1.50 4.00
13 Ichiro Suzuki 01 1.50 4.00
14 Cal Ripken 82 3.00 8.00
15 Tom Seaver 68 .75 2.00
16 Johnny Bench 68 .75 2.00
17 Mike Schmidt 73 1.25 3.00
18 Derek Jeter 93 2.00 5.00
19 Bob Gibson 59 .75 2.00
20 Ozzie Smith 79 1.25 3.00
21 Rickey Henderson 80 .75 2.00
22 Tony Gwynn 83 .75 2.00
23 Wade Boggs 83 .75 2.00
24 Ryne Sandberg 83 1.50 4.00
25 Mickey Mantle TBD 4.00 10.00

2006 Topps Stars

COMPLETE SET (15) 6.00 15.00
SER.2 ODDS 1:12 HOBBY, 1:4 HTA
AP Albert Pujols 1.50 4.00
AR Alex Rodriguez 1.25 3.00
AS Alfonso Soriano .30 .75
BB Barry Bonds 1.50 4.00
DJ Derek Jeter 2.00 5.00
DO David Ortiz .75 2.00
HM Hideki Matsui .75 2.00
IS Ichiro Suzuki 1.25 3.00
MC Miguel Cabrera .50 1.25
MR Manny Ramirez .50 1.25
MT Miguel Tejada .30 .75
PM Pedro Martinez .50 1.25
RC Roger Clemens 1.50 4.00
TH Todd Helton .50 1.25
VG Vladimir Guerrero .75 2.00

2006 Topps Target Factory Set Mantle Memorabilia

The card was packaged exclusively with 2006 Topps Factory sets sold in Target stores. Each factory set contained the complete Series 1 and Series 2 sets as well as the Mantle 1952 Topps reprint relic card. The original set SRP was $59.99.

MMR52 Mickey Mantle 52T 20.00 50.00

2006 Topps Team Topps Autographs

ISSUED IN VARIOUS 06 TOPPS PRODUCTS
SEE '03 TOPPS BLUE CHIPS FOR ADD'L INFO
BF Bob Feller 10.00 25.00
CS Chris Snyder 4.00 10.00
DD Doug Drabek 6.00 15.00
DS Duke Snider 15.00 40.00
DZ Don Zimmer 6.00 15.00
ED Eric Davis 6.00 15.00
JF Josh Fields 6.00 15.00
JL Jim Leyritz 4.00 10.00
JP Johnny Podres 6.00 15.00
JP1 Jimmy Piersall 6.00 15.00
MC Mike Cuellar 6.00 15.00
MP Manny Parra 10.00 25.00
MR Mickey Rivers 6.00 15.00
RS Ryan Sweeney 4.00 10.00
SE Scott Elbert 4.00 10.00
TJ Tommy John 6.00 15.00

2006 Topps Trading Places

COMPLETE SET (20) 10.00 25.00
SER.2 ODDS 1:18 H, 1:4 HTA, 1:32 MINI
SER.2 ODDS 1:18 R, 1:8 RACK
AS Alfonso Soriano .60 1.50
BM Bill Mueller .60 1.50
BW Brad Wilkerson .60 1.50
CC Coco Crisp .60 1.50
CD Carlos Delgado .60 1.50
CP Corey Patterson .60 1.50
ER Edgar Renteria .60 1.50
FT Frank Thomas 1.50 4.00
JD Johnny Damon 1.00 2.50
JP Juan Pierre .60 1.50
JT Jim Thome 1.00 2.50
KL Kenny Lofton .60 1.50
MB Milton Bradley .60 1.50
NG Nomar Garciaparra 1.50 4.00
PW Preston Wilson .60 1.50
RF Rafael Furcal .60 1.50
RH Ramon Hernandez .60 1.50
TG Troy Glaus .60 1.50
JDN Juan Encarnacion .60 1.50
MJP Mike Piazza 1.50 4.00

2006 Topps Wal-Mart

These cards were issued in three-card cello packs within sealed series one Wal-Mart Bonus Boxes. Each Bonus Box carried a $9.97 suggested retail price and contained ten mini packs of series one cards plus the aforementioned three-card cello pack. The mini packs each contained six cards, thus each sealed Bonus Box contained 63 cards in all.

COMPLETE SERIES 1 (18) 20.00 40.00
COMPLETE SERIES 2 (18) 50.00 100.00
THREE PER WAL-MART BLASTER BOX
S1 CARDS ISSUED IN SERIES 1 PACKS
S2 CARDS ISSUED IN SERIES 2 PACKS
WM1 Stan Musial 52 S1 1.25 3.00
WM2 Ted Williams 87 S1 1.25 3.00
WM3 Yogi Berra 54 S2 3.00 8.00
WM4 Joe Mauer 96 UPD 1.00 2.50
WM5 Mickey Mantle 02 S1 3.00 8.00
WM6 Mickey Mantle 57 S2 6.00 15.00
WM7 Alex Rodriguez 58 S2 3.00 8.00
WM8 Carlos Zambrano 92 UPD 1.00 2.50
WM9 Gary Carter 60 S2 1.25 3.00
WM10 Roy Oswalt 61 S2 1.25 3.00
WM11 Mickey Mantle 70 UPD 6.00 15.00
WM12 Randy Johnson 62 UPD 1.50 4.00
WM13 Carlos Lee 64 S1 .75 2.00
WM14 Johan Santana 65 S2 1.25 3.00
WM15 Roberto Clemente 66 S2 8.00 20.00
WM16 Carl Yastrzemski 67 S2 6.00 15.00
WM17 Chase Utley 63 UPD 1.50 4.00
WM18 Pedro Martinez 68 UPD 1.00 2.50
WM19 Jason Bay 69 UPD 1.00 2.50
WM20 Alex Rodriguez 59 UPD 2.50 6.00
WM21 Chipper Jones 72 S2 2.00 5.00
WM22 Ichiro Suzuki 01 S1 1.25 3.00
WM23 Bobby Abreu 94 S1 .75 2.00
WM24 Tom Seaver 95 S1 .75 2.00
WM25 Alfonso Soriano 76 S2 1.25 3.00
WM26 Andruw Jones 92 S1 .75 2.00
WM27 Hanley Ramirez 71 UPD 1.50 4.00
WM28 Adam Dunn 91 S1 .75 2.00
WM29 Carl Crawford 00 UPD 1.00 2.50
WM30 Mark Teixeira 81 S1 .75 2.00
WM31 Albert Pujols 82 S2 3.00 8.00
WM32 Cal Ripken 83 S2 4.00 10.00
WM33 Ryne Sandberg 84 S1 1.25 3.00
WM34 Don Mattingly 85 S1 1.25 3.00
WM35 Roger Clemens 86 S1 1.25 3.00
WM36 Jose Reyes 53 S2 1.25 3.00
WM37 Curt Schilling 80 UPD 1.00 2.50
WM38 Derrek Lee 56 S2 1.25 3.00
WM39 Miguel Cabrera 73 S2 1.25 3.00
WM40 Manny Ramirez 88 UPD 1.00 2.50
WM41 Barry Bonds 89 S1 1.25 3.00
WM42 Barry Bonds 74 S2 3.00 8.00
WM43 Jeff Francoeur 98 UPD 1.50 4.00
WM44 Livan Hernandez 75 S2 1.25 3.00
WM45 Derek Jeter 77 S2 4.00 10.00
WM46 David Ortiz 97 S1 .75 2.00
WM47 Carlos Delgado 78 UPD 1.00 2.50
WM48 Ivan Rodriguez 99 S1 .75 2.00
WM49 Todd Helton 05 UPD 1.00 2.50
WM50 Barry Bonds 79 UPD 2.50 6.00
WM51 Miguel Tejada 55 UPD 1.00 2.50
WM52 Alex Rodriguez 03 S1 1.25 3.00
WM53 Vladimir Guerrero 04 S1 .75 2.00
WM54 Paul Konerko 90 UPD 1.00 2.50

2006 Topps Trading Places Autographs

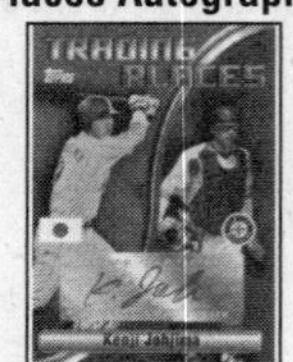

SER.2 A ODDS 1:110,000 HOBBY
SER.2 A ODDS 1:28,000 HTA
SER.2 A ODDS 1:250,000 MINI
SER.2 A ODDS 1:160,000 RACK
SER.2 A ODDS 1:150,000 RETAIL
SER.2 B ODDS 1:18,000 H, 1:5100 HTA
SER.2 B ODDS 1:30,000 MINI, 1:17,000 R
SER.2 B ODDS 1:8700 RACK
SER.2 C ODDS 1:4280 H, 1:1175 HTA
SER.2 C ODDS 1:7200 MINI, 1:4200 R
SER.2 C ODDS 1:2040 RACK
GROUP A PRINT RUN 75 CARDS
GROUP B PRINT RUN 225 SETS
A-B ARE NOT SERIAL-NUMBERED
A-B PRINT RUNS PROVIDED BY TOPPS
BR B.J. Ryan B 15.00 40.00
BW Billy Wagner C 12.50 30.00
JE Johnny Estrada C 4.00 10.00
KJ Kenji Johjima A 90.00 150.00
ML Mike Lowell C 10.00 25.00
PL Paul LoDuca B 15.00 40.00
TS Termel Sledge C 4.00 10.00

2006 Topps Trading Places Autographed Relics

SER.2 ODDS 1:31,500 HOBBY, 1:8000 HTA
SER.2 ODDS 78,000 MINI, 1:52,000 RETAIL
STATED PRINT RUN 25 SERIAL #'d SETS
NO PRICING DUE TO SCARCITY

2006 Topps Trading Places Relics

SER.2 A ODDS 1:645 HOBBY 1:115 HTA
SER.2 A ODDS 1:1355 MINI, 1:810 RETAIL
SER.2 B ODDS 1:410 HOBBY 1:120 HTA
SER.2 B ODDS 1:903 MINI, 1:500 RETAIL
AS Alfonso Soriano Bat A 3.00 8.00
BM Bill Mueller Bat A 3.00 8.00
BR B.J. Ryan Jsy B 3.00 8.00
CP Corey Patterson Bat A 3.00 8.00
ER Edgar Renteria Bat A 3.00 8.00
JD Johnny Damon Jsy B 6.00 15.00
JE Johnny Estrada Bat B 3.00 8.00
JP Juan Pierre Bat A 3.00 8.00
JT Jim Thome Bat A 6.00 15.00
KJ Kenji Johjima Bat B 6.00 15.00
KL Kenny Lofton Bat B 3.00 8.00
MB Milton Bradley Bat B 3.00 8.00
ML Mike Lowell Bat A 3.00 8.00
NG Nomar Garciaparra Bat A 4.00 10.00
PL Paul Lo Duca Bat A 3.00 8.00
PW Preston Wilson Bat A 3.00 8.00
RH Ramon Hernandez Bat B 3.00 8.00
TS Terrmel Sledge Bat B 3.00 8.00
BW1 Billy Wagner Jsy B 3.00 8.00
BW2 Brad Wilkerson Bat B 3.00 8.00

2006 Topps World Series Champion Relics

SER.1 A ODDS 1:23,755 H, 1:9329 HTA
SER.1 A ODDS 1:55,000 MINI, 1:27,000 R
SER.1 B ODDS 1:11,289 H, 1:2544 HTA
SER.1 B ODDS 1:24,000 MINI, 1:11,500 R
SER.1 C ODDS 1:1941 H, 1:880 HTA
SER.1 C ODDS 1:5100 MINI, 1:2500 R
SER.1 D ODDS 1:3144 H, 1:2168 HTA
SER.1 D ODDS 1:9200 MINI, 1:4700 R
SER.1 E ODDS 1:4984 H, 1:3346 HTA
SER.1 E ODDS 1:14,500 MINI, 1:7200 R
SER.1 F ODDS 1:1006 H, 1:617 HTA
SER.1 F ODDS 1:2800 MINI, 1:1430 R
SER.1 G ODDS 1:1396 H, 1:465 HTA
SER.1 G ODDS 1:3500 MINI, 1:1750 R
OVERALL SER.1 AU-GU ODDS 1:137 H/R
OVERALL SER.1 AU-GU ODDS 1:47 HTA
GROUP A PRINT RUN 100 SETS
GROUP A ARE NOT SERIAL-NUMBERED
GROUP A PRINT RUN PROVIDED BY TOPPS
AP A.J. Pierzynski Bat E 10.00 25.00
AR Aaron Rowand Bat D 10.00 25.00
BJ Bobby Jenks Glv A/100 * 250.00 350.00
CEB Carl Everett Bat F 6.00 15.00
CEU Carl Everett Uni A/100 * 60.00 120.00
FT Frank Thomas Uni F 10.00 25.00
JC Joe Crede Bat D 15.00 40.00
JD Jermaine Dye Bat C 10.00 25.00
JG Jon Garland Uni F 6.00 15.00
JU Juan Uribe Bat B 10.00 25.00
MB Mark Buehrle Glv A/100 * 150.00 250.00
PKB Paul Konerko Bat G 6.00 15.00
PKU Paul Konerko Uni G 6.00 15.00
SP Scott Podsednik Bat C 10.00 25.00
TI Tadahito Iguchi Bat C 15.00 30.00
TP Timo Perez Bat C 6.00 15.00
WH Willie Harris Bat F 4.00 10.00

2006 Topps Update

This 330-card set was released in November, 2006. This set was issued in 12-card packs with an $2 SRP and those packs came 36 to a box and 12 boxes to a case. The first 132 cards in this set feature players who were either new to their team in 2006 or made an unexpected impact and were not in the first two Topps series. Cards numbered 133-170 feature 2006 Rookies while cards numbered 171-181 are Season Highlights. Cards number 182-201 are a Postseason Highlight subset, cards 202-217 are an League Leader subset while cards 218-282 form an All-Star subset. Cards numbered 283-290 celebrate players who participated in the Home Run Derby, cards 291-320 were Team Leader cards and the set concluded with Classic Duos (321-330). Cory Lidle, who perished in a plane crash while this set was in production, was issued as an "in memoriam" card.

COMPLETE SET (330) 20.00 50.00
COMMON CARD (1-132) .07 .20
COMMON ROOKIE (133-170) .20 .50
COMMON CARD (171-330) .12 .30
UNLISTED STARS 171-330 .30 .75
1-330 PLATE ODDS 1:85 HTA
PLATE PRINT RUN 1 SET PER COLOR
BLACK-CYAN-MAGENTA-YELLOW ISSUED
NO PLATE PRICING DUE TO SCARCITY
1 Austin Kearns .07 .20
2 Adam Eaton .07 .20
3 Juan Encarnacion .07 .20
4 Jarrod Washburn .07 .20
5 Alex Gonzalez .07 .20
6 Toby Hall .07 .20
7 Preston Wilson .07 .20
8 Ramon Ortiz .07 .20
9 Jason Michaels .07 .20
10 Jeff Weaver .07 .20
11 Russell Branyan .07 .20
12 Brett Tomko .07 .20
13 Doug Mientkiewicz .07 .20
14 David Wells .07 .20
15 Corey Koskie .07 .20
16 Russ Ortiz .07 .20
17 Carlos Pena .07 .20
18 Mark Hendrickson .07 .20
19 Julian Tavarez .07 .20
20 Jeff Conine .07 .20
21 Dioner Navarro .07 .20
22 Bob Wickman .07 .20
23 Felipe Lopez .07 .20
24 Eddie Guardado .07 .20
25 David Dellucci .07 .20
26 Ryan Wagner .07 .20
27 Nick Green .07 .20
28 Gary Majewski .07 .20
29 Shea Hillenbrand .07 .20
30 Jae Seo .07 .20
31 Royce Clayton .07 .20
32 Dave Riske .07 .20
33 Joey Gathright .07 .20
34 Robinson Tejada .07 .20
35 Edwin Jackson .07 .20
36 Aubrey Huff .07 .20
37 Akinori Otsuka .07 .20
38 Juan Castro UER .07 .20
Key Stat does not match actual stat
39 Zach Day .07 .20
40 Jeremy Accardo .07 .20
41 Shawn Green .07 .20
42 Kazuo Matsui .07 .20
43 J.J. Putz .07 .20
44 David Ross .07 .20
45 Scott Williamson .07 .20
46 Joe Borchard .07 .20
47 Elmer Dessens .07 .20
48 Odalis Perez .07 .20
49 Kelly Shoppach .07 .20
50 Brandon Phillips .07 .20
51 Guillermo Mota .07 .20
52 Alex Cintron .07 .20
53 Denny Bautista .07 .20
54 Josh Bard .07 .20
55 Julio Lugo .07 .20
56 Doug Mirabelli .07 .20
57 Kip Wells .07 .20
58 Adrian Gonzalez .07 .20
59 Shawn Chacon .07 .20
60 Marcus Thames .07 .20
61 Craig Wilson .07 .20
62 Cory Sullivan .07 .20
63 Ben Broussard .07 .20
64 Todd Walker .07 .20
65 Greg Maddux .30 .75
66 Xavier Nady .07 .20
67 Oliver Perez .07 .20
68 Sean Casey .07 .20
69 Kyle Lohse .07 .20
70 Carlos Lee .07 .20
71 Rheal Cormier .07 .20
72 Ronnie Belliard .07 .20
73 Cory Lidle 1.50 4.00
74 David Bell .07 .20
75 Wilson Betemit .07 .20
76 Danys Baez .07 .20
77 Mike Stanton .07 .20
78 Kevin Mench .07 .20
79 Sandy Alomar Jr. .07 .20
80 Cesar Izturis .07 .20
81 Jeremy Affeldt .07 .20
82 Matt Stairs .07 .20
83 Hector Luna .07 .20
84 Tony Graffanino .07 .20
85 J.P. Howell .07 .20
86 Bengie Molina .07 .20
87 Maicer Izturis .07 .20
88 Marco Scutaro .07 .20
89 Daryle Ward .07 .20
90 Sal Fasano .07 .20
91 Oscar Villarreal .07 .20
92 Gabe Gross .07 .20
93 Phil Nevin .07 .20
94 Damon Hollins .07 .20
95 Juan Cruz .07 .20
96 Marlon Anderson .07 .20
97 Jason Davis .07 .20
98 Ryan Shealy .07 .20
99 Francisco Cordero .07 .20
100 Bobby Abreu .07 .20
101 Roberto Hernandez .07 .20
102 Gary Bennett .07 .20

103 Aaron Sele .07 .20
104 Nook Logan .07 .20
105 Alfredo Amezaga .07 .20
106 Chris Woodward .07 .20
107 Kevin Jarvis .07 .20
108 B.J. Upton .07 .20
109 Alan Embree .07 .20
110 Milton Bradley .07 .20
111 Pete Orr .07 .20
112 Jeff Cirillo .07 .20
113 Corey Patterson .07 .20
114 Josh Paul .07 .20
115 Fernando Rodney .07 .20
116 Jerry Hairston Jr. .07 .20
117 Scott Proctor .07 .20
118 Ambiorix Burgos .07 .20
119 Jose Bautista .07 .20
120 Livan Hernandez .07 .20
121 John McDonald .07 .20
122 Ronny Cedeno .07 .20
123 Nate Robertson .07 .20
124 Jamey Carroll .07 .20
125 Alex Escobar .07 .20
126 Endy Chavez .07 .20
127 Jorge Julio .07 .20
128 Kenny Lofton .07 .20
129 Matt Diaz .07 .20
130 Dave Bush .07 .20
131 Jose Molina .07 .20
132 Mike MacDougal .07 .20
133 Ben Zobrist (RC) .30 .75
134 Shane Komine RC .30 .75
135 Casey Janssen RC .30 .75
136 Kevin Frandsen (RC) .30 .75
137 John Rheinecker (RC) .20 .50
138 Matt Kemp (RC) .30 .75
139 Scott Mathieson (RC) .20 .50
140 Jered Weaver (RC) 1.00 2.50
141 Joel Guzman (RC) .20 .50
142 Anibal Sanchez (RC) .30 .75
143 Melky Cabrera (RC) .30 .75
144 Howie Kendrick (RC) 1.00 2.50
145 Cole Hamels (RC) .75 2.00
146 Willy Aybar (RC) .20 .50
147 Jamie Shields RC .20 .50
148 Kevin Thompson (RC) .20 .50
149 Jon Lester RC 1.25 3.00
150 Stephen Drew (RC) .50 1.25
151 Andre Ethier (RC) .50 1.25
152 Jordan Tata RC .20 .50
153 Mike Napoli RC .50 1.25
154 Kason Gabbard (RC) .20 .50
155 Lastings Milledge (RC) .30 .75
156 Erick Aybar (RC) .20 .50
157 Fausto Carmona (RC) .20 .50
158 Russ Martin (RC) .30 .75
159 David Pauley (RC) .20 .50
160 Andy Marte (RC) .20 .50
161 Carlos Quentin (RC) .30 .75
162 Franklin Gutierrez (RC) .20 .50
163 Taylor Buchholz (RC) .30 .75
164 Josh Johnson (RC) .30 .75
165 Chad Billingsley (RC) .30 .75
166 Kendry Morales (RC) .50 1.25
167 Adam Loewen (RC) .30 .75
168 Yusmeiro Petit (RC) .20 .50
169 Matt Albers (RC) .20 .50
170 John Maine (RC) .30 .75
171 Alex Rodriguez SH .50 1.25
172 Mike Piazza SH .30 .75
173 Cory Sullivan SH .12 .30
174 Anibal Sanchez SH .12 .30
175 Trevor Hoffman SH .12 .30
176 Barry Bonds SH .60 1.50
177 Derek Jeter SH .75 2.00
178 Jose Reyes SH .30 .75
179 Manny Ramirez SH .20 .50
180 Vladimir Guerrero SH .20 .50
181 Mariano Rivera SH .30 .75
182 Mark Kotsay PH .12 .30
183 Derek Jeter PH .75 2.00
184 Carlos Delgado PH .12 .30
185 Frank Thomas PH .30 .75
186 Albert Pujols PH .60 1.50
187 Magglio Ordonez PH .12 .30
188 Carlos Delgado PH .12 .30
189 Kenny Rogers PH .12 .30
190 Tom Glavine PH .20 .50
191 Placido Polanco .12 .30
Jeff Suppan PH
192 Jose Reyes PH .30 .75
193 Endy Chavez .12 .30
Yadier Molina PH
194 Craig Monroe PH .12 .30
195 Justin Verlander .50 1.25
Joel Zumaya PH
196 Paul LoDuca .12 .30
Carlos Beltran PH
197 Albert Pujols .60 1.50
Jim Edmonds
Scott Rolen PH
198 Anthony Reyes PH .12 .30
199 Chris Carpenter PH .12 .30
200 David Eckstein PH .12 .30
201 Jered Weaver PH .60 1.50
202 David Ortiz .30 .75
Jermaine Dye
Travis Hafner LL
203 Joe Mauer .75 2.00
Derek Jeter
Robinson Cano LL
204 David Ortiz .30 .75
Justin Morneau
Raul Ibanez LL
205 Carl Crawford .50 1.25
Chone Figgins
Ichiro Suzuki LL
206 Johan Santana .50 1.25
Chien-Ming Wang
Jon Garland LL
207 Johan Santana .20 .50
Roy Halladay
C.C. Sabathia LL UER
The heading on the back for ERA was mistakenly labeled for Wins
208 Johan Santana .20 .50
Jeremy Bonderman
John Lackey LL
209 Francisco Rodriguez .12 .30
Bobby Jenks
B.J. Ryan LL
210 Ryan Howard .60 1.50
Albert Pujols
Alfonso Soriano LL
211 Freddy Sanchez .60 1.50
Miguel Cabrera
Albert Pujols LL
212 Ryan Howard .60 1.50
Albert Pujols
Lance Berkman LL
213 Jose Reyes .30 .75
Juan Pierre
Hanley Ramirez LL
214 Derek Lowe .12 .30
Brandon Webb
Carlos Zambrano LL
215 Roy Oswalt .12 .30
Chris Carpenter
Brandon Webb LL
216 Aaron Harang .20 .50
Jake Peavy
John Smoltz LL
217 Trevor Hoffman .12 .30
Billy Wagner
Joe Borowski LL
218 Ichiro Suzuki AS .50 1.25
219 Derek Jeter AS .75 2.00
220 Alex Rodriguez AS .50 1.25
221 David Ortiz AS .30 .75
222 Vladimir Guerrero AS .30 .75
223 Ivan Rodriguez AS .20 .50
224 Vernon Wells AS .12 .30
225 Mark Loretta AS .12 .30
226 Kenny Rogers AS .12 .30
227 Alfonso Soriano AS .12 .30
228 Carlos Beltran AS .12 .30
229 Albert Pujols AS .60 1.50
230 Jason Bay AS .12 .30
231 Edgar Renteria AS .12 .30
232 David Wright AS .50 1.25
233 Chase Utley AS .30 .75
234 Paul LoDuca AS .12 .30
235 Brad Penny AS .12 .30
236 Derrick Turnbow AS .12 .30
237 Mark Redman AS .12 .30
238 Francisco Liriano AS .30 .75
239 A.J. Pierzynski AS .12 .30
240 Grady Sizemore AS .20 .50
241 Jose Contreras AS .12 .30
242 Jermaine Dye AS .12 .30
243 Jason Schmidt AS .12 .30
244 Nomar Garciaparra AS .30 .75
245 Scott Kazmir AS .20 .50
246 Johan Santana AS .20 .50
247 Chris Capuano AS .12 .30
248 Magglio Ordonez AS .12 .30
249 Gary Matthews Jr. AS .12 .30
250 Carlos Lee AS .12 .30
251 David Eckstein AS .12 .30
252 Michael Young AS .12 .30
253 Matt Holliday AS .30 .75
254 Lance Berkman AS .12 .30
255 Scott Rolen AS .20 .50
256 Bronson Arroyo AS .12 .30
257 Barry Zito AS .12 .30
258 Brian McCann AS .12 .30
259 Jose Lopez AS .12 .30
260 Chris Carpenter AS .12 .30
261 Roy Halladay AS .12 .30
262 Jim Thome AS .20 .50
263 Dan Uggla AS .30 .75
264 Mariano Rivera AS .30 .75
265 Roy Oswalt AS .12 .30
266 Tom Gordon AS .12 .30
267 Troy Glaus AS .12 .30
268 Bobby Jenks AS .12 .30
269 Freddy Sanchez AS .12 .30
270 Paul Konerko AS .12 .30
271 Joe Mauer AS .20 .50
272 B.J. Ryan AS .12 .30
273 Ryan Howard AS .50 1.25
274 Brian Fuentes AS .12 .30
275 Miguel Cabrera AS .20 .50
276 Brandon Webb AS .12 .30
277 Mark Buehrle AS .12 .30
278 Trevor Hoffman AS .12 .30
279 Jonathan Papelbon AS .60 1.50
280 Andruw Jones AS .20 .50
281 Miguel Tejada AS .12 .30
282 Carlos Zambrano AS .12 .30
283 Ryan Howard HRD .50 1.25
284 David Wright HRD .50 1.25
285 Miguel Cabrera HRD .20 .50
286 David Ortiz HRD .30 .75
287 Jermaine Dye HRD .12 .30
288 Miguel Tejada HRD .12 .30
289 Lance Berkman HRD .12 .30
290 Troy Glaus HRD .12 .30
291 David Wright .50 1.25
Tom Glavine TL
292 Ryan Howard .50 1.25
Tom Gordon TL
293 Miguel Cabrera .20 .50
Dontrelle Willis TL
294 Andruw Jones .20 .50
John Smoltz TL
295 Alfonso Soriano .12 .30
Alfonso Soriano TL
296 Albert Pujols .60 1.50
Chris Carpenter TL
297 Adam Dunn .12 .30
Bronson Arroyo TL
298 Lance Berkman .12 .30
Roy Oswalt TL
299 Chris Capuano .50 1.25
Prince Fielder TL
300 Freddy Sanchez .12 .30
Jason Bay TL
301 Carlos Zambrano .12 .30
Juan Pierre TL
302 Adrian Gonzalez .12 .30
Trevor Hoffman TL
303 Derek Lowe .12 .30
Rafael Furcal TL
304 Omar Vizquel .20 .50
Jason Schmidt TL
305 Brandon Webb .12 .30
Chad Tracy TL
306 Matt Holliday .30 .75
Garrett Atkins TL
307 Alex Rodriguez .50 1.25
Chien-Ming Wang TL
308 Curt Schilling .30 .75
David Ortiz TL
309 Roy Halladay .12 .30
Vernon Wells TL
310 Miguel Tejada .12 .30
Erik Bedard TL
311 Carl Crawford .20 .50
Scott Kazmir TL
312 Jeremy Bonderman .12 .30
Magglio Ordonez TL
313 Justin Morneau .20 .50
Johan Santana TL
314 Jon Garland .12 .30
Jermaine Dye TL
315 Travis Hafner .12 .30
C.C. Sabathia TL
316 Emil Brown .12 .30
Mark Grudzielanek TL UER
Grudzielanek's name spelled incorrectly
317 Frank Thomas .30 .75
Barry Zito TL
318 Jered Weaver .60 1.50
Vladimir Guerrero TL UER
Ervin Santana was actual team leader in Wins
319 Michael Young .12 .30
Gary Matthews TL
320 Ichiro Suzuki .50 1.25
J.J. Putz TL
321 Derek Jeter .75 2.00
Robinson Cano CD
322 Chris Carpenter .12 .30
Mark Mulder CD
323 Jason Schmidt .12 .30
Trevor Hoffman CD
324 David Wright .50 1.25
Paul Lo Duca CD
325 Lance Berkman .12 .30
Roy Oswalt CD
326 Derek Jeter .30 .75
Jose Reyes CD
327 Cliff Floyd .50 1.25
David Wright CD
328 Francisco Liriano .30 .75
Johan Santana CD
329 J.D. Drew .30 .75
Stephen Drew CD
330 Jeff Weaver .60 1.50
Jered Weaver CD

2006 Topps Update 1st Edition

*1ST ED 1-132: 3X TO 8X BASIC
*1ST ED 133-170: 1.2X TO 3X BASIC RC
*1ST ED 171-330: 2X TO 5X BASIC
STATED ODDS 1:36 HOB, 1:12 HTA
73 Cory Lidle 4.00 10.00

2006 Topps Update Black

COMMON CARD (1-132) 6.00 15.00
COMMON ROOKIE (133-170) 8.00 20.00
COMMON CARD (171-330) 6.00 15.00
STATED ODDS 1:7 HTA
STATED PRINT RUN 55 SER.#'d SETS
1 Austin Kearns 6.00 15.00
2 Adam Eaton 6.00 15.00
3 Juan Encarnacion 6.00 15.00
4 Jarrod Washburn 6.00 15.00
5 Alex Gonzalez 6.00 15.00
6 Toby Hall 6.00 15.00
7 Preston Wilson 6.00 15.00
8 Ramon Ortiz 6.00 15.00
9 Jason Michaels 6.00 15.00
10 Jeff Weaver 6.00 15.00
11 Russell Branyan 6.00 15.00
12 Brett Tomko 6.00 15.00
13 Doug Mientkiewicz 6.00 15.00
14 David Wells 6.00 15.00
15 Corey Koskie 6.00 15.00
16 Russ Ortiz 6.00 15.00
17 Carlos Pena 6.00 15.00
18 Mark Hendrickson 6.00 15.00
19 Julian Tavarez 6.00 15.00
20 Jeff Conine 6.00 15.00
21 Dioner Navarro 6.00 15.00
22 Bob Wickman 6.00 15.00
23 Felipe Lopez 6.00 15.00
24 Eddie Guardado 6.00 15.00
25 David Dellucci 6.00 15.00
26 Ryan Wagner 6.00 15.00
27 Nick Green 6.00 15.00
28 Gary Majewski 6.00 15.00
29 Shea Hillenbrand 6.00 15.00
30 Jae Seo 6.00 15.00
31 Royce Clayton 6.00 15.00
32 Dave Riske 6.00 15.00
33 Joey Gathright 6.00 15.00
34 Robinson Tejada 6.00 15.00
35 Edwin Jackson 6.00 15.00
36 Aubrey Huff 6.00 15.00
37 Akinori Otsuka 6.00 15.00
38 Juan Castro 6.00 15.00
39 Zach Day 6.00 15.00
40 Jeremy Accardo 6.00 15.00
41 Shawn Green 6.00 15.00
42 Kazuo Matsui 6.00 15.00
43 J.J. Putz 6.00 15.00
44 David Ross 6.00 15.00
45 Scott Williamson 6.00 15.00
46 Joe Borchard 6.00 15.00
47 Elmer Dessens 6.00 15.00
48 Odalis Perez 6.00 15.00
49 Kelly Shoppach 6.00 15.00
50 Brandon Phillips 6.00 15.00
51 Guillermo Mota 6.00 15.00
52 Alex Cintron 6.00 15.00
53 Denny Bautista 6.00 15.00
54 Josh Bard 6.00 15.00
55 Julio Lugo 6.00 15.00
56 Doug Mirabelli 6.00 15.00
57 Kip Wells 6.00 15.00
58 Adrian Gonzalez 6.00 15.00
59 Shawn Chacon 6.00 15.00
60 Marcus Thames 6.00 15.00
61 Craig Wilson 6.00 15.00
62 Cory Sullivan 6.00 15.00
63 Ben Broussard 6.00 15.00
64 Todd Walker 6.00 15.00
65 Greg Maddux 20.00 50.00
66 Xavier Nady 6.00 15.00
67 Oliver Perez 6.00 15.00
68 Sean Casey 6.00 15.00
69 Kyle Lohse 6.00 15.00
70 Carlos Lee 6.00 15.00
71 Rheal Cormier 6.00 15.00
72 Ronnie Belliard 6.00 15.00
73 Cory Lidle 12.50 30.00
74 David Bell 6.00 15.00
75 Wilson Betemit 6.00 15.00
76 Danys Baez 6.00 15.00
77 Mike Stanton 6.00 15.00
78 Kevin Mench 6.00 15.00
79 Sandy Alomar Jr. 6.00 15.00
80 Cesar Izturis 6.00 15.00
81 Jeremy Affeldt 6.00 15.00
82 Matt Stairs 6.00 15.00
83 Hector Luna 6.00 15.00
84 Tony Graffanino 6.00 15.00
85 J.P Howell 6.00 15.00
86 Bengie Molina 6.00 15.00
87 Maicer Izturis 6.00 15.00
88 Marco Scutaro 6.00 15.00
89 Daryle Ward 6.00 15.00
90 Sal Fasano 6.00 15.00
91 Oscar Villarreal 6.00 15.00
92 Gabe Gross 6.00 15.00
93 Phil Nevin 6.00 15.00
94 Damon Hollins 6.00 15.00
95 Juan Cruz 6.00 15.00
96 Marlon Anderson 6.00 15.00
97 Jason Davis 6.00 15.00
98 Ryan Shealy 6.00 15.00
99 Francisco Cordero 6.00 15.00
100 Bobby Abreu 6.00 15.00
101 Roberto Hernandez 6.00 15.00
102 Gary Bennett 6.00 15.00
103 Aaron Sele 6.00 15.00
104 Nook Logan 6.00 15.00
105 Alfredo Amezaga 6.00 15.00
106 Chris Woodward 6.00 15.00
107 Kevin Jarvis 6.00 15.00
108 B.J. Upton 6.00 15.00
109 Alan Embree 6.00 15.00
110 Milton Bradley 6.00 15.00
111 Pete Orr 6.00 15.00
112 Jeff Cirillo 6.00 15.00
113 Corey Patterson 6.00 15.00
114 Josh Paul 6.00 15.00
115 Fernando Rodney 6.00 15.00
116 Jerry Hairston Jr. 6.00 15.00
117 Scott Proctor 6.00 15.00
118 Ambiorix Burgos 6.00 15.00
119 Jose Bautista 6.00 15.00
120 Livan Hernandez 6.00 15.00
121 John Mcdonald 6.00 15.00
122 Ronny Cedeno 6.00 15.00
123 Nate Robertson 6.00 15.00
124 Jamey Carroll 6.00 15.00
125 Alex Escobar 6.00 15.00
126 Endy Chavez 6.00 15.00
127 Jorge Julio 6.00 15.00
128 Kenny Lofton 6.00 15.00
129 Matt Diaz 6.00 15.00
130 Dave Bush 6.00 15.00
131 Jose Molina 6.00 15.00
132 Mike MacDougal 6.00 15.00
133 Ben Zobrist 10.00 25.00
134 Shane Komine 10.00 25.00
135 Casey Janssen 10.00 25.00
136 Kevin Frandsen 10.00 25.00
137 John Rheinecker 8.00 20.00
138 Matt Kemp 10.00 25.00
139 Scott Mathieson 8.00 20.00
140 Jered Weaver 12.50 30.00
141 Joel Guzman 8.00 20.00
142 Anibal Sanchez 8.00 20.00
143 Melky Cabrera 12.50 30.00
144 Howie Kendrick 12.50 30.00
145 Cole Hamels 10.00 25.00
146 Willy Aybar 8.00 20.00
147 James Shields 8.00 20.00
148 Kevin Thompson 8.00 20.00
149 Jon Lester 12.50 30.00
150 Stephen Drew 10.00 25.00
151 Andre Ethier 12.50 30.00
152 Jordan Tata 8.00 20.00
153 Mike Napoli 12.50 30.00
154 Kason Gabbard 8.00 20.00
155 Lastings Milledge 10.00 25.00
156 Erick Aybar 8.00 20.00
157 Fausto Carmona 8.00 20.00
158 Russ Martin 10.00 25.00
159 David Pauley 8.00 20.00
160 Andy Marte 8.00 20.00
161 Carlos Quentin 10.00 25.00
162 Franklin Gutierrez 8.00 20.00
163 Taylor Buchholz 10.00 25.00
164 Josh Johnson 10.00 25.00
165 Chad Billingsley 10.00 25.00
166 Kendry Morales 10.00 25.00
167 Akinori Loewen 10.00 25.00
168 Yusmeiro Petit 8.00 20.00
169 Matt Albers 8.00 20.00
170 John Maine 10.00 25.00
171 Alex Rodriguez SH 20.00 50.00
172 Mike Piazza SH 12.50 30.00
173 Cory Sullivan SH 6.00 15.00
174 Anibal Sanchez SH 6.00 15.00
175 Trevor Hoffman SH 6.00 15.00
176 Barry Bonds SH 20.00 50.00
177 Derek Jeter SH 20.00 50.00
178 Jose Reyes SH 6.00 15.00
179 Manny Ramirez SH 8.00 20.00
180 Vladimir Guerrero SH 12.50 30.00
181 Mariano Rivera SH 12.50 30.00
182 Mark Kotsay PH 6.00 15.00
183 Derek Jeter PH 20.00 50.00
184 Carlos Delgado PH 6.00 15.00
185 Frank Thomas PH 12.50 30.00
186 Albert Pujols PH 20.00 50.00
187 Magglio Ordonez PH 6.00 15.00
188 Carlos Delgado PH 6.00 15.00
189 Kenny Rogers PH 6.00 15.00
190 Tom Glavine PH 8.00 20.00
191 Placido Polanco 6.00 15.00
Jeff Suppan PH
192 Jose Reyes PH 6.00 15.00
193 Endy Chavez 6.00 15.00
Yadier Molina PH
194 Craig Monroe PH 6.00 15.00
195 Justin Verlander 20.00 50.00
Joel Zumaya PH
196 Paul LoDuca 6.00 15.00
Carlos Beltran PH
197 Albert Pujols 20.00 50.00
Jim Edmonds
Scott Rolen PH
198 Anthony Reyes PH 6.00 15.00
199 Chris Carpenter PH 6.00 15.00
200 David Eckstein PH 6.00 15.00
201 Jered Weaver PH 20.00 50.00
202 David Ortiz 12.50 30.00
Jermaine Dye
Travis Hafner LL
203 Joe Mauer 20.00 50.00
Derek Jeter
Robinson Cano LL
204 David Ortiz 12.50 30.00
Justin Morneau
Raul Ibanez LL
205 Carl Crawford 20.00 50.00
Chone Figgins
Ichiro Suzuki LL
206 Johan Santana 20.00 50.00
Chien-Ming Wang
Jon Garland LL
207 Johan Santana 8.00 20.00
Roy Halladay
C.C. Sabathia LL
208 Johan Santana 8.00 20.00
Jeremy Bonderman
John Lackey LL
209 Francisco Rodriguez 6.00 15.00
Bobby Jenks
B.J. Ryan LL
210 Ryan Howard 20.00 50.00
Albert Pujols
Alfonso Soriano LL
211 Freddy Sanchez 20.00 50.00
Miguel Cabrera
Albert Pujols LL
212 Ryan Howard 20.00 50.00
Albert Pujols
Lance Berkman LL
213 Jose Reyes 12.50 30.00
Juan Pierre
Hanley Ramirez LL
214 Derek Lowe 6.00 15.00
Brandon Webb
Carlos Zambrano LL
215 Roy Oswalt 6.00 15.00
Chris Carpenter
Brandon Webb LL
216 Aaron Harang 8.00 20.00
Jake Peavy
John Smoltz LL
217 Trevor Hoffman 6.00 15.00
Billy Wagner
Joe Borowski LL
218 Ichiro Suzuki AS 20.00 50.00
219 Derek Jeter AS 20.00 50.00
220 Alex Rodriguez AS 20.00 50.00
221 David Ortiz AS 12.50 30.00
222 Vladimir Guerrero AS 12.50 30.00
223 Ivan Rodriguez AS 8.00 20.00
224 Vernon Wells AS 6.00 15.00
225 Mark Loretta AS 6.00 15.00
226 Kenny Rogers AS 6.00 15.00
227 Alfonso Soriano AS 6.00 15.00
228 Carlos Beltran AS 6.00 15.00
229 Albert Pujols AS 20.00 50.00
230 Jason Bay AS 6.00 15.00
231 Edgar Renteria AS 6.00 15.00
232 David Wright AS 20.00 50.00
233 Chase Utley AS 12.50 30.00
234 Paul LoDuca AS 6.00 15.00
235 Brad Penny AS 6.00 15.00
236 Derrick Turnbow AS 6.00 15.00
237 Mark Redman AS 6.00 15.00
238 Francisco Liriano AS 20.00 50.00
239 A.J. Pierzynski AS 6.00 15.00
240 Grady Sizemore AS 8.00 20.00
241 Jose Contreras AS 6.00 15.00
242 Jermaine Dye AS 6.00 15.00
243 Jason Schmidt AS 6.00 15.00
244 Nomar Garciaparra AS 12.50 30.00
245 Scott Kazmir AS 8.00 20.00
246 Johan Santana AS 8.00 20.00
247 Chris Capuano AS 6.00 15.00
248 Magglio Ordonez AS 6.00 15.00
249 Gary Matthews Jr. AS 6.00 15.00
250 Carlos Lee AS 6.00 15.00
251 David Eckstein AS 6.00 15.00
252 Michael Young AS 6.00 15.00
253 Matt Holliday AS 8.00 20.00
254 Lance Berkman AS 6.00 15.00
255 Scott Rolen AS 8.00 20.00
256 Bronson Arroyo AS 6.00 15.00
257 Barry Zito AS 6.00 15.00
258 Brian McCann AS 6.00 15.00
259 Jose Lopez AS 6.00 15.00
260 Chris Carpenter AS 6.00 15.00
261 Roy Halladay AS 6.00 15.00
262 Jim Thome AS 8.00 20.00
263 Dan Uggla AS 12.50 30.00
264 Mariano Rivera AS 12.50 30.00
265 Roy Oswalt AS 6.00 15.00
266 Tom Gordon AS 6.00 15.00
267 Troy Glaus AS 6.00 15.00
268 Bobby Jenks AS 6.00 15.00
269 Freddy Sanchez AS 6.00 15.00
270 Paul Konerko AS 6.00 15.00
271 Joe Mauer AS 8.00 20.00
272 B.J. Ryan AS 6.00 15.00
273 Ryan Howard AS 20.00 50.00
274 Brian Fuentes AS 6.00 15.00
275 Miguel Cabrera AS 8.00 20.00
276 Brandon Webb AS 6.00 15.00
277 Mark Buehrle AS 6.00 15.00
278 Trevor Hoffman AS 6.00 15.00
279 Jonathan Papelbon AS 20.00 50.00
280 Andruw Jones AS 8.00 20.00
281 Miguel Tejada AS 6.00 15.00
282 Carlos Zambrano AS 6.00 15.00
283 Ryan Howard HRD 20.00 50.00
284 David Wright HRD 20.00 50.00
285 Miguel Cabrera HRD 8.00 20.00
286 David Ortiz HRD 12.50 30.00
287 Jermaine Dye HRD 6.00 15.00
288 Miguel Tejada HRD 6.00 15.00
289 Lance Berkman HRD 6.00 15.00
290 Troy Glaus HRD 6.00 15.00
291 David Wright 20.00 50.00
Tom Glavine TL
292 Ryan Howard 20.00 50.00
Tom Gordon TL
293 Miguel Cabrera 8.00 20.00
Dontrelle Willis TL
294 Andruw Jones 8.00 20.00
John Smoltz TL
295 Alfonso Soriano 6.00 15.00
Alfonso Soriano TL
296 Albert Pujols 20.00 50.00
Chris Carpenter TL
297 Adam Dunn 6.00 15.00
Bronson Arroyo TL
298 Lance Berkman 6.00 15.00
Roy Oswalt TL
299 Chris Capuano 20.00 50.00
Prince Fielder TL
300 Freddy Sanchez 6.00 15.00
Jason Bay TL
301 Carlos Zambrano 6.00 15.00
Juan Pierre TL
302 Adrian Gonzalez 6.00 15.00
Trevor Hoffman TL
303 Derek Lowe 6.00 15.00
Rafael Furcal TL
304 Omar Vizquel 8.00 20.00
Jason Schmidt TL
305 Brandon Webb 6.00 15.00
Chad Tracy TL
306 Matt Holliday 8.00 20.00
Garrett Atkins TL
307 Alex Rodriguez 20.00 50.00
Chien-Ming Wang TL
308 Curt Schilling 12.50 30.00
David Ortiz TL
309 Roy Halladay 6.00 15.00
Vernon Wells TL
310 Miguel Tejada 6.00 15.00
Erik Bedard TL
311 Carl Crawford 8.00 20.00
Scott Kazmir TL
312 Jeremy Bonderman 6.00 15.00
Magglio Ordonez TL
313 Justin Morneau 8.00 20.00
Johan Santana TL
314 Jon Garland 6.00 15.00
Jermaine Dye TL
315 Travis Hafner 6.00 15.00
C.C. Sabathia TL
316 Emil Brown 6.00 15.00
Mark Grundzielanek TL
317 Frank Thomas 12.50 30.00
Barry Zito TL
318 Jered Weaver 20.00 50.00
Vladimir Guerrero TL
319 Michael Young 6.00 15.00
Gary Mathews TL
320 Ichiro Suzuki 20.00 50.00
J.J. Putz TL
321 Derek Jeter 20.00 50.00
Robinson Cano CD
322 Chris Carpenter 6.00 15.00
Mark Mulder CD
323 Jason Schmidt 6.00 15.00
Trevor Hoffman CD
324 David Wright 20.00 50.00
Paul Lo Duca CD
325 Lance Berkman 6.00 15.00
Roy Oswalt CD
326 Derek Jeter 20.00 50.00
Jose Reyes CD
327 Cliff Floyd 20.00 50.00
David Wright CD
328 Francisco Liriano 20.00 50.00
Johan Santana CD
329 J.D. Drew 12.50 30.00
Stephen Drew CD
330 Jeff Weaver 20.00 50.00
Jered Weaver CD

2006 Topps Update Gold

*GOLD 1-132: 2X TO 5X BASIC
*GOLD 133-170: .75X TO 2X BASIC RC
*GOLD 171-330: 1.2X TO 3X BASIC
STATED ODDS 1:4 HOB, 1:2 HTA, 1:6 RET
STATED PRINT RUN 2006 SER.#'d SETS
73 Cory Lidle

2006 Topps Update Platinum

ODDS 1:12,000 H,1:8800 HTA,1:12,000 R
STATED PRINT RUN 1 SERIAL #'d SET
NO PRICING DUE TO SCARCITY

2006 Topps Update All Star Autographs

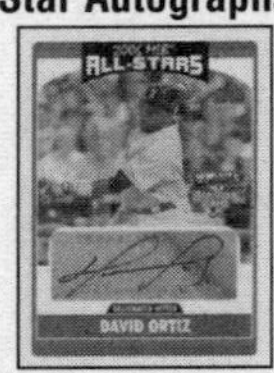

ODDS 1:48,000 H,1:16,000 HTA,1:57,000 R
STATED PRINT RUN 25 SER.#'d SETS
NO PRICING DUE TO SCARCITY
AR Alex Rodriguez
DO David Ortiz
DW David Wright

2006 Topps Update All Star Stitches

STATED ODDS 1:43 H,1:15 HTA,1:53 R
PATCH ODDS 1:2300 HOBBY,1:377 HTA
PATCH PRINT RUN 10 SER. #'d SETS
NO PATCH PRICING DUE TO SCARCITY
AJ Andruw Jones Jsy 5.00 12.00
AJP A.J. Pierzynski Jsy 4.00 10.00
AP Albert Pujols Jsy 12.50 30.00
AR Alex Rodriguez Jsy 6.00 15.00
AS Alfonso Soriano Jsy 5.00 12.00
BA Bronson Arroyo Jsy 5.00 12.00
BF Brian Fuentes Jsy 3.00 8.00
BJ Bobby Jenks Jsy 4.00 10.00
BM Brian McCann Jsy 6.00 15.00
BP Brad Penny Jsy 4.00 10.00
BR B.J. Ryan Jsy 4.00 10.00
BW Brandon Webb Jsy 5.00 12.00
CB Carlos Beltran Jsy 4.00 10.00
CC Chris Carpenter Jsy 5.00 12.00
CFC Chris Capuano Jsy 3.00 8.00
CL Carlos Lee Jsy 4.00 10.00
CU Chase Utley Jsy 5.00 12.00
CZ Carlos Zambrano Jsy 4.00 10.00
DE David Eckstein Jsy 6.00 15.00
DO David Ortiz Jsy 5.00 12.00
DT Derrick Turnbow Jsy 3.00 8.00
DU Dan Uggla Jsy 4.00 10.00
DW David Wright Jsy 8.00 20.00
ER Edgar Renteria Jsy 4.00 10.00
FS Freddy Sanchez Jsy 5.00 12.00
GM Gary Matthews Jr. Jsy 3.00 8.00
GS Grady Sizemore Jsy 5.00 12.00
IR Ivan Rodriguez Jsy 5.00 12.00
JB Jason Bay Jsy 6.00 15.00
JC Jose Contreras Jsy 4.00 10.00
JD Jermaine Dye Jsy 4.00 10.00
JDS Jason Schmidt Jsy 4.00 10.00
JL Jose Lopez Jsy 3.00 8.00
JM Joe Mauer Jsy 5.00 12.00
JP Jonathan Papelbon Jsy 8.00 20.00
JR Jose Reyes Jsy 3.00 8.00
JS Johan Santana Jsy 4.00 10.00
JT Jim Thome Jsy 5.00 12.00
KR Kenny Rogers Jsy 4.00 10.00
LB Lance Berkman Jsy 4.00 10.00
MAR Mark Redman Jsy 4.00 10.00
MB Mark Buehrle Jsy 4.00 10.00
MC Miguel Cabrera Jsy 5.00 12.00
MH Matt Holliday Jsy 5.00 12.00
ML Mark Loretta Jsy 4.00 10.00
MO Magglio Ordonez Jsy 4.00 10.00
MR Mariano Rivera Jsy 5.00 12.00
MT Miguel Tejada Jsy 3.00 8.00
MY Michael Young Jsy 3.00 8.00
PK Paul Konerko Jsy 4.00 10.00
PL Paul LoDuca Jsy 3.00 8.00
RC Robinson Cano Jsy 6.00 15.00
RH Roy Halladay Jsy 4.00 10.00
RJH Ryan Howard Jsy 12.50 30.00
RO Roy Oswalt Jsy 3.00 8.00
SK Scott Kazmir Jsy 4.00 10.00
SR Scott Rolen Jsy 5.00 12.00
TEG Troy Glaus Jsy 3.00 8.00
TG Tom Gordon Jsy 4.00 10.00
TH Trevor Hoffman Jsy 3.00 8.00
TMG Tom Glavine Jsy 5.00 12.00
VG Vladimir Guerrero Jsy 4.00 10.00
VW Vernon Wells Jsy 4.00 10.00

2006 Topps Update All Star Stitches Dual

STATED ODDS 1:2550 HOBBY,1:752 HTA
STATED PRINT RUN 50 SER.#'d SETS
CJ Andruw Jones 10.00 25.00
Miguel Cabrera
HS Johan Santana 10.00 25.00
Roy Halladay
HT Jim Thome Jsy 20.00 50.00
Ryan Howard Jsy
MM Joe Mauer 10.00 25.00
Brian McCann
PW David Wright 30.00 60.00
Albert Pujols
RH Mariano Rivera Jsy 30.00 60.00
Trevor Hoffman Jsy
RO David Ortiz 20.00 50.00
Alex Rodriguez
SS Ichiro Suzuki 20.00 50.00
Alfonso Soriano
TG Miguel Tejada 10.00 25.00
Vladimir Guerrero
WS Grady Sizemore Jsy 12.50 30.00
Vernon Wells Jsy

2006 Topps Update Barry Bonds 715

STATED ODDS 1:36 H,1:36 HTA,1:36 R
BB Barry Bonds 2.00 5.00

2006 Topps Update Barry Bonds Home Run History Autographs

ODDS 1:42,400 H,1:15,141 HTA,1:50,000 R
STATED PRINT RUN 5 SER.#'d SETS
NO PRICING DUE TO SCARCITY

2006 Topps Update Barry Bonds 715 Relics

ODDS 1:5000 H,1:1827 HTA,1:5950 R
STATED PRINT RUN 715 SER.#'d SETS
BB Barry Bonds Jsy 20.00 50.00

2006 Topps Update Derby Digs Jerseys

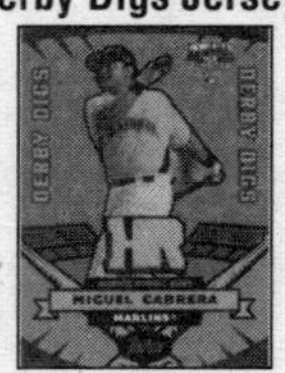

ODDS 1:4200 H,1:1631 HTA, 1:5700 R
NO PRICING DUE TO SCARCITY
DO David Ortiz
DW David Wright
JD Jermaine Dye
LB Lance Berkman
MC Miguel Cabrera
MT Miguel Tejada
RH Ryan Howard
TG Troy Glaus

2006 Topps Update Midsummer Covers Baseball Relics

STATED ODDS 1:7750 HOBBY
STATED PRINT RUN 10 SERIAL #'d SETS
NO PRICING DUE TO SCARCITY
AR Alex Rodriguez
AS Alfonso Soriano
BR B.J. Ryan
CU Chase Utley
DW David Wright
JB Jason Bay
MR Mariano Rivera
MY Michael Young
PK Paul Konerko
VG Vladimir Guerrero

2006 Topps Update Rookie Debut

STATED ODDS 1:4 HOB, 1:4 RET
RD1 Joel Zumaya 1.00 2.50
RD2 Ian Kinsler .60 1.50
RD3 Kenji Johjima 2.00 5.00
RD4 Josh Barfield .40 1.00
RD5 Nick Markakis .60 1.50
RD6 Dan Uggla 1.00 2.50
RD7 Eric Reed .40 1.00
RD8 Carlos Martinez .40 1.00
RD9 Angel Pagan .40 1.00
RD10 Jason Childers .40 1.00
RD11 Ruddy Lugo .40 1.00
RD12 James Loney .60 1.50
RD13 Fernando Nieve .40 1.00
RD14 Reggie Abercrombie .40 1.00
RD15 Boone Logan .40 1.00
RD16 Brian Bannister .40 1.00
RD17 Ricky Nolasco .40 1.00
RD18 Willie Eyre .40 1.00
RD19 Fabio Castro .40 1.00
RD20 Jordan Tata .40 1.00
RD21 Taylor Buchholz .40 1.00
RD22 Sean Marshall .40 1.00
RD23 John Rheinecker .40 1.00
RD24 Casey Janssen .40 1.00
RD25 Russ Martin .40 1.00
RD26 Yusmeiro Petit .40 1.00
RD27 Kendry Morales 1.00 2.50
RD28 Alay Soler .40 1.00
RD29 Jered Weaver 2.00 5.00
RD30 Matt Kemp .60 1.50
RD31 Enrique Gonzalez .40 1.00
RD32 Lastings Milledge .60 1.50
RD33 Jamie Shields .40 1.00
RD34 David Pauley .40 1.00
RD35 Zach Jackson .40 1.00
RD36 Zach Minor .40 1.00
RD37 Jon Lester 3.00 8.00
RD38 Chad Billingsley .40 1.00
RD39 Scott Thorman .40 1.00
RD40 Anibal Sanchez .40 1.00
RD41 Mike Thompson .40 1.00
RD42 T.J. Beam .40 1.00
RD43 Stephen Drew 1.00 2.50
RD44 Joe Saunders .40 1.00
RD45 Carlos Quentin .60 1.50

2006 Topps Update Rookie Debut Autographs

A ODDS 1:10,600 H,1:4416 HTA,1:15,500 R
B ODDS 1:5600 H, 1:2163 HTA,1:7500 R
C ODDS 1:2200 H, 1:815 HTA,1:2650 R
D ODDS 1:1180 H, 1:415 HTA,1:1500 R
NO GROUP A PRICING DUE TO SCARCITY
AL Adam Loewen B 20.00 50.00
BL Bobby Livingston C 6.00 15.00
EF Emiliano Fruto C 6.00 15.00
FC Fausto Carmona C 6.00 15.00
IK Ian Kinsler A
JL Jon Lester D 15.00 40.00
JS Jeremy Sowers B 6.00 15.00
MA Matt Albers A
MN Mike Napoli D 15.00 40.00
MP Martin Prado D 6.00 15.00
RA Reggie Abercrombie A
RN Ricky Nolasco D 6.00 15.00
ST Scott Thorman C 6.00 15.00
YP Yusmeiro Petit D 6.00 15.00

2006 Topps Update Signature Moves

A ODDS 1:300,000 H,1:53,000 HTA,1:57,000 R
B ODDS 1:100,000 H,1:30,000 HTA,1:57,000 R
C-D ODDS 1:17,500 H,1:6624 HTA,1:22,000 R
E ODDS 1:9800 H,1:2600 HTA,1:10,500 R
NO PRICING DUE TO SCARCITY
AH Aubrey Huff C
BP Brandon Phillips E
BW Brad Wilkerson C
CW Craig Wilson B
JD Johnny Damon A
JL Julio Lugo D

2006 Topps Update Touch 'Em All Base Relics

STATED ODDS 1:610 HOBBY,1:90 HTA
AP Albert Pujols 12.50 30.00
AR Alex Rodriguez 10.00 25.00
CB Carlos Beltran 5.00 12.00
DO David Ortiz 8.00 20.00
DW David Wright 10.00 25.00
IS Ichiro Suzuki 10.00 25.00
JM Joe Mauer 6.00 15.00
MT Miguel Tejada 5.00 12.00
MY Michael Young 5.00 12.00
RH Ryan Howard 10.00 25.00

2007 Topps Pre-Production

This three-card set was released to hobby dealers and media in January, 2007 to preview the upcoming 2007 Topps Series I product.

COMPLETE SET (3) 4.00 10.00
1 David Ortiz 1.25 3.00
2 David Wright 2.00 5.00
3 Ryan Howard 2.00 5.00

2007 Topps

This 661-card set was released over two series. The first series was issued in February, 2007 while the second series

COMP.HOLIDAY SET (661) 40.00 80.00
COMP.CARDINALS SET (661) 40.00 80.00
COMP.CUBS SET (661) 40.00 80.00
COMP.DODGERS SET (661) 40.00 80.00
COMP.RED SOX SET (661) 40.00 80.00
COMP.YANKEES SET (661) 40.00 80.00
COMP.SET w/o VAR. (661) 40.00 80.00
COMPLETE SERIES 1 (330) 15.00 40.00
COMP.SERIES 1 w/o #40 (329) 10.00 25.00
COMPLETE SERIES 2 (331) 25.00 50.00
COMMON CARD (1-330) .07 .20
COMMON RC .20 .50
SER.1 VAR. ODDS 1:3700 WAL-MART
SER.2 VAR.ODDS 1:30 HOBBY
NO SER.1 VAR.PRICING DUE TO SCARTIY
OVERALL PLATE SER.1 ODDS 1:98 HTA
OVERALL PLATE SER.2 ODDS 1:139 HTA
PLATE PRINT RUN 1 SET PER COLOR
BLACK-CYAN-MAGENTA-YELLOW ISSUED
NO PLATE PRICING DUE TO SCARCITY
1 John Lackey .07 .20
2 Nick Swisher .07 .20
3 Brad Lidge .07 .20
4 Bengie Molina .07 .20
5 Bobby Abreu .07 .20
6 Edgar Renteria .07 .20
7 Mickey Mantle 1.00 2.50
8 Preston Wilson .07 .20
9 Ryan Dempster .07 .20
10 C.C. Sabathia .07 .20
11 Julio Lugo .07 .20
12 J.D. Drew .07 .20
13 Miguel Batista .07 .20
14 Eliezer Alfonzo .07 .20
15a Andrew Miller RC 1.25 3.00
15b Andrew Miller RC 1.25 3.00
Posed
16 Jason Varitek .20 .50
17 Saul Rivera .07 .20
18 Orlando Hernandez .07 .20
19 Alfredo Amezaga .07 .20
20a Delmon Young (RC) .30 .75
Face Right
20b Delmon Young (RC) .30 .75
Face Left
21 Chris Britton .07 .20
22 Corey Patterson .07 .20
23 Josh Bard .07 .20
24 Tom Gordon .07 .20
25 Gary Matthews .07 .20
26 Jason Jennings .07 .20
27 Joey Gathright .07 .20
28 Brandon Inge .07 .20
29 Pat Neshek .30 .75
30 Bronson Arroyo .07 .20
31 Jay Payton .07 .20
32 Andy Pettitte .12 .30
33 Ervin Santana .07 .20
Fascimile signature is Johan Santana
34 Paul Konerko .07 .20
35 Joel Zumaya .12 .30
36 Gregg Zaun .07 .20
37 Tony Gwynn Jr. .07 .20
38 Adam LaRoche .07 .20
39 Jim Edmonds .12 .30
40a Derek Jeter 6.00 15.00
Mickey Mantle and George W.Bush in background
40b Derek Jeter .50 1.25
41 Rich Hill .07 .20
42 Livan Hernandez .07 .20
43 Aubrey Huff .07 .20
44 Todd Greene .07 .20
45 Andre Ethier .12 .30
46 Jeremy Sowers .07 .20
47 Ben Broussard .07 .20
48 Darren Oliver .07 .20
49 Nook Logan .07 .20
50 Miguel Cabrera .12 .30
51 Carlos Lee .07 .20
52 Jose Castillo .07 .20
53 Mike Piazza .20 .50
54 Daniel Cabrera .07 .20
55 Cole Hamels .20 .50
56 Mark Loretta .07 .20
57 Brian Fuentes .07 .20
58 Todd Coffey .07 .20
59 Brent Clevlen .07 .20
60 John Smoltz .12 .30
61 Jason Grilli .07 .20
62 Dan Wheeler .07 .20
63 Scott Proctor .07 .20
64 Bobby Kielty .07 .20
65 Dan Uggla .12 .30
66 Lyle Overbay .07 .20
67 Geoff Jenkins .07 .20
68 Michael Barrett .07 .20
69 Casey Fossum .07 .20
70 Ivan Rodriguez .12 .30
71 Jose Lopez .07 .20
72 Jake Westbrook .07 .20
73 Moises Alou .07 .20
74 Jose Valverde .07 .20
75 Jered Weaver .12 .30
76 Lastings Milledge .12 .30
77 Austin Kearns .07 .20
78 Adam Loewen .07 .20
79 Josh Barfield .07 .20
80 Johan Santana .12 .30
81 Ian Kinsler .07 .20
82 Ian Snell .07 .20
83 Mike Lowell .07 .20
84 Elizardo Ramirez .07 .20
85 Scott Rolen .12 .30
86 Shannon Stewart .07 .20
87 Alexis Gomez .07 .20
88 Jimmy Gobble .07 .20
89 Jamey Carroll .07 .20
90 Chipper Jones .20 .50
91 Carlos Silva .07 .20
92 Joe Crede .07 .20
93 Mike Napoli .07 .20
94 Willy Taveras .07 .20
95 Rafael Furcal .07 .20
96 Phil Nevin .07 .20
97 Dave Bush .07 .20
98 Marcus Giles .07 .20
99 Joe Blanton .07 .20
100 Dontrelle Willis .07 .20
101 Scott Kazmir .12 .30
102 Jeff Kent .07 .20
103 Pedro Feliz .07 .20
104 Johnny Estrada .07 .20
105 Travis Hafner .07 .20
106 Ryan Garko .07 .20
107 Rafael Soriano .07 .20
108 Wes Helms .07 .20
109 Billy Wagner .07 .20
110 Aaron Rowand .07 .20
111 Felipe Lopez .07 .20
112 Jeff Conine .07 .20
113 Nick Markakis .12 .30
114 John Koronka .07 .20
115 B.J. Ryan .07 .20
116 Tim Wakefield .07 .20
117 David Ross .07 .20
118 Emil Brown .07 .20
119 Michael Cuddyer .07 .20
120 Jason Giambi .07 .20
121 Alex Cintron .07 .20
122 Luke Scott .07 .20
123 Chone Figgins .07 .20
124 Huston Street .07 .20
125 Carlos Delgado .07 .20
126 Daryle Ward .07 .20
127 Chris Duncan .07 .20
128 Damian Miller .07 .20
129 Aramis Ramirez .07 .20
130 Albert Pujols .40 1.00
131 Chris Snyder .07 .20
132 Ray Durham .07 .20
133 Gary Sheffield .07 .20
134 Mike Jacobs .07 .20
135a Troy Tulowitzki (RC) .50 1.25
135b Troy Tulowitzki (RC) .50 1.25
Throw
136 Jon Rauch .07 .20
137 Jay Gibbons .07 .20
138 Adrian Gonzalez .07 .20
139 Prince Fielder .20 .50
140 Freddy Sanchez .07 .20
141 Rich Aurilia .07 .20
142 Trot Nixon .07 .20
143 Vicente Padilla .07 .20
144 Jack Wilson .07 .20
145 Jake Peavy .07 .20
146 Luke Hudson .07 .20
147 Javier Vazquez .07 .20
148 Scott Podsednik .07 .20
149 Magglio Ordonez .12 .30
Ivan Rodriguez CC
150 Todd Helton .12 .30
151 Kendry Morales .12 .30
152 Adam Everett .07 .20
153 Bob Wickman .07 .20
154 Bill Hall .07 .20
155 Jeremy Bonderman .07 .20
156 Ryan Theriot .07 .20
157 Rocco Baldelli .07 .20
158 Noah Lowry .07 .20
159 Jason Michaels .07 .20
160 Justin Verlander .20 .50
161 Eduardo Perez .07 .20
162 Chris Ray .07 .20
163 Dave Roberts .07 .20
164 Zach Duke .07 .20
165 Mark Buehrle .07 .20
166 Hank Blalock .07 .20
167 Royce Clayton .07 .20
168 Mark Teahen .07 .20
169 Todd Jones .07 .20
170 Chien-Ming Wang .30 .75
171 Nick Punto .07 .20
172 Morgan Ensberg .07 .20
173 Rob Mackowiak .07 .20
174 Frank Catalanotto .07 .20
175 Matt Murton .07 .20
176 Alfonso Soriano .07 .20
Carlos Beltran CC
177 Francisco Cordero .07 .20
178 Jason Marquis .07 .20
179 Joe Nathan .07 .20
180 Roy Halladay UER .07 .20
Bio is Joe Nathan's
181 Melvin Mora .07 .20
182 Ramon Ortiz .07 .20
183 Jose Valentin .07 .20
184 Gil Meche .07 .20
185 B.J. Upton .07 .20
186 Grady Sizemore .12 .30
187 Matt Cain .12 .30
188 Eric Byrnes .07 .20
189 Carl Crawford .07 .20
190 J.J. Putz .07 .20
191 Cla Meredith .07 .20
192 Matt Capps .07 .20
193 Rod Barajas .07 .20
194 Edwin Encarnacion .07 .20
195 James Loney .12 .30
196 Johnny Damon .12 .30
197 Freddy Garcia .07 .20
198 Mike Redmond .07 .20
199 Ryan Shealy .07 .20
200 Carlos Beltran .07 .20
201 Chuck James .07 .20
202 Mark Ellis .07 .20
203 Brad Ausmus .07 .20
204 Juan Rivera .07 .20
205 Cory Sullivan .07 .20
206 Ben Sheets .07 .20
207 Mark Mulder .07 .20
208 Carlos Quentin .07 .20
209 Jonathan Broxton .07 .20
210 Kazuo Matsui .07 .20
211 Armando Benitez .07 .20
212 Richie Sexson .07 .20
213 Josh Johnson .07 .20
214 Brian Schneider .07 .20
215 Craig Monroe .07 .20
216 Chris Duffy .07 .20
217 Chris Coste .07 .20
218 Clay Hensley .07 .20
219 Chris Gomez .07 .20
220 Hideki Matsui .20 .50
221 Robinson Tejeda UER .07 .20
Tejeda is misspelled on front
222 Scott Hatteberg .07 .20
223 Jeff Francis .07 .20
224 Matt Thornton .07 .20
225 Robinson Cano .12 .30
226 Chicago White Sox .07 .20
227 Oakland Athletics .07 .20
228 St. Louis Cardinals .07 .20
229 New York Mets .07 .20
230 Barry Zito .07 .20
231 Baltimore Orioles .07 .20
232 Seattle Mariners .07 .20
233 Houston Astros .07 .20
234 Pittsburgh Pirates .07 .20
235 Reed Johnson .07 .20
236 Boston Red Sox .30 .75
237 Cincinnati Reds .07 .20
238 Philadelphia Phillies .07 .20
239 New York Yankees .20 .50
240 Chris Carpenter .07 .20
241 Atlanta Braves .12 .30
242 San Francisco Giants .07 .20
243 Joe Torre MG .12 .30
244 Tampa Bay Devil Rays .07 .20
245 Chad Tracy .07 .20
246 Clint Hurdle MG .07 .20
247 Mike Scioscia MG UER .07 .20
Incorrect Career Stats
248 Ron Gardenhire MG UER .07 .20
Incorrect Career Stats
249 Tony LaRussa MG UER .07 .20
Stats in header and in text do not agree
250 Anibal Sanchez .07 .20
251 Charlie Manuel MG .07 .20
252 John Gibbons MG .07 .20
253 Jim Tracy MG .07 .20
254 Jerry Narron MG .07 .20
255 Brad Penny .07 .20
256 Bobby Cox MG .07 .20
257 Bob Melvin MG .07 .20
258 Mike Hargrove MG UER .07 .20
Stats are those of Tony LaRussa
259 Phil Garner MG UER .07 .20
Stats are those of Tony LaRussa
260 David Wright .30 .75
261 Vinny Rottino (RC) .20 .50
262 Ryan Braun RC .20 .50
263 Kevin Kouzmanoff (RC) .20 .50
264 David Murphy (RC) .20 .50
265 Jimmy Rollins .07 .20
266 Joe Maddon MG .12 .30

267 Grady Little MG .07 .20
268 Ryan Sweeney (RC) .20 .50
269 Fred Lewis (RC) .30 .75
270 Alfonso Soriano .07 .20
271a Delwyn Young (RC) .20 .50
271b Delwyn Young (RC) .20 .50
Swing
272 Jeff Salazar (RC) .20 .50
273 Miguel Montero (RC) .20 .50
274 Shawn Riggans (RC) .20 .50
275 Greg Maddux .30 .75
276 Brian Stokes (RC) .20 .50
277 Philip Humber (RC) .20 .50
278 Scott Moore (RC) .20 .50
279 Adam Lind (RC) .20 .50
280 Curt Schilling .12 .30
281 Chris Narveson (RC) .20 .50
282 Oswaldo Navarro RC .20 .50
283 Drew Anderson RC .20 .50
284 Jerry Owens (RC) .20 .50
285 Stephen Drew .12 .30
286 Joaquin Arias (RC) .20 .50
287 Jose Garcia RC .20 .50
288 Shane Youman RC .20 .50
289 Brian Burres (RC) UER .20 .50
Height and Weight amounts are incorrect
290 Matt Holliday .20 .50
291 Ryan Feierabend (RC) .20 .50
292a Josh Fields (RC) .20 .50
292b Josh Fields (RC) .20 .50
Running
293 Glen Perkins (RC) .20 .50
294 Mike Rabelo RC .20 .50
295 Jorge Posada .12 .30
296 Ubaldo Jimenez (RC) .20 .50
297 Brad Ausmus GG .07 .20
298 Eric Chavez GG .07 .20
299 Orlando Hudson GG .07 .20
300 Vladimir Guerrero .07 .20
301 Derek Jeter GG .50 1.25
302 Scott Rolen GG .12 .30
303 Mark Grudzielanek GG .07 .20
304 Kenny Rogers GG .07 .20
305 Frank Thomas .20 .50
306 Mike Cameron GG .07 .20
307 Torii Hunter GG .07 .20
308 Albert Pujols GG .40 1.00
309 Mark Teixeira GG .12 .30
310 Jonathan Papelbon .20 .50
311 Greg Maddux GG .30 .75
312 Carlos Beltran GG .07 .20
313 Ichiro Suzuki GG .30 .75
314 Andruw Jones GG .12 .30
315 Manny Ramirez .12 .30
316 Vernon Wells GG .07 .20
317 Omar Vizquel GG .12 .30
318 Ivan Rodriguez GG .12 .30
319 Brandon Webb CY .07 .20
320 Magglio Ordonez .07 .20
321 Johan Santana CY .12 .30
322 Ryan Howard MVP .30 .75
323 Justin Morneau MVP .07 .20
324 Hanley Ramirez ROY .12 .30
325 Joe Mauer .12 .30
326 Justin Verlander ROY .20 .50
327 Bobby Abreu .50 1.25
Derek Jeter CC UER
Abreu's career homer total is incorrect
328 Carlos Delgado .30 .75
David Wright CC
329 Yadier Molina .40 1.00
Albert Pujols CC
330 Ryan Howard .30 .75
331 Kelly Johnson .07 .20
332 Chris Young .07 .20
333 Mark Kotsay .07 .20
334 A.J. Burnett .07 .20
335 Brian McCann .07 .20
336 Woody Williams .07 .20
337 Jason Isringhausen .07 .20
338 Juan Pierre .07 .20
339 Jonny Gomes .07 .20
340 Roger Clemens .30 .75
341 Akinori Iwamura RC .50 1.25
342 Bengie Molina .07 .20
343 Shin-Soo Choo .12 .30
344 Kenji Johjima .20 .50
345 Joe Borowski .07 .20
346 Shawn Green .07 .20
347 Chicago Cubs .12 .30
348 Rodrigo Lopez .07 .20
349 Brian Giles .07 .20
350 Chase Utley .20 .50
351 Mark DeRosa .07 .20
352 Carl Pavano .07 .20
353 Kyle Lohse .07 .20
354 Chris Iannetta .07 .20
355 Oliver Perez .07 .20
356 Curtis Granderson .20 .50
357 Sean Casey .07 .20
358 Jason Tyner .07 .20
359 Jon Garland .07 .20
360 David Ortiz .20 .50
361 Adam Kennedy .07 .20
362 Chris Burke .07 .20
363 Bobby Crosby .07 .20
364 Conor Jackson .07 .20
365 Tim Hudson .07 .20
366 Rickie Weeks .07 .20
367 Cristian Guzman .07 .20
368 Mark Prior .12 .30
369 Ben Zobrist .07 .20
370 Troy Glaus .07 .20
371 Kenny Lofton .07 .20
372 Shane Victorino .07 .20
373 Cliff Lee .07 .20
374 Adrian Beltre .07 .20
375 Miguel Olivo .07 .20
376 Endy Chavez .07 .20
377 Zack Segovia (RC) .20 .50
378 Ramon Hernandez .07 .20
379 Chris Young .07 .20
380 Jason Schmidt .07 .20
381 Ronny Paulino .07 .20
382 Kevin Millwood .07 .20
383 Jon Lester .12 .30
384 Alex Gonzalez .07 .20
385 Brad Hawpe .07 .20
386 Placido Polanco .07 .20
387 Nate Robertson .07 .20
388 Torii Hunter .07 .20
389 Gavin Floyd .07 .20
390 Roy Oswalt .07 .20
391 Kelvim Escobar .07 .20
392 Craig Wilson .07 .20
393 Milton Bradley .07 .20
394 Aaron Hill .07 .20
395 Matt Diaz .07 .20
396 Chris Capuano .07 .20
397 Juan Encarnacion .07 .20
398 Jacque Jones .07 .20
399 James Shields .07 .20
400 Ichiro Suzuki .30 .75
401 Matt Kemp .07 .20
402 Matt Morris .07 .20
403 Casey Blake .07 .20
404 Corey Hart .07 .20
405 Josh Willingham .07 .20
406 Ryan Madson .07 .20
407 Nick Johnson .07 .20
408 Kevin Millar .07 .20
409 Khalil Greene .12 .30
410 Tom Glavine .12 .30
411a Jason Bay .07 .20
411b Jason Bay No Sig 2.00 5.00
412 Gerald Laird .07 .20
413 Coco Crisp .07 .20
414 Brandon Phillips .07 .20
415 Aaron Cook .07 .20
416 Mark Redman .07 .20
417 Mike Maroth .07 .20
418 Boof Bonser .07 .20
419 Jorge Cantu .07 .20
420 Jeff Weaver .07 .20
421 Melky Cabrera .07 .20
422 Francisco Rodriguez .07 .20
423 Mike Lamb .07 .20
424 Dan Haren .07 .20
425 Tomo Ohka .07 .20
426 Jeff Francoeur .20 .50
427 Randy Wolf .07 .20
428 So Taguchi .07 .20
429 Carlos Zambrano .07 .20
430 Justin Morneau .07 .20
431 Luis Gonzalez .07 .20
432 Takashi Saito .07 .20
433 Brandon Morrow RC .50 1.25
434 Victor Martinez .07 .20
435 Felix Hernandez .12 .30
436 Ricky Nolasco .07 .20
437 Paul LoDuca .07 .20
437b Paul LoDuca No Sig 2.00 5.00
438 Chad Cordero .07 .20
439 Miguel Tejada .07 .20
440 Mark Teixeira .12 .30
441 Pat Burrell .07 .20
442 Paul Maholm .07 .20
443 Mike Cameron .07 .20
444 Josh Beckett .12 .30
445 Pablo Ozuna .07 .20
446 Jaret Wright .07 .20
447 Angel Berroa .07 .20
448 Fernando Rodney .07 .20
449 Francisco Liriano .20 .50
450 Ken Griffey Jr. .30 .75
451 Bobby Jenks .07 .20
452 Mike Mussina .12 .30
453 Howie Kendrick .07 .20
454 Milwaukee Brewers .07 .20
455 Dan Johnson .07 .20
456 Ted Lilly .07 .20
457 Mike Hampton .07 .20
458 J.J. Hardy .07 .20
459 Jeff Suppan .07 .20
460 Jose Reyes .07 .20
461 Jae Seo .07 .20
462 Edgar Gonzalez .07 .20
463 Russell Martin .07 .20
464 Omar Vizquel .12 .30
465 Jhonny Peralta .07 .20
466 Raul Ibanez .07 .20
467 Hanley Ramirez .12 .30
468 Kerry Wood .07 .20
469 Ryan Church .07 .20
470 Gary Sheffield .07 .20
471 David Wells .07 .20
472 David Dellucci .07 .20
473 Xavier Nady .07 .20
474 Michael Young .07 .20
475 Kevin Youkilis .07 .20
476 Aaron Harang .07 .20
477 Brian Lawrence .07 .20
478 Octavio Dotel .07 .20
479 Chris Shelton .07 .20
480 Matt Garza .07 .20
481a Jim Thome .12 .30
481b Jim Thome No Sig 2.00 5.00
482 Jose Contreras .07 .20
483 Kris Benson .07 .20
484 John Maine .07 .20
485 Tadahito Iguchi .07 .20
486 Wandy Rodriguez .07 .20
487 Eric Chavez .07 .20
488 Vernon Wells .07 .20
489 Doug Davis .07 .20
490 Andruw Jones .12 .30
491 David Eckstein .07 .20
492 Michael Barrett .07 .20
493 Greg Norton .07 .20
494 Orlando Hudson .07 .20
495 Wilson Betemit .07 .20
496 Ryan Klesko .07 .20
497 Fausto Carmona .07 .20
498 Jarrod Washburn .07 .20
499 Aaron Boone .07 .20
500 Pedro Martinez .12 .30
501 Mike O'Connor .07 .20
502 Brian Roberts .07 .20
503 Jeff Cirillo .07 .20
504 Brett Myers .07 .20
505 Jose Bautista .07 .20
506 Akinori Otsuka .07 .20
507 Shea Hillenbrand .07 .20
508 Ryan Langerhans .07 .20
509 Josh Fogg .07 .20
510 Alex Rodriguez .30 .75
511 Kenny Rogers .07 .20
512 Jason Kubel .07 .20
513 Jermaine Dye .07 .20
514 Mark Grudzielanek .07 .20
515 Josh Phelps .07 .20
516 Bartolo Colon .07 .20
517 Craig Biggio .12 .30
518 Esteban Loaiza .07 .20
519 Alex Rios .07 .20
520 Adam Dunn .07 .20
521 Derrick Turnbow .07 .20
522 Anthony Reyes .07 .20
523 Derrek Lee .07 .20
524 Ty Wigginton .07 .20
525 Jeremy Hermida .07 .20
526 Derek Lowe .07 .20
527 Randy Winn .07 .20
528 Paul Byrd .07 .20
529 Chris Snelling .07 .20
530 Brandon Webb .07 .20
531 Julio Franco .07 .20
532 Jose Vidro .07 .20
533 Erik Bedard .07 .20
534 Terrmel Sledge .07 .20
535 Jon Lieber .07 .20
536 Tom Gorzelanny .07 .20
537 Kip Wells .07 .20
538 Wily Mo Pena .07 .20
539 Eric Milton .07 .20
540 Chad Billingsley .07 .20
541 David DeJesus .07 .20
542 Omar Infante .07 .20
543 Rondell White .07 .20
544 Juan Uribe .07 .20
545 Miguel Cairo .07 .20
546 Orlando Cabrera .07 .20
547 Byung-Hyun Kim .07 .20
548 Jason Kendall .07 .20
549 Horacio Ramirez .07 .20
550 Trevor Hoffman .07 .20
551 Ronnie Belliard .07 .20
552 Chris Woodward .07 .20
553 Ramon Martinez .07 .20
554 Elizardo Ramirez .07 .20
555 Andy Marte .07 .20
556 John Patterson .07 .20
557 Scott Olsen .07 .20
558 Steve Trachsel .07 .20
559 Doug Mientkiewicz .07 .20
560 Randy Johnson .20 .50
561 Chan Ho Park .07 .20
562 Jamie Moyer .07 .20
563 Mike Gonzalez .07 .20
564 Nelson Cruz .07 .20
565 Alex Cora .07 .20
566 Ryan Freel .07 .20
567 Chris Stewart RC .20 .50
568 Carlos Guillen .07 .20
569 Jason Bartlett .07 .20
570 Mariano Rivera .20 .50
571 Norris Hopper .07 .20
572 Alex Escobar .07 .20
573 Gustavo Chacin .07 .20
574 Brandon McCarthy .07 .20
575 Seth McClung .07 .20
576 Yuniesky Betancourt .07 .20
577 Jason LaRue .07 .20
578 Dustin Pedroia .30 .75
579 Taylor Tankersley .07 .20
580 Garret Anderson .07 .20
581 Mike Sweeney .07 .20
582 Scott Thorman .07 .20
583 Joe Inglett .07 .20
584 Clint Barmes .07 .20
585 Willie Bloomquist .07 .20
586 Willy Aybar .07 .20
587 Brian Bannister .07 .20
588 Jose Guillen .07 .20
589 Brad Wilkerson .07 .20
590 Lance Berkman .07 .20
591 Toronto Blue Jays .07 .20
592 Florida Marlins .07 .20
593 Washington Nationals .07 .20
594 Los Angeles Angels .07 .20
595 Cleveland Indians .07 .20
596 Texas Rangers .07 .20
597 Detroit Tigers .07 .20
598 Arizona Diamondbacks .07 .20
599 Kansas City Royals .07 .20
600 Ryan Zimmerman .20 .50
601 Colorado Rockies .07 .20
602 Minnesota Twins .07 .20
603 Los Angeles Dodgers .07 .20
604 San Diego Padres .07 .20
605 Bruce Bochy MG .07 .20
606 Ron Washington MG .07 .20
607 Manny Acta MG .07 .20
608 Sam Perlozzo MG .07 .20
609 Terry Francona MG .07 .20
610 Jim Leyland MG .07 .20
611 Eric Wedge MG .07 .20
612 Ozzie Guillen MG .07 .20
613 Buddy Bell MG .07 .20
614 Bob Geren MG .07 .20
615 Lou Piniella MG .07 .20
616 Fredi Gonzalez MG .07 .20
617 Ned Yost MG .07 .20
618 Willie Randolph MG .07 .20
619 Bud Black MG .07 .20
620 Garrett Atkins .07 .20
621 Alexi Casilla RC .30 .75
622 Matt Chico (RC) .20 .50
623 Alejandro De Aza RC .20 .50
624 Jeremy Brown .07 .20
625 Josh Hamilton (RC) .50 1.25
626 Doug Slaten RC .20 .50
627 Andy Cannizaro RC .20 .50
628 Juan Salas (RC) .20 .50
629 Levale Speigner RC .20 .50
630a Daisuke Matsuzaka English RC 3.00 8.00
630b Daisuke Matsuzaka Japanese 5.00 12.00
630c Daisuke Matsuzaka No Sig 5.00 12.00
631 Elijah Dukes RC .30 .75
632 Kevin Cameron RC .20 .50
633 Juan Perez RC .20 .50
634a Alex Gordon RC 1.25 3.00
634b Alex Gordon No Sig 3.00 8.00
635 Juan Lara RC .20 .50
636 Mike Rabelo RC .20 .50
637 Justin Hampson (RC) .20 .50
638 Cesar Jimenez RC .20 .50
639 Joe Smith RC .20 .50
640 Kei Igawa RC .50 1.25
641 Hideki Okajima RC 1.00 2.50
642 Sean Henn (RC) .20 .50
643 Jay Marshall RC .20 .50
644 Jared Burton RC .20 .50
645 Angel Sanchez RC .20 .50
646 Devern Hansack RC .20 .50
647 Juan Morillo (RC) .20 .50
648 Hector Gimenez (RC) .20 .50
649 Brian Barden RC .20 .50
650 Alex Rodriguez .30 .75
Jason Giambi CC
651 Jason Michaels .07 .20
Travis Hafner CC
652 Josh Johnson .07 .20
Miguel Olivo CC
653 Sean Casey .07 .20
Placido Polanco CC
654 Ivan Rodriguez .12 .30
Fernando Rodney CC
655 Dan Uggla .12 .30
Hanley Ramirez CC
656 Carlos Beltran .07 .20
Jose Reyes CC
657 Alex Rodriguez .50 1.25
Derek Jeter CC
658 Aaron Rowand .07 .20
Jimmy Rollins CC
659 Angel Berroa .07 .20
Andres Blanco CC
660a Yadier Molina .07 .20
660b Yadier Molina No Sig 2.00 5.00
661 Barry Bonds 4.00 10.00

2007 Topps 1st Edition

*1st ED: 3X TO 8X BASIC
*1st ED RC: 1.25X TO 3X BASIC
SER.1 ODDS 1:36 HOBBY, 1:5 HTA
SER.2 ODDS 1:36 HOBBY, 1:5 HTA
7 Mickey Mantle 6.00 15.00
15 Andrew Miller 4.00 10.00
29 Pat Neshek 3.00 8.00
40 Derek Jeter 100.00 200.00
625 Josh Hamilton 4.00 10.00
630 Daisuke Matsuzaka 12.50 30.00

2007 Topps Copper

COMMON CARD (1-660) 6.00 15.00
UNLISTED STARS 10.00 25.00
SER.1 ODDS 1:7 HTA
SER.2 ODDS 1:10 HTA
STATED PRINT RUN 56 SERIAL #'d SETS
7 Mickey Mantle 75.00 150.00
15 Andrew Miller 100.00 150.00
29 Pat Neshek 30.00 60.00
40 Derek Jeter 1000.00 1300.00
53 Mike Piazza 15.00 40.00
58 Todd Coffey 10.00 25.00
130 Albert Pujols 30.00 60.00
170 Chien-Ming Wang 30.00 60.00
236 Boston Red Sox CL 6.00 15.00
239 New York Yankees CL 10.00 25.00
260 David Wright 15.00 40.00
275 Greg Maddux 15.00 40.00
301 Derek Jeter GG 40.00 80.00
305 Frank Thomas 15.00 40.00
308 Albert Pujols GG 30.00 60.00
311 Greg Maddux GG 15.00 40.00
313 Ichiro Suzuki GG 15.00 40.00
322 Ryan Howard MVP 15.00 40.00
327 Bobby Abreu 20.00 50.00
Derek Jeter CC
328 Carlos Delgado 15.00 40.00
David Wright CC
329 Yadier Molina 10.00 25.00
Albert Pujols CC
330 Ryan Howard 15.00 40.00
340 Roger Clemens 20.00 50.00
341 Akinori Iwamura 15.00 40.00
360 David Ortiz 20.00 50.00
362 Chris Burke 10.00 25.00
400 Ichiro Suzuki 30.00 60.00
403 Casey Blake 15.00 40.00
413 Coco Crisp 10.00 25.00
444 Josh Beckett 10.00 25.00
450 Ken Griffey Jr. 30.00 60.00
460 Jose Reyes 10.00 25.00
475 Kevin Youkilis 10.00 25.00
510 Alex Rodriguez 20.00 50.00
625 Josh Hamilton 30.00 60.00
630 Daisuke Matsuzaka 100.00 150.00
634 Alex Gordon 15.00 40.00
641 Hideki Okajima 20.00 50.00
650 Alex Rodriguez 15.00 40.00
Jason Giambi CC
657 Alex Rodriguez 20.00 50.00
Derek Jeter CC

2007 Topps Gold

*GOLD: 6X TO 15X BASIC
*GOLD RC: 2.5X TO 6X BASIC RC
SER.1 ODDS 1:11 H, 1:3 HTA, 1:24 K-MART
SER.1 ODDS 1:6 RACK, 1:11 TARGET
SER.1 ODDS 1:24 WAL-MART
SER.2 ODDS 1:11 HOBBY, 1:2 HTA
STATED PRINT RUN 2007 SER.#'d SETS
7 Mickey Mantle 12.50 30.00
15 Andrew Miller 8.00 20.00

29 Pat Neshek 6.00 15.00
40 Derek Jeter 150.00 250.00
130 Albert Pujols 4.00 10.00
170 Chien-Ming Wang 3.00 8.00
260 David Wright 3.00 8.00
275 Greg Maddux 3.00 8.00
301 Derek Jeter GG 8.00 20.00
308 Albert Pujols GG 4.00 10.00
311 Greg Maddux GG 3.00 8.00
313 Ichiro Suzuki GG 3.00 8.00
322 Ryan Howard MVP 3.00 8.00
327 Bobby Abreu 6.00 15.00
Derek Jeter CC
328 Carlos Delgado 3.00 8.00
David Wright CC
329 Yadier Molina 3.00 8.00
Albert Pujols CC
330 Ryan Howard 3.00 8.00
340 Roger Clemens 5.00 12.00
341 Akinori Iwamura 3.00 8.00
372 Shane Victorino 2.50 6.00
413 Coco Crisp 2.00 5.00
475 Kevin Youkilis 1.50 4.00
625 Josh Hamilton 6.00 15.00
630 Daisuke Matsuzaka 8.00 20.00
634 Alex Gordon 6.00 15.00
641 Hideki Okajima 5.00 12.00
657 Alex Rodriguez 6.00 15.00
Derek Jeter CC

2007 Topps Platinum

SER.1 ODDS 1:26,000 H, 1:3200 HTA
SER.1 ODDS 1:45000 K-MART,1:8500 RACK
SER.1 ODDS 1:26000 TAR,1:45000 WAL-MART
SER.2 ODDS 1:24,000 HOBBY , 1:2900 HTA
STATED PRINT RUN 1 SERIAL #'d SET
NO PRICING DUE TO SCARCITY

2007 Topps Red Back

COMP.SERIES 1 (330) 40.00 80.00
COMP.SERIES 2 (330) 40.00 80.00
*RED: 1X TO 2.5X BASIC
*RED RC: .5X TO 1.2X BASIC RC
SER.1 ODDS 2:1 H, 10:1 HTA, 3:1 RACK
15 Andrew Miller 3.00 8.00
40 Derek Jeter 15.00 40.00
170 Chien-Ming Wang 1.25 3.00

2007 Topps 1952 Mantle Reprint Relic

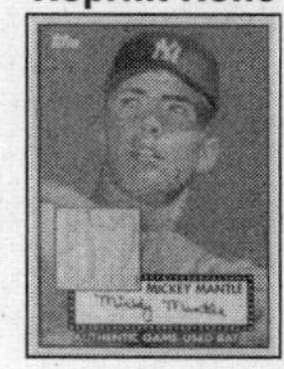

SER.1 ODDS 1:158,700 H, 1:8721 HTA
SER.1 ODDS 1:602,600 K-MART
SER.1 ODDS 1:127,100 TARGET
SER 1 ODDS 1:602,600 WAL-MART
STATED PRINT RUN 52 SERIAL #'d SETS
NO PRICING DUE TO SCARCITY
52MM Mickey Mantle Bat

2007 Topps 1953 Mantle Reprint Relic

SER.2 ODDS 1:199,750 HOBBY, 1:10,500 HTA
STATED PRINT RUN 53 SER.#'d SETS
NO PRICING DUE TO SCARCITY
53MM Mickey Mantle

2007 Topps Alex Rodriguez Road to 500

COMMON CARD (1-75/101-425) 1.25 3.00
COMMON CARD (76-100) 15.00 40.00
COMMON CARD (401-425) 6.00 15.00
COMMON CARD (451-475) 4.00 10.00
COMMON CARD (476-499) 4.00 10.00
SER.1 ODDS 1:36 H, 1:5 HTA, 1:36 K-MART
SER.1 ODDS 1:36 RACK, 1:36 TARGET
SER.1 ODDS 1:36 WAL-MART

FINEST ODDS TWO PER AROD BOX TOPPER
HERITAGE ODDS 1:24 HOBBY/RETAIL
OPENING DAY ODDS 1:36 H, 1:36 R
MOMENTS ODDS TWO PER BOX TOPPER
CO-SIG ODDS TWO PER AROD BOX TOPPER
BOWMAN ODDS 1:6 HOBBY, 1:2 HTA
SER.2 ODDS 1:36 HOBBY, 1:5 HTA
T.CHROME ODDS TWO PER BOX TOPPER
ALLEN AND GINTER ODDS 1:24 H, 1:24 R
BOW.CHR. ODDS 1:9 HOBBY
TURKEY RED ODDS 1:24 HOBBY/RETAIL
BOW.HER ODDS TWO PER BOX TOPPER
UPDATE ODDS 1:36 H, 1:5 HTA, 1:36 R
TOPPS 52 ODDS 1:20 H, 1:20 R
CARDS 1-25 ISSUED IN SERIES 1
CARDS 26-50 ISSUED IN FINEST
CARDS 51-75 ISSUED IN HERITAGE
CARDS 76-100 ISSUED IN OPENING DAY
CARDS 101-125 ISSUED IN MOMENTS
CARDS 126-175 ISSUED IN BOWMAN
CARDS 176-200 ISSUED IN CO-SIGNERS
CARDS 201-225 ISSUED IN SERIES 2
CARDS 226-250 ISSUED IN TOP.CHROME
CARDS 251-275 ISSUED IN ALLEN GINTER
CARDS 276-300 ISSUED IN BOW.CHR.
CARDS 301-325 ISSUSED IN TUR.RED
CARDS 326-350 ISSUED IN 08 FINEST
CARDS 351-375 ISSUED IN BOW.HER.
CARDS 376-400 ISSUED IN UPDATE
CARDS 401-425 ISSUED IN BOW.BEST
CARDS 426-450 ISSUED IN BOW.DRAFT
CARDS 451-475 ISSUED IN BOW.STERL.
CARDS 476-500 ISSUED IN TOPPS 52
ARHR500 Alex Rodriguez 500HR 10.00 25.00

2007 Topps Alex Rodriguez Road to 500 Autographs

SER.1 ODDS 1:1,111,000 H, 1:122,100 HTA
SER.1 ODDS 1:1,000,000 K-MART
SER.1 ODDS 1:127,100 TARGET
SER.1 ODDS 1,000,000 WAL-MART
FINEST ODDS 1:788 BOXES
HERITAGE ODDS 1:100,500 HOBBY/RETAIL
OPEN.DAY ODDS 1:171,146 H, 1:256,960 R
MOMENTS ODDS 1:803 BOX TOPPERS
BOWMAN ODDS 34,931 H, 1:11,000 HTA
CO-SIG ODDS 1:1687 BOX TOPPERS
SER.2 ODDS 1:750,000 HOBBY
SER.2 ODDS 1:173,160 HTA
ALLEN GINTER ODDS 1:64,496 HOBBY
CHROME ODDS 1:1866 BOX TOPPERS
ALLEN GINTER ODDS 1:122,200 RETAIL
BOW.CHR. ODDS 1:57,500 HOBBY
TURKEY RED ODDS 1:50,000 HOBBY
TURKEY RED ODDS 1:50,000 RETAIL
BOW.HER ODDS 1:773 HOBBY BOXES
UPD.ODDS 1:500,000 H, 1:33,500 HTA
UPD.ODDS 1:11,000 RETAIL
TOPPS 52 ODDS 1:16,000 H, 1:77,000 R
CARDS 1-25 ISSUED IN SERIES 1
CARDS 26-50 ISSUED IN FINEST
CARDS 51-75 ISSUED IN HERITAGE
CARDS 76-100 ISSUED IN OPENING DAY
CARDS 101-125 ISSUED IN MOMENTS
CARDS 126-175 ISSUED IN BOWMAN
CARDS 176-200 ISSUED IN CO-SIGNERS
CARDS 201-225 ISSUED IN SER.2
CARDS 226-250 ISSUED IN TOPPS CHROME
CARDS 251-275 ISSUED IN ALLEN GINTER
CARDS 276-300 ISSUED IN BOWMAN CHROME
CARDS 301-325 ISSUED IN TURKEY RED
CARDS 326-250 ISSUED IN 08 FINEST
CARDS 351-375 ISSUED IN BOW.HERITAGE
CARDS 376-400 ISSUED IN UPDATE
CARDS 401-425 ISSUED IN BOW.BEST
CARDS 426-450 ISSUED IN BOW.DRAFT
CARDS 451-475 ISSUED IN BOW.STERL.
CARDS 476-500 ISSUED IN TOPPS 52
STATED PRINT RUN 1 SER.#'d SET
NO PRICING DUE TO SCARCITY

2007 Topps All Stars

COMPLETE SET (12) 6.00 15.00
SER.1 ODDS ONE PER RACK PACK
AS1 Alfonso Soriano .60 1.50
AS2 Paul Konerko .60 1.50
AS3 Carlos Beltran .60 1.50
AS4 Troy Glaus .60 1.50
AS5 Jason Bay .60 1.50
AS6 Vladimir Guerrero .75 2.00
AS7 Chase Utley .75 2.00
AS8 Michael Young .60 1.50
AS9 David Wright 1.25 3.00
AS10 Gary Matthews .60 1.50
AS11 Brad Penny .60 1.50
AS12 Roy Halladay UER .60 1.50
Header line for stats is in incorrect order

2007 Topps All Star Rookies

COMPLETE SET (10) 6.00 15.00
SER.1 ODDS ONE PER RACK PACK
ASR1 Prince Fielder .75 2.00
ASR2 Dan Uggla .60 1.50
ASR3 Ryan Zimmerman 1.00 2.50
ASR4 Hanley Ramirez .60 1.50
ASR5 Melky Cabrera .60 1.50
ASR6 Andre Ethier .60 1.50
ASR7 Nick Markakis .60 1.50
ASR8 Justin Verlander .75 2.00
ASR9 Francisco Liriano .75 2.00
ASR10 Russell Martin .60 1.50

2007 Topps DiMaggio Streak

COMPLETE SET (56) 20.00 50.00
COMMON CARD .60 1.50
SER.2 ODDS 1:9 HOBBY

2007 Topps DiMaggio Streak Before the Streak

COMPLETE SET (61) 20.00 50.00
COMMON CARD .60 1.50
SER.2 ODDS 1:9 HOBBY

2007 Topps Distinguished Service

COMPLETE SET (30) 10.00 25.00
COMP.SERIES 1 (1-20) 6.00 15.00
COMP.SERIES 2 (21-30) 5.00 12.00
SER.1 ODDS 1:12 H, 1:12 HTA, 1:12 K-MART
SER.1 ODDS 1:12 RACK, 1:12 WAL-MART
SER.2 ODDS 1:12 HOBBY, 1:2 HTA
DS1 Duke Snider .60 1.50
DS2 Yogi Berra .75 2.00
DS3 Bob Feller .60 1.50
DS4 Bobby Doerr .60 1.50
DS5 Monte Irvin .60 1.50
DS6 Dwight D. Eisenhower .60 1.50
DS7 George Marshall .60 1.50
DS8 Franklin D. Roosevelt .60 1.50
DS9 Harry Truman .60 1.50
DS10 Douglas Macarthur .60 1.50
DS11 Ralph Kiner .60 1.50
DS12 Hank Sauer .60 1.50
DS13 Elmer Valo .60 1.50
DS14 Sibby Sisti .60 1.50
DS15 Hoyt Wilhelm .60 1.50
DS16 James Doolittle .60 1.50
DS17 Curtis Lemay .60 1.50
DS18 Omar Bradley .60 1.50
DS19 Chester Nimitz .60 1.50
DS20 Mark Clark .60 1.50
DS21 Joe DiMaggio 1.25 3.00
DS22 Warren Spahn .60 1.50
DS23 Stan Musial 1.00 2.50
DS24 Red Schoendienst .60 1.50
DS25 Ted Williams 1.50 4.00
DS26 Winston Churchill .60 1.50
DS27 Charles de Gaulle .60 1.50
DS28 George Bush .60 1.50
DS29 John F. Kennedy .75 2.00
DS30 Richard Bong .60 1.50

2007 Topps Distinguished Service Autographs

SER.1 ODDS 1:20,000 H, 1:830 HTA
SER.1 ODDS 1:41,225 K-MART,1:9200 RACK
SER.1 ODDS 1:20,000 TARGET
SER.1 ODDS 1:41,225 WAL-MART
BD Bobby Doerr 20.00 50.00

BF Bob Feller 30.00 60.00
DS Duke Snider 40.00 80.00
MI Monte Irvin 30.00 60.00
RK Ralph Kiner 40.00 80.00

2007 Topps Distinguished Service Cuts

SER.1 ODDS 1:505,600 H, 1:61,000 HTA
SER.1 ODDS 1:1,000,000 K-MART
SER.1 ODDS 1:138,000 TARGET
SER.1 ODDS 1:1,000,000 WAL-MART
SER.2 ODDS 1:165,000 HOBBY
SER.2 ODDS 1:57,720 HTA
STATED PRINT RUN 1 SER.#'d SET
NO PRICING DUE TO SCARCITY
BB Bill Butland
BP Bill Posedel
BT Birdie Tebbetts
BK Bob Kennedy
BL Bob Lemon
BM Buster Maynard
CG Charlie Gilbert
DB Dick Bartell
EJ Earl Johnson
EV Elmer Valo
ED Emerson Dickman
EW Ernie White
EB Ewell Blackwell
HW Hal Wagner
HH Hank Helf
HS Hank Sauer
HB Herman Besse
HE Hoot Evers
JHW Hoyt Wilhelm
JW Johnnie Wittig
JG Johnny Gorsica
LN Lou Novikoff
RM Ray Mack
RR Red Ruffing
RW Roy Weatherly
SS Sibby Sisti
TW Taffy Wright
TL Ted Lyons
WS Warren Spahn
WR Woody Rich
AB Al Barlick
AZ Al Zarilla
BH Billy Herman
BJ Billy Johnson
BO Buck O'Neill
BS Bill Sayles
BV Bill Veeck
BW Burgess Whitehead
DC Dolf Camilli
DG Denny Galehouse
EF Elbie Fletcher
ES Enos Slaughter
FL Frank LaManna
FP Frankie Pytlak
GS George Selkirk
GW Gene Woodling
HG Harry Gumbert
JB Johnny Beazley
JD Joe DiMaggio
JL Johnny Lanning
JT Jim Tabor
KH Kirby Higbe
KK Ken Keltner
KT Ken Trinkle
LA Luke Appling
MD Murry Dickson
MH Myril Hoag
MM Max Macon
MR Marius Russo
MW Max West
PM Phil Marchildon
PR Pete Reiser
RJ Rankin Johnson
RP Ray Poole
SG Sid Gordon
SR Schoolboy Rowe
TC Tom Carey
TE Tom Earley
TM Terry Moore
TT Tom Turner
AEB Al Brazle
CLG Charlie Gehringer
EWY Early Wynn
HGW Hal White
HWW Harry Walker
JAB Al Benton
JAH Buddy Hassett
JFW Jake Wade
JGD Joe Dobson
JGR Johnny Grodzicki
JLG Joe Gordon
JPW Joe Wood
JVM Johnny Vander Meer
JWA Jack Wallaesa
NJW Mickey Witek
SOS Stan Spence
TSW Ted Williams
WBM Barney McCosky

2007 Topps Factory Set All Star Bonus

1 Alex Rodriguez
2 David Wright
3 David Ortiz
4 Ichiro Suzuki
5 Ryan Howard

2007 Topps Factory Set Cardinals Team Bonus

1 Skip Schumaker
2 Josh Hancock
3 Tyler Johnson
4 Randy Keisler
5 Randy Flores

2007 Topps Factory Set Cubs Team Bonus

1 Ronny Cedeno
2 Cesar Izturis
3 Neal Cotts
4 Wade Miller
5 Michael Wuertz

2007 Topps Factory Set Dodgers Team Bonus

1 Chin-Hui Tsao
2 Olmedo Saenz
3 Brett Tomko
4 Marlon Anderson
5 Brady Clark

2007 Topps Factory Set Red Sox Team Bonus

1 Daisuke Matsuzaka
2 Eric Hinske
3 Brendan Donnelly
4 Hideki Okajima
5 J.C. Romero

2007 Topps Factory Set Rookie Bonus

COMPLETE SET (20) 12.50 30.00
1 Felix Pie .30 .75
2 Rick Vanden Hurk .50 1.25
3 Jeff Baker .30 .75
4 Don Kelly .30 .75
5 Matt Lindstrom .30 .75
6 Chase Wright .75 2.00
7 Jon Coutlangus .30 .75
8 Lee Gardner .30 .75
9 Gustavo Molina .30 .75
10 Kory Casto .30 .75
11 Daisuke Matsuzaka 3.00 8.00
12 Tim Lincecum 2.50 6.00
13 Phil Hughes 1.50 4.00
14 Ryan Braun 2.00 5.00
15 Billy Butler .50 1.25
16 Jarrod Saltalamacchia .50 1.25
17 Hideki Okajima 1.50 4.00
18 Akinori Iwamura .75 2.00
19a Joba Chamberlain 3.00 8.00
19b Joba Chamberlain Houston Astros UER 3.00 8.00
20 Hunter Pence 1.50 4.00

2007 Topps Factory Set Yankees Team Bonus

1 Darrell Rasner
2 Phil Hughes
3 Wil Nieves
4 Kei Igawa
5 Kevin Thompson

2007 Topps Flashback Fridays

COMPLETE SET (25) 6.00 15.00
ISSUED VIA HTA SHOPS
FF1 Ryan Howard .75 2.00
FF2 Derek Jeter 1.25 3.00
FF3 Ken Griffey Jr .75 2.00
FF4 Miguel Tejada .20 .50
FF5 David Wright .75 2.00
FF6 Alfonso Soriano .20 .50
FF7 Matt Holliday .50 1.25
FF8 Jason Bay .20 .50
FF9 Ryan Zimmerman .50 1.25
FF10 Alex Rodriguez .75 2.00
FF11 Jermaine Dye .20 .50
FF12 Miguel Cabrera .30 .75
FF13 Johan Santana .30 .75
FF14 Brandon Webb .20 .50
FF15 Ivan Rodriguez .30 .75
FF16 Ichiro Suzuki .75 2.00
FF17 Michael Young .20 .50
FF18 David Ortiz .50 1.25
FF19 Roger Clemens .75 2.00
FF20 Frank Thomas .50 1.25
FF21 Trevor Hoffman .20 .50
FF22 Gary Matthews .20 .50
FF23 Rafael Furcal .20 .50
FF24 Chipper Jones .50 1.25
FF25 Albert Pujols 1.00 2.50

2007 Topps Generation Now

COMMON J.BARFIELD .40 1.00
COMMON A.ETHIER .40 1.00
COMMON P.FIELDER .60 1.50
COMMON C.GRANDERSON .40 1.00
COMMON R.HOWARD .75 2.00
COMMON K.JOHJIMA .60 1.50
COMMON I.KINSLER .40 1.00
COMMON R.MARTIN .40 1.00
COMMON J.MORNEAU .40 1.00
COMMON M.NAPOLI .40 1.00
COMMON J.PAPELBON .60 1.50
COMMON H.RAMIREZ .40 1.00
COMMON J.REYES .60 1.50
COMMON N.SWISHER .40 1.00
COMMON C.UTLEY .60 1.50
COMMON J.VERLANDER .60 1.50
COMMON C.WANG .75 2.00
COMMON JER.WEAVER .40 1.00
COMMON D.WRIGHT .75 2.00
COMMON D.YOUNG .40 1.00
COMMON R.ZIMMERMAN .60 1.50
SER.1 ODDS 1:4 H, 1:4 K-MART, 1:4 RACK
SER.1 ODDS 1:4 TARGET, 1:4 WAL-MART
SER.2 ODDS 1:4 HOBBY
UPDATE ODDS 1:4 HOB, 1:4 RET

2007 Topps Generation Now Autographs

SER.1 ODDS 1:50,850 H, 1:2070 HTA
SER.1 ODDS 1:101,000 K-MART,1:18,396 RACK
SER.1 ODDS 1:50,850 TARGET
SER.1 ODDS 1:101,000 WAL-MART
SER.2 ODDS 1:94,000 HOBBY
SER.2 ODDS 1:1370 HTA
UPDATE ODDS 1:11,000 H, 1:5500 HTA
UPDATE ODDS 1:10,800 RETAIL
STATED PRINT RUN 1 SERIAL #'d SET
NO PRICING DUE TO SCARCITY

2007 Topps Generation Now Vintage

RANDOM INSERTS IN K-MART PACKS
1-18 ISSUED IN SER.1 PACKS
19-36 ISSUED IN SER.2 PACKS
37-54 ISSUED IN 07 UPDATE PACKS
GNV1 Ryan Howard .75 2.00
GNV2 Jeff Francoeur .50 1.25
GNV3 Nick Swisher .20 .50
GNV4 Joey Gathright .20 .50
GNV5 Jhonny Peralta .20 .50
GNV6 Willy Taveras .20 .50
GNV7 Cory Sullivan .20 .50
GNV8 Chris Young .20 .50
GNV9 Jered Weaver .30 .75
GNV10 Jonathan Papelbon .50 1.25
GNV11 Russell Martin .20 .50
GNV12 Hanley Ramirez .30 .75
GNV13 Justin Verlander .50 1.25
GNV14 Matt Cain .30 .75
GNV15 Kenji Johjima .50 1.25
GNV16 Angel Pagan .20 .50
GNV17 Brandon Phillips .20 .50
GNV18 Mark Teahen .20 .50
GNV19 Stephen Drew .30 .75
GNV20 Nick Markakis .30 .75
GNV21 Anibal Sanchez .20 .50
GNV22 Jeremy Hermida .20 .50
GNV23 James Loney .30 .75
GNV24 Prince Fielder .50 1.25
GNV25 Josh Barfield .20 .50
GNV26 Ian Kinsler .20 .50
GNV27 Ryan Zimmerman .50 1.25
GNV28 David Wright .75 2.00
GNV29 Jose Reyes .50 1.25
GNV30 Delmon Young .30 .75
GNV31 Zach Duke .20 .50
GNV32 Brian McCann .20 .50
GNV33 Bobby Jenks .20 .50
GNV34 Robinson Cano .30 .75
GNV35 Jose Lopez .20 .50
GNV36 Daisuke Matsuzaka 2.00 5.00
GNV37 Alex Rios .20 .50
GNV38 Cole Hamels .50 1.25
GNV39 Matt Kemp .20 .50
GNV40 Dan Uggla .30 .75
GNV41 Scott Kazmir .30 .75
GNV42 J.J. Hardy .20 .50
GNV43 Hunter Pence 1.00 2.50
GNV44 Jason Bay .20 .50
GNV45 James Shields .20 .50
GNV46 Chase Utley .50 1.25
GNV47 Justin Morneau .20 .50
GNV48 Chien-Ming Wang .75 2.00
GNV49 Troy Tulowitzki .50 1.25
GNV50 Joe Mauer .30 .75
GNV51 Brandon Webb .20 .50
GNV52 Matt Holliday .50 1.25
GNV53 Grady Sizemore .30 .75
GNV54 Homer Bailey .30 .75

2007 Topps Gibson Home Run History

COMPLETE SET (110) 60.00 120.00
COMMON GIBSON .60 1.50
SER.1 ODDS 1:9 H, 1:2 HTA, 1:9 K-MART
SER.1 ODDS 1:9 RACK, 1:9 TARGET
SER.1 ODDS 1:9 WAL-MART
CARDS 1-110 ISSUED IN SERIES 1 PACKS

2007 Topps Highlights Autographs

SER.1 A 1:50,842 H, 1:2105 HTA
SER.1 A 1:101,000 K-MART,1:18,396 RACK
SER.1 A 1:50,842 TARGET
SER.1 A 1:101,000 WAL-MART
SER.2 A 1:37,162 HOBBY, 1:523 HTA
SER.1 B 1:24,150 H, 1:1034 HTA
SER.1 B 1:51,800 K-MART, 1:12,264 RACK
SER.1 B 1:25,420 TARGET
SER.1 B 1:51,800 WAL-MART
SER.2 B 1:7330 HOBBY, 1:105 HTA
SER.1 C 1:13,000 H, 1:555 HTA
SER.1 C 1:27,300 K-MART, 1:7350 RACK
SER.1 C 1:13,600 TARGET
SER.1 C 1:27,300 WAL-MART
SER.2 C 1:7330 HOBBY, 1:105 HTA
SER.1 D 1:4916 H, 1:208 HTA
SER.1 D 1:10,250 K-MART, 1:2628 RACK
SER.1 D 1:5100 TARGET, 1:10,250 WAL-MART
SER.2 D 1:12,198 HOBBY, 1:174 HTA
SER.1 E 1:2460 H, 1:52 HTA, 1:5125 K-MART
SER.1 E 1:1314 RACK, 1:2550 TARGET
SER.1 E 1:5125 WAL-MART
SER.2 E 1:1410 HOBBY, 1:20 HTA
SER.1 F 1:1256 H, 1:52 HTA, 1:2564 K-MART
SER.1 F 1:657 RACK, 1:1277 TARGET
SER.1 F 1:2564 WAL-MART
SER.1 G 1:376 H, 1:16 HTA, 1:789 K-MART
SER.1 G 1:203 RACK,1:393 TARGET
SER.1 G 1:789 WAL-MART
GROUP A1 PRINT RUN B/WN 25-50 PER
GROUP B1 PRINT RUN 100 SETS
GROUP C1 PRINT RUN 250 SETS
A1-C1 ARE NOT SERIAL-NUMBERED
A1-C1 PRINT RUNS PROVIDED BY TOPPS
NO GROUP A1 PRICING DUE TO SCARCITY
EXCH * = PARTIAL EXCHANGE
EXCHANGE DEADLINE 02/28/09
AB Aaron Boone E2 4.00 10.00
AJ Andruw Jones B2 12.50 30.00
AM Andrew Miller G 12.50 30.00
AP Albert Pujols A2 150.00 200.00
AP Albert Pujols A/25 *
APA Angel Pagan G 4.00 10.00
AR Alex Rodriguez A/25 *
AR Anthony Reyes E2 6.00 15.00
AGS Alfonso Soriano B/100 * EXCH * 50.00100.00
AS Anibal Sanchez G 4.00 10.00
CG Curtis Granderson B2 15.00 40.00
CMS Curt Schilling A/25 *
CQ Carlos Quentin F 6.00 15.00
CU Chase Utley D EXCH * 30.00 60.00
CW Chien-Ming Wang B/100 * 100.00 200.00
CW Craig Wilson E2 6.00 15.00
DO David Ortiz B/100 * 60.00 120.00
DO David Ortiz B2 30.00 60.00
DT Derrick Turnbow D2 6.00 15.00
DU Dan Uggla E2 8.00 20.00
DW David Wright D 30.00 60.00
DW David Wright C2 30.00 60.00
DWW Dontrelle Willis E 10.00 25.00
DWW Dontrelle Willis C2 6.00 15.00
DY Delmon Young E 10.00 25.00
EC Endy Chavez B2 20.00 50.00
EF Emiliano Fruto G EXCH * 4.00 10.00
ES Ervin Santana E2 4.00 10.00
GS Gary Sheffield A/25 *
HR Hanley Ramirez G 8.00 20.00
JAS John Smoltz C/250 * 20.00 50.00
JD Johnny Damon A/25 *
JD Johnny Damon B2 40.00 80.00
JEM Justin Morneau E 10.00 25.00
JF Josh Fields F 6.00 15.00
JG Jon Garland E2 4.00 10.00
JH John Hattig G 4.00 10.00
JL James Loney G 6.00 15.00
JM John Maine F 10.00 25.00
JS Johan Santana C/250 * 40.00 80.00
JT Jim Thome A2 20.00 50.00
JV Justin Verlander B2 15.00 40.00
JZ Joel Zumaya E2 8.00 20.00
KE Kelvim Escobar C2 6.00 15.00
KM Kevin Mench D 4.00 10.00
KM Kendry Morales B2 4.00 10.00
LM Lastings Milledge E2 4.00 10.00
MC Miguel Cabrera C/250 * 15.00 40.00
MC Melky Cabrera E2 8.00 20.00
MG Matt Garza F EXCH 8.00 20.00
MH Matt Holliday G 8.00 20.00
MN Mike Napoli G 4.00 10.00
MP Mike Piazza A/50 * 90.00 150.00
MTC Matt Cain D2 6.00 15.00
PL Paul LoDuca B2 12.50 30.00
RC Robinson Cano E2 12.50 30.00
RH Ryan Howard B/100 * 75.00 150.00
RH Ryan Howard A2 40.00 80.00
RM Russell Martin C2 10.00 25.00
RZ Ryan Zimmerman E 15.00 40.00
RZ Ryan Zimmerman C2 12.50 30.00
SC Shawn Chacon E2 4.00 10.00
SP Scott Podsednik E2 4.00 10.00
SR Shawn Riggans E2 4.00 10.00
SSC Shin-Soo Choo B2 4.00 10.00
ST Steve Trachsel A2 10.00 25.00
TG Tom Glavine B2 30.00 60.00
TH Travis Hafner D 10.00 25.00
TT Troy Tulowitzki G 12.50 30.00
VG Vladimir Guerrero A/25 *
VG Vladimir Guerrero A2 40.00 80.00

2007 Topps Highlights Relics

SER.1 A 1:933 H, 1:33 HTA, 1:2160 K-MART
SER.1 A 1:1070 TARGET, 1:2160 WAL-MART
SER.2 A 1:2435 HOBBY, 1:138 HTA
SER.1 B 1:726 H, 1:19 HTA, 1:1270 K-MART
SER.1 B 1:631 TARGET, 1:1270 WAL-MART
SER.2 B 1:609 HOBBY, 1:35 HTA
SER.1 C 1:2468 H, 1:87 HTA, 1:5675 K-MART
SER.1 C 1:2825 TARGET, 1:5675 WAL-MART
SER.2 C 1:1420 HOBBY, 1:80 HTA
SER.2 D 1:533 HOBBY, 1:30 HTA
SER.2 E 1:1705 HOBBY, 1:96 HTA
AB Adrian Beltre B2 3.00 8.00
AER Alex Rodriguez C2 8.00 20.00
AJ Andruw Jones E2 3.00 8.00
ALR Anthony Reyes B2 4.00 10.00
AP Albert Pujols Pants B 8.00 20.00
AP Albert Pujols B2 8.00 20.00
AP2 Albert Pujols Jsy B 8.00 20.00
AR Alex Rodriguez Jsy B 8.00 20.00
AR Aramis Ramirez D2 3.00 8.00
AR2 Alex Rodriguez Bat A 8.00 20.00
AS Alfonso Soriano Bat A 4.00 10.00
AS Alfonso Soriano A2 4.00 10.00
BB Barry Bonds B2
BM Brian McCann Bat A 3.00 8.00
CB Craig Biggio Pants A 4.00 10.00
CD Carlos Delgado Bat B 3.00 8.00
CIB Carlos Beltran Jsy B 3.00 8.00
CJ Chipper Jones B2 3.00 8.00
CQ Carlos Quentin Bat A 3.00 8.00
CS Curt Schilling Jsy A 3.00 8.00
DE David Eckstein A2 5.00 12.00
DO David Ortiz Bat B 4.00 10.00
DO David Ortiz D2 4.00 10.00
DW Dontrelle Willis Jsy B 4.00 10.00
DW David Wright D2 5.00 12.00
DW2 Dontrelle Willis Pants B 4.00 10.00
DWW Dontrelle Willis E2 4.00 10.00
ER Edgar Renteria Bat B 3.00 8.00
FT Frank Thomas Bat B 4.00 10.00
GA Garrett Atkins A2 3.00 8.00
GS Gary Sheffield Bat B 3.00 8.00
GS Grady Sizemore A2 5.00 12.00
IR Ivan Rodriguez Bat C 3.00 8.00
IS Ichiro Suzuki Bat A 8.00 20.00
JAS John Smoltz Pants A 4.00 10.00
JB Jason Bay Jsy A 3.00 8.00
JB2 Jason Bay Bat A 3.00 8.00
JD Jermaine Dye C2 3.00 8.00
JDD Johnny Damon A2 4.00 10.00
JM Justin Morneau Bat B 3.00 8.00
JPM Joe Mauer Bat A 4.00 10.00
JR Jose Reyes Jsy A 3.00 8.00
JS Johan Santana Jsy A 4.00 10.00
JT Jim Thome B2 5.00 12.00
JV Justin Verlander A2 5.00 12.00
LB Lance Berkman C2 3.00 8.00
MAR Manny Ramirez Jsy B 3.00 8.00
MAR2 Manny Ramirez Bat C 3.00 8.00
MC Matt Cain B2 3.00 8.00
MCT Mark Teixeira B2 3.00 8.00
MEC Melky Cabrera B2 4.00 10.00
MO Magglio Ordonez Bat B 4.00 10.00
MR Mariano Rivera Jsy A 4.00 10.00
MR Manny Ramirez D2 3.00 8.00
MT Miguel Tejada Bat A 3.00 8.00
MT Miguel Tejada B2 3.00 8.00
NS Nick Swisher D2 4.00 10.00
PK Paul Konerko Bat A 3.00 8.00
PK Paul Konerko B2 3.00 8.00
PM Pedro Martinez D2 3.00 8.00
RC Robinson Cano Pants A 4.00 10.00
RC Robinson Cano B2 4.00 10.00
RH Ryan Howard Bat B 6.00 15.00
RH Roy Halladay B2 3.00 8.00
RJH Ryan Howard B2 6.00 15.00
RO Roy Oswalt Jsy A 3.00 8.00
SK Scott Kazmir Jsy B 3.00 8.00
SK Scott Kazmir C2 3.00 8.00
SR Scott Rolen Jsy A 4.00 10.00
TG Tom Glavine A2 4.00 10.00
TG1 Tom Glavine Jsy A 4.00 10.00
TG2 Troy Glaus Bat B 3.00 8.00
VG Vladimir Guerrero D2 4.00 10.00
VW Vernon Wells Bat A 3.00 8.00
VW Vernon Wells D2 3.00 8.00

2007 Topps Hit Parade

SER.2 ODDS 1:9 HOBBY, 1:2 HTA
HP1 Barry Bonds 2.50 6.00
HP2 Ken Griffey Jr. 2.00 5.00
HP3 Frank Thomas 1.25 3.00
HP4 Jim Thome .75 2.00
HP5 Manny Ramirez .75 2.00
HP6 Alex Rodriguez 2.00 5.00
HP7 Gary Sheffield .50 1.25
HP8 Mike Piazza 1.25 3.00

HP9 Carlos Delgado .50 1.25
HP10 Chipper Jones 1.25 3.00
HP11 Barry Bonds 2.50 6.00
HP12 Ken Griffey Jr. 2.00 5.00
HP13 Frank Thomas 1.25 3.00
HP14 Manny Ramirez .75 2.00
HP15 Gary Sheffield .50 1.25
HP16 Jeff Kent .50 1.25
HP17 Alex Rodriguez 2.00 5.00
HP18 Luis Gonzalez .50 1.25
HP19 Jim Thome .75 2.00
HP20 Mike Piazza 1.25 3.00
HP21 Craig Biggio .75 2.00
HP22 Barry Bonds 2.50 6.00
HP23 Julio Franco .50 1.25
HP24 Steve Finley .50 1.25
HP25 Omar Vizquel .75 2.00
HP26 Ken Griffey Jr. 2.00 5.00
HP27 Gary Sheffield .50 1.25
HP28 Luis Gonzalez .50 1.25
HP29 Ivan Rodriguez .75 2.00
HP30 Bernie Williams .75 2.00

2007 Topps Hobby Masters

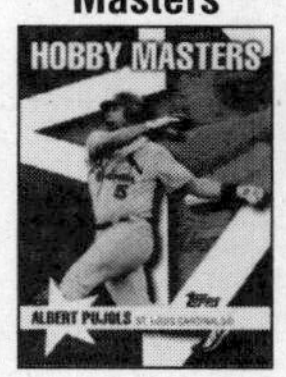

COMPLETE SET (20) 10.00 25.00
SER.1 ODDS 1:6 H, 1:4 HTA
HM1 David Wright 1.25 3.00
HM2 Albert Pujols 1.50 4.00
HM3 David Ortiz .75 2.00
HM4 Ryan Howard 1.25 3.00
HM5 Alfonso Soriano .60 1.50
HM6 Delmon Young .60 1.50
HM7 Jered Weaver .60 1.50
HM8 Derek Jeter 2.00 5.00
HM9 Freddy Sanchez .60 1.50
HM10 Alex Rodriguez 1.25 3.00
HM11 Johan Santana .60 1.50
HM12 Ichiro Suzuki 1.25 3.00
HM13 Andruw Jones .60 1.50
HM14 Vladimir Guerrero .75 2.00
HM15 Miguel Cabrera .60 1.50
HM16 Todd Helton .60 1.50
HM17 Manny Ramirez .60 1.50
HM18 Carlos Beltran .60 1.50
HM19 Justin Morneau .60 1.50
HM20 Francisco Liriano 1.50 4.00

2007 Topps Homerun Derby Contest

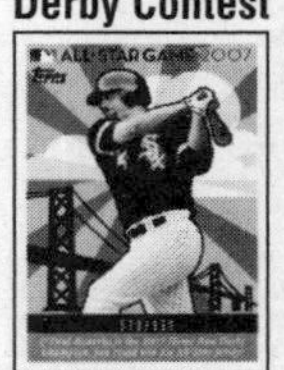

RANDOM INSERTS IN SER.2 PACKS
STATED ODDS 999 SER.#'d SETS
AB Adrian Beltre 1.25 3.00
AD Adam Dunn 1.25 3.00
AER Alex Rodriguez 5.00 12.00
AJ Andruw Jones 2.00 5.00
AL Adam LaRoche 1.25 3.00
AP Albert Pujols 6.00 15.00
AR Aramis Ramirez 1.25 3.00
AS Alfonso Soriano 1.25 3.00
BH Bill Hall 1.25 3.00
CB Carlos Beltran 1.25 3.00
CD Carlos Delgado 1.25 3.00
CL Carlos Lee 1.25 3.00
CM Craig Monroe 1.25 3.00
CU Chase Utley 3.00 8.00
DO David Ortiz 3.00 8.00
DU Dan Uggla 2.00 5.00
DW David Wright 3.00 8.00
DY Delmon Young 3.00 8.00
FT Frank Thomas 5.00 12.00
GA Garrett Atkins 1.25 3.00
GS Grady Sizemore 2.00 5.00
JB Jason Bay 1.25 3.00
JC Joe Crede 1.25 3.00
JD Jermaine Dye 1.25 3.00
JDD Johnny Damon 2.00 5.00
JF Jeff Francoeur 3.00 8.00
JG Jason Giambi 3.00 8.00
JM Justin Morneau 1.25 3.00
JT Jim Thome 2.00 5.00
KG Ken Griffey Jr 5.00 12.00
LB Lance Berkman 1.25 3.00
MC Miguel Cabrera 2.00 5.00
MH Matt Holliday 1.50 4.00
MMT Marcus Thames 1.25 3.00
MOT Miguel Tejada 1.25 3.00
MP Mike Piazza 3.00 8.00
MR Manny Ramirez 2.00 5.00
MT Mark Teixeira 2.00 5.00
NS Nick Swisher 1.25 3.00
PB Pat Burrell 1.25 3.00
PF Prince Fielder 5.00 12.00
PK Paul Konerko 1.25 3.00
RH Ryan Howard 5.00 12.00
RI Raul Ibanez 1.25 3.00
RS Richie Sexson 1.25 3.00
TG Troy Glaus 1.25 3.00
TH Travis Hafner 1.25 3.00
TKH Torii Hunter 1.25 3.00
VG Vladimir Guerrero 10.00 25.00
VW Vernon Wells 1.25 3.00

2007 Topps In the Name Letter Relics

SER.1 ODDS 1:8292 H, 1:488 HTA
STATED PRINT RUN 1 SERIAL #'d SET
NO PRICING DUE TO SCARCITY

2007 Topps Mickey Mantle Story

COMPLETE SET (57) 50.00 100.00
COMP.SERIES 1 (1-15) 8.00 20.00
COMP.SERIES 2 (16-30) 8.00 20.00
COMP.UPD.SET (31-45) 12.50 30.00
COMP.08 SER.1 SET (46-57) 6.00 15.00
COMP.08 SER.2 SET (58-67) 6.00 15.00
COMP.08 UPD SET (68-77) 6.00 15.00
COMMON MANTLE (1-77) .75 2.00
SER.1 ODDS 1:18 H, 1:18 HTA, 1:18 K-MART
SER.1 ODDS 1:18 RACK, 1:18 TARGET
SER.1 ODDS 1:18 WAL-MART
SER.2 ODDS 1:18 H,1:3 HTA,1:18 R
UPDATE ODDS 1:18 H, 1:3 HTA, 1:18 R
08 SER.1 ODDS 1:18 H, 1:3 HTA
08 SER.2 ODDS 1:18 H,1:3 HTA, 1:18 R
08 UPD.ODDS 1:18 HOBBY
1-15 ISSUED IN SERIES 1
16-30 ISSUED IN SERIES 2
31-45 ISSUED IN UPDATE
46-57 ISSSUED IN 08 SERIES 1
58-65 ISSUED IN 08 SERIES 2
66-77 ISSUED IN 08 UPDATE

2007 Topps Opening Day Team vs. Team

COMPLETE SET (15) 6.00 15.00
COMMON CARD .60 1.50
SER.2 ODDS 1:12 HOBBY, 1:3 HTA
OD1 New York Mets .60 1.50
St. Louis Cardinals
OD2 Atlanta Braves .60 1.50
Philadelphia Phillies
OD3 Florida Marlins .60 1.50
Washington Nationals
OD4 Tampa Bay Devil Rays .60 1.50
New York Yankees
OD5 Toronto Blue Jays .60 1.50
Detroit Tigers
OD6 Cleveland Indians .60 1.50
Chicago White Sox
OD7 Los Angeles Dodgers .60 1.50
Milwaukee Brewers
OD8 Chicago Cubs .60 1.50
Cincinnati Reds
OD9 Arizona Diamondbacks .60 1.50
Colorado Rockies
OD10 Boston Red Sox .60 1.50
Kansas City Royals
OD11 Oakland Athletics .60 1.50
Seattle Mariners
OD12 Baltimore Orioles .60 1.50
Minnesota Twins
OD13 Pittsburgh Pirates .60 1.50
Houston Astros
OD14 Texas Rangers .60 1.50
Los Angeles Angels
OD15 San Diego Padres .60 1.50
San Francisco Giants

2007 Topps Own the Game

COMPLETE SET (25) 10.00 25.00
SER.1 ODDS 1:6 H, 1:2 HTA, 1:6 K-MART
SER.1 ODDS 1:6 RACK, 1:6 TARGET
SER.1 ODDS 1:6 WAL-MART
OTG1 Ryan Howard 1.25 3.00
OTG2 David Ortiz .75 2.00
OTG3 Alfonso Soriano .60 1.50
OTG4 Albert Pujols 1.50 4.00
OTG5 Lance Berkman .60 1.50
OTG6 Jermaine Dye .60 1.50
OTG7 Travis Hafner .60 1.50
OTG8 Jim Thome .60 1.50
OTG9 Carlos Beltran .60 1.50
OTG10 Adam Dunn .60 1.50
OTG11 Ryan Howard 1.25 3.00
OTG12 David Ortiz .75 2.00
OTG13 Albert Pujols 1.50 4.00
OTG14 Lance Berkman .60 1.50
OTG15 Justin Morneau .60 1.50
OTG16 Andruw Jones .60 1.50
OTG17 Jermaine Dye .60 1.50
OTG18 Travis Hafner .60 1.50
OTG19 Alex Rodriguez 1.25 3.00
OTG20 David Wright 1.25 3.00
OTG21 Johan Santana .60 1.50
OTG22 Chris Carpenter .60 1.50
OTG23 Brandon Webb .60 1.50
OTG24 Roy Oswalt .60 1.50
OTG25 Roy Halladay .60 1.50

2007 Topps Rookie Stars

COMPLETE SET (10) 6.00 15.00
SER.2 ODDS 1:9 HOBBY
RS1 Daisuke Matsuzaka 2.50 6.00
RS2 Kevin Kouzmanoff .60 1.50
RS3 Elijah Dukes .75 2.00
RS4 Andrew Miller 2.00 5.00
RS5 Kei Igawa .75 2.00
RS6 Troy Tulowitzki .75 2.00
RS7 Ubaldo Jimenez .60 1.50
RS8 Alex Gordon 1.50 4.00
RS9 Josh Hamilton 1.50 4.00
RS10 Delmon Young .75 2.00

2007 Topps Stars

COMPLETE SET (15) 6.00 15.00
SER.2 ODDS 1:9 HOBBY
TS1 Ryan Howard 1.25 3.00
TS2 Alfonso Soriano .30 .75
TS3 Todd Helton .50 1.25
TS4 Johan Santana .50 1.25
TS5 David Wright 1.25 3.00
TS6 Albert Pujols 1.50 4.00
TS7 Daisuke Matsuzaka 2.50 6.00
TS8 Miguel Cabrera .50 1.25
TS9 David Ortiz .75 2.00
TS10 Alex Rodriguez 1.25 3.00
TS11 Vladimir Guerrero .75 2.00
TS12 Ichiro Suzuki 1.25 3.00
TS13 Derek Jeter 2.00 5.00
TS14 Lance Berkman .30 .75
TS15 Ryan Zimmerman .75 2.00

2007 Topps Target Factory Set Mantle Memorabilia

COMMON MANTLE MEMORABILIA 15.00 40.00
DISTRIBUTED WITH TOPPS TARGET FACT.SETS
MMR53 Mickey Mantle 53T 15.00 40.00
MMR56 Mickey Mantle 56T 15.00 40.00
MMR57 Mickey Mantle 57T 15.00 40.00

2007 Topps Target Factory Set Red Backs

1 Mickey Mantle
2 Ted Williams

2007 Topps Trading Places

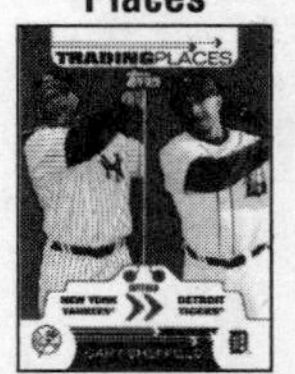

COMPLETE SET (25) 6.00 15.00
SER.2 ODDS 1:9 HOBBY
TP1 Jeff Weaver .40 1.00
TP2 Frank Thomas 1.00 2.50
TP3 Mike Piazza 1.00 2.50
TP4 Alfonso Soriano .40 1.00
TP5 Freddy Garcia .40 1.00
TP6 Jason Marquis .40 1.00
TP7 Ted Lilly .40 1.00
TP8 Mark Loretta .40 1.00
TP9 Marcus Giles .40 1.00
TP10 Barry Zito .40 1.00
TP11 Andy Pettitte .60 1.50
TP12 J.D. Drew .40 1.00
TP13 Gary Matthews .40 1.00
TP14 Jay Payton .40 1.00
TP15 Aubrey Huff .40 1.00
TP16 Brian Bannister .40 1.00
TP17 Jeff Conine .40 1.00
TP18 Gary Sheffield .40 1.00
TP19 Shea Hillenbrand .40 1.00
TP20 Wes Helms .40 1.00
TP21 Frank Catalanotto .40 1.00
TP22 Adam LaRoche .40 1.00
TP23 Mike Gonzalez .40 1.00
TP24 Greg Maddux 1.50 4.00
TP25 Jason Schmidt .40 1.00

2007 Topps Trading Places Autographs

SER.2 ODDS 1:3,055 HOBBY, 1:44 HTA
AH Aubrey Huff 6.00 15.00
AL Adam LaRoche 4.00 10.00
BB Brian Bannister 5.00 12.00
FC Frank Catalanotto 4.00 10.00
FG Freddy Garcia 6.00 15.00
GS Gary Sheffield 15.00 40.00
JS Jason Schmidt 6.00 15.00
MG Mike Gonzalez 4.00 10.00
SH Shea Hillenbrand 4.00 10.00
WH Wes Helms 4.00 10.00

2007 Topps Trading Places Relics

SER.2 ODDS 1:2,435 HOBBY, 1:137 HTA
AP Andy Pettitte 5.00 12.00
AS Alfonso Soriano 5.00 12.00
BZ Barry Zito 4.00 10.00
FT Frank Thomas 5.00 12.00
GM Greg Maddux 5.00 12.00
GS Gary Sheffield 5.00 12.00
JW Jeff Weaver 4.00 10.00
MG Marcus Giles 4.00 10.00
ML Mark Loretta 4.00 10.00
MP Mike Piazza 6.00 15.00

2007 Topps Unlock the Mick

COMPLETE SET (5) 3.00 8.00
COMMON MANTLE 1.00 2.50
SER.1 ODDS 1:18 H, 1:18 HTA, 1:18 K-MART
SER.1 ODDS 1:18 RACK, 1:18 TARGET
SER.1 ODDS 1:18 WAL-MART

2007 Topps Wal-Mart

COMP.SERIES 1 (18) 15.00 40.00
STATED ODDS 1:4 WAL-MART
SER.1 ODDS 3 PER $9.99 WAL-MART BOX
SER.1 ODDS 6 PER $19.99 WAL-MART BOX
1-18 ISSUED IN SERIES 1
19-36 ISSUED IN SERIES 2
37-54 ISSUED IN UPDATE
WM1 Frank Thomas 41 PB .75 2.00
WM2 Mike Piazza 34 DS .75 2.00
WM3 Ivan Rodriguez 22 Caramel .75 2.00
WM4 David Ortiz T207 .75 2.00
WM5 David Wright 1887 AG 1.25 3.00
WM6 Greg Maddux 52T 1.25 3.00
WM7 Mickey Mantle 51T 4.00 10.00
WM8 Jose Reyes 65T .75 2.00
WM9 John Smoltz T205 .75 2.00
WM10 Jim Edmonds 56T .75 2.00
WM11 Ryan Howard 58T 1.25 3.00
WM12 Miguel Cabrera T206 .75 2.00
WM13 Carlos Delgado 10 Turkey .75 2.00
WM14 Miguel Tejada 55B .75 2.00
WM15 Ichiro Suzuki 33 DeLong 1.25 3.00
WM16 Albert Pujols 49B 1.50 4.00
WM17 Derek Jeter 91 SC 2.00 5.00
WM18 Vladimir Guerrero 61 Baz .75 2.00
WM19 Lance Berkman .75 2.00
WM20 Chase Utley .75 2.00
WM21 Gary Matthews .75 2.00
WM22 Johan Santana .75 2.00
WM23 Todd Helton .75 2.00
WM24 Carlos Beltran .75 2.00
WM25 Alex Rodriguez 1.25 3.00
WM26 Cole Hamels .75 2.00
WM27 Daisuke Matsuzaka 2.50 6.00
WM28 Kei Igawa .75 2.00
WM29 Hanley Ramirez .75 2.00
WM30 Joe Mauer .75 2.00
WM31 Brandon Webb .75 2.00
WM32 Michael Young .75 2.00
WM33 Nick Swisher .75 2.00
WM34 Jason Bay .75 2.00
WM35 Manny Ramirez .75 2.00
WM36 Ryan Zimmerman .75 2.00
WM37 Grady Sizemore .75 2.00
WM38 Matt Holliday .75 2.00
WM39 Jimmy Rollins .75 2.00
WM40 Magglio Ordonez .75 2.00
WM41 Prince Fielder .75 2.00
WM42 Jorge Posada .75 2.00
WM43 Hideki Okajima 1.00 2.50
WM44 Dan Uggla .75 2.00
WM45 Jake Peavy .75 2.00
WM46 Carlos Lee .75 2.00
WM47 C.C. Sabathia .75 2.00
WM48 Gary Sheffield .75 2.00
WM49 Tim Lincecum 2.50 6.00
WM50 J.J. Putz .75 2.00
WM51 Justin Verlander .75 2.00
WM52 Akinori Iwamura .75 2.00
WM53 Adam LaRoche .75 2.00
WM54 Alfonso Soriano .75 2.00

2007 Topps Williams 406

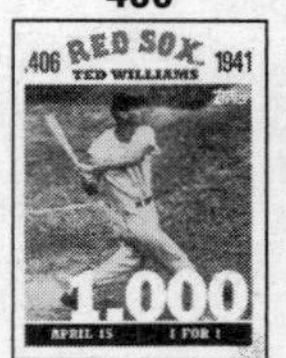

COMPLETE SET (36) 12.50 30.00
COMP.SERIES 1 (18) 6.00 15.00
COMP.SERIES 2 (18) 6.00 15.00
COMMON WILLIAMS .60 1.50
SER.1 ODDS 1:4 TARGET

2007 Topps World Champion Relics

SER.1 ODDS 1:7550 H, 1:226 HTA
SER.1 ODDS 1:14,750 K-MART
SER.1 ODDS 1:7550 TARGET
SER.1 ODDS 1:14,750 WAL-MART
STATED PRINT RUN 100 SETS
CARDS ARE NOT SERIAL NUMBERED
PRINT RUNS PROVIDED BY TOPPS
WCR1 Jeff Weaver Jsy/100 * 20.00 50.00
WCR2 Chris Duncan Jsy/100 * 40.00 80.00
WCR3 Chris Carpenter Jsy/100 * 60.00 120.00
WCR4 Yadier Molina Jsy/100 * 60.00 120.00
WCR5 Albert Pujols Bat/100 * 75.00 150.00
WCR6 Jim Edmonds Jsy/100 * 40.00 80.00
WCR7 Ronnie Belliard Bat/100 * 40.00 80.00
WCR8 So Taguchi Bat/100 * 60.00 120.00
WCR9 Juan Encarnacion Bat/100 * 20.00 50.00
WCR10 Scott Rolen Jsy/100 * 40.00 80.00
WCR11 Anthony Reyes Jsy/100 * 40.00 80.00
WCR12 Preston Wilson Bat/100 * 30.00 60.00
WCR13 Jeff Suppan Jsy/100 * 30.00 60.00
WCR14 Adam Wainwright Jsy/100 * 40.00 80.00
WCR15 David Eckstein Bat/100 * 20.00 50.00

2007 Topps World Domination

WD1 Ryan Howard 1.25 3.00
WD2 Justin Morneau .60 1.50
WD3 Ivan Rodriguez .60 1.50
WD4 Albert Pujols 1.50 4.00
WD5 Jorge Cantu .60 1.50
WD6 Johan Santana .60 1.50
WD7 Ichiro Suzuki 1.25 3.00
WD8 Chien-Ming Wang 1.25 3.00
WD9 Mariano Rivera .75 2.00
WD10 Andruw Jones .60 1.50

2007 Topps Update

This 334-card set was released in October, 2007. The set was issued through both hobby and retail channels. The hobby packs were created in two forms: 10-card wax packs with an $1.59 SRP which came 36 packs to a box and 12 boxes per case. The other form were the 50-card HTA pack with an $10 SRP which came 10 packs per box and six boxes per case. While a few rookies were interspersed throughout the set, most of the 2007 rookies were issued betwwen cards 147-202. The other subset is a Classic Combos grouping (275-284).

COMP.SET w/o SPs (330) 20.00 50.00
COMMON CARD (1-330) .12 .30
COMMON ROOKIE (1-330) .20 .50
1-330 PLATE ODDS 1:54 HTA
PLATE PRINT RUN 1 SET PER COLOR
BLACK-CYAN-MAGENTA-YELLOW ISSUED
NO PLATE PRICING DUE TO SCARCITY
1 Tony Armas Jr. .12 .30
2 Shannon Stewart .12 .30
3 Jason Marquis .12 .30
4 Josh Wilson .12 .30
5 Steve Trachsel .12 .30
6 J.D. Drew .12 .30
7 Ronnie Belliard .12 .30
8 Trot Nixon .12 .30
9 Adam LaRoche .12 .30
10 Mark Loretta .12 .30
11 Matt Morris .12 .30
12 Marlon Anderson .12 .30
13 Jorge Julio .12 .30
14 Brady Clark .12 .30
15 David Wells .12 .30
16 Francisco Rosario .12 .30
17 Jason Ellison .12 .30
18 Adam Jones .12 .30
19 Russell Branyan .12 .30
20 Rob Bowen .12 .30
21 J.D. Durbin .12 .30
22 Jeff Salazar .12 .30
23 Tadahito Iguchi .12 .30
24 Brad Hennessey .12 .30
25 Mark Hendrickson .12 .30
26 Kameron Loe .12 .30
27 Yusmeiro Petit .12 .30
28 Olmedo Saenz .12 .30
29 Carlos Silva .12 .30
30 Kevin Frandsen .12 .30
31 Tony Pena .12 .30
32 Russ Ortiz .12 .30
33 Hong-Chih Kuo .12 .30
34 Paul McAnulty .12 .30
35 Hiram Bocachica .12 .30
36 Justin Germano .12 .30
37 Jason Simontacchi .12 .30
38 Jose Cruz .12 .30
39 Wilfredo Ledezma .12 .30
40 Chris Denorfia .12 .30
41 Ryan Langerhans .12 .30
42 Chris Snelling .12 .30
43 Ubaldo Jimenez .12 .30
44 Scott Spiezio .12 .30
45 Byung-Hyun Kim .12 .30
46 Brandon Lyon .12 .30
47 Scott Hairston .12 .30
48 Chad Durbin .12 .30
49 Sammy Sosa .30 .75
50 Jason Smith .12 .30
51 Zack Greinke .12 .30
52 Armando Benitez .12 .30
53 Randy Messenger .12 .30
54 Mark Teixeira .20 .50
55 Mike Maroth .12 .30
56 Jamie Burke .12 .30
57 Carlos Marmol .12 .30
58 David Weathers .12 .30
59 Ryan Doumit .12 .30
60 Michael Barrett .12 .30
61 Shawn Chacon .12 .30
62 Mike Fontenot .12 .30
63 Cesar Izturis .12 .30
64 Cliff Floyd .12 .30
65 Angel Pagan .12 .30
66 Aaron Miles .12 .30
67 Tony Graffanino .12 .30
68 Kevin Mench .12 .30
69 Claudio Vargas .12 .30
70 Jose Capellan .12 .30
71 A.J. Pierzynski .12 .30
72 Darin Erstad .12 .30
73 Boone Logan .12 .30
74 Luis Castillo .12 .30
75 Marcus Thames .12 .30
76 Neifi Perez .12 .30
77 Esteban German .12 .30
78 Tony Pena .12 .30
79 Adam Wainwright .12 .30
80 Reggie Sanders .12 .30
81 Kelly Shoppach .12 .30
82 Rafael Betancourt .12 .30
83 Tom Mastny .12 .30
84 Kyle Farnsworth .12 .30
85 Rick Ankiel .20 .50
86 Kevin Thompson .12 .30
87 Jeff Karstens .12 .30
88 Eric Hinske .12 .30
89 Doug Mirabelli .12 .30
90 Julian Tavarez .12 .30
91 Carlos Pena .12 .30
92 Brendan Harris .12 .30
93 Chris Sampson .12 .30
94 Al Reyes .12 .30
95 Dmitri Young .12 .30
96 Jason Bergmann .12 .30
97 Shawn Hill .12 .30
98 Greg Dobbs .12 .30
99 Carlos Ruiz .12 .30
100a Abraham Nunez .12 .30
100b Jacoby Ellsbury (RC) 60.00 120.00
101 Jayson Werth .12 .30
102 Adam Eaton .12 .30
103 Antonio Alfonseca .12 .30
104 Jorge Sosa .12 .30
105 Ramon Castro .12 .30
106 Ruben Gotay .12 .30
107 Damion Easley .12 .30
108 David Newhan .12 .30
109 Jason Wood .12 .30
110 Reggie Abercrombie .12 .30
111 Kevin Gregg .12 .30
112 Henry Owens .12 .30
113 Willie Harris .12 .30
114 Pete Orr .12 .30
115 Casey Janssen .12 .30
116 Jason Frasor .12 .30
117 Jeremy Accardo .12 .30
118 John McDonald .12 .30
119 Matt Stairs .12 .30
120 Jason Phillips .12 .30
121 Justin Duchscherer .12 .30
122 Rich Harden .12 .30
123 Jack Cust .12 .30
124 Lenny DiNardo .12 .30
125 Joe Kennedy .12 .30
126 Chad Gaudin .12 .30
127 Marco Scutaro .12 .30
128 Brad Thompson .12 .30
129 Dustin Moseley .12 .30
130 Eric Gagne .12 .30
131 Marlon Byrd .12 .30
132 Scot Shields .12 .30
133 Victor Diaz .12 .30
134 Reggie Willits .12 .30
135 Jose Molina .12 .30
136 Ramon Vazquez .12 .30
137 Erick Aybar .12 .30
138 Sean Marshall .12 .30
139 Casey Kotchman .12 .30
140 Ryan Spilborghs .12 .30

141 Cameron Maybin RC 1.00 2.50
142 Jeremy Guthrie .12 .30
143 Jeff Baker .12 .30
144 Edwin Jackson .12 .30
145 Macay McBride .12 .30
146 Freddie Bynum .12 .30
147 Eric Patterson .12 .30
148 Dustin McGowan .12 .30
149 Homer Bailey (RC) .30 .75
150 Ryan Braun (RC) 1.25 3.00
151 Tony Abreu RC .50 1.25
152 Tyler Clippard (RC) .30 .75
153 Mark Reynolds RC .75 2.00
154 Jesse Litsch RC .30 .75
155 Carlos Gomez RC .30 .75
156 Matt DeSalvo (RC) .20 .50
157 Andy LaRoche (RC) .20 .50
158 Tim Lincecum RC 1.50 4.00
159 Jarrod Saltalamacchia (RC) .30 .75
160 Hunter Pence (RC) 1.00 2.50
161 Brandon Wood (RC) .20 .50
162 Phil Hughes (RC) 1.00 2.50
163 Rocky Cherry RC .50 1.25
164 Chase Wright RC .50 1.25
165 Dallas Braden RC .30 .75
166 Felix Pie (RC) .20 .50
167 Zach McClellan RC .20 .50
168 Rick Vanden Hurk RC .30 .75
169 Micah Owings (RC) .20 .50
170 Jon Coutlangus (RC) .20 .50
171 Andy Sonnanstine RC .20 .50
172 Yunel Escobar (RC) .20 .50
173 Kevin Slowey (RC) .50 1.25
174 Curtis Thigpen (RC) .20 .50
175 Masumi Kuwata RC 1.50 4.00
176 Kurt Suzuki (RC) .20 .50
177 Travis Buck (RC) .20 .50
178 Matt Lindstrom (RC) .20 .50
179 Jesus Flores RC .20 .50
180 Joakim Soria RC .20 .50
181 Nathan Haynes (RC) .20 .50
182 Matthew Brown RC .20 .50
183 Travis Metcalf RC .30 .75
184 Yovani Gallardo (RC) .60 1.50
185 Nate Schierholtz (RC) .20 .50
186 Kyle Kendrick RC .50 1.25
187 Kevin Melillo (RC) .20 .50
188 Ryan Rowland-Smith .12 .30
189 Lee Gronkiewicz RC .20 .50
190 Eulogio De La Cruz (RC) .20 .50
191 Brett Carroll RC .20 .50
192 Terry Evans RC .20 .50
193 Chase Headley (RC) .20 .50
194 Guillermo Rodriguez RC .20 .50
195 Marcus McBeth (RC) .20 .50
196 Brian Wolfe (RC) .20 .50
197 Troy Cate RC .20 .50
198 Mike Zagurski RC .20 .50
199 Yoel Hernandez RC .12 .30
200 Brad Salmon RC .20 .50
201 Alberto Arias RC .20 .50
202 Danny Putnam (RC) .20 .50
203 Jamie Vermilyea RC .20 .50
204 Kyle Lohse .12 .30
205 Sammy Sosa .30 .75
206 Tom Glavine .20 .50
207 Prince Fielder .30 .75
208 Mark Buehrle .12 .30
209 Troy Tulowitzki .30 .75
210 Daisuke Matsuzaka RC 2.00 5.00
211 Randy Johnson .30 .75
212 Justin Verlander .30 .75
213 Trevor Hoffman .12 .30
214 Alex Rodriguez .50 1.25
215 Ivan Rodriguez .20 .50
216 David Ortiz .30 .75
217 Placido Polanco .12 .30
218 Derek Jeter .75 2.00
219 Alex Rodriguez .50 1.25
220 Vladimir Guerrero .30 .75
221 Magglio Ordonez .12 .30
222 Ichiro Suzuki .50 1.25
223 Russell Martin .12 .30
224 Prince Fielder .30 .75
225 Chase Utley .30 .75
226 Jose Reyes .30 .75
227 David Wright .50 1.25
228 Carlos Beltran .12 .30
229 Barry Bonds .60 1.50
230 Ken Griffey Jr. .50 1.25
231 Torii Hunter .12 .30
232 Jonathan Papelbon .30 .75
233 J.J. Putz .12 .30
234 Francisco Rodriguez .12 .30
235 C.C. Sabathia .12 .30
236 Johan Santana .20 .50
237 Justin Verlander .30 .75
238 Francisco Cordero .12 .30
239 Mike Lowell .12 .30
240 Cole Hamels .30 .75
241 Trevor Hoffman .12 .30
242 Manny Ramirez .20 .50
243 Jake Peavy .12 .30
244 Brad Penny .12 .30
245 Takashi Saito .12 .30
246 Ben Sheets .12 .30
247 Hideki Okajima .60 1.50
248 Roy Oswalt .12 .30
249 Billy Wagner .12 .30
250 Carl Crawford .12 .30
251 Chris Young .12 .30
252 Brian McCann .12 .30
253 Derrek Lee .12 .30
254 Albert Pujols .60 1.50
255 Dmitri Young .12 .30
256 Orlando Hudson .12 .30
257 J.J. Hardy .12 .30
258 Miguel Cabrera .20 .50
259 Freddy Sanchez .12 .30
260 Matt Holliday .30 .75
261 Carlos Lee .12 .30
262 Aaron Rowand .12 .30
263 Alfonso Soriano .12 .30
264 Victor Martinez .12 .30
265 Jorge Posada .20 .50
266 Justin Morneau .12 .30
267 Brian Roberts .12 .30
268 Carlos Guillen .12 .30
269 Grady Sizemore .20 .50
270 Josh Beckett .20 .50
271 Dan Haren .12 .30
272 Bobby Jenks .12 .30
273 John Lackey .12 .30
274 Gil Meche .12 .30
275 Mike Fontenot .12 .30
Khalil Greene
276 Alex Rodriguez .50 1.25
Russell Martin
277 Troy Tulowitzki .30 .75
Jose Reyes
278 Jorge Posada .75 2.00
Derek Jeter
Alex Rodriguez
279 Chase Utley .50 1.25
Ichiro Suzuki
280 Carl Crawford .12 .30
Carlos Guillen
281 Cole Hamels .30 .75
Russell Martin
282 Jonathan Papelbon .30 .75
Jorge Posada
283 Carl Crawford .12 .30
Victor Martinez
284 Alfonso Soriano .12 .30
J.J. Hardy
285 Justin Morneau .12 .30
286 Prince Fielder .30 .75
287 Alex Rios .12 .30
288 Vladimir Guerrero .30 .75
289 Albert Pujols .60 1.50
290 Ryan Howard .50 1.25
291 Magglio Ordonez .12 .30
292 Matt Holliday .30 .75
293 Wilson Betemit .12 .30
294 Todd Wellemeyer .12 .30
295 Scott Baker .12 .30
296 Edgar Gonzalez .12 .30
297 J.P. Howell .12 .30
298 Shaun Marcum .12 .30
299 Edinson Volquez .12 .30
300 Kason Gabbard .12 .30
301 Bob Howry .12 .30
302 J.A. Happ .12 .30
303 Scott Feldman .12 .30
304 D'Angelo Jimenez .12 .30
305 Orlando Palmeiro .12 .30
306 Paul Bako .12 .30
307 Kyle Davies .12 .30
308 Gabe Gross .12 .30
309 John Wasdin .12 .30
310 Jon Knott .12 .30
311 Josh Phelps .12 .30
312a Joba Chamberlain RC 4.00 10.00
312b Joba Chamberlain 90.00 150.00
Reverse Negative
312c Joba Chamberlain UER
Houston Astros
313 Octavio Dotel .12 .30
314 Craig Monroe .12 .30
315 Edward Mujica .12 .30
316 Brandon Watson .12 .30
317 Chris Schroder .12 .30
318 Scott Proctor .12 .30
319 Ty Wigginton .12 .30
320 Troy Percival .12 .30
321 Scott Linebrink .12 .30
322 David Murphy .12 .30
323 Jorge Cantu .12 .30
324 Dan Wheeler .12 .30
325 Jason Kendall .12 .30
326 Milton Bradley .12 .30
327 Justin Upton RC 1.25 3.00
328 Kenny Lofton .12 .30
329 Roger Clemens .50 1.25
330 Brian Burres .12 .30
SO1 Poley Walnuts 12.50 30.00

2007 Topps Update 1st Edition

*1ST ED VET: 2X TO 5X BASIC
*1ST ED RC: 1.2X TO 3X BASIC RC
STATED ODDS 1:36 HOB, 1:5 HTA
210 Daisuke Matsuzaka 5.00 12.00
312 Joba Chamberlain 15.00 40.00

2007 Topps Update Copper

COMMON CARD 6.00 15.00
STATED ODDS 1:4 HTA
STATED PRINT RUN 56 SER.#'d SETS
141 Cameron Maybin 20.00 50.00
150 Ryan Braun 20.00 50.00
158 Tim Lincecum 40.00 80.00
160 Hunter Pence 20.00 50.00
162 Phil Hughes 20.00 50.00
175 Masumi Kuwata 15.00 40.00
210 Daisuke Matsuzaka 20.00 50.00
214 Alex Rodriguez 10.00 25.00
218 Derek Jeter 15.00 40.00
219 Alex Rodriguez 10.00 25.00
222 Ichiro Suzuki 15.00 40.00
227 David Wright 10.00 25.00
229 Barry Bonds 30.00 60.00
230 Ken Griffey Jr. 15.00 40.00
247 Hideki Okajima 10.00 25.00
254 Albert Pujols 12.50 30.00
276 Alex Rodriguez 10.00 25.00
Russell Martin
278 Jorge Posada 15.00 40.00
Derek Jeter
Alex Rodriguez
279 Chase Utley 15.00 40.00
Ichiro Suzuki
289 Albert Pujols 12.50 30.00
290 Ryan Howard 10.00 25.00
312 Joba Chamberlain 60.00 120.00
327 Justin Upton 30.00 60.00
329 Roger Clemens 12.50 30.00

2007 Topps Update Gold

*GOLD VET: 2.5X TO 6X BASIC
*GOLD RC: 1.5X TO 4X BASIC RC
STATED ODDS 1:4 HOB, 1:4 RET
STATED PRINT RUN 2007 SER.#'d SETS
312 Joba Chamberlain 12.50 30.00

2007 Topps Update Platinum

STATED ODDS 1:9700 H, 1:1085 HTA
STATED ODDS 1:9700 RETAIL
STATED PRINT RUN 1 SER.#'d SET
NO PRICING DUE TO SCARCITY

2007 Topps Update Red Back

COMPLETE SET (330) 30.00 60.00
*RED VET: .5X TO 1.2X BASIC
*RED RC: .5X TO 1.2X BASIC RC
STATED ODDS XXX
312 Joba Chamberlain 6.00 15.00

2007 Topps Update 1954 Mantle Reprint Relic

STATED ODDS 1:73,000 HOBBY
STATED ODDS 1:67,200 HTA
STATED ODDS 1:10,800 RETAIL
STATED PRINT RUN 54 SER.#'d SETS
NO PRICING DUE TO SCARCITY

2007 Topps Update 2007 Highlights Autographs

GROUP A ODDS 1:14,900 H, 1:252 HTA
GROUP A ODDS 1:14,900 RETAIL
GROUP B ODDS 1:925 H, 19 HTA
GROUP B ODDS 1:1,165 RETAIL
GROUP C ODDS 1:10,100 H, 1:165 HTA
GROUP C ODDS 1:9,700 RETAIL
GROUP D ODDS 1:22,000 H,1:88 HTA
GROUP D ODDS 1:18,400 RETAIL
GROUP E ODDS 1:7,200 H, 1:125 HTA
GROUP E ODDS 1:7,605 RETAIL
GROUP F ODDS 1:7,000 H, 1:123 HTA
GROUP F ODDS 1:7,352 RETAIL
GROUP G ODDS 1:5,025 H, 1:105 HTA
GROUP G ODDS 1:6,563 RETAIL
AC Asdrubal Cabrera G 6.00 15.00
AE Andre Ethier B 4.00 10.00
AG Alex Gordon B 15.00 40.00
AH Aaron Heilman B 4.00 10.00
AJ Andruw Jones A 10.00 25.00
AL Anthony Lerew B 4.00 10.00
AP Albert Pujols A 150.00 200.00
AR Alex Rodriguez A 150.00 200.00
AS Alfonso Soriano A
BB Brian Bruney B 4.00 10.00
CJ Conor Jackson B 4.00 10.00
CS C.C. Sabathia B 6.00 15.00
DE Damion Easley F 4.00 10.00
DW David Wright A 40.00 80.00
FC Francisco Cordero B 4.00 10.00
GS Gary Sheffield B 10.00 25.00
JR Jimmy Rollins B 12.50 30.00
JS Jarrod Saltalamacchia B 4.00 10.00
JT Jim Thome A 30.00 60.00
MC Miguel Cairo E 4.00 10.00
PF Prince Fielder B 15.00 40.00
RB Rod Barajas C 4.00 10.00
RC Robinson Cano B 12.50 30.00
RH Ryan Howard A 40.00 80.00
RW Ron Washington D 4.00 10.00
TT Troy Tulowitzki B 10.00 25.00

2007 Topps Update All-Star Patches

STATED ODDS 1:2,500 H,1:249 HTA
STATED PRINT RUN 10 SER.#'d SETS
NO PRICING DUE TO SCARCITY

2007 Topps Update All-Star Stitches

STATED ODDS 1:45 H,1:10 HTA,1:55 R
AIR Alex Rios 3.00 8.00
AP Albert Pujols 8.00 20.00
AR Alex Rodriguez 6.00 15.00
ARR Aaron Rowand 3.00 8.00
BF Brian Fuentes 3.00 8.00
BJ Bobby Jenks 3.00 8.00
BM Brian McCann 5.00 12.00
BR Brian Roberts 3.00 8.00
BS Ben Sheets 3.00 8.00

BW Brandon Webb 3.00 8.00
CB Carlos Beltran 3.00 8.00
CC Carl Crawford 3.00 8.00
CH Cole Hamels 4.00 10.00
CL Carlos Lee 3.00 8.00
CS C.C. Sabathia 5.00 12.00
CU Chase Utley 5.00 12.00
CY Chris Young 3.00 8.00
DO David Ortiz 6.00 15.00
DW David Wright 6.00 15.00
DY Dmitri Young 3.00 8.00
FC Francisco Cordero 3.00 8.00
FR Francisco Rodriguez 3.00 8.00
FS Freddy Sanchez 3.00 8.00
GM Gil Meche 3.00 8.00
GS Grady Sizemore 5.00 12.00
HO Hideki Okajima 5.00 12.00
IR Ivan Rodriguez 5.00 12.00
IS Ichiro Suzuki 10.00 25.00
JB Josh Beckett 5.00 12.00
JEP Jake Peavy 3.00 8.00
JH J.J. Hardy 3.00 8.00
JL John Lackey 3.00 8.00
JM Justin Morneau 3.00 8.00
JP J.J. Putz 3.00 8.00
JR Jose Reyes 5.00 12.00
JRP Jorge Posada 5.00 12.00
JRV Jose Valverde 3.00 8.00
JS Johan Santana 5.00 12.00
JV Justin Verlander 5.00 12.00
MH Matt Holliday 5.00 12.00
ML Mike Lowell 5.00 12.00
MR Manny Ramirez 5.00 12.00
MY Michael Young
OH Orlando Hudson 3.00 8.00
PF Prince Fielder 5.00 12.00
RH Ryan Howard 6.00 15.00
RM Russell Martin 5.00 12.00
RO Roy Oswalt 3.00 8.00
TH Torii Hunter 3.00 8.00
TS Takashi Saito 5.00 12.00
TWH Trevor Hoffman 3.00 8.00
VM Victor Martinez 3.00 8.00

2007 Topps Update All-Star Stitches Dual

STATED ODDS 1:5600 H, 1:490 HTA
STATED PRINT RUN 25 SER.#'d SETS
NO PRICING DUE TO SCARCITY

2007 Topps Update All-Star Stitches Triple

STATED ODDS 1:5600 H, 1:490 HTA
STATED PRINT RUN 25 SER.#'d SETS
NO PRICING DUE TO SCARCITY

2007 Topps Update Barry Bonds 756

STATED ODDS 1:36 H, 1:5 HTA, 1:36 R
HRK Barry Bonds 1.25 3.00

2007 Topps Update Barry Bonds 756 Relic

STATED ODDS 1:5,145 H,1:1,400 HTA
STATED ODDS 1:5,145 RETAIL
STATED PRINT RUN 756 SER.#'d SETS
HRKR Barry Bonds 20.00 50.00

2007 Topps Update Barry Bonds 756 Relic Autographs

STATED ODDS 1:278,000 HOBBY
STATED ODDS 1:67,200 HTA
STATED PRINT RUN 20 SER.#'d SETS
NO PRICING DUE TO SCARCITY

2007 Topps Update Chrome

STATED ODDS XXX
STATED PRINT RUN 415 SER.#'d SETS
TRC1 Homer Bailey 2.50 6.00
TRC2 Ryan Braun 10.00 25.00
TRC3 Tony Abreu 2.50 6.00
TRC4 Tyler Clippard 2.50 6.00
TRC5 Mark Reynolds 10.00 25.00
TRC6 Jesse Litsch 2.50 6.00
TRC7 Carlos Gomez 6.00 15.00
TRC8 Matt DeSalvo 1.50 4.00
TRC9 Andy LaRoche 4.00 10.00
TRC10 Tim Lincecum 6.00 15.00
TRC11 Jarrod Saltalamacchia 4.00 10.00
TRC12 Hunter Pence 8.00 20.00
TRC13 Brandon Wood 2.50 6.00
TRC14 Phil Hughes 6.00 15.00
TRC15 Rocky Cherry 1.50 4.00
TRC16 Chase Wright 2.50 6.00
TRC17 Dallas Braden 2.50 6.00
TRC18 Felix Pie 1.50 4.00
TRC19 Zach McClellan 1.50 4.00
TRC20 Rick Vanden Hurk 1.50 4.00
TRC21 Micah Owings 2.50 6.00
TRC22 Jon Coutlangus 1.50 4.00
TRC23 Andy Sonnanstine 1.50 4.00
TRC24 Yunel Escobar 1.50 4.00
TRC25 Kevin Slowey 4.00 10.00
TRC26 Curtis Thigpen 1.50 4.00
TRC27 Masumi Kuwata 6.00 15.00
TRC28 Kurt Suzuki 2.50 6.00
TRC29 Travis Buck 2.50 6.00
TRC30 Matt Lindstrom 2.50 6.00
TRC31 Jesus Flores 1.50 4.00
TRC32 Joakim Soria 2.50 6.00
TRC33 Nathan Haynes 1.50 4.00
TRC34 Matthew Brown 1.50 4.00
TRC35 Travis Metcalf 1.50 4.00
TRC36 Yovani Gallardo 2.50 6.00
TRC37 Nate Schierholtz 2.50 6.00
TRC38 Kyle Kendrick 2.50 6.00
TRC39 Kevin Melillo 2.50 6.00
TRC40 Cameron Maybin 8.00 20.00
TRC41 Lee Gronkiewicz 1.50 4.00
TRC42 Eulogio De La Cruz 1.50 4.00
TRC43 Brett Carroll 1.50 4.00
TRC44 Terry Evans 1.50 4.00
TRC45 Chase Headley 1.50 4.00
TRC46 Guillermo Rodriguez 1.50 4.00
TRC47 Marcus McBeth 1.50 4.00
TRC48 Brian Wolfe 1.50 4.00
TRC49 Troy Cate 1.50 4.00
TRC50 Justin Upton 15.00 40.00
TRC51 Joba Chamberlain 30.00 60.00
TRC52 Brad Salmon 1.50 4.00
TRC53 Alberto Arias 1.50 4.00
TRC54 Danny Putnam 1.50 4.00
TRC55 Jamie Vermilyea 1.50 4.00

2007 Topps Update Target

COMMON CARD .75 2.00

2007 Topps Update World Series Watch

COMPLETE SET (15) 8.00 20.00
STATED ODDS 1:36 H, 1:5 HTA, 1:36 R
WSW1 New York Mets .75 2.00
WSW2 Detroit Tigers .75 2.00
WSW3 Boston Red Sox 3.00 8.00
WSW4 Milwaukee Brewers .75 2.00
WSW5 Cleveland Indians .75 2.00
WSW6 Los Angeles Angels .75 2.00
WSW7 San Diego Padres .75 2.00
WSW8 Los Angeles Dodgers .75 2.00
WSW9 Philadelphia Phillies .75 2.00
WSW10 Chicago Cubs .75 2.00
WSW11 St. Louis Cardinals .75 2.00
WSW12 Arizona Diamondbacks .75 2.00
WSW13 New York Yankees .75 2.00
WSW14 Seattle Mariners .75 2.00
WSW15 Atlanta Braves .75 2.00

2008 Topps

This 330-card first series was released in February, 2008. The set was issued in myriad forms both in and outside the hobby. The packs were issued into the hobby in 10-card packs, with an $1.59 SRP, which came 36 packs to a box and 12 boxes to a case. The HTA packs had 46-cards (44 cards if a relic card was inserted), with an $10 SRP, which came 10 packs to a box and six boxes to a case. Card number 234, which featured the Boston Red Sox celebrating their 2007 World Series victory was issued in a regular version and in a photoshopped version in which Presidential Candidate (and noted Yankee fan) Rudy Giuliani was placed into the celebration. The Guiliani card was issued at an officially announced stated rate of one in two of the earliest boxes.

COMP.HOBBY SET (660) 40.00 80.00
COMP.CUBS SET (660) 40.00 80.00
COMP.DODGERS SET (660) 40.00 80.00
COMP.METS SET (660) 40.00 80.00
COMP.RED SOX SET (660) 40.00 80.00
COMP.TIGERS SET (660) 40.00 80.00
COMP.YANKEES SET (660) 40.00 80.00
COMP.SET w/o VAR (660) 40.00 80.00
COMP.SERIES 1 (331) 15.00 40.00
COMP.SERIES 2 (330) 15.00 40.00
COMMON CARD (1-660) .12 .30
COMMON RC (1-660) .25 .60
SERIES 1 SET DOES NOT INCLUDE FS1
SERIES 1 SET DOES NOT INCLUDE #234C
SER.2 SET DOES NOT INCLUDE #661
SER.2 SET DOES NOT INCLUDE NNO CARDS
SER.1 PLATE ODDS 1:1348 HOBBY
SER.2 PLATE ODDS 1:900 HOBBY
PLATE PRINT RUN 1 SET PER COLOR
BLACK-CYAN-MAGENTA-YELLOW ISSUED
NO PLATE PRICING DUE TO SCARCITY
1 Alex Rodriguez .50 1.25
2 Barry Zito .12 .30
3 Jeff Suppan .12 .30
4 Rick Ankiel .12 .30
5 Scott Kazmir .20 .50
6 Felix Pie .12 .30
7 Mickey Mantle 1.25 3.00
8 Stephen Drew .12 .30
9 Randy Wolf .12 .30
10 Miguel Cabrera .20 .50
11 Yorvit Torrealba .12 .30
12 Jason Bartlett .12 .30
13 Kendry Morales .12 .30
14 Lenny DiNardo .12 .30
15 Magglio Ordonez .50 1.25
Ichiro Suzuki
Placido Polanco
16 Kevin Gregg .12 .30
17 Cristian Guzman .12 .30
18 J.D. Durbin .12 .30
19 Robinson Tejeda .12 .30
20 Daisuke Matsuzaka .50 1.25
21 Edwin Encarnacion .12 .30
22 Ron Washington MG .12 .30
23 Chin-Lung Hu (RC) .40 1.00
24 Alex Rodriguez .30 .75
Magglio Ordonez
Vladimir Guerrero
25 Kaz Matsui .12 .30
26 Manny Ramirez .30 .75
27 Bob Melvin MG .12 .30
28 Kyle Kendrick .12 .30
29 Anibal Sanchez .12 .30
30 Jimmy Rollins .20 .50
31 Ronny Paulino .12 .30
32 Howie Kendrick .12 .30
33 Joe Mauer .20 .50
34 Aaron Cook .12 .30
35 Cole Hamels .30 .75
36 Brendan Harris .12 .30
37 Jason Marquis .12 .30
38 Preston Wilson .12 .30
39 Yovanni Gallardo .12 .30
40 Miguel Tejada .12 .30
41 Rich Aurilia .12 .30
42 Corey Hart .12 .30
43 Ryan Dempster .12 .30
44 Jonathan Broxton .12 .30
45 Dontrelle Willis .12 .30
46 Zack Greinke .12 .30
47 Orlando Cabrera .12 .30
48 Zach Duke .12 .30
49 Orlando Hernandez .12 .30
50 Jake Peavy .20 .50
51 Erik Bedard .12 .30
52 Trevor Hoffman .12 .30
53 Hank Blalock .12 .30
54 Victor Martinez .12 .30
55 Chris Young .12 .30
56 Seth Smith (RC) .25 .60
57 Wladimir Balentien (RC) .25 .60
58 Matt Holliday .40 1.00
Ryan Howard
Miguel Cabrera
59 Grady Sizemore .20 .50
60 Jose Reyes .20 .50
61 Alex Rodriguez .30 .75
Carlos Pena
David Ortiz
62 Rich Thompson RC .40 1.00
63 Jason Michaels .12 .30
64 Mike Lowell .12 .30
65 Billy Wagner .12 .30
66 Brad Wilkerson .12 .30
67 Wes Helms .12 .30
68 Kevin Millar .12 .30
69 Bobby Cox MG .12 .30
70 Dan Uggla .20 .50
71 Jarrod Washburn .12 .30
72 Mike Piazza .30 .75
73 Mike Napoli .12 .30
74 Garrett Atkins .12 .30
75 Felix Hernandez .20 .50
76 Ivan Rodriguez .20 .50
77 Angel Guzman .12 .30
78 Radhames Liz RC .40 1.00
79 Omar Vizquel .12 .30
80 Alex Rios .12 .30
81 Ray Durham .12 .30
82 So Taguchi .12 .30
83 Mark Reynolds .12 .30
84 Brian Fuentes .12 .30
85 Jason Bay .12 .30
86 Scott Podsednik .12 .30
87 Maicer Izturis .12 .30
88 Jack Cust .12 .30
89 Josh Willingham .12 .30
90 Vladimir Guerrero .30 .75
91 Marcus Giles .12 .30
92 Ross Detwiler RC .60 1.50
93 Kenny Lofton .12 .30
94 Bud Black MG .12 .30
95 John Lackey .12 .30
96 Sam Fuld RC .25 .60
97 Clint Sammons (RC) .25 .60
98 Ryan Howard .40 1.00
Chase Utley
99 David Ortiz .30 .75
Manny Ramirez
100 Ryan Howard .40 1.00
101 Ryan Braun ROY .40 1.00
102 Ross Ohlendorf RC .40 1.00
103 Jonathan Albaladejo RC .40 1.00
104 Kevin Youkilis .20 .50
105 Roger Clemens .40 1.00
106 Josh Bard .12 .30
107 Shawn Green .12 .30
108 B.J. Ryan .12 .30
109 Joe Nathan .12 .30
110 Justin Morneau .20 .50
111 Ubaldo Jimenez .12 .30
112 Jacque Jones .12 .30
113 Kevin Frandsen .12 .30
114 Mike Fontenot .12 .30
115 Johan Santana .20 .50
116 Chuck James .12 .30
117 Boof Bonser .12 .30
118 Marco Scutaro .12 .30
119 Jeremy Hermida .12 .30
120 Andruw Jones .12 .30
121 Mike Cameron .12 .30
122 Jason Varitek .30 .75
123 Terry Francona MG .12 .30
124 Bob Geren MG .12 .30
125 Tim Hudson .12 .30
126 Brandon Jones RC .60 1.50
127 Steve Pearce RC .40 1.00
128 Kenny Lofton .12 .30
129 Kevin Hart (RC) .25 .60
130 Justin Upton .30 .75
131 Norris Hopper .12 .30
132 Ramon Vazquez .12 .30
133 Mike Bacsik .12 .30
134 Matt Stairs .12 .30
135 Brad Penny .12 .30

136 Robinson Cano .20 .50
137 Jamey Carroll .12 .30
138 Dan Wheeler .12 .30
139 Johnny Estrada .12 .30
140 Brandon Webb .20 .50
141 Ryan Klesko .12 .30
142 Chris Duncan .12 .30
143 Willie Harris .12 .30
144 Jerry Owens .12 .30
145 Magglio Ordonez .20 .50
146 Aaron Hill .12 .30
147 Marlon Anderson .12 .30
148 Gerald Laird .12 .30
149 Luke Hochevar RC .60 1.50
150 Alfonso Soriano .20 .50
151 Adam Loewen .12 .30
152 Bronson Arroyo .12 .30
153 Luis Mendoza (RC) .25 .60
154 David Ross .12 .30
155 Carlos Zambrano .12 .30
156 Brandon McCarthy .12 .30
157 Tim Redding .12 .30
158 Jose Bautista .12 .30
159 Luke Scott .12 .30
160 Ben Sheets .20 .50
161 Matt Garza .12 .30
162 Andy Laroche .12 .30
163 Doug Davis .12 .30
164 Nate Schierholtz .12 .30
165 Tim Lincecum .30 .75
166 Andy Sonnanstine .12 .30
167 Jason Hirsh .12 .30
168 Phil Hughes .30 .75
169 Adam Lind .12 .30
170 Scott Rolen .20 .50
171 John Maine .12 .30
172 Chris Ray .12 .30
173 Jamie Moyer .12 .30
174 Julian Tavarez .12 .30
175 Delmon Young .20 .50
176 Troy Patton (RC) .25 .60
177 Josh Anderson (RC) .25 .60
178 Dustin Pedroia ROY .50 1.25
179 Chris B. Young .12 .30
180 Jose Valverde .12 .30
181 Joe Borowski .12 .30
Bobby Jenks
J.J. Putz
182 Billy Buckner (RC) .25 .60
183 Paul Byrd .12 .30
184 Tadahito Iguchi .12 .30
185 Yunel Escobar .12 .30
186 Lastings Milledge .12 .30
187 Dustin McGowan .12 .30
188 Kei Igawa .12 .30
189 Esteban German .12 .30
190 Russell Martin .12 .30
191 Orlando Hudson .12 .30
192 Jim Edmonds .20 .50
193 J.J. Hardy .12 .30
194 Chad Billingsley .12 .30
195 Todd Helton .20 .50
196 Ross Gload .12 .30
197 Melky Cabrera .12 .30
198 Shannon Stewart .12 .30
199 Adrian Beltre .12 .30
200 Manny Ramirez .30 .75
201 Matt Capps .12 .30
202 Mike Lamb .12 .30
203 Jason Tyner .12 .30
204 Rafael Furcal .12 .30
205 Gil Meche .12 .30
206 Geoff Jenkins .12 .30
207 Jeff Kent .12 .30
208 David DeJesus .12 .30
209 Andy Phillips .12 .30
210 Mark Teahen .12 .30
211 Lyle Overbay .12 .30
212 Moises Alou .12 .30
213 Michael Barrett .12 .30
214 C.J. Wilson .12 .30
215 Bobby Jenks .12 .30
216 Ryan Garko .12 .30
217 Josh Beckett .20 .50
218 Clint Hurdle MG .12 .30
219 Kevin Kouzmanoff .12 .30
220 Roy Oswalt .12 .30
221 Ian Snell .12 .30
222 Mark Grudzielanek .12 .30
223 Odalis Perez .12 .30
224 Mark Buehrle .12 .30
225 Hunter Pence .30 .75
226 Kurt Suzuki .12 .30
227 Alfredo Amezaga .12 .30
228 Geoff Blum .12 .30
229 Dustin Pedroia .50 1.25
230 Roy Halladay .12 .30
231 Casey Blake .12 .30
232 Clay Buchholz (RC) .60 1.50
233 Jimmy Rollins MVP .20 .50
234a Boston Red Sox .50 1.25
234b Boston Red Sox 3.00 8.00
Rudy Giuliani celebrating with team
234c Boston Red Sox 30.00 60.00
Rudy Giuliani celebrating with team Red
235 Rich Harden .12 .30
236 Joe Koshansky (RC) .25 .60
237 Eric Wedge MG .12 .30
238 Shane Victorino .12 .30
239 Richie Sexson .12 .30
240 Jim Thome .20 .50
241 Ervin Santana .12 .30
242 Manny Acta .12 .30
243 Akinori Iwamura .12 .30
244 Adam Wainwright .12 .30
245 Dan Haren .12 .30
246 Jason Isringhausen .12 .30
247 Edgar Gonzalez .12 .30
248 Jose Contreras .12 .30
249 Chris Sampson .12 .30
250 Jonathan Papelbon .20 .50
251 Dan Johnson .12 .30
252 Dmitri Young .12 .30
253 Bronson Sardinha (RC) .25 .60
254 David Murphy .12 .30
255 Brandon Phillips .12 .30
256 Alex Rodriguez MVP .50 1.25
257 Austin Kearns .12 .30
Dimitri Young
258 Manny Ramirez .20 .50
Kevin Youkilis
259 Emilio Bonifacio RC .40 1.00
260 Chad Cordero .12 .30
261 Josh Barfield .12 .30
262 Brett Myers .12 .30
263 Nook Logan .12 .30
264 Byung-Hyun Kim .12 .30
265 Fredi Gonzalez .12 .30
266 Ryan Doumit .12 .30
267 Chris Burke .12 .30
268 Daric Barton (RC) .25 .60
269 James Loney .20 .50
270 C.C. Sabathia .12 .30
271 Chad Tracy .12 .30
272 Anthony Reyes .12 .30
273 Rafael Soriano .12 .30
274 Jermaine Dye .12 .30
275 C.C. Sabathia .12 .30
276 Brad Ausmus .12 .30
277 Aubrey Huff .12 .30
278 Xavier Nady .12 .30
279 Damion Easley .12 .30
280 Willie Randolph MG .12 .30
281 Carlos Ruiz .12 .30
282 Jon Lester .20 .50
283 Jorge Sosa .12 .30
284 Lance Broadway (RC) .25 .60
285 Tony LaRussa MG .12 .30
286 Jeff Clement (RC) .25 .60
287 Justin Morneau .20 .50
Johan Santana
Joe Mauer
288 Ivan Rodriguez .20 .50
Justin Verlander
289 Justin Ruggiano RC .40 1.00
290 Edgar Renteria .12 .30
291 Eugenio Velez RC .25 .60
292 Mark Loretta .12 .30
293 Gavin Floyd .12 .30
294 Brian McCann .20 .50
295 Tim Wakefield .12 .30
296 Paul Konerko .12 .30
297 Jorge Posada .20 .50
298 Prince Fielder .40 1.00
Ryan Howard
Adam Dunn
299 Cesar Izturis .12 .30
300 Chien-Ming Wang .40 1.00
301 Chris Duffy .12 .30
302 Horacio Ramirez .12 .30
303 Jose Lopez .12 .30
304 Jose Vidro .12 .30
305 Carlos Delgado .12 .30
306 Scott Olsen .12 .30
307 Shawn Hill .12 .30
308 Felipe Lopez .12 .30
309 Ryan Church .12 .30
310 Kelvim Escobar .12 .30
311 Jeremy Guthrie .12 .30
312 Ramon Hernandez .12 .30
313 Kameron Loe .12 .30
314 Ian Kinsler .20 .50
315 David Weathers .12 .30
316 Scott Hatteberg .12 .30
317 Cliff Lee .12 .30
318 Ned Yost MG .12 .30
319 Joey Votto (RC) .60 1.50
320 Ichiro Suzuki .50 1.25
321 J.R. Towles RC .60 1.50
322 Scott Kazmir .20 .50
Johan Santana
Erik Bedard
323 Jose Valverde .12 .30
Francisco Cordero
Trevor Hoffman
324 Jake Peavy .20 .50
325 Jim Leyland MG .12 .30
326 Matt Holliday .40 1.00
Chipper Jones
Hanley Ramirez
327 Jake Peavy .20 .50
Aaron Harang
John Smoltz
328 Nyjer Morgan (RC) .25 .60
329 Lou Piniella MG .12 .30
330 Curtis Granderson .12 .30
331 Dave Roberts .12 .30
332 Grady Sizemore .20 .50
Jhonny Peralta
333 Jayson Nix (RC) .25 .60
334 Oliver Perez .12 .30
335 Eric Byrnes .12 .30
336 Jhonny Peralta .12 .30
337 Livan Hernandez .12 .30
338 Matt Diaz .12 .30
339 Troy Percival .12 .30
340 David Wright .40 1.00
341 Daniel Cabrera .12 .30
342 Matt Belisle .12 .30
343 Kason Gabbard .12 .30
344 Mike Rabelo .12 .30
345 Carl Crawford .12 .30
346 Adam Everett .12 .30
347 Chris Capuano .12 .30
348 Craig Monroe .12 .30
349 Mike Mussina .12 .30
350 Mark Teixeira .20 .50
351 Bobby Crosby .12 .30
352 Miguel Batista .12 .30
353 Brendan Ryan .12 .30
354 Edwin Jackson .12 .30
355 Brian Roberts .20 .50
356 Manny Corpas .12 .30
357 Jeremy Accardo .12 .30
358 John Patterson .12 .30
359 Evan Meek RC .25 .60
360 David Ortiz .30 .75
361 Wesley Wright RC .25 .60
362 Fernando Hernandez RC .25 .60
363 Brian Barton RC .40 1.00
364 Al Reyes .12 .30
365 Derrek Lee .20 .50
366 Jeff Weaver .12 .30
367 Khalil Greene .20 .50
368 Michael Bourn .12 .30
369 Luis Castillo .12 .30
370 Adam Dunn .12 .30
371 Rickie Weeks .12 .30
372 Matt Kemp .12 .30
373 Casey Kotchman .12 .30
374 Jason Jennings .12 .30
375 Fausto Carmona .12 .30
376 Willy Taveras .12 .30
377 Jake Westbrook .12 .30
378 Ozzie Guillen .12 .30
379 Hideki Okajima .12 .30
380 Grady Sizemore .20 .50
381 Jeff Francoeur .20 .50
382 Micah Owings .12 .30
383 Jered Weaver .12 .30
384 Carlos Quentin .12 .30
385 Troy Tulowitzki .20 .50
386 Julio Lugo .12 .30
387 Sean Marshall .12 .30
388 Jorge Cantu .12 .30
389 Callix Crabbe (RC) .25 .60
390 Troy Glaus .20 .50
391 Nick Markakis .20 .50
392 Joey Gathright .12 .30
393 Michael Cuddyer .12 .30
394 Mark Ellis .12 .30
395 Lance Berkman .20 .50
396 Randy Johnson .30 .75
397 Brian Wilson .12 .30
398 Kenji Johjima .12 .30
399 Jarrod Saltalamacchia .12 .30
400 Matt Holliday .20 .50
401 Scott Hairston .12 .30
402 Taylor Buchholz .12 .30
403 Nate Robertson .12 .30
404 Cecil Cooper .12 .30
405 Travis Hafner .12 .30
406 Takashi Saito .12 .30
407 Johnny Damon .20 .50
408 Edinson Volquez .12 .30
409 Jason Giambi .20 .50
410 Alex Gordon .30 .75
411 Jason Kubel .12 .30
412 Joel Zumaya .12 .30
413 Wandy Rodriguez .12 .30
414 Andrew Miller .20 .50
415 Derek Lowe .12 .30
416 Elijah Dukes .12 .30
417 Brian Bass (RC) .25 .60
418 Dioner Navarro .12 .30
419 Bengie Molina .12 .30
420 Nick Swisher .12 .30
421 Brandon Backe .12 .30
422 Erick Aybar .12 .30
423 Mike Scioscia MG .12 .30
424 Aaron Harang .12 .30
425 Hanley Ramirez .30 .75
426 Franklin Gutierrez .12 .30
427 Carlos Guillen .12 .30
428 Jair Jurrjens .12 .30
429 Billy Butler .12 .30
430 Ryan Braun .40 1.00
431 Delwyn Young .12 .30
432 Jason Kendall .12 .30
433 Carlos Silva .12 .30
434 Ron Gardenhire MG .12 .30
435 Torii Hunter .12 .30
436 Joe Blanton .12 .30
437 Brandon Wood .12 .30
438 Jay Payton .12 .30
439 Josh Hamilton .40 1.00
440 Pedro Martinez .20 .50
441 Miguel Olivo .12 .30
442 Luis Gonzalez .12 .30
443 Greg Dobbs .12 .30
444 Jack Wilson .12 .30
445 Hideki Matsui .30 .75
446 Randor Bierd RC .25 .60
447 Chipper Jones .40 1.00
Mark Teixeira
448 Cameron Maybin .30 .75
449 Braden Looper .12 .30
450 Prince Fielder .30 .75
451 Brian Giles .12 .30
452 Kevin Slowey .12 .30
453 Josh Fogg .12 .30
454 Mike Hampton .12 .30
455 Derek Jeter .75 2.00
456 Chone Figgins .12 .30
457 Josh Fields .12 .30
458 Brad Hawpe .12 .30
459 Mike Sweeney .12 .30
460 Chase Utley .30 .75
461 Jacoby Ellsbury .50 1.25
462 Freddy Sanchez .12 .30
463 John McLaren .12 .30
464 Rocco Baldelli .12 .30
465 Huston Street .12 .30
466 Miguel Cabrera .20 .50
Ivan Rodriguez
467 Nick Blackburn RC .40 1.00
468 Gregor Blanco (RC) .25 .60
469 Brian Bocock RC .25 .60
470 Tom Gorzelanny .12 .30
471 Brian Schneider .12 .30
472 Shaun Marcum .12 .30
473 Joe Maddon .12 .30
474 Yuniesky Betancourt .12 .30
475 Adrian Gonzalez .20 .50
476 Johnny Cueto RC .40 1.00
477 Ben Broussard .12 .30
478 Geovany Soto .30 .75
479 Bobby Abreu .12 .30
480 Matt Cain .12 .30
481 Manny Parra .12 .30
482 Kazuo Fukumori RC .40 1.00
483 Mike Jacobs .12 .30
484 Todd Jones .12 .30
485 J.J. Putz .12 .30
486 Javier Vazquez .12 .30
487 Corey Patterson .12 .30
488 Mike Gonzalez .12 .30
489 Joakim Soria .12 .30
490 Albert Pujols .60 1.50
491 Cliff Floyd .12 .30
492 Harvey Garcia (RC) .25 .60
493 Steve Holm RC .25 .60
494 Paul Maholm .12 .30
495 James Shields .12 .30
496 Brad Lidge .12 .30
497 Cla Meredith .12 .30
498 Matt Chico .12 .30
499 Milton Bradley .12 .30
500 Chipper Jones .40 1.00
501 Elliot Johnson (RC) .25 .60
502 Alex Cora .12 .30
503 Jeremy Bonderman .12 .30
504 Conor Jackson .12 .30
505 B.J. Upton .20 .50
506 Jay Gibbons .12 .30
507 Mark DeRosa .12 .30
508 John Danks .12 .30
509 Alex Gonzalez .12 .30
510 Justin Verlander .20 .50
511 Jeff Francis .12 .30
512 Placido Polanco .12 .30
513 Rick Vanden Hurk .12 .30
514 Tony Pena .12 .30
515 A.J. Burnett .12 .30
516 Jason Schmidt .12 .30
517 Bill Hall .12 .30
518 Ian Stewart .12 .30
519 Travis Buck .12 .30
520 Vernon Wells .12 .30
521 Jayson Werth .12 .30
522 Nate McLouth .12 .30
523 Noah Lowry .12 .30
524 Raul Ibanez .12 .30
525 Gary Matthews .12 .30
526 Juan Encarnacion .12 .30
527 Marlon Byrd .12 .30
528 Paul Lo Duca .12 .30
529 Masahide Kobayashi RC .40 1.00
530 Ryan Zimmerman .20 .50
531 Hiroki Kuroda RC .40 1.00
532 Tim Lahey RC .25 .60
533 Kyle McClellan RC .25 .60
534 Matt Tupman RC .25 .60
535 Francisco Rodriguez .12 .30
536 Albert Pujols .60 1.50
Prince Fielder
537 Scott Moore .12 .30
538 Alex Romero (RC) .40 1.00
539 Clete Thomas RC .40 1.00
540 John Smoltz .30 .75
541 Adam Jones .12 .30
542 Adam Kennedy .12 .30
543 Carlos Lee .12 .30
544 Chad Gaudin .12 .30
545 Chris Young .12 .30
546 Francisco Liriano .20 .50
547 Fred Lewis .12 .30
548 Garrett Olson .12 .30
549 Gregg Zaun .12 .30
550 Curt Schilling .20 .50
551 Erick Threets (RC) .25 .60
552 J.D. Drew .12 .30
553 Jo-Jo Reyes .12 .30
554 Joe Borowski .12 .30
555 Josh Beckett .20 .50
556 John Gibbons .12 .30
557 John McDonald .12 .30
558 John Russell .12 .30
559 Jonny Gomes .12 .30
560 Aramis Ramirez .12 .30
561 Matt Tolbert RC .40 1.00
562 Ronnie Belliard .12 .30
563 Ramon Troncoso RC .25 .60
564 Frank Catalanotto .12 .30
565 A.J. Pierzynski .12 .30
566 Kevin Millwood .12 .30
567 David Eckstein .12 .30
568 Jose Guillen .12 .30
569 Brad Hennessey .12 .30
570 Homer Bailey .20 .50
571 Eric Gagne .12 .30
572 Adam Eaton .12 .30
573 Tom Gordon .12 .30
574 Scott Baker .12 .30
575 Ty Wigginton .12 .30
576 Dave Bush .12 .30
577 John Buck .12 .30
578 Ricky Nolasco .12 .30
579 Jesse Litsch .12 .30
580 Ken Griffey Jr. .50 1.25
581 Kazuo Matsui .12 .30
582 Dusty Baker .12 .30
583 Nick Punto .12 .30
584 Ryan Theriot .12 .30
585 Brian Bannister .12 .30
586 Coco Crisp .12 .30
587 Chris Snyder .12 .30
588 Tony Gwynn .12 .30
589 Dave Trembley .12 .30
590 Mariano Rivera .30 .75
591 Rico Washington (RC) .25 .60
592 Matt Morris .12 .30
593 Randy Wells RC .25 .60
594 Mike Morse .12 .30
595 Francisco Cordero .12 .30
596 Joba Chamberlain .40 1.00
597 Kyle Davies .12 .30
598 Bruce Bochy .12 .30
599 Austin Kearns .12 .30
600 Tom Glavine .20 .50
601 Felipe Paulino RC .40 1.00
602 Lyle Overbay .12 .30
Vernon Wells
603 Blake DeWitt (RC) .60 1.50
604 Wily Mo Pena .12 .30
605 Andre Ethier .20 .50
606 Jason Bergmann .12 .30
607 Ryan Spilborghs .12 .30
608 Brian Burres .12 .30
609 Ted Lilly .12 .30
610 Carlos Beltran .12 .30
611 Garret Anderson .12 .30
612 Kelly Johnson .12 .30
613 Melvin Mora .12 .30
614 Rich Hill .12 .30
615 Pat Burrell .12 .30
616 Jon Garland .12 .30
617 Asdrubal Cabrera .12 .30
618 Pat Neshek .12 .30
619 Sergio Mitre .12 .30
620 Gary Sheffield .12 .30
621 Denard Span .20 .50
622 Jorge De La Rosa .12 .30
623 Trey Hillman MG .12 .30
624 Joe Torre MG .20 .50
625 Greg Maddux .40 1.00
626 Mike Redmond .12 .30
627 Mike Pelfrey .12 .30
628 Andy Pettitte .20 .50
629 Eric Chavez .12 .30
630 Chris Carpenter .12 .30
631 Joe Girardi MG .12 .30
632 Charlie Manuel MG .12 .30
633 Adam LaRoche .12 .30
634 Kenny Rogers .12 .30
635 Michael Young .12 .30
636 Rafael Betancourt .12 .30
637 Jose Castillo .12 .30
638 Juan Pierre .12 .30
639 Juan Uribe .12 .30
640 Carlos Pena .30 .75
641 Marcus Thames .12 .30
642 Mark Kotsay .12 .30
643 Matt Murton .12 .30
644 Reggie Willits .12 .30
645 Andy Marte .12 .30
646 Rajai Davis .12 .30
647 Randy Winn .12 .30
648 Ryan Freel .12 .30
649 Joe Crede .12 .30
650 Frank Thomas .30 .75
651 Martin Prado .12 .30
652 Rod Barajas .12 .30
653 Endy Chavez .12 .30
654 Willy Aybar .12 .30
655 Aaron Rowand .12 .30
656 Darin Erstad .12 .30
657 Jeff Keppinger .12 .30
658 Kerry Wood .12 .30
659 Vicente Padilla .12 .30
660 Yadier Molina .20 .50
661 Johan Santana 150.00 250.00
Front of card reads Santana Tosses 1st No-No
FS1 Kazuo Uzuki .75 2.00
NNO Alexei Ramirez 50.00 100.00
NNO Kosuke Fukudome 40.00 80.00
NNO Yasuhiko Yabuta 40.00 80.00

2008 Topps Black

SER.1 ODDS 1:95 HOBBY
SER.2 ODDS 1:63 HOBBY
STATED PRINT RUN 57 SER.#'d SETS

1 Alex Rodriguez 15.00 40.00
2 Barry Zito 6.00 15.00
3 Jeff Suppan 6.00 15.00
4 Rick Ankiel 6.00 15.00
5 Scott Kazmir 6.00 15.00
6 Felix Pie 6.00 15.00
7 Mickey Mantle 60.00 120.00
8 Stephen Drew 6.00 15.00
9 Randy Wolf 6.00 15.00
10 Miguel Cabrera 10.00 25.00
11 Yorvit Torrealba 6.00 15.00
12 Jason Bartlett 6.00 15.00
13 Kendry Morales 6.00 15.00
14 Lenny DiNardo 6.00 15.00
15 Magglio Ordonez 15.00 40.00
Ichiro Suzuki
Placido Polanco
16 Kevin Gregg 6.00 15.00
17 Cristian Guzman 6.00 15.00
18 J.D. Durbin 6.00 15.00
19 Robinson Tejeda 6.00 15.00
20 Daisuke Matsuzaka 15.00 40.00
21 Edwin Encarnacion 6.00 15.00
22 Ron Washington MG 6.00 15.00
23 Chin-Lung Hu 30.00 60.00
24 Alex Rodriguez 10.00 25.00
Magglio Ordonez
Vladimir Guerrero
25 Kaz Matsui 6.00 15.00
26 Manny Ramirez 10.00 25.00
27 Bob Melvin MG 6.00 15.00
28 Kyle Kendrick 6.00 15.00
29 Anibal Sanchez 6.00 15.00
30 Jimmy Rollins 10.00 25.00
31 Ronny Paulino 6.00 15.00
32 Howie Kendrick 6.00 15.00
33 Joe Mauer 10.00 25.00
34 Aaron Cook 6.00 15.00
35 Cole Hamels 10.00 25.00
36 Brendan Harris 6.00 15.00
37 Jason Marquis 6.00 15.00
38 Preston Wilson 6.00 15.00
39 Yovanni Gallardo 6.00 15.00
40 Miguel Tejada 6.00 15.00
41 Rich Aurilia 6.00 15.00
42 Corey Hart 6.00 15.00
43 Ryan Dempster 6.00 15.00
44 Jonathan Broxton 6.00 15.00
45 Dontrelle Willis 6.00 15.00
46 Zack Greinke 6.00 15.00
47 Orlando Cabrera 6.00 15.00
48 Zach Duke 6.00 15.00
49 Orlando Hernandez 6.00 15.00
50 Jake Peavy 10.00 25.00
51 Erik Bedard 6.00 15.00
52 Trevor Hoffman 6.00 15.00
53 Hank Blalock 6.00 15.00
54 Victor Martinez 6.00 15.00
55 Chris Young 6.00 15.00
56 Seth Smith 6.00 15.00
57 Wladimir Balentien 6.00 15.00
58 Matt Holliday 10.00 25.00
Ryan Howard
Miguel Cabrera
59 Grady Sizemore 10.00 25.00
60 Jose Reyes 10.00 25.00
61 Alex Rodriguez 10.00 25.00
Carlos Pena
David Ortiz
62 Rich Thompson 6.00 15.00
63 Jason Michaels 6.00 15.00
64 Mike Lowell 10.00 25.00
65 Billy Wagner 6.00 15.00
66 Brad Wilkerson 6.00 15.00
67 Wes Helms 6.00 15.00
68 Kevin Millar 6.00 15.00
69 Bobby Cox MG 6.00 15.00
70 Dan Uggla 6.00 15.00
71 Jarrod Washburn 6.00 15.00
72 Mike Piazza 20.00 50.00
73 Mike Napoli 6.00 15.00
74 Garrett Atkins 6.00 15.00
75 Felix Hernandez 10.00 25.00
76 Ivan Rodriguez 10.00 25.00
77 Angel Guzman 6.00 15.00
78 Radhames Liz 10.00 25.00
79 Omar Vizquel 6.00 15.00
80 Alex Rios 6.00 15.00
81 Ray Durham 6.00 15.00
82 So Taguchi 6.00 15.00
83 Mark Reynolds 6.00 15.00
84 Brian Fuentes 6.00 15.00
85 Jason Bay 10.00 25.00
86 Scott Podsednik 6.00 15.00
87 Maicer Izturis 6.00 15.00
88 Jack Cust 6.00 15.00
89 Josh Willingham 6.00 15.00
90 Vladimir Guerrero 10.00 25.00
91 Marcus Giles 6.00 15.00
92 Ross Detwiler 10.00 25.00
93 Kenny Lofton 6.00 15.00
94 Bud Black MG 6.00 15.00
95 John Lackey 6.00 15.00
96 Sam Fuld 6.00 15.00
97 Clint Sammons 6.00 15.00
98 Ryan Howard 12.50 30.00
Chase Utley
99 David Ortiz 12.50 30.00
Manny Ramirez
100 Ryan Howard 12.50 30.00
101 Ryan Braun ROY 12.50 30.00
102 Ross Ohlendorf 10.00 25.00
103 Jonathan Albaladejo 6.00 15.00
104 Kevin Youkilis 10.00 25.00
105 Roger Clemens 12.00 30.00
106 Josh Bard 6.00 15.00
107 Shawn Green 6.00 15.00
108 B.J. Ryan 6.00 15.00
109 Joe Nathan 6.00 15.00
110 Justin Morneau 6.00 15.00
111 Ubaldo Jimenez 6.00 15.00
112 Jacque Jones 6.00 15.00
113 Kevin Frandsen 6.00 15.00
114 Mike Fontenot 6.00 15.00
115 Johan Santana 12.50 30.00
116 Chuck James 6.00 15.00
117 Boof Bonser 6.00 15.00
118 Marco Scutaro 6.00 15.00
119 Jeremy Hermida 6.00 15.00
120 Andruw Jones 6.00 15.00
121 Mike Cameron 6.00 15.00
122 Jason Varitek 10.00 25.00
123 Terry Francona MG 6.00 15.00
124 Bob Geren MG 6.00 15.00
125 Tim Hudson 6.00 15.00
126 Brandon Jones 6.00 15.00
127 Steve Pearce 10.00 25.00
128 Kenny Lofton 6.00 15.00
129 Kevin Hart 6.00 15.00
130 Justin Upton 10.00 25.00
131 Norris Hopper 6.00 15.00
132 Ramon Vazquez 6.00 15.00
133 Mike Bacsik 6.00 15.00
134 Matt Stairs 6.00 15.00
135 Brad Penny 6.00 15.00
136 Robinson Cano 10.00 25.00
137 Jamey Carroll 6.00 15.00
138 Dan Wheeler 6.00 15.00
139 Johnny Estrada 6.00 15.00
140 Brandon Webb 6.00 15.00
141 Ryan Klesko 6.00 15.00
142 Chris Duncan 6.00 15.00
143 Willie Harris 6.00 15.00
144 Jerry Owens 6.00 15.00
145 Magglio Ordonez 10.00 25.00
146 Aaron Hill 6.00 15.00
147 Marlon Anderson 6.00 15.00
148 Gerald Laird 6.00 15.00
149 Luke Hochevar 10.00 25.00
150 Alfonso Soriano 10.00 25.00
151 Adam Loewen 6.00 15.00
152 Bronson Arroyo 6.00 15.00
153 Luis Mendoza 6.00 15.00
154 David Ross 6.00 15.00
155 Carlos Zambrano 6.00 15.00
156 Brandon McCarthy 6.00 15.00
157 Tim Redding 6.00 15.00
158 Jose Bautista 6.00 15.00
159 Luke Scott 6.00 15.00
160 Ben Sheets 6.00 15.00
161 Matt Garza 6.00 15.00
162 Andy Laroche 6.00 15.00
163 Doug Davis 6.00 15.00
164 Nate Schierholtz 6.00 15.00
165 Tim Lincecum 10.00 25.00
166 Andy Sonnanstine 6.00 15.00
167 Jason Hirsh 6.00 15.00
168 Phil Hughes 12.50 30.00
169 Adam Lind 6.00 15.00
170 Scott Rolen 10.00 25.00
171 John Maine 6.00 15.00
172 Chris Ray 6.00 15.00
173 Jamie Moyer 6.00 15.00
174 Julian Tavarez 6.00 15.00
175 Delmon Young 10.00 25.00
176 Troy Patton 6.00 15.00
177 Josh Anderson 6.00 15.00
178 Dustin Pedroia ROY 10.00 25.00
179 Chris Young 6.00 15.00
180 Jose Valverde 6.00 15.00
181 Joe Borowski 6.00 15.00
Bobby Jenks
J.J. Putz
182 Billy Buckner 6.00 15.00
183 Paul Byrd 6.00 15.00
184 Tadahito Iguchi 6.00 15.00
185 Yunel Escobar 6.00 15.00
186 Lastings Milledge 6.00 15.00
187 Dustin McGowan 6.00 15.00
188 Kei Igawa 6.00 15.00
189 Esteban German 6.00 15.00
190 Russell Martin 6.00 15.00
191 Orlando Hudson 6.00 15.00
192 Jim Edmonds 6.00 15.00
193 J.J. Hardy 6.00 15.00
194 Chad Billingsley 6.00 15.00
195 Todd Helton 10.00 25.00
196 Ross Gload 6.00 15.00
197 Melky Cabrera 6.00 15.00
198 Shannon Stewart 6.00 15.00
199 Adrian Beltre 6.00 15.00
200 Manny Ramirez 10.00 25.00
201 Matt Capps 6.00 15.00
202 Mike Lamb 6.00 15.00
203 Jason Tyner 6.00 15.00
204 Rafael Furcal 6.00 15.00
205 Gil Meche 6.00 15.00
206 Geoff Jenkins 6.00 15.00
207 Jeff Kent 6.00 15.00
208 David DeJesus 6.00 15.00
209 Andy Phillips 6.00 15.00
210 Mark Teahen 6.00 15.00
211 Lyle Overbay 6.00 15.00

212 Moises Alou 6.00 15.00
213 Michael Barrett 6.00 15.00
214 C.J. Wilson 6.00 15.00
215 Bobby Jenks 6.00 15.00
216 Ryan Garko 6.00 15.00
217 Josh Beckett 15.00 40.00
218 Clint Hurdle MG 6.00 15.00
219 Kevin Kouzmanoff 6.00 15.00
220 Roy Oswalt 6.00 15.00
221 Ian Snell 6.00 15.00
222 Mark Grudzielanek 6.00 15.00
223 Odalis Perez 6.00 15.00
224 Mark Buehrle 6.00 15.00
225 Hunter Pence 12.50 30.00
226 Kurt Suzuki 6.00 15.00
227 Alfredo Amezaga 6.00 15.00
228 Geoff Blum 6.00 15.00
229 Dustin Pedroia 12.50 30.00
230 Roy Halladay 6.00 15.00
231 Casey Blake 6.00 15.00
232 Clay Buchholz 30.00 60.00
233 Jimmy Rollins MVP 10.00 25.00
234 Boston Red Sox 30.00 60.00
235 Rich Harden 6.00 15.00
236 Joe Koshansky 6.00 15.00
237 Eric Wedge MG 6.00 15.00
238 Shane Victorino 6.00 15.00
239 Richie Sexson 6.00 15.00
240 Jim Thome 10.00 25.00
241 Ervin Santana 6.00 15.00
242 Manny Acta 6.00 15.00
243 Akinori Iwamura 6.00 15.00
244 Adam Wainwright 6.00 15.00
245 Dan Haren 6.00 15.00
246 Jason Isringhausen 6.00 15.00
247 Edgar Gonzalez 6.00 15.00
248 Jose Contreras 6.00 15.00
249 Chris Sampson 6.00 15.00
250 Jonathan Papelbon 12.50 30.00
251 Dan Johnson 6.00 15.00
252 Dmitri Young 6.00 15.00
253 Bronson Sardinha 6.00 15.00
254 David Murphy 6.00 15.00
255 Brandon Phillips 6.00 15.00
256 Alex Rodriguez MVP 15.00 40.00
257 Austin Kearns 6.00 15.00
Dimitri Young
258 Manny Ramirez 10.00 25.00
Kevin Youkilis
259 Emilio Bonifacio 6.00 15.00
260 Chad Cordero 6.00 15.00
261 Josh Banfield 6.00 15.00
262 Brett Myers 6.00 15.00
263 Nook Logan 6.00 15.00
264 Byung-Hyun Kim 6.00 15.00
265 Fredi Gonzalez 6.00 15.00
266 Ryan Doumit 6.00 15.00
267 Chris Burke 6.00 15.00
268 Daric Barton 6.00 15.00
269 James Loney 12.50 30.00
270 C.C. Sabathia 6.00 15.00
271 Chad Tracy 6.00 15.00
272 Anthony Reyes 6.00 15.00
273 Rafael Soriano 6.00 15.00
274 Jermaine Dye 6.00 15.00
275 C.C. Sabathia 6.00 15.00
276 Brad Ausmus 6.00 15.00
277 Aubrey Huff 6.00 15.00
278 Xavier Nady 6.00 15.00
279 Damion Easley 6.00 15.00
280 Willie Randolph MG 6.00 15.00
281 Carlos Ruiz 6.00 15.00
282 Jon Lester 10.00 25.00
283 Jorge Sosa 6.00 15.00
284 Lance Broadway 6.00 15.00
285 Tony LaRussa MG 6.00 15.00
286 Jeff Clement 6.00 15.00
287 Justin Morneau 12.50 30.00
Johan Santana
Joe Mauer
288 Ivan Rodriguez 10.00 25.00
Justin Verlander
289 Justin Ruggiano 6.00 15.00
290 Edgar Renteria 6.00 15.00
291 Eugenio Velez 6.00 15.00
292 Mark Loretta 6.00 15.00
293 Gavin Floyd 6.00 15.00
294 Brian McCann 6.00 15.00
295 Tim Wakefield 6.00 15.00
296 Paul Konerko 6.00 15.00
297 Jorge Posada 10.00 25.00
298 Prince Fielder 10.00 25.00
Ryan Howard
Adam Dunn
299 Cesar Izturis 6.00 15.00
300 Chien-Ming Wang 12.50 30.00
301 Chris Duffy 6.00 15.00
302 Horacio Ramirez 6.00 15.00
303 Jose Lopez 6.00 15.00
304 Jose Vidro 6.00 15.00
305 Carlos Delgado 6.00 15.00
306 Scott Olsen 6.00 15.00
307 Shawn Hill 6.00 15.00
308 Felipe Lopez 6.00 15.00
309 Ryan Church 6.00 15.00
310 Kelvim Escobar 6.00 15.00
311 Jeremy Guthrie 6.00 15.00
312 Ramon Hernandez 6.00 15.00
313 Kameron Loe 6.00 15.00
314 Ian Kinsler 6.00 15.00
315 David Weathers 6.00 15.00
316 Scott Hatteberg 6.00 15.00
317 Cliff Lee 6.00 15.00
318 Ned Yost MG 6.00 15.00
319 Joey Votto 10.00 25.00
320 Ichiro Suzuki 20.00 50.00
321 J.R. Towles 10.00 25.00
322 Scott Kazmir 10.00 25.00
Johan Santana
Erik Bedard
323 Jose Valverde 6.00 15.00
Francisco Cordero
Trevor Hoffman
324 Jake Peavy 10.00 25.00
325 Jim Leyland MG 6.00 15.00
326 Matt Holliday 10.00 25.00
Chipper Jones
Hanley Ramirez
327 Jake Peavy 10.00 25.00
Aaron Harang
John Smoltz
328 Nyjer Morgan 6.00 15.00
329 Lou Piniella 6.00 15.00
330 Curtis Granderson 10.00 25.00
331 Dave Roberts 6.00 15.00
332 Grady Sizemore 10.00 25.00
Jhonny Peralta
333 Jayson Nix 6.00 15.00
334 Oliver Perez 6.00 15.00
335 Eric Byrnes 6.00 15.00
336 Jhonny Peralta 6.00 15.00
337 Livan Hernandez 6.00 15.00
338 Matt Diaz 6.00 15.00
339 Troy Percival 6.00 15.00
340 David Wright 12.50 30.00
341 Daniel Cabrera 6.00 15.00
342 Matt Belisle 6.00 15.00
343 Kason Gabbard 6.00 15.00
344 Mike Rabelo 6.00 15.00
345 Carl Crawford 6.00 15.00
346 Adam Everett 6.00 15.00
347 Chris Capuano 6.00 15.00
348 Craig Monroe 6.00 15.00
349 Mike Mussina 6.00 15.00
350 Mark Teixeira 10.00 25.00
351 Bobby Crosby 6.00 15.00
352 Miguel Batista 6.00 15.00
353 Brendan Ryan 15.00 40.00
354 Edwin Jackson 6.00 15.00
355 Brian Roberts 6.00 15.00
356 Manny Corpas 6.00 15.00
357 Jeremy Accardo 6.00 15.00
358 John Patterson 6.00 15.00
359 Evan Meek 6.00 15.00
360 David Ortiz 12.50 30.00
361 Wesley Wright 10.00 25.00
362 Fernando Hernandez 6.00 15.00
363 Brian Barton 12.50 30.00
364 Al Reyes 6.00 15.00
365 Derek Lee 6.00 15.00
366 Jeff Weaver 6.00 15.00
367 Khalil Greene 6.00 15.00
368 Michael Bourn 6.00 15.00
369 Luis Castillo 6.00 15.00
370 Adam Dunn 6.00 15.00
371 Rickie Weeks 6.00 15.00
372 Matt Kemp 6.00 15.00
373 Casey Kotchman 6.00 15.00
374 Jason Jennings 6.00 15.00
375 Fausto Carmona 6.00 15.00
376 Willy Taveras 6.00 15.00
377 Jake Westbrook 6.00 15.00
378 Ozzie Guillen 6.00 15.00
379 Hideki Okajima 10.00 25.00
380 Grady Sizemore 10.00 25.00
381 Jeff Francoeur 10.00 25.00
382 Micah Owings 10.00 25.00
383 Jered Weaver 6.00 15.00
384 Carlos Quentin 6.00 15.00
385 Troy Tulowitzki 6.00 15.00
386 Julio Lugo 6.00 15.00
387 Sean Marshall 6.00 15.00
388 Jorge Cantu 6.00 15.00
389 Callix Crabbe 6.00 15.00
390 Troy Glaus 6.00 15.00
391 Nick Markakis 10.00 25.00
392 Joey Gathright 6.00 15.00
393 Michael Cuddyer 6.00 15.00
394 Mark Ellis 6.00 15.00
395 Lance Berkman 6.00 15.00
396 Randy Johnson 10.00 25.00
397 Brian Wilson 6.00 15.00
398 Kenji Johjima 6.00 15.00
399 Jarrod Saltalamacchia 6.00 15.00
400 Matt Holliday 6.00 15.00
401 Scott Hairston 6.00 15.00
402 Taylor Buchholz 6.00 15.00
403 Nate Robertson 6.00 15.00
404 Cecil Cooper 6.00 15.00
405 Travis Hafner 6.00 15.00
406 Takashi Saito 10.00 25.00
407 Johnny Damon 6.00 15.00
408 Edinson Volquez 10.00 25.00
409 Jason Giambi 10.00 25.00
410 Alex Gordon 12.50 30.00
411 Jason Kubel 6.00 15.00
412 Joel Zumaya 6.00 15.00
413 Wandy Rodriguez 6.00 15.00
414 Andrew Miller 6.00 15.00
415 Derek Lowe 10.00 25.00
416 Elijah Dukes 6.00 15.00
417 Brian Bass 6.00 15.00
418 Dioner Navarro 6.00 15.00
419 Bengie Molina 6.00 15.00
420 Nick Swisher 6.00 15.00
421 Brandon Backe 6.00 15.00
422 Erick Aybar 6.00 15.00
423 Mike Scioscia 6.00 15.00
424 Aaron Harang 6.00 15.00
425 Hanley Ramirez 10.00 25.00
426 Franklin Gutierrez 6.00 15.00
427 Carlos Guillen 6.00 15.00
428 Jair Jurrjens 6.00 15.00
429 Billy Butler 6.00 15.00
430 Ryan Braun 15.00 40.00
431 Delwyn Young 6.00 15.00
432 Jason Kendall 6.00 15.00
433 Carlos Silva 6.00 15.00
434 Ron Gardenhire MG 6.00 15.00
435 Torii Hunter 6.00 15.00
436 Joe Blanton 6.00 15.00
437 Brandon Wood 6.00 15.00
438 Jay Payton 6.00 15.00
439 Josh Hamilton 30.00 60.00
440 Pedro Martinez 10.00 25.00
441 Miguel Olivo 6.00 15.00
442 Luis Gonzalez 6.00 15.00
443 Greg Dobbs 6.00 15.00
444 Jack Wilson 6.00 15.00
445 Hideki Matsui 12.50 30.00
446 Randor Bierd 6.00 15.00
447 Chipper Jones 10.00 25.00
Mark Teixeira
448 Cameron Maybin 12.50 30.00
449 Braden Looper 6.00 15.00
450 Prince Fielder 12.50 30.00
451 Brian Giles 6.00 15.00
452 Kevin Slowey 10.00 25.00
453 Josh Fogg 6.00 15.00
454 Mike Hampton 6.00 15.00
455 Derek Jeter 40.00 80.00
456 Chone Figgins 6.00 15.00
457 Josh Fields 6.00 15.00
458 Brad Hawpe 6.00 15.00
459 Mike Sweeney 6.00 15.00
460 Chase Utley 12.50 30.00
461 Jacoby Ellsbury 20.00 50.00
462 Freddy Sanchez 6.00 15.00
463 John McLaren 6.00 15.00
464 Rocco Baldelli 6.00 15.00
465 Huston Street 6.00 15.00
466 Miguel Cabrera 10.00 25.00
Ivan Rodriguez
467 Nick Blackburn 15.00 40.00
468 Gregor Blanco 6.00 15.00
469 Brian Bocock 10.00 25.00
470 Tom Gorzelanny 6.00 15.00
471 Brian Schneider 6.00 15.00
472 Shaun Marcum 6.00 15.00
473 Joe Maddon 6.00 15.00
474 Yuniesky Betancourt 6.00 15.00
475 Adrian Gonzalez 6.00 15.00
476 Johnny Cueto 12.50 30.00
477 Ben Broussard 6.00 15.00
478 Geovany Soto 15.00 40.00
479 Bobby Abreu 6.00 15.00
480 Matt Cain 6.00 15.00
481 Manny Parra 6.00 15.00
482 Kazuo Fukumori 10.00 25.00
483 Mike Jacobs 6.00 15.00
484 Todd Jones 6.00 15.00
485 J.J. Putz 6.00 15.00
486 Javier Vazquez 6.00 15.00
487 Corey Patterson 6.00 15.00
488 Mike Gonzalez 6.00 15.00
489 Joakim Soria 6.00 15.00
490 Albert Pujols 20.00 50.00
491 Cliff Floyd 6.00 15.00
492 Harvey Garcia 6.00 15.00
493 Steve Holm 6.00 15.00
494 Paul Maholm 6.00 15.00
495 James Shields 6.00 15.00
496 Brad Lidge 6.00 15.00
497 Cla Meredith 6.00 15.00
498 Matt Chico 6.00 15.00
499 Milton Bradley 6.00 15.00
500 Chipper Jones 12.50 30.00
501 Elliot Johnson 6.00 15.00
502 Alex Cora 6.00 15.00
503 Jeremy Bonderman 10.00 25.00
504 Conor Jackson 6.00 15.00
505 B.J. Upton 6.00 15.00
506 Jay Gibbons 6.00 15.00
507 Mark DeRosa 6.00 15.00
508 John Danks 6.00 15.00
509 Alex Gonzalez 6.00 15.00
510 Justin Verlander 10.00 25.00
511 Jeff Francis 6.00 15.00
512 Placido Polanco 6.00 15.00
513 Rick Vanden Hurk 6.00 15.00
514 Tony Pena 6.00 15.00
515 A.J. Burnett 6.00 15.00
516 Jason Schmidt 6.00 15.00
517 Bill Hall 6.00 15.00
518 Ian Stewart 6.00 15.00
519 Travis Buck 6.00 15.00
520 Vernon Wells 6.00 15.00
521 Jayson Werth 6.00 15.00
522 Nate McLouth 15.00 40.00
523 Noah Lowry 6.00 15.00
524 Raul Ibanez 6.00 15.00
525 Gary Matthews 6.00 15.00
526 Juan Encarnacion 6.00 15.00
527 Marlon Byrd 6.00 15.00
528 Paul Lo Duca 6.00 15.00
529 Masahide Kobayashi 10.00 25.00
530 Ryan Zimmerman 6.00 15.00
531 Hiroki Kuroda 12.50 30.00
532 Tim Lahey 6.00 15.00
533 Kyle McClellan 6.00 15.00
534 Matt Tupman 6.00 15.00
535 Francisco Rodriguez 6.00 15.00
536 Albert Pujols 12.50 30.00
Prince Fielder
537 Scott Moore 6.00 15.00
538 Alex Romero 6.00 15.00
539 Clete Thomas 6.00 15.00
540 John Smoltz 10.00 25.00
541 Adam Jones 6.00 15.00
542 Adam Kennedy 6.00 15.00
543 Carlos Lee 6.00 15.00
544 Chad Gaudin 6.00 15.00
545 Chris Young 6.00 15.00
546 Francisco Liriano 6.00 15.00
547 Fred Lewis 6.00 15.00
548 Garrett Olson 6.00 15.00
549 Gregg Zaun 6.00 15.00
550 Curt Schilling 10.00 25.00
551 Erick Threets 6.00 15.00
552 J.D. Drew 6.00 15.00
553 Jo-Jo Reyes 6.00 15.00
554 Joe Borowski 6.00 15.00
555 Josh Beckett 10.00 25.00
556 John Gibbons 6.00 15.00
557 John McDonald 6.00 15.00
558 John Russell 6.00 15.00
559 Jonny Gomes 6.00 15.00
560 Aramis Ramirez 6.00 15.00
561 Matt Tolbert 10.00 25.00
562 Ronnie Belliard 6.00 15.00
563 Ramon Troncoso 6.00 15.00
564 Frank Catalanotto 6.00 15.00
565 A.J. Pierzynski 6.00 15.00
566 Kevin Millwood 6.00 15.00
567 David Eckstein 6.00 15.00
568 Jose Guillen 6.00 15.00
569 Brad Hennessey 6.00 15.00
570 Homer Bailey 6.00 15.00
571 Eric Gagne 6.00 15.00
572 Adam Eaton 6.00 15.00
573 Tom Gordon 6.00 15.00
574 Scott Baker 6.00 15.00
575 Ty Wigginton 6.00 15.00
576 Dave Bush 6.00 15.00
577 John Buck 6.00 15.00
578 Ricky Nolasco 6.00 15.00
579 Jesse Litsch 6.00 15.00
580 Ken Griffey Jr. 20.00 50.00
581 Kazuo Matsui 6.00 15.00
582 Dusty Baker 6.00 15.00
583 Nick Punto 6.00 15.00
584 Ryan Theriot 6.00 15.00
585 Brian Bannister 10.00 25.00
586 Coco Crisp 10.00 25.00
587 Chris Snyder 6.00 15.00
588 Tony Gwynn 6.00 15.00
589 Dave Trembley 6.00 15.00
590 Mariano Rivera 12.50 30.00
591 Rico Washington 6.00 15.00
592 Matt Morris 6.00 15.00
593 Randy Wells 6.00 15.00
594 Mike Morse 6.00 15.00
595 Francisco Cordero 6.00 15.00
596 Joba Chamberlain 20.00 50.00
597 Kyle Davies 6.00 15.00
598 Bruce Bochy 6.00 15.00
599 Austin Kearns 6.00 15.00
600 Tom Glavine 10.00 25.00
601 Felipe Paulino 6.00 15.00
602 Lyle Overbay 6.00 15.00
Vernon Wells
603 Blake DeWitt 15.00 40.00
604 Wily Mo Pena 6.00 15.00
605 Andre Ethier 10.00 25.00
606 Jason Bergmann 6.00 15.00
607 Ryan Spilborghs 6.00 15.00
608 Brian Burres 6.00 15.00
609 Ted Lilly 6.00 15.00
610 Carlos Beltran 6.00 15.00
611 Garret Anderson 6.00 15.00
612 Kelly Johnson 6.00 15.00
613 Melvin Mora 6.00 15.00
614 Rich Hill 6.00 15.00
615 Pat Burrell 6.00 15.00
616 Jon Garland 6.00 15.00
617 Asdrubal Cabrera 6.00 15.00
618 Pat Neshek 6.00 15.00
619 Sergio Mitre 6.00 15.00
620 Gary Sheffield 6.00 15.00
621 Denard Span 6.00 15.00
622 Jorge De La Rosa 6.00 15.00
623 Trey Hillman MG 6.00 15.00
624 Joe Torre MG 12.50 30.00
625 Greg Maddux 15.00 40.00
626 Mike Redmond 6.00 15.00
627 Mike Pelfrey 6.00 15.00
628 Andy Pettitte 10.00 25.00
629 Eric Chavez 6.00 15.00
630 Chris Carpenter 6.00 15.00
631 Joe Girardi MG 6.00 15.00
632 Charlie Manuel MG 6.00 15.00
633 Adam LaRoche 6.00 15.00
634 Kenny Rogers 6.00 15.00
635 Michael Young 6.00 15.00
636 Rafael Betancourt 6.00 15.00
637 Jose Castillo 6.00 15.00
638 Juan Pierre 6.00 15.00
639 Juan Uribe 6.00 15.00
640 Carlos Pena 6.00 15.00
641 Marcus Thames 6.00 15.00
642 Mark Kotsay 6.00 15.00
643 Matt Murton 6.00 15.00
644 Reggie Willits 6.00 15.00
645 Andy Marte 6.00 15.00
646 Rajai Davis 6.00 15.00
647 Randy Winn 6.00 15.00
648 Ryan Freel 6.00 15.00
649 Joe Crede 6.00 15.00
650 Frank Thomas 12.50 30.00
651 Martin Prado 6.00 15.00
652 Rod Barajas 6.00 15.00
653 Endy Chavez 6.00 15.00
654 Willy Aybar 6.00 15.00
655 Aaron Rowand 6.00 15.00
656 Darin Erstad 6.00 15.00
657 Jeff Keppinger 6.00 15.00
658 Kerry Wood 6.00 15.00
659 Vicente Padilla 6.00 15.00
660 Yadier Molina 6.00 15.00

2008 Topps Gold Border

*GOLD: 3X TO 8X BASIC
*GOLD RC: 2X TO 5X BASIC RC
SER.1 ODDS 1:9 H,1:3 HTA,1:13 R
SER.2 ODDS 1:5 H,1:2 HTA,1:12 R
STATED PRINT RUN 2008 SER.#'d SETS
234b Boston Red Sox
Rudy Giuliani celebrating with team

2008 Topps Gold Foil

*GOLD FOIL: 1X TO 2.5X BASIC
*GOLD FOIL RC: .6X TO 1.5X BASIC RC
RANDOM INSERTS IN PACKS
234b Boston Red Sox 4.00 10.00
Rudy Giuliani celebrating with team

2008 Topps Platinum

SER.1 ODDS 1:16,500 H,1:10,000 HTA
SER.1 ODDS 1:25,000 RETAIL
SER.2 ODDS 1:12,500 H,1:2950 HTA
SER.2 ODDS 1:21,000 RETAIL
STATED PRINT RUN 1 SER.#'d SET
NO PRICING DUE TO SCARCITY

2008 Topps 1955 Reprint Relic

STATED ODDS 1:400,000 H,1:11,000 HTA
STATED ODDS 1:176,000 RETAIL
STATED PRINT RUN 55 SER.#'d SETS
NO PRICING DUE TO SCARCITY
MM55 Mickey Mantle Bat

2008 Topps 1956 Reprint Relic

SER.2 ODDS 1:43,030 HOBBY
SER.2 ODDS 1:5249 HTA
STATED PRINT RUN 56 SER.#'d SETS
56MM Mickey Mantle 90.00 150.00

2008 Topps 50th Anniversary All Rookie Team

COMPLETE SET (110) 50.00 100.00
COMP.SER.1 SET (55) 20.00 50.00
COMP.SER.2 SET (55) 20.00 50.00
SER.1 ODDS 1:5 HOB, 1:5 RET
SER.2 ODDS 1:5 H,1:5 HTA,1:5 RET
AR1 Darryl Strawberry .40 1.00
AR2 Gary Sheffield .40 1.00
AR3 Dwight Gooden .40 1.00
AR4 Melky Cabrera .40 1.00
AR5 Gary Carter .40 1.00
AR6 Lou Piniella .40 1.00
AR7 Dave Justice .40 1.00
AR8 Andre Dawson .40 1.00
AR9 Mark Ellis .40 1.00
AR10 Dave Johnson .40 1.00
AR11 Jermaine Dye .40 1.00
AR12 Dan Johnson .40 1.00
AR13 Alfonso Soriano .60 1.50
AR14 Prince Fielder 1.00 2.50
AR15 Hanley Ramirez 1.00 2.50
AR16 Matt Holliday .60 1.50
AR17 Justin Verlander .60 1.50
AR18 Mark Teixeira .60 1.50
AR19 Julio Franco .40 1.00
AR20 Ivan Rodriguez .60 1.50
AR21 Jason Bay .40 1.00
AR22 Brandon Webb .60 1.50
AR23 Dontrelle Willis .40 1.00
AR24 Brad Wilkerson .40 1.00
AR25 Dan Uggla .60 1.50
AR26 Ozzie Smith 1.50 4.00
AR27 Andruw Jones .40 1.00
AR28 Garret Anderson .40 1.00
AR29 Jimmy Rollins .60 1.50
AR30 Brian McCann .60 1.50
AR31 Scott Podsednik .40 1.00
AR32 Garrett Atkins .40 1.00
AR33 Billy Wagner .40 1.00
AR34 Chipper Jones 1.25 3.00
AR35 Roger McDowell .40 1.00
AR36 Austin Kearns .40 1.00
AR37 Boog Powell .40 1.00
AR38 Ron Swoboda .40 1.00
AR39 Roy Oswalt .40 1.00
AR40 Mike Piazza 1.00 2.50
AR41 Albert Pujols 2.00 5.00
AR42 Ichiro Suzuki 1.50 4.00
AR43 C.C. Sabathia .40 1.00
AR44 Todd Helton .60 1.50
AR45 Scott Rolen .60 1.50
AR46 Derek Jeter 2.50 6.00
AR47 Shawn Green .40 1.00
AR48 Manny Ramirez 1.00 2.50
AR49 Tom Seaver UER .60 1.50
Position listed as shortstop
AR50 Kenny Lofton .40 1.00
AR51 Francisco Liriano .60 1.50
AR52 Ryan Zimmerman .60 1.50
AR53 Jeff Francoeur .60 1.50
AR54 Joe Mauer .60 1.50
AR55 Magglio Ordonez .60 1.50
AR56 Carlos Beltran .40 1.00
AR57 Andre Ethier .60 1.50
AR58 Brian Bannister .40 1.00
AR59 Chris Young .40 1.00
AR60 Troy Tulowitzki .60 1.50
AR61 Hideki Okajima .40 1.00
AR62 Delmon Young .60 1.50
AR63 Craig Wilson .40 1.00
AR64 Hunter Pence 1.00 2.50
AR65 Tadahito Iguchi .40 1.00
AR66 Mark Kotsay .40 1.00
AR67 Nick Markakis .60 1.50
AR68 Russ Adams .40 1.00
AR69 Russ Martin .60 1.50
AR70 James Loney .60 1.50
AR71 Ryan Braun 1.25 3.00
AR72 Jonny Gomes .40 1.00
AR73 Carlos Ruiz .40 1.00
AR74 Willy Taveras .40 1.00
AR75 Joe Torre .60 1.50
AR76 Jeff Kent .40 1.00
AR77 Huston Street .40 1.00
AR78 Dustin Pedroia 1.50 4.00
AR79 Gustavo Chacin .40 1.00
AR80 Adam Dunn .40 1.00
AR81 Pat Burrell .40 1.00
AR82 Rocco Baldelli .40 1.00
AR83 Chad Tracy .40 1.00
AR84 Adam LaRoche .40 1.00
AR85 Aaron Miles .40 1.00
AR86 Khalil Greene .60 1.50
AR87 Daniel Cabrera .40 1.00
AR88 Mike Gonzalez .40 1.00
AR89 Ty Wigginton .40 1.00
AR90 Angel Berroa .40 1.00
AR91 Moises Alou .40 1.00
AR92 Miguel Olivo .40 1.00
AR93 Nick Johnson .40 1.00
AR94 Eric Hinske .40 1.00
AR95 Ramon Santiago .40 1.00
AR96 Jason Jennings .40 1.00
AR97 Adam Kennedy .40 1.00
AR98 Mike Lamb .40 1.00
AR99 Rafael Furcal .40 1.00
AR100 Jay Payton .40 1.00
AR101 Bengie Molina .40 1.00
AR102 Mark Redman .40 1.00
AR103 Alex Gonzalez .40 1.00
AR104 Ray Durham .40 1.00
AR105 Miguel Cairo .40 1.00
AR106 Kerry Wood .40 1.00
AR107 Dmitri Young .40 1.00
AR108 Jose Cruz .40 1.00
AR109 Jose Guillen .40 1.00
AR110 Scott Hatteberg .40 1.00

2008 Topps 50th Anniversary All Rookie Team Gold

COMMON CARD 5.00 12.00
SEMISTARS 8.00 20.00
UNLISTED STARS 12.50 30.00
SER.1 ODDS 1:1290 H,1:1100 HTA
SER.1 ODDS 1:1290 RETAIL
SER.2 ODDS 1:740 HOB,1:505 HTA
SER.2 ODDS 1:1100 RETAIL
STATED PRINT RUN 99 SER.#'d SETS
AR1 Darryl Strawberry 5.00 12.00
AR2 Gary Sheffield 5.00 12.00
AR3 Dwight Gooden 5.00 12.00
AR4 Melky Cabrera 5.00 12.00
AR5 Gary Carter 5.00 12.00
AR6 Lou Piniella 5.00 12.00
AR7 Dave Justice 5.00 12.00
AR8 Andre Dawson 5.00 12.00
AR9 Mark Ellis 5.00 12.00
AR10 Dave Johnson 5.00 12.00
AR11 Jermaine Dye 5.00 12.00
AR12 Dan Johnson 5.00 12.00
AR13 Alfonso Soriano 8.00 20.00
AR14 Prince Fielder 12.00 30.00
AR15 Hanley Ramirez 12.00 30.00
AR16 Matt Holliday 8.00 20.00
AR17 Justin Verlander 8.00 20.00
AR18 Mark Teixeira 8.00 20.00
AR19 Julio Franco 5.00 12.00
AR20 Ivan Rodriguez 8.00 20.00
AR21 Jason Bay 5.00 12.00
AR22 Brandon Webb 8.00 20.00
AR23 Dontrelle Willis 5.00 12.00
AR24 Brad Wilkerson 5.00 12.00
AR25 Dan Uggla 8.00 20.00
AR26 Ozzie Smith 15.00 40.00
AR27 Andruw Jones 5.00 12.00
AR28 Garret Anderson 5.00 12.00
AR29 Jimmy Rollins 8.00 20.00
AR30 Brian McCann 8.00 20.00
AR31 Scott Podsednik 5.00 12.00
AR32 Garrett Atkins 5.00 12.00
AR33 Billy Wagner 5.00 12.00
AR34 Chipper Jones 15.00 40.00
AR35 Roger McDowell 5.00 12.00
AR36 Austin Kearns 5.00 12.00
AR37 Boog Powell 5.00 12.00
AR38 Ron Swoboda 5.00 12.00
AR39 Roy Oswalt 5.00 12.00
AR40 Mike Piazza 12.00 30.00
AR41 Albert Pujols 20.00 50.00
AR42 Ichiro Suzuki 15.00 40.00
AR43 C.C. Sabathia 5.00 12.00
AR44 Todd Helton 8.00 20.00
AR45 Scott Rolen 8.00 20.00
AR46 Derek Jeter 20.00 50.00
AR47 Shawn Green 5.00 12.00
AR48 Manny Ramirez 12.00 30.00
AR49 Tom Seaver 8.00 20.00
AR50 Kenny Lofton 5.00 12.00
AR51 Francisco Liriano 8.00 20.00
AR52 Ryan Zimmerman 8.00 20.00
AR53 Jeff Francoeur 8.00 20.00
AR54 Joe Mauer 8.00 20.00
AR55 Magglio Ordonez 8.00 20.00
AR56 Carlos Beltran 5.00 12.00
AR57 Andre Ethier 8.00 20.00
AR58 Brian Bannister 5.00 12.00
AR59 Chris Young 5.00 12.00
AR60 Troy Tulowitzki 8.00 20.00
AR61 Hideki Okajima 5.00 12.00
AR62 Delmon Young 8.00 20.00
AR63 Craig Wilson 15.00 40.00
AR64 Hunter Pence 12.00 30.00
AR65 Tadahito Iguchi 5.00 12.00
AR66 Mark Kotsay 5.00 12.00
AR67 Nick Markakis 8.00 20.00
AR68 Russ Adams 5.00 12.00
AR69 Russ Martin 10.00 25.00
AR70 James Loney 8.00 20.00
AR71 Ryan Braun 12.50 30.00
AR72 Jonny Gomes 5.00 12.00
AR73 Carlos Ruiz 5.00 12.00
AR74 Willy Taveras 5.00 12.00
AR75 Joe Torre 8.00 20.00
AR76 Jeff Kent 5.00 12.00
AR77 Huston Street 5.00 12.00
AR78 Dustin Pedroia 20.00 50.00
AR79 Gustavo Chacin 5.00 12.00
AR80 Adam Dunn 5.00 12.00
AR81 Pat Burrell 5.00 12.00
AR82 Rocco Baldelli 5.00 12.00
AR83 Chad Tracy 5.00 12.00
AR84 Adam LaRoche 5.00 12.00
AR85 Aaron Miles 5.00 12.00
AR86 Khalil Greene 8.00 20.00
AR87 Daniel Cabrera 5.00 12.00
AR88 Mike Gonzalez 5.00 12.00
AR89 Ty Wigginton 5.00 12.00
AR90 Angel Berroa 5.00 12.00
AR91 Moises Alou 5.00 12.00
AR92 Miguel Olivo 5.00 12.00
AR93 Nick Johnson 5.00 12.00
AR94 Eric Hinske 5.00 12.00
AR95 Ramon Santiago 5.00 12.00
AR96 Jason Jennings 5.00 12.00
AR97 Adam Kennedy 8.00 20.00
AR98 Mike Lamb 5.00 12.00
AR99 Rafael Furcal 5.00 12.00
AR100 Jay Payton 5.00 12.00
AR101 Bengie Molina 5.00 12.00
AR102 Mark Redman 5.00 12.00
AR103 Alex Gonzalez 5.00 12.00
AR104 Ray Durham 5.00 12.00
AR105 Miguel Cairo 5.00 12.00
AR106 Kerry Wood 5.00 12.00
AR107 Dmitri Young 10.00 25.00
AR108 Jose Cruz 5.00 12.00
AR109 Jose Guillen 5.00 12.00
AR110 Scott Hatteberg 5.00 12.00

2008 Topps 50th Anniversary All Rookie Team Autographs

SER.1 ODDS 1:7194 H, 1:365 HTA
SER.1 ODDS 1:50,000 RETAIL
SER.2 ODDS 1:13,017 HOB,1:432 HTA
SER.2 ODDS 1:34,310 RETAIL
STATED PRINT RUN 25 SER.#'d SETS
NO PRICING DUE TO SCARCITY
AD Andre Dawson
AE Andre Ethier S2
AJ Andruw Jones
AK Austin Kearns
AP Albert Pujols S2
AS Alfonso Soriano
BB Brian Bannister S2
BM Brian McCann
BP Boog Powell
BTW Brandon Webb
BW Billy Wagner
CB Carlos Beltran S2
CJ Chipper Jones
CR Carlos Ruiz S2
CW Craig Wilson S2
CY Chris Young S2
DG Dwight Gooden
DJ Dave Justice
DJ Dave Johnson
DS Darryl Strawberry
DU Dan Uggla
DW Dontrelle Willis
FL Francisco Liriano S2
GA Garret Anderson
GBA Garrett Atkins
GC Gary Carter
GS Gary Sheffield
HO Hideki Okajima S2
HP Hunter Pence S2
HR Hanley Ramirez
IR Ivan Rodriguez
JB Jason Bay
JD Jermaine Dye
JF Julio Franco
JL James Loney S2
JR Jimmy Rollins
JT Joe Torre S2
JV Justin Verlander
LP Lou Piniella
MC Melky Cabrera
ME Mark Ellis
MH Matt Holliday S2
MH Matt Holliday
MK Mark Kotsay S2
MP Mike Piazza
MT Mark Teixeira
NM Nick Markakis S2
OS Ozzie Smith
PF Prince Fielder
RB Ryan Braun S2
RM Russ Martin S2
RM Roger McDowell
RO Roy Oswalt S2
RO Roy Oswalt
RS Ron Swoboda
RZ Ryan Zimmerman S2
SBW Brad Wilkerson
SG Shawn Green S2
SP Scott Podsednik
TS Tom Seaver

2008 Topps 50th Anniversary All Rookie Team Relics

SER.1 ODDS 1:7178 H, 1:366 HTA
SER.1 ODDS 1:50,700 RETAIL
SER.2 ODDS 1:2378 H,1:290 HTA
STATED PRINT RUN 50 SER.#'d SETS

AD Adam Dunn	12.50	30.00
AD Andre Dawson	30.00	60.00
AE Andre Ethier	20.00	50.00
AJ Andruw Jones	12.50	30.00
AP Albert Pujols		
AS Alfonso Soriano	12.50	30.00
BM Brian McCann	10.00	25.00
BW Brandon Webb	15.00	40.00
CJ Chipper Jones	15.00	40.00
CS C.C. Sabathia	12.50	30.00
DG Dwight Gooden	10.00	25.00
DJ Dave Justice	12.50	30.00
DS Darryl Strawberry	20.00	50.00
DU Dan Uggla	12.50	30.00
DW Dontrelle Willis	12.50	30.00
FL Francisco Liriano	15.00	40.00
GA Garret Anderson	10.00	25.00
GC Gary Carter	20.00	50.00
GS Gary Sheffield	30.00	60.00
HR Hanley Ramirez	10.00	25.00
IR Ivan Rodriguez	12.50	30.00
IS Ichiro Suzuki	30.00	60.00
JB Jason Bay	30.00	60.00
JM Joe Mauer	12.50	30.00
JR Jimmy Rollins	15.00	40.00
JV Justin Verlander	15.00	40.00
MH Matt Holliday	20.00	50.00
MO Magglio Ordonez	20.00	50.00
MP Mike Piazza	20.00	50.00
MT Mark Teixeira	15.00	40.00
NJ Nick Johnson	30.00	60.00
NM Nick Markakis	40.00	80.00
OS Ozzie Smith	15.00	40.00
PB Pat Burrell	12.50	30.00
PF Prince Fielder	15.00	40.00
RB Rocco Baldelli	12.50	30.00
RO Roy Oswalt	10.00	25.00
SP Scott Podsednik		
TH Todd Helton	10.00	25.00
TS Tom Seaver	12.50	30.00

2008 Topps Barry Bonds Home Run Triple Relic

RANDOM INSERTS IN PACKS
NO PRICING DUE TO SCARCITY
BB Barry Bonds

2008 Topps Campaign 2008

COMPLETE SET (12)	8.00	20.00
STATED ODDS 1:9 H,1:2 HTA,1:9 R		
AG Al Gore		
AS Arnold Schwarzenegger		
BO Barack Obama	8.00	20.00
BR Bill Richardson	.60	1.50
DK Dennis Kucinich	.60	1.50
FT Fred Thompson	.60	1.50
HC Hillary Clinton	2.00	5.00
JB Joseph Biden	2.00	5.00
JE John Edwards	1.00	2.50
JM John McCain	2.00	5.00
MH Mike Huckabee	1.00	2.50
MR Mitt Romney	1.00	2.50
RG Rudy Giuliani	1.00	2.50
RP Ron Paul	.60	1.50
SP Sarah Palin	10.00	25.00
SP Sarah Palin Pageant	20.00	50.00

2008 Topps Campaign 2008 Gold

COMPLETE SET	50.00	100.00
*GOLD: .75X TO 2X BASIC		
STATED ODDS 1:5 HTA		
BO Barack Obama	20.00	50.00
JB Joseph Biden	5.00	12.00

2008 Topps Campaign 2008 Cut Signatures

STATED ODDS 1:125,000 H,1:7500 HTA
STATED ODDS 1:170,000 RETAIL
PRINT RUNS b/wn 15-18 COPIES PER
NO PRICING DUE TO SCARCITY
BO Barack Obama/15
FT Fred Thompson/15
HC Hillary Clinton/18
JE John Edwards/15
JM John McCain/13

2008 Topps Campaign 2008 Letter Patches

SER.2 ODDS 1:2642 H,1:322 HTA
STATED PRINT RUN 50 SER.#'d SETS

BO Barack Obama O	100.00	200.00
BO Barack Obama B	100.00	200.00
BO Barack Obama A	100.00	200.00
BO Barack Obama M	100.00	200.00
BO Barack Obama A	100.00	200.00
HC Hillary Clinton O	30.00	60.00
HC Hillary Clinton N	30.00	60.00
HC Hillary Clinton C	30.00	60.00
HC Hillary Clinton L	30.00	60.00
HC Hillary Clinton I	30.00	60.00
HC Hillary Clinton N	30.00	60.00
HC Hillary Clinton T	30.00	60.00
JM John McCain M	30.00	60.00
JM John McCain c	30.00	60.00
JM John McCain C	30.00	60.00
JM John McCain A	30.00	60.00
JM John McCain I	30.00	60.00
JM John McCain N	30.00	60.00

2008 Topps Commemorative Patch Relics

SER.2 ODDS 1:792 HOB,1:97 HTA
STATED PRINT RUN 100 SER.#'d SETS

AP Andy Pettitte	30.00	60.00
AR Alex Rodriguez	50.00	100.00
BA Bobby Abreu	20.00	50.00
BS Brian Schneider	10.00	25.00
BW Billy Wagner	10.00	25.00
CB Carlos Beltran	10.00	25.00
CD Carlos Delgado	10.00	25.00
CMW Chien-Ming Wang	50.00	100.00
DJ Derek Jeter	60.00	120.00
DW David Wright	20.00	50.00
EC Endy Chavez	8.00	20.00
HM Hideki Matsui	50.00	100.00
JC Joba Chamberlain	50.00	100.00
JD Johnny Damon	30.00	60.00
JG Jason Giambi	40.00	80.00
JM John Maine	10.00	25.00
JP Jorge Posada	20.00	50.00
JR Jose Reyes	12.50	30.00
LC Luis Castillo	8.00	20.00
MA Moises Alou	8.00	20.00
MC Melky Cabrera	20.00	50.00
MM Mike Mussina	40.00	80.00
MP Mike Pelfrey	12.50	30.00
MR Mariano Rivera	20.00	50.00
OH Orlando Hernandez	8.00	20.00
OP Oliver Perez	8.00	20.00
PH Phil Hughes	20.00	50.00
PM Pedro Martinez	10.00	25.00
RC Robinson Cano	30.00	60.00
RMC Ryan Church	10.00	25.00

2008 Topps Dick Perez

WMDP1 Manny Ramirez	.60	1.50
WMDP2 Cameron Maybin	.60	1.50
WMDP3 Ryan Howard	.75	2.00
WMDP4 David Ortiz	.60	1.50
WMDP5 Tim Lincecum	.60	1.50
WMDP6 David Wright	.75	2.00
WMDP7 Mickey Mantle	2.50	6.00
WMDP8 Joba Chamberlain	.75	2.00
WMDP9 Ichiro Suzuki	1.00	2.50
WMDP10 Prince Fielder	.60	1.50
WMDP11 Jacoby Ellsbury	1.00	2.50
WMDP12 Jake Peavy	.40	1.00
WMDP13 Miguel Cabrera	.40	1.00
WMDP14 Josh Beckett	.40	1.00
WMDP15 Jimmy Rollins	.40	1.00
WMDP16 Torii Hunter	.25	.60
WMDP17 Alfonso Soriano	.40	1.00
WMDP18 Jose Reyes	.40	1.00
WMDP19 C.C. Sabathia	.25	.60
WMDP20 Alex Rodriguez	1.00	2.50
WMDP21 Ryan Braun	.75	2.00
WMDP22 Johan Santana	.40	1.00
WMDP23 Matt Holliday	.40	1.00
WMDP24 Ervin Santana	.25	.60
WMDP25 Daisuke Matsuzaka	1.00	2.50
WMDP26 Josh Hamilton	.75	2.00
WMDP27 Chipper Jones	.75	2.00
WMDP28 Lance Berkman	.40	1.00
WMDP29 Hanley Ramirez	.60	1.50
WMDP30 Mariano Rivera	.60	1.50

2008 Topps Highlights Autographs

SER.1 A ODDS 1:32,000 H,1:1463 HTA
SER.1 A ODDS 1:159,000 RETAIL
SER.2 A ODDS 1:28,927 H,1:965 HTA
SER.2 A ODDS 1:76,245 RETAIL
UPD.A ODDS 1:38,362 HOBBY
SER.1 B ODDS 1:4792 H,1:244 HTA
SER.1 B ODDS 1:33,333 RETAIL
SER.2 B ODDS 1:923 H,1:31 HTA
SER.2 B ODDS 1:2451 RETAIL
UPD.B ODDS 1:11,066 HOBBY
SER.1 C ODDS 1:958 H,1:49 HTA
SER.1 C ODDS 1:6470 RETAIL
SER.2 C ODDS 1:651 H,1:87 HTA
SER.2 C ODDS 1:6862 RETAIL
UPD.C ODDS 1:4082 HOBBY
SER.1 D ODDS 1:1425 H,1:70 HTA
SER.1 D ODDS 1:14,250 RETAIL
SER.2 D ODDS 1:15,370 H,1:181 HTA
SER.2 D ODDS 1:14,296 RETAIL
UPD.D ODDS 1:5587 HOBBY
SER.1 E ODDS 1:1075 H,1:117 HTA
SER.1 E ODDS 1:880 RETAIL
SER.2 E ODDS 1:814 H,1:27 HTA
SER.2 E ODDS 1:2144 RETAIL
UPD.E ODDS 1:6851 HOBBY
SER.1 F ODDS 1:895 H,1:23 HTA
SER.1 F ODDS 1:1370 RETAIL
SER.2 F ODDS 1:3254 H,1:108 HTA
SER.2 F ODDS 1:8578 RETAIL
UPD.F ODDS 1:1116 HOBBY
SER.1 G ODDS 1:3070 H,1:224 HTA
SER.1 G ODDS 1:4055 RETAIL
UPD.G ODDS 1:1109 HOBBY
UPD.H ODDS 1:1985 HOBBY
NO GROUP A PRICING AVAILABLE
NO GROUP A2 PRICING AVAILABLE

AC Asdrubal Cabrera C UPD	6.00	15.00
AG Armando Galarraga D UPD	6.00	15.00
AH Aaron Heilman B2	6.00	15.00
AK Austin Kearns F2	4.00	10.00
AL Adam Lind C	4.00	10.00
AP Albert Pujols A		
AS Alfonso Soriano A		
BB Billy Butler C UPD	10.00	25.00
BC Bobby Crosby B2	6.00	15.00
BD Blake DeWitt C UPD	12.50	30.00
BDB Brian Barton F UPD	4.00	10.00
BP Brandon Phillips B UPD	4.00	10.00
BP Brad Penny B	10.00	25.00
BR B.J. Ryan D UPD	4.00	10.00
CB Clay Buchholz C	30.00	60.00
CC Carl Crawford B2	8.00	20.00
CD Carlos Delgado A2		
CF Chone Figgins B2	6.00	15.00
CG Carlos Gomez C UPD	4.00	10.00
CJ Chipper Jones A UPD		
CK Clayton Kershaw B UPD	40.00	80.00
CM Craig Monroe B2	6.00	15.00
CMW Chien-Ming Wang A2		
CMW Chien-Ming Wang B	100.00	150.00
CP Carlos Pena C	8.00	20.00
CR Carlos Ruiz F UPD	4.00	10.00
CV Claudio Vargas C2	4.00	10.00
CV Carlos Villanueva F	4.00	10.00
CW Chase Wright E2	4.00	10.00
DB Dallas Braden C2	4.00	10.00
DB Daric Barton G	4.00	10.00
DE Darin Erstad B2	4.00	10.00
DH Dan Haren B	6.00	15.00
DM Dustin McGowan C UPD	6.00	15.00
DM Dustin Moseley F	4.00	10.00
DO David Ortiz A2		
DW David Wright A2		
DW David Wright A UPD		
DW David Wright B	30.00	60.00
DY Delwyn Young E2	4.00	10.00
EC Eric Chavez B2	4.00	10.00
ED Eulogio De La Cruz C	4.00	10.00
EL Evan Longoria A UPD		
ES Ervin Santana E2	4.00	10.00
ES Ervin Santana C	4.00	10.00
EV Edinson Volquez D UPD	8.00	20.00
FC Fausto Carmona E2	4.00	10.00
FC Fausto Carmona C	6.00	15.00
FL Francisco Liriano B2	6.00	15.00
FS Freddy Sanchez C	6.00	15.00
GS Greg Smith UPD		
GS Gary Sheffield B	10.00	25.00
HCK Hong-Chih Kuo C2	6.00	15.00
HK Howie Kendrick D	4.00	10.00
HR Hanley Ramirez B	15.00	40.00
JA Josh Anderson E	4.00	10.00
JAB Jason Bartlett D2	4.00	10.00
JAR Jo-Jo Reyes C2	4.00	10.00
JB Jeremy Bonderman B2	6.00	15.00
JB Jay Bruce B UPD		
JBR John Buck D	4.00	10.00
JBR Jose Reyes B	30.00	60.00
JC Joba Chamberlain B2	40.00	80.00
JD Johnny Damon A2		
JD Johnny Damon A		
JEM Justin Morneau B	10.00	25.00
JF Josh Fields C	4.00	10.00
JH Josh Hamilton B UPD	50.00	100.00
JKM John Maine B2	6.00	15.00
JL John Lackey C	4.00	10.00
JLC Jorge Cantu C2	4.00	10.00
JM Justin Morneau A2		
JM Jose Molina D	4.00	10.00
JP Jake Peavy B	15.00	40.00
JR Jimmy Rollins A2		
JR Jo-Jo Reyes E UPD	4.00	10.00
JR Jimmy Rollins B	40.00	80.00
JS Jeff Salazar G UPD	4.00	10.00
JTD Jermaine Dye B2	4.00	10.00
JTD Jermaine Dye B	4.00	10.00
JV Joey Votto C UPD	15.00	40.00
JV Jason Varitek B	40.00	80.00
JW Josh Willingham B2	6.00	15.00
JZ Joel Zumaya B2	6.00	15.00
KM Kendry Morales B2	4.00	10.00
LB Lance Broadway E	4.00	10.00
LC Luis Castillo C	4.00	10.00
MB Mike Bacsik F	4.00	10.00
MC Melky Cabrera B2	10.00	25.00
ME Mark Ellis F	4.00	10.00
MG Matt Garza B2	4.00	10.00
MG Matt Garza C	4.00	10.00
MK Masa Kobayashi C UPD	6.00	15.00
MMT Marcus Thames B2	4.00	10.00
MR Manny Ramirez A		
MS Max Scherzer B UPD	10.00	25.00
MT Mark Teixeira A2		
MW Mark Worrell H UPD	4.00	10.00
MY Michael Young B	6.00	15.00
NJM Nyjer Morgan E	4.00	10.00
NM Nick Markakis B2	6.00	15.00
NM Nick Markakis B UPD	12.50	30.00
NM Nick Markakis C	10.00	25.00
NR Nate Robertson B2	4.00	10.00
PF Prince Fielder B2	15.00	40.00
PF Prince Fielder B	30.00	60.00
PH Philip Humber D2	4.00	10.00
PJF Pedro Feliciano B2	6.00	15.00
RB Ryan Braun B2	20.00	50.00
RB Ryan Braun A UPD	60.00	120.00
RC Robinson Cano B2	10.00	25.00
RC Ramon Castro D	4.00	10.00
RH Rich Hill D	6.00	15.00
RJC Robinson Cano B	30.00	60.00
RJM Randy Messenger F	4.00	10.00
RM Russ Martin B2	6.00	15.00
RM Russell Martin C	6.00	15.00
RN Ricky Nolasco B2	4.00	10.00
RP Ronny Paulino E2	4.00	10.00
RR Ryan Roberts E2	4.00	10.00
SF Sam Fuld E	10.00	25.00
SH Steve Holm F UPD	4.00	10.00
SM Scott Moore F	4.00	10.00
SS Seth Smith G UPD	4.00	10.00
SS Seth Smith E	4.00	10.00
SV Shane Victorino B2	12.50	30.00
TG Tom Gorzelanny E2	4.00	10.00
TG Tom Gorzelanny F	4.00	10.00
TT Taylor Tankersley B2	4.00	10.00
UJ Ubaldo Jimenez F	4.00	10.00
VG Vladimir Guerrero A2		
VG Vladimir Guerrero A		
WN Wil Nieves C	4.00	10.00
YG Yovani Gallardo C	6.00	15.00
YP Yusmeiro Petit UPD		
ZG Zack Greinke E2	4.00	10.00
ZG Zack Greinke C UPD	4.00	10.00

2008 Topps Highlights Relics

SER.1 A ODDS 1:3597 H,1:183 HTA
SER.1 A ODDS 1:25,000 RETAIL
SER.2 A ODDS 1:85 H, 1:11 HTA
SER.1 B ODDS 1:21,250 H,1:958 HTA
SER.1 B ODDS 1:7500 RETAIL
SER.2 B ODDS 1:108 H, 1:14 HTA
SER.1 C ODDS 1:1725 H,1:705 HTA
SER.1 C ODDS 1:3050 RETAIL
SER.2 C ODDS 1:651 H, 1:80 HTA
SER.1 D ODDS 1:244 RETAIL
SER.1 D ODDS 1:1965 H,1:33 HTA

AG Alex Gordon B2	5.00	12.00
AP Albert Pujols B2	6.00	15.00
AP Albert Pujols D	6.00	15.00
AR Aramis Ramirez B2	3.00	8.00
BP Brandon Phillips B2	3.00	8.00
BU B.J. Upton C2	3.00	8.00
BW Brandon Webb C2	3.00	8.00
CB Carlos Beltran Bat C	3.00	8.00
CC Carl Crawford Pants B2	3.00	8.00
CC Carl Crawford D	3.00	8.00
CM Cameron Maybin Bat C2	3.00	8.00
CM Cameron Maybin D	3.00	8.00
CMW Chien-Ming Wang Jsy B2	8.00	20.00
CS Curt Schilling Jsy D	4.00	10.00
CU Chase Utley Jsy B2	5.00	12.00
DL Derrek Lee B2	3.00	8.00
DO David Ortiz D	4.00	10.00
DO1 David Ortiz B2	4.00	10.00
DO2 David Ortiz B2	4.00	10.00
DU Dan Uggla Jsy B2	3.00	8.00
DW David Wright Jsy C2	5.00	12.00
DW David Wright D	5.00	12.00
DWW Dontrelle Willis D	3.00	8.00
DY Delmon Young Jsy B2	3.00	8.00
EC Eric Chavez D	3.00	8.00
HR Hanley Ramirez B2	3.00	8.00
IR Ivan Rodriguez D	5.00	12.00
IS Ichiro Suzuki C2	6.00	15.00
IS Ichiro Suzuki D	6.00	15.00
JB Jeremy Bonderman B2	3.00	8.00
JL James Loney B2	3.00	8.00
JP Jake Peavy B2	3.00	8.00
JR Jose Reyes A2	5.00	12.00
JR Jose Reyes A	5.00	12.00
JT Jim Thome C2	3.00	8.00
JV Justin Verlander D	5.00	12.00
LB Lance Berkman C	3.00	8.00
MH Matt Holliday B	3.00	8.00
MR Manny Ramirez D	4.00	10.00
MT Miguel Tejada D	3.00	8.00
PF Prince Fielder B2	4.00	10.00
PF Prince Fielder A	4.00	10.00
RB Ryan Braun B2	6.00	15.00
RF Rafael Furcal C2	3.00	8.00
RH Ryan Howard B2	5.00	12.00
RO Roy Oswalt A2	3.00	8.00
RZ Ryan Zimmerman B2	3.00	8.00
ST Scott Thorman B2	3.00	8.00
TH Todd Helton D	3.00	8.00
VG Vladimir Guerrero B2	4.00	10.00
VG Vladimir Guerrero A	4.00	10.00

2008 Topps Highlights Relics Autographs

SER.2 ODDS 1:17,356 H,1:577 HTA
SER.2 ODDS 1:45,747 RETAIL
STATED PRINT RUN 25 SER.#'d SETS
NO PRICING DUE TO SCARCITY
AP Albert Pujols
CC Carl Crawford
DW David Wright
JC Joba Chamberlain
JD Jermaine Dye
JM Justin Morneau
MC Melky Cabrera
MR Manny Ramirez
NM Nick Markakis
PF Prince Fielder
RB Ryan Braun
RH Ryan Howard
RM Russ Martin
VG Vladimir Guerrero
YG Yovani Gallardo

2008 Topps Highlights Relics Dual

SER.2 ODDS 1:6342 HOB,1:773 HTA
STATED PRINT RUN 25 SER.#'d SETS
NO PRICING DUE TO SCARCITY
CW Melky Cabrera
Chien-Ming Wang
CY Carl Crawford
Delmon Young
FB Prince Fielder
Ryan Braun
HR Ryan Howard
Jimmy Rollins
ML Russ Martin
James Loney
MM Justin Morneau
Joe Mauer
OR David Ortiz
Manny Ramirez
RL Aramis Ramirez
Derrek Lee
RM Brian Roberts
Nick Markakis
RU Jimmy Rollins
Chase Utley
SJ Ichiro Suzuki
Kenji Johjima
TD Jim Thome
Jermaine Dye
UR Dan Uggla
Hanley Ramirez
WB David Wright
Carlos Beltran
WR David Wright
Jose Reyes

2008 Topps Historical Campaign Match-Ups

COMPLETE SET (55)	20.00	50.00
SER.2 ODDS 1:6 HOB,1:6 HTA,1:6 RET		
1792 George Washington	1.00	2.50
John Adams		
1796 John Adams	1.00	2.50
Thomas Jefferson		
1800 Thomas Jefferson	.75	2.00
Aaron Burr		
1804 Thomas Jefferson	.75	2.00
Charles Pinckney		
1808 James Madison	.60	1.50
Charles Pinckney		
1812 James Madison	.60	1.50
DeWitt Clinton		
1816 James Monroe	.60	1.50
Rufus King		
1820 James Monroe	.60	1.50
John Quincy Adams		
1824 John Quincy Adams	.60	1.50
Andrew Jackson		
1828 Andrew Jackson	.60	1.50
John Quincy Adams		
1832 Andrew Jackson	.40	1.00
Henry Clay		
1836 Martin Van Buren	.40	1.00
William Henry Harrison		
1840 William Henry Harrison	.50	1.25
Martin Van Buren		
1844 James K. Polk	.40	1.00
Henry Clay		
1848 Zachary Taylor	.40	1.00
Lewis Cass		
1852 Franklin Pierce	.40	1.00
Winfield Scott		
1856 James Buchanan	.50	1.25
John C. Fremont		
1860 Abraham Lincoln	.75	2.00
John C. Breckinridge		
1864 Abraham Lincoln	.75	2.00
George B. McClellan		
1868 Ulysses S. Grant	.50	1.25
Horatio Seymour		
1872 Ulysses S. Grant	.50	1.25
Horace Greeley		
1876 Rutherford B. Hayes	.40	1.00
Samuel J. Tilden		
1880 James Garfield	.40	1.00
Winfield Scott Hancock		
1884 Grover Cleveland	.40	1.00
James G. Blaine		
1888 Benjamin Harrison	.40	1.00
Grover Cleveland		
1892 Grover Cleveland	.40	1.00
Benjamin Harrison		
1896 William McKinley	.50	1.25
William Jennings Bryan		
1900 William McKinley	.40	1.00
William Jennings Bryan		
1904 Theodore Roosevelt	.60	1.50
Alton B. Parker		
1908 William H. Taft	.50	1.25
William Jennings Bryan		
1912 Woodrow Wilson	.60	1.50
Theodore Roosevelt		
1916 Woodrow Wilson	.40	1.00
Charles Evans Hughes		
1920 Warren G. Harding	.40	1.00
James M. Cox		
1924 Calvin Coolidge	.40	1.00
John W. Davis		
1928 Herbert Hoover	.40	1.00
Al Smith		
1932 Franklin D. Roosevelt	.60	1.50
Herbert Hoover		
1936 Franklin D. Roosevelt	.50	1.25
Alf Landon		
1940 Franklin D. Roosevelt	.60	1.50
Wendell Willkie		
1944 Franklin D. Roosevelt	.50	1.25
Thomas E. Dewey		
1948 Harry S Truman	.50	1.25
Thomas E. Dewey		
1952 Dwight D. Eisenhower	.60	1.50
Adlai Stevenson		
1956 Dwight D. Eisenhower	.60	1.50
Adlai Stevenson		
1960 John F. Kennedy	1.25	3.00
Richard Nixon		
1964 Lyndon B. Johnson	.60	1.50
Barry Goldwater		
1968 Richard Nixon	.40	1.00
Hubert H. Humphrey		
1972 Richard Nixon	.60	1.50
George McGovern		
1976 Jimmy Carter	.75	2.00
Gerald Ford		
1980 Ronald Reagan	1.25	3.00
Jimmy Carter		
1984 Ronald Reagan	.75	2.00
Walter Mondale		
1988 George Bush	.60	1.50
Michael Dukakis		
1992 Bill Clinton	.75	2.00
George Bush		
1996 Bill Clinton	.75	2.00
Bob Dole		
2000 George W. Bush	.75	2.00
Al Gore		
2004 George W. Bush	.75	2.00
John Kerry		
2008D Hillary Clinton	1.25	3.00
Barack Obama		

2008 Topps Historical Campaign Match-Ups Cut Signatures

SER.2 ODDS 1:80,000 HOBBY
SER.2 ODDS 1:14,000 HTA
SER.2 ODDS 1:96,000 RETAIL
STATED PRINT RUN 1 SER.#'d SETS
NO PRICING DUE TO SCARCITY
AE Spiro Agnew
Thomas Eagleton
BB James G. Blaine
Benjamin Butler
BE John Bell
Edward Everett
BF George Bush
Geraldine Ferraro
BG George W. Bush
Al Gore
CD Calvin Coolidge
John W. Davis
CE Dick Cheney
John Edwards
CF Henry Clay
Theodore Frelinghuysen
CHC John C. Calhoun
Henry Clay
CL George Clinton
John Langdon
CO Hillary Clinton
Barack Obama
CR Charles Curtis
Joseph T. Robinson
CWC John C. Calhoun
William H. Crawford
DD Charles G. Dawes
John W. Davis
DK Bob Dole
Jack Kemp
ES Dwight D. Eisenhower
Adlai Stevenson
FP Charles W. Fairbanks
Alton Parker
GB Horace Greeley
B. Gratz Brown
GC Elbridge Gerry
DeWitt Clinton
GD Al Gore
Dan Quayle
GH Ulysses S. Grant
Thomas A. Hendricks
GL John N. Garner
Alf Landon
HB Garret A. Hobart
Simon Bolivar Buckner
HE Winfield Scott Hancock
William H. English
HG Hubert H. Humphrey
Barry Goldwater
HL Hannibal Hamlin
Joseph Lane
HM Hubert H. Humphrey
Edmund Muskie
HR Benjamin Harrison
Whitelaw Reid
HS Herbert Hoover
Alfred E. Smith
JFG Richard M. Johnson
Francis Granger
JG Lyndon B. Johnson
Barry Goldwater
KG William R. King
William A. Graham
KN John F. Kennedy
Richard Nixon
LM Abraham Lincoln
George McClellan
LW Robert M. LaFollette
Burton K. Wheeler
MB William McKinley

William Jennings Bryan
MS George McGovern
Sargent Shriver
NL Ralph Nader
Joe Lieberman
PS Ross Perot
James Stockdale
QB Dan Quayle
Lloyd Bentsen
RB Ronald Reagan
George Bush
RC Ronald Reagan
Jimmy Carter
RG Franklin D. Roosevelt
John N. Garner
SB Horatio Seymour
Francis P. Blair Jr.
SK Adlai Stevenson
Estes Kefauver
SW John Sergeant
William Wilkins
TC Zachary Taylor
Lewis Cass
TD Harry S Truman
Thomas E. Dewey
TPC Samuel J. Tilden
Peter Cooper
TW Strom Thurmond
Fielding L. Wright
WH Henry Wilson
Thomas A. Hendricks
WL George Wallace
Curtis LeMay
WM Daniel Webster
W.P. Mangum
WT Earl Warren
Glen Taylor
WW Henry A. Wallace
Wendell Willkie

2008 Topps In the Name Relics

STATED ODDS 1:17,908 HOBBY
STATED ODDS 1:1046 HTA
EACH CARD IS #'d ONE-OF-ONE
TOTAL PRINT RUNS LISTED BELOW
PRINT RUNS PROVIDED BY TOPPS
NO PRICING DUE TO SCARCITY
AIR Alex Rios/4 *
AP Albert Pujols/6 *
AR Alex Rodriguez/9 *
ARR Aaron Rowand/6 *
BF Brian Fuentes/7 *
BJ Bobby Jenks/5 *
BM Brian McCann/6 *
BR Brian Roberts/7 *
BS Ben Sheets/6 *
BW Brandon Webb/4 *
CB Carlos Beltran/7 *
CC Carl Crawford/8 *
CH Cole Hamels/6 *
CL Carlos Lee/3 *
CS C.C. Sabathia/8 *
CU Chase Utley/5 *
CY Chris Young/5 *
DO David Ortiz/5 *
DW David Wright/6 *
DY Dmitri Young/5 *
FC Francisco Cordero/7 *
FR Francisco Rodriguez/9 *
FS Freddy Sanchez/7 *
GM Gil Meche/5 *
GS Grady Sizemore/8 *
HO Hideki Okajima/7 *
IR Ivan Rodriguez/9 *
IS Ichiro Suzuki/6 *
JB Josh Beckett/7 *
JEP Jake Peavy/5 *
JL John Lackey/6 *
JM Justin Morneau/7 *
JP J.J. Putz/4 *
JR J.J. Hardy/5 *
JR Jose Reyes/5 *
JRP Jorge Posada/6 *
JRV Jose Valverde/8 *
JS Johan Santana/7 *
JV Justin Verlander/9 *
MH Matt Holliday/8 *
ML Mike Lowell/6 *
MR Manny Ramirez/7 *
MY Michael Young/5 *
OH Orlando Hudson/6 *
PF Prince Fielder/7 *
RH Ryan Howard/6 *
RM Russell Martin/6 *
RO Roy Oswalt/6 *
TH Torii Hunter/6 *
TS Takashi Saito/5 *
TWH Trevor Hoffman/7 *
VM Victor Martinez/8 *

2008 Topps of the Class

RANDOM INSERTS IN PACKS
NNO David Wright .60 1.50

2008 Topps Own the Game

COMPLETE SET (25) 6.00 15.00
STATED ODDS 1:6 HOB, 1:6 RET
OTG1 Alex Rodriguez 1.25 3.00
OTG2 Prince Fielder .75 2.00
OTG3 Ryan Howard 1.00 2.50
OTG4 Carlos Pena .75 2.00
OTG5 Adam Dunn .30 .75
OTG6 Matt Holliday .50 1.25

OTG7 David Ortiz .75 2.00
OTG8 Jim Thome .50 1.25
OTG9 Lance Berkman .50 1.25
OTG10 Miguel Cabrera .50 1.25
OTG11 Alex Rodriguez 1.25 3.00
OTG12 Magglio Ordonez .50 1.25
OTG13 Matt Holliday .50 1.25
OTG14 Ryan Howard 1.00 2.50
OTG15 Vladimir Guerrero .75 2.00
OTG16 Carlos Pena .75 2.00
OTG17 Mike Lowell .30 .75
OTG18 Miguel Cabrera .50 1.25
OTG19 Prince Fielder .75 2.00
OTG20 Carlos Lee .30 .75
OTG21 Jake Peavy .50 1.25
OTG22 John Lackey .30 .75
OTG23 Brandon Webb .50 1.25
OTG24 Brad Penny .30 .75
OTG25 Fausto Carmona .30 .75

2008 Topps Presidential Stamp Collection

SER.1 ODDS 1:1950 H, 1:1240 HTA
SER.1 ODDS 1:3300 RETAIL
SER.2 ODDS 1:1600 H,1:700 HTA
SER.2 ODDS 1:2000 RETAIL
PRINT RUNS B/WN 1-90 COPIES PER
NO PRICING ON QTY OF 1
AJ1 Andrew Jackson/90 40.00 80.00
AJO1 Andrew Johnson 20.00 50.00
AL1 Abraham Lincoln 60.00 120.00
AL2 Abraham Lincoln/90 60.00 120.00
AL3 Abraham Lincoln/90 60.00 120.00
AL4 Abraham Lincoln 60.00 120.00
BH1 Benjamin Harrison/90 30.00 60.00
CAA1 Chester A. Arthur 50.00 100.00
DDE1 Dwight D. Eisenhower/90 40.00 80.00
FDR1 Franklin Delano Roosevelt/90 40.00 80.00
FP1 Franklin Pierce 30.00 60.00
GC1 Grover Cleveland 40.00 80.00
GW1 George Washington/90 30.00 60.00
GW10 George Washington 30.00 60.00
GW11 George Washington
GW12 George Washington 30.00 60.00
GW13 George Washington 30.00 60.00
GW2 George Washington/90 30.00 60.00
GW3 George Washington/90 30.00 60.00
GW4 George Washington/90 30.00 60.00
GW5 George Washington
GW6 George Washington/90 30.00 60.00
GW7 George Washington 30.00 60.00
GW8 George Washington 30.00 60.00
GW9 George Washington 30.00 60.00
HH1 Herbert Hoover/90 20.00 50.00
HST1 Harry S. Truman 30.00 60.00
JB1 James Buchanan/90 50.00 100.00
JFK1 John F. Kennedy/90 50.00 100.00
JFK2 John F. Kennedy/90 50.00 100.00
JG1 James Garfield 30.00 60.00
JG2 James Garfield 30.00 60.00
JKP1 James K. Polk 30.00 60.00
JM1 James Monroe/90 30.00 60.00
JM2 James Monroe 30.00 60.00
JMA1 James Madison 50.00 100.00
JQA1 John Quincy Adams/90 20.00 50.00
JT1 John Tyler/90 20.00 50.00
LBJ1 Lyndon B. Johnson 30.00 60.00
MF1 Millard Fillmore 30.00 60.00
MVB1 Martin Van Buren 30.00 60.00
RBH1 Rutherford B. Hayes 50.00 100.00
RBH2 Rutherford B. Hayes 50.00 100.00
RN1 Richard Nixon 30.00 60.00
RR1 Ronald Reagan 30.00 60.00
TJ1 Thomas Jefferson/90 50.00 100.00
TJ2 Thomas Jefferson/90 50.00 100.00
TJ3 Thomas Jefferson/90 50.00 100.00
TJ4 Thomas Jefferson/90 50.00 100.00
TR1 Teddy Roosevelt/90 30.00 60.00
TR2 Theodore Roosevelt 30.00 60.00
TR3 Theodore Roosevelt 30.00 60.00
USG1 Ulysses S. Grant 30.00 60.00
USG2 Ulysses S. Grant 30.00 60.00
WGH1 Warren G. Harding/90 30.00 60.00
WGH2 Warren G. Harding 30.00 60.00
WHH1 William Henry Harrison/90 30.00 60.00
WHT1 William Howard Taft 30.00 60.00
WM1 William McKinley 20.00 50.00
WW1 Woodrow Wilson/90 30.00 60.00
WW2 Woodrow Wilson 20.00 50.00
ZT1 Zachary Taylor/90 20.00 50.00

2008 Topps Red Hot Rookie Redemption

COMMON EXCH 6.00 15.00
RANDOM INSERTS IN SER.2 PACKS
EXCHANGE DEADLINE 5/30/2010
1 Jay Bruce AU EXCH 40.00 80.00
2 Justin Masterson EXCH 4.00 10.00
3 John Bowker EXCH 3.00 8.00
4 Kosuke Fukudome EXCH 6.00 15.00
5 Mike Aviles EXCH 6.00 15.00
6 Chris Davis EXCH 3.00 8.00
7 Chris Volstad EXCH 2.00 5.00
8 Jeff Samardzija EXCH 6.00 15.00
9 Brad Ziegler EXCH 12.50 30.00
10 Gio Gonzalez EXCH 2.50 6.00
11 Clayton Kershaw EXCH 3.00 8.00
12 Daniel Murphy EXCH 6.00 15.00
13 Chris Dickerson EXCH 5.00 12.00
14 Pablo Sandoval EXCH 6.00 15.00
15 Nick Evans EXCH 5.00 12.00
16 Clayton Richard EXCH 4.00 10.00
17 Evan Longoria AU EXCH 40.00 80.00
18 Taylor Teagarden EXCH 6.00 15.00
19 Collin Balester EXCH 6.00 15.00
20 Lou Montanez EXCH 6.00 15.00

2008 Topps Replica Mini Jerseys

STATED ODDS 1:412 H,1:19 HTA
STATED ODDS 1:8300 RETAIL
PRINT RUNS B/WN 379-539 COPIES PER
AIR Alex Rios/539 5.00 12.00
AP Albert Pujols 10.00 25.00
AR Alex Rodriguez/539 10.00 25.00
BW Brandon Webb 5.00 12.00
CC Carl Crawford/539 5.00 12.00
CH Cole Hamels 6.00 15.00
CMS Curt Schilling 6.00 15.00
CS C.C. Sabathia/539 5.00 12.00
CU Chase Utley 6.00 15.00
DAO David Ortiz 8.00 20.00
DO David Ortiz 8.00 20.00
DP Dustin Pedroia 10.00 25.00
DW David Wright 8.00 20.00
GS Grady Sizemore/539 6.00 15.00
HO Hideki Okajima 8.00 20.00
IS Ichiro Suzuki 10.00 25.00
JAV Jason Varitek 6.00 15.00
JB Josh Beckett 10.00 25.00
JCL Julio Lugo 6.00 15.00
JDD J.D. Drew 6.00 15.00
JE Jacoby Ellsbury 15.00 40.00
JL Jon Lester 8.00 20.00
JM Justin Morneau/539 5.00 12.00
JP Jake Peavy 6.00 15.00
JR Jose Reyes 6.00 15.00
JRP Jonathan Papelbon 8.00 20.00
JV Justin Verlander/539 6.00 15.00
KY Kevin Youkilis 6.00 15.00
MH Matt Holliday 6.00 15.00
ML Mike Lowell 10.00 25.00
MR Manny Ramirez 10.00 25.00
MT Mike Timlin 6.00 15.00
PF Prince Fielder 8.00 20.00
RH Ryan Howard/379 8.00 20.00
RM Russell Martin 5.00 12.00

2008 Topps Retail Relics

ONE PER RETAIL BLASTER BOX
NO PRICING ON SOME DUE TO SCARCITY
AB Angel Berroa UPD 3.00 8.00
AC Asdrubal Cabrera UPD 3.00 8.00
AD Adam Dunn 3.00 8.00
AH Aaron Harang 3.00 8.00
AL Adam LaRoche 3.00 8.00
AR Aaron Rowand 3.00 8.00
AR Aramis Ramirez UPD 3.00 8.00
BA Bronson Arroyo 3.00 8.00
BC Bobby Crosby 3.00 8.00
BG Brian Giles 3.00 8.00
BH Brad Hawpe 3.00 8.00
BJ Bobby Jenks 3.00 8.00
BKA Bobby Abreu 3.00 8.00
BP Brad Penny 3.00 8.00
BS Ben Sheets 3.00 8.00
BW Brandon Webb 3.00 8.00
CB Carlos Beltran 3.00 8.00
CC Chris Capuano 3.00 8.00
CD Carlos Delgado 3.00 8.00
CDC Carl Crawford 3.00 8.00
CG Curtis Granderson UPD 3.00 8.00
CJC Chris Carpenter 3.00 8.00
CK Casey Kotchman 3.00 8.00
DE Darin Erstad 3.00 8.00
DN Dioner Navarro UPD 3.00 8.00
DP Dustin Pedroia UPD 5.00 12.00
DW David Wright UPD 5.00 12.00
EB Erik Bedard UPD 3.00 8.00
EC Eric Chavez 3.00 8.00
EC Eric Chavez UPD 3.00 8.00
EE Edwin Encarnacion 3.00 8.00
FR Francisco Rodriguez 3.00 8.00
GA Garrett Atkins 3.00 8.00
HB Hank Blalock 3.00 8.00
HK Hong-Chih Kuo UPD 4.00 10.00
IK Ian Kinsler UPD 3.00 8.00
IR Ivan Rodriguez 3.00 8.00
IS Ian Snell 3.00 8.00
JB Jason Bay 4.00 10.00
JD Jermaine Dye 3.00 8.00
JE Jim Edmonds 3.00 8.00
JE Johnny Estrada UPD 3.00 8.00
JF Jeff Francis UPD 3.00 8.00
JL Jon Lester UPD 4.00 10.00
JL Jon Lester 4.00 10.00
JM John Maine UPD 3.00 8.00
JP Jake Peavy 3.00 8.00
JR Jimmy Rollins 3.00 8.00
JR Justin Ruggiano UPD 3.00 8.00
JRH Rich Harden 3.00 8.00
KG Khalil Greene 3.00 8.00
KH Kevin Hart UPD 3.00 8.00
KM Kendry Morales 3.00 8.00
KW Kerry Wood 3.00 8.00
KW Kerry Wood UPD 3.00 8.00
LB Lance Berkman 3.00 8.00
LH Livan Hernandez 3.00 8.00
LM Lastings Milledge UPD 3.00 8.00
MB Mark Buehrle 3.00 8.00
MH Mike Hampton 3.00 8.00
MK Matt Kemp UPD 3.00 8.00
MM Mark Mulder UPD 3.00 8.00
MM Melvin Mora 3.00 8.00
MMM Mike Mussina 3.00 8.00
MS Mike Sweeney 3.00 8.00
MT Mark Teahen 3.00 8.00
MY Michael Young 3.00 8.00
OG Ozzie Guillen 3.00 8.00
OG Ozzie Guillen UPD 3.00 8.00
PB Pat Burrell 3.00 8.00
PM Pedro Martinez 3.00 8.00
RB Rocco Baldelli UPD 3.00 8.00
RF Rafael Furcal 3.00 8.00
RF Rafael Furcal UPD 3.00 8.00
RH Roy Halladay 3.00 8.00
RW Rickie Weeks 3.00 8.00
SC Sean Casey UPD 3.00 8.00
SK Scott Kazmir 3.00 8.00
TG Troy Glaus 3.00 8.00
TH Todd Helton 3.00 8.00
TH Todd Helton UPD 3.00 8.00
TP Tony Pena 3.00 8.00
VW Vernon Wells 3.00 8.00
ZG Zack Greinke 3.00 8.00

2008 Topps Silk Collection

SER.2 ODDS 1:300 HOB, 1:139 RET
STATED PRINT RUN 100 SER.#'d SETS
1-100 FOUND IN SERIES 2
UPD ODDS 1:246 HOBBY
STATED PRINT RUN 100 SER.#'d SETS
101-200 FOUND IN UPDATE
SC1 Alex Rodriguez 30.00 60.00
SC2 Scott Kazmir 8.00 20.00
SC3 Ivan Rodriguez 8.00 20.00
SC4 Joe Mauer 15.00 40.00
SC5 Ken Griffey Jr. 20.00 50.00
SC6 Nick Markakis 6.00 15.00
SC7 Mickey Mantle 50.00 100.00
SC8 Erik Bedard 6.00 15.00
SC9 Derrek Lee 15.00 40.00
SC10 Miguel Cabrera 8.00 20.00
SC11 Yovani Gallardo 6.00 15.00
SC12 Victor Martinez 6.00 15.00
SC13 Curtis Granderson 10.00 25.00
SC14 Chris Young 6.00 15.00
SC15 Jimmy Rollins 15.00 40.00
SC16 Dan Uggla 6.00 15.00
SC17 Felix Hernandez 6.00 15.00
SC18 Alex Rios 15.00 40.00
SC19 Jason Bay 40.00 80.00
SC20 Jose Reyes 10.00 25.00
SC21 Mike Lowell 10.00 25.00
SC22 Carl Crawford 6.00 15.00
SC23 Chipper Jones 20.00 50.00
SC24 Troy Glaus 10.00 25.00
SC25 Cole Hamels 20.00 50.00
SC26 Chris Young 8.00 20.00
SC27 Torii Hunter 8.00 20.00
SC28 Hideki Matsui 10.00 25.00
SC29 Freddy Sanchez 6.00 15.00
SC30 Josh Beckett 10.00 25.00
SC31 Mark Buehrle 6.00 15.00
SC32 Brian Bannister 15.00 40.00
SC33 Carlos Beltran 8.00 20.00
SC34 Dontrelle Willis 6.00 15.00
SC35 Vladimir Guerrero 15.00 40.00
SC36 Matt Holliday 8.00 20.00
SC37 Adam Dunn 8.00 20.00
SC38 Gary Matthews 6.00 15.00
SC39 Travis Hafner 15.00 40.00
SC40 Chase Utley 20.00 50.00
SC41 Vernon Wells 6.00 15.00
SC42 Lance Berkman 10.00 25.00
SC43 Jeff Francis 6.00 15.00
SC44 Curt Schilling 10.00 25.00
SC45 Alfonso Soriano 15.00 40.00
SC46 Jarrod Saltalamacchia 6.00 15.00
SC47 Hideki Okajima 10.00 25.00
SC48 Pedro Martinez 20.00 50.00
SC49 Jorge Posada 15.00 40.00
SC50 Justin Upton 15.00 40.00
SC51 Tom Gorzelanny 10.00 25.00
SC52 Carlos Delgado 6.00 15.00
SC53 Edgar Renteria 6.00 15.00
SC54 Chien-Ming Wang 30.00 60.00
SC55 C.C. Sabathia 6.00 15.00
SC56 B.J. Upton 6.00 15.00
SC57 Delmon Young 8.00 20.00
SC58 Tim Lincecum 20.00 50.00
SC59 Carlos Zambrano 6.00 15.00
SC60 Magglio Ordonez 6.00 15.00
SC61 Brandon Webb 20.00 50.00
SC62 Ben Sheets 6.00 15.00
SC63 Brad Penny 20.00 50.00
SC64 John Lackey 6.00 15.00
SC65 Hanley Ramirez 8.00 20.00
SC66 Gary Sheffield 20.00 50.00
SC67 Ubaldo Jimenez 6.00 15.00
SC68 Barry Zito 6.00 15.00
SC69 Daisuke Matsuzaka 20.00 50.00
SC70 Justin Morneau 10.00 25.00
SC71 Jacoby Ellsbury 60.00 120.00
SC72 John Smoltz 20.00 50.00
SC73 Chris Carpenter 10.00 25.00
SC74 Ryan Braun 20.00 50.00
SC75 Prince Fielder 10.00 25.00
SC76 Carlos Lee 6.00 15.00
SC77 Ryan Zimmerman 15.00 40.00
SC78 Troy Tulowitzki 6.00 15.00
SC79 Michael Young 6.00 15.00
SC80 Johan Santana 15.00 40.00
SC81 Hunter Pence 6.00 15.00
SC82 Adrian Gonzalez 6.00 15.00
SC83 Jake Peavy 6.00 15.00
SC84 Derek Jeter 60.00 120.00
SC85 Ichiro Suzuki 20.00 50.00
SC86 Miguel Tejada 6.00 15.00
SC87 Trevor Hoffman 6.00 15.00
SC88 Kevin Youkilis 20.00 50.00
SC89 David Wright 20.00 50.00
SC90 Albert Pujols 60.00 120.00
SC91 Todd Helton 10.00 25.00
SC92 Rich Harden 6.00 15.00
SC93 Fausto Carmona 6.00 15.00
SC94 Mark Teixeira 6.00 15.00
SC95 Justin Verlander 10.00 25.00
SC96 Tim Hudson 6.00 15.00
SC97 Jeff Francoeur 15.00 40.00
SC98 Manny Ramirez 15.00 40.00
SC99 David Ortiz 15.00 40.00
SC100 Ryan Howard 15.00 40.00
SC101 Johan Santana 6.00 15.00
SC102 Cristian Guzman 4.00 10.00
SC103 Brendan Harris 4.00 10.00
SC104 Randy Wolf 4.00 10.00
SC105 Cliff Lee 6.00 15.00
SC106 Roy Halladay 6.00 15.00
SC107 Dustin Pedroia 10.00 25.00
SC108 Chris Iannetta 4.00 10.00
SC109 Kerry Wood 6.00 15.00
SC110 Jim Edmonds 6.00 15.00
SC111 Jon Rauch 4.00 10.00
SC112 Ryan Sweeney 4.00 10.00
SC113 Ryan Ludwick 6.00 15.00
SC114 George Sherrill 5.00 12.00
SC115 Matt Garza 5.00 12.00
SC116 Nate McLouth 30.00 60.00
SC117 Eric Hinske 6.00 15.00
SC118 Adrian Gonzalez 4.00 10.00
SC119 Carlos Marmol 5.00 12.00
SC120 Jose Valverde 4.00 10.00
SC121 Shane Victorino 10.00 25.00
SC122 Brad Wilkerson 5.00 12.00
SC123 Dana Eveland 6.00 15.00
SC124 Luke Scott 5.00 12.00
SC125 Mike Cameron 5.00 12.00
SC126 Ervin Santana 10.00 25.00
SC127 Ryan Dempster 5.00 12.00
SC128 Geoff Jenkins 4.00 10.00
SC129 Billy Wagner 6.00 15.00
SC130 Pedro Feliz 4.00 10.00
SC131 Stephen Drew 4.00 10.00
SC132 Mark Hendrickson 4.00 10.00
SC133 Orlando Hudson 4.00 10.00
SC134 Pat Burrell 6.00 15.00
SC135 Russ Martin 12.50 30.00
SC136 James Loney 5.00 12.00
SC137 Justin Masterson 20.00 50.00
SC138 Matt Kemp 6.00 15.00
SC139 Hiroki Kuroda 6.00 15.00
SC140 Joe Crede 4.00 10.00
SC141 Joakim Soria 4.00 10.00
SC142 Armando Galarraga 6.00 15.00
SC143 Jason Varitek 6.00 15.00
SC144 Aaron Cook 5.00 12.00
SC145 Orlando Cabrera 4.00 10.00
SC146 Ian Kinsler 6.00 15.00
SC147 Carlos Gomez 6.00 15.00
SC148 Mike Aviles 10.00 25.00
SC149 Carlos Guillen 5.00 12.00
SC150 Erik Bedard 4.00 10.00
SC151 J.D. Drew 5.00 12.00
SC152 Marco Scutaro 4.00 10.00
SC153 James Shields 6.00 15.00
SC154 Cesar Izturis 4.00 10.00
SC155 Akinori Iwamura 8.00 20.00
SC156 Aramis Ramirez 5.00 12.00
SC157 Joe Mauer 6.00 15.00
SC158 Brad Lidge 8.00 20.00
SC159 Milton Bradley 4.00 10.00
SC160 Jay Bruce 12.50 30.00
SC161 Andrew Miller 5.00 12.00
SC162 Mark Reynolds 4.00 10.00
SC163 Johnny Damon 8.00 20.00
SC164 Michael Bourn 6.00 15.00
SC165 Andre Ethier 10.00 25.00
SC166 Carlos Pena 6.00 15.00
SC167 Joe Nathan 6.00 15.00
SC168 Cody Ross 4.00 10.00
SC169 Joba Chamberlain 10.00 25.00
SC170 Clayton Kershaw 8.00 20.00
SC171 Francisco Rodriguez 6.00 15.00
SC172 Mark DeRosa 5.00 12.00
SC173 Ben Sheets 4.00 10.00
SC174 Brian Wilson 4.00 10.00
SC175 Emil Brown 4.00 10.00
SC176 Geovany Soto 8.00 20.00
SC177 Jason Giambi 6.00 15.00
SC178 Shaun Marcum 5.00 12.00
SC179 Edinson Volquez 5.00 12.00
SC180 Max Scherzer 8.00 20.00
SC181 Kelly Johnson 5.00 12.00
SC182 Mariano Rivera 10.00 25.00
SC183 Chris Perez 8.00 20.00
SC184 Jose Guillen 4.00 10.00
SC185 Kyle Lohse 10.00 25.00
SC186 Kosuke Fukudome 12.50 30.00
SC187 Takashi Saito 12.50 30.00
SC188 Mike Mussina 12.50 30.00
SC189 J.J. Putz 4.00 10.00
SC190 Evan Longoria 20.00 50.00
SC191 Jered Weaver 5.00 12.00
SC192 Grady Sizemore 12.50 30.00
SC193 Carlos Gonzalez 6.00 15.00
SC194 Brian McCann 5.00 12.00
SC195 Jonathan Papelbon 5.00 12.00
SC196 Dioner Navarro 5.00 12.00
SC197 Bobby Abreu 5.00 12.00
SC198 Carlos Quentin 5.00 12.00
SC199 Josh Hamilton 20.00 50.00
SC200 Dan Haren 4.00 10.00

2008 Topps Stars

COMPLETE SET (25) 8.00 20.00
SER.2 ODDS 1:6 HOB, 1:6 RET
TS1 Alex Rodriguez 1.25 3.00
TS2 Magglio Ordonez .50 1.25
TS3 Justin Morneau .30 .75
TS4 Josh Beckett .50 1.25
TS5 David Wright 1.00 2.50
TS6 Jimmy Rollins .50 1.25
TS7 Ichiro Suzuki 1.25 3.00
TS8 Chipper Jones 1.00 2.50
TS9 Brandon Webb .50 1.25
TS10 Ryan Howard 1.00 2.50
TS11 Derek Jeter 2.00 5.00
TS12 Vladimir Guerrero .75 2.00
TS13 Manny Ramirez .75 2.00
TS14 Jake Peavy .50 1.25
TS15 David Ortiz .75 2.00
TS16 Jose Reyes .50 1.25
TS17 Miguel Cabrera .50 1.25
TS18 Victor Martinez .30 .75
TS19 C.C. Sabathia .30 .75
TS20 Prince Fielder .75 2.00
TS21 Alfonso Soriano .50 1.25
TS22 Grady Sizemore .50 1.25
TS23 Albert Pujols 1.50 4.00
TS24 Pedro Martinez .50 1.25
TS25 Matt Holliday .50 1.25

2008 Topps T205 Relics

TCR1 Albert Pujols
TCR2 Clay Buchholz
TCR3 Matt Holliday
TCR4 Luke Hochevar
TCR5 Alex Rodriguez
TCR6 Joey Votto
TCR7 Chin-lung Hu
TCR8 Ryan Braun
TCR9 Joba Chamberlain
TCR10 Ryan Howard
TCR11 Ichiro Suzuki
TCR12 Steve Pearce
TCR13 Vladimir Guerrero
TCR14 Wladimir Balentien
TCR15 David Ortiz
TCR16 Jacoby Ellsbury
TCR17 David Wright
TCR18 Chase Utley
TCR19 Manny Ramirez
TCR20 Dan Haren
TCR21 Nick Markakis
TCR22 Grady Sizemore
TCR23 Hanley Ramirez
TCR24 Daisuke Matsuzaka
TCR25 Troy Tulowitzki
TCR26 Jose Reyes
TCR27 Tim Lincecum
TCR28 Prince Fielder
TCR29 Alfonso Soriano
TCR30 Andrew Miller

2008 Topps Trading Card History

COMPLETE SET (75) 20.00 50.00
SER.1 ODDS 1:12 HOBBY
SER.2 ODDS 1:6 HOBBY
TCH1 Jacoby Ellsbury 1.50 4.00
TCH2 Joba Chamberlain 1.25 3.00
TCH3 Daisuke Matsuzaka 1.50 4.00
TCH4 Price Fielder 1.00 2.50
TCH5 Clay Buchholz 1.00 2.50
TCH6 Alex Rodriguez 1.50 4.00
TCH7 Mickey Mantle 2.50 6.00
TCH8 Ryan Braun 1.25 3.00
TCH9 Albert Pujols 2.00 5.00
TCH10 Joe Mauer .60 1.50
TCH11 Jose Reyes .60 1.50
TCH12 Joey Votto 1.00 2.50
TCH13 Johan Santana .60 1.50
TCH14 Hunter Pence 1.00 2.50
TCH15 Hideki Okajima .40 1.00
TCH16 Cameron Maybin 1.00 2.50
TCH17 Roger Clemens 1.25 3.00
TCH18 Tim Lincecum 1.00 2.50
TCH19 Mark Teixeira .60 1.50
Jeff Francoeur
TCH20 Justin Upton 1.00 2.50
TCH21 Alfonso Soriano .60 1.50
TCH22 Pedro Martinez .60 1.50
TCH23 Chien-Ming Wang 1.25 3.00
TCH24 Ichiro Suzuki 1.50 4.00
TCH25 Grady Sizemore .60 1.50
TCH26 Ryan Howard 1.25 3.00
TCH27 David Wright 1.25 3.00
TCH28 Chin-Lung Hu .60 1.50
TCH29 Jimmy Rollins .60 1.50
TCH30 Ken Griffey Jr 1.50 4.00
TCH31 Chipper Jones 1.25 3.00
TCH32 Justin Verlander .60 1.50
TCH33 Manny Ramirez 1.00 2.50
TCH34 Chase Utley 1.00 2.50
TCH35 Ivan Rodriguez .60 1.50
TCH36 Josh Beckett .60 1.50
TCH37 Tom Glavine .60 1.50
TCH38 Vladimir Guerrero 1.00 2.50
TCH39 Lance Berkman .60 1.50
TCH40 Gary Sheffield .40 1.00
TCH41 Luke Hochevar 1.00 2.50
TCH42 David Ortiz 1.00 2.50
TCH43 Miguel Cabrera .60 1.50
TCH44 Andruw Jones .40 1.00
TCH45 Hideki Matsui 1.00 2.50
TCH46 C.C. Sabathia .40 1.00
TCH47 Magglio Ordonez .60 1.50
TCH48 Pedro Martinez .60 1.50
TCH49 Curtis Granderson .40 1.00
TCH50 Derek Jeter 2.50 6.00
TCH51 Victor Martinez .40 1.00
TCH52 Hanley Ramirez 1.00 2.50
TCH53 Jake Peavy .60 1.50
TCH54 Brandon Webb .60 1.50
TCH55 Matt Holliday .60 1.50
TCH56 Hiroki Kuroda .60 1.50
TCH57 Mike Lowell .40 1.00
TCH58 Carlos Lee .40 1.00
TCH59 Nick Markakis .60 1.50
TCH60 Carlos Beltran .60 1.50
TCH61 Francisco Rodriguez .40 1.00
TCH62 Troy Tulowitzki .60 1.50
TCH63 Russ Martin .60 1.50
TCH64 Justin Morneau .40 1.00
TCH65 Phil Hughes 1.00 2.50
TCH66 Torii Hunter .40 1.00
TCH67 Adam Dunn .40 1.00
TCH68 Raul Ibanez .40 1.00
TCH69 Robinson Cano .60 1.50
TCH70 Brad Hawpe .40 1.00

TCH71 Michael Young .40 1.00
TCH72 Jim Thome .60 1.50
TCH73 Chris Young .40 1.00
TCH74 Carlos Zambrano .40 1.00
TCH75 Felix Hernandez .60 1.50

2008 Topps World Champion Relics

STATED ODDS 1:4792 H, 1:244 HTA
STATED ODDS 1:33,333 RETAIL
STATE PRINT RUN 100 SER.#'d SETS
WCR1 Josh Beckett 50.00 100.00
WCR2 Hideki Okajima 30.00 60.00
WCR3 Curt Schilling 40.00 80.00
WCR4 Jason Varitek 40.00 80.00
WCR5 Mike Lowell 30.00 60.00
WCR6 Jacoby Ellsbury 60.00 120.00
WCR7 Dustin Pedroia 30.00 60.00
WCR8 Jonathan Papelbon 30.00 60.00
WCR9 Julio Lugo 20.00 50.00
WCR10 Manny Ramirez 30.00 60.00
WCR11 David Ortiz 30.00 60.00
WCR12 Eric Gagne 30.00 60.00
WCR13 Jon Lester 30.00 60.00
WCR14 J.D. Drew 30.00 60.00
WCR15 Kevin Youkilis 40.00 80.00

2008 Topps World Champion Relics Autographs

STATED ODDS 1:14,417 H, 1:732 HTA
STATED ODDS 1:99,000 RETAIL
PRINT RUNS B/WN 25-50 COPIES PER
NO PRICING ON MOST DUE TO SCARCITY
WCAR1 Josh Beckett/50
WCAR2 Hideki Okajima/50
WCAR3 Curt Schilling/50
WCAR4 Jason Varitek/50
WCAR5 Mike Lowell/50
WCAR6 Jacoby Ellsbury/25
WCAR7 Dustin Pedroia/25
WCAR8 Jonathan Papelbon/50
WCAR9 Julio Lugo/50
WCAR10 Manny Ramirez/50 100.00 200.00

2008 Topps Year in Review

COMPLETE SET (178) 50.00 100.00
COMP.SER.1 SET (60) 12.50 30.00
COMP.SER.2 SET (60) 12.50 30.00
COMP.UPD SET (58) 12.50 30.00
SER.1 ODDS 1:6 HOB, 1:6 RET
SER.2 ODDS 1:6 HOB, 1:6 RET
UPD ODDS 1:6 HOBBY
YR1 Paul Lo Duca .30 .75
YR2 Felix Hernandez .50 1.25
YR3 Ian Snell .30 .75
YR4 Carlos Beltran .30 .75
YR5 Daisuke Matsuzaka 1.25 3.00
YR6 Jose Reyes .50 1.25
YR7 Alex Rodriguez 1.25 3.00
YR8 Scott Kazmir .50 1.25
YR9 Adam Everett .30 .75
YR10 Josh Beckett 1.00 2.50
Josh Hamilton
YR11 Craig Monroe .30 .75
YR12 Justin Morneau .50 1.25
YR13 Roy Halladay .30 .75
YR14 Jeff Suppan .30 .75
YR15 Marco Scutaro .30 .75
YR16 Ivan Rodriguez .50 1.25
YR17 Dimtri Young .30 .75
YR18 Mark Buehrle .30 .75
YR19 Alex Rodriguez 1.25 3.00
YR20 Joe Saunders .30 .75
YR21 Russell Martin .30 .75
YR22 Manny Ramirez .75 2.00
YR23 Chase Utley .75 2.00
YR24 Travis Hafner .30 .75
YR25 Jake Peavy .50 1.25
YR26 Shawn Hill .30 .75
YR27 Daisuke Matsuzaka 1.25 3.00
YR28 Matt Belisle .30 .75
YR29 Troy Tulowitzki .50 1.25
YR30 Andruw Jones .30 .75
YR31 Phil Hughes .75 2.00
YR32 Derrek Lee .50 1.25
YR33 Ichiro Suzuki 1.25 3.00
YR34 Julio Franco .30 .75
YR35 Chien-Ming Wang 1.00 2.50
YR36 Hideki Matsui .75 2.00
YR37 Brad Penny .30 .75
YR38 Jack Wilson .30 .75
YR39 Francisco Cordero .30 .75
YR40 Omar Vizquel .30 .75
YR41 Tim Lincecum .75 2.00
YR42 Bartolo Colon .30 .75
YR43 Fred Lewis .30 .75
YR44 Jeff Kent .30 .75
YR45 Randy Johnson .75 2.00
YR46 Rafael Furcal .30 .75
YR47 Delmon Young .50 1.25
YR48 Andrew Miller .50 1.25
YR49 David Ortiz .75 2.00
Mike Lowell
YR50 Justin Verlander .50 1.25
YR51 C.C. Sabathia .30 .75
YR52 Felipe Lopez .30 .75
YR53 Oliver Perez .30 .75
YR54 John Smoltz .75 2.00
YR55 Mark Reynolds .30 .75
YR56 Jeremy Accardo .30 .75
YR57 Todd Helton .50 1.25
YR58 Adrian Beltre .30 .75
YR59 Carlos Delgado .30 .75
YR60 Chris Young .30 .75
YR61 Roy Halladay .30 .75
YR62 Kevin Youkilis .50 1.25
YR63 Joe Blanton .30 .75
YR64 Chad Gaudin .30 .75
YR65 Derek Lowe .30 .75
YR66 C.C. Sabathia .30 .75
YR67 Luis Castillo .30 .75
YR68 Curt Schilling .50 1.25
YR69 Pedro Feliz .30 .75
YR70 James Shields .30 .75
YR71 Masumi Kuwata .30 .75
YR72 Raul Ibanez .30 .75
YR73 Justin Verlander .50 1.25
YR74 Tim Lincecum .75 2.00
YR75 Hideki Matsui .75 2.00
YR76 Julio Franco .30 .75
YR77 Russell Branyan .30 .75
YR78 Chipper Jones 1.00 2.50
YR79 Chone Figgins .30 .75
YR80 Chris Young .30 .75
YR81 Sammy Sosa .50 1.25
YR82 Miguel Tejada .30 .75
YR83 Wil Ledezma .30 .75
YR84 Victor Martinez .30 .75
YR85 Dustin McGowan .30 .75
YR86 Mike Fontenot .30 .75
YR87 Mark Ellis .30 .75
YR88 Ryan Howard 1.00 2.50
YR89 Frank Thomas .75 2.00
YR90 Aubrey Huff .30 .75
YR91 Jake Peavy .50 1.25
YR92 Dan Haren .30 .75
YR93 Damian Miller .30 .75
YR94 Billy Butler .30 .75
YR95 Dmitri Young .30 .75
YR96 Chipper Jones 1.00 2.50
YR97 Justin Morneau .50 1.25
YR98 Erik Bedard .30 .75
YR99 Scott Hatteberg .30 .75
YR100 Vladimir Guerrero .75 2.00
YR101 Ichiro Suzuki 1.25 3.00
YR102 Jose Reyes .50 1.25
YR103 Ryan Garko .30 .75
YR104 Jeff Francoeur .50 1.25
YR105 Joe Mauer .50 1.25
YR106 Manny Ramirez .75 2.00
YR107 Chase Utley .75 2.00
YR108 Magglio Ordonez .50 1.25
YR109 Chris Young .30 .75
YR110 B.J. Upton .50 1.25
YR111 Willie Harris .30 .75
YR112 Shelley Duncan .30 .75
YR113 Jon Lester .50 1.25
YR114 Travis Buck .30 .75
YR115 Ryan Raburn .30 .75
YR116 Eric Byrnes .30 .75
YR117 Kenny Lofton .30 .75
YR118 Jason Isringhausen .30 .75
YR119 Todd Helton .50 1.25
YR120 Carl Crawford .50 1.25
YR121 Mark Teixeira .50 1.25
YR122 Alex Gordon .75 2.00
YR123 Jermaine Dye .30 .75
YR124 Vladimir Guerrero .75 2.00
YR125 Alex Rodriguez 1.25 3.00
YR126 Tom Glavine .50 1.25
YR127 Scott Rolen .50 1.25
YR128 Billy Wagner .30 .75
YR129 Rick Ankiel .30 .75
YR130 Jack Cust .30 .75
YR131 Mike Mussina .30 .75
YR132 Magglio Ordonez .50 1.25
YR133 Placido Polanco .30 .75
YR134 Russell Branyan .30 .75
YR135 David Price .75 2.00
YR136 Mike Cameron .30 .75
YR137 Brandon Webb .50 1.25
YR138 Cameron Maybin .75 2.00
YR139 Johan Santana .50 1.25
YR140 Bobby Jenks .30 .75
YR141 Garret Anderson .30 .75
YR142 Jarrod Saltalamacchia .30 .75
YR143 Adrian Gonzalez .50 1.25
YR144 Carlos Guillen .30 .75
YR145 Tom Shearn .30 .75
YR146 John Lackey .30 .75
YR147 Jayson Werth .30 .75
YR148 Aaron Harang .30 .75
YR149 Chien-Ming Wang 1.00 2.50
YR150 Scott Baker .30 .75
YR151 Clay Buchholz .75 2.00
YR152 Tom Glavine .50 1.25
YR153 Pedro Martinez .50 1.25
YR154 Doug Davis .30 .75
YR155 Brandon Phillips .30 .75
YR156 Jason Varitek .75 2.00
YR157 Jim Thome .50 1.25
YR158 Alex Rodriguez 1.25 3.00
YR159 Curtis Granderson .30 .75
YR160 Scott Kazmir .50 1.25
YR161 Marlon Byrd .30 .75
YR162 David Ortiz .75 2.00
YR163 Greg Maddux 1.00 2.50
YR164 Johnny Damon .50 1.25
YR165 Carlos Lee .30 .75
YR166 Jim Thome .50 1.25
YR167 Frank Thomas .75 2.00
YR168 Greg Maddux 1.00 2.50
YR169 Matt Holliday .50 1.25
YR170 J.R. Towles .75 2.00
YR171 Lance Berkman .50 1.25
YR172 Melky Cabrera .30 .75
YR173 Vladimir Guerrero .75 2.00
YR174 Nick Markakis .50 1.25
YR175 Prince Fielder .75 2.00
YR176 Moises Alou .30 .75
YR177 Micah Owings .30 .75
YR178 Carlos Zambrano .30 .75

2008 Topps All-Star FanFest

COMPLETE SET (8) 20.00 50.00
1 Babe Ruth 5.00 12.00
2 Jackie Robinson 2.00 5.00
3 Alex Rodriguez 3.00 8.00
4 David Wright 2.50 6.00
5 Lou Gehrig 4.00 10.00
6 Joba Chamberlain 2.50 6.00
7 Mickey Mantle 8.00 20.00
8 Johan Santana 1.25 3.00

2008 Topps All-Star FanFest Patch

STATED PRINT RUN 375 SER.#'d SETS
NO CARD NUMBERS
CARDS LISTED ALPHABETICALLY
1 Lou Gehrig 50.00 100.00
2 Mickey Mantle 50.00 100.00
3 Thurman Munson 30.00 60.00
4 Jose Reyes 20.00 50.00
5 Babe Ruth 50.00 100.00
6 Johan Santana 20.00 50.00
7 Tom Seaver 20.00 50.00
8 David Wright 20.00 50.00

2008 Topps Update

This set was released on October 22, 2008. The base set consists of 330 cards.

COMP.SET w/o VAR (330) 20.00 50.00
COMMON CARD (1-330) .12 .30
COMMON ROOKIE (1-330) .20 .50
1-330 PLATE ODDS 1:457 HOBBY
PLATE PRINT RUN 1 SET PER COLOR
BLACK-CYAN-MAGENTA-YELLOW ISSUED
NO PLATE PRICING DUE TO SCARCITY
UH1A Kosuke Fukudome RC .75 2.00
UH1B Kosuke Fukudome VAR 15.00 40.00
Upside-down photo
UH2 Sean Casey .12 .30
UH3 Freddie Bynum .12 .30
UH4 Brent Lillibridge (RC) .20 .50
UH5 Chipper Jones AS .40 1.00
UH6 Yamid Haad .12 .30
UH7 Josh Anderson .12 .30
UH8 Jeff Mathis .12 .30
UH9 Shawn Riggans .12 .30
UH10A Evan Longoria RC 1.50 4.00
UH10B Evan Longoria VAR 40.00 80.00
Upside-down photo
UH11 Matt Holliday AS .20 .50
UH12 Trot Nixon .12 .30
UH13 Geoff Blum .12 .30
UH14 Bartolo Colon .12 .30
UH15 Kevin Cash .12 .30
UH16 Paul Janish (RC) .20 .50
UH17 Russell Martin AS .12 .30
UH18 Andy Phillips .12 .30
UH19 Johnny Estrada .12 .30
UH20 Justin Masterson RC 1.00 2.50
UH21 Darrell Rasner .12 .30
UH22 Brian Moehler .12 .30
UH23 Cristian Guzman AS .12 .30
UH24 Tony Armas Jr. .12 .30
UH25 Lance Berkman AS .20 .50
UH26 Chris Iannetta .12 .30
UH27 Reid Brignac .20 .50
UH28 Miguel Tejada AS .12 .30
UH29 Ryan Ludwick AS .12 .30
UH30 Brendan Harris .12 .30
UH31 Marco Scutaro .12 .30
UH32 Cody Ross .12 .30
UH33 Carlos Marmol .12 .30
UH34 Nate McLouth AS .12 .30
UH35 Hanley Ramirez AS .30 .75
UH36 Xavier Nady .12 .30
UH37 Connor Robertson .12 .30
UH38 Carlos Villanueva .12 .30
UH39 Jose Molina .12 .30
UH40 Jon Rauch .12 .30
UH41 Joe Mauer AS .20 .50
UH42 Chip Ambres .12 .30
UH43 Jason Bartlett .12 .30
UH44 Ryan Sweeney .12 .30
UH45 Eric Hurley (RC) .20 .50
UH46 Kevin Youkilis AS .20 .50
UH47 Dustin Pedroia AS .50 1.25
UH48 Grant Balfour .12 .30
UH49 Ryan Ludwick .12 .30
UH50 Matt Garza .12 .30
UH51 Fernando Tatis .12 .30
UH52 Derek Jeter AS .75 2.00
UH53 Justin Duchscherer AS .12 .30
UH54 Matt Ginter .12 .30
UH55 Cesar Izturis .12 .30
UH56 Roy Halladay AS .20 .50
UH57 Ramon Castro .12 .30
UH58 Scott Kazmir AS .20 .50
UH59 Cliff Lee AS .20 .50
UH60 Jim Edmonds .20 .50
UH61 Randy Wolf .12 .30
UH62 Matt Albers .12 .30
UH63 Eric Bruntlett .12 .30
UH64 Joe Nathan AS .12 .30
UH65 Alex Rodriguez AS .50 1.25
UH66 Robinson Cancel .12 .30
UH67 Jamey Carroll .12 .30
UH68 Jonathan Papelbon AS .20 .50
UH69 Chad Moeller .12 .30
UH70 George Sherrill .12 .30
UH71 Mariano Rivera AS .30 .75
UH72 Pete Orr .12 .30
UH73 Jonathan Albaladejo RC .30 .75
UH74 Corey Patterson .12 .30
UH75 Matt Treanor .12 .30
UH76 Francisco Rodriguez AS .12 .30
UH77 Ervin Santana AS .12 .30
UH78 Dallas Braden .12 .30
UH79 Willie Harris .12 .30
UH80 Erik Bedard .12 .30
UH81 J.C. Romero .12 .30
UH82 Joe Saunders AS .12 .30
UH83 George Sherrill AS .12 .30
UH84 Julian Tavarez .12 .30
UH85 Chad Gaudin .12 .30
UH86 David Aardsma .12 .30
UH87 Ryan Langerhans .12 .30
UH88 Dan Haren .12 .30
Russell Martin
UH89 Joakim Soria AS .12 .30
UH90 Dan Haren .12 .30
UH91 Billy Buckner .12 .30
UH92 Eric Hinske .12 .30
UH93 Chris Coste .12 .30
UH94 Edinson Volquez .12 .30
Russell Martin
UH95 Ichiro Suzuki AS .50 1.25
UH96 Vladimir Nunez .12 .30
UH97 Sean Gallagher .12 .30
UH98 Denny Bautista .12 .30
UH99 Hanley Ramirez .30 .75
David Ortiz
UH100 Jay Bruce (RC) .75 2.00
UH100B Jay Bruce VAR 20.00 50.00
Upside-down photo
UH101 Dioner Navarro AS .12 .30
UH102 Matt Murton .12 .30
UH103 Chris Burke .12 .30
UH104 Omar Infante .12 .30
UH105 Dan Giese (RC) .20 .50
UH106 Carlos Guillen .40 1.00
Josh Hamilton
UH107 Jason Varitek AS .30 .75
UH108 Shin- Soo Choo .12 .30
UH109 Alberto Callaspo .12 .30
UH110 Jose Valverde .12 .30
UH111 Brandon Boggs (RC) .30 .75
UH112 Josh Hamilton .40 1.00
J.D. Drew
UH113 Justin Morneau AS .20 .50
UH114 Billy Traber .12 .30
UH115 Mike Lamb .12 .30
UH116 Odalis Perez .12 .30
UH117 Jed Lowrie (RC) .50 1.25
UH118 Justin Morneau .30 .75
David Ortiz
UH119 Ken Griffey Jr. HL .50 1.25
UH120 Angel Berroa .12 .30
UH121 Jacque Jones .12 .30
UH122 DeWayne Wise .12 .30
UH123 Matt Joyce RC .50 1.25
UH124 Alex Rodriguez 1.00 2.50
Evan Longoria
UH125 John Smoltz HL .30 .75
UH126 Morgan Ensberg .12 .30
UH127 Michael Young .75 2.00
Derek Jeter
UH128 LaTroy Hawkins .12 .30
UH129 Nick Adenhart (RC) .20 .50
UH130 Mike Cameron .12 .30
UH131 Manny Ramirez HL .30 .75
UH132 Jorge De La Rosa .12 .30
UH133 Tadahito Iguchi .12 .30
UH134 Joey Devine .12 .30
UH135 Jose Arredondo RC .30 .75
UH136 Hanley Ramirez .60 1.50
Albert Pujols
UH137 Evan Longoria HL 1.00 2.50
UH138 T.J. Beam .12 .30
UH139 Jon Lieber .12 .30
UH140 Dana Eveland .12 .30
UH141 Michael Aubrey RC .30 .75
UH142 Adrian Gonzalez .20 .50
Matt Holliday
UH143 Chipper Jones HL .40 1.00
UH144 Robinson Tejeda .12 .30
UH145 Kip Wells .12 .30
UH146 Carlos Gonzalez (RC) .20 .50
UH147 Josh Banks (RC) .20 .50
UH148 David Wright AS .40 1.00
UH149 Paul Hoover .12 .30
UH150 Jon Lester HL .20 .50
UH151 Darin Erstad .12 .30
UH152 Steve Trachsel .12 .30
UH153 Armando Galarraga RC .30 .75
UH154 Grady Sizemore HRD .20 .50
UH155 Jay Bruce HL .50 1.25
UH156 Juan Rincon .12 .30
UH157 Mark Hendrickson .12 .30
UH158 Chad Durbin .12 .30
UH159 Mike Aviles RC .30 .75
UH160 Orlando Cabrera .12 .30
UH161 Asdrubal Cabrera HL .12 .30
UH162 Eric Stults .12 .30
UH163 Miguel Cairo .12 .30
UH164 Jason LaRue .12 .30
UH165 Burke Badenhop RC .30 .75
UH166 Ryan Braun HRD .40 1.00
UH167 Justin Morneau HRD .20 .50
UH168 Ben Zobrist .12 .30
UH169 Eulogio De La Cruz .12 .30
UH170 Greg Smith (RC) .20 .50
UH171 Brian Bixler (RC) .20 .50
UH172 Evan Longoria HRD 1.00 2.50
UH173 Randy Johnson HL .30 .75
UH174 D.J. Carrasco .12 .30
UH175 Luis Vizcaino .12 .30
UH176 Brad Wilkerson .12 .30
UH177 Emmanuel Burriss RC .30 .75
UH178 Lance Berkman HRD .20 .50
UH179 Johnny Damon HL .20 .50
UH180 Scott Rolen .20 .50
UH181 Runelvys Hernandez .12 .30
UH182 Sidney Ponson .12 .30
UH183 Greg Reynolds RC .30 .75
UH184 Chase Utley HRD .30 .75
UH185 Joey Votto HL .30 .75
UH186 Wes Littleton .12 .30
UH187 Rod Barajas .12 .30
UH188 Ray Durham .12 .30
UH189 Micah Hoffpauir RC .30 .75
UH190 Manny Ramirez AS .30 .75
UH191 Ian Kinsler AS .20 .50
UH192 Craig Hansen .12 .30
UH193 Jeremy Affeldt .12 .30
UH194 Gary Bennett .12 .30
UH195 Chris Carter (RC) .20 .50
UH196 Dan Uggla HRD .20 .50
UH197 Michael Young AS .12 .30
UH198 Andy LaRoche .12 .30
UH199 Lance Cormier .12 .30
UH200 Luke Scott .12 .30
UH201 Travis Denker RC .30 .75
UH202 Josh Hamilton .40 1.00
UH203 Joe Crede AS .12 .30
UH204 Franquelis Osoria .12 .30
UH205 Octavio Dotel .12 .30
UH206 Russell Branyan .12 .30
UH207 Alberto Gonzalez RC .30 .75
UH208 Kerry Wood AS .12 .30
UH209 Carlos Guillen AS .12 .30
UH210 Joe Saunders .12 .30
UH211 Brett Tomko .12 .30
UH212 Guillermo Mota .12 .30
UH213 German Duran RC .30 .75
UH214 Carlos Zambrano AS .12 .30
UH215 Josh Hamilton AS .40 1.00
UH216 Jason Bay .12 .30
UH217 Willy Aybar .12 .30
UH218 Salomon Torres .12 .30
UH219 Damaso Marte .12 .30
UH220 Geoff Jenkins .12 .30
UH221 J.D. Drew AS .12 .30
UH222 Dave Borkowski .12 .30
UH223 Jeff Ridgway RC .30 .75
UH224 Angel Pagan .12 .30
UH225 Ryan Tucker (RC) .20 .50
UH226 Brian McCann AS .12 .30
UH227 Carlos Quentin AS .12 .30
UH228 Joe Blanton .12 .30
UH229 Adrian Gonzalez AS .20 .50
UH230 Jason Jennings .12 .30
UH231 Chris Davis RC .50 1.25
UH232 Geovany Soto AS .30 .75
UH233 Grady Sizemore AS .20 .50
UH234 Carl Pavano .12 .30
UH235 Eddie Guardado .12 .30
UH236 Chris Snelling .12 .30
UH237 Manny Ramirez .30 .75
UH238 Dan Uggla AS .20 .50
UH239 Milton Bradley AS .12 .30
UH240 Clayton Kershaw RC .60 1.50
UH241 Chase Utley AS .30 .75
UH242 Raul Chavez .12 .30
UH243 Joe Mather RC .30 .75
UH244 Brandon Webb AS .20 .50
UH245 Ryan Braun .40 1.00
UH246 Kelvin Jimenez .12 .30
UH247 Scott Podsednik .12 .30
UH248 Doug Mientkiewicz .12 .30
UH249 Chris Volstad (RC) .20 .50
UH250 Pedro Feliz .12 .30
UH251 Mark Redman .12 .30
UH252 Tony Clark .12 .30
UH253 Josh Johnson .12 .30
UH254 Jose Castillo .12 .30
UH255 Brian Horwitz RC .20 .50
UH256 Aramis Ramirez AS .12 .30
UH257 Casey Blake .12 .30
UH258 Arthur Rhodes .12 .30
UH259 Aaron Boone .12 .30
UH260 Emil Brown .12 .30
UH261 Matt Macri (RC) .20 .50
UH262 Brian Wilson AS .12 .30
UH263 Eric Patterson .12 .30
UH264 David Ortiz .30 .75
UH265 Tony Abreu .12 .30
UH266 Rob Mackowiak .12 .30
UH267 Gregorio Petit RC .30 .75
UH268 Alfonso Soriano AS .20 .50
UH269 Robert Andino .12 .30
UH270 Justin Duchscherer .12 .30
UH271 Brad Thompson .12 .30
UH272 Guillermo Quiroz .12 .30
UH273 Chris Perez RC .30 .75
UH274 Albert Pujols AS .60 1.50
UH275 Rich Harden .12 .30
UH276 Corey Hart AS .12 .30
UH277 John Rheinecker .12 .30
UH278 So Taguchi .12 .30
UH279 Alex Hinshaw RC .30 .75
UH280 Max Scherzer RC .50 1.25
UH281 Chris Aguila .12 .30
UH282 Carlos Marmol AS .12 .30
UH283 Alex Cintron .12 .30
UH284 Curtis Thigpen .12 .30
UH285 Kosuke Fukudome AS .50 1.25
UH286 Aaron Cook AS .12 .30
UH287 Chase Headley .12 .30
UH288 Evan Longoria AS 1.00 2.50
UH289 Chris Gomez .12 .30
UH290 Carlos Gomez .12 .30
UH291 Jonathan Herrera RC .30 .75
UH292 Ryan Dempster AS .12 .30
UH293 Adam Dunn .12 .30
UH294 Mark Teixeira .20 .50
UH295 Aaron Miles .12 .30
UH296 Gabe Gross .12 .30
UH297 Cory Wade (RC) .20 .50
UH298 Dan Haren AS .12 .30
UH299 Jolbert Cabrera .12 .30
UH300 C.C. Sabathia .12 .30
UH301 Tony Pena .12 .30
UH302 Brandon Moss .12 .30
UH303 Taylor Teagarden RC .30 .75
UH304 Brad Lidge AS .12 .30
UH305 Ben Francisco .12 .30
UH306 Casey Kotchman .12 .30
UH307 Greg Norton .12 .30
UH308 Shelley Duncan .12 .30
UH309 John Bowker (RC) .20 .50
UH310 Kyle Lohse .12 .30
UH311 Oscar Salazar .12 .30
UH312 Ivan Rodriguez .20 .50
UH313 Tim Lincecum AS .30 .75
UH314 Wilson Betemit .12 .30
UH315 Sean Rodriguez (RC) .20 .50
UH316 Ben Sheets AS .20 .50
UH317 Brian Buscher .12 .30
UH318 Kyle Farnsworth .12 .30
UH319 Ruben Gotay .12 .30
UH320 Heath Bell .12 .30
UH321 Jeff Niemann (RC) .20 .50
UH322 Edinson Volquez AS .12 .30
UH323 Jorge Velandia .12 .30
UH324 Ken Griffey Jr. .50 1.25
UH325 Clay Hensley .12 .30
UH326 Kevin Mench .12 .30
UH327 Hernan Iribarren (RC) .20 .50
UH328 Billy Wagner AS .12 .30
UH329 Jeremy Sowers .12 .30
UH330 Johan Santana .20 .50

2008 Topps Update Black

COMMON CARD (1-330) 4.00 10.00
STATED ODDS 1:59 HOBBY
STATED PRINT RUN 57 SER.#'d SETS
UH1 Kosuke Fukudome 15.00 40.00
UH2 Sean Casey 10.00 25.00
UH3 Freddie Bynum 4.00 10.00
UH4 Brent Lillibridge 4.00 10.00
UH5 Chipper Jones AS 6.00 15.00
UH6 Yamid Haad 4.00 10.00
UH7 Josh Anderson 4.00 10.00
UH8 Jeff Mathis 4.00 10.00
UH9 Shawn Riggans 4.00 10.00
UH10 Evan Longoria 20.00 50.00
UH11 Matt Holliday AS 6.00 15.00
UH12 Trot Nixon 4.00 10.00
UH13 Geoff Blum 4.00 10.00
UH14 Bartolo Colon 4.00 10.00
UH15 Kevin Cash 4.00 10.00
UH16 Paul Janish 4.00 10.00
UH17 Russ Martin AS 15.00 40.00
UH18 Andy Phillips 4.00 10.00
UH19 Johnny Estrada 4.00 10.00
UH20 Justin Masterson 30.00 60.00
UH21 Darrell Rasner 4.00 10.00
UH22 Brian Moehler 4.00 10.00
UH23 Cristian Guzman AS 4.00 10.00
UH24 Tony Armas Jr. 4.00 10.00
UH25 Lance Berkman AS 6.00 15.00
UH26 Chris Iannetta 4.00 10.00
UH27 Reid Brignac 6.00 15.00
UH28 Miguel Tejada AS 4.00 10.00
UH29 Ryan Ludwick AS 4.00 10.00
UH30 Brendan Harris 4.00 10.00
UH31 Marco Scutaro 4.00 10.00
UH32 Cody Ross 4.00 10.00
UH33 Carlos Marmol 4.00 10.00
UH34 Nate McLouth AS 12.50 30.00
UH35 Hanley Ramirez AS 10.00 25.00
UH36 Xavier Nady 4.00 10.00
UH37 Connor Robertson 4.00 10.00
UH38 Carlos Villanueva 4.00 10.00
UH39 Jose Molina 4.00 10.00
UH40 Jon Rauch 4.00 10.00
UH41 Joe Mauer AS 6.00 15.00
UH42 Chip Ambres 4.00 10.00
UH43 Jason Bartlett 4.00 10.00
UH44 Ryan Sweeney 4.00 10.00
UH45 Eric Hurley 4.00 10.00
UH46 Kevin Youkilis AS 10.00 25.00
UH47 Dustin Pedroia AS 10.00 25.00
UH48 Grant Balfour 4.00 10.00
UH49 Ryan Ludwick 6.00 15.00
UH50 Matt Garza 4.00 10.00
UH51 Fernando Tatis 4.00 10.00
UH52 Derek Jeter AS 25.00 60.00
UH53 Justin Duchscherer AS 4.00 10.00
UH54 Matt Ginter 4.00 10.00
UH55 Cesar Izturis 4.00 10.00
UH56 Roy Halladay AS 4.00 10.00
UH57 Ramon Castro 4.00 10.00
UH58 Scott Kazmir AS 6.00 15.00
UH59 Cliff Lee AS 4.00 10.00
UH60 Jim Edmonds 6.00 15.00
UH61 Randy Wolf 4.00 10.00
UH62 Matt Albers 4.00 10.00
UH63 Eric Bruntlett 4.00 10.00
UH64 Joe Nathan AS 4.00 10.00
UH65 Alex Rodriguez AS 10.00 25.00
UH66 Robinson Cancel 4.00 10.00
UH67 Jamey Carroll 4.00 10.00
UH68 Jonathan Papelbon AS 6.00 15.00
UH69 Chad Moeller 4.00 10.00
UH70 George Sherrill 4.00 10.00
UH71 Mariano Rivera AS 10.00 25.00
UH72 Pete Orr 4.00 10.00
UH73 Jonathan Albaladejo 6.00 15.00
UH74 Corey Patterson 4.00 10.00
UH75 Matt Treanor 4.00 10.00
UH76 Francisco Rodriguez AS 4.00 10.00
UH77 Ervin Santana AS 4.00 10.00
UH78 Dallas Braden 4.00 10.00
UH79 Willie Harris 4.00 10.00
UH80 Erik Bedard 4.00 10.00
UH81 J.C. Romero 4.00 10.00
UH82 Joe Saunders AS 4.00 10.00
UH83 George Sherrill AS 4.00 10.00
UH84 Julian Tavarez 4.00 10.00
UH85 Chad Gaudin 4.00 10.00
UH86 David Aardsma 4.00 10.00
UH87 Ryan Langerhans 4.00 10.00
UH88 Dan Haren 4.00 10.00
Russ Martin
UH89 Joakim Soria AS 4.00 10.00
UH90 Dan Haren 4.00 10.00
UH91 Billy Buckner 4.00 10.00
UH92 Eric Hinske 4.00 10.00
UH93 Chris Coste 4.00 10.00
UH94 Edinson Volquez 4.00 10.00
Russ Martin
UH95 Ichiro Suzuki AS 20.00 50.00
UH96 Vladimir Nunez 4.00 10.00
UH97 Sean Gallagher 4.00 10.00
UH98 Denny Bautista 4.00 10.00
UH99 Hanley Ramirez 10.00 25.00
David Ortiz
UH100 Jay Bruce 10.00 25.00
UH101 Dioner Navarro AS 4.00 10.00
UH102 Matt Murton 4.00 10.00
UH103 Chris Burke 4.00 10.00
UH104 Omar Infante 4.00 10.00
UH105 Dan Giese 4.00 10.00
UH106 Carlos Guillen 12.50 30.00
Josh Hamilton
UH107 Jason Varitek AS 10.00 25.00
UH108 Shin- Soo Choo 4.00 10.00
UH109 Alberto Callaspo 4.00 10.00
UH110 Jose Valverde 4.00 10.00
UH111 Brandon Boggs 6.00 15.00
UH112 Josh Hamilton 12.50 30.00
J.D. Drew
UH113 Justin Morneau AS 6.00 15.00
UH114 Billy Traber 4.00 10.00
UH115 Mike Lamb 4.00 10.00
UH116 Odalis Perez 4.00 10.00
UH117 Jed Lowrie 12.50 30.00
UH118 Justin Morneau 10.00 25.00
David Ortiz

UH119 Ken Griffey Jr. HL 15.00 40.00
UH120 Angel Berroa 4.00 10.00
UH121 Jacque Jones 4.00 10.00
UH122 DeWayne Wise 4.00 10.00
UH123 Matt Joyce 10.00 25.00
UH124 Alex Rodriguez 20.00 50.00
Evan Longoria
UH125 John Smoltz HL 10.00 25.00
UH126 Morgan Ensberg 4.00 10.00
UH127 Michael Young 25.00 60.00
Derek Jeter
UH128 LaTroy Hawkins 4.00 10.00
UH129 Nick Adenhart 10.00 25.00
UH130 Mike Cameron 4.00 10.00
UH131 Manny Ramirez HL 12.50 30.00
UH132 Jorge De La Rosa 4.00 10.00
UH133 Tadahito Iguchi 4.00 10.00
UH134 Joey Devine 4.00 10.00
UH135 Jose Arredondo 6.00 15.00
UH136 Hanley Ramirez 20.00 50.00
Albert Pujols
UH137 Evan Longoria HL 15.00 40.00
UH138 T.J. Beam 4.00 10.00
UH139 Jon Lieber 4.00 10.00
UH140 Dana Eveland 4.00 10.00
UH141 Michael Aubrey 6.00 15.00
UH142 Adrian Gonzalez 6.00 15.00
Matt Holliday
UH143 Chipper Jones HL 6.00 15.00
UH144 Robinson Tejeda 4.00 10.00
UH145 Kip Wells 4.00 10.00
UH146 Carlos Gonzalez 4.00 10.00
UH147 Josh Banks 4.00 10.00
UH148 David Wright AS 12.50 30.00
UH149 Paul Hoover 4.00 10.00
UH150 Jon Lester HL 12.50 30.00
UH151 Darin Erstad 4.00 10.00
UH152 Steve Trachsel 4.00 10.00
UH153 Armando Galarraga 6.00 15.00
UH154 Grady Sizemore HRD 6.00 15.00
UH155 Jay Bruce HL 10.00 25.00
UH156 Juan Rincon 4.00 10.00
UH157 Mark Hendrickson 4.00 10.00
UH158 Chad Durbin 4.00 10.00
UH159 Mike Aviles 6.00 15.00
UH160 Orlando Cabrera 4.00 10.00
UH161 Asdrubal Cabrera HL 4.00 10.00
UH162 Eric Stults 4.00 10.00
UH163 Miguel Cairo 4.00 10.00
UH164 Jason LaRue 4.00 10.00
UH165 Burke Badenhop 6.00 15.00
UH166 Ryan Braun HRD 12.50 30.00
UH167 Justin Morneau HRD 6.00 15.00
UH168 Ben Zobrist 4.00 10.00
UH169 Eulogio De La Cruz 4.00 10.00
UH170 Greg Smith 4.00 10.00
UH171 Brian Bixler 4.00 10.00
UH172 Evan Longoria HRD 15.00 40.00
UH173 Randy Johnson HL 10.00 25.00
UH174 D.J. Carrasco 4.00 10.00
UH175 Luis Vizcaino 4.00 10.00
UH176 Brad Wilkerson 4.00 10.00
UH177 Emmanuel Burriss 6.00 15.00
UH178 Lance Berkman HRD 6.00 15.00
UH179 Johnny Damon HL 6.00 15.00
UH180 Scott Rolen 6.00 15.00
UH181 Runelvys Hernandez 4.00 10.00
UH182 Sidney Ponson 4.00 10.00
UH183 Greg Reynolds 6.00 15.00
UH184 Chase Utley HRD 10.00 25.00
UH185 Joey Votto HL 10.00 25.00
UH186 Wes Littleton 4.00 10.00
UH187 Rod Barajas 4.00 10.00
UH188 Ray Durham 4.00 10.00
UH189 Micah Hoffpauir 6.00 15.00
UH190 Manny Ramirez AS 10.00 25.00
UH191 Ian Kinsler AS 6.00 15.00
UH192 Craig Hansen 4.00 10.00
UH193 Jeremy Affeldt 4.00 10.00
UH194 Gary Bennett 4.00 10.00
UH195 Chris Carter 6.00 15.00
UH196 Dan Uggla HRD 6.00 15.00
UH197 Michael Young AS 6.00 15.00
UH198 Andy LaRoche 4.00 10.00
UH199 Lance Cormier 4.00 10.00
UH200 Luke Scott 4.00 10.00
UH201 Travis Denker 6.00 15.00
UH202 Josh Hamilton 12.50 30.00
UH203 Joe Crede AS 4.00 10.00
UH204 Franquelis Osoria 4.00 10.00
UH205 Octavio Dotel 4.00 10.00
UH206 Russell Branyan 4.00 10.00
UH207 Alberto Gonzalez 6.00 15.00
UH208 Kerry Wood AS 4.00 10.00
UH209 Carlos Guillen AS 4.00 10.00
UH210 Joe Saunders 4.00 10.00
UH211 Brett Tomko 4.00 10.00
UH212 Guillermo Mota 4.00 10.00
UH213 German Duran 6.00 15.00
UH214 Carlos Zambrano AS 4.00 10.00
UH215 Josh Hamilton AS 12.50 30.00
UH216 Jason Bay 12.50 30.00
UH217 Willy Aybar 4.00 10.00
UH218 Salomon Torres 4.00 10.00
UH219 Damaso Marte 4.00 10.00
UH220 Geoff Jenkins 4.00 10.00
UH221 J.D. Drew AS 4.00 10.00
UH222 Dave Borkowski 4.00 10.00
UH223 Jeff Ridgway 6.00 15.00
UH224 Angel Pagan 4.00 10.00
UH225 Ryan Tucker 4.00 10.00
UH226 Brian McCann AS 6.00 15.00
UH227 Carlos Quentin AS 4.00 10.00
UH228 Joe Blanton 4.00 10.00
UH229 Adrian Gonzalez AS 6.00 15.00
UH230 Jason Jennings 4.00 10.00
UH231 Chris Davis 10.00 25.00
UH232 Geovany Soto AS 10.00 25.00
UH233 Grady Sizemore AS 6.00 15.00
UH234 Carl Pavano 4.00 10.00
UH235 Eddie Guardado 4.00 10.00
UH236 Chris Snelling 4.00 10.00
UH237 Manny Ramirez 20.00 50.00
UH238 Dan Uggla AS 6.00 15.00
UH239 Milton Bradley AS 4.00 10.00
UH240 Clayton Kershaw 20.00 50.00
UH241 Chase Utley AS 10.00 25.00
UH242 Raul Chavez 4.00 10.00
UH243 Joe Mather 6.00 15.00
UH244 Brandon Webb AS 6.00 15.00
UH245 Ryan Braun 12.50 30.00
UH246 Kelvin Jimenez 4.00 10.00
UH247 Scott Podsednik 4.00 10.00
UH248 Doug Mientkiewicz 4.00 10.00
UH249 Chris Volstad 4.00 10.00
UH250 Pedro Feliz 4.00 10.00
UH251 Mark Redman 4.00 10.00
UH252 Tony Clark 4.00 10.00
UH253 Josh Johnson 4.00 10.00
UH254 Jose Castillo 4.00 10.00
UH255 Brian Horwitz 4.00 10.00
UH256 Aramis Ramirez AS 4.00 10.00
UH257 Casey Blake 10.00 25.00
UH258 Arthur Rhodes 4.00 10.00
UH259 Aaron Boone 4.00 10.00
UH260 Emil Brown 4.00 10.00
UH261 Matt Macri 4.00 10.00
UH262 Brian Wilson AS 4.00 10.00
UH263 Eric Patterson 4.00 10.00
UH264 David Ortiz 10.00 25.00
UH265 Tony Abreu 4.00 10.00
UH266 Rob Mackowiak 4.00 10.00
UH267 Gregorio Petit 6.00 15.00
UH268 Alfonso Soriano AS 6.00 15.00
UH269 Robert Andino 4.00 10.00
UH270 Justin Duchscherer 4.00 10.00
UH271 Brad Thompson 4.00 10.00
UH272 Guillermo Quiroz 4.00 10.00
UH273 Chris Perez 6.00 15.00
UH274 Albert Pujols AS 12.50 30.00
UH275 Rich Harden 4.00 10.00
UH276 Corey Hart AS 4.00 10.00
UH277 John Rheinecker 4.00 10.00
UH278 So Taguchi 4.00 10.00
UH279 Alex Hinshaw 6.00 15.00
UH280 Max Scherzer 10.00 25.00
UH281 Chris Aguila 4.00 10.00
UH282 Carlos Marmol AS 4.00 10.00
UH283 Alex Cintron 4.00 10.00
UH284 Curtis Thigpen 4.00 10.00
UH285 Kosuke Fukudome AS 10.00 25.00
UH286 Aaron Cook AS 4.00 10.00
UH287 Chase Headley 4.00 10.00
UH288 Evan Longoria AS 15.00 40.00
UH289 Chris Gomez 4.00 10.00
UH290 Carlos Gomez 6.00 15.00
UH291 Jonathan Herrera 6.00 15.00
UH292 Ryan Dempster AS 4.00 10.00
UH293 Adam Dunn 4.00 10.00
UH294 Mark Teixeira 6.00 15.00
UH295 Aaron Miles 4.00 10.00
UH296 Gabe Gross 4.00 10.00
UH297 Cory Wade 4.00 10.00
UH298 Dan Haren AS 4.00 10.00
UH299 Jolbert Cabrera 4.00 10.00
UH300 C.C. Sabathia 4.00 10.00
UH301 Tony Pena 4.00 10.00
UH302 Brandon Moss 4.00 10.00
UH303 Taylor Teagarden 6.00 15.00
UH304 Brad Lidge AS 4.00 10.00
UH305 Ben Francisco 4.00 10.00
UH306 Casey Kotchman 4.00 10.00
UH307 Greg Norton 4.00 10.00
UH308 Shelley Duncan 4.00 10.00
UH309 John Bowker 4.00 10.00
UH310 Kyle Lohse 4.00 10.00
UH311 Oscar Salazar 4.00 10.00
UH312 Ivan Rodriguez 6.00 15.00
UH313 Tim Lincecum AS 10.00 25.00
UH314 Wilson Betemit 4.00 10.00
UH315 Sean Rodriguez 4.00 10.00
UH316 Ben Sheets AS 6.00 15.00
UH317 Brian Buscher 4.00 10.00
UH318 Kyle Farnsworth 4.00 10.00
UH319 Ruben Gotay 4.00 10.00
UH320 Heath Bell 4.00 10.00
UH321 Jeff Niemann 4.00 10.00
UH322 Edinson Volquez AS 4.00 10.00
UH323 Jorge Velandia 4.00 10.00
UH324 Ken Griffey Jr. 15.00 40.00
UH325 Clay Hensley 4.00 10.00
UH326 Kevin Mench 4.00 10.00
UH327 Hernan Iribarren 6.00 15.00
UH328 Billy Wagner AS 4.00 10.00
UH329 Jeremy Sowers 4.00 10.00
UH330 Johan Santana 6.00 15.00

2008 Topps Update Gold Border

*GLD BDR VET: 2X TO 5X BASIC
*GLD BDR RC: 1.2X TO 3X BASIC RC
STATED ODDS 1:5 HOBBY
STATED PRINT RUN 2008 SER.#'d SETS

2008 Topps Update Gold Foil

*GLD FOIL VET: 1X TO 2.5X BASIC
*GLD FOIL RC: .6X TO 1.5X BASIC RC
STATED ODDS 1:2 HOBBY

2008 Topps Update Platinum

STATED ODDS 1:9434 HOBBY
STATED PRINT RUN 1 SER.#'d SET
NO PRICING DUE TO SCARCITY

2008 Topps Update 1957 Mickey Mantle Reprint Relic

STATED ODDS 17,982 HOBBY
STATED PRINT RUN 57 SER.#'d SETS
MMR57 Mickey Mantle Bat/57 60.00 120.00

2008 Topps Update 2008 Presidential Picks

STATED ODDS 1:15,984 HOBBY
STATED PRINT RUN 100 SER.#'d SETS
BO Barack Obama 150.00 250.00
JM John McCain 40.00 80.00

2008 Topps Update All-Star Jumbo Patches

STATED ODDS 1:4496 HOBBY
STATED PRINT RUN 6 SER.#'d SETS
NO PRICING DUE TO SCARCITY

2008 Topps Update All-Star Jumbo Patches Autographs

STATED ODDS 1:23,017 HOBBY
STATED PRINT RUN 6 SER.#'d SETS
NO PRICING DUE TO SCARCITY

2008 Topps Update All-Star Stitches

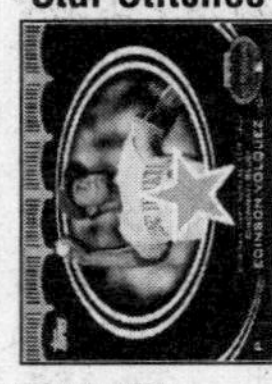

STATED ODDS 1:44 HOBBY
AC Aaron Cook 3.00 8.00
AER Alex Rodriguez 6.00 15.00
AG Adrian Gonzalez 3.00 8.00
AP Albert Pujols 6.00 15.00
AR Aramis Ramirez 3.00 8.00
AS Alfonso Soriano 3.00 8.00
BL Brad Lidge 5.00 12.00
BM Brian McCann 4.00 10.00
BS Ben Sheets 3.00 8.00
BTW Brandon Webb 3.00 8.00
BW Brian Wilson
CAG Carlos Guillen 3.00 8.00
CG Cristian Guzman 3.00 8.00
CH Corey Hart 3.00 8.00
CJ Chipper Jones 4.00 10.00
CL Cliff Lee 4.00 10.00
CM Carlos Marmol 3.00 8.00
CQ Carlos Quentin 3.00 8.00
CU Chase Utley 4.00 10.00
CZ Carlos Zambrano 4.00 10.00
DH Dan Haren 3.00 8.00
DN Dioner Navarro 4.00 10.00
DO David Ortiz 4.00 10.00
DP Dustin Pedroia 5.00 12.00
DU Dan Uggla 3.00 8.00
DW David Wright 5.00 12.00
EL Evan Longoria 12.50 30.00
ES Ervin Santana 3.00 8.00
EV Edinson Volquez 3.00 8.00
FR Francisco Rodriguez 4.00 10.00
GFS George Sherrill 3.00 8.00
GPS Geovany Soto 5.00 12.00
GS Grady Sizemore 4.00 10.00
HR Hanley Ramirez 3.00 8.00
IK Ian Kinsler 3.00 8.00
IS Ichiro Suzuki 8.00 20.00
JC Joe Crede 3.00 8.00
JCD Justin Duchscherer 4.00 10.00
JD J.D. Drew 4.00 10.00
JEM Justin Morneau 4.00 10.00
JES Joe Saunders
JH Josh Hamilton 8.00 20.00
JM Joe Mauer 4.00 10.00
JN Joe Nathan 3.00 8.00
JP Jonathan Papelbon 4.00 10.00
JS Joakim Soria 3.00 8.00
JV Jason Varitek 4.00 10.00
KF Kosuke Fukudome 10.00 25.00
KW Kerry Wood 3.00 8.00
KY Kevin Youkilis 3.00 8.00
LB Lance Berkman 4.00 10.00
MB Milton Bradley 3.00 8.00
MH Matt Holliday 3.00 8.00
MR Manny Ramirez 4.00 10.00
MSR Mariano Rivera 4.00 10.00
MT Miguel Tejada 3.00 8.00
MY Michael Young 3.00 8.00
NM Nate McLouth 5.00 12.00
RB Ryan Braun 4.00 10.00
RD Ryan Dempster 3.00 8.00
RH Roy Halladay 3.00 8.00
RL Ryan Ludwick 5.00 12.00
RM Russ Martin 3.00 8.00
SK Scott Kazmir 3.00 8.00
TL Tim Lincecum 6.00 15.00
WW Billy Wagner 3.00 8.00

2008 Topps Update All-Star Stitches Gold

*GOLD: .75X TO 2X BASIC
STATED ODDS 1:373 HOBBY
STATED PRINT RUN 50 SER.#'d SETS
AER Alex Rodriguez 30.00 60.00
EL Evan Longoria 20.00 50.00
IS Ichiro Suzuki 20.00 50.00
KY Kevin Youkilis 30.00 60.00

2008 Topps Update All-Star Stitches Platinum

STATED ODDS 1:23,017 HOBBY
STATED PRINT RUN 1 SER.#'d SET
NO PRICING DUE TO SCARCITY

2008 Topps Update All-Star Stitches Autographs

STATED ODDS 1:6394 HOBBY
STATED PRINT RUN 25 SER.#'d SETS
CJ Chipper Jones 100.00 200.00
DP Dustin Pedroia 75.00 150.00
DU Dan Uggla 20.00 50.00
EV Edinson Volquez 30.00 60.00
HR Hanley Ramirez 30.00 60.00
JH Josh Hamilton 100.00 200.00
JV Jason Varitek 50.00 100.00
RB Ryan Braun 40.00 80.00
RM Russ Martin 100.00 175.00
TL Tim Lincecum 100.00 200.00

2008 Topps Update All-Star Stitches Dual

STATED ODDS 1:5994
STATED PRINT RUN 25 SER.#'d SETS
NO PRICING ON FEW DUE TO SCARCITY
BP Lance Berkman
Albert Pujols
FL Kosuke Fukudome 40.00 80.00
Ichiro Suzuki
HB Josh Hamilton 12.50 30.00
Ryan Braun
HW Dan Haren
Brandon Webb
LS Cliff Lee 10.00 25.00
Ben Sheets
IV Tim Lincecum 12.50 30.00
Edinson Volquez
RR Alex Rodriguez
Manny Ramirez
RR Mariano Rivera 30.00 60.00
Francisco Rodriguez
RT Hanley Ramirez 8.00 20.00
Miguel Tejada
UU Chase Utley 20.00 50.00
Dan Uggla

2008 Topps Update All-Star Stitches Triple

STATED ODDS 1:5994 HOBBY
STATED PRINT RUN 25 SER.#'d SETS
NO PRICING ON FEW DUE TO SCARCITY
HFB Matt Holliday/Kosuke Fukudome
/Ryan Braun 20.00 50.00
HRS Josh Hamilton/Manny Ramirez
/Ichiro Suzuki 30.00 60.00
KHY Ian Kinsler/Milton Bradley
/Michael Young 8.00 20.00
MMN Joe Mauer/Justin Morneau/Joe Nathan
MNM Russ Martin/Dioner Navarro
/Brian McCann 40.00 80.00
PDY Dustin Pedroia/J.D. Drew
/David Ortiz 20.00 50.00
PGB Albert Pujols/Adrian Gonzalez
/Lance Berkman 30.00 60.00
RSS Francisco Rodriguez/Ervin Santana
/Joe Saunders 30.00 60.00
RWJ Alex Rodriguez/David Wright
/Chipper Jones 40.00 80.00
WLW Kerry Wood/Brad Lidge
/Billy Wagner 20.00 50.00
ZSD Carlos Zambrano/Aramis Ramirez
/Ryan Dempster 50.00 100.00

2008 Topps Update Chrome

ONE PER BOX TOPPER
CHR1 Jay Bruce 5.00 12.00
CHR2 Dan Giese 2.00 5.00
CHR3 Brandon Boggs 3.00 8.00
CHR4 Jed Lowrie 5.00 12.00
CHR5 Matt Joyce 5.00 12.00
CHR6 Nick Adenhart 2.00 5.00
CHR7 Jose Arredondo 3.00 8.00
CHR8 Michael Aubrey 3.00 8.00
CHR9 Josh Banks 2.00 5.00
CHR10 Armando Galarraga 3.00 8.00
CHR11 Mike Aviles 3.00 8.00
CHR12 Burke Badenhop 3.00 8.00
CHR13 Reid Brignac 3.00 8.00
CHR14 Emmanuel Burriss 3.00 8.00
CHR15 Greg Reynolds 3.00 8.00
CHR16 Chris Volstad 2.00 5.00
CHR17 Brian Bixler 2.00 5.00
CHR18 Chris Carter 3.00 8.00
CHR19 Travis Denker 3.00 8.00
CHR20 Alberto Gonzalez 3.00 8.00
CHR21 Robinzon Diaz 2.00 5.00
CHR22 Brett Gardner 5.00 12.00
CHR23 Micah Hoffpauir 3.00 8.00
CHR24 Hernan Iribarren 3.00 8.00
CHR25 Greg Smith 2.00 5.00
CHR26 German Duran 3.00 8.00
CHR27 Kosuke Fukudome 6.00 15.00
CHR28 Ryan Tucker 2.00 5.00
CHR29 Paul Janish 2.00 5.00
CHR30 Clayton Kershaw 5.00 12.00
CHR31 Chris Davis 5.00 12.00
CHR32 Joe Mather 3.00 8.00
CHR33 Nick Hundley 2.00 5.00
CHR34 Brian Horwitz 2.00 5.00
CHR35 Carlos Gonzalez 2.00 5.00
CHR36 Matt Macri 2.00 5.00
CHR37 Gregorio Petit 3.00 8.00
CHR38 Chris Perez 3.00 8.00
CHR39 Alex Hinshaw 3.00 8.00
CHR40 Max Scherzer 5.00 12.00
CHR41 Jonathan Van Every 2.00 5.00
CHR42 Jonathan Herrera 3.00 8.00
CHR43 Cory Wade 2.00 5.00
CHR44 Max Ramirez 2.00 5.00
CHR45 John Bowker 2.00 5.00
CHR46 Sean Rodriguez 2.00 5.00
CHR47 Jeff Niemann 2.00 5.00
CHR48 Taylor Teagarden 3.00 8.00
CHR49 Mark Worrell 2.00 5.00
CHR50 Evan Longoria 10.00 25.00
CHR51 Chris Smith 2.00 5.00
CHR52 Brent Lillibridge 2.00 5.00
CHR53 Colt Morton 3.00 8.00
CHR54 Eric Hurley 2.00 5.00
CHR55 Justin Masterson 5.00 12.00

2008 Topps Update First Couples

COMPLETE SET (41) 15.00 40.00
STATED ODDS 1:6 HOBBY
FC1 George Washington .75 2.00
Martha Washington
FC2 John Adams .60 1.50
Abagail Adams
FC3 Thomas Jefferson .60 1.50
Martha Jefferson
FC4 James Madison .40 1.00
Dolley Madison
FC5 James Monroe .40 1.00
Elizabeth Kotright Monroe
FC6 John Quincy Adams .40 1.00
Louisa Catherine Adams
FC7 Andrew Jackson .40 1.00
Rachel Jackson
FC8 Martin Van Buren .40 1.00
Hannah Van Buren
FC9 William Henry Harrison .40 1.00
Anna Harrison
FC10 John Tyler .40 1.00
Julia Tyler
FC11 James K. Polk .40 1.00
(Sarah Polk
FC12 Zachary Taylor .40 1.00
Margaret Taylor
FC13 Millard Fillmore .40 1.00
Abigail Fillmore
FC14 Franklin Pierce .40 1.00
Jane M. Pierce
FC15 Abraham Lincoln .75 2.00
Mary Lincoln
FC16 Andrew Johnson .40 1.00
Eliza Johnson
FC17 Ulysses S. Grant .40 1.00
Julia Grant
FC18 Rutherford B. Hayes .40 1.00
Lucy Hayes
FC19 James A. Garfield .40 1.00
Lucretia Garfield
FC20 Chester A. Arthur .40 1.00
Ellen Arthur
FC21 Grover Cleveland .40 1.00
Frances Cleveland
FC22 Benjamin Harrison .40 1.00
Caroline Harrison
FC23 William McKinley .40 1.00
Ida McKinley
FC24 Theodore Roosevelt .60 1.50
Edith Roosevelt
FC25 William H. Taft .40 1.00
Helen Taft
FC26 Woodrow Wilson .40 1.00
Edith Wilson
FC27 Warren G. Harding .40 1.00
(Florence Harding
FC28 Calvin Coolidge .40 1.00
Grace Coolidge
FC29 Herbert Hoover .40 1.00
Lou Hoover
FC30 Franklin D. Roosevelt .60 1.50
(Eleanor Roosevelt
FC31 Harry S. Truman .40 1.00
(Bess Truman
FC32 Dwight D. Eisenhower .60 1.50
Mamie Eisenhower
FC33 John F. Kennedy 1.00 2.50
Jacqueline Kennedy Onassis
FC34 Lyndon B. Johnson .60 1.50
(Lady Bird Johnson
FC35 Richard M. Nixon .60 1.50
(Pat Nixon
FC36 Gerald R. Ford .60 1.50
(Betty Ford
FC37 Jimmy Carter .60 1.50
(Rosalynn Carter
FC38 Ronald Reagan 1.00 2.50
(Nancy Reagan
FC39 George Bush .60 1.50
(Barbara Bush
FC40 Bill Clinton .75 2.00
(Hillary Rodham Clinton
FC41 George W. Bush .75 2.00
(Laura Bush

2008 Topps Update First Lady Cut Signatures

STATED ODDS 1:47,952 HOBBY
STATED PRINT RUN 1 SER.#'d SETS
NO PRICING DUE TO SCARCITY

2008 Topps Update Ring of Honor 1986 New York Mets

STATED ODDS 1:18 HOBBY
GOLD ODDS 1:11,743 HOBBY
GOLD PRINT RUN 25 SER.#'d SETS
NO GOLD PRICING AVAILABLE
DG Dwight Gooden .60 1.50
DJ Davey Johnson .60 1.50
DS Darryl Strawberry .60 1.50
GC Gary Carter .60 1.50
HJ Howard Johnson .60 1.50
JO Jesse Orosco .60 1.50
KH Keith Hernandez .60 1.50
KM Kevin Mitchell .60 1.50
RD Ron Darling .60 1.50
RK Ray Knight .60 1.50

2008 Topps Update Ring of Honor 1986 New York Mets Autographs

STATED ODDS 1:2849 HOBBY
DG Dwight Gooden 12.50 30.00
DJ Davey Johnson 10.00 25.00
DS Darryl Strawberry 15.00 40.00
GC Gary Carter 15.00 40.00
HJ Howard Johnson 12.50 30.00
JO Jesse Orosco 15.00 40.00
KH Keith Hernandez 15.00 40.00
KM Kevin Mitchell 12.50 30.00
RD Ron Darling 10.00 25.00
RK Ray Knight 12.50 30.00

2008 Topps Update Ring of Honor World Series Champions

COMPLETE SET (10) 5.00 12.00
STATED ODDS 1:18 HOBBY
GOLD ODDS 1:11,743 HOBBY
GOLD PRINT RUN 25 SER.#'d SETS
NO GOLD PRICING AVAILABLE
BS Bruce Sutter .60 1.50
DC David Cone COR .60 1.50
DC1 David Cone UER .60 1.50
Last name misspelled
DJ David Justice .60 1.50
DS Duke Snider 1.00 2.50
JP Johnny Podres .60 1.50
LA Luis Aparicio .60 1.50
MI Monte Irvin .60 1.50
ML Mike Lowell .60 1.50
OC Orlando Cepeda .60 1.50
WF Whitey Ford 1.00 2.50

2008 Topps Update Ring of Honor World Series Champions Autographs

STATED ODDS 1:2569 HOBBY
BS Bruce Sutter 30.00 60.00
DC David Cone 30.00 60.00
DJ David Justice 30.00 60.00
DS Duke Snider 30.00 60.00
JP Johnny Podres 15.00 40.00
LA Luis Aparicio 15.00 40.00
MI Monte Irvin 15.00 40.00
ML Mike Lowell 20.00 50.00
OC Orlando Cepeda 30.00 60.00
WF Whitey Ford 30.00 60.00

2008 Topps Update Sketch Cards

STATED ODDS 1:214 HOBBY
ANNCD PRINT RUN 1 COPY PER
MULTIPLE VERSIONS OF EACH
NO PRICING DUE TO SCARCITY

2008 Topps Update Take Me Out To The Ballgame

STATED ODDS 1:72 HOBBY
BG 100th Anniversary .75 2.00

2008 Topps Update World Baseball Classic Preview

STATED ODDS 1:9 HOBBY
WBC1 Daisuke Matsuzaka 1.00 2.50
WBC2 Alexei Ramirez 1.50 4.00
WBC3 Derrek Lee .40 1.00
WBC4 Akinori Iwamura .25 .60
WBC5 Chase Utley .60 1.50
WBC6 Jose Reyes .40 1.00
WBC7 Jake Peavy .40 1.00
WBC8 Justin Huber .25 .60
WBC9 Justin Morneau .40 1.00
WBC10 Ichiro Suzuki 1.00 2.50
WBC11 Adrian Gonzalez .40 1.00
WBC12 Carlos Zambrano .25 .60
WBC13 Miguel Cabrera .40 1.00
WBC14 Carlos Beltran .25 .60
WBC15 Albert Pujols 1.25 3.00
WBC16 Paul Bell .25 .60

WBC17 Frank Catalanotto .25 .60
WBC18 Jason Varitek .60 1.50
WBC19 Andruw Jones .25 .60
WBC20 Johan Santana .40 1.00
WBC21 Carlos Lee .25 .60
WBC22 David Ortiz .60 1.50
WBC23 Francisco Rodriguez .25 .60
WBC24 Chin-Lung Hu .40 1.00
WBC25 Kosuke Fukudome 1.00 2.50

2003 Topps 205

This 165 card series one set was released in July, 2003. The 175 card series two set was released several months later in February, 204. These cards were issued in eight-card packs which came 20 packs to a box and 10 boxes to a case. Cards number 1 through 120 feature veterans. Please note that 15 of these cards were issued with variations and we have notated the differences in these cards in our checklist. Cards number 121 through 130 feature prospects who were about ready to jump into the majors. Cards numbered 131 through 144 feature some players in their first year of cards. Card number number 145 features Louis Sockalexis who was supposedly the player the Cleveland Indians named their team in honor of. (This supposition has been buttressed by recently redisovered newspaper clippings from 1897). Cards numbered 146 to 150 feature various "reprints" of some of the tougher T-205 cards. Also randomly inserted in packs were cards featuring "repurchased" tobacco cards. Those cards were inserted at a stated rate of one in 336 for 1st series cards and one in 295 for second series cards. The second series featured the following subsets: T205 Reprints from cards 151 through 154, retired players from card 155 through 160; prospects from cards 161 through 169. First year players from cards 170 through 192. In addition, 10 players had 2 variations in the second series and we have notated this information along with some players who were issued in shorter quantity we have put an SP next to that player's name.

COMPLETE SERIES 1 (165) 15.00 40.00
COMPLETE SERIES 2 (175) 75.00 125.00
COMP.SERIES 2 w/o SP's (155) 15.00 40.00
COM (1-130/161-169/193-315) .20 .50
COMMON (131-145/170-192) .20 .50
COMMON (146-150) .40 1.00
COMMON SP 1.00 2.50
SERIES 2 SP STATED ODDS 1:5
1A Barry Bonds w/Cap 1.25 3.00
1B Barry Bonds w/Helmet 1.25 3.00
2 Bret Boone .20 .50
3A Albert Pujols Clear Logo 1.00 2.50
3B Albert Pujols White Logo 1.00 2.50
4 Carl Crawford .20 .50
5 Bartolo Colon .20 .50
6 Cliff Floyd .20 .50
7 John Olerud .20 .50
8A Jason Giambi Full Jkt .20 .50
8B Jason Giambi Partial Jkt .20 .50
9 Edgardo Alfonzo .20 .50
10 Ivan Rodriguez .30 .75
11 Jim Edmonds .20 .50
12A Mike Piazza Orange .75 2.00
12B Mike Piazza Yellow .75 2.00
13 Greg Maddux .75 2.00
14 Jose Vidro .20 .50
15A Vlad Guerrero Clear Logo .50 1.25
15B V.Guerrero White Logo .50 1.25
16 Bernie Williams .30 .75
17 Roger Clemens 1.00 2.50
18A Miguel Tejada Blue .20 .50
18B Miguel Tejada Green .20 .50
19 Carlos Delgado .20 .50
20A Alfonso Soriano w/Bat .20 .50
20B Alf. Soriano Sunglasses .20 .50
21 Bobby Cox MG .20 .50
22 Mike Scioscia .20 .50
23 John Smoltz .30 .75
24 Luis Gonzalez .20 .50
25 Shawn Green .20 .50
26 Raul Ibanez .20 .50
27 Andruw Jones .30 .75
28 Josh Beckett .20 .50
29 Derek Lowe .20 .50
30 Todd Helton .30 .75
31 Barry Larkin .30 .75
32 Jason Jennings .20 .50
33 Darin Erstad .20 .50
34 Magglio Ordonez .20 .50
35 Mike Sweeney .20 .50
36 Kazuhisa Ishii .20 .50
37 Ron Gardenhire MG .20 .50
38 Tim Hudson .20 .50
39 Tim Salmon .30 .75
40A Pat Burrell Black Bat .20 .50
40B Pat Burrell Brown Bat .20 .50
41 Manny Ramirez .30 .75
42 Nick Johnson .20 .50
43 Tom Glavine .30 .75
44 Mark Mulder .20 .50
45 Brian Jordan .20 .50
46 Rafael Palmeiro .30 .75
47 Vernon Wells .20 .50
48 Bob Brenly MG .20 .50
49 C.C. Sabathia .20 .50
50A A.Rodriguez Look Ahead .75 2.00
50B A.Rodriguez Look Away .75 2.00
51A Sammy Sosa Head Duck .50 1.25
51B Sammy Sosa Head Left .50 1.25
52 Paul Konerko .20 .50
53 Craig Biggio .30 .75
54 Moises Alou .20 .50
55 Johnny Damon .30 .75
56 Torii Hunter .20 .50
57 Omar Vizquel .30 .75
58 Orlando Hernandez .20 .50
59 Barry Zito .20 .50
60 Lance Berkman .20 .50
61 Carlos Beltran .20 .50
62 Edgar Renteria .20 .50
63 Ben Sheets .20 .50
64 Doug Mientkiewicz .20 .50
65 Troy Glaus .20 .50
66 Preston Wilson .20 .50
67 Kerry Wood .20 .50
68 Frank Thomas .50 1.25
69 Jimmy Rollins .20 .50
70 Brian Giles .20 .50
71 Bobby Higginson .20 .50
72 Larry Walker .20 .50
73 Randy Johnson .50 1.25
74 Tony LaRussa MG .20 .50
75A Derek Jeter w/Gold Trim 1.25 3.00
75B D.Jeter w/o Gold Trim 1.25 3.00
76 Bobby Abreu .20 .50
77A A.Dunn Closed Mouth .20 .50
77B Adam Dunn Open Mouth .20 .50
78 Ryan Klesko .20 .50
79 Francisco Rodriguez .20 .50
80 Scott Rolen .30 .75
81 Roberto Alomar .30 .75
82 Joe Torre MG .30 .75
83 Jim Thome .30 .75
84 Kevin Millwood .20 .50
85 J.T. Snow .20 .50
86 Trevor Hoffman .20 .50
87 Jay Gibbons .20 .50
88A Mark Prior New Logo .30 .75
88B Mark Prior Old Logo .30 .75
89 Rich Aurilia .20 .50
90 Chipper Jones .50 1.25
91 Richie Sexson .20 .50
92 Gary Sheffield .20 .50
93 Pedro Martinez .30 .75
94 Rodrigo Lopez .20 .50
95 Al Leiter .20 .50
96 Jorge Posada .30 .75
97 Luis Castillo .20 .50
98 Aubrey Huff .20 .50
99 A.J. Pierzynski .20 .50
100A I.Suzuki Look Ahead 1.00 2.50
100B Ichiro Suzuki Look Right 1.00 2.50
101 Eric Chavez .20 .50
102 Brett Myers .20 .50
103 Jason Kendall .20 .50
104 Jeff Kent .20 .50
105 Eric Hinske .20 .50
106 Jacque Jones .20 .50
107 Phil Nevin .20 .50
108 Roy Oswalt .20 .50
109 Curt Schilling .20 .50
110A N.Garciaparra w/Gold Trim .75 2.00
110B N.Garciaparra w/o Gold Trim .75 2.00
111 Garret Anderson .20 .50
112 Eric Gagne .20 .50
113 Javier Vazquez .20 .50
114 Jeff Bagwell .30 .75
115 Mike Lowell .20 .50
116 Carlos Pena .20 .50
117 Ken Griffey Jr. .75 2.00
118 Tony Batista .20 .50
119 Edgar Martinez .30 .75
120 Austin Kearns .20 .50
121 Jason Stokes PROS .20 .50
122 Jose Reyes PROS .20 .50
123 Rocco Baldelli PROS .20 .50
124 Joe Borchard PROS .20 .50
125 Joe Mauer PROS .50 1.25
126 Gavin Floyd PROS .20 .50
127 Mark Teixeira PROS .30 .75
128 Jeremy Guthrie PROS .20 .50
129 B.J. Upton PROS .50 1.25
130 Khalil Greene PROS .50 1.25
131 Hanley Ramirez FY RC 2.00 5.00
132 Andy Marte FY RC 1.50 4.00
133 J.D. Durbin FY RC .20 .50
134 Jason Kubel FY RC .50 1.25
135 Craig Brazell FY RC .20 .50
136 Bryan Bullington FY RC .20 .50
137 Jose Contreras FY RC .40 1.00
138 Brian Burgamy FY RC .20 .50
139 E.Bastida-Martinez FY RC .20 .50
140 Joey Gomes FY RC .20 .50
141 Ismael Castro FY RC .25 .60
142 Travis Wong FY RC .25 .60
143 Mi.Garciaparra FY RC .20 .50
144 Arnaldo Munoz FY RC .20 .50
145 Louis Sockalexis FY XRC .20 .50
146 Richard Hoblitzell REP .40 1.00
147 George Graham REP .40 1.00
148 Hal Chase REP .40 1.00
149 John McGraw REP .60 1.50
150 Bobby Wallace REP .40 1.00
151 David Shean REP .40 1.00
152 Richard Hoblitzell REP SP 1.00 2.50
153 Hal Chase REP .40 1.00
154 Hooks Wiltse REP .40 1.00
155 George Brett RET 1.25 3.00
156 Willie Mays RET 1.25 3.00
157 Honus Wagner RET SP 4.00 10.00
158 Nolan Ryan RET 1.50 4.00
159 Reggie Jackson RET .60 1.50
160 Mike Schmidt RET 1.25 3.00
161 Josh Barfield PROS .20 .50
162 Grady Sizemore PROS .50 1.25
163 Justin Morneau PROS .20 .50
164 Laynce Nix PROS .20 .50
165 Zack Greinke PROS .20 .50
166 Victor Martinez PROS .30 .75
167 Jeff Mathis PROS .20 .50
168 Casey Kotchman PROS .20 .50
169 Gabe Gross PROS .20 .50
170 Edwin Jackson FY RC .25 .60
171 Delmon Young FY SP RC 4.00 10.00
172 Eric Duncan FY SP RC 2.50 6.00
173 Brian Snyder FY SP RC 2.00 5.00
174 Chris Lubanski FY SP RC 2.00 5.00
175 Ryan Harvey FY SP RC 2.50 6.00
176 Nick Markakis FY SP RC 3.00 8.00
177 Chad Billingsley FY SP RC 3.00 8.00
178 Elizardo Ramirez FY RC .25 .60
179 Ben Francisco FY RC .20 .50
180 Franklin Gutierrez FY SP RC 2.00 5.00
181 Aaron Hill FY SP RC 2.00 5.00
182 Kevin Correia FY RC .20 .50
183 Kelly Shoppach FY RC .40 1.00
184 Felix Pie FY SP RC 3.00 8.00
185 Adam Loewen FY SP RC 2.00 5.00
186 Danny Garcia FY RC .20 .50
187 Rickie Weeks FY SP RC 3.00 8.00
188 Robby Hammock FY SP RC 1.50 4.00
189 Ryan Wagner FY SP RC 1.50 4.00
190 Matt Kata FY SP RC 1.50 4.00
191 Bo Hart FY SP RC 1.50 4.00
192 Brandon Webb FY SP RC 2.50 6.00
193 Bengie Molina .20 .50
194 Junior Spivey .20 .50
195 Gary Sheffield .20 .50
196 Jason Johnson .20 .50
197 David Ortiz .50 1.25
198 Roberto Alomar .30 .75
199 Wily Mo Pena .20 .50
200 Sammy Sosa .50 1.25
201 Jay Payton .20 .50
202 Dmitri Young .20 .50
203 Derrek Lee .30 .75
204A Jeff Bagwell w/Hat .30 .75
204B Jeff Bagwell w/o Hat .30 .75
205 Runelvys Hernandez .20 .50
206 Kevin Brown .20 .50
207 Wes Helms .20 .50
208 Eddie Guardado .20 .50
209 Orlando Cabrera .20 .50
210 Alfonso Soriano .20 .50
211 Ty Wigginton .20 .50
212A Rich Harden Look Left .30 .75
212B Rich Harden Look Right .30 .75
213 Mike Lieberthal .20 .50
214 Brian Giles .20 .50
215 Jason Schmidt .20 .50
216 Jamie Moyer .20 .50
217 Matt Morris .20 .50
218 Victor Zambrano .20 .50
219 Roy Halladay .20 .50
220 Mike Hampton .20 .50
221 Kevin Millar Sox .20 .50
222 Hideo Nomo .50 1.25
223 Milton Bradley .20 .50
224 Jose Guillen .20 .50
225 Derek Jeter 1.25 3.00
226 Rondell White .20 .50
227A Hank Blalock Blue Jsy .20 .50
227B Hank Blalock White Jsy .20 .50
228 Shigetoshi Hasegawa .20 .50
229 Mike Mussina .30 .75
230 Cristian Guzman .20 .50
231A Todd Helton Blue .30 .75
231B Todd Helton Green .30 .75
232 Kenny Lofton .20 .50
233 Carl Everett .20 .50
234 Shea Hillenbrand .20 .50
235 Brad Fullmer .20 .50
236 Bernie Williams .30 .75
237 Vicente Padilla .20 .50
238 Tim Worrell .20 .50
239 Juan Gonzalez .20 .50
240 Ichiro Suzuki 1.00 2.50
241 Aaron Boone .20 .50
242 Shannon Stewart .20 .50
243A Barry Zito Blue .20 .50
243B Barry Zito Green .20 .50
244 Reggie Sanders .20 .50
245 Scott Podsednik .20 .50
246 Miguel Cabrera .50 1.25
247 Angel Berroa .20 .50
248 Carlos Zambrano .20 .50
249 Marlon Byrd .20 .50
250 Mark Prior .30 .75
251 Esteban Loaiza .20 .50
252 David Eckstein .20 .50
253 Alex Cintron .20 .50
254 Melvin Mora .20 .50
255 Russ Ortiz .20 .50
256 Carlos Lee .20 .50
257 Tino Martinez .30 .75
258 Randy Wolf .20 .50
259 Jason Phillips .20 .50
260 Vladimir Guerrero .50 1.25
261 Brad Wilkerson .20 .50
262 Ivan Rodriguez .30 .75
263 Matt Lawton .20 .50
264 Adam Dunn .20 .50
265 Joe Borowski .20 .50
266 Jody Gerut .20 .50
267 Alex Rodriguez .75 2.00
268 Brendan Donnelly .20 .50
269A Randy Johnson Grey .50 1.25
269B Randy Johnson Pink .50 1.25
270 Nomar Garciaparra .75 2.00
271 Javy Lopez .20 .50
272 Travis Hafner .20 .50
273 Juan Pierre .20 .50
274 Morgan Ensberg .20 .50
275 Albert Pujols 1.00 2.50
276 Jason LaRue .20 .50
277 Paul Lo Duca .20 .50
278 Andy Pettitte .30 .75
279 Mike Piazza .75 2.00
280A Jim Thome Blue .30 .75
280B Jim Thome Green .30 .75
281 Marquis Grissom .20 .50
282 Woody Williams .20 .50
283A Curt Schilling Look Ahead .20 .50
283B Curt Schilling Look Right .20 .50
284A Chipper Jones Blue .50 1.25
284B Chipper Jones Yellow .50 1.25
285 Deivi Cruz .20 .50
286 Johnny Damon .30 .75
287 Chin-Hui Tsao .20 .50
288 Alex Gonzalez .20 .50
289 Billy Wagner .20 .50
290 Jason Giambi .20 .50
291 Keith Foulke .20 .50
292 Jerome Williams .20 .50
293 Livan Hernandez .20 .50
294 Aaron Guiel .20 .50
295 Randall Simon .20 .50
296 Byung-Hyun Kim .20 .50
297 Jorge Julio .20 .50
298 Miguel Batista .20 .50
299 Rafael Furcal .20 .50
300A Dontrelle Willis No Smile .50 1.25
300B Dontrelle Willis Smile SP 1.50 4.00
301 Alex Sanchez .20 .50
302 Shawn Chacon .20 .50
303 Matt Clement .20 .50
304 Luis Matos .20 .50
305 Steve Finley .20 .50
306 Marcus Giles .20 .50
307 Boomer Wells .20 .50
308 Jeromy Burnitz .20 .50
309 Mike MacDougal .20 .50
310 Mariano Rivera .50 1.25
311 Adrian Beltre .20 .50
312 Mark Loretta .20 .50
313 Ugueth Urbina .20 .50
314 Bill Mueller .20 .50
315 Johan Santana .30 .75
NNO Vintage Buyback

2003 Topps 205 American Beauty

*AMER.BTY: 1.25X TO 3X BASIC
RANDOM INSERTS IN PACKS
*AMER.BTY PURPLE: 4X TO 10X BASIC
PURPLE CARDS ARE 10% OF PRINT RUN
CL: 1/20/50/51/100/146-150

2003 Topps 205 Bazooka Blue

SERIES 2 STATED ODDS 1:2744 PACKS
SERIES 2 STATED ODDS 1:208 MINI BOXES
STATED PRINT RUN 1 SET
NO PRICING DUE TO SCARCITY

2003 Topps 205 Bazooka Red

SERIES 1 STATED ODDS 1:1573 PACKS
SERIES 2 STATED ODDS 1:691 PACKS
SERIES 2 STATED ODDS 1:52 MINI BOXES
SERIES 1 STATED PRINT RUN 5 SETS
SERIES 2 STATED PRINT RUN 4 SETS
NO PRICING DUE TO SCARCITY

2003 Topps 205 Brooklyn

*BROOKLYN C 1-130: .75X TO 2X BASIC
*BROOKLYN U 1-130: 1.25X TO 3X BASIC
*BROOKLYN U 131-144: 1.25X TO 3X BASIC
*BROOKLYN R 1-130: 2X TO 5X BASIC
*BROOKLYN R 131-144: 2X TO 5X BASIC
BROOKLYN 5 PRINT RUN 5 SETS
NO BROOKLYN 5 PRICING DUE TO SCARCITY
1-150 RANDOM INSERTS IN SER.1 PACKS
SEE BECKETT.COM FOR C/U/R/5 SCHEMATIC
SCHEMATIC IS IN OPG SUBSCRIPTION AREA
*BRKLYN 151-315: 2X TO 5X BASIC
*BRKLYN 151-315: .6X TO 1.5X BASIC SP
151-315 SERIES 2 STATED ODDS 1:12
151-315 STATED PRINT RUN 205 SETS
151-315 ARE NOT SERIAL-NUMBERED
151-315 PRINT RUN PROVIDED BY TOPPS

2003 Topps 205 Brooklyn Exclusive Pose

*BROOKLYN EP: 1X TO 2.5X POLAR EP
OVERALL BROOKLYN SERIES 2 ODDS 1:12
STATED PRINT RUN 205 SETS
CARDS ARE NOT SERIAL-NUMBERED
PRINT RUN PROVIDED BY TOPPS

2003 Topps 205 Cycle

*CYCLE 121-145: 1.25X TO 3X BASIC
RANDOM INSERTS IN PACKS
*CYCLE PURPLE 121-130: 4X TO 10X BASIC
*CYCLE PURPLE 131-145: 3X TO 8X BASIC
PURPLE CARDS ARE 10% OF PRINT RUN

2003 Topps 205 Drum

*DRUM: 2X TO 5X BASIC
*DRUM: .6X TO 1.5X BASIC SP
RANDOM INSERTS IN PACKS

2003 Topps 205 Drum Exclusive Pose

*DRUM EP: 1X TO 2.5X POLAR EP
RANDOM INSERTS IN SERIES 2 PACKS

2003 Topps 205 Honest

*HONEST: 1.25X TO 3X BASIC
RANDOM INSERTS IN PACKS
*HONEST PURPLE: 4X TO 10X BASIC
PURPLE CARDS ARE 10% OF PRINT RUN
CL: 1/3/8/12/15/18/20/40/50/51/75/77/88
CL: 100/110

2003 Topps 205 Piedmont

*PIEDMONT: 1.25X TO 3X BASIC
RANDOM INSERTS IN PACKS
*PIEDMONT PURPLE: 4X TO 10X BASIC
PURPLE CARDS ARE 10% OF PRINT RUN
CL: 2-19/21-49/

2003 Topps 205 Polar Bear

*POLAR BEAR: .75X TO 2X BASIC
*POLAR BEAR: .25X TO .6X BASIC SP
RANDOM INSERTS IN PACKS

2003 Topps 205 Polar Bear Exclusive Pose

RANDOM INSERTS IN SERIES 2 PACKS
316 Willie Mays EP 2.50 6.00
317 Delmon Young EP 3.00 8.00
318 Rickie Weeks EP 2.50 6.00
319 Ryan Wagner EP .75 2.00

320 Brandon Webb EP 1.00 2.50
321 Chris Lubanski EP 1.00 2.50
322 Ryan Harvey EP 2.00 5.00
323 Nick Markakis EP 2.50 6.00
324 Chad Billingsley EP 2.50 6.00
325 Aaron Hill EP .75 2.00
326 Brian Snyder EP .75 2.00
327 Eric Duncan EP 2.50 6.00
328 Sammy Sosa EP 1.00 2.50
329 Alfonso Soriano EP .75 2.00
330 Ichiro Suzuki EP 2.00 5.00
331 Alex Rodriguez EP 1.50 4.00
332 Nomar Garciaparra EP 1.50 4.00
333 Albert Pujols EP 2.00 5.00
334 Jim Thome EP .75 2.00
335 Dontrelle Willis EP 1.00 2.50

2003 Topps 205 Sovereign

*SOVEREIGN: 1.25X TO 3X BASIC
*SOVEREIGN: .4X TO 1X BASIC SP
RANDOM INSERTS IN PACKS
*SOV.GREEN: 2.5X TO 6X BASIC
*SOV.GREEN: 1.25X TO 3X BASIC SP
SOV.GREEN CARDS ARE 25% OF PRINT RUN

2003 Topps 205 Sovereign Exclusive Pose

*SOVEREIGN EP: .6X TO 1.5X POLAR EP
RANDOM INSERTS IN SERIES 2 PACKS
*SOV.GREEN EP: 1.25X TO 3X POLAR EP
SOV.GREEN CARDS ARE 25% OF PRINT RUN

2003 Topps 205 Sweet Caporal

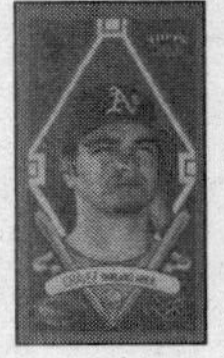

*SWEET CAP: 1.25X TO 3X BASIC
RANDOM INSERTS IN PACKS
*SWEET CAP PURPLE: 4X TO 10X BASIC
PURPLE CARDS ARE 10% OF PRINT RUN
CL: 70-99/101-120

2003 Topps 205 Autographs

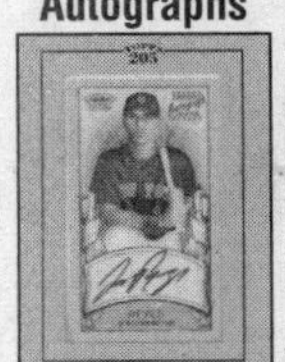

These cards feature autographs of leading players. These cards were inserted at varying odds and we have noted what group the player belongs to in our checklist. Though lacking serial numbering, representatives at Topps publicly announced only 50 copies of Hank Aaron's card were produced - making it, by far, the scarcest card in this set.

SER.1 GROUP A1 ODDS 1:2434
SER.1 GROUP B1 ODDS 1:608
SER.1 GROUP C1 ODDS 1:1460
SER.1 GROUP D1 ODDS 1:122
SER.2 GROUP A2 ODDS 1:5816
SER.2 GROUP B2 ODDS 1:646
SER.2 GROUP C2 ODDS 1:49
A2 STATED PRINT RUN 50 CARDS
A2 IS NOT SERIAL-NUMBERED
A2 PRINT RUN PROVIDED BY TOPPS
CF Cliff Floyd B1 8.00 20.00

DW Dontrelle Willis C2 10.00 25.00
ED Eric Duncan C2 8.00 20.00
FP Felix Pie C2 15.00 40.00
HA Hank Aaron A2 SP/50 150.00 250.00
JR Jose Reyes D1 6.00 15.00
JW Jerome Williams B2 6.00 15.00
LB Lance Berkman B1 12.50 30.00
LC Luis Castillo C2 4.00 10.00
MB Marlon Byrd D1 4.00 10.00
MO Magglio Ordonez C1 8.00 20.00
MS Mike Sweeney B1 8.00 20.00
PL Paul Lo Duca D1 6.00 15.00
RH Rich Harden C2 12.50 30.00
RWA Ryan Wagner C2 6.00 15.00
SR Scott Rolen A1 15.00 40.00
TH Torii Hunter D1 6.00 15.00

2003 Topps 205 Relics

Randomly inserted into packs, these 43 cards feature game-used memorabilia pieces of the featured players. Please note that many of these cards were inserted in different rates and we have noted both the insert ratio as well as the group the player belongs to in our checklisting information.

COM.UNI A1/RELIC A2 6.00 15.00
COM.BAT B-D1/UNI E1/RELIC B2 4.00 10.00
COMMON BAT E-H1/UNI F-M1 3.00 8.00
SER.1 BAT GROUP A1 ODDS 1:1216
SER.1 BAT GROUP B1 ODDS 1:972
SER.1 BAT GROUP C1 ODDS 1:270
SER.1 BAT GROUP D1 ODDS 1:365
SER.1 BAT GROUP E1 ODDS 1:561
SER.1 BAT GROUP F1 ODDS 1:486
SER.1 BAT GROUP G1 ODDS 1:91
SER.1 BAT GROUP H1 ODDS 1:203
SER.1 UNI GROUP A1 ODDS 1:4884
SER.1 UNI GROUP B1 ODDS 1:456
SER.1 UNI GROUP C1 ODDS 1:1460
SER.1 UNI GROUP D1 ODDS 1:1216
SER.1 UNI GROUP E1 ODDS 1:973
SER.1 UNI GROUP F1 ODDS 1:608
SER.1 UNI GROUP G1 ODDS 1:61
SER.1 UNI GROUP H1 ODDS 1:183
SER.1 UNI GROUP I1 ODDS 1:83
SER.1 UNI GROUP J1 ODDS 1:324
SER.1 UNI GROUP K1 ODDS 1:317
SER.1 UNI GROUP L1 ODDS 1:243
SER.1 UNI GROUP M1 ODDS 1:221
SER.2 RELIC GROUP A ODDS 1:79
SER.2 RELIC GROUP B ODDS 1:16
AB A.J. Burnett Jsy G1 3.00 8.00
AD Adam Dunn Bat G1 3.00 8.00
AJ Andruw Jones Jsy B2 UER 6.00 15.00
Chipper Jones is pictured
AL Al Leiter Jsy I1 3.00 8.00
APB Albert Pujols Bat A2 10.00 25.00
AP1 Albert Pujols Uni E1 8.00 20.00
AP2 Albert Pujols Hat A2 10.00 25.00
ARA Aramis Ramirez Bat B2 4.00 10.00
AR1 Alex Rodriguez Jsy H1 6.00 15.00
AR2 Alex Rodriguez Bat B2 6.00 15.00
AS1 Alfonso Soriano Uni G1 3.00 8.00
AS2 Alfonso Soriano Bat A2 6.00 15.00
BB1 Barry Bonds Uni B1 10.00 25.00
BB2 Bret Boone Bat A2 6.00 15.00
BD Brandon Duckworth Jsy B2 4.00 10.00
BG1 Brian Giles Bat G1 3.00 8.00
BG2 Brian Giles Bat A2 6.00 15.00
BP Brad Penny Jsy B2 4.00 10.00
BW1 Bernie Williams Bat D1 6.00 15.00
BW2 Bernie Williams Jsy A2 8.00 20.00
BZ Barry Zito Jsy K1 3.00 8.00
CB Craig Biggio Uni B2 6.00 15.00
CD Carlos Delgado Jsy B2 4.00 10.00
CG Cristian Guzman Jsy B2 4.00 10.00
CJB Chipper Jones Bat A2 8.00 20.00
CP Corey Patterson Bat A2 6.00 15.00
CS1 Curt Schilling Jsy B1 4.00 10.00
CS2 Curt Schilling Bat B2 4.00 10.00
DE Darin Erstad Uni A2 6.00 15.00
DL Derek Lowe Hat A1 6.00 15.00
DW Dontrelle Willis Uni B2 6.00 15.00
EC Eric Chavez Bat G1 3.00 8.00
EG Eric Gagne Jsy G1 3.00 8.00
EMA Edgar Martinez Jsy B2 6.00 15.00
EMU Eddie Murray Bat A2 10.00 25.00
FM Fred McGriff Bat B2 6.00 15.00
FR Frank Robinson Bat A2 8.00 20.00
FT Frank Thomas Jsy B2 6.00 15.00
GA Garret Anderson Uni L1 3.00 8.00
GB George Brett Jsy A2 12.50 30.00
GC Gary Carter Bat A2 6.00 15.00
GM1 Greg Maddux Jsy B1 6.00 15.00
GM2 Greg Maddux Bat A2 8.00 20.00
GS Gary Sheffield Bat B2 4.00 10.00
HB Hank Blalock Bat B2 4.00 10.00
IR Ivan Rodriguez Bat A2 8.00 20.00
JB1 Jeff Bagwell Uni G1 4.00 10.00
JB2 Jeff Bagwell Bat A2 8.00 20.00
JC Jose Canseco Bat B2 6.00 15.00
JD Johnny Damon Bat B1 6.00 15.00
JE Jim Edmonds Jsy A2 6.00 15.00
JG Jason Giambi Bat A2 6.00 15.00
JGI Jeremy Giambi Jsy B2 4.00 10.00
JGO Juan Gonzalez Bat B2 4.00 10.00
JJ Jason Jennings Jsy G1 3.00 8.00
JK Jeff Kent Bat C1 4.00 10.00
JO John Olerud Jsy B2 4.00 10.00
JP Jorge Posada Bat A2 8.00 20.00
JS John Smoltz Jsy B1 6.00 15.00
JT Jim Thome Bat F1 4.00 10.00
KB Kevin Brown Jsy B2 4.00 10.00
KI Kazuhisa Ishii Jsy I1 3.00 8.00
KL1 Kenny Lofton Bat G1 3.00 8.00
KL2 Kenny Lofton Uni B2 4.00 10.00
LB Lance Berkman Bat C1 4.00 10.00
LC Luis Castillo Jsy G1 3.00 8.00
LG1 Luis Gonzalez Jsy J1 3.00 8.00
LG2 Luis Gonzalez Bat A2 6.00 15.00
LW Larry Walker Jsy B2 4.00 10.00
MC Mike Cameron Jsy B2 4.00 10.00
MG Mark Grace Bat A2 8.00 20.00
MGR Marquis Grissom Bat B2 4.00 10.00
MM Mark Mulder Uni A2 6.00 15.00
MO Magglio Ordonez Jsy M1 3.00 8.00
MP1 Mike Piazza Bat C1 6.00 15.00
MP2 Mike Piazza Bat A2 8.00 20.00
MR Manny Ramirez Bat H1 4.00 10.00
MSC Mike Schmidt Bat A2 12.50 30.00
MSW Mike Sweeney Bat H1 3.00 8.00
MTE Miguel Tejada Bat B2 4.00 10.00
MTI Mark Teixeira Bat B2 6.00 15.00
MV Mo Vaughn Jsy I1 3.00 8.00
NG1 Nomar Garciaparra Jsy G1 6.00 15.00
NG2 Nomar Garciaparra Bat A2 8.00 20.00
NJ Nick Johnson Bat D1 4.00 10.00
NR Nolan Ryan Uni A2 30.00 60.00
PM1 Pedro Martinez Jsy F1 4.00 10.00
PM2 Pedro Martinez Jsy A2 8.00 20.00
PO Paul O'Neill Uni B2 6.00 15.00
RA1 Roberto Alomar Bat G1 4.00 10.00
RA2 Roberto Alomar Uni B2 6.00 15.00
RBB Rocco Baldelli Bat B2 4.00 10.00
RBJ Rocco Baldelli Jsy B2 4.00 10.00
RC Roger Clemens Uni A2 8.00 20.00
RF1 Rafael Furcal Bat E1 3.00 8.00
RF2 Rafael Furcal Bat A2 6.00 15.00
RH Rickey Henderson Bat B2 6.00 15.00
RJ1 Randy Johnson Jsy C1 6.00 15.00
RJ2 Randy Johnson Jsy A2 8.00 20.00
RO Roy Oswalt Jsy I1 3.00 8.00
RP1 Rafael Palmeiro Jsy H1 4.00 10.00
RP2 Rafael Palmeiro Bat A2 8.00 20.00
RV Robin Ventura Bat B2 4.00 10.00
SB Sean Burroughs Bat B2 4.00 10.00
SR1 Scott Rolen Bat A1 6.00 15.00
SR2 Scott Rolen Uni A2 8.00 20.00
SS Sammy Sosa Jsy A2 8.00 20.00
SST Shannon Stewart Bat B2 4.00 10.00
TG Troy Glaus Uni A2 6.00 15.00
TH Todd Helton Jsy D1 6.00 15.00
TM Tino Martinez Bat B2 6.00 15.00
TP Troy Percival Uni G1 3.00 8.00
TS Tsuyoshi Shinjo Bat B2 4.00 10.00
VG Vladimir Guerrero Bat A2 8.00 20.00
VW Vernon Wells Jsy A2 6.00 15.00
WB Wade Boggs Bat A2 8.00 20.00

2003 Topps 205 Triple Folder Polar Bear

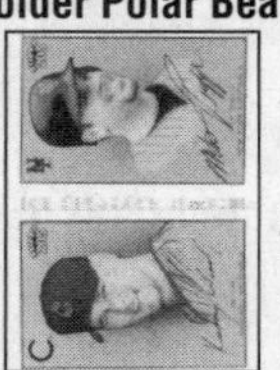

COMPLETE SET (100) 20.00 50.00
COMPLETE SERIES 1 (50) 10.00 25.00
COMPLETE SERIES 2 (50) 10.00 25.00
ONE PER PACK
*BROOKLYN: 3X TO 8X BASIC
SERIES 1 BROOKLYN ODDS 1:72
SERIES 2 BROOKLYN ODDS 1:29
TF1 Barry Bonds 1.00 2.50
Jason LaRue
TF2 Alfonso Soriano 1.00 2.50
Derek Jeter
TF3 Alex Rodriguez .60 1.50
Miguel Tejada
TF4 Nomar Garciaparra 1.00 2.50
Derek Jeter
TF5 Omar Vizquel .60 1.50
Alex Rodriguez
TF6 Paul Konerko .40 1.00
Omar Vizquel
TF7 Paul Konerko .40 1.00
Magglio Ordonez
TF8 Doug Mientkiewicz .40 1.00
Darin Erstad
TF9 Jason Kendall .40 1.00
Jimmy Rollins
TF10 Shawn Green .40 1.00
Roberto Alomar
TF11 Derek Jeter 1.00 2.50
Roberto Alomar
TF12 Bobby Abreu .40 1.00
Luis Castillo
TF13 Randy Johnson .40 1.00
Curt Schilling
TF14 Mike Piazza .60 1.50
Kerry Wood
TF15 Roger Clemens .75 2.00
Jorge Posada
TF16 Ichiro Suzuki .75 2.00
Ryan Klesko
TF17 Alfonso Soriano .40 1.00
Chipper Jones
TF18 Barry Bonds 1.00 2.50
Nick Johnson
TF19 Chipper Jones .40 1.00
Andruw Jones
TF20 Bobby Abreu .40 1.00
Paul Konerko
TF21 Rafael Palmeiro .60 1.50
Alex Rodriguez
TF22 Eric Hinske .40 1.00
Carlos Delgado
TF23 Nomar Garciaparra .40 1.00
Jay Gibbons
TF24 Mike Piazza .60 1.50
Luis Gonzalez
TF25 J.T. Snow .40 1.00
Vladimir Guerrero
TF26 Jason Giambi .40 1.00
Bernie Williams
TF27 Miguel Tejada .40 1.00
Richie Sexson
TF28 Doug Mientkiewicz .40 1.00
Jimmy Rollins
TF29 Eric Chavez 1.00 2.50
Derek Jeter
TF30 Alfonso Soriano .40 1.00
Bret Boone
TF31 Chipper Jones .60 1.50
Mike Piazza
TF32 Ichiro Suzuki .75 2.00
Bret Boone
TF33 Bobby Abreu .60 1.50
Mike Piazza
TF34 Jimmy Rollins .40 1.00
Pat Burell
TF35 Ichiro Suzuki .75 2.00
Miguel Tejada
TF36 Jason LaRue 1.00 2.50
Barry Bonds
TF37 Derek Jeter 1.00 2.50
Alfonso Soriano
TF38 Miguel Tejada .60 1.50
Alex Rodriguez
TF39 Derek Jeter 1.00 2.50
Nomar Garciaparra
TF40 Alex Rodriguez .60 1.50
Omar Vizquel
TF41 Curt Schilling .40 1.00
Randy Johnson
TF42 Jorge Posada .75 2.00
Roger Clemens
TF43 Ryan Klesko .75 2.00
Ichiro Suzuki
TF44 Nick Johnson 1.00 2.50
Barry Bonds
TF45 Alex Rodriguez .60 1.50
Rafael Palmeiro
TF46 Vladimir Guerrero .40 1.00
J.T. Snow
TF47 Derek Jeter 1.00 2.50
Eric Chavez
TF48 Bret Boone .75 2.00
Ichiro Suzuki
TF49 Mike Piazza .60 1.50
Bobby Abreu
TF50 Miguel Tejada .75 2.00
Ichiro Suzuki
TF51 Juan Pierre .40 1.00
Jim Thome
TF52 Kevin Millwood .40 1.00
Jim Thome
TF53 Hank Blalock .40 1.00
Jorge Posada
TF54 Deivi Cruz .40 1.00
Hank Blalock
TF55 Rafael Furcal .40 1.00
Ty Wigginton
TF56 Jim Thome .40 1.00
Nomar Garciaparra
TF57 Craig Biggio .40 1.00
Jason Giambi
TF58 Aaron Boone .40 1.00
Jason Giambi
TF59 Jason Giambi .40 1.00
Bernie Williams
TF60 Cristian Guzman .40 1.00
Jody Gerut
TF61 Todd Helton .40 1.00
Jose Reyes
TF62 Derek Jeter 1.00 2.50
Hank Blalock
TF63 Mike Piazza .40 1.00
Jimmy Rollins
TF64 Bernie Williams 1.00 2.50
Derek Jeter
TF65 Andruw Jones .40 1.00
Rafael Furcal
TF66 Mike Piazza .60 1.50
Andruw Jones
TF67 Mike Piazza .60 1.50
Cliff Floyd
TF68 Jason Kendall .75 2.00
Albert Pujols
TF69 Nomar Garciaparra .60 1.50
Manny Ramirez
TF70 Jorge Posada .60 1.50
Alex Rodriguez
TF71 Derek Jeter 1.00 2.50
Alex Rodriguez
TF72 Mike Sweeney .60 1.50
Alex Rodriguez
TF73 Marquis Grissom .40 1.00
Ivan Rodriguez
TF74 Jason Phillips .40 1.00
Gary Sheffield
TF75 Chipper Jones .40 1.00
Gary Sheffield
TF76 Junior Spivey .40 1.00
Gary Sheffield
TF77 Al Leiter .75 2.00
Ichiro Suzuki
TF78 Jose Vidro .40 1.00
Jim Thome
TF79 Jimmy Rollins .40 1.00
Paul Lo Duca
TF80 Alex Rodriguez .60 1.50
Rafael Palmeiro
TF81 Albert Pujols .75 2.00
Jim Edmonds
TF82 Eric Chavez .40 1.00
Mike Sweeney
TF83 Cristian Guzman .40 1.00
Jimmy Rollins
TF84 Alfonso Soriano .40 1.00
Bernie Williams
TF85 Ichiro Suzuki .75 2.00
Derek Jeter
TF86 Jimmy Rollins .40 1.00
Derrek Lee
TF87 Shawn Green .40 1.00
Paul Lo Duca
TF88 Carlos Delgado .40 1.00
Jorge Posada
TF89 Dmitri Young .40 1.00
C.C. Sabathia
TF90 Dontrelle Willis .40 1.00
Shawn Chacon
TF91 Edgar Martinez .60 1.50
Alex Rodriguez
TF92 Edgar Martinez .40 1.00
Carlos Delgado
TF93 Edgar Martinez .40 1.00
Esteban Loaiza
TF94 Roy Halladay .40 1.00
C.C. Sabathia
TF95 Ichiro Suzuki .75 2.00
Albert Pujols
TF96 Ichiro Suzuki .75 2.00
Shigetoshi Hasegawa
TF97 Geoff Jenkins .40 1.00
Aaron Boone
TF98 Nomar Garciaparra .60 1.50
Alfonso Soriano
TF99 Jorge Posada .40 1.00
Alfonso Soriano
TF100 Vernon Wells .40 1.00
Garret Anderson

2003 Topps 205 Triple Folder Autographs

SERIES 2 STATED ODDS 1:355 HOBBY
STATED PRINT RUN 205 SETS
CARDS ARE NOT SERIAL-NUMBERED
PRINT RUN PROVIDED BY TOPPS
DW Dontrelle Willis 20.00 50.00
JW Jerome Williams 15.00 40.00
RH Rich Harden 30.00 60.00
RW Ryan Wagner 15.00 40.00

2003 Topps 205 World Series Line-Ups

SERIES 2 ODDS 1:27,440 PACKS
SERIES 2 ODDS 1:1960 MINI BOXES
STATED PRINT RUN 1 SET
NO PRICING DUE TO SCARCITY
AL1 David Wells
AL2 Jorge Posada
AL3 Nick Johnson
AL4 Alfonso Soriano
AL5 Aaron Boone
AL6 Derek Jeter
AL7 Juan Rivera
AL8 Bernie Williams
AL9 Karim Garcia
AL10 Jason Giambi
NL1 Brad Penny
NL2 Ivan Rodriguez
NL3 Derrek Lee
NL4 Luis Castillo
NL5 Mike Lowell
NL6 Alex Gonzalez
NL7 Miguel Cabrera
NL8 Juan Pierre
NL9 Juan Encarnacion
NL10 Jeff Conine

2002 Topps 206 Olbermann Promos

This five card set, issued exclusively through Beckett Sports Collectibles Vintage magazine, featured famed television sports announcer and noted card collector Keith Olbermann. These five cards feature Olbermann in a variety of poses similar to poses of the old tobacco cards.

COMPLETE SET 2.00 5.00
COMMON CARD .40 1.00

2002 Topps 206

Issued in three separate series this 526-card set featured a mix of veterans, rookies and retired greats in the general style of the classic T-206 set issued more than 90 years prior. Series one consists of cards 1-180 and went live in February, 2002, series two consists of cards 181-307 - including 96 variations - and went live in early August, 2002 and series three consists of cards 308-456 - including 15 variations and a total of 55 short prints seeded at a rate of one per pack - and went live in January, 2003. Each pack contained eight cards with an SRP of $4. Packs were issued 20 per box and each case had 10 boxes. The following subsets were issued as part of the set: Prospects (131-140/261-270/399-418); First Year Players (141-155/271-285/419-432); Retired Stars (156-170/286-298/433-448) and Reprints (171-180/299-307/449-456). The First Year Player subset cards 141-155 and 277-285 were inserted at stated odds of one in two packs making them short-prints in comparison to other cards in the set. According to press release notes, Topps purchased more than 4,000 original Tobacco cards and also randomly inserted those in packs. They created a "holder" for these smaller cards inside the standard-size cards of the Topps 206 set. Stated pack odds for these "repurchased" Tobacco cards was 1:110 for series one, 1:179 for series two and 1:101 for series three.

COMPLETE SET (525) 110.00 220.00
COMPLETE SERIES 1 (180) 25.00 60.00
COMPLETE SERIES 2 (180) 25.00 60.00
COMPLETE SERIES 3 (165) 50.00 100.00
COM(1-140/181-270/308-418) .20 .50
COMMON (141-155/271-285) .20 .50
COMMON RC (308-418) .20 .50
COMMON SP (308-398) .75 2.00
COMMON FYP SP (.40 1.00
COMMON RET SP (433-447) .75 2.00
1 Vladimir Guerrero .50 1.25
2 Sammy Sosa .50 1.25
3 Garret Anderson .20 .50
4 Rafael Palmeiro .30 .75
5 Juan Gonzalez .20 .50
6 John Smoltz .30 .75
7 Mark Mulder .20 .50
8 Jon Lieber .20 .50
9 Greg Maddux .75 2.00
10 Moises Alou .20 .50
11 Joe Randa .20 .50
12 Bobby Abreu .20 .50
13 Juan Pierre .20 .50
14 Kerry Wood .20 .50
15 Craig Biggio .30 .75
16 Curt Schilling .20 .50
17 Brian Jordan .20 .50
18 Edgardo Alfonzo .20 .50
19 Darren Dreifort .20 .50
20 Todd Helton .30 .75
21 Ramon Ortiz .20 .50
22 Ichiro Suzuki 1.00 2.50
23 Jimmy Rollins .20 .50
24 Darin Erstad .20 .50
25 Shawn Green .20 .50
26 Tino Martinez .30 .75
27 Bret Boone .20 .50
28 Alfonso Soriano .20 .50
29 Chan Ho Park .20 .50
30 Roger Clemens 1.00 2.50
31 Cliff Floyd .20 .50
32 Johnny Damon .30 .75
33 Frank Thomas .50 1.25
34 Barry Bonds 1.25 3.00
35 Luis Gonzalez .20 .50
36 Carlos Lee .20 .50
37 Roberto Alomar .30 .75
38 Carlos Delgado .20 .50
39 Nomar Garciaparra .75 2.00
40 Jason Kendall .20 .50
41 Scott Rolen .30 .75
42 Tom Glavine .30 .75
43 Ryan Klesko .20 .50
44 Brian Giles .20 .50
45 Bud Smith .20 .50
46 Charles Nagy .20 .50
47 Tony Gwynn .60 1.50
48 C.C. Sabathia UER .20 .50
Credited with incorrect victory total in 2001
49 Frank Catalanotto .20 .50
50 Jerry Hairston .20 .50
51 Jeromy Burnitz .20 .50
52 David Justice .20 .50
53 Bartolo Colon .20 .50
54 Andres Galarraga .20 .50
55 Jeff Weaver .20 .50
56 Terrence Long .20 .50
57 Tsuyoshi Shinjo .20 .50
58 Barry Zito .20 .50
59 Mariano Rivera .50 1.25
60 John Olerud .20 .50
61 Randy Johnson .50 1.25
62 Kenny Lofton .20 .50
63 Jermaine Dye .20 .50
64 Troy Glaus .20 .50
65 Larry Walker .20 .50
66 Hideo Nomo .50 1.25
67 Mike Mussina .30 .75
68 Paul LoDuca .20 .50
69 Magglio Ordonez .20 .50
70 Paul O'Neill .30 .75
71 Sean Casey .20 .50
72 Lance Berkman .20 .50
73 Adam Dunn .20 .50
74 Aramis Ramirez .20 .50
75 Rafael Furcal .20 .50
76 Gary Sheffield .20 .50
77 Todd Hollandsworth .20 .50
78 Chipper Jones .50 1.25
79 Bernie Williams .30 .75
80 Richard Hidalgo .20 .50
81 Eric Chavez .20 .50
82 Mike Piazza .75 2.00
83 J.D. Drew .20 .50
84 Ken Griffey Jr. .75 2.00
85 Joe Kennedy .20 .50
86 Joel Pineiro .20 .50
87 Josh Towers .20 .50
88 Andruw Jones .30 .75
89 Carlos Beltran .20 .50
90 Mike Cameron .20 .50
91 Albert Pujols 1.00 2.50
92 Alex Rodriguez .75 2.00
93 Omar Vizquel .30 .75
94 Juan Encarnacion .20 .50
95 Jeff Bagwell .30 .75
96 Jose Canseco .30 .75
97 Ben Sheets .30 .75
98 Mark Grace .30 .75
99 Mike Sweeney .20 .50
100 Mark McGwire 1.25 3.00
101 Ivan Rodriguez .30 .75
102 Rich Aurilia .20 .50
103 Cristian Guzman .20 .50
104 Roy Oswalt .20 .50
105 Tim Hudson .20 .50
106 Brent Abernathy .20 .50
107 Mike Hampton .20 .50
108 Miguel Tejada .20 .50
109 Bobby Higginson .20 .50
110 Edgar Martinez .30 .75
111 Jorge Posada .30 .75
112 Jason Giambi Yankees .20 .50
113 Pedro Astacio .20 .50
114 Kazuhiro Sasaki .20 .50
115 Preston Wilson .20 .50
116 Jason Bere .20 .50
117 Mark Quinn .20 .50
118 Pokey Reese .20 .50
119 Derek Jeter 1.25 3.00
120 Shannon Stewart .20 .50
121 Jeff Kent .20 .50
122 Jeremy Giambi .20 .50
123 Pat Burrell .20 .50
124 Jim Edmonds .20 .50
125 Mark Buehrle .20 .50
126 Kevin Brown .20 .50
127 Raul Mondesi .20 .50
128 Pedro Martinez .30 .75
129 Jim Thome .30 .75
130 Russ Ortiz .20 .50
131 Br.Duckworth PROS .20 .50
132 Ryan Jamison PROS .20 .50
133 Brandon Inge PROS .20 .50
134 Felipe Lopez PROS .20 .50
135 Jason Lane PROS .20 .50
136 F.Johnson PROS RC .20 .50
137 Greg Nash PROS .20 .50
138 Covelli Crisp PROS .75 2.00
139 Nick Neugebauer PROS .20 .50
140 Dustan Mohr PROS .20 .50
141 Freddy Sanchez FYP RC .75 2.00
142 Justin Backsmeyer FYP RC .20 .50
143 Jorge Julio FYP .20 .50
144 Ryan Mottl FYP RC .20 .50
145 Chris Tritle FYP RC .20 .50
146 Noochie Varner FYP RC .20 .50
147 Brian Rogers FYP .20 .50
148 Michael Hill FYP RC .20 .50
149 Luis Pineda FYP .20 .50
150 Rich Thompson FYP RC .20 .50
151 Bill Hall FYP .20 .50
152 Juan Dominguez FYP RC .20 .50
153 Justin Woodrow FYP .20 .50
154 Nic Jackson FYP RC .20 .50
155 Laynce Nix FYP RC .60 1.50
156 Hank Aaron RET 2.00 5.00
157 Ernie Banks RET 1.00 2.50
158 Johnny Bench RET 1.00 2.50
159 George Brett RET 2.00 5.00
160 Carlton Fisk RET .60 1.50
161 Bob Gibson RET .60 1.50
162 Reggie Jackson RET .60 1.50
163 Don Mattingly RET 2.00 5.00
164 Kirby Puckett RET 1.00 2.50
165 Frank Robinson RET .60 1.50
166 Nolan Ryan RET 2.50 6.00
167 Tom Seaver RET .60 1.50
168 Mike Schmidt RET 2.00 5.00
169 Dave Winfield RET .40 1.00
170 Carl Yastrzemski RET 1.25 3.00
171 Frank Chance REP .40 1.00
172 Ty Cobb REP 2.00 5.00
173 Sam Crawford REP .40 1.00
174 Johnny Evers REP .40 1.00
175 John McGraw REP .60 1.50
176 Eddie Plank REP 1.00 2.50
177 Tris Speaker REP 1.00 2.50
178 Joe Tinker REP .40 1.00
179 H.Wagner Orange REP 3.00 8.00
180 Cy Young REP 1.00 2.50
181 Javier Vazquez .20 .50
182A Mark Mulder Green Jsy .20 .50
182B Mark Mulder White Jsy .20 .50
183A R.Clemens Blue Jsy 1.00 2.50
183B R.Clemens Pinstripes 1.00 2.50
184 Kazuhisa Ishii RC .30 .75
185 Roberto Alomar .30 .75
186 Lance Berkman .20 .50
187A A.Dunn Arms Folded .20 .50
187B Adam Dunn w/Bat .20 .50
188A Aramis Ramirez w/Bat .20 .50
188B Aramis Ramirez w/o Bat .20 .50
189 Chuck Knoblauch .20 .50
190 Nomar Garciaparra .75 2.00
191 Brad Penny .20 .50
192A Gary Sheffield w/Bat .20 .50
192B Gary Sheffield w/o Bat .20 .50
193 Alfonso Soriano .20 .50
194 Andruw Jones .30 .75
195A R.Johnson Black Jsy .50 1.25
195B R.Johnson Purple Jsy .50 1.25
196A C.Patterson Blue Jsy .20 .50
196B C.Patterson Pinstripes .20 .50
197 Milton Bradley .20 .50
198A J.Damon Blue Jsy/Cap .30 .75
198B J.Damon Blue Jsy/Hlmt .30 .75
198C J.Damon White Jsy .30 .75
199A Paul Lo Duca Blue Jsy .20 .50
199B Paul Lo Duca White Jsy .20 .50
200A Albert Pujols Red Jsy 1.00 2.50
200B Albert Pujols Running 1.00 2.50
200C Albert Pujols w/Bat 1.00 2.50
201 Scott Rolen .30 .75
202A J.D. Drew Running .20 .50
202B J.D. Drew w/Bat .20 .50
202C J.D. Drew White Jsy .20 .50
203 Vladimir Guerrero .50 1.25
204A Jason Giambi Blue Jsy .20 .50
204B Jason Giambi Grey Jsy .20 .50
204C Jason Giambi Pinstripes .20 .50
205A Moises Alou Grey Jsy .20 .50
205B Moises Alou Pinstripes .20 .50
206A Mag. Ordonez Signing .20 .50
206B Magglio Ordonez w/Bat .20 .50
207 Carlos Febles .20 .50
208 So Taguchi RC .30 .75
209A Raf. Palmeiro One Hand .30 .75
209B Raf. Palmeiro Two Hands .30 .75
210 David Wells .20 .50
211 Orlando Cabrera .20 .50
212 Sammy Sosa .50 1.25
213 Armando Benitez .20 .50
214 Wes Helms .20 .50
215A Mar. Rivera Arms Folded .50 1.25
215B Mar. Rivera Holding Ball .50 1.25
216 Jimmy Rollins .20 .50
217 Matt Lawton .20 .50
218A Shawn Green w/Bat .20 .50
218B Shawn Green w/o Bat .20 .50
219A Bernie Williams w/Bat .30 .75
219B Bernie Williams w/o Bat .30 .75
220A Bret Boone Blue Jsy .20 .50
220B Bret Boone White Jsy .20 .50
221A Alex Rodriguez Blue Jsy .75 2.00
221B Alex Rodriguez One Hand .75 2.00
221C Alex Rodriguez Two Hands .75 2.00
222 Roger Cedeno .20 .50

223 Marty Cordova	.20	.50
224 Fred McGriff	.30	.75
225A Chipper Jones Batting	.50	1.25
225B Chipper Jones Running	.50	1.25
226 Kerry Wood	.20	.50
227A Larry Walker Grey Jsy	.20	.50
227B Larry Walker Purple Jsy	.20	.50
228 Robin Ventura	.20	.50
229 Robert Fick	.20	.50
230A Tino Martinez Black Glove	.30	.75
230B Tino Martinez Throwing	.30	.75
230C Tino Martinez w/Bat	.30	.75
231 Ben Petrick	.20	.50
232 Neifi Perez	.20	.50
233 Pedro Martinez	.30	.75
234A Brian Jordan.Grey Jsy	.20	.50
234B Brian Jordan White Jsy	.20	.50
235 Freddy Garcia	.20	.50
236A Derek Jeter Batting	1.25	3.00
236B Derek Jeter Blue Jsy	1.25	3.00
236C Derek Jeter Kneeling	1.25	3.00
237 Ben Grieve	.20	.50
238A Barry Bonds Black Jsy	1.25	3.00
238B B.Bonds w/Wrist Band	1.25	3.00
238C B.Bonds w/o Wrist Band	1.25	3.00
239 Luis Gonzalez	.20	.50
240 Shane Halter	.20	.50
241A Brian Giles Black Jsy	.20	.50
241B Brian Giles Grey Jsy	.20	.50
242 Bud Smith	.20	.50
243 Richie Sexson	.20	.50
244A Barry Zito Green Jsy	.20	.50
244B Barry Zito White Jsy	.20	.50
245 Eric Milton	.20	.50
246A Ivan Rodriguez Blue Jsy	.30	.75
246B I.Rodriguez Grey Jsy	.30	.75
246C I.Rodriguez White Jsy	.30	.75
247 Toby Hall	.20	.50
248A Mike Piazza Black Jsy	.75	2.00
248B Mike Piazza Grey Jsy	.75	2.00
249 Ruben Sierra	.20	.50
250A Tsuyoshi Shinjo Cap	.20	.50
250B Tsuyoshi Shinjo Helmet	.20	.50
251A Jer. Dye Green Jsy	.20	.50
251B Jermaine Dye White Jsy	.20	.50
252 Roy Oswalt	.20	.50
253 Todd Helton	.30	.75
254 Adrian Beltre	.20	.50
255 Doug Mientkiewicz	.20	.50
256A Ichiro Suzuki Blue Jsy	1.00	2.50
256B Ichiro Suzuki w/Bat	1.00	2.50
256C Ichiro Suzuki White Jsy	1.00	2.50
257A C.C. Sabathia Blue Jsy	.20	.50
257B C.C. Sabathia White Jsy	.20	.50
258 Paul Konerko	.20	.50
259 Ken Griffey Jr.	.75	2.00
260A Jeromy Burnitz w/Bat	.20	.50
260B Jeromy Burnitz w/o Bat	.20	.50
261 Hank Blalock PROS	.30	.75
262 Mark Prior PROS	.30	.75
263 Josh Beckett PROS	.20	.50
264 Carlos Pena PROS	.20	.50
265 Sean Burroughs PROS	.20	.50
266 Austin Kearns PROS	.20	.50
267 Chin-Hui Tsao PROS	.20	.50
268 Dewon Brazelton PROS	.20	.50
269 J.D. Martin PROS	.20	.50
270 Marlon Byrd PROS	.20	.50
271 Joe Mauer FYP RC	4.00	10.00
272 Jason Botts FYP RC	.20	.50
273 Mauricio Lara FYP RC	.20	.50
274 Jonny Gomes FYP RC	1.00	2.50
275 Gavin Floyd FYP RC	.40	1.00
276 Alex Requena FYP RC	.20	.50
277 Jimmy Gobble FYP RC	.20	.50
278 Chris Duffy FYP RC	.20	.50
279 Colt Griffin FYP RC	.20	.50
280 Ryan Church FYP RC	.40	1.00
281 Beltran Perez FYP RC	.20	.50
282 Clint Nageotte FYP RC	.30	.75
283 Justin Schuda FYP RC	.20	.50
284 Scott Hairston FYP RC	.30	.75
285 Mario Ramos FYP RC	.20	.50
286A Tom Seaver White Sox RET	.60	1.50
286B Tom Seaver Mets RET	.60	1.50
287A H.Aaron White Jsy RET	2.00	5.00
287B H.Aaron Blue Jsy RET	2.00	5.00
288 Mike Schmidt RET	2.00	5.00
289A R.Yount Blue Jsy RET	1.00	2.50
289B R.Yount P'stripes RET	1.00	2.50
290 Joe Morgan RET	.40	1.00
291 Frank Robinson RET	.60	1.50
292A Reggie Jackson A's RET	.60	1.50
292B Reggie Jackson Yanks RET	.60	1.50
293A Nolan Ryan Astros RET	2.50	6.00
293B N.Ryan Rangers RET	2.50	6.00
294 Dave Winfield RET	.40	1.00
295 Willie Mays RET	2.00	5.00
296 Brooks Robinson RET	.60	1.50
297A Mark McGwire A's RET	2.50	6.00
297B M.McGwire Cards RET	2.50	6.00
298 Honus Wagner RET	1.00	2.50
299A Sherry Magee REP	.40	1.00
299B Sherry Magie UER REP	.40	1.00
300 Frank Chance REP	.40	1.00
301A Joe Doyle NY REP	.40	1.00
301B Joe Doyle NY Nat'l REP	.40	1.00
302 John McGraw REP	.60	1.50
303 Jimmy Collins REP	.40	1.00
304 Buck Herzog REP	.40	1.00
305 Sam Crawford REP	.40	1.00
306 Cy Young REP	1.00	2.50
307 Honus Wagner Blue REP	3.00	8.00
308A A.Rodriguez Blue Jsy SP	1.50	4.00
308B A.Rodriguez White Jsy	.75	2.00
309 Vernon Wells	.20	.50
310A B.Bonds w/Elbow Pad	1.25	3.00
310B B.Bonds w/o Elbow Pad SP	2.50	6.00
311 Vicente Padilla	.20	.50
312A A.Soriano w/Wristband	.20	.50
312B A.Soriano w/o Wristband SP	.75	2.00
313 Mike Piazza	.75	2.00
314 Jacque Jones	.20	.50
315 Shawn Green SP	.75	2.00
316 Paul Byrd	.20	.50
317 Lance Berkman	.20	.50
318 Larry Walker	.20	.50
319 Ken Griffey Jr. SP	1.50	4.00
320 Shea Hillenbrand	.20	.50
321 Jay Gibbons	.20	.50
322 Andruw Jones	.30	.75
323 Luis Gonzalez SP	.75	2.00
324 Garret Anderson	.20	.50
325 Roy Halladay	.20	.50
326 Randy Winn	.20	.50
327 Matt Morris	.20	.50
328 Robb Nen	.20	.50
329 Trevor Hoffman	.20	.50
330 Kip Wells	.20	.50
331 Orlando Hernandez	.20	.50
332 Rey Ordonez	.20	.50
333 Torii Hunter	.20	.50
334 Geoff Jenkins	.20	.50
335 Eric Karros	.20	.50
336 Mike Lowell	.20	.50
337 Nick Johnson	.20	.50
338 Randall Simon	.20	.50
339 Ellis Burks	.20	.50
340A S.Sosa Blue Jsy SP	1.00	2.50
340B Sammy Sosa White Jsy	.50	1.25
341 Pedro Martinez	.30	.75
342 Junior Spivey	.20	.50
343 Vinny Castilla	.20	.50
344 Randy Johnson SP	1.00	2.50
345 Chipper Jones SP	1.00	2.50
346 Orlando Hudson	.20	.50
347 Albert Pujols SP	2.00	5.00
348 Rondell White	.20	.50
349 Vladimir Guerrero	.50	1.25
350A Mark Prior Red SP	.60	1.50
350B Mark Prior Yellow	.30	.75
351 Eric Gagne	.20	.50
352 Todd Zeile	.20	.50
353 Manny Ramirez SP	.75	2.00
354 Kevin Millwood	.20	.50
355 Troy Percival	.20	.50
356A Jason Giambi Batting SP	.75	2.00
356B Jason Giambi Throwing	.20	.50
357 Bartolo Colon	.20	.50
358 Jeremy Giambi	.20	.50
359 Jose Cruz Jr.	.20	.50
360A I.Suzuki Blue Jsy SP	2.00	5.00
360B I.Suzuki White Jsy	1.00	2.50
361 Eddie Guardado	.20	.50
362 Ivan Rodriguez	.30	.75
363 Carl Crawford	.20	.50
364 Jason Simontacchi RC	.20	.50
365 Kenny Lofton	.20	.50
366 Raul Mondesi	.20	.50
367 A.J. Pierzynski	.20	.50
368 Ugueth Urbina	.20	.50
369 Rodrigo Lopez	.20	.50
370A N.Garciaparra One Bat SP	1.50	4.00
370B N.Garciaparra Two Bats	.75	2.00
371 Craig Counsell	.20	.50
372 Barry Larkin	.30	.75
373 Carlos Pena	.20	.50
374 Luis Castillo	.20	.50
375 Raul Ibanez	.20	.50
376 Kazuhisa Ishii SP	.75	2.00
377 Derek Lowe	.20	.50
378 Curt Schilling	.20	.50
379 Jim Thome Phillies	.30	.75
380A Derek Jeter Blue SP	2.50	6.00
380B Derek Jeter Seats	1.25	3.00
381 Pat Burrell	.20	.50
382 Jamie Moyer	.20	.50
383 Eric Hinske	.20	.50
384 Scott Rolen	.30	.75
385 Miguel Tejada SP	.75	2.00
386 Andy Pettitte	.30	.75
387 Mike Lieberthal	.20	.50
388 Al Leiter	.20	.50
389 Todd Helton SP	.75	2.00
390A Adam Dunn Bat SP	.75	2.00
390B Adam Dunn Glove	.20	.50
391 Cliff Floyd	.20	.50
392 Tim Salmon	.30	.75
393 Joe Torre MG	.30	.75
394 Bobby Cox MG	.20	.50
395 Tony LaRussa MG	.20	.50
396 Art Howe MG	.20	.50
397 Bob Brenly MG	.20	.50
398 Ron Gardenhire MG	.20	.50
399 Mike Cuddyer PROS	.20	.50
400 Joe Mauer PROS	4.00	10.00
401 Mark Teixeira PROS	.50	1.25
402 Hee Seop Choi PROS	.20	.50
403 Angel Berroa PROS	.20	.50
404 Jesse Foppert PROS RC	.30	.75
405 Bobby Crosby PROS	.50	1.25
406 Jose Reyes PROS	.30	.75
407 C.Kotchman PROS RC	.40	1.00
408 Aaron Heilman PROS	.20	.50
409 Adrian Gonzalez PROS	.20	.50
410 Delwyn Young PROS RC	.40	1.00
411 Brett Myers PROS	.20	.50
412 Justin Huber PROS RC	.30	.75
413 Drew Henson PROS	.20	.50
414 T.Bozied PROS RC	.30	.75
415 Dontrelle Willis PROS RC	2.00	5.00
416 Rocco Baldelli PROS	.20	.50
417 Jason Stokes PROS RC	.20	.50
418 Brandon Phillips PROS	.20	.50
419 Jake Blalock FYP RC	.20	.50
420 Micah Schilling FYP RC	.40	1.00
421 Denard Span FYP RC	.40	1.00
422A J.Loney Red FYP RC	1.50	4.00
422B J.Loney w/Sky FYP RC	1.50	4.00
423A W.Bankston Blue FYP RC	.75	2.00
423B W.Bankston w/Sky FYP RC	.75	2.00
424 Jeremy Hermida FYP RC	2.00	5.00
425 C.Granderson FYP RC	1.25	3.00
426A J.Pridie Red FYP RC	.40	1.00
426B J.Pridie w/Sky FYP RC	.40	1.00
427 Larry Broadway FYP RC	.20	.50
428A K.Greene Green FYP RC	3.00	8.00
428B K.Greene Red FYP RC	3.00	8.00
429 Joey Votto FYP RC	1.25	3.00
430A B.Upton Grey FYP RC	2.00	5.00
430B B.Upton w/People FYP RC	2.00	5.00
431A S.Santos Gold FYP RC	.40	1.00
431B S.Santos Grey FYP RC	.40	1.00
432 Brian Dopirak FYP RC	.40	1.00
433 Ozzie Smith RET SP	1.50	4.00
434 Wade Boggs RET SP	1.00	2.50
435 Yogi Berra RET SP	1.50	4.00
436 Al Kaline RET SP	1.50	4.00
437 Robin Roberts RET SP	.75	2.00
438 Rob. Clemente RET SP	3.00	8.00
439 Gary Carter RET SP	.75	2.00
440 Fergie Jenkins RET SP	.75	2.00
441 Orlando Cepeda RET SP	.75	2.00
442 Rod Carew RET SP	1.00	2.50
443 Ha. Killebrew RET SP	1.50	4.00
444 Duke Snider RET SP	1.00	2.50
445 Stan Musial RET SP	2.50	6.00
446 Hank Greenberg RET SP	1.50	4.00
447 Lou Brock RET SP	1.00	2.50
448 Jim Palmer RET	.40	1.00
449 John McGraw REP	.60	1.50
450 Mordecai Brown REP	.40	1.00
451 Christy Mathewson REP	.60	1.50
452 Sam Crawford REP	.40	1.00
453 Bill O'Hara REP	.40	1.00
454 Joe Tinker REP	.40	1.00
455 Nap Lajoie REP	.60	1.50
456 Honus Wagner Red REP	3.00	8.00
NNO Repurchased Tobacco Card		

2002 Topps 206 American Beauty

Inserted into third series packs as a stated rate of one in 15,316 these five cards were issued with the very scarce American Beauty back. These cards were issued to a stated print run of five sets so no pricing is provided due to scarcity.

308 A.Rodriguez White Jsy
310 B.Bonds w/Elbow Pad
312 A.Soriano w/Wristband
370 N.Garciaparra Two Bats
456 Honus Wagner Red REP

2002 Topps 206 Bazooka

This quasi-parallel skip-numbered set was inserted at stated odds of one 1185 first series packs, one in 1989 second series packs and one in 825 third series packs. Though the cards are not serial-numbered in any manner, officials at Topps did publicly release a statement verifying that only 30 copies of each card were produced. This set was limited to 15 key players from each series of the 206 set making the set complete at 45 cards. These cards feature a "Bazooka" back, which is the only back on these parallel cards which was not a tobacco producer during the original tobacco card era. Due to market scarcity, no pricing is currently provided.

22 Ichiro Suzuki Portrait
23 Jimmy Rollins
34 Barry Bonds
47 Tony Gwynn
57 Tsuyoshi Shinjo
73 Adam Dunn
91 Albert Pujols
100 Mark McGwire
104 Roy Oswalt
112 Jason Giambi Yankees
119 Derek Jeter
131 Brandon Duckworth PROS
154 Nic Jackson FYP
166 Nolan Ryan RET
172 Ty Cobb REP
185 Roberto Alomar
190 Nomar Garciaparra
203 Vladimir Guerrero
212 Sammy Sosa
221B A.Rodriguez One Hand
233 Pedro Martinez
244B Barry Zito White Jsy
248A Mike Piazza Black Jsy
253 Todd Helton
259 Ken Griffey Jr.
262 Mark Prior Blue PROS
271 Joe Mauer FYP
288 Mike Schmidt RET
306 Cy Young REP
307 Honus Wagner Blue REP
308 A.Rodriguez White Jsy
310 B.Bonds w/Elbow Pad
312 A.Soriano w/Wristband
315 Shawn Green
337 Nick Johnson
350 Mark Prior Yellow
360 Ichiro Suzuki White Jsy
381 Pat Burrell
385 Miguel Tejada
393 Joe Torre MG
413 Drew Henson PROS
430 B.J. Upton Grey FYP
438 Roberto Clemente RET
454 Joe Tinker REP
456 Honus Wagner Red REP

2002 Topps 206 Carolina Brights

Randomly inserted in second series packs and using the "Carolina Brights" backs, these cards parallel the Topps 206 second series cards.

*CAROLINA 181-270: 3X TO 8X BASIC
*CAROLINA RC's 181-270: 1X TO 2.5X
*CAROLINA 271-285: 1.25X TO 3X BASIC
*CAROLINA 286-307: 2X TO 5X BASIC

2002 Topps 206 Cycle

Randomly inserted in first series packs and using the "Cycle" backs, this is a complete parallel of the Topps 206 first series.

*CYCLE 1-140: 5X TO 12X BASIC CARDS
*CYCLE 141-155: 1.25X TO 3X BASIC
*CYCLE 156-180: 3X TO 8X BASIC

2002 Topps 206 Drum

Issued at a stated rate of one in 3711 third series packs, these five cards feature "Drum" backs. These cards have a stated print run of 20 sets and no pricing is provided due to market scarcity.

324 Garret Anderson
356 Jason Giambi Batting
360 I.Suzuki White Jsy
390 Adam Dunn Glove
400 Joe Mauer PROS

2002 Topps 206 Lenox

Issued at a stated rate of one in 7422 third series packs, these five cards feature "Lenox" backs. These cards have a stated print run of 10 sets and no pricing is provided due to market scarcity.

308 A.Rodriguez Blue Jsy
340 Sammy Sosa White Jsy
349 Vladimir Guerrero
353 Manny Ramirez
416 Rocco Baldelli PROS

2002 Topps 206 Piedmont Black

Randomly inserted in second series packs and using the "Piedmont" backs, these cards parallel the Topps 206 second series cards. The words on the back are in black ink and thus these cards are called Piedmont Black

*P'MONT.BLACK 181-270: 1.5X TO 4X BASIC
*P'MONT.BLACK RC's 181-270: .5X TO 1.2X
*P'MONT.BLACK 271-285: .6X TO 1.5X
*P'MONT.BLACK 286-307: 1X TO 2.5X

2002 Topps 206 Piedmont Red

Randomly inserted in second series packs and using the "Piedmont" backs, these cards parallel the Topps 206 second series cards. The words on the back are in black ink and thus these cards are called Piedmont Red.

*P'MONT.RED 181-270: 3X TO 8X BASIC
*P'MONT.RED RC's 181-270: 1X TO 2.5X
*P'MONT.RED 271-285: 1.25X TO 3X
*P'MONT.RED 286-307: 2X TO 5X BASIC

2002 Topps 206 Polar Bear

Randomly inserted into approximately two out of every three packs and using the "Polar Bear" backs,

this is a complete parallel of the Topps 206 set. Cards 1-180 were distributed in first series packs, 181-307 in second series packs and 308-456 in third series packs. The set is actually complete at 525 cards, but the checklist runs from 1-307 with 96 variations intermingled within.

*POLAR 1-140/181-270/308-418: 1.25X TO 3X
*RC 1-140/181-270/308-418: .5X TO 1.2X
*FYP 141-155/271-285: .5X TO 1.2X
*SP 308-418: .6X TO 1.5X SP
*FYP 419-432: .5X TO 1.2X
*RT/RP 156-180/286-307/448-456: .75X TO 2X
*RET 443-447: .75X TO 2X

2002 Topps 206 Sweet Caporal Black

Randomly inserted into packs, this is a parallel to the T206 third series. These cards have the words "Sweet Caporal" in black on the back.

*BLACK 308-418: 2.5X TO 6X BASIC
*BLACK SP 308-418: 1.25X TO 3X BASIC
*BLACK RC 308-418: 1X TO 2.5X BASIC
*BLACK 419-432: 1.25X TO 3X BASIC
*BLACK 433-447: .75X TO 2X BASIC
*BLACK 448-456: 1.5X TO 4X BASIC

2002 Topps 206 Sweet Caporal Blue

Randomly inserted into packs, this is a parallel to the T206 third series. These cards have the words "Sweet Caporal" in blue on the back.

*BLUE 308-418: 2X TO 5X BASIC
*BLUE SP 308-418: 1X TO 2.5X BASIC
*BLUE RC 308-418: .75X TO 2X BASIC
*BLUE 419-432: 1X TO 2.5X BASIC
*BLUE 433-447: .6X TO 1.5X BASIC
*BLUE 448-456: 1.25X TO 3X BASIC

2002 Topps 206 Sweet Caporal Red

Randomly inserted into packs, this is a parallel to the T206 third series. These cards have the words "Sweet Caporal" in blue on the back.

*RED 308-418: 1.5X TO 4X BASIC
*RED SP 308-418: .75X TO 2X BASIC
*RED RC 308-418: .6X TO 1.5X BASIC
*RED 419-432: .75X TO 2X BASIC
*RED 433-447: .5X TO 1.2X BASIC
*RED 448-456: 1X TO 2.5X BASIC

2002 Topps 206 Tolstoi

Randomly inserted in first series packs and using the "Tolstoi" backs, this is a complete parallel of the Topps 206 first series.

*TOLSTOI 1-140: 1.5X TO 4X BASIC
*TOLSTOI 141-155: .4X TO 1X BASIC
*TOLSTOI 156-180: 1X TO 2.5X BASIC

2002 Topps 206 Tolstoi Red

Randomly inserted in packs and using the "Tolstoi" backs, this is a complete parallel of the Topps 206 first series. These cards are differentiated from the more common Tolstoi backs as the color on the back is red. These cards were printed at a stated rate of 25 percent of the total Tolstoi run.

*TOLSTOI RED 1-140: 3X TO 8X BASIC
*TOLSTOI RED 141-155: .6X TO 1.5X BASIC
*TOLSTOI RED 156-180: 2X TO 5X BASIC

2002 Topps 206 Uzit

Randomly inserted into packs, this is a parallel to the T206 third series. These cards have "Uzit" on the back.

*UZIT 308-418: 3X TO 8X BASIC
*UZIT SP 308-418: 1.5X TO 4X BASIC
*UZIT RC 308-418: 1.5X TO 4X BASIC
*UZIT 419-432: 1.5X TO 4X BASIC
*UZIT 433-447: 1X TO 2.5X BASIC
*UZIT 448-456: 2X TO 5X BASIC

2002 Topps 206 Autographs

Inserted at an overall stated rate of one in 41 series one packs, one in 55 series two packs and varying group specific odds in series three packs (see details below), these cards feature a mix of young players and veteran stars who autographed cards for the T206 product.

SER.1 GROUP A1 ODDS 1:1067
SER.1 GROUP B1 ODDS 1:1122
SER.1 GROUP C1 ODDS 1:532
SER.1 GROUP D1 ODDS 1:444
SER.1 GROUP E1 ODDS 1:532
SER.1 GROUP F1 ODDS 1:121
SER.1 GROUP G1 ODDS 1:118
SER.2 GROUP A2 ODDS 1:511
SER.2 GROUP B2 ODDS 1:893
SER.2 GROUP C2 ODDS 1:1557
SER.2 GROUP D2 ODDS 1:106
SER.2 GROUP E2 ODDS 1:638
SER.2 GROUP F2 ODDS 1:596
SER.2 GROUP G2 ODDS 1:526
SER.3 GROUP A3 ODDS 1:810
SER.3 GROUP B3 ODDS 1:442
SER.3 GROUP C3 ODDS 1:411
SER.3 GROUP D3 ODDS 1:393
SER.3 GROUP E3 ODDS 1:393
SER.3 GROUP F3 ODDS 1:384
SER.3 GROUP G3 ODDS 1:383

AP Albert Pujols A2	200.00	350.00
AR Alex Rodriguez A1	75.00	150.00
BB Barry Bonds A1	150.00	250.00
BG Brian Giles G1	6.00	15.00
BI Brandon Inge D1	6.00	15.00
BS Ben Sheets E2	6.00	15.00
BSM Bud Smith B2	6.00	15.00
BZ Barry Zito D1	12.50	30.00
CG Cristian Guzman G1	4.00	10.00
CT Chris Tritle G2	4.00	10.00
DB Dewon Brazelton D2	4.00	10.00
DE David Eckstein G3	12.50	30.00
DH Drew Henson D3	4.00	10.00
EC Eric Chavez A2	10.00	25.00
FJ Forrest Johnson F1	4.00	10.00
FL Felipe Lopez C1	6.00	15.00
GF Gavin Floyd D2	6.00	15.00
GN Greg Nash F1	4.00	10.00
HB Hank Blalock D2	6.00	15.00
JC Jose Cruz Jr. A3	6.00	15.00
JD Johnny Damon Sox B2	15.00	40.00
JDM J.D. Martin D2	4.00	10.00
JE Jim Edmonds C1	15.00	40.00
JJ Jorge Julio F1	4.00	10.00
JM Joe Mauer D2	50.00	100.00
JR Jimmy Rollins G1	10.00	25.00
JV Jose Vidro B3	6.00	15.00
KI Kazuhisa Ishii A2	15.00	40.00
LB Lance Berkman A2	20.00	50.00
LG Luis Gonzalez C2	10.00	25.00
MA Moises Alou A2	10.00	25.00
MB Milton Bradley C3	6.00	15.00
MB Marlon Byrd D2	4.00	10.00
ML Mike Lamb F3	4.00	10.00
MO Magglio Ordonez E1	6.00	15.00
MP Mark Prior D2	6.00	15.00

MT Marcus Thames E3 4.00 10.00
RC Roger Clemens B1 75.00 150.00
RJ Ryan Jamison F1 4.00 10.00
RS Richie Sexson F2 6.00 15.00
SR Scott Rolen A2 15.00 40.00
ST So Taguchi A2 15.00 40.00

2002 Topps 206 Relics

Issued in first series packs at overall stated odds of one in 11 and second series packs at overall stated odds of one in 12 and third series packs at various odds, these 109 cards feature either a bat sliver or a jersey/uniform swatch. Representatives at Topps announced that only 25 copies of the Honus Wagner blue Bat and Honus Wagner Red Bat and 100 copies of the Ty Cobb Bat card (both seeded into second series packs) were produced. In addition, in early 2005, the Beckett staff managed to confirm with Topps that 300 copies of Wagner's Orange background card were also produced. Please note, all first series Relics feature light yellow frames (surrounding the mini-sized card), all second series Relics feature light blue frames and third series Relics feature light pink frames.

SER.1 BAT GROUP A1 ODDS 1:166
SER.1 BAT GROUP B1 ODDS 1:1780
SER.2 BAT GROUP A2 ODDS 1:35,217
SER.2 BAT GROUP B2 ODDS 1:8991
SER.2 BAT GROUP C2 ODDS 1:2097
SER.2 BAT GROUP D2 ODDS 1:75
SER.2 BAT GROUP E2 ODDS 1:1377
SER.2 BAT GROUP F2 ODDS 1:893
SER.2 BAT GROUP G2 ODDS 1:248
SER.2 BAT GROUP H2 ODDS 1:319
SER.2 BAT GROUP I2 ODDS 1:447
SER.2 BAT OVERALL ODDS 1:40
SER.3 BAT GROUP A3 ODDS 1:15,316
SER.3 BAT GROUP B3 ODDS 1:390
SER.3 BAT GROUP C3 ODDS 1:370
SER.3 BAT GROUP D3 ODDS 1:34
SER.3 BAT GROUP E3 ODDS 1:187
SER.3 BAT GROUP F3 ODDS 1:185
SER.1 UNI GROUP A1 ODDS 1:14
SER.1 UNI GROUP B1 ODDS 1:74
SER.2 UNI GROUP A2 ODDS 1:372
SER.2 UNI GROUP B2 ODDS 1:27
SER.2 UNI GROUP C2 ODDS 1:62
SER.2 UNI GROUP D2 ODDS 1:447
SER.2 UNI OVERALL ODDS 1:18
SER.3 UNI GROUP A3 ODDS 1:247
SER.3 UNI GROUP B3 ODDS 1:185
SER.3 UNI GROUP C3 ODDS 1:62
SER.3 UNI GROUP D3 ODDS 1:187
SER.3 UNI GROUP E3 ODDS 1:27
SER.3 UNI GROUP F3 ODDS 1:176
AB A.J. Burnett Jsy B2 3.00 8.00
AD2 Adam Dunn Bat D2 6.00 15.00
AD3 Adam Dunn Bat C3 6.00 15.00
AJ1 Andruw Jones Jsy A1 4.00 10.00
AJ2 Andruw Jones Jsy C2 4.00 10.00
AJ3 Andruw Jones Uni E3 4.00 10.00
AP1 Albert Pujols Bat A1 8.00 20.00
AP2 Albert Pujols Jsy B2 8.00 20.00
AP3 Albert Pujols Bat D3 8.00 20.00
ARA Aramis Ramirez Bat D2 6.00 15.00
AR2 Alex Rodriguez Bat D2 8.00 20.00
AR3 Alex Rodriguez Bat D3 6.00 15.00
AS1 Alfonso Soriano Bat A1 6.00 15.00
AS2 Alfonso Soriano Bat I2 3.00 8.00
AS3 Alfonso Soriano Bat D3 3.00 8.00
BB1 Barry Bonds Jsy A1 10.00 25.00
BB2 Barry Bonds Uni C2 10.00 25.00
BD Brandon Duckworth Jsy B2 3.00 8.00
BH Buck Herzog Bat G2 20.00 50.00
BL Barry Larkin Jsy B2 4.00 10.00
BP Brad Penny Jsy B2 3.00 8.00
BW1 Bernie Williams Jsy A1 4.00 10.00
BW2 Bernie Williams Jsy B2 4.00 10.00
BW3 Bernie Williams Uni A3 6.00 15.00
BZ1 Barry Zito Jsy A1 3.00 8.00
BZ3 Barry Zito Uni C3 3.00 8.00
CB Craig Biggio Jsy B1 4.00 10.00
CD Carlos Delgado Jsy A1 3.00 8.00
CF1 Cliff Floyd Jsy A1 3.00 8.00
CF2 Cliff Floyd Jsy B2 3.00 8.00
CG Cristian Guzman Jsy B2 3.00 8.00
CJ1 Chipper Jones Jsy A1 6.00 15.00
CJ2 Chipper Jones Jsy B2 6.00 15.00
CJ3 Chipper Jones Uni B3 6.00 15.00
CL Carlos Lee Jsy A1 3.00 8.00
CP Corey Patterson Bat F3 3.00 8.00
CS2 Curt Schilling Bat D2 6.00 15.00
CS3 Curt Schilling Bat D3 3.00 8.00
DE Darin Erstad Jsy B2 3.00 8.00
DM Doug Mientkiewicz Uni D3 3.00 8.00
EC2 Eric Chavez Bat H2 3.00 8.00
EC3 Eric Chavez Uni E3 3.00 8.00
EM1 Edgar Martinez Jsy A1 4.00 10.00
EM2 Edgar Martinez Jsy B2 4.00 10.00
FM Fred McGriff Bat D2 4.00 10.00
FT1 Frank Thomas Jsy A1 6.00 15.00
FT2 Frank Thomas Jsy B2 6.00 15.00
FT3 Frank Thomas Uni C3 6.00 15.00
GM1 Greg Maddux Jsy A1 6.00 15.00
GM2 Greg Maddux Jsy C2 6.00 15.00
GS2 Gary Sheffield Bat D2 6.00 15.00
GS3 Gary Sheffield Bat B3 6.00 15.00
HW1 H.Wag Oran Bat B1/300 * 250.00 400.00
HW2 H.Wagner Blue Bat A2/25 *
HW3 H.Wagner Red Bat A3/25 *
IR1 Ivan Rodriguez Jsy A1 4.00 10.00
IR2 Ivan Rodriguez Uni A2 4.00 10.00
IR3 Ivan Rodriguez Bat D3 4.00 10.00
JB1 Jeff Bagwell Jsy A1 4.00 10.00
JB2 Jeff Bagwell Uni C2 4.00 10.00
JB3 Jeff Bagwell Bat D3 4.00 10.00
JD J.Damon Sox Bat D2 4.00 10.00
JE1 Jim Edmonds Jsy A1 3.00 8.00
JE3 Jim Edmonds Uni F3 3.00 8.00
JG Juan Gonzalez Bat D2 6.00 15.00
JH Josh Hamilton Bat D2 8.00 20.00
JJ Jason Jennings Jsy B2 3.00 8.00
JK Jeff Kent Uni B2 3.00 8.00
JO1 John Olerud Jsy A1 3.00 8.00
JO2 John Olerud Jsy B2 3.00 8.00
JT Joe Tinker Bat G2 30.00 60.00
JW Jeff Weaver Jsy A1 3.00 8.00
KB Kevin Brown Jsy B2 3.00 8.00
KL Kenny Lofton Jsy B1 3.00 8.00
LG Luis Gonzalez Uni E3 3.00 8.00
LW1 Larry Walker Jsy A1 3.00 8.00
LW2 Larry Walker Jsy B2 3.00 8.00
MC Mike Cameron Jsy A1 3.00 8.00
MG Mark Grace Bat D2 6.00 15.00
MO Magglio Ordonez Jsy A1 3.00 8.00
MP1 Mike Piazza Jsy A1 6.00 15.00
MP2 Mike Piazza Uni C2 6.00 15.00
MP3 Mike Piazza Uni C3 6.00 15.00
MT2 Miguel Tejada Bat H2 3.00 8.00
MT3 Miguel Tejada Uni E3 3.00 8.00
MV2 Mo Vaughn Bat D2 6.00 15.00
MV3 Mo Vaughn Uni E3 3.00 8.00
MW Matt Williams Jsy B2 3.00 8.00
NG Nomar Garciaparra Bat C3 8.00 20.00
NJ Nick Johnson Bat E3 3.00 8.00
PB Pat Burrell Bat B3 6.00 15.00
PM Pedro Martinez Uni A3 6.00 15.00
PO Paul O'Neill Jsy A1 4.00 10.00
PW Preston Wilson Jsy B2 3.00 8.00
RA1 Roberto Alomar Jsy A1 4.00 10.00
RA2 Roberto Alomar Bat D2 6.00 15.00
RA3 Roberto Alomar Bat D3 4.00 10.00
RD Ryan Dempster Jsy B2 3.00 8.00
RH2 Rickey Henderson Bat D2 8.00 20.00
RH3 Rickey Henderson Bat D3 6.00 15.00
RJ1 Randy Johnson Jsy A1 6.00 15.00
RJ2 Randy Johnson Jsy C2 6.00 15.00
RJ3 Randy Johnson Uni A3 8.00 20.00
RP2 Rafael Palmeiro Jsy B2 4.00 10.00
RP3 Rafael Palmeiro Uni B3 4.00 10.00
RV Robin Ventura Bat D2 6.00 15.00
SB Sean Burroughs Bat D2 4.00 10.00
SC Sam Crawford Bat A1 30.00 60.00
SCR Sam Crawford Bat C2 30.00 60.00
SG1 Shawn Green Jsy A1 3.00 8.00
SG2 Shawn Green Jsy C2 3.00 8.00
SR Scott Rolen Bat D3 4.00 10.00
SS Shannon Stewart Bat A1 6.00 15.00
TC Ty Cobb Bat B2/100 * 550.00 700.00
TL Travis Lee Bat D2 4.00 10.00
TM1 Tino Martinez Jsy A1 4.00 10.00
TM2 Tino Martinez Bat D2 6.00 15.00
WB Wilson Betemit Bat D3 3.00 8.00
BBO1 Bret Boone Jsy B1 3.00 8.00
BBO2 Bret Boone Jsy D2 3.00 8.00
CHP Chan Ho Park Bat A1 6.00 15.00
JCA Jose Canseco Bat A1 6.00 15.00
JCO Jimmy Collins Bat F2 UER 40.00 80.00
Eddie Collins pictured
JEV1 Johnny Evers Jsy A1 30.00 60.00
JEV2 Johnny Evers Bat G2 30.00 60.00
JMA Joe Mays Jsy B2 3.00 8.00
JMC1 John McGraw Bat A1 40.00 80.00
JMC2 John McGraw Bat E2 40.00 80.00
JTH1 Jim Thome Jsy A1 4.00 10.00
JTH2 Jim Thome Bat D2 6.00 15.00
JTH3 Jim Thome Uni C3 4.00 10.00
TGL1 Tom Glavine Jsy A1 4.00 10.00
TGL2 Tom Glavine Jsy A2 4.00 10.00
TGW1 Tony Gwynn Jsy A1 6.00 15.00
TGW2 Tony Gwynn Jsy B2 6.00 15.00
TGW3 Tony Gwynn Uni E3 6.00 15.00
THA Toby Hall Jsy B2 3.00 8.00
THE1 Todd Helton Jsy A1 4.00 10.00
THE2 Todd Helton Jsy C2 4.00 10.00
THE3 Todd Helton Uni E3 4.00 10.00
TSH2 Tsuyoshi Shinjo Bat D2 6.00 15.00
TSH3 Tsuyoshi Shinjo Bat D3 3.00 8.00
TSP Tris Speaker Bat A1 75.00 150.00
JAGI Jason Giambi Jsy A1 3.00 8.00
JEGI Jeremy Giambi Jsy A1 3.00 8.00

2002 Topps 206 Team 206 Series 1

Inserted at an approximate rate of one per pack (only not in a pack when an autograph or relic card was inserted), these 20 cards feature the leading players from the 206 first series in a more modern design.

COMPLETE SET (20) 6.00 15.00
T2061 Barry Bonds 1.00 2.50
T2062 Ivan Rodriguez .25 .60
T2063 Luis Gonzalez .20 .50
T2064 Jason Giambi Yankees .20 .50
T2065 Pedro Martinez .25 .60
T2066 Larry Walker .20 .50
T2067 Bob Abreu .20 .50
T2068 Derek Jeter 1.00 2.50
T2069 Bret Boone .20 .50
T20610 Mike Piazza .60 1.50
T20611 Alex Rodriguez .60 1.50
T20612 Roger Clemens .75 2.00
T20613 Albert Pujols .75 2.00
T20614 Randy Johnson .40 1.00
T20615 Sammy Sosa .40 1.00
T20616 Cristian Guzman .20 .50
T20617 Shawn Green .20 .50
T20618 Curt Schilling .20 .50
T20619 Ichiro Suzuki .75 2.00
T20620 Chipper Jones .40 1.00

2002 Topps 206 Team 206 Series 2

Inserted at an approximate rate of one per pack (only not in a pack when an autograph or relic card was inserted), these 20 cards feature the leading players from the 206 second series in a more modern design.

COMPLETE SET (25) 6.00 15.00
T2061 Alex Rodriguez .60 1.50
T2062 Sammy Sosa .40 1.00
T2063 Jason Giambi .20 .50
T2064 Nomar Garciaparra .60 1.50
T2065 Ichiro Suzuki .75 2.00
T2066 Chipper Jones .40 1.00
T2067 Derek Jeter 1.00 2.50
T2068 Barry Bonds 1.00 2.50
T2069 Mike Piazza .60 1.50
T20610 Randy Johnson .40 1.00
T20611 Shawn Green .20 .50
T20612 Todd Helton .25 .60
T20613 Luis Gonzalez .20 .50
T20614 Albert Pujols .75 2.00
T20615 Curt Schilling .20 .50
T20616 Scott Rolen .25 .60
T20617 Ivan Rodriguez .25 .60
T20618 Roberto Alomar .25 .60
T20619 Cristian Guzman .20 .50
T20620 Bret Boone .20 .50
T20621 Barry Zito .20 .50
T20622 Larry Walker .20 .50
T20623 Eric Chavez .20 .50
T20624 Roger Clemens .75 2.00
T20625 Pedro Martinez .25 .60

2002 Topps 206 Team 206 Series 3

Inserted at an approximate rate of one per pack (only not in a pack when an autograph or relic card was inserted), these 30 cards feature the leading players from the 206 third series in a more modern design.

COMPLETE SET (30) 6.00 15.00
1 Ichiro Suzuki .75 2.00
2 Kazuhisa Ishii .25 .60
3 Alex Rodriguez .60 1.50
4 Mark Prior .25 .60
5 Derek Jeter 1.00 2.50
6 Sammy Sosa .40 1.00
7 Nomar Garciaparra .60 1.50
8 Mike Piazza .60 1.50
9 Jason Giambi .20 .50
10 Vladimir Guerrero .40 1.00
11 Curt Schilling .20 .50
12 Jim Thome Phillies .25 .60
13 Adam Dunn .20 .50
14 Albert Pujols .75 2.00
15 Pat Burrell .20 .50
16 Chipper Jones .40 1.00
17 Randy Johnson .40 1.00
18 Todd Helton .25 .60
19 Luis Gonzalez .20 .50
20 Alfonso Soriano .20 .50
21 Shawn Green .20 .50
22 Pedro Martinez .25 .60
23 Lance Berkman .20 .50
24 Ivan Rodriguez .25 .60
25 Larry Walker .20 .50
26 Andruw Jones .20 .50
27 Ken Griffey Jr. .60 1.50
28 Manny Ramirez .25 .60
29 Barry Bonds 1.00 2.50
30 Miguel Tejada .20 .50

2006 Topps 52

This 327-card set was released in January, 2007. This product was issued in eight-card packs with an $5 SRP which came 20 packs per box and eight boxes for a case. With the exception of Mickey Mantle (card #311), every player in the set was qualified to be a Topps Rookie Card in 2006. A few players were issued with either their team's current logo or the logo that team used in 1952 and Mantle was issued in six different colors. In addition, a few cards were short printed and those cards were inserted into packs at a stated rate of one in five.

COMP.SET w/o SPs (275) 40.00 80.00
COMMON CARD (1-275) .20 .50
COMMON LOGO VAR. 1.50 4.00
LOGO VAR.STATED ODDS 1:5 H,1:5 R
COMMON SP 2.50 6.00
SP STATED ODDS 1:5 H, 1:5 R
1 Howie Kendrick (RC) .50 1.25
2 Enrique Gonzalez (RC) .20 .50
3 Chuck James (RC) .30 .75
4 Chris Britton RC .20 .50
5 David Pauley (RC) .20 .50
6 Angel Pagan (RC) .20 .50
7 Pat Neshek RC 2.00 5.00
8 Walter Young (RC) .20 .50
9 Chris Denorfia (RC) .20 .50
10 Rafael Perez RC .20 .50
11 Ryan Spilborghs (RC) .30 .75
12 Jon Huber RC .20 .50
13 Jordan Tata RC .20 .50
14 Eric Reed (RC) .20 .50
15 Norris Hopper RC .20 .50
16 Scott Olsen (RC) .20 .50
17 Fernando Nieve (RC) .20 .50
18 Chris Booker (RC) .20 .50
19 Chad Billingsley (RC) .30 .75
20 Carlos Villanueva RC .20 .50
21 Craig Hansen RC .75 2.00
22 Dave Gassner (RC) .20 .50
23 Mike Pelfrey RC .75 2.00
24 Matt Smith RC .30 .75
25 Chris Roberson (RC) .20 .50
26 John Van Benschoten (RC) .20 .50
27 Kevin Frandsen (RC) .20 .50
28 Les Walrond (RC) .20 .50
29 James Shields RC .20 .50
30 Russell Martin (RC) .30 .75
31 Ben Zobrist (RC) .30 .75
32 John Rheinecker (RC) .20 .50
33 Francisco Rosario (RC) .20 .50
34 Santiago Ramirez (RC) .20 .50
35 Mike Napoli RC .50 1.25
36 Tony Pena Jr. (RC) .20 .50
37A Jeff Karstens RC .50 1.25
37B Jeff Karstens 52 Logo 1.50 4.00
38 Phil Stockman (RC) .20 .50
39 Kurt Birkins RC .20 .50
40 Dustin Pedroia (RC) 4.00 10.00
41 Buck Coats (RC) .20 .50
42 Jim Johnson RC .20 .50
43 Angel Guzman (RC) .20 .50
44 Kelly Shoppach (RC) .20 .50
45 Josh Wilson (RC) .20 .50
46 Jack Hannahan RC .20 .50
47 Ricky Nolasco (RC) .20 .50
48 T.J. Bohn (RC) .20 .50
49 Joel Zumaya (RC) .50 1.25
50 Phil Barzilla RC .20 .50
51 Justin Huber (RC) .20 .50
52A Willy Aybar (RC) .20 .50
52B Willy Aybar 52 Logo 1.50 4.00
53 Tony Gwynn Jr. (RC) .50 1.25
54 Chris Barnwell RC .20 .50
55 Henry Owens RC .30 .75
56 Jeff Bajenaru (RC) .20 .50
57 Jonah Bayliss RC .20 .50
58 Josh Sharpless RC .20 .50
59 Eliezer Alfonzo RC .20 .50
60 Bobby Livingston (RC) .20 .50
61 John Gall (RC) .20 .50
62 Ruddy Lugo (RC) .20 .50
63 Fabio Castro RC .20 .50
64 Casey Janssen RC .30 .75
65 Mike O'Connor RC .20 .50
66 Kendry Morales (RC) .30 .75
67 James Hoey RC .30 .75
68 Dustin Moseley (RC) .20 .50
69 Peter Moylan RC .20 .50
70 Manny Delcarmen (RC) .20 .50
71 Rich Hill (RC) .20 .50
72 Boone Logan RC .20 .50
73 Cody Ross (RC) .20 .50
74 Fausto Carmona (RC) .20 .50
75 Ramon Ramirez (RC) .20 .50
76 Zach Miner (RC) .20 .50
77 Hanley Ramirez (RC) .50 1.25
78 Josh Johnson (RC) .30 .75
79 Taylor Buchholz (RC) .20 .50
80 Joe Nelson (RC) .20 .50
81 Hong-Chih Kuo (RC) .50 1.25
82 Chris Mabeus (RC) .20 .50
83 Willie Eyre (RC) .20 .50
84 John Maine (RC) .30 .75
85 Yurendell DeCaster (RC) .20 .50
86 Mike Thompson RC .20 .50
87 Brian Wilson RC .20 .50
88A Matt Cain (RC) .30 .75
88B Matt Cain 52 Logo 2.00 5.00
89 Sean Green RC .20 .50
90 Tyler Johnson (RC) .20 .50
91 Jason Childers RC .20 .50
92 Wes Littleton (RC) .20 .50
93 Ty Taubenheim RC .30 .75
94 Saul Rivera (RC) .20 .50
95 Reggie Willits RC .75 2.00
96 Carlos Quentin (RC) .30 .75
97 Macay McBride (RC) .20 .50
98 Brandon Fahey RC .20 .50
99 Sean Marshall (RC) .20 .50
100 Sean Tracey (RC) .20 .50
101 Brian Slocum (RC) .20 .50
102 Choo Freeman (RC) .20 .50
103 Brent Clevlen (RC) .30 .75
104 Josh Willingham (RC) .20 .50
105 Chris Resop (RC) .20 .50
106 Chris Sampson RC .20 .50
107A James Loney (RC) .30 .75
107B James Loney 52 Logo 2.00 5.00
108 Matt Kemp (RC) .30 .75
109 Jason Kubel (RC) .20 .50
110 Brian Bannister (RC) .20 .50
111 Kevin Thompson (RC) .20 .50
112 Jeremy Brown (RC) .20 .50
113 Brian Sanches (RC) .20 .50
114 Nate McLouth (RC) .20 .50
115 Ben Johnson (RC) .20 .50
116 Jonathan Sanchez (RC) .20 .50
117 Mark Lowe (RC) .20 .50
118 Skip Schumaker (RC) .20 .50
119 Jason Hammel (RC) .20 .50
120 Drew Meyer (RC) .20 .50
121 Melvin Dorta RC .20 .50
122 Jeff Mathis (RC) .20 .50
123 Davis Romero (RC) .20 .50
124 Joey Devine RC .20 .50
125 Sendy Rleal RC .20 .50
126 Freddie Bynum (RC) .20 .50
127 Brian Anderson (RC) .20 .50
128 Jeremy Sowers (RC) .20 .50
129 Ryan Shealy (RC) .20 .50
130 Reggie Abercrombie (RC) .20 .50
131 Matt Albers (RC) .20 .50
132 Lastings Milledge (RC) .30 .75
133 Robert Andino RC .20 .50
134 Chris Demaria RC .20 .50
135 Boof Bonser (RC) .30 .75
136 Alay Soler RC .20 .50
137 Wil Nieves (RC) .20 .50
138 Mike Rouse (RC) .20 .50
139 Carlos Ruiz (RC) .20 .50
140 Matt Capps (RC) .20 .50
141 Travis Ishikawa (RC) .20 .50
142 Josh Kinney RC .20 .50
143 Josh Rupe (RC) .20 .50
144 Shaun Marcum (RC) .20 .50
145 Jason Bergmann RC .20 .50
146 Tommy Murphy (RC) .20 .50
147 Martin Prado (RC) .20 .50
148 Val Majewski (RC) .20 .50
149 Ian Kinsler (RC) .30 .75
150 Joe Winkelsas (RC) .20 .50
151 Agustin Montero (RC) .20 .50
152 Joe Inglett RC .20 .50
153 Manuel Corpas RC .20 .50
154 Yusmeiro Petit (RC) .20 .50
155 Mark Woodyard (RC) .20 .50
156 Jeff Fulchino RC .20 .50
157 Stephen Andrade (RC) .20 .50
158 Tim Hamulack (RC) .20 .50
159 Colter Bean (RC) .20 .50
160 Anderson Hernandez (RC) .20 .50
161 Kevin Reese (RC) .20 .50
162 Jason Windsor (RC) .20 .50
163A Paul Maholm (RC) .20 .50
163B Paul Maholm 52 Logo 2.00 5.00
164 Jeremy Accardo RC .20 .50
165 Joel Guzman (RC) .20 .50
166 Erick Aybar (RC) .20 .50
167 Scott Thorman (RC) .20 .50
168 Adam Loewen (RC) .20 .50
169 Carlos Marmol RC .20 .50
170 Bill Bray (RC) .20 .50
171 Edward Mujica RC .20 .50
172 Jeremy Hermida (RC) .20 .50
173 Taylor Tankersley (RC) .20 .50
174 Bobby Keppel (RC) .20 .50
175 Chris B. Young (RC) .20 .50
176 Josh Rabe RC .20 .50
177 T.J. Beam (RC) .20 .50
178A Shane Komine RC .30 .75
178B Shane Komine 52 Logo 2.00 5.00
179 Scott Mathieson (RC) .20 .50
180 Josh Barfield (RC) .20 .50
181 Justin Knoedler (RC) .20 .50
182 Emiliano Fruto RC .20 .50
183 Adam Wainwright (RC) .20 .50
184 Nick Masset (RC) .20 .50
185 Ryan Roberts RC .20 .50
186 Brandon Watson (RC) .20 .50
187 Chris Bootcheck (RC) .20 .50
188 Dan Ortmeier (RC) .20 .50
189 Kevin Barry (RC) .20 .50
190 Cory Morris RC .20 .50
191 Kason Gabbard (RC) .20 .50
192 Tom Mastny (RC) .20 .50
193 David Aardsma (RC) .20 .50
194 Anthony Reyes (RC) .30 .75
195 Mike Jacobs (RC) .20 .50
196 Conor Jackson (RC) .30 .75
197 Kenji Johjima RC 1.00 2.50
198 Jack Taschner (RC) .20 .50
199 Renyel Pinto (RC) .20 .50
200 Chad Santos (RC) .20 .50
201 Aaron Rakers (RC) .20 .50
202 Franklin Gutierrez (RC) .20 .50
203 Chris Coste RC .75 2.00
204 Chris Iannetta RC .20 .50
205 Mike Vento (RC) .20 .50
206 Ryan O'Malley RC .20 .50
207 Jason Botts (RC) .20 .50
208 John Hattig (RC) .20 .50
209 Brandon Harper RC .20 .50
210 Ryan Theriot RC 2.00 5.00
211 Travis Hughes (RC) .20 .50
212 Paul Hoover (RC) .20 .50
213 Brayan Pena (RC) .20 .50
214 Craig Breslow RC .20 .50
215 Eude Brito (RC) .20 .50
216A Melky Cabrera (RC) .30 .75
216B Melky Cabrera 52 Logo 2.00 5.00
217A Jonathan Broxton (RC) .20 .50
217B Jonathan Broxton 52 Logo 1.50 4.00
218 Bryan Corey (RC) .20 .50
219 Ron Flores RC .20 .50
220 Andrew Brown (RC) .20 .50
221 Jaime Bubela (RC) .20 .50
222 Jason Bulger (RC) .20 .50
223 Alberto Callaspo (RC) .20 .50
224 Jose Capellan (RC) .20 .50
225A Cole Hamels (RC) .50 1.25
225B Cole Hamels 52 Logo 3.00 8.00
226 Bernie Castro (RC) .20 .50
227 Shin-Soo Choo (RC) .30 .75
228 Doug Clark (RC) .20 .50
229 Roy Corcoran RC .20 .50
230 Tim Corcoran RC .20 .50
231 Nelson Cruz (RC) .20 .50
232 Rajai Davis (RC) .20 .50
233A Chris Duncan (RC) .30 .75
233B Chris Duncan 52 Logo 2.00 5.00
234 Scott Dunn (RC) .20 .50
235 Mike Esposito (RC) .20 .50
236 Scott Feldman RC .20 .50
237 Luis Figueroa RC .20 .50
238 Bartolome Fortunato (RC) .20 .50
239 Alejandro Freire RC .20 .50
240 J.J. Furmaniak (RC) .20 .50
241 Nick Markakis (RC) .30 .75
242 Matt Garza (RC) .30 .75
243 Justin Germano (RC) .20 .50
244 Alexis Gomez (RC) .20 .50
245 Tom Gorzelanny (RC) .20 .50
246 Dan Uggla (RC) .50 1.25
247 Jeremy Guthrie (RC) .20 .50
248 Stephen Drew (RC) .50 1.25
249 Brendan Harris (RC) .20 .50
250 Jeff Harris RC .20 .50
251 Corey Hart (RC) .20 .50
252 Chris Heintz RC .20 .50
253 Prince Fielder (RC) .75 2.00
254 Francisco Liriano (RC) 1.00 2.50
255 Jason Hirsh (RC) .20 .50
256 J.R. House (RC) .20 .50
257 Zach Jackson (RC) .20 .50
258 Charlton Jimerson (RC) .20 .50
259 Greg Jones (RC) .20 .50
260 Mitch Jones (RC) .20 .50
261 Ryan Jorgensen RC .20 .50
262 Logan Kensing (RC) .20 .50
263 John Koronka (RC) .20 .50
264 Anthony Lerew (RC) .20 .50
265 Anibal Sanchez (RC) .30 .75
266 Juan Mateo RC .20 .50
267 Paul McAnulty (RC) .20 .50
268 Dustin McGowan (RC) .20 .50
269 Marty McLeary (RC) .20 .50
270 Ryan Zimmerman (RC) 1.25 3.00
271 Dustin Nippert (RC) .20 .50
272 Eric O'Flaherty RC .20 .50
273 Ronny Paulino (RC) .20 .50
274 Tony Pena (RC) .20 .50
275 Hayden Penn (RC) .20 .50
276 Miguel Perez SP (RC) 2.50 6.00
277 Paul Phillips SP (RC) 2.50 6.00
278 Omar Quintanilla SP (RC) 2.50 6.00
279 Guillermo Quiroz SP (RC) 2.50 6.00
280 Darrell Rasner SP (RC) 2.50 6.00
281 Kenny Ray SP (RC) 2.50 6.00
282 Royce Ring SP (RC) 2.50 6.00
283 Brian Rogers SP RC 3.00 8.00
284 Ed Rogers SP (RC) 2.50 6.00
285 Danny Sandoval SP RC 2.50 6.00
286 Joe Saunders SP (RC) 2.50 6.00
287 Chris Schroder SP RC 2.50 6.00
288 Mike Smith SP (RC) 3.00 8.00
289 Travis Smith SP (RC) 2.50 6.00
290 Geovany Soto SP (RC) 2.50 6.00
291 Brian Sweeney SP (RC) 2.50 6.00
292 Jon Switzer SP (RC) 2.50 6.00
293 Joe Thurston SP (RC) 2.50 6.00
294 Jermaine Van Buren SP (RC) 2.50 6.00
295 Ryan Garko SP (RC) 2.50 6.00
296 Cla Meredith SP (RC) 3.00 8.00
297 Luke Scott SP (RC) 2.50 6.00
298 Andy Marte SP (RC) 2.50 6.00
299 Jered Weaver SP (RC) 4.00 10.00
300 Freddy Guzman SP (RC) 2.50 6.00
301 Jonathan Papelbon SP (RC) 4.00 10.00
302 John-Ford Griffin SP (RC) UER 2.50 6.00
Photo is Anthony Lerew
303 Jon Lester SP RC 4.00 10.00
304 Shawn Hill SP (RC) 2.50 6.00
305 Brian Myrow SP RC 2.50 6.00
306 Anderson Garcia SP RC 2.50 6.00
307 Andre Ethier SP (RC) 3.00 8.00
308 Ben Hendrickson SP (RC) 2.50 6.00
309 Alejandro Machado SP (RC) 2.50 6.00
310 Justin Verlander SP (RC) 4.00 10.00
311A Mickey Mantle SP Blue 20.00 50.00
311B Mickey Mantle Black 4.00 10.00
311C Mickey Mantle Green 4.00 10.00
311D Mickey Mantle Orange 4.00 10.00
311E Mickey Mantle Red 4.00 10.00
311F Mickey Mantle Yellow 4.00 10.00
312 Steve Stemle SP RC 2.50 6.00

2006 Topps 52 Chrome

COMMON CARD 1.25 3.00
SEMISTARS 1.50 4.00
UNLISTED STARS 2.00 5.00
STATED ODDS 1:5 H, 1:7 R
STATED PRINT RUN 1952 SER.#'d SETS
6 Craig Hansen 2.50 6.00
7 Mickey Mantle 10.00 25.00
21 Hong-Chih Kuo 3.00 8.00
74 Prince Fielder 2.50 6.00

2006 Topps 52 Chrome Refractors

*CHROME REF: .6X TO 1.5X CHROME
STATED ODDS 1:19 H, 1:20 R
STATED PRINT RUN 552 SER.#'d SETS
6 Craig Hansen 3.00 8.00
7 Mickey Mantle 30.00 60.00
21 Hong-Chih Kuo 4.00 10.00
57 Cole Hamels 3.00 8.00
74 Prince Fielder 3.00 8.00

2006 Topps 52 Chrome Gold Refractors

COMMON CARD 5.00 12.00
SEMISTARS 6.00 15.00
UNLISTED STARS 10.00 25.00
STATED ODDS 1:207 H, 1:207 R
STATED PRINT RUN 52 SER.#'d SETS
6 Craig Hansen 15.00 40.00
7 Mickey Mantle 200.00 300.00
21 Hong-Chih Kuo 40.00 80.00
50 Kenji Johjima 20.00 50.00

72 Nick Markakis 20.00 50.00
74 Prince Fielder 15.00 40.00

2006 Topps 52 Debut Flashbacks

COMPLETE SET (20) 15.00 40.00
STATED ODDS 1:6 H, 1:6 R
*CHROME: .75X TO 2X BASIC
CHROME ODDS 1:25 H, 1:25 R
CHR.PRINT RUN 1952 SER.#'d SETS
DF1 Dontrelle Willis .75 2.00
DF2 Carlos Beltran .75 2.00
DF3 Albert Pujols 2.50 6.00
DF4 Ichiro Suzuki 2.00 5.00
DF5 Mike Piazza 1.25 3.00
DF6 Nomar Garciaparra 1.25 3.00
DF7 Scott Rolen .75 2.00
DF8 Mariano Rivera 1.25 3.00
DF9 David Ortiz 1.25 3.00
DF10 Johnny Damon .75 2.00
DF11 Tom Glavine .75 2.00
DF12 David Wright 2.00 5.00
DF13 Greg Maddux 2.00 5.00
DF14 Manny Ramirez .75 2.00
DF15 Alex Rodriguez 2.00 5.00
DF16 Roger Clemens 2.50 6.00
DF17 Alfonso Soriano .75 2.00
DF18 Frank Thomas 1.25 3.00
DF19 Chipper Jones 1.25 3.00
DF20 Ivan Rodriguez .75 2.00

2006 Topps 52 Debut Flashbacks Chrome Refractors

*CHROME REF: 1.25X TO 3X BASIC
STATED ODDS 1:87 H, 1:88 R
STATED PRINT RUN 552 SER.#'d SETS
DF3 Albert Pujols 10.00 25.00
DF13 Greg Maddux 4.00 10.00
DF16 Roger Clemens 6.00 15.00

2006 Topps 52 Debut Flashbacks Chrome Gold Refractors

GOLD REF: 4X TO 10X BASIC
STATED ODDS 1:931 H, 1:931 R
STATED PRINT RUN 52 SER.#'d SETS
DF3 Albert Pujols 60.00 120.00
DF4 Ichiro Suzuki 40.00 80.00
DF16 Roger Clemens 20.00 50.00
DF18 Frank Thomas 15.00 40.00

2006 Topps 52 Dynamic Duos

COMPLETE SET (15) 8.00 20.00
STATED ODDS 1:4 H, 1:4 R
DD1 Stephen Drew 1.25 3.00
Carlos Quentin
DD2 Jonathan Papelbon 1.50 4.00
Jon Lester
DD3 Joel Zumaya 1.50 4.00
Justin Verlander
DD4 Dan Uggla 1.25 3.00
Hanley Ramirez
DD5 Jonathan Broxton .75 2.00
Chad Billingsley
DD6 Francisco Liriano 1.50 4.00
Matt Garza
DD7 Lastings Milledge .75 2.00
John Maine
DD8 Chris Coste 1.25 3.00
Cole Hamels
DD9 Mike Napoli 1.25 3.00
Howie Kendrick
DD10 Joe Inglett .50 1.25
Andy Marte
DD11 Jeremy Hermida .50 1.25
Josh Willingham
DD12 Matt Kemp .75 2.00
James Loney
DD13 Andre Ethier 1.25 3.00
Russell Martin
DD14 Melky Cabrera 1.25 3.00
Jeff Karstens
DD15 Ricky Nolasco .75 2.00
Scott Olsen
Josh Johnson
Anibal Sanchez

2006 Topps 52 Ticket to Stardom

STATED ODDS 1:6068 H, 1:6068 R
STATED PRINT RUN 10 SER.#'d SETS
NO PRICING DUE TO SCARCITY
CB Chad Billingsley
CJ Casey Janssen
CQ Carlos Quentin
HK Howie Kendrick
IK Ian Kinsler
JR John Rheinecker
JS Jeremy Sowers
JW Jered Weaver
JZ Joel Zumaya
KM Kendry Morales
MK Matt Kemp
MP Mike Pelfrey
MT Mike Thompson
SD Stephen Drew
ST Scott Thorman
TJB T.J. Beam

2006 Topps 52 Signatures

GROUP A ODDS 1:11,000 H, 1:52,000 R
GROUP B ODDS 1:2580 H, 1:9500 R
GROUP C ODDS 1:130 H, 1:410 R
GROUP D ODDS 1:912 H, 1:3000 R
GROUP E ODDS 1:111 H, 1:372 R
GROUP F ODDS 1:104 H, 1:358 R
GROUP G ODDS 1:32 H, 1:115 R
GROUP H ODDS 1:85 H, 1:300 R
GROUP I ODDS 1:30 H, 1:111 R
GROUP J ODDS 1:20 H, 1:76 R
NO A-B PRICING DUE TO SCARCITY
EXCH DEADLINE 12/31/08
ASTERISK = PARTIAL EXCHANGE
AG Angel Guzman E 3.00 8.00
AL Anthony Lerew H 3.00 8.00
AP Angel Pagan F 6.00 15.00
AR Alex Rodriguez A
AS Anibal Sanchez H 6.00 15.00
BA Brian Anderson D 5.00 12.00
BB Boof Bonser C 8.00 20.00
BC Buck Coats G 3.00 8.00
BPB Brian Bannister E 10.00 25.00
BS Brian Slocum I 3.00 8.00
BZ Ben Zobrist J 3.00 8.00
CHJ Chuck James F 6.00 15.00
CI Chris Iannetta E 5.00 12.00
CJ Chipper Jones B EXCH
CM Chris Mabeus I 3.00 8.00
DO David Ortiz B EXCH
DU Dan Uggla E 8.00 20.00
DW David Wright B
DWW Dontrelle Willis B EXCH
EA Erick Aybar J 3.00 8.00
EF Emiliano Fruto J EXCH * 3.00 8.00
EG Enrique Gonzalez J 3.00 8.00
EM Edward Mujica J 3.00 8.00
FC Fabio Castro G 3.00 8.00
FG Franklin Gutierrez H 6.00 15.00
HCK Hong-Chih Kuo G EXCH 20.00 50.00
HK Howie Kendrick C 12.50 30.00
JAP Albert Pujols A
JD Johnny Damon A
JFS Joe Saunders C 8.00 20.00
JG Joel Guzman F 3.00 8.00
JK Josh Kinney J 5.00 12.00
JM Jeff Mathis F EXCH 3.00 8.00
JP Jonathan Papelbon G 15.00 40.00
JS Josh Sharpless I 3.00 8.00
JV Justin Verlander C 20.00 50.00
JVB John Van Benschoten I 3.00 8.00
JW Jered Weaver C EXCH 15.00 40.00
JWK Jeff Karstens G 8.00 20.00
JZ Joel Zumaya C 20.00 50.00
KF Kevin Frandsen J EXCH 3.00 8.00
KM Kendry Morales G 6.00 15.00
MA Matt Albers I 3.00 8.00
MC Melky Cabrera C EXCH 12.50 30.00
MG Matt Garza C 10.00 25.00
MK Matt Kemp G EXCH 6.00 15.00
MN Mike Napoli G EXCH 5.00 12.00
MR Manny Ramirez B EXCH
MTC Matt Cain C 10.00 25.00
RA Reggie Abercrombie G 3.00 8.00
RO Ryan O'Malley G 3.00 8.00
RZ Ryan Zimmerman C EXCH 30.00 60.00
SD Stephen Drew C 20.00 50.00
SM Scott Mathieson I 3.00 8.00
TJB T.J. Bohn I 3.00 8.00
TM Tom Mastny J 3.00 8.00
WB Bill Bray E 3.00 8.00
YD Yurendell DeCaster J 3.00 8.00
YP Yusmeiro Petit E 3.00 8.00

2006 Topps 52 Signatures Red Ink

STATED ODDS 1:235 H, 1:840 R
STATED PRINT RUN 52 SER.#'d SETS
EXCH DEADLINE 12/31/08
AG Angel Guzman 12.50 30.00
AL Anthony Lerew 20.00 50.00
AP Angel Pagan 30.00 60.00
AR Alex Rodriguez
AS Anibal Sanchez 20.00 50.00
BA Brian Anderson 12.50 30.00
BB Boof Bonser 20.00 50.00
BC Buck Coats 12.50 30.00
BPB Brian Bannister 50.00 100.00
BS Brian Slocum 20.00 50.00
BZ Ben Zobrist 12.50 30.00
CHJ Chuck James 20.00 50.00
CI Chris Iannetta 30.00 60.00
CJ Chipper Jones EXCH
CM Chris Mabeus 12.50 30.00
DO David Ortiz EXCH
DU Dan Uggla 20.00 50.00
DW David Wright
DWW Dontrelle Willis EXCH
EA Erick Aybar 12.50 30.00
EF Emiliano Fruto 12.50 30.00
EG Enrique Gonzalez 12.50 30.00
EM Edward Mujica 12.50 30.00
FC Fabio Castro 30.00 60.00
FG Franklin Gutierrez 12.50 30.00
HCK Hong-Chih Kuo EXCH
HK Howie Kendrick 30.00 60.00
JAP Albert Pujols
JD Johnny Damon
JFS Joe Saunders 12.50 30.00
JG Joel Guzman 12.50 30.00
JK Josh Kinney 20.00 50.00
JM Jeff Mathis EXCH 12.50 30.00
JP Jonathan Papelbon 60.00 120.00
JS Josh Sharpless 12.50 30.00
JV Justin Verlander 40.00 80.00
JVB John Van Benschoten 12.50 30.00
JW Jered Weaver EXCH 30.00 60.00
JWK Jeff Karstens 20.00 50.00
JZ Joel Zumaya 50.00 100.00
KF Kevin Frandsen EXCH 12.50 30.00
KM Kendry Morales 20.00 50.00
MA Matt Albers 12.50 30.00
MC Melky Cabrera EXCH 30.00 60.00
MG Matt Garza 20.00 50.00
MK Matt Kemp EXCH 30.00 60.00
MN Mike Napoli EXCH 20.00 50.00
MR Manny Ramirez EXCH
MTC Matt Cain 20.00 50.00
RA Reggie Abercrombie 12.50 30.00
RO Ryan O'Malley 20.00 50.00
RZ Ryan Zimmerman EXCH 60.00 120.00
SD Stephen Drew 50.00 100.00
SM Scott Mathieson 20.00 50.00
TJB T.J. Bohn 12.50 30.00
TM Tom Mastny 20.00 50.00
WB Bill Bray 12.50 30.00
YD Yurendell DeCaster 12.50 30.00
YP Yusmeiro Petit 20.00 50.00

2007 Topps 52

This 227-card set was released in December, 2007. The set was issued in both hobby and retail channels. The hobby packs consisted of eight cards with an $3 SRP which came 20 packs to a box and eight boxes to a case. Some of the more popular 2007 rookies were also created in shorter printed action variations and the final fourteen cards in the set were also short-printed. These shorter printed cards were inserted into packs at a stated rate of one in six for either hobby or retail. No cards numbered 198-200 were printed in this set.

COMP.SET w/o SPs (202) 20.00 50.00
COMMON CARD (1-227) .25 .60
COMMON ACTION VARIATION 2.00 5.00
ACT.VAR.STATED ODDS 1:6 H, 1:6 R
COMMON SP 2.00 5.00
SP STATED ODDS 1:6 H, 1:6 R
1 Akinori Iwamura RC .60 1.50
2 Angel Sanchez RC .25 .60
3 Luis Hernandez (RC) .25 .60
4 Joaquin Arias (RC) .25 .60
5a Troy Tulowitzki (RC) .60 1.50
5b Troy Tulowitzki 2.50 6.00
Action SP
6 Jesus Flores RC .25 .60
7 Mickey Mantle 2.50 6.00
8 Kory Casto (RC) .25 .60
9 Tony Abreu RC .60 1.50
10 Kevin Kouzmanoff (RC) .25 .60
11 Travis Buck (RC) .25 .60
12 Kurt Suzuki (RC) .25 .60
13 Matt DeSalvo (RC) .25 .60
14 Jerry Owens (RC) .25 .60
15 Alex Gordon RC 1.25 3.00
16 Jeff Baker (RC) .25 .60
17 Ben Francisco (RC) .25 .60
18 Nate Schierholtz (RC) .25 .60
19 Nathan Haynes (RC) .25 .60
20a Ryan Braun (RC) 1.50 4.00
20b Ryan Braun 3.00 8.00
Action SP
21 Brian Barden RC .25 .60
22 Sean Barker RC .25 .60
23 Alejandro De Aza RC .40 1.00
24 Jamie Burke (RC) .25 .60
25 Michael Bourn (RC) .25 .60
26 Jeff Salazar (RC) .25 .60
27 Chase Headley (RC) .25 .60
28 Chris Basak RC .25 .60
29 Mike Fontenot (RC) .25 .60
30a Hunter Pence (RC) 1.25 3.00
30b Hunter Pence 3.00 8.00
Action SP
31 Masumi Kuwata RC 2.00 5.00
32 Ryan Rowland-Smith RC .25 .60
33 Tyler Clippard (RC) .40 1.00
34 Matt Lindstrom (RC) .25 .60
35 Fred Lewis (RC) .40 1.00
36 Brett Carroll RC .25 .60
37 Alexi Casilla RC .40 1.00
38 Nick Gorneault (RC) .25 .60
39 Dennis Sarfate (RC) .25 .60
40 Felix Pie (RC) .25 .60
41 Miguel Montero (RC) .25 .60
42 Danny Putnam (RC) .25 .60
43 Shane Youman RC .25 .60
44 Andy LaRoche (RC) .25 .60
45 Jarrod Saltalamacchia (RC) .40 1.00
46 Kei Igawa RC .60 1.50
47 Don Kelly (RC) .25 .60
48 Fernando Cortez (RC) .25 .60
49 Travis Metcalf RC .40 1.00
50a Daisuke Matsuzaka RC 2.50 6.00
50b Daisuke Matsuzaka 3.00 8.00
Action SP
51 Edwar Ramirez RC .60 1.50
52 Ryan Sweeney (RC) .25 .60
53 Shawn Riggans (RC) .25 .60
54 Billy Sadler (RC) .25 .60
55 Billy Butler (RC) .40 1.00
56 Andy Cavazos RC .25 .60
57 Sean Henn (RC) .25 .60
58 Brian Esposito (RC) .25 .60
59 Brandon Morrow RC .60 1.50
60 Adam Lind (RC) .25 .60
61 Joe Smith RC .25 .60
62 Chris Stewart RC .25 .60
63 Eulogio De La Cruz (RC) .25 .60
64 Sean Gallagher (RC) .25 .60
65 Carlos Gomez RC .40 1.00
66 Jailen Peguero RC .25 .60
67 Juan Perez RC .25 .60
68 Levale Speigner RC .25 .60
69 Jamie Vermilyea RC .25 .60
70a Delmon Young (RC) .40 1.00
70b Delmon Young 2.00 5.00
Action SP
71 Jo-Jo Reyes (RC) .25 .60
72 Zack Segovia (RC) .25 .60
73 Andy Sonnanstine RC .25 .60
74 Chase Wright RC .60 1.50
75 Josh Fields (RC) .25 .60
76 Jon Knott (RC) .25 .60
77 Guillermo Rodriguez RC .25 .60
78 Jon Coutlangus (RC) .25 .60
79 Kevin Cameron RC .25 .60
80 Mark Reynolds RC 1.00 2.50
81 Brian Stokes (RC) .25 .60
82 Alberto Arias RC .25 .60
83 Yoel Hernandez RC .25 .60
84 David Murphy (RC) .25 .60
85 Josh Hamilton (RC) .60 1.50
86 Justin Hampson (RC) .25 .60
87 Doug Slaten RC .25 .60
88 Joseph Bisenius RC .25 .60
89 Troy Cate RC .25 .60
90 Homer Bailey (RC) .40 1.00
91 Jacoby Ellsbury (RC) 2.50 6.00
92 Devern Hansack RC .25 .60
93 Zach McClellan RC .25 .60
94 Vinny Rottino (RC) .25 .60
95 Elijah Dukes RC .40 1.00
96 Ryan Z. Braun UER RC .25 .60
Facsimile auto of Ryan J. Braun
97 Lee Gardner (RC) .25 .60
98 Joakim Soria RC .25 .60
99 Jason Miller (RC) .25 .60
100a Hideki Okajima RC 1.25 3.00
100b Hideki Okajima 3.00 8.00
Action SP
101 John Danks RC .25 .60
102 Garrett Jones (RC) .25 .60
103 Jensen Lewis RC .25 .60
104 Clay Rapada RC .25 .60
105 Kyle Kendrick RC .60 1.50
106 Eric Stults RC .25 .60
107 Jared Burton RC .25 .60
108 Julio DePaula RC .40 1.00
109 Jesse Litsch RC .40 1.00
110 Micah Owings (RC) .25 .60
111 Cory Doyne (RC) .25 .60
112 Jay Marshall RC .25 .60
113 Mike Schultz RC .25 .60
114 Juan Salas (RC) .25 .60
115 Matt Chico (RC) .25 .60
116 Brad Salmon RC .25 .60
117 Jeff Bailey (RC) .25 .60
118 Gustavo Molina RC .25 .60
119 Brian Burres (RC) .25 .60
120 Yovani Gallardo (RC) .75 2.00
121 Hector Gimenez (RC) .25 .60
122 Kelvin Jimenez RC .25 .60
123 Rick Vanden Hurk RC .40 1.00
124 Billy Petrick (RC) .25 .60
125 Andrew Miller RC 1.50 4.00
126 Rocky Cherry RC .60 1.50
127 Jonathan De Jong RC .25 .60
128 Eric Hull RC .25 .60
129 Kevin Mahar RC .25 .60
130a Tim Lincecum RC 2.00 5.00
130b Tim Lincecum 3.00 8.00
Action SP
131 Garrett Olson (RC) .25 .60
132 Neal Musser RC .25 .60
133 Mike Rabelo RC .25 .60
134 Dennis Dove (RC) .25 .60
135 J.D. Durbin (RC) .25 .60
136 Jose Garcia RC .25 .60
137 Marcus McBeth (RC) .25 .60
138 Curtis Thigpen (RC) .25 .60
139 Mike Zagurski RC .25 .60
140 Kevin Slowey (RC) .60 1.50
141 Dewon Day RC .25 .60
142 Glen Perkins (RC) .25 .60
143 Brian Wolfe (RC) .25 .60
144 Dallas Braden RC .40 1.00
145 J.A. Happ (RC) .25 .60
146 Lee Gronkiewicz RC .25 .60
147 Cesar Jimenez RC .25 .60
148 Mark McLemore (RC) .25 .60
149 Connor Robertson RC .25 .60
150a Phil Hughes (RC) 1.25 3.00
150b Phil Hughes 3.00 8.00
Action SP
151 Matthew Brown RC .25 .60
152 Ryan Feierabend (RC) .25 .60
153 Brendan Ryan (RC) .25 .60
154 Terry Evans RC .25 .60
155 Eric Patterson (RC) .25 .60
156 Patrick Misch (RC) .25 .60
157 Darren Clarke RC .25 .60
158 Kevin Melillo (RC) .25 .60
159 Edwin Bellorin RC .25 .60
160 Ubaldo Jimenez (RC) .25 .60
161 Ryan Budde (RC) .25 .60
162 Brian Buscher RC .40 1.00
163 Juan Gutierrez RC .25 .60
164 Franklin Morales (RC) .25 .60
165 Carmen Pignatiello (RC) .25 .60
166 Jair Jurrjens (RC) .25 .60
167 Manny Acosta (RC) .25 .60
168 Ian Stewart (RC) .25 .60
169 Daniel Barone (RC) .25 .60
170a Justin Upton RC 1.50 4.00
170b Justin Upton 3.00 8.00
Action SP
171 Tommy Watkins RC .40 1.00
172 Ross Wolf RC .25 .60
173 Jack Cassel RC .25 .60
174 Asdrubal Cabrera RC .25 .60
175 Mauro Zarate RC .25 .60
176 Aaron Laffey RC .60 1.50
177 Marcus Gwyn RC .25 .60
178 Danny Richar RC .25 .60
179 Joel Hanrahan (RC) .25 .60
180 Cameron Maybin RC 1.25 3.00
181 John Lannan RC .25 .60
182 Shelley Duncan (RC) .60 1.50
183 Brandon Wood (RC) .25 .60
184 Delwyn Young (RC) .25 .60
185 Manny Parra (RC) .25 .60
186 Ehren Wassermann RC .25 .60
187 Jose A. Reyes RC .25 .60
188 Jose Ascanio RC .25 .60
190a Alvin Colina RC .60 1.50
190b Joba Chamberlain 5.00 12.00
Action SP
191 Lee Escobar (RC) .25 .60
192 Carlos Maldonado (RC) .25 .60
193 Dan Meyer (RC) .25 .60
194 Scott Moore (RC) .25 .60
195 Romulo Sanchez RC .25 .60
196 Tom Shearn (RC) .25 .60
197 Craig Stansberry (RC) .25 .60
201 Joba Chamberlain RC 2.50 6.00
202 John Nelson SP (RC) 2.00 5.00
203 Phil Dumatrait (RC) .25 .60
204 Brandon Moss (RC) .25 .60
205 Beltran Perez (RC) .25 .60
206 Drew Anderson RC .25 .60
207 Brett Campbell RC .25 .60
208 Andy Cannizaro SP RC 2.00 5.00
209 Travis Chick SP (RC) 2.00 5.00
210 Francisco Cruceta SP (RC) 2.00 5.00
211 Jose Diaz SP (RC) 2.00 5.00
212 Jeff Fiorentino SP (RC) 2.00 5.00
213 Tim Gradoville SP RC 2.00 5.00
214 Kevin Hooper SP (RC) 2.00 5.00
215 Philip Humber SP (RC) 2.00 5.00
216 Juan Lara SP RC 2.00 5.00
217 Mitch Maier SP RC 2.00 5.00
218 Juan Morillo SP (RC) 2.00 5.00
219 A.J. Murray SP RC 2.00 5.00
220 Chris Narveson SP (RC) 2.00 5.00
221 Oswaldo Navarro SP RC 2.00 5.00

2007 Topps 52 Black Back

STATED ODDS 1:6 HOBBY
1 Akinori Iwamura 2.50 6.00
2 Angel Sanchez 2.00 5.00
3 Luis Hernandez 2.00 5.00
4 Joaquin Arias 2.00 5.00
5 Troy Tulowitzki 2.50 6.00
6 Jesus Flores 2.00 5.00
7 Mickey Mantle 3.00 8.00
8 Kory Casto 2.00 5.00
9 Tony Abreu 2.50 6.00
10 Kevin Kouzmanoff 2.00 5.00
11 Travis Buck 2.00 5.00
12 Kurt Suzuki 2.00 5.00
13 Matt DeSalvo 2.00 5.00
14 Jerry Owens 2.00 5.00
15 Alex Gordon 3.00 8.00
16 Jeff Baker 2.00 5.00
17 Ben Francisco 2.00 5.00
18 Nate Schierholtz 2.00 5.00
19 Nathan Haynes 2.00 5.00
20 Ryan Braun 3.00 8.00
21 Brian Barden 2.00 5.00
22 Sean Barker 2.00 5.00
23 Alejandro De Aza 2.00 5.00
24 Jamie Burke 2.00 5.00
25 Michael Bourn 2.00 5.00
26 Jeff Salazar 2.00 5.00
27 Chase Headley 2.00 5.00
28 Chris Basak 2.00 5.00
29 Mike Fontenot 2.00 5.00
30 Hunter Pence 3.00 8.00
31 Masumi Kuwata 2.50 6.00
32 Ryan Rowland-Smith 2.00 5.00
33 Tyler Clippard 2.00 5.00
34 Matt Lindstrom 2.00 5.00
35 Fred Lewis 2.00 5.00
36 Brett Carroll 2.00 5.00
37 Alexi Casilla 2.00 5.00
38 Nick Gorneault 2.00 5.00
39 Dennis Sarfate 2.00 5.00
40 Felix Pie 2.00 5.00
41 Miguel Montero 2.00 5.00
42 Danny Putnam 2.00 5.00
43 Shane Youman 2.00 5.00
44 Andy LaRoche 2.00 5.00
45 Jarrod Saltalamacchia 2.00 5.00
46 Kei Igawa 2.50 6.00
47 Don Kelly 2.00 5.00
48 Fernando Cortez 2.00 5.00
49 Travis Metcalf 2.00 5.00
50 Daisuke Matsuzaka 3.00 8.00
51 Edwar Ramirez 2.50 6.00
52 Ryan Sweeney 2.00 5.00
53 Shawn Riggans 2.00 5.00
54 Billy Sadler 2.00 5.00
55 Billy Butler 2.00 5.00
56 Andy Cavazos 2.00 5.00
57 Sean Henn 2.00 5.00
58 Brian Esposito 2.00 5.00
59 Brandon Morrow 2.00 5.00
60 Adam Lind 2.00 5.00
61 Joe Smith 2.00 5.00
62 Chris Stewart 2.00 5.00
63 Eulogio De La Cruz 2.00 5.00
64 Sean Gallagher 2.00 5.00
65 Carlos Gomez 2.00 5.00
66 Jailen Peguero 2.00 5.00
67 Juan Perez 2.00 5.00
68 Levale Speigner 2.00 5.00
69 Jamie Vermilyea 2.00 5.00
70 Delmon Young 2.00 5.00
71 Jo-Jo Reyes 2.00 5.00
72 Zack Segovia 2.00 5.00
73 Andy Sonnanstine 2.00 5.00
74 Chase Wright 2.50 6.00
75 Josh Fields 2.00 5.00
76 Jon Knott 2.00 5.00
77 Guillermo Rodriguez 2.00 5.00
78 Jon Coutlangus 2.00 5.00
79 Kevin Cameron 2.00 5.00
80 Mark Reynolds 2.50 6.00
81 Brian Stokes 2.00 5.00
82 Alberto Arias 2.00 5.00
83 Yoel Hernandez 2.00 5.00
84 David Murphy 2.00 5.00
85 Josh Hamilton 5.00 12.00
86 Justin Hampson 2.00 5.00
87 Doug Slaten 2.00 5.00
88 Joseph Bisenius 2.00 5.00
89 Troy Cate 2.00 5.00
90 Homer Bailey 2.00 5.00
91 Jacoby Ellsbury 5.00 12.00
92 Devern Hansack 2.00 5.00
93 Zach McClellan 2.00 5.00
94 Vinny Rottino 2.00 5.00
95 Elijah Dukes 2.00 5.00
96 Ryan Z. Braun UER 2.00 5.00
Facsimile auto of Ryan J.Braun
97 Lee Gardner 2.00 5.00
98 Joakim Soria 2.00 5.00
99 Jason Miller 2.00 5.00
100 Hideki Okajima 3.00 8.00
101 John Danks 2.00 5.00
102 Garrett Jones 2.00 5.00
103 Jensen Lewis 2.00 5.00
104 Clay Rapada 2.00 5.00
105 Kyle Kendrick 2.50 6.00
106 Eric Stults 2.00 5.00
110 Micah Owings 2.00 5.00
113 Mike Schultz 2.00 5.00
115 Matt Chico 2.00 5.00
120 Yovani Gallardo 2.50 6.00
125 Andrew Miller 3.00 8.00

2007 Topps 52 Chrome

STATED ODDS 1:3 H, 1:6 R
STATED PRINT RUN 1952 SER.#'d SETS
1 Akinori Iwamura 2.00 5.00
2 Angel Sanchez 1.25 3.00
3 Luis Hernandez 1.25 3.00
4 Troy Tulowitzki 2.00 5.00
5 Joaquin Arias 1.25 3.00
6 Jesus Flores 1.25 3.00
7 Brandon Wood 1.25 3.00
8 Kory Casto 1.25 3.00
9 Kevin Kouzmanoff 1.25 3.00
10 Tony Abreu 2.00 5.00
11 Travis Buck 1.25 3.00
12 Kurt Suzuki 1.25 3.00
13 Alejandro De Aza 1.25 3.00
14 Alex Gordon 3.00 8.00
15 Jerry Owens 1.25 3.00
16 Ryan J. Braun 3.00 8.00
17 Michael Bourn 1.25 3.00
18 Hunter Pence 2.00 5.00

19 Jeff Baker 1.25 3.00
20 Ben Francisco 1.25 3.00
21 Nate Schierholtz 1.25 3.00
22 Nathan Haynes 1.25 3.00
23 Andrew Miller 2.00 5.00
24 Sean Barker 1.25 3.00
25 Matt DeSalvo 1.25 3.00
26 Fred Lewis 1.25 3.00
27 Jamie Burke 1.25 3.00
28 Jeff Salazar 1.25 3.00
29 Chase Headley 1.25 3.00
30 Chris Basak 1.25 3.00
31 Mike Fontenot 1.25 3.00
32 Felix Pie 1.25 3.00
33 Masumi Kuwata 3.00 8.00
34 Daisuke Matsuzaka 4.00 10.00
35 Tim Lincecum 3.00 8.00
36 Jarrod Saltalamacchia 1.25 3.00
37 Tyler Clippard 1.25 3.00
38 Billy Butler 1.25 3.00
39 Matt Lindstrom 1.25 3.00
40 Brett Carroll 1.25 3.00
41 Alexi Casilla 1.25 3.00
42 Nick Gorneault 1.25 3.00
43 Matt Chico 1.25 3.00
44 Adam Lind 1.25 3.00
45 Miguel Montero 1.25 3.00
46 Danny Putnam 1.25 3.00
47 Delmon Young 1.25 3.00
48 Josh Fields 1.25 3.00
49 Carlos Gomez 1.25 3.00
50 Mark Reynolds 2.00 5.00
51 Shane Youman 1.25 3.00
52 Andy LaRoche 1.25 3.00
53 Kei Igawa 2.00 5.00
54 Don Kelly 1.25 3.00
55 Cameron Maybin 3.00 8.00
56 Travis Metcalf 1.25 3.00
57 Ubaldo Jimenez 1.25 3.00
58 Ryan Sweeney 1.25 3.00
59 Shawn Riggans 1.25 3.00
60 Jacoby Ellsbury 6.00 15.00
61 Andy Cavazos 1.25 3.00
62 Josh Hamilton 4.00 10.00
63 Homer Bailey 1.25 3.00
64 Sean Henn 1.25 3.00
65 Elijah Dukes 1.25 3.00
66 Brian Esposito 1.25 3.00
67 Brandon Morrow 1.25 3.00
68 Joe Smith 1.25 3.00
69 Chris Stewart 1.25 3.00
70 Eulogio De La Cruz 1.25 3.00
71 Sean Gallagher 1.25 3.00
72 Jailen Peguero 1.25 3.00
73 Juan Perez 1.25 3.00
74 Levale Speigner 1.25 3.00
75 Jamie Vermilyea 1.25 3.00
76 Hideki Okajima 3.00 8.00
77 Eric Patterson 1.25 3.00
78 Zack Segovia 1.25 3.00
79 Kyle Kendrick 2.00 5.00
80 Andy Sonnanstine 1.25 3.00
81 Chase Wright 2.00 5.00
82 Jon Knott 1.25 3.00
83 Guillermo Rodriguez 1.25 3.00
84 Jon Coutlangus 1.25 3.00
85 Kevin Cameron 1.25 3.00
86 Brian Stokes 1.25 3.00
87 Alberto Arias 1.25 3.00
88 Delwyn Young 1.25 3.00
89 David Murphy 1.25 3.00
90 Micah Owings 1.25 3.00
91 Yovani Gallardo 2.00 5.00
92 Justin Hampson 1.25 3.00
93 Doug Slaten 1.25 3.00
94 Justin Upton 4.00 10.00
95 Joba Chamberlain 8.00 20.00

2007 Topps 52 Chrome Refractors

*CHR.REF: .6X TO 1.5X BASIC CHROME
STATED ODDS 1:9 H, 1:25 R
STATED PRINT RUN 552 SER.#'d SETS
14 Alex Gordon 4.00 10.00
16 Ryan J. Braun 6.00 15.00
33 Masumi Kuwata 4.00 10.00
34 Daisuke Matsuzaka 5.00 12.00
55 Cameron Maybin 4.00 10.00
76 Hideki Okajima 4.00 10.00
94 Justin Upton 5.00 12.00
95 Joba Chamberlain 15.00 40.00

2007 Topps 52 Chrome Gold Refractors

STATED ODDS 1:89 H, 1:300 R
STATED PRINT RUN 52 SER.#'d SETS
1 Akinori Iwamura 6.00 15.00
2 Angel Sanchez 5.00 12.00
3 Luis Hernandez 5.00 12.00
4 Troy Tulowitzki 6.00 15.00
5 Joaquin Arias 5.00 12.00
6 Jesus Flores 5.00 12.00
7 Brandon Wood 5.00 12.00
8 Kory Casto 5.00 12.00
9 Kevin Kouzmanoff 5.00 12.00
10 Tony Abreu 6.00 15.00
11 Travis Buck 5.00 12.00
12 Kurt Suzuki 5.00 12.00
13 Alejandro De Aza 6.00 15.00
14 Alex Gordon 12.50 30.00
15 Jerry Owens 5.00 12.00
16 Ryan J. Braun 20.00 50.00
17 Michael Bourn 5.00 12.00
18 Hunter Pence 20.00 50.00
19 Jeff Baker 5.00 12.00
20 Ben Francisco 5.00 12.00
21 Nate Schierholtz 5.00 12.00
22 Nathan Haynes 5.00 12.00
23 Andrew Miller 10.00 25.00
24 Sean Barker 5.00 12.00
25 Matt DeSalvo 5.00 12.00
26 Fred Lewis 6.00 15.00
27 Jamie Burke 5.00 12.00
28 Jeff Salazar 5.00 12.00
29 Chase Headley 5.00 12.00
30 Chris Basak 5.00 12.00
31 Mike Fontenot 5.00 12.00
32 Felix Pie 5.00 12.00
33 Masumi Kuwata 30.00 60.00
34 Daisuke Matsuzaka 30.00 60.00
35 Tim Lincecum 20.00 50.00
36 Jarrod Saltalamacchia 6.00 15.00
37 Tyler Clippard 6.00 15.00
38 Billy Butler 6.00 15.00
39 Matt Lindstrom 5.00 12.00
40 Brett Carroll 5.00 12.00
41 Alexi Casilla 6.00 15.00
42 Nick Gorneault 5.00 12.00
43 Matt Chico 5.00 12.00
44 Adam Lind 5.00 12.00
45 Miguel Montero 5.00 12.00
46 Danny Putnam 5.00 12.00
47 Delmon Young 6.00 15.00
48 Josh Fields 5.00 12.00
49 Carlos Gomez 6.00 15.00
50 Mark Reynolds 6.00 15.00
51 Shane Youman 5.00 12.00
52 Andy LaRoche 5.00 12.00
53 Kei Igawa 6.00 15.00
54 Don Kelly 5.00 12.00
55 Cameron Maybin 12.50 30.00
56 Travis Metcalf 6.00 15.00
57 Ubaldo Jimenez 5.00 12.00
58 Ryan Sweeney 5.00 12.00
59 Shawn Riggans 5.00 12.00
60 Jacoby Ellsbury 40.00 80.00
61 Andy Cavazos 5.00 12.00
62 Josh Hamilton 12.50 30.00
63 Homer Bailey 6.00 15.00
64 Sean Henn 5.00 12.00
65 Elijah Dukes 6.00 15.00
66 Brian Esposito 5.00 12.00
67 Brandon Morrow 6.00 15.00
68 Joe Smith 5.00 12.00
69 Chris Stewart 5.00 12.00
70 Eulogio De La Cruz 5.00 12.00
71 Sean Gallagher 5.00 12.00
72 Jailen Peguero 5.00 12.00
73 Juan Perez 5.00 12.00
74 Levale Speigner 5.00 12.00
75 Jamie Vermilyea 5.00 12.00
76 Hideki Okajima 15.00 40.00
77 Eric Patterson 5.00 12.00
78 Zack Segovia 5.00 12.00
79 Kyle Kendrick 6.00 15.00
80 Andy Sonnanstine 5.00 12.00
81 Chase Wright 6.00 15.00
82 Jon Knott 5.00 12.00
83 Guillermo Rodriguez 5.00 12.00
84 Jon Coutlangus 5.00 12.00
85 Kevin Cameron 5.00 12.00
86 Brian Stokes 5.00 12.00
87 Alberto Arias 5.00 12.00
88 Delwyn Young 5.00 12.00
89 David Murphy 5.00 12.00
90 Micah Owings 5.00 12.00
91 Yovani Gallardo 6.00 15.00
92 Justin Hampson 5.00 12.00
93 Doug Slaten 5.00 12.00
94 Justin Upton 20.00 50.00
95 Joba Chamberlain 50.00 100.00

2007 Topps 52 Debut Flashbacks

COMPLETE SET (15) 6.00 15.00
STATED ODDS 1:6 H, 1:6 R
COMPLETE CHR.SET (15) 10.00 25.00
*CHROME: .6X TO 1.5X BASIC
CHROME ODDS 1:16 H, 1:46 R
CHR.PRINT RUN 1952 SER.#'d SETS
CHR.REF: 1X TO 2.5X BASIC
CHR.REF ODDS 1:55 H, 1:170 R
CHR.REF PRINT RUN 552 SER.#'d SETS
DFC1 Vladimir Guerrero .75 2.00
DFC2 Ken Griffey Jr. 1.25 3.00
DFC3 Pedro Martinez .75 2.00
DFC4 Carlos Delgado .75 2.00
DFC5 Gary Sheffield .75 2.00
DFC6 Curt Schilling .75 2.00
DFC7 Paul Lo Duca .75 2.00
DFC8 Miguel Tejada .75 2.00
DFC9 Trevor Hoffman .75 2.00
DFC10 Francisco Cordero .75 2.00
DFC11 Travis Hafner .75 2.00
DFC12 Jorge Posada .75 2.00
DFC13 Jimmy Rollins .75 2.00
DFC14 Magglio Ordonez .75 2.00
DFC15 Jim Edmonds .75 2.00

2007 Topps 52 Debut Flashbacks Chrome Gold Refractors

*GOLD REF: 3X TO 8X BASIC
STATED ODDS 1:609 H, 1:1700 R
STATED PRINT RUN 52 SER.#'d SETS
DFC2 Ken Griffey Jr. 15.00 40.00

2007 Topps 52 Diamond Debut Tix

STATED ODDS 1:649 HOBBY
STATED PRINT RUN 20 SER.#'d SETS
NO PRICING DUE TO SCARCITY
AD Alejandro De Aza
AG Alex Gordon
AL Andy LaRoche
BB Billy Butler
DB Dallas Braden
DM Daisuke Matsuzaka
HB Homer Bailey
JAH J.A. Happ
JC Joba Chamberlain
JE Jacoby Ellsbury
JH Josh Hamilton
JL Jesse Litsch
JM Jay Marshall
JS Jarrod Saltalamacchia
JU Justin Upton
KS Kevin Slowey
RB Ryan Braun
TA Tony Abreu
TB Travis Buck
TC Tyler Clippard
TL Tim Lincecum
YG Yovani Gallardo

2007 Topps 52 Dynamic Duos

COMPLETE SET (15) 6.00 15.00
STATED ODDS 1:4 H, 1:4 R
DD1 Tim Lincecum 1.50 4.00
Nate Schierholtz
DD2 Joba Chamberlain 2.00 5.00
Phil Hughes
DD3 Ryan Braun 1.25 3.00
Yovani Gallardo
DD4 Kyle Kendrick .75 2.00
Michael Bourn
DD5 Delmon Young .75 2.00
Elijah Dukes
DD6 Hideki Okajima 2.00 5.00
Daisuke Matsuzaka
DD7 Justin Upton .75 2.00
Mark Reynolds
DD8 Eric Patterson .50 1.25
Felix Pie
DD9 Josh Hamilton 1.50 4.00
Homer Bailey
DD10 Ubaldo Jimenez .75 2.00
Troy Tulowitzki
DD11 Alex Gordon 1.00 2.50
Billy Butler
DD12 Delwyn Young .50 1.25
Andy LaRoche
DD13 Andrew Miller 1.25 3.00
Cameron Maybin
DD14 Joe Smith .75 2.00
Carlos Gomez
DD15 David Murphy .75 2.00
Jarrod Saltalamacchia

2007 Topps 52 Signatures

GROUP A ODDS 1:4750 H, 1:13,401 R
GROUP B ODDS 1:150 H, 1:429 R
GROUP C ODDS 1:3149 H, 1:19,065 R
GROUP D ODDS 1:1049 H, 1:3000 R
GROUP E ODDS 1:54 H, 1:162 R
GROUP F ODDS 1:9 H, 1:29 R
EXCHANGE DEADLINE 11/30/09
AA Alberto Arias F 3.00 8.00
AC Alexi Casilla F 3.00 8.00
AG Alex Gordon B 40.00 80.00
AI Akinori Iwamura B EXCH 8.00 20.00
AL Andy LaRoche B 10.00 25.00
AM Andrew Miller B EXCH 12.50 30.00
AS Angel Sanchez E 3.00 8.00
ASL Aaron Laffey F 6.00 15.00
BB Brian Barden F 3.00 8.00
BC Brett Carroll F 3.00 8.00
BE Brian Esposito F 3.00 8.00
BF Ben Francisco F 3.00 8.00
BP Billy Petrick E 3.00 8.00
BPB Brian Buscher E 3.00 8.00
BS Brian Stokes B EXCH 5.00 12.00
BW Brian Wolfe E 3.00 8.00
CD Cory Doyne F 3.00 8.00
CH Chase Headley E 5.00 12.00
CM Cameron Maybin B 20.00 50.00
CS Chris Stewart B 3.00 8.00
CW Chase Wright B 8.00 20.00
DC Darren Clarke F 3.00 8.00
ER Edwar Ramirez F 5.00 12.00
FC Francisco Cordero A 50.00 100.00
FL Fred Lewis B 5.00 12.00
FP Felix Pie B 10.00 25.00
GS Gary Sheffield A 20.00 50.00
HO Hideki Okajima B 30.00 60.00
HP Hunter Pence B 20.00 50.00
JA Joaquin Arias B 3.00 8.00
JB Jared Burton B 8.00 20.00
JC Jon Coutlangus B 3.00 8.00
JCH Joba Chamberlain B 150.00 250.00
JH Joel Hanrahan D 10.00 25.00
JJR Jo-Jo Reyes B 3.00 8.00
JL Jensen Lewis F 3.00 8.00
JM Jason Miller D 5.00 12.00
JP Jorge Posada A 60.00 120.00
JR Jimmy Rollins A
JRB Joseph Bisenius F 3.00 8.00
JSS Jarrod Saltalamacchia B 10.00 25.00
JU Justin Upton B 30.00 60.00
KK Kevin Kouzmanoff B EXCH 6.00 15.00
KS Kurt Suzuki B 3.00 8.00
LS Levale Speigner F 3.00 8.00
MB Michael Bourn B 10.00 25.00
MBB Matthew Brown F 3.00 8.00
MJZ Mike Zagurski E 3.00 8.00
ML Matt Lindstrom B 6.00 15.00
MM Mark McLemore E 3.00 8.00
NG Nick Gorneault B 6.00 15.00
NH Nathan Haynes F 3.00 8.00
PD Phil Dumatrait E 3.00 8.00
PH Phil Hughes B EXCH 40.00 80.00
PL Paul Lo Duca A EXCH 10.00 25.00
RB Ryan Braun B 50.00 100.00
RC Rocky Cherry C 5.00 12.00
RDB Ryan Budde E 3.00 8.00
RZB Ryan Z. Braun B 3.00 8.00
TB Travis Buck B 5.00 12.00
TC Tyler Clippard B EXCH 12.50 30.00
TL Tim Lincecum B 30.00 60.00
TM Travis Metcalf B 10.00 25.00
TPC Troy Cate F 3.00 8.00
YG Yovani Gallardo B 10.00 25.00
ZS Zack Segovia E 3.00 8.00

2007 Topps 52 Signatures Red Ink

STATED ODDS 1:88 HOBBY
STATED PRINT RUN 52 SER.#'d SETS
EXCH DEADLINE 12/31/08
AA Alberto Arias 10.00 25.00
AC Alexi Casilla 10.00 25.00
AG Alex Gordon 75.00 150.00
AI Akinori Iwamura 30.00 60.00
AL Andy LaRoche 30.00 60.00
AM Andrew Miller 30.00 60.00
AS Angel Sanchez 10.00 25.00
ASL Aaron Laffey 20.00 50.00
BB Brian Barden 10.00 25.00
BC Brett Carroll 10.00 25.00
BE Brian Esposito 10.00 25.00
BF Ben Francisco 10.00 25.00
BP Billy Petrick 10.00 25.00
BPB Brian Buscher 10.00 25.00
BS Brian Stokes 10.00 25.00
BW Brian Wolfe 10.00 25.00
CD Cory Doyne 10.00 25.00
CH Chase Headley 20.00 50.00
CM Cameron Maybin 40.00 80.00
CS Chris Stewart 10.00 25.00
CW Chase Wright 30.00 60.00
DC Darren Clarke 10.00 25.00
ER Edwar Ramirez 15.00 40.00
FC Francisco Cordero 100.00 200.00
FL Fred Lewis 10.00 25.00
FP Felix Pie 20.00 50.00
GS Gary Sheffield 40.00 80.00
HO Hideki Okajima 50.00 100.00
HP Hunter Pence 75.00 150.00
JA Joaquin Arias 10.00 25.00
JB Jared Burton 15.00 40.00
JC Jon Coutlangus 10.00 25.00
JCH Joba Chamberlain 200.00 300.00
JH Joel Hanrahan 20.00 50.00
JJR Jo-Jo Reyes 10.00 25.00
JL Jensen Lewis 10.00 25.00
JM Jason Miller 10.00 25.00
JP Jorge Posada 100.00 200.00
JR Jimmy Rollins
JRB Joseph Bisenius 10.00 25.00
JSS Jarrod Saltalamacchia 20.00 50.00
JU Justin Upton 75.00 150.00
KK Kevin Kouzmanoff 10.00 25.00
KS Kurt Suzuki 20.00 50.00
LS Levale Speigner 10.00 25.00
MB Michael Bourn 30.00 60.00
MBB Matthew Brown 10.00 25.00
MJZ Mike Zagurski 20.00 50.00
ML Matt Lindstrom 15.00 40.00
MM Mark McLemore 10.00 25.00
NG Nick Gorneault 15.00 40.00
NH Nathan Haynes 10.00 25.00
PD Phil Dumatrait 10.00 25.00
PH Phil Hughes 60.00 120.00
PL Paul Lo Duca 20.00 50.00
RB Ryan Braun 100.00 175.00
RC Rocky Cherry 20.00 50.00
RDB Ryan Budde 10.00 25.00
RZB Ryan Braun 15.00 40.00
TB Travis Buck 15.00 40.00
TC Tyler Clippard 30.00 60.00
TL Tim Lincecum 60.00 120.00
TM Travis Metcalf 20.00 50.00
TPC Troy Cate 10.00 25.00
YG Yovani Gallardo 40.00 80.00
ZS Zack Segovia 20.00 50.00

2007 Topps 52 Signatures Combos

STATED ODDS 1:1094 HOBBY
STATED PRINT RUN 25 SER.#'d SETS
NO PRICING DUE TO SCARCITY
EXCHANGE DEADLINE 11/30/09
BP Ryan Braun
Hunter Pence
GB Alex Gordon
Ryan Braun
LB Matt Lindstrom
Michael Bourn EXCH
LG Andy LaRoche
Alex Gordon
LI Andy LaRoche
Akinori Iwamura
LM Tim Lincecum
Andrew Miller
LO Tim Lincecum
Hideki Okajima EXCH
ML Andrew Miller
Matt Lindstrom EXCH
OI Hideki Okajima
Akinori Iwamura
PB Hunter Pence
Michael Bourn

2006 Topps AFLAC

COMMON CARD 8.00 20.00
EACH PLAYER ISSUED 100 OF OWN CARD
APPX.250 SETS DIST.AT 06 AFLAC GAME
BB Blake Beavan 20.00 50.00
BK Brett Krill 10.00 25.00

CC Christian Colon 10.00 25.00
CR Cameron Rupp 10.00 25.00
DB Drake Britton 8.00 20.00
DD Derek Dietrich 15.00 40.00
DM D.J. LeMahieu 8.00 20.00
DR Danny Rams 8.00 20.00
ED Evan Danieli 10.00 25.00
EG Erik Goeddel 10.00 25.00
FF Freddie Freeman 10.00 25.00
GP Greg Peavey 12.50 30.00
HM Hunter Morris 15.00 40.00
JG Jon Gilmore 12.50 30.00
JH Jason Heyward 50.00 100.00
JL Joe Leftridge 8.00 20.00
JS Josh Smoker 20.00 50.00
JT John Tolisano 12.50 30.00
JV Josh Vitters 50.00 100.00
KB Kyle Blair 8.00 20.00
KK Kevin Keyes 8.00 20.00
MB Madison Bumgarner 50.00 100.00
MH Matt Harvey 20.00 50.00
MM Michael Main 20.00 50.00
NN Nick Noonan 12.50 30.00
NR Neil Ramirez 15.00 40.00
PD Paul Demny 8.00 20.00
RP Rick Porcello 40.00 80.00
RS Robert Stock 40.00 80.00
SB Steven Brooks 10.00 25.00
SS Sequoyah Stonecipher 30.00 60.00
TA Tim Alderson 12.50 30.00
YG Yasmani Grandal 10.00 25.00

2006 Topps AFLAC Promo

BB Blake Beavan 5.00 12.00
BK Brett Krill 3.00 8.00
CC Christian Colon 2.50 6.00
CR Cameron Rupp 3.00 8.00
DB Drake Britton 3.00 8.00
DD Derek Dietrich 5.00 12.00
DM D.J. LeMahieu 2.50 6.00
DR Danny Rams 4.00 10.00
ED Evan Danieli 2.50 6.00
EG Erik Goeddel 3.00 8.00
FF Freddie Freeman 5.00 12.00
GP Greg Peavey 4.00 10.00
HM Hunter Morris 4.00 10.00
JG Jon Gilmore 5.00 12.00
JH Jason Heyward 20.00 50.00
JJ Justin Jackson 5.00 12.00
JL Joe Leftridge 3.00 8.00
JS Josh Smoker 10.00 25.00
JT John Tolisano 4.00 10.00
JV Josh Vitters 12.50 30.00
KB Kyle Blair 2.50 6.00
KD Kentrail Davis 4.00 10.00
KK Kevin Keyes 2.50 6.00
MB Madison Bumgarner 20.00 50.00
MB2 Michael Burgess 10.00 25.00
MH Matt Harvey 4.00 10.00
MM Michael Main 4.00 10.00
NN Nick Noonan 5.00 12.00
NR Neil Ramirez 3.00 8.00
PD Paul Demny 5.00 12.00
RP Rick Porcello 30.00 60.00
RS Robert Stock 6.00 15.00
SB Steven Brooks 2.50 6.00
SR Sam Runion 4.00 10.00
SS Sequoyah Stonecipher 3.00 8.00
TA Tim Alderson 6.00 15.00
TR Tanner Robles 2.50 6.00
YG Yasmani Grandal 2.50 6.00

2007 Topps AFLAC

AB Andy Burns
AF Anthony Ferrara 10.00 25.00
AH Aaron Hicks 12.50 30.00
AM Alex Meyer 6.00 15.00
AN Adrian Nieto 8.00 20.00
AW Austin Wright 6.00 15.00
BD Brett DeVall 8.00 20.00
BH B.J. Hermsen 5.00 12.00
BN Billy Nicholson CO
BW Brett Warren 6.00 15.00
CA Chris Amezquita 5.00 12.00
CE Cecil Espy CO
CM Clark Murphy 5.00 12.00
DH Destin Hood 8.00 20.00
DM Daniel Marrs 5.00 12.00
EM Ethan Martin 10.00 25.00
GC Gerrit Cole 15.00 40.00
GL Garrison Lassiter 5.00 12.00
HM Harold Martinez 8.00 20.00
IG Isaac Galloway 5.00 12.00
JA Jack Armstrong 5.00 12.00
JC Jarred Cosart 8.00 20.00
JS Jordan Swagerty 5.00 12.00
KM Kevin Maris CO
KS Kyle Skipworth 15.00 40.00
MH Manny Hermosillo CO
MP Michael Palazzone 5.00 12.00
MS Mike Sheppard Jr. CO 8.00 20.00
QM Quinton Miller 10.00 25.00
RO Ricky Oropesa 5.00 12.00
ROS Ryan O'Sullivan 5.00 12.00
SG Sonny Gray 5.00 12.00
SS Scott Silverstein 6.00 15.00
TB Tim Beckham 40.00 80.00
TH Taylor Hightower 5.00 12.00
TM Tim Melville 8.00 20.00
WF Wesley Freeman 5.00 12.00
WK Walker Kelly 10.00 25.00
XA Xavier Avery 6.00 15.00

2003 Topps All-Time Fan Favorites

This 150-card set was released in May, 2003. This set was issued in six card packs with an $3 SRP which came 24 packs to a box and eight boxes to a case. These cards were issued in different styles with photos purporting to be from that era in which the faux card was issued. While most of the photos are close to the era they are supposed to be from, some photos such as the 64 Brooks Robinson design and the 54 Tom Lasorda are obviously not from the correct time period. The Monte Irvin card was issued in equal quantities with or without the facsmile autograph. A set is considered complete with only one of the Irvin cards. A notable card in this set is the first mainstream card of legendary broadcaster Ernie Harwell who was the Tigers announcers for more than 40 years.

COMPLETE SET (150) 20.00 50.00
1 Willie Mays 1.25 3.00
2 Whitey Ford .40 1.00
3 Stan Musial 1.00 2.50
4 Paul Blair .15 .40
5 Harold Reynolds .25 .60
6 Bob Friend .25 .60
7 Rod Carew .40 1.00
8 Kirk Gibson .25 .60
9 Graig Nettles .25 .60
10 Ozzie Smith 1.00 2.50
11 Tony Perez .25 .60
12 Tim Wallach .15 .40
13 Bert Campaneris .25 .60
14 Cory Snyder .15 .40
15 Dave Parker .25 .60
16 Darrell Evans .25 .60
17 Joe Pepitone .25 .60
18 Don Sutton .25 .60
19 Dale Murphy .40 1.00
20 George Brett 1.25 3.00
21 Carlton Fisk .40 1.00
22 Bob Watson .15 .40
23 Wally Joyner .25 .60
24 Paul Molitor .25 .60
25 Keith Hernandez .25 .60
26 Jerry Koosman .25 .60
27 George Bell .25 .60
28 Boog Powell .40 1.00
29 Bruce Sutter .25 .60
30 Ernie Banks .60 1.50
31 Steve Lyons .15 .40
32 Earl Weaver .25 .60
33 Dave Stieb .25 .60
34 Alan Trammell .25 .60
35 Bret Saberhagen .25 .60
36 J.R. Richard .25 .60
37 Mickey Rivers .15 .40
38 Juan Marichal .25 .60
39 Gaylord Perry .25 .60
40 Don Mattingly 1.25 3.00
41 Bob Grich .25 .60
42 Steve Sax .25 .60
43 Sparky Anderson .25 .60
44 Luis Aparicio .25 .60
45 Fergie Jenkins .25 .60
46 Jim Palmer .25 .60
47 Howard Johnson .25 .60
48 Dwight Evans .40 1.00
49 Bill Buckner .25 .60
50 Cal Ripken 2.00 5.00
51 Jose Cruz .25 .60
52 Tony Oliva .25 .60
53 Bobby Richardson .25 .60
54 Luis Tiant .25 .60
55 Warren Spahn .40 1.00
56 Phil Rizzuto .40 1.00
57 Eric Davis .25 .60
58 Vida Blue .25 .60
59 Steve Balboni .15 .40
60 Mike Schmidt 1.25 3.00
61 Ken Griffey Sr. .25 .60
62 Jim Abbott .40 1.00
63 Whitey Herzog .25 .60
64 Rich Gossage .25 .60
65 Tony Armas .25 .60
66 Bill Skowron .40 1.00
67 Don Newcombe .25 .60
68 Bill Madlock .25 .60
69 Lance Parrish .25 .60
70 Reggie Jackson .40 1.00
71 Willie Wilson .25 .60
72 Terry Pendleton .25 .60
73 Jim Piersall .25 .60
74 George Foster .25 .60
75 Bob Horner .25 .60
76 Chris Sabo .25 .60
77 Fred Lynn .25 .60
78 Jim Rice .25 .60
79 Maury Wills .25 .60
80 Yogi Berra .60 1.50
81 Johnny Sain .40 1.00
82 Tom Lasorda .25 .60
83 Bill Mazeroski .40 1.00
84 John Kruk .25 .60
85 Bob Feller .25 .60
86 Frank Robinson .40 1.00
87 Red Schoendienst .25 .60
88 Gary Carter .25 .60
89 Andre Dawson .25 .60
90 Tim McCarver .25 .60
91 Robin Yount .60 1.50
92 Phil Niekro .25 .60
93 Joe Morgan .25 .60
94 Darren Daulton .25 .60
95 Bobby Thomson .25 .60
96 Alvin Davis .15 .40
97 Robin Roberts .40 1.00

98 Kirby Puckett .60 1.50
99 Jack Clark .25 .60
100 Hank Aaron 1.25 3.00
101 Orlando Cepeda .25 .60
102 Vern Law .25 .60
103 Cecil Cooper .25 .60
104 Don Larsen .25 .60
105 Mario Mendoza .15 .40
106 Tony Gwynn .75 2.00
107 Ernie Harwell .25 .60
108A Monte Irvin .25 .60
108B Monte Irvin NO AU ERR .25 .60
109 Tommy John .25 .60
110 Rollie Fingers .25 .60
111 Johnny Podres .25 .60
112 Jeff Reardon .25 .60
113 Buddy Bell .25 .60
114 Dwight Gooden .25 .60
115 Garry Templeton .25 .60
116 Johnny Bench .60 1.50
117 Joe Rudi .25 .60
118 Ron Guidry .25 .60
119 Vince Coleman .25 .60
120 Al Kaline .60 1.50
121 Carl Yastrzemski 1.00 2.50
122 Hank Bauer .25 .60
123 Mark Fidrych .25 .60
124 Paul O'Neill .40 1.00
125 Ron Cey .25 .60
126 Willie McGee .25 .60
127 Harmon Killebrew .60 1.50
128 Dave Concepcion .25 .60
129 Harold Baines .25 .60
130 Lou Brock .40 1.00
131 Lee Smith .25 .60
132 Willie McCovey .25 .60
133 Steve Garvey .25 .60
134 Kent Tekulve .25 .60
135 Tom Seaver .40 1.00
136 Bo Jackson .60 1.50
137 Walt Weiss .15 .40
138 Brook Jacoby .15 .40
139 Dennis Eckersley .25 .60
140 Duke Snider .40 1.00
141 Lenny Dykstra .25 .60
142 Greg Luzinski .25 .60
143 Jim Bunning .25 .60
144 Jose Canseco .40 1.00
145 Ron Santo .40 1.00
146 Bert Blyleven .25 .60
147 Wade Boggs .40 1.00
148 Brooks Robinson .40 1.00
149 Ray Knight .25 .60
150 Nolan Ryan 1.50 4.00

2003 Topps All-Time Fan Favorites Chrome Refractors

Inserted at a stated rate of one in 18, this is a parallel to the basic set. These cards were produced using the Topps Chrome technology and were issued to a stated print run of 299 serial numbered sets.

*CHROME REF: 3X TO 8X BASIC

2003 Topps All-Time Fan Favorites Archives Autographs

This 165-card set was issued at different odds depending on what group the player belonged to. Please note that exchange cards with a redemption deadline of April 30th, 2005, were seeded into packs for the following players: Dave Concepcion, Bob Feller, Tug McGraw, Paul O'Neill and Kirby Puckett. In addition, exchange cards were produced for a small percentage of Eric Davis cards (though the bulk of his real autographs did make pack out).

GROUP A STATED ODDS 1:218
GROUP B STATED ODDS 1:759
GROUP C STATED ODDS 1:116
GROUP D STATED ODDS 1:45
GROUP E STATED ODDS 1:87
GROUP F STATED ODDS 1:1028
GROUP G STATED ODDS 1:838
GROUP H STATED ODDS 1:818
GROUP I STATED ODDS 1:796
GROUP J STATED ODDS 1:111
GROUP K STATED ODDS 1:759
GROUP L STATED ODDS 1:744
AD Alvin Davis D 4.00 10.00
ADA Andre Dawson A 40.00 80.00
AK Al Kaline A 75.00 150.00
AO Al Oliver D 6.00 15.00
AT Alan Trammell C 10.00 25.00
BB Bert Blyleven D 6.00 15.00
BBE Buddy Bell C 6.00 15.00
BBI Buddy Biancalana D 4.00 10.00
BBU Bill Buckner C 6.00 15.00
BC Bert Campaneris E 4.00 10.00
BF Bob Feller C 6.00 15.00
BFR Bob Friend D 4.00 10.00
BGR Bob Grich D 4.00 10.00
BH Bob Horner J 6.00 15.00
BJ Bo Jackson A 40.00 80.00
BJA Brook Jacoby E 4.00 10.00
BL Bill Lee D 4.00 10.00
BMA Bill Madlock D 4.00 10.00
BMZ Bill Mazeroski A 50.00 100.00
BP Boog Powell D 6.00 15.00
BRO Brooks Robinson A 50.00 100.00
BS Bill Skowron D 6.00 15.00
BSA Bret Saberhagen A 20.00 50.00
BSU Bruce Sutter C 10.00 25.00
BT Bobby Thomson A 40.00 80.00
BW Bob Watson C 6.00 15.00
CC Cecil Cooper E 4.00 10.00
CF Carlton Fisk A 50.00 100.00
CL Carney Lansford C 6.00 15.00
CLE Chet Lemon D 4.00 10.00
CN Cory Snyder C 6.00 15.00
CR Cal Ripken A 175.00 300.00
CS Chris Sabo H 6.00 15.00
CSP Chris Speier C 6.00 15.00
CY Carl Yastrzemski A 100.00 200.00
DC Dave Concepcion A 40.00 80.00
DD Darren Daulton C 6.00 15.00
DDE Doug DeCinces C 6.00 15.00
DE Darrell Evans D 4.00 10.00
DEC Dennis Eckersley A 40.00 80.00
DEV Dwight Evans A 50.00 100.00
DG Dwight Gooden A 40.00 80.00
DL Don Larsen D 6.00 15.00
DM Dale Murphy A 50.00 100.00
DN Don Newcombe A 40.00 80.00
DON Don Mattingly A 75.00 150.00
DP Dave Parker A 40.00 80.00
DS Dave Stieb C 10.00 25.00
DSN Duke Snider A 50.00 100.00
DSU Don Sutton A 40.00 80.00
EB Ernie Banks A 75.00 150.00
ED Eric Davis I 6.00 15.00
EH Ernie Harwell C 20.00 50.00
EW Earl Weaver D 4.00 10.00
FJ Fergie Jenkins C 6.00 15.00
FL Fred Lynn A 30.00 60.00
FR Frank Robinson A 50.00 100.00
GB George Bell D 4.00 10.00
GBR George Brett A 175.00 300.00
GC Gary Carter A 40.00 80.00
GF George Foster D 6.00 15.00
GL Greg Luzinski C 6.00 15.00
GN Graig Nettles D 6.00 15.00
GP Gaylord Perry B 10.00 25.00
GT Garry Templeton C 6.00 15.00
HA Hank Aaron A 175.00 300.00
HB Hank Bauer A 40.00 80.00
HBA Harold Baines C 6.00 15.00
HJ Howard Johnson K 4.00 10.00
HK Harmon Killebrew A 75.00 150.00
HR Harold Reynolds A 40.00 80.00
JA Jim Abbott D 6.00 15.00
JB Jim Bunning A 75.00 150.00
JBE Johnny Bench A 75.00 150.00
JC Jack Clark B 10.00 25.00
JCA Joe Carter A 40.00 80.00
JCR Jose Cruz D 4.00 10.00
JK Jerry Koosman F 10.00 25.00
JKR John Kruk A 50.00 100.00
JM Joe Morgan A 40.00 80.00
JMA Juan Marichal A 50.00 100.00
JMO John Montefusco D 4.00 10.00
JOS Jose Canseco A 50.00 100.00
JP Jim Palmer A 50.00 100.00
JPE Joe Pepitone E 4.00 10.00
JR J.R. Richard E 4.00 10.00
JRE Jeff Reardon D 4.00 10.00
JRI Jim Rice A 40.00 80.00
JRU Joe Rudi E 4.00 10.00
KG Ken Griffey Sr. A 40.00 80.00
KGI Kirk Gibson A 40.00 80.00
KH Keith Hernandez A 40.00 80.00
KM Kevin Mitchell L 4.00 10.00
KP Kirby Puckett A 60.00 120.00
KS Kevin Seitzer D 4.00 10.00
KT Kent Tekulve C 6.00 15.00
LA Luis Aparicio D 10.00 25.00
LB Lou Brock A 50.00 100.00
LD Lenny Dykstra G 6.00 15.00
LDU Leon Durham D 4.00 10.00
LP Lance Parrish D 4.00 10.00
LS Lee Smith J 6.00 15.00
LT Luis Tiant A 40.00 80.00
MCG Willie McGee A 50.00 100.00
MF Mark Fidrych J 4.00 10.00
MI Monte Irvin A 40.00 80.00
MM Mario Mendoza E 4.00 10.00
MP Mike Pagliarulo E 4.00 10.00
MR Mickey Rivers E 4.00 10.00
MS Mike Schmidt A 150.00 250.00
MW Maury Wills E 4.00 10.00
NR Nolan Ryan A 175.00 300.00
OC Orlando Cepeda A 50.00 100.00
OS Ozzie Smith A 75.00 150.00
PB Paul Blair J 4.00 10.00
PM Paul Molitor A 40.00 80.00
PN Phil Niekro A 40.00 80.00
PO Paul O'Neill A 50.00 100.00
PR Phil Rizzuto A 50.00 100.00
RCA Rod Carew A 50.00 100.00
RCE Ron Cey D 4.00 10.00
RD Rob Dibble C 6.00 15.00
RDA Ron Darling C 6.00 15.00
RF Rollie Fingers A 40.00 80.00
RG Rich Gossage A 40.00 80.00
RGU Ron Guidry C 6.00 15.00
RJ Reggie Jackson A 75.00 150.00
RK Ralph Kiner A 50.00 100.00
RKI Ron Kittle D 4.00 10.00
RR Robin Roberts B 10.00 25.00
RS Red Schoendienst C 6.00 15.00
RSA Ron Santo D 10.00 25.00
RY Ray Knight J 4.00 10.00
RYO Robin Yount A 75.00 150.00
SA Sparky Anderson A 40.00 80.00
SB Steve Balboni E 4.00 10.00
SG Steve Garvey B 10.00 25.00
SL Steve Lyons C 6.00 15.00
SM Stan Musial A 100.00 200.00
SS Steve Sax D 4.00 10.00
SY Steve Yeager E 4.00 10.00
TA Tony Armas D 4.00 10.00
TG Tony Gwynn A 75.00 150.00
TH Tom Herr D 4.00 10.00
TJ Tommy John B 6.00 15.00
TL Tom Lasorda A 40.00 80.00
TM Tim McCarver A 40.00 80.00
TMC Tug McGraw D 10.00 25.00
TP Terry Pendleton B 6.00 15.00
TPE Tony Perez A 50.00 100.00
TSE Tom Seaver A 75.00 150.00
TW Tim Wallach E 4.00 10.00
VB Vida Blue C 6.00 15.00
VC Vince Coleman J 4.00 10.00
WB Wade Boggs A 50.00 100.00
WF Whitey Ford A 75.00 150.00
WH Whitey Herzog C 10.00 25.00
WHE Willie Hernandez D 4.00 10.00
WJ Wally Joyner J 4.00 10.00
WM Willie Mays A 175.00 300.00
WMC Willie McCovey A 50.00 100.00
WS Warren Spahn D 15.00 40.00
WW Walt Weiss D 4.00 10.00
WWI Willie Wilson A 40.00 80.00
YB Yogi Berra A 75.00 150.00

2003 Topps All-Time Fan Favorites Best Seat in the House Relics

Inserted at a stated rate of one in 13 special relic packs, these five cards feature a group of stars from a team along with a piece of a set from a now retired ballpark.

BS1 Brooks Robinson 10.00 25.00
Frank Robinson
Jim Palmer
BS2 Bob Grich 10.00 25.00
Rod Carew
Wally Joyner
BS3 Dave Parker 10.00 25.00
Kent Tekulve
Willie Stargell
Phil Garner
BS4 Paul Molitor 10.00 25.00
Robin Yount
Rollie Fingers
BS5 Bob Horner 10.00 25.00
Dale Murphy
Phil Niekro

2003 Topps All-Time Fan Favorites Relics

Issued one per special "relic" box-topper pack, these 43 cards feature players from the basic set along with a game-used memorabilia piece.

ADA Andre Dawson Bat 4.00 10.00
AT Alan Trammell Bat 4.00 10.00
BFR Bob Friend Jsy 4.00 10.00
BH Bob Horner Bat 4.00 10.00
BJ Bo Jackson Bat 10.00 25.00
BR Bobby Richardson Bat 6.00 15.00
CF Curt Flood Bat 4.00 10.00
CS Chris Sabo Bat 4.00 10.00
DEC Dennis Eckersley Uni 4.00 10.00
DM Dale Murphy Bat 4.00 10.00
DON Don Mattingly Bat 12.50 30.00
DP Dave Parker Bat 4.00 10.00
FL Fred Lynn Bat 4.00 10.00
GBR George Brett Uni 12.50 30.00
GC Gary Carter Bat 4.00 10.00
GF George Foster Bat 4.00 10.00
GL Greg Luzinski Bat 4.00 10.00
HBA Harold Baines Bat 6.00 15.00
HR Harold Reynolds Bat 4.00 10.00
JCR Jose Cruz Bat 4.00 10.00
JM Joe Morgan Bat 4.00 10.00
JOS Jose Canseco Bat 6.00 15.00
JRI Jim Rice Bat 4.00 10.00
JRU Joe Rudi Bat 4.00 10.00
KGI Kirk Gibson Bat 4.00 10.00
KH Keith Hernandez Bat 4.00 10.00
KM Kevin Mitchell Bat 4.00 10.00
KP Kirby Puckett Bat 10.00 25.00
LD Lenny Dykstra Bat 4.00 10.00
LP Lance Parrish Bat 6.00 15.00
MCG Willie McGee Bat 6.00 15.00
MS Mike Schmidt Bat 12.50 30.00
MW Maury Wills Bat 4.00 10.00
NC Norm Cash Jsy 20.00 50.00
PO Paul O'Neill Bat 6.00 15.00
RCA Rod Carew Bat 6.00 15.00
RDA Ron Darling Jsy 4.00 10.00
SG Steve Garvey Bat 4.00 10.00
TMC Tug McGraw Jsy 4.00 10.00
VC Vince Coleman Bat 4.00 10.00
WHE Willie Hernandez Jsy 4.00 10.00
WJ Wally Joyner Bat 4.00 10.00
WS Willie Stargell Bat 6.00 15.00

2003 Topps All-Time Fan Favorites Don Zimmer AutoProofs

Inserted at a stated rate of one in 4971, these 13 cards feature authentic signed versions of Don

Zimmer's cards issued between 1955 and 1978. We have notated the print run next to the player's name in our checklist and note that due to market scarcity there is no pricing.

1 Don Zimmer 55 Bow/1
2 Don Zimmer 55/5
3 Don Zimmer 56/9
4 Don Zimmer 58/5
5 Don Zimmer 59/17
6 Don Zimmer 60/14
7 Don Zimmer 61/24
8 Don Zimmer 62/1
9 Don Zimmer 63/29
10 Don Zimmer 64/14
11 Don Zimmer 65/14
12 Don Zimmer 73 MG/3
13 Don Zimmer 78 MG/11

2004 Topps All-Time Fan Favorites

This 150-card set was released in June, 2004. This set was issued in six card packs with an $5 SRP which came 24 packs to a box and 10 boxes to a case. This set has several noticable 1st cards including former commissioners Peter Ueberroth and Fay Vincent, long-time umpire Eric Gregg and long time Yankee Stadium public address announcer legend Bob Shepard.

COMPLETE SET (150) 20.00 50.00
1 Willie Mays 1.50 4.00
2 Bob Gibson .50 1.25
3 Dave Stieb .30 .75
4 Tim McCarver .30 .75
5 Reggie Jackson .50 1.25
6 John Candelaria .30 .75
7 Lenny Dykstra .30 .75
8 Tony Oliva .30 .75
9 Frank Viola .30 .75
10 Don Mattingly 1.50 4.00
11 Garry Maddox .30 .75
12 Randy Jones .20 .50
13 Joe Carter .30 .75
14 Orlando Cepeda .30 .75
15 Bob Sheppard ANC .50 1.25
16 Bobby Grich .30 .75
17 George Scott .20 .50
18 Mickey Rivers .20 .50
19 Ron Santo .50 1.25
20 Mike Schmidt 1.50 4.00
21 Luis Aparicio .30 .75
22 Cesar Geronimo .20 .50
23 Jack Morris .30 .75
24 Jeffrey Loria OWNER .20 .50
25 George Brett 1.50 4.00
26 Paul O'Neill .50 1.25
27 Reggie Smith .30 .75
28 Robin Yount .75 2.00
29 Andre Dawson .30 .75
30 Whitey Ford .50 1.25
31 Ralph Kiner .30 .75
32 Will Clark .50 1.25
33 Keith Hernandez .30 .75
34 Tony Fernandez .20 .50
35 Willie McGee .30 .75
36 Harmon Killebrew .75 2.00
37 Dave Kingman .30 .75
38 Kirk Gibson .30 .75
39 Terry Steinbach .20 .50
40 Frank Robinson .30 .75
41 Chet Lemon .30 .75
42 Mike Cuellar .30 .75
43 Darrell Evans .30 .75
44 Don Kessinger .20 .50
45 Dave Concepcion .30 .75
46 Sparky Anderson .30 .75
47 Bret Saberhagen .30 .75
48 Brett Butler .30 .75
49 Kent Hrbek .30 .75
50 Hank Aaron 1.50 4.00
51 Rudolph Giuliani .75 2.00
52 Clete Boyer .30 .75
53 Mookie Wilson .30 .75
54 Dave Stewart .30 .75
55 Gary Matthews Sr. .30 .75
56 Roy Face .30 .75
57 Vida Blue .30 .75
58 Jimmy Key .50 1.25
59 Al Hrabosky .30 .75
60 Al Kaline .75 2.00
61 Mike Scott .30 .75
62 Jack McDowell .30 .75
63 Reggie Jackson .50 1.25
64 Earl Weaver .30 .75
65 Ernie Harwell ANC .50 1.25
66 David Justice .30 .75
67 Wilbur Wood .30 .75
68 Mike Boddicker .30 .75
69 Don Zimmer .30 .75
70 Jim Palmer .30 .75
71 Doug DeCinces .30 .75
72 Ryne Sandberg 1.50 4.00
73 Don Newcombe .30 .75
74 Denny Martinez .30 .75
75 Carl Yastrzemski 1.25 3.00
76 Bake McBride .30 .75
77 Andy Van Slyke .50 1.25
78 Bruce Sutter .30 .75
79 Bobby Valentine .30 .75
80 Johnny Bench .75 2.00
81 Orel Hershiser .30 .75
82 Cecil Fielder .30 .75
83 Lou Whitaker .30 .75
84 Alan Trammell .30 .75
85 Sam McDowell .30 .75
86 Ray Knight .30 .75
87 Gregg Jefferies .20 .50
88 Ben Oglivie .20 .50
89 Billy Beane .20 .50
90 Yogi Berra .75 2.00
91 Jose Canseco .50 1.25
92 Bobby Bonilla .30 .75
93 Darren Daulton .30 .75
94 Harold Reynolds .30 .75
95 Lou Brock .50 1.25
96 Pete Incaviglia .20 .50
97 Eric Gregg UMP .20 .50
98 Devon White .20 .50
99 Kelly Gruber .20 .50
100 Nolan Ryan 2.00 5.00
101 Carlton Fisk .50 1.25
102 George Foster .30 .75
103 Dennis Eckersley .50 1.25
104 Rick Sutcliffe .30 .75
105 Cal Ripken 2.50 6.00
106 Norm Cash .30 .75
107 Charlie Hough .20 .50
108 Paul Molitor .30 .75
109 Maury Wills .30 .75
110 Tom Seaver .50 1.25
111 Brooks Robinson .50 1.25
112 Jim Rice .30 .75
113 Dwight Gooden .30 .75
114 Harold Baines .30 .75
115 Tim Raines .30 .75
116 Roy Smalley .20 .50
117 Richie Allen .30 .75
118 Ron Swoboda .30 .75
119 Ron Guidry .50 1.25
120 Duke Snider .50 1.25
121 Ferguson Jenkins .30 .75
122 Mark Fidrych UER .30 .75
Posing as a lefty
123 Buddy Bell .30 .75
124 Bo Jackson .75 2.00
125 Stan Musial 1.25 3.00
126 Jesse Barfield .20 .50
127 Tony Gwynn 1.00 2.50
128 Phil Garner .30 .75
129 Dale Murphy .50 1.25
130 Wade Boggs .50 1.25
131 Sid Fernandez .30 .75
132 Monte Irvin .30 .75
133 Peter Ueberroth COM .20 .50
134 Gary Gaetti .30 .75
135 Gorman Thomas .30 .75
136 Dave Lopes .30 .75
137 Sy Berger .30 .75
138 Buck O'Neil UER .30 .75
Wrong birth year on back
139 Herb Score .30 .75
140 Rod Carew .50 1.25
141 Joe Buck ANC .50 1.25
142 Willie Horton .30 .75
143 Hal McRae .30 .75
144 Rollie Fingers .30 .75
145 Tom Brunansky .20 .50
146 Fay Vincent COM .20 .50
147 Gary Carter .30 .75
148 Bobby Richardson .30 .75
149 Jesse Garvey .30 .75
150 Don Larsen .30 .75

2004 Topps All-Time Fan Favorites Refractors

*REFRACTORS: 3X TO 8X BASIC
STATED ODDS 1:19
STATED PRINT RUN 299 SERIAL #'d SETS

2004 Topps All-Time Fan Favorites Autographs

A few players did not return their autograph in time for inclusion in packs and those autographs could be redeemed until May 31, 2006. Please note, Topps was unable to fulfill the Richie Allen exchange card with the promised player and sent out a selection of 2004 Topps World Series Heroes Autographs including Whitey Ford and Duke Snider in their place.

GROUP A ODDS 1:69,360
GROUP B ODDS 1:648
GROUP C ODDS 1:102
GROUP D ODDS 1:5662
GROUP E ODDS 1:181
GROUP F ODDS 1:208
GROUP G ODDS 1:509
GROUP H ODDS 1:356
GROUP I ODDS 1:58
GROUP J ODDS 1:148
GROUP K ODDS 1:128
GROUP L ODDS 1:135
GROUP M ODDS 1:104
GROUP N ODDS 1:228
OVERALL AUTO ODDS 1:12
GROUP A PRINT RUN 10 CARDS
GROUP B PRINT RUN 50 SETS
GROUP C PRINT RUN 100 SETS
GROUP D PRINT RUN 150 CARDS
CARDS ARE NOT SERIAL-NUMBERED
PRINT RUNS PROVIDED BY TOPPS
NO GROUP A PRICING DUE TO SCARCITY
R.ALLEN EXCH UNABLE TO BE FULFILLED
04 WS HL AU'S REPLACE ALLEN EXCH
AD Andre Dawson C 15.00 40.00
AH Al Hrabosky L 4.00 10.00
AK Al Kaline B 60.00 120.00
AT Alan Trammell C 15.00 40.00
AV Andy Van Slyke C 30.00 60.00
BB Billy Beane C 10.00 25.00
BBE Buddy Bell N 4.00 10.00
BG Bob Gibson C 30.00 60.00
BGR Bobby Grich I 4.00 10.00
BJ Bo Jackson B 60.00 120.00
BMB Bobby Bonilla C EXCH 10.00 25.00
BO Ben Oglivie I 4.00 10.00
BON Buck O'Neil K 30.00 60.00
BR Bobby Richardson F 10.00 25.00
BRO Brooks Robinson B 30.00 60.00
BS Bob Sheppard A/10 EXCH
BSA Bret Saberhagen C 15.00 40.00
BSU Bruce Sutter F 12.50 30.00
BV Bobby Valentine C 15.00 40.00
CF Carlton Fisk B 40.00 80.00
CG Cesar Geronimo C 15.00 40.00
CH Charlie Hough G 6.00 15.00
CL Chet Lemon M 4.00 10.00
CR Cal Ripken B 175.00 300.00
CY Carl Yastrzemski B 75.00 150.00
DC Dave Concepcion C 15.00 40.00
DD Darren Daulton L 4.00 10.00
DDE Doug DeCinces E 6.00 15.00
DE Darrell Evans I 4.00 10.00
DEC Dennis Eckersley C 20.00 50.00
DG Dwight Gooden B 20.00 50.00
DJ David Justice E 10.00 25.00
DK Dave Kingman E 15.00 40.00
DKE Don Kessinger M 6.00 15.00
DL Dave Lopes M 4.00 10.00
DLA Don Larsen L 10.00 25.00
DM Dale Murphy B 40.00 80.00
DON Don Mattingly B 75.00 150.00
DS Dave Stewart H 4.00 10.00
DSN Duke Snider C 30.00 60.00
DST Dave Stieb J 4.00 10.00
DZ Don Zimmer I 10.00 25.00
EG Eric Gregg I 6.00 15.00
EH Ernie Harwell E 10.00 25.00
EW Earl Weaver M 6.00 15.00
FJ Ferguson Jenkins F 10.00 25.00
FR Frank Robinson C 30.00 60.00
FVI Fay Vincent C 30.00 60.00
FVI1 Frank Viola I 6.00 15.00
GB George Brett B 125.00 200.00
GC Gary Carter B 20.00 50.00
GF George Foster I 4.00 10.00
GMA Gary Matthews Sr. J 4.00 10.00
GS George Scott K EXCH 6.00 15.00
HA Hank Aaron B 175.00 300.00
HB Harold Baines C 15.00 40.00
HK Harmon Killebrew C 50.00 100.00
HR Harold Reynolds C 15.00 40.00
JB Jesse Barfield J 4.00 10.00
JB1 Joe Buck C 15.00 40.00
JBE Johnny Bench C 60.00 120.00
JC Joe Carter C 15.00 40.00
JCA Jose Canseco C 30.00 60.00
JKE Jimmy Key C 10.00 25.00
JM Jack McDowell K 4.00 10.00
JMO Jack Morris K 4.00 10.00
JP Jim Palmer B 40.00 80.00
JR Jim Rice C 15.00 40.00
KG Kirk Gibson B 20.00 50.00
KH Keith Hernandez B 20.00 50.00
LA Luis Aparicio C 15.00 40.00
LB Lou Brock C 30.00 60.00
LD Lenny Dykstra C 10.00 25.00
MB Mike Boddicker J 4.00 10.00
MF Mark Fidrych C 12.50 30.00
MI Monte Irvin C 12.50 30.00
MR Mickey Rivers M 4.00 10.00
MS Mike Schmidt B
MSC Mike Scott M 4.00 10.00
MW Maury Wills I 4.00 10.00
MWI Mookie Wilson L 4.00 10.00
NR Nolan Ryan D 90.00 150.00
OC Orlando Cepeda C 30.00 60.00
OH Orel Hershiser C 15.00 40.00
PI Pete Incaviglia E 6.00 15.00
PM Paul Molitor B 20.00 50.00
PO Paul O'Neill B 40.00 80.00
PU Peter Ueberroth C 60.00 120.00
RA Richie Allen I EXCH UER
RC Rod Carew C 30.00 60.00
RF Rollie Fingers C 15.00 40.00
RG Ron Guidry C 15.00 40.00
RJO Randy Jones L 4.00 10.00
RJ2 Reggie Jackson C 50.00 100.00
RK Ralph Kiner G 15.00 40.00
RKN Ray Knight C 10.00 25.00
RS Ron Santo I 6.00 15.00
RSU Rick Sutcliffe C 30.00 60.00
RSW Ron Swoboda N 6.00 15.00
RY Robin Yount B 75.00 150.00
RYN Ryne Sandberg C 75.00 150.00
SA Sparky Anderson C 15.00 40.00
SB Sy Berger H 10.00 25.00
SF Sid Fernandez C 10.00 25.00
SG Steve Garvey C 15.00 40.00
SM Stan Musial C 75.00 150.00
SM1 Sam McDowell C 15.00 40.00
TB Tom Brunansky F 4.00 10.00
TF Tony Fernandez F 4.00 10.00
TG Tony Gwynn B 75.00 150.00
TM Tim McCarver E 10.00 25.00
TO Tony Oliva E 15.00 40.00
TR Tim Raines E 4.00 10.00

TSE Tom Seaver B 60.00 120.00
VB Vida Blue F 6.00 15.00
WB Wade Boggs B 40.00 80.00
WF Whitey Ford C 40.00 80.00
WH Willie Horton K 6.00 15.00
WM Willie Mays B
WMC Willie McGee C 15.00 40.00
WW Wilbur Wood I 6.00 15.00
YB Yogi Berra C 50.00 100.00

2004 Topps All-Time Fan Favorites Best Seat in the House Relics

STATED ODDS 1:10 RELIC PACKS
BS1 Tom Seaver 10.00 25.00
George Foster
Johnny Bench
BS2 Frank Robinson 6.00 15.00
Jim Palmer
Brooks Robinson
BS3 Dave Parker 6.00 15.00
Bill Madlock
Bill Mazeroski
BS4 Kent Hrbek 10.00 25.00
Rod Carew
Harmon Killebrew

2004 Topps All-Time Fan Favorites Relics

ONE PER RELIC PACK
BR Brooks Robinson Bat 4.00 10.00
BS Bret Saberhagen Jsy 3.00 8.00
CF Carlton Fisk Bat 4.00 10.00
CY Carl Yastrzemski Bat 10.00 25.00
DE Dennis Eckersley Uni 4.00 10.00
DJ David Justice Bat 3.00 8.00
DP Dave Parker Uni 3.00 8.00
DS Darryl Strawberry Bat 3.00 8.00
EW Earl Weaver Jsy 3.00 8.00
FR Frank Robinson Jsy 3.00 8.00
FRB Frank Robinson Bat 3.00 8.00
GB George Brett Uni 8.00 20.00
GC Gary Carter Jsy 3.00 8.00
GF George Foster Bat 3.00 8.00
GN Graig Nettles Bat 3.00 8.00
HK Harmon Killebrew Jsy 10.00 25.00
HR Harold Reynolds Bat 3.00 8.00
JC Jose Canseco Jsy 4.00 10.00
JCB Jose Canseco Bat 4.00 10.00
JM Joe Morgan Bat 3.00 8.00
JP Jim Palmer Uni 3.00 8.00
JR Jim Rice Jsy 3.00 8.00
KG Kirk Gibson Bat 3.00 8.00
KH Keith Hernandez Bat 3.00 8.00
KP Kirby Puckett Jsy 6.00 15.00
LB Lou Brock Jsy 4.00 10.00
MS Mike Schmidt Bat 8.00 20.00
MW Maury Wills Jsy 3.00 8.00
NR Nolan Ryan Jsy 15.00 40.00
RC Rod Carew Bat 4.00 10.00
RJ Reggie Jackson Bat 4.00 10.00
TP Tony Perez Bat 3.00 8.00
WB Wade Boggs Uni 4.00 10.00
WM Willie Mays Uni 20.00 50.00

2005 Topps All-Time Fan Favorites

This 142-card set was released in June, 2005. The set was issued in six-card hobby and retail packs. The hobby packs had an $5 SRP and came 24 packs to a box and eight boxes to a case. The retail packs had an $3 SRP and also came 24 packs to a box and eight boxes to a case. Please note that the retail boxes had no "memorabilia" cards in them. Sid Bream used three different Bible verses during the course of signing his cards.

COMPLETE SET (142) 25.00 50.00
COMMON CARD (1-142) .25 .60
OVERALL PLATE ODDS 1:1414 HOB/RET
PLATE PRINT RUN 1 SET PER COLOR
BLACK-CYAN-MAGENTA-YELLOW ISSUED
NO PLATE PRICING DUE TO SCARCITY
1 Andy Van Slyke .40 1.00
2 Bill Freehan .40 1.00
3 Bo Jackson 1.00 2.50
4 Mark Grace .60 1.50
5 Chuck Knoblauch .40 1.00
6 Candy Maldonado .25 .60
7 David Cone .40 1.00
8 Don Mattingly 2.00 5.00
9 Darryl Strawberry .40 1.00
10 Dick Williams .40 1.00
11 Frank Robinson .60 1.50
12 Glenn Hubbard .25 .60
13 Jim Abbott .40 1.00
14 Jeff Brantley .25 .60
15 John Elway UER 2.50 6.00
Back has him drafted by wrong Football team
16 Jim Leyland .25 .60
17 Jesse Orosco .25 .60
18 Joe Pepitone .40 1.00
19 J.R. Richard .40 1.00
20 Jerome Walton .25 .60
21 Kevin Maas .25 .60
22 Lou Brock .60 1.50
23 Lou Whitaker .40 1.00
24 Carl Erskine .40 1.00
25 John Candelaria .40 1.00
26 Mike Norris .25 .60
27 Nolan Ryan 2.50 6.00
28 Pedro Guerrero .40 1.00
29 Roger Craig .40 1.00
30 Ron Gant .40 1.00
31 Sid Bream .25 .60
32 Sid Fernandez .25 .60
33 Tony LaRussa .40 1.00
34 Tom Seaver .60 1.50
35 Yogi Berra 1.00 2.50
36 Andre Dawson .40 1.00
37 Al Kaline 1.00 2.50
38 Brett Butler .40 1.00
39 Bob Gibson .60 1.50
40 Bill Mazeroski .60 1.50
41 Matty Alou .25 .60
42 Chet Lemon .40 1.00
43 Cal Ripken 3.00 8.00
44 Dusty Baker .40 1.00
45 Dwight Gooden .40 1.00
46 Dave Winfield .40 1.00
47 Ernie Banks 1.00 2.50
48 Gary Carter .40 1.00
49 Howard Johnson .40 1.00
50 Mike Schmidt 2.00 5.00
51 Matt Williams .40 1.00
52 Ozzie Smith 1.50 4.00
53 Atlee Hammaker .25 .60
54 Cleon Jones .25 .60
55 Dave Johnson .25 .60
56 Denny McLain .40 1.00
57 Don Zimmer .40 1.00
58 Gregg Jefferies .25 .60
59 Jay Buhner .40 1.00
60 Johnny Bench 1.00 2.50
61 George Brett 2.00 5.00
62 Dale Murphy .60 1.50
63 Bob Welch .40 1.00
64 Paul O'Neill .60 1.50
65 Mark Lemke .25 .60
66 Kevin McReynolds .40 1.00
67 Jesus Alou .25 .60
68 Joe Pignatano .25 .60
69 Jim Lonborg .40 1.00
70 Jerry Grote .25 .60
71 Joaquin Andujar .40 1.00
72 Gary Gaetti .40 1.00
73 Edgar Martinez .60 1.50
74 Ron Darling .40 1.00
75 Duke Snider .60 1.50
76 Dave Magadan .25 .60
77 Doug Drabek .40 1.00
78 Carl Yastrzemski 1.50 4.00
79 Mitch Williams .40 1.00
80 Marvin Miller PA .25 .60
81 Michael Kay ANC .25 .60
82 Lonnie Smith .25 .60
83 John Wetteland .40 1.00
84 Johnny Podres .40 1.00
85 Joe Morgan .40 1.00
86 Juan Marichal .40 1.00
87 Jeffrey Leonard .25 .60
88 Bob Feller .60 1.50
89 Brooks Robinson .60 1.50
90 Clem Labine .25 .60
91 Barry Lyons .25 .60
92 Harmon Killebrew 1.00 2.50
93 Jim Frey .25 .60
94 John Kruk .60 1.50
95 Ed Kranepool .25 .60
96 Jose Oquendo .25 .60
97 Johnny Pesky .40 1.00
98 John Tudor .25 .60
99 Keith Hernandez .40 1.00
100 Monte Irvin .40 1.00
101 Marty Barrett .25 .60
102 Oscar Gamble .25 .60
103 Hank Bauer .40 1.00
104 Ron Blomberg .25 .60
105 Rod Carew .60 1.50
106 Rick Dempsey .25 .60
107 Walt Jockety GM .25 .60
108 Tom Kelly .25 .60
109 Steve Carlton .40 1.00
110 Rick Monday .40 1.00
111 Rob Dibble .25 .60
112 Shawon Dunston .25 .60
113 Tony Gwynn 1.25 3.00
114 Tom Niedenfuer .25 .60
115 Bob Dernier .25 .60
116 Anthony Young .25 .60
117 Reggie Jackson .60 1.50
118 Steve Garvey .40 1.00
119 Tim Raines .40 1.00
120 Whitey Ford .60 1.50
121 Rafael Santana .25 .60
122 Scott Brosius .40 1.00
123 Stan Musial 1.50 4.00
124 Ron Santo .60 1.50
125 Wade Boggs .60 1.50
126 Jose Canseco 1.00 2.50
127 Brady Anderson .40 1.00
128 Vida Blue .40 1.00
129 Charlie Hough .25 .60
130 Jim Kaat .40 1.00
131 Zane Smith .25 .60
132 Bob Boone .40 1.00
133 Travis Fryman .40 1.00
134 Harold Baines .40 1.00
135 Orlando Cepeda .40 1.00
136 Mike Cuellar .40 1.00
137 Tito Fuentes .25 .60
138 Daryl Boston .25 .60
139 Jim Leyritz .25 .60
140 Moose Skowron .40 1.00
141 Theo Epstein GM .25 .60
142 Barry Bonds 2.50 6.00

2005 Topps All-Time Fan Favorites Refractors

*REF: 2.5X TO 6X BASIC
STATED ODDS 1:19 H, 1:19 R
STATED PRINT RUN 299 SERIAL #'d SETS

2005 Topps All-Time Fan Favorites Refractors Gold

STATED ODDS 1:225 H, 1:225 R
STATED PRINT RUN 25 SERIAL #'d SETS
NO PRICING DUE TO SCARCITY

2005 Topps All-Time Fan Favorites Autographs

Among players and other personages signing their first major manufacturer autographs for this product included Dr. Jim Beckett, John Elway (first as a baseball player); Marvin Miller and Walt Jockety. Unfortunately, Red Sox GM Theo Epstien di not honor his commitment to sign cards for this set. An exchange card for Epstein was originally placed into packs and Topps sent a variety of different signed cards to collectors that sent in their Epstein exchange as a replacement.

GROUP A ODDS 1:34,438 H, 1:93,312 R
GROUP B ODDS 1:1456 H, 1:1421 R
GROUP C ODDS 1:397 H, 1:462 R
GROUP D ODDS 1:1467 H, 1:1414 R
GROUP E ODDS 1:43 H, 1:233 R
GROUP F ODDS 1:37 H, 1:122 R
GROUP G ODDS 1:1165 H, 1079 R
GROUP H ODDS 1:57 H, 1:97 R
GROUP I ODDS 1:108 H, 1:153 R
OVERALL AUTO ODDS 1:12
GROUP A PRINT RUN 15 CARDS
GROUP B PRINT RUN 40 SETS
GROUP C PRINT RUN 90 SETS
CARDS ARE NOT SERIAL-NUMBERED
PRINT RUNS PROVIDED BY TOPPS
NO GROUP A PRICING DUE TO SCARCITY
EXCHANGE DEADLINE 05/31/07
AD Andre Dawson B/40 *
AH Atlee Hammaker H 4.00 10.00
AK Al Kaline E 20.00 50.00
AV Andy Van Slyke F EXCH 10.00 25.00
AY Anthony Young F 4.00 10.00
BB Brett Butler F 4.00 10.00
BF Bill Freehan H 4.00 10.00
BFE Bob Feller E 30.00 60.00
BG Bob Gibson C/90 * 50.00 100.00
BJ Bo Jackson E 30.00 60.00
BL Barry Lyons G 4.00 10.00
BLB Barry Bonds A/15 *
BM Bill Mazeroski E 30.00 60.00
BR Brooks Robinson C/90 * 75.00 150.00
BS B.Sabean GM C/90 * EXCH 40.00 80.00
BW Bob Welch F 4.00 10.00
CH Charlie Hayes F 4.00 10.00
CJ Cleon Jones H 10.00 25.00
CK Chuck Knoblauch E EXCH 15.00 40.00
CL Clem Labine E 10.00 25.00
CLE Chet Lemon H 4.00 10.00
CM Candy Maldonado H 4.00 10.00
CR Cal Ripken C/90 * 140.00 200.00
CY Carl Yastrzemski C/90 * 75.00 150.00
DB Dusty Baker E EXCH 10.00 25.00
DC David Cone E 6.00 15.00
DD Doug Drabek E 6.00 15.00
DG Dwight Gooden D 10.00 25.00
DJ Dave Johnson E 6.00 15.00
DM Don Mattingly D 50.00 100.00
DMA Dave Magadan F 4.00 10.00
DMC Denny McLain F 10.00 25.00
DMU Dale Murphy F 10.00 25.00
DS Darryl Strawberry E 10.00 25.00
DSN Duke Snider B/40 *
DW Dave Winfield C/90 * 50.00 100.00
DWI Dick Williams C/90 * 15.00 40.00
DZ Don Zimmer B/40 *
EB Ernie Banks B/40 *
EM Edgar Martinez E 10.00 25.00
FR Frank Robinson D 30.00 60.00
GB George Brett B/40 * EXCH
GC Gary Carter E 10.00 25.00
GG Gary Gaetti H 4.00 10.00
GH Glenn Hubbard F 4.00 10.00
GJ Gregg Jefferies E 6.00 15.00
HJ Howard Johnson F 4.00 10.00
HK Harmon Killebrew E 30.00 60.00
JA Jim Abbott E 10.00 25.00
JAN Joaquin Andujar H 4.00 10.00
JB Johnny Bench B/40 * EXCH
JBE Dr. Jim Beckett C/90 * 50.00 100.00
JBR Jeff Brantley E 10.00 25.00
JBU Jay Buhner E 10.00 25.00
JE John Elway B/40 *
JG Jerry Grote F 10.00 25.00
JK John Kruk F 4.00 10.00
JLE Jim Leyland F 4.00 10.00
JLO Jim Lonborg F 6.00 15.00
JMA Juan Marichal C/90 * 20.00 50.00
JO Jesse Orosco E 10.00 25.00
JOQ Jose Oquendo I 4.00 10.00
JP Joe Pignatano F 6.00 15.00
JPE Joe Pepitone F 6.00 15.00
JPO Johnny Podres B/40 *
JPY Johnny Pesky F 15.00 40.00
JR J.R. Richard E 10.00 25.00
JT John Tudor F 4.00 10.00
JW Jerome Walton F 4.00 10.00
JWE John Wetteland E 10.00 25.00
KM Kevin Maas E 6.00 15.00
KMC Kevin McReynolds F 4.00 10.00
LS Lonnie Smith I 4.00 10.00
LW Lou Whitaker C/90 * 10.00 25.00
MB Marty Barrett H 4.00 10.00
MI Monte Irvin E 10.00 25.00
MK Michael Kay ANC C/90 * 20.00 50.00
MLE Mark Lemke H 6.00 15.00
MM M.Miller PA C/90 * EXCH 20.00 50.00
MNO Mike Norris I 4.00 10.00
MS Mike Schmidt B/40 *
MW Matt Williams F 10.00 25.00
MWI Mitch Williams E 6.00 15.00
NR Nolan Ryan B/40 *
OG Oscar Gamble H 6.00 15.00
OS Ozzie Smith E 30.00 60.00
PO Paul O'Neill E 15.00 40.00
RB Ron Blomberg F 4.00 10.00
RCR Roger Craig E 10.00 25.00
RD Rick Dempsey I 4.00 10.00
RG Ron Gant C/90 * 20.00 50.00
RJ Reggie Jackson B/40 *
RM Rick Monday E 10.00 25.00
RS Rafael Santana F 4.00 10.00
RSA Ron Santo C/90 * 20.00 50.00
SB Sid Bream F 6.00 15.00
SBR Scott Brosius C/90 * 20.00 50.00
SC Steve Carlton C/90 * 30.00 60.00
SD Shawon Dunston E 10.00 25.00
SF Sid Fernandez E 6.00 15.00
SG Steve Garvey E 15.00 40.00
SM Stan Musial B/40 *
TE T.Epstein GM C/90 * EXCH
TG Tony Gwynn C/90 * 50.00 100.00
TK Tom Kelly F 6.00 15.00
TL Tony LaRussa E 15.00 40.00
TN Tom Niedenfuer H 4.00 10.00
TR Tim Raines E 10.00 25.00
TS Tom Seaver B/40 *
WB Wade Boggs B/40 *
WF Whitey Ford C/90 * 75.00 150.00
WJ W.Jockety GM C/90 * EXCH 15.00 40.00
YB Yogi Berra C/90 * 40.00 80.00

2005 Topps All-Time Fan Favorites Autographs Rainbow

STATED ODDS 1:543 H, 1:933 R
STATED PRINT RUN 10 SERIAL #'d SETS
NO PRICING DUE TO SCARCITY
EXCHANGE DEADLINE 05/31/07

2005 Topps All-Time Fan Favorites Best Seat in the House Relics

GROUP A ODDS 1:170 BOX LOADER
GROUP B ODDS 1:14 BOX LOADER
GROUP A PRINT RUN 50 CARDS
GROUP B PRINT RUN 125 SETS
RAINBOW ODDS 1:56 BOX LOADER
RAINBOW PRINT RUN 25 SERIAL #'d SETS
NO RAINBOW PRICING DUE TO SCARCITY
CR Cal Ripken 10.00 25.00
Frank Robinson B/125
JD Dave Johnson 6.00 15.00
Rick Dempsey B/125
KMLW Al Kaline 10.00 25.00
Lou Whitaker
Chet Lemon
Denny McLain B/125
MFBJ Don Mattingly 15.00 40.00
Whitey Ford
Yogi Berra
Reggie Jackson A/50
RR Brooks Robinson 10.00 25.00
Cal Ripken B/125
RRRD Brooks Robinson 10.00 25.00
Rick Dempsey
Frank Robinson
Cal Ripken B/125

2005 Topps All-Time Fan Favorites League Leaders Tri-Signers

STATED ODDS 1:5194 H, 1:5632 R
STATED PRINT RUN 50 SERIAL #'d SETS
EXCHANGE DEADLINE 05/31/07
JSB Reggie Jackson
Mike Schmidt
George Brett EXCH
MBG Don Mattingly 150.00 250.00
Wade Boggs
Dwight Gooden
RSM Frank Robinson
Duke Snider
Stan Musial

2005 Topps All-Time Fan Favorites Originals Relics

STATED ODDS 1:17 BOX-LOADER
STATED PRINT RUN 50 SERIAL #'d SETS
PRINT RUNS INTERMINGLE DIFT.CARDS
ACTUAL VINTAGE CARDS USED
AD Andre Dawson Bat 10.00 25.00
BJ Bo Jackson Jsy 20.00 50.00
DM Dale Murphy Bat 15.00 40.00
GC Gary Carter Bat 10.00 25.00
JR Jim Rice Bat 10.00 25.00
NR Nolan Ryan Jsy 30.00 60.00
RC Rod Carew Bat 15.00 40.00
RJ Reggie Jackson Bat 15.00 40.00
TG Tony Gwynn Jsy 20.00 50.00
WB Wade Boggs Bat 15.00 40.00

2005 Topps All-Time Fan Favorites Relics

GROUP A ODDS 1:83 BOX-LOADER
GROUP B ODDS 1:31 BOX-LOADER
GROUP C ODDS 1:3 BOX-LOADER
GROUP D ODDS 1:3 BOX-LOADER
GROUP A PRINT RUN 50 SERIAL #'d SETS
GROUP B PRINT RUN 135 SERIAL #'d SETS
GROUP C PRINT RUN 200 SERIAL #'d SETS
GROUP D PRINT RUN 350 SERIAL #'d SETS
RAINBOW ODDS 1:13 BOX-LOADER
RAINBOW PRINT RUN 25 SERIAL #'d SETS
NO RAINBOW PRICING DUE TO SCARCITY
AD Andre Dawson Bat D/350 4.00 10.00
BD Bucky Dent Bat C/200 4.00 10.00
BJ Bo Jackson Bat C/200 6.00 15.00
BR Brooks Robinson Bat D/350 6.00 15.00
BS Bruce Sutter Jsy D/350 4.00 10.00
CF Cecil Fielder Bat C/200 6.00 15.00
CY Carl Yastrzemski Bat A/50
DM Dale Murphy Bat C/200 6.00 15.00
DS Darryl Strawberry Bat D/350 4.00 10.00
ED Eric Davis Bat C/200 4.00 10.00
GC Gary Carter Bat D/350 4.00 10.00
JC Joe Carter Bat D/350 4.00 10.00
JCC Jose Canseco Bat D/350 5.00 15.00
JR Jim Rice Bat C/200 4.00 10.00
KH Keith Hernandez Bat C/200 4.00 10.00
LD Lenny Dykstra Bat C/200 4.00 10.00
MW Mookie Wilson Bat B/135 4.00 10.00
NR Nolan Ryan Jsy B/135 15.00 40.00
PO Paul O'Neill Bat C/200 6.00 15.00
RC Rod Carew Bat C/200 6.00 15.00
RJ Reggie Jackson Bat D/350 6.00 15.00
SM Stan Musial Bat A/50
TG Tony Gwynn Jsy C/200 6.00 15.00
VC Vince Coleman Bat C/200 4.00 10.00
WB Wade Boggs Bat C/200 6.00 15.00
WJ Wally Joyner Bat C/200 4.00 10.00
WM Willie McGee Bat D/350 6.00 15.00

2005 Topps All-Time Fan Favorites Rookie Dual Autographs

STATED ODDS 1:8356 H, 1:8448 R
STATED PRINT RUN 50 SERIAL #'d SETS
EXCHANGE DEADLINE 05/31/07
RB Nolan Ryan
Johnny Bench
SC Tom Seaver 75.00 150.00
Rod Carew EXCH

2007 Topps All-Star FanFest

This seven card set was given to attendees of the 2007 MLB All-Star FanFest in San Francisco.

COMPLETE SET (7) 3.00 8.00
1 Tim Lincecum .60 1.50
2 Barry Bonds .40 1.00
3 Alex Rodriguez .30 .75
4 David Wright .30 .75
5 Ryan Howard .30 .75
6 Daisuke Matsuzaka .75 2.00
7 Mickey Mantle 1.00 2.50

2006 Topps Allen and Ginter

This 350-card set was release in August, 2006. The set was issued in seven-card hobby packs with an $4 SRP. Those packs came 24 to a box and there were 12 boxes in a case. In addition, there were also six-card retail packs issued and those packs came 24 packs to a box and 20 boxes to a case. There were some subsets included in this set including Rookies (251-265); Retired Greats (266-290); Managers (291-300); Modern Personalities (301-314); Reprinted Allen and Ginters (316-319); Famous People of the Past (326-349).

COMPLETE SET (350) 60.00 120.00
COMP.SET w/o SP's (300) 15.00 40.00
SP STATED ODDS 1:2 HOBBY, 1:2 RETAIL
SP CL: 5/15/25/35/45/50-59/65/85/105/115.
SP CL: 125/135/145/150-159/165/175/185
SP CL: 205/215/235/245/251/255-256/265
SP CL: 285/295/305/315/325/335/345
FRAMED ORIGINALS ODDS 1:3227 H, 1:3227 R
1 Albert Pujols .60 1.50
2 Aubrey Huff .07 .20
3 Mark Teixeira .25 .60
4 Vernon Wells .15 .40
5 Ken Griffey Jr. SP 2.00 5.00
6 Nick Swisher .15 .40
7 Jose Reyes .40 1.00
8 David Wright .60 1.50
9 Vladimir Guerrero .40 1.00
10 Andruw Jones .25 .60
11 Ramon Hernandez .15 .40
12 Miguel Tejada .15 .40
13 Juan Pierre .15 .40
14 Jim Thome .25 .60
15 Austin Kearns SP 1.25 3.00
16 Jhonny Peralta .15 .40
17 Clint Barmes .15 .40
18 Angel Berroa .15 .40
19 Nomar Garciaparra .40 1.00
20 Joe Nathan .15 .40
21 Brandon Webb .15 .40
22 Chad Tracy .15 .40
23 Derek Jeter 1.00 2.50
24 Conor Jackson (RC) .25 .60
25 Jason Giambi SP 1.25 3.00
26 Johnny Estrada .15 .40
27 Luis Gonzalez .15 .40
28 Javier Vazquez .15 .40
29 Orlando Hudson .15 .40
30 Shawn Green .15 .40
31 Mark Buehrle .15 .40
32 Wily Mo Pena .15 .40
33 C.C. Sabathia .15 .40
34 Ronnie Belliard .15 .40
35 Travis Hafner SP 1.25 3.00
36 Mike Jacobs (RC) .15 .40
37 Roy Oswalt .15 .40
38 Zack Greinke .15 .40
39 J.D. Drew .15 .40
40 Jeff Kent .15 .40
41 Ben Sheets .15 .40
42 Luis Castillo .15 .40
43 Carlos Delgado .15 .40
44 Cliff Floyd .15 .40
45 Danny Haren SP 1.25 3.00
46 Bobby Abreu .15 .40
47 Jeromy Burnitz .15 .40
48 Khalil Greene .25 .60
49 Moises Alou .15 .40
50 Alex Rodriguez SP 2.00 5.00
51 Ervin Santana SP 1.25 3.00
52 Bartolo Colon SP 1.25 3.00
53 John Smoltz SP 1.25 3.00
54 David Ortiz SP 1.25 3.00
55 Hideki Matsui SP 1.25 3.00
56 Jermaine Dye SP 1.25 3.00
57 Victor Martinez SP 1.25 3.00
58 Willy Taveras SP 1.25 3.00
59 Brady Clark SP 1.25 3.00
60 Justin Morneau .15 .40
61 Xavier Nady .15 .40
62 Rich Harden .15 .40
63 Jack Wilson .15 .40
64 Brian Giles .15 .40
65 Jon Lieber SP 1.25 3.00
66 Dan Johnson .15 .40
67 Billy Wagner .15 .40
68 Rickie Weeks .15 .40
69 Chris Ray (RC) .15 .40
70 Chris Shelton .15 .40
71 Dmitri Young .15 .40
72 Ivan Rodriguez .25 .60
73 Jeremy Bonderman .15 .40
74 Justin Verlander (RC) .60 1.50
75 Randy Johnson .40 1.00
76 Magglio Ordonez .15 .40
77 Brandon Inge .15 .40
78 Placido Polanco .15 .40
79 Ryan Howard .60 1.50
80 Jason Bay .15 .40
81 Sean Casey .15 .40
82 Jeremy Hermida (RC) .15 .40
83 Mike Cameron .15 .40
84 Trevor Hoffman .15 .40
85 Mike Matheny SP 1.25 3.00
86 Steve Finley .15 .40
87 Adam Everett .15 .40
88 Jason Isringhausen .15 .40
89 Jonny Gomes .15 .40
90 Barry Zito .15 .40
91 Bobby Crosby .15 .40
92 Eric Chavez .15 .40
93 Frank Thomas .40 1.00
94 Huston Street .15 .40
95 Jorge Posada .25 .60
96 Casey Kotchman UER .15 .40
Birthdate is incorrect
97 Darin Erstad .15 .40
98 Chipper Jones .40 1.00
99 Jeff Francoeur .40 1.00
100 Barry Bonds .75 2.00
101 Alfonso Soriano .15 .40
102 Brandon Claussen .15 .40
103 Aaron Boone .15 .40
104 Roger Clemens .60 1.50
105 Andy Pettitte SP 1.25 3.00
106 Nick Johnson .15 .40
107 Tom Gordon .15 .40
108 Orlando Hernandez .15 .40
109 Francisco Rodriguez .15 .40
110 Orlando Cabrera .15 .40
111 Edgar Renteria .15 .40
112 Tim Hudson .15 .40
113 Coco Crisp .15 .40
114 Matt Clement .15 .40
115 Greg Maddux SP 2.00 5.00
116 Paul Konerko .15 .40
117 Felipe Lopez .15 .40
118 Garrett Atkins .15 .40
119 Akinori Otsuka .15 .40

120 Craig Biggio .25 .60
121 Danys Baez .15 .40
122 Brad Penny .15 .40
123 Eric Gagne .15 .40
124 Lew Ford .15 .40
125 Mariano Rivera SP 1.25 3.00
126 Carlos Beltran .15 .40
127 Pedro Martinez .25 .60
128 Todd Helton .25 .60
129 Aaron Rowand .15 .40
130 Mike Lieberthal .15 .40
131 Oliver Perez .15 .40
132 Ryan Klesko .15 .40
133 Randy Winn .15 .40
134 Yuniesky Betancourt .15 .40
135 David Eckstein SP 1.25 3.00
136 Chad Orvella .15 .40
137 Toby Hall .15 .40
138 Hank Blalock .15 .40
139 B.J. Ryan .15 .40
140 Roy Halladay .15 .40
141 Livan Hernandez .15 .40
142 John Patterson .15 .40
143 Bengie Molina .15 .40
144 Brad Wilkerson .15 .40
145 Jorge Cantu SP 1.25 3.00
146 Mark Mulder .15 .40
147 Felix Hernandez .25 .60
148 Paul Lo Duca .15 .40
149 Prince Fielder (RC) .60 1.50
150 Johnny Damon SP 1.25 3.00
151 Ryan Langerhans SP 1.25 3.00
152 Kris Benson SP 1.25 3.00
153 Curt Schilling SP 1.25 3.00
154 Manny Ramirez SP 1.25 3.00
155 Robinson Cano SP 1.25 3.00
156 Derrek Lee SP 1.25 3.00
157 A.J. Pierzynski SP 1.25 3.00
158 Adam Dunn SP 1.25 3.00
159 Cliff Lee SP 1.25 3.00
160 Grady Sizemore .25 .60
161 Jeff Francis .15 .40
162 Dontrelle Willis .15 .40
163 Brad Ausmus .15 .40
164 Preston Wilson .15 .40
165 Derek Lowe SP 1.25 3.00
166 Chris Capuano .15 .40
167 Joe Mauer .25 .60
168 Torii Hunter .15 .40
169 Chase Utley .40 1.00
170 Zach Duke .15 .40
171 Jason Schmidt .15 .40
172 Adrian Beltre .15 .40
173 Eddie Guardado .15 .40
174 Richie Sexson .15 .40
175 Miguel Cabrera SP 1.25 3.00
176 Julio Lugo .15 .40
177 Francisco Cordero .15 .40
178 Kevin Millwood .15 .40
179 A.J. Burnett .15 .40
180 Jose Guillen .15 .40
181 Larry Bigbie .15 .40
182 Raul Ibanez .15 .40
183 Jake Peavy .15 .40
184 Pat Burrell .15 .40
185 Tom Glavine SP 1.25 3.00
186 J.J. Hardy .15 .40
187 Emil Brown .15 .40
188 Lance Berkman .15 .40
189 Marcus Giles .15 .40
190 Scott Podsednik .15 .40
191 Chone Figgins .15 .40
192 Melvin Mora .15 .40
193 Mark Loretta .15 .40
194 Carlos Zambrano .15 .40
195 Chien-Ming Wang .60 1.50
196 Mark Prior .25 .60
197 Bobby Jenks .15 .40
198 Brian Fuentes .15 .40
199 Garret Anderson .15 .40
200 Ichiro Suzuki .60 1.50
201 Brian Roberts .15 .40
202 Jason Kendall .15 .40
203 Milton Bradley .15 .40
204 Jimmy Rollins .15 .40
205 Brett Myers SP 1.25 3.00
206 Joe Randa .15 .40
207 Mike Piazza .40 1.00
208 Matt Morris .15 .40
209 Omar Vizquel .25 .60
210 Jeremy Reed .15 .40
211 Chris Carpenter .15 .40
212 Jim Edmonds .25 .60
213 Scott Kazmir .25 .60
214 Travis Lee .15 .40
215 Michael Young SP 1.25 3.00
216 Rod Barajas .15 .40
217 Gustavo Chacin .15 .40
218 Lyle Overbay .15 .40
219 Troy Glaus .15 .40
220 Chad Cordero .15 .40
221 Jose Vidro .15 .40
222 Scott Rolen .25 .60
223 Carl Crawford .15 .40
224 Rocco Baldelli .15 .40
225 Mike Mussina .25 .60
226 Kelvim Escobar .15 .40
227 Corey Patterson .15 .40
228 Javy Lopez .15 .40
229 Jonathan Papelbon (RC) .75 2.00
230 Aramis Ramirez .15 .40
231 Tadahito Iguchi .15 .40
232 Morgan Ensberg .15 .40
233 Mark Grudzielanek .15 .40
234 Mike Sweeney .15 .40
235 Shawn Chacon SP 1.25 3.00
236 Nick Punto .15 .40
237 Geoff Jenkins .15 .40
238 Carlos Lee .15 .40
239 David DeJesus .15 .40
240 Brad Lidge .15 .40
241 Bob Wickman .15 .40
242 Jon Garland .15 .40
243 Kerry Wood .15 .40
244 Bronson Arroyo .15 .40
245 Matt Holliday SP 1.50 4.00
246 Josh Beckett .15 .40
247 Johan Santana .25 .60
248 Rafael Furcal .15 .40
249 Shannon Stewart .15 .40
250 Gary Sheffield .15 .40
251 Josh Barfield SP (RC) 1.25 3.00
252 Kenji Johjima RC .75 2.00
253 Ian Kinsler (RC) .25 .60
254 Brian Anderson (RC) .15 .40
255 Matt Cain SP (RC) 1.25 3.00
256 Josh Willingham SP (RC) 1.25 3.00
257 John Koronka (RC) .15 .40
258 Chris Duffy (RC) .15 .40
259 Brian McCann (RC) .15 .40
260 Hanley Ramirez (RC) .40 1.00
261 Hong-Chih Kuo (RC) .40 1.00
262 Francisco Liriano (RC) .40 1.00
263 Anderson Hernandez (RC) .15 .40
264 Ryan Zimmerman (RC) 1.00 2.50
265 Brian Bannister SP (RC) 1.25 3.00
266 Nolan Ryan 1.00 2.50
267 Frank Robinson .15 .40
268 Roberto Clemente 1.25 3.00
269 Hank Greenberg .40 1.00
270 Napolean Lajoie .25 .60
271 Lloyd Waner .25 .60
272 Paul Waner .25 .60
273 Frankie Frisch .25 .60
274 Moose Skowron .15 .40
275 Mickey Mantle 2.00 5.00
276 Brooks Robinson .25 .60
277 Carl Yastrzemski .60 1.50
278 Johnny Pesky .15 .40
279 Stan Musial .60 1.50
280 Bill Mazeroski .25 .60
281 Harmon Killebrew .40 1.00
282 Monte Irvin .15 .40
283 Bob Gibson .25 .60
284 Ted Williams 1.00 2.50
285 Yogi Berra SP 1.25 3.00
286 Ernie Banks .40 1.00
287 Bobby Doerr .15 .40
288 Josh Gibson .25 .60
289 Bob Feller .15 .40
290 Cal Ripken 1.50 4.00
291 Bobby Cox MG .15 .40
292 Terry Francona MG .15 .40
293 Dusty Baker MG .15 .40
294 Ozzie Guillen MG .15 .40
295 Jim Leyland MG SP 1.25 3.00
296 Willie Randolph MG .15 .40
297 Joe Torre MG .25 .60
298 Felipe Alou MG .15 .40
299 Tony La Russa MG .15 .40
300 Frank Robinson MG .15 .40
301 Mike Tyson .60 1.50
302 Duke Paoa Kahanamoku .15 .40
303 Jennie Finch 1.00 2.50
304 Brandi Chastain .15 .40
305 Danica Patrick SP 3.00 8.00
306 Wendy Guey .15 .40
307 Hulk Hogan .50 1.25
308 Carl Lewis .10 .30
309 John Wooden .25 .60
310 Randy Couture .15 .40
311 Andy Irons .15 .40
312 Takeru Kobayashi .50 1.25
313 Leon Spinks .10 .30
314 Jim Thorpe .25 .60
315 Jerry Bailey SP 1.25 3.00
316 Adrian C. Anson REP .25 .60
317 John M. Ward REP .15 .40
318 Mike Kelly REP
319 Capt. Jack Glasscock REP .15 .40
320 Aaron Hill .15 .40
321 Derrick Turnbow .15 .40
322 Nick Markakis (RC) .25 .60
323 Brad Hawpe .15 .40
324 Kevin Mench .15 .40
325 John Lackey SP 1.25 3.00
326 Chester A. Arthur .07 .20
327 Ulysses S. Grant .10 .20
328 Abraham Lincoln .10 .30
329 Grover Cleveland .10 .20
330 Benjamin Harrison .10 .20
331 Theodore Roosevelt .10 .30
332 Rutherford B. Hayes .10 .20
333 Chancellor Otto Von Bismarck .15 .40
334 Kaiser Wilhelm II .15 .40
335 Queen Victoria SP 1.25 3.00
336 Pope Leo XIII .15 .40
337 Thomas Edison .10 .20
338 Orville Wright .10 .20
339 Wilbur Wright .10 .20
340 Nathaniel Hawthorne .15 .40
341 Herman Melville .15 .40
342 Stonewall Jackson .10 .20
343 Robert E. Lee .10 .20
344 Andrew Carnegie .10 .20
345 John Rockefeller SP 1.25 3.00
346 Bob Fitzsimmons .10 .20
347 Billy The Kid .10 .20
348 Buffalo Bill .15 .40
349 Jesse James .10 .20
350 Statue Of Liberty .15 .40
NNO Framed Originals 60.00 120.00

2006 Topps Allen and Ginter Mini

*MINI 1-350: 1X TO 2.5X BASIC
*MINI 1-350: 1X TO 2.5X BASIC RC's
APPX.15 MINIS PER 24-CT SEALED BOX
*MINI SP 1-350: .6X TO 1.5X BASIC SP
*MINI SP 1-350: .6X TO 1.5X BASIC SP RC's
MINI SP ODDS 1:13 H, 1:13 R
COMMON CARD (351-375) 20.00 50.00
SEMISTARS 351-375 30.00 60.00
UNLISTED STARS 351-375 30.00 60.00
351-375 RANDOM WITHIN RIP CARDS
OVERALL PLATE ODDS 1:865 H, 1:865 R
PLATE PRINT RUN 1 SET PER COLOR
BLACK-CYAN-MAGENTA-YELLOW ISSUED
NO PLATE PRICING DUE TO SCARCITY
351 Albert Pujols EXT 75.00 150.00
352 Alex Rodriguez EXT 40.00 80.00
353 Andruw Jones EXT 20.00 50.00
354 Barry Bonds EXT 40.00 80.00
355 Cal Ripken EXT 75.00 150.00
356 David Ortiz EXT 40.00 80.00
357 David Wright EXT 50.00 100.00
358 Derek Jeter EXT 75.00 150.00
359 Derrek Lee EXT 20.00 50.00
360 Hideki Matsui EXT 30.00 60.00
361 Ichiro Suzuki EXT 40.00 80.00
362 Johan Santana EXT 30.00 60.00
363 Josh Gibson EXT 20.00 50.00
364 Ken Griffey Jr. EXT 60.00 120.00
365 Manny Ramirez EXT 30.00 60.00
366 Mickey Mantle EXT 75.00 150.00
367 Miguel Cabrera EXT 20.00 50.00
368 Miguel Tejada EXT 20.00 50.00
369 Mike Piazza EXT 30.00 60.00
370 Nolan Ryan EXT 60.00 120.00
371 Roberto Clemente EXT 125.00 200.00
372 Roger Clemens EXT 40.00 80.00
373 Scott Rolen EXT 30.00 60.00
374 Ted Williams EXT 50.00 100.00
375 Vladimir Guerrero EXT 30.00 60.00

2006 Topps Allen and Ginter Mini A and G Back

*A & G BACK: 2X TO 5X BASIC
*A & G BACK: 1.5X TO 4X BASIC RC's
STATED ODDS 1:5 H, 1:5 R
*A & G BACK SP: 1X TO 2.5X BASIC SP
*A & G BACK SP: 1X TO 2.5X BASIC SP RC's
SP STATED ODDS 1:65 H, 1:65 R

2006 Topps Allen and Ginter Mini Bazooka

STATED ODDS 1:125 H, 1:266 R
STATED PRINT RUN 25 SERIAL #'d SETS
NO PRICING DUE TO SCARCITY

2006 Topps Allen and Ginter Mini Black

*BLACK: 4X TO 10X BASIC
*BLACK: 2.5X TO 6X BASIC RC's
STATED ODDS 1:10 H, 1:10 R
*BLACK SP: 1.5X TO 4X BASIC SP
*BLACK SP: 1.5X TO 4X BASIC SP RC's
SP STATED ODDS 1:130 H, 1:130 R

2006 Topps Allen and Ginter Mini No Card Number

*NO NBR: 6X TO 15X BASIC
*NO NBR: 4X TO 10X BASIC RC's
*NO NBR: 2X TO 5X BASIC SP
*NO NBR: 2X TO 5X BASIC SP RC's
STATED ODDS 1:60 H, 1:168 R
STATED PRINT RUN 50 SETS
CARDS ARE NOT SERIAL-NUMBERED
PRINT RUN INFO PROVIDED BY TOPPS

2006 Topps Allen and Ginter Mini Wood

STATED ODDS 1:3100 H, 1:6800 R
STATED PRINT RUN 1 SERIAL #'d SET
NO PRICING DUE TO SCARCITY

2006 Topps Allen and Ginter Autographs

GROUP A ODDS 1:2467 H, 1:3850 R
GROUP B ODDS 1:14,500 H, 1:32,000 R
GROUP C ODDS 1:2200 H, 1:4300 R
GROUP D ODDS 1:548 H, 1:1090 R
GROUP E ODDS 1:473 H, 1:1000 R
GROUP F ODDS 1:250 H, 1:520 R
GROUP G ODDS 1:158 H, 1:299 R
GROUP A PRINT RUN 50 CARDS PER
GROUP A BONDS PRINT RUN 25 CARDS
GROUP B PRINT RUN 75 CARDS PER
GROUP C PRINT RUN 100 CARDS PER
GROUP D PRINT RUN 200 CARDS PER
GROUP A-D ARE NOT SERIAL-NUMBERED
A-D PRINT RUNS PROVIDED BY TOPPS
NO BONDS PRICING DUE TO SCARCITY
AI Andy Irons D/200 * 10.00 25.00
AR Alex Rodriguez A/50 * 400.00 500.00
BB Barry Bonds A/25 *
BC Brandi Chastain D/200 * 30.00 60.00
BF Bob Feller E 20.00 50.00
BJR B.J. Ryan E 8.00 20.00
BW Billy Wagner F 10.00 25.00
CB Clint Barmes F 8.00 20.00
CL Carl Lewis D/200 * 60.00 120.00
CMW Chien-Ming Wang C/100 * 500.00 600.00
CR Cal Ripken A/50 * 350.00 400.00
CU Chase Utley E 40.00 80.00
CY Carl Yastrzemski A/50 * 250.00 400.00
DL Derrek Lee E 15.00 40.00
DP Danica Patrick C/100 * 400.00 600.00
DW David Wright E 75.00 150.00
DWI Dontrelle Willis C/100 * 15.00 40.00
EC Eric Chavez G 6.00 15.00
ES Ervin Santana F 6.00 15.00
FL Francisco Liriano G 20.00 50.00
GS Gary Sheffield A/50 * 60.00 120.00
HH Hulk Hogan D/200 * 90.00 150.00
HS Huston Street E 10.00 25.00
JB Jerry Bailey D/200 * 50.00 100.00
JB1 Josh Barfield G 6.00 15.00
JF Jennie Finch D/200 * 90.00 150.00
JG Jonny Gomes G 6.00 15.00
JS Johan Santana C/100 * 75.00 150.00
JW John Wooden D/200 * 90.00 150.00
KJ Kenji Johjima A/50 * 250.00 350.00
LF Lew Ford G 5.00 12.00
LS Leon Spinks D/200 * 40.00 80.00
MC Miguel Cabrera C/100 * 75.00 150.00
MT Mike Tyson D/200 * 250.00 350.00
MY Michael Young E 10.00 25.00
NR Nolan Ryan A/50 * 350.00 450.00
OS Ozzie Smith B/75 * 100.00 200.00
PF Prince Fielder F 20.00 50.00
RA Randy Couture E 125.00 250.00
RC Robinson Cano G 15.00 40.00
RH Ryan Howard F 50.00 100.00
RZ Ryan Zimmerman F 30.00 60.00
SK Scott Kazmir F 10.00 25.00
SM Stan Musial A/50 * 300.00 400.00
TG Tony Gwynn A/50 * 200.00 300.00
TH Travis Hafner F 8.00 20.00
TK Takeru Kobayashi D/200 * 60.00 120.00
VG Vladimir Guerrero A/50 * 200.00 300.00
VM Victor Martinez E 15.00 40.00
WG Wendy Guey F 8.00 20.00
WMP Wily Mo Pena G 8.00 20.00

2006 Topps Allen and Ginter Autographs Red Ink

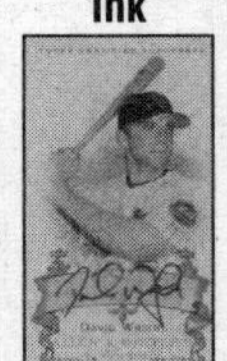

RANDOM INSERTS WITHIN RIP CARDS
STATED PRINT RUN 10 SETS
CARDS ARE NOT SERIAL-NUMBERED
PRINT RUN IFNO PROVIDED BY TOPPS
NO PRICING DUE TO SCARCITY
AR Alex Rodriguez
DW David Wright

2006 Topps Allen and Ginter N43

COMPLETE SET (15) 50.00 100.00
STATED ODDS 1:2 SEALED HOBBY BOXES
1 Alex Rodriguez 3.00 8.00
2 Barry Bonds 4.00 10.00
3 Albert Pujols 4.00 10.00

4 Josh Gibson 2.00 5.00
5 Nolan Ryan 5.00 12.00
6 Ichiro Suzuki 3.00 8.00
7 Mickey Mantle 8.00 20.00
8 Ted Williams 5.00 12.00
9 David Wright 3.00 8.00
10 Ken Griffey Jr. 3.00 8.00
11 Mark Teixeira 1.50 4.00
12 Adrian C. Anson 3.00 8.00
13 Mike Tyson 3.00 8.00
14 Kenji Johjima 4.00 10.00
15 Ryan Zimmerman 5.00 12.00

2006 Topps Allen and Ginter N43 Autographs

STATED ODDS 1:1970 HOBBY BOXES
STATED PRINT RUN 10 SERIAL #'d SETS
NO PRICING DUE TO SCARCITY
AR Alex Rodriguez
BB Barry Bonds

2006 Topps Allen and Ginter N43 Relics

STATED ODDS 1:379 HOBBY BOXES
STATED PRINT RUN 50 SERIAL #'d SETS
AP Albert Pujols Uni 40.00 80.00
JG Josh Gibson Model Bat 200.00 300.00

2006 Topps Allen and Ginter Dick Perez Sketches

COMPLETE SET (30) 10.00 25.00
ONE PEREZ OR DECOY PER PACK
ORIGINALS RANDOM WITHIN RIP CARDS
ORIGINALS PRINT RUN 1 SERIAL #'d SET
NO ORIG. PRICING DUE TO SCARCITY
1 Shawn Green .25 .60
2 Andruw Jones .40 1.00
3 Miguel Tejada .25 .60
4 David Ortiz .60 1.50
5 Derrek Lee .25 .60
6 Paul Konerko .25 .60
7 Ken Griffey Jr. 1.00 2.50
8 Travis Hafner .25 .60
9 Todd Helton .40 1.00
10 Ivan Rodriguez .40 1.00
11 Miguel Cabrera .40 1.00
12 Lance Berkman .25 .60
13 Mike Sweeney .25 .60
14 Vladimir Guerrero .60 1.50
15 Rafael Furcal .25 .60
16 Carlos Lee .25 .60
17 Johan Santana .40 1.00
18 David Wright 1.00 2.50
19 Alex Rodriguez 1.00 2.50
20 Huston Street .25 .60
21 Bobby Abreu .25 .60
22 Jason Bay .25 .60
23 Jake Peavy .25 .60
24 Ichiro Suzuki 1.00 2.50
25 Barry Bonds 1.25 3.00
26 Albert Pujols 1.25 3.00
27 Aubrey Huff .25 .60
28 Mark Teixeira .40 1.00
29 Vernon Wells .25 .60
30 Alfonso Soriano .25 .60

2006 Topps Allen and Ginter Postcards

STATED ODDS 1:2 HOBBY BOXES
PERSONALIZED ODDS 1:3000 HOB.BOXES
PERSONALIZED PRINT RUN 1 #'d SET
NO PERSONALIZED PRICING AVAILABLE
AP Albert Pujols 3.00 8.00
AR Alex Rodriguez 2.50 6.00
BB Barry Bonds 3.00 8.00
CR Cal Ripken 6.00 15.00
DJ Derek Jeter 4.00 10.00

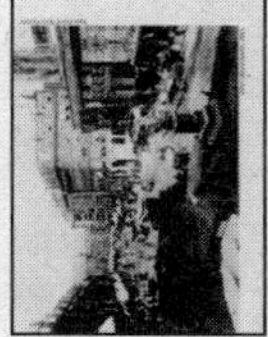

DO David Ortiz 1.50 4.00
DW David Wright 2.50 6.00
IS Ichiro Suzuki 2.50 6.00
JG Josh Gibson 1.50 4.00
KG Ken Griffey Jr. 2.50 6.00
MM Mickey Mantle 6.00 15.00
MR Manny Ramirez 1.50 4.00
MT Miguel Tejada 1.50 4.00
TW Ted Williams 4.00 10.00
VG Vladimir Guerrero 1.50 4.00

2006 Topps Allen and Ginter Relics

GROUP A ODDS 1:2800 H, 1:4950 R
GROUP B ODDS 1:2000 H, 1:3900 R
GROUP C ODDS 1:140 H, 1:248 R
GROUP D ODDS 1:178 H, 1:413 R
GROUP E ODDS 1:128 H, 1:275 R
GROUP F ODDS 1:60 H, 1:118 R
GROUP G ODDS 1:66 H, 1:152 R
GROUP H ODDS 1:111 H, 1:174 R
GROUP I ODDS 1:178 H, 1:413 R
GROUP A ARE NOT SERIAL-NUMBERED
GROUP A QTY PROVIDED BY TOPPS
AP Albert Pujols Uni F 8.00 20.00
APE Andy Pettitte Jsy F 4.00 10.00
AR Alex Rodriguez Jsy C 8.00 20.00
BB Barry Bonds Uni G 10.00 25.00
BC Bobby Crosby Uni E 3.00 8.00
BM Brandon McCarthy Jsy E 3.00 8.00
CB Carlos Beltran Jsy H 3.00 8.00
CBA Clint Barmes Jsy G 3.00 8.00
CD Carlos Delgado Jsy F 3.00 8.00
CMW Chien-Ming Wang Jsy F 20.00 50.00
CS Curt Schilling Jsy F 4.00 10.00
CU Chase Utley Jsy G 6.00 15.00
DO David Ortiz Jsy G 4.00 10.00
DW David Wright Jsy H 6.00 15.00
DWI Dontrelle Willis Jsy I 3.00 8.00
EC Eric Chavez Uni E 3.00 8.00
FH Felix Hernandez Jsy C 4.00 10.00
FT Frank Thomas Bat F 6.00 15.00
GB George W. Bush Tie A/150 * 200.00 300.00
GS Gary Sheffield Bat E 3.00 8.00
HCK Hong-Chih Kuo Jsy D 8.00 20.00
HM Hideki Matsui Uni G 6.00 15.00
HS Huston Street Jsy D 3.00 8.00
JC Jorge Cantu Jsy E 3.00 8.00
JD Johnny Damon Jsy C 4.00 10.00
JDY Jermaine Dye Uni G 3.00 8.00
JF Jeff Francoeur Bat C 6.00 15.00
JG Jonny Gomes Jsy F 3.00 8.00
JK John F. Kennedy Sweater A/250 * 200.00300.00
JP Jake Peavy Jsy C 3.00 8.00
JS Johan Santana Jsy G 4.00 10.00
JT Jim Thome Uni C 4.00 10.00
MB Mark Buehrle Uni F 3.00 8.00
MC Miguel Cabrera Uni B 6.00 15.00
MH Matt Holliday Jsy F 4.00 10.00
MM Mickey Mantle Uni D 75.00 150.00
MP Mark Prior Jsy G 3.00 8.00
MPZ Mike Piazza Bat C 4.00 10.00
MR Manny Ramirez Jsy H 4.00 10.00
MT Miguel Tejada Uni E 3.00 8.00
NS Nick Swisher Jsy E 3.00 8.00
PK Paul Konerko Uni D 3.00 8.00
PM Pedro Martinez Jsy I 4.00 10.00
RC Robinson Cano Uni F 8.00 20.00
RH Ryan Howard Bat C 12.50 30.00
RL Ryan Langerhans Bat C 3.00 8.00
RO Roy Oswalt Jsy G 3.00 8.00
TH Travis Hafner Jsy D 3.00 8.00
VG Vladimir Guerrero Bat F 4.00 10.00
VM Victor Martinez Jsy D 3.00 8.00
WT Willy Taveras Jsy H 3.00 8.00
ZD Zach Duke Jsy C 3.00 8.00

2006 Topps Allen and Ginter Rip Cards

1-50 STATED ODDS 1:265 HOBBY
1-4 PRINT RUN 10 SERIAL #'d SETS
5-9 PRINT RUN 15 SERIAL #'d SETS
10-19 PRINT RUN 25 SERIAL #'d SETS
20-50 PRINT RUN 99 SERIAL #'d SETS
1-19 NO PRICING DUE TO SCARCITY
ALL LISTED PRICES ARE FOR RIPPED
UNRIPPED HAVE ADD'L CARDS WITHIN
COMMON UNRIPPED (20-50) 75.00 150.00
UNRIPPED (30/35/43) 100.00 200.00
UNRIPPED (45/47/49) 100.00 200.00

RIP1 Mickey Mantle Back/10
RIP2 Dontrelle Willis/10
RIP3 Ivan Rodriguez/10
RIP4 Johan Santana/10
RIP5 Mike Piazza/15
RIP6 Randy Johnson/15
RIP7 Robinson Cano/15
RIP8 Scott Rolen/15
RIP9 Todd Helton/15
RIP10 Alex Rodriguez Back/25
RIP11 Alfonso Soriano/25
RIP12 David Ortiz
Alex Rodriguez
RIP13 Barry Bonds Back/25
RIP14 Carlos Beltran
Carlos Delgado
RIP15 David Wright/25
RIP16 Derrek Lee/25
RIP17 Huston Street/25
RIP18 Mariano Rivera/25
RIP19 Nolan Ryan/25
RIP20 Kenji Johjima/99 15.00 40.00
RIP21 Cap Anson/99 15.00 40.00
RIP22 Ryan Zimmerman/99 20.00 50.00
RIP23 Andruw Jones/99 10.00 25.00
RIP24 Barry Bonds at Wall/99 15.00 40.00
RIP25 Cal Ripken/99 30.00 60.00
RIP26 David Ortiz/99 10.00 25.00
RIP27 Hideki Matsui/99 10.00 25.00
RIP28 Ken Griffey Jr./99 15.00 40.00
RIP29 Manny Ramirez/99 10.00 25.00
RIP30 Mickey Mantle w/Bat/99 50.00 100.00
RIP31 Alex Rodriguez Bat Out/99 15.00 40.00
RIP32 Miguel Cabrera/99 6.00 15.00
RIP33 Miguel Tejada/99 6.00 15.00
RIP34 Pedro Martinez/99 10.00 25.00
RIP35 Albert Pujols w/Bat/99 30.00 60.00
RIP36 Alex Rodriguez Hands Out/99 15.00 40.00
RIP37 Alex Rodriguez 15.00 40.00
Derek Jeter
RIP38 Barry Bonds 700/99 15.00 40.00
RIP39 Derek Jeter/99 20.00 50.00
RIP40 Ichiro Suzuki/99 15.00 40.00
RIP41 Ichiro Suzuki 15.00 40.00
Hideki Matsui
RIP42 Josh Gibson/99 15.00 40.00
RIP43 Mickey Mantle Swing/99 50.00 100.00
RIP44 Jonathan Papelbon/99 20.00 50.00
RIP45 Mickey Mantle 50.00 100.00
Ted Williams
RIP46 Albert Pujols Back/99 30.00 60.00
RIP47 Roberto Clemente/99 30.00 60.00
RIP48 Roger Clemens/99 15.00 40.00
RIP49 Ted Williams/99 30.00 60.00
RIP50 Vladimir Guerrero/99 10.00 25.00

2007 Topps Allen and Ginter

This 350-card set was released in August, 2007. The set was issued in both hobby and retail versions. The hobby packs, which had an $4 SRP, consisted of eight-cards which came 24 packs to a box and 12 boxes to a case. Similar to the 2006 set, many non-baseball players were interspersed throughout this set. There were also a group of short-printed cards, which were inserted at a stated rate of one in two hobby or retail packs. In addition, some original 19th century Allen and Ginter cards were repurchased for this product and those original cards (featuring both sports and non-sport subjects) were inserted at a stated rate of one in 17, 072 hobby and one in 34, 654 retail packs.

COMPLETE SET (350) 60.00 120.00
COMP.SET w/o SP's (300) 20.00 50.00
COMMON CARD .12 .30
COMMON RC .20 .50
COMMON SP 1.25 3.00
SP STATED ODDS 1:2 HOBBY, 1:2 RETAIL
SP CL: 5/43/48/58/63/107/110/119/130/137
SP CL: 152/159/178/193/194/203/219/222
SP CL: 224/243/263/301/302/303/306/307
SP CL: 308/309/310/316/317/318/319/320
SP CL: 321/322/325/326/327/330/331/334
SP CL: 335/336/339/340/345/348/349/350
FRAMED ORIGINALS ODDS 1:17,072 HOBBY
FRAMED ORIGINALS ODDS 1:34,654 RETAIL
1 Ryan Howard .50 1.25
2 Mike Gonzalez .12 .30
3 Austin Kearns .12 .30
4 Josh Hamilton (RC) .50 1.25
5 Stephen Drew SP 1.25 3.00
6 Matt Murton .12 .30
7 Mickey Mantle 1.50 4.00
8 Howie Kendrick .12 .30
9 Alexander Graham Bell .12 .30
10 Jason Bay .12 .30
11 Hank Blalock .12 .30
12 Johan Santana .20 .50
13 Eleanor Roosevelt .12 .30
14 Kei Igawa RC .50 1.25
15 Jeff Francoeur .30 .75
16 Carl Crawford .12 .30
17 Jhonny Peralta .12 .30
18 Mariano Rivera .30 .75
19 Mario Andretti .30 .75
20 Vladimir Guerrero .30 .75
21 Adam Wainwright .12 .30
22 Huston Street .12 .30
23 Cael Sanderson .12 .30
24 Susan B. Anthony .12 .30
25 Jay Payton .12 .30
26 P.T. Barnum .12 .30
27 Scott Podsednik .12 .30
28 Willie Randolph .12 .30
29 Sean Casey .12 .30
30 Eiffel Tower .12 .30
31 Kenji Johjima .30 .75
32 Felix Hernandez .20 .50
33 Elijah Dukes RC .30 .75
34 Mark Grudzielanek .12 .30
35 J.D. Drew .12 .30
36 Kevin Kouzmanoff .12 .30
37 Jonathan Papelbon .30 .75
38 Bobby Crosby .12 .30
39 Brooklyn Bridge .12 .30
40 Adam Dunn .12 .30
41 Lyle Overbay .12 .30
42 Brian Fuentes .12 .30
43 Scott Rolen SP 1.25 3.00
44 Matt Lindstrom (RC) .20 .50
45 Carlos Zambrano .12 .30
46 Cole Hamels .30 .75
47 Matt Kemp .12 .30
48 Gary Matthews SP 1.25 3.00
49 J.J. Putz .12 .30
50 Albert Pujols .60 1.50
51 Dan Haren .12 .30
52 Aaron Harang .12 .30
53 Ferris Wheel .12 .30
54 Juan Rivera .12 .30
55 Ken Griffey Jr. .50 1.25
56 Chien-Ming Wang .50 1.25
57 Sean Henn (RC) .20 .50
58 Mike Mussina SP 1.25 3.00
59 Ian Snell .12 .30
60 Josh Barfield .12 .30
61 Justin Morneau .12 .30
62 Dwight D. Eisenhower .12 .30
63 Bengie Molina SP 1.25 3.00
64 Brett Myers .12 .30
65 Andy Marte .12 .30
66 Bill Hall .12 .30
67 Ryan Shealy .12 .30
68 Joe B. Scott .12 .30
69 Mike Rabelo RC .20 .50
70 Jermaine Dye .12 .30
71 Andre Ethier .20 .50
72 Bruce Lee .50 1.25
73 Nick Punto .12 .30
74 Ervin Santana .12 .30
75 Troy Tulowitzki (RC) .50 1.25
76 Garret Anderson .12 .30
77 Ryan Freel .12 .30
78 Carlos Guillen .12 .30
79 John Smoltz .20 .50
80 Chase Utley .30 .75
81 Mike Sweeney .12 .30
82 Joe Frazier .30 .75
83 Brad Lidge .12 .30
84 Casey Blake .12 .30
85 Ivan Rodriguez .20 .50
86 Roy Oswalt .12 .30
87 Akinori Iwamura RC .50 1.25
88 Francisco Rodriguez .12 .30
89 John Lackey .12 .30
90 Miguel Cabrera .20 .50
91 Kevin Mench .12 .30
92 Victor Martinez .12 .30
93 Chad Tracy .12 .30
94 Charlie Manuel .12 .30
95 Hanley Ramirez .20 .50
96 Dontrelle Willis .12 .30
97 Doug Slaten RC .20 .50
98 Noah Lowry .12 .30
99 Shawn Green .12 .30
100 David Ortiz .30 .75
101 Mark Reynolds RC .75 2.00
102 Preston Wilson .12 .30
103 Mohandas Gandhi .12 .30
104 Jeff Kent .12 .30
105 Lance Berkman .12 .30
106 C.C. Sabathia .12 .30
107 Jason Varitek SP 1.25 3.00
108 Mark Twain .12 .30
109 Melvin Mora .12 .30
110 Michael Young SP 1.25 3.00
111 Scott Hatteberg .12 .30
112 Erik Bedard .12 .30
113 Sitting Bull .12 .30
114 Homer Bailey (RC) .30 .75
115 Mark Teahen .12 .30
116 Ryan Braun (RC) 1.00 2.50
117 John Miles .12 .30
118 Coco Crisp .12 .30
119 Hunter Pence SP (RC) 2.00 5.00
120 Delmon Young (RC) .30 .75
121 Aramis Ramirez .12 .30
122 Maggio Ordonez .12 .30
123 Tadahito Iguchi .12 .30
124 Mark Selby .12 .30
125 Gil Meche .12 .30
126 Curt Schilling .20 .50
127 Brandon Phillips .12 .30
128 Milton Bradley .12 .30
129 Craig Monroe .12 .30
130 Jason Schmidt SP 1.25 3.00
131 Nick Markakis .20 .50
132 Paul Konerko .12 .30
133 Carlos Gomez RC .30 .75
134 Garrett Atkins .12 .30
135 Jered Weaver .20 .50
136 Edgar Renteria .12 .30
137 Jason Isringhausen SP 1.25 3.00
138 Ray Durham .12 .30
139 Bob Baffert .12 .30
140 Nick Swisher .12 .30
141 Brian McCann .12 .30
142 Orlando Hudson .12 .30
143 Brian Bannister .12 .30
144 Manny Acta .12 .30
145 Jose Vidro .12 .30
146 Carlos Quentin .12 .30
147 Billy Butler (RC) .30 .75
148 Kenny Rogers .12 .30
149 Tom Gordon .12 .30
150 Derek Jeter .75 2.00
151 Bob Wickman .12 .30
152 Carlos Lee SP 1.25 3.00
153 Willy Taveras .12 .30
154 Paul LoDuca .12 .30
155 Ben Sheets .12 .30
156 Brian Roberts .12 .30
157 Freddy Adu .30 .75
158 Jason Kendall .12 .30
159 Michael Barrett SP 1.25 3.00
160 Frank Thomas .30 .75
161 Manny Ramirez .20 .50
162 Stanley Glenn .12 .30
163 Robinson Cano .20 .50
164 Phil Hughes (RC) 1.00 2.50
165 Joe Mauer .20 .50
166 Derrek Lee .12 .30
167 Jeff Weaver .12 .30
168 Joe Smith RC .12 .30
169 Louis Pasteur .12 .30
170 Gary Sheffield .12 .30
171 Luis Castillo .12 .30
172 Joe Torre .20 .50
173 Andy LaRoche (RC) .20 .50
174 Jamie Fischer .12 .30
175 Carlos Beltran .12 .30
176 Bronson Arroyo .12 .30
177 Rafael Furcal .12 .30
178 Juan Pierre SP 1.25 3.00
179 Matt Cain .20 .50
180 Alfonso Soriano .12 .30
181 Joe Borowski .12 .30
182 Conor Jackson .12 .30
183 Groundhog Day .12 .30
184 Pat Burrell .12 .30
185 Troy Glaus .12 .30
186 Joel Zumaya .20 .50
187 Russell Martin .12 .30
188 Josh Willingham .12 .30
189 Jarrod Saltalamacchia (RC) .30 .75
190 Scott Kazmir .20 .50
191 Jeremy Hermida .12 .30
192 Tower Bridge .12 .30
193 Rich Hill SP 1.25 3.00
194 Francisco Cordero SP 1.25 3.00
195 Mike Piazza .30 .75
196 Brad Ausmus .12 .30
197 Greg Louganis .12 .30
198 Frank Catalanotto .12 .30
199 Alejandro De Aza RC .30 .75
200 David Wright .50 1.25
201 Freddy Sanchez .12 .30
202 Shea Hillenbrand .12 .30
203 Justin Verlander SP 1.25 3.00
204 Alex Gordon RC 1.00 2.50
205 Jimmy Rollins .12 .30
206 Mike Napoli .12 .30
207 Chris Burke .12 .30
208 Chipper Jones .30 .75
209 Randy Johnson .30 .75
210 Daisuke Matsuzaka RC 2.00 5.00
211 Orlando Cabrera .12 .30
212 B.J. Upton .12 .30
213 Lou Piniella MG .12 .30
214 Mike Cameron .12 .30
215 Luis Gonzalez .12 .30
216 Rickie Weeks .12 .30
217 Hideki Okajima RC 1.00 2.50
218 Johnny Estrada .12 .30
219 Dan Uggla SP 1.25 3.00
220 Ryan Zimmerman .30 .75
221 Tony Gwynn Jr. .12 .30
222 Rocco Baldelli SP 1.25 3.00
223 Xavier Nady .12 .30
224 Josh Bard SP 1.25 3.00
225 Raul Ibanez .12 .30
226 Chris Carpenter .12 .30
227 Matt DeSalvo (RC) .20 .50
228 Jack the Ripper .12 .30
229 Eric Chavez .12 .30
230 Jose Reyes .30 .75
231 Glen Perkins (RC) .20 .50
232 Gregg Zaun .12 .30
233 Jim Thome .20 .50
234 Joe Crede .12 .30
235 Barry Zito .12 .30
236 Yoel Hernandez RC .20 .50
237 Kelly Johnson .12 .30
238 Chris Young .12 .30
239 Fyodor Dostoevsky .12 .30
240 Miguel Tejada .12 .30
241 Doug Mientkiewicz .12 .30
242 Bobby Jenks .12 .30
243 Brad Hawpe SP 1.25 3.00
244 Jay Marshall RC .20 .50
245 Brad Penny .12 .30
246 Johnny Damon .20 .50
247 Dave Roberts .12 .30
248 Ron Washington .12 .30
249 Mike Aponte .12 .30
250 Brandon Webb .12 .30
251 Andy Pettitte .20 .50
252 Bud Black .12 .30
253 Michael Cuddyer .12 .30
254 Chris Stewart RC .20 .50
255 Mark Teixeira .20 .50
256 Hideki Matsui .30 .75
257 Curtis Granderson .12 .30
258 A.J. Pierzynski .12 .30
259 Tony La Russa .12 .30
260 Andruw Jones .20 .50
261 Torii Hunter .12 .30
262 Mark Loretta .12 .30
263 Jim Edmonds SP 1.25 3.00
264 Aaron Rowand .12 .30
265 Roy Halladay .12 .30
266 Freddy Garcia .12 .30
267 Reggie Sanders .12 .30
268 Washington Monument .12 .30
269 Franklin D. Roosevelt .12 .30
270 Alex Rodriguez .50 1.25
271 Wes Helms .12 .30
272 Mia Hamm .30 .75
273 Jorge Posada .20 .50
274 Tim Lincecum RC 1.50 4.00
275 Bobby Abreu .12 .30
276 Zach Duke .12 .30
277 Carlos Delgado .12 .30
278 Julio Juarez .12 .30
279 Brandon Inge .12 .30
280 Todd Helton .20 .50
281 Marcus Giles .12 .30
282 Josh Johnson .12 .30
283 Chris Capuano .12 .30
284 B.J. Ryan .12 .30
285 Nick Johnson .12 .30
286 Khalil Greene .20 .50
287 Travis Hafner .12 .30
288 Ted Lilly .12 .30
289 Jim Leyland .12 .30
290 Prince Fielder .30 .75
291 Trevor Hoffman .12 .30
292 Brian Giles .12 .30
293 Omar Vizquel .20 .50
294 Julio Lugo .12 .30
295 Jake Peavy .12 .30
296 Adrian Beltre .12 .30
297 Josh Beckett .20 .50
298 Harry S. Truman .12 .30
299 Mark Buehrle .12 .30
300 Ichiro Suzuki .50 1.25
301 Chris Duncan SP 1.25 3.00
302 Augie Garrido SP CO 1.25 3.00
303 Tyler Clippard SP (RC) 1.25 3.00
304 Ramon Hernandez .12 .30
305 Jeremy Bonderman .12 .30
306 Morgan Ensberg SP 1.25 3.00
307 J.J. Hardy SP 1.25 3.00
308 Mark Zupan SP 1.25 3.00
309 Laila Ali SP 1.25 3.00
310 Greg Maddux SP 1.50 4.00
311 David Ross .12 .30
312 Chris Duffy .12 .30
313 Moises Alou .12 .30
314 Yadier Molina .12 .30
315 Corey Patterson .12 .30
316 Dan O'Brien SP 1.25 3.00
317 Michael Bourn SP (RC) 1.25 3.00
318 Jonny Gomes SP 1.25 3.00
319 Ken Jennings SP 1.25 3.00
320 Barry Bonds SP 1.50 4.00
321 Gary Hall Jr. SP 1.25 3.00
322 Kerri Walsh SP 1.25 3.00
323 Craig Biggio .20 .50
324 Ian Kinsler .12 .30
325 Grady Sizemore SP 1.25 3.00
326 Alex Rios SP 1.25 3.00
327 Ted Toles SP 1.25 3.00
328 Jason Jennings .12 .30
329 Vernon Wells .12 .30
330 Bob Geren SP MG 1.25 3.00
331 Dennis Rodman SP 1.25 3.00
332 Tom Glavine .20 .50
333 Pedro Martinez .20 .50
334 Gustavo Molina SP RC 1.25 3.00
335 Bartolo Colon SP 1.25 3.00
336 Misty May-Treanor SP 1.25 3.00
337 Randy Winn .12 .30
338 Eric Byrnes .12 .30
339 Jason McElwain SP 1.25 3.00
340 Placido Polanco SP 1.25 3.00
341 Adrian Gonzalez .12 .30
342 Chad Cordero .12 .30
343 Jeff Francis .12 .30
344 Lastings Milledge .20 .50
345 Sammy Sosa SP 1.25 3.00
346 Jacque Jones .12 .30
347 Anibal Sanchez .12 .30
348 Roger Clemens SP 1.50 4.00
349 Jesse Litsch SP RC 1.25 3.00
350 Adam LaRoche SP 1.25 3.00
NNO Framed Originals 50.00 100.00

2007 Topps Allen and Ginter Mini

*MINI 1-350: 1X TO 2.5X BASIC
*MINI 1-350: .6X TO 1.5X BASIC RC's
APPX. ONE MINI PER PACK
*MINI SP 1-350: .6X TO 1.5X BASIC SP
*MINI SP 1-350: .6X TO 1.5X BASIC SP RC's
MINI SP ODDS 1:13 H, 1:13 R
COMMON CARD (351-390) 15.00 40.00
351-390 RANDOM WITHIN RIP CARDS
OVERALL PLATE ODDS 1:788 HOBBY
PLATE PRINT RUN 1 SET PER COLOR
BLACK-CYAN-MAGENTA-YELLOW ISSUED
NO PLATE PRICING DUE TO SCARCITY
351 Alex Rodriguez EXT 40.00 80.00
352 Ryan Zimmerman EXT 20.00 50.00
353 Prince Fielder EXT 40.00 80.00
354 Gary Sheffield EXT 15.00 40.00
355 Jermaine Dye EXT 15.00 40.00
356 Hanley Ramirez EXT 15.00 40.00
357 Jose Reyes EXT 30.00 60.00
358 Miguel Tejada EXT 20.00 50.00
359 Elijah Dukes EXT 15.00 40.00
360 Ryan Howard EXT 30.00 60.00
361 Vladimir Guerrero EXT 15.00 40.00
362 Ichiro Suzuki EXT 40.00 80.00
363 Jason Bay EXT 15.00 40.00
364 Justin Morneau EXT 15.00 40.00
365 Michael Young EXT 15.00 40.00
366 Adam Dunn EXT 15.00 40.00
367 Alfonso Soriano EXT 20.00 50.00
368 Jake Peavy EXT 20.00 50.00
369 Nick Swisher EXT 20.00 50.00
370 David Wright EXT 30.00 60.00
371 Brandon Webb EXT 20.00 50.00
372 Brian McCann EXT 20.00 50.00
373 Frank Thomas EXT 20.00 50.00
374 Albert Pujols EXT 30.00 60.00
375 Russell Martin EXT 20.00 50.00
376 Felix Hernandez EXT 15.00 40.00
377 Barry Bonds EXT 40.00 80.00
378 Lance Berkman EXT 15.00 40.00
379 Joe Mauer EXT 30.00 60.00
380 B.J. Upton EXT 15.00 40.00
381 Todd Helton EXT 15.00 40.00
382 Paul Konerko EXT 20.00 50.00
383 Grady Sizemore EXT 20.00 50.00
384 Magglio Ordonez EXT 15.00 40.00
385 Dan Uggla EXT 20.00 50.00
386 J.D. Drew EXT 15.00 40.00
387 Adam LaRoche EXT 15.00 40.00
388 Carlos Beltran EXT 15.00 40.00
389 Derek Jeter EXT 40.00 80.00
390 Daisuke Matsuzaka EXT 75.00 200.00

2007 Topps Allen and Ginter Mini A and G Back

*A & G BACK: 1.25X TO 3X BASIC
*A & G BACK: .75X TO 2X BASIC RC's
STATED ODDS 1:5 H, 1:5 R
*A & G BACK SP: .75X TO 2X BASIC SP
*A & G BACK SP: .75X TO 2X BASIC SP RC's
SP STATED ODDS 1:65 H, 1:65 R

2007 Topps Allen and Ginter Mini Bazooka

STATED ODDS 1:213 H, 1:214 R
STATED PRINT RUN 25 SERIAL #'d SETS
NO PRICING DUE TO SCARCITY

2007 Topps Allen and Ginter Mini Black

*BLACK: 2X TO 5X BASIC
*BLACK: 1.5X TO 4X BASIC RC's
STATED ODDS 1:10 H, 1:10 R
*BLACK SP: 1.5X TO 4X BASIC SP
*BLACK SP: 1.5X TO 4X BASIC SP RC's
SP STATED ODDS 1:130 H, 1:130 R

2007 Topps Allen and Ginter Mini Black No Number

*BLK NO NBR: 2.5X TO 6X BASIC
*BLK NO NBR: 2X TO 5X BASIC RC's
*BLK NO NBR: 1.5X TO 4X BASIC SP
*BLK NO NBR: 1.5X TO 4X BASIC SP RC's
RANDOM INSERTS IN PACKS
210 Daisuke Matsuzaka 6.00 15.00

2007 Topps Allen and Ginter Mini No Card Number

*NO NBR: 10X TO 25X BASIC
*NO NBR: 6X TO 15X BASIC RC's
*NO NBR: 2.5X TO 6X BASIC SP
*NO NBR: 2.5X TO 6X BASIC SP RC's
STATED ODDS 1:106 H, 1:108 R
STATED PRINT RUN 50 SETS
CARDS ARE NOT SERIAL-NUMBERED
PRINT RUN INFO PROVIDED BY TOPPS
7 Mickey Mantle 40.00 80.00
50 Albert Pujols 30.00 60.00
55 Ken Griffey Jr. 40.00 80.00
56 Chien-Ming Wang 30.00 60.00
150 Derek Jeter 40.00 80.00
270 Alex Rodriguez 30.00 60.00
300 Ichiro Suzuki 40.00 80.00
320 Barry Bonds SP 40.00 80.00

2007 Topps Allen and Ginter Mini Wood

STATED ODDS 1:3507 HOBBY
STATED PRINT RUN 1 SERIAL #'d SET
NO PRICING DUE TO SCARCITY

2007 Topps Allen and Ginter Autographs

GROUP A ODDS 1:64,496 H, 1:122200 R
GROUP B ODDS 1:3261 H, 1:6522 R
GROUP C ODDS 1:13,987 H, 1:27,642 R
GROUP D ODDS 1:288 H, 1:578 R
GROUP E ODDS 1:6789 H, 1:13,578 R
GROUP F ODDS 1:162 H, 1:324 R
GROUP G ODDS 1:680 H, 1:1362 R
GROUP A PRINT RUN 25 CARDS PER
GROUP B PRINT RUN 100 CARDS PER
GROUP C PRINT RUN 120 CARDS PER
GROUP D PRINT RUN 200 CARDS PER
GROUP A-D ARE NOT SERIAL-NUMBERED
A-D PRINT RUNS PROVIDED BY TOPPS
NO PUJOLS PRICING DUE TO SCARCITY
EXCH DEADLINE 7/31/2009
AE Andre Ethier F 10.00 25.00
AG Augie Garrido D/200 * 30.00 60.00
AG2 Adrian Gonzalez F 6.00 15.00
AI Akinori Iwamura F 10.00 25.00
AP Albert Pujols A/25 *
AR Alex Rodriguez E/225 * 250.00 300.00
BB Bob Baffert D/200 * 30.00 60.00
BC Brian Cashman B/100 * 40.00 80.00
BH Bill Hall G 6.00 15.00
BPB Brian Bannister F 10.00 25.00
CG Curtis Granderson F 10.00 25.00
CH Cole Hamels F 15.00 40.00
CMW Chien-Ming Wang D/200 * 150.00 250.00
CS Cael Sanderson D/200 * 30.00 60.00
DO Dan O'Brien D/200 * 12.50 30.00
DR Dennis Rodman D/200 * 30.00 60.00
DW David Wright D/200 * 60.00 120.00
ES Ervin Santana F 6.00 15.00
FA Freddy Adu D/200 * 30.00 60.00
GH Gary Hall Jr. D/200 * 20.00 50.00
GL Greg Louganis D/200 * EXCH 30.00 60.00
HK Howie Kendrick F 6.00 15.00
HR Hanley Ramirez F 15.00 40.00
JBS Joe B. Scott D/200 * 40.00 80.00
JF Jamie Fischer D/200 * 20.00 50.00
JH Jeremy Hermida G 5.00 12.00
JJ Julio Juarez D/200 * EXCH 15.00 40.00
JM Justin Morneau F 8.00 20.00
JMC Jason McElwain D/200 * 20.00 50.00
JMM John Miles D/200 * 30.00 60.00
JP Jonathan Papelbon F 15.00 40.00
JS Johan Santana B/100 * 60.00 120.00
JT Jim Thome B/100 * 100.00 200.00
KJ Ken Jennings D/200 * 30.00 60.00
KW Kerri Walsh D/200 * 40.00 80.00
LA Laila Ali D/200 * 60.00 120.00
MA Mike Aponte D/200 * 15.00 40.00
MC Miguel Cabrera B/100 * EXCH 60.00 120.00
MEI Maicer Izturis F 6.00 15.00
MGA Mario Andretti D/200 * 40.00 80.00
MH Mia Hamm D/200 * EXCH 100.00 200.00
MMT Misty May-Treanor D/200 * 50.00 100.00
MN Mike Napoli F 5.00 12.00
MS Mark Selby D/200 * 12.50 30.00
MZ Mark Zupan D/200 * 10.00 25.00
NL Nook Logan G 5.00 12.00
NM Nick Markakis F 8.00 20.00
RH Ryan Howard B/100 * 50.00 100.00
RM Russell Martin F 10.00 25.00
RZ Ryan Zimmerman F 12.50 30.00
SG Stanley Glenn D/200 * 40.00 80.00
SJF Joe Frazier C/120 * 150.00 250.00
TH Torii Hunter F 8.00 20.00
TS Tommie Smith D/200 * 40.00 80.00
TT Ted Toles D/200 * 15.00 40.00
TTT Troy Tulowitzki F 40.00 80.00
VW Vernon Wells F EXCH 10.00 25.00

2007 Topps Allen and Ginter Autographs Red Ink

UNFRAMED RANDOM INSERTS IN RIP CARDS
FRAMED RANDOM INSERTS IN PACKS
STATED PRINT RUN 10 SETS
NO PRICING DUE TO SCARCITY
UNF EQUALS UNFRAMED
AE Andre Ethier
AG Augie Garrido
AG2 Adrian Gonzalez
AI Akinori Iwamura
AP Albert Pujols
AR Alex Rodriguez
BB Bob Baffert
BC Brian Cashman UNF
BH Bill Hall
BPB Brian Bannister
CG Curtis Granderson
CH Cole Hamels UNF
CMW Chien-Ming Wang
CS Cael Sanderson
DO Dan O'Brien UNF
DR Dennis Rodman
DW David Wright
ES Ervin Santana UNF
FA Freddy Adu UNF
GH Gary Hall Jr.
GL Greg Louganis
HK Howie Kendrick UNF
HR Hanley Ramirez
JBS Joe B. Scott UNF
JF Jamie Fischer
JH Jeremy Hermida
JJ Julio Juarez
JM Justin Morneau
JMC Jason McElwain UNF
JMM John Miles
JP Jonathan Papelbon
JS Johan Santana
JT Jim Thome UNF
KJ Ken Jennings UNF
KW Kerri Walsh UNF
LA Laila Ali
MA Mike Aponte UNF
MC Miguel Cabrera
MEI Maicer Izturis UNF
MGA Mario Andretti
MH Mia Hamm
MMT Misty May-Treanor
MN Mike Napoli UNF
MS Mark Selby
MZ Mark Zupan
NL Nook Logan
NM Nick Markakis
RH Ryan Howard UNF
RM Russell Martin
RZ Ryan Zimmerman
SG Stanley Glenn UNF
SJF Joe Frazier UNF
TH Torii Hunter
TS Tommie Smith UNF
TT Ted Toles

TTT Troy Tulowitzki
VW Vernon Wells

2007 Topps Allen and Ginter Cut Signatures

STATED ODDS 1:145,116 HOBBY
STATED ODDS 1:290,232 RETAIL
STATED PRINT RUN 1 SER.#'d SET
NO PRICING DUE TO SCARCITY
1 Franklin D. Roosevelt
2 Jack Dempsey
3 Orville Wright
4 General James Doolittle
5 Admiral Richard E. Byrd
6 Mother Teresa
7 Fidel Castro
8 Charles Lindbergh
9 Roy Rogers
10 William Randolph Hearst

2007 Topps Allen and Ginter Dick Perez Sketches

COMPLETE SET (30) 6.00 15.00
APPX.ONE PEREZ PER PACK
ORIGINALS RANDOM WITHIN RIP CARDS
ORIGINALS PRINT RUN 1 SERIAL #'d SET
NO ORIG. PRICING DUE TO SCARCITY
1 Brandon Webb .20 .50
2 Chipper Jones .50 1.25
3 Nick Markakis .30 .75
4 Daisuke Matsuzaka 2.00 5.00
5 Alfonso Soriano .20 .50
6 Jermaine Dye .20 .50
7 Adam Dunn .20 .50
8 Grady Sizemore .30 .75
9 Troy Tulowitzki .50 1.25
10 Gary Sheffield .20 .50
11 Hanley Ramirez .30 .75
12 Carlos Lee .20 .50
13 Mark Teahen .20 .50
14 Gary Matthews .20 .50
15 Andre Ethier .30 .75
16 Prince Fielder .50 1.25
17 Joe Mauer .30 .75
18 Jose Reyes .50 1.25
19 Derek Jeter 1.25 3.00
20 Nick Swisher .20 .50
21 Ryan Howard .75 2.00
22 Freddy Sanchez .20 .50
23 Greg Maddux .75 2.00
24 Raul Ibanez .20 .50
25 Barry Zito .20 .50
26 Jim Edmonds .30 .75
27 Delmon Young .30 .75
28 Michael Young .20 .50
29 Roy Halladay .20 .50
30 Ryan Zimmerman .50 1.25

2007 Topps Allen and Ginter Mini Emperors

STATED ODDS 1:72 H, 1:72 R
1 Julius Caesar 2.00 5.00
2 Caesar Augustus 2.00 5.00
3 Tiberius 2.00 5.00
4 Caligula 2.00 5.00
5 Claudius 2.00 5.00
6 Nero 2.00 5.00
7 Titus 2.00 5.00
8 Hadrian 2.00 5.00
9 Marcus Aurelius 2.00 5.00
10 Septimus Severus 2.00 5.00

2007 Topps Allen and Ginter Mini Flags

COMPLETE SET (50) 100.00 175.00
STATED ODDS 1:12 H, 1:12 R
1 Algeria 1.50 4.00
2 Argentina 1.50 4.00
3 Australia 1.50 4.00
4 Austria 1.50 4.00
5 Belgium 1.50 4.00
6 Brazil 1.50 4.00
7 Bulgaria 1.50 4.00
8 Canada 1.50 4.00
9 Chile 1.50 4.00
10 China 1.50 4.00
11 Colombia 1.50 4.00
12 Costa Rica 1.50 4.00
13 Denmark 1.50 4.00
14 Dominican Republic 1.50 4.00
15 Ecuador 1.50 4.00
16 Egypt 1.50 4.00
17 France 1.50 4.00
18 Germany 1.50 4.00
19 Greece 1.50 4.00
20 Greenland 1.50 4.00
21 Honduras 1.50 4.00
22 Iceland 1.50 4.00
23 India 1.50 4.00
24 Indonesia 1.50 4.00
25 Ireland 1.50 4.00
26 Israel 1.50 4.00
27 Italy 1.50 4.00
28 Ivory Coast 1.50 4.00
29 Jamaica 1.50 4.00
30 Japan 1.50 4.00
31 Kenya 1.50 4.00
32 Mexico 1.50 4.00
33 Morocco 1.50 4.00
34 Netherlands 1.50 4.00
35 Nigeria 1.50 4.00
36 Norway 1.50 4.00
37 Panama 1.50 4.00
38 Peru 1.50 4.00
39 Philippines 1.50 4.00
40 Portugal 1.50 4.00
41 Puerto Rico 1.50 4.00
42 Russian Federation 1.50 4.00
43 Spain 1.50 4.00
44 Switzerland 1.50 4.00
45 Taiwan 1.50 4.00
46 Thailand 1.50 4.00
47 Turkey 1.50 4.00
48 United Arab Emirates 1.50 4.00
49 United Kingdom 1.50 4.00
50 United States of America 1.50 4.00

2007 Topps Allen and Ginter Mini Snakes

STATED ODDS 1:144 H, 1:144 R
1 Arizona Coral Snake 8.00 20.00
2 Copperhead 8.00 20.00
3 Black Mamba 8.00 20.00
4 King Cobra 8.00 20.00
5 Cottonmouth 8.00 20.00

2007 Topps Allen and Ginter N43

STATED ODDS 1:3 HOBBY BOX LOADER
AP Albert Pujols 3.00 8.00
AR Alex Rodriguez 2.50 6.00
BB Barry Bonds 3.00 8.00
BL Bruce Lee 2.50 6.00
DJ Ch Felicity's Diamond Jim 4.00 10.00
DM Daisuke Matsuzaka 4.00 10.00
DW David Wright 2.50 6.00
GL Greg Louganis 1.25 3.00
IS Ichiro Suzuki 2.50 6.00
JF Joe Frazier 1.50 4.00
MA Mario Andretti 1.50 4.00
PF Prince Fielder 1.50 4.00
RH Ryan Howard 2.50 6.00
RZ Ryan Zimmerman 1.50 4.00
VG Vladimir Guerrero 1.50 4.00

2007 Topps Allen and Ginter N43 Autographs

GROUP A ODDS 1:1747 HOBBY BOX LOADER
GROUP B ODDS 1:1034 HOBBY BOX LOADER
GROUP A PRINT RUN 10 SER.#'d SETS
GROUP B PRINT RUN 50 SER.#'d SETS
NO GROUP A PRICING AVAILABLE
AR Alex Rodriguez A/10
DJ Ch Felicity's Diamond Jim B/50 300.00 450.00
DW David Wright A/10
RH Ryan Howard A/10

2007 Topps Allen and Ginter N43 Relics

STATED ODDS 1:205 HOBBY BOX LOADER
STATED PRINT RUN 25 SER.#'d SETS
NO PRICING DUE TO SCARCITY
AP Albert Pujols
AR Alex Rodriguez Jsy
BB Barry Bonds Pants
CG Curtis Granderson
DW David Wright Bat
NM Nick Markakis Bat
PF Prince Fielder Jsy
RH Ryan Howard Jsy
RZ Ryan Zimmerman Bat
VG Vladimir Guerrero Jsy

2007 Topps Allen and Ginter National Pride

STATED ODDS 1:2 HOBBY BOX LOADER
1 Kei Igawa 5.00 12.00
Daisuke Matsuzaka
Hideki Matsui
Ichiro Suzuki
2 Hideki Okajima 4.00 10.00
Akinori Iwamura
Kenji Johjima
Tadahito Iguchi
3 Bobby Abreu 2.00 5.00
Miguel Cabrera
Felix Hernandez
Johan Santana
4 Shin-Soo Choo 2.00 5.00
Chan Ho Park
Byung-Hyun Kim
Jae Kuk Ryu
5 Jason Bay 1.50 4.00
Russell Martin
Justin Morneau
Rich Harden
6 Hanley Ramirez 2.00 5.00
Manny Ramirez
Aramis Ramirez
Vladimir Guerrero
7 Jose Reyes 4.00 10.00
Pedro Martinez
David Ortiz
Albert Pujols
8 Carlos Beltran 2.00 5.00
Carlos Delgado
Ivan Rodriguez
Jorge Posada
9 Prince Fielder 3.00 8.00
Alex Rodriguez
Ryan Howard
David Wright
10 Brandon Webb 3.00 8.00
Justin Verlander
Greg Maddux
John Smoltz

2007 Topps Allen and Ginter Relics

GROUP A ODDS 1:1,160,000 H
GROUP A ODDS 1:243,648 R
GROUP B ODDS 1:31,376 H, 1:62,750 R
GROUP C ODDS 1:15,275 H, 1:30,550 R
GROUP D ODDS 1:383 H, 1:766 R
GROUP E ODDS 1:1530 H, 1:3068 R
GROUP F ODDS 1:510 H, 1:1022 R
GROUP G ODDS 1:109 H, 1:218 R
GROUP H ODDS 1:69 H, 1:140 R
GROUP I ODDS 1:340 H, 1:680 R
GROUP J ODDS 1:25 H, 1:48 R
GROUP B PRINT RUN 50 COPIES PER
GROUP C PRINT RUN 100 COPIES PER
GROUP D PRINT RUN 250 COPIES PER
GROUP B-D ARE NOT SERIAL-NUMBERED
GROUP B-D QTY PROVIDED BY TOPPS
NO WASHINGTON PRICING AVAILABLE
AER Alex Rodriguez Bat D/250 * 15.00 40.00
AL Adam LaRoche J 3.00 8.00
AP Albert Pujols Bat E 10.00 25.00
AR Aramis Ramirez J 3.00 8.00
AS Arthur Shorin B/50 * 300.00 400.00
BB Barry Bonds Pants D/250 * 20.00 50.00
BC Brian Cashman D/250 * 15.00 40.00
BL Bruce Lee D/250 * 225.00 325.00
BR Brian Roberts J 3.00 8.00
BZ Barry Zito Pants J 3.00 8.00
CB Carlos Beltran Bat I 3.00 8.00
CC Carl Crawford Bat H 3.00 8.00
CK Casey Kotchman J 3.00 8.00
CLC Coco Crisp Bat D 3.00 8.00
CMS Curt Schilling J 4.00 10.00
CP Corey Patterson Bat F 3.00 8.00
CT Chad Tracy Bat G 3.00 8.00
DAO David Ortiz Bat D/250 * 6.00 15.00
DL Derrek Lee Bat H 3.00 8.00
DO Dan O'Brien D/250 * 10.00 25.00
DW Dontrelle Willis J 3.00 8.00
EC Eric Chavez Pants J 3.00 8.00
EG Eric Gagne J 3.00 8.00
GH Gary Hall Jr. D/250 * 10.00 25.00
GW1 George Washington Hair A/1 *
GW2 George Washington Hair A/1 *
GW3 George Washington Hair A/1 *
HB Hank Blalock J 3.00 8.00
HR Hanley Ramirez Bat G 4.00 10.00
IR Ivan Rodriguez J 4.00 10.00
JB Jason Bay Bat H 3.00 8.00
JF Jamie Fischer D/250 * 10.00 25.00
JG Jason Giambi Bat H 3.00 8.00
JJ Julio Juarez D/250 * 8.00 20.00
KJ Ken Jennings D/250 * 10.00 25.00
KO Keith Olbermann C/100 * 75.00 200.00
KW Kerri Walsh D/250 * 30.00 60.00
LA Laila Ali D/250 * 20.00 50.00
MC1 Miguel Cabrera G 4.00 10.00
MC2 Miguel Cabrera Bat G 4.00 10.00
MCM Mike Mussina Pants J 4.00 10.00
MG Marcus Giles J 3.00 8.00
MH Mia Hamm D/250 * 30.00 60.00
MM Mickey Mantle Bat D/250 * 60.00 120.00
MMU Mark Mulder Pants J 3.00 8.00
MP Mike Piazza Bat H 4.00 10.00
MR Manny Ramirez Bat H 4.00 10.00
MT Miguel Tejada J 3.00 8.00
NS Nick Swisher Bat H 3.00 8.00
PF Prince Fielder Bat G 6.00 15.00
PK Paul Konerko Bat H 3.00 8.00
PL Paul LoDuca J 3.00 8.00
RA Rich Aurilia Bat G 3.00 8.00
RC Robinson Cano Bat F 4.00 10.00
RH Rich Harden Pants J 3.00 8.00
RW Randy Winn J 3.00 8.00
SD Stephen Drew J 3.00 8.00
SJF Joe Frazier D/250 * 20.00 50.00
SP Scott Podsednik Bat G 3.00 8.00
SR1 Scott Rolen G 4.00 10.00
SR2 Scott Rolen Bat G 4.00 10.00
SS Sammy Sosa Bat I 4.00 10.00
TG Troy Glaus Bat H 3.00 8.00
TN Trot Nixon Bat G 3.00 8.00
TS Tommie Smith D/250 * 12.50 30.00
VG Vladimir Guerrero Bat H 4.00 10.00

2007 Topps Allen and Ginter Rip Card

STATED ODDS 1:285 HOBBY
PRINT RUNS B/WN 10-99 COPIES PER
NO PRICING ON QTY 10 OR LESS
ALL LISTED PRICED ARE FOR RIPPED
UNRIPPED HAVE ADD'L CARDS WITHIN
1 Grady Sizemore/90 10.00 25.00
2 Miguel Cabrera/75 10.00 25.00
3 Adam Dunn/95 6.00 15.00
4 Jose Reyes/99 10.00 25.00
5 Alfonso Soriano/90 6.00 15.00
6 Chase Utley/99 10.00 25.00
7 Frank Thomas/95 10.00 25.00
8 Andruw Jones/95 10.00 25.00
9 Nick Markakis/75 10.00 25.00
10 Felix Hernandez/99 10.00 25.00
11 Jered Weaver/99 10.00 25.00
12 Ivan Rodriguez/99 10.00 25.00
13 Joe Mauer/99 10.00 25.00
14 Derek Jeter/99 20.00 50.00
15 Delmon Young/
16 Brandon Webb/10
17 Miguel Tejada/95 6.00 15.00
18 Vladimir Guerrero/75 10.00 25.00
19 Greg Maddux/99 15.00 40.00
20 Michael Young/99 6.00 15.00
21 Barry Zito/99 6.00 15.00
22 Russell Martin/95 6.00 15.00
23 Daisuke Matsuzaka/99 90.00 150.00
24 Stephen Drew/95 10.00 25.00
25 Alex Rodriguez/99 15.00 40.00
26 J.D. Drew/99 6.00 15.00
27 Paul Konerko/99 6.00 15.00
28 Josh Hamilton /90 20.00 50.00
29 Mike Piazza /99 10.00 25.00
30 Ryan Howard/10
31 Carl Crawford/99 6.00 15.00
32 Adam LaRoche/99 6.00 15.00
33 Bill Hall/95 6.00 15.00
34 Scott Kazmir/95 10.00 25.00
35 Gary Matthews/99 6.00 15.00
36 Gary Sheffield/99 6.00 15.00
37 Francisco Rodriguez/95 6.00 15.00
38 Todd Helton/99 10.00 25.00
39 Dontrelle Willis/10
40 David Wright/99 15.00 40.00
41 David Ortiz/10
42 Barry Bonds/99 20.00 50.00
43 Johan Santana/75 10.00 25.00
44 Albert Pujols/90 20.00 50.00
45 Carlos Lee/99 6.00 15.00
46 Cole Hamels/95 10.00 25.00
47 Prince Fielder/99 10.00 25.00
48 Hanley Ramirez/99 10.00 25.00
49 Ryan Zimmerman/90 10.00 25.00
50 Kei Igawa/75 10.00 25.00

2008 Topps Allen and Ginter

COMP.SET w/o FUKU.(350) 50.00 100.00
COMP.SET w/o SPs (300) 15.00 40.00
COMMON CARD (1-300) .15 .40
COMMON RC (1-300) .40 1.00
COMMON SP (301-350) 1.25 3.00
SP STATED ODDS 1:2 HOBBY
FRAMED ORIG.ODDS 1:26,500 HOBBY
1 Alex Rodriguez .60 1.50
2 Juan Pierre .15 .40
3 Benjamin Franklin .25 .60
4 Roy Halladay .15 .40
5 C.C. Sabathia .15 .40
6 Brian Barton RC .60 1.50
7 Mickey Mantle 1.50 4.00
8 Brian Bass (RC) .40 1.00
9 Ian Kinsler .25 .60
10 Manny Ramirez .40 1.00
11 Michael Cuddyer .15 .40
12 Ian Snell .15 .40
13 Mike Lowell .15 .40
14 Adrian Gonzalez .25 .60
15 B.J. Upton .25 .60
16 Hiroki Kuroda RC .60 1.50
17 Kenji Johjima .15 .40
18 James Loney .25 .60
19 Albert Einstein .25 .60
20 Vladimir Guerrero .40 1.00
21 Miguel Tejada .25 .60
22 Chin-Lung Hu (RC) .60 1.50
23 A.J. Burnett .15 .40
24 Bobby Jenks .15 .40
25 Aramis Ramirez .15 .40
26 Corey Hart .15 .40
27 Brad Hawpe .15 .40
28 Adam LaRoche .15 .40
29 Empire State Building .25 .60
30 Miguel Cabrera .25 .60
31 Ryan Zimmerman .25 .60
32 Mark Ellis .15 .40
33 Nick Swisher .15 .40
34 Bill Hall .15 .40
35 Eric Byrnes .15 .40
36 Michael Young .15 .40
37 Pedro Martinez .25 .60
38 Andruw Jones .15 .40
39 J.R. Towles RC 1.00 2.50
40 Justin Upton .40 1.00
41 Paul Konerko .15 .40
42 Luke Scott .15 .40
43 Rickie Weeks .15 .40
44 Adam Wainwright .15 .40
45 Justin Morneau .25 .60
46 Chris Young .15 .40
47 Chad Billingsley .15 .40
48 Kazuo Matsui .15 .40
49 Shane Victorino .15 .40
50 Albert Pujols .75 2.00
51 Brian McCann .25 .60
52 Carlos Delgado .15 .40
53 Chien-Ming Wang .50 1.25
54 Takashi Saito .15 .40
55 Josh Beckett .25 .60
56 Nick Johnson .15 .40
57 Ben Sheets .25 .60
58 Johnny Damon .25 .60
59 Nicky Hayden .25 .60
60 Prince Fielder .40 1.00
61 Adam Dunn .15 .40
62 Dustin Pedroia .60 1.50
63 Jacoby Ellsbury .60 1.50
64 Brad Penny .15 .40
65 Victor Martinez .15 .40
66 Joe Mauer .25 .60
67 Kevin Kouzmanoff .15 .40
68 Frank Thomas .40 1.00
69 Stevie Williams .25 .60
70 Matt Holliday .25 .60
71 Fausto Carmona .15 .40
72 Clayton Kershaw RC 1.25 3.00
73 Tadahito Iguchi .15 .40
74 Khalil Greene .25 .60
75 Travis Hafner .15 .40
76 Jim Thome .25 .60
77 Joba Chamberlain .50 1.25
78 Ivan Rodriguez .25 .60
79 Jose Guillen .15 .40
80 Hanley Ramirez .40 1.00
81 Vernon Wells .15 .40
82 Jayson Nix (RC) .40 1.00
83 Masahide Kobayashi RC .60 1.50
84 Bonnie Blair .25 .60
85 Curtis Granderson .15 .40
86 Kelvim Escobar .15 .40
87 Aaron Rowand .15 .40
88 Troy Glaus .25 .60
89 Billy Wagner .15 .40
90 Jose Reyes .25 .60
91 Scott Rolen .25 .60
92 Dan Jansen .25 .60
93 David Eckstein .15 .40
94 Tom Gorzelanny .15 .40
95 Garrett Atkins .15 .40
96 Carlos Zambrano .15 .40
97 Jeff Francis .15 .40
98 Kazuo Fukumori RC .60 1.50
99 John Bowker (RC) .40 1.00
100 David Wright .50 1.25
101 Adrian Beltre .15 .40
102 Ray Durham .15 .40
103 Kerri Strug .25 .60
104 Orlando Hudson .15 .40
105 Jonathan Papelbon .25 .60
106 Brian Schneider .15 .40
107 Matt Biondi .25 .60
108 Alex Romero (RC) .60 1.50
109 Joey Chestnut .25 .60
110 Chase Utley .40 1.00
111 Dan Uggla .25 .60
112 Akinori Iwamura .15 .40
113 Curt Schilling .25 .60
114 Trevor Hoffman .15 .40
115 Alex Rios .15 .40
116 Mariano Rivera .40 1.00
117 Jeff Niemann (RC) .40 1.00
118 Geovany Soto .40 1.00
119 Billy Mitchell .25 .60
120 Derek Jeter 1.00 2.50
121 Yovani Gallardo .15 .40
122 The Gateway Arch .25 .60
123 Josh Willingham .15 .40
124 Greg Maddux .50 1.25
125 John Lackey .15 .40
126 Chris Young .15 .40
127 Billy Butler .15 .40
128 Golden Gate Bridge .25 .60
129 Joey Votto (RC) 1.00 2.50
130 Tim Wakefield .15 .40
131 Todd Helton .25 .60
132 Gary Matthews .15 .40
133 Wild Bill Hickok .25 .60
134 Jason Varitek .40 1.00
135 Robinson Cano .25 .60
136 Javier Vazquez .15 .40
137 Annie Oakley .25 .60
138 Andy Pettitte .25 .60
139 Greg Reynolds RC .60 1.50
140 Jimmy Rollins .25 .60
141 Jermaine Dye .15 .40
142 Eugenio Velez RC .40 1.00
143 J.J. Hardy .15 .40
144 Grand Canyon .25 .60
145 Bobby Abreu .15 .40
146 Scott Kazmir .25 .60
147 James Fenimore Cooper .25 .60
148 Mark Buehrle .15 .40
149 Freddy Sanchez .15 .40
150 Johan Santana .25 .60
151 Orlando Cabrera .15 .40
152 Lyle Overbay .15 .40
153 Clay Buchholz (RC) 1.00 2.50
154 Jesse Carlson RC .60 1.50
155 Troy Tulowitzki .25 .60
156 Delmon Young .25 .60
157 Ross Ohlendorf RC .60 1.50
158 Mary Shelley .25 .60
159 James Shields .15 .40
160 Alfonso Soriano .25 .60
161 Randy Winn .15 .40
162 Austin Kearns .15 .40
163 Jeremy Hermida .15 .40
164 Jorge Posada .25 .60
165 Justin Verlander .25 .60
166 Bram Stoker .25 .60
167 Marie Curie .25 .60
168 Melky Cabrera .15 .40
169 Howie Kendrick .15 .40
170 Jake Peavy .25 .60
171 J.D. Drew .15 .40
172 Pablo Picasso .25 .60
173 Rick Ankiel .15 .40
174 Jose Valverde .15 .40
175 Chipper Jones .50 1.25
176 Claude Monet .25 .60
177 Evan Longoria RC 3.00 8.00
178 Jose Vidro .15 .40
179 Hideki Matsui .40 1.00
180 Ryan Braun .50 1.25
181 Moises Alou .15 .40
182 Nate McLouth .15 .40
183 Harriet Tubman .25 .60
184 Felix Hernandez .25 .60
185 Carlos Pena .40 1.00
186 Jarrod Saltalamacchia .15 .40
187 Les Miles .25 .60
188 Kelly Johnson .15 .40
189 Rampage Jackson .40 1.00
190 Grady Sizemore .25 .60
191 Francisco Cordero .15 .40
192 Yunel Escobar .15 .40
193 Edwin Encarnacion .15 .40
194 Melvin Mora .15 .40
195 Russ Martin .15 .40
196 Edgar Renteria .15 .40
197 Bigfoot .40 1.00
198 Steve Holm RC .40 1.00
199 Daric Barton (RC) .40 1.00
200 David Ortiz .40 1.00
201 Tim Lincecum .40 1.00
202 Jeff King .25 .60
203 Jhonny Peralta .15 .40
204 Julio Lugo .15 .40
205 J.J. Putz .15 .40
206 Jeff Francoeur .25 .60
207 Yuniesky Betancourt .15 .40
208 Bruce Jenner .25 .60
209 Clete Thomas RC .60 1.50
210 Carlos Lee .15 .40
211 Josh Hamilton .50 1.25
212 Pyotr Ilyich Tchaikovsky .25 .60
213 Brendan Harris .15 .40
214 Dustin McGowan .15 .40
215 Aaron Harang .15 .40
216 Brett Myers .15 .40
217 Friedrich Nietzsche .25 .60
218 John Maine .15 .40
219 Charles Dickens .25 .60
220 Erik Bedard .15 .40
221 Tim Hudson .15 .40
222 Jeremy Bonderman .15 .40
223 Nyjer Morgan (RC) .40 1.00
224 Johnny Cueto RC .60 1.50
225 Roy Oswalt .15 .40
226 Rich Hill .15 .40
227 Frederick Douglass .25 .60
228 Derek Lowe .15 .40
229 Joe Blanton .15 .40
230 Carlos Beltran .15 .40
231 Huston Street .15 .40
232 Davy Crockett .25 .60
233 Pluto .25 .60
234 Jered Weaver .15 .40
235 Dan Haren .15 .40
236 Alex Gordon .40 1.00
237 Zack Greinke .15 .40
238 Todd Clever .25 .60
239 Brian Bannister .15 .40
240 Magglio Ordonez .25 .60
241 Ryan Garko .15 .40
242 Takudzwa Ngwenya .25 .60
243 Gil Meche .15 .40
244 Mark Teahen .15 .40
245 Carlos Guillen .15 .40
246 Jeff Kent .15 .40
247 Lisa Leslie .40 1.00
248 Lastings Milledge .15 .40
249 Serena Williams .50 1.25
250 Ichiro Suzuki .60 1.50
251 Matt Cain .15 .40
252 Callix Crabbe (RC) .40 1.00
253 Nick Blackburn RC .60 1.50
254 Hunter Pence .40 1.00
255 Cole Hamels .40 1.00
256 Garret Anderson .15 .40
257 Luis Gonzalez .15 .40
258 Eric Chavez .15 .40
259 Francisco Rodriguez .15 .40
260 Mark Teixeira .25 .60
261 Bob Motley .25 .60
262 Mark Spitz .25 .60
263 Yadier Molina .25 .60
264 Adam Jones .15 .40
265 Brian Roberts .15 .40
266 Matt Kemp .25 .60
267 Andrew Miller .25 .60
268 Dean Karnazes .25 .60
269 Gary Sheffield .15 .40
270 Lance Berkman .25 .60
271 Paul Lo Duca .15 .40
272 Matt Tolbert RC .60 1.50
273 Jay Bruce (RC) 1.50 4.00
274 John Smoltz .40 1.00
275 Nick Markakis .25 .60
276 Oscar Wilde .25 .60
277 Dontrelle Willis .15 .40
278 Kevin Van Dam .25 .60
279 Jim Edmonds .25 .60
280 Brandon Webb .25 .60
281 Joe Nathan .15 .40
282 Jeanette Lee .25 .60
283 Andrew Litz .25 .60
284 Daisuke Matsuzaka .60 1.50
285 Brandon Phillips .15 .40
286 Pat Burrell .15 .40
287 Chris Carpenter .15 .40
288 Pete Weber .25 .60
289 Derrek Lee .25 .60
290 Ken Griffey Jr. .60 1.50
291 Rich Thompson RC .60 1.50

292 Elijah Dukes .15 .40
293 Pedro Feliz .15 .40
294 Torii Hunter .15 .40
295 Chone Figgins .15 .40
296 Hideki Okajima .15 .40
297 Max Scherzer RC 1.00 2.50
298 Greg Smith RC .40 1.00
299 Rafael Furcal .15 .40
300 Ryan Howard .50 1.25
301 Felix Pie SP 1.25 3.00
302 Brad Lidge SP 1.25 3.00
303 Jason Bay SP 1.25 3.00
304 Victor Hugo SP 1.25 3.00
305 Randy Johnson SP 1.25 3.00
306 Carlos Gomez SP 1.25 3.00
307 Pat Neshek SP 1.25 3.00
308 Jed Lowrie SP (RC) 1.25 3.00
309 Ryan Church SP 1.25 3.00
310 Michael Bourn SP 1.25 3.00
311 B.J. Ryan SP 1.25 3.00
312 Brandon Wood SP 1.25 3.00
313 Harriet Beecher Stowe SP 1.25 3.00
314 Mike Cameron SP 1.25 3.00
315 Tom Glavine SP 1.25 3.00
316 Ervin Santana SP 1.25 3.00
317 Geoff Jenkins SP 1.25 3.00
318 Andre Ethier SP 1.25 3.00
319 Jason Giambi SP 1.25 3.00
320 Dmitri Young SP 1.25 3.00
321 Wily Mo Pena SP 1.25 3.00
322 Hank Blalock SP 1.25 3.00
323 James Bowie SP 1.25 3.00
324 Casey Kotchman SP 1.25 3.00
325 Stephen Drew SP 1.25 3.00
326 Adam Kennedy SP 1.25 3.00
327 A.J. Pierzynski SP 1.25 3.00
328 Richie Sexson SP 1.25 3.00
329 Jeff Clement SP (RC) 1.25 3.00
330 Luke Hochevar SP RC 1.25 3.00
331 Luis Castillo SP 1.25 3.00
332 Dave Roberts SP 1.25 3.00
333 Coco Crisp SP 1.25 3.00
334 Jo-Jo Reyes SP 1.25 3.00
335 Phil Hughes SP 1.25 3.00
336 Allen Fisher SP 1.25 3.00
337 Jason Schmidt SP 1.25 3.00
338 Placido Polanco SP 1.25 3.00
339 Jack Cust SP 1.25 3.00
340 Carl Crawford SP 1.25 3.00
341 Ty Wigginton SP 1.25 3.00
342 Aubrey Huff SP 1.25 3.00
343 Bengie Molina SP 1.25 3.00
344 Matt Diaz SP 1.25 3.00
345 Francisco Liriano SP 1.25 3.00
346 Brandon Boggs SP (RC) 1.25 3.00
347 David DeJesus SP 1.25 3.00
348 Justin Masterson SP RC 1.50 4.00
349 Frank Morris SP 1.25 3.00
350 Kevin Youkilis SP 1.25 3.00
NNO Kosuke Fukudome SP 10.00 25.00
NNO Framed Original 50.00 100.00

2008 Topps Allen and Ginter Mini

*MINI 1-300: .75X TO 2X BASIC
*MINI 1-300 RC: .5X TO 1.2X BASIC RC's
APPX. ONE MINI PER PACK
*MINI SP 300-350: .75X TO 2X BASIC SP
MINI SP ODDS 1:13 HOBBY
351-390 RANDOM WITHIN RIP CARDS
OVERALL PLATE ODDS 1:961 HOBBY
PLATE PRINT RUN 1 SET PER COLOR
BLACK-CYAN-MAGENTA-YELLOW ISSUED
NO PLATE PRICING DUE TO SCARCITY
351 Prince Fielder EXT 20.00 50.00
352 Justin Upton EXT 20.00 50.00
353 Russell Martin EXT 30.00 60.00
354 Cy Young EXT 20.00 50.00
355 Hanley Ramirez EXT 20.00 50.00
356 Grady Sizemore EXT 20.00 50.00
357 David Ortiz EXT 40.00 80.00
358 Dan Haren EXT 15.00 40.00
359 Honus Wagner EXT 30.00 60.00
360 Albert Pujols EXT 30.00 60.00
361 Hiroki Kuroda EXT 15.00 40.00
362 Evan Longoria EXT 30.00 60.00
363 Tris Speaker EXT 20.00 50.00
364 Josh Hamilton EXT 30.00 60.00
365 Johan Santana EXT 20.00 50.00
366 Derek Jeter EXT 40.00 80.00
367 Jake Peavy EXT 30.00 60.00
368 Troy Glaus EXT 15.00 40.00
369 Nick Swisher EXT 20.00 50.00
370 George Sisler EXT 20.00 50.00
371 Ichiro Suzuki EXT 40.00 80.00
372 Mark Teixeira EXT 20.00 50.00
373 Justin Verlander EXT 15.00 40.00
374 Jackie Robinson EXT 30.00 60.00
375 Vladimir Guerrero EXT 30.00 60.00
376 Delmon Young EXT 20.00 50.00
377 Lou Gehrig EXT 30.00 60.00
378 Tim Lincecum EXT 30.00 60.00
379 Ryan Zimmerman EXT 15.00 40.00
380 David Wright EXT 40.00 80.00
381 Matt Holliday EXT 20.00 50.00
382 Jose Reyes EXT 30.00 60.00
383 Christy Mathewson EXT 30.00 60.00
384 Hunter Pence EXT 20.00 50.00
385 Chase Utley EXT 20.00 50.00
386 Daisuke Matsuzaka EXT 40.00 80.00
387 Miguel Cabrera EXT 15.00 40.00
388 Torii Hunter EXT 15.00 40.00
389 Carlos Zambrano EXT 20.00 50.00
390 Alex Rodriguez EXT 30.00 60.00
391 Victor Martinez EXT 15.00 40.00
392 Justin Morneau EXT 15.00 40.00
393 Carlos Beltran EXT 15.00 40.00
394 Ryan Braun EXT 20.00 50.00
395 Alfonso Soriano EXT 20.00 50.00
396 Joba Chamberlain EXT 30.00 60.00
397 Nick Markakis EXT 20.00 50.00
398 Ty Cobb EXT 40.00 80.00
399 B.J. Upton EXT 15.00 40.00
400 Ryan Howard EXT 12.50 30.00

2008 Topps Allen and Ginter Mini A and G Back

*A & G BACK: 1X TO 2.5X BASIC
*A & G BACK RCs: .6X TO 1.5X BASIC RCs
STATED ODDS 1:5 HOBBY
*A & G BACK SP: 1X TO 2.5X BASIC SP
SP STATED ODDS 1:65 HOBBY

2008 Topps Allen and Ginter Mini Bazooka

STATED ODDS 1:301 HOBBY
STATED PRINT RUN 25 SER.#'d SETS
NO PRICING DUE TO SCARCITY

2008 Topps Allen and Ginter Mini Black

*BLACK: 1.5X TO 4X BASIC
*BLACK RCs: .75X TO 2X BASIC RCs
STATED ODDS 1:10 HOBBY
*BLACK SP: 1.2X TO 3X BASIC SP
SP STATED ODDS 1:130 HOBBY

2008 Topps Allen and Ginter Mini Framed Cloth

STATED ODDS 1:439 HOBBY
STATED PRINT RUN 10 SER.#'d SETS
NO PRICING DUE TO SCARCITY

2008 Topps Allen and Ginter Mini No Card Number

*NO NBR: 10X TO 25X BASIC
*NO NBR RCs: 4X TO 10X BASIC RCs
*NO NBR: 1.5X TO 4X BASIC SP
STATED ODDS 1:151 HOBBY
STATED PRINT RUN 50 SETS
CARDS ARE NOT SERIAL-NUMBERED
PRINT RUN INFO PROVIDED BY TOPPS
7 Mickey Mantle 30.00 60.00
16 Hiroki Kuroda 6.00 15.00
22 Chin-Lung Hu 6.00 15.00
39 J.R. Towles 6.00 15.00
72 Clayton Kershaw 6.00 15.00
153 Clay Buchholz 10.00 25.00
177 Evan Longoria 15.00 40.00
224 Johnny Cueto 10.00 25.00
253 Nick Blackburn 6.00 15.00
273 Jay Bruce 10.00 25.00
297 Max Scherzer 6.00 15.00

2008 Topps Allen and Ginter Mini Wood

STATED ODDS 1:4395 HOBBY
SOME CARDS FOUND IN RIP PACKS
STATED PRINT RUN 1 SER.#'d SETS
NO PRICING DUE TO SCARCITY

2008 Topps Allen and Ginter Autographs

GROUP A ODDS 1:277 HOBBY
GROUP B ODDS 1:256 HOBBY
GROUP C ODDS 1:135 HOBBY
GRP A PRINT RUNS B/W 90-240 COPIES PER
CARDS ARE NOT SERIAL-NUMBERED
PRINT RUNS PROVIDED BY TOPPS
EXCHANGE DEADLINE 7/31/2010
AE Andre Ethier C 5.00 12.00
AF Andrea Farina A/190 * 15.00 40.00
AFI Allen Fisher A/190 * 12.50 30.00
AIR Alex Rios B 6.00 15.00
AL Andrew Litz A/190 * 15.00 40.00
AM Adriano Moraes A/190 * EXCH 15.00 40.00
BB Bonnie Blair A/190 * 20.00 50.00
BJ Bruce Jenner A/190 * 30.00 60.00
BM Bob Motley A/190 * 30.00 60.00
BP Brad Penny A/240 * 10.00 25.00
BPB Brian Bannister C 5.00 12.00
BPM Billy Mitchell A/190 * 30.00 60.00
CB Clay Buchholz B 10.00 25.00
CC Carl Crawford A/240 * 12.50 30.00
CG Curtis Granderson B 10.00 25.00
DB Murray Campbell A/190 * 20.00 50.00
DJ Dan Jansen A/190 * 20.00 50.00
DK Dean Karnazes A/190 * 20.00 50.00
DO David Ortiz A/90 * 60.00 120.00
DW David Wright A/240 * 40.00 80.00
ES Ervin Santana C 5.00 12.00
FC Francisco Cordero C EXCH 5.00 12.00
FCC Fausto Carmona C 5.00 12.00
FM Frank Morris A/190 * 15.00 40.00
GJ Geoff Jenkins B 5.00 12.00
HP Hunter Pence A/90 * 30.00 60.00
HR Hanley Ramirez A/240 * 20.00 50.00
IK Ian Kinsler C 8.00 20.00
JBF Jeff Francoeur C 6.00 15.00
JC Joba Chamberlain B 40.00 80.00
JF Jeff Francis B 5.00 12.00
JJC Joey Chestnut A/190 * 30.00 60.00
JK Jeff King A/190 * EXCH 12.50 30.00
JL Jeanette Lee A/190 * 75.00 150.00
JR Jose Reyes A/90 * 60.00 120.00
JS Jarrod Saltalamacchia C 5.00 12.00
KS Kerri Strug A/190 * 30.00 60.00
KVD Kevin Van Dam A/190 * 20.00 50.00
LL Lisa Leslie A/190 * 20.00 50.00
LM Les Miles A/190 * EXCH 30.00 60.00
MB Matt Biondi A/190 * 20.00 50.00
MK Matt Kemp B 6.00 15.00
MR Manny Ramirez A/90 * 90.00 150.00
MS Mark Spitz A/190 * 30.00 60.00
MTH Matt Holliday A/90 * 100.00 150.00
NH Nicky Hayden A/240 * 20.00 50.00
NM Nick Markakis B 10.00 25.00
OH Orlando Hudson B 5.00 12.00
PF Prince Fielder A/90 * 40.00 80.00
PW Pete Weber A/190 * 30.00 60.00
RH Ryan Howard A/90 * 75.00 150.00
RJ Rampage Jackson A/190 * 60.00 120.00
SJW Serena Williams A/190 * 50.00 100.00
SW Stevie Williams A/240 * 15.00 40.00
TC Todd Clever A/190 * 20.00 50.00
TH Torii Hunter A/240 * 12.50 30.00
TLH Travis Hafner A/240 * 10.00 25.00
TN Takudzwa Ngwenya A/190 * 20.00 50.00

2008 Topps Allen and Ginter Autographs Red Ink

RANDOM INSERTS IN PACKS
SOME FOUND ONLY IN RIP PACKS
STATED PRINT RUN 10 SER.#'d SETS
NO PRICING DUE TO SCARCITY
EXCHANGE DEADLINE 7/31/2010
AE Andre Ethier
AF Andrea Farina RIP
AL Andrew Litz RIP
AM Adriano Moraes
BB Bonnie Blair RIP
BJ Bruce Jenner
BM Bob Motley RIP
BP Brad Penny
CB Clay Buchholz
CC Carl Crawford RIP
CG Curtis Granderson RIP
DB Deep Blue RIP
DJ Dan Jansen RIP
DK Dean Karnazes
DO David Ortiz
DW David Wright RIP
ES Ervin Santana
FC Francisco Cordero
FM Frank Morris RIP
GJ Geoff Jenkins RIP
HP Hunter Pence
HR Hanley Ramirez RIP
IK Ian Kinsler
JC Joba Chamberlain
JF Jeff Francis
JK Jeff King
JL Jeanette Lee RIP
JR Jose Reyes
JS Jarrod Saltalamacchia
KS Kerri Strug RIP
LL Lisa Leslie
LM Les Miles
MB Matt Biondi RIP
MK Matt Kemp RIP
MR Manny Ramirez RIP
MS Mark Spitz
NH Nicky Hayden
NM Nick Markakis
OH Orlando Hudson RIP
PF Prince Fielder RIP
PW Pete Weber RIP
RH Ryan Howard RIP
RJ Rampage Jackson
SW Stevie Williams RIP
TC Todd Clever
TH Torii Hunter RIP
TN Takudzwa Ngwenya
AFI Allen Fisher RIP
AIR Alex Rios
BPB Brian Bannister
BPM Billy Mitchell RIP
FCC Fausto Carmona RIP
JBF Jeff Francoeur RIP
JJC Joey Chestnut RIP
KVD Kevin Van Dam
MTH Matt Holliday
SJW Serena Williams RIP
TLH Travis Hafner

2008 Topps Allen and Ginter Cabinet Boxloader

STATED ODDS 1:3 HOBBY BOXES
BH1 Matt Holliday 3.00 8.00
Jamey Carroll
Michael Barrett
Brian Giles
BH2 Mike Lowell 4.00 10.00
Manny Ramirez
Jonathan Papelbon
Josh Beckett
BH3 Ryan Howard 4.00 10.00
Jimmy Rollins
Chase Utley
Cole Hamels
BH4 Alex Rodriguez 5.00 12.00
Frank Thomas
Jim Thome
BH5 Justin Verlander 4.00 10.00
Mark Buehrle
Clay Buchholz
HB1 General George Washington 3.00 8.00
General Nathanael Greene
HB2 General Horatio Gates 3.00 8.00
General John Burgoyne
HB3 General George Meade 3.00 8.00
General Robert E. Lee
HB4 Lt. Col. William B. Travis 3.00 8.00
Colonel James Bowie
Colonel Davy Crockett
General Antonio Lopez de Santa Anna
HB5 General Dwight Eisenhower 3.00 8.00
Field Marshal Bernard Montgomery

2008 Topps Allen and Ginter Cabinet Boxloader Autograph

STATED ODDS 1:322 HOBBY BOXES
STATED PRINT RUN 200 SER.#'d SETS
BF Bigfoot 30.00 60.00

2008 Topps Allen and Ginter Cut Signatures

STATED ODDS 1:138,500 HOBBY
STATED PRINT RUN 1 SER.#'d SET
NO PRICING DUE TO SCARCITY
CS1 Arthur Conan Doyle
CS2 Frederick Pabst
CS3 J. Edgar Hoover
CS4 John Glenn
CS5 Thurgood Marshall
CS6 Buffalo Bill
CS7 John Paul Getty
CS8 Eddie Rickenbacker
CS9 Henry Kissinger
CS10 King George III
CS11 Norman Schwarzkopf
CS12 Daniel Webster
CS13 Walter Winchell
CS14 Edgar Rice Burroughs
CS15 John D. Rockefeller
CS16 Thomas Nast
CS17 Boss Tweed
CS18 Jack London
CS19 Adolph Coors
CS20 Oliver Wolcott

2008 Topps Allen and Ginter Dick Perez Original Sketches

RANDOM INSERTS IN PACKS
STATED PRINT RUN 1 SER.#'d SET
NO PRICING DUE TO SCARCITY
DP1 Justin Upton
DP2 Russ Martin
DP3 Ryan Braun
DP4 Victor Martinez
DP5 Hiroki Kuroda
DP6 Mark Teixeira
DP7 Mickey Mantle
DP8 Evan Longoria
DP9 Matt Holliday
DP10 B.J. Upton
DP11 Scott Rolen
DP12 Hideki Matsui
DP13 Frank Thomas
DP14 Carlos Zambrano
DP15 Clay Buchholz
DP16 John Smoltz
DP17 Magglio Ordonez
DP18 Cole Hamels
DP19 Brandon Phillips
DP20 Dontrelle Willis
DP21 Erik Bedard
DP22 Fausto Carmona
DP23 Jorge Posada
DP24 Troy Glaus
DP25 Jonathan Papelbon
DP26 Aaron Rowand
DP27 Adrian Gonzalez
DP28 Francisco Liriano
DP29 Carl Crawford
DP30 Robinson Cano

2008 Topps Allen and Ginter DNA Relics

GROUP A ODDS 1:203,317 HOBBY
GROUP B ODDS 1:264,312 HOBBY
GROUP A PRINT RUN ONE SET
GROUP B PRINT RUN TEN SETS
CARDS ARE NOT SERIAL NUMBERED
PRINT RUN INFO PROVIDED BY TOPPS
NO PRICING DUE TO SCARCITY
AH Alexander Hamilton A
AJ Andrew Jackson A
AL Abraham Lincoln A
CCD Carcharodontosaurus A
CD Charles Dickens A
ET1 Meteorite A
JA John Adams A
JFK John F. Kennedy A
JK Jacqueline Kennedy A
KE King Edward VII A
LB Ludwig van Beethoven A
MS Megalodon A
RR Ronald Reagan A
WM Woolly Mammoth B/10 *

2008 Topps Allen and Ginter Mini Ancient Icons

COMPLETE SET (20) 60.00 120.00
STATED ODDS 1:48 HOBBY
A1 Gilgamesh 3.00 8.00
A2 Marduk 3.00 8.00
A3 Beowulf 3.00 8.00
A4 Poseidon 3.00 8.00
A5 The Sphinx 3.00 8.00
A6 Tutankhamen 3.00 8.00
A7 Alexander the Great 3.00 8.00
A8 Cleopatra 3.00 8.00
A9 Sun Tzu 3.00 8.00
A10 Quetzalcoatl 3.00 8.00
A11 Isis 3.00 8.00
A12 Hercules 3.00 8.00
A13 King Arthur 3.00 8.00
A14 Miyamoto Musashi 3.00 8.00
A15 Genghis Khan 3.00 8.00
A16 Zeus 3.00 8.00
A17 Achilles 3.00 8.00
A18 Confucius 3.00 8.00
A19 Attila the Hun 3.00 8.00
A20 Romulus and Remus 3.00 8.00

2008 Topps Allen and Ginter Mini Baseball Icons

COMPLETE SET (17) 50.00 100.00
STATED ODDS 1:48 HOBBY
BI1 Cy Young 4.00 10.00
BI2 Walter Johnson 4.00 10.00
BI3 Jackie Robinson 5.00 12.00
BI4 Thurman Munson 4.00 10.00
BI5 Mel Ott 3.00 8.00
BI6 Honus Wagner 4.00 10.00
BI7 Pee Wee Reese 3.00 8.00
BI8 Tris Speaker 3.00 8.00
BI9 Christy Mathewson 4.00 10.00
BI10 Ty Cobb 4.00 10.00
BI11 Johnny Mize 3.00 8.00
BI12 Jimmie Foxx 4.00 10.00
BI13 Lou Gehrig 5.00 12.00
BI14 Roy Campanella 3.00 8.00
BI15 George Sisler 3.00 8.00
BI16 Rogers Hornsby 3.00 8.00
BI17 Babe Ruth 8.00 20.00

2008 Topps Allen and Ginter Mini Pioneers of Aviation

COMPLETE SET (5) 15.00 40.00
STATED ODDS 1:XX
PA1 Ornithopter 4.00 10.00
PA2 Linen Balloon 4.00 10.00
PA3 Piloted Glider 4.00 10.00
PA4 Aerial Steam Carriage 4.00 10.00
PA5 Aerodrome 4.00 10.00

2008 Topps Allen and Ginter Mini Team Orange

COMPLETE SET (10) 50.00 100.00
STATED ODDS 1:144 HOBBY
TO1 Cornelius Franks 4.00 10.00
TO2 Mittens McCluskey 4.00 10.00
TO3 Capt. W.P. Mantooth 4.00 10.00
TO4 Wheelbarrow Walker 4.00 10.00
TO5 Archibald Clinker 4.00 10.00
TO6 Minty Beans 4.00 10.00
TO7 Francisco Fiasco 4.00 10.00
TO8 Thurgood Cartwright IV 4.00 10.00
TO9 Enzo DiStubbs 4.00 10.00
TO10 Sir Wagonwheel Stevens 4.00 10.00

2008 Topps Allen and Ginter Mini World's Deadliest Sharks

COMPLETE SET (5) 20.00 50.00
STATED ODDS 1:XX
WDS1 Great White Shark 5.00 12.00
WDS2 Tiger Shark 5.00 12.00
WDS3 Bull Shark 5.00 12.00
WDS4 Oceanic Whitetip Shark 5.00 12.00
WDS5 Mako Shark 5.00 12.00

2008 Topps Allen and Ginter Mini World Leaders

COMPLETE SET (50) 30.00 60.00
STATED ODDS 1:12 HOBBY
WL1 Cristina Fernandez de Kirchner 1.50 4.00
WL2 Kevin Rudd 1.50 4.00
WL3 Guy Verhofstadt 1.50 4.00
WL4 Luiz Inacio Lula da Silva 1.50 4.00
WL5 Stephen Harper 1.50 4.00
WL6 Michelle Bachelet Jeria 1.50 4.00
WL7 Oscar Arias Sanchez 1.50 4.00
WL8 Mirek Topolanek 1.50 4.00

WL9 Anders Fogh Rasmussen 1.50 4.00
WL10 Leonel Fernandez Reyna 1.50 4.00
WL11 Mohamed Hosni Mubarak 1.50 4.00
WL12 Tarja Halonen 1.50 4.00
WL13 Nicolas Sarkozy 1.50 4.00
WL14 Yahya A.J.J. Jammeh 1.50 4.00
WL15 Angela Merkel 1.50 4.00
WL16 Konstandinos Karamanlis 1.50 4.00
WL17 Benedict XVI 2.00 5.00
WL18 Geir H. Haarde 1.50 4.00
WL19 Manmohan Singh 1.50 4.00
WL20 Susilo Bambang Yudhoyono 1.50 4.00
WL21 Bertie Ahern 1.50 4.00
WL22 Ehud Olmert 1.50 4.00
WL23 Bruce Golding 1.50 4.00
WL24 Yasuo Fukuda 1.50 4.00
WL25 Mwai Kibaki 1.50 4.00
WL26 Felipe de Jesus Calderon Hinojosa 1.50 4.00
WL27 Sanjaa Bayar 1.50 4.00
WL28 Armando Guebuza 1.50 4.00
WL29 Girija Prasad Koirala 1.50 4.00
WL30 Jan Peter Balkenende 1.50 4.00
WL31 Helen Clark 1.50 4.00
WL32 Jens Stoltenberg 1.50 4.00
WL33 Qaboos bin Said al-Said 1.50 4.00
WL34 Alan Garcia Perez 1.50 4.00
WL35 Gloria Macapagal-Arroyo 1.50 4.00
WL36 Donald Tusk 1.50 4.00
WL37 Vladimir Vladimirovich Putin 2.50 6.00
WL38 Robert Fico 1.50 4.00
WL39 Thabo Mbeki 1.50 4.00
WL40 Lee Myung-bak 1.50 4.00
WL41 Jose Luis Rodriguez Zapatero 1.50 4.00
WL42 Fredrik Reinfeldt 1.50 4.00
WL43 Pascal Couchepin 1.50 4.00
WL44 Jakaya Kikwete 1.50 4.00
WL45 Samak Sundaravej 1.50 4.00
WL46 Tenzin Gyatso 1.50 4.00
WL47 Patrick Manning 1.50 4.00
WL48 Gordon Brown 2.50 6.00
WL49 George W. Bush 3.00 8.00
WL50 Nguyen Tan Dung 1.50 4.00

2008 Topps Allen and Ginter N43

STATED ODDS 1:3 HOBBY BOXES
CG Curtis Granderson 1.25 3.00
CU Chase Utley 3.00 8.00
DO David Ortiz 3.00 8.00
DW David Wright 4.00 10.00
HR Hanley Ramirez 3.00 8.00
IS Ichiro Suzuki 5.00 12.00
JC Joba Chamberlain 4.00 10.00
JR Jose Reyes 2.00 5.00
MH Matt Holliday 2.00 5.00
MR Manny Ramirez 3.00 8.00
PF Prince Fielder 3.00 8.00
RB Ryan Braun 4.00 10.00
RH Ryan Howard 4.00 10.00
RZ Ryan Zimmerman 2.00 5.00
VG Vladimir Guerrero 3.00 8.00

2008 Topps Allen and Ginter N43 Autographs

STATED PRINT RUN 15 SER.#'d SETS
STATED ODDS 1:428 HOBBY BOXES
NO PRICING DUE TO SCARCITY
EXCHANGE DEADLINE 7/31/2010
CG Curtis Granderson
DO David Ortiz
DW David Wright
HR Hanley Ramirez
JC Joba Chamberlain EXCH
JR Jose Reyes
MH Matt Holliday
MR Manny Ramirez
PF Prince Fielder
RH Ryan Howard

2008 Topps Allen and Ginter N43 Relics

STATED PRINT RUN 25 SER.#'d SETS
STATED ODDS 1:256 HOBBY BOXES
NO PRICING DUE TO SCARCITY
CU Chase Utley
DW David Wright Jsy
HR Hanley Ramirez Jsy
IS Ichiro Suzuki Jsy
JR Jose Reyes Jsy
PF Prince Fielder Jsy
RB Ryan Braun Jsy
RH Ryan Howard Jsy
RZ Ryan Zimmerman Jsy
VG Vladimir Guerrero Jsy

2008 Topps Allen and Ginter N43 Relics Autographs

STATED PRINT RUN 5 SER.#'d SETS
STATED ODDS 1:2565 HOBBY BOXES
NO PRICING DUE TO SCARCITY
EXCHANGE DEADLINE 7/31/2010

DO David Ortiz
DW David Wright
MR Manny Ramirez
PF Prince Fielder
RH Ryan Howard

2008 Topps Allen and Ginter Relics

GROUP A ODDS 1:280 HOBBY
GROUP B ODDS 1:71 HOBBY
GROUP C ODDS 1:20 HOBBY
RELIC AU ODDS 1:26,431 HOBBY
GROUP A B/W 100-250 COPIES PER
CARDS ARE NOT SERIAL NUMBERED
PRINT RUN INFO PROVIDED BY TOPPS
AD1 Adam Dunn Jsy 3.00 8.00
AD2 Adam Dunn Bat 3.00 8.00
AER Alex Rodriguez Bat A 12.50 30.00
AF Andrea Farina A/250 * 5.00 12.00
AFI Allen Fisher A/250 * 8.00 20.00
AIR Alex Rios Bat B 3.00 8.00
AJP A.J. Pierzynski Jsy C 3.00 8.00
AK Austin Kearns Bat B 3.00 8.00
AL Andrew Litz A/250 * 8.00 20.00
AM Archie Moore A/100 * 15.00 40.00
AP1 Albert Pujols Jsy 6.00 15.00
AP2 Albert Pujols Bat 10.00 25.00
APB Aaron Pryor A/100 * 20.00 50.00
AR Aramis Ramirez Jsy B 3.00 8.00
ASM Adriano Moraes A/250 * 12.50 30.00
ATK Adam Kennedy Jsy C 3.00 8.00
AW Andre Ward A/100 * 15.00 40.00
BA Bobby Abreu Bat B 3.00 8.00
BB Bonnie Blair A/250 * 10.00 25.00
BC Bobby Crosby Jsy C 3.00 8.00
BF Bigfoot A/250 * 30.00 60.00
BH Brad Hawpe Jsy C 3.00 8.00
BJ Bruce Jenner A/250 * 6.00 15.00
BM Billy Mitchell A/250 * 20.00 50.00
BMM Brian McCann Jsy C 3.00 8.00
BR1 Brian Roberts Jsy 3.00 8.00
BR2 Brian Roberts Bat 3.00 8.00
CAM Carlos Marmol Jsy C 3.00 8.00
CC1 Carl Crawford Jsy 3.00 8.00
CC2 Carl Crawford Bat 3.00 8.00
CG Curtis Granderson Jsy C 3.00 8.00
CJ Chipper Jones Jsy C 4.00 10.00
CK Casey Kotchman Jsy B 3.00 8.00
CS Curt Schilling Jsy B 3.00 8.00
CU Chase Utley Jsy C 4.00 10.00
CZ Carlos Zambrano Jsy C 3.00 8.00
DG Danny Green A/100 * 30.00 60.00
DJ Dan Jansen A/250 * 8.00 20.00
DK Dean Karnazes A/250 * 10.00 25.00
DM Daisuke Matsuzaka Jsy A 12.50 30.00
DO1 David Ortiz Jsy 4.00 10.00
DO2 David Ortiz Bat 4.00 10.00
DRY Delwyn Young Jsy C 3.00 8.00
DW David Wright Jsy C 6.00 15.00
DY Dmitri Young Bat B 3.00 8.00
EC Eric Chavez Jsy A 3.00 8.00
EM Edison Miranda A/100 * 15.00 40.00
ER Edgar Renteria Bat B 3.00 8.00
FM Frank Morris A/250 * 6.00 15.00
GA Garret Anderson Jsy C 3.00 8.00
HB Hank Blalock Jsy B 3.00 8.00
IR1 Ivan Rodriguez Jsy B 3.00 8.00
IR2 Ivan Rodriguez Bat B 3.00 8.00
IS Ichiro Suzuki Jsy C 6.00 15.00
JB Jason Bay Jsy C 4.00 10.00
JC Joey Chestnut A/250 * 10.00 25.00
JCJ Joel Casamayor A/100 * 12.50 30.00
JD J.D. Drew Bat B 3.00 8.00
JDD Johnny Damon Bat C 3.00 8.00
JF Jeff Francoeur Jsy C 3.00 8.00
JFB Jeff Fenech A/100 * 15.00 40.00
JG Jay Gibbons Bat B 3.00 8.00
JJH J.J. Hardy Jsy C 3.00 8.00
JK Jeff Kent Bat B 3.00 8.00
JKI Jeff King A/250 * 10.00 25.00
JL Jeanette Lee A/250 * 30.00 60.00
JM Joe Mauer Jsy C 4.00 10.00
JS John Smoltz Jsy C 3.00 8.00
JT Jim Thome Jsy C 4.00 10.00
JTD Jermaine Dye Jsy C 3.00 8.00
JV1 Jason Varitek Bat 4.00 10.00
JV2 Jason Varitek Jsy 4.00 10.00
KP Kelly Pavlik A/100 * 40.00 80.00
KS Kerri Strug A/250 * 15.00 40.00
KVD Kevin Van Dam A/250 * 10.00 25.00
LB Lance Berkman Jsy C 3.00 8.00
LL Lisa Leslie A/250 * 12.50 30.00
LM Les Miles A/250 * 10.00 25.00
MB Matt Biondi A/250 * 8.00 20.00
MC Melky Cabrera Jsy C 3.00 8.00
MDC Matt Capps Jsy C 3.00 8.00
MH Mike Hampton Jsy C 3.00 8.00
MH Marcus Henderson AU/100 * 150.00 250.00
MK Matt Kemp Jsy C 3.00 8.00
MR Manny Ramirez Jsy C 4.00 10.00
MS Mark Spitz A/250 * 12.50 30.00
MT Mark Teixeira Jsy C 3.00 8.00
MY Michael Young Jsy C 3.00 8.00
NH Nicky Hayden A/250 * 10.00 25.00
PF Prince Fielder Bat B 3.00 8.00
PK Paul Konerko Jsy C 3.00 8.00
PL Paul Lo Duca Bat B 3.00 8.00
PW Pete Weber A/250 * 15.00 40.00
RF Rafael Furcal Bat B 3.00 8.00
RH Ryan Howard Jsy C 5.00 12.00
RJ Rampage Jackson A/250 * 15.00 40.00
RM Ray Mancini A/100 * 40.00 80.00
RO Roy Oswalt Jsy C 3.00 8.00
RS Richie Sexson Jsy C 3.00 8.00
SD Stephen Drew Jsy B 3.00 8.00
SJW Serena Williams A/250 * 12.50 30.00
SP Samuel Peter A/100 * 10.00 25.00
SW Stevie Williams A/250 * 8.00 20.00
TC Todd Clever A/250 * 10.00 25.00
TG Tom Glavine Jsy C 3.00 8.00
TH Tim Hudson Jsy C 3.00 8.00
TLH Todd Helton Jsy C 3.00 8.00
TN Takudzwa Ngwenya A/250 * 8.00 20.00
TPH Travis Hafner Jsy C 3.00 8.00
TSG Tom Gorzelanny Jsy C 3.00 8.00
TT Troy Tulowitzki Jsy C 3.00 8.00
VG Vladimir Guerrero Bat B 3.00 8.00
VM Victor Martinez Jsy C 3.00 8.00
WMP Wily Mo Pena Bat B 3.00 8.00

2008 Topps Allen and Ginter Rip Cards

STATED ODDS 1:189 HOBBY
PRINT RUNS B/WN 10-99 COPIES PER
NO PRICING ON QTY 10 OR LESS
ALL LISTED PRICED ARE FOR RIPPED
UNRIPPED HAVE ADD'L CARDS WITHIN
COMMON UNRIPPED p/r 99 50.00 120.00
COMMON UNRIPPED p/r 75 60.00 150.00
COMMON UNRIPPED p/r 50 75.00 200.00
COMMON UNRIPPED p/r 28 100.00 250.00
RC1 Erik Bedard/99 6.00 15.00
RC2 Jacoby Ellsbury/75 10.00 25.00
RC3 Chris Carpenter/99 6.00 15.00
RC4 Brandon Phillips/99 6.00 15.00
RC5 Daric Barton/99 6.00 15.00
RC6 Brian McCann/99 6.00 15.00
RC7 Mickey Mantle/10
RC8 Dan Uggla/75 6.00 15.00
RC9 James Loney/99 10.00 25.00
RC10 James Shields/99 6.00 15.00
RC11 Curtis Granderson/75 10.00 25.00
RC12 Jason Bay/99 6.00 15.00
RC13 Alex Gordon/75 10.00 25.00
RC14 Travis Hafner/99 6.00 15.00
RC15 Derek Jeter/28
RC16 Pedro Feliz/99 6.00 15.00
RC17 Thurman Munson/50 10.00 25.00
RC18 Grady Sizemore/75 10.00 25.00
RC19 Alex Rios/99 6.00 15.00
RC20 David Ortiz/50 10.00 25.00
RC21 Walter Johnson/28
RC22 Scott Rolen/99 10.00 25.00
RC23 John Smoltz/99 10.00 25.00
RC24 Mel Ott/28
RC25 Ryan Howard/50 10.00 25.00
RC26 Hiroki Kuroda/99 10.00 25.00
RC27 Johnny Damon/99 6.00 15.00
RC28 Jose Reyes/75 10.00 25.00
RC29 Felix Hernandez/99 10.00 25.00
RC30 John Lackey/99 6.00 15.00
RC31 Albert Pujols/10
RC32 Mark Teixeira/99 10.00 25.00
RC33 Jim Edmonds/99 6.00 15.00
RC34 Prince Fielder/50 10.00 25.00
RC35 Brian Bannister/99 6.00 15.00
RC36 Chipper Jones/50 10.00 25.00
RC37 Edgar Renteria/99 6.00 15.00
RC38 Roy Campanella/50 10.00 25.00
RC39 Troy Tulowitzki/99 10.00 25.00
RC40 Adam LaRoche/99 6.00 15.00
RC41 Phil Hughes/99 10.00 25.00
RC42 Pee Wee Reese/50 10.00 25.00
RC43 Adam Jones/99 6.00 15.00
RC44 Huston Street/99 6.00 15.00
RC45 Cliff Lee/99 6.00 15.00
RC46 Delmon Young/99 10.00 25.00
RC47 Joe Mauer/99 10.00 25.00
RC48 Johan Santana/28
RC49 Dmitri Young/99 6.00 15.00
RC50 Todd Helton/99 10.00 25.00
RC51 Carlos Beltran/75 6.00 15.00
RC52 J.J. Putz/99 6.00 15.00
RC53 Carlos Lee/99 6.00 15.00
RC54 Billy Butler/99 6.00 15.00
RC55 Miguel Cabrera/99 10.00 25.00
RC56 Derrek Lee/99 6.00 15.00
RC57 Alfonso Soriano/75 10.00 25.00
RC58 Cole Hamels/99 10.00 25.00
RC59 Hanley Ramirez/75 10.00 25.00
RC60 Adrian Gonzalez/99 6.00 15.00
RC61 B.J. Upton/99 6.00 15.00
RC62 Tim Lincecum/75 10.00 25.00
RC63 Gary Matthews/99 6.00 15.00
RC64 Justin Upton/75 10.00 25.00
RC65 Zack Greinke/99 6.00 15.00
RC66 Roy Oswalt/75 6.00 15.00
RC67 Jimmy Rollins/28
RC68 Miguel Tejada/99 6.00 15.00
RC69 Clay Buchholz/99 10.00 25.00
RC70 Andruw Jones/99 6.00 15.00
RC71 Chase Utley/75 10.00 25.00
RC72 Aaron Rowand/99 6.00 15.00
RC73 Johnny Mize/50 10.00 25.00
RC74 Jonathan Papelbon/75 10.00 25.00
RC75 Jarrod Saltalamacchia/99 6.00 15.00
RC76 Lance Berkman/50 6.00 15.00
RC77 Vernon Wells/99 6.00 15.00
RC78 Dontrelle Willis/99 6.00 15.00
RC79 Jim Thome/99 10.00 25.00
RC80 Torii Hunter/99 6.00 15.00
RC81 Russ Martin/75 6.00 15.00
RC82 Jake Peavy/99 10.00 25.00
RC83 Carlos Zambrano/99 6.00 15.00
RC84 Troy Glaus/99 6.00 15.00
RC85 Ryan Zimmerman/75 10.00 25.00
RC86 Evan Longoria/75 10.00 25.00
RC87 Yovani Gallardo/99 6.00 15.00
RC88 Jimmie Foxx/10
RC89 Josh Hamilton/75 10.00 25.00
RC90 Matt Holliday/50 10.00 25.00
RC91 Matt Cain/99 6.00 15.00
RC92 Francisco Cordero/99 6.00 15.00
RC93 Derek Lowe/99 6.00 15.00
RC94 Brandon Webb/75 6.00 15.00
RC95 Carlos Pena/99 6.00 15.00
RC96 Ichiro Suzuki/10
RC97 Khalil Greene/99 10.00 25.00
RC98 Rogers Hornsby/10
RC99 C.C. Sabathia/75 6.00 15.00
RC100 Victor Martinez/99 6.00 15.00

2008 Topps Allen and Ginter United States

COMPLETE SET (50) 10.00 25.00
STATED ODDS 1:XX
US1 Alex Rios .25 .60
US2 Curt Schilling .40 1.00
US3 Brian Bannister .25 .60
US4 Torii Hunter .25 .60
US5 Chase Utley .60 1.50
US6 Roy Halladay .25 .60
US7 Brad Ausmus .25 .60
US8 Ian Snell .25 .60
US9 Lastings Milledge .25 .60
US10 Nick Markakis .40 1.00
US11 Shane Victorino .25 .60
US12 Jason Schmidt .25 .60
US13 Curtis Granderson .25 .60
US14 Scott Rolen .40 1.00
US15 Casey Blake .25 .60
US16 Nate Robertson .25 .60
US17 Brandon Webb .40 1.00
US18 Jonathan Papelbon .40 1.00
US19 Tim Stauffer .25 .60
US20 Mark Teixeira .40 1.00
US21 Chris Capuano .25 .60
US22 Jason Varitek .60 1.50
US23 Joe Mauer .40 1.00
US24 Dmitri Young .25 .60
US25 Ryan Howard .75 2.00
US26 Taylor Tankersley .25 .60
US27 Alex Gordon .60 1.50
US28 Barry Zito .25 .60
US29 Chris Carpenter .25 .60
US30 Derek Jeter 1.50 4.00
US31 Cody Ross .25 .60
US32 Alex Rodriguez 1.00 2.50
US33 Ryan Zimmerman .40 1.00
US34 Travis Hafner .25 .60
US35 Nick Swisher .25 .60
US36 Matt Holliday .40 1.00
US37 Jacoby Ellsbury 1.00 2.50
US38 Ken Griffey Jr. 1.00 2.50
US39 Paul Konerko .25 .60
US40 Orlando Hudson .25 .60
US41 Mark Ellis .25 .60
US42 Todd Helton .40 1.00
US43 Adam Dunn .25 .60
US44 Brandon Lyon .25 .60
US45 Daric Barton .25 .60
US46 David Wright .75 2.00
US47 Grady Sizemore .40 1.00
US48 Seth McClung .25 .60
US49 Pat Neshek .25 .60
US50 John Buck .25 .60

2008 Topps Allen and Ginter World's Greatest Victories

STATED ODDS 1:24 HOBBY
WGV1 Kerri Strug 2.50 6.00
WGV2 Mark Spitz 2.50 6.00
WGV3 Jonas Salk 2.00 5.00
WGV4 Man Walks on the Moon 2.00 5.00
WGV5 Jon Lester 3.00 8.00
WGV6 The Fall of the Berlin Wall 2.00 5.00
WGV7 David and Goliath 2.00 5.00
WGV8 Gary Carter and the '86 Mets 2.50 6.00
WGV9 The Battle of Gettysburg 2.00 5.00
WGV10 Deep Blue 2.00 5.00
WGV11 The Allied Forces 2.00 5.00
WGV12 Don Larsen 2.50 6.00
WGV13 Truman Defeats Dewey 2.00 5.00
WGV14 The American Revolution 2.00 5.00
WGV15 2004 ALCS 3.00 8.00
WGV16 The Battle of Thermopylae 2.00 5.00
WGV17 Brown v. Board of Education 2.00 5.00
WGV18 Team Orange 2.50 6.00
WGV19 Bill Mazeroski 2.50 6.00
WGV20 Cinderella 2.00 5.00

2008 Topps Big Stix

Released in August of 2008 and measuring roughly 5"x7", each pack contained five movable stickers. The blank-backed stickers have checklisted alphabetically. The packs had an SRP of $9.99. There several 20-pack box configurations. The first pack configuration featured packs with five random stickers from the 100 sticker checklist. The second pack configuration was a "Mets only" pack. Each Mets pack contained Johan Santana, David Wright, Carlos Beltran, Pedro Martinez and Jose Reyes. The third pack configuration was a "Yankees only" pack. Each of these packs contained the stickers of Robinson Cano, Joba Chamberlain, Alex Rodriguez, Chien-Ming Wang and Derek Jeter.

COMPLETE SET (100) 75.00 200.00
CARDS LISTED ALPHABETICALLY
1 Jason Bay .75 2.00
2 Josh Beckett 1.25 3.00
3 Erik Bedard .75 2.00
4 Carlos Beltran .75 2.00
5 Adrian Beltre .75 2.00
6 Lance Berkman 1.25 3.00
7 Hank Blalock .75 2.00
8 Ryan Braun 2.50 6.00
9 Jay Bruce 3.00 8.00
10 Billy Butler .75 2.00
11 Eric Byrnes .75 2.00
12 Miguel Cabrera 1.25 3.00
13 Matt Cain .75 2.00
14 Robinson Cano 1.25 3.00
15 Joba Chamberlain 2.50 6.00
16 Eric Chavez .75 2.00
17 Carl Crawford .75 2.00
18 Bobby Crosby .75 2.00
19 Adam Dunn .75 2.00
20 Jacoby Ellsbury 3.00 8.00
21 Prince Fielder 2.00 5.00
22 Troy Glaus 1.25 3.00
23 Jonny Gomes .75 2.00
24 Adrian Gonzalez 1.25 3.00
25 Alex Gordon 2.00 5.00
26 Curtis Granderson .75 2.00
27 Ken Griffey Jr. 3.00 8.00
28 Vladimir Guerrero 2.00 5.00
29 Travis Hafner .75 2.00
30 Roy Halladay .75 2.00
31 Cole Hamels 2.00 5.00
32 J.J. Hardy .75 2.00
33 Todd Helton 1.25 3.00
34 Felix Hernandez 1.25 3.00
35 Luke Hochevar 2.00 5.00
36 Matt Holliday 1.25 3.00
37 Ryan Howard 2.50 6.00
38 Torii Hunter .75 2.00
39 Derek Jeter 5.00 12.00
40 Kenji Johjima .75 2.00
41 Chipper Jones 2.50 6.00
42 Andruw Jones .75 2.00
43 Paul Konerko .75 2.00
44 Hiroki Kuroda 1.25 3.00
45 Derrek Lee 1.25 3.00
46 Carlos Lee .75 2.00
47 Tim Lincecum 2.00 5.00
48 Evan Longoria 6.00 15.00
49 Nick Markakis 1.25 3.00
50 Russ Martin 1.25 3.00
51 Victor Martinez .75 2.00
52 Pedro Martinez 1.25 3.00
53 Hideki Matsui 2.00 5.00
54 Daisuke Matsuzaka 3.00 8.00
55 Joe Mauer 1.25 3.00
56 Brian McCann 1.25 3.00
57 Justin Morneau 1.25 3.00
58 Magglio Ordonez 1.25 3.00
59 David Ortiz 2.00 5.00
60 Jonathan Papelbon 1.25 3.00
61 Jake Peavy 1.25 3.00
62 Carlos Pena 2.00 5.00
63 Hunter Pence 2.00 5.00
64 Jorge Posada 1.25 3.00
65 Albert Pujols 4.00 10.00
66 Manny Ramirez 2.00 5.00
67 Hanley Ramirez 2.00 5.00
68 Jose Reyes 1.25 3.00
69 Alex Rios .75 2.00
70 Brian Roberts 1.25 3.00
71 Ivan Rodriguez 1.25 3.00
72 Alex Rodriguez 3.00 8.00
73 Jimmy Rollins 1.25 3.00
74 C.C. Sabathia .75 2.00
75 Johan Santana 1.25 3.00
76 Grady Sizemore 1.25 3.00
77 John Smoltz 2.00 5.00
78 Alfonso Soriano 1.25 3.00
79 Ichiro Suzuki 3.00 8.00
80 Nick Swisher .75 2.00
81 Mark Teixeira 1.25 3.00
82 Miguel Tejada .75 2.00
83 Troy Tulowitzki 1.25 3.00
84 Dan Uggla 1.25 3.00
85 Justin Upton 2.00 5.00
86 B.J. Upton .75 2.00
87 Chase Utley 2.00 5.00
88 Justin Verlander 2.00 5.00
89 Joey Votto 2.00 5.00
90 Chien-Ming Wang 2.50 6.00
91 Brandon Webb 1.25 3.00
92 Vernon Wells .75 2.00
93 Dontrelle Willis .75 2.00
94 David Wright 2.50 6.00
95 Chris Young .75 2.00
96 Delmon Young 1.25 3.00
97 Michael Young .75 2.00
98 Carlos Zambrano .75 2.00
99 Ryan Zimmerman 1.25 3.00
100 Barry Zito .75 2.00

1996 Topps Chrome

The 1996 Topps Chrome set was issued in one series totalling 165 cards and features a selection of players from the 1996 Topps regular set. The four-card packs retailed for $3.00 each. Each chromium card is a replica of its regular version with the exception of the Topps Chrome logo replacing the traditional logo. Included in the set is a Mickey Mantle number 7 Commemorative card and a Cal Ripken Tribute card.

COMPLETE SET (165) 20.00 50.00
1 Tony Gwynn STP .50 1.25
2 Mike Piazza STP .75 2.00
3 Greg Maddux STP .75 2.00
4 Jeff Bagwell STP .30 .75
5 Larry Walker STP .30 .75
6 Barry Larkin STP .30 .75
7 Mickey Mantle COMM 4.00 10.00
8 Tom Glavine STP .30 .75
9 Craig Biggio STP .30 .75
10 Barry Bonds STP 1.00 2.50
11 H.Slocumb STP .30 .75
12 Matt Williams STP .30 .75
13 Todd Helton 1.50 4.00
14 Paul Molitor .30 .75
15 Glenallen Hill .30 .75
16 Troy Percival .30 .75
17 Albert Belle .30 .75
18 Mark Wohlers .30 .75
19 Kirby Puckett .75 2.00
20 Mark Grace .50 1.25
21 J.T. Snow .30 .75
22 David Justice .30 .75
23 Mike Mussina .50 1.25
24 Bernie Williams .50 1.25
25 Ron Gant .30 .75
26 Carlos Baerga .30 .75
27 Gary Sheffield .30 .75
28 Cal Ripken 2131 2.50 6.00
29 Frank Thomas .75 2.00
30 Kevin Seitzer .30 .75
31 Joe Carter .30 .75
32 Jeff King .30 .75
33 David Cone .30 .75
34 Eddie Murray .75 2.00
35 Brian Jordan .30 .75
36 Garret Anderson .30 .75
37 Hideo Nomo .75 2.00
38 Steve Finley .30 .75
39 Ivan Rodriguez .50 1.25
40 Quilvio Veras .30 .75
41 Mark McGwire 2.00 5.00
42 Greg Vaughn .30 .75
43 Randy Johnson .75 2.00
44 David Segui .30 .75
45 Derek Bell .30 .75
46 John Valentin .30 .75
47 Steve Avery .30 .75
48 Tino Martinez .50 1.25
49 Shane Reynolds .30 .75
50 Jim Edmonds .30 .75
51 Raul Mondesi .30 .75
52 Chipper Jones .75 2.00
53 Gregg Jefferies .30 .75
54 Ken Caminiti .30 .75
55 Brian McRae .30 .75
56 Don Mattingly 2.00 5.00
57 Marty Cordova .30 .75
58 Vinny Castilla .30 .75
59 John Smoltz .50 1.25
60 Travis Fryman .30 .75
61 Ryan Klesko .30 .75
62 Alex Fernandez .30 .75
63 Dante Bichette .30 .75
64 Eric Karros .30 .75
65 Roger Clemens 1.50 4.00
66 Randy Myers .30 .75
67 Cal Ripken 2.50 6.00
68 Rod Beck .30 .75
69 Jack McDowell .30 .75
70 Ken Griffey Jr. 1.25 3.00
71 Ramon Martinez .30 .75
72 Jason Giambi .30 .75
73 Nomar Garciaparra FS 1.25 3.00
74 Billy Wagner .30 .75
75 Todd Greene .30 .75
76 Paul Wilson .30 .75
77 Johnny Damon .50 1.25
78 Alan Benes .30 .75
79 Karim Garcia FS .30 .75
80 Derek Jeter FS 2.00 5.00
81 Kirby Puckett STP .50 1.25
82 Cal Ripken STP 1.25 3.00
83 Albert Belle STP .30 .75
84 Randy Johnson STP .50 1.25
85 Wade Boggs STP .30 .75
86 Carlos Baerga STP .30 .75
87 Ivan Rodriguez STP .30 .75
88 Mike Mussina STP .30 .75
89 Frank Thomas STP .50 1.25
90 Ken Griffey Jr. STP .75 2.00
91 Jose Mesa STP .30 .75
92 Matt Morris RC 2.00 5.00
93 Mike Piazza 1.25 3.00
94 Edgar Martinez .50 1.25
95 Chuck Knoblauch .30 .75
96 Andres Galarraga .30 .75
97 Tony Gwynn 1.00 2.50
98 Lee Smith .30 .75
99 Sammy Sosa .75 2.00
100 Jim Thome .50 1.25
101 Bernard Gilkey .30 .75
102 Brady Anderson .30 .75
103 Rico Brogna .30 .75
104 Len Dykstra .30 .75
105 Tom Glavine .50 1.25
106 John Olerud .30 .75
107 Terry Steinbach .30 .75
108 Brian Hunter .30 .75
109 Jay Buhner .30 .75
110 Mo Vaughn .30 .75
111 Jose Mesa .30 .75
112 Brett Butler .30 .75
113 Chili Davis .30 .75
114 Paul O'Neill .50 1.25
115 Roberto Alomar .50 1.25
116 Barry Larkin .50 1.25
117 Marquis Grissom .30 .75
118 Will Clark .50 1.25
119 Barry Bonds 2.00 5.00
120 Ozzie Smith 1.25 3.00
121 Pedro Martinez .50 1.25
122 Craig Biggio .50 1.25
123 Moises Alou .30 .75
124 Robin Ventura .30 .75
125 Greg Maddux 1.25 3.00
126 Tim Salmon .50 1.25
127 Wade Boggs .50 1.25
128 Ismael Valdes .30 .75
129 Juan Gonzalez .30 .75
130 Ray Lankford .30 .75
131 Bobby Bonilla .30 .75
132 Reggie Sanders .30 .75
133 Alex Ochoa .30 .75
134 Mark Loretta .30 .75
135 Jason Kendall .30 .75
136 Brooks Kieschnick .30 .75
137 Chris Snopek .30 .75
138 Ruben Rivera NOW .30 .75
139 Jeff Suppan .30 .75
140 John Wasdin .30 .75
141 Jay Payton .30 .75
142 Rick Krivda .30 .75
143 Jimmy Haynes .30 .75
144 Ryne Sandberg 1.25 3.00
145 Matt Williams .30 .75
146 Jose Canseco .50 1.25
147 Larry Walker .30 .75
148 Kevin Appier .30 .75
149 Javy Lopez .30 .75
150 Dennis Eckersley .30 .75
151 Jason Isringhausen .30 .75
152 Dean Palmer .30 .75
153 Jeff Bagwell .50 1.25
154 Rondell White .30 .75
155 Wally Joyner .30 .75
156 Fred McGriff .50 1.25
157 Cecil Fielder .30 .75
158 Rafael Palmeiro .50 1.25
159 Rickey Henderson .75 2.00
160 Shawon Dunston .30 .75
161 Manny Ramirez .50 1.25
162 Alex Gonzalez .30 .75
163 Shawn Green .30 .75
164 Kenny Lofton .30 .75
165 Jeff Conine .30 .75

1996 Topps Chrome Refractors

Randomly inserted at the rate of one in every 12 packs, this 165-card set is parallel to the regular Chrome set. The difference in design is the refractive quality of the cards.

*STARS: 2.5X TO 6X BASIC CARDS
*ROOKIES: 1.5X TO 4X BASIC CARDS

1996 Topps Chrome Masters of the Game

Randomly inserted in packs at a rate of one in 12, this 20-card set honors players who are masters of their playing positions. The fronts feature color action photography with brilliant color metallization.

COMPLETE SET (20) 25.00 60.00
*REF: 1X TO 2.5X BASIC CHR.MASTERS
REF.STATED ODDS 1:36 HOBBY
1 Dennis Eckersley .75 2.00
2 Denny Martinez .75 2.00
3 Eddie Murray 2.00 5.00
4 Paul Molitor .75 2.00
5 Ozzie Smith 3.00 8.00
6 Rickey Henderson 2.00 5.00
7 Tim Raines .75 2.00
8 Lee Smith .75 2.00
9 Cal Ripken 6.00 15.00
10 Chili Davis .75 2.00
11 Wade Boggs 1.25 3.00
12 Tony Gwynn 2.50 6.00
13 Don Mattingly 5.00 12.00
14 Bret Saberhagen .75 2.00
15 Kirby Puckett 2.00 5.00
16 Joe Carter .75 2.00
17 Roger Clemens 4.00 10.00
18 Barry Bonds 5.00 12.00
19 Greg Maddux 3.00 8.00
20 Frank Thomas 2.00 5.00

1996 Topps Chrome Wrecking Crew

Randomly inserted in packs at a rate of one in 24, this 15-card set features baseball's top hitters and is printed in color action photography with brilliant color metallization.

COMPLETE SET (15) 30.00 80.00
*REF: 1X TO 2.5X BASIC CHR.WRECKING
REF.STATED ODDS 1:72 HOBBY
WC1 Jeff Bagwell 1.50 4.00
WC2 Albert Belle 1.00 2.50
WC3 Barry Bonds 6.00 15.00
WC4 Jose Canseco 1.50 4.00
WC5 Joe Carter 1.00 2.50
WC6 Cecil Fielder 1.00 2.50
WC7 Ron Gant 1.00 2.50
WC8 Juan Gonzalez 1.00 2.50
WC9 Ken Griffey Jr. 4.00 10.00
WC10 Fred McGriff 1.50 4.00
WC11 Mark McGwire 6.00 15.00
WC12 Mike Piazza 4.00 10.00
WC13 Frank Thomas 2.50 6.00

WC14 Mo Vaughn 1.00 2.50
WC15 Matt Williams 1.00 2.50

1997 Topps Chrome

The 1997 Topps Chrome set was issued in one series totalling 165 cards and was distributed in four-card packs with a suggested retail price of $3.00. Using Chromium technology to highlight the cards, this set features a metalized version of the cards of some of the best players from the 1997 regular Topps Series one and two. An attractive 8 1/2" by 11" chrome promo sheet was sent to dealers advertising this set.

COMPLETE SET (165) 20.00 50.00
1 Barry Bonds 2.00 5.00
2 Jose Valentin .30 .75
3 Brady Anderson .30 .75
4 Wade Boggs .50 1.25
5 Andres Galarraga .30 .75
6 Rusty Greer .30 .75
7 Derek Jeter 2.00 5.00
8 Ricky Bottalico .30 .75
9 Mike Piazza 1.25 3.00
10 Garret Anderson .30 .75
11 Jeff King .30 .75
12 Kevin Appier .30 .75
13 Mark Grace .50 1.25
14 Jeff D'Amico .30 .75
15 Jay Buhner .30 .75
16 Hal Morris .30 .75
17 Harold Baines .30 .75
18 Jeff Cirillo .30 .75
19 Tom Glavine .50 1.25
20 Andy Pettitte .50 1.25
21 Mark McGwire 2.00 5.00
22 Chuck Knoblauch .30 .75
23 Raul Mondesi .30 .75
24 Albert Belle .30 .75
25 Trevor Hoffman .30 .75
26 Eric Young .30 .75
27 Brian McRae .30 .75
28 Jim Edmonds .30 .75
29 Robb Nen .30 .75
30 Reggie Sanders .30 .75
31 Mike Lansing .30 .75
32 Craig Biggio .50 1.25
33 Ray Lankford .30 .75
34 Charles Nagy .30 .75
35 Paul Wilson .30 .75
36 John Wetteland .30 .75
37 Derek Bell .30 .75
38 Edgar Martinez .50 1.25
39 Rickey Henderson .75 2.00
40 Jim Thome .50 1.25
41 Frank Thomas .75 2.00
42 Jackie Robinson .75 2.00
43 Terry Steinbach .30 .75
44 Kevin Brown .30 .75
45 Joey Hamilton .30 .75
46 Travis Fryman .30 .75
47 Juan Gonzalez .30 .75
48 Ron Gant .30 .75
49 Greg Maddux 1.25 3.00
50 Wally Joyner .30 .75
51 John Valentin .30 .75
52 Bret Boone .30 .75
53 Paul Molitor .30 .75
54 Rafael Palmeiro .50 1.25
55 Todd Hundley .30 .75
56 Ellis Burks .30 .75
57 Bernie Williams .50 1.25
58 Roberto Alomar .50 1.25
59 Jose Mesa .30 .75
60 Troy Percival .30 .75
61 John Smoltz .50 1.25
62 Jeff Conine .30 .75
63 Bernard Gilkey .30 .75
64 Mickey Tettleton .30 .75
65 Justin Thompson .30 .75
66 Tony Phillips .30 .75
67 Ryne Sandberg 1.25 3.00
68 Geronimo Berroa .30 .75
69 Todd Hollandsworth .30 .75
70 Rey Ordonez .30 .75
71 Marquis Grissom .30 .75
72 Tino Martinez .50 1.25
73 Steve Finley .30 .75
74 Andy Benes .30 .75
75 Jason Kendall .30 .75
76 Johnny Damon .50 1.25
77 Jason Giambi .30 .75
78 Henry Rodriguez .30 .75
79 Edgar Renteria .30 .75
80 Ray Durham .30 .75
81 Gregg Jefferies .30 .75
82 Roberto Hernandez .30 .75
83 Joe Carter .30 .75
84 Jermaine Dye .30 .75
85 Julio Franco .30 .75
86 David Justice .30 .75
87 Jose Canseco .50 1.25
88 Paul O'Neill .50 1.25
89 Mariano Rivera .75 2.00
90 Bobby Higginson .30 .75
91 Mark Grudzielanek .30 .75
92 Lance Johnson .30 .75
93 Ken Caminiti .30 .75
94 Gary Sheffield .30 .75
95 Luis Castillo .30 .75
96 Scott Rolen .50 1.25
97 Chipper Jones .75 2.00
98 Darryl Strawberry .30 .75
99 Nomar Garciaparra 1.25 3.00
100 Jeff Bagwell .50 1.25
101 Ken Griffey Jr. 1.25 3.00
102 Sammy Sosa .75 2.00
103 Jack McDowell .30 .75
104 James Baldwin .30 .75
105 Rocky Coppinger .30 .75
106 Manny Ramirez .50 1.25
107 Tim Salmon .50 1.25
108 Eric Karros .30 .75
109 Brett Butler .30 .75
110 Randy Johnson .75 2.00
111 Pat Hentgen .30 .75
112 Rondell White .30 .75
113 Eddie Murray .75 2.00
114 Ivan Rodriguez .50 1.25
115 Jermaine Allensworth .30 .75
116 Ed Sprague .30 .75
117 Kenny Lofton .30 .75
118 Alan Benes .30 .75
119 Fred McGriff .50 1.25
120 Alex Fernandez .30 .75
121 Al Martin .30 .75
122 Devon White .30 .75
123 David Cone .30 .75
124 Karim Garcia .30 .75
125 Chili Davis .30 .75
126 Roger Clemens 1.50 4.00
127 Bobby Bonilla .30 .75
128 Mike Mussina .50 1.25
129 Todd Walker .30 .75
130 Dante Bichette .30 .75
131 Carlos Baerga .30 .75
132 Matt Williams .30 .75
133 Will Clark .50 1.25
134 Dennis Eckersley .30 .75
135 Ryan Klesko .30 .75
136 Dean Palmer .30 .75
137 Javy Lopez .30 .75
138 Greg Vaughn .30 .75
139 Vinny Castilla .30 .75
140 Cal Ripken 2.50 6.00
141 Ruben Rivera .30 .75
142 Mark Wohlers .30 .75
143 Tony Clark .30 .75
144 Jose Rosado .30 .75
145 Tony Gwynn 1.00 2.50
146 Cecil Fielder .30 .75
147 Brian Jordan .30 .75
148 Bob Abreu .50 1.25
149 Barry Larkin .50 1.25
150 Robin Ventura .30 .75
151 John Olerud .30 .75
152 Rod Beck .30 .75
153 Vladimir Guerrero .75 2.00
154 Marty Cordova .30 .75
155 Todd Stottlemyre .30 .75
156 Hideo Nomo .75 2.00
157 Denny Neagle .30 .75
158 John Jaha .30 .75
159 Mo Vaughn .30 .75
160 Andruw Jones .50 1.25
161 Moises Alou .30 .75
162 Larry Walker .30 .75
163 Eddie Murray SH .50 1.25
164 Paul Molitor SH .30 .75
165 Checklist .30 .75

1997 Topps Chrome Refractors

Randomly inserted in packs at a rate of one in 12, this 165-card set is a parallel version of the regular Topps Chrome set and is similar in design. The difference is found in the refractive quality of the cards.

*STARS: 2.5X TO 6X BASE CARDS

1997 Topps Chrome All-Stars

Randomly inserted in packs at a rate of one in 24, this 22-card set features color player photos printed on rainbow foilboard. The set showcases the top three players from each position from both the American and National leagues as voted on by the Topps Sports Department.

COMPLETE SET (22) 40.00 100.00
*REF: 1X TO 2.5X BASIC CHROME AS
REFRACTOR STATED ODDS 1:72
AS1 Ivan Rodriguez 1.50 4.00
AS2 Todd Hundley 1.00 2.50
AS3 Frank Thomas 2.50 6.00
AS4 Andres Galarraga 1.00 2.50
AS5 Chuck Knoblauch 1.00 2.50
AS6 Eric Young 1.00 2.50
AS7 Jim Thome 1.50 4.00
AS8 Chipper Jones 2.50 6.00
AS9 Cal Ripken 8.00 20.00
AS10 Barry Larkin 1.50 4.00
AS11 Albert Belle 1.00 2.50
AS12 Barry Bonds 6.00 15.00
AS13 Ken Griffey Jr. 4.00 10.00
AS14 Ellis Burks 1.00 2.50
AS15 Juan Gonzalez 1.00 2.50
AS16 Gary Sheffield 1.00 2.50
AS17 Andy Pettitte 1.50 4.00
AS18 Tom Glavine 1.50 4.00
AS19 Pat Hentgen 1.00 2.50
AS20 John Smoltz 1.50 4.00
AS21 Roberto Hernandez 1.00 2.50
AS22 Mark Wohlers 1.00 2.50

1997 Topps Chrome Diamond Duos

Randomly inserted in packs at a rate of one in 36, this 10-card set features color player photos of two superstar teammates on double sided chromium cards.

COMPLETE SET (10) 20.00 50.00
*REF: 1X TO 2.5X BASIC DIAM.DUOS
REFRACTOR STATED ODDS 1:108
DD1 Chipper Jones / Andruw Jones 2.00 5.00
DD2 Derek Jeter / Bernie Williams 5.00 12.00
DD3 Ken Griffey Jr. / Jay Buhner 3.00 8.00
DD4 Kenny Lofton / Manny Ramirez 1.25 3.00
DD5 Jeff Bagwell / Craig Biggio 1.25 3.00
DD6 Juan Gonzalez / Ivan Rodriguez 1.25 3.00
DD7 Cal Ripken / Brady Anderson 6.00 15.00
DD8 Mike Piazza / Hideo Nomo 3.00 8.00
DD9 Andres Galarraga / Dante Bichette .75 2.00
DD10 Frank Thomas / Albert Belle 2.00 5.00

1997 Topps Chrome Season's Best

Randomly inserted in packs at a rate of one in 18, this 25-card set features color player photos of the five top players from five statistical categories: most steals (Leading Looters), most home runs (Bleacher Reachers), most wins (Hill Toppers), most RBIs (Number Crunchers), and best slugging percentage (Kings of Swing).

COMPLETE SET (25) 25.00 60.00
*REF: 1X TO 2.5X BASIC SEAS.BEST
REFRACTOR STATED ODDS 1:54
1 Tony Gwynn 2.50 6.00
2 Frank Thomas 2.00 5.00
3 Ellis Burks .75 2.00
4 Paul Molitor .75 2.00
5 Chuck Knoblauch .75 2.00
6 Mark McGwire 5.00 12.00
7 Brady Anderson .75 2.00
8 Ken Griffey Jr. 3.00 8.00
9 Albert Belle .75 2.00
10 Andres Galarraga .75 2.00
11 Andres Galarraga .75 2.00
12 Albert Belle .75 2.00
13 Juan Gonzalez .75 2.00
14 Mo Vaughn .75 2.00
15 Rafael Palmeiro 1.25 3.00
16 John Smoltz 1.25 3.00
17 Andy Pettitte 1.25 3.00
18 Pat Hentgen .75 2.00
19 Mike Mussina 1.25 3.00
20 Andy Benes .75 2.00
21 Kenny Lofton .75 2.00
22 Tom Goodwin .75 2.00
23 Otis Nixon .75 2.00
24 Eric Young .75 2.00
25 Lance Johnson .75 2.00

1997 Topps Chrome Jumbos

This six-card set contains jumbo versions of the six featured players' regular Topps Chrome cards and measures approximately 3 3/4" by 5 1/4". One of these cards was found in a special box with five Topps Chrome packs issued through Wal-Mart. The cards are numbered according to their corresponding number in the regular set.

COMPLETE SET (6) 6.00 15.00
9 Mike Piazza 1.25 3.00
94 Gary Sheffield .50 1.25
97 Chipper Jones 1.00 2.50
101 Ken Griffey Jr. 1.00 2.50
102 Sammy Sosa .60 1.50
140 Cal Ripken Jr. 2.00 5.00

1998 Topps Chrome

The 1998 Topps Chrome set was issued in two separate series of 282 and 221 cards respectively with design and content paralleling the base 1998 Topps set. Four-card packs carried a suggested retail price of $3 each. Card fronts feature color action player photos printed wtih Chromium technology on metalized cards. The backs carry player information. As is tradition with Topps sets since 1996, card number seven was excluded from the set in honor of Mickey Mantle. Subsets are as follows: Prospects/Draft Picks (245-264/484-501), Season Highlights (265-269/474-478), Inter-League (270-274/479-483), Checklists (275-276/502-503) and World Series (277-283). After four years of being excluded from Topps products, superstar Alex Rodriguez finally made his Topps debut as card number 504. Notable Rookie Cards include Ryan Anderson, Michael Cuddyer, Jack Cust and Troy Glaus.

COMPLETE SET (503) 60.00 150.00
COMP. SERIES 1 (282) 30.00 80.00
COMP. SERIES 2 (221) 30.00 80.00
1 Tony Gwynn 1.00 2.50
2 Larry Walker .30 .75
3 Billy Wagner .30 .75
4 Denny Neagle .30 .75
5 Vladimir Guerrero .75 2.00
6 Kevin Brown .50 1.25
8 Mariano Rivera .75 2.00
9 Tony Clark .30 .75
10 Deion Sanders .50 1.25
11 Francisco Cordova .30 .75
12 Matt Williams .30 .75
13 Carlos Baerga .30 .75
14 Mo Vaughn .30 .75
15 Bobby Witt .30 .75
16 Matt Stairs .30 .75
17 Chan Ho Park .30 .75
18 Mike Bordick .30 .75
19 Michael Tucker .30 .75
20 Frank Thomas .75 2.00
21 Roberto Clemente 2.00 5.00
22 Dmitri Young .30 .75
23 Steve Trachsel .30 .75
24 Jeff Kent .30 .75
25 Scott Rolen .50 1.25
26 John Thomson .30 .75
27 Joe Vitiello .30 .75
28 Eddie Guardado .30 .75
29 Charlie Hayes .30 .75
30 Juan Gonzalez .30 .75
31 Garret Anderson .30 .75
32 John Jaha .30 .75
33 Omar Vizquel .50 1.25
34 Brian Hunter .30 .75
35 Jeff Bagwell .50 1.25
36 Mark Lemke .30 .75
37 Doug Glanville .30 .75
38 Dan Wilson .30 .75
39 Steve Cooke .30 .75
40 Chili Davis .30 .75
41 Mike Cameron .30 .75
42 F.P. Santangelo .30 .75
43 Brad Ausmus .30 .75
44 Gary DiSarcina .30 .75
45 Pat Hentgen .30 .75
46 Wilton Guerrero .30 .75
47 Devon White .30 .75
48 Danny Patterson .30 .75
49 Pat Meares .30 .75
50 Rafael Palmeiro .50 1.25
51 Mark Gardner .30 .75
52 Jeff Blauser .30 .75
53 Dave Hollins .30 .75
54 Carlos Garcia .30 .75
55 Ben McDonald .30 .75
56 John Mabry .30 .75
57 Trevor Hoffman .30 .75
58 Tony Fernandez .30 .75
59 Rich Loiselle RC .30 .75
60 Mark Leiter .30 .75
61 Pat Kelly .30 .75
62 John Flaherty .30 .75
63 Roger Bailey .30 .75
64 Tom Gordon .30 .75
65 Ryan Klesko .30 .75
66 Darryl Hamilton .30 .75
67 Jim Eisenreich .30 .75
68 Butch Huskey .30 .75
69 Mark Grudzielanek .30 .75
70 Marquis Grissom .30 .75
71 Mark McLemore .30 .75
72 Gary Gaetti .30 .75
73 Greg Gagne .30 .75
74 Lyle Mouton .30 .75
75 Jim Edmonds .30 .75
76 Shawn Green .30 .75
77 Greg Vaughn .30 .75
78 Terry Adams .30 .75
79 Kevin Polcovich .30 .75
80 Troy O'Leary .30 .75
81 Jeff Shaw .30 .75
82 Rich Becker .30 .75
83 David Wells .30 .75
84 Steve Karsay .30 .75
85 Charles Nagy .30 .75
86 B.J. Surhoff .30 .75
87 Jamey Wright .30 .75
88 James Baldwin .30 .75
89 Edgardo Alfonzo .30 .75
90 Jay Buhner .30 .75
91 Brady Anderson .30 .75
92 Scott Servais .30 .75
93 Edgar Renteria .30 .75
94 Mike Lieberthal .30 .75
95 Rick Aguilera .30 .75
96 Walt Weiss .30 .75
97 Deivi Cruz .30 .75
98 Kurt Abbott .30 .75
99 Henry Rodriguez .30 .75
100 Mike Piazza 1.25 3.00
101 Billy Taylor .30 .75
102 Todd Zeile .30 .75
103 Rey Ordonez .30 .75
104 Willie Greene .30 .75
105 Tony Womack .30 .75
106 Mike Sweeney .30 .75
107 Jeffrey Hammonds .30 .75
108 Kevin Orie .30 .75
109 Alex Gonzalez .30 .75
110 Jose Canseco .50 1.25
111 Paul Sorrento .30 .75
112 Joey Hamilton .30 .75
113 Brad Radke .30 .75
114 Steve Avery .30 .75
115 Esteban Loaiza .30 .75
116 Stan Javier .30 .75
117 Chris Gomez .30 .75
118 Royce Clayton .30 .75
119 Orlando Merced .30 .75
120 Kevin Appier .30 .75
121 Mel Nieves .30 .75
122 Joe Girardi .30 .75
123 Rico Brogna .30 .75
124 Kent Mercker .30 .75
125 Manny Ramirez .50 1.25
126 Jeromy Burnitz .30 .75
127 Kevin Foster .30 .75
128 Matt Morris .30 .75
129 Jason Dickson .30 .75
130 Tom Glavine .50 1.25
131 Wally Joyner .30 .75
132 Rick Reed .30 .75
133 Todd Jones .30 .75
134 Dave Martinez .30 .75
135 Sandy Alomar Jr. .30 .75
136 Mike Lansing .30 .75
137 Sean Berry .30 .75
138 Doug Jones .30 .75
139 Todd Stottlemyre .30 .75
140 Jay Bell .30 .75
141 Jaime Navarro .30 .75
142 Chris Hoiles .30 .75
143 Joey Cora .30 .75
144 Scott Spiezio .30 .75
145 Joe Carter .30 .75
146 Jose Guillen .30 .75
147 Damion Easley .30 .75
148 Lee Stevens .30 .75
149 Alex Fernandez .30 .75
150 Randy Johnson .75 2.00
151 J.T. Snow .30 .75
152 Chuck Finley .30 .75
153 Bernard Gilkey .30 .75
154 David Segui .30 .75
155 Dante Bichette .30 .75
156 Kevin Stocker .30 .75
157 Carl Everett .30 .75
158 Jose Valentin .30 .75
159 Pokey Reese .30 .75
160 Derek Jeter 2.00 5.00
161 Roger Pavlik .30 .75
162 Mark Wohlers .30 .75
163 Ricky Bottalico .30 .75
164 Ozzie Guillen .30 .75
165 Mike Mussina .50 1.25
166 Gary Sheffield .30 .75
167 Hideo Nomo .75 2.00
168 Mark Grace .50 1.25
169 Aaron Sele .30 .75
170 Darryl Kile .30 .75
171 Shawn Estes .30 .75
172 Vinny Castilla .30 .75
173 Ron Coomer .30 .75
174 Jose Rosado .30 .75
175 Kenny Lofton .30 .75
176 Jason Giambi .30 .75
177 Hal Morris .30 .75
178 Darren Bragg .30 .75
179 Orel Hershiser .30 .75
180 Ray Lankford .30 .75
181 Hideki Irabu .30 .75
182 Kevin Young .30 .75
183 Javy Lopez .30 .75
184 Jeff Montgomery .30 .75
185 Mike Holtz .30 .75
186 George Williams .30 .75
187 Cal Eldred .30 .75
188 Tom Candiotti .30 .75
189 Glenallen Hill .30 .75
190 Brian Giles .30 .75
191 Dave Mlicki .30 .75
192 Garrett Stephenson .30 .75
193 Jeff Frye .30 .75
194 Joe Oliver .30 .75
195 Bob Hamelin .30 .75
196 Luis Sojo .30 .75
197 LaTroy Hawkins .30 .75
198 Kevin Elster .30 .75
199 Jeff Reed .30 .75
200 Dennis Eckersley .30 .75
201 Bill Mueller .30 .75
202 Russ Davis .30 .75
203 Armando Benitez .30 .75
204 Quilvio Veras .30 .75
205 Tim Naehring .30 .75
206 Quinton McCracken .30 .75
207 Raul Casanova .30 .75
208 Matt Lawton .30 .75
209 Luis Alicea .30 .75
210 Luis Gonzalez .30 .75
211 Allen Watson .30 .75
212 Gerald Williams .30 .75
213 David Bell .30 .75
214 Todd Hollandsworth .30 .75
215 Wade Boggs .50 1.25
216 Jose Mesa .30 .75
217 Jamie Moyer .30 .75
218 Darren Daulton .30 .75
219 Mickey Morandini .30 .75
220 Rusty Greer .30 .75
221 Jim Bullinger .30 .75
222 Jose Offerman .30 .75
223 Matt Karchner .30 .75
224 Woody Williams .30 .75
225 Mark Loretta .30 .75
226 Mike Hampton .30 .75
227 Willie Adams .30 .75
228 Scott Hatteberg .30 .75
229 Rich Amaral .30 .75
230 Terry Steinbach .30 .75
231 Glendon Rusch .30 .75
232 Bret Boone .30 .75
233 Robert Person .30 .75
234 Jose Hernandez .30 .75
235 Doug Drabek .30 .75
236 Jason McDonald .30 .75
237 Chris Widger .30 .75
238 Tom Martin .30 .75
239 Dave Burba .30 .75
240 Pete Rose Jr. RC .30 .75
241 Bobby Ayala .30 .75
242 Tim Wakefield .30 .75
243 Dennis Springer .30 .75
244 Tim Belcher .30 .75
245 Jon Garland / Geoff Goetz .40 1.00
246 Glenn Davis / Lance Berkman .40 1.00
247 Vernon Wells / Aaron Akin .40 1.00
248 Adam Kennedy / Jason Romano .40 1.00
249 Jason Dellaero / Troy Cameron .40 1.00
250 Alex Sanchez / Jared Sandberg .40 1.00
251 Pablo Ortega / James Manias .40 1.00
252 Jason Conti RC / Mike Stoner .40 1.00
253 John Patterson / Larry Rodriguez .40 1.00
254 Adrian Beltre / Ryan Minor RC / Aaron Boone .40 1.00
255 Ben Grieve / Brian Buchanan / Dermal Brown .40 1.00
256 Kerry Wood / Carl Pavano / Gil Meche .40 1.00
257 David Ortiz / Daryle Ward / Richie Sexson 2.00 5.00
258 Randy Winn / Juan Encarnacion / Andrew Vessel .40 1.00
259 Kris Benson / Travis Smith / Courtney Duncan RC .40 1.00
260 Chad Hermansen RC / Brent Butler / Warren Morris .40 1.00
261 Ben Davis / Eli Marrero / Ramon Hernandez .40 1.00
262 Eric Chavez / Russell Branyan / Russ Johnson .40 1.00
263 Todd Dunwoody RC / John Barnes / Ryan Jackson .40 1.00
264 Matt Clement / Roy Halladay / Brian Fuentes RC .40 1.00
265 Randy Johnson SH .50 1.25
266 Kevin Brown SH .30 .75
267 Ricardo Rincon SH .30 .75
268 N.Garciaparra SH .75 2.00
269 Tino Martinez SH .30 .75
270 Chuck Knoblauch IL .30 .75
271 Pedro Martinez IL .50 1.25
272 Denny Neagle IL .30 .75
273 Juan Gonzalez IL .30 .75
274 Andres Galarraga IL .30 .75
275 Checklist .30 .75
276 Checklist .30 .75
277 Moises Alou WS .30 .75
278 Sandy Alomar Jr. WS .30 .75
279 Gary Sheffield WS .30 .75
280 Matt Williams WS .30 .75
281 Livan Hernandez WS .30 .75
282 Chad Ogea WS .30 .75
283 Marlins Champs .30 .75
284 Tino Martinez .50 1.25
285 Roberto Alomar .50 1.25
286 Jeff King .30 .75
287 Brian Jordan .30 .75
288 Darin Erstad .30 .75
289 Ken Caminiti .30 .75
290 Jim Thome .50 1.25
291 Paul Molitor .30 .75
292 Ivan Rodriguez .50 1.25
293 Bernie Williams .50 1.25
294 Todd Hundley .30 .75
295 Andres Galarraga .30 .75
296 Greg Maddux 1.25 3.00
297 Edgar Martinez .50 1.25
298 Ron Gant .30 .75
299 Derek Bell .30 .75
300 Roger Clemens 1.50 4.00
301 Rondell White .30 .75
302 Barry Larkin .50 1.25
303 Robin Ventura .30 .75
304 Jason Kendall .30 .75
305 Chipper Jones .75 2.00
306 John Franco .30 .75
307 Sammy Sosa .75 2.00
308 Troy Percival .30 .75
309 Chuck Knoblauch .30 .75
310 Ellis Burks .30 .75
311 Al Martin .30 .75
312 Tim Salmon .50 1.25
313 Moises Alou .30 .75
314 Lance Johnson .30 .75
315 Justin Thompson .30 .75
316 Will Clark .50 1.25
317 Barry Bonds 2.00 5.00
318 Craig Biggio .50 1.25
319 John Smoltz .50 1.25
320 Cal Ripken 2.50 6.00
321 Ken Griffey Jr. 1.25 3.00
322 Paul O'Neill .50 1.25
323 Todd Helton .50 1.25
324 John Olerud .30 .75
325 Mark McGwire 2.00 5.00
326 Jose Cruz Jr. .30 .75

327 Jeff Cirillo .30 .75
328 Dean Palmer .30 .75
329 John Wetteland .30 .75
330 Steve Finley .30 .75
331 Albert Belle .30 .75
332 Curt Schilling .30 .75
333 Raul Mondesi .30 .75
334 Andruw Jones .50 1.25
335 Nomar Garciaparra 1.25 3.00
336 David Justice .30 .75
337 Andy Pettitte .50 1.25
338 Pedro Martinez .50 1.25
339 Travis Miller .30 .75
340 Chris Stynes .30 .75
341 Gregg Jefferies .30 .75
342 Jeff Fassero .30 .75
343 Craig Counsell .30 .75
344 Wilson Alvarez .30 .75
345 Bip Roberts .30 .75
346 Kelvim Escobar .30 .75
347 Mark Bellhorn .30 .75
348 Cory Lidle RC 3.00 8.00
349 Fred McGriff .50 1.25
350 Chuck Carr .30 .75
351 Bob Abreu .30 .75
352 Juan Guzman .30 .75
353 Fernando Vina .30 .75
354 Andy Benes .30 .75
355 Dave Nilsson .30 .75
356 Bobby Bonilla .30 .75
357 Ismael Valdes .30 .75
358 Carlos Perez .30 .75
359 Kirk Rueter .30 .75
360 Bartolo Colon .30 .75
361 Mel Rojas .30 .75
362 Johnny Damon .50 1.25
363 Geronimo Berroa .30 .75
364 Reggie Sanders .30 .75
365 Jermaine Allensworth .30 .75
366 Orlando Cabrera .30 .75
367 Jorge Fabregas .30 .75
368 Scott Stahoviak .30 .75
369 Ken Cloude .30 .75
370 Donovan Osborne .30 .75
371 Roger Cedeno .30 .75
372 Neifi Perez .30 .75
373 Chris Holt .30 .75
374 Cecil Fielder .30 .75
375 Marty Cordova .30 .75
376 Tom Goodwin .30 .75
377 Jeff Suppan .30 .75
378 Jeff Brantley .30 .75
379 Mark Langston .30 .75
380 Shane Reynolds .30 .75
381 Mike Fetters .30 .75
382 Todd Greene .30 .75
383 Ray Durham .30 .75
384 Carlos Delgado .30 .75
385 Jeff D'Amico .30 .75
386 Brian McRae .30 .75
387 Alan Benes .30 .75
388 Heathcliff Slocumb .30 .75
389 Eric Young .30 .75
390 Travis Fryman .30 .75
391 David Cone .30 .75
392 Otis Nixon .30 .75
393 Jeremi Gonzalez .30 .75
394 Jeff Juden .30 .75
395 Jose Vizcaino .30 .75
396 Ugueth Urbina .30 .75
397 Ramon Martinez .30 .75
398 Robb Nen .30 .75
399 Harold Baines .30 .75
400 Delino DeShields .30 .75
401 John Burkett .30 .75
402 Sterling Hitchcock .30 .75
403 Mark Clark .30 .75
404 Terrell Wade .30 .75
405 Scott Brosius .30 .75
406 Chad Curtis .30 .75
407 Brian Johnson .30 .75
408 Roberto Kelly .30 .75
409 Dave Dellucci RC .50 1.25
410 Michael Tucker .30 .75
411 Mark Kotsay .30 .75
412 Mark Lewis .30 .75
413 Ryan McGuire .30 .75
414 Shawon Dunston .30 .75
415 Brad Rigby .30 .75
416 Scott Erickson .30 .75
417 Bobby Jones .30 .75
418 Darren Oliver .30 .75
419 John Smiley .30 .75
420 T.J. Mathews .30 .75
421 Dustin Hermanson .30 .75
422 Mike Timlin .30 .75
423 Willie Blair .30 .75
424 Manny Alexander .30 .75
425 Bob Tewksbury .30 .75
426 Pete Schourek .30 .75
427 Reggie Jefferson .30 .75
428 Ed Sprague .30 .75
429 Jeff Conine .30 .75
430 Roberto Hernandez .30 .75
431 Tom Pagnozzi .30 .75
432 Jaret Wright .30 .75
433 Livan Hernandez .30 .75
434 Andy Ashby .30 .75
435 Todd Dunn .30 .75
436 Bobby Higginson .30 .75
437 Rod Beck .30 .75
438 Jim Leyritz .30 .75
439 Matt Williams .30 .75
440 Brett Tomko .30 .75
441 Joe Randa .30 .75
442 Chris Carpenter .30 .75
443 Dennis Reyes .30 .75
444 Al Leiter .30 .75
445 Jason Schmidt .30 .75
446 Ken Hill .30 .75
447 Shannon Stewart .30 .75
448 Enrique Wilson .30 .75
449 Fernando Tatis .30 .75
450 Jimmy Key .30 .75
451 Darrin Fletcher .30 .75
452 John Valentin .30 .75
453 Kevin Tapani .30 .75
454 Eric Karros .30 .75
455 Jay Bell .30 .75
456 Walt Weiss .30 .75
457 Devon White .30 .75
458 Carl Pavano .30 .75
459 Mike Lansing .30 .75
460 John Flaherty .30 .75
461 Richard Hidalgo .30 .75
462 Quinton McCracken .30 .75
463 Karim Garcia .30 .75
464 Miguel Cairo .30 .75
465 Edwin Diaz .30 .75
466 Bobby Smith .30 .75
467 Yamil Benitez .30 .75
468 Rich Butler RC .30 .75
469 Ben Ford RC .30 .75
470 Bubba Trammell .30 .75
471 Brent Brede .30 .75
472 Brooks Kieschnick .30 .75
473 Carlos Castillo .30 .75
474 Brad Radke SH .30 .75
475 Roger Clemens SH .75 2.00
476 Curt Schilling SH .30 .75
477 John Olerud SH .30 .75
478 Mark McGwire SH 1.00 2.50
479 Mike Piazza IL .75 2.00
Ken Griffey Jr.
480 Jeff Bagwell .50 1.25
Frank Thomas
481 Chipper Jones .50 1.25
Nomar Garciaparra IL
482 Larry Walker IL .30 .75
Juan Gonzalez IL
483 Gary Sheffield IL .30 .75
Tino Martinez IL
484 Derrick Gibson .40 1.00
Michael Coleman
Norm Hutchins
485 Braden Looper .40 1.00
Cliff Politte
Brian Rose
486 Eric Milton .40 1.00
Jason Marquis
Corey Lee
487 A.J.Hinch .40 1.00
Mark Osborne RC
Robert Fick
488 Aramis Ramirez .40 1.00
Alex Gonzalez
Sean Casey
489 Donnie Bridges .40 1.00
Tim Drew RC
490 Ntema Ndungidi RC .40 1.00
Darnell McDonald
491 Ryan Anderson RC .40 1.00
Mark Mangum
492 J.J.Davis 2.00 5.00
Troy Glaus RC
493 Jayson Werth RC .40 1.00
Dan Reichert
494 John Curtice RC 1.00 2.50
Michael Cuddyer RC
495 Jack Cust RC .75 2.00
Jason Standridge
496 Brian Anderson .40 1.00
497 Tony Saunders .40 1.00
498 Vladimir Nunez .40 1.00
Jhensy Sandoval
499 Brad Penny .40 1.00
Nick Bierbrodt
500 Dustin Carr .40 1.00
Luis Cruz RC
501 Cedric Bowers .40 1.00
Marcus McCain
502 Checklist .30 .75
503 Checklist .30 .75
504 Alex Rodriguez 1.50 4.00

1998 Topps Chrome Refractors

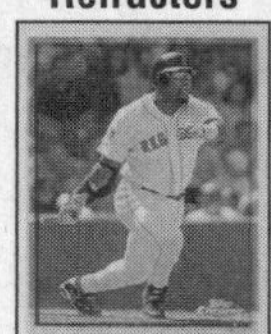

Randomly inserted in first and second series packs at the rate of one in 12, this set is parallel to the base set and is similar in design. The difference is found in the refractive quality of the cards.

*STARS: 2.5X TO 6X BASIC CARDS
*ROOKIES: 1.25X TO 3X BASIC

1998 Topps Chrome Baby Boomers

Randomly inserted in first series packs at the rate of one in 24, this 15 card set features color action photos printed on metalized cards with Chromium technology of young players who have already made their mark in the game with less than three years in the majors.

COMPLETE SET (15) 30.00 80.00
*REF: .75X TO 2X BASIC CHR.BOOMERS
REFRACTOR SER.1 STATED ODDS 1:72
BB1 Derek Jeter 6.00 15.00
BB2 Scott Rolen 1.50 4.00
BB3 Nomar Garciaparra 4.00 10.00
BB4 Jose Cruz Jr. 1.00 2.50
BB5 Darin Erstad 1.00 2.50
BB6 Todd Helton 1.50 4.00
BB7 Tony Clark 1.00 2.50
BB8 Jose Guillen 1.00 2.50
BB9 Andruw Jones 1.50 4.00
BB10 Vladimir Guerrero 2.50 6.00
BB11 Mark Kotsay 1.00 2.50
BB12 Todd Greene 1.00 2.50
BB13 Andy Pettitte 1.50 4.00
BB14 Justin Thompson 1.00 2.50
BB15 Alan Benes 1.00 2.50

1998 Topps Chrome Clout Nine

Randomly seeded at a rate of one in 24 second series packs, cards from this nine-card set feature a selection of the league's top sluggers. The cards are a straight parallel of the previously released 1998 Topps Clout 9 set, except of course for the Chromium stock fronts.

COMPLETE SET (9) 25.00 60.00
*REF: .75X TO 2X BASIC CHR.CLOUT
REFRACTOR SER.2 STATED ODDS 1:72
C1 Edgar Martinez 1.50 4.00
C2 Mike Piazza 4.00 10.00
C3 Frank Thomas 2.50 6.00
C4 Craig Biggio 1.50 4.00
C5 Vinny Castilla 1.00 2.50
C6 Jeff Blauser 1.00 2.50
C7 Barry Bonds 6.00 15.00
C8 Ken Griffey Jr. 4.00 10.00
C9 Larry Walker 1.00 2.50

1998 Topps Chrome Flashback

Randomly inserted in first series packs at the rate of one in 24, this 10-card set features two-sided cards with color action photos of top players printed on metalized cards with Chromium technology. One side displays how they looked "then" as rookies, while the other side shows how they look "now" as stars.

COMPLETE SET (10) 30.00 80.00
*REF: .75X TO 2X BASIC CHR.FLASHBACK
REFRACTOR SER.1 STATED ODDS 1:72
FB1 Barry Bonds 6.00 15.00
FB2 Ken Griffey Jr. 4.00 10.00
FB3 Paul Molitor 1.00 2.50
FB4 Randy Johnson 2.50 6.00
FB5 Cal Ripken 8.00 20.00
FB6 Tony Gwynn 3.00 8.00
FB7 Kenny Lofton 1.00 2.50
FB8 Gary Sheffield 1.00 2.50
FB9 Deion Sanders 1.50 4.00
FB10 Brady Anderson 1.00 2.50

1998 Topps Chrome HallBound

Randomly inserted in first series packs at the rate of one in 24, this 15-card set features color photos printed on metalized cards with Chromium technology of top stars who are bound for the Hall of Fame in Cooperstown, New York.

COMPLETE SET (15) 60.00 150.00
*REF: .75X TO 2X BASIC HALLBOUND
REFRACTOR SER.1 STATED ODDS 1:72
HB1 Paul Molitor 1.25 3.00
HB2 Tony Gwynn 4.00 10.00
HB3 Wade Boggs 2.00 5.00
HB4 Roger Clemens 6.00 15.00
HB5 Dennis Eckersley 1.25 3.00
HB6 Cal Ripken 10.00 25.00
HB7 Greg Maddux 5.00 12.00
HB8 Rickey Henderson 2.00 5.00
HB9 Ken Griffey Jr. 5.00 12.00
HB10 Frank Thomas 3.00 8.00
HB11 Mark McGwire 8.00 20.00
HB12 Barry Bonds 8.00 20.00
HB13 Mike Piazza 5.00 12.00
HB14 Juan Gonzalez 1.25 3.00
HB15 Randy Johnson 3.00 8.00

1998 Topps Chrome Milestones

Randomly seeded at a rate of one in every 24 second series packs, these 10 cards feature a selection of veteran stars that achieved specific career milestones in 1997. The cards are a straight parallel from the previously released 1998 Topps Milestones inserts except, of course, for the Chromium finish on the fronts.

COMPLETE SET (10) 50.00 120.00
*REF: .75X TO 2X BASIC CHR.MILE
REFRACTOR SER.2 STATED ODDS 1:72
MS1 Barry Bonds 5.00 12.00
MS2 Roger Clemens 4.00 10.00
MS3 Dennis Eckersley .75 2.00
MS4 Juan Gonzalez .75 2.00
MS5 Ken Griffey Jr. 3.00 8.00
MS6 Tony Gwynn 2.50 6.00
MS7 Greg Maddux 3.00 8.00
MS8 Mark McGwire 5.00 12.00
MS9 Cal Ripken 6.00 15.00
MS10 Frank Thomas 2.00 5.00

1998 Topps Chrome Rookie Class

Randomly seeded at a rate of one in 12 second series packs, cards from this 10-card set feature a selection of the league's top rookies for 1998. The cards are a straight parallel of the previously released 1998 Topps Rookie Class set, except of course for the Chromium stock fronts.

COMPLETE SET (10) 8.00 20.00
*REF: .75X TO 2X BASIC CHR.RK.CLASS
REFRACTOR SER.2 STATED ODDS 1:24
R1 Travis Lee .75 2.00
R2 Richard Hidalgo .75 2.00
R3 Todd Helton 1.25 3.00
R4 Paul Konerko .75 2.00
R5 Mark Kotsay .75 2.00
R6 Derrek Lee .75 2.00
R7 Eli Marrero .75 2.00
R8 Fernando Tatis .75 2.00
R9 Juan Encarnacion .75 2.00
R10 Ben Grieve .75 2.00

1999 Topps Chrome

1999 Topps Chrome

The 1999 Topps Chrome set totaled 462 cards (though is numbered 1-463 - card number 7 was never issued in honor of Mickey Mantle). The product was distributed in first and second series four-card packs each carrying a suggested retail price of $3. The first series cards were 1-6/8-242, second series cards 243-463. The card fronts feature action color player photos. The backs carry player information. The set contains the following subsets: Season Highlights (200-204), Prospects (205-212/425-437), Draft Picks (213-219/438-444), League Leaders (221-232), World Series (233-240), Strikeout Kings (445-449), All-Topps (450-460) and four Checklist Cards (241-242/462-463). The Mark McGwire Home Run Record Breaker card (220) was released in 70 different variations highlighting every home run that he hit in 1998. The Sammy Sosa Home Run Parade card (461) was issued in 66 different variations. A 462 card set of 1999 Topps Chrome is considered complete with any version of the McGwire 220 and Sosa 461. Rookie Cards of note include Pat Burrell and Alex Escobar

COMPLETE SET (462) 50.00 120.00
COMP. SERIES 1 (241) 25.00 60.00
COMP. SERIES 2 (221) 25.00 60.00
COMMON (1-6/8-463) .20 .50
COMMON (205-212/425-437) .40 1.00
1 Roger Clemens 1.50 4.00
2 Andres Galarraga .30 .75
3 Scott Brosius .30 .75
4 John Flaherty .20 .50
5 Jim Leyritz .20 .50
6 Ray Durham .30 .75
8 Jose Vizcaino .20 .50
9 Will Clark .50 1.25
10 David Wells .30 .75
11 Jose Guillen .30 .75
12 Scott Hatteberg .20 .50
13 Edgardo Alfonzo .20 .50
14 Mike Bordick .20 .50
15 Manny Ramirez .50 1.25
16 Greg Maddux 1.25 3.00
17 David Segui .20 .50
18 Darryl Strawberry .30 .75
19 Brad Radke .30 .75
20 Kerry Wood .30 .75
21 Matt Anderson .20 .50
22 Derrek Lee .50 1.25
23 Mickey Morandini .20 .50
24 Paul Konerko .30 .75
25 Travis Lee .20 .50
26 Ken Hill .20 .50
27 Kenny Rogers .30 .75
28 Paul Sorrento .20 .50
29 Quilvio Veras .20 .50
30 Todd Walker .20 .50
31 Ryan Jackson .20 .50
32 John Olerud .30 .75
33 Doug Glanville .20 .50
34 Nolan Ryan 2.50 6.00
35 Ray Lankford .30 .75
36 Mark Loretta .20 .50
37 Jason Dickson .20 .50
38 Sean Bergman .20 .50
39 Quinton McCracken .20 .50
40 Bartolo Colon .20 .50
41 Brady Anderson .30 .75
42 Chris Stynes .20 .50
43 Jorge Posada .50 1.25
44 Justin Thompson .20 .50
45 Johnny Damon .50 1.25
46 Armando Benitez .20 .50
47 Brant Brown .20 .50
48 Charlie Hayes .20 .50
49 Darren Dreifort .20 .50
50 Juan Gonzalez .30 .75
51 Chuck Knoblauch .30 .75
52 Todd Helton .50 1.25
53 Rick Reed .20 .50
54 Chris Gomez .20 .50
55 Gary Sheffield .30 .75
56 Rod Beck .20 .50
57 Rey Sanchez .20 .50
58 Garret Anderson .30 .75
59 Jimmy Haynes .20 .50
60 Steve Woodard .20 .50
61 Rondell White .30 .75
62 Vladimir Guerrero .75 2.00
63 Eric Karros .30 .75
64 Russ Davis .20 .50
65 Mo Vaughn .30 .75
66 Sammy Sosa .75 2.00
67 Troy Percival .30 .75
68 Kenny Lofton .30 .75
69 Bill Taylor .20 .50
70 Mark McGwire 2.00 5.00
71 Roger Cedeno .20 .50
72 Javy Lopez .30 .75
73 Damion Easley .20 .50
74 Andy Pettitte .50 1.25
75 Tony Gwynn 1.00 2.50
76 Ricardo Rincon .20 .50
77 F.P. Santangelo .20 .50
78 Jay Bell .30 .75
79 Scott Servais .20 .50
80 Jose Canseco .50 1.25
81 Roberto Hernandez .20 .50
82 Todd Dunwoody .20 .50
83 John Wetteland .30 .75
84 Mike Caruso .20 .50
85 Derek Jeter 2.00 5.00
86 Aaron Sele .20 .50
87 Jose Lima .20 .50
88 Ryan Christenson .20 .50
89 Jeff Cirillo .20 .50
90 Jose Hernandez .20 .50
91 Mark Kotsay .30 .75
92 Darren Bragg .20 .50
93 Albert Belle .30 .75
94 Matt Lawton .20 .50
95 Pedro Martinez .50 1.25
96 Greg Vaughn .20 .50
97 Neifi Perez .20 .50
98 Gerald Williams .20 .50
99 Derek Bell .20 .50
100 Ken Griffey Jr. 1.25 3.00
101 David Cone .30 .75
102 Brian Johnson .20 .50
103 Dean Palmer .30 .75
104 Javier Valentin .20 .50
105 Trevor Hoffman .30 .75
106 Butch Huskey .20 .50
107 Dave Martinez .20 .50
108 Billy Wagner .30 .75
109 Shawn Green .30 .75
110 Ben Grieve .20 .50
111 Tom Goodwin .20 .50
112 Jaret Wright .20 .50
113 Aramis Ramirez .30 .75
114 Dmitri Young .30 .75
115 Hideki Irabu .20 .50
116 Roberto Kelly .20 .50
117 Jeff Fassero .20 .50
118 Mark Clark .20 .50
119 Jason McDonald .20 .50
120 Matt Williams .30 .75
121 Dave Burba .20 .50
122 Bret Saberhagen .30 .75
123 Deivi Cruz .20 .50
124 Chad Curtis .20 .50
125 Scott Rolen .50 1.25
126 Lee Stevens .20 .50
127 J.T. Snow .30 .75
128 Rusty Greer .30 .75
129 Brian Meadows .20 .50
130 Jim Edmonds .30 .75
131 Ron Gant .30 .75
132 A.J. Hinch .20 .50
133 Shannon Stewart .30 .75
134 Brad Fullmer .20 .50
135 Cal Eldred .20 .50
136 Matt Walbeck .20 .50
137 Carl Everett .30 .75
138 Walt Weiss .20 .50
139 Fred McGriff .50 1.25
140 Darin Erstad .30 .75
141 Dave Nilsson .20 .50
142 Eric Young .20 .50
143 Dan Wilson .20 .50
144 Jeff Reed .20 .50
145 Brett Tomko .20 .50
146 Terry Steinbach .20 .50
147 Seth Greisinger .20 .50
148 Pat Meares .20 .50
149 Livan Hernandez .30 .75
150 Jeff Bagwell .50 1.25
151 Bob Wickman .20 .50
152 Omar Vizquel .50 1.25
153 Eric Davis .30 .75
154 Larry Sutton .20 .50
155 Magglio Ordonez .30 .75
156 Eric Milton .20 .50
157 Darren Lewis .20 .50
158 Rick Aguilera .20 .50
159 Mike Lieberthal .30 .75
160 Robb Nen .30 .75
161 Brian Giles .30 .75
162 Jeff Brantley .20 .50
163 Gary DiSarcina .20 .50
164 John Valentin .20 .50
165 Dave Dellucci .20 .50
166 Chan Ho Park .30 .75
167 Masato Yoshii .20 .50
168 Jason Schmidt .30 .75
169 LaTroy Hawkins .20 .50
170 Bret Boone .30 .75
171 Jerry DiPoto .20 .50
172 Mariano Rivera .75 2.00
173 Mike Cameron .20 .50
174 Scott Erickson .20 .50
175 Charles Johnson .30 .75
176 Bobby Jones .20 .50
177 Francisco Cordova .20 .50
178 Todd Jones .20 .50
179 Jeff Montgomery .20 .50
180 Mike Mussina .50 1.25
181 Bob Abreu .30 .75
182 Ismael Valdes .20 .50
183 Andy Fox .20 .50
184 Woody Williams .20 .50
185 Denny Neagle .20 .50
186 Jose Valentin .20 .50
187 Darrin Fletcher .20 .50
188 Gabe Alvarez .20 .50
189 Eddie Taubensee .20 .50
190 Edgar Martinez .50 1.25
191 Jason Kendall .30 .75
192 Darryl Kile .30 .75
193 Jeff King .20 .50
194 Rey Ordonez .20 .50
195 Andruw Jones .50 1.25
196 Tony Fernandez .20 .50
197 Jamey Wright .20 .50
198 B.J. Surhoff .30 .75
199 Vinny Castilla .30 .75
200 David Wells HL .20 .50
201 Mark McGwire HL 1.00 2.50
202 Sammy Sosa HL .50 1.25
203 Roger Clemens HL .75 2.00
204 Kerry Wood HL .20 .50
205 Gabe Kapler .40 1.00
Lance Berkman
Mike Frank
206 Alex Escobar RC .40 1.00
Ricky Ledee
Mike Stoner
207 Peter Bergeron RC .40 1.00
Jeremy Giambi
George Lombard
208 Michael Barrett .40 1.00
Ben Davis
Robert Fick
209 Jayson Werth .40 1.00
Ramon Hernandez
Pat Cline
210 Ryan Anderson .40 1.00
Bruce Chen
Chris Enochs
211 Brad Penny .40 1.00
Octavio Dotel
Mike Lincoln
212 Chuck Abbott RC .40 1.00
Brent Butler
Danny Klassen
213 Chris C.Jones .40 1.00
Jeff Urban RC
214 Arturo McDowell RC .40 1.00
Tony Torcato
215 Josh McKinley RC .40 1.00
Jason Tyner
216 Matt Burch .40 1.00
Seth Etheron RC
217 Mamon Tucker RC .40 1.00
Rick Elder
218 J.M.Gold .40 1.00
Ryan Mills RC
219 Andy Brown .40 1.00
Choo Freeman RC
220A Mark McGwire HR 1 20.00 50.00
220B Mark McGwire HR 2 12.50 30.00
220C Mark McGwire HR 3 12.50 30.00
220D Mark McGwire HR 4 12.50 30.00
220E Mark McGwire HR 5 12.50 30.00
220F Mark McGwire HR 6 12.50 30.00
220G Mark McGwire HR 7 12.50 30.00
220H Mark McGwire HR 8 12.50 30.00
220I Mark McGwire HR 9 12.50 30.00
220J M.McGwire HR 10 12.50 30.00
220K M.McGwire HR 11 12.50 30.00
220L M.McGwire HR 12 12.50 30.00
220M M.McGwire HR 13 12.50 30.00
220N M.McGwire HR 14 12.50 30.00
220O M.McGwire HR 15 12.50 30.00
220P M.McGwire HR 16 12.50 30.00
220Q M.McGwire HR 17 12.50 30.00
220R M.McGwire HR 18 12.50 30.00
220S M.McGwire HR 19 12.50 30.00
220T M.McGwire HR 20 12.50 30.00
220U M.McGwire HR 21 12.50 30.00
220V M.McGwire HR 22 12.50 30.00
220W M.McGwire HR 23 12.50 30.00
220X M.McGwire HR 24 12.50 30.00
220Y M.McGwire HR 25 12.50 30.00
220Z M.McGwire HR 26 12.50 30.00
220AA M.McGwire HR 27 12.50 30.00
220AB M.McGwire HR 28 12.50 30.00
220AC M.McGwire HR 29 12.50 30.00
220AD M.McGwire HR 30 12.50 30.00
220AE M.McGwire HR 31 12.50 30.00
220AF M.McGwire HR 32 12.50 30.00
220AG M.McGwire HR 33 12.50 30.00
220AH M.McGwire HR 34 12.50 30.00
220AI M.McGwire HR 35 12.50 30.00
220AJ M.McGwire HR 36 12.50 30.00
220AK M.McGwire HR 37 12.50 30.00
220AL M.McGwire HR 38 12.50 30.00
220AM M.McGwire HR 39 12.50 30.00
220AN M.McGwire HR 40 12.50 30.00
220AO M.McGwire HR 41 12.50 30.00
220AP M.McGwire HR 42 12.50 30.00
220AQ M.McGwire HR 43 12.50 30.00
220AR M.McGwire HR 44 12.50 30.00
220AS M.McGwire HR 45 12.50 30.00
220AT M.McGwire HR 46 12.50 30.00
220AU M.McGwire HR 47 12.50 30.00

220AV M.McGwire HR 48 12.50 30.00
220AW M.McGwire HR 49 12.50 30.00
220AX M.McGwire HR 50 12.50 30.00
220AY M.McGwire HR 51 12.50 30.00
220AZ M.McGwire HR 52 12.50 30.00
220BB M.McGwire HR 53 12.50 30.00
220CC M.McGwire HR 54 12.50 30.00
220DD M.McGwire HR 55 12.50 30.00
220EE M.McGwire HR 56 12.50 30.00
220FF M.McGwire HR 57 12.50 30.00
220GG M.McGwire HR 58 12.50 30.00
220HH M.McGwire HR 59 12.50 30.00
220II M.McGwire HR 60 12.50 30.00
220JJ M.McGwire HR 61 20.00 50.00
220KK M.McGwire HR 62 40.00 80.00
220LL M.McGwire HR 63 20.00 50.00
220MM M.McGwire HR 64 20.00 50.00
220NN M.McGwire HR 65 20.00 50.00
220OO M.McGwire HR 66 20.00 50.00
220PP M.McGwire HR 67 20.00 50.00
220QQ M.McGwire HR 68 20.00 50.00
220RR M.McGwire HR 69 20.00 50.00
220SS M.McGwire HR 70 60.00 120.00
221 Larry Walker LL .20 .50
222 Bernie Williams LL .30 .75
223 Mark McGwire LL 1.00 2.50
224 Ken Griffey Jr. LL .75 2.00
225 Sammy Sosa LL .50 1.25
226 Juan Gonzalez LL .20 .50
227 Dante Bichette LL .20 .50
228 Alex Rodriguez LL .75 2.00
229 Sammy Sosa LL .50 1.25
230 Derek Jeter LL 1.00 2.50
231 Greg Maddux LL .75 2.00
232 Roger Clemens LL .75 2.00
233 Ricky Ledee WS .20 .50
234 Chuck Knoblauch WS .20 .50
235 Bernie Williams WS .30 .75
236 Tino Martinez WS .30 .75
237 Orl. Hernandez WS .30 .75
238 Scott Brosius WS .20 .50
239 Andy Pettitte WS .30 .75
240 Mariano Rivera WS .50 1.25
241 Checklist .20 .50
242 Checklist .20 .50
243 Tom Glavine .50 1.25
244 Andy Benes .20 .50
245 Sandy Alomar Jr. .20 .50
246 Wilton Guerrero .20 .50
247 Alex Gonzalez .20 .50
248 Roberto Alomar .50 1.25
249 Ruben Rivera .20 .50
250 Eric Chavez .30 .75
251 Ellis Burks .30 .75
252 Richie Sexson .30 .75
253 Steve Finley .30 .75
254 Dwight Gooden .30 .75
255 Dustin Hermanson .20 .50
256 Kirk Rueter .20 .50
257 Steve Trachsel .20 .50
258 Gregg Jefferies .20 .50
259 Matt Stairs .20 .50
260 Shane Reynolds .20 .50
261 Gregg Olson .20 .50
262 Kevin Tapani .20 .50
263 Matt Morris .30 .75
264 Carl Pavano .30 .75
265 Nomar Garciaparra 1.25 3.00
266 Kevin Young .30 .75
267 Rick Helling .20 .50
268 Matt Franco .20 .50
269 Brian McRae .20 .50
270 Cal Ripken 2.50 6.00
271 Jeff Abbott .20 .50
272 Tony Batista .20 .50
273 Bill Simas .20 .50
274 Brian Hunter .20 .50
275 John Franco .30 .75
276 Devon White .30 .75
277 Rickey Henderson .75 2.00
278 Chuck Finley .30 .75
279 Mike Blowers .20 .50
280 Mark Grace .50 1.25
281 Randy Winn .20 .50
282 Bobby Bonilla .30 .75
283 David Justice .30 .75
284 Shane Monahan .20 .50
285 Kevin Brown .50 1.25
286 Todd Zeile .30 .75
287 Al Martin .20 .50
288 Troy O'Leary .20 .50
289 Darryl Hamilton .20 .50
290 Tino Martinez .50 1.25
291 David Ortiz .75 2.00
292 Tony Clark .20 .50
293 Ryan Minor .20 .50
294 Mark Leiter .20 .50
295 Wally Joyner .30 .75
296 Cliff Floyd .30 .75
297 Shawn Estes .20 .50
298 Pat Hentgen .20 .50
299 Scott Elarton .20 .50
300 Alex Rodriguez 1.25 3.00
301 Ozzie Guillen .30 .75
302 Hideo Nomo .75 2.00
303 Ryan McGuire .20 .50
304 Brad Ausmus .30 .75
305 Alex Gonzalez .20 .50
306 Brian Jordan .30 .75
307 John Jaha .30 .75
308 Mark Grudzielanek .20 .50
309 Juan Guzman .20 .50
310 Tony Womack .20 .50
311 Dennis Reyes .20 .50
312 Marty Cordova .20 .50
313 Ramiro Mendoza .20 .50
314 Robin Ventura .30 .75
315 Rafael Palmeiro .50 1.25
316 Ramon Martinez .20 .50
317 Pedro Astacio .20 .50
318 Dave Hollins .20 .50
319 Tom Candiotti .20 .50
320 Al Leiter .30 .75
321 Rico Brogna .20 .50
322 Reggie Jefferson .20 .50
323 Bernard Gilkey .20 .50
324 Jason Giambi .30 .75
325 Craig Biggio .50 1.25
326 Troy Glaus .50 1.25
327 Delino DeShields .20 .50
328 Fernando Vina .20 .50
329 John Smoltz .50 1.25
330 Jeff Kent .30 .75
331 Roy Halladay .30 .75
332 Andy Ashby .20 .50
333 Tim Wakefield .30 .75
334 Roger Clemens 1.50 4.00
335 Bernie Williams .50 1.25
336 Desi Relaford .20 .50
337 John Burkett .20 .50
338 Mike Hampton .30 .75
339 Royce Clayton .20 .50
340 Mike Piazza 1.25 3.00
341 Jeremi Gonzalez .20 .50
342 Mike Lansing .20 .50
343 Jamie Moyer .30 .75
344 Ron Coomer .20 .50
345 Barry Larkin .50 1.25
346 Fernando Tatis .20 .50
347 Chili Davis .30 .75
348 Bobby Higginson .30 .75
349 Hal Morris .20 .50
350 Larry Walker .30 .75
351 Carlos Guillen .30 .75
352 Miguel Tejada .30 .75
353 Travis Fryman .30 .75
354 Jarrod Washburn .20 .50
355 Chipper Jones .75 2.00
356 Todd Stottlemyre .20 .50
357 Henry Rodriguez .20 .50
358 Eli Marrero .20 .50
359 Alan Benes .20 .50
360 Tim Salmon .50 1.25
361 Luis Gonzalez .30 .75
362 Scott Spiezio .20 .50
363 Chris Carpenter .30 .75
364 Bobby Howry .20 .50
365 Raul Mondesi .30 .75
366 Ugueth Urbina .20 .50
367 Tom Evans .20 .50
368 Kerry Ligtenberg RC .30 .75
369 Adrian Beltre .30 .75
370 Ryan Klesko .30 .75
371 Wilson Alvarez .20 .50
372 John Thomson .20 .50
373 Tony Saunders .20 .50
374 Dave Mlicki .20 .50
375 Ken Caminiti .30 .75
376 Jay Buhner .30 .75
377 Bill Mueller .30 .75
378 Jeff Blauser .20 .50
379 Edgar Renteria .30 .75
380 Jim Thome .50 1.25
381 Joey Hamilton .20 .50
382 Calvin Pickering .20 .50
383 Marquis Grissom .30 .75
384 Omar Daal .20 .50
385 Curt Schilling .30 .75
386 Jose Cruz Jr. .20 .50
387 Chris Widger .20 .50
388 Pete Harnisch .20 .50
389 Charles Nagy .20 .50
390 Tom Gordon .20 .50
391 Bobby Smith .20 .50
392 Derrick Gibson .20 .50
393 Jeff Conine .30 .75
394 Carlos Perez .20 .50
395 Barry Bonds 2.00 5.00
396 Mark McLemore .20 .50
397 Juan Encarnacion .20 .50
398 Wade Boggs .50 1.25
399 Ivan Rodriguez .50 1.25
400 Moises Alou .30 .75
401 Jeromy Burnitz .30 .75
402 Sean Casey .30 .75
403 Jose Offerman .20 .50
404 Joe Fontenot .20 .50
405 Kevin Millwood .30 .75
406 Lance Johnson .20 .50
407 Richard Hidalgo .20 .50
408 Mike Jackson .20 .50
409 Brian Anderson .20 .50
410 Jeff Shaw .20 .50
411 Preston Wilson .30 .75
412 Todd Hundley .20 .50
413 Jim Parque .20 .50
414 Justin Baughman .20 .50
415 Dante Bichette .30 .75
416 Paul O'Neill .50 1.25
417 Miguel Cairo .20 .50
418 Randy Johnson .75 2.00
419 Jesus Sanchez .20 .50
420 Carlos Delgado .30 .75
421 Ricky Ledee .20 .50
422 Orlando Hernandez .30 .75
423 Frank Thomas .75 2.00
424 Pokey Reese .20 .50
425 Carlos Lee .40 1.00
Mike Lowell
Kit Pellow RC
426 Michael Cuddyer .40 1.00
Mark DeRosa
Jerry Hairston Jr.
427 Marlon Anderson .40 1.00
Ron Belliard
Orlando Cabrera
428 Micah Bowie .40 1.00
Phil Norton RC
Randy Wolf
429 Jack Cressend RC .40 1.00
Jason Rakers
John Rocker
430 Ruben Mateo .40 1.00
Scott Morgan
Mike Zywica RC
431 Jason LaRue .40 1.00
Matt LeCroy
Mitch Meluskey
432 Gabe Kapler .40 1.00
Armando Rios
Fernando Seguignol
433 Adam Kennedy .40 1.00
Mickey Lopez RC
Jackie Rexrode
434 Jose Fernandez RC .40 1.00
Jeff Liefer
Chris Truby
435 Corey Koskie .60 1.50
Doug Mientkiewicz RC
Damon Minor
436 Roosevelt Brown RC .40 1.00
Dernell Stenson
Vernon Wells
437 A.J. Burnett RC .75 2.00
Billy Koch
John Nicholson
438 Matt Belisle .40 1.00
Matt Roney RC
439 Austin Kearns 1.50 4.00
Chris George RC
440 Nate Bump RC .40 1.00
Nate Cornejo
441 Brad Lidge 1.50 4.00
Mike Nannini RC
442 Matt Holliday 3.00 8.00
Jeff Winchester RC
443 Adam Everett .60 1.50
Chip Ambres RC
444 Pat Burrell 1.50 4.00
Eric Valent RC
445 Roger Clemens SK .75 2.00
446 Kerry Wood SK .20 .50
447 Curt Schilling SK .20 .50
448 Randy Johnson SK .50 1.25
449 Pedro Martinez SK .50 1.25
450 Jeff Bagwell AT .75 2.00
Andres Galarraga
Mark McGwire
451 John Olerud AT .30 .75
Jim Thome
Tino Martinez
452 Alex Rodriguez AT 1.00 2.50
Nomar Garciaparra
Derek Jeter
453 Vinny Castilla AT .50 1.25
Chipper Jones
Scott Rolen
454 Sammy Sosa AT .75 2.00
Ken Griffey Jr.
Juan Gonzalez
455 Barry Bonds AT 1.00 2.50
Manny Ramirez
Larry Walker
456 Frank Thomas AT .75 2.00
Tim Salmon
David Justice
457 Travis Lee AT .30 .75
Todd Helton
Ben Grieve
458 Vladimir Guerrero AT .30 .75
Greg Vaughn
Bernie Williams
459 Mike Piazza AT .75 2.00
Ivan Rodriguez
Jason Kendall
460 Roger Clemens AT .75 2.00
Kerry Wood
Greg Maddux
461A Sammy Sosa HR 1 8.00 20.00
461B Sammy Sosa HR 2 5.00 12.00
461C Sammy Sosa HR 3 5.00 12.00
461D Sammy Sosa HR 4 5.00 12.00
461E Sammy Sosa HR 5 5.00 12.00
461F Sammy Sosa HR 6 5.00 12.00
461G Sammy Sosa HR 7 5.00 12.00
461H Sammy Sosa HR 8 5.00 12.00
461I Sammy Sosa HR 9 5.00 12.00
461J Sammy Sosa HR 10 5.00 12.00
461K Sammy Sosa HR 11 5.00 12.00
461L Sammy Sosa HR 12 5.00 12.00
461M Sammy Sosa HR 13 5.00 12.00
461N Sammy Sosa HR 14 5.00 12.00
461O Sammy Sosa HR 15 5.00 12.00
461P Sammy Sosa HR 16 5.00 12.00
461Q Sammy Sosa HR 17 5.00 12.00
461R Sammy Sosa HR 18 5.00 12.00
461S Sammy Sosa HR 19 5.00 12.00
461T Sammy Sosa HR 20 5.00 12.00
461U Sammy Sosa HR 21 5.00 12.00
461V Sammy Sosa HR 22 5.00 12.00
461W Sammy Sosa HR 23 5.00 12.00
461X Sammy Sosa HR 24 5.00 12.00
461Y Sammy Sosa HR 25 5.00 12.00
461Z Sammy Sosa HR 26 5.00 12.00
461AA S.Sosa HR 27 5.00 12.00
461AB S.Sosa HR 28 5.00 12.00
461AC S.Sosa HR 29 5.00 12.00
461AD S.Sosa HR 30 5.00 12.00
461AE S.Sosa HR 31 5.00 12.00
461AF S.Sosa HR 32 5.00 12.00
461AG S.Sosa HR 33 5.00 12.00
461AH S.Sosa HR 34 5.00 12.00
461AI S.Sosa HR 35 5.00 12.00
461AJ S.Sosa HR 36 5.00 12.00
461AK S.Sosa HR 37 5.00 12.00
461AL S.Sosa HR 38 5.00 12.00
461AM S.Sosa HR 39 5.00 12.00
461AN S.Sosa HR 40 5.00 12.00
461AO S.Sosa HR 41 5.00 12.00
461AP S.Sosa HR 42 5.00 12.00
461AR S.Sosa HR 43 5.00 12.00
461AS S.Sosa HR 44 5.00 12.00
461AT S.Sosa HR 45 5.00 12.00
461AU S.Sosa HR 46 5.00 12.00
461AV S.Sosa HR 47 5.00 12.00
461AW S.Sosa HR 48 5.00 12.00
461AX S.Sosa HR 49 5.00 12.00
461AY S.Sosa HR 50 5.00 12.00
461AZ S.Sosa HR 51 5.00 12.00
461BB S.Sosa HR 52 5.00 12.00
461CC S.Sosa HR 53 5.00 12.00
461DD S.Sosa HR 54 5.00 12.00
461EE S.Sosa HR 55 5.00 12.00
461FF S.Sosa HR 56 5.00 12.00
461GG S.Sosa HR 57 5.00 12.00
461HH S.Sosa HR 58 5.00 12.00
461II S.Sosa HR 59 5.00 12.00
461JJ S.Sosa HR 60 5.00 12.00
461KK S.Sosa HR 61 8.00 20.00
461LL S.Sosa HR 62 12.50 30.00
461MM S.Sosa HR 63 8.00 20.00
461NN S.Sosa HR 64 8.00 20.00
461OO S.Sosa HR 65 8.00 20.00
461PP S.Sosa HR 66 30.00 60.00
462 Checklist .20 .50
463 Checklist .20 .50

1999 Topps Chrome Refractors

Randomly inserted in packs at the rate of one in 12, this 462-card set is parallel to the base set and is similar in design. The difference is found in the refractive quality of the card. It's estimated that only around 15 to 25 of each McGwire number 220 refractor was produced.

*STARS: 2.5X TO 6X BASIC CARDS
*ROOKIES: 1.25X TO 3X BASIC CARDS
MCGWIRE 220 HR 1 125.00 250.00
MCGWIRE 220 HR 2-60 60.00 120.00
MCGWIRE 220 HR 61 100.00 200.00
MCGWIRE 220 HR 62 150.00 300.00
MCGWIRE 220 HR 63-69 60.00 120.00
MCGWIRE 220 HR 70 200.00 400.00
SOSA 461 HR 1 30.00 60.00
SOSA 461 HR 2-60 10.00 25.00
SOSA 461 HR 61 20.00 50.00
SOSA 461 HR 62 40.00 80.00
SOSA 461 HR 63-65 10.00 25.00
SOSA 461 HR 66 60.00 120.00
442 Matt Holliday 15.00 40.00
Jeff Winchester

1999 Topps Chrome All-Etch

Randomly inserted in Series two packs at the rate of one in six, this 30-card set features color player photos printed on All-Etch technology. A refractive parallel version of this set was also produced with an insertion rate of 1:24 packs.

COMPLETE SET (30) 40.00 100.00
*REFRACTORS: .75X TO 2X BASIC ALL-ETCH
SER.2 REFRACTOR ODDS 1:24
AE1 Mark McGwire 5.00 12.00
AE2 Sammy Sosa 2.00 5.00
AE3 Ken Griffey Jr. 3.00 8.00
AE4 Greg Vaughn .50 1.25
AE5 Albert Belle .75 2.00
AE6 Vinny Castilla .75 2.00
AE7 Jose Canseco 1.25 3.00
AE8 Juan Gonzalez .75 2.00
AE9 Manny Ramirez 1.25 3.00
AE10 Andres Galarraga .75 2.00
AE11 Rafael Palmeiro 1.25 3.00
AE12 Alex Rodriguez 3.00 8.00
AE13 Mo Vaughn .75 2.00
AE14 Eric Chavez .75 2.00
AE15 Gabe Kapler 1.00 2.50
AE16 Calvin Pickering .50 1.25
AE17 Ruben Mateo 1.00 2.50
AE18 Roy Halladay 1.00 2.50
AE19 Jeremy Giambi .50 1.25
AE20 Alex Gonzalez .50 1.25
AE21 Ron Belliard 1.00 2.50
AE22 Marlon Anderson 1.00 2.50
AE23 Carlos Lee 1.00 2.50
AE24 Kerry Wood .75 2.00
AE25 Roger Clemens 4.00 10.00
AE26 Curt Schilling .75 2.00
AE27 Kevin Brown 1.25 3.00
AE28 Randy Johnson 2.00 5.00
AE29 Pedro Martinez 1.25 3.00
AE30 Orlando Hernandez .75 2.00

1999 Topps Chrome Early Road to the Hall

Randomly inserted in Series one packs at the rate of one in 12, this 10-card set features color photos of ten players with less than 10 years in the Majors but are already headed towards the Hall of Fame in Cooperstown, New York.

COMPLETE SET (10) 25.00 60.00
*REFRACTORS: 3X TO 8X BASIC ROAD
SER.1 REFRACTOR ODDS 1:944 HOBBY
REF.PRINT RUN 100 SERIAL #'d SETS
ER1 Nomar Garciaparra 3.00 8.00
ER2 Derek Jeter 5.00 12.00
ER3 Alex Rodriguez 3.00 8.00
ER4 Juan Gonzalez .75 2.00
ER5 Ken Griffey Jr. 3.00 8.00
ER6 Chipper Jones 2.00 5.00
ER7 Vladimir Guerrero 2.00 5.00
ER8 Jeff Bagwell 1.25 3.00
ER9 Ivan Rodriguez 1.25 3.00
ER10 Frank Thomas 2.00 5.00

1999 Topps Chrome Fortune 15

Randomly inserted into Series two packs at the rate of one in 12, this 15-card set features color photos of the League's most elite veteran and rookie players. A refractor parallel version of this set was also produced with an insertion rate of 1:627 packs and sequentially numnbered to 100.

COMPLETE SET (15) 40.00 100.00
*REFRACTORS: 4X TO 8X BASIC FORT.15
5.00
SER.2 REFRACTOR ODDS 1:627
REF.PRINT RUN 100 SERIAL #'d SETS
FF1 Alex Rodriguez 3.00 8.00
FF2 Nomar Garciaparra 3.00 8.00
FF3 Derek Jeter 5.00 12.00
FF4 Troy Glaus 1.25 3.00
FF5 Ken Griffey Jr. 3.00 8.00
FF6 Vladimir Guerrero 2.00 5.00
FF7 Kerry Wood .75 2.00
FF8 Eric Chavez .75 2.00
FF9 Greg Maddux 3.00 8.00
FF10 Mike Piazza 3.00 8.00
FF11 Sammy Sosa 2.00 5.00
FF12 Mark McGwire 5.00 12.00
FF13 Ben Grieve .50 1.25
FF14 Chipper Jones 2.00 5.00
FF15 Manny Ramirez 1.25 3.00

1999 Topps Chrome Lords of the Diamond

Randomly inserted in Series one packs at the rate of one in eight, this 15-card set features color photos of some of the true masters of the ballfield. A refractive parallel version of this set was also produced with an insertion rate of 1:24.

COMPLETE SET (15) 20.00 50.00
*REFRACTORS: .6X TO 1.5X BASIC LORDS
SER.1 REFRACTOR ODDS 1:24
LD1 Ken Griffey Jr. 1.50 4.00
LD2 Chipper Jones 1.00 2.50
LD3 Sammy Sosa 1.00 2.50
LD4 Frank Thomas 1.00 2.50
LD5 Mark McGwire 2.50 6.00
LD6 Jeff Bagwell .60 1.50
LD7 Alex Rodriguez 1.50 4.00
LD8 Juan Gonzalez .40 1.00
LD9 Barry Bonds 2.50 6.00
LD10 Nomar Garciaparra 1.50 4.00
LD11 Darin Erstad .40 1.00
LD12 Tony Gwynn 1.25 3.00
LD13 Andres Galarraga .40 1.00
LD14 Mike Piazza 1.50 4.00
LD15 Greg Maddux 1.50 4.00

1999 Topps Chrome New Breed

Randomly inserted in Series one packs at the rate of one in 24, this 15-card set features color photos of some of today's young stars in Major League Baseball. A refractive parallel version of this set was also produced with an insertion rate of 1:72.

COMPLETE SET (15) 40.00 100.00
*REFRACTORS: .6X TO 1.5X BASIC BREED
SER.1 REFRACTOR ODDS 1:72
NB1 Darin Erstad 1.25 3.00
NB2 Brad Fullmer .75 2.00
NB3 Kerry Wood 1.25 3.00
NB4 Nomar Garciaparra 5.00 12.00
NB5 Travis Lee .75 2.00
NB6 Scott Rolen 2.00 5.00
NB7 Todd Helton 2.00 5.00
NB8 Vladimir Guerrero 3.00 8.00
NB9 Derek Jeter 8.00 20.00
NB10 Alex Rodriguez 5.00 12.00
NB11 Ben Grieve .75 2.00
NB12 Andruw Jones 2.00 5.00
NB13 Paul Konerko 1.25 3.00
NB14 Aramis Ramirez 1.25 3.00
NB15 Adrian Beltre 1.25 3.00

1999 Topps Chrome Record Numbers

Randomly inserted in Series two packs at the rate of one in 36, this 10-card set features color photos of top Major League record-setters. A refractive parallel version of this set was also produced with an insertion rate of 1:144.

COMPLETE SET (10) 60.00 150.00
*REFRACTORS: .75X TO 2X BASIC REC.NUM.
SER.2 REFRACTOR ODDS 1:144
RN1 Mark McGwire 8.00 20.00

RN2 Mike Piazza 5.00 12.00
RN3 Curt Schilling 1.25 3.00
RN4 Ken Griffey Jr. 5.00 12.00
RN5 Sammy Sosa 3.00 8.00
RN6 Nomar Garciaparra 5.00 12.00
RN7 Kerry Wood 1.25 3.00
RN8 Roger Clemens 6.00 15.00
RN9 Cal Ripken 10.00 25.00
RN10 Mark McGwire 8.00 20.00

1999 Topps Chrome Traded

This 121-card set features color photos on Chromium cards of 46 of the most notable transactions of the 1999 season and 75 newcomers accented with the Topps "Rookie Card" logo. The set was distributed only in factory boxes. Due to a very late ship date (January, 2000) this set caused some commotion in the hobby as to its status as a 1999 or 2000 product. Notable Rookie Cards include Carl Crawford, Adam Dunn, Josh Hamilton, Corey Patterson and Alfonso Soriano.

COMP.FACT SET (121) 50.00 100.00
T1 Seth Etherton .15 .40
T2 Mark Harriger RC .20 .50
T3 Matt Wise RC .20 .50
T4 Carlos E. Hernandez RC .30 .75
T5 Julio Lugo RC .50 1.25
T6 Mike Nannini .15 .40
T7 Justin Bowles RC .20 .50
T8 Mark Mulder RC 1.25 3.00
T9 Roberto Vaz RC .20 .50
T10 Felipe Lopez RC 1.25 3.00
T11 Matt Belisle .15 .40
T12 Micah Bowie .15 .40
T13 Ruben Quevedo RC .20 .50
T14 Jose Garcia RC .20 .50
T15 David Kelton RC .20 .50
T16 Phil Norton .15 .40
T17 Corey Patterson RC .75 2.00
T18 Ron Walker RC .20 .50
T19 Paul Hoover RC .20 .50
T20 Ryan Rupe RC .20 .50
T21 J.D. Closser RC .30 .75
T22 Rob Ryan RC .20 .50
T23 Steve Colyer RC .20 .50
T24 Bubba Crosby RC .50 1.25
T25 Luke Prokopec RC .20 .50
T26 Matt Blank RC .20 .50
T27 Josh McKinley .15 .40
T28 Nate Bump .20 .50
T29 G.Chiaramonte RC .20 .50
T30 Arturo McDowell .15 .40
T31 Tony Torcato .15 .40
T32 Dave Roberts RC .50 1.25
T33 C.C. Sabathia RC 2.00 5.00
T34 Sean Spencer RC .20 .50
T35 Chip Ambres .15 .40
T36 A.J. Burnett .75 2.00
T37 Mo Bruce RC .20 .50
T38 Jason Tyner .15 .40
T39 Mamon Tucker .15 .40
T40 Sean Burroughs RC .50 1.25
T41 Kevin Eberwein RC .20 .50
T42 Junior Herndon RC .20 .50
T43 Bryan Wolff RC .20 .50
T44 Pat Burrell 1.25 3.00
T45 Eric Valent .30 .75
T46 Carlos Pena RC .40 1.00
T47 Mike Zywica .15 .40
T48 Adam Everett .40 1.00
T49 Juan Pena RC .20 .50
T50 Adam Dunn RC 3.00 8.00
T51 Austin Kearns 1.25 3.00
T52 Jacobo Sequea RC .20 .50
T53 Choo Freeman .25 .60
T54 Jeff Winchester .15 .40
T55 Matt Burch .20 .50
T56 Chris George .15 .40
T57 Scott Mullen RC .20 .50
T58 Kit Pellow .20 .50
T59 Mark Quinn RC .20 .50
T60 Nate Cornejo .20 .50
T61 Ryan Mills .15 .40
T62 Kevin Beirne RC .20 .50
T63 Kip Wells RC .30 .75
T64 Juan Rivera RC .75 2.00
T65 Alfonso Soriano RC 4.00 10.00
T66 Josh Hamilton RC 6.00 15.00
T67 Josh Girdley RC .20 .50
T68 Kyle Snyder RC .20 .50
T69 Mike Paradis RC .20 .50
T70 Jason Jennings RC .50 1.25
T71 David Walling RC .20 .50
T72 Omar Ortiz RC .20 .50
T73 Jay Gehrke RC .20 .50
T74 Casey Burns RC .20 .50
T75 Carl Crawford RC 3.00 8.00
T76 Reggie Sanders .25 .60
T77 Will Clark .40 1.00
T78 David Wells .25 .60
T79 Paul Konerko .25 .60
T80 Armando Benitez .25 .60
T81 Brant Brown .15 .40

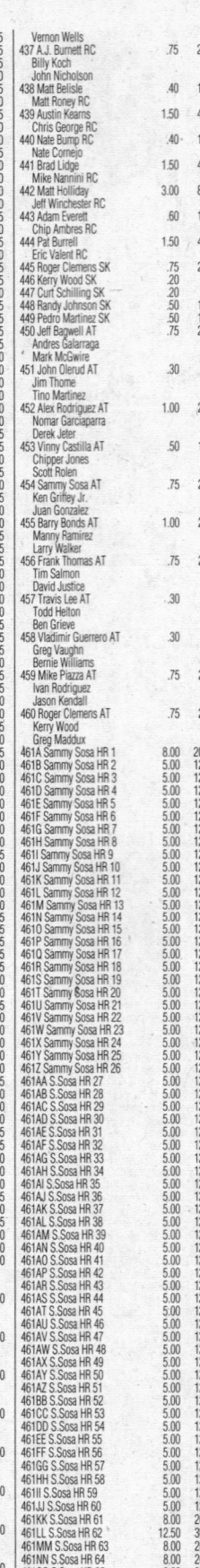

Card	Low	High
T82 Mo Vaughn	.25	.60
T83 Jose Canseco	.40	1.00
T84 Albert Belle	.25	.60
T85 Dean Palmer	.25	.60
T86 Greg Vaughn	.15	.40
T87 Mark Clark	.15	.40
T88 Pat Meares	.15	.40
T89 Eric Davis	.25	.60
T90 Brian Giles	.25	.60
T91 Jeff Brantley	.15	.40
T92 Bret Boone	.25	.60
T93 Ron Gant	.25	.60
T94 Mike Cameron	.15	.40
T95 Charles Johnson	.25	.60
T96 Denny Neagle	.15	.40
T97 Brian Hunter	.15	.40
T98 Jose Hernandez	.15	.40
T99 Rick Aguilera	.15	.40
T100 Tony Batista	.15	.40
T101 Roger Cedeno	.15	.40
T102 C.Gubanich RC	.20	.50
T103 Tim Belcher	.15	.40
T104 Bruce Aven	.15	.40
T105 Brian Daubach RC	.30	.75
T106 Ed Sprague	.15	.40
T107 Michael Tucker	.15	.40
T108 Homer Bush	.15	.40
T109 Armando Reynoso	.15	.40
T110 Brook Fordyce	.15	.40
T111 Matt Mantei	.15	.40
T112 Dave Mlicki	.15	.40
T113 Kenny Rogers	.25	.60
T114 Livan Hernandez	.25	.60
T115 Butch Huskey	.15	.40
T116 David Segui	.15	.40
T117 Darryl Hamilton	.15	.40
T118 Terry Mulholland	.15	.40
T119 Randy Velarde	.15	.40
T120 Bill Taylor	.15	.40
T121 Kevin Appier	.25	.60

2000 Topps Chrome

These cards parallel the regular Topps set and are issued using Topps' Chromium technology and color metallization. The first series product was released in February, 2000 and second series in May, 2000. Four card packs for each series carried an SRP of $3.00. Similar to the regular set, no card number 7 was issued and a Mark McGwire rookie reprint card was also inserted into packs. Also, like the base Topps set all of the Magic Moments subset cards (235-239 and 475-479) are available in five variations - each detailing a different highlight in the featured player's career. The base Chrome set is considered complete with any of the Magic Moments variations (for each player). Notable Rookie Cards include Rick Asadoorian, Ben Sheets and Barry Zito.

Card	Low	High
COMPLETE SET (478)	60.00	160.00
COMP. SERIES 1 (240)	30.00	80.00
COMP. SERIES 2 (240)	30.00	80.00
MCGWIRE MM SET (5)	20.00	50.00
AARON MM SET (5)	15.00	40.00
RIPKEN MM SET (5)	25.00	60.00
BOGGS MM SET (5)	5.00	12.00
GWYNN MM SET (5)	10.00	25.00
GRIFFEY MM SET (5)	12.50	30.00
BONDS MM SET (5)	20.00	50.00
SOSA MM SET (5)	12.50	30.00
JETER MM SET (5)	20.00	50.00
A.ROD MM SET (5)	15.00	40.00
1 Mark McGwire	2.00	5.00
2 Tony Gwynn	1.00	2.50
3 Wade Boggs	.50	1.25
4 Cal Ripken	2.50	6.00
5 Matt Williams	.30	.75
6 Jay Buhner	.30	.75
7 Does Not Exist		
8 Jeff Conine	.30	.75
9 Todd Greene	.30	.75
10 Mike Lieberthal	.30	.75
11 Steve Avery	.30	.75
12 Bret Saberhagen	.30	.75
13 Magglio Ordonez	.30	.75
14 Brad Radke	.30	.75
15 Derek Jeter	2.00	5.00
16 Javy Lopez	.30	.75
17 Russ Davis	.30	.75
18 Armando Benitez	.30	.75
19 B.J. Surhoff	.30	.75
20 Darryl Kile	.30	.75
21 Mark Lewis	.30	.75
22 Mike Williams	.30	.75
23 Mark McLemore	.30	.75
24 Sterling Hitchcock	.30	.75
25 Darin Erstad	.30	.75
26 Ricky Gutierrez	.30	.75
27 John Jaha	.30	.75
28 Homer Bush	.30	.75
29 Darrin Fletcher	.30	.75
30 Mark Grace	.50	1.25
31 Fred McGriff	.50	1.25
32 Omar Daal	.30	.75
33 Eric Karros	.30	.75
34 Orlando Cabrera	.30	.75
35 J.T. Snow	.30	.75
36 Luis Castillo	.30	.75
37 Rey Ordonez	.30	.75
38 Bob Abreu	.30	.75
39 Warren Morris	.30	.75
40 Juan Gonzalez	.30	.75
41 Mike Lansing	.30	.75
42 Chili Davis	.30	.75
43 Dean Palmer	.30	.75
44 Hank Aaron	1.50	4.00
45 Jeff Bagwell	.50	1.25
46 Jose Valentin	.30	.75
47 Shannon Stewart	.30	.75
48 Kent Bottenfield	.30	.75
49 Jeff Shaw	.30	.75
50 Sammy Sosa	.75	2.00
51 Randy Johnson	.75	2.00
52 Benny Agbayani	.30	.75
53 Dante Bichette	.30	.75
54 Pete Harnisch	.30	.75
55 Frank Thomas	.75	2.00
56 Jorge Posada	.50	1.25
57 Todd Walker	.30	.75
58 Juan Encarnacion	.30	.75
59 Mike Sweeney	.30	.75
60 Pedro Martinez	.50	1.25
61 Lee Stevens	.30	.75
62 Brian Giles	.30	.75
63 Chad Ogea	.30	.75
64 Ivan Rodriguez	.50	1.25
65 Roger Cedeno	.30	.75
66 David Justice	.30	.75
67 Steve Trachsel	.30	.75
68 Eli Marrero	.30	.75
69 Dave Nilsson	.30	.75
70 Ken Caminiti	.30	.75
71 Tim Raines	.30	.75
72 Brian Jordan	.30	.75
73 Jeff Blauser	.30	.75
74 Bernard Gilkey	.30	.75
75 John Flaherty	.30	.75
76 Brent Mayne	.30	.75
77 Jose Vidro	.30	.75
78 David Bell	.30	.75
79 Bruce Aven	.30	.75
80 John Olerud	.30	.75
81 Pokey Reese	.30	.75
82 Woody Williams	.30	.75
83 Ed Sprague	.30	.75
84 Joe Girardi	.30	.75
85 Barry Larkin	.50	1.25
86 Mike Caruso	.30	.75
87 Bobby Higginson	.30	.75
88 Roberto Kelly	.30	.75
89 Edgar Martinez	.50	1.25
90 Mark Kotsay	.30	.75
91 Paul Sorrento	.30	.75
92 Eric Young	.30	.75
93 Carlos Delgado	.30	.75
94 Troy Glaus	.30	.75
95 Ben Grieve	.30	.75
96 Jose Lima	.30	.75
97 Garret Anderson	.30	.75
98 Luis Gonzalez	.30	.75
99 Carl Pavano	.30	.75
100 Alex Rodriguez	1.25	3.00
101 Preston Wilson	.30	.75
102 Ron Gant	.30	.75
103 Brady Anderson	.30	.75
104 Rickey Henderson	.75	2.00
105 Gary Sheffield	.30	.75
106 Mickey Morandini	.30	.75
107 Jim Edmonds	.30	.75
108 Kris Benson	.30	.75
109 Adrian Beltre	.30	.75
110 Alex Fernandez	.30	.75
111 Dan Wilson	.30	.75
112 Mark Clark	.30	.75
113 Greg Vaughn	.30	.75
114 Neifi Perez	.30	.75
115 Paul O'Neill	.50	1.25
116 Jermaine Dye	.30	.75
117 Todd Jones	.30	.75
118 Terry Steinbach	.30	.75
119 Greg Norton	.30	.75
120 Curt Schilling	.30	.75
121 Todd Zeile	.30	.75
122 Edgardo Alfonzo	.30	.75
123 Ryan McGuire	.30	.75
124 Rich Aurilia	.30	.75
125 John Smoltz	.50	1.25
126 Bob Wickman	.30	.75
127 Richard Hidalgo	.30	.75
128 Chuck Finley	.30	.75
129 Billy Wagner	.30	.75
130 Todd Hundley	.30	.75
131 Dwight Gooden	.30	.75
132 Russ Ortiz	.30	.75
133 Mike Lowell	.30	.75
134 Reggie Sanders	.30	.75
135 John Valentin	.30	.75
136 Brad Ausmus	.30	.75
137 Chad Kreuter	.30	.75
138 David Cone	.30	.75
139 Brook Fordyce	.30	.75
140 Roberto Alomar	.50	1.25
141 Charles Nagy	.30	.75
142 Brian Hunter	.30	.75
143 Mike Mussina	.50	1.25
144 Robin Ventura	.50	1.25
145 Kevin Brown	.50	1.25
146 Pat Hentgen	.30	.75
147 Ryan Klesko	.30	.75
148 Derek Bell	.30	.75
149 Andy Sheets	.30	.75
150 Larry Walker	.30	.75
151 Scott Williamson	.30	.75
152 Jose Offerman	.30	.75
153 Doug Mientkiewicz	.30	.75
154 John Snyder RC	.40	1.00
155 Sandy Alomar Jr.	.30	.75
156 Joe Nathan	.30	.75
157 Lance Johnson	.30	.75
158 Odalis Perez	.30	.75
159 Hideo Nomo	.75	2.00
160 Steve Finley	.30	.75
161 Dave Martinez	.30	.75
162 Matt Walbeck	.30	.75
163 Bill Spiers	.30	.75
164 Fernando Tatis	.30	.75
165 Kenny Lofton	.30	.75
166 Paul Byrd	.30	.75
167 Aaron Sele	.30	.75
168 Eddie Taubensee	.30	.75
169 Reggie Jefferson	.30	.75
170 Roger Clemens	1.50	4.00
171 Francisco Cordova	.30	.75
172 Mike Bordick	.30	.75
173 Wally Joyner	.30	.75
174 Marvin Benard	.30	.75
175 Jason Kendall	.30	.75
176 Mike Stanley	.30	.75
177 Chad Allen	.30	.75
178 Carlos Beltran	.30	.75
179 Deivi Cruz	.30	.75
180 Chipper Jones	.75	2.00
181 Vladimir Guerrero	.75	2.00
182 Dave Burba	.30	.75
183 Tom Goodwin	.30	.75
184 Brian Daubach	.30	.75
185 Jay Bell	.30	.75
186 Roy Halladay	.30	.75
187 Miguel Tejada	.30	.75
188 Armando Rios	.30	.75
189 Fernando Vina	.30	.75
190 Eric Davis	.30	.75
191 Henry Rodriguez	.30	.75
192 Joe McEwing	.30	.75
193 Jeff Kent	.30	.75
194 Mike Jackson	.30	.75
195 Mike Morgan	.30	.75
196 Jeff Montgomery	.30	.75
197 Jeff Zimmerman	.30	.75
198 Tony Fernandez	.30	.75
199 Jason Giambi	.30	.75
200 Jose Canseco	.50	1.25
201 Alex Gonzalez	.30	.75
202 Jack Cust	.40	1.00
Mike Colangelo		
Dee Brown		
203 Felipe Lopez	.75	2.00
Alfonso Soriano		
Pablo Ozuna		
204 Erubiel Durazo	.60	1.50
Pat Burrell		
Nick Johnson		
205 John Sneed RC	.40	1.00
Kip Wells		
Matt Blank		
206 Josh Kalinowski	.40	1.00
Michael Tejera		
Chris Mears RC		
207 Roosevelt Brown	.60	1.50
Corey Patterson		
Lance Berkman		
208 Kit Pellow	.40	1.00
Kevin Barker		
Russ Branyan		
209 B.J. Garbe	1.00	2.50
Larry Bigbie RC		
210 Eric Munson	.40	1.00
Bobby Bradley RC		
211 Josh Girdley	.40	1.00
Kyle Snyder		
212 Chance Caple RC	.40	1.00
Jason Jennings		
213 Ryan Christianson	1.50	4.00
Brett Myers RC		
214 Jason Stumm	.40	1.00
Rob Purvis RC		
215 David Walling	.40	1.00
Mike Paradis		
216 Omar Ortiz	.40	1.00
Jay Gehrke		
217 David Cone HL	.30	.75
218 Jose Jimenez HL	.30	.75
219 Chris Singleton HL	.30	.75
220 Fernando Tatis HL	.30	.75
221 Todd Helton HL	.30	.75
222 Kevin Millwood DIV	.30	.75
223 Todd Pratt DIV	.30	.75
224 Orl. Hernandez DIV	.30	.75
225 Pedro Martinez DIV	.50	1.25
226 Tom Glavine LCS	.30	.75
227 Bernie Williams LCS	.30	.75
228 Mariano Rivera WS	.50	1.25
229 Tony Gwynn 20CB	1.00	2.50
230 Wade Boggs 20CB	.50	1.25
231 Lance Johnson CB	.30	.75
232 Mark McGwire 20CB	2.00	5.00
233 R.Henderson 20CB	.75	2.00
234 R.Henderson 20CB	.75	2.00
235 Roger Clemens 20CB	1.50	4.00
236A Mark McGwire MM	5.00	12.00
1st HR		
236B Mark McGwire MM	5.00	12.00
1987 ROY		
236C Mark McGwire MM	5.00	12.00
62nd HR		
236D Mark McGwire MM	5.00	12.00
70th HR		
236E Mark McGwire MM	5.00	12.00
500th HR		
237A Hank Aaron MM	4.00	10.00
1st Career HR		
237B Hank Aaron MM	4.00	10.00
1957 MVP		
237C Hank Aaron MM	4.00	10.00
3000th Hit		
237D Hank Aaron MM	4.00	10.00
715th HR		
237E Hank Aaron	4.00	10.00
MM 755th HR		
238A Cal Ripken MM	6.00	15.00
1982 ROY		
238B Cal Ripken MM	6.00	15.00
1991 MVP		
238C Cal Ripken MM	6.00	15.00
2131 Game		
238D Cal Ripken MM	6.00	15.00
Streak Ends		
238E Cal Ripken MM	6.00	15.00
400th HR		
239A Wade Boggs MM	1.25	3.00
1983 Batting		
239B Wade Boggs MM	1.25	3.00
1988 Batting		
239C Wade Boggs MM	1.25	3.00
2000th Hit		
239D Wade Boggs MM	1.25	3.00
1996 Champs		
239E Wade Boggs MM	1.25	3.00
3000th Hit		
240A Tony Gwynn MM	2.50	6.00
1984 Batting		
240B Tony Gwynn MM	2.50	6.00
1984 NLCS		
240C Tony Gwynn MM	2.50	6.00
1995 Batting		
240D Tony Gwynn MM	2.50	6.00
1998 NLCS		
240E Tony Gwynn MM	2.50	6.00
3000th Hit		
241 Tom Glavine	.50	1.25
242 David Wells	.30	.75
243 Kevin Appier	.30	.75
244 Troy Percival	.30	.75
245 Ray Lankford	.30	.75
246 Marquis Grissom	.30	.75
247 Randy Winn	.30	.75
248 Miguel Batista	.30	.75
249 Darren Dreifort	.30	.75
250 Barry Bonds	1.50	4.00
251 Harold Baines	.30	.75
252 Cliff Floyd	.30	.75
253 Freddy Garcia	.30	.75
254 Kenny Rogers	.30	.75
255 Ben Davis	.30	.75
256 Charles Johnson	.30	.75
257 Bubba Trammell	.30	.75
258 Desi Relaford	.30	.75
259 Al Martin	.30	.75
260 Andy Pettitte	.50	1.25
261 Carlos Lee	.30	.75
262 Matt Lawton	.30	.75
263 Andy Fox	.30	.75
264 Chan Ho Park	.30	.75
265 Billy Koch	.30	.75
266 Dave Roberts	.30	.75
267 Carl Everett	.30	.75
268 Orel Hershiser	.30	.75
269 Trot Nixon	.30	.75
270 Rusty Greer	.30	.75
271 Will Clark	.50	1.25
272 Quilvio Veras	.30	.75
273 Rico Brogna	.30	.75
274 Devon White	.30	.75
275 Tim Hudson	.30	.75
276 Mike Hampton	.30	.75
277 Miguel Cairo	.30	.75
278 Darren Oliver	.30	.75
279 Jeff Cirillo	.30	.75
280 Al Leiter	.30	.75
281 Shane Andrews	.30	.75
282 Carlos Febles	.30	.75
283 Pedro Astacio	.30	.75
284 Juan Guzman	.30	.75
285 Orlando Hernandez	.30	.75
286 Paul Konerko	.30	.75
287 Tony Clark	.30	.75
288 Aaron Boone	.30	.75
289 Ismael Valdes	.30	.75
290 Moises Alou	.30	.75
291 Kevin Tapani	.30	.75
292 John Franco	.30	.75
293 Todd Zeile	.30	.75
294 Jason Schmidt	.30	.75
295 Johnny Damon	.50	1.25
296 Scott Brosius	.30	.75
297 Travis Fryman	.30	.75
298 Jose Vizcaino	.30	.75
299 Eric Chavez	.30	.75
300 Mike Piazza	1.25	3.00
301 Matt Clement	.30	.75
302 Cristian Guzman	.30	.75
303 C.J. Nitkowski	.30	.75
304 Michael Tucker	.30	.75
305 Brett Tomko	.30	.75
306 Mike Lansing	.30	.75
307 Eric Owens	.30	.75
308 Livan Hernandez	.30	.75
309 Rondell White	.30	.75
310 Todd Stottlemyre	.30	.75
311 Chris Carpenter	.30	.75
312 Ken Hill	.30	.75
313 Mark Loretta	.30	.75
314 John Rocker	.30	.75
315 Richie Sexson	.30	.75
316 Ruben Mateo	.30	.75
317 Joe Randa	.30	.75
318 Mike Sirotka	.30	.75
319 Jose Rosado	.30	.75
320 Matt Mantei	.30	.75
321 Kevin Millwood	.30	.75
322 Gary DiSarcina	.30	.75
323 Dustin Hermanson	.30	.75
324 Mike Stanton	.30	.75
325 Kirk Rueter	.30	.75
326 Damian Miller RC	.60	1.50
327 Doug Glanville	.30	.75
328 Scott Rolen	.50	1.25
329 Ray Durham	.30	.75
330 Butch Huskey	.30	.75
331 Mariano Rivera	.75	2.00
332 Darren Lewis	.30	.75
333 Mike Timlin	.30	.75
334 Mark Grudzielanek	.30	.75
335 Mike Cameron	.30	.75
336 Kelvim Escobar	.30	.75
337 Bret Boone	.30	.75
338 Mo Vaughn	.30	.75
339 Craig Biggio	.50	1.25
340 Michael Barrett	.30	.75
341 Marlon Anderson	.30	.75
342 Bobby Jones	.30	.75
343 John Halama	.30	.75
344 Todd Ritchie	.30	.75
345 Chuck Knoblauch	.30	.75
346 Rick Reed	.30	.75
347 Kelly Stinnett	.30	.75
348 Tim Salmon	.50	1.25
349 A.J. Hinch	.30	.75
350 Jose Cruz Jr.	.30	.75
351 Roberto Hernandez	.30	.75
352 Edgar Renteria	.30	.75
353 Jose Hernandez	.30	.75
354 Brad Fullmer	.30	.75
355 Trevor Hoffman	.50	1.25
356 Troy O'Leary	.30	.75
357 Justin Thompson	.30	.75
358 Kevin Young	.30	.75
359 Hideki Irabu	.30	.75
360 Jim Thome	.50	1.25
361 Steve Karsay	.30	.75
362 Octavio Dotel	.30	.75
363 Omar Vizquel	.50	1.25
364 Raul Mondesi	.30	.75
365 Shane Reynolds	.30	.75
366 Bartolo Colon	.30	.75
367 Chris Widger	.30	.75
368 Gabe Kapler	.30	.75
369 Bill Simas	.30	.75
370 Tino Martinez	.50	1.25
371 John Thomson	.30	.75
372 Delino DeShields	.30	.75
373 Carlos Perez	.30	.75
374 Eddie Perez	.30	.75
375 Jeromy Burnitz	.30	.75
376 Jimmy Haynes	.30	.75
377 Travis Lee	.30	.75
378 Darryl Hamilton	.30	.75
379 Jamie Moyer	.30	.75
380 Alex Gonzalez	.30	.75
381 John Wetteland	.30	.75
382 Vinny Castilla	.30	.75
383 Jeff Suppan	.30	.75
384 Jim Leyritz	.30	.75
385 Robb Nen	.30	.75
386 Wilson Alvarez	.30	.75
387 Andres Galarraga	.30	.75
388 Mike Remlinger	.30	.75
389 Geoff Jenkins	.30	.75
390 Matt Stairs	.30	.75
391 Bill Mueller	.30	.75
392 Mike Lowell	.30	.75
393 Andy Ashby	.30	.75
394 Ruben Rivera	.30	.75
395 Todd Helton	.50	1.25
396 Bernie Williams	.50	1.25
397 Royce Clayton	.30	.75
398 Manny Ramirez	.50	1.25
399 Kerry Wood	.30	.75
400 Ken Griffey Jr.	1.25	3.00
401 Enrique Wilson	.30	.75
402 Joey Hamilton	.30	.75
403 Shawn Estes	.30	.75
404 Ugueth Urbina	.30	.75
405 Albert Belle	.30	.75
406 Rick Helling	.30	.75
407 Steve Parris	.30	.75
408 Eric Milton	.30	.75
409 Dave Mlicki	.30	.75
410 Shawn Green	.30	.75
411 Jaret Wright	.30	.75
412 Tony Womack	.30	.75
413 Vernon Wells	.30	.75
414 Ron Belliard	.30	.75
415 Ellis Burks	.30	.75
416 Scott Erickson	.30	.75
417 Rafael Palmeiro	.50	1.25
418 Damion Easley	.30	.75
419 Jamey Wright	.30	.75
420 Corey Koskie	.30	.75
421 Bobby Howry	.30	.75
422 Ricky Ledee	.30	.75
423 Dmitri Young	.30	.75
424 Sidney Ponson	.30	.75
425 Greg Maddux	1.25	3.00
426 Jose Guillen	.30	.75
427 Jon Lieber	.30	.75
428 Andy Benes	.30	.75
429 Randy Velarde	.30	.75
430 Sean Casey	.30	.75
431 Torii Hunter	.30	.75
432 Ryan Rupe	.30	.75
433 David Segui	.30	.75
434 Todd Pratt	.30	.75
435 Nomar Garciaparra	1.25	3.00
436 Denny Neagle	.30	.75
437 Ron Coomer	.30	.75
438 Chris Singleton	.30	.75
439 Tony Batista	.30	.75
440 Andruw Jones	.50	1.25
441 Aubrey Huff	.30	.75
Sean Burroughs		
Adam Piatt		
442 Rafael Furcal	.60	1.50
Travis Dawkins		
Jason Dellaero		
443 Mike Lamb RC	1.50	4.00
Joe Crede		
Wilton Veras		
444 Julio Zuleta RC	.40	1.00
Jorge Toca		
Dernell Stenson		
445 Garry Maddox Jr. RC	.40	1.00
Gary Matthews Jr.		
Tim Raines Jr.		
446 Mark Mulder	.60	1.50
C.C. Sabathia		
Matt Riley		
447 Scott Downs RC	.40	1.00
Chris George		
Matt Belisle		
448 Doug Mirabelli	.40	1.00
Ben Petrick		
Jayson Werth		
449 Josh Hamilton	.60	1.50
Corey Myers RC		
450 Ben Christensen RC	.40	1.00
Richard Stahl		
451 Ben Sheets RC	4.00	10.00
Barry Zito RC		
452 Kurt Ainsworth	.40	1.00
Ty Howington RC		
453 Vince Faison RC	.60	1.50
Rick Asadoorian		
454 Keith Reed RC	.40	1.00
Jeff Heaverlo		
455 Mike MacDougal	.40	1.00
Brad Baker RC		
456 Mark McGwire SH	1.00	2.50
457 Cal Ripken SH	1.25	3.00
458 Wade Boggs SH	.30	.75
459 Tony Gwynn SH	.50	1.25
460 Jesse Orosco SH	.30	.75
461 Larry Walker	.50	1.25
Nomar Garciaparra LL		
462 Ken Griffey Jr.	.75	2.00
Mark McGwire LL		
463 Manny Ramirez	.75	2.00
Mark McGwire LL		
464 Pedro Martinez	.50	1.25
Randy Johnson LL		
465 Pedro Martinez	.50	1.25
Randy Johnson LL		
466 Derek Jeter	.75	2.00
Luis Gonzalez LL		
467 Larry Walker	.50	1.25
Manny Ramirez LL		
468 Tony Gwynn 20CB	1.00	2.50
469 Mark McGwire 20CB	2.00	5.00
470 Frank Thomas 20CB	.50	1.25
471 Harold Baines 20CB	.30	.75
472 Roger Clemens 20CB	1.50	4.00
473 John Franco 20CB	.30	.75
474 John Franco 20CB	.30	.75
475A Ken Griffey Jr. MM	3.00	8.00
350th HR		
475B Ken Griffey Jr. MM	3.00	8.00
1997 MVP		
475C Ken Griffey Jr. MM	3.00	8.00
HR Dad		
475D Ken Griffey Jr. MM	3.00	8.00
1992 AS MVP		
475E Ken Griffey Jr. MM	3.00	8.00
50 HR 1997		
476A Barry Bonds MM	5.00	12.00
400HR/400SB		
476B Barry Bonds MM	5.00	12.00
40HR/40SB		
476C Barry Bonds MM	5.00	12.00
1993 MVP		
476D Barry Bonds MM	5.00	12.00
1990 MVP		
476E Barry Bonds MM	5.00	12.00
1992 MVP		
477A Sammy Sosa	3.00	8.00
MM 20 HR June		
477B Sammy Sosa MM	3.00	8.00
66 HR 1998		
477C Sammy Sosa MM	3.00	8.00
60 HR 1999		
477D Sammy Sosa MM	3.00	8.00
1998 MVP		
477E Sammy Sosa MM	3.00	8.00
HR's 61/62		
478A Derek Jeter MM	5.00	12.00
1996 ROY		
478B Derek Jeter MM	5.00	12.00
Wins 1999 WS		
478C Derek Jeter MM	5.00	12.00
Wins 1998 WS		
478D Derek Jeter MM	5.00	12.00
Wins 1996 WS		
478E Derek Jeter MM	5.00	12.00
17 GM Hit Streak		
479A Alex Rodriguez MM	4.00	10.00
40HR/40SB		
479B Alex Rodriguez MM	4.00	10.00
100th HR		
479C Alex Rodriguez	4.00	10.00
MM 1996 POY		
479D Alex Rodriguez	4.00	10.00
MM Wins 1 Million		
479E Alex Rodriguez MM	4.00	10.00
1996 Batting Leader		
NNO M.McGwire 85 Reprint	3.00	8.00

2000 Topps Chrome Refractors

These cards which parallel the regular Topps Chrome set were issued at a rate of one in 12 packs. The Mark McGwire rookie reprint card was issued at a rate of one in 12,116 first series packs and are serial numbered to 70.

Card	Low	High
*STARS: 2.5X TO 6X BASIC CARDS		
*PROSPECTS 202-216: 2.5X TO 6X BASIC		
*ROOKIES 202-216: 2X TO 5X BASIC		
*PROSPECTS 441-455: 2.5X TO 6X BASIC		
*ROOKIES 441-455: 2X TO 5X BASIC		
MCGWIRE MM SET (5)	75.00	150.00
MCGWIRE MM (236A-236E)	15.00	40.00
AARON MM SET (5)	60.00	120.00
AARON MM (237A-237E)	12.50	30.00
RIPKEN MM SET (5)	100.00	200.00
RIPKEN MM (238A-238E)	20.00	50.00
BOGGS MM SET (5)	15.00	40.00
BOGGS MM (239A-239E)	4.00	10.00
GWYNN MM SET (5)	40.00	80.00
GWYNN MM (240A-240E)	8.00	20.00
GRIFFEY MM SET (5)	50.00	100.00
GRIFFEY MM (475A-475E)	10.00	25.00
BONDS MM SET (5)	75.00	150.00
BONDS MM (476A-476E)	15.00	40.00
SOSA MM SET (5)	50.00	100.00
SOSA MM (477A-477E)	10.00	25.00
JETER MM SET (5)	75.00	150.00
JETER MM (478A-478E)	15.00	40.00
A.ROD MM SET (5)	60.00	120.00
A.ROD MM (479A-479E)	12.50	30.00

2000 Topps Chrome 21st Century

Inserted at a rate of one in 16, this 10 cards feature players who are expected to be the best in the first part of the 21st century. Card backs carry a "C" prefix.

Card	Low	High
COMPLETE SET (10)	15.00	40.00
*REF: 1X TO 2.5X BASIC 21ST CENT.	1.50	4.00
SER.1 REFRACTOR ODDS 1:80		
C1 Ben Grieve	.60	1.50
C2 Alex Gonzalez	.60	1.50
C3 Derek Jeter	4.00	10.00
C4 Sean Casey	.60	1.50
C5 Nomar Garciaparra	2.50	6.00
C6 Alex Rodriguez	2.50	6.00
C7 Scott Rolen	1.00	2.50

C8 Andruw Jones 1.00 2.50
C9 Vladimir Guerrero 1.50 4.00
C10 Todd Helton 1.00 2.50

2000 Topps Chrome All-Star Rookie Team

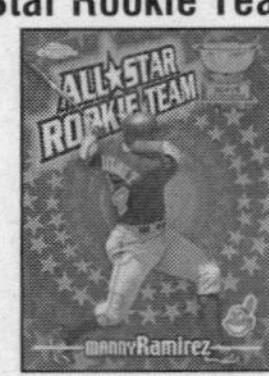

Randomly inserted into packs at one in 16, this 10-card insert set features players that made the All-Star game their rookie season. Card backs carry a "RT" prefix.

COMPLETE SET (10) 20.00 50.00
*REF: 1X TO 2.5X BASIC ASR TEAM 1.50 4.00
REFRACTOR STATED ODDS 1:80
RT1 Mark McGwire 4.00 10.00
RT2 Chuck Knoblauch .60 1.50
RT3 Chipper Jones 1.50 4.00
RT4 Cal Ripken 5.00 12.00
RT5 Manny Ramirez 1.00 2.50
RT6 Jose Canseco 1.00 2.50
RT7 Ken Griffey Jr. 2.50 6.00
RT8 Mike Piazza 2.50 6.00
RT9 Dwight Gooden .60 1.50
RT10 Billy Wagner .60 1.50

2000 Topps Chrome All-Topps

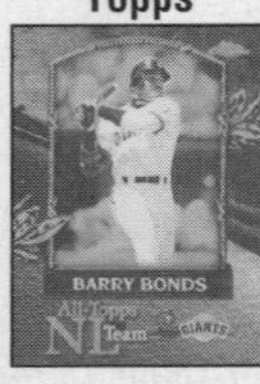

Inserted at a rate of one in 32 first and second series packs, these 10 cards feature the best players in the American and National Leagues. National League cards 91-10) were distributed in series one and American league (11-20) in series two. Card backs carry an "AT" prefix.

COMPLETE SET (20) 60.00 160.00
COMPLETE N.L. (10) 30.00 80.00
COMPLETE A.L.(10) 30.00 80.00
*REFRACTORS: 1X TO 2.5X BASIC ALL NL
REFRACTOR ODDS 1:160
AT1 Greg Maddux 4.00 10.00
AT2 Mike Piazza 4.00 10.00
AT3 Mark McGwire 6.00 15.00
AT4 Craig Biggio 1.50 4.00
AT5 Chipper Jones 2.50 6.00
AT6 Barry Larkin 1.50 4.00
AT7 Barry Bonds 5.00 12.00
AT8 Andruw Jones 1.50 4.00
AT9 Sammy Sosa 2.50 6.00
AT10 Larry Walker 1.00 2.50
AT11 Pedro Martinez 1.50 4.00
AT12 Ivan Rodriguez 1.50 4.00
AT13 Rafael Palmeiro 1.50 4.00
AT14 Roberto Alomar 1.50 4.00
AT15 Cal Ripken 8.00 20.00
AT16 Derek Jeter 6.00 15.00
AT17 Albert Belle 1.00 2.50
AT18 Ken Griffey Jr. 4.00 10.00
AT19 Manny Ramirez 1.50 4.00
AT20 Jose Canseco 1.50 4.00

2000 Topps Chrome Allegiance

This Topps Chrome exclusive set features 20 players who have spent their entire career with just one team. The Allegiance cards were issued at a rate of one in 16 and have a "TA" prefix.

COMPLETE SET (20) 50.00 120.00
*REF: 4X TO 10X BASIC ALLEGIANCE
SER.1 REFRACTOR ODDS 1:424 HOBBY
REFRACTOR PRINT RUN 100 SERIAL #'d SETS
TA1 Derek Jeter 6.00 15.00
TA2 Ivan Rodriguez 1.50 4.00
TA3 Alex Rodriguez 4.00 10.00
TA4 Cal Ripken 8.00 20.00
TA5 Mark Grace 1.50 4.00
TA6 Tony Gwynn 3.00 8.00
TA7 Tom Glavine 1.50 4.00
TA8 Frank Thomas 2.50 6.00
TA9 Manny Ramirez 1.50 4.00
TA10 Barry Larkin 1.50 4.00
TA11 Bernie Williams 1.50 4.00
TA12 Eric Karros 1.00 2.50
TA13 Vladimir Guerrero 2.50 6.00
TA14 Craig Biggio 1.50 4.00
TA15 Nomar Garciaparra 4.00 10.00
TA16 Andruw Jones 1.50 4.00
TA17 Jim Thome 1.50 4.00
TA18 Scott Rolen 1.50 4.00
TA19 Chipper Jones 2.50 6.00
TA20 Ken Griffey Jr. 4.00 10.00

2000 Topps Chrome Combos

Randomly inserted into series two packs at one in 16, this 10-card insert features a variety of player combinations, such as the 1999 MVP's. Card backs carry a "TC" prefix.

COMPLETE SET (10) 30.00 80.00
*REFRACTORS: 1X TO 2.5X BASIC COMBO
REFRACTOR ODDS 1:80
TC1 Roberto Alomar 1.00 2.50
Manny Ramirez
Kenny Lofton
Jim Thome
TC2 Tom Glavine 2.50 6.00
Greg Maddux
John Smoltz
TC3 Paul O'Neill 4.00 10.00
Derek Jeter
Bernie Williams
Tino Martinez
TC4 Ivan Rodriguez 2.50 6.00
Mike Piazza
TC5 Nomar Garciaparra 4.00 10.00
Alex Rodriguez
Derek Jeter
TC6 Sammy Sosa 4.00 10.00
Mark McGwire
TC7 Pedro Martinez 1.00 2.50
Randy Johnson
TC8 Barry Bonds 2.50 6.00
Ken Griffey Jr.
TC9 Chipper Jones 1.50 4.00
Ivan Rodriguez
TC10 Cal Ripken 5.00 12.00
Tony Gwynn
Wade Boggs

2000 Topps Chrome Kings

Randomly inserted into series two packs at one in 32, this 10-card insert features some of the greatest players in major league baseball. Card backs carry a "CK" prefix.

COMPLETE SET (10) 30.00 80.00
CK1 Mark McGwire 6.00 15.00
CK2 Sammy Sosa 2.50 6.00
CK3 Ken Griffey Jr. 4.00 10.00
CK4 Mike Piazza 4.00 10.00
CK5 Alex Rodriguez 4.00 10.00
CK6 Manny Ramirez 1.50 4.00
CK7 Barry Bonds 5.00 12.00
CK8 Nomar Garciaparra 4.00 10.00
CK9 Chipper Jones 2.50 6.00
CK10 Vladimir Guerrero 2.50 6.00

2000 Topps Chrome Kings Refractors

Randomly inserted into series two packs at one in 514, this 10-card insert is a complete parallel of the Chrome Kings insert. Each card was produced using Topps' "refractor" technology. Please note that each card was serial numbered to the amount of homeruns that the individual players had after the 1999 season. Production runs are listed below. Card backs carry a "CK" prefix.

COMPLETE SET (10) 125.00 300.00
CK1 Mark McGwire/522 12.50 30.00
CK2 Sammy Sosa/366 8.00 20.00
CK3 Ken Griffey Jr./398 10.00 25.00
CK4 Mike Piazza/240 10.00 25.00
CK5 Alex Rodriguez/148 20.00 50.00
CK6 Manny Ramirez/198 6.00 15.00
CK7 Barry Bonds/445 10.00 25.00
CK8 N.Garciaparra/96 20.00 50.00
CK9 Chipper Jones/153 8.00 20.00
CK10 V.Guerrero/92 15.00 40.00

2000 Topps Chrome New Millennium Stars

Randomly inserted into series two packs at one in 32, this 10-card insert features some of the major league's hottest young talent. Card backs carry a "NMS" prefix.

COMPLETE SET (10) 15.00 40.00
*REFRACTORS: 1X TO 2.5X BASIC MILL. 2.50 6.00
SER.2 REFRACTOR ODDS 1:160

NMS1 Nomar Garciaparra 4.00 10.00
NMS2 Vladimir Guerrero 2.50 6.00
NMS3 Sean Casey 1.00 2.50
NMS4 Richie Sexson 1.00 2.50
NMS5 Todd Helton 1.50 4.00
NMS6 Carlos Beltran 1.00 2.50
NMS7 Kevin Millwood 1.00 2.50
NMS8 Ruben Mateo 1.00 2.50
NMS9 Pat Burrell 2.00 5.00
NMS10 Alfonso Soriano 1.00 2.50

2000 Topps Chrome Own the Game

Randomly inserted into series two packs at one in 11, this 30-card insert features players that are amoung the major league's statistical leaders year after year. Card backs carry an "OTG" prefix.

COMPLETE SET (30) 80.00 200.00
*REFRACTORS: 1X TO 2.5X BASIC OWN 2.50 6.00
SER.2 REFRACTOR ODDS 1:55
OTG1 Derek Jeter 6.00 15.00
OTG2 B.J. Surhoff 1.00 2.50
OTG3 Luis Gonzalez 1.00 2.50
OTG4 Manny Ramirez 1.50 4.00
OTG5 Rafael Palmeiro 1.50 4.00
OTG6 Mark McGwire 6.00 15.00
OTG7 Mark McGwire 6.00 15.00
OTG8 Sammy Sosa 2.50 6.00
OTG9 Ken Griffey Jr. 4.00 10.00
OTG10 Larry Walker 1.00 2.50
OTG11 Nomar Garciaparra 4.00 10.00
OTG12 Derek Jeter 6.00 15.00
OTG13 Larry Walker 1.00 2.50
OTG14 Mark McGwire 6.00 15.00
OTG15 Manny Ramirez 1.50 4.00
OTG16 Pedro Martinez 1.50 4.00
OTG17 Randy Johnson 2.50 6.00
OTG18 Kevin Millwood 1.00 2.50
OTG19 Randy Johnson 2.50 6.00
OTG20 Pedro Martinez 1.50 4.00
OTG21 Kevin Brown 1.50 4.00
OTG22 Chipper Jones 2.50 6.00
OTG23 Ivan Rodriguez 1.50 4.00
OTG24 Mariano Rivera 2.50 6.00
OTG25 Scott Williamson 1.00 2.50
OTG26 Carlos Beltran 1.00 2.50
OTG27 Randy Johnson 2.50 6.00
OTG28 Pedro Martinez 1.50 4.00
OTG29 Sammy Sosa 2.50 6.00
OTG30 Manny Ramirez 1.50 4.00

2000 Topps Chrome Power Players

This 20 card set, issued at a rate of one in eight packs, features players who are the leading power hitters in the majors. Card backs carry a "P" prefix.

COMPLETE SET (20) 40.00 100.00
*REFRACTORS: 1X TO 2.5X BASIC POWER 1.50 4.00
SER.1 REFRACTOR ODDS 1:40
P1 Juan Gonzalez .60 1.50
P2 Ken Griffey Jr. 2.50 6.00
P3 Mark McGwire 4.00 10.00
P4 Nomar Garciaparra 2.50 6.00
P5 Barry Bonds 3.00 8.00
P6 Mo Vaughn .60 1.50
P7 Larry Walker .60 1.50
P8 Alex Rodriguez 2.50 6.00
P9 Jose Canseco 1.00 2.50
P10 Jeff Bagwell 1.00 2.50
P11 Manny Ramirez 1.00 2.50
P12 Albert Belle .60 1.50
P13 Frank Thomas 1.50 4.00
P14 Mike Piazza 2.50 6.00
P15 Chipper Jones 1.50 4.00
P16 Sammy Sosa 1.50 4.00
P17 Vladimir Guerrero 1.50 4.00
P18 Scott Rolen 1.00 2.50
P19 Raul Mondesi .60 1.50
P20 Derek Jeter 4.00 10.00

2000 Topps Chrome Traded

The 2000 Topps Chrome Traded set was released in late November, 2000 and features a 135-card base set. The set is an exact parallel of the Topps Traded set. This set was produced using Topps' chrome technology. Please note that card backs carry a "T" prefix. Each set came with 135 cards and carried a $99.99 suggested retail price. Notable Rookie Cards include Miguel Cabrera.

COMP.FACT.SET (135) 40.00 80.00
T1 Mike MacDougal .30 .75
T2 Andy Tracy RC .20 .50
T3 Brandon Phillips RC 1.00 2.50
T4 Brandon Inge RC 1.50 4.00
T5 Robbie Morrison RC .20 .50
T6 Josh Pressley RC .20 .50
T7 Todd Moser RC .20 .50
T8 Rob Purvis .25 .60
T9 Chance Caple .15 .40
T10 Ben Sheets 1.00 2.50
T11 Russ Jacobson RC .20 .50
T12 Brian Cole RC .20 .50
T13 Brad Baker .15 .40
T14 Alex Cintron RC .30 .75
T15 Lyle Overbay RC .75 2.00
T16 Mike Edwards RC .20 .50
T17 Sean McGowan RC .20 .50
T18 Jose Molina .15 .40
T19 Marcos Castillo RC .20 .50
T20 Josue Espada RC .20 .50
T21 Alex Gordon RC .20 .50
T22 Rob Pugmire RC .20 .50
T23 Jason Stumm .20 .50
T24 Ty Howington .15 .40
T25 Brett Myers .60 1.50
T26 Maicer Izturis RC .30 .75
T27 John McDonald .15 .40
T28 W.Rodriguez RC .20 .50
T29 Carlos Zambrano RC 4.00 10.00
T30 Alejandro Diaz RC .20 .50
T31 Geraldo Guzman RC .20 .50
T32 J.R. House RC .20 .50
T33 Elvin Nina RC .20 .50
T34 Juan Pierre RC .75 2.00
T35 Ben Johnson RC 1.25 3.00
T36 Jeff Bailey RC .20 .50
T37 Miguel Olivo RC .50 1.25
T38 F.Rodriguez RC 1.50 4.00
T39 Tony Pena Jr. RC .20 .50
T40 Miguel Cabrera RC 12.50 30.00
T41 Asdrubal Oropeza RC .20 .50
T42 Junior Zamora RC .30 .75
T43 Jovanny Cedeno RC .20 .50
T44 John Sneed .25 .60
T45 Josh Kalinowski .25 .60
T46 Mike Young RC 4.00 10.00
T47 Rico Washington RC .20 .50
T48 Chad Durbin RC .20 .50
T49 Junior Brignac RC .20 .50
T50 Carlos Hernandez RC .30 .75
T51 Cesar Izturis RC .50 1.25
T52 Oscar Salazar RC .20 .50
T53 Pat Strange RC .20 .50
T54 Rick Asadoorian .30 .75
T55 Keith Reed .15 .40
T56 Leo Estrella RC .20 .50
T57 Wascar Serrano RC .20 .50
T58 Richard Gomez RC .20 .50
T59 Ramon Santiago RC .20 .50
T60 Jovanny Sosa RC .20 .50
T61 Aaron Rowand RC 1.25 3.00
T62 Junior Guerrero RC .20 .50
T63 Luis Terrero RC .30 .75
T64 Brian Sanches RC .20 .50
T65 Scott Sobkowiak RC .20 .50
T66 Gary Majewski RC .30 .75
T67 Barry Zito 1.25 3.00
T68 Ryan Christianson .20 .50
T69 Cristian Guerrero RC .20 .50
T70 T.De La Rosa RC .20 .50
T71 Andrew Beinbrink RC .20 .50
T72 Ryan Knox RC .20 .50
T73 Alex Graman RC .20 .50
T74 Juan Guzman RC .20 .50
T75 Ruben Salazar RC .20 .50
T76 Luis Matos RC .30 .75
T77 Tony Mota RC .20 .50
T78 Doug Davis .25 .60
T79 Ben Christensen .15 .40
T80 Mike Lamb .50 1.25
T81 Adrian Gonzalez RC 2.00 5.00
T82 Mike Stodolka RC .20 .50
T83 Adam Johnson RC .20 .50
T84 Matt Wheatland RC .20 .50
T85 Corey Smith RC .20 .50
T86 Rocco Baldelli RC 1.50 4.00
T87 Keith Bucktrot RC .20 .50
T88 Adam Wainwright RC .75 2.00
T89 Scott Thorman RC .75 2.00
T90 Tripper Johnson RC .20 .50
T91 Jim Edmonds Cards .25 .60
T92 Masato Yoshii .15 .40
T93 Adam Kennedy .15 .40
T94 Darryl Kile .25 .60
T95 Mark McLemore .15 .40
T96 Ricky Gutierrez .15 .40
T97 Juan Gonzalez .25 .60
T98 Melvin Mora .25 .60
T99 Dante Bichette .25 .60
T100 Lee Stevens .15 .40
T101 Roger Cedeno .15 .40
T102 John Olerud .25 .60
T103 Eric Young .15 .40
T104 Mickey Morandini .15 .40
T105 Travis Lee .15 .40
T106 Greg Vaughn .15 .40
T107 Todd Zeile .25 .60
T108 Chuck Finley .25 .60
T109 Ismael Valdes .15 .40
T110 Reggie Sanders .25 .60
T111 Pat Hentgen .15 .40
T112 Ryan Klesko .25 .60
T113 Derek Bell .15 .40
T114 Hideo Nomo .60 1.50
T115 Aaron Sele .15 .40
T116 Fernando Vina .15 .40
T117 Wally Joyner .25 .60
T118 Brian Hunter .15 .40
T119 Joe Girardi .15 .40
T120 Omar Daal .15 .40
T121 Brook Fordyce .15 .40
T122 Jose Valentin .15 .40
T123 Curt Schilling .25 .60
T124 B.J. Surhoff .25 .60
T125 Henry Rodriguez .15 .40
T126 Mike Bordick .15 .40
T127 David Justice .25 .60
T128 Charles Johnson .25 .60
T129 Will Clark .40 1.00
T130 Dwight Gooden .25 .60
T131 David Segui .15 .40
T132 Denny Neagle .25 .60
T133 Jose Canseco .40 1.00
T134 Bruce Chen .15 .40
T135 Jason Bere .15 .40

2001 Topps Chrome

The 2001 Topps Chrome product was released in two separate series. The first series shipped in February 2001, and features a 331-card base set produced with Topps' special chrome technology. This set parallels the regular 2001 Topps base set in card design and photography but card numbering differs due to the fact that the manufacturer decided to select only the best 331 cards of the 405 card basic Topps set to be featured in this upgraded Chrome product. Each Topps Chrome pack contains four cards, and carried a suggested retail price of $2.99. Please note, card number 7 does not exist. The number was retired in Topps and Topps Chrome brands back in 1996 in honor of Yankees legend Mickey Mantle. Notable Rookie Cards include Hee Seop Choi.

COMPLETE SET (661) 150.00 300.00
COMP. SERIES 1 (331) 75.00 150.00
COMP. SERIES 2 (330) 75.00 150.00
1 Cal Ripken 2.50 6.00
2 Chipper Jones .75 2.00
3 Roger Cedeno .20 .50
4 Garret Anderson .30 .75
5 Robin Ventura .30 .75
6 Daryle Ward .20 .50
7 Does Not Exist
8 Phil Nevin .30 .75
9 Jermaine Dye .30 .75
10 Chris Singleton .20 .50
11 Mike Redmond .20 .50
12 Jim Thome .50 1.25
13 Brian Jordan .30 .75
14 Dustin Hermanson .20 .50
15 Shawn Green .30 .75
16 Todd Stottlemyre .20 .50
17 Dan Wilson .20 .50
18 Derek Lowe .30 .75
19 Juan Gonzalez .30 .75
20 Pat Meares .20 .50
21 Paul O'Neill .50 1.25
22 Jeffrey Hammonds .20 .50
23 Pokey Reese .20 .50
24 Mike Mussina .50 1.25
25 Rico Brogna .20 .50
26 Jay Buhner .30 .75
27 Steve Cox .20 .50
28 Quilvio Veras .20 .50
29 Marquis Grissom .30 .75
30 Shigetoshi Hasegawa .20 .50
31 Shane Reynolds .20 .50
32 Adam Piatt .20 .50
33 Preston Wilson .30 .75
34 Ellis Burks .30 .75
35 Armando Rios .20 .50
36 Chuck Finley .30 .75
37 Shannon Stewart .30 .75
38 Mark McGwire 2.00 5.00
39 Gerald Williams .20 .50
40 Eric Young .20 .50
41 Peter Bergeron .20 .50
42 Arthur Rhodes .20 .50
43 Bobby Jones .20 .50
44 Matt Clement .30 .75
45 Pedro Martinez .50 1.25
46 Jose Canseco .50 1.25
47 Matt Anderson .20 .50
48 Torii Hunter .30 .75
49 Carlos Lee .30 .75
50 Eric Chavez .30 .75
51 Rick Helling .20 .50
52 John Franco .30 .75
53 Mike Bordick .20 .50
54 Andres Galarraga .30 .75
55 Jose Cruz Jr. .20 .50
56 Mike Matheny .20 .50
57 Randy Johnson .75 2.00
58 Richie Sexson .30 .75
59 Vladimir Nunez .20 .50
60 Aaron Boone .30 .75
61 Darin Erstad .30 .75
62 Alex Gonzalez .20 .50
63 Gil Heredia .20 .50
64 Shane Andrews .20 .50
65 Todd Hundley .20 .50
66 Bill Mueller .30 .75
67 Mark McLemore .20 .50
68 Scott Spiezio .20 .50
69 Kevin McGlinchy .20 .50
70 Manny Ramirez .50 1.25
71 Mike Lamb .20 .50
72 Brian Buchanan .20 .50
73 Mike Sweeney .30 .75
74 John Wetteland .30 .75
75 Rob Bell .20 .50
76 John Burkett .20 .50
77 Derek Jeter 2.00 5.00
78 J.D. Drew .30 .75
79 Jose Offerman .20 .50
80 Rick Reed .20 .50
81 Will Clark .50 1.25
82 Rickey Henderson .75 2.00
83 Kirk Rueter .20 .50
84 Lee Stevens .20 .50
85 Jay Bell .20 .50
86 Fred McGriff .50 1.25
87 Julio Zuleta .20 .50
88 Brian Anderson .20 .50
89 Orlando Cabrera .30 .75
90 Alex Fernandez .20 .50
91 Derek Bell .20 .50
92 Eric Owens .20 .50
93 Dennys Reyes .20 .50
94 Mike Stanley .20 .50
95 Jorge Posada .50 1.25
96 Paul Konerko .30 .75
97 Mike Remlinger .20 .50
98 Travis Lee .20 .50
99 Ken Caminiti .30 .75
100 Kevin Barker .20 .50
101 Ozzie Guillen .30 .75
102 Randy Wolf .20 .50
103 Michael Tucker .20 .50
104 Darren Lewis .20 .50
105 Joe Randa .30 .75
106 Jeff Cirillo .20 .50
107 David Ortiz .75 2.00
108 Herb Perry .20 .50
109 Jeff Nelson .20 .50
110 Chris Stynes .20 .50
111 Johnny Damon .50 1.25
112 Jason Schmidt .30 .75
113 Charles Johnson .20 .50
114 Pat Burrell .30 .75
115 Gary Sheffield .30 .75
116 Tom Glavine .50 1.25
117 Jason Isringhausen .30 .75
118 Chris Carpenter .30 .75
119 Jeff Suppan .20 .50
120 Ivan Rodriguez .50 1.25
121 Luis Sojo .20 .50
122 Ron Villone .20 .50
123 Mike Sirotka .20 .50
124 Chuck Knoblauch .30 .75
125 Jason Kendall .30 .75
126 Bobby Estalella .20 .50
127 Jose Guillen .30 .75
128 Carlos Delgado .30 .75
129 Benji Gil .20 .50
130 Einar Diaz .20 .50
131 Andy Benes .20 .50
132 Adrian Beltre .30 .75
133 Roger Clemens 1.50 4.00
134 Scott Williamson .20 .50
135 Brad Penny .20 .50
136 Troy Glaus .30 .75
137 Kevin Appier .30 .75
138 Walt Weiss .20 .50
139 Michael Barrett .20 .50
140 Mike Hampton .30 .75
141 Francisco Cordova .20 .50
142 David Segui .20 .50
143 Carlos Febles .20 .50
144 Roy Halladay .30 .75
145 Seth Etherton .20 .50
146 Fernando Tatis .20 .50
147 Livan Hernandez .30 .75
148 B.J. Surhoff .30 .75
149 Barry Larkin .50 1.25
150 Bobby Howry .20 .50
151 Dmitri Young .30 .75
152 Brian Hunter .20 .50
153 Alex Rodriguez 1.25 3.00
154 Hideo Nomo .75 2.00
155 Warren Morris .20 .50
156 Antonio Alfonseca .20 .50
157 Edgardo Alfonzo .20 .50
158 Mark Grudzielanek .20 .50
159 Fernando Vina .20 .50
160 Homer Bush .20 .50
161 Jason Giambi .30 .75
162 Steve Karsay .20 .50
163 Matt Lawton .20 .50
164 Rusty Greer .30 .75
165 Billy Koch .20 .50
166 Todd Hollandsworth .20 .50
167 Raul Ibanez .30 .75
168 Tony Gwynn 1.00 2.50
169 Carl Everett .30 .75
170 Hector Carrasco .20 .50
171 Jose Valentin .20 .50
172 Deivi Cruz .20 .50
173 Bret Boone .30 .75
174 Melvin Mora .20 .50
175 Danny Graves .20 .50
176 Jose Jimenez .20 .50
177 James Baldwin .20 .50
178 C.J. Nitkowski .20 .50
179 Jeff Zimmerman .20 .50
180 Mike Lowell .30 .75
181 Hideki Irabu .20 .50
182 Greg Vaughn .20 .50
183 Omar Daal .20 .50
184 Darren Dreifort .20 .50
185 Gil Meche .20 .50
186 Damian Jackson .20 .50
187 Frank Thomas .75 2.00
188 Luis Castillo .20 .50
189 Bartolo Colon .30 .75
190 Craig Biggio .50 1.25
191 Scott Schoeneweis .20 .50
192 Dave Veres .20 .50
193 Ramon Martinez .20 .50
194 Jose Vidro .20 .50
195 Todd Helton .50 1.25
196 Greg Norton .20 .50
197 Jacque Jones .30 .75
198 Jason Grimsley .20 .50
199 Dan Reichert .20 .50
200 Robb Nen .30 .75
201 Scott Hatteberg .20 .50
202 Terry Shumpert .20 .50
203 Kevin Millar .30 .75
204 Ismael Valdes .20 .50
205 Richard Hidalgo .20 .50
206 Randy Velarde .20 .50
207 Bengie Molina .20 .50
208 Tony Womack .20 .50
209 Enrique Wilson .20 .50
210 Jeff Brantley .20 .50
211 Rick Ankiel .20 .50
212 Terry Mulholland .20 .50
213 Ron Belliard .20 .50
214 Terrence Long .20 .50
215 Alberto Castillo .20 .50
216 Royce Clayton .20 .50
217 Joe McEwing .20 .50
218 Jason McDonald .20 .50
219 Ricky Bottalico .20 .50

220 Keith Foulke .30 .75
221 Brad Radke .30 .75
222 Gabe Kapler .30 .75
223 Pedro Astacio .20 .50
224 Armando Reynoso .20 .50
225 Darryl Kile .30 .75
226 Reggie Sanders .30 .75
227 Esteban Yan .20 .50
228 Joe Nathan .30 .75
229 Jay Payton .20 .50
230 Francisco Cordero .20 .50
231 Gregg Jefferies .20 .50
232 LaTroy Hawkins .20 .50
233 Jacob Cruz .20 .50
234 Chris Holt .20 .50
235 Vladimir Guerrero .75 2.00
236 Marvin Benard .20 .50
237 Alex Ramirez .20 .50
238 Mike Williams .20 .50
239 Sean Bergman .20 .50
240 Juan Encarnacion .20 .50
241 Russ Davis .20 .50
242 Ramon Hernandez .20 .50
243 Sandy Alomar Jr. .20 .50
244 Eddie Guardado .20 .50
245 Shane Halter .20 .50
246 Geoff Jenkins .20 .50
247 Brian Meadows .20 .50
248 Damian Miller .20 .50
249 Darrin Fletcher .20 .50
250 Rafael Furcal .30 .75
251 Mark Grace .50 1.25
252 Mark Mulder .30 .75
253 Joe Torre MG .50 1.25
254 Bobby Cox MG .20 .50
255 Mike Scioscia MG .20 .50
256 Mike Hargrove MG .20 .50
257 Jimy Williams MG .20 .50
258 Jerry Manuel MG .20 .50
259 Charlie Manuel MG .20 .50
260 Don Baylor MG .30 .75
261 Phil Garner MG .30 .75
262 Tony Muser MG .20 .50
263 Buddy Bell MG .30 .75
264 Tom Kelly MG .20 .50
265 John Boles MG .20 .50
266 Art Howe MG .20 .50
267 Larry Dierker MG .20 .50
268 Lou Piniella MG .30 .75
269 Larry Rothschild MG .20 .50
270 Davey Lopes MG .30 .75
271 Johnny Oates MG .20 .50
272 Felipe Alou MG .20 .50
273 Bobby Valentine MG .20 .50
274 Tony LaRussa MG .30 .75
275 Bruce Bochy MG .20 .50
276 Dusty Baker MG .30 .75
277 Adrian Gonzalez .40 1.00
Adam Johnson
278 Matt Wheatland .40 1.00
Bryan Digby
279 Tripper Johnson .40 1.00
Scott Thorman
280 Phil Dumatrait .40 1.00
Adam Wainwright
281 Scott Heard .40 1.00
David Parrish RC
282 Rocco Baldelli .60 1.50
Mark Folsom
283 Dominic Rich RC .40 1.00
Aaron Herr
284 Mike Stodolka .40 1.00
Sean Burnett
285 Derek Thompson .40 1.00
Corey Smith
286 Danny Borrell .40 1.00
Jason Bourgeois RC
287 Chin-Feng Chen .75 2.00
Corey Patterson
Josh Hamilton
288 Ryan Anderson .75 2.00
Barry Zito
C.C. Sabathia
289 Scott Sobkowiak .75 2.00
David Walling
Ben Sheets
290 Ty Howington .40 1.00
Josh Kalinowski
Josh Girdley
291 Hee Seop Choi .75 2.00
Aaron McNeal
Jason Hart
292 Bobby Bradley .60 1.50
Kurt Ainsworth
Chin-Hui Tsao
293 Mike Glendenning .40 1.00
Kenny Kelly
Juan Silvestre
294 J.R. House .40 1.00
Ramon Castro
Ben Davis
295 Chance Caple .60 1.50
Rafael Soriano
Pasqual Coco
296 Travis Hafner RC 4.00 10.00
Eric Munson
Bucky Jacobsen
297 Jason Conti .40 1.00
Chris Wakeland
Brian Cole
298 Scott Seabol 1.00 2.50
Aubrey Huff
Joe Crede
299 Adam Everett .40 1.00
Jose Ortiz
Keith Ginter
300 Carlos Hernandez .40 1.00
Geraldo Guzman
Adam Eaton
301 Bobby Kielty .60 1.50
Milton Bradley
Juan Rivera
302 Mark McGwire GM 1.00 2.50
303 Don Larsen GM .30 .75
304 Bobby Thomson GM .30 .75
305 Bill Mazeroski GM .30 .75
306 Reggie Jackson GM .50 1.25
307 Kirk Gibson GM .30 .75
308 Roger Maris GM .50 1.25
309 Cal Ripken GM 1.25 3.00
310 Hank Aaron GM .75 2.00
311 Joe Carter GM .30 .75
312 Cal Ripken SH 1.25 3.00
313 Randy Johnson SH .50 1.25
314 Ken Griffey Jr. SH .75 2.00
315 Troy Glaus SH .30 .75
316 Kazuhiro Sasaki SH .30 .75
317 Sammy Sosa .50 1.25
Troy Glaus LL
318 Todd Helton .30 .75
Edgar Martinez LL
319 Todd Helton .75 2.00
Nomar Garciaparra LL
320 Barry Bonds .75 2.00
Jason Giambi LL
321 Todd Helton .30 .75
Manny Ramirez LL
322 Todd Helton .30 .75
Darin Erstad LL
323 Kevin Brown .50 1.25
Pedro Martinez LL
324 Randy Johnson .50 1.25
Pedro Martinez LL
325 Will Clark HL .50 1.25
326 New York Mets HL .75 2.00
327 New York Yankees HL 1.25 3.00
328 Seattle Mariners HL .30 .75
329 Mike Hampton HL .30 .75
330 New York Yankees HL 1.50 4.00
331 N.Y. Yankees Champs 3.00 8.00
332 Jeff Bagwell .50 1.25
333 Andy Pettitte .50 1.25
334 Tony Armas Jr. .20 .50
335 Jeromy Burnitz .30 .75
336 Javier Vazquez .30 .75
337 Eric Karros .30 .75
338 Brian Giles .30 .75
339 Scott Rolen .50 1.25
340 David Justice .30 .75
341 Ray Durham .30 .75
342 Todd Zeile .30 .75
343 Cliff Floyd .30 .75
344 Barry Bonds 2.00 5.00
345 Matt Williams .30 .75
346 Steve Finley .30 .75
347 Scott Elarton .20 .50
348 Bernie Williams .50 1.25
349 David Wells .30 .75
350 J.T. Snow .30 .75
351 Al Leiter .30 .75
352 Magglio Ordonez .30 .75
353 Raul Mondesi .30 .75
354 Tim Salmon .50 1.25
355 Jeff Kent .30 .75
356 Mariano Rivera .75 2.00
357 John Olerud .30 .75
358 Javy Lopez .30 .75
359 Ben Grieve .20 .50
360 Ray Lankford .30 .75
361 Ken Griffey Jr. 1.25 3.00
362 Rich Aurilia .20 .50
363 Andruw Jones .50 1.25
364 Ryan Klesko .30 .75
365 Roberto Alomar .50 1.25
366 Miguel Tejada .30 .75
367 Mo Vaughn .30 .75
368 Albert Belle .30 .75
369 Jose Canseco .50 1.25
370 Kevin Brown .30 .75
371 Rafael Palmeiro .50 1.25
372 Mark Redman .20 .50
373 Larry Walker .30 .75
374 Greg Maddux 1.25 3.00
375 Nomar Garciaparra 1.25 3.00
376 Kevin Millwood .30 .75
377 Edgar Martinez .50 1.25
378 Sammy Sosa .75 2.00
379 Tim Hudson .30 .75
380 Jim Edmonds .30 .75
381 Mike Piazza 1.25 3.00
382 Brant Brown .20 .50
383 Brad Fullmer .20 .50
384 Alan Benes .20 .50
385 Mickey Morandini .20 .50
386 Troy Percival .30 .75
387 Eddie Perez .20 .50
388 Vernon Wells .30 .75
389 Ricky Gutierrez .20 .50
390 Rondell White .30 .75
391 Kelvim Escobar .20 .50
392 Tony Batista .20 .50
393 Jimmy Haynes .20 .50
394 Billy Wagner .30 .75
395 A.J. Hinch .20 .50
396 Matt Morris .30 .75
397 Lance Berkman .30 .75
398 Jeff D'Amico .20 .50
399 Octavio Dotel .20 .50
400 Olmedo Saenz .20 .50
401 Esteban Loaiza .20 .50
402 Adam Kennedy .20 .50
403 Moises Alou .30 .75
404 Orlando Palmeiro .20 .50
405 Kevin Young .20 .50
406 Tom Goodwin .20 .50
407 Mac Suzuki .20 .50
408 Pat Hentgen .20 .50
409 Kevin Stocker .20 .50
410 Mark Sweeney .20 .50
411 Tony Eusebio .20 .50
412 Edgar Renteria .30 .75
413 John Rocker .30 .75
414 Jose Lima .20 .50
415 Kerry Wood .30 .75
416 Mike Timlin .20 .50
417 Jose Hernandez .20 .50
418 Jeremy Giambi .20 .50
419 Luis Lopez .20 .50
420 Mitch Meluskey .20 .50
421 Garrett Stephenson .20 .50
422 Jamey Wright .20 .50
423 John Jaha .20 .50
424 Placido Polanco .20 .50
425 Marty Cordova .20 .50
426 Joey Hamilton .20 .50
427 Travis Fryman .30 .75
428 Mike Cameron .20 .50
429 Matt Mantei .20 .50
430 Chan Ho Park .30 .75
431 Shawn Estes .20 .50
432 Danny Bautista .20 .50
433 Wilson Alvarez .20 .50
434 Kenny Lofton .30 .75
435 Russ Ortiz .20 .50
436 Dave Burba .20 .50
437 Felix Martinez .20 .50
438 Jeff Shaw .20 .50
439 Mike DiFelice .20 .50
440 Roberto Hernandez .20 .50
441 Bryan Rekar .20 .50
442 Ugueth Urbina .20 .50
443 Vinny Castilla .30 .75
444 Carlos Perez .20 .50
445 Juan Guzman .20 .50
446 Ryan Rupe .20 .50
447 Mike Mordecai .20 .50
448 Ricardo Rincon .20 .50
449 Curt Schilling .30 .75
450 Alex Cora .20 .50
451 Turner Ward .20 .50
452 Omar Vizquel .50 1.25
453 Russ Branyan .20 .50
454 Russ Johnson .20 .50
455 Greg Colbrunn .20 .50
456 Charles Nagy .20 .50
457 Wil Cordero .20 .50
458 Jason Tyner .20 .50
459 Devon White .30 .75
460 Kelvim Escobar .20 .50
461 Wilton Guerrero .20 .50
462 Jason Bere .20 .50
463 Calvin Murray .20 .50
464 Miguel Batista .20 .50
466 Luis Gonzalez .30 .75
467 Jaret Wright .30 .75
468 Chad Kreuter .20 .50
469 Armando Benitez .20 .50
470 Erubiel Durazo .20 .50
470 Sidney Ponson .20 .50
471 Adrian Brown .20 .50
472 Sterling Hitchcock .20 .50
473 Timo Perez .20 .50
474 Jamie Moyer .30 .75
475 Delino DeShields .20 .50
476 Glendon Rusch .20 .50
477 Chris Gomez .20 .50
478 Adam Eaton .20 .50
479 Pablo Ozuna .20 .50
480 Bob Abreu .30 .75
481 Kris Benson .20 .50
482 Keith Osik .20 .50
483 Darryl Hamilton .20 .50
484 Marlon Anderson .20 .50
485 Jimmy Anderson .20 .50
486 John Halama .20 .50
487 Nelson Figueroa .20 .50
488 Alex Gonzalez .20 .50
489 Benny Agbayani .20 .50
490 Ed Sprague .20 .50
491 Scott Erickson .20 .50
492 Doug Glanville .20 .50
493 Jesus Sanchez .20 .50
494 Mike Lieberthal .30 .75
495 Aaron Sele .20 .50
496 Pat Mahomes .20 .50
497 Ruben Rivera .20 .50
498 Wayne Gomes .20 .50
499 Freddy Garcia .30 .75
500 Al Martin .20 .50
501 Woody Williams .20 .50
502 Paul Byrd .20 .50
503 Rick White .20 .50
504 Trevor Hoffman .30 .75
505 Brady Anderson .30 .75
506 Robert Person .20 .50
507 Jeff Conine .30 .75
508 Chris Truby .20 .50
509 Emil Brown .20 .50
510 Ryan Dempster .20 .50
511 Ruben Mateo .20 .50
512 Alex Ochoa .20 .50
513 Jose Rosado .20 .50
514 Masato Yoshii .20 .50
515 Brian Daubach .20 .50
516 Jeff D'Amico .20 .50
517 Brent Mayne .20 .50
518 John Thomson .20 .50
519 Todd Ritchie .20 .50
520 John VanderWal .20 .50
521 Neifi Perez .20 .50
522 Chad Curtis .20 .50
523 Kenny Rogers .30 .75
524 Trot Nixon .30 .75
525 Sean Casey .30 .75
526 Wilton Veras .20 .50
527 Troy O'Leary .20 .50
528 Dante Bichette .30 .75
529 Jose Silva .20 .50
530 Darren Oliver .20 .50
531 Steve Parris .20 .50
532 David McCarty .20 .50
533 Todd Walker .20 .50
534 Brian Rose .20 .50
535 Pete Schourek .20 .50
536 Ricky Ledee .20 .50
537 Justin Thompson .20 .50
538 Benito Santiago .30 .75
539 Carlos Beltran .30 .75
540 Gabe White .20 .50
541 Bret Saberhagen .30 .75
542 Ramon Martinez .20 .50
543 John Valentin .20 .50
544 Frank Catalanotto .20 .50
545 Tim Wakefield .30 .75
546 Michael Tucker .20 .50
547 Juan Pierre .30 .75
548 Rich Garces .20 .50
549 Luis Ordaz .20 .50
550 Jerry Spradlin .20 .50
551 Corey Koskie .20 .50
552 Cal Eldred .20 .50
553 Alfonso Soriano .50 1.25
554 Kip Wells .20 .50
555 Orlando Hernandez .30 .75
556 Bill Simas .20 .50
557 Jim Parque .20 .50
558 Joe Mays .30 .75
559 Tim Belcher .20 .50
560 Shane Spencer .20 .50
561 Glenallen Hill .20 .50
562 Matt LeCroy .20 .50
563 Tino Martinez .50 1.25
564 Eric Milton .20 .50
565 Ron Coomer .20 .50
566 Cristian Guzman .20 .50
567 Kazuhiro Sasaki .30 .75
568 Mark Quinn .20 .50
569 Eric Gagne .30 .75
570 Kerry Ligtenberg .20 .50
571 Rolando Arrojo .20 .50
572 Jon Lieber .20 .50
573 Jose Vizcaino .20 .50
574 Jeff Abbott .20 .50
575 Carlos Hernandez .20 .50
576 Scott Sullivan .20 .50
577 Matt Stairs .20 .50
578 Tom Lampkin .20 .50
579 Donnie Sadler .20 .50
580 Desi Relaford .20 .50
581 Scott Downs .20 .50
582 Mike Mussina .50 1.25
583 Ramon Ortiz .20 .50
584 Mike Myers .20 .50
585 Frank Castillo .20 .50
586 Manny Ramirez Sox .50 1.25
587 Alex Rodriguez 1.25 3.00
588 Andy Ashby .20 .50
589 Felipe Crespo .20 .50
590 Bobby Bonilla .30 .75
591 Denny Neagle .20 .50
592 Dave Martinez .20 .50
593 Mike Hampton .30 .75
594 Gary DiSarcina .20 .50
595 Tsuyoshi Shinjo RC .75 2.00
596 Albert Pujols RC 20.00 50.00
597 Roy Oswalt 1.00 2.50
Pat Strange
Jon Rauch
598 Phil Wilson RC 4.00 10.00
Jake Peavy RC
Darwin Cubillan RC UER
Peavy is spelled incorrectly
599 Nathan Haynes .40 1.00
Steve Smyth RC
Mike Bynum
600 Joe Lawrence .40 1.00
Choo Freeman
Michael Cuddyer
601 Larry Barnes .40 1.00
DeWayne Wise
Carlos Pena
602 Feilpe Lopez .40 1.00
Gookie Dawkins
Eric Almonte RC
603 Brad Wilkerson .40 1.00
Alex Escobar
Eric Valent
604 Jeff Goldbach .40 1.00
Toby Hall
Rod Barajas
605 Marcus Giles .60 1.50
Pablo Ozuna
Jason Romano
606 Vernon Wells .40 1.00
Jack Cust
Dee Brown
607 Luis Montanez RC .40 1.00
David Espinosa
608 Anthony Pluta RC .40 1.00
Justin Wayne RC
609 Josh Axelson RC .40 1.00
Carmen Cali RC
610 Shaun Boyd RC .40 1.00
Chris Morris RC
611 Dan Moylan RC .40 1.00
Tommy Arko RC
612 Luis Cotto RC .40 1.00
Luis Escobar
613 Blake Williams RC .40 1.00
Brandon Mims RC
614 Chris Russ RC .40 1.00
Bryan Edwards
615 Joe Torres .40 1.00
Ben Diggins
616 Hugh Quattlebaum RC 4.00 10.00
Edwin Encarnacion RC
617 Brian Bass RC .40 1.00
Odannis Ayala RC
618 Jason Kaanoi .40 1.00
Michael Matthews RC UER
name misspelled Mathews
619 Stuart McFarland RC .40 1.00
Adam Sterrett RC
620 David Krynzel 2.00 5.00
Grady Sizemore
621 Keith Bucktrot .40 1.00
Dane Sardinha
622 Anaheim Angels TC .30 .75
623 Ariz. Diamondbacks TC .30 .75
624 Atlanta Braves TC .30 .75
625 Baltimore Orioles TC .30 .75
626 Boston Red Sox TC .30 .75
627 Chicago Cubs TC .30 .75
628 Chicago White Sox TC .30 .75
629 Cincinnati Reds TC .30 .75
630 Cleveland Indians TC .30 .75
631 Colorado Rockies TC .30 .75
632 Detroit Tigers TC .30 .75
633 Florida Marlins TC .30 .75
634 Houston Astros TC .30 .75
635 K.C. Royals TC .30 .75
636 L.A. Dodgers TC .30 .75
637 Milw. Brewers TC .30 .75
638 Minnesota Twins TC .30 .75
639 Montreal Expos TC .30 .75
640 New York Mets TC .30 .75
641 New York Yankees TC 1.50 4.00
642 Oakland Athletics TC .30 .75
643 Phil. Phillies TC .30 .75
644 Pittsburgh Pirates TC .30 .75
645 San Diego Padres TC .30 .75
646 S.F. Giants TC .30 .75
647 Seattle Mariners TC .30 .75
648 St. Louis Cardinals TC .30 .75
649 T. Bay Devil Rays TC .30 .75
650 Texas Rangers TC .30 .75
651 Toronto Blue Jays TC .30 .75
652 Bucky Dent GM .20 .50
653 Jackie Robinson GM .75 2.00
654 Roberto Clemente GM 1.00 2.50
655 Nolan Ryan GM 1.25 3.00
656 Kerry Wood GM .30 .75
657 Rickey Henderson GM .75 2.00
658 Lou Brock GM .50 1.25
659 David Wells GM .20 .50
660 Andruw Jones GM .30 .75
661 Carlton Fisk GM .30 .75

2001 Topps Chrome Retrofractors

Randomly inserted into packs at one in 12, this 661-card set is a complete parallel set of the 2001 Topps Chrome base set. Please note that these cards were produced with Topps Refractor technology.

*STARS: 2.5X TO 6X BASIC CARDS
*PROSPECTS 277-301/595-621: 2X TO 5X
*ROOKIES 277-301/595-621: 2X TO 5X
596 Albert Pujols 150.00 250.00
598 Phil Wilson 30.00 60.00
Jake Peavy
Darwin Cubillan
616 Hugh Quattlebaum 40.00 80.00
Edwin Encarnacion

2001 Topps Chrome Before There Was Topps

This set parallels the regular Before There Was Topps insert cards. These cards were inserted at a rate of one in 20 2001 Topps Chrome series two hobby/retail packs.

COMPLETE SET (10) 30.00 80.00
*REFRACTORS: 1.25X TO 3X BASIC BEFORE
SER.2 REFRACTOR ODDS 1:200 HOB/RET
BT1 Lou Gehrig 5.00 12.00
BT2 Babe Ruth 8.00 20.00
BT3 Cy Young 2.50 6.00
BT4 Walter Johnson 2.50 6.00
BT5 Ty Cobb 4.00 10.00
BT6 Rogers Hornsby 2.50 6.00
BT7 Honus Wagner 2.50 6.00
BT8 Christy Mathewson 2.50 6.00
BT9 Grover Alexander 2.50 6.00
BT10 Joe DiMaggio 5.00 12.00

2001 Topps Chrome Combos

Randomly insert into packs at 1:12 Hobby/Retail and 1:4 HTA, this 10-card insert pairs up players that have put up similar statistics throughout their careers. Card backs carry a "TC" prefix. Please note that these cards feature Topps' special chrome technology.

COMPLETE SET (20) 60.00 120.00
COMPLETE SERIES 1 (10) 30.00 60.00
COMPLETE SERIES 2 (10) 30.00 60.00
*REFRACTORS: 1.5X TO 4X BASIC COMBO
REFRACTOR ODDS 1:120 H/R
TC1 Derek Jeter 4.00 10.00
Yogi Berra
Whitey Ford
Don Mattingly
Reggie Jackson
TC2 Chipper Jones 1.25 3.00
Mike Schmidt
TC3 Brooks Robinson 3.00 8.00
Cal Ripken
TC4 Bob Gibson 1.25 3.00
Pedro Martinez
TC5 Ivan Rodriguez 1.25 3.00
Johnny Bench
TC6 Ernie Banks 2.00 5.00
Alex Rodriguez
TC7 Joe Morgan 1.25 3.00
Ken Griffey Jr.
Barry Larkin
Johnny Bench
TC8 Vladimir Guerrero 1.25 3.00
Roberto Clemente
TC9 Ken Griffey Jr. 2.00 5.00
Hank Aaron
TC10 Casey Stengel MG 1.25 3.00
Joe Torre
TC11 Kevin Brown 2.50 6.00
Sandy Koufax
Don Drysdale UER
Card states the Dodgers swept the 1965 World Series
They won the Series in 7 games
TC12 Mark McGwire 3.00 8.00
Sammy Sosa
Roger Maris
Babe Ruth
TC13 Ted Williams 2.00 5.00
Carl Yastrzemski
Nomar Garciaparra
TC14 Greg Maddux 2.00 5.00
Roger Clemens
Cy Young
TC15 Tony Gwynn 2.50 6.00
Ted Williams
TC16 Cal Ripken 4.00 10.00
Lou Gehrig
TC17 Sandy Koufax 4.00 10.00
Randy Johnson
Warren Spahn
Steve Carlton
TC18 Mike Piazza 1.50 4.00
Josh Gibson
TC19 Barry Bonds 3.00 8.00
Willie Mays
TC20 Jackie Robinson 1.25 3.00
Larry Doby

2001 Topps Chrome Golden Anniversary

Randomly inserted into packs at 1:10 Hobby/Retail, this 50-card insert celebrates Topp's 50th Anniversary by taking a look at some of the all-time greats. Card backs carry a "GA" prefix. Please note that these cards feature Topps' special chrome technology.

COMPLETE SET (50) 150.00 300.00
*REFRACTORS: 1.5X TO 4X BASIC ANNV.
SER.1 REFRACTOR ODDS 1:100
GA1 Hank Aaron 4.00 10.00
GA2 Ernie Banks 2.00 5.00
GA3 Mike Schmidt 4.00 10.00
GA4 Willie Mays 4.00 10.00
GA5 Johnny Bench 2.00 5.00
GA6 Tom Seaver 1.25 3.00
GA7 Frank Robinson 1.25 3.00
GA8 Sandy Koufax 6.00 15.00
GA9 Bob Gibson 1.25 3.00
GA10 Ted Williams 4.00 10.00
GA11 Cal Ripken 6.00 15.00
GA12 Tony Gwynn 2.50 6.00
GA13 Mark McGwire 5.00 12.00
GA14 Ken Griffey Jr. 3.00 8.00
GA15 Greg Maddux 3.00 8.00
GA16 Roger Clemens 4.00 10.00
GA17 Barry Bonds 5.00 12.00
GA18 Rickey Henderson 2.00 5.00
GA19 Mike Piazza 3.00 8.00
GA20 Jose Canseco 1.25 3.00
GA21 Derek Jeter 5.00 12.00
GA22 Nomar Garciaparra 3.00 8.00
GA23 Alex Rodriguez 3.00 8.00
GA24 Sammy Sosa 2.00 5.00
GA25 Ivan Rodriguez 1.25 3.00
GA26 Vladimir Guerrero 2.00 5.00
GA27 Chipper Jones 2.00 5.00
GA28 Jeff Bagwell 1.25 3.00
GA29 Pedro Martinez 1.25 3.00
GA30 Randy Johnson 2.00 5.00
GA31 Pat Burrell .75 2.00
GA32 Josh Hamilton 1.50 4.00
GA33 Ryan Anderson .75 2.00
GA34 Corey Patterson .75 2.00
GA35 Eric Munson .75 2.00
GA36 Sean Burroughs .75 2.00
GA37 C.C. Sabathia .75 2.00
GA38 Chin-Feng Chen .75 2.00
GA39 Barry Zito 1.25 3.00
GA40 Adrian Gonzalez .75 2.00
GA41 Mark McGwire 5.00 12.00
GA42 Nomar Garciaparra 3.00 8.00
GA43 Todd Helton 1.25 3.00
GA44 Matt Williams .75 2.00
GA45 Troy Glaus .75 2.00
GA46 Geoff Jenkins .75 2.00
GA47 Frank Thomas 2.00 5.00
GA48 Mo Vaughn .75 2.00
GA49 Barry Larkin 1.25 3.00
GA50 J.D. Drew .75 2.00

2001 Topps Chrome King Of Kings

Randomly inserted into packs at 1:5,157 series one hobby and 1:5,209 series one retail and 1:6383 series two hobby and 1:6,520 series two retail, this seven-card insert features game-used memorabilia from major superstars. Please note that a special fourth card containing game-used memorabilia of all three were inserted into Hobby packs at 1:59,220. Card backs carry a "KKR" prefix.

KKR1 Hank Aaron 60.00 120.00
KKR2 Nolan Ryan Rangers 50.00 100.00
KKR3 Rickey Henderson 15.00 40.00
KKR5 Bob Gibson 10.00 25.00
KKR6 Nolan Ryan Angels 50.00 100.00
KKGE Hank Aaron
Nolan Ryan
Rickey Henderson

2001 Topps Chrome King Of Kings Refractors

This insert is a complete parallel of the Chrome King of Kings insert set produced with Topps patented refractor technology. The first three cards were randomly inserted exclusively into first series hobby packs at 1:16,920. Cards 5 and 6 were randomly seeded exclusively into second series hobby packs at a rate of 1:23,022. Card number 4 in the set (intended to feature Mark McGwire) was never produced. Only ten of each card was printed and each is hand-numbered in thein blue pen on back.

Please note that a special "Golden Edition" card containing game-used memorabilia of Aaron, Ryan and Henderson was inserted into first series hobby packs at a rate of 1:212,169. Only 5 copies of this card were produced. Card backs carry a "KKR" prefix. Due to scarcity, no pricing is provided.

KKR1 Hank Aaron/10
KKR2 Nolan Ryan Rangers/10
KKR3 Rickey Henderson/10
KKR5 Bob Gibson/10
KKR6 Nolan Ryan Angels/10
KKGE Hank Aaron
Nolan Ryan
Rickey Henderson/5

2001 Topps Chrome Originals

Randomly inserted into Hobby packs at 1:1783 and Retail packs at 1:1788, this ten-card insert features game-used jersey cards of players like Roberto Clemente and Carl Yastrzemski produced with Topps patented chrome technology.

REFRACT.1-5 SER.1 ODDS 1:9644 HOBBY
REFRACT.6-10 SER.2 ODDS 1:8372 HOBBY
REFRACTOR PRINT RUN 10 #'d SETS
NO REFRACTOR PRICE DUE TO SCARCITY
1 Roberto Clemente 175.00 300.00
2 Carl Yastrzemski 125.00 200.00
3 Mike Schmidt 75.00 150.00
4 Wade Boggs 30.00 60.00
5 Chipper Jones 40.00 80.00
6 Willie Mays 175.00 300.00
7 Lou Brock 30.00 60.00
8 Dave Parker 20.00 50.00
9 Barry Bonds 75.00 150.00
10 Alex Rodriguez 60.00 120.00

2001 Topps Chrome Past to Present

Randomly insert into packs at 1:18 Hobby/Retail, this 10-card insert pairs up players that have put up similar statistics throughout their careers. Card backs carry a "PTP" prefix. Please note that these cards feature Topps' special chrome technology.

COMPLETE SET (10) 30.00 60.00
*REFRACTORS: 1.5X TO 4X BASIC PAST
SER.1 REFRACTOR ODDS 1:180
PTP1 Phil Rizzuto 5.00 12.00
Derek Jeter
PTP2 Warren Spahn 3.00 8.00
Greg Maddux
PTP3 Yogi Berra 4.00 10.00
Jorge Posada
PTP4 Willie Mays 8.00 20.00
Barry Bonds
PTP5 Red Schoendienst 1.50 4.00
Fernando Vina
PTP6 Duke Snider 1.50 4.00
Shawn Green
PTP7 Bob Feller 1.50 4.00
Bartolo Colon
PTP8 Johnny Mize 1.50 4.00
Tino Martinez
PTP9 Larry Doby 1.50 4.00
Manny Ramirez
PTP10 Eddie Mathews 2.00 5.00
Chipper Jones

2001 Topps Chrome Through the Years Reprints

Randomly inserted into packs at 1:10 Hobby/Retail, this 50-card set takes a look at some of the best players to every make it onto a Topps trading card. Please note that these cards were produced with Topps chrome technology.

COMPLETE SET (50) 150.00 300.00
*REFRACTORS: 1.5X TO 4X BASIC THROUGH
SER.1 REFRACTOR ODDS 1:100
1 Yogi Berra 57 2.50 6.00
2 Roy Campanella 56 2.50 6.00
3 Willie Mays 53 4.00 10.00
4 Andy Pafko 52 2.50 6.00
5 Jackie Robinson 52 2.50 6.00
6 Stan Musial 59 3.00 8.00
7 Duke Snider 56 2.00 5.00
8 Warren Spahn 56 2.00 5.00
9 Ted Williams 54 6.00 15.00
10 Eddie Mathews 55 2.50 6.00
11 Willie McCovey 60 2.00 5.00
12 Frank Robinson 69 2.00 5.00
13 Ernie Banks 66 2.50 6.00
14 Hank Aaron 65 4.00 10.00
15 Sandy Koufax 61 5.00 12.00
16 Bob Gibson 68 2.00 5.00
17 Harmon Killebrew 67 2.50 6.00
18 Whitey Ford 64 2.00 5.00
19 Roberto Clemente 63 6.00 15.00
20 Juan Marichal 61 2.00 5.00
21 Johnny Bench 70 2.50 6.00
22 Willie Stargell 73 2.00 5.00
23 Joe Morgan 74 2.00 5.00
24 Carl Yastrzemski 71 3.00 8.00
25 Reggie Jackson 76 2.00 5.00
26 Tom Seaver 78 2.00 5.00
27 Steve Carlton 77 2.00 5.00
28 Jim Palmer 79 2.00 5.00
29 Rod Carew 72 2.00 5.00
30 George Brett 75 6.00 15.00
31 Roger Clemens 85 5.00 12.00
32 Don Mattingly 84 6.00 15.00
33 Ryne Sandberg 89 4.00 10.00
34 Mike Schmidt 81 4.00 10.00
35 Cal Ripken 82 8.00 20.00
36 Tony Gwynn 83 3.00 8.00
37 Ozzie Smith 87 4.00 10.00
38 Wade Boggs 88 2.00 5.00
39 Nolan Ryan 80 6.00 15.00
40 Robin Yount 86 2.50 6.00
41 Mark McGwire 99 5.00 12.00
42 Ken Griffey Jr. 92 3.00 8.00
43 Sammy Sosa 90 2.50 6.00
44 Alex Rodriguez 98 3.00 8.00
45 Barry Bonds 94 5.00 12.00
46 Mike Piazza 95 3.00 8.00
47 Chipper Jones 91 2.50 6.00
48 Greg Maddux 96 3.00 8.00
49 Nomar Garciaparra 97 3.00 8.00
50 Derek Jeter 93 6.00 15.00

2001 Topps Chrome What Could Have Been

Inserted a rate of one in 30 hobby/retail packs, these 10 cards parallel the regular What Could Have Been retail set.

COMPLETE SET (10) 15.00 40.00
*REFRACTORS: 1.5X TO 4X BASIC WHAT
SER.2 REFRACTOR ODDS 1:300 HOB/RET
WCB1 Josh Gibson 4.00 10.00
WCB2 Satchel Paige 1.50 4.00
WCB3 Buck Leonard 1.50 4.00
WCB4 James Bell 1.50 4.00
WCB5 Rube Foster 1.50 4.00
WCB6 Martin DiHigo 1.50 4.00
WCB7 William Johnson 1.50 4.00
WCB8 Mule Suttles 1.50 4.00
WCB9 Ray Dandridge 1.50 4.00
WCB10 John Lloyd 1.50 4.00

2001 Topps Chrome Traded

This set is a parallel to the 2001 Topps Traded set. Inserted into the 2001 Topps Traded at a rate of two per pack, these cards feature the patented "Chrome" technology which Topps uses.

COMPLETE SET (266) 75.00 150.00
COMMON (1-99/145-266) .30 .75
COMMON (100-144) .50 1.25
T1 Sandy Alomar Jr. .30 .75
T2 Kevin Appier .50 1.25
T3 Brad Ausmus .50 1.25
T4 Derek Bell .30 .75
T5 Bret Boone .50 1.25
T6 Rico Brogna .30 .75
T7 Ellis Burks .50 1.25
T8 Ken Caminiti .50 1.25
T9 Roger Cedeno .30 .75
T10 Royce Clayton .30 .75
T11 Enrique Wilson .30 .75
T12 Rheal Cormier .30 .75
T13 Eric Davis .50 1.25
T14 Shawon Dunston .30 .75
T15 Andres Galarraga .50 1.25
T16 Tom Gordon .30 .75
T17 Mark Grace .75 2.00
T18 Jeffrey Hammonds .30 .75
T19 Dustin Hermanson .30 .75
T20 Quinton McCracken .30 .75
T21 Todd Hundley .30 .75
T22 Charles Johnson .50 1.25
T23 Marquis Grissom .50 1.25
T24 Jose Mesa .30 .75
T25 Brian Boehringer .30 .75
T26 John Rocker .50 1.25
T27 Jeff Frye .30 .75
T28 Reggie Sanders .50 1.25
T29 David Segui .30 .75
T30 Mike Sirotka .30 .75
T31 Fernando Tatis .30 .75
T32 Steve Trachsel .30 .75
T33 Ismael Valdes .30 .75
T34 Randy Velarde .30 .75
T35 Ryan Kohlmeier .30 .75
T36 Mike Bordick .50 1.25
T37 Kent Bottenfield .30 .75
T38 Pat Rapp .30 .75
T39 Jeff Nelson .30 .75
T40 Ricky Bottalico .30 .75
T41 Luke Prokopec .30 .75
T42 Hideo Nomo 1.25 3.00
T43 Bill Mueller .50 1.25
T44 Roberto Kelly .30 .75
T45 Chris Holt .30 .75
T46 Mike Jackson .30 .75
T47 Devon White .50 1.25
T48 Gerald Williams .30 .75
T49 Eddie Taubensee .30 .75
T50 Brian Hunter UER .30 .75
Brian R Hunter pictured
Brian L Hunter stats
T51 Nelson Cruz .30 .75
T52 Jeff Fassero .30 .75
T53 Bubba Trammell .30 .75
T54 Bo Porter .30 .75
T55 Greg Norton .30 .75
T56 Benito Santiago .50 1.25
T57 Ruben Rivera .30 .75
T58 Dee Brown .30 .75
T59 Jose Canseco .75 2.00
T60 Chris Michalak .30 .75
T61 Tim Worrell .30 .75
T62 Matt Clement .50 1.25
T63 Bill Pulsipher .30 .75
T64 Troy Brohawn RC .40 1.00
T65 Mark Kotsay .50 1.25
T66 Jimmy Rollins .50 1.25
T67 Shea Hillenbrand .50 1.25
T68 Ted Lilly .30 .75
T69 Jermaine Dye .50 1.25
T70 Jerry Hairston Jr. .30 .75
T71 John Mabry .30 .75
T72 Kurt Abbott .30 .75
T73 Eric Owens .30 .75
T74 Jeff Brantley .30 .75
T75 Roy Oswalt 1.25 3.00
T76 Doug Mientkiewicz .50 1.25
T77 Rickey Henderson 1.25 3.00
T78 Jason Grimsley .30 .75
T79 Christian Parker RC .40 1.00
T80 Donne Wall .30 .75
T81 Alex Arias .30 .75
T82 Willis Roberts .30 .75
T83 Ryan Minor .30 .75
T84 Jason LaRue .30 .75
T85 Ruben Sierra .50 1.25
T86 Johnny Damon .75 2.00
T87 Juan Gonzalez .50 1.25
T88 C.C. Sabathia .50 1.25
T89 Tony Batista .30 .75
T90 Jay Witasick .30 .75
T91 Brent Abernathy .30 .75
T92 Paul LoDuca .50 1.25
T93 Wes Helms .30 .75
T94 Mark Wohlers .30 .75
T95 Rob Bell .30 .75
T96 Tim Redding .30 .75
T97 Bud Smith RC .40 1.00
T98 Adam Dunn .75 2.00
T99 Ichiro Suzuki 12.50 30.00
Albert Pujols ROY
T100 Carlton Fisk 81 .75 2.00
T101 Tim Raines 81 .50 1.25
T102 Juan Marichal 74 .50 1.25
T103 Dave Winfield 81 .50 1.25
T104 Reggie Jackson 82 .75 2.00
T105 Cal Ripken 82 4.00 10.00
T106 Ozzie Smith 82 2.00 5.00
T107 Tom Seaver 83 .75 2.00
T108 Lou Piniella 74 .50 1.25
T109 Dwight Gooden 84 .50 1.25
T110 Bret Saberhagen 84 .50 1.25
T111 Gary Carter 85 .50 1.25
T112 Jack Clark 85 .50 1.25
T113 Rickey Henderson 85 1.25 3.00
T114 Barry Bonds 86 3.00 8.00
T115 Bobby Bonilla 86 .50 1.25
T116 Jose Canseco 86 .75 2.00
T117 Will Clark 86 .75 2.00
T118 Andres Galarraga 86 .50 1.25
T119 Bo Jackson 86 1.25 3.00
T120 Wally Joyner 86 .50 1.25
T121 Ellis Burks 87 .50 1.25
T122 David Cone 87 .50 1.25
T123 Greg Maddux 87 2.00 5.00
T124 Willie Randolph 76 .50 1.25
T125 Dennis Eckersley 87 .50 1.25
T126 Matt Williams 87 .50 1.25
T127 Joe Morgan 81 .50 1.25
T128 Fred McGriff 87 .75 2.00
T129 Roberto Alomar 88 .75 2.00
T130 Lee Smith 88 .50 1.25
T131 David Wells 88 .50 1.25
T132 Ken Griffey Jr. 89 2.00 5.00
T133 Deion Sanders 89 .75 2.00
T134 Nolan Ryan 89 3.00 8.00
T135 David Justice 90 .50 1.25
T136 Joe Carter 91 .50 1.25
T137 Jack Morris 92 .50 1.25
T138 Mike Piazza 93 2.00 5.00
T139 Barry Bonds 93 3.00 8.00
T140 Terrence Long 94 .50 1.25
T141 Ben Grieve 94 .50 1.25
T142 Richie Sexson 95 .50 1.25
George Arias
Mark Sweeney
Brian Schneider
T143 Sean Burroughs 99 .50 1.25
T144 Alfonso Soriano 99 .75 2.00
T145 Bob Boone MG .30 .75
T146 Larry Bowa MG .30 .75
T147 Bob Brenly MG .30 .75
T148 Buck Martinez MG .30 .75
T149 L. McClendon MG .30 .75
T150 Jim Tracy MG .30 .75
T151 Jared Abruzzo RC .40 1.00
T152 Kurt Ainsworth .30 .75
T153 Willie Bloomquist .50 1.25
T154 Ben Broussard .30 .75
T155 Bobby Bradley .30 .75
T156 Mike Bynum .30 .75
T157 A.J. Hinch .30 .75
T158 Ryan Christianson .30 .75
T159 Carlos Silva .30 .75
T160 Joe Crede 1.25 3.00
T161 Jack Cust .30 .75
T162 Ben Diggins .30 .75
T163 Phil Dumatrait .30 .75
T164 Alex Escobar .30 .75
T165 Miguel Olivo .30 .75
T166 Chris George .30 .75
T167 Marcus Giles .50 1.25
T168 Keith Ginter .30 .75
T169 Josh Girdley .30 .75
T170 Tony Alvarez .30 .75
T171 Scott Seabol .30 .75
T172 Josh Hamilton .60 1.50
T173 Jason Hart .30 .75
T174 Israel Alcantara .30 .75
T175 Jake Peavy 3.00 8.00
T176 Stubby Clapp RC .40 1.00
T177 D'Angelo Jimenez .30 .75
T178 Nick Johnson .50 1.25
T179 Ben Johnson .50 1.25
T180 Larry Bigbie .30 .75
T181 Allen Levrault .30 .75
T182 Felipe Lopez .50 1.25
T183 Sean Burnett .30 .75
T184 Nick Neugebauer .30 .75
T185 Austin Kearns .50 1.25
T186 Corey Patterson .30 .75
T187 Carlos Pena .30 .75
T188 R. Rodriguez RC .40 1.00
T189 Juan Rivera .30 .75
T190 Grant Roberts .30 .75
T191 Adam Pettyjohn RC .40 1.00
T192 Jared Sandberg .30 .75
T193 Xavier Nady .30 .75
T194 Dane Sardinha .30 .75
T195 Shawn Sonnier .30 .75
T196 Rafael Soriano .40 1.00
T197 Brian Specht RC .40 1.00
T198 Aaron Myette .30 .75
T199 Juan Uribe RC .50 1.25
T200 Jayson Werth .30 .75
T201 Brad Wilkerson .30 .75
T202 Horacio Estrada .30 .75
T203 Joel Pineiro .50 1.25
T204 Matt LeCroy .30 .75
T205 Michael Coleman .30 .75
T206 Ben Sheets .75 2.00
T207 Eric Byrnes .30 .75
T208 Sean Burroughs .30 .75
T209 Ken Harvey .30 .75
T210 Travis Hafner 3.00 8.00
T211 Erick Almonte .40 1.00
T212 Jason Belcher RC .40 1.00
T213 Wilson Betemit RC 1.50 4.00
T214 Hank Blalock RC 2.50 6.00
T215 Danny Borrell .40 1.00
T216 John Buck RC .50 1.25
T217 Freddie Bynum RC .40 1.00
T218 Noel Devarez RC .40 1.00
T219 Juan Diaz RC .40 1.00
T220 Felix Diaz RC .40 1.00
T221 Josh Fogg RC .40 1.00
T222 Matt Ford RC .40 1.00
T223 Scott Heard .30 .75
T224 Ben Hendrickson RC .40 1.00
T225 Cody Ross RC .40 1.00
T226 A. Hernandez RC .40 1.00
T227 Alfredo Amezaga RC .40 1.00
T228 Bob Keppel RC .40 1.00
T229 Ryan Madson RC .75 2.00
T230 Octavio Martinez RC .40 1.00
T231 Hee Seop Choi .50 1.25
T232 Thomas Mitchell .30 .75
T233 Luis Montanez .40 1.00
T234 Andy Morales RC .40 1.00
T235 Justin Morneau RC 5.00 12.00
T236 Toe Nash RC .40 1.00
T237 V. Pascucci RC .40 1.00
T238 Roy Smith RC .40 1.00
T239 Antonio Perez RC .50 1.25
T240 Chad Petty RC .40 1.00
T241 Steve Smyth .40 1.00
T242 Jose Reyes RC 12.50 30.00
T243 Eric Reynolds RC .40 1.00
T244 Dominic Rich .40 1.00
T245 J. Richardson RC .40 1.00
T246 Ed Rogers RC .40 1.00
T247 Albert Pujols 30.00 60.00
T248 Esix Snead RC .40 1.00
T249 Luis Torres RC .40 1.00
T250 Matt White RC .40 1.00
T251 Blake Williams .40 1.00
T252 Chris Russ .40 1.00
T253 Joe Kennedy RC .50 1.25
T254 Jeff Randazzo RC .40 1.00
T255 Beau Hale RC .40 1.00
T256 Brad Hennessey RC .75 2.00
T257 Jake Gautreau RC .40 1.00
T258 Jeff Mathis RC .50 1.25
T259 Aaron Heilman RC .50 1.25
T260 B. Sardinha RC .40 1.00
T261 Irvin Guzman RC 3.00 8.00
T262 Gabe Gross RC .50 1.25
T263 J.D. Martin RC .40 1.00
T264 Chris Smith RC .40 1.00
T265 Kenny Baugh RC .40 1.00
T266 Ichiro Suzuki RC 10.00 25.00

2001 Topps Chrome Traded Retrofractors

This set is a parallel to the 2001 Topps Chrome Traded set. Inserted into the 2001 Topps Traded at a rate of one in 12, these cards feature grayback card stock with refractor technology on the front.

*STARS: 1.5X TO 4X BASIC CARDS
*REPRINTS: 1X TO 2.5X BASIC
*ROOKIES: 2.5X TO 6X BASIC
T99 Ichiro Suzuki 60.00 120.00
Albert Pujols ROY
T210 Travis Hafner 20.00 50.00
T235 Justin Morneau 30.00 60.00
T242 Jose Reyes 75.00 150.00
T247 Albert Pujols 150.00 250.00
T261 Irvin Guzman 50.00 100.00
T266 Ichiro Suzuki 50.00 100.00

2002 Topps Chrome

This product's first series, consisting of cards 1-6 and 8-331, was released in late January, 2002. The second series, consisting of cards 366-695, was released in early June, 2002. Both first and second series packs contained four cards and carried an SRP of $3. Sealed boxes contained 24 packs. The set parallels the 2002 Topps set except, of course, for the upgraded chrome card stock. Unlike the 1999 Topps Chrome product, featuring 70 variations of Mark McGwire's Home Run record card, the 2002 first series product did not include different variations of the Barry Bonds Home Run record cards. Please note, that just as in the basic 2002 Topps set there is no card number 7 as it is still retired in honor of Mickey Mantle. In addition, the foil-coated subset cards from the basic Topps set (cards 332-365 and 696-719) were NOT replicated for this Chrome set, thus it's considered complete at 660 cards. Notable Rookie Cards include Kazuhisa Ishii and Joe Mauer.

COMPLETE SET (660) 100.00 250.00
COMPLETE SERIES 1 (330) 50.00 125.00
COMPLETE SERIES 2 (330) 50.00 125.00
COMMON (1-331/366-695) .20 .50
COMMON (307-326/671-690) .60 1.50
COMMON (327-331/691-695) .60 1.50
1 Pedro Martinez .60 1.50
2 Mike Stanton .20 .50
3 Brad Penny .20 .50
4 Mike Matheny .20 .50
5 Johnny Damon .60 1.50
6 Bret Boone .40 1.00
7 Does Not Exist
8 Chris Truby .20 .50
9 B.J. Surhoff .40 1.00
10 Mike Hampton .40 1.00
11 Juan Pierre .40 1.00
12 Mark Buehrle .40 1.00
13 Bob Abreu .40 1.00
14 David Cone .40 1.00
15 Aaron Sele .20 .50
16 Fernando Tatis .20 .50
17 Bobby Jones .20 .50
18 Rick Helling .20 .50
19 Dmitri Young .40 1.00
20 Mike Mussina .60 1.50
21 Mike Sweeney .40 1.00
22 Cristian Guzman .20 .50
23 Ryan Kohlmeier .20 .50
24 Adam Kennedy .20 .50
25 Larry Walker .40 1.00
26 Eric Davis .40 1.00
27 Jason Tyner .20 .50
28 Eric Young .20 .50
29 Jason Marquis .20 .50
30 Luis Gonzalez .40 1.00
31 Kevin Tapani .20 .50
32 Orlando Cabrera .40 1.00
33 Marty Cordova .20 .50
34 Brad Ausmus .40 1.00
35 Livan Hernandez .40 1.00
36 Alex Gonzalez .20 .50
37 Edgar Renteria .40 1.00
38 Bengie Molina .20 .50
39 Frank Menechino .20 .50
40 Rafael Palmeiro .60 1.50
41 Brad Fullmer .20 .50
42 Julio Zuleta .20 .50
43 Darren Dreifort .20 .50
44 Trot Nixon .40 1.00
45 Trevor Hoffman .40 1.00
46 Vladimir Nunez .20 .50
47 Mark Kotsay .40 1.00
48 Kenny Rogers .40 1.00
49 Ben Petrick .20 .50
50 Jeff Bagwell .60 1.50
51 Juan Encarnacion .20 .50
52 Ramiro Mendoza .20 .50
53 Brian Meadows .20 .50
54 Chad Curtis .20 .50
55 Aramis Ramirez .40 1.00
56 Mark McLemore .20 .50
57 Dante Bichette .40 1.00
58 Scott Schoeneweis .20 .50
59 Jose Cruz Jr. .20 .50
60 Roger Clemens 2.00 5.00
61 Jose Guillen .40 1.00
62 Darren Oliver .20 .50
63 Chris Reitsma .20 .50
64 Jeff Abbott .20 .50
65 Robin Ventura .40 1.00
66 Denny Neagle .20 .50
67 Al Martin .20 .50
68 Benito Santiago .40 1.00
69 Roy Oswalt .40 1.00
70 Juan Gonzalez .40 1.00
71 Garret Anderson .40 1.00
72 Bobby Bonilla .40 1.00
73 Danny Bautista .20 .50
74 J.T. Snow .40 1.00
75 Derek Jeter 2.50 6.00
76 John Olerud .40 1.00
77 Kevin Appier .40 1.00
78 Phil Nevin .40 1.00
79 Sean Casey .40 1.00
80 Troy Glaus .40 1.00
81 Joe Randa .40 1.00
82 Jose Valentin .20 .50
83 Ricky Bottalico .20 .50
84 Todd Zeile .40 1.00
85 Barry Larkin .60 1.50
86 Bob Wickman .20 .50
87 Jeff Shaw .20 .50
88 Greg Vaughn .20 .50
89 Fernando Vina .20 .50
90 Mark Mulder .40 1.00
91 Paul Bako .20 .50
92 Aaron Boone .40 1.00
93 Esteban Loaiza .20 .50
94 Richie Sexson .40 1.00
95 Alfonso Soriano .40 1.00
96 Tony Womack .20 .50
97 Paul Shuey .20 .50
98 Melvin Mora .40 1.00
99 Tony Gwynn 1.25 3.00
100 Vladimir Guerrero 1.00 2.50
101 Keith Osik .20 .50
102 Bud Smith .20 .50
103 Scott Williamson .20 .50
104 Daryle Ward .20 .50
105 Doug Mientkiewicz .40 1.00
106 Stan Javier .20 .50
107 Russ Ortiz .20 .50
108 Wade Miller .20 .50
109 Luke Prokopec .20 .50
110 Andruw Jones .60 1.50
111 Ron Coomer .20 .50
112 Dan Wilson .20 .50
113 Luis Castillo .20 .50
114 Derek Bell .20 .50
115 Gary Sheffield .40 1.00
116 Ruben Rivera .20 .50
117 Paul O'Neill .60 1.50
118 Craig Paquette .20 .50
119 Kelvim Escobar .20 .50
120 Brad Radke .40 1.00
121 Jorge Fabregas .20 .50
122 Randy Winn .20 .50
123 Tom Goodwin .20 .50
124 Jaret Wright .20 .50
125 Barry Bonds HR 73 15.00 40.00
126 Al Leiter .20 .50
127 Ben Davis .20 .50
128 Frank Catalanotto .20 .50
129 Jose Cabrera .20 .50
130 Magglio Ordonez .40 1.00
131 Jose Macias .20 .50
132 Ted Lilly .20 .50
133 Chris Holt .20 .50
134 Eric Milton .20 .50
135 Shannon Stewart .40 1.00
136 Omar Olivares .20 .50
137 David Segui .20 .50
138 Jeff Nelson .20 .50
139 Matt Williams .40 1.00
140 Ellis Burks .40 1.00
141 Jason Bere .20 .50
142 Jimmy Haynes .20 .50
143 Ramon Hernandez .20 .50
144 Craig Counsell .20 .50
145 John Smoltz .60 1.50
146 Homer Bush .20 .50
147 Quilvio Veras .20 .50
148 Esteban Yan .20 .50
149 Ramon Ortiz .20 .50
150 Carlos Delgado .40 1.00
151 Lee Stevens .20 .50
152 Wil Cordero .20 .50
153 Mike Bordick .40 1.00
154 John Flaherty .20 .50
155 Omar Daal .20 .50
156 Todd Ritchie .20 .50
157 Carl Everett .40 1.00
158 Scott Sullivan .20 .50
159 Deivi Cruz .20 .50
160 Albert Pujols 2.00 5.00
161 Royce Clayton .20 .50
162 Jeff Suppan .20 .50
163 C.C. Sabathia .40 1.00
164 Jimmy Rollins .40 1.00
165 Rickey Henderson 1.00 2.50
166 Rey Ordonez .20 .50
167 Shawn Estes .20 .50
168 Reggie Sanders .40 1.00
169 Jon Lieber .20 .50
170 Armando Benitez .20 .50
171 Mike Remlinger .20 .50
172 Billy Wagner .40 1.00
173 Troy Percival .40 1.00
174 Devon White .40 1.00
175 Ivan Rodriguez .60 1.50
176 Dustin Hermanson .20 .50
177 Brian Anderson .20 .50
178 Graeme Lloyd .20 .50
179 Russell Branyan .20 .50
180 Bobby Higginson .40 1.00
181 Alex Gonzalez .20 .50
182 John Franco .40 1.00
183 Sidney Ponson .20 .50
184 Jose Mesa .20 .50
185 Todd Hollandsworth .20 .50
186 Kevin Young .20 .50
187 Tim Wakefield .40 1.00
188 Craig Biggio .60 1.50
189 Jason Isringhausen .40 1.00
190 Mark Quinn .20 .50
191 Glendon Rusch .20 .50
192 Damian Miller .20 .50
193 Sandy Alomar Jr. .20 .50
194 Scott Brosius .40 1.00
195 Dave Martinez .20 .50
196 Danny Graves .20 .50
197 Shea Hillenbrand .40 1.00
198 Jimmy Anderson .20 .50
199 Travis Lee .20 .50
200 Randy Johnson 1.00 2.50
201 Carlos Beltran .40 1.00
202 Jerry Hairston .20 .50
203 Jesus Sanchez .20 .50
204 Eddie Taubensee .20 .50
205 David Wells .40 1.00
206 Russ Davis .20 .50
207 Michael Barrett .20 .50
208 Marquis Grissom .40 1.00
209 Byung-Hyun Kim .40 1.00

210 Hideo Nomo 1.00 2.50
211 Ryan Rupe .20 .50
212 Ricky Gutierrez .20 .50
213 Darryl Kile .40 1.00
214 Rico Brogna .20 .50
215 Terrence Long .20 .50
216 Mike Jackson .20 .50
217 Jamey Wright .20 .50
218 Adrian Beltre .40 1.00
219 Benny Agbayani .20 .50
220 Chuck Knoblauch .40 1.00
221 Randy Wolf .20 .50
222 Andy Ashby .20 .50
223 Corey Koskie .20 .50
224 Roger Cedeno .20 .50
225 Ichiro Suzuki 2.00 5.00
226 Keith Foulke .40 1.00
227 Ryan Minor .20 .50
228 Shawon Dunston .20 .50
229 Alex Cora .20 .50
230 Jeromy Burnitz .40 1.00
231 Mark Grace .60 1.50
232 Aubrey Huff .40 1.00
233 Jeffrey Hammonds .20 .50
234 Olmedo Saenz .20 .50
235 Brian Jordan .40 1.00
236 Jeremy Giambi .20 .50
237 Joe Girardi .20 .50
238 Eric Gagne .40 1.00
239 Masato Yoshii .20 .50
240 Greg Maddux 1.50 4.00
241 Bryan Rekar .20 .50
242 Ray Durham .40 1.00
243 Torii Hunter .40 1.00
244 Derrek Lee .60 1.50
245 Jim Edmonds .40 1.00
246 Einar Diaz .20 .50
247 Brian Bohanon .20 .50
248 Ron Belliard .20 .50
249 Mike Lowell .40 1.00
250 Sammy Sosa 1.00 2.50
251 Richard Hidalgo .20 .50
252 Bartolo Colon .40 1.00
253 Jorge Posada .60 1.50
254 Latroy Hawkins .20 .50
255 Paul LoDuca .40 1.00
256 Carlos Febles .20 .50
257 Nelson Cruz .20 .50
258 Edgardo Alfonzo .20 .50
259 Joey Hamilton .20 .50
260 Cliff Floyd .40 1.00
261 Wes Helms .20 .50
262 Jay Bell .40 1.00
263 Mike Cameron .20 .50
264 Paul Konerko .40 1.00
265 Jeff Kent .40 1.00
266 Robert Fick .20 .50
267 Allen Levrault .20 .50
268 Placido Polanco .20 .50
269 Marlon Anderson .20 .50
270 Mariano Rivera 1.00 2.50
271 Chan Ho Park .40 1.00
272 Jose Vizcaino .20 .50
273 Jeff D'Amico .20 .50
274 Mark Gardner .20 .50
275 Travis Fryman .40 1.00
276 Darren Lewis .20 .50
277 Bruce Bochy MG .20 .50
278 Jerry Manuel MG .20 .50
279 Bob Brenly MG .20 .50
280 Don Baylor MG .40 1.00
281 Davey Lopes MG .40 1.00
282 Jerry Narron MG .20 .50
283 Tony Muser MG .20 .50
284 Hal McRae MG .40 1.00
285 Bobby Cox MG .40 1.00
286 Larry Dierker MG .20 .50
287 Phil Garner MG .40 1.00
288 Joe Kerrigan MG .20 .50
289 Bobby Valentine MG .20 .50
290 Dusty Baker MG .40 1.00
291 Lloyd McClendon MG .20 .50
292 Mike Scioscia MG .20 .50
293 Buck Martinez MG .20 .50
294 Larry Bowa MG .40 1.00
295 Tony LaRussa MG .40 1.00
296 Jeff Torborg MG .20 .50
297 Tom Kelly MG .20 .50
298 Mike Hargrove MG .20 .50
299 Art Howe MG .20 .50
300 Lou Piniella MG .40 1.00
301 Charlie Manuel MG .20 .50
302 Buddy Bell MG .40 1.00
303 Tony Perez MG .40 1.00
304 Bob Boone MG .40 1.00
305 Joe Torre MG .60 1.50
306 Jim Tracy MG .20 .50
307 Jason Lane PROS .60 1.50
308 Chris George PROS .60 1.50
309 Hank Blalock PROS 1.00 2.50
310 Joe Borchard PROS .60 1.50
311 Marlon Byrd PROS .60 1.50
312 Ray. Cabrera PROS RC .60 1.50
313 Fr. Sanchez PROS RC 2.50 6.00
314 Scott Wiggins PROS RC .60 1.50
315 Jason Maule PROS RC .60 1.50
316 Dionys Cesar PROS RC .60 1.50
317 Boof Bonser PROS .60 1.50
318 Juan Tolentino PROS RC .60 1.50
319 Earl Snyder PROS RC .60 1.50
320 Travis Wade PROS RC .60 1.50
321 Nap. Calzado PROS RC .60 1.50
322 Eric Glaser PROS .60 1.50
323 Craig Kuzmic PROS RC .60 1.50
324 Nic Jackson PROS RC .60 1.50
325 Mike Rivera PROS .60 1.50
326 Jason Bay PROS RC 3.00 8.00
327 Chris Smith DP .60 1.50
328 Jake Gautreau DP .60 1.50
329 Gabe Gross DP .60 1.50
330 Kenny Baugh DP .60 1.50
331 J.D. Martin DP .60 1.50
366 Pat Meares .20 .50
367 Mike Lieberthal .40 1.00
368 Larry Bigbie .20 .50
369 Ron Gant .40 1.00
370 Moises Alou .40 1.00
371 Chad Kreuter .20 .50
372 Willis Roberts .20 .50
373 Toby Hall .20 .50
374 Miguel Batista .20 .50
375 John Burkett .20 .50
376 Cory Lidle .20 .50
377 Nick Neugebauer .20 .50
378 Jay Payton .20 .50
379 Steve Karsay .20 .50
380 Eric Chavez .40 1.00
381 Kelly Stinnett .20 .50
382 Jarrod Washburn .20 .50
383 Rick White .20 .50
384 Jeff Conine .40 1.00
385 Fred McGriff .60 1.50
386 Marvin Benard .20 .50
387 Joe Crede .40 1.00
388 Dennis Cook .20 .50
389 Rick Reed .20 .50
390 Tom Glavine .60 1.50
391 Rondell White .40 1.00
392 Matt Morris .40 1.00
393 Pat Rapp .20 .50
394 Robert Person .20 .50
395 Omar Vizquel .60 1.50
396 Jeff Cirillo .20 .50
397 Dave Mlicki .20 .50
398 Jose Ortiz .20 .50
399 Ryan Dempster .20 .50
400 Curt Schilling .40 1.00
401 Peter Bergeron .20 .50
402 Kyle Lohse .20 .50
403 Craig Wilson .20 .50
404 David Justice .40 1.00
405 Darin Erstad .40 1.00
406 Jose Mercedes .20 .50
407 Carl Pavano .40 1.00
408 Albie Lopez .20 .50
409 Alex Ochoa .20 .50
410 Chipper Jones 1.00 2.50
411 Tyler Houston .20 .50
412 Dean Palmer .40 1.00
413 Damian Jackson .20 .50
414 Josh Towers .20 .50
415 Rafael Furcal .40 1.00
416 Mike Morgan .20 .50
417 Herb Perry .20 .50
418 Mike Sirotka .20 .50
419 Mark Wohlers .20 .50
420 Nomar Garciaparra 1.50 4.00
421 Felipe Lopez .20 .50
422 Joe McEwing .20 .50
423 Jacque Jones .40 1.00
424 Julio Franco .40 1.00
425 Frank Thomas 1.00 2.50
426 So Taguchi RC 1.00 2.50
427 Kazuhisa Ishii RC 1.00 2.50
428 D'Angelo Jimenez .20 .50
429 Chris Stynes .20 .50
430 Kerry Wood .40 1.00
431 Chris Singleton .20 .50
432 Erubiel Durazo .20 .50
433 Matt Lawton .20 .50
434 Bill Mueller .40 1.00
435 Jose Canseco .60 1.50
436 Ben Grieve .20 .50
437 Terry Mulholland .20 .50
438 David Bell .20 .50
439 A.J. Pierzynski .40 1.00
440 Adam Dunn .40 1.00
441 Jon Garland .20 .50
442 Jeff Fassero .20 .50
443 Julio Lugo .20 .50
444 Carlos Guillen .40 1.00
445 Orlando Hernandez .40 1.00
446 Mark Loretta .20 .50
447 Scott Spiezio .20 .50
448 Kevin Millwood .40 1.00
449 Jamie Moyer .40 1.00
450 Todd Helton .60 1.50
451 Todd Walker .20 .50
452 Jose Lima .20 .50
453 Brook Fordyce .20 .50
454 Aaron Rowand .40 1.00
455 Barry Zito .40 1.00
456 Eric Owens .20 .50
457 Charles Nagy .20 .50
458 Raul Ibanez .20 .50
459 Joe Mays .20 .50
460 Jim Thome .60 1.50
461 Adam Eaton .20 .50
462 Felix Martinez .20 .50
463 Vernon Wells .40 1.00
464 Donnie Sadler .20 .50
465 Tony Clark .20 .50
466 Jose Hernandez .20 .50
467 Ramon Martinez .20 .50
468 Rusty Greer .40 1.00
469 Rod Barajas .20 .50
470 Lance Berkman .40 1.00
471 Brady Anderson .40 1.00
472 Pedro Astacio .20 .50
473 Shane Halter .20 .50
474 Bret Prinz .20 .50
475 Edgar Martinez .60 1.50
476 Steve Trachsel .20 .50
477 Gary Matthews Jr. .20 .50
478 Ismael Valdes .20 .50
479 Juan Uribe .20 .50
480 Shawn Green .40 1.00
481 Kirk Rueter .20 .50
482 Damion Easley .20 .50
483 Chris Carpenter .40 1.00
484 Kris Benson .20 .50
485 Antonio Alfonseca .20 .50
486 Kyle Farnsworth .20 .50
487 Brandon Lyon .20 .50
488 Hideki Irabu .20 .50
489 David Ortiz 1.00 2.50
490 Mike Piazza 1.50 4.00
491 Derek Lowe .40 1.00
492 Chris Gomez .20 .50
493 Mark Johnson .20 .50
494 John Rocker .40 1.00
495 Eric Karros .40 1.00
496 Bill Haselman .20 .50
497 Dave Veres .20 .50
498 Pete Harnisch .20 .50
499 Tomokazu Ohka .20 .50
500 Barry Bonds 2.50 6.00
501 David Dellucci .20 .50
502 Wendell Magee .20 .50
503 Tom Gordon .20 .50
504 Jose Vazquez .40 1.00
505 Ben Sheets .40 1.00
506 Wilton Guerrero .20 .50
507 John Halama .20 .50
508 Mark Redman .20 .50
509 Jack Wilson .20 .50
510 Bernie Williams .60 1.50
511 Miguel Cairo .20 .50
512 Denny Hocking .20 .50
513 Tony Batista .20 .50
514 Mark Grudzielanek .20 .50
515 Jose Vidro .20 .50
516 Sterling Hitchcock .20 .50
517 Billy Koch .20 .50
518 Matt Clement .40 1.00
519 Bruce Chen .20 .50
520 Roberto Alomar .60 1.50
521 Orlando Palmeiro .20 .50
522 Steve Finley .40 1.00
523 Danny Patterson .20 .50
524 Terry Adams .20 .50
525 Tino Martinez .60 1.50
526 Tony Armas Jr. UER .20 .50
Career stats do not include pre-2001
527 Geoff Jenkins .20 .50
528 Kerry Robinson .20 .50
529 Corey Patterson .20 .50
530 Brian Giles .40 1.00
531 Jose Jimenez .20 .50
532 Joe Kennedy .20 .50
533 Armando Rios .20 .50
534 Osvaldo Fernandez .20 .50
535 Ruben Sierra .40 1.00
536 Octavio Dotel .20 .50
537 Luis Sojo .20 .50
538 Brent Butler .20 .50
539 Pablo Ozuna .20 .50
540 Freddy Garcia .40 1.00
541 Chad Durbin .20 .50
542 Orlando Merced .20 .50
543 Michael Tucker .20 .50
544 Roberto Hernandez .20 .50
545 Pat Burrell .40 1.00
546 A.J. Burnett .40 1.00
547 Bubba Trammell .20 .50
548 Scott Elarton .20 .50
549 Mike Darr .20 .50
550 Ken Griffey Jr. 1.50 4.00
551 Ugueth Urbina .20 .50
552 Todd Jones .20 .50
553 Delino Deshields .20 .50
554 Adam Piatt .20 .50
555 Jason Kendall .40 1.00
556 Hector Ortiz .20 .50
557 Turk Wendell .20 .50
558 Rob Bell .20 .50
559 Sun Woo Kim .20 .50
560 Raul Mondesi .40 1.00
561 Brent Abernathy .20 .50
562 Seth Etherton .20 .50
563 Shawn Wooten .20 .50
564 Jay Buhner .40 1.00
565 Andres Galarraga .40 1.00
566 Shane Reynolds .20 .50
567 Rod Beck .20 .50
568 Dee Brown .20 .50
569 Pedro Feliz .20 .50
570 Ryan Klesko .40 1.00
571 John Vander Wal .20 .50
572 Nick Bierbrodt .20 .50
573 Joe Nathan .40 1.00
574 James Baldwin .20 .50
575 J.D. Drew .40 1.00
576 Greg Colbrunn .20 .50
577 Doug Glanville .20 .50
578 Brandon Duckworth .20 .50
579 Shawn Chacon .20 .50
580 Rich Aurilia .20 .50
581 Chuck Finley .40 1.00
582 Abraham Nunez .20 .50
583 Kenny Lofton .40 1.00
584 Brian Daubach .20 .50
585 Miguel Tejada .40 1.00
586 Nate Cornejo .20 .50
587 Kazuhiro Sasaki .40 1.00
588 Chris Richard .20 .50
589 Armando Reynoso .20 .50
590 Tim Hudson .40 1.00
591 Neifi Perez .20 .50
592 Steve Cox .20 .50
593 Henry Blanco .20 .50
594 Ricky Ledee .20 .50
595 Tim Salmon .60 1.50
596 Luis Rivas .20 .50
597 Jeff Zimmerman .20 .50
598 Matt Stairs .20 .50
599 Preston Wilson .40 1.00
600 Mark McGwire 2.50 6.00
601 Timo Perez .20 .50
602 Matt Anderson .20 .50
603 Todd Hundley .20 .50
604 Rick Ankiel .20 .50
605 Tsuyoshi Shinjo .40 1.00
606 Woody Williams .20 .50
607 Jason LaRue .20 .50
608 Carlos Lee .40 1.00
609 Russ Johnson .20 .50
610 Scott Rolen .60 1.50
611 Brent Mayne .20 .50
612 Darrin Fletcher .20 .50
613 Ray Lankford .40 1.00
614 Troy O'Leary .20 .50
615 Javier Lopez .40 1.00
616 Randy Velarde .20 .50
617 Vinny Castilla .40 1.00
618 Milton Bradley .40 1.00
619 Ruben Mateo .20 .50
620 Jason Giambi Yankees .40 1.00
621 Andy Benes .20 .50
622 Joe Mauer RC 6.00 15.00
623 Andy Pettitte .60 1.50
624 Jose Offerman .20 .50
625 Mo Vaughn .40 1.00
626 Steve Sparks UER .20 .50
No 2001 Stats listed
627 Mike Matthews .20 .50
628 Robb Nen .40 1.00
629 Kip Wells .20 .50
630 Kevin Brown .40 1.00
631 Arthur Rhodes .20 .50
632 Gabe Kapler .40 1.00
633 Jermaine Dye .40 1.00
634 Josh Beckett .40 1.00
635 Pokey Reese .20 .50
636 Benji Gil .20 .50
637 Marcus Giles .40 1.00
638 Julian Tavarez .20 .50
639 Jason Schmidt .40 1.00
640 Alex Rodriguez 1.50 4.00
641 Anaheim Angels TC .40 1.00
642 Ariz. Diamondbacks TC .60 1.50
643 Atlanta Braves TC .40 1.00
644 Baltimore Orioles TC .40 1.00
645 Boston Red Sox TC .40 1.00
646 Chicago Cubs TC .40 1.00
647 Chicago White Sox TC .40 1.00
648 Cincinnati Reds TC .40 1.00
649 Cleveland Indians TC .40 1.00
650 Colorado Rockies TC .40 1.00
651 Detroit Tigers TC .40 1.00
652 Florida Marlins TC .40 1.00
653 Houston Astros TC .40 1.00
654 Kansas City Royals TC .40 1.00
655 Los Angeles Dodgers TC .40 1.00
656 Milwaukee Brewers TC .40 1.00
657 Minnesota Twins TC .40 1.00
658 Montreal Expos TC .40 1.00
659 New York Mets TC .40 1.00
660 New York Yankees TC 1.00 2.50
661 Oakland Athletics TC .40 1.00
662 Philadelphia Phillies TC .40 1.00
663 Pittsburgh Pirates TC .40 1.00
664 San Diego Padres TC .40 1.00
665 San Francisco Giants TC .40 1.00
666 Seattle Mariners TC .60 1.50
667 St. Louis Cardinals TC .40 1.00
668 T.B. Devil Rays TC .40 1.00
669 Texas Rangers TC .40 1.00
670 Toronto Blue Jays TC .40 1.00
671 Juan Cruz PROS .60 1.50
672 Kevin Cash PROS RC .60 1.50
673 Jimmy Gobble PROS RC .60 1.50
674 Mike Hill PROS RC .60 1.50
675 T.Buchholz PROS RC .60 1.50
676 Bill Hall PROS .60 1.50
677 B.Roneberg PROS RC .60 1.50
678 R.Huffman PROS RC .60 1.50
679 Chris Tritle PROS RC .60 1.50
680 Nate Espy PROS .60 1.50
681 Nick Alvarez PROS RC .60 1.50
682 Jason Botts PROS RC .60 1.50
683 Ryan Gripp PROS RC .60 1.50
684 Dan Phillips PROS RC .60 1.50
685 Pablo Arias PROS RC .60 1.50
686 J.Rodriguez PROS RC 1.00 2.50
687 Rich Harden PROS RC 3.00 8.00
688 Neal Frendling PROS RC .60 1.50
689 R.Thompson PROS RC .60 1.50
690 G.Montalbano PROS RC .60 1.50
691 Len Dinardo DP RC .60 1.50
692 Ryan Raburn DP RC .60 1.50
693 Josh Barfield DP RC 2.00 5.00
694 David Bacani DP RC .60 1.50
695 Dan Johnson DP RC 1.00 2.50

2002 Topps Chrome Black Refractors

Issued in second series hobby packs at a stated rate of one in 21, these cards parallel the 2002 Topps Chrome set. Black Refractors can be differentiated from the regular cards by their black borders. In addition, each card was serial-numbered to 50 in thin gold foil on the card back.

*BLACK: 6X TO 15X BASIC CARDS
*BLACK 307-331/671-695: 5X TO 12X BASIC
125 Barry Bonds HR 73 175.00 300.00
622 Joe Mauer 175.00 300.00

2002 Topps Chrome Gold Refractors

Inserted into first and second series packs at stated odds of one in four, these cards parallel the 2002 Topps Chrome set. The cards can be differentiated by their striking gold borders and refractive sheen on front.

*GOLD: 2X TO 5X BASIC
*GOLD 307-331/671-695: 1.25X TO 3X BASIC
622 Joe Mauer 20.00 50.00

2002 Topps Chrome 1952 Reprints

Issued in packs at stated odds of one in eight, these nineteen reprint cards feature players who participated in the 1952 World Series which was won by the New York Yankees.

COMPLETE SET (19) 20.00 50.00
COMPLETE SERIES 1 (9) 10.00 25.00
COMPLETE SERIES 2 (10) 10.00 25.00
*REF: .75X TO 2X BASIC 52 REPRINTS
52R1 Roy Campanella 2.00 5.00
52R2 Duke Snider 1.50 4.00
52R3 Carl Erskine 1.50 4.00
52R4 Andy Pafko 1.50 4.00
52R5 Johnny Mize 1.50 4.00
52R6 Billy Martin 1.50 4.00
52R7 Phil Rizzuto 2.00 5.00
52R8 Gil McDougald 1.50 4.00
52R9 Allie Reynolds 1.50 4.00
52R10 Jackie Robinson 2.00 5.00
52R11 Preacher Roe 1.50 4.00
52R12 Gil Hodges 2.00 5.00
52R13 Billy Cox 1.50 4.00
52R14 Yogi Berra 2.00 5.00
52R15 Gene Woodling 1.50 4.00
52R16 Johnny Sain 1.50 4.00
52R17 Ralph Houk 1.50 4.00
52R18 Joe Collins 1.50 4.00
52R19 Hank Bauer 1.50 4.00

2002 Topps Chrome 5-Card Stud Aces Relics

Inserted in second series packs at a stated rate of one in 140, these five cards feature leading pitchers along with a game-worn jersey swatch.

5AAL Al Leiter Jsy 6.00 15.00
5ABZ Barry Zito Jsy 6.00 15.00
5ACS Curt Schilling Jsy 6.00 15.00
5AKB Kevin Brown Jsy 6.00 15.00
5ATH Tim Hudson Jsy 6.00 15.00

2002 Topps Chrome 5-Card Stud Deuces are Wild Relics

Inserted in second series packs at an overall stated rate of one in 428, these three cards feature teammates as well as a piece of game-used memorabilia from each player.

SER.2 BAT ODDS 1:1098
SER.2 UNIFORM ODDS 1:704
5DBT Bernie Williams Bat 15.00 40.00
Tino Martinez Bat
5DCA Chipper Jones Bat 20.00 50.00
Andruw Jones Bat
5DRC Ryan Dempster Uni 6.00 15.00
Cliff Floyd Uni

2002 Topps Chrome 5-Card Stud Jack of all Trades Relics

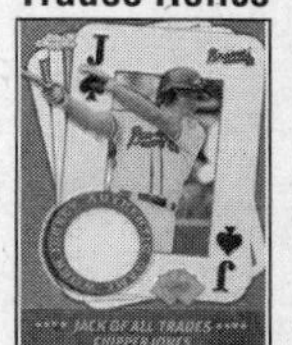

Inserted in second series packs at a stated rate of one in 428, these three cards feature players who have all five tools along with a piece of game-used memorabilia of that player.

SER.2 BAT ODDS 1:1098
SER.2 JERSEY ODDS 1:704
5JAR Alex Rodriguez Bat
5JCJ Chipper Jones Jsy 10.00 25.00
5JMO Maggio Ordonez Bat 6.00 15.00

2002 Topps Chrome 5-Card Stud Kings of the Clubhouse Relics

Inserted in second series packs at a stated rate of one in 303, these three cards feature three of the best team leaders along with a piece of game-used memorabilia from the featured player.

SER.2 BAT ODDS 1:2204
SER.2 JERSEY ODDS 1:704
SER.2 UNIFORM ODDS 1:704
5KAR Alex Rodriguez Bat
5KJB Jeff Bagwell Uniform 8.00 20.00
5KTG Tony Gwynn Jsy 12.50 30.00

2002 Topps Chrome 5-Card Stud Three of a Kind Relics

Inserted into second series packs at a stated rate of one in 689, these three cards feature a group of three teammates along with a piece of game-used memorabilia from each player.

B ='s Bat, J ='s Jsy, U ='s Uniform
5TAIR Alex Rodriguez Bat 40.00 80.00
Ivan Rodriguez Jsy
Rafael Palmeiro Uni
5TBEJ Bret Boone Bat 40.00 80.00
Edgar Martinez Bat
John Olerud Bat
5TJCL Jeff Bagwell Uni 40.00 80.00
Craig Biggio Bat
Lance Berkman Bat

2002 Topps Chrome Summer School Like Father Like Son Relics

Issued in packs at stated odds of one in 790, this card features memorabilia from Preston and Mookie Wilson.

FSCWI Preston Wilson Uni 6.00 15.00
Mookie Wilson Jsy

2002 Topps Chrome Summer School Battery Mates Relics

Inserted at overall odds of one in 349, these two cards feature memorabilia from a pitcher and catcher from the same team. The Hampton/Petrick card was seeded at a rate of 1:716 and the Glavine/Lopez at 1:681.

BMCGL Tom Glavine Jsy 10.00 25.00
Javier Lopez Jsy B
BMCHP Mike Hampton Jsy 6.00 15.00
Ben Petrick Jsy A UER
Card has two jersey swatches on it
but states jersey and bat

2002 Topps Chrome Summer School Top of the Order Relics

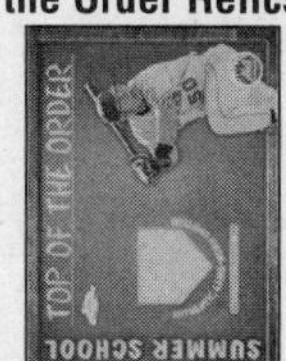

Inserted into packs at an overall rate of one in 106, these 12 cards featured players who lead off for their teams along with a memorabilia piece. Uniforms (a.k.a. pants), jerseys and bats were utilized for this set. Bat cards were seeded into five different groups at the following ratios: Group A 1:1383, Group B 1:1538, Group C 1:3170, Group D 1:2902, Group E 1:2544. Jersey cards were seeded into two groups as follows: Group A 1:790 and Group B 1:659. Uniform cards were seeded into three groups as follows: Group A 1:920, Group B 1:651 and Group C 1:614.

TOCBA Benny Agbayani Uni C 6.00 15.00
TOCCB Craig Biggio Uni A 10.00 25.00
TOCCK Chuck Knoblauch Bat E 6.00 15.00

TOCJD Johnny Damon Bat B 10.00 25.00
TOCJK Jason Kendall Bat D 6.00 15.00
TOCJP Juan Pierre Bat A 6.00 15.00
TOCKL Kenny Lofton Uni B 6.00 15.00
TOCPB Peter Bergeron Jsy A 6.00 15.00
TOCPL Paul LoDuca Bat A 6.00 15.00
TOCRF Rafael Furcal Bat C 6.00 15.00
TOCRH R.Henderson Bat B 10.00 25.00
TOCSS Shannon Stewart Jsy B 6.00 15.00

2002 Topps Chrome Traded

Inserted at a stated rate of two per 2002 Topps Traded Hobby or Retail Pack and sever per 2002 Topps Traded HTA pack, this is a complete parallel of the 2002 Topps Traded set. Unlike the regular Topps Traded set, all cards are printed in equal quantities.

COMPLETE SET (275) 60.00 120.00
T1 Jeff Weaver .20 .50
T2 Jay Powell .20 .50
T3 Alex Gonzalez .20 .50
T4 Jason Isringhausen .30 .75
T5 Tyler Houston .20 .50
T6 Ben Broussard .20 .50
T7 Chuck Knoblauch .30 .75
T8 Brian L. Hunter .20 .50
T9 Dustan Mohr .20 .50
T10 Eric Hinske .20 .50
T11 Roger Cedeno .20 .50
T12 Eddie Perez .20 .50
T13 Jeromy Burnitz .30 .75
T14 Bartolo Colon .30 .75
T15 Rick Helling .20 .50
T16 Dan Plesac .20 .50
T17 Scott Strickland .20 .50
T18 Antonio Alfonseca .20 .50
T19 Ricky Gutierrez .20 .50
T20 John Valentin .20 .50
T21 Raul Mondesi .30 .75
T22 Ben Davis .20 .50
T23 Nelson Figueroa .20 .50
T24 Earl Snyder .20 .50
T25 Robin Ventura .30 .75
T26 Jimmy Haynes .20 .50
T27 Kenny Kelly .20 .50
T28 Morgan Ensberg .30 .75
T29 Reggie Sanders .30 .75
T30 Shigetoshi Hasegawa .30 .75
T31 Mike Timlin .20 .50
T32 Russell Branyan .20 .50
T33 Alan Embree .20 .50
T34 D'Angelo Jimenez .20 .50
T35 Kent Mercker .20 .50
T36 Jesse Orosco .20 .50
T37 Gregg Zaun .20 .50
T38 Reggie Taylor .20 .50
T39 Andres Galarraga .30 .75
T40 Chris Truby .20 .50
T41 Bruce Chen .20 .50
T42 Darren Lewis .20 .50
T43 Ryan Kohlmeier .20 .50
T44 John McDonald .20 .50
T45 Omar Daal .20 .50
T46 Matt Clement .30 .75
T47 Glendon Rusch .20 .50
T48 Chan Ho Park .30 .75
T49 Benny Agbayani .20 .50
T50 Juan Gonzalez .30 .75
T51 Carlos Baerga .20 .50
T52 Tim Raines .30 .75
T53 Kevin Appier .30 .75
T54 Marty Cordova .20 .50
T55 Jeff D'Amico .20 .50
T56 Dmitri Young .30 .75
T57 Roosevelt Brown .20 .50
T58 Dustin Hermanson .20 .50
T59 Jose Rijo .20 .50
T60 Todd Ritchie .20 .50
T61 Lee Stevens .20 .50
T62 Placido Polanco .20 .50
T63 Eric Young .20 .50
T64 Chuck Finley .30 .75
T65 Dicky Gonzalez .20 .50
T66 Jose Macias .20 .50
T67 Gabe Kapler .30 .75
T68 Sandy Alomar Jr. .20 .50
T69 Henry Blanco .20 .50
T70 Julian Tavarez .20 .50
T71 Paul Bako .20 .50
T72 Scott Rolen .50 1.25
T73 Brian Jordan .30 .75
T74 Rickey Henderson .75 2.00
T75 Kevin Mench .20 .50
T76 Hideo Nomo .75 2.00
T77 Jeremy Giambi .20 .50
T78 Brad Fullmer .20 .50
T79 Carl Everett .30 .75
T80 David Wells .30 .75
T81 Aaron Sele .20 .50
T82 Todd Hollandsworth .20 .50
T83 Vicente Padilla .20 .50
T84 Kenny Lofton .30 .75
T85 Corky Miller .20 .50
T86 Josh Fogg .20 .50
T87 Cliff Floyd .30 .75
T88 Craig Paquette .20 .50
T89 Jay Payton .20 .50
T90 Carlos Pena .20 .50
T91 Juan Encarnacion .20 .50
T92 Rey Sanchez .20 .50
T93 Ryan Dempster .20 .50
T94 Mario Encarnacion .20 .50
T95 Jorge Julio .20 .50
T96 John Mabry .20 .50
T97 Todd Zeile .30 .75
T98 Johnny Damon .50 1.25
T99 Deivi Cruz .20 .50
T100 Gary Sheffield .30 .75
T101 Ted Lilly .20 .50
T102 Todd Van Poppel .20 .50
T103 Shawn Estes .20 .50
T104 Cesar Izturis .20 .50
T105 Ron Coomer .20 .50
T106 Grady Little MG RC .20 .50
T107 Jimy Williams MGR .20 .50
T108 Tony Pena MGR .20 .50
T109 Frank Robinson MGR .50 1.25
T110 Ron Gardenhire MGR .20 .50
T111 Dennis Tankersley .20 .50
T112 Alejandro Cadena RC .40 1.00
T113 Justin Reid RC .40 1.00
T114 Nate Field RC .40 1.00
T115 Rene Reyes RC .40 1.00
T116 Nelson Castro RC .40 1.00
T117 Miguel Olivo .20 .50
T118 David Espinosa .20 .50
T119 Chris Bootcheck RC .40 1.00
T120 Rob Henkel RC .40 1.00
T121 Steve Bechler RC .40 1.00
T122 Mark Outlaw RC .40 1.00
T123 Henry Pichardo RC .40 1.00
T124 Michael Floyd RC .40 1.00
T125 Richard Lane RC .40 1.00
T126 Pete Zamora RC .40 1.00
T127 Javier Colina .20 .50
T128 Greg Sain RC .40 1.00
T129 Ronnie Merrill .20 .50
T130 Gavin Floyd RC 1.00 2.50
T131 Josh Bonifay RC .40 1.00
T132 Tommy Marx RC .40 1.00
T133 Gary Cates Jr. RC .40 1.00
T134 Neal Cotts RC 1.00 2.50
T135 Angel Berroa .20 .50
T136 Elio Serrano RC .40 1.00
T137 J.J. Putz RC .50 1.25
T138 Ruben Gotay RC .50 1.25
T139 Eddie Rogers .20 .50
T140 Wily Mo Pena .30 .75
T141 Tyler Yates RC .40 1.00
T142 Colin Young RC .30 .75
T143 Chance Caple .20 .50
T144 Ben Howard RC .40 1.00
T145 Ryan Bukvich RC .40 1.00
T146 Cliff Bartosh RC .40 1.00
T147 Brandon Claussen .20 .50
T148 Cristian Guerrero .20 .50
T149 Derrick Lewis .20 .50
T150 Eric Miller RC .40 1.00
T151 Justin Huber RC .75 2.00
T152 Adrian Gonzalez .20 .50
T153 Brian West RC .40 1.00
T154 Chris Baker RC .40 1.00
T155 Drew Henson .20 .50
T156 Scott Hairston RC .50 1.25
T157 Jason Simontacchi RC .40 1.00
T158 Jason Arnold RC .40 1.00
T159 Brandon Phillips .20 .50
T160 Adam Roller RC .40 1.00
T161 Scotty Layfield RC .40 1.00
T162 Freddie Money RC .40 1.00
T163 Noochie Varner RC .40 1.00
T164 Terrance Hill RC .40 1.00
T165 Jeremy Hill RC .40 1.00
T166 Carlos Cabrera RC .40 1.00
T167 Jose Morban RC .40 1.00
T168 Kevin Frederick RC .40 1.00
T169 Mark Teixeira 1.50 4.00
T170 Brian Rogers .20 .50
T171 Anastacio Martinez RC .40 1.00
T172 Bobby Jenks RC 1.50 4.00
T173 David Gil RC .40 1.00
T174 Andres Torres .20 .50
T175 James Barrett RC .40 1.00
T176 Jimmy Journell .20 .50
T177 Brett Kay RC .40 1.00
T178 Jason Young RC .40 1.00
T179 Mark Hamilton RC .40 1.00
T180 Jose Bautista RC 1.00 2.50
T181 Blake McGinley RC .40 1.00
T182 Ryan Mottl RC .40 1.00
T183 Jeff Austin RC .40 1.00
T184 Xavier Nady .20 .50
T185 Kyle Kane RC .40 1.00
T186 Travis Foley RC .40 1.00
T187 Nathan Kaup RC .40 1.00
T188 Eric Cyr .20 .50
T189 Josh Cisneros RC .40 1.00
T190 Brad Nelson RC .40 1.00
T191 Clint Weibl RC .40 1.00
T192 Ron Calloway RC .40 1.00
T193 Jung Bong .20 .50
T194 Rolando Viera RC .40 1.00
T195 Jason Bulger RC .40 1.00
T196 Chone Figgins RC 1.50 4.00
T197 Jimmy Alvarez RC .40 1.00
T198 Joel Crump RC .40 1.00
T199 Ryan Doumit RC .60 1.50
T200 Demetrius Heath RC .40 1.00
T201 John Ennis RC .40 1.00
T202 Doug Sessions RC .40 1.00
T203 Clinton Hosford RC .40 1.00
T204 Chris Narveson RC .40 1.00
T205 Ross Peeples RC .40 1.00
T206 Alex Requena RC .40 1.00
T207 Matt Erickson RC .40 1.00
T208 Brian Forystek RC .40 1.00
T209 Dewon Brazelton .20 .50
T210 Nathan Haynes .20 .50
T211 Jack Cust .20 .50
T212 Jesse Foppert RC .50 1.25
T213 Jesus Cota RC .40 1.00
T214 Juan M. Gonzalez RC .40 1.00
T215 Tim Kalita RC .40 1.00
T216 Manny Delcarmen RC .50 1.25
T217 Jim Kavourias RC .40 1.00
T218 C.J. Wilson RC .40 1.00
T219 Edwin Yan RC .40 1.00
T220 Andy Van Hekken .20 .50
T221 Michael Cuddyer .20 .50
T222 Jeff Verplancke RC .40 1.00
T223 Mike Wilson RC .40 1.00
T224 Corwin Malone RC .40 1.00
T225 Chris Snelling RC .60 1.50
T226 Joe Rogers RC .40 1.00
T227 Jason Bay 3.00 8.00
T228 Ezequiel Astacio RC .40 1.00
T229 Joey Hammond RC .40 1.00
T230 Chris Duffy RC .40 1.00
T231 Mark Prior .50 1.25
T232 Hansel Izquierdo RC .40 1.00
T233 Franklyn German RC .40 1.00
T234 Alexis Gomez .20 .50
T235 Jorge Padilla RC .40 1.00
T236 Ryan Snare RC .40 1.00
T237 Deivis Santos .20 .50
T238 Taggert Bozied RC .50 1.25
T239 Mike Peeples RC .40 1.00
T240 Ronald Acuna RC .40 1.00
T241 Koyie Hill .20 .50
T242 Garrett Guzman RC .40 1.00
T243 Ryan Church RC 1.00 2.50
T244 Tony Fontana RC .40 1.00
T245 Keto Anderson RC .40 1.00
T246 Brad Bouras RC .40 1.00
T247 Jason Dubois RC .50 1.25
T248 Angel Guzman RC .75 2.00
T249 Joel Hanrahan RC .40 1.00
T250 Joe Jiannetti RC .40 1.00
T251 Sean Pierce RC .40 1.00
T252 Jake Mauer RC .40 1.00
T253 Marshall McDougall RC .40 1.00
T254 Edwin Almonte RC .40 1.00
T255 Shawn Riggans RC .40 1.00
T256 Steven Shell RC .40 1.00
T257 Kevin Hooper RC .40 1.00
T258 Michael Frick RC .40 1.00
T259 Travis Chapman RC .40 1.00
T260 Tim Hummel RC .40 1.00
T261 Adam Morrissey RC .40 1.00
T262 Dontrelle Willis RC 4.00 10.00
T263 Justin Sherrod RC .40 1.00
T264 Gerald Smiley RC .40 1.00
T265 Tony Miller RC .40 1.00
T266 Nolan Ryan WW 2.00 5.00
T267 Reggie Jackson WW .50 1.25
T268 Steve Garvey WW .30 .75
T269 Wade Boggs WW .50 1.25
T270 Sammy Sosa WW .75 2.00
T271 Curt Schilling WW .30 .75
T272 Mark Grace WW .50 1.25
T273 Jason Giambi WW .20 .50
T274 Ken Griffey Jr. WW 1.25 3.00
T275 Roberto Alomar WW .50 1.25

2002 Topps Chrome Traded Black Refractors

Inserted at a stated rate of one in 56 Topps Traded hobby or retail packs and one in 16 HTA packs, this is a parallel of the Topps Chrome Traded set. These cards can be differentiated from the regular cards by their black borders and are printed to a stated print run of 100 serial numbered sets.

*BLACK REF: 4X TO 10X BASIC
*BLACK REF RC'S: 4X TO 10X BASIC RC'S
T262 Dontrelle Willis 75.00 150.00

2002 Topps Chrome Traded Refractors

nserted at a stated rate of one in 12 Topps Traded packs, this is a parallel of the Topps Chrome Traded set. These cards can be differentiated from the regular cards by their "refractive" sheen and are notated as refractors on the back of the card.

*REF: 2X TO 5X BASIC
*REF RC'S: 1.5X TO 4X BASIC RC'S
STATED ODDS 1:12 HOB/RET, 1:12 HTA
T262 Dontrelle Willis 15.00 40.00

2003 Topps Chrome

The first series of 2003 Topps Chrome was released in January, 2003. These cards were issued in four card packs which came 24 packs to a box and 10 boxes to a case with an SRP of $3 per pack. Cards numbered 201 through 220 feature players in their first year of Topps cards. The second series, which also consisted of 220 cards, was released in May, 2003. Cards number 421 through 430 were draft pick cards while cards 431 through 440 were two player prospect cards.

COMPLETE SET (440) 80.00 200.00
COMPLETE SERIES 1 (220) 40.00 100.00
COMPLETE SERIES 2 (220) 40.00 100.00
COMMON (1-200/221-420) .40 1.00
COMMON (201-220/421-440) .60 1.50
1 Alex Rodriguez 1.50 4.00
2 Eddie Guardado .40 1.00
3 Curt Schilling .40 1.00
4 Andruw Jones .60 1.50
5 Magglio Ordonez .40 1.00
6 Todd Helton .60 1.50
7 Odalis Perez .40 1.00
8 Edgardo Alfonzo .40 1.00
9 Eric Hinske .40 1.00
10 Danny Bautista .40 1.00
11 Sammy Sosa 1.00 2.50
12 Roberto Alomar .60 1.50
13 Roger Clemens 2.00 5.00
14 Austin Kearns .40 1.00
15 Luis Gonzalez .40 1.00
16 Mo Vaughn .40 1.00
17 Alfonso Soriano .40 1.00
18 Orlando Cabrera .40 1.00
19 Hideo Nomo 1.00 2.50
20 Omar Vizquel .60 1.50
21 Greg Maddux 1.50 4.00
22 Fred McGriff .60 1.50
23 Frank Thomas 1.00 2.50
24 Shawn Green .40 1.00
25 Jacque Jones .40 1.00
26 Bernie Williams .60 1.50
27 Corey Patterson .40 1.00
28 Cesar Izturis .40 1.00
29 Larry Walker .40 1.00
30 Darren Dreifort .40 1.00
31 Al Leiter .40 1.00
32 Jason Marquis .40 1.00
33 Sean Casey .40 1.00
34 Craig Counsell .40 1.00
35 Albert Pujols 2.00 5.00
36 Kyle Lohse .40 1.00
37 Paul Lo Duca .40 1.00
38 Roy Oswalt .40 1.00
39 Danny Graves .40 1.00
40 Kevin Millwood .40 1.00
41 Lance Berkman .40 1.00
42 Denny Hocking .40 1.00
43 Jose Valentin .40 1.00
44 Josh Beckett .40 1.00
45 Nomar Garciaparra 1.50 4.00
46 Craig Biggio .60 1.50
47 Omar Daal .40 1.00
48 Jimmy Rollins .40 1.00
49 Jermaine Dye .40 1.00
50 Edgar Renteria .40 1.00
51 Brandon Duckworth .40 1.00
52 Luis Castillo .40 1.00
53 Andy Ashby .40 1.00
54 Mike Williams .40 1.00
55 Benito Santiago .40 1.00
56 Bret Boone .40 1.00
57 Randy Wolf .40 1.00
58 Ivan Rodriguez .60 1.50
59 Shannon Stewart .40 1.00
60 Jose Cruz Jr. .40 1.00
61 Billy Wagner .40 1.00
62 Alex Gonzalez .40 1.00
63 Ichiro Suzuki 2.00 5.00
64 Joe McEwing .40 1.00
65 Mark Mulder .40 1.00
66 Mike Cameron .40 1.00
67 Corey Koskie .40 1.00
68 Marlon Anderson .40 1.00
69 Jason Kendall .40 1.00
70 J.T. Snow .40 1.00
71 Edgar Martinez .60 1.50
72 Vernon Wells .40 1.00
73 Vladimir Guerrero 1.00 2.50
74 Adam Dunn .40 1.00
75 Barry Zito .40 1.00
76 Jeff Kent .40 1.00
77 Russ Ortiz .40 1.00
78 Phil Nevin .40 1.00
79 Carlos Beltran .40 1.00
80 Mike Lowell .40 1.00
81 Bob Wickman .40 1.00
82 Junior Spivey .40 1.00
83 Melvin Mora .40 1.00
84 Derrek Lee .60 1.50
85 Chuck Knoblauch .40 1.00
86 Eric Gagne .40 1.00
87 Orlando Hernandez .40 1.00
88 Robert Person .40 1.00
89 Elmer Dessens .40 1.00
90 Wade Miller .40 1.00
91 Adrian Beltre .40 1.00
92 Kazuhiro Sasaki .40 1.00
93 Timo Perez .40 1.00
94 Jose Vidro .40 1.00
95 Geronimo Gil .40 1.00
96 Trot Nixon .40 1.00
97 Denny Neagle .40 1.00
98 Roberto Hernandez .40 1.00
99 David Ortiz 1.00 2.50
100 Robb Nen .40 1.00
101 Sidney Ponson .40 1.00
102 Kevin Appier .40 1.00
103 Javier Lopez .40 1.00
104 Jeff Conine .40 1.00
105 Mark Buehrle .40 1.00
106 Jason Simontacchi .40 1.00
107 Jose Jimenez .40 1.00
108 Brian Jordan .40 1.00
109 Brad Wilkerson .40 1.00
110 Scott Hatteberg .40 1.00
111 Matt Morris .40 1.00
112 Miguel Tejada .40 1.00
113 Rafael Furcal .40 1.00
114 Steve Cox .40 1.00
115 Roy Halladay .40 1.00
116 David Eckstein .40 1.00
117 Tomo Ohka .40 1.00
118 Jack Wilson .40 1.00
119 Randall Simon .40 1.00
120 Jamie Moyer .40 1.00
121 Andy Benes .40 1.00
122 Tino Martinez .60 1.50
123 Esteban Yan .40 1.00
124 Jason Isringhausen .40 1.00
125 Chris Carpenter .40 1.00
126 Aaron Rowand .40 1.00
127 Brandon Inge .40 1.00
128 Jose Vizcaino .40 1.00
129 Jose Mesa .40 1.00
130 Troy Percival .40 1.00
131 Jon Lieber .40 1.00
132 Brian Giles .40 1.00
133 Aaron Boone .40 1.00
134 Bobby Higginson .40 1.00
135 Luis Rivas .40 1.00
136 Troy Glaus .40 1.00
137 Jim Thome .60 1.50
138 Ramon Martinez .40 1.00
139 Jay Gibbons .40 1.00
140 Mike Lieberthal .40 1.00
141 Juan Uribe .40 1.00
142 Gary Sheffield .40 1.00
143 Ramon Santiago .40 1.00
144 Ben Sheets .40 1.00
145 Tony Armas Jr. .40 1.00
146 Kazuhisa Ishii .40 1.00
147 Erubiel Durazo .40 1.00
148 Jerry Hairston Jr. .40 1.00
149 Byung-Hyun Kim .40 1.00
150 Marcus Giles .40 1.00
151 Johnny Damon .60 1.50
152 Terrence Long .40 1.00
153 Juan Pierre .40 1.00
154 Aramis Ramirez .40 1.00
155 Brent Abernathy .40 1.00
156 Ismael Valdes .40 1.00
157 Mike Mussina .60 1.50
158 Ramon Hernandez .40 1.00
159 Adam Kennedy .40 1.00
160 Tony Womack .40 1.00
161 Tony Batista .40 1.00
162 Kip Wells .40 1.00
163 Jeromy Burnitz .40 1.00
164 Todd Hundley .40 1.00
165 Tim Wakefield .40 1.00
166 Derek Lowe .40 1.00
167 Jorge Posada .60 1.50
168 Ramon Ortiz .40 1.00
169 Brent Butler .40 1.00
170 Shane Halter .40 1.00
171 Matt Lawton .40 1.00
172 Alex Sanchez .40 1.00
173 Eric Milton .40 1.00
174 Vicente Padilla .40 1.00
175 Steve Karsay .40 1.00
176 Mark Prior .60 1.50
177 Kerry Wood .40 1.00
178 Jason LaRue .40 1.00
179 Danys Baez .40 1.00
180 Nick Neugebauer .40 1.00
181 Andres Galarraga .40 1.00
182 Jason Giambi .40 1.00
183 Aubrey Huff .40 1.00
184 Juan Gonzalez .40 1.00
185 Ugueth Urbina .40 1.00
186 Rickey Henderson 1.00 2.50
187 Brad Fullmer .40 1.00
188 Todd Zeile .40 1.00
189 Jason Jennings .40 1.00
190 Vladimir Nunez .40 1.00
191 David Justice .40 1.00
192 Brian Lawrence .40 1.00
193 Pat Burrell .40 1.00
194 Pokey Reese .40 1.00
195 Robert Fick .40 1.00
196 C.C. Sabathia .40 1.00
197 Fernando Vina .40 1.00
198 Sean Burroughs .40 1.00
199 Ellis Burks .40 1.00
200 Joe Randa .40 1.00
201 Chris Duncan FY RC 2.50 6.00
202 Franklin Gutierrez FY RC 1.25 3.00
203 Adam LaRoche FY RC .60 1.50
204 Manuel Ramirez FY RC 1.00 2.50
205 Il Kim FY RC .60 1.50
206 Daryl Clark FY RC .60 1.50
207 Sean Pierce FY .60 1.50
208 Andy Marte FY RC 3.00 8.00
209 Bernie Castro FY RC .60 1.50
210 Jason Perry FY RC 1.00 2.50
211 Jaime Bubela FY RC .60 1.50
212 Alexis Rios FY RC 1.00 2.50
213 Brendan Harris FY RC 1.00 2.50
214 R.Nivar-Martinez FY RC .60 1.50
215 Terry Tiffee FY RC .60 1.50
216 Kevin Youkilis FY RC 1.50 4.00
217 Derell McCall FY RC .60 1.50
218 Scott Tyler FY RC 1.00 2.50
219 Craig Brazell FY RC .60 1.50
220 Walter Young FY .60 1.50
221 Francisco Rodriguez .40 1.00
222 Chipper Jones 1.00 2.50
223 Chris Singleton .40 1.00
224 Cliff Floyd .40 1.00
225 Bobby Hill .40 1.00
226 Antonio Osuna .40 1.00
227 Barry Larkin .60 1.50
228 Dean Palmer .40 1.00
229 Eric Owens .40 1.00
230 Randy Johnson 1.00 2.50
231 Jeff Suppan .40 1.00
232 Eric Karros .40 1.00
233 Johan Santana .60 1.50
234 Javier Vazquez .40 1.00
235 John Thomson .40 1.00
236 Nick Johnson .40 1.00
237 Mark Ellis .40 1.00
238 Doug Glanville .40 1.00
239 Ken Griffey Jr. 1.50 4.00
240 Bubba Trammell .40 1.00
241 Livan Hernandez .40 1.00
242 Desi Relaford .40 1.00
243 Eli Marrero .40 1.00
244 Jared Sandberg .40 1.00
245 Barry Bonds 2.50 6.00
246 Aaron Sele .40 1.00
247 Derek Jeter 2.50 6.00
248 Eric Byrnes .40 1.00
249 Rich Aurilia .40 1.00
250 Joel Pineiro .40 1.00
251 Chuck Finley .40 1.00
252 Bengie Molina .40 1.00
253 Steve Finley .40 1.00
254 Marty Cordova .40 1.00
255 Shea Hillenbrand .40 1.00
256 Milton Bradley .40 1.00
257 Carlos Pena .40 1.00
258 Brad Ausmus .40 1.00
259 Carlos Delgado .40 1.00
260 Kevin Mench .40 1.00
261 Joe Kennedy .40 1.00
262 Mark McLemore .40 1.00
263 Bill Mueller .40 1.00
264 Ricky Ledee .40 1.00
265 Ted Lilly .40 1.00
266 Sterling Hitchcock .40 1.00
267 Scott Strickland .40 1.00
268 Damion Easley .40 1.00
269 Torii Hunter .40 1.00
270 Brad Radke .40 1.00
271 Geoff Jenkins .40 1.00
272 Paul Byrd .40 1.00
273 Morgan Ensberg .40 1.00
274 Mike Maroth .40 1.00
275 Mike Hampton .40 1.00
276 Flash Gordon .40 1.00
277 John Burkett .40 1.00
278 Rodrigo Lopez .40 1.00
279 Tim Spooneybarger .40 1.00
280 Quinton McCracken .40 1.00
281 Tim Salmon .60 1.50
282 Jarrod Washburn .40 1.00
283 Pedro Martinez .60 1.50
284 Julio Lugo .40 1.00
285 Armando Benitez .40 1.00
286 Raul Mondesi .40 1.00
287 Robin Ventura .40 1.00
288 Bobby Abreu .40 1.00
289 Josh Fogg .40 1.00
290 Ryan Klesko .40 1.00
291 Tsuyoshi Shinjo .40 1.00
292 Jim Edmonds .40 1.00
293 Chan Ho Park .40 1.00
294 John Mabry .40 1.00
295 Woody Williams .40 1.00
296 Scott Schoeneweis .40 1.00
297 Brian Anderson .40 1.00
298 Brett Tomko .40 1.00
299 Scott Erickson .40 1.00
300 Kevin Millar Sox .40 1.00
301 Danny Wright .40 1.00
302 Jason Schmidt .40 1.00
303 Scott Williamson .40 1.00
304 Einar Diaz .40 1.00
305 Jay Payton .40 1.00
306 Juan Acevedo .40 1.00
307 Ben Grieve .40 1.00
308 Raul Ibanez .40 1.00
309 Richie Sexson .40 1.00
310 Rick Reed .40 1.00
311 Pedro Astacio .40 1.00
312 Bud Smith .40 1.00
313 Tomas Perez .40 1.00
314 Rafael Palmeiro .60 1.50
315 Jason Tyner .40 1.00
316 Scott Rolen .60 1.50
317 Randy Winn .40 1.00
318 Ryan Jensen .40 1.00
319 Trevor Hoffman .40 1.00
320 Craig Wilson .40 1.00
321 Jeremy Giambi .40 1.00
322 Andy Pettitte .60 1.50
323 John Franco .40 1.00
324 Felipe Lopez .40 1.00
325 Mike Piazza 1.50 4.00
326 Cristian Guzman .40 1.00
327 Jose Hernandez .40 1.00
328 Octavio Dotel .40 1.00
329 Brad Penny .40 1.00
330 Dave Veres .40 1.00
331 Ryan Dempster .40 1.00
332 Joe Crede .40 1.00
333 Chad Hermansen .40 1.00
334 Gary Matthews Jr. .40 1.00
335 Frank Catalanotto .40 1.00
336 Darin Erstad .40 1.00
337 Matt Williams .40 1.00
338 B.J. Surhoff .40 1.00
339 Kerry Ligtenberg .40 1.00
340 Mike Bordick .40 1.00
341 Joe Girardi .40 1.00
342 D'Angelo Jimenez .40 1.00
343 Paul Konerko .40 1.00
344 Joe Mays .40 1.00
345 Marquis Grissom .40 1.00
346 Neifi Perez .40 1.00
347 Preston Wilson .40 1.00
348 Jeff Weaver .40 1.00
349 Eric Chavez .40 1.00
350 Placido Polanco .40 1.00
351 Matt Mantei .40 1.00
352 James Baldwin .40 1.00
353 Toby Hall .40 1.00
354 Benji Gil .40 1.00
355 Damian Moss .40 1.00
356 Jorge Julio .40 1.00
357 Matt Clement .40 1.00
358 Lee Stevens .40 1.00
359 Dave Roberts .40 1.00
360 J.C. Romero .40 1.00
361 Bartolo Colon .40 1.00
362 Roger Cedeno .40 1.00
363 Mariano Rivera 1.00 2.50
364 Billy Koch .40 1.00
365 Manny Ramirez .60 1.50
366 Travis Lee .40 1.00
367 Oliver Perez .40 1.00
368 Tim Worrell .40 1.00
369 Damian Miller .40 1.00
370 John Smoltz .60 1.50
371 Willis Roberts .40 1.00
372 Tim Hudson .40 1.00
373 Moises Alou .40 1.00
374 Corky Miller .40 1.00
375 Ben Broussard .40 1.00
376 Gabe Kapler .40 1.00
377 Chris Woodward .40 1.00
378 Todd Hollandsworth .40 1.00
379 So Taguchi .40 1.00
380 John Olerud .40 1.00
381 Reggie Sanders .40 1.00
382 Jake Peavy .40 1.00
383 Kris Benson .40 1.00
384 Ray Durham .40 1.00
385 Boomer Wells .40 1.00
386 Tom Glavine .60 1.50
387 Antonio Alfonseca .40 1.00
388 Keith Foulke .40 1.00
389 Shawn Estes .40 1.00
390 Mark Grace .60 1.50
391 Dmitri Young .40 1.00
392 A.J. Burnett .40 1.00
393 Richard Hidalgo .40 1.00
394 Mike Sweeney .40 1.00
395 Doug Mientkiewicz .40 1.00
396 Cory Lidle .40 1.00
397 Jeff Bagwell .60 1.50
398 Steve Sparks .40 1.00
399 Sandy Alomar Jr. .40 1.00
400 John Lackey .40 1.00
401 Rick Helling .40 1.00
402 Carlos Lee .40 1.00
403 Garrett Anderson .40 1.00
404 Vinny Castilla .40 1.00
405 David Bell .40 1.00
406 Freddy Garcia .40 1.00

407 Scott Spiezio .40 1.00
408 Russell Branyan .40 1.00
409 Jose Contreras RC 1.25 3.00
410 Kevin Brown .40 1.00
411 Tyler Houston .40 1.00
412 A.J. Pierzynski .40 1.00
413 Peter Bergeron .40 1.00
414 Brett Myers .40 1.00
415 Kenny Lofton .40 1.00
416 Ben Davis .40 1.00
417 J.D. Drew .40 1.00
418 Ricky Gutierrez .40 1.00
419 Mark Redman .40 1.00
420 Juan Encarnacion .40 1.00
421 Bryan Bullington DP RC .60 1.50
422 Jeremy Guthrie DP .60 1.50
423 Joey Gomes DP RC .60 1.50
424 E.Bastida-Martinez DP RC .60 1.50
425 Brian Wright DP RC .60 1.50
426 B.J. Upton DP 1.00 2.50
427 Jeff Francis DP .60 1.50
428 Jeremy Hermida DP 1.00 2.50
429 Khalil Greene DP 1.00 2.50
430 Darrell Rasner DP RC .60 1.50
431 Brandon Phillips 1.00 2.50
Victor Martinez
432 Hee Seop Choi .60 1.50
Nic Jackson
433 Dontrelle Willis 1.00 2.50
Jason Stokes
434 Chad Tracy .60 1.50
Lyle Overbay
435 Joe Borchard .60 1.50
Corwin Malone
436 Joe Mauer 1.00 2.50
Justin Morneau
437 Drew Henson .60 1.50
Brandon Claussen
438 Chase Utley 1.00 2.50
Gavin Floyd
439 Taggert Bozied .60 1.50
Xavier Nady
440 Aaron Heilman .60 1.50
Jose Reyes

2003 Topps Chrome Black Refractors

Issued at a stated rate of one in 20 for first series cards and one in 17 for second series cards, this is a parallel to the Topps Chrome set. These cards have black borders and were issued to a stated print run of 199 serial numbered sets.

*BLACK 1-200/221-420: 2X TO 5X
*BLACK 201-220/409/421-440: 2.5X TO 6X

2003 Topps Chrome Gold Refractors

Issued at a stated rate of one in eight for first series cards and two in eight for second series cards, this is a parallel to the Topps Chrome set. These cards have gold borders and were issued to a stated print run of 449 serial numbered sets.

*GOLD 1-200/221-420: 1.25X TO 3X
*GOLD 201-220/409/421-440: 1.5X TO 4X

2003 Topps Chrome Refractors

Issued at a stated rate of one in five, this is a parallel to the Topps Chrome set. These cards use the patented Topps Chrome technology and were issued to a stated print run of 699 serial numbered sets.

*REF 1-200/201-420: 1X TO 2.5X
*REF 201-220/409/421-440: 1.25X TO 3X

2003 Topps Chrome Silver Refractors

*SILVER REF 221-420: 1.25X TO 3X BASIC
*SILVER REF 421-440: 1.5X TO 4X BASIC
ONE PER SER.2 RETAIL EXCH.CARD
CARDS WERE ONLY PRODUCED FOR SER.2

2003 Topps Chrome Uncirculated X-Fractors

Issued at a box-topper, this is a parallel to the Topps Chrome set. Each of these cards were issued in a special case and each of these cards were issued to

a stated print run of 50 serial numbered sets for first series cards and a stated print run of 57 serial numbered cards for second series cards.

*X-FRACT 1-200/221-420: 4X TO 10X
*X-FRACT 201-220/409/421-440: 5X TO 12X

2003 Topps Chrome Blue Backs Relics

Randomly inserted into packs, these 20 cards are authentic game-used memorabilia attached to a card which was in 1951 Blue Back design. These cards were issued in three different odds and we have notated those odds as well as what group the player belonged to in our checklist.

BAT ODDS 1:236 HOB/RET
UNI GROUP A ODDS 1:69 HOB/RET
UNI GROUP B ODDS 1:662 HOB/RET
AD Adam Dunn Uni B 6.00 15.00
AP Albert Pujols Uni A 10.00 25.00
AR Alex Rodriguez Bat 10.00 25.00
AS Alfonso Soriano Bat 6.00 15.00
BW Bernie Williams Bat 6.00 15.00
EC Eric Chavez Uni A 4.00 10.00
FT Frank Thomas Uni A 6.00 15.00
JB Josh Beckett Uni A 4.00 10.00
JBA Jeff Bagwell Uni A 4.00 10.00
JR Jimmy Rollins Uni A 4.00 10.00
KW Kerry Wood Uni A 4.00 10.00
LB Lance Berkman Bat 6.00 15.00
MO Magglio Ordonez Uni A 4.00 10.00
MP Mike Piazza Uni A 8.00 20.00
NG Nomar Garciaparra Bat 10.00 25.00
NJ Nick Johnson Bat 6.00 15.00
PK Paul Konerko Uni A 4.00 10.00
RA Roberto Alomar Bat 6.00 15.00
SG Shawn Green Uni A 4.00 10.00
TS Tsuyoshi Shinjo Bat 6.00 15.00

2003 Topps Chrome Record Breakers Relics

Randomly inserted into packs, these 40 cards feature a mix of active and retired players along with a game-used memorabilia piece. These cards were issued in a few different group and we have notated that information next to the player's name in our checklist.

BAT 1 ODDS 1:364 HOB/RET
BAT 2 ODDS 1:131 HOB/RET
UNI GROUP A1 ODDS 1:413 HOB/RET
UNI GROUP B1 ODDS 1:50 HOB/RET
UNI GROUP A2 ODDS 1:1707 HOB/RET
UNI GROUP B2 ODDS 1:127 HOB/RET
AR1 Alex Rodriguez Uni B1 6.00 15.00
AR2 Alex Rodriguez Bat 2 6.00 15.00
BB Barry Bonds Walks Uni B2 10.00 25.00
BB2 Barry Bonds Slg Uni B2 10.00 25.00
BB3 Barry Bonds Bat 2 10.00 25.00
CB Craig Biggio Uni B1 4.00 10.00
CD Carlos Delgado Uni B1 4.00 10.00
CF Cliff Floyd Bat 1 4.00 10.00
DE Darin Erstad Bat 2 4.00 10.00
DLE Dennis Eckersley Uni A2 6.00 15.00
DM Don Mattingly Bat 2 15.00 40.00
FT Frank Thomas Uni B1 6.00 15.00
HK Harmon Killebrew Uni B1 10.00 25.00
HR Harold Reynolds Bat 2 4.00 10.00
JB1 Jeff Bagwell Slg Uni B1 4.00 10.00
JB2 Jeff Bagwell RBI Uni B2 4.00 10.00
JC Jose Canseco Bat 2 6.00 15.00
JG Juan Gonzalez Uni B1 4.00 10.00
JM Joe Morgan Bat 1 4.00 10.00
JS John Smoltz Uni B2 4.00 10.00
KS Kazuhiro Sasaki Uni B1 4.00 10.00
LB Lou Brock Bat 1 8.00 20.00
LG1 Luis Gonzalez RBI Bat 1 4.00 10.00
LG2 Luis Gonzalez Avg Bat 2 4.00 10.00
LW Larry Walker Bat 1 4.00 10.00
MP Mike Piazza Uni B1 8.00 20.00
MR Manny Ramirez Bat 2 6.00 15.00
MS Mike Schmidt Uni A1 15.00 40.00
PM Paul Molitor Bat 2 4.00 10.00
RC Rod Carew Avg Bat 2 6.00 15.00
RC2 Rod Carew Hits Bat 2 6.00 15.00
RH1 R.Henderson A's Bat 1 6.00 15.00
RH2 R.Henderson Yanks Bat 2 6.00 15.00
RJ1 Randy Johnson ERA Uni B1 6.00 15.00
RJ2 Randy Johnson Wins Uni B2 6.00 15.00
RY Robin Yount Uni B1 10.00 25.00
SM Stan Musial Uni A1 20.00 50.00
SS Sammy Sosa Bat 2 6.00 15.00
TH Todd Helton Bat 1 6.00 15.00
TS Tom Seaver Uni B2 8.00 20.00

2003 Topps Chrome Red Backs Relics

Randomly inserted into packs, these 20 cards are authentic game-used memorabilia attached to a card which was in 1951 Red Back design. These cards were issued in three different odds and we have notated those odds as well as what group the player belonged to in our checklist.

SERIES 2 BAT A ODDS 1:342 HOB/RET
SERIES 2 BAT B ODDS 1:383 HOB/RET
SERIES 2 JERSEY ODDS 1:49 HOB/RET
AD Adam Dunn Jsy 4.00 10.00
AJ Andruw Jones Jsy 4.00 10.00
AP Albert Pujols Bat B 8.00 20.00
AR Alex Rodriguez Jsy 6.00 15.00
AS Alfonso Soriano Bat A 6.00 15.00
CJ Chipper Jones Jsy 6.00 15.00
CS Curt Schilling Jsy 4.00 10.00
GA Garrett Anderson Bat A 6.00 15.00
JB Jeff Bagwell Jsy 4.00 10.00
MP Mike Piazza Jsy 6.00 15.00
MR Manny Ramirez Bat B 4.00 10.00
MS Mike Sweeney Jsy 4.00 10.00
NG Nomar Garciaparra Bat A 10.00 25.00
PB Pat Burrell Bat A 6.00 15.00
PM Pedro Martinez Jsy 4.00 10.00
RA Roberto Alomar Jsy 4.00 10.00
RJ Randy Johnson Jsy 6.00 15.00
SR Scott Rolen Bat A 6.00 15.00
TH Todd Helton Jsy 4.00 10.00
TKH Torii Hunter Jsy 4.00 10.00

2003 Topps Chrome Traded

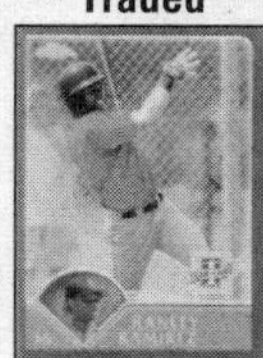

These cards were issued at a stated rate of two per 2003 Topps Traded pack. Cards numbered 1 through 115 feature veterans who were traded while cards 116 through 120 feature managers. Cards numbered 121 through 165 featured prospects and cards 166 through 275 feature Rookie Cards. All of these cards were issued with a "T" prefix.

COMPLETE SET (275) 60.00 120.00
COMMON CARD (1-120) .30 .75
COMMON CARD (121-165) .40 1.00
COMMON CARD (166-275) .40 1.00
2 PER 2003 TOPPS TRADED HOBBY PACK
2 PER 2003 TOPPS TRADED HTA PACK
2 PER 2003 TOPPS TRADED RETAIL PACK
T1 Juan Pierre .30 .75
T2 Mark Grudzielanek .30 .75
T3 Tanyon Sturtze .30 .75
T4 Greg Vaughn .30 .75
T5 Greg Myers .30 .75
T6 Randall Simon .30 .75
T7 Todd Hundley .30 .75
T8 Marlon Anderson .30 .75
T9 Jeff Reboulet .30 .75
T10 Alex Sanchez .30 .75
T11 Mike Rivera .30 .75
T12 Todd Walker .30 .75
T13 Ray King .30 .75
T14 Shawn Estes .30 .75
T15 Gary Matthews Jr. .30 .75
T16 Jaret Wright .30 .75
T17 Edgardo Alfonzo .30 .75
T18 Omar Daal .30 .75
T19 Ryan Rupe .30 .75
T20 Tony Clark .30 .75
T21 Jeff Suppan .30 .75
T22 Mike Stanton .30 .75
T23 Ramon Martinez .30 .75
T24 Armando Rios .30 .75
T25 Johnny Estrada .30 .75
T26 Joe Girardi .30 .75
T27 Ivan Rodriguez .50 1.25
T28 Robert Fick .30 .75
T29 Rick White .30 .75
T30 Robert Person .30 .75
T31 Alan Benes .30 .75
T32 Chris Carpenter .30 .75
T33 Chris Widger .30 .75
T34 Travis Hafner .30 .75
T35 Mike Venafro .30 .75
T36 Jon Lieber .30 .75
T37 Orlando Hernandez .30 .75
T38 Aaron Myette .30 .75
T39 Paul Bako .30 .75
T40 Erubiel Durazo .30 .75
T41 Mark Guthrie .30 .75
T42 Steve Avery .30 .75
T43 Damian Jackson .30 .75
T44 Rey Ordonez .30 .75
T45 John Flaherty .30 .75
T46 Byung-Hyun Kim .30 .75
T47 Tom Goodwin .30 .75
T48 Elmer Dessens .30 .75
T49 Al Martin .30 .75
T50 Gene Kingsale .30 .75
T51 Lenny Harris .30 .75
T52 David Ortiz Sox .75 2.00
T53 Jose Lima .30 .75
T54 Mike Difelice .30 .75
T55 Jose Hernandez .30 .75
T56 Todd Zeile .30 .75
T57 Roberto Hernandez .30 .75
T58 Albie Lopez .30 .75
T59 Roberto Alomar .50 1.25
T60 Russ Ortiz .30 .75
T61 Brian Daubach .30 .75
T62 Carl Everett .30 .75
T63 Jeromy Burnitz .30 .75
T64 Mark Bellhorn .30 .75
T65 Ruben Sierra .30 .75
T66 Mike Fetters .30 .75
T67 Armando Benitez .30 .75
T68 Deivi Cruz .30 .75
T69 Jose Cruz Jr. .30 .75
T70 Jeremy Fikac .30 .75
T71 Jeff Kent .30 .75
T72 Andres Galarraga .30 .75
T73 Rickey Henderson .75 2.00
T74 Royce Clayton .30 .75
T75 Troy O'Leary .30 .75
T76 Ron Coomer .30 .75
T77 Greg Colbrunn .30 .75
T78 Wes Helms .30 .75
T79 Kevin Millwood .30 .75
T80 Damion Easley .30 .75
T81 Bobby Kielty .30 .75
T82 Keith Osik .30 .75
T83 Ramiro Mendoza .30 .75
T84 Shea Hillenbrand .30 .75
T85 Shannon Stewart .30 .75
T86 Eddie Perez .30 .75
T87 Ugueth Urbina .30 .75
T88 Orlando Palmeiro .30 .75
T89 Graeme Lloyd .30 .75
T90 John Vander Wal .30 .75
T91 Gary Bennett .30 .75
T92 Shane Reynolds .30 .75
T93 Steve Parris .30 .75
T94 Julio Lugo .30 .75
T95 John Halama .30 .75
T96 Carlos Baerga .30 .75
T97 Jim Parque .30 .75
T98 Mike Williams .30 .75
T99 Fred McGriff .50 1.25
T100 Kenny Rogers .30 .75
T101 Matt Herges .30 .75
T102 Jay Bell .30 .75
T103 Esteban Yan .30 .75
T104 Eric Owens .30 .75
T105 Aaron Fultz .30 .75
T106 Rey Sanchez .30 .75
T107 Jim Thome .50 1.25
T108 Aaron Boone .30 .75
T109 Raul Mondesi .30 .75
T110 Kenny Lofton .30 .75
T111 Jose Guillen .30 .75
T112 Aramis Ramirez .30 .75
T113 Sidney Ponson .30 .75
T114 Scott Williamson .30 .75
T115 Robin Ventura .30 .75
T116 Dusty Baker MG .30 .75
T117 Felipe Alou MG .30 .75
T118 Buck Showalter MG .30 .75
T119 Jack McKeon MG .30 .75
T120 Art Howe MG .30 .75
T121 Bobby Crosby PROS .40 1.00
T122 Adrian Gonzalez PROS .40 1.00
T123 Kevin Cash PROS .40 1.00
T124 Shin-Soo Choo PROS .40 1.00
T125 Chin-Feng Chen PROS 1.00 2.50
T126 Miguel Cabrera PROS 1.00 2.50
T127 Jason Young PROS .40 1.00
T128 Alex Herrera PROS .40 1.00
T129 Jason Dubois PROS .40 1.00
T130 Jeff Mathis PROS .40 1.00
T131 Casey Kotchman PROS .40 1.00
T132 Ed Rogers PROS .40 1.00
T133 Wilson Betemit PROS .40 1.00
T134 Jim Kavourias PROS .40 1.00
T135 Taylor Buchholz PROS .40 1.00
T136 Adam LaRoche PROS .40 1.00
T137 D.McPherson PROS .40 1.00
T138 Jesus Cota PROS .40 1.00
T139 Clint Nageotte PROS .40 1.00
T140 Boof Bonser PROS .40 1.00
T141 Walter Young PROS .40 1.00
T142 Joe Crede PROS .40 1.00
T143 Denny Bautista PROS .40 1.00
T144 Victor Diaz PROS .40 1.00
T145 Chris Narveson PROS .40 1.00
T146 Gabe Gross PROS .40 1.00
T147 Jimmy Journell PROS .40 1.00
T148 Rafael Soriano PROS .40 1.00
T149 Jerome Williams PROS .40 1.00
T150 Aaron Cook PROS .40 1.00
T151 An. Martinez PROS .40 1.00
T152 Scott Hairston PROS .40 1.00
T153 John Buck PROS .40 1.00
T154 Ryan Ludwick PROS .40 1.00
T155 Chris Bootcheck PROS .40 1.00
T156 John Rheinecker PROS .40 1.00
T157 Jason Lane PROS .40 1.00
T158 Shelley Duncan PROS .75 2.00
T159 Adam Wainwright PROS .40 1.00
T160 Jason Arnold PROS .40 1.00
T161 Jonny Gomes PROS .60 1.50
T162 James Loney PROS .50 1.25
T163 Mike Fontenot PROS .40 1.00
T164 Khalil Greene PROS 1.00 2.50
T165 Sean Burnett PROS .40 1.00
T166 David Martinez FY RC .40 1.00
T167 Felix Pie FY RC 4.00 10.00
T168 Joe Valentine FY RC .40 1.00
T169 Brandon Webb FY RC 3.00 8.00
T170 Matt Diaz FY RC .60 1.50
T171 Lew Ford FY RC .50 1.25
T172 Jeremy Griffiths FY RC .40 1.00
T173 Matt Hensley FY RC .40 1.00
T174 Charlie Manning FY RC .40 1.00
T175 Elizardo Ramirez FY RC .50 1.25
T176 Greg Aquino FY RC .40 1.00
T177 Felix Sanchez FY RC .40 1.00
T178 Kelly Shoppach FY RC .75 2.00
T179 Bubba Nelson FY RC .50 1.25
T180 Mike O3 ™Keefe FY RC .40 1.00
T181 Hanley Ramirez FY RC 5.00 12.00
T182 T.Wellemeyer FY RC .40 1.00
T183 Dustin Moseley FY RC .40 1.00
T184 Eric Crozier FY RC .50 1.25
T185 Ryan Shealy FY RC 2.00 5.00
T186 Jer. Bonderman FY RC 3.00 8.00
T187 T.Story-Harden FY RC .40 1.00
T188 Dusty Brown FY RC .40 1.00
T189 Rob Hammock FY RC .40 1.00
T190 Jorge Piedra FY RC .50 1.25
T191 Chris De La Cruz FY RC .40 1.00
T192 Eli Whiteside FY RC .40 1.00
T193 Jason Kubel FY RC 1.25 3.00
T194 Jon Schuerholz FY RC .40 1.00
T195 St. Randolph FY RC .40 1.00
T196 Andy Sisco FY RC .40 1.00
T197 Sean Smith FY RC .50 1.25
T198 Jon-Mark Sprowl FY RC .40 1.00
T199 Matt Kata FY RC .40 1.00
T200 Robinson Cano FY RC 6.00 15.00
T201 Nook Logan FY RC .50 1.25
T202 Ben Francisco FY RC .40 1.00
T203 Arnie Munoz FY RC .40 1.00
T204 Ozzie Chavez FY RC .40 1.00
T205 Eric Riggs FY RC .50 1.25
T206 Beau Kemp FY RC .40 1.00
T207 Travis Wong FY RC .50 1.25
T208 Dustin Yount FY RC .50 1.25
T209 Brian McCann FY RC 6.00 15.00
T210 Wilton Reynolds FY RC .50 1.25
T211 Matt Bruback FY RC .40 1.00
T212 Andrew Brown FY RC .50 1.25
T213 Edgar Gonzalez FY RC .40 1.00
T214 Eider Torres FY RC .40 1.00
T215 Aquilino Lopez FY RC .40 1.00
T216 Bobby Basham FY RC .40 1.00
T217 Tim Olson FY RC .40 1.00
T218 Nathan Panther FY RC .40 1.00
T219 Bryan Grace FY RC .40 1.00
T220 Dusty Gomon FY RC .50 1.25
T221 Wil Ledezma FY RC .40 1.00
T222 Josh Willingham FY RC 1.00 2.50
T223 David Cash FY RC .40 1.00
T224 Oscar Villarreal FY RC .40 1.00
T225 Jeff Duncan FY RC .40 1.00
T226 Kade Johnson FY RC .40 1.00
T227 L.Steidlmayer FY RC .40 1.00
T228 Brandon Watson FY RC .40 1.00
T229 Jose Morales FY RC .40 1.00
T230 Mike Gallo FY RC .40 1.00
T231 Tyler Adamczyk FY RC .40 1.00
T232 Adam Stern FY RC .40 1.00
T233 Brennan King FY RC .40 1.00
T234 Dan Haren FY RC .75 2.00
T235 Mi. Hernandez FY RC .40 1.00
T236 Ben Fritz FY RC .40 1.00
T237 Clay Hensley FY RC .40 1.00
T238 Tyler Johnson FY RC .40 1.00
T239 Pete LaForest FY RC .40 1.00
T240 Tyler Martin FY RC .40 1.00
T241 J.D. Durbin FY RC .40 1.00
T242 Shane Victorino FY RC .75 2.00
T243 Rajai Davis FY RC .40 1.00
T244 Ismael Castro FY RC .40 1.00
T245 C.Wang FY RC 4.00 10.00
T246 Travis Ishikawa FY RC .75 2.00
T247 Corey Shafer FY RC .40 1.00
T248 G.Schneidmiller FY RC .40 1.00
T249 Dave Pember FY RC .40 1.00
T250 Keith Stamler FY RC .40 1.00
T251 Tyson Graham FY RC .40 1.00
T252 Ryan Cameron FY RC .40 1.00
T253 Eric Eckenstahler FY .40 1.00
T254 Ma. Peterson FY RC .40 1.00
T255 Dustin McGowan FY RC .50 1.25
T256 Pr. Redman FY RC .40 1.00
T257 Haj Turay FY RC .40 1.00
T258 Carlos Guzman FY RC .50 1.25
T259 Matt DeMarco FY RC .40 1.00
T260 Derek Michaelis FY RC .40 1.00
T261 Brian Burgamy FY RC .40 1.00
T262 Jay Sitzman FY RC .40 1.00
T263 Chris Fallon FY RC .40 1.00
T264 Mike Adams FY RC .40 1.00
T265 Clint Barmes FY RC 1.00 2.50
T266 Eric Reed FY RC .40 1.00
T267 Willie Eyre FY RC .40 1.00
T268 Carlos Duran FY RC .40 1.00
T269 Nick Trzesniak FY RC .40 1.00
T270 Ferdin Tejeda FY RC .40 1.00
T271 Mi. Garciaparra FY RC .40 1.00
T272 Michael Hinckley FY RC .50 1.25
T273 Br. Florence FY RC .40 1.00
T274 Trent Oeltjen FY RC .50 1.25
T275 Mike Neu FY RC .40 1.00

2003 Topps Chrome Traded Refractors

*REF 1-120: 2X TO 5X BASIC
*REF 121-165: 1.5X TO 4X BASIC
*REF 166-275: 1.5X TO 4X BASIC
STATED ODDS 1:12 HOB/RET, 1:4 HTA
T181 Hanley Ramirez FY 30.00 60.00
T245 Chien-Ming Wang FY 15.00 40.00

2003 Topps Chrome Traded Uncirculated X-Fractors

ONE PER TOPPS TRADED HTA BOX
STATED PRINT RUN 25 SERIAL #'d SETS
NO PRICING DUE TO SCARCITY

2004 Topps Chrome

This 233 card first series was released in January, 2004. A matching second series of 233 cards was released in May, 2004. This set was issued in four-card packs with an $3 SRP which came 20 packs to a box and 10 boxes to a case. The first 210 cards of the first series are veterans while the final 23 cards of the set feature first year cards. Please note that cards 221 through 233 were autographed by the featured players and those cards were issued to a stated rate of one in 21 hobby packs and one in 33 retail packs. In the second series cards numbered 234 through 246 feature autographs of the rookie pictured and those cards were inserted at a stated rate of one in 22 hobby packs and one in 35 retail packs. Bradley Sullivan (#234) was issued with either the correct back or an incorrect back numbered to 345 which consistitued about 20 percent of the total press run.

COMP.SERIES 1 w/o SP's (220) 40.00 80.00
COMP.SERIES 2 w/o SP's (220) 40.00 80.00
COMMON (1-210/257-466) .40 1.00
COMMON (211-220/247-256) .75 2.00
COMMON AU (221-233) 4.00 10.00
1 Jim Thome .60 1.50
2 Reggie Sanders .40 1.00
3 Mark Kotsay .40 1.00
4 Edgardo Alfonzo .40 1.00
5 Tim Wakefield .40 1.00
6 Moises Alou .40 1.00
7 Jorge Julio .40 1.00
8 Bartolo Colon .40 1.00
9 Chan Ho Park .40 1.00
10 Ichiro Suzuki 2.00 5.00
11 Kevin Millwood .40 1.00
12 Preston Wilson .40 1.00
13 Tom Glavine .60 1.50
14 Junior Spivey .40 1.00
15 Marcus Giles .40 1.00
16 David Segui .40 1.00
17 Kevin Millar .40 1.00
18 Corey Patterson .40 1.00
19 Aaron Rowand .40 1.00
20 Derek Jeter 2.00 5.00
21 Luis Castillo .40 1.00
22 Manny Ramirez .60 1.50
23 Jay Payton .40 1.00
24 Bobby Higginson .40 1.00
25 Lance Berkman .40 1.00
26 Juan Pierre .40 1.00
27 Mike Mussina .60 1.50
28 Fred McGriff .60 1.50
29 Richie Sexson .40 1.00
30 Tim Hudson .40 1.00
31 Mike Piazza 1.50 4.00
32 Brad Radke .40 1.00
33 Jeff Weaver .40 1.00
34 Ramon Hernandez .40 1.00
35 David Bell .40 1.00
36 Randy Wolf .40 1.00
37 Jake Peavy .40 1.00
38 Tim Worrell .40 1.00
39 Gil Meche .40 1.00
40 Albert Pujols 2.00 5.00
41 Michael Young .40 1.00
42 Josh Phelps .40 1.00
43 Brendan Donnelly .40 1.00
44 Steve Finley .40 1.00
45 John Smoltz .60 1.50
46 Jay Gibbons .40 1.00
47 Trot Nixon .40 1.00
48 Carl Pavano .40 1.00
49 Frank Thomas 1.00 2.50
50 Mark Prior .60 1.50
51 Danny Graves .40 1.00
52 Milton Bradley .40 1.00
53 Kris Benson .40 1.00
54 Ryan Klesko .40 1.00
55 Mike Lowell .40 1.00
56 Geoff Blum .40 1.00
57 Michael Tucker .40 1.00
58 Paul Lo Duca .40 1.00
59 Vicente Padilla .40 1.00
60 Jacque Jones .40 1.00
61 Fernando Tatis .40 1.00
62 Ty Wigginton .40 1.00
63 Rich Aurilia .40 1.00
64 Andy Pettitte .60 1.50
65 Terrence Long .40 1.00
66 Cliff Floyd .40 1.00
67 Mariano Rivera 1.00 2.50
68 Kelvim Escobar .40 1.00
69 Marlon Byrd .40 1.00
70 Mark Mulder .40 1.00
71 Francisco Cordero .40 1.00

72 Carlos Guillen .40 1.00
73 Fernando Vina .40 1.00
74 Lance Carter .40 1.00
75 Hank Blalock .40 1.00
76 Jimmy Rollins .40 1.00
77 Francisco Rodriguez .40 1.00
78 Javy Lopez .40 1.00
79 Jerry Hairston Jr. .40 1.00
80 Andruw Jones .60 1.50
81 Rodrigo Lopez .40 1.00
82 Johnny Damon .60 1.50
83 Hee Seop Choi .40 1.00
84 Kazuhiro Sasaki .40 1.00
85 Danny Bautista .40 1.00
86 Matt Lawton .40 1.00
87 Juan Uribe .40 1.00
88 Rafael Furcal .40 1.00
89 Kyle Farnsworth .40 1.00
90 Jose Vidro .40 1.00
91 Luis Rivas .40 1.00
92 Hideo Nomo 1.00 2.50
93 Javier Vazquez .40 1.00
94 Al Leiter .40 1.00
95 Jose Valentin .40 1.00
96 Alex Cintron .40 1.00
97 Zach Day .40 1.00
98 Jorge Posada .60 1.50
99 C.C. Sabathia .40 1.00
100 Alex Rodriguez 1.50 4.00
101 Brad Penny .40 1.00
102 Brad Ausmus .40 1.00
103 Raul Ibanez .40 1.00
104 Mike Hampton .40 1.00
105 Adrian Beltre .40 1.00
106 Ramiro Mendoza .40 1.00
107 Rocco Baldelli .40 1.00
108 Esteban Loaiza .40 1.00
109 Russell Branyan .40 1.00
110 Todd Helton .60 1.50
111 Braden Looper .40 1.00
112 Octavio Dotel .40 1.00
113 Mike MacDougal .40 1.00
114 Cesar Izturis .40 1.00
115 Johan Santana 1.00 2.50
116 Jose Contreras .40 1.00
117 Placido Polanco .40 1.00
118 Jason Phillips .40 1.00
119 Orlando Hudson .40 1.00
120 Vernon Wells .40 1.00
121 Ben Grieve .40 1.00
122 Dave Roberts .40 1.00
123 Ismael Valdes .40 1.00
124 Eric Owens .40 1.00
125 Curt Schilling .40 1.00
126 Russ Ortiz .40 1.00
127 Mark Buehrle .40 1.00
128 Doug Mientkiewicz .40 1.00
129 Dmitri Young .40 1.00
130 Kazuhisa Ishii .40 1.00
131 A.J. Pierzynski .40 1.00
132 Brad Wilkerson .40 1.00
133 Joe McEwing .40 1.00
134 Alex Cora .40 1.00
135 Jose Cruz Jr. .40 1.00
136 Carlos Zambrano .40 1.00
137 Jeff Kent .40 1.00
138 Shigetoshi Hasegawa .40 1.00
139 Jarrod Washburn .40 1.00
140 Greg Maddux 1.50 4.00
141 Josh Beckett .40 1.00
142 Miguel Batista .40 1.00
143 Omar Vizquel .60 1.50
144 Alex Gonzalez .40 1.00
145 Billy Wagner .40 1.00
146 Brian Jordan .40 1.00
147 Wes Helms .40 1.00
148 Deivi Cruz .40 1.00
149 Alex Gonzalez .40 1.00
150 Jason Giambi .40 1.00
151 Erubiel Durazo .40 1.00
152 Mike Lieberthal .40 1.00
153 Jason Kendall .40 1.00
154 Xavier Nady .40 1.00
155 Kirk Rueter .40 1.00
156 Mike Cameron .40 1.00
157 Miguel Cairo .40 1.00
158 Woody Williams .40 1.00
159 Toby Hall .40 1.00
160 Bernie Williams .60 1.50
161 Darin Erstad .40 1.00
162 Matt Mantei .40 1.00
163 Shawn Chacon .40 1.00
164 Bill Mueller .40 1.00
165 Damian Miller .40 1.00
166 Tony Graffanino .40 1.00
167 Sean Casey .40 1.00
168 Brandon Phillips .40 1.00
169 Runelvys Hernandez .40 1.00
170 Adam Dunn .40 1.00
171 Carlos Lee .40 1.00
172 Juan Encarnacion .40 1.00
173 Angel Berroa .40 1.00
174 Desi Relaford .40 1.00
175 Joe Mays .40 1.00
176 Ben Sheets .40 1.00
177 Eddie Guardado .40 1.00
178 Rocky Biddle .40 1.00
179 Eric Gagne .40 1.00
180 Eric Chavez .40 1.00
181 Jason Michaels .40 1.00
182 Dustan Mohr .40 1.00
183 Kip Wells .40 1.00
184 Brian Lawrence .40 1.00
185 Bret Boone .40 1.00
186 Tino Martinez .60 1.50
187 Aubrey Huff .40 1.00
188 Kevin Mench .40 1.00
189 Tim Salmon .60 1.50
190 Carlos Delgado .40 1.00
191 John Lackey .40 1.00
192 Eric Byrnes .40 1.00
193 Luis Matos .40 1.00
194 Derek Lowe .40 1.00
195 Mark Grudzielanek .40 1.00
196 Tom Gordon .40 1.00
197 Matt Clement .40 1.00
198 Byung-Hyun Kim .40 1.00
199 Brandon Inge .40 1.00
200 Nomar Garciaparra 1.50 4.00
201 Frank Catalanotto .40 1.00
202 Cristian Guzman .40 1.00
203 Bo Hart .40 1.00
204 Jack Wilson .40 1.00
205 Ray Durham .40 1.00
206 Freddy Garcia .40 1.00
207 J.D. Drew .40 1.00
208 Orlando Cabrera .40 1.00
209 Roy Halladay .40 1.00
210 David Eckstein .40 1.00
211 Matt Falcon FY RC .75 2.00
212 Todd Self FY RC 1.25 3.00
213 David Murphy FY RC 1.25 3.00
214 Dioner Navarro FY RC 1.25 3.00
215 Marcus McBeth FY RC .75 2.00
216 Chris O'Riordan FY RC .75 2.00
217 Rodney Choy Foo FY RC .75 2.00
218 Tim Frend FY RC .75 2.00
219 Yadier Molina FY RC 2.50 6.00
220 Zach Duke FY RC 2.00 5.00
221 Anthony Lerew FY AU RC 6.00 15.00
222 B.Hawksworth FY AU RC 6.00 15.00
223 Brayan Pena FY AU RC 4.00 10.00
224 Craig Ansman FY AU RC 4.00 10.00
225 Jon Knott FY AU RC 4.00 10.00
226 Josh Labandeira FY AU RC 4.00 10.00
227 Khalid Ballouli FY AU RC 4.00 10.00
228 Kyle Davies FY AU RC 10.00 25.00
229 Matt Creighton FY AU RC 4.00 10.00
230 Mike Gosling FY AU RC 4.00 10.00
231 Nic Ungs FY AU RC 4.00 10.00
232 Zach Miner FY AU RC 10.00 25.00
233 Donald Levinski FY AU RC 4.00 10.00
234A Bradley Sullivan FY AU RC 6.00 15.00
234B B.Sullivan FY AU ERR 345 10.00 25.00
235 Carlos Quentin FY AU RC 15.00 40.00
236 Conor Jackson FY AU RC 12.50 30.00
237 Estee Harris FY AU RC 6.00 15.00
238 Jeffrey Allison FY AU RC 4.00 10.00
239 Kyle Sleeth FY AU RC 6.00 15.00
240 Matthew Moses FY AU RC 6.00 15.00
241 Tim Stauffer FY AU RC 4.00 10.00
242 Brad Snyder FY AU RC 5.00 12.00
243 Jason Hirsh FY AU RC 10.00 25.00
244 L.Milledge FY AU RC 20.00 50.00
245 Logan Kensing FY AU RC 4.00 10.00
246 Kory Casto FY AU RC 6.00 15.00
247 David Aardsma FY RC 1.25 3.00
248 Omar Quintanilla FY RC 1.25 3.00
249 Ervin Santana FY RC 2.00 5.00
250 Merkin Valdez FY RC .75 2.00
251 Vito Chiaravalloti FY RC .75 2.00
252 Travis Blackley FY RC .75 2.00
253 Chris Shelton FY RC 1.25 3.00
254 Rudy Guillen FY RC 1.25 3.00
255 Bobby Brownlie FY RC 1.00 2.50
256 Paul Maholm FY RC 1.50 4.00
257 Roger Clemens 2.00 5.00
258 Laynce Nix .40 1.00
259 Eric Hinske .40 1.00
260 Ivan Rodriguez .60 1.50
261 Brandon Webb .40 1.00
262 Jhonny Peralta .40 1.00
263 Adam Kennedy .40 1.00
264 Tony Batista .40 1.00
265 Jeff Suppan .40 1.00
266 Kenny Lofton .40 1.00
267 Scott Sullivan .40 1.00
268 Ken Griffey Jr. 1.50 4.00
269 Juan Rivera .40 1.00
270 Larry Walker .40 1.00
271 Todd Hollandsworth .40 1.00
272 Carlos Beltran .40 1.00
273 Carl Crawford .40 1.00
274 Karim Garcia .40 1.00
275 Jose Reyes .40 1.00
276 Brandon Duckworth .40 1.00
277 Brian Giles .40 1.00
278 J.T. Snow .40 1.00
279 Jamie Moyer .40 1.00
280 Julio Lugo .40 1.00
281 Mark Teixeira .60 1.50
282 Cory Lidle .40 1.00
283 Lyle Overbay .40 1.00
284 Troy Percival .40 1.00
285 Robby Hammock .40 1.00
286 Jason Johnson .40 1.00
287 Damian Rolls .40 1.00
288 Antonio Alfonseca .40 1.00
289 Tom Goodwin .40 1.00
290 Paul Konerko .40 1.00
291 D'Angelo Jimenez .40 1.00
292 Ben Broussard .40 1.00
293 Magglio Ordonez .40 1.00
294 Carlos Pena .40 1.00
295 Chad Fox .40 1.00
296 Jeriome Robertson .40 1.00
297 Travis Hafner .40 1.00
298 Joe Randa .40 1.00
299 Brady Clark .40 1.00
300 Barry Zito .40 1.00
301 Ruben Sierra .40 1.00
302 Brett Myers .40 1.00
303 Oliver Perez .40 1.00
304 Benito Santiago .40 1.00
305 David Ross .40 1.00
306 Joe Nathan .40 1.00
307 Jim Edmonds .40 1.00
308 Matt Kata .40 1.00
309 Vinny Castilla .40 1.00
310 Marty Cordova .40 1.00
311 Aramis Ramirez .40 1.00
312 Carl Everett .40 1.00
313 Ryan Freel .40 1.00
314 Mark Bellhorn Sox .40 1.00
315 Joe Mauer 1.00 2.50
316 Tim Redding .40 1.00
317 Jeromy Burnitz .40 1.00
318 Miguel Cabrera .60 1.50
319 Ramon Nivar .40 1.00
320 Casey Blake .40 1.00
321 Adam LaRoche .40 1.00
322 Jermaine Dye .40 1.00
323 Jerome Williams .40 1.00
324 John Olerud .40 1.00
325 Scott Rolen .60 1.50
326 Bobby Kielty .40 1.00
327 Travis Lee .40 1.00
328 Jeff Cirillo .40 1.00
329 Scott Spiezio .40 1.00
330 Melvin Mora .40 1.00
331 Mike Timlin .40 1.00
332 Kerry Wood .40 1.00
333 Tony Womack .40 1.00
334 Jody Gerut .40 1.00
335 Morgan Ensberg .40 1.00
336 Odalis Perez .40 1.00
337 Michael Cuddyer .40 1.00
338 Jose Hernandez .40 1.00
339 LaTroy Hawkins .40 1.00
340 Marquis Grissom .40 1.00
341 Matt Morris .40 1.00
342 Juan Gonzalez .40 1.00
343 Jose Valverde .40 1.00
344 Joe Borowski .40 1.00
345 Josh Bard .40 1.00
346 Austin Kearns .40 1.00
347 Chin-Hui Tsao .40 1.00
348 Wil Ledezma .40 1.00
349 Aaron Guiel .40 1.00
350 Alfonso Soriano .40 1.00
351 Ted Lilly .40 1.00
352 Sean Burroughs .40 1.00
353 Rafael Palmeiro .60 1.50
354 Quinton McCracken .40 1.00
355 David Ortiz 1.00 2.50
356 Randall Simon .40 1.00
357 Wily Mo Pena .40 1.00
358 Brian Anderson .40 1.00
359 Corey Koskie .40 1.00
360 Keith Foulke Sox .40 1.00
361 Sidney Ponson .40 1.00
362 Gary Matthews Jr. .40 1.00
363 Herbert Perry .40 1.00
364 Shea Hillenbrand .40 1.00
365 Craig Biggio .60 1.50
366 Barry Larkin .60 1.50
367 Arthur Rhodes .40 1.00
368 Sammy Sosa 1.00 2.50
369 Joe Crede .40 1.00
370 Gary Sheffield .40 1.00
371 Coco Crisp .40 1.00
372 Torii Hunter .40 1.00
373 Derrek Lee .60 1.50
374 Adam Everett .40 1.00
375 Miguel Tejada .40 1.00
376 Jeremy Affeldt .40 1.00
377 Robin Ventura .40 1.00
378 Scott Podsednik .40 1.00
379 Matthew LeCroy .40 1.00
380 Vladimir Guerrero 1.00 2.50
381 Steve Karsay .40 1.00
382 Jeff Nelson .40 1.00
383 Chase Utley .60 1.50
384 Bobby Abreu .40 1.00
385 Josh Fogg .40 1.00
386 Trevor Hoffman .40 1.00
387 Matt Stairs .40 1.00
388 Edgar Martinez .60 1.50
389 Edgar Renteria .40 1.00
390 Chipper Jones 1.00 2.50
391 Eric Munson .40 1.00
392 Dewon Brazelton .40 1.00
393 John Thomson .40 1.00
394 Chris Woodward .40 1.00
395 Joe Kennedy .40 1.00
396 Reed Johnson .40 1.00
397 Johnny Estrada .40 1.00
398 Damian Moss .40 1.00
399 Victor Zambrano .40 1.00
400 Dontrelle Willis .60 1.50
401 Troy Glaus .40 1.00
402 Raul Mondesi .40 1.00
403 Jeff Davanon .40 1.00
404 Kurt Ainsworth .40 1.00
405 Pedro Martinez .60 1.50
406 Eric Karros .40 1.00
407 Billy Koch .40 1.00
408 Luis Gonzalez .40 1.00
409 Jack Cust .40 1.00
410 Mike Sweeney .40 1.00
411 Jason Bay .40 1.00
412 Mark Redman .40 1.00
413 Jason Jennings .40 1.00
414 Rondell White .40 1.00
415 Todd Hundley .40 1.00
416 Shannon Stewart .40 1.00
417 Jae Weong Seo .40 1.00
418 Livan Hernandez .40 1.00
419 Mark Ellis .40 1.00
420 Pat Burrell .40 1.00
421 Mark Loretta .40 1.00
422 Robb Nen .40 1.00
423 Joel Pineiro .40 1.00
424 Todd Walker .40 1.00
425 Jeremy Bonderman .40 1.00
426 A.J. Burnett .40 1.00
427 Greg Myers .40 1.00
428 Roy Oswalt .40 1.00
429 Carlos Baerga .40 1.00
430 Garret Anderson .40 1.00
431 Horacio Ramirez .40 1.00
432 Brian Roberts .40 1.00
433 Kevin Brown .40 1.00
434 Eric Milton .40 1.00
435 Ramon Vazquez .40 1.00
436 Alex Escobar .40 1.00
437 Alex Sanchez .40 1.00
438 Jeff Bagwell .60 1.50
439 Claudio Vargas .40 1.00
440 Shawn Green .40 1.00
441 Geoff Jenkins .40 1.00
442 David Wells .40 1.00
443 Nick Johnson .40 1.00
444 Jose Guillen .40 1.00
445 Scott Hatteberg .40 1.00
446 Phil Nevin .40 1.00
447 Jason Schmidt .40 1.00
448 Ricky Ledee .40 1.00
449 So Taguchi .40 1.00
450 Randy Johnson 1.00 2.50
451 Eric Young .40 1.00
452 Chone Figgins .40 1.00
453 Larry Bigbie .40 1.00
454 Scott Williamson .40 1.00
455 Ramon Martinez .40 1.00
456 Roberto Alomar .60 1.50
457 Ryan Dempster .40 1.00
458 Ryan Ludwick .40 1.00
459 Ramon Santiago .40 1.00
460 Jeff Conine .40 1.00
461 Brad Lidge .40 1.00
462 Ken Harvey .40 1.00
463 Guillermo Mota .40 1.00
464 Rick Reed .40 1.00
465 Armando Benitez .40 1.00
466 Wade Miller .40 1.00

2004 Topps Chrome Black Refractors

*BLACK 1-210/257-466: 1.5X TO 4X BASIC
*BLACK 211-220/247-256: 1.5X TO 4X BASIC
1-220 SERIES 1 ODDS 1:10 H, 1:20 R
247-466 SERIES 2 ODDS 1:19 H, 1:20 R
221-233 SERIES 1 ODDS 1:1527 H, 1:2480 R
234-246 SERIES 2 ODDS 1:1579 H, 1:2549 R
221-246 PRINT RUN 25 SERIAL #'d SETS
221-246 NO PRICING DUE TO SCARCITY

2004 Topps Chrome Gold Refractors

*GOLD 1-210/257-466: 1.25X TO 3X BASIC
*GOLD 211-220/247-256: 1.25X TO 3X BASIC
1-220 SERIES 1 ODDS 1:5 H, 1:10 R
247-466 SERIES 2 ODDS 1:9 H, 1:10 R
*GOLD AU 221-246: 2X TO 4X BASIC AU
221-233 SERIES 1 ODDS 1:759 H, 1:1208 R
234-246 SERIES 2 ODDS 1:790 H, 1:1324 R
221-246 PRINT RUN 50 SERIAL #'d SETS
232 Zach Miner FY AU 50.00 100.00
235 Carlos Quentin FY AU 100.00 200.00
244 Lastings Milledge FY AU 150.00 250.00

2004 Topps Chrome Red X-Fractors

*RED XF 1-210/257-466: 3X TO 8X BASIC
*RED XF 211-220/247-256: 3X TO 8X BASIC
1-220 ONE PER SER.1 PARALLEL HOT PACK
247-466 1 PER SER.2 PARALLEL HOT PACK
ONE HOT PACK PER SEALED HOBBY BOX
1-220 STATED PRINT RUN 63 SETS
247-466 STATED PRINT RUN 61 SETS
1-220/247-466 ARE NOT SERIAL #'d
1-220/247-466 PRINT RUN GIVEN BY TOPPS
221-233 SERIES 1 ODDS 1:21,371 HOBBY
234-246 SERIES 2 ODDS 1:20,800 HOBBY
221-246 PRINT RUN 1 SERIAL #'d SET
221-246 NO PRICING DUE TO SCARCITY

2004 Topps Chrome Refractors

*REF 1-210/257-466: 1X TO 2.5X BASIC
*REF 211-220/247-256: 1X TO 2.5X BASIC
1-220 SERIES 1 ODDS 1:4 H/R
247-466 SERIES 2 ODDS 1:4 H/R
*REF AU 221-246: 1X TO 2.5X BASIC AU
221-233 SERIES 1 ODDS 1:380 H, 1:597 R
234-246 SERIES 2 ODDS 1:375 H, 1:680 R
221-246 PRINT RUN 100 SERIAL #'d SETS
232 Zach Miner FY AU 30.00 60.00
235 Carlos Quentin FY AU 60.00 120.00
244 Lastings Milledge FY AU 90.00 150.00

2004 Topps Chrome Fashionably Great Relics

ONE RELIC PER SER.1 GU HOBBY PACK
GROUP A 1:59 SER.1 RETAIL
GROUP B 1:107 SER.1 RETAIL
AD Adam Dunn Jsy A 3.00 8.00
AJ Andruw Jones Uni A 4.00 10.00
AP Albert Pujols Jsy A 10.00 25.00
AR Alex Rodriguez Uni A 6.00 15.00
BM Brett Myers Jsy A 3.00 8.00
BW Billy Wagner Jsy B 3.00 8.00
CB Craig Biggio Uni A 4.00 10.00
CD Carlos Delgado Jsy A 3.00 8.00
CF Cliff Floyd Jsy A 3.00 8.00
CJ Chipper Jones Uni A 4.00 10.00
CS Curt Schilling Jsy A 3.00 8.00
DL Derek Lowe Uni B 3.00 8.00
EC Eric Chavez Uni B 3.00 8.00
FG Freddy Garcia Jsy A 3.00 8.00
FM Fred McGriff Jsy A 4.00 10.00
FT Frank Thomas Uni A 4.00 10.00
HB Hank Blalock Jsy A 3.00 8.00
IR Ivan Rodriguez Uni B 4.00 10.00
JB Jeff Bagwell Uni A 4.00 10.00
JBO Joe Borchard Jsy A 3.00 8.00
JO John Olerud Jsy A 3.00 8.00
JR Juan Rivera Jsy A 3.00 8.00
JS John Smoltz Uni A 4.00 10.00
JV Jose Vidro Jsy A 3.00 8.00
KB Kevin Brown Jsy B 3.00 8.00
MM Mark Mulder Uni A 3.00 8.00
MP Mike Piazza Uni A 6.00 15.00
MR Manny Ramirez Uni A 4.00 10.00
MS Mike Sweeney Uni A 3.00 8.00
NG Nomar Garciaparra Uni B 6.00 15.00
PM Pedro Martinez Jsy A 4.00 10.00
RP Rafael Palmeiro Jsy A 4.00 10.00
SS Sammy Sosa Jsy A 4.00 10.00
TH Tim Hudson Uni B 3.00 8.00
THO Trevor Hoffman Uni A 3.00 8.00
VW Vernon Wells Jsy B 3.00 8.00
WP Wily Mo Pena Jsy A 3.00 8.00

2004 Topps Chrome Handle With Care Bat Knob Relics

STATED PRINT RUN 5 SERIAL #'d SETS
1 OF 1 PRINT RUN 1 SERIAL #'d SET
NO PRICING DUE TO SCARCITY
RANDOM IN SERIES 1 HOBBY RELIC PACKS
AK Al Kaline
AP Albert Pujols
AR Alex Rodriguez
AS Alfonso Soriano
BR Brooks Robinson
CF Carlton Fisk
CY Carl Yastrzemski
FR Frank Robinson
GB George Brett
HK Harmon Killebrew
JB Johnny Bench
JG Jason Giambi
JT Jim Thome
LB Lance Berkman
LBR Lou Brock
LG Luis Gonzalez
MT Miguel Tejada
NG Nomar Garciaparra
PM Paul Molitor
RJ Reggie Jackson
RY Robin Yount
TH Torii Hunter
WB Wade Boggs
WM Willie Mays
WS Willie Stargell

2004 Topps Chrome Presidential First Pitch Seat Relics

SERIES 2 ODDS 1:15 BOX-LOADER HOBBY
SERIES 2 ODDS 1:633 HOBBY
STATED PRINT RUN 100 SETS
CARDS ARE NOT SERIAL-NUMBERED
PRINT RUN INFO PROVIDED BY TOPPS
BC Bill Clinton 20.00 50.00
CC Calvin Coolidge 10.00 25.00
DE Dwight Eisenhower 10.00 25.00
FR Franklin D. Roosevelt 15.00 40.00
GB George W. Bush 20.00 50.00
GF Gerald Ford 15.00 40.00
GHB George H.W. Bush 15.00 40.00
HH Herbert Hoover 10.00 25.00
HT Harry Truman 10.00 25.00
JK John F. Kennedy 20.00 50.00
LJ Lyndon B. Johnson 10.00 25.00
RN Richard Nixon 20.00 50.00
RR Ronald Reagan 30.00 60.00
WH Warren Harding 10.00 25.00
WT William Taft 10.00 25.00
WW Woodrow Wilson 10.00 25.00

2004 Topps Chrome Presidential Pastime Refractors

COMPLETE SET (42) 60.00 120.00
SERIES 2 ODDS 1:9 HOBBY
*X-FRACTOR p/r 26-43: 2X TO 5X BASIC
X-FRACTOR SER.2 ODDS 1:400 H, 1:791 R
X-F PRINT RUNS B/WN 1-43 COPIES PER
NO X-F PRICING ON QTY OF 25 OR LESS
PP1 George Washington 2.50 6.00
PP2 John Adams 1.50 4.00
PP3 Thomas Jefferson 2.50 6.00
PP4 James Madison 1.50 4.00

PP5 James Monroe 1.50 4.00
PP6 John Quincy Adams 1.50 4.00
PP7 Andrew Jackson 1.50 4.00
PP8 Martin Van Buren 1.50 4.00
PP9 William Harrison 1.50 4.00
PP10 John Tyler 1.50 4.00
PP11 James Polk 1.50 4.00
PP12 Zachary Taylor 1.50 4.00
PP13 Millard Fillmore 1.50 4.00
PP14 Franklin Pierce 1.50 4.00
PP15 James Buchanan 1.50 4.00
PP16 Abraham Lincoln 2.50 6.00
PP17 Andrew Johnson 1.50 4.00
PP18 Ulysses S. Grant 2.00 5.00
PP19 Rutherford B. Hayes 1.50 4.00
PP20 James Garfield 1.50 4.00
PP21 Chester Arthur 1.50 4.00
PP22 Grover Cleveland 1.50 4.00
PP23 Benjamin Harrison 1.50 4.00
PP24 William McKinley 1.50 4.00
PP25 Theodore Roosevelt 2.00 5.00
PP26 William Taft 1.50 4.00
PP27 Woodrow Wilson 1.50 4.00
PP28 Warren Harding 1.50 4.00
PP29 Calvin Coolidge 1.50 4.00
PP30 Herbert Hoover 1.50 4.00
PP31 Franklin D. Roosevelt 2.00 5.00
PP32 Harry Truman 1.50 4.00
PP33 Dwight Eisenhower 1.50 4.00
PP34 John F. Kennedy 2.00 5.00
PP35 Lyndon B. Johnson 1.50 4.00
PP36 Richard Nixon 2.00 5.00
PP37 Gerald Ford 2.00 5.00
PP38 Jimmy Carter 1.50 4.00
PP39 Ronald Reagan 5.00 12.00
PP40 George H.W. Bush 2.00 5.00
PP41 Bill Clinton 2.50 6.00
PP42 George W. Bush 2.50 6.00

2004 Topps Chrome Town Heroes Relics

SER.2 ODDS 1 PER HOBBY BOX-LOADER
SER.2 ODDS 1:48 RETAIL
AP Albert Pujols Bat 6.00 15.00
AR Alex Rodriguez Bat 6.00 15.00
BZ Barry Zito Uni 3.00 8.00
CJ Chipper Jones Jsy 4.00 10.00
EC Eric Chavez Uni 3.00 8.00
FT Frank Thomas Jsy 4.00 10.00
HN Hideo Nomo Jsy 4.00 10.00
JG Jason Giambi Uni 3.00 8.00
JR Jose Reyes Bat 3.00 8.00
KW Kerry Wood Jsy 3.00 8.00
LB Lance Berkman Jsy 3.00 8.00
MM Mark Mulder Uni 3.00 8.00
MP Mark Prior Bat 4.00 10.00
MR Manny Ramirez Bat 4.00 10.00
MT Miguel Tejada Bat 3.00 8.00
NG Nomar Garciaparra Bat 4.00 10.00
RH Rich Harden Uni 3.00 8.00
RP Rafael Palmeiro Jsy 4.00 10.00
SS Sammy Sosa Jsy 4.00 10.00
SST Shannon Stewart Jsy 3.00 8.00
TH Tim Hudson Uni 3.00 8.00

2004 Topps Chrome Traded

These cards were issued at a stated rate of two per 2004 Topps Traded pack. Cards numbered 1 through 65 feature veterans who were traded while cards 66 through 70 feature managers. Cards numbered 71 through 90 feature high draft picks, cards numbered 91 through 110 feature prospect and cards 111 through 220 feature Rookie Cards. All of these cards were issued with a "T" prefix.

COMPLETE SET (220) 60.00 120.00
COMMON CARD (1-70) .30 .75
COMMON CARD (71-90) .40 1.00
COMMON CARD (91-110) .40 1.00
COMMON CARD (111-220) .40 1.00
2 PER 2004 TOPPS TRADED HOBBY PACK
2 PER 2004 TOPPS TRADED HTA PACK
2 PER 2004 TOPPS TRADED RETAIL PACK
PLATE ODDS 1:1151 H, 1:1173 R, 1:327 HTA
PLATE PRINT RUN 1 SET PER COLOR
BLACK-CYAN-MAGENTA-YELLOW ISSUED
NO PLATE PRICING DUE TO SCARCITY
T1 Pokey Reese .30 .75
T2 Tony Womack .30 .75
T3 Richard Hidalgo .30 .75

T4 Juan Uribe .30 .75
T5 J.D. Drew .30 .75
T6 Alex Gonzalez .30 .75
T7 Carlos Guillen .30 .75
T8 Doug Mientkiewicz .30 .75
T9 Fernando Vina .30 .75
T10 Milton Bradley .30 .75
T11 Kelvim Escobar .30 .75
T12 Ben Grieve .30 .75
T13 Brian Jordan .30 .75
T14 A.J. Pierzynski .30 .75
T15 Billy Wagner .30 .75
T16 Terrence Long .30 .75
T17 Carlos Beltran .30 .75
T18 Carl Everett .30 .75
T19 Reggie Sanders .30 .75
T20 Javy Lopez .30 .75
T21 Jay Payton .30 .75
T22 Octavio Dotel .30 .75
T23 Eddie Guardado .30 .75
T24 Andy Pettitte .50 1.25
T25 Richie Sexson .30 .75
T26 Ronnie Belliard .30 .75
T27 Michael Tucker .30 .75
T28 Brad Fullmer .30 .75
T29 Freddy Garcia .30 .75
T30 Bartolo Colon .30 .75
T31 Larry Walker Cards .50 1.25
T32 Mark Kotsay .30 .75
T33 Jason Marquis .30 .75
T34 Dustan Mohr .30 .75
T35 Javier Vazquez .30 .75
T36 Nomar Garciaparra 1.25 3.00
T37 Tino Martinez .50 1.25
T38 Hee Seop Choi .30 .75
T39 Damian Miller .30 .75
T40 Jose Lima .30 .75
T41 Ty Wigginton .30 .75
T42 Raul Ibanez .30 .75
T43 Danys Baez .30 .75
T44 Tony Clark .30 .75
T45 Greg Maddux 1.25 3.00
T46 Victor Zambrano .30 .75
T47 Orlando Cabrera Sox .30 .75
T48 Jose Cruz Jr. .30 .75
T49 Kris Benson .30 .75
T50 Alex Rodriguez 1.50 4.00
T51 Steve Finley .30 .75
T52 Ramon Hernandez .30 .75
T53 Esteban Loaiza .30 .75
T54 Ugueth Urbina .30 .75
T55 Jeff Weaver .30 .75
T56 Flash Gordon .30 .75
T57 Jose Contreras .30 .75
T58 Paul Lo Duca .30 .75
T59 Junior Spivey .30 .75
T60 Curt Schilling .50 1.25
T61 Brad Penny .30 .75
T62 Braden Looper .30 .75
T63 Miguel Cairo .30 .75
T64 Juan Encarnacion .30 .75
T65 Miguel Batista .30 .75
T66 Terry Francona MG .30 .75
T67 Lee Mazzilli MG .30 .75
T68 Al Pedrique MG .30 .75
T69 Ozzie Guillen MG .75 2.00
T70 Phil Garner MG .30 .75
T71 Matt Bush DP RC 1.50 4.00
T72 Homer Bailey DP RC 2.50 6.00
T73 Greg Golson DP RC 1.25 3.00
T74 Kyle Waldrop DP RC 1.00 2.50
T75 Richie Robnett DP RC 1.25 3.00
T76 Jay Rainville DP RC 1.50 4.00
T77 Bill Bray DP RC .40 1.00
T78 Philip Hughes DP RC 4.00 10.00
T79 Scott Elbert DP RC 1.00 2.50
T80 Josh Fields DP RC 2.00 5.00
T81 Justin Orenduff DP RC .75 2.00
T82 Dan Putnam DP RC .75 2.00
T83 Chris Nelson DP RC 2.00 5.00
T84 Blake DeWitt DP RC 1.50 4.00
T85 J.P. Howell DP RC 1.00 2.50
T86 Huston Street DP RC 2.50 6.00
T87 Kurt Suzuki DP RC 1.25 3.00
T88 Erick San Pedro DP RC .40 1.00
T89 Matt Tuiasosopo DP RC 2.00 5.00
T90 Matt Macri DP RC 1.00 2.50
T91 Chad Tracy PROS .40 1.00
T92 Scott Hairston PROS .40 1.00
T93 Jonny Gomes PROS .40 1.00
T94 Chin-Feng Chen PROS .40 1.00
T95 Chien-Ming Wang PROS 1.25 3.00
T96 Dustin McGowan PROS .40 1.00
T97 Chris Burke PROS .40 1.00
T98 Denny Bautista PROS .40 1.00
T99 Preston Larrison PROS .40 1.00
T100 Kevin Youkilis PROS .40 1.00
T101 John Maine PROS .40 1.00
T102 Guillermo Quiroz PROS .40 1.00
T103 Dave Krynzel PROS .40 1.00
T104 David Kelton PROS .40 1.00
T105 Edwin Encarnacion PROS .40 1.00
T106 Chad Gaudin PROS .40 1.00
T107 Sergio Mitre PROS .40 1.00
T108 Laynce Nix PROS .40 1.00
T109 David Parrish PROS .40 1.00
T110 Brandon Claussen PROS .40 1.00
T111 Frank Francisco FY RC .40 1.00
T112 Brian Dallimore FY RC .40 1.00
T113 Jim Crowell FY RC .50 1.25
T114 Andres Blanco FY RC .40 1.00
T115 Eduardo Villacis FY RC .40 1.00
T116 Kazuhito Tadano FY RC .50 1.25
T117 Aarom Baldiris FY RC .50 1.25
T118 Justin Germano FY RC .40 1.00
T119 Joey Gathright FY RC 1.25 3.00
T120 Franklyn Gracesqui FY RC .40 1.00
T121 Chin-Lung Hu FY RC 1.25 3.00
T122 Scott Olsen FY RC 1.50 4.00
T123 Tyler Davidson FY RC .50 1.25
T124 Fausto Carmona FY RC 2.00 5.00
T125 Tim Hutting FY RC .40 1.00
T126 Ryan Meaux FY RC .40 1.00
T127 Jon Connolly FY RC 1.00 2.50
T128 Hector Made FY RC .75 2.00
T129 Jamie Brown FY RC .40 1.00
T130 Paul McAnulty FY RC .75 2.00
T131 Chris Saenz FY RC .40 1.00
T132 Marland Williams FY RC .50 1.25
T133 Mike Huggins FY RC .40 1.00
T134 Jesse Crain FY RC .75 2.00
T135 Chad Bentz FY RC .40 1.00
T136 Kazuo Matsui FY RC .75 2.00
T137 Paul Maholm FY 1.00 2.50
T138 Brock Jacobsen FY RC .40 1.00
T139 Casey Daigle FY RC .40 1.00
T140 Nyjer Morgan FY RC .40 1.00
T141 Tom Mastny FY RC .40 1.00
T142 Kody Kirkland FY RC .50 1.25
T143 Jose Capellan FY RC .50 1.25
T144 Felix Hernandez FY RC 10.00 25.00
T145 Shawn Hill FY RC .40 1.00
T146 Danny Gonzalez FY RC .40 1.00
T147 Scott Dohmann FY RC .40 1.00
T148 Tommy Murphy FY RC .40 1.00
T149 Akinori Otsuka FY RC .40 1.00
T150 Miguel Perez FY RC .40 1.00
T151 Mike Rouse FY RC .40 1.00
T152 Ramon Ramirez FY RC .40 1.00
T153 Luke Hughes FY RC .40 1.00
T154 Howie Kendrick FY RC 20.00 30.00
T155 Ryan Budde FY RC .40 1.00
T156 Charlie Zink FY RC .40 1.00
T157 Warner Madrigal FY RC .75 2.00
T158 Jason Szuminski FY RC .40 1.00
T159 Chad Chop FY RC .40 1.00
T160 Shingo Takatsu FY RC .75 2.00
T161 Matt Lemanczyk FY RC .40 1.00
T162 Wardell Starling FY RC .40 1.00
T163 Nick Gorneault FY RC .50 1.25
T164 Scott Proctor FY RC .50 1.25
T165 Brooks Conrad FY RC .50 1.25
T166 Hector Gimenez FY RC .40 1.00
T167 Kevin Howard FY RC .50 1.25
T168 Vince Perkins FY RC .50 1.25
T169 Brock Peterson FY RC .40 1.00
T170 Chris Shelton FY .75 2.00
T171 Erick Aybar FY RC .75 2.00
T172 Paul Bacot FY RC .50 1.25
T173 Matt Capps FY RC .40 1.00
T174 Kory Casto FY .50 1.25
T175 Juan Cedeno FY RC .40 1.00
T176 Vito Chiaravalloti FY .40 1.00
T177 Alec Zumwalt FY RC .40 1.00
T178 J.J. Furmaniak FY RC .75 2.00
T179 Lee Gwaltney FY RC .40 1.00
T180 Donald Kelly FY RC .40 1.00
T181 Benji DeQuin FY RC .40 1.00
T182 Brant Colamarino FY RC .75 2.00
T183 Juan Gutierrez FY RC .40 1.00
T184 Carl Loadenthal FY RC .50 1.25
T185 Ricky Nolasco FY RC 1.25 3.00
T186 Jeff Salazar FY RC 1.00 2.50
T187 Rob Tejeda FY RC .75 2.00
T188 Alex Romero FY RC .40 1.00
T189 Yoann Torrealba FY RC .40 1.00
T190 Carlos Sosa FY RC .40 1.00
T191 Tim Bittner FY RC .40 1.00
T192 Chris Aguila FY RC .40 1.00
T193 Jason Frasor FY RC .40 1.00
T194 Reid Gorecki FY RC .40 1.00
T195 Dustin Nippert FY RC .50 1.25
T196 Javier Guzman FY RC .50 1.25
T197 Harvey Garcia FY RC .40 1.00
T198 Ivan Ochoa FY RC .40 1.00
T199 David Wallace FY RC .50 1.25
T200 Joel Zumaya FY RC 3.00 8.00
T201 Casey Kopitzke FY RC .40 1.00
T202 Lincoln Holdzkom FY RC .40 1.00
T203 Chad Santos FY RC .40 1.00
T204 Brian Pilkington FY RC .40 1.00
T205 Terry Jones FY RC .50 1.25
T206 Jerome Gamble FY RC .40 1.00
T207 Brad Eldred FY RC .50 1.25
T208 David Pauley FY RC 1.25 3.00
T209 Kevin Davidson FY RC .40 1.00
T210 Damaso Espino FY RC .40 1.00
T211 Tom Farmer FY RC .40 1.00
T212 Michael Mooney FY RC .40 1.00
T213 James Tomlin FY RC .40 1.00
T214 Greg Thissen FY RC .40 1.00
T215 Calvin Hayes FY RC .50 1.25
T216 Fernando Cortez FY RC .40 1.00
T217 Sergio Silva FY RC .40 1.00
T218 Jon de Vries FY RC .40 1.00
T219 Don Sutton FY RC 1.00 2.50
T220 Leo Nunez FY RC .40 1.00

2004 Topps Chrome Traded Blue Refractors

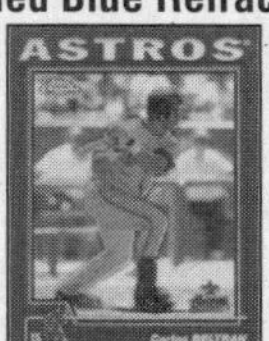

ODDS 1:4574 H, 1:4925 R, 1:1238 HTA
STATED PRINT RUN 1 SERIAL #'d SET
NO PRICING DUE TO SCARCITY

2004 Topps Chrome Traded Refractors

*REF 1-70: 2X TO 5X BASIC
*REF 71-90: 1X TO 2.5X BASIC
*REF 91-110: 1.5X TO 4X BASIC
*REF [illegible]20: 1.5X TO 4X BASIC
STATED ODDS 1:12 HOB/RET, 1:4 HTA
STATED PRINT RUN 355 SETS
CARDS ARE NOT SERIAL-NUMBERED
PRINT RUN INFO PROVIDED BY TOPPS
T72 Homer Bailey DP 12.50 30.00
T78 Philip Hughes DP 15.00 40.00
T121 Chin-Lung Hu FY 12.50 30.00
T144 Felix Hernandez FY 40.00 80.00
T154 Howie Kendrick FY 60.00 120.00

2004 Topps Chrome Traded X-Fractors

*XF 1-70: 8X TO 20X BASIC
*XF 91-110: 6X TO 15X BASIC
ONE XF PACK PER SEALED HTA BOX
ONE XF CARD PER XF PACK
STATED PRINT RUN 20 SERIAL #'d SETS
NO PRICING ON 71-90 DUE TO SCARCITY
NO PRICING ON 91-110 DUE TO SCARCITY

2005 Topps Chrome

This 234-card first series was released in January, 2005 while the 238-card second series was released in April, 2005. The cards were issued in four card hobby or retail packs with an $3 SRP which came 20 packs to a box and eight boxes to a case. Cards numbered 1-210 feature veteran players while cards 211-220 feature Rookie Cards and cards numbered 221-234 feature players in their first year with Topps who signed cards for this product. Cards numbered 221-234 were issued to a stated print run of 1771 sets (although these cards were not serial numbered) and were inserted at a stated rate of one in 28 hobby and one in 33 retail packs. In the second series, cards numbered 235 through 252 feature autographs and those cards were issued at a stated rate of one in two mini-boxes and one in 55 retail packs. In addition, these cards were issued to a stated print run of 1770 sets although these cards were not serial numbered.

COMP.SET w/o AU'S (440) 80.00 160.00
COMP.SERIES 1 w/o AU'S (220) 40.00 80.00
COMP.SERIES 2 w/o AU'S (220) 40.00 80.00
COMMON (1-210/253-467) .40 1.00
COMMON (211-220/468-472) .75 2.00
221-252 PRINT RUN PROVIDED BY TOPPS
EXCHANGE DEADLINE 05/31/07
1-234 PLATE ODDS 1:310 SER.1 HOBBY
235-252 PLATE ODDS 1:350 SER.2 MINI BOX
253-472 PLATE ODDS 1:29 SER.2 MINI BOX
PLATE PRINT RUN 1 SET PER COLOR
BLACK-CYAN-MAGENTA-YELLOW ISSUED
NO PLATE PRICING DUE TO SCARCITY
1 Alex Rodriguez 1.50 4.00
2 Placido Polanco .40 1.00
3 Torii Hunter .40 1.00
4 Lyle Overbay .40 1.00
5 Johnny Damon .60 1.50
6 Johnny Estrada .40 1.00
7 Rich Harden .40 1.00
8 Francisco Rodriguez .40 1.00
9 Jarrod Washburn .40 1.00
10 Sammy Sosa 1.00 2.50
11 Randy Wolf .40 1.00
12 Jason Bay .40 1.00
13 Tom Glavine .60 1.50
14 Michael Tucker .40 1.00
15 Brian Giles .40 1.00
16 Chad Tracy .40 1.00
17 Jim Edmonds .40 1.00
18 John Smoltz .60 1.50
19 Roy Halladay .40 1.00
20 Hank Blalock .40 1.00
21 Darin Erstad .40 1.00
22 Todd Walker .40 1.00
23 Mike Hampton .40 1.00
24 Mark Bellhorn .40 1.00
25 Jim Thome .60 1.50
26 Shingo Takatsu .40 1.00
27 Jody Gerut .40 1.00
28 Vinny Castilla .40 1.00
29 Luis Castillo .40 1.00
30 Ivan Rodriguez .60 1.50
31 Craig Biggio .60 1.50
32 Joe Randa .40 1.00
33 Adrian Beltre .40 1.00
34 Scott Podsednik .40 1.00
35 Cliff Floyd .40 1.00
36 Livan Hernandez .40 1.00
37 Eric Byrnes .40 1.00
38 Jose Acevedo .40 1.00
39 Jack Wilson .40 1.00
40 Gary Sheffield .40 1.00
41 Chan Ho Park .40 1.00
42 Carl Crawford .40 1.00
43 Shawn Estes .40 1.00
44 David Bell .40 1.00
45 Jeff DaVanon .40 1.00
46 Brandon Webb .40 1.00
47 Lance Berkman .40 1.00
48 Melvin Mora .40 1.00
49 David Ortiz 1.00 2.50
50 Andruw Jones .60 1.50
51 Chone Figgins .40 1.00
52 Danny Graves .40 1.00
53 Preston Wilson .40 1.00
54 Jeremy Bonderman .40 1.00
55 Carlos Guillen .40 1.00
56 Cesar Izturis .40 1.00
57 Kazuo Matsui .40 1.00
58 Jason Schmidt .40 1.00
59 Jason Marquis .40 1.00
60 Jose Vidro .40 1.00
61 Al Leiter .40 1.00
62 Javier Vazquez .40 1.00
63 Erubiel Durazo .40 1.00
64 Scott Spiezio .40 1.00
65 Scot Shields .40 1.00
66 Edgardo Alfonzo .40 1.00
67 Miguel Tejada .40 1.00
68 Francisco Cordero .40 1.00
69 Brett Myers .40 1.00
70 Curt Schilling .60 1.50
71 Matt Kata .40 1.00
72 Bartolo Colon .40 1.00
73 Rodrigo Lopez .40 1.00
74 Tim Wakefield .40 1.00
75 Frank Thomas 1.00 2.50
76 Jimmy Rollins .40 1.00
77 Barry Zito .40 1.00
78 Hideo Nomo 1.00 2.50
79 Brad Wilkerson .40 1.00
80 Adam Dunn .40 1.00
81 Derrek Lee .60 1.50
82 Joe Crede .40 1.00
83 Nate Robertson .40 1.00
84 John Thomson .40 1.00
85 Mike Sweeney .40 1.00
86 Kip Wells .40 1.00
87 Eric Gagne .40 1.00
88 Zach Day .40 1.00
89 Alex Sanchez .40 1.00
90 Bret Boone .40 1.00
91 Mark Loretta .40 1.00
92 Miguel Cabrera .60 1.50
93 Randy Winn .40 1.00
94 Adam Everett .40 1.00
95 Aubrey Huff .40 1.00
96 Kevin Mench .40 1.00
97 Frank Catalanotto .40 1.00
98 Flash Gordon .40 1.00
99 Scott Hatteberg .40 1.00
100 Albert Pujols 2.00 5.00
101 Jose Molina .40 1.00
Bengie Molina
102 Jason Johnson .40 1.00
103 Jay Gibbons .40 1.00
104 Byung-Hyun Kim .40 1.00
105 Joe Borowski .40 1.00
106 Mark Grudzielanek .40 1.00
107 Mark Buehrle .40 1.00
108 Paul Wilson .40 1.00
109 Ronnie Belliard .40 1.00
110 Reggie Sanders .40 1.00
111 Tim Redding .40 1.00
112 Brian Lawrence .40 1.00
113 Travis Hafner .40 1.00
114 Jose Hernandez .40 1.00
115 Ben Sheets .40 1.00
116 Johan Santana 1.00 2.50
117 Billy Wagner .40 1.00
118 Mariano Rivera 1.00 2.50
119 Steve Trachsel .40 1.00
120 Akinori Otsuka .40 1.00
121 Jose Valentin .40 1.00
122 Orlando Hernandez .40 1.00
123 Raul Ibanez .40 1.00
124 Mike Matheny .40 1.00
125 Vernon Wells .40 1.00
126 Jason Isringhausen .40 1.00
127 Jose Guillen .40 1.00
128 Danny Bautista .40 1.00
129 Marcus Giles .40 1.00
130 Javy Lopez .40 1.00
131 Kevin Millar .40 1.00
132 Kyle Farnsworth .40 1.00
133 Carl Pavano .40 1.00
134 Rafael Furcal .40 1.00
135 Casey Blake .40 1.00
136 Matt Holliday .50 1.25
137 Bobby Higginson .40 1.00
138 Adam Kennedy .40 1.00
139 Alex Gonzalez .40 1.00
140 Jeff Kent .40 1.00
141 Aaron Guiel .40 1.00
142 Shawn Green .40 1.00
143 Bill Hall .40 1.00
144 Shannon Stewart .40 1.00
145 Juan Rivera .40 1.00
146 Coco Crisp .40 1.00
147 Mike Mussina .60 1.50
148 Eric Chavez .40 1.00
149 Jon Lieber .40 1.00
150 Vladimir Guerrero 1.00 2.50
151 Alex Cintron .40 1.00
152 Luis Matos .40 1.00
153 Sidney Ponson .40 1.00
154 Trot Nixon .40 1.00
155 Greg Maddux 1.50 4.00
156 Edgar Renteria .40 1.00
157 Ryan Freel .40 1.00
158 Matt Lawton .40 1.00
159 Mark Prior .60 1.50
160 Josh Beckett .40 1.00
161 Ken Harvey .40 1.00
162 Angel Berroa .40 1.00
163 Juan Encarnacion .40 1.00
164 Wes Helms .40 1.00
165 Brad Radke .40 1.00
166 Phil Nevin .40 1.00
167 Mike Cameron .40 1.00
168 Billy Koch .40 1.00
169 Bobby Crosby .40 1.00
170 Mike Lieberthal .40 1.00
171 Rob Mackowiak .40 1.00
172 Sean Burroughs .40 1.00
173 J.T. Snow .40 1.00
174 Paul Konerko .40 1.00
175 Luis Gonzalez .40 1.00
176 John Lackey .40 1.00
177 Oliver Perez .40 1.00
178 Brian Roberts .40 1.00
179 Bill Mueller .40 1.00
180 Carlos Lee .40 1.00
181 Corey Patterson .40 1.00
182 Sean Casey .40 1.00
183 Cliff Lee .40 1.00
184 Jason Jennings .40 1.00
185 Dmitri Young .40 1.00
186 Juan Uribe .40 1.00
187 Andy Pettitte .60 1.50
188 Juan Gonzalez .40 1.00
189 Orlando Hudson .40 1.00
190 Jason Phillips .40 1.00
191 Braden Looper .40 1.00
192 Lew Ford .40 1.00
193 Mark Mulder .40 1.00
194 Bobby Abreu .40 1.00
195 Jason Kendall .40 1.00
196 Khalil Greene .60 1.50
197 A.J. Pierzynski .40 1.00
198 Tim Worrell .40 1.00
199 So Taguchi .40 1.00
200 Jason Giambi .40 1.00
201 Tony Batista .40 1.00
202 Carlos Zambrano .40 1.00
203 Trevor Hoffman .40 1.00
204 Odalis Perez .40 1.00
205 Jose Cruz Jr. .40 1.00
206 Michael Barrett .40 1.00
207 Chris Carpenter .40 1.00
208 Michael Young UER .40 1.00
Player sliding is Rod Barajas
209 Toby Hall .40 1.00
210 Woody Williams .40 1.00
211 Chris Denorfia FY RC 1.25 3.00
212 Darren Fenster FY RC .75 2.00
213 Elvys Quezada FY RC .75 2.00
214 Ian Kinsler FY RC 2.00 5.00
215 Matthew Lindstrom FY RC .75 2.00
216 Ryan Goleski FY RC 1.25 3.00
217 Ryan Sweeney FY RC 1.50 4.00
218 Sean Marshall FY RC 2.00 5.00
219 Steve Doetsch FY RC 1.25 3.00
220 Wade Robinson FY RC .75 2.00
221 Andre Ethier FY AU RC 15.00 40.00
222 Brandon Moss FY AU RC 8.00 20.00
223 Chadd Blasko FY AU RC 6.00 15.00
224 Chris Roberson FY AU RC 4.00 10.00
225 Chris Seddon FY AU RC 4.00 10.00
226 Ian Bladergroen FY AU RC 6.00 15.00
227 Jake Dittler FY AU 4.00 10.00
228 Jose Vaquedano FY AU RC 4.00 10.00
229 Jeremy West FY AU RC 6.00 15.00
230 Kole Strayhorn FY AU RC 4.00 10.00
231 Kevin West FY AU RC 4.00 10.00
232 Luis Ramirez FY AU RC 4.00 10.00
233 Melky Cabrera FY AU RC 20.00 40.00
234 Nate Schierholtz FY AU 4.00 10.00
235 Billy Butler FY AU RC 20.00 50.00
236 B.Szymanski FY AU EXCH 4.00 10.00
237 Chad Orvella FY AU RC 4.00 10.00
238 Chip Cannon FY AU RC 8.00 20.00
239 Eric Nielsen FY AU RC 4.00 10.00
240 Erik Cordier FY AU RC 4.00 10.00
241 Glen Perkins FY AU RC 8.00 20.00
242 Justin Verlander FY AU RC 30.00 50.00
243 Kevin Melillo FY AU RC 6.00 15.00
244 Landon Powell FY AU RC 6.00 15.00
245 Matt Campbell FY AU RC 4.00 10.00
246 Michael Rogers FY AU RC 4.00 10.00
247 Nate McLouth FY AU RC 8.00 20.00
248 Scott Mathieson FY AU RC 4.00 10.00
249 Shane Costa FY AU RC 4.00 10.00
250 Tony Giarratano FY AU RC 4.00 10.00
251 Tyler Pelland FY AU RC 6.00 15.00
252 Wes Swackhamer FY AU RC 4.00 10.00
253 Garret Anderson .40 1.00
254 Randy Johnson 1.00 2.50
255 Charles Thomas .40 1.00
256 Rafael Palmeiro .60 1.50
257 Kevin Youkilis .40 1.00
258 Freddy Garcia .40 1.00
259 Magglio Ordonez .40 1.00
260 Aaron Harang .40 1.00
261 Grady Sizemore .60 1.50
262 Chin-hui Tsao .40 1.00
263 Eric Munson .40 1.00
264 Juan Pierre .40 1.00
265 Brad Lidge .40 1.00
266 Brian Anderson .40 1.00
267 Todd Helton .60 1.50
268 Chad Cordero .40 1.00
269 Kris Benson .40 1.00
270 Brad Halsey .40 1.00
271 Jermaine Dye .40 1.00
272 Manny Ramirez .60 1.50
273 Adam Eaton .40 1.00
274 Brett Tomko .40 1.00
275 Bucky Jacobsen .40 1.00
276 Dontrelle Willis .40 1.00
277 B.J. Upton .40 1.00
278 Rocco Baldelli .40 1.00
279 Ryan Drese .40 1.00
280 Ichiro Suzuki 2.00 5.00
281 Brandon Lyon .40 1.00
282 Nick Green .40 1.00
283 Jerry Hairston Jr. .40 1.00
284 Mike Lowell .40 1.00
285 Kerry Wood .40 1.00
286 Omar Vizquel .60 1.50
287 Carlos Beltran .40 1.00
288 Carlos Pena .40 1.00
289 Jeff Weaver .40 1.00
290 Chad Moeller .40 1.00
291 Joe Mays .40 1.00
292 Termel Sledge .40 1.00
293 Richard Hidalgo .40 1.00
294 Justin Duchscherer .40 1.00
295 Eric Milton .40 1.00
296 Ramon Hernandez .40 1.00
297 Jose Reyes .40 1.00
298 Joel Pineiro .40 1.00
299 Matt Morris .40 1.00
300 John Halama .40 1.00
301 Gary Matthews Jr. .40 1.00
302 Ryan Madson .40 1.00
303 Mark Kotsay .40 1.00
304 Carlos Delgado .40 1.00
305 Casey Kotchman .40 1.00
306 Greg Aquino .40 1.00
307 LaTroy Hawkins .40 1.00
308 Jose Contreras .40 1.00
309 Ken Griffey Jr. 1.50 4.00
310 C.C. Sabathia .40 1.00
311 Brandon Inge .40 1.00
312 John Buck .40 1.00
313 Hee Seop Choi .40 1.00
314 Chris Capuano .40 1.00
315 Jesse Crain .40 1.00
316 Geoff Jenkins .40 1.00
317 Mike Piazza 1.00 2.50
318 Jorge Posada .60 1.50
319 Nick Swisher .40 1.00
320 Kevin Millwood .40 1.00
321 Mike Gonzalez .40 1.00
322 Jake Peavy .40 1.00
323 Dustin Hermanson .40 1.00
324 Jeremy Reed .40 1.00
325 Alfonso Soriano .40 1.00
326 Alexis Rios .40 1.00
327 David Eckstein .40 1.00
328 Shea Hillenbrand .40 1.00
329 Russ Ortiz .40 1.00
330 Kurt Ainsworth .40 1.00
331 Orlando Cabrera .40 1.00
332 Carlos Silva .40 1.00
333 Ross Gload .40 1.00
334 Josh Phelps .40 1.00
335 Mike Maroth .40 1.00
336 Guillermo Mota .40 1.00
337 Chris Burke .40 1.00
338 David DeJesus .40 1.00
339 Jose Lima .40 1.00
340 Cristian Guzman .40 1.00
341 Nick Johnson .40 1.00
342 Victor Zambrano .40 1.00
343 Rod Barajas .40 1.00
344 Damian Miller .40 1.00
345 Chase Utley .60 1.50
346 Sean Burnett .40 1.00
347 David Wells .40 1.00
348 Dustan Mohr .40 1.00
349 Bobby Madritsch .40 1.00
350 Reed Johnson .40 1.00
351 R.A. Dickey .40 1.00
352 Scott Kazmir .40 1.00
353 Tony Womack .40 1.00
354 Tomas Perez .40 1.00
355 Esteban Loaiza .40 1.00
356 Tomokazu Ohka .40 1.00
357 Ramon Ortiz .40 1.00
358 Richie Sexson .40 1.00
359 J.D. Drew .40 1.00
360 Barry Bonds 2.50 6.00
361 Aramis Ramirez .40 1.00
362 Wily Mo Pena .40 1.00
363 Jeromy Burnitz .40 1.00
364 Nomar Garciaparra 1.00 2.50
365 Brandon Backe .40 1.00
366 Derek Lowe .40 1.00
367 Doug Davis .40 1.00
368 Joe Mauer 1.00 2.50
369 Endy Chavez .40 1.00
370 Bernie Williams .60 1.50
371 Jason Michaels .40 1.00
372 Craig Wilson .40 1.00
373 Ryan Klesko .40 1.00
374 Ray Durham .40 1.00
375 Jose Lopez .40 1.00
376 Jeff Suppan .40 1.00
377 David Bush .40 1.00
378 Marlon Byrd .40 1.00
379 Roy Oswalt .40 1.00
380 Rondell White .40 1.00
381 Troy Glaus .40 1.00
382 Scott Hairston .40 1.00
383 Chipper Jones 1.00 2.50
384 Daniel Cabrera .40 1.00
385 Jon Garland .40 1.00
386 Austin Kearns .40 1.00
387 Jake Westbrook .40 1.00
388 Aaron Miles .40 1.00
389 Omar Infante .40 1.00
390 Paul Lo Duca .40 1.00
391 Morgan Ensberg .40 1.00
392 Tony Graffanino .40 1.00
393 Milton Bradley .40 1.00
394 Keith Ginter .40 1.00
395 Justin Morneau .40 1.00
396 Tony Armas Jr. .40 1.00
397 Kevin Brown .40 1.00
398 Marco Scutaro .40 1.00
399 Tim Hudson .40 1.00
400 Pat Burrell .40 1.00
401 Jeff Cirillo .40 1.00
402 Larry Walker .60 1.50
403 Dewon Brazelton .40 1.00
404 Shigetoshi Hasegawa .40 1.00
405 Octavio Dotel .40 1.00
406 Michael Cuddyer .40 1.00
407 Junior Spivey .40 1.00
408 Zack Greinke .40 1.00
409 Roger Clemens 1.50 4.00
410 Chris Shelton .60 1.50
411 Ugueth Urbina .40 1.00
412 Rafael Betancourt .40 1.00
413 Willie Harris .40 1.00
414 Keith Foulke .40 1.00
415 Larry Bigbie .40 1.00
416 Paul Byrd .40 1.00
417 Troy Percival .40 1.00
418 Pedro Martinez .60 1.50
419 Matt Clement .40 1.00
420 Ryan Wagner .40 1.00
421 Jeff Francis .40 1.00
422 Jeff Conine .40 1.00
423 Wade Miller .40 1.00
424 Gavin Floyd .40 1.00
425 Kazuhisa Ishii .40 1.00
426 Victor Santos .40 1.00
427 Jacque Jones .40 1.00
428 Hideki Matsui 1.50 4.00
429 Cory Lidle .40 1.00
430 Jose Castillo .40 1.00
431 Alex Gonzalez .40 1.00
432 Kirk Rueter .40 1.00
433 Jolbert Cabrera .40 1.00
434 Erik Bedard .40 1.00
435 Ricky Ledee .40 1.00
436 Mark Hendrickson .40 1.00
437 Laynce Nix .40 1.00
438 Jason Frasor .40 1.00
439 Kevin Gregg .40 1.00
440 Derek Jeter 2.00 5.00
441 Jaret Wright .40 1.00
442 Edwin Jackson .40 1.00
443 Moises Alou .40 1.00
444 Aaron Rowand .40 1.00
445 Kazuhito Tadano .40 1.00

446 Luis Gonzalez .40 1.00
447 A.J. Burnett .40 1.00
448 Jeff Bagwell .60 1.50
449 Brad Penny .40 1.00
450 Corey Koskie .40 1.00
451 Mark Ellis .40 1.00
452 Hector Luna .40 1.00
453 Miguel Olivo .40 1.00
454 Scott Rolen .60 1.50
455 Ricardo Rodriguez .40 1.00
456 Eric Hinske .40 1.00
457 Tim Salmon .60 1.50
458 Adam LaRoche .40 1.00
459 B.J. Ryan .40 1.00
460 Steve Finley .40 1.00
461 Joe Nathan .40 1.00
462 Vicente Padilla .40 1.00
463 Yadier Molina .40 1.00
464 Tino Martinez .60 1.50
465 Mark Teixeira .60 1.50
466 Kelvim Escobar .40 1.00
467 Pedro Feliz .40 1.00
468 Ryan Garko FY RC 2.00 5.00
469 Bobby Livingston FY RC .75 2.00
470 Yorman Bazardo FY RC .75 2.00
471 Mike Bourn FY RC 1.25 3.00
472 Andy LaRoche FY RC 3.00 8.00

2005 Topps Chrome Black Refractors

*BLACK 1-210/253-467: 1.5X TO 4X BASIC
*BLACK 211-220/468-472: 1.5X TO 4X BASIC
1-220 SER.1 ODDS 1:10 H, 1:20 R
253-472 SER.2 ODDS 1:1 MINI BOX, 1:36 R
1-220/253-472 PRINT RUN 225 #'d SETS
*BLACK AU 221-252: 1X TO 2.5X BASIC AU
221-234 SER.1 ODDS 1:250 H, 1:291 R
235-252 SER.2 ODDS 1:12 MINI BOX, 1:508 R
221-252 PRINT RUN 200 SERIAL #'d SETS
214 Ian Kinsler FY 10.00 25.00
221 Andre Ethier FY AU 30.00 60.00
233 Melky Cabrera FY AU 50.00 100.00
235 Billy Butler FY AU 60.00 120.00
242 Justin Verlander FY AU 60.00 120.00
247 Nate McLouth FY AU 50.00 100.00
360 Barry Bonds 15.00 40.00

2005 Topps Chrome Gold Super-Fractors

1-220 SER.1 ODDS 1:1234 HOBBY
235-252 SER.2 AU ODDS 1:1397 MINI BOXES
253-472 SER.2 ODDS 1:56 BOX LOADER
STATED PRINT RUN 1 SERIAL #'d SET
NO PRICING DUE TO SCARCITY

2005 Topps Chrome Red X-Fractors

*RED XF 1-210/253-467: 6X TO 15X BASIC
1-220 SER.1 ODDS 1:50 HOBBY
221-234 SER.1 AU ODDS 1:779 HOBBY
235-252 SER.2 AU ODDS 1:91 MINI BOX
235-252 SER.2 AU ODDS 1:4042 RETAIL
253-472 SER.2 ODDS 1:3 BOX LOADER
STATED PRINT RUN 25 SERIAL #'d SETS
211-252/468-472 NO PRICING AVAILABLE
360 Barry Bonds 125.00 200.00

2005 Topps Chrome Refractors

*REF 1-210/253-467: 1X TO 2.5X BASIC
*REF 211-220/468-472: 1X TO 2.5X BASIC
1-220 SER.1 ODDS 1:6 H, 1:4 R
253-472 SER.2 ODDS 2 PER MINI BOX, 1:5 R
*REF AU 221-252: .5X TO 1.2X BASIC AU
221-234 SER.1 AU ODDS 1:100 H, 1:118 R
235-252 SER.2 AU ODDS 1:5 MINI BOXES
235-252 SER.2 AU ODDS 1:199 RETAIL
221-252 PRINT RUN 500 SERIAL #'d SETS
214 Ian Kinsler FY 5.00 12.00
221 Andre Ethier FY AU 20.00 50.00
233 Melky Cabrera FY AU 30.00 60.00
235 Billy Butler FY AU 50.00 80.00
242 Justin Verlander FY AU 50.00 80.00
247 Nate McLouth FY AU 15.00 40.00

2005 Topps Chrome A-Rod Throwbacks

COMPLETE SET (4) 3.00 8.00
COMMON CARD (1-4) 1.25 3.00
SER.2 ODDS 2 PER MINI BOX, 1:5 R
*BLACK REF: 2X TO 5X BASIC
BLACK REF SER.2 ODDS 1:14 BOX LOADER
BLACK REF PRINT RUN 225 #'d SETS
GOLD SUPER SER.2 ODDS 1:2968 BOX LDR
GOLD SUPER PRINT RUN 1 #'d SET
NO GOLD SUPER PRICING AVAILABLE
*RED XF: 6X TO 15X BASIC
RED XF SER.2 ODDS 1:124 BOX LOADER
RED XF PRINT RUN 25 #'d SETS
*REFRACTOR: 1X TO 2.5X BASIC
REFRACTOR SER.2 ODDS 1:3 BOX LOADER
1 Alex Rodriguez 1994 1.25 3.00
2 Alex Rodriguez 1995 1.25 3.00
3 Alex Rodriguez 1996 1.25 3.00
4 Alex Rodriguez 1997 1.25 3.00

2005 Topps Chrome Dem Bums Autographs

SERIES 1 ODDS 1:1816 H, 1:7270 R
STATED PRINT RUN 50 SETS
CARDS ARE NOT SERIAL-NUMBERED
PRINT RUN INFO PROVIDED BY TOPPS
CE Carl Erskine 30.00 60.00
CL Clem Labine 30.00 60.00
DS Duke Snider 50.00 100.00
DZ Don Zimmer 30.00 60.00
JP Johnny Podres 30.00 60.00

2005 Topps Chrome the Game Relics

SER.1 GROUP A ODDS 1:15 BOX-LOADER
SER.1 GROUP B ODDS 1:2 BOX-LOADER
AR Alex Rodriguez Bat A 6.00 15.00
AS Alfonso Soriano Uni B 3.00 8.00
JB Jeff Bagwell Uni B 4.00 10.00
JP Jorge Posada Uni B 4.00 10.00
JS John Smoltz Uni B 4.00 10.00
MP Mark Prior Jsy B 4.00 10.00
MPI Mike Piazza Jsy B 4.00 10.00
MY Michael Young Bat A 3.00 8.00
SS Sammy Sosa Jsy B 4.00 10.00
TH Torii Hunter Jsy B 3.00 8.00
WB Wade Boggs Uni B 4.00 10.00

2005 Topps Chrome the Game Patch Relics

*3-COLOR ADD: ADD 20% PREMIUM
SER.1 ODDS 1:8 BOX-LOADER
STATED PRINT RUN 70 SETS
CARDS ARE NOT SERIAL-NUMBERED
PRINT RUN INFO PROVIDED BY TOPPS
AD1 Adam Dunn Pose 6.00 15.00
AD2 Adam Dunn Fielding 6.00 15.00
AP Albert Pujols 20.00 50.00
AR Alex Rodriguez 15.00 40.00
BB Bret Boone 6.00 15.00
CJ Chipper Jones 10.00 25.00
CS C.C. Sabathia 6.00 15.00
DW Dontrelle Willis 6.00 15.00
FT Frank Thomas 10.00 25.00
HN Hideo Nomo 10.00 25.00
JB Jeff Bagwell 10.00 25.00
JBE Josh Beckett 6.00 15.00
KI Kazuhisa Ishii 6.00 15.00
KW Kerry Wood 6.00 15.00
LB Lance Berkman 6.00 15.00
ML Mike Lowell 6.00 15.00
MO Maggio Ordonez 6.00 15.00
MPI Mike Piazza 10.00 25.00
MT Mark Teixeira 10.00 25.00
PL Paul Lo Duca 6.00 15.00
PM Pedro Martinez 10.00 25.00
SS Sammy Sosa 10.00 25.00
TG Troy Glaus 6.00 15.00
TH Todd Helton 10.00 25.00

2005 Topps Chrome Update

This 237-card set was released in January, 2006. This set was issued in four-card hobby and retail packs with an $3 SRP which came 24 packs per retail box with 20 retail boxes per case. The hobby boxes are actually two 10-count boxes which come eight full (or 16 mini) boxes to a case. Cards numbered 1-85 feature players who switched teams from when their regular Chrome card was printed. Cards numbered 86-105 feature leading prospects while cards numbered 106 through 216 feature players with their first year on Topps cards. Cards numbered 216 through 220 feature players who accomplished important feats during the 2005 season. Cards numbered 221 through 237 feature signed Rookie Cards. Those cards were inserted at differing odds depending on whether the player was a group A or a group B autograph.

COMPLETE SET (237) 200.00 300.00
COMP.SET w/o SP's (220) 40.00 80.00
COM (1-85/216-220) .30 .75
COMMON (86-105) .30 .75
COM (14/65/106-215) .40 1.00
221-237 GROUP A ODDS 1:25 H, 1:49 R
221-237 GROUP B ODDS 1:29 H, 1:57 R
1-220 PLATE ODDS 1:347 H
221-237 PLATE AU ODDS 1:4857 H
PLATE PRINT RUN 1 SET PER COLOR
BLACK-CYAN-MAGENTA-YELLOW ISSUED
NO PLATE PRICING DUE TO SCARCITY
1 Sammy Sosa .75 2.00
2 Jeff Francoeur 1.00 2.50
3 Tony Clark .30 .75
4 Michael Tucker .30 .75
5 Mike Matheny .30 .75
6 Eric Young .30 .75
7 Jose Valentin .30 .75
8 Matt Lawton .30 .75
9 Juan Rivera .30 .75
10 Shawn Green .30 .75
11 Aaron Boone .30 .75
12 Woody Williams .30 .75
13 Brad Wilkerson .30 .75
14 Anthony Reyes RC 2.00 5.00
15 Gustavo Chacin .30 .75
16 Michael Restovich .30 .75
17 Humberto Quintero .30 .75
18 Matt Ginter .30 .75
19 Scott Podsednik .30 .75
20 Byung-Hyun Kim .30 .75
21 Orlando Hernandez .30 .75
22 Mark Grudzielanek .30 .75
23 Jody Gerut .30 .75
24 Adrian Beltre .30 .75
25 Scott Schoeneweis .30 .75
26 Marlon Anderson .30 .75
27 Jason Vargas .30 .75
28 Claudio Vargas .30 .75
29 Jason Kendall .30 .75
30 Aaron Small .30 .75
31 Juan Cruz .30 .75
32 Placido Polanco .30 .75
33 Jorge Sosa .30 .75
34 John Olerud .30 .75
35 Ryan Langerhans .30 .75
36 Randy Winn .30 .75
37 Zach Duke .75 2.00
38 Garrett Atkins .30 .75
39 Al Leiter .30 .75
40 Shawn Chacon .30 .75
41 Mark DeRosa .30 .75
42 Miguel Ojeda .30 .75
43 A.J. Pierzynski .30 .75
44 Carlos Lee .30 .75
45 LaTroy Hawkins .30 .75
46 Nick Green .30 .75
47 Shawn Estes .30 .75
48 Eli Marrero .30 .75
49 Jeff Kent .30 .75
50 Joe Randa .30 .75
51 Jose Hernandez .30 .75
52 Joe Blanton .30 .75
53 Huston Street .75 2.00
54 Marlon Byrd .30 .75
55 Alex Sanchez .30 .75
56 Livan Hernandez .30 .75
57 Chris Young .30 .75
58 Brad Eldred .30 .75
59 Terrence Long .30 .75
60 Phil Nevin .30 .75
61 Kyle Farnsworth .30 .75
62 Jon Lieber .30 .75
63 Antonio Alfonseca .30 .75
64 Tony Graffanino .30 .75
65 Tadahito Iguchi RC 1.25 3.00
66 Brad Thompson .30 .75
67 Jose Vidro .30 .75
68 Jason Phillips .30 .75
69 Carl Pavano .30 .75
70 Pokey Reese .30 .75
71 Jerome Williams .30 .75
72 Kazuhisa Ishii .30 .75
73 Felix Hernandez 1.25 3.00
74 Edgar Renteria .30 .75
75 Mike Myers .30 .75
76 Jeff Cirillo .30 .75
77 Endy Chavez .30 .75
78 Jose Guillen .30 .75
79 Ugueth Urbina .30 .75
80 Zach Day .30 .75
81 Javier Vazquez .30 .75
82 Willy Taveras .30 .75
83 Mark Mulder .30 .75
84 Vinny Castilla .30 .75
85 Russ Adams .30 .75
86 Homer Bailey PROS .30 .75
87 Ervin Santana PROS .30 .75
88 Bill Bray PROS .30 .75
89 Thomas Diamond PROS .30 .75
90 Trevor Plouffe PROS .30 .75
91 James Houser PROS .30 .75
92 Jake Stevens PROS .30 .75
93 Anthony Whittington PROS .30 .75
94 Philip Hughes PROS .30 .75
95 Greg Golson PROS .30 .75
96 Paul Maholm PROS .30 .75
97 Carlos Quentin PROS .30 .75
98 Dan Johnson PROS .30 .75
99 Mark Rogers PROS .30 .75
100 Neil Walker PROS .30 .75
101 Omar Quintanilla PROS .30 .75
102 Blake DeWitt PROS .30 .75
103 Taylor Tankersley PROS .30 .75
104 David Murphy PROS .30 .75
105 Chris Lambert PROS .30 .75
106 Drew Anderson FY RC .40 1.00
107 Luis Hernandez FY RC .40 1.00
108 Jim Burt FY RC .40 1.00
109 Mike Morse FY RC .75 2.00
110 Elliot Johnson FY RC .40 1.00
111 C.J. Smith FY RC .40 1.00
112 Casey McGehee FY RC .40 1.00
113 Brian Miller FY RC .40 1.00
114 Chris Vines FY RC .40 1.00
115 D.J. Houlton FY RC .40 1.00
116 Chuck Tiffany FY RC 1.25 3.00
117 Humberto Sanchez FY RC 1.50 4.00
118 Baltazar Lopez FY RC .40 1.00
119 Russ Martin FY RC 1.25 3.00
120 Dana Eveland FY RC .40 1.00
121 Johan Silva FY RC .40 1.00
122 Adam Harben FY RC .50 1.25
123 Brian Bannister FY RC 1.25 3.00
124 Adam Boeve FY RC .40 1.00
125 Thomas Oldham FY RC .40 1.00
126 Cody Haerther FY RC .40 1.00
127 Dan Santin FY RC .40 1.00
128 Daniel Haigwood FY RC .75 2.00
129 Craig Tatum FY RC .40 1.00
130 Martin Prado FY RC .40 1.00
131 Errol Simonitsch FY RC .50 1.25
132 Lorenzo Scott FY RC .40 1.00
133 Hayden Penn FY RC .75 2.00
134 Heath Totten FY RC .40 1.00
135 Nick Masset FY RC .40 1.00
136 Pedro Lopez FY RC .40 1.00
137 Ben Harrison FY RC .40 1.00
138 Mike Spidale FY RC .40 1.00
139 Jeremy Harts FY RC .40 1.00
140 Danny Zell FY RC .40 1.00
141 Kevin Collins FY RC .40 1.00
142 Tony Arnerich FY RC .40 1.00
143 Matt Albers FY RC 1.00 2.50
144 Ricky Barrett FY RC .40 1.00
145 Hernan Iribarren FY RC .50 1.25
146 Sean Tracey FY RC .40 1.00
147 Jerry Owens FY RC .50 1.25
148 Steve Nelson FY RC .40 1.00
149 Brandon McCarthy FY RC 1.00 2.50
150 David Shepard FY RC .40 1.00
151 Steven Bondurant FY RC .40 1.00
152 Billy Sadler FY RC .40 1.00
153 Ryan Feierabend FY RC .40 1.00
154 Stuart Pomeranz FY RC .40 1.00
155 Shaun Marcum FY .40 1.00
156 Erik Schindewolf FY RC .40 1.00
157 Stefan Bailie FY RC .40 1.00
158 Mike Esposito FY RC UER .40 1.00
Front photo is of a Kansas City Royal
159 Buck Coats FY RC .40 1.00
160 Andy Sides FY RC .40 1.00
161 Micah Schnurstein FY RC .40 1.00
162 Jesse Gutierrez FY RC .40 1.00
163 Jake Postlewait FY RC .40 1.00
164 Willy Mota FY RC .40 1.00
165 Ryan Speier FY RC .40 1.00
166 Frank Mata FY RC .40 1.00
167 Jair Jurrjens FY RC 1.00 2.50
168 Nick Touchstone FY RC .40 1.00
169 Matthew Kemp FY RC 3.00 8.00
170 Vinny Rottino FY RC .40 1.00
171 J.B. Thurmond FY RC .40 1.00
172 Kelvin Pichardo FY RC .40 1.00
173 Scott Mitchinson FY RC .40 1.00
174 Darwinson Salazar FY RC .40 1.00
175 George Kottaras FY RC .75 2.00
176 Kenny Durost FY RC .40 1.00
177 Jonathan Sanchez FY RC 1.25 3.00
178 Brandon Moorhead FY RC .40 1.00
179 Kennard Bibbs FY RC .40 1.00
180 David Gassner FY RC .40 1.00
181 Micah Furtado FY RC .40 1.00
182 Ismael Ramirez FY RC .40 1.00
183 Carlos Gonzalez FY RC 2.50 6.00
184 Brandon Sing FY RC .50 1.25
185 Jason Motte FY RC .40 1.00
186 Chuck James FY RC 2.00 5.00
187 Andy Santana FY RC .40 1.00
188 Manny Parra FY RC 1.50 4.00
189 Chris B.Young FY RC 1.50 4.00
190 Juan Senreiso FY RC .40 1.00
191 Franklin Morales FY RC .75 2.00
192 Jared Gothreaux FY RC .40 1.00
193 Jayce Tingler FY RC .40 1.00
194 Matt Brown FY RC .40 1.00
195 Frank Diaz FY RC .40 1.00
196 Stephen Drew FY RC 4.00 10.00
197 Jered Weaver FY RC 4.00 10.00
198 Ryan Braun FY RC 8.00 20.00
199 John Mayberry Jr. FY RC 1.00 2.50
200 Aaron Thompson FY RC .75 2.00
201 Ben Copeland FY RC 1.50 4.00
202 Jacoby Ellsbury FY RC 8.00 20.00
203 Garrett Olson FY RC .75 2.00
204 Cliff Pennington FY RC .75 2.00
205 Colby Rasmus FY RC 6.00 15.00
206 Chris Volstad FY RC 1.00 2.50
207 Ricky Romero FY RC .75 2.00
208 Ryan Zimmerman FY RC 6.00 15.00
209 C.J. Henry FY RC 1.50 4.00
210 Nelson Cruz FY RC 1.25 3.00
211 Josh Wall FY RC .50 1.25
212 Nick Webber FY RC .40 1.00
213 Paul Kelly FY RC .50 1.25
214 Kyle Winters FY RC .50 1.25
215 Mitch Boggs FY RC .40 1.00
216 Craig Biggio HL .30 .75
217 Greg Maddux HL .75 2.00
218 Bobby Abreu HL .30 .75
219 Alex Rodriguez HL .75 2.00
220 Trevor Hoffman HL .30 .75
221 Trevor Bell FY AU A RC 6.00 15.00
222 Jay Bruce FY AU A RC 40.00 80.00
223 Travis Buck FY AU B RC 6.00 15.00
224 Cesar Carrillo FY AU B RC 6.00 15.00
225 Mike Costanzo FY AU A RC 8.00 20.00
226 Brent Cox FY AU A RC 4.00 10.00
227 Matt Garza FY AU A RC 12.50 30.00
228 Josh Geer FY AU A RC 4.00 10.00
229 Tyler Greene FY AU A RC 6.00 15.00
230 Eli Iorg FY AU A RC 4.00 10.00
231 Craig Italiano FY AU B RC 4.00 10.00
232 Beau Jones FY AU B RC 6.00 15.00
233 M.McCormick FY AU B RC 4.00 10.00
234 A.McCutchen FY AU B RC 20.00 40.00
235 Micah Owings FY AU B RC 8.00 20.00
236 Cesar Ramos FY AU B RC 4.00 10.00
237 Chaz Roe FY AU A RC 4.00 10.00

2005 Topps Chrome Update Refractors

*REF 1-85: 1.25X TO 3X BASIC
*REF 86-105: 1.25X TO 3X BASIC
*REF 14/65/106-215: 1X TO 2.5X BASIC
*REF 216-220: 2X TO 5X BASIC
1-220 ODDS 1:5 HOBBY, 1:5 RETAIL
*REF AU 221-237: .6X TO 1.5X BASIC AU
221-237 AU ODDS 1:53 H, 1:115 R
221-237 AU PRINT RUN 500 #'d SETS
119 Russ Martin FY 6.00 15.00
123 Brian Bannister FY 4.00 10.00
169 Matthew Kemp FY 10.00 25.00
188 Manny Parra FY 6.00 15.00
191 Franklin Morales FY 6.00 15.00
196 Stephen Drew FY 8.00 20.00
198 Ryan Braun FY 30.00 60.00
202 Jacoby Ellsbury FY 30.00 60.00
208 Ryan Zimmerman FY 15.00 30.00
222 Jay Bruce FY AU 60.00 120.00
223 Travis Buck FY AU 12.50 30.00
227 Matt Garza FY AU 15.00 40.00
234 Andrew McCutchen FY AU 30.00 60.00

2005 Topps Chrome Update Black Refractors

There have been several copies of card number 235 Micah Owings in existence that does not have the serial number on back. Furthermore, the backs are coated with an extra amount of gloss. The back also features "Black Refractor" written over what seems to be the text "Refractor". This is considered to have been a production error and recorded as card number 235B. There is no information on the print run on this variation.

*BLACK 1-85: 2X TO 5X BASIC
*BLACK 86-105: 2X TO 5X BASIC
*BLACK 14/65/106-215: 1.5X TO 4X BASIC
*BLACK 216-220: 2.5X TO 6X BASIC
1-220 ODDS 1:10 HOBBY, 1:19 RETAIL
1-220 PRINT RUN 250 #'d SETS
*BLACK AU 221-237: 1X TO 2.5X BASIC AU
221-237 AU ODDS 1:140 H, 1:279 R
221-237 AU PRINT RUN 200 #'d SETS
119 Russ Martin FY 10.00 25.00
123 Brian Bannister FY 6.00 15.00
169 Matthew Kemp FY 30.00 60.00
183 Carlos Gonzalez FY 20.00 50.00
188 Manny Parra FY 10.00 25.00
191 Franklin Morales FY 12.50 30.00
196 Stephen Drew FY 15.00 40.00
198 Ryan Braun FY 60.00 120.00
202 Jacoby Ellsbury FY 60.00 120.00
205 Colby Rasmus FY 50.00 100.00
208 Ryan Zimmerman FY 30.00 60.00
222 Jay Bruce FY AU 125.00 250.00
223 Travis Buck FY AU 30.00 60.00
227 Matt Garza FY AU 20.00 50.00
234 Andrew McCutchen FY AU 60.00 120.00
235A Micah Owings FY AU 40.00 80.00
235B Micah Owings FY AU
No Serial Number

2005 Topps Chrome Update Gold Super-Fractors

1-220 ODDS 1:1482 HOBBY
221-237 AU ODDS 1:19,730 HOBBY
STATED PRINT RUN 1 SERIAL #'d SET
NO PRICING DUE TO SCARCITY

2005 Topps Chrome Update Red X-Fractors

*RED 1-85: 4X TO 10X BASIC
*RED 86-105: 4X TO 10X BASIC
*RED 14/65/106-215: 5X TO 12X BASIC
*RED 216-220: 5X TO 12X BASIC
1-220 ODDS 1:5 HOBBY
1-220 PRINT RUN 65 #'d SETS
221-237 AU ODDS 1:766 HOBBY
221-237 AU PRINT RUN 25 #'d SETS
221-237 NO PRICING DUE TO SCARCITY
2 Jeff Francoeur 25.00 50.00
73 Felix Hernandez 30.00 60.00
119 Russ Martin FY 30.00 60.00
123 Brian Bannister FY 20.00 50.00
169 Matthew Kemp FY 90.00 150.00
191 Franklin Morales FY 40.00 80.00
196 Stephen Drew FY 50.00 100.00
198 Ryan Braun FY 100.00 200.00
202 Jacoby Ellsbury FY 60.00 120.00
208 Ryan Zimmerman FY 90.00 150.00

2005 Topps Chrome Update Barry Bonds Home Run History

COMPLETE SET (29) 20.00 50.00
COMPLETE SERIES 1 (15) 12.50 30.00
COMPLETE SERIES 2 (14) 8.00 20.00
COMMON CARD 1.25 3.00
1-350 ODDS 1:12 HOBBY, 1:23 RETAIL
375-700 ODDS 1:6 HOBBY, 1:23 RETAIL
1-350 PLATE ODDS 1:347 H
375-700 PLATE ODDS 1:300 BOX LDR
PLATE PRINT RUN 1 SET PER COLOR
BLACK-CYAN-MAGENTA-YELLOW ISSUED
*REF: 1.25X TO 3X BASIC
1-350 REF ODDS 1:71 H, 1:141 R
375-700 REF ODDS 1:70 H, 1:350 R
375-700 REF PRINT RUN 500 #'d SETS
*BLACK REF: 2X TO 5X BASIC
1-350 BLACK REF ODDS 1:178 H, 1:365 R
375-700 BLACK REF ODDS 1:175 H, 1:950 R
BLACK REF PRINT RUN 200 #'d SETS
*BLUE: 4X TO 10X BASIC
375-700 BLUE REF ODDS 1:300 RETAIL
BLUE REF PRINT RUN 100 #'d SETS
1-350 GOLD SUPER ODDS 1:22,548 H
375-700 GOLD SUP.ODDS 1:1234 BOX LDR
GOLD SUPER PRINT RUN 1 #'d SET
NO GOLD SUP.PRICING DUE TO SCARCITY
*RED X-F: 6X TO 15X BASIC
1-350 RED X-F ODDS 1:872 H
375-700 RED X-F ODDS 1:48 BOX LDR
RED X-F PRINT RUN 25 #'d SETS
1-350 ISSUED IN '05 CHROME UPDATE
375-700 ISSUED IN '06 CHROME

2006 Topps Chrome

This 355-card set was released in July, 2006. In a change from previous years, this chrome set was issued all in one series. The set was issued in four-card packs with an $3 SRP and those packs came 24 to a box and 10 boxes to a case. The first 252 cards in this set feature veterans while cards numbered 253-275 feature Award Winners, 276-330 feature rookies and 331-354 feature signed rookies. Card number 285 Kenji Johjima also comes in a signed version. The overall odds of securing a signed rookie card was stated to be one in fifteen hobby packs.

COMP.SET w/o AU's (330) 40.00 80.00
COMMON CARD (1-252) .25 .60
COMMON CARD (253-275) .15 .40
COMMON ROOKIE (276-330) .40 1.00
COMMON AUTO (285b/331-354) 4.00 10.00

AU 331-354 ODDS 1:15 HOBBY
JOHJIMA AU ODDS 1:1650 HOBBY
1-330 PLATES 1:25 HOBBY BOX LDR
331-354 AU PLATES 1:324 HOBBY BOX LDR
PLATE PRINT RUN 1 SET PER COLOR
BLACK-CYAN-MAGENTA-YELLOW ISSUED
NO PLATE PRICING DUE TO SCARCITY
1 Alex Rodriguez 1.00 2.50
2 Garrett Atkins .25 .60
3 Carl Crawford .25 .60
4 Clint Barmes .25 .60
5 Tadahito Iguchi .25 .60
6 Brian Roberts .25 .60
7 Mickey Mantle UER 3.00 8.00
Distance of 1953 homer in cartoon is wrong
Highest seasonal home run total noted for wrong year
8 David Wright 1.00 2.50
9 Jeremy Reed .25 .60
10 Bobby Abreu .25 .60
11 Lance Berkman .25 .60
12 Jonny Gomes .25 .60
13 Jason Marquis .25 .60
14 Chipper Jones .60 1.50
15 Jon Garland .25 .60
16 Brad Wilkerson .25 .60
17 Rickie Weeks .25 .60
18 Jorge Posada .40 1.00
19 Greg Maddux 1.00 2.50
20 Jeff Francis .25 .60
21 Felipe Lopez .25 .60
22 Dan Johnson .25 .60
23 Manny Ramirez .40 1.00
24 Joe Mauer .40 1.00
25 Randy Winn .25 .60
26 Pedro Feliz .25 .60
27 Kenny Rogers .25 .60
28 Rocco Baldelli .25 .60
29 Nomar Garciaparra .60 1.50
30 Carlos Lee .25 .60
31 Tom Glavine .40 1.00
32 Craig Biggio .40 1.00
33 Steve Finley .25 .60
34 Eric Gagne .25 .60
35 Dallas McPherson .25 .60
36 Mark Kotsay .25 .60
37 Kerry Wood .25 .60
38 Huston Street .25 .60
39 Hank Blalock .25 .60
40 Brad Radke .25 .60
41 Chien-Ming Wang 1.00 2.50
42 Mark Buehrle .25 .60
43 Andy Pettitte .40 1.00
44 Bernie Williams .40 1.00
45 Victor Martinez .25 .60
46 Darin Erstad .25 .60
47 Gustavo Chacin .25 .60
48 Carlos Guillen .25 .60
49 Lyle Overbay .25 .60
50 Barry Bonds 1.25 3.00
51 Nook Logan .25 .60
52 Mark Teahen .25 .60
53 Mike Lamb .25 .60
54 Jayson Werth .25 .60
55 Mariano Rivera .60 1.50
56 Julio Lugo .25 .60
57 Adam Dunn .25 .60
58 Troy Percival .25 .60
59 Chad Tracy .25 .60
60 Edgar Renteria .25 .60
61 Jason Giambi .25 .60
62 Justin Morneau .25 .60
63 Carlos Delgado .25 .60
64 John Buck .25 .60
65 Shannon Stewart .25 .60
66 Mike Cameron .25 .60
67 Richie Sexson .25 .60
68 Russ Adams .25 .60
69 Josh Beckett .25 .60
70 Ryan Freel .25 .60
71 Victor Zambrano .25 .60
72 Ronnie Belliard .25 .60
73 Brian Giles .25 .60
74 Randy Wolf .25 .60
75 Robinson Cano .40 1.00
76 Joe Blanton .25 .60
77 Esteban Loaiza .25 .60
78 Troy Glaus .25 .60
79 Matt Clement .25 .60
80 Geoff Jenkins .25 .60
81 Roy Oswalt .25 .60
82 A.J. Pierzynski .25 .60
83 Pedro Martinez .40 1.00
84 Roger Clemens 1.25 3.00
85 Jack Wilson .25 .60
86 Mike Piazza .60 1.50
87 Paul Lo Duca .25 .60
88 Jeff Bagwell .40 1.00
89 Carlos Zambrano .25 .60
90 Brandon Claussen .25 .60
91 Travis Hafner .25 .60
92 Chris Shelton .25 .60
93 Rafael Furcal .25 .60
94 Frank Thomas .60 1.50
95 Noah Lowry .25 .60
96 Jhonny Peralta .25 .60
97 Vernon Wells .25 .60
98 Jorge Cantu .25 .60
99 Willy Taveras .25 .60
100 Ivan Rodriguez .40 1.00
101 Jose Reyes .60 1.50
102 Barry Zito .25 .60
103 Mark Teixeira .40 1.00
104 Chone Figgins .25 .60
105 Todd Helton .40 1.00
106 Tim Wakefield .25 .60
107 Mike Maroth .25 .60
108 Johnny Damon .40 1.00
109 David DeJesus .25 .60
110 Ryan Klesko .25 .60
111 Nick Johnson .25 .60
112 Freddy Garcia .25 .60
113 Torii Hunter .25 .60
114 Mike Sweeney .25 .60
115 Scott Rolen .40 1.00
116 Jim Thome .40 1.00
117 Adam Kennedy .25 .60
118 Albert Pujols 1.25 3.00
119 Kazuo Matsui .25 .60
120 Zack Greinke .25 .60
121 Jimmy Rollins .25 .60
122 Edgardo Alfonzo .25 .60
123 Billy Wagner .25 .60
124 B.J. Ryan .25 .60
125 Orlando Hudson .25 .60
126 Preston Wilson .25 .60
127 Melvin Mora .25 .60
128 Alfonso Soriano .25 .60
129 Javy Lopez .25 .60
130 Wilson Betemit .25 .60
131 Garret Anderson .25 .60
132 Jason Bay .25 .60
133 Adam LaRoche .25 .60
134 C.C. Sabathia .25 .60
135 Bartolo Colon .25 .60
136 Ichiro Suzuki 1.00 2.50
137 Jim Edmonds .40 1.00
138 David Eckstein .25 .60
139 Cristian Guzman .25 .60
140 Jeff Kent .25 .60
141 Chris Capuano .25 .60
142 Cliff Floyd .25 .60
143 Zach Duke .25 .60
144 Matt Morris .25 .60
145 Jose Vidro .25 .60
146 David Wells .25 .60
147 John Smoltz .40 1.00
148 Felix Hernandez .60 1.50
149 Orlando Cabrera .25 .60
150 Mark Prior .40 1.00
151 Ted Lilly .25 .60
152 Michael Young .25 .60
153 Livan Hernandez .25 .60
154 Yadier Molina .25 .60
155 Eric Chavez .25 .60
156 Miguel Batista .25 .60
157 Ben Sheets .25 .60
158 Oliver Perez .25 .60
159 Doug Davis .25 .60
160 Andruw Jones .40 1.00
161 Hideki Matsui .60 1.50
162 Reggie Sanders .25 .60
163 Joe Nathan .25 .60
164 John Lackey .25 .60
165 Matt Murton .25 .60
166 Grady Sizemore .40 1.00
167 Brad Thompson .25 .60
168 Kevin Millwood .25 .60
169 Orlando Hernandez .25 .60
170 Mark Mulder .25 .60
171 Chase Utley .60 1.50
172 Moises Alou .25 .60
173 Wily Mo Pena .25 .60
174 Brian McCann .25 .60
175 Jermaine Dye .25 .60
176 Ryan Madson .25 .60
177 Aramis Ramirez .25 .60
178 Khalil Greene .40 1.00
179 Mike Hampton .25 .60
180 Mike Mussina .40 1.00
181 Rich Harden .25 .60
182 Woody Williams .25 .60
183 Chris Carpenter .25 .60
184 Brady Clark .25 .60
185 Luis Gonzalez .25 .60
186 Raul Ibanez .25 .60
187 Magglio Ordonez .25 .60
188 Adrian Beltre .25 .60
189 Marcus Giles .25 .60
190 Odalis Perez .25 .60
191 Derek Jeter 1.50 4.00
192 Jason Schmidt .25 .60
193 Toby Hall .25 .60
194 Danny Haren .25 .60
195 Tim Hudson .25 .60
196 Jake Peavy .25 .60
197 Casey Blake .25 .60
198 J.D. Drew .25 .60
199 Ervin Santana .25 .60
200 J.J. Hardy .25 .60
201 Austin Kearns .25 .60
202 Pat Burrell .25 .60
203 Jason Vargas .25 .60
204 Ryan Howard 1.00 2.50
205 Joe Crede .25 .60
206 Vladimir Guerrero .60 1.50
207 Roy Halladay .25 .60
208 David Dellucci .25 .60
209 Brandon Webb .25 .60
210 Ryan Church .25 .60
211 Miguel Tejada .25 .60
212 Mark Kinsler .25 .60
213 Kevin Youkilis .25 .60
214 Jon Lieber .25 .60
215 Miguel Cabrera .40 1.00
216 A.J. Burnett .25 .60
217 David Bell .25 .60
218 Eric Byrnes .25 .60
219 Lance Niekro .25 .60
220 Shawn Green .25 .60
221 Ken Griffey Jr. 1.00 2.50
222 Johnny Estrada .25 .60
223 Omar Vizquel .40 1.00
224 Gary Sheffield .25 .60
225 Brad Halsey .25 .60
226 Aaron Cook .25 .60
227 David Ortiz .60 1.50
228 Scott Kazmir .40 1.00
229 Dustin McGowan .25 .60
230 Gregg Zaun .25 .60
231 Carlos Beltran .25 .60
232 Bob Wickman .25 .60
233 Brett Myers .25 .60
234 Casey Kotchman .25 .60
235 Jeff Francoeur .60 1.50
236 Paul Konerko .25 .60
237 Juan Rivera .25 .60
238 Bobby Crosby .25 .60
239 Derrek Lee .25 .60
240 Curt Schilling .40 1.00
241 Jake Westbrook .25 .60
242 Dontrelle Willis .25 .60
243 Brad Lidge .25 .60
244 Randy Johnson .60 1.50
245 Nick Swisher .25 .60
246 Johan Santana .40 1.00
247 Jeremy Bonderman .25 .60
248 Ramon Hernandez .25 .60
249 Mike Lowell .25 .60
250 Javier Vazquez .25 .60
251 Jose Contreras .25 .60
252 Aubrey Huff .25 .60
253 Kenny Rogers AW .15 .40
254 Mark Teixeira AW .25 .60
255 Orlando Hudson AW .15 .40
256 Derek Jeter AW 1.00 2.50
257 Eric Chavez AW .15 .40
258 Torii Hunter AW .15 .40
259 Vernon Wells AW .15 .40
260 Ichiro Suzuki AW .60 1.50
261 Greg Maddux AW .60 1.50
262 Mike Matheny AW .15 .40
263 Derrek Lee AW .15 .40
264 Luis Castillo AW .15 .40
265 Omar Vizquel AW .25 .60
266 Mike Lowell AW .15 .40
267 Andruw Jones AW .25 .60
268 Jim Edmonds AW .25 .60
269 Bobby Abreu AW .15 .40
270 Bartolo Colon AW .15 .40
271 Chris Carpenter AW .15 .40
272 Alex Rodriguez AW .60 1.50
273 Albert Pujols AW .75 2.00
274 Huston Street AW .15 .40
275 Ryan Howard AW .60 1.50
276 Jose Denorfia (RC) .40 1.00
277 John Van Benschoten (RC) .40 1.00
278 Russ Martin (RC) .60 1.50
279 Fausto Carmona (RC) .40 1.00
280 Freddie Bynum (RC) .40 1.00
281 Kelly Shoppach (RC) .40 1.00
282 Chris Demaria RC .40 1.00
283 Jordan Tata RC .40 1.00
284 Ryan Zimmerman (RC) 2.50 6.00
285a Kenji Johjima RC 2.00 5.00
285b Kenji Johjima AU 50.00 100.00
286 Ruddy Lugo (RC) .40 1.00
287 Tommy Murphy (RC) .40 1.00
288 Bobby Livingston (RC) .40 1.00
289 Anderson Hernandez (RC) .40 1.00
290 Brian Slocum (RC) .40 1.00
291 Sendy Rleal RC .40 1.00
292 Ryan Spilborghs (RC) .60 1.50
293 Brandon Fahey RC .40 1.00
294 Jason Kubel (RC) .40 1.00
295 James Loney (RC) .60 1.50
296 Jeremy Accardo RC .40 1.00
297 Fabio Castro RC .40 1.00
298 Matt Capps (RC) .40 1.00
299 Casey Janssen RC .40 1.00
300 Martin Prado (RC) .40 1.00
301 Ronny Paulino (RC) .40 1.00
302 Josh Barfield (RC) .40 1.00
303 Joel Zumaya (RC) 1.00 2.50
304 Matt Cain (RC) .60 1.50
305 Conor Jackson (RC) .60 1.50
306 Brian Anderson (RC) .40 1.00
307 Prince Fielder (RC) 1.50 4.00
308 Jeremy Hermida (RC) .40 1.00
309 Justin Verlander (RC) 1.50 4.00
310 Brian Bannister (RC) .40 1.00
311 Josh Willingham (RC) .40 1.00
312 John Rheinecker (RC) .40 1.00
313 Nick Markakis (RC) .60 1.50
314 Jonathan Papelbon (RC) 2.00 5.00
315 Mike Jacobs (RC) .40 1.00
316 Jose Capellan (RC) .40 1.00
317 Mike Napoli RC 1.00 2.50
318 Ricky Nolasco (RC) .40 1.00
319 Ben Johnson (RC) .40 1.00
320 Paul Maholm (RC) .40 1.00
321 Drew Meyer (RC) .40 1.00
322 Jeff Mathis (RC) .40 1.00
323 Fernando Nieve (RC) .40 1.00
324 John Koronka (RC) .40 1.00
325 Wil Nieves (RC) .40 1.00
326 Nate McLouth (RC) .40 1.00
327 Howie Kendrick (RC) 2.00 5.00
328 Sean Marshall (RC) .40 1.00
329 Brandon Watson (RC) .40 1.00
330 Skip Schumaker (RC) .40 1.00
331 Ryan Garko AU (RC) 4.00 10.00
332 Jason Bergmann AU RC 4.00 10.00
333 Chuck James AU (RC) 6.00 15.00
334 Adam Wainwright AU (RC) 4.00 10.00
335 Dan Ortmeier AU (RC) 4.00 10.00
336 Francisco Liriano AU (RC) 12.50 30.00
337 Craig Breslow AU RC 4.00 10.00
338 Darrell Rasner AU (RC) 4.00 10.00
339 Jason Botts AU (RC) 4.00 10.00
340 Ian Kinsler AU (RC) 6.00 15.00
341 Joey Devine AU RC 4.00 10.00
342 Miguel Perez AU (RC) 4.00 10.00
343 Scott Olsen AU (RC) 6.00 15.00
344 Tyler Johnson AU (RC) 4.00 10.00
345 Anthony Lerew AU (RC) 4.00 10.00
346 Nelson Cruz AU (RC) 4.00 10.00
347 Willie Eyre AU (RC) 4.00 10.00
348 Josh Johnson AU (RC) 8.00 20.00
349 Shaun Marcum AU (RC) 4.00 10.00
350 Dustin Nippert AU (RC) 4.00 10.00
351 Josh Wilson AU (RC) 4.00 10.00
352 Hanley Ramirez AU (RC) 12.50 30.00
353 Reggie Abercrombie AU (RC) 4.00 10.00
354 Dan Uggla AU (RC) 8.00 20.00

2006 Topps Chrome Refractors

*REF 1-275: .6X TO 1.5X BASIC
*REF 276-330: .6X TO 1.5X BASIC RC
1-330 STATED ODDS 1:4 H, 1:4 R
*REF AU 331-354: .5X TO 1.2X BASIC AU
331-354 AU ODDS 1:65 HOBBY
331-354 PRINT RUN 500 SERIAL #'d SETS
340 Ian Kinsler AU 10.00 25.00
354 Dan Uggla AU 12.50 30.00

2006 Topps Chrome Black Refractors

*BLACK REF 1-275: 1.25X TO 3X BASIC
*BLACK REF 276-330: 1.25X TO 3X BASIC RC
1-330 STATED ODDS 1:6 H, 1:19 R
1-330 PRINT RUN 549 SERIAL #'d SETS
*BLK REF AU 331-354: .6X TO 1.5X BASIC AU
331-354 AU ODDS 1:162 HOBBY
331-354 PRINT RUN 200 SERIAL #'d SETS
340 Ian Kinsler AU 20.00 50.00
354 Dan Uggla AU 15.00 40.00

2006 Topps Chrome Blue Refractors

*BLUE REF 1-275: 2X TO 5X BASIC
*BLUE REF 276-330: 2X TO 5X BASIC RC
STATED ODDS 1:8 RETAIL

2006 Topps Chrome Gold Super-Fractors

1-330 ODDS 1:97 HOBBY BOX LOADER
311-354 AU ODDS 1:1335 HOBBY BOX LDR
STATED PRINT RUN 1 SERIAL #'d SET
NO PRICING DUE TO SCARCITY

2006 Topps Chrome Red Refractors

*RED REF 1-275: 4X TO 10X BASIC
*RED REF 276-330: 3X TO 8X BASIC RC
1-330 ODDS 1:2 HOBBY BOX LOADER
1-330 PRINT RUN 90 SERIAL #'d SETS
331-354 AU ODDS 1:52 HOBBY BOX LOADER
331-354 AU PRINT RUN 25 SERIAL #'d SETS
NO AU PRICING DUE TO SCARCITY

2006 Topps Chrome X-Fractors

*X-FRAC: 1-275: 1.5X TO 4X BASIC
*X-FRAC: 276-330: 1.5X TO 4X BASIC RC
STATED ODDS 1:6 RETAIL

2006 Topps Chrome Declaration of Independence

COMPLETE SET (56) 60.00 120.00
STATED ODDS 1:7 H, 1:7 R
*REF: .5X TO 1.2X BASIC
REF ODDS 1:11 HOBBY, 1:44 RETAIL
AC Abraham Clark 1.25 3.00
AM Arthur Middleton 1.25 3.00
BF Benjamin Franklin 2.00 5.00
BG Button Gwinnett 1.25 3.00
BH Benjamin Harrison 1.25 3.00
BR Benjamin Rush 1.25 3.00
CB Carter Braxton 1.25 3.00
CC Charles Carroll 1.25 3.00
CR Caesar Rodney 1.25 3.00
EG Elbridge Gerry 1.25 3.00
ER Edward Rutledge 1.25 3.00
FH Francis Hopkinson 1.25 3.00
FL Francis Lewis 1.25 3.00
FLL Francis Lightfoot Lee 1.25 3.00
GC George Clymer 1.25 3.00
GR George Ross 1.25 3.00
GRE George Read 1.25 3.00
GT George Taylor 1.25 3.00
GW George Walton 1.25 3.00
GWY George Wythe 1.25 3.00
JA John Adams 1.25 3.00
JB Josiah Bartlett 1.25 3.00
JH John Hancock 1.25 3.00
JHA John Hart 1.25 3.00
JHE Joseph Hewes 1.25 3.00
JM John Morton 1.25 3.00
JP John Penn 1.25 3.00
JS James Smith 1.25 3.00
JW James Wilson 1.25 3.00
JWI John Witherspoon 1.25 3.00
LH Lyman Hall 1.25 3.00
LM Lewis Morris 1.25 3.00
MT Matthew Thornton 1.25 3.00
OW Oliver Wolcott 1.25 3.00
PL Philip Livingston 1.25 3.00
RHL Richard Henry Lee 1.25 3.00
RM Robert Morris 1.25 3.00
RS Roger Sherman 1.25 3.00
RST Richard Stockton 1.25 3.00
RTP Robert Treat Paine 1.25 3.00
SA Samuel Adams 1.25 3.00
SC Samuel Chase 1.25 3.00
SH Stephen Hopkins 1.25 3.00
SHU Samuel Huntington 1.25 3.00
TH Thomas Heyward Jr. 1.25 3.00
TJ Thomas Jefferson 2.00 5.00
TL Thomas Lynch Jr. 1.25 3.00
TM Thomas McKean 1.25 3.00
TN Thomas Nelson Jr. 1.25 3.00
TS Thomas Stone 1.25 3.00
WE William Ellery 1.25 3.00
WF William Floyd 1.25 3.00
WH William Hooper 1.25 3.00
WP William Paca 1.25 3.00
WW William Whipple 1.25 3.00
WWI William Williams 1.25 3.00
HDR1 Declaration of Independence 1.25 3.00

2006 Topps Chrome Mantle Home Run History

COMPLETE SET (59) 40.00 80.00
COMP.07TCH SET (13) 8.00 20.00
COMP.07TCH SET (29) 15.00 40.00
COMP.08TCH SET (17) 8.00 20.00
COMMON CARD (1-59) 1.00 2.50
STATED 06 ODDS 1:6 HOBBY, 1:23 RETAIL
STATED 07 ODDS 1:8 HOBBY, 1:24 RETAIL
06 PLATE ODDS 1:300 HOBBY BOX LOADER
07 PLATE ODDS 1:116 HOBBY BOX LOADER
08 PLATE ODDS 1:1971 HOBBY
PLATE PRINT RUN 1 SET PER COLOR
BLACK-CYAN-MAGENTA-YELLOW ISSUED
NO PLATE PRICING DUE TO SCARCITY
*REF: .75X TO 2X BASIC
06 REF ODDS 1:70 HOBBY, 1:350 RETAIL
07 REF ODDS 1:27 HOBBY, 1:71 RETAIL
08 REF ODDS 1:31 HOBBY
REF PRINT RUN 500 SERIAL #'d SETS
08 REF PRINT RUN 400 SER.#'d SETS
*BLACK REF: 2.5X TO 6X BASIC
BLACK ODDS 1:175 HOBBY, 1:950 RETAIL
BLACK PRINT RUN 200 SERIAL #'d SETS
*06-07 BLUE REF: 3X TO 8X BASIC
*08 BLUE REF: 2.5X TO 6X BASIC
06 BLUE ODDS 1:300 RETAIL
07 BLUE ODDS 1:72 RETAIL
06-07 BLUE PRINT RUN 100 SERIAL #'d SETS
08 BLUE PRINT RUN 200 SERIAL #'d SETS
*COPPER REF: 3X TO 8X BASIC
COPPER ODDS 1:117 HOBBY
STATED PRINT RUN 100 SERIAL #'d SETS
06 GOLD SF ODDS 1:1234 HOBBY BOX LDR
08 GOLD SF ODDS 1:7885 HOBBY
GOLD SF PRINT RUN 1 SERIAL #'d SET
NO GOLD SF PRICING DUE TO SCARCITY
*07 RED REF: 3X TO 8X BASIC
*08 RED REF: 12X TO 30X BASIC
08 RED REF ODDS 1:315 HOBBY
07 RED REF PRINT RUN 99 SER.#'d SETS
08 RED REF PRINT RUN 25 SER.#'d SETS
*RED XF: 12X TO 30X BASIC
RED XF ODDS 1:48 HOBBY BOX LOADER
RED XF PRINT RUN 25 SERIAL #'d SETS
*WHITE REF: 2.5X TO 6X BASIC
07 WHITE REF ODDS 1:67 HOBBY, 1:185 RETAIL
WHITE REF PRINT RUN 200 SER.#'d SETS
MHRC536 Mickey Mantle 1.00

2006 Topps Chrome Rookie Logos

ONE PER UPDATE HOB.BOX LOADER
STATED PRINT RUN 599 SER.#'d SETS
1 Ben Zobrist 2.50 6.00

2 Shane Komine 2.50 6.00
3 Casey Janssen 2.50 6.00
4 Kevin Frandsen 2.50 6.00
5 John Rheinecker 1.50 4.00
6 Matt Kemp 2.50 6.00
7 Scott Mathieson 1.50 4.00
8 Jered Weaver 4.00 10.00
9 Joel Guzman 1.50 4.00
10 Anibal Sanchez 1.50 4.00
11 Melky Cabrera 5.00 12.00
12 Howie Kendrick 4.00 10.00
13 Cole Hamels 4.00 10.00
14 Willy Aybar 1.50 4.00
15 James Shields 1.50 4.00
16 Kevin Thompson 1.50 4.00
17 Jon Lester 8.00 20.00
18 Stephen Drew 4.00 10.00
19 Andre Ethier 4.00 10.00
20 Jordan Tata 1.50 4.00
21 Mike Napoli 5.00 12.00
22 Kason Gabbard 1.50 4.00
23 Lastings Milledge 2.50 6.00
24 Erick Aybar 1.50 4.00
25 Fausto Carmona 1.50 4.00
26 Russ Martin 2.50 6.00
27 David Pauley 1.50 4.00
28 Andy Marte 2.50 6.00
29 Carlos Quentin 2.50 6.00
30 Franklin Gutierrez 1.50 4.00
31 Taylor Buchholz 2.50 6.00
32 Josh Johnson 2.50 6.00
33 Chad Billingsley 2.50 6.00
34 Kendry Morales 1.50 4.00
35 Adam Loewen 1.50 4.00
36 Yusmeiro Petit 1.50 4.00
37 Matt Albers 1.50 4.00
38 John Maine 2.50 6.00
39 Josh Willingham 1.50 4.00
40 Taylor Tankersley 1.50 4.00
41 Pat Neshek 30.00 60.00
42 Francisco Rosario 2.50 6.00
43 Matt Smith 2.50 6.00
44 Jonathan Sanchez 1.50 4.00
45 Chris Demaria 1.50 4.00
46 Manuel Corpas 1.50 4.00
47 Kevin Reese 2.50 6.00
48 Brent Clevlen 2.50 6.00
49 Anderson Hernandez 2.50 6.00
50 Chris Roberson 1.50 4.00

2006 Topps Chrome Rookie Logos Refractors

STATED ODDS 1:25 UPD.HOB.BOX LDR
STATED PRINT RUN 25 SER. #'d SETS
NO PRICING DUE TO SCARCITY

2006 Topps Chrome United States Constitution

COMPLETE SET (42) 30.00 60.00
STATED ODDS 1:15 H, 1:15 R
*REF: .5X TO 1.2X BASIC
REF ODDS 1:9 HOBBY, 1:36 RETAIL
AB Abraham Baldwin .75 2.00
AH Alexander Hamilton .75 2.00
BF Benjamin Franklin 1.25 3.00
CCP Charles Cotesworth Pinckney .75 2.00
CP Charles Pinckney .75 2.00
DB David Brearly .75 2.00
DC Daniel Carroll .75 2.00
DJ Daniel of St. Thomas Jenifer .75 2.00
GB Gunning Bedford Jr. .75 2.00
GC George Clymer .75 2.00
GM Gouverneur Morris .75 2.00
GR George Read .75 2.00
GW George Washington 1.25 3.00
HW Hugh Williamson .75 2.00
JB John Blair .75 2.00
JBR Jacob Broom .75 2.00
JD Jonathan Dayton .75 2.00
JDI John Dickinson .75 2.00
JI Jared Ingersoll .75 2.00
JL John Langdon .75 2.00
JM James Madison .75 2.00
JMC James McHenry .75 2.00
JR John Rutledge .75 2.00
JW James Wilson .75 2.00
NG Nicholas Gilman .75 2.00
NGO Nathaniel Gorham .75 2.00
PB Pierce Butler .75 2.00

RB Richard Bassett .75 2.00
RDS Richard Dobbs Spaight .75 2.00
RK Rufus King .75 2.00
RM Robert Morris .75 2.00
RS Roger Sherman .75 2.00
TF Thomas Fitzsimons .75 2.00
TM Thomas Mifflin .75 2.00
WB William Blount .75 2.00
WF William Few .75 2.00
WJ William Samuel Johnson .75 2.00
WL William Livingston .75 2.00
WP William Paterson .75 2.00
HDR1 United States Constitution .75 2.00
HDR2 .75 2.00
HDR3 .75 2.00

2007 Topps Chrome

This 369-card set was released in July, 2007. The set was issued in both hobby and retail versions. The hobby packs consisted of four-card packs (with an $3 SRP) which came 24 packs to a box and 12 boxes to a case. Cards numbered 1-275 featured veterans while cards 276-330 featured rookies and cards 331-355 (and a featured signed Rookie Cards. The signed cards were inserted into packs at a stated rate of one in 16 hobby and one in 122 retail. In addition, the players in this set who were originally from Japan all were issued in American and Japanese versions and the Japanese cards were issued at a stated rate of one in 82 hobby packs.

COMP.SET w/o AU's (330) 40.00 80.00
COMMON CARD .20 .50
COMMON ROOKIE .40 1.00
JAPANESE VARIATION ODDS 1:82 H
COMMON AUTO 3.00 8.00
AUTO ODDS 1:16 HOBBY, 1:122 RETAIL
PRINT.PLATE ODDS 1:36 HOBBY BOX LDR
VAR.PLATES 1:1943 HOBBY BOX LDR
AU PLATES 1:343 HOBBY BOX LDR
PLATE PRINT RUN 1 SET PER COLOR
BLACK-CYAN-MAGENTA-YELLOW ISSUED
NO PLATE PRICING DUE TO SCARCITY
EXCHANGE DEADLINE 07/31/09
1 Nick Swisher .20 .50
2 Bobby Abreu .20 .50
3 Edgar Renteria .20 .50
4 Mickey Mantle 1.50 4.00
5 Preston Wilson .20 .50
6 C.C. Sabathia .20 .50
7 Julio Lugo .20 .50
8 J.D. Drew .20 .50
9 Jason Varitek .50 1.25
10 Orlando Hernandez .20 .50
11 Corey Patterson .20 .50
12 Josh Bard .20 .50
13 Gary Matthews .20 .50
14 Jason Jennings .20 .50
15 Bronson Arroyo .20 .50
16 Andy Pettitte .30 .75
17 Ervin Santana .20 .50
18 Paul Konerko .20 .50
19 Adam LaRoche .20 .50
20 Jim Edmonds .30 .75
21 Derek Jeter 1.25 3.00
22 Aubrey Huff .20 .50
23 Andre Ethier .30 .75
24 Jeremy Sowers .20 .50
25 Miguel Cabrera .30 .75
26 Carlos Lee .20 .50
27 Mike Piazza .50 1.25
28 Cole Hamels .50 1.25
29 Mark Loretta .20 .50
30 John Smoltz .30 .75
31 Dan Uggla .30 .75
32 Lyle Overbay .20 .50
33 Michael Barrett .20 .50
34 Ivan Rodriguez .30 .75
35 Jake Westbrook .20 .50
36 Moises Alou .20 .50
37 Jered Weaver .30 .75
38 Lastings Milledge .30 .75
39 Austin Kearns .20 .50
40 Adam Loewen .20 .50
41 Josh Barfield .20 .50
42 Johan Santana .30 .75
43 Ian Kinsler .20 .50
44 Mike Lowell .20 .50
45 Scott Rolen .30 .75
46 Chipper Jones .50 1.25
47 Joe Crede .20 .50
48 Rafael Furcal .20 .50
49 Dave Bush .20 .50
50 Marcus Giles .20 .50
51 Joe Blanton .20 .50
52 Dontrelle Willis .20 .50
53 Scott Kazmir .30 .75
54 Jeff Kent .20 .50
55 Travis Hafner .20 .50
56 Ryan Garko .20 .50
57 Nick Markakis .30 .75
58 Michael Cuddyer .20 .50
59 Jason Giambi .20 .50
60 Chone Figgins .20 .50
61 Carlos Delgado .20 .50
62 Aramis Ramirez .20 .50
63 Albert Pujols 1.00 2.50
64 Gary Sheffield .20 .50
65 Adrian Gonzalez .20 .50
66 Prince Fielder .50 1.25
67 Freddy Sanchez .20 .50
68 Jack Wilson .20 .50
69 Jake Peavy .20 .50
70 Javier Vazquez .20 .50
71 Todd Helton .30 .75
72 Bill Hall .20 .50
73 Jeremy Bonderman .20 .50
74 Rocco Baldelli .20 .50
75 Noah Lowry .20 .50
76 Justin Verlander .50 1.25
77 Mark Buehrle .20 .50
78 Hank Blalock .20 .50
79 Mark Teahen .20 .50
80 Chien-Ming Wang .75 2.00
81 Roy Halladay .20 .50
82 Melvin Mora .20 .50
83 Grady Sizemore .30 .75
84 Matt Cain .20 .50
85 Carl Crawford .20 .50
86 Johnny Damon .30 .75
87 Freddy Garcia .20 .50
88 Ryan Shealy .20 .50
89 Carlos Beltran .20 .50
90 Chuck James .20 .50
91 Ben Sheets .20 .50
92 Mark Mulder .20 .50
93 Carlos Quentin .20 .50
94 Richie Sexson .20 .50
95 Brian Schneider .20 .50
96a Hideki Matsui .50 1.25
96b Hideki Matsui Japanese 2.00 5.00
97 Robinson Tejeda .20 .50
98 Scott Hatteberg .20 .50
99 Jeff Francis .20 .50
100 Robinson Cano .30 .75
101 Barry Zito .20 .50
102 Reed Johnson .20 .50
103 Chris Carpenter .20 .50
104 Chad Tracy .20 .50
105 Anibal Sanchez .20 .50
106 Brad Penny .20 .50
107 David Wright .75 2.00
108 Jimmy Rollins .20 .50
109 Alfonso Soriano .20 .50
110 Greg Maddux .75 2.00
111 Curt Schilling .30 .75
112 Stephen Drew .30 .75
113 Matt Holliday .50 1.25
114 Jorge Posada .30 .75
115 Vladimir Guerrero .50 1.25
116 Frank Thomas .50 1.25
117 Jonathan Papelbon .50 1.25
118 Manny Ramirez .30 .75
119 Magglio Ordonez .30 .75
120 Joe Mauer .30 .75
121 Ryan Howard .75 2.00
122 Chris Young .20 .50
123 A.J. Burnett .20 .50
124 Brian McCann .20 .50
125 Juan Pierre .20 .50
126 Jonny Gomes .20 .50
127 Roger Clemens .75 2.00
128 Chad Billingsley .20 .50
129a Kenji Johjima .50 1.25
129b Kenji Johjima Japanese 2.00 5.00
130 Brian Giles .20 .50
131 Chase Utley .50 1.25
132 Carl Pavano .20 .50
133 Curtis Granderson .20 .50
134 Sean Casey .20 .50
135 Jon Garland .20 .50
136 David Ortiz .50 1.25
137 Bobby Crosby .20 .50
138 Conor Jackson .20 .50
139 Tim Hudson .20 .50
140 Rickie Weeks .20 .50
141 Mark Prior .20 .50
142 Ben Zobrist .20 .50
143 Troy Glaus .20 .50
144 Cliff Lee .20 .50
145 Adrian Beltre .20 .50
146 Endy Chavez .20 .50
147 Ramon Hernandez .20 .50
148 Chris Young .20 .50
149 Jason Schmidt .20 .50
150 Kevin Millwood .20 .50
151 Placido Polanco .20 .50
152 Torii Hunter .20 .50
153 Roy Oswalt .20 .50
154 Kelvim Escobar .20 .50
155 Milton Bradley .20 .50
156 Chris Capuano .20 .50
157 Juan Encarnacion .20 .50
158a Ichiro Suzuki .75 2.00
158b Ichiro Suzuki Japanese 3.00 8.00
159 Matt Kemp .20 .50
160 Matt Morris .20 .50
161 Casey Blake .20 .50
162 Josh Willingham .20 .50
163 Nick Johnson .20 .50
164 Khalil Greene .20 .50
165 Tom Glavine .30 .75
166 Jason Bay .20 .50
167 Brandon Phillips .20 .50
168 Jorge Cantu .20 .50
169 Jeff Weaver .20 .50
170 Melky Cabrera .20 .50
171 Dan Haren .20 .50
172 Jeff Francoeur .50 1.25
173 Randy Wolf .20 .50
174 Carlos Zambrano .20 .50
175 Justin Morneau .20 .50
176 Takashi Saito .20 .50
177 Victor Martinez .20 .50
178 Felix Hernandez .30 .75
179 Paul LoDuca .20 .50
180 Miguel Tejada .20 .50
181 Mark Teixeira .30 .75
182 Pat Burrell .20 .50
183 Mike Cameron .20 .50
184 Josh Beckett .30 .75
185 Francisco Liriano .50 1.25
186 Ken Griffey Jr. .75 2.00
187 Mike Mussina .30 .75
188 Howie Kendrick .20 .50
189 Ted Lilly .20 .50
190 Mike Hampton .20 .50
191 Jeff Suppan .20 .50
192 Jose Reyes .50 1.25
193 Russell Martin .20 .50
194 Jhonny Peralta .20 .50
195 Raul Ibanez .20 .50
196 Hanley Ramirez .30 .75
197 Kerry Wood .20 .50
198 Gary Sheffield .20 .50
199 David Dellucci .20 .50
200 Xavier Nady .20 .50
201 Michael Young .20 .50
202 Kevin Youkilis .20 .50
203 Aaron Harang .20 .50
204 Matt Garza .20 .50
205 Jim Thome .30 .75
206 Jose Contreras .20 .50
207 Tadahito Iguchi .20 .50
208 Eric Chavez .20 .50
209 Vernon Wells .20 .50
210 Doug Davis .20 .50
211 Andruw Jones .30 .75
212 David Eckstein .20 .50
213 J.J. Hardy .20 .50
214 Orlando Hudson .20 .50
215 Pedro Martinez .30 .75
216 Brian Roberts .20 .50
217 Brett Myers .20 .50
218 Alex Rodriguez .75 2.00
219 Kenny Rogers .20 .50
220 Jason Kubel .20 .50
221 Jermaine Dye .20 .50
222 Bartolo Colon .20 .50
223 Craig Biggio .30 .75
224 Alex Rios .20 .50
225 Adam Dunn .20 .50
226 Anthony Reyes .20 .50
227 Derrek Lee .20 .50
228 Jeremy Hermida .20 .50
229 Derek Lowe .20 .50
230 Randy Winn .20 .50
231 Brandon Webb .20 .50
232 Jose Vidro .20 .50
233 Erik Bedard .20 .50
234 Jon Lieber .20 .50
235 Wily Mo Pena .20 .50
236 Kelly Johnson .20 .50
237 David DeJesus .20 .50
238 Andy Marte .20 .50
239 Scott Olsen .20 .50
240 Randy Johnson .50 1.25
241 Nelson Cruz .30 .75
242 Carlos Guillen .20 .50
243 Brandon McCarthy .20 .50
244 Garret Anderson .20 .50
245 Mike Sweeney .20 .50
246 Brian Bannister .20 .50
247 Jose Lopez .20 .50
248 Brad Wilkerson .20 .50
249 Lance Berkman .20 .50
250 Ryan Zimmerman .50 1.25
251 Garrett Atkins .20 .50
252 Johan Santana .30 .75
253 Brandon Webb .20 .50
254 Justin Verlander .50 1.25
255 Hanley Ramirez .30 .75
256 Justin Morneau .50 1.25
257 Ryan Howard .75 2.00
258 Eric Chavez .20 .50
259 Scott Rolen .30 .75
260 Derek Jeter 1.25 3.00
261 Omar Vizquel .30 .75
262 Mark Grudzielanek .20 .50
263 Orlando Hudson .20 .50
264 Mark Teixeira .30 .75
265 Albert Pujols 1.00 2.50
266 Ivan Rodriguez .30 .75
267 Brad Ausmus .20 .50
268 Torii Hunter .20 .50
269 Mike Cameron .20 .50
270 Ichiro Suzuki .75 2.00
271 Carlos Beltran .20 .50
272 Vernon Wells .20 .50
273 Andruw Jones .30 .75
274 Kenny Rogers .20 .50
275 Greg Maddux .75 2.00
276 Danny Putnam (RC) .40 1.00
277 Chase Wright RC 1.00 2.50
278 Zach McClellan RC .40 1.00
279 Jamie Vermilyea RC .40 1.00
280 Felix Pie (RC) .40 1.00
281 Phil Hughes (RC) 2.00 5.00
282 Jon Knott (RC) .40 1.00
283 Micah Owings (RC) .40 1.00
284 Devern Hansack RC .40 1.00
285 Andy Cannizaro RC .40 1.00
286 Lee Gardner (RC) .40 1.00
287 Josh Hamilton (RC) 1.00 2.50
288a Angel Sanchez RC
288b Angel Sanchez AU 3.00 8.00
289 J.D. Durbin (RC) .40 1.00
290 Jaime Burke (RC) .40 1.00
291 Joe Bisenius RC .40 1.00
292 Rick Vanden Hurk RC .60 1.50
293 Brian Barden RC .40 1.00
294 Levale Speigner RC .40 1.00
295 Kevin Cameron RC .40 1.00
296 Don Kelly (RC) .40 1.00
297a Hideki Okajima RC 2.00 5.00
297b Hideki Okajima Japanese 3.00 8.00
298 Andrew Miller RC 2.50 6.00
299 Delmon Young (RC) 1.00 2.50
300 Vinny Rottino (RC) .40 1.00
301 Philip Humber (RC) .40 1.00
302 Drew Anderson RC .40 1.00
303 Jerry Owens (RC) .40 1.00
304 Jose Garcia RC .40 1.00
305 Shane Youman RC .40 1.00
306 Ryan Feierabend (RC) .40 1.00
307 Mike Rabelo RC .40 1.00
308 Josh Fields (RC) .40 1.00
309 Jon Coutlangus (RC) .40 1.00
310 Travis Buck (RC) .40 1.00
311 Doug Slaten RC .40 1.00
312 Ryan Braun RC .40 1.00
313 Juan Salas (RC) .40 1.00
314 Matt Lindstrom (RC) .40 1.00
315 Cesar Jimenez RC .40 1.00
316 Jay Marshall RC .40 1.00
317 Jared Burton RC .40 1.00
318 Juan Perez RC .40 1.00
319 Elijah Dukes RC .60 1.50
320 Juan Lara RC .40 1.00
321 Justin Hampson (RC) .40 1.00
322a Kei Igawa RC 1.00 2.50
322b Kei Igawa Japanese 2.00 5.00
323 Zack Segovia (RC) .40 1.00
324 Alejandro De Aza RC .60 1.50
325 Brandon Morrow RC 1.00 2.50
326 Gustavo Molina RC .40 1.00
327 Joe Smith RC .40 1.00
328 Jesus Flores RC .40 1.00
329 Jeff Baker (RC) .40 1.00
330a Daisuke Matsuzaka RC 4.00 10.00
330b Daisuke Matsuzaka Japanese 8.00 20.00
331 Troy Tulowitzki AU (RC) 12.50 30.00
332 John Danks AU RC 4.00 10.00
333 Kevin Kouzmanoff AU (RC) 3.00 8.00
334 David Murphy AU (RC) 3.00 8.00
335 Ryan Sweeney AU (RC) 3.00 8.00
336 Fred Lewis AU (RC) 4.00 10.00
337 Delwyn Young AU (RC) 3.00 8.00
338 Matt Chico AU (RC) 3.00 8.00
339 Miguel Montero AU (RC) 3.00 8.00
340 Shawn Riggans AU (RC) 3.00 8.00
341 Brian Stokes AU (RC) 3.00 8.00
342 Scott Moore AU (RC) 3.00 8.00
343 Adam Lind AU (RC) 3.00 8.00
344 Chris Narveson AU (RC) 3.00 8.00
345 Alex Gordon AU RC 15.00 40.00
346 Joaquin Arias AU (RC) 3.00 8.00
347 Brian Burres AU (RC) 3.00 8.00
348 Glen Perkins AU (RC) 3.00 8.00
349 Ubaldo Jimenez AU (RC) 10.00 25.00
350 Chris Stewart AU RC 3.00 8.00
351 Beltran Perez AU (RC) 3.00 8.00
352 Dennis Sarfate AU (RC) 3.00 8.00
353 Carlos Maldonado AU (RC) 3.00 8.00
354 Mitch Maier AU RC 3.00 8.00
355 Kory Casto AU (RC) 3.00 8.00
356 Juan Morillo AU (RC) 3.00 8.00
357 Hector Gimenez AU (RC) 3.00 8.00
358 Alexi Casilla AU RC 4.00 10.00
359 Michael Bourn AU (RC) 4.00 10.00
360 Sean Henn AU (RC) 3.00 8.00
361 Tim Gradoville AU RC 3.00 8.00
362 Akinori Iwamura AU RC EXCH 8.00 20.00
363 Oswaldo Navarro AU RC 3.00 8.00

2007 Topps Chrome Refractors

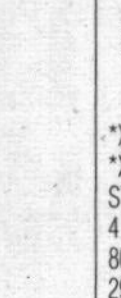

*REF: 1.2X TO 3X BASIC
REF ODDS 1:3 HOB,1:2 RET
*REF RC: .6X TO 1.5X BASIC RC
REF RC ODDS 1:3 HOB, 1:2 RET
*REF VAR: .5X TO 1.2X BASIC VARIATION
REF VAR ODDS 1:73 HOBBY
REF VAR PRINT RUN 500 SER.#'d SETS
*REF AU: .5X TO 1.2X BASIC AUTO
REF AU ODDS 1:71 HOB, 1:570 RET
REF AU PRINT RUN 500 SER.#'d SETS
EXCHANGE DEADLINE 07/31/09
330a Daisuke Matsuzaka 6.00 15.00
345 Alex Gordon AU 15.00 40.00

2007 Topps Chrome Blue Refractors

*BLUE: 4X TO 10X BASIC
*BLUE RC: 2.5X TO 6X BASIC RC
STATED ODDS 1:6 RETAIL
4 Mickey Mantle 30.00 60.00
80 Chien-Ming Wang 20.00 50.00
186 Ken Griffey Jr. 10.00 25.00
218 Alex Rodriguez 10.00 25.00
298 Andrew Miller 30.00 60.00
325 Brandon Morrow 10.00 25.00
330 Daisuke Matsuzaka 50.00 100.00

2007 Topps Chrome Red Refractors

*RED REF: 4X TO 10X BASIC
*RED REF RC: 2.5X TO 6X BASIC RC
STATED ODDS 1:2 HOB.BOX LDR
STATED PRINT RUN 99 SER.#'d SETS
STATED VAR.ODDS 1:311 HOB.BOX LDR
STATED VAR.PRINT RUN 25 SER.#'d SETS
NO VARIATION PRICING AVAILABLE
STATED AU ODDS 1:55 HOB.BOX LDR
STATED AU PRINT RUN 25 SER.#'d SETS
NO AU PRICING AVAILABLE
EXCHANGE DEADLINE 07/31/09
4 Mickey Mantle 30.00 60.00
80 Chien-Ming Wang 20.00 50.00
186 Ken Griffey Jr. 10.00 25.00
218 Alex Rodriguez 10.00 25.00
298 Andrew Miller 15.00 40.00
325 Brandon Morrow 10.00 25.00
330a Daisuke Matsuzaka 30.00 60.00

2007 Topps Chrome White Refractors

*WHITE REF: 1.5X TO 4X BASIC
WHITE REF ODDS 1:6 HOB,1:23 RET
WHITE REF PRINT RUN 660 SER.#'d SETS
*WHITE REF RC: .75X TO 2X BASIC RC
WHITE REF RC ODDS 1:6 HOB, 1:23 RET
WHITE REF RC PRINT RUN 660 SER.#'d SETS
*WHITE REF VAR: .6X TO 1.5X BASIC VAR
WHITE REF VAR ODDS 1:932 HOBBY
WHITE REF VAR PRINT RUN 200 SER.#'d SETS
*WHITE REF AU: .75X TO 2X BASIC AUTO

WHITE REF AU ODDS 1:177 HOB, 1:1475 RET
WHITE REF AU PRINT RUN 200 SER.#'d SETS
EXCHANGE DEADLINE 07/31/09
297b Hideki Okajima Japanese 15.00 40.00
330a Daisuke Matsuzaka 12.50 30.00
330b Daisuke Matsuzaka Japanese 40.00 80.00
345 Alex Gordon AU 30.00 60.00

2007 Topps Chrome SuperFractors

STATED ODDS 1:108 HOB.BOX LDR
STATED VAR.ODDS 1:7775 HOB.BOX LDR
STATED AU ODDS 1:1372 HOB.BOX LDR
STATED PRINT RUN 1 SER.#'d SET
NO PRICING DUE TO SCARCITY
EXCHANGE DEADLINE 07/31/09

2007 Topps Chrome X-Fractors

*X-F: 1.5X TO 4X BASIC
*X-F RC: 1.5X TO 4X BASIC RC
STATED ODDS 1:3 RETAIL
4 Mickey Mantle 6.00 15.00
80 Chien-Ming Wang 6.00 15.00
297 Hideki Okajima 4.00 10.00
298 Andrew Miller 5.00 12.00
330 Daisuke Matsuzaka 8.00 20.00

2007 Topps Chrome Generation Now

COMPLETE SET (41) 10.00 25.00
COMMON A.ETHIER .50 1.25
COMMON R.HOWARD .75 2.00
COMMON N.MARKAKIS .50 1.25
COMMON R.MARTIN .50 1.25
COMMON J.MORNEAU .50 1.25
COMMON M.NAPOLI .50 1.25
COMMON H.RAMIREZ .50 1.25
COMMON N.SWISHER .50 1.25
COMMON C.UTLEY .50 1.25
COMMON J.VERLANDER .60 1.50
COMMON C.WANG 1.00 2.50
COMMON JER.WEAVER .50 1.25
COMMON D.YOUNG .50 1.25
COMMON R.ZIMMERMAN .60 1.50
STATED ODDS 1:5 HOBBY,1:17 RETAIL
PLATE ODDS 1:116 HOB.BOXLOADER
PLATE PRINT RUN 1 SET PER COLOR
BLACK-CYAN-MAGENTA-YELLOW ISSUED
NO PLATE PRICING DUE TO SCARCITY
SUPERFRAC.PRINT RUN 1 SER.#'d SET
NO SUPERFRAC.PRICING DUE TO SCARCITY

2007 Topps Chrome Generation Now Refractors

*REF: 1X TO 2.5X BASIC
STATED ODDS 1:27 H, 1:71 R
STATED PRINT RUN 500 SER.#'d SETS
GN210 Chien-Ming Wang 10.00 25.00

2007 Topps Chrome Generation Now Blue Refractors

*BLUE REF: 2.5X TO 6X BASIC
STATED ODDS 1:72 RETAIL
STATED PRINT RUN 100 SER.#'d SETS
GN210 Chien-Ming Wang 40.00 60.00

2007 Topps Chrome Generation Now Red Refractors

*RED REF: 2.5X TO 6X BASIC
STATED ODDS
STATED PRINT RUN 99 SER.#'d SETS
GN210 Chien-Ming Wang 40.00 60.00

2007 Topps Chrome Generation Now White Refractors

*WHITE REF: 1.25X TO 3X BASIC
STATED ODDS 1:67 HOBBY,1:185 RETAIL
STATED PRINT RUN 200 SER.#'d SETS
GN210 Chien-Ming Wang 12.50 30.00

2007 Topps Chrome Mickey Mantle Story

COMMON MANTLE (1-40) .75 2.00
1-30 STATED ODDS 1:7 H, :23 R
46-55 STATED ODDS 1:20 HOBBY
1-30 PLATE ODDS 1:116 HOB.BOXLDR
46-55 PLATE ODDS 1:1971 HOBBY
PLATE PRINT RUN 1 SET PER COLOR
BLACK-CYAN-MAGENTA-YELLOW ISSUED
NO PLATE PRICING DUE TO SCARCITY
*REF: 1X TO 2.5X BASIC
1-30 REF.ODDS 1:27 H, 1:71 R
46-55 REF.ODDS 1:31 HOBBY
1-30 REF PRINT RUN 500 SER.#'d SETS
46-55 REF PRINT RUN 400 SER.#'d SETS
*07 BLUE REF: 2.5X TO 6X BASIC
*08 BLUE REF: 1.2X TO 3X BASIC
07 BLUE REF ODDS 1:72 RETAIL
07 BLUE REF PRINT RUN 100 SER.#'d SETS
08 BLUE REF PRINT RUN 200 SER.#'d SETS
*COPPER: 2.5X TO 6X BASIC
STATED ODDS 1:117 HOBBY
STATED PRINT RUN 100 SER.#'d SETS
*1-30 RED REF: 2.5X TO 6X BASIC
46-55 RED REF ODDS 1:315 HOBBY
1-30 RED REF 99 SER.#'d SETS
46-55 RED REF 25 SER.#'d SETS
NO 46-55 RED PRICING AVAILABLE
*WHITE REF: 1.2X TO 3X BASIC
WHITE REF.ODDS 1:67 HOBBY,1:185 RETAIL
WHITE REF PRINT RUN 200 SER.#'d SETS
46-55 SUP.FRAC. ODDS 1:7885
SUPERFRAC.PRINT RUN 1 SER.#'d SET
NO SUPERFRAC.PRICING DUE TO SCARCITY
1-30 ISSUED IN 07 TOPPS CHROME
46-55 ISSUED IN 08 TOPPS CHROME

2008 Topps Chrome

COMP.SET w/o AU's (220) 30.00 60.00
COMMON CARD .20 .50
COMMON ROOKIE .60 1.50
COMMON AUTO 4.00 10.00
AUTO ODDS 1:15 HOBBY
PRINT.PLATE ODDS 1:1896 HOBBY
AU PLATES 1:10,961 HOBBY
PLATE PRINT RUN 1 SET PER COLOR
BLACK-CYAN-MAGENTA-YELLOW ISSUED
NO PLATE PRICING DUE TO SCARCITY
EXCHANGE DEADLINE 6/30/2010
1 Alex Rodriguez .75 2.00
2 Barry Zito .20 .50
3 Scott Kazmir .30 .75
4 Stephen Drew .20 .50
5 Miguel Cabrera .30 .75
6 Daisuke Matsuzaka .75 2.00
7 Mickey Mantle 2.00 5.00
8 Jimmy Rollins .30 .75

9 Joe Mauer .30 .75
10 Cole Hamels .50 1.25
11 Yovani Gallardo .20 .50
12 Miguel Tejada .20 .50
13 Dontrelle Willis .20 .50
14 Orlando Cabrera .20 .50
15 Jake Peavy .30 .75
16 Erik Bedard .20 .50
17 Victor Martinez .20 .50
18 Chris Young .20 .50
19 Jose Reyes .30 .75
20 Mike Lowell .20 .50
21 Dan Uggla .30 .75
22 Garrett Atkins .20 .50
23 Felix Hernandez .30 .75
24 Ivan Rodriguez .30 .75
25 Alex Rios .20 .50
26 Jason Bay .20 .50
27 Vladimir Guerrero .50 1.25
28 John Lackey .20 .50
29 Ryan Howard .60 1.50
30 Kevin Youkilis .30 .75
31 Justin Morneau .30 .75
32 Johan Santana .30 .75
33 Jeremy Hermida .20 .50
34 Andruw Jones .20 .50
35 Mike Cameron .20 .50
36 Jason Varitek .50 1.25
37 Tim Hudson .20 .50
38 Justin Upton .50 1.25
39 Brad Penny .20 .50
40 Robinson Cano .30 .75
41 Brandon Webb .30 .75
42 Magglio Ordonez .30 .75
43 Aaron Hill .20 .50
44 Alfonso Soriano .30 .75
45 Carlos Zambrano .20 .50
46 Ben Sheets .30 .75
47 Tim Lincecum .50 1.25
48 Phil Hughes .50 1.25
49 Scott Rolen .30 .75
50 John Maine .20 .50
51 Delmon Young .30 .75
52 Tadahito Iguchi .20 .50
53 Yunel Escobar .20 .50
54 Russell Martin .20 .50
55 Orlando Hudson .20 .50
56 Jim Edmonds .30 .75
57 Todd Helton .30 .75
58 Melky Cabrera .20 .50
59 Adrian Beltre .20 .50
60 Manny Ramirez .50 1.25
61 Gil Meche .20 .50
62 David DeJesus .20 .50
63 Roy Oswalt .20 .50
64 Mark Buehrle .20 .50
65 Hunter Pence .50 1.25
66 Dustin Pedroia .75 2.00
67 Roy Halladay .20 .50
68 Rich Harden .20 .50
69 Jim Thome .30 .75
70 Akinori Iwamura .20 .50
71 Dan Haren .20 .50
72 Brandon Phillips .20 .50
73 Brett Myers .20 .50
74 James Loney .30 .75
75 C.C. Sabathia .20 .50
76 Jermaine Dye .20 .50
77 Carlos Ruiz .20 .50
78 Brian McCann .30 .75
79 Paul Konerko .20 .50
80 Jorge Posada .30 .75
81 Chien-Ming Wang .60 1.50
82 Carlos Delgado .20 .50
83 Ichiro Suzuki .75 2.00
84 Elijah Dukes .20 .50
85 David Wright .60 1.50
86 Carl Crawford .20 .50
87 Mark Teixeira .30 .75
88 Bobby Crosby .20 .50
89 Brian Roberts .30 .75
90 David Ortiz .50 1.25
91 Derrek Lee .30 .75
92 Adam Dunn .20 .50
93 Fausto Carmona .20 .50
94 Grady Sizemore .30 .75
95 Jeff Francoeur .30 .75
96 Jered Weaver .20 .50
97 Troy Tulowitzki .30 .75
98 Troy Glaus .30 .75
99 Nick Markakis .30 .75
100 Lance Berkman .30 .75
101 Randy Johnson .50 1.25
102 Kenji Johjima .20 .50
103 Jarrod Saltalamacchia .20 .50
104 Matt Holliday .30 .75
105 Travis Hafner .20 .50
106 Johnny Damon .30 .75
107 Alex Gordon .50 1.25
108 Derek Lowe .20 .50
109 Nick Swisher .20 .50
110 Aaron Harang .20 .50
111 Hanley Ramirez .50 1.25
112 Carlos Guillen .20 .50
113 Ryan Braun .60 1.50
114 Torii Hunter .20 .50
115 Joe Blanton .20 .50
116 Josh Hamilton .60 1.50
117 Pedro Martinez .30 .75
118 Hideki Matsui .50 1.25
119 Cameron Maybin .50 1.25
120 Prince Fielder .50 1.25
121 Derek Jeter 1.25 3.00
122 Chone Figgins .20 .50
123 Chase Utley .50 1.25
124 Jacoby Ellsbury .75 2.00
125 Freddy Sanchez .20 .50
126 Rocco Baldelli .20 .50
127 Tom Gorzelanny .20 .50
128 Adrian Gonzalez .30 .75
129 Geovany Soto .50 1.25
130 Bobby Abreu .20 .50
131 Albert Pujols 1.00 2.50
132 Chipper Jones .60 1.50
133 Jeremy Bonderman .20 .50
134 B.J. Upton .30 .75
135 Justin Verlander .30 .75
136 Jeff Francis .20 .50
137 A.J. Burnett .20 .50
138 Travis Buck .20 .50
139 Vernon Wells .20 .50
140 Raul Ibanez .20 .50
141 Ryan Zimmerman .30 .75
142 John Smoltz .50 1.25
143 Carlos Lee .20 .50
144 Chris Young .20 .50
145 Francisco Liriano .30 .75
146 Curt Schilling .30 .75
147 Josh Beckett .30 .75
148 Aramis Ramirez .20 .50
149 Ronnie Belliard .20 .50
150 Homer Bailey .20 .50
151 Curtis Granderson .20 .50
152 Ken Griffey Jr. .75 2.00
153 Kazuo Matsui .20 .50
154 Brian Bannister .20 .50
155 Joba Chamberlain .60 1.50
156 Tom Glavine .30 .75
157 Carlos Beltran .20 .50
158 Kelly Johnson .20 .50
159 Rich Hill .20 .50
160 Pat Burrell .20 .50
161 Asdrubal Cabrera .20 .50
162 Gary Sheffield .20 .50
163 Greg Maddux .60 1.50
164 Eric Chavez .20 .50
165 Chris Carpenter .20 .50
166 Michael Young .20 .50
167 Carlos Pena .50 1.25
168 Frank Thomas .50 1.25
169 Aaron Rowand .20 .50
170 Yadier Molina .30 .75
171 Luis Castillo .20 .50
172 Ryan Theriot .20 .50
173 Andre Ethier .30 .75
174 Casey Kotchman .20 .50
175 Rickie Weeks .20 .50
176 Milton Bradley .20 .50
177 Daniel Cabrera .20 .50
178 Jo-Jo Reyes .20 .50
179 Livan Hernandez .20 .50
180 Hideki Okajima .20 .50
181 Matt Kemp .20 .50
182 Jonny Gomes .20 .50
183 Billy Butler .20 .50
184 Adam LaRoche .20 .50
185 Brad Hawpe .20 .50
186 Paul Maholm .20 .50
187 Placido Polanco .20 .50
188 Noah Lowry .20 .50
189 Gregg Zaun .20 .50
190 Nate McLouth .20 .50
191 Edinson Volquez .20 .50
192 Jeff Niemann (RC) .60 1.50
193 Evan Longoria RC 5.00 12.00
194 Adam Jones .20 .50
195 Eugenio Velez RC .60 1.50
196 Joey Votto (RC) 1.50 4.00
197 Nick Blackburn RC 1.00 2.50
198 Harvey Garcia (RC) .60 1.50
199 Hiroki Kuroda RC 1.00 2.50
200 Elliot Johnson (RC) .60 1.50
201 Luis Mendoza (RC) .60 1.50
202 Alex Romero (RC) 1.00 2.50
203 Gregor Blanco (RC) .60 1.50
204 Rico Washington (RC) .60 1.50
205 Brian Bocock RC .60 1.50
206 Evan Meek RC .60 1.50
207 Stephen Holm RC .60 1.50
208 Matt Tupman RC .60 1.50
209 Fernando Hernandez RC .60 1.50
210 Randor Bierd RC .60 1.50
211 Blake DeWitt (RC) 1.50 4.00
212 Randy Wells RC .60 1.50
213 Wesley Wright RC .60 1.50
214 Clete Thomas RC 1.00 2.50
215 Kyle McClellan RC .60 1.50
216 Brian Bixler (RC) .60 1.50
217 Kazuo Fukumori RC 1.00 2.50
218 Burke Badenhop RC 1.00 2.50
219 Denard Span (RC) 1.00 2.50
220 Brian Bass (RC) .60 1.50
221 J.R. Towles AU RC 4.00 10.00
222 Felipe Paulino AU RC 4.00 10.00
223 Sam Fuld AU RC 4.00 10.00
224 Kevin Hart AU (RC) 4.00 10.00
225 Nyjer Morgan AU (RC) 4.00 10.00
226 Daric Barton AU (RC) 4.00 10.00
227 Armando Galarraga AU RC 8.00 20.00
228 Chin-Lung Hu AU (RC) 6.00 15.00
229 Clay Buchholz AU (RC) EXCH 10.00 25.00
230 Rich Thompson AU RC 4.00 10.00
231 Brian Barton AU RC 5.00 12.00
232 Ross Ohlendorf AU RC 4.00 10.00
233 Masahide Kobayashi AU RC 5.00 12.00
234 Callix Crabbe AU (RC) 4.00 10.00
235 Matt Tolbert AU RC 4.00 10.00
236 Jayson Nix AU (RC) 4.00 10.00
237 Johnny Cueto AU RC 10.00 25.00
238 Evan Meek AU RC 4.00 10.00
239 Randy Wells AU (RC) 4.00 10.00

2008 Topps Chrome Refractors

*REF: 1.2X TO 3X BASIC
REF ODDS 1:3 HOBBY
*REF RC: .6X TO 1.5X BASIC RC
REF RC ODDS 1:3 HOBBY
*REF AU: .5X TO 1.2X BASIC AUTO
REF AU ODDS 1:95 HOBBY
REF AU PRINT RUN 500 SER.#'d SETS
EXCHANGE DEADLINE 6/30/2010

2008 Topps Chrome Blue Refractors

*BLUE REF: 4X TO 10X BASIC
*BLUE REF RC: 1.2X TO 3X BASIC RC
*BLUE REF AU: .6X TO 1.5X BASIC AUTO
BLUE REF AU ODDS 1:230 HOBBY
BLUE REF AU PRINT RUN 200 SER.#'d SETS
EXCHANGE DEADLINE 6/30/2010
227 Armando Galarraga AU 20.00 50.00
228 Chin-Lung Hu AU 15.00 40.00
229 Clay Buchholz AU 20.00 50.00
231 Brian Barton AU 12.50 30.00
237 Johnny Cueto AU 20.00 50.00

2008 Topps Chrome Copper Refractors

*COPPER REF: 2X TO 5X BASIC
COPPER REF ODDS 1:12 HOBBY
*COPPER REF RC: 1X TO 2.5X BASIC RC
REF RC ODDS 1:12 HOBBY
COPPER REF PRINT RUN 599 SER.#'d SETS
*COPPER REF AU: 1X TO 2.5X BASIC AUTO
COPPER REF AU ODDS 1:980 HOBBY
COPPER REF AU PRINT RUN 100 SER.#'d SETS
EXCHANGE DEADLINE 6/30/2010
227 Armando Galarraga AU 40.00 80.00
228 Chin-Lung Hu AU 40.00 80.00
229 Clay Buchholz AU 30.00 60.00
231 Brian Barton AU 30.00 60.00
233 Masahide Kobayashi AU 20.00 50.00
237 Johnny Cueto AU 30.00 60.00

2008 Topps Chrome Red Refractors

RED 1-220 ODDS 1:143 HOBBY
RED AU 221-239 ODDS 1:2185 HOBBY
STATED PRINT RUN 25 SER.#'d SETS
NO PRICING DUE TO SCARCITY

2008 Topps Chrome SuperFractors

SF 1-220 ODDS 1:3584 HOBBY
SF AU 221-239 ODDS 1:41,500 HOBBY
STATED PRINT RUN 1 SER.#'d SET
NO PRICING DUE TO SCARCITY

2008 Topps Chrome 50th Anniversary All Rookie Team

COMPLETE SET (23) 12.50 30.00
STATED ODDS 1:9 HOBBY
PRINTING PLATE ODDS 1:1971 HOBBY
PLATE PRINT RUN 1 SET PER COLOR
BLACK-CYAN-MAGENTA-YELLOW ISSUED
NO PLATE PRICING DUE TO SCARCITY
*REF: .75X TO 2X BASIC
REF ODDS 1:31 HOBBY
REF PRINT RUN 400 SER.#'d SETS
*BLUE REF: 1.2X TO 3X BASIC
BLUE REF PRINT RUN 200 SER.#'d SETS
*COP.REF: 1X TO 2.5X BASIC
COP.REF ODDS 1:117 HOBBY
COP.REF PRINT RUN 100 SER.#'d SETS
RED.REF ODDS 1:315 HOBBY
RED PRINT RUN 25 SER.#'d SETS
NO RED PRICING DUE TO SCARCITY
SUPFRAC.ODDS 1:7885 HOBBY
SUPFRAC.PRINT RUN 1 SER.#'d SET
NO SUPFRAC.PRICING DUE TO SCARCITY
ARC1 Gary Sheffield .40 1.00
ARC2 Ivan Rodriguez .60 1.50
ARC3 Mike Piazza 1.00 2.50
ARC4 Manny Ramirez 1.00 2.50
ARC5 Chipper Jones 1.25 3.00
ARC6 Derek Jeter 2.50 6.00
ARC7 Andruw Jones .40 1.00
ARC8 Alfonso Soriano .60 1.50
ARC9 Jimmy Rollins .60 1.50
ARC10 Albert Pujols 2.00 5.00
ARC11 Ichiro Suzuki 1.50 4.00
ARC12 Mark Teixeira .60 1.50
ARC13 Matt Holliday .60 1.50
ARC14 Joe Mauer .60 1.50
ARC15 Prince Fielder 1.00 2.50
ARC16 Hideki Okajima .40 1.00
ARC17 Roy Oswalt .40 1.00
ARC18 Hunter Pence 1.00 2.50
ARC19 Nick Markakis .60 1.50
ARC20 Ryan Zimmerman .60 1.50
ARC21 Ryan Braun 1.25 3.00
ARC22 C.C. Sabathia .40 1.00
ARC23 Dustin Pedroia 1.50 4.00

2008 Topps Chrome Dick Perez

EXCLUSIVE TO WALMART PACKS
WMDPC1 Manny Ramirez 2.00 5.00
WMDPC2 Cameron Maybin 2.00 5.00
WMDPC3 Ryan Howard 2.50 6.00
WMDPC4 David Ortiz 2.00 5.00
WMDPC5 Tim Lincecum 2.00 5.00
WMDPC6 David Wright 2.50 6.00
WMDPC7 Mickey Mantle 3.00 8.00
WMDPC8 Joba Chamberlain 2.50 6.00
WMDPC9 Ichiro Suzuki 3.00 8.00
WMDPC10 Prince Fielder 2.00 5.00
WMDPC11 Jacoby Ellsbury 5.00 12.00
WMDPC12 Jake Peavy 1.25 3.00
WMDPC13 Miguel Cabrera 1.25 3.00
WMDPC14 Josh Beckett 1.25 3.00
WMDPC15 Jimmy Rollins 1.25 3.00
WMDPC16 Torii Hunter .75 2.00
WMDPC17 Alfonso Soriano 1.25 3.00
WMDPC18 Jose Reyes 1.25 3.00
WMDPC19 C.C. Sabathia .75 2.00
WMDPC20 Alex Rodriguez 3.00 8.00

2008 Topps Chrome T205

EXCLUSIVE TO TARGET PACKS
TCCP1 Albert Pujols 4.00 10.00
TCCP2 Clay Buchholz 2.00 5.00
TCCP3 Matt Holliday 1.25 3.00
TCCP4 Luke Hochevar 2.00 5.00
TCCP5 Alex Rodriguez 3.00 8.00
TCCP6 Joey Votto 2.00 5.00
TCCP7 Chin-Lung Hu 1.25 3.00
TCCP8 Ryan Braun 2.50 6.00
TCCP9 Joba Chamberlain 2.50 6.00
TCCP10 Ryan Howard 2.50 6.00
TCCP11 Ichiro Suzuki 3.00 8.00
TCCP12 Steve Pearce 1.25 3.00
TCCP13 Vladimir Guerrero 2.00 5.00
TCCP14 Wladimir Balentien .75 2.00
TCCP15 David Ortiz 2.00 5.00
TCCP16 Jacoby Ellsbury 5.00 12.00
TCCP17 David Wright 2.50 6.00
TCCP18 Chase Utley 2.00 5.00
TCCP19 Manny Ramirez 2.00 5.00
TCCP20 Dan Haren .75 2.00
TCCP21 Nick Markakis 1.25 3.00
TCCP22 Grady Sizemore 1.25 3.00
TCCP23 Hanley Ramirez 2.00 5.00
TCCP24 Daisuke Matsuzaka 3.00 8.00
TCCP25 Troy Tulowitzki 1.25 3.00
TCCP26 Jose Reyes 1.25 3.00
TCCP27 Tim Lincecum 2.00 5.00
TCCP28 Prince Fielder 2.00 5.00
TCCP29 Alfonso Soriano 1.25 3.00
TCCP30 Andrew Miller 1.25 3.00

2008 Topps Chrome Trading Card History

COMPLETE SET (50) 30.00 60.00
STATED ODDS 1:9 HOBBY
PRINTING PLATE ODDS 1:1971 HOBBY
PLATE PRINT RUN 1 SET PER COLOR
BLACK-CYAN-MAGENTA-YELLOW ISSUED
NO PLATE PRICING DUE TO SCARCITY
*REF: .75X TO 2X BASIC
REF ODDS 1:31 HOBBY
REF.PRINT RUN 400 SER.#'d SETS
RED.REF ODDS 1:315 HOBBY
RED PRINT RUN 25 SER.#'d SETS
NO RED PRICING DUE TO SCARCITY
SUPFRAC.ODDS 1:7885 HOBBY
SUPFRAC.PRINT RUN 1 SER.#'d SET
NO SUPFRAC.PRICING DUE TO SCARCITY
TCHC1 Jacoby Ellsbury 1.50 4.00
TCHC2 Joba Chamberlain 1.25 3.00
TCHC3 Daisuke Matsuzaka 1.50 4.00
TCHC4 Prince Fielder 1.00 2.50
TCHC5 Alex Rodriguez 1.50 4.00
TCHC6 Mickey Mantle 2.50 6.00
TCHC7 Ryan Braun 1.25 3.00
TCHC8 Albert Pujols 2.00 5.00
TCHC9 Joe Mauer .60 1.50
TCHC10 Jose Reyes .60 1.50
TCHC11 Johan Santana .60 1.50
TCHC12 Hunter Pence 1.00 2.50
TCHC13 Hideki Okajima .40 1.00
TCHC14 Cameron Maybin 1.00 2.50
TCHC15 Tim Lincecum 1.00 2.50
TCHC16 Mark Teixeira .60 1.50
Jeff Francoeur
TCHC17 Justin Upton 1.00 2.50
TCHC18 Alfonso Soriano .60 1.50
TCHC19 Ichiro Suzuki 1.50 4.00
TCHC20 Grady Sizemore .60 1.50
TCHC21 Ryan Howard 1.25 3.00
TCHC22 David Wright 1.25 3.00
TCHC23 Jimmy Rollins .60 1.50
TCHC24 Ken Griffey Jr 1.50 4.00
TCHC25 Chipper Jones 1.25 3.00
TCHC26 Justin Verlander .60 1.50
TCHC27 Manny Ramirez 1.00 2.50
TCHC28 Chase Utley 1.00 2.50
TCHC29 Ivan Rodriguez .60 1.50
TCHC30 Josh Beckett .60 1.50
TCHC31 Vladimir Guerrero 1.00 2.50
TCHC32 Lance Berkman .60 1.50
TCHC33 Gary Sheffield .40 1.00
TCHC34 David Ortiz 1.00 2.50
TCHC35 Andruw Jones .40 1.00
TCHC36 Hideki Matsui 1.00 2.50
TCHC37 C.C. Sabathia .40 1.00
TCHC38 Magglio Ordonez .60 1.50
TCHC39 Pedro Martinez .60 1.50
TCHC40 Derek Jeter 2.50 6.00
TCHC41 Hanley Ramirez 1.00 2.50
TCHC42 Jake Peavy .60 1.50
TCHC43 Brandon Webb .60 1.50
TCHC44 Matt Holliday .60 1.50
TCHC45 Carlos Beltran .40 1.00
TCHC46 Troy Tulowitzki .60 1.50
TCHC47 Justin Morneau .60 1.50
TCHC48 Phil Hughes 1.00 2.50
TCHC49 Torii Hunter .40 1.00
TCHC50 Brad Hawpe .40 1.00

2008 Topps Chrome Trading Card History Blue Refractors

*BLUE REF: 1.2X TO 3X BASIC
STATED PRINT RUN 200 SER.#'d SETS
TCHC1 Jacoby Ellsbury 30.00 60.00

2008 Topps Chrome Trading Card History Copper Refractors

*COP.REF: 1X TO 2.5X BASIC
STATED ODDS 1:117 HOBBY
STATED PRINT RUN 100 SER.#'d SETS
TCHC1 Jacoby Ellsbury 20.00 50.00

2006 Topps Co-Signers

This 120-card set was released in May, 2006. The set was issued only in six-card hobby packs with an $10 SRP. The packs came 12 to a box and 24 boxes to a case. Cards numbered 1-100 feature veteran players while cards numbered 101-120 feature signed cards of 2006 rookies.

COMP.SET w/o AU's (100) 15.00 40.00
COMMON CARD (1-100) .30 .75
101-120 GROUP A ODDS 1:2025
101-120 GROUP B ODDS 1:1625
101-120 GROUP C ODDS 1:920
101-120 GROUP D ODDS 1:81
101-120 GROUP E ODDS 1:270
101-120 GROUP F ODDS 1:68
101-120 GROUP G ODDS 1:12
101-120 GROUP A PRINT RUN 200 CARDS
101-120 GROUP B PRINT RUN 250 CARDS
101-120 GROUP C PRINT RUN 440 CARDS
A-C CARDS ARE NOT SERIAL NUMBERED
A-C PRINT RUNS PROVIDED BY TOPPS
1 Albert Pujols 1.50 4.00
2 Roger Clemens 1.50 4.00
3 Paul Konerko .30 .75
4 Jeff Francouer .75 2.00
5 Miguel Tejada .30 .75
6 Curt Schilling .50 1.25
7 Mickey Mantle 2.00 5.00
8 Miguel Cabrera .50 1.25
9 Derrek Lee .30 .75
10 Jeff Kent .30 .75
11 Gary Sheffield .30 .75
12 Rich Harden .30 .75
13 Scott Rolen .50 1.25
14 David Wright 1.25 3.00
15 Troy Glaus .30 .75
16 Torii Hunter .30 .75
17 Nolan Ryan 2.00 5.00
18 Alfonso Soriano .30 .75
19 Hank Blalock .30 .75
20 Chase Utley .75 2.00
21 Ryan Howard 1.25 3.00
22 Robinson Cano .50 1.25
23 Derek Jeter 2.00 5.00
24 Huston Street .30 .75
25 Jason Giambi .30 .75
26 Rafael Furcal .30 .75
27 Rickie Weeks .30 .75
28 Ivan Rodriguez .50 1.25
29 Travis Hafner .30 .75
30 Greg Maddux 1.25 3.00
31 Andruw Jones .50 1.25
32 Andy Pettitte .50 1.25
33 Scott Podsednik .30 .75
34 Francisco Rodriguez .30 .75
35 Josh Beckett .30 .75
36 Lance Berkman .30 .75
37 Roy Oswalt .30 .75
38 Pedro Martinez .50 1.25
39 Jimmy Rollins .30 .75
40 Johan Santana .50 1.25
41 Randy Johnson .75 2.00
42 Mariano Rivera .75 2.00
43 Nick Johnson .30 .75
44 Josh Gibson .75 2.00
45 Shawn Green .30 .75
46 Adrian Beltre .30 .75
47 Johnny Damon .50 1.25
48 Joe Mauer .50 1.25
49 Todd Helton .50 1.25
50 Alex Rodriguez 1.25 3.00
51 Jake Peavy .30 .75
52 David Ortiz .75 2.00
53 Mark Buehrle .30 .75
54 Eric Gagne .30 .75
55 Hideki Matsui 1.25 3.00
56 Bobby Abreu .30 .75
57 Victor Martinez .30 .75
58 Brian Roberts .30 .75
59 Chipper Jones .75 2.00
60 Carlos Beltran .30 .75
61 Tim Hudson .30 .75
62 Carlos Lee .30 .75
63 Barry Zito .30 .75
64 Moises Alou .30 .75
65 Mark Teixeira .50 1.25
66 Lyle Overbay .30 .75
67 Kerry Wood .30 .75
68 B.J. Ryan .30 .75
69 Jim Edmonds .50 1.25
70 Carlos Delgado .30 .75
71 Magglio Ordonez .30 .75
72 Juan Pierre .30 .75
73 Manny Ramirez .50 1.25
74 Dontrelle Willis .30 .75
75 Ichiro Suzuki 1.25 3.00
76 Nomar Garciaparra .75 2.00
77 Zach Duke .30 .75
78 Chris Carpenter .30 .75
79 A.J. Burnett .30 .75
80 Scott Kazmir .50 1.25
81 Carl Crawford .30 .75
82 Mark Prior .50 1.25
83 Adam Dunn .30 .75
84 Justin Morneau .30 .75
85 Morgan Ensberg .30 .75
86 Pat Burrell .30 .75
87 Paul Lo Duca .30 .75
88 Jason Bay .30 .75
89 Aubrey Huff .30 .75
90 Kevin Millwood .30 .75
91 Vernon Wells .30 .75
92 Javy Lopez .30 .75
93 Michael Young .30 .75
94 Felix Hernandez .50 1.25
95 Ken Griffey Jr. 1.25 3.00
96 Bartolo Colon .30 .75
97 Billy Wagner .30 .75
98 Vladimir Guerrero .75 2.00
99 Jose Reyes .75 2.00
100 Barry Bonds 2.00 5.00
101 Anthony LeRew AU G (RC) 4.00 10.00
102 R.Zimm AU C/440 (RC) * 20.00 50.00
103 C.Hansen AU B/250 RC * 20.00 50.00
104 Francisco Liriano AU G (RC) 15.00 40.00
105 Jason Botts AU G (RC) 4.00 10.00
106 Josh Johnson AU G (RC) 6.00 15.00
107 Hanley Ramirez AU G (RC) 10.00 25.00
108 Adam Wainwright AU G (RC) 6.00 15.00
109 K.Johjima AU A/200 RC * 50.00 100.00
110 Dan Ortmeier AU G (RC) 4.00 10.00
111 Darrell Rasner AU G (RC) 4.00 10.00
112 Chuck James AU F (RC) 6.00 15.00
113 Nelson Cruz AU F (RC) 4.00 10.00
114 Hong-Chih Kuo AU E (RC) 15.00 40.00
115 Ryan Garko AU G (RC) 4.00 10.00
116 Reggie Abercrombie AU D (RC) 4.00 10.00
117 Ian Kinsler AU D (RC) 6.00 15.00
118 Joel Zumaya AU D (RC) 10.00 25.00
119 Willie Eyre AU D (RC) 4.00 10.00
120 Dan Uggla AU D (RC) 6.00 15.00

2006 Topps Co-Signers Changing Faces Blue

*BLUE: .75X TO 2X BASIC
STATED ODDS 1:11
STATED PRINT RUN 125 SERIAL #'d SETS

2006 Topps Co-Signers Changing Faces Bronze

*BRONZE: .75X TO 2X BASIC
STATED ODDS 1:9
STATED PRINT RUN 150 SERIAL #'d SETS

2006 Topps Co-Signers Changing Faces Gold

*GOLD: .75X TO 2X BASIC
STATED ODDS 1:12
STATED PRINT RUN 115 SERIAL #'d SETS

2006 Topps Co-Signers Changing Faces Red

*RED: .75X TO 2X BASIC
STATED ODDS 1:9
STATED PRINT RUN 150 SERIAL #'d SETS

2006 Topps Co-Signers Changing Faces Silver Blue

*SILVER BLUE: 1X TO 2.5X BASIC
STATED ODDS 1:18
STATED PRINT RUN 75 SERIAL #'d SETS

2006 Topps Co-Signers Changing Faces Silver Bronze

*SILVER BRONZE: .75X TO 2X BASIC
STATED ODDS 1:11
STATED PRINT RUN 125 SERIAL #'d SETS

2006 Topps Co-Signers Changing Faces Silver Gold

*SILVER GOLD: 1.25X TO 3X BASIC
STATED ODDS 1:27
STATED PRINT RUN 50 SERIAL #'d SETS

2006 Topps Co-Signers Changing Faces Silver Red

*SILVER RED: .75X TO 2X BASIC
STATED ODDS 1:14
STATED PRINT RUN 100 SERIAL #'d SETS

2006 Topps Co-Signers Changing Faces HyperSilver Blue

STATED ODDS 1:135
STATED PRINT RUN 10 SERIAL #'d SETS
NO PRICING DUE TO SCARCITY

2006 Topps Co-Signers Changing Faces HyperSilver Bronze

*HYPER BRONZE: 1X TO 2.5X BASIC
STATED ODDS 1:18
STATED PRINT RUN 75 SERIAL #'d SETS

2006 Topps Co-Signers Changing Faces HyperSilver Gold

STATED ODDS 1:270
STATED PRINT RUN 5 SERIAL #'d SETS
NO PRICING DUE TO SCARCITY

2006 Topps Co-Signers Changing Faces HyperSilver Red

*HYPER RED: 2X TO 5X BASIC
STATED ODDS 1:54
STATED PRINT RUN 25 SERIAL #'d SETS
NO BONDS PRICING DUE TO VOLATILITY

2006 Topps Co-Signers Dual Autographs

GROUP A ODDS 1:11,375
GROUP B ODDS 1:20,350
GROUP C ODDS 1:522
GROUP D ODDS 1:1013
GROUP E ODDS 1:2705
GROUP F ODDS 1:580
GROUP G ODDS 1:3223
GROUP H ODDS 1:2025
GROUP I ODDS 1:540
GROUP J ODDS 1:1352
GROUP K ODDS 1:1158
GROUP L ODDS 1:950
GROUP M ODDS 1:902
GROUP N ODDS 1:162
GROUP O ODDS 1:624
GROUP P ODDS 1:270
GROUP Q ODDS 1:68
GROUP R ODDS 1:90
GROUP S ODDS 1:29
GROUP A PRINT RUN 18 SETS
GROUP B PRINT RUN 20 SETS
GROUP C PRINT RUN 25 SETS
GROUP D PRINT RUN 50 SETS
GROUP E PRINT RUN 75 SETS
GROUP F PRINT RUN 100 SETS
GROUP G PRINT RUN 125 SETS
GROUP H PRINT RUN 200 SETS
GROUP I PRINT RUN 250 SETS
AROD/BONDS PRINT RUN 25 SERIAL #'d SETS
CARDS ARE NOT SERIAL NUMBERED
PRINT RUN INFO PROVIDED BY TOPPS
NO GROUP A-C PRICING DUE TO SCARCITY
CS1 Alex Rodriguez / Barry Bonds C/25
CS2 David Wright / Alex Rodriguez C/25 *
CS3 Victor Martinez / Kenji Johjima C/25 *
CS4 Kenji Johjima / Felix Hernandez A/18 *
CS5 David Ortiz / Manny Ramirez C/25 *
CS6 Nolan Ryan / Roger Clemens C/25 *
CS7 David Ortiz / Albert Pujols C/25 *
CS8 Chipper Jones / Dale Murphy C/25 *
CS9 Wade Boggs / Don Mattingly C/25 *
CS10 Nolan Ryan / Felix Hernandez A/18 *
CS11 Stan Musial / Albert Pujols B/20 *
CS12 Robinson Cano / Rod Carew C/25 *
CS13 Cal Ripken / Brooks Robinson C/25 *
CS14 Dave Winfield / Johnny Damon C/25 *
CS15 Prince Fielder / Ryan Zimmerman I/250 * 40.00 80.00
CS16 Cal Ripken / Ozzie Smith C/25 *
CS17 Alex Rodriguez / Don Mattingly C/25 *
CS18 Don Larsen / Yogi Berra C/25 *
CS19 Mike Schmidt / Brooks Robinson C/25 *
CS20 Ryan Zimmerman / Wade Boggs C/25 *
CS21 Dwight Gooden / Keith Hernandez C/25 *
CS22 Ryan Howard / Derrek Lee E/75 * 40.00 80.00
CS23 Jeff Mathis / Chris Snyder S 4.00 10.00
CS24 Dontrelle Willis / Miguel Cabrera C/25 *
CS25 Ray Knight / Keith Hernandez F/100 * 10.00 25.00
CS26 Mike Schmidt / Chase Utley C/25 *
CS27 Billy Wagner / Paul Lo Duca D/50 * 40.00 80.00
CS28 Tony Gwynn / Wade Boggs C/25 *
CS29 Mike Schmidt / Ozzie Smith C/25 *
CS30 Dwight Gooden / Darryl Strawberry D/50 * 20.00 50.00
CS31 Ryan Howard / Huston Street N 30.00 60.00
CS32 Mariano Rivera / Huston Street C/25 *
CS33 Prince Fielder / Ryan Howard D/50 * 40.00 80.00
CS34 Robinson Cano / Chase Utley E/75 * 30.00 60.00
CS35 Johnny Podres / Duke Snider C/25 *
CS36 David Justice / Chipper Jones C/25 *
CS37 David Wright / Jose Reyes D/50 * 150.00 250.00
CS38 Jeff Mathis / Ryan Garko S 4.00 10.00
CS39 Brandon McCarthy / Pedro Lopez S 4.00 10.00
CS40 David Justice / Dale Murphy F/100 * 30.00 60.00
CS41 Dave Winfield / Gary Sheffield C/25 *
CS42 Joe Mauer / Francisco Liriano Q 30.00 60.00
CS43 Jim Leyritz / Reggie Jackson C/25 *
CS44 Ryan Zimmerman / David Wright F/100 * 60.00 120.00
CS45 Rick Rhoden / Dave Parker F/100 * 15.00 40.00
CS46 Jonathan Papelbon / Craig Breslow R 10.00 25.00
CS47 Ryan Zimmerman / Kenji Johjima C/25 *
CS48 Dan Johnson / Prince Fielder F/100 * 15.00 40.00
CS49 Victor Martinez / Ryan Garko N 8.00 20.00
CS50 Ben Hendrickson / Anthony Reyes Q 6.00 15.00
CS51 Nelson Cruz / Prince Fielder F/100 * 15.00 40.00
CS52 Jonathan Papelbon / Anthony Reyes R 10.00 25.00
CS53 Ben Hendrickson / Rich Hill Q 6.00 15.00
CS54 Shin-Soo Choo / Kenji Johjima C/25 *
CS55 Francisco Liriano / Johan Santana F/100 * 75.00 150.00
CS56 Brandon McCarthy / Zach Duke S 6.00 15.00
CS57 Josh Johnson / Scott Olsen S 10.00 25.00
CS58 Tommy John / Bob Welch K 6.00 15.00
CS59 Roy White / Joe Pepitone N 10.00 25.00
CS60 Cecil Fielder / Prince Fielder N 20.00 50.00
CS61 Andre Dawson / Derrek Lee C/25 *
CS62 Conor Jackson / Ryan Howard Q 15.00 40.00
CS63 Dontrelle Willis / Zach Duke D/50 * 15.00 40.00
CS64 Mariano Rivera / Billy Wagner C/25 *
CS65 Hong-Chih Kuo / Shin-Soo Choo Q 15.00 40.00
CS66 Jim Leyritz / Cecil Fielder G/125 * 20.00 50.00
CS67 Scott Kazmir / Francisco Liriano P 10.00 25.00
CS68 Scott Kazmir / Roy Oswalt D/50 * 15.00 40.00
CS69 Chuck James / Anthony LeRew S 6.00 15.00
CS70 Cecil Fielder / Ryan Howard I/250 * 30.00 60.00
CS71 Chien-Ming Wang / Hong-Chih Kuo C/25 *
CS72 Shin-Soo Choo / Chien-Ming Wang D/50 * 100.00 175.00
CS73 Nelson Cruz / Jason Botts Q 6.00 15.00
CS74 Francisco Liriano / Ervin Santana S 6.00 15.00
CS75 Adam Wainwright / Anthony Reyes S 15.00 40.00
CS76 Scott Kazmir / Ervin Santana H/200 * 12.50 30.00
CS77 Robinson Cano / Gary Sheffield I/250 * 30.00 60.00
CS78 David Wright / Miguel Cabrera D/50 * 60.00 120.00
CS79 Dan Johnson / Conor Jackson P 6.00 15.00
CS80 Frank Tanana / Mickey Tettleton R 6.00 15.00
CS81 Andruw Jones / Chipper Jones J 30.00 60.00
CS82 Morgan Ensberg / Roy Oswalt M 10.00 25.00
CS83 Michael Young / Ozzie Smith O 15.00 40.00
CS84 Grady Sizemore / Nick Swisher L 10.00 25.00
CS85 Garrett Atkins / Clint Barmes N 6.00 15.00

2006 Topps Co-Signers Dual Cut Signatures

GROUP A ODDS 1:30,000
GROUP B ODDS 1:6800
GROUP C ODDS 1:43,000
GROUP D ODDS 1:21,000
GROUP E ODDS 1:1125
GROUP F ODDS 1:4450
GROUP G ODDS 1:875
GROUP H ODDS 1:3650
GROUP I ODDS 1:5150
GROUP J ODDS 1:1980
GROUP A PRINT RUN 1 SERIAL #'d SET
NO A-F PRICING DUE TO SCARCITY
GWTJ A.B. Chandler / Billy Herman H 60.00 120.00
ABCFF A.B. Chandler / Ford Frick A
ABCJC A.B. Chandler / Jocko Conlon E
ABCJJ A.B. Chandler / Judy Johnson B
ABCLB A.B. Chandler / Lou Boudreau B
ABCRF A.B. Chandler / Rick Ferrell B
ABCWG A.B. Chandler / Warren Giles B
ABCWH A.B. Chandler / Will Harridge G 125.00 200.00
AETE Albert Einstein / Thomas Edison A
ALLA Al Lopez / Luke Appling E
BDWH Bill Dickey / Waite Hoyt A
BHJM Billy Herman / Joe McCarthy B
BLHW Bob Lemon / Hoyt Wilhelm E
BLJH Bob Lemon / Jim 'Catfish' Hunter G 100.00 175.00
BLJJ Buck Leonard / Judy Johnson J 125.00 200.00
BLJS Bob Lemon / Joe Sewell E
BLLB Bob Lemon / Lou Boudreau I 75.00 150.00
BLRF Bob Lemon / Rick Ferrell G 75.00 150.00
BTGK Bill Terry / George Kelly E
BTSM Bill Terry / Sal Maglie E
BTTJ Bill Terry / Travis Jackson E
BTTW Bill Terry / Ted Williams A
CGFF Charles Gehringer / Frankie Frisch B
CGHN Charles Gehringer / Hal Newhouser C
CGRF Charles Gehringer / Rick Ferrell G 75.00 150.00
CHBH Charles Gehringer / Billy Herman G 75.00 150.00
CHWH Catfish Hunter / Waite Hoyt E
DGGM David Ben Gurion / Golda Meir A
EALB Earl Averill / Lou Boudreau F
FCGW Frank Crosetti / Gene Woodling G 100.00 175.00
GWTJ George Washington / Thomas Jefferson A
HGCG Hank Greenberg / Charles Gehringer A
HKCG Harvey Kuenn / Charles Gehringer J 75.00 150.00
HKLB Harvey Kuenn / Lou Boudreau B
HTBT Harry Truman / Bess Truman A
HWHN Hoyt Wilhelm / Hal Newhouser B
HWTL Hoyt Wilhelm / Ted Lyons B
JCAB Jocko Conlon / Al Barlick B
JFKRFK John F. Kennedy / Robert F. Kennedy A
JSGW Joe Sewell / Gene Woodling E
JSLA Joe Sewell / Luke Appling G 100.00 175.00
JSLB Joe Sewell / Lou Boudreau G 60.00 120.00
JSSC Joe Sewell / Stanley Coveleski F
Coveleski's name is spelled incorrectly
LABH Luke Appling / Billy Herman E
LBBH Lou Boudreau / Billy Herman B
LBCG Lou Boudreau / Charles Gehringer F
LBRF Lou Boudreau / Rick Ferrell B
LWBT Lloyd Waner / Bill Terry E
LWCG Lloyd Waner / Charles Gehringer G 75.00 150.00
LWWS Lloyd Waner / {Willie Stargell A
MMTW Mickey Mantle / Ted Williams A
RFJJ Rick Ferrell / Judy Johnson E
RNGF Richard Nixon / Gerald Ford A
RRNR Ronald Reagan / Nancy Reagan A
SMHW Sal Maglie / Hoyt Wilhelm D
TJBH Travis Jackson / Billy Herman E
TJGK Travis Jackson / George Kelly E

2006 Topps Co-Signers Solo Sigs

GROUP A ODDS 1:2528
GROUP B ODDS 1:1790
GROUP C ODDS 1:2025
GROUP D ODDS 1:2700
GROUP E ODDS 1:2025
GROUP F ODDS 1:2025
GROUP G ODDS 1:540
GROUP H ODDS 1:135
GROUP I ODDS 1:600
GROUP J ODDS 1:108
GROUP K ODDS 1:45
GROUP A PRINT RUN 20 SETS
GROUP B PRINT RUN 25 SETS
GROUP C PRINT RUN 50 SETS
GROUP D PRINT RUN 75 SETS
GROUP E PRINT RUN 100 SETS
GROUP F-G PRINT RUN 250 SETS
CARDS ARE NOT SERIAL NUMBERED
PRINT RUN INFO PROVIDED BY TOPPS
NO A-B PRICING DUE TO SCARCITY
AD Andre Dawson H 4.00 10.00
AK Al Kaline E/100 * 15.00 40.00
AP Albert Pujols A/20 *
AR Alex Rodriguez A/20 *
ARE Anthony Reyes K 6.00 15.00
CB Clint Barmes J 4.00 10.00
CBR Craig Breslow K 4.00 10.00
CF Cecil Fielder J 6.00 15.00
CJ Chipper Jones B/25 *
CM Craig Monroe K 4.00 10.00
CR Cal Ripken A/20 *
CS Chris Snyder K 4.00 10.00
CY Carl Yastrzemski B/25 *
DJ Dan Johnson F/250 * 4.00 10.00
DL Don Larsen H 6.00 15.00
DLE Derrek Lee C/50 * 20.00 50.00
DM Don Mattingly C/50 * 60.00 120.00
DO David Ortiz B/25 *
DS Darryl Strawberry J 6.00 15.00
DW David Wright D/75 * 40.00 80.00
DWI Dontrelle Willis H 6.00 15.00
ES Ervin Santana G/250 * 4.00 10.00
GC Gustavo Chacin K 4.00 10.00
HS Huston Street G/250 * 6.00 15.00
JC Jack Clark H 4.00 10.00
JD Johnny Damon B/25 *
JM Jeff Mathis K 4.00 10.00
JMA Joe Mauer D/75 * 15.00 40.00
JP Jonathan Papelbon H 20.00 50.00
JS Johan Santana C/50 * 20.00 50.00
MC Miguel Cabrera B/25 *
MR Mariano Rivera B/25 *
MRA Manny Ramirez A/20 *
NR Nolan Ryan A/20 *
OS Ozzie Smith B/25 *
PF Prince Fielder G/250 * 15.00 40.00
RC Robinson Cano J 15.00 40.00
RCL Roger Clemens A/20 *
RH Ryan Howard E/100 * 40.00 80.00
RHI Rich Hill K 12.50 30.00
RJ Reggie Jackson B/25 *
RR Rick Rhoden J 4.00 10.00
SK Scott Kazmir H 10.00 25.00
SO Scott Olsen K 4.00 10.00
SSC Shin-Soo Choo K 4.00 10.00
TG Tony Gwynn A/20 *
VG Vladimir Guerrero A/20 *
VM Victor Martinez C/50 * 12.50 30.00
YB Yogi Berra B/25 *
ZD Zach Duke I 6.00 15.00

2007 Topps Co-Signers

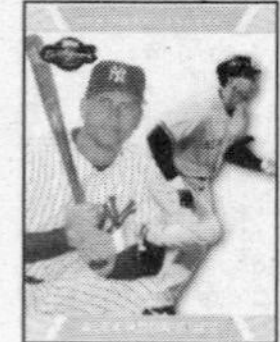

This 127-card set was released in June, 2007. This set was issued in six-card packs which came 12 packs to a box; 12 boxes to a carton and two cartons to a case. Cards numbered 1-93 feature rookies; while cards 94-121 feature rookies. Cards numbered 96-100 came in both signed and unsigned versions and cards 101-121 were all signed by the player featured. The signed rookie cards were inserted at a stated rate of one in 28 and the signed rookie variation cards were inserted at a stated rate of one in 198.

COMP.SET w/o AU's (100) 12.50 30.00
COMMON CARD (1-92) .25 .60
COMMON ROOKIE (93-100) .60 1.50
COMMON ROOKIE AU (96-121) 3.00 8.00
ROOKIE AUTO ODDS 1:28
ROOKIE AUTO VARIATION ODDS 1:198
PRINTING PLATE ODDS 1:705
PRINTING PLATE AUTO ODDS 1:21,168
PLATE PRINT RUN 1 SET PER COLOR
BLACK-CYAN-MAGENTA-SPOT-YELLOW ISSUED
NO PLATE PRICING DUE TO SCARCITY
1 Ryan Howard 1.00 2.50
2 Jered Weaver .40 1.00
3 Brian McCann .25 .60
4 Garrett Atkins .25 .60
5 Travis Hafner .25 .60
6 Jason Schmidt .25 .60
7 Curtis Granderson .25 .60
8 Ben Sheets .25 .60
9 Chien-Ming Wang 1.00 2.50
10 Francisco Liriano .60 1.50
11 Freddy Sanchez .25 .60
12 Roy Oswalt .25 .60
13 Jim Edmonds .40 1.00
14 Matt Cain .40 1.00
15 Jake Peavy .25 .60
16 Ryan Zimmerman .60 1.50
17 Troy Glaus .25 .60
18 Kenji Johjima .60 1.50
19 Curt Schilling .40 1.00
20 Alfonso Soriano .25 .60
21 Adam Dunn .25 .60
22 Hanley Ramirez .40 1.00
23 Mark Teahen .25 .60
24 Todd Helton .40 1.00
25 Alex Rodriguez 1.00 2.50
26 Mike Mussina .40 1.00
27 Jason Bay .25 .60
28 Carl Crawford .25 .60
29 Vernon Wells .25 .60
30 Rich Harden .25 .60
31 Justin Morneau .25 .60
32 Andre Ethier .40 1.00
33 Ramon Hernandez .25 .60
34 Erik Bedard .25 .60
35 Vladimir Guerrero .60 1.50
36 Stephen Drew .40 1.00
37 Felix Hernandez .40 1.00
38 C.C. Sabathia .25 .60
39 Adrian Gonzalez .25 .60
40 Prince Fielder .60 1.50
41 Carlos Delgado .25 .60
42 Jimmy Rollins .25 .60
43 Raul Ibanez .25 .60
44 Jorge Cantu .25 .60
45 Michael Young .25 .60
46 Austin Kearns .25 .60
47 Ivan Rodriguez .40 1.00
48 Mark Teixeira .25 .60
49 David Ortiz .60 1.50
50 David Wright 1.00 2.50
51 Justin Verlander .60 1.50
52 Nick Markakis .40 1.00
53 Miguel Cabrera .40 1.00
54 Lance Berkman .25 .60
55 Robinson Cano .40 1.00
56 Jon Lieber .25 .60
57 Andruw Jones .40 1.00
58 Dan Haren .25 .60
59 Grady Sizemore .40 1.00
60 Gary Sheffield .25 .60
61 Paul Lo Duca .25 .60
62 Cole Hamels .40 1.00
63 Richie Sexson .25 .60
64 David Eckstein .25 .60
65 Carlos Zambrano .25 .60
66 Scott Kazmir .40 1.00
67 Anthony Reyes .25 .60
68 Mark Kotsay .25 .60
69 Miguel Tejada .25 .60
70 Pedro Martinez .40 1.00
71 Jack Wilson .25 .60
72 Joe Mauer .40 1.00
73 Brian Giles .25 .60
74 Jonathan Papelbon .60 1.50
75 Albert Pujols 1.25 3.00
76 Nick Swisher .25 .60
77 Bill Hall .25 .60
78 Jose Contreras .25 .60
79 David DeJesus .25 .60
80 Bobby Abreu .25 .60
81 John Smoltz .40 1.00
82 Chipper Jones .60 1.50
83 Mark Buehrle .25 .60
84 Josh Barfield .25 .60
85 Derrek Lee .25 .60
86 Jim Thome .40 1.00
87 Kenny Rogers .25 .60
88 Jeremy Sowers .25 .60
89 Brandon Webb .25 .60
90 Roy Halladay .25 .60
91 Tadahito Iguchi .25 .60
92 Jeff Kent .25 .60
93 Johnny Damon .40 1.00
94 Daisuke Matsuzaka RC 3.00 8.00
95 Kei Igawa RC 1.00 2.50
96a Delmon Young (RC) .75 2.00
96b Delmon Young AU 8.00 20.00
97a Jeff Baker (RC) .60 1.50
97b Jeff Baker AU 3.00 8.00
98a Michael Bourn (RC) .60 1.50
98b Michael Bourn AU 4.00 10.00
99a Ubaldo Jimenez (RC) .60 1.50
99b Ubaldo Jimenez AU 6.00 15.00
100a Andrew Miller RC 1.50 4.00
100b Andrew Miller AU 15.00 40.00
101 Angel Sanchez AU RC 3.00 8.00
102 Troy Tulowitzki AU (RC) 12.50 30.00
103 Joaquin Arias AU (RC) 3.00 8.00
104 Beltran Perez AU (RC) 3.00 8.00
105 Josh Fields AU (RC) 4.00 10.00
106 Hector Gimenez AU (RC) 3.00 8.00
107 Kevin Kouzmanoff AU (RC) 4.00 10.00
108 Miguel Montero AU (RC) 3.00 8.00
109 Philip Humber AU (RC) 4.00 10.00
110 Jerry Owens AU (RC) 3.00 8.00
111 Shawn Riggans AU (RC) 3.00 8.00
112 Brian Stokes AU (RC) 3.00 8.00
113 Scott Moore AU (RC) 3.00 8.00
114 David Murphy AU (RC) 3.00 8.00
115 Mitch Maier AU RC 3.00 8.00
116 Adam Lind AU (RC) 4.00 10.00
117 Glen Perkins AU (RC) 4.00 10.00
118 Dennis Sarfate AU (RC) 3.00 8.00
119 Elijah Dukes AU RC 6.00 15.00
120 Josh Hamilton AU (RC) 12.50 30.00
121 Alex Gordon AU RC 15.00 40.00
122 Barry Bonds 3.00 8.00

2007 Topps Co-Signers Blue

*BLUE: .75X TO 2X BASIC
*BLUE RC: .5X TO 1.2X BASIC
*BLUE AUTO: .4X TO 1X BASIC
BASE/ROOKIE CARD ODDS 1:10
ROOKIE AUTO ODDS 1:104
BASE/RC PRINT RUN 250 SER.#'d SETS
RC AUTO PRINT RUN 225 SER.#'d SETS

2007 Topps Co-Signers Bronze

*BRONZE: .75X TO 2X BASIC
*BRONZE RC: .5X TO 1.2X BASIC
*BRONZE AUTO: .4X TO 1X BASIC
BASE/ROOKIE CARD ODDS 1:9
ROOKIE AUTO ODDS 1:94
BASE/RC PRINT RUN 275 SER.#'d SETS
RC AUTO PRINT RUN 250 SER.#'d SETS

2007 Topps Co-Signers Gold

*GOLD: .75X TO 2X BASIC
*GOLD RC: .5X TO 1.2X BASIC
*GOLD AUTO: .4X TO 1X BASIC
BASE/ROOKIE CARD ODDS 1:11
ROOKIE AUTO ODDS 1:117
BASE/RC PRINT RUN 225 SER.#'d SETS
RC AUTO PRINT RUN 200 SER.#'d SETS

2007 Topps Co-Signers Red

*RED: .75X TO 2X BASIC
*RED RC: .5X TO 1.2X BASIC
*RED AUTO: .4X TO 1X BASIC
BASE/ROOKIE CARD ODDS 1:9
ROOKIE AUTO ODDS 1:85
BASE/RC PRINT RUN 299 SER.#'d SETS
RC AUTO PRINT RUN 275 SER.#'d SETS

2007 Topps Co-Signers Hyper Plaid Silver

BASE/ROOKIE CARD ODDS 1:2490
ROOKIE AUTO ODDS 1:25,872
STATED PRINT RUN 1 SERIAL #'d SET
NO PRICING DUE TO SCARCITY

2007 Topps Co-Signers Hyper Silver Blue

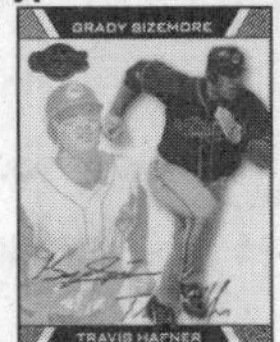

BASE/ROOKIE CARD ODDS 1:165
ROOKIE AUTO ODDS 1:938
BASE/ROOKIE PRINT RUN 15 SER.#'d SETS
ROOKIE AUTO PRINT RUN 25 SER.#'d SETS
NO PRICING DUE TO SCARCITY

2007 Topps Co-Signers Hyper Silver Bronze

*HS BRONZE: 1.2X TO 3X BASIC
*HS BRONZE RC: 1.2X TO 3X BASIC
*HS BRONZE AUTO: .6X TO 1.5X BASIC
BASE/ROOKIE CARD ODDS 1:49
ROOKIE AUTO ODDS 1:468
STATED PRINT RUN 50 SER.#'d SETS

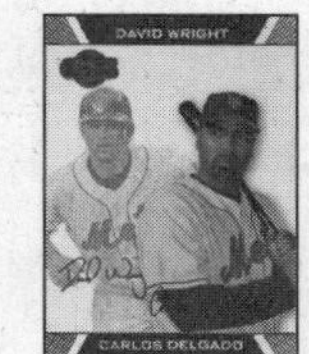

94B Daisuke Matsuzaka 20.00 50.00
Hideki Okajima
100A Andrew Miller 20.00 50.00
Daisuke Matsuzaka

2007 Topps Co-Signers Hyper Silver Gold

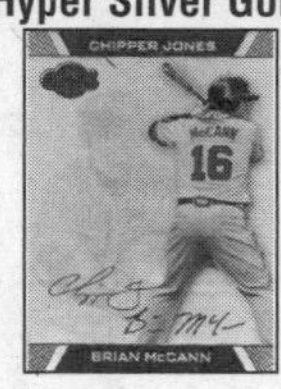

BASE/ROOKIE CARD ODDS 1:493
ROOKIE AUTO ODDS 1:4800
STATED PRINT RUN 5 SERIAL #'d SETS
NO PRICING DUE TO SCARCITY

2007 Topps Co-Signers Hyper Silver Red

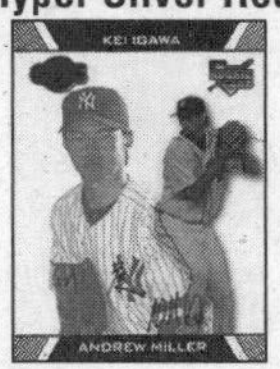

*HS RED: 1X TO 2.5X BASIC
*HS RED RC: .75X TO 2X BASIC
*HS RED AUTO: .6X TO 1.5X BASIC
BASE/ROOKIE CARD ODDS 1:33
ROOKIE AUTO ODDS 1:312
STATED PRINT RUN 75 SER.#'d SETS

2007 Topps Co-Signers Silver Blue

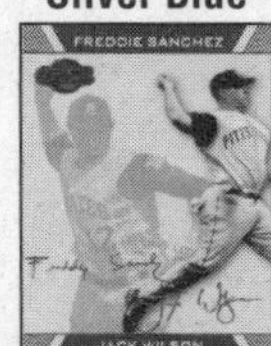

*SIL BLUE: .75X TO 2X BASIC
*SIL BLUE RC: .5X TO 1.2X BASIC
*SIL BLUE AUTO: .5X TO 1.2X BASIC
BASE/ROOKIE CARD ODDS 1:17
ROOKIE AUTO ODDS 1:187
BASE/RC PRINT RUN 150 SER.#'d SETS
RC AUTO PRINT RUN 125 SER.#'d SETS

2007 Topps Co-Signers Silver Bronze

*SIL BRONZE: .75X TO 2X BASIC
*SIL BRONZE RC: .5X TO 1.2X BASIC
*SIL BRONZE AUTO: .5X TO 1.2X BASIC
BASE/ROOKIE CARD ODDS 1:14
ROOKIE AUTO ODDS 1:156
BASE/RC PRINT RUN 175 SER.#'d SETS
RC AUTO PRINT RUN 150 SER.#'d SETS

2007 Topps Co-Signers Silver Gold

*SIL GOLD: 1X TO 2.5X BASIC
*SIL GOLD RC: .75X TO 2X BASIC
*SIL GOLD AUTO: .5X TO 1.2X BASIC
BASE/ROOKIE CARD ODDS 1:20
ROOKIE AUTO ODDS 1:234
BASE/RC PRINT RUN 125 SER.#'d SETS
RC AUTO PRINT RUN 100 SER.#'d SETS

2007 Topps Co-Signers Silver Red

*SIL RED: .75X TO 2X BASIC
*SIL RED RC: .5X TO 1.2X BASIC
*SIL RED AUTO: .5X TO 1.2X BASIC
BASE/ROOKIE CARD ODDS 1:13
ROOKIE AUTO ODDS 1:134
BASE/RC PRINT RUN 199 SER.#'d SETS
RC AUTO PRINT RUN 175 SER.#'d SETS

2007 Topps Co-Signers Cut Signatures Dual

STATED ODDS 1:46,569
NO PRICING DUE TO SCARCITY
CM Chipper Jones
Mickey Mantle
DM Joe DiMaggio
Mickey Mantle
EM Dwight Eisenhower
Mickey Mantle
HM Ryan Howard
Mickey Mantle
JM Lyndon B. Johnson
Mickey Mantle
RM Alex Rodriguez
Mickey Mantle
SM Duke Snider
Mickey Mantle
TM Harry Truman
Mickey Mantle
WM David Wright
Mickey Mantle
ADM Abner Doubleday
Mickey Mantle

2007 Topps Co-Signers Dual Autographs

GROUP A ODDS 1:17
GROUP B ODDS 1:49
GROUP C ODDS 1:1646
GROUP D ODDS 1:2464
GROUP E ODDS 1:328
AH Garrett Atkins 12.50 30.00
Matt Holliday B
AI Matt Albers 4.00 10.00
Chris Iannetta A
AS Matt Albers 4.00 10.00
Brian Slocum A
BB Brian Bannister 10.00 25.00
Floyd Bannister A
BDE Erik Bedard 6.00 15.00
Zach Duke A
BG Jeremy Bonderman 15.00 40.00
{Curtis Granderson B
BS Jeff Baker 4.00 10.00
Jeff Salazar B
BV Jeremy Bonderman 20.00 50.00
Justin Verlander E
CC Melky Cabrera 30.00 60.00
Robinson Cano E
CJ Chris Carpenter 20.00 50.00
{Tyler Johnson E
CK Robinson Cano 15.00 40.00
Chuck Knoblach E
CM Fabio Castro 4.00 10.00
Scott Mathieson A
CW Miguel Cabrera 15.00 40.00
Dontrelle Willis B
CY Alberto Callaspo 8.00 20.00
Chris Young B
CZ Alberto Callaspo 4.00 10.00
Ben Zobrist A
GB Garrett Atkins 4.00 10.00
Clint Barmes B
GC Curtis Granderson 10.00 25.00
Melky Cabrera A
GM Hector Gimenez 4.00 10.00
Miguel Montero A
GS Dwight Gooden 15.00 40.00
Darryl Strawberry E
HH Bill Hall 10.00 25.00
J.J. Hardy A
HO Ryan Howard 50.00 100.00
David Ortiz E
IK Chris Iannetta 6.00 15.00
Matt Kemp A
IM Chirs Iannetta 6.00 15.00
Miguel Montero A
JJ Andruw Jones 40.00 80.00
David Justice E
JS Ubaldo Jimenez 4.00 10.00
Dennis Sarfate A
JY Conor Jackson 30.00 60.00
Chris Young D
KA Howie Kendrick 10.00 25.00
Erick Aybar A
KF Kevin Kouzmanoff 6.00 15.00
Josh Fields B
KG Matt Kemp 6.00 15.00
Franklin Gutierrez A
KM Josh Kinney 4.00 10.00
Tom Mastny A
KMA Jeff Karstens 4.00 10.00
Scott Mathieson A
KZ Austin Kearns 15.00 40.00
Ryan Zimmerman A
LG Adam LaRoche 6.00 15.00
Tom Gorzelanny A
LK Francisco Liriano 10.00 25.00
Jim Kaat B
LL Tony Larussa 30.00 60.00
Jim Leyland E
LP Francisco Liriano 15.00 40.00
Jonathan Papelbon C
LV Francisco Liriano 12.50 30.00
Justin Verlander B
LY Adam Lind 6.00 15.00
Delwyn Young A
MB Nick Markakis 20.00 50.00
Brian Roberts B
MC Omar Minaya 40.00 80.00
Brian Cashman E
MCA Nick Markakis 15.00 40.00
Melky Cabrera B
MG Craig Monroe 6.00 15.00
Curtis Granderson A
MH John Maine 12.50 30.00
Philip Humber B
MM Lastings Milledge 12.50 30.00
{John Maine B
MMA David Murphy 4.00 10.00
Mitch Maier A
MP Andrew Miller 10.00 25.00
Glen Perkins B
MQ Nick Markakis 10.00 25.00
Carlos Quetin B
MS Justin Morneau 12.50 30.00
Nick Swisher B
MSL Tom Mastny 4.00 10.00
Brian Slocum A
MW Lastings Milledge 20.00 50.00
David Wright E
OB Jerry Owens 4.00 10.00
Mike Bourn B
PC Angel Pagan 6.00 15.00
Buck Coats A
PS Yusmeiro Petit 4.00 10.00
Anibal Sanchez A
PV Jonathan Papelbon 20.00 50.00
Justin Verlander B
SH Jonathan Sanchez 6.00 15.00
Brad Hennessey A
SM Freddy Sanchez 10.00 25.00
Joe Mauer E
SMA Chris Stewart 4.00 10.00
Carlos Maldonado A
SR Brian Stokes 4.00 10.00
Shawn Riggans A
VF Justin Verlander 20.00 50.00
Mark Fidrych B
VM John Van Benschoten 4.00 10.00
Scott Mathieson A
VP Jason Varitek 40.00 80.00
{Jorge Posada E
WC David Wright 40.00 80.00
Robinson Cano E
WS Dontrelle Willis 6.00 15.00
Anibal Sanchez E
YL Chris Young 6.00 15.00
Nook Logan B
YU Delmon Young 20.00 50.00
B.J. Upton E
ZG Ben Zobrist 4.00 10.00
Joel Guzman A

2007 Topps Co-Signers Moon Shots Autographs

STATED ODDS 1:339
AW Alfred Worden 50.00 100.00
BA Buzz Aldrin 125.00 250.00
CD Charles Duke 50.00 100.00
EM Edgar Mitchell 50.00 100.00
FH Fred Haise 60.00 120.00
RC Robert Crippen 50.00 100.00
RG Richard Gordon 50.00 100.00
SC Scott Carpenter 60.00 120.00
WC Walt Cunningham 50.00 100.00
WS Wally Schirra 75.00 150.00

2007 Topps Co-Signers Moon Shots Autographs Dual

STATED ODDS 1:1028
NO PRICING DUE TO SCARCITY
AC Garrett Atkins
Scott Carpenter
AD Andre Dawson
Alfred Worden
DG Jermaine Dye
Richard Gordon
HC Ryan Howard
Walt Cunnigham
OS David Ortiz
Wally Schirra
RA Alex Rodriguez
Buzz Aldrin
SC Alfonso Soriano
Robert Crippen
SH Duke Snider
Fred Haise
WD David Wright
Charles Duke
WM Dave Winfield
Edgar Mitchell

2007 Topps Co-Signers Solo Sigs

GROUP A ODDS 1:25
GROUP B ODDS 1:164
GROUP C ODDS 1:2464
GROUP D ODDS 1:9908
AH Aaron Hill A 4.00 10.00
AL Anthony Lerew B 4.00 10.00
AS Anibal Sanchez A 4.00 10.00
BB Boof Bonser A 4.00 10.00
CB Clint Barmes A 4.00 10.00
CH Cole Hamels A 10.00 25.00
CJ Chuck James A 4.00 10.00
CQ Carlos Quentin A 5.00 12.00
DH Dave Henderson A 4.00 10.00
DU Dan Uggla A 6.00 15.00
ES Ervin Santana B 4.00 10.00
FL Francisco Liriano A 6.00 15.00
FS Freddy Sanchez A 4.00 10.00
GA Garrett Atkins A 4.00 10.00
HK Howie Kendrick B 6.00 15.00
HM Hideki Matsui D
HR Hanley Ramirez A 6.00 15.00
JM Justin Morneau B 10.00 25.00
JS Jeremy Sowers A 4.00 10.00
MC Matt Cain A 4.00 10.00
MH Matt Holliday A 8.00 20.00
NM Nick Markakis A 8.00 20.00
RC Robinson Cano A 12.50 30.00
RG Ryan Garko A 4.00 10.00
RH Ryan Howard B 25.00 50.00
RR Rick Rhoden A 4.00 10.00
VG Vladimir Guerrero C 15.00 40.00
RCE Ronny Cedeno B 4.00 10.00

2007 Topps Co-Signers Tri-Signers

STATED ODDS 1:264
ANS Joaquin Arias/Oswaldo Navarro
/Angel Sanchez 10.00 25.00
CPC Melky Cabrera/Wily Mo Pena
/Miguel Cabrera 20.00 50.00
HLC Brad Hennessey/Jonathan Sanchez
/Matt Cain 15.00 40.00
JGK Conor Jackson/Ryan Garko
/Howie Kendrick 15.00 40.00
JHS Chuck James/Cole Hamels
/Jeremy Sowers 20.00 50.00
LNB Francisco Liriano/Joe Nathan
/Boof Bonser 20.00 50.00
MAR Justin Morneau/Garrett Atkins
/Brian Roberts 15.00 40.00
MLM Justin Morneau/Francisco Liriano
/Matt Garza 30.00 60.00
MLP Justin Morneau/Francisco Liriano
/Glen Perkins 15.00 40.00
MSG Justin Morneau/Nick Swisher
/Adrian Gonzalez 15.00 40.00
MYT Andrew Miller/Delmon Young
/Troy Tulowitzki 15.00 40.00
OPV David Ortiz/Jonathan Papelbon
/Jason Varitek 100.00 175.00
OWH David Ortiz/David Wright
/Ryan Howard 100.00 175.00
QJY Carlos Quentin/Conor Jackson
/Chris Young 15.00 40.00
RCC Alex Rodriguez/Melky Cabrera
/Robinson Cano 175.00 250.00
RWH Alex Rodriguez/David Wright
/Ryan Howard 200.00 300.00
SHH Huston Street/Rich Harden
/Dan Haren 20.00 50.00
TPW Taylor Tankersley/Yusmerio Petit
/Dontrelle Willis 10.00 25.00
URW Dan Uggla/Hanley Ramirez
/Dontrelle Willis 20.00 50.00

2007 Topps Co-Signers Yankees Cut Signatures

A-ROD MANTLE ODDS 1:66,528
A-ROD DIMAGGIO ODDS 1:93,139
TRIPLE CUT SIG ODDS 1:232,848
PRINT RUNS B/WN 3-7 COPIES PER
NO PRICING DUE TO SCARCITY
YCS1 Alex Rodriguez
Mickey Mantle/7
YCS2 Alex Rodriguez
Joe DiMaggio/6
YCS3 Alex Rodriguez
Mickey Mantle
Joe DiMaggio/3

2008 Topps Co-Signers

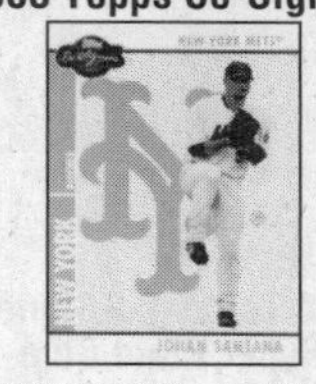

COMP.SET w/o AU's (100) 12.50 30.00
COMMON CARD (1-95) .25 .60
COMMON RC (96-100) .60 1.50
AU RC VAR ODDS 1:315 HOBBY
COMMON AU RC 3.00 8.00
AU RC ODDS 1:22 HOBBY
PRINTING PLATE VET/RC ODDS 1:445
PRINTING PLATE AU RC VAR ODDS 1:29,736
PRINTING PLATE AU RC ODDS 1:5216
PLATE PRINT RUN 1 SET PER COLOR
5TH-BLACK-CYAN-MAGENTA-YELLOW ISSUED
NO PLATE PRICING DUE TO SCARCITY
1 Jacoby Ellsbury 1.00 2.50
2 Michael Young .25 .60
3 Cameron Maybin .60 1.50
4 Dmitri Young .25 .60
5 Grady Sizemore .40 1.00
6 Brandon Webb .40 1.00
7 Derrek Lee .40 1.00
8 Jeff Francis .25 .60
9 Aaron Harang .25 .60
10 John Smoltz .60 1.50
11 Nick Markakis .40 1.00
12 Tom Gorzelanny .25 .60
13 Miguel Cabrera .40 1.00
14 Josh Beckett .40 1.00
15 Magglio Ordonez .40 1.00
16 Joe Mauer .40 1.00
17 Carl Crawford .25 .60
18 Barry Zito .25 .60
19 Brad Penny .25 .60
20 C.C. Sabathia .25 .60
21 Mark Buehrle .25 .60
22 Carlos Lee .25 .60
23 Chipper Jones .75 2.00
24 Chase Utley .60 1.50
25 David Ortiz .60 1.50
26 Justin Morneau .25 .60
27 Erik Bedard .25 .60
28 Greg Maddux .75 2.00
29 Joba Chamberlain .75 2.00
30 Vernon Wells .25 .60
31 Orlando Hudson .25 .60
32 Kevin Youkilis .40 1.00
33 Curtis Granderson .25 .60
34 Chone Figgins .25 .60
35 Jorge Posada .40 1.00
36 Ken Griffey Jr. 1.00 2.50
37 Tim Hudson .25 .60
38 Nick Swisher .25 .60
39 Carlos Beltran .25 .60
40 Alex Gordon .60 1.50
41 Andre Ethier .40 1.00
42 Todd Helton .40 1.00
43 Miguel Tejada .25 .60
44 Yadier Molina .40 1.00
45 Hanley Ramirez .60 1.50
46 Justin Verlander .40 1.00
47 Adam Dunn .25 .60
48 Raul Ibanez .25 .60
49 Scott Rolen .40 1.00
50 Alex Rodriguez 1.00 2.50
51 Garret Anderson .25 .60
52 Andruw Jones .25 .60
53 Matt Cain .25 .60
54 Daisuke Matsuzaka 1.25 3.00
55 Ichiro Suzuki 1.00 2.50
56 Scott Kazmir .40 1.00
57 Jeff Kent .25 .60
58 Aubrey Huff .25 .60
59 Justin Upton .60 1.50
60 Prince Fielder .60 1.50
61 Alex Rios .25 .60
62 Alfonso Soriano .40 1.00
63 Paul Konerko .25 .60
64 Matt Holliday .40 1.00
65 Felix Hernandez .40 1.00
66 Ivan Rodriguez .40 1.00
67 John Maine .25 .60
68 Roy Oswalt .25 .60
69 Brian McCann .40 1.00
70 Albert Pujols 1.25 3.00
71 John Lackey .25 .60
72 Travis Hafner .25 .60
73 Gil Meche .25 .60
74 Ben Sheets .40 1.00
75 Ryan Howard .75 2.00
76 Hideki Matsui .60 1.50
77 Mike Lowell .25 .60
78 Dan Haren .25 .60
79 Adrian Gonzalez .40 1.00
80 David Wright .75 2.00
81 Jason Bay .25 .60
82 Carlos Zambrano .25 .60
83 Johan Santana .40 1.00
84 David DeJesus .25 .60
85 Ryan Zimmerman .40 1.00
86 Bobby Abreu .25 .60
87 Richie Sexson .25 .60
88 Eric Chavez .25 .60
89 Derek Lowe .25 .60
90 Jake Peavy .40 1.00
91 Joe Blanton .25 .60
92 Jermaine Dye .25 .60
93 Pedro Martinez .40 1.00
94 B.J. Upton .40 1.00
95 Vladimir Guerrero .60 1.50
96 Ross Ohlendorf RC 1.00 2.50
97 J.R. Towles RC 1.50 4.00
98 Jonathan Meloan RC 1.00 2.50
99a Chin-Lung Hu (RC) 1.00 2.50
99b Chin-Lung Hu AU 10.00 25.00

100a Clay Buchholz (RC) 1.50 4.00
100b Clay Buchholz AU 12.50 30.00
101 Willie Collazo AU RC 3.00 8.00
102 David Davidson AU RC 3.00 8.00
103 Joe Koshansky AU (RC) 3.00 8.00
104 Sam Fuld AU RC 3.00 8.00
105 Nyjer Morgan AU (RC) 3.00 8.00
106 Clint Sammons AU (RC) 3.00 8.00
107 Josh Anderson AU (RC) 3.00 8.00
108 Bronson Sardinha AU (RC) 3.00 8.00
109 Wladimir Balentien AU (RC) 3.00 8.00
110 Kevin Hart AU (RC) 3.00 8.00
111 Felipe Paulino AU RC 3.00 8.00
112 Rob Johnson AU (RC) 3.00 8.00

2008 Topps Co-Signers Hyper Plaid Blue

*HS BLUE VET: 1.2X TO 3X BASIC
STATED VET ODDS 1:32 HOBBY
VET PRINT RUN 50 SER.#'D SETS
*HS BLUE RC: 1.5X TO 4X BASIC
STATED RC ODDS 1:32 HOBBY
RC PRINT RUN 50 SER.#'D SETS
*HS BLUE AU: .5X TO 1.2X BASIC AU RC
STATED AU RC ODDS 1:540 HOBBY
AU PRINT RUN 50 SER.#'d SETS

2008 Topps Co-Signers Hyper Plaid Bronze

*HS BRONZE VET: 1X TO 2.5X BASIC
STATED VET ODDS 1:21 HOBBY
VET PRINT RUN 75 SER.#'D SETS
*HS BRONZE RC: 1X TO 2.5X BASIC
STATED RC ODDS 1:21 HOBBY
RC PRINT RUN 100 SER.#'D SETS
*HS BRONZE AU: .5X TO 1.2X BASIC AU RC
STATED AU RC ODDS 1:355 HOBBY
AU PRINT RUN 75 SER.#'d SETS

2008 Topps Co-Signers Hyper Plaid Gold

1-100 A/B ODDS 1:155 HOBBY
101-112 AUTO ODDS 1:3267 HOBBY
STATED PRINT RUN 10 SER.#'d SETS
NO PRICING DUE TO SCARCTIY
EXCHANGE DEADLINE 4/30/10

2008 Topps Co-Signers Hyper Plaid Green

1-100 A/B ODDS 1:63 HOBBY
101-112 AUTO ODDS 1:1130 HOBBY
STATED PRINT RUN 25 SER.#'d SETS
NO PRICING DUE TO SCARCTIY
EXCHANGE DEADLINE 4/30/10

2008 Topps Co-Signers Hyper Plaid Red

*HS RED VET: 1X TO 2.5X BASIC
STATED VET ODDS 1:16 HOBBY
VET PRINT RUN 100 SER.#'D SETS
*HS RED RC: 1X TO 2.5X BASIC
STATED RC ODDS 1:16 HOBBY
RC PRINT RUN 100 SER.#'D SETS
*HS RED AU: .4X TO 1X BASIC AU RC
STATED AU RC ODDS 1:264 HOBBY
AU PRINT RUN 100 SER.#'d SETS

2008 Topps Co-Signers Hyper Plaid Silver

1-100 A/B ODDS 1:1556 HOBBY
101-112 AUTO ODDS 1:24,780 HOBBY
STATED PRINT RUN 1 SER.#'d SET
NO PRICING DUE TO SCARCTIY
EXCHANGE DEADLINE 4/30/10

2008 Topps Co-Signers Silver Blue

*BLUE VET: .6X TO 1.5X BASIC
STATED VET ODDS 1:7 HOBBY
VET PRINT RUN 250 SER.#'D SETS
*BLUE RC: .6X TO 1.5X BASIC
STATED RC ODDS 1:7 HOBBY
RC PRINT RUN 250 SER.#'D SETS
*BLUE AU: .4X TO 1X BASIC AU RC
STATED AU RC ODDS 1:87 HOBBY
AU PRINT RUN 300 SER.#'d SETS

2008 Topps Co-Signers Silver Bronze

*BRONZE VET: .6X TO 1.5X BASIC
STATED VET ODDS 1:6 HOBBY
VET PRINT RUN 300 SER.#'D SETS
*BRONZE RC: .6X TO 1.5X BASIC
STATED RC ODDS 1:6 HOBBY
RC PRINT RUN 300 SER.#'D SETS
*BRONZE AU: .4X TO 1X BASIC AU RC
STATED AU RC ODDS 1:65 HOBBY
AU PRINT RUN 400 SER.#'d SETS

2008 Topps Co-Signers Silver Gold

*GOLD VET: .75X TO 2X BASIC
STATED VET ODDS 1:11 HOBBY
VET PRINT RUN 150 SER.#'D SETS
*GOLD RC: .75X TO 2X BASIC
STATED RC ODDS 1:11 HOBBY
RC PRINT RUN 150 SER.#'D SETS
*GOLD AU: .4X TO 1X BASIC AU RC
STATED AU RC ODDS 1:175 HOBBY
AU PRINT RUN 150 SER.#'d SETS

2008 Topps Co-Signers Silver Green

*GREEN VET: .75X TO 2X BASIC
STATED VET ODDS 1:8 HOBBY
VET PRINT RUN 200 SER.#'D SETS
*GREEN RC: .75X TO 2X BASIC
STATED RC ODDS 1:8 HOBBY
RC PRINT RUN 200 SER.#'D SETS
*GREEN AU: .4X TO 1X BASIC AU RC
STATED AU RC ODDS 1:131 HOBBY
AU PRINT RUN 200 SER.#'d SETS

2008 Topps Co-Signers Silver Red

*RED VET: .6X TO 1.5X BASIC
STATED VET ODDS 1:4 HOBBY
VET PRINT RUN 400 SER.#'d SETS
*RED RC: .6X TO 1.5X BASIC
STATED RC ODDS 1:4 HOBBY
RC PRINT RUN 400 SER.#'d SETS
*RED AU: .4X TO 1X BASIC AU RC
STATED AU RC ODDS 1:52 HOBBY
AU PRINT RUN 500 SER.#'d SETS

2008 Topps Co-Signers Cowhide Dual Signatures

STATED ODDS 1:29,736 HOBBY
STATED PRINT RUN 1 SER.#'d SET
NO PRICING DUE TO SCARCITY
BR Johnny Bench
Ivan Rodriguez
CH Steve Carlton
Cole Hamels
CW Gary Carter
David Wright
MO Paul Molitor
David Ortiz
MT Paul Molitor
Frank Thomas
RR Frank Robinson
Alex Rodriguez
SD Ryne Sandberg
Andre Dawson
SW Mike Schmidt
David Wright
YB Robin Yount
Ryan Braun
YF Robin Yount
Prince Fielder

2008 Topps Co-Signers Cut Signatures Dual

STATED ODDS 1:21,240 HOBBY
STATED PRINT RUN 1 SER.#'d SET
NO PRICING DUE TO SCARCITY
DT Thomas Dewey
Harry Truman
EN Dwight Eisenhower
Richard Nixon
FP Lucius Fairchild
Halbert E. Paine
FR Malcolm Forbes
Alex Rodriguez
GB Carlo Gambino
Charles Boles
HC Matt Holliday
Adolph Coors
HW John Hartranft
William Wells
MR Mickey Mantle
Alex Rodriguez
NF Richard Nixon
Gerald Ford
RP Alex Rodriguez
Albert Pujols
RW Norma L. McCorvey
(Henry Wade
SS John Sherman
William T. Sherman
WH Marinus Willett
Jedidiah Huntington
WP George Washington
John J. Pershing

2008 Topps Co-Signers Cut Signatures Quad

STATED ODDS 1:237,600 HOBBY
STATED PRINT RUN 1 SER.#'d SET
NO PRICING DUE TO SCARCITY
MEMB Douglas MacArthur
Dwight Eisenhower
George Marshall
Omar Bradley
OHGM Barack Obama
Hillary Clinton
Rudy Giuliani
John McCain

2008 Topps Co-Signers Dual Autographs

GROUP A ODDS 1:23 HOBBY
GROUP B ODDS 1:39 HOBBY
GROUP C ODDS 1:101 HOBBY
GROUP D ODDS 1:443 HOBBY
GROUP E ODDS 1:3912 HOBBY
AC Jorge Arce 6.00 15.00
Ivan Calderon C
BA Josh Banks 4.00 10.00
Jeremy Accardo A
BB Daric Barton 10.00 25.00
Clay Buchholz A
BJ Erik Bedard 12.50 30.00
Adam Jones B
BM Bill Buck 6.00 15.00
Cameron Maybin B
BZ Jason Bartlett 8.00 20.00
Ben Zobrist A
CB Steve Cunningham 4.00 10.00
Shannon Briggs C
CC Robinson Cano 10.00 25.00
Asdrubal Cabrera A
CE Jack Cust 4.00 10.00
Mark Ellis A
CG Jerome Cochran 6.00 15.00
Curtis Granderson B
DB Chad Dawson 10.00 25.00
Andre Berto C
DD Juan Diaz 6.00 15.00
Julio Diaz C
DG Vic Darchinyan 4.00 10.00
Danny Green C EXCH
DR Chris Duncan 10.00 25.00
Brendan Ryan A
EH Bob Engle 10.00 25.00
Felix Hernandez B
FC Chone Figgins 6.00 15.00
Carl Crawford D
FH Jeff Francis 4.00 10.00
Jason Hirsh A
FJ Jeff Francis 4.00 10.00
Ubaldo Jimenez B
FP Sam Fuld 4.00 10.00
Felix Pie A
GS Tom Gorzelanny 4.00 10.00
Freddy Sanchez A
HC Felix Hernandez 30.00 60.00
Joba Chamberlain A
JA Brandon Jones 4.00 10.00
Josh Anderson A
JM Dave Jennings 4.00 10.00
Nick Markakis B
KA Roman Karmazin 6.00 15.00
Arthur Abraham C
KC Tim Kelly 30.00 60.00
Joba Chamberlain B
LG Don Lyle 4.00 10.00
Ryan Garko B
LH Andy LaRoche 10.00 25.00
Chin-Lung Hu B
MB Edison Miranda 4.00 10.00
O'Neil Bell C EXCH
MD Lastings Milledge 4.00 10.00
Elijah Dukes B
MM Andrew Miller 6.00 15.00
Cameron Maybin A
MP Joe Mason 6.00 15.00
Jonathan Papelbon B
MS Carlos Marmol 20.00 50.00
Geovany Soto A
MV Rafael Marquez 20.00 50.00
Israel Vasquez C
OB Garrett Olsen 4.00 10.00
Brian Burres A
PG Daniel Ponce de Leon 10.00 25.00
Joan Guzman C
PO Jonathan Papelbon 30.00 60.00
Hideki Okajima D
PP Samuel Peter 12.50 30.00
Aaron Pryor C
PS Steve Pearce 4.00 10.00
Freddy Sanchez A
RM Alex Rios 10.00 25.00
Nick Markakis B
RO Edwar Ramirez 6.00 15.00
Ross Ohlendorf A
RR Jimmy Rollins 40.00 80.00
Jose Reyes D
RW Jose Reyes 75.00 150.00
David Wright D
SC Brian Schneider 6.00 15.00
Ramon Castro A
SE Arthur Shorin 50.00 100.00
Michael Eisner E
SG Andy Sonnanstine 12.50 30.00
Matt Garza A
SP Geovany Soto 12.50 30.00
Felix Pie A
SZ Alex Smith 6.00 15.00
Ryan Zimmerman B
VC Joey Votto 10.00 25.00
Daric Barton B
WB David Wright 50.00 100.00
Ryan Braun D
WF Dontrelle Willis 6.00 15.00
Mark Fidrych D
BMP Ray Mancini 75.00 150.00
Kelly Pavlik E
CCC Martin Castillo 12.50 30.00
Julio Cesar Chavez Jr. C
CLC Joel Casamayor 10.00 25.00
Jose Luis Castillo C
FHO Prince Fielder 40.00 80.00
Ryan Howard D
HCA Josue Herrera 4.00 10.00
Fausto Carmona B
MMJ Juan Manuel Marquez 10.00 25.00
Chris John C
OBA Dan Ontiveros 4.00 10.00
Daric Barton B
PKS Glen Perkins 4.00 10.00
Kevin Slowey A

2008 Topps Co-Signers Quad Signers

STATED ODDS 1:1436 HOBBY
NO PRICING DUE TO SCARCITY
EXCHANGE DEADLINE 4/30/10
BHHF Ryan Braun
J.J. Hardy
Bill Hall
Prince Fielder EXCH
CSHW Steve Carlton
Johan Santana
Cole Hamels
Dontrelle Willis
LKFW Francisco Liriano
Scott Kazmir
Jeff Francis
Dontrelle Willis
RWZB Brooks Robinson
David Wright
Ryan Zimmerman
Ryan Braun EXCH
SRRR Ozzie Smith
Jose Reyes
Jimmy Rollins
Hanley Ramirez
VHCP Justin Verlander
Felix Hernandez
Joba Chamberlain
Jake Peavy
WHCP Chien-Ming Wang
Phil Hughes
Joba Chamberlain
Jorge Posada
WRCD David Wright
Jose Reyes
Luis Castillo
Carlos Delgado EXCH
YYUU Dmitri Young
Delmon Young
Justin Upton
B.J. Upton

2008 Topps Co-Signers Solo Sigs

STATED ODDS 1:21 HOBBY
EXCHANGE DEADLINE 4/30/10
AA Arthur Abraham 6.00 15.00
AB Andre Berto 6.00 15.00
AP Aaron Pryor 10.00 25.00
AW Andre Ward 6.00 15.00
BS Bert Sugar EXCH 8.00 20.00
CD Chad Dawson 5.00 12.00
CJ Chris John 4.00 10.00
DP Daniel Ponce de Leon 5.00 12.00
EM Edison Miranda 6.00 15.00
FM Fernando Montiel 4.00 10.00
IC Ivan Calderon 6.00 15.00
IV Israel Vasquez 6.00 15.00
JA Jorge Arce 6.00 15.00
JC Joel Casamayor 6.00 15.00
JD Juan Diaz 6.00 15.00
JF Jeff Fenech 4.00 10.00
JG Joan Guzman 4.00 10.00
JM Juan Manuel Marquez 8.00 20.00
KP Kelly Pavlik 30.00 60.00
MC Martin Castillo 4.00 10.00
OB O'Neil Bell C EXCH 4.00 10.00
RK Roman Karmazin 4.00 10.00
RM Rafael Marquez 6.00 15.00
SB Shannon Briggs 5.00 12.00
SC Steve Cunningham 4.00 10.00
SP Samuel Peter 6.00 15.00
TA Teddy Atlas 8.00 20.00
VD Vic Darchinyan 4.00 10.00
DAG Danny Green EXCH 4.00 10.00
JCC Julio Cesar Chavez Jr. EXCH 8.00 20.00
JLC Jose Luis Castillo 5.00 12.00
JUD Julio Diaz 4.00 10.00
RBBM Ray Mancini 30.00 60.00

2008 Topps Co-Signers Tri Signers

STATED ODDS 1:317 HOBBY
EXCHANGE DEADLINE 4/30/10
BHH Clay Buchholz 20.00 50.00
Phil Hughes
Felix Hernandez
CEC Asdrubal Cabrera 15.00 40.00
Yunel Escobar
Robinson Cano
CHC Joba Chamberlain 50.00 100.00
Phil Hughes
Melky Cabrera
GFH Tom Gorzelanny 20.00 50.00
Jeff Francis
Cole Hamels
HSY Josh Hamilton 15.00 40.00
Jarrod Saltalamacchia
Michael Young
MGY Cameron Maybin 30.00 60.00
Curtis Granderson
Chris Young
MHR Nick Markakis 20.00 50.00
Matt Holliday
Alex Rios
MRH Cameron Maybin 30.00 60.00
Hanley Ramirez
Jeremy Hermida EXCH
PBG Manny Parra 50.00 100.00
Ryan Braun
Yovani Gallardo EXCH
WZB David Wright 60.00 120.00
Ryan Zimmerman
Ryan Braun EXCH

2004 Topps Cracker Jack

This 250 card set was released in April, 2004. The set was issued in nine-card packs which came 20 packs to a box and 10 boxes to a case. Please note that many cards in this set were issued in shorter supply than others (we have notated those cards with an SP) or have variation poses. In addition, to mirror the original Cracker Jack set the managers of the 2003 World Series were included as well as the Marlins Owner, Jeffrey Loria. In addition, to acknowledge the late trade of Alex Rodriguez to the Yankees a Rodriguez card in a Yankee uniform was a late addition to this set and was issued without a card number. In addition, 550 original cracker jacks were inserted into packs, those cards were issued at a stated rate of one in 2598 hobby and one in 3084 retail packs.

COMPLETE SET (250) 125.00 200.00
COMP.SET w/o SP's (200) 15.00 40.00
COMMON CARD .15 .40
COMMON SP 1.50 4.00
COMMON SP RC 1.50 4.00
SP STATED ODDS 1:3
SP CL: 226/229B/232/236A-236B
1 Jose Reyes SP 1.50 4.00
2 Edgar Renteria .15 .40
3A Albert Pujols Portrait .75 2.00
3B Albert Pujols Swinging SP 3.00 8.00
4 Garret Anderson .15 .40
5 Bobby Abreu .15 .40
6 Andruw Jones .25 .60
7 Jeff Kent .15 .40
8 Magglio Ordonez .15 .40
9 Kris Benson .15 .40
10 Luis Gonzalez .15 .40
11 Corey Patterson .15 .40
12 Connie Mack MG .15 .40
13 Vernon Wells SP 1.50 4.00
14 Jim Edmonds .15 .40
15 Bret Boone .15 .40
16 Travis Lee .15 .40
17 Alex Rodriguez Yanks SP 3.00 8.00
18 Erubiel Durazo .15 .40
19 Brett Myers .15 .40
20 Scott Rolen SP 2.00 5.00
21 Paul Lo Duca .15 .40
22 Geoff Jenkins .15 .40
23 Charles Comiskey .15 .40
24 Cliff Floyd .15 .40
25A Jim Thome Batting .25 .60
25B Jim Thome Fielding SP 2.00 5.00
26 Russ Ortiz .15 .40
27 Bill Mueller .15 .40
28 Kenny Lofton .15 .40
29 Jay Gibbons .15 .40
30 Ken Griffey Jr. .60 1.50
31 Jeff Bagwell .25 .60
32 Jose Lima .15 .40
33 Brad Radke .15 .40
34 Ramon Hernandez .15 .40
35 Brian Giles SP 1.50 4.00
36 Jeremy Bonderman .15 .40
37 Jerome Williams .15 .40
38 Rafael Palmeiro .25 .60
39 Scott Podsednik .15 .40
40 Rafael Furcal .15 .40
41 Roy Oswalt .15 .40
42 Orlando Hudson .15 .40
43 Todd Helton .25 .60
44 Kerry Wood .15 .40
45 Tom Glavine .25 .60
46 David Eckstein .15 .40
47 Trot Nixon .15 .40
48 Preston Wilson .15 .40
49 Bernie Williams .25 .60
50 Eric Gagne SP 1.50 4.00
51 Ichiro Suzuki SP 3.00 8.00
52 Juan Gonzalez .15 .40
53 Torii Hunter .15 .40
54 Bartolo Colon .15 .40
55A Dick Hoblitzel ERR .15 .40
55B Dick Hoblitzell COR .15 .40
56 Al Leiter .15 .40
57 Johnny Damon .25 .60
58 Larry Walker .15 .40
59 Brian Jordan .15 .40
60 Richie Sexson SP 1.50 4.00
61 Orlando Cabrera .15 .40
62 Jason Phillips .15 .40
63 Phil Nevin .15 .40
64 John Olerud .15 .40
65 Miguel Tejada .15 .40
66A Nap La Joie ERR .40 1.00
66B Nap Lajoie COR .40 1.00
67 C.C. Sabathia .15 .40
68 Ty Wigginton .15 .40
69 Troy Glaus .15 .40
70 Mike Piazza .60 1.50
71 Craig Biggio .25 .60
72 Cristian Guzman .15 .40
73 Dmitri Young .15 .40
74 Roger Clemens .60 1.50
75 Runelvys Hernandez .15 .40
76 Nomar Garciaparra .60 1.50
77 Mark Mulder .15 .40
78 Derek Lowe .15 .40
79 Paul Konerko .15 .40
80A Sammy Sosa SP 2.00 5.00
80B Felix Pie SP 2.00 5.00
81 Vladimir Guerrero .40 1.00
82 Xavier Nady .15 .40
83 Joel Pineiro .15 .40
84 Chipper Jones .40 1.00
85 Manny Ramirez .25 .60
86A Burt Shotten ERR .15 .40
86B Burt Shotton COR UER .15 .40
Began his playing career in 1997; should be 1907
87 Raul Ibanez SP 1.50 4.00
88 Eric Chavez .15 .40
89 Frank Catalanotto .15 .40
90 Dontrelle Willis .25 .60
91 Roy Halladay .15 .40
92 Jermaine Dye .15 .40
93 Jason Kendall .15 .40
94 Jacque Jones .15 .40
95A Gary Sheffield Braves .15 .40
95B Gary Sheffield Yanks SP 2.00 5.00
96 Mike Lieberthal .15 .40
97 Adam Dunn .15 .40
98 Carl Crawford .15 .40
99 Reggie Sanders .15 .40
100 Mark Prior SP 2.00 5.00
101 Luis Matos .15 .40
102 Barry Zito .15 .40
103 Randy Johnson .40 1.00
104A Kevin Brown .15 .40
104B Edwin Jackson SP 1.50 4.00
105 Pat Burrell .15 .40
106 Steve Finley .15 .40
107 Moises Alou .15 .40
108 David Ortiz SP 2.50 6.00
109 Austin Kearns SP 1.50 4.00
110 Carlos Beltran .15 .40
111 Shawn Green .15 .40
112 Javier Vazquez .15 .40
113 Hideo Nomo .40 1.00
114 Kazuhisa Ishii .15 .40
115 Corey Koskie .15 .40
116 Kevin Millwood .15 .40
117 Randy Wolf .15 .40
118 Darin Erstad .15 .40
119 Fernando Vina .15 .40
120 Pedro Martinez .25 .60
121 Melvin Mora .15 .40
122 Carl Everett .15 .40
123 Matt Morris .15 .40
124 Greg Maddux .60 1.50
125 Jason Schmidt .15 .40
126 Mark Teixeira SP 2.00 5.00
127 Randy Winn .15 .40
128 Rich Aurilia .15 .40
129 Vicente Padilla .15 .40
130 Tim Hudson .15 .40
131 Marlon Byrd .15 .40
132 Jae Weong Seo .15 .40
133 Branch Rickey MG .15 .40
134 A.J. Pierzynski .15 .40
135 Ryan Klesko .15 .40
136 Eric Hinske .15 .40
137 Mike Cameron .15 .40
138 Roberto Alomar .25 .60
139 Jarrod Washburn .15 .40
140A Curt Schilling D'backs .15 .40
140B Curt Schilling Sox SP 2.00 5.00
141 Omar Vizquel .25 .60
142 Mike Sweeney .15 .40
143 Wade Miller .15 .40
144 Jose Vidro .15 .40
145 Rich Harden SP 1.50 4.00
146 Eric Munson .15 .40
147 Lance Berkman .15 .40
148 Mark Buehrle .15 .40
149 Carlos Delgado .15 .40
150 Sean Burroughs .15 .40
151 Kevin Millar .15 .40
152 Frank Thomas .40 1.00
153 Adrian Beltre .15 .40
154 Shannon Stewart .15 .40
155 Johan Santana .40 1.00
156 Edgardo Alfonzo .15 .40
157 Jose Cruz Jr. .15 .40
158 Sidney Ponson .15 .40
159 Edgar Martinez .25 .60
160 Jamie Moyer .15 .40
161 Tony Batista .15 .40
162 Wes Helms .15 .40
163 Brandon Webb SP 1.50 4.00
164 Gil Meche .15 .40
165 Marcus Giles SP 1.50 4.00
166 Angel Berroa SP 1.50 4.00
167 Rocco Baldelli SP 1.50 4.00
168 Michael Young .15 .40
169 Esteban Loaiza .15 .40
170 Casey Blake .15 .40
171 Jody Gerut .15 .40
172 Bo Hart SP 1.50 4.00
173 Kelvim Escobar .15 .40
174 Aaron Guiel .15 .40
175 Javy Lopez SP 1.50 4.00
176 Aubrey Huff .15 .40
177 Hank Blalock .15 .40
178 Edwin Jackson .15 .40
179 Delmon Young SP 2.00 5.00
180 Bobby Jenks .15 .40
181 Felix Pie .25 .60
182 Jeremy Reed SP 1.50 4.00
183 Aaron Hill .15 .40
184 Casey Kotchman SP 1.50 4.00
185 Grady Sizemore .40 1.00
186 Joe Mauer SP 2.00 5.00
187 Ryan Harvey .15 .40
188 Neal Cotts .15 .40
189 Victor Martinez .15 .40
190 Rene Reyes .15 .40
191 Eric Duncan .15 .40
192 B.J. Upton SP 2.00 5.00
193 Khalil Greene SP 2.00 5.00
194 Bobby Crosby .15 .40
195 Rickie Weeks SP 1.50 4.00
196 Zack Greinke SP 1.50 4.00
197 Laynce Nix .15 .40
198 Vito Chiaravalloti SP RC 1.50 4.00
199 Estee Harris RC .40 1.00
200 Jon Knott SP RC 1.50 4.00
201 Dioner Navarro RC .30 .75
202 Craig Ansman RC .30 .75
203 Travis Blackley RC .30 .75
204 Yadier Molina RC .75 2.00
205 Rodney Choy Foo RC .20 .50
206 Kyle Sleeth SP RC 2.00 5.00
207 Jeff Allison RC .30 .75
208 Josh Labandeira RC .30 .75
209 Lastings Milledge SP RC 3.00 8.00
210 Rudy Guillen SP RC 2.00 5.00
211 Blake Hawksworth SP RC 2.00 5.00
212 David Aardsma RC .40 1.00
213 Shawn Hill RC .30 .75
214 Erick Aybar SP RC 2.00 5.00
215 Ervin Santana RC .75 2.00
216 Tim Stauffer SP RC 2.00 5.00
217 Merkin Valdez RC .40 1.00
218 Jack McKeon MG .15 .40
219 Jeff Conine .15 .40
220 Josh Beckett SP 1.50 4.00
221 Luis Castillo .15 .40
222 Mike Lowell .15 .40
223 Juan Pierre .15 .40
224A Ivan Rodriguez Marlins .25 .60
224B Ivan Rodriguez Tigers SP 2.00 5.00
225 A.J. Burnett .15 .40
226 Miguel Cabrera SP 2.00 5.00
227 Jeffrey Loria .15 .40
228 Joe Torre MG .25 .60
229A Jason Giambi Portrait .15 .40
229B Jason Giambi Fielding SP 1.50 4.00
230 Aaron Boone .15 .40
231 Jose Contreras .15 .40
232 Derek Jeter SP 3.00 8.00
233 Ruben Sierra .15 .40
234 Mike Mussina .25 .60
235 Mariano Rivera .40 1.00
236A Jorge Posada SP 2.00 5.00
236B Dioner Navarro SP 2.00 5.00
237 Alfonso Soriano .15 .40
NNO Alex Rodriguez Yanks 1.25 3.00
VB Vintage Buyback

2004 Topps Cracker Jack Mini

COMP.SET w/o SP's (200) 40.00 80.00
*MINI: .75X TO 2X BASIC
*MINI: .75X TO 2X BASIC RC
*MINI SP: .6X TO 1.5X BASIC SP

*MINI SP: .5X TO 1.2X BASIC SP RC
MINI STATED ODDS ONE PER PACK
MINI SP STATED ODDS 1:20
SP'S ARE SAME AS IN BASIC SET

2004 Topps Cracker Jack Mini Autographs

Luis Castillo did not return his cards in time for pack-out and those cards could be redeemed until March 31st, 2006.

STATED ODDS 1:258 HOBBY/RETAIL
SHEFFIELD PRINT RUN 50 CARDS
SHEFFIELD IS NOT SERIAL NUMBERED
SHEFFIELD INFO PROVIDED BY TOPPS
95 Gary Sheffield SP/50
112 Javier Vazquez 15.00 40.00
163 Brandon Webb 6.00 15.00
165 Marcus Giles 8.00 20.00
221 Luis Castillo 4.00 10.00
226 Miguel Cabrera 15.00 40.00

2004 Topps Cracker Jack Mini Blue

*BLUE: 4X TO 10X BASIC
*BLUE: 2.5X TO 6X BASIC RC
*BLUE SP: 1.25X TO 3X BASIC SP
*BLUE SP: 1X TO 2.5X BASIC SP RC
BLUE STATED ODDS 1:10
BLUE SP STATED ODDS 1:60
SP'S ARE SAME AS IN BASIC SET

2004 Topps Cracker Jack Mini Stickers

*STICKERS: .75X TO 2X BASIC
*STICKERS: .75X TO 2X BASIC RC
*SP STICKERS: .4X TO 1X BASIC SP
*SP STICKERS: .4X TO 1X BASIC SP RC
ONE PER SURPRISE PACK
SP ODDS 1:10 SURPRISE PACKS
SP'S ARE SAME AS IN BASIC SET

2004 Topps Cracker Jack Mini White

STATED ODDS 1:6189 HOB, 1:6413 RET
STATED PRINT RUN 1 SET
CARDS ARE NOT SERIAL-NUMBERED
PRINT RUN INFO PROVIDED BY TOPPS
NO PRICING DUE TO SCARCITY

2004 Topps Cracker Jack 1-2-3 Strikes You're Out Relics

GROUP A 1:5045 H, 1:5310 R SURPRISE
GROUP B 1:103 H, 1:109 R SURPRISE
GROUP C 1:177 H, 1:202 R SURPRISE
GROUP D 1:157 H, 1:191 R SURPRISE
BM Brett Myers Jsy C 3.00 8.00
BW Billy Wagner Jsy B 3.00 8.00
BZ Barry Zito Jsy B 3.00 8.00
CCS C.C. Sabathia Jsy C 3.00 8.00
CS Curt Schilling Jsy A 6.00 15.00
DL Derek Lowe Jsy B 3.00 8.00
EG Eric Gagne Jsy C 3.00 8.00
HN Hideo Nomo Jsy B 4.00 10.00
JB Josh Beckett Uni B 3.00 8.00
JS John Smoltz Jsy D 4.00 10.00
KB Kevin Brown Uni B 3.00 8.00
KM Kevin Millwood Jsy D 3.00 8.00
KW Kerry Wood Jsy C 3.00 8.00
MAM Mark Mulder Uni D 3.00 8.00
MM Mike Mussina Uni A 8.00 20.00
PM Pedro Martinez Jsy B 4.00 10.00
RH Rich Harden Jsy B 3.00 8.00
RJ Randy Johnson Jsy B 4.00 10.00

2004 Topps Cracker Jack Secret Surprise Signatures

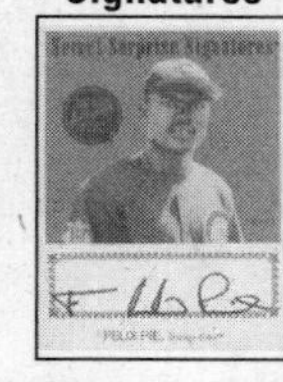

Scott Rolen did not return his cards in time for pack-out and those cards could be redeemed until March 31st, 2006.

GROUP A 1:1448 H, 1:1657 R SURPRISE
GROUP B 1:451 H, 1:524 R SURPRISE
GROUP C 1:323 H, 1:368 R SURPRISE
GROUP D 1:372 H, 1:404 R SURPRISE
AH Aubrey Huff B 6.00 15.00
BG Brian Giles D 6.00 15.00
CF Cliff Floyd B 6.00 15.00
DM Dustin McGowan B 4.00 10.00
DW Dontrelle Willis A 10.00 25.00
FP Felix Pie C 10.00 25.00
JW Jerome Williams A 4.00 10.00
ML Mike Lamb C 4.00 10.00
MV Merkin Valdez B 6.00 15.00
SP Scott Podsednik D 10.00 25.00
SR Scott Rolen C 10.00 25.00

2004 Topps Cracker Jack Take Me Out to the Ballgame Relics

GROUP A 1:654 SURPRISE
GROUP B 1:645 H, 1:645 R SURPRISE
GROUP C 1:152 H, 1:194 R SURPRISE
GROUP D 1:131 H, 1:223 R SURPRISE
GROUP E 1:99 H, 1:125 R SURPRISE
GROUP F 1:201 H, 1:264 R SURPRISE
GROUP G 1:211 H, 1:297 R SURPRISE
GROUP H 1:190 H, 1:226 R SURPRISE
GROUP I 1:126 H, 1:154 R SURPRISE
GROUP J 1:149 H, 1:189 R SURPRISE
GROUP K 1:89 H, 1:93 R SURPRISE
AB Angel Berroa Bat I 3.00 8.00
AD Adam Dunn Jsy C 3.00 8.00
AP Albert Pujols Uni G 6.00 15.00
AP2 Albert Pujols Bat C 6.00 15.00
AR Alex Rodriguez Jsy H 4.00 10.00
AR2 A.Rodriguez Yanks Bat C 8.00 20.00
AS Alfonso Soriano Uni G 3.00 8.00
AS2 Alfonso Soriano Bat A 4.00 10.00
BA Bob Abreu Jsy E 3.00 8.00
BB1 Bret Boone Bat C 3.00 8.00
BB2 Bret Boone Jsy K 3.00 8.00
CB Craig Biggio Jsy E 4.00 10.00
CJ Chipper Jones Jsy K 4.00 10.00
EC Eric Chavez Uni F 3.00 8.00
GA Garrett Anderson Bat B 4.00 10.00
HB Hank Blalock Bat C 3.00 8.00
IR Ivan Rodriguez Bat D 4.00 10.00
JB Jeff Bagwell Uni E 4.00 10.00
JE Jim Edmonds Jsy E 3.00 8.00
JGA Jason Giambi Jsy C 3.00 8.00
JGH Jason Giambi Uni F 3.00 8.00
JL Javy Lopez Jsy E 3.00 8.00
JL2 Javy Lopez Bat A 4.00 10.00
JR Jose Reyes Jsy D 3.00 8.00
JRO Jimmy Rollins Jsy E 3.00 8.00
JT Jim Thome Jsy I 4.00 10.00
KW Kerry Wood Jsy G 3.00 8.00
LB Lance Berkman Bat F 3.00 8.00
LB2 Lance Berkman Jsy K 3.00 8.00
LG Luis Gonzalez Jsy B 4.00 10.00
LW Larry Walker Jsy J 3.00 8.00
MA Moises Alou Jsy J 3.00 8.00
MC Miguel Cabrera Bat H 4.00 10.00
MCT Mark Teixeira Jsy I 4.00 10.00
MG Marcus Giles Jsy E 3.00 8.00
MP Mike Piazza Jsy F 4.00 10.00
MR Manny Ramirez Uni C 4.00 10.00
MS Mike Sweeney Jsy A 4.00 10.00
MT Miguel Tejada Bat K 3.00 8.00
MY Michael Young Jsy D 3.00 8.00
NG Nomar Garciaparra Jsy B 6.00 15.00
NG2 Nomar Garciaparra Bat A 6.00 15.00
PB Pat Burrell Jsy E 3.00 8.00
PL Paul Lo Duca Uni D 3.00 8.00
RB Rocco Baldelli Bat H 3.00 8.00
RF Rafael Furcal Jsy J 3.00 8.00
SG Shawn Green Uni D 3.00 8.00
SG2 Shawn Green Bat C 3.00 8.00
SS Sammy Sosa Bat D 4.00 10.00
SS2 Sammy Sosa Jsy E 4.00 10.00
TG Troy Glaus Jsy I 3.00 8.00
TH Todd Helton Jsy K 4.00 10.00
TKH Torii Hunter Jsy B 4.00 10.00
VW Vernon Wells Jsy D 3.00 8.00

2005 Topps Cracker Jack

This 250-card set was released in April, 2004. These cards were issued in nine-card packs with a $3 SRP which came 20 packs to a box and 12 boxes to a

case. There were random short prints sprinkled throughout the set and these cards are notated in our checklist as SP's and were issued to a stated rate of one in three.

COMPLETE SET (250) 100.00 200.00
COMP.SET w/o SP'S (200) 15.00 40.00
SP STATED ODDS 1:3 HOBBY/RETAIL
SP CL: 1/3B/4/6/11/13/21/26/30/31/41/51
SP CL: 56/60B/71/75A/75B/84/85B/106/110
SP CL: 111/112/126/135A/135B/146/151/156
SP CL: 164B/166/176/181/186/191/196/201
SP CL: 211/216/221A/221B/225/226/228B
SP CL: 231/235/236A/236B
1 David Wright SP 3.00 8.00
2 Rafael Furcal .15 .40
3A Alex Rodriguez Portrait .60 1.50
3B Alex Rodriguez Fielding SP 2.50 6.00
4 Victor Martinez SP 1.50 4.00
5 Ken Griffey Jr. .60 1.50
6 Bobby Crosby SP 1.50 4.00
7 Ivan Rodriguez .25 .60
8 Darin Erstad .15 .40
9 Javy Lopez .15 .40
10 Brian Giles .15 .40
11 Aaron Rowand SP 1.50 4.00
12 Joe Torre MG .25 .60
13 Zack Greinke SP 1.50 4.00
14 Shannon Stewart .15 .40
15 Jack Wilson .15 .40
16 Jose Vidro .15 .40
17 Josh Beckett .15 .40
18 Barry Zito .15 .40
19 Bret Boone .15 .40
20 Greg Maddux .60 1.50
21 Carl Crawford SP 1.50 4.00
22 Mark Teixeira .25 .60
23 Jason Schmidt .15 .40
24 Kazuhisa Ishii .15 .40
25 Mike Piazza .40 1.00
26 Daniel Cabrera SP 1.50 4.00
27 Mike Lieberthal .15 .40
28 Gil Meche .15 .40
29 Phil Nevin .15 .40
30 Adrian Beltre SP 1.50 4.00
31 Chipper Jones SP 2.00 5.00
32 Zach Day .15 .40
33 Ben Sheets .15 .40
34 Carlos Zambrano .15 .40
35 Melvin Mora .15 .40
36 Joe Mauer .40 1.00
37 Ken Harvey .15 .40
38 Bernie Williams .15 .40
39 Mike Maroth .15 .40
40 Eric Chavez .15 .40
41 Matt Lawton SP 1.50 4.00
42 Ray Durham .15 .40
43 Vernon Wells .15 .40
44 Mike Lowell .15 .40
45 Jim Thome .25 .60
46 Joel Pineiro .15 .40
47 Lance Berkman .15 .40
48 Ryan Klesko .15 .40
49 Adam Dunn .15 .40
50 Vladimir Guerrero .40 1.00
51 Eric Gagne SP 1.50 4.00
52 Richie Sexson .15 .40
53 Javier Vazquez .15 .40
54 Roy Oswalt .15 .40
55 Carlos Delgado .15 .40
56 John Buck SP 1.50 4.00
57 Kenny Rogers .15 .40
58 Sidney Ponson .15 .40
59 Vicente Padilla .15 .40
60A Mark Prior Leg Up .25 .60
60B Mark Prior Portrait SP 2.00 5.00
61 A.J. Pierzynski .15 .40
62 Aubrey Huff .15 .40
63 Shea Hillenbrand .15 .40
64 Carlos Guillen .15 .40
65 Lyle Overbay .15 .40
66 Al Leiter .15 .40
67 Eric Hinske .15 .40
68 Laynce Nix .15 .40
69 Scott Hairston .15 .40
70 Roger Clemens .60 1.50
71 Cesar Izturis SP 1.50 4.00
72 Shawn Green .15 .40
73 Marcus Giles .15 .40
74 Rafael Palmeiro .25 .60
75A Gary Sheffield SP 1.50 4.00
75B Melky Cabrera SP 3.00 8.00
76 Juan Pierre .15 .40
77 Pat Burrell .15 .40
78 Sean Burroughs .15 .40
79 Frank Thomas .40 1.00
80 Andruw Jones .25 .60
81 C.C. Sabathia .15 .40
82 Jeff Bagwell .25 .60
83 Tom Glavine .25 .60
84 Craig Wilson SP 1.50 4.00
85A Johan Santana Throwing .40 1.00
85B Johan Santana Portrait SP 2.50 6.00
86 Raul Ibanez .15 .40
87 Sean Casey .15 .40
88 Bucky Jacobsen .15 .40
89 B.J. Upton .25 .60
90 Bobby Abreu .15 .40
91 Geoff Jenkins .15 .40
92 Troy Glaus .15 .40
93 Dontrelle Willis .15 .40
94 Jose Lima .15 .40
95 Rocco Baldelli .15 .40
96 Aramis Ramirez .15 .40
97 Paul Lo Duca .15 .40
98 Torii Hunter .15 .40
99 Jay Payton .15 .40
100 Carlos Beltran .15 .40
101 Jaret Wright .15 .40
102 Jason Bay .15 .40
103 Cliff Floyd .15 .40
104 Mike Sweeney .15 .40
105 Sammy Sosa .40 1.00
106 Khalil Greene SP 2.00 5.00
107 David DeJesus .15 .40
108 Jermaine Dye .15 .40
109 Miguel Cabrera .25 .60
110 Miguel Tejada SP 1.50 4.00
111 Johnny Estrada SP 1.50 4.00
112 Ronnie Belliard SP 1.50 4.00
113 Austin Kearns .15 .40
114 Erubiel Durazo .15 .40
115 Preston Wilson .15 .40
116 Hideo Nomo .40 1.00
117 Dmitri Young .15 .40
118 Jon Lieber .15 .40
119 Derrek Lee .25 .60
120 Todd Helton .25 .60
121 Omar Vizquel .25 .60
122 Wily Mo Pena .15 .40
123 J.D. Drew .15 .40
124 Matt Holliday .20 .50
125 Ichiro Suzuki .75 2.00
126 Mark Buehrle SP 1.50 4.00
127 Barry Bonds 1.00 2.50
128 Jeff Kent .15 .40
129 Kerry Wood .15 .40
130 Mariano Rivera .40 1.00
131 Nick Johnson .15 .40
132 Randy Winn .15 .40
133 Phil Garner MG .15 .40
134 Jose Reyes .15 .40
135A Michael Young SP 1.50 4.00
135B Ian Kinsler SP 4.00 10.00
136 Jose Contreras .15 .40
137 Oliver Perez .15 .40
138 Roy Halladay .15 .40
139 Kevin Millwood .15 .40
140 Jorge Posada .25 .60
141 Mike Cameron .15 .40
142 Edgardo Alfonzo .15 .40
143 Chris Shelton .25 .60
144 Luis Castillo .15 .40
145 Alfonso Soriano .15 .40
146 Ryan Drese SP 1.50 4.00
147 Mark Mulder .15 .40
148 Jason Giambi .15 .40
149 Travis Hafner .15 .40
150 Randy Johnson .40 1.00
151 Paul Konerko SP 1.50 4.00
152 Mike Mussina .25 .60
153 Brad Wilkerson .15 .40
154 Tim Hudson .15 .40
155 Garret Anderson .15 .40
156 Chase Utley SP 2.00 5.00
157 Jamie Moyer .15 .40
158 Scott Kazmir .15 .40
159 Brett Myers .15 .40
160 Kazuo Matsui .15 .40
161 Orlando Hudson .15 .40
162 Luis Gonzalez .15 .40
163 Kevin Youkilis .15 .40
164A Jason Kendall .15 .40
164B Landon Powell SP 2.00 5.00
165 Hank Blalock .15 .40
166 Mark Loretta SP 1.50 4.00
167 Miguel Cairo .15 .40
168 Corey Patterson .15 .40
169 Victor Zambrano .15 .40
170 Magglio Ordonez .15 .40
171 J.T. Snow .15 .40
172 Randy Wolf .15 .40
173 Rich Harden .15 .40
174 Bartolo Colon .15 .40
175 Derek Jeter .75 2.00
176 Casey Kotchman SP 1.50 4.00
177 Val Majewski .15 .40
178 Grady Sizemore .25 .60
179 Rickie Weeks .15 .40
180 Robinson Cano .25 .60
181 Nick Swisher SP 1.50 4.00
182 Ryan Howard 1.00 2.50
183 John Van Benschoten .15 .40
184 Delmon Young .25 .60
185 Aaron Hill .15 .40
186 Chris Burke SP 1.50 4.00
187 Merkin Valdez .15 .40
188 Jeremy Reed .15 .40
189 Conor Jackson .25 .60
190 Mark Teahen .15 .40
191 Joey Gathright SP 1.50 4.00
192 Gavin Floyd .15 .40
193 Joe Blanton .15 .40
194 Jason Kubel .15 .40
195 Jeff Francis .15 .40
196 Angel Guzman SP 1.50 4.00
197 Dallas McPherson .15 .40
198 Melky Cabrera RC .75 2.00
199 Jake Dittler .20 .50
200 Elvys Quezada RC .30 .75
201 Ian Kinsler SP RC 4.00 10.00
202 Nate McLouth RC .40 1.00
203 Chris Seddon RC .30 .75
204 Chad Orvella RC .30 .75
205 Ian Bladergroen RC .40 1.00
206 James Jurries SP RC 2.00 5.00
207 Landon Powell RC .40 1.00
208 Eric Nielsen RC .30 .75
209 Chris Roberson RC .30 .75
210 Andre Ethier RC 2.00 5.00
211 Chris Denorfia SP RC 2.00 5.00
212 Darren Fenster RC .30 .75
213 Jeremy West RC .40 1.00
214 Sean Marshall RC 1.00 2.50
215 Ryan Sweeney RC .50 1.25
216 Steve Doetsch SP RC 2.00 5.00
217 Kevin Melillo RC .40 1.00
218 Chip Cannon RC .40 1.00
219 Tony La Russa MG .15 .40
220 Chris Carpenter .15 .40
221A Edgar Renteria Sox SP 1.50 4.00
221B Edgar Renteria Cards SP 1.50 4.00
222 Albert Pujols .75 2.00
223 Jim Edmonds .15 .40
224 Jason Marquis .15 .40
225 Scott Rolen SP 2.00 5.00
226 Larry Walker SP 2.00 5.00
227 Matt Morris .15 .40
228A Mike Matheny Giants .15 .40
228B Mike Matheny Cards SP 1.50 4.00
229 Jeromy Burnitz .15 .40
230 Terry Francona MG .25 .60
231 Johnny Damon SP 2.00 5.00
232 Keith Foulke .15 .40
233 Trot Nixon .15 .40
234 Manny Ramirez .25 .60
235 David Ortiz SP 2.00 5.00
236A Pedro Martinez Sox SP 2.00 5.00
236B Pedro Martinez Mets SP 2.00 5.00
237 Curt Schilling .25 .60
238 Kevin Millar .15 .40
239 Bill Mueller .15 .40
240 Mark Bellhorn .15 .40
NNO Josh Beckett NNO SP 1.50 4.00

2005 Topps Cracker Jack Mini Blue

*BLUE: 8X TO 20X BASIC
*BLUE: 5X TO 12X BASIC RC
STATED ODDS 1:75 HOBBY/RETAIL
STATED PRINT RUN 50 SERIAL #'d SETS
1 David Wright 12.50 30.00
3B Alex Rodriguez Fielding 12.50 30.00
4 Victor Martinez 3.00 8.00
6 Bobby Crosby 3.00 8.00
11 Aaron Rowand 3.00 8.00
13 Zack Greinke 3.00 8.00
21 Carl Crawford 3.00 8.00
26 Daniel Cabrera 3.00 8.00
30 Adrian Beltre 3.00 8.00
31 Chipper Jones 8.00 20.00
41 Matt Lawton 3.00 8.00
51 Eric Gagne 3.00 8.00
56 John Buck 3.00 8.00
60A Mark Prior Leg Up 5.00 12.00
60B Mark Prior Portrait 5.00 12.00
71 Cesar Izturis 3.00 8.00
75A Gary Sheffield 3.00 8.00
75B Melky Cabrera 8.00 20.00
84 Craig Wilson 3.00 8.00
85B Johan Santana Portrait 8.00 20.00
106 Khalil Greene 5.00 12.00
110 Miguel Tejada 3.00 8.00
111 Johnny Estrada 3.00 8.00
112 Ronnie Belliard 3.00 8.00
126 Mark Buehrle 3.00 8.00
135A Michael Young 3.00 8.00
135B Ian Kinsler 10.00 25.00
146 Ryan Drese 3.00 8.00
151 Paul Konerko 3.00 8.00
156 Chase Utley 5.00 12.00
164B Landon Powell 5.00 12.00
166 Mark Loretta 3.00 8.00
176 Casey Kotchman 3.00 8.00
181 Nick Swisher 3.00 8.00
186 Chris Burke 3.00 8.00
191 Joey Gathright 3.00 8.00
196 Angel Guzman 3.00 8.00
201 Ian Kinsler 10.00 25.00
206 James Jurries 5.00 12.00
216 Steve Doetsch 5.00 12.00
221A Edgar Renteria Sox 3.00 8.00
221B Edgar Renteria Cards 3.00 8.00
225 Scott Rolen 5.00 12.00
226 Larry Walker 5.00 12.00
228B Mike Matheny Cards 3.00 8.00
231 Johnny Damon 5.00 12.00
235 David Ortiz 5.00 12.00
236A Pedro Martinez Sox 5.00 12.00
236B Pedro Martinez Mets 5.00 12.00
NNO Josh Beckett NNO 3.00 8.00

2005 Topps Cracker Jack Mini Grey

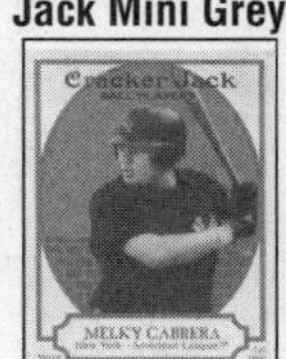

STATED ODDS 1:151 HOBBY, 1:150 RETAIL
STATED PRINT RUN 25 SERIAL #'d SETS
NO PRICING DUE TO SCARCITY

2005 Topps Cracker Jack Mini Red

COMP.SET w/o SP'S (200) 40.00 80.00
*RED: .75X TO 2X BASIC
*RED: .75X TO 2X BASIC RC
ONE PER PACK
*RED SP: .6X TO 1.5X BASIC SP
*RED SP: .5X TO 1.2X BASIC SP RC
SP STATED ODDS 1:20 HOBBY/RETAIL

2005 Topps Cracker Jack Mini Stickers

COMP.SET w/o SP'S (200) 40.00 80.00
*STICKER: .75X TO 2X BASIC
*STICKER: .75X TO 2X BASIC RC
ONE PER PACK
*STICKER SP: .6X TO 1.5X BASIC SP
*STICKER SP: .5X TO 1.2X BASIC SP RC
SP STATED ODDS 1:20 HOBBY/RETAIL

2005 Topps Cracker Jack Mini White

STATED ODDS 1:3763 HOB, 1:3813 RET
STATED PRINT RUN 1 SERIAL #'d SET
NO PRICING DUE TO SCARCITY

2005 Topps Cracker Jack 1-2-3 Strikes You're Out Mini Relics

STATED ODDS 1:204 HOBBY/RETAIL
BR Brad Radke Jsy 3.00 8.00
CS Curt Schilling Jsy 6.00 15.00
JB Josh Beckett Uni 3.00 8.00
JW Jaret Wright Jsy 3.00 8.00
RD Ryan Drese Jsy 3.00 8.00
RO Russ Ortiz Jsy 3.00 8.00

2005 Topps Cracker Jack Autographs

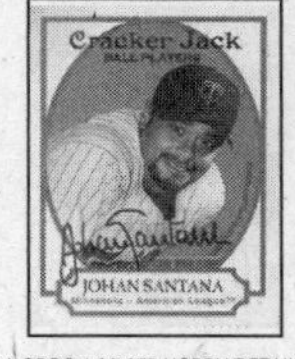

GROUP A ODDS 1:38,675 HOBBY/RETAIL
GROUP B ODDS 1:1864 HOBBY/RETAIL
GROUP A PRINT RUN 25 SERIAL #'d SETS
GROUP B PRINT RUN 50 SERIAL #'d SETS
NO GROUP A PRICING DUE TO SCARCITY
AR Alex Rodriguez B/50 300.00 500.00
BB Barry Bonds A/25
CC Carl Crawford B/50 30.00 60.00
CS C.C. Sabathia B/50 30.00 60.00
CW Craig Wilson B/50 15.00 40.00
DW David Wright B/50 125.00 200.00
EC Eric Chavez B/50 30.00 60.00
EG Eric Gagne B/50 40.00 80.00
GA Garrett Anderson B/50 30.00 60.00
JS Johan Santana B/50 30.00 60.00

2005 Topps Cracker Jack Secret Surprise Mini Autographs

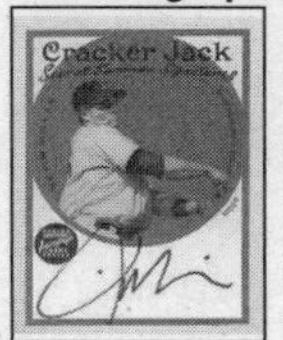

GROUP A ODDS 1:2328 HOBBY/RETAIL
GROUP B ODDS 1:517 HOBBY/RETAIL
GROUP C ODDS 1:1864 HOBBY/RETAIL
GROUP D ODDS 1:163 HOBBY/RETAIL
GROUP E ODDS 1:930 HOBBY/RETAIL
GROUP F ODDS 1:155 HOBBY/RETAIL
GROUP A PRINT RUN 100 COPIES PER
GROUP A ARE NOT SERIAL-NUMBERED
GROUP A PRINT RUN PROVIDED BY TOPPS
AG Angel Guzman F 4.00 10.00
AR Alex Rodriguez A/100 * 200.00 350.00
CC Carl Crawford D 6.00 15.00

CN Chris Nelson F 8.00 20.00
CS C.C. Sabathia D 6.00 15.00
CT Curtis Thigpen B 6.00 15.00
CW Craig Wilson D 4.00 10.00
DM Dallas McPherson A/100 * 10.00 25.00
DW David Wright D 20.00 50.00
EC Eric Chavez B 10.00 25.00
EG Eric Gagne D 8.00 20.00
GA Garret Anderson B 10.00 25.00
HB Hank Blalock D 6.00 15.00
JS Johan Santana B 15.00 40.00
KM Kevin Millar F 12.50 30.00
MK Mark Kotsay A/100 * 10.00 25.00
ML Mark Loretta A/100 * 10.00 25.00
MM Melvin Mora E 6.00 15.00
RR Richie Robnett F 6.00 15.00
SK Scott Kazmir C 10.00 25.00

2005 Topps Cracker Jack Take Me Out to the Ballgame Mini Relics

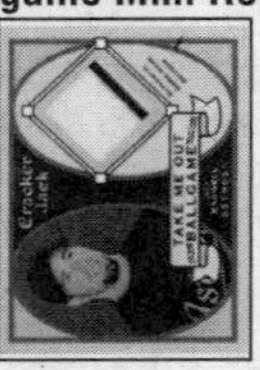

STATED ODDS 1:16 HOBBY/RETAIL
AB Adrian Beltre Bat 3.00 8.00
AB1 Angel Berroa Bat 3.00 8.00
AB2 Angel Berroa Uni 3.00 8.00
AD Adam Dunn Bat 3.00 8.00
AL Adam LaRoche Bat 3.00 8.00
AP Albert Pujols Jsy 8.00 20.00
AR Alex Rodriguez Bat 6.00 15.00
ARA Aramis Ramirez Bat 3.00 8.00
AS Alfonso Soriano Bat 3.00 8.00
BB Barry Bonds Uni 12.50 30.00
BC Bobby Cox Uni 3.00 8.00
BCR Bobby Crosby Bat 3.00 8.00
BK Bobby Kielty Bat 3.00 8.00
BS Benito Santiago Bat 4.00 10.00
BW Bernie Williams Uni 4.00 10.00
CB Carlos Beltran Bat 3.00 8.00
CBI Craig Biggio Uni 4.00 10.00
CC Coco Crisp Bat 3.00 8.00
CG Cristian Guzman Bat 3.00 8.00
CP Corey Patterson Bat 3.00 8.00
CT Charles Thomas Bat 3.00 8.00
DE Darin Erstad Bat 3.00 8.00
DM Doug Mientkiewicz Bat 3.00 8.00
DO David Ortiz Bat 4.00 10.00
DW Dontrelle Willis Bat 3.00 8.00
EC1 Eric Chavez Bat 3.00 8.00
EC2 Eric Chavez Uni 3.00 8.00
GS Gary Sheffield Bat 3.00 8.00
HB1 Hank Blalock Bat 3.00 8.00
HB2 Hank Blalock Uni 3.00 8.00
HB3 Hank Blalock Jsy 3.00 8.00
IR1 Ivan Rodriguez Bat 4.00 10.00
IR2 Ivan Rodriguez Jsy 4.00 10.00
JB Jeff Bagwell Uni 4.00 10.00
JE Johnny Estrada Jsy 3.00 8.00
JE1 Jim Edmonds Bat 3.00 8.00
JE2 Jim Edmonds Jsy 3.00 8.00
JG Jody Gerut Bat 3.00 8.00
JGI Jay Gibbons Bat 3.00 8.00
JGU Jose Guillen Bat 3.00 8.00
JJ Jacque Jones Bat 3.00 8.00
JK Jason Kendall Bat 3.00 8.00
JP1 Jorge Posada Bat 4.00 10.00
JP2 Jorge Posada Jsy 4.00 10.00
JR Jeremy Reed Bat 3.00 8.00
JT Jim Thome Bat 4.00 10.00
JTO Joe Torre Uni 6.00 15.00
KM Kevin Millar Bat 4.00 10.00
KME Kevin Mench Jsy 3.00 8.00
LB1 Lance Berkman Bat 3.00 8.00
LB2 Lance Berkman Jsy 3.00 8.00
LG Luis Gonzalez Bat 3.00 8.00
LN Laynce Nix Jsy 3.00 8.00
MC Miguel Cabrera Bat 4.00 10.00
MG Marcus Giles Bat 3.00 8.00
MK Mark Kotsay Bat 3.00 8.00
MM Melvin Mora Bat 3.00 8.00
MO Magglio Ordonez Bat 3.00 8.00
MP Mike Piazza Uni 4.00 10.00
MR Manny Ramirez Bat 4.00 10.00
MRE Mike Restovich Bat 3.00 8.00
MTE1 Miguel Tejada Uni 3.00 8.00
MTE2 Miguel Tejada Bat 3.00 8.00
MT1 Mark Teixeira Uni 4.00 10.00
MT2 Mark Teixeira Jsy 4.00 10.00
MT3 Mark Teixeira Bat 4.00 10.00
MY Michael Young Jsy 3.00 8.00
NG Nick Green Jsy 3.00 8.00
OV Omar Vizquel Bat 4.00 10.00
PK Paul Konerko Bat 3.00 8.00
PN Phil Nevin Bat 3.00 8.00
RB Ron Belliard Bat 3.00 8.00
RF Rafael Furcal Jsy 3.00 8.00
RK Ryan Klesko Jsy 3.00 8.00
RP Rafael Palmeiro Bat 4.00 10.00
RS Reggie Sanders Bat 3.00 8.00
SB Sean Burroughs Bat 3.00 8.00
SG Shawn Green Bat 3.00 8.00
TG Troy Glaus Bat 3.00 8.00
TH Todd Helton Bat 4.00 10.00
THU Torii Hunter Bat 3.00 8.00
VC Vinny Castilla Bat 3.00 8.00
VG Vladimir Guerrero Bat 4.00 10.00
VM Victor Martinez Bat 3.00 8.00

1996 Topps Gallery

The 1996 Topps Gallery set was issued in one series totalling 180 cards. The eight-card packs retailed for $3.00 each. The set is divided into five themes: Classics (1-90), New Editions (91-108), Modernists (109-126), Futurists (127-144) and Masters (145-180). Each theme features a different design on front, but the bulk of the set has full-bleed, color action shots. A Mickey Mantle Masterpiece was

inserted into these packs at a rate of one every 48 packs. It is priced at the bottom of these listings.

COMPLETE SET (180) 20.00 40.00
1 Tom Glavine .30 .75
2 Carlos Baerga .20 .50
3 Dante Bichette .20 .50
4 Mark Langston .20 .50
5 Ray Lankford .20 .50
6 Moises Alou .20 .50
7 Marquis Grissom .20 .50
8 Ramon Martinez .20 .50
9 Steve Finley .20 .50
10 Todd Hundley .20 .50
11 Brady Anderson .20 .50
12 John Valentin .20 .50
13 Heathcliff Slocumb .20 .50
14 Ruben Sierra .20 .50
15 Jeff Conine .20 .50
16 Jay Buhner .20 .50
17 Sammy Sosa .50 1.25
18 Doug Drabek .20 .50
19 Jose Mesa .20 .50
20 Jeff King .20 .50
21 Mickey Tettleton .20 .50
22 Jeff Montgomery .20 .50
23 Alex Fernandez .20 .50
24 Greg Vaughn .20 .50
25 Chuck Finley .20 .50
26 Terry Steinbach .20 .50
27 Rod Beck .20 .50
28 Jack McDowell .20 .50
29 Mark Wohlers .20 .50
30 Len Dykstra .20 .50
31 Bernie Williams .30 .75
32 Travis Fryman .20 .50
33 Jose Canseco .30 .75
34 Ken Caminiti .20 .50
35 Devon White .20 .50
36 Bobby Bonilla .20 .50
37 Paul Sorrento .20 .50
38 Ryne Sandberg .75 2.00
39 Derek Bell .20 .50
40 Bobby Jones .20 .50
41 J.T. Snow .20 .50
42 Denny Neagle .20 .50
43 Tim Wakefield .20 .50
44 Andres Galarraga .20 .50
45 David Segui .20 .50
46 Lee Smith .20 .50
47 Mel Rojas .20 .50
48 John Franco .20 .50
49 Pete Schourek .20 .50
50 John Wetteland .20 .50
51 Paul Molitor .20 .50
52 Ivan Rodriguez .30 .75
53 Chris Hoiles .20 .50
54 Mike Greenwell .20 .50
55 Orel Hershiser .20 .50
56 Brian McRae .20 .50
57 Geronimo Berroa .20 .50
58 Craig Biggio .30 .75
59 David Justice .20 .50
60 Lance Johnson .20 .50
61 Andy Ashby .20 .50
62 Randy Myers .20 .50
63 Gregg Jefferies .20 .50
64 Kevin Appier .20 .50
65 Rick Aguilera .20 .50
66 Shane Reynolds .20 .50
67 John Smoltz .30 .75
68 Ron Gant .20 .50
69 Eric Karros .20 .50
70 Jim Thome .30 .75
71 Terry Pendleton .20 .50
72 Kenny Rogers .20 .50
73 Robin Ventura .20 .50
74 Dave Nilsson .20 .50
75 Brian Jordan .20 .50
76 Glenallen Hill .20 .50
77 Greg Colbrunn .20 .50
78 Roberto Alomar .20 .50
79 Rickey Henderson .50 1.25
80 Carlos Garcia .20 .50
81 Dean Palmer .20 .50
82 Mike Stanley .20 .50
83 Hal Morris .20 .50
84 Wade Boggs .30 .75
85 Chad Curtis .20 .50
86 Roberto Hernandez .20 .50
87 John Olerud .20 .50
88 Frank Castillo .20 .50
89 Rafael Palmeiro .30 .75
90 Trevor Hoffman .20 .50
91 Marty Cordova .20 .50
92 Hideo Nomo .50 1.25
93 Johnny Damon .30 .75
94 Bill Pulsipher .20 .50
95 Garret Anderson .20 .50
96 Ray Durham .20 .50
97 Ricky Bottalico .20 .50
98 Carlos Perez .20 .50
99 Troy Percival .20 .50
100 Chipper Jones .50 1.25
101 Esteban Loaiza .20 .50
102 John Mabry .20 .50
103 Jon Nunnally .20 .50
104 Andy Pettitte .30 .75
105 Lyle Mouton .20 .50
106 Jason Isringhausen .20 .50
107 Brian L.Hunter .20 .50
108 Quilvio Veras .20 .50
109 Jim Edmonds .20 .50
110 Ryan Klesko .20 .50
111 Pedro Martinez .30 .75
112 Joey Hamilton .20 .50
113 Vinny Castilla .20 .50
114 Alex Gonzalez .20 .50
115 Raul Mondesi .20 .50
116 Rondell White .20 .50
117 Dan Miceli .20 .50
118 Tom Goodwin .20 .50
119 Bret Boone .20 .50
120 Shawn Green .20 .50
121 Jeff Cirillo .20 .50
122 Rico Brogna .20 .50
123 Chris Gomez .20 .50
124 Ismael Valdes .20 .50
125 Javy Lopez .20 .50
126 Manny Ramirez .30 .75
127 Paul Wilson .20 .50
128 Billy Wagner .20 .50
129 Eric Owens .20 .50
130 Todd Greene .20 .50
131 Karim Garcia .20 .50
132 Jimmy Haynes .20 .50
133 Michael Tucker .20 .50
134 John Wasdin .20 .50
135 Brooks Kieschnick .20 .50
136 Alex Ochoa .20 .50
137 Ariel Prieto .20 .50
138 Tony Clark .20 .50
139 Mark Loretta .20 .50
140 Rey Ordonez .20 .50
141 Chris Snopek .20 .50
142 Roger Cedeno .20 .50
143 Derek Jeter 1.25 3.00
144 Jeff Suppan .20 .50
145 Greg Maddux .75 2.00
146 Ken Griffey Jr. .75 2.00
147 Tony Gwynn .60 1.50
148 Darren Daulton .20 .50
149 Will Clark .30 .75
150 Mo Vaughn .20 .50
151 Reggie Sanders .20 .50
152 Kirby Puckett .50 1.25
153 Paul O'Neill .30 .75
154 Tim Salmon .30 .75
155 Mark McGwire 1.25 3.00
156 Barry Bonds 1.25 3.00
157 Albert Belle .20 .50
158 Edgar Martinez .30 .75
159 Mike Mussina .30 .75
160 Cecil Fielder .20 .50
161 Kenny Lofton .20 .50
162 Randy Johnson .50 1.25
163 Juan Gonzalez .20 .50
164 Jeff Bagwell .30 .75
165 Joe Carter .20 .50
166 Mike Piazza .75 2.00
167 Eddie Murray .50 1.25
168 Cal Ripken 1.50 4.00
169 Barry Larkin .30 .75
170 Chuck Knoblauch .20 .50
171 Chili Davis .20 .50
172 Fred McGriff .30 .75
173 Matt Williams .20 .50
174 Roger Clemens 1.00 2.50
175 Frank Thomas .50 1.25
176 Dennis Eckersley .20 .50
177 Gary Sheffield .20 .50
178 David Cone .20 .50
179 Larry Walker .20 .50
180 Mark Grace .30 .75
NNO M. Mantle Masterpiece 8.00 20.00

1996 Topps Gallery Players Private Issue

Randomly inserted in packs at a rate of one in 12, this 180-card parallel is foil stamped. The backs are sequentially numbered 0-999, with the first 100 cards (numbers 0-99) sent to the players and the balance inserted in packs. Topps released a statement at the end of the 1996 season, claiming that they destroyed 400 sets.

*STARS: 6X TO 15X BASIC CARDS
*ROOKIES: 5X TO 12X BASIC CARDS

1996 Topps Gallery Expressionists

Randomly inserted in packs at a rate of one in 24, this 20-card set features leaders printed on triple foil stamped and texture embossed cards. Card backs contain a second photo and narrative about the player.

COMPLETE SET (20) 30.00 80.00
1 Mike Piazza 3.00 8.00
2 J.T. Snow .75 2.00
3 Ken Griffey Jr. 3.00 8.00
4 Kirby Puckett 2.00 5.00
5 Carlos Baerga .75 2.00
6 Chipper Jones 2.00 5.00
7 Hideo Nomo 2.00 5.00
8 Mark McGwire 5.00 12.00
9 Gary Sheffield .75 2.00
10 Randy Johnson 2.00 5.00
11 Ray Lankford .75 2.00
12 Sammy Sosa 2.00 5.00
13 Denny Martinez .75 2.00
14 Jose Canseco 1.25 3.00
15 Tony Gwynn 2.50 6.00
16 Edgar Martinez 1.25 3.00
17 Reggie Sanders .75 2.00
18 Andres Galarraga .75 2.00
19 Albert Belle .75 2.00
20 Barry Larkin 1.25 3.00

1996 Topps Gallery Photo Gallery

Randomly inserted in packs at a rate of one in 30, this 15-card set features top photography chronicling baseball's biggest stars and greatest moments from last year. Each double foil stamped card is printed on 24 pt. stock with customized designs to accentuate the photography.

COMPLETE SET (15) 30.00 80.00
PG1 Eddie Murray 2.50 6.00
PG2 Randy Johnson 2.50 6.00
PG3 Cal Ripken 8.00 20.00
PG4 Bret Boone 1.00 2.50
PG5 Frank Thomas 2.50 6.00
PG6 Jeff Conine 1.00 2.50
PG7 Johnny Damon 1.50 4.00
PG8 Roger Clemens 5.00 12.00
PG9 Albert Belle 1.00 2.50
PG10 Ken Griffey Jr. 4.00 10.00
PG11 Kirby Puckett 2.50 6.00
PG12 David Justice 1.00 2.50
PG13 Bobby Bonilla 1.00 2.50
PG14 Colorado Rockies 1.00 2.50
PG15 Atlanta Braves 1.00 2.50

1997 Topps Gallery Promos

This four-card set was distributed as a promotion for the 1997 Topps Gallery set and features color player pictures in four different frame designs with a player portrait, biographical, and career statistics on the backs.

COMPLETE SET (4) 4.00 10.00
PP1 Andruw Jones 1.25 3.00
PP2 Derek Jeter 2.50 6.00
PP3 Mike Piazza 1.50 4.00
PP4 Craig Biggio .40 1.00

1997 Topps Gallery

The 1997 Topps Gallery set was issued in one series totalling 180 cards. The eight-card packs retailed for $4.00 each. This hobby only set is divided into four themes: Veterans, Prospects, Rising Stars and Young Stars. Printed on 24-point card stock with a high-gloss film and etch stamped with one or more foils, each theme features a different design on front with a variety of informative statistics and revealing player text on the back.

COMPLETE SET (180) 20.00 50.00
1 Paul Molitor .20 .50
2 Devon White .20 .50
3 Andres Galarraga .20 .50
4 Cal Ripken 1.50 4.00
5 Tony Gwynn .60 1.50
6 Mike Stanley .20 .50
7 Orel Hershiser .20 .50
8 Jose Canseco .30 .75
9 Chili Davis .20 .50
10 Harold Baines .20 .50
11 Rickey Henderson .50 1.25
12 Darryl Strawberry .20 .50
13 Todd Worrell .20 .50
14 Cecil Fielder .20 .50
15 Gary Gaetti .20 .50
16 Bobby Bonilla .20 .50
17 Will Clark .30 .75
18 Kevin Brown .20 .50
19 Tom Glavine .30 .75
20 Wade Boggs .30 .75
21 Edgar Martinez .30 .75
22 Lance Johnson .20 .50
23 Gregg Jefferies .20 .50
24 Bip Roberts .20 .50
25 Tony Phillips .20 .50
26 Greg Maddux .75 2.00
27 Mickey Tettleton .20 .50
28 Terry Steinbach .20 .50
29 Ryne Sandberg .75 2.00
30 Wally Joyner .20 .50
31 Joe Carter .20 .50
32 Ellis Burks .20 .50
33 Fred McGriff .30 .75
34 Barry Larkin .30 .75
35 John Franco .20 .50
36 Rafael Palmeiro .30 .75
37 Mark McGwire 1.25 3.00
38 Ken Caminiti .20 .50
39 David Cone .20 .50
40 Julio Franco .20 .50
41 Roger Clemens 1.00 2.50
42 Barry Bonds 1.25 3.00
43 Dennis Eckersley .20 .50
44 Eddie Murray .50 1.25
45 Paul O'Neill .30 .75
46 Craig Biggio .30 .75
47 Roberto Alomar .30 .75
48 Mark Grace .30 .75
49 Matt Williams .20 .50
50 Jay Buhner .20 .50
51 John Smoltz .30 .75
52 Randy Johnson .50 1.25
53 Ramon Martinez .20 .50
54 Curt Schilling .20 .50
55 Gary Sheffield .20 .50
56 Jack McDowell .20 .50
57 Brady Anderson .20 .50
58 Dante Bichette .20 .50
59 Ron Gant .20 .50
60 Alex Fernandez .20 .50
61 Moises Alou .20 .50
62 Travis Fryman .20 .50
63 Dean Palmer .20 .50
64 Todd Hundley .20 .50
65 Jeff Brantley .20 .50
66 Bernard Gilkey .20 .50
67 Geronimo Berroa .20 .50
68 John Wetteland .20 .50
69 Robin Ventura .20 .50
70 Ray Lankford .20 .50
71 Kevin Appier .20 .50
72 Larry Walker .20 .50
73 Juan Gonzalez .20 .50
74 Jeff King .20 .50
75 Greg Vaughn .20 .50
76 Steve Finley .20 .50
77 Brian McRae .20 .50
78 Paul Sorrento .20 .50
79 Ken Griffey Jr. .75 2.00
80 Omar Vizquel .30 .75
81 Jose Mesa .20 .50
82 Albert Belle .20 .50
83 Glenallen Hill .20 .50
84 Sammy Sosa .50 1.25
85 Andy Benes .20 .50
86 David Justice .20 .50
87 Marquis Grissom .20 .50
88 John Olerud .20 .50
89 Tino Martinez .30 .75
90 Frank Thomas .50 1.25
91 Raul Mondesi .20 .50
92 Steve Trachsel .20 .50
93 Jim Edmonds .20 .50
94 Rusty Greer .20 .50
95 Joey Hamilton .20 .50
96 Ismael Valdes .20 .50
97 Dave Nilsson .20 .50
98 John Jaha .20 .50
99 Alex Gonzalez .20 .50
100 Javy Lopez .20 .50
101 Ryan Klesko .20 .50
102 Tim Salmon .30 .75
103 Bernie Williams .30 .75
104 Roberto Hernandez .20 .50
105 Chuck Knoblauch .20 .50
106 Mike Lansing .20 .50
107 Vinny Castilla .20 .50
108 Reggie Sanders .20 .50
109 Mo Vaughn .20 .50
110 Rondell White .20 .50
111 Ivan Rodriguez .30 .75
112 Mike Mussina .30 .75
113 Carlos Baerga .20 .50
114 Jeff Conine .20 .50
115 Jim Thome .30 .75
116 Manny Ramirez .30 .75
117 Kenny Lofton .20 .50
118 Wilson Alvarez .20 .50
119 Eric Karros .20 .50
120 Robb Nen .20 .50
121 Mark Wohlers .20 .50
122 Ed Sprague .20 .50
123 Pat Hentgen .20 .50
124 Juan Guzman .20 .50
125 Derek Bell .20 .50
126 Jeff Bagwell .30 .75
127 Eric Young .20 .50
128 John Valentin .20 .50
129 Al Martin UER .20 .50
Picture of Javy Lopez
130 Trevor Hoffman .20 .50
131 Henry Rodriguez .20 .50
132 Pedro Martinez .30 .75
133 Mike Piazza .75 2.00
134 Brian Jordan .20 .50
135 Jose Valentin .20 .50
136 Jeff Cirillo .20 .50
137 Chipper Jones .50 1.25
138 Ricky Bottalico .20 .50
139 Hideo Nomo .50 1.25
140 Troy Percival .20 .50
141 Rey Ordonez .20 .50
142 Edgar Renteria .20 .50
143 Luis Castillo .20 .50
144 Vladimir Guerrero .50 1.25
145 Jeff D'Amico .20 .50
146 Andruw Jones .30 .75
147 Darin Erstad .20 .50
148 Bob Abreu .30 .75
149 Carlos Delgado .20 .50
150 Jamey Wright .20 .50
151 Nomar Garciaparra .75 2.00
152 Jason Kendall .20 .50
153 Jermaine Allensworth .20 .50
154 Scott Rolen .30 .75
155 Rocky Coppinger .20 .50
156 Paul Wilson .20 .50
157 Garret Anderson .20 .50
158 Mariano Rivera .50 1.25
159 Ruben Rivera .20 .50
160 Andy Pettitte .30 .75
161 Derek Jeter 1.25 3.00
162 Neifi Perez .20 .50
163 Ray Durham .20 .50
164 James Baldwin .20 .50
165 Marty Cordova .20 .50
166 Tony Clark .20 .50
167 Michael Tucker .20 .50
168 Mike Sweeney .20 .50
169 Johnny Damon .30 .75
170 Jermaine Dye .20 .50
171 Alex Ochoa .20 .50
172 Jason Isringhausen .20 .50
173 Mark Grudzielanek .20 .50
174 Jose Rosado .20 .50
175 Todd Hollandsworth .20 .50
176 Alan Benes .20 .50
177 Jason Giambi .20 .50
178 Billy Wagner .20 .50
179 Justin Thompson .20 .50
180 Todd Walker .20 .50

1997 Topps Gallery Player's Private Issue

Randomly inserted in packs at a rate of one in 12, this 180-card set is a foil-stamped parallel version of the regular Topps Gallery set, limited to 250, with some of the cards sent to the players. The cards are spot UV coated on the photo only to allow for autographing.

*STARS: 6X TO 15X BASIC CARDS

1997 Topps Gallery Gallery of Heroes

Randomly inserted in packs at a rate of one in 36, this 10-card set features color player photos designed to command the attention paid to works hanging in art museums. The backs carry player information.

COMPLETE SET (10) 60.00 150.00
GH1 Derek Jeter 10.00 25.00
GH2 Chipper Jones 4.00 10.00
GH3 Frank Thomas 4.00 10.00
GH4 Ken Griffey Jr. 6.00 15.00
GH5 Cal Ripken 12.50 30.00
GH6 Mark McGwire 10.00 25.00
GH7 Mike Piazza 6.00 15.00
GH8 Jeff Bagwell 2.50 6.00
GH9 Tony Gwynn 5.00 12.00
GH10 Mo Vaughn 1.50 4.00

1997 Topps Gallery Peter Max Serigraphs

Randomly inserted in packs at a rate of one in 24, this 10-card set features painted renditions of ten superstars by the artist, Peter Max. The backs carry his commentary about the player.

COMPLETE SET (10) 30.00 80.00
*AUTOS: 8X TO 20X BASIC SERIGRAPHS
AUTOS RANDOM INSERTS IN PACKS
AUTOS STATED PRINT RUN 40 SETS
AU'S SIGNED BY MAX BENEATH UV COATING
1 Derek Jeter 5.00 12.00
2 Albert Belle .75 2.00
3 Ken Caminiti .75 2.00
4 Chipper Jones 2.00 5.00
5 Ken Griffey Jr. 3.00 8.00
6 Frank Thomas 2.00 5.00
7 Cal Ripken 6.00 15.00
8 Mark McGwire 5.00 12.00
9 Barry Bonds 5.00 12.00
10 Mike Piazza 3.00 8.00

1997 Topps Gallery Photo Gallery

Randomly inserted in packs at a rate of one in 24, this 16-card set features color photos of some of baseball's hottest stars and their most memorable moments. Each card is enhanced by customized designs and double foil-stamping.

COMPLETE SET (16) 40.00 100.00
PG1 John Wetteland 1.00 2.50
PG2 Paul Molitor 1.00 2.50
PG3 Eddie Murray 2.50 6.00
PG4 Ken Griffey Jr. 4.00 10.00
PG5 Chipper Jones 2.50 6.00
PG6 Derek Jeter 6.00 15.00
PG7 Frank Thomas 2.50 6.00
PG8 Mark McGwire 6.00 15.00

PG9 Kenny Lofton 1.00 2.50
PG10 Gary Sheffield 1.00 2.50
PG11 Mike Piazza 4.00 10.00
PG12 Vinny Castilla 1.00 2.50
PG13 Andres Galarraga 1.00 2.50
PG14 Andy Pettitte 1.50 4.00
PG15 Robin Ventura 1.00 2.50
PG16 Barry Larkin 1.50 4.00

1998 Topps Gallery

The 1998 Topps Gallery hobby-only set was issued in one series totalling 150 cards. The six-card packs retailed for $3.00 each. The set is divided by five subset groupings: Expressionists, Exhibitionists, Impressions, Portraits and Permanent Collection. Each theme features a different design with informative stats and text on each player.

COMPLETE SET (150) 20.00 50.00
1 Andruw Jones .30 .75
2 Fred McGriff .30 .75
3 Wade Boggs .30 .75
4 Pedro Martinez .30 .75
5 Matt Williams .20 .50
6 Wilson Alvarez .20 .50
7 Henry Rodriguez .20 .50
8 Jay Bell .20 .50
9 Marquis Grissom .20 .50
10 Darryl Kile .20 .50
11 Chuck Knoblauch .20 .50
12 Kenny Lofton .20 .50
13 Quinton McCracken .20 .50
14 Andres Galarraga .20 .50
15 Brian Jordan .20 .50
16 Mike Lansing .20 .50
17 Travis Fryman .20 .50
18 Tony Saunders .20 .50
19 Moises Alou .20 .50
20 Travis Lee .20 .50
21 Garret Anderson .20 .50
22 Ken Caminiti .20 .50
23 Pedro Astacio .20 .50
24 Ellis Burks .20 .50
25 Albert Belle .20 .50
26 Alan Benes .20 .50
27 Jay Buhner .20 .50
28 Derek Bell .20 .50
29 Jeromy Burnitz .20 .50
30 Kevin Appier .20 .50
31 Jeff Cirillo .20 .50
32 Bernard Gilkey .20 .50
33 David Cone .20 .50
34 Jason Dickson .20 .50
35 Jose Cruz Jr. .20 .50
36 Marty Cordova .20 .50
37 Ray Durham .20 .50
38 Jaret Wright .20 .50
39 Billy Wagner .20 .50
40 Roger Clemens 1.00 2.50
41 Juan Gonzalez .20 .50
42 Jeremi Gonzalez .20 .50
43 Mark Grudzielanek .20 .50
44 Tom Glavine .30 .75
45 Barry Larkin .30 .75
46 Lance Johnson .20 .50
47 Bobby Higginson .20 .50
48 Mike Mussina .30 .75
49 Al Martin .20 .50
50 Mark McGwire 1.25 3.00
51 Todd Hundley .20 .50
52 Ray Lankford .20 .50
53 Jason Kendall .20 .50
54 Javy Lopez .20 .50
55 Ben Grieve .20 .50
56 Randy Johnson .50 1.25
57 Jeff King .20 .50
58 Mark Grace .30 .75
59 Rusty Greer .20 .50
60 Greg Maddux .75 2.00
61 Jeff Kent .20 .50
62 Rey Ordonez .20 .50
63 Hideo Nomo .50 1.25
64 Charles Nagy .20 .50
65 Rondell White .20 .50
66 Todd Helton .30 .75
67 Jim Thome .30 .75
68 Denny Neagle .20 .50
69 Ivan Rodriguez .30 .75
70 Vladimir Guerrero .50 1.25
71 Jorge Posada .30 .75
72 J.T. Snow .20 .50
73 Reggie Sanders .20 .50
74 Scott Rolen .30 .75
75 Robin Ventura .20 .50
76 Mariano Rivera .50 1.25
77 Cal Ripken 1.50 4.00
78 Justin Thompson .20 .50
79 Mike Piazza .75 2.00
80 Kevin Brown .30 .75
81 Sandy Alomar Jr. .20 .50
82 Craig Biggio .30 .75
83 Vinny Castilla .20 .50
84 Eric Young .20 .50
85 Bernie Williams .30 .75
86 Brady Anderson .20 .50
87 Bobby Bonilla .20 .50
88 Tony Clark .20 .50
89 Dan Wilson .20 .50
90 John Wetteland .20 .50
91 Barry Bonds 1.25 3.00
92 Chan Ho Park .20 .50
93 Carlos Delgado .20 .50
94 David Justice .20 .50
95 Chipper Jones .50 1.25
96 Shawn Estes .20 .50
97 Jason Giambi .20 .50
98 Ron Gant .20 .50
99 John Olerud .20 .50
100 Frank Thomas .50 1.25
101 Jose Guillen .20 .50
102 Brad Radke .20 .50
103 Troy Percival .20 .50
104 John Smoltz .30 .75
105 Edgardo Alfonzo .20 .50
106 Dante Bichette .20 .50
107 Larry Walker .20 .50
108 John Valentin .20 .50
109 Roberto Alomar .30 .75
110 Mike Cameron .20 .50
111 Eric Davis .20 .50
112 Johnny Damon .30 .75
113 Darin Erstad .20 .50
114 Omar Vizquel .30 .75
115 Derek Jeter 1.25 3.00
116 Tony Womack .20 .50
117 Edgar Renteria .20 .50
118 Raul Mondesi .20 .50
119 Tony Gwynn .60 1.50
120 Ken Griffey Jr. .75 2.00
121 Jim Edmonds .20 .50
122 Brian Hunter .20 .50
123 Neifi Perez .20 .50
124 Dean Palmer .20 .50
125 Alex Rodriguez .75 2.00
126 Tim Salmon .30 .75
127 Curt Schilling .20 .50
128 Kevin Orie .20 .50
129 Andy Pettitte .30 .75
130 Gary Sheffield .20 .50
131 Jose Rosado .20 .50
132 Manny Ramirez .30 .75
133 Rafael Palmeiro .30 .75
134 Sammy Sosa .50 1.25
135 Jeff Bagwell .30 .75
136 Delino DeShields .20 .50
137 Ryan Klesko .20 .50
138 Mo Vaughn .20 .50
139 Steve Finley .20 .50
140 Nomar Garciaparra .75 2.00
141 Paul Molitor .20 .50
142 Pat Hentgen .20 .50
143 Eric Karros .20 .50
144 Bobby Jones .20 .50
145 Tino Martinez .30 .75
146 Matt Morris .20 .50
147 Livan Hernandez .20 .50
148 Edgar Martinez .30 .75
149 Paul O'Neill .30 .75
150 Checklist .20 .50

1998 Topps Gallery Gallery Proofs

Randomly inserted in packs at a rate of one in 34, this 150-card set is a parallel to the Topps Gallery base set. The set is sequentially numbered to 125.

*STARS: 10X TO 25X BASIC CARDS

1998 Topps Gallery Player's Private Issue

Randomly inserted in packs at a rate of one in 17, this 150-card set is a parallel to the Topps Gallery base set. The set is sequentially numbered to 250.

*STARS: 5X TO 12X BASIC CARDS

1998 Topps Gallery Player's Private Issue Auction

Seeded at a rate of one per pack, these standard-sized cards loosely parallel the far more scarce Player's Private Issue cards. Two glaring differences, however, are readily apparent: 1) The Auction cards are printed on thin paper stock (compared to the thick 20 pt board for PPI cards) and 2) The Auction card backs contain rules and guidelines for the auction promotion (compared to the normal statistics and player photo on the PPI cards). Collectors who obtained Auction cards were supposed to "bid" on a selection of ten different pieces of framed artwork (one for each of the following players: J.Gonzalez, M.McGwire, C.Ripken, M.Piazza, C.Jones, F.Thomas, D.Jeter, K.Griffey Jr., A.Rodriguez and N.Garciaparra). Bidding points were available in 25, 50, 75 and 100 point increments detailed at the top right corner of each Auction card back. Point totals were doubled, however, when the player featured on the Auction card was the same player actually being bid on. The auction period ran from July 4th, 1998 through October 16th, 1998. During that time period, collectors had to mail in their accumulated bid points and specify which of the ten pieces they were bidding upon. An "800" number was available for collectors to check upon the status of the current high bid, allowing them the opportunity to submit additional bid points prior to the October 16th closing date. Winners were notified 30 days after the closing date.

COMPLETE SET (150) 50.00 100.00
*STARS: .75X TO 2X BASIC CARDS

1998 Topps Gallery Awards Gallery

Randomly inserted in packs at a rate of one in 24, this 10-card set honors the achievements of the majors top stars.

COMPLETE SET (10) 25.00 60.00
AG1 Ken Griffey Jr. 4.00 10.00
AG2 Larry Walker 1.00 2.50
AG3 Roger Clemens 5.00 12.00
AG4 Pedro Martinez 1.50 4.00
AG5 Nomar Garciaparra 4.00 10.00
AG6 Scott Rolen 1.50 4.00
AG7 Frank Thomas 2.50 6.00
AG8 Tony Gwynn 3.00 8.00
AG9 Mark McGwire 6.00 15.00
AG10 Livan Hernandez 1.00 2.50

1998 Topps Gallery Gallery of Heroes

Randomly inserted in packs at a rate of one in 24, this 15-card set is an insert to the Topps Gallery base set. The fronts feature a translucent stain-glass design that helps showcase some of today's high performance players.

COMPLETE SET (15) 60.00 150.00
*JUMBOS: .3X TO .8X BASIC HEROES
ONE JUMBO PER HOBBY BOX
GH1 Ken Griffey Jr. 5.00 12.00
GH2 Derek Jeter 8.00 20.00
GH3 Barry Bonds 8.00 20.00
GH4 Alex Rodriguez 5.00 12.00
GH5 Frank Thomas 3.00 8.00
GH6 Nomar Garciaparra 5.00 12.00
GH7 Mark McGwire 8.00 20.00
GH8 Mike Piazza 5.00 12.00
GH9 Cal Ripken 10.00 25.00
GH10 Jose Cruz Jr. 1.25 3.00
GH11 Jeff Bagwell 2.00 5.00
GH12 Chipper Jones 3.00 8.00
GH13 Juan Gonzalez 1.25 3.00
GH14 Hideo Nomo 3.00 8.00
GH15 Greg Maddux 5.00 12.00

1998 Topps Gallery Photo Gallery

Randomly inserted in packs at a rate of one in 24, this 10-card set features a selection of top stars in riveting game action.

COMPLETE SET (10) 30.00 80.00
PG1 Alex Rodriguez 4.00 10.00
PG2 Frank Thomas 2.50 6.00
PG3 Derek Jeter 6.00 15.00
PG4 Cal Ripken 8.00 20.00
PG5 Ken Griffey Jr. 4.00 10.00
PG6 Mike Piazza 4.00 10.00
PG7 Nomar Garciaparra 4.00 10.00
PG8 Tim Salmon 1.50 4.00
PG9 Jeff Bagwell 1.50 4.00
PG10 Barry Bonds 6.00 15.00

1999 Topps Gallery Previews

This three-card standard-size set was released to preview the 1999 Topps Gallery set. The set features a regular design as well as a couple of the subsets involved in this set.

COMPLETE SET (3) 2.00 5.00
PP1 Scott Rolen 1.00 2.50
PP2 A.Galarrraga MAS .60 1.50
PP3 Brad Fullmer ART .40 1.00

1999 Topps Gallery

The 1999 Topps Gallery set was issued in one series totalling 150 cards and was distributed in six-card packs for a suggested retail price of $3. The set features 100 veteran stars and 50 subset cards finely crafted and printed on 24-pt. stock, with serigraph textured frame, etched foil stamping, and spot UV finish. The set contains the following subsets: Masters (101-115), Artisans (116-127), and Apprentices (128-150). Rookie Cards inlcude Pat Burrell, Nick Johnson and Alfonso Soriano.

COMPLETE SET (150) 20.00 50.00
COMP.SET w/o SP's (100) 10.00 25.00
COMMON CARD (1-100) .10 .30
COMMON (101-150) .30 .75
1 Mark McGwire .75 2.00
2 Jim Thome .20 .50
3 Bernie Williams .20 .50
4 Larry Walker .10 .30
5 Juan Gonzalez .10 .30
6 Ken Griffey Jr. .50 1.25
7 Raul Mondesi .10 .30
8 Sammy Sosa .30 .75
9 Greg Maddux .50 1.25
10 Jeff Bagwell .20 .50
11 Vladimir Guerrero .30 .75
12 Scott Rolen .20 .50
13 Nomar Garciaparra .50 1.25
14 Mike Piazza .50 1.25
15 Travis Lee .10 .30
16 Carlos Delgado .10 .30
17 Darin Erstad .10 .30
18 David Justice .10 .30
19 Cal Ripken 1.00 2.50
20 Derek Jeter .75 2.00
21 Tony Clark .10 .30
22 Barry Larkin .20 .50
23 Greg Vaughn .10 .30
24 Jeff Kent .10 .30
25 Wade Boggs .20 .50
26 Andres Galarraga .10 .30
27 Ken Caminiti .10 .30
28 Jason Kendall .10 .30
29 Todd Helton .20 .50
30 Chuck Knoblauch .10 .30
31 Roger Clemens .60 1.50
32 Jeromy Burnitz .10 .30
33 Javy Lopez .10 .30
34 Roberto Alomar .20 .50
35 Eric Karros .10 .30
36 Ben Grieve .10 .30
37 Eric Davis .10 .30
38 Rondell White .10 .30
39 Dmitri Young .10 .30
40 Ivan Rodriguez .20 .50
41 Paul O'Neill .20 .50
42 Jeff Cirillo .10 .30
43 Kerry Wood .10 .30
44 Albert Belle .10 .30
45 Frank Thomas .30 .75
46 Manny Ramirez .20 .50
47 Tom Glavine .20 .50
48 Mo Vaughn .10 .30
49 Jose Cruz Jr. .10 .30
50 Sandy Alomar Jr. .10 .30
51 Edgar Martinez .20 .50
52 John Olerud .10 .30
53 Todd Walker .10 .30
54 Tim Salmon .20 .50
55 Derek Bell .10 .30
56 Matt Williams .10 .30
57 Alex Rodriguez .50 1.25
58 Rusty Greer .10 .30
59 Vinny Castilla .10 .30
60 Jason Giambi .10 .30
61 Mark Grace .20 .50
62 Jose Canseco .20 .50
63 Gary Sheffield .10 .30
64 Brad Fullmer .10 .30
65 Trevor Hoffman .10 .30
66 Mark Kotsay .10 .30
67 Mike Mussina .20 .50
68 Johnny Damon .20 .50
69 Tino Martinez .20 .50
70 Curt Schilling .10 .30
71 Jay Buhner .10 .30
72 Kenny Lofton .10 .30
73 Randy Johnson .30 .75
74 Kevin Brown .20 .50
75 Brian Jordan .10 .30
76 Craig Biggio .20 .50
77 Barry Bonds .75 2.00
78 Tony Gwynn .40 1.00
79 Jim Edmonds .10 .30
80 Shawn Green .10 .30
81 Todd Hundley .10 .30
82 Cliff Floyd .10 .30
83 Jose Guillen .10 .30
84 Dante Bichette .10 .30
85 Moises Alou .10 .30
86 Chipper Jones .30 .75
87 Ray Lankford .10 .30
88 Fred McGriff .20 .50
89 Rod Beck .10 .30
90 Dean Palmer .10 .30
91 Pedro Martinez .20 .50
92 Andruw Jones .20 .50
93 Robin Ventura .10 .30
94 Ugueth Urbina .10 .30
95 Orlando Hernandez .10 .30
96 Sean Casey .10 .30
97 Denny Neagle .10 .30
98 Troy Glaus .20 .50
99 John Smoltz .20 .50
100 Al Leiter .10 .30
101 Ken Griffey Jr. MAS 1.00 2.50
102 Frank Thomas MAS .60 1.50
103 Mark McGwire MAS 1.50 4.00
104 Sammy Sosa MAS .60 1.50
105 Chipper Jones MAS .60 1.50
106 Alex Rodriguez MAS 1.00 2.50
107 N.Garciaparra MAS 1.00 2.50
108 Juan Gonzalez MAS .30 .75
109 Derek Jeter MAS 1.50 4.00
110 Mike Piazza MAS 1.00 2.50
111 Barry Bonds MAS 1.50 4.00
112 Tony Gwynn MAS .75 2.00
113 Cal Ripken MAS 2.00 5.00
114 Greg Maddux MAS 1.00 2.50
115 Roger Clemens MAS 1.25 3.00
116 Brad Fullmer ART .30 .75
117 Kerry Wood ART .30 .75
118 Ben Grieve ART .30 .75
119 Todd Helton ART .40 1.00
120 Kevin Millwood ART .30 .75
121 Sean Casey ART .30 .75
122 V.Guerrero ART .60 1.50
123 Travis Lee ART .30 .75
124 Troy Glaus ART .40 1.00
125 Bartolo Colon ART .30 .75
126 Andruw Jones ART .40 1.00
127 Scott Rolen ART .40 1.00
128 A.Soriano APP RC 2.00 5.00
129 Nick Johnson APP RC .75 2.00
130 Matt Belisle APP RC .30 .75
131 Jorge Toca APP RC .30 .75
132 Masao Kida APP RC .30 .75
133 Carlos Pena APP RC .40 1.00
134 Adrian Beltre APP .30 .75
135 Eric Chavez APP .30 .75
136 Carlos Beltran APP .40 1.00
137 Alex Gonzalez APP .30 .75
138 Ryan Anderson APP .30 .75
139 Ruben Mateo APP .30 .75
140 Bruce Chen APP .30 .75
141 Pat Burrell APP RC 1.25 3.00
142 Michael Barrett APP .30 .75
143 Carlos Lee APP .30 .75
144 Mark Mulder APP RC 1.00 2.50
145 C.Freeman APP RC .30 .75
146 Gabe Kapler APP .30 .75
147 J.Encarnacion APP .30 .75
148 Jeremy Giambi APP .30 .75
149 Jason Tyner APP RC .30 .75
150 George Lombard APP .30 .75

1999 Topps Gallery Player's Private Issue

Randomly inserted in packs at the rate of one in 17, this 150-card set is parallel to the base set with a "Players Private Issue" foil stamp and sequentially numbered to 250.

*STARS 1-100: 8X TO 20X BASIC CARDS
*MASTERS 101-115: 4X TO 10X BASIC
*ARTISANS 116-127: 3X TO 8X BASIC
*APPRENTICES 128-150: 3X TO 8X BASIC
*APP.RC'S 128-150: 2X TO 5X BASIC

1999 Topps Gallery Autographs

Randomly inserted into packs at the rate of one in 209, this three-card set features color photos of three of baseball's top prospects printed on 24-point stock with the "Topps Certified Autograph" foil stamp logo.

GA1 Troy Glaus 10.00 25.00
GA2 Adrian Beltre 6.00 15.00
GA3 Eric Chavez 6.00 15.00

1999 Topps Gallery Awards Gallery

Randomly inserted into packs at the rate of one in 12, this 10-card set features color photos of the game's HR Champs, Cy Young award winners, RBI Leaders, MVP winnners, and Rookies of the year from 1998.

COMPLETE SET (10) 12.50 30.00
AG1 Kerry Wood .50 1.25
AG2 Ben Grieve .50 1.25
AG3 Roger Clemens 2.50 6.00
AG4 Tom Glavine .75 2.00
AG5 Juan Gonzalez .50 1.25
AG6 Sammy Sosa 1.25 3.00
AG7 Ken Griffey Jr. 2.00 5.00
AG8 Mark McGwire 3.00 8.00
AG9 Bernie Williams .75 2.00
AG10 Larry Walker .50 1.25

1999 Topps Gallery Exhibitions

Randomly inserted in packs at the rate of one in 48, this 20-card set features color photos of top players printed on textured 24-point card stock with the look and feel of brushstrokes on canvas.

COMPLETE SET (20) 80.00 200.00
E1 Sammy Sosa 3.00 8.00
E2 Mark McGwire 8.00 20.00
E3 Greg Maddux 5.00 12.00
E4 Roger Clemens 6.00 15.00
E5 Ben Grieve 1.25 3.00
E6 Kerry Wood 1.25 3.00
E7 Ken Griffey Jr. 5.00 12.00
E8 Tony Gwynn 4.00 10.00
E9 Cal Ripken 10.00 25.00
E10 Frank Thomas 3.00 8.00
E11 Jeff Bagwell 2.00 5.00
E12 Derek Jeter 8.00 20.00
E13 Alex Rodriguez 5.00 12.00
E14 Nomar Garciaparra 5.00 12.00
E15 Manny Ramirez 2.00 5.00
E16 Vladimir Guerrero 3.00 8.00
E17 Darin Erstad 1.25 3.00
E18 Scott Rolen 2.00 5.00
E19 Mike Piazza 5.00 12.00
E20 Andres Galarraga 1.25 3.00

1999 Topps Gallery Gallery of Heroes

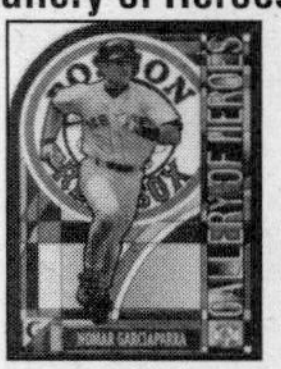

Randomly inserted into packs at the rate of one in 24, this 10-card set features some of the game's top players depicted on clear Polycarbonate stock simulating the appearance of stained glass.

COMPLETE SET (10) 30.00 80.00
GH1 Mark McGwire 5.00 12.00
GH2 Sammy Sosa 2.00 5.00
GH3 Ken Griffey Jr. 3.00 8.00
GH4 Mike Piazza 3.00 8.00
GH5 Derek Jeter 5.00 12.00
GH6 Nomar Garciaparra 3.00 8.00
GH7 Kerry Wood .75 2.00
GH8 Ben Grieve .75 2.00
GH9 Chipper Jones 2.00 5.00
GH10 Alex Rodriguez 3.00 8.00

1999 Topps Gallery Heritage

Randomly inserted into packs at the rate of one in 12, this 20-card set features color photos of legendary stars printed on 24-point conventional card stock depicting the 1953 Topps design. This was one of the most popular insert sets issued in 1999 as hobbyists responded well to the gorgeous 1953 retro art. Interestingly, the back of the Aaron card was written as if it were 1953 while the modern players were written about their current accomplishments.

COMPLETE SET (20) 75.00 200.00
*PROOFS: .4X TO 1X BASIC HERITAGE
PROOFS STATED ODDS 1:48
TH1 Hank Aaron 12.50 30.00
TH2 Ben Grieve 3.00 8.00
TH3 Nomar Garciaparra 10.00 25.00
TH4 Roger Clemens 12.50 30.00
TH5 Travis Lee 3.00 8.00
TH6 Tony Gwynn 8.00 20.00
TH7 Alex Rodriguez 10.00 25.00
TH8 Ken Griffey Jr. 10.00 25.00
TH9 Derek Jeter 15.00 40.00
TH10 Sammy Sosa 6.00 15.00
TH11 Scott Rolen 4.00 10.00
TH12 Chipper Jones 6.00 15.00
TH13 Cal Ripken 20.00 50.00
TH14 Kerry Wood 4.00 8.00
TH15 Barry Bonds 15.00 40.00

TH16 Juan Gonzalez	4.00	8.00
TH17 Mike Piazza	10.00	25.00
TH18 Greg Maddux	10.00	25.00
TH19 Frank Thomas	6.00	15.00
TH20 Mark McGwire	20.00	50.00

1999 Topps Gallery Heritage Postcards

This seven-card postcard-sized set was issued by Topps in 1999. The set features superstar players painted by James Fiorentino.

COMPLETE SET (7)	15.00	40.00
1 Mark McGwire	2.00	5.00
2 Sammy Sosa	1.25	3.00
3 Roger Clemens	2.00	5.00
4 Mike Piazza	2.50	6.00
5 Cal Ripken	4.00	10.00
6 Derek Jeter	4.00	10.00
7 Ken Griffey Jr.	2.00	5.00

2000 Topps Gallery Pre-Production

This three card set was issued in a sealed cello pack to dealers and hobby media several weeks prior to the products release. The cards have a "PP" prefix so they can be differentiated from the regular cards.

COMPLETE SET (3)	2.50	6.00
PP1 Derek Jeter	1.60	4.00
PP2 Mark McGwire	.75	2.00
PP3 Josh Hamilton	1.25	3.00

2000 Topps Gallery

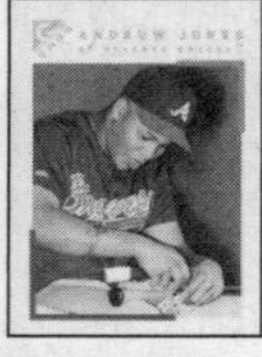

The 2000 Topps Gallery product was released in early June, 2000 as a 150-card set. The set features 100 player cards, a 20-card Masters of the Game subset, and a 30-card Students of the Game subset. Please note that cards 101-150 were issued at a rate of one per pack. Each pack contained six cards and carried a suggested retail price of $3.00. Notable Rookie Cards include Bobby Bradley.

COMPLETE SET (150)	40.00	100.00
COMP.SET w/o SP's (100)	10.00	25.00
COMMON CARD (1-100)	.10	.30
COMMON (101-150)	.40	1.00
1 Nomar Garciaparra	.50	1.25
2 Kevin Millwood	.10	.30
3 Jay Bell	.10	.30
4 Rusty Greer	.10	.30
5 Bernie Williams	.20	.50
6 Barry Larkin	.20	.50
7 Carlos Beltran	.10	.30
8 Damion Easley	.10	.30
9 Magglio Ordonez	.10	.30
10 Matt Williams	.10	.30
11 Shannon Stewart	.10	.30
12 Ray Lankford	.10	.30
13 Vinny Castilla	.10	.30
14 Miguel Tejada	.10	.30
15 Craig Biggio	.20	.50
16 Chipper Jones	.30	.75
17 Albert Belle	.10	.30
18 Doug Glanville	.10	.30
19 Brian Giles	.10	.30
20 Shawn Green	.10	.30
21 Bret Boone	.10	.30
22 Luis Gonzalez	.10	.30
23 Carlos Delgado	.10	.30
24 J.D. Drew	.10	.30
25 Ivan Rodriguez	.20	.50
26 Tino Martinez	.20	.50
27 Erubiel Durazo	.10	.30
28 Scott Rolen	.20	.50
29 Gary Sheffield	.10	.30
30 Manny Ramirez	.20	.50
31 Luis Castillo	.10	.30
32 Fernando Tatis	.10	.30
33 Darin Erstad	.10	.30
34 Tim Hudson	.10	.30
35 Sammy Sosa	.30	.75
36 Jason Kendall	.10	.30
37 Todd Walker	.10	.30
38 Orlando Hernandez	.10	.30
39 Pokey Reese	.10	.30
40 Mike Piazza	.50	1.25
41 B.J. Surhoff	.10	.30
42 Tony Gwynn	.40	1.00
43 Kevin Brown	.10	.30
44 Preston Wilson	.10	.30
45 Kenny Lofton	.10	.30
46 Rondell White	.10	.30
47 Frank Thomas	.30	.75
48 Neifi Perez	.10	.30
49 Edgardo Alfonzo	.05	.15
50 Ken Griffey Jr.	.50	1.25
51 Barry Bonds	.75	2.00
52 Brian Jordan	.10	.30
53 Raul Mondesi	.10	.30
54 Troy Glaus	.10	.30
55 Curt Schilling	.10	.30
56 Mike Mussina	.20	.50
57 Brian Daubach	.10	.30
58 Roger Clemens	.60	1.50
59 Carlos Febles	.10	.30
60 Todd Helton	.20	.50
61 Mark Grace	.20	.50
62 Randy Johnson	.30	.75
63 Jeff Bagwell	.20	.50
64 Tom Glavine	.20	.50
65 Adrian Beltre	.10	.30
66 Rafael Palmeiro	.20	.50
67 Paul O'Neill	.20	.50
68 Robin Ventura	.10	.30
69 Ray Durham	.10	.30
70 Mark McGwire	.75	2.00
71 Greg Vaughn	.10	.30
72 Javy Lopez	.10	.30
73 Ryan Klesko	.10	.30
74 Mike Lieberthal	.10	.30
75 Cal Ripken	1.00	2.50
76 Juan Gonzalez	.10	.30
77 Sean Casey	.10	.30
78 Jermaine Dye	.10	.30
79 John Olerud	.10	.30
80 Jose Canseco	.20	.50
81 Eric Karros	.10	.30
82 Roberto Alomar	.20	.50
83 Ben Grieve	.10	.30
84 Greg Maddux	.50	1.25
85 Pedro Martinez	.20	.50
86 Tony Clark	.10	.30
87 Richie Sexson	.10	.30
88 Cliff Floyd	.10	.30
89 Eric Chavez	.10	.30
90 Andruw Jones	.20	.50
91 Vladimir Guerrero	.30	.75
92 Alex Gonzalez	.10	.30
93 Jim Thome	.20	.50
94 Bob Abreu	.10	.30
95 Derek Jeter	.75	2.00
96 Larry Walker	.10	.30
97 Mike Hampton	.10	.30
98 Mo Vaughn	.10	.30
99 Jason Giambi	.10	.30
100 Alex Rodriguez	.50	1.25
101 Mark McGwire MAS	1.50	4.00
102 Sammy Sosa MAS	.60	1.50
103 Alex Rodriguez MAS	1.00	2.50
104 Derek Jeter MAS	1.50	4.00
105 Greg Maddux MAS	1.00	2.50
106 Jeff Bagwell MAS	.40	1.00
107 N.Garciaparra MAS	1.00	2.50
108 Mike Piazza MAS	1.00	2.50
109 Pedro Martinez MAS	.40	1.00
110 Chipper Jones MAS	.60	1.50
111 Randy Johnson MAS	.60	1.50
112 Barry Bonds MAS	1.50	4.00
113 Ken Griffey Jr. MAS	1.00	2.50
114 Manny Ramirez MAS	.40	1.00
115 Ivan Rodriguez MAS	.40	1.00
116 Juan Gonzalez MAS	.40	1.00
117 V.Guerrero MAS	.60	1.50
118 Tony Gwynn MAS	.75	2.00
119 Larry Walker MAS	.40	1.00
120 Cal Ripken MAS	2.00	5.00
121 Josh Hamilton SG	1.00	2.50
122 Corey Patterson SG	.40	1.00
123 Pat Burrell SG	.40	1.00
124 Nick Johnson SG	.40	1.00
125 Adam Piatt SG	.40	1.00
126 Rick Ankiel SG	.40	1.00
127 A.J. Burnett SG	.40	1.00
128 Ben Petrick SG	.40	1.00
129 Rafael Furcal SG	.40	1.00
130 Alfonso Soriano SG	.60	1.50
131 Dee Brown SG	.40	1.00
132 Ruben Mateo SG	.40	1.00
133 Pablo Ozuna SG	.40	1.00
134 S.Burroughs SG UER	.40	1.00
Eric Munson's bio on back		
135 Mark Mulder SG	.40	1.00
136 Jason Jennings SG	.40	1.00
137 Eric Munson SG	.40	1.00
138 Vernon Wells SG	.40	1.00
139 Brett Myers SG RC	.75	2.00
140 B.Christensen SG RC	.40	1.00
141 Bobby Bradley SG RC	.40	1.00
142 Ruben Salazar SG RC	.40	1.00
143 R.Christianson SG RC	.40	1.00
144 Corey Myers SG RC	.40	1.00
145 Aaron Rowand SG RC	1.00	2.50
146 Julio Zuleta SG RC	.40	1.00
147 Kurt Ainsworth SG RC	.40	1.00
148 Scott Downs SG RC	.40	1.00
149 Larry Bigbie SG RC	.40	1.00
150 Chance Caple SG RC	.40	1.00

2000 Topps Gallery Player's Private Issue

Randomly inserted into packs at one in 20, this 150-card set is a complete parallel of the Topps Gallery base set. Each card in the set is individually serial numbered to 250. The cards are serial numbered in gold foil on the back of the cards.

*STARS 1-100: 6X TO 15X BASIC CARDS
*MASTERS 101-120: 3X TO 8X BASIC
*STUDENTS 121-138: 1.5X TO 4X BASIC
*STUDENTS RC's 139-150: 2X TO 5X BASIC

2000 Topps Gallery Autographs

Randomly inserted into packs at one in 153, this insert set features autographed cards from five of the major league's top prospects. Card backs are numbered using the players initials.

BP Ben Petrick	4.00	10.00
CP Corey Patterson	4.00	10.00
RA Rick Ankiel	10.00	25.00
RM Ruben Mateo	4.00	10.00
VW Vernon Wells	6.00	15.00

2000 Topps Gallery Exhibits

Randomly inserted into packs at one in 18, this 30-card insert captures some of baseball's best on canvas texturing. Card backs carry a "GE" prefix.

COMPLETE SET (30)	125.00	300.00
GE1 Mark McGwire	8.00	20.00
GE2 Jeff Bagwell	2.00	5.00
GE3 Mike Piazza	5.00	12.00
GE4 Alex Rodriguez	5.00	12.00
GE5 Nomar Garciaparra	5.00	12.00
GE6 Ivan Rodriguez	2.00	5.00
GE7 Chipper Jones	3.00	8.00
GE8 Cal Ripken	10.00	25.00
GE9 Tony Gwynn	4.00	10.00
GE10 Jose Canseco	2.00	5.00
GE11 Albert Belle	1.25	3.00
GE12 Greg Maddux	5.00	12.00
GE13 Barry Bonds	8.00	20.00
GE14 Ken Griffey Jr.	5.00	12.00
GE15 Juan Gonzalez	1.25	3.00
GE16 Rickey Henderson	6.00	15.00
GE17 Craig Biggio	2.00	5.00
GE18 Vladimir Guerrero	3.00	8.00
GE19 Rey Ordonez	4.00	10.00
GE20 Roberto Alomar	2.00	5.00
GE21 Derek Jeter	8.00	20.00
GE22 Manny Ramirez	2.00	5.00
GE23 Shawn Green	1.25	3.00
GE24 Sammy Sosa	3.00	8.00
GE25 Larry Walker	1.25	3.00
GE26 Pedro Martinez	2.00	5.00
GE27 Randy Johnson	3.00	8.00
GE28 Pat Burrell	1.25	3.00
GE29 Josh Hamilton	3.00	8.00
GE30 Corey Patterson	1.25	3.00

2000 Topps Gallery Gallery of Heroes

Randomly inserted into packs at one in 24, this insert features ten celestial superstars on clear, die-cut polycarbonate stock, creating a stained glass effect. Card backs carry a "GH" prefix.

COMPLETE SET (10)	30.00	80.00
GH1 Alex Rodriguez	3.00	8.00
GH2 Chipper Jones	2.00	5.00
GH3 Pedro Martinez	1.25	3.00
GH4 Sammy Sosa	2.00	5.00
GH5 Mark McGwire	5.00	12.00
GH6 Nomar Garciaparra	3.00	8.00
GH7 Vladimir Guerrero	2.00	5.00
GH8 Ken Griffey Jr.	3.00	8.00
GH9 Mike Piazza	3.00	8.00
GH10 Derek Jeter	5.00	12.00

2000 Topps Gallery Heritage

Randomly inserted into packs at one in 12, this 20-card insert set was influenced by the 1954 Topps set, the set features many of baseball's elite players as illustrated artist renderings. Card backs carry a "TGH" prefix.

COMPLETE SET (20)	60.00	150.00
*PROOFS: .6X TO 1.5X BASIC HERITAGE	4.00	10.00
PROOFS STATED ODDS 1:27		
TGH1 Mark McGwire	10.00	25.00
TGH2 Sammy Sosa	4.00	10.00
TGH3 Greg Maddux	6.00	15.00
TGH4 Mike Piazza	6.00	15.00
TGH5 Ivan Rodriguez	2.50	6.00
TGH6 Manny Ramirez	2.50	6.00
TGH7 Jeff Bagwell	2.50	6.00
TGH8 Sean Casey	1.50	4.00
TGH9 Orlando Hernandez	1.50	4.00
TGH10 Randy Johnson	4.00	10.00
TGH11 Pedro Martinez	2.50	6.00
TGH12 Vladimir Guerrero	4.00	10.00
TGH13 Shawn Green	1.50	4.00
TGH14 Ken Griffey Jr.	6.00	15.00
TGH15 Alex Rodriguez	6.00	15.00
TGH16 Nomar Garciaparra	6.00	15.00
TGH17 Derek Jeter	10.00	25.00
TGH18 Tony Gwynn	5.00	12.00
TGH19 Chipper Jones	4.00	10.00
TGH20 Cal Ripken	12.50	30.00

2000 Topps Gallery Proof Positive

Randomly insert into packs at one in 48, these ten cards couple one master of the game with one student of the game by way of positive and negative photography. Card backs carry a "P" prefix.

COMPLETE SET (10)	40.00	100.00
P1 Ken Griffey Jr.	4.00	10.00
Ruben Mateo		
P2 Derek Jeter	6.00	15.00
Alfonso Soriano		
P3 Mark McGwire	6.00	15.00
Pat Burrell		
P4 Pedro Martinez	1.50	4.00
A.J.Burnett		
P5 Alex Rodriguez	4.00	10.00
Rafael Furcal		
P6 Sammy Sosa	2.50	6.00
Corey Patterson		
P7 Randy Johnson	2.50	6.00
Rick Ankiel		
P8 Chipper Jones	2.50	6.00
Adam Piatt		
P9 Nomar Garciaparra	4.00	10.00
Pablo Ozuna		
P10 Mike Piazza	4.00	10.00
Eric Munson		

2001 Topps Gallery

This 150 card set was issued in six card packs with an SRP of $3. The packs were issued 24 packs to a box with eight boxes to a case. Cards numbered 102-150 were short printed in these ratios: Prospects from 102-141 were issued one every 2.5 packs, rookies from 102-141 were issued one every 3.5 packs and cards numbered 142-150 were issued one every five packs. Card number 50 was supposedly only available to people who could show their dealers that that was the only card they were missing for the set. However, a retail version of that card was issued so many collectors did not get to share in the surprise of finding out the missing card was Willie Mays. In addition, a special Ichiro card was randomly included in packs, these cards were good for either an American or a Japanese version of what would become card number 151. The deadline to receive the Mays HTA version was October 24th, 2001 while the Ichiro exchange deadline was June 30th, 2003.

COMPLETE SET (150)	50.00	80.00
COMP.SET w/o SP's (100)	15.00	40.00
COMMON (1-49/51-101)	.20	.50
COMMON (102-150)	1.25	3.00
1 Darin Erstad	.20	.50
2 Chipper Jones	.50	1.25
3 Nomar Garciaparra	.75	2.00
4 Fernando Vina	.20	.50
5 Bartolo Colon	.20	.50
6 Bobby Higginson	.20	.50
7 Antonio Alfonseca	.20	.50
8 Mike Sweeney	.20	.50
9 Kevin Brown	.20	.50
10 Jose Vidro	.20	.50
11 Derek Jeter	1.25	3.00
12 Jason Giambi	.20	.50
13 Pat Burrell	.20	.50
14 Jeff Kent	.20	.50
15 Alex Rodriguez	.75	2.00
16 Rafael Palmeiro	.30	.75
17 Garret Anderson	.20	.50
18 Brad Fullmer	.20	.50
19 Doug Glanville	.20	.50
20 Mark Quinn	.20	.50
21 Mo Vaughn	.20	.50
22 Andruw Jones	.30	.75
23 Pedro Martinez	.30	.75
24 Ken Griffey Jr.	.75	2.00
25 Roberto Alomar	.30	.75
26 Dean Palmer	.20	.50
27 Jeff Bagwell	.30	.75
28 Jermaine Dye	.20	.50
29 Chan Ho Park	.20	.50
30 Vladimir Guerrero	.50	1.25
31 Bernie Williams	.30	.75
32 Ben Grieve	.20	.50
33 Jason Kendall	.20	.50
34 Barry Bonds	1.25	3.00
35 Jim Edmonds	.20	.50
36 Ivan Rodriguez	.30	.75
37 Javy Lopez	.20	.50
38 J.T. Snow	.20	.50
39 Erubiel Durazo	.20	.50
40 Terrence Long	.20	.50
41 Tim Salmon	.30	.75
42 Greg Maddux	.75	2.00
43 Sammy Sosa	.50	1.25
44 Sean Casey	.20	.50
45 Jeff Cirillo	.20	.50
46 Juan Gonzalez	.20	.50
47 Richard Hidalgo	.20	.50
48 Shawn Green	.20	.50
49 Jeromy Burnitz	.20	.50
50 Willie Mays HTA	6.00	15.00
N.Y. Giants		
50 Willie Mays RETAIL	15.00	40.00
S.F. Giants		
51 David Justice	.20	.50
52 Tim Hudson	.20	.50
53 Brian Giles	.20	.50
54 Robb Nen	.20	.50
55 Fernando Tatis	.20	.50
56 Tony Batista	.20	.50
57 Pokey Reese	.20	.50
58 Ray Durham	.20	.50
59 Greg Vaughn	.20	.50
60 Kazuhiro Sasaki	.20	.50
61 Troy Glaus	.20	.50
62 Rafael Furcal	.20	.50
63 Magglio Ordonez	.20	.50
64 Jim Thome	.30	.75
65 Todd Helton	.30	.75
66 Preston Wilson	.20	.50
67 Moises Alou	.20	.50
68 Gary Sheffield	.20	.50
69 Geoff Jenkins	.20	.50
70 Mike Piazza	.75	2.00
71 Jorge Posada	.30	.75
72 Bobby Abreu	.20	.50
73 Phil Nevin	.20	.50
74 John Olerud	.20	.50
75 Mark McGwire	1.25	3.00
76 Jose Cruz Jr.	.20	.50
77 David Segui	.20	.50
78 Neifi Perez	.20	.50
79 Omar Vizquel	.30	.75
80 Rick Ankiel	.20	.50
81 Randy Johnson	.50	1.25
82 Albert Belle	.20	.50
83 Frank Thomas	.50	1.25
84 Manny Ramirez Sox	.30	.75
85 Larry Walker	.30	.75
86 Luis Castillo	.20	.50
87 Johnny Damon	.30	.75
88 Adrian Beltre	.20	.50
89 Cristian Guzman	.20	.50
90 Jay Payton	.20	.50
91 Miguel Tejada	.20	.50
92 Scott Rolen	.30	.75
93 Ryan Klesko	.20	.50
94 Edgar Martinez	.30	.75
95 Fred McGriff	.30	.75
96 Carlos Delgado	.20	.50
97 Barry Zito	.30	.75
98 Mike Lieberthal	.20	.50
99 Trevor Hoffman	.20	.50
100 Gabe Kapler	.20	.50
101 Edgardo Alfonzo	.20	.50
102 Corey Patterson	1.25	3.00
103 Alfonso Soriano	1.25	3.00
104 Keith Ginter	1.25	3.00
105 Keith Reed	1.25	3.00
106 Nick Johnson	1.25	3.00
107 Carlos Pena	1.25	3.00
108 Vernon Wells	1.25	3.00
109 Roy Oswalt	1.50	4.00
110 Alex Escobar	1.25	3.00
111 Adam Everett	1.25	3.00
112 Jimmy Rollins	1.25	3.00
113 Marcus Giles	1.25	3.00
114 Jack Cust	1.25	3.00
115 Chin-Feng Chen	1.25	3.00
116 Pablo Ozuna	1.25	3.00
117 Ben Sheets	1.25	3.00
118 Adrian Gonzalez	1.25	3.00
119 Ben Davis	1.25	3.00
120 Eric Valent	1.25	3.00
121 Scott Heard	1.25	3.00
122 David Parrish RC	1.25	3.00
123 Sean Burnett	1.25	3.00
124 Derek Thompson	1.25	3.00
125 Tim Christman RC	1.25	3.00
126 Mike Jacobs RC	3.00	8.00
127 Luis Montanez RC	1.25	3.00
128 Chris Bass RC	1.25	3.00
129 Will Smith RC	1.25	3.00
130 Justin Wayne RC	1.25	3.00
131 Shawn Fagan RC	1.25	3.00
132 Chad Petty RC	1.25	3.00
133 J.R. House	1.25	3.00
134 Joel Pineiro	1.25	3.00
135 Albert Pujols RC	15.00	40.00
136 Carmen Cali RC	1.25	3.00
137 Steve Smyth RC	1.25	3.00
138 John Lackey	1.25	3.00
139 Bob Keppel RC	1.25	3.00
140 Dominic Rich RC	1.25	3.00
141 Josh Hamilton	2.50	6.00
142 Nolan Ryan	2.50	6.00
143 Tom Seaver	1.50	4.00
144 Reggie Jackson	1.50	4.00
145 Johnny Bench	1.50	4.00
146 Warren Spahn	1.50	4.00
147 Brooks Robinson	1.50	4.00
148 Carl Yastrzemski	2.00	5.00
149 Al Kaline	1.50	4.00
150 Bob Feller	1.25	3.00
151A I. Suzuki English RC	8.00	20.00
151B I.Suzuki Japan RC	8.00	20.00

2001 Topps Gallery Press Plates

Randomly inserted into packs at one in 1347, this 150-card insert is a complete parallel of the base set. The set features the actual press plates used to make all of the 150-card base set. There are four colored press plates inserted for each player: black, cyan, magenta, and yellow.

NO PRICING DUE TO SCARCITY

2001 Topps Gallery Autographs

Inserted at overall odds of one in 232, these six cards feature cards signed by active professionals. All of these cards are all also the special painted cards for this product. Rick Ankiel did not return his cards in time for inclusion in this product. Those cards were redeemable until June 30, 2003.

GROUP A STATED ODDS 1:1066		
GROUP B STATED ODDS 1:1144		
GROUP C STATED ODDS 1:400		
GAAG Adrian Gonzalez B	8.00	20.00
GAAR Alex Rodriguez A	75.00	150.00
GABB Barry Bonds A	100.00	175.00
GAIR Ivan Rodriguez A	40.00	80.00
GAPB Pat Burrell C	8.00	20.00
GARA R. Ankiel C EXCH	15.00	40.00

2001 Topps Gallery Bucks

Issued at a rate of one in 102, this "Buck" was good for $5 towards purchase of Topps Memorabilia.

1 Johnny Bench $5	2.00	5.00

2001 Topps Gallery Heritage

Inserted one per 12 packs, these 12 cards feature a mix of active and retired players in the design Topps used for their 1965 set.

COMPLETE SET (10)	30.00	60.00
GH1 Todd Helton	1.25	3.00
GH2 Greg Maddux	3.00	8.00
GH3 Pedro Martinez	1.25	3.00
GH4 Orlando Cepeda	1.25	3.00
GH5 Willie McCovey	1.25	3.00
GH6 Ken Griffey Jr.	3.00	8.00
GH7 Alex Rodriguez	3.00	8.00
GH8 Derek Jeter	5.00	12.00
GH9 Mark McGwire	5.00	12.00
GH10 Vladimir Guerrero	2.00	5.00

2001 Topps Gallery Heritage Game Jersey

Inserted at a rate of one in 133 packs, these five cards feature pieces of game-worn uniforms along with the Gallery Heritage design.

GHRGM Greg Maddux	10.00	25.00
GHRMR Mystery Jersey	.40	1.00
GHROC Orlando Cepeda	6.00	15.00
GHRPM Pedro Martinez	10.00	25.00
GHRVG Vladimir Guerrero	10.00	25.00
GHRWM Willie McCovey	6.00	15.00

2001 Topps Gallery Heritage Game Jersey Autographs

Issued at a rate of one in 16,313 these two cards feature not only the Heritage design and a game-

worn jersey piece but they also feature an autograph by the featured player. Orlando Cepeda did not return his cards in time for inclusion in this set so those cards were redeemable until June 30, 2003. These cards are serial numbered to 25.

GHRAOC Orlando Cepeda
GHRAWM W.McCovey

2001 Topps Gallery Originals Game Bat

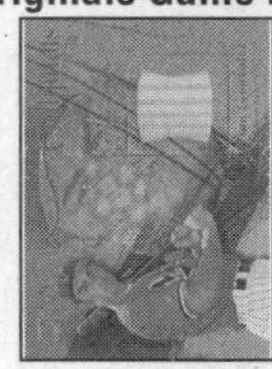

Issued at a rate of one per 133 packs these 15 cards feature game-used bat cards from 15 leading active hitters today. These cards display the genuine issue sticker. Sammy Sosa and Jason Giambi were the two players made available through the Mystery Exchange redemption cards.

GRAG Adrian Gonzalez 4.00 10.00
GRAJ Andruw Jones 6.00 15.00
GRBW Bernie Williams 6.00 15.00
GRDE Darin Erstad 4.00 10.00
GRJD Jermaine Dye 4.00 10.00
GRJG Jason Giambi 4.00 10.00
GRJK Jason Kendall 4.00 10.00
GRJFK Jeff Kent 4.00 10.00
GRMR1 Mystery Relic .40 1.00
GRMR2 Mystery Relic .40 1.00
GRPR Pokey Reese 4.00 10.00
GRPW Preston Wilson 4.00 10.00
GRRA Roberto Alomar 6.00 15.00
GRRP Rafael Palmeiro 6.00 15.00
GRRV Robin Ventura 4.00 10.00
GRSG Shawn Green 4.00 10.00
GRSS Sammy Sosa 6.00 15.00

2001 Topps Gallery Star Gallery

Issued at a rate of one in eight, these 10 cards feature some of the most popular players in the game.

COMPLETE SET (10) 15.00 40.00
SG1 Vladimir Guerrero 1.00 2.50
SG2 Alex Rodriguez 1.50 4.00
SG3 Derek Jeter 2.50 6.00
SG4 Nomar Garciaparra 1.50 4.00
SG5 Ken Griffey Jr. 1.50 4.00
SG6 Mark McGwire 2.50 6.00
SG7 Chipper Jones 1.00 2.50
SG8 Sammy Sosa 1.00 2.50
SG9 Barry Bonds 2.50 6.00
SG10 Mike Piazza 1.50 4.00

2002 Topps Gallery

This 200 card set was released in June, 2002. The set was issued in five-card packs, with an SRP of $3, which came packaged 24 packs to a box and eight boxes to a case. The first 150 cards of this set featured veterans while cards 1511 through 190 featured rookies and cards 191-200 featured retired stars.

COMPLETE SET (200) 40.00 100.00
COMMON CARD (1-150) .20 .50
COMMON CARD (151-190) .40 1.00
COMMON CARD (191-200) .75 2.00
1 Jason Giambi .20 .50
2 Mark Grace .30 .75
3 Bret Boone .20 .50
4 Antonio Alfonseca .20 .50
5 Kevin Brown .20 .50
6 Cristian Guzman .20 .50
7 Magglio Ordonez .20 .50
8 Luis Gonzalez .20 .50
9 Jorge Posada .30 .75
10 Roberto Alomar .30 .75
11 Mike Sweeney .20 .50
12 Jeff Kent .20 .50
13 Matt Morris .20 .50
14 Alfonso Soriano .20 .50
15 Adam Dunn .20 .50
16 Neifi Perez .20 .50
17 Todd Walker .20 .50
18 J.D. Drew .20 .50
19 Eric Chavez .20 .50
20 Alex Rodriguez .75 2.00
21 Ray Lankford .20 .50
22 Roger Cedeno .20 .50
23 Chipper Jones .50 1.25
24 Josh Beckett .20 .50
25 Mike Piazza .75 2.00
26 Freddy Garcia .20 .50
27 Todd Helton .30 .75
28 Tino Martinez .30 .75
29 Kazuhiro Sasaki .20 .50
30 Curt Schilling .20 .50
31 Mark Buehrle .20 .50
32 John Olerud .20 .50
33 Brad Radke .20 .50
34 Steve Sparks .20 .50
35 Jason Tyner .20 .50
36 Jeff Shaw .20 .50
37 Mariano Rivera .50 1.25
38 Russ Ortiz .20 .50
39 Richard Hidalgo .20 .50
40 Carl Everett .20 .50
41 John Burkett .20 .50
42 Tim Hudson .20 .50
43 Mike Hampton .20 .50
44 Orlando Cabrera .20 .50
45 Barry Zito .20 .50
46 C.C. Sabathia .20 .50
47 Chan Ho Park .20 .50
48 Tom Glavine .30 .75
49 Aramis Ramirez .20 .50
50 Lance Berkman .20 .50
51 Al Leiter .20 .50
52 Phil Nevin .20 .50
53 Javier Vazquez .20 .50
54 Troy Glaus .20 .50
55 Tsuyoshi Shinjo .20 .50
56 Albert Pujols 1.00 2.50
57 John Smoltz .30 .75
58 Derek Jeter 1.25 3.00
59 Robb Nen .20 .50
60 Jason Kendall .20 .50
61 Eric Gagne .20 .50
62 Vladimir Guerrero .50 1.25
63 Corey Patterson .20 .50
64 Rickey Henderson .50 1.25
65 Jack Wilson .20 .50
66 Jason LaRue .20 .50
67 Sammy Sosa .50 1.25
68 Ken Griffey Jr. .75 2.00
69 Randy Johnson .50 1.25
70 Nomar Garciaparra .75 2.00
71 Ivan Rodriguez .30 .75
72 J.T. Snow .20 .50
73 Darryl Kile .20 .50
74 Andruw Jones .30 .75
75 Brian Giles .20 .50
76 Pedro Martinez .30 .75
77 Jeff Bagwell .30 .75
78 Rafael Palmeiro .30 .75
79 Ryan Dempster .20 .50
80 Jeff Cirillo .20 .50
81 Geoff Jenkins .20 .50
82 Brandon Duckworth .20 .50
83 Roger Clemens 1.00 2.50
84 Fred McGriff .30 .75
85 Hideo Nomo .50 1.25
86 Larry Walker .20 .50
87 Sean Casey .20 .50
88 Trevor Hoffman .20 .50
89 Robert Fick .20 .50
90 Armando Benitez .20 .50
91 Jeromy Burnitz .20 .50
92 Bernie Williams .30 .75
93 Carlos Delgado .20 .50
94 Troy Percival .20 .50
95 Nate Cornejo .20 .50
96 Derrek Lee .30 .75
97 Jose Ortiz .20 .50
98 Brian Jordan .20 .50
99 Jose Cruz Jr. .20 .50
100 Ichiro Suzuki 1.00 2.50
101 Jose Mesa .20 .50
102 Tim Salmon .30 .75
103 Bud Smith .20 .50
104 Paul LoDuca .20 .50
105 Juan Pierre .20 .50
106 Ben Grieve .20 .50
107 Russell Branyan .20 .50
108 Bob Abreu .20 .50
109 Moises Alou .20 .50
110 Richie Sexson .20 .50
111 Jerry Hairston Jr. .20 .50
112 Marlon Anderson .20 .50
113 Juan Gonzalez .20 .50
114 Craig Biggio .30 .75
115 Carlos Beltran .20 .50
116 Eric Milton .20 .50
117 Cliff Floyd .20 .50
118 Rich Aurilia .20 .50
119 Adrian Beltre .20 .50
120 Jason Bere .20 .50
121 Darin Erstad .20 .50
122 Ben Sheets .20 .50
123 Johnny Damon Sox .30 .75
124 Jimmy Rollins .20 .50
125 Shawn Green .20 .50
126 Greg Maddux .75 2.00
127 Mark Mulder .20 .50
128 Bartolo Colon .20 .50
129 Shannon Stewart .20 .50
130 Ramon Ortiz .20 .50
131 Kerry Wood .20 .50
132 Ryan Klesko .20 .50
133 Preston Wilson .20 .50
134 Roy Oswalt .20 .50
135 Rafael Furcal .30 .75
136 Eric Karros .20 .50
137 Nick Neugebauer .20 .50
138 Doug Mientkiewicz .20 .50
139 Paul Konerko .20 .50
140 Bobby Higginson .20 .50
141 Garret Anderson .20 .50
142 Wes Helms .20 .50
143 Brent Abernathy .20 .50
144 Scott Rolen .30 .75
145 Dmitri Young .20 .50
146 Jim Thome .30 .75
147 Raul Mondesi .20 .50
148 Pat Burrell .20 .50
149 Gary Sheffield .20 .50
150 Miguel Tejada .20 .50
151 Brandon Inge PROS .40 1.00
152 Carlos Pena PROS .40 1.00
153 Jason Lane PROS .40 1.00
154 Nathan Haynes PROS .40 1.00
155 Hank Blalock PROS .60 1.50
156 Juan Cruz PROS .40 1.00
157 Morgan Ensberg PROS .40 1.00
158 Sean Burroughs PROS .40 1.00
159 Ed Rogers PROS .40 1.00
160 Nick Johnson PROS .40 1.00
161 Orlando Hudson PROS .40 1.00
162 A.Martinez PROS RC .40 1.00
163 Jeremy Affeldt PROS .40 1.00
164 Brandon Claussen PROS .40 1.00
165 Deivis Santos PROS .40 1.00
166 Mike Rivera PROS .40 1.00
167 Carlos Silva PROS .40 1.00
168 Val Pascucci PROS .40 1.00
169 Xavier Nady PROS .40 1.00
170 David Espinosa PROS .40 1.00
171 Dan Phillips FYP RC .40 1.00
172 Tony Fontana FYP RC .40 1.00
173 Juan Silvestre FYP .40 1.00
174 Henry Pichardo FYP RC .40 1.00
175 Pablo Arias FYP RC .40 1.00
176 Brett Roneberg FYP RC .40 1.00
177 Chad Qualls FYP RC .60 1.50
178 Greg Sain FYP RC .40 1.00
179 Rene Reyes FYP RC .40 1.00
180 So Taguchi FYP RC .60 1.50
181 Dan Johnson FYP RC .75 2.00
182 J.Backsmeyer FYP RC .40 1.00
183 J.M. Gonzalez FYP RC .40 1.00
184 Jason Ellison FYP RC .60 1.50
185 Kazuhisa Ishii FYP RC .60 1.50
186 Joe Mauer FYP RC 5.00 12.00
187 James Shanks FYP RC .40 1.00
188 Kevin Cash FYP RC .40 1.00
189 J.J. Trujillo FYP RC .40 1.00
190 Jorge Padilla FYP RC .40 1.00
191 Nolan Ryan RET 2.50 6.00
192 George Brett RET 2.00 5.00
193 Ryne Sandberg RET 2.00 5.00
194 Robin Yount RET 1.00 2.50
195 Tom Seaver RET .75 2.00
196 Mike Schmidt RET 2.00 5.00
197 Frank Robinson RET .75 2.00
198 Harmon Killebrew RET 1.00 2.50
199 Kirby Puckett RET 1.00 2.50
200 Don Mattingly RET 2.00 5.00

2002 Topps Gallery Veteran Variation 1

Inserted at stated odds of one in 24, these 10 cards feature the most important players from the Gallery set featuring a variation from the regular issue cards. Since these were not announced until after the product went live, we have put the information about the variation next to the player's name.

1 Jason Giambi Solid Blue 1.00 2.50
20 Alex Rodriguez Grey Jsy 4.00 10.00
25 Mike Piazza Black Jsy 4.00 10.00
27 Todd Helton Solid Blue 1.50 4.00
56 Albert Pujols Red Hat 5.00 12.00
58 Derek Jeter Solid Blue 6.00 15.00
67 Sammy Sosa Black Bat 2.50 6.00
71 Ivan Rodriguez Blue Jsy 1.50 4.00
76 Pedro Martinez Red Shirt 1.50 4.00
100 Ichiro Suzuki Empty Dugout 5.00 12.00

2002 Topps Gallery Autographs

Issued at overall stated odds of one in 240, these 10 cards feature players who have added their signature to these painted cards. The players belong to three different groups and we have put that information about their group next to their name in our checklist.

GROUP A ODDS 1:815 HOB/RET
GROUP B ODDS 1:1017 HOB, 1:1023 RET
GROUP C ODDS 1:509 HOB/RET
GABBO Bret Boone A 10.00 25.00
GAJD J.D. Drew B 10.00 25.00
GAJL Jason Lane C 4.00 10.00
GAJP Jorge Posada A 20.00 50.00
GAJS Juan Silvestre C 4.00 10.00
GALB Lance Berkman A 12.50 30.00
GALG Luis Gonzalez B 10.00 25.00
GAMO Magglio Ordonez A 10.00 25.00
GASG Shawn Green A 15.00 40.00

2002 Topps Gallery Bucks

Inserted at stated odds of one in 27, this $5 buck could be used for redemption towards purchasing

original Topps Gallery artwork.

NNO Nolan Ryan $5 3.00 8.00

2002 Topps Gallery Heritage

Inserted at stated odds of one in 12, these 25 cards feature drawings of players in the style of their Topps rookie card. We have put the year of the players "Topps" rookie card next to their name in our checklist.

COMPLETE SET (25) 50.00 120.00
GHAK Al Kaline 54 2.00 5.00
GHAR Alex Rodriguez 98 3.00 8.00
GHBR Brooks Robinson 57 1.25 3.00
GHBBO Bret Boone 93 1.25 3.00
GHCJ Chipper Jones 91 2.00 5.00
GHCY Carl Yastrzemski 60 3.00 8.00
GHGM Greg Maddux 87 3.00 8.00
GHJG Jason Giambi 91 1.25 3.00
GHKG Ken Griffey Jr. 89 3.00 8.00
GHLG Luis Gonzalez 91 1.25 3.00
GHMM Mark McGwire 85 6.00 15.00
GHMP Mike Piazza 93 3.00 8.00
GHMS Mike Schmidt 73 4.00 10.00
GHNR Nolan Ryan 68 5.00 12.00
GHPM Pedro Martinez 93 1.25 3.00
GHRA Roberto Alomar 88 1.25 3.00
GHRC Roger Clemens 85 4.00 10.00
GHRJ Reggie Jackson 69 1.25 3.00
GHRY Robin Yount 75 2.00 5.00
GHSG Shawn Green 92 1.25 3.00
GHSM Stan Musial 58 3.00 8.00
GHSS Sammy Sosa 90 2.00 5.00
GHTG Tony Gwynn 83 2.50 6.00
GHTS Tom Seaver 67 1.25 3.00
GHTSH Tsuyoshi Shinjo 01 1.25 3.00

2002 Topps Gallery Heritage Autographs

Inserted at stated odds of one in 13,595 hobby and one in 14,064 retail, these three cards feature authentic autographs of the players. These cards have a stated print run of 25 serial numbered sets and due to market scarcity, no pricing is provided for these cards.

GHALG Luis Gonzalez 91
GHASG Shawn Green 92
GHABBO Bret Boone 93

2002 Topps Gallery Heritage Uniform Relics

Inserted in packs at an overall stated rate of one in 85, these nine cards are a partial parallel to the Heritage insert set. Each card contains not only the player's photo but also a game-worn uniform piece. The players were broken up into two groups and we have notated the groups the player belonged to as well as their stated odds in our set information.

GROUP A ODDS 1:106 HOB/RET
GROUP B ODDS 1:424 HOB/RET
GHRAR Alex Rodriguez 98 A 8.00 20.00
GHRCJ Chipper Jones 91 B 6.00 15.00
GHRGM Greg Maddux 87 A 6.00 15.00
GHRLG Luis Gonzalez 91 A 4.00 10.00
GHRMP Mike Piazza 93 A 6.00 15.00
GHRPM Pedro Martinez 93 A 6.00 15.00
GHRTG Tony Gwynn 83 A 6.00 15.00
GHRTS Tsuyoshi Shinjo 01 A 4.00 10.00
GHRBBO Bret Boone 93 A 4.00 10.00

2002 Topps Gallery Original Bat Relics

Inserted at overall stated odds of one in 169, these 15 cards feature not only the player's photo featured

but also a game-used bat piece.

GOAJ Andruw Jones 6.00 15.00
GOAP Albert Pujols 15.00 40.00
GOAR Alex Rodriguez 6.00 15.00
GOAS Alfonso Soriano 4.00 10.00
GOBW Bernie Williams 6.00 15.00
GOBBO Bret Boone 4.00 10.00
GOCD Carlos Delgado 4.00 10.00
GOCJ Chipper Jones 6.00 15.00
GOJC Jose Canseco 6.00 15.00
GOJG Juan Gonzalez 4.00 10.00
GOLG Luis Gonzalez 4.00 10.00
GOMP Mike Piazza 10.00 25.00
GOTG Tony Gwynn 8.00 20.00
GOTH Todd Helton 6.00 15.00
GOTM Tino Martinez 6.00 15.00

2003 Topps Gallery

This 200 card set was released in August, 2003. These cards were issued in four card packs with an $5 SRP which came 20 packs to a box and eight boxes to a case. Cards numbered 1 through 150 featured veterans while cards 151 through 167 featured first year cards, cards 168 through 190 featured leading prospects and cards numbered 191 through 200 featured legendary retired players. In addition, 20 variations (seeded at a stated rate of one in 20) were also included in this set.

COMP.SET w/o SP's (200) 40.00 100.00
COMMON (1-150/168-190) .20 .50
COMMON CARD (151-167) .25 .60
VARIATION STATED ODDS 1:20
COMMON CARD (191-200) .50 1.25
1 Jason Giambi .20 .50
1A Jason Giambi Blue Jsy 2.00 5.00
2 Miguel Tejada .20 .50
3 Mike Lieberthal .20 .50
4 Jason Kendall .20 .50
5 Robb Nen .20 .50
6 Freddy Garcia .20 .50
7 Scott Rolen .30 .75
8 Boomer Wells .20 .50
9 Rafael Palmeiro .30 .75
10 Garret Anderson .20 .50
11 Curt Schilling .20 .50
12 Greg Maddux .75 2.00
13 Rodrigo Lopez .20 .50
14 Nomar Garciaparra .75 2.00
14A N.Garciaparra Btg Glv 3.00 8.00
15 Kerry Wood .20 .50
16 Frank Thomas .50 1.25
17 Ken Griffey Jr. .75 2.00
18 Jim Thome .30 .75
19 Todd Helton .30 .75
20 Lance Berkman .20 .50
21 Robert Fick .20 .50
22 Kevin Brown .20 .50
23 Richie Sexson .20 .50
24 Eddie Guardado .20 .50
25 Vladimir Guerrero .50 1.25
26 Mike Piazza .75 2.00
27 Bernie Williams .30 .75
28 Eric Chavez .20 .50
29 Jimmy Rollins .20 .50
30 Ichiro Suzuki 1.00 2.50
30A I.Suzuki Black Sleeve 3.00 8.00
31 J.D. Drew .20 .50
32 Nick Johnson .20 .50
33 Shannon Stewart .20 .50
34 Tim Salmon .30 .75
35 Andruw Jones .30 .75
36 Jay Gibbons .20 .50
37 Johnny Damon .30 .75
38 Fred McGriff .30 .75
39 Carlos Lee .20 .50
40 Adam Dunn .20 .50
40A Adam Dunn Red Sleeve 2.00 5.00
41 Jason Jennings .20 .50
42 Mike Lowell .20 .50
43 Mike Sweeney .20 .50
44 Shawn Green .20 .50
45 Doug Mientkiewicz .20 .50
46 Bartolo Colon .20 .50
47 Edgardo Alfonzo .20 .50
48 Roger Clemens 1.00 2.50
49 Randy Wolf .20 .50
50 Alex Rodriguez .75 2.00
50A Alex Rodriguez Red Shirt 3.00 8.00
51 Vernon Wells .20 .50
52 Kenny Lofton .20 .50
53 Mariano Rivera .50 1.25
54 Brian Jordan .20 .50
55 Roberto Alomar .30 .75
56 Carlos Pena .20 .50
57 Moises Alou .20 .50
58 John Smoltz .30 .75
59 Adam Kennedy .20 .50
60 Randy Johnson .50 1.25
61 Mark Buehrle .20 .50
62 C.C. Sabathia .20 .50
63 Craig Biggio .30 .75
64 Eric Karros .20 .50
65 Jose Vidro .20 .50
66 Tim Hudson .20 .50
67 Trevor Hoffman .20 .50
68 Bret Boone .20 .50
69 Carl Crawford .20 .50
70 Derek Jeter 1.25 3.00
71 Troy Percival .20 .50
72 Gary Sheffield .20 .50
73 Rickey Henderson .50 1.25
74 Paul Konerko .20 .50
75 Larry Walker .20 .50
76 Pat Burrell .20 .50
77 Brian Giles .20 .50
78 Jeff Kent .20 .50
79 Kazuhiro Sasaki .20 .50
80 Chipper Jones .50 1.25
81 Darin Erstad .20 .50
82 Sean Casey .20 .50
83 Luis Gonzalez .20 .50
84 Roy Oswalt .20 .50
85 Dustan Mohr .20 .50
86 Al Leiter .20 .50
87 Mike Mussina .30 .75
88 Vicente Padilla .20 .50
89 Rich Aurilia .20 .50
90 Albert Pujols 1.00 2.50
91 John Olerud .20 .50
92 Ivan Rodriguez .30 .75
93 Eric Hinske .20 .50
94 Phil Nevin .20 .50
95 Barry Zito .20 .50
96 Armando Benitez .20 .50
97 Torii Hunter .20 .50
98 Paul Lo Duca .20 .50
99 Preston Wilson .20 .50
100 Sammy Sosa .50 1.25
100A Sammy Sosa Black Bat 2.00 5.00
101 Jarrod Washburn .20 .50
102 Steve Finley .20 .50
103 Cliff Floyd .20 .50
104 Mark Prior .30 .75
105 Austin Kearns .20 .50
106 Jeff Bagwell .30 .75
107 A.J. Pierzynski .20 .50
108 Pedro Martinez .30 .75
109 Orlando Cabrera .20 .50
110 Raul Mondesi .20 .50
111 Russ Ortiz .20 .50
112 Ruben Sierra .20 .50
113 Tino Martinez .30 .75
114 Manny Ramirez .30 .75
115 Troy Glaus .20 .50
116 Magglio Ordonez .20 .50
117 Omar Vizquel .30 .75
118 Carlos Beltran .20 .50
119 Jose Hernandez .20 .50
120 Javier Vazquez .20 .50
121 Jorge Posada .30 .75
122 Aramis Ramirez .20 .50
123 Jason Schmidt .20 .50
124 Jamie Moyer .20 .50
125 Jim Edmonds .20 .50
126 Aubrey Huff .20 .50
127 Carlos Delgado .20 .50
128 Junior Spivey .20 .50
129 Tom Glavine .30 .75
130 Marty Cordova .20 .50
131 Derek Lowe .20 .50
132 Ellis Burks .20 .50
133 Barry Bonds 1.25 3.00
134 Josh Beckett .20 .50
135 Raul Ibanez .20 .50
136 Kazuhisa Ishii .20 .50
137 Geoff Jenkins .20 .50
138 Eric Milton .20 .50
139 Mo Vaughn .20 .50
140 Mark Mulder .20 .50
141 Bobby Abreu .20 .50
142 Ryan Klesko .20 .50
143 Tsuyoshi Shinjo .20 .50
144 Jose Mesa .20 .50
145 Shea Hillenbrand .20 .50
146 Edgar Renteria .20 .50
147 Juan Gonzalez .20 .50
148 Edgar Martinez .30 .75
149 Matt Morris .20 .50
150 Alfonso Soriano .20 .50
150A Alfonso Soriano No Pad 2.00 5.00
151 Bryan Bullington FY RC .25 .60
151A B.Bullington Red Back FY 2.00 5.00
152 Andy Marte FY RC 2.00 5.00
152A A.Marte No Necklace FY 3.00 8.00
153 Brendan Harris FY RC .40 1.00
154 Juan Camacho FY RC .25 .60
155 Byron Gettis FY RC .25 .60
156 Daryl Clark FY RC .25 .60
157 J.D. Durbin FY RC .25 .60
158 Craig Brazell FY RC .25 .60
158A Craig Brazell Black Jsy 2.00 5.00
159 Jason Kubel FY RC 1.00 2.50
160 Br. Roberson FY RC .25 .60
161 Jose Contreras FY RC .60 1.50
162 Hanley Ramirez FY RC 2.00 5.00
163 Jaime Bubela FY RC .25 .60
164 Chris Duncan FY RC 2.50 6.00
165 Tyler Johnson FY RC .25 .60
166 Joey Gomes FY RC .25 .60
167 Ben Francisco FY RC .25 .60
168 Adam LaRoche PROS .20 .50
169 Tommy Whiteman PROS .20 .50
170 Trey Hodges PROS .20 .50
171 Fr. Rodriguez PROS .20 .50
172 Jason Arnold PROS .20 .50
173 Brett Myers PROS .20 .50
174 Rocco Baldelli PROS .20 .50
175 Adrian Gonzalez PROS .20 .50
176 Dontrelle Willis PROS .50 1.25
177 Walter Young PROS .20 .50
178 Marlon Byrd PROS .20 .50
179 Aaron Heilman PROS .20 .50
180 Casey Kotchman PROS .20 .50
181 Miguel Cabrera PROS .50 1.25
182 Hee Seop Choi PROS .20 .50
183 Drew Henson PROS .20 .50
184 Jose Reyes PROS .20 .50
185 Michael Cuddyer PROS .20 .50
186 Brandon Phillips PROS .20 .50
187 Victor Martinez PROS .30 .75
188 Joe Mauer PROS .50 1.25
189 Hank Blalock PROS .20 .50
190 Mark Teixeira PROS .30 .75
191 Willie Mays RET 1.50 4.00
192 George Brett RET 1.50 4.00

193 Tony Gwynn RET 1.00 2.50
194 Carl Yastrzemski RET 1.25 3.00
195 Nolan Ryan RET 2.00 5.00
196 Reggie Jackson RET .50 1.25
197 Mike Schmidt RET 1.50 4.00
198 Cal Ripken RET 2.50 6.00
199 Don Mattingly RET 1.50 4.00
200 Tom Seaver RET .50 1.25

2003 Topps Gallery Artist's Proofs

*AP 1-150/168-190: .75X TO 2X BASIC
*AP 151-167: .75X TO 2X BASIC
*AP 191-200: 1X TO 2.5X BASIC
ONE PER PACK
AP'S FEATURE SILVER HOLO-FOIL

2003 Topps Gallery Press Plates

RANDOM INSERTS IN PACKS
STATED PRINT RUN 4 SERIAL #'d SETS
NO PRICING DUE TO SCARCITY

2003 Topps Gallery Bucks

Inserted at a stated rate of one in 41, this one "card" insert set featured a photo of Willie Mays along with a $5 gift certificate good for Topps product.

5 Willie Mays $5 2.00 5.00

2003 Topps Gallery Currency Collection Coin Relics

Inserted in each hobby box as a "box-topper" these 25 cards feature players from throughout the world along with a coin from their homeland.

AJ Andruw Jones 3.00 8.00
AP Albert Pujols 6.00 15.00
AS Alfonso Soriano 3.00 8.00
BA Bobby Abreu 3.00 8.00
BC Bartolo Colon 3.00 8.00
ER Edgar Renteria 3.00 8.00
FR Francisco Rodriguez 3.00 8.00
HC Hee Seop Choi 3.00 8.00
HN Hideo Nomo 4.00 10.00
IS Ichiro Suzuki 6.00 15.00
JR Jose Reyes 3.00 8.00
KI Kazuhisa Ishii 3.00 8.00
KS Kazuhiro Sasaki 3.00 8.00
LW Larry Walker 3.00 8.00
MO Magglio Ordonez 3.00 8.00
MR Manny Ramirez 3.00 8.00
MRI Mariano Rivera 4.00 10.00
OC Orlando Cabrera 3.00 8.00
OV Omar Vizquel 3.00 8.00
PM Pedro Martinez 3.00 8.00
RL Rodrigo Lopez 3.00 8.00
RM Raul Mondesi 3.00 8.00
SS Sammy Sosa 4.00 10.00
VG Vladimir Guerrero 4.00 10.00
VP Vicente Padilla 3.00 8.00

2003 Topps Gallery Heritage

STATED ODDS 1:10
AD Adam Dunn 1.25 3.00
AS Alfonso Soriano 1.25 3.00
BW Bernie Williams 2.00 5.00
CY Carl Yastrzemski 3.00 8.00
DJ Derek Jeter 5.00 12.00
DS Duke Snider 2.00 5.00
GB George Brett 3.00 8.00
HK Harmon Killebrew 2.00 5.00

HN Hideo Nomo 2.00 5.00
IR Ivan Rodriguez 2.00 5.00
IS Ichiro Suzuki 4.00 10.00
JC Jose Canseco 2.00 5.00
JT Jim Thome 2.00 5.00
KP Kirby Puckett 2.00 5.00
KR Jerry Koosman 6.00 15.00
Nolan Ryan
MJ Miguel Tejada 1.25 3.00
NG Nomar Garciaparra 3.00 8.00
RC Roger Clemens 4.00 10.00
RH Rickey Henderson 2.00 5.00
RJ Randy Johnson 2.00 5.00
SG Shawn Green 1.25 3.00
TG Tom Glavine 2.00 5.00
TGW Tony Gwynn 2.50 6.00
WB Wade Boggs 2.00 5.00
WM Willie Mays 4.00 10.00

2003 Topps Gallery Heritage Autograph Relics

Randomly inserted into packs, these four cards feature not only a game-used memorabilia piece but also an authentic autograph of the featured player. Each of these cards were issued to a stated print run of 25 copies and no pricing is available due to market scarcity.

NO PRICING DUE TO SCARCITY
GB George Brett Bat
KP Kirby Puckett Bat
TG Tony Gwynn Jsy
WB Wade Boggs Uni

2003 Topps Gallery Heritage Relics

Inserted at varying odds depending what group the card belonged to, this 10 card set featured game-used memorabilia pieces of the featured player.

GROUP A ODDS 1:141
GROUP B ODDS 1:67
GB George Brett Bat A 10.00 25.00
HK Harmon Killebrew Bat A 10.00 25.00
HN Hideo Nomo Jsy A 6.00 15.00
JC Jose Canseco Bat B 4.00 10.00
KP Kirby Puckett Bat A 6.00 15.00
RC Roger Clemens Jsy A 6.00 15.00
RH Rickey Henderson Bat B 4.00 10.00
SG Shawn Green Jsy B 3.00 8.00
TG Tony Gwynn Jsy B 6.00 15.00
WB Wade Boggs Uni B 4.00 10.00

2003 Topps Gallery Originals Bat Relics

GROUP A ODDS 1:131
GROUP B ODDS 1:81
GROUP C ODDS 1:15
AD Adam Dunn C 3.00 8.00
AJ Andruw Jones C 4.00 10.00
AP Albert Pujols B 8.00 20.00
AR Alex Rodriguez C 6.00 15.00
AS Alfonso Soriano B 3.00 8.00
BB Bret Boone C 3.00 8.00
BW Bernie Williams C 4.00 10.00
CJ Chipper Jones C 4.00 10.00
CY Carl Yastrzemski A 8.00 20.00
DH Drew Henson B 3.00 8.00
FT Frank Thomas C 4.00 10.00
GS Gary Sheffield C 3.00 8.00
IR Ivan Rodriguez C 4.00 10.00
JM Joe Mauer A 8.00 20.00
JT Jim Thome C 4.00 10.00
LB Lance Berkman C 3.00 8.00
LG Luis Gonzalez A 4.00 10.00
MA Moises Alou B 3.00 8.00
MJ Miguel Tejada A 4.00 10.00
MO Magglio Ordonez C 3.00 8.00
MP Mike Piazza C 6.00 15.00
MR Manny Ramirez C 4.00 10.00
NG Nomar Garciaparra B 6.00 15.00
RA Roberto Alomar C 4.00 10.00
RH Rickey Henderson C 4.00 10.00
RP Rafael Palmeiro C 4.00 10.00
SG Shawn Green B 3.00 8.00
TG Tony Gwynn C 4.00 10.00
TH Todd Helton C 4.00 10.00
THU Torii Hunter A 4.00 10.00

2005 Topps Gallery

This 205-card set was released in January, 2005. The set was issued in five-card packs with an $10 SRP which came 20 packs to a box and 12 boxes to a case. Cards numbered 1-150 feature veterans while cards 151 through 170 feature players in their first year in Topps. Cards numbered 171 through 185 feature leading prospects while cards 186-195 feature retired players. Cards numbered 151 through 195 were issued at a stated rate of five per "mini-box" and there are some short print "variations" which came one in eight mini-boxes.

COMP.SET w/o SP'S (150) 30.00 60.00
COMMON CARD (1-150) .30 .75
COMMON CARD (151-170) 2.00 5.00
COMMON CARD (171-185) 2.00 5.00
COMMON CARD (186-195) 2.00 5.00
151-195 ODDS FIVE PER MINI-BOX
VARIATION ODDS 1:8 MINI-BOXES
VARIATION STATED PRINT RUN 517 SETS
VARIATIONS ARE NOT SERIAL-NUMBERED
PRINT RUN INFO PROVIDED BY TOPPS
VAR CL: 1/40/100/154-155/157/
VAR CL: 167-168/187
SEE BECKETT.COM FOR VARIATION INFO
PLATE ODDS 1:48 MINI-BOXES
PLATE PRINT RUN 1 SET PER COLOR
BLACK-CYAN-MAGENTA-YELLOW ISSUED
NO PLATE PRICING DUE TO SCARCITY
1A A.Rodriguez White Glv 1.25 3.00
1B A.Rodriguez Blk Glv SP 3.00 8.00
2 Eric Chavez .30 .75
3 Mike Piazza .75 2.00
4 Bret Boone .30 .75
5 Albert Pujols 1.50 4.00
6 Vernon Wells .30 .75
7 Andruw Jones .50 1.25
8 Miguel Tejada .30 .75
9 Johnny Damon .50 1.25
10 Nomar Garciaparra .75 2.00
11 Pat Burrell .30 .75
12 Bartolo Colon .30 .75
13 Johnny Estrada .30 .75
14 Luis Gonzalez .30 .75
15 Jay Gibbons .30 .75
16 Curt Schilling .50 1.25
17 Aramis Ramirez .30 .75
18 Frank Thomas .75 2.00
19 Adam Dunn .30 .75
20 Sammy Sosa .75 2.00
21 Matt Lawton .30 .75
22 Preston Wilson UER .30 .75
Preston is listed as his own father in text
23 Carlos Pena .30 .75
24 Josh Beckett .30 .75
25 Carlos Beltran .30 .75
26 Juan Gonzalez .30 .75
27 Adrian Beltre .30 .75
28 Lyle Overbay .30 .75
29 Justin Morneau .30 .75
30 Derek Jeter 1.50 4.00
31 Barry Zito .30 .75
32 Bobby Abreu .30 .75
33 Jason Bay .30 .75
34 Jose Reyes .30 .75
35 Nick Johnson .30 .75
36 Lew Ford .30 .75
37 Scott Podsednik .30 .75
38 Rocco Baldelli .30 .75
39 Eric Hinske .30 .75
40A Ichiro Black Wall 1.50 4.00
40B Ichiro Writing on Wall SP 4.00 10.00
41 Larry Walker .50 1.25
42 Mark Teixeira .50 1.25
43 Khalil Greene .50 1.25
44 Edgardo Alfonzo .30 .75
45 Javier Vazquez .30 .75
46 Cliff Floyd .30 .75
47 Geoff Jenkins .30 .75
48 Ken Griffey Jr. 1.25 3.00
49 Vinny Castilla .30 .75
50 Mark Prior .50 1.25
51 Jose Guillen .30 .75
52 J.D. Drew .30 .75
53 Rafael Palmeiro .50 1.25
54 Kevin Youkilis .30 .75
55 Derrek Lee .50 1.25
56 Freddy Garcia .30 .75
57 Wily Mo Pena .30 .75
58 C.C. Sabathia .30 .75
59 Craig Biggio .50 1.25
60 Ivan Rodriguez .50 1.25
61 Angel Berroa .30 .75
62 Ben Sheets .30 .75
63 Johan Santana .75 2.00
64 Al Leiter .30 .75
65 Bernie Williams .50 1.25
66 Bobby Crosby .30 .75
67 Jack Wilson .30 .75
68 A.J. Pierzynski .30 .75
69 Jimmy Rollins .30 .75
70 Jason Giambi .30 .75
71 Tom Glavine .50 1.25
72 Kevin Brown .30 .75
73 B.J. Upton .50 1.25
74 Edgar Renteria .30 .75
75 Alfonso Soriano .30 .75
76 Mike Lieberthal .30 .75
77 Kazuo Matsui .30 .75
78 Phil Nevin .30 .75
79 Shawn Green .30 .75
80 Miguel Cabrera .50 1.25
81 Todd Helton .50 1.25
82 Magglio Ordonez .30 .75
83 Manny Ramirez .50 1.25
84 Bill Mueller .30 .75
85 Troy Glaus .30 .75
86 Richie Sexson .30 .75
87 Javy Lopez .30 .75
88 David Ortiz .75 2.00
89 Greg Maddux 1.25 3.00
90 Vladimir Guerrero .75 2.00
91 Jeromy Burnitz .30 .75
92 Jeff Kent .30 .75
93 Travis Hafner .30 .75
94 Mark Buehrle .30 .75
95 Paul Lo Duca .30 .75
96 Roy Oswalt .30 .75
97 Torii Hunter .30 .75
98 Gary Sheffield .30 .75
99 Erubiel Durazo .30 .75
100A J.Thome Kid's Shirt Blue .50 1.25
100B J.Thome Kid's Shirt Red SP 3.00 8.00
101 Ken Harvey .30 .75
102 Shannon Stewart .30 .75
103 Dmitri Young .30 .75
104 Kevin Millar .30 .75
105 Kerry Wood .30 .75
106 Paul Konerko .30 .75
107 Ronnie Belliard .30 .75
108 Mike Lowell .30 .75
109 Hee Seop Choi .30 .75
110 Joe Mauer .75 2.00
111 David Wright 1.25 3.00
112 Jorge Posada .50 1.25
113 Tim Hudson .30 .75
114 Brian Giles .30 .75
115 Jason Schmidt .30 .75
116 Aubrey Huff .30 .75
117 Hank Blalock .30 .75
118 Jim Edmonds .30 .75
119 Raul Ibanez .30 .75
120 Carlos Delgado .30 .75
121 Craig Wilson .30 .75
122 Ryan Klesko .30 .75
123 Mark Mulder .30 .75
124 Jose Vidro .30 .75
125 Mike Sweeney .30 .75
126 Lance Berkman .30 .75
127 Juan Pierre .30 .75
128 Austin Kearns .30 .75
129 Moises Alou .30 .75
130 Garret Anderson .30 .75
131 Pedro Martinez .50 1.25
132 Melvin Mora .30 .75
133 Marcus Giles .30 .75
134 Corey Patterson .30 .75
135 Carlos Lee .30 .75
136 Sean Casey .30 .75
137 Jody Gerut .30 .75
138 Jose Valentin .30 .75
139 Aaron Miles .30 .75
140 Randy Johnson .75 2.00
141 Carlos Guillen .30 .75
142 Dontrelle Willis .30 .75
143 Jeff Bagwell .50 1.25
144 Jason Kendall .30 .75
145 Mark Loretta .30 .75
146 Scott Rolen .50 1.25
147 Carl Crawford .30 .75
148 Michael Young .30 .75
149 Jermaine Dye .30 .75
150 Chipper Jones .75 2.00
151 Melky Cabrera FY RC 4.00 10.00
152 Chris Seddon FY RC 2.00 5.00
153 Nate Schierholtz FY 2.00 5.00
154A Ian Kinsler FY Green RC 5.00 12.00
154B Ian Kinsler FY Gold SP 8.00 20.00
155A B.Moss FY Black Hat RC 3.00 8.00
155B B.Moss FY Red Hat SP 4.00 10.00
156 Chadd Blasko FY RC 2.00 5.00
157A J.West FY Red Jsy RC 2.00 5.00
157B J.West FY Navy Jsy SP 3.00 8.00
158 Sean Marshall FY RC 2.50 6.00
159 Ryan Sweeney FY RC 3.00 8.00
160 Matthew Lindstrom FY RC 2.00 5.00
161 Ryan Goleski FY RC 2.00 5.00
162 Brett Harper FY RC 2.00 5.00
163 Chris Roberson FY RC 2.00 5.00
164 Andre Ethier FY RC 6.00 15.00
165A I.Bladergroen FY Pose RC 2.00 5.00
165B I.Bladergroen FY Swing SP 3.00 8.00
166 James Jurries FY RC 2.00 5.00
167A Billy Butler FY Vest RC 6.00 15.00
167B B.Butler FY Black Uni SP 8.00 20.00
168A M.Rogers FY Ball/Air RC 2.00 5.00
168B M.Rogers FY Ball/Hand SP 3.00 8.00
169 Tyler Clippard FY RC 10.00 25.00
170 Luis Ramirez FY RC 2.00 5.00
171 Casey Kotchman PROS 2.00 5.00
172 Chris Burke PROS 2.00 5.00
173 Dallas McPherson PROS 2.00 5.00
174 Edwin Jackson PROS 2.00 5.00
175 Felix Hernandez PROS 4.00 10.00
176 Gavin Floyd PROS 2.00 5.00
177 Guillermo Quiroz PROS 2.00 5.00
178 Jason Kubel PROS 2.00 5.00
179 Jeff Mathis PROS 2.00 5.00
180 Rickie Weeks PROS 2.00 5.00
181 Ryan Howard PROS 3.00 8.00
182 Franklin Gutierrez PROS 2.00 5.00
183 Jeremy Reed PROS 2.00 5.00
184 Carlos Quentin PROS 2.00 5.00
185 Jeff Francis PROS 2.00 5.00
186 Nolan Ryan RET 6.00 15.00
187A Hank Aaron RET w/o 755 4.00 10.00
187B Hank Aaron RET w/755 SP 6.00 15.00
188 Duke Snider RET 3.00 8.00
189 Mike Schmidt RET 4.00 10.00
190 Ernie Banks RET 3.00 8.00
191 Frank Robinson RET 2.00 5.00
192 Harmon Killebrew RET 3.00 8.00
193 Al Kaline RET 3.00 8.00
194 Rod Carew RET 3.00 8.00
195 Johnny Bench RET 3.00 8.00

2005 Topps Gallery Artist's Proof

*AP 1-150: 1X TO 2.5X BASIC
1-150 ODDS FIVE PER MINI-BOX
*AP 151-195: .75X TO 2X BASIC
151-195 ODDS 1:4 MINI-BOXES
151-195 STATED PRINT RUN 259 SETS
151-195 ARE NOT SERIAL-NUMBERED
*AP VAR: .75X TO 2X BASIC VAR
VARIATION ODDS 1:29 MINI-BOXES
VARIATION STATED PRINT RUN 130 SETS
VARIATIONS ARE NOT SERIAL-NUMBERED
PRINT RUN INFO PROVIDED BY TOPPS
169 Tyler Clippard FY 20.00 50.00

2005 Topps Gallery Murray Olderman Sketches

STATED ODDS 1:203 MINI-BOXES
STATED PRINT RUN 1 SERIAL #'d SET
NO PRICING DUE TO SCARCITY

2005 Topps Gallery Cut Signatures

STATED ODDS 1:1376 MINI-BOXES
CARDS ARE SERIAL #'d AS 1 OF 1's
ACTUAL PRINT RUNS B/WN 1-7 COPIES PER
NO PRICING DUE TO SCARCITY
BW Benjamin West/1
ED Eugene Delacroix/1
FB Frederic Bartholdi/2
FC Frederic Church/1
FF Friz Freleng/1
FR Frederic Remington/1
GM Grandma Moses/1
JF James Earl Fraser/1
JM Joan Miro/2
JW James Whistler/1
MC Marc Chagall/2
ME Max Ernst/1
NR Norman Rockwell/2
PP Pablo Picasso/1
RK Rockwell Kent/1
SD Salvador Dali/2
TN Thomas Nast/7
WD Walt Disney/1

2005 Topps Gallery Gallo's Gallery

STATED ODDS 1:3 MINI-BOXES
AP Albert Pujols 4.00 10.00
AR Alex Rodriguez 3.00 8.00
AS Alfonso Soriano 2.00 5.00
CJ Chipper Jones 3.00 8.00
DJ Derek Jeter 4.00 10.00
HA Hank Aaron 6.00 15.00
HB Hank Blalock 2.00 5.00
IR Ivan Rodriguez 3.00 8.00
IS Ichiro Suzuki 4.00 10.00
JT Jim Thome 3.00 8.00
MP Mark Prior 3.00 8.00
MPI Mike Piazza 3.00 8.00
MS Mike Schmidt 4.00 10.00
MT Miguel Tejada 2.00 5.00
NG Nomar Garciaparra 3.00 8.00
NR Nolan Ryan 6.00 15.00
RJ Randy Johnson 3.00 8.00
SS Sammy Sosa 3.00 8.00
TH Todd Helton 3.00 8.00
VG Vladimir Guerrero 3.00 8.00

2005 Topps Gallery Heritage

STATED ODDS 1:3 MINI-BOXES
AK Al Kaline 59 Thrill 3.00 8.00
AP Albert Pujols 01 TT 3.00 8.00
BG Bob Gibson 59 3.00 8.00
BR Brooks Robinson 72 Boy 3.00 8.00
CB Carlos Beltran 95 DP 2.00 5.00
CS Curt Schilling 90 2.00 5.00
DM Don Mattingly 84 3.00 8.00
DS Darryl Strawberry 84 2.00 5.00
DSN Duke Snider 59 Thrill 3.00 8.00
DW Dontrelle Willis 02 TT 2.00 5.00
EB Ernie Banks 54 3.00 8.00
FR Frank Robinson 57 2.00 5.00
GB George Brett 77 RB 3.00 8.00
HB Hank Blalock 01 2.00 5.00
IR Ivan Rodriguez 04 3.00 8.00
JB Johnny Bench 69 3.00 8.00
JC Jose Canseco 87 3.00 8.00
JP Jim Palmer 73 Boy 2.00 5.00
MS Mike Schmidt 83 SV 3.00 8.00
NR Nolan Ryan 90 HL 5.00 12.00
OS Ozzie Smith 79 3.00 8.00
RJ Alex Rodriguez 8.00 20.00
Derek Jeter
Kings of New York
RP Rafael Palmeiro 87 3.00 8.00
RR Frank Robinson 3.00 8.00
Brooks Robinson
68 Bird Belters
TS Jim Thome 4.00 10.00
Mike Schmidt
South Philly Sluggers

2005 Topps Gallery Heritage Relics

STATED ODDS 1:8 MINI BOXES
AP Albert Pujols 01 TT Jsy 8.00 20.00
AR Alex Rodriguez 04 Bat 6.00 15.00
DM Don Mattingly 84 Bat 8.00 20.00
DS Darryl Strawberry 84 Bat 3.00 8.00
DW Dontrelle Willis 02 TT Jsy 3.00 8.00
GB George Brett 77 RB Bat 6.00 15.00
IR Ivan Rodriguez 04 Bat 4.00 10.00
JC Jose Canseco 87 Bat 4.00 10.00
NR Nolan Ryan 90 HL Jsy 10.00 25.00
OS Ozzie Smith 79 Bat 6.00 15.00

2005 Topps Gallery Heritage Relics Autographs

STATED ODDS 1:396 MINI-BOXES
STATED PRINT RUN 25 SERIAL #'d SETS
EXCHANGE DEADLINE 01/31/07
NO PRICING DUE TO SCARCITY
AR Alex Rodriguez 04 Bat
DM Don Mattingly 84 Bat
IR I.Rodriguez 04 Bat EXCH
NR Nolan Ryan 90 HL Uni

2005 Topps Gallery Originals Relics

STATED ODDS 1:2 MINI-BOXES
AB Angel Berroa Bat 3.00 8.00
AP Albert Pujols Jsy 8.00 20.00
AR Alex Rodriguez Uni 6.00 15.00
AS Alfonso Soriano Bat 3.00 8.00
BU B.J. Upton Bat 4.00 10.00
BW Bernie Williams Bat 4.00 10.00
CJ Chipper Jones Jsy 4.00 10.00
DO David Ortiz Bat 4.00 10.00
DW Dontrelle Willis Jsy 3.00 8.00
FT Frank Thomas Bat 4.00 10.00
HB Hank Blalock Jsy 3.00 8.00

HBB Hank Blalock Bat 3.00 8.00
IR Ivan Rodriguez Bat 4.00 10.00
JB Jeff Bagwell Uni 4.00 10.00
JBE Josh Beckett Bat 3.00 8.00
JD Johnny Damon Bat 4.00 10.00
JG Jason Giambi Bat 3.00 8.00
JL Javy Lopez Bat 3.00 8.00
JR Jose Reyes Bat 3.00 8.00
KM Kazuo Matsui Bat 4.00 10.00
KW Kerry Wood Jsy 3.00 8.00
LB Lance Berkman Jsy 3.00 8.00
LN Laynce Nix Jsy 3.00 8.00
MC Miguel Cabrera Jsy 4.00 10.00
MG Marcus Giles Jsy 3.00 8.00
ML Mike Lowell Jsy 3.00 8.00
MP Mike Piazza Jsy 4.00 10.00
MPB Mike Piazza Bat 4.00 10.00
MPR Mark Prior Jsy 4.00 10.00
MR Manny Ramirez Bat 4.00 10.00
MT Mark Teixeira Jsy 4.00 10.00
MTE Miguel Tejada Bat 3.00 8.00
MY Michael Young Jsy 3.00 8.00
PM Pedro Martinez Jsy 4.00 10.00
RB Rocco Baldelli Bat 3.00 8.00
RD Ryan Drese Jsy 3.00 8.00
RH Rich Harden Uni 3.00 8.00
SS Sammy Sosa Jsy 4.00 10.00
TH Todd Helton Jsy 4.00 10.00
VG Vladimir Guerrero Bat 4.00 10.00

2005 Topps Gallery Penmanship Autographs

GROUP A ODDS 1:786 MINI-BOXES
GROUP B ODDS 1:132 MINI-BOXES
GROUP C ODDS 1:39 MINI-BOXES
GROUP D ODDS 1:39 MINI-BOXES
GROUP E ODDS 1:5 MINI-BOXES
GROUP A STATED PRINT RUN 25 SETS
GROUP A PRINT RUN PROVIDED BY TOPPS
NO GROUP A PRICING DUE TO SCARCITY
EXCHANGE DEADLINE 01/31/07
AH Aubrey Huff C 4.00 10.00
AR Alex Rodriguez A/25 *
DM Dallas McPherson E 4.00 10.00
EC Eric Chavez D 6.00 15.00
FH Felix Hernandez E 20.00 40.00
IR Ivan Rodriguez A/25 * EXCH
JB Jason Bartlett E 4.00 10.00
JJ Justin Jones B 4.00 10.00
TB Taylor Buchholz E 4.00 10.00
VW Vernon Wells C 6.00 15.00

2003 Topps Gallery HOF

This set was released in April, 2003. Each card in the set was actually issued in different versions, some of each were easy to identify and others had far more subtle differences. This set was issued in five card packs with an $5 SRP. The packs were issued in 20 pack boxes which came six boxes to a case.

COMPLETE SET (74) 15.00 40.00
COMMON CARD (1-74) .30 .75
COMMON VARIATION (1-74) .60 1.50
1 Willie Mays Bleachers 1.25 3.00
1B Willie Mays Gold 2.50 6.00
2 Al Kaline Stripes .60 1.50
2B Al Kaline No Stripes 1.25 3.00
3 Hank Aaron Black Hat 1.25 3.00
3B Hank Aaron Blue Hat 2.50 6.00
4 Carl Yastrzemski Black Ltr 1.00 2.50
4B Carl Yastrzemski Red Ltr 2.00 5.00
5 Luis Aparicio Wood Bat .30 .75
5B Luis Aparicio Black Bat .60 1.50
6 Sam Crawford Grey Uni .30 .75
6B Sam Crawford Navy Uni .60 1.50
7 Tom Lasorda Trees .30 .75
7B Tom Lasorda Red .60 1.50
8 John McGraw MG No Logo .40 1.00
8B J.McGraw MG NY Logo .75 2.00
9 Edd Roush White C .30 .75
9B Edd Roush Red C .60 1.50
10 Reggie Jackson Grass .40 1.00
10B Reggie Jackson Red .75 2.00
11 Catfish Hunter Yellow Jsy .40 1.00
11B Catfish Hunter White Jsy .75 2.00
12 Rob. Clemente White Uni 1.50 4.00
12B Rob. Clemente Yellow Uni 3.00 8.00
13 Eddie Collins Grey Uni .30 .75
13B Eddie Collins Navy Uni .60 1.50
14 Frankie Frisch Olive .30 .75
14B Frankie Frisch Blue .60 1.50
15 Nolan Ryan Leather Glv 1.50 4.00
15B Nolan Ryan Black Glv 3.00 8.00
16 Brooks Robinson Yellow .40 1.00
16B Brooks Robinson Green .75 2.00
17 Phil Niekro Black Hat .30 .75
17B Phil Niekro Blue Hat .60 1.50
18 Joe Cronin Blue Sleeve .30 .75
18B Joe Cronin White Sleeve .60 1.50
19 Joe Tinker White Hat .30 .75
19B Joe Tinker Blue Hat .60 1.50
20 Johnny Bench Day .60 1.50
20B Johnny Bench Night 1.25 3.00
21 Harry Heilmann Day .30 .75
21B Harry Heilmann Night .60 1.50
22 Ernie Harwell BRD Red Tie .30 .75
22B Ernie Harwell BRD Blue Tie .60 1.50
23 Warren Spahn Patch .40 1.00
23B Warren Spahn No Patch .75 2.00
24 George Kelly Blue Bill .30 .75
24B George Kelly Red Bill .60 1.50
25 Phil Rizzuto Bleachers .40 1.00
25B Phil Rizzuto Green .75 2.00
26 Robin Roberts Day .30 .75
26B Robin Roberts Night .60 1.50
27 Ozzie Smith Red Sleeve 1.00 2.50
27B Ozzie Smith Blue Sleeve 2.00 5.00
28 Jim Palmer White Hat .30 .75
28B Jim Palmer Black Hat .60 1.50
29 Duke Snider No Patch .40 1.00
29B Duke Snider Flag Patch .75 2.00
30 Bob Feller White Uni .30 .75
30B Bob Feller Grey Uni .60 1.50
31 Buck Leonard Bleachers .30 .75
31B Buck Leonard Red .60 1.50
32 Kirby Puckett Wood Bat .60 1.50
32B Kirby Puckett Black Bat 1.25 3.00
33 Monte Irvin Black Sleeve .30 .75
33B Monte Irvin White Sleeve .60 1.50
34 Chuck Klein Black Socks .30 .75
34B Chuck Klein Red Socks .60 1.50
35 Willie Stargell Yellow Uni .40 1.00
35B Willie Stargell White Uni .75 2.00
36 Juan Marichal Ballpark .30 .75
36B Juan Marichal Gold .60 1.50
37 Lou Brock Day .40 1.00
37B Lou Brock Night .75 2.00
38 Bucky Harris Black W .30 .75
38B Bucky Harris Red W .60 1.50
39 Bobby Doerr Ballpark .30 .75
39B Bobby Doerr Red .60 1.50
40 Lee MacPhail Blue Tie .30 .75
40B Lee MacPhail Red Tie .60 1.50
41 H.Manush Grey Sleeve .30 .75
41B H.Manush Navy Sleeve .60 1.50
42 George Brett Patch 1.25 3.00
42B George Brett No Patch 2.50 6.00
43 Harmon Killebrew Blue Hat .60 1.50
43B Har. Killebrew Red Hat 1.25 3.00
44 Whitey Ford Day .40 1.00
44B Whitey Ford Night .75 2.00
45 Eddie Mathews Day .60 1.50
45B Eddie Mathews Night 1.25 3.00
46 Gaylord Perry Leather Glv .30 .75
46B Gaylord Perry Black Glv .60 1.50
47 Red Schoendienst Stripes .30 .75
47B R.Schoendienst No Stripes .60 1.50
48 Earl Weaver MG Day .30 .75
48B Earl Weaver MG Night .60 1.50
49 Joe Morgan Day .30 .75
49B Joe Morgan Night .60 1.50
50 Mike Schmidt Grey Uni 1.25 3.00
50B Mike Schmidt White Uni 2.50 6.00
51 Willie McCovey Wood Bat .30 .75
51B Willie McCovey Black Bat .60 1.50
52 Stan Musial Day 1.00 2.50
52B Stan Musial Night 2.00 5.00
53 Don Sutton Ballpark .30 .75
53B Don Sutton Gray .60 1.50
54 Hank Greenberg w/Player .60 1.50
54B H.Greenberg No Player 1.25 3.00
55 Robin Yount w/Player .60 1.50
55B Robin Yount No Player 1.25 3.00
56 Tom Seaver Leather Glv .40 1.00
56B Tom Seaver Black Glv .75 2.00
57 Tony Perez Wood Bat .30 .75
57B Tony Perez Black Bat .60 1.50
58 George Sisler w/Ad .30 .75
58B George Sisler No Ad .60 1.50
59 Jim Bottomley White Hat .30 .75
59B Jim Bottomley Red Hat .60 1.50
60 Yogi Berra Leather Chest .60 1.50
60B Yogi Berra Navy Chest 1.25 3.00
61 Fred Lindstrom Blue Bill .30 .75
61B Fred Lindstrom Red Bill .60 1.50
62 Napoleon Lajoie White Uni .60 1.50
62B Nap. Lajoie Navy Uni 1.25 3.00
63 Frank Robinson Wood Bat .40 1.00
63B Fr. Robinson Black Bat .75 2.00
64 Carlton Fisk Red Ltr .40 1.00
64B Carlton Fisk Black Ltr .75 2.00
65 Orlando Cepeda Blue Sky .30 .75
65B Orlando Cepeda Sunset .60 1.50
66 Fergie Jenkins Leather Glv .30 .75
66B Fergie Jenkins Black Glv .60 1.50
67 Ernie Banks Day .60 1.50
67B Ernie Banks Night 1.25 3.00
68 Bill Mazeroski No Sleeves .40 1.00
68B Bill Mazeroski w/Sleeves .75 2.00
69 Jim Bunning Grey Uni .30 .75
69B Jim Bunning White Uni .60 1.50
70 Rollie Fingers Day .30 .75
70B Rollie Fingers Night .60 1.50
71 Jimmie Foxx Black Sleeve .60 1.50
71B Ji. Foxx White Sleeve 1.25 3.00
72 Rod Carew Red Btg Glv .40 1.00
72B Rod Carew Blue Btg Glv .75 2.00
73 Sparky Anderson Blue Sky .30 .75
73B Sparky Anderson Yellow .60 1.50
74 George Kell Red D .30 .75
74B George Kell White D .60 1.50

2003 Topps Gallery HOF Artist's Proofs

Inserted in packs at a rate of one per for basic cards and one in 20 for variations cards, this is a complete parallel of the Topps Gallery set. The Artist Proof cards can be differentiated by the presence of silver foil and those are also much heavier than the regular cards.

*ARTIST'S PROOFS: .75X TO 2X BASIC
*VARIATIONS: 2X TO 5X BASIC VAR

2003 Topps Gallery HOF Accent Mark Autographs

Issued at various odds depending on who signed the cards, these six cards featured authentic autographs of the featured HOFer. Each person signed a different amount of cards and we have notated the group of the signed card next to their name in our checklist.

GROUP A ODDS 1:3446
GROUP B ODDS 1:2074
GROUP C ODDS 1:1483
GROUP D ODDS 1:1149
GROUP E ODDS 1:941
GROUP F ODDS 1:545
ARTIST'S PROOFS ODDS 1:1723
ARTIST'S PROOFS PRINT RUN 25 #'d SETS
NO AP PRICING DUE TO SCARCITY
AP'S FEATURE SILVER HOLO-FOIL
BD Bobby Doerr B 15.00 40.00
LM Lee MacPhail D 15.00 40.00
RR Robin Roberts E 15.00 40.00
RS Red Schoendienst C 15.00 40.00
WS Warren Spahn F 15.00 40.00
YB Yogi Berra A 40.00 80.00

2003 Topps Gallery HOF ARTifact Relics

Inserted in packs at differing rates depending on what group the relic belong to, this is a 57-card insert set featuring game-used relic pieces of various Hall of Famers. We have notated next to the player's name both the relic piece as well as what group the relic piece belonged to.

BAT GROUP A ODDS 1:1812
BAT GROUP B ODDS 1:469
BAT GROUP C ODDS 1:242
BAT GROUP D ODDS 1:111
BAT GROUP E ODDS 1:96
BAT GROUP F ODDS 1:28
BAT GROUP G ODDS 1:62
JSY/UNI GROUP A ODDS 1:1812
JSY/UNI GROUP B ODDS 1:2353
JSY/UNI GROUP C ODDS 1:728
JSY/UNI GROUP D ODDS 1:151
JSY/UNI GROUP E ODDS 1:145
ARTIST'S PROOFS BAT ODDS 1:345
ARTIST'S PROOFS JSY/UNI ODDS 1:967
ARTIST'S PROOFS PRINT RUN 25 #'d SETS
NO AP PRICING DUE TO SCARCITY
AP'S FEATURE SILVER HOLO-FOIL
AK Al Kaline Bat F 6.00 15.00
BD Bobby Doerr Jsy D 4.00 10.00
BH Bucky Harris Bat F 6.00 15.00
BR Babe Ruth Bat B 90.00 180.00
BRO Brooks Robinson Bat D 6.00 15.00
CF Carlton Fisk Bat G 6.00 15.00
CK Chuck Klein Bat F 6.00 15.00
CY Carl Yastrzemski Bat F 8.00 20.00
DS Duke Snider Bat F 6.00 15.00
DSU Don Sutton Bat D 4.00 10.00
EB Ernie Banks Uni B 15.00 40.00
EC Eddie Collins Bat B 15.00 40.00
EM Eddie Mathews Jsy A
ER Edd Roush Bat B 12.50 30.00
FF Frankie Frisch Bat E 6.00 15.00
FR Frank Robinson Bat G 6.00 15.00
GB George Brett Jsy D 12.50 30.00
GK George Kelly Bat D 8.00 20.00
GP Gaylord Perry Uni E 4.00 10.00
GS George Sisler Bat F 6.00 15.00
HA Hank Aaron Bat F 10.00 25.00
HG Hank Greenberg Bat D 15.00 40.00
HH Harry Heilmann Bat B 8.00 20.00
HK Harmon Killebrew Jsy E 8.00 20.00
HM Heinie Manush Bat B 8.00 20.00
HW Honus Wagner Bat A
HWI Hoyt Wilhelm Uni D 4.00 10.00
JB Jim Bottomley Bat E 6.00 15.00
JBE Johnny Bench Bat G 6.00 15.00
JF Jimmie Foxx Bat A
JM Joe Morgan Bat E 4.00 10.00
JP Jim Palmer Jsy A
JR Jackie Robinson Bat C 20.00 50.00
JT Joe Tinker Bat E 20.00 50.00
KP Kirby Puckett Bat E 8.00 20.00
LA Luis Aparicio Bat A
LB Lou Brock Bat A
LG Lou Gehrig Bat C 75.00 150.00
MS Mike Schmidt Uni E 12.50 30.00
NR Nolan Ryan Bat C 30.00 60.00
OC Orlando Cepeda Bat F 4.00 10.00
OS Ozzie Smith Bat E 8.00 20.00
PN Phil Niekro Uni D 4.00 10.00
PW Paul Waner Bat C 10.00 25.00
RCA Rod Carew Jsy E 6.00 15.00
RJ Reggie Jackson Bat F 6.00 15.00
RY Robin Yount Bat F 6.00 15.00
SA Sparky Anderson Uni A
SC Sam Crawford Bat D 10.00 25.00
SM Stan Musial Bat D 12.50 30.00
TC Ty Cobb Bat C 60.00 120.00
TLA Tom Lasorda Jsy A
TP Tony Perez Bat F 4.00 10.00
TS Tom Seaver Bat C 8.00 20.00
WM Willie Mays Jsy C 20.00 50.00
WMC Willie McCovey Bat F 4.00 10.00
WS Willie Stargell Jsy C 8.00 20.00

2003 Topps Gallery HOF ARTifact Relics Autographs

Inserted at different rates depending on which group the player belonged to, these 11 cards feature not only a game-used relic piece of the featured player but also an authentic autograph. We have notated next to the player's name not only what type of memorabilia piece but also what group the card belongs to.

GROUP A ODDS 1:3446
GROUP B ODDS 1:691
GROUP C ODDS 1:691
ARTIST'S PROOFS ODDS 1:941
ARTIST'S PROOFS PRINT RUN 25 #'d SETS
NO AP PRICING DUE TO SCARCITY
AP'S FEATURE SILVER HOLO-FOIL
AK Al Kaline Bat C 50.00 100.00
BD Bobby Doerr Jsy C 20.00 50.00
BRO Brooks Robinson Bat C 40.00 80.00
DS Duke Snider Bat B 40.00 80.00
HK Harmon Killebrew Jsy B 40.00 80.00
JM Joe Morgan Bat B 20.00 50.00
JP Jim Palmer Jsy A
MS Mike Schmidt Uni B
OC Orlando Cepeda Bat B
RS Red Schoendienst Jsy A
RY Robin Yount Bat A

2003 Topps Gallery HOF Currency Connection Coin Relics

Issued as a box topper, these 12 cards feature not only a player but an authentic coin from a key point in their career.

STATED ODDS ONE PER BOX
BF B.Feller 1945 Dime B 6.00 15.00
BR B.Ruth 1916 Dime A 40.00 80.00
EB E.Banks 1958 Penny B 10.00 25.00
HG H.Greenberg 1945 Nickel B 10.00 25.00
JR J.Robinson 1946 Dime B 10.00 25.00
LG L.Gehrig 1938 Nickel A 15.00 40.00
OC O.Cepeda 1958 Penny B 6.00 15.00
SM S.Musial 1943 Penny B 15.00 40.00
TC T.Cobb 1909 Penny A 20.00 50.00
WM W.Mays 1958 Penny B 10.00 25.00
WMA W.Mays 1954 Nickel B 10.00 25.00
WMC W.McCovey 1959 Penny B 6.00 15.00

2003 Topps Gallery HOF Paint by Number Patch Relics

Inserted into packs at a stated rate of one in 1037, these 14 cards feature prime patch swatches of game-worn jerseys on specially designed art cards. These cards were issued to a stated print run of 25 serial numbered sets and no pricing is available due to market scarcity.

CH Catfish Hunter
CY Carl Yastrzemski
DS Don Sutton
EM Eddie Mathews
FJ Fergie Jenkins
GB George Brett
HK Harmon Killebrew
JP Jim Palmer
MS Mike Schmidt
NR Nolan Ryan
OS Ozzie Smith
RY Robin Yount
TL Tom Lasorda
WM Willie McCovey

2001 Topps Heritage

The 2001 Topps Heritage product was released in February 2001. Each pack contained eight cards and carried a $1.99 SRP. The base set features 407 cards. Please note that all low series cards 1-80, feature both red and black back variations and are in shorter supply than mid-series cards 81-310. Also, high series cards 311-407 are short-printed with an announced seeding ratio of 1:2 packs. Finally, the following mid-series cards were erroneously printed exclusively in black back format: 103, 159, 171, 176, 179, 188, 201, 212, 224 and 241. All told, a master set of all red and black variations consists of 487-cards (397 red backs and 90 black backs). Most collectors in pursuit of a 407-card complete set typically intermingle red and black back cards.

COMP.MASTER SET (487) 350.00 500.00
COMPLETE SET (407) 250.00 400.00
COMP.SET w/o SP's (230) 40.00 80.00
COMMON CARD (81-310) .20 .50
COMMON CARD (1-80) 1.00 2.50
COMMON (311-407) 2.00 5.00
1 Kris Benson 1.00 2.50
1 Kris Benson Black 1.00 2.50
2 Brian Jordan 1.00 2.50
2 Brian Jordan Black 1.00 2.50
3 Fernando Vina 1.00 2.50
3 Fernando Vina Black 1.00 2.50
4 Mike Sweeney 1.00 2.50
4 Mike Sweeney Black 1.00 2.50
5 Rafael Palmeiro 1.00 2.50
5 Rafael Palmeiro Black 1.00 2.50
6 Paul O'Neill 1.00 2.50
6 Paul O'Neill Black 1.00 2.50
7 Todd Helton 1.00 2.50
7 Todd Helton Black 1.00 2.50
8 Ramiro Mendoza 1.00 2.50
8 Ramiro Mendoza Black 1.00 2.50
9 Kevin Millwood 1.00 2.50
9 Kevin Millwood Black 1.00 2.50
10 Chuck Knoblauch 1.00 2.50
10 Chuck Knoblauch Black 1.00 2.50
11 Derek Jeter 4.00 10.00
11 Derek Jeter Black 4.00 10.00
12 A.Rodriguez Rangers 2.50 6.00
12 A.Rod Black Rangers 2.50 6.00
13 Geoff Jenkins 1.00 2.50
13 Geoff Jenkins Black 1.00 2.50
14 David Justice 1.00 2.50
14 David Justice Black 1.00 2.50
15 David Cone 1.00 2.50
15 David Cone Black 1.00 2.50
16 Andres Galarraga 1.00 2.50
16 Andres Galarraga Black 1.00 2.50
17 Garret Anderson 1.00 2.50
17 Garret Anderson Black 1.00 2.50
18 Roger Cedeno 1.00 2.50
18 Roger Cedeno Black 1.00 2.50
19 Randy Velarde 1.00 2.50
19 Randy Velarde Black 1.00 2.50
20 Carlos Delgado 1.00 2.50
20 Carlos Delgado Black 1.00 2.50
21 Quilvio Veras 1.00 2.50
21 Quilvio Veras Black 1.00 2.50
22 Jose Vidro 1.00 2.50
22 Jose Vidro Black 1.00 2.50
23 Corey Patterson 1.00 2.50
23 Corey Patterson Black 1.00 2.50
24 Jorge Posada 1.00 2.50
24 Jorge Posada Black 1.00 2.50
25 Eddie Perez 1.00 2.50
25 Eddie Perez Black 1.00 2.50
26 Jack Cust 1.00 2.50
26 Jack Cust Black 1.00 2.50
27 Sean Burroughs 1.00 2.50
27 Sean Burroughs Black 1.00 2.50
28 Randy Wolf 1.00 2.50
28 Randy Wolf Black 1.00 2.50
29 Mike Lamb 1.00 2.50
29 Mike Lamb Black 1.00 2.50
30 Rafael Furcal 1.00 2.50
30 Rafael Furcal Black 1.00 2.50
31 Barry Bonds 4.00 10.00
31 Barry Bonds Black 4.00 10.00
32 Tim Hudson 1.00 2.50
32 Tim Hudson Black 1.00 2.50
33 Tom Glavine 1.00 2.50
33 Tom Glavine Black 1.00 2.50
34 Javy Lopez 1.00 2.50
34 Javy Lopez Black 1.00 2.50
35 Aubrey Huff 1.00 2.50
35 Aubrey Huff Black 1.00 2.50
36 Wally Joyner 1.00 2.50
36 Wally Joyner Black 1.00 2.50
37 Magglio Ordonez 1.00 2.50
37 Magglio Ordonez Black 1.00 2.50
38 Matt Lawton 1.00 2.50
38 Matt Lawton Black 1.00 2.50
39 Mariano Rivera 1.50 4.00
39 Mariano Rivera Black 1.50 4.00
40 Andy Ashby 1.00 2.50
40 Andy Ashby Black 1.00 2.50
41 Mark Buehrle 1.00 2.50
41 Mark Buehrle Black 1.00 2.50
42 Esteban Loaiza 1.00 2.50
42 Esteban Loaiza Black 1.00 2.50
43 Mark Redman 1.00 2.50
43 Mark Redman Black 1.00 2.50
44 Mark Quinn 1.00 2.50
44 Mark Quinn Black 1.00 2.50
45 Tino Martinez 1.00 2.50
45 Tino Martinez Black 1.00 2.50
46 Joe Mays 1.00 2.50
46 Joe Mays Black 1.00 2.50
47 Walt Weiss 1.00 2.50
47 Walt Weiss Black 1.00 2.50
48 Roger Clemens 3.00 8.00
48 Roger Clemens Black 3.00 8.00
49 Greg Maddux 2.50 6.00
49 Greg Maddux Black 2.50 6.00
50 Richard Hidalgo 1.00 2.50
50 Richard Hidalgo Black 1.00 2.50
51 Orlando Hernandez 1.00 2.50
51 O.Hernandez Black 1.00 2.50
52 Chipper Jones 1.50 4.00
52 Chipper Jones Black 1.50 4.00
53 Ben Grieve 1.00 2.50
53 Ben Grieve Black 1.00 2.50
54 Jimmy Haynes 1.00 2.50
54 Jimmy Haynes Black 1.00 2.50
55 Ken Caminiti 1.00 2.50
55 Ken Caminiti Black 1.00 2.50
56 Tim Salmon 1.00 2.50
56 Tim Salmon Black 1.00 2.50
57 Andy Pettitte 1.00 2.50
57 Andy Pettitte Black 1.00 2.50
58 Darin Erstad 1.00 2.50
58 Darin Erstad Black 1.00 2.50
59 Marquis Grissom 1.00 2.50
59 Marquis Grissom Black 1.00 2.50
60 Raul Mondesi 1.00 2.50
60 Raul Mondesi Black 1.00 2.50
61 Bengie Molina 1.00 2.50
61 Bengie Molina Black 1.00 2.50
62 Miguel Tejada 1.00 2.50
62 Miguel Tejada Black 1.00 2.50
63 Jose Cruz Jr. 1.00 2.50
63 Jose Cruz Jr. Black 1.00 2.50
64 Billy Koch 1.00 2.50
64 Billy Koch Black 1.00 2.50
65 Troy Glaus 1.00 2.50
65 Troy Glaus Black 1.00 2.50
66 Cliff Floyd 1.00 2.50
66 Cliff Floyd Black 1.00 2.50
67 Tony Batista 1.00 2.50
67 Tony Batista Black 1.00 2.50
68 Jeff Bagwell 1.00 2.50
68 Jeff Bagwell Black 1.00 2.50
69 Billy Wagner 1.00 2.50
69 Billy Wagner Black 1.00 2.50
70 Eric Chavez 1.00 2.50
70 Eric Chavez Black 1.00 2.50
71 Troy Percival 1.00 2.50
71 Troy Percival Black 1.00 2.50
72 Andruw Jones 1.00 2.50
72 Andruw Jones Black 1.00 2.50
73 Shane Reynolds 1.00 2.50
73 Shane Reynolds Black 1.00 2.50
74 Barry Zito 1.00 2.50
74 Barry Zito Black 1.00 2.50
75 Roy Halladay 1.00 2.50
75 Roy Halladay Black 1.00 2.50
76 David Wells 1.00 2.50
76 David Wells Black 1.00 2.50
77 Jason Giambi 1.00 2.50
77 Jason Giambi Black 1.00 2.50
78 Scott Elarton 1.00 2.50
78 Scott Elarton Black 1.00 2.50
79 Moises Alou 1.00 2.50
79 Moises Alou Black 1.00 2.50
80 Adam Piatt 1.00 2.50
80 Adam Piatt Black 1.00 2.50
81 Wilton Veras .20 .50
82 Darryl Kile .25 .60
83 Johnny Damon .40 1.00
84 Tony Armas Jr. .20 .50
85 Ellis Burks .25 .60
86 Jamey Wright .20 .50
87 Jose Vizcaino .20 .50
88 Bartolo Colon .25 .60
89 Carmen Cali RC .20 .50
90 Kevin Brown .25 .60
91 Josh Hamilton .40 1.00
92 Jay Buhner .25 .60
93 Scott Pratt RC .25 .60
94 Alex Cora .20 .50
95 Luis Montanez RC .25 .60
96 Dmitri Young .25 .60
97 J.T. Snow .25 .60
98 Damion Easley .20 .50
99 Greg Norton .20 .50
100 Matt Wheatland .20 .50
101 Chin-Feng Chen .25 .60
102 Tony Womack .20 .50
103 Adam Kennedy Black .20 .50
104 J.D. Drew .25 .60
105 Carlos Febles .20 .50
106 Jim Thome .40 1.00
107 Danny Graves .20 .50
108 Dave Mlicki .20 .50
109 Ron Coomer .20 .50
110 James Baldwin .20 .50
111 Shaun Boyd RC .20 .50
112 Brian Bohanon .20 .50
113 Jacque Jones .25 .60
114 Alfonso Soriano .40 1.00
115 Tony Clark .20 .50
116 Terrence Long .20 .50
117 Todd Hundley .20 .50
118 Kazuhiro Sasaki .25 .60
119 Brian Sellier RC .20 .50
120 John Olerud .25 .60
121 Javier Vazquez .25 .60
122 Sean Burnett .20 .50
123 Matt LeCroy .20 .50
124 Erubiel Durazo .20 .50
125 Juan Encarnacion .20 .50
126 Pablo Ozuna .20 .50
127 Russ Ortiz .20 .50
128 David Segui .20 .50
129 Mark McGwire 1.50 4.00
130 Mark Grace .40 1.00
131 Fred McGriff .40 1.00
132 Carl Pavano .25 .60
133 Derek Thompson .20 .50
134 Shawn Green .25 .60
135 B.J. Surhoff .25 .60
136 Michael Tucker .20 .50
137 Jason Isringhausen .25 .60
138 Eric Milton .20 .50
139 Mike Stodolka .20 .50
140 Milton Bradley .25 .60
141 Curt Schilling .25 .60
142 Sandy Alomar Jr. .20 .50
143 Brent Mayne .20 .50
144 Todd Jones .20 .50
145 Charles Johnson .20 .50
146 Dean Palmer .25 .60
147 Masato Yoshii .20 .50
148 Edgar Renteria .25 .60
149 Joe Randa .25 .60
150 Adam Johnson .20 .50

Card		
151 Greg Vaughn	.20	.50
152 Adrian Beltre	.25	.60
153 Glenallen Hill	.20	.50
154 David Parrish RC	.20	.50
155 Neifi Perez	.20	.50
156 Pete Harnisch	.20	.50
157 Paul Konerko	.25	.60
158 Dennys Reyes	.20	.50
159 Jose Lima Black	.20	.50
160 Eddie Taubensee	.20	.50
161 Miguel Cairo	.20	.50
162 Jeff Kent	.25	.60
163 Dustin Hermanson	.20	.50
164 Alex Gonzalez	.20	.50
165 Hideo Nomo	.60	1.50
166 Sammy Sosa	.60	1.50
167 C.J. Nitkowski	.20	.50
168 Cal Eldred	.20	.50
169 Jeff Abbott	.20	.50
170 Jim Edmonds	.25	.60
171 Mark Mulder Black	.25	.60
172 Dominic Rich RC	.25	.60
173 Ray Lankford	.25	.60
174 Danny Borrell RC	.20	.50
175 Rick Aguilera	.20	.50
176 S.Stewart Black	.25	.60
177 Steve Finley	.25	.60
178 Jim Parque	.20	.50
179 Kevin Appier Black	.25	.60
180 Adrian Gonzalez	.20	.50
181 Tom Goodwin	.20	.50
182 Kevin Tapani	.20	.50
183 Fernando Tatis	.20	.50
184 Mark Grudzielanek	.20	.50
185 Ryan Anderson	.20	.50
186 Jeffrey Hammonds	.20	.50
187 Corey Koskie	.20	.50
188 Brad Fullmer Black	.20	.50
189 Rey Sanchez	.20	.50
190 Michael Barrett	.20	.50
191 Rickey Henderson	.60	1.50
192 Jermaine Dye	.25	.60
193 Scott Brosius	.25	.60
194 Matt Anderson	.20	.50
195 Brian Buchanan	.20	.50
196 Derrek Lee	.40	1.00
197 Larry Walker	.25	.60
198 Dan Moylan RC	.20	.50
199 Vinny Castilla	.25	.60
200 Ken Griffey Jr.	1.00	2.50
201 Matt Stairs Black	.20	.50
202 Ty Howington	.20	.50
203 Andy Benes	.20	.50
204 Luis Gonzalez	.25	.60
205 Brian Moehler	.20	.50
206 Harold Baines	.25	.60
207 Pedro Astacio	.20	.50
208 Cristian Guzman	.20	.50
209 Kip Wells	.20	.50
210 Frank Thomas	.60	1.50
211 Jose Rosado	.20	.50
212 Vernon Wells Black	.25	.60
213 Bobby Higginson	.25	.60
214 Juan Gonzalez	.25	.60
215 Omar Vizquel	.40	1.00
216 Bernie Williams	.40	1.00
217 Aaron Sele	.20	.50
218 Shawn Estes	.20	.50
219 Roberto Alomar	.40	1.00
220 Rick Ankiel	.20	.50
221 Josh Kalinowski	.20	.50
222 David Bell	.20	.50
223 Keith Foulke	.25	.60
224 Craig Biggio Black	.40	1.00
225 Josh Axelson RC	.20	.50
226 Scott Williamson	.20	.50
227 Ron Belliard	.20	.50
228 Chris Singleton	.20	.50
229 Alex Serrano RC	.20	.50
230 Deivi Cruz	.20	.50
231 Eric Munson	.20	.50
232 Luis Castillo	.20	.50
233 Edgar Martinez	.40	1.00
234 Jeff Shaw	.20	.50
235 Jeromy Burnitz	.25	.60
236 Richie Sexson	.25	.60
237 Will Clark	.40	1.00
238 Ron Villone	.20	.50
239 Kerry Wood	.25	.60
240 Rich Aurilia	.20	.50
241 Mo Vaughn Black	.25	.60
242 Travis Fryman	.25	.60
243 M. Ramirez Sox	.40	1.00
244 Chris Stynes	.20	.50
245 Ray Durham	.25	.60
246 Juan Uribe RC	.40	1.00
247 Juan Guzman	.20	.50
248 Lee Stevens	.20	.50
249 Devon White	.20	.50
250 Kyle Lohse RC	.40	1.00
251 Bryan Wolff	.20	.50
252 Matt Galante RC	.25	.60
253 Eric Young	.20	.50
254 Freddy Garcia	.25	.60
255 Jay Bell	.25	.60
256 Steve Cox	.20	.50
257 Torii Hunter	.25	.60
258 Jose Canseco	.40	1.00
259 Brad Ausmus	.25	.60
260 Jeff Cirillo	.20	.50
261 Brad Penny	.20	.50
262 Antonio Alfonseca	.20	.50
263 Russ Branyan	.20	.50
264 Chris Morris RC	.20	.50
265 John Lackey	.20	.50
266 Justin Wayne RC	.25	.60
267 Brad Radke	.25	.60
268 Todd Stottlemyre	.20	.50
269 Mark Loretta	.20	.50
270 Matt Williams	.25	.60
271 Kenny Lofton	.25	.60
272 Jeff D'Amico	.20	.50
273 Jamie Moyer	.25	.60
274 Darren Dreifort	.20	.50
275 Denny Neagle	.20	.50
276 Orlando Cabrera	.25	.60
277 Chuck Finley	.25	.60
278 Miguel Batista	.25	.60
279 Carlos Beltran	.25	.60
280 Eric Karros	.25	.60
281 Mark Kotsay	.25	.60
282 Ryan Dempster	.20	.50
283 Barry Larkin	.40	1.00
284 Jeff Suppan	.20	.50
285 Gary Sheffield	.25	.60
286 Jose Valentin	.20	.50
287 Robb Nen	.25	.60
288 Chan Ho Park	.25	.60
289 John Halama	.20	.50
290 Steve Smyth RC	.25	.60
291 Gerald Williams	.20	.50
292 Preston Wilson	.25	.60
293 Victor Hall RC	.25	.60
294 Ben Sheets	.40	1.00
295 Eric Davis	.25	.60
296 Kirk Rueter	.20	.50
297 Chad Petty RC	.20	.50
298 Kevin Millar	.25	.60
299 Marvin Benard	.20	.50
300 Vladimir Guerrero	.60	1.50
301 Livan Hernandez	.25	.60
302 Travis Baptist RC	.20	.50
303 Bill Mueller	.25	.60
304 Mike Cameron	.20	.50
305 Randy Johnson UER	.60	1.50
Facsimile signature is Randall K. Johnson		
306 Alan Mahaffey RC	.20	.50
307 Timo Perez UER	.20	.50
No facsimile autograph on card		
308 Pokey Reese	.20	.50
309 Ryan Rupe	.20	.50
310 Carlos Lee	.25	.60
311 Doug Glanville SP	2.00	5.00
312 Jay Payton SP	2.00	5.00
313 Troy O'Leary SP	2.00	5.00
314 Francisco Cordero SP	2.00	5.00
315 Rusty Greer SP	2.00	5.00
316 Cal Ripken SP	10.00	25.00
317 Ricky Ledee SP	2.00	5.00
318 Brian Daubach SP	2.00	5.00
319 Robin Ventura SP	2.00	5.00
320 Todd Zeile SP	2.00	5.00
321 Francisco Cordova SP	2.00	5.00
322 Henry Rodriguez SP	2.00	5.00
323 Pat Meares SP	2.00	5.00
324 Glendon Rusch SP	2.00	5.00
325 Keith Osik SP	2.00	5.00
326 Robert Keppel SP RC	2.00	5.00
327 Bobby Jones SP	2.00	5.00
328 Alex Ramirez SP	2.00	5.00
329 Robert Person SP	2.00	5.00
330 Ruben Mateo SP	2.00	5.00
331 Rob Bell SP	2.00	5.00
332 Carl Everett SP	2.00	5.00
333 Jason Schmidt SP	2.00	5.00
334 Scott Rolen SP	3.00	8.00
335 Jimmy Anderson SP	2.00	5.00
336 Bret Boone SP	2.00	5.00
337 Delino DeShields SP	2.00	5.00
338 Trevor Hoffman SP	2.00	5.00
339 Bob Abreu SP	2.00	5.00
340 Mike Williams SP	2.00	5.00
341 Mike Hampton SP	2.00	5.00
342 John Wetteland SP	2.00	5.00
343 Scott Erickson SP	2.00	5.00
344 Enrique Wilson SP	2.00	5.00
345 Tim Wakefield SP	2.00	5.00
346 Mike Lowell SP	2.00	5.00
347 Todd Pratt SP	2.00	5.00
348 Brook Fordyce SP	2.00	5.00
349 Benny Agbayani SP	2.00	5.00
350 Gabe Kapler SP	2.00	5.00
351 Sean Casey SP	2.00	5.00
352 Darren Oliver SP	2.00	5.00
353 Todd Ritchie SP	2.00	5.00
354 Kenny Rogers SP	2.00	5.00
355 Jason Kendall SP	2.00	5.00
356 John Vander Wal SP	2.00	5.00
357 Ramon Martinez SP	2.00	5.00
358 Edgardo Alfonzo SP	2.00	5.00
359 Phil Nevin SP	2.00	5.00
360 Albert Belle SP	2.00	5.00
361 Ruben Rivera SP	2.00	5.00
362 Pedro Martinez SP	3.00	8.00
363 Derek Lowe SP	2.00	5.00
364 Pat Burrell SP	2.00	5.00
365 Mike Mussina SP	3.00	8.00
366 Brady Anderson SP	2.00	5.00
367 Darren Lewis SP	2.00	5.00
368 Sidney Ponson SP	2.00	5.00
369 Adam Eaton SP	2.00	5.00
370 Eric Owens SP	2.00	5.00
371 Aaron Boone SP	2.00	5.00
372 Matt Clement SP	2.00	5.00
373 Derek Bell SP	2.00	5.00
374 Trot Nixon SP	2.00	5.00
375 Travis Lee SP	2.00	5.00
376 Mike Benjamin SP	2.00	5.00
377 Jeff Zimmerman SP	2.00	5.00
378 Mike Lieberthal SP	2.00	5.00
379 Rick Reed SP	2.00	5.00
380 N.Garciaparra SP	5.00	12.00
381 Omar Daal SP	2.00	5.00
382 Ryan Klesko SP	2.00	5.00
383 Rey Ordonez SP	2.00	5.00
384 Kevin Young SP	2.00	5.00
385 Rick Helling SP	2.00	5.00
386 Brian Giles SP	2.00	5.00
387 Tony Gwynn SP	4.00	10.00
388 Ed Sprague SP	2.00	5.00
389 J.R. House SP	2.00	5.00
390 Scott Hatteberg SP	2.00	5.00
391 John Valentin SP	2.00	5.00
392 Melvin Mora SP	2.00	5.00
393 Royce Clayton SP	2.00	5.00
394 Jeff Fassero SP	2.00	5.00
395 Manny Alexander SP	2.00	5.00
396 John Franco SP	2.00	5.00
397 Luis Alicea SP	2.00	5.00
398 Ivan Rodriguez SP	3.00	8.00
399 Kevin Jordan SP	2.00	5.00
400 Jose Offerman SP	2.00	5.00
401 Jeff Conine SP	2.00	5.00
402 Seth Etherton SP	2.00	5.00
403 Mike Bordick SP	2.00	5.00
404 Al Leiter SP	2.00	5.00
405 Mike Piazza SP	5.00	12.00
406 Armando Benitez SP	2.00	5.00
407 Warren Morris SP	2.00	5.00
NNO 1952 Card Redemption EXCH		
NNO Replica Hat-Jsy EXCH		

2001 Topps Heritage Chrome

Randomly inserted into packs at one in 25 Hob/Ret, this 110-card insert is a partial parallel of the 2001 Topps Heritage base set. Each card was produced using Topps Chrome technology. Please note that each card is also individually serial numbered to 552.

STATED ODDS 1:25 HOB/RET
STATED PRINT RUN 552 SERIAL #'d SETS

Card		
CP1 Cal Ripken	20.00	50.00
CP2 Jim Thome	4.00	10.00
CP3 Derek Jeter	15.00	40.00
CP4 Andres Galarraga	3.00	8.00
CP5 Carlos Delgado	3.00	8.00
CP6 Roberto Alomar	4.00	10.00
CP7 Tom Glavine	4.00	10.00
CP8 Gary Sheffield	3.00	8.00
CP9 Mo Vaughn	3.00	8.00
CP10 Preston Wilson	3.00	8.00
CP11 Mike Mussina	4.00	10.00
CP12 Greg Maddux	10.00	25.00
CP13 Ivan Rodriguez	4.00	10.00
CP14 Al Leiter	3.00	8.00
CP15 Seth Etherton	3.00	8.00
CP16 Edgardo Alfonzo	3.00	8.00
CP17 Richie Sexson	3.00	8.00
CP18 Andruw Jones	4.00	10.00
CP19 Bartolo Colon	3.00	8.00
CP20 Darin Erstad	3.00	8.00
CP21 Kevin Brown	3.00	8.00
CP22 Mike Sweeney	3.00	8.00
CP23 Mike Piazza	10.00	25.00
CP24 Rafael Palmeiro	4.00	10.00
CP25 Terrence Long	3.00	8.00
CP26 Kazuhiro Sasaki	3.00	8.00
CP27 John Olerud	3.00	8.00
CP28 Mark McGwire	15.00	40.00
CP29 Fred McGriff	4.00	10.00
CP30 Todd Helton	4.00	10.00
CP31 Curt Schilling	3.00	8.00
CP32 Alex Rodriguez	10.00	25.00
CP33 Jeff Kent	3.00	8.00
CP34 Pat Burrell	3.00	8.00
CP35 Jim Edmonds	3.00	8.00
CP36 Mark Mulder	3.00	8.00
CP37 Troy Glaus	3.00	8.00
CP38 Jay Payton	3.00	8.00
CP39 Jermaine Dye	3.00	8.00
CP40 Larry Walker	3.00	8.00
CP41 Ken Griffey Jr.	10.00	25.00
CP42 Jeff Bagwell	4.00	10.00
CP43 Rick Ankiel	3.00	8.00
CP44 Mark Redman	3.00	8.00
CP45 Edgar Martinez	4.00	10.00
CP46 Mike Hampton	3.00	8.00
CP47 Manny Ramirez Sox	4.00	10.00
CP48 Ray Durham	3.00	8.00
CP49 Rafael Furcal	3.00	8.00
CP50 Sean Casey	3.00	8.00
CP51 Jose Canseco	4.00	10.00
CP52 Barry Bonds	15.00	40.00
CP53 Tim Hudson	3.00	8.00
CP54 Barry Zito	4.00	10.00
CP55 Chuck Finley	3.00	8.00
CP56 Magglio Ordonez	3.00	8.00
CP57 David Wells	3.00	8.00
CP58 Jason Giambi	3.00	8.00
CP59 Tony Gwynn	8.00	20.00
CP60 Vladimir Guerrero	6.00	15.00
CP61 Randy Johnson	6.00	15.00
CP62 Bernie Williams	4.00	10.00
CP63 Craig Biggio	4.00	10.00
CP64 Jason Kendall	3.00	8.00
CP65 Pedro Martinez	4.00	10.00
CP66 Mark Quinn	3.00	8.00
CP67 Frank Thomas	6.00	15.00
CP68 Nomar Garciaparra	10.00	25.00
CP69 Brian Giles	3.00	8.00
CP70 Shawn Green	3.00	8.00
CP71 Roger Clemens	12.50	30.00
CP72 Sammy Sosa	6.00	15.00
CP73 Juan Gonzalez	3.00	8.00
CP74 Orlando Hernandez	3.00	8.00
CP75 Chipper Jones	6.00	15.00
CP76 Josh Hamilton	6.00	15.00
CP77 Adam Johnson	3.00	8.00
CP78 Shaun Boyd	3.00	8.00
CP79 Alfonso Soriano	4.00	10.00
CP80 Derek Thompson	3.00	8.00
CP81 Adrian Gonzalez	3.00	8.00
CP82 Ryan Anderson	3.00	8.00
CP83 Corey Patterson	3.00	8.00
CP84 J.R. House	3.00	8.00
CP85 Sean Burroughs	3.00	8.00
CP86 Bryan Wolff	3.00	8.00
CP87 John Lackey	3.00	8.00
CP88 Ben Sheets	4.00	10.00
CP89 Timo Perez	3.00	8.00
CP90 Robert Keppel	3.00	8.00
CP91 Luis Montanez	3.00	8.00
CP92 Sean Burnett	3.00	8.00
CP93 Justin Wayne	3.00	8.00
CP94 Eric Munson	3.00	8.00
CP95 Steve Smyth	3.00	8.00
CP96 Matt Galante	3.00	8.00
CP97 Carmen Cali	3.00	8.00
CP98 Brian Sellier	3.00	8.00
CP99 David Parrish	3.00	8.00
CP100 Danny Borrell	3.00	8.00
CP101 Chad Petty	3.00	8.00
CP102 Dominic Rich	3.00	8.00
CP103 Josh Axelson	3.00	8.00
CP104 Alex Serrano	3.00	8.00
CP105 Juan Uribe	4.00	10.00
CP106 Travis Baptist	3.00	8.00
CP107 Alan Mahaffey	3.00	8.00
CP108 Kyle Lohse	4.00	10.00
CP109 Victor Hall	3.00	8.00
CP110 Scott Pratt	3.00	8.00

2001 Topps Heritage Autographs

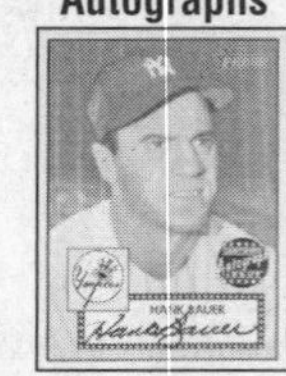

Randomly inserted into packs at one in 142 HOB/RET, this 51-card insert set features authentic autographs from many of the Major League's top players. Please note that a few of the players packed out as exchange cards, and must be redeemed by 1/31/02. Due to the untimely passing of Eddie Mathews, please note the exchange card issued for him went unredeemed. In addition, Larry Doby's card was originally seeded in packs as exchange cards (of which carried a January 31st, 2002 deadline).

*RED INK: .75X TO 1.5X BASIC AU
RED INK ODDS 1:545 HOB, 1:546 RET
RED INK PRINT RUN 52 SERIAL #'d SETS

Card		
THAAH Aubrey Huff	20.00	50.00
THAAP Andy Pafko	50.00	100.00
THAAR Alex Rodriguez	200.00	350.00
THABB Barry Bonds	225.00	350.00
THABS Bobby Shantz	30.00	60.00
THABT Bobby Thomson	60.00	120.00
THACD Carlos Delgado	40.00	80.00
THACF Cliff Floyd	40.00	80.00
THACJ Chipper Jones	100.00	200.00
THACP Corey Patterson	15.00	40.00
THACS Curt Simmons	40.00	80.00
THADD Dom DiMaggio	100.00	200.00
THADG Dick Groat	50.00	100.00
THADS Duke Snider	150.00	250.00
THAEM Eddie Mathews EXCH		
THAES Enos Slaughter	60.00	120.00
THAFV Fernando Vina	15.00	40.00
THAGJ Geoff Jenkins	15.00	40.00
THAGM Gil McDougald	50.00	100.00
THAHB Hank Bauer	60.00	120.00
THAHS Hank Sauer	60.00	120.00
THAHW Hoyt Wilhelm	60.00	120.00
THAJG Joe Garagiola	50.00	100.00
THAJM Joe Mays	15.00	40.00
THAJS Johnny Sain	60.00	120.00
THAJV Jose Vidro	15.00	40.00
THAKB Kris Benson	15.00	40.00
THAMB Mark Buehrle	40.00	80.00
THAMI Monte Irvin	50.00	100.00
THAML Mike Lamb	15.00	40.00
THAML Matt Lawton	15.00	40.00
THAMM Minnie Minoso	60.00	120.00
THAMO Magglio Ordonez	20.00	50.00
THAMQ Mark Quinn	15.00	40.00
THAMR Mark Redman	15.00	40.00
THAMS Mike Sweeney	20.00	50.00
THAMV Mickey Vernon	30.00	60.00
THANG Nomar Garciaparra	150.00	250.00
THAPR Preacher Roe	75.00	150.00
THAPFR Phil Rizzuto	100.00	175.00
THARH Richard Hidalgo	15.00	40.00
THARR Robin Roberts	50.00	100.00
THARS Red Schoendienst	50.00	100.00
THARW Randy Wolf	15.00	40.00
THASPB Sean Burroughs	15.00	40.00
THATG Tom Glavine	60.00	120.00
THATH Todd Helton	50.00	100.00
THATL Terrence Long	15.00	40.00
THAVL Vernon Law	50.00	100.00
THAWM Willie Mays	200.00	300.00
THAWS Warren Spahn	75.00	150.00

2001 Topps Heritage Autographs Red Ink

Randomly inserted into packs at 1:545 Hobby and 1:546 Retail, this 52-card insert set is a complete parallel of the Heritage Autographs signed in red ink. Please note that each of these cards are individually serial numbered to 52. Also note Larry Doby and Eddie Mathews packed out as exchange cards with a redemption deadline of 1/31/02. Due to his untimely death, the Eddie Mathews exchange card went unredeemed. The Willie Mays autograph cards come with or without serial numbering.

Card		
THAAP Andy Pafko	200.00	300.00
THACJ Chipper Jones	400.00	500.00
THAGM Gil McDougald	100.00	200.00
THAHS Hank Sauer	150.00	300.00
THAHW Hoyt Wilhelm	150.00	250.00
THAJG Joe Garagiola	150.00	300.00
THAJS Johnny Sain	100.00	200.00
THAMV Mickey Vernon	100.00	200.00
THAVL Vernon Law	150.00	300.00

2001 Topps Heritage AutoProofs

Randomly inserted at approximately 1 in every 5749 boxes, this card is an actual 1952 Topps Willie Mays card that was bought from the Topps Company, then individually autographed by Willie

Mays, and distributed into packs. Please note that each card is individually serial numbered to 25.

NO PRICING DUE TO SCARCITY
AUTOPROOF IS A REAL '52 TOPPS CARD
AP1 Willie Mays '52T AU/25

2001 Topps Heritage Classic Renditions

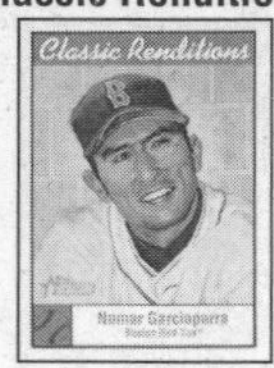

Randomly inserted into packs at one in 5 Hobby, and one in 9 Retail, this 10-card insert set features artist drawn sketches of some of the best modern day ballplayers. Card backs carry a "CR" prefix.

Card		
COMPLETE SET (10)	8.00	20.00
CR1 Mark McGwire	1.50	4.00
CR2 Nomar Garciaparra	1.00	2.50
CR3 Barry Bonds	1.50	4.00
CR4 Sammy Sosa	.60	1.50
CR5 Chipper Jones	.60	1.50
CR6 Pat Burrell	.40	1.00
CR7 Frank Thomas	.60	1.50
CR8 Manny Ramirez	.40	1.00
CR9 Derek Jeter	1.50	4.00
CR10 Ken Griffey Jr.	1.00	2.50

2001 Topps Heritage Classic Renditions Autograph

Randomly inserted into packs at one in 19,710 Hobby, and 1:20,926 Retail, this three-card insert set is a partial parallel of the Classic Renditions insert. Each of these cards have been autographed by the given player and are individually serial numbered to 25. Due to market scarcity, no pricing is provided.

CRABB Barry Bonds
CRACJ Chipper Jones
CRANG Nomar Garciaparra

2001 Topps Heritage Clubhouse Collection

Randomly inserted into packs, this 22-card insert features game-used memorabilia cards from past and present stars. Included in the set are game-used bat and jersey cards. Please note that a numbered of the players have autographed 25 of each of these cards. Also note that a few of the cards packed out as exchange cards, and must have been redeemed by 01/31/02. Common Bat cards were inserted at a rate of 1:590 and Jersey cards at 1:798 Hobby/1:799 Retail. Dual Bat cards were inserted at 1:5701 Hobby/1:5772 Retail. Dual Jersey cards were inserted into packs at 1:28,744 Hobby/1:29,820 Retail. Autographed Bat cards were inserted at 1:19,710 Hobby/1:20,928 Retail, and Autographed Jerseys at 1:62,714 Hobby/1:83,712 Retail. Exchange cards - with a deadline of Janury 31st, 2002 - were seeded into packs for the following cards: Eddie Mathews Bat, Duke Snider Bat AU and Willie Mays Bat AU.

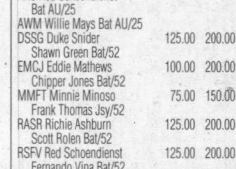

Card		
BB Barry Bonds Bat	40.00	80.00
CJ Chipper Jones Bat	20.00	50.00
DS Duke Snider Bat	20.00	50.00
EM Eddie Mathews Bat	20.00	50.00
FT Frank Thomas Jsy	20.00	50.00
FV Fernando Vina Bat	15.00	40.00
MM Minnie Minoso Jsy	15.00	40.00
RA Richie Ashburn Bat	20.00	50.00
RS Red Schoendienst Bat	15.00	40.00
SG Shawn Green Bat	15.00	40.00
SR Scott Rolen Bat	20.00	50.00
WM Willie Mays Bat	75.00	150.00
ADS Duke Snider Bat AU/25		
AMM Minnie Minoso Jsy AU/25		
ARS Red Schoendienst Bat AU/25		
AWM Willie Mays Bat AU/25		
DSSG Duke Snider Shawn Green Bat/52	125.00	200.00
EMCJ Eddie Mathews Chipper Jones Bat/52	100.00	200.00
MMFT Minnie Minoso Frank Thomas Jsy/52	75.00	150.00
RASR Richie Ashburn Scott Rolen Bat/52	125.00	200.00
RSFV Red Schoendienst Fernando Vina Bat/52	125.00	200.00
WMBB Willie Mays Barry Bonds Bat/52	200.00	350.00

2001 Topps Heritage Grandstand Glory

Randomly inserted into packs at 1:211 Hobby/Retail, this seven-card insert set features a swatch of original stadium seating. Card backs carry the player's initials as numbering.

Card		
JR Jackie Robinson	20.00	50.00
NF Nellie Fox	10.00	25.00
PR Phil Rizzuto	15.00	40.00
RA Richie Ashburn	10.00	25.00
RR Robin Roberts	10.00	25.00
WM Willie Mays	40.00	80.00
YB Yogi Berra	15.00	40.00

2001 Topps Heritage New Age Performers

Randomly inserted into packs at 1:8 Hobby, 1:15 Retail, this 15-card insert set features players that have become the superstars of the future. Card backs carry a "NAP" prefix.

Card		
COMPLETE SET (15)	20.00	50.00
NAP1 Mike Piazza	1.50	4.00
NAP2 Sammy Sosa	1.00	2.50
NAP3 Alex Rodriguez	1.50	4.00
NAP4 Barry Bonds	2.50	6.00
NAP5 Ken Griffey Jr.	1.50	4.00
NAP6 Chipper Jones	1.00	2.50
NAP7 Randy Johnson	1.00	2.50
NAP8 Derek Jeter	2.50	6.00
NAP9 Nomar Garciaparra	1.50	4.00
NAP10 Mark McGwire	2.50	6.00
NAP11 Jeff Bagwell	1.00	2.50
NAP12 Pedro Martinez	1.00	2.50
NAP13 Todd Helton	1.00	2.50
NAP14 Vladimir Guerrero	1.00	2.50
NAP15 Greg Maddux	1.50	4.00

2001 Topps Heritage Then and Now

Randomly inserted into Hobby packs at 1:8 and Retail packs at 1:15, this 10-card set pairs up modern day heroes with players from the past that compare statistically. Card backs carry a "TH" prefix.

Card		
COMPLETE SET (10)	15.00	30.00
TH1 Yogi Berra Mike Piazza	1.25	3.00
TH2 Duke Snider Sammy Sosa	.75	2.00
TH3 Willie Mays Ken Griffey Jr.	1.50	4.00
TH4 Phil Rizzuto Derek Jeter	2.00	5.00
TH5 Pee Wee Reese Nomar Garciaparra	1.25	3.00
TH6 Jackie Robinson Alex Rodriguez	1.25	3.00
TH7 Johnny Mize Mark McGwire	2.00	5.00
TH8 Bob Feller Pedro Martinez	.75	2.00
TH9 Robin Roberts Greg Maddux	1.25	3.00
TH10 Warren Spahn Randy Johnson	.75	2.00

2001 Topps Heritage Time Capsule

This unique set features swatches of fabric taken from actual combat uniforms from the 1952 Korean War. It's important to note that though these cards do indeed feature patches of vintage Korean War uniforms, they were not worn by the athlete featured on the card. Stated odds for the four single-player cards was 1:369. Unlike the other cards in this set, the lone dual-player Willie Mays-Ted Williams card is hand-numbered on back. Only 52 copies of this card were produced, and each is marked by hand on back in black pen "X/52". The stated odds for this dual-player card is 1:28,744 packs.

Card		
DN Don Newcombe	10.00	25.00
TW Ted Williams UER	40.00	80.00
Card says 525 career homers, Williams hit 521		
WF Whitey Ford	15.00	40.00
WM Willie Mays	40.00	80.00
WMTW Willie Mays Ted Williams/52	125.00	200.00

2002 Topps Heritage

Issued in early February 2002, this set was the second year that Topps used their Heritage brand and achieved success in the secondary market. These cards were issued in eight card packs which were packed 24 to a box and had a SRP of $3 per pack. The set consists of 440 cards with seven short prints among the low numbers as well as all cards

from 364 through 446 as short prints. Those cards were all inserted at a rate of one in two packs. In addition, there was an unannounced variation in which 10 cards were printed in both day and night versions. The night versions were also inserted into packs at a rate of one in two.

COMPLETE SET (440) 200.00 400.00
COMP.SET w/o SP's (350) 40.00 80.00
COMMON CARD (1-363) .20 .50
COMMON SP (364-446) 2.00 5.00
1 Ichiro Suzuki SP 6.00 15.00
2 Darin Erstad .25 .60
3 Rod Beck .25 .60
4 Doug Mientkiewicz .25 .60
5 Mike Sweeney .25 .60
6 Roger Clemens 1.25 3.00
7 Jason Tyner .20 .50
8 Alex Gonzalez .20 .50
9 Eric Young .20 .50
10 Randy Johnson .60 1.50
10N Randy Johnson Night SP 3.00 8.00
11 Aaron Sele .20 .50
12 Tony Clark .20 .50
13 C.C. Sabathia .25 .60
14 Melvin Mora .25 .60
15 Tim Hudson .25 .60
16 Ben Petrick .20 .50
17 Tom Glavine .40 1.00
18 Jason Lane .25 .60
19 Larry Walker .25 .60
20 Mark Mulder .25 .60
21 Steve Finley .25 .60
22 Bengie Molina .20 .50
23 Rob Bell .20 .50
24 Nathan Haynes .20 .50
25 Rafael Furcal .25 .60
25N Rafael Furcal Night SP 2.00 5.00
26 Mike Mussina .40 1.00
27 Paul LoDuca .25 .60
28 Torii Hunter .25 .60
29 Carlos Lee .25 .60
30 Jimmy Rollins .25 .60
31 Arthur Rhodes .20 .50
32 Ivan Rodriguez .40 1.00
33 Wes Helms .20 .50
34 Cliff Floyd .25 .60
35 Julian Tavarez .20 .50
36 Mark McGwire 1.50 4.00
37 Chipper Jones SP 3.00 8.00
38 Denny Neagle .20 .50
39 Odalis Perez .20 .50
40 Antonio Alfonseca .20 .50
41 Edgar Renteria .25 .60
42 Troy Glaus .25 .60
43 Scott Brosius .25 .60
44 Abraham Nunez .20 .50
45 Jamey Wright .20 .50
46 Bobby Bonilla .25 .60
47 Ismael Valdes .20 .50
48 Chris Reitsma .20 .50
49 Neifi Perez .20 .50
50 Juan Cruz .20 .50
51 Kevin Brown .25 .60
52 Ben Grieve .20 .50
53 Alex Rodriguez SP 5.00 12.00
54 Charles Nagy .20 .50
55 Reggie Sanders .25 .60
56 Nelson Figueroa .20 .50
57 Felipe Lopez .20 .50
58 Bill Ortega .20 .50
59 Jeffrey Hammonds .25 .60
60 Johnny Estrada .20 .50
61 Bob Wickman .20 .50
62 Doug Glanville .20 .50
63 Jeff Cirillo .20 .50
63N Jeff Cirillo Night SP 2.00 5.00
64 Corey Patterson .20 .50
65 Aaron Myette .20 .50
66 Magglio Ordonez .25 .60
67 Ellis Burks .25 .60
68 Miguel Tejada .25 .60
69 John Olerud .25 .60
69N John Olerud Night SP 2.00 5.00
70 Greg Vaughn .20 .50
71 Andy Pettitte .40 1.00
72 Mike Matheny .20 .50
73 Brandon Duckworth .20 .50
74 Scott Schoeneweis .20 .50
75 Mike Lowell .25 .60
76 Einar Diaz .20 .50
77 Tino Martinez .40 1.00
78 Matt Williams .25 .60
79 Jason Young RC .40 1.00
80 Nate Cornejo .20 .50
81 Andres Galarraga .25 .60
82 Bernie Williams SP 3.00 8.00
83 Ryan Klesko .25 .60
84 Dan Wilson .20 .50
85 Henry Pichardo RC .40 1.00
86 Ray Durham .25 .60
87 Omar Daal .20 .50
88 Derrek Lee .40 1.00
89 Al Leiter .25 .60
90 Darrin Fletcher .20 .50
91 Josh Beckett .25 .60
92 Johnny Damon .40 1.00
92N Johnny Damon Night SP 3.00 8.00
93 Abraham Nunez .20 .50
94 Ricky Ledee .20 .50
95 Richie Sexson .25 .60
96 Adam Kennedy .20 .50
97 Raul Mondesi .25 .60
98 John Burkett .25 .60
99 Ben Sheets .25 .60
99N Ben Sheets Night SP 2.00 5.00
100 Preston Wilson .25 .60
100N Pr. Wilson Night SP 2.00 5.00
101 Boof Bonser .20 .50
102 Shigetoshi Hasegawa .25 .60
103 Carlos Febles .20 .50
104 Jorge Posada SP 3.00 8.00
105 Michael Tucker .20 .50
106 Roberto Hernandez .25 .60
107 John Rodriguez RC .40 1.00
108 Danny Graves .20 .50
109 Rich Aurilia .20 .50
110 Jon Lieber .20 .50
111 Tim Hummel RC .40 1.00
112 J.T. Snow .25 .60
113 Kris Benson .20 .50
114 Derek Jeter 1.50 4.00
115 John Franco .25 .60
116 Matt Stairs .20 .50
117 Ben Davis .20 .50
118 Darryl Kile .25 .60
119 Mike Peeples RC .40 1.00
120 Kevin Tapani .20 .50
121 Armando Benitez .20 .50
122 Damian Miller .20 .50
123 Jose Jimenez .20 .50
124 Pedro Astacio .20 .50
125 Marlyn Tisdale RC .40 1.00
126 Deivi Cruz .20 .50
127 Paul O'Neill .40 1.00
128 Jermaine Dye .25 .60
129 Marcus Giles .25 .60
130 Mark Loretta .20 .50
131 Garret Anderson .25 .60
132 Todd Ritchie .20 .50
133 Joe Crede .25 .60
134 Kevin Millwood .25 .60
135 Shane Reynolds .20 .50
136 Mark Grace .40 1.00
137 Shannon Stewart .25 .60
138 Nick Neugebauer .20 .50
139 Nic Jackson RC .40 1.00
140 Robb Nen UER .25 .60
Name spelled Rob on front
141 Dmitri Young .25 .60
142 Kevin Appier .25 .60
143 Jack Cust .20 .50
144 Andres Torres .20 .50
145 Frank Thomas .60 1.50
146 Jason Kendall .25 .60
147 Greg Maddux 1.00 2.50
148 David Justice .25 .60
149 Hideo Nomo .60 1.50
150 Bret Boone .25 .60
151 Wade Miller .25 .60
152 Jeff Kent .25 .60
153 Scott Williamson .20 .50
154 Julio Lugo .20 .50
155 Bobby Higginson .25 .60
156 Geoff Jenkins .20 .50
157 Darren Dreifort .20 .50
158 Freddy Sanchez RC 1.25 3.00
159 Bud Smith .20 .50
160 Phil Nevin .25 .60
161 Cesar Izturis .20 .50
162 Sean Casey .25 .60
163 Jose Ortiz .20 .50
164 Brent Abernathy .20 .50
165 Kevin Young .20 .50
166 Daryle Ward .20 .50
167 Trevor Hoffman .25 .60
168 Rondell White .25 .60
169 Kip Wells .20 .50
170 John Vander Wal .20 .50
171 Jose Lima .20 .50
172 Wilton Guerrero .20 .50
173 Aaron Dean RC .40 1.00
174 Rick Helling .20 .50
175 Juan Pierre .25 .60
176 Jay Bell .25 .60
177 Craig House .20 .50
178 David Bell .20 .50
179 Pat Burrell .25 .60
180 Eric Gagne .25 .60
181 Adam Pettyjohn .20 .50
182 Ugueth Urbina .20 .50
183 Peter Bergeron .20 .50
184 Adrian Gonzalez UER .20 .50
Birthdate is wrong
184N Adrian Gonzalez 2.00 5.00
Night SP UER
Birthdate is wrong
185 Damion Easley .20 .50
186 Gookie Dawkins .20 .50
187 Matt Lawton .20 .50
188 Frank Catalanotto .20 .50
189 David Wells .25 .60
190 Roger Cedeno .20 .50
191 Brian Giles .25 .60
192 Julio Zuleta .20 .50
193 Timo Perez .20 .50
194 Billy Wagner .25 .60
195 Craig Counsell .20 .50
196 Bart Miadich .20 .50
197 Gary Sheffield .25 .60
198 Richard Hidalgo .20 .50
199 Juan Uribe .20 .50
200 Curt Schilling .25 .60
201 Jay Lopez .25 .60
202 Jimmy Haynes .20 .50
203 Jim Edmonds .25 .60
204 Pokey Reese .20 .50
204N Pokey Reese Night SP 2.00 5.00
205 Matt Clement .25 .60
206 Dean Palmer .25 .60
207 Nick Johnson .25 .60
208 Nate Espy RC .40 1.00
209 Pedro Feliz .20 .50
210 Aaron Rowand .25 .60
211 Masato Yoshii .20 .50
212 Jose Cruz Jr. .20 .50
213 Paul Byrd .20 .50
214 Mark Phillips RC .40 1.00
215 Benny Agbayani .20 .50
216 Frank Menechino .20 .50
217 John Flaherty .20 .50
218 Brian Boehringer .20 .50
219 Todd Hollandsworth .20 .50
220 Sammy Sosa SP 3.00 8.00
221 Steve Sparks .20 .50
222 Homer Bush .20 .50
223 Mike Hampton .25 .60
224 Bobby Abreu .25 .60
225 Barry Larkin .40 1.00
226 Ryan Rupe .20 .50
227 Bubba Trammell .20 .50
228 Todd Zeile .25 .60
229 Jeff Shaw .20 .50
230 Alex Ochoa .20 .50
231 Orlando Cabrera .25 .60
232 Jeremy Giambi .20 .50
233 Tomo Ohka .20 .50
234 Luis Castillo .20 .50
235 Chris Holt .20 .50
236 Shawn Green .25 .60
237 Sidney Ponson .20 .50
238 Lee Stevens .20 .50
239 Hank Blalock .40 1.00
240 Randy Winn .20 .50
241 Pedro Martinez .40 1.00
242 Vinny Castilla .25 .60
243 Steve Karsay .20 .50
244 Barry Bonds SP 8.00 20.00
245 Jason Bere .20 .50
246 Scott Rolen .40 1.00
246N Scott Rolen Night SP 3.00 8.00
247 Ryan Kohlmeier .20 .50
248 Kerry Wood .25 .60
249 Aramis Ramirez .25 .60
250 Lance Berkman .25 .60
251 Omar Vizquel .40 1.00
252 Juan Encarnacion .20 .50
253 Does Not Exist
254 David Segui .20 .50
255 Brian Anderson .20 .50
256 Jay Payton .20 .50
257 Mark Grudzielanek .25 .60
258 Jimmy Anderson .20 .50
259 Eric Valent .20 .50
260 Chad Durbin .20 .50
261 Does Not Exist
262 Alex Gonzalez .20 .50
263 Scott Dunn .20 .50
264 Scott Elarton .20 .50
265 Tom Gordon .20 .50
266 Moises Alou .25 .60
267 Does Not Exist
268 Does Not Exist
269 Mark Buehrle .25 .60
270 Jerry Hairston .20 .50
271 Does Not Exist
272 Luke Prokopec .20 .50
273 Graeme Lloyd .20 .50
274 Bret Prinz .20 .50
275 Does Not Exist
276 Chris Carpenter .25 .60
277 Ryan Minor .20 .50
278 Jeff D'Amico .20 .50
279 Raul Ibanez .20 .50
280 Joe Mays .20 .50
281 Livan Hernandez .25 .60
282 Robin Ventura .25 .60
283 Gabe Kapler .25 .60
284 Tony Batista .20 .50
285 Ramon Hernandez .20 .50
286 Craig Paquette .20 .50
287 Mark Kotsay .25 .60
288 Mike Lieberthal .25 .60
289 Joe Borchard .20 .50
290 Cristian Guzman .20 .50
291 Craig Biggio .40 1.00
292 Joaquin Benoit .20 .50
293 Ken Caminiti .25 .60
294 Sean Burroughs .20 .50
295 Eric Karros .25 .60
296 Eric Chavez .25 .60
297 LaTroy Hawkins .20 .50
298 Alfonso Soriano .25 .60
299 John Smoltz .40 1.00
300 Adam Dunn .25 .60
301 Ryan Dempster .20 .50
302 Travis Hafner .25 .60
303 Russell Branyan .20 .50
304 Dustin Hermanson .20 .50
305 Jim Thome .40 1.00
306 Carlos Beltran .25 .60
307 Jason Botts RC .25 .60
308 David Cone .25 .60
309 Ivanon Coffie .20 .50
310 Brian Jordan .20 .50
311 Todd Walker .20 .50
312 Jeromy Burnitz .25 .60
313 Tony Armas Jr. .20 .50
314 Jeff Conine .25 .60
315 Todd Jones .20 .50
316 Roy Oswalt .25 .60
317 Aubrey Huff .25 .60
318 Josh Fogg .20 .50
319 Jose Vidro .20 .50
320 Jace Brewer .20 .50
321 Mike Redmond .20 .50
322 Noochie Varner RC .40 1.00
323 Russ Ortiz .25 .60
324 Edgardo Alfonzo .20 .50
325 Ruben Sierra .25 .60
326 Calvin Murray .20 .50
327 Marlon Anderson .20 .50
328 Albie Lopez .20 .50
329 Chris Gomez .20 .50
330 Fernando Tatis .20 .50
331 Stubby Clapp .20 .50
332 Rickey Henderson .60 1.50
333 Brad Radke .25 .60
334 Brent Mayne .20 .50
335 Cory Lidle .20 .50
336 Edgar Martinez .40 1.00
337 Aaron Boone .25 .60
338 Jay Witasick .20 .50
339 Benito Santiago .25 .60
340 Jose Mercedes .25 .60
341 Fernando Vina .20 .50
342 A.J. Pierzynski .25 .60
343 Jeff Bagwell .40 1.00
344 Brian Bohanon .20 .50
345 Adrian Beltre .25 .60
346 Troy Percival .25 .60
347 Napoleon Calzado RC .40 1.00
348 Ruben Rivera .20 .50
349 Rafael Soriano .20 .50
350 Damian Jackson .20 .50
351 Joe Randa .25 .60
352 Chan Ho Park .20 .50
353 Dante Bichette .25 .60
354 Bartolo Colon .25 .60
355 Jason Bay RC 2.00 5.00
356 Shea Hillenbrand .25 .60
357 Matt Morris .25 .60
358 Brad Penny .20 .50
359 Mark Quinn .20 .50
360 Marquis Grissom .25 .60
361 Henry Blanco .20 .50
362 Billy Koch .20 .50
363 Mike Cameron .20 .50
364 Albert Pujols SP 6.00 15.00
365 Paul Konerko SP 2.00 5.00
366 Eric Milton SP 2.00 5.00
367 Nick Bierbrodt SP 2.00 5.00
368 Rafael Palmeiro SP 3.00 8.00
369 Jorge Padilla SP RC 2.00 5.00
370 Jason Giambi 2.00 5.00
Yankees SP
Stats on back are Jeremy Giambi's
371 Mike Piazza SP 5.00 12.00
372 Alex Cora SP 2.00 5.00
373 Todd Helton SP 3.00 8.00
374 Juan Gonzalez SP 2.00 5.00
375 Mariano Rivera SP 3.00 8.00
376 Shannon LaRue SP 2.00 5.00
377 Tony Gwynn SP 4.00 10.00
378 Wilson Betemit SP 2.00 5.00
379 J.J. Trujillo SP RC 2.00 5.00
380 Brad Ausmus SP 2.00 5.00
381 Chris George SP 2.00 5.00
382 Jose Canseco SP 3.00 8.00
383 Ramon Ortiz SP 2.00 5.00
384 John Rocker SP 2.00 5.00
385 Rey Ordonez SP 2.00 5.00
386 Ken Griffey Jr. SP 5.00 12.00
387 Juan Pena SP 2.00 5.00
388 Michael Barrett SP 2.00 5.00
389 J.D. Drew SP 2.00 5.00
390 Corey Koskie SP 2.00 5.00
391 Vernon Wells SP 2.00 5.00
392 Juan Tolentino SP RC 2.00 5.00
393 Luis Gonzalez SP 2.00 5.00
394 Terrence Long SP 2.00 5.00
395 Travis Lee SP 2.00 5.00
396 Earl Snyder SP RC 2.00 5.00
397 Nomar Garciaparra SP 5.00 12.00
398 Jason Schmidt SP 2.00 5.00
399 David Espinosa SP 2.00 5.00
400 Steve Green SP 2.00 5.00
401 Jack Wilson SP 2.00 5.00
402 Chris Tritle SP RC 2.00 5.00
403 Angel Berroa SP 2.00 5.00
404 Josh Towers SP 2.00 5.00
405 Andruw Jones SP 3.00 8.00
406 Brent Butler SP 2.00 5.00
407 Craig Kuzmic SP 2.00 5.00
408 Derek Bell SP 2.00 5.00
409 Eric Glaser SP RC 2.00 5.00
410 Joel Pineiro SP 2.00 5.00
411 Alexis Gomez SP 2.00 5.00
412 Mike Rivera SP 2.00 5.00
413 Shawn Estes SP 2.00 5.00
414 Milton Bradley SP 2.00 5.00
415 Carl Everett SP 2.00 5.00
416 Kazuhiro Sasaki SP 2.00 5.00
417 Tony Fontana SP RC 2.00 5.00
418 Josh Pearce SP 2.00 5.00
419 Gary Matthews Jr. SP 2.00 5.00
420 Raymond Cabrera SP RC 2.00 5.00
421 Joe Kennedy SP 2.00 5.00
422 Jason Maule SP RC 2.00 5.00
423 Casey Fossum SP 2.00 5.00
424 Christian Parker SP 2.00 5.00
425 Laynce Nix SP RC 4.00 10.00
426 Byung-Hyun Kim SP 2.00 5.00
427 Freddy Garcia SP 2.00 5.00
428 Herbert Perry SP 2.00 5.00
429 Jason Marquis SP 2.00 5.00
430 Sandy Alomar Jr. SP 2.00 5.00
431 Roberto Alomar SP 3.00 8.00
432 Tsuyoshi Shinjo SP 2.00 5.00
433 Tim Wakefield SP 2.00 5.00
434 Robert Fick SP 2.00 5.00
435 Vladimir Guerrero SP 3.00 8.00
436 Jose Mesa SP 2.00 5.00
437 Scott Spiezio SP 2.00 5.00
438 Jose Hernandez SP 2.00 5.00
439 Jose Acevedo SP 2.00 5.00
440 Brian West SP RC 2.00 5.00
441 Barry Zito SP 2.00 5.00
442 Luis Maza SP 2.00 5.00
443 Marlon Byrd SP 2.00 5.00
444 A.J. Burnett SP 2.00 5.00
445 Dee Brown SP 2.00 5.00
446 Carlos Delgado SP 2.00 5.00
NNO 1953 Repurchased EXCH.

2002 Topps Heritage Chrome

Inserted into packs at stated odds of one in 29, these 100 cards feature the "Chrome" technology and have a stated print run of 553 copies.

THC1 Darin Erstad 3.00 8.00
THC2 Doug Mientkiewicz 3.00 8.00
THC3 Mike Sweeney 3.00 8.00
THC4 Roger Clemens 10.00 25.00
THC5 C.C. Sabathia 3.00 8.00
THC6 Tim Hudson 3.00 8.00
THC7 Jason Lane 3.00 8.00
THC8 Larry Walker 3.00 8.00
THC9 Mark Mulder 3.00 8.00
THC10 Mike Mussina 3.00 8.00
THC11 Paul LoDuca 3.00 8.00
THC12 Jimmy Rollins 3.00 8.00
THC13 Ivan Rodriguez 3.00 8.00
THC14 Mark McGwire 12.50 30.00
THC15 Edgar Renteria 3.00 8.00
THC16 Scott Brosius 3.00 8.00
THC17 Juan Cruz 3.00 8.00

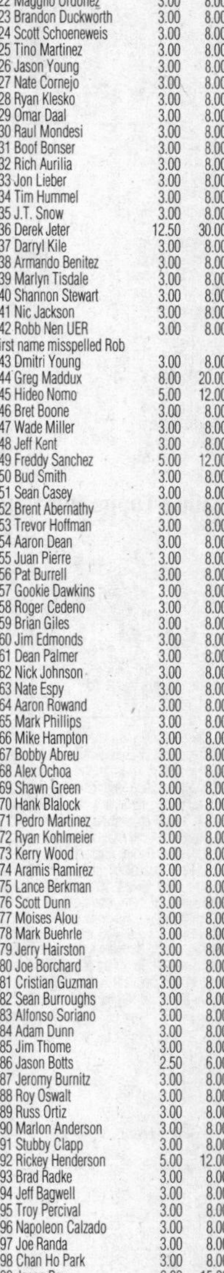

THC18 Kevin Brown 3.00 8.00
THC19 Charles Nagy 3.00 8.00
THC20 Bill Ortega 3.00 8.00
THC21 Corey Patterson 3.00 8.00
THC22 Magglio Ordonez 3.00 8.00
THC23 Brandon Duckworth 3.00 8.00
THC24 Scott Schoeneweis 3.00 8.00
THC25 Tino Martinez 3.00 8.00
THC26 Jason Young 3.00 8.00
THC27 Nate Cornejo 3.00 8.00
THC28 Ryan Klesko 3.00 8.00
THC29 Omar Daal 3.00 8.00
THC30 Raul Mondesi 3.00 8.00
THC31 Boof Bonser 3.00 8.00
THC32 Rich Aurilia 3.00 8.00
THC33 Jon Lieber 3.00 8.00
THC34 Tim Hummel 3.00 8.00
THC35 J.T. Snow 3.00 8.00
THC36 Derek Jeter 12.50 30.00
THC37 Darryl Kile 3.00 8.00
THC38 Armando Benitez 3.00 8.00
THC39 Marlyn Tisdale 3.00 8.00
THC40 Shannon Stewart 3.00 8.00
THC41 Nic Jackson 3.00 8.00
THC42 Robb Nen UER 3.00 8.00
First name misspelled Rob
THC43 Dmitri Young 3.00 8.00
THC44 Greg Maddux 8.00 20.00
THC45 Hideo Nomo 5.00 12.00
THC46 Bret Boone 3.00 8.00
THC47 Wade Miller 3.00 8.00
THC48 Jeff Kent 3.00 8.00
THC49 Freddy Sanchez 5.00 12.00
THC50 Bud Smith 3.00 8.00
THC51 Sean Casey 3.00 8.00
THC52 Brent Abernathy 3.00 8.00
THC53 Trevor Hoffman 3.00 8.00
THC54 Aaron Dean 3.00 8.00
THC55 Juan Pierre 3.00 8.00
THC56 Pat Burrell 3.00 8.00
THC57 Gookie Dawkins 3.00 8.00
THC58 Roger Cedeno 3.00 8.00
THC59 Brian Giles 3.00 8.00
THC60 Jim Edmonds 3.00 8.00
THC61 Dean Palmer 3.00 8.00
THC62 Nick Johnson 3.00 8.00
THC63 Nate Espy 3.00 8.00
THC64 Aaron Rowand 3.00 8.00
THC65 Mark Phillips 3.00 8.00
THC66 Mike Hampton 3.00 8.00
THC67 Bobby Abreu 3.00 8.00
THC68 Alex Ochoa 3.00 8.00
THC69 Shawn Green 3.00 8.00
THC70 Hank Blalock 3.00 8.00
THC71 Pedro Martinez 3.00 8.00
THC72 Ryan Kohlmeier 3.00 8.00
THC73 Kerry Wood 3.00 8.00
THC74 Aramis Ramirez 3.00 8.00
THC75 Lance Berkman 3.00 8.00
THC76 Scott Dunn 3.00 8.00
THC77 Moises Alou 3.00 8.00
THC78 Mark Buehrle 3.00 8.00
THC79 Jerry Hairston 3.00 8.00
THC80 Joe Borchard 3.00 8.00
THC81 Cristian Guzman 3.00 8.00
THC82 Sean Burroughs 3.00 8.00
THC83 Alfonso Soriano 3.00 8.00
THC84 Adam Dunn 3.00 8.00
THC85 Jim Thome 3.00 8.00
THC86 Jason Botts 2.50 6.00
THC87 Jeromy Burnitz 3.00 8.00
THC88 Roy Oswalt 3.00 8.00
THC89 Russ Ortiz 3.00 8.00
THC90 Marlon Anderson 3.00 8.00
THC91 Stubby Clapp 3.00 8.00
THC92 Rickey Henderson 5.00 12.00
THC93 Brad Radke 3.00 8.00
THC94 Jeff Bagwell 3.00 8.00
THC95 Troy Percival 3.00 8.00
THC96 Napoleon Calzado 3.00 8.00
THC97 Joe Randa 3.00 8.00
THC98 Chan Ho Park 3.00 8.00
THC99 Jason Bay 6.00 15.00
THC100 Mark Quinn 3.00 8.00

2002 Topps Heritage Classic Renditions

Inserted into packs at stated odds of one in 12, these 10 cards show how current players might look like if they played in their 1953 team uniforms. These cards are printed on grayback paper stock.

COMPLETE SET (10) 8.00 20.00
CR1 Kerry Wood .75 2.00
CR2 Brian Giles .75 2.00
CR3 Roger Cedeno .75 2.00
CR4 Jason Giambi .75 2.00
CR5 Albert Pujols 2.00 5.00
CR6 Mark Buehrle .75 2.00
CR7 Cristian Guzman .75 2.00
CR8 Jimmy Rollins .75 2.00
CR9 Jim Thome .75 2.00
CR10 Shawn Green .75 2.00

2002 Topps Heritage Classic Renditions Autographs

Partially paralleling the Classic Rendition set, these three cards were all autographed by the player and have a stated print run of 25 sets. Due to market scarcity, no pricing is provided for these cards.

CRABG Brian Giles
CRACG Cristian Guzman
CRAJR Jimmy Rollins

2002 Topps Heritage Clubhouse Collection

Inserted into packs at a rate for jersey cards of one in 332 and bat cards at a rate of one in 498, these 12 cards feature a mix of active and retired players with a memorabilia swatch.

CCAD Alvin Dark Bat 10.00 25.00
CCBB Barry Bonds Bat 40.00 80.00
CCCP Corey Patterson Bat 10.00 25.00
CCEM Eddie Mathews Jsy 15.00 40.00
CCGK George Kell Jsy 15.00 40.00
CCGM Greg Maddux Jsy 15.00 40.00
CCHS Hank Sauer Bat 10.00 25.00
CCJP Jorge Posada Bat 15.00 40.00
CCNG Nomar Garciaparra Bat 20.00 50.00
CCRA Rich Aurilia Bat 10.00 25.00
CCWM Willie Mays Bat 50.00 100.00
CCYB Yogi Berra Jsy 15.00 40.00

2002 Topps Heritage Clubhouse Collection Autographs

These four cards parallel the Clubhouse Collection insert set. These cards feature autographs from the noted players are are serial numbered to 25. Due to market scarcity, no pricing is provided for these players.

CCAAD Alvin Dark Bat
CCAGK George Kell Jsy
CCAWM Willie Mays Bat
CCAYB Yogi Berra Jsy

2002 Topps Heritage Clubhouse Collection Duos

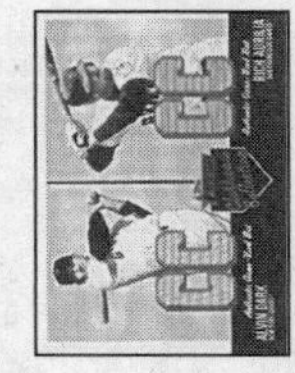

Inserted into packs at stated odds of one in 5016, these six cards feature one current player and one 1953 franchise alum from that same team with a relic from each player. These cards have a stated print run of 53 serial numbered sets. Due to market scarcity, no pricing is provided for these cards.

CC2BP Yogi Berra Jsy 75.00 150.00
Jorge Posada Bat
CC2DA Alvin Dark Bat 50.00 100.00
Rich Aurilia Bat
CC2KR George Kell Jsy 75.00 150.00
Nomar Garciaparra Bat
CC2MB Willie Mays Bat 150.00 250.00
Barry Bonds Bat UER
Card states Bonds is Mays' godfather
It is the other way around
CC2SM Eddie Mathews Jsy 100.00 200.00
Greg Maddux Jsy
CC2SP Hank Sauer Bat 50.00 100.00
Corey Patterson Bat

2002 Topps Heritage Grandstand Glory

Inserted into packs at different rates depending on which group the player is from, these 12 cards feature retired 1950's players along with an authentic relic from an historic 1950's stadium.

GROUP A STATED ODDS 1:4115
GROUP B STATED ODDS 1:531
GROUP C STATED ODDS 1:1576
GROUP D STATED ODDS 1:370
GROUP E STATED ODDS 1:483

GGBF Bob Feller E	10.00	25.00
GGBM Billy Martin B	10.00	25.00
GGBP Billy Pierce B	8.00	20.00
GGBS Bobby Shantz D	8.00	20.00
GGEW Early Wynn E	10.00	25.00
GGHN Hal Newhouser B	10.00	25.00
GGHS Hank Sauer C	8.00	20.00
GGRC Roy Campanella D	15.00	40.00
GGSP Satchel Paige A	40.00	80.00
GGTK Ted Kluszewski E	15.00	40.00
GGWF Whitey Ford D	10.00	25.00
GGWS Warren Spahn D	15.00	40.00

2002 Topps Heritage New Age Performers

Inserted into packs at stated odds of one in 15, these 15 cards feature powerhouse players whose accomplishments have cemented their names in major league history.

COMPLETE SET (15)	20.00	50.00
NA1 Luis Gonzalez	.75	2.00
NA2 Mark McGwire	2.50	6.00
NA3 Barry Bonds	2.50	6.00
NA4 Ken Griffey Jr.	1.50	4.00
NA5 Ichiro Suzuki	2.00	5.00
NA6 Sammy Sosa	1.00	2.50
NA7 Andruw Jones	.75	2.00
NA8 Derek Jeter	2.50	6.00
NA9 Todd Helton	.75	2.00
NA10 Alex Rodriguez	1.50	4.00
NA11 Jason Giambi Yankees	.75	2.00
NA12 Bret Boone	.75	2.00
NA13 Roberto Alomar	.75	2.00
NA14 Albert Pujols	2.00	5.00
NA15 Vladimir Guerrero	1.00	2.50

2002 Topps Heritage Real One Autographs

Inserted into packs at different odds depending on which group the player belongs to, this 28 card set features a mix of authentic autographs between active players and those who were active in the 1953 season. Please note that the group which each player belongs to is listed next to their name in our checklist. The Roger Clemens card has been signed in both blue and black, please let us know if any other players are signed in more than one color.

GROUP 1 STATED ODDS 1:346
GROUP 2 STATED ODDS 1:6363
GROUP 3 STATED ODDS 1:4908
GROUP 4 STATED ODDS 1:3196
GROUP 5 STATED ODDS 1:498
*RED INK: .75X TO 1.5X BASIC AUTO'S
RED INK ODDS 1:306
RED INK PRINT RUN 53 SERIAL #'d SETS

ROAC Andy Carey 1	15.00	40.00
ROAD Alvin Dark 1	30.00	60.00
ROAR Al Rosen 1	50.00	100.00
ROARO Alex Rodriguez 2	100.00	200.00
ROASC Al Schoendienst 1	30.00	60.00
ROBF Bob Feller 1	50.00	100.00
ROBG Brian Giles 5	10.00	25.00
ROBS Bobby Shantz 1	30.00	60.00
ROCG Cristian Guzman 5	6.00	15.00
RODD Dom DiMaggio 1	50.00	100.00
ROES Enos Slaughter 1	50.00	100.00
ROGK George Kell 1	30.00	60.00
ROGM Gil McDougald 1	50.00	100.00
ROHW Hoyt Wilhelm 1	50.00	100.00
ROJB Joe Black 1	30.00	60.00
ROJE Jim Edmonds 4	15.00	40.00
ROJP John Podres 1	30.00	60.00
ROMI Monte Irvin 1	30.00	60.00
ROOM Minnie Minoso 1	30.00	60.00
ROPR Phil Rizzuto 1	50.00	100.00
ROPRO Preacher Roe 1	30.00	60.00
RORB Ray Boone 1	50.00	100.00
RORF Roy Face 1	30.00	60.00
RORCL Roger Clemens 3	100.00	175.00
ROWF Whitey Ford 1	90.00	150.00
ROWM Willie Mays 1	150.00	250.00
ROWS Warren Spahn 1	60.00	120.00
ROYB Yogi Berra 1	90.00	150.00

2002 Topps Heritage Then and Now

Inserted into packs at stated odds of one in 15, these 10 cards feature a 1953 player as well as a current stand-out. These cards offer statistical comparisions in major stat categories and are printed in greyback paper stock.

COMPLETE SET (10)	12.50	30.00
TN1 Eddie Mathews Barry Bonds	2.50	6.00
TN2 Al Rosen Alex Rodriguez	1.50	4.00
TN3 Carl Furillo Larry Walker	.75	2.00
TN4 Minnie Minoso Ichiro Suzuki	2.00	5.00
TN5 Richie Ashburn Rich Aurilia	.75	2.00
TN6 Al Rosen Bret Boone	.75	2.00
TN7 Duke Snider Sammy Sosa	1.00	2.50
TN8 Al Rosen Alex Rodriguez	1.50	4.00
TN9 Robin Roberts Randy Johnson	1.00	2.50
TN10 Billy Pierce Hideo Nomo	1.00	2.50

2003 Topps Heritage

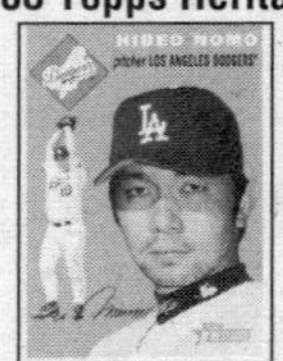

This 430-card set, which was designed to honor the 1954 Topps set, was released in February, 2003. These cards were issued in five card packs with an $3 SRP. These packs were issued in 24 pack boxes which came eight boxes to a case. In addition, many cards in the set were issued in two varieties. A few cards were issued featuring either a logo used today or a scarcer version in which the logo was used in the 1954 set. In addition, some cards were printed with either the originally designed version or a black background. The black background version is the tougher of the two versions of each card. A few cards between 1 and 363 were produced in less quantities and all cards from 364 on up were short printed as well. In a nod to the 1954 set, Alex Rodriguez had both cards 1 and 250; just as Ted Williams had in the original 1954 Topps set.

COMPLETE SET (450)	175.00	300.00
COMP SET w/o SP's (350)	40.00	80.00
COMMON CARD	.20	.50
COMMON RC	.40	1.00
COMMON SP	2.00	5.00
COMMON SP RC	2.00	5.00
1A Alex Rodriguez Red	1.00	2.50
1B Alex Rodriguez Black SP	5.00	12.00
2 Jose Cruz Jr.	.20	.50
3 Ichiro Suzuki SP	6.00	15.00
4 Rich Aurilia	.20	.50
5 Trevor Hoffman	.25	.60
6A Brian Giles New Logo	.25	.60
6B Brian Giles Old Logo SP	2.00	5.00
7A Albert Pujols Orange	1.25	3.00
7B Albert Pujols Black SP	6.00	15.00
8 Vicente Padilla	.20	.50
9 Bobby Crosby	.25	.60
10A Derek Jeter New Logo	1.50	4.00
10B Derek Jeter Old Logo SP	6.00	15.00
11A Pat Burrell New Logo	.25	.60
11B Pat Burrell Old Logo SP	2.00	5.00
12 Armando Benitez	.20	.50
13 Javier Vazquez	.25	.60
14 Justin Morneau	.25	.60
15 Doug Mientkiewicz	.25	.60
16 Kevin Brown	.25	.60
17 Alexis Gomez	.20	.50
18A Lance Berkman Blue	.25	.60
18B Lance Berkman Black SP	2.00	5.00
19 Adrian Gonzalez	.20	.50
20A Todd Helton Green	.40	1.00
20B Todd Helton Black SP	3.00	8.00
21 Carlos Pena	.20	.50
22 Matt Lawton	.20	.50
23 Elmer Dessens	.20	.50
24 Hee Seop Choi	.20	.50
25 Chris Duncan SP RC	5.00	12.00
26 Ugueth Urbina	.20	.50
27A Rodrigo Lopez New Logo	.20	.50
27B Ro. Lopez Old Logo SP	2.00	5.00
28 Damian Moss	.20	.50
29 Steve Finley	.25	.60
30A Sammy Sosa New Logo	.60	1.50
30B S.Sosa Old Logo SP	3.00	8.00
31 Kevin Cash	.20	.50
32 Kenny Rogers	.25	.60
33 Ben Grieve	.20	.50
34 Jason Simontacchi	.20	.50
35 Shin-Soo Choo	.20	.50
36 Freddy Garcia	.25	.60
37 Jesse Foppert	.20	.50
38 Tony LaRussa MG	.25	.60
39 Mark Kotsay	.25	.60
40 Barry Zito	.25	.60
41 Josh Fogg	.20	.50
42 Marlon Byrd	.20	.50
43 Marcus Thames	.20	.50
44 Al Leiter	.25	.60
45 Michael Barrett	.20	.50
46 Jake Peavy	.25	.60
47 Dustan Mohr	.20	.50
48 Alex Sanchez	.20	.50
49 Chin-Feng Chen	.25	.60
50A Kazuhisa Ishii Blue	.25	.60
50B Kazuhisa Ishii Black SP	2.00	5.00
51 Carlos Beltran	.25	.60
52 Franklin Gutierrez RC	.40	1.00
53 Miguel Cabrera	.60	1.50
54 Roger Clemens	1.25	3.00
55 Juan Cruz	.20	.50
56 Jason Young	.20	.50
57 Alex Herrera	.20	.50
58 Aaron Boone	.25	.60
59 Mark Buehrle	.25	.60
60 Larry Walker	.25	.60
61 Morgan Ensberg	.25	.60
62 Barry Larkin	.40	1.00
63 Joe Borchard	.20	.50
64 Jason Dubois	.20	.50
65 Shea Hillenbrand	.25	.60
66 Jay Gibbons	.20	.50
67 Vinny Castilla	.25	.60
68 Jeff Mathis	.20	.50
69 Curt Schilling	.25	.60
70 Garret Anderson	.25	.60
71 Josh Phelps	.20	.50
72 Chan Ho Park	.25	.60
73 Edgar Renteria	.25	.60
74 Kazuhiro Sasaki	.25	.60
75 Lloyd McClendon MG	.20	.50
76 Jon Lieber	.20	.50
77 Rolando Viera	.20	.50
78 Jeff Conine	.25	.60
79 Kevin Millwood	.25	.60
80A Randy Johnson Green	.60	1.50
80B Randy Johnson Black SP	5.00	12.00
81 Troy Percival	.25	.60
82 Cliff Floyd	.25	.60
83 Tony Graffanino	.20	.50
84 Austin Kearns	.25	.60
85 Manuel Ramirez SP RC	3.00	8.00
86 Jim Tracy MG	.20	.50
87 Rondell White	.25	.60
88 Trot Nixon	.25	.60
89 Carlos Lee	.25	.60
90 Mike Lowell	.25	.60
91 Raul Ibanez	.20	.50
92 Ricardo Rodriguez	.20	.50
93 Ben Sheets	.25	.60
94 Jason Perry SP RC	3.00	8.00
95 Mark Teixeira	.40	1.00
96 Brad Fullmer	.20	.50
97 Casey Kotchman	.25	.60
98 Craig Counsell	.20	.50
99 Jason Marquis	.20	.50
100A N.Garciaparra New Logo	1.00	2.50
100B N.Garciaparra Old Logo SP	5.00	12.00
101 Ed Rogers	.20	.50
102 Wilson Betemit	.20	.50
103 Wayne Lydon RC	.40	1.00
104 Jack Cust	.20	.50
105 Derrek Lee	.40	1.00
106 Jim Kavourias	.20	.50
107 Joe Randa	.20	.50
108 Taylor Buchholz	.20	.50
109 Gabe Kapler	.25	.60
110 Preston Wilson	.25	.60
111 Craig Biggio	.40	1.00
112 Paul Lo Duca	.25	.60
113 Eddie Guardado	.20	.50
114 Andres Galarraga	.40	1.00
115 Edgardo Alfonzo	.20	.50
116 Robin Ventura	.25	.60
117 Jeremy Giambi	.20	.50
118 Ray Durham	.25	.60
119 Mariano Rivera	.60	1.50
120 Jimmy Rollins	.25	.60
121 Dennis Tankersley	.20	.50
122 Jason Schmidt	.25	.60
123 Bret Boone	.25	.60
124 Josh Hamilton	.40	1.00
125 Scott Rolen	.40	1.00
126 Steve Cox	.20	.50
127 Larry Bowa MG	.25	.60
128 Adam LaRoche SP	2.00	5.00
129 Ryan Klesko	.25	.60
130 Tim Hudson	.25	.60
131 Brandon Claussen	.20	.50
132 Craig Brazell SP RC	2.00	5.00
133 Grady Little MG	.20	.50
134 Jarrod Washburn	.20	.50
135 Lyle Overbay	.20	.50
136 John Burkett	.20	.50
137 Daryl Clark RC	.40	1.00
138 Kirk Rueter	.20	.50
139A Joe Mauer Jake Mauer Green	.60	1.50
139B Joe Mauer Jake Mauer Black SP	4.00	10.00
140 Troy Glaus	.25	.60
141 Trey Hodges SP	2.00	5.00
142 Dallas McPherson	.25	.60
143 Art Howe MG	.20	.50
144 Jesus Cota	.20	.50
145 J.R. House	.20	.50
146 Reggie Sanders	.25	.60
147 Clint Nageotte	.20	.50
148 Jim Edmonds	.25	.60
149 Carl Crawford	.25	.60
150A Mike Piazza Blue	1.00	2.50
150B Mike Piazza Black SP	5.00	12.00
151 Seung Song	.20	.50
152 Roberto Hernandez	.25	.60
153 Marquis Grissom	.25	.60
154 Billy Wagner	.25	.60
155 Josh Beckett	.25	.60
156A R.Simon New Logo	.20	.50
156B R.Simon Old Logo SP	2.00	5.00
157 Ben Broussard	.20	.50
158 Russell Branyan	.20	.50
159 Frank Thomas	.60	1.50
160 Alex Escobar	.20	.50
161 Mark Bellhorn	.20	.50
162 Melvin Mora	.25	.60
163 Andruw Jones	.40	1.00
164 Danny Bautista	.20	.50
165 Ramon Ortiz	.20	.50
166 Wily Mo Pena	.25	.60
167 Jose Jimenez	.20	.50
168 Mark Redman	.20	.50
169 Angel Berroa	.20	.50
170 Andy Marte SP RC	5.00	12.00
171 Juan Gonzalez	.25	.60
172 Fernando Vina	.20	.50
173 Joel Pineiro	.20	.50
174 Boof Bonser	.20	.50
175 Bernie Castro SP RC	2.00	5.00
176 Bobby Cox MG	.20	.50
177 Jeff Kent	.25	.60
178 Oliver Perez	.25	.60
179 Chase Utley	.60	1.50
180 Mark Mulder	.25	.60
181 Bobby Abreu	.25	.60
182 Ramiro Mendoza	.20	.50
183 Aaron Heilman	.20	.50
184 A.J. Pierzynski	.25	.60
185 Eric Gagne	.25	.60
186 Kirk Saarloos	.20	.50
187 Ron Gardenhire MG	.20	.50
188 Dmitri Young	.25	.60
189 Todd Zeile	.25	.60
190A Jim Thome New Logo	.40	1.00
190B Jim Thome Old Logo SP	3.00	8.00
191 Cliff Lee	.20	.50
192 Matt Morris	.25	.60
193 Robert Fick	.25	.60
194 C.C. Sabathia	.25	.60
195 Alexis Rios	.25	.60
196 D'Angelo Jimenez	.20	.50
197 Edgar Martinez	.40	1.00
198 Robb Nen	.25	.60
199 Taggert Bozied	.20	.50
200 Vladimir Guerrero SP	3.00	8.00
201 Walter Young SP	2.00	5.00
202 Brendan Harris RC	.40	1.00
203 Mike Hargrove MG	.20	.50
204 Vernon Wells	.25	.60
205 Hank Blalock	.25	.60
206 Mike Cameron	.20	.50
207 Tony Batista	.20	.50
208 Matt Williams	.25	.60
209 Tony Womack	.20	.50
210 R.Nivar-Martinez RC	.40	1.00
211 Aaron Sele	.20	.50
212 Mark Grace	.40	1.00
213 Joe Crede	.25	.60
214 Ryan Dempster	.20	.50
215 Omar Vizquel	.40	1.00
216 Juan Pierre	.20	.50
217 Denny Bautista	.25	.60
218 Chuck Knoblauch	.25	.60
219 Eric Karros	.25	.60
220 Victor Diaz	.20	.50
221 Jacque Jones	.25	.60
222 Jose Vidro	.20	.50
223 Joe McEwing	.20	.50
224 Nick Johnson	.25	.60
225 Eric Chavez	.25	.60
226 Jose Mesa	.20	.50
227 Aramis Ramirez	.25	.60
228 John Lackey	.20	.50
229 David Bell	.20	.50
230 John Olerud	.25	.60
231 Tino Martinez	.40	1.00
232 Randy Winn	.20	.50
233 Todd Hollandsworth	.20	.50
234 Ruddy Lugo RC	.40	1.00
235 Carlos Delgado	.25	.60
236 Chris Narveson	.25	.60
237 Tim Salmon	.40	1.00
238 Orlando Palmeiro	.20	.50
239 Jeff Clark SP RC	2.00	5.00
240 Byung-Hyun Kim	.25	.60
241 Mike Remlinger	.20	.50
242 Johnny Damon	.40	1.00
243 Corey Patterson	.20	.50
244 Paul Konerko	.25	.60
245 Danny Graves	.20	.50
246 Ellis Burks	.25	.60
247 Gavin Floyd	.20	.50
248 Jaime Bubela RC	.40	1.00
249 Sean Burroughs	.20	.50
250 Alex Rodriguez SP	5.00	12.00
251 Gabe Gross	.20	.50
252 Rafael Palmeiro	.40	1.00
253 Dewon Brazelton	.20	.50
254 Jimmy Journell	.20	.50
255 Rafael Soriano	.20	.50
256 Jerome Williams	.20	.50
257 Xavier Nady	.20	.50
258 Mike Williams	.20	.50
259 Randy Wolf	.20	.50
260A Miguel Tejada Orange	.25	.60
260B Miguel Tejada Black SP	2.00	5.00
261 Juan Rivera	.20	.50
262 Rey Ordonez	.20	.50
263 Bartolo Colon	.25	.60
264 Eric Milton	.20	.50
265 Jeffrey Hammonds	.20	.50
266 Odalis Perez	.20	.50
267 Mike Sweeney	.25	.60
268 Richard Hidalgo	.20	.50
269 Alex Gonzalez	.20	.50
270 Aaron Cook	.20	.50
271 Earl Snyder	.20	.50
272 Todd Walker	.20	.50
273 Aaron Rowand	.20	.50
274 Matt Clement	.25	.60
275 Anastacio Martinez	.20	.50
276 Mike Bordick	.25	.60
277 John Smoltz	.40	1.00
278 Scott Hairston	.20	.50
279 David Eckstein	.20	.50
280 Shannon Stewart	.25	.60
281 Carl Everett	.25	.60
282 Aubrey Huff	.20	.50
283 Mike Mussina	.40	1.00
284 Ruben Sierra	.25	.60
285 Russ Ortiz	.20	.50
286 Brian Lawrence	.20	.50
287 Kip Wells	.20	.50
288 Placido Polanco	.20	.50
289 Ted Lilly	.20	.50
290 Andy Pettitte	.40	1.00
291 John Buck	.20	.50
292 Orlando Cabrera	.25	.60
293 Cristian Guzman	.20	.50
294 Ruben Quevedo	.20	.50
295 Cesar Izturis	.20	.50
296 Ryan Ludwick	.20	.50
297 Roy Oswalt	.25	.60
298 Jason Stokes	.25	.60
299 Mike Hampton	.25	.60
300 Pedro Martinez	.40	1.00
301 Nic Jackson	.20	.50
302A Mag. Ordonez New Logo	.25	.60
302B Mag. Ordonez Old Logo SP	2.00	5.00
303 Manny Ramirez	.40	1.00
304 Jorge Julio	.20	.50
305 Javy Lopez	.25	.60
306 Roy Halladay	.25	.60
307 Kevin Mench	.20	.50
308 Jason Isringhausen	.25	.60
309 Carlos Guillen	.25	.60
310 Tsuyoshi Shinjo	.25	.60
311 Phil Nevin	.25	.60
312 Pokey Reese	.20	.50
313 Jorge Padilla	.20	.50
314 Jermaine Dye	.25	.60
315 David Wells	.25	.60
316 Mo Vaughn	.25	.60
317 Bernie Williams	.40	1.00
318 Michael Restovich	.20	.50
319 Jose Hernandez	.20	.50
320 Richie Sexson	.25	.60
321 Daryle Ward	.20	.50
322 Luis Castillo	.20	.50
323 Rene Reyes	.20	.50
324 Victor Martinez	.40	1.00
325A Adam Dunn New Logo	.25	.60
325B Adam Dunn Old Logo SP	2.00	5.00
326 Corwin Malone	.20	.50
327 Kerry Wood	.25	.60
328 Rickey Henderson	.60	1.50
329 Marty Cordova	.20	.50
330 Greg Maddux	1.00	2.50
331 Miguel Batista	.20	.50
332 Chris Bootcheck	.20	.50
333 Carlos Baerga	.20	.50
334 Antonio Alfonseca	.20	.50
335 Shane Halter	.20	.50
336 Juan Encarnacion	.20	.50
337 Tom Gordon	.20	.50
338 Hideo Nomo	.60	1.50
339 Torii Hunter	.20	.50
340A Alfonso Soriano Yellow	.25	.60
340B Alf. Soriano Black SP	2.00	5.00
341 Roberto Alomar	.40	1.00
342 David Justice	.25	.60
343 Mike Lieberthal	.25	.60
344 Jeff Weaver	.20	.50
345 Timo Perez	.20	.50
346 Travis Lee	.25	.60
347 Sean Casey	.25	.60
348 Willie Harris	.20	.50
349 Derek Lowe	.25	.60
350 Tom Glavine	.40	1.00
351 Eric Hinske	.20	.50
352 Rocco Baldelli	.25	.60
353 J.D. Drew	.20	.50
354 Jamie Moyer	.25	.60
355 Todd Linden	.20	.50
356 Benito Santiago	.25	.60
357 Brad Baker	.20	.50
358 Alex Gonzalez	.20	.50
359 Brandon Duckworth	.20	.50
360 John Rheinecker	.20	.50
361 Orlando Hernandez	.25	.60
362 Pedro Astacio	.20	.50
363 Brad Wilkerson	.20	.50
364 David Ortiz SP	3.00	8.00
365 Geoff Jenkins SP	2.00	5.00
366 Brian Jordan SP	2.00	5.00
367 Paul Byrd SP	2.00	5.00
368 Jason Lane SP	2.00	5.00
369 Jeff Bagwell SP	3.00	8.00
370 Bobby Higginson SP	2.00	5.00
371 Juan Uribe SP	2.00	5.00
372 Lee Stevens SP	2.00	5.00
373 Jimmy Haynes SP	2.00	5.00
374 Jose Valentin SP	2.00	5.00
375 Ken Griffey Jr. SP	5.00	12.00
376 Barry Bonds SP	8.00	20.00
377 Gary Matthews Jr. SP	2.00	5.00
378 Gary Sheffield SP	2.00	5.00
379 Rick Helling SP	2.00	5.00
380 Junior Spivey SP	2.00	5.00
381 Francisco Rodriguez SP	2.00	5.00
382 Chipper Jones SP	3.00	8.00
383 Orlando Hudson SP	2.00	5.00
384 Ivan Rodriguez SP	3.00	8.00
385 Chris Snelling SP	2.00	5.00
386 Kenny Lofton SP	2.00	5.00
387 Eric Cyr SP	2.00	5.00
388 Jason Kendall SP	2.00	5.00
389 Marlon Anderson SP	2.00	5.00
390 Billy Koch SP	2.00	5.00
391 Shelley Duncan SP	5.00	12.00
392 Jose Reyes SP	2.00	5.00
393 Fernando Tatis SP	2.00	5.00
394 Michael Cuddyer SP	2.00	5.00
395 Mark Prior SP	3.00	8.00
396 Dontrelle Willis SP	3.00	8.00
397 Jay Payton SP	2.00	5.00
398 Brandon Phillips SP	2.00	5.00
399 Dustin Moseley SP RC	2.00	5.00
400 Jason Giambi SP	2.00	5.00
401 John Mabry SP	2.00	5.00
402 Ron Gant SP	2.00	5.00
403 J.T. Snow SP	2.00	5.00
404 Jeff Cirillo SP	2.00	5.00
405 Darin Erstad SP	2.00	5.00
406 Luis Gonzalez SP	2.00	5.00
407 Marcus Giles SP	2.00	5.00
408 Brian Daubach SP	2.00	5.00
409 Moises Alou SP	2.00	5.00
410 Raul Mondesi SP	2.00	5.00
411 Adrian Beltre SP	2.00	5.00
412 A.J. Burnett SP	2.00	5.00
413 Jason Jennings SP	2.00	5.00
414 Edwin Almonte SP	2.00	5.00
415 Fred McGriff SP	3.00	8.00
416 Tim Raines Jr. SP	2.00	5.00
417 Rafael Furcal SP	2.00	5.00
418 Erubiel Durazo SP	2.00	5.00
419 Drew Henson SP	2.00	5.00
420 Kevin Appier SP	2.00	5.00
421 Chad Tracy SP	2.00	5.00
422 Adam Wainwright SP	2.00	5.00
423 Choo Freeman SP	2.00	5.00
424 Sandy Alomar Jr. SP	2.00	5.00
425 Corey Koskie SP	2.00	5.00
426 Jeromy Burnitz SP	2.00	5.00
427 Jorge Posada SP	3.00	8.00
428 Jason Arnold SP	2.00	5.00
429 Brett Myers SP	2.00	5.00
430 Shawn Green SP	2.00	5.00

2003 Topps Heritage Chrome

Inserted at a stated rate of one in eight, this is a partial parallel to the basic Topps Heritage set. These cards feature Topps special Chrome technology and were printed to a stated print run of 1954 serial numbered sets.

THC1 Alex Rodriguez	4.00	10.00
THC2 Ichiro Suzuki	4.00	10.00
THC3 Brian Giles	1.50	4.00
THC4 Albert Pujols	5.00	12.00
THC5 Derek Jeter	6.00	15.00
THC6 Pat Burrell	1.50	4.00
THC7 Lance Berkman	1.50	4.00
THC8 Todd Helton	2.00	5.00
THC9 Chris Duncan	8.00	20.00
THC10 Rodrigo Lopez	1.50	4.00
THC11 Sammy Sosa	2.50	6.00
THC12 Barry Zito	1.50	4.00
THC13 Marlon Byrd	1.50	4.00
THC14 Al Leiter	1.50	4.00
THC15 Kazuhisa Ishii	1.50	4.00
THC16 Franklin Gutierrez	2.00	5.00
THC17 Roger Clemens	4.00	10.00
THC18 Mark Buehrle	1.50	4.00
THC19 Larry Walker	1.50	4.00
THC20 Curt Schilling	1.50	4.00
THC21 Garret Anderson	1.50	4.00
THC22 Randy Johnson	2.50	6.00
THC23 Cliff Floyd	1.50	4.00
THC24 Austin Kearns	1.50	4.00
THC25 Manuel Ramirez	1.50	4.00
THC26 Raul Ibanez	1.50	4.00
THC27 Jason Perry	2.00	5.00
THC28 Mark Teixeira	2.00	5.00
THC29 Nomar Garciaparra	2.50	6.00
THC30 Wayne Lydon	1.50	4.00
THC31 Preston Wilson	1.50	4.00
THC32 Paul Lo Duca	1.50	4.00
THC33 Edgardo Alfonzo	1.50	4.00
THC34 Jeremy Giambi	1.50	4.00
THC35 Mariano Rivera	2.50	6.00
THC36 Jimmy Rollins	1.50	4.00
THC37 Bret Boone	1.50	4.00
THC38 Scott Rolen	2.00	5.00
THC39 Adam LaRoche	1.50	4.00
40 Tim Hudson	1.50	4.00
THC41 Craig Brazell	1.50	4.00
THC42 Daryl Clark	1.50	4.00
THC43 Joe Mauer Jake Mauer	2.50	6.00
THC44 Troy Glaus	1.50	4.00
THC45 Trey Hodges	1.50	4.00
THC46 Carl Crawford	1.50	4.00
THC47 Mike Piazza	2.50	6.00
THC48 Josh Beckett	1.50	4.00
THC49 Randall Simon	1.50	4.00
THC50 Frank Thomas	2.50	6.00
THC51 Andruw Jones	2.00	5.00
THC52 Andy Marte	5.00	12.00
THC53 Bernie Castro	1.50	4.00
THC54 Jim Thome	1.50	4.00
THC55 Alexis Rios	1.50	4.00
THC56 Vladimir Guerrero	2.50	6.00
THC57 Walter Young	1.50	4.00
THC58 Hank Blalock	1.50	4.00
THC59 Ramon Nivar-Martinez	1.50	4.00
THC60 Jacque Jones	1.50	4.00
THC61 Nick Johnson	1.50	4.00
THC62 Ruddy Lugo	1.50	4.00
THC63 Carlos Delgado	1.50	4.00
THC64 Jeff Clark	1.50	4.00
THC65 Johnny Damon	2.00	5.00
THC66 Jaime Bubela	1.50	4.00
THC67 Alex Rodriguez	4.00	40.00
THC68 Rafael Palmeiro	2.00	5.00
THC69 Miguel Tejada	1.50	4.00
THC70 Bartolo Colon	1.50	4.00
THC71 Mike Sweeney	1.50	4.00
THC72 John Smoltz	2.00	5.00
THC73 Shannon Stewart	1.50	4.00
THC74 Mike Mussina	2.00	5.00
THC75 Roy Oswalt	1.50	4.00
THC76 Pedro Martinez	2.00	5.00
THC77 Magglio Ordonez	1.50	4.00
THC78 Manny Ramirez	2.00	5.00
THC79 David Wells	1.50	4.00
THC80 Richie Sexson	1.50	4.00
THC81 Adam Dunn	1.50	4.00
THC82 Greg Maddux	4.00	10.00
THC83 Alfonso Soriano	1.50	4.00
THC84 Roberto Alomar	2.00	5.00
THC85 Derek Lowe	1.50	4.00
THC86 Tom Glavine	2.00	5.00
THC87 Jeff Bagwell	2.00	5.00
THC88 Ken Griffey Jr.	4.00	10.00
THC89 Barry Bonds	6.00	15.00
THC90 Gary Sheffield	1.50	4.00
THC91 Chipper Jones	2.50	6.00
THC92 Orlando Hudson	1.50	4.00
THC93 Jose Cruz Jr.	1.50	4.00
THC94 Mark Prior	2.00	5.00
THC95 Jason Giambi	1.50	4.00
THC96 Luis Gonzalez	1.50	4.00
THC97 Drew Henson	1.50	4.00
THC98 Cristian Guzman	1.50	4.00
THC99 Shawn Green	1.50	4.00
THC100 Jose Vidro	1.50	4.00

2003 Topps Heritage Clubhouse Collection Relics

Inserted at different odds depending on the relic, these 12 cards feature a mix of active and retire players and various game-used relics used during their career.

BAT A STATED ODDS 1:2569
BAT B STATED ODDS 1:2506
BAT C STATED ODDS 1:2464
BAT D STATED ODDS 1:1989
UNI A STATED ODDS 1:4223
UNI B STATED ODDS 1:1207
UNI C STATED ODDS 1:921
UNI D STATED ODDS 1:171
AD Adam Dunn Uni D 6.00 15.00
AK Al Kaline Bat D 12.50 30.00
AP Albert Pujols Uni D 8.00 20.00
AR Alex Rodriguez Uni D 8.00 20.00
CJ Chipper Jones Uni D 6.00 15.00
DS Duke Snider Uni A 15.00 40.00
EB Ernie Banks Bat C 12.50 30.00
EM Eddie Mathews Bat B 12.50 30.00
JG Jim Gilliam Uni B 6.00 15.00
KW Kerry Wood Uni D 6.00 15.00
SG Shawn Green Uni C 6.00 15.00
WM Willie Mays Bat A 20.00 50.00

2003 Topps Heritage Clubhouse Collection Autograph Relics

Inserted in packs at a stated rate of one in 15,424, these four cards feature not only a game used relic from the featured player but also an authentic autograph. These cards were issued to a stated print run of 25 serial numbered sets and no pricing is provided due to market scarcity.

AK Al Kaline Bat
DS Duke Snider Uni
EB Ernie Banks Bat
WM Willie Mays Bat

2003 Topps Heritage Clubhouse Collection Dual Relics

Issued at a stated rate of one in 9.521, these three cards feature game-used relics from both a legendary player and a current star of the same franchise. These cards were issued to a stated print run of 54 serial numbered sets.

BW Ernie Banks Bat
Kerry Wood Uni
MJ Eddie Mathews Bat
Chipper Jones Uni
SG Duke Snider Uni
Shawn Green Uni

2003 Topps Heritage Flashbacks

Inserted at a stated rate of one in 12, these 10 cards feature thrilling moments from the 1954 season.

COMPLETE SET 10) 8.00 20.00
F1 Willie Mays 2.00 5.00
F2 Yogi Berra 1.00 2.50
F3 Ted Kluszewski .75 2.00
F4 Stan Musial 1.50 4.00
F5 Hank Aaron 2.00 5.00
F6 Duke Snider .75 2.00
F7 Richie Ashburn .75 2.00
F8 Robin Roberts .75 2.00
F9 Mickey Vernon .75 2.00
F10 Don Larsen .75 2.00

2003 Topps Heritage Flashbacks Autographs

Inserted at a stated rate of one in 65,384 this card features an authentic autograph of Willie Mays. This card was issued to a stated print run of 25 serial numbered cards and no pricing is available due to market scarcity.

WM Willie Mays

2003 Topps Heritage Grandstand Glory Stadium Relics

Inserted at different odds depending on the group, these 12 cards feature a player photo along with a seat relic from any of nine historic ballparks involved in their career.

GROUP A ODDS 1:2804
GROUP B ODDS 1:514
GROUP C ODDS 1:1446
GROUP D ODDS 1:1356
GROUP E ODDS 1:654
GROUP F ODDS 1:214
AK Al Kaline F 8.00 20.00
AP Andy Pafko F 4.00 10.00
DG Dick Groat D 6.00 15.00
DS Duke Snider A 10.00 25.00
EB Ernie Banks C 10.00 25.00
EM Eddie Mathews F 6.00 15.00
PR Phil Rizzuto E 8.00 20.00
RA Richie Ashburn B 8.00 20.00
TK Ted Kluszewski B 8.00 20.00
WM Willie Mays B 15.00 40.00
WS Warren Spahn F 8.00 20.00
YB Yogi Berra E 10.00 25.00

2003 Topps Heritage New Age Performers

Issued at a stated rate of one in 15, these 15 cards feature prominent active players who have taken the game of baseball to new levels.

NA1 Mike Piazza 1.50 4.00
NA2 Ichiro Suzuki 2.00 5.00
NA3 Derek Jeter 2.50 6.00
NA4 Alex Rodriguez 1.50 4.00
NA5 Sammy Sosa 1.00 2.50
NA6 Jason Giambi .75 2.00
NA7 Vladimir Guerrero 1.00 2.50
NA8 Albert Pujols 2.00 5.00
NA9 Todd Helton .75 2.00
NA10 Nomar Garciaparra 1.50 4.00
NA11 Randy Johnson 1.00 2.50
NA12 Jim Thome .75 2.00
NA13 Barry Bonds 2.50 6.00
NA14 Miguel Tejada .75 2.00
NA15 Alfonso Soriano .75 2.00

2003 Topps Heritage Real One Autographs

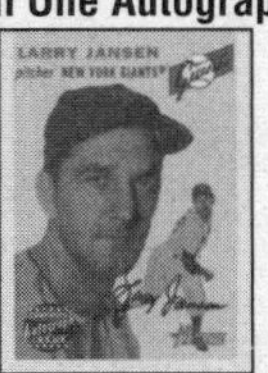

Inserted at various odds depending on what group the player belonged to, these cards feature authentic autographs from the featured player. Topps made an effort to secure autographs from every person who was still living that was in the 1954 Topps set. Hank Aaron, Yogi Berra and Johnny Sain did not return their cards in time for inclusion in this set and a collector could redeem these cards until February 28th, 2005. Sain never did sign his cards before his passing in November, 2006.

RETIRED ODDS 1:188
ACTIVE A ODDS 1:6168
ACTIVE B ODDS 1:1540
ACTIVE C ODDS 1:2802
*RED INK: 1X TO 2X BASIC RETIRED
*RED INK: .75X TO 1.5X BASIC ACTIVE A
*RED INK: .75X TO 1.5X BASIC ACTIVE B
*RED INK: .75X TO 1.5X BASIC ACTIVE C
RED INK STATED ODDS 1:696
RED INK PRINT RUN 54 SERIAL #'d SETS
AK Al Kaline 50.00 100.00
AP Andy Pafko 30.00 60.00
BR Bob Ross 10.00 25.00
BS Bill Skowron 15.00 40.00
BSH Bobby Shantz 15.00 40.00
BT Bob Talbot 10.00 25.00
BWE Bill Werle 10.00 25.00
CH Cal Hogue 10.00 25.00
CK Charlie Kress 10.00 25.00
CS Carl Scheib 10.00 25.00
DG Dick Groat 30.00 60.00
DK Dick Kryhoski 10.00 25.00
DL Don Lenhardt 10.00 25.00
DLU Don Lund 10.00 25.00
DS Duke Snider 50.00 100.00
EB Ernie Banks 75.00 150.00
EM Eddie Mayo 10.00 25.00
GH Gene Hermanski 10.00 25.00
HA Hank Aaron 200.00 350.00
HB Hank Bauer 15.00 40.00
JC Jose Cruz Jr. B 10.00 25.00
JP Joe Presko 10.00 25.00
JPO Johnny Podres 15.00 40.00
JR Jimmy Rollins C 15.00 40.00
JS Johnny Sain 15.00 40.00
Sain, due to ill health, never was able to sign cards for this product
JV Jose Vidro B 10.00 25.00
JW Jim Willis 10.00 25.00
LB Lance Berkman A 40.00 80.00
LJ Larry Jansen 15.00 40.00
LW Leroy Wheat 10.00 25.00
MB Matt Batts 10.00 25.00
MBL Mike Blyzka 10.00 25.00
MI Monte Irvin 30.00 60.00
MM Mickey Micelotta 10.00 25.00
MS Mike Sandlock 10.00 25.00
PP Paul Penson 10.00 25.00
PR Phil Rizzuto 30.00 60.00
PRO Preacher Roe 15.00 40.00
RF Roy Face 15.00 40.00
RM Ray Murray 10.00 25.00
TL Tom Lasorda 50.00 100.00
VL Vern Law 15.00 40.00
WF Whitey Ford 30.00 60.00
WM Willie Mays 150.00 250.00
YB Yogi Berra 50.00 100.00

2003 Topps Heritage Then and Now

Issued at a stated rate of one in 15, these 10 cards feature an 1954 star along with a current standout. The backs compare 10 league leaders of 1954 to the league leaders of 2002. Interestingly enough, Ted Kluszewski and Alex Rodriguez are on both the first two cards in this set.

COMPLETE SET (10) 12.50 30.00
TN1 Ted Kluszewski 1.50 4.00
Alex Rodriguez HR
TN2 Ted Kluszewski 1.50 4.00
Alex Rodriguez RBI
TN3 Willie Mays 2.50 6.00
Barry Bonds Batting
TN4 Don Mueller .75 2.00
Alfonso Soriano
TN5 Stan Musial 1.50 4.00
Garret Anderson
TN6 Minnie Minoso .75 2.00
Johnny Damon
TN7 Willie Mays 2.50 6.00
Barry Bonds Slugging
TN8 Duke Snider 1.50 4.00
Alex Rodriguez
TN9 Robin Roberts 1.00 2.50
Randy Johnson
TN10 Johnny Antonelli .75 2.00
Pedro Martinez

2004 Topps Heritage

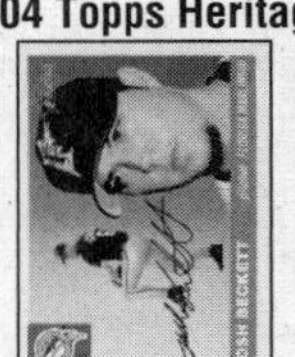

This 495 card set was released in February, 2004. As this was the fourth year this set was issued, the cards were designed in the style of the 1955 Topps set. This set was issued in eight card packs which came 24 packs to a box and eight boxes to a case. This set features a mix of cards printed to standard amounts as well as various Short Prints and then even some variation short prints. Any type of short printed card was issued to a stated rate of one in two. We have delineated in our checklist what the various variations are. In addition, all cards from 398 through 475 are SP's.

COMPLETE SET (495) 200.00 350.00
COMP.SET w/o SP's (385) 30.00 60.00
1A Jim Thome Fielding .40 1.00
1B Jim Thome Hitting SP 3.00 8.00
2 Nomar Garciaparra SP 4.00 10.00
3 Aramis Ramirez .25 .60
4 Rafael Palmeiro SP 3.00 8.00
5 Danny Graves .20 .50
6 Casey Blake .20 .50
7 Juan Uribe .20 .50
8A Dmitri Young New Logo .25 .60
8B Dmitri Young Old Logo SP 2.00 5.00
9 Billy Wagner .25 .60
10A Jason Giambi Swinging .25 .60
10B Jason Giambi Btg Stance SP 2.00 5.00
11 Carlos Beltran .25 .60
12 Chad Hermansen .20 .50
13 B.J. Upton .40 1.00
14 Dustan Mohr .20 .50
15 Endy Chavez .20 .50
16 Cliff Floyd .25 .60
17 Bernie Williams .40 1.00
18 Eric Chavez .25 .60
19 Chase Utley .40 1.00
20 Randy Johnson .60 1.50
21 Vernon Wells .25 .60
22 Juan Gonzalez .25 .60
23 Joe Kennedy .20 .50
24 Bengie Molina .20 .50
25 Carlos Lee .25 .60
26 Horacio Ramirez .20 .50
27 Anthony Acevedo RC .30 .75
28 Sammy Sosa SP 3.00 8.00
29 Jon Garland .25 .60
30A Adam Dunn Fielding .25 .60
30B Adam Dunn Hitting SP 2.00 5.00
31 Aaron Rowand .25 .60
32 Jody Gerut .20 .50
33 Chin-Hui Tsao .25 .60
34 Alex Sanchez .20 .50
35 A.J. Burnett .25 .60
36 Brad Ausmus .25 .60
37 Blake Hawksworth RC .40 1.00
38 Francisco Rodriguez .25 .60
39 Alex Cintron .20 .50
40A Chipper Jones Pointing .60 1.50
40B Chipper Jones Fielding SP 3.00 8.00
41 Deivi Cruz .20 .50
42 Bill Mueller .25 .60
43 Joe Borowski .20 .50
44 Jimmy Haynes .20 .50
45 Mark Loretta .20 .50
46 Jerome Williams .20 .50
47 Gary Sheffield Yanks SP 3.00 8.00
48 Richard Hidalgo .20 .50
49A Jason Kendall New Logo .25 .60
49B Jason Kendall Old Logo SP 2.00 5.00
50 Ichiro Suzuki SP 5.00 12.00
51 Jim Edmonds .25 .60
52 Frank Catalanotto .20 .50
53 Jose Contreras .20 .50
54 Mo Vaughn .25 .60
55 Brendan Donnelly .20 .50
56 Luis Gonzalez .25 .60
57 Robert Fick .20 .50
58 Laynce Nix .20 .50
59 Johnny Damon .40 1.00
60A Magglio Ordonez Running .25 .60
60B Magglio Ordonez Hitting SP 2.00 5.00
61 Matt Clement .25 .60
62 Ryan Ludwick .20 .50
63 Luis Castillo .20 .50
64 Dave Crouthers RC .30 .75
65 Dave Berg .20 .50
66 Kyle Davies RC 1.50 4.00
67 Tim Salmon .40 1.00
68 Marcus Giles .25 .60
69 Marty Cordova .20 .50
70A Todd Helton White Jsy .40 1.00
70B Todd Helton Purple Jsy SP 3.00 8.00
71 Jeff Kent .25 .60
72 Michael Tucker .20 .50
73 Cesar Izturis .20 .50
74 Paul Quantrill .20 .50
75 Conor Jackson RC 1.25 3.00
76 Placido Polanco .20 .50
77 Adam Eaton .20 .50
78 Ramon Hernandez .25 .60
79 Edgardo Alfonzo .20 .50
80 Dioner Navarro RC .40 1.00
81 Woody Williams .20 .50
82 Rey Ordonez .20 .50
83 Randy Winn .20 .50
84 Casey Myers RC .30 .75
85A R.Choy Foo New Logo RC .30 .75
85B R.Choy Foo Old Logo SP 2.00 5.00
86 Ray Durham .25 .60
87 Sean Burroughs .20 .50
88 Tim Frend RC .30 .75
89 Shigetoshi Hasegawa .25 .60
90 Jeffrey Allison RC .30 .75
91 Orlando Hudson .20 .50
92 Matt Creighton SP RC 2.00 5.00
93 Tim Worrell .20 .50
94 Kris Benson .20 .50
95 Mike Lieberthal .25 .60
96 David Wells .25 .60
97 Jason Phillips .20 .50
98 Bobby Cox MGR .20 .50
99 Johan Santana .60 1.50
100A Alex Rodriguez Hitting 1.00 2.50
100B Alex Rodriguez Throwing SP 4.00 10.00
101 John Vander Wal .20 .50
102 Orlando Cabrera .25 .60
103 Hideo Nomo .60 1.50
104 Todd Walker .20 .50
105 Jason Johnson .20 .50
106 Matt Mantei .20 .50
107 Jarrod Washburn .20 .50
108 Preston Wilson .25 .60
109 Carl Pavano .25 .60
110 Geoff Blum .20 .50
111 Eric Gagne .25 .60
112 Geoff Jenkins .20 .50
113 Joe Torre MG .40 1.00
114 Jon Knott RC .30 .75
115 Hank Blalock .25 .60
116 John Olerud .25 .60
117A Pat Burrell New Logo .25 .60
117B Pat Burrell Old Logo SP 2.00 5.00
118 Aaron Boone .25 .60
119 Zach Day .20 .50
120A Frank Thomas New Logo .60 1.50
120B Frank Thomas Old Logo SP 3.00 8.00
121 Kyle Farnsworth .20 .50
122 Derek Lowe .25 .60
123 Zach Miner SP RC 3.00 8.00
124 Matthew Moses SP RC 3.00 8.00
125 Jesse Roman RC .30 .75
126 Josh Phelps .20 .50
127 Nic Ungs RC .30 .75
128 Dan Haren .20 .50
129 Kirk Rueter .20 .50
130 Jack McKeon MGR .25 .60
131 Keith Foulke .25 .60
132 Garrett Stephenson .20 .50
133 Wes Helms .20 .50
134 Raul Ibanez .20 .50
135 Morgan Ensberg .25 .60
136 Jay Payton .25 .60
137 Billy Koch .20 .50
138 Mark Grudzielanek .20 .50
139 Rodrigo Lopez .20 .50
140 Corey Patterson .20 .50
141 Troy Percival .25 .60
142 Shea Hillenbrand .25 .60
143 Brad Fullmer .25 .60
144 Ricky Nolasco RC .60 1.50
145 Mark Teixeira .40 1.00
146 Tydus Meadows RC .30 .75
147 Toby Hall .20 .50
148 Orlando Palmeiro .20 .50
149 Khalid Ballouli RC .30 .75
150 Grady Little MGR .20 .50
151 David Eckstein .25 .60
152 Kenny Perez RC .30 .75
153 Ben Grieve .20 .50
154 Ismael Valdes .20 .50
155 Bret Boone .25 .60
156 Jesse Foppert .20 .50
157 Vicente Padilla .20 .50
158 Bobby Abreu .25 .60
159 Scott Hatteberg .20 .50
160 Carlos Quentin RC 1.00 2.50
161 Anthony Lerew RC .40 1.00
162 Lance Carter .20 .50
163 Robb Nen .25 .60
164 Zach Duke SP RC 4.00 10.00
165 Xavier Nady .20 .50
166 Kip Wells .20 .50
167 Kevin Millwood .25 .60
168 Jon Lieber .20 .50
169 Jose Reyes .25 .60
170 Eric Byrnes .20 .50
171 Paul Konerko .25 .60
172 Chris Lubanski .25 .60
173 Jae Weong Seo .20 .50
174 Corey Koskie .20 .50
175 Tim Stauffer RC 4.00 1.00
176 John Lackey .20 .50
177 Danny Bautista .20 .50
178 Shane Reynolds .20 .50
179 Jorge Julio .20 .50
180A Manny Ramirez New Logo .40 1.00
180B Manny Ramirez Old Logo SP 3.00 8.00
181 Alex Gonzalez .20 .50
182A Moises Alou New Logo .25 .60
182B Moises Alou Old Logo SP 2.00 5.00
183 Mark Buehrle .25 .60
184 Carlos Guillen .25 .60
185 Nate Cornejo .20 .50
186 Billy Traber .20 .50
187 Jason Jennings .20 .50
188 Eric Munson .20 .50
189 Braden Looper .20 .50
190 Juan Encarnacion .20 .50
191 Dusty Baker MGR .25 .60
192 Travis Lee .20 .50
193 Miguel Cairo .20 .50
194 Rich Aurilia SP 2.00 5.00
195 Tom Gordon .20 .50
196 Freddy Garcia .25 .60
197 Brian Lawrence .20 .50
198 Jorge Posada SP 3.00 8.00
199 Javier Vazquez .25 .60
200A Albert Pujols New Logo 1.25 3.00
200B Albert Pujols Old Logo SP 5.00 12.00
201 Victor Zambrano .20 .50
202 Eli Marrero .20 .50
203 Joel Pineiro .20 .50
204 Rondell White .25 .60
205 Craig Ansman RC .30 .75
206 Michael Young .25 .60
207 Carlos Baerga .20 .50
208 Andruw Jones .40 1.00
209 Jerry Hairston Jr. .20 .50
210 Shawn Green SP 2.00 5.00
211 Ron Gardenhire MGR .20 .50
212 Darin Erstad .25 .60
213A Brandon Webb Glove Chest .20 .50
213B Brandon Webb Glove Out SP 2.00 5.00
214 Greg Maddux 1.00 2.50
215 Reed Johnson .20 .50
216 John Thomson .20 .50
217 Tino Martinez .40 1.00
218 Mike Cameron UER .20 .50
Card has facsimile autograph of Troy Cameron
219 Edgar Martinez .40 1.00
220 Eric Young .20 .50
221 Reggie Sanders .25 .60
222 Randy Wolf .20 .50
223 Erubiel Durazo .20 .50
224 Mike Mussina .40 1.00
225 Tom Glavine .40 1.00
226 Troy Glaus .25 .60
227 Oscar Villarreal .20 .50
228 David Segui .20 .50
229 Jeff Suppan .20 .50
230 Kenny Lofton .25 .60
231 Esteban Loaiza .20 .50
232 Felipe Lopez .20 .50
233 Matt Lawton .20 .50
234 Mark Bellhorn .25 .60
235 Wil Ledezma .20 .50
236 Todd Hollandsworth .20 .50
237 Octavio Dotel .20 .50
238 Darren Dreifort .20 .50
239 Paul Lo Duca .25 .60
240 Richie Sexson .25 .60
241 Doug Mientkiewicz .25 .60
242 Luis Rivas .20 .50
243 Claudio Vargas .20 .50
244 Mark Ellis .20 .50
245 Brett Myers .25 .60
246 Jake Peavy .25 .60
247 Marquis Grissom .25 .60
248 Armando Benitez .20 .50
249 Ryan Franklin .20 .50
250A Alfonso Soriano Throwing .25 .60
250B Alfonso Soriano Fielding SP 2.00 5.00
251 Tim Hudson .25 .60
252 Shannon Stewart .25 .60
253 A.J. Pierzynski .25 .60
254 Runelvys Hernandez .20 .50
255 Roy Oswalt .25 .60
256 Shawn Chacon .20 .50
257 Tony Graffanino .20 .50
258 Tim Wakefield .25 .60
259 Damian Miller .20 .50
260 Joe Crede .25 .60
261 Jason LaRue .20 .50
262 Jose Jimenez .20 .50
263 Juan Pierre .25 .60
264 Wade Miller .20 .50
265 Odalis Perez .20 .50
266 Eddie Guardado .20 .50
267 Rocky Biddle .20 .50
268 Jeff Nelson .20 .50
269 Terrence Long .20 .50
270 Ramon Ortiz .20 .50
271 Raul Mondesi .25 .60
272 Ugueth Urbina .20 .50
273 Jeromy Burnitz .25 .60
274 Brad Radke .25 .60
275 Jose Vidro .20 .50
276 Bobby Jenks .25 .60
277 Ty Wigginton .20 .50
278 Jose Guillen .25 .60
279 Delmon Young .40 1.00
280 Brian Giles .25 .60
281 Jason Schmidt .25 .60
282 Nick Markakis .25 .60
283 Felipe Alou MGR .25 .60
284 Carl Crawford .25 .60
285 Neifi Perez .20 .50
286 Miguel Tejada .25 .60
287 Victor Martinez .25 .60
288 Adam Kennedy .20 .50
289 Kerry Ligtenberg .20 .50
290 Scott Williamson .20 .50
291 Tony Womack .20 .50
292 Travis Hafner .25 .60
293 Bobby Crosby .25 .60
294 Chad Billingsley .25 .60
295 Russ Ortiz .20 .50
296 John Burkett .20 .50
297 Carlos Zambrano .25 .60
298 Randall Simon .20 .50
299 Juan Castro .20 .50
300 Mike Lowell .25 .60
301 Fred McGriff .40 1.00
302 Glendon Rusch .20 .50
303 Sung Jung RC .30 .75
304 Rocco Baldelli .25 .60
305 Fernando Vina .20 .50
306 Gil Meche .20 .50
307 Jose Cruz Jr. .20 .50
308 Bernie Castro .20 .50
309 Scott Spiezio .20 .50
310 Paul Byrd .20 .50
311A Jay Gibbons New Logo .20 .50
311B Jay Gibbons Old Logo SP 2.00 5.00
312 Trot Nixon .25 .60
313 Chris O'Riordan RC .30 .75
314 Julio Lugo .20 .50
315 Ben Davis .20 .50
316 Mike Williams .20 .50
317 Trevor Hoffman .25 .60
318 Andy Pettitte .40 1.00
319 Orlando Hernandez .25 .60
320 Juan Rivera .20 .50
321 Elizardo Ramirez .20 .50
322 Junior Spivey .20 .50
323 Tony Batista .20 .50
324 Mike Remlinger .20 .50
325 Alex Gonzalez .20 .50
326 Aaron Hill .20 .50
327 Steve Finley .25 .60
328 Vinny Castilla .25 .60
329 Eric Duncan .25 .60
330 Mike Gosling RC .30 .75
331 Eric Hinske .20 .50
332 Scott Rolen .40 1.00
333 Benito Santiago .25 .60
334 Jimmy Gobble .20 .50
335 Bobby Higginson .25 .60
336 Kelvim Escobar .20 .50
337 Mike DeJean .20 .50
338 Sidney Ponson .20 .50
339 Todd Self RC .40 1.00
340 Jeff Cirillo .20 .50
341 Jimmy Rollins .25 .60
342A Barry Zito White Jsy .25 .60
342B Barry Zito Green Jsy SP 2.00 5.00
343 Felix Pie .40 1.00
344 Matt Morris .25 .60
345 Kazuhiro Sasaki .25 .60
346 Jack Wilson .20 .50
347 Nick Johnson .25 .60
348 Wil Cordero .20 .50
349 Ryan Madson .20 .50
350 Torii Hunter .25 .60
351 Andy Ashby .20 .50
352 Aubrey Huff .25 .60
353 Brad Lidge .25 .60
354 Derrek Lee .40 1.00
355 Yadier Molina RC 1.00 2.50
356 Paul Wilson .20 .50
357 Omar Vizquel .40 1.00
358 Rene Reyes .20 .50
359 Marlon Anderson .20 .50
360 Bobby Kielty .20 .50
361A Ryan Wagner New Logo .20 .50
361B Ryan Wagner Old Logo SP 2.00 5.00
362 Justin Morneau .25 .60
363 Shane Spencer .20 .50
364 David Bell .20 .50
365 Matt Stairs .20 .50
366 Joe Borchard .20 .50
367 Mark Redman .20 .50
368 Dave Roberts .20 .50
369 Desi Relaford .20 .50
370 Rich Harden .25 .60
371 Fernando Tatis .20 .50
372 Eric Karros .25 .60
373 Eric Milton .20 .50
374 Mike Sweeney .25 .60
375 Brian Daubach .20 .50
376 Brian Snyder .20 .50
377 Chris Reitsma .20 .50

Card	Low	High
378 Kyle Lohse	.20	.50
379 Livan Hernandez	.25	.60
380 Robin Ventura	.25	.60
381 Jacque Jones	.25	.60
382 Danny Kolb	.20	.50
383 Casey Kotchman	.25	.60
384 Cristian Guzman	.20	.50
385 Josh Beckett	.25	.60
386 Khalil Greene	.40	1.00
387 Greg Myers	.20	.50
388 Francisco Cordero	.20	.50
389 Donald Levinski RC	.30	.75
390 Roy Halladay	.25	.60
391 J.D. Drew	.25	.60
392 Jamie Moyer	.25	.60
393 Ken Macha MGR	.20	.50
394 Jeff Davanon	.20	.50
395 Matt Kata	.20	.50
396 Jack Cust	.20	.50
397 Mike Timlin	.20	.50
398 Zack Greinke SP	2.00	5.00
399 Byung-Hyun Kim SP	2.00	5.00
400 Kazuhisa Ishii SP	2.00	5.00
401 Brayan Pena SP RC	2.00	5.00
402 Garret Anderson SP	2.00	5.00
403 Kyle Sleeth SP RC	3.00	8.00
404 Javy Lopez SP	2.00	5.00
405 Damian Moss SP	2.00	5.00
406 David Ortiz SP	3.00	8.00
407 Pedro Martinez SP	3.00	8.00
408 Hee Seop Choi SP	2.00	5.00
409 Carl Everett SP	2.00	5.00
410 Dontrelle Willis SP	3.00	8.00
411 Ryan Harvey SP	2.00	5.00
412 Russell Branyan SP	2.00	5.00
413 Milton Bradley SP	2.00	5.00
414 Marcus McBeth SP RC	2.00	5.00
415 Carlos Pena SP	2.00	5.00
416 Ivan Rodriguez SP	3.00	8.00
417 Craig Biggio SP	3.00	8.00
418 Angel Berroa SP	2.00	5.00
419 Brian Jordan SP	2.00	5.00
420 Scott Podsednik SP	2.00	5.00
421 Omar Falcon SP RC	2.00	5.00
422 Joe Mays SP	2.00	5.00
423 Brad Wilkerson SP	2.00	5.00
424 Al Leiter SP	2.00	5.00
425 Derek Jeter SP	5.00	12.00
426 Mark Mulder SP	2.00	5.00
427 Marlon Byrd SP	2.00	5.00
428 David Murphy SP RC	3.00	8.00
429 Phil Nevin SP	2.00	5.00
430 J.T. Snow SP	2.00	5.00
431 Brad Sullivan SP RC	3.00	8.00
432 Bo Hart SP	2.00	5.00
433 Josh Labandeira SP RC	2.00	5.00
434 Chan Ho Park SP	2.00	5.00
435 Carlos Delgado SP	2.00	5.00
436 Curt Schilling Sox SP	3.00	8.00
437 John Smoltz SP	3.00	8.00
438 Luis Matos SP	2.00	5.00
439 Mark Prior SP	3.00	8.00
440 Roberto Alomar SP	3.00	8.00
441 Coco Crisp SP	2.00	5.00
442 Austin Kearns SP	2.00	5.00
443 Larry Walker SP	2.00	5.00
444 Neal Cotts SP	2.00	5.00
445 Jeff Bagwell SP	3.00	8.00
446 Adrian Beltre SP	2.00	5.00
447 Grady Sizemore SP	3.00	8.00
448 Keith Ginter SP	2.00	5.00
449 Vladimir Guerrero SP	3.00	8.00
450 Lyle Overbay SP	2.00	5.00
451 Rafael Furcal SP	2.00	5.00
452 Melvin Mora SP	2.00	5.00
453 Kerry Wood SP	2.00	5.00
454 Jose Valentin SP	2.00	5.00
455 Ken Griffey Jr. SP	4.00	10.00
456 Brandon Phillips SP	2.00	5.00
457 Miguel Cabrera SP	3.00	8.00
458 Edwin Jackson SP	2.00	5.00
459 Eric Owens SP	2.00	5.00
460 Miguel Batista SP	2.00	5.00
461 Mike Hampton SP	2.00	5.00
462 Kevin Millar SP	2.00	5.00
463 Bartolo Colon SP	2.00	5.00
464 Sean Casey SP	2.00	5.00
465 C.C. Sabathia SP	2.00	5.00
466 Rickie Weeks SP	2.00	5.00
467 Brad Penny SP	2.00	5.00
468 Mike MacDougal SP	2.00	5.00
469 Kevin Brown SP	2.00	5.00
470 Lance Berkman SP	2.00	5.00
471 Ben Sheets SP	2.00	5.00
472 Mariano Rivera SP	3.00	8.00
473 Mike Piazza SP	4.00	10.00
474 Ryan Klesko SP	2.00	5.00
475 Edgar Renteria SP	2.00	5.00

2004 Topps Heritage Chrome

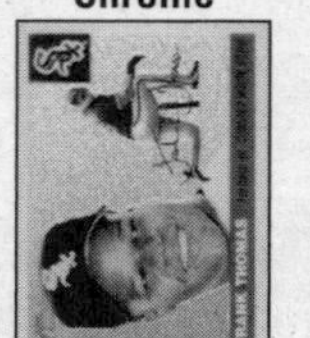

COMPLETE SET (110) 150.00 250.00
STATED ODDS 1:7
STATED PRINT RUN 1955 SERIAL #'d SETS

Card	Low	High
THC1 Sammy Sosa	2.50	6.00
THC2 Nomar Garciaparra	2.50	6.00
THC3 Ichiro Suzuki	4.00	10.00
THC4 Rafael Palmeiro	2.00	5.00
THC5 Carlos Delgado	1.50	4.00
THC6 Troy Glaus	1.50	4.00
THC7 Jay Gibbons	1.50	4.00
THC8 Frank Thomas	2.50	6.00
THC9 Pat Burrell	1.50	4.00
THC10 Albert Pujols	5.00	12.00
THC11 Brandon Webb	1.50	4.00
THC12 Chipper Jones	2.50	6.00
THC13 Magglio Ordonez	1.50	4.00
THC14 Adam Dunn	1.50	4.00
THC15 Todd Helton	2.00	5.00
THC16 Jason Giambi	1.50	4.00
THC17 Alfonso Soriano	1.50	4.00
THC18 Barry Zito	1.50	4.00
THC19 Jim Thome	2.00	5.00
THC20 Alex Rodriguez	4.00	10.00
THC21 Hee Seop Choi	1.50	4.00
THC22 Pedro Martinez	2.00	5.00
THC23 Kerry Wood	1.50	4.00
THC24 Bartolo Colon	1.50	4.00
THC25 Austin Kearns	1.50	4.00
THC26 Ken Griffey Jr.	4.00	10.00
THC27 Coco Crisp	1.50	4.00
THC28 Larry Walker	1.50	4.00
THC29 Ivan Rodriguez	2.00	5.00
THC30 Dontrelle Willis	2.00	5.00
THC31 Miguel Cabrera	2.00	5.00
THC32 Jeff Bagwell	2.00	5.00
THC33 Lance Berkman	1.50	4.00
THC34 Shawn Green	1.50	4.00
THC35 Kevin Brown	1.50	4.00
THC36 Vladimir Guerrero	2.50	6.00
THC37 Mike Piazza	2.50	6.00
THC38 Derek Jeter	6.00	15.00
THC39 John Smoltz	2.00	5.00
40 Mark Prior	2.00	5.00
THC41 Gary Sheffield Yanks	1.50	4.00
THC42 Curt Schilling Sox	2.00	5.00
THC43 Randy Johnson	2.50	6.00
THC44 Luis Gonzalez	1.50	4.00
THC45 Andruw Jones	2.00	5.00
THC46 Greg Maddux	4.00	10.00
THC47 Tony Batista	1.50	4.00
THC48 Esteban Loaiza	1.50	4.00
THC49 Chin-Hui Tsao	1.50	4.00
THC50 Mike Lowell	1.50	4.00
THC51 Jeff Kent	1.50	4.00
THC52 Richie Sexson	1.50	4.00
THC53 Torii Hunter	1.50	4.00
THC54 Jose Vidro	1.50	4.00
THC55 Jose Reyes	1.50	4.00
THC56 Jimmy Rollins	1.50	4.00
THC57 Bret Boone	1.50	4.00
THC58 Rocco Baldelli	1.50	4.00
THC59 Hank Blalock	1.50	4.00
THC60 Rickie Weeks	1.50	4.00
THC61 Rodney Choy Foo	1.50	4.00
THC62 Zach Miner	3.00	8.00
THC63 Brayan Pena	1.50	4.00
THC64 David Murphy	2.00	5.00
THC65 Matt Creighton	1.50	4.00
THC66 Kyle Sleeth	2.00	5.00
THC67 Matthew Moses	2.00	5.00
THC68 Josh Labandeira	1.50	4.00
THC69 Grady Sizemore	2.50	6.00
THC70 Edwin Jackson	1.50	4.00
THC71 Marcus McBeth	1.50	4.00
THC72 Brad Sullivan	2.00	5.00
THC73 Zach Duke	4.00	10.00
THC74 Omar Falcon	1.50	4.00
THC75 Conor Jackson	4.00	10.00
THC76 Carlos Quentin	3.00	8.00
THC77 Craig Ansman	1.50	4.00
THC78 Mike Gosling	1.50	4.00
THC79 Kyle Davies	3.00	8.00
THC80 Anthony Lerew	2.50	6.00
THC81 Sung Jung	1.50	4.00
THC82 Dave Crouthers	1.50	4.00
THC83 Kenny Perez	1.50	4.00
THC84 Jeffrey Allison	1.50	4.00
THC85 Nic Ungs	1.50	4.00
THC86 Donald Levinski	1.50	4.00
THC87 Anthony Acevedo	1.50	4.00
THC88 Todd Self	2.00	5.00
THC89 Tim Frend	1.50	4.00
THC90 Tydus Meadows	1.50	4.00
THC91 Khalid Ballouli	1.50	4.00
THC92 Dioner Navarro	2.00	5.00
THC93 Casey Myers	1.50	4.00
THC94 Jon Knott	1.50	4.00
THC95 Tim Stauffer	2.00	5.00
THC96 Ricky Nolasco	3.00	8.00
THC97 Blake Hawksworth	2.00	5.00
THC98 Jesse Roman	1.50	4.00
THC99 Yadier Molina	3.00	8.00
THC100 Chris O'Riordan	1.50	4.00
THC101 Cliff Floyd	1.50	4.00
THC102 Nick Johnson	1.50	4.00
THC103 Edgar Martinez	2.00	5.00
THC104 Brett Myers	1.50	4.00
THC105 Francisco Rodriguez	1.50	4.00
THC106 Scott Rolen	2.00	5.00
THC107 Mark Teixeira	2.00	5.00
THC108 Miguel Tejada	1.50	4.00
THC109 Vernon Wells	1.50	4.00
THC110 Jerome Williams	1.50	4.00

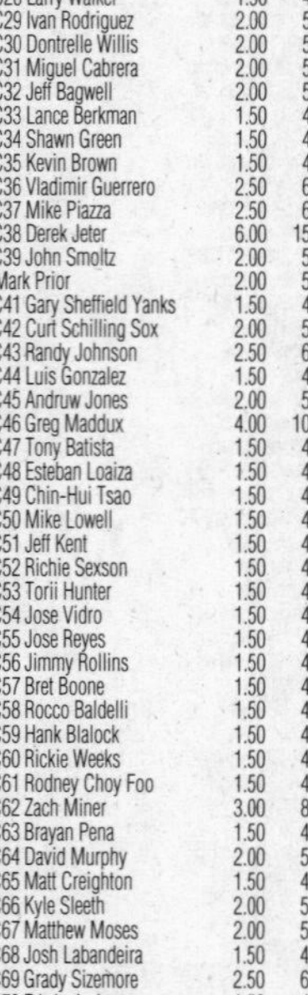

2004 Topps Heritage Chrome Black Refractors

*BLACK REF: 3X TO 6X CHROME
*BLACK REF: 4X TO 8X CHROME RC YR
STATED ODDS 1:251
STATED PRINT RUN 55 SERIAL #'d SETS

Card	Low	High
THC67 Matthew Moses	20.00	40.00

2004 Topps Heritage Chrome Refractors

*REFRACTOR: .6X TO 1.5X CHROME
*REFRACTOR: .75X TO 2X CHROME RC YR
STATED ODDS 1:25
STATED PRINT RUN 555 SERIAL #'d SETS

2004 Topps Heritage Clubhouse Collection Relics

GROUP A ODDS 1:3037
GROUP B ODDS 1:4142
GROUP C ODDS 1:138
GROUP D ODDS 1:92
GROUP A STATED PRINT RUN 100 SETS
GROUP A PRINT RUN PROVIDED BY TOPPS
GROUP A ARE NOT SERIAL-NUMBERED

Card	Low	High
AD Adam Dunn Jsy D	3.00	8.00
AJ Andruw Jones Jsy C	4.00	10.00
AK Al Kaline Bat A	20.00	50.00
AP Albert Pujols Uni C	6.00	15.00
AR Alex Rodriguez Jsy C	4.00	10.00
AS Alfonso Soriano Uni D	3.00	8.00
BA Bobby Abreu Jsy D	3.00	8.00
BB Bret Boone Jsy D	3.00	8.00
BM Brett Myers Jsy D	3.00	8.00
BZ Barry Zito Uni C	3.00	8.00
CJ Chipper Jones Jsy D	4.00	10.00
CS C.C. Sabathia Jsy D	3.00	8.00
DS Duke Snider Bat A	15.00	40.00
EC Eric Chavez Uni D	3.00	8.00
EG Eric Gagne Uni D	3.00	8.00
FM Fred McGriff Bat C	4.00	10.00
GM Greg Maddux Jsy C	6.00	15.00
GS Gary Sheffield Uni D	3.00	8.00
HB Hank Blalock Jsy D	3.00	8.00
HK Harmon Killebrew Jsy C	10.00	25.00
IR Ivan Rodriguez Bat C	4.00	10.00
JD Johnny Damon Uni D	4.00	10.00
JG Jason Giambi Uni D	3.00	8.00
JL Javy Lopez Jsy D	3.00	8.00
JR Jimmy Rollins Jsy D	3.00	8.00
JRE Jose Reyes Jsy D	3.00	8.00
JS John Smoltz Jsy C	4.00	10.00
JT Jim Thome Bat D	4.00	10.00
KB Kevin Brown Uni D	3.00	8.00
KI Kazuhisa Ishii Uni D	3.00	8.00
KW Kerry Wood Jsy D	3.00	8.00
LB Lance Berkman Jsy C	3.00	8.00
LG Luis Gonzalez Jsy D	3.00	8.00
MG Marcus Giles Jsy C	3.00	8.00
MM Mark Mulder Uni D	3.00	8.00
MR Manny Ramirez Jsy C	4.00	10.00
MS Mike Sweeney Jsy D	3.00	8.00
MT Miguel Tejada Uni D	3.00	8.00
MTB Miguel Tejada Bat C	3.00	8.00
MTE Mark Teixeira Jsy D	4.00	10.00
NG Nomar Garciaparra Uni C	6.00	15.00
PL Paul Lo Duca Uni C	3.00	8.00
PM Pedro Martinez Jsy D	4.00	10.00
RB Rocco Baldelli Jsy D	3.00	8.00
RC Roger Clemens Uni D	6.00	15.00
RF Rafael Furcal Jsy D	3.00	8.00
RJ Randy Johnson Jsy C	4.00	10.00
SG Shawn Green Uni C	3.00	8.00
SM Stan Musial Bat A	30.00	60.00
SR Scott Rolen Uni B	4.00	10.00
SRB Scott Rolen Bat C	4.00	10.00
SS Sammy Sosa Jsy C	4.00	10.00
TG Troy Glaus Uni C	3.00	8.00
TH Tim Hudson Uni D	3.00	8.00
THU Torii Hunter Bat C	3.00	8.00
VW Vernon Wells Jsy C	3.00	8.00
WM Willie Mays Uni A	50.00	100.00
YB Yogi Berra Jsy A	20.00	50.00

2004 Topps Heritage Clubhouse Collection Autograph Relics

STATED ODDS 1:15,186
STATED PRINT RUN 25 SERIAL #'d SETS
NO PRICING DUE TO SCARCITY
AK Al Kaline Bat
DS Duke Snider Bat
EB Ernie Banks Uni
WM Willie Mays Uni

2004 Topps Heritage Clubhouse Collection Dual Relics

STATED ODDS 1:9244
STATED PRINT RUN 55 SERIAL #'d SETS

Card	Low	High
BC Yogi Berra Uni	75.00	150.00
Roger Clemens Uni		
GS Shawn Green Jsy	75.00	150.00
Duke Snider Uni		
MP Albert Pujols Jsy	150.00	250.00
Stan Musial Uni		

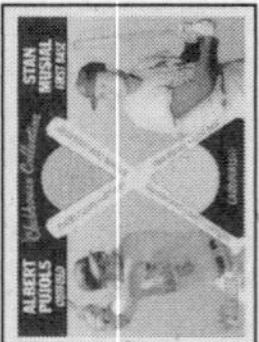

2004 Topps Heritage Doubleheader

ONE PER SEALED HOBBY BOX
VINTAGE D-HEADERS RANDOMLY SEEDED

Card	Low	High
12 Alex Rodriguez	3.00	8.00
Nomar Garciaparra		
34 Ichiro Suzuki	4.00	10.00
Albert Pujols		
56 Sammy Sosa	4.00	10.00
Derek Jeter		
78 Jim Thome	3.00	8.00
Adam Dunn		
910 Jason Giambi	3.00	8.00
Ivan Rodriguez		
1112 Todd Helton	3.00	8.00
Luis Gonzalez		
1314 Jeff Bagwell	3.00	8.00
Lance Berkman		
1516 Alfonso Soriano	3.00	8.00
Dontrelle Willis		
1718 Mark Prior	3.00	8.00
Vladimir Guerrero		
1920 Mike Piazza	4.00	10.00
Roger Clemens		
2122 Randy Johnson	3.00	8.00
Curt Schilling		
2324 Gary Sheffield	3.00	8.00
Pedro Martinez		
2526 Carlos Delgado	2.00	5.00
Jimmy Rollins		
2728 Andruw Jones	3.00	8.00
Chipper Jones		
2930 Rocco Baldelli	2.00	5.00
Hank Blalock		
NNO Vintage Buyback		

2004 Topps Heritage Flashbacks

Card	Low	High
COMPLETE SET (10)	6.00	15.00
STATED ODDS 1:12		
F1 Duke Snider	1.25	3.00
F2 Johnny Podres	.75	2.00
F3 Don Newcombe	.75	2.00
F4 Al Kaline	1.25	3.00
F5 Willie Mays	2.00	5.00
F6 Stan Musial	1.50	4.00
F7 Harmon Killebrew	1.25	3.00
F8 Herb Score	.75	2.00
F9 Whitey Ford	1.25	3.00
F10 Robin Roberts	.75	2.00

2004 Topps Heritage Flashbacks Autographs

STATED ODDS 1:30,373
STATED PRINT RUN 25 SERIAL #'d SETS
NO PRICING DUE TO SCARCITY
AK Al Kaline
NPS Don Newcombe
Johnny Podres
Duke Snider

2004 Topps Heritage Grandstand Glory Stadium Seat Relics

GROUP A ODDS 1:27,731
GROUP A ODDS 1:606
GROUP A STATED PRINT RUN 55 CARDS
GROUP A PRINT RUN PROVIDED BY TOPPS
GROUP A IS NOT SERIAL-NUMBERED

Card	Low	High
AK Al Kaline B	10.00	25.00
HK Harmon Killebrew B	10.00	25.00
SM Stan Musial B	15.00	40.00
WM Willie Mays A	90.00	150.00
WS Warren Spahn B	10.00	25.00
YB Yogi Berra B	10.00	25.00

2004 Topps Heritage New Age Performers

Card	Low	High
COMPLETE SET (15)	12.50	30.00
STATED ODDS 1:15		
NA1 Jason Giambi	.75	2.00
NA2 Ichiro Suzuki	2.00	5.00
NA3 Alex Rodriguez	1.50	4.00
NA4 Alfonso Soriano	.75	2.00
NA5 Albert Pujols	2.00	5.00
NA6 Nomar Garciaparra	1.50	4.00
NA7 Mark Prior	.75	2.00
NA8 Derek Jeter	2.00	5.00
NA9 Sammy Sosa	1.00	2.50
NA10 Carlos Delgado	.75	2.00
NA11 Jim Thome	.75	2.00
NA12 Todd Helton	.75	2.00
NA13 Gary Sheffield	.75	2.00
NA14 Vladimir Guerrero	1.00	2.50
NA15 Josh Beckett	.75	2.00

2004 Topps Heritage Real One Autographs

These autograph cards feature a mix of players who are active today; players who had cards in the 1955 Topps set and Stan Musial signing cards as if he were in the 1955 set. Scott Rolen did not return his cards in time for pack out and those exchange cards could be redeemed until February 28th, 2006.

STATED ODDS 1:230
STATED PRINT RUN 200 SETS
PRINT RUN INFO PROVIDED BY TOPPS
BASIC AUTOS ARE NOT SERIAL-NUMBERED
*RED INK: .75X TO 1.5X RETIRED
*RED INK MAYS: 1.25X TO 2X BASIC MAYS
*RED INK: .75X TO 1.5X ACTIVE
RED INK ODDS 1:835
RED INK PRINT RUN 55 #'d SETS
RED INK ALSO CALLED SPECIAL EDITION

Card	Low	High
AH Aubrey Huff	15.00	40.00
AK Al Kaline	50.00	100.00
BB Bob Borkowski	15.00	40.00
BC Billy Consolo	15.00	40.00
BG Bill Glynn	15.00	40.00
BK Bob Kline	15.00	40.00
BM Bob Milliken	15.00	40.00
BW Bill Wilson	20.00	50.00
CF Cliff Floyd	15.00	40.00
DN Don Newcombe	30.00	60.00
DP Duane Pillette	15.00	40.00
DS Duke Snider	50.00	100.00
DW Dontrelle Willis	15.00	40.00
EB Ernie Banks	70.00	120.00
FS Frank Smith	15.00	40.00
GA Gair Allie	15.00	40.00
HE Harry Elliott	15.00	40.00
HK Harmon Killebrew	50.00	100.00
HP Harry Perkowski	15.00	40.00
HV Corky Valentine	20.00	50.00
JG Johnny Gray	15.00	40.00
JP Jim Pearce	20.00	50.00
JPO Johnny Podres	30.00	60.00
LL Lou Limmer	30.00	60.00
ML Mike Lowell	15.00	40.00
MO Magglio Ordonez	15.00	40.00
SK Steve Kraly	30.00	60.00
SM Stan Musial	60.00	120.00
SR Scott Rolen	15.00	40.00
TK Thornton Kipper	20.00	50.00
TW Tom Wright	15.00	40.00
VT Jake Thies	20.00	50.00
WM Willie Mays	125.00	200.00
YB Yogi Berra	100.00	200.00

2004 Topps Heritage Then and Now

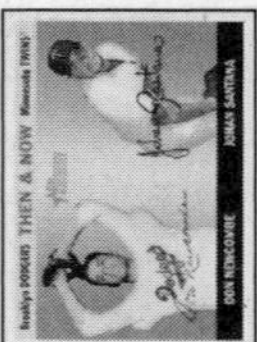

Card	Low	High
COMPLETE SET (6)	4.00	10.00
STATED ODDS 1:15		
TN1 Willie Mays	2.00	5.00
Jim Thome		
TN2 Al Kaline	2.00	5.00
Albert Pujols		
TN3 Duke Snider	1.25	3.00
Carlos Delgado		
TN4 Robin Roberts	.75	2.00
Roy Halladay		
TN5 Don Newcombe	1.25	3.00
Johan Santana		
TN6 Herb Score	.75	2.00
Kerry Wood		

2005 Topps Heritage

This 495-card set was released in February, 2005. This set was issued in eight-card hobby/retail packs with an $3 SRP which came 24 packs to a box and eight boxes to a case. The 2005 version of Heritage honored the 1956 Topps set. Sprinkled throughout the set was a grouping of variation cards and other short printed cards. The Short print cards were issued at a stated rate of one in two hobby/retail packs.

Card	Low	High
COMPLETE SET (495)	250.00	400.00
COMP.SET w/o SP's (385)	30.00	60.00
COMMON CARD	.20	.50
COMMON RC	.20	.50
COMMON TEAM CARD	.20	.50
COMMON SP	3.00	8.00
COMMON SP RC	3.00	8.00

SP STATED ODDS 1:2 HOBBY/RETAIL
BASIC SP: 5/20/30/31/33/79/101/110/130
BASIC SP: 135/260/292/398-475
VARIATION SP: 3/6/7/31/50/69/78/82/118
VARIATION SP: 125/135/155/261/273/286
VARIATION SP: 296/300/312/353/389
SEE BECKETT.COM FOR VAR.DESCRIPTIONS

Card	Low	High
1 Will Harridge	.20	.50
2 Warren Giles	.20	.50
3A Alfonso Soriano Fldg	.20	.50
3B Alfonso Soriano Running SP	3.00	8.00
4 Mark Mulder	.20	.50
5 Todd Helton SP	3.00	8.00
6A Jason Bay Black Cap	.20	.50
6B Jason Bay Yellow Cap SP	3.00	8.00
7A Ichiro Suzuki Running	.60	1.50
7B Ichiro Suzuki Crouch SP	4.00	10.00
8 Jim Tracy MG	.20	.50
9 Gavin Floyd	.20	.50
10 John Smoltz	.30	.75
11 Chicago Cubs TC	.30	.75
12 Darin Erstad	.20	.50
13 Chad Tracy	.20	.50
14 Charles Thomas	.20	.50
15 Miguel Tejada	.20	.50
16 Andre Ethier RC	2.00	5.00
17 Jeff Francis	.20	.50
18 Derrek Lee	.30	.75
19 Juan Uribe	.20	.50
20 Jim Edmonds SP	3.00	8.00
21 Kenny Lofton	.20	.50
22 Brad Ausmus	.20	.50
23 Jon Garland	.20	.50
24 Edwin Jackson	.20	.50
25 Joe Mauer	.40	1.00
26 Wes Helms	.20	.50
27 Brian Schneider	.20	.50
28 Kazuo Matsui	.20	.50
29 Flash Gordon	.20	.50
30 Hideo Nomo SP	3.00	8.00
31A Albert Pujols Red Hat SP	5.00	12.00
31B Albert Pujols Blue Hat SP	5.00	12.00
32 Carl Crawford	.20	.50
33 Vladimir Guerrero SP	3.00	8.00
34 Nick Green	.20	.50
35 Jay Gibbons	.20	.50
36 Kevin Youkilis	.20	.50
37 Billy Wagner	.20	.50
38 Terrence Long	.20	.50
39 Kevin Mench	.20	.50
40 Garret Anderson	.20	.50
41 Reed Johnson	.20	.50
42 Reggie Sanders	.20	.50
43 Kirk Rueter	.20	.50
44 Jay Payton	.20	.50
45 Tike Redman	.20	.50
46 Mike Lieberthal	.20	.50
47 Damian Miller	.20	.50
48 Zach Day	.20	.50
49 Juan Rincon	.20	.50
50A Jim Thome At Bat	.30	.75
50B Jim Thome Fldg SP	3.00	8.00
51 Jose Guillen	.20	.50
52 Richie Sexson	.20	.50
53 Juan Cruz	.20	.50
54 Byung-Hyun Kim	.20	.50
55 Carlos Zambrano	.20	.50
56 Carlos Lee	.20	.50
57 Adam Dunn	.20	.50
58 David Riske	.20	.50
59 Carlos Guillen	.20	.50
60 Larry Bowa MG	.20	.50
61 Barry Bonds	3.00	8.00
62 Chris Woodward	.20	.50
63 Matt DeSalvo RC	.30	.75
64 Brian Stavisky RC	.20	.50
65 Scot Shields	.20	.50
66 J.D. Drew	.20	.50
67 Erik Bedard	.20	.50

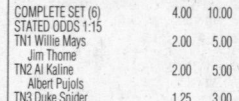

68 Scott Williamson .20 .50
69A M.Prior New C on Cap .30 .75
69B M.Prior Old C on Cap SP 3.00 8.00
70 Ken Griffey Jr. .60 1.50
71 Kazuhito Tadano .20 .50
72 Philadelphia Phillies TC .20 .50
73 Jeremy Reed .20 .50
74 Ricardo Rodriguez .20 .50
75 Carlos Delgado .20 .50
76 Eric Milton .20 .50
77 Miguel Olivo .20 .50
78A E.Alfonzo No Socks .20 .50
78B E.Alfonzo Black Socks SP 3.00 8.00
79 Kazuhisa Ishii SP 3.00 8.00
80 Jason Giambi .20 .50
81 Cliff Floyd .20 .50
Facsimile autograph is Jeff Abbott
82A Torii Hunter Twins Cap .20 .50
82B Torii Hunter Wash Cap SP 3.00 8.00
83 Odalis Perez .20 .50
84 Scott Podsednik .20 .50
85 Cleveland Indians TC .20 .50
86 Jeff Suppan .20 .50
87 Ray Durham .20 .50
88 Tyler Clippard RC 8.00 20.00
89 Ryan Howard 1.00 2.50
90 Cincinnati Reds TC .20 .50
91 Bengie Molina .20 .50
92 Danny Bautista .20 .50
93 Eli Marrero .20 .50
94 Larry Bigbie .20 .50
95 Atlanta Braves TC .20 .50
96 Merkin Valdez .20 .50
97 Rocco Baldelli .20 .50
98 Woody Williams .20 .50
99 Jason Frasor .20 .50
100 Baltimore Orioles TC .20 .50
101 Ivan Rodriguez SP 3.00 8.00
102 Joe Kennedy .20 .50
103 Mike Lowell .20 .50
104 Armando Benitez .20 .50
105 Craig Biggio .30 .75
106 David DeJesus .20 .50
107 Adrian Beltre .20 .50
108 Phil Nevin .20 .50
109 Cristian Guzman .20 .50
110 Jorge Posada SP 3.00 8.00
111 Boston Red Sox TC .40 1.00
112 Jeff Mathis .20 .50
113 Bartolo Colon .20 .50
114 Alex Cintron .20 .50
115 Russ Ortiz .20 .50
116 Doug Mientkiewicz .20 .50
117 Placido Polanco .20 .50
118A M.Ordonez Black Uni .20 .50
118B M.Ordonez White Uni SP 3.00 8.00
119 Chris Seddon RC .20 .50
120 Bobby Abreu .20 .50
121 Pittsburgh Pirates TC .20 .50
122 Dallas McPherson .20 .50
123 Rodrigo Lopez .20 .50
124 Mark Bellhorn .20 .50
125A N.Garciaparra Red Cap .40 1.00
125B N.Garciaparra Blue Cap SP 3.00 8.00
126 Sean Casey .20 .50
127 Ronnie Belliard .20 .50
128 Tom Goodwin .20 .50
129 Preston Wilson .20 .50
130 Andruw Jones SP 3.00 8.00
131 Roberto Alomar .30 .75
132 John Buck .20 .50
133 Jason LaRue .20 .50
134 St. Louis Cardinals TC .30 .75
135A Alex Rodriguez Fldg SP 4.00 10.00
135B Alex Rodriguez At Bat SP 4.00 10.00
136 Nate Robertson .20 .50
137 Juan Pierre .20 .50
138 Morgan Ensberg .20 .50
139 Vinny Castilla .20 .50
140 Jake Dittler .20 .50
141 Chan Ho Park .20 .50
142 Felix Hernandez 1.25 3.00
143 Jason Isringhausen .20 .50
144 Dustan Mohr .20 .50
145 Khalil Greene .30 .75
146 Minnesota Twins TC .20 .50
147 Vicente Padilla .20 .50
148 Oliver Perez .20 .50
149 Brian Giles .20 .50
150 Shawn Green .20 .50
151 Matt Lawton .20 .50
152 Casey Blake .20 .50
153 Frank Thomas .40 1.00
154 Orlando Hernandez .20 .50
155A Eric Chavez Green Cap .20 .50
155B Eric Chavez Blue Cap SP 3.00 8.00
156 Chase Utley .30 .75
157 John Olerud .20 .50
158 Adam Eaton .20 .50
159 Josh Fogg .20 .50
160 Michael Tucker .20 .50
161 Kevin Brown .20 .50
162 Bobby Crosby .20 .50
163 Jason Schmidt .20 .50
164 Shannon Stewart .20 .50
165 Tony Womack .20 .50
166 Los Angeles Dodgers TC .30 .75
167 Franklin Gutierrez .20 .50
168 Ted Lilly .20 .50
169 Mark Teixeira .30 .75
170 Matt Morris .20 .50
171 Bucky Jacobsen .20 .50
172 Steve Doetsch RC .30 .75
173 Jeff Weaver .20 .50
174 Tony Graffanino .20 .50
175 Jeff Bagwell .30 .75
176 Carl Pavano .20 .50
177 Junior Spivey .20 .50
178 Carlos Silva .20 .50
179 Tim Redding .20 .50
180 Brett Myers .20 .50
181 Mike Mussina .30 .75
182 Richard Hidalgo .20 .50
183 Nick Johnson .20 .50
184 Lew Ford .20 .50
185 Barry Zito .20 .50
186 Jimmy Rollins .20 .50
187 Jack Wilson .20 .50
188 Chicago White Sox TC .20 .50
189 Guillermo Quiroz .20 .50
190 Mark Hendrickson .20 .50
191 Jeremy Bonderman .20 .50
192 Jason Jennings .20 .50
193 Paul Lo Duca .20 .50
194 A.J. Burnett .20 .50
195 Ken Harvey .20 .50
196 Geoff Jenkins .20 .50
197 Joe Mays .20 .50
198 Jose Vidro .20 .50
199 David Wright .75 2.00
200 Randy Johnson .40 1.00
201 Jeff DaVanon .20 .50
202 Paul Byrd .20 .50
203 David Ortiz .40 1.00
204 Kyle Farnsworth .20 .50
205 Keith Foulke .20 .50
206 Joe Crede .20 .50
207 Austin Kearns .20 .50
208 Jody Gerut .20 .50
209 Shawn Chacon .20 .50
210 Carlos Pena .20 .50
211 Luis Castillo .20 .50
212 Chris Denorfia RC .40 1.00
213 Detroit Tigers TC .20 .50
214 Aubrey Huff .20 .50
215 Brad Fullmer .20 .50
216 Frank Catalanotto .20 .50
217 Raul Ibanez .20 .50
218 Ryan Klesko .20 .50
219 Octavio Dotel .20 .50
220 Rob Mackowiak .20 .50
221 Scott Hatteberg .20 .50
222 Pat Burrell .20 .50
223 Bernie Williams .30 .75
224 Kris Benson .20 .50
225 Eric Gagne .20 .50
226 San Francisco Giants TC .30 .75
227 Roy Oswalt .20 .50
228 Josh Beckett .20 .50
229 Lee Mazzilli MG .20 .50
230 Rickie Weeks .20 .50
231 Troy Glaus .20 .50
232 Chone Figgins .20 .50
233 John Thomson .20 .50
234 Trot Nixon .20 .50
235 Brad Penny .20 .50
236 Oakland A's TC .20 .50
237 Miguel Batista .20 .50
238 Ryan Drese .20 .50
239 Aaron Miles .20 .50
240 Randy Wolf .20 .50
241 Brian Lawrence .20 .50
242 A.J. Pierzynski .20 .50
243 Jamie Moyer .20 .50
244 Chris Carpenter .20 .50
245 So Taguchi .20 .50
246 Rob Bell .20 .50
247 Francisco Cordero .20 .50
248 Tom Glavine .30 .75
249 Jermaine Dye .20 .50
250 Cliff Lee .20 .50
251 New York Yankees TC .40 1.00
252 Vernon Wells .20 .50
253 R.A. Dickey .20 .50
254 Larry Walker .30 .75
255 Randy Winn .20 .50
256 Pedro Feliz .20 .50
257 Mark Loretta .20 .50
258 Tim Worrell .20 .50
259 Kip Wells .20 .50
260 Cesar Izturis SP 3.00 8.00
261A Carlos Beltran Fldg .20 .50
261B Carlos Beltran At Bat SP 3.00 8.00
262 Juan Encarnacion .20 .50
263 Luis A. Gonzalez .20 .50
Facsimile autograph is of other Luis Gonzalez
264 Grady Sizemore .30 .75
265 Paul Wilson .20 .50
266 Mark Buehrle .20 .50
267 Todd Hollandsworth .20 .50
268 Orlando Cabrera .20 .50
269 Sidney Ponson .20 .50
270 Mike Hampton .20 .50
271 Luis Gonzalez .20 .50
Facsimile autographs is of other Luis Gonzalez
272 Brendan Donnelly .20 .50
273A Chipper Jones Slide .40 1.00
273B Chipper Jones Fldg SP 3.00 8.00
274 Brandon Webb .20 .50
275 Marty Cordova .20 .50
276 Greg Maddux .60 1.50
277 Jose Contreras .20 .50
278 Aaron Harang .20 .50
279 Coco Crisp .20 .50
280 Bobby Higginson .20 .50
281 Guillermo Mota .20 .50
282 Andy Pettitte .30 .75
283 Jeremy West RC .30 .75
284 Craig Brazell .20 .50
285 Eric Hinske .20 .50
286A Hank Blalock Hitting .20 .50
286B Hank Blalock Fldg SP 3.00 8.00
287 B.J. Upton .30 .75
288 Jason Marquis .20 .50
289 Matt Herges .20 .50
290 Ramon Hernandez .20 .50
291 Marlon Byrd .20 .50
292 Ryan Sweeney SP RC 3.00 8.00
293 Esteban Loaiza .20 .50
294 Al Leiter .20 .50
295 Alex Gonzalez .20 .50
296A J.Santana Twins Cap .40 1.00
296B J.Santana Wash Cap SP 3.00 8.00
297 Milton Bradley .20 .50
298 Mike Sweeney .20 .50
299 Wade Miller .20 .50
300A Sammy Sosa Hitting .40 1.00
300B Sammy Sosa Standing SP 3.00 8.00
301 Wily Mo Pena .20 .50
302 Tim Wakefield .20 .50
303 Rafael Palmeiro .30 .75
304 Rafael Furcal .20 .50
305 David Eckstein .20 .50
306 David Segui .20 .50
307 Kevin Millar .20 .50
308 Matt Clement .20 .50
309 Wade Robinson RC .20 .50
310 Brad Radke .20 .50
311 Steve Finley .20 .50
312A Lance Berkman Hitting .20 .50
312B Lance Berkman Fldg SP 3.00 8.00
313 Joe Randa .20 .50
314 Miguel Cabrera .30 .75
315 Billy Koch .20 .50
316 Alex Sanchez .20 .50
317 Chin-Hui Tsao .20 .50
318 Omar Vizquel .30 .75
319 Ryan Freel .20 .50
320 LaTroy Hawkins .20 .50
321 Aaron Rowand .20 .50
322 Paul Konerko .20 .50
323 Joe Borowski .20 .50
324 Jarrod Washburn .20 .50
325 Jaret Wright .20 .50
326 Johnny Damon .30 .75
327 Corey Patterson .20 .50
328 Travis Hafner .20 .50
329 Shingo Takatsu .20 .50
330 Dmitri Young .20 .50
331 Matt Holliday .25 .60
332 Jeff Kent .20 .50
333 Desi Relaford .20 .50
334 Jose Hernandez .20 .50
335 Lyle Overbay .20 .50
336 Jacque Jones .20 .50
337 Terrmel Sledge .20 .50
338 Victor Zambrano .20 .50
339 Gary Sheffield .20 .50
340 Brad Wilkerson .20 .50
341 Ian Kinsler RC 1.25 3.00
342 Jesse Crain .20 .50
343 Orlando Hudson .20 .50
344 Laynce Nix .20 .50
345 Jose Cruz Jr. .20 .50
346 Edgar Renteria .20 .50
347 Eddie Guardado .20 .50
348 Jerome Williams .20 .50
349 Trevor Hoffman .20 .50
350 Mike Piazza .40 1.00
351 Jason Kendall .20 .50
352 Kevin Millwood .20 .50
353A Tim Hudson Atl Cap .20 .50
353B Tim Hudson Milw Cap SP 3.00 8.00
354 Paul Quantrill .20 .50
355 Jon Lieber .20 .50
356 Braden Looper .20 .50
357 Chad Cordero .20 .50
358 Joe Nathan .20 .50
359 Doug Davis .20 .50
360 Ian Bladergroen RC .30 .75
361 Val Majewski .20 .50
362 Francisco Rodriguez .20 .50
363 Kelvim Escobar .20 .50
364 Marcus Giles .20 .50
365 Darren Fenster RC .20 .50
366 David Bell .20 .50
367 Shea Hillenbrand .20 .50
368 Manny Ramirez .30 .75
369 Ben Broussard .20 .50
370 Luis Ramirez RC .30 .75
371 Dustin Hermanson .20 .50
372 Akinori Otsuka .20 .50
373 Chadd Blasko RC .30 .75
374 Michael Young .20 .50
375 Michael Young .20 .50
376 Bret Boone .20 .50
377 Jake Peavy .20 .50
378 Matthew Lindstrom RC .20 .50
379 Sean Burroughs .20 .50
380 Rich Harden .20 .50
381 Chris Roberson RC .20 .50
382 John Lackey .20 .50
383 Johnny Estrada .20 .50
384 Matt Rogelstad RC .20 .50
385 Toby Hall .20 .50
386 Adam LaRoche .20 .50
387 Bill Hall .20 .50
388 Tim Salmon .20 .50
389A Curt Schilling Throw .30 .75
389B Curt Schilling Glove Up SP 3.00 8.00
390 Michael Barrett .20 .50
391 Jose Acevedo .20 .50
392 Nate Schierholtz .30 .75
393 J.T. Snow Jr. .20 .50
394 Mark Redman .20 .50
395 Ryan Madson .20 .50
396 Kevin West RC .20 .50
397 Ramon Ortiz .20 .50
398 Derek Lowe SP 3.00 8.00
399 Kerry Wood SP 3.00 8.00
400 Derek Jeter SP 5.00 12.00
401 Livan Hernandez SP 3.00 8.00
402 Casey Kotchman SP 3.00 8.00
403 Chaz Lytle SP RC 3.00 8.00
404 Alexis Rios SP 3.00 8.00
405 Scott Spiezio SP 3.00 8.00
406 Craig Wilson SP 3.00 8.00
407 Felix Rodriguez SP 3.00 8.00
408 D'Angelo Jimenez SP 3.00 8.00
409 Rondell White SP 3.00 8.00
410 Shawn Estes SP 3.00 8.00
411 Troy Percival SP 3.00 8.00
412 Melvin Mora SP 3.00 8.00
413 Aramis Ramirez SP 3.00 8.00
414 Carl Everett SP 3.00 8.00
415 Elvys Quezada SP RC 3.00 8.00
416 Ben Sheets SP 3.00 8.00
417 Matt Stairs SP 3.00 8.00
418 Adam Everett SP 3.00 8.00
419 Jason Johnson SP 3.00 8.00
420 Billy Butler SP RC 4.00 10.00
421 Justin Morneau SP 3.00 8.00
422 Jose Reyes SP 3.00 8.00
423 Mariano Rivera SP 3.00 8.00
424 Jose Vaquedano SP RC 3.00 8.00
425 Gabe Gross SP 3.00 8.00
426 Scott Rolen SP 3.00 8.00
427 Ty Wigginton SP 3.00 8.00
428 James Jurries SP RC 3.00 8.00
429 Pedro Martinez SP 3.00 8.00
430 Mark Grudzielanek SP 3.00 8.00
431 Josh Phelps SP 3.00 8.00
432 Ryan Goleski SP RC 3.00 8.00
433 Mike Matheny SP 3.00 8.00
434 Bobby Kielty SP 3.00 8.00
435 Tony Batista SP 3.00 8.00
436 Corey Koskie SP 3.00 8.00
437 Brad Lidge SP 3.00 8.00
438 Dontrelle Willis SP 3.00 8.00
439 Angel Berroa SP 3.00 8.00
440 Jason Kubel SP 3.00 8.00
441 Roy Halladay SP 3.00 8.00
442 Brian Roberts SP 3.00 8.00
443 Bill Mueller SP 3.00 8.00
444 Adam Kennedy SP 3.00 8.00
445 Brandon Moss SP RC 3.00 8.00
446 Sean Burnett SP 3.00 8.00
447 Eric Byrnes SP 3.00 8.00
448 Matt Campbell SP RC 3.00 8.00
449 Ryan Webb SP 3.00 8.00
450 Jose Valentin SP 3.00 8.00
451 Jake Westbrook SP 3.00 8.00
452 Glen Perkins SP RC 3.00 8.00
453 Alex Gonzalez SP 3.00 8.00
454 Jeromy Burnitz SP 3.00 8.00
455 Zack Greinke SP 3.00 8.00
456 Sean Marshall SP RC 2.50 6.00
457 Erubiel Durazo SP 3.00 8.00
458 Michael Cuddyer SP 3.00 8.00
459 Hee Seop Choi SP 3.00 8.00
460 Melky Cabrera SP RC 4.00 10.00
461 Jerry Hairston Jr. SP 3.00 8.00
462 Moises Alou SP 3.00 8.00
463 Michael Rogers SP RC 3.00 8.00
464 Javy Lopez SP 3.00 8.00
465 Freddy Garcia SP 3.00 8.00
466 Brett Harper SP RC 3.00 8.00
467 Juan Gonzalez SP 3.00 8.00
468 Kevin Melillo SP RC 3.00 8.00
469 Todd Walker SP 3.00 8.00
470 C.C. Sabathia SP 3.00 8.00
471 Kole Strayhorn SP RC 3.00 8.00
472 Mark Kotsay SP 3.00 8.00
473 Javier Vazquez SP 3.00 8.00
474 Mike Cameron SP 3.00 8.00
475 Wes Swackhamer SP RC 3.00 8.00

2005 Topps Heritage White Backs

COMPLETE SET (220) 75.00 150.00
*WHITE BACKS: .75X TO 2X BASIC
RANDOM INSERTS IN PACKS
SEE BECKETT.COM FOR FULL CHECKLIST
61 Barry Bonds 4.00 10.00

2005 Topps Heritage Chrome

COMPLETE SET (110)
STATED ODDS 1:7 HOBBY/RETAIL
STATED PRINT RUN 1956 SERIAL #'d SETS
1 Will Harridge 1.50 4.00
THC2 Warren Giles 1.50 4.00
THC3 Alex Rodriguez 4.00 10.00
THC4 Alfonso Soriano 1.50 4.00
THC5 Barry Bonds 6.00 15.00
THC6 Todd Helton 2.00 5.00
THC7 Kazuo Matsui 1.50 4.00
THC8 Garret Anderson 1.50 4.00
THC9 Mark Prior 2.00 5.00
THC10 Jim Thome 2.00 5.00
THC11 Jason Giambi 1.50 4.00
THC12 Ivan Rodriguez 2.00 5.00
THC13 Mike Lowell 1.50 4.00
THC14 Vladimir Guerrero 2.50 6.00
THC15 Adrian Beltre 1.50 4.00
16 Andruw Jones 2.00 5.00
THC17 Jose Vidro 1.50 4.00
THC18 Josh Beckett 1.50 4.00
THC19 Mike Sweeney 1.50 4.00
THC20 Sammy Sosa 2.50 6.00
THC21 Scott Rolen 2.00 5.00
THC22 Javy Lopez 1.50 4.00
THC23 Albert Pujols 5.00 12.00
THC24 Adam Dunn 1.50 4.00
THC25 Ken Griffey Jr. 4.00 10.00
THC26 Torii Hunter 1.50 4.00
THC27 Jorge Posada 2.00 5.00
THC28 Magglio Ordonez 1.50 4.00
THC29 Shawn Green 1.50 4.00
THC30 Frank Thomas 2.50 6.00
THC31 Barry Zito 1.50 4.00
THC32 David Ortiz 2.50 6.00
THC33 Pat Burrell 1.50 4.00
THC34 Luis Gonzalez 1.50 4.00
THC35 Chipper Jones 2.50 6.00
THC36 Hank Blalock 1.50 4.00
THC37 Rafael Palmeiro 2.00 5.00
THC38 Lance Berkman 1.50 4.00
THC39 Miguel Cabrera 2.00 5.00
THC40 Paul Konerko 1.50 4.00
THC41 Jeff Kent 1.50 4.00
THC42 Gary Sheffield 1.50 4.00
THC43 Mike Piazza 2.50 6.00
THC44 Bret Boone 1.50 4.00
THC45 Kerry Wood 1.50 4.00
THC46 Derek Jeter 6.00 15.00
THC47 Pedro Martinez 2.00 5.00
THC48 Jason Bay 1.50 4.00
THC49 Ichiro Suzuki 4.00 10.00
THC50 Miguel Tejada 1.50 4.00
THC51 Richie Sexson 1.50 4.00
THC52 Jeff Bagwell 2.00 5.00
THC53 Lew Ford 1.50 4.00
THC54 Randy Johnson 2.50 6.00
THC55 Carlos Beltran 1.50 4.00
THC56 Greg Maddux 4.00 10.00
THC57 Lyle Overbay 1.50 4.00
THC58 Michael Young 1.50 4.00
THC59 Curt Schilling 2.00 5.00
THC60 Jose Reyes 1.50 4.00
THC61 Dontrelle Willis 1.50 4.00
THC62 Nomar Garciaparra 2.50 6.00
THC63 Paul Lo Duca 1.50 4.00
THC64 Larry Walker 2.00 5.00
THC65 Andre Ethier 6.00 15.00
THC66 Matt DeSalvo 2.00 5.00
THC67 Brian Stavisky 1.50 4.00
THC68 Tyler Clippard 12.50 30.00
THC69 Chris Seddon 1.50 4.00
THC70 Steve Doetsch 2.00 5.00
THC71 Chris Denorfia 2.00 5.00
THC72 Jeremy West 2.00 5.00
THC73 Ryan Sweeney 2.00 5.00
THC74 Ian Kinsler 4.00 10.00
THC75 Ian Bladergroen 2.00 5.00
THC76 Darren Fenster 1.50 4.00
THC77 Luis Ramirez 1.50 4.00
THC78 Chadd Blasko 2.00 5.00
THC79 Matthew Lindstrom 1.50 4.00
THC80 Chris Roberson 1.50 4.00
THC81 Matt Rogelstad 1.50 4.00
THC82 Nate Schierholtz 2.00 5.00
THC83 Kevin West 1.50 4.00
THC84 Chaz Lytle 2.00 5.00
THC85 Elvys Quezada 1.50 4.00
THC86 Billy Butler 4.00 10.00
THC87 Jose Vaquedano 1.50 4.00
THC88 James Jurries 2.00 5.00
THC89 Ryan Goleski 2.00 5.00
THC90 Brandon Moss 3.00 8.00
THC91 Matt Campbell 1.50 4.00
THC92 Ryan Webb 1.50 4.00
THC93 Glen Perkins 2.00 5.00
THC94 Sean Marshall 2.50 6.00
THC95 Melky Cabrera 3.00 8.00
THC96 Michael Rogers 1.50 4.00
THC97 Brett Harper 2.00 5.00
THC98 Kevin Melillo 2.00 5.00
THC99 Kole Strayhorn 1.50 4.00
THC100 Wes Swackhamer 1.50 4.00
THC101 Rickie Weeks 1.50 4.00
THC102 Delmon Young 2.00 5.00
THC103 Kazuhito Tadano 1.50 4.00
THC104 Kazuhisa Ishii 1.50 4.00
THC105 David Wright 3.00 8.00
THC106 Eric Gagne 1.50 4.00
THC107 So Taguchi 1.50 4.00
THC108 B.J. Upton 2.00 5.00
THC109 Shingo Takatsu 1.50 4.00
THC110 Akinori Otsuka 1.50 4.00

2005 Topps Heritage Chrome Black Refractors

*BLACK REF: 4X TO 8X CHROME
*BLACK REF: 4X TO 8X CHROME RC YR
STATED ODDS 1:250 HOBBY/RETAIL
STATED PRINT RUN 56 SERIAL #'d SETS
THC3 Alex Rodriguez 50.00 100.00
THC5 Barry Bonds 125.00 200.00
THC23 Albert Pujols 90.00 150.00
THC46 Derek Jeter 90.00 150.00
THC65 Andre Ethier 50.00 100.00
THC68 Tyler Clippard 60.00 120.00

2005 Topps Heritage Chrome Refractors

*REFRACTOR: .6X TO 1.5X CHROME
*REFRACTOR: .6X TO 1.5X CHROME RC YR
STATED ODDS 1:25 HOBBY/RETAIL
STATED PRINT RUN 556 SERIAL #'d SETS
THC68 Tyler Clippard 30.00 60.00

2005 Topps Heritage 1956 Cuts

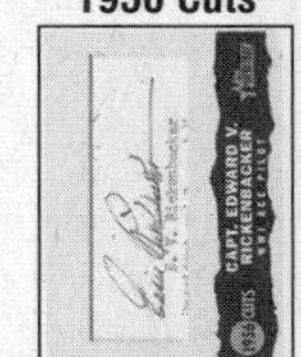

STATED ODDS 1:92,490 HOBBY
STATED PRINT RUN 1 SERIAL #'d SET
NO PRICING DUE TO SCARCITY
DE Dwight Eisenhower
ER Eleanor Roosevelt
EW Earl Warren
JH J. Edgar Hoover
RN Richard Nixon
ERI Capt. Edward V. Rickenbacker
JSA Jonas Salk

2005 Topps Heritage Clubhouse Collection Relics

GROUP A ODDS 1:291 H, 1:292 R
GROUP B ODDS 1:384 H, 1:387 R
GROUP C ODDS 1:1303 H, 1:1307 R
GROUP D ODDS 1:497 H, 1:499 R
GROUP E ODDS 1:384 H, 1:387 R
AK Al Kaline Bat A 8.00 20.00

AP Albert Pujols Bat B 8.00 20.00
AR Alex Rodriguez Bat D 6.00 15.00
AS Alfonso Soriano Bat C 3.00 8.00
BW Bernie Williams Bat A 4.00 10.00
DW Dontrelle Willis Jsy E 3.00 8.00
EB Ernie Banks Bat A 8.00 20.00
GS Gary Sheffield Bat B 3.00 8.00
HK Harmon Killebrew Bat A 8.00 20.00
LA Luis Aparicio Bat A 4.00 10.00
LB Lance Berkman Bat D 3.00 8.00
MC Miguel Cabrera Bat A 4.00 10.00
MR Manny Ramirez Jsy E 4.00 10.00
MT Miguel Tejada Bat B 3.00 8.00
RS Red Schoendienst Bat B 4.00 10.00

2005 Topps Heritage Clubhouse Collection Autograph Relics

STATED ODDS 1:12,216 H, 1:13,728 R
STATED PRINT RUN 25 SERIAL #'d SETS
NO PRICING DUE TO SCARCITY
AK Al Kaline Bat
EB Ernie Banks Bat
HK Harmon Killebrew Bat
LA Luis Aparicio Bat
RS Red Schoendienst Bat

2005 Topps Heritage Clubhouse Collection Dual Relics

STATED ODDS 1:9249 H, 1:9490 R
STATED PRINT RUN 56 SERIAL #'d SETS
BG Ernie Banks Bat 75.00 150.00
Nomar Garciaparra Bat
KR Al Kaline Bat 75.00 150.00
Ivan Rodriguez Bat
MP Stan Musial Jsy 125.00 200.00
Albert Pujols Jsy

2005 Topps Heritage Flashbacks

COMPLETE SET (10) 6.00 15.00
STATED ODDS 1:12 HOBBY/RETAIL
AK Al Kaline 1.25 3.00
BF Bob Feller 1.25 3.00
DL Don Larsen 1.25 3.00
DS Duke Snider 1.25 3.00
EB Ernie Banks 1.25 3.00
FR Frank Robinson .75 2.00
HA Hank Aaron 2.00 5.00
HS Herb Score .75 2.00
LA Luis Aparicio .75 2.00
SM Stan Musial 1.50 4.00

2005 Topps Heritage Flashbacks Autographs

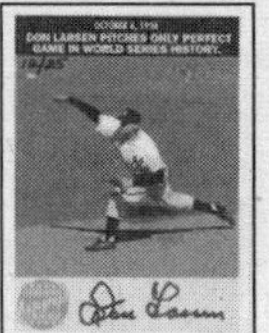

STATED ODDS 1:6166 H, 1:6864 R
STATED PRINT RUN 25 SERIAL #'d SETS
NO PRICING DUE TO SCARCITY

2005 Topps Heritage Flashbacks Seat Relics

STATED ODDS 1:96 HOBBY/RETAIL
AK Al Kaline 6.00 15.00
BF Bob Feller 6.00 15.00
DL Don Larsen 6.00 15.00
DS Duke Snider 6.00 15.00
EB Ernie Banks 6.00 15.00
FR Frank Robinson 4.00 10.00
HA Hank Aaron 8.00 20.00
HS Herb Score 4.00 10.00
LA Luis Aparicio 4.00 10.00
SM Stan Musial 8.00 20.00

2005 Topps Heritage Flashbacks Autograph Seat Relics

STATED ODDS 1:6166 H, 1:6864 R
STATED PRINT RUN 25 SERIAL #'d SETS
NO PRICING DUE TO SCARCITY

2005 Topps Heritage New Age Performers

COMPLETE SET (15) 12.50 30.00
STATED ODDS 1:15 HOBBY/RETAIL
1 Alfonso Soriano .75 2.00
2 Alex Rodriguez 1.50 4.00
3 Ichiro Suzuki 1.50 4.00
4 Albert Pujols 2.00 5.00
5 Vladimir Guerrero 1.00 2.50
6 Jim Thome .75 2.00
7 Derek Jeter 2.00 5.00
8 Sammy Sosa 1.00 2.50
9 Ivan Rodriguez .75 2.00
10 Manny Ramirez .75 2.00
11 Todd Helton .75 2.00
12 David Ortiz .75 2.00
13 Gary Sheffield .75 2.00
14 Nomar Garciaparra 1.00 2.50
15 Randy Johnson 1.00 2.50

2005 Topps Heritage Real One Autographs

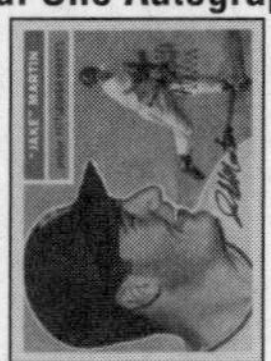

STATED ODDS 1:333 H, 1:332 R
STATED PRINT RUN 200 SETS
PRINT RUN INFO PROVIDED BY TOPPS
BASIC AUTOS ARE NOT SERIAL-NUMBERED
*RED INK: .75X TO 1.5X BASIC
RED INK ODDS 1:1195 H, 1:1196 R
RED INK PRINT RUN 56 SERIAL #'d SETS
RED INK ALSO CALLED SPECIAL EDITION
AS Art Swanson 20.00 50.00
BF Bob Feller 40.00 80.00
BN Bob Nelson 20.00 50.00
BT Bill Tremel 20.00 50.00
CD Chuck Diering 20.00 50.00
DS Duke Snider 50.00 100.00
EB Ernie Banks 60.00 120.00
FM Fred Marsh 20.00 50.00
HA Hank Aaron 150.00 250.00
JA Joe Astroth 20.00 50.00
JB Jim Brady 20.00 50.00
JG Jim Greengrass 20.00 50.00
JM Jake Martin 20.00 50.00
JS Johnny Schmitz 20.00 50.00
JSA Jose Santiago 20.00 50.00
LP Laurin Pepper 20.00 50.00
LPO Leroy Powell 20.00 50.00
MI Monte Irvin 30.00 60.00
PM Paul Minner 20.00 50.00
RM Rudy Minarcin 20.00 50.00
SJ Spook Jacobs 20.00 50.00
WW Wally Westlake 20.00 50.00
YB Yogi Berra 60.00 120.00

2005 Topps Heritage Then and Now

COMPLETE SET (10) 8.00 20.00
STATED ODDS 1:15 HOBBY/RETAIL
TN1 Hank Aaron 2.00 5.00
Ichiro Suzuki
TN2 Don Newcombe 1.25 3.00
Curt Schilling
TN3 Robin Roberts .75 2.00
Livan Hernandez
TN4 Bob Friend .75 2.00
Livan Hernandez
TN5 Herb Score 1.25 3.00
Randy Johnson
TN6 Whitey Ford 1.25 3.00
Jake Peavy
TN7 Jimmy Piersall .75 2.00
Lyle Overbay
TN8 Clem Labine 1.25 3.00
Mariano Rivera
TN9 Billy Bruton .75 2.00
Carl Crawford
TN10 Ed Yost .75 2.00
Bob Abreu

2006 Topps Heritage

This 494-card set was released in February, 2006. This set, using the same design as the 1957 Topps baseball set, was issued in eight-card hobby and retail packs, both with an $3 SRP which came 24 packs to a box and eight boxes to a case. Card number 297, which was intended to be Alex Gordon had to be pulled from production as there was no approval to print that card as he had yet to particpate in a major league game. In addition, cards numbered 265-352, with the curious exception of card #329 were short printed similar to the original 1957 Topps set in which those cards were issued in shorter quantities than the rest of the 57 set. A few variation and short prints were scattered around the rest of the set.

COMPLETE SET (494) 250.00 400.00
COMP.SET w/o SP's (384) 30.00 60.00
SP STATED ODDS 1:2 HOBBY/RETAIL
SP CL: 1/2/10/18/20B/23B/25/35/55
SP CL: 70/76/80B/91/95A/95B/99/106
SP CL: 123/127/165B/200B/212B/265-269
SP CL: 271-274/276-316/318-323/325A
SP CL: 325B/326-328/330-349/350A/350B
SP CL: 351-352/400/407/475B
VARIATION CL: 20/23/80/95/165/200
VARIATION CL: 212/325/350/475
TWO VERSIONS OF EACH VARIATION EXIST
SEE BECKETT.COM FOR VAR.DESCRIPTIONS
CARD 255 NOT INTENDED FOR RELEASE
COMP.SET EXCLUDES CARD 255 CUT OUT
1 David Ortiz SP 3.00 8.00
2 Mike Piazza SP 4.00 10.00
3 Daryle Ward .20 .50
4 Rafael Furcal .20 .50
5 Derek Lowe .20 .50
6 Eric Chavez .20 .50
7 Juan Uribe .20 .50
8 C.C. Sabathia .20 .50
9 Sean Casey .20 .50
10 Barry Bonds SP 5.00 12.00
11 Gary Sheffield .20 .50
12 Ted Lilly .20 .50
13 Lew Ford .20 .50
14 Tom Gordon .20 .50
15 Curt Schilling .40 1.00
16 Jason Kendall .20 .50
17 Frank Catalanotto .20 .50
18 Pedro Martinez SP 3.00 8.00
19 David Dellucci .20 .50
20A A.Jones w/o Seats .40 1.00
20B A.Jones w/Seats SP 3.00 8.00
21 Brad Halsey .20 .50
22 Vernon Wells .20 .50
23A D.Jeter Yellow/White Ltr 1.50 4.00
23B D.Jeter Blue Ltr SP 5.00 12.00
24 Todd Helton .40 1.00
25 Randy Johnson SP 4.00 10.00
26 Jay Gibbons .20 .50
27 Joe Mays .20 .50
28 Paul Konerko .20 .50
29 Lyle Overbay .20 .50
30 Jorge Posada .40 1.00
31 Brandon Webb .20 .50
32 Marcus Giles .20 .50
33 J.T. Snow .20 .50
34 Todd Walker .20 .50
35 Wily Mo Pena SP 3.00 8.00
36 Carlos Delgado .20 .50
37 David Wright .60 1.50
38 Shea Hillenbrand .20 .50
39 Daniel Cabrera .20 .50
40 Trevor Hoffman .20 .50
41 Matt Morris .20 .50
42 Mariano Rivera .60 1.50
43 Jeff Bagwell .40 1.00
44 J.D. Drew .20 .50
45 Carl Pavano .20 .50
46 Placido Polanco .20 .50
47 Adrian Beltre .20 .50
48 J.D. Closser .20 .50
49 Paul Lo Duca .20 .50
50 Scott Rolen .20 .50
51 Bernie Williams .40 1.00
52 Jose Guillen .20 .50
53 Aubrey Huff .20 .50
54 Greg Maddux 1.00 2.50
55 Derrek Lee SP 3.00 8.00
56 Hideki Matsui .60 1.50
57 Jose Bautista .20 .50
58 Kyle Farnsworth .20 .50
59 Nate Robertson .20 .50
60 Sammy Sosa .60 1.50
61 Javier Vazquez .20 .50
62 Jeff Mathis .20 .50
63 Mark Buehrle .20 .50
64 Orlando Hernandez .20 .50
65 Brandon Claussen .20 .50
66 Miguel Batista .20 .50
67 Eddie Guardado .20 .50
68 Alex Gonzalez .20 .50
69 Kris Benson .20 .50
70 Bobby Abreu SP 3.00 8.00
71 Vinny Castilla .20 .50
72 Ben Broussard .20 .50
73 Travis Hafner .20 .50
74 Dmitri Young .20 .50
75 Alex S. Gonzalez .20 .50
76 Jason Bay SP 3.00 8.00
77 Charlton Jimerson .20 .50
78 Ryan Garko .20 .50
79 Lance Berkman .20 .50
80A T.Hudson Red/Blue Ltr .20 .50
80B T.Hudson Blue Ltr SP 3.00 8.00
81 Guillermo Mota .20 .50
82 Chris B. Young .20 .50
83 Brad Lidge .20 .50
84 A.J. Pierzynski .20 .50
85 Maicer Izturis .20 .50
86 Vladimir Guerrero .60 1.50
87 J.J. Hardy .20 .50
88 Cesar Izturis .20 .50
89 Mark Ellis .20 .50
90 Chipper Jones .60 1.50
91 Chris Snelling SP 3.00 8.00
92 Jose Reyes .20 .50
93 Mike Lieberthal .20 .50
94 Octavio Dotel .20 .50
95A A.Rodriguez Fielding SP 4.00 10.00
95B A.Rodriguez w/Bat SP 4.00 10.00
96 Brett Myers .20 .50
97 New York Yankees TC .40 1.00
98 Ryan Klesko .20 .50
99 Brian Jordan SP 3.00 8.00
100 William Harridge .20 .50
Warren Giles
101 Adam Eaton .20 .50
102 Aaron Boone .20 .50
103 Alex Rios .20 .50
104 Andy Pettitte .40 1.00
105 Barry Zito .20 .50
106 Bengie Molina SP 3.00 8.00
107 Austin Kearns .20 .50
108 Adam Everett .20 .50
109 A.J. Burnett .20 .50
110 Mark Prior .40 1.00
111 Russ Ortiz .20 .50
112 Adam Dunn .20 .50
113 Byung-Hyun Kim .20 .50
114 Atlanta Braves TC .20 .50
115 Carlos Silva .20 .50
116 Chad Cordero .20 .50
117 Chone Figgins .20 .50
118 Chris Reitsma .20 .50
119 Coco Crisp .20 .50
120 David DeJesus .20 .50
121 Chris Snyder .20 .50
122 Brad Eldred .20 .50
123 Humberto Cota SP 3.00 8.00
124 Erubiel Durazo .20 .50
125 Josh Beckett .20 .50
126 Kenny Lofton .20 .50
127 Joe Nathan SP 3.00 8.00
128 Bryan Bullington .20 .50
129 Jim Thome .40 1.00
130 Shawn Green .20 .50
131 LaTroy Hawkins .20 .50
132 Mark Kotsay .20 .50
133 Matt Lawton .20 .50
134 Luis Castillo .20 .50
135 Michael Barrett .20 .50
136 Preston Wilson .20 .50
137 Orlando Cabrera .20 .50
138 Chuck James .20 .50
139 Raul Ibanez .20 .50
140 Frank Thomas .60 1.50
141 Orlando Hudson .20 .50
142 Scott Kazmir .20 .50
143 Steve Finley .20 .50
144 Danny Sandoval RC .20 .50
145 Javy Lopez .20 .50
146 Tony Giarratano .20 .50
147 Terrence Long .20 .50
148 Victor Martinez .20 .50
149 Toby Hall .20 .50
150 Fausto Carmona .20 .50
151 Tim Wakefield .20 .50
152 Troy Percival .20 .50
153 Chris Denorfia .20 .50
154 Junior Spivey .20 .50
155 Desi Relaford .20 .50
156 Francisco Liriano 1.25 3.00
157 Corey Koskie .20 .50
158 Chris Carpenter .20 .50
159 Robert Andino RC .20 .50
160 Cliff Floyd .20 .50
161 Pittsburgh Pirates TC .20 .50
162 Anderson Hernandez .20 .50
163 Mike Maroth .20 .50
164 Aaron Rowand .20 .50
165A A.Pujols Grey Shirt 1.25 3.00
165B A.Pujols Red Shirt SP 5.00 12.00
166 David Bell .20 .50
167 Angel Berroa .20 .50
168 B.J. Ryan .20 .50
169 Bartolo Colon .20 .50
170 Hong-Chih Kuo .60 1.50
171 Cincinnati Reds TC .20 .50
172 Bill Mueller .20 .50
173 John Koronka .20 .50
174 Billy Wagner .20 .50
175 Zack Greinke .20 .50
176 Rick Short .20 .50
177 Yadier Molina .20 .50
178 Willy Taveras .20 .50
179 Wes Helms .20 .50
180 Wade Miller .20 .50
181 Luis Gonzalez .20 .50
182 Victor Zambrano .20 .50
183 Chicago Cubs TC .20 .50
184 Victor Santos .20 .50
185 Tyler Walker .20 .50
186 Bobby Crosby .20 .50
187 Trot Nixon .20 .50
188 Nick Johnson .20 .50
189 Nick Swisher .20 .50
190 Brian Roberts .20 .50
191 Nomar Garciaparra .60 1.50
192 Oliver Perez .20 .50
193 Ramon Hernandez .20 .50
194 Randy Winn .20 .50
195 Ryan Church .20 .50
196 Ryan Wagner .20 .50
197 Todd Hollandsworth .20 .50
198 Detroit Tigers TC .20 .50
199 Tino Martinez .40 1.00
200A R.Clemens On Mound 1.25 3.00
200B R.Clemens Red Shirt SP 4.00 10.00
201 Shawn Estes .20 .50
202 Justin Morneau .20 .50
203 Jeff Francis .20 .50
204 Oakland Athletics TC .20 .50
205 Jeff Francoeur .60 1.50
206 C.J. Wilson .20 .50
207 Francisco Rodriguez .20 .50
208 Edgardo Alfonzo .20 .50
209 David Eckstein .20 .50
210 Cory Lidle .20 .50
211 Chase Utley .40 1.00
212A R.Baldelli Yellow/White Ltr .20 .50
212B R.Baldelli Blue Ltr SP 3.00 8.00
213 So Taguchi .20 .50
214 Philadelphia Phillies TC .20 .50
215 Brad Hawpe .20 .50
216 Walter Young .20 .50
217 Tom Gorzelanny .20 .50
218 Shaun Marcum .20 .50
219 Ryan Howard 1.00 2.50
220 Damian Jackson .20 .50
221 Craig Counsell .20 .50
222 Damian Miller .20 .50
223 Derrick Turnbow .20 .50
224 Hank Blalock .20 .50
225 Brayan Pena .20 .50
226 Grady Sizemore .40 1.00
227 Ivan Rodriguez .40 1.00
228 Jason Isringhausen .20 .50
229 Brian Fuentes .20 .50
230 Jason Phillips .20 .50
231 Jason Schmidt .20 .50
232 Javier Valentin .20 .50
233 Jeff Kent .20 .50
234 John Buck .20 .50
235 Mike Matheny .20 .50
236 Jorge Cantu .20 .50
237 Jose Castillo .20 .50
238 Kenny Rogers .20 .50
239 Kerry Wood .20 .50
240 Kevin Mench .20 .50
241 Tim Stauffer .20 .50
242 Eric Milton .20 .50
243 St. Louis Cardinals TC .20 .50
244 Shawn Chacon .20 .50
245 Mike Jacobs .20 .50
246 Ryan Dempster .20 .50
247 Todd Jones .20 .50
248 Tom Glavine .40 1.00
249 Tony Graffanino .20 .50
250 Ichiro Suzuki 1.00 2.50
251 Baltimore Orioles TC .20 .50
252 Brad Radke .20 .50
253 Brad Wilkerson .20 .50
254 Carlos Lee .20 .50
255 Alex Gordon Cut Out 100.00 200.00
256 Gustavo Chacin .20 .50
257 Jermaine Dye .20 .50
258 Jose Mesa .20 .50
259 Julio Lugo .20 .50
260 Mark Redman .20 .50
261 Brandon Watson .20 .50
262 Pedro Feliz .20 .50
263 Esteban Loaiza .20 .50
264 Anthony Reyes .40 1.00
265 Jose Contreras SP 3.00 8.00
266 Tadahito Iguchi SP 3.00 8.00
267 Mark Loretta SP 3.00 8.00
268 Ray Durham SP 3.00 8.00
269 Neifi Perez SP 3.00 8.00
270 Washington Nationals TC .20 .50
271 Troy Glaus SP 3.00 8.00
272 Matt Holliday SP 4.00 10.00
273 Kevin Millwood SP 3.00 8.00
274 Jon Lieber SP 3.00 8.00
275 Cleveland Indians TC .20 .50
276 Jeremy Reed SP 3.00 8.00
277 Garrett Atkins SP 3.00 8.00
278 Geoff Jenkins SP 3.00 8.00
279 Joey Gathright SP 3.00 8.00
280 Ben Sheets SP 3.00 8.00
281 Melvin Mora SP 3.00 8.00
282 Jonathan Papelbon SP 4.00 10.00
283 John Smoltz SP 3.00 8.00
284 Jake Peavy SP 3.00 8.00
285 Felix Hernandez SP 3.00 8.00
286 Alfonso Soriano SP 3.00 8.00
287 Bronson Arroyo SP 3.00 8.00
288 Adam LaRoche SP 3.00 8.00
289 Aramis Ramirez SP 3.00 8.00
290 Brad Hennessey SP 3.00 8.00
291 Conor Jackson SP 3.00 8.00
292 Rod Barajas SP 3.00 8.00
293 Chris R. Young SP 3.00 8.00
294 Jeremy Bonderman SP 3.00 8.00
295 Jack Wilson SP 3.00 8.00
296 Jay Payton SP 3.00 8.00
297 Danys Baez SP 3.00 8.00
298 Jose Lima SP 3.00 8.00
299 Luis A. Gonzalez SP 3.00 8.00
300 Mike Sweeney SP 3.00 8.00
301 Nelson Cruz SP 3.00 8.00
302 Eric Gagne SP 3.00 8.00
303 Juan Castro SP 3.00 8.00
304 Joe Mauer SP 3.00 8.00
305 Richie Sexson SP 3.00 8.00
306 Roy Oswalt SP 3.00 8.00
307 Rickie Weeks SP 3.00 8.00
308 Pat Borders SP 3.00 8.00
309 Mike Morse SP 3.00 8.00
310 Matt Stairs SP 3.00 8.00
311 Chad Tracy SP 3.00 8.00
312 Matt Cain SP 3.00 8.00
313 Mark Mulder SP 3.00 8.00
314 Mark Grudzielanek SP 3.00 8.00
315 Johnny Damon Yanks SP 4.00 10.00
316 Casey Kotchman SP 3.00 8.00
317 San Francisco Giants TC .20 .50
318 Chris Burke SP 3.00 8.00
319 Carl Crawford SP 3.00 8.00
320 Edgar Renteria SP 3.00 8.00
321 Chan Ho Park SP 3.00 8.00
322 Boston Red Sox TC SP 3.00 8.00
323 Robinson Cano SP 3.00 8.00
324 Los Angeles Dodgers TC .20 .50
325A M.Tejada w/Bat SP 3.00 8.00
325B M.Tejada Hand Up SP 3.00 8.00
326 Jimmy Rollins SP 3.00 8.00
327 Juan Pierre SP 3.00 8.00
328 Dan Johnson SP 3.00 8.00
329 Chicago White Sox TC .40 1.00
330 Pat Burrell SP 3.00 8.00
331 Ramon Ortiz SP 3.00 8.00
332 Rondell White SP 3.00 8.00
333 David Wells SP 3.00 8.00
334 Michael Young SP 3.00 8.00
335 Mike Mussina SP 3.00 8.00
336 Moises Alou SP 3.00 8.00
337 Scott Podsednik SP 3.00 8.00
338 Rich Harden SP 3.00 8.00
339 Mark Teahen SP 3.00 8.00
340 Jacque Jones SP 3.00 8.00
341 Jason Giambi SP 3.00 8.00
342 Bill Hall SP 3.00 8.00
343 Jon Garland SP 3.00 8.00
344 Dontrelle Willis SP 3.00 8.00
345 Danny Haren SP 3.00 8.00
346 Brian Giles SP 3.00 8.00
347 Brad Penny SP 3.00 8.00
348 Brandon McCarthy SP 3.00 8.00
349 Chien-Ming Wang SP 4.00 10.00
350A T.Hunter Red/Blue Ltr SP 3.00 8.00
350B T.Hunter Blue Ltr SP 3.00 8.00
351 Yhency Brazoban SP 3.00 8.00
352 Rodrigo Lopez SP 3.00 8.00
353 Paul McAnulty .20 .50
354 Francisco Cordero .20 .50
355 Brandon Inge .20 .50
356 Jason Lane .20 .50
357 Brian Schneider .20 .50
358 Dustin Hermanson .20 .50
359 Eric Hinske .20 .50
360 Jarrod Washburn .20 .50
361 Jayson Werth .20 .50
362 Craig Breslow RC .20 .50
363 Jeff Weaver .20 .50
364 Jeromy Burnitz .20 .50
365 Jhonny Peralta .20 .50
366 Joe Crede .20 .50
367 Johan Santana .60 1.50
368 Jose Valentin .20 .50
369 Keith Foulke .20 .50
370 Larry Bigbie .20 .50
371 Manny Ramirez .40 1.00
372 Jim Edmonds .20 .50
373 Horacio Ramirez .20 .50
374 Garret Anderson .20 .50
375 Felipe Lopez .20 .50
376 Eric Byrnes .20 .50
377 Darin Erstad .20 .50
378 Carlos Zambrano .20 .50
379 Craig Biggio .40 1.00
380 Darrell Rasner .20 .50
381 Dave Roberts .20 .50
382 Hanley Ramirez .20 .50
383 Geoff Blum .20 .50
384 Joel Pineiro .20 .50
385 Kip Wells .20 .50
386 Kelvim Escobar .20 .50
387 John Patterson .20 .50
388 Jody Gerut .20 .50
389 Marshall McDougall .20 .50
390 Mike MacDougal .20 .50
391 Orlando Palmeiro .20 .50
392 Rich Aurilia .20 .50
393 Ronnie Belliard .20 .50
394 Rich Hill .20 .50
395 Scott Hatteberg .20 .50
396 Ryan Langerhans .20 .50
397 Richard Hidalgo .20 .50
398 Omar Vizquel .40 1.00
399 Mike Lowell .20 .50
400 Astros Aces SP 3.00 8.00
Roy Oswalt
Roger Clemens
Andy Pettitte
401 Mike Cameron .20 .50
402 Matt Clement .20 .50
403 Miguel Cabrera .40 1.00
404 Milton Bradley .20 .50
405 Laynce Nix .20 .50
406 Rob Mackowiak .20 .50
407 White Sox Power Hitters SP 3.00 8.00
Jermaine Dye
Paul Konerko
408 Mark Teixeira .40 1.00
409 Brady Clark .20 .50
410 Johnny Estrada .20 .50
411 Juan Encarnacion .20 .50
412 Morgan Ensberg .20 .50
413 Nook Logan .20 .50
414 Phil Nevin .20 .50
415 Reggie Sanders .20 .50
416 Roy Halladay .20 .50
417 Livan Hernandez .20 .50
418 Jose Vidro .20 .50
419 Shannon Stewart .20 .50
420 Brian Bruney .20 .50
421 Royce Clayton .20 .50
422 Chris Demaria RC .20 .50
423 Eduardo Perez .20 .50
424 Jeff Suppan .20 .50
425 Jaret Wright .20 .50
426 Joe Randa .20 .50
427 Bobby Kielty .20 .50
428 Jason Ellison .20 .50
429 Gregg Zaun .20 .50
430 Runelvys Hernandez .20 .50
431 Joe McEwing .20 .50
432 Jason LaRue .20 .50
433 Aaron Miles .20 .50
434 Adam Kennedy .20 .50
435 Ambiorix Burgos .20 .50
436 Armando Benitez .20 .50
437 Brad Ausmus .20 .50
438 Brandon Backe .20 .50
439 Brian James Anderson .20 .50
440 Bruce Chen .20 .50
441 Carlos Guillen .20 .50
442 Casey Blake .20 .50
443 Chris Capuano .20 .50
444 Chris Duffy .20 .50
445 Chris Ray .20 .50
446 Clint Barmes .20 .50
447 Andrew Sisco .20 .50
448 Dallas McPherson .20 .50
449 Tanyon Sturtze .20 .50
450 Carlos Beltran .20 .50
451 Jason Vargas .20 .50
452 Ervin Santana .20 .50
453 Jason Marquis .20 .50
454 Juan Rivera .20 .50
455 Jake Westbrook .20 .50
456 Jason Johnson .20 .50
457 Joe Blanton .20 .50
458 Kevin Millar .20 .50
459 John Thomson .20 .50
460 J.P. Howell .20 .50
461 Justin Verlander 1.00 2.50
462 Kelly Johnson .20 .50
463 Kyle Davies .20 .50
464 Lance Niekro .20 .50
465 Magglio Ordonez .20 .50
466 Melky Cabrera .20 .50
467 Nick Punto .20 .50
468 Paul Byrd .20 .50
469 Randy Wolf .20 .50
470 Ruben Gotay .20 .50
471 Ryan Madson .20 .50
472 Victor Diaz .20 .50
473 Xavier Nady .20 .50
474 Zach Duke .20 .50
475A H.Street Yellow/White Ltr .20 .50
475B H.Street Blue Ltr SP 3.00 8.00
476 Brad Thompson .20 .50
477 Jonny Gomes .20 .50
478 B.J. Upton .20 .50
479 Jamey Carroll .20 .50
480 Mike Hampton .20 .50
481 Tony Clark .20 .50
482 Antonio Alfonseca .20 .50
483 Justin Duchscherer .20 .50
484 Mike Timlin .20 .50
485 Joe Saunders .20 .50

2006 Topps Heritage Checklists

COMPLETE SET (5) .75 2.00
COMMON CARD (1-5) .20 .50
RANDOM INSERTS IN PACKS

2006 Topps Heritage Chrome

COMPLETE SET (109) 200.00 300.00
COMMON (1-102/104-110) 1.50 4.00
STATED ODDS 1:9 HOBBY, 1:10 RETAIL
STATED PRINT RUN 1957 SERIAL #'d SETS
CARD 103 DOES NOT EXIST
1 Rafael Furcal 1.50 4.00
2 C.C. Sabathia 1.50 4.00
3 Sean Casey 1.50 4.00
4 Gary Sheffield 1.50 4.00
5 William Harridge 1.50 4.00
Warren Giles
6 Curt Schilling 2.00 5.00
7 Jay Gibbons 1.50 4.00
8 Paul Konerko 1.50 4.00
9 Lyle Overbay 1.50 4.00
10 Jorge Posada 2.00 5.00
11 Todd Walker 1.50 4.00
12 Carlos Delgado 1.50 4.00
13 David Wright 2.50 6.00
14 Matt Morris 1.50 4.00
15 Mariano Rivera 2.50 6.00
16 Jeff Bagwell 2.00 5.00
17 Carl Pavano 1.50 4.00
18 Adrian Beltre 1.50 4.00
19 Scott Rolen 2.00 5.00
20 Aubrey Huff 1.50 4.00
21 Hideki Matsui 2.50 6.00
22 Andruw Jones 2.00 5.00
23 Sammy Sosa 2.50 6.00
24 Mark Buehrle 1.50 4.00
25 Orlando Hernandez 1.50 4.00
26 Travis Hafner 1.50 4.00
27 Vladimir Guerrero 2.50 6.00

28 Chipper Jones 2.50 6.00
29 Jose Reyes 1.50 4.00
30 Roger Clemens 4.00 10.00
31 Aaron Boone 1.50 4.00
32 Andy Pettitte 2.00 5.00
33 David DeJesus 1.50 4.00
34 Shawn Green 1.50 4.00
35 Luis Castillo 1.50 4.00
36 Frank Thomas 2.50 6.00
37 Javy Lopez 1.50 4.00
38 Victor Martinez 1.50 4.00
39 Tim Wakefield 1.50 4.00
40 Cliff Floyd 1.50 4.00
41 Bartolo Colon 1.50 4.00
42 Billy Wagner 1.50 4.00
43 Dmitri Young 1.50 4.00
44 Mark Prior 2.00 5.00
45 Nick Johnson 1.50 4.00
46 Brian Roberts 1.50 4.00
47 Nomar Garciaparra 2.50 6.00
48 Jorge Cantu 1.50 4.00
49 Jeff Francoeur 2.50 6.00
50 Barry Bonds 6.00 15.00
51 Francisco Rodriguez 1.50 4.00
52 Rocco Baldelli 1.50 4.00
53 Ryan Howard 4.00 10.00
54 Hank Blalock 1.50 4.00
55 Ivan Rodriguez 2.00 5.00
56 Jason Schmidt 1.50 4.00
57 Jeff Kent 1.50 4.00
58 Jose Castillo 1.50 4.00
59 Kerry Wood 1.50 4.00
60 Chase Utley 2.00 5.00
61 Shawn Chacon 1.50 4.00
62 Tom Glavine 2.00 5.00
63 Ichiro Suzuki 4.00 10.00
64 Carlos Lee 1.50 4.00
65 Jeff Weaver 1.50 4.00
66 Jeremy Burnitz 1.50 4.00
67 Jhonny Peralta 1.50 4.00
68 Johan Santana 2.50 6.00
69 Keith Foulke 1.50 4.00
70 Manny Ramirez 2.00 5.00
71 Jim Edmonds 1.50 4.00
72 Garret Anderson 1.50 4.00
73 Felipe Lopez 1.50 4.00
74 Craig Biggio 2.00 5.00
75 Ryan Langerhans 1.50 4.00
76 Mike Cameron 1.50 4.00
77 Matt Clement 1.50 4.00
78 Miguel Cabrera 2.00 5.00
79 Mark Teixeira 2.00 5.00
80 Johnny Estrada 1.50 4.00
81 Nook Logan 1.50 4.00
82 Livan Hernandez 1.50 4.00
83 Roy Halladay 1.50 4.00
84 Jose Vidro 1.50 4.00
85 Shannon Stewart 1.50 4.00
86 Brian Bruney 1.50 4.00
87 Jaret Wright 1.50 4.00
88 Gregg Zaun 1.50 4.00
89 Jason LaRue 1.50 4.00
90 Adam Kennedy 1.50 4.00
91 Armando Benitez 1.50 4.00
92 Chris Ray 1.50 4.00
93 Clint Barmes 1.50 4.00
94 Ervin Santana 1.50 4.00
95 Justin Verlander 4.00 10.00
96 Magglio Ordonez 1.50 4.00
97 Todd Helton 2.00 5.00
98 Zach Duke 1.50 4.00
99 Huston Street 1.50 4.00
100 Alex Rodriguez 4.00 10.00
101 Mike Hampton 1.50 4.00
102 Tony Clark 1.50 4.00
104 Barry Zito 1.50 4.00
105 Anderson Hernandez 1.50 4.00
106 B.J. Upton 1.50 4.00
107 Albert Pujols 5.00 12.00
108 Tim Hudson 1.50 4.00
109 Derek Jeter 6.00 15.00
110 Greg Maddux 4.00 10.00

2006 Topps Heritage Chrome Refractors

*CHROME REF: .6X TO 1.5X CHROME
STATED ODDS 1:33 HOBBY, 1:34 RETAIL
STATED PRINT RUN 557 SERIAL #'d SETS
CARD 103 DOES NOT EXIST

2006 Topps Heritage Chrome Black Refractors

*BLACK: 6X TO 15X CHROME
STATED ODDS 1:328 HOBBY, 1:328 RETAIL
STATED PRINT RUN 57 SERIAL #'d SETS
CARD 103 DOES NOT EXIST
30 Roger Clemens 50.00 100.00
50 Barry Bonds 125.00 200.00
63 Ichiro Suzuki 50.00 100.00
95 Justin Verlander 40.00 80.00
100 Alex Rodriguez 90.00 150.00
107 Albert Pujols 90.00 150.00
109 Derek Jeter 125.00 200.00

2006 Topps Heritage Clubhouse Collection Relics

GROUP A ODDS 1:3440 H, 1:3457 R
GROUP B ODDS 1:8164 H, 1:8232 R
GROUP C ODDS 1:1639 H, 1:1650 R
GROUP D ODDS 1:2928 H, 1:2935 R
GROUP E ODDS 1:4082 H, 1:4116 R
GROUP F ODDS 1:3404 H, 1:3426 R
GROUP G ODDS 1:487 H, 1:490 R
GROUP H ODDS 1:2583 H, 1:2600 R
GROUP I ODDS 1:206 H, 1:207 R
GROUP J ODDS 1:257 H, 1:255 R
GROUP K ODDS 1:1370 H, 1:1364 R
GROUP L ODDS 1:421 H, 1:419 R
OVERALL AU-RELIC ODDS 1:36 H, 1:36 R
GROUP A PRINT RUN 99 COPIES PER
GROUP B PRINT RUN 125 COPIES PER
GROUP A-B CARDS ARE NOT SERIAL #'d
A-B PRINT RUN INFO PROVIDED BY TOPPS
AD Adam Dunn Bat G 3.00 8.00
AJ Andruw Jones Uni G 4.00 10.00
AK Al Kaline Bat B/125 * 30.00 60.00
AP Albert Pujols Jsy I 8.00 20.00
AR Alex Rodriguez Bat A/99 * 40.00 80.00
AR2 Alex Rodriguez Jsy D 20.00 50.00
AS Alfonso Soriano Bat I 3.00 8.00
BB Barry Bonds Uni A/99 * 30.00 60.00
BM Bill Mazeroski Jsy A/99 * 50.00 100.00
BR Brian Roberts Bat I 3.00 8.00
BRO Brooks Robinson Bat A/99 * 15.00 40.00
BR2 Brian Roberts Jsy J 3.00 8.00
CB Clint Barmes Jsy J 3.00 8.00
CC Carl Crawford Bat I 3.00 8.00
CJ Conor Jackson Bat I 3.00 8.00
CS Curt Schilling Jsy C 4.00 10.00
DL Derrek Lee Bat I 4.00 10.00
DO David Ortiz Jsy C 4.00 10.00
DW David Wright Jsy L 4.00 10.00
DWI Dontrelle Willis Jsy J 3.00 8.00
EC Eric Chavez Uni L 3.00 8.00
EG Eric Gagne Jsy F 3.00 8.00
FJF Jeff Francis Jsy L 3.00 8.00
FR Frank Robinson Bat B/125 * 20.00 50.00
GS Gary Sheffield Bat I 3.00 8.00
JD Johnny Damon Bat E 4.00 10.00
JD2 Johnny Damon Jsy G 4.00 10.00
JE Jim Edmonds Jsy H 3.00 8.00
JP Jake Peavy Jsy J 3.00 8.00
JS Johan Santana Jsy J 4.00 10.00
KG Khalil Greene Jsy D 4.00 10.00
MC Miguel Cabrera Jsy G 4.00 10.00
ME Morgan Ensberg Bat I 3.00 8.00
MH Matt Holliday Bat I 4.00 10.00
MM Mickey Mantle Bat A/99 * 125.00 200.00
MMU Mark Mulder Uni K 3.00 8.00
MP Mike Piazza Bat C 6.00 15.00
MR Manny Ramirez Jsy C 4.00 10.00
MR2 Manny Ramirez Bat J 4.00 10.00
MT Miguel Tejada Uni I 3.00 8.00
MTE Mark Teixeira Jsy G 4.00 10.00
PM Pedro Martinez Jsy C 4.00 10.00
RC Robinson Cano Bat I 4.00 10.00
RW Rickie Weeks Bat G 3.00 8.00
SC Shin-Soo Choo Bat I 3.00 8.00
SM Stan Musial Bat A/99 * 15.00 40.00
TI Tadahito Iguchi Jsy J 3.00 8.00
VG Vladimir Guerrero Bat J 4.00 10.00

2006 Topps Heritage Clubhouse Collection Autograph Relics

STATED ODDS 1:16,400 H, 1:16,400 R
STATED PRINT RUN 25 SERIAL #'d SETS
EXCHANGE DEADLINE 02/28/08
NO PRICING DUE TO SCARCITY
1 Bill Mazeroski Jsy EXCH
2 Frank Robinson Jsy
3 Brooks Robinson Jsy
4 Al Kaline Jsy
6 Stan Musial Jsy

2006 Topps Heritage Clubhouse Collection Cut Signature Relic

STATED ODDS 1:963,072 HOBBY
STATED PRINT RUN 1 SERIAL #'d CARD
NO PRICING DUE TO SCARCITY
5 Mickey Mantle Bat

2006 Topps Heritage Clubhouse Collection Dual Relics

STATED ODDS 1:12,067 H, 1:12,067 R
STATED PRINT RUN 57 SERIAL #'d SETS

BR Brooks Robinson Bat 50.00 100.00
Brian Roberts Jsy
MP Stan Musial Bat 125.00 200.00
Albert Pujols Jsy
MR Mickey Mantle Bat 150.00 300.00
Alex Rodriguez Jsy

2006 Topps Heritage Flashbacks

COMPLETE SET (10) 10.00 25.00
STATED ODDS 1:12 HOBBY, 1:12 RETAIL
AK Al Kaline 1.25 3.00
BM Bill Mazeroski 1.25 3.00
BR Bobby Richardson .75 2.00
BR Brooks Robinson 1.25 3.00
EB Ernie Banks 1.25 3.00
FR Frank Robinson .75 2.00
MM Mickey Mantle 3.00 8.00
SM Stan Musial 1.50 4.00
WF Whitey Ford 1.25 3.00
YB Yogi Berra 1.25 3.00

2006 Topps Heritage Flashbacks Autographs

STATED ODDS 1:16,400 H, 1:16,400 R
STATED PRINT RUN 25 SERIAL #'d SETS
NO PRICING DUE TO SCARCITY
BR Brooks Robinson
DS Duke Snider
EB Ernie Banks
FR Frank Robinson
SM Stan Musial

2006 Topps Heritage Flashbacks Autograph Seat Relics

STATED ODDS 1:16,400 H, 1:16,400 R
STATED PRINT RUN 25 SERIAL #'d SETS
NO PRICING DUE TO SCARCITY
BR Brooks Robinson
DS Duke Snider
EB Ernie Banks
FR Frank Robinson
SM Stan Musial

2006 Topps Heritage Flashbacks Seat Relics

GROUP A ODDS 1:14,607 H, 1:14,607 R
GROUP B ODDS 1:6225 H, 1:6175 R
GROUP C ODDS 1:721 H, 1:719 R
GROUP D ODDS 1:1711 H, 1:1703 R
GROUP E ODDS 1:308 H, 1:306 R
OVERALL AU-RELIC ODDS 1:36 H, 1:36 R
GROUP A PRINT RUN 140 COPIES
GROUP A CARD IS NOT SERIAL #'d
GROUP A PRINT RUN PROVIDED BY TOPPS
AK Al Kaline E 6.00 15.00
BM Bill Mazeroski B 10.00 25.00
BR Brooks Robinson E 6.00 15.00
BR Bobby Richardson C 10.00 25.00
EB Ernie Banks D 10.00 25.00
FR Frank Robinson E 4.00 10.00
MM Mickey Mantle E 20.00 50.00
SM Stan Musial A/140 * 40.00 80.00
WF Whitey Ford C 6.00 15.00
YB Yogi Berra C 10.00 25.00

2006 Topps Heritage New Age Performers

COMPLETE SET (15) 15.00 40.00
STATED ODDS 1:15 HOBBY, 1:15 RETAIL
AP Albert Pujols 2.00 5.00
AR Alex Rodriguez 1.50 4.00
BB Barry Bonds 2.00 5.00
CL Carlos Lee .75 2.00
DL Derrek Lee 1.25 3.00
DO David Ortiz 1.50 4.00
GM Mark Prior 1.25 3.00
GS Gary Sheffield .75 2.00
IS Ichiro Suzuki 1.50 4.00
MC Miguel Cabrera 1.25 3.00
MR Manny Ramirez 1.25 3.00
MT Mark Teixeira 1.25 3.00
PM Pedro Martinez 1.25 3.00
RC Roger Clemens 1.50 4.00
VG Vladimir Guerrero 1.25 3.00

2006 Topps Heritage Real One Autographs

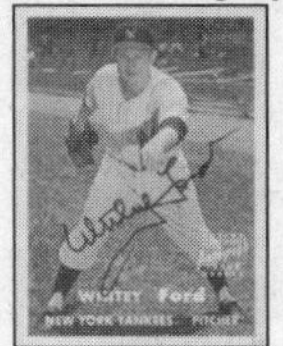

Charley Thompson and Red Murff cards were originally seeded into packs as redemption cards with an exchange deadline of February 28th, 2008.

STATED ODDS 1:366 HOBBY, 1:366 RETAIL
STATED PRINT RUN 200 SETS
CARDS ARE NOT SERIAL-NUMBERED
PRINT RUN INFO PROVIDED BY TOPPS
*RED INK: .75X TO 1.5X BASIC
RED INK ODDS 1:1280 H, 1:1288 R
RED INK PRINT RUN 57 SERIAL #'d SETS
RED INK ALSO CALLED SPECIAL EDITION
EXCHANGE DEADLINE 02/28/08
BC Bob Chakales 20.00 50.00
BW Bob Wiesler 20.00 50.00
CT Charley Thompson EXCH 20.00 50.00
DK Don Kaiser 20.00 50.00
DR Dusty Rhodes 30.00 60.00
DS Duke Snider 50.00 100.00
EB Ernie Banks 75.00 150.00
EO Ernie Oravetz 20.00 50.00
EOB Eddie O'Brien 30.00 60.00
FR Frank Robinson 50.00 100.00
JAC Jackie Collum 20.00 50.00
JCR Jack Crimian 20.00 50.00
JD Jack Dittmer 20.00 50.00
JM Joe Margoneri 20.00 50.00
JP Jim Pyburn 20.00 50.00
JRM Red Murff EXCH 20.00 50.00
JSM Jim Small 20.00 50.00
JSN Jerry Snyder UER 30.00 60.00
Photo is actually Ed Fitzgerald
KO Karl Olson 20.00 50.00
LK Lou Kretlow 20.00 50.00
MP Mel Parnell 30.00 60.00
NK Nellie King 20.00 50.00
PL Paul LaPalme 20.00 50.00
RN Ron Negray 20.00 50.00
SM Stan Musial 75.00 150.00
TB Tommy Byrne 30.00 60.00
WF Whitey Ford 50.00 100.00
WM Windy McCall 20.00 50.00
YB Yogi Berra 60.00 120.00

2006 Topps Heritage Real One Cut Signatures

STATED ODDS 1:481,536 HOBBY
STATED PRINT RUN 1 SERIAL #'d SET
NO PRICING DUE TO SCARCITY
MM Mickey Mantle
TW Ted Williams

2006 Topps Heritage Team Topps Autographs

SEE 06 TOPPS TEAM TOPPS FOR PRICING

2006 Topps Heritage Then and Now

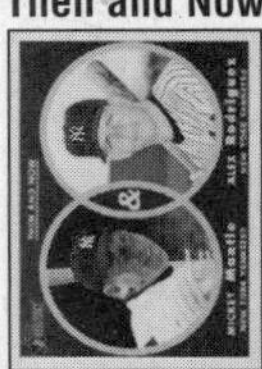

COMPLETE SET (10) 10.00 25.00
STATED ODDS 1:15 HOBBY, 1:15 RETAIL
TN1 Mickey Mantle 3.00 8.00
Alex Rodriguez
TN2 Ted Williams 2.00 5.00
Michael Young
TN3 Mickey Mantle 3.00 8.00
Jason Giambi
TN4 Luis Aparicio .75 2.00
Chone Figgins
TN5 Ted Williams 2.00 5.00
Alex Rodriguez
TN6 Stan Musial 1.50 4.00
Derrek Lee
TN7 Stan Musial 1.50 4.00
Derrek Lee
TN8 Red Schoendienst 1.25 3.00
Derrek Lee
TN9 Johnny Podres 1.50 4.00
Roger Clemens
TN10 Clem Labine .75 2.00
Chad Cordero

2007 Topps Heritage

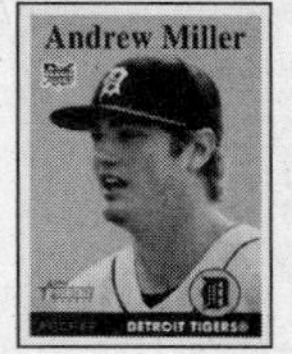

This 527-card set was released in March, 2007. This set was issued through both hobby and retail channels. The set was issued in eight-card hobby packs (with an $3 SRP) which came 24 packs to a box and 12 boxes to a case. Each pack also included a sealed piece of bubble gum. In the tradition of previous Heritage sets, this product honored the 1958 Topps set. In addition, in homage to the original 1958 set, some cards issued between 1-110 were issued in two varieties (a white and yellow letter version). Those yellow cards were inserted at a stated rate of one in six hobby or retail packs. Also, just like the original 1958 Topps set, there was no card #145 issued. In another long-standing Heritage tradition, many cards throughout the set were short-printed. Those short prints were inserted at a stated rate of one in two. In other tributes to the original 1958 sets, many multi-player cards and team checklist cards were inserted in the same card number as the original set and the set concludes with a 20-card All-Star set (476-495).

COMPLETE SET (527) 250.00 400.00
COMP.SET w/o SP's (384) 30.00 60.00
COMMON CARD .20 .50
COMMON RC .20 .50
COMMON TEAM CARD .20 .50
COMMON SP 2.50 6.00
SP STATED ODDS 1:2 HOBBY/RETAIL
SEE BECKETT.COM FOR SP CHECKLIST
COMMON YELLOW 2.00 5.00
YELLOW STATED ODDS 1:6 HOBBY/RETAIL
SEE BECKETT.COM FOR YELLOW CL
CARD 145 DOES NOT EXIST
1 David Ortiz .50 1.25
2a Roger Clemens .75 2.00
2b Roger Clemens YT 3.00 8.00
3 David Wells .20 .50
4 Ronny Paulino SP 2.50 6.00
5 Derek Jeter SP 6.00 15.00
6 Felix Hernandez .30 .75
7 Todd Helton .30 .75
8a David Eckstein .20 .50
8b David Eckstein YN 2.00 5.00
9 Craig Wilson .20 .50
10 John Smoltz .30 .75
11a Rob Mackowiak .20 .50
11b Rob Mackowiak YT 2.00 5.00
12 Scott Hatteberg .20 .50
13a Wilfredo Ledezma SP 2.50 6.00
13b Wilfredo Ledezma YT 2.00 5.00
14 Bobby Abreu SP 2.50 6.00
15 Mike Stanton .20 .50
16 Wilson Betemit .20 .50
17 Darren Oliver .20 .50
18 Josh Beckett .30 .75
19 San Francisco Giants TC .20 .50
20a Robinson Cano .30 .75
20b Robinson Cano YT 2.50 6.00
21 Matt Cain .30 .75
22 Jason Kendall SP 2.50 6.00
23a Mark Kotsay SP 2.50 6.00
23b Mark Kotsay YN 2.00 5.00
24a Yadier Molina .20 .50
24b Yadier Molina YN 2.00 5.00
25 Brad Penny .20 .50
26 Adrian Gonzalez .20 .50
27 Danny Haren .20 .50
28 Brian Giles .20 .50
29 Jose Lopez .20 .50
30a Ichiro Suzuki .75 2.00
30b Ichiro Suzuki YN 3.00 8.00
31 Beltran Perez SP (RC) 2.50 6.00
32 Brad Hawpe SP 2.50 6.00
33a Jim Thome .30 .75
33b Jim Thome YT 2.50 6.00
34 Mark DeRosa .20 .50
35a Woody Williams .20 .50
35b Woody Williams YT 2.00 5.00
36 Luis Gonzalez .20 .50
37 Billy Sadler (RC) .20 .50
38 Dave Roberts .20 .50
39 Mitch Maier RC .20 .50
40 Francisco Cordero SP 2.50 6.00
41 Anthony Reyes SP 2.50 6.00
42 Russell Martin .20 .50
43 Scott Proctor .20 .50
44 Washington Nationals TC .20 .50
45 Shane Victorino .20 .50
46a Joel Zumaya .30 .75
46b Joel Zumaya YN 2.50 6.00
47 Delmon Young (RC) .50 1.25
48 Alex Rios .20 .50
49 Willy Taveras SP 2.50 6.00
50a Mark Buehrle SP 2.50 6.00
50b Mark Buehrle YT 2.00 5.00
51 Livan Hernandez .20 .50
52a Jason Bay .20 .50
52b Jason Bay YT 2.00 5.00
53a Jose Valentin .20 .50
53b Jose Valentin YN 2.00 5.00
54 Kevin Reese .20 .50
55 Felipe Lopez .20 .50
56 Ryan Sweeney (RC) .20 .50
57a Kelvim Escobar .20 .50
57b Kelvim Escobar YN 2.00 5.00
58a Nick Swisher SP 2.50 6.00
Oakland Athletics in small print
58b Nick Swisher YT 2.00 5.00
Oakland Athletics in large print
59 Kevin Millwood SP 2.50 6.00
60a Preston Wilson .20 .50
60b Preston Wilson YN 2.00 5.00
61a Mariano Rivera .50 1.25
61b Mariano Rivera YN 2.50 6.00
62 Josh Barfield .20 .50
63 Ryan Freel .20 .50
64 Tim Hudson .20 .50
65a Chris Narveson (RC) .20 .50
65b Chris Narveson YN (RC) 2.00 5.00
66 Matt Murton .20 .50
67 Melvin Mora SP 2.50 6.00
68 Jason Jennings SP 2.50 6.00
69 Emil Brown .20 .50
70a Magglio Ordonez .20 .50
70b Magglio Ordonez YN 2.00 5.00
71 Los Angeles Dodgers TC .20 .50
72 Ross Gload .20 .50
73 David Ross .20 .50
74 Juan Uribe .20 .50
75 Scott Podsednik .20 .50
76a Cole Hamels SP 3.00 8.00
76b Cole Hamels YT 2.50 6.00
77a Rafael Furcal SP 2.50 6.00
77b Rafael Furcal YT 2.00 5.00
78a Ryan Theriot .20 .50
78b Ryan Theriot YN 2.00 5.00
79a Corey Patterson .20 .50
79b Corey Patterson YT 2.00 5.00
80 Jered Weaver .30 .75
81a Stephen Drew .30 .75
81b Stephen Drew YT 2.50 6.00
82 Adam Kennedy .20 .50
83 Tony Gwynn Jr. .20 .50
84 Kazuo Matsui .20 .50
85a Omar Vizquel SP 3.00 8.00
85b Omar Vizquel YT 2.50 6.00
86 Fred Lewis SP (RC) 2.50 6.00
87a Shawn Chacon .20 .50
87b Shawn Chacon YN 2.00 5.00
88 Frank Catalanotto .20 .50
89 Orlando Hudson .20 .50
90 Pat Burrell .20 .50
91 David DeJesus .20 .50
92a David Wright .75 2.00
92b David Wright YN 3.00 8.00
93 Conor Jackson .20 .50
94 Xavier Nady SP 2.50 6.00
95 Bill Hall SP 2.50 6.00
96 Kip Wells .20 .50
97a Jeff Suppan .20 .50
97b Jeff Suppan YN 2.00 5.00
98a Ryan Zimmerman .50 1.25
98b Ryan Zimmerman YN 2.50 6.00
99 Wes Helms .20 .50
100a Jose Contreras .20 .50
100b Jose Contreras YT 2.00 5.00
101a Miguel Cairo .20 .50
101b Miguel Cairo YN 2.00 5.00
102 Brian Roberts .20 .50
103 Carl Crawford SP 2.50 6.00
104 Mike Lamb SP 2.50 6.00
105 Mark Ellis .20 .50
106 Scott Rolen .30 .75
107 Garrett Atkins .20 .50
108a Hanley Ramirez .30 .75
108b Hanley Ramirez YT 2.50 6.00
109 Trot Nixon .20 .50
110 Edgar Renteria .20 .50
111 Jeff Francis .20 .50
112 Marcus Thames SP 2.50 6.00
113 Brian Burres SP (RC) 2.50 6.00
114 Brian Schneider .20 .50
115 Jeremy Bonderman .20 .50
116 Ryan Madson .20 .50
117 Gerald Laird .20 .50
118 Roy Halladay .20 .50
119 Victor Martinez .20 .50
120 Greg Maddux .75 2.00
121 Jay Payton SP 2.50 6.00
122 Jacque Jones SP 2.50 6.00
123 Juan Lara RC .20 .50
124 Derrick Turnbow .20 .50
125 Adam Everett .20 .50
126 Michael Cuddyer .20 .50
127 Gil Meche .20 .50
128 Willy Aybar .20 .50
129 Jerry Owens (RC) .20 .50
130 Manny Ramirez SP 3.00 8.00
131 Howie Kendrick SP 2.50 6.00
132 Byung-Hyun Kim .20 .50
133 Kevin Kouzmanoff (RC) .20 .50
134 Philadelphia Phillies TC .20 .50
135 Joe Blanton .20 .50
136 Ray Durham .20 .50
137 Luke Hudson .20 .50
138 Eric Byrnes .20 .50
139 Ryan Braun SP RC 2.50 6.00
140 Johnny Damon SP 3.00 8.00
141 Ambiorix Burgos .20 .50
142 Hideki Matsui .50 1.25
143 Josh Johnson .20 .50
144 Miguel Cabrera .30 .75
146 Delwyn Young (RC) .20 .50
147 Chuck James .20 .50
148 Morgan Ensberg .20 .50
149 Jose Vidro SP 2.50 6.00
150 Alex Rodriguez SP 5.00 12.00
151 Carlos Maldonado (RC) .20 .50
152 Jason Schmidt .20 .50
153 Alex Escobar .20 .50
154 Chris Gomez .20 .50
155 Jeremy Chavez .20 .50
156 Kris Benson .20 .50
157 Bronson Arroyo .20 .50
158 Cleveland Indians TC SP 2.50 6.00
159 Chris Ray SP 2.50 6.00
160 Richie Sexson .20 .50

161 Huston Street .20 .50
162 Kevin Youkilis .20 .50
163 Armando Benitez .20 .50
164 Vinny Rottino (RC) .20 .50
165 Garrett Anderson .20 .50
166 Todd Greene .20 .50
167 Brian Stokes SP (RC) 2.50 6.00
168 Albert Pujols SP 6.00 15.00
169 Todd Coffey .20 .50
170 Jason Michaels .20 .50
171 David Dellucci .20 .50
172 Eric Milton .20 .50
173 Austin Kearns .20 .50
174 Oakland Athletics TC .20 .50
175 Andy Cannizaro RC .20 .50
176 David Weathers SP 2.50 6.00
177 Jermaine Dye SP 2.50 6.00
178 Wily Mo Pena .20 .50
179 Chris Burke .20 .50
180 Jeff Weaver .20 .50
181 Edwin Encarnacion .20 .50
182 Jeremy Hermida .20 .50
183 Tim Wakefield .20 .50
184 Rich Hill .20 .50
185 Aaron Hill SP 2.50 6.00
186 Scot Shields SP 2.50 6.00
187 Randy Johnson .50 1.25
188 Dan Johnson .20 .50
189 Sean Marshall .20 .50
190 Marcus Giles .20 .50
191 Jonathan Broxton .20 .50
192 Mike Piazza .50 1.25
193 Carlos Quentin .20 .50
194 Derek Lowe SP 2.50 6.00
195 Russell Branyan SP 2.50 6.00
196 Jason Marquis .20 .50
197 Khalil Greene .30 .75
198 Ryan Dempster .20 .50
199 Ronnie Belliard .20 .50
200 Josh Fogg .20 .50
201 Carlos Lee .20 .50
202 Chris Denorfia .20 .50
203 Kendry Morales SP 3.00 8.00
204 Rafael Soriano SP 2.50 6.00
205 Brandon Phillips .20 .50
206 Andrew Miller RC 1.25 3.00
207 John Koronka .20 .50
208 Luis Castillo .20 .50
209 Angel Guzman .20 .50
210 Jim Edmonds .30 .75
211 Patrick Misch (RC) .20 .50
212 Ty Wigginton SP 2.50 6.00
213 Brandon Inge SP 2.50 6.00
214 Royce Clayton .20 .50
215 Ben Broussard .20 .50
216 St. Louis Cardinals TC .20 .50
217 Mark Mulder .20 .50
218 Kenji Johjima .50 1.25
219 Joe Crede .20 .50
220 Shea Hillenbrand .20 .50
221 Josh Fields SP (RC) 2.50 6.00
222 Pat Neshek SP 3.00 8.00
223 Reed Johnson .20 .50
224 Mike Mussina .30 .75
225 Randy Winn .20 .50
226 Brian Rogers .20 .50
227 Juan Rivera .20 .50
228 Shawn Green .20 .50
229 Mike Napoli .20 .50
230 Chase Utley SP 3.00 8.00
231 John Nelson SP (RC) 2.50 6.00
232 Casey Blake .20 .50
233 Lyle Overbay .20 .50
234 Adam LaRoche .20 .50
235 Julio Lugo .20 .50
236 Johnny Estrada .20 .50
237 James Shields .20 .50
238 Jose Castillo .20 .50
239 Doug Davis SP 2.50 6.00
240 Jason Giambi SP 2.50 6.00
241 Mike Gonzalez .20 .50
242 Scott Downs .20 .50
243 Joe Inglett .20 .50
244 Matt Kemp .20 .50
245 Ted Lilly .20 .50
246 New York Yankees TC .50 1.25
247 Jamey Carroll .20 .50
248 Adam Wainwright SP 2.50 6.00
249 Matt Thornton SP 2.50 6.00
250 Alfonso Soriano .20 .50
251 Tom Gordon .20 .50
252 Dennis Sarfate (RC) .20 .50
253 Zach Duke .20 .50
254 Hank Blalock .20 .50
255 Johan Santana .30 .75
256 Chicago White Sox TC .20 .50
257 Aaron Cook SP 2.50 6.00
258 Cliff Lee SP 2.50 6.00
259 Miguel Tejada .20 .50
260 Mike Lowell .20 .50
261 Ian Snell .20 .50
262 Jason Tyner .20 .50
263 Troy Tulowitzki (RC) .50 1.25
264 Ervin Santana .20 .50
265 Jon Lester .30 .75
266 Andy Pettitte SP 3.00 8.00
267 A.J. Pierzynski SP 2.50 6.00
268 Rich Aurilia .20 .50
269 Phil Nevin .20 .50
270 Tom Glavine .30 .75
271 Chris Coste .20 .50
272 Moises Alou .20 .50
273 J.D. Drew .20 .50
274 Abraham Nunez .20 .50
275 Jorge Posada SP 3.00 8.00
276 Jeff Conine SP 2.50 6.00
277 Chad Cordero .20 .50
278 Nick Johnson .20 .50
279 Kevin Millar .20 .50
280 Mark Grudzielanek .20 .50
281 Chris Stewart RC .20 .50
282 Nate Robertson .20 .50
283 Drew Anderson RC .20 .50
284 Doug Mientkiewicz SP 2.50 6.00
285 Ken Griffey Jr. SP 4.00 10.00
286 Cory Sullivan .20 .50
287 Chris Carpenter .20 .50
288 Gary Matthews .20 .50
289 Justin Verlander .50 1.25
Jeff Weaver
290 Vicente Padilla UER .20 .50
Vincente on front, Vicente on back
291 Chris Roberson .20 .50
292 Chris R. Young .20 .50
293 Ryan Garko SP 2.50 6.00
294 Miguel Batista SP 2.50 6.00
295 B.J. Upton .20 .50
296 Justin Verlander .50 1.25
297 Ben Zobrist .20 .50
298 Ben Sheets UER .20 .50
Listed as an San Diego Padre
299 Eric Chavez .20 .50
300 Scott Schoeneweis .20 .50
301 Placido Polanco .20 .50
302 Angel Sanchez SP RC 2.50 6.00
303 Freddy Sanchez SP 2.50 6.00
304 Magglio Ordonez .20 .50
Craig Monroe
305 A.J. Burnett .20 .50
306 Juan Perez RC .20 .50
307 Chris Britton .20 .50
308 Jon Garland .20 .50
309 Pedro Feliz .20 .50
310 Ryan Howard .75 2.00
311 Aaron Harang SP 2.50 6.00
312 Boston Red Sox TC SP 3.00 8.00
313 Chad Billingsley .20 .50
314 Chipper Jones .50 1.25
Bobby Cox MG
315 Bengie Molina .20 .50
316 Juan Pierre .20 .50
317 Luke Scott .20 .50
318 Javier Valentin .20 .50
319 Mark Loretta .20 .50
320 Kenny Lofton SP 2.50 6.00
321 Vladimir Guerrero 3.00 8.00
Ivan Rodriguez SP
322 Josh Willingham .20 .50
323 Lance Berkman .20 .50
324 Anibal Sanchez .20 .50
325 Maicer Izturis .20 .50
326 Brett Myers .20 .50
327 Chicago Cubs TC .30 .75
328 Francisco Liriano 1.00 2.50
329 Craig Monroe SP 2.50 6.00
330 Paul LoDuca SP 2.50 6.00
331 Steve Trachsel .20 .50
332 Bernie Williams .30 .75
333 Carlos Guillen .20 .50
334 Chien-Ming Wang .75 2.00
Mike Mussina
335 Dave Bush .20 .50
336 Carlos Beltran .20 .50
337 Jason Isringhausen .20 .50
338 Todd Walker SP 2.50 6.00
339 Jarrod Washburn SP 2.50 6.00
340 Brandon Webb .20 .50
341 Pittsburgh Pirates TC .20 .50
342 Daryle Ward .20 .50
343 Chad Santos .20 .50
344 Brad Lidge .20 .50
345 Brad Ausmus .20 .50
346 Carlos Delgado .20 .50
347 Boone Logan SP 2.50 6.00
348 Jimmy Rollins SP 2.50 6.00
349 Orlando Hernandez .20 .50
350 Gary Sheffield .20 .50
351 Albert Pujols 1.00 2.50
Chris Duncan
Jim Edmonds
Yadier Molina
352 Jake Peavy .20 .50
353 Jason Varitek .50 1.25
354 Freddy Garcia .20 .50
355 Matt Diaz .20 .50
356 Bernie Castro SP 2.50 6.00
357 Eric Stults SP RC 2.50 6.00
358 John Lackey .20 .50
359 Bobby Jenks .20 .50
360 Mark Teixeira .30 .75
361 Jonathan Papelbon .50 1.25
362 Paul Konerko .20 .50
363 Erik Bedard .20 .50
364 Eliezer Alfonzo .20 .50
365 Fernando Rodney SP 2.50 6.00
366 Chris Duncan SP 2.50 6.00
367 Jose Diaz (RC) .20 .50
368 Travis Hafner .20 .50
369 Matt Capps .20 .50
370 Ivan Rodriguez .30 .75
371 David Murphy (RC) .20 .50
372 Carlos Zambrano .20 .50
373 Chris Iannetta .20 .50
374 Jose Mesa SP 2.50 6.00
375 Michael Young SP 2.50 6.00
376 Bill Bray .20 .50
377 Atlanta Braves TC .30 .75
378 Jeff Cirillo .20 .50
379 Barry Zito .20 .50
380 Clay Hensley .20 .50
381 J.J. Putz .20 .50
382 C.C. Sabathia .20 .50
383 Eduardo Perez SP 2.50 6.00
384 Scott Moore SP (RC) 2.50 6.00
385 Scott Olsen .20 .50
386 Ryan Howard .75 2.00
Chase Utley
387 Aaron Rowand .20 .50
388 Mike Rouse .20 .50
389 Alexis Gomez .20 .50
390 Brian McCann .20 .50
391 Ryan Shealy .20 .50
392 Shane Youman SP RC 2.50 6.00
393 Melky Cabrera SP 2.50 6.00
394 Jeremy Sowers .20 .50
395 Casey Janssen .20 .50
396 Travis Chick (RC) .20 .50
397 Detroit Tigers TC UER .20 .50
Listed as being in the National League
398 Reggie Abercrombie .20 .50
399 Ricky Nolasco .20 .50
400 Tadahito Iguchi .20 .50
401 Jose Reyes SP 2.50 6.00
402 Juan Encarnacion SP 2.50 6.00
403 Brandon Harper .20 .50
404 Torii Hunter .20 .50
405 Dan Uggla .30 .75
406 Orlando Cabrera .20 .50
407 Jose Capellan .20 .50
408 Baltimore Orioles TC .20 .50
409 Frank Thomas .50 1.25
410 Francisco Rodriguez SP 2.50 6.00
411 Ian Kinsler SP 3.00 8.00
412 Billy Wagner .20 .50
413 Andy Marte .20 .50
414 Mike Jacobs .20 .50
415 Raul Ibanez .20 .50
416 Jhonny Peralta .20 .50
417 Chris B. Young .20 .50
418 Albert Pujols 1.00 2.50
Magglio Ordonez
419 Scott Kazmir SP 3.00 8.00
420 Norris Hopper SP 2.50 6.00
421 Chris Capuano .20 .50
422 Troy Glaus .20 .50
423 Roy Oswalt .20 .50
424 Grady Sizemore .30 .75
425 Chone Figgins .20 .50
426 Chad Tracy .20 .50
427 Brian Fuentes .20 .50
428 Cincinnati Reds TC SP 2.50 6.00
429 Ramon Hernandez SP 2.50 6.00
430 Mike Cameron .20 .50
431 Dontrelle Willis .20 .50
432 Josh Sharpless .20 .50
433 Adrian Beltre .20 .50
434 Curtis Granderson .20 .50
435 B.J. Ryan .20 .50
436 David Wright .75 2.00
Ryan Howard
437 Vernon Wells SP 2.50 6.00
438 Vladimir Guerrero SP 3.00 8.00
439 Jake Westbrook .20 .50
440 Chipper Jones .50 1.25
441 James Loney .30 .75
442 Nook Logan .20 .50
443 Oswaldo Navarro RC .20 .50
444 Joe Mauer .30 .75
445 Miguel Montero (RC) .20 .50
446 Franklin Gutierrez SP 2.50 6.00
447 Mark Redman SP 2.50 6.00
448 Mike Rabelo RC .20 .50
449 Philip Humber (RC) .30 .75
450 Justin Morneau .20 .50
451 Hector Gimenez (RC) .20 .50
452 Matt Holliday .50 1.25
453 Akinori Otsuka .20 .50
454 Prince Fielder .50 1.25
455 Chien-Ming Wang SP 4.00 10.00
456 Shawn Riggans SP 2.50 6.00
457 John Maine .20 .50
458 Adam Lind (RC) .20 .50
459 Ubaldo Jimenez (RC) .20 .50
460 Jaret Wright .20 .50
461 Cla Meredith .20 .50
462 Joaquin Arias (RC) .20 .50
463 Kenny Rogers .20 .50
464 Jose Garcia SP RC 2.50 6.00
465 Pedro Martinez SP 3.00 8.00
466 Jeff Salazar (RC) .20 .50
467 Glen Perkins .20 .50
468 Travis Ishikawa .20 .50
469 Joe Borowski .20 .50
470 Jeremy Brown .20 .50
471 Andre Ethier .30 .75
472 Taylor Tankersley .20 .50
473 Lastings Milledge SP 3.00 8.00
474 Brian Sanches SP 2.50 6.00
475 Ozzie Guillen AS MG .20 .50
Phil Garner AS MG
476 Albert Pujols AS 1.00 2.50
477 David Ortiz AS .50 1.25
478 Chase Utley AS .50 1.25
479 Mark Loretta AS .20 .50
480 David Wright AS .75 2.00
481 Alex Rodriguez AS .75 2.00
482 Edgar Renteria AS SP 2.50 6.00
483 Derek Jeter AS SP 5.00 12.00
484 Alfonso Soriano AS .20 .50
485 Vladimir Guerrero AS .50 1.25
486 Carlos Beltran AS .20 .50
487 Vernon Wells AS .20 .50
488 Jason Bay AS .20 .50
489 Ichiro Suzuki AS .75 2.00
490 Paul LoDuca AS .20 .50
491 Ivan Rodriguez AS SP 3.00 8.00
492 Brad Penny AS SP 2.50 6.00
493 Roy Halladay AS .20 .50
494 Brian Fuentes AS .20 .50
495 Kenny Rogers AS .20 .50

2007 Topps Heritage Chrome

STATED ODDS 1:11 HOBBY, 1:12 RETAIL
STATED PRINT RUN 1958 SERIAL #'d SETS
THC1 David Ortiz 2.50 6.00
THC2 John Smoltz 2.00 5.00
THC3 San Francisco Giants TC 1.50 4.00
THC4 Brian Giles 1.50 4.00
THC5 Billy Sadler 1.50 4.00
THC6 Joel Zumaya 2.00 5.00
THC7 Felipe Lopez 1.50 4.00
THC8 Tim Hudson 1.50 4.00
THC9 David Ross 1.50 4.00
THC10 Adam Kennedy 1.50 4.00
THC11 David DeJesus 1.50 4.00
THC12 Jose Contreras 1.50 4.00
THC13 Trot Nixon 1.50 4.00
THC14 Roy Halladay 1.50 4.00
THC15 Gil Meche 1.50 4.00
THC16 Ray Durham 1.50 4.00
THC17 Delwyn Young 1.50 4.00
THC18 Endy Chavez 1.50 4.00
THC19 Vinny Rottino 1.50 4.00
THC20 Austin Kearns 1.50 4.00
THC21 Jeremy Hermida 1.50 4.00
THC22 Jonathan Broxton 1.50 4.00
THC23 Josh Fogg 1.50 4.00
THC24 Angel Guzman 1.50 4.00
THC25 Kenji Johjima 2.50 6.00
THC26 Juan Rivera 1.50 4.00
THC27 Johnny Estrada 1.50 4.00
THC28 Ted Lilly 1.50 4.00
THC29 Hank Blalock 1.50 4.00
THC30 Troy Tulowitzki 2.50 6.00
THC31 Moises Alou 1.50 4.00
THC32 Chris Stewart 1.50 4.00
THC33 Vicente Padilla 1.50 4.00
THC34 Eric Chavez 1.50 4.00
THC35 Jon Garland 1.50 4.00
THC36 Luke Scott 1.50 4.00
THC37 Brett Myers 1.50 4.00
THC38 Dave Bush 1.50 4.00
THC39 Brad Lidge 1.50 4.00
THC40 Jason Varitek 2.50 6.00
THC41 Paul Konerko 1.50 4.00
THC42 David Murphy 1.50 4.00
THC43 Clay Hensley 1.50 4.00
THC44 Alexis Gomez 1.50 4.00
THC45 Reggie Abercrombie 1.50 4.00
THC46 Jose Capellan 1.50 4.00
THC47 Jhonny Peralta 1.50 4.00
THC48 Chone Figgins 1.50 4.00
THC49 Curtis Granderson 1.50 4.00
THC50 Oswaldo Navarro 1.50 4.00
THC51 Matt Holliday 2.00 5.00
THC52 Cla Meredith 1.50 4.00
THC53 Jeremy Brown 1.50 4.00
THC54 Mark Loretta AS 1.50 4.00
THC55 Jason Bay AS 1.50 4.00
THC56 Roger Clemens 3.00 8.00
THC57 Rob Mackowiak 1.50 4.00
THC58 Robinson Cano 2.00 5.00
THC59 Jose Lopez 1.50 4.00
THC60 Dave Roberts 1.50 4.00
THC61 Delmon Young 2.50 6.00
THC62 Ryan Sweeney 1.50 4.00
THC63 Chris Narveson 1.50 4.00
THC64 Juan Uribe 1.50 4.00
THC65 Tony Gwynn Jr. 1.50 4.00
THC66 David Wright 3.00 8.00
THC67 Miguel Cairo 1.50 4.00
THC68 Edgar Renteria 1.50 4.00
THC69 Victor Martinez 1.50 4.00
THC70 Willy Aybar 1.50 4.00
THC71 Luke Hudson 1.50 4.00
THC72 Chuck James 1.50 4.00
THC73 Kris Benson 1.50 4.00
THC74 Garret Anderson 1.50 4.00
THC75 Oakland Athletics TC 1.50 4.00
THC76 Tim Wakefield 1.50 4.00
THC77 Mike Piazza 2.50 6.00
THC78 Carlos Lee 1.50 4.00
THC79 Jim Edmonds 2.00 5.00
THC80 Joe Crede 1.50 4.00
THC81 Shawn Green 1.50 4.00
THC82 James Shields 1.50 4.00
THC83 New York Yankees TC 3.00 8.00
THC84 Johan Santana 2.50 6.00
THC85 Ervin Santana 1.50 4.00
THC86 J.D. Drew 1.50 4.00
THC87 Nate Robertson 1.50 4.00
THC88 Chris Roberson 1.50 4.00
THC89 Scott Schoeneweis 1.50 4.00
THC90 Pedro Feliz 1.50 4.00
THC91 Javier Valentin 1.50 4.00
THC92 Chicago Cubs TC 2.00 5.00
THC93 Carlos Beltran 1.50 4.00
THC94 Brad Ausmus 1.50 4.00
THC95 Freddy Garcia 1.50 4.00
THC96 Erik Bedard 1.50 4.00
THC97 Carlos Zambrano 1.50 4.00
THC98 J.J. Putz 1.50 4.00
THC99 Brian McCann 1.50 4.00
THC100 Ricky Nolasco 1.50 4.00
THC101 Baltimore Orioles TC 1.50 4.00
THC102 Chris B. Young 1.50 4.00
THC103 Chad Tracy 1.50 4.00
THC104 B.J. Ryan 1.50 4.00
THC105 Joe Mauer 2.00 5.00
THC106 Akinori Otsuka 1.50 4.00
THC107 Joaquin Arias 1.50 4.00
THC108 Andre Ethier 2.00 5.00
THC109 David Wright AS 3.00 8.00
THC110 Ichiro Suzuki AS 3.00 8.00

2007 Topps Heritage Chrome Refractors

*CHROME REF: 1X TO 2.5X
STATED ODDS 1:39 HOBBY, 1:40 RETAIL
STATED PRINT RUN 558 SERIAL #'d SETS

2007 Topps Heritage Chrome Black Refractors

STATED ODDS 1:383 HOBBY/RETAIL
STATED PRINT RUN 58 SERIAL #'d SETS
THC1 David Ortiz 40.00 80.00
THC2 John Smoltz 30.00 60.00
THC3 San Francisco Giants TC 20.00 50.00
THC4 Brian Giles 20.00 50.00
THC5 Billy Sadler 20.00 50.00
THC6 Joel Zumaya 40.00 80.00
THC7 Felipe Lopez 20.00 50.00
THC8 Tim Hudson 30.00 60.00
THC9 David Ross 20.00 50.00
THC10 Adam Kennedy 30.00 60.00
THC11 David DeJesus 20.00 50.00
THC12 Jose Contreras 30.00 60.00
THC13 Trot Nixon 20.00 50.00
THC14 Roy Halladay 30.00 60.00
THC15 Gil Meche 20.00 50.00
THC16 Ray Durham 20.00 50.00
THC17 Delwyn Young 20.00 50.00
THC18 Endy Chavez 30.00 60.00
THC19 Vinny Rottino 20.00 50.00
THC20 Austin Kearns 30.00 60.00
THC21 Jeremy Hermida 30.00 60.00
THC22 Jonathan Broxton 40.00 80.00
THC23 Josh Fogg 20.00 50.00
THC24 Angel Guzman 20.00 50.00
THC25 Kenji Johjima 40.00 80.00
THC26 Juan Rivera 20.00 50.00
THC27 Johnny Estrada 30.00 60.00
THC28 Ted Lilly 30.00 60.00
THC29 Hank Blalock 20.00 50.00
THC30 Troy Tulowitzki 40.00 80.00
THC31 Moises Alou 20.00 50.00
THC32 Chris Stewart 40.00 80.00
THC33 Vicente Padilla 30.00 60.00
THC34 Eric Chavez 40.00 80.00
THC35 Jon Garland 20.00 50.00
THC36 Luke Scott 20.00 50.00
THC37 Brett Myers 30.00 60.00
THC38 Dave Bush 30.00 60.00
THC39 Brad Lidge 40.00 80.00
THC40 Jason Varitek 30.00 60.00
THC41 Paul Konerko 40.00 80.00
THC42 David Murphy 20.00 50.00
THC43 Clay Hensley 20.00 50.00
THC44 Alexis Gomez 20.00 50.00
THC45 Reggie Abercrombie 30.00 60.00
THC46 Jose Capellan 20.00 50.00
THC47 Jhonny Peralta 20.00 50.00
THC48 Chone Figgins 20.00 50.00
THC49 Curtis Granderson 30.00 60.00
THC50 Oswaldo Navarro 20.00 50.00
THC51 Matt Holliday 30.00 60.00
THC52 Cla Meredith 30.00 60.00
THC53 Jeremy Brown 30.00 60.00
THC54 Mark Loretta AS 20.00 50.00
THC55 Jason Bay AS 40.00 80.00
THC56 Roger Clemens 60.00 150.00
THC57 Rob Mackowiak 20.00 50.00
THC58 Robinson Cano 30.00 60.00
THC59 Jose Lopez 20.00 50.00
THC60 Dave Roberts 30.00 60.00
THC61 Delmon Young 40.00 80.00
THC62 Ryan Sweeney 20.00 50.00
THC63 Chris Narveson 20.00 50.00
THC64 Juan Uribe 20.00 50.00
THC65 Tony Gwynn Jr. 20.00 50.00
THC66 David Wright 60.00 120.00
THC67 Miguel Cairo 20.00 50.00
THC68 Edgar Renteria 20.00 50.00
THC69 Victor Martinez 30.00 60.00
THC70 Willy Aybar 40.00 80.00
THC71 Luke Hudson 20.00 50.00
THC72 Chuck James 20.00 50.00
THC73 Kris Benson 20.00 50.00
THC74 Garret Anderson 40.00 80.00
THC75 Oakland Athletics TC 40.00 80.00
THC76 Tim Wakefield 20.00 50.00
THC77 Mike Piazza 40.00 80.00
THC78 Carlos Lee 20.00 50.00
THC79 Jim Edmonds 40.00 80.00
THC80 Joe Crede 20.00 50.00
THC81 Shawn Green 20.00 50.00
THC82 James Shields 20.00 50.00
THC83 New York Yankees TC 40.00 80.00
THC84 Johan Santana 40.00 80.00
THC85 Ervin Santana 30.00 60.00
THC86 J.D. Drew 20.00 50.00
THC87 Nate Robertson 20.00 50.00
THC88 Chris Roberson 20.00 50.00
THC89 Scott Schoeneweis 20.00 50.00
THC90 Pedro Feliz 20.00 50.00
THC91 Javier Valentin 20.00 50.00
THC92 Chicago Cubs TC 30.00 60.00
THC93 Carlos Beltran 20.00 50.00
THC94 Brad Ausmus 20.00 50.00
THC95 Freddy Garcia 20.00 50.00
THC96 Erik Bedard 20.00 50.00
THC97 Carlos Zambrano 20.00 50.00
THC98 J.J. Putz 20.00 50.00
THC99 Brian McCann 20.00 50.00
THC100 Ricky Nolasco 40.00 80.00
THC101 Baltimore Orioles TC 20.00 50.00
THC102 Chris B. Young 20.00 50.00
THC103 Chad Tracy 20.00 50.00
THC104 B.J. Ryan 20.00 50.00
THC105 Joe Mauer 30.00 60.00
THC106 Akinori Otsuka 40.00 80.00
THC107 Joaquin Arias 20.00 50.00
THC108 Andre Ethier 30.00 60.00
THC109 David Wright AS 60.00 120.00
THC110 Ichiro Suzuki AS 90.00 120.00

2007 Topps Heritage 1958 Cut Signature

STATED ODDS 1:403,200 HOBBY
STATED PRINT RUN 1 SER.#'d SET
NO PRICING DUE TO SCARCITY
MM Mickey Mantle
RM Roger Maris
TW Ted Williams

2007 Topps Heritage 1958 Home Run Champion

COMPLETE SET (42) 20.00 50.00
COMMON MANTLE .60 1.50
STATED ODDS 1:6 HOBBY, 1:6 RETAIL

2007 Topps Heritage Clubhouse Collection Relics

GROUP A ODDS 1:2425 HOBBY/RETAIL
GROUP B ODDS 1:202 HOBBY/RETAIL
GROUP C ODDS 1:67 HOBBY/RETAIL
GROUP D ODDS 1:808 HOBBY/RETAIL
AJP Albert Pujols Pants C 8.00 20.00
AK Al Kaline Bat C 8.00 20.00
ALR Anthony Reyes Jsy C 3.00 8.00
AR Alex Rodriguez Bat C 8.00 20.00
AW Adam Wainwright Jsy C 4.00 10.00
BR Brian Roberts Jsy B 3.00 8.00
BR Brooks Robinson Pants C 6.00 15.00
BS Ben Sheets Bat B 4.00 10.00
BU B.J. Upton Bat C 3.00 8.00
BW Billy Wagner Jsy C 3.00 8.00
BZ Barry Zito Pants D 3.00 8.00
CC Chris Carpenter Jsy C 3.00 8.00
CD Chris Duncan Jsy C 6.00 15.00
CJ Chipper Jones Jsy C 4.00 10.00
CJ Conor Jackson Bat B 3.00 8.00
CU Chase Utley Jsy B 8.00 20.00
DE David Eckstein Bat B 6.00 15.00
DM Doug Mientkiewicz Bat C 3.00 8.00
DO David Ortiz Jsy C 4.00 10.00
DS Duke Snider Pants C 6.00 15.00
DW David Wright Jsy A 12.50 30.00
DWW Dontrelle Willis Jsy C 3.00 8.00
DY Delmon Young Bat C 3.00 8.00
EC Eric Chavez Pants C 3.00 8.00
ER Edgar Renteria Bat C 3.00 8.00
ES Ervin Santana Jsy C 3.00 8.00
FL Francisco Liriano Jsy C 4.00 10.00
FR Frank Robinson Pants C 6.00 15.00
GS Gary Sheffield Bat C 3.00 8.00
HB Hank Blalock Jsy B 3.00 8.00
IR Ivan Rodriguez Jsy B 10.00 25.00
JBR Jose Reyes Jsy A 8.00 20.00
JD Johnny Damon Bat C 4.00 10.00
JM Justin Morneau Bat A 6.00 15.00
JP Juan Pierre Bat B 3.00 8.00
JR Jimmy Rollins Jsy C 3.00 8.00
JRP Jorge Posada Pants C 4.00 10.00
JS Jeff Suppan Jsy C 3.00 8.00
JSA Johan Santana Jsy C 4.00 10.00
JV Jose Vidro Bat B 3.00 8.00
JW Jeff Weaver Jsy C 3.00 8.00
LB Lance Berkman Jsy B 3.00 8.00
LG Luis Gonzalez Bat C 3.00 8.00
MA Moises Alou Bat C 3.00 8.00
MC Miguel Cabrera Bat B 4.00 10.00
MK Mark Kotsay Bat B 3.00 8.00
MM Melvin Mora Jsy C 3.00 8.00
MO Magglio Ordonez Bat C 3.00 8.00
MOT Miguel Tejada Pants C 3.00 8.00
MP Mike Piazza Bat B 6.00 15.00
MR Manny Ramirez Jsy C 4.00 10.00
MT Mark Teixeira Jsy B 4.00 10.00
NS Nick Swisher Jsy C 3.00 8.00
OV Omar Vizquel Bat C 4.00 10.00
PB Pat Burrell Bat B 3.00 8.00
PP Placido Polanco Bat B 10.00 25.00
RB Ronnie Belliard Bat B 3.00 8.00
RF Rafael Furcal Bat D 3.00 8.00
RH Ryan Howard Bat A 12.50 30.00
RS Richie Sexson Bat B 3.00 8.00
SM Stan Musial Pants B 12.50 30.00
TH Todd Helton Jsy B 4.00 10.00
TKH Torii Hunter Jsy B 3.00 8.00
VM Victor Martinez Jsy B 3.00 8.00
YB Yogi Berra Bat B 12.50 30.00
YM Yadier Molina Jsy B 10.00 25.00

2007 Topps Heritage Clubhouse Collection Relics Autographs

STATED ODDS 1:16,100 HOBBY
STATED ODDS 1:16,275 RETAIL
STATED PRINT RUN 25 SER.#'d SETS
NO PRICING DUE TO SCARCITY
BR Brooks Robinson Pants
DS Duke Snider Pants
FR Frank Robinson Pants
LA Luis Aparicio Bat
SM Stan Musial Pants
YB Yogi Berra Bat

2007 Topps Heritage Clubhouse Collection Relics Dual

STATED ODDS 1:13,900 HOBBY
STATED ODDS 1:14,000 RETAIL
STATED PRINT RUN 58 SER.#'d SETS

BR Yogi Berra Pants	125.00	250.00
Alex Rodriguez Pants		
KR Al Kaline Bat	75.00	150.00
Ivan Rodriguez Bat		
MP Stan Musial Pants	125.00	250.00
Albert Pujols Pants		

2007 Topps Heritage Felt Logos

COMPLETE SET (13)	20.00	50.00
1 PER HOBBY BOX TOPPER		
BOS Boston Red Sox	3.00	8.00
CHC Chicago Cubs	2.00	5.00
CHW Chicago White Sox	2.00	5.00
CIN Cincinnati Redlegs	2.00	5.00
KCA Kansas City Athletics	2.00	5.00
LAD Los Angeles Dodgers	2.00	5.00
NYY New York Yankees	3.00	8.00
PHI Philadelphia Phillies	2.00	5.00
PIT Pittsburgh Pirates	2.00	5.00
SFG San Francisco Giants	2.00	5.00
STL St. Louis Cardinals	2.00	5.00
WAS Washington Senators	2.00	5.00
BAL Baltimore Orioles	2.00	5.00

2007 Topps Heritage Flashbacks

COMPLETE SET (10)	5.00	12.00
STATED ODDS 1:12 HOBBY, 1:12 RETAIL		
FB1 Al Kaline	.75	2.00
FB2 Brooks Robinson	.75	2.00
FB3 Red Schoendienst	.75	2.00
FB4 Warren Spahn	.75	2.00
FB5 Stan Musial	1.25	3.00
FB6 Lew Burdette	.75	2.00
FB7 Eddie Yost	.75	2.00
FB8 Jim Bunning	.75	2.00
FB9 Richie Ashburn	.75	2.00
FB10 Hoyt Wilhelm	.75	2.00

2007 Topps Heritage Flashbacks Autographs

STATED ODDS 1:19,500 HOBBY/RETAIL
STATED PRINT RUN 25 SER.#'d SETS
NO PRICING DUE TO SCARCITY
AK Al Kaline
BR Brooks Robinson
LA Luis Aparicio
RS Red Schoendienst
SM Stan Musial

2007 Topps Heritage Flashbacks Seat Relics

STATED ODDS 1:484 HOBBY, 1:484 RETAIL		
AK Al Kaline	10.00	25.00
BR Brooks Robinson	10.00	25.00
EY Eddie Yost	8.00	20.00
HW Hoyt Wilhelm	8.00	20.00
JB Jim Bunning	10.00	25.00
RA Richie Ashburn	8.00	20.00
LB Lew Burdette	8.00	20.00
RS Red Schoendienst	8.00	20.00
SM Stan Musial	15.00	40.00
WS Warren Spahn	10.00	25.00

2007 Topps Heritage Flashbacks Seat Relics Autographs

STATED ODDS 1:19,500 HOBBY/RETAIL
STATED PRINT RUN 25 SER.#'d SETS
NO PRICING DUE TO SCARCITY
AK Al Kaline
BR Brooks Robinson
LA Luis Aparicio
RS Red Schoendienst
SM Stan Musial

2007 Topps Heritage Flashbacks Seat Relics Dual

STATED ODDS 1:82,544 HOBBY/RETAIL
STATED PRINT RUN 10 SER.#'d SETS
NO PRICING DUE TO SCARCITY
DS Duke Snider
HS Hank Sauer
SS Duke Snider
Hank Sauer

2007 Topps Heritage New Age Performers

COMPLETE SET (15)	10.00	25.00
STATED ODDS 1:15 HOBBY, 1:15 RETAIL		
NP1 Ryan Howard	1.25	3.00
NP2 Alex Rodriguez	1.25	3.00
NP3 Alfonso Soriano	.75	2.00
NP4 David Ortiz	.75	2.00
NP5 Trevor Hoffman	.75	2.00
NP6 Derek Jeter	1.50	4.00
NP7 Anibal Sanchez	.75	2.00
NP8 Roger Clemens	1.25	3.00
NP9 Johan Santana	.75	2.00
NP10 Albert Pujols	1.50	4.00
NP11 Chipper Jones	.75	2.00
NP12 Frank Thomas	.75	2.00
NP13 Ivan Rodriguez	.75	2.00
NP14 Ichiro Suzuki	1.25	3.00
NP15 Craig Biggio	.75	2.00

2007 Topps Heritage Real One Autographs

STATED ODDS 1:327 HOBBY, 1:328 RETAIL
STATED PRINT RUN 200 SETS
CARDS ARE NOT SERIAL-NUMBERED
PRINT RUN INFO PROVIDED BY TOPPS
EXCHANGE DEADLINE 02/28/09

AK Al Kaline	60.00	120.00
BH Bob Henrich	20.00	50.00
BM Bobby Morgan	30.00	60.00
BP Buddy Pritchard	30.00	60.00
BR Brooks Robinson	60.00	120.00
BT Bill Taylor	20.00	50.00
BW Bill Wight	20.00	50.00
CH Chuck Harmon EXCH	20.00	50.00
CR Charley Rabe	20.00	50.00
DM Dave Melton	20.00	50.00
DS Duke Snider	40.00	80.00
DW David Wright	90.00	150.00
DWW Dontrelle Willis	20.00	50.00
DY Delmon Young	30.00	60.00
DZ Don Zimmer	30.00	60.00
EN Ed Mayer	20.00	50.00
GK George Kell	40.00	80.00
HP Harding Peterson	30.00	60.00
JB Jim Bunning	40.00	80.00
JC Joe Caffie	30.00	60.00
JD Joe Durham	30.00	60.00
JL Joe Lonnett	30.00	60.00
JM Justin Morneau	30.00	60.00
JP Johnny Podres	50.00	100.00
LA Luis Aparicio	50.00	100.00
LM Lloyd Merritt	20.00	50.00
LS Lou Sleater	20.00	50.00
MB Milt Bolling	40.00	80.00
MEB Mack Burk	20.00	50.00
OH Orlando Hudson	20.00	50.00
PS Paul Smith	20.00	50.00
RC Ray Crone	30.00	60.00
RH Ryan Howard	75.00	150.00
RS Red Schoendienst	50.00	100.00
SP Stan Palys	20.00	50.00
TT Tim Thompson	20.00	50.00
CJD Jim Derrington	30.00	60.00

2007 Topps Heritage Real One Autographs Red Ink

STATED ODDS 1:1129 HOBBY/RETAIL
STATED PRINT RUN 58 SERIAL #'d SETS
RED INK ALSO CALLED SPECIAL EDITION
EXCHANGE DEADLINE 02/28/09

AK Al Kaline	125.00	250.00
BH Bob Henrich	50.00	100.00
BM Bobby Morgan	60.00	120.00
BP Buddy Pritchard	60.00	120.00
BR Brooks Robinson	75.00	150.00
BT Bill Taylor	60.00	120.00
BW Bill Wight	50.00	100.00
CH Chuck Harmon	50.00	100.00
CR Charley Rabe	50.00	100.00
DM Dave Melton	60.00	120.00
DS Duke Snider	100.00	200.00
DW David Wright	250.00	350.00
DY Delmon Young	60.00	120.00
DZ Don Zimmer	60.00	120.00
EN Ed Mayer	50.00	100.00
GK George Kell	75.00	150.00
HP Harding Peterson	60.00	120.00
JB Jim Bunning	75.00	150.00
JC Joe Caffie	60.00	120.00
JD Joe Durham	75.00	150.00
JL Joe Lonnett	50.00	100.00
JM Justin Morneau	50.00	100.00
JP Johnny Podres	90.00	150.00
LA Luis Aparicio	100.00	200.00
LM Lloyd Merritt	60.00	120.00
LS Lou Sleater	50.00	100.00
MB Milt Bolling	60.00	120.00
OH Orlando Hudson	50.00	100.00
PS Paul Smith	50.00	100.00
RC Ray Crone	40.00	80.00
RH Ryan Howard	150.00	300.00
RS Red Schoendienst	100.00	200.00
SP Stan Palys	50.00	100.00
TT Tim Thompson	40.00	80.00
CJD Jim Derrington	60.00	120.00
DWW Dontrelle Willis	50.00	100.00
MEB Mack Burk	50.00	100.00

2007 Topps Heritage Then and Now

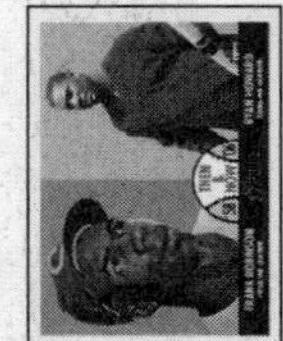

COMPLETE SET (10)	8.00	20.00
STATED ODDS 1:15 HOBBY, 1:15 RETAIL		
TN1 Frank Robinson	1.25	3.00
Ryan Howard		
TN2 Mickey Mantle	1.50	4.00
David Ortiz		
TN3 Ted Williams	1.25	3.00
Joe Mauer		
TN4 Luis Aparicio	.75	2.00
Jose Reyes		
TN5 Lew Burdette	.75	2.00
Johan Santana		
TN6 Johnny Podres	.75	2.00
Aaron Harang		
TN7 Richie Ashburn	1.25	3.00
Ichiro Suzuki		
TN8 Stan Musial	1.25	3.00
Travis Hafner		
TN9 Jim Bunning	.75	2.00
Anibal Sanchez		
TN10 Warren Spahn	1.25	3.00
Chien-Ming Wang		

2008 Topps Heritage

COMP.SET w/o SP's (425)	40.00	80.00
COMP.HN SET (220)	125.00	200.00
COMP.HN SET w/o SP's (150)	12.50	30.00
COMMON CARD	.15	.40
COMMON RC	.40	1.00
COMMON TEAM CARD	.15	.40
COMMON GB SP	.40	1.00
COMMON SP	2.50	6.00
SP STATED ODDS 1:3 HOBBY/RETAIL		
HN SP ODDS 1:3 HOBBY/RETAIL		
1 Vladimir Guerrero	.40	1.00
2 Placido Polanco GB SP	.40	1.00
3 Eric Byrnes GB SP	.40	1.00
4 Mark Teixeira	.25	.60
5 Javier Vazquez GB SP	.40	1.00
6 Jacoby Ellsbury	.60	1.50
7 Joey Gathright GB SP	.40	1.00
8 Philadelphia Phillies GB SP	.40	1.00
9 Andre Ethier GB SP	.60	1.50
10 Alex Rodriguez	.60	1.50
11 Luke Scott SP	2.50	6.00
12 Curt Schilling GB SP	.60	1.50
13 Billy Wagner GB SP	.40	1.00
14 Gary Matthews GB SP	.40	1.00
15 Sean Marshall	.15	.40
16 Ichiro Suzuki GB SP	1.50	4.00
17 Jack Wilson	.15	.40
Jason Bay		
Freddy Sanchez		
18 Dontrelle Willis GB SP	.40	1.00
19 Josh Willingham	.15	.40
20 Jeff Kent	.15	.40
21 Troy Tulowitzki GB SP	.60	1.50
22 Brian Fuentes GB SP	.40	1.00
23 Robinson Cano GB SP	.60	1.50
24 Felix Hernandez GB SP	.60	1.50
25 Edwin Encarnacion	.15	.40
26 Fausto Carmona	.15	.40
27 Greg Maddux	.50	1.25
28 Ivan Rodriguez GB SP	.60	1.50
29 Joe Nathan	.15	.40
30 Paul Konerko	.15	.40
31 Nook Logan	.15	.40
32 Derek Lowe	.15	.40
33 Jose Lopez	.15	.40
34 Magglio Ordonez	.40	1.00
Curtis Granderson GB SP		
35 Adam LaRoche GB SP	.40	1.00
36 Kenny Lofton	.15	.40
37 Matt Capps	.15	.40
38 Mark Reynolds	.15	.40
39 Joe Mauer	.25	.60
40 Tim Hudson GB SP	.40	1.00
41 Kelvim Escobar GB SP	.40	1.00
42 Jason Jennings GB SP	.40	1.00
43 Victor Martinez	.15	.40
44 Jason Kendall	.15	.40
45 Chris Ray GB SP	.40	1.00
46 Jason Bergmann	.15	.40
47 Jason Marquis	.15	.40
48 Baltimore Orioles	.15	.40
49 Bill Hall GB SP	.40	1.00
50 Ken Griffey Jr.	.60	1.50
51 Chad Cordero	.15	.40
52 Omar Vizquel GB SP	.40	1.00
53 Jim Edmonds	.25	.60
54 Justin Upton GB SP	1.00	2.50
55 Josh Beckett	.25	.60
56 Jeff Francis	.15	.40
57 Brad Lidge GB SP	.40	1.00
58 Paul Lo Duca GB SP	.40	1.00
59 John Patterson	.15	.40
60 Andy Pettitte GB SP	.60	1.50
61 Brendan Harris GB SP	.40	1.00
62 Chris Young GB SP	.40	1.00
63 Eric Chavez	.15	.40
64 Francisco Rodriguez	.15	.40
65 Jason Giambi GB SP	.60	1.50
66 B.J. Ryan	.15	.40
67 Rich Hill GB SP	.40	1.00
68 Derek Jeter	1.00	2.50
69 San Francisco Giants GB SP	.40	1.00
70 Carlos Guillen	.15	.40
71 Trevor Hoffman GB SP	.40	1.00
72 Zach Duke	.15	.40
73 Dustin Pedroia	.60	1.50
74 Dmitri Young	.25	.60
Ryan Zimmerman		
75 Cole Hamels	.40	1.00
76 Carlos Delgado	.15	.40
77 Jonathan Broxton	.15	.40
78 Josh Hamilton GB SP	1.25	3.00
79 Mark Loretta GB SP	.40	1.00
80 Grady Sizemore	.25	.60
81 Torii Hunter GB SP	.40	1.00
82 Carlos Beltran GB SP	.40	1.00
83 Jason Isringhausen GB SP	.40	1.00
84 Brad Penny GB SP	.40	1.00
85 Jayson Werth	.15	.40
86 Alex Gordon	.40	1.00
87 David DeJesus	.15	.40
88 Clay Buchholz	.40	1.00
89 Conor Jackson	.15	.40
90 Hideki Matsui GB SP	1.00	2.50
91 Matt Garza GB SP	.40	1.00
92 Phil Hughes GB SP	1.00	2.50
93 Mike Piazza	.40	1.00
94 Chicago White Sox GB SP	.40	1.00
95 Buddy Carlyle	.15	.40
96 Mark DeRosa	.15	.40
97 Brandon Webb	.25	.60
98 Jon Garland GB SP	.40	1.00
99 Mariano Rivera	.40	1.00
100 Jack Cust	.15	.40
101 Carlos Ruiz	.15	.40
102 Moises Alou GB SP	.40	1.00
103 Bengie Molina	.15	.40
104 Adam Jones	.15	.40
105 Alfonso Soriano	.25	.60
106 Troy Glaus	.25	.60
107 John Maine	.15	.40
108 Pat Burrell	.15	.40
109 David Eckstein	.15	.40
110 Homer Bailey	.25	.60
111 Cincinnati Reds	.15	.40
112 Corey Hart	.15	.40
113 Orlando Hernandez	.15	.40
114 Orlando Cabrera	.15	.40
115 Ryan Garko	.15	.40
116 Wladimir Balentien GB SP (RC)	.40	1.00
117 Daric Barton GB SP (RC)	.40	1.00
118 Emilio Bonifacio RC	.60	1.50
119 Lance Broadway (RC)	.40	1.00
120 Jeff Clement (RC)	.40	1.00
121 Dave Davidson RC	.60	1.50
122 Ross Detwiler GB SP RC	1.00	2.50
123 Sam Fuld RC	.40	1.00
124 Armando Galarraga RC	.60	1.50
125 Harvey Garcia (RC)	.40	1.00
126 Dan Giese GB SP (RC)	.40	1.00
127 Alberto Gonzalez GB SP RC	.60	1.50
128 Kevin Hart (RC)	.40	1.00
129 Luke Hochevar GB SP RC	1.00	2.50
130 Chin-Lung Hu GB SP (RC)	.60	1.50
131 Brandon Jones RC	1.00	2.50
132 Joe Koshansky (RC)	.40	1.00
133 Radhames Liz RC	.60	1.50
134 Donny Lucy (RC)	.40	1.00
135 Mitch Stetter GB SP RC	.60	1.50
136 Nyjer Morgan (RC)	.40	1.00
137 Ross Ohlendorf RC	.60	1.50
138 Steve Pearce RC	.60	1.50
139 Jeff Ridgway RC	.60	1.50
140 Bronson Sardinha (RC)	.40	1.00
141 Seth Smith (RC)	.40	1.00
142 Rich Thompson RC	.60	1.50
143 Erick Threets (RC)	.40	1.00
144 J.R. Towles RC	1.00	2.50
145 Eugenio Velez RC	.40	1.00
146 Joey Votto (RC)	1.00	2.50
147 Alfonso Soriano	.25	.60
Aramis Ramirez		
Derrick Lee		
148 Hunter Pence	.40	1.00
149 Barry Zito	.15	.40
150 Albert Pujols	2.00	5.00
151 Sammy Sosa	.25	.60
152 Brian Bannister	.15	.40
153 Reggie Willits	.15	.40
154 Bobby Abreu	.15	.40
155 Johnny Damon GB SP	.60	1.50
156 Brandon Webb	.25	.60
Jake Peavy		
157 Aramis Ramirez	.15	.40
158 Aaron Cook	.15	.40
159 David Weathers	.15	.40
160 Jack Wilson	.15	.40
161 Josh Fogg	.15	.40
162 Garrett Atkins	.15	.40
163 Brad Ausmus	.15	.40
164 Gil Meche	.15	.40
165 Jeff Francoeur	.25	.60
166 Victor Martinez	.25	.60
Travis Hafner		
Grady Sizemore		
167 Juan Pierre	.15	.40
168 Rafael Furcal	.15	.40
169 J.J. Hardy	.15	.40
170 Nick Markakis	.25	.60
171 Delmon Young	.25	.60
172 Oakland Athletics	.15	.40
173 Ronny Paulino GB SP	.40	1.00
174 Mike Cameron GB SP	.40	1.00
175 Jeff Weaver GB SP	.40	1.00
176 Preston Wilson GB SP	.40	1.00
177 Robinson Tejeda GB SP	.40	1.00
178 Adam Lind GB SP	.40	1.00
179 Austin Kearns GB SP	.40	1.00
180 Jorge Posada GB SP	.60	1.50
181 Tadahito Iguchi	.15	.40
182 Matt Cain	.15	.40
183 Yuniesky Betancourt	.15	.40
184 Bronson Arroyo	.15	.40
185 Brad Hawpe GB SP	.40	1.00
186 Rickie Weeks GB SP	.40	1.00
187 Carlos Silva GB SP	.40	1.00
188 Adrian Gonzalez	.25	.60
189 Kenji Johjima	.15	.40
190 Chris Duncan	.15	.40
191 James Shields	.15	.40
192 Akinori Iwamura	.15	.40
193 David Murphy	.15	.40
194 Alex Rios	.15	.40
195 Carlos Quentin GB SP	.40	1.00
196 Jose Valverde GB SP	.40	1.00
197 Derrek Lee GB SP	.60	1.50
198 Jerry Owens GB SP	.40	1.00
199 Russell Martin	.15	.40
200 Yovani Gallardo	.15	.40
201a Johan Santana Twins	.25	.60
201b Johan Santana Mets	50.00	100.00
202 Nick Swisher	.15	.40
203 So Taguchi	.15	.40
204 Justin Morneau	.25	.60
205 Milton Bradley	.15	.40
206 Jake Westbrook	.15	.40
207 Dave Roberts	.15	.40
208 Billy Butler	.15	.40
209 Lance Berkman	.25	.60
210 J.J. Putz GB SP	.40	1.00
211 Mike Sweeney GB SP	.40	1.00
212 Andruw Jones	.50	1.25
Chipper Jones		
213 Ricky Nolasco	.15	.40
214 Andy LaRoche	.15	.40
215 Ray Durham	.15	.40
216 Francisco Cordero	.15	.40
217 Jered Weaver	.15	.40
218 Rafael Soriano	.15	.40
219 Orlando Hudson	.15	.40
220 Mike Lowell	.15	.40
221 Chris Snyder	.15	.40
222 Cesar Izturis	.15	.40
223 St. Louis Cardinals	.15	.40
224 David Wright GB SP	1.25	3.00
225 Pedro Martinez GB SP	.60	1.50
226 Rich Harden GB SP	.40	1.00
227 Shane Victorino GB SP	.40	1.00
228 Andrew Miller GB SP	.60	1.50
229 Chris Young	.15	.40
230 Andruw Jones	.15	.40
231 Kevin Gregg SP	2.50	6.00
232 C.C. Sabathia	.15	.40
233 Hanley Ramirez	.40	1.00
234 Wandy Rodriguez	.15	.40
235 Roy Oswalt	.15	.40
236 Mark Grudzielanek	.15	.40
237 Derek Jeter	1.00	2.50
Chien-Ming Wang		
Robinson Cano		
238 Todd Helton	.25	.60
239 Zack Greinke	.15	.40
240 Carlos Gomez	.15	.40
241 Lastings Milledge	.15	.40
242 Huston Street	.15	.40
243 Dan Haren	.15	.40
244 Carlos Pena	.40	1.00
245 Brad Wilkerson	.15	.40
246 Roy Halladay	.15	.40
247 Dmitri Young	.15	.40
248 Boston Red Sox	.60	1.50
249 Jonathan Papelbon	.25	.60
250 Felix Pie	.15	.40
251 Alex Gonzalez	.15	.40
252 Bobby Crosby	.15	.40
253 Justin Ruggiano RC	.60	1.50
254 Freddy Garcia	.15	.40
255 Khalil Greene	.25	.60
256 Rich Aurilia	.15	.40
257 Jarrod Washburn	.15	.40
258 B.J. Upton	.25	.60
259 Michael Young	.15	.40
260 Carlos Zambrano	.15	.40
261 Livan Hernandez	.15	.40
262 Chad Billingsley	.40	1.00
Derek Lowe		
Brad Penny GB SP		
263 Melky Cabrera GB SP	.40	1.00
264 Shannon Stewart GB SP	.40	1.00
265 Aaron Rowand GB SP	.40	1.00
266 Matt Morris GB SP	.40	1.00
267 Xavier Nady GB SP	.40	1.00
268 Jim Thome	.25	.60
269 Horacio Ramirez	.15	.40
270 Prince Fielder	.40	1.00
271 Andy Phillips	.15	.40
272 Aaron Harang	.15	.40
273 Josh Barfield	.15	.40
274 Ubaldo Jimenez	.15	.40
275 Anibal Sanchez	.15	.40
276 Carlos Lee	.15	.40
277 Mark Teahen	.15	.40
278 Delwyn Young	.15	.40
279 Kurt Suzuki	.15	.40
280 Nate Schierholtz	.15	.40
281 Raul Ibanez	.15	.40
282 Jose Vidro	.15	.40
283 Miguel Cabrera GB SP	.60	1.50
284 Luis Gonzalez GB SP	.40	1.00
285 Chad Billingsley GB SP	.40	1.00
286 Tony Gwynn GB SP	.40	1.00
287 Matt Kemp	.15	.40
288 James Loney	.25	.60
289 Brett Myers	.15	.40
290 Nate McLouth	.15	.40
291 Matt Chico	.40	1.00
Jason Bergmann GB SP		
292 Chad Tracy	.15	.40
293 Edgar Renteria	.15	.40
294 Jay Payton	.15	.40
295 Josh Johnson	.15	.40
296 Josh Banks (RC)	.40	1.00
297 Bill Murphy (RC)	.40	1.00
298 Ben Sheets	.25	.60
299 Jose Reyes	.25	.60
300 Chase Utley	.40	1.00
301 Ronnie Belliard GB SP	.40	1.00
302 Wily Mo Pena	.15	.40
303 Tim Lincecum	.40	1.00
304 Chicago Cubs	.25	.60
305 John Lackey	.15	.40
306 Stephen Drew	.15	.40
307 Kelly Johnson	.15	.40
308 Daisuke Matsuzaka	.60	1.50
309 Craig Monroe	.15	.40
310 Jerry Owens	.15	.40
311 Jeff Suppan	.15	.40
312 Tom Glavine	.25	.60
313 Kei Igawa	.15	.40
314 Mark Kotsay	.15	.40
315 Jacque Jones SP	2.50	6.00
316 Melvin Mora	.15	.40
317 Matt Holliday	.40	1.00
Hanley Ramirez		
318 Jarrod Saltalamacchia	.15	.40
319 A.J. Burnett	.15	.40
320 Casey Kotchman	.15	.40
321 Randy Winn GB SP	.40	1.00
322 Richie Sexson GB SP	.40	1.00
323 Juan Encarnacion GB SP	.40	1.00
324 Rick Ankiel GB SP	.40	1.00
325 Dan Wheeler GB SP	.40	1.00
326 Brian Roberts	.25	.60
327 David Ortiz	.40	1.00
328 Garret Anderson	.15	.40
329 Detroit Tigers	.15	.40
330 Ty Wigginton GB SP	.40	1.00
331 Travis Hafner	.15	.40
332 Howie Kendrick GB SP	.40	1.00
333 Kevin Kouzmanoff GB SP	.40	1.00
334 Matt Holliday GB SP	.60	1.50
335 Brandon Phillips GB SP	.40	1.00
336 Ian Kinsler GB SP	.60	1.50
337 Lyle Overbay GB SP	.40	1.00
338 Justin Verlander GB SP	.60	1.50
339 Ian Snell	.15	.40
340 Hank Blalock	.15	.40
341 Vernon Wells	.15	.40
342 Matt Chico	.15	.40
343 Tim Wakefield	.15	.40
344 Michael Bourn	.15	.40
345 Chris Carpenter	.15	.40
346 Daisuke Matsuzaka	.60	1.50
Josh Beckett		
347 Chuck James GB SP	.40	1.00
348 Joba Chamberlain	.50	1.25
349 Erik Bedard	.15	.40
350 Jimmy Rollins GB SP	.60	1.50
351 Anthony Reyes	.15	.40
352 Carl Crawford	.15	.40
353 Jeremy Hermida	.15	.40
354 Ervin Santana	.15	.40
355 Edgar Gonzalez	.15	.40
356 Yunel Escobar	.15	.40
357 Yorvit Torrealba	.15	.40
358 Hideki Okajima	.15	.40
359 Paul Byrd	.15	.40
360 Magglio Ordonez GB SP	.60	1.50
361 Joe Borowski	.15	.40
362 Clint Sammons (RC)	.40	1.00
363 Chris Duffy	.15	.40
364 Fred Lewis	.15	.40
365 Adrian Beltre	.15	.40
366 Alex Rodriguez BT	.60	1.50
367 Troy Tulowitzki BT	.25	.60
368 Prince Fielder BT	.40	1.00
369 Clay Buchholz BT	.40	1.00
370 Justin Verlander BT GB SP	.60	1.50
371 Pedro Martinez BT GB SP	.60	1.50
372 Ryan Howard BT GB SP	1.25	3.00
373 Ichiro Suzuki BT	.60	1.50
374 Kenny Lofton BT	.15	.40
375 Manny Ramirez BT	.40	1.00
376 Randy Johnson	.40	1.00
377 Chris Capuano	.15	.40
378 Johnny Estrada	.15	.40
379 Franklin Morales	.15	.40
380 Ryan Howard	.50	1.25
381 Casey Blake SP	2.50	6.00
382 Coco Crisp	.15	.40
383 John Maine	.15	.40

Willie Randolph MG
384 Jeremy Guthrie .15 .40
385 Geoff Jenkins .15 .40
386 Marlon Byrd .15 .40
387 Jeremy Bonderman .15 .40
388 Jason Varitek .40 1.00
389 Joe Girardi MG .15 .40
390 Ryan Braun .50 1.25
391 Ryan Zimmerman .15 .40
392 Mike Lowell .60 1.50
Kevin Youkilis
Dustin Pedroia
393 Pittsburgh Pirates .15 .40
394 Ryan Spilborghs .15 .40
395 Eric Gagne .15 .40
396 Joe Blanton .15 .40
397 Washington Nationals .15 4.00
398 Ryan Church .15 .40
399 Ted Lilly .15 .40
400 Manny Ramirez .40 1.00
401 Chad Gaudin .15 .40
402 Dustin McGowan .15 .40
403 Scott Baker .15 .40
404 Franklin Gutierrez .15 .40
405 Dave Bush .15 .40
406 Aubrey Huff .15 .40
407 Jermaine Dye .15 .40
408 Chase Utley .40 1.00
Jimmy Rollins
409 Jon Lester SP 3.00 8.00
410 Mark Buehrle .15 .40
411 Sergio Mitre .15 .40
412 Jason Bartlett .15 .40
413 Edwin Jackson .15 .40
414 J.D. Drew .15 .40
415 Freddy Sanchez GB SP .40 1.00
416 Asdrubal Cabrera .15 .40
417 Nate Robertson .15 .40
418 Shaun Marcum .15 .40
419 Atlanta Braves .25 .60
420 Noah Lowry .15 .40
421 Jamie Moyer .15 .40
422 Michael Cuddyer .15 .40
423 Randy Wolf .15 .40
424 Juan Uribe .15 .40
425 Brian McCann .25 .60
426 Kyle Lohse SP 2.50 6.00
427 Doug Davis SP 2.50 6.00
428 Ian Snell 2.50 6.00
Matt Capps
Tom Gorzelanny
Paul Maholm SP
429 Miguel Batista SP 2.50 6.00
430 Chien-Ming Wang SP 4.00 10.00
431 Jeff Salazar SP 2.50 6.00
432 Yadier Molina SP 2.50 6.00
433 Adam Wainwright SP 2.50 6.00
434 Scott Kazmir SP 2.50 6.00
435 Adam Dunn SP 2.50 6.00
436 Ryan Freel SP 2.50 6.00
437 Jhonny Peralta SP 2.50 6.00
438 Kazuo Matsui SP 2.50 6.00
439 Daniel Cabrera .15 .40
440a John Smoltz .40 1.00
440b John Smoltz 60.00 120.00
Name misspelled Jon
441 Emil Brown SP 2.50 6.00
442 Gary Sheffield SP 2.50 6.00
443 Jake Peavy SP 3.00 8.00
444 Scott Rolen SP 3.00 8.00
445 Kason Gabbard SP 2.50 6.00
446 Aaron Hill SP 2.50 6.00
447 Felipe Lopez SP 2.50 6.00
448 Dan Uggla SP 2.50 6.00
449 Willy Taveras SP 2.50 6.00
450 Chipper Jones SP 3.00 8.00
451 Josh Anderson SP (RC) 3.00 8.00
452 Chris Young 3.00 8.00
Justin Upton
Eric Byrnes SP
453 Braden Looper SP 2.50 6.00
454 Brandon Inge SP 2.50 6.00
455 Brian Giles SP 2.50 6.00
456 Corey Patterson SP 2.50 6.00
457 Los Angeles Dodgers SP 3.00 8.00
458 Sean Casey SP 2.50 6.00
459 Pedro Feliz SP 2.50 6.00
460 Tom Gorzelanny .15 .40
461 Chone Figgins SP 2.50 6.00
462 Kyle Kendrick SP 2.50 6.00
463 Tony Pena SP 2.50 6.00
464 Marcus Giles SP 2.50 6.00
465 Augie Ojeda SP 2.50 6.00
466 Micah Owings SP 2.50 6.00
467 Ryan Theriot SP 2.50 6.00
468 Shawn Green SP 2.50 6.00
469 Frank Thomas SP 3.00 8.00
470 Lenny DiNardo SP 2.50 6.00
471 Jose Bautista SP 2.50 6.00
472 Manny Corpas SP 2.50 6.00
473 Kevin Millwood SP 2.50 6.00
474 Kevin Youkilis SP 2.50 6.00
475 Jose Contreras SP 2.50 6.00
476 Cleveland Indians .15 .40
477 Julio Lugo SP 2.50 6.00
478 Jason Bay .15 .40
479 Tony LaRussa AS MG SP 2.50 6.00
480 Jim Leyland AS MG SP 2.50 6.00
481 Derrek Lee AS SP 2.50 6.00
482 Justin Morneau AS SP 2.50 6.00
483 Orlando Hudson AS SP 2.50 6.00
484 Brian Roberts AS SP 2.50 6.00
485 Miguel Cabrera AS SP 3.00 8.00
486 Mike Lowell AS SP 2.50 6.00
487 J.J. Hardy AS SP 2.50 6.00
488 Carlos Guillen AS SP 2.50 6.00
489 Ken Griffey Jr. AS SP 4.00 10.00
490 Vladimir Guerrero AS SP 3.00 8.00
491 Alfonso Soriano AS SP 3.00 8.00
492 Ichiro Suzuki AS SP 4.00 10.00
493 Matt Holliday AS SP 3.00 8.00
494 Magglio Ordonez AS SP 3.00 8.00
495 Brian McCann AS SP 2.50 6.00
496 Victor Martinez AS SP 2.50 6.00
497 Brad Penny AS SP 2.50 6.00
498 Josh Beckett AS SP 3.00 8.00
499 Cole Hamels AS SP 3.00 8.00
500 Justin Verlander AS SP 3.00 8.00
501 John Danks .15 .40
502 Jamey Wright .15 .40
503 Johnny Cueto RC .60 1.50
504 Todd Wellemeyer .15 .40
505 Chase Headley .15 .40
506 Takashi Saito .15 .40
507 Skip Schumaker .15 .40
508 Tampa Bay Rays .15 .40
509 Marcus Thames .15 .40
510 Joe Saunders .15 .40
511 Jair Jurrjens .15 .40
512 Ryan Sweeney .15 .40
513 Darin Erstad .15 .40
514 Brandon Backe .40 1.00
515 Chris Volstad (RC) .40 1.00
516 Salomon Torres .15 .40
517 Brian Burres .15 .40
518 Brandon Boggs (RC) .60 1.50
519 Max Scherzer RC 1.00 2.50
520 Cliff Lee .15 .40
521 Angel Pagan .15 .40
522 Jason Kubel .15 .40
523 Jose Molina .40 1.00
524 Hiroki Kuroda RC .60 1.50
525 Matt Harrison (RC) .40 1.00
526 C.J. Wilson .15 .40
527 Robb Quinlan .15 .40
528 Darrell Rasner .40 1.00
529 Frank Catalanotto .40 1.00
530 Mike Mussina .15 .40
531 Ryan Doumit .40 1.00
532 Willie Bloomquist .40 1.00
533 Jonny Gomes .15 .40
534 Jesse Litsch .15 .40
535 Curtis Granderson .15 .40
536 A.J. Pierzynski .15 .40
537 Toronto Blue Jays .15 .40
538 Brian Buscher .40 1.00
539 Kelly Shoppach .40 1.00
540 Edinson Volquez .15 .40
541 Jon Rauch .40 1.00
542 Ramon Castro .40 1.00
543 Greg Smith RC .40 1.00
544 Sean Gallagher .15 .40
545 Justin Masterson RC 2.00 5.00
546 Milwaukee Brewers .15 .40
547 Jay Bruce (RC) 1.50 4.00
548 Glendon Rusch .15 .40
549 Jeremy Sowers .40 1.00
550 Ryan Dempster .15 .40
551 Clete Thomas RC .60 1.50
552 Jose Castillo .15 .40
553 Brandon Lyon .15 .40
554 Vicente Padilla .15 .40
555 Jeff Keppinger .15 .40
556 Colorado Rockies .15 .40
557 Dallas Braden .40 1.00
558 Adam Kennedy .15 .40
559 Luis Mendoza (RC) .40 1.00
560 Justin Duchscherer .15 .40
561 Mike Aviles RC .60 1.50
562 Jed Lowrie (RC) 1.00 2.50
563 Doug Mientkiewicz .40 1.00
564 Chris Burke .15 .40
565 Dana Eveland .15 .40
566 Bryan LaHair RC .40 1.00
567 Denard Span (RC) .60 1.50
568 Damion Easley .15 .40
569 Josh Fields .15 .40
570 Geovany Soto .40 1.00
571 Gerald Laird UER .15 .40
Pictured as rookie prospect
572 Bobby Jenks .15 .40
573 Andy Marte .15 .40
574 Mike Pelfrey .15 .40
575 Jerry Hairston .15 .40
576 Mike Lamb .15 .40
577 Ben Zobrist .15 .40
578 Carlos Gonzalez (RC) .40 1.00
579 Jose Guillen .40 1.00
580 Kosuke Fukudome RC 1.50 4.00
581 Gabe Kapler .40 1.00
582 Florida Marlins .15 .40
583 Ramon Vazquez .40 1.00
584 Wes Helms .40 1.00
585 Minnesota Twins .15 .40
586 Cody Ross .15 .40
587 Mike Napoli .15 .40
588 Alexi Casilla .15 .40
589 Emmanuel Burriss RC .60 1.50
590 Brian Wilson .15 .40
591 Rod Barajas .15 .40
592 Mike Hampton .40 1.00
593 Nick Blackburn RC .60 1.50
594 Joe Mather RC .60 1.50
595 Clayton Kershaw RC 1.25 3.00
596 Cliff Floyd .40 1.00
597 Sidney Ponson .40 1.00
598 Brian Anderson .15 .40
599 Joe Inglett .15 .40
600 Miguel Tejada .15 .40
601 San Diego Padres .15 .40
602 Scott Hairston .40 1.00
603 Joel Pineiro .15 .40
604 Fernando Tatis .15 .40
605 Greg Reynolds RC .60 1.50
606 Brian Moehler .15 .40
607 Kevin Millar .40 1.00
608 Ben Francisco .15 .40
609 Troy Percival .15 .40
610 Kerry Wood .15 .40
611 Max Ramirez RC .40 1.00
612 Jeff Baker .15 .40
613 Houston Astros .15 .40
614 Russell Branyan .15 .40
615 Todd Jones .15 .40
616 Brian Schneider .15 .40
617 Gregorio Petit RC .60 1.50
618 Matt Diaz .15 .40
619 Blake DeWitt (RC) 1.00 2.50
620 Cristian Guzman .15 .40
621 Jeff Samardzija RC 1.25 3.00
622 John Baker (RC) .40 1.00
623 Eric Hinske .15 .40
624 Scott Olsen .15 .40
625 Greg Dobbs .15 .40
626 Carlos Marmol .40 1.00
627 Kansas City Royals .15 .40
628 Esteban German .15 .40
629 Dennis Sarfate .15 .40
630 Ryan Ludwick .15 .40
631 Mike Jacobs .15 .40
632 Tyler Yates .15 .40
633 Joel Hanrahan .15 .40
634 Manny Parra .15 .40
635 Maicer Izturis .15 .40
636 Juan Rivera .15 .40
637 Tim Redding .15 .40
638 Jose Arredondo RC .60 1.50
639 Mike Redmond .40 1.00
640 Joe Crede .15 .40
641 Omar Infante .15 .40
642 Nick Punto .15 .40
643 Jeff Mathis .15 .40
644 Andy Sonnanstine .15 .40
645 Masahide Kobayashi RC .60 1.50
646 Marco Scutaro .15 .40
647 Matt Macri (RC) .40 1.00
648 Ian Stewart SP 2.50 6.00
649 David Dellucci .40 1.00
650 Evan Longoria RC 3.00 8.00
651 Martin Prado .40 1.00
652 Glen Perkins .15 .40
653 Alfredo Amezaga .40 1.00
654 Brett Gardner (RC) 1.00 2.50
655 Angel Berroa .40 1.00
656 Pablo Sandoval RC .40 1.00
657 Jody Gerut .15 .40
658 Arizona Diamondbacks .15 4.00
659 Ryan Freel .40 1.00
660 Dioner Navarro .15 .40
661 Endy Chavez .40 1.00
662 Jorge Campillo .15 .40
663 Mark Ellis .15 .40
664 John Buck .15 .40
665 Texas Rangers .15 .40
666 Jason Michaels .15 .40
667 Chris Dickerson RC .60 1.50
668 Kevin Mench .15 .40
669 Aaron Miles .15 .40
670 Joakim Soria .15 .40
671 Chris Davis RC 1.00 2.50
672 Taylor Teagarden RC .60 1.50
673 Willy Aybar .15 .40
674 Paul Maholm .15 .40
675 Mike Gonzalez .15 .40
676 Seattle Mariners .15 .40
677 Ryan Langerhans SP 2.50 6.00
678 Alex Romero (RC) .60 1.50
679 Erick Aybar .15 .40
680 George Sherrill .15 .40
681 John Bowker (RC) .40 1.00
682 Zach Miner .40 1.00
683 Jorge Cantu .15 .40
684 Jo-Jo Reyes .15 .40
685 Ryan Raburn .15 .40
686 Gavin Floyd SP 2.50 6.00
687 Kevin Slowey SP 2.50 6.00
688 Gio Gonzalez SP (RC) 2.50 6.00
689 Eric Patterson SP 2.50 6.00
690 Jonathan Sanchez SP 2.50 6.00
691 Oliver Perez SP 2.50 6.00
692 John Lannan SP 2.50 6.00
693 Ramon Hernandez SP 2.50 6.00
694 Mike Fontenot SP 2.50 6.00
695 Ross Gload SP 2.50 6.00
696 Mark Sweeney SP 2.50 6.00
697 Nick Hundley SP (RC) 2.50 6.00
698 Kevin Correia SP 2.50 6.00
699 Jeremy Reed SP 2.50 6.00
700 Eddie Kunz SP RC 2.50 6.00
701 Miguel Montero SP 2.50 6.00
702 Gabe Gross SP 2.50 6.00
703 Matt Stairs SP 2.50 6.00
704 Kenny Rogers SP 2.50 6.00
705 Mark Hendrickson SP 2.50 6.00
706 Heath Bell SP 2.50 6.00
707 Wilson Betemit SP 2.50 6.00
708 Brandon Morrow SP 2.50 6.00
709 Brendan Ryan SP 2.50 6.00
710 Eric Hurley SP (RC) 2.50 6.00
711 Los Angeles Angels SP 2.50 6.00
712 Jack Hannahan SP 2.50 6.00
713 Seth McClung SP 2.50 6.00
714 New York Mets SP 2.50 6.00
715 Chris Perez SP RC 2.50 6.00
716 Clayton Richard SP (RC) 2.50 6.00
717 Jaime Garcia SP RC 2.50 6.00
718 Matt Joyce SP RC 2.50 6.00
719 Brad Ziegler SP RC 2.50 6.00
720 Ivan Ochoa (RC) .60 1.50

2008 Topps Heritage Black Back

*BLK BACK VET: .4X TO 1X BASIC
*BLK BACK RC: .4X TO 1X BASIC RC
RANDOM INSERTS IN PACKS

2008 Topps Heritage Chrome

1-100 ODDS 1:8 HOBBY, 1:18 RETAIL
1-100 INSERTED IN 08 HERITAGE
101-200 ODDS 1:6 HOBBY
101-200 INSERTED IN 08 TOPPS CHROME
201-300 ODDS 1:3 HOBBY
201-300 INSERTED IN 08 HERITAGE HN
STATED PRINT RUN 1959 SERIAL #'d SETS
C1 Hunter Pence 2.50 6.00
C2 Andre Ethier 2.00 5.00
C3 Curt Schilling 2.00 5.00
C4 Gary Matthews 1.50 4.00
C5 Dontrelle Willis 1.50 4.00
C6 Troy Tulowitzki 2.00 5.00
C7 Robinson Cano 2.00 5.00
C8 Felix Hernandez 2.00 5.00
C9 Josh Hamilton 2.50 6.00
C10 Justin Upton 2.50 6.00
C11 Brad Penny 1.50 4.00
C12 Hideki Matsui 2.50 6.00
C13 J.J. Putz 1.50 4.00
C14 Jorge Posada 2.00 5.00
C15 Albert Pujols 4.00 10.00
C16 Aaron Rowand 1.50 4.00
C17 Ronnie Belliard 1.50 4.00
C18 Rick Ankiel 1.50 4.00
C19 Ian Kinsler 2.00 5.00
C20 Justin Verlander 2.00 5.00
C21 Lyle Overbay 1.50 4.00
C22 Tim Hudson 1.50 4.00
C23 Ryan Zimmerman 2.00 5.00
C24 Ryan Braun 2.50 6.00
C25 Jimmy Rollins 2.00 5.00
C26 Kelvim Escobar 1.50 4.00
C27 Adam LaRoche 1.50 4.00
C28 Ivan Rodriguez 2.00 5.00
C29 Billy Wagner 1.50 4.00
C30 Ichiro Suzuki 3.00 8.00
C31 Chris Young 1.50 4.00
C32 Trevor Hoffman 1.50 4.00
C33 Torii Hunter 1.50 4.00
C34 Jason Isringhausen 1.50 4.00
C35 Jose Valverde 1.50 4.00
C36 Derrek Lee 2.00 5.00
C37 Rich Harden 1.50 4.00
C38 Andrew Miller 2.00 5.00
C39 Miguel Cabrera 2.00 5.00
C40 David Wright 2.50 6.00
C41 Brandon Phillips 1.50 4.00
C42 Magglio Ordonez 2.00 5.00
C43 Eric Byrnes 1.50 4.00
C44 John Smoltz 2.50 6.00
C45 Brandon Webb 2.00 5.00
C46 Barry Zito 1.50 4.00
C47 Sammy Sosa 2.00 5.00
C48 James Shields 1.50 4.00
C49 Alex Rios 1.50 4.00
C50 Matt Holliday 2.00 5.00
C51 Chris Young 1.50 4.00
C52 Roy Oswalt 1.50 4.00
C53 Matt Kemp 1.50 4.00
C54 Tim Lincecum 2.50 6.00
C55 Hanley Ramirez 2.50 6.00
C56 Vladimir Guerrero 2.50 6.00
C57 Mark Teixeira 2.00 5.00
C58 Fausto Carmona 1.50 4.00
C59 B.J. Ryan 1.50 4.00
C60 Manny Ramirez 2.50 6.00
C61 Carlos Delgado 1.50 4.00
C62 Matt Cain 1.50 4.00
C63 Brian Bannister 1.50 4.00
C64 Russell Martin 1.50 4.00
C65 Todd Helton 2.00 5.00
C66 Roy Halladay 1.50 4.00
C67 Lance Berkman 2.00 5.00
C68 John Lackey 1.50 4.00
C69 Daisuke Matsuzaka 3.00 8.00
C70 Joe Mauer 2.00 5.00
C71 Francisco Rodriguez 1.50 4.00
C72 Derek Jeter 5.00 12.00
C73 Homer Bailey 2.00 5.00
C74 Jonathan Papelbon 2.00 5.00
C75 Billy Butler 1.50 4.00
C76 B.J. Upton 2.00 5.00
C77 Ubaldo Jimenez 1.50 4.00
C78 Erik Bedard 1.50 4.00
C79 Jeff Kent 1.50 4.00
C80 Ken Griffey Jr. 3.00 8.00
C81 Josh Beckett 2.00 5.00
C82 Jeff Francis 1.50 4.00
C83 Grady Sizemore 2.00 5.00
C84 John Maine 1.50 4.00
C85 Cole Hamels 2.50 6.00
C86 Nick Markakis 2.00 5.00
C87 Ben Sheets 1.50 4.00
C88 Jose Reyes 2.00 5.00
C89 Vernon Wells 1.50 4.00
C90 Justin Morneau 2.00 5.00
C91 Brian McCann 2.00 5.00
C92 Jacoby Ellsbury 3.00 8.00
C93 Clay Buchholz 2.50 6.00
C94 Prince Fielder 2.50 6.00
C95 David Ortiz 2.50 6.00
C96 Joba Chamberlain 2.50 6.00
C97 Chien-Ming Wang 2.50 6.00
C98 Chipper Jones 2.50 6.00
C99 Chase Utley 2.50 6.00
C100 Alex Rodriguez 4.00 10.00
C101 Phil Hughes 2.50 6.00
C102 Hideki Okajima 1.50 4.00
C103 Chone Figgins 1.50 4.00
C104 Jose Vidro 1.50 4.00
C105 Johan Santana 2.00 5.00
C106 Paul Konerko 1.50 4.00
C107 Alfonso Soriano 2.00 5.00
C108 Kei Igawa 1.50 4.00
C109 Lastings Milledge 1.50 4.00
C110 Asdrubal Cabrera 1.50 4.00
C111 Brandon Jones 2.50 6.00
C112 Tom Gorzelanny 1.50 4.00
C113 Delmon Young 2.00 5.00
C114 Daric Barton 1.50 4.00
C115 David DeJesus 1.50 4.00
C116 Ryan Howard 2.50 6.00
C117 Tom Glavine 2.50 6.00
C118 Frank Thomas 2.50 6.00
C119 J.R. Towles 2.50 6.00
C120 Jeremy Bonderman 1.50 4.00
C121 Adrian Beltre 1.50 4.00
C122 Dan Haren 1.50 4.00
C123 Kazuo Matsui 1.50 4.00
C124 Joe Blanton 1.50 4.00
C125 Dan Uggla 2.00 5.00
C126 Stephen Drew 1.50 4.00
C127 Daniel Cabrera 1.50 4.00
C128 Jeff Clement 1.50 4.00
C129 Pedro Martinez 2.00 5.00
C130 Josh Anderson 1.50 4.00
C131 Orlando Hudson 1.50 4.00
C132 Jason Bay 1.50 4.00
C133 Eric Chavez 1.50 4.00
C134 Johnny Damon 2.00 5.00
C135 Lance Broadway 1.50 4.00
C136 Jake Peavy 2.00 5.00
C137 Carl Crawford 1.50 4.00
C138 Kenji Johjima 1.50 4.00
C139 Melky Cabrera 1.50 4.00
C140 Aaron Hill 1.50 4.00
C141 Carlos Lee 1.50 4.00
C142 Mark Buehrle 1.50 4.00
C143 Carlos Beltran 1.50 4.00
C144 Chin-Lung Hu 2.00 5.00
C145 C.C. Sabathia 1.50 4.00
C146 Dustin Pedroia 3.00 8.00
C147 Freddy Sanchez 1.50 4.00
C148 Kevin Youkilis 2.00 5.00
C149 Radhames Liz 2.00 5.00
C150 Jim Thome 2.00 5.00
C151 Greg Maddux 2.50 6.00
C152 Rich Hill 1.50 4.00
C153 Andy LaRoche 1.50 4.00
C154 Gil Meche 1.50 4.00
C155 Victor Martinez 1.50 4.00
C156 Mariano Rivera 2.50 6.00
C157 Kyle Kendrick 1.50 4.00
C158 Jarrod Saltalamacchia 1.50 4.00
C159 Tadahito Iguchi 1.50 4.00
C160 Eric Gagne 1.50 4.00
C161 Garrett Atkins 1.50 4.00
C162 Pat Burrell 1.50 4.00
C163 Akinori Iwamura 1.50 4.00
C164 Melvin Mora 1.50 4.00
C165 Joey Votto 2.50 6.00
C166 Brian Roberts 2.00 5.00
C167 Brett Myers 1.50 4.00
C168 Michael Young 1.50 4.00
C169 Adam Jones 1.50 4.00
C170 Carlos Zambrano 1.50 4.00
C171 Jeff Francoeur 2.00 5.00
C172 Brad Hawpe 1.50 4.00
C173 Andy Pettitte 2.00 5.00
C174 Ryan Garko 1.50 4.00
C175 Adrian Gonzalez 2.00 5.00
C176 Ted Lilly 1.50 4.00
C177 J.J. Hardy 1.50 4.00
C178 Jon Lester 2.00 5.00
C179 Carlos Pena 2.50 6.00
C180 Ross Detwiler 2.50 6.00
C181 Andruw Jones 1.50 4.00
C182 Gary Sheffield 1.50 4.00
C183 Dmitri Young 1.50 4.00
C184 Carlos Guillen 1.50 4.00
C185 Yovani Gallardo 1.50 4.00
C186 Alex Gordon 2.50 6.00
C187 Aaron Harang 1.50 4.00
C188 Travis Hafner 1.50 4.00
C189 Orlando Cabrera 1.50 4.00
C190 Bobby Abreu 1.50 4.00
C191 Randy Johnson 2.50 6.00
C192 Scott Kazmir 2.00 5.00
C193 Jason Varitek 2.50 6.00
C194 Mike Lowell 1.50 4.00
C195 A.J. Burnett 1.50 4.00
C196 Garret Anderson 1.50 4.00
C197 Chris Carpenter 1.50 4.00
C198 Jermaine Dye 1.50 4.00
C199 Luke Hochevar 2.50 6.00
C200 Steve Pearce 2.00 5.00
C201 Joe Saunders 1.50 4.00
C202 Cliff Lee 1.50 4.00
C203 Mike Mussina 1.50 4.00
C204 Ryan Dempster 1.50 4.00
C205 Edinson Volquez 1.50 4.00
C206 Justin Duchscherer 1.50 4.00
C207 Geovany Soto 2.50 6.00
C208 Brian Wilson 1.50 4.00
C209 Kerry Wood 1.50 4.00
C210 Kosuke Fukudome 3.00 8.00
C211 Cristian Guzman 1.50 4.00
C212 Ryan Ludwick 1.50 4.00
C213 Joe Crede 1.50 4.00
C214 Dioner Navarro 1.50 4.00
C215 Miguel Tejada 1.50 4.00
C216 Joakim Soria 1.50 4.00
C217 George Sherrill 1.50 4.00
C218 John Danks 1.50 4.00
C219 Jair Jurrjens 1.50 4.00
C220 Evan Longoria 6.00 15.00
C221 Hiroki Kuroda 2.00 5.00
C222 Greg Smith 1.50 4.00
C223 Dana Eveland 1.50 4.00
C224 Ryan Sweeney 1.50 4.00
C225 Mike Pelfrey 1.50 4.00
C226 Nick Blackburn 2.00 5.00
C227 Scott Olsen 1.50 4.00
C228 Manny Parra 1.50 4.00
C229 Tim Redding 1.50 4.00
C230 Paul Maholm 1.50 4.00
C231 Todd Wellemeyer 1.50 4.00
C232 Jesse Litsch 1.50 4.00
C233 Andy Sonnanstine 1.50 4.00
C234 Johnny Cueto 2.00 5.00
C235 Vicente Padilla 1.50 4.00
C236 Glen Perkins 1.50 4.00
C237 Brian Burres 1.50 4.00
C238 Jamey Wright 1.50 4.00
C239 Chase Headley 1.50 4.00
C240 Takashi Saito 1.50 4.00
C241 Skip Schumaker 1.50 4.00
C242 Curtis Granderson 1.50 4.00
C243 A.J. Pierzynski 1.50 4.00
C244 Jorge Cantu 1.50 4.00
C245 Maicer Izturis 1.50 4.00
C246 Kevin Mench 1.50 4.00
C247 Jason Kubel 1.50 4.00
C248 Rod Barajas 1.50 4.00
C249 Jed Lowrie 2.50 6.00
C250 Bobby Jenks 1.50 4.00
C251 Jonny Gomes 1.50 4.00
C252 Clete Thomas 2.00 5.00
C253 Eric Hinske 1.50 4.00
C254 Brett Gardner 3.00 8.00
C255 Denard Span 2.00 5.00
C256 Brian Anderson 1.50 4.00
C257 Troy Percival 1.50 4.00
C258 Darrell Rasner 1.50 4.00
C259 Willy Aybar 1.50 4.00
C260 John Bowker 1.50 4.00
C261 Marco Scutaro 1.50 4.00
C262 Adam Kennedy 1.50 4.00
C263 Nick Punto 1.50 4.00
C264 Mike Napoli 1.50 4.00
C265 Carlos Gonzalez 1.50 4.00
C266 Matt Macri 1.50 4.00
C267 Marcus Thames 1.50 4.00
C268 Ben Zobrist 1.50 4.00
C269 Mark Ellis 1.50 4.00
C270 Mike Aviles 2.00 5.00
C271 Angel Pagan 1.50 4.00
C272 Erick Aybar 1.50 4.00
C273 Todd Jones 1.50 4.00
C274 Brandon Boggs 2.50 6.00
C275 Mike Jacobs 1.50 4.00
C276 Mike Gonzalez 1.50 4.00
C277 Mike Lamb 1.50 4.00
C278 Robb Quinlan 1.50 4.00
C279 Salomon Torres 1.50 4.00
C280 Jose Castillo 1.50 4.00
C281 Damion Easley 1.50 4.00
C282 Jo-Jo Reyes 1.50 4.00
C283 Cody Ross 1.50 4.00
C284 Alexi Casilla 1.50 4.00
C285 Jerry Hairston
C286 Brandon Lyon 1.50 4.00
C287 Greg Dobbs 1.50 4.00
C288 Joel Pineiro 1.50 4.00
C289 Chris Davis 3.00 8.00
C290 Masahide Kobayashi 2.00 5.00
C291 Darin Erstad 1.50 4.00
C292 Matt Diaz 1.50 4.00
C293 Brian Schneider 1.50 4.00
C294 Gerald Laird 1.50 4.00
C295 Ben Francisco 1.50 4.00
C296 Brian Moehler 1.50 4.00
C297 Aaron Miles 1.50 4.00
C298 Max Scherzer 2.50 6.00
C299 C.J. Wilson 1.50 4.00
C300 Jay Bruce 3.00 8.00

2008 Topps Heritage Chrome Refractors

*CHROME REF: .6X TO 1.5X
1-100 ODDS 1:29 HOBBY, 1:59 RETAIL
1-100 INSERTED IN 08 TOPPS HERITAGE
101-200 ODDS 1:21 HOBBY
101-200 INSERTED IN 08 TOPPS CHROME
201-300 ODDS 1:11 HOBBY
201-300 INSERTED IN 08 HERITAGE HN
STATED PRINT RUN 559 SERIAL #'d SETS
C72 Derek Jeter 12.50 30.00
C100 Alex Rodriguez 12.50 30.00
C220 Evan Longoria 8.00 20.00

2008 Topps Heritage Chrome Refractors Black

1-100 ODDS 1:315 HOB,1:450 RET
1-100 INSERTED IN 08 TOPPS HERITAGE
101-200 ODDS 1:196 HOBBY
201-300 INSERTED IN 08 HERITAGE HN
201-300 ODDS 1:99 HOBBY
101-200 INSERTED IN 08 TOPPS CHROME
STATED PRINT RUN 59 SERIAL #'d SETS
C1 Hunter Pence 30.00 60.00
C2 Andre Ethier 20.00 50.00
C3 Curt Schilling 20.00 50.00
C4 Gary Matthews 20.00 50.00
C5 Dontrelle Willis 20.00 50.00
C6 Troy Tulowitzki 20.00 50.00
C7 Robinson Cano 20.00 50.00
C8 Felix Hernandez 20.00 50.00
C9 Josh Hamilton 50.00 100.00
C10 Justin Upton 20.00 50.00
C11 Brad Penny 20.00 50.00
C12 Hideki Matsui 30.00 60.00
C13 J.J. Putz 20.00 50.00
C14 Jorge Posada 20.00 50.00
C15 Albert Pujols 100.00 200.00
C16 Aaron Rowand 20.00 50.00
C17 Ronnie Belliard 20.00 50.00
C18 Rick Ankiel 20.00 50.00
C19 Ian Kinsler 20.00 50.00
C20 Justin Verlander 20.00 50.00
C21 Lyle Overbay 20.00 50.00
C22 Tim Hudson 20.00 50.00
C23 Ryan Zimmerman 20.00 50.00
C24 Ryan Braun 30.00 60.00
C25 Jimmy Rollins 20.00 50.00
C26 Kelvim Escobar 20.00 50.00
C27 Adam LaRoche 20.00 50.00
C28 Ivan Rodriguez 20.00 50.00
C29 Billy Wagner 20.00 50.00
C30 Ichiro Suzuki 60.00 120.00
C31 Chris Young 20.00 50.00
C32 Trevor Hoffman 20.00 50.00
C33 Torii Hunter 20.00 50.00
C34 Jason Isringhausen 20.00 50.00
C35 Jose Valverde 20.00 50.00
C36 Derrek Lee 20.00 50.00
C37 Rich Harden 20.00 50.00
C38 Andrew Miller 20.00 50.00
C39 Miguel Cabrera 20.00 50.00
C40 David Wright 40.00 80.00
C41 Brandon Phillips 20.00 50.00
C42 Magglio Ordonez 20.00 50.00
C43 Eric Byrnes 20.00 50.00
C44 John Smoltz 20.00 50.00
C45 Brandon Webb 20.00 50.00
C46 Barry Zito 20.00 50.00
C47 Sammy Sosa 20.00 50.00
C48 James Shields 20.00 50.00
C49 Alex Rios 20.00 50.00
C50 Matt Holliday 20.00 50.00
C51 Chris Young 20.00 50.00
C52 Roy Oswalt 20.00 50.00
C53 Matt Kemp 20.00 50.00
C54 Tim Lincecum 30.00 60.00
C55 Hanley Ramirez 20.00 50.00
C56 Vladimir Guerrero 20.00 50.00
C57 Mark Teixeira 20.00 50.00
C58 Fausto Carmona 20.00 50.00
C59 B.J. Ryan 20.00 50.00
C60 Manny Ramirez 20.00 50.00
C61 Carlos Delgado 20.00 50.00
C62 Matt Cain 20.00 50.00
C63 Brian Bannister 20.00 50.00
C64 Russell Martin 20.00 50.00
C65 Todd Helton 20.00 50.00
C66 Roy Halladay 20.00 50.00
C67 Lance Berkman 20.00 50.00
C68 John Lackey 20.00 50.00
C69 Daisuke Matsuzaka 40.00 80.00
C70 Joe Mauer 20.00 50.00
C71 Francisco Rodriguez 20.00 50.00
C72 Derek Jeter 60.00 120.00
C73 Homer Bailey 20.00 50.00
C74 Jonathan Papelbon 20.00 50.00
C75 Billy Butler 20.00 50.00
C76 B.J. Upton 20.00 50.00
C77 Ubaldo Jimenez 20.00 50.00
C78 Erik Bedard 20.00 50.00

C79 Jeff Kent 20.00 50.00
C80 Ken Griffey Jr. 60.00 120.00
C81 Josh Beckett 20.00 50.00
C82 Jeff Francis 20.00 50.00
C83 Grady Sizemore 20.00 50.00
C84 John Maine 20.00 50.00
C85 Cole Hamels 20.00 50.00
C86 Nick Markakis 20.00 50.00
C87 Ben Sheets 20.00 50.00
C88 Jose Reyes 20.00 50.00
C89 Vernon Wells 20.00 50.00
C90 Justin Morneau 20.00 50.00
C91 Brian McCann 20.00 50.00
C92 Jacoby Ellsbury 60.00 120.00
C93 Clay Buchholz 40.00 80.00
C94 Prince Fielder 30.00 60.00
C95 David Ortiz 30.00 60.00
C96 Joba Chamberlain 60.00 120.00
C97 Chien-Ming Wang 40.00 80.00
C98 Chipper Jones 20.00 50.00
C99 Chase Utley 20.00 50.00
C100 Alex Rodriguez 100.00 200.00
C101 Phil Hughes 20.00 50.00
C102 Hideki Okajima 12.50 30.00
C103 Chone Figgins 12.50 30.00
C104 Jose Vidro 12.50 30.00
C105 Johan Santana 20.00 50.00
C106 Paul Konerko 12.50 30.00
C107 Alfonso Soriano 15.00 40.00
C108 Kei Igawa 12.50 30.00
C109 Lastings Milledge 12.50 30.00
C110 Asdrubal Cabrera 12.50 30.00
C111 Brandon Jones 20.00 50.00
C112 Tom Gorzelanny 12.50 30.00
C113 Delmon Young 15.00 40.00
C114 Daric Barton 15.00 40.00
C115 David DeJesus 12.50 30.00
C116 Ryan Howard 60.00 120.00
C117 Tom Glavine 20.00 50.00
C118 Frank Thomas 20.00 50.00
C119 J.R. Towles 15.00 40.00
C120 Jeremy Bonderman 12.50 30.00
C121 Adrian Beltre 12.50 30.00
C122 Dan Haren 12.50 30.00
C123 Kazuo Matsui 12.50 30.00
C124 Joe Blanton 12.50 30.00
C125 Dan Uggla 12.50 30.00
C126 Stephen Drew 12.50 30.00
C127 Daniel Cabrera 12.50 30.00
C128 Jeff Clement 12.50 30.00
C129 Pedro Martinez 15.00 40.00
C130 Josh Anderson 12.50 30.00
C131 Orlando Hudson 12.50 30.00
C132 Jason Bay 12.50 30.00
C133 Eric Chavez 12.50 30.00
C134 Johnny Damon 12.50 30.00
C135 Lance Broadway 12.50 30.00
C136 Jake Peavy 15.00 40.00
C137 Carl Crawford 12.50 30.00
C138 Kenji Johjima 12.50 30.00
C139 Melky Cabrera 12.50 30.00
C140 Aaron Hill 12.50 30.00
C141 Carlos Lee 12.50 30.00
C142 Mark Buehrle 12.50 30.00
C143 Carlos Beltran 12.50 30.00
C144 Chin-Lung Hu 20.00 50.00
C145 C.C. Sabathia 12.50 30.00
C146 Dustin Pedroia 15.00 40.00
C147 Freddy Sanchez 12.50 30.00
C148 Kevin Youkilis 12.50 30.00
C149 Radhames Liz 15.00 40.00
C150 Jim Thome 15.00 40.00
C151 Greg Maddux 30.00 60.00
C152 Rich Hill 12.50 30.00
C153 Andy LaRoche 12.50 30.00
C154 Gil Meche 12.50 30.00
C155 Victor Martinez 12.50 30.00
C156 Mariano Rivera 20.00 50.00
C157 Kyle Kendrick 12.50 30.00
C158 Jarrod Saltalamacchia 12.50 30.00
C159 Tadahito Iguchi 12.50 30.00
C160 Eric Gagne 12.50 30.00
C161 Garrett Atkins 12.50 30.00
C162 Pat Burrell 12.50 30.00
C163 Akinori Iwamura 12.50 30.00
C164 Melvin Mora 12.50 30.00
C165 Joey Votto 15.00 40.00
C166 Brian Roberts 12.50 30.00
C167 Brett Myers 12.50 30.00
C168 Michael Young 12.50 30.00
C169 Adam Jones 12.50 30.00
C170 Carlos Zambrano 12.50 30.00
C171 Jeff Francoeur 15.00 40.00
C172 Brad Hawpe 12.50 30.00
C173 Andy Pettitte 15.00 40.00
C174 Ryan Garko 12.50 30.00
C175 Adrian Gonzalez 12.50 30.00
C176 Ted Lilly 12.50 30.00
C177 J.J. Hardy 12.50 30.00
C178 Jon Lester 15.00 40.00
C179 Carlos Pena 12.50 30.00
C180 Ross Detwiler 20.00 50.00
C181 Andruw Jones 12.50 30.00
C182 Gary Sheffield 12.50 30.00
C183 Dmitri Young 12.50 30.00
C184 Carlos Guillen 12.50 30.00
C185 Yovani Gallardo 12.50 30.00
C186 Alex Gordon 20.00 50.00
C187 Aaron Harang 12.50 30.00
C188 Travis Hafner 12.50 30.00
C189 Orlando Cabrera 12.50 30.00
C190 Bobby Abreu 12.50 30.00
C191 Randy Johnson 20.00 50.00
C192 Scott Kazmir 15.00 40.00
C193 Jason Varitek 20.00 50.00
C194 Mike Lowell 15.00 40.00
C195 A.J. Burnett 12.50 30.00
C196 Garret Anderson 12.50 30.00
C197 Chris Carpenter 12.50 30.00
C198 Jermaine Dye 12.50 30.00
C199 Luke Hochevar 15.00 40.00
C200 Steve Pearce 20.00 50.00
C201 Joe Saunders 12.50 30.00
C202 Cliff Lee 12.50 30.00
C203 Mike Mussina 12.50 30.00
C204 Ryan Dempster 12.50 30.00
C205 Edinson Volquez 12.50 30.00
C206 Justin Duchscherer 12.50 30.00
C207 Geovany Soto 12.50 30.00
C208 Brian Wilson 12.50 30.00
C209 Kerry Wood 12.50 30.00
C210 Kosuke Fukudome 20.00 50.00
C211 Cristian Guzman 12.50 30.00
C212 Ryan Ludwick 12.50 30.00
C213 Joe Crede 12.50 30.00
C214 Dioner Navarro 12.50 30.00
C215 Miguel Tejada 12.50 30.00
C216 Joakim Soria 12.50 30.00
C217 George Sherrill 12.50 30.00
C218 John Danks 12.50 30.00
C219 Jair Jurrjens 12.50 30.00
C220 Evan Longoria 60.00 120.00
C221 Hiroki Kuroda 15.00 40.00
C222 Greg Smith 12.50 30.00
C223 Dana Eveland 12.50 30.00
C224 Ryan Sweeney 12.50 30.00
C225 Mike Pelfrey 12.50 30.00
C226 Nick Blackburn 15.00 40.00
C227 Scott Olsen 12.50 30.00
C228 Manny Parra 12.50 30.00
C229 Tim Redding 12.50 30.00
C230 Paul Maholm 12.50 30.00
C231 Todd Wellemeyer 12.50 30.00
C232 Jesse Litsch 12.50 30.00
C233 Andy Sonnanstine 12.50 30.00
C234 Johnny Cueto 12.50 30.00
C235 Vicente Padilla 12.50 30.00
C236 Glen Perkins 12.50 30.00
C237 Brian Burres 12.50 30.00
C238 Jamey Wright 12.50 30.00
C239 Chase Headley 12.50 30.00
C240 Takashi Saito 20.00 50.00
C241 Skip Schumaker 12.50 30.00
C242 Curtis Granderson 12.50 30.00
C243 A.J. Pierzynski 12.50 30.00
C244 Jorge Cantu 12.50 30.00
C245 Maicer Izturis 12.50 30.00
C246 Kevin Mench 12.50 30.00
C247 Jason Kubel 12.50 30.00
C248 Rod Barajas 12.50 30.00
C249 Jed Lowrie 15.00 40.00
C250 Bobby Jenks 12.50 30.00
C251 Jonny Gomes 12.50 30.00
C252 Clete Thomas 15.00 40.00
C253 Eric Hinske 12.50 30.00
C254 Brett Gardner 15.00 40.00
C255 Denard Span 15.00 40.00
C256 Brian Anderson 12.50 30.00
C257 Troy Percival 12.50 30.00
C258 Darrell Rasner 12.50 30.00
C259 Willy Aybar 12.50 30.00
C260 John Bowker 12.50 30.00
C261 Marco Scutaro 12.50 30.00
C262 Adam Kennedy 12.50 30.00
C263 Nick Punto 12.50 30.00
C264 Mike Napoli 12.50 30.00
C265 Carlos Gonzalez 12.50 30.00
C266 Matt Macri 12.50 30.00
C267 Marcus Thames 12.50 30.00
C268 Ben Zobrist 12.50 30.00
C269 Mark Ellis 12.50 30.00
C270 Mike Aviles 15.00 40.00
C271 Angel Pagan 12.50 30.00
C272 Erick Aybar 12.50 30.00
C273 Todd Jones 12.50 30.00
C274 Brandon Boggs 12.50 30.00
C275 Mike Jacobs 12.50 30.00
C276 Mike Gonzalez 12.50 30.00
C277 Mike Lamb 12.50 30.00
C278 Robb Quinlan 12.50 30.00
C279 Salomon Torres 12.50 30.00
C280 Jose Castillo 12.50 30.00
C281 Damion Easley 12.50 30.00
C282 Jo-Jo Reyes 12.50 30.00
C283 Cody Ross 12.50 30.00
C284 Alexi Casilla 12.50 30.00
C285 Jerry Hairston 12.50 30.00
C286 Brandon Lyon 12.50 30.00
C287 Greg Dobbs 12.50 30.00
C288 Joel Pineiro 12.50 30.00
C289 Chris Davis 15.00 40.00
C290 Masahide Kobayashi 15.00 40.00
C291 Darin Erstad 12.50 30.00
C292 Matt Diaz 12.50 30.00
C293 Brian Schneider 12.50 30.00
C294 Gerald Laird 12.50 30.00
C295 Ben Francisco 12.50 30.00
C296 Brian Moehler 12.50 30.00
C297 Aaron Miles 12.50 30.00
C298 Max Scherzer 15.00 40.00
C299 C.J. Wilson 12.50 30.00
C300 Jay Bruce 20.00 50.00

2008 Topps Heritage 1959 Buybacks

RANDOM INSERTS IN PACKS
NO PRICING DUE TO SCARCITY

2008 Topps Heritage 1959 Cut Signature

STATED ODDS 1:98,200 HOBBY
HN ODDS 1:65,000 HOBBY
STATED PRINT RUN 1 SER.#'d SET
NO PRICING DUE TO SCARCITY
BA Bob Allison
DD Don Drysdale
DH Don Hoak HN
EM Eddie Mathews
ES Enos Slaughter HN
EW Early Wynn
FF Ford Frick
HB Hank Bauer HN
JJ Jackie Jensen HN
KB Ken Boyer HN
LB Lew Burdette
MM Mickey Mantle
RA Richie Ashburn
RC Roberto Clemente
WA Walter Alston HN
WS Warren Spahn

2008 Topps Heritage 1959 Cut Signature Relics

STATED ODDS 1:100,000 HOBBY
STATED PRINT RUN 1 SER.#'d SET
NO PRICING DUE TO SCARCITY
EM Eddie Mathews HN
LB Lou Burdette HN
MM Mickey Mantle HN
RA Richie Ashburn HN

2008 Topps Heritage 2008 Flashbacks

jon lester
LESTER TOSSES NO-HITTER AGAINST ROYALS

COMPLETE SET (10) 6.00 15.00
STATED ODDS 1:12 HOBBY
FB1 Mark Teixeira .75 2.00
FB2 Tim Lincecum 1.25 3.00
FB3 Jon Lester .75 2.00
FB4 Ken Griffey Jr. 2.00 5.00
FB5 Kosuke Fukudome 2.00 5.00
FB6 Albert Pujols 2.50 6.00
FB7 Ichiro Suzuki 2.00 5.00
FB8 Felix Hernandez .75 2.00
FB9 Carlos Delgado .50 1.25
FB10 Josh Hamilton 1.50 4.00

2008 Topps Heritage Baseball Flashbacks

brooks robinson
BREAKS UP 0-0 GAME WITH WALK-OFF HIT IN 16TH

STATED ODDS 1:12 HOBBY,1:12 RETAIL
BF1 Minnie Minoso .50 1.25
BF2 Luis Aparicio .50 1.25
BF3 Ernie Banks 1.25 3.00
BF4 Bill Mazeroski .75 2.00
BF5 Bob Gibson .75 2.00
BF6 Frank Robinson .50 1.25
BF7 Brooks Robinson .75 2.00
BF8 Mickey Mantle 2.00 5.00
BF9 Orlando Cepeda .50 1.25
BF10 Eddie Mathews 1.25 3.00

2008 Topps Heritage Clubhouse Collection Relics

GROUP A ODDS 1:4100 H,1:7400 R
GROUP B ODDS 1:18,000 H,1:7800 R
GROUP C ODDS 1:90 H,1:182 R
GROUP D ODDS 1:54 H,1:108 R
HN GROUP A ODDS 1:3600 HOBBY
HN GROUP B ODDS 1:74 HOBBY
HN GROUP C ODDS 1:55 HOBBY
NO HN GRP A PRICING AVAILABLE
AD Adam Dunn C 3.00 8.00
AG Alex Gordon HN C 4.00 10.00
AJ Andruw Jones C 3.00 8.00
AJ Andruw Jones HN B 3.00 8.00
AL Al Kaline HN A
AP Albert Pujols HN B 6.00 15.00
AR Aramis Ramirez C 3.00 8.00
AR Aramis Ramirez HN B 3.00 8.00
BA Bobby Abreu C 3.00 8.00
BD Blake DeWitt HN B 6.00 15.00
BG Bob Gibson A 30.00 60.00
BG Bob Gibson HN B 10.00 25.00
BM Bill Mazeroski HN B 10.00 25.00
BR Brooks Robinson HN B 10.00 25.00
BS Bill Skowron HN A
CAB Craig Biggio C 4.00 10.00
CB Carlos Beltran C 3.00 8.00
CB Carlos Beltran HN B 3.00 8.00
CC Carl Crawford C 3.00 8.00
CD Carlos Delgado C 3.00 8.00
CG Curtis Granderson HN C 3.00 8.00
CL Carlos Lee C 3.00 8.00
CL Carlos Lee HN B 3.00 8.00
DH Dan Haren HN C 3.00 8.00
DL Derrek Lee C 3.00 8.00
DL Derrek Lee HN B 3.00 8.00
DO David Ortiz C 4.00 10.00
DO David Ortiz HN B 4.00 10.00
DS Duke Snider HN A
DY Dmitri Young C 3.00 8.00
DY Dmitri Young HN B 3.00 8.00
EB Erik Bedard HN C 3.00 8.00
EC Eric Chavez C 3.00 8.00
FR Frank Robinson HN A
FT Frank Thomas C 4.00 10.00
FT Frank Thomas HN B 4.00 10.00
GA Garret Anderson D 3.00 8.00
HB Hank Blalock D 3.00 8.00
IR Ivan Rodriguez C 4.00 10.00
JB Jeremy Bonderman HN C 3.00 8.00
JD Johnny Damon C 3.00 8.00
JD Jermaine Dye HN C 3.00 8.00
JE Jim Edmonds D 3.00 8.00
JE Johnny Estrada HN C 3.00 8.00
JL Julio Lugo HN C 3.00 8.00
JP Jorge Posada C 4.00 10.00
JS John Smoltz D 4.00 10.00
JV Justin Verlander C 4.00 10.00
LA Luis Aparicio A 60.00 120.00
LB Lance Berkman D 3.00 8.00
MC Miguel Cabrera D 4.00 10.00
MIM Minnie Minoso B 50.00 100.00
MM Mike Mussina D 3.00 8.00
MT Miguel Tejada D 3.00 8.00
MT Miguel Tejada HN B 3.00 8.00
NF Nellie Fox HN B 12.50 30.00
OC Orlando Cepeda HN A
PM Pedro Martinez D 4.00 10.00
PM Pedro Martinez HN B 3.00 8.00
RH Ryan Howard D 5.00 12.00
RO Roy Oswalt D 3.00 8.00
RO Roy Oswalt HN B 3.00 8.00
RR Robin Roberts HN B 8.00 20.00
RS Richie Sexson D 3.00 8.00
RS Darrell Rasner HN B 3.00 8.00
RZ Ryan Zimmerman D 4.00 10.00
RZ Ryan Zimmerman HN B 3.00 8.00
SG Shawn Green C 3.00 8.00
ST Steve Pearce HN C 3.00 8.00
TH Todd Helton C 4.00 10.00
TKH Torii Hunter D 3.00 8.00
TLH Travis Hafner D 3.00 8.00
WM Bill Mazeroski A 60.00 120.00
YB Yogi Berra A 60.00 120.00

2008 Topps Heritage Clubhouse Collection Relics Autographs

STATED ODDS 1:6875 HOBBY
STATED ODDS 1:14,200 RETAIL
HN ODDS 1:1815 HOBBY
STATED PRINT RUN 25 SER.#'d SETS
NO PRICING DUE TO SCARCITY
EXCHANGE DEADLINE 2/28/2010
HN EXCH DEADLINE 11/30/2010
AK Al Kaline HN
AR Aramis Ramirez
BG Bob Gibson
BM Brian McCann HN
BS Bill Skowron HN
CG Curtis Granderson HN
CK Clayton Kershaw HN
DR Darrell Rasner HN
DS Duke Snider HN
FL Fred Lewis HN
FR Frank Robinson HN
FS Freddy Sanchez EXCH
JB Jay Bruce HN
JC Joba Chamberlain
LA Luis Aparicio
MM Minnie Minoso EXCH
OC Orlando Cepeda HN
SP Scott Podsednik EXCH
WM Bill Mazeroski
YB Yogi Berra

2008 Topps Heritage Clubhouse Collection Relics Dual

STATED ODDS 1:5582 H,1:11,000 R
HN STATED ODDS 1:1900 HOBBY
HN PRINT RUN 59 SER.#'d SETS
AK Luis Aparicio 60.00 120.00
Paul Konerko
BL Ernie Banks 100.00 200.00
Derrek Lee
CL Orlando Cepeda 100.00 200.00
Fred Lewis HN
GE Bob Gibson 60.00 120.00
Jim Edmonds
KG Al Kaline 100.00 200.00
Curtis Granderson HN
MB Bill Mazeroski 60.00 120.00
Jason Bay
MH Minnie Minoso 60.00 120.00
Travis Hafner
RB Frank Robinson 150.00 250.00
Jay Bruce HN
SK Duke Snider 300.00 350.00
Clayton Kershaw HN
SR Bill Skowron 90.00 150.00
Darrell Rasner HN

2008 Topps Heritage Dick Perez

COMPLETE SET (10) 30.00 60.00
THREE PER $9.99 WALMART BOX
SIX PER $19.99 WALMART BOX
HDP1 Manny Ramirez 2.50 6.00
HDP2 Cameron Maybin 2.50 6.00
HDP3 Ryan Howard 3.00 8.00
HDP4 David Ortiz 2.50 6.00
HDP5 Tim Lincecum 2.50 6.00
HDP6 David Wright 3.00 8.00
HDP7 Mickey Mantle 6.00 15.00
HDP8 Joba Chamberlain 3.00 8.00
HDP9 Ichiro Suzuki 4.00 10.00
HDP10 Prince Fielder 2.50 6.00

2008 Topps Heritage Flashbacks Autographs

STATED ODDS 1:14,900 HOBBY
STATED ODDS 1:20,000 RETAIL
STATED PRINT RUN 25 SER.#'d SETS
NO PRICING DUE TO SCARCITY
EXCHANGE DEADLINE 2/28/10
BG Bob Gibson
EB Ernie Banks
LA Luis Aparicio
MM Minnie Minoso EXCH
WM Bill Mazeroski

2008 Topps Heritage Flashbacks Seat Relics

STATED ODDS 1:162 H,1:327 R
HN ODDS 1:3175 HOBBY
HN PRINT RUN 59 SER.#'d SETS
BG Bob Gibson 10.00 25.00
BR Brooks Robinson 10.00 25.00
DE Dwight D. Eisenhower HN 60.00 120.00
EB Ernie Banks 10.00 25.00
EM Eddie Mathews 10.00 25.00
FR Frank Robinson 8.00 20.00
LA Luis Aparicio 8.00 20.00
MIM Minnie Minoso 8.00 20.00
MM Mickey Mantle 30.00 60.00
MO Motown HN 40.00 80.00
NK Nikita Khrushchev HN 150.00 200.00
OC Orlando Cepeda 8.00 20.00
WM Bill Mazeroski 10.00 25.00

2008 Topps Heritage Flashbacks Seat Relics Autographs

STATED ODDS 1:22,100 HOBBY
STATED ODDS 1:50,000 RETAIL
STATED PRINT RUN 25 SER.#'d SETS
NO PRICING DUE TO SCARCITY
EXCHANGE DEADLINE 2/28/10
BG Bob Gibson
MM Minnie Minoso EXCH
WM Bill Mazeroski

2008 Topps Heritage Flashbacks Seat Relics Dual

STATED ODDS 1:55,000 HOBBY
STATED ODDS 1:40,000 RETAIL
STATED PRINT RUN 10 SER.#'d SETS
NO PRICING DUE TO SCARCITY
AM Luis Aparicio
Minnie Minoso
BG Bob Gibson
MC Eddie Mathews
Orlando Cepeda
MM Minnie Minoso
MR Mickey Mantle
Brooks Robinson

2008 Topps Heritage High Numbers Then and Now

COMPLETE SET (10) 6.00 15.00
STATED ODDS 1:12 HOBBY
TN1 Ernie Banks 1.25 3.00
Jimmy Rollins
TN2 Nellie Fox 2.00 5.00
Alex Rodriguez
TN3 Larry Sherry .50 1.25
Mike Lowell
TN4 Willie McCovey 1.50 4.00
Ryan Braun
TN5 Bob Allison 2.00 5.00
Dustin Pedroia
TN6 Del Crandall .50 1.25
Russ Martin
TN7 Luis Aparicio .50 1.25
Orlando Cabrera
TN8 Early Wynn 2.00 5.00
Alex Rodriguez
TN9 Early Wynn .75 2.00
Jake Peavy
TN10 Sam Jones .50 1.25
CC Sabathia

2008 Topps Heritage New Age Performers

COMPLETE SET (15) 10.00 25.00
STATED ODDS 1:15 HOBBY,1:15 RETAIL
NAP1 Magglio Ordonez .75 2.00
NAP2 Ichiro Suzuki 2.00 5.00
NAP3 Matt Holliday .75 2.00
NAP4 Prince Fielder 1.25 3.00
NAP5 David Wright 1.50 4.00
NAP6 Jake Peavy .75 2.00
NAP7 Alex Rodriguez 2.00 5.00
NAP8 John Lackey .50 1.25
NAP9 Vladimir Guerrero 1.25 3.00
NAP10 Ryan Howard 1.50 4.00
NAP11 Brandon Webb .75 2.00
NAP12 Manny Ramirez 1.25 3.00
NAP13 Josh Beckett .75 2.00
NAP14 Jimmy Rollins .75 2.00
NAP15 David Ortiz 1.25 3.00

2008 Topps Heritage News Flashbacks

COMPLETE SET (10) 4.00 10.00
STATED ODDS 1:12 HOBBY,1:12 RETAIL
NF1 Alaska becomes the 49th state .60 1.50
NF2 The Day the Music Died .60 1.50
NF3 Fidel Castro becomes Prime Minister of Cuba .60 1.50
NF4 The Dalai Lama flees to India .60 1.50
NF5 NASA introduces the first seven astronauts .60 1.50

NF6 Kitchen Debate between Nixon and Khrushchev .60 1.50
NF7 Hawaii becomes the 50th state .60 1.50
NF8 USSR's Luna 2 becomes the first man-made object on the moon .60 1.50
NF9 In Cold Blood murders committed .60 1.50
NF10 Antarctic Treaty signed .60 1.50

2008 Topps Heritage Real One Autographs

STATED ODDS 1:247 H,1:495 R
HN ODDS 1:110 HOBBY
EXCHANGE DEADLINE 02/28/2010
HN EXCH DEADLINE 11/30/2010
AJ Al Jackson HN 20.00 50.00
AK Al Kaline HN 40.00 80.00
AR Aramis Ramirez 15.00 40.00
BB Bob Blaylock 20.00 50.00
BM Bob Martyn 15.00 40.00
BM Brian McCann HN 15.00 40.00
BMS Bill Skowron HN 20.00 50.00
BR Bill Renna 20.00 50.00
BS Bob Smith 20.00 50.00
BS Barney Schultz HN 15.00 40.00
BSP Bob Speake 20.00 50.00
CE Carl Erskine 30.00 60.00
CE Chuck Essegian HN 20.00 50.00
CG Curtis Granderson HN 15.00 40.00
CK Chick King 30.00 60.00
CK Clayton Kershaw HN 20.00 50.00
DP Dustin Pedroia HN 40.00 80.00
DR Dusty Rhodes HN 15.00 40.00
DS Duke Snider HN 50.00 100.00
FL Fred Lewis HN 15.00 40.00
FR Frank Robinson HN 40.00 80.00
FS Freddy Sanchez EXCH 15.00 40.00
GEZ Gus Zernial 30.00 60.00
GS Geovany Soto HN 20.00 50.00
GZ George Zuverink 20.00 50.00
HL Hector Lopez HN 15.00 40.00
HP Herb Plews 20.00 50.00
JAB Jay Bruce HN 20.00 50.00
JB Jim Bolger 20.00 50.00
JB Jim Brosnan HN 30.00 60.00
JC Joba Chamberlain 75.00 150.00
JF Jack Fisher HN 20.00 50.00
JH Jay Hook HN 15.00 40.00
JK Jim Kaat HN 20.00 50.00
JO Johnny O'Brien 20.00 50.00
JP J.W. Porter 20.00 50.00
KL Ken Lehman 20.00 50.00
LA Luis Aparicio 40.00 80.00
LM Les Moss 20.00 50.00
LT Lee Tate 20.00 50.00
MB Mike Baxes 20.00 50.00
MIM Minnie Minoso EXCH 30.00 60.00
MM Morrie Martin 20.00 50.00
MW Maury Wills HN 20.00 50.00
OC Orlando Cepeda HN 30.00 60.00
PC Phil Clark 20.00 50.00
PG Pumpsie Green HN 20.00 50.00
RC Roger Craig HN 30.00 60.00
RH Russ Heman 20.00 50.00
RJ Randy Jackson 20.00 50.00
SP Scott Podsednik EXCH 20.00 50.00
TC Tom Carroll 20.00 50.00
TD Tommy Davis HN 30.00 60.00
TK Ted Kazanski 20.00 50.00
TQ Tom Qualters 20.00 50.00
VV Vito Valentinetti 15.00 40.00
WM Bill Mazeroski 30.00 60.00
YB Yogi Berra 60.00 120.00

2008 Topps Heritage Real One Autographs Dual

STATED ODDS 1:6869 HOBBY
HN ODDS 1:850 HOBBY
STATED PRINT RUN 25 SER.#'d SETS
NO PRICING DUE TO SCARCITY
EXCHANGE DEADLINE 2/28/2010
EXCHANGE DEADLINE 11/30/2010
BC Yogi Berra
Joba Chamberlain
BK Ernie Banks
Chick King
BM Yogi Berra
Les Moss
BR Ernie Banks
Aramis Ramirez
CL Orlando Cepeda
Fred Lewis HN
CS Roger Craig
Duke Snider HN
HR Jay Hook
Frank Robinson HN
KG Al Kaline
Curtis Granderson HN
MBS Bill Mazeroski
Bob Smith
MS Bill Mazeroski
Freddy Sanchez EXCH
RB Frank Robinson
Jay Bruce HN
RC Dusty Rhodes
Orlando Cepeda HN
SAK Barney Schultz
Al Kaline HN EXCH
SK Duke Snider
Clayton Kershaw HN
SR Bill Skowron
Darrell Rasner HN

2008 Topps Heritage Real One Autographs Red Ink

*RED INK: .6X TO 1.5X BASIC
STATED ODDS 1:835 H,1:1650 R
HN ODDS 1:439 HOBBY
STATED PRINT RUN 59 SERIAL #'d SETS
RED INK ALSO CALLED SPECIAL EDITION
EXCHANGE DEADLINE 02/28/2010
HN EXCH DEADLINE 11/30/2010

CK Clayton Kershaw HN	100.00	200.00
DP Dustin Pedroia HN	75.00	150.00
DS Duke Snider HN	100.00	200.00
GS Geovany Soto HN	50.00	100.00
JAB Jay Bruce HN	60.00	120.00
JC Joba Chamberlain	200.00	300.00
MIM Minnie Minoso EXCH	60.00	120.00
RC Roger Craig HN	60.00	120.00
WM Bill Mazeroski	125.00	250.00

2008 Topps Heritage Rookie Performers

COMPLETE SET (15)	12.50	30.00
STATED ODDS 1:12 HOBBY		
RP1 Clayton Kershaw	1.50	4.00
RP2 Mike Aviles	.75	2.00
RP3 Armando Galarraga	.75	2.00
RP4 Joey Votto	1.25	3.00
RP5 Kosuke Fukudome	2.00	5.00
RP6 Chris Davis	1.25	3.00
RP7 Jeff Samardzija	1.50	4.00
RP8 Carlos Gonzalez	.50	1.25
RP9 Max Scherzer	1.25	3.00
RP10 Evan Longoria	4.00	10.00
RP11 Johnny Cueto	.75	2.00
RP12 Hiroki Kuroda	.75	2.00
RP13 John Bowker	.50	1.25
RP14 Justin Masterson	2.50	6.00
RP15 Jay Bruce	2.00	5.00

2008 Topps Heritage T205 Mini

THREE PER $9.99 TARGET BOX
SIX PER $19.99 TARGET BOX

HTCP1 Albert Pujols	3.00	8.00
HTCP2 Clay Buchholz	3.00	8.00
HTCP3 Matt Holliday	1.25	3.00
HTCP4 Luke Hochevar	2.00	5.00
HTCP5 Alex Rodriguez	3.00	8.00
HTCP6 Joey Votto	2.00	5.00
HTCP7 Chin-Lung Hu	1.25	3.00
HTCP8 Ryan Braun	2.50	6.00
HTCP9 Joba Chamberlain	2.50	6.00
HTCP10 Ryan Howard	2.50	6.00
HTCP11 Ichiro Suzuki	3.00	8.00
HTCP12 Steve Pearce	1.25	3.00
HTCP13 Vladimir Guerrero	2.00	5.00
HTCP14 Wladimir Balentien	.75	2.00
HTCP15 David Ortiz	2.00	5.00

2008 Topps Heritage Then and Now

COMPLETE SET (10)	6.00	15.00
STATED ODDS 1:15 HOBBY,1:15 RETAIL		
TN1 Alex Rodriguez Eddie Mathews	2.00	5.00
TN2 Alex Rodriguez Ernie Banks	1.25	3.00
TN3 Magglio Ordonez Orlando Cepeda	.75	2.00
TN4 Jose Reyes Luis Aparicio	.50	1.25
TN5 David Ortiz Mickey Mantle	2.50	6.00
TN6 Erik Bedard Johnny Podres	.50	1.25
TN7 Josh Beckett Early Wynn	.75	2.00
TN8 Ichiro Suzuki Minnie Minoso	2.00	5.00
TN9 David Ortiz Frank Robinson	1.25	3.00
TN10 Jake Peavy Don Drysdale	.75	2.00

2007 Topps Moments and Milestones

This 193-card set was released in April, 2007. However, in reality the set consisted of far more than 193 cards as each card was actually printed as many variations of the milestone or moment featured on the cards. Therefore there were as few as two variations (300 total cards) or as many as 364 variations (54, 600 total cards) for each card. This schematic covered cards 1-169 while cards 170-193 featured rookies and each rookie was issued in a triplet of cards and each of those cards were also issued to a stated print run of 150 cards making the total print run for all of the rookies 450 cards. This

product was issued in six-card packs, with an $6 SRP, which came 18 packs to a box; six boxes to a carton and two cartons to a case.

COMMON p/r 11250-54600	.30	.75
COMMON p/r 1650-10350	.40	1.00
COMMON p/r 900-1500	3.00	8.00
COMMON p/r 300-450	4.00	10.00
COMMON ROOKIE	4.00	10.00

STATED PRINT RUN 150 SER. #'d SETS
(# OF VARIATONS/TOTAL PRINT RUN)
PRICING BASED ON TOTAL PRINT RUN
OVERALL PLATE ODDS 1:473 HOBBY
PLATE PRINT RUN 1 SET PER COLOR
BLACK-CYAN-MAGENTA-YELLOW ISSUED
NO PLATE PRICING DUE TO SCARCITY

1 Albert Pujols (37/5550)	1.00	2.50
2 Albert Pujols (130/19500)	.75	2.00
3 Albert Pujols (194/29100)	.75	2.00
4 Albert Pujols (112/16800)	.75	2.00
5 Albert Pujols (47/7050)	1.00	2.50
6 Ichiro Suzuki (242/36300)	.60	1.50
7 Ichiro Suzuki (34/5100)	.75	2.00
8 Ichiro Suzuki (8/1200)	4.00	10.00
9 Ichiro Suzuki (56/8400)	.75	2.00
10 Ichiro Suzuki (69/10350)	.75	2.00
11 Ichiro Suzuki (8/1200)	4.00	10.00
12 Greg Maddux (20/3000)	.75	2.00
13 Greg Maddux (199/29850)	.60	1.50
14 Greg Maddux (20/3000)	.75	2.00
15 Greg Maddux (197/29550)	.60	1.50
16 Roger Clemens (24/3600)	.75	2.00
17 Roger Clemens (10/1500)	5.00	12.00
18 Roger Clemens (238/35700)	.60	1.50
19 Roger Clemens (20/3000)	.75	2.00
20 Roger Clemens (256/38400)	.60	1.50
21 Chipper Jones (45/6750)	.60	1.50
22 Chipper Jones (110/16500)	.50	1.25
23 Chipper Jones (181/27150)	.50	1.25
24 Chipper Jones (116/17400)	.50	1.25
25 Chipper Jones (41/6150)	.60	1.50
26 Chipper Jones (25/3750)	.60	1.50
27 Alex Rodriguez (47/7050)	.75	2.00
28 Alex Rodriguez (118/17700)	.60	1.50
29 Alex Rodriguez (181/27150)	.60	1.50
30 Alex Rodriguez (124/18600)	.60	1.50
31 Alex Rodriguez (30/4500)	.75	2.00
32 Alex Rodriguez (17/2550)	.75	2.00
33 Alex Rodriguez (48/7200)	.75	2.00
34 Alex Rodriguez (130/19500)	.60	1.50
35 Alex Rodriguez (194/29100)	.60	1.50
36 Alex Rodriguez (124/18600)	.60	1.50
37 Alex Rodriguez (29/4350)	.75	2.00
38 Alex Rodriguez (21/3150)	.75	2.00
39 Vladimir Guerrero (39/5850)	.60	1.50
40 Vladimir Guerrero (126/18900)	.50	1.25
41 Vladimir Guerrero (206/30900)	.50	1.25
42 Vladimir Guerrero (124/18600)	.50	1.25
43 Vladimir Guerrero (39/5850)	.60	1.50
44 Vladimir Guerrero (13/1950)	.60	1.50
45 Ken Griffey Jr. (56/8400)	.75	2.00
46 Ken Griffey Jr. (147/22050)	.60	1.50
47 Ken Griffey Jr. (185/27750)	.60	1.50
48 Barry Zito (23/3450)	.40	1.00
49 Barry Zito (182/27300)	.30	.75
50 Randy Johnson (18/2700)	.60	1.50
51 Randy Johnson (294/44100)	.50	1.25
52 Randy Johnson (6/900)	3.00	8.00
53 Randy Johnson (3/450)	30.00	60.00
54 Randy Johnson (17/2550)	.60	1.50
55 Randy Johnson (364/54600)	.50	1.25
56 Randy Johnson (12/1800)	.60	1.50
57 Randy Johnson (2/300)	30.00	60.00
58 Prince Fielder (35/5250)	.60	1.50
59 Prince Fielder (81/12150)	.50	1.25
60 Dan Uggla (26/3900)	.60	1.50
61 Dan Uggla (27/4050)	.60	1.50
62 Dan Uggla (172/25800)	.50	1.25
63 Justin Verlander (17/2550)	.60	1.50
64 Justin Verlander (124/18600)	.50	1.25
65 Francisco Liriano (12/1800)	.60	1.50
66 Francisco Liriano (144/21600)	.50	1.25
67 Ryan Zimmerman (176/26400)	.50	1.25
68 Ryan Zimmerman (110/16500)	.50	1.25
69 Ryan Zimmerman (84/12600)	.50	1.25
70 Hanley Ramirez (51/7650)	.60	1.50
71 Hanley Ramirez (119/17850)	.50	1.25
72 Hanley Ramirez (185/27750)	.50	1.25
73 Russ Martin (65/9750)	.40	1.00
74 Russ Martin (26/3900)	.40	1.00
75 Mickey Mantle (173/25950)	2.00	5.00
76 Mickey Mantle (121/18150)	2.00	5.00
77 Mickey Mantle (146/21900)	2.00	5.00
78 Mickey Mantle (94/14100)	2.00	5.00
79 Mike Piazza (35/5250)	.60	1.50
80 Mike Piazza (112/16800)	.50	1.25
81 Derek Jeter (10/1500)	6.00	15.00
82 Derek Jeter (78/11700)	1.00	2.50
83 Derek Jeter (183/27450)	1.00	2.50
84 Dontrelle Willis (14/2100)	.40	1.00
85 Dontrelle Willis (142/21300)	.30	.75
86 Dontrelle Willis (2/300)	30.00	60.00
87 Bobby Crosby (22/3300)	.40	1.00
88 Bobby Crosby (64/9600)	.40	1.00
89 Ryan Howard (22/3300)	.75	2.00
90 Ryan Howard (63/9450)	.75	2.00
91 Curt Schilling (21/3150)	.60	1.50
92 Curt Schilling (203/30450)	.50	1.25
93 Andruw Jones (52/7800)	.60	1.50
94 Andruw Jones (128/19200)	.50	1.25
95 Andruw Jones (11/1650)	.60	1.50
96 Hideki Matsui (23/3450)	.60	1.50
97 Hideki Matsui (116/17400)	.50	1.25
98 Hideki Matsui (192/28800)	.50	1.25
99 David Wright (27/4050)	.75	2.00
100 David Wright (102/15300)	.60	1.50
101 David Wright (42/6300)	.75	2.00
102 David Wright (17/2550)	.75	2.00
103 David Ortiz (75/11250)	.50	1.25
104 David Ortiz (47/7050)	.60	1.50
105 David Ortiz (11/1650)	.60	1.50
106 Frank Thomas (38/5700)	.60	1.50
107 Frank Thomas (101/15150)	.50	1.25
108 Craig Biggio (40/6000)	.60	1.50
109 Miguel Cabrera (33/4950)	.60	1.50
110 Miguel Cabrera (116/17400)	.50	1.25
111 Vernon Wells (12/1800)	.40	1.00
112 Michael Young (24/3600)	.40	1.00
113 Michael Young (40/6000)	.40	1.00
114 Joe Mauer (144/21600)	.50	1.25
115 Gary Sheffield (34/5100)	.40	1.00
116 Jim Edmonds (42/6300)	.60	1.50
117 Jorge Posada (19/2850)	.60	1.50
118 Jorge Posada (23/3450)	.60	1.50
119 Pat Burrell (32/4800)	.40	1.00
120 Adam Dunn (40/6000)	.40	1.00
121 Johnny Damon (35/5250)	.60	1.50
122 Scott Rolen (34/5100)	.60	1.50
123 Paul Konerko (6/900)	3.00	8.00
124 Roy Halladay (22/3300)	.40	1.00
125 Grady Sizemore (22/3300)	.60	1.50
126 Grady Sizemore (37/5550)	.60	1.50
127 John Smoltz (24/3600)	.60	1.50
128 Jeff Kent (29/4350)	.40	1.00
129 Billy Wagner (38/5700)	.40	1.00
130 Mark Prior (18/2700)	.60	1.50
131 Eric Chavez (32/4800)	.40	1.00
132 Jimmy Rollins (41/6150)	.40	1.00
133 Manny Ramirez (7/1050)	3.00	8.00
134 Manny Ramirez (45/6750)	.60	1.50
135 Manny Ramirez (144/21600)	.50	1.25
136 Derrek Lee (46/6900)	.40	1.00
137 Derrek Lee (107/16050)	.30	.75
138 Tom Glavine (14/2100)	.60	1.50
139 Tom Glavine (20/3000)	.60	1.50
140 Jose Reyes (17/2550)	.40	1.00
141 Pedro Martinez (15/2250)	.60	1.50
142 Pedro Martinez (208/31200)	.50	1.25
143 Mark Teixeira (43/6450)	.60	1.50
144 Jake Peavy (13/1950)	.40	1.00
145 Carlos Lee (32/4800)	.40	1.00
146 Josh Beckett (16/2400)	.60	1.50
147 Johan Santana (20/3000)	.60	1.50
148 Todd Helton (33/4950)	.60	1.50
149 Mariano Rivera (43/6450)	.60	1.50
150 Travis Hafner (33/4950)	.40	1.00
151 Jason Bay (24/3600)	.40	1.00
152 Bobby Abreu (30/4500)	.40	1.00
153 Mike Mussina (13/1950)	.60	1.50
154 Miguel Tejada (34/5100)	.40	1.00
155 Miguel Tejada (150/22500)	.30	.75
156 Robinson Cano (14/2100)	.60	1.50
157 Robinson Cano (34/5100)	.60	1.50
158 Ryan Zimmerman (23/3450)	.60	1.50
159 Carlos Beltran (16/2400)	.40	1.00
160 Carlos Beltran (17/2550)	.40	1.00
161 Roger Clemens (18/2700)	.75	2.00
162 Roger Clemens (218/32700)	.60	1.50
163 Mickey Mantle (52/7800)	2.50	6.00
164 Mickey Mantle (130/19500)	2.00	5.00
165 Mickey Mantle (188/28200)	2.00	5.00
166 Mickey Mantle (132/19800)	2.00	5.00
167 Mickey Mantle (42/6300)	2.50	6.00
168 Mickey Mantle (97/14550)	2.00	5.00
169 Mickey Mantle (127/19050)	2.00	5.00
170 Daisuke Matsuzaka RC	30.00	60.00
171 Daisuke Matsuzaka RC	30.00	60.00
172 Daisuke Matsuzaka RC	30.00	60.00
173 Delmon Young (RC)	5.00	12.00
174 Delmon Young (RC)	5.00	12.00
175 Delmon Young (RC)	5.00	12.00
176 Andrew Miller RC	10.00	25.00
177 Andrew Miller RC	10.00	25.00
178 Andrew Miller RC	10.00	25.00
179 Troy Tulowitzki (RC)	5.00	12.00
180 Troy Tulowitzki (RC)	5.00	12.00
181 Troy Tulowitzki (RC)	5.00	12.00
182 Josh Fields (RC)	4.00	10.00
183 Josh Fields (RC)	4.00	10.00
184 Josh Fields (RC)	4.00	10.00
185 Jeff Baker (RC)	4.00	10.00
186 Jeff Baker (RC)	4.00	10.00
187 Jeff Baker (RC)	4.00	10.00
188 Philip Humber (RC)	4.00	10.00
189 Philip Humber (RC)	4.00	10.00
190 Philip Humber (RC)	4.00	10.00
191 Kevin Kouzmanoff (RC)	4.00	10.00
192 Kevin Kouzmanoff (RC)	4.00	10.00
193 Kevin Kouzmanoff (RC)	4.00	10.00

2007 Topps Moments and Milestones Black

*BLACK p/r 2175-10556 :1.2X TO 3X BASIC
*BLACK p/r 841-2001 :1.5X TO 4X BASIC
*BLACK p/r 319-783 :2X TO 5X BASIC
*BLACK p/r 174-290 :5X TO 1.2X BASIC
*BLACK p/r 58-87 :.5X TO 1.2X BASIC
STATED PRINT RUN 29 SER. #'d SETS
(# OF VARIATONS/TOTAL PRINT RUN)
PRICING BASED ON TOTAL PRINT RUN
NO RC PRICING DUE TO SCARCITY

75 Mickey Mantle (173/5017)	4.00	10.00
76 Mickey Mantle (121/3509)	4.00	10.00
77 Mickey Mantle (146/4234)	4.00	10.00
78 Mickey Mantle (94/2726)	4.00	10.00
163 Mickey Mantle (52/1508)	6.00	15.00
164 Mickey Mantle (130/3770)	4.00	10.00
165 Mickey Mantle (188/5452)	4.00	10.00
166 Mickey Mantle (132/3828)	4.00	10.00
167 Mickey Mantle (42/1218)	6.00	15.00
168 Mickey Mantle (97/2813)	4.00	10.00
169 Mickey Mantle (127/3683)	4.00	10.00

2007 Topps Moments and Milestones Red

STATED PRINT RUN 1 SER. #'d SET
TOTAL PRINT RUN IN PARENTHESIS
PRICING BASED ON TOTAL PRINT RUN
NO PRICING ON TOTAL QTY UNDER 25

1 Albert Pujols (37)	30.00	60.00
2 Albert Pujols (130)	30.00	60.00
3 Albert Pujols (194)	30.00	60.00
4 Albert Pujols (112)	30.00	60.00
5 Albert Pujols (47)	30.00	60.00
6 Ichiro Suzuki (242)	40.00	80.00
7 Ichiro Suzuki (34)	40.00	80.00
8 Ichiro Suzuki (8)		
9 Ichiro Suzuki (56)	40.00	80.00
10 Ichiro Suzuki (69)	40.00	80.00
11 Ichiro Suzuki (8)		
12 Greg Maddux (20)		
13 Greg Maddux (199)	15.00	40.00
14 Greg Maddux (20)		
15 Greg Maddux (197)	15.00	40.00
16 Roger Clemens (24)		
17 Roger Clemens (10)		
18 Roger Clemens (238)	20.00	50.00
19 Roger Clemens (20)		
20 Roger Clemens (256)	20.00	50.00
21 Chipper Jones (45)	15.00	40.00
22 Chipper Jones (110)	15.00	40.00
23 Chipper Jones (181)	15.00	40.00
24 Chipper Jones (116)	15.00	40.00
25 Chipper Jones (41)	15.00	40.00
26 Chipper Jones (25)		
27 Alex Rodriguez (47)	30.00	60.00
28 Alex Rodriguez (118)	30.00	60.00
29 Alex Rodriguez (181)	30.00	60.00
30 Alex Rodriguez (124)	30.00	60.00
31 Alex Rodriguez (30)	30.00	60.00
32 Alex Rodriguez (17)		
33 Alex Rodriguez (48)	30.00	60.00
34 Alex Rodriguez (130)	30.00	60.00
35 Alex Rodriguez (194)	30.00	60.00
36 Alex Rodriguez (124)	30.00	60.00
37 Alex Rodriguez (29)	30.00	60.00
38 Alex Rodriguez (21)		
39 Vladimir Guerrero (39)	15.00	40.00
40 Vladimir Guerrero (126)	15.00	40.00
41 Vladimir Guerrero (206)	15.00	40.00
42 Vladimir Guerrero (124)	15.00	40.00
43 Vladimir Guerrero (39)	15.00	40.00
44 Vladimir Guerrero (13)		
45 Ken Griffey Jr. (56)	150.00	250.00
46 Ken Griffey Jr. (147)	150.00	250.00
47 Ken Griffey Jr. (185)	150.00	250.00
48 Barry Zito (23)		
49 Barry Zito (182)	6.00	15.00
50 Randy Johnson (18)		
51 Randy Johnson (294)	15.00	40.00
52 Randy Johnson (6)		
53 Randy Johnson (3)		
54 Randy Johnson (17)		
55 Randy Johnson (364)	15.00	40.00
56 Randy Johnson (12)		
57 Randy Johnson (2)		
58 Prince Fielder (35)	15.00	40.00
59 Prince Fielder (81)	15.00	40.00
60 Dan Uggla (26)	10.00	25.00
61 Dan Uggla (27)	10.00	25.00
62 Dan Uggla (172)	10.00	25.00
63 Justin Verlander (17)		
64 Justin Verlander (124)	15.00	40.00
65 Francisco Liriano (12)		
66 Francisco Liriano (144)	15.00	40.00
67 Ryan Zimmerman (176)	15.00	40.00
68 Ryan Zimmerman (110)	15.00	40.00
69 Ryan Zimmerman (84)	15.00	40.00
70 Hanley Ramirez (51)	10.00	25.00
71 Hanley Ramirez (119)	10.00	25.00
72 Hanley Ramirez (185)	10.00	25.00
73 Russ Martin (65)	6.00	15.00
74 Russ Martin (26)	6.00	15.00
75 Mickey Mantle (173)	20.00	50.00
76 Mickey Mantle (121)	20.00	50.00
77 Mickey Mantle (146)	20.00	50.00
78 Mickey Mantle (94)	20.00	50.00
79 Mike Piazza (35)	15.00	40.00
80 Mike Piazza (112)	15.00	40.00
81 Derek Jeter (10)		
82 Derek Jeter (78)	30.00	60.00
83 Derek Jeter (183)	30.00	60.00
84 Dontrelle Willis (14)		
85 Dontrelle Willis (142)	6.00	15.00
86 Dontrelle Willis (2)		
87 Bobby Crosby (22)		
88 Bobby Crosby (64)	6.00	15.00
89 Ryan Howard (22)		
90 Ryan Howard (63)	20.00	50.00
91 Curt Schilling (21)		
92 Curt Schilling (203)	10.00	25.00
93 Andruw Jones (52)	10.00	25.00
94 Andruw Jones (128)	10.00	25.00
95 Andruw Jones (11)		
96 Hideki Matsui (23)		
97 Hideki Matsui (116)	15.00	40.00
98 Hideki Matsui (192)	15.00	40.00
99 David Wright (27)	20.00	50.00
100 David Wright (102)	20.00	50.00
101 David Wright (42)	20.00	50.00
102 David Wright (17)		
103 David Ortiz (75)	15.00	40.00
104 David Ortiz (47)	15.00	40.00
105 David Ortiz (11)		
106 Frank Thomas (38)	15.00	40.00
107 Frank Thomas (101)	15.00	40.00
108 Craig Biggio (40)	10.00	25.00
109 Miguel Cabrera (33)	10.00	25.00
110 Miguel Cabrera (116)	10.00	25.00
111 Vernon Wells (12)		
112 Michael Young (24)		
113 Michael Young (40)	20.00	50.00
114 Joe Mauer (144)	10.00	25.00
115 Gary Sheffield (34)	6.00	15.00
116 Jim Edmonds (42)	10.00	25.00
117 Jorge Posada (19)		
118 Jorge Posada (23)		
119 Pat Burrell (32)	6.00	15.00
120 Adam Dunn (40)	6.00	15.00
121 Johnny Damon (35)	10.00	25.00
122 Scott Rolen (34)	10.00	25.00
123 Paul Konerko (6)		
124 Roy Halladay (22)		
125 Grady Sizemore (22)		
126 Grady Sizemore (37)	10.00	25.00
127 John Smoltz (24)		
128 Jeff Kent (29)	6.00	15.00
129 Billy Wagner (38)	6.00	15.00
130 Mark Prior (18)		
131 Eric Chavez (32)	6.00	15.00
132 Jimmy Rollins (41)	6.00	15.00
133 Manny Ramirez (7)		
134 Manny Ramirez (45)	10.00	25.00
135 Manny Ramirez (144)	10.00	25.00
136 Derrek Lee (46)	6.00	15.00
137 Derrek Lee (107)	6.00	15.00
138 Tom Glavine (14)		
139 Tom Glavine (20)		
140 Jose Reyes (17)		
141 Pedro Martinez (15)		
142 Pedro Martinez (208)	10.00	25.00
143 Mark Teixeira (43)	10.00	25.00
144 Jake Peavy (13)		
145 Carlos Lee (32)	6.00	15.00
146 Josh Beckett (16)		
147 Johan Santana (20)		
148 Todd Helton (33)	10.00	25.00
149 Mariano Rivera (43)	15.00	40.00
150 Travis Hafner (33)	6.00	15.00
151 Jason Bay (24)		
152 Bobby Abreu (30)	6.00	15.00
153 Mike Mussina (13)		
154 Miguel Tejada (34)	6.00	15.00
155 Miguel Tejada (150)	6.00	15.00
156 Robinson Cano (14)		
157 Robinson Cano (34)	10.00	25.00
158 Ryan Zimmerman (23)		
159 Carlos Beltran (16)		
160 Carlos Beltran (17)		
161 Roger Clemens (18)		
162 Roger Clemens (218)	20.00	50.00
163 Mickey Mantle (52)	20.00	50.00
164 Mickey Mantle (130)	20.00	50.00
165 Mickey Mantle (188)	20.00	50.00
166 Mickey Mantle (132)	20.00	50.00
167 Mickey Mantle (42)	20.00	50.00
168 Mickey Mantle (97)	20.00	50.00
169 Mickey Mantle (127)	20.00	50.00
170 Daisuke Matsuzaka		
171 Daisuke Matsuzaka		
172 Daisuke Matsuzaka		
173 Delmon Young		
174 Delmon Young		
175 Delmon Young		
176 Andrew Miller		
177 Andrew Miller		
178 Andrew Miller		
179 Troy Tulowitzki		
180 Troy Tulowitzki		
181 Troy Tulowitzki		
182 Josh Fields		
183 Josh Fields		
184 Josh Fields		
185 Jeff Baker		
186 Jeff Baker		
187 Jeff Baker		
188 Philip Humber		
189 Philip Humber		
190 Philip Humber		
191 Kevin Kouzmanoff		
192 Kevin Kouzmanoff		
193 Kevin Kouzmanoff		

2007 Topps Moments and Milestones Milestone Autographs

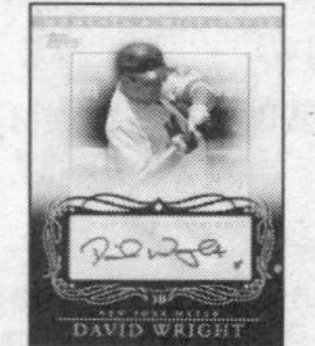

GROUP A ODDS 1:63 HOBBY
GROUP B ODDS 1:64 HOBBY
GROUP C ODDS 1:192 HOBBY
GROUP D ODDS 1:74 HOBBY
GROUP E ODDS 1:479 HOBBY
GROUP F ODDS 1:1112 HOBBY
GROUP E PRINT RUN 200 CARDS
GROUP F PRINT RUN 100 CARDS
E-F ARE NOT SERIAL-NUMBERED
E-F PRINT RUNS PROVIDED BY TOPPS
OVERALL PLATE ODDS 1:2361 HOBBY
PLATE PRINT RUN 1 SET PER COLOR
BLACK-CYAN-MAGENTA-YELLOW ISSUED
NO PLATE PRICING DUE TO SCARCITY

AJ Andruw Jones F/100 *	20.00	50.00
AR Alex Rodriguez F/100 *	100.00	175.00
BP Brandon Phillips C	3.00	8.00
BR Brian Roberts D	4.00	10.00
CJ Conor Jackson D	4.00	10.00
DO David Ortiz D	20.00	50.00
DW David Wright D	30.00	60.00
GA Garrett Atkins B	6.00	15.00
GS Gary Sheffield F/100 *	15.00	40.00
HS Huston Street E UER Huston is spelled as Houston	6.00	15.00
JF Jeff Francoeur D	20.00	50.00
JG Jason Giambi F/100 *	20.00	50.00
JJG Jonny Gomes D	3.00	8.00
JL Julio Lugo D	3.00	8.00
JP Jonathan Papelbon B	12.50	30.00
JR Jose Reyes E/200 *	20.00	50.00
JS Jeremy Sowers A	4.00	10.00
KJ Kenji Johjima D	15.00	40.00
KM Kendry Morales B	3.00	8.00
LM Lastings Milledge D	6.00	15.00
MK Matt Kemp B	4.00	10.00
MN Mike Napoli C	3.00	8.00
MP Martin Prado A	3.00	8.00
NS Nick Swisher D	6.00	15.00
RH Ryan Howard E/200 *	30.00	60.00
RP Ronny Paulino A	3.00	8.00
TH Travis Hafner D	6.00	15.00
VG Vladimir Guerrero F/100 *	20.00	50.00
WP Wily Mo Pena F/100 *	6.00	15.00

2007 Topps Moments and Milestones Milestone Autographs Black

*BLACK: .5X TO 1.2X BASIC
STATED ODDS 1:235 HOBBY
STATED PRINT RUN 40 SER.#'d SETS

AR Alex Rodriguez	150.00	200.00
DO David Ortiz	40.00	80.00
DW David Wright	50.00	100.00
JF Jeff Francoeur	40.00	80.00
JR Jose Reyes	40.00	80.00
RH Ryan Howard	50.00	100.00
TH Travis Hafner	12.50	30.00

2007 Topps Moments and Milestones Milestone Autographs Red

STATED ODDS 1:9624 HOBBY
STATED PRINT RUN 1 SER.#'d SET
NO PRICING DUE TO SCARCITY

2007 Topps Moments and Milestones Rookie Autographs

STATED ODDS 1:19 HOBBY
OVERALL PLATE ODDS 1:2361 HOBBY
PLATE PRINT RUN 1 SET PER COLOR
BLACK-CYAN-MAGENTA-YELLOW ISSUED
NO PLATE PRICING DUE TO SCARCITY

AL Adam Lind	6.00	15.00
AM Andrew Miller	20.00	50.00
DM David Murphy	4.00	10.00
HG Hector Gimenez	3.00	8.00
JA Joaquin Arias	3.00	8.00
KK Kevin Kouzmanoff	4.00	10.00
MB Michael Bourn	3.00	8.00
MM Miguel Montero	3.00	8.00
SR Shawn Riggans	3.00	8.00
TT Troy Tulowitzki	12.50	30.00

2007 Topps Moments and Milestones Rookie Autographs Black

*BLACK: .75X TO 2X BASIC
STATED ODDS 1:235 HOBBY
STATED PRINT RUN 40 SER.#'d SETS

AL Adam Lind	20.00	50.00
AM Andrew Miller	60.00	120.00
TT Troy Tulowitzki	15.00	40.00

2007 Topps Moments and Milestones Rookie Autographs Red

STATED ODDS 1:9624 HOBBY
STATED PRINT RUN 1 SER.#'d SET
NO PRICING DUE TO SCARCITY

2008 Topps Moments and Milestones

COMMON p/r 11250-78600	.15	.40
COMMON p/r 1650-8100	.25	.60
COMMON ROOKIE	2.00	5.00

STATED PRINT RUN 150 SER.#'d SETS
MILESTONE X 150 = TOTAL PRINT RUN

PRICING BASED ON TOTAL PRINT RUN
ALL VARIATIONS EQUALLY PRICED
PLATES RANDOMLY INSERTED
PLATE PRINT RUN 1 SET PER COLOR
BLACK-CYAN-MAGENTA-YELLOW ISSUED
NO PLATE PRICING DUE TO SCARCITY
1-1 Alex Rodriguez .60 1.50
145 Joey Votto (RC) 6.00 15.00
146 Joey Votto (RC) 6.00 15.00
147 Joey Votto (RC) 6.00 15.00
148 Luke Hochevar RC 6.00 15.00
149 Luke Hochevar RC 6.00 15.00
150 Luke Hochevar RC 6.00 15.00
151 Clay Buchholz (RC) 5.00 12.00
152 Clay Buchholz (RC) 5.00 12.00
153 Clay Buchholz (RC) 5.00 12.00
154 Billy Buckner (RC) 2.00 5.00
155 Billy Buckner (RC) 2.00 5.00
156 Billy Buckner (RC) 2.00 5.00
157 Jeff Clement (RC) 2.50 6.00
158 Jeff Clement (RC) 2.50 6.00
159 Jeff Clement (RC) 2.50 6.00
160 Radhames Liz RC 2.00 5.00
161 Radhames Liz RC 2.00 5.00
162 Radhames Liz RC 2.00 5.00
163 Bronson Sardinha (RC) 2.00 5.00
164 Bronson Sardinha (RC) 2.00 5.00
165 Bronson Sardinha (RC) 2.00 5.00
166 Seth Smith (RC) 2.00 5.00
167 Seth Smith (RC) 2.00 5.00
168 Seth Smith (RC) 2.00 5.00
169 Chris Seddon (RC) 2.00 5.00
170 Chris Seddon (RC) 2.00 5.00
171 Chris Seddon (RC) 2.00 5.00
172 Wladimir Balentien (RC) 2.50 6.00
173 Wladimir Balentien (RC) 2.50 6.00
174 Wladimir Balentien (RC) 2.50 6.00
175 Josh Banks (RC) 2.00 5.00
176 Josh Banks (RC) 2.00 5.00
177 Josh Banks (RC) 2.00 5.00
178 Ross Detwiler RC 2.00 5.00
179 Ross Detwiler RC 2.00 5.00
180 Ross Detwiler RC 2.00 5.00
181 Felipe Paulino RC 2.00 5.00
182 Felipe Paulino RC 2.00 5.00
183 Felipe Paulino RC 2.00 5.00
184 Troy Patton (RC) 2.00 5.00
185 Troy Patton (RC) 2.00 5.00
186 Troy Patton (RC) 2.00 5.00
187 Brandon Jones RC 2.00 5.00
188 Brandon Jones RC 2.00 5.00
189 Brandon Jones RC 2.00 5.00
2-1 Alex Rodriguez 1.00 2.50
3-1 Frank Thomas .40 1.00
4-1 Mickey Mantle .75 2.00
5-1 Mickey Mantle .75 2.00
6-1 Mickey Mantle .60 1.50
7-1 Mickey Mantle .75 2.00
8-1 Greg Maddux .50 1.25
9-1 Troy Tulowitzki .25 .60
10-1 Hunter Pence .40 1.00
11-1 Hunter Pence .60 1.50
12-1 Albert Pujols .60 1.50
13-1 Albert Pujols .60 1.50
14-1 Albert Pujols 1.00 2.50
15-1 Albert Pujols .60 1.50
16-1 David Ortiz .60 1.50
17-1 David Ortiz .60 1.50
18-1 David Wright .75 2.00
19-1 David Wright .75 2.00
20-1 Aaron Hill .25 .60
21-1 Eric Byrnes .25 .60
22-1 Dmitri Young .25 .60
23-1 Garret Anderson .25 .60
24-1 Jimmy Rollins .40 1.00
25-1 Jimmy Rollins .40 1.00
26-1 Joba Chamberlain .75 2.00
27-1 Magglio Ordonez .40 1.00
28-1 Ryan Howard .50 1.25
29-1 Ryan Howard .75 2.00
30-1 Ryan Howard .50 1.25
31-1 Ryan Howard .75 2.00
32-1 Trevor Hoffman .15 .40
33-1 Ken Griffey Jr. .60 1.50
34-1 Travis Hafner .15 .40
35-1 Joe Mauer .40 1.00
36-1 Daisuke Matsuzaka 50.00 100.00
37-1 Daisuke Matsuzaka 1.25 3.00
38-1 Curtis Granderson .25 .60
39-1 Curtis Granderson .25 .60
40-1 Curtis Granderson .25 .60
41-1 Curtis Granderson .25 .60
42-1 Alex Gordon .60 1.50
43-1 Aramis Ramirez .15 .40
44-1 Jonathan Papelbon .25 .60
45-1 B.J. Upton .40 1.00
46-1 C.C. Sabathia .25 .60
47-1 Carl Crawford .25 .60
48-1 Jason Bay .25 .60
49-1 Carlos Beltran .25 .60
50-1 Carlos Guillen .25 .60
51-1 C.C. Sabathia .15 .40
52-1 Gary Sheffield .15 .40
53-1 Chris Young .25 .60
54-1 Dontrelle Willis .25 .60
55-1 Dustin Pedroia 1.00 2.50
56-1 Alfonso Soriano .25 .60
57-1 Derek Jeter 1.00 2.50
58-1 Chase Utley .60 1.50
59-1 Chase Utley .60 1.50
60-1 Chase Utley .40 1.00
61-1 Chase Utley .60 1.50
62-1 Ichiro Suzuki 40.00 80.00
63-1 Ichiro Suzuki .60 1.50
64-1 Jorge Posada .40 1.00
65-1 Jorge Posada .40 1.00
66-1 Jose Reyes .25 .60
67-1 Miguel Tejada .25 .60
68-1 Miguel Tejada .25 .60
69-1 Nick Swisher .25 .60
70-1 Robinson Cano .25 .60
71-1 Roy Halladay .25 .60
72-1 Ryan Zimmerman .40 1.00
73-1 Scott Rolen .40 1.00
74-1 Tim Lincecum .40 1.00
75-1 Vernon Wells .25 .60
76-1 Roger Clemens .75 2.00
77-1 Roger Clemens .75 2.00
78-1 Roger Clemens .75 2.00
79-1 Roger Clemens .75 2.00
80-1 Roger Clemens .75 2.00
81-1 Roger Clemens .75 2.00
82-1 Roger Clemens .75 2.00
83-1 Michael Young .25 .60
84-1 John Smoltz .40 1.00
85-1 Jim Thome .25 .60
86-1 Johan Santana .25 .60
87-1 Johan Santana .25 .60
88-1 Jack Cust .25 .60
89-1 Jack Cust .25 .60
90-1 Jake Peavy .40 1.00
91-1 Hanley Ramirez .60 1.50
92-1 Hanley Ramirez .40 1.00
93-1 Hideki Okajima .40 1.00
94-1 Grady Sizemore .40 1.00
95-1 Erik Bedard .15 .40
96-1 Derrek Lee .40 1.00
97-1 Derrek Lee .40 1.00
98-1 Delmon Young .40 1.00
99-1 Delmon Young .40 1.00
100-1 Cole Hamels .60 1.50
101-1 Brad Hawpe .15 .40
102-1 Mike Lowell .15 .40
103-1 Placido Polanco .15 .40
104-1 Nick Swisher .15 .40
105-1 Adrian Gonzalez .40 1.00
106-1 Adrian Gonzalez .25 .60
107-1 Scott Kazmir .25 .60
108-1 Freddy Sanchez .15 .40
109-1 Jeremy Guthrie .15 .40
110-1 Chipper Jones .75 2.00
111-1 Chris Carpenter .25 .60
112-1 Andy Pettitte .25 .60
113-1 Andruw Jones .25 .60
114-1 Bobby Abreu .25 .60
115-1 Eric Chavez .25 .60
116-1 Eric Chavez .25 .60
117-1 Josh Hamilton .75 2.00
118-1 Manny Ramirez .40 1.00
119-1 Manny Ramirez .40 1.00
120-1 Mariano Rivera .60 1.50
121-1 Kelly Johnson .25 .60
122-1 Jeff Kent .15 .40
123-1 Mark Teixeira .25 .60
124-1 Matt Holliday .40 1.00
125-1 Matt Holliday .25 .60
126-1 Huston Street .25 .60
127-1 Carlos Lee .25 .60
128-1 Brian Bannister .25 .60
129-1 Carlos Pena .60 1.50
130-1 Brian McCann .40 1.00
131-1 Prince Fielder .60 1.50
132-1 Randy Johnson .60 1.50
133-1 Russell Martin .25 .60
134-1 Ryan Braun .75 2.00
135-1 Vladimir Guerrero .40 1.00
136-1 Vladimir Guerrero .60 1.50
137-1 Tom Glavine .25 .60
138-1 Miguel Cabrera .25 .60
139-1 Miguel Cabrera .25 .60
140-1 Miguel Cabrera .40 1.00
141-1 Pedro Martinez .25 .60
142-1 Daisuke Matsuzaka .75 2.00
143-1 Garrett Atkins .25 .60
144-1 Brian Roberts .40 1.00

2008 Topps Moments and Milestones Black

*BLACK p/r 1950-13100 :1.2X TO 3X BASIC
*BLACK p/r 625-1350 : 1.2X TO 3X BASIC
BLACK RC: .5X TO 1.2X BASIC RC
STATED ODDS 1:2 HOBBY
STATED PRINT RUN 25 SER. #'d SETS
MILESTONE X 25 = TOTAL PRINT RUN
PRICING BASED ON TOTAL PRINT RUN
ALL VARIATIONS EQUALLY PRICED
NO PRICING ON QTY 25 OR LESS
145 Joey Votto 8.00 20.00
146 Joey Votto 8.00 20.00
147 Joey Votto 8.00 20.00
148 Luke Hochevar 8.00 20.00
149 Luke Hochevar 8.00 20.00
150 Luke Hochevar 8.00 20.00
151 Clay Buchholz 6.00 15.00
152 Clay Buchholz 6.00 15.00
153 Clay Buchholz 6.00 15.00
154 Billy Buckner 2.50 6.00
155 Billy Buckner 2.50 6.00
156 Billy Buckner 2.50 6.00
157 Jeff Clement 3.00 8.00
158 Jeff Clement 3.00 8.00
159 Jeff Clement 3.00 8.00
160 Radhames Liz 2.50 6.00
161 Radhames Liz 2.50 6.00
162 Radhames Liz 2.50 6.00
163 Bronson Sardinha 2.50 6.00
164 Bronson Sardinha 2.50 6.00
165 Bronson Sardinha 2.50 6.00
166 Seth Smith 2.50 6.00
167 Seth Smith 2.50 6.00
168 Seth Smith 2.50 6.00
169 Chris Seddon 2.50 6.00
170 Chris Seddon 2.50 6.00
171 Chris Seddon 2.50 6.00
172 Wladimir Balentien 3.00 8.00
173 Wladimir Balentien 3.00 8.00
174 Wladimir Balentien 3.00 8.00
175 Josh Banks 2.50 6.00
176 Josh Banks 2.50 6.00
177 Josh Banks 2.50 6.00
178 Ross Detwiler 2.50 6.00
179 Ross Detwiler 2.50 6.00
180 Ross Detwiler 2.50 6.00
181 Felipe Paulino 2.50 6.00
182 Felipe Paulino 2.50 6.00
183 Felipe Paulino 2.50 6.00
184 Troy Patton 2.50 6.00
185 Troy Patton 2.50 6.00
186 Troy Patton 2.50 6.00
187 Brandon Jones 2.50 6.00
188 Brandon Jones 2.50 6.00
189 Brandon Jones 2.50 6.00
36-1 Daisuke Matsuzaka
62-1 Ichiro Suzuki

2008 Topps Moments and Milestones Blue

*BLUE p/r 750-5240 : 2.5X TO 6X BASIC
*BLUE p/r 110-540 : 2.5X TO 6X BASIC
BLUE RC: .6X TO 1.5X BASIC RC
STATED ODDS 1:4 HOBBY
STATED PRINT RUN 10 SER. #'d SETS
MILESTONE X 10 = TOTAL PRINT RUN
PRICING BASED ON TOTAL PRINT RUN
ALL VARIATIONS EQUALLY PRICED
NO PRICING ON QTY 25 OR LESS
157 Jeff Clement 6.00 15.00
158 Jeff Clement 6.00 15.00
159 Jeff Clement 6.00 15.00

2008 Topps Moments and Milestones Alex Rodriguez 500 HR Wall Relic

STATED ODDS 1:109
*BLACK: 1X TO 2.5X BASIC
BLACK ODDS 1:4125 HOBBY
BLACK PRINT RUN 99 SER.#'d SETS
BLUE ODDS 1:19,000 HOBBY
BLUE PRINT RUN 25 SER.#'d SETS
NO BLUE PRICING DUE TO SCARCITY
RED ODDS 1:316,440 HOBBY
RED PRINT RUN 1 SER.#'d SET
NO RED PRICING DUE TO SCARCITY
AR Alex Rodriguez 10.00 25.00

2008 Topps Moments and Milestones Milestone Autographs

NO GROUP D PRICING AVAILABLE
GROUP A ODDS 1:69 HOBBY
GROUP B ODDS 1:67 HOBBY
GROUP C ODDS 1:147 HOBBY
GROUP D ODDS 1:9251 HOBBY
OVERALL PLATE ODDS 1:1832 HOBBY
PLATE PRINT RUN 1 SET PER COLOR
BLACK-CYAN-MAGENTA-YELLOW ISSUED
NO PLATE PRICING DUE TO SCARCITY
AC Asdrubal Cabrera B 5.00 12.00
AL Adam Lind A 3.00 8.00
AR Alex Rodriguez D
AS Alfonso Soriano C 15.00 40.00
BC Bobby Crosby B 3.00 8.00
BH Brad Hawpe B 4.00 10.00
BR B.J. Ryan A 3.00 8.00
CC Carl Crawford C 5.00 12.00
CM Cameron Maybin B 6.00 15.00
CP Carlos Pena B 4.00 10.00
CR Carlos Ruiz A 3.00 8.00
DH Dan Haren C 3.00 8.00
DW David Wright C 30.00 60.00
FC Fausto Carmona B 5.00 12.00
FS Freddy Sanchez B 3.00 8.00
HR Hanley Ramirez C 8.00 20.00
JD Jermaine Dye B 3.00 8.00
JH Josh Hamilton C 20.00 50.00
JP Jorge Posada C 30.00 60.00
JR Jose Reyes C 20.00 50.00
LM Lastings Milledge B 3.00 8.00
MC Melky Cabrera A 6.00 15.00
MH Matt Holliday C 8.00 20.00
RB Ryan Braun B 15.00 40.00
RC Robinson Cano B 10.00 25.00
RG Ryan Garko C 3.00 8.00
RH Rich Harden C 3.00 8.00
RM Russell Martin B 5.00 12.00
TG Tom Gorzelanny A 3.00 8.00
TH Tim Hudson C 6.00 15.00
TJ Todd Jones B 3.00 8.00
MCA Matt Cain A 4.00 10.00
MIC Miguel Cabrera C 10.00 25.00
RJH Ryan Howard D

2008 Topps Moments and Milestones Milestone Autographs Black

STATED ODDS 1:332 HOBBY
STATED PRINT RUN 25 SER.#'d SETS
NO PRICING DUE TO SCARCITY

2008 Topps Moments and Milestones Milestone Autographs Blue

STATED ODDS 1:763 HOBBY
STATED PRINT RUN 10 SER.#'d SETS
NO PRICING DUE TO SCARCITY

2008 Topps Moments and Milestones Milestone Autographs Red

STATED ODDS 1:7740 HOBBY
STATED PRINT RUN 1 SER.#'d SET
NO PRICING DUE TO SCARCITY

2008 Topps Moments and Milestones Rookie Autographs

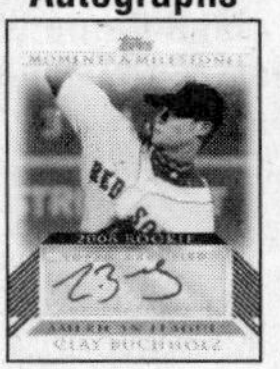

STATED ODDS 1:11 HOBBY
OVERALL PLATE ODDS 1:1832 HOBBY
PLATE PRINT RUN 1 SET PER COLOR
BLACK-CYAN-MAGENTA-YELLOW ISSUED
NO PLATE PRICING DUE TO SCARCITY
AG Armando Galarraga 3.00 8.00
BJ Brandon Jones 3.00 8.00
CB Clay Buchholz 12.50 30.00
CH Chin-Lung Hu 15.00 40.00
DB Daric Barton 4.00 10.00
FP Felipe Paulino 3.00 8.00
JA Josh Anderson 3.00 8.00
JK Joe Koshansky 3.00 8.00
JM Jonathan Meloan 3.00 8.00
JR Justin Ruggiano 3.00 8.00
JT J.R. Towles 5.00 12.00
LB Lance Broadway 3.00 8.00
NM Nyjer Morgan 3.00 8.00
RJ Rob Johnson 3.00 8.00
RO Ross Ohlendorf 4.00 10.00
RT Rich Thompson 3.00 8.00
SF Sam Fuld 3.00 8.00
SP Steve Pearce 5.00 12.00
WB Wladimir Balentien 3.00 8.00
JMM Jose Morales 3.00 8.00

2008 Topps Moments and Milestones Rookie Autographs Black

STATED ODDS 1:332 HOBBY
STATED PRINT RUN 25 SER.#'d SETS
NO PRICING DUE TO SCARCITY

2008 Topps Moments and Milestones Rookie Autographs Blue

STATED ODDS 1:763 HOBBY
STATED PRINT RUN 10 SER.#'d SETS
NO PRICING DUE TO SCARCITY

2008 Topps Moments and Milestones Rookie Autographs Red

STATED ODDS 1:7740 HOBBY
STATED PRINT RUN 1 SER.#'d SET
NO PRICING DUE TO SCARCITY

1998 Topps Opening Day

This 165-card set is a parallel version of basic 1998 Topps cards and features 110 cards from Series 1 and 55 cards from Series 2. Cards were issued in special retail seven-card "Opening Day" packs carrying an SRP of $0.99. The cards are an exact parallel of the 1998 Topps base cards except, of course, for the bold Opening Day foil logo on front and the different numbering on back.

COMPLETE SET (165) 30.00 50.00
*OPEN.DAY: .75X TO 2X BASIC TOPPS
ISSUED IN OPENING DAY PACKS

1999 Topps Opening Day

This 165-card set is a parallel version of basic 1999 Topps cards. Cards were issued in special retail seven-card "Opening Day" packs carrying an SRP of $0.99. The cards are an exact parallel of the 1999 Topps base cards except, of course, for the bold Opening Day foil logo on front and the different numbering on back. A Hank Aaron autograph card was inserted one every 29,462 packs.

COMPLETE SET (165) 15.00 40.00
*OPEN.DAY: .75X TO 2X BASIC TOPPS
ISSUED IN OPENING DAY PACKS
AARON AUTO STATED ODDS 1:29,642
1 Hank Aaron 1.00 2.50
NNO Hank Aaron AU 150.00 250.00

1999 Topps Opening Day Oversize

Randomly inserted one per retail box of 1999 Topps Opening Day base set, this three-card set features color player photos printed on 4 1/2" by 3 1/4" cards.

COMPLETE SET (3) 4.00 8.00
1 Sammy Sosa .50 1.25
2 Mark McGwire 1.25 3.00
3 Ken Griffey Jr. .75 2.00

2000 Topps Opening Day

The Topps Opening Day set was released in March, 2000 as a retail only 165-card set that featured 153 player cards, 10 Memorable Moments, 1 Hank Aaron 1954 reprint, and 1 checklist. Each pack contained seven cards and carried a suggested retail price of .99.

COMPLETE SET (165) 15.00 40.00
*OPEN.DAY: .75X TO 2X BASIC TOPPS
ISSUED IN OPENING DAY PACKS
UER 110 AARON '54 REPRINT #'d 128
NO MM VARIATIONS IN OPENING DAY

2000 Topps Opening Day Autographs

Randomly inserted in packs, this insert set features autographs of five major league players. There were three levels of autographs. Level A were inserted into packs at one in 4207, Level B were inserted at one in 48074, Level C were inserted at one in 6280. Card backs carry an "ODA" prefix.

ODA1 Edgardo Alfonzo A 15.00 40.00
ODA2 Wade Boggs A 40.00 80.00
ODA3 Robin Ventura A 15.00 40.00
ODA4 Josh Hamilton B 20.00 50.00
ODA5 Vernon Wells C 15.00 40.00

2001 Topps Opening Day

The 2001 Topps Opening Day product packed out in early March, 2001 and offers a 165-card base set. The base set features 150 Veteran players (1-150), four Prospects (151-154), 10 Golden Moments cards (155-164), and one checklist card (165). Each pack contained seven cards, and carries a suggested retail price of 1.99.

COMPLETE SET (165) 15.00 40.00
*OPEN.DAY: .75X TO 2X BASIC TOPPS
ISSUED IN OPENING DAY PACKS

2001 Topps Opening Day Autographs

Randomly inserted into packs, this 4-card insert set features authentic autographs from four of the Major League's top players. The set is brol. - down into four groups: Group A is Chipper Jones (1:31,680), Group B is Todd Helton (1:15,020), Group C is Magglio Ordonez (1:10,004), and Group D is Corey Patterson (1:5,940). Card backs carry an "ODA" prefix followed by the player's initials.

ODACJ Chipper Jones A 60.00 120.00
ODACP Corey Patterson D 15.00 30.00
ODAMO Magglio Ordonez C 15.00 30.00
ODATH Todd Helton B 25.00 50.00

2001 Topps Opening Day Stickers

Randomly inserted into packs at approximately one in two, this 30-card insert features stickers of all 30 Major League Franchises. Card backs are not numbered and are listed below in alphabetical order for convenience.

COMPLETE SET (30) 2.50 6.00
COMMON TEAM (1-30) .08 .25

2002 Topps Opening Day

Released in early 2002, this 165 card set, which was issued in seven-card packs is a partial parallel of the 2002 Topps set. These cards all have an opening day logo on the front. The Barry Bonds card issued at card numbered 73 only featured the 73 home run logo. Unlike the regular set, this was the only version of that card issued.

COMPLETE SET (165) 15.00 40.00
*OPEN.DAY: .75X TO X2 BASIC TOPPS
ISSUED IN OPENING DAY PACKS

2002 Topps Opening Day Autographs

Randomly inserted into packs, these three cards feature autographs of players in the Opening Day set. These cards were all inserted at differening odds and we have notated that information next to the player's name.

GROUP A STATED ODDS 1:6069
GROUP B STATED ODDS 1:3036
GROUP C STATED ODDS 1:2014
NO PRICING DUE TO SCARCITY
ODABS Ben Sheets B
ODAGJ Geoff Jenkins A
ODANJ Nick Johnson C

2003 Topps Opening Day

This 165-card set was issued in February, 2003. These cards were issued in six card packs which came 22 packs to a box and 20 boxes to a case. These cards can be notated by the special Topps Opening Day logo printed on the front.

COMPLETE SET (165) 15.00 40.00
*OPEN.DAY: .75X TO 2X BASIC TOPPS
ISSUED IN OPENING DAY PACKS

2003 Topps Opening Day Stickers

Issued one per pack, these 72 cards partially parallel the Opening Day set. Each of the fronts is designed exactly as the basic 2003 Topps card.

*OD STICKERS: 1.5X TO 4X BASIC TOPPS
ONE PER PACK

2003 Topps Opening Day Autographs

Inserted at different odds depending on which group the players were assigned to, these cards feature authentic autographs of the featured players.

GROUP A ODDS 1:10,623
GROUP B ODDS 1:3539
GROUP C ODDS 1:2654
JD Johnny Damon B 15.00 40.00
LB Lance Berkman A 20.00 50.00
RF Rafael Furcal C 10.00 25.00

2004 Topps Opening Day

This 165-card set, which is a mini-parallel to the basic Topps set was released in February, 2004. The set was issued in six card packs which came 36 packs to a box and 20 boxes to a case. Each of these cards have a special "Opening Day" logo embossed on them.

COMPLETE SET (165) 15.00 40.00
*OPEN.DAY 1-165: .75X TO 2X BASIC TOPPS
ISSUED IN OPENING DAY PACKS

2004 Topps Opening Day Autographs

STATED ODDS 1:629
AT Andres Torres 6.00 15.00
DW Dontrelle Willis 15.00 40.00
JD Jeff Duncan 6.00 15.00
JW Jerome Williams 6.00 15.00
RH Rich Harden 10.00 25.00
RW Ryan Wagner 6.00 15.00

2005 Topps Opening Day

This 165-card set was released early in 2005. The set features a mix of players from either series of the 2005 basic Topps set with the only difference being an opening day logo on the card.

COMPLETE SET (165) 15.00 40.00
COMMON CARD (1-165) .15 .40
ISSUED IN OPENING DAY PACKS
1 Alex Rodriguez .60 1.50
2 Placido Polanco .15 .40
3 Torii Hunter .15 .40
4 Lyle Overbay .15 .40
5 Johnny Damon .25 .60
6 Mike Cameron .15 .40
7 Ichiro Suzuki .75 2.00
8 Francisco Rodriguez .15 .40
9 Bobby Crosby .15 .40
10 Sammy Sosa .40 1.00
11 Randy Wolf .15 .40
12 Jason Bay .15 .40
13 Mike Lieberthal .15 .40
14 Paul Konerko .15 .40
15 Brian Giles .15 .40
16 Luis Gonzalez .15 .40
17 Jim Edmonds .15 .40
18 Carlos Lee .15 .40
19 Corey Patterson .15 .40
20 Hank Blalock .15 .40
21 Sean Casey .15 .40
22 Dmitri Young .15 .40
23 Mark Mulder .15 .40
24 Bobby Abreu .15 .40
25 Jim Thome .25 .60
26 Jason Kendall .15 .40
27 Jason Giambi .15 .40
28 Vinny Castilla .15 .40
29 Tony Batista .15 .40
30 Ivan Rodriguez .25 .60
31 Craig Biggio .25 .60
32 Chris Carpenter .15 .40
33 Adrian Beltre .15 .40
34 Scott Podsednik .15 .40
35 Cliff Floyd .15 .40
36 Chad Tracy .15 .40
37 John Smoltz .25 .60
38 Shingo Takatsu .15 .40
39 Jack Wilson .15 .40
40 Gary Sheffield .15 .40
41 Lance Berkman .15 .40
42 Carl Crawford .15 .40
43 Carlos Guillen .15 .40
44 David Bell .15 .40
45 Kazuo Matsui .15 .40
46 Jason Schmidt .15 .40
47 Jason Marquis .15 .40
48 Melvin Mora .15 .40
49 David Ortiz .40 1.00
50 Andruw Jones .25 .60
51 Miguel Tejada .15 .40
52 Bartolo Colon .15 .40
53 Derrek Lee .25 .60
54 Eric Gagne .15 .40
55 Miguel Cabrera .25 .60
56 Travis Hafner .15 .40
57 Jose Valentin .15 .40
58 Mark Prior .25 .60
59 Phil Nevin .15 .40
60 Jose Vidro .15 .40
61 Khalil Greene .25 .60
62 Carlos Zambrano .15 .40
63 Erubiel Durazo .15 .40
64 Michael Young UER .15 .40
Player sliding is Rod Barajas
65 Woody Williams .15 .40
66 Edgardo Alfonzo .15 .40
67 Troy Glaus .15 .40
68 Garret Anderson .15 .40
69 Richie Sexson .15 .40
70 Curt Schilling .25 .60
71 Randy Johnson .40 1.00
72 Chipper Jones .40 1.00
73 J.D. Drew .15 .40
74 Russ Ortiz .15 .40
75 Frank Thomas .40 1.00
76 Jimmy Rollins .15 .40
77 Barry Zito .15 .40
78 Rafael Palmeiro .25 .60
79 Brad Wilkerson .15 .40
80 Adam Dunn .15 .40
81 Doug Mientkiewicz .15 .40
82 Manny Ramirez .25 .60
83 Pedro Martinez .25 .60
84 Moises Alou .15 .40
85 Mike Sweeney .15 .40
86 Boston Red Sox WC .40 1.00
87 Matt Clement .15 .40
88 Nomar Garciaparra .40 1.00
89 Magglio Ordonez .15 .40
90 Bret Boone .15 .40
91 Mark Loretta .15 .40
92 Jose Contreras .15 .40
93 Randy Winn .15 .40
94 Austin Kearns .15 .40
95 Ken Griffey Jr. .60 1.50
96 Jake Westbrook .15 .40
97 Kazuhito Tadano .15 .40
98 C.C. Sabathia .15 .40
99 Todd Helton .25 .60
100 Albert Pujols .75 2.00
101 Jose Molina .15 .40
Bengie Molina
102 Aaron Miles .15 .40
103 Mike Lowell .15 .40
104 Paul Lo Duca .15 .40
105 Juan Pierre .15 .40
106 Dontrelle Willis .15 .40
107 Jeff Bagwell .25 .60
108 Carlos Beltran .15 .40
109 Ronnie Belliard .15 .40
110 Roy Oswalt .15 .40
111 Zack Greinke .15 .40
112 Steve Finley .15 .40
113 Kazuhisa Ishii .15 .40
114 Justin Morneau .15 .40
115 Ben Sheets .15 .40
116 Johan Santana .40 1.00
117 Billy Wagner .15 .40
118 Mariano Rivera .40 1.00
119 Corey Koskie .15 .40
120 Akinori Otsuka .15 .40
121 Joe Mauer .40 1.00
122 Jacque Jones .15 .40
123 Joe Nathan .15 .40
124 Nick Johnson .15 .40
125 Vernon Wells .15 .40
126 Mike Piazza .40 1.00
127 Jose Guillen .15 .40
128 Jose Reyes .15 .40
129 Marcus Giles .15 .40
130 Javy Lopez .15 .40
131 Kevin Millar .15 .40
132 Jorge Posada .25 .60
133 Carl Pavano .15 .40
134 Bernie Williams .25 .60
135 Kerry Wood .15 .40
136 Matt Holliday .20 .50
137 Kevin Brown .15 .40
138 Derek Jeter .75 2.00
139 Barry Bonds 1.00 2.50
140 Jeff Kent .15 .40
141 Mark Kotsay .15 .40
142 Shawn Green .15 .40
143 Tim Hudson .15 .40
144 Shannon Stewart .15 .40
145 Pat Burrell .15 .40
146 Gavin Floyd .15 .40
147 Mike Mussina .25 .60
148 Eric Chavez .15 .40
149 Jon Lieber .15 .40
150 Vladimir Guerrero .40 1.00
151 Vicente Padilla .15 .40
152 Ryan Klesko .15 .40
153 Jake Peavy .15 .40
154 Scott Rolen .25 .60
155 Greg Maddux .60 1.50
156 Edgar Renteria .15 .40
157 Larry Walker .25 .60
158 Scott Kazmir .15 .40
159 B.J. Upton .25 .60
160 Mark Teixeira .25 .60
161 Ken Harvey .15 .40
162 Alfonso Soriano .15 .40
163 Carlos Delgado .15 .40
164 Alexis Rios .15 .40
165 Checklist .15 .40

2005 Topps Opening Day Chrome Refractors

RANDOM INSERTS IN PACKS
1 Albert Pujols 4.00 10.00
2 Alex Rodriguez 3.00 8.00
3 Ivan Rodriguez 2.00 5.00
4 Jim Thome 2.00 5.00
5 Sammy Sosa 2.00 5.00
6 Vladimir Guerrero 2.00 5.00
7 Alfonso Soriano 1.25 3.00
8 Ichiro Suzuki 4.00 10.00
9 Derek Jeter 4.00 10.00
10 Chipper Jones 2.00 5.00

2005 Topps Opening Day Autographs

GROUP A ODDS 1:852
GROUP B ODDS 1:1192
EXCHANGE DEADLINE 02/28/07
AH Aaron Hill B 4.00 10.00
AW Anthony Whittington A 4.00 10.00
CC Chad Cordero A 6.00 15.00
FH Felix Hernandez A EXCH 15.00 40.00
OQ Omar Quintanilla B 6.00 15.00
PM Paul Maholm A 4.00 10.00

2005 Topps Opening Day MLB Game Worn Jersey Collection

RANDOM INSERTS IN TARGET RETAIL
37 Vladimir Guerrero 3.00 8.00
38 Albert Pujols 6.00 15.00
39 Torii Hunter 2.00 5.00
40 Alfonso Soriano 2.00 5.00
41 Bobby Abreu 2.00 5.00
42 Moises Alou 2.00 5.00
43 Sean Burroughs 2.00 5.00
44 Shannon Stewart 2.00 5.00
45 Troy Glaus 2.00 5.00
46 Fernando Vina 2.00 5.00
47 Dan Wilson 2.00 5.00
48 Paul Konerko 2.00 5.00
49 Jimmy Rollins 2.00 5.00
50 Livan Hernandez 2.00 5.00
51 Sean Casey 2.00 5.00
52 Paul LoDuca 2.00 5.00
53 Richie Sexson 2.00 5.00
54 Aubrey Huff 2.00 5.00

2006 Topps Opening Day

This 165-card set was released in March, 2006. This set was issued six-card hobby and retail packs with an 99 cent SRP which came 36 packs to a box and 20 boxes to a case. Cards numbered 1-134 feature veterans while cards 135-164 feature players who qualified for the rookie card status in 2006,

COMPLETE SET (165) 15.00 40.00
COMMON CARD (1-165) .15 .40
OVERALL PLATE SER.1 ODDS 1:246 HTA
PLATE PRINT RUN 1 SET PER COLOR
BLACK-CYAN-MAGENTA-YELLOW ISSUED
NO PLATE PRICING DUE TO SCARCITY
1 Alex Rodriguez .60 1.50
2 Jhonny Peralta .20 .50
3 Garrett Atkins .15 .40
4 Vernon Wells .15 .40
5 Carl Crawford .15 .40
6 Josh Beckett .15 .40
7 Mickey Mantle 3.00 8.00
8 Willy Taveras .15 .40
9 Ivan Rodriguez .25 .60
10 Clint Barmes .15 .40
11 Jose Reyes .40 1.00
12 Travis Hafner .15 .40
13 Tadahito Iguchi .15 .40
14 Barry Zito .15 .40
15 Brian Roberts .15 .40
16 David Wright .60 1.50
17 Mark Teixeira .25 .60
18 Roy Halladay .15 .40
19 Scott Rolen .25 .60
20 Bobby Abreu .15 .40
21 Lance Berkman .15 .40
22 Moises Alou .15 .40
23 Chone Figgins .15 .40
24 Aaron Rowand .15 .40
25 Chipper Jones .40 1.00
26 Johnny Damon .25 .60
27 Matt Clement .15 .40
28 Nick Johnson .15 .40
29 Freddy Garcia .15 .40
30 Jon Garland .15 .40
31 Torii Hunter .15 .40
32 Mike Sweeney .15 .40
33 Mike Lieberthal .15 .40
34 Rafael Furcal .15 .40
35 Brad Wilkerson .15 .40
36 Brad Penny .15 .40
37 Jorge Cantu .15 .40
38 Paul Konerko .15 .40
39 Rickie Weeks .15 .40
40 Jorge Posada .25 .60
41 Albert Pujols .75 2.00
42 Zack Greinke .15 .40
43 Jimmy Rollins .15 .40
44 Mark Prior .25 .60
45 Greg Maddux .60 1.50
46 Jeff Francis .15 .40
47 Felipe Lopez .15 .40
48 Dan Johnson .15 .40
49 B.J. Ryan .15 .40
50 Manny Ramirez .25 .60
51 Melvin Mora .15 .40
52 Javy Lopez .15 .40
53 Garret Anderson .15 .40
54 Jason Bay .15 .40
55 Joe Mauer .25 .60
56 C.C. Sabathia .15 .40
57 Bartolo Colon .15 .40
58 Ichiro Suzuki .60 1.50
59 Andruw Jones .25 .60
60 Rocco Baldelli .15 .40
61 Jeff Kent .15 .40
62 Cliff Floyd .15 .40
63 John Smoltz .25 .60
64 Shawn Green .15 .40
65 Nomar Garciaparra .40 1.00
66 Miguel Cabrera .25 .60
67 Vladimir Guerrero .40 1.00
68 Gary Sheffield .15 .40
69 Jake Peavy .15 .40
70 Carlos Lee .15 .40
71 Tom Glavine .25 .60
72 Craig Biggio .25 .60
73 Steve Finley .15 .40
74 Adrian Beltre .15 .40
75 Eric Gagne .15 .40
76 Aubrey Huff .15 .40
77 Livan Hernandez .15 .40
78 Scott Podsednik .15 .40
79 Todd Helton .25 .60
80 Kerry Wood .15 .40
81 Randy Johnson .40 1.00
82 Huston Street .15 .40
83 Pedro Martinez .25 .60
84 Roger Clemens .75 2.00
85 Hank Blalock .15 .40
86 Carlos Beltran .15 .40
87 Chien-Ming Wang .60 1.50
88 Rich Harden .15 .40
89 Mike Mussina .25 .60
90 Mark Buehrle .15 .40
91 Michael Young .15 .40
92 Mark Mulder .15 .40
93 Khalil Greene .25 .60
94 Johan Santana .25 .60
95 Andy Pettitte .25 .60
96 Derek Jeter 1.00 2.50
97 Jack Wilson .15 .40
98 Ben Sheets .15 .40
99 Miguel Tejada .15 .40
100 Barry Bonds 1.00 2.50
101 Dontrelle Willis .15 .40
102 Curt Schilling .25 .60
103 Jose Contreras .15 .40
104 Jeremy Bonderman .15 .40
105 David Ortiz .40 1.00
106 Lyle Overbay .15 .40
107 Robinson Cano .25 .60
108 Tim Hudson .15 .40
109 Paul Lo Duca .15 .40
110 Mariano Rivera .25 .60
111 Derrek Lee .15 .40
112 Morgan Ensberg .15 .40
113 Wily Mo Pena .15 .40
114 Roy Oswalt .15 .40
115 Adam Dunn .15 .40
116 Hideki Matsui .60 1.50
117 Pat Burrell .15 .40
118 Jason Schmidt .15 .40
119 Alfonso Soriano .15 .40
120 Aramis Ramirez .15 .40
121 Jason Giambi .15 .40
122 Orlando Hernandez .15 .40
123 Magglio Ordonez .15 .40
124 Troy Glaus .15 .40
125 Carlos Delgado .15 .40
126 Kevin Millwood .15 .40
127 Shannon Stewart .15 .40
128 Luis Castillo .15 .40
129 Jim Edmonds .25 .60
130 Richie Sexson .15 .40
131 Dmitri Young .15 .40
132 Russ Adams .15 .40
133 Nick Swisher .15 .40
134 Jermaine Dye .15 .40
135 Anderson Hernandez (RC) .15 .40
136 Justin Huber (RC) .15 .40
137 Jason Botts (RC) .15 .40
138 Jeff Mathis (RC) .15 .40
139 Ryan Garko (RC) .15 .40
140 Charlton Jimerson (RC) .15 .40
141 Chris Denorfia (RC) .15 .40
142 Anthony Reyes (RC) .15 .40
143 Bryan Bullington (RC) .15 .40
144 Chuck James (RC) .25 .60
145 Danny Sandoval RC .15 .40
146 Walter Young (RC) .15 .40
147 Fausto Carmona (RC) .15 .40
148 Francisco Liriano (RC) .75 2.00
149 Hong-Chih Kuo (RC) .40 1.00
150 Joe Saunders (RC) .15 .40
151 John Koronka (RC) .15 .40
152 Robert Andino RC .15 .40
153 Shaun Marcum (RC) .15 .40
154 Tom Gorzelanny (RC) .15 .40
155 Craig Breslow RC .15 .40
156 Chris Demaria RC .15 .40
157 Brayan Pena (RC) .15 .40
158 Rich Hill (RC) .15 .40
159 Rick Short (RC) .15 .40
160 Darrell Rasner (RC) .15 .40
161 C.J. Wilson (RC) .15 .40
162 Brandon Watson (RC) .15 .40
163 Paul McAnulty (RC) .15 .40
164 Marshall McDougall (RC) .15 .40
165 Checklist .15 .40

2006 Topps Opening Day Red Foil

*RED FOIL: 3X TO 8X BASIC
*RED FOIL: 3X TO 8X BASIC RC
STATED ODDS 1:8 HOBBY, 1:11 RETAIL
STATED PRINT RUN 2006 SERIAL #'d SETS
7 Mickey Mantle 10.00 25.00

2006 Topps Opening Day Autographs

GROUP A ODDS 1:10928 H, 1:11668 R
GROUP B ODDS 1:3491 H, 1:3491 R
GROUP C ODDS 1:978 H, 1:1185 R
BE Brad Eldred B 4.00 10.00
EM Eli Marrero C 4.00 10.00
JE Johnny Estrada A 6.00 15.00
MK Mark Kotsay B 6.00 15.00
TH Toby Hall C 4.00 10.00
VZ Victor Zambrano C 4.00 10.00

2006 Topps Opening Day Sports Illustrated For Kids

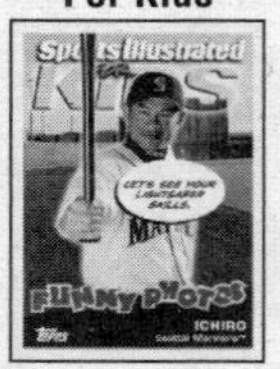

COMPLETE SET (25) 4.00 10.00
STATED ODDS 1:1
1 Vladimir Guerrero .60 1.50
2 Marcus Giles .25 .60
3 Michael Young .25 .60
4 Derek Jeter 1.50 4.00
5 Barry Bonds 1.50 4.00
6 Ivan Rodriguez .40 1.00
7 Miguel Cabrera .40 1.00
8 Jim Edmonds .40 1.00
9 Jack Wilson .25 .60
10 Khalil Greene .40 1.00
11 Miguel Tejada .25 .60
12 Eric Chavez .25 .60
13 Shannon Stewart .25 .60
14 Julio Lugo .25 .60
15 Andruw Jones .40 1.00
16 Nick Johnson .60 1.50
Randy Johnson
17 Tadahito Iguchi .40 1.00
Ivan Rodriguez
18 Roy Oswalt .60 1.50
Jose Reyes
19 Manny Ramirez .40 1.00
Ronnie Belliard
20 Todd Helton .40 1.00
Khalil Greene
21 David Ortiz .60 1.50
Dontrelle Willis
22 Ichiro Suzukii 1.00 2.50
Johnny Damon
23 Craig Biggio .40 1.00
Jack Wilson
24 Brian Roberts .25 .60
Richie Sexson
25 Chipper Jones .60 1.50
Marcus Giles

2007 Topps Opening Day

This 220-card set was released in March, 2007. This set was issued in six-card packs, with an 99 cent SRP, which came 36 packs to a box and 20 boxes to a case. The Derek Jeter (#46) card, which featured Mickey Mantle and President George W Bush in the regular Topps set; did not feature either personage in the background.

COMPLETE SET (220) 20.00 50.00
COMMON CARD (1-220) .15 .40
COMMON RC .20 .50
OVERALL PLATE ODDS 1:370 HOBBY
PLATE PRINT RUN 1 SET PER COLOR
BLACK-CYAN-MAGENTA-YELLOW ISSUED
NO PLATE PRICING DUE TO SCARCITY
1 Bobby Abreu .15 .40
2 Mike Piazza .40 1.00
3 Jake Westbrook .15 .40
4 Zach Duke .15 .40
5 David Wright .60 1.50
6 Adrian Gonzalez .15 .40
7 Mickey Mantle 2.00 5.00
8 Bill Hall .15 .40
9 Robinson Cano .25 .60
10 Dontrelle Willis .15 .40
11 J.D. Drew .15 .40
12 Paul Konerko .15 .40
13 Austin Kearns .15 .40
14 Mike Lowell .15 .40
15 Magglio Ordonez .15 .40
16 Rafael Furcal .15 .40
17 Matt Cain .25 .60
18 Craig Monroe .15 .40
19 Matt Holliday .20 .50
20 Edgar Renteria .15 .40
21 Mark Buehrle .15 .40
22 Carlos Quentin .15 .40
23 C.C. Sabathia .15 .40
24 Nick Markakis .25 .60
25 Chipper Jones .40 1.00
26 Jason Giambi .15 .40
27 Barry Zito .15 .40
28 Jake Peavy .15 .40
29 Hank Blalock .15 .40
30 Johnny Damon .25 .60
31 Chad Tracy .15 .40
32 Nick Swisher .15 .40
33 Willy Taveras .15 .40
34 Chuck James .15 .40
35 Carlos Delgado .15 .40
36 Livan Hernandez .15 .40
37 Freddy Garcia .15 .40
38 Bronson Arroyo .15 .40
39 Jack Wilson .15 .40
40 Dan Uggla .25 .60
41 Chris Carpenter .15 .40
42 Jorge Posada .25 .60
43 Joe Mauer .25 .60
44 Corey Patterson .15 .40
45 Chien-Ming Wang .60 1.50
46 Derek Jeter 6.00 15.00
47 Carlos Beltran .15 .40
48 Jim Edmonds .25 .60
49 Jeremy Sowers .15 .40
50 Randy Johnson .40 1.00
51 Jered Weaver .25 .60
52 Josh Barfield .15 .40
53 Scott Rolen .25 .60
54 Ryan Shealy .15 .40
55 Freddy Sanchez .15 .40
56 Javier Vazquez .15 .40
57 Jeremy Bonderman .15 .40
58 Miguel Cabrera .25 .60
59 Kazuo Matsui .15 .40
60 Curt Schilling .25 .60
61 Alfonso Soriano .15 .40
62 Orlando Hernandez .15 .40
63 Joe Blanton .15 .40
64 Aramis Ramirez .15 .40
65 Ben Sheets .15 .40
66 Jimmy Rollins .15 .40
67 Mark Loretta .15 .40
68 Cole Hamels .25 .60
69 Albert Pujols .75 2.00
70 Moises Alou .15 .40
71 Mark Teahen .15 .40
72 Roy Halladay .15 .40
73 Cory Sullivan .15 .40
74 Frank Thomas .40 1.00
75 Ryan Howard .60 1.50
76 Rocco Baldelli .15 .40
77 Manny Ramirez .25 .60
78 Ray Durham .15 .40
79 Gary Sheffield .15 .40
80 Jay Gibbons .15 .40
81 Todd Helton .25 .60
82 Gary Matthews .15 .40
83 Brandon Inge .15 .40
84 Jonathan Papelbon .40 1.00
85 John Smoltz .25 .60
86 Chone Figgins .15 .40
87 Hideki Matsui .40 1.00
88 Carlos Lee .15 .40
89 Jose Reyes .15 .40
90 Lyle Overbay .15 .40
91 Johan Santana .25 .60
92 Ian Kinsler .15 .40
93 Scott Kazmir .25 .60
94 Hanley Ramirez .25 .60
95 Greg Maddux .60 1.50
96 Johnny Estrada .15 .40
97 B.J. Upton .15 .40
98 Francisco Liriano .40 1.00
99 Chase Utley .40 1.00
100 Preston Wilson .15 .40
101 Marcus Giles .15 .40
102 Jeff Kent .15 .40
103 Grady Sizemore .25 .60
104 Ken Griffey .60 1.50
105 Garret Anderson .15 .40
106 Brian McCann .15 .40
107 Jon Garland .15 .40
108 Troy Glaus .15 .40
109 Brandon Webb .15 .40
110 Jason Schmidt .15 .40
111 Ramon Hernandez .15 .40
112 Justin Morneau .15 .40
113 Mike Cameron .15 .40
114 Andruw Jones .25 .60
115 Russell Martin .15 .40
116 Vernon Wells .15 .40
117 Orlando Hudson .15 .40
118 Derek Lowe .15 .40
119 Alex Rodriguez .60 1.50
120 Chad Billingsley .15 .40
121 Kenji Johjima .40 1.00
122 Nick Johnson .15 .40
123 Dan Haren .15 .40
124 Mark Teixeira .25 .60
125 Jeff Francoeur .40 1.00
126 Ted Lilly .15 .40
127 Jhonny Peralta .15 .40
128 Aaron Harang .15 .40
129 Ryan Zimmerman .40 1.00
130 Jermaine Dye .15 .40
131 Orlando Cabrera .15 .40
132 Juan Pierre .15 .40
133 Brian Giles .15 .40
134 Jason Bay .15 .40
135 David Ortiz .40 1.00
136 Chris Capuano .15 .40
137 Carlos Zambrano .15 .40
138 Luis Gonzalez .15 .40
139 Jeff Weaver .15 .40
140 Lance Berkman .15 .40
141 Raul Ibanez .15 .40
142 Jim Thome .25 .60
143 Jose Contreras .15 .40
144 David Eckstein .15 .40
145 Adam Dunn .15 .40
146 Alex Rios .15 .40
147 Garrett Atkins .15 .40
148 A.J. Burnett .15 .40
149 Jeremy Hermida .15 .40
150 Conor Jackson .15 .40
151 Adrian Beltre .15 .40
152 Torii Hunter .15 .40
153 Andrew Miller RC 1.50 4.00
154 Ichiro Suzuki .60 1.50
155 Mark Redman .15 .40
156 Paul LoDuca .15 .40
157 Xavier Nady .15 .40

158 Stephen Drew .25 .60
159 Eric Chavez .15 .40
160 Pedro Martinez .25 .60
161 Derrek Lee .15 .40
162 David DeJesus .15 .40
163 Troy Tulowitzki (RC) .50 1.25
164 Vinny Rottino (RC) .20 .50
165 Philip Humber (RC) .30 .75
166 Jerry Owens (RC) .20 .50
167 Ubaldo Jimenez (RC) .20 .50
168 Michael Young .15 .40
169 Ryan Braun RC .20 .50
170 Kevin Kouzmanoff (RC) .20 .50
171 Oswaldo Navarro RC .20 .50
172 Miguel Montero (RC) .20 .50
173 Roy Oswalt .15 .40
174 Shane Youman RC .20 .50
175 Josh Fields (RC) .20 .50
176 Adam Lind (RC) .20 .50
177 Miguel Tejada .15 .40
178 Delwyn Young (RC) .20 .50
179 Scott Moore (RC) .20 .50
180 Fred Lewis (RC) .20 .50
181 Glen Perkins (RC) .20 .50
182 Vladimir Guerrero .40 1.00
183 Drew Anderson RC .20 .50
184 Jeff Salazar (RC) .20 .50
185 Tom Gordon .15 .40
186 The Bird .15 .40
187 Justin Verlander .40 1.00
188 Delmon Young (RC) .50 1.25
189 Homer .15 .40
190 Wally the Green Monster .15 .40
191 Southpaw .15 .40
192 Dinger .15 .40
193 Carl Crawford .15 .40
194 Slider .15 .40
195 Gapper .15 .40
196 Paws .15 .40
197 Billy the Marlin .15 .40
198 Ivan Rodriguez .25 .60
199 Slugger .15 .40
200 Junction Jack .15 .40
201 Bernie Brewer .15 .40
202 Travis Hafner .15 .40
203 Stomper .15 .40
204 Mr. Met .15 .40
205 The Moose .15 .40
206 Phillie Phanatic .15 .40
207 Prince Fielder .40 1.00
208 Julio Lugo .15 .40
209 Pirate Parrot .15 .40
210 Joel Zumaya .25 .60
211 Swinging Friar .15 .40
212 Jay Payton .15 .40
213 Lou Seal .15 .40
214 Fredbird .15 .40
215 Screech .15 .40
216 TC Bear .15 .40
217 Andre Ethier .25 .60
218 Ervin Santana .15 .40
219 Melvin Mora .15 .40
220 Checklist .15 .40

2007 Topps Opening Day Gold

COMPLETE SET (219) 75.00 150.00
*GOLD: 1.25X TO 3X BASIC
*GOLD: 1X TO 2.5X BASIC RC
STATED ODDS APPX. 1 PER HOBBY PACK
STATED PRINT RUN 2007 SERIAL #'d SETS
46 Derek Jeter 12.50 30.00

2007 Topps Opening Day Autographs

STATED ODDS 1:965 HOBBY, 1:965 RETAIL
EF Emiliano Fruto 10.00 25.00
HK Howie Kendrick 20.00 50.00
JM Juan Morillo 6.00 15.00
JT Jordan Tata
MC Matt Cain 10.00 25.00
MK Matt Kemp 10.00 25.00
MN Mike Napoli
OH Orlando Hudson 10.00 25.00
RM Rob Mackowiak
SS Shannon Stewart 6.00 15.00

2007 Topps Opening Day Diamond Stars

COMPLETE SET (25) 6.00 15.00
STATED ODDS 1:4 HOBBY, 1:4 RETAIL
DS1 Ryan Howard 1.00 2.50
DS2 Alfonso Soriano .25 .60
DS3 Alex Rodriguez 1.00 2.50
DS4 David Ortiz .60 1.50
DS5 Raul Ibanez .25 .60
DS6 Matt Holliday .30 .75
DS7 Delmon Young .60 1.50
DS8 Derrick Turnbow .25 .60
DS9 Freddy Sanchez .25 .60
DS10 Troy Glaus .25 .60
DS11 A.J. Pierzynski .25 .60
DS12 Dontrelle Willis .25 .60
DS13 Justin Morneau .25 .60
DS14 Jose Reyes .25 .60
DS15 Derek Jeter 1.50 4.00
DS16 Ivan Rodriguez .40 1.00
DS17 Jay Payton .25 .60
DS18 Adrian Gonzalez .25 .60
DS19 David Eckstein .25 .60
DS20 Chipper Jones .60 1.50
DS21 Aramis Ramirez .25 .60
DS22 David Wright 1.00 2.50
DS23 Mark Teixeira .40 1.00
DS24 Stephen Drew .40 1.00
DS25 Ichiro Suzuki 1.00 2.50

2007 Topps Opening Day Movie Gallery

STATED ODDS 1:6 HOBBY
NNO Alex Rodriguez .40 1.00

2007 Topps Opening Day Puzzle

COMPLETE SET (28) 6.00 15.00
STATED ODDS 1:3 HOBBY, 1:3 RETAIL
P1 Adam Dunn .25 .60
P2 Adam Dunn .25 .60
P3 Miguel Tejada .25 .60
P4 Miguel Tejada .25 .60
P5 Hanley Ramirez .25 .60
P6 Hanley Ramirez .25 .60
P7 Johan Santana .25 .60
P8 Johan Santana .25 .60
P9 Brandon Webb .25 .60
P10 Brandon Webb .25 .60
P11 David Wright .60 1.50
P12 David Wright .60 1.50
P13 Alex Rodriguez .60 1.50
P14 Alex Rodriguez .60 1.50
P15 Ryan Howard .60 1.50
P16 Ryan Howard .60 1.50
P17 Albert Pujols .75 2.00
P18 Albert Pujols .75 2.00
P19 Andruw Jones .25 .60
P20 Andruw Jones .25 .60
P21 Alfonso Soriano .25 .60
P22 Alfonso Soriano .25 .60
P23 Vladimir Guerrero .40 1.00
P24 Vladimir Guerrero .40 1.00
P25 David Ortiz .40 1.00
P26 David Ortiz .40 1.00
P27 Ichiro Suzuki .60 1.50
P28 Ichiro Suzuki .60 1.50

2008 Topps Opening Day

COMPLETE SET (220) 15.00 40.00
COMMON CARD (1-194) .12 .30
COMMON RC (195-220) .20 .50
OVERALL PLATE ODDS 1:546 HOBBY
PLATE PRINT RUN 1 SET PER COLOR
BLACK-CYAN-MAGENTA-YELLOW ISSUED
NO PLATE PRICING DUE TO SCARCITY
1 Alex Rodriguez .50 1.25
2 Barry Zito .12 .30
3 Jeff Suppan .12 .30
4 Placido Polanco .12 .30
5 Scott Kazmir .20 .50
6 Ivan Rodriguez .20 .50
7 Mickey Mantle 1.25 3.00
8 Stephen Drew .12 .30
9 Ken Griffey Jr. .50 1.25
10 Miguel Cabrera .20 .50
11 Yorvit Torrealba .12 .30
12 Daisuke Matsuzaka .60 1.50
13 Kyle Kendrick .12 .30
14 Jimmy Rollins .20 .50
15 Joe Mauer .20 .50
16 Cole Hamels .30 .75
17 Yovani Gallardo .12 .30
18 Miguel Tejada .12 .30
19 Corey Hart .12 .30
20 Nick Markakis .20 .50
21 Zack Greinke .12 .30
22 Orlando Cabrera .12 .30
23 Jake Peavy .20 .50
24 Erik Bedard .12 .30
25 Trevor Hoffman .12 .30
26 Derrek Lee .20 .50
27 Hank Blalock .12 .30
28 Victor Martinez .12 .30
29 Chris Young .12 .30
30 Jose Reyes .20 .50
31 Mike Lowell .12 .30
32 Curtis Granderson .12 .30
33 Dan Uggla .20 .50
34 Mike Piazza .30 .75
35 Garrett Atkins .12 .30
36 Felix Hernandez .20 .50
37 Alex Rios .12 .30
38 Mark Reynolds .12 .30
39 Jason Bay .12 .30
40 Josh Beckett .20 .50
41 Jack Cust .12 .30
42 Vladimir Guerrero .30 .75
43 Marcus Giles .12 .30
44 Kenny Lofton .12 .30
45 John Lackey .12 .30
46 Ryan Howard .40 1.00
47 Kevin Youkilis .20 .50
48 Gary Sheffield .12 .30
49 Justin Morneau .12 .30
50 Albert Pujols .50 1.25
51 Ubaldo Jimenez .12 .30
52 Johan Santana .20 .50
53 Chuck James .12 .30
54 Jeremy Hermida .12 .30
55 Andruw Jones .12 .30
56 Jason Varitek .30 .75
57 Tim Hudson .12 .30
58 Justin Upton .30 .75
59 Brad Penny .12 .30
60 Robinson Cano .20 .50
61 Johnny Estrada .12 .30
62 Brandon Webb .20 .50
63 Chris Duncan .12 .30
64 Aaron Hill .12 .30
65 Alfonso Soriano .20 .50
66 Carlos Zambrano .12 .30
67 Ben Sheets .20 .50
68 Andy LaRoche .12 .30
69 Tim Lincecum .30 .75
70 Phil Hughes .40 1.00
71 Magglio Ordonez .20 .50
72 Scott Rolen .20 .50
73 John Maine .12 .30
74 Delmon Young .20 .50
75 Chase Utley .30 .75
76 Jose Valverde .12 .30
77 Tadahito Iguchi .12 .30
78 Checklist .12 .30
79 Russell Martin .12 .30
80 B.J. Upton .20 .50
81 Orlando Hudson .12 .30
82 Jim Edmonds .20 .50
83 J.J. Hardy .12 .30
84 Todd Helton .20 .50
85 Melky Cabrera .12 .30
86 Adrian Beltre .12 .30
87 Manny Ramirez .30 .75
88 Rafael Furcal .12 .30
89 Gil Meche .12 .30
90 Grady Sizemore .20 .50
91 Jeff Kent .12 .30
92 David DeJesus .12 .30
93 Lyle Overbay .12 .30
94 Moises Alou .12 .30
95 Frank Thomas .30 .75
96 Ryan Garko .12 .30
97 Kevin Kouzmanoff .12 .30
98 Roy Oswalt .12 .30
99 Mark Buehrle .12 .30
100 David Ortiz .30 .75
101 Hunter Pence .30 .75
102 David Wright .40 1.00
103 Dustin Pedroia .50 1.25
104 Roy Halladay .12 .30
105 Derek Jeter .75 2.00
106 Casey Blake .12 .30
107 Rich Harden .12 .30
108 Shane Victorino .12 .30
109 Richie Sexson .12 .30
110 Jim Thome .20 .50
111 Akinori Iwamura .12 .30
112 Dan Haren .12 .30
113 Jose Contreras .12 .30
114 Jonathan Papelbon .20 .50
115 Prince Fielder .30 .75
116 Dan Johnson .12 .30
117 Dmitri Young .12 .30
118 Brandon Phillips .12 .30
119 Brett Myers .12 .30
120 James Loney .20 .50
121 C.C. Sabathia .12 .30
122 Jermaine Dye .12 .30
123 Aubrey Huff .12 .30
124 Carlos Ruiz .12 .30
125 Hanley Ramirez .30 .75
126 Edgar Renteria .12 .30
127 Mark Loretta .12 .30
128 Brian McCann .20 .50
129 Paul Konerko .20 .50
130 Jorge Posada .20 .50
131 Chien-Ming Wang .50 1.25
132 Jose Vidro .12 .30
133 Carlos Delgado .12 .30
134 Kelvim Escobar .12 .30
135 Pedro Martinez .20 .50
136 Jeremy Guthrie .20 .50
137 Ramon Hernandez .12 .30
138 Ian Kinsler .20 .50
139 Ichiro Suzuki .50 1.25
140 Garret Anderson .12 .30
141 Tom Gorzelanny .12 .30
142 Bobby Crosby .12 .30
143 Jeff Francoeur .20 .50
144 Josh Hamilton .40 1.00
145 Mark Teixeira .20 .50
146 Fausto Carmona .12 .30
147 Alex Gordon .30 .75
148 Nick Swisher .12 .30
149 Justin Verlander .20 .50
150 Pat Burrell .12 .30
151 Chris Carpenter .12 .30
152 Matt Holliday .20 .50
153 Adam Dunn .12 .30
154 Curt Schilling .20 .50
155 Kelly Johnson .12 .30
156 Aaron Rowand .12 .30
157 Brian Roberts .20 .50
158 Bobby Abreu .12 .30
159 Carlos Beltran .12 .30
160 Lance Berkman .20 .50
161 Gary Matthews .12 .30
162 Jeff Francis .12 .30
163 Vernon Wells .12 .30
164 Dontrelle Willis .12 .30
165 Travis Hafner .12 .30
166 Brian Bannister .12 .30
167 Carlos Pena .30 .75
168 Raul Ibanez .12 .30
169 Aramis Ramirez .12 .30
170 Eric Byrnes .12 .30
171 Greg Maddux .40 1.00
172 John Smoltz .30 .75
173 Jarrod Saltalamacchia .12 .30
174 Hideki Okajima .20 .50
175 Javier Vazquez .12 .30
176 Aaron Harang .12 .30
177 Jhonny Peralta .12 .30
178 Carlos Lee .12 .30
179 Ryan Braun .40 1.00
180 Torii Hunter .12 .30
181 Hideki Matsui .30 .75
182 Eric Chavez .12 .30
183 Freddy Sanchez .12 .30
184 Adrian Gonzalez .20 .50
185 Bengie Molina .12 .30
186 Kenji Johjima .12 .30
187 Carl Crawford .12 .30
188 Chipper Jones .40 1.00
189 Chris Young .12 .30
190 Michael Young .12 .30
191 Troy Glaus .20 .50
192 Ryan Zimmerman .20 .50
193 Brian Giles .12 .30
194 Troy Tulowitzki .20 .50
195 Chin-Lung Hu (RC) .30 .75
196 Seth Smith (RC) .30 .75
197 Wladimir Balentien (RC) .20 .50
198 Rich Thompson RC .30 .75
199 Radhames Liz RC .30 .75
200 Ross Detwiler RC .50 1.25
201 Sam Fuld RC .20 .50
202 Clint Sammons (RC) .20 .50
203 Ross Ohlendorf RC .30 .75
204 Jonathan Albaladejo RC .30 .75
205 Brandon Jones RC .50 1.25
206 Steve Pearce RC .30 .75
207 Kevin Hart (RC) .20 .50
208 Luke Hochevar RC .50 1.25
209 Troy Patton (RC) .20 .50
210 Josh Anderson (RC) .20 .50
211 Clay Buchholz (RC) .50 1.25
212 Joe Koshansky (RC) .20 .50
213 Bronson Sardinha (RC) .20 .50
214 Emilio Bonifacio RC .30 .75
215 Daric Barton (RC) .20 .50
216 Lance Broadway (RC) .20 .50
217 Jeff Clement (RC) .20 .50
218 Joey Votto (RC) .50 1.25
219 J.R. Towles RC .50 1.25
220 Nyjer Morgan (RC) .20 .50

2008 Topps Opening Day Gold

COMPLETE SET (220) 50.00 100.00
*GOLD VET: 1X TO 2.5X BASIC
*GOLD RC: 1X TO 2.5X BASIC RC
STATED ODDS APPX. ONE PER PACK
STATED PRINT RUN 2199 SERIAL #'d SETS
7 Mickey Mantle 3.00 8.00

2008 Topps Opening Day Autographs

GROUP A ODDS 1:359
GROUP B ODDS 1:7800
AAL Adam Lind A 6.00 15.00
AL Anthony Lerew A 6.00 15.00
GP Glen Perkins A 3.00 8.00
JAB Jason Bartlett A 3.00 8.00
JB Jeff Baker A 3.00 8.00
JCB Jason Botts B 6.00 15.00
JRB John Buck A 3.00 8.00
KG Kevin Gregg A 5.00 12.00
NS Nate Schierholtz A 5.00 12.00

2008 Topps Opening Day Flapper Cards

COMPLETE SET (18) 6.00 15.00
STATED ODDS 1:8
AP Albert Pujols 1.00 2.50
AR Alex Rodriguez 1.00 2.50
CJ Chipper Jones .75 2.00
DJ Derek Jeter 1.50 4.00
DM Daisuke Matsuzaka 1.25 3.00
DO David Ortiz .60 1.50
DW David Wright .75 2.00
GM Greg Maddux .75 2.00
IS Ichiro Suzuki 1.00 2.50
JB Josh Beckett .40 1.00
JR Jose Reyes .40 1.00
KG Ken Griffey Jr 1.00 2.50
MM Mickey Mantle 1.50 4.00
MR Manny Ramirez .60 1.50
PF Prince Fielder .60 1.50
RC Roger Clemens .75 2.00
RH Ryan Howard .75 2.00
VG Vladimir Guerrero .60 1.50

2008 Topps Opening Day Puzzle

COMPLETE SET (28) 5.00 12.00
STATED ODDS 1:3
P1 Matt Holliday .30 .75
P2 Matt Holliday .30 .75
P3 Vladimir Guerrero .50 1.25
P4 Vladimir Guerrero .50 1.25
P5 Jose Reyes .30 .75
P6 Jose Reyes .30 .75
P7 Josh Beckett .30 .75
P8 Josh Beckett .30 .75
P9 Albert Pujols .75 2.00
P10 Albert Pujols .75 2.00
P11 Alex Rodriguez .75 2.00
P12 Alex Rodriguez .75 2.00
P13 Jake Peavy .30 .75
P14 Jake Peavy .30 .75
P15 David Ortiz .50 1.25
P16 David Ortiz .50 1.25
P17 Ryan Howard .60 1.50
P18 Ryan Howard .60 1.50
P19 Ichiro Suzuki .75 2.00
P20 Ichiro Suzuki .75 2.00
P21 Hanley Ramirez .50 1.25
P22 Hanley Ramirez .50 1.25
P23 Grady Sizemore .30 .75
P24 Grady Sizemore .30 .75
P25 David Wright .60 1.50
P26 David Wright .60 1.50
P27 Alex Rios .20 .50
P28 Alex Rios .20 .50

2008 Topps Opening Day Tattoos

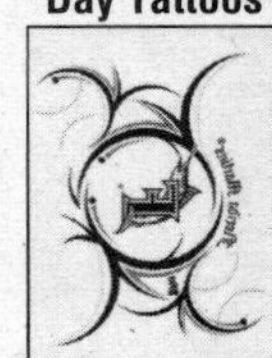

STATED ODDS 1:12
AB Atlanta Braves .60 1.50
AD Arizona Diamondbacks .60 1.50
BB Bernie Brewer .60 1.50
BM Billy the Marlin .60 1.50
BRS Boston Red Sox .60 1.50
CC Chicago Cubs .60 1.50
CI Cleveland Indians .60 1.50
CR Cincinnati Reds .60 1.50
CWS Chicago White Sox .60 1.50
FB Fredbird .60 1.50
FM Florida Marlins .60 1.50
JJ Junction Jack .60 1.50
LAA Los Angeles Angels .60 1.50
LS Lou Seal .60 1.50
MM Mr. Met .60 1.50
NYM New York Mets .60 1.50
NYY New York Yankees .60 1.50
PIP Pirate Parrot .60 1.50
PP Phillie Phanatic .60 1.50
PW Paws .60 1.50
SF Swinging Friar .60 1.50
SFG San Francisco Giants .60 1.50
SL Slider .60 1.50
ST Stomper .60 1.50
TB TC Bear .60 1.50
TBJ Toronto Blue Jays .60 1.50
TDR Tampa Bay Rays .60 1.50
TM The Moose .60 1.50
TR Texas Rangers .60 1.50
WM Wally the Green Monster .60 1.50

2004 Topps Originals Signature

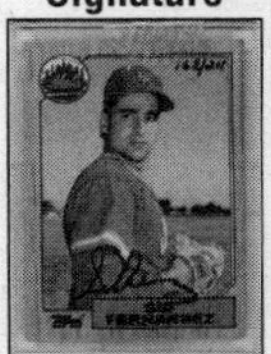

This 1179-card set was released in July, 2004. The set was released in one-card packs with an $50 SRP which came six packs to a box and 4 boxes to a case. All of the cards used in the set were original Topps cards which Topps bought back and the players signed. All of the players signed one copy of each of their rookie cards.

ONE AUTO PER PACK
PRINT RUNS B/WN 1-339 COPIES PER
NO PRICING ON QTY OF 14 OR LESS
AD1 Andre Dawson 77/1
AD2 Andre Dawson 79/3
AD3 Andre Dawson 80/27 15.00 40.00
AD4 Andre Dawson 81/37 10.00 25.00
AD5 Andre Dawson 82/55 10.00 25.00
AD6 Andre Dawson 83/47 10.00 25.00
AD7 Andre Dawson 84/25 15.00 40.00
AD8 Andre Dawson 85/22 15.00 40.00
AD9 Andre Dawson 86/24 15.00 40.00
AD10 Andre Dawson 88/9
AH1 Al Hrabosky 71/1
AH2 Al Hrabosky 74/2
AH3 Al Hrabosky 75/1
AH4 Al Hrabosky 76/5
AH5 Al Hrabosky 77/5
AH6 Al Hrabosky 78/20 12.50 30.00
AH7 Al Hrabosky 79/40 10.00 25.00
AH8 Al Hrabosky 80/61 10.00 25.00
AH9 Al Hrabosky 81/38 6.00 15.00
AH10 Al Hrabosky 82/62 6.00 15.00
AH11 Al Hrabosky 89 Sr./20 10.00 25.00
AK1 Al Kaline 54/1
AK2 Al Kaline 59/1
AK3 Al Kaline 60/1
AK4 Al Kaline 60 AS/1
AK5 Al Kaline 61/3
AK6 Al Kaline 62/3
AK7 Al Kaline 62 AS/2
AK8 Al Kaline 64/4
AK9 Al Kaline 66/1
AK10 Al Kaline 67/18 60.00 120.00
AK11 Al Kaline 68/6
AK12 Al Kaline 69/7
AK13 Al Kaline 70/3
AK14 Al Kaline 71/7
AK15 Al Kaline 72/11
AK16 Al Kaline 73/25 50.00 100.00
AK17 Al Kaline 74/11
AK18 Al Kaline 75 HL/1
AO1 Al Oliver 69/1
AO2 Al Oliver 74/2
AO3 Al Oliver 75/2
AO4 Al Oliver 76/2
AO5 Al Oliver 78/3
AO6 Al Oliver 79/42 10.00 25.00
AO7 Al Oliver 80/6
AO8 Al Oliver 81/54 6.00 15.00
AO9 Al Oliver 82/45 6.00 15.00
AO10 Al Oliver 83/50 6.00 15.00
AO11 Al Oliver 84/51 6.00 15.00
AO12 Al Oliver 85/46 6.00 15.00
AO13 Al Oliver 86/44 6.00 15.00
AT1 Alan Trammell 79/12
AT2 Alan Trammell 80/17 20.00 50.00
AT3 Alan Trammell 81/26 12.50 30.00
AT4 Alan Trammell 82/40 10.00 25.00
AT5 Alan Trammell 83/21 15.00 40.00
AT6 Alan Trammell 84/57 10.00 25.00
AT7 Alan Trammell 85/39 10.00 25.00
AT8 Alan Trammell 86/23 15.00 40.00
AT9 Alan Trammell 87/15 15.00 40.00
AV1 Andy Van Slyke 84/1
AV2 Andy Van Slyke 85/35 20.00 50.00
AV3 Andy Van Slyke 86/37 15.00 40.00
AV4 Andy Van Slyke 87/178 10.00 25.00
AV5 Andy Van Slyke 87 TR/130 10.00 25.00
BB1 Buddy Bell 73/1
BB2 Buddy Bell 75/1
BB3 Buddy Bell 76/1
BB4 Buddy Bell 78/3
BB5 Buddy Bell 79/135 6.00 15.00
BB6 Buddy Bell 80/10
BB7 Buddy Bell 81/11
BB8 Buddy Bell 82/34 8.00 20.00
BB9 Buddy Bell 83/83 4.00 10.00
BB10 Buddy Bell 84/22 10.00 25.00
BB11 Buddy Bell 85/13
BB12 Buddy Bell 86/32 8.00 20.00
BBL1 Bert Blyleven 71/1
BBL2 Bert Blyleven 75/1
BBL3 Bert Blyleven 76/4
BBL4 Bert Blyleven 79/45 15.00 40.00
BBL5 Bert Blyleven 80/12
BBL6 Bert Blyleven 81/29 12.50 30.00
BBL7 Bert Blyleven 82 NNO/51 15.00 40.00
BBL8 Bert Blyleven 83/41 10.00 25.00
BBL9 Bert Blyleven 84/10
BBL10 Bert Blyleven 85/40 10.00 25.00
BBL11 Bert Blyleven 86/62 10.00 25.00
BBL12 Bert Blyleven 87/54 10.00 25.00
BC1 Bert Campaneris 65/1
BC2 Bert Campaneris 72/5
BC3 Bert Campaneris 74/1
BC4 Bert Campaneris 78/2
BC5 Bert Campaneris 79/107 6.00 15.00
BC6 Bert Campaneris 80/6
BC7 Bert Campaneris 84/28 8.00 20.00
BD1 Bucky Dent 74/1
BD2 Bucky Dent 78/1
BD3 Bucky Dent 79/14
BD4 Bucky Dent 80/9
BD5 Bucky Dent 81/16 15.00 40.00
BD6 Bucky Dent 82/49 10.00 25.00
BD7 Bucky Dent 83/92 4.00 10.00
BD8 Bucky Dent 84/63 6.00 15.00
BD9 Bucky Dent 90 MG/10
BG1 Bob Grich 71/1
BG2 Bob Grich 79/29 10.00 25.00
BG3 Bob Grich 80/70 6.00 15.00
BG4 Bob Grich 81/14
BG5 Bob Grich 82/45 6.00 15.00
BG6 Bob Grich 83/85 4.00 10.00
BG7 Bob Grich 84/57 6.00 15.00
BG8 Bob Grich 85/36 6.00 15.00
BG9 Bob Grich 86/13
BH1 Bob Horner 79/1
BH2 Bob Horner 80/14
BH3 Bob Horner 81/11
BH4 Bob Horner 82/21 15.00 40.00
BH5 Bob Horner 83/69 6.00 15.00

Card	Low	High
BH6 Bob Horner 84/63	10.00	25.00
BH7 Bob Horner 85/15	15.00	40.00
BH8 Bob Horner 86/118	6.00	15.00
BH9 Bob Horner 87/38	10.00	25.00
BJ1 Bo Jackson 86 TR/1		
BJ2 Bo Jackson 87/100	30.00	60.00
BJA1 Brook Jacoby 85/1		
BJA2 Brook Jacoby 86/133	4.00	10.00
BJA3 Brook Jacoby 87/191	4.00	10.00
BJA4 Brook Jacoby 88/9		
BM1 Bill Madlock 74/1		
BM2 Bill Madlock 75/7		
BM3 Bill Madlock 76/4		
BM4 Bill Madlock 79/6		
BM5 Bill Madlock 80/11		
BM6 Bill Madlock 81/11		
BM7 Bill Madlock 82/26	8.00	20.00
BM8 Bill Madlock 83/55	6.00	15.00
BM9 Bill Madlock 84/69	4.00	10.00
BM10 Bill Madlock 85/60	6.00	15.00
BM11 Bill Madlock 86/63	6.00	15.00
BM12 Bill Madlock 87/42	6.00	15.00
BP1 Boog Powell 62/1		
BP2 Boog Powell 64/4		
BP3 Boog Powell 65/7		
BP4 Boog Powell 66/4		
BP5 Boog Powell 67/3		
BP6 Boog Powell 69/5		
BP7 Boog Powell 70/6		
BP8 Boog Powell 72/13		
BP9 Boog Powell 73/17	20.00	50.00
BP10 Boog Powell 74/7		
BP11 Boog Powell 75/19	20.00	50.00
BP12 Boog Powell 76/6		
BP13 Boog Powell 77/15	20.00	50.00
BR1 Brooks Robinson 57/1		
BR2 Brooks Robinson 59/1		
BR3 Brooks Robinson 60/2		
BR4 Brooks Robinson 61/1		
BR5 Brooks Robinson 69/6		
BR6 Brooks Robinson 69 AS/2		
BR7 Brooks Robinson 70/8		
BR8 Brooks Robinson 70 AS/3		
BR9 Brooks Robinson 72/6		
BR10 Brooks Robinson 73/14		
BR11 Brooks Robinson 74/20	50.00	100.00
BR12 Brooks Robinson 75/10		
BR13 Brooks Robinson 76/17	50.00	100.00
BR14 Brooks Robinson 77/13		
BS1 Bret Saberhagen 85/1		
BS2 Bret Saberhagen 86/23	15.00	40.00
BS3 Bret Saberhagen 87/230	6.00	15.00
BSU1 Bruce Sutter 77/1		
BSU2 Bruce Sutter 78/5		
BSU3 Bruce Sutter 79/8		
BSU4 Bruce Sutter 80/9		
BSU5 Bruce Sutter 81/11		
BSU6 Bruce Sutter 82/111	10.00	25.00
BSU7 Bruce Sutter 83/45	15.00	40.00
BSU8 Bruce Sutter 84/24	30.00	60.00
BSU9 Bruce Sutter 85/19	30.00	60.00
BSU10 Bruce Sutter 86/78	10.00	25.00
BSU11 Bruce Sutter 87/36	15.00	40.00
BU1 Bill Buckner 70/1		
BU2 Bill Buckner 74/5		
BU3 Bill Buckner 75/1		
BU4 Bill Buckner 76/1		
BU5 Bill Buckner 78/1		
BU6 Bill Buckner 79/11		
BU7 Bill Buckner 80/8		
BU8 Bill Buckner 81/39	10.00	25.00
BU9 Bill Buckner 82/38	10.00	25.00
BU10 Bill Buckner 83/47	10.00	25.00
BU11 Bill Buckner 84/31	12.50	30.00
BU12 Bill Buckner 84 TR/24	15.00	40.00
BU13 Bill Buckner 85/80	6.00	15.00
BU14 Bill Buckner 86/63	10.00	25.00
BW1 Bob Watson 69/1		
BW2 Bob Watson 74/1		
BW3 Bob Watson 79/77	6.00	15.00
BW4 Bob Watson 80/8		
BW5 Bob Watson 81/16	10.00	25.00
BW6 Bob Watson 82/23	10.00	25.00
BW7 Bob Watson 83/93	4.00	10.00
BW8 Bob Watson 84/64	6.00	15.00
BW9 Bob Watson 85/68	4.00	10.00
CF1 Cecil Fielder 86/1		
CF2 Cecil Fielder 87/208	6.00	15.00
CF3 Cecil Fielder 88/26	12.50	30.00
CF4 Cecil Fielder 89/16	15.00	40.00
CFI1 Carlton Fisk 72/1		
CFI2 Carlton Fisk 78/3		
CFI3 Carlton Fisk 79/24	40.00	80.00
CFI4 Carlton Fisk 80/32	30.00	60.00
CFI5 Carlton Fisk 81/15		
CFI6 Carlton Fisk 82/30	20.00	50.00
CG1 Cesar Geronimo 71/1		
CG2 Cesar Geronimo 74/1		
CG3 Cesar Geronimo 79/28	10.00	25.00
CG4 Cesar Geronimo 80/11		
CG5 Cesar Geronimo 81/21	10.00	25.00
CG6 Cesar Geronimo 82/52	6.00	15.00
CG7 Cesar Geronimo 83/67	4.00	10.00
CG8 Cesar Geronimo 84/70	4.00	10.00
CH1 Charlie Hough 72/1		
CH2 Charlie Hough 83/19	10.00	25.00
CH3 Charlie Hough 84/50	6.00	15.00
CH4 Charlie Hough 85/57	6.00	15.00
CH5 Charlie Hough 86/66	4.00	10.00
CH6 Charlie Hough 87/46	6.00	15.00
CH7 Charlie Hough 88/19	10.00	25.00
CH8 Charlie Hough 91 TR/70	4.00	10.00
CH9 Charlie Hough 92/25	10.00	25.00
CH10 Charlie Hough 94/8		
CL1 Carney Lansford 79/1		
CL2 Carney Lansford 80/12		
CL3 Carney Lansford 81/184	4.00	10.00
CL4 Carney Lansford 82/6		
CL5 Carney Lansford 83/40	6.00	15.00
CL6 Carney Lansford 85/35	8.00	20.00
CL7 Carney Lansford 86/76	4.00	10.00
CLE1 Chet Lemon 76/1		
CLE2 Chet Lemon 78/3		
CLE3 Chet Lemon 79/24	12.50	30.00
CLE4 Chet Lemon 80/16	12.50	30.00
CLE5 Chet Lemon 81/12		
CLE6 Chet Lemon 82/23	10.00	25.00
CLE7 Chet Lemon 83/35	8.00	20.00
CLE8 Chet Lemon 84/42	6.00	15.00
CLE9 Chet Lemon 85/32	8.00	20.00
CLE10 Chet Lemon 86/136	4.00	10.00
CLE11 Chet Lemon 87/27	8.00	20.00
CR1 Cal Ripken 82/1		
CR2 Cal Ripken 84/10		
CR3 Cal Ripken 85/15		
CR4 Cal Ripken 86/74	60.00	120.00
CS1 Cory Snyder 85 OLY/1		
CS2 Cory Snyder 87/291	4.00	10.00
CS3 Cory Snyder 91/39	6.00	15.00
CS4 Cory Snyder 91 TR/8		
CS5 Cory Snyder 93/8		
CS6 Cory Snyder 93 Gold/8		
CS7 Cory Snyder 94/10		
CY1 Carl Yastrzemski 60/1		
CY2 Carl Yastrzemski 78/3		
CY3 Carl Yastrzemski 79/2		
CY4 Carl Yastrzemski 80/60	50.00	100.00
CY5 Carl Yastrzemski 81/35	60.00	120.00
DC1 Dave Concepcion 71/1		
DC2 Dave Concepcion 75/2		
DC3 Dave Concepcion 76/1		
DC4 Dave Concepcion 78/3		
DC5 Dave Concepcion 79/3		
DC6 Dave Concepcion 80/21	20.00	50.00
DC7 Dave Concepcion 81/8		
DC8 Dave Concepcion 82/43	10.00	25.00
DC9 Dave Concepcion 83/34	12.50	30.00
DC10 Dave Concepcion 84/24	15.00	40.00
DC11 Dave Concepcion 85/41	10.00	25.00
DC12 Dave Concepcion 86/69	6.00	15.00
DD1 Darren Daulton 86/1		
DD2 Darren Daulton 87/269	4.00	10.00
DD3 Darren Daulton 90/8		
DD4 Darren Daulton 92/32	8.00	20.00
DD5 Darren Daulton 94/17	10.00	25.00
DD6 Darren Daulton 96/22	10.00	25.00
DDE1 Doug DeCinces 75/1		
DDE2 Doug DeCinces 79/38	10.00	25.00
DDE3 Doug DeCinces 80/24	12.50	30.00
DDE4 Doug DeCinces 81/24	10.00	25.00
DDE5 Doug DeCinces 82/42	6.00	15.00
DDE6 Doug DeCinces 83/75	4.00	10.00
DDE7 Doug DeCinces 84/19	10.00	25.00
DDE8 Doug DeCinces 85/54	6.00	15.00
DDE9 Doug DeCinces 86/74	4.00	10.00
DE1 Dennis Eckersley 76/1		
DE2 Dennis Eckersley 78/10		
DE3 Dennis Eckersley 79/44	30.00	60.00
DE4 Dennis Eckersley 80/40	30.00	60.00
DE5 Dennis Eckersley 81/9		
DEV1 Darrell Evans 70/1		
DEV2 Darrell Evans 74/5		
DEV3 Darrell Evans 75/3		
DEV4 Darrell Evans 78/2		
DEV5 Darrell Evans 79/19	12.50	30.00
DEV6 Darrell Evans 80/5		
DEV7 Darrell Evans 81/15	10.00	25.00
DEV8 Darrell Evans 82/25	10.00	25.00
DEV9 Darrell Evans 83/63	6.00	15.00
DEV10 Darrell Evans 84/81	4.00	10.00
DEV11 Darrell Evans 85/48	6.00	15.00
DEV12 Darrell Evans 86/82	4.00	10.00
DG1 Dwight Gooden 85/1		
DG2 Dwight Gooden 86/16	15.00	40.00
DG3 Dwight Gooden 87/52	10.00	25.00
DG4 Dwight Gooden 89/19	15.00	40.00
DJ1 David Justice 90 DB/69	6.00	15.00
DJ2 David Justice 90 TR/1		
DJ3 David Justice 93/32	12.50	30.00
DK1 Dave Kingman 72/1		
DK2 Dave Kingman 79/9		
DK3 Dave Kingman 80/8		
DK4 Dave Kingman 81/25	15.00	40.00
DK5 Dave Kingman 82/5		
DK6 Dave Kingman 83/32	12.50	30.00
DK7 Dave Kingman 86/25	15.00	40.00
DL1 Davey Lopes 73/1		
DL2 Davey Lopes 76/1		
DL3 Davey Lopes 78/1		
DL4 Davey Lopes 79/71	6.00	15.00
DL5 Davey Lopes 80/19	12.50	30.00
DL6 Davey Lopes 81/12		
DL7 Davey Lopes 82/17	10.00	25.00
DL8 Davey Lopes 83/65	6.00	15.00
DL9 Davey Lopes 84/15	10.00	25.00
DL10 Davey Lopes 85/24	10.00	25.00
DL11 Davey Lopes 86/40	6.00	15.00
DL12 Davey Lopes 01 MG/67	4.00	10.00
DL13 Davey Lopes 02 MG/19	10.00	25.00
DM1 Don Mattingly 84/1		
DM2 Don Mattingly 85/16		
DM3 Don Mattingly 87/84	50.00	100.00
DMU1 Dale Murphy 77/1		
DMU2 Dale Murphy 79/38	30.00	60.00
DMU3 Dale Murphy 80/11		
DMU4 Dale Murphy 82/1		
DMU5 Dale Murphy 83/10		
DMU6 Dale Murphy 84/29	20.00	50.00
DMU7 Dale Murphy 85/18	30.00	60.00
DMU8 Dale Murphy 86/25	30.00	60.00
DMU9 Dale Murphy 87/91	10.00	25.00
DMU10 Dale Murphy 88/11		
DMU11 Dale Murphy 89/14		
DP1 Dave Parker 74/1		
DP2 Dave Parker 75/2		
DP3 Dave Parker 79/6		
DP4 Dave Parker 80/9		
DP5 Dave Parker 81/19	15.00	40.00
DP6 Dave Parker 82/73	6.00	15.00
DP7 Dave Parker 83/30	12.50	30.00
DP8 Dave Parker 84/14		
DP9 Dave Parker 85/45	10.00	25.00
DP10 Dave Parker 86/29	12.50	30.00
DP11 Dave Parker 87/12		
DP12 Dave Parker 88/11		
DS1 Duke Snider 52/1		
DS2 Duke Snider 58/3		
DS3 Duke Snider 59/4		
DS4 Duke Snider 60/2		
DS5 Duke Snider 61/13		
DS6 Duke Snider 62/4		
DS7 Duke Snider 63/4		
DS8 Duke Snider 64/18	60.00	120.00
DSE1 Dave Stieb 80/1		
DSE2 Dave Stieb 81/21	15.00	40.00
DSE3 Dave Stieb 82/34	12.50	30.00
DSE4 Dave Stieb 83/70	6.00	15.00
DSE5 Dave Stieb 84/20	15.00	40.00
DSE6 Dave Stieb 85/55	10.00	25.00
DSE7 Dave Stieb 86/69	6.00	15.00
DSE8 Dave Stieb 87/75	6.00	15.00
DSE9 Dave Stieb 88/11		
DSR1 Darryl Strawberry 84/1		
DSR2 Darryl Strawberry 85/32	12.50	30.00
DSR3 Darryl Strawberry 86/24	15.00	40.00
DSR4 Darryl Strawberry 87/183	6.00	15.00
DSR5 Darryl Strawberry 87 AS/110	6.00	15.00
DSW1 Dave Stewart 82/1		
DSW2 Dave Stewart 83/41	6.00	15.00
DSW3 Dave Stewart 84/60	6.00	15.00
DSW4 Dave Stewart 85/24	10.00	25.00
DSW5 Dave Stewart 86/53	6.00	15.00
DSW6 Dave Stewart 87/171	4.00	10.00
EB1 Ernie Banks 54/1		
EB2 Ernie Banks 58 AS/1		
EB3 Ernie Banks 59/1		
EB4 Ernie Banks 59 AS/1		
EB5 Ernie Banks 60/2		
EB6 Ernie Banks 61/2		
EB7 Ernie Banks 61 MVP/7		
EB8 Ernie Banks 62/3		
EB9 Ernie Banks 64/5		
EB10 Ernie Banks 66/7		
EB11 Ernie Banks 67/4		
EB12 Ernie Banks 68/7		
EB13 Ernie Banks 69/7		
EB14 Ernie Banks 70/2		
ED1 Eric Davis 85/1		
ED2 Eric Davis 86/13		
ED3 Eric Davis 87/336	6.00	15.00
EW1 Earl Weaver 69 MG/1		
EW2 Earl Weaver 72 MG/1		
EW3 Earl Weaver 74 MG/1		
EW4 Earl Weaver 78 MG/52	10.00	25.00
EW5 Earl Weaver 83 MG/38	6.00	15.00
EW6 Earl Weaver 85 TR MG/12		
EW7 Earl Weaver 86 MG/107	4.00	10.00
EW8 Earl Weaver 87 MG/175	4.00	10.00
FJ1 Fergie Jenkins 66/1		
FJ2 Fergie Jenkins 68/2		
FJ3 Fergie Jenkins 70/1		
FJ4 Fergie Jenkins 71/1		
FJ5 Fergie Jenkins 72/4		
FJ6 Fergie Jenkins 76/10		
FJ7 Fergie Jenkins 77/11		
FJ8 Fergie Jenkins 78/17	20.00	50.00
FJ9 Fergie Jenkins 79/9		
FJ10 Fergie Jenkins 80/37	15.00	40.00
FJ11 Fergie Jenkins 81/32	12.50	30.00
FJ12 Fergie Jenkins 82/65	10.00	25.00
FJ13 Fergie Jenkins 83/22	15.00	40.00
FJ14 Fergie Jenkins 84/42	10.00	25.00
FR1 Frank Robinson 57/1		
FR2 Frank Robinson 63/1		
FR3 Frank Robinson 65/1		
FR4 Frank Robinson 69/4		
FR5 Frank Robinson 71/2		
FR6 Frank Robinson 72/16	40.00	80.00
FR7 Frank Robinson 73/4		
FR8 Frank Robinson 74/4		
FR9 Frank Robinson 75/1		
FR10 Frank Robinson 83 MG/13		
FR11 Frank Robinson 84 MG/3		
FV1 Frank Viola 83/1		
FV2 Frank Viola 84/1		
FV3 Frank Viola 85/25	15.00	40.00
FV4 Frank Viola 86/99	6.00	15.00
FV5 Frank Viola 87/209	6.00	15.00
FV6 Frank Viola 88/10		
GB1 George Bell 82/1		
GB2 George Bell 84/67	4.00	10.00
GB3 George Bell 85/32	8.00	20.00
GB4 George Bell 86/46	6.00	15.00
GB5 George Bell 87/204	4.00	10.00
GBR1 George Brett 75/1		
GBR2 George Brett 79/16		
GBR3 George Brett 80/9		
GBR4 George Brett 81/19	90.00	150.00
GBR5 George Brett 82/6		
GC1 Gary Carter 75/1		
GC2 Gary Carter 78/9		
GC3 Gary Carter 79/21	20.00	50.00
GC4 Gary Carter 80/24	20.00	50.00
GC5 Gary Carter 81/22	15.00	40.00
GC6 Gary Carter 82/12		
GC7 Gary Carter 83/2		
GC8 Gary Carter 84/9		
GF1 George Foster 71/1		
GF2 George Foster 74/5		
GF3 George Foster 75/3		
GF4 George Foster 76/1		
GF5 George Foster 78/3		
GF6 George Foster 79/20	12.50	30.00
GF7 George Foster 80/7		
GF8 George Foster 81/10		
GF9 George Foster 82/14		
GF10 George Foster 83/39	6.00	15.00
GF11 George Foster 84/112	4.00	10.00
GF12 George Foster 85/76	4.00	10.00
GF13 George Foster 86/64	6.00	15.00
GL1 Greg Luzinski 71/1		
GL2 Greg Luzinski 72/5		
GL3 Greg Luzinski 75/6		
GL4 Greg Luzinski 76/1		
GL5 Greg Luzinski 78/5		
GL6 Greg Luzinski 79/14		
GL7 Greg Luzinski 80/21	20.00	50.00
GL8 Greg Luzinski 81/11		
GL9 Greg Luzinski 82/34	12.50	30.00
GL10 Greg Luzinski 83/75	6.00	15.00
GL11 Greg Luzinski 84/85	6.00	15.00
GL12 Greg Luzinski 85/92	6.00	15.00
GM1 Gary Matthews Sr. 73/1		
GM2 Gary Matthews Sr. 82/10		
GM3 Gary Matthews Sr. 83/20	10.00	25.00
GM4 Gary Matthews Sr. 84/43	6.00	15.00
GM5 Gary Matthews Sr. 85/39	6.00	15.00
GM6 Gary Matthews Sr. 86/38	6.00	15.00
GM7 Gary Matthews Sr. 87/82	4.00	10.00
GM8 Gary Matthews Sr. 88/30	8.00	20.00
HA1 Hank Aaron 54/1		
HA2 Hank Aaron 58 AS/2		
HA3 Hank Aaron 59/1		
HA4 Hank Aaron 60 AS/1		
HA5 Hank Aaron 61/1		
HA6 Hank Aaron 61 MVP/1		
HA7 Hank Aaron 62 AS/1		
HA8 Hank Aaron 65/1		
HA9 Hank Aaron 68/1		
HA10 Hank Aaron 69/1		
HA11 Hank Aaron 70/6		
HA12 Hank Aaron 70 AS/3		
HA13 Hank Aaron 71/3		
HA14 Hank Aaron 72/2		
HA15 Hank Aaron 73/8		
HA16 Hank Aaron 75/5		
HA17 Hank Aaron 75 HL/1		
HA18 Hank Aaron 76/12		
HB1 Harold Baines 81/1		
HB2 Harold Baines 82/31	12.50	30.00
HB3 Harold Baines 83/19	15.00	40.00
HB4 Harold Baines 84/5		
HB5 Harold Baines 85/97	6.00	15.00
HB6 Harold Baines 86/93	6.00	15.00
HB7 Harold Baines 87/115	6.00	15.00
HK1 Harmon Killebrew 55/1		
HK2 Harmon Killebrew 60/1		
HK3 Harmon Killebrew 61/1		
HK4 Harmon Killebrew 62/2		
HK5 Harmon Killebrew 64/2		
HK6 Harmon Killebrew 66/2		
HK7 Harmon Killebrew 68/2		
HK8 Harmon Killebrew 68 AS/2		
HK9 Harmon Killebrew 69/5		
HK10 Harmon Killebrew 70/3		
HK11 Harmon Killebrew 71/3		
HK12 Harmon Killebrew 72/12		
HK13 Harmon Killebrew 73/4		
HK14 Harmon Killebrew 74/6		
HK15 Harmon Killebrew 75/9		
HR1 Harold Reynolds 86/1		
HR2 Harold Reynolds 87/255	6.00	15.00
JA1 Jim Abbott 88 TR/339	10.00	25.00
JA2 Jim Abbott 89/1		
JA3 Jim Abbott 90 DB/50	15.00	40.00
JB1 Jesse Barfield 82/1		
JB2 Jesse Barfield 83/45	6.00	15.00
JB3 Jesse Barfield 84/12		
JB4 Jesse Barfield 85/60	6.00	15.00
JB5 Jesse Barfield 86/37	6.00	15.00
JB6 Jesse Barfield 87/180	4.00	10.00
JB7 Jesse Barfield 88/10		
JBE1 Johnny Bench 68/1		
JBE2 Johnny Bench 79/14		
JBE3 Johnny Bench 80/10		
JBE4 Johnny Bench 81/8		
JBE5 Johnny Bench 82/16	40.00	80.00
JBE6 Johnny Bench 83/2		
JC1 John Candelaria 76/1		
JC2 John Candelaria 79/77	10.00	25.00
JC3 John Candelaria 80/8		
JC4 John Candelaria 81/19	15.00	40.00
JC5 John Candelaria 82/42	10.00	25.00
JC6 John Candelaria 83/77	6.00	15.00
JC7 John Candelaria 84/18	15.00	40.00
JC8 John Candelaria 85/61	10.00	25.00
JC9 John Candelaria 86/36	10.00	25.00
JC10 John Candelaria 87/13		
JCA1 Jose Canseco 86 TR/1		
JCA2 Jose Canseco 87/99	20.00	50.00
JCR1 Joe Carter 85/1		
JCR2 Joe Carter 86/24	30.00	60.00
JCR3 Joe Carter 87/23	30.00	60.00
JCR4 Joe Carter 90/2		
JCU1 Jose Cruz Sr. 72/1		
JCU2 Jose Cruz Sr. 74/2		
JCU3 Jose Cruz Sr. 76/1		
JCU4 Jose Cruz Sr. 78/5		
JCU5 Jose Cruz Sr. 79/7		
JCU6 Jose Cruz Sr. 80/14		
JCU7 Jose Cruz Sr. 81/14		
JCU8 Jose Cruz Sr. 82/28	8.00	20.00
JCU9 Jose Cruz Sr. 83/102	4.00	10.00
JCU10 Jose Cruz Sr. 84/67	4.00	10.00
JCU11 Jose Cruz Sr. 85/68	4.00	10.00
JCU12 Jose Cruz Sr. 86/31	8.00	20.00
JK1 Jimmy Key 85/1		
JK2 Jimmy Key 86/21	15.00	40.00
JK3 Jimmy Key 87/263	6.00	15.00
JK4 Jimmy Key 88/15	15.00	40.00
JK5 Jimmy Key 92/37	10.00	25.00
JK6 Jimmy Key 94/11		
JKR1 John Kruk 86 TR/1		
JKR2 John Kruk 87/214	10.00	25.00
JKR3 John Kruk 92/22	30.00	60.00
JKR4 John Kruk 93/13		
JL1 Jim Leyritz 90 TR/1		
JL2 Jim Leyritz 91/38	6.00	15.00
JL3 Jim Leyritz 93/49	6.00	15.00
JL4 Jim Leyritz 94/16	10.00	25.00
JL5 Jim Leyritz 95/14		
JL6 Jim Leyritz 97/62	6.00	15.00
JL7 Jim Leyritz 98/20	10.00	25.00
JL8 Jim Leyritz 99/124	4.00	10.00
JL9 Jim Leyritz 00/40	6.00	15.00
JM1 Jack McDowell 88 TR/1		
JM2 Jack McDowell 89/36	6.00	15.00
JM3 Jack McDowell 90 TR/61	6.00	15.00
JM4 Jack McDowell 91/33	8.00	20.00
JM5 Jack McDowell 92/38	6.00	15.00
JM6 Jack McDowell 93/27	8.00	20.00
JM7 Jack McDowell 94/3		
JM8 Jack McDowell 95/9		
JM9 Jack McDowell 96/15	10.00	25.00
JM10 Jack McDowell 97/27	8.00	20.00
JMO1 Joe Morgan 65/1		
JMO2 Joe Morgan 74/2		
JMO3 Joe Morgan 75/1		
JMO4 Joe Morgan 76/5		
JMO5 Joe Morgan 77/6		
JMO6 Joe Morgan 78/3		
JMO7 Joe Morgan 79/4		
JMO8 Joe Morgan 80/12		
JMO9 Joe Morgan 81/32	12.50	30.00
JMO10 Joe Morgan 82/18	15.00	40.00
JMO11 Joe Morgan 83/49	10.00	25.00
JMO12 Joe Morgan 83 TR/4		
JMO13 Joe Morgan 84/73	6.00	15.00
JMO14 Joe Morgan 85/40	10.00	25.00
JP1 Jim Palmer 66/1		
JP2 Jim Palmer 79/4		
JP3 Jim Palmer 80/33	15.00	40.00
JP4 Jim Palmer 81/23	15.00	40.00
JP5 Jim Palmer 82/24	15.00	40.00
JP6 Jim Palmer 83/7		
JP7 Jim Palmer 84/9		
JR1 Jim Rice 75/1		
JR2 Jim Rice 76/2		
JR3 Jim Rice 77/4		
JR4 Jim Rice 78/3		
JR5 Jim Rice 79/5		
JR6 Jim Rice 80/9		
JR7 Jim Rice 81/123	10.00	25.00
JR8 Jim Rice 82/24	15.00	40.00
JR9 Jim Rice 83/71	10.00	25.00
JR10 Jim Rice 84/12		
JRU1 Joe Rudi 69/1		
JRU2 Joe Rudi 72/2		
JRU3 Joe Rudi 73/9		
JRU4 Joe Rudi 74/6		
JRU5 Joe Rudi 75/7		
JRU6 Joe Rudi 76/4		
JRU7 Joe Rudi 77/7		
JRU8 Joe Rudi 78/14		
JRU9 Joe Rudi 79/24	12.50	30.00
JRU10 Joe Rudi 80/45	10.00	25.00
JRU11 Joe Rudi 82/26	8.00	20.00
JRU12 Joe Rudi 83/75	4.00	10.00
KB1 Kevin Bass 79/1		
KB2 Kevin Bass 84/71	4.00	10.00
KB3 Kevin Bass 85/30	8.00	20.00
KB4 Kevin Bass 86/44	6.00	15.00
KB5 Kevin Bass 87/74	4.00	10.00
KB6 Kevin Bass 90 TR/35	8.00	20.00
KG1 Ken Griffey Sr. 74/1		
KG2 Ken Griffey Sr. 75/2		
KG3 Ken Griffey Sr. 76/2		
KG4 Ken Griffey Sr. 79/3		
KG5 Ken Griffey Sr. 80/15	20.00	50.00
KG6 Ken Griffey Sr. 81/11		
KG7 Ken Griffey Sr. 82/18	15.00	40.00
KG8 Ken Griffey Sr. 83/70	6.00	15.00
KG9 Ken Griffey Sr. 84/64	10.00	25.00
KG10 Ken Griffey Sr. 85/32	12.50	30.00
KG11 Ken Griffey Sr. 86 TR/32	12.50	30.00
KGI1 Kirk Gibson 81/1		
KGI2 Kirk Gibson 82/35	12.50	30.00
KGI3 Kirk Gibson 83/35	12.50	30.00
KGI4 Kirk Gibson 84/5		
KGI5 Kirk Gibson 85/44	10.00	25.00
KGI6 Kirk Gibson 86/44	10.00	25.00
KGI7 Kirk Gibson 87/65	10.00	25.00
KGI8 Kirk Gibson 89/14		
KGI9 Kirk Gibson 90/12		
KGU1 Kelly Gruber 87/1		
KGU2 Kelly Gruber 88/77	4.00	10.00
KGU3 Kelly Gruber 89/44	6.00	15.00
KGU4 Kelly Gruber 90/86	4.00	10.00
KGU5 Kelly Gruber 91/52	6.00	15.00
KGU6 Kelly Gruber 92/55	6.00	15.00
KGU7 Kelly Gruber 93/26	8.00	20.00
KGU8 Kelly Gruber 93 Gold/9		
KH1 Keith Hernandez 75/1		
KH2 Keith Hernandez 79/8		
KH3 Keith Hernandez 80/38	15.00	40.00
KH4 Keith Hernandez 81/19	15.00	40.00
KH5 Keith Hernandez 82/156	6.00	15.00
KH6 Keith Hernandez 83/17	15.00	40.00
KH7 Keith Hernandez 84/4		
KH8 Keith Hernandez 86/7		
KS1 Kevin Seitzer 87 TR/1		
KS2 Kevin Seitzer 88/88	4.00	10.00
KS3 Kevin Seitzer 89/39	6.00	15.00
KS4 Kevin Seitzer 90/18	10.00	25.00
KS5 Kevin Seitzer 91/39	6.00	15.00
KS6 Kevin Seitzer 92/49	6.00	15.00
KS7 Kevin Seitzer 92 Gold/2		
KS8 Kevin Seitzer 92 TR/9		
KS9 Kevin Seitzer 93/38	6.00	15.00
KS10 Kevin Seitzer 94/22	10.00	25.00
KS11 Kevin Seitzer 95/16	10.00	25.00
KS12 Kevin Seitzer 96/13		
KS13 Kevin Seitzer 97/24	10.00	25.00
KT1 Kent Tekulve 76/1		
KT2 Kent Tekulve 78/2		
KT3 Kent Tekulve 79/14		
KT4 Kent Tekulve 80/6		
KT5 Kent Tekulve 81/17	15.00	40.00
KT6 Kent Tekulve 82/36	10.00	25.00
KT7 Kent Tekulve 83/52	10.00	25.00
KT8 Kent Tekulve 84/71	6.00	15.00
KT9 Kent Tekulve 85/43	10.00	25.00
KT10 Kent Tekulve 86/57	10.00	25.00
KT11 Kent Tekulve 87/32	12.50	30.00
KT12 Kent Tekulve 88/20	15.00	40.00
LA1 Luis Aparicio 56/1		
LA2 Luis Aparicio 60/1		
LA3 Luis Aparicio 61/3		
LA4 Luis Aparicio 62/2		
LA5 Luis Aparicio 63/3		
LA6 Luis Aparicio 66/3		
LA7 Luis Aparicio 67/2		
LA8 Luis Aparicio 68/14		
LA9 Luis Aparicio 69/49	15.00	40.00
LA10 Luis Aparicio 70/2		
LA11 Luis Aparicio 71/1		
LA12 Luis Aparicio 72/15	20.00	50.00
LA13 Luis Aparicio 73/3		
LA14 Luis Aparicio 74/3		
LB1 Lou Brock 62/1		
LB2 Lou Brock 66/1		
LB3 Lou Brock 68/2		
LB4 Lou Brock 70/20	40.00	80.00
LB5 Lou Brock 71/3		
LB6 Lou Brock 72/3		
LB7 Lou Brock 73/4		
LB8 Lou Brock 74/5		
LB9 Lou Brock 75/9		
LB10 Lou Brock 76/5		
LB11 Lou Brock 77/11		
LB12 Lou Brock 78/11		
LB13 Lou Brock 79/27	30.00	60.00
LD1 Leon Durham 81/1		
LD2 Leon Durham 82/51	6.00	15.00
LD3 Leon Durham 83/52	6.00	15.00
LD4 Leon Durham 84/151	4.00	10.00
LD5 Leon Durham 85/2		
LD6 Leon Durham 86/19	10.00	25.00
LD7 Leon Durham 87/87	4.00	10.00
LDY1 Len Dykstra 86/1		
LDY2 Len Dykstra 87/200	6.00	15.00
LDY3 Len Dykstra 88/30	12.50	30.00
LDY4 Len Dykstra 89/17	15.00	40.00
LDY5 Len Dykstra 92/7		
LS1 Lee Smith 82/1		
LS2 Lee Smith 83/39	10.00	25.00
LS3 Lee Smith 84/5		
LS4 Lee Smith 85/9		
LS5 Lee Smith 86/29	12.50	30.00
LS6 Lee Smith 87/237	6.00	15.00
LS7 Lee Smith 88/27	12.50	30.00
LS8 Lee Smith 92/12		
LT1 Luis Tiant 65/1		
LT2 Luis Tiant 68/16	20.00	50.00
LT3 Luis Tiant 70/9		
LT4 Luis Tiant 71/2		
LT5 Luis Tiant 73/12		
LT6 Luis Tiant 74/19	20.00	50.00
LT7 Luis Tiant 75/10		
LT8 Luis Tiant 76/3		
LT9 Luis Tiant 77/3		
LT10 Luis Tiant 78/6		
LT11 Luis Tiant 79/22	12.50	30.00
LT12 Luis Tiant 80/23	12.50	30.00
LT13 Luis Tiant 81/20	10.00	25.00
LT14 Luis Tiant 82/51	6.00	15.00
LT15 Luis Tiant 83/58	6.00	15.00
MB1 Mike Boddicker 81/1		
MB2 Mike Boddicker 84/56	6.00	15.00
MB3 Mike Boddicker 85/139	4.00	10.00
MB4 Mike Boddicker 86/66	4.00	10.00
MB5 Mike Boddicker 87/88	4.00	10.00
MF1 Mark Fidrych 77/1		
MF2 Mark Fidrych 78/3		
MF3 Mark Fidrych 79/74	10.00	25.00
MF4 Mark Fidrych 80/16	20.00	50.00
MF5 Mark Fidrych 81/11		
MR1 Mickey Rivers 72/1		
MR2 Mickey Rivers 79/35	10.00	25.00
MR3 Mickey Rivers 80/14		
MR4 Mickey Rivers 81/13		
MR5 Mickey Rivers 82/49	6.00	15.00
MR6 Mickey Rivers 83/79	4.00	10.00
MR7 Mickey Rivers 84/91	4.00	10.00
MR8 Mickey Rivers 85/34	8.00	20.00
MS1 Mike Schmidt 73/1		
MS2 Mike Schmidt 80/100	30.00	60.00
MSC1 Mike Scott 80/1		
MSC2 Mike Scott 81/6		
MSC3 Mike Scott 82/32	8.00	20.00
MSC4 Mike Scott 83/58	6.00	15.00
MSC5 Mike Scott 84/28	8.00	20.00
MSC6 Mike Scott 86/73	4.00	10.00
MSC7 Mike Scott 87/36	6.00	15.00
MSC8 Mike Scott 88/21	10.00	25.00
MT1 Paul Molitor Alan Trammell 78/1		
MW1 Mookie Wilson 81/1		
MW2 Mookie Wilson 82/20	15.00	40.00
MW3 Mookie Wilson 83/41	10.00	25.00
MW4 Mookie Wilson 84/11		
MW5 Mookie Wilson 85/51	10.00	25.00
MW6 Mookie Wilson 86/47	10.00	25.00
MW7 Mookie Wilson 87/67	6.00	15.00
MW8 Mookie Wilson 88/12		
NR1 Nolan Ryan 68/1		
NR2 Nolan Ryan 80/10		
NR3 Nolan Ryan 81/13		
NR4 Nolan Ryan 82/11		
NR5 Nolan Ryan 83/23	100.00	175.00
NR6 Nolan Ryan 84/20	100.00	175.00
NR7 Nolan Ryan 85/4		
NR8 Nolan Ryan 86/20	100.00	175.00
OH1 Orel Hershiser 85/1		
OH2 Orel Hershiser 86/23	30.00	60.00
OH3 Orel Hershiser 87/218	10.00	25.00
OH4 Orel Hershiser 88/9		
OS1 Ozzie Smith 79/1		
OS2 Ozzie Smith 81/28	50.00	100.00
OS3 Ozzie Smith 82/27	50.00	100.00
OS4 Ozzie Smith 83/6		
OS5 Ozzie Smith 84/19	60.00	120.00
OS6 Ozzie Smith 85/16	60.00	120.00
OS7 Ozzie Smith 86/3		
PI1 Pete Incaviglia 86 TR/1		
PI2 Pete Incaviglia 87/311	4.00	10.00
PM1 Paul Molitor 79/15	50.00	100.00
PM2 Paul Molitor 80/26	40.00	80.00
PM3 Paul Molitor 81/12		
PM4 Paul Molitor 82/32	20.00	50.00
PM5 Paul Molitor 83/14		
PO1 Paul O'Neill 88/1		
PO2 Paul O'Neill 89/24	30.00	60.00
PO3 Paul O'Neill 90/18	30.00	60.00
PO4 Paul O'Neill 91/24	30.00	60.00
PO5 Paul O'Neill 97/33	20.00	50.00
RC1 Rod Carew 67/1		
RC2 Rod Carew 70/10		
RC3 Rod Carew 78/2		
RC4 Rod Carew 79/29	30.00	60.00
RC5 Rod Carew 80/10		
RC6 Rod Carew 81/21	30.00	60.00
RC7 Rod Carew 82/18	30.00	60.00
RC8 Rod Carew 84/9		
RCE1 Ron Cey 72/1		
RCE2 Ron Cey 75/4		
RCE3 Ron Cey 79/55	10.00	25.00
RCE4 Ron Cey 80/8		
RCE5 Ron Cey 81/16	10.00	25.00
RCE6 Ron Cey 82/34	8.00	20.00
RCE7 Ron Cey 83/87	4.00	10.00
RCE8 Ron Cey 83 TR/68	4.00	10.00
RCE9 Ron Cey 84/15	10.00	25.00
RCE10 Ron Cey 85/19	10.00	25.00
RCE11 Ron Cey 86/43	6.00	15.00
RD1 Ron Darling 85/1		
RD2 Ron Darling 86/12		
RD3 Ron Darling 87/224	6.00	15.00
RD4 Ron Darling 93/13		
RDI1 Rob Dibble 89/1		
RDI2 Rob Dibble 90/31	8.00	20.00
RDI3 Rob Dibble 91/62	6.00	15.00
RDI4 Rob Dibble 92/56	6.00	15.00
RDI5 Rob Dibble 92 Gold/17	10.00	25.00
RDI6 Rob Dibble 93/47	6.00	15.00
RDI7 Rob Dibble 94/37	6.00	15.00
RF1 Rollie Fingers 69/1		
RF2 Rollie Fingers 78/6		
RF3 Rollie Fingers 79/52	15.00	40.00
RF4 Rollie Fingers 80/15	20.00	50.00
RF5 Rollie Fingers 81/18	15.00	40.00
RF6 Rollie Fingers 82/8		
RG1 Rich Gossage 73/1		
RG2 Rich Gossage 74/6		
RG3 Rich Gossage 76/3		
RG4 Rich Gossage 78/2		
RG5 Rich Gossage 79/11		
RG6 Rich Gossage 80/15	20.00	50.00
RG7 Rich Gossage 81/21	10.00	25.00
RG8 Rich Gossage 82/30	12.50	30.00
RG9 Rich Gossage 83/34	12.50	30.00
RG10 Rich Gossage 84/90	6.00	15.00
RG11 Rich Gossage 85/7		
RG12 Rich Gossage 86/30	12.50	30.00
RGU1 Ron Guidry 76/1		
RGU2 Ron Guidry 78/9		

RGU3 Ron Guidry 79/10
RGU4 Ron Guidry 80/22 20.00 50.00
RGU5 Ron Guidry 81/104 6.00 15.00
RGU6 Ron Guidry 82/53 10.00 25.00
RGU7 Ron Guidry 83/46 10.00 25.00
RGU8 Ron Guidry 84/40 10.00 25.00
RGU9 Ron Guidry 85/50 10.00 25.00
RGU10 Ron Guidry 86/15 15.00 40.00
RJ1 Reggie Jackson 69/1
RJ2 Reggie Jackson 73/3
RJ3 Reggie Jackson 75/1
RJ4 Reggie Jackson 76/2
RJ5 Reggie Jackson 79/2
RJ6 Reggie Jackson 80/7
RJ7 Reggie Jackson 81/12
RJ8 Reggie Jackson 82/21 50.00 100.00
RJ9 Reggie Jackson 83/14
RJ10 Reggie Jackson 84/3
RJ11 Reggie Jackson 85/17 40.00 80.00
RJ12 Reggie Jackson 86/17 40.00 80.00
RK1 Ron Kittle 84/1
RK2 Ron Kittle 85/86 4.00 10.00
RK3 Ron Kittle 86/55 6.00 15.00
RK4 Ron Kittle 87/201 4.00 10.00
RKN1 Ray Knight 78/1
RKN2 Ray Knight 79/10
RKN3 Ray Knight 80/5
RKN4 Ray Knight 81/7
RKN5 Ray Knight 82/25 15.00 40.00
RKN6 Ray Knight 83/36 10.00 25.00
RKN7 Ray Knight 84/26 12.50 30.00
RKN8 Ray Knight 85/68 6.00 15.00
RKN9 Ray Knight 86/80 6.00 15.00
RKN10 Ray Knight 87 TR/90 6.00 15.00
RM1 Reggie Smith 67/1
RM2 Reggie Smith 69/1
RM3 Reggie Smith 73/7
RM4 Reggie Smith 74/4
RM5 Reggie Smith 75/2
RM6 Reggie Smith 76/3
RM7 Reggie Smith 77/2
RM8 Reggie Smith 79/15 12.50 30.00
RM9 Reggie Smith 80/16 12.50 30.00
RM10 Reggie Smith 81/14
RM11 Reggie Smith 82/32 8.00 20.00
RM12 Reggie Smith 83/48 6.00 15.00
RS1 Ryne Sandberg 83/1
RS2 Ryne Sandberg 84/37 50.00 100.00
RS3 Ryne Sandberg 85/4
RS4 Ryne Sandberg 86/1
RS5 Ryne Sandberg 87/32 50.00 100.00
RS6 Ryne Sandberg 88/6
RS7 Ryne Sandberg 89/9
RS8 Ryne Sandberg 92/10
RSA1 Ron Santo 61/1
RSA2 Ron Santo 67/2
RSA3 Ron Santo 68/6
RSA4 Ron Santo 69/2
RSA5 Ron Santo 70/1
RSA6 Ron Santo 70 AS/1
RSA7 Ron Santo 71/2
RSA8 Ron Santo 72/2
RSA9 Ron Santo 72 IA/3
RSA10 Ron Santo 73/13
RSA11 Ron Santo 74/2
RSA12 Ron Santo 74 TR/1
RSA13 Ron Santo 75/12
RU1 Rick Sutcliffe 80/1
RU2 Rick Sutcliffe 81/9
RU3 Rick Sutcliffe 82/53 6.00 15.00
RU4 Rick Sutcliffe 83/43 6.00 15.00
RU5 Rick Sutcliffe 84/33 8.00 20.00
RU6 Rick Sutcliffe 85/82 4.00 10.00
RU7 Rick Sutcliffe 86/10
RU8 Rick Sutcliffe 87/19 10.00 25.00
RY1 Robin Yount 75/1
RY2 Robin Yount 77/1
RY3 Robin Yount 78/3
RY4 Robin Yount 79/1
RY5 Robin Yount 80/18 50.00 100.00
RY6 Robin Yount 81/23 50.00 100.00
RY7 Robin Yount 82/11
RY8 Robin Yount 83/2
RY9 Robin Yount 84/15 50.00 100.00
RY10 Robin Yount 85/5
RY11 Robin Yount 86/21 50.00 100.00
SA1 Sparky Anderson 59/1
SA2 Sparky Anderson 60/2
SA3 Sparky Anderson 74 MG/3
SA4 Sparky Anderson 78 MG/6
SA5 Sparky Anderson 83 MG/67 6.00 15.00
SA6 Sparky Anderson 84 MG/97 6.00 15.00
SA7 Sparky Anderson 85 MG/73 6.00 15.00
SA8 Sparky Anderson 86 MG/6
SF1 Sid Fernandez 85/1
SF2 Sid Fernandez 86/18 15.00 40.00
SF3 Sid Fernandez 87/211 6.00 15.00
SF4 Sid Fernandez 93/20 15.00 40.00
SG1 Steve Garvey 71/1
SG2 Steve Garvey 75/1
SG3 Steve Garvey 76/4
SG4 Steve Garvey 79/26 15.00 40.00
SG5 Steve Garvey 80/5
SG6 Steve Garvey 81/10
SG7 Steve Garvey 82/122 6.00 15.00
SG8 Steve Garvey 83/19 15.00 40.00
SG9 Steve Garvey 84/32 12.50 30.00
SG10 Steve Garvey 85/129 6.00 15.00
SM1 Stan Musial 58 AS/15 150.00 250.00
SM2 Stan Musial 59/1
SM3 Stan Musial 60/5
SM4 Stan Musial 61/13
SM5 Stan Musial 62/16 150.00 250.00
SM6 Stan Musial 63/1
SS1 Steve Sax 82/1
SS2 Steve Sax 83/34 8.00 20.00
SS3 Steve Sax 84/14
SS4 Steve Sax 85/33 8.00 20.00
SS5 Steve Sax 86/45 6.00 15.00
SS6 Steve Sax 87/215 4.00 10.00
SS7 Steve Sax 88/10
SY1 Steve Yeager 73/1
SY2 Steve Yeager 74/1
SY3 Steve Yeager 76/1
SY4 Steve Yeager 78/18 12.50 30.00
SY5 Steve Yeager 79/23 12.50 30.00
SY6 Steve Yeager 80/10
SY7 Steve Yeager 81/12
SY8 Steve Yeager 82/18 10.00 25.00
SY9 Steve Yeager 83/80 4.00 10.00
SY10 Steve Yeager 84/15 10.00 25.00
SY11 Steve Yeager 85/4
SY12 Steve Yeager 86/47 6.00 15.00
SY13 Steve Yeager 86 TR/100 4.00 10.00
TB1 Tom Brunansky 82/1
TB2 Tom Brunansky 83/27 8.00 20.00
TB3 Tom Brunansky 84/62 6.00 15.00
TB4 Tom Brunansky 85/13
TB5 Tom Brunansky 86/28 8.00 20.00
TB6 Tom Brunansky 87/193 4.00 10.00
TB7 Tom Brunansky 88/18 10.00 25.00
TB8 Tom Brunansky 90/8
TF1 Tony Fernandez 85/1
TF2 Tony Fernandez 86/41 6.00 15.00
TF3 Tony Fernandez 87/228 4.00 10.00
TF4 Tony Fernandez 88/10
TF5 Tony Fernandez 90/11
TG1 Tony Gwynn 83/1
TG2 Tony Gwynn 84/95 30.00 60.00
TG3 Tony Gwynn 85/4
TH1 Tom Herr 80/1
TH2 Tom Herr 81/22 10.00 25.00
TH3 Tom Herr 82/42 6.00 15.00
TH4 Tom Herr 83/80 4.00 10.00
TH5 Tom Herr 84/30 8.00 20.00
TH6 Tom Herr 85/17 10.00 25.00
TH7 Tom Herr 86/28 8.00 20.00
TH8 Tom Herr 87/134 4.00 10.00
TM1 Tim McCarver 62/1
TM2 Tim McCarver 76/5
TM3 Tim McCarver 77/8
TM4 Tim McCarver 78/12
TM5 Tim McCarver 79/22 12.50 30.00
TM6 Tim McCarver 80/4
TO1 Tony Oliva 63/1
TO2 Tony Oliva 68/1
TO3 Tony Oliva 69/4
TO4 Tony Oliva 69 AS/1
TO5 Tony Oliva 70/9
TO6 Tony Oliva 71/2
TO7 Tony Oliva 72/5
TO8 Tony Oliva 73/18 20.00 50.00
TO9 Tony Oliva 74/11
TO10 Tony Oliva 75/10
TO11 Tony Oliva 76/1
TR1 Tim Raines 81/5
TR2 Tim Raines 82/43 10.00 25.00
TR3 Tim Raines 83/26 12.50 30.00
TR4 Tim Raines 84/10
TR5 Tim Raines 85/43 10.00 25.00
TR6 Tim Raines 86/21 15.00 40.00
TR7 Tim Raines 87/211 6.00 15.00
TS1 Tom Seaver 67/1
TS2 Tom Seaver 79/44 40.00 80.00
TS3 Tom Seaver 80/9
TS4 Tom Seaver 81/16 40.00 80.00
TS5 Tom Seaver 82/25 40.00 80.00
TS6 Tom Seaver 83/4
TS7 Tom Seaver 85/6
TW1 Tim Wallach 82/1
TW2 Tim Wallach 83/49 6.00 15.00
TW3 Tim Wallach 84/13
TW4 Tim Wallach 85/46 6.00 15.00
TW5 Tim Wallach 86/44 6.00 15.00
TW6 Tim Wallach 87/197 4.00 10.00
VB1 Vida Blue 70/1
VB2 Vida Blue 72/1
VB3 Vida Blue 75/1
VB4 Vida Blue 78/10
VB5 Vida Blue 79/21 12.50 30.00
VB6 Vida Blue 80/10
VB7 Vida Blue 81/227 4.00 10.00
VB8 Vida Blue 82/53 6.00 15.00
VB9 Vida Blue 83/45 6.00 15.00
VC1 Vince Coleman 85 TR/1
VC2 Vince Coleman 87/299 6.00 15.00
VC3 Vince Coleman 88/34 12.50 30.00
VC4 Vince Coleman 91 TR/23 15.00 40.00
WB1 Wade Boggs 83/1
WB2 Wade Boggs 84/20 40.00 80.00
WB3 Wade Boggs 85/25 40.00 80.00
WB4 Wade Boggs 86/9
WB5 Wade Boggs 87/45 30.00 60.00
WF1 Whitey Ford 53/1
WF2 Whitey Ford 58/1
WF3 Whitey Ford 59/3
WF4 Whitey Ford 60/5
WF5 Whitey Ford 61/6
WF6 Whitey Ford 62/5
WF7 Whitey Ford 62 AS/2
WF8 Whitey Ford 62 WS/3
WF9 Whitey Ford 63/1
WF10 Whitey Ford 65/1
WF11 Whitey Ford 66/9
WF12 Whitey Ford 67/13
WH1 Whitey Herzog 57/1
WH2 Whitey Herzog 61/13
WH3 Whitey Herzog 62/1
WH4 Whitey Herzog 83 MG/63 6.00 15.00
WH5 Whitey Herzog 84 MG/85 4.00 10.00
WH6 Whitey Herzog 85 MG/75 4.00 10.00
WH7 Whitey Herzog 86 MG/66 4.00 10.00
WH8 Whitey Herzog 87 MG/29 8.00 20.00
WH9 Whitey Herzog 88 MG/35 8.00 20.00
WJ1 Wally Joyner 86 TR/1
WJ2 Wally Joyner 87/335 6.00 15.00
WJ3 Wally Joyner 94/14
WM1 Willie Mays 52/1
WM2 Willie Mays 60/1
WM3 Willie Mays 61/3
WM4 Willie Mays 61 MVP/4
WM5 Willie Mays 62/1
WM6 Willie Mays 62 AS/3
WM7 Willie Mays 69/1
WM8 Willie Mays 70/2
WM9 Willie Mays 72/25 200.00 350.00
WM10 Willie Mays 72 IA/5
WM11 Willie Mays 73/5
WMC1 Willie McGee 83/1
WMC2 Willie McGee 84/66 6.00 15.00
WMC3 Willie McGee 85/44 10.00 25.00
WMC4 Willie McGee 86/24 15.00 40.00
WMC5 Willie McGee 87/117 6.00 15.00
WW1 Walt Weiss 88 TR/1
WW2 Walt Weiss 89/34 8.00 20.00
WW3 Walt Weiss 91/30 8.00 20.00
WW4 Walt Weiss 92/71 4.00 10.00
WW5 Walt Weiss 93/10
WW6 Walt Weiss 94/21 10.00 25.00
WW7 Walt Weiss 97/49 6.00 15.00
WW8 Walt Weiss 98 Rockies/23 10.00 25.00
WW9 Walt Weiss 98 Braves/21 10.00 25.00
WW10 Walt Weiss 99/40 6.00 15.00
WW11 Walt Weiss 01/51 6.00 15.00
YB1 Yogi Berra 52/1
YB2 Yogi Berra 59/1
YB3 Yogi Berra 60/1
YB4 Yogi Berra 61/2
YB5 Yogi Berra 62/3
YB6 Yogi Berra 64 MG/3
YB7 Yogi Berra 65 CO/1
YB8 Yogi Berra 73 MG/5
YB9 Yogi Berra 74 MG/6
YB10 Yogi Berra 85 MG/27 40.00 80.00

2002 Topps Pristine

This 210 card set was issued in October, 2002. This set was issued in eight card packs with an $40 SRP which came five packs to a box and six boxes to a case. The first 140 cards feature active veterans stars while cards 141-150 feature retired greats and cards numbered 151-210 feature three different versions of each rookie. Each rookie has a common version, a uncommon version which has a print run of 1999 serial numbered sets and a rare version which has a stated print run of 799 serial numbered sets.

COMMON CARD (1-140) .50 1.25
COMMON CARD (141-150) .75 2.00
COMMON C CARD (151-210) .50 1.25
COMMON U CARD (151-210) 1.00 2.50
COMMON R CARD (151-210) 1.50 4.00
1 Alex Rodriguez 2.00 5.00
2 Carlos Delgado .50 1.25
3 Jimmy Rollins .50 1.25
4 Jason Kendall .50 1.25
5 John Olerud .50 1.25
6 Albert Pujols 2.50 6.00
7 Curt Schilling .50 1.25
8 Gary Sheffield .50 1.25
9 Johnny Damon Sox .75 2.00
10 Ichiro Suzuki 2.50 6.00
11 Pat Burrell .50 1.25
12 Garret Anderson .50 1.25
13 Andruw Jones .75 2.00
14 Kerry Wood .50 1.25
15 Kenny Lofton .50 1.25
16 Adam Dunn .50 1.25
17 Juan Pierre .50 1.25
18 Josh Beckett .50 1.25
19 Roy Oswalt .50 1.25
20 Derek Jeter 3.00 8.00
21 Jose Vidro .50 1.25
22 Richie Sexson .50 1.25
23 Mike Sweeney .50 1.25
24 Jeff Kent .50 1.25
25 Jason Giambi .50 1.25
26 Bret Boone .50 1.25
27 J.D. Drew .50 1.25
28 Shannon Stewart .50 1.25
29 Miguel Tejada .50 1.25
30 Barry Bonds 3.00 8.00
31 Randy Johnson 1.25 3.00
32 Pedro Martinez .75 2.00
33 Magglio Ordonez .50 1.25
34 Todd Helton .75 2.00
35 Craig Biggio .75 2.00
36 Shawn Green .50 1.25
37 Vladimir Guerrero 1.25 3.00
38 Mo Vaughn .50 1.25
39 Alfonso Soriano .50 1.25
40 Barry Zito .50 1.25
41 Aramis Ramirez .50 1.25
42 Ryan Klesko .50 1.25
43 Ruben Sierra .50 1.25
44 Tino Martinez .75 2.00
45 Toby Hall .50 1.25
46 Ivan Rodriguez .75 2.00
47 Raul Mondesi .50 1.25
48 Carlos Pena .50 1.25
49 Darin Erstad .50 1.25
50 Sammy Sosa 1.25 3.00
51 Bartolo Colon .50 1.25
52 Robert Fick .50 1.25
53 Cliff Floyd .50 1.25
54 Brian Jordan .50 1.25
55 Torii Hunter .50 1.25
56 Roberto Alomar .75 2.00
57 Roger Clemens 2.50 6.00
58 Mark Mulder .50 1.25
59 Brian Giles .50 1.25
60 Mike Piazza 2.00 5.00
61 Rich Aurilia .50 1.25
62 Freddy Garcia .50 1.25
63 Jim Edmonds .50 1.25
64 Eric Hinske .50 1.25
65 Vicente Padilla .50 1.25
66 Javier Vazquez .50 1.25
67 Cristian Guzman .50 1.25
68 Paul Lo Duca .50 1.25
69 Bobby Abreu .50 1.25
70 Nomar Garciaparra 2.00 5.00
71 Troy Glaus .50 1.25
72 Chipper Jones 1.25 3.00
73 Scott Rolen .75 2.00
74 Lance Berkman .75 2.00
75 C.C. Sabathia .50 1.25
76 Bernie Williams .75 2.00
77 Rafael Palmeiro .75 2.00
78 Phil Nevin .50 1.25
79 Kazuhiro Sasaki .50 1.25
80 Eric Chavez .50 1.25
81 Jorge Posada .75 2.00
82 Edgardo Alfonzo .50 1.25
83 Geoff Jenkins .50 1.25
84 Preston Wilson .50 1.25
85 Jim Thome .75 2.00
86 Frank Thomas 1.25 3.00
87 Jeff Bagwell .75 2.00
88 Greg Maddux 2.00 5.00
89 Mark Prior .75 2.00
90 Larry Walker .50 1.25
91 Luis Gonzalez .50 1.25
92 Tim Hudson .50 1.25
93 Tsuyoshi Shinjo .50 1.25
94 Juan Gonzalez .50 1.25
95 Shea Hillenbrand .50 1.25
96 Paul Konerko .50 1.25
97 Tom Glavine .75 2.00
98 Marty Cordova .50 1.25
99 Moises Alou .50 1.25
100 Ken Griffey Jr. 2.00 5.00
101 Hank Blalock .75 2.00
102 Matt Morris .50 1.25
103 Robb Nen .50 1.25
104 Mike Cameron .50 1.25
105 Mark Buehrle .50 1.25
106 Sean Burroughs .50 1.25
107 Orlando Cabrera .50 1.25
108 Jeromy Burnitz .50 1.25
109 Juan Uribe .50 1.25
110 Eric Milton .50 1.25
111 Carlos Lee .50 1.25
112 Jose Mesa .50 1.25
113 Morgan Ensberg .50 1.25
114 Derek Lowe .50 1.25
115 Juan Cruz .50 1.25
116 Mike Lieberthal .50 1.25
117 Armando Benitez .50 1.25
118 Vinny Castilla .50 1.25
119 Russ Ortiz .50 1.25
120 Mike Lowell .50 1.25
121 Corey Patterson .50 1.25
122 Mike Mussina .75 2.00
123 Rafael Furcal .50 1.25
124 Mark Grace .75 2.00
125 Ben Sheets .50 1.25
126 John Smoltz .75 2.00
127 Fred McGriff .75 2.00
128 Nick Johnson .50 1.25
129 J.T. Snow .50 1.25
130 Jeff Cirillo .50 1.25
131 Trevor Hoffman .50 1.25
132 Kevin Brown .50 1.25
133 Mariano Rivera 1.25 3.00
134 Marlon Anderson .50 1.25
135 Al Leiter .50 1.25
136 Doug Mientkiewicz .50 1.25
137 Eric Karros .50 1.25
138 Bobby Higginson .50 1.25
139 Sean Casey .50 1.25
140 Troy Percival .50 1.25
141 Willie Mays 2.50 6.00
142 Carl Yastrzemski 2.00 5.00
143 Stan Musial 2.00 5.00
144 Harmon Killebrew 1.25 3.00
145 Mike Schmidt 2.50 6.00
146 Duke Snider .75 2.00
147 Brooks Robinson .75 2.00
148 Frank Robinson .75 2.00
149 Nolan Ryan 3.00 8.00
150 Reggie Jackson .75 2.00
151 Joe Mauer C RC 5.00 12.00
152 Joe Mauer U 8.00 20.00
153 Joe Mauer R 12.50 30.00
154 Colt Griffin C RC .50 1.25
155 Colt Griffin U 1.00 2.50
156 Colt Griffin R 1.50 4.00
157 Jason Simontacchi C RC .50 1.25
158 Jason Simontacchi U 1.00 2.50
159 Jason Simontacchi R 1.50 4.00
160 Casey Kotchman C RC 1.25 3.00
161 Casey Kotchman U 2.50 6.00
162 Casey Kotchman R 4.00 10.00
163 Greg Sain C RC .50 1.25
164 Greg Sain U 1.00 2.50
165 Greg Sain R 1.50 4.00
166 David Wright C RC 12.50 30.00
167 David Wright U 20.00 50.00
168 David Wright R 30.00 60.00
169 Scott Hairston C RC .75 2.00
170 Scott Hairston U 1.50 4.00
171 Scott Hairston R 2.50 6.00
172 Rolando Viera C RC .50 1.25
173 Rolando Viera U 1.00 2.50
174 Rolando Viera R 1.50 4.00
175 Tyrell Godwin C RC .50 1.25
176 Tyrell Godwin U 1.00 2.50
177 Tyrell Godwin R 1.50 4.00
178 Jesus Cota C RC .50 1.25
179 Jesus Cota U 1.00 2.50
180 Jesus Cota R 1.50 4.00
181 Dan Johnson C RC 1.25 3.00
182 Dan Johnson U 2.50 6.00
183 Dan Johnson R 4.00 10.00
184 Mario Ramos C RC .50 1.25
185 Mario Ramos U 1.00 2.50
186 Mario Ramos R 1.50 4.00
187 Jason Dubois C RC .75 2.00
188 Jason Dubois U 1.50 4.00
189 Jason Dubois R 2.50 6.00
190 Jonny Gomes C RC 1.50 4.00
191 Jonny Gomes U 3.00 8.00
192 Jonny Gomes R 5.00 12.00
193 Chris Snelling C RC .60 1.50
194 Chris Snelling U 1.25 3.00
195 Chris Snelling R 2.00 5.00
196 Hansel Izquierdo C RC .50 1.25
197 Hansel Izquierdo U 1.00 2.50
198 Hansel Izquierdo R 1.50 4.00
199 So Taguchi C RC .75 2.00
200 So Taguchi U 1.50 4.00
201 So Taguchi R 2.50 6.00
202 Kazuhisa Ishii C RC .75 2.00
203 Kazuhisa Ishii U 1.50 4.00
204 Kazuhisa Ishii R 2.50 6.00
205 Jorge Padilla C RC .50 1.25
206 Jorge Padilla U 1.00 2.50
207 Jorge Padilla R 1.50 4.00
208 Earl Snyder C RC .50 1.25
209 Earl Snyder U 1.00 2.50
210 Earl Snyder R 1.50 4.00

2002 Topps Pristine Gold Refractors

Inserted one per hobby box, this is a parallel of the regular set. Each card has a stated print run of 70 serial numbered sets.

*GOLD 1-140: 2.5X TO 6X BASIC

*GOLD 141-150: 2.5X TO 6X BASIC
*GOLD C 151-210: 4X TO 10X BASIC C
*GOLD U 151-210: 2X TO 5X BASIC U
*GOLD R 151-210: 1.25X TO 3X BASIC R
166 David Wright C 125.00 250.00
167 David Wright U 125.00 250.00
168 David Wright R 125.00 250.00

2002 Topps Pristine Refractors

Issued at different odds depending on the card number, these cards parallel the regular pristine set. The veterans and retired players were issued to a stated print run of 149 serial numbered sets. The rookie cards were issued to stated print runs of 1999 for the common versions, 799 for the uncommon versions and 149 for the rare version.

*REFRACTORS 1-140: 1.5X TO 4X
*REFRACTORS 141-150: 1.5X TO 4X
1-150 STATED ODDS 1:4
*REFRACTORS C 151-210: 1X TO 2.5X
COMMON 151-210 STATED ODDS 1:2
*REFRACTORS U 151-210: .75X TO 2X
UNCOMMON 151-210 STATED ODDS 1:5
*REFRACTORS R 151-210: .75X TO 2X
RARE 151-210 STATED ODDS 1:27
166 David Wright C 40.00 80.00
167 David Wright U 50.00 100.00
168 David Wright R 60.00 120.00

2002 Topps Pristine Fall Memories

Issued at different odds depending on which group the insert card belonged to, these cards feature players who had participated in post-season play and a piece of game-used memorabilia pertaining to that player. We have listed the stated print run information for that player as well as what type of memorabilia next to the player's name in our checklist.

GROUP A ODDS 1:21
GROUP B ODDS 1:8
GROUP C ODDS 1:49
GROUP A PRINT RUN 425 SERIAL #'d SETS
GROUP B PRINT RUN 1000 SERIAL #'d SETS
GROUP C PRINT RUN 1600 SERIAL #'d SETS
AJ Andruw Jones Uni B 4.00 10.00
AS Alfonso Soriano Bat B 3.00 8.00
BB Barry Bonds Bat A 15.00 40.00
BW Bernie Williams Bat B 4.00 10.00
CJ Chipper Jones Bat A 6.00 15.00
CS Curt Schilling Jsy B 3.00 8.00
EM Eddie Murray Bat A 6.00 15.00
GB George Brett Jsy B 10.00 25.00
GS Gary Sheffield Bat C 3.00 8.00
JB Johnny Bench Jsy B 6.00 15.00
JP Jorge Posada Bat B 4.00 10.00
KP Kirby Puckett Bat A 6.00 15.00
LG Luis Gonzalez Bat B 3.00 8.00
MG Mark Grace Bat A 6.00 15.00
RJ Reggie Jackson Bat A 6.00 15.00
SG Shawn Green Bat A 4.00 10.00
TG Tom Glavine Jsy B 4.00 10.00
TH Todd Helton Jsy B 4.00 10.00
TM Tino Martinez Bat A 6.00 15.00
WM Willie Mays Jsy A 15.00 40.00

2002 Topps Pristine In the Gap

Inserted at a stated rate of one in 12 for group A cards and one in five for group B cards, these 30 cards feature players along with a game-used memorabilia piece. We have notated next to the player's name not only what type of memorabilia but also what grouping they belonged to.

GROUP A PRINT RUN 425 SERIAL #'d SETS
GROUP B PRINT RUN 1000 SERIAL #'d SETS
AD Adam Dunn Jsy B 3.00 8.00
AJ Andruw Jones Jsy B 4.00 10.00
AP Albert Pujols Uni B 8.00 20.00
AR Alex Rodriguez Bat A 6.00 15.00
ARA Aramis Ramirez Bat A 4.00 10.00
AS Alfonso Soriano Bat A 4.00 10.00
BB Bret Boone Bat B 3.00 8.00
BBO Barry Bonds Uni B 12.50 30.00
BW Bernie Williams Bat A 6.00 15.00
CD Carlos Delgado Bat A 4.00 10.00
DE Darin Erstad Bat A 4.00 10.00
EC Eric Chavez Bat A 4.00 10.00
IR Ivan Rodriguez Bat A 6.00 15.00
JE Jim Edmonds Jsy B 3.00 8.00
JK Jeff Kent Jsy B 3.00 8.00
LB Lance Berkman Bat A 4.00 10.00
LW Larry Walker Jsy B 3.00 8.00
MP Mike Piazza Bat A 6.00 15.00
NG Nomar Garciaparra Bat A 6.00 15.00
PL Paul Lo Duca Bat A 4.00 10.00
PW Preston Wilson Jsy B 3.00 8.00
RA Roberto Alomar Bat B 4.00 10.00
RH Rickey Henderson Bat A 6.00 15.00
RK Ryan Klesko Bat A 4.00 10.00
RP Rafael Palmeiro Bat A 6.00 15.00
TG Tony Gwynn Jsy B 6.00 15.00
TH Todd Helton Bat B 4.00 10.00
TS Tsuyoshi Shinjo Bat B 3.00 8.00
WB Wade Boggs Uni B 4.00 10.00
WBE Wilson Betemit Bat B 3.00 8.00

2002 Topps Pristine Patches

Inserted at stated odds of one in 126, these 25 cards feature game-used patches of the featured player. Each of these cards were issued to a stated print run of 25 serial numbered sets and no pricing is provided due to scarcity.

AD Adam Dunn
AJ Andruw Jones
AP Albert Pujols
AR Alex Rodriguez
BB Bret Boone
BBO Barry Bonds
CD Carlos Delgado
CJ Chipper Jones
CS Curt Schilling
DM Don Mattingly
EC Eric Chavez
FT Frank Thomas
GB George Brett
GM Greg Maddux
KS Kazuhiro Sasaki
LW Larry Walker
MP Mike Piazza
NG Nomar Garciaparra
PM Pedro Martinez
RP Rafael Palmeiro
SR Scott Rolen
TG Tony Gwynn
TGL Tom Glavine
TH Todd Helton
WB Wade Boggs

2002 Topps Pristine Personal Endorsements

Inserted at different odds depending on the group the player belonged to, these cards feature authentic player autographs on a clear acrylic like card surface. We have notated what group the player belongs to next to their name in our checklist.

GROUP A ODDS 1:396
GROUP B ODDS 1:63
GROUP C ODDS 1:79
GROUP D ODDS 1:33
GROUP E ODDS 1:9
GROUP F ODDS 1:53
AP Albert Pujols A 175.00 250.00
BB Barry Bonds E 100.00 175.00
BS Ben Sheets B 8.00 20.00
CG Cristian Guzman C 4.00 10.00
CK Casey Kotchman E 6.00 15.00
CM Corwin Malone E 4.00 10.00
DB Dewon Brazelton D 4.00 10.00
GF Gavin Floyd D 6.00 15.00
IG Irvin Guzman E 30.00 50.00
JD Johnny Damon Sox B 15.00 40.00
JL Jason Lane E 6.00 15.00
JR Jimmy Rollins C 8.00 20.00
JS Juan Silvestre E 4.00 10.00
KB Kenny Baugh F 4.00 10.00
KI Kazuhisa Ishii A 15.00 40.00
LB Lance Berkman B 12.50 30.00
MT Marcus Thames E 4.00 10.00
NN Nick Neugebauer E 4.00 10.00
OH Orlando Hudson D 4.00 10.00
RA Roberto Alomar B 12.50 30.00
ST So Taguchi B 12.50 30.00

2002 Topps Pristine Popular Demand

Inserted at a stated print run of one in four, these 20 cards feature some of the leading players in the game along with a game-used memorabilia piece. Each card was issued to a stated print run of 1000 serial numbered sets.

AD Adam Dunn Jsy 3.00 8.00
AP Albert Pujols Jsy 8.00 20.00
AR Alex Rodriguez Bat 6.00 15.00
BB Bret Boone Jsy 3.00 8.00
BBO Barry Bonds Uni 12.50 30.00
CD Carlos Delgado Uni 3.00 8.00
CJ Chipper Jones Jsy 6.00 15.00
CS Curt Schilling Jsy 3.00 8.00
DM Don Mattingly Jsy 15.00 40.00
FT Frank Thomas Jsy 6.00 15.00
IR Ivan Rodriguez Uni 4.00 10.00
JB Jeff Bagwell Jsy 4.00 10.00
LW Larry Walker Jsy 3.00 8.00
MP Mike Piazza Jsy 6.00 15.00
NG Nomar Garciaparra Bat 6.00 15.00
RA Roberto Alomar Jsy 4.00 10.00
SG Shawn Green Jsy 3.00 8.00
TG Tony Gwynn Jsy 6.00 15.00
TH Todd Helton Jsy 4.00 10.00
WB Wade Boggs Jsy 4.00 10.00

2002 Topps Pristine Portions

Issued at different odds depending on which group the insert card belonged to, these cards feature some leading players along with a piece of game-used memorabilia pertaining to that player. We have listed the stated print run information for that player as well as what type of memorabilia next to the player's name in our checklist.

GROUP A ODDS 1:21
GROUP B ODDS 1:4
GROUP C ODDS 1:33
GROUP A PRINT RUN 425 SERIAL #'d SETS
GROUP B PRINT RUN 1000 SERIAL #'d SETS
GROUP C PRINT RUN 2400 SERIAL #'d SETS
AD Adam Dunn Bat B 4.00 10.00
AP Albert Pujols Uni B 8.00 20.00
AR Alex Rodriguez Jsy B 6.00 15.00
BB Bret Boone Jsy B 4.00 10.00
BBO Barry Bonds Uni C 8.00 20.00
CB Craig Biggio Jsy B 6.00 15.00
CD Carlos Delgado Jsy B 4.00 10.00
CF Cliff Floyd Jsy B 4.00 10.00
CG Cristian Guzman Jsy B 3.00 8.00
EM Edgar Martinez Bat A 6.00 15.00
GM Greg Maddux Jsy A 6.00 15.00
IR Ivan Rodriguez Bat A 6.00 15.00
JB Jeff Bagwell Uni A 6.00 15.00
JP Jorge Posada Bat A 6.00 15.00
KS Kazuhiro Sasaki Jsy A 6.00 15.00
LB Lance Berkman Bat A 6.00 15.00
LD Paul Lo Duca Jsy B 4.00 10.00
MM Mike Mussina Uni B 6.00 15.00
MO Magglio Ordonez Jsy B 4.00 10.00
MP Mike Piazza Bat A 6.00 15.00
NG Nomar Garciaparra Jsy B 6.00 15.00
NJ Nick Johnson Bat B 4.00 10.00
NR Nolan Ryan Uni B 20.00 50.00
RA Roberto Alomar Bat A 6.00 15.00
RD Ryan Dempster Jsy B 3.00 8.00
RF Rafael Furcal Jsy B 4.00 10.00
RP Rafael Palmeiro Jsy B 6.00 15.00
TH Todd Helton Jsy B 6.00 15.00

2003 Topps Pristine

This 190 card pack was issued in special eight-card packs, which actually came as a few packs within a large pack. Each pack contained a mix of cards from the base set as well as an encased special. In the basic set, cards numbered 1 through 95 featured veterans, cards numbered 96 through 100 featured retired greats and cards 101 through 190 featured rookies. Each of the rookies were issued in three forms as "Common", "Uncommon" or "Rare". The "Uncommon" rookies were issued to a stated print run of 1499 serial numbered sets while the "rare" rookies were issued to a stated print run of 499 serial numbered sets.

COMMON CARD (1-100) .60 1.50
COMMON C (101-190) .50 1.25
C 101-190 APPX. 2X EASIER THAN 1-100
COMMON U (101-190) 1.00 2.50
UNCOMMON 101-190 STATED ODDS 1:2
UNCOMMON PRINT 1499 SERIAL #'d SETS
COMMON R (101-190) 2.00 5.00
RARE 101-190 STATED ODDS 1:6
RARE PRINT RUN 499 SERIAL #'d SETS
1 Pedro Martinez 1.00 2.50
2 Derek Jeter 4.00 10.00
3 Alex Rodriguez 2.50 6.00
4 Miguel Tejada .60 1.50
5 Nomar Garciaparra 2.50 6.00
6 Austin Kearns .60 1.50
7 Jose Vidro .60 1.50
8 Bret Boone .60 1.50
9 Scott Rolen 1.00 2.50
10 Mike Sweeney .60 1.50
11 Jason Schmidt .60 1.50
12 Alfonso Soriano .60 1.50
13 Tim Hudson .60 1.50
14 A.J. Pierzynski .60 1.50
15 Lance Berkman .60 1.50
16 Frank Thomas 1.50 4.00
17 Gary Sheffield .60 1.50
18 Jarrod Washburn .60 1.50
19 Hideo Nomo 1.50 4.00
20 Barry Zito .60 1.50
21 Kevin Millwood .60 1.50
22 Matt Morris .60 1.50
23 Carl Crawford .60 1.50
24 Carlos Delgado .60 1.50
25 Mike Piazza 2.50 6.00
26 Brad Radke .60 1.50
27 Richie Sexson .60 1.50
28 Kevin Brown .60 1.50
29 Carlos Beltran .60 1.50
30 Curt Schilling .60 1.50
31 Chipper Jones 1.50 4.00
32 Paul Konerko .60 1.50
33 Larry Walker .60 1.50
34 Jeff Bagwell 1.00 2.50
35 Jason Giambi .60 1.50
36 Mark Mulder .60 1.50
37 Vicente Padilla .60 1.50
38 Kris Benson .60 1.50
39 Bernie Williams 1.00 2.50
40 Jim Thome 1.00 2.50
41 Roger Clemens 3.00 8.00
42 Roberto Alomar 1.00 2.50
43 Torii Hunter .60 1.50
44 Bobby Abreu .60 1.50
45 Jeff Kent .60 1.50
46 Roy Oswalt .60 1.50
47 Bartolo Colon .60 1.50
48 Greg Maddux 2.50 6.00
49 Tom Glavine 1.00 2.50
50 Sammy Sosa 1.50 4.00
51 Ichiro Suzuki 3.00 8.00
52 Mark Prior 1.00 2.50
53 Manny Ramirez 1.00 2.50
54 Andruw Jones 1.00 2.50
55 Randy Johnson 1.50 4.00
56 Garret Anderson .60 1.50
57 Roy Halladay .60 1.50
58 Rafael Palmeiro 1.00 2.50
59 Rocco Baldelli .60 1.50
60 Albert Pujols 3.00 8.00
61 Edgar Renteria .60 1.50
62 John Olerud .60 1.50
63 Rich Aurilia .60 1.50
64 Ryan Klesko .60 1.50
65 Brian Giles .60 1.50
66 Eric Chavez .60 1.50
67 Jorge Posada 1.00 2.50
68 Cliff Floyd .60 1.50
69 Vladimir Guerrero 1.50 4.00
70 Cristian Guzman .60 1.50
71 Raul Ibanez .60 1.50
72 Paul Lo Duca .60 1.50
73 A.J. Burnett .60 1.50
74 Ken Griffey Jr. 2.50 6.00
75 Mark Buehrle .60 1.50
76 Moises Alou .60 1.50
77 Adam Dunn .60 1.50
78 Tony Batista .60 1.50
79 Troy Glaus .60 1.50
80 Luis Gonzalez .60 1.50
81 Shea Hillenbrand .60 1.50
82 Kerry Wood .60 1.50
83 Magglio Ordonez .60 1.50
84 Omar Vizquel 1.00 2.50
85 Bobby Higginson .60 1.50
86 Mike Lowell .60 1.50
87 Runelvys Hernandez .60 1.50
88 Shawn Green .60 1.50
89 Erubiel Durazo .60 1.50
90 Pat Burrell .60 1.50
91 Todd Helton 1.00 2.50
92 Jim Edmonds .60 1.50
93 Aubrey Huff .60 1.50
94 Eric Hinske .60 1.50
95 Barry Bonds 4.00 10.00
96 Willie Mays 3.00 8.00
97 Bo Jackson 1.50 4.00
98 Carl Yastrzemski 2.50 6.00
99 Don Mattingly 3.00 8.00
100 Gary Carter 1.00 2.50
101 Jose Contreras C RC .75 2.00
102 Jose Contreras U 1.50 4.00
103 Jose Contreras R 3.00 8.00
104 Dan Haren C RC .75 2.00
105 Dan Haren U 1.50 4.00
106 Dan Haren R 3.00 8.00
107 Michel Hernandez C RC .50 1.25
108 Michel Hernandez U 1.00 2.50
109 Michel Hernandez R 2.00 5.00
110 Bobby Basham C RC .50 1.25
111 Bobby Basham U 1.00 2.50
112 Bobby Basham R 2.00 5.00
113 Bryan Bullington C RC .50 1.25
114 Bryan Bullington U 1.00 2.50
115 Bryan Bullington R 2.00 5.00
116 Bernie Castro C RC .50 1.25
117 Bernie Castro U 1.00 2.50
118 Bernie Castro R 2.00 5.00
119 Chien-Ming Wang C RC 2.00 5.00
120 Chien-Ming Wang U 10.00 25.00
121 Chien-Ming Wang R 15.00 40.00
122 Eric Crozier C RC .50 1.25
123 Eric Crozier U 1.00 2.50
124 Eric Crozier R 2.00 5.00
125 Mi. Garciaparra C RC .50 1.25
126 Michael Garciaparra U 1.00 2.50
127 Michael Garciaparra R 2.00 5.00
128 Joey Gomes C RC .50 1.25
129 Joey Gomes U 1.00 2.50
130 Joey Gomes R 2.00 5.00
131 Wil Ledezma C RC .50 1.25
132 Wil Ledezma U 1.00 2.50
133 Wil Ledezma R 2.00 5.00
134 Branden Florence C RC .50 1.25
135 Branden Florence U 1.00 2.50
136 Branden Florence R 2.00 5.00
137 Jeremy Bonderman C RC 2.00 5.00
138 Jeremy Bonderman U 4.00 10.00
139 Jeremy Bonderman R 8.00 20.00
140 Travis Ishikawa C RC .75 2.00
141 Travis Ishikawa U 1.50 4.00
142 Travis Ishikawa R 3.00 8.00
143 Ben Francisco C RC .50 1.25
144 Ben Francisco U 1.00 2.50
145 Ben Francisco R 2.00 5.00
146 Jason Kubel C RC 1.00 2.50
147 Jason Kubel U 2.00 5.00
148 Jason Kubel R 4.00 10.00
149 Tyler Martin C RC .50 1.25
150 Tyler Martin U 1.00 2.50
151 Tyler Martin R 2.00 5.00
152 Jason Perry C RC .50 1.25
153 Jason Perry U 1.00 2.50
154 Jason Perry R 2.00 5.00
155 Ryan Shealy C RC 2.00 5.00
156 Ryan Shealy U 3.00 8.00
157 Ryan Shealy R 6.00 15.00
158 Hanley Ramirez C RC 2.50 6.00
159 Hanley Ramirez U 5.00 12.00
160 Hanley Ramirez R 10.00 25.00
161 Rajai Davis C RC .50 1.25
162 Rajai Davis U 1.00 2.50
163 Rajai Davis R 2.00 5.00
164 Gary Schneidmiller C RC .50 1.25
165 Gary Schneidmiller U 1.00 2.50
166 Gary Schneidmiller R 2.00 5.00
167 Haj Turay C RC .50 1.25
168 Haj Turay U 1.00 2.50
169 Haj Turay R 2.00 5.00
170 Kevin Youkilis C RC 1.25 3.00
171 Kevin Youkilis U 2.50 6.00
172 Kevin Youkilis R 5.00 12.00
173 Shane Bazzell C RC .50 1.25
174 Shane Bazzell U 1.00 2.50
175 Shane Bazzell R 2.00 5.00
176 Elizardo Ramirez C RC .50 1.25
177 Elizardo Ramirez U 1.00 2.50
178 Elizardo Ramirez R 2.00 5.00
179 Robinson Cano C RC 4.00 10.00
180 Robinson Cano U 8.00 20.00
181 Robinson Cano R 15.00 40.00
182 Nook Logan C RC .50 1.25
183 Nook Logan U 1.00 2.50
184 Nook Logan R 2.00 5.00
185 Dustin McGowan C RC .50 1.25
186 Dustin McGowan U 1.00 2.50
187 Dustin McGowan R 2.00 5.00
188 Ryan Howard C RC 6.00 15.00
189 Ryan Howard U 8.00 20.00
190 Ryan Howard R 15.00 40.00

2003 Topps Pristine Gold Refractors

*GOLD 1-95: 2.5X TO 6X BASIC
*GOLD 96-100: 2.5X TO 6X BASIC
*GOLD C 101-190: 4X TO 10X BASIC C
*GOLD U 101-190: 2X TO 5X BASIC U
*GOLD R 101-190: 1X TO 2.5X BASIC R
ONE PER SEALED HOBBY BOX
STATED PRINT RUN 69 SERIAL #'d SETS
119 Chien-Ming Wang C 60.00 120.00
120 Chien-Ming Wang U 60.00 120.00
121 Chien-Ming Wang R 60.00 120.00
188 Ryan Howard C 50.00 100.00
189 Ryan Howard U 50.00 100.00
190 Ryan Howard R 50.00 100.00

2003 Topps Pristine Plates

STATED ODDS 1:83
STATED PRINT RUN 4 SETS
BLACK, CYAN, MAGENTA AND YELLOW EXIST
NO PRICING DUE TO SCARCITY

2003 Topps Pristine Refractors

*REFRACTORS 1-95: 2X TO 5X BASIC
*REFRACTORS 96-100: 2X TO 5X BASIC
REFRACTORS 1-100 ODDS 1:8
REFRACTORS 1-100 PRINT RUN 99 #'d SETS
*REFRACTORS C 101-190: .75X TO 2X
COMMON 101-190 RANDOM IN PACKS
COMMON 101-190 PRINT RUN 1599 #'d SETS
*REFRACTORS U 101-190: .75X TO 2X
UNCOMMON 101-190 ODDS 1:6
UNCOMMON 101-190 PRINT 499 #'d SETS
*REFRACTORS R 101-190: .75X TO 2X
RARE 101-190 ODDS 1:27
RARE 101-190 PRINT RUN 99 #'d SETS
119 Chien-Ming Wang C 12.50 30.00
120 Chien-Ming Wang U 15.00 40.00
121 Chien-Ming Wang R 30.00 80.00
179 Robinson Cano C 8.00 20.00
180 Robinson Cano U 15.00 40.00
181 Robinson Cano R 40.00 80.00
188 Ryan Howard C 15.00 40.00
189 Ryan Howard U 20.00 50.00
190 Ryan Howard R 40.00 80.00

2003 Topps Pristine Bonds Jersey Relics

REFRACTOR ODDS 1:787
REFRACTOR PRINT RUN 25 SERIAL #'d SETS
NO REFRACTOR PRICING DUE TO SCARCITY
BB Barry Bonds BB 15.00 40.00
GG Barry Bonds GG 15.00 40.00
HR Barry Bonds HR 15.00 40.00
MVP Barry Bonds MVP 15.00 40.00

2003 Topps Pristine Bonds Dual Relics

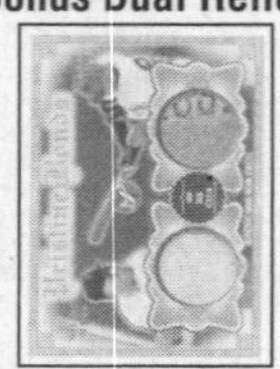

REFRACTOR STATED ODDS 1:787
REFRACTOR PRINT RUN 25 SERIAL #'d SETS
NO REFRACTOR PRICING DUE TO SCARCITY
BJ Barry Bonds Jsy 20.00 50.00
Randy Johnson Jsy
BM Willie Mays Jsy 60.00 120.00
Barry Bonds Jsy
BR Alex Rodriguez Jsy 20.00 50.00
Barry Bonds Jsy
BT Miguel Tejada Bat 20.00 50.00
Barry Bonds Bat

2003 Topps Pristine Bomb Squad Relics

GROUP A ODDS 1:3
GROUP B ODDS 1:5
GROUP C ODDS 1:9
REFRACTOR ODDS 1:59
REFRACTOR PRINT RUN 25 SERIAL #'d SETS
NO REFRACTOR PRICING DUE TO SCARCITY
AD Adam Dunn Jsy A 3.00 8.00
AJ Andruw Jones Bat B 6.00 15.00
AP1 Albert Pujols Bat A 8.00 20.00
AP2 Albert Pujols Uni B 10.00 25.00
AR1 Alex Rodriguez Bat C 4.00 10.00
AR2 Alex Rodriguez Jsy A 4.00 10.00
AS Alfonso Soriano Uni A 3.00 8.00
BB Barry Bonds Jsy B 10.00 25.00
CC Carl Crawford Bat C 3.00 8.00
CF Cliff Floyd Bat B 4.00 10.00
CJ Chipper Jones Bat B 6.00 15.00
DE1 Darin Erstad Uni B 4.00 10.00
DE2 Darin Erstad Jsy B 4.00 10.00
EC1 Eric Chavez Gray Uni A 3.00 8.00
EC2 Eric Chavez White Uni A 3.00 8.00
FT Frank Thomas Bat C 4.00 10.00
GA1 Garret Anderson Bat A 3.00 8.00
GA2 Garret Anderson Uni B 4.00 10.00
GB1 George Brett Bat A 8.00 20.00
GB2 George Brett Bat B 8.00 20.00
GC Gary Carter Bat C 3.00 8.00
GS Gary Sheffield Bat A 3.00 8.00
HB Hank Blalock Bat B 4.00 10.00
JAG Juan Gonzalez Jsy B 4.00 10.00
JB Johnny Bench Bat A 4.00 10.00
JG Jason Giambi Bat A 3.00 8.00
JK Jeff Kent Bat B 4.00 10.00
JRB Jeff Bagwell Bat B 6.00 15.00
JT Jim Thome Bat B 6.00 15.00
LB1 Lance Berkman Jsy C 3.00 8.00
LB2 Lance Berkman Bat C 3.00 8.00
LG Luis Gonzalez Jsy B 4.00 10.00
MO Magglio Ordonez Jsy A 3.00 8.00
MO1 Moises Alou Uni A 3.00 8.00
MO2 Moises Alou Bat B 4.00 10.00
MP Mike Piazza Jsy B 6.00 15.00
MR Manny Ramirez Bat A 3.00 8.00
MS1 Mike Schmidt Bat A 8.00 20.00
MS2 Mike Schmidt Uni A 8.00 20.00
MT Miguel Tejada Bat B 4.00 10.00
NG1 Nomar Garciaparra Bat B 6.00 15.00
NG2 Nomar Garciaparra Jsy B 6.00 15.00
RH Rickey Henderson Bat B 6.00 15.00
RP Rafael Palmeiro Jsy B 6.00 15.00
SG Shawn Green Bat B 4.00 10.00
SS1 Sammy Sosa Bat B 6.00 15.00
SS2 Sammy Sosa Jsy A 4.00 10.00
TG1 Troy Glaus Bat A 3.00 8.00
TG2 Troy Glaus Uni B 4.00 10.00
TH Todd Helton Bat B 6.00 15.00
TS Tim Salmon Uni B 6.00 15.00
VG1 Vladimir Guerrero Jsy A 4.00 10.00
VG2 Vladimir Guerrero Bat A 4.00 10.00

2003 Topps Pristine Borders Relics

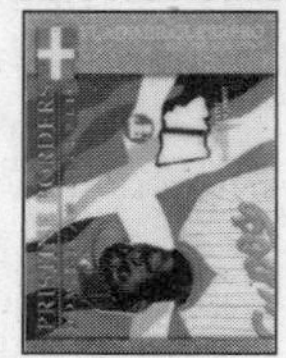

REFRACTOR ODDS 1:210
REFRACTOR PRINT RUN 25 SERIAL #'d SETS
NO REFRACTOR PRICING DUE TO SCARCITY
AJ Andruw Jones Uni 4.00 10.00
AP Albert Pujols Jsy 8.00 20.00
AS Alfonso Soriano Bat 3.00 8.00
BW Bernie Williams Bat 4.00 10.00
CC Chin Feng Chen Jsy 15.00 40.00
CG Cristian Guzman Bat 3.00 8.00
IR Ivan Rodriguez Bat 4.00 10.00
KI Kazuhisa Ishii Jsy 3.00 8.00
MO Magglio Ordonez Jsy 3.00 8.00
MR Manny Ramirez Jsy 4.00 10.00
MT Miguel Tejada Bat 3.00 8.00
PM Pedro Martinez Jsy 4.00 10.00
SS Sammy Sosa Jsy 4.00 10.00
TS Tsuyoshi Shinjo Bat 3.00 8.00
VG Vladimir Guerrero Jsy 4.00 10.00

2003 Topps Pristine Corners Relics

STATED ODDS 1:12
REFRACTOR ODDS 1:285
REFRACTOR PRINT RUN 25 SERIAL #'d SETS
NO REFRACTOR PRICING DUE TO SCARCITY
AS Edgardo Alfonzo Bat 4.00 10.00
J.T. Snow Bat
BK Sean Burroughs Jsy 4.00 10.00
Ryan Klesko Bat
BM Adrian Beltre Bat 4.00 10.00
Fred McGriff Bat
BT David Bell Bat 6.00 15.00
Jim Thome Bat
CD Eric Chavez Bat 4.00 10.00
Erubiel Durazo Bat
GS Troy Glaus Jsy 4.00 10.00
Scott Spiezio Jsy
KM Corey Koskie Bat 4.00 10.00
Doug Mientkiewicz Bat
RM Scott Rolen Bat 10.00 25.00
Tino Martinez Bat
TP Mark Teixeira Bat 6.00 15.00
Rafael Palmeiro Bat
VG Robin Ventura Bat 4.00 10.00
Jason Giambi Bat
WG Matt Williams Bat 6.00 15.00
Mark Grace Bat

2003 Topps Pristine Factor Bat Relics

STATED ODDS 1:9
REFRACTOR ODDS 1:210
REFRACTOR PRINT RUN 25 SERIAL #'d SETS
NO REFRACTOR PRICING DUE TO SCARCITY
AD Adam Dunn 3.00 8.00
AR Alex Rodriguez 4.00 10.00
AS Alfonso Soriano 3.00 8.00
DE Darin Erstad 3.00 8.00
JG Jason Giambi 3.00 8.00
LB Lance Berkman 3.00 8.00
MO Magglio Ordonez 3.00 8.00
MP Mike Piazza 6.00 15.00
MR Manny Ramirez 4.00 10.00
NG Nomar Garciaparra 6.00 15.00
SS Sammy Sosa 4.00 10.00
TG Troy Glaus 3.00 8.00
TH Todd Helton 4.00 10.00
TKH Torii Hunter 3.00 8.00
VG Vladimir Guerrero 4.00 10.00

2003 Topps Pristine Mini

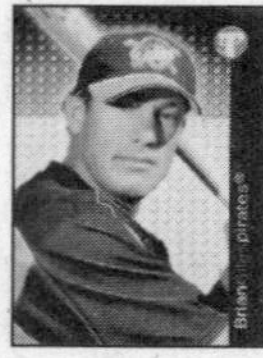

VETERAN STATED ODDS 1:8
ROOKIE STATED ODDS 1:16
AK Austin Kearns V 1.25 3.00
AR Alex Rodriguez V 4.00 10.00
AS Alfonso Soriano V 1.25 3.00
BB Barry Bonds V 6.00 15.00
BC Bernie Castro R 1.25 3.00
BG Brian Giles V 1.25 3.00
BPB Bryan Bullington R 1.25 3.00
BWB Bobby Basham R 1.25 3.00
CW Chien-Ming Wang R 10.00 25.00
DH Dan Haren R 2.00 5.00
DJ Derek Jeter V 6.00 15.00
DM Dustin McGowan R 1.50 4.00
EC Eric Chavez V 1.25 3.00
ELC Eric Crozier R 1.50 4.00
ER Elizardo Ramirez R 1.50 4.00
IS Ichiro Suzuki V 5.00 12.00
JB Jeremy Bonderman R 4.00 10.00
JC Jose Contreras R 2.00 5.00
JG Jason Giambi V 1.25 3.00
JJK Jason Kubel R 3.00 8.00
JK Jeff Kent V 1.25 3.00
JT Jim Thome V 1.50 4.00
KY Kevin Youkilis R 3.00 8.00
MH Michel Hernandez R 1.25 3.00
MJP Mike Piazza V 4.00 10.00
MO Magglio Ordonez V 1.25 3.00
MP Mark Prior V 1.50 4.00
MT Miguel Tejada V 1.25 3.00
NG Nomar Garciaparra V 4.00 10.00
NL Nook Logan R 1.50 4.00
RB Rocco Baldelli V 1.25 3.00
RC Roger Clemens V 5.00 12.00
RD Rajai Davis R 1.25 3.00
RH Ryan Howard R 15.00 40.00
RJC Robinson Cano R 8.00 20.00
RS Ryan Shealy R 4.00 10.00
SS Sammy Sosa V 2.50 6.00
TM Tyler Martin R 1.25 3.00
VG Vladimir Guerrero V 2.50 6.00
WL Wil Ledezma R 1.25 3.00

2003 Topps Pristine Mini Autograph

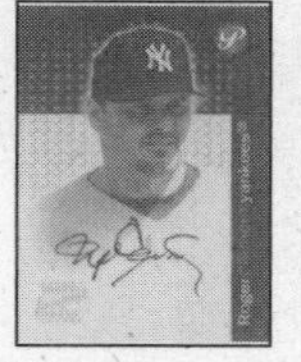

STATED ODDS 1:636
STATED PRINT RUN 100 CARDS
PRINT RUN INFO PROVIDED BY TOPPS
CARD IS NOT SERIAL-NUMBERED
RC Roger Clemens/100 * 60.00 120.00

2003 Topps Pristine Personal Endorsements

STATED ODDS 1:5
GOLD STATED ODDS 1:184
GOLD PRINT RUN 25 SERIAL #'d SETS
NO GOLD PRICING DUE TO SCARCITY
AB Andrew Brown 6.00 15.00
BM Brett Myers 6.00 15.00
DE David Eckstein 12.50 30.00
FS Felix Sanchez 4.00 10.00
FV Fernando Vina 4.00 10.00
JG Jay Gibbons 4.00 10.00
JP Josh Phelps 4.00 10.00
KH Ken Harvey 4.00 10.00
KS Kelly Shoppach 6.00 15.00
LF Lew Ford 6.00 15.00
ML Mike Lowell 6.00 15.00
MS Mike Sweeney 6.00 15.00
PK Paul Konerko 10.00 25.00
RJH Rich Harden 10.00 25.00
RYC Ryan Church 6.00 15.00
SR Scott Rolen 10.00 25.00
VM Victor Martinez 10.00 25.00

2003 Topps Pristine Primary Elements Patch Relics

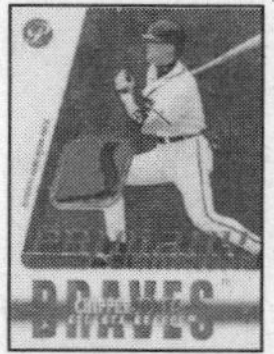

STATED ODDS 1:45
STATED PRINT RUN 50 SETS
CARDS ARE NOT SERIAL-NUMBERED
PRINT RUN INFO PROVIDED BY TOPPS
NO PRICING DUE TO SCARCITY
REFRACTOR ODDS 1:224
REFRACTOR PRINT RUN 10 SERIAL #'d SETS
NO REFRACTOR PRICING DUE TO SCARCITY
AD Adam Dunn
AJ Andruw Jones
AP Albert Pujols

AR Alex Rodriguez
BB Barry Bonds
BRB Bret Boone
BZ Barry Zito
CD Carlos Delgado
CJ Chipper Jones
CR Cal Ripken
CS Curt Schilling
EC Eric Chavez
EG Eric Gagne
GM Greg Maddux
JB Jeff Bagwell
KI Kazuhisa Ishii
LB Lance Berkman
LG Luis Gonzalez
MM Mark Mulder
MO Magglio Ordonez
MP Mike Piazza
MR Manny Ramirez
MRO Moises Alou
MT Miguel Tejada
NG Nomar Garciaparra
PK Paul Konerko
PM Pedro Martinez
RJ Randy Johnson
RO Roy Oswalt
RP Rafael Palmeiro
SG Shawn Green
SS Sammy Sosa
TG Tony Gwynn
TH Todd Helton
TKH Torii Hunter

2004 Topps Pristine

This 190-card set was released in October, 2004. The set was issued, in what has been traditional for this product, in a pack within a pack concept. The "full" pack, is an eight card pack with an $30 SRP which came five packs to a box and six boxes to a case. Cards numbered 1 through 100 feature veterans while cards 101 through 190 feature three cards each of the same rookie with decreasing print runs for each card. The Common Rookie Cards were printed in the approximate same print run as the veterans while the uncommon cards were issued to a stated rate of one in two with a stated print run of 999 serial numbered sets and the rare rookies were issued with a stated print run of 499 serial numbered sets and were issued at a stated rate of one in four. There are some reports that the #168 and #169 Chris Saenz cards were never produced.

COMMON CARD (1-100) .60 1.50
COMMON C (101-190) .75 2.00
C 101-190 APPROX.EQUAL TO 1-100
COMMON U (101-190) 1.25 3.00
UNCOMMON 101-190 STATED ODDS 1:2
UNCOMMON 101-190 PRINT 999 #'d SETS
COMMON R (101-190) 2.00 5.00
RARE 101-190 STATED ODDS 1:4
RARE 101-190 PRINT RUN 499 #'d SETS
OVERALL PLATES ODDS 1:52 HOBBY
PLATE PRINT RUN 1 SET PER COLOR
BLACK-CYAN-MAGENTA-YELLOW ISSUED
NO PLATE PRICING DUE TO SCARCITY
1 Jim Thome 1.00 2.50
2 Ryan Klesko .60 1.50
3 Ichiro Suzuki 3.00 8.00
4 Rocco Baldelli .60 1.50
5 Vernon Wells .60 1.50
6 Javier Vazquez .60 1.50
7 Billy Wagner .60 1.50
8 Jose Reyes .60 1.50
9 Lance Berkman .60 1.50
10 Alex Rodriguez 2.50 6.00
11 Pat Burrell .60 1.50
12 Mark Mulder .60 1.50
13 Mike Piazza 2.50 6.00
14 Miguel Cabrera 1.00 2.50
15 Larry Walker .60 1.50
16 Carlos Lee .60 1.50
17 Mark Prior 1.00 2.50
18 Pedro Martinez 1.00 2.50
19 Melvin Mora .60 1.50
20 Sammy Sosa 1.50 4.00
21 Bartolo Colon .60 1.50
22 Luis Gonzalez .60 1.50
23 Marcus Giles .60 1.50
24 Ken Griffey Jr. 2.50 6.00
25 Ivan Rodriguez 1.00 2.50
26 Carlos Beltran .60 1.50
27 Geoff Jenkins .60 1.50
28 Nick Johnson .60 1.50
29 Gary Sheffield .60 1.50
30 Alfonso Soriano .60 1.50
31 Scott Rolen 1.00 2.50
32 Garret Anderson .60 1.50
33 Richie Sexson .60 1.50
34 Curt Schilling 1.00 2.50
35 Greg Maddux 2.50 6.00
36 Adam Dunn .60 1.50
37 Preston Wilson .60 1.50
38 Josh Beckett .60 1.50
39 Roy Oswalt .60 1.50
40 Derek Jeter 3.00 8.00
41 Jason Kendall .60 1.50
42 Bret Boone .60 1.50
43 Torii Hunter .60 1.50
44 Roy Halladay .60 1.50
45 Edgar Renteria .60 1.50
46 Troy Glaus .60 1.50
47 Chipper Jones 1.50 4.00
48 Manny Ramirez 1.00 2.50
49 C.C. Sabathia .60 1.50
50 Albert Pujols 3.00 8.00
51 Randy Wolf .60 1.50
52 Eric Chavez .60 1.50
53 Kevin Brown .60 1.50
54 Cliff Floyd .60 1.50
55 Jeff Bagwell 1.00 2.50
56 Frank Thomas 1.50 4.00
57 David Ortiz 1.50 4.00
58 Rafael Palmeiro 1.00 2.50
59 Randy Johnson 1.50 4.00
60 Vladimir Guerrero 1.50 4.00
61 Carlos Delgado .60 1.50
62 Hank Blalock .60 1.50
63 Jim Edmonds .60 1.50
64 Jason Schmidt .60 1.50
65 Mike Lieberthal .60 1.50
66 Tim Hudson .60 1.50
67 Jorge Posada 1.00 2.50
68 Jose Vidro .60 1.50
69 Eric Gagne .60 1.50
70 Roger Clemens 3.00 8.00
71 Mike Lowell .60 1.50
72 Dontrelle Willis 1.00 2.50
73 Austin Kearns .60 1.50
74 Kerry Wood .60 1.50
75 Miguel Tejada .60 1.50
76 Bobby Abreu .60 1.50
77 Edgar Martinez 1.00 2.50
78 Joe Mauer 1.50 4.00
79 Mike Sweeney .60 1.50
80 Jason Giambi .60 1.50
81 Mark Teixeira 1.00 2.50
82 Aubrey Huff .60 1.50
83 Brian Giles .60 1.50
84 Barry Zito .60 1.50
85 Mike Mussina 1.00 2.50
86 Brandon Webb .60 1.50
87 Andruw Jones 1.00 2.50
88 Javy Lopez .60 1.50
89 Bill Mueller .60 1.50
90 Scott Podsednik .60 1.50
91 Moises Alou .60 1.50
92 Esteban Loaiza .60 1.50
93 Magglio Ordonez .60 1.50
94 Jeff Kent .60 1.50
95 Todd Helton 1.00 2.50
96 Juan Pierre .60 1.50
97 Jody Gerut .60 1.50
98 Angel Berroa .60 1.50
99 Shawn Green .60 1.50
100 Nomar Garciaparra 2.50 6.00
101 David Aardsma C RC .75 2.00
102 David Aardsma U 1.25 3.00
103 David Aardsma R 2.00 5.00
104 Erick Aybar C RC 1.25 3.00
105 Erick Aybar U 2.00 5.00
106 Erick Aybar R 3.00 8.00
107 Chad Bentz C RC .75 2.00
108 Chad Bentz U 1.25 3.00
109 Chad Bentz R 2.00 5.00
110 Travis Blackley C RC .75 2.00
111 Travis Blackley U 1.25 3.00
112 Travis Blackley R 2.00 5.00
113 Bobby Brownlie C RC 1.00 2.50
114 Bobby Brownlie U 1.50 4.00
115 Bobby Brownlie R 2.50 6.00
116 Alberto Callaspo C RC 1.25 3.00
117 Alberto Callaspo U 2.00 5.00
118 Alberto Callaspo R 3.00 8.00
119 Kazuo Matsui C RC .75 2.00
120 Kazuo Matsui U 1.25 3.00
121 Kazuo Matsui R 2.00 5.00
122 Jesse Crain C RC 1.25 3.00
123 Jesse Crain U 2.00 5.00
124 Jesse Crain R 3.00 8.00
125 Howie Kendrick C RC 10.00 25.00
126 Howie Kendrick U 12.50 30.00
127 Howie Kendrick R 20.00 50.00
128 Blake Hawksworth C RC .75 2.00
129 Blake Hawksworth U 1.25 3.00
130 Blake Hawksworth R 2.00 5.00
131 Conor Jackson C RC 3.00 8.00
132 Conor Jackson U 5.00 12.00
133 Conor Jackson R 8.00 20.00
134 Paul Maholm C RC 1.50 4.00
135 Paul Maholm U 2.50 6.00
136 Paul Maholm R 4.00 10.00
137 Lastings Milledge C RC 2.00 5.00
138 Lastings Milledge U 3.00 8.00
139 Lastings Milledge R 5.00 12.00
140 Matt Moses C RC 1.00 2.50
141 Matt Moses U 1.50 4.00
142 Matt Moses R 2.50 6.00
143 David Murphy C RC 1.25 3.00
144 David Murphy U 2.00 5.00
145 David Murphy R 3.00 8.00
146 Dioner Navarro C RC 1.25 3.00
147 Dioner Navarro U 2.00 5.00
148 Dioner Navarro R 3.00 8.00
149 Dustin Nippert C RC .75 2.00
150 Dustin Nippert U 1.25 3.00
151 Dustin Nippert R 2.00 5.00
152 Vito Chiaravalloti C RC .75 2.00
153 Vito Chiaravalloti U 1.25 3.00
154 Vito Chiaravalloti R 2.00 5.00
155 Akinori Otsuka C RC .75 2.00
156 Akinori Otsuka U 1.25 3.00
157 Akinori Otsuka R 2.00 5.00
158 Casey Daigle C RC .75 2.00
159 Casey Daigle U 1.25 3.00
160 Casey Daigle R 2.00 5.00
161 Carlos Quentin C RC 2.50 6.00
162 Carlos Quentin U 4.00 10.00
163 Carlos Quentin R 6.00 15.00
164 Omar Quintanilla C RC .75 2.00
165 Omar Quintanilla U 1.25 3.00
166 Omar Quintanilla R 2.00 5.00
167 Chris Saenz C RC .75 2.00
168 Chris Saenz U
169 Chris Saenz R
170 Ervin Santana C RC 2.00 5.00
171 Ervin Santana U 3.00 8.00
172 Ervin Santana R 5.00 12.00
173 Chris Shelton C RC 1.25 3.00
174 Chris Shelton U 1.50 4.00
175 Chris Shelton R 2.50 6.00
176 Kyle Sleeth C RC .75 2.00
177 Kyle Sleeth U 1.25 3.00
178 Kyle Sleeth R 2.00 5.00
179 Brad Snyder C RC 1.00 2.50
180 Brad Snyder U 1.50 4.00
181 Brad Snyder R 2.50 6.00
182 Tim Stauffer C RC 1.00 2.50
183 Tim Stauffer U 1.50 4.00
184 Tim Stauffer R 2.50 6.00
185 Shingo Takatsu C RC 1.25 3.00
186 Shingo Takatsu U 2.00 5.00
187 Shingo Takatsu R 3.00 8.00
188 Merkin Valdez C RC .75 2.00
189 Merkin Valdez U 1.25 3.00
190 Merkin Valdez R 2.00 5.00

2004 Topps Pristine Gold Refractors

*GOLD 1-100: 2.5X TO 6X BASIC
*GOLD C 101-190: 2.5X TO 6X BASIC
*GOLD U 101-190: 1.5X TO 4X BASIC
*GOLD R 101-190: 1X TO 2.5X BASIC
ONE PER SEALED HOBBY BOX
STATED PRINT RUN 41 SERIAL #'d SETS
125 Howie Kendrick C 125.00 200.00
126 Howie Kendrick U 125.00 200.00
127 Howie Kendrick R 125.00 200.00
131 Conor Jackson C 20.00 50.00
132 Conor Jackson U 20.00 50.00
133 Conor Jackson R 20.00 50.00
137 Lastings Milledge C 20.00 50.00
138 Lastings Milledge U 20.00 50.00
139 Lastings Milledge R 20.00 50.00
161 Carlos Quentin C 15.00 40.00
162 Carlos Quentin U 15.00 40.00
163 Carlos Quentin R 15.00 40.00
173 Chris Shelton C 10.00 25.00
174 Chris Shelton U 10.00 25.00
175 Chris Shelton R 10.00 25.00

2004 Topps Pristine Refractors

*REFRACTORS 1-100: 2.5X TO 6X BASIC
1-100 STATED ODDS 1:11
1-100 PRINT RUN 49 SERIAL #'d SETS
*REFRACTORS C 101-190: .6X TO 1.5X BASIC
COMMON 101-190 RANDOM IN PACKS
COMMON 101-190 PRINT RUN 999 #'d SETS
*REFRACTORS U 101-190: .6X TO 1.5X BASIC
UNCOMMON 101-190 ODDS 1:5
UNCOMMON 101-190 PRINT 399 #'d SETS
*REFRACTORS R 101-190: 1X TO 2.5X BASIC
RARE 101-190 ODDS 1:35
RARE 101-190 PRINT RUN 49 #'d SETS
125 Howie Kendrick C 15.00 40.00
126 Howie Kendrick U 20.00 50.00
127 Howie Kendrick R 60.00 120.00
131 Conor Jackson C 5.00 12.00
132 Conor Jackson U 8.00 20.00
133 Conor Jackson R 20.00 50.00
137 Lastings Milledge C 3.00 8.00
138 Lastings Milledge U 5.00 12.00
139 Lastings Milledge R 20.00 50.00
161 Carlos Quentin C 4.00 10.00
162 Carlos Quentin U 6.00 15.00
163 Carlos Quentin R 15.00 40.00

2004 Topps Pristine 1-2-3 Triple Relics

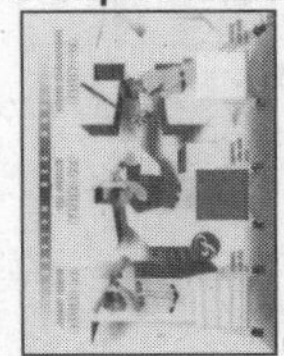

STATED ODDS 1:171
*REFRACTOR: X TO X BASIC
REFRACTOR ODDS 1:686
REFRACTOR PRINT RUN 25 #'d SETS
B ='S BAT; J ='S JSY
BOS Johnny Damon Bat 20.00 50.00
Bill Mueller Jsy
Nomar Garciaparra Jsy
CHC Mark Grudzielanek Bat 15.00 40.00
Alex Gonzalez Bat
Sammy Sosa Bat
NYY Kenny Lofton Bat 20.00 50.00
Derek Jeter Bat
Alex Rodriguez Bat

2004 Topps Pristine Fantasy Favorites Relics

RANDOM INSERTS IN PACKS
*REFRACTOR: 2X TO 5X BASIC
REFRACTOR STATED ODDS 1:59
REFRACTOR PRINT RUN 25 #'d SETS
AB Angel Berroa Bat 2.00 5.00
AJ Andruw Jones Jsy 3.00 8.00
AP Albert Pujols Jsy 6.00 15.00
AR Alex Rodriguez Bat 4.00 10.00
BB Bret Boone Jsy 2.00 5.00
BW Brandon Webb Uni 2.00 5.00
CD Carlos Delgado Jsy 2.00 5.00
CJ Chipper Jones Jsy 4.00 10.00
CK Corey Koskie Bat 2.00 5.00
DJ Derek Jeter Bat 8.00 20.00
EG Eric Gagne Jsy 2.00 5.00
FT Frank Thomas Jsy 4.00 10.00
JB Jeff Bagwell Uni 3.00 8.00
JD Johnny Damon Bat 3.00 8.00
JR Jimmy Rollins Jsy 2.00 5.00
JT Jim Thome Uni 3.00 8.00
JV Jose Vidro Bat 2.00 5.00
KL Kenny Lofton Bat 2.00 5.00
KW Kerry Wood Jsy 2.00 5.00
LW Larry Walker Jsy 2.00 5.00
MA Moises Alou Jsy 2.00 5.00
MG Mark Grudzielanek Bat 2.00 5.00
MP Mark Prior Jsy 3.00 8.00
MPI Mike Piazza Jsy 4.00 10.00
MT Mark Teixeira Bat 3.00 8.00
NG Nomar Garciaparra Jsy 4.00 10.00
PM Pedro Martinez Jsy 3.00 8.00
PW Preston Wilson Jsy 2.00 5.00
RB Rocco Baldelli Bat 2.00 5.00
RF Rafael Furcal Bat 2.00 5.00
RFJ Rafael Furcal Jsy 2.00 5.00
SG Shawn Green Jsy 2.00 5.00
TH Tim Hudson Jsy 2.00 5.00
THE Todd Helton Jsy 3.00 8.00
VG Vladimir Guerrero Bat 4.00 10.00

2004 Topps Pristine Going Going Gone Bat Relics

GROUP A ODDS 1:6
GROUP B ODDS 1:11
*REFRACTOR: 2X TO 5X BASIC
REFRACTOR STATED ODDS 1:93
REFRACTOR PRINT RUN 25 #'d SETS
AD Adam Dunn B 2.00 5.00
AP Albert Pujols A 6.00 15.00
AR Alex Rodriguez A 4.00 10.00
AS Alfonso Soriano A 2.00 5,00
BB Bret Boone A 2.00 5.00
CJ Chipper Jones A 4.00 10.00
DO David Ortiz B 4.00 10.00
FT Frank Thomas B 4.00 10.00
JG Juan Gonzalez A 2.00 5.00
JJ Jacque Jones A 2.00 5.00
JK Jeff Kent A 2.00 5.00
JT Jim Thome A 3.00 8.00
LB Lance Berkman A 2.00 5.00
LG Luis Gonzalez A 2.00 5.00
MO Magglio Ordonez A 2.00 5.00
MP Mike Piazza B 4.00 10.00
MR Manny Ramirez B 3.00 8.00
RK Ryan Klesko B 2.00 5.00
SR Scott Rolen A 3.00 8.00
SS Sammy Sosa A 4.00 10.00
VG Vladimir Guerrero A 4.00 10.00
VW Vernon Wells A 2.00 5.00

2004 Topps Pristine Key Acquisition Bat Relics

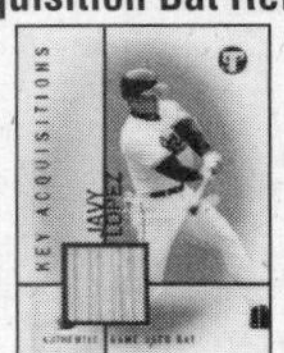

STATED ODDS 1:8
*REFRACTOR: 2X TO 5X BASIC
REFRACTOR ODDS 1:256
REFRACTOR PRINT RUN 25 #'d SETS
AR Alex Rodriguez 4.00 10.00
AS Alfonso Soriano 2.00 5.00
GS Gary Sheffield 2.00 5.00
HC Hee Seop Choi 2.00 5.00
IR Ivan Rodriguez 3.00 8.00
JG Juan Gonzalez 2.00 5.00
JL Javy Lopez 2.00 5.00
VG Vladimir Guerrero 4.00 10.00

2004 Topps Pristine Mini

STATED ODDS 1:5
AO Akinori Otsuka R 1.25 3.00
AP Albert Pujols V 4.00 10.00
AR Alex Rodriguez V 3.00 8.00
BH Blake Hawksworth R 1.25 3.00
CJ Chipper Jones V 2.00 5.00
CJA Conor Jackson R 3.00 8.00
DA David Aardsma R 1.25 3.00
DJ Derek Jeter V 4.00 10.00
DM David Murphy R 1.50 4.00
DN Dioner Navarro R 1.50 4.00
DW Dontrelle Willis V 1.25 3.00
EA Erick Aybar R 1.25 3.00
HK Howie Kendrick R 15.00 30.00
IS Ichiro Suzuki V 4.00 10.00
JG Jason Giambi V 1.25 3.00
JT Jim Thome V 1.25 3.00
KM Kazuo Matsui R 1.50 4.00
KS Kyle Sleeth R 1.25 3.00
KW Kerry Wood V 1.25 3.00
LM Lastings Milledge R 3.00 8.00
MM Matt Moses R 1.50 4.00
MP Mark Prior V 1.25 3.00
MPI Mike Piazza V 3.00 8.00
MV Merkin Valdez R 1.50 4.00
NG Nomar Garciaparra V 3.00 8.00
SS Sammy Sosa V 2.00 5.00
ST Shingo Takatsu R 1.50 4.00
TS Tim Stauffer R 1.50 4.00
VC Vito Chiaravalloti R 1.25 3.00
VG Vladimir Guerrero V 2.00 5.00

2004 Topps Pristine Mini Relics

STATED ODDS 1:51
STATED PRINT RUN 100 SETS
CARDS ARE NOT SERIAL-NUMBERED
PRINT RUN INFO PROVIDED BY TOPPS
AP Albert Pujols Jsy 10.00 25.00
CJ Chipper Jones Jsy 6.00 15.00
EG Eric Gagne Jsy 3.00 8.00
JB Jeff Bagwell Uni 5.00 12.00
KW Kerry Wood Jsy 3.00 8.00
MP Mark Prior Jsy 5.00 12.00
NG Nomar Garciaparra Jsy 6.00 15.00
PM Pedro Martinez Jsy 5.00 12.00
PW Preston Wilson Jsy 3.00 8.00
MPI Mike Piazza Jsy 6.00 15.00

2004 Topps Pristine Patch Place Relics

GROUP A ODDS 1:30
GROUP B ODDS 1:34
REFRACTOR STATED ODDS 1:155
REFRACTOR PRINT RUN 10 #'d SETS
NO REF.PRICING DUE TO SCARCITY
LISTED PRICES ARE SINGLE COLOR PATCH
*MULTI-COLOR: ADD 100% PREMIUM
AD Adam Dunn A 4.00 10.00
AJ Andruw Jones A 6.00 15.00
AK Austin Kearns A 4.00 10.00
AP Albert Pujols B 15.00 40.00
BB Bret Boone B 4.00 10.00
BZ Barry Zito A 4.00 10.00
CC Chin-Feng Chen A 20.00 50.00
CD Carlos Delgado A 4.00 10.00
CJ Chipper Jones B 6.00 15.00
DW Dontrelle Willis A 6.00 15.00
EG Eric Gagne A 4.00 10.00
FT Frank Thomas A 6.00 15.00
JB Jeff Bagwell B 6.00 15.00
JBE Josh Beckett B 4.00 10.00
JR Jose Reyes A 4.00 10.00
JS John Smoltz A 6.00 15.00
KW Kerry Wood A 4.00 10.00
LC Luis Castillo A 4.00 10.00
LG Luis Gonzalez B 4.00 10.00
ML Mike Lowell A 4.00 10.00
MP Mark Prior B 6.00 15.00
MPI Mike Piazza B 6.00 15.00
NG Nomar Garciaparra A 6.00 15.00
PL Paul Lo Duca A 4.00 10.00
PM Pedro Martinez B 6.00 15.00
PW Preston Wilson A 4.00 10.00
RB Rocco Baldelli A 4.00 10.00
RF Rafael Furcal A 4.00 10.00
RJ Randy Johnson B 6.00 15.00
SG Shawn Green A 4.00 10.00
SS Sammy Sosa A 6.00 15.00
TH Tim Hudson A 4.00 10.00
THE Todd Helton B 6.00 15.00

2004 Topps Pristine Personal Endorsements

GROUP A ODDS 1:39
GROUP B ODDS 1:41
GROUP C ODDS 1:7
GOLD STATED ODDS 1:73
GOLD PRINT RUN 25 SERIAL #'d SETS
NO GOLD PRICING DUE TO SCARCITY
AH Aubrey Huff C 4.00 10.00
AR Alex Rodriguez A 75.00 150.00

BC Bobby Crosby C 4.00 10.00
BM Brett Myers A 6.00 15.00
BW Brandon Webb B 4.00 10.00
CJ Conor Jackson C 8.00 20.00
CL Chris Lubanski C 4.00 10.00
DA David Aardsma C 6.00 15.00
DM Dustin McGowan C 4.00 10.00
DY Delmon Young A 10.00 25.00
EH Estee Harris C 6.00 15.00
ES Ervin Santana C 10.00 25.00
GA Garret Anderson A 6.00 15.00
GS Gary Sheffield A 15.00 40.00
GSI Grady Sizemore C 10.00 25.00
HB Hank Blalock B 6.00 15.00
IR Ivan Rodriguez A 15.00 40.00
JF Jennie Finch A 100.00 175.00
JM Joe Mauer B 12.50 30.00
JP Jorge Posada A 15.00 40.00
JV Javier Vazquez A 6.00 15.00
LB Lance Berkman A 10.00 25.00
MC Miguel Cabrera B 10.00 25.00
MG Marcus Giles A 6.00 15.00
SP Scott Podsednik B 10.00 25.00
VC Vito Chiaravalloti C 4.00 10.00
VG Vladimir Guerrero A 20.00 50.00
WM Willie Mays A 125.00 200.00

2004 Topps Pristine Two of a Kind Dual Autographs

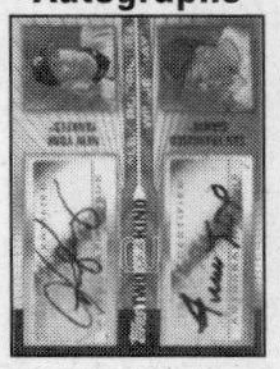

STATED ODDS 1:3705
STATED PRINT RUN 13 SERIAL #'d CARDS
AROD/CANSECO NOT SER.#'d
NO PRICING DUE TO SCARCITY
RM Alex Rodriguez
Willie Mays
RC Alex Rodriguez
Jose Canseco

2005 Topps Pristine

This 210-card set was released in October, 2005. The set was issued in eight-card packs which came as a multi-pack concept. Cards numbered 1-100 feature active veterans while cards 101 through 130 feature Rookie Cards. Cards numbered 131 through 180 feature game-used cards of veterans while cards 181 through 205 feature signed cards of players (Most of whom are Rookies or Prospects). Cards numbered 206 through 210 feature both an autograph and a game-worn jersey piece. Cards numbered 131 through 180 were issued to a stated print run of 500 serial numbered sets and were issued to stated odds of one in three. Cards numbered 181 through 205 were issued at stated odds of one in 22 and were issued to a stated print run of 100 serial numbered sets. Cards numbered 206 through 210 were issued at a stated rate of one in 219 and those cards were issued to a stated print run of 49 serial numbered sets. A couple of players did not return their cards in time for pack-out and those cards could be exchanged until October 31, 2007.

COMMON CARD (1-100) .40 1.00
COMMON RC (101-130) .60 1.50
OVERALL PLATE ODDS 1:53 HOBBY
PLATE PRINT RUN 1 SET PER COLOR
BLACK-CYAN-MAGENTA-YELLOW ISSUED
NO PLATE PRICING DUE TO SCARCITY
1 Alex Rodriguez 1.50 4.00
2 Jake Peavy .40 1.00
3 Bobby Crosby .40 1.00
4 J.D. Drew .40 1.00
5 Scott Rolen .60 1.50
6 Bobby Abreu .40 1.00
7 Ken Griffey Jr. 1.50 4.00
8 Jeremy Bonderman .40 1.00
9 Mike Sweeney .40 1.00
10 Mark Prior .60 1.50
11 Tim Hudson .40 1.00
12 Clint Barmes .40 1.00
13 Jeff Bagwell .60 1.50
14 Andruw Jones .60 1.50
15 Carlos Delgado .40 1.00
16 Rocco Baldelli .40 1.00
17 Adam Dunn .40 1.00
18 Greg Maddux 1.50 4.00
19 Torii Hunter .40 1.00
20 Miguel Tejada .40 1.00
21 Lyle Overbay .40 1.00
22 Craig Wilson .40 1.00

23 Scott Kazmir .40 1.00
24 Alex Rios .40 1.00
25 Ichiro Suzuki 2.00 5.00
26 Jorge Posada .60 1.50
27 Jose Reyes .40 1.00
28 Hank Blalock .40 1.00
29 Troy Glaus .40 1.00
30 Todd Helton .60 1.50
31 Javy Lopez .40 1.00
32 Barry Zito .40 1.00
33 Jimmy Rollins .40 1.00
34 Mark Loretta .40 1.00
35 Richie Sexson .40 1.00
36 Nick Johnson .40 1.00
37 Ivan Rodriguez .60 1.50
38 Jeff Kent .40 1.00
39 Jake Westbrook .40 1.00
40 Carlos Beltran .40 1.00
41 Rich Harden .40 1.00
42 Joe Mauer 1.00 2.50
43 Luis Gonzalez .40 1.00
44 Frank Thomas 1.00 2.50
45 Michael Young .40 1.00
46 Jason Schmidt .40 1.00
47 Eric Chavez .40 1.00
48 Vinny Castilla .40 1.00
49 John Smoltz .60 1.50
50 Barry Bonds 2.50 6.00
51 Jim Edmonds .40 1.00
52 Edgar Renteria .40 1.00
53 Jose Vidro .40 1.00
54 Chipper Jones 1.00 2.50
55 Curt Schilling .60 1.50
56 Victor Martinez .40 1.00
57 Josh Beckett .40 1.00
58 Derrek Lee .60 1.50
59 Shawn Green .40 1.00
60 Roger Clemens 1.50 4.00
61 Orlando Cabrera .40 1.00
62 Mike Piazza 1.00 2.50
63 Gary Sheffield .40 1.00
64 Carl Crawford .40 1.00
65 Johan Santana 1.00 2.50
66 Oliver Perez .40 1.00
67 Manny Ramirez .60 1.50
68 Paul Konerko .40 1.00
69 Preston Wilson .40 1.00
70 Sammy Sosa 1.00 2.50
71 Eric Gagne .40 1.00
72 Geoff Jenkins .40 1.00
73 Magglio Ordonez .40 1.00
74 Kerry Wood .40 1.00
75 Albert Pujols 2.00 5.00
76 Roy Halladay .40 1.00
77 Aubrey Huff .40 1.00
78 Nomar Garciaparra 1.00 2.50
79 Brian Roberts .40 1.00
80 Randy Johnson 1.00 2.50
81 Pat Burrell .40 1.00
82 Brian Giles .40 1.00
83 Mike Mussina .60 1.50
84 Mark Teixeira .60 1.50
85 Pedro Martinez .60 1.50
86 Jason Bay .40 1.00
87 Mark Buehrle .40 1.00
88 Rafael Furcal .40 1.00
89 Juan Pierre .40 1.00
90 Jim Thome .60 1.50
91 Ben Sheets .40 1.00
92 Alfonso Soriano .40 1.00
93 Adrian Beltre .40 1.00
94 Miguel Cabrera .60 1.50
95 Derek Jeter 2.00 5.00
96 Vernon Wells .40 1.00
97 Lance Berkman .40 1.00
98 Hideki Matsui 1.50 4.00
99 David Ortiz 1.00 2.50
100 Vladimir Guerrero 1.00 2.50
101 Justin Verlander FY RC 3.00 8.00
102 Billy Butler FY RC 3.00 8.00
103 Wladimir Balentien FY RC 1.25 3.00
104 Jeremy West FY RC 1.25 3.00
105 Philip Humber FY RC 1.25 3.00
106 Tyler Pelland FY RC .75 2.00
107 Andy LaRoche FY RC 3.00 8.00
108 Hernan Iribarren FY RC .75 2.00
109 Luke Scott FY RC 1.50 4.00
110 Landon Powell FY RC .75 2.00
111 Alexander Smit FY RC .60 1.50
112 Ryan Garko FY RC 1.50 4.00
113 Bear Bay FY RC .75 2.00
114 Ian Bladergroen FY RC .75 2.00
115 Manny Parra FY RC .50 1.25
116 Andy Sides FY RC .60 1.50
117 Travis Chick FY RC .75 2.00
118 Stefan Bailie FY RC .60 1.50
119 Chuck Tiffany FY RC 1.25 3.00
120 Buck Coats FY RC .60 1.50
121 Jeff Niemann FY RC 1.25 3.00
122 Jake Postlewait FY RC .60 1.50
123 Matt Campbell FY RC .60 1.50
124 Kevin Melillo FY RC 1.25 3.00
125 Mike Morse FY RC 1.25 3.00
126 Anthony Reyes FY RC 2.00 5.00
127 Casey McGehee FY RC .60 1.50
128 Cody Haerther FY RC .60 1.50
129 Brandon McCarthy FY RC 1.50 4.00
130 Glen Perkins FY RC 1.25 3.00
131 Moises Alou Bat 2.00 5.00
132 Nomar Garciaparra Bat 4.00 10.00
133 Scott Rolen Jsy 3.00 8.00
134 Miguel Tejada Uni 2.00 5.00
135 Alex Rodriguez Bat 6.00 15.00
136 Michael Young Jsy 2.00 5.00
137 Tim Hudson Uni 2.00 5.00
138 Troy Glaus Bat 2.00 5.00
139 Eric Chavez Uni 2.00 5.00
140 David Ortiz Bat 3.00 8.00
141 Andruw Jones Jsy 3.00 8.00
142 Richie Sexson Bat 2.00 5.00
143 Jim Thome Bat 3.00 8.00
144 Javy Lopez Bat 2.00 5.00
145 Lance Berkman Jsy 2.00 5.00
146 Gary Sheffield Bat 2.00 5.00
147 Dontrelle Willis Jsy 2.00 5.00
148 Curt Schilling Jsy 3.00 8.00
149 Jorge Posada Jsy 3.00 8.00
150 Vladimir Guerrero Bat 4.00 10.00
151 Adam Dunn Jsy 2.00 5.00
152 Ryan Drese Jsy 2.00 5.00
153 Hank Blalock Uni 2.00 5.00
154 Kerry Wood Jsy 2.00 5.00
155 Alfonso Soriano Bat 2.00 5.00
156 Aramis Ramirez Bat 2.00 5.00
157 Mark Mulder Uni 2.00 5.00
158 Paul Konerko Bat 2.00 5.00
159 Jim Edmonds Jsy 2.00 5.00
160 Roger Clemens Jsy 5.00 12.00
161 Mariano Rivera Jsy 4.00 10.00
162 Rafael Palmeiro Bat 3.00 8.00
163 Mark Teixeira Bat 3.00 8.00
164 Eric Gagne Jsy 2.00 5.00
165 Sammy Sosa Bat 4.00 10.00
166 Brett Myers Jsy 2.00 5.00
167 Kazuhisa Ishii Uni 2.00 5.00
168 Ken Harvey Bat 2.00 5.00
169 Johnny Estrada Jsy 2.00 5.00
170 Todd Helton Jsy 3.00 8.00
171 Rich Harden Jsy 2.00 5.00
172 Johnny Damon Bat 3.00 8.00
173 Manny Ramirez Bat 3.00 8.00
174 Benito Santiago Bat 2.00 5.00
175 Albert Pujols Jsy 6.00 15.00
176 Chipper Jones Jsy 4.00 10.00
177 Miguel Cabrera Bat 3.00 8.00
178 Jeff Bagwell Uni 3.00 8.00
179 Ivan Rodriguez Jsy 3.00 8.00
180 Mike Piazza Uni 4.00 10.00
181 Chip Cannon FY AU RC 15.00 40.00
182 Erik Cordier FY AU RC 10.00 25.00
183 Billy Butler FY AU 50.00 80.00
184 C.J. Smith FY AU RC 10.00 25.00
185 Alfonso Soriano AU 12.50 30.00
186 Bobby Livingston FY AU RC 10.00 25.00
187 Wladimir Balentien FY AU 15.00 40.00
188 Mike Morse FY AU 10.00 25.00
189 W.Swackhamer FY AU RC 10.00 25.00
190 Justin Verlander FY AU 25.00 50.00
191 Jake Postlewait FY AU 10.00 25.00
192 Michael Rogers FY AU RC 10.00 25.00
193 Matt Campbell FY AU 10.00 25.00
194 Eric Nielsen FY AU RC 10.00 25.00
195 Gary Sheffield AU 20.00 50.00
196 Glen Perkins FY AU 15.00 40.00
197 Kevin Melillo FY AU 10.00 25.00
198 Chad Orvella FY AU RC 10.00 25.00
199 Jeff Niemann FY AU 15.00 40.00
200 Alex Rodriguez AU 125.00 200.00
201 Brian Stavisky FY AU RC 10.00 25.00
202 Brian Miller FY AU RC 10.00 25.00
203 Landon Powell FY AU 15.00 40.00
204 Philip Humber FY AU 15.00 40.00
205 Mariano Rivera AU 60.00 120.00
206 Curt Schilling AU Jsy EXCH 50.00 100.00
207 Nolan Ryan AU Jsy 60.00 120.00
208 Albert Pujols AU Jsy 175.00 300.00
209 Stan Musial AU Bat 60.00 120.00
210 B.Bonds AU Jsy * EXCH 250.00 400.00

2005 Topps Pristine Die Cut Red

*DC RED 1-100: 2.5X TO 6X BASIC
*DC RED 101-130: 1.5X TO 4X BASIC
1-130 ODDS 1:2 HOBBY BOXES
1-130 PRINT RUN 66 SERIAL #'d SETS
GU 131-180 ODDS 1:59 HOBBY BOXES
AU 181-205 ODDS 1:117 HOBBY BOXES
AU-GU 206-210 ODDS 1:595 HOBBY BOXES
AU-GU 206-210 EXCH.DEADLINE 10/31/07
131-210 PRINT RUN 3 SERIAL #'d SETS
181-210 NO PRICING DUE TO SCARCITY

2005 Topps Pristine Uncirculated Bronze

*BRZ 1-100: 1.5X TO 4X BASIC
*BRZ 101-130: 1X TO 2.5X BASIC
1-130 STATED ODDS 1:2
1-130 PRINT RUN 375 SERIAL #'d SETS
*BRZ 131-180: .6X TO 1.5X BASIC
GU 131-180 STATED ODDS 1:11
GU 131-180 PRINT RUN 100 SERIAL #'d SETS
AU 181-205 STATED ODDS 1:121
AU 181-205 PRINT RUN 18 SERIAL #'d SETS
AU-GU 206-210 STATED ODDS 1:3482
AU-GU 206-210 PRINT RUN 10 #'d SETS
AU-GU 206-210 EXCH.DEADLINE 10/31/07
181-205 NO PRICING DUE TO SCARCITY

2005 Topps Pristine Doubles Act Autographs

GROUP A ODDS 1:579
GROUP B ODDS 1:8705
STATED PRINT RUN 5 SERIAL #'d SETS
NO PRICING DUE TO SCARCITY
EXCHANGE DEADLINE 10/31/07
BJ Barry Bonds
Jay-Z B EXCH
BM Barry Bonds
Willie McCovey A EXCH
BP Barry Bonds
Albert Pujols A EXCH
BR Barry Bonds
Alex Rodriguez A EXCH
GM Dwight Gooden
Pedro Martinez A
GS Dwight Gooden
Darryl Strawberry A
JP Reggie Jackson
Albert Pujols A
JR Reggie Jackson
Alex Rodriguez A
KB Harmon Killebrew
Barry Bonds A EXCH
KM Harmon Killebrew
Stan Musial A
MB Stan Musial
Barry Bonds A EXCH
MP Stan Musial
Albert Pujols A
MS Pedro Martinez
Curt Schilling A
RJ Alex Rodriguez
Jay-Z B
RP Alex Rodriguez
Albert Pujols A
RR Alex Rodriguez
Mariano Rivera A
RS Nolan Ryan
Curt Schilling A
SG Tom Seaver
Dwight Gooden A
SM Tom Seaver
Pedro Martinez A
SR Tom Seaver
Nolan Ryan A
SS Tom Seaver
Curt Schilling A

2005 Topps Pristine Fielder's Choice Glove Relics

STATED ODDS 1:139
STATED PRINT RUN 9 SERIAL #'d SETS
NO PRICING DUE TO SCARCITY
AM Andy Marte
BA Bobby Abreu
CB Craig Biggio
CC Carl Crawford
CM Chad Moeller
CS Chris Singleton
DH Damon Hollins
DM Damian Miller
DR Desi Relaford
DW Dan Wilson
DWA Daryle Ward
HC Humberto Cota
JB Jason Bay
JDC J.D. Closser
JH John Halama
JJ Jacque Jones
JL Jason Lane
JM Justin Morneau
JR Jimmy Rollins
JS John Smoltz
KL Kenny Lofton
KM Kevin Millar
KY Kevin Youkilis
LB Lance Berkman
MB Marlon Byrd
MC Michael Cuddyer
MH Mike Hampton
ML Mike Lieberthal
MLE Matt LeCroy
MM Mike Maroth
MO Miguel Olivo
MR Mike Redmond
PW Preston Wilson
RB Rocco Baldelli
RBA Rod Barajas
RH Ryan Howard
RHE Ramon Hernandez
RO Roy Oswalt
SS Shannon Stewart
TG Todd Greene
TH Tim Hudson
TR Tike Redman
WG Wiki Gonzalez

2005 Topps Pristine In the Name Letter Patch Relics

STATED ODDS 1:803
STATED PRINT RUN 1 SERIAL #'d SET
ONE CARD MADE FOR EACH LETTER
NO PRICING DUE TO SCARCITY
AJ1 Andruw Jones A
AJ2 Andruw Jones J
AJ3 Andruw Jones O
AJ4 Andruw Jones N
AJ5 Andruw Jones E
AJ6 Andruw Jones S
AP1 Albert Pujols P
AP2 Albert Pujols U
AP3 Albert Pujols J
AP4 Albert Pujols O
AP5 Albert Pujols L
AP6 Albert Pujols S
BJ1 Brian Jordan J
BJ2 Brian Jordan O
BJ3 Brian Jordan R
BJ4 Brian Jordan D
BJ5 Brian Jordan A
BJ6 Brian Jordan N
BM1 Brett Myers M
BM2 Brett Myers Y
BM3 Brett Myers E
BM4 Brett Myers R
BM5 Brett Myers S
CB1 Carlos Beltran B
CB2 Carlos Beltran E
CB3 Carlos Beltran L
CB4 Carlos Beltran T
CB5 Carlos Beltran R
CB6 Carlos Beltran A
CB7 Carlos Beltran N
CJ1 Chipper Jones J
CJ2 Chipper Jones O
CJ3 Chipper Jones N
CJ4 Chipper Jones E
CJ5 Chipper Jones S
EG1 Eric Gagne G
EG2 Eric Gagne A
EG3 Eric Gagne G
EG4 Eric Gagne N
EG5 Eric Gagne E
JE1 Jim Edmonds E
JE2 Jim Edmonds D
JE3 Jim Edmonds M
JE4 Jim Edmonds O
JE5 Jim Edmonds N
JE6 Jim Edmonds D
JE7 Jim Edmonds S
PM1 Pedro Martinez M
PM2 Pedro Martinez A
PM3 Pedro Martinez R
PM4 Pedro Martinez T
PM5 Pedro Martinez I
PM6 Pedro Martinez N
PM7 Pedro Martinez E
PM8 Pedro Martinez Z
RC1 Roger Clemens C
RC2 Roger Clemens L
RC3 Roger Clemens E
RC4 Roger Clemens M
RC5 Roger Clemens E
RC6 Roger Clemens N
RC7 Roger Clemens S
SR1 Scott Rolen R
SR2 Scott Rolen O
SR3 Scott Rolen L
SR4 Scott Rolen E
SR5 Scott Rolen N

2005 Topps Pristine Personal Endorsements Common

STATED ODDS 1:6
STATED PRINT RUN 497 SERIAL #'d SETS
UNCIRCULATED ODDS 1:916
UNCIRCULATED PRINT RUN 3 #'d SETS
NO UNCIRC PRICING DUE TO SCARCITY
BB Billy Butler 15.00 40.00
BJ Blake Johnson 4.00 10.00
BL Bobby Livingston 4.00 10.00
CJS C.J. Smith 4.00 10.00
CO Chad Orvella 4.00 10.00
GP Glen Perkins 6.00 15.00
JF Josh Fields 6.00 15.00
JPH J.P. Howell 4.00 10.00
JS Jeremy Sowers 6.00 15.00
JV Justin Verlander 20.00 50.00
LC Lance Cormier 4.00 10.00
LH Livan Hernandez 6.00 15.00
LP Landon Powell 6.00 15.00
MB Milton Bradley 6.00 15.00
MR Mike Rodriguez 4.00 10.00
MRO Mark Rogers 4.00 10.00
PH Philip Humber 6.00 15.00
SE Scott Elbert 4.00 10.00
TS Termel Sledge 4.00 10.00
ZJ Zach Jackson 4.00 10.00

2005 Topps Pristine Personal Endorsements Uncommon

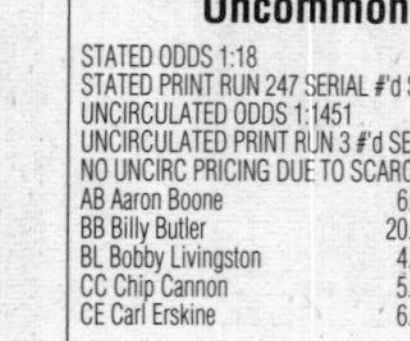

STATED ODDS 1:18
STATED PRINT RUN 247 SERIAL #'d SETS
UNCIRCULATED ODDS 1:1451
UNCIRCULATED PRINT RUN 3 #'d SETS
NO UNCIRC PRICING DUE TO SCARCITY
AB Aaron Boone 6.00 15.00
BB Billy Butler 20.00 50.00
BL Bobby Livingston 4.00 10.00
CC Chip Cannon 5.00 12.00
CE Carl Erskine 6.00 15.00

CW Craig Wilson 4.00 10.00
DO David Ortiz 20.00 50.00
DW David Wright 30.00 60.00
DZ Don Zimmer 10.00 25.00
HK Harmon Killebrew 15.00 40.00
JB Jason Bay 6.00 15.00
MB Matt Bush 6.00 15.00
ML Mark Loretta 4.00 10.00

2005 Topps Pristine Personal Endorsements Rare

STATED ODDS 1:95
STATED PRINT RUN 97 SERIAL #'d SETS
UNCIRCULATED ODDS 1:3072
UNCIRCULATED PRINT RUN 3 #'d SETS
NO UNCIRC PRICING DUE TO SCARCITY
AS Alfonso Soriano 10.00 25.00
EB Ernie Banks 30.00 60.00
GA Garret Anderson 10.00 25.00
MR Mariano Rivera 60.00 120.00
SM Stan Musial 30.00 60.00
TS Tom Seaver 15.00 40.00

2005 Topps Pristine Personal Endorsements Scarce

STATED ODDS 1:1226
STATED PRINT RUN 22 SERIAL #'d SETS
UNCIRCULATED ODDS 1:10,466
UNCIRCULATED PRINT RUN 3 #'d SETS
NO PRICING DUE TO SCARCITY
EXCHANGE DEADLINE 10/31/07
AP Albert Pujols
BB Barry Bonds EXCH

2005 Topps Pristine Personal Pieces Common Relics

STATED ODDS 1:3
STATED PRINT RUN 425 SERIAL #'d SETS
HAFNER PRINT RUN 400 SERIAL #'d CARDS
UNCIRCULATED ODDS 1:363
UNCIRCULATED PRINT RUN 3 #'d SETS
NO UNCIRC PRICING DUE TO SCARCITY
AB Adrian Beltre Bat 2.00 5.00
AD Adam Dunn Bat 2.00 5.00
AJ Andruw Jones Bat 3.00 8.00
AP Albert Pujols Jsy 6.00 15.00
AS Alfonso Soriano Bat 2.00 5.00
BC Bobby Crosby Bat 2.00 5.00
BJU B.J. Upton Bat 2.00 5.00
BM Brett Myers Jsy 2.00 5.00
BR Brad Radke Jsy 2.00 5.00
BW Bernie Williams Bat 3.00 8.00
BZ Barry Zito Uni 2.00 5.00
CG Cristian Guzman Bat 2.00 5.00
CJ Chipper Jones Bat 4.00 10.00
CS Curt Schilling Jsy 3.00 8.00
EC Eric Chavez Uni 2.00 5.00
ER Edgar Renteria Bat 2.00 5.00
FT Frank Thomas Jsy 4.00 10.00
GS Gary Sheffield Bat 2.00 5.00
HB Hank Blalock Jsy 2.00 5.00
JB Jeff Bagwell Jsy 3.00 8.00
JDD J.D. Drew Jsy 2.00 5.00
JE Jim Edmonds Jsy 2.00 5.00
JES Johnny Estrada Jsy 2.00 5.00
JG Jason Giambi Uni 2.00 5.00
JGI Jay Gibbons Bat 2.00 5.00
JL Javy Lopez Bat 2.00 5.00
JT Jim Thome Jsy 3.00 8.00
KM Kevin Millar Bat 2.00 5.00
KW Kerry Wood Jsy 2.00 5.00
LB Lance Berkman Jsy 2.00 5.00
LN Laynce Nix Jsy 2.00 5.00
ML Mark Loretta Bat 2.00 5.00
MLO Mike Lowell Jsy 2.00 5.00
MM Mark Mulder Uni 2.00 5.00
MP Mike Piazza Uni 4.00 10.00
MPR Mark Prior Jsy 3.00 8.00
MR Manny Ramirez Bat 3.00 8.00
MRI Mariano Rivera Jsy 4.00 10.00
MT Miguel Tejada Uni 2.00 5.00
MTE Mark Teixeira Jsy 3.00 8.00
PM Pedro Martinez Jsy 3.00 8.00
RB Ronnie Belliard Bat 2.00 5.00
RC Roger Clemens Jsy 5.00 12.00
SG Shawn Green Bat 2.00 5.00
SR Scott Rolen Jsy 3.00 8.00
TH Todd Helton Jsy 3.00 8.00
THA Travis Hafner Bat/400 2.00 5.00
THU Tim Hudson Uni 2.00 5.00
VG Vladimir Guerrero Bat 4.00 10.00
VM Victor Martinez Bat 2.00 5.00

2005 Topps Pristine Personal Pieces Uncommon Relics

STATED ODDS 1:11
STATED PRINT RUN 200 SERIAL #'d SETS
UNCIRCULATED ODDS 1:726
UNCIRCULATED PRINT RUN 3 #'d SETS
NO UNCIRC PRICING DUE TO SCARCITY
AB Adrian Beltre Bat 2.00 5.00
AJ Andruw Jones Bat 3.00 8.00
AP Albert Pujols Jsy 6.00 15.00
AR Alex Rodriguez Jsy 6.00 15.00
AS Alfonso Soriano Uni 2.00 5.00
CB Carlos Beltran Jsy 2.00 5.00
CJ Chipper Jones Jsy 4.00 10.00
CS Curt Schilling Jsy 3.00 8.00
DO David Ortiz Jsy 4.00 10.00
EG Eric Gagne Jsy 2.00 5.00
IR Ivan Rodriguez Jsy 3.00 8.00
JE Jim Edmonds Jsy 2.00 5.00
JP Jorge Posada Uni 3.00 8.00
JT Jim Thome Jsy 3.00 8.00
MC Miguel Cabrera Jsy 3.00 8.00
MM Mark Mulder Uni 2.00 5.00
MO Magglio Ordonez Bat 2.00 5.00
MP Mike Piazza Jsy 4.00 10.00
MR Manny Ramirez Jsy 3.00 8.00
MRI Mariano Rivera Jsy 4.00 10.00
RC Roger Clemens Jsy 5.00 12.00
SR Scott Rolen Jsy 3.00 8.00
SS Sammy Sosa Bat 4.00 10.00
TG Troy Glaus Bat 2.00 5.00
TH Torii Hunter Jsy 2.00 5.00

2005 Topps Pristine Personal Pieces Rare Relics

STATED ODDS 1:72
STATED PRINT RUN 75 SERIAL #'d SETS
UNCIRCULATED ODDS 1:1801
UNCIRCULATED PRINT RUN 3 #'d SETS
NO UNCIRC PRICING DUE TO SCARCITY
AP Albert Pujols Jsy 12.50 30.00
AR Alex Rodriguez Jsy 12.50 30.00
BB Barry Bonds AS Jsy * 40.00 80.00
CB Carlos Beltran Jsy 4.00 10.00
EG Eric Gagne Jsy 4.00 10.00
JD Johnny Damon Jsy 6.00 15.00
PM Pedro Martinez Jsy 6.00 15.00
RC Roger Clemens Jsy 10.00 25.00
TH Todd Helton Jsy 6.00 15.00
VG Vladimir Guerrero Jsy 6.00 15.00

2005 Topps Pristine Personal Pieces Scarce Relics

STATED ODDS 1:1088
STATED PRINT RUN 10 SERIAL #'d SETS
UNCIRCULATED ODDS 1:3731
UNCIRCULATED PRINT RUN 3 #'d SETS
NO PRICING DUE TO SCARCITY
AP Albert Pujols Jsy
AR Alex Rodriguez Jsy
BB Barry Bonds AS Jsy *
RC Roger Clemens Jsy
VG Vladimir Guerrero Jsy

2005 Topps Pristine Power Core Bat Knob Relics

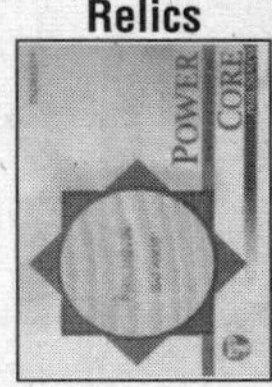

STATED ODDS 1:69
PRINT RUNS B/WN 3-10 COPIES PER
NO PRICING DUE TO SCARCITY
AB Adrian Beltre/6
ABE Angel Berroa/5
AD Adam Dunn/6
ADA Andre Dawson/5
AG Alex Gonzalez/6
AJ Andruw Jones/6
AK Al Kaline/5
AL Adam LaRoche/6
AP Albert Pujols/5
AR Alex Rodriguez/5
ARA Aramis Ramirez/5
AS Alfonso Soriano/5
ASC Red Schoendienst/7
BC Bobby Crosby/6
BJU B.J. Upton/6
BK Bobby Kielty/6
BM Bill Mueller/4
BR Brooks Robinson/5
BS Benito Santiago/7
BW Bernie Williams/7
CB Carlos Beltran/5
CC Coco Crisp/7
CE Carl Everett/5
CF Chone Figgins/5
CG Carlos Guillen/5
CGU Cristian Guzman/7
CJ Chipper Jones/6
CP Corey Patterson/5
CS Curt Schilling/6
CT Charles Thomas/5
DE Darin Erstad/6
DEV Darrell Evans/6
DJ David Justice/6
DL Derrek Lee/5
DM Doug Mientkiewicz/5
DO David Ortiz/6
DR Dave Roberts/5
DS Darryl Strawberry/5
DW Dontrelle Willis/6
EB Ernie Banks/6
EC Eric Chavez/6
ER Edgar Renteria/6
GB George Brett/5
GC Gary Carter/3
GM Greg Maddux/4
GS Gary Sheffield/7
HB Hank Blalock/6
HBA Harold Baines/6
HK Harmon Killebrew/5
HR Harold Reynolds/5
IR Ivan Rodriguez/6
JB Jason Bay/6
JBU Jeromy Burnitz/5
JC Jose Canseco/6
JCJ Jose Cruz Jr./8
JCO Jeff Conine/6
JD Johnny Damon/7
JE Jim Edmonds/5
JES Johnny Estrada/10
JF Julio Franco/6
JG Jason Giambi/5
JGE Jody Gerut/4
JGI Jay Gibbons/6
JJ Jacque Jones/6
JK Jeff Kent/4
JKE Jason Kendall/5
JL Javy Lopez/6
JLE Jim Leyritz/6
JP Jorge Posada/5
JR Jeremy Reed/4
JT Jim Thome/10
JV Jose Vidro/6
JVA Jose Valentin/7
JW Jayson Werth/5
KH Ken Harvey/5
KM Kevin Millar/7
KY Kevin Youkilis/5
LA Luis Aparicio/5
LB Lance Berkman/6
LH Livan Hernandez/6
LW Larry Walker/6
MC Miguel Cabrera/6
ME Morgan Ensberg/6
MG Marcus Giles/6
MK Mark Kotsay/7
ML Mark Loretta/5
MLO Mike Lowell/6
MM Melvin Mora/5
MO Magglio Ordonez/6
MP Mike Piazza/3
MR Manny Ramirez/6
MRI Mickey Rivers/7
MS Mike Schmidt/5
MT Miguel Tejada/8
MTE Mark Teixeira/5
MTU Matt Tuiasosopo/5
MY Michael Young/5
NG Nomar Garciaparra/6
NGR Nick Green/6
OC Orlando Cabrera/6
OV Omar Vizquel/5
PK Paul Konerko/7
PM Pedro Martinez/7
PN Phil Nevin/5
PR Pokey Reese/4
PW Preston Wilson/5
RA Roberto Alomar/8
RB Rocco Baldelli/6
RBE Ronnie Belliard/6
RH Richard Hidalgo/6
RJ Reggie Jackson/5
RK Ron Kittle/9
RP Rafael Palmeiro/9
RS Richie Sexson/6
RSA Reggie Sanders/6
RSI Ruben Sierra/6
SB Sean Burroughs/7
SG Shawn Green/4
SR Scott Rolen/6
SS Sammy Sosa/6
TC Tony Clark/5
TG Troy Glaus/7
TH Todd Helton/5
THU Torii Hunter/5
TL Travis Lee/7
TM Tino Martinez/5
TN Trot Nixon/5
TO Tony Oliva/7
TR Tim Raines/7
VC Vinny Castilla/6
VG Vladimir Guerrero/6
VM Victor Martinez/6
WB Wade Boggs/6
WM Willie McGee/8
WW Walt Weiss/6

2005 Topps Pristine Power Stick Bat Knob Relics

STATED ODDS 1:395
STATED PRINT RUN 1 SERIAL #'d SET
NO PRICING DUE TO SCARCITY
AB Adrian Beltre
ABE Angel Berroa
AD Adam Dunn
ADA Andre Dawson
AG Alex Gonzalez
AJ Andruw Jones
AK Al Kaline
AL Adam LaRoche
AP Albert Pujols
AR Alex Rodriguez
ARA Aramis Ramirez
AS Alfonso Soriano
ASC Red Schoendienst
BC Bobby Crosby
BJU B.J. Upton
BK Bobby Kielty
BM Bill Mueller
BR Brooks Robinson
BS Benito Santiago
BW Bernie Williams
CB Carlos Beltran
CC Coco Crisp
CE Carl Everett
CF Chone Figgins
CG Carlos Guillen
CGU Cristian Guzman
CJ Chipper Jones
CP Corey Patterson
CS Curt Schilling
CT Charles Thomas
DE Darin Erstad
DEV Darrell Evans
DJ David Justice
DL Derrek Lee
DM Doug Mientkiewicz
DO David Ortiz
DR Dave Roberts
DS Darryl Strawberry
DW Dontrelle Willis
EB Ernie Banks
EC Eric Chavez
ER Edgar Renteria
GB George Brett
GC Gary Carter
GM Greg Maddux
GS Gary Sheffield
HB Hank Blalock
HBA Harold Baines
HK Harmon Killebrew
HR Harold Reynolds
IR Ivan Rodriguez
JB Jason Bay
JBU Jeromy Burnitz
JC Jeff Conine
JCJ Jose Cruz Jr.
JCO Jose Canseco
JD Johnny Damon
JE Jim Edmonds
JES Johnny Estrada
JF Julio Franco
JG Jason Giambi
JGE Jody Gerut
JGI Jay Gibbons
JJ Jacque Jones
JK Jeff Kent
JKE Jason Kendall
JL Javy Lopez
JLE Jim Leyritz
JM Justin Morneau
JP Jorge Posada
JR Jeremy Reed
JT Jim Thome
JV Jose Vidro
JVA Jose Valentin
JW Jayson Werth
KH Ken Harvey
KM Kevin Millar
KY Kevin Youkilis
LA Luis Aparicio
LB Lance Berkman
LH Livan Hernandez
LW Larry Walker
MC Miguel Cabrera
ME Morgan Ensberg
MG Marcus Giles
MK Mark Kotsay
ML Mark Loretta
MLO Mike Lowell
MM Melvin Mora
MO Magglio Ordonez
MP Mike Piazza
MR Manny Ramirez
MRI Mickey Rivers
MS Mike Schmidt
MT Miguel Tejada
MTE Mark Teixeira
MTU Matt Tuiasosopo
MY Michael Young
NG Nomar Garciaparra
NGR Nick Green
OC Orlando Cabrera
OV Omar Vizquel
PK Paul Konerko
PM Pedro Martinez
PN Phil Nevin
PR Pokey Reese
PW Preston Wilson
RA Roberto Alomar
RB Rocco Baldelli
RBE Ronnie Belliard
RH Richard Hidalgo
RJ Reggie Jackson
RK Ron Kittle
RP Rafael Palmeiro
RS Richie Sexson
RSA Reggie Sanders
RSI Ruben Sierra
SB Sean Burroughs
SG Shawn Green
SR Scott Rolen
SS Sammy Sosa
TC Tony Clark
TG Troy Glaus
TH Todd Helton
THU Torii Hunter
TL Travis Lee
TM Tino Martinez
TN Trot Nixon
TO Tony Oliva
TR Tim Raines
VC Vinny Castilla
VG Vladimir Guerrero
VM Victor Martinez
WB Wade Boggs
WM Willie McGee
WW Walt Weiss

2005 Topps Pristine Selective Swatch Letter-Number Patch Relics

OVERALL SELECTIVE SWATCH ODDS 1:768
STATED PRINT RUN 1 SERIAL #'d SET
NO PRICING DUE TO SCARCITY
AP1 Albert Pujols P
AP2 Albert Pujols T
AP3 Albert Pujols L
AP4 Albert Pujols O
AP5 Albert Pujols U
AP6 Albert Pujols I
AP7 Albert Pujols S
BM1 Brett Myers 3
BM2 Brett Myers 9
DO1 David Ortiz R
DO2 David Ortiz E
DO3 David Ortiz D
DO4 David Ortiz S
DO5 David Ortiz O
DO6 David Ortiz X
JD1 Johnny Damon R
JD2 Johnny Damon E
JD3 Johnny Damon D
JD4 Johnny Damon S
JD5 Johnny Damon O
JD6 Johnny Damon X
JE1 Jim Edmonds C
JE2 Jim Edmonds T
JE3 Jim Edmonds L
JE4 Jim Edmonds O
JE5 Jim Edmonds U
JE6 Jim Edmonds I
JE7 Jim Edmonds S
MR1 Mariano Rivera N
MR2 Mariano Rivera E
MR3 Mariano Rivera W
MR4 Mariano Rivera Y
MR5 Mariano Rivera O
MR6 Mariano Rivera R
MR7 Mariano Rivera K
SR1 Scott Rolen S
SR2 Scott Rolen T
SR3 Scott Rolen L
SR4 Scott Rolen O
SR5 Scott Rolen U
SR6 Scott Rolen I
SR7 Scott Rolen S

2005 Topps Pristine Selective Swatch Logo Patch Relics

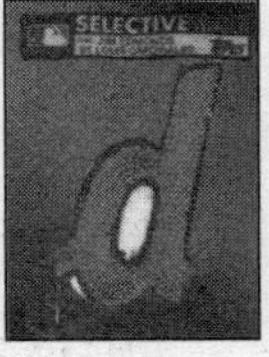

OVERALL SELECTIVE SWATCH ODDS 1:768
STATED PRINT RUN 1 SERIAL #'d SET
NO PRICING DUE TO SCARCITY

2005 Topps Pristine Legends

This 140-card set was released in August, 2005. The set was issued in eight-card hobby packs with an $30 SRP which came five packs per box and six boxes per case. The set was also issued in eight-card retail packs with an $30 SRP which came one pack per case. Cards numbered 1-100 feature common retired veterans. Cards numbered 101-125, which were inserted at a stated rate of four in five packs, feature players in college photos and were printed to a stated print run of 1999 serial numbered sets. Cards numbered 126 through 135 feature Negro League greats, were issued at a stated rate of one in seven, and were issued to a stated print run of 999 serial numbered sets. Cards numbered 136-140 feature players during their Little League days and were issued at a stated rate of one in 26. Those cards were issued to a stated print run of 499 serial numbered sets.

COMP. SET w/o SP's (100) 60.00 120.00
COMMON C (1-100) .60 1.50
COMMON U (101-125) 1.25 3.00
COMMON R (126-135) 1.50 4.00
COMMON S (136-140) 2.00 5.00
OVERALL PLATE ODDS 1:82 HOBBY
PLATE PRINT RUN 1 SET PER COLOR
BLACK-CYAN-MAGENTA-YELLOW ISSUED
NO PLATE PRICING DUE TO SCARCITY
1 Vida Blue C .60 1.50
2 Bert Blyleven C .60 1.50
3 Joe Carter C .60 1.50
4 Bill Buckner C .60 1.50
5 Luis Aparicio C .60 1.50
6 Ernie Banks C 1.25 3.00
7 Wade Boggs C .75 2.00
8 George Brett C 2.00 5.00
9 Lou Brock C .75 2.00
10 Rod Carew C .75 2.00
11 Gary Carter C .60 1.50
12 Andre Dawson C .60 1.50
13 Dennis Eckersley C .60 1.50
14 Rollie Fingers C .60 1.50
15 Steve Garvey C .60 1.50
16 Dwight Gooden C .60 1.50
17 Goose Gossage C .60 1.50
18 Ron Guidry C .60 1.50
19 Keith Hernandez C .60 1.50
20 Charlie Hough C .60 1.50
21 Bo Jackson C 1.25 3.00
22 Monte Irvin C .60 1.50
23 Reggie Jackson C .75 2.00
24 Ferguson Jenkins C .60 1.50
25 Ralph Kiner C .60 1.50
26 Juan Marichal C .60 1.50
27 Stan Musial C 1.50 4.00
28 Tony Oliva C .60 1.50
29 Jim Palmer C .60 1.50
30 Dave Parker C .60 1.50
31 Gaylord Perry C .60 1.50
32 Jimmy Piersall C .60 1.50
33 Johnny Podres C .60 1.50
34 Brooks Robinson C .75 2.00
35 Frank Robinson C .60 1.50
36 Nolan Ryan C 2.50 6.00
37 Tom Seaver C .75 2.00
38 Ozzie Smith C 1.50 4.00
39 Duke Snider C .75 2.00
40 Bobby Thomson C .60 1.50
41 Carl Yastrzemski C 1.25 3.00
42 Maury Wills C .60 1.50
43 Robin Yount C 1.25 3.00
44 Matt Williams C .75 2.00
45 Orel Hershiser C .60 1.50
46 Tim McCarver C .60 1.50
47 Don Newcombe C .60 1.50
48 Paul O'Neill C .75 2.00
49 Al Kaline C 1.25 3.00
50 Harmon Killebrew C 1.25 3.00
51 Dave Kingman C .60 1.50
52 Ken Griffey Sr. C .60 1.50
53 George Foster C .60 1.50
54 Mark Fidrych C .60 1.50
55 Orlando Cepeda C .60 1.50
56 Don Larsen C .60 1.50
57 Bill Madlock C .60 1.50
58 Dale Murphy C .75 2.00
59 Graig Nettles C .60 1.50
60 Phil Niekro C .60 1.50
61 Al Oliver C .60 1.50
62 Harold Reynolds C .60 1.50
63 Bobby Richardson C .75 2.00
64 Mike Scott C .60 1.50
65 Dave Stewart C .60 1.50
66 Rick Sutcliffe C .60 1.50
67 Bruce Sutter C .60 1.50
68 Luis Tiant C .60 1.50
69 Bob Watson C .60 1.50
70 Walt Weiss C .60 1.50
71 Don Zimmer C .60 1.50
72 Tommy John C .60 1.50
73 Ray Knight C .60 1.50
74 Jack Morris C .60 1.50
75 Mickey Rivers C .60 1.50
76 Lee Smith C .60 1.50
77 Darryl Strawberry C .60 1.50
78 Dave Justice C .75 2.00
79 Wally Joyner C .60 1.50
80 Jimmy Key C .60 1.50
81 John Kruk C .60 1.50
82 Greg Luzinski C .60 1.50
83 Mookie Wilson C .60 1.50
84 Wilbur Wood C .60 1.50
85 Tim Raines C .60 1.50
86 Jim Rice C .60 1.50
87 Tony Armas C .60 1.50
88 Harold Baines C .60 1.50
89 Bucky Dent C .60 1.50
90 Darrell Evans C .60 1.50
91 Cecil Fielder C .60 1.50
92 Jose Cruz C .60 1.50
93 Dave Concepcion C .60 1.50
94 Ron Cey C .60 1.50
95 Davey Lopes C .60 1.50
96 Boog Powell C .60 1.50
97 Buddy Bell C .60 1.50
98 George Bell C .60 1.50
99 Bert Campaneris C .60 1.50
100 Chet Lemon C .60 1.50
101 Bo Jackson U 3.00 8.00
102 Will Clark U 2.00 5.00
103 Cecil Fielder U 1.25 3.00
104 Ron Cey U 1.25 3.00
105 Tony Gwynn U 2.00 5.00
106 Orel Hershiser U 1.25 3.00
107 Jimmy Key U 1.25 3.00
108 Paul Molitor U 1.25 3.00
109 Pete Incaviglia U 1.25 3.00
110 Wally Joyner U 1.25 3.00
111 Dave Kingman U 1.25 3.00
112 Ron Guidry U 1.25 3.00
113 Ron Darling U 1.25 3.00
114 Mookie Wilson U 1.25 3.00
115 Reggie Jackson U 2.00 5.00
116 Walt Weiss U 1.25 3.00
117 Joe Carter U 1.25 3.00
118 Cory Snyder U 1.25 3.00
119 Dave Winfield U 1.25 3.00
120 Terry Steinbach U 1.25 3.00
121 Matt Williams U 2.00 5.00
122 Ozzie Smith U 2.50 6.00
123 Jack McDowell U 1.25 3.00
124 Bob Horner U 1.25 3.00
125 Don Kessinger U 1.25 3.00
126 Minnie Minoso R 1.50 4.00
127 Josh Gibson R 2.50 6.00
128 Buck O'Neil R 1.50 4.00
129 Monte Irvin R 1.50 4.00
130 Jim Gilliam R 1.50 4.00
131 Josh Gibson R 2.50 6.00
132 Ernie Banks R 3.00 8.00
133 Don Newcombe R 1.50 4.00
134 Josh Gibson R 2.50 6.00
135 Josh Gibson R 2.50 6.00
136 Gary Carter S 2.00 5.00
137 Bo Jackson S 4.00 10.00
138 George Brett S 6.00 15.00
139 Joe Carter S 2.00 5.00
140 Nolan Ryan S 6.00 15.00

2005 Topps Pristine Legends Refractors

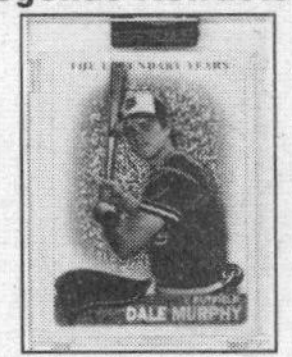

*REF 1-100: 1X TO 2.5X BASIC
1-100 ONE PER PACK
1-100 PRINT RUN 549 SERIAL #'d SETS
*REF 101-125: 1X TO 2.5X BASIC
101-125 ODDS 1:13 HOBBY/RETAIL
101-125 PRINT RUN 199 SERIAL #'d SETS
*REF 126-135: 1X TO 2.5X BASIC
126-135 ODDS 1:64 HOBBY/RETAIL
126-135 PRINT RUN 99 SERIAL #'d SETS
136-140 ODDS 1:514 HOBBY, 1:480 RETAIL
136-140 PRINT RUN 25 SERIAL #'d SETS
136-140 NO PRICING DUE TO SCARCITY

2005 Topps Pristine Legends Gold Die Cut Refractors

*GOLD DC 1-100: 2X TO 5X BASIC
*GOLD DC 101-125: 1.25X TO 3X BASIC
*GOLD DC 126-135: 1X TO 2.5X BASIC
*GOLD DC 136-140: .6X TO 1.5X BASIC
ONE PER SEALED HOBBY BOX
STATED PRINT RUN 65 SERIAL #'d SETS
8 George Brett C 15.00 40.00
21 Bo Jackson C 10.00 25.00
36 Nolan Ryan C 15.00 40.00
127 Josh Gibson R 10.00 25.00
131 Josh Gibson R 10.00 25.00
132 Ernie Banks R 10.00 25.00
134 Josh Gibson R 10.00 25.00
135 Josh Gibson R 10.00 25.00
137 Bo Jackson S 10.00 25.00
138 George Brett S 15.00 40.00
140 Nolan Ryan S 15.00 40.00

2005 Topps Pristine Legends SuperFractors

STATED ODDS 1:455 HOBBY, 1:480 RETAIL
STATED PRINT RUN 1 SERIAL #'d SET
NO PRICING DUE TO SCARCITY

2005 Topps Pristine Legends Celebrity Threads

STATED ODDS 1:18 HOBBY/RETAIL
REFRACTOR ODDS 1:1284 H, 1:1440 R
REF PRINT RUN 25 SERIAL #'d SETS
NO REF PRICING DUE TO SCARCITY
EP Elvis Presley Shirt 30.00 60.00
MM Marilyn Monroe Dress 40.00 80.00

2005 Topps Pristine Legends Leading Indicators Relics

GROUP A ODDS 1:210 HOBBY/RETAIL
GROUP B ODDS 1:71 HOBBY/RETAIL
GROUP C ODDS 1:7 HOBBY/RETAIL
GROUP D ODDS 1:20 HOBBY/RETAIL
GROUP E ODDS 1:8 HOBBY/RETAIL
GROUP A PRINT RUN 99 SERIAL #'d SETS
REF GROUP A ODDS 1:14,550 HOBBY
REF GROUP B ODDS 1:111 HOBBY/RETAIL
REF A PRINT RUN 1 SERIAL #'d SET
REF B PRINT RUN 25 SERIAL #'d SETS
NO REF PRICING DUE TO SCARCITY
AD Andre Dawson Bat C 3.00 8.00
AK Al Kaline Bat C 4.00 10.00
BF Bob Feller Uni D 4.00 10.00
CF Cecil Fielder Bat C 3.00 8.00
CY Carl Yastrzemski Bat C 6.00 15.00
DBM Dale Murphy Bat C 4.00 10.00
DK Dave Kingman Bat C 3.00 8.00
DM Don Mattingly Bat D 6.00 15.00
DP Dave Parker Bat E 3.00 8.00
DS Darryl Strawberry Bat C 3.00 8.00
GF George Foster Bat C 3.00 8.00
GP Gaylord Perry Jsy E 3.00 8.00
JR Jim Rice Bat B 3.00 8.00
LB Lou Brock Bat A/99 6.00 15.00
MS Mike Scott Jsy E 3.00 8.00
MW Maury Wills Bat A/99 4.00 10.00
NR Nolan Ryan Jsy C 6.00 15.00
PO Paul O'Neill Bat E 4.00 10.00
RC Rod Carew Bat C 4.00 10.00
RM Roger Maris Bat B 15.00 40.00
TG Tony Gwynn Jsy E 4.00 10.00
TO Tony Oliva Bat D 3.00 8.00
TR Tim Raines Uni C 3.00 8.00
TR2 Tim Raines Bat C 3.00 8.00
TS Tom Seaver Jsy A/99 6.00 15.00
WB Wade Boggs Bat E 4.00 10.00

2005 Topps Pristine Legends Personal Endorsements

GROUP A ODDS 1:40 HOBBY/RETAIL
GROUP B ODDS 1:16 HOBBY/RETAIL
GROUP C ODDS 1:9 HOBBY/RETAIL
GOLD ODDS 1:85 HOBBY/RETAIL
GOLD PRINT RUN 25 SERIAL #'d SETS
NO GOLD PRICING DUE TO SCARCITY
AD Andre Dawson A 6.00 15.00
AK Al Kaline A 15.00 40.00
BB Bert Blyleven B 4.00 10.00
BG Bobby Grich C 4.00 10.00
BJ Bo Jackson A 30.00 60.00
BR Brooks Robinson A 10.00 25.00
CF Carlton Fisk A 10.00 25.00

CR Cal Ripken A 60.00 120.00
CY Carl Yastrzemski A 20.00 50.00
DE Dennis Eckersley A 6.00 15.00
DL Don Larsen B 4.00 10.00
DS Duke Snider A 15.00 40.00
DWE Darrell Evans C 4.00 10.00
EW Earl Weaver C 4.00 10.00
GB George Brett A 30.00 60.00
GC Gary Carter B 4.00 10.00
GF George Foster C 4.00 10.00
GG Goose Gossage B 10.00 25.00
GN Graig Nettles B 4.00 10.00
JA Jim Abbott C 4.00 10.00
JAP Jimmy Piersall B 6.00 15.00
JM Jack McDowell C 4.00 10.00
JO Jesse Orosco C 4.00 10.00
JP Jim Palmer A 6.00 15.00
KH Keith Hernandez A 6.00 15.00
LA Luis Aparicio B 6.00 15.00
NR Nolan Ryan A 50.00 100.00
RD Ron Darling B 4.00 10.00
RJ Reggie Jackson A 15.00 40.00
RY Robin Yount A 15.00 40.00
SM Stan Musial A 20.00 50.00

2005 Topps Pristine Legends Signature Marks

STATED ODDS 1:4850 HOBBY
STATED PRINT RUN 1 SERIAL #'d SET
NO PRICING DUE TO SCARCITY
AA Arthur Ashe
BH Ben Hogan
EP Elvis Presley
JD Jack Dempsey
JL Joe Louis
JO Jesse Owens
MM Marilyn Monroe
MS Mark Spitz
RM Rocky Marciano
RR Sugar Ray Robinson

2005 Topps Pristine Legends Title Threads Relics

GROUP A ODDS 1:66 HOBBY/RETAIL
GROUP B ODDS 1:9 HOBBY/RETAIL
GROUP C ODDS 1:6 HOBBY/RETAIL
REFRACTOR ODDS 1:111 HOBBY/RETAIL
REF PRINT RUN 25 SERIAL #'d SETS
NO REF PRICING DUE TO SCARCITY
BD Bucky Dent Uni B 3.00 8.00
CS Cesar Geronimo Bat C 3.00 8.00
DJ Dave Justice Uni A 4.00 10.00
DS Darryl Strawberry Bat B 3.00 8.00
EK Ed Kranepool Uni C 3.00 8.00
GC Gary Carter Bat C 3.00 8.00
GF George Foster Bat B 3.00 8.00
GG Goose Gossage Uni C 3.00 8.00
GN Graig Nettles Uni C 3.00 8.00
JC Joe Carter Bat B 3.00 8.00
JK Jimmy Key Uni C 3.00 8.00
JP Jim Palmer Uni B 3.00 8.00
KG Ken Griffey Sr. Bat B 3.00 8.00
LD Len Dykstra Bat B 3.00 8.00
MI Monte Irvin Bat B 3.00 8.00
MW Mookie Wilson Uni B 3.00 8.00
OC Orlando Cepeda Jsy C 3.00 8.00
OH Orel Hershiser Jsy A 3.00 8.00
PO Paul O'Neill Uni C 3.00 8.00
RF Rollie Fingers Uni C 3.00 8.00
TM Tim McCarver Uni C 3.00 8.00
WB Wade Boggs Uni C 4.00 10.00
WH Willie Horton Jsy B 3.00 8.00

2005 Topps Pristine Legends Valuable Performance Relics

GROUP A ODDS 1:7275 HOBBY
GROUP B ODDS 1:6 HOBBY/RETAIL
GROUP C ODDS 1:12 HOBBY/RETAIL
GROUP A PRINT RUN 9 SERIAL #'d CARDS
NO GROUP A PRICING DUE TO SCARCITY
REF GROUP A ODDS 1:43,650 HOBBY
REF GROUP B ODDS 1:128 H, 1:125 R
REF A PRINT RUN 1 SERIAL #'d SET
REF B PRINT RUN 25 SERIAL #'d SETS
NO REF PRICING DUE TO SCARCITY
AD Andre Dawson Uni C 3.00 8.00
CF Cecil Fielder Bat B 3.00 8.00
CR Cal Ripken Bat B 8.00 20.00
CY Carl Yastrzemski Bat B 4.00 10.00
DBM Don Mattingly Uni C 6.00 15.00
DE Dennis Eckersley Jsy C 3.00 8.00
DM Dale Murphy Bat B 4.00 10.00
DP Dave Parker Uni C 3.00 8.00
FR Frank Robinson Bat B 3.00 8.00
HK Harmon Killebrew Bat B 4.00 10.00
JC Jose Canseco Bat B 4.00 10.00
JM Joe Morgan Bat B 3.00 8.00
JR Jim Rice Bat B 3.00 8.00
KH Keith Hernandez Bat B 3.00 8.00
MS Mike Schmidt Bat C 6.00 15.00
RC Roberto Clemente Bat A/9
RJ Reggie Jackson Bat B 4.00 10.00
RY Robin Yount Bat B 4.00 10.00
SG Steve Garvey Bat B 3.00 8.00
SM Stan Musial Bat B 6.00 15.00
YB Yogi Berra Bat B 4.00 10.00

2003 Topps Retired Signature

This 110-card set was released in July, 2003. The set was issued in five card packs with an $30 SRP which came five packs to a box and six boxes to a case.

COMPLETE SET (110) 100.00 200.00
1 Willie Mays 2.50 6.00
2 Tony Perez .50 1.25
3 Tom Seaver .75 2.00
4 Johnny Bench 1.25 3.00
5 Rod Carew .75 2.00
6 Red Schoendienst .50 1.25
7 Phil Rizzuto .75 2.00
8 Ozzie Smith 2.00 5.00
9 Maury Wills .50 1.25
10 Hank Aaron 2.50 6.00
11 Jim Palmer .50 1.25
12 Jose Cruz Sr. .50 1.25
13 Dave Parker .50 1.25
14 Don Sutton .50 1.25
15 Brooks Robinson .75 2.00
16 Bo Jackson 1.25 3.00
17 Andre Dawson .50 1.25
18 Fergie Jenkins .50 1.25
19 George Foster .50 1.25
20 George Brett 2.50 6.00
21 Jerry Koosman .50 1.25
22 John Kruk .50 1.25
23 Kent Tekulve .50 1.25
24 Lee Smith .50 1.25
25 Nolan Ryan 3.00 8.00
26 Paul O'Neill .50 1.25
27 Rich Gossage .50 1.25
28 Ron Santo .50 1.25
29 Tom Lasorda .50 1.25
30 Tony Gwynn 1.50 4.00
31 Vida Blue .50 1.25
32 Whitey Herzog .50 1.25
33 Willie McGee .50 1.25
34 Bill Mazeroski .50 1.25
35 Al Kaline 1.25 3.00
36 Bobby Richardson .50 1.25
37 Carlton Fisk .75 2.00
38 Darrell Evans .50 1.25
39 Dave Concepcion .50 1.25
40 Cal Ripken 4.00 10.00
41 Dwight Evans .75 2.00
42 Earl Weaver .50 1.25
43 Fred Lynn .50 1.25
44 Greg Luzinski .50 1.25
45 Duke Snider .75 2.00
46 Hank Bauer .50 1.25
47 Jim Rice .50 1.25
48 Johnny Sain .50 1.25
49 Lenny Dykstra .50 1.25
50 Mike Schmidt 2.50 6.00
51 Orlando Cepeda .50 1.25
52 Ralph Kiner .50 1.25
53 Robin Roberts .50 1.25
54 Ron Guidry .50 1.25
55 Steve Garvey .50 1.25
56 Tony Oliva .50 1.25
57 Whitey Ford .75 2.00
58 Willie McCovey .50 1.25
59 Phil Niekro .50 1.25
60 Stan Musial 2.00 5.00
61 Rollie Fingers .50 1.25
62 Robin Yount 1.25 3.00
63 Alan Trammell .50 1.25
64 Bill Buckner .50 1.25
65 Bob Feller .50 1.25
66 Bruce Sutter .50 1.25
67 Dale Murphy .75 2.00
68 Dennis Eckersley .50 1.25
69 Don Newcombe .50 1.25
70 Don Mattingly 2.50 6.00
71 Dwight Gooden .50 1.25
72 Frank Robinson .75 2.00
73 Gary Carter .50 1.25
74 Graig Nettles .50 1.25
75 Harmon Killebrew 1.25 3.00
76 Jim Bunning .50 1.25
77 Joe Morgan .50 1.25
78 Joe Rudi .50 1.25
79 Jose Canseco .75 2.00
80 Ernie Banks 1.25 3.00
81 Luis Aparicio .50 1.25
82 Luis Tiant .50 1.25
83 Mark Fidrych .50 1.25
84 Kirk Gibson .50 1.25
85 Lou Brock .75 2.00
86 Juan Marichal .50 1.25
87 Monte Irvin .50 1.25
88 Paul Molitor .50 1.25
89 Tommy John .50 1.25
90 Warren Spahn .75 2.00
91 Wade Boggs .75 2.00
92 Reggie Jackson .75 2.00
93 Kirby Puckett 1.25 3.00
94 Boog Powell .75 2.00
95 Carl Yastrzemski 2.00 5.00
96 Bobby Thomson .50 1.25
97 Bill Skowron .50 1.25
98 Bill Madlock .50 1.25
99 Sparky Anderson .50 1.25
100 Yogi Berra 1.25 3.00
101 Bobby Boerr .50 1.25
102 Gaylord Perry .50 1.25
103 George Kell .50 1.25
104 Harold Reynolds .50 1.25
105 Joe Carter .50 1.25
106 Johnny Podres .50 1.25
107 Ron Cey .50 1.25
*108 Tim McCarver .50 1.25
109 Tug McGraw .50 1.25
110 Don Larsen .50 1.25

2003 Topps Retired Signature Black

*BLACK: 2.5X TO 6X BASIC
STATED ODDS 1:8
STATED PRINT RUN 99 SERIAL #'d SETS

2003 Topps Retired Signature Autographs

Inserted at a stated rate of one per pack, these 120 cards feature signatures from some of the most famous retired players. The cards were signed in different ratios and we have notated the insert odds as well as what group the player belonged to in our checklist.

ONE AUTOGRAPH PER PACK
A-B PRINT RUNS PROVIDED BY TOPPS
GROUPS A-B ARE NOT SERIAL-NUMBERED
NO GROUP A PRICING DUE TO SCARCITY
AD Andre Dawson D 10.00 25.00
AK Al Kaline C 40.00 80.00
AT Alan Trammell E 6.00 15.00
BB Bert Blyleven F 6.00 15.00
BBU Bill Buckner C 12.50 30.00
BD Bobby Doerr C 20.00 50.00
BF Bob Feller F 10.00 25.00
BGR Bobby Grich C 12.50 30.00
BH Bob Horner C 20.00 50.00
BJ Bo Jackson C 50.00 100.00
BM Bill Madlock G 4.00 10.00
BMA Bill Mazeroski C 30.00 60.00
BP Boog Powell G 6.00 15.00
BR Bobby Richardson G 6.00 15.00
BRO Brooks Robinson B/75 125.00 200.00
BS Bill Skowron G 6.00 15.00
BSA Bret Saberhagen C 20.00 50.00
BSU Bruce Sutter E 10.00 25.00
BT Bobby Thomson D 10.00 25.00
BW Bob Watson C 12.50 30.00
CF Carlton Fisk C 30.00 60.00
CR Cal Ripken A/25
CY Carl Yastrzemski C 60.00 120.00
DE Darrell Evans F 4.00 10.00
DEC Dennis Eckersley C 20.00 50.00
DEV Dwight Evans B/78 125.00 200.00
DG Dwight Gooden C 20.00 50.00
DL Don Larsen G 6.00 15.00
DM Dale Murphy C 30.00 60.00
DN Don Newcombe C 12.50 30.00
DON Don Mattingly B/81 125.00 250.00
DP Dave Parker C 20.00 50.00
DS Dave Stieb C 20.00 50.00
DSN Duke Snider B/75 125.00 200.00
DSU Don Sutton C 20.00 50.00
EB Ernie Banks A/24
EW Earl Weaver G 4.00 10.00
FJ Fergie Jenkins D 10.00 25.00
FL Fred Lynn C 20.00 50.00
FR Frank Robinson C 30.00 60.00
GB George Brett A/25
GC Gary Carter B/77 90.00 150.00
GF George Foster G 6.00 15.00
GK George Kell C 20.00 50.00
GL Greg Luzinski D 10.00 25.00
GN Graig Nettles G 6.00 15.00
GP Gaylord Perry C 12.50 30.00
HA Hank Aaron A/30
HB Harold Baines F 6.00 15.00
HBA Hank Bauer C 20.00 50.00
HK Harmon Killebrew B/76 125.00 200.00
HR Harold Reynolds C 12.50 30.00
JA Jim Abbott E 6.00 15.00
JB Jim Bunning B/76 125.00 200.00
JBE Johnny Bench C 40.00 80.00
JC Joe Carter C 20.00 50.00
JCA Jose Canseco C 30.00 60.00
JCR Jose Cruz Sr. D 6.00 15.00
JK Jerry Koosman C 12.50 30.00
JKR John Kruk C 20.00 50.00
JM Joe Morgan C 20.00 50.00
JMA Juan Marichal C 15.00 40.00
JP Jim Palmer C 30.00 60.00
JPI Jim Piersall G 6.00 15.00
JPO Johnny Podres G 6.00 15.00
JR Jim Rice C 15.00 40.00
JRU Joe Rudi F 4.00 10.00
KG Kirk Gibson C 20.00 50.00
KGR Ken Griffey Sr. C 20.00 50.00
KP Kirby Puckett B/75
KT Kent Tekulve C 12.50 30.00
LA Luis Aparicio G 6.00 15.00
LB Lou Brock B/76 60.00 120.00
LD Lenny Dykstra D 10.00 25.00
LP Lance Parrish G 6.00 15.00
LS Lee Smith E 6.00 15.00
LT Luis Tiant G 4.00 10.00
MF Mark Fidrych D 10.00 25.00
MI Monte Irvin C 30.00 60.00
MS Mike Schmidt B/83 150.00 250.00
MW Maury Wills F 6.00 15.00
NR Nolan Ryan B/77 200.00 300.00
OC Orlando Cepeda B/75 125.00 200.00
OS Ozzie Smith C 50.00 100.00
PM Paul Molitor C 20.00 50.00
PN Phil Niekro D 10.00 25.00
PO Paul O'Neill C 30.00 60.00
PR Phil Rizzuto B/77 125.00 200.00
RCA Rod Carew C 30.00 60.00
RCE Ron Cey F 4.00 10.00
RF Rollie Fingers C 20.00 50.00
RG Rich Gossage C 12.50 30.00
RGU Ron Guidry D 15.00 40.00
RJ Reggie Jackson C 50.00 100.00
RK Ralph Kiner B/80 125.00 200.00
RR Robin Roberts C 20.00 50.00
RS Red Schoendienst B/83 125.00 200.00
RSA Ron Santo G 10.00 25.00
RY Robin Yount A/25
SA Sparky Anderson C 12.50 30.00
SG Steve Garvey D 10.00 25.00
SM Stan Musial A/28
TG Tony Gwynn A/25
TJ Tommy John C 12.50 30.00
TL Tom Lasorda B/76 90.00 150.00
TM Tim McCarver C 20.00 50.00
TMC Tug McGraw D 20.00 50.00
TO Tony Oliva C 20.00 50.00
TP Tony Perez C 15.00 40.00
TPE Terry Pendleton D 6.00 15.00
TS Tom Seaver C 40.00 80.00
VB Vida Blue E 4.00 10.00
WB Wade Boggs B/77 125.00 200.00
WF Whitey Ford C 30.00 60.00
WH Whitey Herzog D 6.00 15.00
WM Willie Mays A/25
WMC Willie McCovey C 30.00 60.00
WMG Willie McGee D 10.00 25.00
WS Warren Spahn F 20.00 50.00
YB Yogi Berra A/25

2003 Topps Retired Signature Autographs Refractors

STATED ODDS 1:27
STATED PRINT RUN 25 SERIAL #'d SETS
NO PRICING DUE TO SCARCITY

2004 Topps Retired Signature

This 110-card set was released in September, 2004. The set was issued in four card packs (of which one card was autographed) with an $30 SRP which came five packs to a box and six boxes to a case.

COMPLETE SET (110) 100.00 200.00
1 Willie Mays 2.50 6.00
2 Tony Gwynn 2.00 5.00
3 Dale Murphy .75 2.00
4 Lenny Dykstra .50 1.25
5 Johnny Bench 1.25 3.00
6 Bill Buckner .50 1.25
7 Ferguson Jenkins .50 1.25
8 George Brett 2.50 6.00
9 Ralph Kiner .75 2.00
10 Ernie Banks 1.25 3.00
11 Hal McRae .50 1.25
12 Lou Brock .75 2.00
13 Keith Hernandez .50 1.25
14 Jose Canseco .75 2.00
15 Whitey Ford .75 2.00
16 Dave Kingman .50 1.25
17 Tim Raines .40 1.00
18 Paul O'Neill .75 2.00
19 Lou Whitaker .50 1.25
20 Mike Schmidt 2.50 6.00
21 Wally Joyner .40 1.00
22 Kirk Gibson .50 1.25
23 Ryne Sandberg 2.50 6.00
24 Luis Tiant .50 1.25
25 Al Kaline 1.25 3.00
26 Brooks Robinson .75 2.00
27 Don Zimmer .50 1.25
28 Nolan Ryan 3.00 8.00
29 Maury Wills .50 1.25
30 Stan Musial 2.00 5.00
31 Garry Maddox .40 1.00
32 Tom Brunansky .40 1.00
33 Don Mattingly 2.50 6.00
34 Earl Weaver .50 1.25
35 Bobby Grich .50 1.25
36 Orlando Cepeda .50 1.25
37 Alan Trammell .50 1.25
38 Al Hrabosky .40 1.00
39 Dave Lopes .40 1.00
40 Rod Carew .75 2.00
41 Robin Yount 1.25 3.00
42 Dwight Gooden .50 1.25
43 Andre Dawson .50 1.25
44 Hank Aaron 2.50 6.00
45 Norm Cash .75 2.00
46 Reggie Jackson .75 2.00
47 Jim Rice .50 1.25
48 Carlton Fisk .75 2.00
49 Dave Parker .50 1.25
50 Cal Ripken 4.00 10.00
51 Roy Face .40 1.00
52 Bob Gibson .75 2.00
53 Jimmy Key .50 1.25
54 Al Oliver .40 1.00
55 Don Larsen .50 1.25
56 Tom Seaver .75 2.00
57 Tony Armas .40 1.00
58 Dave Stieb .50 1.25
59 Will Clark .75 2.00
60 Duke Snider .75 2.00
61 Cesar Geronimo .40 1.00
62 Ron Kittle .40 1.00
63 Ron Santo .75 2.00
64 Mickey Rivers .40 1.00
65 Jim Piersall .50 1.25
66 Ron Swoboda .50 1.25
67 Kent Hrbek .50 1.25
68 Dennis Eckersley .75 2.00
69 Greg Luzinski .50 1.25
70 Harmon Killebrew 1.25 3.00
71 Ron Guidry .50 1.25
72 Steve Garvey .50 1.25
73 Andy Van Slyke .75 2.00
74 Goose Gossage .50 1.25
75 Ozzie Smith 2.00 5.00
76 Richie Allen .50 1.25
77 Vida Blue .40 1.00
78 Tony Oliva .50 1.25
79 Darryl Strawberry .50 1.25
80 Frank Robinson .50 1.25
81 Bruce Sutter .50 1.25
82 Dave Concepcion .50 1.25
83 Darrell Evans .40 1.00
84 Jack Morris .50 1.25
85 Bo Jackson 1.25 3.00
86 Orel Hershiser .50 1.25
87 Rob Dibble .40 1.00
88 Wade Boggs .75 2.00
89 Fernando Valenzuela .50 1.25
90 Jim Palmer .50 1.25
91 George Foster .50 1.25
92 Mike Scott .40 1.00
93 Paul Molitor .50 1.25
94 Gary Carter .50 1.25
95 Bobby Richardson .50 1.25
96 Rollie Fingers .50 1.25
97 Tim McCarver .50 1.25
98 John Candelaria .40 1.00
99 Dave Winfield .50 1.25
100 Yogi Berra 1.25 3.00
101 Bill Madlock .50 1.25
102 Jack McDowell .40 1.00
103 Luis Aparicio .50 1.25
104 Graig Nettles .50 1.25
105 Dave Stewart .50 1.25
106 Darren Daulton .50 1.25
107 Gary Gaetti .50 1.25
108 Tony Fernandez .40 1.00
109 Buddy Bell .40 1.00
110 Carl Yastrzemski 2.00 5.00

2004 Topps Retired Signature Black

*BLACK: 2.5X TO 6X BASIC
STATED ODDS 1:7
STATED PRINT RUN 99 SERIAL #'d SETS

2004 Topps Retired Signature Autographs

GROUP A ODDS 1:675
GROUP B ODDS 1:338
GROUP C ODDS 1:82
GROUP D ODDS 1:25
GROUP E ODDS 1:8
GROUP F ODDS 1:46
GROUP G ODDS 1:2
GROUP H ODDS 1:33
GROUP A PRINT RUN 25 SETS
GROUP B PRINT RUN 50 SETS
GROUP C PRINT RUN 75 SETS
GROUP A-C ARE NOT SERIAL-NUMBERED
A-C PRINT RUNS PROVIDED BY TOPPS
OVERALL PRESS PLATE ODDS 1:222
PLATE PRINT RUN 1 SET PER COLOR
BLACK-CYAN-MAGENTA-YELLOW ISSUED
NO PLATE PRICING DUE TO SCARCITY
AH Al Hrabosky E 4.00 10.00
AO Al Oliver G 6.00 15.00
AT Alan Trammell E 6.00 15.00
BB Bill Buckner G 6.00 15.00
BBE Buddy Bell E 6.00 15.00
BD Bucky Dent E 6.00 15.00
BG Bob Gibson C 60.00 120.00
BGR Bobby Grich G 4.00 10.00
BM Bill Madlock G 4.00 10.00
BR Bobby Richardson G 6.00 15.00
BRO Brooks Robinson C 75.00 150.00
BS Bruce Sutter G 10.00 25.00
CF Carlton Fisk D 20.00 50.00
CG Cesar Geronimo E 6.00 15.00
CR Cal Ripken A 300.00 500.00
CY Carl Yastrzemski A 175.00 300.00
DD Darren Daulton G 4.00 10.00
DE Darrell Evans G 4.00 10.00
DEC Dennis Eckersley E 10.00 25.00
DG Dwight Gooden C 60.00 120.00
DL Davey Lopes F 4.00 10.00
DM Don Mattingly C 125.00 200.00
DMU Dale Murphy G 10.00 25.00
DP Dave Parker E 6.00 15.00
DS Darryl Strawberry D 20.00 50.00
DSN Duke Snider B 125.00 200.00
DST Dave Stieb G 4.00 10.00
DZ Don Zimmer D 15.00 40.00
EB Ernie Banks B 125.00 200.00
EW Earl Weaver G 6.00 15.00
FJ Ferguson Jenkins G 6.00 15.00
FR Frank Robinson D 30.00 60.00
GC Gary Carter D 20.00 50.00
GF George Foster E 4.00 10.00
GG Goose Gossage E 6.00 15.00
GL Greg Luzinski E 4.00 10.00
GN Graig Nettles G 6.00 15.00
HA Hank Aaron B 200.00 350.00
JB Johnny Bench C 100.00 175.00
JC John Candelaria D 10.00 25.00
JCA Jose Canseco D 20.00 50.00
JK Jimmy Key G 4.00 10.00
JM Jack McDowell G 4.00 10.00
JP Jim Piersall E 4.00 10.00
KG Kirk Gibson E 6.00 15.00
LT Luis Tiant G 4.00 10.00
MS Mike Schmidt C 125.00 200.00
MW Maury Wills G 4.00 10.00
NR Nolan Ryan A 250.00 400.00
OC Orlando Cepeda G 6.00 15.00
OH Orel Hershiser E 6.00 15.00
OS Ozzie Smith C 60.00 120.00
PM Paul Molitor D 15.00 40.00
PO Paul O'Neill D 20.00 50.00
RC Rod Carew E 15.00 40.00
RD Rob Dibble E 4.00 10.00
RF Rollie Fingers E 6.00 15.00
RFA Roy Face H 6.00 15.00
RK Ralph Kiner D 20.00 50.00
RKI Ron Kittle G 4.00 10.00
RS Ron Swoboda G 4.00 10.00
RSA Ryne Sandberg D 40.00 80.00
RSN Ron Santo G 10.00 25.00
RY Robin Yount A 175.00 300.00
SM Stan Musial B 150.00 250.00
TA Tony Armas G 4.00 10.00
TB Tom Brunansky G 4.00 10.00
TF Tony Fernandez E 6.00 15.00
TG Tony Gwynn C 60.00 120.00
TO Tony Oliva E 10.00 25.00
TS Tom Seaver C 75.00 150.00
VB Vida Blue G 4.00 10.00
WB Wade Boggs D 40.00 80.00
WF Whitey Ford C 60.00 120.00
WJ Wally Joyner G 4.00 10.00
YB Yogi Berra C 125.00 200.00

2004 Topps Retired Signature Autographs Refractors

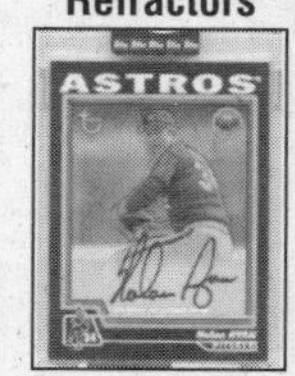

STATED ODDS 1:36
STATED PRINT RUN 25 SERIAL #'d SETS
AH Al Hrabosky 30.00 60.00
AO Al Oliver 40.00 80.00
AT Alan Trammell 40.00 80.00
BB Bill Buckner 40.00 80.00
BBE Buddy Bell 30.00 60.00
BD Bucky Dent 30.00 60.00
BG Bob Gibson 60.00 120.00
BGR Bobby Grich 30.00 60.00
BM Bill Madlock 30.00 60.00
BR Bobby Richardson 40.00 80.00
BRO Brooks Robinson 60.00 120.00
BS Bruce Sutter 60.00 120.00
CF Carlton Fisk 60.00 120.00
CG Cesar Geronimo 40.00 80.00
CR Cal Ripken 300.00 500.00
CY Carl Yastrzemski 150.00 250.00
DD Darren Daulton 30.00 60.00
DE Darrell Evans 30.00 60.00
DEC Dennis Eckersley 40.00 80.00
DG Dwight Gooden 40.00 80.00
DL Davey Lopes 30.00 60.00
DM Don Mattingly 175.00 300.00
DMU Dale Murphy 60.00 120.00
DP Dave Parker 40.00 80.00
DS Darryl Strawberry 40.00 80.00
DSN Duke Snider 60.00 120.00
DST Dave Stieb 40.00 80.00
DZ Don Zimmer 40.00 80.00
EB Ernie Banks 150.00 250.00
EW Earl Weaver 30.00 60.00
FJ Ferguson Jenkins 40.00 80.00
FR Frank Robinson 60.00 120.00
GC Gary Carter 60.00 120.00
GF George Foster 30.00 60.00
GG Goose Gossage 40.00 80.00
GL Greg Luzinski 30.00 60.00
GN Graig Nettles 40.00 80.00
HA Hank Aaron 350.00 600.00
JB Johnny Bench 75.00 150.00
JC John Candelaria 40.00 80.00
JCA Jose Canseco 60.00 120.00
JK Jimmy Key 40.00 80.00
JM Jack McDowell 30.00 60.00
JP Jim Piersall 30.00 60.00
KG Kirk Gibson 40.00 80.00
LT Luis Tiant 30.00 60.00
MS Mike Schmidt 175.00 300.00
MW Maury Wills 40.00 80.00
NR Nolan Ryan 300.00 500.00
OC Orlando Cepeda 60.00 120.00
OH Orel Hershiser 40.00 80.00
OS Ozzie Smith 125.00 200.00
PM Paul Molitor 40.00 80.00
PO Paul O'Neill 40.00 80.00

RC Rod Carew 60.00 120.00
RD Rob Dibble 30.00 60.00
RF Rollie Fingers 40.00 80.00
RFA Roy Face 40.00 80.00
RK Ralph Kiner 40.00 80.00
RKI Ron Kittle 30.00 60.00
RS Ron Swoboda 40.00 80.00
RSA Ryne Sandberg 125.00 200.00
RSN Ron Santo 60.00 120.00
RY Robin Yount 150.00 250.00
SM Stan Musial 200.00 350.00
TA Tony Armas 30.00 60.00
TB Tom Brunansky 30.00 60.00
TF Tony Fernandez 30.00 60.00
TG Tony Gwynn 125.00 200.00
TO Tony Oliva 30.00 60.00
TS Tom Seaver 75.00 150.00
VB Vida Blue 30.00 60.00
WB Wade Boggs 75.00 150.00
WF Whitey Ford 75.00 150.00
WJ Wally Joyner 30.00 60.00
YB Yogi Berra 75.00 150.00

2004 Topps Retired Signature Co-Signers

STATED ODDS 1:675
STATED PRINT RUN 25 SERIAL #'d SETS
NO PRICING DUE TO SCARCITY
MAA Willie Mays
Hank Aaron
MBA Willie Mays
Ernie Banks
MMU Willie Mays
Stan Musial
MSN Willie Mays
Duke Snider

2005 Topps Retired Signature

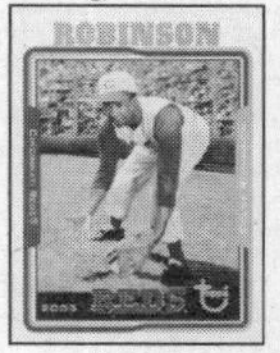

This 110-card set was released in September, 2005. The set was issued in four-card packs (of which one card was an autograph), with an $30 SRP which came five packs to a box and six boxes to a case.

PLATE ODDS 1:126 HOBBY, 1:127 RETAIL
PLATE PRINT RUN 1 SET PER COLOR
BLACK-CYAN-MAGENTA-YELLOW ISSUED
NO PLATE PRICING DUE TO SCARCITY
1 Josh Gibson 2.00 5.00
2 Andre Dawson .75 2.00
3 Al Kaline 2.00 5.00
4 Andy Van Slyke 1.25 3.00
5 Brett Butler .75 2.00
6 Bob Gibson 1.25 3.00
7 Bo Jackson 2.00 5.00
8 Carlton Fisk 1.25 3.00
9 Chuck Knoblauch .75 2.00
10 Cal Ripken 6.00 15.00
11 Carl Yastrzemski 2.50 6.00
12 Tom Niedenfuer .75 2.00
13 Dennis Eckersley .75 2.00
14 Darryl Strawberry .75 2.00
15 Dwight Gooden .75 2.00
16 Davey Johnson .75 2.00
17 Don Mattingly 4.00 10.00
18 Dave Winfield .75 2.00
19 Don Zimmer .75 2.00
20 Ernie Banks 2.00 5.00
21 George Brett 4.00 10.00
22 Gary Carter .75 2.00
23 Gregg Jefferies .75 2.00
24 Harold Baines .75 2.00
25 Ryne Sandberg 4.00 10.00
26 Howard Johnson .75 2.00
27 Jim Abbott .75 2.00
28 Johnny Bench 2.00 5.00
29 Jay Buhner .75 2.00
30 Johnny Podres .75 2.00
31 Jose Canseco 1.25 3.00
32 Keith Hernandez .75 2.00
33 Lou Brock Cubs 2.00 5.00
34 Lou Whitaker .75 2.00
35 Mark Fidrych .75 2.00
36 Orlando Cepeda .75 2.00
37 Ozzie Smith 3.00 8.00
38 Paul O'Neill 1.25 3.00
39 Reggie Jackson 1.25 3.00
40 Sid Fernandez .75 2.00
41 Tony Gwynn 2.50 6.00
42 Tim Raines .75 2.00
43 Tom Seaver 1.25 3.00
44 Vida Blue .75 2.00
45 Brady Anderson .75 2.00
46 Bob Brenly .75 2.00
47 Bob Feller .75 2.00
48 Bill Mazeroski 1.25 3.00
49 Brooks Robinson 1.25 3.00
50 Harmon Killebrew 2.00 5.00
51 Bob Welch .75 2.00
52 Carl Erskine .75 2.00
53 Dale Murphy 1.25 3.00
54 Denny McLain .75 2.00
55 Dave Magadan .75 2.00
56 Duke Snider 1.25 3.00
57 Ed Kranepool .75 2.00
58 Frank Robinson .75 2.00
59 Jesus Alou .75 2.00
60 Joe Girardi .75 2.00
61 John Kruk 1.25 3.00
62 Jimmy Leyland MG .75 2.00
63 Juan Marichal .75 2.00
64 Johnny Pesky .75 2.00
65 Jesse Orosco .75 2.00
66 Ken Singleton .75 2.00
67 Matty Alou .75 2.00
68 Monte Irvin .75 2.00
69 Matt Williams 1.25 3.00
70 Pedro Guerrero .75 2.00
71 Ron Blomberg .75 2.00
72 Rod Carew 1.25 3.00
73 Rafael Santana .75 2.00
74 Ralph Kiner .75 2.00
75 Wade Boggs 1.25 3.00
76 Roger Craig .75 2.00
77 Robin Yount 2.00 5.00
78 Steve Carlton .75 2.00
79 Shawon Dunston .75 2.00
80 Steve Garvey .75 2.00
81 Stan Musial 3.00 8.00
82 Travis Fryman .75 2.00
83 Tito Fuentes .75 2.00
84 Mike Cuellar .75 2.00
85 Roberto Clemente 5.00 12.00
86 Whitey Ford 1.25 3.00
87 Yogi Berra 2.00 5.00
88 Atlee Hammaker .75 2.00
89 Bill Freehan .75 2.00
90 Brian Cashman GM .75 2.00
91 Bobby Richardson 1.25 3.00
92 Bob Boone .75 2.00
93 Charlie Hough .75 2.00
94 Glenn Hubbard .75 2.00
95 Grady Little MG .75 2.00
96 Jimmy Piersall .75 2.00
97 Jim Frey MG .75 2.00
98 Jerry Grote .75 2.00
99 Jim Leyritz .75 2.00
100 Nolan Ryan 4.00 10.00
101 Jim Kaat .75 2.00
102 Joe Pepitone .75 2.00
103 J.R. Richard .75 2.00
104 John Candelaria .75 2.00
105 Moose Skowron .75 2.00
106 Rick Cerone .75 2.00
107 Ron Santo 1.25 3.00
108 Rick Dempsey .75 2.00
109 Roy White .75 2.00
110 Tippy Martinez .75 2.00

2005 Topps Retired Signature Black

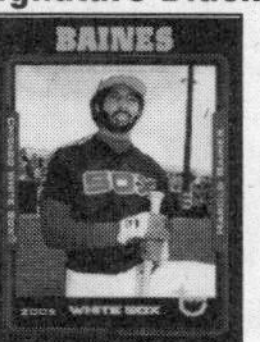

*BLACK: 2X TO 5X BASIC
STATED ODDS 1:9 HOBBY, 1:11 RETAIL
STATED PRINT RUN 54 SERIAL #'d SETS

2005 Topps Retired Signature Foilboard

STATED ODDS 1:497 HOBBY, 1:528 RETAIL
STATED PRINT RUN 1 SERIAL #'d SET
NO PRICING DUE TO SCARCITY

2005 Topps Retired Signature Gold

*GOLD: .5X TO 1.2X BASIC
STATED ODDS 1:2 HOBBY/RETAIL
STATED PRINT RUN 500 SERIAL #'d SETS

2005 Topps Retired Signature Autographs

GROUP A ODDS 1:205 HOBBY/RETAIL
GROUP B ODDS 1:35 HOBBY, 1:34 RETAIL
GROUP C ODDS 1:65 HOBBY, 1:64 RETAIL
GROUP D ODDS 1:11 HOBBY/RETAIL
GROUP E ODDS 1:149 HOBBY/RETAIL
GROUP F ODDS 1:5 HOBBY/RETAIL
GROUP G ODDS 1:16 HOBBY/RETAIL
GROUP H ODDS 1:64 HOBBY/RETAIL
GROUP I ODDS 1:4 HOBBY/RETAIL
GROUP J ODDS 1:6 HOBBY/RETAIL
GROUP A PRINT RUNS B/WN 24-35 PER
GROUP B PRINT RUNS B/WN 60-70 PER
GROUP C PRINT RUNS B/WN 170-175 PER
GROUP D PRINT RUN 220 SETS
A-D ARE NOT SERIAL-NUMBERED
A-D PRINT RUNS PROVIDED BY TOPPS
AU PLATE ODDS 1:121 HOBBY
AU PLATE PRINT RUN 1 SET PER COLOR
BLACK-CYAN-MAGENTA-YELLOW ISSUED
NO AU PLATE PRICING DUE TO SCARCITY
AD Andre Dawson D/220 * 10.00 25.00
AH Atlee Hammaker I 4.00 10.00
AK Al Kaline D/220 * 20.00 50.00
AY Anthony Young H 4.00 10.00
BA Brady Anderson F 6.00 15.00
BAF Bill Freehan I 6.00 15.00
BB Brett Butler F 6.00 15.00
BC Brian Cashman GM B/70 * 50.00 100.00
BCR Bobby Richardson F 6.00 15.00
BD Bob Dernier F 10.00 25.00
BEB Bob Brenly F 6.00 15.00
BF Bob Feller D/220 * 15.00 40.00
BG Bob Gibson A/35 *
BJ Bo Jackson B/70 * 75.00 150.00
BM Bill Mazeroski B/70 * 30.00 60.00
BR Brooks Robinson D/220 * 20.00 50.00
BRB Bob Boone F 6.00 15.00
BW Bob Welch F 6.00 15.00
CDH Charlie Hayes F 4.00 10.00
CE Carl Erskine D/220 * 10.00 25.00
CF Carlton Fisk C/170 * 15.00 40.00
CH Charlie Hough I 4.00 10.00
CR Cal Ripken B/70 * 150.00 250.00
CY Carl Yastrzemski B/70 * 60.00 120.00
DBM Dale Murphy F 10.00 25.00
DDM Denny McLain F 6.00 15.00
DES Darryl Strawberry B/70 * 20.00 50.00
DG Dwight Gooden F 6.00 15.00
DJ Davey Johnson B/70 * 15.00 40.00
DJM Dave Magadan F 4.00 10.00
DLB Daryl Boston J 4.00 10.00
DM Don Mattingly B/70 * 75.00 150.00
DS Duke Snider C/170 * 40.00 80.00
DW Dave Winfield B/70 * 30.00 60.00
DZ Don Zimmer D/220 * 10.00 25.00
EB Ernie Banks A/35 *
EK Ed Kranepool F 6.00 15.00
FR Frank Robinson B/70 * 30.00 60.00
GB George Brett B/70 * 75.00 150.00
GC Gary Carter D/220 * 10.00 25.00
GH Glenn Hubbard I 4.00 10.00
GJ Gregg Jefferies F 4.00 10.00
GL Grady Little MG I 4.00 10.00
HB Harold Baines F 6.00 15.00
HJ Howard Johnson D/220 * 6.00 15.00
HK Harmon Killebrew B/70 * 60.00 120.00
JA Jesus Alou F 6.00 15.00
JAA Jim Abbott F 6.00 15.00
JAP Jimmy Piersall J 6.00 15.00
All of these cards were issued without the Topps certification
JB Johnny Bench A/35 *
JC Jose Canseco D/220 * 20.00 50.00
JCB Jay Buhner D/220 * 10.00 25.00
JF Jim Frey MG I 4.00 10.00
JG Jerry Grote I 4.00 10.00
JJL Jim Leyritz I 4.00 10.00
JJP Johnny Podres B/70 * 20.00 50.00
JK John Kruk D/220 * 6.00 15.00
JL Jimmy Leyland MG J 4.00 10.00
JLK Jim Kaat I 6.00 15.00
JM Juan Marichal D/220 * 10.00 25.00
JMP Johnny Pesky F 10.00 25.00
JO Jesse Orosco F 4.00 10.00
JP Joe Pepitone J 6.00 15.00
JR J.R. Richard I 6.00 15.00
JRC John Candelaria I 4.00 10.00
JRL Jim Lonborg I 4.00 10.00
KH Keith Hernandez D/220 * 10.00 25.00
KS Ken Singleton G 6.00 15.00
LB Lou Brock Cubs F 15.00 40.00
LW Lou Whitaker C/175 * 15.00 40.00
MA Matty Alou F 6.00 15.00
MC Mike Cuellar J 6.00 15.00
MI Monte Irvin B/70 * 30.00 60.00
MS Moose Skowron I 6.00 15.00
MW Matt Williams B/70 * 20.00 50.00
NR Nolan Ryan A/35 *
OC Orlando Cepeda D/220 * 10.00 25.00
OS Ozzie Smith B/70 * 50.00 100.00
PG Pedro Guerrero F 6.00 15.00
PO Paul O'Neill B/70 * 30.00 60.00
RB Ron Blomberg D/220 * 6.00 15.00
RC Rick Cerone I 4.00 10.00
RCC Rod Carew B/70 * 30.00 60.00
RD Ron Darling I 6.00 15.00
REG Ron Gant D/220 * 20.00 50.00
RES Ron Santo I 10.00 25.00
RFS Rafael Santana G 4.00 10.00
RG Rusty Greer B/70 * 20.00 50.00
RJ Reggie Jackson B/60 * 75.00 150.00
RK Ralph Kiner D/220 * 20.00 50.00
RKD Rob Dibble D/220 * 6.00 15.00
RLC Roger Craig G 6.00 15.00
RRD Rick Dempsey I 4.00 10.00
RS Ryne Sandberg C/170 * 40.00 80.00
RW Roy White J 4.00 10.00
RY Robin Yount B/70 * 60.00 120.00
SC Steve Carlton D/220 * 20.00 50.00
SD Shawon Dunston D/220 * 10.00 25.00
SF Sid Fernandez D/220 * 6.00 15.00
SG Steve Garvey F 10.00 25.00
SM Stan Musial A/35 *
TDF Travis Fryman F 6.00 15.00
TF Tito Fuentes D/220 * 10.00 25.00
TG Tony Gwynn B/70 * 60.00 120.00
TH Toby Harrah G 4.00 10.00
TL Tony LaRussa D/220 * 10.00 25.00
TM Tippy Martinez J 4.00 10.00
TN Tom Niedenfuer E 6.00 15.00
TR Tim Raines B/70 * 20.00 50.00
TS Tom Seaver A/24 *
VB Vida Blue D/220 * 6.00 15.00
WB Wade Boggs C/170 * 20.00 50.00
WF Whitey Ford A/35 *
YB Yogi Berra A/35 *
ZS Zane Smith G 4.00 10.00

2005 Topps Retired Signature Autographs Refractors

GROUP A ODDS 1:788 HOBBY/RETAIL
GROUP B ODDS 1:21 HOBBY/RETAIL
GROUP A PRINT RUN 10 SERIAL #'d SETS
GROUP B PRINT RUN 25 SERIAL #'d SETS
NO GROUP A PRICING DUE TO SCARCITY
AD Andre Dawson B/25 30.00 60.00
AH Atlee Hammaker B/25 20.00 50.00
AK Al Kaline B/25 75.00 150.00
AY Anthony Young B/25 20.00 50.00
BA Brady Anderson B/25 30.00 60.00
BAF Bill Freehan B/25 30.00 60.00
BB Brett Butler B/25 30.00 60.00
BC Brian Cashman GM B/25 60.00 120.00
BCR Bobby Richardson B/25 30.00 60.00
BD Bob Dernier B/25 30.00 60.00
BEB Bob Brenly B/25 30.00 60.00
BF Bob Feller B/25 50.00 100.00
BG Bob Gibson A/10
BJ Bo Jackson B/25 75.00 150.00
BM Bill Mazeroski B/25 50.00 100.00
BR Brooks Robinson B/25 50.00 100.00
BRB Bob Boone B/25 30.00 60.00
BW Bob Welch B/25 30.00 60.00
CDH Charlie Hayes B/25 20.00 50.00
CE Carl Erskine B/25 30.00 60.00
CF Carlton Fisk B/25 30.00 60.00
CH Charlie Hough B/25 20.00 50.00
CR Cal Ripken B/25 250.00 400.00
CY Carl Yastrzemski B/25 125.00 200.00
DBM Dale Murphy B/25 50.00 100.00
DDM Denny McLain B/25 30.00 60.00
DES Darryl Strawberry B/25 30.00 60.00
DG Dwight Gooden B/25 30.00 60.00
DJ Davey Johnson B/25 20.00 50.00
DJM Dave Magadan B/25 20.00 50.00
DLB Daryl Boston B/25 20.00 50.00
DM Don Mattingly B/25 125.00 200.00
DS Duke Snider B/25 75.00 150.00
DW Dave Winfield B/25 50.00 100.00
DZ Don Zimmer B/25 30.00 60.00
EB Ernie Banks A/10
EK Ed Kranepool B/25 30.00 60.00
FR Frank Robinson B/25 50.00 100.00
GB George Brett B/25
GC Gary Carter B/25 30.00 60.00
GH Glenn Hubbard B/25 20.00 50.00
GJ Gregg Jefferies B/25 20.00 50.00
GL Grady Little MG B/25 20.00 50.00
HB Harold Baines B/25 30.00 60.00
HJ Howard Johnson B/25 20.00 50.00
HK Harmon Killebrew B/25 75.00 150.00
JA Jesus Alou B/25 30.00 60.00
JAA Jim Abbott B/25 30.00 60.00
JAP Jimmy Piersall B/25 30.00 60.00
JB Johnny Bench A/10
JC Jose Canseco B/25 75.00 150.00
JCB Jay Buhner B/25 30.00 60.00
JF Jim Frey MG B/25 20.00 50.00
JG Jerry Grote B/25 20.00 50.00
JJL Jim Leyritz B/25 20.00 50.00
JJP Johnny Podres B/25 30.00 60.00
JK John Kruk B/25 30.00 60.00
JL Jimmy Leyland MG B/25 30.00 60.00
JLK Jim Kaat B/25 30.00 60.00
JM Juan Marichal B/25 30.00 60.00
JMP Johnny Pesky B/25 50.00 100.00
JO Jesse Orosco B/25 20.00 50.00
JP Joe Pepitone B/25 30.00 60.00
JR J.R. Richard B/25 30.00 60.00
JRC John Candelaria B/25 20.00 50.00
JRL Jim Lonborg B/25 20.00 50.00
KH Keith Hernandez B/25 30.00 60.00
KS Ken Singleton B/25 30.00 60.00
LB Lou Brock Cubs B/25 50.00 100.00
LW Lou Whitaker B/25 30.00 60.00
MA Matty Alou B/25 30.00 60.00
MC Mike Cuellar B/25 30.00 60.00
MI Monte Irvin B/25 50.00 100.00
MS Moose Skowron B/25 30.00 60.00
MW Matt Williams B/25 30.00 60.00
NR Nolan Ryan A/10
OC Orlando Cepeda B/25 30.00 60.00
OS Ozzie Smith B/25
PG Pedro Guerrero B/25 30.00 60.00
PO Paul O'Neill B/25 50.00 100.00
RB Ron Blomberg B/25 20.00 50.00
RC Rick Cerone B/25 20.00 50.00
RCC Rod Carew B/25 50.00 100.00
RD Ron Darling B/25 30.00 60.00
REG Ron Gant B/25 30.00 60.00
RES Ron Santo B/25 50.00 100.00
RFS Rafael Santana B/25 20.00 50.00
RG Rusty Greer B/25 20.00 50.00
RJ Reggie Jackson B/25 75.00 150.00
RK Ralph Kiner B/25 50.00 100.00
RKD Rob Dibble B/25 30.00 60.00
RLC Roger Craig B/25 30.00 60.00
RRD Rick Dempsey B/25 20.00 50.00
RS Ryne Sandberg B/25 100.00 175.00
RW Roy White B/25 20.00 50.00
RY Robin Yount B/25 75.00 150.00
SC Steve Carlton B/25 50.00 100.00
SD Shawon Dunston B/25 30.00 60.00
SF Sid Fernandez B/25 30.00 60.00
SG Steve Garvey B/25 50.00 100.00
SM Stan Musial A/10
TDF Travis Fryman B/25 50.00 100.00
TF Tito Fuentes B/25 30.00 60.00
TG Tony Gwynn B/25
TH Toby Harrah B/25 20.00 50.00
TL Tony LaRussa B/25 30.00 60.00
TM Tippy Martinez B/25 20.00 50.00
TN Tom Niedenfuer B/25 30.00 60.00
TR Tim Raines B/25 30.00 60.00
TS Tom Seaver B/25 125.00 200.00
VB Vida Blue B/25 20.00 50.00
WB Wade Boggs B/25 50.00 100.00
WF Whitey Ford A/10
YB Yogi Berra A/10
ZS Zane Smith B/25 20.00 50.00

2005 Topps Retired Signature Co-Signers

GROUP A ODDS 1:6295 H, 1:6192 R
GROUP B ODDS 1:224 HOBBY/RETAIL
GROUP A PRINT RUN 9 SERIAL #'d SETS
GROUP B PRINT RUN 49 SERIAL #'d SETS
NO GROUP A PRICING DUE TO SCARCITY
REFRACTOR ODDS 1:9443 H, 1:12,384 R
REFRACTOR PRINT RUN 1 SERIAL #'d SET
NO REF PRICING DUE TO SCARCITY
BF Johnny Bench 75.00 150.00
Carlton Fisk B/49
BJ Barry Bonds
Reggie Jackson A/9
BS Wade Boggs 75.00 150.00
Ryne Sandberg B/49
GF Bob Gibson 60.00 120.00
Whitey Ford B/49
MS Stan Musial 100.00 175.00
Duke Snider B/49
SR Tom Seaver 200.00 350.00
Nolan Ryan B/49

2005 Topps Rookie Cup

COMP.SET w/o AU's (150) 20.00 40.00
COMMON CARD (1-150) .20 .50
AU 151-160 ODDS 1:62 H, 1:155 R
1-150 OVERALL PLATE ODDS 1:251 H
151-160 OVERALL AU PLATE ODDS 1:3752 H
BLACK-CYAN-MAGENTA-YELLOW ISSUED
NO PLATE PRICING DUE TO SCARCITY
1 Pat Corrales .20 .50
2 Ron Santo .60 1.50
3 Joe Torre .60 1.50
4 Boog Powell .40 1.00
5 Tom Tresh .40 1.00
6 Jonny Gomes .40 1.00
7 Rico Carty .20 .50
8 Bert Campaneris .40 1.00
9 Tony Oliva .40 1.00
10 Ron Swoboda .40 1.00
11 Tony Perez .40 1.00
12 Joe Morgan .40 1.00
13 Davey Johnson .20 .50
14 Cleon Jones .20 .50
15 Tom Seaver .60 1.50
16 Rod Carew .60 1.50
17 Rick Monday .40 1.00
18 Johnny Bench 1.00 2.50
19 Bobby Cox .40 1.00
20 Jerry Koosman .40 1.00
21 Al Oliver .40 1.00
22 Lou Piniella .40 1.00
23 Larry Bowa .40 1.00
24 Chris Chambliss .40 1.00
25 Bill Buckner .40 1.00
26 Don Baylor .40 1.00
27 Buddy Bell .40 1.00
28 Carlton Fisk .60 1.50
29 Gary Matthews .40 1.00
30 Dave Lopes .40 1.00
31 Bob Boone .40 1.00
32 Bill Madlock .40 1.00
33 Claudell Washington .20 .50
34 Jim Rice .40 1.00
35 Gary Carter .40 1.00
36 Willie Randolph .40 1.00
37 Chet Lemon .20 .50
38 Andre Dawson .40 1.00
39 Eddie Murray 1.00 2.50
40 Paul Molitor .40 1.00
41 Ozzie Smith 1.50 4.00
42 Jeffrey Leonard .20 .50
43 Lonnie Smith .20 .50
44 Mookie Wilson .40 1.00
45 Tim Wallach .20 .50
46 Tim Raines .40 1.00
47 Fernando Valenzuela .40 1.00
48 Cal Ripken 3.00 8.00
49 Ryne Sandberg 2.00 5.00
50 Willie McGee .40 1.00
51 Darryl Strawberry .40 1.00
52 Julio Franco .40 1.00
53 Brook Jacoby .20 .50
54 Dwight Gooden .40 1.00
55 Roger McDowell .20 .50
56 Ozzie Guillen .40 1.00
57 Vince Coleman .20 .50
58 Pete Incaviglia .20 .50
59 Wally Joyner .40 1.00
60 Jose Canseco 1.00 2.50
61 Cory Snyder .20 .50
62 Devon White .20 .50
63 Walt Weiss .20 .50
64 Mark Grace .60 1.50
65 Ron Gant .40 1.00
66 Chris Sabo .40 1.00
67 Jay Buhner .40 1.00
68 Gary Sheffield .60 1.50
69 Gregg Jefferies .20 .50
70 Ken Griffey Jr. 1.50 4.00
71 Tom Gordon .20 .50
72 Jim Abbott .40 1.00
73 Dave Justice .60 1.50
74 Larry Walker .40 1.00
75 Sandy Alomar Jr. .20 .50
76 Chuck Knoblauch .40 1.00
77 Jeff Bagwell .60 1.50
78 Luis Gonzalez .40 1.00
79 Ivan Rodriguez .60 1.50
80 Eric Karros .40 1.00
81 Jeff Kent .40 1.00
82 Kenny Lofton .40 1.00
83 Moises Alou .40 1.00
84 Reggie Sanders .40 1.00
85 Jeff Conine .40 1.00
86 J.T. Snow .40 1.00
87 Tim Salmon .40 1.00
88 Mike Piazza 1.00 2.50
89 Manny Ramirez .60 1.50
90 Ryan Klesko .40 1.00
91 Javy Lopez .40 1.00
92 Chipper Jones 1.00 2.50
93 Ray Durham .40 1.00
94 Garret Anderson .40 1.00
95 Shawn Green .40 1.00
96 Hideo Nomo 1.00 2.50
97 Jermaine Dye .40 1.00
98 Tony Clark .20 .50
99 Joe Randa .40 1.00
100 Derek Jeter 2.00 5.00
101 Jason Kendall .40 1.00
102 Billy Wagner .40 1.00
103 Andruw Jones .60 1.50
104 Dmitri Young .40 1.00
105 Scott Rolen .60 1.50
106 Nomar Garciaparra 1.00 2.50
107 Jose Cruz Jr. .20 .50
108 Scott Hatteberg .20 .50
109 Mark Kotsay .40 1.00
110 Todd Helton .60 1.50
111 Miguel Cairo .20 .50
112 Magglio Ordonez .40 1.00
113 Kerry Wood .40 1.00
114 Preston Wilson .40 1.00
115 Alex Gonzalez .20 .50
116 Carlos Beltran .40 1.00
117 Rafael Furcal .40 1.00
118 Pat Burrell .40 1.00
119 Adam Kennedy .20 .50
120 Terrence Long .20 .50
121 Jay Payton .20 .50
122 Bengie Molina .20 .50
123 Albert Pujols 2.00 5.00
124 Craig Wilson .20 .50
125 Alfonso Soriano .40 1.00
126 Jimmy Rollins .40 1.00
127 Adam Dunn .40 1.00
128 Ichiro Suzuki 1.50 4.00
129 Roy Oswalt .40 1.00
130 C.C. Sabathia .40 1.00
131 Brad Wilkerson .20 .50
132 Nick Johnson .40 1.00
133 Eric Hinske .20 .50
134 Austin Kearns .40 1.00
135 Dontrelle Willis .40 1.00
136 Mark Teixeira .60 1.50
137 Rocco Baldelli .40 1.00
138 Scott Podsednik .40 1.00
139 Brandon Webb .20 .50
140 Jason Bay .40 1.00
141 Adam LaRoche .20 .50
142 Khalil Greene .60 1.50
143 Joe Mauer 1.00 2.50
144 Matt Holliday .25 .60
145 Chad Tracy .20 .50
146 Garrett Atkins .20 .50
147 Tadahito Iguchi RC 1.25 3.00
148 Russ Adams .20 .50
149 Huston Street .60 1.50
150 Dan Johnson .40 1.00
151 J. Brent Cox AU RC 6.00 15.00
152 John Drennen AU RC 10.00 25.00
153 Ryan Tucker AU RC 6.00 15.00
154 Yunel Escobar AU RC 20.00 50.00
155 Jacob Marceaux AU RC 4.00 10.00
156 Mark Pawelek AU RC 12.50 30.00
157 Brandon Snyder AU RC 10.00 25.00
158 Wade Townsend AU RC 6.00 15.00
159 Troy Tulowitzki AU RC 50.00 100.00
160 Kevin Whelan AU RC 6.00 15.00

2005 Topps Rookie Cup Blue

*BLUE 1-150: 3X TO 8X BASIC
*BLUE 1-150: 2X TO 5X BASIC RC
1-150 ODDS 1:29 HOBBY, 1:130 RETAIL
*BLUE 151-160: 1X TO 2.5X BASIC AU
151-160 AU ODDS 1:548 H, 1:1385 R
STATED PRINT RUN 50 SERIAL #'d SETS

2005 Topps Rookie Cup Gold

1-150 ODDS 1:1004 HOBBY
151-160 AU ODDS 1:15,840 HOBBY
STATED PRINT RUN 1 SERIAL #'d SET
NO PRICING DUE TO SCARCITY

2005 Topps Rookie Cup Green

*GREEN 1-150: 2X TO 5X BASIC
*BLUE 1-150: 1.25X TO 3X BASIC RC
1-150 ODDS 1:8 HOBBY, 1:33 RETAIL
1-150 PRINT RUN 199 SERIAL #'d SETS
*GREEN 151-160: .75X TO 2X BASIC AU
151-160 AU ODDS 1:274 H, 1:703 R
151-160 PRINT RUN 99 SERIAL #'d SETS

2005 Topps Rookie Cup Orange

*ORANGE 1-150: 1.25X TO 3X BASIC
*BLUE 1-150: .75X TO 2X BASIC RC
1-150 ODDS 1:4 HOBBY, 1:18 RETAIL
1-150 PRINT RUN 399 SERIAL #'d SETS
*ORANGE 151-160: .4X TO 1X BASIC AU
151-160 AU ODDS 1:91 H, 1:232 R
151-160 PRINT RUN 299 SERIAL #'d SETS
154 Yunel Escobar AU 20.00 50.00

2005 Topps Rookie Cup Red

*RED 1-150: 1X TO 2.5X BASIC
*BLUE 1-150: .6X TO 1.5X BASIC RC
1-150 RANDOM INSERTS IN PACKS
1-150 PRINT RUN 499 SERIAL #'d SETS
*RED 151-160: .4X TO 1X BASIC AU
151-160 AU ODDS 1:68 H, 1:174 R
151-160 PRINT RUN 399 SERIAL #'d SETS
154 Yunel Escobar AU 20.00 50.00

2005 Topps Rookie Cup Silver

1-150 ODDS 1:300 HOBBY, 1:1200 RETAIL
151-160 AU ODDS 1:5483 H, 1:13,454 R
STATED PRINT RUN 5 SERIAL #'d SETS
NO PRICING DUE TO SCARCITY

2005 Topps Rookie Cup Yellow

*YELLOW 1-150: 1.5X TO 4X BASIC
*BLUE 1-150: 1X TO 2.5X BASIC RC
1-150 ODDS 1:5 HOBBY, 1:21 RETAIL
1-150 PRINT RUN 299 SERIAL #'d SETS
*YELLOW 151-160: .5X TO 1.2X BASIC AU
151-160 AU ODDS 1:137 H, 1:349 R
151-160 PRINT RUN 199 SERIAL #'d SETS
154 Yunel Escobar AU 20.00 50.00

2005 Topps Rookie Cup Autographs

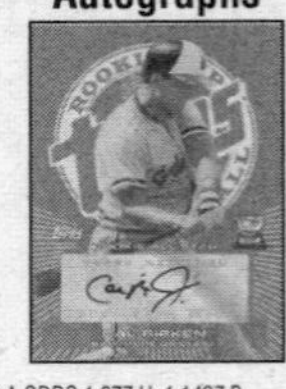

GROUP A ODDS 1:677 H, 1:1427 R
GROUP B ODDS 1:45 H, 1:51 R
GOLD ODDS 1:5281 HOBBY
GOLD PRINT RUN 1 SERIAL #'d SET
NO GOLD PRICING DUE TO SCARCITY
SILVER ODDS 1:2458 H, 1:3622 R
SILVER PRINT RUN 5 SERIAL #'d SETS
NO SILVER PRICING DUE TO SCARCITY
EXCHANGE DEADLINE 12/31/07
AD Andre Dawson B 6.00 15.00
AJ Andruw Jones A 20.00 50.00
AP Albert Pujols A 150.00 250.00
BP Boog Powell B 6.00 15.00
BW Brad Wilkerson B 4.00 10.00
CJ Chipper Jones B 20.00 50.00
CK Chuck Knoblauch B 6.00 15.00
CR Cal Ripken A 150.00 250.00
DJ Davey Johnson B 4.00 10.00
DJ Dave Justice B 6.00 15.00
DRJ Dan Johnson B 6.00 15.00
DS Darryl Strawberry B 6.00 15.00
DW Dontrelle Willis B 10.00 25.00
EK Eric Karros B 6.00 15.00
GS Gary Sheffield A 15.00 40.00
JB Johnny Bench A 30.00 60.00
JBA Jason Bay B 6.00 15.00
JD Jermaine Dye B EXCH 6.00 15.00
JR Jim Rice A 10.00 25.00
JT Joe Torre A 30.00 60.00
MG Mark Grace B 10.00 25.00
MK Mark Kotsay B 4.00 10.00
MR Manny Ramirez A 20.00 50.00
PM Paul Molitor A 10.00 25.00
RF Rafael Furcal B 6.00 15.00
RM Roger McDowell B 4.00 10.00
RS Ron Swoboda B 6.00 15.00
RSA Ron Santo B 15.00 40.00
TS Tom Seaver A 30.00 60.00

2005 Topps Rookie Cup Dual Autographs

STATED ODDS 1:118 HOBBY
BW Jason Bay 12.50 30.00
Dontrelle Willis
CS J. Brent Cox 20.00 50.00
Tom Seaver
DR John Drennen 20.00 50.00
Manny Ramirez
EF Yunel Escobar 10.00 25.00
Rafael Furcal
GS Mark Grace 40.00 80.00
Ron Santo
MM Jacob Marceaux 8.00 20.00
Roger McDowell
PG Mark Pawelek 30.00 60.00
Mark Grace
RTW Ryan Tucker 12.50 30.00
Dontrelle Willis
SP Brandon Snyder 10.00 25.00
Boog Powell
TS Wade Townsend 20.00 50.00
Tom Seaver
TW Troy Tulowitzki 15.00 40.00
Walt Weiss
WD Brad Wilkerson 10.00 25.00
Andre Dawson
WM Kevin Whelan 12.50 30.00
Roger McDowell

2005 Topps Rookie Cup Original Relics

GROUP A ODDS 1:957 HOBBY
GROUP B ODDS 1:1004 HOBBY
GROUP C ODDS 1:587 HOBBY
GROUP D ODDS 1:3033 HOBBY
GROUP E ODDS 1:474 HOBBY
GROUP F ODDS 1:673 HOBBY
GROUP G ODDS 1:1004 HOBBY
PRINT RUNS B/WN 1-10 COPIES PER
NO PRICING DUE TO SCARCITY
EXCHANGE DEADLINE 12/31/07

2005 Topps Rookie Cup Reprints

COMPLETE SET (150) 40.00 80.00
*REPRINTS: .75X TO 2X BASIC
*REPRINTS: .4X TO 1X BASIC RC
TWO PER HOBBY PACK
ONE PER RETAIL PACK
CHROME ODDS 1:2 BOX-LOADERS
CHROME PRINT RUN 25 #'d SETS
NO CHROME PRICING DUE TO SCARCITY
CHROME REF ODDS 1:3 BOX-LOADERS
CHROME REF PRINT RUN 15 #'d SETS
NO CHR.REF PRICING DUE TO SCARCITY
CHROME GOLD ODDS 1:42 BOX-LOADERS
CHROME GOLD PRINT RUN 1 #'d SET
NO CHR.GOLD PRICING DUE TO SCARCITY

2006 Topps Sterling

This 200-card set was releasedin November, 2006. The set was issued in a special "cherry wood player specific box" which had three base cards plus an autographed relic or relic card of the featured player,. In addition, each box had an mystery pack with either an cut signature or an framed parallel card of the featured player. These "boxes" had an $250 SRP and were issued 10 to a case. Each base card in this set had a stated print run of 250 serial numbered sets.

B.BONDS (1-19) 5.00 12.00
B.BONDS ODDS 1:10
M.MANTLE (20-39) 6.00 15.00
M.MANTLE ODDS 1:10
J.GIBSON (40-43) 12.50 30.00
J.GIBSON ODDS 1:191
R.HENDERSON (44-53) 4.00 10.00
R.HENDERSON ODDS 1:22
T.WILLIAMS (54-62) 5.00 12.00
T.WILLIAMS ODDS 1:27
R.CLEMENTE (63-67) 10.00 25.00
R.CLEMENTE ODDS 1:40
N.RYAN (68-77) 8.00 20.00
N.RYAN ODDS 1:20
C.RIPKEN (78-96) 8.00 20.00
C.RIPKEN ODDS 1:10
S.MUSIAL (97-101) 4.00 10.00
S.MUSIAL ODDS 1:40
R.JACKSON (102-106) 4.00 10.00
R.JACKSON ODDS 1:40
J.BENCH (107-111) 4.00 10.00
J.BENCH ODDS 1:43
G.BRETT (112-121) 4.00 10.00
G.BRETT ODDS 1:20
D.MATTINGLY (122-131) 5.00 12.00
D.MATTINGLY ODDS 1:20
R.MARIS (132-136) 5.00 12.00
R.MARIS ODDS 1:40
R.CAREW (137-146) 4.00 10.00
R.CAREW ODDS 1:20
Y.BERRA (147-151) 4.00 10.00
Y.BERRA ODDS 1:40
M.SCHMIDT (152-156) 4.00 10.00
M.SCHMIDT ODDS 1:40
C.YASTRZEMSKI (157-175) 4.00 10.00
C.YASTRZEMSKI ODDS 1:10
T.GWYNN (176-185 4.00 10.00
T.GWYNN ODDS 1:20
R.SANDBERG (186-190) 4.00 10.00
R.SANDBERG ODDS 1:40
O.SMITH (191-200) 4.00 10.00
O.SMITH ODDS 1:20
STATED PRINT RUN 250 SER.#'d SETS

2006 Topps Sterling Framed Burgundy

B.BONDS (1-19) 30.00 60.00
M.MANTLE (20-39) 50.00 100.00
J.GIBSON (40-43) 30.00 60.00
R.HENDERSON (44-53) 20.00 50.00
T.WILLIAMS (54-62) 30.00 60.00
R.CLEMENTE (63-67) 40.00 80.00
N.RYAN (68-77) 75.00 150.00
C.RIPKEN (78-96) 75.00 150.00
S.MUSIAL (97-101) 20.00 50.00
R.JACKSON (102-106) 20.00 50.00
J.BENCH (107-111) 20.00 50.00
G.BRETT (112-121) 30.00 60.00
D.MATTINGLY (122-131) 30.00 60.00
R.MARIS (132-136) 30.00 60.00
R.CAREW (137-146) 10.00 25.00
Y.BERRA (147-151) 20.00 50.00
M.SCHMIDT (152-156) 20.00 50.00
C.YASTRZEMSKI (157-175) 20.00 50.00
T.GWYNN (176-185 20.00 50.00
R.SANDBERG (186-190) 20.00 50.00
O.SMITH (191-200) 20.00 50.00
RANDOM INSERTS IN BONUS PACKS
STATED PRINT RUN 10 SER.#'d SETS

2006 Topps Sterling Framed Cherry Wood

RANDOM INSERTS IN BONUS PACKS
STATED PRINT RUN 1 SER.#'d SET
NO PRICING DUE TO SCARCITY

2006 Topps Sterling Framed Silver

RANDOM INSERTS IN BONUS PACKS
STATED PRINT RUN 1 SER.#'d SET
NO PRICING DUE TO SCARCITY

2006 Topps Sterling Framed White

*FRAMED WHITE: .6X TO 1.5X BASIC
RANDOM INSERTS IN BONUS PACKS
STATED PRINT RUN 50 SER.#'d SETS

2006 Topps Sterling Baseball Cut Signatures

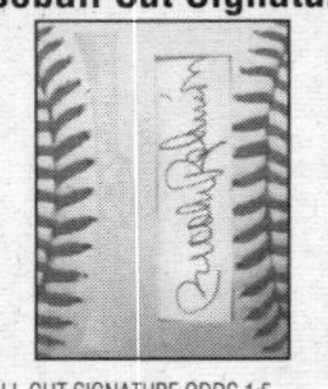

OVERALL CUT SIGNATURE ODDS 1:5
AK Al Kaline 30.00 60.00
BF Bob Feller 15.00 40.00
BG Bob Gibson 30.00 60.00
BR Brooks Robinson 20.00 50.00
CF Carlton Fisk 30.00 60.00
CY Carl Yastrzemski
DE Dennis Eckersley
DS Duke Snider 30.00 60.00
DW Dave Winfield
EB Ernie Banks
EM Eddie Murray
EW Earl Weaver 15.00 40.00
FR Frank Robinson
GC Gary Carter 30.00 60.00
GK George Kell 15.00 40.00
GP Gaylord Perry 15.00 40.00
HK Harmon Killebrew 30.00 60.00
JB Johnny Bench
JM Juan Marichal
JMO Joe Morgan 15.00 40.00
JP Jim Palmer 15.00 40.00
LA Luis Aparicio 15.00 40.00
LB Lou Brock 20.00 50.00
MI Monte Irvin 15.00 40.00
MS Mike Schmidt
NR Nolan Ryan
OC Orlando Cepeda 15.00 40.00
OS Ozzie Smith
PM Paul Molitor
PN Phil Niekro 15.00 40.00
RC Rod Carew 20.00 50.00
RF Rollie Fingers 15.00 40.00
RJ Reggie Jackson
RK Ralph Kiner 20.00 50.00
RR Robin Roberts 15.00 40.00
RS Ryne Sandberg 40.00 80.00
RSH Red Schoendienst 20.00 50.00
RY Robin Yount 30.00 60.00
SA Sparky Anderson 15.00 40.00
SC Steve Carlton
SM Stan Musial
TP Tony Perez
TS Tom Seaver
WB Wade Boggs
WF Whitey Ford
YB Yogi Berra

2006 Topps Sterling Career Stats Relics

OVERALL AU/GU ODDS 1:3
STATED PRINT RUN 10 SERIAL #'d SETS
NO PRICING DUE TO SCARCITY
PRIME PRINT RUN 1 SERIAL #'d SET

NO PRIME PRICING DUE TO SCARCITY
STER.SIL. PRINT RUN 1 SER. #'d SET
NO STER.SIL. PRICING DUE TO SCARCITY
SS PRIME PRINT RUN 1 SER.#'d SET
NO SS PRIME PRICING DUE TO SCARCITY
BB Barry Bonds 500 500
CY Carl Yastrzemski 3308
GB George Brett 665 2B
JB Johnny Bench 389 HR
MS Mike Schmidt 548 HR
NR Nolan Ryan 5714
RC Roberto Clemente 3000
RJ Reggie Jackson 563 HR
RM Roger Maris 2MVP
TW Ted Williams 482 OBP
YB Yogi Berra 358 HR

2006 Topps Sterling Career Stats Relics Autographs

OVERALL AU/GU ODDS 1:3
STATED PRINT RUN 10 SERIAL #'d SETS
NO PRICING DUE TO SCARCITY
PRIME PRINT RUN 1 SERIAL #'d SET
NO PRIME PRICING DUE TO SCARCITY
STER.SIL. PRINT RUN 1 SER. #'d SET
NO STER.SIL. PRICING DUE TO SCARCITY
SS PRIME PRINT RUN 1 SER.#'d SET
NO SS PRIME PRICING DUE TO SCARCITY
CR Cal Ripken 3184
CY Carl Yastrzemski 3308
GB George Brett 665 2B
JB Johnny Bench 389 HR
MS Mike Schmidt 548 HR
NR Nolan Ryan 5714
OS Ozzie Smith 978
RCA Rod Carew 3053
RS Ryne Sandberg 989
TG Tony Gwynn 3141
YB Yogi Berra 358 HR

2006 Topps Sterling Cut from the Same Cloth Signatures

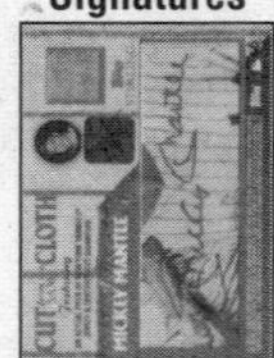

OVERALL CUT SIGNATURES ODDS 1:5
PRINT RUNS B/WN 1-5 COPIES PER
NO PRICING DUE TO SCARCITY
SC1 Mickey Mantle
Roger Maris/5
SC2 Mickey Mantle
Ted Williams/5
SC3 Mickey Mantle
Roberto Clemente/1
SC4 Ted Williams
Roberto Clemente/1
SC5 Ted Williams
Roger Maris/1

2006 Topps Sterling Cut Signatures

OVERALL CUT SIGNATURE ODDS 1:5
1 Bobby Brown
2 Bucky Harris
3 Calvin Coolidge
4 Charley Lau
5 John F. Kennedy
6 Dutch Leonard
7 Earl Torgeson
8 Eddie Stanky
9 Ferris Fain
10 Gene Woodling
11 Hal Reniff
12 Harry Truman
13 Herbert Hoover
14 Hoot Evers
15 Bill Clinton
16 James Garfield
17 James Buchanan
18 Johnny Roseboro
19 Luke Sewell
20 Marv Throneberry
21 Dwight Eisenhower
22 Moe Drabowsky
23 Pete Gray
24 Sam Jethroe
25 Walker Cooper
26 Richard Nixon
27 Jimmy Carter
28 Cal Abrams
29 Ed Lopat
30 Frank Crosetti
31 Joe Black
32 John Jorgensen
33 Lefty Gomez
34 Bob Grim
35 Joe Adcock
36 Red Rolfe
37 Smokey Burgess
38 Vern Stephens
39 Harvey Haddix
40 Jocko Conlon
41 Joe Collins
42 Joe Medwick
43 Mark Belanger
44 Red Ruffing
45 Birdie Tebbetts
46 Elmer Valo
47 Ewell Blackwell
48 Jack Sanford
49 Jesse Haines
50 Max Carey
51 Wes Westrum
52 Al Lopez
53 Carl Furillo
54 Daffy Dean
55 Danny Murtaugh
56 Harry Walker
57 Mark Koenig
58 Joe McCarthy
59 Ted Lyons
60 George Kelly
61 Hal Newhouser
62 Harry Hooper
63 Allie Reynolds
64 Dick Sisler
65 Frank Shea
66 Monty Stratton
67 Lloyd Waner 75.00 150.00
68 Sal Maglie 40.00 80.00
69 Waite Hoyt 40.00 80.00
70 Warren Spahn 75.00 150.00
71 Hank Sauer
72 A.B. Chandler 40.00 80.00
73 Al Barlick 40.00 80.00
74 Bill Dickey 60.00 120.00
75 Bill Terry 40.00 80.00
76 Billy Herman 30.00 60.00
77 Bob Lemon 30.00 60.00
78 Buck Leonard 40.00 80.00
79 Charles Gehringer 60.00 120.00
80 Dave DeBusschere
81 Earl Averill
82 Hoyt Wilhelm 40.00 80.00
83 Catfish Hunter 50.00 100.00
84 Joe Sewell 40.00 80.00
85 Judy Johnson 40.00 80.00
86 Carl Hubbell 50.00 100.00
87 Lou Boudreau 40.00 80.00
88 Luke Appling 40.00 80.00
89 Ray Dandridge 40.00 80.00
90 Rick Ferrell 30.00 60.00
91 Stan Coveleski 40.00 80.00
92 Willie Stargell 75.00 150.00

2006 Topps Sterling Five Relics

OVERALL AU/GU ODDS 1:3
STATED PRINT RUN 10 SERIAL #'d SETS
NO PRICING DUE TO SCARCITY
PRIME PRINT RUN 10 SERIAL #'d SETS
NO PRIME PRICING DUE TO SCARCITY
STER.SIL. PRINT RUN 1 SER. #'d SET
NO STER.SIL. PRICING DUE TO SCARCITY
SS PRIME PRINT RUN 1 SER.#'d SET
NO SS PRIME PRICING DUE TO SCARCITY
BB Barry Bonds
GB George Brett
NR Nolan Ryan
RC Roberto Clemente
RH Rickey Henderson
RM Roger Maris
TW Ted Williams

2006 Topps Sterling Five Relics Autographs

OVERALL AU/GU ODDS 1:3
STATED PRINT RUN 10 SERIAL #'d SETS
NO PRICING DUE TO SCARCITY

PRIME PRINT RUN 10 SERIAL #'d SETS
NO PRIME PRICING DUE TO SCARCITY
STER.SIL. PRINT RUN 1 SER. #'d SET
NO STER.SIL. PRICING DUE TO SCARCITY
SS PRIME PRINT RUN 1 SER.#'d SET
NO SS PRIME PRICING DUE TO SCARCITY
CR Cal Ripken
CY Carl Yastrzemski
JB Johnny Bench
MS Mike Schmidt
OS Ozzie Smith
RS Ryne Sandberg
TG Tony Gwynn

2006 Topps Sterling Josh Gibson Bat Barrel

OVERALL AU/GU ODDS 1:3
STATED PRINT RUN 1 SERIAL #'d SETS
NO PRICING DUE TO SCARCITY

2006 Topps Sterling Jumbo Jersey

OVERALL AU/GU ODDS 1:3
STATED PRINT RUN 10 SERIAL #'d SETS
NO PRICING DUE TO SCARCITY
PRIME PRINT RUN 1 SERIAL #'d SET
NO PRIME PRICING DUE TO SCARCITY
PATCH PRINT RUN 10 SER.#'d SETS
NO PATCH PRICING DUE TO SCARCITY
STER.SIL. PRINT RUN 1 SER. #'d SET
NO STER.SIL. PRICING DUE TO SCARCITY
SS PRIME PRINT RUN 1 SER.#'d SET
NO SS PRIME PRICING DUE TO SCARCITY
SS PATCH PRINT RUN 1 SER.#'d SET
NO PATCH PRICING DUE TO SCARCITY
BB Barry Bonds
CR Cal Ripken
CY Carl Yastrzemski
GB George Brett
JB Johnny Bench
MM Mickey Mantle
RH Rickey Henderson

2006 Topps Sterling Moments Relics

B.BONDS 30.00 80.00
M.MANTLE 3 or 4 RELIC 150.00 250.00
M.MANTLE 5 or 6 RELIC 300.00 600.00
J.GIBSON 250.00 500.00
R.HENDERSON 30.00 80.00
T.WILLIAMS 60.00 150.00
R.CLEMENTE 100.00 200.00
N.RYAN 60.00 150.00
C.RIPKEN 40.00 80.00
S.MUSIAL 30.00 80.00
R.JACKSON 25.00 60.00
J.BENCH 25.00 60.00
G.BRETT 25.00 60.00
R.MARIS 50.00 120.00
Y.BERRA 30.00 80.00
M.SCHMIDT 25.00 60.00
C.YASTRZEMSKI 20.00 50.00
T.GWYNN 25.00 60.00
R.SANDBERG 25.00 60.00
OVERALL AU/GU ODDS 1:3
STATED PRINT RUN 10 SER.#'d SETS
PRIME PRIME RUN 1 SER.#'d SET
NO PRIME PRICING DUE TO SCARCITY

2006 Topps Sterling Moments Relics Autographs

R.HENDERSON 75.00 150.00
N.RYAN 150.00 300.00
C.RIPKEN 150.00 300.00
S.MUSIAL 90.00 150.00
R.JACKSON 75.00 150.00
J.BENCH 75.00 150.00
G.BRETT 75.00 150.00
D.MATTINGLY 75.00 150.00
R.CAREW 40.00 80.00
Y.BERRA 90.00 150.00
M.SCHMIDT 75.00 150.00
C.YASTRZEMSKI 60.00 120.00
T.GWYNN 50.00 100.00
R.SANDBERG 75.00 150.00
O.SMITH 50.00 100.00
OVERALL AU-GU ODDS 1:3

STATED PRINT RUN 10 SERIAL #'d SETS
NO BONDS PRICING DUE TO SCARCITY
PRIME PRINT RUN 1 SER.#'d SET
NO PRIME PRICING DUE TO SCARCITY

2006 Topps Sterling Moments Relics Cut Signatures

OVERALL CUT SIGNATURE ODDS 1:5
STATED PRINT RUN 10 SER.#'d SETS
NO PRICING DUE TO SCARCITY
PRIME PRINT RUN 1 SER.#'d SET
NO PRIME PRICING DUE TO SCARCITY
MMAS1 Mickey Mantle 1952
MMHR1 Mickey Mantle HR 1
MMHR7 Mickey Mantle HR 7
RMHR1 Roger Maris HR 1
TWBA15 Ted Williams 406
TW42HR1 Ted Williams HR 1

2006 Topps Sterling Quad Relics

OVERALL AU/GU ODDS 1:3
STATED PRINT RUN 10 SERIAL #'d SETS
NO PRICING DUE TO SCARCITY
PRIME PRINT RUN 10 SERIAL #'d SETS
NO PRIME PRICING DUE TO SCARCITY
STER.SIL. PRINT RUN 1 SER. #'d SET
NO STER.SIL. PRICING DUE TO SCARCITY
SS PRIME PRINT RUN 1 SER.#'d SET
NO SS PRIME PRICING DUE TO SCARCITY
BB Barry Bonds
NR Nolan Ryan
RC Roberto Clemente
RH Rickey Henderson
RM Roger Maris
TW Ted Williams

2006 Topps Sterling Quad Relics Autographs

OVERALL AU/GU ODDS 1:3
STATED PRINT RUN 10 SERIAL #'d SETS
NO PRICING DUE TO SCARCITY
PRIME PRINT RUN 10 SERIAL #'d SETS
NO PRIME PRICING DUE TO SCARCITY
STER.SIL. PRINT RUN 1 SER. #'d SET
NO STER.SIL. PRICING DUE TO SCARCITY
SS PRIME PRINT RUN 1 SER.#'d SET
NO SS PRIME PRICING DUE TO SCARCITY
MS Mike Schmidt
OS Ozzie Smith
RS Ryne Sandberg
TG Tony Gwynn

2006 Topps Sterling Season Stats Relics

OVERALL AU/GU ODDS 1:3
STATED PRINT RUN 10 SERIAL #'d SETS
NO PRICING DUE TO SCARCITY
PRIME PRINT RUN 1 SERIAL #'d SET
NO PRIME PRICING DUE TO SCARCITY
STER.SIL. PRINT RUN 1 SER. #'d SET
NO STER.SIL. PRICING DUE TO SCARCITY
SS PRIME PRINT RUN 1 SER.#'d SET
NO SS PRIME PRICING DUE TO SCARCITY
BB Barry Bonds 232 BB
CY Carl Yastrzemski 326 BA
GB George Brett 390 BA
JB Johnny Bench 45 HR
MM Mickey Mantle 365 BA
NR Nolan Ryan 169 ERA
RC Roberto Clemente 357 BA
RM Roger Maris 142 RBI
TW Ted Williams 159 RBI
YB Yogi Berra 28HR 12SO

2006 Topps Sterling Season Stats Relics Autographs

OVERALL AU/GU ODDS 1:3
STATED PRINT RUN 10 SERIAL #'d SETS
NO PRICING DUE TO SCARCITY
PRIME PRINT RUN 1 SERIAL #'d SET
NO PRIME PRICING DUE TO SCARCITY
STER.SIL. PRINT RUN 1 SER. #'d SET
NO STER.SIL. PRICING DUE TO SCARCITY
SS PRIME PRINT RUN 1 SER.#'d SET
NO SS PRIME PRICING DUE TO SCARCITY
CR Cal Ripken 211H
JB Johnny Bench 45 HR
MS Mike Schmidt 48 HR
NR Nolan Ryan 169 ERA
OS Ozzie Smith 75 RBI
RS Ryne Sandberg 54 SB
TG Tony Gwynn 394 BA
YB Yogi Berra 28HR 12SO
RCA Rod Carew 388 BA

2006 Topps Sterling Six Relics

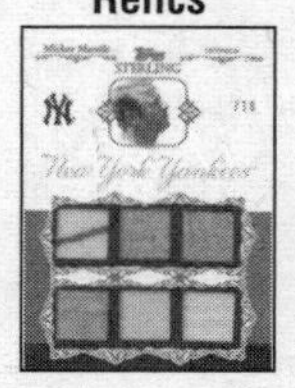

OVERALL AU/GU ODDS 1:3
STATED PRINT RUN 10 SERIAL #'d SETS
NO PRICING DUE TO SCARCITY
PRIME PRINT RUN 10 SERIAL #'d SETS
NO PRIME PRICING DUE TO SCARCITY
STER.SIL. PRINT RUN 1 SER. #'d SET
NO STER.SIL. PRICING DUE TO SCARCITY
SS PRIME PRINT RUN 1 SER.#'d SET
NO SS PRIME PRICING DUE TO SCARCITY
BB Barry Bonds
CR Cal Ripken
GB George Brett
JB Johnny Bench
MM Mickey Mantle
NR Nolan Ryan
RC Roberto Clemente
RH Rickey Henderson
RM Roger Maris
TW Ted Williams

2006 Topps Sterling Six Relics Autographs

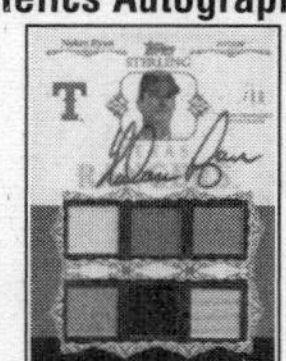
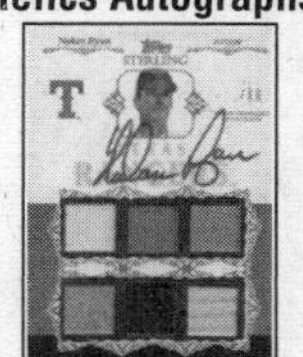

OVERALL AU/GU ODDS 1:3
STATED PRINT RUN 10 SERIAL #'d SETS
NO PRICING DUE TO SCARCITY
PRIME PRINT RUN 10 SERIAL #'d SETS
NO PRIME PRICING DUE TO SCARCITY
STER.SIL. PRINT RUN 1 SER. #'d SET
NO STER.SIL. PRICING DUE TO SCARCITY
SS PRIME PRINT RUN 1 SER.#'d SET
NO SS PRIME PRICING DUE TO SCARCITY
CR Cal Ripken
CY Carl Yastrzemski
GB George Brett
JB Johnny Bench
MS Mike Schmidt
NR Nolan Ryan
OS Ozzie Smith
RCA Rod Carew
RJ Reggie Jackson
RS Ryne Sandberg
TG Tony Gwynn

2006 Topps Sterling Triple Relics Autographs

OVERALL AU/GU ODDS 1:3
STATED PRINT RUN 10 SERIAL #'d SETS
NO PRICING DUE TO SCARCITY
PRIME PRINT RUN 10 SERIAL #'d SETS
NO PRIME PRICING DUE TO SCARCITY
STER.SIL. PRINT RUN 1 SER. #'d SET
NO STER.SIL. PRICING DUE TO SCARCITY
SS PRIME PRINT RUN 1 SER.#'d SET
NO SS PRIME PRICING DUE TO SCARCITY
OS Ozzie Smith
RS Ryne Sandberg
TG Tony Gwynn

2007 Topps Sterling

This 254-card set was released in December, 2007. The set was issued in "box" form which consisted of a player specific wood box and a mystery pack which also pertained to the player one recieved in the wood box. Each full box had five total cards in them and those boxes came five per carton and two cartons per full case.

COMMON MANTLE (1-24) 5.00 12.00
COMMON BONDS (25-48) 5.00 12.00
COMMON ICHIRO (49-56) 4.00 10.00
COMMON YAZ (57-64) 3.00 8.00
COMMON WRIGHT (65-76) 3.00 8.00
COMMON CLEMENTE (77-81) 6.00 15.00
COMMON SANTANA (82-89) 3.00 8.00
COMMON MORNEAU (90-101) 3.00 8.00
COMMON R.JACKSON (102-109) 3.00 8.00
COMMON CLEMENS (110-117) 4.00 10.00
COMMON T.WILLIAMS (118-122) 5.00 12.00
COMMON BERRA (123-130) 3.00 8.00
COMMON MATSUI (131-135) 3.00 8.00
COMMON HOWARD (136-143) 3.00 8.00
COMMON GWYNN (144-151) 3.00 8.00
COMMON ORTIZ (152-159) 2.50 6.00
COMMON SEAVER (160-167) 2.50 6.00
COMMON PUJOLS (168-175) 4.00 10.00
COMMON MUSIAL (176-183) 3.00 8.00
COMMON WANG (184-191) 5.00 12.00
COMMON SANDBERG (192-199) 4.00 10.00
COMMON N.RYAN (200-207) 8.00 20.00
COMMON B.GIBSON (208-215) 2.50 6.00
COMMON MARIS (216-220) 3.00 8.00
COMMON M.RAMIREZ (221-228) 3.00 8.00
COMMON SCHMIDT (229-236) 4.00 10.00
COMMON A.ROD (237-244) 3.00 8.00
COMMON MATSUZAKA (245-249) 6.00 15.00
COMMON DIMAGGIO (250-254) 4.00 10.00
THREE BASE CARDS PER BOX
STATED PRINT RUN 250 SER.#'d SETS

1 Mickey Mantle 5.00 12.00
2 Mickey Mantle 5.00 12.00
3 Mickey Mantle 5.00 12.00
4 Mickey Mantle 5.00 12.00
5 Mickey Mantle 5.00 12.00
6 Mickey Mantle 5.00 12.00
7 Mickey Mantle 5.00 12.00
8 Mickey Mantle 5.00 12.00
9 Mickey Mantle 5.00 12.00
10 Mickey Mantle 5.00 12.00
11 Mickey Mantle 5.00 12.00
12 Mickey Mantle 5.00 12.00
13 Mickey Mantle 5.00 12.00
14 Mickey Mantle 5.00 12.00
15 Mickey Mantle 5.00 12.00
16 Mickey Mantle 5.00 12.00
17 Mickey Mantle 5.00 12.00
18 Mickey Mantle 5.00 12.00
19 Mickey Mantle 5.00 12.00
20 Mickey Mantle 5.00 12.00
21 Mickey Mantle 5.00 12.00
22 Mickey Mantle 5.00 12.00
23 Mickey Mantle 5.00 12.00
24 Mickey Mantle 5.00 12.00
25 Barry Bonds 5.00 12.00
26 Barry Bonds 5.00 12.00
27 Barry Bonds 5.00 12.00
28 Barry Bonds 5.00 12.00
29 Barry Bonds 5.00 12.00
30 Barry Bonds 5.00 12.00
31 Barry Bonds 5.00 12.00
32 Barry Bonds 5.00 12.00
33 Barry Bonds 5.00 12.00
34 Barry Bonds 5.00 12.00
35 Barry Bonds 5.00 12.00
36 Barry Bonds 5.00 12.00
37 Barry Bonds 5.00 12.00
38 Barry Bonds 5.00 12.00
39 Barry Bonds 5.00 12.00
40 Barry Bonds 5.00 12.00
41 Barry Bonds 5.00 12.00
42 Barry Bonds 5.00 12.00
43 Barry Bonds 5.00 12.00
44 Barry Bonds 5.00 12.00
45 Barry Bonds 5.00 12.00
46 Barry Bonds 5.00 12.00
47 Barry Bonds 5.00 12.00
48 Barry Bonds 5.00 12.00
49 Ichiro Suzuki 4.00 10.00
50 Ichiro Suzuki 4.00 10.00
51 Ichiro Suzuki 4.00 10.00
52 Ichiro Suzuki 4.00 10.00
53 Ichiro Suzuki 4.00 10.00
54 Ichiro Suzuki 4.00 10.00
55 Ichiro Suzuki 4.00 10.00
56 Ichiro Suzuki 4.00 10.00
57 Carl Yastrzemski 3.00 8.00
58 Carl Yastrzemski 3.00 8.00
59 Carl Yastrzemski 3.00 8.00
60 Carl Yastrzemski 3.00 8.00
61 Carl Yastrzemski 3.00 8.00
62 Carl Yastrzemski 3.00 8.00
63 Carl Yastrzemski 3.00 8.00
64 Carl Yastrzemski 3.00 8.00
65 David Wright 3.00 8.00
66 David Wright 3.00 8.00
67 David Wright 3.00 8.00
68 David Wright 3.00 8.00
69 David Wright 3.00 8.00
70 David Wright 3.00 8.00
71 David Wright 3.00 8.00
72 David Wright 3.00 8.00
73 David Wright 3.00 8.00
74 David Wright 3.00 8.00
75 David Wright 3.00 8.00
76 David Wright 3.00 8.00
77 Roberto Clemente 6.00 15.00
78 Roberto Clemente 6.00 15.00
79 Roberto Clemente 6.00 15.00
80 Roberto Clemente 6.00 15.00
81 Roberto Clemente 6.00 15.00
82 Johan Santana 3.00 8.00
83 Johan Santana 3.00 8.00
84 Johan Santana 3.00 8.00
85 Johan Santana 3.00 8.00
86 Johan Santana 3.00 8.00
87 Johan Santana 3.00 8.00
88 Johan Santana 3.00 8.00
89 Johan Santana 3.00 8.00
90 Justin Morneau 3.00 8.00
91 Justin Morneau 3.00 8.00
92 Justin Morneau 3.00 8.00
93 Justin Morneau 3.00 8.00
94 Justin Morneau 3.00 8.00
95 Justin Morneau 3.00 8.00
96 Justin Morneau 3.00 8.00
97 Justin Morneau 3.00 8.00
98 Justin Morneau 3.00 8.00
99 Justin Morneau 3.00 8.00
100 Justin Morneau 3.00 8.00
101 Justin Morneau 3.00 8.00
102 Reggie Jackson 3.00 8.00
103 Reggie Jackson 3.00 8.00
104 Reggie Jackson 3.00 8.00
105 Reggie Jackson 3.00 8.00
106 Reggie Jackson 3.00 8.00
107 Reggie Jackson 3.00 8.00
108 Reggie Jackson 3.00 8.00
109 Reggie Jackson 3.00 8.00
110 Roger Clemens 4.00 10.00
111 Roger Clemens 4.00 10.00
112 Roger Clemens 4.00 10.00
113 Roger Clemens 4.00 10.00
114 Roger Clemens 4.00 10.00
115 Roger Clemens 4.00 10.00
116 Roger Clemens 4.00 10.00
117 Roger Clemens 4.00 10.00
118 Ted Williams 5.00 12.00
119 Ted Williams 5.00 12.00
120 Ted Williams 5.00 12.00
121 Ted Williams 5.00 12.00
122 Ted Williams 5.00 12.00
123 Yogi Berra 3.00 8.00
124 Yogi Berra 3.00 8.00
125 Yogi Berra 3.00 8.00
126 Yogi Berra 3.00 8.00
127 Yogi Berra 3.00 8.00
128 Yogi Berra 3.00 8.00
129 Yogi Berra 3.00 8.00
130 Yogi Berra 3.00 8.00
131 Hideki Matsui 3.00 8.00
132 Hideki Matsui 3.00 8.00
133 Hideki Matsui 3.00 8.00
134 Hideki Matsui 3.00 8.00
135 Hideki Matsui 3.00 8.00
136 Ryan Howard 3.00 8.00
137 Ryan Howard 3.00 8.00
138 Ryan Howard 3.00 8.00
139 Ryan Howard 3.00 8.00
140 Ryan Howard 3.00 8.00
141 Ryan Howard 3.00 8.00
142 Ryan Howard 3.00 8.00
143 Ryan Howard 3.00 8.00
144 Tony Gwynn 3.00 8.00
145 Tony Gwynn 3.00 8.00
146 Tony Gwynn 3.00 8.00
147 Tony Gwynn 3.00 8.00
148 Tony Gwynn 3.00 8.00
149 Tony Gwynn 3.00 8.00
150 Tony Gwynn 3.00 8.00
151 Tony Gwynn 3.00 8.00
152 David Ortiz 2.50 6.00
153 David Ortiz 2.50 6.00
154 David Ortiz 2.50 6.00
155 David Ortiz 2.50 6.00
156 David Ortiz 2.50 6.00
157 David Ortiz 2.50 6.00
158 David Ortiz 2.50 6.00
159 David Ortiz 2.50 6.00
160 Tom Seaver 2.50 6.00
161 Tom Seaver 2.50 6.00
162 Tom Seaver 2.50 6.00
163 Tom Seaver 2.50 6.00
164 Tom Seaver 2.50 6.00
165 Tom Seaver 2.50 6.00
166 Tom Seaver 2.50 6.00
167 Tom Seaver 2.50 6.00
168 Albert Pujols 4.00 10.00
169 Albert Pujols 4.00 10.00
170 Albert Pujols 4.00 10.00
171 Albert Pujols 4.00 10.00
172 Albert Pujols 4.00 10.00
173 Albert Pujols 4.00 10.00
174 Albert Pujols 4.00 10.00
175 Albert Pujols 4.00 10.00
176 Stan Musial 3.00 8.00
177 Stan Musial 3.00 8.00
178 Stan Musial 3.00 8.00
179 Stan Musial 3.00 8.00
180 Stan Musial 3.00 8.00
181 Stan Musial 3.00 8.00
182 Stan Musial 3.00 8.00
183 Stan Musial 3.00 8.00
184 Chien-Ming Wang 5.00 12.00
185 Chien-Ming Wang 5.00 12.00
186 Chien-Ming Wang 5.00 12.00
187 Chien-Ming Wang 5.00 12.00
188 Chien-Ming Wang 5.00 12.00
189 Chien-Ming Wang 5.00 12.00
190 Chien-Ming Wang 5.00 12.00
191 Chien-Ming Wang 5.00 12.00
192 Ryne Sandberg 4.00 10.00
193 Ryne Sandberg 4.00 10.00
194 Ryne Sandberg 4.00 10.00
195 Ryne Sandberg 4.00 10.00
196 Ryne Sandberg 4.00 10.00
197 Ryne Sandberg 4.00 10.00
198 Ryne Sandberg 4.00 10.00
199 Ryne Sandberg 4.00 10.00
200 Nolan Ryan 8.00 20.00
201 Nolan Ryan 8.00 20.00
202 Nolan Ryan 8.00 20.00
203 Nolan Ryan 8.00 20.00
204 Nolan Ryan 8.00 20.00
205 Nolan Ryan 8.00 20.00
206 Nolan Ryan 8.00 20.00
207 Nolan Ryan 8.00 20.00
208 Bob Gibson 2.50 6.00
209 Bob Gibson 2.50 6.00
210 Bob Gibson 2.50 6.00
211 Bob Gibson 2.50 6.00
212 Bob Gibson 2.50 6.00
213 Bob Gibson 2.50 6.00
214 Bob Gibson 2.50 6.00
215 Bob Gibson 2.50 6.00
216 Roger Maris 3.00 8.00
217 Roger Maris 3.00 8.00
218 Roger Maris 3.00 8.00
219 Roger Maris 3.00 8.00
220 Roger Maris 3.00 8.00
221 Manny Ramirez 3.00 8.00
222 Manny Ramirez 3.00 8.00
223 Manny Ramirez 3.00 8.00
224 Manny Ramirez 3.00 8.00
225 Manny Ramirez 3.00 8.00
226 Manny Ramirez 3.00 8.00
227 Manny Ramirez 3.00 8.00
228 Manny Ramirez 3.00 8.00
229 Mike Schmidt 4.00 10.00
230 Mike Schmidt 4.00 10.00
231 Mike Schmidt 4.00 10.00
232 Mike Schmidt 4.00 10.00
233 Mike Schmidt 4.00 10.00
234 Mike Schmidt 4.00 10.00
235 Mike Schmidt 4.00 10.00
236 Mike Schmidt 4.00 10.00
237 Alex Rodriguez 3.00 8.00
238 Alex Rodriguez 3.00 8.00
239 Alex Rodriguez 3.00 8.00
240 Alex Rodriguez 3.00 8.00
241 Alex Rodriguez 3.00 8.00
242 Alex Rodriguez 3.00 8.00
243 Alex Rodriguez 3.00 8.00
244 Alex Rodriguez 3.00 8.00
245 Daisuke Matsuzaka RC 6.00 15.00
246 Daisuke Matsuzaka RC 6.00 15.00
247 Daisuke Matsuzaka RC 6.00 15.00
248 Daisuke Matsuzaka RC 6.00 15.00
249 Daisuke Matsuzaka RC 6.00 15.00
250 Joe DiMaggio 4.00 10.00
251 Joe DiMaggio 4.00 10.00
252 Joe DiMaggio 4.00 10.00
253 Joe DiMaggio 4.00 10.00
254 Joe DiMaggio 4.00 10.00

2007 Topps Sterling Framed Burgundy

COMMON MANTLE (1-24) 20.00 50.00
COMMON BONDS (25-48) 12.50 30.00
COMMON ICHIRO (49-56) 12.50 30.00
COMMON YAZ (57-64) 12.50 30.00
COMMON WRIGHT (65-76) 10.00 25.00
COMMON CLEMENTE (77-81) 20.00 50.00
COMMON SANTANA (82-89) 8.00 20.00
COMMON MORNEAU (90-101) 6.00 15.00
COMMON R.JACKSON (102-109) 10.00 25.00
COMMON CLEMENS (110-117) 10.00 25.00
COMMON T.WILLIAMS (118-122) 12.50 30.00
COMMON BERRA (123-130) 6.00 15.00
COMMON MATSUI (131-135) 8.00 20.00
COMMON HOWARD (136-143) 10.00 25.00
COMMON GWYNN (144-151) 20.00 50.00
COMMON ORTIZ (152-159) 6.00 15.00
COMMON SEAVER (160-167) 8.00 20.00
COMMON PUJOLS (168-175) 12.50 30.00
COMMON MUSIAL (176-183) 10.00 25.00
COMMON WANG (184-191) 15.00 40.00
COMMON SANDBERG (192-199) 12.50 30.00
COMMON N.RYAN (200-207) 30.00 60.00
COMMON B.GIBSON (208-215) 8.00 20.00
COMMON MARIS (216-220) 12.50 30.00
COMMON M.RAMIREZ (221-228) 6.00 15.00
COMMON SCHMIDT (229-236) 15.00 40.00
COMMON A.ROD (237-244) 20.00 50.00
COMMON MATSUZAKA (245-249) 20.00 50.00
COMMON DIMAGGIO (250-254) 15.00 40.00
RANDOMLY INSERTED IN MYSTERY PACKS
STATED PRINT RUN 14 SER.#'d SETS

2007 Topps Sterling Framed Cherry Wood

RANDOM INSERTS IN MYSTERY PACKS
STATED PRINT RUN 1 SER.#'d SET
NO PRICING DUE TO SCARCITY

2007 Topps Sterling Framed Gold

COMPLETE SET (254)
COMMON MANTLE (1-24) 40.00 80.00
COMMON BONDS (25-48) 30.00 60.00
COMMON ICHIRO (49-56) 20.00 50.00
COMMON YAZ (57-64) 15.00 40.00
COMMON WRIGHT (65-76) 15.00 40.00
COMMON CLEMENTE (77-81) 30.00 60.00
COMMON SANTANA (82-89) 10.00 25.00
COMMON MORNEAU (90-101) 6.00 15.00
COMMON R.JACKSON (102-109) 12.50 30.00
COMMON CLEMENS (110-117) 12.50 30.00
COMMON T.WILLIAMS (118-122) 15.00 40.00
COMMON BERRA (123-130) 10.00 25.00
COMMON MATSUI (131-135) 15.00 40.00
COMMON HOWARD (136-143) 12.50 30.00
COMMON GWYNN (144-151) 30.00 60.00
COMMON ORTIZ (152-159) 8.00 20.00
COMMON SEAVER (160-167) 10.00 25.00
COMMON PUJOLS (168-175) 20.00 50.00
COMMON MUSIAL (176-183) 12.50 30.00
COMMON WANG (184-191) 30.00 60.00
COMMON SANDBERG (192-199) 15.00 40.00
COMMON N.RYAN (200-207) 30.00 60.00
COMMON B.GIBSON (208-215) 12.50 30.00
COMMON MARIS (216-220) 12.50 30.00
COMMON M.RAMIREZ (221-228) 8.00 20.00
COMMON SCHMIDT (229-236) 20.00 50.00
COMMON A.ROD (237-244) 20.00 50.00
COMMON MATSUZAKA (245-249) 30.00 60.00
COMMON DIMAGGIO (250-254) 20.00 50.00
RANDOMLY INSERTED IN MYSTERY PACKS
STATED PRINT RUN 9 SER.#'d SETS

2007 Topps Sterling Framed Sterling Silver

RANDOM INSERTS IN MYSTERY PACKS
STATED PRINT RUN 1 SER.#'d SET
NO PRICING DUE TO SCARCITY

NO STER.SIL. PRICING DUE TO SCARCITY
SS PRIME PRINT RUN 1 SER.#'d SET
NO SS PRIME PRICING DUE TO SCARCITY
OS Ozzie Smith
RS Ryne Sandberg
TG Tony Gwynn

2007 Topps Sterling Framed White Suede

*FRAMED WHITE: .6X TO 1.5X BASIC
RANDOM INSERTS IN MYSTERY PACKS
STATED PRINT RUN 50 SER.#'d SETS

2007 Topps Sterling Bat Barrels

RANDOM INSERTS IN BOXES
OVERALL ONE AUTO OR MEM PER BOX
STATED PRINT RUN 1 SER.#'d SET
NO PRICING DUE TO SCARCITY

2007 Topps Sterling Career Stats Relics Five

COMMON MANTLE 100.00 175.00
COMMON BONDS 30.00 60.00
COMMON ICHIRO 75.00 150.00
COMMON YAZ 30.00 60.00
COMMON WRIGHT 40.00 80.00
COMMON CLEMENTE 90.00 150.00
COMMON MORNEAU 12.50 30.00
COMMON CLEMENS 20.00 50.00
COMMON T.WILLIAMS 75.00 150.00
COMMON MATSUI 50.00 100.00
COMMON HOWARD 30.00 60.00
COMMON ORTIZ 20.00 50.00
COMMON PUJOLS 30.00 60.00
COMMON WANG 40.00 80.00
COMMON RYAN 50.00 100.00
COMMON GIBSON 20.00 50.00
COMMON MARIS 50.00 100.00
COMMON M.RAMIREZ 15.00 40.00
COMMON SCHMIDT 40.00 80.00
COMMON A.ROD 60.00 120.00
COMMON MATSUZAKA 60.00 120.00
COMMON DIMAGGIO 60.00 120.00
RANDOM INSERTS IN BOXES
OVERALL ONE AUTO OR MEM PER BOX
STATED PRINT RUN 10 SER.#'d SETS
NO BERRA,GWYNN PRICING
NO SEAVER,SANDBERG PRICING

2007 Topps Sterling Career Stats Relics Five Sterling Silver

RANDOM INSERTS IN BOXES
OVERALL ONE AUTO OR MEM PER BOX
OVERALL ONE OF ONE RELICS 1:10 BOXES
STATED PRINT RUN ONE SER.#'d SET
NO PRICING DUE TO SCARCITY

2007 Topps Sterling Career Stats Relics Quad

COMMON MANTLE 100.00 175.00
COMMON BONDS 20.00 50.00
COMMON ICHIRO 60.00 120.00
COMMON YAZ 30.00 60.00
COMMON CLEMENTE 90.00 150.00
COMMON SANTANA 15.00 40.00
COMMON CLEMENS 15.00 40.00
COMMON T.WILLIAMS 75.00 150.00
COMMON MATUSI 40.00 80.00
COMMON ORTIZ 15.00 40.00
COMMON SEAVER 30.00 60.00
COMMON PUJOLS 20.00 50.00
COMMON GIBSON 20.00 50.00
COMMON MARIS 50.00 100.00
COMMON SCHMIDT 40.00 80.00
COMMON MATSUZAKA 60.00 120.00
COMMON DIMAGGIO 60.00 120.00
RANDOM INSERTS IN BOXES
OVERALL ONE AUTO OR MEM PER BOX
STATED PRINT RUN 10 SER.#'d SETS
NO WRIGHT,MORNEAU,JACKSON PRICING
NO HOWARD,MUSIAL,WANG PRICING
NO SANDBERG PRICING

2007 Topps Sterling Career Stats Relics Quad Sterling Silver

RANDOM INSERTS IN BOXES
OVERALL ONE AUTO OR MEM PER BOX
OVERALL ONE OF ONE RELICS 1:10 BOXES
STATED PRINT RUN ONE SER.#'d SET
NO PRICING DUE TO SCARCITY

2007 Topps Sterling Career Stats Relics Six

COMMON MANTLE 100.00 200.00
COMMON BONDS 30.00 60.00
COMMON ICHIRO 75.00 150.00
COMMON D.WRIGHT 40.00 80.00
COMMON CLEMENTE 100.00 200.00
COMMON SANTANA 20.00 50.00
COMMON MORNEAU 12.50 30.00
COMMON R.JACKSON 30.00 60.00
COMMON CLEMENS 20.00 50.00
COMMON T.WILLIAMS 100.00 200.00
COMMON MATSUI 50.00 100.00
COMMON ORTIZ 20.00 50.00
COMMON PUJOLS 40.00 80.00
COMMON WANG 50.00 100.00
COMMON SANDBERG 20.00 50.00
COMMON RYAN 50.00 100.00
COMMON MARIS 50.00 100.00
COMMON M.RAMIREZ 20.00 50.00
COMMON SCHMIDT 40.00 80.00
COMMON AROD 75.00 150.00
COMMON MATSUZAKA 75.00 150.00
COMMON DIMAGGIO 75.00 150.00
RANDOM INSERTS IN BOXES
OVERALL ONE AUTO OR MEM PER BOX
STATED PRINT RUN 10 SER.#'d SETS
NO YAZ,BERRA,GWYNN PRICING
NO MUSIAL OR GIBSON PRICING

2007 Topps Sterling Career Stats Relics Six Sterling Silver

RANDOM INSERTS IN BOXES
OVERALL ONE AUTO OR MEM PER BOX
OVERALL ONE OF ONE RELICS 1:10 BOXES
STATED PRINT RUN ONE SER.#'d SET
NO PRICING DUE TO SCARCITY

2007 Topps Sterling Career Stats Relics Triple

COMMON MANTLE 90.00 150.00
COMMON BONDS 20.00 50.00
COMMON ICHIRO 60.00 120.00
COMMON D.WRIGHT 30.00 60.00
COMMON CLEMENTE 75.00 150.00
COMMON MORNEAU 10.00 25.00
COMMON CLEMENS 15.00 40.00
COMMON T.WILLIAMS 50.00 100.00
COMMON BERRA 30.00 60.00
COMMON MATSUI 30.00 60.00
COMMON ORTIZ 15.00 40.00
COMMON SEAVER 20.00 50.00
COMMON PUJOLS 20.00 50.00
COMMON MUSIAL 30.00 60.00
COMMON GIBSON 15.00 40.00
COMMON MARIS 40.00 80.00
COMMON SCHMIDT 40.00 80.00
COMMON MATSUZAKA 60.00 120.00
COMMON DIMAGGIO 60.00 120.00
RANDOM INSERTS IN BOXES
OVERALL ONE AUTO OR MEM PER BOX
STATED PRINT RUN 10 SER.#'d SETS
NO YAZ,JACKSON,GWYNN PRICING
NO SANDBERG,RYAN PRICING

2007 Topps Sterling Career Stats Relics Triple Sterling Silver

RANDOM INSERTS IN BOXES
OVERALL ONE AUTO OR MEM PER BOX
OVERALL ONE OF ONE RELICS 1:10 BOXES
STATED PRINT RUN ONE SER.#'d SET
NO PRICING DUE TO SCARCITY

2007 Topps Sterling Career Stats Relics Autographs Quad

COMMON YAZ 50.00 100.00
COMMON D.WRIGHT 75.00 150.00
COMMON SANTANA 50.00 100.00
COMMON MORNEAU 20.00 50.00
COMMON R.JACKSON 40.00 80.00
COMMON R.CLEMENS 60.00 120.00
COMMON Y.BERRA 60.00 120.00
COMMON R.HOWARD 50.00 100.00
COMMON T.GWYNN 60.00 120.00
COMMON ORTIZ 50.00 100.00
COMMON T.SEAVER 40.00 80.00
COMMON PUJOLS 175.00 300.00
COMMON MUSIAL 60.00 120.00
COMMON WANG 150.00 250.00
COMMON SANDBERG 60.00 120.00
COMMON RYAN 75.00 150.00
COMMON GIBSON 30.00 60.00
COMMON M.RAMIREZ 40.00 80.00
COMMON SCHMIDT 60.00 120.00
COMMON AROD 175.00 300.00
RANDOM INSERTS IN BOXES
OVERALL ONE AUTO OR MEM PER BOX
STATED PRINT RUN 10 SER.#'d SETS
NO MATSUI PRICING DUE TO SCARCITY

2007 Topps Sterling Career Stats Relics Autographs Quad Sterling Silver

RANDOM INSERTS IN BOXES
OVERALL ONE AUTO OR MEM PER BOX
OVERALL ONE OF ONE AUTO 1:10 BOXES
STATED PRINT RUN ONE SER.#'d SET
NO PRICING DUE TO SCARCITY

2007 Topps Sterling Career Stats Relics Autographs Triple

COMMON BONDS 175.00 300.00
COMMON YAZ 40.00 80.00
COMMON D.WRIGHT 60.00 120.00
COMMON SANTANA 40.00 80.00
COMMON MORNEAU 20.00 50.00
COMMON R.JACKSON 30.00 60.00
COMMON R.CLEMENS 60.00 120.00
COMMON Y.BERRA 50.00 100.00
COMMON R.HOWARD 50.00 100.00
COMMON T.GWYNN 50.00 100.00
COMMON ORTIZ 40.00 80.00
COMMON T.SEAVER 40.00 80.00
COMMON PUJOLS 175.00 300.00
COMMON MUSIAL 50.00 100.00
COMMON WANG 150.00 250.00
COMMON SANDBERG 50.00 100.00
COMMON RYAN 60.00 120.00
COMMON GIBSON 30.00 60.00
COMMON M.RAMIREZ 30.00 60.00
COMMON SCHMIDT 60.00 120.00
COMMON AROD 175.00 300.00
RANDOM INSERTS IN BOXES
OVERALL ONE AUTO OR MEM PER BOX
STATED PRINT RUN 10 SER.#'d SETS

2007 Topps Sterling Career Stats Relics Autographs Triple Sterling Silver

RANDOM INSERTS IN BOXES
OVERALL ONE AUTO OR MEM PER BOX
OVERALL ONE OF ONE AUTO 1:10 BOXES
STATED PRINT RUN ONE SER.#'d SET
NO PRICING DUE TO SCARCITY

2007 Topps Sterling Cut Signatures

RANDOM INSERTS IN BOXES
OVERALL ONE AUTO OR MEM PER BOX
STATED PRINT RUN 1 SER.#'d SET
NO PRICING DUE TO SCARCITY

2007 Topps Sterling Jumbo Swatch

RANDOM INSERTS IN BOXES
OVERALL ONE AUTO OR MEM PER BOX
STATED PRINT RUN 10 SER.#'d SETS
NO PRICING DUE TO SCARCITY
SJS1 Barry Bonds
SJS2 Ichiro Suzuki
SJS3 David Wright
SJS4 Johan Santana
SJS5 Justin Morneau
SJS6 Reggie Jackson
SJS7 Roger Clemens
SJS8 Hideki Matsui
SJS9 Ryan Howard
SJS10 Ryan Howard
SJS11 David Ortiz
SJS12 David Ortiz
SJS13 Tom Seaver
SJS14 Albert Pujols
SJS15 Stan Musial
SJS16 Chien-Ming Wang
SJS17 Ryne Sandberg
SJS18 Nolan Ryan
SJS19 Mike Schmidt
SJS20 Alex Rodriguez

2007 Topps Sterling Jumbo Swatch Autographs

RANDOM INSERTS IN BOXES
OVERALL ONE AUTO OR MEM PER BOX
STATED PRINT RUN 10 SER.#'d SETS
NO PRICING DUE TO SCARCITY

2007 Topps Sterling Letter Patch

RANDOM INSERTS IN MYSTERY PACKS
OVERALL LETTER ODDS 1:10 BOXES
STATED PRINT RUN 1 SER.#'d SET
TOTAL LETTER PRINT RUNS LISTED BELOW
CARDS LISTED ALPHABETICALLY
NO PRICING DUE TO SCARCITY

2007 Topps Sterling Moments Relics Eight

COMMON MANTLE 275.00 375.00
COMMON BONDS 150.00 250.00
COMMON MATSUI 75.00 150.00
COMMON ORTIZ 40.00 80.00
RANDOM INSERTS IN BOXES
OVERALL ONE AUTO OR MEM PER BOX
STATED PRINT RUN 10 SER.#'d SETS
NO PRICING ON MOST DUE TO SCARCITY

2007 Topps Sterling Moments Relics Eight Sterling Silver

RANDOM INSERTS IN BOXES
OVERALL ONE AUTO OR MEM PER BOX
OVERALL ONE OF ONE RELICS 1:10 BOXES
STATED PRINT RUN ONE SER.#'d SET
NO PRICING DUE TO SCARCITY

2007 Topps Sterling Moments Relics Five

COMMON MANTLE 100.00 175.00
COMMON BONDS 30.00 60.00
COMMON ICHIRO 75.00 150.00
COMMON YAZ 30.00 60.00
COMMON WRIGHT 40.00 80.00
COMMON CLEMENTE 90.00 150.00
COMMON MORNEAU 12.50 30.00
COMMON CLEMENS 20.00 50.00
COMMON T.WILLIAMS 75.00 150.00
COMMON MATSUI 50.00 100.00
COMMON HOWARD 30.00 60.00
COMMON ORTIZ 20.00 50.00
COMMON PUJOLS 30.00 60.00
COMMON WANG 40.00 80.00
COMMON RYAN 50.00 100.00
COMMON GIBSON 20.00 50.00
COMMON MARIS 50.00 100.00
COMMON M.RAMIREZ 15.00 40.00
COMMON SCHMIDT 40.00 80.00
COMMON A.ROD 60.00 120.00
COMMON MATSUZAKA 60.00 120.00
COMMON DIMAGGIO 60.00 120.00
RANDOM INSERTS IN BOXES
OVERALL ONE AUTO OR MEM PER BOX
STATED PRINT RUN 10 SER.#'d SETS
NO JOHAN,SEAVER,MUSIAL PRICING

2007 Topps Sterling Moments Relics Five Sterling Silver

RANDOM INSERTS IN BOXES
OVERALL ONE AUTO OR MEM PER BOX
OVERALL ONE OF ONE RELICS 1:10 BOXES
STATED PRINT RUN ONE SER.#'d SET
NO PRICING DUE TO SCARCITY

2007 Topps Sterling Moments Relics Quad

COMMON MANTLE 100.00 175.00
COMMON BONDS 20.00 50.00
COMMON ICHIRO 60.00 120.00
COMMON YAZ 30.00 60.00
COMMON CLEMENTE 90.00 150.00
COMMON SANTANA 15.00 40.00
COMMON CLEMENS 15.00 40.00
COMMON T.WILLIAMS 75.00 150.00
COMMON MATUSI 40.00 80.00
COMMON ORTIZ 15.00 40.00
COMMON SEAVER 30.00 60.00
COMMON PUJOLS 20.00 50.00
COMMON GIBSON 20.00 50.00
COMMON MARIS 50.00 100.00
COMMON SCHMIDT 40.00 80.00
COMMON MATSUZAKA 60.00 120.00
COMMON DIMAGGIO 60.00 120.00
RANDOM INSERTS IN BOXES
OVERALL ONE AUTO OR MEM PER BOX
STATED PRINT RUN 10 SER.#'d SETS
NO WRIGHT,MORNEAU,BERRA PRICING
NO GWYNN OR MUSIAL PRICING

2007 Topps Sterling Moments Relics Quad Sterling Silver

RANDOM INSERTS IN BOXES
OVERALL ONE AUTO OR MEM PER BOX
OVERALL ONE OF ONE RELICS 1:10 BOXES
STATED PRINT RUN ONE SER.#'d SET
NO PRICING DUE TO SCARCITY

2007 Topps Sterling Moments Relics Six

COMMON MANTLE 100.00 200.00
COMMON BONDS 30.00 60.00
COMMON ICHIRO 75.00 150.00
COMMON D.WRIGHT 40.00 100.00
COMMON CLEMENTE 100.00 200.00
COMMON SANTANA 20.00 50.00
COMMON MORNEAU 12.50 30.00
COMMON R.JACKSON 30.00 60.00
COMMON CLEMENS 20.00 50.00
COMMON T.WILLIAMS 100.00 200.00
COMMON MATSUI 50.00 100.00
COMMON ORTIZ 20.00 50.00
COMMON PUJOLS 40.00 80.00
COMMON WANG 50.00 100.00
COMMON SANDBERG 20.00 50.00
COMMON RYAN 50.00 100.00
COMMON MARIS 50.00 100.00
COMMON M.RAMIREZ 20.00 50.00
COMMON SCHMIDT 40.00 80.00
COMMON AROD 75.00 150.00
COMMON MATSUZAKA 75.00 150.00
COMMON DIMAGGIO 75.00 150.00
RANDOM INSERTS IN BOXES
OVERALL ONE AUTO OR MEM PER BOX
STATED PRINT RUN 10 SER.#'d SETS
NO HOWARD PRICING

2007 Topps Sterling Moments Relics Six Sterling Silver

RANDOM INSERTS IN BOXES
OVERALL ONE AUTO OR MEM PER BOX
OVERALL ONE OF ONE RELICS 1:10 BOXES
STATED PRINT RUN ONE SER.#'d SET
NO PRICING DUE TO SCARCITY

2007 Topps Sterling Moments Relics Triple

COMMON MANTLE 90.00 150.00
COMMON BONDS 20.00 50.00
COMMON ICHIRO 60.00 120.00
COMMON D.WRIGHT 30.00 60.00
COMMON CLEMENTE 75.00 150.00
COMMON MORNEAU 10.00 25.00
COMMON CLEMENS 15.00 40.00
COMMON T.WILLIAMS 50.00 100.00
COMMON BERRA 30.00 60.00
COMMON MATSUI 30.00 60.00
COMMON ORTIZ 15.00 40.00
COMMON SEAVER 20.00 50.00
COMMON PUJOLS 20.00 50.00
COMMON MUSIAL 30.00 60.00
COMMON GIBSON 15.00 40.00
COMMON MARIS 40.00 80.00
COMMON SCHMIDT 40.00 80.00
COMMON MATSUZAKA 60.00 120.00
COMMON DIMAGGIO 60.00 120.00
RANDOM INSERTS IN BOXES
OVERALL ONE AUTO OR MEM PER BOX
STATED PRINT RUN 10 SER.#'d SETS
NO JACKSON OR GWYNN PRICING

2007 Topps Sterling Moments Relics Triple Sterling Silver

RANDOM INSERTS IN BOXES
OVERALL ONE AUTO OR MEM PER BOX
OVERALL ONE OF ONE RELICS 1:10 BOXES
STATED PRINT RUN ONE SER.#'d SET
NO PRICING DUE TO SCARCITY

2007 Topps Sterling Moments Relics Autographs Eight

COMMON M.RAMIREZ 60.00 120.00
RANDOM INSERTS IN BOXES
OVERALL ONE AUTO OR MEM PER BOX
STATED PRINT RUN 10 SER.#'d SETS
NO PRICING ON MOST DUE TO SCARCITY

2007 Topps Sterling Moments Relics Autographs Eight Sterling Silver

RANDOM INSERTS IN BOXES
OVERALL ONE AUTO OR MEM PER BOX
OVERALL ONE OF ONE AUTO 1:10 BOXES
STATED PRINT RUN ONE SER.#'d SET
NO PRICING DUE TO SCARCITY

2007 Topps Sterling Moments Relics Autographs Quad

COMMON YAZ 50.00 100.00
COMMON D.WRIGHT 75.00 150.00
COMMON SANTANA 50.00 100.00
COMMON MORNEAU 20.00 50.00
COMMON R.JACKSON 40.00 80.00
COMMON R.CLEMENS 60.00 120.00
COMMON Y.BERRA 60.00 120.00
COMMON R.HOWARD 50.00 100.00
COMMON T.GWYNN 60.00 120.00
COMMON ORTIZ 50.00 100.00
COMMON T.SEAVER 40.00 80.00
COMMON PUJOLS 175.00 300.00
COMMON MUSIAL 60.00 120.00
COMMON WANG 150.00 250.00
COMMON SANDBERG 60.00 120.00
COMMON RYAN 75.00 150.00
COMMON GIBSON 30.00 60.00
COMMON M.RAMIREZ 40.00 80.00
COMMON SCHMIDT 60.00 120.00
COMMON AROD 175.00 300.00
RANDOM INSERTS IN BOXES
OVERALL ONE AUTO OR MEM PER BOX
STATED PRINT RUN 10 SER.#'d SETS
NO BONDS PRICING DUE TO SCARCITY

2007 Topps Sterling Moments Relics Autographs Quad Sterling Silver

RANDOM INSERTS IN BOXES
OVERALL ONE AUTO OR MEM PER BOX
OVERALL ONE OF ONE AUTO 1:10 BOXES
STATED PRINT RUN ONE SER.#'d SET
NO PRICING DUE TO SCARCITY

2007 Topps Sterling Moments Relics Autographs Triple

COMMON BONDS 175.00 300.00
COMMON YAZ 40.00 80.00
COMMON D.WRIGHT 60.00 120.00
COMMON SANTANA 40.00 80.00
COMMON MORNEAU 20.00 50.00
COMMON R.JACKSON 30.00 60.00
COMMON R.CLEMENS 60.00 120.00
COMMON Y.BERRA 50.00 100.00
COMMON R.HOWARD 50.00 100.00
COMMON T.GWYNN 50.00 100.00
COMMON ORTIZ 40.00 80.00
COMMON T.SEAVER 40.00 80.00
COMMON PUJOLS 175.00 300.00
COMMON MUSIAL 50.00 100.00
COMMON WANG 150.00 250.00
COMMON SANDBERG 50.00 100.00
COMMON RYAN 60.00 120.00
COMMON GIBSON 30.00 60.00
COMMON M.RAMIREZ 30.00 60.00
COMMON SCHMIDT 60.00 120.00
COMMON AROD 175.00 300.00
RANDOM INSERTS IN BOXES
OVERALL ONE AUTO OR MEM PER BOX
STATED PRINT RUN 10 SER.#'d SETS

2007 Topps Sterling Moments Relics Autographs Triple Sterling Silver

RANDOM INSERTS IN BOXES
OVERALL ONE AUTO OR MEM PER BOX
OVERALL ONE OF ONE AUTO 1:10 BOXES
STATED PRINT RUN ONE SER.#'d SET
NO PRICING DUE TO SCARCITY

2007 Topps Sterling Stardom Relics Eight

COMMON MANTLE 275.00 375.00
COMMON BONDS 150.00 250.00
COMMON MATSUI 75.00 150.00
COMMON ORTIZ 40.00 80.00
RANDOM INSERTS IN BOXES
OVERALL ONE AUTO OR MEM PER BOX
STATED PRINT RUN 10 SER.#'d SETS
NO PRICING ON MOST DUE TO SCARCITY

2007 Topps Sterling Stardom Relics Eight Sterling Silver

RANDOM INSERTS IN BOXES
OVERALL ONE AUTO OR MEM PER BOX
OVERALL ONE OF ONE RELICS 1:10 BOXES
STATED PRINT RUN ONE SER.#'d SET
NO PRICING DUE TO SCARCITY

2007 Topps Sterling Stardom Relics Five

COMMON MANTLE 100.00 175.00
COMMON BONDS 30.00 60.00
COMMON ICHIRO 75.00 150.00
COMMON YAZ 30.00 60.00
COMMON WRIGHT 40.00 80.00
COMMON CLEMENTE 90.00 150.00
COMMON MORNEAU 12.50 30.00
COMMON CLEMENS 20.00 50.00
COMMON T.WILLIAMS 75.00 150.00
COMMON MATSUI 50.00 100.00
COMMON HOWARD 30.00 60.00
COMMON ORTIZ 20.00 50.00
COMMON PUJOLS 30.00 60.00
COMMON WANG 40.00 80.00
COMMON RYAN 50.00 100.00
COMMON GIBSON 20.00 50.00
COMMON MARIS 50.00 100.00
COMMON M.RAMIREZ 15.00 40.00
COMMON SCHMIDT 40.00 80.00
COMMON A.ROD 60.00 120.00
COMMON MATSUZAKA 60.00 120.00
COMMON DIMAGGIO 60.00 120.00
RANDOM INSERTS IN BOXES
OVERALL ONE AUTO OR MEM PER BOX
STATED PRINT RUN 10 SER.#'d SETS
NO JOHAN,JACKSON,BERRA PRICING

2007 Topps Sterling Stardom Relics Five Sterling Silver

RANDOM INSERTS IN BOXES
OVERALL ONE AUTO OR MEM PER BOX
OVERALL ONE OF ONE RELICS 1:10 BOXES
STATED PRINT RUN ONE SER.#'d SET
NO PRICING DUE TO SCARCITY

2007 Topps Sterling Stardom Relics Quad

COMMON MANTLE 100.00 175.00
COMMON BONDS 20.00 50.00
COMMON ICHIRO 60.00 120.00
COMMON YAZ 30.00 60.00
COMMON CLEMENTE 90.00 150.00
COMMON SANTANA 15.00 40.00
COMMON CLEMENS 15.00 40.00
COMMON T.WILLIAMS 75.00 150.00
COMMON MATUSI 40.00 80.00
COMMON ORTIZ 15.00 40.00
COMMON SEAVER 30.00 60.00
COMMON PUJOLS 20.00 50.00
COMMON GIBSON 20.00 50.00
COMMON MARIS 50.00 100.00
COMMON SCHMIDT 40.00 80.00
COMMON MATSUZAKA 60.00 120.00
COMMON DIMAGGIO 60.00 120.00
RANDOM INSERTS IN BOXES
OVERALL ONE AUTO OR MEM PER BOX
STATED PRINT RUN 10 SER.#'d SETS
NO BERRA,HOWARD,GWYNN PRICING
NO WANG,SANDBERG, AROD PRICING

2007 Topps Sterling Stardom Relics Quad Sterling Silver

RANDOM INSERTS IN BOXES
OVERALL ONE AUTO OR MEM PER BOX
OVERALL ONE OF ONE RELICS 1:10 BOXES
STATED PRINT RUN ONE SER.#'d SET
NO PRICING DUE TO SCARCITY

2007 Topps Sterling Stardom Relics Six

COMMON MANTLE 100.00 200.00
COMMON BONDS 30.00 60.00
COMMON ICHIRO 75.00 150.00
COMMON D.WRIGHT 40.00 100.00
COMMON CLEMENTE 100.00 200.00
COMMON SANTANA 20.00 50.00
COMMON MORNEAU 12.50 30.00
COMMON R.JACKSON 30.00 60.00
COMMON CLEMENS 20.00 50.00
COMMON T.WILLIAMS 100.00 200.00
COMMON MATSUI 50.00 100.00
COMMON ORTIZ 20.00 50.00
COMMON PUJOLS 40.00 80.00
COMMON WANG 50.00 100.00
COMMON SANDBERG 20.00 50.00
COMMON RYAN 50.00 100.00
COMMON MARIS 50.00 100.00
COMMON M.RAMIREZ 20.00 50.00
COMMON SCHMIDT 40.00 80.00
COMMON AROD 75.00 150.00
COMMON MATSUZAKA 75.00 150.00
COMMON DIMAGGIO 75.00 150.00
RANDOM INSERTS IN BOXES
OVERALL ONE AUTO OR MEM PER BOX
STATED PRINT RUN 10 SER.#'d SETS
NO HOWARD PRICING

2007 Topps Sterling Stardom Relics Six Sterling Silver

RANDOM INSERTS IN BOXES
OVERALL ONE AUTO OR MEM PER BOX
OVERALL ONE OF ONE RELICS 1:10 BOXES
STATED PRINT RUN ONE SER.#'d SET
NO PRICING DUE TO SCARCITY

2007 Topps Sterling Stardom Relics Triple

COMPLETE SET (73)
COMMON MANTLE 90.00 150.00
COMMON BONDS 20.00 50.00
COMMON ICHIRO 60.00 120.00
COMMON D.WRIGHT 30.00 60.00
COMMON CLEMENTE 75.00 150.00
COMMON MORNEAU 10.00 25.00
COMMON CLEMENS 15.00 40.00
COMMON T.WILLIAMS 50.00 100.00
COMMON BERRA 30.00 60.00
COMMON MATSUI 30.00 60.00
COMMON ORTIZ 15.00 40.00
COMMON SEAVER 20.00 50.00
COMMON PUJOLS 20.00 50.00
COMMON MUSIAL 30.00 60.00
COMMON GIBSON 15.00 40.00
COMMON MARIS 40.00 80.00
COMMON SCHMIDT 40.00 80.00
COMMON MATSUZAKA 60.00 120.00
COMMON DIMAGGIO 60.00 120.00
RANDOM INSERTS IN BOXES
OVERALL ONE AUTO OR MEM PER BOX
STATED PRINT RUN 10 SER.#'d SETS
NO YAZ OR RYAN PRICING

2007 Topps Sterling Stardom Relics Triple Sterling Silver

RANDOM INSERTS IN BOXES
OVERALL ONE AUTO OR MEM PER BOX

OVERALL ONE OF ONE RELICS 1:10 BOXES
STATED PRINT RUN ONE SER.#'d SET
NO PRICING DUE TO SCARCITY

2007 Topps Sterling Stardom Relics Autographs Eight

COMMON M.RAMIREZ 60.00 120.00
RANDOM INSERTS IN BOXES
OVERALL ONE AUTO OR MEM PER BOX
STATED PRINT RUN 10 SER.#'d SETS
NO PRICING ON MOST DUE TO SCARCITY

2007 Topps Sterling Stardom Relics Autographs Eight Sterling Silver

RANDOM INSERTS IN BOXES
OVERALL ONE AUTO OR MEM PER BOX
OVERALL ONE OF ONE AUTO 1:10 BOXES
STATED PRINT RUN ONE SER.#'d SET
NO PRICING DUE TO SCARCITY

2007 Topps Sterling Stardom Relics Autographs Quad

COMMON YAZ 50.00 100.00
COMMON D.WRIGHT 75.00 150.00
COMMON SANTANA 50.00 100.00
COMMON MORNEAU 20.00 50.00
COMMON R.JACKSON 40.00 80.00
COMMON R.CLEMENS 60.00 120.00
COMMON Y.BERRA 60.00 120.00
COMMON R.HOWARD 50.00 100.00
COMMON T.GWYNN 60.00 120.00
COMMON ORTIZ 50.00 100.00
COMMON T.SEAVER 40.00 80.00
COMMON PUJOLS 175.00 300.00
COMMON MUSIAL 60.00 120.00
COMMON WANG 150.00 250.00
COMMON SANDBERG 60.00 120.00
COMMON RYAN 75.00 150.00
COMMON GIBSON 30.00 60.00
COMMON M.RAMIREZ 40.00 80.00
COMMON SCHMIDT 60.00 120.00
COMMON AROD 175.00 300.00
RANDOM INSERTS IN BOXES
OVERALL ONE AUTO OR MEM PER BOX
STATED PRINT RUN 10 SER.#'d SETS
NO BONDS OR MATSUI PRICING

2007 Topps Sterling Stardom Relics Autographs Quad Sterling Silver

RANDOM INSERTS IN BOXES
OVERALL ONE AUTO OR MEM PER BOX
OVERALL ONE OF ONE AUTO 1:10 BOXES
STATED PRINT RUN ONE SER.#'d SET
NO PRICING DUE TO SCARCITY

2007 Topps Sterling Stardom Relics Autographs Triple

COMMON BONDS 175.00 300.00
COMMON YAZ 40.00 80.00
COMMON D.WRIGHT 60.00 120.00
COMMON SANTANA 40.00 80.00
COMMON MORNEAU 20.00 50.00
COMMON R.JACKSON 30.00 60.00
COMMON R.CLEMENS 60.00 120.00
COMMON Y.BERRA 50.00 100.00
COMMON R.HOWARD 50.00 100.00
COMMON T.GWYNN 50.00 100.00
COMMON ORTIZ 40.00 80.00
COMMON T.SEAVER 40.00 80.00
COMMON PUJOLS 175.00 300.00
COMMON MUSIAL 50.00 100.00
COMMON WANG 150.00 250.00
COMMON SANDBERG 50.00 100.00
COMMON RYAN 60.00 120.00
COMMON GIBSON 30.00 60.00
COMMON M.RAMIREZ 30.00 60.00
COMMON SCHMIDT 60.00 120.00
COMMON AROD 175.00 300.00
RANDOM INSERTS IN BOXES
OVERALL ONE AUTO OR MEM PER BOX
STATED PRINT RUN 10 SER.#'d SETS

2007 Topps Sterling Stardom Relics Autographs Triple Sterling Silver

RANDOM INSERTS IN BOXES
OVERALL ONE AUTO OR MEM PER BOX
OVERALL ONE OF ONE AUTO 1:10 BOXES
STATED PRINT RUN ONE SER.#'d SET
NO PRICING DUE TO SCARCITY

2002 Topps Total

This 990 card set was issued in June, 2002. These cards were issued in 10 card packs which came 36 packs to a box and six boxes to a case. Each card was numbered not only in a numerical sequence but also in a team sequence.

COMPLETE SET (990) 75.00 150.00
1 Joe Mauer RC 4.00 10.00
2 Derek Jeter .75 2.00
3 Shawn Green .10 .30
4 Vladimir Guerrero .30 .75
5 Mike Piazza .50 1.25
6 Brandon Duckworth .07 .20
7 Aramis Ramirez .10 .30
8 Josh Barfield RC 1.00 2.50
9 Troy Glaus .10 .30
10 Sammy Sosa .30 .75
11 Rod Barajas .07 .20
12 Tsuyoshi Shinjo .10 .30
13 Larry Bigbie .07 .20
14 Tino Martinez .20 .50
15 Craig Biggio .20 .50
16 Anastacio Martinez RC .15 .40
17 John McDonald .07 .20
18 Kyle Kane RC .08 .25
19 Aubrey Huff .10 .30
20 Juan Cruz .07 .20
21 Doug Creek .07 .20
22 Luther Hackman .07 .20
23 Rafael Furcal .10 .30
24 Andres Torres .07 .20
25 Jason Giambi .10 .30
26 Jose Paniagua .07 .20
27 Jose Offerman .07 .20
28 Alex Arias .07 .20
29 J.M. Gold .07 .20
30 Jeff Bagwell .20 .50
31 Brent Cookson .07 .20
32 Kelly Wunsch .07 .20
33 Larry Walker .10 .30
34 Luis Gonzalez .10 .30
35 John Franco .10 .30
36 Roy Oswalt .10 .30
37 Tom Glavine .20 .50
38 C.C. Sabathia .10 .30
39 Jay Gibbons .07 .20
40 Wilson Betemit .07 .20
41 Tony Armas Jr. .07 .20
42 Mo Vaughn .10 .30
43 Gerard Oakes RC .15 .40
44 Dmitri Young .10 .30
45 Tim Salmon .20 .50
46 Barry Zito .10 .30
47 Adrian Gonzalez .07 .20
48 Joe Davenport .07 .20
49 Adrian Hernandez .07 .20
50 Randy Johnson .30 .75
52 Adam Pettyjohn .07 .20
53 Alex Escobar .07 .20
54 Stevenson Agosto RC .08 .25
55 Omar Daal .07 .20
56 Mike Buddie .07 .20
57 Dave Williams .07 .20
58 Marquis Grissom .10 .30
59 Pat Burrell .10 .30
60 Mark Prior .20 .50
61 Mike Bynum .07 .20
62 Mike Hill RC .15 .40
63 Brandon Backe RC .20 .50
64 Dan Wilson .07 .20
65 Nick Johnson .10 .30
66 Jason Grimsley .07 .20
67 Russ Johnson .07 .20
68 Todd Walker .07 .20
69 Kyle Farnsworth .07 .20
70 Ben Broussard .07 .20
71 Garrett Guzman RC .15 .40
72 Terry Mulholland .07 .20
73 Tyler Houston .07 .20
74 Jace Brewer .07 .20
75 Chris Baker RC .15 .40
76 Frank Catalanotto .07 .20
77 Mike Redmond .07 .20
78 Matt Wise .07 .20
79 Fernando Vina .07 .20
80 Kevin Brown .10 .30
81 Grant Balfour .07 .20
82 Clint Nageotte RC .20 .50
83 Jeff Tam .07 .20
84 Steve Trachsel .07 .20
85 Tomo Ohka .07 .20
86 Keith McDonald .07 .20
87 Jose Ortiz .07 .20
88 Rusty Greer .10 .30
89 Jeff Suppan .07 .20
90 Moises Alou .10 .30
91 Juan Encarnacion .07 .20
92 Tyler Yates RC .15 .40
93 Scott Strickland .07 .20
94 Brent Butler .07 .20
95 Jon Rauch .07 .20
96 Brian Mallette RC .08 .25
97 Joe Randa .10 .30
98 Cesar Crespo .07 .20
99 Felix Rodriguez .07 .20
100 Chipper Jones .30 .75
101 Victor Martinez .30 .75
102 Danny Graves .07 .20
103 Brandon Berger .07 .20
104 Carlos Garcia .07 .20
105 Alfonso Soriano .10 .30
106 Allan Simpson RC .08 .25
107 Brad Thomas .07 .20
108 Devon White .10 .30
109 Scott Chiasson .07 .20
110 Cliff Floyd .10 .30
111 Scott Williamson .07 .20
112 Julio Zuleta .07 .20
113 Terry Adams .07 .20
114 Zach Day .07 .20
115 Ben Grieve .07 .20
116 Mark Ellis .07 .20
117 Bobby Jenks RC .60 1.50
118 LaTroy Hawkins .07 .20
119 Tim Raines Jr. .07 .20
120 Juan Uribe .07 .20
121 Bob Scanlan .07 .20
122 Brad Nelson RC .15 .40
123 Adam Johnson .07 .20
124 Raul Casanova .07 .20
125 Jeff D'Amico .07 .20
126 Aaron Cook RC .15 .40
127 Alan Benes .07 .20
128 Mark Little .07 .20
129 Randy Wolf .07 .20
130 Phil Nevin .10 .30
131 Guillermo Mota .07 .20
132 Nick Neugebauer .07 .20
133 Pedro Borbon Jr. .07 .20
134 Doug Mientkiewicz .10 .30
135 Edgardo Alfonzo .07 .20
136 Dustan Mohr .07 .20
137 Dan Reichert .07 .20
138 Dewon Brazelton .07 .20
139 Orlando Cabrera .10 .30
140 Todd Hollandsworth .07 .20
141 Darren Dreifort .07 .20
142 Jose Valentin .07 .20
143 Josh Kalinowski .07 .20
144 Randy Keisler .07 .20
145 Bret Boone .10 .30
146 Roosevelt Brown .07 .20
147 Brent Abernathy .07 .20
148 Jorge Julio .07 .20
149 Alex Gonzalez .07 .20
150 Juan Pierre .10 .30
151 Roger Cedeno .07 .20
152 Javier Vazquez .10 .30
153 Armando Benitez .07 .20
154 Dave Burba .07 .20
155 Brad Penny .07 .20
156 Ryan Jensen .07 .20
157 Jeromy Burnitz .10 .30
158 Matt Childers RC .15 .40
159 Wilmy Caceres .07 .20
160 Roger Clemens .60 1.50
161 Jamie Cerda RC .15 .40
162 Jason Christiansen .07 .20
163 Pokey Reese .07 .20
164 Ivanon Coffie .07 .20
165 Joaquin Benoit .07 .20
166 Mike Matheny .07 .20
167 Eric Cammack .07 .20
168 Alex Graman .07 .20
169 Brook Fordyce .07 .20
170 Mike Lieberthal .10 .30
171 Giovanni Carrara .07 .20
172 Antonio Perez .07 .20
173 Fernando Tatis .07 .20
174 Jason Bay RC 2.00 5.00
175 Jason Botts RC .20 .50
176 Danys Baez .07 .20
177 Shea Hillenbrand .10 .30
178 Jack Cust .07 .20
179 Clay Bellinger .07 .20
180 Roberto Alomar .20 .50
181 Graeme Lloyd .07 .20
182 Clint Weibl RC .08 .25
183 Royce Clayton .07 .20
184 Ben Davis .07 .20
185 Brian Adams RC .08 .25
186 Jack Wilson .07 .20
187 David Coggin .07 .20
188 Derrick Turnbow .07 .20
189 Vladimir Nunez .07 .20
190 Mariano Rivera .30 .75
191 Wilson Guzman .07 .20
192 Michael Barrett .07 .20
193 Corey Patterson .07 .20
194 Luis Sojo .07 .20
195 Scott Elarton .07 .20
196 Charles Thomas RC .15 .40
197 Ricky Bottalico .07 .20
198 Wilfredo Rodriguez .07 .20
199 Ricardo Rincon .07 .20
200 John Smoltz .20 .50
201 Travis Miller .07 .20
202 Ben Weber .07 .20
203 T.J. Tucker .07 .20
204 Terry Shumpert .07 .20
205 Bernie Williams .20 .50
206 Russ Ortiz .07 .20
207 Nate Rolison .07 .20
208 Jose Cruz Jr. .07 .20
209 Bill Ortega .07 .20
210 Carl Everett .10 .30
211 Luis Lopez .07 .20
212 Brian Wolfe RC .15 .40
213 Doug Davis .07 .20
214 Troy Mattes .07 .20
215 Al Leiter .10 .30
216 Joe Mays .07 .20
217 Bobby Smith .07 .20
218 J.J. Trujillo RC .15 .40
219 Hideo Nomo .30 .75
220 Jimmy Rollins .10 .30
221 Bobby Seay .07 .20
222 Mike Thurman .07 .20
223 Bartolo Colon .10 .30
224 Jesus Sanchez .07 .20
225 Ray Durham .10 .30
226 Juan Diaz .07 .20
227 Lee Stevens .07 .20
228 Ben Howard RC .15 .40
229 James Mouton .07 .20
230 Paul Quantrill .07 .20
231 Randy Knorr .07 .20
232 Abraham Nunez .07 .20
233 Mike Fetters .07 .20
234 Mario Encarnacion .07 .20
235 Jeremy Fikac .07 .20
236 Travis Lee .07 .20
237 Bob File .07 .20
238 Pete Harnisch .07 .20
239 Randy Galvez RC .15 .40
240 Geoff Goetz .07 .20
241 Gary Glover .07 .20
242 Troy Percival .10 .30
243 Len Dinardo RC .15 .40
244 Jonny Gomes RC 1.00 2.50
245 Jesus Medrano RC .15 .40
246 Rey Ordonez .07 .20
247 Juan Gonzalez .10 .30
248 Jose Guillen .10 .30
249 Franklyn German RC .15 .40
250 Mike Mussina .20 .50
251 Ugueth Urbina .07 .20
252 Melvin Mora .10 .30
253 Gerald Williams .07 .20
254 Jared Sandberg .07 .20
255 Darrin Fletcher .07 .20
256 A.J. Pierzynski .10 .30
257 Lenny Harris .07 .20
258 Blaine Neal .07 .20
259 Denny Neagle .07 .20
260 Jason Hart .07 .20
261 Henry Mateo .07 .20
262 Rheal Cormier .07 .20
263 Luis Terrero .07 .20
264 Shigetoshi Hasegawa .10 .30
265 Bill Haselman .07 .20
266 Scott Hatteberg .07 .20
267 Adam Hyzdu .07 .20
268 Mike Williams .07 .20
269 Marlon Anderson .07 .20
270 Bruce Chen .07 .20
271 Eli Marrero .07 .20
272 Jimmy Haynes .07 .20
273 Bronson Arroyo .10 .30
274 Kevin Jordan .07 .20
275 Rick Helling .07 .20
276 Mark Loretta .07 .20
277 Dustin Hermanson .07 .20
278 Pablo Ozuna .07 .20
279 Keto Anderson RC .15 .40
280 Jermaine Dye .10 .30
281 Will Smith .07 .20
282 Brian Daubach .07 .20
283 Eric Hinske .07 .20
284 Joe Jiannetti RC .15 .40
285 Chan Ho Park .10 .30
286 Curtis Legendre RC .15 .40
287 Jeff Reboulet .07 .20
288 Scott Rolen .20 .50
289 Chris Richard .07 .20
290 Eric Chavez .10 .30
291 Scot Shields .07 .20
292 Donnie Sadler .07 .20
293 Dave Veres .07 .20
294 Craig Counsell .07 .20
295 Armando Reynoso .07 .20
296 Kyle Lohse .07 .20
297 Arthur Rhodes .07 .20
298 Sidney Ponson .07 .20
299 Trevor Hoffman .10 .30
300 Kerry Wood .10 .30
301 Danny Bautista .07 .20
302 Scott Sauerbeck .07 .20
303 Johnny Estrada .07 .20
304 Mike Timlin .07 .20
305 Orlando Hernandez .10 .30
306 Tony Clark .07 .20
307 Tomas Perez .07 .20
308 Marcus Giles .10 .30
309 Mike Bordick .10 .30
310 Jorge Posada .20 .50
311 Jason Conti .07 .20
312 Kevin Millar .10 .30
313 Paul Shuey .07 .20
314 Jake Mauer RC .15 .40
315 Luke Hudson .07 .20
316 Angel Berroa .07 .20
317 Fred Bastardo RC .15 .40
318 Shawn Estes .07 .20
319 Andy Ashby .07 .20
320 Ryan Klesko .10 .30
321 Kevin Appier .10 .30
322 Juan Pena .07 .20
323 Alex Herrera .07 .20
324 Robb Nen .10 .30
325 Orlando Hudson .07 .20
326 Lyle Overbay .07 .20
327 Ben Sheets .10 .30
328 Mike DiFelice .07 .20
329 Pablo Arias RC .15 .40
330 Mike Sweeney .10 .30
331 Rick Ankiel .07 .20
332 Tomas De La Rosa .07 .20
333 Kazuhisa Ishii RC .20 .50
334 Jose Reyes .20 .50
335 Jeremy Giambi .07 .20
336 Jose Mesa .07 .20
337 Ralph Roberts RC .15 .40
338 Jose Nunez .07 .20
339 Curt Schilling .10 .30
340 Sean Casey .10 .30
341 Bob Wells .07 .20
342 Carlos Beltran .10 .30
343 Alexis Gomez .07 .20
344 Brandon Claussen .07 .20
345 Buddy Groom .07 .20
346 Mark Phillips RC .15 .40
347 Francisco Cordova .07 .20
348 Joe Oliver .07 .20
349 Danny Patterson .07 .20
350 Joel Pineiro .07 .20
351 J.R. House .07 .20
352 Benny Agbayani .07 .20
353 Jose Vidro .07 .20
354 Reed Johnson RC .40 1.00
355 Mike Lowell .10 .30
356 Scott Schoeneweis .07 .20
357 Brian Jordan .10 .30
358 Steve Finley .10 .30
359 Randy Choate .07 .20
360 Jose Lima .07 .20
361 Miguel Olivo .07 .20
362 Kenny Rogers .10 .30
363 David Justice .10 .30
364 Brandon Knight .07 .20
365 Joe Kennedy .07 .20
366 Eric Valent .07 .20
367 Nelson Cruz .07 .20
368 Brian Giles .10 .30
369 Charles Gipson RC .08 .25
370 Juan Pena .07 .20
371 Mark Redman .07 .20
372 Billy Koch .07 .20
373 Ted Lilly .07 .20
374 Craig Paquette .07 .20
375 Kevin Jarvis .07 .20
376 Scott Erickson .07 .20
377 Josh Paul .07 .20
378 Darwin Cubillan .07 .20
379 Nelson Figueroa .07 .20
380 Darin Erstad .10 .30
381 Jeremy Hill RC .15 .40
382 Elvin Nina .07 .20
383 David Wells .10 .30
384 Jay Caligiuri RC .15 .40
385 Freddy Garcia .10 .30
386 Damian Miller .07 .20
387 Bobby Higginson .10 .30
388 Alejandro Giron RC .15 .40
389 Ivan Rodriguez .20 .50
390 Ed Rogers .07 .20
391 Andy Benes .07 .20
392 Matt Blank .07 .20
393 Ryan Vogelsong .07 .20
394 Kelly Ramos RC .08 .25
395 Eric Karros .10 .30
396 Bobby J. Jones .07 .20
397 Omar Vizquel .20 .50
398 Matt Perisho .07 .20
399 Delino DeShields .07 .20
400 Carlos Hernandez .07 .20
401 Derrek Lee .20 .50
402 Kirk Rueter .07 .20
403 David Wright RC 12.50 30.00
404 Paul LoDuca .10 .30
405 Brian Schneider .07 .20
406 Milton Bradley .10 .30
407 Daryle Ward .07 .20
408 Cody Ransom .07 .20
409 Fernando Rodney .07 .20
410 John Suomi RC .15 .40
411 Joe Girardi .07 .20
412 Demetrius Heath RC .15 .40
413 John Foster RC .15 .40
414 Doug Glanville .07 .20
415 Ryan Kohlmeier .07 .20
416 Mike Matthews .07 .20
417 Craig Wilson .07 .20
418 Jay Witasick .07 .20
419 Jay Payton .07 .20
420 Andruw Jones .20 .50
421 Benji Gil .07 .20
422 Jeff Liefer .07 .20
423 Kevin Young .07 .20
424 Richie Sexson .10 .30
425 Cory Lidle .07 .20
426 Shane Halter .07 .20
427 Jesse Foppert RC .20 .50
428 Jose Molina .07 .20
429 Nick Alvarez RC .15 .40
430 Brian L. Hunter .07 .20
431 Cliff Bartosh RC .15 .40
432 Junior Spivey .07 .20
433 Eric Good RC .15 .40
434 Chin-Feng Chen .10 .30
435 T.J. Mathews .07 .20
436 Rich Rodriguez .07 .20
437 Bobby Abreu .10 .30
438 Joe McEwing .07 .20
439 Michael Tucker .07 .20
440 Preston Wilson .10 .30
441 Mike MacDougal .07 .20
442 Shannon Stewart .10 .30
443 Bob Howry .07 .20
444 Mike Benjamin .07 .20
445 Erik Hiljus .07 .20
446 Ryan Gripp RC .15 .40
447 Jose Vizcaino .07 .20
448 Shawn Wooten .07 .20
449 Steve Kent RC .15 .40
450 Ramiro Mendoza .07 .20
451 Jake Westbrook .07 .20
452 Joe Lawrence .07 .20
453 Jae Seo .07 .20
454 Ryan Fry RC .15 .40
455 Darren Lewis .07 .20
456 Brad Wilkerson .07 .20
457 Gustavo Chacin RC .40 1.00
458 Adrian Brown .07 .20
459 Mike Cameron .07 .20
460 Bud Smith .07 .20
461 Derrick Lewis .07 .20
462 Derek Lowe .10 .30
463 Matt Williams .10 .30
464 Jason Jennings .07 .20
465 Albie Lopez .07 .20
466 Felipe Lopez .07 .20
467 Luke Allen .07 .20
468 Brian Anderson .07 .20
469 Matt Riley .07 .20
470 Ryan Dempster .07 .20
471 Matt Ginter .07 .20
472 David Ortiz .30 .75
473 Cole Barthel RC .08 .25
474 Damian Jackson .07 .20
475 Andy Van Hekken .07 .20
476 Doug Brocail .07 .20
477 Denny Hocking .07 .20
478 Sean Douglass .07 .20
479 Eric Owens .07 .20
480 Ryan Ludwick .07 .20
481 Todd Pratt .07 .20
482 Aaron Sele .07 .20
483 Edgar Renteria .10 .30
484 Raymond Cabrera RC .15 .40
485 Brandon Lyon .07 .20
486 Chase Utley 1.00 2.50
487 Robert Fick .07 .20
488 Wilfredo Cordero .07 .20
489 Octavio Dotel .07 .20
490 Paul Abbott .07 .20
491 Jason Kendall .10 .30
492 Jarrod Washburn .07 .20
493 Dane Sardinha .07 .20
494 Jung Bong .07 .20
495 J.D. Drew .10 .30
496 Jason Schmidt .10 .30
497 Mike Magnante .07 .20
498 Jorge Padilla RC .15 .40
499 Eric Gagne .10 .30
500 Todd Helton .20 .50
501 Jeff Weaver .07 .20
502 Alex Sanchez .07 .20
503 Ken Griffey Jr. .50 1.25
504 Abraham Nunez .07 .20
505 Reggie Sanders .10 .30
506 Casey Kotchman RC .40 1.00
507 Jim Mann .07 .20
508 Matt LeCroy .07 .20
509 Frank Castillo .07 .20
510 Geoff Jenkins .07 .20
511 Jayson Durocher RC .08 .25
512 Ellis Burks .10 .30
513 Aaron Fultz .07 .20
514 Hiram Bocachica .07 .20
515 Nate Espy RC .15 .40
516 Placido Polanco .07 .20
517 Kerry Ligtenberg .07 .20
518 Doug Nickle .07 .20
519 Ramon Ortiz .07 .20
520 Greg Swindell .07 .20
521 J.J. Davis .07 .20
522 Sandy Alomar Jr. .07 .20
523 Chris Carpenter .10 .30
524 Vance Wilson .07 .20
525 Nomar Garciaparra .50 1.25
526 Jim Mecir .07 .20
527 Taylor Buchholz RC .20 .50
528 Brent Mayne .07 .20
529 John Rodriguez RC .20 .50
530 David Segui .07 .20
531 Nate Cornejo .07 .20
532 Gil Heredia .07 .20
533 Esteban Loaiza .07 .20
534 Pat Mahomes .07 .20
535 Matt Morris .10 .30
536 Todd Stottlemyre .07 .20
537 Brian Lesher .07 .20
538 Arturo McDowell .07 .20
539 Felix Diaz .07 .20
540 Mark Mulder .10 .30
541 Kevin Frederick RC .15 .40
542 Andy Fox .07 .20
543 Dionys Cesar RC .08 .25
544 Justin Miller .07 .20
545 Keith Osik .07 .20
546 Shane Reynolds .07 .20
547 Mike Myers .07 .20
548 Raul Chavez RC .08 .25
549 Joe Nathan .10 .30
550 Ryan Anderson .07 .20
551 Jason Marquis .07 .20
552 Marty Cordova .07 .20
553 Kevin Tapani .07 .20
554 Jimmy Anderson .07 .20
555 Pedro Martinez .20 .50
556 Rocky Biddle .07 .20
557 Alex Ochoa .07 .20
558 D'Angelo Jimenez .07 .20
559 Wilkin Ruan .07 .20
560 Terrence Long .07 .20
561 Mark Lukasiewicz .07 .20
562 Jose Santiago .07 .20
563 Brad Fullmer .07 .20
564 Corky Miller .07 .20
565 Matt White .07 .20
566 Mark Grace .20 .50
567 Raul Ibanez .07 .20
568 Josh Towers .07 .20
569 Juan M. Gonzalez RC .15 .40
570 Brian Buchanan .07 .20
571 Ken Harvey .07 .20
572 Jeffrey Hammonds .07 .20
573 Wade Miller .07 .20
574 Elpidio Guzman .07 .20
575 Kevin Olsen .07 .20
576 Austin Kearns .07 .20
577 Tim Kalita RC .15 .40
578 David Dellucci .07 .20
579 Alex Gonzalez .07 .20
580 Joe Orloski RC .15 .40
581 Gary Matthews Jr. .07 .20
582 Ryan Mills .07 .20
583 Erick Almonte .07 .20
584 Jeremy Affeldt .07 .20
585 Chris Tritle RC .08 .25
586 Michael Cuddyer .07 .20
587 Kris Foster .07 .20
588 Russell Branyan .07 .20
589 Darren Oliver .07 .20
590 Freddie Money RC .15 .40
591 Carlos Lee .10 .30
592 Tim Wakefield .10 .30
593 Bubba Trammell .07 .20
594 John Koronka RC .40 1.00
595 Geoff Blum .07 .20
596 Darryl Kile .10 .30
597 Neifi Perez .07 .20
598 Torii Hunter .10 .30
599 Luis Castillo .07 .20
600 Mark Buehrle .10 .30
601 Jeff Zimmerman .07 .20
602 Mike DeJean .07 .20
603 Julio Lugo .07 .20
604 Chad Hermansen .07 .20
605 Keith Foulke .10 .30
606 Lance Davis .07 .20
607 Jeff Austin RC .15 .40
608 Brandon Inge .07 .20
609 Orlando Merced .07 .20
610 Johnny Damon Sox .20 .50
611 Doug Henry .07 .20
612 Adam Kennedy .07 .20
613 Wiki Gonzalez .07 .20
614 Brian West RC .15 .40
615 Andy Pettitte .20 .50
616 Chone Figgins RC .60 1.50
617 Matt Lawton .07 .20
618 Paul Rigdon .07 .20
619 Keith Lockhart .07 .20
620 Tim Redding .07 .20
621 John Parrish .07 .20
622 Homer Bush .07 .20
623 Todd Greene .07 .20
624 David Eckstein .10 .30
625 Greg Montalbano RC .15 .40
626 Joe Beimel .07 .20
627 Adrian Beltre .10 .30
628 Charles Nagy .07 .20
629 Cristian Guzman .07 .20
630 Toby Hall .07 .20
631 Jose Hernandez .07 .20
632 Jose Macias .10 .30
633 Jaret Wright .07 .20
634 Steve Parris .07 .20
635 Gene Kingsale .07 .20
636 Tim Worrell .07 .20
637 Billy Martin .07 .20
638 Jovanny Cedeno .07 .20
639 Curtis Leskanic .07 .20
640 Tim Hudson .10 .30
641 Juan Castro .07 .20
642 Rafael Soriano .07 .20
643 Juan Rincon .07 .20
644 Mark DeRosa .07 .20
645 Carlos Pena .07 .20
646 Robin Ventura .10 .30
647 Odalis Perez .07 .20
648 Damion Easley .07 .20
649 Benito Santiago .10 .30
650 Alex Rodriguez .50 1.25
651 Aaron Rowand .10 .30
652 Alex Cora .07 .20
653 Bobby Kielty .07 .20
654 Jose Rodriguez RC .15 .40
655 Herbert Perry .07 .20

656 Jeff Urban .07 .20
657 Paul Bako .07 .20
658 Shane Spencer .07 .20
659 Pat Hentgen .07 .20
660 Jeff Kent .10 .30
661 Mark McLemore .07 .20
662 Chuck Knoblauch .10 .30
663 Blake Stein .07 .20
664 Brett Roneberg RC .15 .40
665 Josh Phelps .07 .20
666 Byung-Hyun Kim .10 .30
667 Dave Martinez .07 .20
668 Mike Maroth .07 .20
669 Shawn Chacon .07 .20
670 Billy Wagner .10 .30
671 Luis Alicea .07 .20
672 Sterling Hitchcock .07 .20
673 Adam Piatt .07 .20
674 Ryan Franklin .07 .20
675 Luke Prokopec .07 .20
676 Alfredo Amezaga .07 .20
677 Gookie Dawkins .07 .20
678 Eric Byrnes .07 .20
679 Barry Larkin .20 .50
680 Albert Pujols .60 1.50
681 Edwards Guzman .07 .20
682 Jason Bere .07 .20
683 Adam Everett .07 .20
684 Greg Colbrunn .07 .20
685 Brandon Puffer RC .15 .40
686 Mark Kotsay .10 .30
687 Willie Bloomquist .07 .20
688 Hank Blalock .20 .50
689 Travis Hafner .10 .30
690 Lance Berkman .10 .30
691 Joe Crede .10 .30
692 Chuck Finley .10 .30
693 John Grabow .07 .20
694 Randy Winn .07 .20
695 Mike James .07 .20
696 Kris Benson .07 .20
697 Bret Prinz .07 .20
698 Jeff Williams .07 .20
699 Eric Munson .07 .20
700 Mike Hampton .10 .30
701 Ramon E. Martinez .07 .20
702 Hansel Izquierdo RC .15 .40
703 Nathan Haynes .07 .20
704 Eddie Taubensee .07 .20
705 Esteban German .07 .20
706 Ross Gload .07 .20
707 Matt Merricks RC .15 .40
708 Chris Piersoll RC .08 .25
709 Seth Greisinger .07 .20
710 Ichiro Suzuki .60 1.50
711 Cesar Izturis .07 .20
712 Brad Cresse .07 .20
713 Carl Pavano .10 .30
714 Steve Sparks .07 .20
715 Dennis Tankersley .07 .20
716 Kelvim Escobar .07 .20
717 Jason LaRue .07 .20
718 Corey Koskie .07 .20
719 Vinny Castilla .10 .30
720 Tim Drew .07 .20
721 Chin-Hui Tsao .10 .30
722 Paul Byrd .07 .20
723 Alex Cintron .07 .20
724 Orlando Palmeiro .07 .20
725 Ramon Hernandez .07 .20
726 Mark Johnson .07 .20
727 B.J. Ryan .07 .20
728 Wendell Magee .07 .20
729 Michael Coleman .07 .20
730 Mario Ramos RC .15 .40
731 Mike Stanton .07 .20
732 Dee Brown .07 .20
733 Brad Ausmus .10 .30
734 Napoleon Calzado RC .15 .40
735 Woody Williams .07 .20
736 Paxton Crawford .07 .20
737 Jason Karnuth .07 .20
738 Michael Restovich .07 .20
739 Ramon Castro .07 .20
740 Magglio Ordonez .10 .30
741 Tom Gordon .07 .20
742 Mark Grudzielanek .07 .20
743 Jaime Moyer .10 .30
744 Marlyn Tisdale RC .15 .40
745 Steve Kline .07 .20
746 Adam Eaton .07 .20
747 Eric Glaser RC .15 .40
748 Sean DePaula .07 .20
749 Greg Norton .07 .20
750 Steve Reed .07 .20
751 Ricardo Aramboles .07 .20
752 Matt Mantei .07 .20
753 Gene Stechschulte .07 .20
754 Chuck McElroy .07 .20
755 Barry Bonds .75 2.00
756 Matt Anderson .07 .20
757 Yorvit Torrealba .07 .20
758 Jason Standridge .07 .20
759 Desi Relaford .07 .20
760 Jolbert Cabrera .07 .20
761 Chris George .07 .20
762 Erubiel Durazo .07 .20
763 Paul Konerko .10 .30
764 Tike Redman .07 .20
765 Chad Ricketts RC .08 .25
766 Roberto Hernandez .07 .20
767 Mark Lewis .07 .20
768 Livan Hernandez .10 .30
769 Carlos Brackley RC .15 .40
770 Kazuhiro Sasaki .10 .30
771 Bill Hall .10 .30
772 Nelson Castro RC .15 .40
773 Eric Milton .07 .20
774 Tom Davey .07 .20
775 Todd Ritchie .07 .20
776 Seth Etherton .07 .20
777 Chris Singleton .07 .20
778 Robert Averette RC .08 .25
779 Robert Person .07 .20
780 Fred McGriff .20 .50
781 Richard Hidalgo .07 .20
782 Kris Wilson .07 .20
783 John Rocker .10 .30
784 Justin Kaye .07 .20
785 Glendon Rusch .07 .20
786 Greg Vaughn .07 .20
787 Mike Lamb .07 .20
788 Greg Myers .07 .20
789 Nate Field RC .15 .40
790 Jim Edmonds .10 .30
791 Olmedo Saenz .07 .20
792 Jason Johnson .07 .20
793 Mike Lincoln .07 .20
794 Todd Coffey RC .15 .40
795 Jesus Sanchez .07 .20
796 Aaron Myette .07 .20
797 Tony Womack .07 .20
798 Chad Kreuter .07 .20
799 Brady Clark .07 .20
800 Adam Dunn .10 .30
801 Jacque Jones .10 .30
802 Kevin Millwood .10 .30
803 Mike Rivera .07 .20
804 Jim Thome .20 .50
805 Jeff Conine .10 .30
806 Elmer Dessens .07 .20
807 Randy Velarde .07 .20
808 Carlos Delgado .10 .30
809 Steve Karsay .07 .20
810 Casey Fossum .07 .20
811 J.C. Romero .07 .20
812 Chris Truby .07 .20
813 Tony Graffanino .07 .20
814 Wascar Serrano .07 .20
815 Delvin James .07 .20
816 Pedro Feliz .07 .20
817 Damian Rolls .07 .20
818 Scott Linebrink .07 .20
819 Rafael Palmeiro .20 .50
820 Javy Lopez .10 .30
821 Larry Barnes .07 .20
822 Brian Lawrence .07 .20
823 Scotty Layfield RC .15 .40
824 Jeff Cirillo .07 .20
825 Willis Roberts .07 .20
826 Rich Harden RC 1.25 3.00
827 Chris Snelling RC .25 .60
828 Gary Sheffield .10 .30
829 Jeff Heaverlo .07 .20
830 Matt Clement .10 .30
831 Rich Garces .07 .20
832 Rondell White .10 .30
833 Henry Pichardo RC .15 .40
834 Aaron Boone .10 .30
835 Ruben Sierra .10 .30
836 Deivis Santos .07 .20
837 Tony Batista .07 .20
838 Rob Bell .07 .20
839 Frank Thomas .30 .75
840 Jose Silva .07 .20
841 Dan Johnson RC .40 1.00
842 Steve Cox .07 .20
843 Jose Acevedo .07 .20
844 Jay Bell .10 .30
845 Mike Sirotka .07 .20
846 Garret Anderson .10 .30
847 James Shanks RC .15 .40
848 Trot Nixon .10 .30
849 Keith Ginter .07 .20
850 Tim Spooneybarger .07 .20
851 Matt Stairs .07 .20
852 Chris Stynes .07 .20
853 Marvin Benard .07 .20
854 Raul Mondesi .10 .30
855 Jeremy Owens .07 .20
856 Jon Garland .10 .30
857 Mitch Meluskey .07 .20
858 Chad Durbin .07 .20
859 John Burkett .07 .20
860 Jon Switzer RC .15 .40
861 Peter Bergeron .07 .20
862 Jesus Colome .07 .20
863 Todd Hundley .07 .20
864 Ben Petrick .07 .20
865 So Taguchi RC .20 .50
866 Ryan Drese .07 .20
867 Mike Trombley .07 .20
868 Rick Reed .07 .20
869 Mark Teixeira .30 .75
870 Corey Thurman RC .15 .40
871 Brian Roberts .10 .30
872 Mike Timlin .07 .20
873 Chris Reitsma .07 .20
874 Jeff Fassero .07 .20
875 Carlos Valderrama .07 .20
876 John Lackey .07 .20
877 Travis Fryman .10 .30
878 Ismael Valdes .07 .20
879 Rick White .07 .20
880 Edgar Martinez .20 .50
881 Dean Palmer .10 .30
882 Matt Allegra RC .15 .40
883 Greg Sain RC .15 .40
884 Carlos Silva .07 .20
885 Jose Valverde RC .15 .40
886 Dernell Stenson .07 .20
887 Todd Van Poppel .07 .20
888 Wes Anderson .07 .20
889 Bill Mueller .10 .30
890 Morgan Ensberg .10 .30
891 Marcus Thames .07 .20
892 Adam Walker RC .15 .40
893 John Halama .07 .20
894 Frank Menechino .07 .20
895 Greg Maddux .50 1.25
896 Gary Bennett .07 .20
897 Mauricio Lara RC .15 .40
898 Mike Young .30 .75
899 Travis Phelps .07 .20
900 Rich Aurilia .07 .20
901 Henry Blanco .07 .20
902 Carlos Febles .07 .20
903 Scott MacRae .07 .20
904 Lou Merloni .07 .20
905 Dicky Gonzalez .07 .20
906 Jeff DaVanon .07 .20
907 A.J. Burnett .10 .30
908 Einar Diaz .07 .20
909 Julio Franco .10 .30
910 John Olerud .10 .30
911 Mark Hamilton RC .15 .40
912 David Riske .07 .20
913 Jason Tyner .07 .20
914 Britt Reames .07 .20
915 Vernon Wells .10 .30
916 Eddie Perez .07 .20
917 Edwin Almonte RC .15 .40
918 Enrique Wilson .07 .20
919 Chris Gomez .07 .20
920 Jayson Werth .07 .20
921 Jeff Nelson .07 .20
922 Freddy Sanchez RC .75 2.00
923 John Vander Wal .07 .20
924 Chad Qualls RC .20 .50
925 Gabe White .07 .20
926 Chad Harville .07 .20
927 Ricky Gutierrez .07 .20
928 Carlos Guillen .10 .30
929 B.J. Surhoff .10 .30
930 Chris Woodward .07 .20
931 Ricardo Rodriguez .07 .20
932 Jimmy Gobble RC .15 .40
933 Jon Lieber .07 .20
934 Craig Kuzmic RC .15 .40
935 Eric Young .07 .20
936 Greg Zaun .07 .20
937 Miguel Batista .07 .20
938 Danny Wright .07 .20
939 Todd Zeile .10 .30
940 Chad Zerbe .07 .20
941 Jason Young RC .08 .25
942 Ronnie Belliard .07 .20
943 John Ennis RC .15 .40
944 John Flaherty .07 .20
945 Jerry Hairston Jr. .07 .20
946 Al Levine .07 .20
947 Antonio Alfonseca .07 .20
948 Brian Moehler .07 .20
949 Calvin Murray .07 .20
950 Nick Bierbrodt .07 .20
951 Sun Woo Kim .07 .20
952 Noochie Varner RC .15 .40
953 Luis Rivas .07 .20
954 Donnie Bridges .07 .20
955 Ramon Vazquez .07 .20
956 Luis Garcia .07 .20
957 Mark Quinn .07 .20
958 Armando Rios .07 .20
959 Chad Fox .07 .20
960 Hee Seop Choi .07 .20
961 Turk Wendell .07 .20
962 Adam Roller RC .15 .40
963 Grant Roberts .07 .20
964 Ben Molina .07 .20
965 Juan Rivera .07 .20
966 Matt Kinney .07 .20
967 Rod Beck .07 .20
968 Xavier Nady .07 .20
969 Masato Yoshii .07 .20
970 Miguel Tejada .10 .30
971 Danny Kolb .07 .20
972 Mike Remlinger .07 .20
973 Ray Lankford .10 .30
974 Ryan Minor .07 .20
975 J.T. Snow .10 .30
976 Brad Radke .10 .30
977 Jason Lane .10 .30
978 Jamey Wright .07 .20
979 Tom Goodwin .07 .20
980 Erik Bedard .10 .30
981 Gabe Kapler .10 .30
982 Brian Reith .07 .20
983 Nic Jackson RC .15 .40
984 Kurt Ainsworth .07 .20
985 Jason Isringhausen .10 .30
986 Willie Harris .07 .20
987 David Cone .10 .30
988 Bob Wickman .07 .20
989 Wes Helms .07 .20
990 Josh Beckett .10 .30

2002 Topps Total Award Winners

Issued at a stated rate of one in six, these 30 cards honored players who have won major awards during their career.

COMPLETE SET (30) 15.00 40.00
AW1 Ichiro Suzuki 1.50 4.00
AW2 Albert Pujols 1.50 4.00
AW3 Barry Bonds 2.00 5.00
AW4 Ichiro Suzuki 1.50 4.00
AW5 Randy Johnson .75 2.00
AW6 Roger Clemens 1.50 4.00
AW7 Jason Giambi A's .30 .75
AW8 Bret Boone .30 .75
AW9 Troy Glaus .30 .75
AW10 Alex Rodriguez 1.25 3.00
AW11 Juan Gonzalez .30 .75
AW12 Ichiro Suzuki 1.50 4.00
AW13 Jorge Posada .50 1.25
AW14 Edgar Martinez .50 1.25
AW15 Todd Helton .50 1.25
AW16 Jeff Kent .30 .75
AW17 Albert Pujols 1.50 4.00
AW18 Rich Aurilia .30 .75
AW19 Barry Bonds 2.00 5.00
AW20 Luis Gonzalez .30 .75
AW21 Sammy Sosa .75 2.00
AW22 Mike Piazza 1.25 3.00
AW23 Mike Hampton .30 .75
AW24 Ruben Sierra .30 .75
AW25 Matt Morris .30 .75
AW26 Curt Schilling .30 .75
AW27 Alex Rodriguez 1.25 3.00
AW28 Barry Bonds 2.00 5.00
AW29 Jim Thome .50 1.25
AW30 Barry Bonds 2.00 5.00

2002 Topps Total Production

Issued at a stated rate of one in 12, these 10 cards feature players who are among the best in the game in producing large offensive numbers.

COMPLETE SET (10) 8.00 20.00
TP1 Alex Rodriguez 1.25 3.00
TP2 Barry Bonds 2.00 5.00
TP3 Ichiro Suzuki 1.50 4.00
TP4 Edgar Martinez .50 1.25
TP5 Jason Giambi .50 1.25
TP6 Todd Helton .50 1.25
TP7 Nomar Garciaparra 1.25 3.00
TP8 Vladimir Guerrero .75 2.00
TP9 Sammy Sosa .75 2.00
TP10 Chipper Jones .75 2.00

2002 Topps Total Team Checklists

Seeded at a rate of approximately two in every three packs, these 30 cards feature team checklists for the 990-card Topps Total set. The card fronts are identical to the corresponding basic issue Topps Total cards. But the card backs feature a checklist of players (unlike basic issue cards of which feature statistics and career information on the specific player pictured on front). In addition, unlike basic issue Topps Total cards, these Team Checklist cards do not feature glossy coating on front and back.

COMPLETE SET (30) 4.00 10.00
TTC1 Troy Glaus .07 .20
TTC2 Randy Johnson .20 .50
TTC3 Chipper Jones .20 .50
TTC4 Scott Erickson .07 .20
TTC5 Nomar Garciaparra .30 .75
TTC6 Sammy Sosa .20 .50
TTC7 Magglio Ordonez .07 .20
TTC8 Ken Griffey Jr. .30 .75
TTC9 Jim Thome .10 .30
TTC10 Todd Helton .10 .30
TTC11 Bobby Higginson .07 .20
TTC12 Josh Beckett .07 .20
TTC13 Jeff Bagwell .10 .30
TTC14 Mike Sweeney .07 .20
TTC15 Shawn Green .07 .20
TTC16 Geoff Jenkins .07 .20
TTC17 Cristian Guzman .07 .20
TTC18 Vladimir Guerrero .20 .50
TTC19 Mike Piazza .30 .75
TTC20 Derek Jeter .50 1.25
TTC21 Eric Chavez .07 .20
TTC22 Pat Burrell .07 .20
TTC23 Brian Giles .07 .20
TTC24 Phil Nevin .07 .20
TTC25 Ichiro Suzuki .40 1.00
TTC26 Barry Bonds .50 1.25
TTC27 J.D. Drew .07 .20
TTC28 Carlos Delgado .07 .20
TTC29 Toby Hall .07 .20
TTC30 Alex Rodriguez

2002 Topps Total Topps

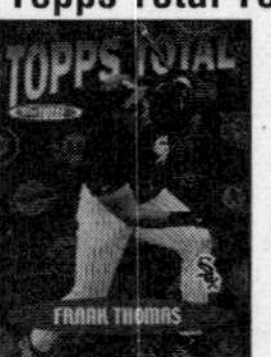

Inserted in packs at a stated rate of one in three, these 50 cards feature some of the leading players in the game.

COMPLETE SET (50) 20.00 50.00
TT1 Roberto Alomar .50 1.25
TT2 Moises Alou .30 .75
TT3 Jeff Bagwell .50 1.25
TT4 Lance Berkman .30 .75
TT5 Barry Bonds 2.00 5.00
TT6 Bret Boone .30 .75
TT7 Kevin Brown .30 .75
TT8 Eric Chavez .30 .75
TT9 Roger Clemens 1.50 4.00
TT10 Carlos Delgado .30 .75
TT11 Cliff Floyd .30 .75
TT12 Nomar Garciaparra 1.25 3.00
TT13 Jason Giambi .30 .75
TT14 Brian Giles .30 .75
TT15 Troy Glaus .30 .75
TT16 Tom Glavine .50 1.25
TT17 Luis Gonzalez .30 .75
TT18 Juan Gonzalez .30 .75
TT19 Shawn Green .30 .75
TT20 Ken Griffey Jr. 1.25 3.00
TT21 Vladimir Guerrero .75 2.00
TT22 Jorge Posada .50 1.25
TT23 Todd Helton .50 1.25
TT24 Tim Hudson .30 .75
TT25 Derek Jeter 2.00 5.00
TT26 Randy Johnson .75 2.00
TT27 Andruw Jones .50 1.25
TT28 Chipper Jones .75 2.00
TT29 Jeff Kent .30 .75
TT30 Greg Maddux 1.25 3.00
TT31 Edgar Martinez .50 1.25
TT32 Pedro Martinez .50 1.25
TT33 Magglio Ordonez .30 .75
TT34 Rafael Palmeiro .50 1.25
TT35 Mike Piazza 1.25 3.00
TT36 Albert Pujols 1.50 4.00
TT37 Aramis Ramirez .30 .75
TT38 Mariano Rivera .75 2.00
TT39 Alex Rodriguez 1.25 3.00
TT40 Ivan Rodriguez .50 1.25
TT41 Curt Schilling .30 .75
TT42 Gary Sheffield .30 .75
TT43 Sammy Sosa .75 2.00
TT44 Ichiro Suzuki 1.50 4.00
TT45 Miguel Tejada .30 .75
TT46 Frank Thomas .75 2.00
TT47 Jim Thome .50 1.25
TT48 Larry Walker .30 .75
TT49 Bernie Williams .50 1.25
TT50 Kerry Wood .30 .75

2003 Topps Total

For the second straight year, Topps issued this 990 card set which was designed to be a comprehensive look at who was in the majors at the time of issue. This set was released in May, 2003. This set was issued in 10 card packs with an 99 cent SRP which came 36 packs to a box and 6 boxes to a case.

COMPLETE SET (990) 100.00 200.00
COMMON CARD (1-990) .07 .20
COMMON RC .08 .25
1 Brent Abernathy .07 .20
2 Bobby Hill .07 .20
3 Victor Martinez .20 .50
4 Chip Ambres .07 .20
5 Matt Anderson .07 .20
6 Ricardo Aramboles .07 .20
7 Carlos Pena .07 .20
8 Aaron Guiel .07 .20
9 Luke Allen .07 .20
10 Francisco Rodriguez .10 .30
11 Jason Marquis .07 .20
12 Edwin Almonte .07 .20
13 Grant Balfour .07 .20
14 Adam Piatt .07 .20
15 Andy Phillips .07 .20
16 Adrian Beltre .10 .30
17 Brandon Backe .07 .20
18 Dave Berg .07 .20
19 Brett Myers .10 .30
20 Brian Meadows .07 .20
21 Chin-Feng Chen .10 .30
22 Blake Williams .07 .20
23 Josh Bard .07 .20
24 Josh Beckett .10 .30
25 Tommy Whiteman .07 .20
26 Matt Childers .07 .20
27 Adam Everett .07 .20
28 Mike Bordick .10 .30
29 Antonio Alfonseca .07 .20
30 Doug Creek .07 .20
31 J.D. Drew .10 .30
32 Milton Bradley .10 .30
33 David Wells .10 .30
34 Vance Wilson .07 .20
35 Jeff Fassero .07 .20
36 Sandy Alomar Jr. .07 .20
37 Ryan Vogelsong .07 .20
38 Roger Clemens .60 1.50
39 Juan Gonzalez .10 .30
40 Dustin Hermanson .07 .20
41 Andy Ashby .07 .20
42 Adam Hyzdu .07 .20
43 Ben Broussard .07 .20
44 Ryan Klesko .10 .30
45 Chris Buglovsky FY RC .15 .40
46 Bud Smith .07 .20
47 Aaron Boone .10 .30
48 Cliff Floyd .10 .30
49 Alex Cora .07 .20
50 Curt Schilling .10 .30
51 Michael Cuddyer .07 .20
52 Joe Valentine FY RC .15 .40
53 Carlos Guillen .10 .30
54 Angel Berroa .07 .20
55 Eli Marrero .07 .20
56 A.J. Burnett .10 .30
57 Oliver Perez .10 .30
58 Matt Morris .10 .30
59 Valerio De Los Santos .07 .20
60 Austin Kearns .07 .20
61 Darren Dreifort .07 .20
62 Jason Standridge .07 .20
63 Carlos Silva .07 .20
64 Moises Alou .10 .30
65 Jason Anderson .07 .20
66 Russell Branyan .07 .20
67 B.J. Ryan .07 .20
68 Cory Aldridge .07 .20
69 Ellis Burks .10 .30
70 Troy Glaus .10 .30
71 Kelly Wunsch .07 .20
72 Brad Wilkerson .07 .20
73 Jayson Durocher .07 .20
74 Tony Fiore .07 .20
75 Brian Giles .10 .30
76 Billy Wagner .10 .30
77 Neifi Perez .07 .20
78 Jose Valverde .07 .20
79 Brent Butler .07 .20
80 Mario Ramos .07 .20
81 Kerry Robinson .07 .20
82 Brent Mayne .07 .20
83 Sean Casey .10 .30
84 Danys Baez .07 .20
85 Chase Utley .30 .75
86 Jared Sandberg .07 .20
87 Terrence Long .07 .20
88 Kevin Walker .07 .20
89 Royce Clayton .07 .20
90 Shea Hillenbrand .10 .30
91 Brad Lidge .10 .30
92 Shawn Chacon .07 .20
93 Kenny Rogers .10 .30
94 Chris Snelling .07 .20
95 Omar Vizquel .20 .50
96 Joe Borchard .07 .20
97 Matt Belisle .07 .20
98 Steve Smyth .07 .20
99 Raul Mondesi .10 .30
100 Chipper Jones .30 .75
101 Victor Alvarez .07 .20
102 J.M. Gold .07 .20
103 Willis Roberts .07 .20
104 Eddie Guardado .07 .20
105 Brad Voyles .07 .20
106 Bronson Arroyo .10 .30
107 Juan Castro .07 .20
108 Dan Plesac .07 .20
109 Ramon Castro .07 .20
110 Tim Salmon .20 .50
111 Gene Kingsale .07 .20
112 J.D. Closser .07 .20
113 Mark Buehrle .10 .30
114 Steve Karsay .07 .20
115 Cristian Guerrero .07 .20
116 Brad Ausmus .10 .30
117 Cristian Guzman .07 .20
118 Dan Wilson .07 .20
119 Jake Westbrook .07 .20
120 Manny Ramirez .20 .50
121 Jason Giambi .10 .30
122 Bob Wickman .07 .20
123 Aaron Cook .07 .20
124 Alfredo Amezaga .07 .20
125 Corey Thurman .07 .20
126 Brandon Puffer .07 .20
127 Hee Seop Choi .07 .20
128 Javier Vazquez .10 .30
129 Carlos Valderrama .07 .20
130 Jerome Williams .07 .20
131 Wilson Betemit .07 .20
132 Luke Prokopec .07 .20
133 Esteban Yan .07 .20
134 Brandon Berger .07 .20
135 Bill Hall .07 .20
136 LaTroy Hawkins .07 .20
137 Nate Cornejo .07 .20
138 Jim Mecir .07 .20
139 Joe Crede .10 .30
140 Andres Galarraga .10 .30
141 Reggie Sanders .10 .30
142 Joey Eischen .07 .20
143 Mike Timlin .07 .20
144 Jose Cruz Jr. .07 .20
145 Wes Helms .07 .20
146 Brian Roberts .10 .30
147 Bret Prinz .07 .20
148 Brian Hunter .07 .20
149 Chad Hermansen .07 .20
150 Andruw Jones .20 .50
151 Kurt Ainsworth .07 .20
152 Cliff Bartosh .07 .20
153 Kyle Lohse .07 .20
154 Brian Jordan .10 .30
155 Coco Crisp .20 .50
156 Tomas Perez .07 .20
157 Keith Foulke .10 .30
158 Chris Carpenter .10 .30
159 Mike Remlinger .07 .20
160 Dewon Brazelton .07 .20
161 Brook Fordyce .07 .20
162 Rusty Greer .10 .30
163 Scott Downs .07 .20
164 Jason Dubois .07 .20
165 David Coggin .07 .20
166 Mike DeJean .07 .20
167 Carlos Hernandez .07 .20
168 Matt Williams .10 .30
169 Rheal Cormier .07 .20
170 Duaner Sanchez .07 .20
171 Craig Counsell .07 .20
172 Edgar Martinez .20 .50
173 Zack Greinke .07 .20
174 Pedro Feliz .07 .20
175 Randy Choate .07 .20
176 Jon Garland .10 .30
177 Keith Ginter .07 .20
178 Carlos Febles .07 .20
179 Kerry Wood .10 .30
180 Jack Cust .07 .20
181 Koyie Hill .07 .20
182 Ricky Gutierrez .07 .20
183 Ben Grieve .07 .20
184 Scott Eyre .07 .20
185 Jason Isringhausen .10 .30
186 Gookie Dawkins .07 .20
187 Roberto Alomar .20 .50
188 Eric Junge .07 .20
189 Carlos Beltran .10 .30
190 Denny Hocking .07 .20
191 Jason Schmidt .10 .30
192 Cory Lidle .07 .20
193 Rob Mackowiak .07 .20
194 Charlton Jimerson RC .15 .40
195 Darin Erstad .10 .30
196 Jason Davis .07 .20
197 Luis Castillo .07 .20
198 Juan Encarnacion .07 .20
199 Jeffrey Hammonds .07 .20
200 Nomar Garciaparra .50 1.25
201 Ryan Christianson .07 .20
202 Robert Person .07 .20
203 Damian Moss .07 .20
204 Chris Richard .07 .20
205 Todd Hundley .07 .20
206 Paul Bako .07 .20
207 Adam Kennedy .07 .20
208 Scott Hatteberg .07 .20
209 Andy Pratt .07 .20
210 Ken Griffey Jr. .50 1.25
211 Chris George .07 .20
212 Lance Niekro .07 .20
213 Greg Colbrunn .07 .20
214 Herbert Perry .07 .20
215 Cody Ransom .07 .20
216 Craig Biggio .20 .50

Card	Low	High
217 Miguel Batista	.07	.20
218 Alex Escobar	.07	.20
219 Willie Harris	.07	.20
220 Scott Strickland	.07	.20
221 Felix Rodriguez	.07	.20
222 Torii Hunter	.10	.30
223 Tyler Houston	.07	.20
224 Darrell May	.07	.20
225 Benito Santiago	.10	.30
226 Ryan Dempster	.07	.20
227 Andy Fox	.07	.20
228 Jung Bong	.07	.20
229 Jose Macias	.07	.20
230 Shannon Stewart	.10	.30
231 Buddy Groom	.07	.20
232 Eric Valent	.07	.20
233 Scott Schoeneweis	.07	.20
234 Corey Hart	.07	.20
235 Brett Tomko	.07	.20
236 Shane Bazzell RC	.15	.40
237 Tim Hummel	.07	.20
238 Matt Stairs	.07	.20
239 Pete Munro	.07	.20
240 Ismael Valdes	.07	.20
241 Brian Fuentes	.07	.20
242 Cesar Izturis	.07	.20
243 Mark Bellhorn	.10	.30
244 Geoff Jenkins	.07	.20
245 Derek Jeter	.75	2.00
246 Anderson Machado	.07	.20
247 Dave Roberts	.07	.20
248 Jaime Cerda	.07	.20
249 Woody Williams	.07	.20
250 Vernon Wells	.10	.30
251 Jon Lieber	.07	.20
252 Franklyn German	.07	.20
253 David Segui	.07	.20
254 Freddy Garcia	.10	.30
255 James Baldwin	.07	.20
256 Tony Alvarez	.07	.20
257 Walter Young	.07	.20
258 Alex Herrera	.07	.20
259 Robert Fick	.07	.20
260 Rob Bell	.07	.20
261 Ben Petrick	.07	.20
262 Dee Brown	.07	.20
263 Mike Bacsik	.07	.20
264 Corey Patterson	.07	.20
265 Marvin Benard	.07	.20
266 Eddie Rogers	.07	.20
267 Elio Serrano	.07	.20
268 D'Angelo Jimenez	.07	.20
269 Adam Johnson	.07	.20
270 Gregg Zaun	.07	.20
271 Nick Johnson	.10	.30
272 Geoff Goetz	.07	.20
273 Ryan Drese	.07	.20
274 Eric Dubose	.07	.20
275 Barry Zito	.10	.30
276 Mike Crudale	.07	.20
277 Paul Byrd	.07	.20
278 Eric Gagne	.10	.30
279 Aramis Ramirez	.10	.30
280 Ray Durham	.10	.30
281 Tony Graffanino	.07	.20
282 Jeremy Guthrie	.07	.20
283 Erik Bedard	.07	.20
284 Vince Faison	.07	.20
285 Bobby Kielty	.07	.20
286 Francis Beltran	.07	.20
287 Alexis Gomez	.07	.20
288 Vladimir Guerrero	.30	.75
289 Kevin Appier	.10	.30
290 Gil Meche	.07	.20
291 Marquis Grissom	.10	.30
292 John Burkett	.07	.20
293 Vinny Castilla	.10	.30
294 Tyler Walker	.07	.20
295 Shane Halter	.07	.20
296 Geronimo Gil	.07	.20
297 Eric Hinske	.07	.20
298 Adam Dunn	.10	.30
299 Mike Kinkade	.07	.20
300 Mark Prior	.20	.50
301 Corey Koskie	.07	.20
302 David Dellucci	.07	.20
303 Todd Helton	.20	.50
304 Greg Miller	.07	.20
305 Delvin James	.07	.20
306 Humberto Cota	.07	.20
307 Aaron Harang	.07	.20
308 Jeremy Hill	.07	.20
309 Billy Koch	.07	.20
310 Brandon Claussen	.07	.20
311 Matt Ginter	.07	.20
312 Jason Lane	.07	.20
313 Ben Weber	.07	.20
314 Alan Benes	.07	.20
315 Matt Walbeck	.07	.20
316 Danny Graves	.07	.20
317 Jason Johnson	.07	.20
318 Jason Grimsley	.07	.20
319 Steve Kline	.07	.20
320 Johnny Damon	.20	.50
321 Jay Gibbons	.07	.20
322 J.J. Putz	.07	.20
323 Stephen Randolph RC	.15	.40
324 Bobby Higginson	.10	.30
325 Kazuhisa Ishii	.10	.30
326 Carlos Lee	.10	.30
327 J.R. House	.07	.20
328 Mark Loretta	.07	.20
329 Mike Matheny	.07	.20
330 Ben Diggins	.07	.20
331 Seth Etherton	.07	.20
332 Eli Whiteside FY RC	.15	.40
333 Juan Rivera	.07	.20
334 Jeff Conine	.10	.30
335 John McDonald	.07	.20
336 Erik Hiljus	.07	.20
337 David Eckstein	.10	.30
338 Jeff Bagwell	.20	.50
339 Matt Holliday	.08	.25
340 Jeff Liefer	.07	.20
341 Greg Myers	.07	.20
342 Scott Sauerbeck	.07	.20
343 Omar Infante	.07	.20
344 Ryan Langerhans	.10	.30
345 Abraham Nunez	.07	.20
346 Mike MacDougal	.07	.20
347 Travis Phelps	.07	.20
348 Terry Shumpert	.07	.20
349 Alex Rodriguez	.50	1.25
350 Bobby Seay	.07	.20
351 Ichiro Suzuki	.60	1.50
352 Brandon Inge	.07	.20
353 Jack Wilson	.07	.20
354 John Ennis	.07	.20
355 Jamal Strong	.07	.20
356 Jason Jennings	.07	.20
357 Jeff Kent	.10	.30
358 Scott Chiasson	.07	.20
359 Jeremy Griffiths RC	.15	.40
360 Paul Konerko	.10	.30
361 Jeff Austin	.07	.20
362 Todd Van Poppel	.07	.20
363 Sun Woo Kim	.07	.20
364 Jerry Hairston Jr.	.07	.20
365 Tony Torcato	.07	.20
366 Arthur Rhodes	.07	.20
367 Jose Jimenez	.07	.20
368 Matt LeCroy	.07	.20
369 Curtis Leskanic	.07	.20
370 Ramon Vazquez	.07	.20
371 Joe Randa	.10	.30
372 John Franco	.10	.30
373 Bobby Estalella	.07	.20
374 Craig Wilson	.07	.20
375 Michael Young	.20	.50
376 Mark Ellis	.07	.20
377 Joe Mauer	.30	.75
378 Checklist 1	.07	.20
379 Jason Kendall	.10	.30
380 Checklist 2	.07	.20
381 Alex Gonzalez	.07	.20
382 Tom Gordon	.07	.20
383 John Buck	.07	.20
384 Shigetoshi Hasegawa	.10	.30
385 Scott Stewart	.07	.20
386 Luke Hudson	.07	.20
387 Todd Jones	.07	.20
388 Fred McGriff	.20	.50
389 Mike Sweeney	.10	.30
390 Marlon Anderson	.07	.20
391 Terry Adams	.07	.20
392 Mark DeRosa	.07	.20
393 Doug Mientkiewicz	.10	.30
394 Miguel Cairo	.07	.20
395 Jamie Moyer	.10	.30
396 Jose Leon	.07	.20
397 Matt Clement	.10	.30
398 Bengie Molina	.07	.20
399 Marcus Thames	.07	.20
400 Nick Bierbrodt	.07	.20
401 Tim Kalita	.07	.20
402 Corwin Malone	.07	.20
403 Jesse Orosco	.07	.20
404 Brandon Phillips	.07	.20
405 Eric Cyr	.07	.20
406 Jason Michaels	.07	.20
407 Julio Lugo	.07	.20
408 Gabe Kapler	.10	.30
409 Mark Mulder	.10	.30
410 Adam Eaton	.07	.20
411 Ken Harvey	.07	.20
412 Jolbert Cabrera	.07	.20
413 Eric Milton	.07	.20
414 Josh Hall RC	.15	.40
415 Bob File	.07	.20
416 Brett Evert	.07	.20
417 Ron Chiavacci	.07	.20
418 Jorge De La Rosa	.07	.20
419 Quinton McCracken	.07	.20
420 Luther Hackman	.07	.20
421 Gary Knotts	.07	.20
422 Kevin Brown	.10	.30
423 Jeff Cirillo	.07	.20
424 Damaso Marte	.07	.20
425 Chan Ho Park	.10	.30
426 Nathan Haynes	.07	.20
427 Matt Lawton	.07	.20
428 Mike Stanton	.07	.20
429 Bernie Williams	.20	.50
430 Kevin Jarvis	.07	.20
431 Joe McEwing	.07	.20
432 Mark Kotsay	.10	.30
433 Juan Cruz	.07	.20
434 Russ Ortiz	.07	.20
435 Jeff Nelson	.07	.20
436 Alan Embree	.07	.20
437 Miguel Tejada	.10	.30
438 Kirk Saarloos	.07	.20
439 Cliff Lee	.07	.20
440 Ryan Ludwick	.07	.20
441 Derrek Lee	.20	.50
442 Bobby Abreu	.10	.30
443 Dustan Mohr	.07	.20
444 Nook Logan RC	.20	.50
445 Seth McClung	.07	.20
446 Miguel Olivo	.07	.20
447 Henry Blanco	.07	.20
448 Seung Song	.07	.20
449 Kris Wilson	.07	.20
450 Xavier Nady	.07	.20
451 Corky Miller	.07	.20
452 Jim Thome	.20	.50
453 George Lombard	.07	.20
454 Rey Ordonez	.07	.20
455 Deivis Santos	.07	.20
456 Mike Myers	.07	.20
457 Edgar Renteria	.10	.30
458 Braden Looper	.07	.20
459 Guillermo Mota	.07	.20
460 Scott Rolen	.20	.50
461 Lance Berkman	.10	.30
462 Jeff Heaverlo	.07	.20
463 Ramon Hernandez	.07	.20
464 Jason Simontacchi	.07	.20
465 So Taguchi	.10	.30
466 Dave Veres	.07	.20
467 Shane Loux	.07	.20
468 Rodrigo Lopez	.07	.20
469 Bubba Trammell	.07	.20
470 Scott Sullivan	.07	.20
471 Mike Mussina	.20	.50
472 Ramon Ortiz	.07	.20
473 Lyle Overbay	.07	.20
474 Mike Lowell	.10	.30
475 Al Martin	.07	.20
476 Larry Bigbie	.07	.20
477 Rey Sanchez	.07	.20
478 Magglio Ordonez	.10	.30
479 Rondell White	.10	.30
480 Jay Witasick	.07	.20
481 Jimmy Rollins	.10	.30
482 Mike Maroth	.07	.20
483 Alejandro Machado	.07	.20
484 Nick Neugebauer	.07	.20
485 Victor Zambrano	.07	.20
486 Travis Lee	.07	.20
487 Bobby Bradley	.07	.20
488 Marcus Giles	.10	.30
489 Steve Trachsel	.07	.20
490 Derek Lowe	.10	.30
491 Hideo Nomo	.30	.75
492 Brad Hawpe	.10	.30
493 Jesus Medrano	.07	.20
494 Rick Ankiel	.07	.20
495 Pasqual Coco	.07	.20
496 Michael Barrett	.07	.20
497 Joe Beimel	.07	.20
498 Marty Cordova	.07	.20
499 Aaron Sele	.07	.20
500 Sammy Sosa	.30	.75
501 Ivan Rodriguez	.20	.50
502 Keith Osik	.07	.20
503 Hank Blalock	.10	.30
504 Hiram Bocachica	.07	.20
505 Junior Spivey	.07	.20
506 Edgardo Alfonzo	.07	.20
507 Alex Graman	.07	.20
508 J.J. Davis	.07	.20
509 Roger Cedeno	.07	.20
510 Joe Roa	.07	.20
511 Wily Mo Pena	.10	.30
512 Eric Munson	.07	.20
513 Arnie Munoz RC	.15	.40
514 Albie Lopez	.07	.20
515 Andy Pettitte	.20	.50
516 Jim Edmonds	.10	.30
517 Jeff Davanon	.07	.20
518 Aaron Myette	.07	.20
519 C.C. Sabathia	.10	.30
520 Gerardo Garcia	.07	.20
521 Brian Schneider	.07	.20
522 Wes Obermueller	.07	.20
523 John Mabry	.07	.20
524 Casey Fossum	.07	.20
525 Toby Hall	.07	.20
526 Denny Neagle	.07	.20
527 Willie Bloomquist	.10	.30
528 A.J. Pierzynski	.10	.30
529 Bartolo Colon	.10	.30
530 Chad Harville	.07	.20
531 Blaine Neal	.07	.20
532 Luis Terrero	.07	.20
533 Reggie Taylor	.07	.20
534 Melvin Mora	.10	.30
535 Tino Martinez	.20	.50
536 Peter Bergeron	.07	.20
537 Jorge Padilla	.07	.20
538 Oscar Villarreal RC	.15	.40
539 David Weathers	.07	.20
540 Mike Lamb	.07	.20
541 Greg Norton	.07	.20
542 Michael Tucker	.07	.20
543 Ben Kozlowski	.07	.20
544 Alex Sanchez	.07	.20
545 Trey Lunsford	.07	.20
546 Abraham Nunez	.07	.20
547 Mike Lincoln	.07	.20
548 Orlando Hernandez	.10	.30
549 Kevin Mench	.07	.20
550 Garret Anderson	.10	.30
551 Kyle Farnsworth	.07	.20
552 Kevin Olsen	.07	.20
553 Joel Pineiro	.10	.30
554 Jorge Julio	.07	.20
555 Jose Mesa	.07	.20
556 Jorge Posada	.20	.50
557 Jose Ortiz	.07	.20
558 Mike Tonis	.07	.20
559 Gabe White	.07	.20
560 Rafael Furcal	.10	.30
561 Matt Franco	.07	.20
562 Trey Hodges	.07	.20
563 Esteban German	.07	.20
564 Josh Fogg	.07	.20
565 Fernando Tatis	.07	.20
566 Alex Cintron	.07	.20
567 Grant Roberts	.07	.20
568 Gene Stechschulte	.07	.20
569 Rafael Palmeiro	.20	.50
570 Mike Hampton	.10	.30
571 Ben Davis	.07	.20
572 Dean Palmer	.10	.30
573 Jerrod Riggan	.07	.20
574 Nate Frese	.07	.20
575 Josh Phelps	.20	.50
576 Freddie Bynum	.07	.20
577 Morgan Ensberg	.10	.30
578 Juan Rincon	.07	.20
579 Kazuhiro Sasaki	.10	.30
580 Yorvit Torrealba	.07	.20
581 Tim Wakefield	.10	.30
582 Sterling Hitchcock	.07	.20
583 Craig Paquette	.20	.50
584 Kevin Millwood	.10	.30
585 Damian Rolls	.07	.20
586 Brad Baisley	.07	.20
587 Kyle Snyder	.07	.20
588 Paul Quantrill	.07	.20
589 Trot Nixon	.10	.30
590 J.T. Snow	.10	.30
591 Kevin Young	.07	.20
592 Tomo Ohka	.10	.30
593 Brian Boehringer	.07	.20
594 Danny Patterson	.07	.20
595 Jeff Tam	.07	.20
596 Anastacio Martinez	.07	.20
597 Rod Barajas	.07	.20
598 Octavio Dotel	.07	.20
599 Jason Tyner	.07	.20
600 Gary Sheffield	.07	.20
601 Ruben Quevedo	.07	.20
602 Jay Payton	.07	.20
603 Mo Vaughn	.10	.30
604 Pat Burrell	.10	.30
605 Fernando Vina	.07	.20
606 Wes Anderson	.07	.20
607 Alex Gonzalez	.07	.20
608 Ted Lilly	.07	.20
609 Nick Punto	.07	.20
610 Ryan Madson	.07	.20
611 Odalis Perez	.07	.20
612 Chris Woodward	.07	.20
613 John Olerud	.10	.30
614 Brad Cresse	.07	.20
615 Chad Zerbe	.07	.20
616 Brad Penny	.07	.20
617 Barry Larkin	.20	.50
618 Brandon Duckworth	.07	.20
619 Brad Radke	.10	.30
620 Troy Brohawn	.07	.20
621 Juan Pierre	.10	.30
622 Rick Reed	.07	.20
623 Omar Daal	.07	.20
624 Jose Hernandez	.07	.20
625 Greg Maddux	.50	1.25
626 Henry Mateo	.07	.20
627 Kip Wells	.07	.20
628 Kevin Cash	.07	.20
629 Wil Ledezma FY RC	.15	.40
630 Luis Gonzalez	.10	.30
631 Jason Conti	.07	.20
632 Ricardo Rincon	.07	.20
633 Mike Bynum	.07	.20
634 Mike Redmond	.07	.20
635 Chance Caple	.07	.20
636 Chris Widger	.07	.20
637 Michael Restovich	.07	.20
638 Mark Grudzielanek	.07	.20
639 Brandon Larson	.07	.20
640 Rocco Baldelli	.10	.30
641 Javy Lopez	.10	.30
642 Rene Reyes	.07	.20
643 Orlando Merced	.07	.20
644 Jason Phillips	.07	.20
645 Luis Ugueto	.07	.20
646 Ron Calloway	.07	.20
647 Josh Paul	.07	.20
648 Todd Greene	.07	.20
649 Joe Girardi	.07	.20
650 Todd Ritchie	.07	.20
651 Kevin Millar Sox	.10	.30
652 Shawn Wooten	.07	.20
653 David Riske	.07	.20
654 Luis Rivas	.07	.20
655 Roy Halladay	.10	.30
656 Travis Driskill	.07	.20
657 Ricky Ledee	.07	.20
658 Timo Perez	.07	.20
659 Fernando Rodney	.07	.20
660 Trevor Hoffman	.10	.30
661 Pat Hentgen	.07	.20
662 Bret Boone	.10	.30
663 Ryan Jensen	.07	.20
664 Ricardo Rodriguez	.07	.20
665 Jeremy Lambert	.07	.20
666 Troy Percival	.10	.30
667 Jon Rauch	.07	.20
668 Mariano Rivera	.30	.75
669 Jason LaRue	.07	.20
670 J.C. Romero	.07	.20
671 Cody Ross	.07	.20
672 Eric Byrnes	.07	.20
673 Paul Lo Duca	.10	.30
674 Brad Fullmer	.07	.20
675 Cliff Politte	.07	.20
676 Justin Miller	.07	.20
677 Nic Jackson	.07	.20
678 Kris Benson	.07	.20
679 Carl Sadler	.07	.20
680 Joe Nathan	.10	.30
681 Julio Santana	.07	.20
682 Wade Miller	.07	.20
683 Josh Pearce	.07	.20
684 Tony Armas Jr.	.07	.20
685 Al Leiter	.10	.30
686 Raul Ibanez	.07	.20
687 Danny Bautista	.07	.20
688 Travis Hafner	.10	.30
689 Carlos Zambrano	.10	.30
690 Pedro Martinez	.20	.50
691 Ramon Santiago	.07	.20
692 Felipe Lopez	.07	.20
693 David Ross	.07	.20
694 Chone Figgins	.07	.20
695 Antonio Osuna	.07	.20
696 Jay Powell	.07	.20
697 Ryan Church	.07	.20
698 Alexis Rios	.10	.30
699 Tanyon Sturtze	.07	.20
700 Turk Wendell	.07	.20
701 Richard Hidalgo	.07	.20
702 Joe Mays	.07	.20
703 Jorge Sosa	.07	.20
704 Eric Karros	.10	.30
705 Steve Finley	.10	.30
706 Sean Smith FY RC	.20	.50
707 Jeremy Giambi	.07	.20
708 Scott Hodges	.07	.20
709 Vicente Padilla	.07	.20
710 Erubiel Durazo	.07	.20
711 Aaron Rowand	.10	.30
712 Dennis Tankersley	.07	.20
713 Rick Bauer	.07	.20
714 Tim Olson FY RC	.15	.40
715 Jeff Urban	.07	.20
716 Steve Sparks	.07	.20
717 Glendon Rusch	.07	.20
718 Ricky Stone	.07	.20
719 Benji Gil	.07	.20
720 Pete Walker	.07	.20
721 Tim Worrell	.07	.20
722 Michael Tejera	.07	.20
723 David Kelton	.07	.20
724 Britt Reames	.07	.20
725 John Stephens	.07	.20
726 Mark McLemore	.07	.20
727 Jeff Zimmerman	.07	.20
728 Checklist 3	.07	.20
729 Andres Torres	.07	.20
730 Checklist 4	.07	.20
731 Johan Santana	.20	.50
732 Dane Sardinha	.07	.20
733 Rodrigo Rosario	.07	.20
734 Frank Thomas	.30	.75
735 Tom Glavine	.20	.50
736 Doug Mirabelli	.07	.20
737 Juan Uribe	.07	.20
738 Ryan Anderson	.07	.20
739 Sean Burroughs	.07	.20
740 Eric Chavez	.10	.30
741 Enrique Wilson	.07	.20
742 Elmer Dessens	.07	.20
743 Marlon Byrd	.07	.20
744 Brendan Donnelly	.07	.20
745 Gary Bennett	.07	.20
746 Roy Oswalt	.10	.30
747 Andy Van Hekken	.07	.20
748 Jesus Colome	.07	.20
749 Erick Almonte	.07	.20
750 Frank Catalanotto	.07	.20
751 Kenny Lofton	.10	.30
752 Carlos Delgado	.10	.30
753 Ryan Franklin	.07	.20
754 Wilkin Ruan	.07	.20
755 Kelvim Escobar	.07	.20
756 Tim Drew	.07	.20
757 Jarrod Washburn	.07	.20
758 Runelvys Hernandez	.07	.20
759 Cory Vance	.07	.20
760 Doug Glanville	.07	.20
761 Ryan Rupe	.07	.20
762 Jermaine Dye	.10	.30
763 Mike Cameron	.07	.20
764 Scott Erickson	.07	.20
765 Richie Sexson	.10	.30
766 Jose Vidro	.07	.20
767 Brian West	.07	.20
768 Shawn Estes	.07	.20
769 Brian Tallet	.07	.20
770 Larry Walker	.10	.30
771 Josh Hamilton	.15	.40
772 Orlando Hudson	.07	.20
773 Justin Morneau	.10	.30
774 Ryan Bukvich	.07	.20
775 Mike Gonzalez	.07	.20
776 Tsuyoshi Shinjo	.10	.30
777 Matt Mantei	.07	.20
778 Jimmy Journell	.07	.20
779 Brian Lawrence	.07	.20
780 Mike Lieberthal	.10	.30
781 Scott Mullen	.07	.20
782 Zach Day	.07	.20
783 John Thomson	.07	.20
784 Ben Sheets	.10	.30
785 Damon Minor	.07	.20
786 Jose Valentin	.07	.20
787 Armando Benitez	.07	.20
788 Jamie Walker RC	.08	.25
789 Preston Wilson	.10	.30
790 Josh Wilson	.07	.20
791 Phil Nevin	.10	.30
792 Roberto Hernandez	.07	.20
793 Mike Williams	.07	.20
794 Jake Peavy	.10	.30
795 Paul Shuey	.07	.20
796 Chad Bradford	.07	.20
797 Bobby Jenks	.10	.30
798 Sean Douglass	.07	.20
799 Damian Miller	.07	.20
800 Mark Wohlers	.07	.20
801 Ty Wigginton	.07	.20
802 Alfonso Soriano	.10	.30
803 Randy Johnson	.30	.75
804 Placido Polanco	.07	.20
805 Drew Henson	.07	.20
806 Tony Womack	.07	.20
807 Pokey Reese	.07	.20
808 Albert Pujols	.60	1.50
809 Henri Stanley	.07	.20
810 Mike Rivera	.07	.20
811 John Lackey	.10	.30
812 Brian Wright FY RC	.15	.40
813 Eric Good	.07	.20
814 Dernell Stenson	.07	.20
815 Kirk Rueter	.07	.20
816 Todd Zeile	.07	.20
817 Brad Thomas	.07	.20
818 Shawn Sedlacek	.07	.20
819 Garrett Stephenson	.07	.20
820 Mark Teixeira	.20	.50
821 Tim Hudson	.10	.30
822 Mike Koplove	.07	.20
823 Chris Reitsma	.07	.20
824 Rafael Soriano	.07	.20
825 Ugueth Urbina	.07	.20
826 Lance Carter	.07	.20
827 Colin Young	.07	.20
828 Pat Strange	.07	.20
829 Juan Pena	.07	.20
830 Joe Thurston	.07	.20
831 Shawn Green	.10	.30
832 Pedro Astacio	.07	.20
833 Danny Wright	.07	.20
834 Wes O'Brien FY RC	.15	.40
835 Luis Lopez	.07	.20
836 Randall Simon	.07	.20
837 Jaret Wright	.07	.20
838 Jayson Werth	.07	.20
839 Endy Chavez	.07	.20
840 Checklist 5	.07	.20
841 Chad Paronto	.07	.20
842 Randy Winn	.07	.20
843 Sidney Ponson	.07	.20
844 Robin Ventura	.10	.30
845 Rich Aurilia	.07	.20
846 Joaquin Benoit	.07	.20
847 Barry Bonds	.75	2.00
848 Carl Crawford	.10	.30
849 Jeromy Burnitz	.10	.30
850 Orlando Cabrera	.10	.30
851 Luis Vizcaino	.07	.20
852 Randy Wolf	.07	.20
853 Todd Walker	.07	.20
854 Jeremy Affeldt	.07	.20
855 Einar Diaz	.07	.20
856 Carl Everett	.10	.30
857 Wiki Gonzalez	.07	.20
858 Mike Paradis	.07	.20
859 Travis Harper	.07	.20
860 Mike Piazza	.50	1.25
861 Will Ohman	.07	.20
862 Eric Young	.07	.20
863 Jason Grabowski	.07	.20
864 Rett Johnson RC	.15	.40
865 Aubrey Huff	.10	.30
866 John Smoltz	.20	.50
867 Mickey Callaway	.07	.20
868 Joe Kennedy	.07	.20
869 Tim Redding	.07	.20
870 Colby Lewis	.07	.20
871 Salomon Torres	.07	.20
872 Marco Scutaro	.07	.20
873 Tony Batista	.07	.20
874 Dmitri Young	.10	.30
875 Scott Williamson	.07	.20
876 Scott Spiezio	.07	.20
877 John Webb	.07	.20
878 Jose Acevedo	.07	.20
879 Kevin Orie	.07	.20
880 Jacque Jones	.10	.30
881 Ben Francisco FY RC	.15	.40
882 Bobby Basham FY RC	.15	.40
883 Corey Shafer FY RC	.15	.40
884 J.D. Durbin FY RC	.15	.40
885 Chien-Ming Wang FY RC	3.00	8.00
886 Adam Stern FY RC	.08	.25
887 Wayne Lydon FY RC	.15	.40
888 Derell McCall FY RC	.15	.40
889 Jon Nelson FY RC	.20	.50
890 Willie Eyre FY RC	.15	.40
891 R.Nivar-Martinez FY RC	.15	.40
892 Adrian Myers FY RC	.08	.25
893 Jamie Athas FY RC	.15	.40
894 Ismael Castro FY RC	.20	.50
895 David Martinez FY RC	.15	.40
896 Terry Tiffee FY RC	.15	.40
897 Nathan Panther FY RC	.15	.40
898 Kyle Roat FY RC	.15	.40
899 Kason Gabbard FY RC	.15	.40
900 Hanley Ramirez FY RC	2.00	5.00
901 Bryan Grace FY RC	.15	.40
902 B.J. Barns FY RC	.15	.40
903 Greg Bruso FY RC	.15	.40
904 Mike Neu FY RC	.15	.40
905 Dustin Yount FY RC	.20	.50
906 Shane Victorino FY RC	.40	1.00
907 Brian Burgamy FY RC	.15	.40
908 Beau Kemp FY RC	.15	.40
909 David Corrente FY RC	.15	.40
910 Dexter Cooper FY RC	.15	.40
911 Chris Colton FY RC	.15	.40
912 David Cash FY RC	.15	.40
913 Bernie Castro FY RC	.15	.40
914 Luis Hodge FY RC	.15	.40
915 Jeff Clark FY RC	.15	.40
916 Jason Kubel FY RC	.40	1.00
917 T.J. Bohn FY RC	.15	.40
918 Luke Steidlmayer FY RC	.15	.40
919 Matthew Peterson FY RC	.15	.40
920 Darrell Rasner FY RC	.15	.40
921 Scott Tyler FY RC	.20	.50
922 G.Schneidmiller FY RC	.15	.40
923 Gregor Blanco FY RC	.15	.40
924 Ryan Cameron FY RC	.15	.40
925 Wilfredo Rodriguez FY	.07	.20
926 Rajai Davis FY RC	.15	.40
927 E.Bastida-Martinez FY RC	.15	.40
928 Chris Duncan FY RC	1.50	4.00
929 Dave Pember FY RC	.15	.40
930 Branden Florence FY RC	.15	.40
931 Eric Eckenstahler FY	.07	.20
932 Hong-Chih Kuo FY RC	2.00	5.00
933 Il Kim FY RC	.15	.40
934 Mi. Garciaparra FY RC	.15	.40
935 Kip Bouknight FY RC	.20	.50
936 Gary Harris FY RC	.15	.40
937 Derry Hammond FY RC	.15	.40
938 Joey Gomes FY RC	.15	.40
939 Donnie Hood FY RC	.20	.50
940 Clay Hensley FY RC	.15	.40
941 David Pahucki FY RC	.15	.40
942 Wilton Reynolds FY RC	.15	.40
943 Michael Hinckley FY RC	.20	.50
944 Josh Willingham FY RC	.40	1.00
945 Pete LaForest FY RC	.15	.40
946 Pete Smart FY RC	.15	.40
947 Jay Sitzman FY RC	.15	.40
948 Mark Malaska FY RC	.15	.40
949 Mike Gallo FY RC	.15	.40
950 Matt Diaz FY RC	.30	.75
951 Brennan King FY RC	.15	.40
952 Ryan Howard FY RC	6.00	15.00
953 Daryl Clark FY RC	.15	.40
954 Dayton Buller FY RC	.15	.40
955 Rylan Reed FY RC	.15	.40
956 Chris Booker FY	.07	.20
957 Brandon Watson FY RC	.15	.40
958 Matt DeMarco FY RC	.15	.40
959 Doug Waechter FY RC	.20	.50
960 Callix Crabbe FY RC	.20	.50
961 Jairo Garcia FY RC	.20	.50
962 Jason Perry FY RC	.20	.50
963 Eric Riggs FY RC	.20	.50
964 Travis Ishikawa FY RC	.30	.75
965 Simon Pond FY RC	.15	.40
966 Manuel Ramirez FY RC	.20	.50
967 Tyler Johnson FY RC	.15	.40
968 Jaime Bubela FY RC	.15	.40
969 Haj Turay FY RC	.08	.25
970 Tyson Graham FY RC	.15	.40
971 David DeJesus FY RC	.30	.75
972 Franklin Gutierrez FY RC	.40	1.00
973 Craig Brazell FY RC	.15	.40
974 Keith Stamler FY RC	.15	.40
975 Jemel Spearman FY RC	.15	.40
976 Ozzie Chavez FY RC	.15	.40
977 Nick Trzesniak FY RC	.15	.40
978 Bill Simon FY RC	.15	.40
979 Matthew Hagen FY RC	.15	.40
980 Chris Kroski FY RC	.15	.40
981 Prentice Redman FY RC	.15	.40
982 Kevin Randel FY RC	.15	.40
983 Tho. Story-Harden FY RC	.15	.40
984 Brian Shackelford FY RC	.15	.40
985 Mike Adams FY RC	.15	.40
986 Brian McCann FY RC	2.00	5.00
987 Mike McNutt FY RC	.15	.40
988 Aron Weston FY RC	.15	.40
989 Dustin Moseley FY RC	.15	.40
990 Bryan Bullington FY RC	.15	.40

2003 Topps Total Silver

*SILVER: 1X TO 2.5X BASIC
*SILVER RC'S: 1X TO 2.5X BASIC
STATED ODDS 1:1

Card	Low	High
885 Chien-Ming Wang FY	8.00	20.00
952 Ryan Howard FY	20.00	50.00

2003 Topps Total Award Winners

Card	Low	High
COMPLETE SET (30)	15.00	40.00
STATED ODDS 1:12		
AW1 Barry Zito	.30	.75
AW2 Randy Johnson	.75	2.00
AW3 Miguel Tejada	.30	.75
AW4 Barry Bonds	2.00	5.00
AW5 Sammy Sosa	.75	2.00
AW6 Barry Bonds	2.00	5.00
AW7 Mike Piazza	1.25	3.00
AW8 Todd Helton	.50	1.25
AW9 Jeff Kent	.30	.75
AW10 Edgar Renteria	.30	.75
AW11 Scott Rolen	.50	1.25
AW12 Vladimir Guerrero	.75	2.00
AW13 Mike Hampton	.30	.75
AW14 Jason Giambi	.30	.75
AW15 Alfonso Soriano	.30	.75
AW16 Alex Rodriguez	1.25	3.00
AW17 Eric Chavez	.30	.75
AW18 Jorge Posada	.50	1.25
AW19 Bernie Williams	.50	1.25
AW20 Magglio Ordonez	.30	.75
AW21 Garret Anderson	.30	.75
AW22 Manny Ramirez	.50	1.25
AW23 Jason Jennings	.30	.75
AW24 Eric Hinske	.30	.75
AW25 Billy Koch	.30	.75
AW26 John Smoltz	.50	1.25
AW27 Alex Rodriguez	1.25	3.00
AW28 Barry Bonds	2.00	5.00
AW29 Tony La Russa MG	.30	.75
AW30 Mike Scioscia MG	.30	.75

2003 Topps Total Production

Card	Low	High
COMPLETE SET (10)	6.00	15.00
STATED ODDS 1:18		
TP1 Barry Bonds	2.00	5.00
TP2 Manny Ramirez	.50	1.25
TP3 Albert Pujols	1.50	4.00
TP4 Jason Giambi	.30	.75
TP5 Magglio Ordonez	.30	.75
TP6 Lance Berkman	.30	.75
TP7 Todd Helton	.50	1.25
TP8 Miguel Tejada	.30	.75
TP9 Sammy Sosa	.75	2.00
TP10 Alex Rodriguez	1.25	3.00

2003 Topps Total Signatures

Card	Low	High
STATED ODDS 1:176		
TSBP Brandon Phillips	4.00	10.00
TSEM Eli Marrero	4.00	10.00
TSMB Marlon Byrd	4.00	10.00
TSMT Marcus Thames	4.00	10.00
TSTT Tony Torcato	4.00	10.00

2003 Topps Total Team Checklists

Card	Low	High
COMPLETE SET (30)	6.00	15.00
RANDOM INSERTS IN PACKS		
1 Troy Glaus	.10	.30
2 Randy Johnson	.30	.75
3 Greg Maddux	.50	1.25
4 Jay Gibbons	.10	.30
5 Nomar Garciaparra	.50	1.25
6 Sammy Sosa	.30	.75
7 Paul Konerko	.10	.30
8 Ken Griffey Jr.	.50	1.25
9 Omar Vizquel	.20	.50
10 Todd Helton	.20	.50
11 Carlos Pena	.10	.30
12 Mike Lowell	.10	.30
13 Lance Berkman	.10	.30
14 Mike Sweeney	.10	.30
15 Shawn Green	.10	.30
16 Richie Sexson	.10	.30
17 Torii Hunter	.10	.30
18 Vladimir Guerrero	.30	.75
19 Mike Piazza	.50	1.25
20 Jason Giambi	.10	.30
21 Eric Chavez	.10	.30
22 Jim Thome	.20	.50
23 Brian Giles	.10	.30
24 Ryan Klesko	.10	.30
25 Barry Bonds	.75	2.00
26 Ichiro Suzuki	.60	1.50
27 Albert Pujols	.60	1.50
28 Carl Crawford	.10	.30
29 Alex Rodriguez	.50	1.25
30 Carlos Delgado	.10	.30

2003 Topps Total Team Logo Stickers

Card	Low	High
COMPLETE SET (3)	2.00	5.00
STATED ODDS 1:24		
1 Anaheim Angels	.75	2.00
Arizona Diamondbacks		
Atlanta Braves		
Baltimore Orioles		
Boston Red Sox		
Chicago Cubs		
Chicago White Sox		
Cincinnati Reds		
Cleveland Indians		
Colorado Rockies		
2 Detroit Tigers	.75	2.00
Florida Marlins		
Houston Astros		
Kansas City Royals		
Los Angeles Dodgers		
Milwaukee Brewers		
Minnesota Twins		
Montreal Expos		
New York Mets		
New York Yankees		
3 Oakland Athletics	.75	2.00
Philadelphia Phillies		
Pittsburgh Pirates		
San Diego Padres		
San Francisco Giants		
Seattle Mariners		
St. Louis Cardinals		
Tampa Bay Devil Rays		
Texas Rangers		
Toronto Blue Jays		

2003 Topps Total Topps

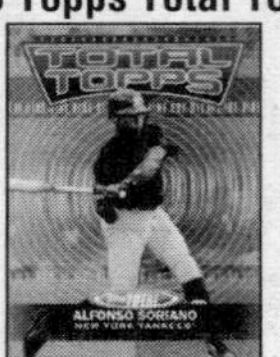

Card	Low	High
COMPLETE SET (50)	15.00	40.00
STATED ODDS 1:7		
TT1 Ichiro Suzuki	1.50	4.00
TT2 Alex Rodriguez	1.25	3.00
TT3 Barry Bonds	2.00	5.00
TT4 Jason Giambi	.30	.75
TT5 Troy Glaus	.30	.75
TT6 Greg Maddux	1.25	3.00
TT7 Albert Pujols	1.50	4.00
TT8 Randy Johnson	.75	2.00
TT9 Chipper Jones	.75	2.00
TT10 Magglio Ordonez	.30	.75
TT11 Jim Thome	.50	1.25
TT12 Jeff Kent	.30	.75
TT13 Curt Schilling	.30	.75
TT14 Alfonso Soriano	.30	.75
TT15 Rafael Palmeiro	.50	1.25
TT16 Carlos Delgado	.30	.75
TT17 Torii Hunter	.30	.75
TT18 Pat Burrell	.30	.75
TT19 Adam Dunn	.30	.75
TT20 Roberto Alomar	.50	1.25
TT21 Eric Chavez	.30	.75
TT22 Derek Jeter	1.50	4.00
TT23 Nomar Garciaparra	1.25	3.00
TT24 Lance Berkman	.30	.75
TT25 Jim Edmonds	.30	.75
TT26 Todd Helton	.50	1.25
TT27 Sammy Sosa	.75	2.00
TT28 Phil Nevin	.30	.75
TT29 Andruw Jones	.50	1.25
TT30 Barry Zito	.30	.75
TT31 Richie Sexson	.30	.75
TT32 Ken Griffey Jr.	1.25	3.00
TT33 Gary Sheffield	.30	.75
TT34 Shawn Green	.30	.75
TT35 Mike Sweeney	.30	.75
TT36 Mike Lowell	.30	.75
TT37 Larry Walker	.30	.75
TT38 Manny Ramirez	.50	1.25
TT39 Miguel Tejada	.30	.75
TT40 Mike Piazza	1.25	3.00
TT41 Scott Rolen	.50	1.25
TT42 Brian Giles	.30	.75
TT43 Garret Anderson	.30	.75
TT44 Vladimir Guerrero	.75	2.00
TT45 Bartolo Colon	.30	.75
TT46 Jorge Posada	.50	1.25
TT47 Ivan Rodriguez	.50	1.25
TT48 Ryan Klesko	.30	.75
TT49 Jose Vidro	.30	.75
TT50 Pedro Martinez	.50	1.25

2004 Topps Total

This 880-card set was released in May, 2004. This set was issued in 10 card packs with an $1 SRP which came 36 packs to box and six boxes to a case. Cards numbered 781 through 875 feature Rookie Cards while cards numbered 876 through 880 are checklists.

Card	Low	High
COMPLETE SET (880)	75.00	150.00
OVERALL PRESS PLATES ODDS 1:159		
PLATES PRINT RUN 1 #'d SET PER COLOR		
PLATES: BLACK, CYAN, MAGENTA & YELLOW		
NO PLATES PRICING DUE TO SCARCITY		
1 Kevin Brown	.10	.30
2 Mike Mordecai	.10	.30
3 Seung Song	.10	.30
4 Mike Maroth	.10	.30
5 Mike Lieberthal	.10	.30
6 Billy Koch	.10	.30
7 Mike Stanton	.10	.30
8 Brad Penny	.10	.30
9 Brooks Kieschnick	.10	.30
10 Carlos Delgado	.10	.30
11 Brady Clark	.10	.30
12 Ramon Martinez	.10	.30
13 Dan Wilson	.10	.30
14 Guillermo Mota	.10	.30
15 Trevor Hoffman	.10	.30
16 Tony Batista	.10	.30
17 Rusty Greer	.10	.30
18 David Weathers	.10	.30
19 Horacio Ramirez	.10	.30
20 Aubrey Huff	.10	.30
21 Casey Blake	.10	.30
22 Ryan Bukvich	.10	.30
23 Garrett Atkins	.10	.30
24 Jose Contreras	.10	.30
25 Chipper Jones	.30	.75
26 Neifi Perez	.10	.30
27 Scott Linebrink	.10	.30
28 Matt Kinney	.10	.30
29 Michael Restovich	.10	.30
30 Scott Rolen	.20	.50
31 John Franco	.10	.30
32 Toby Hall	.10	.30
33 Wily Mo Pena	.10	.30
34 Dennis Tankersley	.10	.30
35 Robb Nen	.10	.30
36 Jose Valverde	.10	.30
37 Chin-Feng Chen	.10	.30
38 Gary Knotts	.10	.30
39 Mark Sweeney	.10	.30
40 Bret Boone	.10	.30
41 Josh Phelps	.10	.30
42 Jason LaRue	.10	.30
43 Tim Redding	.10	.30
44 Greg Myers	.10	.30
45 Darin Erstad	.10	.30
46 Kip Wells	.10	.30
47 Matt Ford	.10	.30
48 Jerome Williams	.10	.30
49 Brian Meadows	.10	.30
50 Albert Pujols	.60	1.50
51 Kirk Saarloos	.10	.30
52 Scott Eyre	.10	.30
53 John Flaherty	.10	.30
54 Rafael Soriano	.10	.30
55 Shea Hillenbrand	.10	.30
56 Kyle Farnsworth	.10	.30
57 Nate Cornejo	.10	.30
58 Julian Tavarez	.10	.30
59 Ryan Vogelsong	.10	.30
60 Ryan Klesko	.10	.30
61 Luke Hudson	.10	.30
62 Justin Morneau	.10	.30
63 Frank Catalanotto	.10	.30
64 Derrick Turnbow	.10	.30
65 Marcus Giles	.10	.30
66 Mark Mulder	.10	.30
67 Matt Anderson	.10	.30
68 Mike Matheny	.10	.30
69 Brian Lawrence	.10	.30
70 Bobby Abreu	.10	.30
71 Damian Moss	.10	.30
72 Richard Hidalgo	.10	.30
73 Mark Kotsay	.10	.30
74 Mike Cameron	.10	.30
75 Troy Glaus	.10	.30
76 Matt Holliday	.15	.40
77 Byung-Hyun Kim	.10	.30
78 Aaron Sele	.10	.30
79 Danny Graves	.10	.30
80 Barry Zito	.10	.30
81 Matt LeCroy	.10	.30
82 Jason Isringhausen	.10	.30
83 Colby Lewis	.10	.30
84 Franklyn German	.10	.30
85 Luis Matos	.10	.30
86 Mike Timlin	.10	.30
87 Miguel Batista	.10	.30
88 John McDonald	.10	.30
89 Joey Eischen	.10	.30
90 Mike Mussina	.20	.50
91 Jack Wilson	.10	.30
92 Aaron Cook	.10	.30
93 John Parrish	.10	.30
94 Jose Valentin	.10	.30
95 Johnny Damon	.20	.50
96 Pat Burrell	.10	.30
97 Brendan Donnelly	.10	.30
98 Lance Carter	.10	.30
99 Omar Daal	.10	.30
100 Ichiro Suzuki	.60	1.50
101 Robin Ventura	.10	.30
102 Brian Shouse	.10	.30
103 Kevin Jarvis	.10	.30
104 Jason Young	.10	.30
105 Moises Alou	.10	.30
106 Wes Obermueller	.10	.30
107 David Segui	.10	.30
108 Mike MacDougal	.10	.30
109 John Buck	.10	.30
110 Gary Sheffield	.10	.30
111 Yorvit Torrealba	.10	.30
112 Matt Kata	.10	.30
113 David Bell	.10	.30
114 Juan Gonzalez	.10	.30
115 Kelvim Escobar	.10	.30
116 Ruben Sierra	.10	.30
117 Todd Wellemeyer	.10	.30
118 Jamie Walker	.10	.30
119 Will Cunnane	.10	.30
120 Cliff Floyd	.10	.30
121 Aramis Ramirez	.10	.30
122 Damaso Marte	.10	.30
123 Juan Castro	.10	.30
124 Chris Woodward	.10	.30
125 Andruw Jones	.20	.50
126 Ben Weber	.10	.30
127 Dee Brown	.10	.30
128 Steve Reed	.10	.30
129 Gabe Kapler	.10	.30
130 Miguel Cabrera	.20	.50
131 Billy McMillon	.10	.30
132 Julio Mateo	.10	.30
133 Preston Wilson	.10	.30
134 Tony Clark	.10	.30
135 Carlos Lee	.10	.30
136 Carlos Baerga	.10	.30
137 Mike Crudale	.10	.30
138 David Ross	.10	.30
139 Josh Fogg	.10	.30
140 Dmitri Young	.10	.30
141 Cliff Lee	.10	.30
142 Mike Lowell	.10	.30
143 Jason Lane	.10	.30
144 Pedro Feliz	.10	.30
145 Ken Griffey Jr.	.50	1.25
146 Dustin Hermanson	.10	.30
147 Scott Hodges	.10	.30
148 Aquilino Lopez	.10	.30
149 Wes Helms	.10	.30
150 Jason Giambi	.10	.30
151 Erasmo Ramirez	.10	.30
152 Sean Burroughs	.10	.30
153 J.T. Snow	.10	.30
154 Eddie Guardado	.10	.30
155 C.C. Sabathia	.10	.30
156 Kyle Lohse	.10	.30
157 Roberto Hernandez	.10	.30
158 Jason Simontacchi	.10	.30
159 Tim Spooneybarger	.10	.30
160 Alfonso Soriano	.10	.30
161 Mike Gonzalez	.10	.30
162 Alex Cora	.10	.30
163 Kevin Gryboski	.10	.30
164 Mike Lincoln	.10	.30
165 Luis Castillo	.10	.30
166 Odalis Perez	.10	.30
167 Alex Sanchez	.10	.30
168 Rob Mackowiak	.10	.30
169 Francisco Rodriguez	.10	.30
170 Roy Oswalt	.10	.30
171 Omar Infante	.10	.30
172 Ryan Jensen	.10	.30
173 Ben Broussard	.10	.30
174 Mark Hendrickson	.10	.30
175 Manny Ramirez	.20	.50
176 Rob Bell	.10	.30
177 Adam Everett	.10	.30
178 Chris George	.10	.30
179 Ronnie Belliard	.10	.30
180 Eric Gagne	.10	.30
181 Scott Schoeneweis	.10	.30
182 Kris Benson	.10	.30
183 Amaury Telemaco	.10	.30
184 John Riedling	.10	.30
185 Juan Pierre	.10	.30
186 Ramon Ortiz	.10	.30
187 Luis Rivas	.10	.30
188 Larry Bigbie	.10	.30
189 Robby Hammock	.10	.30
190 Geoff Jenkins	.10	.30
191 Chad Cordero	.10	.30
192 Mark Ellis	.10	.30
193 Mark Loretta	.10	.30
194 Ryan Drese	.10	.30
195 Lance Berkman	.10	.30
196 Kevin Appier	.10	.30
197 Kiko Calero	.10	.30
198 Mickey Callaway	.10	.30
199 Chase Utley	.20	.50
200 Nomar Garciaparra	.50	1.25
201 Kevin Cash	.10	.30
202 Ramiro Mendoza	.10	.30
203 Shane Reynolds	.10	.30
204 Chris Spurling	.10	.30
205 Aaron Guiel	.10	.30
206 Mark DeRosa	.10	.30
207 Adam Kennedy	.10	.30
208 Andy Pettitte	.20	.50
209 Rafael Palmeiro	.20	.50
210 Luis Gonzalez	.10	.30
211 Ryan Franklin	.10	.30
212 Bob Wickman	.10	.30
213 Ron Calloway	.10	.30
214 Jae Weong Seo	.10	.30
215 Kazuhisa Ishii	.10	.30
216 Sterling Hitchcock	.10	.30
217 Jimmy Gobble	.10	.30
218 Chad Moeller	.10	.30
219 Jake Peavy	.10	.30
220 John Smoltz	.20	.50
221 Donovan Osborne	.10	.30
222 David Wells	.10	.30
223 Brad Lidge	.10	.30
224 Carlos Zambrano	.10	.30
225 Kerry Wood	.10	.30
226 Alex Cintron	.10	.30
227 Javier A. Lopez	.10	.30
228 Jeremy Griffiths	.10	.30
229 Jon Garland	.10	.30
230 Curt Schilling	.20	.50
231 Alex Scott Gonzalez	.10	.30
232 Jay Gibbons	.10	.30
233 Aaron Miles	.10	.30
234 Mike Gallo	.10	.30
235 Johan Santana	.30	.75
236 Jose Guillen	.10	.30
237 Jeff Conine	.10	.30
238 Matt Roney	.10	.30
239 Desi Relaford	.10	.30
240 Frank Thomas	.30	.75
241 Danny Patterson	.10	.30
242 Kevin Mench	.10	.30
243 Mike Redmond	.10	.30
244 Jeff Suppan	.10	.30
245 Carl Everett	.10	.30
246 Jack Cressend	.10	.30
247 Matt Mantei	.10	.30
248 Enrique Wilson	.10	.30
249 Craig Counsell	.10	.30
250 Mark Prior	.20	.50
251 Jared Sandberg	.10	.30
252 Scott Strickland	.10	.30
253 Lew Ford	.10	.30
254 Hee Seop Choi	.10	.30
255 Jason Phillips	.10	.30
256 Jason Jennings	.10	.30
257 Todd Pratt	.10	.30
258 Matt Herges	.10	.30
259 Kerry Ligtenberg	.10	.30
260 Austin Kearns	.10	.30
261 Jay Witasick	.10	.30
262 Tony Armas Jr.	.10	.30
263 Tom Martin	.10	.30
264 Oliver Perez	.10	.30
265 Jorge Posada	.20	.50
266 Jason Boyd	.10	.30
267 Ben Hendrickson	.10	.30
268 Reggie Sanders	.10	.30
269 Julio Lugo	.10	.30
270 Pedro Martinez	.20	.50
271 Kyle Snyder	.10	.30
272 Felipe Lopez	.10	.30
273 Kevin Millar	.10	.30
274 Travis Hafner	.10	.30
275 Magglio Ordonez	.10	.30
276 Marlon Byrd	.10	.30
277 Scott Spiezio	.10	.30
278 Mark Corey	.10	.30
279 Tim Salmon	.20	.50
280 Alex Gonzalez	.10	.30
281 Marquis Grissom	.10	.30
282 Miguel Olivo	.10	.30
283 Orlando Hudson	.10	.30
284 Rondell White	.10	.30
285 Jermaine Dye	.10	.30
286 Paul Shuey	.10	.30
287 Brandon Inge	.10	.30
288 B.J. Surhoff	.10	.30
289 Edgar Gonzalez	.10	.30
290 Angel Berroa	.10	.30
291 Claudio Vargas	.10	.30
292 Cesar Izturis	.10	.30
293 Brandon Phillips	.10	.30
294 Jeff Duncan	.10	.30
295 Randy Wolf	.10	.30
296 Barry Larkin	.20	.50
297 Felix Rodriguez	.10	.30
298 Robb Quinlan	.10	.30
299 Brian Jordan	.10	.30
300 Dontrelle Willis	.20	.50
301 Doug Davis	.10	.30
302 Ricky Stone	.10	.30
303 Travis Harper	.10	.30
304 Jaret Wright	.10	.30
305 Edgardo Alfonzo	.10	.30
306 Quinton McCracken	.10	.30
307 Jason Bay	.10	.30
308 Joe Randa	.10	.30
309 Steve Sparks	.10	.30
310 Roy Halladay	.10	.30
311 Antonio Alfonseca	.10	.30
312 Michael Cuddyer	.10	.30
313 John Patterson	.10	.30
314 Chris Widger	.10	.30
315 Shigetoshi Hasegawa	.10	.30
316 Tim Wakefield	.10	.30
317 Scott Hatteberg	.10	.30
318 Mike Remlinger	.10	.30
319 Jose Vizcaino	.10	.30
320 Rocco Baldelli	.10	.30
321 David Riske	.10	.30
322 Steve Karsay	.10	.30
323 Peter Bergeron	.10	.30
324 Jeff Weaver	.10	.30
325 Larry Walker	.10	.30
326 Jack Cust	.10	.30
327 Bo Hart	.10	.30
328 Rod Beck	.10	.30
329 Jose Acevedo	.10	.30
330 Hank Blalock	.10	.30
331 Tom Gordon	.10	.30
332 Brian Fuentes	.10	.30
333 Tomas Perez	.10	.30
334 Lenny Harris	.10	.30
335 Matt Morris	.10	.30
336 Jeremi Gonzalez	.10	.30
337 David Eckstein	.10	.30
338 Aaron Rowand	.10	.30
339 Rick Bauer	.10	.30
340 Jim Edmonds	.10	.30
341 Joe Borowski	.10	.30
342 Eric DuBose	.10	.30
343 D'Angelo Jimenez	.10	.30
344 Tomo Ohka	.10	.30
345 Victor Zambrano	.10	.30
346 Joe McEwing	.10	.30
347 Jorge Sosa	.10	.30
348 Keith Ginter	.10	.30
349 A.J. Pierzynski	.10	.30
350 Mike Sweeney	.10	.30
351 Shawn Chacon	.10	.30
352 Matt Clement	.10	.30
353 Vance Wilson	.10	.30
354 Benito Santiago	.10	.30
355 Eric Hinske	.10	.30
356 Vladimir Guerrero	.30	.75
357 Kenny Rogers	.10	.30
358 Travis Lee	.10	.30
359 Jay Powell	.10	.30
360 Phil Nevin	.10	.30
361 Willie Harris	.10	.30
362 Ty Wigginton	.10	.30
363 Chad Fox	.10	.30
364 Junior Spivey	.10	.30
365 Brandon Webb	.10	.30
366 Brett Myers	.10	.30
367 Alexis Gomez	.10	.30
368 Dave Roberts	.10	.30
369 LaTroy Hawkins	.10	.30
370 Kevin Millwood	.10	.30
371 Brian Schneider	.10	.30
372 Blaine Neal	.10	.30
373 Jeromy Burnitz	.10	.30
374 Ted Lilly	.10	.30
375 Shawn Green	.10	.30
376 Carlos Pena	.10	.30
377 Gil Meche	.10	.30
378 Jeff Bagwell	.20	.50
379 Alex Escobar	.10	.30
380 Erubiel Durazo	.10	.30
381 Cristian Guzman	.10	.30
382 Rocky Biddle	.10	.30
383 Craig Wilson	.10	.30
384 Rey Sanchez	.10	.30
385 Russ Ortiz	.10	.30
386 Freddy Garcia	.10	.30
387 Luis Vizcaino	.10	.30
388 David Ortiz	.30	.75
389 Jose Molina	.10	.30
390 Edgar Martinez	.20	.50
391 Nate Bump	.10	.30
392 Brent Mayne	.10	.30
393 Ray King	.10	.30
394 Paul Wilson	.10	.30
395 Melvin Mora	.10	.30
396 Morgan Ensberg	.10	.30
397 Ramon Hernandez	.10	.30
398 Juan Rincon	.10	.30
399 Ron Mahay	.10	.30
400 Jeff Kent	.10	.30
401 Cal Eldred	.10	.30
402 Mike Difelice	.10	.30
403 Valerio De Los Santos	.10	.30
404 Steve Finley	.10	.30
405 Trot Nixon	.10	.30
406 Akinori Otsuka RC	.15	.40
407 Ryan Freel	.10	.30
408 Ray Durham	.10	.30
409 Aaron Heilman	.10	.30
410 Edgar Renteria	.10	.30
411 Mike Hampton	.10	.30
412 Kirk Rueter	.10	.30
413 Jim Mecir	.10	.30
414 Brian Roberts	.10	.30
415 Paul Konerko	.10	.30
416 Reed Johnson	.10	.30
417 Roger Clemens	.60	1.50
418 Coco Crisp	.10	.30
419 Carlos Hernandez	.10	.30
420 Scott Podsednik	.10	.30
421 Miguel Cairo	.10	.30
422 Abraham Nunez	.10	.30
423 Endy Chavez	.10	.30
424 Eric Munson	.10	.30
425 Torii Hunter	.10	.30
426 Ben Howard	.10	.30
427 Chris Gomez	.10	.30
428 Francisco Cordero	.10	.30
429 Jeffrey Hammonds	.10	.30
430 Shannon Stewart	.10	.30
431 Einar Diaz	.10	.30
432 Eric Byrnes	.10	.30
433 Marty Cordova	.10	.30
434 Matt Ginter	.10	.30
435 Victor Martinez	.10	.30
436 Geronimo Gil	.10	.30
437 Grant Balfour	.10	.30
438 Ramon Vazquez	.10	.30
439 Jose Cruz Jr.	.10	.30
440 Orlando Cabrera	.10	.30
441 Joe Kennedy	.10	.30
442 Scott Williamson	.10	.30
443 Troy Percival	.10	.30
444 Derrek Lee	.20	.50
445 Runelvys Hernandez	.10	.30
446 Mark Grudzielanek	.10	.30
447 Trey Hodges	.10	.30
448 Jimmy Haynes	.10	.30
449 Eric Milton	.10	.30
450 Todd Helton	.20	.50
451 Greg Zaun	.10	.30
452 Woody Williams	.10	.30
453 Todd Walker	.10	.30
454 Juan Cruz	.10	.30
455 Fernando Vina	.10	.30
456 Omar Vizquel	.20	.50
457 Roberto Alomar	.20	.50
458 Bill Hall	.10	.30
459 Juan Rivera	.10	.30
460 Tom Glavine	.20	.50
461 Ramon Castro	.10	.30
462 Cory Vance	.10	.30
463 Dan Miceli	.10	.30
464 Lyle Overbay	.10	.30
465 Craig Biggio	.20	.50
466 Ricky Ledee	.10	.30
467 Michael Barrett	.10	.30
468 Jason Anderson	.10	.30
469 Matt Stairs	.10	.30
470 Jarrod Washburn	.10	.30
471 Todd Hundley	.10	.30
472 Grant Roberts	.10	.30
473 Randy Winn	.10	.30
474 Pat Hentgen	.10	.30
475 Jose Vidro	.10	.30
476 Tony Torcato	.10	.30
477 Jeremy Affeldt	.10	.30
478 Carlos Guillen	.10	.30
479 Paul Quantrill	.10	.30
480 Rafael Furcal	.10	.30
481 Adam Melhuse	.10	.30
482 Jerry Hairston Jr.	.10	.30
483 Adam Bernero	.10	.30
484 Terrence Long	.10	.30
485 Paul Lo Duca	.10	.30
486 Corey Koskie	.10	.30
487 John Lackey	.10	.30
488 Chad Zerbe	.10	.30
489 Vinny Castilla	.10	.30
490 Corey Patterson	.10	.30
491 John Olerud	.10	.30
492 Josh Bard	.10	.30

Card	Low	High
493 Darren Dreifort	.10	.30
494 Jason Standridge	.10	.30
495 Ben Sheets	.10	.30
496 Jose Castillo	.10	.30
497 Jay Payton	.10	.30
498 Rob Bowen	.10	.30
499 Bobby Higginson	.10	.30
500 Alex Rodriguez Yanks	.50	1.25
501 Octavio Dotel	.10	.30
502 Rheal Cormier	.10	.30
503 Felix Heredia	.10	.30
504 Dan Wright	.10	.30
505 Michael Young	.10	.30
506 Wilfredo Ledezma	.10	.30
507 Sun Woo Kim	.10	.30
508 Michael Tejera	.10	.30
509 Herbert Perry	.10	.30
510 Esteban Loaiza	.10	.30
511 Alan Embree	.10	.30
512 Ben Davis	.10	.30
513 Greg Colbrunn	.10	.30
514 Josh Hall	.10	.30
515 Raul Ibanez	.10	.30
516 Jason Kershner	.10	.30
517 Corky Miller	.10	.30
518 Jason Marquis	.10	.30
519 Roger Cedeno	.10	.30
520 Adam Dunn	.10	.30
521 Paul Byrd	.10	.30
522 Sandy Alomar Jr.	.10	.30
523 Salomon Torres	.10	.30
524 John Halama	.10	.30
525 Mike Piazza	.50	1.25
526 Buddy Groom	.10	.30
527 Adrian Beltre	.10	.30
528 Chad Harville	.10	.30
529 Javier Vazquez	.10	.30
530 Jody Gerut	.10	.30
531 Elmer Dessens	.10	.30
532 B.J. Ryan	.10	.30
533 Chad Durbin	.10	.30
534 Doug Mirabelli	.10	.30
535 Bernie Williams	.20	.50
536 Jeff DaVanon	.10	.30
537 Dave Berg	.10	.30
538 Geoff Blum	.10	.30
539 John Thomson	.10	.30
540 Jeremy Bonderman	.10	.30
541 Jeff Zimmerman	.10	.30
542 Derek Lowe	.10	.30
543 Scot Shields	.10	.30
544 Michael Tucker	.10	.30
545 Tim Hudson	.10	.30
546 Ryan Ludwick	.10	.30
547 Rick Reed	.10	.30
548 Placido Polanco	.10	.30
549 Tony Graffanino	.10	.30
550 Garret Anderson	.10	.30
551 Timo Perez	.10	.30
552 Jesus Colome	.10	.30
553 R.A. Dickey	.10	.30
554 Tim Worrell	.10	.30
555 Jason Kendall	.10	.30
556 Tom Goodwin	.10	.30
557 Joaquin Benoit	.10	.30
558 Stephen Randolph	.10	.30
559 Miguel Tejada	.10	.30
560 A.J. Burnett	.10	.30
561 Ben Diggins	.10	.30
562 Kent Mercker	.10	.30
563 Zach Day	.10	.30
564 Antonio Perez	.10	.30
565 Jason Schmidt	.10	.30
566 Armando Benitez	.10	.30
567 Denny Neagle	.10	.30
568 Eric Eckenstahler	.10	.30
569 Chan Ho Park	.10	.30
570 Carlos Beltran	.10	.30
571 Brett Tomko	.10	.30
572 Henry Mateo	.10	.30
573 Ken Harvey	.10	.30
574 Matt Lawton	.10	.30
575 Mariano Rivera	.30	.75
576 Darrell May	.10	.30
577 Jamie Moyer	.10	.30
578 Paul Bako	.10	.30
579 Cory Lidle	.10	.30
580 Jacque Jones	.10	.30
581 Jolbert Cabrera	.10	.30
582 Jason Grimsley	.10	.30
583 Danny Kolb	.10	.30
584 Billy Wagner	.10	.30
585 Rich Aurilia	.10	.30
586 Vicente Padilla	.10	.30
587 Oscar Villarreal	.10	.30
588 Rene Reyes	.10	.30
589 Jon Lieber	.10	.30
590 Nick Johnson	.10	.30
591 Bobby Crosby	.10	.30
592 Steve Trachsel	.10	.30
593 Brian Boehringer	.10	.30
594 Juan Uribe	.10	.30
595 Bartolo Colon	.10	.30
596 Bobby Hill	.10	.30
597 Chris Shelton RC	.40	1.00
598 Carl Pavano	.10	.30
599 Kurt Ainsworth	.10	.30
600 Derek Jeter	.60	1.50
601 Doug Mientkiewicz	.10	.30
602 Orlando Palmeiro	.10	.30
603 J.C. Romero	.10	.30
604 Scott Sullivan	.10	.30
605 Brad Radke	.10	.30
606 Fernando Rodney	.10	.30
607 Jim Brower	.10	.30
608 Josh Towers	.10	.30
609 Brad Fullmer	.10	.30
610 Jose Reyes	.10	.30
611 Ryan Wagner	.10	.30
612 Joe Mays	.10	.30
613 Jung Bong	.10	.30
614 Curtis Leskanic	.10	.30
615 Al Leiter	.10	.30
616 Wade Miller	.10	.30
617 Keith Foulke Sox	.10	.30
618 Casey Fossum	.10	.30
619 Craig Monroe	.10	.30
620 Hideo Nomo	.30	.75
621 Bob File	.10	.30
622 Steve Kline	.10	.30
623 Bobby Kielty	.10	.30
624 Dewon Brazelton	.10	.30
625 Eric Chavez	.10	.30
626 Chris Carpenter	.10	.30
627 Alexis Rios	.10	.30
628 Jason Davis	.10	.30
629 Jose Jimenez	.10	.30
630 Vernon Wells	.10	.30
631 Kenny Lofton	.10	.30
632 Chad Bradford	.10	.30
633 Brad Wilkerson	.10	.30
634 Pokey Reese	.10	.30
635 Richie Sexson	.10	.30
636 Chin-Hui Tsao	.10	.30
637 Eli Marrero	.10	.30
638 Chris Reitsma	.10	.30
639 Daryle Ward	.10	.30
640 Mark Teixeira	.20	.50
641 Corwin Malone	.10	.30
642 Adam Eaton	.10	.30
643 Jimmy Rollins	.10	.30
644 Brian Anderson	.10	.30
645 Bill Mueller	.10	.30
646 Jake Westbrook	.10	.30
647 Bengie Molina	.10	.30
648 Jorge Julio	.10	.30
649 Billy Traber	.10	.30
650 Randy Johnson	.30	.75
651 Javy Lopez	.10	.30
652 Doug Glanville	.10	.30
653 Jeff Cirillo	.10	.30
654 Tino Martinez	.20	.50
655 Mark Buehrle	.10	.30
656 Jason Michaels	.10	.30
657 Damian Rolls	.10	.30
658 Rosman Garcia	.10	.30
659 Scott Hairston	.10	.30
660 Carl Crawford	.10	.30
661 Livan Hernandez	.10	.30
662 Danny Bautista	.10	.30
663 Brad Ausmus	.10	.30
664 Juan Acevedo	.10	.30
665 Sean Casey	.10	.30
666 Josh Beckett	.10	.30
667 Milton Bradley	.10	.30
668 Braden Looper	.10	.30
669 Paul Abbott	.10	.30
670 Joel Pineiro	.10	.30
671 Luis Terrero	.10	.30
672 Rodrigo Lopez	.10	.30
673 Joe Crede	.10	.30
674 Mike Koplove	.10	.30
675 Brian Giles	.10	.30
676 Jeff Nelson	.10	.30
677 Russell Branyan	.10	.30
678 Mike DeJean	.10	.30
679 Brian Daubach	.10	.30
680 Ellis Burks	.10	.30
681 Ryan Dempster	.10	.30
682 Cliff Politte	.10	.30
683 Brian Reith	.10	.30
684 Scott Stewart	.10	.30
685 Allan Simpson	.10	.30
686 Shawn Estes	.10	.30
687 Jason Johnson	.10	.30
688 Wil Cordero	.10	.30
689 Kelly Stinnett	.10	.30
690 Jose Lima	.10	.30
691 Gary Bennett	.10	.30
692 T.J. Tucker	.10	.30
693 Shane Spencer	.10	.30
694 Chris Hammond	.10	.30
695 Raul Mondesi	.10	.30
696 Xavier Nady	.10	.30
697 Cody Ransom	.10	.30
698 Ron Villone	.10	.30
699 Brook Fordyce	.10	.30
700 Sammy Sosa	.30	.75
701 Terry Adams	.10	.30
702 Ricardo Rincon	.10	.30
703 Tike Redman	.10	.30
704 Chris Stynes	.10	.30
705 Mark Redman	.10	.30
706 Juan Encarnacion	.10	.30
707 Jhonny Peralta	.10	.30
708 Denny Hocking	.10	.30
709 Ivan Rodriguez	.20	.50
710 Jose Hernandez	.10	.30
711 Brandon Duckworth	.10	.30
712 Dave Burba	.10	.30
713 Joe Nathan	.10	.30
714 Dan Smith	.10	.30
715 Karim Garcia	.10	.30
716 Arthur Rhodes	.10	.30
717 Shawn Wooten	.10	.30
718 Ramon Santiago	.10	.30
719 Luis Ugueto	.10	.30
720 Danys Baez	.10	.30
721 Alfredo Amezaga PROS	.10	.30
722 Sidney Ponson	.10	.30
723 Joe Mauer PROS	.30	.75
724 Jesse Foppert PROS	.10	.30
725 Todd Greene	.10	.30
726 Dan Haren PROS	.10	.30
727 Brandon Larson PROS	.10	.30
728 Bobby Jenks PROS	.10	.30
729 Grady Sizemore PROS	.30	.75
730 Ben Grieve	.10	.30
731 Khalil Greene PROS	.20	.50
732 Chad Gaudin PROS	.10	.30
733 Johnny Estrada PROS	.10	.30
734 Joe Valentine PROS	.10	.30
735 Tim Raines Jr. PROS	.10	.30
736 Brandon Claussen PROS	.10	.30
737 Sam Marsonek PROS	.10	.30
738 Delmon Young PROS	.20	.50
739 David Dellucci	.10	.30
740 Sergio Mitre PROS	.10	.30
741 Nick Neugebauer PROS	.10	.30
742 Laynce Nix PROS	.10	.30
743 Joe Thurston PROS	.10	.30
744 Ryan Langerhans PROS	.10	.30
745 Pete LaForest PROS	.10	.30
746 Arnie Munoz PROS	.10	.30
747 Rickie Weeks PROS	.10	.30
748 Neal Cotts PROS	.10	.30
749 Jonny Gomes PROS	.10	.30
750 Jim Thome	.20	.50
751 Jon Rauch PROS	.10	.30
752 Edwin Jackson PROS	.10	.30
753 Ryan Madson PROS	.10	.30
754 Andrew Good PROS	.10	.30
755 Eddie Perez	.10	.30
756 Joe Borchard PROS	.10	.30
757 Jeremy Guthrie PROS	.10	.30
758 Jose Mesa	.10	.30
759 Doug Waechter PROS	.10	.30
760 J.D. Drew	.10	.30
761 Adam LaRoche PROS	.10	.30
762 Rich Harden PROS	.10	.30
763 Justin Speier	.10	.30
764 Todd Zeile	.10	.30
765 Turk Wendell	.10	.30
766 Mark Bellhorn Sox	.10	.30
767 Mike Jackson	.10	.30
768 Chone Figgins	.10	.30
769 Mike Neu	.10	.30
770 Greg Maddux	.50	1.25
771 Frank Menechino	.10	.30
772 Alec Zumwalt RC	.10	.30
773 Eric Young	.10	.30
774 Dustan Mohr	.10	.30
775 Shane Halter	.10	.30
776 Brian Buchanan	.10	.30
777 So Taguchi	.10	.30
778 Eric Karros	.10	.30
779 Ramon Nivar	.10	.30
780 Marlon Anderson	.10	.30
781 Brayan Pena FY RC	.15	.40
782 Chris O'Riordan FY RC	.15	.40
783 Dioner Navarro FY RC	.30	.75
784 Alberto Callaspo FY RC	.30	.75
785 Hector Gimenez FY RC	.10	.30
786 Yadier Molina FY RC	.75	2.00
787 Kevin Richardson FY RC	.10	.30
788 Brian Pilkington FY RC	.10	.30
789 Adam Greenberg FY RC	.30	.75
790 Ervin Santana FY RC	.75	2.00
791 Brant Colamarino FY RC	.30	.75
792 Ben Himes FY RC	.10	.30
793 Todd Self FY RC	.20	.50
794 Brad Vericker FY RC	.15	.40
795 Donald Kelly FY RC	.15	.40
796 Brock Jacobsen FY RC	.10	.30
797 Brock Peterson FY RC	.15	.40
798 Carlos Sosa FY RC	.15	.40
799 Chad Chop FY RC	.15	.40
800 Matt Moses FY RC	.40	1.00
801 Chris Aguila FY RC	.15	.40
802 David Murphy FY RC	.30	.75
803 Don Sutton FY RC	.40	1.00
804 Jereme Milons FY RC	.20	.50
805 Jon Coutlangus FY RC	.10	.30
806 Greg Thissen FY RC	.15	.40
807 Jose Capellan FY RC	.20	.50
808 Chad Santos FY RC	.15	.40
809 Wardell Starling FY RC	.15	.40
810 Kevin Kouzmanoff FY RC	.75	2.00
811 Kevin Davidson FY RC	.10	.30
812 Michael Mooney FY RC	.15	.40
813 Rodney Choy Foo FY RC	.10	.30
814 Reid Gorecki FY RC	.15	.40
815 Rudy Guillen FY RC	.30	.75
816 Harvey Garcia FY RC	.15	.40
817 Warner Madrigal FY RC	.30	.75
818 Kenny Perez FY RC	.15	.40
819 Joaquin Arias FY RC	.30	.75
820 Benji DeQuin FY RC	.10	.30
821 Lastings Milledge FY RC	2.00	5.00
822 Blake Hawksworth FY RC	.20	.50
823 Estee Harris FY RC	.20	.50
824 Bobby Brownlie FY RC	.40	1.00
825 Wanell Severino FY RC	.10	.30
826 Bobby Madritsch FY	.10	.30
827 Travis Hanson FY RC	.20	.50
828 Brandon Medders FY RC	.15	.40
829 Kevin Howard FY RC	.20	.50
830 Brian Steffek FY RC	.10	.30
831 Terry Jones FY RC	.20	.50
832 Anthony Acevedo FY RC	.15	.40
833 Kory Casto FY RC	.20	.50
834 Brooks Conrad FY RC UER	.15	.40
Anthony Acevedo Pictured on front		
835 Juan Gutierrez FY RC	.15	.40
836 Charlie Zink FY RC	.10	.30
837 David Aardsma FY RC	.20	.50
838 Carl Loadenthal FY RC	.20	.50
839 Donald Levinski FY RC	.10	.30
840 Dustin Nippert FY RC	.20	.50
841 Calvin Hayes FY RC	.20	.50
842 Felix Hernandez FY RC	3.00	8.00
843 Tyler Davidson FY RC	.20	.50
844 George Sherrill FY RC	.15	.40
845 Craig Ansman FY RC	.15	.40
846 Jeff Allison FY RC	.15	.40
847 Tommy Murphy FY RC	.15	.40
848 Jerome Gamble FY RC	.15	.40
849 Jesse English FY RC	.15	.40
850 Alex Romero FY RC	.15	.40
851 Joel Zumaya FY RC	1.25	3.00
852 Carlos Quentin FY RC	1.00	2.50
853 Jose Valdez FY RC	.15	.40
854 J.J. Furmaniak FY RC	.30	.75
855 Juan Cedeno FY RC	.15	.40
856 Kyle Sleeth FY RC	.20	.50
857 Josh Labandeira FY RC	.15	.40
858 Lee Gwaltney FY RC	.10	.30
859 Lincoln Holdzkom FY RC	.15	.40
860 Ivan Ochoa FY RC	.15	.40
861 Luke Anderson FY RC	.10	.30
862 Conor Jackson FY RC	1.25	3.00
863 Matt Capps FY RC	.15	.40
864 Merkin Valdez FY RC	.20	.50
865 Paul Bacot FY RC	.20	.50
866 Erick Aybar FY RC	.40	1.00
867 Scott Proctor FY RC	.20	.50
868 Tim Stauffer FY RC	.40	1.00
869 Matt Creighton FY RC	.15	.40
870 Zach Miner FY RC	.50	1.25
871 Danny Gonzalez FY RC	.10	.30
872 Tom Farmer FY RC	.15	.40
873 John Santor FY RC	.15	.40
874 Logan Kensing FY RC	.15	.40
875 Vito Chiaravalloti FY RC	.15	.40
876 Checklist	.10	.30
877 Checklist	.10	.30
878 Checklist	.10	.30
879 Checklist	.10	.30
880 Checklist	.10	.30

2004 Topps Total Silver

*PARALLEL: 1X TO 2.5X BASIC
*PARALLEL RC's: 1X TO 2.5X BASIC RC's
ONE PER PACK

2004 Topps Total Award Winners

Card	Low	High
COMPLETE SET (30)	12.50	30.00
STATED ODDS 1:12		
OVERALL PRESS PLATES ODDS 1:159		
PLATES PRINT RUN 1 #'d SET PER COLOR		
PLATES: BLACK, CYAN, MAGENTA & YELLOW		
NO PLATES PRICING DUE TO SCARCITY		
AW1 Roy Halladay CY	.30	.75
AW2 Eric Gagne CY	.30	.75
AW3 Alex Rodriguez MVP	1.25	3.00
AW4 Albert Pujols POY	1.50	4.00
AW5 Alex Rodriguez POY	1.25	3.00
AW6 Jorge Posada SS	.50	1.25
AW7 Javy Lopez SS	.30	.75
AW8 Carlos Delgado SS	.30	.75
AW9 Todd Helton SS	.50	1.25
AW10 Bret Boone SS	.30	.75
AW11 Jose Vidro SS	.30	.75
AW12 Bill Mueller SS	.30	.75
AW13 Mike Lowell SS	.30	.75
AW14 Alex Rodriguez SS	1.25	3.00
AW15 Edgar Renteria SS	.30	.75
AW16 Garret Anderson SS	.30	.75
AW17 Albert Pujols SS	1.50	4.00
AW18 Manny Ramirez SS	.50	1.25
AW19 Vernon Wells SS	.30	.75
AW20 Gary Sheffield SS	.30	.75
AW21 Edgar Martinez SS	.50	1.25
AW22 Mike Hampton SS	.30	.75
AW23 Angel Berroa ROY	.30	.75
AW24 Dontrelle Willis ROY	.50	1.25
AW25 Keith Foulke Rolaids	.30	.75
AW26 Eric Gagne Rolaids	.30	.75
AW27 Alex Rodriguez HA	1.25	3.00
AW28 Albert Pujols HA	1.50	4.00
AW29 Tony Pena MG	.30	.75
AW30 Jack McKeon MG	.30	.75

2004 Topps Total Production

Card	Low	High
COMPLETE SET (10)	6.00	15.00
STATED ODDS 1:18		
OVERALL PRESS PLATES ODDS 1:159		
PLATES PRINT RUN 1 #'d SET PER COLOR		
PLATES: BLACK, CYAN, MAGENTA & YELLOW		
NO PLATES PRICING DUE TO SCARCITY		
TP1 Alex Rodriguez	1.25	3.00
TP2 Albert Pujols	1.50	4.00
TP3 Sammy Sosa	.75	2.00
TP4 Carlos Delgado	.30	.75
TP5 Gary Sheffield	.30	.75
TP6 Manny Ramirez	.50	1.25
TP7 Jim Thome	.50	1.25
TP8 Todd Helton	.50	1.25
TP9 Garret Anderson	.30	.75
TP10 Nomar Garciaparra	1.25	3.00

2004 Topps Total Signatures

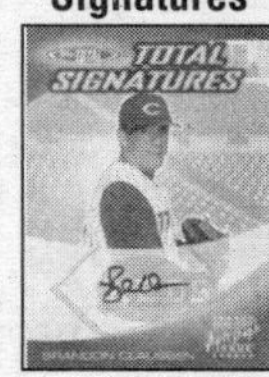

Card	Low	High
STATED ODDS 1:414		
BC Brandon Claussen	4.00	10.00
GB Grant Balfour	4.00	10.00
JJ Jimmy Journell	4.00	10.00
LB Larry Bigbie	6.00	15.00
TB Toby Hall	4.00	10.00

2004 Topps Total Team Checklists

Card	Low	High
COMPLETE SET (30)	6.00	15.00
STATED ODDS 1:4		
OVERALL PRESS PLATES ODDS 1:159		
PLATES PRINT RUN 1 #'d SET PER COLOR		
PLATES: BLACK, CYAN, MAGENTA & YELLOW		
NO PLATES PRICING DUE TO SCARCITY		
TTC1 Garret Anderson	.10	.30
TTC2 Randy Johnson	.30	.75
TTC3 Chipper Jones	.30	.75
TTC4 Miguel Tejada	.10	.30
TTC5 Nomar Garciaparra	.50	1.25
TTC6 Mark Prior	.20	.50
TTC7 Magglio Ordonez	.10	.30
TTC8 Ken Griffey Jr.	.50	1.25
TTC9 C.C. Sabathia	.10	.30
TTC10 Todd Helton	.20	.50
TTC11 Ivan Rodriguez	.20	.50
TTC12 Dontrelle Willis	.20	.50
TTC13 Roger Clemens	.60	1.50
TTC14 Mike Sweeney	.10	.30
TTC15 Shawn Green	.10	.30
TTC16 Geoff Jenkins	.10	.30
TTC17 Torii Hunter	.10	.30
TTC18 Jose Vidro	.10	.30
TTC19 Mike Piazza	.50	1.25
TTC20 Alex Rodriguez	.75	2.00
TTC21 Eric Chavez	.10	.30
TTC22 Jim Thome	.20	.50
TTC23 Jason Kendall	.10	.30
TTC24 Brian Giles	.10	.30
TTC25 Jason Schmidt	.10	.30
TTC26 Ichiro Suzuki	.60	1.50
TTC27 Albert Pujols	.60	1.50
TTC28 Aubrey Huff	.10	.30
TTC29 Hank Blalock	.10	.30
TTC30 Carlos Delgado	.10	.30

2004 Topps Total Topps

Card	Low	High
COMPLETE SET (50)	20.00	50.00
STATED ODDS 1:7		
OVERALL PRESS PLATES ODDS 1:159		
PLATES PRINT RUN 1 SERIAL #'d SET		
NO PLATES PRICING DUE TO SCARCITY		
TT1 Derek Jeter	1.50	4.00
TT2 Jose Reyes	.30	.75
TT3 Miguel Tejada	.30	.75
TT4 Larry Walker	.30	.75
TT5 Frank Thomas	.75	2.00
TT6 Carlos Delgado	.30	.75
TT7 Vernon Wells	.30	.75
TT8 Jeff Bagwell	.50	1.25
TT9 Jason Giambi	.30	.75
TT10 Mike Lowell	.30	.75
TT11 Shannon Stewart	.30	.75
TT12 Mike Piazza	1.25	3.00
TT13 Todd Helton	.50	1.25
TT14 Austin Kearns	.30	.75
TT15 Jim Edmonds	.30	.75
TT16 Jose Vidro	.30	.75
TT17 Andruw Jones	.50	1.25
TT18 Gary Sheffield	.30	.75
TT19 Eric Chavez	.30	.75
TT20 Magglio Ordonez	.30	.75
TT21 Geoff Jenkins	.30	.75
TT22 Ken Griffey Jr.	1.25	3.00
TT23 Jeff Kent	.30	.75
TT24 Jorge Posada	.50	1.25
TT25 Albert Pujols	1.50	4.00
TT26 Javy Lopez	.30	.75
TT27 Alfonso Soriano	.30	.75
TT28 Brian Giles	.30	.75
TT29 Mike Sweeney	.30	.75
TT30 Miguel Cabrera	.50	1.25
TT31 Luis Gonzalez	.30	.75
TT32 Scott Rolen	.50	1.25
TT33 Jim Thome	.50	1.25
TT34 Garret Anderson	.30	.75
TT35 Vladimir Guerrero	.75	2.00
TT36 Shawn Green	.30	.75
TT37 Hank Blalock	.30	.75
TT38 Marcus Giles	.30	.75
TT39 Torii Hunter	.30	.75
TT40 Sammy Sosa	.75	2.00
TT41 Nomar Garciaparra	1.25	3.00
TT42 Bobby Abreu	.30	.75
TT43 Richie Sexson	.30	.75
TT44 Manny Ramirez	.50	1.25
TT45 Troy Glaus	.30	.75
TT46 Preston Wilson	.30	.75
TT47 Ivan Rodriguez	.50	1.25
TT48 Ichiro Suzuki	1.50	4.00
TT49 Chipper Jones	.75	2.00
TT50 Alex Rodriguez	2.00	5.00

2005 Topps Total

This massive 770-card set lays claim to the most comprehensive selection of players for any product issued in 2005 with just over 950 athletes featured. The set is structured with veterans as 1-575, dual-player veterans 576-690, prospects 691-720, "First Year" minor leaguers 721-765 and checklists 766-770. Oddly enough, card 666 (a number feared by some as the sign of the devil) is a single player card featuring Red Sox closer Keith Foulke - indicating a serious dislike for the Red Sox by whomever at Topps was responsible for constructing the checklist. The set was issued within 10-card packs carrying an affordable SRP of $1.00. Each box contained 36 packs. The actual printing plates used to create each card (barring the checklists) were cut up and seeded into packs. Black, Cyan, Magenta and Yellow plates were produced, each labeled as a 1 of 1. In a move deemed about as popular as bad breath by most collectors, the plates for the card backs were incorporated alongside the far more popular card fronts - harkening back to the card back plates issued eight years earlier in forgettable products such as New Pinnacle. Though these plates are too scarce to price for individual stars, most common fronts can be had between $15-$40 per and back between $8-$25 per.

Card	Low	High
COMPLETE SET (770)	75.00	150.00
COMMON (1-575/666)	.10	.30
COMMON CARD (576-690)	.10	.30
COM (269/588/691-765)	.20	.50
COMMON CL (766-770)	.10	.30
OVERALL PLATE ODDS 1:85 HOBBY		
PLATE PRINT RUN 1 SET PER COLOR		
BLACK-CYAN-MAGENTA-YELLOW ISSUED		
FRONT AND BACK PLATES PRODUCED		
NO PLATE PRICING DUE TO SCARCITY		
1 Rafael Furcal	.10	.30
2 Tony Clark	.10	.30
3 Hideki Matsui	.50	1.25
4 Zach Day	.10	.30
5 Garret Anderson	.10	.30
6 B.J. Surhoff	.10	.30
7 Trevor Hoffman	.10	.30
8 Kenny Lofton	.10	.30
9 Ross Gload	.10	.30
10 Jorge Cantu	.10	.30
11 Joel Pineiro	.10	.30
12 Alex Cintron	.10	.30
13 Mike Matheny	.10	.30
14 Rod Barajas	.10	.30
15 Ray Durham	.10	.30
16 Danys Baez	.10	.30
17 Brian Schneider	.10	.30
18 Tike Redman	.10	.30
19 Ricardo Rodriguez	.10	.30
20 Mike Sweeney	.10	.30
21 Greg Myers	.10	.30
22 Chone Figgins	.10	.30
23 Brian Lawrence	.10	.30
24 Joe Nathan	.10	.30
25 Placido Polanco	.10	.30
26 Yadier Molina	.10	.30
27 Gary Bennett	.10	.30
28 Yorvit Torrealba	.10	.30
29 Javier Valentin	.10	.30
30 Jason Giambi	.10	.30
31 Brandon Claussen	.10	.30
32 Miguel Olivo	.10	.30
33 Josh Bard	.10	.30
34 Ramon Hernandez	.10	.30
35 Geoff Jenkins	.10	.30
36 Bobby Kielty	.10	.30
37 Luis A. Gonzalez	.10	.30
38 Benito Santiago	.10	.30
39 Brandon Inge	.10	.30
40 Mark Prior	.20	.50
41 Mike Lieberthal	.10	.30
42 Toby Hall	.10	.30
43 Brad Ausmus	.10	.30
44 Damian Miller	.10	.30
45 Mark Kotsay	.10	.30
46 John Buck	.10	.30
47 Oliver Perez	.10	.30
48 Matt Morris	.10	.30
49 Raul Chavez	.10	.30
50 Randy Johnson	.30	.75
51 Dave Bush	.10	.30
52 Jose Macias	.10	.30
53 Paul Wilson	.10	.30
54 Wilfredo Ledezma	.10	.30
55 J.D. Drew	.10	.30
56 Pedro Martinez	.20	.50
57 Josh Towers	.10	.30
58 Jamie Moyer	.10	.30
59 Scott Elarton	.10	.30
60 Ken Griffey Jr.	.50	1.25
61 Steve Trachsel	.10	.30
62 Bubba Crosby	.10	.30
63 Michael Barrett	.10	.30
64 Odalis Perez	.10	.30
65 B.J. Upton	.10	.30
66 Eric Bruntlett	.10	.30
67 Victor Zambrano	.10	.30
68 Brandon League	.10	.30
69 Carlos Silva	.10	.30
70 Lyle Overbay	.10	.30
71 Runelvys Hernandez	.10	.30
72 Brad Penny	.10	.30
73 Ty Wigginton	.10	.30
74 Orlando Hudson	.10	.30
75 Roy Oswalt	.10	.30
76 Jason LaRue	.10	.30
77 Ismael Valdez	.10	.30
78 Calvin Pickering	.10	.30
79 Bill Hall	.10	.30
80 Carl Crawford	.10	.30
81 Tomas Perez	.10	.30
82 Joe Kennedy	.10	.30
83 Chris Woodward	.10	.30
84 Jason Lane	.10	.30
85 Steve Finley	.10	.30
86 Jeff Francis	.10	.30
87 Felipe Lopez	.10	.30

88 Chan Ho Park .10 .30
89 Joe Crede .10 .30
90 Jose Vidro .10 .30
91 Casey Kotchman .10 .30
92 Brandon Backe .10 .30
93 Mike Hampton .10 .30
94 Ryan Dempster .10 .30
95 Wily Mo Pena .10 .30
96 Matt Holliday .15 .40
97 A.J. Pierzynski .10 .30
98 Jason Jennings .10 .30
99 Eli Marrero .10 .30
100 Carlos Beltran .10 .30
101 Scott Kazmir .10 .30
102 Kenny Rogers .10 .30
103 Roy Halladay .10 .30
104 Alex Cora .10 .30
105 Richie Sexson .10 .30
106 Ben Sheets .10 .30
107 Bartolo Colon .10 .30
108 Eddie Perez .10 .30
109 Vicente Padilla .10 .30
110 Sammy Sosa .30 .75
111 Mark Ellis .10 .30
112 Woody Williams .10 .30
113 Todd Greene .10 .30
114 Nook Logan .10 .30
115 Francisco Rodriguez .10 .30
116 Miguel Batista .10 .30
117 Livan Hernandez .10 .30
118 Chris Aguila .10 .30
119 Coco Crisp .10 .30
120 Jose Reyes .10 .30
121 Ricky Ledee .10 .30
122 Brad Radke .10 .30
123 Carlos Guillen .10 .30
124 Paul Bako .10 .30
125 Tom Glavine .20 .50
126 Chad Moeller .10 .30
127 Mark Buehrle .10 .30
128 Casey Blake .10 .30
129 Juan Rivera .10 .30
130 Preston Wilson .10 .30
131 Nate Robertson .10 .30
132 Julio Franco .10 .30
133 Derek Lowe .10 .30
134 Rob Bell .10 .30
135 Javy Lopez .10 .30
136 Javier Vazquez .10 .30
137 Desi Relaford .10 .30
138 Danny Graves .10 .30
139 Josh Fogg .10 .30
140 Bobby Crosby .10 .30
141 Ramon Castro .10 .30
142 Jerry Hairston Jr. .10 .30
143 Morgan Ensberg .10 .30
144 Brandon Webb .10 .30
145 Jack Wilson .10 .30
146 Bill Mueller .10 .30
147 Troy Glaus .10 .30
148 Armando Benitez .10 .30
149 Adam LaRoche .10 .30
150 Hank Blalock .10 .30
151 Ryan Franklin .10 .30
152 Kevin Millwood .10 .30
153 Jason Marquis .10 .30
154 Dewon Brazelton .10 .30
155 Al Leiter .10 .30
156 Garrett Atkins .10 .30
157 Todd Walker .10 .30
158 Kris Benson .10 .30
159 Eric Milton .10 .30
160 Bret Boone .10 .30
161 Matt LeCroy .10 .30
162 Chris Widger .10 .30
163 Ruben Gotay .10 .30
164 Craig Monroe .10 .30
165 Travis Hafner .10 .30
166 Vance Wilson .10 .30
167 Jason Grabowski .10 .30
168 Tim Salmon .20 .50
169 Henry Blanco .10 .30
170 Josh Beckett .10 .30
171 Jake Westbrook .10 .30
172 Paul Lo Duca .10 .30
173 Julio Lugo .10 .30
174 Juan Cruz .10 .30
175 Mark Mulder .10 .30
176 Juan Castro .10 .30
177 Damion Easley .10 .30
178 LaTroy Hawkins .10 .30
179 Jon Lieber .10 .30
180 Vernon Wells .10 .30
181 Jeff DaVanon .10 .30
182 Dustan Mohr .10 .30
183 Ryan Freel .10 .30
184 Doug Davis .10 .30
185 Sean Casey .10 .30
186 Robb Quinlan .10 .30
187 J.D. Closser .10 .30
188 Tim Wakefield .10 .30
189 Brian Jordan .10 .30
190 Adam Dunn .10 .30
191 Antonio Perez .10 .30
192 Brett Tomko .10 .30
193 John Flaherty .10 .30
194 Michael Cuddyer .10 .30
195 Ronnie Belliard .10 .30
196 Tony Womack .10 .30
197 Jason Johnson .10 .30
198 Victor Santos .10 .30
199 Danny Haren .10 .30
200 Derek Jeter .60 1.50
201 Brian Anderson .10 .30
202 Carlos Pena .10 .30
203 Jaret Wright .10 .30
204 Paul Byrd .10 .30
205 Shannon Stewart .10 .30
206 Chris Carpenter .10 .30
207 Matt Stairs .10 .30
208 Brad Hawpe .10 .30
209 Bobby Higginson .10 .30
210 Torii Hunter .10 .30
211 Shawn Green .10 .30
212 Todd Hollandsworth .10 .30
213 Scott Erickson .10 .30
214 C.C. Sabathia .10 .30
215 Mike Mussina .20 .50
216 Jason Kendall .10 .30
217 Todd Pratt .10 .30
218 Danny Kolb .10 .30
219 Tony Armas .10 .30
220 Edgar Renteria .10 .30
221 Dave Roberts .10 .30
222 Luis Rivas .10 .30
223 Adam Everett .10 .30
224 Jeff Cirillo .10 .30
225 Orlando Hernandez .10 .30
226 Ken Harvey .10 .30
227 Corey Patterson .10 .30
228 Humberto Cota .10 .30
229 A.J. Burnett .10 .30
230 Roger Clemens .50 1.25
231 Joe Randa .10 .30
232 David Dellucci .10 .30
233 Troy Percival .10 .30
234 Dustin Hermanson .10 .30
235 Eric Gagne .10 .30
236 Terry Tiffee .10 .30
237 Tony Graffanino .10 .30
238 Jayson Werth .10 .30
239 Mark Sweeney .10 .30
240 Chipper Jones .30 .75
241 Aramis Ramirez .10 .30
242 Frank Catalanotto .10 .30
243 Mike Maroth .10 .30
244 Kelvim Escobar .10 .30
245 Bobby Abreu .10 .30
246 Kyle Lohse .10 .30
247 Jason Isringhausen .10 .30
248 Jose Lima .10 .30
249 Adrian Gonzalez .10 .30
250 Alex Rodriguez .50 1.25
251 Ramon Ortiz .10 .30
252 Frank Menechino .10 .30
253 Keith Ginter .10 .30
254 Kip Wells .10 .30
255 Dmitri Young .10 .30
256 Craig Biggio .20 .50
257 Ramon E. Martinez .10 .30
258 Jason Bartlett .10 .30
259 Brad Lidge .10 .30
260 Brian Giles .10 .30
261 Luis Terrero .10 .30
262 Miguel Ojeda .10 .30
263 Rich Harden .10 .30
264 Jacque Jones .10 .30
265 Marcus Giles .10 .30
266 Carlos Zambrano .10 .30
267 Michael Tucker .10 .30
268 Wes Obermueller .10 .30
269 Pete Orr RC .20 .50
270 Jim Thome .20 .50
271 Omar Vizquel .20 .50
272 Jose Valentin .10 .30
273 Juan Uribe .10 .30
274 Doug Mirabelli .10 .30
275 Jeff Kent .10 .30
276 Brad Wilkerson .10 .30
277 Chris Burke .10 .30
278 Endy Chavez .10 .30
279 Richard Hidalgo .10 .30
280 John Smoltz .20 .50
281 Jarrod Washburn .10 .30
282 Larry Bigbie .10 .30
283 Edgardo Alfonzo .10 .30
284 Cliff Lee .10 .30
285 Carlos Lee .10 .30
286 Olmedo Saenz .10 .30
287 Tomo Ohka .10 .30
288 Ruben Sierra .10 .30
289 Nick Swisher .10 .30
290 Frank Thomas .30 .75
291 Aaron Cook .10 .30
292 Cody McKay .10 .30
293 Hee-Seop Choi .10 .30
294 Carl Pavano .10 .30
295 Scott Rolen .20 .50
296 Matt Kata .10 .30
297 Terrence Long .10 .30
298 Jimmy Gobble .10 .30
299 Jason Repko .10 .30
300 Manny Ramirez .20 .50
301 Dan Wilson .10 .30
302 Jhonny Peralta .10 .30
303 John Mabry .10 .30
304 Adam Melhuse .10 .30
305 Kerry Wood .10 .30
306 Ryan Langerhans .10 .30
307 Antonio Alfonseca .10 .30
308 Marco Scutaro .10 .30
309 Jamey Carroll .10 .30
310 Lance Berkman .10 .30
311 Willie Harris .10 .30
312 Phil Nevin .10 .30
313 Gregg Zaun .10 .30
314 Michael Ryan .10 .30
315 Zack Greinke .10 .30
316 Ted Lilly .10 .30
317 David Eckstein .10 .30
318 Tony Torcato .10 .30
319 Rob Mackowiak .10 .30
320 Mark Teixeira .20 .50
321 Jason Phillips .10 .30
322 Jeremy Reed .10 .30
323 Bengie Molina .10 .30
324 Termel Sledge .10 .30
325 Justin Morneau .10 .30
326 Sandy Alomar Jr. .10 .30
327 Jon Garland .10 .30
328 Jay Payton .10 .30
329 Tino Martinez .20 .50
330 Jason Bay .10 .30
331 Jeff Conine .10 .30
332 Shawn Chacon .10 .30
333 Angel Berroa .10 .30
334 Reggie Sanders .10 .30
335 Kevin Brown .10 .30
336 Brady Clark .10 .30
337 Casey Fossum .10 .30
338 Raul Ibanez .10 .30
339 Derrek Lee .20 .50
340 Victor Martinez .10 .30
341 Kazuhisa Ishii .10 .30
342 Royce Clayton .10 .30
343 Trot Nixon .10 .30
344 Eric Young .10 .30
345 Aubrey Huff .10 .30
346 Brett Myers .10 .30
347 Joey Gathright .10 .30
348 Mark Grudzielanek .10 .30
349 Scott Spiezio .10 .30
350 Eric Chavez .10 .30
351 Einar Diaz .10 .30
352 Dallas McPherson .10 .30
353 John Thomson .10 .30
354 Neifi Perez .10 .30
355 Larry Walker .20 .50
356 Billy Wagner .10 .30
357 Mike Cameron .10 .30
358 Jimmy Rollins .10 .30
359 Kevin Mench .10 .30
360 Joe Mauer .30 .75
361 Jose Molina .10 .30
362 Joe Borchard .10 .30
363 Kevin Cash .10 .30
364 Jay Gibbons .10 .30
365 Khalil Greene .20 .50
366 Justin Leone .10 .30
367 Eddie Guardado .10 .30
368 Mike Lamb .10 .30
369 Matt Riley .10 .30
370 Luis Gonzalez .10 .30
371 Alfredo Amezaga .10 .30
372 J.J. Hardy .10 .30
373 Hector Luna .10 .30
374 Greg Aquino .10 .30
375 Jim Edmonds .10 .30
376 Joe Blanton .10 .30
377 Russell Branyan .10 .30
378 J.T. Snow .10 .30
379 Magglio Ordonez .10 .30
380 Rafael Palmeiro .20 .50
381 Andruw Jones .20 .50
382 David DeJesus .10 .30
383 Marquis Grissom .10 .30
384 Bobby Hill .10 .30
385 Kazuo Matsui .10 .30
386 Mark Loretta .10 .30
387 Chris Shelton .15 .40
388 Johnny Estrada .10 .30
389 Adam Hyzdu .10 .30
390 Nomar Garciaparra .30 .75
391 Mark Teahen .10 .30
392 Chris Capuano .10 .30
393 Ben Broussard .10 .30
394 Daniel Cabrera .10 .30
395 Jeremy Bonderman .10 .30
396 Darin Erstad .10 .30
397 Alex S. Gonzalez .10 .30
398 Kevin Millar .10 .30
399 Freddy Garcia .10 .30
400 Alfonso Soriano .10 .30
401 Koyie Hill .10 .30
402 Omar Infante .10 .30
403 Alex Gonzalez .10 .30
404 Pat Burrell .10 .30
405 Wes Helms .10 .30
406 Junior Spivey .10 .30
407 Joe Mays .10 .30
408 Jason Stanford .10 .30
409 Gil Meche .10 .30
410 Tim Hudson .10 .30
411 Chase Utley .20 .50
412 Matt Clement .10 .30
413 Nick Green .10 .30
414 Jose Vizcaino .10 .30
415 Ryan Klesko .10 .30
416 Vinny Castilla .10 .30
417 Brian Roberts .10 .30
418 Geronimo Gil .10 .30
419 Gary Matthews .10 .30
420 Jeff Weaver .10 .30
421 Jerome Williams .10 .30
422 Andy Pettitte .20 .50
423 Randy Wolf .10 .30
424 D'Angelo Jimenez .10 .30
425 Moises Alou .10 .30
426 Eric Byrnes .10 .30
427 Mark Redman .10 .30
428 Jermaine Dye .10 .30
429 Cory Lidle .10 .30
430 Jason Schmidt .10 .30
431 Jason W. Smith .10 .30
432 Jose Castillo .10 .30
433 Pokey Reese .10 .30
434 Matt Lawton .10 .30
435 Jose Guillen .10 .30
436 Craig Counsell .10 .30
437 Jose Hernandez .10 .30
438 Braden Looper .10 .30
439 Scott Hatteberg .10 .30
440 Gary Sheffield .10 .30
441 Gabe Gross .10 .30
442 Chris Gomez .10 .30
443 Dontrelle Willis .10 .30
444 Jamey Wright .10 .30
445 Rocco Baldelli .10 .30
446 Bernie Williams .20 .50
447 Sean Burroughs .10 .30
448 Willie Bloomquist .10 .30
449 Luis Castillo .10 .30
450 Mike Piazza .30 .75
451 Ryan Drese .10 .30
452 Pedro Feliz .10 .30
453 Horacio Ramirez .10 .30
454 Luis Matos .10 .30
455 Craig Wilson .10 .30
456 Russ Ortiz .10 .30
457 Xavier Nady .10 .30
458 Hideo Nomo .30 .75
459 Miguel Cairo .10 .30
460 Mike Lowell .10 .30
461 Corky Miller .10 .30
462 Bobby Madritsch .10 .30
463 Jose Contreras .10 .30
464 Johnny Damon .20 .50
465 Miguel Cabrera .20 .50
466 Eric Hinske .10 .30
467 Marlon Byrd .10 .30
468 Aaron Miles .10 .30
469 Ramon Vazquez .10 .30
470 Michael Young .10 .30
471 Alex Sanchez .10 .30
472 Shea Hillenbrand .10 .30
473 Jeff Bagwell .20 .50
474 Erik Bedard .10 .30
475 Jake Peavy .10 .30
476 Jody Gerut .10 .30
477 Randy Winn .10 .30
478 Kevin Youkilis .10 .30
479 Eric Dubose .10 .30
480 David Wright .50 1.25
481 Wilson Valdez .10 .30
482 Cliff Floyd .10 .30
483 Jose Mesa .10 .30
484 Doug Mientkiewicz .10 .30
485 Jorge Posada .20 .50
486 Sidney Ponson .10 .30
487 Dave Krynzel .10 .30
488 Octavio Dotel .10 .30
489 Matt Treanor .10 .30
490 Johan Santana .30 .75
491 John Patterson .10 .30
492 So Taguchi .10 .30
493 Carl Everett .10 .30
494 Jason Dubois .10 .30
495 Albert Pujols .60 1.50
496 Kirk Rueter .10 .30
497 Geoff Blum .10 .30
498 Juan Encarnacion .10 .30
499 Mark Hendrickson .10 .30
500 Barry Bonds .75 2.00
501 Cesar Izturis .10 .30
502 David Wells .10 .30
503 Jorge Julio .10 .30
504 Cristian Guzman .10 .30
505 Juan Pierre .10 .30
506 Adam Eaton .10 .30
507 Nick Johnson .10 .30
508 Mike Redmond .10 .30
509 Daryle Ward .10 .30
510 Adrian Beltre .10 .30
511 Laynce Nix .10 .30
512 Reed Johnson .10 .30
513 Jeremy Affeldt .10 .30
514 R.A. Dickey .10 .30
515 Alex Rios .10 .30
516 Orlando Palmeiro .10 .30
517 Mark Bellhorn .10 .30
518 Adam Kennedy .10 .30
519 Curtis Granderson .10 .30
520 Todd Helton .20 .50
521 Aaron Boone .10 .30
522 Milton Bradley .10 .30
523 Timo Perez .10 .30
524 Jeff Suppan .10 .30
525 Austin Kearns .10 .30
526 Charles Thomas .10 .30
527 Bronson Arroyo .10 .30
528 Roger Cedeno .10 .30
529 Russ Adams .10 .30
530 Barry Zito .10 .30
531 Bob Wickman .10 .30
532 Deivi Cruz .10 .30
533 Mariano Rivera .30 .75
534 J.J. Davis .10 .30
535 Greg Maddux .50 1.25
536 Ryan Vogelsong .10 .30
537 Josh Phelps .10 .30
538 Scott Hairston .10 .30
539 Vladimir Guerrero .30 .75
540 Ivan Rodriguez .20 .50
541 David Newhan .10 .30
542 David Bell .10 .30
543 Lew Ford .10 .30
544 Grady Sizemore .20 .50
545 David Ortiz .30 .75
546 Jose Cruz Jr. .10 .30
547 Aaron Rowand .10 .30
548 Marcus Thames .10 .30
549 Scott Podsednik .10 .30
550 Ichiro Suzuki .60 1.50
551 Eduardo Perez .10 .30
552 Chris Snyder .10 .30
553 Corey Koskie .10 .30
554 Miguel Tejada .10 .30
555 Orlando Cabrera .10 .30
556 Rondell White .10 .30
557 Wade Miller .10 .30
558 Rodrigo Lopez .10 .30
559 Chad Tracy .10 .30
560 Paul Konerko .10 .30
561 Wil Cordero .10 .30
562 John McDonald .10 .30
563 Jason Ellison .10 .30
564 Jason Michaels .10 .30
565 Melvin Mora .10 .30
566 Ryan Church .10 .30
567 Ryan Ludwick .10 .30
568 Erubiel Durazo .10 .30
569 Noah Lowry .10 .30
570 Curt Schilling .20 .50
571 Esteban Loaiza .10 .30
572 Freddy Sanchez .10 .30
573 Rich Aurilia .10 .30
574 Travis Lee .10 .30
575 Nick Punto .10 .30
576 Jason Christiansen .10 .30
Kevin Correia
577 Brad Baker .10 .30
Tim Redding
578 Terry Adams .10 .30
Gavin Floyd
579 Seth Etherton .10 .30
Dan Meyer
580 Justin Lehr .10 .30
Derrick Turnbow
581 Mike Gosling .10 .30
Brad Halsey
582 Jim Mecir .10 .30
Logan Kensing
583 Brad Hennessey .10 .30
Jeff Fassero
584 Jon Adkins .10 .30
Felix Diaz
585 Jesse Crain .10 .30
Juan Rincon
586 Jamie Cerda .10 .30
Nate Field
587 Bartolome Fortunato .10 .30
Jae Weong Seo
588 Steve Schmoll RC .20 .50
Yhency Brazoban
589 Ugueth Urbina .10 .30
Jamie Walker
590 Jorge De Paula .10 .30
Scott Proctor
591 Jason Davis .10 .30
Bob Howry
592 Tim Worrell .10 .30
Pedro Liriano
593 Jose Acevedo .10 .30
Kent Mercker
594 Chris Hammond .10 .30
Scott Linebrink
595 Fernando Nieve .10 .30
John Franco
596 Randy Flores .10 .30
Mike Lincoln
597 Joe Borowski .10 .30
Sergio Mitre
598 Lance Carter .10 .30
Jesus Colome
599 John Halama .10 .30
Lenny DiNardo
600 Chad Bradford .10 .30
Kiko Calero
601 David Aardsma .10 .30
Jim Brower
602 Geoff Geary .10 .30
Ryan Madson
603 Brian Moehler .10 .30
Nate Bump
604 Chin-Hui Tsao .10 .30
Ryan Speier
605 Ryan Wagner .10 .30
Aaron Harang
606 Steve Kline .10 .30
Rick Bauer
607 Lance Cormier .10 .30
Randy Choate
608 Jon Leicester .10 .30
Todd Wellemeyer
609 Vinnie Chulk .10 .30
Jason Frasor
610 Scott Dohmann .10 .30
Brian Fuentes
611 Steve Colyer .10 .30
Roberto Hernandez
612 Ian Snell .10 .30
Salomon Torres
613 Cal Eldred .10 .30
Adam Wainwright
614 Ryan Bukvich .10 .30
Doug Brocail
615 J.J. Putz .10 .30
Aaron Sele
616 Bruce Chen .10 .30
Todd Williams
617 David Weathers .10 .30
Ben Weber
618 Dennys Reyes .10 .30
Rudy Seanez
619 Tim Harikkala .10 .30
Ricardo Rincon
620 Shawn Camp .10 .30
Denny Bautista
621 Javier A. Lopez .10 .30
Allan Simpson
622 Mike Remlinger .10 .30
Glendon Rusch
623 Roman Colon .10 .30
Kevin Gryboski
624 Tom Martin .10 .30
Chris Reitsma
625 Chad Qualls .10 .30
Dan Wheeler
626 Tommy Phelps .10 .30
Matt Wise
627 Scott Schoeneweis .10 .30
Justin Speier
628 Francisco Cordero .10 .30
Frank Francisco
629 Rafael Soriano .10 .30
Matt Thornton
630 Mike Stanton .10 .30
Steve Karsay
631 Mike MacDougal .10 .30
Scott Sullivan
632 Brian Bruney .10 .30
Oscar Villarreal
633 Mike Adams .10 .30
Ricky Bottalico
634 Eddy Rodriguez .10 .30
Dave Borkowski
635 Rafael Betancourt .10 .30
David Riske
636 Jorge De La Rosa .10 .30
Gary Glover
637 Matt Perisho .10 .30
Ben Howard
638 Jeff Bajenaru .10 .30
Luis Vizcaino
639 Ron Mahay .10 .30
Erasmo Ramirez
640 John Grabow .10 .30
Mike Gonzalez
641 J.C. Romero .10 .30
Matt Guerrier
642 Carlos Hernandez .10 .30
Brandon Duckworth UER
Tim Redding is referred to in the Hernandez informational blurb
643 Travis Harper .10 .30
Seth McClung
644 Matt Herges .10 .30
Tyler Walker
645 Kelly Wunsch .10 .30
Elmer Dessens
646 Mark Malaska .10 .30
Mike Myers
647 Kyle Farnsworth .10 .30
Gary Knotts
648 Justin Duchscherer .10 .30
Jairo Garcia
649 Aaron Rakers .10 .30
Steve Reed
650 Tom Gordon .10 .30
Paul Quantrill
651 Brandon Lyon .10 .30
Shawn Estes
652 Pete Walker .10 .30
Gustavo Chacin
653 John Lackey .10 .30
Scot Shields
654 Doug Waechter .10 .30
Trever Miller
655 Luis Ayala .10 .30
Chad Cordero
656 Ron Villone .10 .30
Julio Mateo
657 Matt Mantei .10 .30
Blaine Neal
658 Damaso Marte .10 .30
Cliff Politte
659 Joe Valentine .10 .30
Luke Hudson
660 Todd Jones .10 .30
John Riedling
661 Heath Bell .10 .30
Aaron Heilman
662 Darrell May .10 .30
Akinori Otsuka
663 Joey Eischen .10 .30
Joe Horgan
664 Andy Sisco .10 .30
Mike Wood
665 Alan Embree .10 .30
Mike Timlin
666 Keith Foulke .10 .30
667 Rheal Cormier .10 .30
Aaron Fultz
668 Jake Woods .10 .30
Kevin Gregg
669 Matt Ginter .10 .30
Franklyn German
670 Scott Eyre .10 .30
Merkin Valdez
671 Brian Meadows .10 .30
Rick White
672 Guillermo Mota .10 .30
Tim Spooneybarger
673 Jason Grimsley .10 .30
B.J. Ryan
674 Neal Cotts .10 .30
Shingo Takatsu
675 Mike DeJean .10 .30
Felix Heredia
676 Matt Belisle .10 .30
Josh Hancock
677 Jon Rauch .10 .30
T.J. Tucker
678 Nick Regilio .10 .30
Brian Shouse
679 Julian Tavarez .10 .30
Ray King
680 Chad Fox .10 .30
Michael Wuertz
681 Jorge Sosa .10 .30
Adam Bernero
682 Jose Valverde .10 .30
Mike Koplove
683 Arthur Rhodes .10 .30
Scott Sauerbeck
684 Felix Rodriguez .10 .30
Tanyon Sturtze
685 Giovanni Carrara .10 .30
Duaner Sanchez
686 Mike Gallo .10 .30
Chad Harville
687 Mike Johnston .10 .30
Sean Burnett
688 Jeff Nelson .10 .30
Shigetoshi Hasegawa
689 Claudio Vargas .10 .30
Antonio Osuna
690 Brendan Donnelly .10 .30
Esteban Yan
691 Jeff Mathis .20 .50
Ervin Santana
692 Clint Everts .20 .50
Bill Bray
693 Jason Kubel .20 .50
Trevor Plouffe
694 Jake Stevens .20 .50
Andy Marte
695 Aaron Hill .20 .50
Chad Gaudin
696 Carlos Quentin .20 .50
Jesus Cota
697 Thomas Diamond .20 .50
Chris Young
698 Omar Quintanilla .20 .50
Dan Johnson
699 John Maine .20 .50
Val Majewski
700 James Houser .20 .50
Jonny Gomes
701 David Murphy .20 .50
Hanley Ramirez
702 Chris Lambert .20 .50
Rick Ankiel
703 Felix Pie .20 .50
Angel Guzman
704 Fred Lewis .20 .50
Nate Schierholtz
705 Arnie Munoz .20 .50
Gio Gonzalez
706 Felix Hernandez .60 1.50
Travis Blackley
707 Ray Olmedo .20 .50
Edwin Encarnacion UER
Photos Reversed
708 Tim Stauffer .20 .50
Justin Germano
709 Jeremy Guthrie .20 .50
Jeremy Sowers
710 Jorge Cortes .20 .50
Tom Gorzelanny
711 Taylor Tankersley .20 .50
Eric Reed
712 Neil Walker .20 .50
Paul Maholm
713 Willy Taveras .60 1.50
Luke Scott RC
714 Ryan Howard .75 2.00
Greg Golson
715 Blake DeWitt .20 .50
Edwin Jackson
716 Huston Street .20 .50
Dan Putnam
717 Rickie Weeks .20 .50
Mark Rogers
718 Robinson Cano .20 .50
Philip Hughes
719 Kyle Waldrop .20 .50
Jay Rainville
720 Craig Brazell .20 .50
Yusmeiro Petit
721 Baltazar Lopez RC .20 .50
Matt Brown RC
722 Daryl Thompson RC .20 .50
Ender Chavez RC
723 Dan Uggla RC 6.00 15.00
Erik Schindewolf RC

724 Ismael Ramirez RC .20 .50
Jayce Tingler RC
725 Tony Giarratano RC .20 .50
Eulogio de la Cruz RC
726 Matt Campbell RC .20 .50
Shane Costa RC
727 Martin Prado RC .20 .50
Bill McCarthy RC
728 Ian Kinsler RC 1.00 2.50
Juan Senreiso RC UER
Kinsler photo is Edinson Volquez
729 Luis Ramirez RC .20 .50
Lorenzo Scott RC
730 Chris Seddon RC .20 .50
Elliot Johnson RC
731 Craig Tatum RC .20 .50
Javon Moran RC
732 Stuart Pomeranz RC .20 .50
Jason Motte RC
733 Jose Vaquedano RC .20 .50
Stefan Bailie RC
734 Matt Albers RC .50 1.25
Wade Robinson RC
735 Matt DeSalvo RC .75 2.00
Melky Cabrera RC
736 Brian Stavisky RC .20 .50
Landon Powell RC
737 Scott Mathieson RC .30 .75
Scott Mitchinson RC
738 Sean Marshall RC .60 1.50
Bear Bay RC
739 Brandon McCarthy RC .50 1.25
Pedro Lopez RC
740 Alexander Smit RC .20 .50
Ricky Barrett RC
741 Matt Rogelstad RC .20 .50
Ryan Feierabend RC
742 Nate McLouth RC .20 .50
Adam Boeve RC
743 Kevin Melillo RC .30 .75
Michael Rogers RC
744 Matthew Kemp RC 1.50 4.00
Heath Totten RC
745 Jai Miller RC .20 .50
Tony Arnerich RC
746 Tyler Pelland RC .20 .50
Jesse Gutierrez RC
747 Jeremy West RC .20 .50
Willy Mota RC
748 Ryan Goleski RC .60 1.50
Ryan Garko RC
749 Bryan Triplett RC .20 .50
Jared Gothreaux RC
750 Kevin West RC .30 .75
Glen Perkins RC
751 Mike Esposito RC .20 .50
Zach Parker RC
752 Ryan Sweeney RC .40 1.00
Brian Miller RC
753 Casey McGehee RC .20 .50
Buck Coats RC
754 Mike Bourn RC .30 .75
Kelvin Pichardo RC
755 Mike Morse RC .30 .75
Bobby Livingston RC
756 Wes Swackhamer RC .20 .50
Brendan Ryan RC
757 Micah Furtado RC .20 .50
Nick Masset RC
758 Peeter Ramos RC .30 .75
George Kottaras RC
759 Elvys Quezada RC .30 .75
T.J. Beam RC
760 Dana Eveland RC .20 .50
Travis Hinton RC
761 James Jurries RC .20 .50
Chris Vines RC
762 Humberto Sanchez RC 2.00 5.00
Justin Verlander RC
763 Philip Humber RC .30 .75
Shawn Bowman RC
764 Pat Misch RC .20 .50
J.B. Thurmond RC
765 Christian Colonel RC .20 .50
Neil Wilson RC
766 Checklist 1 .10 .30
767 Checklist 2 .10 .30
768 Checklist 3 .10 .30
769 Checklist 4 .10 .30
770 Checklist 5 .10 .30

2005 Topps Total Domination

*DOMINATION: .75X TO 2X BASIC
STATED ODDS 1:10 H 1:10 R
CL: 40/50/56/60/100/110/147/150/180/190
CL: 200/230/250/260/270/290/300/345/350
CL: 400/465/490/495/500/510/520/540/545
CL: 575/580

2005 Topps Total Domination Autograph

STATED ODDS 1:494,640 H, 1:257,760 R
STATED PRINT RUN 10 CARDS
NO PRICING DUE TO SCARCITY
EXCHANGE DEADLINE 05/31/07
500 Barry Bonds EXCH

2005 Topps Total Silver

*SILVER 1-575/666: 1X TO 2.5X BASIC
*SILVER 576-690: 1X TO 2.5X BASIC
*SILVER 269/691-765: 1X TO 2.5X BASIC
*SILVER 766-770: 1X TO 2.5X BASIC
ONE PER PACK

2005 Topps Total Award Winners

COMPLETE SET (30) 12.50 30.00
STATED ODDS 1:10 H, 1:10 R
OVERALL INSERT PLATE ODDS 1:726 H
PLATE PRINT RUN 1 SET PER COLOR
BLACK-CYAN-MAGENTA-YELLOW ISSUED
FRONT AND BACK PLATES PRODUCED
NO PLATE PRICING DUE TO SCARCITY
AW1 Barry Bonds MVP 2.00 5.00
AW2 Vladimir Guerrero MVP .75 2.00
AW3 Roger Clemens CY 1.25 3.00
AW4 Johan Santana CY .75 2.00
AW5 Jason Bay ROY .30 .75
AW6 Bobby Crosby ROY .30 .75
AW7 Eric Gagne Rolaids .30 .75
AW8 Mariano Rivera Rolaids .75 2.00
AW9 Albert Pujols SS 1.50 4.00
AW10 Mark Teixeira SS .50 1.25
AW11 Mark Loretta SS .30 .75
AW12 Alfonso Soriano SS .30 .75
AW13 Jack Wilson SS .30 .75
AW14 Miguel Tejada SS .30 .75
AW15 Adrian Beltre SS .30 .75
AW16 Melvin Mora SS .30 .75
AW17 Barry Bonds SS 2.00 5.00
AW18 Jim Edmonds SS .30 .75
AW19 Bobby Abreu SS .30 .75
AW20 Manny Ramirez SS .50 1.25
AW21 Gary Sheffield SS .30 .75
AW22 Vladimir Guerrero SS .75 2.00
AW23 Johnny Estrada SS .30 .75
AW24 Victor Martinez SS .30 .75
AW25 Ivan Rodriguez SS .50 1.25
AW26 Livan Hernandez SS .30 .75
AW27 David Ortiz SS .50 1.25
AW28 Bobby Cox MG .30 .75
AW29 Buck Showalter MG .30 .75
AW30 Barry Bonds Aaron Award 2.00 5.00

2005 Topps Total Production

COMPLETE SET (10) 6.00 15.00
STATED ODDS 1:15 H, 1:15 R
OVERALL INSERT PLATE ODDS 1:726 H
PLATE PRINT RUN 1 SET PER COLOR
BLACK-CYAN-MAGENTA-YELLOW ISSUED
FRONT AND BACK PLATES PRODUCED
NO PLATE PRICING DUE TO SCARCITY
AB Adrian Beltre .30 .75
AP Albert Pujols 1.50 4.00
AR Alex Rodriguez 1.25 3.00
AS Alfonso Soriano .30 .75
BB Barry Bonds 2.00 5.00
JT Jim Thome .50 1.25
MR Manny Ramirez .50 1.25
MT Miguel Tejada .30 .75
TH Todd Helton .50 1.25
VG Vladimir Guerrero .75 2.00

2005 Topps Total Signatures

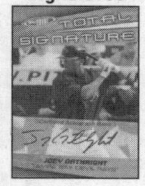

GROUP A ODDS 1:4849 H, 1:5484 R
GROUP B ODDS 1:608 H, 1:697 R
GROUP C ODDS 1:974 H, 1:1117 R
OVERALL AU PLATE ODDS 1:19,024 HOBBY
AU PLATE PRINT RUN 1 SET PER COLOR
BLACK-CYAN-MAGENTA-YELLOW ISSUED
NO AU PLATE PRICING DUE TO SCARCITY
EXCHANGE DEADLINE 05/31/07
BB Brian Bruney B 6.00 15.00
BM Brett Myers A
DW David Wright B 30.00 60.00
JG Joey Gathright B 4.00 10.00
RC Robinson Cano B EXCH 15.00 40.00
TT Terry Tiffee C 4.00 10.00
ZG Zack Greinke C 4.00 10.00

2005 Topps Total Team Checklists

COMPLETE SET (30) 6.00 15.00
STATED ODDS 1:4 H, 1:4 R
1 Luis Gonzalez .10 .30
2 John Smoltz .20 .50
3 Miguel Tejada .10 .30
4 David Ortiz .30 .75
5 Kerry Wood .10 .30
6 Frank Thomas .30 .75
7 Adam Dunn .10 .30
8 Victor Martinez .10 .30
9 Todd Helton .20 .50
10 Ivan Rodriguez .20 .50
11 Miguel Cabrera .20 .50
12 Roger Clemens .50 1.25
13 Zack Greinke .10 .30
14 Vladimir Guerrero .30 .75
15 Eric Gagne .10 .30
16 Ben Sheets .10 .30
17 Johan Santana .30 .75
18 Carlos Beltran .10 .30
19 Alex Rodriguez .50 1.25
20 Eric Chavez .10 .30
21 Jim Thome .20 .50
22 Jason Bay .10 .30
23 Brian Giles .10 .30
24 Barry Bonds .75 2.00
25 Ichiro Suzuki .60 1.50
26 Albert Pujols .60 1.50
27 Carl Crawford .10 .30
28 Alfonso Soriano .10 .30
29 Roy Halladay .10 .30
30 Jose Vidro .10 .30

2005 Topps Total Topps

COMPLETE SET (20) 12.50 30.00
STATED ODDS 1:15 H, 1:15 R
OVERALL INSERT PLATE ODDS 1:726 H
PLATE PRINT RUN 1 SET PER COLOR
BLACK-CYAN-MAGENTA-YELLOW ISSUED
FRONT AND BACK PLATES PRODUCED
NO PLATE PRICING DUE TO SCARCITY
AB Adrian Beltre .30 .75
AP Albert Pujols 1.50 4.00
AR Alex Rodriguez 1.25 3.00
AS Alfonso Soriano .30 .75
BB Barry Bonds 2.00 5.00
CB Carlos Beltran .30 .75
DJ Derek Jeter 1.50 4.00
EC Eric Chavez .30 .75
GM Greg Maddux 1.25 3.00
IR Ivan Rodriguez .50 1.25
JS Johan Santana .75 2.00
JT Jim Thome .50 1.25
MP Mike Piazza .75 2.00
MR Manny Ramirez .50 1.25
MT Miguel Tejada .30 .75
RC Roger Clemens 1.25 3.00
RJ Randy Johnson .75 2.00
SS Sammy Sosa .75 2.00
TH Todd Helton .50 1.25
VG Vladimir Guerrero .75 2.00

2001 Topps Tribute

This hobby-only product was released in mid-December 2001, and featured a 90-card base set that honors Hall of Fame caliber players like Babe Ruth and Mickey Mantle. Each pack contained four-cards, and carried a suggested retail price of 40.00.

COMPLETE SET (90) 100.00 200.00
PSA-GRADED MANTLE EXCH ODDS 1:170
M.MANTLE REPURCHASED ODDS 1:426
J.ROBINSON REPURCHASED ODDS 1:426
T.WILLIAMS REPURCHASED ODDS 1:426
EXCHANGE DEADLINE 11/30/03
1 Pee Wee Reese 2.50 6.00
2 Babe Ruth 8.00 20.00
3 Ralph Kiner 2.00 5.00
4 Brooks Robinson 2.00 5.00
5 Don Sutton 2.00 5.00
6 Carl Yastrzemski 4.00 10.00
7 Roger Maris 2.50 6.00
8 Andre Dawson 2.00 5.00
9 Luis Aparicio 2.00 5.00
10 Wade Boggs 2.00 5.00
11 Johnny Bench 2.50 6.00
12 Ernie Banks 2.50 6.00
13 Thurman Munson 2.50 6.00
14 Harmon Killebrew 2.50 6.00
15 Ted Kluszewski 2.00 5.00
16 Bob Feller 2.00 5.00
17 Mike Schmidt 5.00 12.00
18 Warren Spahn 2.00 5.00
19 Jim Palmer 2.00 5.00
20 Don Mattingly 5.00 12.00
21 Willie Mays 5.00 12.00
22 Gil Hodges 2.50 6.00
23 Juan Marichal 2.00 5.00
24 Robin Yount 2.50 6.00
25 Nolan Ryan Angels 6.00 15.00
26 Dave Winfield 2.00 5.00
27 Hank Greenberg 2.50 6.00
28 Honus Wagner 3.00 8.00
29 Nolan Ryan Rangers 6.00 15.00
30 Phil Niekro 2.00 5.00
31 Robin Roberts 2.00 5.00
32 Casey Stengel Yankees 2.00 5.00
33 Willie McCovey 2.00 5.00
34 Roy Campanella 2.50 6.00
35 Rollie Fingers A's 2.00 5.00
36 Tom Seaver 2.00 5.00
37 Jackie Robinson 2.50 6.00
38 Hank Aaron Braves 5.00 12.00
39 Bob Gibson 2.00 5.00
40 Carlton Fisk Red Sox 2.00 5.00
41 Hank Aaron Brewers 5.00 12.00
42 George Brett 5.00 12.00
43 Orlando Cepeda 2.00 5.00
44 Red Schoendienst 2.00 5.00
45 Don Drysdale 2.00 5.00
46 Mel Ott 2.50 6.00
47 Casey Stengel Mets 2.50 6.00
48 Al Kaline 2.50 6.00
49 Reggie Jackson 2.00 5.00
50 Tony Perez 2.00 5.00
51 Ozzie Smith 4.00 10.00
52 Billy Martin 2.00 5.00
53 Bill Dickey 2.00 5.00
54 Catfish Hunter 2.00 5.00
55 Duke Snider 2.00 5.00
56 Dale Murphy 2.00 5.00
57 Bobby Doerr 2.00 5.00
58 Earl Averill UER 2.00 5.00
Card pictures Earl Averill Jr.
59 Carlton Fisk White Sox 2.00 5.00
60 Tom Lasorda 2.00 5.00
61 Lou Gehrig 5.00 12.00
62 Enos Slaughter 2.00 5.00
63 Jim Bunning 2.00 5.00
64 Rollie Fingers Brewers 2.00 5.00
65 Frank Robinson Reds 2.00 5.00
66 Earl Weaver 2.00 5.00
67 Eddie Mathews 2.50 6.00
68 Kirby Puckett 2.50 6.00
69 Phil Rizzuto 2.50 6.00
70 Lou Brock 2.00 5.00
71 Walt Alston 2.00 5.00
72 Billy Pierce 2.00 5.00
73 Joe Morgan 2.00 5.00
74 Roberto Clemente 6.00 15.00
75 Whitey Ford 2.00 5.00
76 Richie Ashburn 2.00 5.00
77 Elston Howard 2.00 5.00
78 Gary Carter 2.00 5.00
79 Carl Hubbell 2.00 5.00
80 Yogi Berra 2.50 6.00
81 Ken Boyer 2.00 5.00
82 Nolan Ryan Astros 6.00 15.00
83 Bill Mazeroski 2.00 5.00
84 Dizzy Dean 2.50 6.00
85 Nellie Fox 2.00 5.00
86 Stan Musial 4.00 10.00
87 Steve Carlton 2.00 5.00
88 Willie Stargell 2.00 5.00
89 Hal Newhouser 2.00 5.00
90 Frank Robinson Orioles 2.00 5.00
NNO Mickey Mantle
PSA Redemption
NNO Mickey Mantle
Buyback EXCH
NNO Jackie Robinson
Buyback EXCH
NNO Ted Williams
Buyback EXCH

2001 Topps Tribute Dual Relics

This two-card set features relic cards of Casey Stengel and Frank Robinson. Each card was issued at 1:860 packs.

CSYM Casey Stengel Jsy-Jsy 75.00 150.00
FRRO Frank Robinson Bat-Jsy 50.00 100.00

2001 Topps Tribute Franchise Figures Relics

This 19-card set features relic cards of franchise players from teams past. Please note that these cards were broken into two groups: Group A were inserted at a rate of 1:106, while, Group B were inserted at 1:34. Card backs carry a "RM" prefix.

AL Walt Alston Jsy 40.00 80.00
Tommy Lasorda Jsy A
CD Gary Carter 40.00 80.00
Andre Dawson B
FY Carlton Fisk 75.00 150.00
Carl Yastrzemski A
JM Reggie Jackson 75.00 150.00
Billy Martin A
KG Al Kaline 75.00 150.00
Hank Greenberg A
MM Thurman Munson Jsy 150.00 250.00
Don Mattingly Jsy A
PK Kirby Puckett 75.00 150.00
Harmon Killebrew A
RG Babe Ruth 400.00 700.00
Lou Gehrig A
RR Brooks Robinson Bat 60.00 120.00
Frank Robinson Uni A
AFF Luis Aparicio 60.00 120.00
Nellie Fox
Carlton Fisk A
HDB Bill Dickey Jsy 125.00 200.00
Elston Howard Bat
Yogi Berra Jsy A
HSS Gil Hodges Bat 125.00 250.00
Casey Stengel Bat
Tom Seaver Jsy A
MCS Bill Mazeroski 150.00 250.00
Roberto Clemente
Willie Stargell A
MMA Dale Murphy 125.00 200.00
Eddie Mathews
Hank Aaron A
MMC Willie Mays Jsy 125.00 200.00
Willie McCovey Bat
Orlando Cepeda Jsy A
RSC Pee Wee Reese 75.00 150.00
Duke Snider
Roy Campanella A
SAC Mike Schmidt Jsy 75.00 150.00
Richie Ashburn Bat
Steve Carlton Uni A
BPKRM Johnny Bench 150.00 250.00
Tony Perez
Ted Kluszewski
Frank Robinson
Joe Morgan A
SBSM Ozzie Smith 75.00 150.00
Lou Brock
Red Schoendienst
Stan Musial A

2001 Topps Tribute Game Bat Relics

This 31-card set features bat relic cards of classic players like George Brett and Hank Aaron. Please note that these cards were broken into two groups: Group 1 were inserted at a rate of 1:2, while, Group 2 were inserted at 1:35. Card backs carry a "RB" prefix.

BAT LOGO AND STENCIL CUT-OUT SAME QTY
BAT LOGO AND STENCIL CUT-OUT SAME VALUE

RBAK Al Kaline 1 10.00 25.00
RBBM Billy Martin 1 15.00 40.00
RBBR Babe Ruth 2 100.00 200.00
RBBRO B.Robinson 1 10.00 25.00
RBCFR C.Fisk Red Sox 1 10.00 25.00
RBCFW C.Fisk W.Sox 1 10.00 25.00
RBCS Casey Stengel 1 10.00 25.00
RBCY Carl Yastrzemski 1 10.00 25.00
RBDM Don Mattingly 1 10.00 25.00
RBFRR F.Robinson Reds 1 10.00 25.00
RBGB George Brett 1 10.00 25.00
RBGH Gil Hodges 1 15.00 40.00
RBHA H.Aaron Braves 1 20.00 50.00
RBHAB Hank Aaron Brewers 1 20.00 50.00
RBHG Hank Greenberg 1 20.00 50.00
RBHK Harmon Killebrew 1 10.00 25.00
RBHW Honus Wagner 1 75.00 150.00
RBJR Jackie Robinson 1
RBKB Ken Boyer 1 6.00 15.00
RBLA Luis Aparicio 1 6.00 15.00
RBLB Lou Brock 1 10.00 25.00
RBLG Lou Gehrig 1 75.00 150.00
RBOS Ozzie Smith 1 10.00 25.00
RBPWR P.W.Reese 1 10.00 25.00
RBRA Richie Ashburn 1 10.00 25.00
RBRC Roy Campanella 1 10.00 25.00
RBRCL R.Clemente 1 40.00 80.00
RBRJ Reggie Jackson 1 10.00 25.00
RBRM Roger Maris 1 20.00 50.00
RBTM T.Munson 1 10.00 25.00
RBWM Willie McCovey 1 10.00 25.00

2001 Topps Tribute Game Patch-Number Relics

This 23-card set features swatches of actual game-used jersey patches. These cards were issued into packs at 1:61. Card backs carry a "RPN" prefix.

RPNBD Bill Dickey 150.00 250.00
RPNBDO Bobby Doerr 90.00 150.00
RPNCY Carl Yastrzemski 125.00 250.00
RPNDM Don Mattingly 150.00 250.00
RPNDW Dave Winfield 90.00 150.00
RPNEM Eddie Mathews 125.00 200.00
RPNGB George Brett 125.00 200.00
RPNHK Harmon Killebrew 125.00 200.00
RPNJB Johnny Bench 125.00 200.00
RPNJM Juan Marichal 90.00 150.00
RPNJP Jim Palmer 90.00 150.00
RPNKB Kirby Puckett 125.00 200.00
RPNLB Lou Brock 125.00 200.00
RPNMS Mike Schmidt 150.00 300.00
RPNNRA N.Ryan Angels 250.00 500.00
RPNNRH N.Ryan Astros 250.00 500.00
RPNNRR Nolan Ryan Rgr 250.00 500.00
RPNRS Red Schoendienst 90.00 150.00
RPNRY Robin Yount 125.00 200.00
RPNTL Tom Lasorda 90.00 150.00
RPNWA Walt Alston 90.00 150.00
RPNWB Wade Boggs 125.00 200.00
RPNYB Yogi Berra 125.00 200.00

2001 Topps Tribute Game Worn Relics

This 39-card set features swatches of actual game-used jerseys. These cards were issued into packs in two different groups: Group 1 (1:282), and Group 2 (1:13) packs. Card backs carry a "RJ" prefix.

GROUP 1 STATED ODDS 1:282
GROUP 2 STATED ODDS 1:13
GROUP 3 STATED ODDS 1:42
GROUP 4 STATED ODDS 1:12
GROUP 5 STATED ODDS 1:9
OVERALL STATED ODDS 1:2
RJBD Bill Dickey 5 12.50 30.00
RJBDO Bobby Doerr 2 12.50 30.00
RJCS Casey Stengel 5 12.50 30.00
RJCY C.Yastrzemski White 3 15.00 40.00
RJCYA C.Yastrzemski Gray 3 15.00 40.00
RJDD Dizzy Dean Uni 4 20.00 50.00
RJDM Don Mattingly 2 15.00 40.00
RJDW Dave Winfield 2 8.00 20.00
RJEB E.Banks White 2 12.50 30.00
RJEM Eddie Mathews 2 12.50 30.00
RJEBA E.Banks Gray 2 12.50 30.00
RJFR Frank Robinson 2 12.50 30.00
RJGB George Brett 2 15.00 40.00
RJHK H.Killebrew 2 12.50 30.00
RJJB J.Bench White 2 12.50 30.00
RJJP Jim Palmer White 2 8.00 20.00
RJJR Jackie Robinson 1 200.00 350.00
RJJBE Johnny Bench Gray 2 12.50 30.00
RJJMG Juan Marichal 2 8.00 20.00
RJJPA Jim Palmer Gray 2 8.00 20.00
RJKP Kirby Puckett 2 12.50 30.00
RJLB Lou Brock 2 12.50 30.00
RJMSB M.Schmidt Blue 2 15.00 40.00
RJMSW M.Schmidt White 2 15.00 40.00
RJNF Nellie Fox 2 12.50 30.00
RJNRA N.Ryan Angels 2 30.00 60.00
RJNRH N.Ryan Astros 2 30.00 60.00
RJNRR N.Ryan Rangers 2 30.00 60.00
RJRS R.Schoendienst 2 8.00 20.00
RJRY Robin Yount 2 12.50 30.00
RJSC Steve Carlton 2 8.00 20.00
RJSM Stan Musial 2 20.00 50.00
RJTL Tom Lasorda 4 8.00 20.00
RJWA Walt Alston 4 8.00 20.00
RJWB Wade Boggs 2 12.50 30.00
RJWMF W.Mays Gray 2 40.00 80.00
RJWMW W.Mays White 2 40.00 80.00
RJWST Willie Stargell 2 12.50 30.00
RJYB Yogi Berra 2 12.50 30.00

2001 Topps Tribute Tri-Relic

This one-card set features a tri-relic card of Nolan Ryan. This card was issued at 1:1292. Card backs carry a "NR" prefix.

NRAAR Nolan Ryan

2002 Topps Tribute

This 90 card set was released in November, 2002. These cards were issued in five card packs which came six packs to a box and four boxes to a case. Each of these packs had an SRP of $50 per pack.

COMPLETE SET (90) 60.00 120.00
1 Hank Aaron 4.00 10.00
2 Rogers Hornsby 2.00 5.00
3 Bobby Thomson 1.50 4.00
4 Eddie Collins 1.50 4.00
5 Joe Carter 1.50 4.00
6 Jim Palmer 1.50 4.00
7 Willie Mays 4.00 10.00
8 Willie Stargell 1.50 4.00
9 Vida Blue 1.50 4.00
10 Whitey Ford 1.50 4.00
11 Bob Gibson 1.50 4.00
12 Nellie Fox 2.00 5.00

13 Napoleon Lajoie 2.00 5.00
14 Frankie Frisch 1.50 4.00
15 Nolan Ryan 5.00 12.00
16 Brooks Robinson 1.50 4.00
17 Kirby Puckett 2.00 5.00
18 Fergie Jenkins 1.50 4.00
19 Edd Roush 1.50 4.00
20 Honus Wagner 3.00 8.00
21 Richie Ashburn 1.50 4.00
22 Bob Feller 1.50 4.00
23 Joe Morgan 1.50 4.00
24 Orlando Cepeda 1.50 4.00
25 Steve Garvey 1.50 4.00
26 Hank Greenberg 2.00 5.00
27 Stan Musial 3.00 8.00
28 Sam Crawford 1.50 4.00
29 Jim Rice 1.50 4.00
30 Hack Wilson 1.50 4.00
31 Lou Brock 1.50 4.00
32 Mickey Vernon 1.50 4.00
33 Chuck Klein 1.50 4.00
34 Tony Gwynn 2.50 6.00
35 Duke Snider 1.50 4.00
36 Ryne Sandberg 4.00 10.00
37 Johnny Bench 2.00 5.00
38 Sam Rice 1.50 4.00
39 Lou Gehrig 4.00 10.00
40 Robin Yount 2.00 5.00
41 Don Sutton 1.50 4.00
42 Jim Bottomley 1.50 4.00
43 Billy Herman 1.50 4.00
44 Zach Wheat 1.50 4.00
45 Juan Marichal 1.50 4.00
46 Bert Blyleven 1.50 4.00
47 Jackie Robinson 2.00 5.00
48 Gil Hodges 1.50 4.00
49 Mike Schmidt 4.00 10.00
50 Dale Murphy 1.50 4.00
51 Phil Rizzuto 1.50 4.00
52 Ty Cobb 3.00 8.00
53 Andre Dawson 1.50 4.00
54 Fred Lindstrom 1.50 4.00
55 Roy Campanella 2.00 5.00
56 Don Larsen 1.50 4.00
57 Harry Heilmann 1.50 4.00
58 Catfish Hunter 1.50 4.00
59 Frank Robinson 1.50 4.00
60 Bill Mazeroski 1.50 4.00
61 Roger Maris 2.00 5.00
62 Dave Winfield 1.50 4.00
63 Warren Spahn 1.50 4.00
64 Babe Ruth 6.00 15.00
65 Ernie Banks 2.00 5.00
66 Wade Boggs 1.50 4.00
67 Carl Yastrzemski 3.00 8.00
68 Ron Santo 1.50 4.00
69 Dennis Martinez 1.50 4.00
70 Yogi Berra 2.00 5.00
71 Paul Waner 1.50 4.00
72 George Brett 4.00 10.00
73 Eddie Mathews 2.00 5.00
74 Bill Dickey 1.50 4.00
75 Carlton Fisk 1.50 4.00
76 Thurman Munson 2.00 5.00
77 Reggie Jackson 1.50 4.00
78 Phil Niekro 1.50 4.00
79 Luis Aparicio 1.50 4.00
80 Steve Carlton 1.50 4.00
81 Tris Speaker 1.50 4.00
82 Johnny Mize 1.50 4.00
83 Tom Seaver 1.50 4.00
84 Heinie Manush 1.50 4.00
85 Tommy John 1.50 4.00
86 Joe Cronin 1.50 4.00
87 Don Mattingly 4.00 10.00
88 Kirk Gibson 1.50 4.00
89 Bo Jackson 2.00 5.00
90 Mel Ott 2.00 5.00

2002 Topps Tribute First Impressions

Inserted into packs at a stated rate of one in 16, this is a parallel to the Topps Tribute set. Each of these cards were printed to a stated print run which matched the player's major league debut season. For those players who debuted in 1925 or before, no pricing is provided due to market scarcity.

1 Hank Aaron/54 25.00 60.00
2 Rogers Hornsby/15
3 Bobby Thomson/46 12.50 30.00
4 Eddie Collins/6
5 Joe Carter/83 6.00 15.00
6 Jim Palmer/65 10.00 25.00
7 Willie Mays/51 25.00 60.00
8 Willie Stargell/62 10.00 25.00
9 Vida Blue/69 8.00 20.00
10 Whitey Ford/50 12.50 30.00
11 Bob Gibson/59 10.00 25.00
12 Nellie Fox/47 20.00 50.00
13 Napoleon Lajoie/96 8.00 20.00
14 Frankie Frisch/19
15 Nolan Ryan/66 25.00 60.00
16 Brooks Robinson/55 10.00 25.00
17 Kirby Puckett/84 8.00 20.00
18 Fergie Jenkins/65 10.00 25.00
19 Edd Roush/13
20 Honus Wagner/97 12.50 30.00
21 Richie Ashburn/48 12.50 30.00
22 Bob Feller/36 12.50 30.00
23 Joe Morgan/63 10.00 25.00
24 Orlando Cepeda/58 10.00 25.00
25 Steve Garvey/69 8.00 20.00
26 Hank Greenberg/30 20.00 50.00
27 Stan Musial/41 25.00 60.00
28 Sam Crawford/99 6.00 15.00
29 Jim Rice/74 8.00 20.00
30 Hack Wilson/23
31 Lou Brock/61 10.00 25.00
32 Mickey Vernon/39 12.50 30.00
33 Chuck Klein/28 15.00 40.00
34 Tony Gwynn/82 10.00 25.00
35 Duke Snider/47 12.50 30.00
36 Ryne Sandberg/81 30.00 60.00
37 Johnny Bench/67 10.00 25.00
38 Sam Rice/15
39 Lou Gehrig/23
40 Robin Yount/74 10.00 25.00
41 Don Sutton/66 8.00 20.00
42 Jim Bottomley/22
43 Billy Herman/31 15.00 40.00
44 Zach Wheat/9
45 Juan Marichal/60 10.00 25.00
46 Bert Blyleven/70 8.00 20.00
47 Jackie Robinson/47 15.00 40.00
48 Gil Hodges/43 12.50 30.00
49 Mike Schmidt/72 20.00 50.00
50 Dale Murphy/76 20.00 50.00
51 Phil Rizzuto/41 12.50 30.00
52 Ty Cobb/5
53 Andre Dawson/76 8.00 20.00
54 Fred Lindstrom/24
55 Roy Campanella/48 15.00 40.00
56 Don Larsen/53 10.00 25.00
57 Harry Heilmann/14
58 Catfish Hunter/65 10.00 25.00
59 Frank Robinson/56 10.00 25.00
60 Bill Mazeroski/56 10.00 25.00
61 Roger Maris/57 12.50 30.00
62 Dave Winfield/73 8.00 20.00
63 Warren Spahn/42 12.50 30.00
64 Babe Ruth/14
65 Ernie Banks/53 12.50 30.00
66 Wade Boggs/82 6.00 15.00
67 Carl Yastrzemski/61 20.00 50.00
68 Ron Santo/60 10.00 25.00
69 Dennis Martinez/76 8.00 20.00
70 Yogi Berra/46 15.00 40.00
71 Paul Waner/26 15.00 40.00
72 George Brett/73 20.00 50.00
73 Eddie Mathews/52 20.00 50.00
74 Bill Dickey/28 15.00 40.00
75 Carlton Fisk/69 8.00 20.00
76 Thurman Munson/69 10.00 25.00
77 Reggie Jackson/67 8.00 20.00
78 Phil Niekro/64 10.00 25.00
79 Luis Aparicio/56 10.00 25.00
80 Steve Carlton/65 10.00 25.00
81 Tris Speaker/7
82 Johnny Mize/36 12.50 30.00
83 Tom Seaver/67 8.00 20.00
84 Heinie Manush/23
85 Tommy John/63 10.00 25.00
86 Joe Cronin/26 15.00 40.00
87 Don Mattingly/82 15.00 40.00
88 Kirk Gibson/79 8.00 20.00
89 Bo Jackson/86 8.00 20.00
90 Mel Ott/26 20.00 50.00

2002 Topps Tribute Lasting Impressions

Inserted into packs at a stated rate of one in 13, this is a parallel to the Topps Tribute set. Each of these cards were printed to a stated print run which matched the player's major league final season. For those players who retired in 1925 or before (or 2001 or later), no pricing is provided due to market scarcity.

1 Hank Aaron/76 20.00 50.00
2 Rogers Hornsby/37 15.00 40.00
3 Bobby Thomson/60 10.00 25.00
4 Eddie Collins/30 15.00 40.00
5 Joe Carter/98 6.00 15.00
6 Jim Palmer/84 6.00 15.00
7 Willie Mays/73 20.00 50.00
8 Willie Stargell/82 6.00 15.00
9 Vida Blue/86 6.00 15.00
10 Whitey Ford/67 8.00 20.00
11 Bob Gibson/75 8.00 20.00
12 Nellie Fox/65 20.00 50.00
13 Napoleon Lajoie/16
14 Frankie Frisch/37 12.50 30.00
15 Nolan Ryan/93 20.00 50.00
16 Brooks Robinson/77 8.00 20.00
17 Kirby Puckett/95 8.00 20.00
18 Fergie Jenkins/83 6.00 15.00
19 Edd Roush/31 15.00 40.00
20 Honus Wagner/17
21 Richie Ashburn/62 10.00 25.00
22 Bob Feller/56 10.00 25.00
23 Joe Morgan/84 6.00 15.00
24 Orlando Cepeda/74 8.00 20.00
25 Steve Garvey/87 6.00 15.00
26 Hank Greenberg/47 15.00 40.00
27 Stan Musial/63 20.00 50.00
28 Sam Crawford/17
29 Jim Rice/89 6.00 15.00
30 Hack Wilson/34 15.00 40.00
31 Lou Brock/79 8.00 20.00
32 Mickey Vernon/60 10.00 25.00
33 Chuck Klein/44 12.50 30.00
34 Tony Gwynn/1
35 Duke Snider/64 10.00 25.00
36 Ryne Sandberg/97 30.00 60.00
37 Johnny Bench/83 8.00 20.00
38 Sam Rice/34 15.00 40.00
39 Lou Gehrig/39 30.00 80.00
40 Robin Yount/93 8.00 20.00
41 Don Sutton/88 6.00 15.00
42 Jim Bottomley/37 12.50 30.00
43 Billy Herman/47 12.50 30.00
44 Zach Wheat/27 15.00 40.00
45 Juan Marichal/75 8.00 20.00
46 Bert Blyleven/92 6.00 15.00
47 Jackie Robinson/56 12.50 30.00
48 Gil Hodges/63 10.00 25.00
49 Mike Schmidt/89 20.00 50.00
50 Dale Murphy/93 20.00 50.00
51 Phil Rizzuto/56 10.00 25.00
52 Ty Cobb/28 30.00 80.00
53 Andre Dawson/96 6.00 15.00
54 Fred Lindstrom/36 12.50 30.00
55 Roy Campanella/57 12.50 30.00
56 Don Larsen/67 8.00 20.00
57 Harry Heilmann/32 15.00 40.00
58 Catfish Hunter/79 8.00 20.00
59 Frank Robinson/76 8.00 20.00
60 Bill Mazeroski/72 8.00 20.00
61 Roger Maris/68 10.00 25.00
62 Dave Winfield/95 6.00 15.00
63 Warren Spahn/65 10.00 25.00
64 Babe Ruth/35 30.00 80.00
65 Ernie Banks/71 10.00 25.00
66 Wade Boggs/99 6.00 15.00
67 Carl Yastrzemski/83 12.50 30.00
68 Ron Santo/74 8.00 20.00
69 Dennis Martinez/98 6.00 15.00
70 Yogi Berra/65 12.50 30.00
71 Paul Waner/45 12.50 30.00
72 George Brett/99 20.00 50.00
73 Eddie Mathews/68 20.00 50.00
74 Bill Dickey/46 12.50 30.00
75 Carlton Fisk/93 6.00 15.00
76 Thurman Munson/79 10.00 25.00
77 Reggie Jackson/87 6.00 15.00
78 Phil Niekro/87 6.00 15.00
79 Luis Aparicio/79 8.00 20.00
80 Steve Carlton/88 6.00 15.00
81 Tris Speaker/28 15.00 40.00
82 Johnny Mize/53 10.00 25.00
83 Tom Seaver/86 6.00 15.00
84 Heinie Manush/39 12.50 30.00
85 Tommy John/89 6.00 15.00
86 Joe Cronin/45 12.50 30.00
87 Don Mattingly/95 15.00 40.00
88 Kirk Gibson/95 6.00 15.00
89 Bo Jackson/94 8.00 20.00
90 Mel Ott/47 15.00 40.00

2002 Topps Tribute The Catch Dual Relic

Inserted into packs at a stated rate of one in 1023, this card features relics from players involved in Willie Mays' legendary catch during the 1954 World Series when he ran down a well hit ball by Vic Wertz.

JSY NUMBER ODDS 1:3161
JSY NUMBER PRINT RUN 24 #'d CARDS
NO JSY NUM.PRICING DUE TO SCARCITY
*SEASON: .6X TO 1.2X BASIC DUAL RELIC
SEASON ODDS 1:1391
SEASON PRINT RUN 54 SERIAL #'d CARDS
MW Vic Wertz Bat 150.00 300.00
Willie Mays Glove

2002 Topps Tribute Marks of Excellence Autograph

Inserted into packs at a stated rate of one in 61, these six cards feature players who signed cards honoring their signature moment.

DL Don Larsen 20.00 50.00
LB Lou Brock 20.00 50.00
MS Mike Schmidt 60.00 120.00
SC Steve Carlton 20.00 50.00
SM Stan Musial 50.00 100.00
WS Warren Spahn 40.00 80.00

2002 Topps Tribute Marks of Excellence Autograph Relics

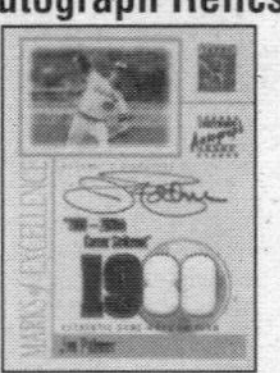

Inserted in packs at a stated rate of one in 61, these six cards feature game-used memorabilia pieces honoring players and their signature moment.

BR Brooks Robinson Bat 40.00 80.00
DM Don Mattingly Jsy 75.00 150.00
DS Duke Snider Uni 40.00 80.00
FJ Fergie Jenkins Jsy 20.00 50.00
JP Jim Palmer Uni 20.00 50.00
RY Robin Yount Uni 40.00 80.00

2002 Topps Tribute Matching Marks Dual Relics

Inserted into packs at an overall stated rate of one in 11, these 22 cards feature two players and a game-used memorabilia piece from each of them.

GROUP A ODDS 1:134
GROUP B ODDS 1:368
GROUP C ODDS 1:123
GROUP D ODDS 1:43
GROUP E ODDS 1:105
GROUP F ODDS 1:82
GROUP G ODDS 1:31
AR Hank Aaron Bat 250.00 400.00
Babe Ruth Bat A
BB Wade Boggs Jsy 20.00 50.00
George Brett Jsy C
BF Johnny Bench Bat 30.00 60.00
Carlton Fisk Bat A
BM Vida Blue Jsy 6.00 15.00
Dennis Martinez Jsy G
BMA George Brett Jsy 75.00 150.00
Don Mattingly Jsy A
BS Bert Blyleven Jsy 8.00 20.00
Don Sutton Jsy C
GA Hank Greenberg Bat 60.00 120.00
Richie Ashburn Bat A
GH Steve Garvey Bat 10.00 25.00
Gil Hodges Bat D
JS Fergie Jenkins Jsy 20.00 50.00
Tom Seaver Jsy B
MA Willie Mays Uni 150.00 250.00
Hank Aaron Bat A
NS Phil Niekro Uni 8.00 20.00
Tom Seaver Uni G
PJ Jim Palmer Jsy 10.00 25.00
Tommy John Jsy D
RJ Frank Robinson Uni 30.00 60.00
Reggie Jackson Bat A
RS Nolan Ryan Jsy 75.00 150.00
Tom Seaver Jsy A
SB Tris Speaker Bat 200.00 300.00
George Brett Bat A
SBA Ron Santo Bat 10.00 25.00
Ernie Banks Bat D
SM Duke Snider Bat 50.00 100.00
Willie Mays Uni A
SR Willie Stargell Uni 8.00 20.00
Jim Rice Uni E
WY Dave Winfield Bat 15.00 40.00
Carl Yastrzemski Bat D
WYO Dave Winfield Uni 8.00 20.00
Robin Yount Uni F
YK Carl Yastrzemski Bat 50.00 100.00
Chuck Klein Bat A
YP Robin Yount Uni 30.00 60.00
Kirby Puckett Uni A

2002 Topps Tribute Memorable Materials

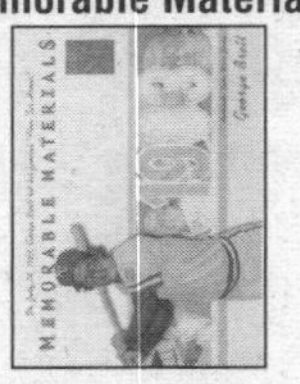

Inserted into packs at different rates depending on what group and game-used memorabilia piece, these 22 cards feature players from the tribute set as well as a memorabilia piece. We have notated next to the player's name what group this memorabilia piece belongs to.

BAT GROUP A ODDS 1:11,592
BAT GROUP B ODDS 1:6
JSY/UNI GROUP A ODDS 1:246
JSY/UNI GROUP B ODDS 1:12
BJ Bo Jackson Jsy B 10.00 25.00
BM Bill Mazeroski Uni B 8.00 20.00
BT Bobby Thomson Bat B 8.00 20.00
CF Carlton Fisk Bat B 10.00 25.00
CK Chuck Klein Bat B 15.00 40.00
CY Carl Yastrzemski Uni B 12.50 30.00
DM Don Mattingly Jsy B 15.00 40.00
GB George Brett Jsy B 15.00 40.00
HA Hank Aaron Bat B 20.00 50.00
HW Hack Wilson Bat B 30.00 60.00
JC Joe Carter Bat B 8.00 20.00
JM Joe Morgan Bat B 8.00 20.00
JR Jackie Robinson Bat B 20.00 50.00
KG Kirk Gibson Bat B 8.00 20.00
KP Kirby Puckett Bat B 15.00 40.00
LG Lou Gehrig Bat A
NR Nolan Ryan Jsy A 20.00 50.00
PR Phil Rizzuto Bat B 10.00 25.00
RC Roy Campanella Bat B 15.00 40.00
RJ Reggie Jackson Bat B 10.00 25.00
RM Roger Maris Bat B 40.00 80.00
TM Thurman Munson Bat B 20.00 50.00

2002 Topps Tribute Memorable Materials Jersey Number

Inserted into packs at a different rate depending on whether it is a bat or a uniform piece, this is a parallel to the Memorable Materials insert set. Each of these cards are issued to a stated print run

matching the uniform number that the player wore during his career. For cards with less than 40 cards printed, no pricing is provided due to market scarcity.

BAT STATED ODDS 1:208
JSY/UNI STATED ODDS 1:644
BJ Bo Jackson Jsy/16
BM Bill Mazeroski Uni/9
BT Bobby Thomson Bat/23
CF Carlton Fisk Bat/27
CK Chuck Klein Bat/1
CY Carl Yastrzemski Uni/27 UER
Yaz jersey number is actually 8
DM Don Mattingly Jsy/23
GB George Brett Jsy/5
HA Hank Aaron Bat/44 50.00 120.00
HW Hack Wilson Bat/1
JC Joe Carter Bat/29
JM Joe Morgan Bat/8
JR Jackie Robinson Bat/42 50.00 120.00
KG Kirk Gibson Bat/23
KP Kirby Puckett Bat/34
LG Lou Gehrig Bat/4
NR Nolan Ryan Jsy/34
PR Phil Rizzuto Bat/10
RC Roy Campanella Bat/39
RJ Reggie Jackson Bat/44 25.00 60.00
RM Roger Maris Bat/9
TM Thurman Munson Bat/15

2002 Topps Tribute Memorable Materials Season

Inserted into packs at a different rate depending on whether it is a bat or a uniform piece, this is a parallel to the Memorable Materials insert set. Each of these cards are issued to a stated print run matching the most memorable season that the player had during his career. For cards with less than 40 cards printed, no pricing is provided due to market scarcity.

BAT STATED ODDS 1:72
JSY/UNI STATED ODDS 1:152
BJ Bo Jackson Jsy/89 30.00 80.00
BM Bill Mazeroski Uni/60 15.00 40.00
BT Bobby Thomson Bat/51 15.00 40.00
CF Carlton Fisk Bat/75 15.00 40.00
CK Chuck Klein Bat/33
CY Carl Yastrzemski Uni/75 UER 20.00 50.00
Card commemorates 1967 season
DM Don Mattingly Jsy/87 25.00 60.00
GB George Brett Jsy/83 30.00 80.00
HA Hank Aaron Bat/74 30.00 80.00
HW Hack Wilson Bat/30
JC Joe Carter Bat/93 12.50 30.00
JM Joe Morgan Bat/76 12.50 30.00
JR Jackie Robinson Bat/47 40.00 100.00
KG Kirk Gibson Bat/88 12.50 30.00
KP Kirby Puckett Bat/91 25.00 60.00
LG Lou Gehrig Bat/39
NR Nolan Ryan Jsy/91 30.00 80.00
PR Phil Rizzuto Bat/50 20.00 50.00
RC Roy Campanella Bat/55 30.00 80.00
RJ Reggie Jackson Bat/77 15.00 40.00
RM Roger Maris Bat/61 60.00 150.00
TM Thurman Munson Bat/76 30.00 80.00

2002 Topps Tribute Milestone Materials

Inserted at different stated odds depending on whether it is a bat or a jersey/uniform piece, these 50 cards feature game-used memorabilia from the feature player's career.

BAT STATED ODDS 1:4
JSY/UNI STATED ODDS 1:5
AD Andre Dawson Jsy 6.00 15.00
BD Bill Dickey Uni 10.00 25.00
BF Bob Feller Bat 10.00 25.00
BG Bob Gibson Uni 8.00 20.00
BH Billy Herman Uni 6.00 15.00
BR Babe Ruth Bat 150.00 250.00
BRO Brooks Robinson Bat 10.00 25.00
CH Catfish Hunter Jsy 8.00 20.00
DM Dale Murphy Jsy 8.00 20.00
DS Duke Snider Uni 8.00 20.00
EB Ernie Banks Uni 10.00 25.00
EC Eddie Collins Bat 75.00 150.00
EM Eddie Mathews Jsy 10.00 25.00
ER Edd Roush Bat 15.00 40.00
FF Frankie Frisch Bat 10.00 25.00
FL Fred Lindstrom Uni 10.00 25.00
FR Frank Robinson Bat 10.00 25.00
HH Harry Heilmann Bat 10.00 25.00
HM Heinie Manush Bat 15.00 40.00
HW Honus Wagner Bat 75.00 150.00
JB Johnny Bench Jsy 10.00 25.00
JBO Jim Bottomley Bat 10.00 25.00
JC Joe Cronin Bat 10.00 25.00
JM Johnny Mize Uni 8.00 20.00
JMA Juan Marichal Jsy 6.00 15.00
JP Jim Palmer Uni 6.00 15.00
LA Luis Aparicio Bat 8.00 20.00
LG Lou Gehrig Bat 100.00 175.00
MO Mel Ott Bat 30.00 60.00
MV Mickey Vernon Bat 8.00 20.00
NF Nellie Fox Uni 10.00 25.00
NL Napoleon Lajoie Bat 90.00 150.00
NR Nolan Ryan Jsy 20.00 50.00
OC Orlando Cepeda Jsy 6.00 15.00
PW Paul Waner Bat 15.00 40.00
RH Rogers Hornsby Bat 30.00 60.00
RJ Reggie Jackson Jsy 8.00 20.00
RS Ryne Sandberg Bat 15.00 40.00
RY Robin Yount Uni 10.00 25.00
SC Sam Crawford Bat 15.00 40.00
SR Sam Rice Bat 10.00 25.00
TC Ty Cobb Bat 75.00 150.00
TS Tom Seaver Jsy 8.00 20.00
TSP Tris Speaker Bat 75.00 150.00
WB Wade Boggs Uni 8.00 20.00
WF Whitey Ford Uni 8.00 20.00
WM Willie Mays Uni 20.00 50.00
WS Willie Stargell Uni 8.00 20.00
YB Yogi Berra Jsy 10.00 25.00
ZW Zach Wheat Bat 15.00 40.00

2002 Topps Tribute Milestone Materials Jersey Number

Inserted into packs at a different rate depending on whether it is a bat or a uniform piece, this is a parallel to the Milestone Materials insert set. Each of these cards are issued to a stated print run matching the uniform number that the player wore during his career. For cards with less than 40 cards printed, no pricing is provided due to market scarcity.

BAT STATED ODDS 1:443
JSY/UNI STATED ODDS 1:148
AD Andre Dawson Jsy/8
BD Bill Dickey Uni/8
BF Bob Feller Bat/19
BG Bob Gibson Uni/45 20.00 50.00
BH Billy Herman Uni/2
BR Babe Ruth Bat/3
BRO Brooks Robinson Bat/5
CH Catfish Hunter Jsy/27
DM Dale Murphy Jsy/3
DS Duke Snider Uni/4
EB Ernie Banks Uni/14
EC Eddie Collins Bat/1
EM Eddie Mathews Jsy/41 25.00 60.00
ER Edd Roush Bat/1
FF Frankie Frisch Bat/3
FL Fred Lindstrom Uni/3
FR Frank Robinson Bat/20
HH Harry Heilmann Bat/1
HM Heinie Manush Bat/3
HW Honus Wagner Bat/33
JB Johnny Bench Jsy/5
JBO Jim Bottomley Bat/4
JC Joe Cronin Bat/4
JM Johnny Mize Uni/36
JMA Juan Marichal Jsy/27
JP Jim Palmer Uni/22
LA Luis Aparicio Bat/11
LG Lou Gehrig Bat/4
MO Mel Ott Bat/4
MV Mickey Vernon Bat/3
NF Nellie Fox Uni/2
NL Napoleon Lajoie Bat/1
NR Nolan Ryan Jsy/34
OC Orlando Cepeda Jsy/30
PW Paul Waner Bat/9
RH Rogers Hornsby Bat/9
RJ Reggie Jackson Jsy/44 20.00 50.00
RS Ryne Sandberg Bat/23
RY Robin Yount Uni/19
SC Sam Crawford Bat/1
SR Sam Rice Bat/1
TC Ty Cobb Bat/1
TS Tom Seaver Jsy/41 20.00 50.00
TSP Tris Speaker Bat/1
WB Wade Boggs Uni/26
WF Whitey Ford Uni/16
WM Willie Mays Uni/24
WS Willie Stargell Uni/8
YB Yogi Berra Jsy/8
ZW Zach Wheat Bat/1

2002 Topps Tribute Milestone Materials Season

Inserted into packs at a different rate depending on whether it is a bat or a uniform piece, this is a parallel to the Memorable Materials insert set. Each of these cards are issued to a stated print run matching the most memorable season that the player had during his career. For cards with less than 40 cards printed, no pricing is provided due to market scarcity.

BAT STATED ODDS 1:73
JSY/UNI STATED ODDS 1:41

AD Andre Dawson Jsy/95 12.50 30.00
BD Bill Dickey Uni/46 25.00 60.00
BF Bob Feller Bat/54 25.00 60.00
BG Bob Gibson Uni/74 15.00 40.00
BH Billy Herman Uni/47 15.00 40.00
BR Babe Ruth Bat/34
BRO Brooks Robinson Bat/74 20.00 50.00
CH Catfish Hunter Jsy/79 15.00 40.00
DM Dale Murphy Jsy/91 20.00 50.00
DS Duke Snider Uni/63 20.00 50.00
EB Ernie Banks Uni/70 20.00 50.00
EC Eddie Collins Bat/25
EM Eddie Mathews Jsy/67 20.00 50.00
ER Edd Roush Bat/31
FF Frankie Frisch Bat/35
FL Fred Lindstrom Uni/36
FR Frank Robinson Bat/71 20.00 50.00
HH Harry Heilmann Bat/32
HM Heinie Manush Bat/39
HW Honus Wagner Bat/14
JB Johnny Bench Jsy/80 20.00 50.00
JBO Jim Bottomley Bat/36
JC Joe Cronin Bat/45 25.00 60.00
JM Johnny Mize Uni/50 20.00 50.00
JMA Juan Marichal Jsy/7
JP Jim Palmer Uni/82 12.50 30.00
LA Luis Aparicio Bat/73 15.00 40.00
LG Lou Gehrig Bat/37
MO Mel Ott Bat/45 60.00 150.00
MV Mickey Vernon Bat/56 20.00 50.00
NF Nellie Fox Uni/41 40.00 100.00
NL Napoleon Lajoie Bat/14
NR Nolan Ryan Jsy/89 40.00 100.00
OC Orlando Cepeda Jsy/73 12.50 30.00
PW Paul Waner Bat/42 40.00 100.00
RH Rogers Hornsby Bat/37
RJ Reggie Jackson Jsy/84 15.00 40.00
RS Ryne Sandberg Bat/93 30.00 80.00
RY Robin Yount Uni/92 15.00 40.00
SC Sam Crawford Bat/16
SR Sam Rice Bat/34
TC Ty Cobb Bat/27
TS Tom Seaver Jsy/81 15.00 40.00
TSP Tris Speaker Bat/25
WB Wade Boggs Uni/99 15.00 40.00
WF Whitey Ford Uni/62 20.00 50.00
WM Willie Mays Uni/69 40.00 100.00
WS Willie Stargell Uni/80 15.00 40.00
YB Yogi Berra Jsy/61 25.00 60.00
ZW Zach Wheat Bat/25

2002 Topps Tribute Pastime Patches

Inserted into packs at a stated overall rate of one in 92, these 12 cards feature game-worn patch relic cards of these baseball legends.

*LOGO PATCHES: 2.5X VALUE
GROUP A ODDS 1:184
GROUP B ODDS 1:184
OVERALL ODDS 1:92
BD Bill Dickey B 125.00 200.00
CY Carl Yastrzemski B 125.00 200.00
DM Don Mattingly A 100.00 200.00
DW Dave Winfield A 60.00 120.00
EM Eddie Mathews A 75.00 150.00
GB George Brett A 125.00 200.00
JB Johnny Bench B 75.00 150.00
JP Jim Palmer B 75.00 150.00
KP Kirby Puckett B 75.00 150.00
RY Robin Yount B 75.00 150.00
WB Wade Boggs B 75.00 150.00
NRR Nolan Ryan B 150.00 250.00

2002 Topps Tribute Signature Cuts

Inserted into packs at a stated rate of one in 9936, these four cards feature cut autographs of four of baseball's most legendary figures. According to Topps, each of these cards were issued to a print run of two cards.

BR Babe Ruth
JR Jackie Robinson
LG Lou Gehrig
TC Ty Cobb

2003 Topps Tribute Contemporary

This 110 card set was released in August, 2003. These cards were issued in five card packs with an

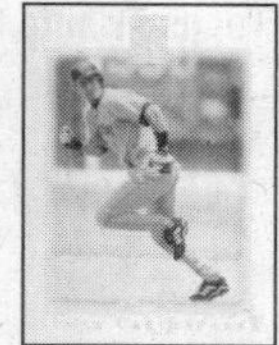

$50 SRP which came six packs to a box and four boxes to a case. Cards numbered 1-90 feature veterans and cards 91-100 feature rookies. Cards numbered 101 through 110 also feature rookies, but those cards are signed and were issued to a stated print run of 499 serial numbered sets and these cards were inserted at a stated rate of one in seven. Jose Contreras did not return his cards in time for inclusion in this product and those cards could be redeemed until August 31, 2005.

COMMON CARD (1-90) .75 2.00
COMMON CARD (91-100) .75 2.00
COMMON CARD (101-110) 4.00 10.00
1 Jim Thome 1.00 2.50
2 Edgardo Alfonzo .75 2.00
3 Edgar Martinez 1.00 2.50
4 Scott Rolen 1.00 2.50
5 Eric Hinske .75 2.00
6 Mark Mulder .75 2.00
7 Jason Giambi .75 2.00
8 Bernie Williams 1.00 2.50
9 Cliff Floyd .75 2.00
10 Ichiro Suzuki 3.00 8.00
11 Pat Burrell .75 2.00
12 Garret Anderson .75 2.00
13 Gary Sheffield .75 2.00
14 Johnny Damon 1.00 2.50
15 Kerry Wood .75 2.00
16 Bartolo Colon .75 2.00
17 Adam Dunn .75 2.00
18 Omar Vizquel 1.00 2.50
19 Todd Helton 1.00 2.50
20 Nomar Garciaparra 2.50 6.00
21 A.J. Burnett .75 2.00
22 Craig Biggio 1.00 2.50
23 Carlos Beltran .75 2.00
24 Kazuhisa Ishii .75 2.00
25 Vladimir Guerrero 1.50 4.00
26 Roberto Alomar 1.00 2.50
27 Roger Clemens 3.00 8.00
28 Tim Hudson .75 2.00
29 Brian Giles .75 2.00
30 Barry Bonds 4.00 10.00
31 Jim Edmonds .75 2.00
32 Rafael Palmeiro 1.00 2.50
33 Francisco Rodriguez .75 2.00
34 Andruw Jones 1.00 2.50
35 Shea Hillenbrand .75 2.00
36 Moises Alou .75 2.00
37 Luis Gonzalez .75 2.00
38 Darin Erstad .75 2.00
39 John Smoltz 1.00 2.50
40 Derek Jeter 4.00 10.00
41 Aubrey Huff .75 2.00
42 Eric Chavez .75 2.00
43 Doug Mientkiewicz .75 2.00
44 Lance Berkman .75 2.00
45 Josh Beckett .75 2.00
46 Austin Kearns .75 2.00
47 Frank Thomas 1.50 4.00
48 Pedro Martinez 1.00 2.50
49 Tim Salmon .75 2.00
50 Alex Rodriguez 2.50 6.00
51 Ryan Klesko .75 2.00
52 Tom Glavine 1.00 2.50
53 Shawn Green .75 2.00
54 Jeff Kent .75 2.00
55 Carlos Pena .75 2.00
56 Paul Konerko .75 2.00
57 Troy Glaus .75 2.00
58 Manny Ramirez 1.00 2.50
59 Jason Jennings .75 2.00
60 Randy Johnson 1.50 4.00
61 Ivan Rodriguez 1.00 2.50
62 Roy Oswalt .75 2.00
63 Kevin Brown .75 2.00
64 Jose Vidro .75 2.00
65 Jorge Posada 1.00 2.50
66 Mike Piazza 2.50 6.00
67 Bret Boone .75 2.00
68 Carlos Delgado .75 2.00
69 Jimmy Rollins .75 2.00
70 Alfonso Soriano .75 2.00
71 Greg Maddux 2.50 6.00
72 Mark Prior 1.00 2.50
73 Jeff Bagwell 1.00 2.50
74 Richie Sexson .75 2.00
75 Sammy Sosa 1.50 4.00
76 Curt Schilling .75 2.00
77 Mike Sweeney .75 2.00
78 Torii Hunter .75 2.00
79 Larry Walker .75 2.00
80 Miguel Tejada .75 2.00
81 Rich Aurilia .75 2.00
82 Bobby Abreu .75 2.00
83 Phil Nevin .75 2.00
84 Rodrigo Lopez .75 2.00
85 Chipper Jones 1.50 4.00
86 Ken Griffey Jr. 2.50 6.00
87 Mike Lowell .75 2.00
88 Magglio Ordonez .75 2.00
89 Barry Zito .75 2.00
90 Albert Pujols 3.00 8.00
91 Corey Shafer FY RC .75 2.00
92 Dan Haren FY RC 1.25 3.00
93 Jeremy Bonderman FY RC 3.00 8.00
94 Branden Florence FY RC .75 2.00
95 E.Bastida-Martinez FY RC .75 2.00
96 Brian Wright FY RC .75 2.00
97 Elizardo Ramirez FY RC 1.25 3.00
98 Mi.Garciaparra FY RC .75 2.00
99 Clay Hensley FY RC .75 2.00
100 Bobby Basham FY RC .75 2.00
101 Jose Contreras FY AU RC 8.00 20.00
102 Br. Bullington FY AU RC 4.00 10.00
103 Joey Gomes FY AU RC 4.00 10.00
104 Craig Brazell FY AU RC 4.00 10.00
105 Andy Marte FY AU RC 30.00 60.00
106 Han. Ramirez FY AU RC 75.00 150.00
107 Ryan Shealy FY AU RC 12.50 30.00
108 Daryl Clark FY AU RC 4.00 10.00
109 Tyler Johnson FY AU RC 4.00 10.00
110 Ben Francisco FY AU RC 4.00 10.00

2003 Topps Tribute Contemporary Gold

Card 101 (Jose Contreras) was issued in packs in the form of an exchange card with a redemption deadline of August 31st, 2005.

RANDOM INSERTS IN PACKS
STATED PRINT RUN 25 SERIAL #'d SETS
NO PRICING DUE TO SCARCITY

2003 Topps Tribute Contemporary Red

*RED 1-90: .6X TO 1.5X BASIC CARDS
*RED 91-100: .75X TO 2X BASIC CARDS
1-100 PRINT RUN 225 SERIAL #'d SETS
*RED 101-110: .6X TO 1.5X BASIC
101-110 PRINT RUN 99 SERIAL #'d SETS
RANDOM INSERTS IN PACKS
106 Hanley Ramirez FY AU 75.00 150.00

2003 Topps Tribute Contemporary Bonds Tribute Relics

*RED BONDS: .6X TO 1.5X BASIC BONDS
RED BONDS PRINT RUN 50 #'d SETS
GOLD BONDS PRINT RUN 1 #'d SET
NO GOLD PRICING DUE TO SCARCITY
RANDOM INSERTS IN PACKS
DB Barry Bonds Bat-Jsy 20.00 50.00
SB Barry Bonds Jsy 15.00 40.00
TB Barry Bonds Bat-Cap-Jsy 40.00 80.00

2003 Topps Tribute Contemporary Bonds Tribute 40-40 Club Relics

RANDOM INSERTS IN PACKS
NO GOLD PRICING DUE TO SCARCITY
CBR Jose Canseco Uni 40.00 80.00
Barry Bonds Uni
Alex Rodriguez Uni
CBRG Jose Canseco Uni
Barry Bonds Uni
Alex Rodriguez Uni Gold/1
CBRR Jose Canseco Uni 60.00 120.00
Barry Bonds Uni
Alex Rodriguez Uni Red/50

2003 Topps Tribute Contemporary Bonds Tribute 600 HR Club Relics

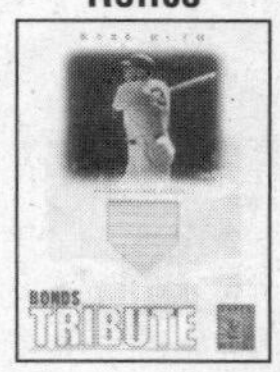

*RED 600: .6X TO 1.5X BASIC
RED 600 PRINT RUN 50 SERIAL #'d SETS
GOLD PRINT RUN 1 SERIAL #'d SET
NO GOLD PRICING DUE TO SCARCITY
RANDOM INSERTS IN PACKS
BB Barry Bonds Bat 15.00 40.00
BR Babe Ruth Bat 75.00 150.00
HA Hank Aaron Bat 15.00 40.00
WM Willie Mays Uni 20.00 50.00

2003 Topps Tribute Contemporary Bonds Tribute 600 HR Club Double Relics

*RED 600 DOUBLE: .6X TO 1.5X BASIC
RED 600 DOUBLE PRINT RUN 50 #'d SETS
GOLD 600 DOUBLE PRINT 1 SERIAL #'d SET
NO GOLD PRICING DUE TO SCARCITY
RANDOM INSERTS IN PACKS
BA Barry Bonds Bat 50.00 100.00
Hank Aaron Bat
BM Barry Bonds Bat 50.00 100.00
Willie Mays Uni
RB Babe Ruth Bat 125.00 200.00
Barry Bonds Bat

2003 Topps Tribute Contemporary Bonds Tribute 600 HR Club Quad Relics

RANDOM INSERTS IN PACKS
PRINT RUNS B/WN 1-50 COPIES PER
NO GOLD/RED PRICING DUE TO SCARCITY
HR Babe Ruth Bat 300.00 500.00
Willie Mays Uni
Hank Aaron Bat
Barry Bonds Bat/50
HRG Babe Ruth Bat
Willie Mays Uni
Hank Aaron Bat
Barry Bonds Bat Gold/1
HRR Babe Ruth Bat
Willie Mays Uni
Hank Aaron Bat
Barry Bonds Bat Red/25

2003 Topps Tribute Contemporary Matching Marks Dual Relics

*RED MARKS: .6X TO 1.5X BASIC
RED MARKS PRINT RUN 50 SERIAL #'d SETS
GOLD MARKS PRINT RUN 1 SERIAL #'d SET
NO GOLD PRICING DUE TO SCARCITY
RANDOM INSERTS IN PACKS
AP Roberto Alomar Bat 6.00 15.00
Rafael Palmeiro Bat
BG Jeff Bagwell Uni 6.00 15.00
Juan Gonzalez Bat
BP Barry Bonds Bat 15.00 40.00
Rafael Palmeiro Bat
GR Nomar Garciaparra Jsy 10.00 25.00
Alex Rodriguez Jsy
HR Rickey Henderson Bat 6.00 15.00
Manny Ramirez Bat
MG Fred McGriff Bat 4.00 10.00
Juan Gonzalez Bat
MP Fred McGriff Bat 6.00 15.00
Rafael Palmeiro Bat
PA Rafael Palmeiro Bat 6.00 15.00
Roberto Alomar Uni
PH Rafael Palmeiro Bat 6.00 15.00
Rickey Henderson Bat
PS Rafael Palmeiro Uni 6.00 15.00
Sammy Sosa Bat
RP Manny Ramirez Jsy 10.00 25.00
Mike Piazza Uni
SB Sammy Sosa Bat 6.00 15.00
Jeff Bagwell Uni
SG Alfonso Soriano Uni 6.00 15.00
Vladimir Guerrero Bat

2003 Topps Tribute Contemporary Memorable Materials Relics

*RED MEM: .6X TO 1.5X BASIC
RED MEM PRINT RUN 50 SERIAL #'d SETS
GOLD MEM PRINT RUN 1 SERIAL #'d SET
NO GOLD PRICING DUE TO SCARCITY
RANDOM INSERTS IN PACKS
AJÂ Andruw Jones Jsy 6.00 15.00
APÂ Albert Pujols Jsy 10.00 25.00
ARÂ Alex Rodriguez Jsy 8.00 20.00
ASÂ Alfonso Soriano Uni 4.00 10.00
BBÂ Barry Bonds Jsy 15.00 40.00
CRÂ Cal Ripken Bat 20.00 50.00
GMÂ Greg Maddux Jsy 6.00 15.00
JGÂ Jason Giambi Jsy 4.00 10.00
JG2 Jason Giambi Bat 4.00 10.00
KWÂ Kerry Wood Jsy 4.00 10.00
LGÂ Luis Gonzalez Bat 4.00 10.00
MTÂ Miguel Tejada Bat 4.00 10.00
RHÂ Rickey Henderson Uni 6.00 15.00
SGÂ Shawn Green Jsy 4.00 10.00
SSÂ Sammy Sosa Bat 6.00 15.00
SS2 Sammy Sosa Jsy 6.00 15.00
TGÂ Troy Glaus Uni 4.00 10.00
THÂ Torii Hunter Jsy 4.00 10.00
VGÂ Vladimir Guerrero Bat 6.00 15.00

2003 Topps Tribute Contemporary Milestone Materials Relics

*RED MILE: .6X TO 1.5X BASIC
RED MILE PRINT RUN 50 SERIAL #'d SETS
GOLD PRINT RUN 1 SERIAL #'d SET
NO GOLD PRICING DUE TO SCARCITY
RANDOM INSERTS IN PACKS
ARÂ Alex Rodriguez Jsy 8.00 20.00
BB1 Barry Bonds 1500 RBI Uni 10.00 25.00
BB2 Barry Bonds 1500 Runs Uni 10.00 25.00
BB3 Barry Bonds 2000 Hits Uni 10.00 25.00
BB4 Barry Bonds 500 2B Uni 10.00 25.00
BB5 Barry Bonds 600 HR Uni 10.00 25.00
CJÂ Chipper Jones Jsy 6.00 15.00
FM1 Fred McGriff Cubs Bat 4.00 10.00
FM2 Fred McGriff 2000 Hits Bat 4.00 10.00
FM3 Fred McGriff 400 HR Bat 4.00 10.00
FTÂ Frank Thomas Jsy 6.00 15.00
JB1 Jeff Bagwell Jsy 4.00 10.00
JB2 Jeff Bagwell Uni 4.00 10.00
JG1 Juan Gonzalez Indians Bat 3.00 8.00
JG2 Juan Gonzalez Rgr Bat 3.00 8.00
MP1 Mike Piazza Bat 6.00 15.00
MP2 Mike Piazza Uni 6.00 15.00
MR1 Manny Ramirez Bat 4.00 10.00
MR2 Manny Ramirez Jsy 4.00 10.00
NGÂ Nomar Garciaparra Jsy 10.00 25.00
RAÂ Roberto Alomar Uni 6.00 15.00
RH1 R.Henderson Mets Bat 4.00 10.00
RH2 R.Henderson Sox Bat 4.00 10.00
RH3 R.Henderson A's Bat 4.00 10.00
RH4 R.Henderson 3000 Hits Bat 4.00 10.00
RH5 R.Henderson 500 2B Bat 4.00 10.00
RP1 R.Palmeiro 1500 RBI Jsy 4.00 10.00
RP2 R.Palmeiro 2500 Hits Bat 4.00 10.00
RP3 R.Palmeiro 500 HR Uni 4.00 10.00
RP4 R.Palmeiro 500 2B Bat 4.00 10.00
SS1 Sammy Sosa 1250 RBI Jsy 6.00 15.00
SS2 Sammy Sosa 2000 Hits Jsy 6.00 15.00
SS3 Sammy Sosa Bat 6.00 15.00
THÂ Todd Helton Jsy 6.00 15.00
VGÂ Vladimir Guerrero Bat 6.00 15.00

2003 Topps Tribute Contemporary Modern Marks Autographs

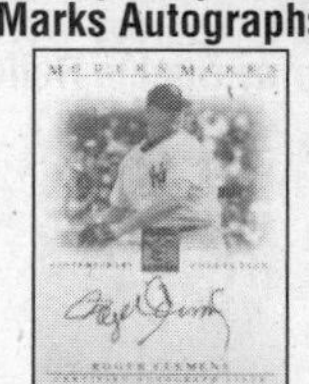

Inserted at a stated rate of one in 19, these nine cards feature authentic autographs from current major leaguers.

STATED ODDS 1:19
*RED MARKS: .5X TO 1.2X BASIC
RED MARKS STATED ODDS 1:38
RED MARKS PRINT RUN 99 SERIAL #'d SETS
GOLD MARKS STATED ODDS 1:149
GOLD MARKS PRINT RUN 25 SERIAL #'d SETS
NO GOLD PRICING DUE TO SCARCITY
CF Cliff Floyd 6.00 15.00
EH Eric Hinske 6.00 15.00
LB Lance Berkman 10.00 25.00
MO Magglio Ordonez 6.00 15.00
MS Mike Sweeney 6.00 15.00
PK Paul Konerko 10.00 25.00
PL Paul Lo Duca 6.00 15.00
RC Roger Clemens 60.00 120.00
TH Torii Hunter 6.00 15.00

2003 Topps Tribute Contemporary Perennial All-Star Relics

*RED AS: .6X TO 1.5X BASIC
RED AS PRINT RUN 50 SERIAL #'d SETS
GOLD AS PRINT RUN 1 SERIAL #'d SET
NO GOLD PRICING DUE TO SCARCITY
RANDOM INSERTS IN PACKS
ARÂ Â Alex Rodriguez Jsy 8.00 20.00
BBÂ Â Barry Bonds Uni 10.00 25.00
BSÂ Â Benito Santiago Bat 4.00 10.00
BWÂ Â Bernie Williams Bat 6.00 15.00
CBÂ Â Craig Biggio Uni 6.00 15.00
CJÂ Â Chipper Jones Jsy 6.00 15.00
CSÂ Â Curt Schilling Jsy 4.00 10.00
EMÂ Â Edgar Martinez Bat 6.00 15.00
FTÂ Â Frank Thomas Bat 6.00 15.00
GMÂ Â Greg Maddux Jsy 6.00 15.00
GSÂ Â Gary Sheffield Bat 4.00 10.00
IRÂ Â Ivan Rodriguez Bat 6.00 15.00
JSÂ Â John Smoltz Uni 6.00 15.00
LWÂ Â Larry Walker Bat 4.00 10.00
MMÂ Â Mike Mussina Uni 6.00 15.00
MPÂ Â Mike Piazza Bat 6.00 15.00
MRÂ Â Manny Ramirez Bat 6.00 15.00
PMÂ Â Pedro Martinez Jsy 6.00 15.00
RAÂ Â Roberto Alomar Bat 6.00 15.00
RCÂ Â Roger Clemens Uni 8.00 20.00
RHÂ Â Rickey Henderson Bat 6.00 15.00
SSÂ Â Sammy Sosa Bat 6.00 15.00

2003 Topps Tribute Contemporary Performance Double Relics

*RED DOUBLE: .6X TO 1.5X BASIC
RED DOUBLE PRINT RUN 50 #'d SETS
GOLD DOUBLE PRINT RUN 1 #'d SET
NO GOLD PRICING DUE TO SCARCITY
RAMDOM INSERTS IN PACKS
BJÂ Barry Bonds Uni 10.00 25.00
Chipper Jones Bat
CMÂ Roger Clemens Uni 15.00 40.00
Greg Maddux Jsy
GGÂ Luis Gonzalez Bat 4.00 10.00
Troy Glaus Uni
JPÂ Chipper Jones Bat 8.00 20.00
Mike Piazza Bat
MMÂ Pedro Martinez Jsy 8.00 20.00
Greg Maddux Uni
PRÂ Mike Piazza Uni 8.00 20.00
Ivan Rodriguez Bat
PSÂ Mike Piazza Bat 8.00 20.00
Benito Santiago Bat
PWÂ Albert Pujols Jsy 10.00 25.00
Kerry Wood Jsy
RGÂ Alex Rodriguez Jsy 15.00 40.00
Nomar Garciaparra Jsy
RRÂ Cal Ripken Bat 30.00 60.00
Alex Rodriguez Jsy
RTÂ Alex Rodriguez Jsy 8.00 20.00
Miguel Tejada Bat
SAÂ Alfonso Soriano Uni 6.00 15.00
Roberto Alomar Uni
SGÂ Sammy Sosa Bat 6.00 15.00
Juan Gonzalez Bat
ZJÂ Barry Zito Uni 6.00 15.00
Randy Johnson Uni

2003 Topps Tribute Contemporary Performance Triple Relics

*RED TRIPLE: .6X TO 1.5X BASIC
RED TRIPLE PRINT RUN 50 #'d SETS
GOLD TRIPLE PRINT RUN 1 #'d SET

NO GOLD PRICING DUE TO SCARCITY
RANDOM INSERTS IN PACKS
BMP Barry Bonds Uni 15.00 40.00
Fred McGriff Bat
Rafael Palmeiro Jsy
CMJ Roger Clemens Uni 15.00 40.00
Greg Maddux Jsy
Randy Johnson Jsy
RPH Manny Ramirez Jsy 15.00 40.00
Mike Piazza Uni
Rickey Henderson Bat
SPM Sammy Sosa Bat 12.50 30.00
Rafael Palmeiro Bat
Fred McGriff Bat
STB Sammy Sosa Jsy 12.50 30.00
Frank Thomas Jsy
Jeff Bagwell Jsy

2003 Topps Tribute Contemporary Team Double Relics

*RED DOUBLE: .6X TO 1.5X BASIC
RED DOUBLE PRINT RUN 50 #'d SETS
GOLD DOUBLE PRINT RUN 1 #'d SET
NO GOLD PRICING DUE TO SCARCITY
RANDOM INSERTS IN PACKS
BBA Craig Biggio Jsy 6.00 15.00
Jeff Bagwell Uni
GRA Nomar Garciaparra Jsy 10.00 25.00
Manny Ramirez Jsy
INA Kazuhisa Ishii Jsy 10.00 25.00
Hideo Nomo Jsy
MSA Greg Maddux Jsy 20.00 50.00
John Smoltz Jsy
RPA Alex Rodriguez Jsy 8.00 20.00
Rafael Palmeiro Jsy
WHA Larry Walker Jsy 6.00 15.00
Todd Helton Jsy

2003 Topps Tribute Contemporary Team Triple Relics

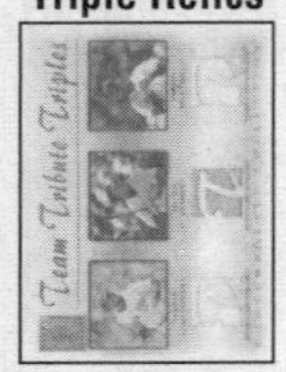

*RED TRIPLE: .6X TO 1.5X BASIC
RED TRIPLE PRINT RUN 50 SERIAL #'d SETS
GOLD TRIPLE PRINT RUN 1 SERIAL #'d SET
NO GOLD PRICING DUE TO SCARCITY
RANDOM INSERTS IN PACKS
ASP Moises Alou Bat 12.50 30.00
Sammy Sosa Jsy
Corey Patterson Bat
BBB Craig Biggio Uni 10.00 25.00
Lance Berkman Bat
Jeff Bagwell Uni
CTM Eric Chavez Uni 10.00 25.00
Miguel Tejada Jsy
Mark Mulder Uni
GRM Nomar Garciaparra Jsy 15.00 40.00
Manny Ramirez Jsy
Pedro Martinez Jsy
HZM Tim Hudson Uni 10.00 25.00
Barry Zito Uni
Mark Mulder Uni
JSJ Andruw Jones Jsy 12.50 30.00
Gary Sheffield Bat
Chipper Jones Jsy
MHM Joe Mauer Bat 12.50 30.00
Torii Hunter Jsy
Doug Mientkiewicz Bat
MOB Edgar Martinez Jsy 10.00 25.00
John Olerud Bat
Bret Boone Jsy
PER Albert Pujols Bat 15.00 40.00
Jim Edmonds Jsy
Scott Rolen Bat
RBT Alex Rodriguez Bat 12.50 30.00
Hank Blalock Bat
Mark Teixeira Bat
RGP Alex Rodriguez Jsy 12.50 30.00
Juan Gonzalez Bat
Rafael Palmeiro Jsy
SGV Alfonso Soriano Bat 10.00 25.00
Jason Giambi Bat
Robin Ventura Bat
TBB Jim Thome Jsy 10.00 25.00
Marlon Byrd Jsy
Pat Burrell Jsy
TOK Frank Thomas Jsy 12.50 30.00
Magglio Ordonez Jsy
Paul Konerko Jsy

2003 Topps Tribute Contemporary Tribute to the Stars Dual Relics

*RED DUAL: .6X TO 1.5X BASIC
RED DUAL PRINT RUN 50 #'d SETS
GOLD DUAL PRINT RUN 1 SERIAL #'d SET
NO GOLD PRICING DUE TO SCARCITY
RANDOM INSERTS IN PACKS
AD Adam Dunn Bat-Jsy 6.00 15.00
AJ Andruw Jones Bat-Jsy 6.00 15.00

AP Albert Pujols Bat-Uni 15.00 40.00
AR Alex Rodriguez Bat-Jsy 12.50 30.00
AS Alfonso Soriano Bat-Uni 6.00 15.00
BB Barry Bonds Bat-Uni 20.00 50.00
CJ Chipper Jones Bat-Jsy 6.00 15.00
EC Eric Chavez Bat-Uni 6.00 15.00
FT Frank Thomas Bat-Jsy 6.00 15.00
GA Garret Anderson Bat-Uni 6.00 15.00
GM Greg Maddux Bat-Jsy 8.00 20.00
JT Jim Thome Bat-Jsy 6.00 15.00
LB Lance Berkman Bat-Jsy 6.00 15.00
LW Larry Walker Bat-Jsy 6.00 15.00
MP Mike Piazza Bat-Uni 8.00 20.00
NG Nomar Garciaparra Bat-Jsy 15.00 40.00
PB Pat Burrell Bat-Jsy 6.00 15.00
RA Roberto Alomar Bat-Uni 6.00 15.00
RH Rickey Henderson Bat-Uni 6.00 15.00
RP Rafael Palmeiro Bat-Jsy 6.00 15.00
SS Sammy Sosa Bat-Jsy 6.00 15.00
TG Troy Glaus Bat-Uni 6.00 15.00
TH Todd Helton Bat-Jsy 6.00 15.00
VG Vladimir Guerrero Bat-Jsy 6.00 15.00
THU Torii Hunter Bat-Jsy 6.00 15.00

2003 Topps Tribute Contemporary Tribute to the Stars Patchworks Dual Relics

STATED ODDS 1:34
STATED PRINT RUN 50 SERIAL #'d SETS
APA Albert Pujols 50.00 100.00
ARA Alex Rodriguez 30.00 60.00
AR2 Alex Rodriguez Blue 30.00 60.00
BBA Barry Bonds 50.00 100.00
CJA Chipper Jones 15.00 40.00
CSA Curt Schilling 10.00 25.00
FTA Frank Thomas 15.00 40.00
GMA Greg Maddux 20.00 50.00
JBA Jeff Bagwell 15.00 40.00
KWA Kerry Wood 10.00 25.00
LGA Luis Gonzalez 10.00 25.00
MRA Manny Ramirez 15.00 40.00
NGA Nomar Garciaparra 20.00 50.00
PMA Pedro Martinez 15.00 40.00
RJA Randy Johnson 15.00 40.00
RPA Rafael Palmeiro 15.00 40.00
SGA Shawn Green 10.00 25.00
SSA Sammy Sosa 15.00 40.00
THA Todd Helton 15.00 40.00
THU Torii Hunter 10.00 25.00

2003 Topps Tribute Contemporary World Series Relics

*RED WS: .6X TO 1.5X BASIC
RED WS PRINT RUN 50 SERIAL #'d SETS
GOLD WS PRINT RUN 1 SERIAL #'d SET
NO GOLD PRICING DUE TO SCARCITY
RANDOM INSERTS IN PACKS
MRA Mariano Rivera Jsy 6.00 15.00
TGA Troy Glaus Uni 4.00 10.00

2003 Topps Tribute Contemporary World Series Double Relics

*RED WS DOUBLE: .6X TO 1.5X BASIC
RED WS DOUBLE PRINT RUN 50 #'d SETS
GOLD WS DOUBLE PRINT RUN 1 #'d SET
NO GOLD PRICING DUE TO SCARCITY
RANDOM INSERTS IN PACKS
BGA Barry Bonds Uni 15.00 40.00
Troy Glaus Uni
LPA John Lackey Uni 4.00 10.00
Troy Percival Uni

PCA Mike Piazza Bat 15.00 40.00
Roger Clemens Uni
PPA Jorge Posada Bat 10.00 25.00
Andy Pettitte Jsy
SJA Curt Schilling Jsy 6.00 15.00
Randy Johnson Jsy
WGA Bernie Williams Bat 6.00 15.00
Luis Gonzalez Bat
WOA Bernie Williams Bat 6.00 15.00
Paul O'Neill Bat

2003 Topps Tribute Contemporary World Series Triple Relics

*RED WS TRIPLE: .6X TO 1.5X BASIC
RED WS TRIPLE PRINT RUN 50 #'d SETS
GOLD WS TRIPLE PRINT RUN 1 #'d SET
NO GOLD PRICING DUE TO SCARCITY
RANDOM INSERTS IN PACKS
EGS Darin Erstad Uni 10.00 25.00
Troy Glaus Uni
Tim Salmon Uni
LGP John Lackey Uni 6.00 15.00
Troy Glaus Bat
Troy Percival Uni

2004 Topps Tribute HOF

This 80-card set was released in January, 2005. The set was issued in five card packs with an $50 SRP which came six packs to a box and four boxes to a case. Each pack contained either a game-used card or some other special card. This set was highlighted by the insertion of a 'cut signature' of but about every Hall of Famer all of which were issued to a stated print run of one serial numbered set.

COMPLETE SET (80) 75.00 150.00
COMMON CARD (1-80) 1.50 4.00
1 Willie Mays 4.00 10.00
2 Richie Ashburn 2.00 5.00
3 Babe Ruth 6.00 15.00
4 Lou Gehrig 4.00 10.00
5 Carl Yastrzemski 3.00 8.00
6 Fergie Jenkins 1.50 4.00
7 Cool Papa Bell 2.00 5.00
8 Johnny Bench 2.00 5.00
9 Satchel Paige 2.00 5.00
10 Ty Cobb 3.00 8.00
11 Robin Roberts 1.50 4.00
12 Eddie Mathews 2.00 5.00
13 Tom Seaver 2.00 5.00
14 Kirby Puckett 2.00 5.00
15 Stan Musial 3.00 8.00
16 Ralph Kiner 2.00 5.00
17 Reggie Jackson 2.00 5.00
18 Walter Johnson 2.00 5.00
19 Phil Niekro 1.50 4.00
20 Mike Schmidt 4.00 10.00
21 Brooks Robinson 2.00 5.00
22 Jimmie Foxx 2.00 5.00
23 Nellie Fox 2.00 5.00
24 Joe Morgan 1.50 4.00
25 Cy Young 2.00 5.00
26 Hank Greenberg 2.00 5.00
27 Josh Gibson 2.00 5.00
28 Robin Yount 2.00 5.00
29 Hoyt Wilhelm 1.50 4.00
30 Yogi Berra 2.00 5.00
31 Rollie Fingers 1.50 4.00
32 Gaylord Perry 1.50 4.00
33 Ozzie Smith 3.00 8.00
34 Jim Palmer 1.50 4.00
35 Harmon Killebrew 2.00 5.00
36 Bob Feller 1.50 4.00
37 Chuck Klein 1.50 4.00
38 Mordecai Brown 1.50 4.00
39 Napoleon Lajoie 2.00 5.00
40 Al Kaline 2.00 5.00
41 Paul Molitor 1.50 4.00
42 Jackie Robinson 2.00 5.00
43 Mel Ott 2.00 5.00
44 Hank Aaron 4.00 10.00
45 Rod Carew 2.00 5.00
46 Rogers Hornsby 2.00 5.00
47 Bob Gibson 2.00 5.00
48 Juan Marichal 1.50 4.00
49 Bill Mazeroski 2.00 5.00
50 Roberto Clemente 5.00 12.00
51 Willie McCovey 2.00 5.00
52 Red Schoendienst 1.50 4.00
53 Nolan Ryan 5.00 12.00
54 Dennis Eckersley 1.50 4.00
55 Monte Irvin 1.50 4.00
56 George Kell 1.50 4.00
57 Gary Carter 1.50 4.00
58 Tony Perez 1.50 4.00
59 Carlton Fisk 2.00 5.00
60 Duke Snider 2.00 5.00
61 Bobby Doerr 1.50 4.00
62 John McGraw 2.00 5.00
63 George Sisler 2.00 5.00
64 Orlando Cepeda 1.50 4.00
65 Earl Weaver 1.50 4.00
66 Roy Campanella 2.00 5.00
67 Tris Speaker 2.00 5.00
68 Sparky Anderson 1.50 4.00
69 Willie Stargell 2.00 5.00
70 Honus Wagner 2.00 5.00
71 Lou Brock 2.00 5.00
72 Whitey Ford 2.00 5.00
73 George Brett 4.00 10.00
74 Luis Aparicio 1.50 4.00
75 Ernie Banks 2.00 5.00
76 Jim Bunning 1.50 4.00
77 Warren Spahn 2.00 5.00
78 Catfish Hunter 2.00 5.00
79 Pee Wee Reese 2.00 5.00
80 Frank Robinson 1.50 4.00

2004 Topps Tribute HOF Gold

*GOLD p/r 80-99: 1.25X TO 3X BASIC
*GOLD p/r 62-79: 1.5X TO 4X BASIC
*GOLD p/r 36-56: 1.25X TO 3X BASIC
GROUP A ODDS 1:2714
GROUP B ODDS 1:74
GROUP C ODDS 1:38
GROUP D ODDS 1:14
GROUP A PRINT RUNS B/WN 1-4 PER
GROUP B PRINT RUNS B/WN 36-56 PER
GROUP C PRINT RUNS B/WN 62-79 PER
GROUP D PRINT RUNS B/WN 80-99 PER
NO PRICING ON QTY OF 4 OR LESS

2004 Topps Tribute HOF Cooperstown Classmates Dual Cut Signatures

STATED ODDS 1:10,854
STATED PRINT RUN 1 SERIAL #'d SET
NO PRICING DUE TO SCARCITY
DT Bill Dickey
Bill Terry
GC Hank Greenberg
Joe Cronin
RC Babe Ruth
Ty Cobb
WS Hoyt Wilhelm
Enos Slaughter

2004 Topps Tribute HOF Cooperstown Classmates Dual Relics

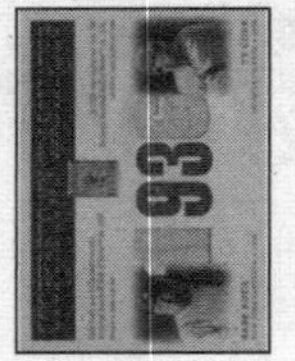

GROUP A ODDS 1:4342
GROUP B ODDS 1:229
GROUP C ODDS 1:122
GROUP A PRINT RUN 5 SERIAL #'d SETS
GROUP B PRINT RUN 50 SERIAL #'d SETS
GROUP C PRINT RUN 75 SERIAL #'d SETS
NO GROUP A PRICING DUE TO SCARCITY
*GOLD: .6X TO 1.5X BASIC C
*GOLD: .5X TO 1.2X BASIC B
GOLD STATED ODDS 1:201
GOLD PRINT RUN 25 SERIAL #'d SETS
GOLD OTT/FOXX PRINT RUN 1 #'d CARD
GOLD RUTH/COBB PRINT RUN 1 #'d CARD
NO GOLD OTT/FOXX, RUTH/COBB PRICING
BY Johnny Bench Uni 30.00 60.00
Carl Yastrzemski Uni C
CR Orlando Cep Bat 30.00 60.00
Nolan Ryan Jsy C
KK Chuck Klein Bat 30.00 60.00
Al Kaline Bat C
ME Paul Molitor Bat 10.00 25.00
Dennis Eckersley Uni C
MP Joe Morgan Bat 10.00 25.00
Jim Palmer Uni C
MR Juan Marichal Uni 20.00 50.00
Brooks Robinson Bat B
OF Mel Ott Bat
Jimmie Foxx Bat A
PC Gaylord Perry Uni 20.00 50.00
Rod Carew Uni B
RB Nolan Ryan Uni 40.00 80.00
George Brett Uni B
RC Babe Ruth Bat
Ty Cobb Uni A
SK Duke Snider Bat 40.00 80.00
Al Kaline Uni B

2004 Topps Tribute HOF Relics

GROUP A ODDS 1:118
GROUP B ODDS 1:36
GROUP C ODDS 1:22
GROUP D ODDS 1:6
GROUP E ODDS 1:5
GROUP F ODDS 1:6
GROUP G ODDS 1:4
GROUP A PRINT RUNS B/WN 20-85 PER
GROUP B PRINT RUNS B/WN 100-175 PER
GROUP C PRINT RUNS B/WN 200-455 PER
A-C PRINT RUNS PROVIDED BY TOPPS
GROUP A-C ARE NOT SERIAL-NUMBERED
AK Al Kaline Uni B/125 * 10.00 25.00
AKB Al Kaline Bat D 6.00 15.00
BG Bob Gibson Uni E 6.00 15.00
BR Babe Ruth Bat B/163 * 100.00 175.00
BRO Brooks Robinson Bat E 6.00 15.00
CF Carlton Fisk Wall C/300 * 15.00 40.00
CK Chuck Klein Bat B/107 * 10.00 25.00
CY C.Yastrzemski Wall C/300 * 20.00 50.00
CYU Carl Yastrzemski Uni E 8.00 20.00
DS Duke Snider Bat E 6.00 15.00
EW Earl Weaver Jsy A/25 * 10.00 25.00
FR Frank Robinson O's Uni E 4.00 10.00
FRA F.Robinson Angels Uni D 4.00 10.00
FRB Frank Robinson Bat D 4.00 10.00
GB George Brett Uni F 8.00 20.00
GBB George Brett Bat D 8.00 20.00
GC G.Carter Mets Jsy C/200 * 6.00 15.00
GCU Gary Carter Expos Uni D 4.00 10.00
GS George Sisler Bat C/455 * 10.00 25.00
HA Hank Aaron Bat D 15.00 40.00
HG Hank Greenberg Bat E 10.00 25.00
HK H.Killebrew Bat B/135 * 15.00 40.00
HW Honus Wagner Bat B/118 * 75.00 150.00
JB J.Bench w/Glv Uni C/250 * 10.00 25.00
JB2 J.Bench w/o Glv Uni G 6.00 15.00
JF Jimmie Foxx Bat A/25 * 100.00 175.00
JM Joe Morgan Bat E 4.00 10.00
JMA Juan Marichal Uni B/125 * 6.00 15.00
JP J.Palmer Arm Up Uni F 4.00 10.00
JP2 J.Palmer Arm Down Uni F 4.00 10.00
JR Jackie Robinson Bat G 10.00 25.00
KP Kirby Puckett Jsy B/175 * 10.00 25.00
KPB Kirby Puckett Bat G 6.00 15.00
LBB Lou Brock Bat E 6.00 15.00
LG Lou Gehrig Bat A/52 * 175.00 300.00
MO Mel Ott Bat A/25 * 60.00 120.00
MS Mike Schmidt Jsy A/50 * 15.00 40.00
MSB Mike Schmidt Bat G 8.00 20.00
NR Nolan Ryan Rgr Uni F 12.50 30.00
NRA N.Ryan Angels Uni C/425 * 15.00 40.00
NRJ Nolan Ryan Astros Jsy F 12.50 30.00
OC Orl Cepeda Bat B/100 * 6.00 15.00
OS Ozzie Smith Bat F 6.00 15.00
PM Paul Molitor Jsy G 4.00 10.00
PMB Paul Molitor Bat D 4.00 10.00
RC Roberto Clemente Bat E 30.00 60.00
RH Rogers Hornsby Bat D 15.00 40.00
RJ R.Jackson Jsy B/110 * 10.00 25.00
RJB R.Jackson Bat C/200 * 10.00 25.00
RY Robin Yount Uni A/50 * 15.00 40.00
SM Stan Musial Jsy G 10.00 25.00
TC Ty Cobb Uni A/20 *
TCB Ty Cobb Bat D 40.00 80.00
TS Tom Seaver Uni D 6.00 15.00
TSP Tris Speaker Bat A/85 * 100.00 175.00
WF Whitey Ford Uni A/50 * 15.00 40.00
WM1 Willie Mays Glove B/110 * 100.00 175.00
WM2 Willie Mays Giants Bat D 15.00 40.00
WM3 Willie Mays Mets Bat D 15.00 40.00
WM4 Willie Mays Uni Gray F 15.00 40.00
WM5 Willie Mays Uni White G 15.00 40.00

2004 Topps Tribute HOF Relics Gold

*GOLD: 1.25X TO 3X GROUP E-G
*GOLD: 1.25X TO 3X GROUP D
*GOLD: .75X TO 2X GROUP C
*GOLD: .75X TO 2X GROUP B
*GOLD: .6X TO 1.5X GROUP A p/r 50-85
*GOLD: .5X TO 1.2X GROUP A p/r 20-25
STATED ODDS 1:33
STATED PRINT RUN 25 SERIAL #'d SETS
E.WEAVER PRINT RUN 1 SERIAL #'d CARD
J.FOXX PRINT RUN 1 SERIAL #'d CARD
M.OTT PRINT RUN 1 SERIAL #'d CARD
T.COBB UNI PRINT RUN 1 SERIAL #'d CARD
W.FORD PRINT RUN 15 SERIAL #'d CARDS
NO PRICING ON QTY OF 15 OR LESS
BR Babe Ruth Bat 175.00 300.00
CY Carl Yastrzemski Wall 40.00 100.00
GB George Brett Uni 30.00 80.00
GBB George Brett Bat 30.00 80.00
HA Hank Aaron Bat 40.00 100.00
HW Honus Wagner Bat 75.00 150.00
JR Jackie Robinson Bat 40.00 100.00
KP Kirby Puckett Jsy 25.00 60.00
KPB Kirby Puckett Bat 25.00 60.00
MS Mike Schmidt Jsy 30.00 80.00
MSB Mike Schmidt Bat 30.00 80.00
NRA Nolan Ryan Angels Uni 40.00 100.00
OS Ozzie Smith Bat 25.00 60.00
RC Roberto Clemente Bat 75.00 150.00
RH Rogers Hornsby Bat 30.00 80.00
SM Stan Musial Jsy 40.00 100.00
TCB Ty Cobb Bat 75.00 150.00
TSP Tris Speaker Bat 100.00 175.00
WF Whitey Ford Uni/15 40.00 100.00
WM1 Willie Mays Glove 200.00 350.00
WM2 Willie Mays Giants Bat 40.00 100.00
WM3 Willie Mays Mets Bat 40.00 100.00
WM4 Willie Mays Uni Gray 40.00 100.00
WM5 Willie Mays Uni White 40.00 100.00

2004 Topps Tribute HOF Relics Autographs

GROUP A ODDS 1:835
GROUP B ODDS 1:120
GROUP A PRINT RUN 55 SERIAL #'d SETS
GROUP B PRINT RUN 95 SERIAL #'d SETS
GOLD STATED ODDS 1:1888
GOLD PRINT RUN 5 SERIAL #'d SETS
NO GOLD PRICING DUE TO SCARCITY
AKB Al Kaline Bat B 30.00 60.00
BRO Brooks Robinson Bat B 30.00 60.00
CYU Carl Yastrzemski Uni B 40.00 80.00
EW Earl Weaver Jsy A 15.00 40.00
NRJ Nolan Ryan Jsy B 75.00 150.00

2004 Topps Tribute HOF Relics Jersey Patch

*3-COLOR PATCH: ADD 20% PREMIUM
GROUP A ODDS 1:172
GROUP B ODDS 1:114
GROUP A PRINT RUNS B/WN 10-50 PER
GROUP B PRINT RUN 100 SERIAL #'d SETS
NO PRICING ON QTY OF 17 OR LESS
*GOLD p/r 25: .75X TO 2X BASIC p/r 100
*GOLD p/r 25: .6X TO 1.5X BASIC p/r 50
GOLD STATED ODDS 1:251
GOLD PRINT RUNS B/WN 1-25 COPIES PER
NO GOLD PRICING ON QTY OF 10 OR LESS
DE Dennis Eckersley A/50 15.00 40.00
FR Frank Robinson A/39 30.00 60.00
GB George Brett A/50 20.00 50.00
LB Lou Brock A/17
MS Mike Schmidt Swing B 20.00 50.00
MS2 Mike Schmidt Stance B 20.00 50.00
NR Nolan Ryan B 30.00 60.00
OS Ozzie Smith A/10
RC Rod Carew B 15.00 40.00
RJ Reggie Jackson A/50 20.00 50.00
RY Robin Yount A/50 20.00 50.00

2004 Topps Tribute HOF Signature Cuts Cooperstown

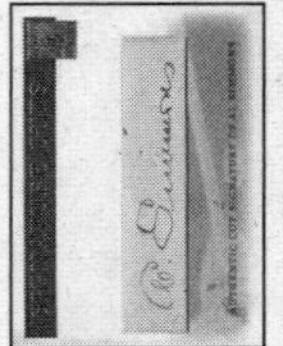

STATED ODDS 1:244
STATED PRINT RUN 1 SERIAL #'d SET
NO PRICING DUE TO SCARCITY
AK Al Kaline
AL Al Lopez
AS Al Simmons
BD Bill Dickey
BD Bobby Doerr
BE Billy Evans
BFE Bob Feller
BG Bob Gibson
BGR Burleigh Grimes
BHA Bucky Harris
BHE Billy Herman
BL Bob Lemon
BLE Buck Leonard
BMC Bill McGowan
BMK Bill McKechnie
BR Babe Ruth
BRI Branch Rickey
BRO Brooks Robinson
BT Bill Terry
BV Bill Veeck
BW Billy Williams
BWA Bobby Wallace
CA Cap Anson
CB Chief Bender
CG Charlie Gehringer
CGR Clark Griffith
CH Cal Hubbard
CHA Chick Hafey
CHU Carl Hubbell

CK Chuck Klein
CMA Connie Mack
CP James Cool Papa Bell
CS Casey Stengel
CY Carl Yastrzemski
CYO Cy Young
DB Dan Brouthers
DBA Dave Bancroft
DD Dizzy Dean
DDR Don Drysdale
DE Dennis Eckersley
DS Don Sutton
DSN Duke Snider
DV Dazzy Vance
EA Earl Averill
EB Ed Barrow
EBA Ernie Banks
EC Earle Combs
ECO Eddie Collins
EF Elmer Flick
EL Ernie Lombardi
EM Eddie Mathews
ERI Eppa Rixey
ES Enos Slaughter
EW Earl Weaver
EWA Ed Walsh
EWY Early Wynn
FB Frank Baker
FC Frank Chance
FCL Fred Clarke
FF Ford Frick
FFR Frankie Frisch
FL Freddy Lindstrom
FR Frank Robinson
GB George Brett
GG Goose Goslin
GH Gabby Hartnett
GK George Kell
GKE George Kelly
GP Gaylord Perry
GS George Sisler
GW George Weiss
GWR George Wright
HA Hank Aaron
HC Happy Chandler
HD Hugh Duffy
HG Hank Greenberg
HH Harry Heilman
HHO Harry Hooper
HJ Hughie Jennings
HK Harmon Killebrew
HM Heinie Manush
HN Hal Newhouser
HP Herb Pennock
HW Hack Wilson
HWA Honus Wagner
HWI Hoyt Wilhelm
JBE Johnny Bench
JBO Jim Bottomley
JBU Jesse Burkett
JCO Jocko Conlan
JCR Joe Cronin
JE Johnny Evers
JF Jimmie Foxx
JH Jesse Haines
JJ Judy Johnson
JK Joe Kelley
JM Joe McCarthy
JMA Juan Marichal
JME Joe Medwick
JMI Johnny Mize
JMO Joe Morgan
JO Jim O'Rourke
JPB Jim Bunning
JR Jackie Robinson
JS Joe Sewell
JT Joe Tinker
KC Kiki Cuyler
KL Kenesaw Mountain Landis
KN Kid Nichols
LA Luis Aparicio
LAP Luke Appling
LB Lou Boudreau
LBR Lou Brock
LDA Leon Day
LDU Leo Durocher
LG Lefty Gomez
LGE Lou Gehrig
LGR Lefty Grove
LM Larry MacPhail
LMA Lee MacPhail
LW Lloyd Waner
MB Mordecai Brown
MC Max Carey
MI Monte Irvin
MM Mickey Mantle
MO Mel Ott
NC Nestor Chylak
NF Nellie Fox
NR Nolan Ryan
OC Orlando Cepeda
OCH Oscar Charleston
PA Grover C. Alexander
PL Pop Lloyd
PM Paul Molitor
PN Phil Niekro
PR Pee Wee Reese
PRI Phil Rizzuto
PT Pie Traynor
PW Paul Waner
RA Richie Ashburn
RB Roger Bresnahan
RC Roberto Clemente
RF Red Faber
RFE Rick Ferrell
RFI Rollie Fingers
RH Rogers Hornsby
RJ Reggie Jackson
RK Ralph Kiner
RM Rabbit Maranville
RMA Rube Marquard
ROY Roy Campanella
RR Red Ruffing
RRO Robin Roberts
RS Ray Schalk
RSC Red Schoendienst
RY Robin Yount
SA Sparky Anderson
SC Sam Crawford
SCA Steve Carlton
SCO Stan Coveleski
SK Sandy Koufax
SM Stan Musial
SP Satchel Paige
SR Sam Rice
TC Tom Connolly
TCL Tom Lasorda
TCO Ty Cobb
TK Tim Keefe
TL Ted Lyons
TP Tony Perez
TS Tom Seaver
TSP Tris Speaker
TW Ted Williams
TY Tom Yawkey
WA Walter Alston
WF Whitey Ford
WG Warren Giles
WH Waite Hoyt
WHA Will Harridge
WJ Walter Johnson
WK Willie Keeler
WM Willie Mays
WMC Willie McCovey
WS Warren Spahn
WST Willie Stargell
WW Willie Wells
YB Yogi Berra
ZW Zach Wheat

2004 Topps Tribute HOF Signature Cuts Personalities

STATED ODDS 1:1034
STATED PRINT RUN 1 SERIAL #'d SET
NO PRICING DUE TO SCARCITY
AP Al Pacino
BC Buster Crabbe
BD Bette Davis
BH Bob Hope
BJ Billy Joel
CC Charlie Chaplin
CCH Chevy Chase
CG Cary Grant
CGA Clark Gable
CH Charlton Heston
DD David Duchovy
DE Dwight Eisenhower
EJ Elton John
ER Edward G. Robinson
FS Frank Sinatra
GA Gillian Anderson
GB George Burns
GG George Gershwin
GM Groucho Marx
HF Harrison Ford
HR Hyman Rickover
JA John Quincy Adams
JC James Cagney
JD James Doolittle
JG John Glenn
JL Jack Lord
JS Jimmy Stewart
JW John Wayne
LA Louis Armstrong
MH Moe Howard
MJ Mick Jagger
MM Marilyn Monroe
OB Omar Bradley
PH Patrick Henry
RB Richard Byrd
RH Rutherford B. Hayes
RHO Ron Howard
RW Robin Williams
SC Sean Connery
SL Stan Laurel
SM Steve Martin
TR Teddy Roosevelt
VP Vincent Price
WA Woody Allen
WT William H. Taft

2004 Topps Tribute HOF Signature Cuts Personalities Dual

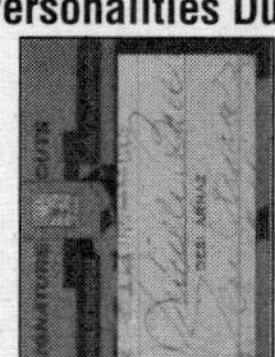

STATED ODDS 1:4824
STATED PRINT RUN 1 SERIAL #'d SET
NO PRICING DUE TO SCARCITY
AC Bud Abbott
Lou Costello
BA Lucille Ball
Desi Arnaz
CH Bing Crosby
Bob Hope
GH Judy Garland
Jack Haley
JH James Earl Jones
Mark Hamill
KR Jack Klugman
Tony Randall
NF Richard Nixon
Gerald Ford
PM George Patton
Douglas MacArthur
RB Ronald Reagan
George H.W. Bush

2003 Topps Tribute Perennial All-Star

This 50 card set was released in February, 2003. These cards were issued in five card packs with an $50 SRP. These packs were issued in six pack boxes which came four boxes to a case. These cards honored players who made at least five trips to the All-Star game during their career.

COMPLETE SET (50)	40.00	100.00
1 Willie Mays	4.00	10.00
2 Don Mattingly	4.00	10.00
3 Hoyt Wilhelm	1.50	4.00
4 Hank Aaron	4.00	10.00
5 Hank Greenberg	2.00	5.00
6 Johnny Bench	2.00	5.00
7 Duke Snider	1.50	4.00
8 Carl Yastrzemski	3.00	8.00
9 Jim Palmer	1.50	4.00
10 Roberto Clemente	5.00	12.00
11 Mike Schmidt	4.00	10.00
12 Joe Cronin	1.50	4.00
13 Lou Brock	1.50	4.00
14 Orlando Cepeda	1.50	4.00
15 Bill Mazeroski	1.50	4.00
16 Whitey Ford	1.50	4.00
17 Rod Carew	1.50	4.00
18 Joe Morgan	1.50	4.00
19 Luis Aparicio	1.50	4.00
20 Nolan Ryan	5.00	12.00
21 Bobby Doerr	1.50	4.00
22 Dale Murphy	1.50	4.00
23 Bob Feller	1.50	4.00
24 Paul Molitor	1.50	4.00
25 Tom Seaver	1.50	4.00
26 Ozzie Smith	3.00	8.00
27 Stan Musial	3.00	8.00
28 Willie McCovey	1.50	4.00
29 Gary Carter	1.50	4.00
30 Reggie Jackson	1.50	4.00
31 Gaylord Perry	1.50	4.00
32 George Brett	4.00	10.00
33 Robin Roberts	1.50	4.00
34 Wade Boggs	1.50	4.00
35 Cal Ripken	6.00	15.00
36 Carlton Fisk	1.50	4.00
37 Al Kaline	2.00	5.00
38 Kirby Puckett	2.00	5.00
39 Phil Rizzuto		
40 Willie Stargell	1.50	4.00
41 Harmon Killebrew	2.00	5.00
42 Red Schoendienst	1.50	4.00
43 Tony Gwynn	2.50	6.00
44 Ralph Kiner	1.50	4.00
45 Yogi Berra	2.00	5.00
46 Catfish Hunter	1.50	4.00
47 Frank Robinson	1.50	4.00
48 Ernie Banks	2.00	5.00
49 Warren Spahn	1.50	4.00
50 Brooks Robinson	1.50	4.00

2003 Topps Tribute Perennial All-Star Gold

This is a parallel to the Topps Tribute set. These cards were issued at different rates depending on what group the card was issued from. We have notated that information next to the player's name in our checklist.

*GOLD p/r 81-86: 1.5X TO 4X BASIC
*GOLD p/r 66-80: 2X TO 5X BASIC
*GOLD p/r 51-65: 2.5X TO 6X BASIC
*GOLD p/r 36-50: 3X TO 8X BASIC
*GOLD p/r 26-35: 4X TO 10X BASIC
GROUP A ODDS 1:106
GROUP B ODDS 1:49
GROUP C ODDS 1:38

2003 Topps Tribute Perennial All-Star Relics

This 65-card insert set was inserted at various odds depending on what type of relic and what group the card belonged to. We have notated the group, the odds for the group as well as the relic in our checklist.

BAT GROUP A ODDS 1:556
BAT GROUP B ODDS 1:
BAT GROUP C ODDS 1:276
BAT GROUP D ODDS 1:61
BAT GROUP E ODDS 1:158
BAT GROUP F ODDS 1:23
BAT GROUP G ODDS 1:111
BAT GROUP H ODDS 1:46
BAT GROUP I ODDS 1:85
BAT GROUP J ODDS 1:16
BAT GROUP K ODDS 1:18
BAT GROUP L ODDS 1:31
BAT GROUP M ODDS 1:50
BAT GROUP N ODDS 1:46
BAT GROUP O ODDS 1:21
BAT GROUP P ODDS 1:37
JSY/UNI GROUP A ODDS 1:368
JSY/UNI GROUP B ODDS 1:148
JSY/UNI GROUP C ODDS 1:92
JSY/UNI GROUP D ODDS 1:185
JSY/UNI GROUP E ODDS 1:69
JSY/UNI GROUP F ODDS 1:55
JSY/UNI GROUP G ODDS 1:79
JSY/UNI GROUP H ODDS 1:61
JSY/UNI GROUP I ODDS 1:55
JSY/UNI GROUP J ODDS 1:25
JSY/UNI GROUP K ODDS 1:46
JSY/UNI GROUP L ODDS 1:43
JSY/UNI GROUP M ODDS 1:21
JSY/UNI GROUP N ODDS 1:8
JSY/UNI GROUP O ODDS 1:29
JSY/UNI GROUP P ODDS 1:10

AD Andre Dawson Bat F	8.00	20.00
AK Al Kaline Bat E	12.50	30.00
BD Bobby Doerr Jsy N	6.00	15.00
BF Bob Feller Bat I	6.00	15.00
BM Bill Mazeroski Uni C	10.00	25.00
BR Babe Ruth Bat J	90.00	180.00
BRO Brooks Robinson Bat J	8.00	20.00
CF Carlton Fisk Bat J	8.00	20.00
CH Catfish Hunter Jsy B	10.00	25.00
CRB Cal Ripken Bat P	15.00	40.00
CY Carl Yastrzemski Jsy E	15.00	40.00
DD Dizzy Dean Uni E	20.00	50.00
DM Dale Murphy Jsy A	12.50	30.00
DMA Don Mattingly Jsy L	12.50	30.00
DN Don Newcombe Bat K	6.00	15.00
DSN Duke Snider Bat F	10.00	25.00
EB Ernie Banks Bat M	8.00	20.00
EM Eddie Mathews Jsy K	8.00	20.00
FR Frank Robinson Uni G	8.00	20.00
GB George Brett Jsy M	12.50	30.00
GC Gary Carter Jsy I	6.00	15.00
HA Hank Aaron Bat O	15.00	40.00
HG Hank Greenberg Bat D	20.00	50.00
HK Harmon Killebrew Jsy J	8.00	20.00
HW Honus Wagner Bat B	100.00	200.00
HWI Hoyt Wilhelm Uni N	6.00	15.00
JBE Johnny Bench Uni F	12.50	30.00
JCR Joe Cronin Bat N	6.00	15.00
JF Jimmie Foxx Bat F	20.00	50.00
JMI Johnny Mize Uni D	8.00	20.00
JMO Joe Morgan Bat K	6.00	15.00
JP Jim Palmer Uni N	6.00	15.00
JR Jackie Robinson Bat L	20.00	50.00
KP Kirby Puckett Jsy N	8.00	20.00
LA Luis Aparicio Bat C	8.00	20.00
LB Lou Brock Bat A	12.50	30.00
LBU Lou Brock Uni H	8.00	20.00
LG Lou Gehrig Bat F	100.00	200.00
MO Mel Ott Bat D	12.50	30.00
MS Mike Schmidt Uni P	8.00	20.00
NL Nap Lajoie Bat D	90.00	150.00
NR Nolan Ryan Rangers Uni O	15.00	40.00
NRA Nolan Ryan Astros Jsy F	20.00	50.00
OC Orlando Cepeda Jsy C	8.00	20.00
OS Ozzie Smith Uni J	8.00	20.00
PM Paul Molitor Bat K	6.00	15.00
PR Phil Rizzuto Bat H	10.00	25.00
RC Roberto Clemente Bat L	30.00	60.00
RCA Roy Campanella Bat F	10.00	25.00
RH Rogers Hornsby Bat G	20.00	50.00
RJ Reggie Jackson Bat O	8.00	20.00
ROD Rod Carew Jsy N	8.00	20.00
RS Red Schoendienst Bat H	6.00	15.00
SM Stan Musial Bat J	15.00	40.00
TC Ty Cobb Bat F	60.00	120.00
TG Tony Gwynn Jsy P	6.00	15.00
TM Thurman Munson Jsy M	12.50	30.00
TS Tris Speaker Bat A	100.00	175.00
TSE Tom Seaver Jsy A	12.50	30.00
WB Wade Boggs Uni C	10.00	25.00
WF Whitey Ford Uni B	10.00	25.00
WM Willie Mays Bat K	15.00	40.00
WMC Willie McCovey Bat J	6.00	15.00
WST Willie Stargell Uni B	10.00	25.00
YB Yogi Berra Jsy A	20.00	50.00

2003 Topps Tribute Perennial All-Star Patch Relics

Inserted at a stated rate of one in 123, these 15 cards feature premium relics from prestigious retired talents. These game-worn uniform patch relic cards display a unique design featuring the player, his relic and the site of an All-Star appearance. These cards were issued to a stated print run of 30 serial numbered sets.

CR Cal Ripken	175.00	300.00
CY Carl Yastrzemski	125.00	200.00
DMU Dale Murphy	40.00	80.00
GB George Brett	150.00	250.00
GC Gary Carter	20.00	50.00
HK Harmon Killebrew	60.00	120.00
JM Joe Morgan	20.00	50.00
MS Mike Schmidt	150.00	250.00
NR Nolan Ryan Rangers	150.00	250.00
NRA Nolan Ryan Astros	150.00	250.00
OS Ozzie Smith	125.00	200.00
TG Tony Gwynn	75.00	150.00
WB Wade Boggs	40.00	80.00
WM Willie McCovey	20.00	50.00
WS Willie Stargell	40.00	80.00

2003 Topps Tribute Perennial All-Star Signing

Issued at a stated rate of one in 34, these cards feature not only a game-used relic from the player's career but also an authentic signature of the featured player.

GOLD STATED ODDS 1:201
GOLD PRINT RUN 25 SERIAL #'d SETS
NO GOLD PRICING DUE TO SCARCITY

AD Andre Dawson Bat	15.00	40.00
AK Al Kaline Bat	40.00	80.00
DM Dale Murphy Jsy	30.00	60.00
DMA Don Mattingly Jsy	60.00	120.00
DSN Duke Snider Bat	40.00	80.00
GC Gary Carter Jsy	15.00	40.00
JP Jim Palmer Uni	15.00	40.00
LB Lou Brock Bat	30.00	60.00
MS Mike Schmidt Uni	60.00	120.00
OC Orlando Cepeda Jsy	15.00	40.00
TG Tony Gwynn Jsy	50.00	100.00

2003 Topps Tribute Perennial All-Star 1st Class Cut Relics

Inserted at a stated rate of one in 7461, these seven cards feature autograph cuts from among the most legendary figures in the game. On back each card is an authentic USPS stamp of the featured player. Each of these cards is a true 1 of 1 and is stamped as such on back.

BR Babe Ruth
DD Dizzy Dean
HW Honus Wagner
JR Jackie Robinson
LG Lou Gehrig
TC Ty Cobb
TS Tris Speaker

2003 Topps Tribute Perennial All-Star Memorable Match-Up Relics

Issued at a stated rate of one in 41, these 10 cards feature two all stars who appeared in the same all-star game along with a game-used relic from each of their career. These cards were issued to a stated print run of 150 serial numbered sets.

GOLD STATED ODDS 1:245
GOLD PRINT RUN 25 SERIAL #'d SETS
NO GOLD PRICING DUE TO SCARCITY

BF Johnny Bench Bat / Carlton Fisk Bat	30.00	60.00
BG Wade Boggs Bat / Tony Gwynn Bat	30.00	60.00
BS George Brett Jsy / Mike Schmidt Uni	60.00	120.00
CM Gary Carter Jsy / Don Mattingly Jsy	40.00	80.00
KA Harmon Killebrew Jsy / Hank Aaron Bat	60.00	120.00
MJ Willie Mays Bat / Reggie Jackson Bat	50.00	100.00
PG Kirby Puckett Bat / Tony Gwynn Bat	30.00	60.00
YB Carl Yastrzemski Jsy / Johnny Bench Bat	40.00	80.00
YBR Carl Yastrzemski Jsy / Lou Brock Bat	30.00	60.00

2003 Topps Tribute World Series

This 150 card set was released in October, 2003. The set was issued in four card packs with an $50 SRP which came six packs to a box and four boxes to a case. Cards numbered 1 through 130 feature players from a year in which their team participated in a World Series while cards 131 through 150 is a Fall Classic sub set featuring key moments in World Series history.

COMMON CARD (1-130)	1.50	4.00
COMMON CARD (131-150)	1.50	4.00
1 Willie Mays 54	4.00	10.00
2 Gary Carter 86	1.50	4.00
3 Yogi Berra 47	2.00	5.00
4 Dennis Eckersley 88	1.50	4.00
5 Willie McCovey 62	1.50	4.00
6 Willie Stargell 71	1.50	4.00
7 Mike Schmidt 80	4.00	10.00
8 Robin Yount 82	2.00	5.00
9 Bucky Harris 24	1.50	4.00
10 Carl Yastrzemski 67	3.00	8.00
11 Lenny Dykstra 86	1.50	4.00
12 Boog Powell 66	1.50	4.00
13 Bill Lee 75	1.50	4.00
14 Lou Brock 64	1.50	4.00
15 Bob Friend 60	1.50	4.00
16 Hank Greenberg 34	2.00	5.00
17 Maury Wills 59	1.50	4.00
18 Tom Lasorda 77	1.50	4.00
19 Moose Skowron 55	1.50	4.00
20 Frank Robinson 61	1.50	4.00
21 Rollie Fingers 72	1.50	4.00
22 Doug DeCinces 79	1.50	4.00
23 Eric Davis 90	1.50	4.00
24 Johnny Podres 53	1.50	4.00
25 Darrell Evans 84	1.50	4.00
26 Ron Cey 74	1.50	4.00
27 Ray Knight 86	1.50	4.00
28 Don Larsen 55	1.50	4.00
29 Harold Baines 90	1.50	4.00
30 Brooks Robinson 66	1.50	4.00
31 Wade Boggs 86	1.50	4.00
32 Joe Morgan 72	1.50	4.00
33 Kirk Gibson 84	1.50	4.00
34 Tommy John 77	1.50	4.00
35 Monte Irvin 51	1.50	4.00
36 Goose Gossage 78	1.50	4.00
37 Tug McGraw 73	1.50	4.00
38 Walt Weiss 88	1.50	4.00
39 Bill Madlock 79	1.50	4.00
40 Juan Marichal 62	1.50	4.00
41 Willie McGee 82	1.50	4.00
42 Joe Cronin 33	1.50	4.00
43 Paul Blair 66	1.50	4.00
44 Norm Cash 59	1.50	4.00
45 Ken Griffey 75	1.50	4.00
46 Bret Saberhagen 85	1.50	4.00
47 Don Sutton 74	1.50	4.00
48 Kirby Puckett 87	2.00	5.00
49 Keith Hernandez 82	1.50	4.00
50 George Brett 80	4.00	10.00
51 Bobby Richardson 57	1.50	4.00
52 Jose Canseco 88	1.50	4.00
53 Greg Luzinski 80	1.50	4.00
54 Bill Mazeroski 60	1.50	4.00
55 Red Schoendienst 46	1.50	4.00
56 Graig Nettles 76	1.50	4.00
57 Jerry Koosman 69	1.50	4.00
58 Tony Perez 70	1.50	4.00
59 Jim Rice 86	1.50	4.00
60 Duke Snider 49	1.50	4.00
61 David Justice 91	1.50	4.00
62 Johnny Sain 48	1.50	4.00
63 Chuck Klein 35	1.50	4.00
64 Sparky Anderson 70	1.50	4.00
65 Alan Trammell 84	1.50	4.00
66 Willie Wilson 80	1.50	4.00
67 Hoyt Wilhelm 54	1.50	4.00
68 Joe Pepitone 63	1.50	4.00
69 Darren Daulton 93	1.50	4.00
70 Tom Seaver 69	1.50	4.00
71 Catfish Hunter 72	1.50	4.00
72 Tim McCarver 64	1.50	4.00
73 Dave Parker 79	1.50	4.00
74 Earl Weaver 69	1.50	4.00
75 Ted Kluszewski 59	1.50	4.00
76 John Kruk 93	1.50	4.00
77 Dwight Evans 75	1.50	4.00
78 Ron Darling 86	1.50	4.00
79 Tony Oliva 65	1.50	4.00
80 Johnny Bench 70	2.00	5.00
81 Sam Crawford 07	1.50	4.00
82 Steve Yeager 74	1.50	4.00
83 Paul Molitor 82	1.50	4.00
84 Bert Campaneris 72	1.50	4.00
85 Mickey Rivers 76	1.50	4.00
86 Vince Coleman 87	1.50	4.00
87 Kent Tekulve 79	1.50	4.00
88 Dwight Gooden 86	1.50	4.00
89 Whitey Herzog 82	1.50	4.00
90 Whitey Ford 50	1.50	4.00
91 Warren Spahn 48	1.50	4.00
92 Fred Lynn 75	1.50	4.00
93 Joe Tinker 06	1.50	4.00
94 Bill Buckner 74	1.50	4.00
95 Bob Feller 48	1.50	4.00
96 Hank Bauer 49	1.50	4.00
97 Joe Rudi 72	1.50	4.00
98 Steve Sax 81	1.50	4.00
99 Bruce Sutter 82	1.50	4.00

100 Nolan Ryan 69 5.00 12.00
101 Bobby Thomson 51 1.50 4.00
102 Bob Watson 81 1.50 4.00
103 Vida Blue 72 1.50 4.00
104 Robin Roberts 50 1.50 4.00
105 Orlando Cepeda 62 1.50 4.00
106 Jim Bottomley 26 1.50 4.00
107 Heinie Manush 33 1.50 4.00
108 Jim Gilliam 53 1.50 4.00
109 Dave Concepcion 70 1.50 4.00
110 Al Kaline 68 2.00 5.00
111 Howard Johnson 84 1.50 4.00
112 Phil Rizzuto 41 1.50 4.00
113 Steve Garvey 74 1.50 4.00
114 George Foster 72 1.50 4.00
115 Carlton Fisk 75 1.50 4.00
116 Don Newcombe 49 1.50 4.00
117 Lance Parrish 84 1.50 4.00
118 Reggie Jackson 73 1.50 4.00
119 Luis Aparicio 59 1.50 4.00
120 Jim Palmer 66 1.50 4.00
121 Ron Guidry 77 1.50 4.00
122 Frankie Frisch 21 1.50 4.00
123 Chet Lemon 84 1.50 4.00
124 Cecil Cooper 75 1.50 4.00
125 Harmon Killebrew 65 2.00 5.00
126 Luis Tiant 75 1.50 4.00
127 John McGraw 05 1.50 4.00
128 Paul O'Neill 90 1.50 4.00
129 Jack Clark 85 1.50 4.00
130 Stan Musial 42 3.00 8.00
131 Mike Schmidt FC 4.00 10.00
132 Kirby Puckett FC 2.00 5.00
133 Carlton Fisk FC 1.50 4.00
134 Bill Mazeroski FC 1.50 4.00
135 Johnny Podres FC 1.50 4.00
136 Robin Yount FC 2.00 5.00
137 David Justice FC 1.50 4.00
138 Bobby Thomson FC 1.50 4.00
139 Joe Carter FC 1.50 4.00
140 Reggie Jackson FC 1.50 4.00
141 Kirk Gibson FC 1.50 4.00
142 Whitey Ford FC 1.50 4.00
143 Don Larsen FC 1.50 4.00
144 Duke Snider FC 1.50 4.00
145 Carl Yastrzemski FC 3.00 8.00
146 Johnny Bench FC 2.00 5.00
147 Lou Brock FC 1.50 4.00
148 Ted Kluszewski FC 1.50 4.00
149 Jim Palmer FC 1.50 4.00
150 Willie Mays FC 4.00 10.00

2003 Topps Tribute World Series Gold

*GOLD 1-130: 1.5X TO 4X BASIC
*GOLD 131-150: 1.5X TO 4X BASIC
RANDOM INSERTS IN PACKS
STATED PRINT RUN 100 SERIAL #'d SETS

2003 Topps Tribute World Series Fall Classic Cuts

STATED ODDS 1:3437
STATED PRINT RUN 1 SERIAL #'d SET
NO PRICING DUE TO SCARCITY
BR Babe Ruth
HG Hank Greenberg
HW Honus Wagner
JF Jimmie Foxx
JR Jackie Robinson
LG Lou Gehrig
MO Mel Ott
RM Roger Maris
TC Ty Cobb
TM Thurman Munson

2003 Topps Tribute World Series Memorable Match-Up Relics

STATED ODDS 1:28
PRINT RUNS B/WN 9-88 COPIES PER
NO PRICING ON QTY OF 19 OR LESS
AM Sparky Anderson Uni 15.00 40.00
  Billy Martin Uni/76
AS Luis Aparicio Bat 20.00 50.00
  Duke Snider Bat/59
CR Eddie Collins Bat
  Edd Roush Bat/19
EG Dennis Eckersley Uni 15.00 40.00
  Kirk Gibson Bat/88
FS Whitey Ford Uni 40.00 80.00
  Duke Snider Bat/52
GF Hank Greenberg Bat 75.00 150.00
  Frankie Frisch Bat/34
GK Hank Greenberg Bat 75.00 150.00
  Chuck Klein Bat/35
KB Al Kaline Uni 40.00 80.00
  Lou Brock Bat/68
MF Bill Mazeroski Jsy 40.00 80.00
  Whitey Ford Uni/64
PR Phil Rizzuto Bat 75.00 150.00
  Willie Mays Uni/51
RBE Brooks Robinson Bat 40.00 80.00
  Johnny Bench Bat/70
RS Frank Robinson Bat 20.00 50.00
  Tom Seaver Uni/69
SB Mike Schmidt Uni 50.00 100.00
  George Brett Uni/80
SP Willie Stargell Bat 15.00 40.00
  Jim Palmer Jsy/79
SRI Mike Schmidt Uni 75.00 150.00
  Cal Ripken Uni/83
SY Ozzie Smith Bat 40.00 80.00
  Robin Yount Jsy/82
TG Alan Trammell Jsy 40.00 80.00
  Tony Gwynn Bat/84
WB Mookie Wilson Bat 20.00 50.00
  Bill Buckner Jsy/86
WC Honus Wagner Bat
  Ty Cobb Bat/9

2003 Topps Tribute World Series Pastime Patches

STATED ODDS 1:146
STATED PRINT RUN 15 SERIAL #'d SETS
NO PRICING DUE TO SCARCITY
AK Al Kaline
AT Alan Trammell
CH Catfish Hunter
CR Cal Ripken
CY Carl Yastrzemski
DE Dennis Eckersley
DP Dave Parker
DS Don Sutton
GB George Brett
JC Jose Canseco
JP Jim Palmer
JR Jim Rice
MS Mike Schmidt
MSK Moose Skowron
RY Robin Yount

2003 Topps Tribute World Series Signature Relics

GROUP A ODDS 1:218
GROUP B ODDS 1:94
GROUP C ODDS 1:9
GROUP D ODDS 1:12
GOLD STATED ODDS 1:88
GOLD PRINT RUN 25 SERIAL #'d SETS
NO GOLD PRICING DUE TO SCARCITY
AK Al Kaline Uni C 20.00 50.00
AT Alan Trammell Jsy C 10.00 25.00
BR Brooks Robinson Bat A 40.00 80.00
DJ David Justice Uni B 20.00 50.00
DN Don Newcombe Bat A 20.00 50.00
EW Earl Weaver Jsy D 10.00 25.00
JC Joe Carter Bat C 10.00 25.00
JP Jim Palmer Jsy D 15.00 40.00
KG Kirk Gibson Bat C 10.00 25.00
MS Moose Skowron Bat C 10.00 25.00
MW Maury Wills Jsy D 10.00 25.00
MWI Mookie Wilson Bat B 15.00 40.00
SA Sparky Anderson Uni C 10.00 25.00
SG Steve Garvey Bat C 10.00 25.00
WF Whitey Ford Uni C 30.00 60.00

2003 Topps Tribute World Series Subway Fan Fare Tokens

ONE PER BOX
BM Billy Martin 6.00 15.00
DJ David Justice 4.00 10.00
DL Don Larsen 4.00 10.00
DN Don Newcombe 4.00 10.00
DS Duke Snider 6.00 15.00
HB Hank Bauer 4.00 10.00
JP Johnny Podres 4.00 10.00
MS Moose Skowron 4.00 10.00
PO Paul O'Neill 6.00 15.00
PR Phil Rizzuto 6.00 15.00
WF Whitey Ford 6.00 15.00
YB Yogi Berra 8.00 20.00

2003 Topps Tribute World Series Team Tribute Relics

GROUP A ODDS 1:436
GROUP B ODDS 1:7
GROUP A PRINT RUN 25 SERIAL #'d SETS
GROUP B PRINT RUN 275 SERIAL #'d SETS
NO GROUP A PRICING DUE TO SCARCITY
CM Orlando Cepeda Bat 12.50 30.00
  Juan Marichal Uni B
CPM Dave Concepcion Bat 20.00 50.00
  Tony Perez Uni
  Joe Morgan Uni B
CYG Ron Cey Bat 12.50 30.00
  Steve Yeager Bat
  Steve Garvey Bat B
EC Dennis Eckersley Jsy 10.00 25.00
  Jose Canseco Jsy B
FB Whitey Ford Uni
  Yogi Berra Jsy A
FPG George Foster Bat 15.00 40.00
  Tony Perez Uni
  Ken Griffey Sr. Bat B
GB Lou Gehrig Bat
  Babe Ruth Bat A
GT Kirk Gibson Bat 10.00 25.00
  Alan Trammell Jsy B
HCD Keith Hernandez Bat 12.50 30.00
  Gary Carter Uni
  Lenny Dykstra Bat B
HJ Catfish Hunter Jsy 12.50 30.00
  Reggie Jackson Bat B
KCA Al Kaline Uni 15.00 40.00
  Norm Cash Bat B
MM Willie Mays Uni 30.00 80.00
  Willie McCovey Bat B
OSD Paul O'Neill Bat 15.00 40.00
  Chris Sabo Bat
  Eric Davis Bat B
SB Bret Saberhagen Jsy 15.00 40.00
  George Brett Bat B
SMC Ozzie Smith Uni 25.00 60.00
  Willie McGee Bat
  Vince Coleman Bat B
SPM Willie Stargell Bat 15.00 40.00
  Dave Parker Jsy
  Bill Madlock Bat B
SR Moose Skowron Bat
  Bobby Richardson Bat A
SRK Tom Seaver Uni 30.00 80.00
  Nolan Ryan Bat
  Jerry Koosman Jsy B
TA Alan Trammell Jsy 10.00 25.00
  Sparky Anderson Uni B
YLK Carl Yastrzemski Jsy 20.00 50.00
  Fred Lynn Jsy
  Carlton Fisk Bat B
YM Robin Yount Jsy 15.00 40.00
  Paul Molitor Bat B

2003 Topps Tribute World Series Tribute Relics

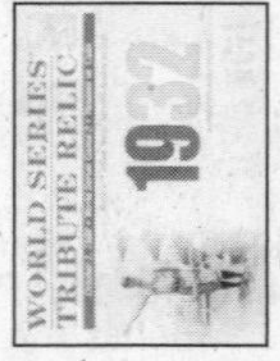

GROUP A ODDS 1:41
GROUP B ODDS 1:3
GROUP A PRINT RUN 50 SERIAL #'d SETS
GROUP B PRINT RUN 425 SERIAL #'d SETS
GOLD STATED ODDS 1:25
GOLD PRINT RUN 25 SERIAL #'d SETS
NO GOLD PRICING DUE TO SCARCITY
BH Bucky Harris Bat B 6.00 15.00
BM Bill Mazeroski Uni B 6.00 15.00
BMA Billy Martin Uni B 6.00 15.00
BR Babe Ruth Bat B 100.00 175.00
BT Bobby Thomson Bat B 4.00 10.00
CF Carlton Fisk Bat-Wall B 20.00 50.00
CH Catfish Hunter Jsy B 6.00 15.00
CK Chuck Klein Bat B 6.00 15.00
CR Cal Ripken Uni B 20.00 50.00
CY Carl Yastrzemski Jsy B 15.00 40.00
ER Edd Roush Bat A 20.00 50.00
FF Frankie Frisch Bat B 10.00 25.00
FR Frank Robinson Bat B 6.00 15.00
GB George Brett Uni B 10.00 25.00
HA Hank Aaron Bat A 30.00 60.00
HB Hank Bauer Bat A 20.00 50.00
HG Hank Greenberg Bat A 40.00 80.00
HK Harmon Killebrew Uni B 10.00 25.00
HM Heinie Manush Bat A 20.00 50.00
HW Honus Wagner Bat A 150.00 250.00
JB Jim Bottomley Bat A 20.00 50.00
JBE Johnny Bench Uni B 10.00 25.00
JC Jose Canseco Jsy B 6.00 15.00
JF Jimmie Foxx Bat A 60.00 120.00
JM Juan Marichal Uni B 4.00 10.00
JR Jackie Robinson Bat B 20.00 50.00
JT Joe Tinker Bat B 20.00 50.00
KP Kirby Puckett Bat B 10.00 25.00
LB Lou Brock Bat B 6.00 15.00
LG Lou Gehrig Bat A 150.00 250.00
MS Mike Schmidt Uni B 10.00 25.00
NC Norm Cash Jsy A 30.00 60.00
OC Orlando Cepeda Bat A 20.00 50.00
OS Ozzie Smith Uni B 10.00 25.00
RC Roberto Clemente Bat A 75.00 150.00
RH Rogers Hornsby Bat B 15.00 40.00
RJ Reggie Jackson Bat B 6.00 15.00
RM Roger Maris Bat A 50.00 100.00
RS Red Schoendienst Bat B 6.00 15.00
RY Robin Yount Jsy B 10.00 25.00
SC Sam Crawford Bat A 20.00 50.00
SM Stan Musial Bat B 15.00 40.00
TC Ty Cobb Uni B 75.00 150.00
TG Tony Gwynn Uni B 10.00 25.00
TK Ted Kluszewski Uni B 6.00 15.00
TM Thurman Munson Bat B 12.50 30.00
TS Tom Seaver Uni B 6.00 15.00
TSP Tris Speaker Bat A 100.00 175.00
WB Wade Boggs Bat B 6.00 15.00
WM Willie Mays Uni B 20.00 50.00
WMC Willie McCovey Uni B 4.00 10.00
WS Willie Stargell Uni A 20.00 50.00
YB Yogi Berra Uni B 10.00 25.00

2003 Topps Tribute World Series Tribute Autograph Relics

STATED ODDS 1:55
GOLD STATED ODDS 1:163
GOLD PRINT RUN 25 SERIAL #'d SETS
NO GOLD PRICING DUE TO SCARCITY
BM Bill Mazeroski Jsy 30.00 60.00
BT Bobby Thomson Bat 15.00 40.00
CF Carlton Fisk Bat-Wall 100.00 200.00
HK Harmon Killebrew Uni 50.00 100.00
JC Jose Canseco Jsy 30.00 60.00
LB Lou Brock Bat 30.00 60.00
MS Mike Schmidt Uni 60.00 120.00
WM Willie Mays Uni 250.00 400.00

2006 Topps Triple Threads

This 120-card set was released in April, 2006. The set was release solely through the hobby in six-card packs with an $80 SRP which came two packs to a box and 18 boxes to a case. The first 100-cards are a mix of veteran players and retired greats. With the exception of Don Mattingly, all of the retired players pictured are in the Hall of Fame. Cards numbered 101-120 feature younger players who both signed these cards and had some game-used memorabilia included on the card. These cards were issued to a stated print run of 225 serial numbered cards.

1-100 THREE PER PACK
101-120 ODDS 1:7 MINI
101-120 PRINT RUN 225 SERIAL #'d SETS
OVERALL 1-100 PLATE ODDS 1:80 MINI
PLATE PRINT RUN 1 SET PER COLOR
BLACK-CYAN-MAGENTA-YELLOW ISSUED
NO PLATE PRICING DUE TO SCARCITY
1 Hideki Matsui 2.00 5.00
2 Josh Gibson HOF 2.00 5.00
3 Roger Clemens 3.00 8.00
4 Paul Konerko 1.25 3.00
5 Brooks Robinson HOF 1.50 4.00
6 Stan Musial HOF 2.00 5.00
7 Dontrelle Willis 1.25 3.00
8 Yogi Berra HOF 2.00 5.00
9 John Smoltz 1.50 4.00
10 Brian Roberts 1.25 3.00
11 Gary Sheffield 1.25 3.00
12 Wade Boggs HOF 1.50 4.00
13 Alex Rodriguez 3.00 8.00
14 Ernie Banks HOF 2.00 5.00
15 Ichiro Suzuki 3.00 8.00
16 Whitey Ford HOF 1.50 4.00
17 Vladimir Guerrero 2.00 5.00
18 Tadahito Iguchi 1.25 3.00
19 Robin Yount HOF 2.00 5.00
20 Jason Schmidt 1.25 3.00
21 Roberto Clemente HOF 4.00 10.00
22 Andruw Jones 1.50 4.00
23 Don Mattingly 4.00 10.00
24 Joe Mauer 1.50 4.00
25 Barry Bonds 5.00 12.00
26 Johnny Damon 1.50 4.00
27 Chris Carpenter 1.25 3.00
28 Garret Anderson 1.25 3.00
29 Scott Rolen 1.50 4.00
30 Tim Hudson 1.25 3.00
31 Dave Winfield HOF 1.25 3.00
32 Steve Carlton HOF 1.25 3.00
33 Miguel Tejada 1.25 3.00
34 Nolan Ryan HOF 4.00 10.00
35 Mark Buehrle 1.25 3.00
36 Travis Hafner 1.25 3.00
37 Rickie Weeks 1.25 3.00
38 Sammy Sosa 2.00 5.00
39 Carlos Beltran 1.25 3.00
40 Todd Helton 1.50 4.00
41 Tom Seaver HOF 1.50 4.00
42 Ted Williams HOF 2.50 6.00
43 Alfonso Soriano 1.25 3.00
44 Reggie Jackson HOF 1.50 4.00
45 Pedro Martinez 1.50 4.00
46 Randy Johnson 2.00 5.00
47 Ted Williams HOF UER 2.50 6.00
  Lifetime stats double his real career stats
48 Torii Hunter 1.25 3.00
49 Manny Ramirez 1.50 4.00
50 George Brett HOF 2.50 6.00
51 Chipper Jones 2.00 5.00
52 Nomar Garciaparra 1.50 4.00
53 Richie Sexson 1.25 3.00
54 David Ortiz 2.00 5.00
55 Derek Jeter 6.00 15.00
56 Mickey Mantle HOF 6.00 15.00
57 Michael Young 1.25 3.00
58 Aramis Ramirez 1.25 3.00
59 Bartolo Colon 1.25 3.00
60 Troy Glaus 1.25 3.00
61 Carlos Delgado 1.25 3.00
62 Mike Sweeney 1.25 3.00
63 Jorge Cantu 1.25 3.00
64 Mike Mussina 1.50 4.00
65 Hank Blalock 1.25 3.00
66 Frank Robinson HOF 1.25 3.00
67 Carl Yastrzemski HOF 2.00 5.00
68 Adam Dunn 1.25 3.00
69 Eric Chavez 1.25 3.00
70 Curt Schilling 1.50 4.00
71 Jeff Francoeur 2.50 6.00
72 C.C. Sabathia 1.25 3.00
73 Roy Oswalt 1.25 3.00
74 Carlos Lee 1.25 3.00
75 Barry Zito 1.25 3.00
76 Derrek Lee 1.50 4.00
77 Greg Maddux 2.50 6.00
78 Ivan Rodriguez 1.50 4.00
79 Jeff Kent 1.25 3.00
80 Gary Carter HOF 1.25 3.00
81 Jose Reyes 1.25 3.00
82 Johan Santana 1.50 4.00
83 Magglio Ordonez 1.25 3.00
84 Mark Prior 1.50 4.00
85 Johnny Bench HOF 2.00 5.00
86 Vernon Wells 1.25 3.00
87 Mark Mulder 1.25 3.00
88 Cal Ripken 6.00 15.00
89 Mark Teixeira 1.50 4.00
90 Miguel Cabrera 1.50 4.00
91 Duke Snider HOF 1.50 4.00
92 Jason Giambi 1.25 3.00
93 Albert Pujols 3.00 8.00
94 Carl Crawford 1.25 3.00
95 Jim Edmonds 1.25 3.00
96 Jose Contreras 1.25 3.00
97 Victor Martinez 1.25 3.00
98 Jeremy Bonderman 1.25 3.00
99 Lance Berkman 1.25 3.00
100 Rocco Baldelli 1.25 3.00
101 Zach Duke AU J-J 10.00 25.00
102 Felix Hernandez AU J-J 15.00 40.00
103 Dan Johnson AU J-J 6.00 15.00
104 Brandon McCarthy AU J-J 10.00 25.00
105 Huston Street AU J-J 10.00 25.00
106 Robinson Cano AU J-J 20.00 50.00
107 Jason Bay AU J-J 10.00 25.00
108 Ryan Howard AU B-B 30.00 60.00
109 Ervin Santana AU J-J 6.00 15.00
110 Rich Harden AU J-J 6.00 15.00
111 Aaron Hill AU J-J 6.00 15.00
112 David Wright AU J-J 30.00 60.00
113 Rich Hill AU J-J (RC) 15.00 40.00
114 Nelson Cruz AU J-J (RC) 6.00 15.00
115 Francisco Liriano AU J-J (RC) 50.00 100.00
116 Hong-Chih Kuo AU J-J (RC) 30.00 60.00
117 Ryan Garko AU J-J (RC) 10.00 25.00
118 Craig Hansen AU J-J RC 20.00 50.00
119 Shin-Soo Choo AU J-J (RC) 6.00 15.00
120 Darrell Rasner AU J-J (RC) 6.00 15.00

2006 Topps Triple Threads White Whale Prospect-Rookie Printing Plate

OVERALL WHALE PLATE ODDS 1:400 MINI
STATED PRINT RUN 1 SERIAL #'d SET
NO PRICING DUE TO SCARCITY

2006 Topps Triple Threads Emerald

*EMERALD 1-100: .75X TO 2X BASIC
1-100 ODDS 1:4 MINI
1-100 PRINT RUN 99 SERIAL #'d SETS
*EMERALD 101-112: .5X TO 1.2X BASIC AU
*EMERALD 113-120: .5X TO 1.2X BASIC AU
101-120 AU ODDS 1:21 MINI
101-120 AU PRINT RUN 75 SERIAL #'d SETS
56 Mickey Mantle HOF 15.00 40.00

2006 Topps Triple Threads Gold

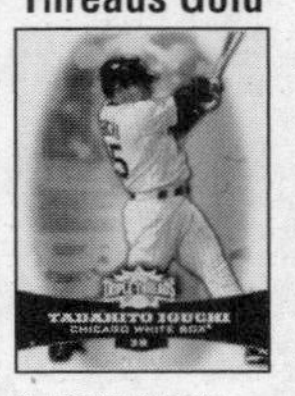

*GOLD 1-100: 1.25X TO 3X BASIC
1-100 ODDS 1:7 MINI
1-100 PRINT RUN 50 SERIAL #'d SETS
*GOLD 101-112: .6X TO 1.5X BASIC AU
*GOLD 113-120: .6X TO 1.5X BASIC AU
101-120 AU ODDS 1:32 MINI
101-120 AU PRINT RUN 50 SERIAL #'d SETS
56 Mickey Mantle HOF 30.00 60.00
116 Hong-Chih Kuo AU J-J 75.00 150.00
118 Craig Hansen AU J-J 30.00 60.00

2006 Topps Triple Threads Platinum

1-100 ODDS 1:322 MINI
101-120 AU ODDS 1:1598 MINI
STATED PRINT RUN 1 SERIAL #'d SET
NO PRICING DUE TO SCARCITY

2006 Topps Triple Threads Sapphire

*SAPHIRE 1-100: 2X TO 5X BASIC
1-100 ODDS 1:13 MINI
1-100 PRINT RUN 25 SERIAL #'d SETS
101-120 AU ODDS 1:63 MINI
101-120 AU PRINT RUN 25 SERIAL #'d SETS
101-120 NO PRICING DUE TO SCARCITY
25 Barry Bonds 50.00 100.00
56 Mickey Mantle HOF 50.00 100.00

2006 Topps Triple Threads Sepia

*SEPIA 1-100: .6X TO 1.5X BASIC
1-100 ODDS 1:3 MINI
1-100 PRINT RUN 150 SERIAL #'d SETS
*SEPIA 101-112: .4X TO 1X BASIC AU
*SEPIA 113-120: .4X TO 1X BASIC AU
101-120 AU ODDS 1:13 MINI
101-120 AU PRINT RUN 125 SERIAL #'d SETS

2006 Topps Triple Threads Heroes

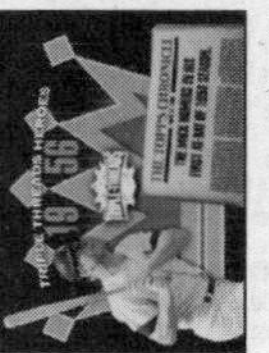

COMM.T.WILL (1-5/42;1-5/47) 3.00 8.00
COMMON MANTLE (1-10) 6.00 15.00
COMMON F.ROB (1-10) 1.50 4.00
COMMON YAZ (1-10) 2.00 5.00
ONE BASIC OR DIE CUT HEROES PER PACK
*DIE CUT: 1X TO 2.5X BASIC
DIE CUT ODDS 1:16 MINI
DIE CUT PRINT RUN 50 SERIAL #'d SETS

2006 Topps Triple Threads Heroes Autograph

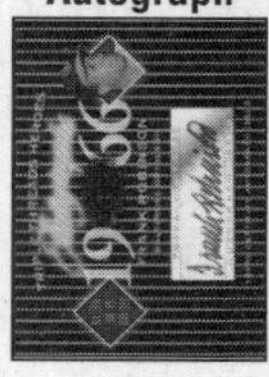

STATED ODDS 1:524 MINI
STATED PRINT RUN 3 SERIAL #'d SETS
NO PRICING DUE TO SCARCITY

2006 Topps Triple Threads Heroes Cut Signature

STATED ODDS 1:10,122 MINI
STATED PRINT RUN 1 SERIAL #'d SET
NO PRICING DUE TO SCARCITY
MM Mickey Mantle
42TW Ted Williams 1942
47TW Ted Williams 1947

2006 Topps Triple Threads Heroes Co-Signer

STATED ODDS 1:10,122 MINI
STATED PRINT RUN 3 SERIAL #'d CARDS
NO PRICING DUE TO SCARCITY
RY Frank Robinson
Carl Yastrzemski

2006 Topps Triple Threads Heroes Triple Signed Hide

STATED ODDS 1:15,183 MINI
STATED PRINT RUN 1 SERIAL #'d SET
NO PRICING DUE TO SCARCITY
MRY Mickey Mantle Cut
Frank Robinson
Carl Yastrzemski
WRY Ted Williams Cut
Frank Robinson
Carl Yastrzemski

2006 Topps Triple Threads Heroes Quad Signer

STATED ODDS 1:10,122 MINI
STATED PRINT RUN 1 SERIAL #'d CARD
NO PRICING DUE TO SCARCITY
QS Mickey Mantle Cut
Ted Williams Cut
Frank Robinson
Carl Yastrzemski

2006 Topps Triple Threads Relic

STATED ODDS 1:7 MINI
STATED PRINT RUN 18 SERIAL #'d SETS
*GOLD: .5X TO 1.2X BASIC
GOLD ODDS 1:15 MINI
GOLD PRINT RUN 9 SERIAL #'d SETS
PLATINUM ODDS 1:43 MINI
PLATINUM PRINT RUN 3 SERIAL #'d SETS
NO PLATINUM PRICING DUE TO SCARCITY

1 Adam Dunn RBI 10.00 25.00
PT-PT-J
2 Adam Dunn CIN 10.00 25.00
PT-PT-PT
3 Adrian Beltre LAD 10.00 25.00
B-B-B
4 Adrian Beltre SEA 10.00 25.00
B-B-B
5 Al Kaline GOLD GLOVE 40.00 80.00
B-B-B
6 Al Kaline HOF 40.00 80.00
B-B-B
7 Al Kaline DET 40.00 80.00
B-B-B
8 Albert Pujols STL 40.00 80.00
J-PT-J
9 Albert Pujols 300 BAT AVG 40.00 80.00
J-J-J
10 Albert Pujols MVP 40.00 80.00
H-J-P
11 Albert Pujols ROY 40.00 80.00
J-J-J
12 Alex Rodriguez NYY 60.00 120.00
J-J-J
13 Alex Rodriguez #13 40.00 80.00
J-J-J
14 Alex Rodriguez MVP 50.00 100.00
J-B-J
15 Alex Rodriguez 400 50.00 100.00
B-B-J
16 Alex Rodriguez SEA 40.00 80.00
B-H-B
17 Alex Rodriguez 40/40 40.00 80.00
H-B-J
18 Alex Rodriguez TEX 50.00 100.00
PT-PT-PT
19 Alex Rodriguez GOLD GLOVE 40.00 80.00
J-PT-J
20 Alex Rodriguez MVP 50.00 100.00
J-B-J
21 Alfonso Soriano NYY 10.00 25.00
B-P-P
22 Alfonso Soriano TEX 10.00 25.00
P-B-S
23 Andruw Jones GOLD GLOVE 15.00 40.00
PT-PT-PT
24 Andruw Jones ATL 15.00 40.00
PT-J-PT
25 Andy Pettitte ACE 15.00 40.00
J-PT-J
26 Andy Pettitte HOU 15.00 40.00
J-J-J
27 Aramis Ramirez CHC 10.00 25.00
B-B-B
28 B.J. Upton MLB 10.00 25.00
B-B-B
29 Barry Bonds 40/40 40.00 80.00
B-B-B
30 Barry Bonds MVP 40.00 80.00
B-B-B
31 Barry Bonds PIT 40.00 80.00
B-B-B
32 Barry Bonds 700 40.00 80.00
ST-ST-ST
33 Barry Bonds SFG 40.00 80.00
P-B-P
34 Barry Bonds 700 40.00 80.00
P-B-P
35 Barry Bonds #25 40.00 80.00
P-B-P
36 Barry Bonds 7MVP 40.00 80.00
P-B-P
37 Barry Zito OAK 10.00 25.00
PT-P-PT
38 Barry Zito CY YOUNG 10.00 25.00
P-PT-P
39 Ben Sheets USA 10.00 25.00
B-B-B
40 Bill Mazeroski PIT 15.00 40.00
B-B-B
41 Bob Feller HOF 15.00 40.00
P-P-P
42 Bobby Abreu PHI 10.00 25.00
J-J-J
43 Bobby Cox ATL 10.00 25.00
J-P-J
44 Bobby Doerr BOS 10.00 25.00
B-B-B
45 Brad Lidge HOU 10.00 25.00
J-J-J
46 Brian Giles SDP 10.00 25.00
B-B-B
47 Brian Roberts BAL 10.00 25.00
J-B-J
48 Cal Ripken CAL 40.00 80.00
J-B-J
49 Cal Ripken MVP 40.00 80.00
J-P-BS
50 Cal Ripken BAL 40.00 80.00
J-P-J
51 Carl Yastrzemski YAZ 30.00 60.00
J-B-J
52 Carl Yastrzemski MVP 30.00 60.00
J-P-J
53 Carl Yastrzemski BOS 30.00 60.00
B-J-S
54 Carlos Beltran ROY 10.00 25.00
B-B-B
55 Carlos Beltran NYM 10.00 25.00
J-PT-J
56 Carlos Delgado RBI 10.00 25.00
B-B-B
57 Carlton Fisk BOS 15.00 40.00
P-B-P
58 Carlton Fisk HOF 15.00 40.00
P-P-P
59 Carlton Fisk CWS 15.00 40.00
P-P-P
60 Chipper Jones MVP 30.00 60.00
J-PT-J
61 Chipper Jones 300 BAT AVG 30.00 60.00
PT-PT-PT
62 Chipper Jones ATL 30.00 60.00
PT-B-PT
63 Chris Carpenter STL 15.00 40.00
J-J-J
64 Craig Biggio HBP 15.00 40.00
J-B-J
65 Craig Biggio HOU 15.00 40.00
J-P-J
66 Curt Schilling World Series 10.00 25.00
J-J-J
67 Curt Schilling ACE 10.00 25.00
PT-J-H
68 Curt Schilling World Series 15.00 40.00
J-J-J
69 Curt Schilling BOS 15.00 40.00
J-J-J
70 Dale Murphy ATL 15.00 40.00
B-B-B
71 Darryl Strawberry NYM 10.00 25.00
J-B-J
72 Darryl Strawberry ROY 10.00 25.00
B-J-B
73 Dave Winfield GOLD GLOVE 10.00 25.00
J-PT-P
74 Dave Winfield NYY 10.00 25.00
P-J-P
75 Dave Winfield HOF 10.00 25.00
B-B-B
76 David Ortiz RBI 15.00 40.00
J-PT-J
77 David Ortiz BOS 15.00 40.00
J-J-J
78 David Ortiz MIN 10.00 25.00
B-B-B
79 Derrek Lee CHC 15.00 40.00
J-J-J
80 Don Mattingly NYY 30.00 60.00
J-B-P
81 Don Mattingly #23 30.00 60.00
J-J-J
82 Don Mattingly MVP 30.00 60.00
J-P-P
83 Dontrelle Willis ROY 10.00 25.00
PT-PT-PT
84 Dontrelle Willis FLA 10.00 25.00
PT-PT-PT
85 Duke Snider HOF 15.00 40.00
P-P-P
86 Dwight Gooden Dr.K 10.00 25.00
J-J-J
87 Dwight Gooden ROY 10.00 25.00
J-J-J
88 Eric Chavez OAK 10.00 25.00
P-P-P
89 Ernie Banks CHC 20.00 50.00
P-P-P
90 Ernie Banks 2MVP 20.00 50.00
P-B-P
91 Ernie Banks 512 20.00 50.00
P-P-P
92 Frank Robinson 586 15.00 40.00
B-B-B
93 Frank Robinson MVP 15.00 40.00
P-P-P
94 Frankie Frisch HOF 20.00 50.00
B-B-B
95 Gary Carter NYM 10.00 25.00
B-PT-B
96 Gary Sheffield NYY 10.00 25.00
J-J-J
97 Gary Sheffield RBI 10.00 25.00
B-B-B
98 George Brett KC5 40.00 80.00
PT-H-B
99 George Brett MVP 40.00 80.00
PT-PT-PT
100 Greg Maddux CHC 40.00 80.00
PT-B-PT
101 Hank Blalock TEX 10.00 25.00
J-PT-J
102 Hank Greenberg HOF 60.00 120.00
B-B-B
103 Hank Greenberg DET 60.00 120.00
B-B-B
104 Hideki Matsui NYY 40.00 80.00
J-PT-J
105 Hideki Matsui MLB 40.00 80.00
J-J-J
106 Hideki Matsui RBI 40.00 80.00
J-J-J
107 Ichiro Suzuki SEA 60.00 120.00
J-J-J
108 Ichiro Suzuki ROY 60.00 120.00
J-J-J
109 Ichiro Suzuki 262 60.00 120.00
B-B-B
110 Ivan Rodriguez GOLD GLOVE 10.00 25.00
J-J-PT
111 Ivan Rodriguez DET 10.00 25.00
J-PT-J
112 Ivan Rodriguez FLA 10.00 25.00
J-B-J
113 Ivan Rodriguez TEX 10.00 25.00
PT-PT-PT
114 Jake Peavy SDP 10.00 25.00
J-J-J
115 Javy Lopez BAL 10.00 25.00
J-J-J
116 Jeff Bagwell HOU 15.00 40.00
P-J-P
117 Jim Edmonds STL 10.00 25.00
J-PT-J
118 Jim Thome PHI 15.00 40.00
PT-P-PT
119 Joe Mauer MIN 10.00 25.00
J-J-J
120 Joe Torre STL 10.00 25.00
J-PT-J
121 Johan Santana CY YOUNG 15.00 40.00
J-J-J
122 Johan Santana MIN 15.00 40.00
J-J-J
123 Johnny Bench ROY 30.00 60.00
P-B-P
124 Johnny Bench CIN 30.00 60.00
P-P-P
125 Johnny Damon BOS 15.00 40.00
J-B-PT
126 Jon Garland World Series 10.00 25.00
P-P-P
127 Jon Garland CWS 10.00 25.00
P-P-P
128 Jorge Posada NYY 15.00 40.00
P-B-P
129 Jorge Posada RBI 15.00 40.00
P-P-P
130 Jose Canseco ROY 40.00 80.00
J-PT-P
131 Jose Reyes NYM 10.00 25.00
J-J-J
132 Juan Marichal SFG 10.00 25.00
J-J-J
133 Kerry Wood ROY 10.00 25.00
PT-J-PT
134 Kerry Wood CHC 10.00 25.00
PT-PT-PT
135 Lance Berkman MLB 10.00 25.00
J-PT-J
136 Lance Berkman HOU 10.00 25.00
PT-J-PT
137 Lloyd Waner HOF 40.00 80.00
B-B-B
138 Lloyd Waner PIT 40.00 80.00
B-B-B
139 Lou Brock HOF 15.00 40.00
B-B-B
140 Manny Ramirez RBI 15.00 40.00
J-B-J
141 Manny Ramirez BOS 15.00 40.00
J-J-J
142 Mariano Rivera NYY 30.00 60.00
J-J-J
143 Mariano Rivera SAV 30.00 60.00
J-J-J
144 Mark Buehrle CWS 10.00 25.00
P-FG-P
145 Mark Mulder OAK 10.00 25.00
PT-PT-PT
146 Mark Mulder STL 10.00 25.00
P-P-P
147 Mark Prior CHC 10.00 25.00
J-J-J
148 Mark Teixeira TEX 15.00 40.00
J-PT-J
149 Michael Young TEX 10.00 25.00
J-PT-J
150 Michael Young BAT CROWN 10.00 25.00
J-J-J
151 Mickey Mantle NYY 200.00 350.00
ST-SH-ST
152 Mickey Mantle 536 200.00 350.00
P-J-P
153 Mickey Mantle HOF 200.00 350.00
J-B-P
154 Mickey Mantle NY7 200.00 350.00
P-P-P
155 Mickey Mantle 3MVP 200.00 350.00
B-B-B
156 Miguel Cabrera FLA 15.00 40.00
J-B-J
157 Miguel Tejada #10 10.00 25.00
P-P-P
158 Miguel Tejada RBI 10.00 25.00
P-B-P
159 Miguel Tejada BAL 10.00 25.00
P-P-P
160 Miguel Tejada MVP 10.00 25.00
P-B-P
161 Mike Mussina NYY 15.00 40.00
P-P-P
162 Mike Mussina ACE 15.00 40.00
P-P-P
163 Mike Piazza LAD 40.00 80.00
H-B-H
164 Mike Piazza NYM 40.00 80.00
PT-J-PT
165 Mike Piazza #31 30.00 60.00
J-PT-J
166 Mike Schmidt 548 30.00 60.00
B-PT-H
167 Mike Schmidt HOF 30.00 60.00
H-S-B
168 Mike Schmidt MVP 30.00 60.00
PT-H-B
169 Monte Irvin HOF 15.00 40.00
B-B-B
170 Morgan Ensberg HOU 10.00 25.00
J-J-J
171 Nolan Ryan HOF 40.00 80.00
J-P-J
172 Nolan Ryan HOU 40.00 80.00
P-B-P
173 Nolan Ryan TEX 40.00 80.00
J-PT-J
174 Nolan Ryan 324 40.00 80.00
J-J-J
175 Wade Boggs WS 15.00 40.00
B-J-B
176 Ozzie Smith GOLD GLOVE 20.00 50.00
B-J-S
177 Ozzie Smith HOF 20.00 50.00
B-S-B
178 Pat Burrell PHI 10.00 25.00
B-PT-B
179 Paul Konerko WS 10.00 25.00
P-PT-P
180 Paul Konerko RBI 10.00 25.00
P-B-P
181 Paul Konerko CWS 10.00 25.00
PT-B-P
182 Paul Molitor HOF 10.00 25.00
J-PT-P
183 Pedro Martinez 3CY 15.00 40.00
PT-PT-PT
184 Pedro Martinez NYM 15.00 40.00
J-B-J
185 Pedro Martinez ACE 15.00 40.00
J-B-J
186 Randy Johnson Triple Crown 15.00 40.00
P-B-J
187 Randy Johnson 5CY 15.00 40.00
P-P-P
188 Reggie Jackson OCT 20.00 50.00
B-B-B
189 Reggie Jackson 563 20.00 50.00
B-PT-B
190 Rickey Henderson NYY 30.00 60.00
B-B-B
191 Rickey Henderson OAK 30.00 60.00
J-P-S
192 Rickey Henderson MVP 30.00 60.00
S-P-S
193 Rickey Henderson 130 30.00 60.00
J-PT-J
194 Rickie Weeks MLB 10.00 25.00
B-B-B
195 Rickie Weeks MIL 10.00 25.00
B-B-B
196 Roberto Clemente 3000 HITS 100.00 175.00
B-P-B
197 Roberto Clemente MVP 100.00 175.00
B-B-B
198 Robin Yount 2MVP 30.00 60.00
J-H-J
199 Rod Carew ROY 15.00 40.00
B-B-B
200 Roger Clemens 7CY 30.00 60.00
J-J-J
201 Roger Clemens CY YOUNG 30.00 60.00
J-J-J
202 Roger Clemens ERA 30.00 60.00
J-J-J
203 Roger Clemens HOU 30.00 60.00
J-J-J
204 Roger Clemens NYY 30.00 60.00
J-H-J
205 Roger Clemens CY 30.00 60.00
J-J-J
206 Roy Halladay CY YOUNG 10.00 25.00
J-J-J
207 Roy Oswalt 20W 10.00 25.00
J-PT-J
208 Roy Oswalt HOU 10.00 25.00
J-J-J
209 Ryne Sandberg HOF 40.00 80.00
B-B-B
210 Ryne Sandberg MVP 40.00 80.00
J-B-B
211 Sammy Sosa 500 30.00 60.00
J-J-B
212 Sammy Sosa BAL 30.00 60.00
J-J-J
213 Sammy Sosa MVP 30.00 60.00
PT-J-PT
214 Sammy Sosa CHC 30.00 60.00
J-J-J
215 Sammy Sosa 500 30.00 60.00
J-J-J
216 Scott Rolen ROY 15.00 40.00
J-B-J
217 Scott Rolen STL 15.00 40.00
J-PT-J
218 Sean Burroughs SDP 10.00 25.00
B-J-B
219 Stan Musial 3MVP 30.00 60.00
P-P-P
220 Steve Carlton PHI 10.00 25.00
P-P-P
221 Steve Carlton 4CY 10.00 25.00
P-S-P
222 Steve Carlton 329 10.00 25.00
P-P-P
223 Steve Garvey MVP 10.00 25.00
B-B-B
224 Tadahito Iguchi CWS 10.00 25.00
J-J-J
225 Ted Williams 0.406 150.00 250.00
B-B-B
226 Ted Williams 521 150.00 250.00
B-B-B
227 Tim Hudson ATL 10.00 25.00
J-B-J
228 Tim Hudson OAK 10.00 25.00
J-P-J
229 Todd Helton GOLD GLOVE 15.00 40.00
PT-PT-PT
230 Todd Helton 300 BAT AVG 15.00 40.00
PT-J-PT
231 Todd Helton COL 15.00 40.00
PT-J-PT
232 Tom Seaver 311 15.00 40.00
P-P-P
233 Tony Gwynn SDP 30.00 60.00
PT-B-PT
234 Tony Gwynn 300 BAT AVG 30.00 60.00
J-J-J
235 Tony Gwynn 3000 HITS 30.00 60.00
J-B-J
236 Torii Hunter GOLD GLOVE 10.00 25.00
J-PT-J
237 Torii Hunter MIN 10.00 25.00
PT-PT-PT
238 Travis Hafner CLE 10.00 25.00
J-J-J
239 Vladimir Guerrero MVP 20.00 50.00
B-PT-B
240 Vladimir Guerrero RBI 20.00 50.00
PT-B-PT
241 Wade Boggs 3000 HITS 15.00 40.00
B-H-S
242 Willie Stargell HOF 15.00 40.00
P-P-P
243 Willie Stargell PIT 15.00 40.00
P-B-H
244 Willie Stargell POP 15.00 40.00
P-B-P
245 Willy Taveras HOU 10.00 25.00
J-J-J

2006 Topps Triple Threads Relic Autograph

STATED ODDS 1:14 MINI
STATED PRINT RUN 18 SERIAL #'d SETS
*GOLD: .5X TO 1.2X BASIC
GOLD ODDS 1:27 MINI
GOLD PRINT RUN 9 SERIAL #'d SETS
PLATINUM ODDS 1:81 MINI
PLATINUM PRINT RUN 3 SERIAL #'d SETS
NO PLATINUM PRICING DUE TO SCARCITY

1 Albert Pujols MVP 300.00 500.00
J-P-J
2 Albert Pujols ROY 300.00 500.00
PT-PT-PT
3 Albert Pujols STL 300.00 500.00
PT-B-PT
4 Alex Rodriguez MVP 200.00 350.00
J-B-J
5 Alex Rodriguez 40/40 200.00 350.00
J-B-H
6 Alex Rodriguez MVP 200.00 350.00
PT-PT-PT
7 Derrek Lee CHC 25.00 60.00
P-B-P
8 Barry Bonds 700 250.00 400.00
J-J-J
9 Ben Sheets MIL 15.00 40.00
B-B-B
10 Ben Sheets USA 15.00 40.00
B-B-B
11 Brad Lidge HOU 15.00 40.00
J-J-J
12 Brad Lidge Pitcher-Ball 15.00 40.00
J-PT-J
13 Cal Ripken BAL 125.00 200.00
P-B-BS
14 Cal Ripken HIT 125.00 200.00
J-J-J
15 Cal Ripken MVP 125.00 200.00
J-P-J
16 Carl Yastrzemski BOS 60.00 120.00
S-B-J
17 Carl Yastrzemski MVP 60.00 120.00
J-S-J
18 Carl Yastrzemski YAZ 60.00 120.00
J-J-B
19 Chase Utley PHI 25.00 60.00
J-J-J
20 Chase Utley RBI 25.00 60.00
J-PT-J
21 C.Wang Chinese 600.00 1000.00
J-PT-J
22 Chien-Ming Wang ERA 300.00 500.00
J-J-J
23 Chien-Ming Wang NYY 300.00 500.00
J-PT-J
24 C.Wang Pitcher-Ball 300.00 500.00
J-J-J
25 Chris Carpenter CY 60.00 120.00
J-J-J
26 Chris Carpenter STL 60.00 120.00
J-PT-J
27 Clint Barmes COL 10.00 25.00
J-PT-J
28 Clint Barmes MLB 10.00 25.00
J-J-J
29 Conor Jackson 1ST 25.00 60.00
B-B-B
30 Conor Jackson ARI 25.00 60.00
B-B-B
31 David Ortiz BOS 50.00 100.00
J-PT-J
32 Don Mattingly #23 60.00 120.00
J-PT-P
33 Don Mattingly MVP 60.00 120.00
J-B-P
34 Don Mattingly NYY 60.00 120.00
J-B-J
35 Duke Snider LAD 30.00 80.00
P-P-P
36 Duke Snider World Series 30.00 80.00
P-P-P
37 Ernie Banks CHC 75.00 150.00
P-P-P
38 Frank Robinson MVP 25.00 60.00
B-B-B
39 Frank Robinson CIN 25.00 60.00
P-B-P
40 Frank Robinson Triple Crown 25.00 60.00
P-P-B
41 Garrett Atkins 3RD 10.00 25.00
B-B-B
42 Garrett Atkins COL 10.00 25.00
B-B-B
43 Derrek Lee BAT 25.00 60.00
J-J-J
44 Derrek Lee LEE 25.00 60.00
J-J-J
45 Derrek Lee OPS 25.00 60.00
J-J-J
46 J.J. Hardy MIL 40.00 80.00
B-B-B
47 J.J. Hardy SS6 40.00 80.00
B-B-B
48 Jake Peavy ERA 25.00 60.00
J-J-J
49 Jake Peavy SDP 25.00 60.00
J-J-J
50 Jeff Francis COL 10.00 25.00
J-PT-J
51 Jeff Francis Pitcher-Ball 10.00 25.00
J-J-J
52 Joe Mauer MIN 15.00 40.00
J-J-J
53 Joe Mauer RBI 15.00 40.00
J-J-J
54 Joey Devine ATL 15.00 40.00
J-PT-J
55 J.Devine Pitcher-Ball 15.00 40.00
J-J-J
56 Johan Santana CY 40.00 80.00
J-PT-J
57 Johan Santana ERA 40.00 80.00
J-J-J
58 Johan Santana MIN 40.00 80.00
J-J-J
59 Johan Santana Strikeouts 40.00 80.00
J-J-J
60 Johnny Bench CIN 50.00 100.00
P-B-P
61 Johnny Bench MVP 50.00 100.00
P-P-P
62 Johnny Bench ROY 50.00 100.00
B-P-B
63 Johnny Damon BOS 50.00 100.00
J-J-P
64 Jonny Gomes MLB 15.00 40.00
J-PT-J
65 Jonny Gomes RBI 15.00 40.00
J-J-J
66 Jose Reyes MLB 20.00 50.00
PT-J-PT
67 Jose Reyes NYM 20.00 50.00
J-B-J
68 Justin Morneau 1ST 15.00 40.00
B-B-B
69 Justin Morneau MIN 15.00 40.00
B-B-B
70 Lou Brock 938 25.00 60.00
B-B-B
71 Lou Brock 3 Stars 25.00 60.00
B-PT-B
72 Lou Brock HOF 25.00 60.00
B-B-B
73 Lou Brock STL 25.00 60.00
PT-B-B
74 Manny Ramirez BOS 50.00 100.00
J-PT-J
75 Mariano Rivera 0.81 125.00 200.00
J-PT-J
76 Mark Prior CHC 15.00 40.00
J-PT-J
77 Miguel Cabrera #24 30.00 80.00
J-B-J
78 Miguel Cabrera FLA 30.00 80.00
B-J-B
79 Miguel Cabrera 300 30.00 80.00
[J-J-J
80 Miguel Cabrera RBI 30.00 80.00
J-PT-J
81 Mike Schmidt HOF 50.00 100.00
PT-B-H
82 Mike Schmidt MVP 50.00 100.00

2006 Topps Triple Threads Relic Combos

B-H-S
83 Mike Schmidt PHI 50.00 100.00
PT-PT-PT
84 Morgan Ensberg 3 Stars 15.00 40.00
J-J-J
85 Morgan Ensberg HOU 15.00 40.00
J-PT-J
86 Nick Swisher OAK 15.00 40.00
B-B-B
87 Nick Swisher RBI 15.00 40.00
B-B-B
88 Nolan Ryan HOF 75.00 150.00
P-B-P
89 Nolan Ryan TEX 75.00 150.00
J-PT-J
90 Nolan Ryan 7 NO NO 75.00 150.00
J-J-J
91 Zach Duke PIT 15.00 40.00
J-J-J
92 Zach Duke WIN 15.00 40.00
J-J-J
93 Ozzie Smith Gold Glove 50.00 100.00
B-J-S
94 Ozzie Smith HOF 50.00 100.00
B-H-P
95 Ozzie Smith STL 50.00 100.00
H-J-P
96 Pedro Martinez NYM 75.00 150.00
J-PT-J
97 Robin Yount HOF 25.00 60.00
PT-PT-PT
98 Robin Yount MIL 25.00 60.00
J-B-J
99 Robin Yount MVP 25.00 60.00
J-J-J
100 Rod Carew BAT 20.00 50.00
B-B-B
101 Rod Carew MIN 20.00 50.00
B-B-B
102 Rod Carew MVP 20.00 50.00
B-B-B
103 Rod Carew ROY 20.00 50.00
B-B-B
104 Roger Clemens CY 125.00 200.00
J-J-J
105 Roger Clemens CY 125.00 200.00
J-J-H
106 Ryan Langerhans ATL 20.00 50.00
B-B-B
107 Ryan Langerhans RBI 20.00 50.00
B-B-B
108 Ryne Sandberg CHC 50.00 100.00
B-B-B
109 Ryne Sandberg HOF 50.00 100.00
S-B-S
110 Ryne Sandberg MVP 50.00 100.00
B-S-B
111 Scott Kazmir ERA 15.00 40.00
J-PT-J
112 Scott Kazmir Pitcher-Ball 15.00 40.00
J-PT-J
113 Stan Musial 3 Stars 60.00 120.00
P-B-P
114 Stan Musial MVP 60.00 120.00
B-P-B
115 Stan Musial STL 60.00 120.00
B-B-B
116 Steve Carlton 329 15.00 40.00
P-P-P
117 Steve Carlton CY 15.00 40.00
P-P-P
118 Steve Carlton PHI 15.00 40.00
P-P-P
119 Steve Garvey LAD 20.00 50.00
B-B-B
120 Steve Garvey MVP 20.00 50.00
B-B-B
121 Tony Gwynn 300 50.00 100.00
PT-PT-PT
122 Tony Gwynn HIT 50.00 100.00
PT-PT-PT
123 Tony Gwynn SDP 50.00 100.00
J-PT-J
124 Travis Hafner CLE 25.00 60.00
J-PT-J
125 Travis Hafner RBI 25.00 60.00
J-J-J
126 Victor Martinez CLE 15.00 40.00
J-J-J
127 Victor Martinez RBI 15.00 40.00
J-J-J
128 Wade Boggs BAT 25.00 60.00
B-S-B
129 Wade Boggs BOS 25.00 60.00
B-J-H
130 Wade Boggs RBI 25.00 60.00
B-S-H

2006 Topps Triple Threads Relic Combos

STATED ODDS 1:7 MINI
STATED PRINT RUN 18 SERIAL #'d SETS
*GOLD: .5X TO 1.2X BASIC
GOLD ODDS 1:14 MINI
GOLD PRINT RUN 9 SERIAL #'d SETS
PLATINUM ODDS 1:42 MINI
PLATINUM PRINT RUN 3 SERIAL #'d SETS
NO PLATINUM PRICING DUE TO SCARCITY

1 Albert Pujols Jsy 60.00 120.00
Alex Rodriguez Patch
Barry Bonds Pants 300
2 Alex Rodriguez Jsy 60.00 120.00
Barry Bonds Jsy
Albert Pujols Jsy 300
3 Albert Pujols Pants 40.00 80.00
Alex Rodriguez Bat
Manny Ramirez Jsy 300
4 Albert Pujols Jsy 125.00 200.00
Barry Bonds Cap
Ted Williams Bat 300
5 Alex Rodriguez Jsy 50.00 100.00
Barry Bonds Pants
Chipper Jones Jsy 300
6 Alex Rodriguez Jsy 60.00 120.00
Roberto Clemente Pants
Barry Bonds Pants 300
7 Alex Rodriguez Jsy 50.00 100.00
Vladimir Guerrero Cap
Ichiro Suzuki Jsy 300
8 Alex Rodriguez Bat 50.00 100.00
Stan Musial Pants
Ted Williams Bat 300
9 Andruw Jones Cap 15.00 40.00
Alfonso Soriano Cleats
Vladimir Guerrero Cap 300
10 Barry Bonds Bat 75.00 150.00
Ichiro Suzuki Jsy
Roberto Clemente Bat 300
11 Barry Bonds Bat 50.00 100.00
Lloyd Waner Bat
Roberto Clemente Bat 300
12 Barry Bonds Bat 30.00 60.00
Manny Ramirez Cleats
Andruw Jones Btg Glv 300
13 Barry Bonds Pants 50.00 100.00
Manny Ramirez Jsy
Ted Williams Bat 300
14 Barry Bonds Pants 75.00 150.00
Roberto Clemente Bat
Willie Stargell Cap 300
15 Carl Yastrzemski Cleats 30.00 60.00
Paul Molitor Cleats
Manny Ramirez Cleats 300
16 Don Mattingly Jsy 30.00 60.00
Paul Molitor Cleats
Wade Boggs Bat 300
17 Don Mattingly Jsy 30.00 60.00
Rod Carew Bat
Tony Gwynn Jsy 300
18 Gary Sheffield Pants 15.00 40.00
Vladimir Guerrero Patch
Ivan Rodriguez Patch 300
19 Hank Greenberg Bat 75.00 150.00
Stan Musial Bat
Ted Williams Bat 300
20 Ichiro Suzuki Jsy 50.00 100.00
Chipper Jones Patch
Barry Bonds Pants 300
21 Ichiro Suzuki Jsy 150.00 250.00
Ted Williams Bat
Roberto Clemente Pants 300
22 Joe Morgan Cap 15.00 40.00
Paul Molitor Cleats
Gary Carter Cap 300
23 Manny Ramirez Jsy 40.00 80.00
Vladimir Guerrero Bat
Roberto Clemente Pants 300
24 Mike Piazza Btg Glv 30.00 60.00
Paul Molitor Btg Glv
Rickey Henderson Btg Glv 300
25 Napoleon Lajoie Bat 75.00 150.00
Stan Musial Bat
Ted Williams Bat 300
26 Paul Molitor Cap 15.00 40.00
Andruw Jones Cap
Robin Yount Cap 300
27 Paul Molitor Cleats 15.00 40.00
Andruw Jones Cleats
Alfonso Soriano Cleats 300
28 Reggie Jackson Patch 20.00 50.00
Vladimir Guerrero Patch
Andruw Jones Patch 300
29 Rickey Henderson Cleats 30.00 60.00
Wade Boggs Cleats
Tony Gwynn Cleats 300
30 Roberto Clemente Bat 75.00 150.00
Ted Williams Bat
Tony Gwynn Bat 300
31 Stan Musial Bat 50.00 100.00
Ted Williams Bat
Tony Gwynn Bat 300
32 Ted Williams Bat 75.00 150.00
Ichiro Suzuki Jsy
Wade Boggs Bat 300
33 Albert Pujols Jsy 150.00 250.00
Ted Williams Bat
Mickey Mantle Jsy 300
34 Andruw Jones Cap 20.00 50.00
George Brett Cap
Chipper Jones Cap 300
35 Greg Maddux Patch 30.00 60.00
Nolan Ryan Bat
Steve Carlton Pants 300
36 Greg Maddux Patch 20.00 50.00
Steve Carlton Pants
Tom Seaver Pants 300
37 Nolan Ryan Jsy 20.00 50.00
Steve Carlton Cleats
Tom Seaver Bat 300
38 Nolan Ryan Jsy 40.00 80.00
Tom Seaver Cap
Roger Clemens Jsy 300
39 Roger Clemens Cap 40.00 80.00
Nolan Ryan Jsy
Tom Seaver Cap 300
40 Barry Bonds Bat 30.00 60.00
Rickey Henderson Cleats
Tony Gwynn Cleats 300
41 Cal Ripken Pants 40.00 80.00
Carl Yastrzemski Jsy
Paul Molitor Jsy 3000
42 Cal Ripken Pants 60.00 120.00
George Brett Bat
Roberto Clemente Pants 3000
43 Cal Ripken Pants 40.00 80.00
George Brett Bat
Tony Gwynn Cleats 3000
44 Cal Ripken Jsy 30.00 60.00
Paul Molitor Patch
Rickey Henderson Jsy 3000
45 Cal Ripken Jsy 30.00 60.00
Paul Molitor Jsy
Tony Gwynn Jsy 3000
46 George Brett Bat 40.00 80.00
Cal Ripken Pants
Rod Carew Bat 3000
47 George Brett Bat 40.00 80.00
Cal Ripken Pants
Rod Carew Patch 3000
48 George Brett Bat 20.00 50.00
Robin Yount Jsy
Rod Carew Bat 3000
49 George Brett Bat 30.00 60.00
Rod Carew Patch
Stan Musial Bat 3000
50 George Brett Bat 30.00 60.00
Tony Gwynn Jsy
Wade Boggs Bat 3000
51 Paul Molitor Cap 20.00 50.00
Robin Yount Jsy
Wade Boggs Jsy 3000
52 Paul Waner Bat 40.00 80.00
Rickey Henderson Cleats
Stan Musial Pants 3000
53 Paul Waner Bat 30.00 60.00
Rickey Henderson Pants
Wade Boggs Bat 3000
54 Paul Waner Bat 15.00 40.00
Rod Carew Bat
Wade Boggs Bat 3000
55 Rickey Henderson Jsy 30.00 60.00
Stan Musial Bat
Wade Boggs Bat 3000
56 Roberto Clemente Pants 50.00 100.00
Robin Yount Cap
Rod Carew Bat 3000
57 Roberto Clemente Pants 50.00 100.00
Robin Yount Cap
Tony Gwynn Cleats 3000
58 Roberto Clemente Bat 50.00 100.00
Stan Musial Bat
Tony Gwynn Bat 3000
59 Rod Carew Jsy 20.00 50.00
Stan Musial Pants
Tony Gwynn Jsy 3000
60 Stan Musial Pants 20.00 50.00
Tony Gwynn Jsy
Wade Boggs Patch 3000
61 Wade Boggs Bat 20.00 50.00
Wade Boggs Bat
Wade Boggs Bat 3000
62 Barry Bonds Bat 100.00 175.00
Mickey Mantle Bat
Frank Robinson Bat 500
63 Barry Bonds Suit 200.00 350.00
Ted Williams Bat
Mickey Mantle Suit 500
64 Barry Bonds Bat 40.00 80.00
Frank Robinson Pants
Reggie Jackson Bat 500
65 Barry Bonds Pants 30.00 60.00
Frank Robinson Bat
Harmon Killebrew Jsy 500
66 Frank Robinson Bat 40.00 80.00
Barry Bonds Pants
Mike Schmidt Jsy 500
67 Frank Robinson Bat 100.00 175.00
Harmon Killebrew Bat
Mickey Mantle Bat 500
68 Josh Gibson Model Bat 200.00 350.00
Barry Bonds Pants
Mickey Mantle Patch 500
69 Josh Gibson Model Bat 125.00 200.00
Barry Bonds Jsy
Ted Williams Bat 500
70 Mike Schmidt Bat 30.00 60.00
Harmon Killebrew Jsy
Reggie Jackson Bat 500
71 Dave Winfield Jsy 15.00 40.00
Vladimir Guerrero Bat
Reggie Jackson Jsy ANA
72 Rod Carew Bat 15.00 40.00
Reggie Jackson Jsy
Vladimir Guerrero Bat ANA
73 Andruw Jones Cleats 30.00 60.00
Chipper Jones Patch
Jeff Francoeur Jsy ATL
74 Bobby Cox Patch 20.00 50.00
Andruw Jones Cleats
Chipper Jones Jsy ATL
75 Chipper Jones Patch 40.00 80.00
Greg Maddux Patch
Andruw Jones Patch ATL
76 Brian Roberts Jsy 15.00 40.00
Sammy Sosa Jsy
Miguel Tejada Pants BAL
77 Brooks Robinson Bat 40.00 80.00
Cal Ripken Pants
Jim Palmer Cap BAL
78 Brooks Robinson Bat 15.00 40.00
Jim Palmer Jsy
Frank Robinson Bat BAL
79 Cal Ripken Pants 30.00 60.00
Brooks Robinson Bat
Miguel Tejada Pants BAL
80 Cal Ripken Pants 30.00 60.00
Frank Robinson Bat
Sammy Sosa Jsy BAL
81 Frank Robinson Bat 20.00 50.00
Reggie Jackson Jsy
Brooks Robinson Bat BAL
82 Jim Palmer Jsy 15.00 40.00
Frank Robinson Bat
Reggie Jackson Jsy BAL
83 Jim Palmer Pants 30.00 60.00
Reggie Jackson Jsy
Sammy Sosa Jsy BAL
84 Jim Palmer Pants 15.00 40.00
Sammy Sosa Bat
Miguel Tejada Pants BAL
85 Miguel Tejada Pants 30.00 60.00
Brian Roberts Jsy
Cal Ripken Pants BAL
86 Reggie Jackson Jsy 30.00 60.00
Frank Robinson Bat
Sammy Sosa Jsy BAL
87 Bobby Doerr Bat 75.00 150.00
Carl Yastrzemski Cleats
Ted Williams Bat BOS
88 Carl Yastrzemski Cleats 30.00 60.00
David Ortiz Jsy
Manny Ramirez Cleats BOS
89 Carl Yastrzemski Pants 75.00 150.00
Ted Williams Bat
David Ortiz Jsy BOS
90 Carl Yastrzemski Jsy 75.00 150.00
Ted Williams Bat
Manny Ramirez Cleats BOS
91 Curt Schilling Jsy 15.00 40.00
David Ortiz Jsy
Johnny Damon Jsy BOS
92 Curt Schilling Patch 15.00 40.00
David Ortiz Bat
Manny Ramirez Jsy BOS
93 Curt Schilling Jsy 15.00 40.00
Manny Ramirez Bat
Johnny Damon Jsy BOS
94 David Ortiz Bat 15.00 40.00
Johnny Damon Pants
Manny Ramirez Bat BOS
95 Johnny Damon Bat 40.00 80.00
Manny Ramirez Jsy
Ted Williams Bat BOS
96 Manny Ramirez Cleats 30.00 60.00
David Ortiz Jsy
Pedro Martinez Patch BOS
97 Manny Ramirez Jsy 60.00 120.00
Ted Williams Bat
David Ortiz Jsy BOS
98 Pedro Martinez Cleats 30.00 60.00
Roger Clemens Cap
Manny Ramirez Cleats BOS
99 Greg Maddux Jsy 50.00 100.00
Randy Johnson Jsy
Roger Clemens Jsy C*Y
100 Johan Santana Jsy 20.00 50.00
Pedro Martinez Cleats
Roger Clemens Jsy C*Y
101 Roger Clemens Jsy 50.00 100.00
Roger Clemens Jsy
Roger Clemens Jsy C*Y
102 Roger Clemens Jsy 75.00 150.00
Roger Clemens Jsy
Roger Clemens Jsy C*Y
103 Randy Johnson Cap 30.00 60.00
Curt Schilling Jsy
Roger Clemens Cap World Series
104 Derrek Lee Jsy 15.00 40.00
Aramis Ramirez Bat
Mark Prior Jsy CHC
105 Derrek Lee Jsy 40.00 80.00
Ryne Sandberg Bat
Sammy Sosa Jsy CHC
106 Ernie Banks Pants 40.00 80.00
Ryne Sandberg Bat
Derrek Lee Jsy CHC
107 Ernie Banks Pants 40.00 80.00
Ryne Sandberg Bat
Sammy Sosa Jsy CHC
108 Greg Maddux Jsy 50.00 100.00
Ryne Sandberg Bat
Ernie Banks Pants CHC
109 Mark Prior Jsy 30.00 60.00
Kerry Wood Patch
Greg Maddux Jsy CHC
110 Sammy Sosa Jsy 40.00 80.00
Ernie Banks Pants
Derrek Lee Jsy CHC
111 Frank Robinson Pants 20.00 50.00
Joe Morgan Cap
Johnny Bench Pants CIN
112 Johnny Bench Pants 20.00 50.00
Frank Robinson Bat
Tom Seaver Cap CIN
113 Johnny Bench Pants 20.00 50.00
Tom Seaver Cap
Joe Morgan Jsy CIN
114 Jermaine Dye Pants 15.00 40.00
Scott Podsednik Bat
Tadahito Iguchi Jsy CWS
115 Jim Thome Bat 30.00 60.00
Paul Konerko Pants
Tadahito Iguchi Bat CWS
116 Jon Garland Pants 15.00 40.00
Scott Podsednik Bat
Mark Buehrle Pants CWS
117 Jon Garland Pants 15.00 40.00
Tadahito Iguchi Jsy
Mark Buehrle Pants CWS
118 Paul Konerko Jsy 30.00 60.00
Sammy Sosa Bat
Carlton Fisk Bat Pants CWS
119 Paul Konerko Pants 15.00 40.00
Tadahito Iguchi Jsy
Jermaine Dye Pants CWS
120 Al Kaline Bat 50.00 100.00
Ivan Rodriguez Jsy
Hank Greenberg Bat DET
121 Greg Maddux Btg Glv 30.00 60.00
Johan Santana Jsy
Roger Clemens Jsy ERA
122 Juan Marichal Jsy 30.00 60.00
Nolan Ryan Pants
Roger Clemens Pants ERA
123 Nolan Ryan Pants 30.00 60.00
Randy Johnson Jsy
Whitey Ford Bat ERA
124 Cal Ripken Jsy 40.00 80.00
Ozzie Smith Bat
Mike Schmidt Jsy Gold Glove
125 Mike Schmidt Bat 40.00 80.00
Cal Ripken Pants
Ozzie Smith Bat Gold Glove
126 Al Kaline Bat 30.00 60.00
Frank Robinson Pants
Paul Waner Bat HOF
127 Al Kaline Bat 30.00 60.00
Harmon Killebrew Pants
Frank Robinson Bat HOF
128 Al Kaline Bat 100.00 175.00
Mickey Mantle Pants
Reggie Jackson Jsy HOF
129 Al Kaline Bat 40.00 80.00
Reggie Jackson Bat
Stan Musial Bat HOF
130 Al Kaline Bat 30.00 60.00
Robin Yount Jsy
Paul Waner Bat HOF
131 Barry Bonds Pants 30.00 60.00
Chipper Jones Patch
Manny Ramirez Wristband OPS
132 Bob Feller Pants 20.00 50.00
Juan Marichal Jsy
Nolan Ryan Jsy HOF
133 Bob Feller Pants 15.00 40.00
Whitey Ford Bat
Steve Carlton Pants HOF
134 Bobby Doerr Bat 40.00 80.00
Ted Williams Bat
Wade Boggs Bat HOF
135 Brooks Robinson Bat 30.00 60.00
Ozzie Smith Bat
Ryne Sandberg Bat HOF
136 Carl Yastrzemski Cleats 30.00 60.00
George Brett Bat
Paul Molitor Cleats HOF
137 Carlton Fisk Bat 20.00 50.00
Carl Yastrzemski Jsy
Wade Boggs Bat HOF
138 Joe Morgan Cap 30.00 60.00
George Brett Cap
Mike Schmidt Cap HOF
139 Yogi Berra Glv 20.00 50.00
Carlton Fisk Bat
Gary Carter Cap HOF
140 Andy Pettitte Jsy 20.00 50.00
Nolan Ryan Pants
Brad Lidge Jsy HOU
141 Andy Pettitte Jsy 20.00 50.00
Nolan Ryan Bat
Randy Johnson Pants HOU
142 Andy Pettitte Jsy 30.00 60.00
Nolan Ryan Pants
Roger Clemens Jsy HOU
143 Andy Pettitte Jsy 15.00 40.00
Randy Johnson Pants
Brad Lidge Jsy HOU
144 Andy Pettitte Jsy 30.00 60.00
Roy Oswalt Jsy
Roger Clemens Jsy HOU
145 Brad Lidge Jsy 15.00 40.00
Roy Oswalt Jsy
Andy Pettitte Jsy HOU
146 Craig Biggio Patch 20.00 50.00
Jeff Bagwell Cap
Lance Berkman Patch HOU
147 Nolan Ryan Pants 50.00 100.00
Roger Clemens Jsy
Randy Johnson Pants HOU
148 Roger Clemens Jsy 20.00 50.00
Brad Lidge Jsy
Andy Pettitte Jsy HOU
149 Roger Clemens Jsy 20.00 50.00
Randy Johnson Pants
Andy Pettitte Jsy HOU
150 Ichiro Suzuki Jsy 100.00 175.00
Hideki Matsui Jsy
Ichiro Suzuki Jsy JPN
151 Ichiro Suzuki Bat 100.00 175.00
Hideki Matsui Jsy
Kaz Matsui Bat JPN
152 Ichiro Suzuki Jsy 100.00 175.00
Tadahito Iguchi Jsy
Hideki Matsui Jsy JPN
153 Eric Gagne Patch 20.00 50.00
Mike Piazza Bat
Duke Snider Pants LAD
154 Gary Sheffield Pants 15.00 40.00
Rickie Weeks Bat
Paul Molitor Jsy MIL
155 Paul Molitor Jsy 20.00 50.00
Gary Sheffield Pants
Robin Yount Patch MIL
156 Robin Yount Bat 15.00 40.00
Paul Molitor Jsy
Rickie Weeks Bat MIL
157 Harmon Killebrew Pants 20.00 50.00
Rod Carew Bat
Johan Santana Jsy MIN
158 Harmon Killebrew Bat 20.00 50.00
Torii Hunter Jsy
Rod Carew Bat MIN
159 Johan Santana Jsy 15.00 40.00
Joe Mauer Jsy
Torii Hunter Jsy MIN
160 Paul Molitor Pants 30.00 60.00
Rod Carew Bat
Harmon Killebrew Bat MIN
161 Albert Pujols Jsy 75.00 150.00
Ichiro Suzuki Jsy
Barry Bonds Pants MVP
162 Alex Rodriguez Jsy 50.00 100.00
Barry Bonds Pants
George Brett Patch MVP
163 Alex Rodriguez Jsy 125.00 200.00
Barry Bonds Pants
Mickey Mantle Jsy MVP
164 Alex Rodriguez Jsy 150.00 250.00
Ichiro Suzuki Jsy
Mickey Mantle Jsy MVP
165 Alex Rodriguez Jsy 50.00 100.00
Reggie Jackson Bat
Yogi Berra Bat MVP
166 Alex Rodriguez Jsy 175.00 300.00
Ted Williams Bat
Mickey Mantle Pants MVP
167 Alex Rodriguez Jsy 60.00 120.00
Yogi Berra Bat
Don Mattingly Pants MVP
168 Alex Rodriguez Cleats 50.00 100.00
Barry Bonds Bat
Don Mattingly Pants MVP
169 Alex Rodriguez Cleats 40.00 80.00
Cal Ripken Pants
Miguel Tejada Pants MVP
170 Barry Bonds Bat 40.00 80.00
Harmon Killebrew Jsy
Reggie Jackson Bat MVP
171 Barry Bonds Bat 75.00 150.00
Roberto Clemente Pants
Willie Stargell Bat MVP
172 Barry Bonds Pants 60.00 120.00
Alex Rodriguez Jsy
Albert Pujols Cap MVP
173 Barry Bonds Pants 125.00 200.00
Cal Ripken Jsy
Mickey Mantle Pants MVP
174 Barry Bonds Pants 75.00 150.00
Josh Gibson Model Bat
Albert Pujols Jsy MVP
175 Barry Bonds Pants 50.00 100.00
Vladimir Guerrero Bat
Ichiro Suzuki Jsy MVP
176 Brooks Robinson Bat 30.00 60.00
George Brett Bat
Mike Schmidt Bat MVP
177 Cal Ripken Bat 100.00 175.00
Barry Bonds Bat
Ichiro Suzuki Bat MVP
178 Cal Ripken Jsy 50.00 100.00
Don Mattingly Jsy
George Brett Bat MVP
179 Cal Ripken Pants 50.00 100.00
George Brett Bat
Don Mattingly Jsy MVP
180 Cal Ripken Jsy 50.00 100.00
Mike Schmidt Bat
Don Mattingly Jsy MVP
181 Cal Ripken Pants 50.00 100.00
Roger Clemens Jsy
Don Mattingly Pants MVP
182 Chipper Jones Patch 40.00 80.00
Dale Murphy Bat
Don Mattingly Pants MVP
183 Don Mattingly Jsy 125.00 200.00
Mickey Mantle Pants
Reggie Jackson Bat MVP
184 George Brett Bat 30.00 60.00
Johnny Bench Pants
Mike Schmidt Bat MVP
185 George Brett Bat 30.00 60.00
Johnny Bench Bat
Mike Schmidt Bat HIT
186 Ichiro Suzuki Bat 150.00 250.00
Barry Bonds Pants
Mickey Mantle Bat MVP
187 Ivan Rodriguez Pants 15.00 40.00
Vladimir Guerrero Bat
Miguel Tejada Pants MVP
188 Ivan Rodriguez Pants 20.00 50.00
Yogi Berra Jsy
Johnny Bench Pants MVP
189 Ivan Rodriguez Pants 20.00 50.00
Yogi Berra Fld Glv
Johnny Bench Pants MVP
190 Johnny Bench Pants 40.00 80.00
Mike Piazza Bat
Yogi Berra Pants MVP
191 Mickey Mantle Bat 200.00 350.00
Barry Bonds Pants
Ted Williams Bat MVP
192 Mickey Mantle Pants 175.00 300.00
Ichiro Suzuki Jsy
Roberto Clemente Pants MVP
193 Mickey Mantle Jsy 125.00 200.00
Roberto Clemente Pants
Stan Musial Pants MVP
194 Mickey Mantle Jsy 250.00 400.00
Ted Williams Bat
Roberto Clemente Pants MVP
195 Mickey Mantle Pants 125.00 200.00
Vladimir Guerrero Bat
Roberto Clemente Pants MVP
196 Miguel Tejada Pants 20.00 50.00
Reggie Jackson Bat
Rickey Henderson Pants MVP
197 Reggie Jackson Bat 50.00 100.00
Alex Rodriguez Jsy
Yogi Berra Bat MVP
198 Roberto Clemente Bat 125.00 200.00
Mickey Mantle Bat
Barry Bonds Bat MVP
199 Buck O'Neil Bat 150.00 250.00
Josh Gibson Model Bat
Monte Irvin Bat N*L
200 Carlos Beltran Jsy 20.00 50.00
Carlos Delgado Bat
David Wright Jsy NYM
201 Carlos Beltran Jsy 15.00 40.00
Carlos Delgado Bat
Jose Reyes Jsy NYM
202 Carlos Beltran Jsy 20.00 50.00
David Wright Jsy
Pedro Martinez Jsy NYM
203 Darryl Strawberry Bat 15.00 40.00
Dwight Gooden Jsy
Gary Carter Bat NYM
204 David Wright Jsy 40.00 80.00
Carlos Beltran Patch
Mike Piazza Jsy NYM
205 David Wright Bat 40.00 80.00
Mike Piazza Patch
Jose Reyes Bat NYM
206 Jose Reyes Jsy 15.00 40.00
Kaz Matsui Bat
David Wright Jsy NYM
207 Alex Rodriguez Jsy 150.00 250.00
Don Mattingly Jsy
Mickey Mantle Jsy NYY
208 Alex Rodriguez Jsy 50.00 100.00
Hideki Matsui Jsy
Joe Torre Pants NYY
209 Alex Rodriguez Jsy 150.00 250.00
Hideki Matsui Jsy
Mickey Mantle Pants NYY
210 Don Mattingly Jsy 75.00 150.00
Mickey Mantle Jsy
Roger Clemens Jsy NYY
211 Hideki Matsui Jsy 50.00 100.00
Gary Sheffield Bat
Alex Rodriguez Jsy NYY
212 Hideki Matsui Jsy 40.00 80.00
Gary Sheffield Bat
Jorge Posada Jsy NYY
213 Jorge Posada Jsy 30.00 60.00
Roger Clemens Jsy
Mike Mussina Pants NYY
214 Mickey Mantle Jsy 150.00 250.00
Whitey Ford Bat
Yogi Berra Fld Glv NYY
215 Mike Mussina Pants 30.00 60.00
Whitey Ford Bat
Roger Clemens Jsy NYY
216 Roger Clemens Jsy 150.00 250.00
Mickey Mantle Pants
Alex Rodriguez Jsy NYY
217 Wade Boggs Cleats 15.00 40.00
Joe Torre Pants
Alfonso Soriano Cleats NYY
218 Barry Zito Pants 15.00 40.00
Mark Mulder Patch
Tim Hudson Jsy OAK
219 Jose Canseco Jsy 20.00 50.00
Reggie Jackson Bat
Rickey Henderson Cleats OAK
220 Mark Mulder Pants 15.00 40.00
Miguel Tejada Pants
Tim Hudson Pants OAK
221 Bob Abreu Jsy 15.00 40.00
Pat Burrell Bat
Jim Thome Patch PHI
222 Curt Schilling Cap 20.00 50.00

Mike Schmidt Bat
Steve Carlton Pants PHI
223 Mike Schmidt Bat 20.00 50.00
Pat Burrell Bat
Scott Rolen Bat PHI
224 Barry Bonds Bat 100.00 175.00
Roberto Clemente Bat
Josh Gibson Model Bat PIT
225 Paul Waner Bat 75.00 150.00
Roberto Clemente Pants
Lloyd Waner Bat PIT
226 Willie Stargell Pants 60.00 120.00
Bill Mazeroski Bat
Roberto Clemente Pants PIT
227 Albert Pujols Pants 30.00 60.00
Carlos Beltran Bat
Dontrelle Willis Patch ROY
228 Albert Pujols Bat 50.00 100.00
Dontrelle Willis Patch
Ichiro Suzuki Bat ROY
229 Cal Ripken Jsy 40.00 80.00
Albert Pujols Pants
Dontrelle Willis Jsy ROY
230 Cal Ripken Jsy 30.00 60.00
Carlton Fisk Bat
Tom Seaver Pants ROY
231 Cal Ripken Pants 30.00 60.00
Rod Carew Bat
Carlton Fisk Pants ROY
232 Cal Ripken Pants 30.00 60.00
Rod Carew Bat
Carlton Fisk Pants 300
233 Jeff Bagwell Cap 30.00 60.00
Albert Pujols Bat
Mike Piazza Cap ROY
234 Mike Piazza Bat 30.00 60.00
Jeff Bagwell Pants
Scott Rolen Jsy ROY
235 Rickey Henderson Cleats 30.00 60.00
Steve Garvey Bat
Tony Gwynn Jsy SDP
236 Adrian Beltre Bat 50.00 100.00
Ichiro Suzuki Jsy
Alex Rodriguez Bat SEA
237 Ichiro Suzuki Jsy 50.00 100.00
Alex Rodriguez Bat
Randy Johnson Cap SEA
238 Barry Bonds Pants 40.00 80.00
Juan Marichal Jsy
Moises Alou Bat SFG
239 Juan Marichal Jsy 15.00 40.00
Monte Irvin Bat
Moises Alou Bat SFG
240 Moises Alou Bat 30.00 60.00
Monte Irvin Bat
Barry Bonds Jsy SFG
241 Albert Pujols Jsy 50.00 100.00
Frankie Frisch Bat
Stan Musial Pants STL
242 Albert Pujols Jsy 30.00 60.00
Mark Mulder Pants
Scott Rolen Jsy STL
243 Scott Rolen Jsy 40.00 80.00
Jim Edmonds Jsy
Albert Pujols Jsy STL
244 Stan Musial Pants 40.00 80.00
Ozzie Smith Bat
Albert Pujols Pants STL
245 Alex Rodriguez Cleats 20.00 50.00
Ivan Rodriguez Patch
Alfonso Soriano Cleats TEX
246 Alex Rodriguez Jsy 20.00 50.00
Mark Teixeira Jsy
Alfonso Soriano Pants TEX
247 Alex Rodriguez Cleats 30.00 60.00
Nolan Ryan Jsy
Alfonso Soriano Cleats TEX
248 Alfonso Soriano Pants 15.00 40.00
Hank Blalock Jsy
Mark Teixeira Jsy TEX
249 Alfonso Soriano Cleats 15.00 40.00
Hank Blalock Jsy
Michael Young Jsy TEX
250 Mark Teixeira Jsy 15.00 40.00
Alfonso Soriano Cleats
Michael Young Jsy TEX

2006 Topps Triple Threads Relic Combos Autograph

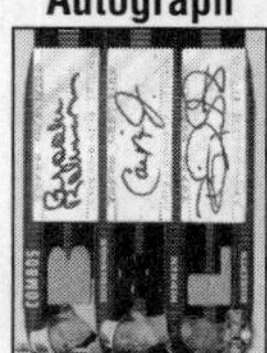

STATED ODDS 1:59 MINI
STATED PRINT RUN 18 SERIAL #'d SETS
*GOLD: .5X TO 1.2X BASIC
GOLD ODDS 1:116 MINI
GOLD PRINT RUN 9 SERIAL #'d SETS
PLATINUM ODDS 1:353 MINI
PLATINUM PRINT RUN 3 SERIAL #'d SETS
NO PLATINUM PRICING DUE TO SCARCITY
1 Albert Pujols Jsy 1000.00 1200.00
Barry Bonds Jsy
Alex Rodriguez Jsy MVP
2 Felix Hernandez Jsy 125.00 200.00
Alex Rodriguez Jsy
Shin-Soo Choo Jsy SEA
3 Nolan Ryan Jsy 175.00 300.00
Roger Clemens Jsy
Felix Hernandez Jsy ERA
4 Johnny Damon Bat 250.00 350.00
Alex Rodriguez Jsy
Robinson Cano Pants NYY
5 Manny Ramirez Jsy 100.00 175.00
Carl Yastrzemski Jsy
David Ortiz Jsy BOS
6 Michael Young Jsy 125.00 200.00
Cal Ripken Jsy
Ozzie Smith Cleats SS6
7 Brian Roberts Jsy 125.00 200.00
Cal Ripken Jsy
Frank Robinson Bat BAL
8 Stan Musial Pants 125.00 200.00
Ozzie Smith Bat
Lou Brock Bat HOF
9 Ozzie Smith Cleats 125.00 200.00
Stan Musial Pants
Lou Brock Bat STL
10 Tony Gwynn Jsy 125.00 200.00
Stan Musial Pants
Rod Carew Patch HOF
11 Brooks Robinson Pants 125.00 200.00
Cal Ripken Jsy
Brian Roberts Jsy BAL
12 Rod Carew Patch 60.00 120.00
Robin Yount Jsy
Paul Molitor Jsy HOF
13 Derrek Lee Jsy 100.00 175.00
Ryne Sandberg Bat
Mark Prior Jsy CHC
14 Chien-Ming Wang Jsy 125.00 250.00
Steve Carlton Pants
Dontrelle Willis Patch Pitcher
15 Brad Lidge Jsy 125.00 200.00
Mariano Rivera Jsy
Huston Street Jsy SAV
16 Morgan Ensberg Jsy 60.00 120.00
Wade Boggs Bat
David Wright Jsy 3RD
17 Ben Sheets Jsy 40.00 80.00
Steve Carlton Pants
Felix Hernandez Jsy Pitcher
18 Victor Martinez Jsy 50.00 100.00
Johnny Bench Pants
Joe Mauer Jsy RBI
19 David Wright Jsy 60.00 120.00
Mike Schmidt Bat
Aaron Hill Jsy 3RD
20 Chase Utley Jsy 150.00 250.00
Mike Schmidt Cleats
Ryan Howard Bat PHI
21 Felix Hernandez Jsy 40.00 80.00
Steve Carlton Pants
Brandon McCarthy Jsy Pitcher
22 David Wright Jsy 60.00 120.00
Miguel Cabrera Jsy
Jason Bay Jsy RBI
23 Robinson Cano Pants 250.00 400.00
Don Mattingly Jsy
Chien-Ming Wang Jsy NYY
24 Justin Morneau Bat 75.00 150.00
Don Mattingly Jsy
Travis Hafner Jsy 1ST
25 Steve Garvey Bat 50.00 100.00
Don Mattingly Jsy
Dan Johnson Jsy 1ST
26 Travis Hafner Patch 50.00 100.00
Miguel Cabrera Jsy
Jason Bay Jsy RBI
27 Ben Sheets Jsy 50.00 100.00
Johan Santana Jsy
Jake Peavy Jsy Pitcher
28 Ervin Santana Jsy 30.00 60.00
Johan Santana Jsy
Ben Sheets Bat Pitcher
29 Chris Carpenter Jsy 40.00 80.00
Johan Santana Jsy
Rich Harden Jsy Pitcher
30 Zach Duke Jsy 30.00 60.00
Johan Santana Jsy
Brandon McCarthy Jsy Pitcher

2006 Topps Triple Threads White Whale Relic

STATED ODDS 1:56 MINI
STATED PRINT RUN 1 SERIAL #'d SET
NO PRICING DUE TO SCARCITY

2006 Topps Triple Threads White Whale Relic Combos

STATED ODDS 1:130 MINI
STATED PRINT RUN 1 SERIAL #'d SET
NO PRICING DUE TO SCARCITY

2006 Topps Triple Threads White Whale Autograph Relic Printing Plate

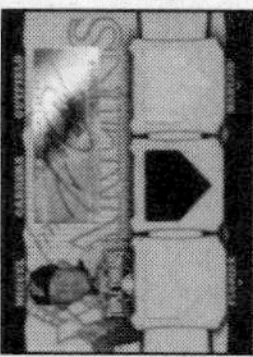

STATED ODDS 1:56 MINI
STATED PRINT RUN 1 SERIAL #'d SET
NO PRICING DUE TO SCARCITY

2006 Topps Triple Threads White Whale Autograph Relic Printing Plate Combos

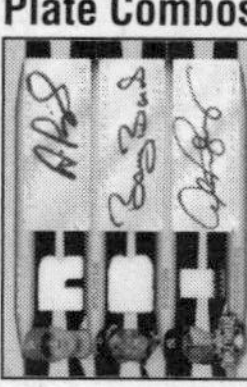

STATED ODDS 1:131 MINI
STATED PRINT RUN 1 SERIAL #'d SET
NO PRICING DUE TO SCARCITY

2007 Topps Triple Threads

This 204-card set was released in June, 2007. This set was issued in three-card mini-boxes with an $65 SRP. Those mini-boxes came two to an display box which came nine boxes to a carton and two cartons to a case. Cards numbered 1-125 feature veterans, while the rest of the set features either just game-used relic cards or game-used relic cards with an autograph as well.

COMP.SET w/o AU's (125) 125.00 200.00
COMMON CARD (1-125) .40 1.00
1-125 STATED PRINT RUN 1350 SER.#'d SETS
COMMON JSY AU 5.00 12.00
126-189 JSY AU ODDS 1:9 MINI
126-189 JSY AU VARIATION ODDS 1:38 MINI
126-189 JSY AU PRINT RUN 99 SER.#'d SETS
TEAM INITIAL DIECUTS ARE VARIATIONS
OVERALL 1-125 PLATE ODDS 1:113 MINI
PLATE PRINT RUN 1 SET PER COLOR
BLACK-CYAN-MAGENTA-YELLOW ISSUED
NO PLATE PRICING DUE TO SCARCITY
1 Alex Rodriguez 1.25 3.00
2 Barry Zito .40 1.00
3 Corey Patterson .40 1.00
4 Roberto Clemente 2.50 6.00
5 David Wright 1.25 3.00
6 Dontrelle Willis .40 1.00
7 Mickey Mantle 3.00 8.00
8 Adam Dunn .40 1.00
9 Richie Ashburn .60 1.50
10 Ryan Howard 1.25 3.00
11 Miguel Tejada .40 1.00
12 Ernie Banks 1.00 2.50
13 Ken Griffey Jr. 1.25 3.00
14 Johnny Bench 1.00 2.50
15 Ichiro Suzuki 1.25 3.00
16 Gil Meche .40 1.00
17 Kazuo Matsui .40 1.00
18 Matt Holliday .50 1.25
19 Juan Pierre .40 1.00
20 Yogi Berra 1.00 2.50
21 Bill Hall .40 1.00
22 Wade Boggs .60 1.50
23 Jason Bay .40 1.00
24 Troy Glaus .40 1.00
25 Paul Konerko .40 1.00
26 Rod Carew .60 1.50
27 Jay Gibbons .40 1.00
28 Frank Thomas 1.00 2.50
29 Joe Mauer .60 1.50
30 Carlos Beltran .40 1.00
31 Frank Robinson .40 1.00
32 Bobby Abreu .40 1.00
33 Roy Oswalt .40 1.00
34 Edgar Renteria .40 1.00
35 Magglio Ordonez .40 1.00
36 Mike Piazza 1.00 2.50
37 Trevor Hoffman .40 1.00
38 Eddie Mathews 1.00 2.50
39 Albert Pujols 1.50 4.00
40 Dennis Eckersley .40 1.00
41 Andruw Jones .60 1.50
42 Alfonso Soriano .40 1.00
43 Bob Feller .40 1.00
44 J.D. Drew .40 1.00
45 Jason Schmidt .40 1.00
46 Vladimir Guerrero 1.00 2.50
47 Reggie Jackson .60 1.50
48 Lance Berkman .40 1.00
49 Michael Young .40 1.00
50 Carlton Fisk .60 1.50
51 Brandon Webb .40 1.00
52 Adrian Beltre .40 1.00
53 Hideki Matsui 1.00 2.50
54 Bronson Arroyo .40 1.00
55 Tony Gwynn 1.00 2.50
56 Ray Durham .40 1.00
57 Garrett Atkins .40 1.00
58 Nolan Ryan 2.00 5.00
59 Daisuke Matsuzaka RC 6.00 15.00
60 Todd Helton .60 1.50
61 Carl Crawford .40 1.00
62 Jake Peavy .40 1.00
63 Rafael Furcal .40 1.00
64 Joe Morgan .40 1.00
65 Greg Maddux 1.25 3.00
66 Luis Aparicio .40 1.00
67 Derrek Lee .40 1.00
68 Johnny Damon .60 1.50
69 Mike Lowell .40 1.00
70 Roger Maris 1.00 2.50
71 Vernon Wells .40 1.00
72 Monte Irvin .40 1.00
73 Jermaine Dye .40 1.00
74 Miguel Cabrera .60 1.50
75 Barry Bonds 1.50 4.00
76 Stan Musial 1.25 3.00
77 Derek Lowe .40 1.00
78 Don Mattingly 1.50 4.00
79 Lyle Overbay .40 1.00
80 Chien-Ming Wang 1.25 3.00
81 Carlos Zambrano .40 1.00
82 Kei Igawa RC 1.25 3.00
83 Cole Hamels .60 1.50
84 Gary Sheffield .40 1.00
85 Nick Johnson .40 1.00
86 Brooks Robinson .60 1.50
87 Curt Schilling .60 1.50
88 Ryne Sandberg 1.50 4.00
89 Mike Cameron .40 1.00
90 Mike Schmidt 1.25 3.00
91 Chris Carpenter .40 1.00
92 Scott Rolen .60 1.50
93 Rocco Baldelli .40 1.00
94 C.C. Sabathia .40 1.00
95 Jeff Francis .40 1.00
96 Ozzie Smith 1.25 3.00
97 Aramis Ramirez .40 1.00
98 Aaron Harang .40 1.00
99 Duke Snider .60 1.50
100 David Ortiz 1.00 2.50
101 Raul Ibanez .40 1.00
102 Bruce Sutter .40 1.00
103 Gary Matthews .40 1.00
104 Chipper Jones 1.00 2.50
105 Craig Biggio .60 1.50
106 Roy Halladay .40 1.00
107 Hoyt Wilhelm .40 1.00
108 Manny Ramirez .60 1.50
109 Randy Johnson 1.00 2.50
110 Carl Yastrzemski 1.25 3.00
111 Mark Teixeira .60 1.50
112 Derek Jeter 2.00 5.00
113 Stephen Drew .60 1.50
114 Darryl Strawberry .40 1.00
115 Travis Hafner .40 1.00
116 Torii Hunter .40 1.00
117 Jim Edmonds .60 1.50
118 John Smoltz .60 1.50
119 Bo Jackson 1.00 2.50
120 Roger Clemens 1.50 4.00
121 Pedro Martinez .60 1.50
122 Rickey Henderson 1.00 2.50
123 Ivan Rodriguez .60 1.50
124 Robin Yount 1.00 2.50
125 Johan Santana .60 1.50
126a Robinson Cano Jsy AU 15.00 40.00
126b Robinson Cano Jsy AU 15.00 40.00
127a Jose Reyes Jsy AU 30.00 60.00
127b Jose Reyes Jsy AU 30.00 60.00
128a Justin Morneau Jsy AU 10.00 25.00
128b Justin Morneau Jsy AU 10.00 25.00
129a Curtis Granderson Jsy AU 12.50 30.00
129b Curtis Granderson Jsy AU 12.50 30.00
130a Justin Verlander Jsy AU 15.00 40.00
130b Justin Verlander Jsy AU 15.00 40.00
131 Prince Fielder Jsy AU 30.00 60.00
132a Ryan Zimmerman Jsy AU 10.00 25.00
132b Ryan Zimmerman Jsy AU 10.00 25.00
133 Mike Napoli Jsy AU 5.00 12.00
134 Melky Cabrera Jsy AU 10.00 25.00
135 Jonathan Papelbon Jsy AU 15.00 40.00
136a Nick Markakis Jsy AU 10.00 25.00
136b Nick Markakis Jsy AU 10.00 25.00
137 B.J. Upton Jsy AU 12.50 30.00
138a Joel Zumaya Jsy AU 10.00 25.00
138b Joel Zumaya Jsy AU 10.00 25.00
140 Nick Swisher Jsy AU 10.00 25.00
141 Andre Ethier Jsy AU 8.00 20.00
142a Jered Weaver Jsy AU 10.00 25.00
142b Jered Weaver Jsy AU 10.00 25.00
143 Matt Cain Jsy AU 12.50 30.00
144 Lastings Milledge Jsy AU 8.00 20.00
145 Brian McCann Jsy AU 15.00 40.00
146 Shin-Soo Choo Jsy AU 6.00 15.00
147a Dan Uggla Jsy AU 12.50 30.00
147b Dan Uggla Jsy AU 12.50 30.00
148 Hanley Ramirez Jsy AU 15.00 40.00
149 Russell Martin Jsy AU 15.00 40.00
150 Francisco Liriano Jsy AU 10.00 25.00
151 Anthony Reyes Jsy AU 5.00 12.00
152 Josh Barfield Jsy AU 6.00 15.00
153 Anibal Sanchez Jsy AU 5.00 12.00
154 Jeremy Hermida Jsy AU 6.00 15.00
155 Kendry Morales Jsy AU 5.00 12.00
156 Matt Kemp Jsy AU 10.00 25.00
157 Freddy Sanchez Jsy AU 6.00 15.00
158 Howie Kendrick Jsy AU 8.00 20.00
159 Scott Thorman Jsy AU 8.00 20.00
160 Franklin Gutierrez Bat AU 6.00 15.00
161 Jason Bartlett Jsy AU 6.00 15.00
162 Chris Duncan Jsy AU 20.00 50.00
163 Maicer Izturis Jsy AU 5.00 12.00
164 Jason Botts Jsy AU 5.00 12.00
165 Tony Gwynn Jr. Jsy AU 15.00 40.00
166 Jorge Cantu Jsy AU 5.00 12.00
167 Adam Jones Jsy AU 15.00 40.00
168 Edinson Volquez Jsy AU 40.00 80.00
169 Joey Gathright Jsy AU 5.00 12.00
170 Carlos Marmol Jsy AU 8.00 20.00
171 Ben Zobrist Jsy AU 6.00 15.00
172 Josh Willingham Jsy AU 5.00 12.00
173 Brad Thompson Jsy AU 10.00 25.00
174a Chris Ray Jsy AU 6.00 15.00
174b Ervin Santana Jsy AU 6.00 15.00
175 Ronny Paulino Jsy AU 5.00 12.00
176 Tyler Johnson Jsy AU 5.00 12.00
177 J.J. Hardy Jsy AU 12.50 30.00
178 Adrian Gonzalez Jsy AU 8.00 20.00
179 Scott Kazmir Jsy AU 10.00 25.00
180 Juan Morillo JSY AU (RC) 5.00 12.00
181a Shawn Riggans JSY AU (RC) 5.00 12.00
181b Shawn Riggans JSY AU (RC) 5.00 12.00
182 Brian Stokes JSY AU (RC) 5.00 12.00
183 Delmon Young JSY AU (RC) 12.50 30.00
184a Troy Tulowitzki JSY AU (RC) 15.00 40.00
184b Troy Tulowitzki JSY AU (RC) 15.00 40.00
185 Adam Lind JSY AU (RC) 6.00 15.00
186 David Murphy JSY AU (RC) 6.00 15.00
187a Philip Humber JSY AU (RC) 6.00 15.00
187b Philip Humber JSY AU (RC) 6.00 15.00
188a Andrew Miller JSY AU RC 30.00 60.00
188b Andrew Miller JSY AU RC 30.00 60.00
189a Glen Perkins JSY AU (RC) 5.00 12.00
189b Glen Perkins JSY AU (RC) 5.00 12.00

2007 Topps Triple Threads Emerald

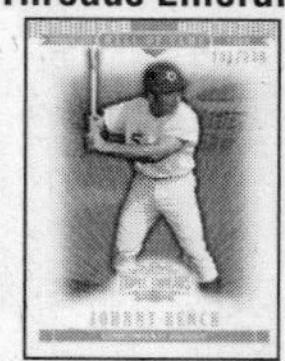

*EMERALD 1-125: .75X TO 2X BASIC
1-125 ODDS 1:2 MINI
1-125 PRINT RUN 239 SERIAL #'d SETS
*EMERALD AUTO: .5X TO 1.2X BASIC AU
*EMERALD VAR AUTO: .5X TO 1.2X BASIC AU VAR
126-189 AU ODDS 1:18 MINI
126-189 AU VARIATION ODDS 1:75 MINI
126-189 AU PRINT RUN 50 SERIAL #'d SETS
TEAM INITIAL DIECUTS ARE VARIATIONS
168 Edinson Volquez Jsy AU 75.00 150.00

2007 Topps Triple Threads Gold

*GOLD 1-125: 1.25X TO 3X BASIC
1-125 ODDS 1:5 MINI
1-125 PRINT RUN 99 SERIAL #'d SETS
*GOLD AUTO: .75X TO 2X BASIC AU
*GOLD VAR AUTO: .75X TO 2X BASIC AU VAR
126-189 AU ODDS 1:35 MINI
126-189 AU VARIATION ODDS 1:149 MINI
126-189 AU PRINT RUN 25 SERIAL #'d SETS
TEAM INITIAL DIECUTS ARE VARIATIONS
15 Ichiro Suzuki 6.00 15.00
80 Chien-Ming Wang 6.00 15.00
168 Edinson Volquez Jsy AU 175.00 300.00

2007 Topps Triple Threads Platinum

1-125 ODDS 1:454 MINI
1-125 PRINT RUN 1 SERIAL #'d SET
126-189 AU ODDS 1:1219 MINI
126-189 AU VARIATION ODDS 1:4878 MINI
126-189 AU PRINT RUN 1 SERIAL #'d SET
TEAM INITIAL DIECUTS ARE VARIATIONS
NO PRICING DUE TO SCARCITY

2007 Topps Triple Threads Sapphire

*SAPPHIRE 1-125: 3X TO 8X BASIC
1-125 ODDS 1:19 MINI
1-125 PRINT RUN 25 SERIAL #'d SETS
126-189 JSY AU ODDS 1:88 MINI
126-189 JSY AU VAR.ODDS 1:372 MINI
126-189 AU PRINT RUN 10 SERIAL #'d SETS
TEAM INITIAL DIECUTS ARE VARIATIONS
NO SAPPHIRE JSY AUTO PRICING AVAILABLE
13 Ken Griffey Jr. 15.00 40.00
15 Ichiro Suzuki 15.00 40.00
58 Nolan Ryan 20.00 50.00
75 Barry Bonds 50.00 100.00
80 Chien-Ming Wang 50.00 100.00

2007 Topps Triple Threads Sepia

*SEPIA 1-125: .5X TO 1.2X BASIC
1-125 PRINT RUN 559 SERIAL #'d SETS
*SEPIA AUTO: .5X TO 1.2X BASIC AU
*SEPIA VAR AUTO: .5X TO 1.2X BASIC AU VAR
126-189 AU ODDS 1:12 MINI
126-189 AU VAR.ODDS 1:50 MINI
126-189 AU PRINT RUN 75 SERIAL #'d SETS
TEAM INITIAL DIECUTS ARE VARIATIONS
59 Daisuke Matsuzaka 12.50 30.00
168 Edinson Volquez Jsy AU 40.00 80.00

2007 Topps Triple Threads White Whale Printing Plate

126-189 JSY AU ODDS 1:333 MINI
126-189 JSY AU VAR.ODDS 1:1330 MINI
STATED PRINT RUN 1 SERIAL #'d SET
TEAM INITIAL DIECUTS ARE VARIATIONS
NO PRICING DUE TO SCARCITY

2007 Topps Triple Threads All-Star Triple Patches

STATED ODDS 1:97 MINI
STATED PRINT RUN 9 SER.#'d SETS
NO PRICING DUE TO SCARCITY
LOGO MAN ODDS 1:879 MINI
LOGO MAN PRINT RUN 1 SER.#'d SET
NO LOGO MAN PRICING DUE TO SCARCITY
PLATINUM ODDS 1:879 MINI
PLATINUM PRINT RUN 1 SER.#'d SET
NO PLATINUM PRICING DUE TO SCARCITY
1 A.J. Pierzynski
2 Albert Pujols
3 Alex Rios
4 Alex Rodriguez
5 Alfonso Soriano
6 Andruw Jones
7 B.J. Ryan
8 Bobby Jenks
9 Brad Penny
10 Brandon Webb
11 Brian Fuentes
12 Brian McCann
13 Bronson Arroyo
14 Carlos Beltran
15 Carlos Lee
16 Carlos Zambrano
17 Chase Utley
18 Chris Capuano
19 Chris Carpenter
20 Dan Uggla
21 David Eckstein
22 David Ortiz
23 David Wright
24 Derrick Turnbow
25 Edgar Renteria
26 Freddy Sanchez
27 Gary Matthews
28 Grady Sizemore
29 Ivan Rodriguez
30 Jason Bay
31 Jason Schmidt
32 Jermaine Dye
33 Jim Thome
34 Joe Mauer
35 Johan Santana
36 Jonathan Papelbon
37 Jose Contreras
38 Jose Lopez
39 Jose Reyes
40 Kenny Rogers
41 Lance Berkman
42 Magglio Ordonez
43 Mariano Rivera
44 Mark Buehrle
45 Mark Loretta
46 Mark Redman
47 Matt Holliday
48 Michael Young
49 Miguel Cabrera
50 Miguel Tejada
51 Paul Konerko
52 Paul LoDuca
53 Robinson Cano
54 Roy Halladay
55 Roy Oswalt
56 Ryan Howard
57 Scott Kazmir
58 Scott Rolen
59 Tom Glavine
60 Tom Gordon
61 Trevor Hoffman
62 Troy Glaus
63 Vernon Wells
64 Vladimir Guerrero

2007 Topps Triple Threads Bat-Barrels

STATED ODDS 1:1729 MINI
STATED PRINT RUN 1 SER.#'d SET
NO PRICING DUE TO SCARCITY

2007 Topps Triple Threads Cut Above

STATED ODDS 1:10,717 MINI
STATED PRINT RUN 1 SER.#'d SET
NO PRICING DUE TO SCARCITY
JD Joe DiMaggio
MM Mickey Mantle
RC Roberto Clemente
RM Roger Maris
TW Ted Williams

2007 Topps Triple Threads Relics

STATED ODDS 1:11 MINI
STATED PRINT RUN 36 SER.#'d SETS
PLATINUM ODDS 1:373 MINI
PLATINUM PRINT RUN 1 SER.#'d SET
NO PLATINUM PRICING DUE TO SCARCITY
SAPPHIRE ODDS 1:125 MINI
SAPPHIRE PRINT RUN 3 SER.#'d SETS
NO SAPPHIRE PRICING DUE TO SCARCITY
*SEPIA: .4X TO 1X BASIC
SEPIA ODDS 1:14 MINI
SEPIA PRINT RUN 27 SER.#'d SETS
ALL DC VARIATIONS PRICED EQUALLY
1 Carl Yastrzemski 12.50 30.00
2 Carl Yastrzemski 12.50 30.00
3 Carl Yastrzemski 12.50 30.00
4 Roberto Clemente 75.00 150.00
5 Roberto Clemente 75.00 150.00
6 Roberto Clemente 75.00 150.00
7 Roberto Clemente 75.00 150.00
8 Roberto Clemente 75.00 150.00
9 Roberto Clemente 75.00 150.00
10 Alex Rodriguez 25.00 60.00
11 Alex Rodriguez 25.00 60.00
12 Alex Rodriguez 25.00 60.00
13 Alex Rodriguez 25.00 60.00
14 Alex Rodriguez 25.00 60.00
15 Alex Rodriguez 25.00 60.00
16 Ryan Howard 20.00 50.00
17 Ryan Howard 20.00 50.00
18 Ryan Howard 20.00 50.00
19 David Wright 20.00 50.00
20 David Wright 20.00 50.00
21 David Wright 20.00 50.00
22 Chien-Ming Wang 75.00 150.00
23 Chien-Ming Wang 75.00 150.00
24 Chien-Ming Wang 75.00 150.00
25 Ichiro Suzuki 60.00 120.00
26 Ichiro Suzuki 60.00 120.00
27 Ichiro Suzuki 60.00 120.00
28 Hideki Matsui 25.00 60.00
29 Hideki Matsui 25.00 60.00
30 Hideki Matsui 25.00 60.00
31 Luis Aparicio 8.00 20.00
32 Luis Aparicio 8.00 20.00
33 Luis Aparicio 8.00 20.00
34 Joe DiMaggio 50.00 100.00
35 Joe DiMaggio 50.00 100.00
36 Joe DiMaggio 50.00 100.00
37 Ted Williams 50.00 100.00
38 Ted Williams 50.00 100.00
39 Ted Williams 50.00 100.00
40 Mickey Mantle 100.00 200.00
41 Mickey Mantle 100.00 200.00
42 Mickey Mantle 100.00 200.00
43 Mickey Mantle 100.00 200.00
44 Mickey Mantle 100.00 200.00
45 Mickey Mantle 100.00 200.00
46 Mickey Mantle 100.00 200.00
47 Mickey Mantle 100.00 200.00
48 Mickey Mantle 100.00 200.00
49 David Ortiz 12.50 30.00
50 David Ortiz 12.50 30.00
51 David Ortiz 12.50 30.00
52 Albert Pujols 25.00 60.00
53 Albert Pujols 25.00 60.00
54 Albert Pujols 25.00 60.00
55 Justin Morneau 10.00 25.00
56 Justin Morneau 10.00 25.00
57 Justin Morneau 10.00 25.00
58 Nolan Ryan 25.00 60.00
59 Nolan Ryan 25.00 60.00
60 Nolan Ryan 25.00 60.00
61 Nolan Ryan 25.00 60.00
62 Nolan Ryan 25.00 60.00
63 Nolan Ryan 25.00 60.00
64 Manny Ramirez 10.00 25.00
65 Manny Ramirez 10.00 25.00
66 Manny Ramirez 10.00 25.00
67 Roger Maris 50.00 100.00
68 Roger Maris 50.00 100.00
69 Roger Maris 50.00 100.00
70 Daisuke Matsuzaka 50.00 100.00
71 Daisuke Matsuzaka 50.00 100.00
72 Daisuke Matsuzaka 50.00 100.00
73 Brian Cashman 8.00 20.00
74 Brian Cashman 8.00 20.00
75 Brian Cashman 8.00 20.00
76 Ernie Banks 20.00 50.00
77 Ernie Banks 20.00 50.00
78 Ernie Banks 20.00 50.00
79 Stan Musial 25.00 60.00
80 Stan Musial 25.00 60.00
81 Stan Musial 25.00 60.00
82 Duke Snider 12.50 30.00
83 Duke Snider 12.50 30.00
84 Duke Snider 12.50 30.00
85 Yogi Berra 20.00 50.00
86 Yogi Berra 20.00 50.00
87 Yogi Berra 20.00 50.00
88 Harmon Killebrew 15.00 40.00
89 Harmon Killebrew 15.00 40.00
90 Harmon Killebrew 15.00 40.00
91 Joe Mauer 8.00 20.00
92 Joe Mauer 8.00 20.00
93 Joe Mauer 8.00 20.00
94 Alfonso Soriano 10.00 25.00
95 Alfonso Soriano 10.00 25.00
96 Alfonso Soriano 10.00 25.00
97 Reggie Jackson 15.00 40.00
98 Reggie Jackson 15.00 40.00
99 Reggie Jackson 15.00 40.00
100 Reggie Jackson 15.00 40.00
101 Reggie Jackson 15.00 40.00
102 Reggie Jackson 15.00 40.00
103 Vladimir Guerrero 10.00 25.00
104 Vladimir Guerrero 10.00 25.00
105 Vladimir Guerrero 10.00 25.00
106 Pedro Martinez 10.00 25.00
107 Pedro Martinez 10.00 25.00
108 Pedro Martinez 10.00 25.00
109 Roger Clemens 12.50 30.00
110 Roger Clemens 12.50 30.00
111 Roger Clemens 12.50 30.00
112 Randy Johnson 10.00 25.00
113 Randy Johnson 10.00 25.00
114 Randy Johnson 10.00 25.00
115 Don Mattingly 15.00 40.00
116 Don Mattingly 15.00 40.00
117 Don Mattingly 15.00 40.00
118 Bill Dickey 20.00 50.00
119 Bill Dickey 20.00 50.00
120 Bill Dickey 20.00 50.00
121a Barry Bonds 60.00 120.00
121b Bruce Sutter 10.00 25.00
122a Barry Bonds 60.00 120.00
122b Bruce Sutter 10.00 25.00
123a Barry Bonds 60.00 120.00
123b Bruce Sutter 10.00 25.00
124 John F. Kennedy 150.00 250.00
125 John F. Kennedy 150.00 250.00
126 John F. Kennedy 150.00 250.00
127 Johnny Bench 12.50 30.00
128 Johnny Bench 12.50 30.00
129 Johnny Bench 12.50 30.00
130 Mark Teixeira 8.00 20.00
131 Mark Teixeira 8.00 20.00
132 Mark Teixeira 8.00 20.00
133 Johan Santana 15.00 40.00
134 Johan Santana 15.00 40.00
135 Johan Santana 15.00 40.00
136 Alex Rodriguez 25.00 60.00
137 Alex Rodriguez 25.00 60.00
138 Alex Rodriguez 25.00 60.00
139 Brooks Robinson 12.50 30.00
140 Brooks Robinson 12.50 30.00
141 Brooks Robinson 12.50 30.00
142 Rickey Henderson 12.50 30.00
143 Rickey Henderson 12.50 30.00
144 Rickey Henderson 12.50 30.00
145 Ozzie Smith 20.00 50.00
146 Ozzie Smith 20.00 50.00
147 Ozzie Smith 20.00 50.00
148 Chipper Jones 12.50 30.00
149 Chipper Jones 12.50 30.00
150 Chipper Jones 12.50 30.00

2007 Topps Triple Threads Relics Emerald

*EMERALD: .5X TO 1.2X BASIC
STATED ODDS 1:21 MINI
STATED PRINT RUN 18 SER.#'d SETS
ALL DC VARIATIONS PRICED EQUALLY
4 Roberto Clemente 75.00 150.00
40 Mickey Mantle 100.00 200.00
121a Barry Bonds 60.00 120.00
124 John F. Kennedy 150.00 250.00

2007 Topps Triple Threads Relics Gold

*GOLD: .6X TO 1.5X BASIC
STATED ODDS 1:42 MINI
STATED PRINT RUN 9 SER.#'d SETS
ALL DC VARIATIONS PRICED EQUALLY
4 Roberto Clemente 100.00 175.00
25 Ichiro Suzuki 150.00 300.00
70 Daisuke Matsuzaka 200.00 250.00
79 Stan Musial 40.00 80.00
118 Bill Dickey 30.00 60.00
121a Barry Bonds 60.00 120.00
124 John F. Kennedy 150.00 250.00
145 Ozzie Smith 30.00 60.00

2007 Topps Triple Threads Relics Autographs

STATED ODDS 1:18 MINI
STATED PRINT RUN 18 SER.#'d SETS
*GOLD: .5X TO 1.2X BASIC
GOLD ODDS 1:34 MINI
GOLD PRINT RUN 9 SER.#'d SETS
PLATINUM ODDS 1:472 MINI
PLATINUM PRINT RUN 1 SER.#'d SET
NO PLATINUM PRICING DUE TO SCARCITY

SAPPHIRE ODDS 1:104 MINI
SAPPHIRE PRINT RUN 3 SER.#'d SETS
NO SAPPHIRE PRICING DUE TO SCARCITY
WHITE WHALE ODDS 1:118 MINI
WHITE WHALE PRINT RUN 1 SER.#'d SET
NO WHITE WHALE PRICING DUE TO SCARCITY
ALL DC VARIATIONS PRICED EQUALLY
1 Alex Rodriguez 150.00 250.00
2 Alex Rodriguez 150.00 250.00
3 Alex Rodriguez 150.00 250.00
4 Chien-Ming Wang 300.00 400.00
5 Chien-Ming Wang 300.00 400.00
6 Chien-Ming Wang 300.00 400.00
7 David Ortiz 50.00 100.00
8 David Ortiz 50.00 100.00
9 David Ortiz 50.00 100.00
10 Manny Ramirez 50.00 100.00
11 Manny Ramirez 50.00 100.00
12 Manny Ramirez 50.00 100.00
13 Johnny Damon 30.00 60.00
14 Johnny Damon 30.00 60.00
15 Johnny Damon 30.00 60.00
16 Miguel Tejada 20.00 50.00
17 Miguel Tejada 20.00 50.00
18 Miguel Tejada 20.00 50.00
19 Carl Crawford 20.00 50.00
20 Carl Crawford 20.00 50.00
21 Carl Crawford 20.00 50.00
22 Johan Santana 30.00 60.00
23 Johan Santana 30.00 60.00
24 Johan Santana 30.00 60.00
25 Francisco Liriano 20.00 50.00
26 Francisco Liriano 20.00 50.00
27 Francisco Liriano 20.00 50.00
28 Bob Feller 40.00 80.00
29 Bob Feller 40.00 80.00
30 Bob Feller 40.00 80.00
31 Vladimir Guerrero 40.00 80.00
32 Vladimir Guerrero 40.00 80.00
33 Vladimir Guerrero 40.00 80.00
34 Ernie Banks 100.00 200.00
35 Ernie Banks 100.00 200.00
36 Ernie Banks 100.00 200.00
37 Yogi Berra 60.00 120.00
38 Yogi Berra 60.00 120.00
39 Yogi Berra 60.00 120.00
40 Nolan Ryan 100.00 200.00
41 Nolan Ryan 100.00 200.00
42 Nolan Ryan 100.00 200.00
43 Ozzie Smith 40.00 80.00
44 Ozzie Smith 40.00 80.00
45 Ozzie Smith 40.00 80.00
46 David Wright 50.00 100.00
47 David Wright 50.00 100.00
48 David Wright 50.00 100.00
49 Albert Pujols 200.00 350.00
50 Albert Pujols 200.00 350.00
51 Albert Pujols 200.00 350.00
52 Ryan Howard 50.00 100.00
53 Ryan Howard 50.00 100.00
54 Ryan Howard 50.00 100.00
55 Don Mattingly 50.00 100.00
56 Don Mattingly 50.00 100.00
57 Don Mattingly 50.00 100.00
58 Brooks Robinson 30.00 60.00
59 Brooks Robinson 30.00 60.00
60 Brooks Robinson 30.00 60.00
61 Robin Yount 30.00 60.00
62 Robin Yount 30.00 60.00
63 Robin Yount 30.00 60.00
64 Mike Schmidt 60.00 120.00
65 Mike Schmidt 60.00 120.00
66 Mike Schmidt 60.00 120.00
67 Carl Yastrzemski 50.00 100.00
68 Carl Yastrzemski 50.00 100.00
69 Carl Yastrzemski 50.00 100.00
70 Wade Boggs 30.00 60.00
71 Wade Boggs 30.00 60.00
72 Wade Boggs 30.00 60.00
73 Andre Dawson 30.00 60.00
74 Andre Dawson 30.00 60.00
75 Andre Dawson 30.00 60.00
76 Reggie Jackson 40.00 80.00
77 Reggie Jackson 40.00 80.00
78 Reggie Jackson 40.00 80.00
79 Miguel Cabrera 30.00 60.00
80 Miguel Cabrera 30.00 60.00
81 Miguel Cabrera 30.00 60.00
82 Tom Seaver 40.00 80.00
83 Tom Seaver 40.00 80.00
84 Tom Seaver 40.00 80.00
85 Ralph Kiner 30.00 60.00
86 Ralph Kiner 30.00 60.00
87 Ralph Kiner 30.00 60.00
88 Chipper Jones 50.00 100.00
89 Chipper Jones 50.00 100.00
90 Chipper Jones 50.00 100.00
91 Andruw Jones 30.00 60.00
92 Andruw Jones 30.00 60.00
93 Andruw Jones 30.00 60.00
94 Dontrelle Willis 20.00 50.00
95 Dontrelle Willis 20.00 50.00
96 Dontrelle Willis 20.00 50.00
97 Bob Gibson 30.00 60.00
98 Bob Gibson 30.00 60.00
99 Bob Gibson 30.00 60.00
100 Johnny Bench 40.00 80.00
101 Johnny Bench 40.00 80.00
102 Johnny Bench 40.00 80.00
103 Joe Morgan 20.00 50.00
104 Joe Morgan 20.00 50.00
105 Joe Morgan 20.00 50.00
106 Ryne Sandberg 50.00 100.00
107 Ryne Sandberg 50.00 100.00
108 Ryne Sandberg 50.00 100.00
109 Dwight Gooden 20.00 50.00
110 Dwight Gooden 20.00 50.00
111 Dwight Gooden 20.00 50.00
112 Johnny Podres 20.00 50.00
113 Johnny Podres 20.00 50.00
114 Johnny Podres 20.00 50.00
115 Monte Irvin 20.00 50.00
116 Monte Irvin 20.00 50.00
117 Monte Irvin 20.00 50.00
118 Orlando Cepeda 20.00 50.00
119 Orlando Cepeda 20.00 50.00
120 Orlando Cepeda 20.00 50.00
121 Bo Jackson 60.00 120.00
122 Bo Jackson 60.00 120.00
123 Bo Jackson 60.00 120.00
124 Gary Sheffield 20.00 50.00
125 Gary Sheffield 20.00 50.00
126 Gary Sheffield 20.00 50.00
127 Tom Glavine 40.00 80.00
128 Tom Glavine 40.00 80.00
129 Tom Glavine 40.00 80.00
130 Tony LaRussa 20.00 50.00
131 Tony LaRussa 20.00 50.00
132 Tony LaRussa 20.00 50.00
133 Jim Leyland 20.00 50.00
134 Jim Leyland 20.00 50.00
135 Jim Leyland 20.00 50.00
136 Joe Torre 30.00 60.00
137 Joe Torre 30.00 60.00
138 Joe Torre 30.00 60.00
139 Gary Carter 30.00 60.00
140 Gary Carter 30.00 60.00
141 Gary Carter 30.00 60.00
142 Roy Oswalt 20.00 50.00
143 Roy Oswalt 20.00 50.00
144 Roy Oswalt 20.00 50.00
145 Carlos Delgado 20.00 50.00
146 Carlos Delgado 20.00 50.00
147 Carlos Delgado 20.00 50.00
148 Jason Varitek 40.00 80.00
149 Jason Varitek 40.00 80.00
150 Jason Varitek 40.00 80.00
151 Bobby Abreu 20.00 50.00
152 Bobby Abreu 20.00 50.00
153 Bobby Abreu 20.00 50.00
154 Juan Marichal 20.00 50.00
155 Juan Marichal 20.00 50.00
156 Juan Marichal 20.00 50.00
157 Frank Robinson 30.00 60.00
158 Frank Robinson 30.00 60.00
159 Frank Robinson 30.00 60.00
160 Jorge Posada 50.00 100.00
161 Jorge Posada 50.00 100.00
162 Jorge Posada 50.00 100.00
163 Luis Aparicio 20.00 50.00
164 Luis Aparicio 20.00 50.00
165 Luis Aparicio 20.00 50.00
166 Carlton Fisk 30.00 60.00
167 Carlton Fisk 30.00 60.00
168 Carlton Fisk 30.00 60.00
169 Dale Murphy 75.00 150.00
170 Dale Murphy 75.00 150.00
171 Dale Murphy 75.00 150.00
172 Mark Teixeira 30.00 60.00
173 Mark Teixeira 30.00 60.00
174 Mark Teixeira 30.00 60.00
175 Darryl Strawberry 20.00 50.00
176 Darryl Strawberry 20.00 50.00
177 Darryl Strawberry 20.00 50.00
178 Justin Morneau 30.00 60.00
179 Justin Morneau 30.00 60.00
180 Justin Morneau 30.00 60.00

2007 Topps Triple Threads Relics Autographs Gold

*GOLD: .5X TO 1.2X BASIC
STATED ODDS 1:34 MINI
STATED PRINT RUN 9 SER.#'d SETS
ALL DC VARIATIONS PRICED EQUALLY
34 Ernie Banks 100.00 200.00
37 Yogi Berra 60.00 120.00
49 Albert Pujols 250.00 350.00
52 Ryan Howard 100.00 150.00
88 Chipper Jones 75.00 150.00
121 Bo Jackson 150.00 250.00

2007 Topps Triple Threads Relics Combos

STATED ODDS 1:16 MINI
STATED PRINT RUN 36 SER.#'d SETS
*EMERALD: .5X TO 1.2X BASIC
EMERALD ODDS 1:31 MINI
EMERALD PRINT RUN 18 SER.#'d SETS
GOLD ODDS 1:62 MINI
GOLD PRINT RUN 9 SER.#'d SETS
NO GOLD PRICING DUE TO SCARCITY
PLATINUM ODDS 1:558 MINI
PLATINUM PRINT RUN 1 SER.#'d SET
NO PLATINUM PRICING DUE TO SCARCITY
SAPPHIRE ODDS 1:186 MINI
SAPPHIRE PRINT RUN 3 SER.#'d SETS
NO SAPPHIRE PRICING DUE TO SCARCITY
*SEPIA: .4X TO 1X BASIC
SEPIA ODDS 1:21 MINI
SEPIA PRINT RUN 27 SER.#'d SETS
WHITE WHALE RANDOMLY INSERTED
WHITE WHALE PRINT RUN 1 SER.#'d SET
NO WHITE WHALE PRICING DUE TO SCARCITY
1 Albert Pujols 20.00 50.00
Manny Ramirez
David Ortiz
2 Albert Pujols 20.00 50.00
Pedro Martinez
Vladimir Guerrero
3 Ivan Rodriguez 30.00 60.00
Carlos Delgado
Carlos Beltran
4 Roberto Clemente 30.00 60.00
Bernie Williams
Carlos Beltran
5 Jose Reyes 8.00 20.00
Alfonso Soriano
Miguel Tejada
6 Carl Crawford 8.00 20.00
Jose Reyes
Juan Pierre
7 Hideki Matsui 40.00 80.00
Ichiro
So Taguchi
8 Miguel Cabrera 12.50 30.00
Johan Santana
Bobby Abreu
9 Alex Rodriguez 30.00 60.00
Mariano Rivera
Hideki Matsui
10 Reggie Jackson 30.00 60.00
Alex Rodriguez
Don Mattingly
11 Yogi Berra 30.00 60.00
Don Mattingly
Reggie Jackson
12 David Ortiz 12.50 30.00
Wade Boggs
Manny Ramirez
13 David Ortiz 12.50 30.00
Manny Ramirez
Pedro Martinez
14 Miguel Tejada 10.00 25.00
Eddie Murray
Brooks Robinson
15 Joe Mauer 15.00 40.00
Justin Morneau
Johan Santana
16 Harmon Killebrew 20.00 50.00
Joe Mauer
Justin Morneau
17 Justin Verlander 12.50 30.00
Ivan Rodriguez
Joel Zumaya
18 Barry Zito 8.00 20.00
Dennis Eckersley
Huston Street
19 Reggie Jackson 10.00 25.00
Rod Carew
Vladimir Guerrero
20 Vladimir Guerrero 12.50 30.00
Pedro Martinez
Moises Alou
21 Michael Young 12.50 30.00
Mark Teixeira
Alex Rodriguez
22 Edgar Martinez 30.00 60.00
Ichiro
Alex Rodriguez
23 David Wright 12.50 30.00
Carlos Delgado
Jose Reyes
24 Jose Reyes 15.00 40.00
Pedro Martinez
David Wright
25 Jose Reyes 15.00 40.00
Carlos Beltran
David Wright
26 Ryan Howard 30.00 60.00
Chase Utley
Jimmy Rollins
27 Jeff Francoeur 15.00 40.00
Chipper Jones
Brian McCann
28 John Smoltz 20.00 50.00
Tom Glavine
Greg Maddux
29 Chipper Jones 15.00 40.00
Jeff Francoeur
Andruw Jones
30 Nolan Ryan 20.00 50.00
Pedro Martinez
Tom Seaver
31 Mike Schmidt 15.00 40.00
Jim Thome
Ryan Howard
32 Stan Musial 30.00 60.00
Albert Pujols
Ozzie Smith
33 Albert Pujols 15.00 40.00
David Eckstein
Jim Edmonds
34 Lance Berkman 12.50 30.00
Roy Oswalt
Craig Biggio
35 Roger Clemens 15.00 40.00
Roy Oswalt
Nolan Ryan
36 Frank Robinson 20.00 50.00
Joe Morgan
Johnny Bench
37 Paul Molitor 15.00 40.00
Prince Fielder
Robin Yount
38 Ernie Banks 20.00 50.00
Alfonso Soriano
Ryne Sandberg
39 Andre Ethier 8.00 20.00
Matt Kemp
Jered Weaver
40 Chien-Ming Wang 50.00 100.00
Alex Rodriguez
Mariano Rivera
41 Albert Pujols 20.00 50.00
Ichiro
Vladimir Guerrero
42 Albert Pujols 40.00 80.00
Alex Rodriguez
Ichiro
43 Ryan Howard 15.00 40.00
Justin Morneau
Albert Pujols
44 Albert Pujols 50.00 100.00
Roberto Clemente
Ichiro
45 Albert Pujols 100.00 200.00
Roberto Clemente
Mickey Mantle
46 Joe DiMaggio 100.00 150.00
Mickey Mantle
Alex Rodriguez
47 Ted Williams 150.00 250.00
Joe DiMaggio
Mickey Mantle
48 Roberto Clemente 75.00 150.00
Mickey Mantle
Reggie Jackson
49 Stan Musial 50.00 100.00
Roberto Clemente
Frank Robinson
50 Albert Pujols 60.00 120.00
Johnny Bench
Mickey Mantle
51 Carl Yastrzemski 100.00 150.00
Ted Williams
Mickey Mantle
52 Brandon Webb 12.50 30.00
Tom Seaver
Johan Santana
53 Roger Clemens 15.00 40.00
Dwight Gooden
Pedro Martinez
54 Johan Santana 12.50 30.00
Greg Maddux
Roger Clemens
55 Johan Santana 12.50 30.00
Pedro Martinez
Roger Clemens
56 Randy Johnson 12.50 30.00
Roger Clemens
Tom Glavine
57 Justin Verlander 20.00 50.00
Ryan Howard
Ichiro
58 Dontrelle Willis 8.00 20.00
Carlos Beltran
Jason Bay
59 Albert Pujols 20.00 50.00
Scott Rolen
Ryan Howard
60 Roberto Clemente 125.00 200.00
Joe DiMaggio
Mickey Mantle
61 Stan Musial 60.00 120.00
Ernie Banks
Mickey Mantle
62 Mike Schmidt 15.00 40.00
Joe Morgan
Johnny Bench
63 George Brett 30.00 60.00
Robin Yount
Ozzie Smith
64 Albert Pujols 30.00 60.00
Ichiro
Rod Carew
65 Alfonso Soriano 60.00 120.00
Mickey Mantle
Alex Rodriguez
66 Don Mattingly 20.00 50.00
Wade Boggs
Tony Gwynn
67 Rod Carew 10.00 25.00
Vladimir Guerrero
Garret Anderson
68 Tony Gwynn 20.00 50.00
Wade Boggs
George Brett
69 Vladimir Guerrero 15.00 40.00
Alfonso Soriano
Bobby Abreu
70 Darryl Strawberry 12.50 30.00
Carlos Beltran
Howard Johnson
71 Jim Thome 12.50 30.00
Manny Ramirez
Frank Thomas
72 Mickey Mantle 60.00 120.00
Mike Piazza
Mike Schmidt
73 Carl Yastrzemski 20.00 50.00
Alex Rodriguez
Dave Winfield
74 Johan Santana 12.50 30.00
Pedro Martinez
Roger Clemens
75 Greg Maddux 30.00 60.00
Nolan Ryan
Tom Seaver
76 Bob Gibson 20.00 50.00
Dwight Gooden
Greg Maddux
77 Roberto Clemente 30.00 60.00
Reggie Jackson
Manny Ramirez
78 Johnny Podres 10.00 25.00
Don Larsen
Lew Burdette
79 Ichiro 30.00 60.00
Kenji Johjima
Tadahito Iguchi
80 Paul Molitor 10.00 25.00
Jimmy Rollins
Chase Utley
81 Gary Carter 30.00 60.00
Paul Lo Duca
Mike Piazza
82 George Brett 30.00 60.00
Alex Rodriguez
David Wright
83 Hoyt Wilhelm 20.00 50.00
Phil Niekro
Tim Wakefield
84 Franklin D. Roosevelt 40.00 80.00
Harry S. Truman
Dwight D. Eisenhower
85 Ichiro 20.00 50.00
Eric Chavez
Torii Hunter
86 Richard Nixon 60.00 120.00
Ronald Reagan
George W. Bush

2007 Topps Triple Threads Cut Above

87 John Smoltz 8.00 20.00
Carlos Delgado
Edgar Martinez
88 Manny Ramirez 12.50 30.00
Vladimir Guerrero
David Ortiz
89 Livan Hernandez 10.00 25.00
Orel Hershiser
Willie Stargell
90 David Ortiz 15.00 40.00
Ryan Howard
Albert Pujols
91 Chien-Ming Wang 40.00 80.00
Johan Santana
Jon Garland
92 Deion Sanders 15.00 40.00
Bo Jackson
Brian Jordan
93 Franklin D. Roosevelt 75.00 150.00
John F. Kennedy
Bill Clinton
94 Vladimir Guerrero 30.00 60.00
Ichiro
Vernon Wells
95 Jim Thome 10.00 25.00
Jermaine Dye
Paul Konerko
96 A.J. Pierzynski 8.00 20.00
Kelvim Escobar
Josh Paul
97 Joe Carter 15.00 40.00
Rickey Henderson
Paul Molitor
98 Kirk Gibson 8.00 20.00
Dennis Eckersley
99 Luis Castillo 8.00 20.00
Moises Alou
Mark Prior
100 Mookie Wilson 20.00 50.00
Ray Knight
Bill Buckner

2007 Topps Triple Threads Relics Combos Autographs

STATED ODDS 1:94 MINI
STATED PRINT RUN 36 SER.#'d SETS
EMERALD: .5X TO 1.2X BASIC
EMERALD ODDS 1:185 MINI
EMERALD PRINT RUN 18 SER.#'d SETS
GOLD ODDS 1:371 MINI
GOLD PRINT RUN 9 SER.#'d SETS
NO GOLD PRICING DUE TO SCARCITY
PLATINUM ODDS 1:2996 MINI
PLATINUM PRINT RUN 1 SER.#'d SET
NO PLATINUM PRICING DUE TO SCARCITY
SAPPHIRE ODDS 1:1145 MINI
SAPPHIRE PRINT RUN 3 SER.#'d SETS
NO SAPPHIRE PRICING DUE TO SCARCITY
*SEPIA: .4X TO 1X BASIC
SEPIA ODDS 1:129 MINI
SEPIA PRINT RUN 27 SER.#'d SETS
WHITE WHALE ODDS 1:1219 MINI
WHITE WHALE PRINT RUN 1 SER.#'d SET
NO WHITE WHALE PRICING DUE TO SCARCITY
1 Brooks Robinson 60.00 120.00
Robin Yount
Johnny Bench
2 Reggie Jackson 60.00 120.00
Joe Morgan
Ryne Sandberg
3 Tom Seaver 125.00 200.00
Bob Gibson
Nolan Ryan
4 Albert Pujols 300.00 400.00
Alex Rodriguez
Vladimir Guerrero
5 Tom Seaver 75.00 150.00
Roger Clemens
Dwight Gooden
6 Johan Santana 150.00 250.00
Tom Glavine
Roger Clemens
7 Alex Rodriguez 250.00 350.00
Chien-Ming Wang
Don Mattingly
8 Ryan Howard 75.00 150.00
Mike Schmidt
Bobby Abreu
9 Ryan Howard 200.00 300.00
David Ortiz
Albert Pujols
10 Alex Rodriguez 200.00 300.00
David Wright
Jose Reyes
11 Miguel Cabrera 60.00 120.00
Manny Ramirez
David Ortiz
12 Justin Verlander 150.00 250.00
Jered Weaver
Chien-Ming Wang
13 Ralph Kiner 60.00 120.00
Duke Snider
Yogi Berra
14 Ryan Howard 150.00 250.00
Alex Rodriguez
Andruw Jones
15 Adam Lind 12.50 30.00
Brian Stokes
David Murphy
16 Andrew Miller 15.00 40.00
Brian Stokes
Glen Perkins
17 Shawn Riggans 20.00 50.00
Troy Tulowitzki
Andrew Miller
18 Glen Perkins 20.00 50.00
Lastings Milledge
Troy Tulowitzki

2007 Topps Triple Threads Relics Combos Double

STATED ODDS 1:31 MINI
STATED PRINT RUN 36 SER.#'d SETS
*EMERALD: .4X TO 1X BASIC
EMERALD ODDS 1:62 MINI
EMERALD PRINT RUN 18 SER.#'d SETS
GOLD ODDS 1:125 MINI
PLATINUM ODDS 1:1140 MINI
PLATINUM PRINT RUN 1 SER.#'d SET
GOLD PRINT RUN 9 SER.#'d SETS
NO GOLD PRICING DUE TO SCARCITY
NO PLATINUM PRICING DUE TO SCARCITY
SAPPHIRE ODDS 1:372 MINI
SAPPHIRE PRINT RUN 3 SER.#'d SETS
NO SAPPHIRE PRICING DUE TO SCARCITY
*SEPIA: .4X TO 1X BASIC
SEPIA ODDS 1:42 MINI
SEPIA PRINT RUN 27 SER.#'d SETS
1 Mickey Mantle 200.00 300.00
Joe DiMaggio
2 Alex Rodriguez 125.00 175.00
Chien-Ming Wang
Johnny Damon
Manny Ramirez
David Ortiz
Jason Varitek
3 David Wright 30.00 60.00
Carlos Beltran
Tom Glavine
Chipper Jones
Andruw Jones
John Smoltz
4 David Wright 30.00 60.00
5 Albert Pujols 50.00 100.00
6 Chien-Ming Wang 100.00 200.00
7 David Wright 30.00 60.00
Ryan Howard
8 Alex Rodriguez 50.00 100.00
9 Ryan Howard 40.00 80.00
10 Ichiro Suzuki 75.00 150.00
11 Albert Pujols 30.00 60.00
Pedro Martinez
David Ortiz
Vladimir Guerrero
Manny Ramirez
Alfonso Soriano
12 Ichiro 100.00 200.00
So Taguchi
Hideki Matsui
Kazuo Matsui
Tadahito Iguchi
Kenji Johjima
13 Roberto Clemente 75.00 150.00
Ivan Rodriguez
Carlos Beltran
Bernie Williams
Carlos Delgado
Javy Lopez
14 Johan Santana 40.00 80.00
Miguel Cabrera
Bobby Abreu
Omar Vizquel
Ozzie Guillen
Luis Aparicio
15 Mickey Mantle 250.00 500.00
Joe DiMaggio
Ted Williams
Ernie Banks
Yogi Berra
Stan Musial
16 Mickey Mantle 250.00 350.00
Albert Pujols
Vladimir Guerrero
Roberto Clemente
Joe DiMaggio
Ted Williams
17 Mickey Mantle 200.00 300.00
Alex Rodriguez
Don Mattingly
Yogi Berra
Chien-Ming Wang
Reggie Jackson
18 Carl Yastrzemski 40.00 80.00
Manny Ramirez
David Ortiz
Pedro Martinez
Johnny Damon
Carlton Fisk
19 Justin Morneau 50.00 100.00
Torii Hunter
Joe Mauer
Johan Santana
Francisco Liriano
Harmon Killebrew
20 Justin Verlander 50.00 100.00
Joel Zumaya
Curtis Granderson
Magglio Ordonez
Ivan Rodriguez
Kenny Rogers
21 Nick Swisher 60.00 120.00
Huston Street
Reggie Jackson
Barry Zito
Jose Canseco
Dennis Eckersley
22 Vladimir Guerrero 40.00 80.00
Rod Carew
Jered Weaver
Reggie Jackson
Garret Anderson
Francisco Rodriguez
23 Vladimir Guerrero 30.00 60.00
Pedro Martinez
Moises Alou
Gary Carter
Andre Dawson
Randy Johnson
24 Nolan Ryan 50.00 100.00
Mark Teixeira
Michael Young
Alex Rodriguez
Ivan Rodriguez
Hank Blalock
25 Kenji Johjima 60.00 120.00
Ichiro
Alex Rodriguez
Randy Johnson
Edgar Martinez
Richie Sexson
26 David Wright 60.00 120.00
Jose Reyes
Carlos Beltran
Pedro Martinez
Tom Glavine
Carlos Delgado
27 David Eckstein 50.00 100.00
Albert Pujols
Chris Carpenter
Stan Musial
Ozzie Smith
Jim Edmonds
28 Nolan Ryan 100.00 200.00
Andy Pettitte
Roger Clemens
Roy Oswalt
Lance Berkman
Craig Biggio
29 Ryan Howard 125.00 175.00
Chase Utley
Mike Schmidt
Jimmy Rollins
Richie Ashburn
Steve Carlton
30 Jeff Francoeur 60.00 120.00
Brian McCann
Chipper Jones
Andruw Jones
John Smoltz
Tim Hudson
31 Alfonso Soriano 40.00 80.00
Ernie Banks
Ryne Sandberg
Kerry Wood
Mark Prior
Andre Dawson
32 David Wright 40.00 80.00
Justin Morneau
Ryan Howard
Chien-Ming Wang
Chase Utley
Jose Reyes
33 David Ortiz 30.00 60.00
34 Roger Maris 125.00 175.00
Stan Musial
Roberto Clemente
Ernie Banks
Johnny Bench
Carl Yastrzemski
35 Albert Pujols 50.00 100.00
Jim Edmonds
Scott Rolen
Ivan Rodriguez
Kenny Rogers
Magglio Ordonez
36 Derrek Lee 40.00 80.00
Juan Pierre
Greg Maddux
Paul Konerko
Jermaine Dye
Jim Thome
37 David Wright 40.00 80.00
Paul Lo Duca
Jose Reyes
Alex Rodriguez
Jason Giambi
Johnny Damon
38 Joe Mauer 30.00 60.00
Freddy Sanchez
Robinson Cano
Miguel Cabrera
Albert Pujols
Miguel Tejada
39 Ryan Howard 40.00 80.00
David Ortiz
Albert Pujols
Alfonso Soriano
Lance Berkman
Jermaine Dye
40 Ryan Howard 40.00 80.00
Albert Pujols
David Ortiz
Lance Berkman
Justin Morneau
Andruw Jones
41 Johan Santana 30.00 60.00
Roy Oswalt
Chris Carpenter
Brandon Webb
Roy Halladay
C.C. Sabathia
42 Chien-Ming Wang 50.00 100.00
Johan Santana
Jon Garland
Randy Johnson
Kenny Rogers
Freddy Garcia
43 Johan Santana 30.00 60.00
Aaron Harang
Jake Peavy
John Smoltz
Carlos Zambrano
Jeremy Bonderman
44 Jeff Suppan 30.00 60.00
Roy Oswalt
Albert Pujols
Placido Polanco
Paul Konerko
David Ortiz
45 Orlando Cepeda 50.00 100.00
Monte Irvin
Bobby Thomson
Duke Snider
Johnny Podres
Don Zimmer
46 Ryne Sandberg 40.00 80.00
Wade Boggs
Dennis Eckersley
Paul Molitor
Gary Carter
Eddie Murray
47 Jermaine Dye 30.00 60.00
Paul Konerko
A.J. Pierzynski
Craig Biggio
Lance Berkman
Morgan Ensberg
48 Roger Clemens 40.00 80.00
Randy Johnson
Greg Maddux
Curt Schilling
Pedro Martinez
John Smoltz
49 David Wright 125.00 175.00
Brooks Robinson
George Brett
Mike Schmidt
Alex Rodriguez
Eddie Mathews
50 Alfonso Soriano 40.00 80.00
Bobby Abreu
Carlos Beltran
Vladimir Guerrero
Alex Rodriguez
Preston Wilson

2007 Topps Triple Threads Triple Signed Hide

STATED ODDS 1:13,396 MINI
STATED PRINT RUN 1 SER.#'d SET
NO PRICING DUE TO SCARCITY
MPR Mickey Mantle
Albert Pujols
Alex Rodriguez
MRW Mickey Mantle
Alex Rodriguez
David Wright
RWP Alex Rodriguez
David Wright
Albert Pujols
WRO Ted Williams
Manny Ramirez
David Ortiz

2008 Topps Triple Threads

COMMON CARD (1-145) .40 1.00
1-145 PRINT RUN 1350 SER.#'d SETS
COMMON JSY AU RC (146-170) 4.00 10.00
JSY AU RC ODDS 1:11 MINI
JSY AU RC VAR.ODDS 1:20 MINI
JSY AU RC PRINT RUN 99 SER.#'d SETS
TEAM INITIAL DIECUTS ARE VARIATIONS
COMMON JSY AU (171-220) 4.00 10.00
JSY AU ODDS 1:11 MINI
JSY AU VAR.ODDS 1:20 MINI
JSY AU PRINT RUN 99 SER.#'d SETS
TEAM INITIAL DIECUTS ARE VARIATIONS
COMMON CARD (221-251) .40 1.00
221-251 PRINT RUN 1350 SER.#'d SETS
COMMON ROOKIE (221-251) .40 1.00
221-251 RC PRINT RUN 1350 SER.#'d SETS
OVERALL 1-145 PLATE ODDS 1:116 MINI
OVERALL 221-251 PLATE ODDS 1:116 MINI
PLATE PRINT RUN 1 SET PER COLOR
BLACK-CYAN-MAGENTA-YELLOW ISSUED
NO PLATE PRICING DUE TO SCARCITY
1 David Wright 1.25 3.00
2 Nolan Ryan 3.00 8.00
3 Johnny Damon .60 1.50
4 Joe Mauer .60 1.50
5 Francisco Rodriguez .40 1.00
6 Carlos Beltran .40 1.00
7 Mickey Mantle 4.00 10.00
8 Brian Roberts .60 1.50
9 Lou Gehrig 2.00 5.00
10 Babe Ruth 2.50 6.00
11 Ryne Sandberg 2.00 5.00
12 Bob Gibson .60 1.50
13 Greg Maddux 1.25 3.00
14 Jered Weaver .40 1.00
15 Johnny Bench 1.00 2.50
16 Magglio Ordonez .60 1.50
17 Carl Yastrzemski 1.50 4.00
18 Derek Jeter 2.50 6.00
19 Gil Meche .40 1.00
20 Hanley Ramirez 1.00 2.50
21 Edgar Martinez .60 1.50
22 Steve Carlton .40 1.00
23 C.C. Sabathia .40 1.00
24 Chase Utley 1.00 2.50
25 Francisco Cordero .40 1.00
26 Mark Ellis .40 1.00
27 Jeff Kent .40 1.00
28 Brian Fuentes .40 1.00
29 Johan Santana .60 1.50
30 Ichiro 1.50 4.00
31 Ken Griffey Jr. 1.50 4.00
32 Steve Garvey .40 1.00
33 Rafael Furcal .40 1.00
34 Chipper Jones 1.25 3.00
35 Roberto Clemente 2.00 5.00
36 Rich Harden .40 1.00
37 Cy Young 1.00 2.50
38 Albert Pujols 2.00 5.00
39 Dontrelle Willis .40 1.00
40 Mark Teixeira .60 1.50
41 Daisuke Matsuzaka 1.50 4.00
42 Harmon Killebrew 1.00 2.50
43 Darryl Strawberry .40 1.00
44 Eric Chavez .40 1.00
45 Don Larsen .40 1.00
46 Huston Street .40 1.00
47 Jake Peavy .60 1.50
48 Prince Fielder 1.00 2.50
49 Garret Anderson .40 1.00
50 Matt Holliday .60 1.50
51 Travis Buck .40 1.00
52 Ben Sheets .60 1.50
53 George Brett 2.00 5.00
54 Dmitri Young .40 1.00
55 Phil Rizzuto .60 1.50
56 Jimmy Rollins .60 1.50
57 Manny Ramirez 1.00 2.50
58 Ozzie Smith 1.50 4.00
59 Dale Murphy .60 1.50
60 Bobby Crosby .40 1.00
61 Trevor Hoffman .40 1.00
62 Chien-Ming Wang 1.25 3.00
63 Jose Reyes .60 1.50
64 Vladimir Guerrero 1.00 2.50
65 Vida Blue .40 1.00
66 Rod Carew .60 1.50
67 Aaron Rowand .40 1.00
68 Hong-Chih Kuo .40 1.00
69 Mike Schmidt 1.50 4.00
70 Rogers Hornsby .60 1.50
71 Alex Rodriguez 1.50 4.00
72 Roger Maris 1.00 2.50
73 Travis Hafner .40 1.00
74 Tom Glavine .60 1.50
75 Pat Burrell .40 1.00
76 Pedro Martinez .60 1.50
77 Joba Chamberlain 1.25 3.00
78 Jason Varitek 1.00 2.50
79 Hideo Nomo 1.00 2.50
80 Frank Thomas 1.00 2.50
81 Rollie Fingers .40 1.00
82 Carl Crawford .40 1.00
83 Bobby Jenks .40 1.00
84 Victor Martinez .40 1.00
85 Ernie Banks 1.00 2.50
86 Josh Beckett .60 1.50
87 Jose Valverde .40 1.00
88 Reggie Jackson .60 1.50
89 Duke Snider .60 1.50
90 Mike Lowell .40 1.00
91 Dom DiMaggio .40 1.00
92 Torii Hunter .40 1.00
93 Alfonso Soriano .60 1.50
94 Justin Morneau .60 1.50
95 Carlos Delgado .40 1.00
96 Ty Cobb 1.50 4.00
97 Andruw Jones .40 1.00
98 Yogi Berra 1.00 2.50
99 Joe DiMaggio 2.50 6.00
100 Willie Randolph .40 1.00
101 Miguel Cabrera .60 1.50
102 Grady Sizemore .60 1.50
103 Michael Young .40 1.00
104 Wade Boggs .60 1.50
105 Goose Gossage .40 1.00
106 Robin Roberts .40 1.00
107 Brooks Robinson .60 1.50
108 Jim Palmer .40 1.00
109 Jorge Posada .60 1.50
110 Keith Hernandez .40 1.00
111 Ivan Rodriguez .60 1.50
112 Carlos Lee .40 1.00
113 John Lackey .40 1.00
114 Alex Rios .40 1.00
115 Carlton Fisk .60 1.50
116 Gary Matthews .40 1.00
117 Billy Martin .60 1.50
118 Paul Molitor 1.00 2.50
119 Hideki Matsui 1.00 2.50
120 Al Kaline 1.00 2.50
121 Takashi Saito .40 1.00
122 Stan Musial 1.50 4.00
123 Ryan Howard 1.25 3.00
124 Whitey Ford .60 1.50
125 John Smoltz 1.00 2.50
126 Roy Oswalt .40 1.00
127 Jim Thome .60 1.50
128 Tony Gwynn .40 1.00
129 Dennis Eckersley .40 1.00
130 Ted Williams 2.50 6.00
131 Justin Verlander .60 1.50
132 David Ortiz 1.00 2.50
133 Tom Gordon .40 1.00
134 Tom Seaver .60 1.50
135 Red Schoendienst .40 1.00
136 Johnny Podres .40 1.00
137 Paul Konerko .40 1.00
138 Robin Yount 1.00 2.50
139 Todd Helton .60 1.50
140 Frank Robinson .40 1.00
141 J.J. Putz .40 1.00
142 Jackie Robinson 1.00 2.50
143 Brandon Webb .60 1.50
144 Eddie Murray 1.00 2.50
145 Freddy Sanchez .40 1.00
146 Josh Anderson Jsy AU (RC) 5.00 12.00
147a Daric Barton Jsy AU (RC) 5.00 12.00
147b Daric Barton Jsy AU (RC) 5.00 12.00
148 Steve Pearce Jsy AU RC 6.00 15.00
149 Chin-Lung Hu Jsy AU (RC) 20.00 50.00
150a Clay Buchholz Jsy AU (RC) 10.00 25.00
150b Clay Buchholz Jsy AU (RC) 10.00 25.00
151a J.R. Towles Jsy AU RC 6.00 15.00
151b J.R. Towles Jsy AU RC 6.00 15.00
152 Brandon Jones Jsy AU RC 5.00 12.00
153 Lance Broadway Jsy AU (RC) 6.00 15.00
154a Nyjer Morgan Jsy AU (RC) 5.00 12.00
154b Nyjer Morgan Jsy AU (RC) 4.00 10.00
155a Ross Ohlendorf Jsy AU RC 5.00 12.00
155b Ross Ohlendorf Jsy AU RC 5.00 12.00
156 Chris Seddon Jsy AU (RC) 4.00 10.00
157 Jonathan Albaladejo Jsy AU RC 5.00 12.00
158a Seth Smith Jsy AU (RC) 4.00 10.00
158b Seth Smith Jsy AU (RC) 4.00 10.00
159a Kevin Hart Jsy AU (RC) 5.00 12.00
159b Kevin Hart Jsy AU (RC) 5.00 12.00
160 Bill White Jsy AU RC 5.00 12.00
161 Wladimir Balentien Jsy AU (RC) 5.00 12.00
162a Justin Ruggiano Jsy AU RC 4.00 10.00
162b Justin Ruggiano Jsy AU RC 4.00 10.00
163a Clint Sammons Jsy AU (RC) 5.00 12.00
163b Clint Sammons Jsy AU (RC) 5.00 12.00
164 Rich Thompson Jsy AU RC 5.00 12.00
165 Dave Davidson Jsy AU RC 4.00 10.00
166 Troy Patton Jsy AU (RC) 5.00 12.00
167 Joe Koshansky Jsy AU (RC) 5.00 12.00
168a Colt Morton Jsy AU RC 5.00 12.00
168b Colt Morton Jsy AU RC 5.00 12.00
169 Armando Galarraga Jsy AU RC 12.50 30.00
170a Sam Fuld Jsy AU RC 5.00 12.00
170b Sam Fuld Jsy AU RC 5.00 12.00
171 Dustin Moseley Bat AU 4.00 10.00
172 Tim Lincecum Jsy AU 30.00 60.00
173a Ryan Braun Jsy AU 30.00 60.00
173b Ryan Braun Jsy AU 30.00 60.00
174 Phil Hughes Jsy AU 15.00 40.00
175a Joba Chamberlain Jsy AU 30.00 60.00
175b Joba Chamberlain Jsy AU 30.00 60.00
176 Hunter Pence Jsy AU 12.50 30.00
177a Fausto Carmona Jsy AU 6.00 15.00
177b Fausto Carmona Jsy AU 6.00 15.00
178a Ubaldo Jimenez Jsy AU 4.00 10.00
178b Ubaldo Jimenez Jsy AU 4.00 10.00
179a Cameron Maybin Jsy AU 8.00 20.00
179b Cameron Maybin Jsy AU 8.00 20.00
180a Adam Jones Jsy AU 10.00 25.00
180b Adam Jones Jsy AU 10.00 25.00
181a Brian Bannister Jsy AU 5.00 12.00
181b Brian Bannister Jsy AU 5.00 12.00
182a Jarrod Saltalamacchia Jsy AU 6.00 15.00
182b Jarrod Saltalamacchia Jsy AU 6.00 15.00
183 Alex Gordon Jsy AU 12.50 30.00
184a Russell Martin Jsy AU 10.00 25.00
184b Russell Martin Jsy AU 10.00 25.00
185 John Maine Jsy AU 10.00 25.00
186a Hideki Okajima Jsy AU 12.50 30.00
186b Hideki Okajima Jsy AU 12.50 30.00
187a Curtis Granderson Jsy AU 10.00 25.00
187b Curtis Granderson Jsy AU 10.00 25.00
188 Delmon Young Jsy AU 5.00 12.00
189a Jo-Jo Reyes Jsy AU 5.00 12.00
189b Jo-Jo Reyes Jsy AU 5.00 12.00
190 Yovani Gallardo Jsy AU 8.00 20.00
191a Ryan Zimmerman Jsy AU 10.00 25.00
191b Ryan Zimmerman Jsy AU 10.00 25.00
192 Jeremy Guthrie Jsy AU 8.00 20.00
193a Dan Uggla Jsy AU 8.00 20.00
193b Dan Uggla Jsy AU 8.00 20.00
194a Andre Ethier Jsy AU 8.00 20.00
194b Andre Ethier Jsy AU 8.00 20.00
195a Chris Young Jsy AU 6.00 15.00
195b Chris Young Jsy AU 6.00 15.00
196a Elijah Dukes Jsy AU 5.00 12.00
196b Elijah Dukes Jsy AU 5.00 12.00
197a Nick Markakis Jsy AU 10.00 25.00
197b Nick Markakis Jsy AU 10.00 25.00
198a Melky Cabrera Jsy AU 8.00 20.00
198b Melky Cabrera Jsy AU 8.00 20.00
199 Cole Hamels Jsy AU 10.00 25.00
200 James Loney Jsy AU 10.00 25.00
201a Kevin Slowey Jsy AU 8.00 20.00
201b Kevin Slowey Jsy AU 8.00 20.00
202 Carlos Marmol Jsy AU 8.00 20.00
203a Akinori Iwamura Jsy AU 10.00 25.00
203b Akinori Iwamura Jsy AU 10.00 25.00
204 Adrian Gonzalez Jsy AU 6.00 15.00
205a Brandon Phillips Jsy AU 10.00 25.00
205b Brandon Phillips Jsy AU 10.00 25.00
206 J.J. Hardy Jsy AU 10.00 25.00
207a Tom Gorzelanny Jsy AU 4.00 10.00
207b Tom Gorzelanny Jsy AU 4.00 10.00
208a Matt Cain Jsy AU 6.00 15.00
208b Matt Cain Jsy AU 6.00 15.00
209a Matt Capps Jsy AU 5.00 12.00
209b Matt Capps Jsy AU 5.00 12.00
210a Jeff Francis Jsy AU 5.00 12.00
210b Jeff Francis Jsy AU 5.00 12.00
211 Brian McCann Jsy AU 10.00 25.00
212 Matt Garza Jsy AU 8.00 20.00
213a Robinson Cano Jsy AU 12.50 30.00
213b Robinson Cano Jsy AU 12.50 30.00
214 Felix Hernandez Jsy AU 10.00 25.00
215 Yunel Escobar Jsy AU 8.00 20.00
216a Francisco Liriano Jsy AU 8.00 20.00
216b Francisco Liriano Jsy AU 8.00 20.00
217a Rich Hill Jsy AU 5.00 12.00
217b Rich Hill Jsy AU 5.00 12.00
218a Taylor Buchholz Jsy AU 4.00 10.00
218b Taylor Buchholz Jsy AU 4.00 10.00
219 Asdrubal Cabrera Jsy AU 5.00 12.00
220a Lastings Milledge Jsy AU 5.00 12.00
220b Lastings Milledge Jsy AU 5.00 12.00
221 Honus Wagner 1.00 2.50
222 Walter Johnson 1.00 2.50
223 Thurman Munson 1.00 2.50
224 Roy Campanella 1.00 2.50
225 George Sisler .60 1.50
226 Pee Wee Reese .60 1.50
227 Johnny Mize .60 1.50
228 Jimmie Foxx 1.00 2.50
229 Tris Speaker .60 1.50
230 Christy Mathewson 1.00 2.50
231 Mel Ott 1.00 2.50
232 Ralph Kiner .60 1.50
233 Joey Votto (RC) 1.00 2.50
234 Hiroki Kuroda RC .60 1.50
235 John Bowker (RC) .40 1.00
236 Lance Berkman .60 1.50
237 Aaron Harang .40 1.00
238 B.J. Upton .60 1.50
239 Zack Greinke .40 1.00
240 Cal Ripken Jr. 4.00 10.00
241 Justin Upton 1.00 2.50
242 Roy Halladay .40 1.00
243 Orlando Hudson .40 1.00
244 Scott Kazmir .60 1.50
245 Matt Kemp .40 1.00
246 Mark Buehrle .40 1.00
247 Adam Dunn .40 1.00
248 Erik Bedard .40 1.00
249 Carlos Zambrano .40 1.00
250 Jeff Francoeur .60 1.50
251 Brad Penny .40 1.00

2008 Topps Triple Threads Black

*BLACK 1-145: 3X TO 8X BASIC
*BLACK 221-251: 3X TO 8X BASIC

1-145/221-251 ODDS 1:16 MINI
1-145/221-251 PNT RUN 30 SER.#'d SETS

2008 Topps Triple Threads Emerald

*EMERALD 1-145: .6X TO 1.5X BASIC
*EMERALD 221-251: .6X TO 1.5X BASIC
1-145/221-251 ODDS 1:2 MINI
1-145/221-251 PNT RUN 240 SER.#'d SETS
*EMERALD AUTO: .5X TO 1.2X BASIC AU
*EMERALD VAR AU: .5X TO 1.2X BASIC AU
146-220 AU ODDS 1:22 MINI
146-220 AU VAR.ODDS 1:39 MINI
146-220 AU PRINT RUN 50 SERIAL #'d SETS
TEAM INITIAL DIECUTS ARE VARIATIONS

2008 Topps Triple Threads Gold

*GOLD 1-145: 1X TO 2.5X BASIC
*GOLD 221-251: 1X TO 2.5X BASIC
1-145/221-251 ODDS 1:5 MINI
1-145/221-251 PNT RUN 99 SER.#'d SETS
*GOLD AUTO: .6X TO 1.5X BASIC AU
*GOLD VAR AU: .6X TO 1.5X BASIC AU
146-220 AU ODDS 1:43 MINI
146-220 AU VAR.ODDS 1:77 MINI
146-220 AU PRINT RUN 25 SERIAL #'d SETS
TEAM INITIAL DIECUTS ARE VARIATIONS

2008 Topps Triple Threads Platinum

1-145 ODDS 1:461 MINI
221-251 ODDS 1:461 MINI
STATED PRINT RUN 1 SER.#'d SET
NO PRICING DUE TO SCARCITY
146-220 AU ODDS 1:1080 MINI
146-220 AU VARIATION ODDS 1:1945 MINI
146-220 AU PRINT RUN 1 SERIAL #'d SET
TEAM INITIAL DIECUTS ARE VARIATIONS
NO PRICING DUE TO SCARCITY

2008 Topps Triple Threads Sapphire

*SAPPHIRE 1-145: 3X TO 8X BASIC
*SAPPHIRE 221-251: 3X TO 8X BASIC
1-145/221-251 ODDS 1:19 MINI
1-145/221-251 PNT RUN 25 SER.#'d SETS
146-220 JSY AU ODDS 1:107 MINI
146-220 JSY AU VAR.ODDS 1:190 MINI
146-220 AU PRINT RUN 10 SERIAL #'d SETS
TEAM INITIAL DIECUTS ARE VARIATIONS
NO SAPPHIRE JSY AUTO PRICING AVAILABLE

2008 Topps Triple Threads Sepia

*SEPIA 1-145: .5X TO 1.2X BASIC
*SEPIA 221-251: .5X TO 1.2X BASIC
1-145/221-251 RANDOMLY INSERTED
1-145/221-251 PNT RUN 525 SER.#'d SETS
*SEPIA AUTO: .4X TO 1X BASIC AU
*SEPIA VAR AU: .4X TO 1X BASIC AU
146-220 AU ODDS 1:15 MINI
146-220 AU VAR.ODDS 1:26 MINI
146-220 AU PRINT RUN 75 SERIAL #'d SETS
TEAM INITIAL DIECUTS ARE VARIATIONS

2008 Topps Triple Threads White Whale Printing Plates

VERSION A ODDS 1:267 MINI
VERSION B ODDS 1:157 MINI
VERSION C ODDS 1:457 MINI
TEAM INITIALS ODDS 1:477 MINI
STATED PRINT RUN 1 SER.#'d SET
NO PRICING DUE TO SCARCITY

2008 Topps Triple Threads All-Star Triple Patches

STATED ODDS 1:171 MINI
STATED PRINT RUN 9 SER.#'d SETS
NO PRICING DUE TO SCARCITY
STATED LOGO ODDS 1:1588 MINI
STATED PRINT RUN 1 SER.#'d SET
NO PRICING DUE TO SCARCITY
STATED PLATINUM ODDS 1:1588 MINI
STATED PRINT RUN 1 SER.#'d SETS
NO PRICING DUE TO SCARCITY
1 Josh Beckett
2 Carlos Beltran
3 Francisco Cordero
4 Carl Crawford
5 Prince Fielder
6 Brian Fuentes
7 Cole Hamels
8 J.J. Hardy
9 Trevor Hoffman
10 Matt Holliday
11 Ryan Howard
12 Orlando Hudson
13 Torii Hunter
14 Bobby Jenks
15 John Lackey
16 Carlos Lee
17 Mike Lowell
18 Russell Martin
19 Victor Martinez
20 Brian McCann
21 Gil Meche
22 Justin Morneau
23 Hideki Okajima
24 David Ortiz
25 Roy Oswalt
26 Jake Peavy
27 Jorge Posada
28 Albert Pujols
29 J.J. Putz
30 Manny Ramirez
31 Jose Reyes
32 Alex Rios
33 Brian Roberts
34 Alex Rodriguez
35 Francisco Rodriguez
36 Ivan Rodriguez
37 Aaron Rowand
38 C.C. Sabathia
39 Takashi Saito
40 Freddy Sanchez
41 Johan Santana
42 Ben Sheets
43 Grady Sizemore
44 Ichiro Suzuki
45 Chase Utley
46 Jose Valverde
47 Justin Verlander
48 Brandon Webb
49 David Wright
50 Chris Young
51 Dmitri Young
52 Michael Young

2008 Topps Triple Threads Bat Barrels

STATED ODDS 1:2358 MINI
STATED PRINT RUN 1 SER.#'d SET
NO PRICING DUE TO SCARCITY

2008 Topps Triple Threads Cut Above

STATED ODDS 1:7781 MINI
STATED PRINT RUN 1 SER.#'d SET
NO PRICING DUE TO SCARCITY

2008 Topps Triple Threads Cut Above Presidential

GROUP A ODDS 1:8646 MINI
GROUP B ODDS 1:77,814 MINI
STATED PRINT RUN 1 SER.#'d SET
NO PRICING DUE TO SCARCITY
1 John F. Kennedy
2 Woodrow Wilson
3 Grover Cleveland
4 George W. Bush
5 Franklin D. Roosevelt
6 Warren G. Harding
7 William H. Taft
8 Herbert Hoover
9 Theodore Roosevelt
10 Calvin Coolidge

2008 Topps Triple Threads Jumbo Plus Relics

STATED ODDS 1:1080 MINI
STATED PRINT RUN 3 SER.#'d SETS
NO PRICING DUE TO SCARCITY
PLATINUM ODDS 1:3112 MINI
PLATINUM PRINT RUN 1 SER.#'d SET
NO PRICING DUE TO SCARCITY

2008 Topps Triple Threads Letter Plus Relics

STATED ODDS 1:1080 MINI
STATED PRINT RUN 3 SER.#'d SETS
NO PRICING DUE TO SCARCITY
PLATINUM ODDS 1:3112 MINI
PLATINUM PRINT RUN 1 SER.#'d SET
NO PRICING DUE TO SCARCITY

2008 Topps Triple Threads Relics

STATED ODDS 1:10 MINI
STATED PRINT RUN 36 SER.#'d SETS
*EMERALD: .5X TO 1.2X BASIC
EMERALD ODDS 1:19 MINI
EMERALD PRINT RUN 18 SER.#'d SETS
NO 226-240 EMERALD PRICING
*GOLD: .6X TO 1.5X BASIC
GOLD ODDS 1:38 MINI
GOLD PRINT RUN 9 SER.#'d SETS
NO 226-240 GOLD PRICING
PLATINUM ODDS 1:334 MINI
PLATINUM PRINT RUN 1 SER.#'d SET
NO PLATINUM PRICING DUE TO SCARCITY
SAPPHIRE ODDS 1:111 MINI
SAPPHIRE PRINT RUN 3 SER.#'d SETS
NO SAPPHIRE PRICING DUE TO SCARCITY
*SEPIA: .4X TO 1X BASIC
SEPIA ODDS 1:13 MINI
SEPIA PRINT RUN 27 SER.#'d SETS
ALL DC VARIATIONS PRICED EQUALLY
1 David Wright 15.00 40.00
2 David Wright 15.00 40.00
3 David Wright 15.00 40.00
4 Alex Rodriguez 20.00 50.00
5 Alex Rodriguez 20.00 50.00
6 Alex Rodriguez 20.00 50.00
7 Mickey Mantle 60.00 120.00
8 Mickey Mantle 60.00 120.00
9 Mickey Mantle 60.00 120.00
10 Duke Snider 12.50 30.00
11 Duke Snider 12.50 30.00
12 Duke Snider 30.00 60.00
13 Carlton Fisk 10.00 25.00
14 Carlton Fisk 10.00 25.00
15 Carlton Fisk 10.00 25.00
16 Ichiro Suzuki 20.00 50.00
17 Ichiro Suzuki 20.00 50.00
18 Ichiro Suzuki 20.00 50.00
19 Wade Boggs 10.00 25.00
20 Wade Boggs 10.00 25.00
21 Wade Boggs 10.00 25.00
22 Chien-Ming Wang 15.00 40.00
23 Chien-Ming Wang 15.00 40.00
24 Chien-Ming Wang 15.00 40.00
25 Alfonso Soriano 8.00 20.00
26 Alfonso Soriano 8.00 20.00
27 Alfonso Soriano 8.00 20.00
28 Ernie Banks 12.50 30.00
29 Ernie Banks 12.50 30.00
30 Ernie Banks 12.50 30.00
31 Jimmy Rollins 8.00 20.00
32 Jimmy Rollins 8.00 20.00
33 Jimmy Rollins 8.00 20.00
34 Bob Gibson 10.00 25.00
35 Bob Gibson 10.00 25.00
36 Bob Gibson 10.00 25.00
37 Brooks Robinson 15.00 40.00
38 Brooks Robinson 15.00 40.00
39 Brooks Robinson 40.00 80.00
40 Joe DiMaggio 50.00 100.00
41 Joe DiMaggio 50.00 100.00
42 Joe DiMaggio 30.00 60.00
43 Hideo Nomo 20.00 50.00
44 Hideo Nomo 20.00 50.00
45 Hideo Nomo 20.00 50.00
46 Ted Williams 30.00 60.00
47 Ted Williams 30.00 60.00
48 Ted Williams 30.00 60.00
49 David Ortiz 8.00 20.00
50 David Ortiz 8.00 20.00
51 David Ortiz 8.00 20.00
52 Frank Robinson 12.50 30.00
53 Frank Robinson 12.50 30.00
54 Frank Robinson 12.50 30.00
55 Tony Gwynn 15.00 40.00
56 Tony Gwynn 15.00 40.00
57 Tony Gwynn 30.00 60.00
58 Jose Reyes 12.50 30.00
59 Jose Reyes 12.50 30.00
60 Jose Reyes 12.50 30.00
61 Roger Maris 30.00 60.00
62 Roger Maris 30.00 60.00
63 Roger Maris 30.00 60.00
64 Mike Schmidt 15.00 40.00
65 Mike Schmidt 15.00 40.00
66 Mike Schmidt 15.00 40.00
67 Eddie Murray 10.00 25.00
68 Eddie Murray 10.00 25.00
69 Eddie Murray 10.00 25.00
70 Johnny Bench 12.50 30.00
71 Johnny Bench 12.50 30.00
72 Johnny Bench 12.50 30.00
73 Roberto Clemente 40.00 80.00
74 Roberto Clemente 40.00 80.00
75 Roberto Clemente 40.00 80.00
76 Steve Carlton 8.00 20.00
77 Steve Carlton 8.00 20.00
78 Steve Carlton 8.00 20.00
79 Grady Sizemore 10.00 25.00
80 Grady Sizemore 10.00 25.00
81 Grady Sizemore 10.00 25.00
82 Robin Yount 10.00 25.00
83 Robin Yount 10.00 25.00
84 Robin Yount 10.00 25.00
85 Hanley Ramirez 8.00 20.00
86 Hanley Ramirez 8.00 20.00
87 Hanley Ramirez 8.00 20.00
88 Al Kaline 12.50 30.00
89 Al Kaline 12.50 30.00
90 Al Kaline 12.50 30.00
91 Vladimir Guerrero 8.00 20.00
92 Vladimir Guerrero 8.00 20.00
93 Vladimir Guerrero 8.00 20.00
94 George Kell 10.00 25.00
95 George Kell 10.00 25.00
96 George Kell 10.00 25.00
97 Reggie Jackson 10.00 25.00
98 Reggie Jackson 10.00 25.00
99 Reggie Jackson 10.00 25.00
100 Tom Seaver 12.50 30.00
101 Tom Seaver 12.50 30.00
102 Tom Seaver 12.50 30.00
103 Johan Santana 8.00 20.00
104 Johan Santana 8.00 20.00
105 Johan Santana 8.00 20.00
106 Jason Varitek 10.00 25.00
107 Jason Varitek 10.00 25.00
108 Jason Varitek 10.00 25.00
109 Ryan Howard 10.00 25.00
110 Ryan Howard 10.00 25.00
111 Ryan Howard 10.00 25.00
112 Manny Ramirez 8.00 20.00
113 Manny Ramirez 8.00 20.00
114 Manny Ramirez 8.00 20.00
115 Miguel Cabrera 8.00 20.00
116 Miguel Cabrera 8.00 20.00
117 Miguel Cabrera 8.00 20.00
118 Jorge Posada 8.00 20.00
119 Jorge Posada 8.00 20.00
120 Jorge Posada 8.00 20.00
121 Nolan Ryan 20.00 50.00
122 Nolan Ryan 20.00 50.00
123 Nolan Ryan 20.00 50.00
124 Paul Molitor 8.00 20.00
125 Paul Molitor 8.00 20.00
126 Paul Molitor 8.00 20.00
127 Chipper Jones 10.00 25.00
128 Chipper Jones 10.00 25.00
129 Chipper Jones 10.00 25.00
130 Carl Yastrzemski 15.00 40.00
131 Carl Yastrzemski 15.00 40.00
132 Carl Yastrzemski 15.00 40.00
133 Whitey Ford 15.00 40.00
134 Whitey Ford 15.00 40.00
135 Whitey Ford 15.00 40.00
136 Yogi Berra 20.00 50.00
137 Yogi Berra 20.00 50.00
138 Yogi Berra 40.00 80.00
139 Albert Pujols 20.00 50.00
140 Albert Pujols 20.00 50.00
141 Albert Pujols 15.00 40.00
142 Jim Palmer 8.00 20.00
143 Jim Palmer 8.00 20.00
144 Jim Palmer 8.00 20.00
145 Harmon Killebrew 20.00 50.00
146 Harmon Killebrew 20.00 50.00
147 Harmon Killebrew 20.00 50.00
148 Ozzie Smith 10.00 25.00
149 Ozzie Smith 10.00 25.00
150 Ozzie Smith 10.00 25.00
151 Stan Musial 15.00 40.00
152 Stan Musial 15.00 40.00
153 Stan Musial 15.00 40.00
154 Ryne Sandberg 12.50 30.00
155 Ryne Sandberg 12.50 30.00
156 Ryne Sandberg 12.50 30.00
157 Matt Holliday 8.00 20.00
158 Matt Holliday 8.00 20.00
159 Matt Holliday 8.00 20.00
160 Carlos Beltran 8.00 20.00
161 Carlos Beltran 8.00 20.00
162 Carlos Beltran 8.00 20.00
163 Prince Fielder 8.00 20.00
164 Prince Fielder 8.00 20.00
165 Prince Fielder 8.00 20.00
166 Ivan Rodriguez 8.00 20.00
167 Ivan Rodriguez 8.00 20.00
168 Ivan Rodriguez 8.00 20.00
169 Victor Martinez 8.00 20.00
170 Victor Martinez 8.00 20.00
171 Victor Martinez 8.00 20.00
172 Justin Verlander 8.00 20.00
173 Justin Verlander 8.00 20.00
174 Justin Verlander 8.00 20.00
175 Reggie Jackson 10.00 25.00
176 Reggie Jackson 10.00 25.00
177 Reggie Jackson 20.00 50.00
178 Alfonso Soriano 8.00 20.00
179 Alfonso Soriano 8.00 20.00
180 Alfonso Soriano 8.00 20.00
181 Prince Fielder 8.00 20.00
182 Prince Fielder 8.00 20.00
183 Prince Fielder 8.00 20.00
184 Ichiro Suzuki 20.00 50.00
185 Ichiro Suzuki 20.00 50.00
186 Ichiro Suzuki 20.00 50.00
187 David Wright 15.00 40.00
188 David Wright 15.00 40.00
189 David Wright 15.00 40.00
190 Eddie Murray 10.00 25.00
191 Eddie Murray 10.00 25.00
192 Eddie Murray 10.00 25.00
193 Manny Ramirez 8.00 20.00
194 Manny Ramirez 8.00 20.00
195 Manny Ramirez 8.00 20.00
196 Mike Schmidt 15.00 40.00
197 Mike Schmidt 15.00 40.00
198 Mike Schmidt 15.00 40.00
199 Johnny Bench 12.50 30.00
200 Johnny Bench 12.50 30.00
201 Johnny Bench 12.50 30.00
202 Matt Holliday 8.00 20.00
203 Matt Holliday 8.00 20.00
204 Matt Holliday 8.00 20.00
205 Alex Rodriguez 20.00 50.00
206 Alex Rodriguez 20.00 50.00
207 Alex Rodriguez 20.00 50.00
208 Jose Reyes 12.50 30.00
209 Jose Reyes 12.50 30.00
210 Jose Reyes 12.50 30.00
211 Jimmy Rollins 8.00 20.00
212 Jimmy Rollins 8.00 20.00
213 Jimmy Rollins 8.00 20.00
214 David Ortiz 8.00 20.00
215 David Ortiz 8.00 20.00
216 David Ortiz 8.00 20.00
217 Robin Yount 10.00 25.00
218 Robin Yount 10.00 25.00
219 Robin Yount 10.00 25.00
220 Nolan Ryan 20.00 50.00
221 Nolan Ryan 20.00 50.00
222 Nolan Ryan 40.00 80.00
223 Ryan Howard 10.00 25.00
224 Ryan Howard 10.00 25.00
225 Ryan Howard 10.00 25.00
226 John F. Kennedy 150.00 200.00
227 Ty Cobb 100.00 200.00
228 Jimmie Foxx 40.00 80.00
229 Rogers Hornsby 40.00 80.00
230 George Sisler 30.00 60.00
231 Mel Ott 60.00 120.00
232 Jackie Robinson 60.00 120.00
233 Tris Speaker 40.00 80.00
234 Honus Wagner 150.00 250.00
235 Lou Gehrig 100.00 150.00
236 Pee Wee Reese 12.50 30.00
237 Roy Campanella 30.00 60.00
238 Johnny Mize 10.00 25.00
239 Thurman Munson 30.00 60.00
240 Babe Ruth 350.00 450.00

2008 Topps Triple Threads Relics Platinum

STATED ODDS 1:727 MINI
STATED PRINT RUN 1 SER.#'d SET
NO PRICING DUE TO SCARCITY

2008 Topps Triple Threads Relics Sapphire

STATED ODDS 1:241 MINI
STATED PRINT RUN 3 SER.#'d SETS
NO PRICING DUE TO SCARCITY

2008 Topps Triple Threads Relics Autographs

STATED ODDS 1:25 MINI
STATED PRINT RUN 18 SER.#'d SETS
*GOLD: .5X TO 1.2X BASIC
GOLD ODDS 1:50 MINI
GOLD PRINT RUN 9 SER.#'d SETS
PLATINUM ODDS 1:447 MINI
PLATINUM PRINT RUN 1 SER.#'d SET
NO PLATINUM PRICING DUE TO SCARCITY
SAPPHIRE ODDS 1:149 MINI
SAPPHIRE PRINT RUN 3 SER.#'d SETS
NO SAPPHIRE PRICING DUE TO SCARCITY
WHITE WHALE ODDS 1:111 MINI
WHITE WHALE PRINT RUN 1 SER.#'d SET
NO WHITE WHALE PRICING DUE TO SCARCITY
ALL DC VARIATIONS PRICED EQUALLY
1 Prince Fielder 30.00 60.00
2 Prince Fielder 30.00 60.00
3 Prince Fielder 30.00 60.00
4 Vladimir Guerrero 30.00 60.00
5 Vladimir Guerrero 30.00 60.00
6 Vladimir Guerrero 30.00 60.00
7 Bob Gibson 30.00 60.00
8 Bob Gibson 30.00 60.00
9 Bob Gibson 30.00 60.00
10 Chien-Ming Wang 90.00 150.00
11 Chien-Ming Wang 90.00 150.00
12 Chien-Ming Wang 90.00 150.00
13 Johnny Podres 20.00 50.00
14 Johnny Podres 20.00 50.00
15 Johnny Podres 20.00 50.00
16 Frank Robinson 20.00 50.00
17 Frank Robinson 20.00 50.00
18 Frank Robinson 20.00 50.00
19 Robin Yount 30.00 60.00
20 Robin Yount 30.00 60.00
21 Robin Yount 30.00 60.00
22 David Ortiz 40.00 80.00
23 David Ortiz 40.00 80.00
24 David Ortiz 40.00 80.00
25 Chipper Jones 60.00 120.00
26 Chipper Jones 60.00 120.00
27 Chipper Jones 60.00 120.00
28 Cal Ripken Jr. 150.00 250.00
29 Cal Ripken Jr. 150.00 200.00
30 Cal Ripken Jr. 150.00 200.00
31 Carlton Fisk 20.00 50.00
32 Carlton Fisk 20.00 50.00
33 Carlton Fisk 20.00 50.00
34 Jason Varitek 30.00 60.00
35 Jason Varitek 30.00 60.00
36 Jason Varitek 30.00 60.00
37 Ernie Banks 60.00 120.00
38 Ernie Banks 60.00 120.00
39 Ernie Banks 60.00 120.00
40 Harmon Killebrew 50.00 100.00
41 Harmon Killebrew 50.00 100.00
42 Harmon Killebrew 50.00 100.00
43 Travis Hafner 20.00 50.00
44 Travis Hafner 20.00 50.00
45 Travis Hafner 20.00 50.00
46 Manny Ramirez 50.00 100.00
47 Manny Ramirez 50.00 100.00
48 Manny Ramirez 50.00 100.00
49 Tony Gwynn 30.00 60.00
50 Tony Gwynn 30.00 60.00
51 Tony Gwynn 30.00 60.00
52 Alfonso Soriano 20.00 50.00
53 Alfonso Soriano 20.00 50.00
54 Alfonso Soriano 20.00 50.00
55 Carl Yastrzemski 60.00 120.00
56 Carl Yastrzemski 60.00 120.00
57 Carl Yastrzemski 60.00 120.00
58 Jim Palmer 20.00 50.00
59 Jim Palmer 20.00 50.00
60 Jim Palmer 20.00 50.00
61 Jimmy Rollins 30.00 60.00
62 Jimmy Rollins 30.00 60.00
63 Jimmy Rollins 30.00 60.00
64 Frank Thomas 50.00 100.00
65 Frank Thomas 50.00 100.00
66 Frank Thomas 50.00 100.00
67 Brooks Robinson 30.00 60.00
68 Brooks Robinson 30.00 60.00
69 Brooks Robinson 30.00 60.00
70 Dom DiMaggio 20.00 50.00
71 Dom DiMaggio 20.00 50.00
72 Dom DiMaggio 20.00 50.00
73 George Kell 20.00 50.00
74 George Kell 20.00 50.00
75 George Kell 20.00 50.00
76 Wade Boggs 20.00 50.00
77 Wade Boggs 20.00 50.00
78 Wade Boggs 20.00 50.00
79 Johan Santana 40.00 80.00
80 Johan Santana 40.00 80.00
81 Johan Santana 40.00 80.00
82 Jose Reyes 30.00 60.00
83 Jose Reyes 30.00 60.00
84 Jose Reyes 30.00 60.00
85 Hanley Ramirez 30.00 60.00
86 Hanley Ramirez 30.00 60.00
87 Hanley Ramirez 30.00 60.00
88 Johnny Bench 40.00 80.00
89 Johnny Bench 40.00 80.00
90 Johnny Bench 40.00 80.00
91 Mike Lowell 20.00 50.00
92 Mike Lowell 20.00 50.00
93 Mike Lowell 20.00 50.00
94 Tom Seaver 30.00 60.00
95 Tom Seaver 30.00 60.00
96 Tom Seaver 30.00 60.00
97 John Smoltz 40.00 80.00
98 John Smoltz 40.00 80.00
99 John Smoltz 40.00 80.00
100 Ozzie Smith 30.00 60.00
101 Ozzie Smith 30.00 60.00
102 Ozzie Smith 30.00 60.00
103 Duke Snider 30.00 60.00
104 Duke Snider 30.00 60.00
105 Duke Snider 30.00 60.00
106 Steve Carlton 20.00 50.00
107 Steve Carlton 20.00 50.00
108 Steve Carlton 20.00 50.00
109 Jorge Posada 20.00 50.00
110 Jorge Posada 20.00 50.00
111 Jorge Posada 20.00 50.00
112 Andruw Jones 20.00 50.00
113 Andruw Jones 20.00 50.00
114 Andruw Jones 20.00 50.00
115 Reggie Jackson 50.00 100.00
116 Reggie Jackson 50.00 100.00
117 Reggie Jackson 50.00 100.00
118 C.C. Sabathia 20.00 50.00
119 C.C. Sabathia 20.00 50.00
120 C.C. Sabathia 20.00 50.00
121 Jim Thome 30.00 60.00
122 Jim Thome 30.00 60.00
123 Jim Thome 30.00 60.00
124 Mike Schmidt 30.00 60.00
125 Mike Schmidt 30.00 60.00
126 Mike Schmidt 30.00 60.00
127 Yogi Berra 50.00 100.00
128 Yogi Berra 50.00 100.00
129 Yogi Berra 50.00 100.00
130 Dontrelle Willis 20.00 50.00
131 Dontrelle Willis 20.00 50.00
132 Dontrelle Willis 20.00 50.00
133 Nolan Ryan 75.00 150.00
134 Nolan Ryan 75.00 150.00
135 Nolan Ryan 75.00 150.00
136 Goose Gossage 30.00 60.00
137 Goose Gossage 30.00 60.00
138 Goose Gossage 30.00 60.00
139 Al Kaline 20.00 50.00
140 Al Kaline 20.00 50.00
141 Al Kaline 20.00 50.00
142 David Wright 50.00 100.00
143 David Wright 50.00 100.00
144 David Wright 50.00 100.00
145 Miguel Cabrera 30.00 60.00
146 Miguel Cabrera 30.00 60.00
147 Miguel Cabrera 30.00 60.00
148 Ryne Sandberg 40.00 80.00
149 Ryne Sandberg 40.00 80.00
150 Ryne Sandberg 40.00 80.00
151 Tom Glavine 30.00 60.00
152 Tom Glavine 30.00 60.00
153 Tom Glavine 30.00 60.00
154 Paul Molitor 30.00 60.00
155 Paul Molitor 30.00 60.00
156 Paul Molitor 30.00 60.00
157 Eddie Murray 30.00 60.00
158 Eddie Murray 30.00 60.00
159 Eddie Murray 30.00 60.00
160 Justin Verlander 20.00 50.00
161 Justin Verlander 20.00 50.00
162 Justin Verlander 20.00 50.00
163 Dale Murphy 50.00 100.00
164 Dale Murphy 50.00 100.00
165 Dale Murphy 50.00 100.00
166 Whitey Ford 30.00 60.00
167 Whitey Ford 30.00 60.00
168 Whitey Ford 30.00 60.00
169 Matt Holliday 20.00 50.00
170 Matt Holliday 20.00 50.00
171 Matt Holliday 20.00 50.00
172 Albert Pujols 150.00 250.00
173 Albert Pujols 150.00 250.00
174 Albert Pujols 150.00 250.00
175 Stan Musial 50.00 100.00
176 Stan Musial 50.00 100.00
177 Stan Musial 50.00 100.00
178 Ryan Howard 50.00 100.00
179 Ryan Howard 50.00 100.00
180 Ryan Howard 50.00 100.00
181 Johnny Cueto 10.00 25.00
182 Johnny Cueto 10.00 25.00
183 Johnny Cueto 10.00 25.00
184 Evan Longoria 100.00 175.00
185 Evan Longoria 100.00 175.00
186 Evan Longoria 100.00 175.00

2008 Topps Triple Threads Relics Autographs Sapphire

STATED ODDS 1:149 MINI
STATED PRINT RUN 3 SER.#'d SETS
NO PRICING DUE TO SCARCITY

2008 Topps Triple Threads Relics Autographs White Whale Printing Plates

STATED ODDS 1:111 MINI
STATED PRINT RUN 1 SER.#'d SET
NO PRICING DUE TO SCARCITY

2008 Topps Triple Threads Relics Combos

STATED ODDS 1:20 MINI
STATED PRINT RUN 36 SER.#'d SETS
EMERALD ODDS 1:41 MINI
EMERALD PRINT RUN 18 SER.#'d SETS
NO EMERALD PRICING AVAILABLE
GOLD ODDS 1:81 MINI
GOLD PRINT RUN 9 SER.#'d SETS
NO GOLD PRICING AVAILABLE
PLATINUM ODDS 1:727 MINI
PLATINUM PRINT RUN 1 SER.#'d SET
NO PLATINUM PRICING AVAILABLE
SAPPHIRE ODDS 1:241 MINI
SAPPHIRE PRINT RUN 3 SER.#'d SETS
NO SAPPHIRE PRICING AVAILABLE
*SEPIA: .4X TO 1X BASIC COMBO
SEPIA ODDS 1:27 MINI
SEPIA PRINT RUN 27 SER.#'d SETS
1 Alex Rodriguez 20.00 50.00
David Wright
Ryan Howard
2 Mickey Mantle 200.00 300.00
Ted Williams
Joe DiMaggio
3 Ted Williams 40.00 80.00
Carl Yastrzemski
Manny Ramirez
4 Magglio Ordonez 12.50 30.00
Ichiro Suzuki
Placido Polanco
5 Alex Rodriguez 20.00 50.00
Prince Fielder
Ryan Howard
6 Alex Rodriguez 20.00 50.00
Matt Holliday
Magglio Ordonez
7 Jose Reyes 8.00 20.00
Juan Pierre
Hanley Ramirez
8 Chien-Ming Wang 20.00 50.00
Alex Rodriguez
Mariano Rivera
9 Jake Peavy 10.00 25.00
Scott Kazmir
Johan Santana
10 Joe DiMaggio 75.00 150.00
Roberto Clemente
Mickey Mantle
11 Mark Buehrle 10.00 25.00
Justin Verlander
Clay Buchholz
12 Magglio Ordonez 15.00 40.00
Al Kaline
Curtis Granderson
13 Russ Martin 8.00 20.00
Andruw Jones
Rafael Furcal
14 Jason Varitek 8.00 20.00
Jorge Posada
Ivan Rodriguez
15 Yogi Berra 100.00 200.00
Mickey Mantle
Roger Maris
16 Gary Matthews 8.00 20.00
Vladimir Guerrero
Torii Hunter
17 Troy Tulowitzki 10.00 25.00
Matt Holliday
Todd Helton

18 Roberto Clemente 50.00 100.00
Carl Yastrzemski
Reggie Jackson
19 Ernie Banks 15.00 40.00
Alfonso Soriano
Ryne Sandberg
20 Mickey Mantle 60.00 120.00
Albert Pujols
Roberto Clemente
21 Lance Berkman 8.00 20.00
Carlos Lee
Hunter Pence
22 Alex Gordon 12.50 30.00
Ryan Braun
Ryan Zimmerman
23 Mickey Mantle 75.00 150.00
Alex Rodriguez
Ted Williams
24 Justin Morneau 15.00 40.00
Harmon Killebrew
Joe Mauer
25 Trevor Hoffman 20.00 50.00
Dennis Eckersley
Mariano Rivera
26 Jose Reyes 20.00 50.00
David Wright
John Maine
27 Daisuke Matsuzaka 40.00 80.00
Ichiro Suzuki
Hideki Matsui
28 Stan Musial 75.00 150.00
Albert Pujols
Rogers Hornsby
29 Vince DiMaggio 60.00 120.00
Joe DiMaggio
Dom DiMaggio
30 Mike Schmidt 30.00 60.00
George Brett
Steve Carlton
31 Nick Markakis 15.00 40.00
Brooks Robinson
Brian Roberts
32 Prince Fielder 15.00 40.00
Paul Molitor
Ryan Braun
33 Tim Lincecum 30.00 60.00
Joba Chamberlain
Brian Bannister
34 Andruw Jones 10.00 25.00
Ryan Howard
Prince Fielder
35 Manny Ramirez 30.00 60.00
Alex Rodriguez
David Ortiz
36 Jim Palmer 15.00 40.00
Pedro Martinez
Tom Seaver
37 Ichiro Suzuki 20.00 50.00
Todd Helton
Albert Pujols
38 Pedro Martinez 10.00 25.00
Roy Oswalt
Greg Maddux
39 Yogi Berra 75.00 150.00
Joe DiMaggio
Phil Rizzuto
40 Ernie Banks 40.00 80.00
Roberto Clemente
Carl Yastrzemski
41 Justin Morneau 10.00 25.00
Ryan Howard
Prince Fielder
42 Alex Gordon 10.00 25.00
George Brett
Brian Bannister
43 Ryan Howard 20.00 50.00
Albert Pujols
Manny Ramirez
44 Alex Rodriguez 20.00 50.00
Vladimir Guerrero
Prince Fielder
45 Randy Johnson 20.00 50.00
Nolan Ryan
Hideo Nomo
46 Rollie Fingers 15.00 40.00
Reggie Jackson
Vida Blue
47 Roberto Clemente 75.00 150.00
Ichiro Suzuki
Mickey Mantle
48 Brooks Robinson 20.00 50.00
Jim Palmer
Frank Robinson
49 Reggie Jackson 10.00 25.00
Steve Garvey
Willie Randolph
50 David Ortiz 30.00 60.00
Ted Williams
Manny Ramirez
51 Mickey Mantle 75.00 150.00
Alex Rodriguez
Joe DiMaggio
52 Duke Snider 15.00 40.00
Russ Martin
Steve Garvey
53 Ichiro Suzuki 10.00 25.00
Alfonso Soriano
Carlos Beltran
54 Chase Utley 12.50 30.00
Dan Uggla
Dustin Pedroia
55 Jose Reyes 8.00 20.00
Jimmy Rollins
Hanley Ramirez
56 Jimmy Rollins 30.00 60.00
Joe DiMaggio
Chase Utley
57 Johnny Bench 10.00 25.00
Ivan Rodriguez
Carlton Fisk
58 Pedro Martinez 15.00 40.00
Nolan Ryan
Johan Santana
59 Jose Reyes 15.00 40.00
Ozzie Smith
Jimmy Rollins
60 Jimmy Rollins 12.50 30.00
Jake Peavy
Ryan Braun
61 Alex Rodriguez 12.50 30.00
C.C. Sabathia
Dustin Pedroia
62 Delmon Young 15.00 40.00
Alex Rodriguez
Justin Upton
63 Alex Rodriguez 20.00 50.00
Frank Thomas
Jim Thome
64 Roger Maris 100.00 200.00
Mickey Mantle
Harmon Killebrew
65 Carlos Beltran 8.00 20.00
Chipper Jones
Jose Reyes
66 Jimmy Rollins 8.00 20.00
Matt Holliday
Prince Fielder
67 Alex Rodriguez 10.00 25.00
Magglio Ordonez
Vladimir Guerrero
68 Jake Peavy 8.00 20.00
Brandon Webb
Brad Penny
69 C.C. Sabathia 10.00 25.00
Josh Beckett
John Lackey
70 Ryan Braun 10.00 25.00
Troy Tulowitzki
Hunter Pence
71 Dustin Pedroia 10.00 25.00
Delmon Young
Brian Bannister
72 Victor Martinez 10.00 25.00
Grady Sizemore
Travis Hafner
73 Magglio Ordonez 10.00 25.00
Ichiro Suzuki
Vladimir Guerrero
74 Dan Uggla 8.00 20.00
Hanley Ramirez
Cameron Maybin
75 Ichiro Suzuki 30.00 60.00
Daisuke Matsuzaka
Akinori Iwamura
76 Jason Varitek 12.50 30.00
Alex Rodriguez
Chase Utley
77 Tris Speaker 20.00 50.00
Manny Ramirez
Travis Hafner
78 Eddie Mathews 40.00 80.00
Chipper Jones
Dale Murphy
79 Mike Schmidt 12.50 30.00
Ryan Howard
Richie Ashburn
80 Jimmy Rollins 10.00 25.00
Ryan Howard
Chase Utley
81 Matt Holliday 8.00 20.00
Carlos Beltran
Carlos Lee
82 Vladimir Guerrero 10.00 25.00
Magglio Ordonez
Ichiro Suzuki
83 Andruw Jones 8.00 20.00
Jeff Francoeur
Carlos Beltran
84 Grady Sizemore 15.00 40.00
Ichiro Suzuki
Torii Hunter
85 Stan Musial 30.00 60.00
Carl Yastrzemski
Ted Williams
86 Alex Rodriguez 20.00 50.00
Alex Rodriguez
Alex Rodriguez
87 Chipper Jones 12.50 30.00
Brian McCann
Jeff Francoeur
88 Nolan Ryan 60.00 120.00
Nolan Ryan
Nolan Ryan
89 David Ortiz 8.00 20.00
Paul Molitor
Edgar Martinez
90 Alex Rodriguez 20.00 50.00
Albert Pujols
Manny Ramirez
91 Randy Johnson 20.00 50.00
Luis Gonzalez
Mariano Rivera
92 Goose Gossage 20.00 50.00
George Brett
Billy Martin
93 Fausto Carmona 8.00 20.00
Joba Chamberlain
Grady Sizemore
94 Brian Giles 8.00 20.00
Matt Holliday
Michael Barrett
95 Franklin D. Roosevelt 40.00 80.00
Harry S Truman
John F. Kennedy
96 George Bush 50.00 100.00
Ronald Reagan
George W. Bush
97 William H. Taft 40.00 80.00
Woodrow Wilson
Warren G. Harding
98 Johnny Damon 10.00 25.00
Chipper Jones
Matt Holliday
99 David Ortiz 10.00 25.00
Jose Reyes
Alfonso Soriano
100 Adrian Beltre 10.00 25.00
Albert Pujols
Placido Polanco
101 Joe DiMaggio 200.00 300.00
Lou Gehrig
Mickey Mantle
102 Ty Cobb 250.00 350.00
Babe Ruth
Honus Wagner
103 Roy Campanella 30.00 60.00
Thurman Munson
Johnny Bench
104 Pee Wee Reese 40.00 80.00
Jackie Robinson
Roy Campanella
105 Roberto Clemente 75.00 150.00
Honus Wagner
Ralph Kiner
106 Johnny Mize 50.00 100.00
Mel Ott
Rogers Hornsby
107 Reggie Jackson 30.00 60.00
Thurman Munson
Billy Martin
108 Jimmie Foxx 100.00 175.00
Lou Gehrig
Mel Ott
109 Roger Maris 250.00 350.00
Babe Ruth
Mickey Mantle
110 Honus Wagner 200.00 300.00
Ty Cobb
Tris Speaker
111 Jimmie Foxx 30.00 60.00
Manny Ramirez
Ted Williams

2008 Topps Triple Threads Relics Combos Autographs

STATED ODDS 1:97 MINI
STATED PRINT RUN 36 SER.#'d SETS
EMERALD ODDS 1:193 MINI
EMERALD PRINT RUN 18 SER.#'d SETS
NO EMERALD PRICING AVAILABLE
GOLD ODDS 1:387 MINI
GOLD PRINT RUN 9 SER.#'d SETS
NO GOLD PRICING AVAILABLE
PLATINUM ODDS 1:3383 MINI
PLAT.PRINT RUN 1 SER.#'d SET
NO PLAT.PRICING AVAILABLE
SAPPHIRE ODDS 1:1179 MINI
SAPP.PRINT RUN 3 SER.#'d SETS
NO SAPP.PRICING AVAILABLE
*SEPIA: .4X TO 1X BASIC
SEPIA ODDS 1:129 MINI
SEPIA PRINT RUN 27 SER.#'d SETS
WHITE WHALE ODDS 1:874 MINI
WHITE WHALE PRINT RUN 1 SER.#'d SET
NO WHITE WHALE PRICING AVAILABLE
1 Jose Reyes 50.00 100.00
Ozzie Smith
Hanley Ramirez
2 Albert Pujols 125.00 250.00
Manny Ramirez
Vladimir Guerrero
3 Keith Hernandez 50.00 100.00
Mike Schmidt
Dale Murphy
4 Frank Robinson 75.00 150.00
Carl Yastrzemski
Harmon Killebrew
5 Bob Gibson 60.00 120.00
Tom Seaver
Steve Carlton
6 Harmon Killebrew 50.00 100.00
Rod Carew
Brooks Robinson
7 David Wright 125.00 250.00
Ryan Howard
Albert Pujols
8 Prince Fielder 60.00 120.00
Eddie Murray
Ryan Howard
9 Nolan Ryan 125.00 250.00
George Brett
Robin Yount
10 Johnny Bench 60.00 120.00
Ivan Rodriguez
Carlton Fisk
11 Yogi Berra 75.00 150.00
Whitey Ford
Jorge Posada
12 Tony Gwynn 60.00 120.00
Dale Murphy
Darryl Strawberry
13 Mike Lowell 60.00 120.00
Manny Ramirez
David Ortiz
14 Joba Chamberlain 125.00 250.00
Jorge Posada
Chien-Ming Wang
15 Jeff Francis 12.50 30.00
Taylor Buchholz
Ubaldo Jimenez
16 Melky Cabrera 20.00 50.00
Ross Ohlendorf
Robinson Cano
17 Dan Uggla 15.00 40.00
Chris Seddon
Hanley Ramirez
18 Alex Gordon 40.00 80.00
Evan Longoria
Ryan Zimmerman
19 Chris Young 12.50 30.00
Melky Cabrera
Lastings Milledge
20 Rich Hill 12.50 30.00
Johnny Cueto
Tom Gorzelanny
21 Dustin Moseley 15.00 40.00
Francisco Liriano
Felix Hernandez
22 Hanley Ramirez 15.00 40.00
James Loney
J.J. Hardy
23 Armando Galarraga 12.50 30.00
Fausto Carmona
Troy Patton

2008 Topps Triple Threads Relics Combos Double

STATED ODDS 1:41 MINI
STATED PRINT RUN 36 SER.#'d SETS
EMERALD ODDS 1:81 MINI
EMERALD PRINT RUN 18 SER.#'d SETS
NO EMERALD PRICING AVAILABLE
GOLD ODDS 1:162 MINI
GOLD PRINT RUN 9 SER.#'d SETS
NO GOLD PRICING AVAILABLE
PLATINUM ODDS 1:1496 MINI
PLAT.PRINT RUN 1 SER.#'d SET
NO PLAT.PRICING AVAILABLE
SAPPHIRE ODDS 1:486 MINI
SAPP.PRINT RUN 3 SER.#'d SETS
NO SAPP.PRICING AVAILABLE
*SEPIA: .4X TO 1X BASIC
SEPIA ODDS 1:54 MINI
SEPIA PRINT RUN 27 SER.#'d SETS
1 Joe DiMaggio 125.00 250.00
Mickey Mantle
Roger Maris
Roberto Clemente
Ted Williams
Tris Speaker
2 Ty Cobb 250.00 350.00
Rogers Hornsby
Joe DiMaggio
Ted Williams
Tony Gwynn
Ichiro Suzuki
3 Troy Tulowitzki 30.00 60.00
Chipper Jones
Troy Tulowitzki
Kelly Johnson
Troy Tulowitzki
Edgar Renteria
4 Albert Pujols 60.00 120.00
Bob Gibson
Rogers Hornsby
Stan Musial
Ozzie Smith
Red Schoendienst
5 Ryan Howard 40.00 80.00
Albert Pujols
Prince Fielder
Vladimir Guerrero
Alex Rodriguez
David Ortiz
6 Tom Seaver 60.00 120.00
Nolan Ryan
Steve Carlton
Dennis Eckersley
Jim Palmer
Whitey Ford
7 Jose Reyes 30.00 60.00
Hanley Ramirez
Jimmy Rollins
Carl Crawford
Brian Roberts
Ichiro Suzuki
8 Russell Martin 30.00 60.00
Brian McCann
Jorge Posada
Mike Piazza
Carlton Fisk
Yogi Berra
9 Joe DiMaggio/Mickey Mantle 100.00 200.00
10 Joe DiMaggio 100.00 200.00
Mickey Mantle
Roger Maris
Billy Martin
Phil Rizzuto
Whitey Ford
11 Frank Robinson 75.00 150.00
Carl Yastrzemski
Roberto Clemente
Mickey Mantle
Ted Williams
Harmon Killebrew
12 Roy Oswalt 20.00 50.00
Peter Munro
Kirk Saarloos
Brad Lidge
Octavio Dotel
Billy Wagner
13 Mickey Mantle 75.00 150.00
Joe DiMaggio
Ted Williams
David Wright
Ryan Howard
Alex Rodriguez
14 Alex Rodriguez 50.00 100.00
Hideki Matsui
Jorge Posada
Johnny Damon
Chien-Ming Wang
Joba Chamberlain
15 Akinori Iwamura 50.00 100.00
Kenji Johjima
Hideki Matsui
Hideki Okajima
Kaz Matsui
Ichiro Suzuki
16 Russell Martin 20.00 50.00
Jason Bay
Erik Bedard
Rich Harden
Justin Morneau
Shawn Hill
17 Carlos Beltran 30.00 60.00
David Wright
Carlos Delgado
Jose Reyes
Pedro Martinez
John Maine
18 Travis Hafner 20.00 50.00
Victor Martinez
Grady Sizemore
C.C. Sabathia
Fausto Carmona
Bob Feller
19 Brooks Robinson 20.00 50.00
Jim Palmer
Eddie Murray
Brian Roberts
Nick Markakis
Melvin Mora
20 David Ortiz 40.00 80.00
Jason Varitek
Josh Beckett
Manny Ramirez
Mike Lowell
Hideki Okajima
21 Jose Vidro 40.00 80.00
Alex Rodriguez
Ichiro Suzuki
J.J. Putz
Edgar Martinez
Kenji Johjima
22 Alex Rodriguez 30.00 60.00
C.C. Sabathia
Dustin Pedroia
Jimmy Rollins
Jake Peavy
Ryan Braun
23 Mickey Mantle 150.00 250.00
24 Joe DiMaggio 60.00 120.00
25 Roberto Clemente 60.00 120.00
26 Carlos Lee 30.00 60.00
Roy Oswalt
Lance Berkman
Hunter Pence
Nolan Ryan
Kaz Matsui
27 Jimmy Rollins 30.00 60.00
Mike Schmidt
Chase Utley
Cole Hamels
Robin Roberts
Ryan Howard
28 Johnny Podres 40.00 80.00
Whitey Ford
Bob Gibson
Frank Robinson
Brooks Robinson
Roberto Clemente
29 Ted Williams 50.00 100.00
30 Justin Morneau 50.00 100.00
Rod Carew
Francisco Liriano
Joe Mauer
Delmon Young
Harmon Killebrew
31 Justin Morneau 30.00 60.00
Ryan Howard
Albert Pujols
Prince Fielder
Carlos Delgado
Mark Teixeira
32 Magglio Ordonez 50.00 100.00
Al Kaline
Ivan Rodriguez
Curtis Granderson
Ty Cobb
Gary Sheffield
33 Carlton Fisk 20.00 50.00
Jim Thome
Jermaine Dye
Mark Buehrle
Paul Konerko
Luis Aparicio
34 Keith Hernandez 20.00 50.00
Dwight Gooden
Darryl Strawberry
David Wright
Pedro Martinez
Jose Reyes
35 Chipper Jones 30.00 60.00
John Smoltz
Brian McCann
Jeff Francoeur
Mark Teixeira
Tom Glavine
36 Alex Rodriguez 40.00 80.00
Jorge Posada
Johnny Damon
David Ortiz
Manny Ramirez
Jason Varitek
37 Roger Maris/Mickey Mantle 200.00 300.00
38 Ichiro Suzuki 40.00 80.00
39 Albert Pujols 30.00 60.00
40 Robin Yount 30.00 60.00
Paul Molitor
Rollie Fingers
Prince Fielder
Ryan Braun
Ben Sheets
41 Nolan Ryan 30.00 60.00
Alex Rodriguez
Ivan Rodriguez
Ian Kinsler
Michael Young
Hank Blalock
42 Vladimir Guerrero 20.00 50.00
John Lackey
Jered Weaver
Garret Anderson
Torii Hunter
Gary Matthews
43 Tim Lincecum 20.00 50.00
Rich Aurilia
Barry Zito
Eric Chavez
Mark Ellis
Bobby Crosby
44 Russell Martin 20.00 50.00
Rafael Furcal
Andruw Jones
Matt Kemp
Jeff Kent
Hong-Chih Kuo
45 David Wright 30.00 60.00
Carlos Beltran
Jose Reyes
Ryan Howard
Jimmy Rollins
Chase Utley
46 Chien-Ming Wang 40.00 80.00
47 Ichiro Suzuki 30.00 60.00
Alex Rodriguez
Magglio Ordonez
David Ortiz
Ivan Rodriguez
Vladimir Guerrero
48 Manny Ramirez 30.00 60.00
David Ortiz
Mike Lowell
Travis Hafner
Victor Martinez
Grady Sizemore
49 Matt Holliday 20.00 50.00
Todd Helton
Troy Tulowitzki
Orlando Hudson
Stephen Drew
Chris Young
50 Manny Ramirez 30.00 60.00
David Ortiz
Mike Lowell
Matt Holliday
Todd Helton
Troy Tulowitzki
51 Alex Rodriguez/Mickey Mantle 40.00 80.00
52 Albert Pujols 30.00 60.00
Vladimir Guerrero
Manny Ramirez
David Ortiz
Pedro Martinez
Alfonso Soriano
53 Joe DiMaggio 450.00 650.00
Ty Cobb
Babe Ruth
Lou Gehrig
Ted Williams
Mickey Mantle
54 George Sisler 100.00 200.00
Rogers Hornsby
Jimmie Foxx
Mel Ott
Johnny Mize
Pee Wee Reese
55 Jackie Robinson 100.00 200.00
Duke Snider
Roy Campanella
Phil Rizzuto
Mickey Mantle
Yogi Berra

2008 Topps Triple Threads Relics Combos Double Autographs

STATED ODDS 1:4323 MINI
STATED PRINT RUN 3 SER.#'d SETS
NO PRICING DUE TO SCARCITY
1 Carlton Fisk
Carl Yastrzemski
Wade Boggs
Manny Ramirez
David Ortiz
Daisuke Matsuzaka
2 Goose Gossage
Brooks Robinson
Robin Yount
Dale Murphy
Reggie Jackson
Nolan Ryan
3 Wade Boggs
Mike Schmidt
Brooks Robinson
David Wright
Miguel Cabrera
Ryan Braun
4 John Smoltz
C.C. Sabathia
Justin Verlander
Johan Santana
Tom Glavine
Chien-Ming Wang
5 Albert Pujols
Ryan Howard
Chipper Jones
Bob Gibson
Mike Schmidt
Dale Murphy
6 Yogi Berra
Whitey Ford
Don Larsen
Jorge Posada
Joba Chamberlain
Chien-Ming Wang

2008 Topps Triple Threads Relics Combos Double Autographs Platinum

STATED ODDS 1:12,969 MINI
STATED PRINT RUN 1 SER.#'d SET
NO PRICING DUE TO SCARCITY

2008 Topps Triple Threads Relics Pairs Autographs

STATED ODDS 1:486 MINI
STATED PRINT RUN 18 SER.#'d SETS
NO PRICING DUE TO SCARCITY
GLD ODDS 1:894 MINI
GLD PRINT RUN 9 SER.#'d SETS
NO GLD PRICING AVAILABLE
PLAT.ODDS 1:7781 MINI
PLAT.PRINT RUN 1 SER.#'d SET
NO PLAT.PRICING AVAILABLE
SAP.ODDS 1:802 MINI
SAP.PRINT RUN 3 SER.#'D SETS
NO SAP.PRICING AVAILABLE
1 Ryan Howard
David Wright
2 Manny Ramirez
David Ortiz
3 Frank Thomas
Jim Thome
4 Eddie Murray
Mike Schmidt
5 Paul Molitor
Prince Fielder
6 Jimmy Rollins
Ryan Howard
7 C.C. Sabathia
Johan Santana
8 Travis Hafner
Fausto Carmona
9 Robin Yount
Ozzie Smith
10 Whitey Ford
Yogi Berra

2008 Topps Triple Threads Relics Pairs Rookie-Stars Autographs

STATED ODDS 1:160 MINI
STATED PRINT RUN 50 SER.#'d SETS
GLD ODDS 1:322 MINI
GLD.PRINT RUN 25 SER.#'d SETS
NO GLD.PRICING AVAILABLE

PLAT.ODDS 1:7781 MINI
PLAT.PRINT RUN 1 SER.#'d SET
NO PLAT.PRICING AVAILABLE
SAP.ODDS 1:802 MINI
SAP.PRINT RUN 10 SER.#'d SETS
NO SAP.PRICING AVAILABLE
1 Steve Pearce 10.00 25.00
Nyjer Morgan
2 Cameron Maybin 12.50 30.00
Curtis Granderson
3 Melky Cabrera 20.00 50.00
Robinson Cano
4 Lastings Milledge 10.00 25.00
Elijah Dukes
5 Rich Hill 10.00 25.00
Sam Fuld
6 J.R. Towles 10.00 25.00
Jarrod Saltalamacchia
7 Clay Buchholz 20.00 50.00
Fausto Carmona
8 Ryan Braun 30.00 60.00
Ryan Zimmerman
9 Phil Hughes 30.00 60.00
Joba Chamberlain
10 Brandon Phillips 12.50 30.00
Homer Bailey

2008 Topps Triple Threads Relics X Autographs Gold

STATED ODDS 1:3890 MINI
STATED PRINT RUN 10 SER.#'d SETS
NO PRICING DUE TO SCARCITY
PLATINUM STATED ODDS 1:38,907 MINI
PLAT.PRINT RUN 1 SER.#'d SET
NO PLAT.PRICING DUE TO SCARCITY
SAPPHIRE STATED ODDS 1:7781 MINI
SAPP.PRINT RUN 5 SER.#'d SETS
NO SAPP.PRICING DUE TO SCARCITY
1 Daisuke Matsuzaka
2 John Elway

2008 Topps Triple Threads Triple Signed Hide

STATED ODDS 1:15,562 MINI
STATED PRINT RUN 1 SER.#'d SET
NO PRICING DUE TO SCARCITY
1 Don Mattingly
Mickey Mantle
Reggie Jackson
2 Joe DiMaggio
Mike Schmidt
Stan Musial
3 Bob Gibson
Roger Maris
Stan Musial
4 Yogi Berra
Joe DiMaggio
Whitey Ford
5 Phil Niekro
Billy Martin
Phil Rizzuto

2008 Topps Triple Threads XXIV Legends Relics

STATED ODDS 1:15,562 MINI
NO PRICING DUE TO SCARCITY
1 Babe Ruth
2 Lou Gehrig
3 Jackie Robinson
4 Tris Speaker
5 Ty Cobb

2008 Topps Triple Threads XXIV Relics

STATED ODDS 1:149 MINI
STATED PRINT RUN 18 SER.#'d SETS
NO PRICING DUE TO SCARCITY
GLD.ODDS 1:297 MINI
GLD.PRINT RUN 9 SER.#'d SETS
NO GLD.PRICING AVAILABLE
PLAT.ODDS 1:2683 MINI
PLAT.PRINT RUN 1 SER.#'d SET
NO PLAT.PRICING AVAILABLE
SAP.ODDS 1:894 MINI
SAP.PRINT RUN 3 SER.#'d SETS
NO SAP.PRICING AVAILABLE

2005 Topps Turkey Red

This 330-card set was released in August, 2005. The set was issued in eight-card packs with a $4 SRP which came 24 packs to a box and eight boxes to a case. Interspersed throughout the set are both short prints and reprinted cards of some of the great players in the original set. The SP's were issued at a stated rate of one in four. Cards numbered 271 through 300 feature Rookie Cards while cards 301 through 315 feature retired greats.

COMPLETE SET (330) 200.00 300.00
COMP.SET w/o SP's (275) 20.00 50.00
COMMON CARD (1-270) .15 .40
COMMON SP (1-270) 3.00 8.00
SP CL: 160A/160B/170/175/181/184/185/193
COMMON REPRINT .30 .75
COMMON RC (271-300) .40 1.00
COMMON RET (301-315) .40 1.00
VAR CL: 1/5/10/16/75/83/100/102/120/125
VAR CL: 130/160/225/230/270
TWO VERSIONS OF EACH VARIATION EXIST
1A B.Bonds Grey Uni SP 6.00 15.00
1B B.Bonds White Uni 1.00 2.50
2 Michael Young .15 .40
3 Jim Edmonds .15 .40
4 Cliff Floyd .15 .40
5A R.Clemens Blue Sky SP 4.00 10.00
5B R.Clemens Yellow Sky SP 4.00 10.00
6 Hal Chase REP .30 .75
7 Shannon Stewart .15 .40
8 Fred Clarke REP .30 .75
9 Travis Hafner .15 .40
10A S.Sosa w/Name SP 3.00 8.00
10B S.Sosa w/o Name SP 3.00 8.00
11 Jermaine Dye .15 .40
12 Lyle Overbay .15 .40
13 Oliver Perez .15 .40
14 Red Dooin REP .30 .75
15 Kid Elberfeld REP .30 .75
16A M.Piazza Blue Uni SP 3.00 8.00
16B M.Piazza Pinstripe .40 1.00
17 Bret Boone .15 .40
18 Hughie Jennings REP .30 .75
19 Jeff Francis .15 .40
20 Manny Ramirez SP 3.00 8.00
21 Russ Ortiz .15 .40
22 Carlos Zambrano .15 .40
23 Luis Castillo .15 .40
24 David DeJesus .15 .40
25 Carlos Beltran SP 3.00 8.00
26 Doug Davis .15 .40
27 Bobby Abreu .15 .40
28 Rich Harden SP 3.00 8.00
29 Brian Giles .15 .40
30 Richie Sexson SP 3.00 8.00
31 Nick Johnson .15 .40
32 Roy Halladay .15 .40
33 Andy Pettitte .25 .60
34 Miguel Cabrera .25 .60
35 Jeff Kent .15 .40
36 Chone Figgins .15 .40
37 Carlos Lee .15 .40
38 Greg Maddux .60 1.50
39 Preston Wilson .15 .40
40 Chipper Jones .40 1.00
41 Coco Crisp .15 .40
42 Adam Dunn .15 .40
43 Out At Second M.Tejada CL .15 .40
44 Sheffield At Bat CL .15 .40
45 Play At the Plate J.Lopez CL .15 .40
46 Rolen Diggin' In CL .15 .40
47 Helton With the Slap Tag CL .15 .40
48 Clemens Bringing Heat CL .40 1.00
49 A Close Play J.Rollins CL .15 .40
50 Ichiro At Bat CL .40 1.00
51 Can of Corn C.Floyd CL .15 .40
52 Pulling String J.Santana CL .40 1.00
53 Mark Teixeira .25 .60
54 Chris Carpenter .15 .40
55 Roy Oswalt SP 3.00 8.00
56 Casey Kotchman .15 .40
57 Torii Hunter .15 .40
58 Jose Reyes .15 .40
59 Wily Mo Pena SP 3.00 8.00
60 Magglio Ordonez SP 3.00 8.00
61 Aaron Miles .15 .40
62 Dallas McPherson .15 .40
63 Javy Lopez .15 .40
64 Luis Gonzalez .15 .40
65 David Ortiz .40 1.00
66 Jorge Posada .25 .60
67 Xavier Nady .15 .40
68 Larry Walker .25 .60
69 Mark Loretta .15 .40
70 Jim Thome SP 3.00 8.00
71 Livan Hernandez .15 .40
72 Garrett Atkins .15 .40
73 Milton Bradley .15 .40
74 B.J. Upton .15 .40
75A I.Suzuki w/Name SP 4.00 10.00
75B I.Suzuki w/o Name SP 4.00 10.00
76 Aramis Ramirez .15 .40
77 Eric Milton .15 .40
78 Troy Glaus SP 3.00 8.00
79 David Newhan .15 .40
80 Delmon Young .25 .60
81 Justin Morneau .15 .40
82 Ramon Ortiz .15 .40
83A E.Chavez Blue Sky .15 .40
83B E.Chavez Purple Sky SP 3.00 8.00
84 Sean Burroughs .15 .40
85 Scott Rolen SP 3.00 8.00
86 Rocco Baldelli .15 .40
87 Joe Mauer SP 4.00 10.00
88 Tony Womack .15 .40
89 Ken Griffey Jr. .60 1.50
90 Alfonso Soriano SP 3.00 8.00
91 Paul Konerko .15 .40
92 Guillermo Mota .15 .40
93 Lance Berkman .15 .40
94 Mark Buehrle .15 .40
95 Matt Clement .15 .40
96 Melvin Mora .15 .40
97 Khalil Greene .25 .60
98 David Wright .60 1.50
99 Jack Wilson .15 .40
100A A.Rodriguez w/Bat SP 4.00 10.00
100B A.Rodriguez w/Glove SP 4.00 10.00
101 Joe Nathan .15 .40
102A A.Beltre Grey Uni SP 3.00 8.00
102B A.Beltre White Uni .15 .40
103 Mike Sweeney .15 .40
104 Brad Lidge .15 .40
105 Shawn Green .15 .40
106 Miguel Tejada SP 3.00 8.00
107 Derrek Lee .25 .60
108 Eric Hinske .15 .40
109 Eric Byrnes .15 .40
110 Hideki Matsui SP 3.00 8.00
111 Tom Glavine .25 .60
112 Jimmy Rollins .15 .40
113 Ryan Drese .15 .40
114 Josh Beckett .15 .40
115 Curt Schilling SP 3.00 8.00
116 Jeremy Bonderman .15 .40
117 Kazuo Matsui .15 .40
118 Chase Utley .25 .60
119 Troy Percival .15 .40
120A V.Guerrero w/Bat SP 3.00 8.00
120B V.Guerrero w/Glove SP 3.00 8.00
121 Gary Sheffield .15 .40
122 Jeromy Burnitz .15 .40
123 Javier Vazquez .15 .40
124 Kevin Millar .15 .40
125A R.Johnson Blue Sky .40 1.00
125B R.Johnson Purple Sky SP 3.00 8.00
126 Pat Burrell .15 .40
127 Jason Schmidt .15 .40
128 Jose Vidro .15 .40
129 Kip Wells .15 .40
130A I.Rodriguez w/Cap .25 .60
130B I.Rodriguez w/Helmet SP 3.00 8.00
131 C.C. Sabathia .15 .40
132 Carlos Delgado SP 3.00 8.00
133 Bartolo Colon .15 .40
134 Andruw Jones .25 .60
135 Kerry Wood .15 .40
136 Sidney Ponson .15 .40
137 Eric Gagne .15 .40
138 Rickie Weeks .15 .40
139 Mariano Rivera .40 1.00
140 Bobby Crosby .15 .40
141 Jamie Moyer .15 .40
142 Corey Koskie .15 .40
143 John Smoltz .25 .60
144 Frank Thomas .40 1.00
145 Cristian Guzman .15 .40
146 Paul Lo Duca .15 .40
147 Geoff Jenkins .15 .40
148 Nick Swisher .15 .40
149 Jason Bay SP 3.00 8.00
150 Albert Pujols SP 6.00 15.00
151 Edwin Jackson .15 .40
152 Carl Crawford .15 .40
153 Mark Mulder .15 .40
154 Rafael Palmeiro .25 .60
155 Pedro Martinez SP 3.00 8.00
156 Jake Westbrook .15 .40
157 Sean Casey .15 .40
158 Aaron Rowand .15 .40
159 J.D. Drew .15 .40
160A J.Sant Glove on Knee SP 3.00 8.00
160B J.Santana Throwing SP 3.00 8.00
161 Gavin Floyd .15 .40
162 Vernon Wells .15 .40
163 Aubrey Huff .15 .40
164 Jeff Bagwell .25 .60
165 Boomer Wells .15 .40
166 Brad Penny .15 .40
167 Austin Kearns .15 .40
168 Mike Mussina .25 .60
169 Randy Wolf .15 .40
170 Tim Hudson SP 3.00 8.00
171 Casey Blake .15 .40
172 Edgar Renteria .15 .40
173 Ben Sheets .15 .40
174 Kevin Brown .15 .40
175 Nomar Garciaparra SP 3.00 8.00
176 Armando Benitez .15 .40
177 Jody Gerut .15 .40
178 Craig Biggio .25 .60
179 Omar Vizquel .25 .60
180 Jake Peavy .15 .40
181 Gustavo Chacin SP 3.00 8.00
182 Johnny Damon .25 .60
183 Mike Lieberthal .15 .40
184 Felix Hernandez SP 6.00 15.00
185 Zach Day SP 3.00 8.00
186 Matt Cain .40 1.00
187 Erubiel Durazo .15 .40
188 Zack Greinke .15 .40
189 Matt Morris .15 .40
190 Billy Wagner .15 .40
191 Al Leiter .15 .40
192 Miguel Olivo .15 .40
193 Jose Capellan SP 3.00 8.00
194 Adam Eaton .15 .40
195 Steven White SP RC 3.00 8.00
196 Jose Randa .15 .40
197 Richard Hidalgo .15 .40
198 Orlando Cabrera .15 .40
199 Joel Guzman SP 3.00 8.00
200 Garret Anderson .15 .40
201 Endy Chavez .15 .40
202 Andy Marte .15 .40
203 Jose Guillen .15 .40
204 Victor Martinez .15 .40
205 Johnny Estrada .15 .40
206 Damian Miller .15 .40
207 Ken Harvey .15 .40
208 Ronnie Belliard .15 .40
209 Chan Ho Park .15 .40
210 Laynce Nix .15 .40
211 Lew Ford .15 .40
212 Moises Alou .15 .40
213 Kris Benson .15 .40
214 Mike Gonzalez SP 3.00 8.00
215 Chris Burke .15 .40
216 Juan Pierre .15 .40
217 Phil Nevin .15 .40
218 Jerry Hairston Jr. .15 .40
219 Jeremy Reed .15 .40
220 Scott Kazmir SP 3.00 8.00
221 Mike Maroth .15 .40
222 Alex Rios .15 .40
223 Esteban Loaiza .15 .40
224 Termel Sledge .15 .40
225A M.Prior Blue Sky SP 3.00 8.00
225B M.Prior Yellow Sky SP 3.00 8.00
226 Hank Blalock .15 .40
227 Craig Wilson .15 .40
228 Cesar Izturis .15 .40
229 Dmitri Young .15 .40
230A D.Jeter Blue Sky SP 6.00 15.00
230B D.Jeter Purple Sky SP 6.00 15.00
231 Mark Kotsay .15 .40
232 Darin Erstad .15 .40
233 Brandon Backe SP 3.00 8.00
234 Mike Lowell .15 .40
235 Scott Podsednik .15 .40
236 Michael Barrett .15 .40
237 Chad Tracy .15 .40
238 David Dellucci .15 .40
239 Brady Clark .15 .40
240 Jorge Cantu .15 .40
241 Wil Ledezma .15 .40
242 Morgan Ensberg .15 .40
243 Omar Infante .15 .40
244 Corey Patterson .15 .40
245 Matt Holliday .20 .50
246 Vinny Castilla .15 .40
247 Jason Bartlett .15 .40
248 Noah Lowry .15 .40
249 Huston Street .25 .60
250 Russell Branyan .15 .40
251 Juan Uribe .15 .40
252 Larry Bigbie .15 .40
253 Grady Sizemore .25 .60
254 Pedro Feliz .15 .40
255 Brad Wilkerson .15 .40
256 Brandon Inge .15 .40
257 Dewon Brazelton .15 .40
258 Rodrigo Lopez .15 .40
259 Jacque Jones .15 .40
260 Jason Giambi .15 .40
261 Clint Barmes .15 .40
262 Willy Taveras .15 .40
263 Marcus Giles .15 .40
264 Joe Blanton .15 .40
265 John Thomson .15 .40
266 Steve Finley SP 3.00 8.00
267 Kevin Millwood .15 .40
268 David Eckstein .15 .40
269 Barry Zito .15 .40
270A T.Helton Purple Sky SP 3.00 8.00
270B T.Helton Yellow Sky SP 3.00 8.00
271 Landon Powell RC .40 1.00
272 Justin Verlander RC 1.50 4.00
273 Wes Swackhamer RC .40 1.00
274 Wladimir Balentien RC .40 1.00
275 Philip Humber RC .40 1.00
276 Kevin Melillo RC .40 1.00
277 Billy Butler RC 1.50 4.00
278 Michael Rogers RC .40 1.00
279 Bobby Livingston RC .40 1.00
280 Glen Perkins RC .40 1.00
281 Mike Bourn RC .40 1.00
282 Tyler Pelland RC .40 1.00
283 Jeremy West RC .40 1.00
284 Brandon McCarthy RC .60 1.50
285 Ian KinslerÂ RC 1.00 2.50
286 Chris Roberson RC .40 1.00
287 Melky Cabrera RC .75 2.00
288 Ryan Sweeney RC .40 1.00
289 Chip Cannon RC .50 1.25
290 Andy LaRoche RC 1.50 4.00
291 Chuck Tiffany RC .50 1.25
292 Ian Bladergroen RC .40 1.00
293 Bear Bay RC .40 1.00
294 Hernan Iribarren RC .50 1.25
295 Stuart Pomeranz RC .40 1.00
296 Luke Scott RC .75 2.00
297 Chuck James RC .75 2.00
298 Kennard Bibbs RC .40 1.00
299 Steven Bondurant RC .40 1.00
300 Thomas Oldham RC .40 1.00
301 Nolan Ryan RET 2.00 5.00
302 Reggie Jackson RET .50 1.25
303 Tom Seaver RET .50 1.25
304 Al Kaline RET .75 2.00
305 Cal Ripken RET 2.50 6.00
306 Josh Gibson RET .75 2.00
307 Frank Robinson RET .40 1.00
308 Duke Snider RET .50 1.25
309 Wade Boggs RET .50 1.25
310 Tony Gwynn RET 1.00 2.50
311 Carl Yastrzemski RET .75 2.00
312 Ryne Sandberg RET 1.25 3.00
313 Gary Carter RET .40 1.00
314 Brooks Robinson RET .50 1.25
315 Ernie Banks RET .75 2.00

2005 Topps Turkey Red Black

COMMON CARD (1-270) 2.00 5.00
*BLACK 1-270: 5X TO 12X BASIC
*BLACK 1-270: .75X TO 2X BASIC SP
*BLACK 1-270: 4X TO 10X BASIC REP
*BLACK 271-300: 2X TO 5X BASIC
*BLACK 301-315: 2.5X TO 6X BASIC
STATED ODDS 1:20 HOBBY/RETAIL
STATED PRINT RUN 142 SETS
CARDS ARE NOT SERIAL-NUMBERED
PRINT RUN INFO PROVIDED BY TOPPS
THERE ARE NO SP'S IN THIS SET
1A Barry Bonds Grey Uni 20.00 50.00
1B Barry Bonds White Uni 20.00 50.00
5A Roger Clemens Blue Sky 8.00 20.00
10A Sammy Sosa w/Name 5.00 12.00
10B Sammy Sosa w/o Name 5.00 12.00
16A Mike Piazza Blue Uni 5.00 12.00
20 Manny Ramirez 5.00 12.00
25 Carlos Beltran 2.00 5.00
28 Rich Harden 2.00 5.00
30 Richie Sexson 2.00 5.00
52 Pulling String J.Santana CL 3.00 8.00
55 Roy Oswalt 2.00 5.00
59 Wily Mo Pena 2.00 5.00
60 Magglio Ordonez 2.00 5.00
70 Jim Thome 3.00 8.00
75A IchiroÂ Suzuki w/Name 10.00 25.00
75B IchiroÂ Suzuki w/o Name 10.00 25.00
78 Troy Glaus 2.00 5.00
83B Eric Chavez Purple Sky 2.00 5.00
85 Scott Rolen 3.00 8.00
87 Joe Mauer 3.00 8.00
90 Alfonso Soriano 2.00 5.00
102A Adrian Beltre Grey Uni 2.00 5.00
106 Miguel Tejada 2.00 5.00
110 Hideki Matsui 8.00 20.00
115 Curt Schilling 3.00 8.00
120A Vladimir Guerrero w/Bat 5.00 12.00
120B Vladimir Guerrero w/Glove 5.00 12.00
125B Randy Johnson Purple Sky 5.00 12.00
130B Ivan Rodriguez w/Helmet 3.00 8.00
132 Carlos Delgado 2.00 5.00
149 Jason Bay 2.00 5.00
150 Albert Pujols 10.00 25.00
155 Pedro Martinez 3.00 8.00
160A J.Santana Glove on Knee 5.00 12.00
160B J.Santana Throwing 5.00 12.00
170 Tim Hudson 2.00 5.00
175 Nomar Garciaparra 5.00 12.00
181 Gustavo Chacin 2.00 5.00
184 Felix Hernandez 8.00 20.00
185 Zach Day 2.00 5.00
193 Jose Capellan 2.00 5.00
195 Steven White 2.00 5.00
199 Joel Guzman 2.00 5.00
214 Mike Gonzalez 2.00 5.00
220 Scott Kazmir 2.00 5.00
225A Mark Prior Blue Sky 3.00 8.00
225B Mark Prior Yellow Sky 3.00 8.00
230A Derek Jeter Blue Sky 15.00 40.00
230B Derek Jeter Purple Sky 15.00 40.00
233 Brandon Backe 2.00 5.00
266 Steve Finley 2.00 5.00
270A Todd Helton Purple Sky 3.00 8.00
270B Todd Helton Yellow Sky 3.00 8.00

2005 Topps Turkey Red Gold

*GOLD 1-270: 12X TO 30X BASIC
*GOLD 1-270: 2X TO 5X BASIC SP
*GOLD 1-270: 10X TO 25X BASIC REP
*GOLD 271-300: 6X TO 15X BASIC
*GOLD 301-315: 5X TO 12X BASIC
STATED ODDS 1:59 HOBBY/RETAIL
STATED PRINT RUN 50 SERIAL #'d SETS
1A Barry Bonds Grey Uni 75.00 150.00
1B Barry Bonds White Uni 75.00 150.00
10A Sammy Sosa w/Name 12.50 30.00
10B Sammy Sosa w/o Name 12.50 30.00
16A Mike Piazza Blue Uni 12.50 30.00
20 Manny Ramirez 8.00 20.00
25 Carlos Beltran 5.00 12.00
28 Rich Harden 5.00 12.00
30 Richie Sexson 5.00 12.00
52 Pulling String J.Santana CL 8.00 20.00
55 Roy Oswalt 5.00 12.00
59 Wily Mo Pena 5.00 12.00
60 Magglio Ordonez 5.00 12.00
70 Jim Thome 8.00 20.00
75A Ichiro Suzuki w/Name 30.00 60.00
75B IchiroÂ Suzuki w/o Name 30.00 60.00
78 Troy Glaus 5.00 12.00
83B Eric Chavez Purple Sky 5.00 12.00
85 Scott Rolen 8.00 20.00
87 Joe Mauer 8.00 20.00
90 Alfonso Soriano 5.00 12.00
102A Adrian Beltre Grey Uni 5.00 12.00
106 Miguel Tejada 5.00 12.00
110 Hideki Matsui 20.00 50.00
115 Curt Schilling 8.00 20.00
120A Vladimir Guerrero w/Bat 12.50 30.00
120B Vladimir Guerrero w/Glove 12.50 30.00
125B Randy Johnson Purple Sky 12.50 30.00
130B Ivan Rodriguez w/Helmet 8.00 20.00
132 Carlos Delgado 5.00 12.00
149 Jason Bay 5.00 12.00
150 Albert Pujols 30.00 60.00
155 Pedro Martinez 8.00 20.00
160A J.Santana Glove on Knee 8.00 20.00
160B J.Santana Throwing 8.00 20.00
170 Tim Hudson 5.00 12.00
175 Nomar Garciaparra 12.50 30.00
181 Gustavo Chacin 5.00 12.00
184 Felix Hernandez 20.00 50.00
185 Zach Day 5.00 12.00
193 Jose Capellan 5.00 12.00
195 Steven White 5.00 12.00
199 Joel Guzman 5.00 12.00
214 Mike Gonzalez 5.00 12.00
220 Scott Kazmir 5.00 12.00
225A Mark Prior Blue Sky 8.00 20.00
225B Mark Prior Yellow Sky 8.00 20.00
230A Derek Jeter Blue Sky 50.00 100.00
230B Derek Jeter Purple Sky 50.00 100.00
233 Brandon Backe 5.00 12.00
270A Todd Helton Purple Sky 8.00 20.00
270B Todd Helton Yellow Sky 8.00 20.00
305 Cal Ripken RET 50.00 100.00

2005 Topps Turkey Red Red

*RED 1-270: 1X TO 2.5X BASIC
*RED 1-270: .2X TO .5X BASIC SP
*RED 1-270: .75X TO 2X BASIC REP
*RED 271-300: .75X TO 2X BASIC
*RED 301-315: .75X TO 2X BASIC
ONE RED OR OTHER PARALLEL PER PACK
THERE ARE NO SP'S IN THIS SET
10A Sammy Sosa w/Name 1.00 2.50
10B Sammy Sosa w/o Name 1.00 2.50
16A Mike Piazza Blue Uni 1.00 2.50
20 Manny Ramirez .60 1.50
25 Carlos Beltran .40 1.00
28 Rich Harden .40 1.00
30 Richie Sexson .40 1.00
52 Pulling String J.Santana CL 1.00 2.50
55 Roy Oswalt .40 1.00
59 Wily Mo Pena .40 1.00
60 Magglio Ordonez .40 1.00
70 Jim Thome .60 1.50
78 Troy Glaus .40 1.00
83B Eric Chavez Purple Sky .40 1.00
85 Scott Rolen .60 1.50
87 Joe Mauer 1.00 2.50
90 Alfonso Soriano .40 1.00
102B Adrian Beltre White Uni .40 1.00
106 Miguel Tejada .40 1.00
115 Curt Schilling .60 1.50
120A Vladimir Guerrero w/Bat 1.00 2.50
120B Vladimir Guerrero w/Glove 1.00 2.50
125B Randy Johnson Purple Sky 1.00 2.50
130B Ivan Rodriguez w/Helmet .60 1.50
132 Carlos Delgado .40 1.00
149 Jason Bay .40 1.00
155 Pedro Martinez .60 1.50
160A J.Santana Glove on Knee 1.00 2.50
160B J.Santana Throwing 1.00 2.50
170 Tim Hudson .40 1.00
175 Nomar Garciaparra 1.00 2.50
181 Gustavo Chacin .40 1.00
185 Zach Day .40 1.00
193 Jose Capellan .40 1.00
195 Steven White .40 1.00
199 Joel Guzman .40 1.00
214 Mike Gonzalez .40 1.00
220 Scott Kazmir .40 1.00
225A Mark Prior Blue Sky .60 1.50
225B Mark Prior Yellow Sky .60 1.50
233 Brandon Backe .40 1.00
266 Steve Finley .40 1.00
270A Todd Helton Purple Sky .60 1.50
270B Todd Helton Yellow Sky .60 1.50

2005 Topps Turkey Red Suede

STATED ODDS 1:2955 H, 1:3072 R
STATED PRINT RUN 1 SERIAL #'d SET
NO PRICING DUE TO SCARCITY

2005 Topps Turkey Red White

*WHITE 1-270: 2X TO 5X BASIC
*WHITE 1-270: .3X TO .8X BASIC SP
*WHITE 1-270: 1.5X TO 4X BASIC REP
*WHITE 271-300: 1X TO 2.5X BASIC
*WHITE 301-315: 1.5X TO 4X BASIC
STATED ODDS 1:4 HOBBY/RETAIL
THERE ARE NO SP'S IN THIS SET
10A Sammy Sosa w/Name 2.00 5.00
10B Sammy Sosa w/o Name 2.00 5.00
16A Mike Piazza Blue Uni 2.00 5.00
20 Manny Ramirez 1.25 3.00
25 Carlos Beltran .75 2.00
28 Rich Harden .75 2.00
30 Richie Sexson .75 2.00
52 Pulling String J.Santana CL 2.00 5.00
55 Roy Oswalt .75 2.00
59 Wily Mo Pena .75 2.00
60 Magglio Ordonez .75 2.00
70 Jim Thome 1.25 3.00
75A IchiroÂ Suzuki w/Name 4.00 10.00
75B IchiroÂ Suzuki w/o Name 4.00 10.00
78 Troy Glaus .75 2.00
83B Eric Chavez Purple Sky .75 2.00
85 Scott Rolen 1.25 3.00
87 Joe Mauer 2.00 5.00
90 Alfonso Soriano .75 2.00
102A Adrian Beltre Grey Uni .75 2.00
106 Miguel Tejada .75 2.00
110 Hideki Matsui 3.00 8.00
115 Curt Schilling 1.25 3.00
120A Vladimir Guerrero w/Bat 2.00 5.00
120B Vladimir Guerrero w/Glove 2.00 5.00
125B Randy Johnson Purple Sky 2.00 5.00
130B Ivan Rodriguez w/Helmet 1.25 3.00
132 Carlos Delgado .75 2.00
149 Jason Bay .75 2.00
150 Albert Pujols 4.00 10.00
155 Pedro Martinez 1.25 3.00
160A J.Santana Glove on Knee 2.00 5.00
160B J.Santana Throwing 2.00 5.00
170 Tim Hudson .75 2.00
175 Nomar Garciaparra 2.00 5.00
181 Gustavo Chacin .75 2.00
184 Felix Hernandez 4.00 10.00
185 Zach Day .75 2.00
193 Jose Capellan .75 2.00
195 Steven White .75 2.00
199 Joel Guzman .75 2.00
214 Mike Gonzalez .75 2.00
220 Scott Kazmir .75 2.00
225A Mark Prior Blue Sky 1.25 3.00
225B Mark Prior Yellow Sky 1.25 3.00
230A Derek Jeter Blue Sky 4.00 10.00
230B Derek Jeter Purple Sky 4.00 10.00
233 Brandon Backe .75 2.00
266 Steve Finley .75 2.00
270A Todd Helton Purple Sky 1.25 3.00
270B Todd Helton Yellow Sky 1.25 3.00

2005 Topps Turkey Red Autographs

GROUP A ODDS 1:6495 H, 1:6262 R
GROUP B ODDS 1:1280 H, 1:4372 R
GROUP C ODDS 1:106 H, 1:1037 R
GROUP D ODDS 1:1270 H, 1:2714 R
GROUP E ODDS 1:816 H, 1:3024 R
GROUP A PRINT RUNS B/WN 17-67 PER
GROUP B PRINT RUNS B/WN 142-192 PER
GROUP A-B ARE NOT SERIAL-NUMBERED
A-B PRINT RUNS PROVIDED BY TOPPS
NO GROUP A PRICING DUE TO SCARCITY
EXCHANGE DEADLINE 08/31/07

AR Alex Rodriguez A/42 *		
AS A.Soriano B/142 * EXCH	15.00	40.00
BJ Blake Johnson C	4.00	10.00
BM Brett Myers A/67 *		
CC Carl Crawford A/17 *		
CN Chris Nelson C	4.00	10.00
DO David Ortiz C	20.00	50.00
DP Dustin Pedroia C	40.00	80.00
EG Eric Gagne B/142 *	15.00	40.00
GS Gary Sheffield C	15.00	40.00
JF Josh Fields C	6.00	15.00
JG Jody Gerut D	4.00	10.00
JJ Jason Jaramillo C	4.00	10.00
JPH J.P. Howell C	4.00	10.00
JS Jeremy Sowers C	6.00	15.00
MB Matt Bush A/17 *		
MK Mark Kotsay A/17 *		
MR M.Rivera B/192 * EXCH	60.00	120.00
MRO Mike Rodriguez E	4.00	10.00
SE Scott Elbert C	6.00	15.00
ZJ Zach Jackson C	4.00	10.00
ZP Zach Parker C	4.00	10.00

2005 Topps Turkey Red Autographs Black

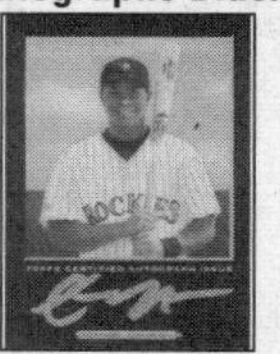

*GROUP B: .6X TO 1.5X BASIC
BONDS ODDS 1:344,256 H
GROUP A ODDS 1:18,119 H, 1:20,032 R
GROUP B ODDS 1:574 H, 1:1809 R
BONDS PRINT RUN 1 SERIAL #'d CARD
GROUP A PRINT RUN 5 SERIAL #'d SETS
GROUP B PRINT RUN 99 SERIAL #'d SETS
NO BONDS PRICING DUE TO SCARCITY
NO GROUP A PRICING DUE TO SCARCITY
EXCHANGE DEADLINE 08/31/07

2005 Topps Turkey Red Autographs Gold

BONDS ODDS 1:344,256 H
GROUP A ODDS 1:46,437 H, 1:60,096 R
GROUP B ODDS 1:3742 H, 1:3840 R
BONDS PRINT RUN 1 SERIAL #'d CARD
GROUP A PRINT RUN 2 SERIAL #'d SETS
GROUP B PRINT RUN 25 SERIAL #'d SETS
NO PRICING DUE TO SCARCITY
EXCHANGE DEADLINE 08/31/07

2005 Topps Turkey Red Autographs Red

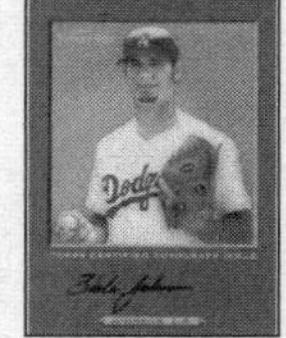

*GROUP B: .4X TO 1X BASIC
BONDS ODDS 1:344,256 H
GROUP A ODDS 1:5935 H, 1:6048 R
GROUP B ODDS 1:153 H, 1:1943R
BONDS PRINT RUN 1 SERIAL #'d CARD
GROUP A PRINT RUN 15 SERIAL #'d SETS
GROUP B PRINT RUN 300 SERIAL #'d SETS
NO BONDS PRICING DUE TO SCARCITY
NO GROUP A PRICING DUE TO SCARCITY
EXCHANGE DEADLINE 08/31/07

2005 Topps Turkey Red Autographs Suede

STATED ODDS 1:40,632 H, 1:60,096 R
STATED PRINT RUN 1 SERIAL #'d SET
NO PRICING DUE TO SCARCITY
EXCHANGE DEADLINE 08/31/07

2005 Topps Turkey Red Autographs White

*GROUP B: .5X TO 1.2X BASIC
BONDS ODDS 1:344,256 H
GROUP A ODDS 1:9563 H, 1:9072 R
GROUP B ODDS 1:242 H, 1:1536 R
BONDS PRINT RUN 1 SERIAL #'d CARD
GROUP A PRINT RUN 10 SERIAL #'d SETS
GROUP B PRINT RUN 200 SERIAL #'d SETS
NO BONDS PRICING DUE TO SCARCITY
NO GROUP A PRICING DUE TO SCARCITY
EXCHANGE DEADLINE 08/31/07

2005 Topps Turkey Red B-18 Blankets

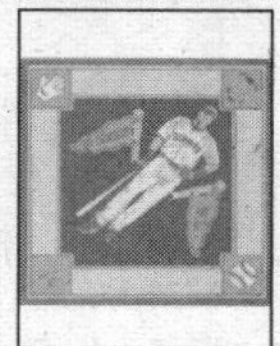

STATED ODDS 1:2 JUMBO
SP STATED ODDS 1:6 JUMBO
REPURCHASED ODDS 1:165 JUMBO

AR1 Alex Rodriguez Blue SP	10.00	25.00
AR2 Alex Rodriguez Green	6.00	15.00
AS1 Alfonso Soriano Red SP	6.00	15.00
AS2 Alfonso Soriano White	4.00	10.00
BB1 Barry Bonds Red SP	15.00	40.00
BB2 Barry Bonds White	10.00	25.00
CS1 Curt Schilling Red SP	6.00	15.00
CS2 Curt Schilling White	4.00	10.00
DJ1 Derek Jeter Blue SP	10.00	25.00
DJ2 Derek Jeter Green	6.00	15.00
IS1 Ichiro Suzuki Green SP	10.00	25.00
IS2 Ichiro Suzuki White	6.00	15.00
RC1 Roger Clemens Purple SP	10.00	25.00
RC2 Roger Clemens White	6.00	15.00
TH1 Todd Helton Green SP	6.00	15.00
TH2 Todd Helton White	4.00	10.00
NNO Repurchased B-18 Blanket		

2005 Topps Turkey Red Cabinet

STATED ODDS 1:2 JUMBO
SP STATED ODDS 1:30 JUMBO
SP STATED PRINT RUNS 118 COPIES PER
SP'S ARE NOT SERIAL-NUMBERED
SP PRINT RUNS PROVIDED BY TOPPS
SP'S HAVE ADVERTISEMENTS ON BACK
REPURCHASED ODDS 1:211 JUMBO

AP Albert Pujols	8.00	20.00
AR1 Alex Rodriguez w/Bat	6.00	15.00
AR2 A.Rod w/Glove SP/118 *	10.00	25.00
BB1 Barry Bonds At Bat SP/118 *	30.00	60.00
BB2 Barry Bonds On Steps	10.00	25.00
GB George W. Bush	10.00	25.00
GW George Washington	10.00	25.00
JS Johan Santana	6.00	15.00
JT Jim Thome	6.00	15.00
MP Mike Piazza	6.00	15.00
MR Manny Ramirez	6.00	15.00
MT Miguel Tejada	4.00	10.00
RJ Randy Johnson	6.00	15.00
SR Scott Rolen	6.00	15.00
SS Sammy Sosa	6.00	15.00
WT William Howard Taft	10.00	25.00
NNO Repurchased T-3 Cabinet		

2005 Topps Turkey Red Cabinet Auto Relics

GROUP A ODDS 1:2869 JUMBO
GROUP B ODDS 1:202 JUMBO
GROUP C ODDS 1:67 JUMBO
GROUP D ODDS 1:101 JUMBO
GROUP E ODDS 1:9 JUMBO
GROUP A PRINT RUN 5 SERIAL #'d SETS
GROUP B PRINT RUN 25 SERIAL #'d SETS
GROUP C PRINT RUN 75 SERIAL #'d SETS
GROUP D PRINT RUN 150 SERIAL #'d SETS
GROUP E PRINT RUN 450 SERIAL #'d SETS
NO GROUP A-B PRICING DUE TO SCARCITY
EXCHANGE DEADLINE 08/31/07

AR Alex Rodriguez Bat B/25		
AS A.Soriano Bat C/75 EXCH	30.00	60.00
BB Barry Bonds Jsy A/5		
BM Brett Myers Jsy D/150	15.00	40.00
CC Carl Crawford Bat E/450	10.00	25.00
DO David Ortiz Bat C/75	60.00	120.00
EG Eric Gagne Jsy C/75	60.00	120.00
GS Gary Sheffield Bat B/25		
JG Jody Gerut Bat E/450	6.00	15.00
MB Matt Bush Jsy E/450	10.00	25.00
MK Mark Kotsay Bat E/450	10.00	25.00
MR M.Rivera Jsy B/25 EXCH		

2005 Topps Turkey Red Cut Signatures

STATED ODDS 1:86,064 HOBBY
STATED PRINT RUN 1 SERIAL #'d SET
NO PRICING DUE TO SCARCITY
DE Dwight D. Eisenhower
FR Franklin D. Roosevelt
TR Theodore Roosevelt
WT William Howard Taft

2005 Topps Turkey Red Relics

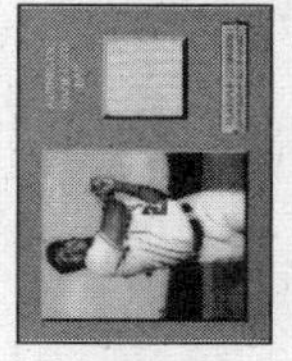

GROUP A ODDS 1:2550 H, 1:2560 R
GROUP B ODDS 1:1776 H, 1:1781 R
GROUP C ODDS 1:1383 H, 1:1398 R
GROUP D ODDS 1:349 H, 1:1202 R
GROUP E ODDS 1:208 H, 1:577 R
GROUP F ODDS 1:65 H, 1:200 R
GROUP G ODDS 1:172 H, 1:427 R
GROUP H ODDS 1:52 H, 1:102 R

AB Adrian Beltre Bat C	4.00	10.00
AP Albert Pujols Bat E	6.00	15.00
AR Alex Rodriguez Uni D	5.00	12.00
AR2 Alex Rodriguez Bat G	4.00	10.00
AS Alfonso Soriano Bat H	2.00	5.00
BB Barry Bonds Pants D	8.00	20.00
CB Carlos Beltran Bat E	3.00	8.00
CJ Chipper Jones Jsy H	3.00	8.00
CS Curt Schilling Jsy F	3.00	8.00
DO David Ortiz Jsy F	3.00	8.00
GS Gary Sheffield Bat H	2.00	5.00
HB Hank Blalock Bat F	2.00	5.00
JB Jeff Bagwell Uni H	3.00	8.00
JD Johnny Damon Bat G	3.00	8.00
JD2 Johnny Damon Jsy E	4.00	10.00
JT Jim Thome Bat F	3.00	8.00
LW Larry Walker Bat B	6.00	15.00
MC Miguel Cabrera Jsy H	3.00	8.00
ML Mike Lowell Jsy H	2.00	5.00
MM Mark Mulder Uni F	2.00	5.00
MO Magglio Ordonez Bat F	2.00	5.00
MP Mike Piazza Uni A	6.00	15.00
MPR Mark Prior Jsy B	6.00	15.00
MR Manny Ramirez Jsy D	4.00	10.00
MT Miguel Tejada Uni F	2.00	5.00
MTE Mark Teixeira Bat G	3.00	8.00
RC Roger Clemens Bat A	8.00	20.00
RC2 Roger Clemens Jsy E	5.00	12.00
RP Rafael Palmeiro Bat F	3.00	8.00
SS Sammy Sosa Bat C	6.00	15.00
TH Todd Helton Jsy H	3.00	8.00
VG Vladimir Guerrero Bat H	3.00	8.00

2005 Topps Turkey Red Relics Black

*BLACK: 1.25X TO 3X BASIC F-H
*BLACK: 1X TO 2.5X BASIC D-E
*BLACK: .6X TO 1.5X BASIC A-C
STATED ODDS 1:608 H, 1:614 R
STATED PRINT RUN 50 SERIAL #'d SETS

2005 Topps Turkey Red Relics Gold

STATED ODDS 1:1217 H, 1:1218 R
STATED PRINT RUN 25 SERIAL #'d SETS
NO PRICING DUE TO SCARCITY

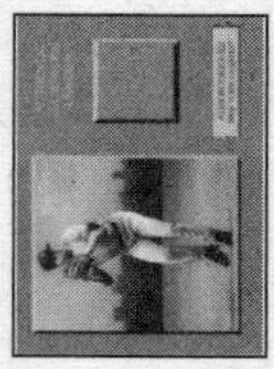

2005 Topps Turkey Red Relics Red

*RED: .75X TO 2X BASIC F-H
*RED: .6X TO 1.5X BASIC D-E
*RED: .4X TO 1X BASIC A-C
STATED ODDS 1:295 H, 1:341 R
STATED PRINT RUN 99 SERIAL #'d SETS

2005 Topps Turkey Red Relics Suede

STATED ODDS 1:38,251 H, 1:36,288 R
STATED PRINT RUN 1 SERIAL #'d SET
NO PRICING DUE TO SCARCITY

2005 Topps Turkey Red Relics White

*WHITE: 1X TO 2.5X BASIC F-H
*WHITE: .75X TO 2X BASIC D-E
*WHITE: .5X TO 1.2X BASIC A-C
STATED ODDS 1:377 H, 1:417 R
STATED PRINT RUN 75 SERIAL #'d SETS

2006 Topps Turkey Red

This 330-card set was released in September, 2006. These cards were issued in eight-card packs with an $4 SRP which came 24 packs to a box and eight boxes to a case. This set was numbered in continuation of the Topps Turkey Red set issued in 2005. Intererspersed throughout the set were some short printed cards as well as some players printed with both their original team and their current team. The short prints were issued at stated odds of one in four hobby or retail packs. Subsets in this product include Checklists (571-580); Retired Players (581-590) and 2006 Rookies (591-630).

COMPLETE SET (330)	150.00	250.00
COMP.SET w/o SP's (275)	15.00	40.00
COMMON CARD (316-580)	.15	.40
COMMON SP (316-580)	3.00	8.00
SP STATED ODDS 1:4 HOBBY, 1:4 RETAIL		
SEE BECKETT.COM FOR SP CHECKLIST		
COMMON CL (571-580)	.07	.20
COMMON RET (581-590)	.30	.75
COMMON RC (591-630)	.40	1.00
OVERALL PLATE ODDS 1:477 H		
PLATE PRINT RUN 1 SET PER COLOR		
BLACK-CYAN-MAGENTA-YELLOW ISSUED		
NO PLATE PRICING DUE TO SCARCITY		
316A Alex Rodriguez Yanks	.60	1.50
316B Alex Rodriguez Rangers SP	4.00	10.00
316C Alex Rodriguez M's SP	4.00	10.00
317 Jeff Francoeur SP	3.00	8.00
318 Shawn Green	.15	.40
319 Daniel Cabrera	.15	.40
320 Craig Biggio	.25	.60
321 Jeremy Bonderman	.15	.40
322 Mark Kotsay	.15	.40
323 Cliff Floyd	.15	.40
324 Jimmy Rollins	.15	.40
325A Magglio Ordonez Tigers	.15	.40
325B Magglio Ordonez White Sox SP	3.00	8.00
326 C.C. Sabathia	.15	.40
327 Oliver Perez	.15	.40
328 Orlando Hudson	.15	.40
329 Chris Ray	.15	.40
330 Manny Ramirez	.25	.60
331 Paul Konerko	.15	.40
332 Joe Mauer SP	3.00	8.00
333 Jorge Posada	.25	.60
334 Mark Ellis	.15	.40
335 A.J. Burnett	.15	.40
336 Mike Sweeney	.15	.40
337 Shannon Stewart	.15	.40
338 Jake Peavy SP	3.00	8.00
339A Carlos Delgado Mets SP	3.00	8.00
339B Carlos Delgado Blue Jays SP	3.00	8.00
340 Brian Roberts	.15	.40
341 Dontrelle Willis	.15	.40
342 Aaron Rowand	.15	.40
343A Richie Sexson M's	.15	.40
343B Richie Sexson Brewers SP	3.00	8.00
344 Chris Carpenter	.15	.40
345 Carlos Zambrano	.15	.40
346 Nomar Garciaparra	.40	1.00
347 Carlos Lee	.15	.40
348A Preston Wilson Astros	.15	.40
348B Preston Wilson Marlins SP	3.00	8.00
349 Mariano Rivera	.40	1.00
350 Ichiro Suzuki SP	4.00	10.00
351A Mike Piazza Padres	.40	1.00
351B Mike Piazza Mets SP	3.00	8.00
352 Jason Schmidt	.15	.40
353 Jeff Weaver	.15	.40
354 Rocco Baldelli	.15	.40
355 Adam Dunn	.15	.40
356 Jeromy Burnitz	.15	.40
357 Chris Shelton SP	3.00	8.00
358 Chone Figgins SP	3.00	8.00
359 Javier Vazquez	.15	.40
360 Chipper Jones	.40	1.00
361 Frank Thomas	.40	1.00
362 Mark Loretta	.15	.40
363 Hideki Matsui	.40	1.00
364 J.J. Hardy SP	3.00	8.00
365 Todd Helton	.25	.60
366 Reggie Sanders	.15	.40
367 Jay Gibbons	.15	.40
368 Johnny Estrada	.15	.40
369 Grady Sizemore	.25	.60
370 Jim Thome	.25	.60
371 Ivan Rodriguez	.25	.60
372 Jason Bay	.15	.40
373 Carl Crawford	.15	.40
374 Adrian Beltre	.15	.40
375 Derrek Lee SP	3.00	8.00
376 Miguel Olivo	.15	.40
377 Roy Oswalt	.15	.40
378 Coco Crisp	.15	.40
379 Moises Alou	.15	.40
380 Kevin Millwood	.15	.40
381 Mark Grudzielanek	.15	.40
382 Justin Morneau	.15	.40
383 Austin Kearns	.15	.40
384 Brad Penny	.15	.40
385 Troy Glaus	.15	.40
386 Cliff Lee	.15	.40
387 Armando Benitez	.15	.40
388 Clint Barmes	.15	.40
389 Orlando Cabrera	.15	.40
390 Jim Edmonds SP	3.00	8.00
391 Jermaine Dye	.15	.40
392 Morgan Ensberg SP	3.00	8.00
393 Paul LoDuca	.15	.40
394 Eric Chavez	.15	.40
395 Greg Maddux SP	4.00	10.00
396 Jack Wilson	.15	.40
397 Omar Vizquel	.25	.60
398 Joe Nathan	.15	.40
399 Bobby Abreu	.15	.40
400 Barry Bonds SP	6.00	15.00
401 Gary Sheffield	.15	.40
402 John Patterson	.15	.40
403 J.D. Drew	.15	.40
404 Bruce Chen	.15	.40
405 Johnny Damon SP	3.00	8.00
406 Aubrey Huff	.15	.40
407 Mark Mulder	.15	.40
408 Jamie Moyer	.15	.40
409 Carlos Guillen	.15	.40
410 Andruw Jones SP	3.00	8.00
411 Jhonny Peralta SP	3.00	8.00
412 Doug Davis	.15	.40
413 Aaron Miles	.15	.40
414 Jon Lieber	.15	.40
415 Aaron Hill	.15	.40
416 Josh Beckett SP	3.00	8.00
417 Bobby Crosby	.15	.40
418 Noah Lowry SP	3.00	8.00
419 Sidney Ponson	.15	.40
420 Luis Castillo	.15	.40
421 Brad Wilkerson	.15	.40
422 Felix Hernandez SP	3.00	8.00
423 Vinny Castilla	.15	.40
424 Tom Glavine	.25	.60
425 Vladimir Guerrero	.40	1.00
426 Javy Lopez	.15	.40
427 Ronnie Belliard	.15	.40
428 Dmitri Young	.15	.40
429 Johan Santana	.25	.60
430A David Ortiz Red Sox SP	3.00	8.00
430B David Ortiz Twins SP	3.00	8.00
431 Ben Sheets	.15	.40
432 Matt Holliday	.40	1.00
433 Brian McCann	.15	.40
434 Joe Blanton	.15	.40
435 Sean Casey	.15	.40
436 Brad Lidge	.15	.40
437 Chad Tracy	.15	.40
438 Brett Myers	.15	.40
439 Matt Morris	.15	.40
440 Brian Giles	.15	.40
441 Zach Duke	.15	.40
442 Jose Lopez	.15	.40
443 Kris Benson	.15	.40
444 Jose Reyes SP	3.00	8.00
445 Travis Hafner	.15	.40
446 Orlando Hernandez	.15	.40
447 Edgar Renteria	.15	.40
448 Scott Podsednik	.15	.40
449 Nick Swisher SP	3.00	8.00
450 Derek Jeter SP	6.00	15.00
451 Scott Kazmir SP	3.00	8.00
452 Hank Blalock	.15	.40
453 Jake Westbrook	.15	.40
454 Miguel Cabrera	.25	.60
455A Ken Griffey Jr. Reds	.60	1.50
455B Ken Griffey Jr. M's SP	4.00	10.00
456 Rafael Furcal	.15	.40
457 Lance Berkman	.15	.40
458 Aramis Ramirez	.15	.40
459A Xavier Nady Mets	.15	.40
459B Xavier Nady Padres SP	3.00	8.00
460A Randy Johnson Yanks	.40	1.00
460B Randy Johnson Astros SP	3.00	8.00
461 Khalil Greene	.25	.60
462 Bartolo Colon	.15	.40
463 Mike Lowell	.15	.40
464 David DeJesus	.15	.40
465 Ryan Howard SP	4.00	10.00
466 Tim Salmon SP	3.00	8.00
467 Mark Buehrle SP	3.00	8.00
468 Curtis Granderson	.15	.40
469 Kerry Wood	.15	.40
470 Miguel Tejada	.15	.40
471 Geoff Jenkins	.15	.40
472 Jeremy Reed	.15	.40
473 David Eckstein	.15	.40
474 Lyle Overbay	.15	.40
475 Michael Young	.15	.40
476A Nick Johnson Nats SP	3.00	8.00
476B Nick Johnson Yanks SP	3.00	8.00
477 Carlos Beltran	.15	.40
478 Huston Street	.15	.40
479 Brandon Webb	.15	.40
480 Phil Nevin	.15	.40
481 Ryan Madson SP	3.00	8.00
482 Jason Giambi	.15	.40
483 Angel Berroa	.15	.40
484 Casey Blake	.15	.40
485 Pat Burrell	.15	.40
486 B.J. Ryan	.15	.40
487 Torii Hunter	.15	.40
488 Garret Anderson	.15	.40
489 Chase Utley SP	3.00	8.00
490 Matt Murton	.15	.40
491 Rich Harden	.15	.40
492 Garrett Atkins	.15	.40
493 Tadahito Iguchi SP	3.00	8.00
494 Jarrod Washburn	.15	.40
495 Carl Everett	.15	.40
496 Kameron Loe	.15	.40
497 Jorge Cantu SP	3.00	8.00
498 Chris Young	.15	.40
499 Marcus Giles	.15	.40
500 Albert Pujols	.75	2.00
501A Alfonso Soriano Nats SP	3.00	8.00
501B Alfonso Soriano Yanks SP	3.00	8.00
502 Randy Winn	.15	.40
503 Roy Halladay	.15	.40
504 Victor Martinez	.15	.40
505 Pedro Martinez	.25	.60
506 Rickie Weeks	.15	.40
507 Dan Johnson	.15	.40
508A Tim Hudson Braves	.15	.40
508B Tim Hudson A's SP	3.00	8.00
509 Mark Prior	.25	.60
510 Melvin Mora	.15	.40
511 Matt Clement	.15	.40
512 Brandon Inge	.15	.40
513 Mike Mussina	.25	.60
514 Mike Cameron	.15	.40
515 Barry Zito	.15	.40
516 Luis Gonzalez	.15	.40
517 Jose Castillo	.15	.40
518 Andy Pettitte	.25	.60
519 Wily Mo Pena	.15	.40
520 Billy Wagner	.15	.40
521 Ervin Santana SP	3.00	8.00
522 Juan Pierre	.15	.40
523 Dan Haren	.15	.40
524 Adrian Gonzalez SP	3.00	8.00
525 Robinson Cano	.25	.60
526 Jeff Kent	.15	.40
527 Cory Sullivan	.15	.40
528 Joe Crede SP	3.00	8.00
529 John Smoltz	.25	.60
530 David Wright	.60	1.50
531 Chad Cordero	.15	.40
532 Scott Rolen SP	3.00	8.00
533 Edwin Jackson	.15	.40
534 Doug Mientkiewicz	.15	.40
535 Mark Teixeira SP	3.00	8.00
536 Kelvim Escobar	.15	.40
537 Alex Rios	.15	.40
538 Jose Vidro	.15	.40
539 Alex Gonzalez	.15	.40
540 Yadier Molina	.15	.40
541 Ronny Cedeno SP	3.00	8.00
542 Mark Hendrickson	.15	.40
543 Russ Adams	.15	.40
544 Chris Capuano	.15	.40
545 Raul Ibanez	.15	.40
546 Vicente Padilla	.15	.40
547 Chris Duffy	.15	.40
548 Bengie Molina	.15	.40
549 Chien-Ming Wang	.60	1.50
550 Curt Schilling	.25	.60
551 Craig Wilson	.15	.40
552 Mike Lieberthal	.15	.40
553 Kazuo Matsui	.15	.40
554 Jeff Francis	.15	.40
555 Brady Clark	.15	.40
556 Willy Taveras	.15	.40
557 Mike Maroth	.15	.40
558 Bernie Williams	.25	.60
559 Edwin Encarnacion	.15	.40
560 Vernon Wells	.15	.40
561A Livan Hernandez Nats	.15	.40
561B Livan Hernandez Giants SP	3.00	8.00
562 Kenny Rogers	.15	.40
563 Steve Finley	.15	.40
564 Trot Nixon	.15	.40
565 Jonny Gomes SP	3.00	8.00
566 Brandon Phillips	.15	.40
567 Shawn Chacon	.15	.40
568 Dave Bush	.15	.40
569 Jose Guillen	.15	.40
570 Gustavo Chacin	.15	.40
571 A.Rod Safe at the Plate CL	.30	.75
572 Pujols At Bat CL	.40	1.00
573 Bonds On Deck CL	.40	1.00
574 Breaking Up Two CL	.07	.20
575 Conference On The Mound CL	.20	.50
576 Touch Em All CL	.30	.75
577 Avoiding The Runner CL	.07	.20
578 Bunting The Runner Over CL	.07	.20
579 In The Hole CL	.07	.20
580 Jeter Steals Third CL	.50	1.25
581 Nolan Ryan RET	2.00	5.00
582 Cal Ripken RET	3.00	8.00
583 Carl Yastrzemski RET	1.25	3.00
584 Duke Snider RET	.50	1.25
585 Tom Seaver RET	.50	1.25
586 Mickey Mantle RET	4.00	10.00
587 Jim Palmer RET	.30	.75
588 Gary Carter RET	.30	.75

Card	Low	High
589 Stan Musial RET	1.25	3.00
590 Luis Aparicio RET	.30	.75
591 Prince Fielder (RC)	1.50	4.00
592 Conor Jackson (RC)	.60	1.50
593 Jeremy Hermida (RC)	.40	1.00
594 Jeff Mathis (RC)	.40	1.00
595 Alay Soler RC	.40	1.00
596 Ryan Spilborghs (RC)	.60	1.50
597 Chuck James (RC)	.60	1.50
598 Josh Barfield (RC)	.40	1.00
599 Ian Kinsler (RC)	.60	1.50
600 Val Majewski (RC)	.40	1.00
601 Brian Slocum (RC)	.40	1.00
602 Matt Kemp (RC)	.60	1.50
603 Nate McLouth (RC)	.40	1.00
604 Sean Marshall (RC)	.40	1.00
605 Brian Bannister (RC)	.40	1.00
606 Ryan Zimmerman (RC)	2.50	6.00
607 Kendry Morales (RC)	1.00	2.50
608 Jonathan Papelbon (RC)	2.00	5.00
609 Matt Cain (RC)	.60	1.50
610 Anderson Hernandez (RC)	.40	1.00
611 Jose Capellan (RC)	.40	1.00
612 Lastings Milledge (RC)	.60	1.50
613 Francisco Liriano (RC)	2.00	5.00
614 Hanley Ramirez (RC)	1.00	2.50
615 Brian Anderson (RC)	.40	1.00
616 Reggie Abercrombie (RC)	.40	1.00
617 Erick Aybar (RC)	.40	1.00
618 James Loney (RC)	.60	1.50
619 Joel Zumaya (RC)	1.00	2.50
620 Travis Ishikawa (RC)	.40	1.00
621 Jason Kubel (RC)	.40	1.00
622 Drew Meyer (RC)	.40	1.00
623 Kenji Johjima RC	2.00	5.00
624 Fausto Carmona (RC)	.40	1.00
625 Nick Markakis (RC)	.60	1.50
626 John Rheinecker (RC)	.40	1.00
627 Melky Cabrera (RC)	.60	1.50
628 Michael Pelfrey RC	1.50	4.00
629 Dan Uggla (RC)	1.00	2.50
630 Justin Verlander (RC)	1.50	4.00

2006 Topps Turkey Red Black

*BLACK 316-580: 4X TO 10X BASIC
*BLACK 316-580: .6X TO 1.5X BASIC SP
*BLACK 581-590: 2X TO 5X BASIC RET
*BLACK 591-630: 1.25X TO 3X BASIC ROOKIE
STATED ODDS 1:20 HOBBY/RETAIL
THERE ARE NO SP'S IN THIS SET

2006 Topps Turkey Red Gold

Card	Low	High
COMMON CARD (316-580)	6.00	15.00
COMMON CL (571-580)	3.00	8.00
COMMON RET (581-590)	6.00	15.00
COMMON ROOKIE (591-630)	8.00	20.00

STATED ODDS 1:60 HOBBY/RETAIL
THERE ARE NO SP'S IN THIS SET

Card	Low	High
316A Alex Rodriguez Yanks	20.00	50.00
316B Alex Rodriguez Rangers	20.00	50.00
316C Alex Rodriguez M's	20.00	50.00
317 Jeff Francoeur	15.00	40.00
318 Shawn Green	6.00	15.00
319 Daniel Cabrera	6.00	15.00
320 Craig Biggio	10.00	25.00
321 Jeremy Bonderman	6.00	15.00
322 Mark Kotsay	6.00	15.00
323 Cliff Floyd	6.00	15.00
324 Jimmy Rollins	6.00	15.00
325A Magglio Ordonez Tigers	6.00	15.00
325B Magglio Ordonez White Sox	6.00	15.00
326 C.C. Sabathia	6.00	15.00
327 Oliver Perez	6.00	15.00
328 Orlando Hudson	6.00	15.00
329 Chris Ray	6.00	15.00
330 Manny Ramirez	10.00	25.00
331 Paul Konerko	6.00	15.00
332 Joe Mauer	10.00	25.00
333 Jorge Posada	10.00	25.00
334 Mark Ellis	6.00	15.00
335 A.J. Burnett	6.00	15.00
336 Mike Sweeney	6.00	15.00
337 Shannon Stewart	6.00	15.00
338 Jake Peavy	6.00	15.00
339A Carlos Delgado Mets	6.00	15.00
339B Carlos Delgado Blue Jays	6.00	15.00
340 Brian Roberts	6.00	15.00
341 Dontrelle Willis	6.00	15.00
342 Aaron Rowand	6.00	15.00
343A Richie Sexson M's	6.00	15.00
343B Richie Sexson Brewers	6.00	15.00
344 Chris Carpenter	6.00	15.00
345 Carlos Zambrano	6.00	15.00
346 Nomar Garciaparra	15.00	40.00
347 Carlos Lee	6.00	15.00
348A Preston Wilson Astros	6.00	15.00
348B Preston Wilson Marlins	6.00	15.00
349 Mariano Rivera	15.00	40.00
350 Ichiro Suzuki	20.00	50.00
351A Mike Piazza Padres	15.00	40.00
351B Mike Piazza Mets	15.00	40.00
352 Jason Schmidt	6.00	15.00
353 Jeff Weaver	6.00	15.00
354 Rocco Baldelli	6.00	15.00
355 Adam Dunn	6.00	15.00
356 Jeremy Burnitz	6.00	15.00
357 Chris Shelton	6.00	15.00
358 Chone Figgins	6.00	15.00
359 Javier Vazquez	6.00	15.00
360 Chipper Jones	15.00	40.00
361 Frank Thomas	15.00	40.00
362 Mark Loretta	6.00	15.00
363 Hideki Matsui	15.00	40.00
364 J.J. Hardy	6.00	15.00
365 Todd Helton	10.00	25.00
366 Reggie Sanders	6.00	15.00
367 Jay Gibbons	6.00	15.00
368 Johnny Estrada	6.00	15.00
369 Grady Sizemore	10.00	25.00
370 Jim Thome	10.00	25.00
371 Ivan Rodriguez	10.00	25.00
372 Jason Bay	6.00	15.00
373 Carl Crawford	6.00	15.00
374 Adrian Beltre	6.00	15.00
375 Derrek Lee	6.00	15.00
376 Miguel Olivo	6.00	15.00
377 Roy Oswalt	6.00	15.00
378 Coco Crisp	6.00	15.00
379 Moises Alou	6.00	15.00
380 Kevin Millwood	6.00	15.00
381 Mark Grudzielanek	6.00	15.00
382 Justin Morneau	6.00	15.00
383 Austin Kearns	6.00	15.00
384 Brad Penny	6.00	15.00
385 Troy Glaus	6.00	15.00
386 Cliff Lee	6.00	15.00
387 Armando Benitez	6.00	15.00
388 Clint Barmes	6.00	15.00
389 Orlando Cabrera	6.00	15.00
390 Jim Edmonds	10.00	25.00
391 Jermaine Dye	6.00	15.00
392 Morgan Ensberg	6.00	15.00
393 Paul LoDuca	6.00	15.00
394 Eric Chavez	6.00	15.00
395 Greg Maddux	20.00	50.00
396 Jack Wilson	6.00	15.00
397 Omar Vizquel	10.00	25.00
398 Joe Nathan	6.00	15.00
399 Bobby Abreu	6.00	15.00
400 Barry Bonds	30.00	60.00
401 Gary Sheffield	6.00	15.00
402 John Patterson	6.00	15.00
403 J.D. Drew	6.00	15.00
404 Bruce Chen	6.00	15.00
405 Johnny Damon	10.00	25.00
406 Aubrey Huff	6.00	15.00
407 Mark Mulder	6.00	15.00
408 Jamie Moyer	6.00	15.00
409 Carlos Guillen	6.00	15.00
410 Andruw Jones	10.00	25.00
411 Jhonny Peralta	6.00	15.00
412 Doug Davis	6.00	15.00
413 Aaron Miles	6.00	15.00
414 Jon Lieber	6.00	15.00
415 Aaron Hill	6.00	15.00
416 Josh Beckett	6.00	15.00
417 Bobby Crosby	6.00	15.00
418 Noah Lowry	6.00	15.00
419 Sidney Ponson	6.00	15.00
420 Luis Castillo	6.00	15.00
421 Brad Wilkerson	6.00	15.00
422 Felix Hernandez	10.00	25.00
423 Vinny Castilla	6.00	15.00
424 Tom Glavine	10.00	25.00
425 Vladimir Guerrero	15.00	40.00
426 Javy Lopez	6.00	15.00
427 Ronnie Belliard	6.00	15.00
428 Dmitri Young	6.00	15.00
429 Johan Santana	10.00	25.00
430A David Ortiz Red Sox	15.00	40.00
430B David Ortiz Twins	15.00	40.00
431 Ben Sheets	6.00	15.00
432 Matt Holliday	8.00	20.00
433 Brian McCann	6.00	15.00
434 Joe Blanton	6.00	15.00
435 Sean Casey	6.00	15.00
436 Brad Lidge	6.00	15.00
437 Chad Tracy	6.00	15.00
438 Brett Myers	6.00	15.00
439 Matt Morris	6.00	15.00
440 Brian Giles	6.00	15.00
441 Zach Duke	6.00	15.00
442 Jose Lopez	6.00	15.00
443 Kris Benson	6.00	15.00
444 Jose Reyes	6.00	15.00
445 Travis Hafner	6.00	15.00
446 Orlando Hernandez	6.00	15.00
447 Edgar Renteria	6.00	15.00
448 Scott Podsednik	6.00	15.00
449 Nick Swisher	6.00	15.00
450 Derek Jeter	30.00	60.00
451 Scott Kazmir	10.00	25.00
452 Hank Blalock	6.00	15.00
453 Jake Westbrook	6.00	15.00
454 Miguel Cabrera	10.00	25.00
455A Ken Griffey Jr. Reds	20.00	50.00
455B Ken Griffey Jr. M's	20.00	50.00
456 Rafael Furcal	6.00	15.00
457 Lance Berkman	6.00	15.00
458 Aramis Ramirez	6.00	15.00
459A Xavier Nady Mets	6.00	15.00
459B Xavier Nady Padres	6.00	15.00
460A Randy Johnson Yanks	15.00	40.00
460B Randy Johnson Astros	15.00	40.00
461 Khalil Greene	10.00	25.00
462 Bartolo Colon	6.00	15.00
463 Mike Lowell	6.00	15.00
464 David DeJesus	6.00	15.00
465 Ryan Howard	20.00	50.00
466 Tim Salmon	6.00	15.00
467 Mark Buehrle	6.00	15.00
468 Curtis Granderson	6.00	15.00
469 Kerry Wood	6.00	15.00
470 Miguel Tejada	6.00	15.00
471 Geoff Jenkins	6.00	15.00
472 Jeremy Reed	6.00	15.00
473 David Eckstein	6.00	15.00
474 Lyle Overbay	6.00	15.00
475 Michael Young	6.00	15.00
476A Nick Johnson Nats	6.00	15.00
476B Nick Johnson Yankees	6.00	15.00
477 Carlos Beltran	6.00	15.00
478 Huston Street	6.00	15.00
479 Brandon Webb	6.00	15.00
480 Phil Nevin	6.00	15.00
481 Ryan Madson	6.00	15.00
482 Jason Giambi	6.00	15.00
483 Angel Berroa	6.00	15.00
484 Casey Blake	6.00	15.00
485 Pat Burrell	6.00	15.00
486 B.J. Ryan	6.00	15.00
487 Torii Hunter	6.00	15.00
488 Garret Anderson	6.00	15.00
489 Chase Utley	15.00	40.00
490 Matt Murton	6.00	15.00
491 Rich Harden	6.00	15.00
492 Garrett Atkins	6.00	15.00
493 Tadahito Iguchi	6.00	15.00
494 Jarrod Washburn	6.00	15.00
495 Carl Everett	6.00	15.00
496 Kameron Loe	6.00	15.00
497 Jorge Cantu	6.00	15.00
498 Chris Young	6.00	15.00
499 Marcus Giles	6.00	15.00
500 Albert Pujols	30.00	60.00
501A Alfonso Soriano Nats	6.00	15.00
501B Alfonso Soriano Yanks	6.00	15.00
502 Randy Winn	6.00	15.00
503 Roy Halladay	6.00	15.00
504 Victor Martinez	6.00	15.00
505 Pedro Martinez	10.00	25.00
506 Rickie Weeks	6.00	15.00
507 Dan Johnson	6.00	15.00
508A Tim Hudson Braves	6.00	15.00
508B Tim Hudson A's	6.00	15.00
509 Mark Prior	10.00	25.00
510 Melvin Mora	6.00	15.00
511 Matt Clement	6.00	15.00
512 Brandon Inge	6.00	15.00
513 Mike Mussina	10.00	25.00
514 Mike Cameron	6.00	15.00
515 Barry Zito	6.00	15.00
516 Luis Gonzalez	6.00	15.00
517 Jose Castillo	6.00	15.00
518 Andy Pettitte	6.00	15.00
519 Wily Mo Pena	6.00	15.00
520 Billy Wagner	6.00	15.00
521 Ervin Santana	6.00	15.00
522 Juan Pierre	6.00	15.00
523 Dan Haren	6.00	15.00
524 Adrian Gonzalez	6.00	15.00
525 Robinson Cano	6.00	15.00
526 Jeff Kent	6.00	15.00
527 Cory Sullivan	6.00	15.00
528 Joe Crede	6.00	15.00
529 John Smoltz	10.00	25.00
530 David Wright	20.00	50.00
531 Chad Cordero	6.00	15.00
532 Scott Rolen	10.00	25.00
533 Edwin Jackson	6.00	15.00
534 Doug Mientkiewicz	6.00	15.00
535 Mark Teixeira	10.00	25.00
536 Kelvim Escobar	6.00	15.00
537 Alex Rios	6.00	15.00
538 Jose Vidro	6.00	15.00
539 Alex Gonzalez	6.00	15.00
540 Yadier Molina	6.00	15.00
541 Ronny Cedeno	6.00	15.00
542 Mark Hendrickson	6.00	15.00
543 Russ Adams	6.00	15.00
544 Chris Capuano	6.00	15.00
545 Raul Ibanez	6.00	15.00
546 Vicente Padilla	6.00	15.00
547 Chris Duffy	6.00	15.00
548 Bengie Molina	6.00	15.00
549 Chien-Ming Wang	20.00	50.00
550 Curt Schilling	10.00	25.00
551 Craig Wilson	6.00	15.00
552 Mike Lieberthal	6.00	15.00
553 Kazuo Matsui	6.00	15.00
554 Jeff Francis	6.00	15.00
555 Brady Clark	6.00	15.00
556 Willy Taveras	6.00	15.00
557 Mike Maroth	6.00	15.00
558 Bernie Williams	10.00	25.00
559 Edwin Encarnacion	6.00	15.00
560 Vernon Wells	6.00	15.00
561A Livan Hernandez Nats	6.00	15.00
561B Livan Hernandez Giants	6.00	15.00
562 Kenny Rogers	6.00	15.00
563 Steve Finley	6.00	15.00
564 Trot Nixon	6.00	15.00
565 Jonny Gomes	6.00	15.00
566 Brandon Phillips	6.00	15.00
567 Shawn Chacon	6.00	15.00
568 Dave Bush	6.00	15.00
569 Jose Guillen	6.00	15.00
570 Gustavo Chacin	6.00	15.00
571 A.Rod Safe at the Plate CL	12.50	30.00
572 Pujols At Bat CL	15.00	40.00
573 Bonds On Deck CL	15.00	40.00
574 Breaking Up Two CL	3.00	8.00
575 Conference On The Mound CL	8.00	20.00
576 Touch Em All CL	12.50	30.00
577 Avoiding The Runner CL	3.00	8.00
578 Bunting The Runner Over CL	3.00	8.00
579 In The Hole CL	3.00	8.00
580 Jeter Steals Third CL	20.00	50.00
581 Nolan Ryan	40.00	80.00
582 Cal Ripken	50.00	100.00
583 Carl Yastrzemski	20.00	50.00
584 Duke Snider	10.00	25.00
585 Tom Seaver	10.00	25.00
586 Mickey Mantle	100.00	200.00
587 Jim Palmer	6.00	15.00
588 Gary Carter	6.00	15.00
589 Stan Musial	20.00	50.00
590 Luis Aparicio	6.00	15.00
591 Prince Fielder	30.00	60.00
592 Conor Jackson	12.50	30.00
593 Jeremy Hermida	12.50	30.00
594 Jeff Mathis	8.00	20.00
595 Alay Soler	8.00	20.00
596 Ryan Spilborghs	12.50	30.00
597 Chuck James	12.50	30.00
598 Josh Barfield	8.00	20.00
599 Ian Kinsler	12.50	30.00
600 Val Majewski	8.00	20.00
601 Brian Slocum	8.00	20.00
602 Matt Kemp	12.50	30.00
603 Nate McLouth	8.00	20.00
604 Sean Marshall	8.00	20.00
605 Brian Bannister	8.00	20.00
606 Ryan Zimmerman	50.00	100.00
607 Kendry Morales	20.00	50.00
608 Jonathan Papelbon	30.00	60.00
609 Matt Cain	12.50	30.00
610 Anderson Hernandez	8.00	20.00
611 Jose Capellan	8.00	20.00
612 Lastings Milledge	12.50	30.00
613 Francisco Liriano	30.00	60.00
614 Hanley Ramirez	12.50	30.00
615 Brian Anderson	8.00	20.00
616 Reggie Abercrombie	8.00	20.00
617 Erick Aybar	8.00	20.00
618 James Loney	12.50	30.00
619 Joel Zumaya	20.00	50.00
620 Travis Ishikawa	8.00	20.00
621 Jason Kubel	8.00	20.00
622 Drew Meyer	8.00	20.00
623 Kenji Johjima	30.00	60.00
624 Fausto Carmona	8.00	20.00
625 Nick Markakis	12.50	30.00
626 John Rheinecker	8.00	20.00
627 Melky Cabrera	20.00	50.00
628 Michael Pelfrey	20.00	50.00
629 Dan Uggla	20.00	50.00
630 Justin Verlander	30.00	60.00

2006 Topps Turkey Red Red

*RED 316-580: 1X TO 2X BASIC
*RED 316-580: .2X TO .5X BASIC SP
*RED 581-590: .5X TO 1.2X BASIC RET
*RED 591-630: .6X TO 1.5X BASIC ROOKIE
ONE RED OR OTHER PARALLEL PER PACK
THERE ARE NO SP'S IN THIS SET

2006 Topps Turkey Red Suede

STATED ODDS 1:1910 HOBBY
STATED PRINT RUN 1 SERIAL #'d SET
NO PRICING DUE TO SCARCITY

2006 Topps Turkey Red White

*WHITE 316-580: 2X TO 5X BASIC
*WHITE 316-580: .25X TO .6X BASIC SP
*WHITE 581-590: .6X TO 1.5X BASIC RET
*WHITE 591-630: .75X TO 2X BASIC ROOKIE
STATED ODDS 1:4 HOBBY/RETAIL
THERE ARE NO SP'S IN THIS SET

2006 Topps Turkey Red Autographs

GROUP A ODDS 1:870 H, 1:880 R
GROUP B ODDS 1:165 H, 1:170 R
EXCHANGE DEADLINE 09/30/08

Card	Low	High
AR Alex Rodriguez EXCH	125.00	250.00
BM Brian McCann B	10.00	25.00
BMC Brandon McCarthy B	4.00	10.00
CB Clint Barmes B	4.00	10.00
CJ Chipper Jones A	40.00	80.00
CJA Conor Jackson B EXCH	6.00	15.00
CV Claudio Vargas B EXCH	4.00	10.00
DJ Dan Johnson B	4.00	10.00
DL Derrek Lee A	15.00	40.00
DW David Wright A	60.00	120.00
GA Garrett Atkins B	4.00	10.00
HS Huston Street A EXCH	15.00	40.00
JB Josh Barfield B	6.00	15.00
JG Jonny Gomes A	15.00	40.00
JS Johan Santana A EXCH	40.00	80.00
KJ Kenji Johjima A	50.00	100.00
MC Miguel Cabrera A	30.00	60.00
MM Mike Morse B	4.00	10.00
NS Nick Swisher B EXCH	6.00	15.00
PL Paul LoDuca A	15.00	40.00
RC Robinson Cano A	30.00	60.00
RH Ryan Howard A	60.00	120.00
RO Roy Oswalt A	15.00	40.00

2006 Topps Turkey Red Autographs Black

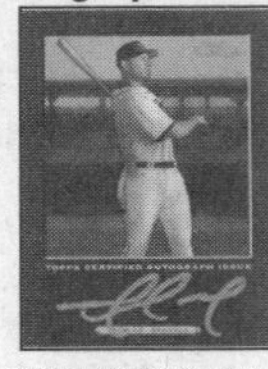

*BLACK GROUP B: .6X TO 1.5X BASIC
GROUP A ODDS 1:6000 H, 1:6200 R
GROUP B ODDS 1:1185 H, 1:1200 R
GROUP A PRINT RUN 15 SERIAL #'d SETS
GROUP B PRINT RUN 99 SERIAL #'d SETS
NO GROUP A PRICING DUE TO SCARCITY
EXCHANGE DEADLINE 09/30/08

2006 Topps Turkey Red Autographs Gold

GROUP A ODDS 1:17,000 H, 1:21,000 R
GROUP B ODDS 1:4500 H, 1:4600 R
GROUP A PRINT RUN 5 SERIAL #'d SETS
GROUP B PRINT RUN 25 SERIAL #'d SETS
NO PRICING DUE TO SCARCITY
EXCHANGE DEADLINE 09/30/08

2006 Topps Turkey Red Autographs Red

*RED GROUP A: .5X TO 1.2X BASIC
*RED GROUP B: .4X TO 1X BASIC
GROUP A ODDS 1:1800 H, 1:1850 R
GROUP B ODDS 1:245 H, 1:250 R
GROUP A PRINT RUN 50 SERIAL #'d SETS
GROUP B PRINT RUN 475 SERIAL #'d SETS
EXCHANGE DEADLINE 09/30/08

Card	Low	High
AR Alex Rodriguez A/50 EXCH	175.00	300.00
DW David Wright A/50	75.00	150.00
KJ Kenji Johjima A/50	50.00	100.00
MC Miguel Cabrera A/50	30.00	60.00
PL Paul LoDuca A/50	15.00	40.00

2006 Topps Turkey Red Autographs Suede

STATED ODDS 1:28,300 HOBBY
STATED PRINT RUN 1 SERIAL #'d SET
NO PRICING DUE TO SCARCITY
EXCHANGE DEADLINE 09/30/08

2006 Topps Turkey Red Autographs White

*WHITE GROUP B: .5X TO 1.2X BASIC
GROUP A ODDS 1:3600 H, 1:3800 R
GROUP B ODDS 1:585 H, 1:600 R
GROUP A PRINT RUN 25 SERIAL #'d SETS
GROUP B PRINT RUN 200 SERIAL #'d SETS
NO GROUP A PRICING DUE TO SCARCITY
EXCHANGE DEADLINE 09/30/08

2006 Topps Turkey Red B-18 Blankets

STATED ODDS 1:2 JUMBO
REPURCHASED ODDS 1:159 JUMBO

Card	Low	High
AR1 Alex Rodriguez White	5.00	12.00
AR2 Alex Rodriguez Blue	6.00	15.00
BB1 Barry Bonds White	5.00	12.00
BB2 Barry Bonds Red	6.00	15.00
DL1 Derrek Lee White	4.00	10.00
DL2 Derrek Lee Red	5.00	12.00
DO1 David Ortiz White	4.00	10.00
DO2 David Ortiz Orange	5.00	12.00
HM1 Hideki Matsui White	4.00	10.00
HM2 Hideki Matsui Blue	5.00	12.00
IS1 Ichiro Suzuki White	5.00	12.00
IS2 Ichiro Suzuki Green	6.00	15.00
KJ1 Kenji Johjima White	5.00	12.00
KJ2 Kenji Johjima Green	6.00	15.00
MM1 Mickey Mantle White	8.00	20.00
MM2 Mickey Mantle Blue	10.00	25.00
MR1 Manny Ramirez White	4.00	10.00
MR2 Manny Ramirez Orange	5.00	12.00
VG1 Vladimir Guerrero White	4.00	10.00
VG2 Vladimir Guerrero Green	5.00	12.00
NNO Repurchased B-18 Blanket		

2006 Topps Turkey Red Cabinet

STATED ODDS 1:2 JUMBO
REPURCHASED ODDS 1:4340 JUMBO
SUEDE ODDS 1:634 JUMBO
SUEDE PRINT RUN 1 SERIAL #'d SET
NO SUEDE PRICING DUE TO SCARCITY

Card	Low	High
AJ Andruw Jones	6.00	15.00
AP Albert Pujols	12.50	30.00
AR Alex Rodriguez	10.00	25.00
AS Alfonso Soriano	4.00	10.00
BB Barry Bonds	10.00	25.00
CC Carl Crawford	4.00	10.00
CCA Chris Carpenter	4.00	10.00
CD Carlos Delgado	4.00	10.00
CY Carl Yastrzemski	10.00	25.00
DJ Derek Jeter	12.50	30.00
DL Derrek Lee	4.00	10.00
DO David Ortiz	6.00	15.00
DS Duke Snider	6.00	15.00
DW David Wright	10.00	25.00
FL Francisco Liriano	6.00	15.00
GC Gary Carter	4.00	10.00
HM Hideki Matsui	6.00	15.00
IR Ivan Rodriguez	6.00	15.00
IS Ichiro Suzuki	10.00	25.00
JB Josh Barfield	4.00	10.00
JBE Josh Beckett	4.00	10.00
JC Jorge Cantu	4.00	10.00
JD Johnny Damon	6.00	15.00
JF Jeff Francoeur	6.00	15.00
JG Jonny Gomes	4.00	10.00
JP Jake Peavy	4.00	10.00
JPA Jonathan Papelbon	10.00	25.00
JR Jimmy Rollins	4.00	10.00
JS Johan Santana	6.00	15.00
JT Jim Thome	6.00	15.00
KG Ken Griffey Jr.	10.00	25.00
MM Mickey Mantle	30.00	60.00
MP Mike Piazza	6.00	15.00
NG Nomar Garciaparra	6.00	15.00
NJ Nick Johnson	4.00	10.00
NM Nick Markakis	6.00	15.00
NR Nolan Ryan	15.00	40.00
PF Prince Fielder	6.00	15.00
PM Pedro Martinez	6.00	15.00
RH Ryan Howard	10.00	25.00
RJ Randy Johnson	6.00	15.00
TG Troy Glaus	4.00	10.00
NNO Repurchased T-3 Cabinet		

2006 Topps Turkey Red Cabinet Auto Relics

STATED ODDS 1:86 JUMBO
NO PRICING DUE TO SCARCITY
EXCHANGE DEADLINE 09/30/08

AR Alex Rodriguez Jsy EXCH
BB Barry Bonds Pants EXCH
BM Brian McCann Bat
CB Clint Barmes Jsy
CJ Conor Jackson Bat EXCH
CJO Chipper Jones Jsy
DL Derrek Lee Jsy
DW David Wright Jsy
HS Huston Street Jsy EXCH
JS Johan Santana Jsy EXCH
NS Nick Swisher Bat
PL Paul LoDuca Jsy
RC Robinson Cano Bat
RH Ryan Howard Bat EXCH
RO Roy Oswalt Jsy

2006 Topps Turkey Red Cabinet Auto Relics Suede

STATED ODDS 1:1730 JUMBO
STATED PRINT RUN 1 SERIAL #'d SET
NO PRICING DUE TO SCARCITY
EXCHANGE DEADLINE 09/30/08

2006 Topps Turkey Red Cabinet Auto Relics Dual

STATED ODDS 1:1368 JUMBO
NO PRICING DUE TO SCARCITY
EXCHANGE DEADLINE 09/30/08
HL Ryan Howard Bat
Derrek Lee Jsy
RB Alex Rodriguez Jsy
Barry Bonds Pants
RJ Alex Rodriguez Jsy
Chipper Jones Jsy EXCH
RW Alex Rodriguez Jsy
David Wright Jsy EXCH
WC David Wright Jsy
Robinson Cano Bat

2006 Topps Turkey Red Cabinet Auto Relics Dual Suede

STATED ODDS 1:6520 JUMBO
STATED PRINT RUN 1 SERIAL #'d SET
NO PRICING DUE TO SCARCITY

2006 Topps Turkey Red Relics

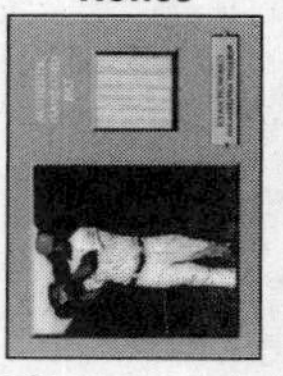

GROUP A ODDS 1:330 H, 1:335 R
GROUP B ODDS 1:205 H, 1:211 R
GROUP C-D ODDS 1:50 H, 1:54 R
GROUP E ODDS 1:88 H, 1:88 R
AJ Andruw Jones Jsy D 3.00 8.00
AP Albert Pujols Jsy D 8.00 20.00
APE Andy Pettitte Jsy B 3.00 8.00
AR Alex Rodriguez Jsy C 8.00 20.00
BL Brad Lidge Jsy C 3.00 8.00
BR Brian Roberts Jsy E 3.00 8.00
BW Bernie Williams Pants C 3.00 8.00
CB Carlos Beltran Jsy C 3.00 8.00
CBA Clint Barmes Jsy A 3.00 8.00
CC Chris Carpenter Jsy D 3.00 8.00
CD Carlos Delgado Bat A 3.00 8.00
CJ Chipper Jones Jsy C 5.00 12.00
DL Derrek Lee Jsy B 3.00 8.00
DO David Ortiz Jsy D 5.00 12.00
DW David Wright Jsy C 6.00 15.00
DWI Dontrelle Willis Jsy D 3.00 8.00
EC Eric Chavez Pants D 3.00 8.00
HB Hank Blalock Jsy D 3.00 8.00
HM Hideki Matsui Jsy C 5.00 12.00
IS Ichiro Suzuki Jsy A 8.00 20.00
JC Jose Contreras Jsy D 3.00 8.00
JD Johnny Damon Bat A 3.00 8.00
JE Jim Edmonds Jsy C 3.00 8.00
JF Jeff Francoeur Jsy E 5.00 12.00
JG Jon Garland Pants D 3.00 8.00
JH Jeremy Hermida Bat A 3.00 8.00
JM Joe Mauer Jsy E 3.00 8.00
JR Jose Reyes Jsy C 3.00 8.00
JS Johan Santana Jsy B 3.00 8.00
LB Lance Berkman Jsy D 3.00 8.00
MC Miguel Cabrera Jsy C 3.00 8.00
ME Morgan Ensberg Jsy E 3.00 8.00
MM Mike Mussina Pants B 3.00 8.00
MP Mike Piazza Bat A 5.00 12.00
MR Manny Ramirez Pants E 3.00 8.00
MRI Mariano Rivera Jsy C 5.00 12.00
MT Mark Teixeira Jsy D 3.00 8.00
MY Michael Young Jsy C 3.00 8.00
PK Paul Konerko Pants C 3.00 8.00
PL Paul LoDuca Jsy D 3.00 8.00
PM Pedro Martinez Jsy C 3.00 8.00
RC Robinson Cano Bat C 5.00 12.00
RH Ryan Howard Bat A 8.00 20.00
RHA Roy Halladay Jsy E 3.00 8.00
RIH Rich Harden Jsy C 3.00 8.00
RO Roy Oswalt Jsy B 3.00 8.00
TH Torii Hunter Jsy E 3.00 8.00
VG Vladimir Guerrero Jsy D 5.00 12.00

2006 Topps Turkey Red Relics Black

*BLACK: .75X TO 2X BASIC
STATED ODDS 1:485 H, 1:500 R
STATED PRINT RUN 50 SERIAL #'d SETS

2006 Topps Turkey Red Relics Gold

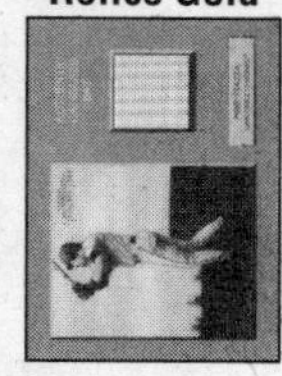

STATED ODDS 1:975 H, 1:1000 R
STATED PRINT RUN 25 SERIAL #'d SETS
NO PRICING DUE TO SCARCITY

2006 Topps Turkey Red Relics Red

*RED: .5X TO 1.2X BASIC
STATED ODDS 1:160 H, 1:170 R
STATED PRINT RUN 150 SERIAL #'d SETS

2006 Topps Turkey Red Relics Suede

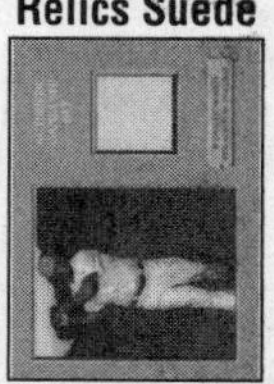

STATED ODDS 1:13,250 HOBBY
STATED PRINT RUN 1 SERIAL #'d SET
NO PRICING DUE TO SCARCITY

2006 Topps Turkey Red Relics White

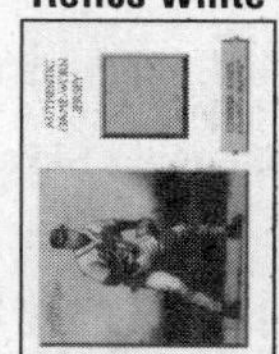

*WHITE: .6X TO 1.5X BASIC
STATED ODDS 1:245 H, 1:250 R
STATED PRINT RUN 99 SERIAL #'d SETS

2007 Topps Turkey Red

This 200-card set was released in September, 2007. The set was issued in both retail and hobby versions. The hobby packs consisted of eight cards (with an $4 SRP) which came 24 packs to a box and eight boxes to a case. Some of the cards in this set were either short printed or had an ad back variation. Either the SP's which are explicitly noted in our checklist or the cards with the ad backs were inserted into packs at a stated rate of one in four hobby or retail packs.

COMPLETE SET (200) 150.00 200.00
COMP.SET w/o SP's (150) 12.50 30.00
COMMON CARD (1-186) .12 .30
COMMON RC (1-186) .15 .40
COMMON SP (1-186) 2.50 6.00
SP ODDS 1:4 HOBBY, 1:4 RETAIL
COMMON AD BACK (1-186) 2.50 6.00
AD BACK ODDS 1:4 HOBBY,1:4 RETAIL
1 Ryan Howard .50 1.25
1b Ryan Howard Ad Back SP 4.00 10.00
2 Dontrelle Willis .12 .30
3 Matt Cain .20 .50
4 John Maine .12 .30
5 Cole Hamels .20 .50
6 Corey Patterson .12 .30
7 Mickey Mantle SP 10.00 25.00
8 Servin Up Strikes Johan Santana CL .20 .50
9 Josh Beckett .12 .30
10 Jimmy Rollins .20 .50
11 Kenji Johjima .30 .75
12 Orlando Hernandez .12 .30
13 Jorge Posada Play at the Plate CL .20 .50
14 Ivan Rodriguez .20 .50
15 Ichiro Suzuki .50 1.25
15b Ichiro Suzuki Ad Back SP 4.00 10.00
16 Stand Up Double Ken Griffey CL .50 1.25
17 Stephen Drew .20 .50
18 B.J. Upton .12 .30
19 Mickey Mantle 1.00 2.50
20 Alex Rodriguez .50 1.25
20b Alex Rodriguez Ad Back SP 4.00 10.00
21 Adam Dunn .12 .30
22 Adam Lind SP (RC) 2.50 6.00
23 Adrian Gonzalez .12 .30
24 Akinori Iwamura RC .40 1.00
25 Albert Pujols .60 1.50
25b Albert Pujols Ad Back SP 4.00 10.00
26 Frank Thomas .30 .75
27 Roy Halladay .12 .30
28 Alejandro De Aza RC .25 .60
29 Alex Gordon RC .75 2.00
30 Barry Bonds .60 1.50
31 Andrew Miller RC 1.00 2.50
32 Andruw Jones .20 .50
33 Kurt Suzuki SP (RC) 2.50 6.00
34 Mickey Mantle 1.00 2.50
35 Andy Pettitte .20 .50
36 Tadahito Iguchi .12 .30
37 Edgar Renteria .12 .30
38 Tim Hudson .12 .30
39 Micah Owings (RC) .15 .40
40 Chipper Jones .30 .75
40b Chipper Jones Ad Back SP 3.00 8.00
41 Barry Zito .12 .30
42 Dice-K Daisuke Matsuzaka CL 1.25 3.00
43 Jarrod Saltalamacchia SP (RC) 2.50 6.00
44 Bill Hall .12 .30
45 Billy Butler (RC) .25 .60
46 Billy Wagner .12 .30
47 Rich Harden SP 2.50 6.00
48 Prince Albert Albert Pujols CL .60 1.50
49 Brandon Inge .12 .30
50 Jason Giambi .12 .30
51 Brandon Webb .12 .30
52 Brandon Wood (RC) .15 .40
53 Swiping Second Carl Crawford CL .12 .30
54 Brian Giles .12 .30
55 Josh Hamilton (RC) .75 2.00
56 Chase Utley Ad Back SP 3.00 8.00
57 Miguel Montero (RC) .15 .40
58 Carl Crawford .12 .30
59 Carlos Beltran .12 .30
60 Mariano Rivera .30 .75
61 Carlos Delgado .12 .30
62 Carlos Lee SP 2.50 6.00
63 Carlos Zambrano SP 2.50 6.00
64 Miguel Tejada .12 .30
65 Mike Cameron .12 .30
66 Chase Utley SP 3.00 8.00
67 Chase Wright RC .40 1.00
68 Chien-Ming Wang .50 1.25
69 Nick Swisher .12 .30
70 David Wright .50 1.25
71 Mike Piazza SP 3.00 8.00
72 Chris Carpenter .12 .30
73 Mark Buehrle SP 2.50 6.00
74 Torii Hunter SP 2.50 6.00
75 Tyler Clippard (RC) .25 .60
76 Nick Markakis .20 .50
77 Mickey Mantle 1.00 2.50
78 Curt Schilling .20 .50
79 Curtis Granderson .12 .30
80 Craig Biggio .20 .50
81 Juan Pierre .12 .30
82 Dallas Braden SP RC 2.50 6.00
83 Dan Haren SP 3.00 8.00
84 Dan Uggla .20 .50
85 Danny Putnam (RC) .15 .40
86 David DeJesus .12 .30
87 David Eckstein .12 .30
88 Tim Lincecum RC 1.25 3.00
89 Johnny Damon SP 2.50 6.00
90 Justin Morneau .12 .30
91 Delmon Young (RC) .25 .60
92 Homer Bailey (RC) .25 .60
93 Carlos Gomez RC .25 .60
94 Josh Fields SP (RC) 2.50 6.00
95 Derek Jeter .75 2.00
95b Derek Jeter Ad Back SP 6.00 15.00
96 Derek Lee .12 .30
97 Don Kelly (RC) .15 .40
98 Doug Slaten RC .15 .40
99 Dustin Moseley .12 .30
100 Gary Sheffield .12 .30
101 Orlando Hudson SP 2.50 6.00
102 Elijah Dukes RC .25 .60
103 Eric Byrnes SP 2.50 6.00
104 Eric Chavez .12 .30
105 Phil Hughes (RC) .75 2.00
105b Phil Hughes Ad Back SP (RC) 4.00 10.00
106 Felix Hernandez SP 2.50 6.00
106b Felix Hernandez Ad Back SP 2.50 6.00
107 Mickey Mantle 1.00 2.50
108 Felix Pie (RC) .15 .40
109 The Captain Derek Jeter CL .75 2.00
110 Daisuke Matsuzaka RC 1.50 4.00
110b Daisuke Matsuzaka Ad Back SP RC 6.00 15.00
111 Francisco Rodriguez .12 .30
112 Ramon Hernandez .12 .30
113 Randy Johnson .30 .75
114 Gary Matthews .12 .30
115 Prince Fielder .30 .75
116 Vladdy Goes Yard Vladimir Guerrero CL .30 .75
117 Mickey Mantle 1.00 2.50
118 Hideki Matsui .30 .75
119 Hideki Okajima RC .75 2.00
120 Manny Ramirez .20 .50
121 Hunter Pence SP (RC) 6.00 15.00
122 Roy Oswalt .12 .30
123 Josh Willingham SP 2.50 6.00
124 Tom Gordon SP 2.50 6.00
125 Michael Young .12 .30
126 J.D. Drew .12 .30
127 Ryan Zimmerman .30 .75
128 James Shields SP 3.00 8.00
129 Jack Wilson .12 .30
130 David Ortiz .30 .75
130b David Ortiz Ad Back SP 3.00 8.00
131 Jose Jose Jose Jose Jose Reyes CL .30 .75
132 Jamie Vermilyea RC .15 .40
133 Jason Bay .12 .30
134 Scott Kazmir SP 2.50 6.00
135 Jason Isringhausen SP 3.00 8.00
136 Jason Marquis SP 2.50 6.00
137 Jason Schmidt .12 .30
138 Shawn Green .12 .30
139 Jeff Francoeur SP 3.00 8.00
140 Alfonso Soriano .12 .30
141 Kevin Kouzmanoff (RC) .15 .40
142 Jered Weaver .20 .50
143 Todd Helton SP 2.50 6.00
144 Jermaine Dye .12 .30
145 Jim Thome .20 .50
146 Tom Glavine SP 2.50 6.00
147 Joe Mauer .20 .50
148 Joe Nathan .12 .30
149 Joe Smith RC .15 .40
150 Ken Griffey Jr. .50 1.25
150b Ken Griffey Jr. Ad Back SP 4.00 10.00
151 Grady Sizemore .20 .50
152 Sammy Sosa SP 3.00 8.00
153 Andy LaRoche (RC) .15 .40
154 Travis Buck (RC) .15 .40
155 Alex Rios .12 .30
156 Travis Hafner .12 .30
157 Jake Peavy .12 .30
158 Jeff Kent .12 .30
159 Johan Santana .20 .50
159b Johan Santana Ad Back SP 2.50 6.00
160 Ivan Rodriguez .20 .50
161 Trevor Hoffman .12 .30
162 Troy Glaus .12 .30
163 Troy Tulowitzki (RC) .40 1.00
164 Jorge Posada .20 .50
165 Kei Igawa SP RC 3.00 8.00
166 Jose Reyes .30 .75
167 Mickey Mantle 1.00 2.50
168 Hit Streak Chase Utley CL .30 .75
169 Justin Verlander .30 .75
170 Hanley Ramirez .20 .50
171 Kelly Johnson SP 2.50 6.00
172 Kelvin Jimenez RC .15 .40
173 Roger Clemens .60 1.50
174 Khalil Greene SP 2.50 6.00
175 Lance Berkman .12 .30
176 Turning Two Hanley Ramirez CL .20 .50
177 Kyle Kendrick RC .40 1.00
178 Magglio Ordonez .12 .30
179 Marcus Giles SP 2.50 6.00
180 Miguel Cabrera .20 .50
180b Miguel Cabrera Ad Back SP 2.50 6.00
181 Mark Teahen .12 .30
182 Mark Teixeira SP 2.50 6.00
183 Matt Chico SP (RC) 2.50 6.00
184 Matt Holliday .15 .40
185 Vladimir Guerrero .30 .75
185b Vladimir Guerrero Ad Back SP 3.00 8.00
186 Yovani Gallardo (RC) .40 1.00

2007 Topps Turkey Red Chrome

STATED ODDS 1:4 HOBBY,1:7 RETAIL
STATED PRINT RUN 1999 SER.#'d SETS
SKIP NUMBERED SET
1 Ryan Howard 3.00 8.00
2 Dontrelle Willis 1.50 4.00
4 John Maine 1.50 4.00
5 Cole Hamels 2.00 5.00
9 Josh Beckett 1.50 4.00
11 Kenji Johjima 2.50 6.00
12 Orlando Hernandez 1.50 4.00
15 Ichiro Suzuki 3.00 8.00
17 Stephen Drew 1.50 4.00
20 Alex Rodriguez 3.00 8.00
21 Adam Dunn 1.50 4.00
24 Akinori Iwamura 1.50 4.00
25 Albert Pujols 4.00 10.00
29 Alex Gordon 3.00 8.00
30 Barry Bonds 4.00 10.00
31 Andrew Miller 3.00 8.00
32 Andruw Jones 2.00 5.00
34 Mickey Mantle 3.00 8.00
35 Andy Pettitte 2.00 5.00
36 Tadahito Iguchi 1.50 4.00
39 Micah Owings 1.50 4.00
40 Chipper Jones 2.50 6.00
41 Barry Zito 1.50 4.00
45 Billy Butler 2.00 5.00
46 Billy Wagner 1.50 4.00
51 Brandon Webb 1.50 4.00
52 Brandon Wood 1.50 4.00
55 Josh Hamilton 5.00 12.00
59 Carlos Beltran 1.50 4.00
60 Mariano Rivera 2.50 6.00
61 Carlos Delgado 1.50 4.00
64 Miguel Tejada 1.50 4.00
68 Chien-Ming Wang 3.00 8.00
70 David Wright 3.00 8.00
72 Chris Carpenter 1.50 4.00
75 Tyler Clippard 2.00 5.00
76 Nick Markakis 2.00 5.00
77 Mickey Mantle 3.00 8.00
81 Juan Pierre 1.50 4.00
84 Dan Uggla 2.00 5.00
85 Danny Putnam 1.50 4.00
87 David Eckstein 1.50 4.00
88 Tim Lincecum 4.00 10.00
90 Justin Morneau 1.50 4.00
91 Delmon Young 2.00 5.00
93 Carlos Gomez 2.00 5.00
95 Derek Jeter 4.00 10.00
96 Derek Lee 1.50 4.00
97 Don Kelly 1.50 4.00
98 Doug Slaten 1.50 4.00
99 Dustin Moseley 1.50 4.00
100 Gary Sheffield 1.50 4.00
102 Elijah Dukes 2.00 5.00
104 Eric Chavez 1.50 4.00
105 Phil Hughes 3.00 8.00
107 Mickey Mantle 3.00 8.00
108 Felix Pie 1.50 4.00
110 Daisuke Matsuzaka 4.00 10.00
111 Francisco Rodriguez 1.50 4.00
113 Randy Johnson 2.50 6.00
114 Gary Matthews 1.50 4.00
115 Prince Fielder 2.50 6.00
117 Mickey Mantle 3.00 8.00
119 Hideki Okajima 3.00 8.00
120 Manny Ramirez 2.00 5.00
122 Roy Oswalt 1.50 4.00
125 Michael Young 1.50 4.00
126 J.D. Drew 1.50 4.00
127 Ryan Zimmerman 2.50 6.00
130 David Ortiz 2.50 6.00
133 Jason Bay 1.50 4.00
137 Jason Schmidt 1.50 4.00
140 Alfonso Soriano 1.50 4.00
141 Kevin Kouzmanoff 1.50 4.00
142 Jered Weaver 2.00 5.00
144 Jermaine Dye 1.50 4.00
147 Joe Mauer 2.00 5.00
149 Joe Smith 1.50 4.00
150 Ken Griffey Jr. 3.00 8.00
151 Grady Sizemore 2.00 5.00
154 Travis Buck 1.50 4.00
155 Alex Rios 1.50 4.00
158 Jeff Kent 1.50 4.00
159 Johan Santana 2.00 5.00
160 Ivan Rodriguez 2.00 5.00
162 Troy Glaus 1.50 4.00
163 Troy Tulowitzki 2.50 6.00
166 Jose Reyes 2.50 6.00
167 Mickey Mantle 3.00 8.00
169 Justin Verlander 2.50 6.00
170 Hanley Ramirez 2.00 5.00
172 Kelvin Jimenez 1.50 4.00
173 Roger Clemens 4.00 10.00
175 Lance Berkman 1.50 4.00
177 Kyle Kendrick 2.50 6.00
178 Magglio Ordonez 1.50 4.00
180 Miguel Cabrera 2.00 5.00
181 Mark Teahen 1.50 4.00
185 Vladimir Guerrero 2.50 6.00
186 Yovani Gallardo 2.50 6.00

2007 Topps Turkey Red Chrome Refractors

*CHROME REF: .5X TO 1.2X BASIC CHROME
STATED ODDS 1:8 HOBBY,1:16 RETAIL
STATED PRINT RUN 999 SER.#'d SETS
SKIP NUMBERED SET

2007 Topps Turkey Red Chrome Black Refractors

*BLACK REF: 1X TO 2.5X BASIC CHROME
STATED ODDS 1:43 HOBBY
STATED PRINT RUN 99 SER.#'d SETS
SKIP NUMBERED SET
15 Ichiro Suzuki 12.50 30.00
25 Albert Pujols 50.00 100.00
29 Alex Gordon 20.00 50.00
30 Barry Bonds 12.50 30.00
31 Andrew Miller 10.00 25.00
34 Mickey Mantle 15.00 40.00
68 Chien-Ming Wang 15.00 40.00
77 Mickey Mantle 15.00 40.00
88 Tim Lincecum 50.00 100.00
95 Derek Jeter 15.00 40.00
105 Phil Hughes 10.00 25.00
107 Mickey Mantle 15.00 40.00
110 Daisuke Matsuzaka 30.00 60.00
117 Mickey Mantle 15.00 40.00
119 Hideki Okajima 6.00 15.00
150 Ken Griffey Jr. 10.00 25.00
163 Troy Tulowitzki 15.00 40.00
167 Mickey Mantle 15.00 40.00

2007 Topps Turkey Red Cabinet

STATED ODDS 1:2 HOB.BOXLOADER
AD Adam Dunn 4.00 10.00
AG Alex Gordon 6.00 15.00
AI Akinori Iwamura 4.00 10.00
AJ Andruw Jones 4.00 10.00
AP Albert Pujols 10.00 25.00
AR Alex Rodriguez 10.00 25.00
AS Alfonso Soriano 4.00 10.00
BW Brandon Webb 4.00 10.00
BZ Barry Zito 4.00 10.00
CC Chris Carpenter 4.00 10.00
CL Carlos Lee 4.00 10.00
CU Chase Utley 5.00 12.00
CW Chien-Ming Wang 5.00 12.00
DJ Derek Jeter 10.00 25.00
DM Daisuke Matsuzaka 6.00 15.00
DO David Ortiz 6.00 15.00
DW David Wright 6.00 15.00
DY Delmon Young 5.00 12.00
ED Elijah Dukes 4.00 10.00
FH Felix Hernandez 4.00 10.00
FR Francisco Rodriguez 4.00 10.00
GS Grady Sizemore 5.00 12.00
HO Hideki Okajima 5.00 12.00
HR Hanley Ramirez 4.00 10.00
IR Ivan Rodriguez 4.00 10.00
IS Ichiro Suzuki 6.00 15.00
JB Jason Bay 5.00 12.00
JD Jermaine Dye 4.00 10.00
JDS Jason Schmidt 4.00 10.00
JEM Justin Morneau 4.00 10.00
JF Jeff Francoeur 5.00 12.00
JM Joe Mauer 4.00 10.00
JR Jose Reyes 5.00 12.00
JS Johan Santana 4.00 10.00
JV Justin Verlander 5.00 12.00
KG Ken Griffey Jr. 6.00 15.00
LB Lance Berkman 4.00 10.00
MC Miguel Cabrera 4.00 10.00
MM Mickey Mantle 12.50 30.00
MP Mike Piazza 5.00 12.00
MR Manny Ramirez 6.00 15.00
MT Miguel Tejada 4.00 10.00
MY Michael Young 4.00 10.00
NM Nick Markakis 4.00 10.00
PF Prince Fielder 5.00 12.00
RC Roger Clemens 6.00 15.00
RH Ryan Howard 6.00 15.00
RZ Ryan Zimmerman 5.00 12.00
SD Stephen Drew 4.00 10.00
TT Troy Tulowitzki 5.00 12.00
VG Vladimir Guerrero 5.00 12.00

2007 Topps Turkey Red Cabinet Dick Perez Autographs

STATED ODDS 1:14 HOB.BOXLOADER
STATED PRINT RUN 25 SER.#'d SETS
CARDS FEATURE DICK PEREZ AUTO
NO PRICING DUE TO SCARCITY
AD Adam Dunn
AG Alex Gordon
AI Akinori Iwamura
AJ Andruw Jones
AP Albert Pujols
AR Alex Rodriguez
AS Alfonso Soriano
BW Brandon Webb
BZ Barry Zito
CC Chris Carpenter
CL Carlos Lee
CU Chase Utley
CW Chien-Ming Wang
DJ Derek Jeter
DM Daisuke Matsuzaka
DO David Ortiz
DW David Wright
DY Delmon Young
ED Elijah Dukes
FH Felix Hernandez
FR Francisco Rodriguez
GS Grady Sizemore
HO Hideki Okajima
HR Hanley Ramirez
IR Ivan Rodriguez
IS Ichiro Suzuki
JB Jason Bay
JD Jermaine Dye
JDS Jason Schmidt
JEM Justin Morneau
JF Jeff Francoeur
JM Joe Mauer
JR Jose Reyes
JS Johan Santana
JV Justin Verlander
KG Ken Griffey Jr.
LB Lance Berkman
MC Miguel Cabrera
MM Mickey Mantle
MP Mike Piazza
MR Manny Ramirez
MT Miguel Tejada
MY Michael Young
NM Nick Markakis
PF Prince Fielder
RC Roger Clemens
RH Ryan Howard
RZ Ryan Zimmerman
SD Stephen Drew
TT Troy Tulowitzki
VG Vladimir Guerrero

2007 Topps Turkey Red Chromographs

GROUP A ODDS 1:3700 HOBBY/RETAIL
GROUP B ODDS 1:292 HOBBY/RETAIL
GROUP C ODDS 1:194 HOBBY/RETAIL
GROUP D ODDS 1:177 HOBBY/RETAIL
NO GROUP A PRICING AVAILABLE
EXCH DEADLINE 9/30/2009
AG Alex Gordon D 20.00 50.00
AK Austin Kearns D 4.00 10.00
AR Alex Rodriguez A
BJ Bobby Jenks C 10.00 25.00
BW Brad Wilkerson B 3.00 8.00
CAH Clay Hensley C 3.00 8.00
CG Curtis Granderson B 50.00 100.00
CH Cole Hamels C 15.00 40.00
CJ Chuck James B 4.00 10.00
DE Darin Erstad B 4.00 10.00
DU Dan Uggla D 8.00 20.00
DW David Wright A
EC Eric Chavez B 6.00 15.00
FP Felix Pie C 6.00 15.00
GS Gary Sheffield A
HCK Hong-Chih Kuo C 6.00 15.00
HR Hanley Ramirez C 12.50 30.00
JB Jason Bay A
JD Johnny Damon A
JM John Maine C 10.00 25.00
JP Jake Peavy A

JZ Joel Zumaya D 6.00 15.00
KE Kelvim Escobar B EXCH 4.00 10.00
LM Lastings Milledge D 6.00 15.00
MC Melky Cabrera D 10.00 25.00
MG Mike Gonzalez C 3.00 8.00
NM Nick Markakis D 10.00 25.00
NR Nate Robertson C 6.00 15.00
PL Paul LoDuca B 4.00 10.00
RC Robinson Cano B 15.00 40.00
RH Ryan Howard A
RJH Rich Hill D 4.00 10.00
RM Rob Mackowiak B 3.00 8.00
RNM Russell Martin D 10.00 25.00
SC Sean Casey B 10.00 25.00
SP Scott Podsednik B 3.00 8.00
SV Shane Victorino C 15.00 40.00
TG Tony Gwynn Jr. B 6.00 15.00
WN Wil Nieves B 6.00 15.00

2007 Topps Turkey Red Presidents

COMPLETE SET (43) 60.00 150.00
STATED ODDS 1:12 HOBBY, 1:12 RETAIL
TRP1 George Washington 2.00 5.00
TRP2 John Adams 1.50 4.00
TRP3 Thomas Jefferson 1.50 4.00
TRP4 James Madison 1.50 4.00
TRP5 James Monroe 1.50 4.00
TRP6 John Quincy Adams 1.50 4.00
TRP7 Andrew Jackson 1.50 4.00
TRP8 Martin Van Buren 1.50 4.00
TRP9 William H. Harrison 1.50 4.00
TRP10 John Tyler 1.50 4.00
TRP11 James K. Polk 1.50 4.00
TRP12 Zachary Taylor 1.50 4.00
TRP13 Millard Fillmore 1.50 4.00
TRP14 Franklin Pierce 1.50 4.00
TRP15 James Buchanan 1.50 4.00
TRP16 Abraham Lincoln 2.00 5.00
TRP17 Andrew Johnson 1.50 4.00
TRP18 Ulysses S. Grant 1.50 4.00
TRP19 Rutherford B. Hayes 1.50 4.00
TRP20 James Garfield 1.50 4.00
TRP21 Chester A. Arthur 1.50 4.00
TRP22 Grover Cleveland 1.50 4.00
TRP23 Benjamin Harrison 1.50 4.00
TRP24 Grover Cleveland 1.50 4.00
TRP25 William McKinley 1.50 4.00
TRP26 Theodore Roosevelt 1.50 4.00
TRP27 William H. Taft 1.50 4.00
TRP28 Woodrow Wilson 1.50 4.00
TRP29 Warren G. Harding 1.50 4.00
TRP30 Calvin Coolidge 1.50 4.00
TRP31 Herbert Hoover 1.50 4.00
TRP32 Franklin D. Roosevelt 1.50 4.00
TRP33 Harry S. Truman 1.50 4.00
TRP34 Dwight D. Eisenhower 1.50 4.00
TRP35 John F. Kennedy 2.00 5.00
TRP36 Lyndon B. Johnson 1.50 4.00
TRP37 Richard Nixon 1.50 4.00
TRP38 Gerald Ford 1.50 4.00
TRP39 Jimmy Carter 1.50 4.00
TRP40 Ronald Reagan 2.00 5.00
TRP41 George H. W. Bush 2.00 5.00
TRP42 Bill Clinton 2.00 5.00
TRP43 George W. Bush 2.00 5.00

2007 Topps Turkey Red Relics

GROUP A ODDS 1:13,000 HOBBY/RETAIL
GROUP B ODDS 1:211 HOBBY/RETAIL
GROUP C ODDS 1:58 HOBBY/RETAIL
GROUP D ODDS 1:155 HOBBY/RETAIL
GROUP E ODDS 1:85 HOBBY/RETAIL
GROUP F ODDS 1:80 HOBBY/RETAIL
GROUP G ODDS 1:53 HOBBY/RETAIL
AB Adrian Beltre Bat D 3.00 8.00
AD Adam Dunn Jsy C 3.00 8.00
AH Aaron Harang Bat D 3.00 8.00
AJ1 Andruw Jones Jsy B 4.00 10.00
AJ2 Andruw Jones Bat F 3.00 8.00
AM Andrew Miller Jsy G 3.00 8.00
ANB Angel Berroa Bat F 3.00 8.00
AS Alfonso Soriano Bat C 4.00 10.00
BB Barry Bonds Bat B 12.50 30.00
BC Bobby Crosby Pants C 3.00 8.00
BJR B.J. Ryan Jsy C 3.00 8.00
BR Brian Roberts Jsy B 5.00 12.00
BS Brian Stokes Jsy E 3.00 8.00
BT Brad Thompson Jsy E 3.00 8.00
BW Brandon Webb Pants B 5.00 12.00
BZ Ben Zobrist Bat B 4.00 10.00
CB1 Carlos Beltran Jsy G 3.00 8.00
CB2 Carlos Beltran Bat B 4.00 10.00
CC Coco Crisp Bat C 3.00 8.00
CD Carlos Delgado Bat B 5.00 12.00
CH Cole Hamels Jsy D 5.00 12.00
CJ Chipper Jones Jsy C 4.00 10.00
CJC Chris Carpenter Jsy C 3.00 8.00
CL Carlos Lee Bat B 4.00 10.00
CR Chris Ray Jsy E 3.00 8.00
CS C.C. Sabathia Jsy E 3.00 8.00
DM Daisuke Matsuzaka Jsy A
DN Dioner Navarro Bat C 3.00 8.00
DO David Ortiz Bat C 4.00 10.00
DR Darrell Rasner Jsy E 3.00 8.00
DU Dan Uggla Jsy C 3.00 8.00
DW David Wright Jsy D 6.00 15.00
DWA Daryle Ward Bat G 3.00 8.00
DWW Dontrelle Willis Jsy G 3.00 8.00
DY Delmon Young Bat C 3.00 8.00
ES Ervin Santana Jsy C 3.00 8.00
GP Glen Perkins Jsy C 3.00 8.00
HB Hank Blalock Jsy C 3.00 8.00
HR Hanley Ramirez Bat B 5.00 12.00
IR Ivan Rodriguez Pants D 4.00 10.00
IS Ichiro Suzuki Bat B 8.00 20.00
JB Josh Beckett Bat G 3.00 8.00
JC Jorge Cantu Bat C 3.00 8.00
JD Jermaine Dye Pants B 5.00 12.00
JE Jim Edmonds Jsy C 3.00 8.00
JF Jeff Francoeur Bat B 6.00 15.00
JG Jon Garland Pants G 3.00 8.00
JH Josh Hamilton Bat G 8.00 20.00
JK Jeff Kent Bat B 4.00 10.00
JM Justin Morneau Bat C 3.00 8.00
JP Josh Paul Bat D 3.00 8.00
JPM Joe Mauer Jsy C 4.00 10.00
JR Jose Reyes Jsy E 3.00 8.00
JRB Jason Bay Jsy B 4.00 10.00
JS John Smoltz Jsy C 4.00 10.00
JV2 Jason Varitek Bat D 4.00 10.00
JW Jered Weaver JsyB 5.00 12.00
JZ Joel Zumaya Jsy D 3.00 8.00
KM Kaz Matsui Bat D 3.00 8.00
LB Lance Berkman Jsy G 3.00 8.00
LC Luis Castillo Bat C 3.00 8.00
MC Melky Cabrera Bat C 3.00 8.00
ME Morgan Ensberg Jsy E 3.00 8.00
MG Marcus Giles Jsy F 3.00 8.00
MJC Miguel Cairo Bat C 3.00 8.00
MM Mickey Mantle Bat B 60.00 120.00
MP Mike Piazza Bat D 5.00 12.00
MR Manny Ramirez Jsy F 4.00 10.00
MT Miguel Tejada Pants C 3.00 8.00
MY Michael Young Jsy C 3.00 8.00
NM Nick Markakis Bat B 6.00 15.00
NP Neifi Perez Bat G 3.00 8.00
NS Nick Swisher Pants E 3.00 8.00
PM Pedro Martinez Bat C 3.00 8.00
PP Placido Polanco Bat D 3.00 8.00
RB1 Rocco Baldelli Jsy F 3.00 8.00
RB2 Rocco Baldelli Jsy C 3.00 8.00
RH Ryan Howard Jsy B 10.00 25.00
RJH Rich Hill Jsy F 3.00 8.00
RK Ryan Klesko Bat C 3.00 8.00
RS Reggie Sanders Bat C 3.00 8.00
RZ Ryan Zimmerman Bat C 5.00 12.00
SR Scott Rolen Jsy F 3.00 8.00
SS Sammy Sosa Bat E 4.00 10.00
ST So Taguchi Bat C 3.00 8.00
TB Travis Buck Jsy F 3.00 8.00
TH Travis Hafner Jsy B 5.00 12.00
TI Tadahito Iguchi Jsy C 3.00 8.00
TJ Tyler Johnson Pants C 3.00 8.00
VG Vladimir Guerrero Jsy B 5.00 12.00
VW Vernon Wells Jsy B 5.00 12.00

2007 Topps Turkey Red Silks

STATED ODDS 1:85 HOBBY
STATED PRINT RUN 99 SER.#'d SETS
AD Adam Dunn 6.00 15.00
AI Akinori Iwamura 8.00 20.00
AIR Alex Rios 8.00 20.00
AP Albert Pujols 30.00 60.00
AR Alex Rodriguez 30.00 60.00
AS Alfonso Soriano 10.00 25.00
BB Billy Butler 12.50 30.00
BLB Barry Bonds 20.00 50.00
CH Cole Hamels 10.00 25.00
CJ Chipper Jones 12.50 30.00
CS C.C. Sabathia 8.00 20.00
CY Adrian Gonzalez 6.00 15.00
DH Dan Haren 6.00 15.00
DJ Derek Jeter 35.00 70.00
DM Daisuke Matsuzaka 30.00 60.00
DO David Ortiz 12.50 30.00
DU Dan Uggla 8.00 20.00
DW David Wright 12.50 30.00
DWW Dontrelle Willis 6.00 15.00
EB Erik Bedard 8.00 20.00
GS Grady Sizemore 10.00 25.00
HP Hunter Pence 15.00 40.00
HR Hanley Ramirez 8.00 20.00
IS Ichiro Suzuki 20.00 50.00
JAS John Smoltz 12.50 30.00
JB Josh Beckett 10.00 25.00
JBR Jose Reyes 12.50 30.00
JD Jermaine Dye 6.00 15.00
JH J.J. Hardy 6.00 15.00
JL John Lackey 6.00 15.00
JM Justin Morneau 6.00 15.00
JP Jake Peavy 10.00 25.00
JR Jimmy Rollins 12.50 30.00
JRB Jason Bay 6.00 15.00
JS Johan Santana 15.00 40.00
JV Justin Verlander 10.00 25.00
KG Ken Griffey Jr. 20.00 50.00
MAR Manny Ramirez 10.00 25.00
MH Matt Holliday 12.50 30.00
MM Mickey Mantle 60.00 120.00
MO Magglio Ordonez 15.00 40.00
MR Mark Reynolds 10.00 25.00
MT Mark Teixeira 8.00 20.00
NS Nick Swisher 8.00 20.00
PF Prince Fielder 15.00 40.00
RH Ryan Howard 20.00 50.00
RM Russell Martin 8.00 20.00
RZ Ryan Zimmerman 8.00 20.00
TH Torii Hunter 6.00 15.00
VG Vladimir Guerrero 8.00 20.00

2008 UD A Piece of History

COMPLETE SET (200) 15.00 40.00
COMMON CARD (1-100) .20 .50
COMMON ROOKIE (101-150) .40 1.00
COMMON HM (151-200) .20 .50
1 Brandon Webb .30 .75
2 Dan Haren .20 .50
3 Justin Upton .50 1.25
4 Chris B. Young .20 .50
5 Mark Teixeira .30 .75
6 Jeff Francoeur .20 .50
7 John Smoltz .50 1.25
8 Tom Glavine .30 .75
9 Brian McCann .30 .75
10 Chipper Jones .60 1.50
11 Erik Bedard .20 .50
12 Nick Markakis .30 .75
13 Josh Beckett .30 .75
14 David Ortiz .50 1.25
15 Manny Ramirez .50 1.25
16 Dustin Pedroia .75 2.00
17 Grady Sizemore .30 .75
18 Jonathan Papelbon .30 .75
19 Daisuke Matsuzaka .75 2.00
20 Curt Schilling .30 .75
21 Alfonso Soriano .30 .75
22 Aramis Ramirez .20 .50
23 Carlos Zambrano .30 .75
24 Nick Swisher .20 .50
25 Jim Thome .30 .75
26 Ken Griffey Jr. .75 2.00
27 Adam Dunn .20 .50
28 Aaron Harang .20 .50
29 Matt Holliday .30 .75
30 Troy Tulowitzki .30 .75
31 Todd Helton .30 .75
32 Magglio Ordonez .30 .75
33 Justin Verlander .30 .75
34 Miguel Cabrera .30 .75
35 Gary Sheffield .20 .50
36 Ivan Rodriguez .30 .75
37 Dontrelle Willis .20 .50
38 Hanley Ramirez .50 1.25
39 Andrew Miller .30 .75
40 Lance Berkman .30 .75
41 Roy Oswalt .20 .50
42 Carlos Lee .20 .50
43 Hunter Pence .50 1.25
44 Alex Gordon .50 1.25
45 Mark Teahen .20 .50
46 Torii Hunter .20 .50
47 Vladimir Guerrero .50 1.25
48 Victor Martinez .20 .50
49 Andruw Jones .20 .50
50 James Loney .30 .75
51 Russell Martin .30 .75
52 Jeff Kent .20 .50
53 Ryan Braun .60 1.50
54 Prince Fielder .50 1.25
55 Joe Mauer .30 .75
56 Justin Morneau .30 .75
57 Delmon Young .30 .75
58 Jose Reyes .30 .75
59 David Wright .60 1.50
60 Carlos Beltran .20 .50
61 Johan Santana .30 .75
62 Pedro Martinez .30 .75
63 Alex Rodriguez .75 2.00
64 Derek Jeter 1.25 3.00
65 Hideki Matsui .50 1.25
66 Robinson Cano .30 .75
67 Joba Chamberlain .60 1.50
68 Phil Hughes .50 1.25
69 Mariano Rivera .50 1.25
70 Rich Harden .20 .50
71 Joe Blanton .20 .50
72 Cole Hamels .50 1.25
73 Ryan Howard .60 1.50
74 Jimmy Rollins .30 .75
75 Chase Utley .50 1.25
76 Jason Bay .20 .50
77 Freddy Sanchez .20 .50
78 Jake Peavy .30 .75
79 Greg Maddux .60 1.50
80 Trevor Hoffman .20 .50
81 Barry Zito .20 .50
82 Tim Lincecum .50 1.25
83 Travis Hafner .20 .50
84 C.C. Sabathia .30 .75
85 Felix Hernandez .30 .75
86 Ichiro Suzuki .75 2.00
87 Troy Glaus .20 .50
88 Albert Pujols 1.00 2.50
89 Chris Carpenter .20 .50
90 Scott Kazmir .30 .75
91 Carl Crawford .20 .50
92 B.J. Upton .30 .75
93 Michael Young .20 .50
94 Josh Hamilton .60 1.50
95 Vernon Wells .20 .50
96 Alex Rios .20 .50
97 Scott Rolen .30 .75
98 Frank Thomas .50 1.25
99 Chad Cordero .20 .50
100 Ryan Zimmerman .30 .75
101 Emilio Bonifacio (RC) .60 1.50
102 Bill Murphy (RC) .40 1.00
103 Billy Buckner (RC) .40 1.00
104 Brandon Jones RC 1.00 2.50
105 Clint Sammons (RC) .40 1.00
106 Clay Buchholz (RC) 1.00 2.50
107 Kevin Hart (RC) .40 1.00
108 Lance Broadway (RC) .40 1.00
109 Donny Lucy (RC) .40 1.00
110 Heath Phillips RC .60 1.50
111 Ryan Hanigan RC .60 1.50
112 Joey Votto (RC) 1.00 2.50
113 Joe Koshansky (RC) .40 1.00
114 Josh Newman RC .60 1.50
115 Seth Smith (RC) .40 1.00
116 Harvey Garcia (RC) .40 1.00
117 Chris Seddon (RC) .40 1.00
118 Josh Anderson (RC) .40 1.00
119 Troy Patton (RC) .40 1.00
120 Felipe Paulino RC .60 1.50
121 J.R. Towles RC 1.00 2.50
122 Luke Hochevar RC 1.00 2.50
123 Chin-Lung Hu (RC) .60 1.50
124 Jonathan Meloan RC .60 1.50
125 Sam Fuld RC .40 1.00
126 Mitch Stetter RC .60 1.50
127 Jose Morales (RC) .40 1.00
128 Carlos Muniz RC .60 1.50
129 Alberto Gonzalez RC .60 1.50
130 Ian Kennedy RC 1.00 2.50
131 Ross Ohlendorf RC .60 1.50
132 Jonathan Albaladejo RC .60 1.50
133 Daric Barton (RC) .40 1.00
134 Jerry Blevins RC .60 1.50
135 Dave Davidson RC .60 1.50
136 Nyjer Morgan (RC) .40 1.00
137 Steve Pearce RC .60 1.50
138 Colt Morton RC .60 1.50
139 Eugenio Velez RC .40 1.00
140 Erick Threets (RC) .40 1.00
141 Bronson Sardinha (RC) .40 1.00
142 Wladimir Balentien (RC) .40 1.00
143 Jeff Clement (RC) .40 1.00
144 Rob Johnson (RC) .40 1.00
145 Jeff Ridgway RC .60 1.50
146 Justin Ruggiano RC .60 1.50
147 Luis Mendoza (RC) .40 1.00
148 Bill White RC .40 1.00
149 Ross Detwiler RC 1.00 2.50
150 Justin Maxwell RC .60 1.50
151 Fall of the Berlin Wall .20 .50
152 Wright Brothers 1st Flight .20 .50
153 Signing of Declaration of Independence .20 .50
154 Columbus Discovers America .20 .50
155 First Space Shuttle launch .20 .50
156 Hawaii becomes 50th state .20 .50
157 Statue of LIberty given to U.S. .20 .50
158 Gettysburg Address .20 .50
159 Completion of Transcontinental Railroad .20 .50
160 Opening of Panama Canal .20 .50
161 U.S. enters World War 1 .20 .50
162 Treaty of Versailes .20 .50
163 Television invented .20 .50
164 Geneva Summit .20 .50
165 Woodstock .20 .50
166 Invention of Cotton Gin .20 .50
167 Eiffel Tower .20 .50
168 Suez Canal opens .20 .50
169 New York City Subway opens .20 .50
170 Polio Vaccine invented .20 .50
171 Bell X-1 Breaks Sound Barrier .20 .50
172 USS Enterprise Aircraft Carrier launched .20 .50
173 Hubble Telescope launches .20 .50
174 N.A.T.O. created .20 .50
175 Sputnik launched by Russia .20 .50
176 U.S.S.R. Crumbles .20 .50
177 Boston Tea Party .20 .50
178 Paul Revere's Ride .20 .50
179 Civil Rights Act Passes .20 .50
180 Hindenburg blows up .20 .50
181 Franklin discovers electricity .20 .50
182 Creation of the Internet .20 .50
183 1st World's Fair - 1851 London .20 .50
184 Pope John Paul II .20 .50
185 1st Heart Transplant .20 .50
186 California Gold Rush .20 .50
187 Creation of the personal computer .20 .50
188 Louisiana Purchase .20 .50
189 1st Dictionary published .20 .50
190 Steam Engine invented .20 .50
191 History of Nobel Prize .20 .50
192 Liberty Bell .20 .50
193 International Space Station .20 .50
194 Human Genome Project .20 .50
195 The Supreme Court .20 .50
196 Lewis and Clark .20 .50
197 Battle of the Alamo .20 .50
198 The creation of baseball .20 .50
199 Juan Ponce De Leon .20 .50
200 Jamestown - 1607 .20 .50

2008 UD A Piece of History Blue

RANDOM INSERTS IN PACKS
STATED PRINT RUN 25 SER.#'d SETS
NO PRICING DUE TO SCARCITY

2008 UD A Piece of History Gold

*GOLD 1-100: 1.5X TO 4X BASIC 1-100
*GOLD RC 101-150: 1.5X TO 4X BASIC RC
*GOLD HM 151-200: 1.5X TO 4X BASIC HM
RANDOM INSERTS IN PACKS
STATED PRINT RUN 75 SER.#'d SETS

2008 UD A Piece of History Red

*RED 1-100: 1X TO 2.5X BASIC 1-100
*RED RC 101-150: 1X TO 2.5X BASIC RC
*RED HM 151-200: 1X TO 2.5X BASIC HM
RANDOM INSERTS IN PACKS
STATED PRINT RUN 149 SER.#'d SETS

2008 UD A Piece of History Silver

*SILVER 1-100: .6X TO 1.5X BASIC 1-100
*SILVER RC 101-150: .6X TO 1.5X BASIC RC
*SILVER HM 151-200: .6X TO 1.5X BASIC HM
RANDOM INSERTS IN PACKS

2008 UD A Piece of History Rookie Autographs

OVERALL AU ODDS 1:16
PRINT RUNS B/W 50-499 COPIES PER
101 Emilio Bonifacio/499 3.00 8.00
102 Bill Murphy/499 3.00 8.00
103 Billy Buckner/149 4.00 10.00
104 Brandon Jones/499 3.00 8.00
105 Clint Sammons/499 3.00 8.00
106 Clay Buchholz/199 8.00 20.00
107 Kevin Hart/499 3.00 8.00
108 Lance Broadway/99 4.00 10.00
111 Ryan Hanigan/499 3.00 8.00
112 Joey Votto/50 8.00 20.00
113 Joe Koshansky/499 3.00 8.00
114 Josh Newman/499 3.00 8.00
115 Seth Smith/499 3.00 8.00
116 Harvey Garcia/499 3.00 8.00
117 Chris Seddon/459 3.00 8.00
118 Josh Anderson/499 3.00 8.00
119 Troy Patton/499 4.00 10.00
120 Felipe Paulino/499 3.00 8.00
121 J.R. Towles/499 4.00 10.00
122 Luke Hochevar/99
123 Chin-Lung Hu/99 12.50 30.00
124 Jonathan Meloan/99
127 Jose Morales/499 3.00 8.00
129 Alberto Gonzalez/499 4.00 10.00
130 Ian Kennedy/199 6.00 15.00
131 Ross Ohlendorf/499 4.00 10.00
132 Jonathan Albaladejo/499 3.00 8.00
133 Daric Barton/99 4.00 10.00
134 Jerry Blevins/499 3.00 8.00
135 Dave Davidson/499 3.00 8.00
136 Nyjer Morgan/499 3.00 8.00
137 Steve Pearce/499 4.00 10.00
138 Colt Morton/499 3.00 8.00
139 Eugenio Velez/499 3.00 8.00
141 Bronson Sardinha/499 3.00 8.00
142 Wladimir Balentien/199 4.00 10.00
144 Rob Johnson/499 3.00 8.00
146 Justin Ruggiano/499 3.00 8.00
147 Luis Mendoza/499 3.00 8.00
148 Bill White/499 3.00 8.00
149 Ross Detwiler/499 3.00 8.00
150 Justin Maxwell/499 4.00 10.00

2008 UD A Piece of History Rookie Autographs Blue

*BLUE: .6X TO 1.5X BASIC
OVERALL AU ODDS 1:16
PRINT RUNS B/WN 15-50 COPIES PER
NO PRICING ON QTY 25 OR LESS

2008 UD A Piece of History Rookie Autographs Copper

OVERALL AUTO ODDS 1:16
PRINT RUNS B/WN 5-10 COPIES PER
NO PRICING DUE TO SCARCITY

2008 UD A Piece of History Rookie Autographs Gold

*GOLD: .6X TO 1.5X BASIC
OVERALL AU ODDS 1:16
PRINT RUNS B/WN 20-75 COPIES PER
NO PRICING ON QTY 25 OR LESS
106 Clay Buchholz/50 15.00 40.00

2008 UD A Piece of History Rookie Autographs Red

*RED: .6X TO 1.5X BASIC
OVERALL AU ODDS 1:16
PRINT RUNS B/WN 25-99 COPIES PER
NO PRICING ON QTY 25 OR LESS

2008 UD A Piece of History Rookie Autographs Silver

OVERALL AUTO ODDS 1:16
PRINT RUNS B/WN 10-25 COPIES PER
NO PRICING DUE TO SCARCITY

2008 UD A Piece of History A Piece of Hollywood Memorablia

STATED ODDS 1:16
1 Amanda Bynes 6.00 15.00
Sydney White Costume
2 Mel Gibson 5.00 12.00
We Were Soldiers Shirt
3 Brad Pitt 5.00 12.00
Spy Game Shirt
4 George Clooney 4.00 10.00
3 Kings Army Jacket
5 Denzell Washington 4.00 10.00
Courage Under Fire Jacket
6 Jamie Foxx 4.00 10.00
Ray Shirt
7 Kevin Costner 5.00 12.00
JFK Shirt
8 Jack Nicholson 5.00 12.00
A Few Good Men Shirt
9 Mike Myers 6.00 15.00
Austin Powers Pants
10 Dana Carvey 6.00 15.00
Wayne's World Hockey Jersey
11 Phillip Seymour Hoffman 4.00 10.00
Capote Sweater
12 Jim Carrey 4.00 10.00
Bruce Almighty Shirt
13 Scarlett Johanson 6.00 15.00
Nanny Diaries T-Shirt
14 Demi Moore 4.00 10.00
GI Jane Jacket
15 Christopher Reeve 12.50 30.00
Superman 3 Cape
16 Mel Gibson 20.00 50.00
We Were Soldiers Shoes SP
17 Denzel Washington 40.00 80.00
Courage Under Fire Hat SP
18 Jim Carrey 4.00 10.00
Bruce Almighty Pants
19 George Clooney 4.00 10.00
3 Kings Army Pants
20 Scarlett Johanson 10.00 25.00
Nanny Diaries Undershirt SP
21 Phillip Seymour Hoffman 4.00 10.00
Capote Jacket
22 Denzell Washington 4.00 10.00
Courage Under Fire Army Pants
23 Mel Gibson 5.00 12.00
We Were Soldiers Pants
24 Woody Harrelson 4.00 10.00
Kingpin Jacket
25 Robin Williams 4.00 10.00
Birdcage Shirt
26 Jennifer Garner 5.00 12.00
Time of Your Life Pajamas
27 Tom Cruise 6.00 15.00
A Few Good Men Shirt

2008 UD A Piece of History Box Score Memories

RANDOM INSERTS IN PACKS
STATED PRINT RUN 699 SER.#'d SETS
*BLUE: .6X TO 1.5X BASIC
BLUE RANDOMLY INSERTED
BLUE PRINT RUN 75 SER.#'d SETS
*COPPER: .6X TO 1.5X BASIC
COPPER RANDOMLY INSERTED
COPPER PRINT RUN 99 SER.#'d SETS
*RED: .5X TO 1.2X BASIC
RED RANDOMLY INSERTED
RED PRINT RUN 149 SER.#'d SETS
SILVER RANDOMLY INSERTED
SILVER PRINT RUN 25 SER.#'d SETS
NO SILVER PRICING DUE TO SCARCITY
BSM1 Chris B. Young .50 1.25
BSM2 Stephen Drew .50 1.25
BSM3 Chipper Jones 1.50 4.00
BSM4 Mark Teixeira .75 2.00
BSM5 Jeff Francoeur .75 2.00
BSM6 David Ortiz 1.25 3.00
BSM7 Dustin Pedroia 2.00 5.00
BSM8 Manny Ramirez 1.25 3.00
BSM9 Mike Lowell .50 1.25
BSM10 Alfonso Soriano .75 2.00
BSM11 Aramis Ramirez .50 1.25
BSM12 Jim Thome .75 2.00
BSM13 Ken Griffey Jr. 2.00 5.00
BSM14 Adam Dunn .50 1.25
BSM15 Grady Sizemore .75 2.00
BSM16 Travis Hafner .50 1.25
BSM17 Victor Martinez .50 1.25
BSM18 Matt Holliday .75 2.00
BSM19 Todd Helton .75 2.00
BSM20 Troy Tulowitzki .75 2.00
BSM21 Ivan Rodriguez .75 2.00
BSM22 Miguel Cabrera .75 2.00
BSM23 Magglio Ordonez .75 2.00
BSM24 Hanley Ramirez 1.25 3.00
BSM25 Hunter Pence 1.25 3.00
BSM26 Lance Berkman .75 2.00
BSM27 Carlos Lee .50 1.25
BSM28 Alex Gordon 1.25 3.00
BSM29 Vladimir Guerrero 1.25 3.00
BSM30 Andruw Jones .50 1.25
BSM31 Jeff Kent .50 1.25
BSM32 Ryan Braun 1.50 4.00
BSM33 Prince Fielder 1.25 3.00
BSM34 Joe Mauer .75 2.00
BSM35 Justin Morneau .75 2.00
BSM36 David Wright 1.50 4.00
BSM37 Carlos Beltran .50 1.25
BSM38 Jose Reyes .75 2.00
BSM39 Derek Jeter 3.00 8.00
BSM40 Alex Rodriguez 2.00 5.00
BSM41 Hideki Matsui 1.25 3.00
BSM42 Bobby Abreu .50 1.25
BSM43 Chase Utley 1.25 3.00
BSM44 Ryan Howard 1.50 4.00
BSM45 Jimmy Rollins .75 2.00
BSM46 Jason Bay .50 1.25
BSM47 Khalil Greene .75 2.00
BSM48 Ichiro Suzuki 2.00 5.00
BSM49 Albert Pujols 2.50 6.00
BSM50 Frank Thomas 1.25 3.00

2008 UD A Piece of History Box Score Memories Button

OVERALL GU ODDS 1:8
PRINT RUNS B/WN 1-5 COPIES PER
NO PRICING DUE TO SCARCITY
BSM1 Chris B. Young/5
BSM2 Stephen Drew/5
BSM3 Chipper Jones/5
BSM4 Mark Teixeira/5
BSM5 Jeff Francoeur/5
BSM6 David Ortiz/5
BSM7 Dustin Pedroia/1
BSM8 Manny Ramirez/5
BSM10 Alfonso Soriano/5
BSM11 Aramis Ramirez/5
BSM12 Jim Thome/5
BSM13 Ken Griffey Jr./5
BSM14 Adam Dunn/5
BSM15 Grady Sizemore/5
BSM16 Travis Hafner/5
BSM17 Victor Martinez/5
BSM18 Matt Holliday/5
BSM19 Todd Helton/5
BSM20 Troy Tulowitzki/5
BSM21 Ivan Rodriguez/5
BSM22 Miguel Cabrera/5
BSM23 Magglio Ordonez/5
BSM24 Hanley Ramirez/5
BSM25 Hunter Pence/5
BSM26 Lance Berkman/5
BSM27 Carlos Lee/5
BSM28 Alex Gordon/5
BSM29 Vladimir Guerrero/5
BSM30 Andruw Jones/5
BSM31 Jeff Kent/5
BSM32 Ryan Braun/5
BSM33 Prince Fielder/5
BSM34 Joe Mauer/5
BSM35 Justin Morneau/5
BSM37 Carlos Beltran/5
BSM38 Jose Reyes/1
BSM39 Derek Jeter/5
BSM40 Alex Rodriguez/5
BSM42 Bobby Abreu/5
BSM43 Chase Utley/5
BSM45 Jimmy Rollins/5
BSM46 Jason Bay/5
BSM47 Khalil Greene/5
BSM49 Albert Pujols/5
BSM50 Frank Thomas/5

2008 UD A Piece of History Box Score Memories Jersey Red

OVERALL GU ODDS 1:8
BSM1 Chris B. Young 3.00 8.00
BSM2 Stephen Drew 3.00 8.00
BSM3 Chipper Jones 3.00 8.00
BSM4 Mark Teixeira 3.00 8.00
BSM5 Jeff Francoeur 3.00 8.00
BSM6 David Ortiz 4.00 10.00
BSM7 Dustin Pedroia 3.00 8.00
BSM8 Manny Ramirez 3.00 8.00
BSM10 Alfonso Soriano 3.00 8.00
BSM11 Aramis Ramirez 3.00 8.00
BSM12 Jim Thome 3.00 8.00
BSM16 Travis Hafner 3.00 8.00
BSM17 Victor Martinez 3.00 8.00
BSM18 Matt Holliday 3.00 8.00
BSM19 Todd Helton 3.00 8.00
BSM20 Troy Tulowitzki 3.00 8.00
BSM21 Ivan Rodriguez 3.00 8.00
BSM23 Magglio Ordonez 3.00 8.00
BSM24 Hanley Ramirez 3.00 8.00
BSM25 Hunter Pence 4.00 10.00
BSM26 Lance Berkman 3.00 8.00
BSM27 Carlos Lee 3.00 8.00
BSM28 Alex Gordon 4.00 10.00
BSM29 Vladimir Guerrero 3.00 8.00
BSM31 Jeff Kent 3.00 8.00
BSM33 Prince Fielder 4.00 10.00
BSM34 Joe Mauer 3.00 8.00
BSM35 Justin Morneau 3.00 8.00
BSM37 Carlos Beltran 3.00 8.00
BSM38 Jose Reyes 3.00 8.00
BSM39 Derek Jeter 8.00 20.00
BSM40 Alex Rodriguez 6.00 15.00
BSM42 Bobby Abreu 3.00 8.00
BSM45 Jimmy Rollins 3.00 8.00
BSM46 Jason Bay 3.00 8.00
BSM47 Khalil Greene 3.00 8.00
BSM49 Albert Pujols 6.00 15.00
BSM50 Frank Thomas 4.00 10.00

2008 UD A Piece of History Box Score Memories Jersey Blue

OVERALL GU ODDS 1:8
STATED PRINT RUN 25 SER.#'D SETS
NO PRICING DUE TO SCARCITY

2008 UD A Piece of History Box Score Memories Jersey Gold

*GOLD: .5X TO 1.2X BASIC
OVERALL GU ODDS 1:8
STATED PRINT RUN 75 SER.#'d SETS
BSM14 Adam Dunn 4.00 10.00
BSM15 Grady Sizemore 4.00 10.00
BSM22 Miguel Cabrera 4.00 10.00
BSM32 Ryan Braun 6.00 15.00
BSM43 Chase Utley 4.00 10.00

2008 UD A Piece of History Box Score Memories Jersey Gold Patch

OVERALL GU ODDS 1:8
STATED PRINT RUN 25 SER.#'D SETS
NO PRICING DUE TO SCARCITY

2008 UD A Piece of History Box Score Memories Jersey Autographs

OVERALL AUTO ODDS 1:16
PRINT RUNS B/WN 10-99 COPIES PER
NO PRICING ON QTY 25 OR LESS
BSM1 Chris B. Young/99
BSM2 Stephen Drew/10
BSM3 Chipper Jones/25
BSM5 Jeff Francoeur/99 12.50 30.00
BSM10 Alfonso Soriano/15
BSM11 Aramis Ramirez/99 10.00 25.00
BSM12 Jim Thome/10
BSM13 Ken Griffey Jr./25
BSM14 Adam Dunn/25
BSM16 Travis Hafner/50 6.00 15.00
BSM17 Victor Martinez/99 6.00 15.00
BSM18 Matt Holliday/25
BSM20 Troy Tulowitzki/99 10.00 25.00
BSM22 Miguel Cabrera/10
BSM24 Hanley Ramirez/50 12.50 30.00
BSM25 Hunter Pence/10
BSM26 Lance Berkman/10
BSM27 Carlos Lee/99 10.00 25.00
BSM28 Alex Gordon/25
BSM30 Andruw Jones/15
BSM32 Ryan Braun/25
BSM33 Prince Fielder/15
BSM34 Joe Mauer/10
BSM39 Derek Jeter/25
BSM46 Jason Bay/99 6.00 15.00
BSM47 Khalil Greene/15
BSM50 Frank Thomas/10

2008 UD A Piece of History Cut From the Same Cloth

RANDOM INSERTS IN PACKS
STATED PRINT RUN 799 SER.#'d SETS
BLUE RANDOMLY INSERTED
BLUE PRINT RUN 25 SER.#'d SETS
NO BLUE PRICING DUE TO SCARCITY
*PEWTER: .6X TO 1.5X BASIC
PEWTER RANDOMLY INSERTED
PEWTER PRINT RUN 75 SER.#'d SETS
*RED: .6X TO 1.5X BASIC
RED RANDOMLY INSERTED
RED PRINT RUN 99 SER.#'d SETS
*SILVER: .5X TO 1.2X BASIC
SILVER RANDOMLY INSERTED
SILVER PRINT RUN 149 SER.#'d SETS
BB Jeremy Bonderman .40 1.00
Joe Blanton
BP A.J. Burnett .60 1.50
Jake Peavy
BR Carlos Beltran .60 1.50
Jose Reyes
BS Mark Buehrle .60 1.50
Johan Santana
BV Mark Buehrle .60 1.50
Justin Verlander
BZ Ryan Zimmerman 1.25 3.00
Ryan Braun
CB Carlos Beltran .40 1.00
Carlos Beltran
CH Trevor Hoffman .40 1.00
Chad Cordero
CS Curt Schilling .60 1.50
Curt Schilling
DD Johnny Damon .60 1.50
Johnny Damon
FT Frank Thomas 1.00 2.50
Frank Thomas
GD Ken Griffey Jr. 1.50 4.00
Adam Dunn
GM Greg Maddux 1.25 3.00
Greg Maddux
GO Magglio Ordonez .40 1.00
Curtis Granderson
GT Ken Griffey Jr. 1.50 4.00
Frank Thomas
HH Todd Helton .60 1.50
Matt Holliday
HJ Matt Holliday .40 1.00
Andruw Jones
HL Francisco Liriano 1.00 2.50
Cole Hamels
HM Greg Maddux 1.25 3.00
Tim Hudson
HP Jake Peavy .60 1.50
Dan Haren
HS John Smoltz 1.00 2.50
Tim Hudson
HY Michael Young .40 1.00
J.J. Hardy
HZ Carlos Zambrano .60 1.50
Felix Hernandez
JB Josh Beckett .60 1.50
Josh Beckett
JD Jason Varitek 1.50 4.00
Daisuke Matsuzaka
JH Andruw Jones .40 1.00
Torii Hunter
JS Randy Johnson .60 1.50
Johan Santana
JT Jim Thome .60 1.50
Jim Thome
JY Derek Jeter 2.50 6.00
Michael Young
JZ Chipper Jones 1.25 3.00
Ryan Zimmerman
KS Johan Santana .60 1.50
Scott Kazmir
LF Derrek Lee .60 1.50
Prince Fielder
MA Joe Mauer .60 1.50
Russell Martin
MJ Mariano Rivera 1.00 2.50
Jonathan Papelbon
MK Justin Morneau .60 1.50
Jason Kubel
MM Victor Martinez .60 1.50
Joe Mauer
MS Curt Schilling 1.50 4.00
Daisuke Matsuzaka
OF David Ortiz 1.00 2.50
Prince Fielder
OG Carlos Guillen .60 1.50
Magglio Ordonez
OP David Ortiz 2.00 5.00
Albert Pujols
OR Manny Ramirez 1.00 2.50
David Ortiz
OV Jason Varitek 1.00 2.50
David Ortiz
PG Vladimir Guerrero 1.00 2.50
Albert Pujols
PH Roy Halladay .60 1.50
Jake Peavy
PM Pedro Martinez .60 1.50
Pedro Martinez
PO Roy Oswalt .60 1.50
Jake Peavy
PS Curt Schilling .60 1.50
Jonathan Papelbon
PV Jason Varitek 1.00 2.50
Jorge Posada
RJ Randy Johnson 1.00 2.50
Randy Johnson
RL Derrek Lee .60 1.50
Aramis Ramirez
RP BJ Ryan .60 1.50
Jonathan Papelbon
RR Jose Reyes 1.00 2.50
Hanley Ramirez
RU Jimmy Rollins 1.00 2.50
Chase Utley
SH Travis Hafner .60 1.50
Grady Sizemore
SL Francisco Liriano .60 1.50
Johan Santana
SM Pedro Martinez .60 1.50
Curt Schilling
TR Roy Halladay .40 1.00
Tim Hudson
UU Chase Utley .60 1.50
Dan Uggla
VR Manny Ramirez 1.00 2.50
Jason Varitek
WS C.C. Sabathia .40 1.00
Dontrelle Willis

2008 UD A Piece of History Cut From the Same Cloth Dual Jersey

OVERALL GU ODDS 1:8
PRINT RUNS B/WN 33-99 COPIES PER
BB Jeremy Bonderman 4.00 10.00
Joe Blanton/99
BP A.J. Burnett 5.00 12.00
Jake Peavy/99
BR Carlos Beltran 5.00 12.00
Jose Reyes/99
BS Mark Buehrle 6.00 15.00
Johan Santana/99
BV Mark Buehrle 6.00 15.00
Justin Verlander/33
BZ Ryan Zimmerman 8.00 20.00
Ryan Braun/99
CB Carlos Beltran 4.00 10.00
Carlos Beltran/70
CH Trevor Hoffman 4.00 10.00
Chad Cordero/99
CS Curt Schilling 5.00 12.00
Curt Schilling/99
DD Johnny Damon 4.00 10.00
Johnny Damon/99
FT Frank Thomas 6.00 15.00
Frank Thomas/99
GM Greg Maddux 8.00 20.00
Greg Maddux/99
GO Magglio Ordonez 5.00 12.00
Curtis Granderson/99
HH Todd Helton 5.00 12.00
Matt Holliday/99
HJ Matt Holliday 5.00 12.00
Andruw Jones/99
HL Francisco Liriano 5.00 12.00
Cole Hamels/99
HM Greg Maddux 8.00 20.00
Tim Hudson/99
HP Jake Peavy 5.00 12.00
Dan Haren/99
HS John Smoltz 5.00 12.00
Tim Hudson/99
HY Michael Young 4.00 10.00
J.J. Hardy/99
HZ Carlos Zambrano 5.00 12.00
Felix Hernandez/99
JB Josh Beckett 5.00 12.00
Josh Beckett/99
JD Jason Varitek 10.00 25.00
Daisuke Matsuzaka/99
JH Andruw Jones 4.00 10.00
Torii Hunter/99
JS Randy Johnson 6.00 15.00
Johan Santana/99
JT Jim Thome 5.00 12.00
Jim Thome/99
JY Derek Jeter 12.50 30.00
Michael Young/99
JZ Chipper Jones 5.00 12.00
Ryan Zimmerman/99
LF Derrek Lee 6.00 15.00
Prince Fielder/99
MA Joe Mauer 5.00 12.00
Russell Martin/99
MJ Mariano Rivera 8.00 20.00
Jonathan Papelbon/99
MK Justin Morneau 5.00 12.00
Jason Kubel/99
MM Victor Martinez 5.00 12.00
Joe Mauer/99
MS Curt Schilling 10.00 25.00
Daisuke Matsuzaka/99
OF David Ortiz 6.00 15.00
Prince Fielder/99
OG Carlos Guillen 5.00 12.00
Magglio Ordonez/99
OP David Ortiz 12.50 30.00
Albert Pujols/99
OR Manny Ramirez 8.00 20.00
David Ortiz/99
OV Jason Varitek 8.00 20.00
David Ortiz/99
PG Vladimir Guerrero 10.00 25.00
Albert Pujols/99
PH Roy Halladay 5.00 12.00
Jake Peavy/99
PM Pedro Martinez 5.00 12.00
Pedro Martinez/99
PO Roy Oswalt 5.00 12.00
Jake Peavy/99
PS Curt Schilling 5.00 12.00
Jonathan Papelbon/99
PV Jason Varitek 6.00 15.00
Jorge Posada/99
RJ Randy Johnson 6.00 15.00
Randy Johnson/99
RL Derrek Lee 4.00 10.00
Aramis Ramirez/99
RP BJ Ryan 5.00 12.00
Jonathan Papelbon/99
RR Jose Reyes 5.00 12.00
Hanley Ramirez/99
RU Jimmy Rollins 5.00 12.00
Chase Utley/99
SH Travis Hafner 5.00 12.00
Grady Sizemore/99
SL Francisco Liriano 6.00 15.00
Johan Santana/99
SM Pedro Martinez 5.00 12.00
Curt Schilling/99
TR Tim Hudson 4.00 10.00
Roy Halladay/99
UU Chase Utley 5.00 12.00
Dan Uggla/99
VR Manny Ramirez 8.00 20.00
Jason Varitek/99
WS C.C. Sabathia 4.00 10.00
Dontrelle Willis/99

2008 UD A Piece of History Franchise History

RANDOM INSERTS IN PACKS
STATED PRINT RUN 699 SER.#'d SETS
*BLUE: .6X TO 1.5X BASIC
BLUE RANDOMLY INSERTED
BLUE PRINT RUN 75 SER.#'d SETS
*COPPER: .6X TO 1.5X BASIC
COPPER RANDOMLY INSERTED
COPPER PRINT RUN 99 SER.#'d SETS
*RED: .5X TO 1.2X BASIC
RED RANDOMLY INSERTED
RED PRINT RUN 149 SER.#'d SETS
SILVER RANDOMLY INSERTED
SILVER PRINT RUN 25 SER.#'d SETS
NO SILVER PRICING DUE TO SCARCITY
FH1 Justin Upton 1.25 3.00
FH2 Randy Johnson 1.25 3.00
FH3 Mark Teixeira .75 2.00
FH4 John Smoltz 1.25 3.00
FH5 Chipper Jones 1.50 4.00
FH6 Jonathan Papelbon .75 2.00
FH7 Manny Ramirez 1.25 3.00
FH8 Daisuke Matsuzaka 2.00 5.00
FH9 Josh Beckett .75 2.00
FH10 David Ortiz 1.25 3.00
FH11 Alfonso Soriano .75 2.00
FH12 Jim Thome .75 2.00
FH13 Adam Dunn .50 1.25
FH14 Ken Griffey Jr. 2.00 5.00
FH15 C.C. Sabathia .50 1.25
FH16 Grady Sizemore .75 2.00
FH17 Travis Hafner .50 1.25
FH18 Matt Holliday .75 2.00
FH19 Troy Tulowitzki .75 2.00
FH20 Magglio Ordonez .75 2.00
FH21 Ivan Rodriguez .75 2.00
FH22 Miguel Cabrera .75 2.00
FH23 Hanley Ramirez 1.25 3.00
FH24 Hunter Pence 1.25 3.00
FH25 Lance Berkman .75 2.00
FH26 Vladimir Guerrero 1.25 3.00
FH27 Andruw Jones .50 1.25
FH28 Prince Fielder 1.25 3.00
FH29 Ryan Braun 1.50 4.00
FH30 Joe Mauer .75 2.00
FH31 Carlos Beltran .50 1.25
FH32 Pedro Martinez .75 2.00
FH33 Johan Santana .75 2.00
FH34 Jose Reyes .75 2.00
FH35 David Wright 1.50 4.00
FH36 Joba Chamberlain 1.50 4.00
FH37 Hideki Matsui 1.25 3.00
FH38 Alex Rodriguez 2.00 5.00
FH39 Derek Jeter 3.00 8.00
FH40 Jimmy Rollins .75 2.00
FH41 Ryan Howard 1.50 4.00
FH42 Chase Utley 1.25 3.00
FH43 Greg Maddux 1.50 4.00
FH44 Jake Peavy .75 2.00
FH45 Trevor Hoffman .50 1.25
FH46 Ichiro Suzuki 2.00 5.00
FH47 Felix Hernandez .75 2.00
FH48 Albert Pujols 2.50 6.00
FH49 Frank Thomas 1.25 3.00
FH50 Vernon Wells .50 1.25

2008 UD A Piece of History Franchise History Button

OVERALL GU ODDS 1:8
PRINT RUNS B/WN 1-5 COPIES PER
NO PRICING DUE TO SCARCITY

2008 UD A Piece of History Franchise History Jersey Red

OVERALL GU ODDS 1:8
FH1 Justin Upton 4.00 10.00
FH2 Randy Johnson 4.00 10.00
FH3 Mark Teixeira 3.00 8.00
FH4 John Smoltz 3.00 8.00
FH5 Chipper Jones 3.00 8.00
FH6 Jonathan Papelbon 3.00 8.00
FH7 Manny Ramirez 3.00 8.00
FH8 Daisuke Matsuzaka 6.00 15.00
FH9 Josh Beckett 3.00 8.00
FH10 David Ortiz 4.00 10.00
FH11 Alfonso Soriano 3.00 8.00
FH12 Jim Thome 3.00 8.00
FH13 Adam Dunn 3.00 8.00
FH14 Ken Griffey Jr. 5.00 12.00
FH15 C.C. Sabathia 3.00 8.00
FH16 Grady Sizemore 3.00 8.00
FH17 Travis Hafner 3.00 8.00
FH18 Matt Holliday 3.00 8.00
FH19 Troy Tulowitzki 3.00 8.00
FH20 Magglio Ordonez 3.00 8.00
FH21 Ivan Rodriguez 3.00 8.00
FH22 Miguel Cabrera 3.00 8.00
FH23 Hanley Ramirez 3.00 8.00
FH24 Hunter Pence 4.00 10.00
FH25 Lance Berkman 3.00 8.00
FH26 Vladimir Guerrero 3.00 8.00
FH27 Andruw Jones 3.00 8.00
FH28 Prince Fielder 4.00 10.00
FH29 Ryan Braun 5.00 12.00
FH30 Joe Mauer 3.00 8.00
FH31 Carlos Beltran 3.00 8.00
FH32 Pedro Martinez 3.00 8.00
FH33 Johan Santana 4.00 10.00
FH34 Jose Reyes 3.00 8.00
FH36 Joba Chamberlain 8.00 20.00
FH38 Alex Rodriguez 6.00 15.00
FH39 Derek Jeter 8.00 20.00
FH40 Jimmy Rollins 3.00 8.00
FH42 Chase Utley 3.00 8.00
FH43 Greg Maddux 5.00 12.00
FH44 Jake Peavy 3.00 8.00
FH45 Trevor Hoffman 3.00 8.00
FH47 Felix Hernandez 3.00 8.00
FH48 Albert Pujols 6.00 15.00
FH49 Frank Thomas 4.00 10.00
FH50 Vernon Wells 3.00 8.00

2008 UD A Piece of History Franchise History Jersey Blue

OVERALL GU ODDS 1:8
STATED PRINT RUN 25 SER.#'d SETS
NO PRICING DUE TO SCARCITY

2008 UD A Piece of History Franchise History Jersey Gold

*GOLD: .5X TO 1.2X BASIC
OVERALL GU ODDS 1:8
STATED PRINT RUN 99 SER.#'d SETS

2008 UD A Piece of History Franchise History Jersey Gold Patch

OVERALL GU ODDS 1:8
STATED PRINT RUN 25 SER.#'D SETS
NO PRICING DUE TO SCARCITY

2008 UD A Piece of History Franchise History Jersey Autographs

OVERALL AUTO ODDS 1:16
PRINT RUNS B/WN 5-99 COPIES PER
NO PRICING ON QTY 25 OR LESS
FH1 Justin Upton/25
FH3 Mark Teixeira/10
FH5 Chipper Jones/25
FH6 Jonathan Papelbon/99 12.50 30.00
FH8 Daisuke Matsuzaka/15
FH9 Josh Beckett/10
FH11 Alfonso Soriano/15
FH12 Jim Thome/10
FH13 Adam Dunn/25
FH14 Ken Griffey Jr./25
FH17 Travis Hafner/50 6.00 15.00
FH18 Matt Holliday/25
FH19 Troy Tulowitzki/50 12.50 30.00
FH21 Ivan Rodriguez/5
FH22 Miguel Cabrera/10
FH23 Hanley Ramirez/50 12.50 30.00
FH24 Hunter Pence/10
FH25 Lance Berkman/10
FH27 Andruw Jones/15
FH28 Prince Fielder/15
FH29 Ryan Braun/25
FH30 Joe Mauer/10
FH36 Joba Chamberlain/20
FH39 Derek Jeter/24
FH44 Jake Peavy/10
FH45 Trevor Hoffman/10
FH47 Felix Hernandez/75 12.50 30.00
FH48 Albert Pujols/5
FH49 Frank Thomas/10

2008 UD A Piece of History Franchise Members Triple

RANDOM INSERTS IN PACKS
STATED PRINT RUN 799 SER.#'d SETS
BLUE RANDOMLY INSERTED
BLUE PRINT RUN 25 SER.#'d SETS
NO BLUE PRICING DUE TO SCARCITY
*PEWTER: .6X TO 1.5X BASIC
PEWTER RANDOMLY INSERTED
PEWTER PRINT RUN 75 SER.#'d SETS
*RED: .6X TO 1.5X BASIC
RED RANDOMLY INSERTED
RED PRINT RUN 99 SER.#'d SETS
*SILVER: .5X TO 1.2X BASIC
SILVER RANDOMLY INSERTED
SILVER PRINT RUN 149 SER.#'d SETS
1 John Smoltz 1.00 2.50
Tim Hudson
Tom Glavine
2 Josh Beckett 1.50 4.00
Daisuke Matsuzaka
Curt Schilling
3 David Ortiz 1.00 2.50
Manny Ramirez
Jason Varitek
4 Ken Griffey Jr. 1.50 4.00
Frank Thomas
Jim Thome
5 Grady Sizemore .60 1.50
Travis Hafner
Victor Martinez
6 Matt Holliday .60 1.50
Carlos Lee
Jason Bay
7 Carlos Guillen .60 1.50
Magglio Ordonez
Miguel Cabrera
8 Roy Oswalt .60 1.50
Jake Peavy
Dan Haren
9 Jered Weaver 1.00 2.50
Vladimir Guerrero
Casey Kotchman
10 Russell Martin .60 1.50
Joe Mauer
Brian McCann
11 Prince Fielder 1.25 3.00
Ryan Braun
JJ Hardy
12 Joe Mauer .60 1.50
Justin Morneau
Joe Nathan
13 Johan Santana .60 1.50
Pedro Martinez
Billy Wagner
14 Derek Jeter 2.50 6.00
Jose Reyes
Hanley Ramirez
15 Derek Jeter 2.50 6.00
Robinson Cano
Jason Giambi
16 Jake Peavy .60 1.50
Greg Maddux
Trevor Hoffman
17 Felix Hernandez .60 1.50
Justin Verlander
Rich Harden
18 Chris Carpenter 1.00 2.50
Randy Johnson
Cole Hamels
19 Albert Pujols .60 1.50
Troy Glaus
Chris Duncan
20 Roy Halladay .40 1.00
A.J. Burnett
Vernon Wells

2008 UD A Piece of History Franchise Members Triple Jersey

OVERALL GU ODDS 1:8
STATED PRINT RUN 99 SER.#'d SETS
1 John Smoltz 5.00 12.00
Tim Hudson
Tom Glavine
2 Josh Beckett 12.50 30.00
Daisuke Matsuzaka
Curt Schilling
3 David Ortiz 10.00 25.00
Manny Ramirez
Jason Varitek
5 Grady Sizemore 5.00 12.00
Travis Hafner
Victor Martinez
6 Matt Holliday 5.00 12.00
Carlos Lee
Jason Bay
7 Carlos Guillen 5.00 12.00
Magglio Ordonez
Miguel Cabrera
8 Roy Oswalt 5.00 12.00
Jake Peavy
Dan Haren
9 Jered Weaver 5.00 12.00
Vladimir Guerrero
Casey Kotchman
10 Russell Martin 5.00 12.00
Joe Mauer
Brian McCann
11 Prince Fielder 8.00 20.00
Ryan Braun
JJ Hardy
12 Joe Mauer 5.00 12.00
Justin Morneau
Joe Nathan
13 Johan Santana 6.00 15.00
Pedro Martinez
Billy Wagner
14 Derek Jeter 12.50 30.00
Jose Reyes
Hanley Ramirez
15 Derek Jeter 15.00 40.00
Robinson Cano
Jason Giambi
16 Jake Peavy 8.00 20.00
Greg Maddux
Trevor Hoffman
17 Felix Hernandez 5.00 12.00
Justin Verlander
Rich Harden
18 Chris Carpenter 6.00 15.00
Randy Johnson
Cole Hamels
19 Albert Pujols 10.00 25.00
Troy Glaus
Chris Duncan
20 Roy Halladay 4.00 10.00
A.J. Burnett
Vernon Wells

2008 UD A Piece of History Franchise Members Quad

RANDOM INSERTS IN PACKS
STATED PRINT RUN 799 SER.#'d SETS
BLUE RANDOMLY INSERTED
BLUE PRINT RUN 25 SER.#'d SETS
NO BLUE PRICING DUE TO SCARCITY
*PEWTER: .6X TO 1.5X BASIC
PEWTER RANDOMLY INSERTED
PEWTER PRINT RUN 75 SER.#'d SETS
*RED: .6X TO 1.5X BASIC
RED RANDOMLY INSERTED
RED PRINT RUN 99 SER.#'d SETS
*SILVER: .5X TO 1.2X BASIC
SILVER RANDOMLY INSERTED
SILVER PRINT RUN 149 SER.#'d SETS
1 Derek Jeter 2.50 6.00
Johnny Damon
Jorge Posada
Jason Giambi
2 Daisuke Matsuzaka 1.50 4.00
Josh Beckett
Jonathan Papelbon
Curt Schilling
3 Jose Reyes .60 1.50
Carlos Beltran
Carlos Delgado
Johan Santana
4 Jeff Francoeur 1.25 3.00
Brian McCann
Mark Teixeira
Chipper Jones
5 Prince Fielder 1.25 3.00
Rickie Weeks
Ryan Braun
JJ Hardy
6 Ken Griffey Jr. 1.50 4.00
Adam Dunn
Brandon Phillips
Aaron Harang
7 Justin Verlander .60 1.50
Joel Zumaya
Jeremy Bonderman
Dontrelle Willis
8 Jim Thome 1.00 2.50
David Ortiz
Frank Thomas
Gary Sheffield
9 Jake Peavy .60 1.50
Greg Maddux
Mark Prior
Chris Young
10 Brandon Webb .60 1.50
Dan Haren
Randy Johnson
Conor Jackson
11 Eric Chavez .40 1.00
Bobby Crosby
Rich Harden
Huston Street
12 Felix Hernandez .60 1.50
Erik Bedard
Adrian Beltre

Kenji Johjima
13 Chone Figgins 1.00 2.50
Vladimir Guerrero
Torii Hunter
Garret Anderson
14 Jose Reyes 2.50 6.00
Rafael Furcal
Derek Jeter
Jhonny Peralta
15 Ken Griffey Jr. .60 1.50
Jim Edmonds
Andruw Jones
Carlos Beltran
16 Ivan Rodriguez 1.00 2.50
Jason Varitek
Joe Mauer
Jorge Posada
17 Hanley Ramirez .60 1.50
Dan Uggla
Josh Willingham
Jeremy Hermida
18 Johan Santana .60 1.50
Cole Hamels
C.C. Sabathia
Francisco Liriano
19 Prince Fielder .60 1.50
Lance Berkman
Derrek Lee
Conor Jackson
20 Rafael Furcal .40 1.00
Matt Kemp
Andruw Jones
Jeff Kent

2008 UD A Piece of History Franchise Members Quad Jersey

OVERALL GU ODDS 1:8
STATED PRINT RUN 99 SER.#'d SETS
1 Derek Jeter 20.00 50.00
Johnny Damon
Jorge Posada
Jason Giambi
2 Daisuke Matsuzaka 15.00 40.00
Josh Beckett
Jonathan Papelbon
Curt Schilling
3 Jose Reyes 6.00 15.00
Carlos Beltran
Carlos Delgado
Johan Santana
4 Jeff Francoeur 5.00 12.00
Brian McCann
Mark Teixeira
Chipper Jones
5 Prince Fielder 8.00 20.00
Rickie Weeks
Ryan Braun
JJ Hardy
7 Justin Verlander 5.00 12.00
Joel Zumaya
Jeremy Bonderman
Dontrelle Willis
8 Jim Thome 6.00 15.00
David Ortiz
Frank Thomas
Gary Sheffield
9 Jake Peavy 8.00 20.00
Greg Maddux
Mark Prior
Chris Young
10 Brandon Webb 6.00 15.00
Dan Haren
Randy Johnson
Conor Jackson
11 Eric Chavez 4.00 10.00
Bobby Crosby
Rich Harden
Huston Street
12 Felix Hernandez 5.00 12.00
Erik Bedard
Adrian Beltre
Kenji Johjima
13 Chone Figgins 5.00 12.00
Vladimir Guerrero
Torii Hunter
Garret Anderson
14 Jose Reyes 12.50 30.00
Rafael Furcal
Derek Jeter
Jhonny Peralta
16 Ivan Rodriguez 6.00 15.00
Jason Varitek
Joe Mauer
Jorge Posada
18 Johan Santana 6.00 15.00
Cole Hamels
C.C. Sabathia
Francisco Liriano
19 Prince Fielder 6.00 15.00
Lance Berkman
Derrek Lee
Conor Jackson
20 Rafael Furcal 4.00 10.00
Matt Kemp
Andruw Jones
Jeff Kent

2008 UD A Piece of History Hair Relics

RANDOM INSERTS IN PACKS
NO PRICING DUE TO SCARCITY

2008 UD A Piece of History Stadium Scenes

RANDOM INSERTS IN PACKS
STATED PRINT RUN 699 SER.#'d SETS
*BLUE: .6X TO 1.5X BASIC
BLUE RANDOMLY INSERTED
BLUE PRINT RUN 75 SER.#'d SETS
*COPPER: .6X TO 1.5X BASIC
COPPER RANDOMLY INSERTED
COPPER PRINT RUN 99 SER.#'d SETS
*RED: .5X TO 1.2X BASIC
RED RANDOMLY INSERTED
RED PRINT RUN 149 SER.#'d SETS
SILVER RANDOMLY INSERTED
SILVER PRINT RUN 25 SER.#'d SETS
NO SILVER PRICING DUE TO SCARCITY
SS1 Randy Johnson 1.25 3.00
SS2 Justin Upton 1.25 3.00
SS3 Mark Teixeira .75 2.00
SS4 Chipper Jones 1.50 4.00
SS5 John Smoltz 1.25 3.00
SS6 David Ortiz 1.25 3.00
SS7 Josh Beckett .75 2.00
SS8 Daisuke Matsuzaka 2.00 5.00
SS9 Manny Ramirez 1.25 3.00
SS10 Jonathan Papelbon .75 2.00
SS11 Alfonso Soriano .75 2.00
SS12 Kerry Wood .50 1.25
SS13 Derrek Lee .75 2.00
SS14 Jim Thome .75 2.00
SS15 Ken Griffey Jr. 2.00 5.00
SS16 Adam Dunn .50 1.25
SS17 Grady Sizemore .75 2.00
SS18 Travis Hafner .50 1.25
SS19 Victor Martinez .50 1.25
SS20 C.C. Sabathia .50 1.25
SS21 Miguel Cabrera .75 2.00
SS22 Justin Verlander .75 2.00
SS23 Ivan Rodriguez .75 2.00
SS24 Magglio Ordonez .75 2.00
SS25 Lance Berkman .75 2.00
SS26 Roy Oswalt .50 1.25
SS27 Vladimir Guerrero 1.25 3.00
SS28 Andruw Jones .50 1.25
SS29 Rickie Weeks .50 1.25
SS30 Ryan Braun 1.50 4.00
SS31 Prince Fielder 1.25 3.00
SS32 Joe Mauer .75 2.00
SS33 Pedro Martinez .75 2.00
SS34 Jose Reyes .75 2.00
SS35 David Wright 1.50 4.00
SS36 Johan Santana .75 2.00
SS37 Derek Jeter 3.00 8.00
SS38 Alex Rodriguez 2.00 5.00
SS39 Hideki Matsui 1.25 3.00
SS40 Joba Chamberlain 1.50 4.00
SS41 Cole Hamels 1.25 3.00
SS42 Chase Utley 1.25 3.00
SS43 Ryan Howard 1.50 4.00
SS44 Jimmy Rollins .75 2.00
SS45 Jake Peavy .75 2.00
SS46 Greg Maddux 1.50 4.00
SS47 Felix Hernandez .75 2.00
SS48 Ichiro Suzuki 2.00 5.00
SS49 Albert Pujols 2.50 6.00
SS50 Frank Thomas 1.25 3.00

2008 UD A Piece of History Stadium Scenes Button

OVERALL GU ODDS 1:8
STATED PRINT RUN 5 SER.#'d SETS
NO PRICING DUE TO SCARCITY

2008 UD A Piece of History Stadium Scenes Jersey Red

OVERALL GU ODDS 1:8
SS1 Randy Johnson 4.00 10.00
SS2 Justin Upton 4.00 10.00
SS3 Mark Teixeira 3.00 8.00
SS4 Chipper Jones 3.00 8.00
SS5 John Smoltz 3.00 8.00
SS6 David Ortiz 4.00 10.00
SS7 Josh Beckett 3.00 8.00
SS8 Daisuke Matsuzaka 6.00 15.00
SS9 Manny Ramirez 3.00 8.00
SS10 Jonathan Papelbon 3.00 8.00
SS11 Alfonso Soriano 3.00 8.00
SS12 Kerry Wood 3.00 8.00
SS13 Derrek Lee 3.00 8.00
SS14 Jim Thome 3.00 8.00
SS15 Ken Griffey Jr. 5.00 12.00
SS16 Adam Dunn 3.00 8.00
SS18 Travis Hafner 3.00 8.00
SS19 Victor Martinez 3.00 8.00
SS20 C.C. Sabathia 3.00 8.00
SS21 Miguel Cabrera 3.00 8.00
SS22 Justin Verlander 3.00 8.00
SS23 Ivan Rodriguez 3.00 8.00
SS24 Magglio Ordonez 3.00 8.00
SS25 Lance Berkman 3.00 8.00
SS26 Roy Oswalt 3.00 8.00
SS27 Vladimir Guerrero 3.00 8.00
SS28 Andruw Jones 3.00 8.00
SS29 Rickie Weeks 3.00 8.00
SS30 Ryan Braun 5.00 12.00
SS31 Prince Fielder 4.00 10.00
SS32 Joe Mauer 3.00 8.00
SS33 Pedro Martinez 3.00 8.00
SS34 Jose Reyes 3.00 8.00
SS36 Johan Santana 4.00 10.00
SS37 Derek Jeter 8.00 20.00
SS38 Alex Rodriguez 6.00 15.00
SS40 Joba Chamberlain 8.00 20.00
SS41 Cole Hamels 3.00 8.00
SS42 Chase Utley 3.00 8.00
SS44 Jimmy Rollins 3.00 8.00
SS45 Jake Peavy 3.00 8.00
SS46 Greg Maddux 5.00 12.00
SS47 Felix Hernandez 3.00 8.00
SS49 Albert Pujols 6.00 15.00
SS50 Frank Thomas 4.00 10.00

2008 UD A Piece of History Stadium Scenes Jersey Blue

OVERALL GU ODDS 1:8
STATED PRINT RUN 25 SER.#'D SETS
NO PRICING DUE TO SCARCITY

2008 UD A Piece of History Stadium Scenes Jersey Gold

*GOLD: .5X TO 1.2X BASIC
OVERALL GU ODDS 1:8
STATED PRINT RUN 99 SER.#'d SETS

2008 UD A Piece of History Stadium Scenes Jersey Gold Patch

OVERALL GU ODDS 1:8
STATED PRINT RUN 25 SER.#'D SETS
NO PRICING DUE TO SCARCITY

2008 UD A Piece of History Stadium Scenes Jersey Autographs

OVERALL AUTO ODDS 1:16
PRINT RUNS B/WN 10-99 COPIES PER
NO PRICING ON QTY 25 OR LESS
SS2 Justin Upton/25
SS3 Mark Teixeira/10
SS4 Chipper Jones/25
SS7 Josh Beckett/10
SS8 Daisuke Matsuzaka/15
SS10 Jonathan Papelbon/99 12.50 30.00
SS11 Alfonso Soriano/15
SS12 Kerry Wood/99 6.00 15.00
SS13 Derrek Lee/25
SS14 Jim Thome/10
SS15 Ken Griffey Jr./25
SS16 Adam Dunn/25
SS18 Travis Hafner/50 6.00 15.00
SS19 Victor Martinez/99 6.00 15.00
SS21 Miguel Cabrera/10
SS22 Justin Verlander/15
SS25 Lance Berkman/10
SS26 Roy Oswalt/25
SS28 Andruw Jones/15
SS29 Rickie Weeks/50 6.00 15.00
SS30 Ryan Braun/25
SS31 Prince Fielder/15
SS32 Joe Mauer/10
SS37 Derek Jeter/25
SS40 Joba Chamberlain/20
SS41 Cole Hamels/25
SS45 Jake Peavy/10
SS47 Felix Hernandez/75 12.50 30.00
SS50 Frank Thomas/10

2008 UD A Piece of History Timeless Moments

RANDOM INSERTS IN PACKS
STATED PRINT RUN 699 SER.#'d SETS
*BLUE: .6X TO 1.5X BASIC
BLUE RANDOMLY INSERTED
BLUE PRINT RUN 75 SER.#'d SETS
*COPPER: .6X TO 1.5X BASIC
COPPER RANDOMLY INSERTED
COPPER PRINT RUN 99 SER.#'d SETS
*RED: .5X TO 1.2X BASIC
RED RANDOMLY INSERTED
RED PRINT RUN 149 SER.#'d SETS
SILVER RANDOMLY INSERTED
SILVER PRINT RUN 25 SER.#'d SETS
NO SILVER PRICING DUE TO SCARCITY
1 Randy Johnson 1.25 3.00
2 Dan Haren .50 1.25
3 John Smoltz 1.25 3.00
4 Chipper Jones 1.50 4.00
5 Mark Teixeira .75 2.00
6 David Ortiz 1.25 3.00
7 Dustin Pedroia 2.00 5.00
8 Josh Beckett .75 2.00
9 Curt Schilling .75 2.00
10 Daisuke Matsuzaka 2.00 5.00
11 Alfonso Soriano .75 2.00
12 Carlos Zambrano .50 1.25
13 Jim Thome .75 2.00
14 Ken Griffey Jr. 2.00 5.00
15 Adam Dunn .50 1.25
16 Grady Sizemore .75 2.00
17 C.C. Sabathia .50 1.25
18 Troy Tulowitzki .75 2.00
19 Matt Holliday .75 2.00
20 Justin Verlander .75 2.00
21 Ivan Rodriguez .75 2.00
22 Hanley Ramirez 1.25 3.00
23 Alex Gordon 1.25 3.00
24 Vladimir Guerrero 1.25 3.00
25 Jeff Kent .50 1.25
26 Nomar Garciaparra 1.25 3.00
27 Prince Fielder 1.25 3.00
28 Joe Mauer .75 2.00
29 Justin Morneau .75 2.00
30 Jose Reyes .75 2.00
31 David Wright 1.50 4.00
32 Pedro Martinez .75 2.00
33 Johan Santana .75 2.00
34 Joba Chamberlain 1.50 4.00
35 Derek Jeter 3.00 8.00
36 Alex Rodriguez 2.00 5.00
37 Hideki Matsui 1.25 3.00
38 Ryan Howard 1.50 4.00
39 Chase Utley 1.25 3.00
40 Jimmy Rollins .75 2.00
41 Cole Hamels 1.25 3.00
42 Jake Peavy .75 2.00
43 Greg Maddux 1.50 4.00
44 Phil Hughes 1.25 3.00
45 Felix Hernandez .75 2.00
46 Ichiro Suzuki 2.00 5.00
47 Albert Pujols 2.50 6.00
48 Chris Carpenter .50 1.25
49 Frank Thomas 1.25 3.00
50 Vernon Wells .50 1.25

2008 UD A Piece of History Timeless Moments Button

OVERALL GU ODDS 1:8
STATED PRINT RUN 5 SER.#'d SETS
NO PRICING DUE TO SCARCITY

2008 UD A Piece of History Timeless Moments Jersey

OVERALL GU ODDS 1:8
1 Randy Johnson 4.00 10.00
2 Dan Haren 3.00 8.00
3 John Smoltz 3.00 8.00
5 Mark Teixeira 3.00 8.00
6 David Ortiz 4.00 10.00
7 Dustin Pedroia 3.00 8.00
8 Josh Beckett 3.00 8.00
9 Curt Schilling 3.00 8.00
10 Daisuke Matsuzaka 6.00 15.00
11 Alfonso Soriano 3.00 8.00
12 Carlos Zambrano 3.00 8.00
13 Jim Thome 3.00 8.00
17 C.C. Sabathia 3.00 8.00
18 Troy Tulowitzki 3.00 8.00
19 Matt Holliday 3.00 8.00
20 Justin Verlander 3.00 8.00
21 Ivan Rodriguez 3.00 8.00
22 Hanley Ramirez 3.00 8.00
23 Alex Gordon 4.00 10.00
24 Vladimir Guerrero 3.00 8.00
25 Jeff Kent 3.00 8.00
27 Prince Fielder 4.00 10.00
28 Joe Mauer 3.00 8.00
29 Justin Morneau 3.00 8.00
30 Jose Reyes 3.00 8.00
32 Pedro Martinez 3.00 8.00
33 Johan Santana 4.00 10.00
34 Joba Chamberlain 8.00 20.00
35 Derek Jeter 8.00 20.00
36 Alex Rodriguez 6.00 15.00
39 Chase Utley 3.00 8.00
40 Jimmy Rollins 3.00 8.00
41 Cole Hamels 3.00 8.00
42 Jake Peavy 3.00 8.00
43 Greg Maddux 5.00 12.00
44 Phil Hughes 4.00 10.00
45 Felix Hernandez 3.00 8.00
47 Albert Pujols 6.00 15.00
48 Chris Carpenter 3.00 8.00
49 Frank Thomas 4.00 10.00
50 Vernon Wells 3.00 8.00

2008 UD A Piece of History Timeless Moments Jersey Blue

OVERALL GU ODDS 1:8
STATED PRINT RUN 25 SER.#'D SETS
NO PRICING DUE TO SCARCITY

2008 UD A Piece of History Timeless Moments Jersey Gold

*GOLD: .5X TO 1.2X BASIC
OVERALL GU ODDS 1:8
STATED PRINT RUN 99 SER.#'d SETS

2008 UD A Piece of History Timeless Moments Jersey Gold Patch

OVERALL GU ODDS 1:8
STATED PRINT RUN 25 SER.#'D SETS
NO PRICING DUE TO SCARCITY

2008 UD A Piece of History Timeless Moments Jersey Autographs

OVERALL AUTO ODDS 1:16
PRINT RUNS B/WN 5-75 COPIES PER
NO PRICING ON QTY 25 OR LESS
2 Dan Haren/50 6.00 15.00
4 Chipper Jones/25
5 Mark Teixeira/10
8 Josh Beckett/10
10 Daisuke Matsuzaka/15
11 Alfonso Soriano/15
13 Jim Thome/10
14 Ken Griffey Jr./25
15 Adam Dunn/25
18 Troy Tulowitzki/50 12.50 30.00
19 Matt Holliday/25
20 Justin Verlander/15
22 Hanley Ramirez/50
23 Alex Gordon/25
27 Prince Fielder/15
28 Joe Mauer/10
29 Justin Morneau/5
34 Joba Chamberlain/50 100.00 150.00
35 Derek Jeter/25
41 Cole Hamels/25
42 Jake Peavy/10
44 Phil Hughes/50 15.00 40.00
45 Felix Hernandez/75 12.50 30.00
47 Albert Pujols/5
49 Frank Thomas/10

2007 UD Black

COMMON JSY AU (1-42) 12.50 30.00
1-42 PRINT RUNS B/WN 16-75 COPIES PER
NO PRICING ON QTY 25 OR LESS
COMMON AU RC (43-72) 10.00 25.00
43-72 PRINT RUN 99 SER.#'d SETS
EXCHANGE DEADLINE 11/26/2009
AUTO PRINTING PLATES RANDOMLY INSERTED
PLATE PRINT RUN 1 SET PER COLOR
BLACK-CYAN-MAGENTA-YELLOW ISSUED
NO PLATE PRICING DUE TO SCARCITY
1 Brandon Webb Jsy AU/75 20.00 50.00
2 Tim Hudson Jsy AU/75 20.00 50.00
3 Cal Ripken Jr. Jsy AU/75 100.00 175.00
4 Nick Markakis Jsy AU/35 30.00 60.00
5 David Ortiz Jsy AU/52 60.00 120.00
6 Jonathan Papelbon Jsy AU/75 30.00 60.00
7 Coco Crisp Jsy AU/43 15.00 40.00
8 Derrek Lee Jsy AU/75 20.00 50.00
9 Paul Konerko Jsy AU/75 15.00 40.00
10 Adam Dunn Jsy AU/75 20.00 50.00
11 Ken Griffey Jr. Jsy AU/75 50.00 100.00
12 Travis Hafner Jsy AU/75 30.00 60.00
13 Victor Martinez Jsy AU/75 15.00 40.00
14 Garrett Atkins Jsy AU/75 12.50 30.00
15 Justin Verlander Jsy AU/75 30.00 60.00
16 Jeremy Bonderman Jsy AU/75 12.50 30.00
17 Curtis Granderson Jsy AU/75 20.00 50.00
18 Hanley Ramirez Jsy AU/75 20.00 50.00
19 Dan Uggla Jsy AU/75 12.50 30.00
20 Lance Berkman Jsy AU/75 30.00 60.00
21 Mark Teahen Jsy AU/75 12.50 30.00
22 John Lackey Jsy AU/75 12.50 30.00
23 Howie Kendrick Jsy AU/75 15.00 40.00
24 Russell Martin Jsy AU/75 20.00 50.00
25 Prince Fielder Jsy AU/75 40.00 80.00
26 Torii Hunter Jsy AU/75 12.50 30.00
27 Justin Morneau Jsy AU/75 20.00 50.00
28 John Maine Jsy AU/75 20.00 50.00
29 Derek Jeter Jsy AU/16
30 Dan Haren Jsy AU/75 12.50 30.00
31 Eric Chavez Jsy AU/75 12.50 30.00
32 Cole Hamels Jsy AU/75 30.00 60.00
33 Jason Bay Jsy AU/75 15.00 40.00
34 Adrian Gonzalez Jsy AU/75 12.50 30.00
35 Chris Young Jsy AU/75 15.00 40.00
36 Matt Cain Jsy AU/75 15.00 40.00
37 Felix Hernandez Jsy AU/75 20.00 50.00
38 Chris Duncan Jsy AU/75 15.00 40.00
39 B.J. Upton Jsy AU/75 20.00 50.00
40 Ian Kinsler Jsy AU/75 20.00 50.00
41 Roy Halladay Jsy AU/75 20.00 50.00
42a Chad Cordero Jsy AU/75 12.50 30.00
42b Chad Cordero Jsy AU/52 12.50 30.00
43 Adam Lind AU (RC) 10.00 25.00
44 Akinori Iwamura AU RC 50.00 100.00
45 Alex Gordon AU RC 60.00 120.00
46 Andy LaRoche AU (RC) 15.00 40.00
47 Billy Butler AU (RC) 30.00 60.00
48 David Murphy AU (RC) 10.00 25.00
49 Brandon Wood AU (RC) 12.50 30.00
50 Carlos Gomez AU RC 20.00 50.00
51 Chase Headley AU (RC) 15.00 40.00
52 Curtis Thigpen AU (RC) 10.00 25.00
53 Joba Chamberlain AU RC 300.00 400.00
54 Delmon Young AU (RC) 20.00 50.00
55 Felix Pie AU (RC) 12.50 30.00
56 Homer Bailey AU (RC) 20.00 50.00
57 Hunter Pence AU (RC) 40.00 80.00
58 Josh Hamilton AU (RC) 50.00 100.00
59 Kei Igawa AU RC 40.00 80.00
60 Kevin Slowey AU (RC) 20.00 50.00
61 Kurt Suzuki AU (RC) 12.50 30.00
62 Mark Reynolds AU RC 75.00 150.00
63 Daisuke Matsuzaka AU RC 450.00 550.00
64 Justin Upton AU RC 75.00 150.00
65 Phil Hughes AU (RC) 50.00 100.00
66 Ryan Braun AU (RC) 60.00 120.00
67 Ryan Sweeney AU (RC) 10.00 25.00
68 Sean Gallagher AU (RC) 10.00 25.00
69 Tim Lincecum AU RC 150.00 250.00
70 Travis Buck AU (RC) 10.00 25.00
71 Troy Tulowitzki AU (RC) 50.00 100.00
72 Yovani Gallardo AU (RC) 30.00 60.00

2007 UD Black Gold Spectrum

RANDOM INSERTS IN PACKS
STATED PRINT RUN 10 SER.#'d SETS
NO PRICING DUE TO SCARCITY
EXCHANGE DEADLINE 11/26/2009

2007 UD Black Natural Pearl

RANDOM INSERTS IN PACKS
STATED PRINT RUN 1 SER.#'d SET
NO PRICING DUE TO SCARCITY
EXCHANGE DEADLINE 11/26/2009

2007 UD Black August Patch Autographs

RANDOM INSERTS IN PACKS
PRINT RUNS B/WN 4-25 COPIES PER
NO PRICING DUE TO SCARCITY
GOLD SPEC.PRINT RUN 5 SER.#'d SETS
NO GOLD PRICING DUE TO SCARCITY
NAT.PEARL PRINT RUN 1 SER.#'d SET
NO PEARL PRICING DUE TO SCARCITY
EXCHANGE DEADLINE 11/26/2009
BS Ben Sheets
BU B.J. Upton
CC Carl Crawford
CD Chris Duncan
CG Curtis Granderson
CH Cole Hamels
CO Chad Cordero
CR Cal Ripken Jr./4
DL Derrek Lee
DW Dontrelle Willis
FH Felix Hernandez
FL Francisco Liriano
FT Frank Thomas
GA Garrett Atkins
GR Khalil Greene
HK Hong-Chih Kuo
HR Hanley Ramirez
IR Ivan Rodriguez
JB Jason Bay
JM Justin Morneau
JT Jim Thome
MC Miguel Cabrera
MH Matt Holliday
PK Paul Konerko
RH Roy Halladay
RM Russell Martin
TH Travis Hafner
VM Victor Martinez

2007 UD Black Bat Barrel Autographs

RANDOM INSERTS IN PACKS
PRINT RUNS B/WN 25-50 COPIES PER
GOLD SPEC.PRINT RUN 10 SER.#'d SETS
NO GOLD PRICING DUE TO SCARCITY
NAT.PEARL PRINT RUN 1 SER.#'d SET
NO PEARL PRICING DUE TO SCARCITY
EXCHANGE DEADLINE 11/26/2009
AD Adam Dunn 15.00 40.00
AE Andre Ethier 10.00 25.00
AI Akinori Iwamura 20.00 50.00
AL Andy LaRoche 10.00 25.00
BO Jeremy Bonderman 12.50 30.00
BU B.J. Upton 30.00 60.00
CC Carl Crawford 10.00 25.00
CL Carlos Lee 15.00 40.00
CR Cal Ripken Jr./25
DJ Derek Jeter 100.00 200.00
DL Derrek Lee 15.00 40.00
DY Delmon Young 12.50 30.00
GA Garrett Atkins 10.00 25.00
HB Homer Bailey 15.00 40.00
HK Howie Kendrick 12.50 30.00
HR Hanley Ramirez 15.00 40.00
HU Torii Hunter 12.50 30.00
IK Ian Kinsler 20.00 50.00
JB Jason Bay 12.50 30.00
JH Josh Hamilton 60.00 120.00
JL John Lackey 12.50 30.00
JM Joe Mauer 20.00 50.00
KG Ken Griffey Jr. 100.00 150.00
KJ Kelly Johnson 12.50 30.00
MO Justin Morneau 15.00 40.00
MT Mark Teixeira 15.00 40.00
RB Ryan Braun 50.00 100.00
RM Russell Martin 20.00 50.00
TH Travis Hafner 20.00 50.00
TT Troy Tulowitzki 50.00 100.00

2007 UD Black Exclusive Eight Autographs

RANDOM INSERTS IN PACKS
STATED PRINT RUN 3 SER.#'d SETS
NO PRICING DUE TO SCARCITY
GOLD SPEC.PRINT RUN 2 SER.#'d SETS
NO GOLD PRICING DUE TO SCARCITY
NAT.PEARL PRINT RUN 1 SER.#'d SET
NO PEARL PRICING DUE TO SCARCITY
EXCHANGE DEADLINE 11/26/2009
EX1 Ken Griffey Jr.
Adam Dunn
Aaron Harang
Homer Bailey
Roy Oswalt
Carlos Lee
Lance Berkman
Hunter Pence
EX2 Roy Halladay
Dan Haren
John Lackey
Justin Verlander
Scott Kazmir
Jered Weaver
Jeremy Bonderman
James Shields
EX3 Ben Sheets
Tim Hudson
Cole Hamels
John Maine
Aaron Harang
Dontrelle Willis
Matt Cain
Chris Young
EX4 Tim Lincecum
Homer Bailey
Yovani Gallardo
Kyle Kendrick
Phil Hughes
Andrew Miller
Glen Perkins
Kei Igawa
EX5 Cal Ripken Jr.
Derek Jeter
Ken Griffey Jr.
Frank Thomas
Jim Thome
Justin Morneau
Mark Teixeira
Lance Berkman
EX6 Delmon Young
Brandon Wood
Billy Butler
Kurt Suzuki
Hunter Pence
Ryan Braun
Chase Headley
Andy LaRoche
EX7 David Ortiz
Josh Beckett
Jonathan Papelbon
Coco Crisp
Derek Jeter
Phil Hughes
Tyler Clippard
Kei Igawa

2007 UD Black Game Day Box Score Autographs

RANDOM INSERTS IN PACKS
STATED PRINT RUN 50 SER.#'d SETS
GOLD SPEC. PRINT RUN 10 SER.#'d SETS
NO GOLD PRICING DUE TO SCARCITY
NAT.PEARL PRINT RUN 1 SER.#'d SET
NO PEARL PRICING DUE TO SCARCITY
EXCHANGE DEADLINE 11/26/2009
AE Andre Ethier 6.00 15.00
AG Adrian Gonzalez 6.00 15.00
AH Aaron Harang 6.00 15.00
AI Akinori Iwamura 20.00 50.00
AL Adam LaRoche 6.00 15.00
AM Andrew Miller 10.00 25.00
AR Aaron Rowand 6.00 15.00
BA Bronson Arroyo 10.00 25.00
BB Billy Butler 10.00 25.00
BP Brandon Phillips 6.00 15.00
BS Ben Sheets 6.00 15.00
CC Coco Crisp 6.00 15.00
CG Curtis Granderson 30.00 60.00
CH Cole Hamels 15.00 40.00
CY Chris Young 6.00 15.00
DH Dan Haren 6.00 15.00
DL Derrek Lee 10.00 25.00
DW Dontrelle Willis 6.00 15.00

DY Delmon Young 10.00 25.00
FC Fausto Carmona 10.00 25.00
FL Fred Lewis 6.00 15.00
GM Greg Maddux 40.00 80.00
GO Alex Gordon 20.00 50.00
HP Hunter Pence 30.00 60.00
JB Joe Blanton 6.00 15.00
JM John Maine 10.00 25.00
JN Joe Nathan 6.00 15.00
JV Justin Verlander 20.00 50.00
KG Ken Griffey Jr. 40.00 80.00
KI Kei Igawa 15.00 40.00
KJ Kelly Johnson 6.00 15.00
LI Francisco Liriano 10.00 25.00
MC Matt Cain 6.00 15.00
MH Matt Holliday 20.00 50.00
MM Melvin Mora 6.00 15.00
NS Nick Swisher 10.00 25.00
PH Phil Hughes 30.00 60.00
RB Ryan Braun 30.00 60.00
RZ Ryan Zimmerman 15.00 40.00
TB Travis Buck 6.00 15.00
TH Tim Hudson 10.00 25.00
TL Tim Lincecum 40.00 80.00

2007 UD Black Game Day Lineup Autographs

RANDOM INSERTS IN PACKS
STATED PRINT RUN 50 SER.#'d SETS
GOLD SPEC. PRINT RUN 10 SER.#'d SETS
NO GOLD PRICING DUE TO SCARCITY
NAT.PEARL PRINT RUN 1 SER.#'d SET
NO PEARL PRICING DUE TO SCARCITY
EXCHANGE DEADLINE 11/26/2009
AE Andre Ethier 6.00 15.00
AG Adrian Gonzalez 6.00 15.00
AH Aaron Harang 6.00 15.00
AI Akinori Iwamura 20.00 50.00
AL Adam LaRoche 6.00 15.00
AM Andrew Miller 10.00 25.00
AR Aaron Rowand 6.00 15.00
BA Bronson Arroyo 10.00 25.00
BB Billy Butler 10.00 25.00
BP Brandon Phillips 6.00 15.00
BS Ben Sheets 6.00 15.00
CC Coco Crisp 6.00 15.00
CG Curtis Granderson 30.00 60.00
CH Cole Hamels 15.00 40.00
CY Chris Young 6.00 15.00
DH Dan Haren 6.00 15.00
DL Derrek Lee 10.00 25.00
DW Dontrelle Willis 6.00 15.00
DY Delmon Young 10.00 25.00
FC Fausto Carmona 10.00 25.00
FL Fred Lewis 6.00 15.00
GM Greg Maddux 40.00 80.00
GO Alex Gordon 20.00 50.00
HP Hunter Pence 30.00 60.00
JB Joe Blanton 6.00 15.00
JM John Maine 10.00 25.00
JN Joe Nathan 6.00 15.00
JV Justin Verlander 20.00 50.00
KG Ken Griffey Jr. 50.00 100.00
KI Kei Igawa 15.00 40.00
KJ Kelly Johnson 6.00 15.00
LI Francisco Liriano 10.00 25.00
MC Matt Cain 6.00 15.00
MH Matt Holliday 20.00 50.00
MM Melvin Mora 6.00 15.00
NS Nick Swisher 6.00 25.00
PH Phil Hughes 30.00 60.00
RB Ryan Braun 30.00 60.00
RZ Ryan Zimmerman 15.00 40.00
TB Travis Buck 6.00 15.00
TH Tim Hudson 10.00 25.00
TL Tim Lincecum 40.00 80.00

2007 UD Black Game Day Ticket Autographs

RANDOM INSERTS IN PACKS
PRINT RUNS B/WN 15-50 COPIES PER
NO PRICING ON QTY OF 15
GOLD SPEC. PRINT RUN 10 SER.#'d SETS
NO GOLD PRICING DUE TO SCARCITY
NAT.PEARL PRINT RUN 1 SER.#'d SET
NO PEARL PRICING DUE TO SCARCITY
EXCHANGE DEADLINE 11/26/2009
AE Andre Ethier 6.00 15.00
AG Adrian Gonzalez 6.00 15.00
AH Aaron Harang 6.00 15.00
AI Akinori Iwamura 10.00 25.00
AL Adam LaRoche 6.00 15.00
AM Andrew Miller 10.00 25.00
AR Aaron Rowand 6.00 15.00
BA Bronson Arroyo 10.00 25.00
BB Billy Butler 10.00 25.00
BP Brandon Phillips 6.00 15.00
BS Ben Sheets 6.00 15.00
CC Coco Crisp 6.00 15.00
CG Curtis Granderson 30.00 60.00
CH Cole Hamels 15.00 40.00
CY Chris Young 6.00 15.00
DH Dan Haren 6.00 15.00
DL Derrek Lee 10.00 25.00
DW Dontrelle Willis 6.00 15.00
DY Delmon Young 10.00 25.00
FC Fausto Carmona 10.00 25.00
FL Fred Lewis 6.00 15.00
GM Greg Maddux 40.00 80.00
GO Alex Gordon 20.00 50.00
HP Hunter Pence 30.00 60.00
JB Joe Blanton 6.00 15.00
JM John Maine/15
JN Joe Nathan 6.00 15.00
JV Justin Verlander 20.00 50.00
KG Ken Griffey Jr./15
KI Kei Igawa 15.00 40.00
KJ Kelly Johnson 6.00 15.00
LI Francisco Liriano 10.00 25.00
MC Matt Cain 6.00 15.00
MH Matt Holliday 20.00 50.00
MM Melvin Mora 6.00 15.00
NS Nick Swisher 6.00 25.00
PH Phil Hughes 30.00 60.00
RB Ryan Braun 30.00 60.00
RZ Ryan Zimmerman 15.00 40.00
TB Travis Buck 6.00 15.00
TH Tim Hudson 10.00 25.00
TL Tim Lincecum 40.00 80.00

2007 UD Black Illustrious Dual Autographs

RANDOM INSERTS IN PACKS
PRINT RUNS B/WN 15-25 COPIES PER
NO PRICING DUE TO SCARCITY
GOLD SPEC.PRINT RUN 15 SER.#'d SETS
NO GOLD PRICING DUE TO SCARCITY
NAT.PEARL PRINT RUN 1 SER.#'d SET
NO PEARL PRICING DUE TO SCARCITY
EXCHANGE DEADLINE 11/26/2009

2007 UD Black Illustrious Dual Materials Autographs

RANDOM INSERTS IN PACKS
PRINT RUNS B/WN 15-50 COPIES PER
NO PRICING ON QTY 15
EXCHANGE DEADLINE 11/26/2009
CI Eric Chavez 20.00 50.00
Akinori Iwamura
CK Carl Crawford 15.00 40.00
Scott Kazmir
CP Coco Crisp 20.00 50.00
Jonathan Papelbon
GB Alex Gordon 40.00 80.00
Ryan Braun
GC Curtis Granderson 20.00 50.00
Coco Crisp
GH Ken Griffey Jr.
Josh Hamilton/15
GY Adrian Gonzalez 12.50 30.00
Chris Young
HH Dan Haren 12.50 30.00
Rich Harden
HM Aaron Harang 12.50 30.00
John Maine
HW Jeremy Hermida 12.50 30.00
Dontrelle Willis
JJ Justin Morneau 20.00 50.00
Jason Bay
LC Tim Lincecum 40.00 80.00
Matt Cain
LK John Lackey 20.00 50.00
Howie Kendrick
LP Carlos Lee 30.00 60.00
Hunter Pence
MM Russell Martin 15.00 40.00
Victor Martinez
NH Joe Nathan 12.50 30.00
Torii Hunter
NM Nick Markakis 12.50 30.00
Melvin Mora
RG Aaron Rowand 12.50 30.00
Brian Giles
RJ Cal Ripken Jr.
Derek Jeter/15
SB Huston Street 12.50 30.00
Joe Blanton
TA Troy Tulowitzki 15.00 40.00
Garrett Atkins
UW Dan Uggla 12.50 30.00
Josh Willingham
UY B.J. Upton 12.50 30.00
Delmon Young
ZB Joel Zumaya 15.00 40.00
Jeremy Bonderman

2007 UD Black Illustrious Dual Patch Autographs

RANDOM INSERTS IN PACKS
PRINT RUNS B/WN 5-15 COPIES PER
NO PRICING DUE TO SCARCITY
EXCHANGE DEADLINE 11/26/2009

2007 UD Black Lustrous Autographs

RANDOM INSERTS IN PACKS
PRINT RUNS B/WN 15-50 COPIES PER
NO PRICING ON QTY 15
GOLD SPEC. PRINT RUN 10 SER.#'d SETS
NO GOLD PRICING DUE TO SCARCITY
NAT.PEARL PRINT RUN 1 SER.#'d SET
NO PEARL PRICING DUE TO SCARCITY
EXCHANGE DEADLINE 11/26/2009
AG Alex Gordon 20.00 50.00
BB Billy Butler 10.00 25.00
BU B.J. Upton 6.00 15.00
CC Carl Crawford 6.00 15.00
CH Cole Hamels 15.00 40.00
CR Cal Ripken Jr./15
DJ Derek Jeter 75.00 150.00
DL Derrek Lee 10.00 25.00
DU Dan Uggla 6.00 15.00
DW Dontrelle Willis 6.00 15.00
GA Garrett Atkins 6.00 15.00
GR Khalil Greene 10.00 25.00
HA Josh Hamilton 40.00 80.00
HP Hunter Pence 30.00 60.00
HR Hanley Ramirez 10.00 25.00
HS Huston Street 6.00 15.00
IK Ian Kinsler 6.00 15.00
JB Jason Bay 10.00 25.00
JF Jeff Francis 6.00 15.00
JH Jeremy Hermida 6.00 15.00
JL Jon Lester 10.00 25.00
JN Joe Nathan 6.00 15.00
JV Justin Verlander 20.00 50.00
KE Howie Kendrick 10.00 25.00
KG Ken Griffey Jr. 50.00 100.00
KI Kei Igawa 15.00 40.00
LA John Lackey 6.00 15.00
MO Justin Morneau 10.00 25.00
MY Michael Young 6.00 15.00
PA Jonathan Papelbon 20.00 50.00
PF Prince Fielder 20.00 50.00
PH Phil Hughes 30.00 60.00
PK Paul Konerko 10.00 25.00
RM Russell Martin 10.00 25.00
RO Roy Oswalt 10.00 25.00
RT Ryan Theriot 10.00 25.00
RW Rickie Weeks 6.00 15.00
RZ Ryan Zimmerman 15.00 40.00
SA Jarrod Saltalamacchia 10.00 25.00
SK Scott Kazmir 8.00 20.00
TH Torii Hunter 6.00 15.00
VW Vernon Wells 6.00 15.00

2007 UD Black Lustrous Materials Autographs

RANDOM INSERTS IN PACKS
PRINT RUNS B/WN 33-50 COPIES PER
GOLD SPEC. PRINT RUN 10 SER.#'d SETS
NO GOLD PRICING DUE TO SCARCITY
NAT.PEARL PRINT RUN 1 SER.#'d SET
NO PEARL PRICING DUE TO SCARCITY
EXCHANGE DEADLINE 11/26/2009
AD Adam Dunn/50 6.00 15.00
AE Andre Ethier/50 6.00 15.00
BO Jeremy Bonderman/50 10.00 25.00
BU B.J. Upton/50 10.00 25.00
CA Melky Cabrera/50 6.00 15.00
CC Carl Crawford/50 6.00 15.00
CL Carlos Lee/50 6.00 15.00
CO Chad Cordero/50 6.00 15.00
CP Coco Crisp/50 6.00 15.00
CR Cal Ripken Jr./50 100.00 150.00
DH Dan Haren/50 6.00 15.00
DJ Derek Jeter/50 100.00 150.00
DL Derrek Lee/50 10.00 25.00
DU Dan Uggla/50 6.00 15.00
DW Dontrelle Willis/50 6.00 15.00
DY Delmon Young/50 10.00 25.00
FH Felix Hernandez/50 20.00 50.00
GR Khalil Greene/50 6.00 15.00
HR Hanley Ramirez/33 10.00 25.00
HS Huston Street/50 6.00 15.00
IK Ian Kinsler/50 10.00 25.00
JB Jason Bay/50 6.00 15.00
JH Jeremy Hermida/50 6.00 15.00
JM Joe Mauer/50 15.00 40.00
JN Joe Nathan/50 6.00 15.00
JV Justin Verlander/50 20.00 50.00
JW Josh Willingham/50 6.00 15.00
JZ Joel Zumaya/50 10.00 25.00
KE Howie Kendrick/50 10.00 25.00
KG Ken Griffey Jr./50 60.00 120.00
KM Kendry Morales/50 6.00 15.00
MC Matt Cain/50 10.00 25.00
MM Melvin Mora/50 6.00 15.00
MP Mike Pelfrey/50 6.00 15.00
NM Nick Markakis/50 15.00 40.00
PA Jonathan Papelbon/50 20.00 50.00
PF Prince Fielder/50 30.00 60.00
RW Rickie Weeks/50 6.00 15.00
RZ Ryan Zimmerman/50 15.00 40.00
SD Stephen Drew/50 10.00 25.00
TH Torii Hunter/50 10.00 25.00
VW Vernon Wells/50 10.00 25.00

2007 UD Black Pride of a Nation Autographs

RANDOM INSERTS IN PACKS
PRINT RUNS B/WN 25-75 COPIES PER
NO PRICING ON QTY 25
GOLD SPEC.PRINT RUN 10 SER.#'d SETS
NO GOLD PRICING DUE TO SCARCITY
NAT.PEARL PRINT RUN 1 SER.#'d SET
NO PEARL PRICING DUE TO SCARCITY
PRINTING PLATES RANDOMLY INSERTED
PLATE PRINT RUN 1 SET PER COLOR
BLACK-CYAN-MAGENTA-YELLOW ISSUED
NO PLATE PRICING DUE TO SCARCITY
EXCHANGE DEADLINE 11/26/2009
AH Aaron Harang 10.00 25.00
AL Adam LaRoche 10.00 25.00
AR Aaron Rowand 10.00 25.00
BO Jeremy Bonderman 12.50 30.00
BP Brandon Phillips 10.00 25.00
CA Carl Crawford 12.50 30.00
CC Coco Crisp 15.00 40.00
CG Curtis Granderson 20.00 50.00
CL Carlos Lee 20.00 50.00
CR Cal Ripken Jr./25
DH Dan Haren 10.00 25.00
DL Derrek Lee 15.00 40.00
DU Dan Uggla 10.00 25.00
DW Dontrelle Willis 12.50 30.00
EC Eric Chavez 12.50 30.00
FH Felix Hernandez 30.00 60.00
FT Frank Thomas 60.00 120.00
HR Hanley Ramirez 20.00 50.00
JB Jason Bay 20.00 50.00
JL John Lackey 10.00 25.00
JM John Maine 15.00 40.00
LB Lance Berkman 20.00 50.00
MM Melvin Mora 10.00 25.00
MO Justin Morneau 20.00 50.00
PF Prince Fielder 30.00 60.00
RM Russell Martin 12.50 30.00
RO Roy Oswalt 15.00 40.00
SK Scott Kazmir 12.50 30.00
VM Victor Martinez 15.00 40.00

2007 UD Black Prodigious Autographs

RANDOM INSERTS IN PACKS
PRINT RUNS B/WN 50-75 COPIES PER
GOLD SPEC. PRINT RUN 25 SER.#'d SETS
NO GOLD PRICING DUE TO SCARCITY
NAT.PEARL PRINT RUN 1 SER.#'d SET
NO PEARL PRICING DUE TO SCARCITY
EXCHANGE DEADLINE 11/26/2009
AE Andre Ethier/75 6.00 15.00
AG Adrian Gonzalez/75 6.00 15.00
AH Aaron Harang/75 6.00 15.00
AI Akinori Iwamura/75 20.00 50.00
AL Adam LaRoche/75 6.00 15.00

AR Aaron Rowand/50 6.00 15.00
BB Billy Butler/75 10.00 25.00
BE Josh Beckett/50 30.00 60.00
BP Brandon Phillips/50 6.00 15.00
BS Ben Sheets/50 6.00 15.00
BU B.J. Upton/75 6.00 15.00
CA Carl Crawford/75 6.00 15.00
CC Coco Crisp/50 6.00 15.00
CG Curtis Granderson/50 30.00 60.00
CH Cole Hamels/50 15.00 40.00
CO Chad Cordero/50 6.00 15.00
CR Cal Ripken Jr./75 50.00 100.00
CY Chris Young/50 6.00 15.00
DH Dan Haren/75 6.00 15.00
DM Daisuke Matsuzaka/75 350.00 500.00
DU Dan Uggla/75 6.00 15.00
DY Delmon Young/75 10.00 25.00
FP Felix Pie/75 10.00 25.00
GA Garrett Atkins/75 6.00 15.00
GO Alex Gordon/75 20.00 50.00
GP Glen Perkins/75 6.00 15.00
HB Homer Bailey/75 10.00 25.00
HK Howie Kendrick/50 10.00 25.00
HP Hunter Pence/75 30.00 60.00
HS Huston Street/50 6.00 15.00
JB Jeremy Bonderman/75 10.00 25.00
JE Johnny Estrada/75 6.00 15.00
JH Josh Hamilton/50 20.00 50.00
JL John Lackey/50 6.00 15.00
JM John Maine/50 10.00 25.00
JP Jonathan Papelbon/75 15.00 40.00
JS Joakim Soria/75 10.00 25.00
JV Justin Verlander/50 20.00 50.00
JW Josh Willingham/50 6.00 15.00
KE Kelvim Escobar/50 6.00 15.00
KI Kei Igawa/75 15.00 40.00
KJ Kelly Johnson/50 6.00 15.00
LE Jon Lester/75 10.00 25.00
MC Matt Cain/75 6.00 15.00
MH Matt Holliday/75 20.00 50.00
MM Melvin Mora/50 6.00 15.00
MO Justin Morneau/75 10.00 25.00
NM Nick Markakis/75 10.00 25.00
NS Nick Swisher/75 10.00 25.00
PK Paul Konerko/75 10.00 25.00
RB Ryan Braun/75 30.00 60.00
RH Rich Harden/50 6.00 15.00
RM Russell Martin/75 10.00 25.00
RZ Ryan Zimmerman/75 15.00 40.00
SK Scott Kazmir/75 8.00 20.00
SM Sergio Mitre/50 6.00 15.00
TH Tim Hudson/75 10.00 25.00
TL Tim Lincecum/75 40.00 80.00
VM Victor Martinez/75 10.00 25.00
YG Yovani Gallardo/50 10.00 25.00

2007 UD Black Prodigious Materials Autographs

RANDOM INSERTS IN PACKS
PRINT RUNS B/WN 35-50 COPIES PER
GOLD SPEC. PRINT RUN 10 SER.#'d SETS
NO GOLD PRICING DUE TO SCARCITY
NAT.PEARL PRINT RUN 1 SER.#'d SET
NO PEARL PRICING DUE TO SCARCITY
EXCHANGE DEADLINE 11/26/2009
AD Adam Dunn 10.00 25.00
AE Andre Ethier 10.00 25.00
AL Adam LaRoche 10.00 25.00
AR Aaron Rowand 10.00 25.00
BO Jeremy Bonderman 10.00 25.00
BP Brandon Phillips 6.00 15.00
BU B.J. Upton 10.00 25.00
CC Coco Crisp 10.00 25.00
CD Chris Duncan 15.00 40.00
CH Cole Hamels 20.00 50.00
CL Cliff Lee 8.00 20.00
CR Carl Crawford 10.00 25.00
CY Chris Young 10.00 25.00
DH Dan Haren 6.00 15.00
DU Dan Uggla 10.00 25.00
DW Dontrelle Willis 10.00 25.00
FH Felix Hernandez 20.00 50.00
GA Garrett Atkins 6.00 15.00
HA Josh Hamilton 20.00 50.00
HK Hong-Chih Kuo 40.00 80.00
HR Hanley Ramirez 10.00 25.00
HS Huston Street 6.00 15.00
IK Ian Kinsler 10.00 25.00
JB Joe Blanton 6.00 15.00
JH Jeremy Hermida 6.00 15.00
JL Jon Lester 10.00 25.00
JN Joe Nathan 6.00 15.00
JS Johan Santana 20.00 50.00
JV Justin Verlander 20.00 50.00
JZ Joel Zumaya 10.00 25.00
KE Howie Kendrick 10.00 25.00
KW Kerry Wood 10.00 25.00
MO Justin Morneau 15.00 40.00
MT Mark Teixeira 10.00 25.00
PA Jonathan Papelbon 20.00 50.00
RI Cal Ripken Jr./35 100.00 150.00
RW Rickie Weeks 6.00 15.00
SK Scott Kazmir 8.00 20.00
SR Scott Rolen 10.00 25.00
TE Miguel Tejada 10.00 25.00
TG Tom Glavine 20.00 50.00
VW Vernon Wells 10.00 25.00

2007 UD Black Prominent Numbers Autographs

RANDOM INSERTS IN PACKS
PRINT RUNS B/WN 1-58 COPIES PER
NO PRICING ON QTY 25 OR LESS
GOLD SPEC. PRINT RUN 10 SER.#'d SETS
NO GOLD PRICING DUE TO SCARCITY
NAT.PEARL PRINT RUN 1 SER.#'d SETS
NO PEARL PRICING DUE TO SCARCITY
EXCHANGE DEADLINE 11/26/2009
AE Andre Ethier/16
AH Aaron Harang/39 6.00 15.00
AI Akinori Iwamura/1
AL Adam LaRoche/25
BB Billy Butler/21
BL Joe Blanton/55 6.00 15.00
BU B.J. Upton/2
CA Chris Carpenter/22
CC Carl Crawford/13
CG Curtis Granderson/28 20.00 50.00
CH Cole Hamels/35 20.00 50.00
CR Cal Ripken Jr./8
CY Chris Young/32 10.00 25.00
DJ Derek Jeter/2
DY Delmon Young/26 10.00 25.00
FH Felix Hernandez/34 20.00 50.00
GA Garrett Atkins/27 10.00 25.00
HK Howie Kendrick/47 6.00 15.00
HR Hanley Ramirez/2
HS Huston Street/20
IK Ian Kinsler/5
JB Jason Bay/38 10.00 25.00
JE Johnny Estrada/33 6.00 15.00
JM Justin Morneau/33 10.00 25.00
JN Joe Nathan/36 6.00 15.00
JP Jonathan Papelbon/58 15.00 40.00
JV Justin Verlander/35 20.00 50.00
JZ Joel Zumaya/54 6.00 15.00
MA John Maine/33 10.00 25.00
MB Michael Bourn/45 6.00 15.00
MC Matt Cain/18
MH Matt Holliday/5
MM Melvin Mora/6
MT Miguel Tejada/3
NM Nick Markakis/21
NS Nick Swisher/18
PK Paul Konerko/14
RH Rich Harden/40 6.00 15.00
RM Russell Martin/55 15.00 40.00
RW Rickie Weeks/23
RZ Ryan Zimmerman/11
SK Scott Kazmir/19

2007 UD Black Pure White Autographs

RANDOM INSERTS IN MYSTERY PACKS
STATED PRINT RUN 1 SER.#'d SET
NO PRICING DUE TO SCARCITY
AUTO PRINTING PLATES RANDOMLY INSERTED
PLATE PRINT RUN 1 SET PER COLOR
BLACK-CYAN-MAGENTA-YELLOW ISSUED
NO PLATE PRICING DUE TO SCARCITY
EXCHANGE DEADLINE 11/26/2009

2007 UD Black Triptych Triple Autographs

RANDOM INSERTS IN PACKS
STATED PRINT RUN 15 SER.#'d SETS
NO PRICING DUE TO SCARCITY
GOLD SPEC.PRINT RUN 5 SER.#'d SETS
NO GOLD PRICING DUE TO SCARCITY
NAT.PEARL PRINT RUN 1 SER.#'d SET
NO PEARL PRICING DUE TO SCARCITY
EXCHANGE DEADLINE 11/26/2009
AKW Garret Anderson
Howie Kendrick
Brandon Wood
BGL Jason Bay
Tom Gorzelanny
Adam LaRoche
BLB Josh Beckett
John Lackey
Jeremy Bonderman
GDH Ken Griffey Jr.
Adam Dunn
Josh Hamilton
HAC Aaron Harang
Bronson Arroyo
Jon Coutlangus
HGC Torii Hunter
Curtis Granderson
Coco Crisp
HMP Phil Hughes
Andrew Miller
Glen Perkins
LBG Tim Lincecum
Homer Bailey
Yovani Gallardo
LPT Derrek Lee
Felix Pie
Ryan Theriot
MEL Russell Martin
Andre Ethier
Andy LaRoche
OHM Roy Oswalt
Aaron Harang
John Maine
PBT Hunter Pence
Ryan Braun
Troy Tulowitzki
SPS Huston Street
Jonathan Papelbon
Joakim Soria
UKK B.J. Upton
Howie Kendrick
Ian Kinsler
VHS Justin Verlander
Dan Haren
James Shields

2007 UD Black Triptych Triple Materials Autographs

RANDOM INSERTS IN PACKS
STATED PRINT RUN 25 SER.#'d SETS
NO PRICING DUE TO SCARCITY
PATCH PRINT RUN 5 SER.#'d SETS
NO PATCH PRICING DUE TO SCARCITY
EXCHANGE DEADLINE 11/26/2009
BU B.J. Upton
CG Curtis Granderson
CL Carlos Lee
DU Dan Uggla
HP Hunter Pence
JB Josh Beckett
JL John Lackey
PF Prince Fielder
TH Torii Hunter
VW Vernon Wells

2007 UD Black Upper Echelon Quad Autographs

RANDOM INSERTS IN PACKS
STATED PRINT RUN 5 SER.#'d SETS
NO PRICING DUE TO SCARCITY
GOLD SPEC.PRINT RUN 3 SER.#'d SETS
NO GOLD PRICING DUE TO SCARCITY
NAT.PEARL PRINT RUN 1 SER.#'d SET
NO PEARL PRICING DUE TO SCARCITY
EXCHANGE DEADLINE 11/26/2009
BLOP Lance Berkman
Carlos Lee
Roy Oswalt
Hunter Pence
GHHB Ken Griffey Jr.
Josh Hamilton
Aaron Harang
Homer Bailey
HWCG Torii Hunter
Vernon Wells
Coco Crisp
Curtis Granderson
IUKY Akinori Iwamura
B.J. Upton
Scott Kazmir
Delmon Young
MGEK Russell Martin
Luis Gonzalez
Andre Ethier
Hong-Chih Kuo
PSCS Jonathan Papelbon
Huston Street
Chad Cordero
Joakim Soria
RTRT Cal Ripken Jr.
Miguel Tejada
Hanley Ramirez
Troy Tulowitzki
TMFL Mark Teixeira
Justin Morneau
Prince Fielder
Derrek Lee
TWHT Frank Thomas
Vernon Wells
Roy Halladay
Curtis Thigpen
YGGH Chris Young
Adrian Gonzalez
Khalil Greene
Chase Headley
YHMC Chris Young
Cole Hamels
John Maine
Matt Cain

2007 UD Black Upper Echelon Quad Materials Autographs

RANDOM INSERTS IN PACKS
PRINT RUNS B/WN 2-5 COPIES PER
NO PRICING DUE TO SCARCITY
PATCH PRINT RUN 1 SER.#'d SET
NO PATCH PRICING DUE TO SCARCITY
EXCHANGE DEADLINE 11/26/2009
CR Cal Ripken Jr./5
DJ Derek Jeter/2
FT Frank Thomas/5
JT Jim Thome/5
KG Ken Griffey Jr./3
RJ Randy Johnson/5

2007 UD Masterpieces

COMPLETE SET (90) 15.00 40.00
COMMON CARD (1-90) .25 .60
COMMON ROOKIE (1-90) .25 .60
PRINTING PLATES RANDOMLY INSERTED
PLATE PRINT RUN 1 SET PER COLOR
BLACK-CYAN-MAGENTA-YELLOW ISSUED
NO PLATE PRICING DUE TO SCARCITY
1 Babe Ruth 1.50 4.00
2 Babe Ruth 1.50 4.00
3 Bobby Thomson .40 1.00
4 Bill Mazeroski .40 1.00
5 Carlton Fisk .40 1.00
6 Kirk Gibson .25 .60
7 Don Larsen .25 .60
8 Lou Gehrig 1.25 3.00
9 Roger Maris .60 1.50
10 Cal Ripken Jr. 2.50 6.00
11 Bucky Dent .25 .60
12 Ryan Howard 1.00 2.50
13 Brooks Robinson .40 1.00
14 David Ortiz .60 1.50
15 Hideki Matsui .60 1.50
16 Roger Clemens 1.00 2.50
17 Sandy Koufax 2.00 5.00
18 Reggie Jackson .40 1.00
19 Ozzie Smith 1.00 2.50
20 Ty Cobb 1.00 2.50
21 Walter Johnson .60 1.50
22 Babe Ruth 1.50 4.00
23 Roy Campanella .60 1.50
24 Jackie Robinson .60 1.50

25 Carl Yastrzemski 1.00 2.50
26 Sandy Koufax 2.00 5.00
27 Daisuke Matsuzaka RC 2.50 6.00
28 Kei Igawa RC .60 1.50
29 Ken Griffey Jr. 1.00 2.50
30 Derek Jeter 1.50 4.00
31 David Ortiz .60 1.50
32 Vladimir Guerrero .60 1.50
33 Chase Utley .60 1.50
34 Troy Tulowitzki (RC) .60 1.50
35 Joe Mauer .40 1.00
36 Travis Hafner .25 .60
37 Miguel Cabrera .40 1.00
38 Albert Pujols 1.25 3.00
39 Frank Thomas .60 1.50
40 Mike Piazza .60 1.50
41 Josh Hamilton .60 1.50
42 Tony Gwynn 2.50 6.00
Cal Ripken Jr.
43 Ichiro Suzuki 1.00 2.50
44 Hideki Matsui .60 1.50
45 Ken Griffey Jr. 1.00 2.50
46 Michael Jordan 1.50 4.00
47 John F. Kennedy 1.00 2.50
48 Randy Johnson .60 1.50
49 Albert Pujols 1.25 3.00
50 Carlos Beltran .25 .60
51 Delmon Young (RC) .40 1.00
52 Johan Santana .40 1.00
53 Cal Ripken Jr. 2.50 6.00
54 Yogi Berra .60 1.50
Jackie Robinson
55 Cal Ripken Jr. 2.50 6.00
56 Hanley Ramirez .40 1.00
57 Victor Martinez .25 .60
58 Cole Hamels .60 1.50
59 Bobby Doerr .25 .60
60 Bruce Sutter .25 .60
61 Jason Bay .25 .60
62 Luis Aparicio .25 .60
63 Stephen Drew .40 1.00
64 Jered Weaver .40 1.00
65 Alex Gordon RC 1.25 3.00
66 Howie Kendrick .25 .60
67 Ryan Zimmerman .60 1.50
68 Akinori Iwamura RC .60 1.50
69 Chien-Ming Wang 1.00 2.50
70 David Wright 1.00 2.50
71 Ryan Howard 1.00 2.50
72 Alex Rodriguez 1.00 2.50
73 Justin Morneau .25 .60
74 Andrew Miller RC 1.50 4.00
75 Richard Nixon .60 1.50
76 Bill Clinton 1.00 2.50
77 Phil Hughes (RC) 1.25 3.00
78 Tom Glavine .40 1.00
79 Chipper Jones .60 1.50
80 Craig Biggio .40 1.00
81 Chris Chambliss .25 .60
82 Tim Lincecum RC 2.00 5.00
83 Billy Butler (RC) .40 1.00
84 Andy LaRoche (RC) .25 .60
85 1969 New York Mets .25 .60
86 2004 Boston Red Sox 1.00 2.50
87 Roberto Clemente 2.00 5.00
88 Chase Utley .60 1.50
89 Reggie Jackson .40 1.00
90 Curt Schilling .40 1.00

2007 UD Masterpieces Artists Proof

RANDOM INSERTS IN PACKS
STATED PRINT RUN 1 SER.#'d SET
NO PRICING DUE TO SCARCITY

2007 UD Masterpieces Black Linen

*BLACK VET: 1.5X TO 4X BASIC
*BLACK RC: 1.5X TO 4X BASIC
RANDOM INSERTS IN PACKS
STATED PRINT RUN 99 SER.#'d SETS
1 Babe Ruth 5.00 12.00
2 Babe Ruth 5.00 12.00
10 Cal Ripken Jr. 15.00 40.00
17 Sandy Koufax 12.50 30.00
22 Babe Ruth 5.00 12.00
26 Sandy Koufax 12.50 30.00
27 Daisuke Matsuzaka 12.50 30.00
29 Ken Griffey Jr. 6.00 15.00
30 Derek Jeter 15.00 40.00
40 Mike Piazza 6.00 15.00
42 Tony Gwynn 15.00 40.00
Cal Ripken Jr.
43 Ichiro Suzuki 6.00 15.00
45 Ken Griffey Jr. 6.00 15.00
46 Michael Jordan 15.00 40.00
53 Cal Ripken Jr. 15.00 40.00
55 Cal Ripken Jr. 15.00 40.00
69 Chien-Ming Wang 12.50 30.00

2007 UD Masterpieces Blue Steel

*BLUE STEEL VET: 1.5X TO 4X BASIC
*BLUE STEEL RC: 1.5X TO 4X BASIC
RANDOM INSERTS IN PACKS
STATED PRINT RUN 50 SER.#'d SETS
1 Babe Ruth 5.00 12.00
2 Babe Ruth 5.00 12.00
10 Cal Ripken Jr. 15.00 40.00
17 Sandy Koufax 12.50 30.00
22 Babe Ruth 5.00 12.00
26 Sandy Koufax 12.50 30.00
27 Daisuke Matsuzaka 12.50 30.00
29 Ken Griffey Jr. 6.00 15.00
30 Derek Jeter 15.00 40.00
40 Mike Piazza 6.00 15.00
42 Tony Gwynn 15.00 40.00
Cal Ripken Jr.
43 Ichiro Suzuki 6.00 15.00
45 Ken Griffey Jr. 6.00 15.00
46 Michael Jordan 15.00 40.00
53 Cal Ripken Jr. 15.00 40.00
55 Cal Ripken Jr. 15.00 40.00
69 Chien-Ming Wang 12.50 30.00

2007 UD Masterpieces Bronze Ore

RANDOM INSERTS IN PACKS
STATED PRINT RUN 1 SER.#'d SET
NO PRICING DUE TO SCARCITY

2007 UD Masterpieces Celestial Blue

RANDOM INSERTS IN PACKS
STATED PRINT RUN 1 SER.#'d SET
NO PRICING DUE TO SCARCITY

2007 UD Masterpieces Deep Blue Linen

*DEEP BLUE VET: 1.5X TO 4X BASIC
*DEEP BLUE RC: 1.5X TO 4X BASIC
RANDOM INSERTS IN PACKS
STATED PRINT RUN 75 SER.#'d SETS
1 Babe Ruth 5.00 12.00
2 Babe Ruth 5.00 12.00
10 Cal Ripken Jr. 15.00 40.00
17 Sandy Koufax 12.50 30.00
22 Babe Ruth 5.00 12.00
26 Sandy Koufax 12.50 30.00
27 Daisuke Matsuzaka 12.50 30.00
29 Ken Griffey Jr. 6.00 15.00
30 Derek Jeter 15.00 40.00
40 Mike Piazza 6.00 15.00
42 Tony Gwynn 15.00 40.00
Cal Ripken Jr.
43 Ichiro Suzuki 6.00 15.00
45 Ken Griffey Jr. 6.00 15.00
46 Michael Jordan 15.00 40.00
53 Cal Ripken Jr. 15.00 40.00
55 Cal Ripken Jr. 15.00 40.00
69 Chien-Ming Wang 12.50 30.00

2007 UD Masterpieces Green Linen

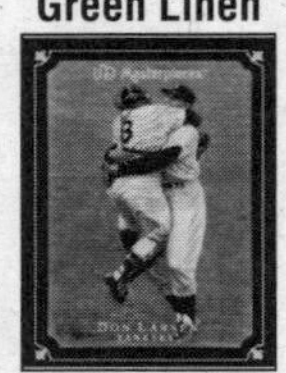

*GREEN VET: .75X TO 2X BASIC
*GREEN RC: .75X TO 2X BASIC
STATED ODDS 1:6 H, 1:48 R, 1:48 BLASTER

2007 UD Masterpieces Hades

*HADES VET: 1.5X TO 4X BASIC
*HADES RC: 1.5X TO 4X BASIC
RANDOM INSERTS IN PACKS
STATED PRINT RUN 50 SER.#'d SETS
1 Babe Ruth 5.00 12.00
2 Babe Ruth 5.00 12.00
10 Cal Ripken Jr. 15.00 40.00
17 Sandy Koufax 12.50 30.00
22 Babe Ruth 5.00 12.00
26 Sandy Koufax 12.50 30.00
27 Daisuke Matsuzaka 12.50 30.00
29 Ken Griffey Jr. 6.00 15.00
30 Derek Jeter 15.00 40.00
40 Mike Piazza 6.00 15.00
42 Tony Gwynn 15.00 40.00
Cal Ripken Jr.
43 Ichiro Suzuki 6.00 15.00
45 Ken Griffey Jr. 6.00 15.00
46 Michael Jordan 15.00 40.00
53 Cal Ripken Jr. 15.00 40.00
55 Cal Ripken Jr. 15.00 40.00
69 Chien-Ming Wang 12.50 30.00

2007 UD Masterpieces Ionised

*IONISED VET: 1.5X TO 4X BASIC
*IONISED RC: 1.5X TO 4X BASIC
RANDOM INSERTS IN PACKS
STATED PRINT RUN 50 SER.#'d SETS
1 Babe Ruth 5.00 12.00
2 Babe Ruth 5.00 12.00
10 Cal Ripken Jr. 15.00 40.00
17 Sandy Koufax 12.50 30.00
22 Babe Ruth 5.00 12.00
26 Sandy Koufax 12.50 30.00
27 Daisuke Matsuzaka 12.50 30.00
29 Ken Griffey Jr. 6.00 15.00
30 Derek Jeter 15.00 40.00
40 Mike Piazza 6.00 15.00
42 Tony Gwynn 15.00 40.00
Cal Ripken Jr.
43 Ichiro Suzuki 6.00 15.00
45 Ken Griffey Jr. 6.00 15.00
46 Michael Jordan 15.00 40.00
53 Cal Ripken Jr. 15.00 40.00
55 Cal Ripken Jr. 15.00 40.00
69 Chien-Ming Wang 12.50 30.00

2007 UD Masterpieces Persian Blue Linen

RANDOM INSERTS IN PACKS
STATED PRINT RUN 1 SER.#'d SET
NO PRICING DUE TO SCARCITY

2007 UD Masterpieces Pinot Red

*PINOT RED VET: 1.5X TO 4X BASIC
*PINOT RED RC: 1.5X TO 4X BASIC
RANDOM INSERTS IN PACKS
STATED PRINT RUN 75 SER.#'d SETS
1 Babe Ruth 5.00 12.00
2 Babe Ruth 5.00 12.00
10 Cal Ripken Jr. 15.00 40.00
17 Sandy Koufax 12.50 30.00
22 Babe Ruth 5.00 12.00
26 Sandy Koufax 12.50 30.00
27 Daisuke Matsuzaka 12.50 30.00
29 Ken Griffey Jr. 6.00 15.00
30 Derek Jeter 15.00 40.00
40 Mike Piazza 6.00 15.00
42 Tony Gwynn 15.00 40.00
Cal Ripken Jr.
43 Ichiro Suzuki 6.00 15.00
45 Ken Griffey Jr. 6.00 15.00
46 Michael Jordan 15.00 40.00
53 Cal Ripken Jr. 15.00 40.00
55 Cal Ripken Jr. 15.00 40.00
69 Chien-Ming Wang 12.50 30.00

2007 UD Masterpieces Red Linen

RANDOM INSERTS IN PACKS
STATED PRINT RUN 1 SER.#'d SET
NO PRICING DUE TO SCARCITY

2007 UD Masterpieces Rusted

*RUSTED VET: 1.5X TO 4X BASIC
*RUSTED RC: 1.5X TO 4X BASIC
RANDOM INSERTS IN PACKS
STATED PRINT RUN 50 SER.#'d SETS
1 Babe Ruth 5.00 12.00
2 Babe Ruth 5.00 12.00
10 Cal Ripken Jr. 15.00 40.00
17 Sandy Koufax 12.50 30.00
22 Babe Ruth 5.00 12.00
26 Sandy Koufax 12.50 30.00
27 Daisuke Matsuzaka 12.50 30.00
29 Ken Griffey Jr. 6.00 15.00
30 Derek Jeter 15.00 40.00
40 Mike Piazza 6.00 15.00
42 Tony Gwynn 15.00 40.00
Cal Ripken Jr.
43 Ichiro Suzuki 6.00 15.00
45 Ken Griffey Jr. 6.00 15.00
46 Michael Jordan 15.00 40.00
53 Cal Ripken Jr. 15.00 40.00
55 Cal Ripken Jr. 15.00 40.00
69 Chien-Ming Wang 12.50 30.00

2007 UD Masterpieces Serious Black

*SER.BLACK VET: 1.5X TO 4X BASIC
*SER.BLACK RC: 1.5X TO 4X BASIC
RANDOM INSERTS IN PACKS
STATED PRINT RUN 99 SER.#'d SETS
1 Babe Ruth 5.00 12.00
2 Babe Ruth 5.00 12.00
10 Cal Ripken Jr. 15.00 40.00
17 Sandy Koufax 12.50 30.00
22 Babe Ruth 5.00 12.00
26 Sandy Koufax 12.50 30.00
27 Daisuke Matsuzaka 12.50 30.00
29 Ken Griffey Jr. 6.00 15.00
30 Derek Jeter 15.00 40.00
40 Mike Piazza 6.00 15.00
42 Tony Gwynn 15.00 40.00
Cal Ripken Jr.
43 Ichiro Suzuki 6.00 15.00
45 Ken Griffey Jr. 6.00 15.00
46 Michael Jordan 15.00 40.00
53 Cal Ripken Jr. 15.00 40.00
55 Cal Ripken Jr. 15.00 40.00
69 Chien-Ming Wang 12.50 30.00

2007 UD Masterpieces Urban Gray

RANDOM INSERTS IN PACKS
STATED PRINT RUN 1 SER.#'d SET
NO PRICING DUE TO SCARCITY

2007 UD Masterpieces Windsor Green

*WIN.GREEN VET: .75X TO 2X BASIC
*WIN.GREEN RC: .75X TO 2X BASIC
STATED ODDS 1:9 H, 1:72 R, 1:750 BLASTER

2007 UD Masterpieces 5x7 Box Topper

STATED ODDS ONE PER HOBBY BOX
MP1 Cal Ripken Jr. 6.00 15.00
MP2 Ken Griffey Jr. 5.00 12.00
MP3 Derek Jeter 6.00 15.00
MP4 Sandy Koufax 6.00 15.00
MP5 Babe Ruth 6.00 15.00
MP6 Lou Gehrig 6.00 15.00
MP7 Travis Hafner 3.00 8.00
MP8 Victor Martinez 3.00 8.00
MP9 Jered Weaver 3.00 8.00
MP10 Phil Hughes 4.00 10.00
MP11 Bobby Doerr 4.00 10.00
MP12 Billy Butler 3.00 8.00
MP13 Andy LaRoche 3.00 8.00
MP14 Josh Hamilton 6.00 15.00
MP15 Reggie Jackson 4.00 10.00
MP16 Hanley Ramirez 3.00 8.00
MP17 Don Larsen 4.00 10.00
MP18 Ken Griffey Jr. 5.00 12.00
MP19 Jason Bay 3.00 8.00
MP20 Daisuke Matsuzaka 10.00 25.00

2007 UD Masterpieces 5x7 Box Topper Signatures

STATED ODDS APPX.ONE PER HOBBY CASE
NO PRICING DUE TO SCARCITY
EXCHANGE DEADLINE 10/10/2009

2007 UD Masterpieces Captured on Canvas

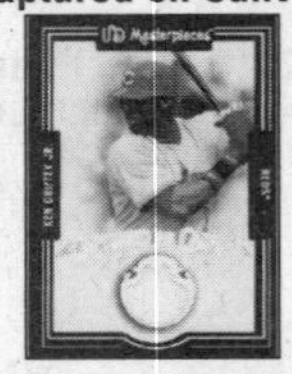

STATED ODDS 1:6 H, 1:24 R, 1:1500 BLAST
BRONZE RANDOMLY INSERTED
BRONZE PRINT RUN 1 SER.#'d SET
NO BRONZE PRICING AVAILABLE
FOR.GREEN RANDOMLY INSERTED
FOR.GREEN PRINT RUN 1 SER.#'d SET
NO FOR.GREEN PRICING AVAILABLE
AB Adrian Beltre 3.00 8.00
AD Adam Dunn 3.00 8.00
AI Akinori Iwamura 4.00 10.00
AJ Andruw Jones 3.00 8.00
AP Albert Pujols 6.00 15.00
BA Bobby Abreu 3.00 8.00
BC Bobby Crosby 3.00 8.00
BE Carlos Beltran 3.00 8.00
BG Brian Giles 3.00 8.00
BL Brad Lidge 3.00 8.00
BO Jeremy Bonderman 3.00 8.00
BR Brian Roberts 3.00 8.00
BS Ben Sheets 3.00 8.00
CA Chris Carpenter 3.00 8.00
CB Craig Biggio 4.00 10.00
CC Carl Crawford 3.00 8.00
CD Carlos Delgado 3.00 8.00
CF Carlton Fisk 4.00 10.00
CJ Chipper Jones 4.00 10.00
CL Carlos Lee 3.00 8.00
CR Coco Crisp 3.00 8.00
CS C.C. Sabathia 4.00 10.00
CU Chase Utley 4.00 10.00
CY Carl Yastrzemski 4.00 10.00
DJ Derek Jeter 8.00 20.00
DL Derrek Lee 3.00 8.00
DM Don Mattingly 6.00 15.00
DO David Ortiz 4.00 10.00
DR J.D. Drew 3.00 8.00
DW Dontrelle Willis 3.00 8.00
EB Erik Bedard 3.00 8.00
EC Eric Chavez 3.00 8.00
EG Eric Gagne 3.00 8.00
FH Felix Hernandez 3.00 8.00
FL Francisco Liriano 4.00 10.00
GA Garrett Atkins 3.00 8.00
GL Tom Glavine 4.00 10.00
GR Khalil Greene 4.00 10.00
GS Grady Sizemore 4.00 10.00
HA Roy Halladay 3.00 8.00
HB Hank Blalock 3.00 8.00
HE Todd Helton 3.00 8.00
HR Hanley Ramirez 3.00 8.00
HS Huston Street 3.00 8.00
IR Ivan Rodriguez 3.00 8.00
JA Jason Bay 3.00 8.00
JB Josh Beckett 3.00 8.00
JH J.J. Hardy 4.00 10.00
JK Jason Kendall 3.00 8.00
JM Joe Mauer 3.00 8.00
JN Joe Nathan 3.00 8.00
JP Jake Peavy 3.00 8.00
JR Jose Reyes 4.00 10.00
JS John Smoltz 4.00 10.00
JV Jason Varitek 4.00 10.00
JW Jered Weaver 3.00 8.00
KG Ken Griffey Jr. 6.00 15.00
LB Lance Berkman 3.00 8.00
MA Daisuke Matsuzaka 10.00 25.00
MC Miguel Cabrera 3.00 8.00
MG Marcus Giles 3.00 8.00
MH Matt Holliday 6.00 15.00
MO Magglio Ordonez 3.00 8.00
MR Mariano Rivera 4.00 10.00
MT Miguel Tejada 3.00 8.00
MY Michael Young 3.00 8.00
PA Jonathan Papelbon 6.00 15.00
RA Manny Ramirez 3.00 8.00
RB Rocco Baldelli 3.00 8.00
RC Roger Clemens 6.00 15.00
RH Rich Harden 3.00 8.00
RI Cal Ripken Jr. 8.00 20.00
RJ Randy Johnson 3.00 8.00
RO Roy Oswalt 4.00 10.00
RW Rickie Weeks 3.00 8.00
RZ Ryan Zimmerman 4.00 10.00
SA Johan Santana 4.00 10.00
SC Curt Schilling 3.00 8.00
SH Gary Sheffield 4.00 10.00
SK Scott Kazmir 3.00 8.00
SR Scott Rolen 4.00 10.00
TE Mark Teixeira 4.00 10.00
TG Tony Gwynn 4.00 10.00
TH Tim Hudson 3.00 8.00
TR Travis Hafner 3.00 8.00
VG Vladimir Guerrero 4.00 10.00
VM Victor Martinez 3.00 8.00
WC Will Clark 6.00 15.00

2007 UD Masterpieces Original Paintings

RANDOM INSERTS IN PACKS
EACH PAINTING IS A ONE-OF-ONE
EXCHANGE DEADLINE 10/10/2009

2007 UD Masterpieces Stroke of Genius Signatures

STATED ODDS 1:18 H, 1:2500 R, 1:2500 BLAST
WIN.GREEN RANDOMLY INSERTED
WIN.GREEN PRINT RUN 1 SER.#'d SET
NO WIN.GREEN PRICING AVAILABLE
PRINTING PLATES RANDOMLY INSERTED
PLATE PRINT RUN 1 SET PER COLOR
BLACK-CYAN-MAGENTA-YELLOW ISSUED
NO PLATE PRICING DUE TO SCARCITY
EXCHANGE DEADLINE 10/10/2009
AD Adam Dunn
AG Adrian Gonzalez 4.00 10.00
AI Akinori Iwamura
AJ Andruw Jones
AK Al Kaline 10.00 25.00
AL Andy LaRoche 4.00 10.00
BA Bronson Arroyo 6.00 15.00
BB Billy Butler 10.00 25.00
BO Boof Bonser 3.00 8.00
BR Brooks Robinson 10.00 25.00
BS Ben Sheets 3.00 8.00
BU B.J. Upton 4.00 10.00
CD Chris Duffy 3.00 8.00
CF Chone Figgins 3.00 8.00
CH Cole Hamels 15.00 40.00
CL Carlos Lee
CQ Carlos Quentin 8.00 20.00
CR Cal Ripken Jr. EXCH 60.00 120.00
DH Dan Haren 4.00 10.00
DJ Derek Jeter EXCH 75.00 150.00
DM Don Mattingly
DO David Ortiz 20.00 50.00
DU Dan Uggla 3.00 8.00
DW Dontrelle Willis 6.00 15.00
DY Delmon Young
EC Eric Chavez 3.00 8.00
FH Felix Hernandez
FT Frank Thomas
GO Alex Gordon 50.00 100.00
GP Glen Perkins 3.00 8.00
GW Tony Gwynn
HA Justin Hampson 3.00 8.00
HI Rich Hill 4.00 10.00
HK Howie Kendrick 4.00 10.00
HP Hunter Pence 15.00 40.00
HR Hanley Ramirez 10.00 25.00
HS Huston Street 4.00 10.00
HU Torii Hunter 6.00 15.00
IK Ian Kinsler 3.00 8.00
JA Jason Bay 4.00 10.00
JB Jeff Baker 3.00 8.00
JH Josh Hamilton 12.50 30.00
JM Joe Mauer
JP Jonathan Papelbon 15.00 40.00
JT Jim Thome 12.50 30.00
JU Justin Morneau 6.00 15.00
JV Justin Verlander 15.00 40.00
JW Jered Weaver 6.00 15.00
JZ Joel Zumaya 4.00 10.00
KE Austin Kearns 3.00 8.00
KG Ken Griffey Jr. EXCH 50.00 100.00
KI Kei Igawa
KK Kevin Kouzmanoff 4.00 10.00
LE Cliff Lee 4.00 10.00
LI Adam Lind 3.00 8.00
MB Michael Bourn 4.00 10.00
MC Matt Cain 4.00 10.00
MO Micah Owings 4.00 10.00
MS Mike Schmidt 20.00 50.00
NR Nolan Ryan
PS Phil Hughes 30.00 60.00
RA Aramis Ramirez 4.00 10.00
RC Roger Clemens 30.00 60.00
RH Rich Harden 3.00 8.00
RO Roy Oswalt 4.00 10.00
RW Rickie Weeks
RZ Ryan Zimmerman 10.00 25.00
SD Stephen Drew 6.00 15.00
SH Sean Henn 3.00 8.00
SK Scott Kazmir 12.50 30.00
SO Jeremy Sowers 3.00 8.00
TG Tom Glavine
TI Tim Hudson 4.00 10.00
TL Tim Lincecum 20.00 50.00
TR Travis Hafner 10.00 25.00
TT Troy Tulowitzki 10.00 25.00
VG Vladimir Guerrero
VM Victor Martinez EXCH 10.00 25.00
WB Wade Boggs
WC Will Clark
XN Xavier Nady 3.00 8.00

2008 UD Masterpieces

COMPLETE SET (120) 60.00 120.00
COMP.SET w/o SPs (90) 12.50 30.00
COMMON CARD (1-90) .20 .50
COMMON ROOKIE (1-90) .40 1.00
COMMON SP (91-120) .40 1.00
SP ODDS 1:2 HOBBY
1 Brandon Webb .30 .75
2 Justin Upton .50 1.25
3 Randy Johnson .50 1.25
4 Chipper Jones .60 1.50
5 Max Scherzer RC 1.00 2.50
6 Mark Teixeira .30 .75
7 Evan Longoria RC 3.00 8.00
8 Jim Palmer .20 .50
9 Brooks Robinson .30 .75
10 Nick Markakis .30 .75
11 Carl Yastrzemski .75 2.00
12 Wade Boggs .30 .75
13 Curt Schilling .30 .75
14 Daisuke Matsuzaka .75 2.00
15 David Ortiz .50 1.25
16 Jonathan Papelbon .30 .75
17 Manny Ramirez .50 1.25
18 Alfonso Soriano .30 .75
19 Ryne Sandberg 1.00 2.50
20 Carlos Zambrano .20 .50
21 Derrek Lee .30 .75
22 Kosuke Fukudome RC 1.50 4.00
23 Jim Thome .30 .75
24 Adam Dunn .20 .50
25 Joe Morgan .20 .50
26 Grady Sizemore .30 .75
27 Victor Martinez .20 .50
28 Travis Hafner .20 .50
29 Troy Tulowitzki .30 .75
30 Matt Holliday .30 .75
31 Todd Helton .30 .75
32 Justin Verlander .30 .75
33 Asdrubal Cabrera .20 .50
34 Gary Sheffield .20 .50
35 Magglio Ordonez .30 .75
36 Miguel Cabrera .30 .75
37 Hanley Ramirez .50 1.25
38 Lance Berkman .30 .75
39 Roy Oswalt .20 .50
40 Alex Gordon .50 1.25
41 Vladimir Guerrero .50 1.25
42 Andruw Jones .20 .50
43 Chin-Lung Hu (RC) .60 1.50
44 James Loney .30 .75
45 Hunter Pence .50 1.25
46 Robin Yount .50 1.25
47 Prince Fielder .50 1.25
48 Ryan Braun .60 1.50
49 Harmon Killebrew .50 1.25
50 Joe Mauer .30 .75
51 Justin Morneau .30 .75
52 Ken Griffey Jr. .75 2.00
53 Carlos Beltran .20 .50
54 David Wright .60 1.50
55 Johan Santana .30 .75
56 Jose Reyes .30 .75
57 Pedro Martinez .30 .75
58 Ian Kennedy RC 1.00 2.50
59 Jay Bruce (RC) 1.50 4.00
60 Whitey Ford .30 .75
61 Mariano Rivera .50 1.25
62 Alex Rodriguez .75 2.00
63 Hideki Matsui .50 1.25
64 Joba Chamberlain .60 1.50
65 Jorge Posada .30 .75
66 Robinson Cano .30 .75
67 Eric Chavez .20 .50
68 Rich Harden .20 .50
69 Chase Utley .50 1.25
70 Jimmy Rollins .30 .75
71 Ryan Howard .60 1.50
72 Bill Mazeroski .30 .75
73 Freddy Sanchez .20 .50
74 Luke Hochevar RC 1.00 2.50
75 Tony Gwynn .20 .50
76 Greg Maddux .60 1.50
77 Jake Peavy .30 .75
78 Barry Zito .20 .50
79 Russell Martin .20 .50
80 Tim Lincecum .50 1.25
81 Ichiro Suzuki .75 2.00
82 Felix Hernandez .30 .75
83 Ozzie Smith .75 2.00
84 Jason Varitek .50 1.25
85 Chris Carpenter .20 .50
86 Carl Crawford .20 .50
87 Michael Young .20 .50
88 Frank Thomas .50 1.25
89 Roy Halladay .20 .50
90 Ryan Zimmerman .30 .75

91 Eddie Murray SP 1.00 2.50
92 Cal Ripken Jr. SP 4.00 10.00
93 Frank Robinson SP .40 1.00
94 Ryne Sandberg SP 2.00 5.00
95 Warren Spahn SP .60 1.50
96 Ernie Banks SP 1.00 2.50
97 Carlton Fisk SP .60 1.50
98 Johnny Bench SP 1.00 2.50
99 Ken Griffey Jr. SP 1.50 4.00
100 Al Kaline SP 1.00 2.50
101 Cal Ripken Jr. SP 4.00 10.00
102 Nolan Ryan SP 3.00 8.00
103 Jack Morris SP .40 1.00
104 Rod Carew SP .60 1.50
105 Tom Seaver SP .60 1.50
106 Don Mattingly SP 2.00 5.00
107 Lou Brock SP .60 1.50
108 Joe DiMaggio SP 2.50 6.00
109 Derek Jeter SP 2.50 6.00
110 Yogi Berra SP 1.00 2.50
111 Reggie Jackson SP .60 1.50
112 Mike Schmidt SP 1.50 4.00
113 Steve Carlton SP .40 1.00
114 Willie Stargell SP .60 1.50
115 Roberto Clemente SP 2.00 5.00
116 Albert Pujols SP 2.00 5.00
117 Stan Musial SP 1.50 4.00
118 Bob Gibson SP .60 1.50
119 Dave Winfield SP .40 1.00
120 Joe Carter SP .40 1.00

2008 UD Masterpieces Framed Black

*BLK 1-90: 1X TO 2.5X BASIC
*BLK RC 1-90: .5X TO 1.2X BASIC
*BLK SP 91-120: .5X TO 1.2X BASIC
APPX.ODDS 1:3 HOBBY
7 Evan Longoria 5.00 12.00
92 Cal Ripken Jr. 8.00 20.00
101 Cal Ripken Jr. 8.00 20.00
102 Nolan Ryan 5.00 12.00

2008 UD Masterpieces Framed Blue 125

*BLUE 1-90: 2X TO 5X BASIC
*BLUE RC 1-90: 1X TO 2.5X BASIC
*BLUE SP 91-120: 1X TO 2.5X BASIC
RANDOM INSERTS IN PACKS
PRINT RUN 125 SER.#'d SETS
7 Evan Longoria 10.00 25.00
92 Cal Ripken Jr. 20.00 50.00
101 Cal Ripken Jr. 20.00 50.00
102 Nolan Ryan 10.00 25.00

2008 UD Masterpieces Framed Blue 50

*BLUE 1-90: 2.5X TO 6X BASIC
*BLUE RC 1-90: 1.2X TO 3X BASIC
*BLUE SP 91-120: 1.2X TO 3X BASIC
RANDOM INSERTS IN PACKS
PRINT RUN 50 SER.#'d SETS
7 Evan Longoria 12.00 30.00
92 Cal Ripken Jr. 25.00 60.00
101 Cal Ripken Jr. 25.00 60.00
102 Nolan Ryan 12.00 30.00

2008 UD Masterpieces Framed Blue 5

RANDOM INSERTS IN PACKS
STATED PRINT RUN 5 SER.#'d SETS
NO PRICING DUE TO SCARCITY

2008 UD Masterpieces Framed Brown 100

*BRN 1-90: 2X TO 5X BASIC
*BRN RC 1-90: 1X TO 2.5X BASIC
*BRN SP 91-120: 1X TO 2.5X BASIC
RANDOM INSERTS IN PACKS
PRINT RUN 100 SER.#'d SETS
7 Evan Longoria 10.00 25.00
92 Cal Ripken Jr. 20.00 50.00
101 Cal Ripken Jr. 20.00 50.00
102 Nolan Ryan 10.00 25.00

2008 UD Masterpieces Framed Green 75

*GRN 1-90: 2X TO 5X BASIC
*GRN RC 1-90: 1X TO 2.5X BASIC
*GRN SP 91-120: 1X TO 2.5X BASIC
RANDOM INSERTS IN PACKS
PRINT RUN 75 SER.#'d SETS
7 Evan Longoria 10.00 25.00
92 Cal Ripken Jr. 20.00 50.00
101 Cal Ripken Jr. 20.00 50.00
102 Nolan Ryan 10.00 25.00

2008 UD Masterpieces Framed Red

*RED 1-90: 1.2X TO 3X BASIC
*RED RC 1-90: .6X TO 1.5X BASIC
*RED SP 91-120: .6X TO 1.5X BASIC
APPX.ODDS 1:12 HOBBY
7 Evan Longoria 6.00 15.00
92 Cal Ripken Jr. 10.00 25.00
101 Cal Ripken Jr. 10.00 25.00
102 Nolan Ryan 6.00 15.00

2008 UD Masterpieces Framed Red 1

RANDOM INSERTS IN PACKS
STATED PRINT RUN 1 SER.#'d SET
NO PRICING DUE TO SCARCITY

2008 UD Masterpieces Framed Silver 25

RANDOM INSERTS IN PACKS
STATED PRINT RUN 25 SER.#'d SETS
NO PRICING DUE TO SCARCITY

2008 UD Masterpieces Captured on Canvas

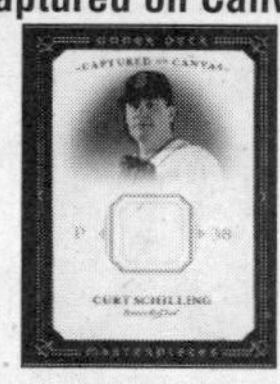

OVERALL MEM ODDS 1:12
AJ Andruw Jones 3.00 8.00
AP Albert Pujols 6.00 15.00
AR Alex Rodriguez 8.00 20.00
BE Carlos Beltran 3.00 8.00
BH Bill Hall 3.00 8.00
BM Brian McCann 3.00 8.00
BP Brandon Phillips 4.00 10.00
BR Brian Roberts 5.00 12.00
BS Ben Sheets 3.00 8.00
BU B.J. Upton 3.00 8.00
CA Matt Cain 3.00 8.00
CB Chad Billingsley 3.00 8.00
CC Chris Carpenter 3.00 8.00
CD Chris Duncan 3.00 8.00
CF Carlton Fisk 3.00 8.00
CH Cole Hamels 3.00 8.00
CJ Chipper Jones 3.00 8.00
CL Carlos Lee 3.00 8.00
CR Cal Ripken Jr. 40.00 80.00
CS C.C. Sabathia 4.00 10.00
CW Rod Carew 3.00 8.00
CZ Carlos Zambrano 3.00 8.00
DJ Derek Jeter 10.00 25.00
DL Derrek Lee 3.00 8.00
DM Don Mattingly 6.00 15.00
DO David Ortiz 3.00 8.00
DU Dan Uggla 3.00 8.00
DW Dontrelle Willis 3.00 8.00
EB Erik Bedard 3.00 8.00
EC Eric Chavez 3.00 8.00
EM Eddie Murray 3.00 8.00
FH Felix Hernandez 3.00 8.00
FR Francisco Rodriguez 3.00 8.00
FS Freddy Sanchez 3.00 8.00
FT Frank Thomas 4.00 10.00
GA Garrett Atkins 3.00 8.00
GL Tom Glavine 5.00 12.00
GM Greg Maddux 8.00 20.00
GR Ken Griffey Jr. 6.00 15.00
GS Gary Sheffield 3.00 8.00
HK Howie Kendrick 3.00 8.00
HR Hanley Ramirez 3.00 8.00
HU Torii Hunter 3.00 8.00
IR Ivan Rodriguez 3.00 8.00
JB Josh Beckett 3.00 8.00
JE Derek Jeter 10.00 25.00
JF Jeff Francoeur 3.00 8.00
JL John Lackey 3.00 8.00
JM Joe Mauer 3.00 8.00
JO Kelly Johnson 3.00 8.00
JP Jake Peavy 3.00 8.00
JR Jose Reyes 4.00 10.00
JS Johan Santana 3.00 8.00
JT Jim Thome 3.00 8.00
JV Jason Varitek 5.00 12.00
JW Jered Weaver 3.00 8.00
KG Khalil Greene 3.00 8.00
KJ Kenji Johjima 3.00 8.00
KY Kevin Youkilis 3.00 8.00
LB Lance Berkman 3.00 8.00
MC Miguel Cabrera 3.00 8.00
MM Mark Mulder 3.00 8.00
MO Justin Morneau 3.00 8.00
MR Manny Ramirez 4.00 10.00
MT Mark Teixeira 3.00 8.00
MY Michael Young 3.00 8.00
NM Nick Markakis 6.00 15.00
NR Nolan Ryan 15.00 40.00
PA Jonathan Papelbon 4.00 10.00
PF Prince Fielder 3.00 8.00
PM Pedro Martinez 3.00 8.00
PO Jorge Posada 3.00 8.00
RA Aramis Ramirez 3.00 8.00
RB Ryan Braun 10.00 25.00
RC Roger Clemens
RH Rich Harden 3.00 8.00
RJ Randy Johnson 3.00 8.00
RO Roy Oswalt 3.00 8.00
RY Nolan Ryan 15.00 40.00
RZ Ryan Zimmerman 3.00 8.00
SC Curt Schilling 3.00 8.00
TG Tony Gwynn
TH Travis Hafner 3.00 8.00
VE Justin Verlander 3.00 8.00
VG Vladimir Guerrero 3.00 8.00
VM Victor Martinez 3.00 8.00
VW Vernon Wells 3.00 8.00
WI Josh Willingham 3.00 8.00
YB Yogi Berra
YE Yunel Escobar

2008 UD Masterpieces Captured on Canvas Autographs

OVERALL AUTO ODDS 1:12
EXCH DEADLINE 9/15/2010
BH Bill Hall 4.00 10.00
BM Brian McCann 6.00 15.00
BP Brandon Phillips 8.00 20.00
BU B.J. Upton 10.00 25.00
CA Matt Cain 6.00 15.00
CB Chad Billingsley 10.00 25.00
CH Cole Hamels 40.00 80.00
CJ Chipper Jones 40.00 80.00
CL Carlos Lee 8.00 20.00
CR Cal Ripken Jr. 150.00 250.00
CW Rod Carew 10.00 25.00
DJ Derek Jeter 90.00 150.00
DL Derrek Lee 6.00 15.00
DM Don Mattingly 20.00 50.00
DU Dan Uggla 6.00 15.00
FH Felix Hernandez 8.00 20.00
GR Ken Griffey Jr. 90.00 150.00
HR Hanley Ramirez 8.00 20.00
JB Josh Beckett 10.00 25.00
JE Derek Jeter 90.00 150.00
JF Jeff Francoeur 8.00 20.00
JO Kelly Johnson 4.00 10.00
KY Kevin Youkilis EXCH 15.00 40.00
LB Lance Berkman 10.00 25.00
MC Miguel Cabrera 15.00 40.00
PA Jonathan Papelbon 12.50 30.00
RA Aramis Ramirez 6.00 15.00
RH Rich Harden 4.00 10.00
RZ Ryan Zimmerman 8.00 20.00
TG Tony Gwynn 30.00 60.00
WI Josh Willingham 6.00 15.00

2008 UD Masterpieces Captured on Canvas Patch

OVERALL MEM ODDS 1:12
PRINT RUNS B/WN 5-25 COPIES PER
NO PRICING DUE TO SCARCITY

2008 UD Masterpieces Captured on Canvas Patch Autographs

OVERALL AUTO ODDS 1:12
PRINT RUNS B/WN 5-25 COPIES PER
EXCH DEADLINE 9/15/2010
NO PRICING DUE TO SCARCITY
AP Albert Pujols/25
BE Carlos Beltran/5
BH Bill Hall/25
BM Brian McCann/25
BP Brandon Phillips/25
BR Brian Roberts/25
BS Ben Sheets/25
BU B.J. Upton/25
CA Matt Cain/25
CB Chad Billingsley/25
CC Chris Carpenter/25
CF Carlton Fisk/25
CH Cole Hamels/25
CJ Chipper Jones/25
CL Carlos Lee/25
CR Cal Ripken Jr./25
CS C.C. Sabathia/25
CW Rod Carew/25
CZ Carlos Zambrano/25
DL Derrek Lee/25
DM Don Mattingly/25
DO David Ortiz/25
DU Dan Uggla/25
DW Dontrelle Willis/25
EB Erik Bedard/25
EC Eric Chavez/25
EM Eddie Murray/25
FR Francisco Rodriguez/25
FT Frank Thomas/25
GA Garrett Atkins/25
GM Greg Maddux/25
GS Gary Sheffield/25
HR Hanley Ramirez/25
HU Torii Hunter/25
IR Ivan Rodriguez/25
JB Josh Beckett/25
JE Derek Jeter/25
JF Jeff Francoeur/25
JL John Lackey/25
JM Joe Mauer/25
JO Kelly Johnson/25
JP Jake Peavy/25
JV Jason Varitek/25
JW Jered Weaver/25
KG Khalil Greene/5
KJ Kenji Johjima/5
LB Lance Berkman/25
MC Miguel Cabrera/25
MM Mark Mulder/5
MR Manny Ramirez/5
MT Mark Teixeira/25
NR Nolan Ryan/10
PA Jonathan Papelbon/10
PF Prince Fielder/25
PM Pedro Martinez/25
RA Aramis Ramirez/25
RB Ryan Braun/25
RH Rich Harden/25
RJ Randy Johnson/25
RO Roy Oswalt/25
RY Nolan Ryan/25
RZ Ryan Zimmerman/10
SC Curt Schilling/25
TG Tony Gwynn/25
TH Travis Hafner/25
VE Justin Verlander/25
VW Vernon Wells/25
YB Yogi Berra/25
YE Yunel Escobar/25

2008 UD Masterpieces Stroke of Genius Signatures

OVERALL AUTO ODDS 1:12
EXCH DEADLINE 9/15/2010
AE Andre Ethier 5.00 12.00
AG Adrian Gonzalez 3.00 8.00
AL Adam LaRoche 3.00 8.00
AR Aramis Ramirez 6.00 15.00
BC Clay Buchholz 8.00 20.00
BH Bill Hall 4.00 10.00
BM Brian McCann 10.00 25.00
BP Brandon Phillips 5.00 12.00
BS Bill Skowron 6.00 15.00
BU B.J. Upton 10.00 25.00
CB Chad Billingsley 6.00 15.00
CF Chone Figgins 4.00 10.00
CH Cole Hamels 20.00 50.00
CR Cal Ripken Jr. 100.00 175.00
CY Chris B. Young 6.00 15.00
DC Daniel Cabrera 3.00 8.00
EE Edwin Encarnacion 3.00 8.00
EL Evan Longoria 60.00 120.00
EV Edinson Volquez 8.00 20.00
FC Fausto Carmona 4.00 10.00
GF Gavin Floyd 5.00 12.00
GJ Geoff Jenkins 10.00 25.00
GL Tom Glavine
GN Graig Nettles 5.00 12.00
GP Glen Perkins 3.00 8.00
HR Hanley Ramirez 10.00 25.00
HU Chin-Lung Hu 30.00 60.00
IA Ian Kinsler 5.00 12.00
JA James Loney 8.00 20.00
JB Joe Blanton 3.00 8.00
JC Jack Cust 3.00 8.00
JF Jeff Francoeur
JG Jeremy Guthrie 10.00 25.00
JK John Kruk 10.00 25.00
JN Joe Nathan 4.00 10.00
JO Josh Hamilton 15.00 40.00
JT J.R. Towles 6.00 15.00
JW Josh Willingham 4.00 10.00
KJ Kelly Johnson 3.00 8.00
KY Kevin Youkilis 8.00 20.00
LE Jon Lester 20.00 50.00
LH Luke Hochevar 5.00 12.00
MA John Maine 4.00 10.00
MC Matt Cain 4.00 10.00
MK Matt Kemp 10.00 25.00
MS Max Scherzer 10.00 25.00
NA Nick Adenhart 5.00 12.00
NB Nick Blackburn 8.00 20.00
NL Noah Lowry 3.00 8.00
NS Nick Swisher 5.00 12.00
PK Paul Konerko 6.00 15.00
RH Rich Hill 3.00 8.00
RM Russell Martin EXCH 20.00 50.00
TG Tom Gorzelanny 3.00 8.00
WB Wladimir Balentien 8.00 20.00
XN Xavier Nady 5.00 12.00
YG Yovani Gallardo 6.00 15.00

2001 Ultimate Collection

This product was released in mid-January 2002, and featured a 120-card base set that was broken up into tiers as follows: 90 Base Veterans, 10 Prospects numbered to 1000, 10 Prospects numbered to 750, and 10 Prospects numbered to 250. Exchange cards were seeded into packs for signed cards of Mark Prior and Mark Teixiera.

COMMON CARD (1-90) 1.50 4.00
COMMON CARD (91-100) 4.00 10.00
COMMON (101-110) 4.00 10.00
COMMON CARD (111-120) 6.00 15.00
1 Troy Glaus 1.50 4.00
2 Darin Erstad 1.50 4.00
3 Jason Giambi 1.50 4.00
4 Barry Zito 1.50 4.00
5 Tim Hudson 1.50 4.00
6 Miguel Tejada 1.50 4.00
7 Carlos Delgado 1.50 4.00
8 Shannon Stewart 1.50 4.00
9 Greg Vaughn 1.50 4.00
10 Toby Hall 1.50 4.00
11 Roberto Alomar 1.50 4.00
12 Juan Gonzalez 1.50 4.00
13 Jim Thome 1.50 4.00
14 Edgar Martinez 1.50 4.00
15 Freddy Garcia 1.50 4.00
16 Bret Boone 1.50 4.00
17 Kazuhiro Sasaki 1.50 4.00
18 Cal Ripken 8.00 20.00
19 Tim Raines Jr. 1.50 4.00
20 Alex Rodriguez 4.00 10.00
21 Ivan Rodriguez 1.50 4.00
22 Rafael Palmeiro 1.50 4.00
23 Pedro Martinez 1.50 4.00
24 Nomar Garciaparra 4.00 10.00
25 Manny Ramirez Sox 1.50 4.00
26 Hideo Nomo 2.50 6.00
27 Mike Sweeney 1.50 4.00
28 Carlos Beltran 1.50 4.00
29 Tony Clark 1.50 4.00
30 Dean Palmer 1.50 4.00
31 Doug Mientkiewicz 1.50 4.00
32 Cristian Guzman 1.50 4.00
33 Corey Koskie 1.50 4.00
34 Frank Thomas 2.50 6.00
35 Magglio Ordonez 1.50 4.00
36 Jose Canseco 1.50 4.00
37 Roger Clemens 5.00 12.00
38 Derek Jeter 6.00 15.00
39 Bernie Williams 1.50 4.00
40 Mike Mussina 1.50 4.00
41 Tino Martinez 1.50 4.00
42 Jeff Bagwell 1.50 4.00
43 Lance Berkman 1.50 4.00
44 Roy Oswalt 2.50 6.00
45 Chipper Jones 2.50 6.00
46 Greg Maddux 4.00 10.00
47 Andruw Jones 1.50 4.00
48 Tom Glavine 1.50 4.00
49 Richie Sexson 1.50 4.00
50 Jeromy Burnitz 1.50 4.00
51 Ben Sheets 1.50 4.00
52 Mark McGwire 6.00 15.00
53 Matt Morris 1.50 4.00
54 Jim Edmonds 1.50 4.00
55 J.D. Drew 1.50 4.00
56 Sammy Sosa 2.50 6.00
57 Fred McGriff 1.50 4.00
58 Kerry Wood 1.50 4.00
59 Randy Johnson 2.50 6.00
60 Luis Gonzalez 1.50 4.00
61 Curt Schilling 1.50 4.00
62 Shawn Green 1.50 4.00
63 Kevin Brown 1.50 4.00
64 Gary Sheffield 1.50 4.00
65 Vladimir Guerrero 2.50 6.00
66 Barry Bonds 6.00 15.00
67 Jeff Kent 1.50 4.00
68 Rich Aurilia 1.50 4.00
69 Cliff Floyd 1.50 4.00
70 Charles Johnson 1.50 4.00
71 Josh Beckett 1.50 4.00
72 Mike Piazza 4.00 10.00
73 Edgardo Alfonzo 1.50 4.00
74 Robin Ventura 1.50 4.00
75 Tony Gwynn 3.00 8.00
76 Ryan Klesko 1.50 4.00
77 Phil Nevin 1.50 4.00
78 Scott Rolen 1.50 4.00
79 Bobby Abreu 1.50 4.00
80 Jimmy Rollins 1.50 4.00
81 Brian Giles 1.50 4.00
82 Jason Kendall 1.50 4.00
83 Aramis Ramirez 1.50 4.00
84 Ken Griffey Jr. 4.00 10.00
85 Adam Dunn 1.50 4.00
86 Sean Casey 1.50 4.00
87 Barry Larkin 1.50 4.00
88 Larry Walker 1.50 4.00
89 Mike Hampton 1.50 4.00
90 Todd Helton 1.50 4.00
91 Ken Harvey T1 4.00 10.00
92 Bill Ortega T1 RC 4.00 10.00
93 Juan Diaz T1 RC 4.00 10.00
94 Greg Miller T1 RC 4.00 10.00
95 Brandon Berger T1 RC 4.00 10.00
96 Brandon Lyon T1 RC 4.00 10.00
97 Jay Gibbons T1 RC 6.00 15.00
98 Rob Mackowiak T1 RC 6.00 15.00
99 Erick Almonte T1 RC 4.00 10.00
100 J.Middlebrook T1 RC 4.00 10.00
101 Johnny Estrada T2 RC 6.00 15.00
102 Juan Uribe T2 RC 6.00 15.00
103 Travis Hafner T2 RC 12.50 30.00
104 M.Ensberg T2 RC 6.00 15.00
105 Mike Rivera T2 RC 4.00 10.00
106 Josh Towers T2 RC 6.00 15.00
107 A.Hernandez T2 RC 4.00 10.00
108 Rafael Soriano T2 RC 4.00 10.00
109 Jackson Melian T2 RC 4.00 10.00
110 Wilkin Ruan T2 RC 4.00 10.00
111 Albert Pujols T3 RC 500.00 700.00
112 T.Shinjo T3 RC 10.00 25.00
113 B.Duckworth T3 RC 6.00 15.00
114 Juan Cruz T3 RC 6.00 15.00
115 D.Brazelton T3 RC 6.00 15.00
116 Mark Prior T3 AU RC 125.00 200.00
117 Mark Teixeira T3 AU RC 150.00 250.00
118 Wilson Betemit T3 RC 10.00 25.00
119 Bud Smith T3 RC 6.00 15.00
120 I.Suzuki T3 AU RC 1800.00 2200.00

2001 Ultimate Collection Game Jersey

These cards feature swatches of actual game-used jerseys from various major league stars. Game Jersey cards (including Copper, Silver and Gold parallel versions) were cumulatively issued into packs at 1:2. Each card is serial-numbered to 150.

COPPER RANDOM INSERTS IN PACKS
COPPER PRINT RUN 24 SERIAL #'d SETS
NO COPPER PRICING DUE TO SCARCITY
GOLD RANDOM INSERTS IN PACKS
GOLD PRINT RUN 15 SERIAL #'d SETS
NO GOLD PRICING DUE TO SCARCITY
SILVER RANDOM INSERTS IN PACKS
SILVER PRINT RUN 20 SERIAL #'d SETS
NO SILVER PRICING DUE TO SCARCITY
UAJ Andruw Jones 10.00 25.00
UAP Albert Pujols 60.00 120.00
UAR Alex Rodriguez 10.00 25.00
UBB Barry Bonds 15.00 40.00
UBW Bernie Williams 10.00 25.00
UCD Carlos Delgado 6.00 15.00
UCJ Chipper Jones 10.00 25.00
UCR Cal Ripken 20.00 50.00
UDE Darin Erstad 6.00 15.00
UFT Frank Thomas 10.00 25.00
UGM Greg Maddux 10.00 25.00
UGS Gary Sheffield 6.00 15.00
UIR Ivan Rodriguez 10.00 25.00
UJAG Jason Giambi 6.00 15.00
UJB Jeff Bagwell 10.00 25.00
UJC Jose Canseco 10.00 25.00
UJG Juan Gonzalez 6.00 15.00
UKG Ken Griffey Jr. 10.00 25.00
ULG Luis Gonzalez 6.00 15.00
ULW Larry Walker 6.00 15.00
UMO Magglio Ordonez 6.00 15.00
UMP Mike Piazza 10.00 25.00
URA Roberto Alomar 10.00 25.00
URC Roger Clemens 10.00 25.00
URJ Randy Johnson 10.00 25.00
USG Shawn Green 6.00 15.00
USR Scott Rolen 10.00 25.00
USS Sammy Sosa 10.00 25.00
UTG Tony Gwynn 10.00 25.00
UTH Todd Helton 10.00 25.00

2001 Ultimate Collection Ichiro Ball

This five-card insert set features game-used ball cards from the 2001 Rookie of the Year, Ichiro Suzuki. There is a Base, Copper, Silver, Gold and Autographed version. Card backs carry a "BB" prefix. Print runs are listed in our checklist. The signed Ichiro Ball card was available via an exchange card seeded into packs. The redemption date for the exchange card was February, 25th, 2004.

BI Ichiro Suzuki AU/25

IA Ichiro Suzuki SP 40.00 80.00
IG Ichiro Suzuki Gold/25
IH I.Suzuki Copper/150 60.00 120.00
IS I.Suzuki Silver/50 75.00 150.00

2001 Ultimate Collection Ichiro Base

This five-card insert set features game-used base cards from the 2001 Rookie of the Year, Ichiro Suzuki. There is a Base, Copper, Silver, Gold and Autographed version. Card backs carry a "U" preifx. Print runs are listed in our checklist. The autograph card was seeded into packs in the form of an exchange card of which carried a redemption deadline of 02/25/04.

SUI Ichiro Suzuki AU/25
UIA Ichiro Suzuki 12.50 30.00
UIC Ichiro Suzuki Copper/150 50.00 100.00
UIG Ichiro Suzuki Gold/25
UIS Ichiro Suzuki Silver/50 60.00 120.00

2001 Ultimate Collection Ichiro Bat

This five-card insert set features game-used bat cards from the 2001 Rookie of the Year, Ichiro Suzuki. There is a Base, Copper, Silver, Gold and Autographed version. Card backs carry a "B" prefix. Print runs are listed in our checklist. The autographed card was seeded into packs in the form of an exchange card of which carried a redemption deadline of 02/25/04.

BIA I.Suzuki Away SP 40.00 80.00
BIC I.Suzuki Home SP 50.00 100.00
BIG I.Suzuki Gold/200 60.00 120.00
BIS I.Suzuki Silver/250 50.00 100.00
SBI Ichiro Suzuki AU/50 1200.00 1500.00

2001 Ultimate Collection Ichiro Batting Glove

This two-card insert set features game-used batting glove cards from the 2001 Rookie of the Year, Ichiro Suzuki. There are two versions available, Base and Gold. Cards carry a "BG" prefix. Print runs are listed in our checklist.

BGI Ichiro Suzuki/75 175.00 300.00
BGIG Ichiro Suzuki Gold/25

2001 Ultimate Collection Ichiro Fielders Glove

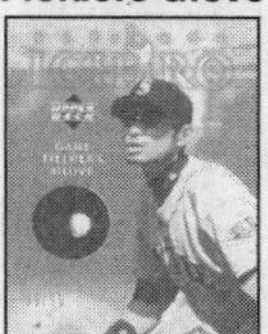

Randomly inserted into Ultimate Collection packs, these two cards feature swatches of Ichiro Suzuki gloves. The cards are printed to different amounts and we have listed those cards in our checklist.

FGI Ichiro Suzuki/75 175.00 300.00
FGIG Ichiro Suzuki Gold/25

2001 Ultimate Collection Ichiro Jersey

This five-card insert set features game-used jersey cards from the 2001 Rookie of the Year, Ichiro Suzuki. There is a Base, Copper, Silver, Gold and Autographed version. Card backs carry a "J" prefix. Print runs listed in our checklist. The autographed card was seeded into packs in the form of an exchange card of which carried a redemption deadline of 02/25/04.

JIA Ichiro Suzuki Away 20.00 50.00
JIG I.Suzuki Gold/200 60.00 120.00
JIH I.Suzuki Home SP 40.00 80.00
JIS I.Suzuki Silver/250 50.00 100.00
SJI Ichiro Suzuki AU/50 1000.00 1400.00

2001 Ultimate Collection Magic Numbers Game Jersey

These cards feature swatches of actual game-used jerseys from various major league stars. They were issued into packs at 1:2. Card backs carry a "MN" prefix.

GAME JERSEY CUMULATIVE ODDS 1:2
STATED PRINT RUN 150 SERIAL #'d SETS
*RED: .75X TO 2X BASIC MAGIC NUMBERS
RED RANDOM INSERTS IN PACKS
RED PRINT RUN 30 SERIAL #'d SETS
NO RED PUJOLS PRICING AVAILABLE
COPPER RANDOM INSERTS IN PACKS
COPPER PRINT RUN 24 SERIAL #'d SETS
NO COPPER PRICING DUE TO SCARCITY
SILVER RANDOM INSERTS IN PACKS
SILVER PRINT RUN 20 SERIAL #'d SETS
NO SILVER PRICING DUE TO SCARCITY
GOLD RANDOM INSERTS IN PACKS
GOLD PRINT RUN 15 SERIAL #'d SETS
NO GOLD PRICING DUE TO SCARCITY
MNG Tony Gwynn 10.00 25.00
MNAJ Andruw Jones 10.00 25.00
MNAP Albert Pujols 75.00 125.00
MNAR Alex Rodriguez 10.00 25.00
MNBB Barry Bonds 15.00 40.00
MNBW Bernie Williams 10.00 25.00
MNCD Carlos Delgado 6.00 15.00
MNCJ Chipper Jones 10.00 25.00
MNCR Cal Ripken 20.00 50.00
MNDE Darin Erstad 6.00 15.00
MNFT Frank Thomas 10.00 25.00
MNGM Greg Maddux 10.00 25.00
MNGS Gary Sheffield 6.00 15.00
MNIR Ivan Rodriguez 10.00 25.00
MNJAG Jason Giambi 6.00 15.00
MNJB Jeff Bagwell 10.00 25.00
MNJC Jose Canseco 10.00 25.00
MNJG Juan Gonzalez 6.00 15.00
MNKG Ken Griffey Jr. 10.00 25.00
MNLG Luis Gonzalez 6.00 15.00
MNLW Larry Walker 6.00 15.00
MNMO Magglio Ordonez 6.00 15.00
MNMP Mike Piazza 10.00 25.00
MNRA Roberto Alomar 10.00 25.00
MNRC Roger Clemens 10.00 25.00
MNRJ Randy Johnson 10.00 25.00
MNSG Shawn Green 6.00 15.00
MNSR Scott Rolen 10.00 25.00
MNSS Sammy Sosa 10.00 25.00
MNTH Todd Helton 10.00 25.00

2001 Ultimate Collection Signatures

These cards feature authentic autographs from various major league stars. They were issued into packs at 1:4. Card backs carry the player's initials as numbering. Please note that there were only 150 sets produced. The following players cards were seeded into packs as exchange cards with a redemption deadline of 02/25/04: Cal Ripken, Edgar Martinez, Ken Griffey Jr. and Tom Glavine.

*COPPER: .75X TO 1.5X BASIC SIG
COPPER PRINT RUN 70 SERIAL #'d SETS
GOLD PRINT RUN 15 SERIAL #'d SETS
NO GOLD PRICING DUE TO SCARCITY
SILVER PRINT RUN 24 SERIAL #'d SETS
NO SILVER PRICING DUE TO SCARCITY
AR Alex Rodriguez 60.00 120.00
BAB Barry Bonds 100.00 175.00
CD Carlos Delgado 10.00 25.00
CF Carlton Fisk 15.00 40.00
CR Cal Ripken 75.00 150.00
DS Duke Snider 15.00 40.00
EB Ernie Banks 20.00 50.00
EM Edgar Martinez 20.00 50.00
FT Frank Thomas 20.00 50.00
GS Gary Sheffield 15.00 40.00
IR Ivan Rodriguez 20.00 50.00
JAG Jason Giambi 10.00 25.00
JT Jim Thome 20.00 50.00
KG Ken Griffey Jr. 60.00 120.00
KP Kirby Puckett 50.00 100.00
LG Luis Gonzalez 10.00 25.00
RA Roberto Alomar 15.00 40.00
RC Roger Clemens 50.00 100.00
RK Ryan Klesko 10.00 25.00
RY Robin Yount 30.00 60.00
SK Sandy Koufax 200.00 350.00
SS Sammy Sosa 50.00 100.00
TG Tony Gwynn 40.00 80.00
TGL Tom Glavine 20.00 50.00
TP Tony Perez 10.00 25.00
TS Tom Seaver 15.00 40.00

2002 Ultimate Collection

This 120 card set was released in late December, 2002. These cards were issued in five card packs which came four packs to a box and four boxes to a case with an SRP of approximately $100 per pack. Card numbered 61 through 120 featured Rookie Cards with cards numbered 110 through 120 being autographed by the player. The cards between 61 and 110 were issued to a stated print run of 500 serial numbered sets while cards numbered 111 through 113 were issued to a stated print run of 300 serial numbered sets and cards numbered 114 through 120 were issued to a stated print run of 550 serial numbered sets. One hundred Mark McGwire Priority Signing exchange cards were randomly seeded in packs (at a believed odds of 1:1000 packs). The bearer of the card was allowed to send in one item of his or her choice to Upper Deck for McGwire to sign.

COMMON CARD (1-60) 1.50 4.00
COMMON CARD (61-110) 4.00 10.00
61-110 PRINT RUN 550 SERIAL #'d SETS
COMMON CARD (111-113) 6.00 15.00
COMMON CARD (114-120) 6.00 15.00
1 Troy Glaus 1.50 4.00
2 Luis Gonzalez 1.50 4.00
3 Curt Schilling 1.50 4.00
4 Randy Johnson 2.50 6.00
5 Andruw Jones 1.50 4.00
6 Greg Maddux 4.00 10.00
7 Chipper Jones 2.50 6.00
8 Gary Sheffield 1.50 4.00
9 Cal Ripken 8.00 20.00
10 Manny Ramirez 1.50 4.00
11 Pedro Martinez 1.50 4.00
12 Nomar Garciaparra 4.00 10.00
13 Sammy Sosa 2.50 6.00
14 Kerry Wood 1.50 4.00
15 Mark Prior 2.50 6.00
16 Magglio Ordonez 1.50 4.00
17 Frank Thomas 2.50 6.00
18 Adam Dunn 1.50 4.00
19 Ken Griffey Jr. 4.00 10.00
20 Jim Thome 1.50 4.00
21 Larry Walker 1.50 4.00
22 Todd Helton 1.50 4.00
23 Nolan Ryan 6.00 15.00
24 Jeff Bagwell 1.50 4.00
25 Roy Oswalt 1.50 4.00
26 Lance Berkman 1.50 4.00
27 Mike Sweeney 1.50 4.00
28 Shawn Green 1.50 4.00
29 Hideo Nomo 2.50 6.00
30 Torii Hunter 1.50 4.00
31 Vladimir Guerrero 2.50 6.00
32 Tom Seaver 1.50 4.00
33 Mike Piazza 4.00 10.00
34 Roberto Alomar 1.50 4.00
35 Derek Jeter 6.00 15.00
36 Alfonso Soriano 1.50 4.00
37 Jason Giambi 1.50 4.00
38 Roger Clemens 5.00 12.00
39 Mike Mussina 1.50 4.00
40 Bernie Williams 1.50 4.00
41 Joe DiMaggio 5.00 12.00
42 Mickey Mantle 10.00 25.00
43 Miguel Tejada 1.50 4.00
44 Eric Chavez 1.50 4.00
45 Barry Zito 1.50 4.00
46 Pat Burrell 1.50 4.00
47 Jason Kendall 1.50 4.00
48 Brian Giles 1.50 4.00
49 Barry Bonds 6.00 15.00
50 Ichiro Suzuki 5.00 12.00
51 Stan Musial 4.00 10.00
52 J.D. Drew 1.50 4.00
53 Scott Rolen 1.50 4.00
54 Albert Pujols 5.00 12.00
55 Mark McGwire 6.00 15.00
56 Alex Rodriguez 4.00 10.00
57 Ivan Rodriguez 1.50 4.00
58 Juan Gonzalez 1.50 4.00
59 Rafael Palmeiro 1.50 4.00
60 Carlos Delgado 1.50 4.00
61 Jose Valverde UR RC 4.00 10.00
62 Doug Devore UR RC 4.00 10.00
63 John Ennis UR RC 4.00 10.00
64 Joey Dawley UR RC 4.00 10.00
65 Trey Hodges UR RC 4.00 10.00
66 Mike Mahoney UR 4.00 10.00
67 Aaron Cook UR RC 4.00 10.00
68 Rene Reyes UR RC 4.00 10.00
69 Mark Corey UR RC 4.00 10.00
70 Hansel Izquierdo UR RC 4.00 10.00
71 Brandon Puffer UR RC 4.00 10.00
72 Jeriome Robertson UR RC 4.00 10.00
73 Jose Diaz UR RC 4.00 10.00
74 David Ross UR RC 4.00 10.00
75 Jayson Durocher UR RC 4.00 10.00
76 Eric Good UR RC 4.00 10.00
77 Satoru Komiyama UR RC 4.00 10.00
78 Tyler Yates UR RC 4.00 10.00
79 Eric Junge UR RC 4.00 10.00
80 Anderson Machado UR RC 4.00 10.00
81 Adrian Burnside UR RC 4.00 10.00
82 Ben Howard UR RC 4.00 10.00
83 Clay Condrey UR RC 4.00 10.00
84 Nelson Castro UR RC 4.00 10.00
85 So Taguchi UR RC 6.00 15.00
86 Mike Crudale UR RC 4.00 10.00
87 Scotty Layfield UR RC 4.00 10.00
88 Steve Bechler UR RC 4.00 10.00
89 Travis Driskill UR RC 4.00 10.00
90 Howie Clark UR RC 4.00 10.00
91 Josh Hancock UR RC 5.00 12.00
92 Jorge De La Rosa UR RC 4.00 10.00
93 Anastacio Martinez UR RC 4.00 10.00
94 Brian Tallet UR RC 4.00 10.00
95 Carl Sadler UR RC 4.00 10.00
96 Cliff Lee UR RC 6.00 15.00
97 Josh Bard UR RC 4.00 10.00
98 Wes Obermueller UR RC 4.00 10.00
99 Juan Brito UR RC 4.00 10.00
100 Aaron Guiel UR RC 4.00 10.00
101 Jeremy Hill UR RC 4.00 10.00
102 Kevin Frederick UR RC 4.00 10.00
103 Nate Field UR RC 4.00 10.00
104 Julio Mateo UR RC 4.00 10.00
105 Chris Snelling UR RC 5.00 12.00
106 Felix Escalona UR RC 4.00 10.00
107 Reynaldo Garcia UR RC 4.00 10.00
108 Mike Smith UR RC 4.00 10.00
109 Ken Huckaby UR RC 4.00 10.00
110 Kevin Cash UR RC 4.00 10.00
111 Kazuhisa Ishii UR AU RC 15.00 40.00
112 Fr. Sanchez UR AU RC 15.00 40.00
113 J.Simontacchi UR AU RC 6.00 15.00
114 Jorge Padilla UR AU RC 6.00 15.00
115 Kirk Saarloos UR AU RC 6.00 15.00
116 Ro. Rosario UR AU RC 6.00 15.00
117 Oliver Perez UR AU RC 15.00 40.00
118 Mi. Asencio UR AU RC 6.00 15.00
119 Fr. German UR AU RC 6.00 15.00
120 Jaime Cerda UR AU RC 6.00 15.00
MM M.McGwire Priority EXCH/100

2002 Ultimate Collection Double Barrel Action

Randomly inserted into packs, these 18 cards feature two bat "barrell" cards of the featured player. As each of these cards have a stated print run of nine or fewer cards, we have not priced these cards due to market scarcity.

BR Jeff Bagwell
Manny Ramirez/1
DG Joe DiMaggio
Ken Griffey Jr./5
DJ Carlos Delgado
Jason Giambi/2
GH Shawn Green
Todd Helton/2
GI Ken Griffey Jr.
Ichiro Suzuki/3
GJ Luis Gonzalez
Randy Johnson/1
GP Juan Gonzalez
Rafael Palmeiro/3
IM Ichiro Suzuki
Edgar Martinez/1
JJ Chipper Jones
Andruw Jones/2
JM Chipper Jones
Greg Maddux/1
RI Alex Rodriguez
Ivan Rodriguez/5
RM Alex Rodriguez
Miguel Tejada/2
RR Alex Rodriguez
Cal Ripken/9
RS Manny Ramirez
Sammy Sosa/1
SC Sammy Sosa
Fred McGriff/3
SM Sammy Sosa
Mark McGwire/1
TD Jim Thome
Carlos Delgado/3
TO Frank Thomas
Magglio Ordonez/4

2002 Ultimate Collection Game Jersey Tier 1

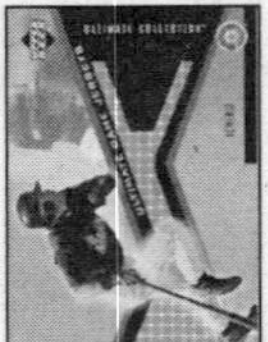

Randomly inserted into packs, these 21 cards were issued to a stated print run of 99 serial numbered sets. These cards can be differentiated from the other game jersey as they have a "JB" numbering prefix as well as featuring batting images and the swatches are on the right side.

AD Adam Dunn 6.00 15.00
AJ Andruw Jones 10.00 25.00
AR Alex Rodriguez 10.00 25.00
AS Alfonso Soriano 6.00 15.00
CJ Chipper Jones 10.00 25.00
CR Cal Ripken 15.00 40.00
IR Ivan Rodriguez 10.00 25.00
IS Ichiro Suzuki 20.00 50.00
JD Joe DiMaggio 50.00 100.00
JG Jason Giambi 6.00 15.00
KG Ken Griffey Jr. 10.00 25.00
KI Kazuhisa Ishii 10.00 25.00
MC Mark McGwire 40.00 80.00
MM Mickey Mantle 75.00 150.00
MP Mike Piazza 10.00 25.00
MR Manny Ramirez 10.00 25.00
PM Pedro Martinez 10.00 25.00
PR Mark Prior 6.00 15.00
RC Roger Clemens 10.00 25.00
RJ Randy Johnson 10.00 25.00
SS Sammy Sosa 10.00 25.00

2002 Ultimate Collection Game Jersey Tier 1 Gold

Randomly inserted into packs, this is a parallel to the Tier 1 set. These cards have a stated print run of 50 serial numbered sets.

*TIER 1 GOLD: .75X TO 1.5X TIER 1 JSY

2002 Ultimate Collection Game Jersey Tier 2

Randomly inserted into packs, these 21 cards were issued to a stated print run of 99 serial numbered sets. These cards can be differentiated from the other game jersey as they have a "JF" numbering prefix as well as featuring fielding images and the swatches are on the left side.

*TIER 2: .4X TO 1X TIER 1 JSY

2002 Ultimate Collection Game Jersey Tier 2 Gold

Randomly inserted into packs, this is a parallel to the Tier 1 set. These cards have a stated print run of 30 serial numbered sets.

*TIER 2 GOLD: .75X TO 2X TIER JSY

2002 Ultimate Collection Game Jersey Tier 3

Randomly inserted into packs, these 21 cards were issued to a stated print run of 199 serial numbered sets. These cards can be differentiated from the other game jersey as they have a "JP" numbering prefix as well as featuring profile images and the swatches are on the right side.

*TIER 3: .3X TO .8X TIER 1 JSY

2002 Ultimate Collection Game Jersey Tier 4

Randomly inserted into packs, these 21 cards were issued to a stated print run of 199 serial numbered sets. These cards can be differentiated from the other game jersey as they have a "JR" numbering prefix as well as featuring running images and the swatches are on the left side.

*TIER 4: .3X TO .8X TIER 1 JSY

2002 Ultimate Collection Patch Card

Randomly inserted into packs, these 10 cards feature game-used patch swatched of the feature player. Each of these cards were issued to a stated print run of 100 serial numbered sets.

*3-COLOR PATCH: 1X TO 1.5X HI COLUMN
CJ Chipper Jones 20.00 50.00
IR Ivan Rodriguez 20.00 50.00
IS Ichiro Suzuki 75.00 150.00
KI Kazuhisa Ishii 20.00 50.00
LG Luis Gonzalez 15.00 40.00
MM Mark McGwire 75.00 150.00
MP Mark Prior 12.50 30.00
SG Shawn Green 15.00 40.00
SS Sammy Sosa 20.00 50.00
TH Todd Helton 20.00 50.00

2002 Ultimate Collection Patch Card Double

Randomly inserted into packs, these nine cards feature two game-used patch swatches of the featured players and were printed to a stated print run of 100 serial numbered sets.

DE J.D. Drew 20.00 50.00
Jim Edmonds
GC Jason Giambi 50.00 100.00
Roger Clemens
IG Ichiro Suzuki 75.00 150.00
Ken Griffey Jr.
JS Randy Johnson 40.00 80.00
Curt Schilling
MG Greg Maddux 50.00 100.00
Tom Glavine
MS Mark McGwire 125.00 200.00
Sammy Sosa
PA Mike Piazza 50.00 100.00
Roberto Alomar
RG Alex Rodriguez 50.00 100.00
Juan Gonzalez
RM Manny Ramirez 40.00 80.00
Pedro Martinez

2002 Ultimate Collection Patch Card Double Gold

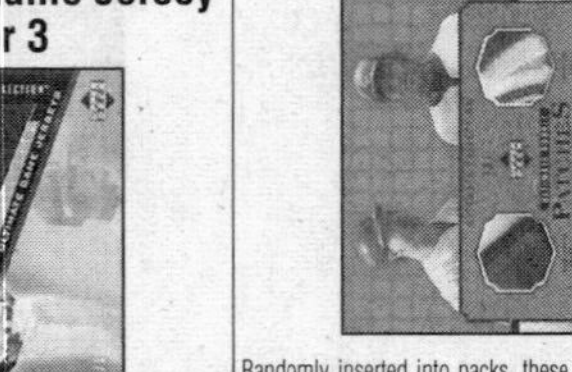

Randomly inserted into packs, these cards parallel the Patch Card Double insert set are were issued to a stated print run of 50 serial numbered sets. Please note that a card featuring Mickey Mantle and Joe DiMaggio was issued to a stated print run of 13 serial numbered sets and is not priced due to market scarcity.

*GOLD: .75X TO 1.5X BASIC PATCH
MD Mickey Mantle
Joe DiMaggio/13

2002 Ultimate Collection Signatures Tier 1

Randomly inserted into packs, these 19 cards feature signatures of some of the leading players in baseball. As the cards are signed to a differing amount of signatures, we have notated that information next to their name in our checklist.

GOLD PRINT RUN 25 SERIAL #'d SETS
NO GOLD PRICING DUE TO SCARCITY
AD1 Adam Dunn/125 20.00 50.00
AR1 Alex Rodriguez/329 60.00 120.00
BG1 Brian Giles/220 8.00 20.00
BZ1 Barry Zito/199 12.50 30.00
CD1 Carlos Delgado/95 12.50 30.00
CR1 Cal Ripken/75 100.00 200.00
GS1 Gary Sheffield/95 20.00 50.00
JD1 J.D. Drew/220 8.00 20.00
JG1 Jason Giambi/295 8.00 20.00
JK1 Jason Kendall/220 8.00 20.00
JT1 Jim Thome/90 30.00 60.00
KG1 Ken Griffey Jr./195 60.00 120.00
LB1 Lance Berkman/179 12.50 30.00
LG1 Luis Gonzalez/199 8.00 20.00
MP1 Mark Prior/160 10.00 25.00
PB1 Pat Burrell/95 12.50 30.00
RA1 Roberto Alomar/155 12.50 30.00
RC1 Roger Clemens/320 50.00 100.00
SR1 Scott Rolen/160 12.50 30.00

2002 Ultimate Collection Signatures Tier 2

Randomly inserted into packs, these 16 cards feature signatures of some of the leading players in baseball. As the cards are signed to a differing amount of signatures, we have notated that information next to their name in our checklist.

GOLD PRINT RUN 10 SERIAL #'d SETS
NO GOLD PRICING DUE TO SCARCITY
AJ2 Andruw Jones/51 30.00 60.00
AR2 Alex Rodriguez/75 75.00 150.00
BZ2 Barry Zito/70 20.00 50.00
DS2 Duke Snider/51 30.00 60.00
FT2 Frank Thomas/51 40.00 80.00
JB2 Jeff Bagwell/51 40.00 80.00
JG2 Jason Giambi/50 20.00 50.00
KG2 Ken Griffey Jr./30 75.00 150.00
KP2 Kirby Puckett/75 50.00 100.00
KW2 Kerry Wood/51 30.00 60.00
LB2 Lance Berkman/85 20.00 50.00
LG2 Luis Gonzalez/70 12.50 30.00
MP2 Mark Prior/60 15.00 40.00
SR2 Scott Rolen/60 30.00 60.00
TG2 Tony Gwynn/51 50.00 100.00
TH2 Todd Helton/51 30.00 60.00

2002 Ultimate Collection Signed Excellence

Randomly inserted into packs, these 20 cards feature signed cards of Upper Deck Spokespeople. Most of the cards were issued to a stated print run of 100 or fewer cards. Mark McGwire added a 583 HR notation to some of his signatures.

*MCGWIRE 583 HR: 1X TO 1.5X HI COLUMN
I1 Ichiro Suzuki/56 400.00 500.00
I2 Ichiro Suzuki/51 400.00 500.00
I3 Ichiro Suzuki/23
I4 Ichiro Suzuki/12
I5 Ichiro Suzuki Batting 400.00 500.00
I6 Ichiro Suzuki Throwing 400.00 500.00
MM1 Mark McGwire/70 175.00 300.00
MM2 Mark McGwire/65 175.00 300.00
MM3 Mark McGwire A's/49 175.00 300.00
MM4 Mark McGwire/25
MM5 Mark McGwire Standing 175.00 300.00
MM6 Mark McGwire Waving 175.00 300.00
MM7 Mark McGwire A's Fldg 175.00 300.00
SS1 Sammy Sosa/66 50.00 100.00
SS2 Sammy Sosa/64 50.00 100.00
SS3 Sammy Sosa/54 50.00 100.00
SS4 Sammy Sosa/21
SS5 Sammy Sosa Running 50.00 100.00
SS6 Sammy Sosa Holding Bat 50.00 100.00
SS7 Sammy Sosa Throwing 50.00 100.00

2002 Ultimate Collection Signed Excellence Gold

Randomly inserted into packs, these cards partially parallel the Signed Excellence insert set and were printed to a stated print run of 1 serial numbered sets. Due to market scarcity, no pricing is provided for these cards.

I4 Ichiro Suzuki
MM4 Mark McGwire
SS4 Sammy Sosa

2003 Ultimate Collection

This 180 card set was released in very early January, 2004. The set was issued in four card packs with an $100 SRP which came four packs to a box and four boxes to a case. Cards numbered 1-84 feature veterans and were issued to a stated print run of 850 serial numbered sets. Cards 85-117 are Tier 1 Rookie Cards and were issued to a stated print run of 625 serial numbered sets. Cards numbered 118 through 140 are Tier 2 Rookie Cards and were issued to a stated print run of 399 serial numbered sets. Cards numbered 141 through 158 are Tier 3 Rookie Cards and were issued to a stated print run of 250 serial numbered sets. Cards numbered 159 through 168 are Tier 4 Rookie Cards and were issued to a stated print run of 100 serial numbered sets. Cards numbered 169 through 180 were each signed and inserted into packs at slightly different odds.

COMMON CARD (1-84) 1.25 3.00
1-84 STATED ODDS TWO PER PACK
COMMON CARD (85-117) 2.00 5.00
COMMON CARD (118-140) 2.00 5.00
118-140 PRINT RUN 399 SERIAL #'d SETS
COMMON CARD (141-158) 2.50 6.00
COMMON CARD (159-168) 5.00 12.00
159-168 PRINT RUN 100 SERIAL #'d SETS
85-168 STATED ODDS ONE PER PACK
COMMON CARD (169-174) 6.00 15.00
169-174 AND ULT.SIG.OVERALL ODDS 1:4
COMMON CARD (175-180) 6.00 15.00
175-180 AND BUYBACK OVERALL ODDS 1:8
169-180 PRINT RUN 250 SERIAL #'d SETS
MATSUI PART LIVE/ PART EXCH
EXCHANGE DEADLINE 12/17/06
1 Ichiro Suzuki 4.00 10.00
2 Ken Griffey Jr. 3.00 8.00
3 Sammy Sosa 2.00 5.00
4 Jason Giambi 1.25 3.00
5 Mike Piazza 3.00 8.00
6 Derek Jeter 4.00 10.00
7 Randy Johnson 2.00 5.00
8 Barry Bonds 5.00 12.00
9 Carlos Delgado 1.25 3.00
10 Mark Prior 2.00 5.00
11 Vladimir Guerrero 2.00 5.00
12 Alfonso Soriano 1.25 3.00
13 Jim Thome 2.00 5.00
14 Pedro Martinez 2.00 5.00
15 Nomar Garciaparra 3.00 8.00
16 Chipper Jones 2.00 5.00
17 Rocco Baldelli 1.25 3.00
18 Dontrelle Willis 2.00 5.00
19 Garret Anderson 1.25 3.00
20 Jeff Bagwell 2.00 5.00
21 Jim Edmonds 1.25 3.00
22 Rickey Henderson 2.00 5.00
23 Torii Hunter 1.25 3.00
24 Tom Glavine 2.00 5.00
25 Hideo Nomo 2.00 5.00
26 Luis Gonzalez 1.25 3.00
27 Alex Rodriguez 3.00 8.00
28 Albert Pujols 4.00 10.00
29 Manny Ramirez 2.00 5.00
30 Rafael Palmeiro 2.00 5.00
31 Bernie Williams 2.00 5.00
32 Curt Schilling 1.25 3.00
33 Roger Clemens 4.00 10.00
34 Andruw Jones 2.00 5.00
35 J.D. Drew 1.25 3.00
36 Kerry Wood 1.25 3.00
37 Scott Rolen 2.00 5.00
38 Darin Erstad 1.25 3.00
39 Joe DiMaggio 3.00 8.00
40 Magglio Ordonez 1.25 3.00
41 Todd Helton 2.00 5.00
42 Barry Zito 1.25 3.00
43 Mickey Mantle 6.00 15.00
44 Miguel Tejada 1.25 3.00
45 Troy Glaus 1.25 3.00
46 Kazuhisa Ishii 1.25 3.00
47 Adam Dunn 1.25 3.00
48 Ted Williams 4.00 10.00
49 Mike Mussina 2.00 5.00
50 Ivan Rodriguez 2.00 5.00
51 Jacque Jones 1.25 3.00
52 Stan Musial 3.00 8.00
53 Mariano Rivera 2.00 5.00
54 Larry Walker 1.25 3.00
55 Aaron Boone 1.25 3.00
56 Hank Blalock 1.25 3.00
57 Rich Harden 2.00 5.00
58 Lance Berkman 1.25 3.00
59 Eric Chavez 1.25 3.00
60 Carlos Beltran 1.25 3.00
61 Roy Oswalt 1.25 3.00
62 Moises Alou 1.25 3.00
63 Nolan Ryan 5.00 12.00
64 Jeff Kent 1.25 3.00
65 Roberto Alomar 2.00 5.00
66 Runelvys Hernandez 1.25 3.00
67 Roy Halladay 1.25 3.00
68 Tim Hudson 1.25 3.00
69 Tom Seaver 2.00 5.00
70 Edgardo Alfonzo 1.25 3.00
71 Andy Pettitte 2.00 5.00
72 Preston Wilson 1.25 3.00
73 Frank Thomas 2.00 5.00
74 Jerome Williams 1.25 3.00
75 Shawn Green 1.25 3.00
76 David Wells 1.25 3.00
77 John Smoltz 2.00 5.00
78 Jorge Posada 2.00 5.00
79 Marlon Byrd 1.25 3.00
80 Austin Kearns 1.25 3.00
81 Bret Boone 1.25 3.00
82 Rafael Furcal 1.25 3.00
83 Jay Gibbons 1.25 3.00
84 Shane Reynolds 1.25 3.00
85 Nate Bland UR T1 RC 2.00 5.00
86 Willie Eyre UR T1 RC 2.00 5.00
87 Jeremy Guthrie UR T1 2.00 5.00
88 Jeremy Wedel UR T1 RC 2.00 5.00
89 Jhonny Peralta UR T1 3.00 8.00
90 Luis Ayala UR T1 RC 2.00 5.00
91 Michael Hessman UR T1 RC 2.00 5.00
92 Michael Nakamura UR T1 RC 2.00 5.00
93 Nook Logan UR T1 RC 3.00 8.00
94 Rett Johnson UR T1 RC 2.00 5.00
95 Josh Hall UR T1 RC 2.00 5.00
96 Julio Manon UR T1 RC 2.00 5.00
97 Heath Bell UR T1 RC 2.00 5.00
98 Ian Ferguson UR T1 RC 2.00 5.00
99 Jason Gilfillan UR T1 RC 2.00 5.00
100 Jason Roach UR T1 RC 2.00 5.00
101 Jason Shiell UR T1 RC 2.00 5.00
102 Termel Sledge UR T1 RC 2.00 5.00
103 Phil Seibel UR T1 RC 2.00 5.00
104 Jeff Duncan UR T1 RC 2.00 5.00
105 Mike Neu UR T1 RC 2.00 5.00
106 Colin Porter UR T1 RC 2.00 5.00
107 David Matranga UR T1 RC 2.00 5.00
108 Aaron Looper UR T1 RC 2.00 5.00
109 Jeremy Bonderman UR T1 RC 6.00 15.00
110 Miguel Ojeda UR T1 RC 2.00 5.00
111 Chad Cordero UR T1 RC 4.00 10.00
112 Shane Bazzell UR T1 RC 2.00 5.00
113 Tim Olson UR T1 RC 2.00 5.00
114 Michel Hernandez UR T1 RC 2.00 5.00
115 Chien-Ming Wang UR T1 RC 20.00 50.00
116 Josh Stewart UR T1 RC 2.00 5.00
117 Clint Barmes UR T1 RC 2.00 5.00
118 Craig Brazell UR T2 RC 2.00 5.00
119 Josh Willingham UR T2 RC 4.00 10.00
120 Brent Hoard UR T2 RC 2.00 5.00
121 Francisco Rosario UR T2 RC 2.00 5.00
122 Rick Roberts UR T2 RC 2.00 5.00
123 Geoff Geary UR T2 RC 2.00 5.00
124 Edgar Gonzalez UR T2 RC 2.00 5.00
125 Kevin Correia UR T2 RC 2.00 5.00
126 Ryan Cameron UR T2 RC 2.00 5.00
127 Beau Kemp UR T2 RC 2.00 5.00
128 Tommy Phelps UR T2 2.00 5.00
129 Mark Malaska UR T2 RC 2.00 5.00
130 Kevin Ohme UR T2 RC 2.00 5.00
131 Humberto Quintero UR T2 RC 2.00 5.00
132 Aquilino Lopez UR T2 RC 2.00 5.00
133 Andrew Brown UR T2 RC 3.00 8.00
134 Wilfredo Ledezma UR T2 RC 2.00 5.00
135 Luis De Los Santos UR T2 2.00 5.00
136 Garrett Atkins UR T2 2.00 5.00
137 Fernando Cabrera UR T2 RC 2.00 5.00
138 D.J. Carrasco UR T2 RC 2.00 5.00
139 Alfredo Gonzalez UR T2 RC 2.00 5.00
140 Alex Prieto UR T2 RC 2.00 5.00
141 Matt Kata UR T3 RC 2.50 6.00
142 Chris Capuano UR T3 RC 6.00 15.00
143 Bobby Madritsch UR T3 RC 2.50 6.00
144 Greg Jones UR T3 RC 2.50 6.00
145 Pete Zoccolillo UR T3 RC 2.50 6.00
146 Chad Gaudin UR T3 RC 2.50 6.00
147 Rosman Garcia UR T3 RC 2.50 6.00
148 Gerald Laird UR T3 2.50 6.00
149 Danny Garcia UR T3 RC 2.50 6.00
150 Stephen Randolph UR T3 RC 2.50 6.00
151 Pete LaForest UR T3 RC 2.50 6.00
152 Brian Sweeney UR T3 RC 2.50 6.00
153 Aaron Miles UR T3 RC 4.00 10.00
154 Jorge DePaula UR T3 UER 2.50 6.00
Real name is Julio DePaula
155 Graham Koonce UR T3 RC 2.50 6.00
156 Tom Gregorio UR T3 RC 2.50 6.00
157 Javier A. Lopez UR T3 RC 2.50 6.00
158 Oscar Villarreal UR T3 RC 2.50 6.00
159 Prentice Redman UR T4 RC 5.00 12.00
160 Francisco Cruceta UR T4 RC 5.00 12.00
161 Guillermo Quiroz UR T4 RC 5.00 12.00
162 Jeremy Griffiths UR T4 RC 5.00 12.00
163 Lew Ford UR T4 RC 8.00 20.00
164 Rob Hammock UR T4 RC 5.00 12.00
165 Todd Wellemeyer UR T4 RC 5.00 12.00
166 Ryan Wagner UR T4 RC 5.00 12.00
167 Edwin Jackson UR T4 RC 8.00 20.00
168 Dan Haren UR T4 RC 8.00 20.00
169 Hideki Matsui AU RC 250.00 350.00
170 Jose Contreras AU RC 20.00 50.00
171 Delmon Young AU RC 225.00 325.00
172 Rickie Weeks AU RC 50.00 100.00
173 Brandon Webb AU RC 100.00 175.00
174 Bo Hart AU RC 6.00 15.00
175 Rocco Baldelli YS AU 10.00 25.00
176 Jose Reyes YS AU 10.00 25.00
177 Dontrelle Willis YS AU 20.00 50.00
178 Bobby Hill YS AU 6.00 15.00
179 Jae Weong Seo YS AU 10.00 25.00
180 Jesse Foppert YS AU 6.00 15.00

2003 Ultimate Collection Gold

*GOLD ACTIVE 1-84: 1.25X TO 3X BASIC
*GOLD RETIRED 1-84: 1.25X TO 3X BASIC
1-84 PRINT RUN 50 SERIAL #'d SETS
*GOLD 84-117: .75X TO 2X BASIC
84-117 PRINT RUN 50 SERIAL #'d SETS
*GOLD 118-140: .75X TO 2X BASIC
118-140 PRINT RUN 35 SERIAL #'d SETS
*GOLD 141-158: .75X TO 2X BASIC
141-158 PRINT RUN 25 SERIAL #'d SETS
159-168 PRINT RUN 10 SERIAL #'d SETS
159-168 NO PRICING DUE TO SCARCITY

169-174 AU PRINT RUN 25 SERIAL #'d SETS
169-174 AU NO PRICING DUE TO SCARCITY
175-180 AU PRINT RUN 25 SERIAL #'d SETS
175-180 AU NO PRICING DUE TO SCARCITY
RANDOM INSERTS IN PACKS
115 Chien-Ming Wang UR T1 60.00 120.00

2003 Ultimate Collection Buybacks

These 231 cards, which were randomly inserted into packs, feature mainly 2003 cards (with a smattering of earlier year cards) from varying Upper Deck products which UD bought back and had the player signed. Please note that for cards with print runs of 15 or fewer copies pricing is not provided due to scarcity of market evidence.

BUYBACKS & YS 175-180 OVERALL ODDS 1:8
1 Rocco Baldelli 03 UDA Blue/10
2 Rocco Baldelli 03 UDA Red/10
3 Hank Blalock 02-3 SUP/10
4 Hank Blalock 02-3 SUP/35 15.00 40.00
5 Hank Blalock 03 40M/25 20.00 50.00
6 Hank Blalock 03 GF/25 20.00 50.00
7 Hank Blalock 03 MVP/10
8 Hank Blalock 03 Patch/25 20.00 50.00
9 Hank Blalock 03 SPA/20 20.00 50.00
10 Hank Blalock 03 SPA/25 20.00 50.00
11 Hank Blalock 03 UD/10
12 Hank Blalock 03 VIN/25 20.00 50.00
13 Carlos Delgado 03 40M/10
14 Carlos Delgado 03 40M Flag/2
15 Carlos Delgado 03 GF/2
16 Carlos Delgado 03 MVP/3
17 Carlos Delgado 03 Patch/2
18 Carlos Delgado 03 PB/5
19 Carlos Delgado 03 PB Red/3
20 Carlos Delgado 03 SPA/11
21 Carlos Delgado 03 UD/1
22 Carlos Delgado 03 UD LS Jsy/4
23 Carlos Delgado 03 UDA/5
24 Carlos Delgado 03 VIN/2
25 Adam Dunn 03 40M Rain/1
26 Adam Dunn 03 40M Rain AS/5
27 Adam Dunn 03 GF/1
28 Adam Dunn 03 MVP/5
29 Adam Dunn 03 Patch/7
30 Adam Dunn 03 PB/9
31 Adam Dunn 03 PB Red/1
32 Adam Dunn 03 UD/7
33 Adam Dunn 03 UDA/5
34 Adam Dunn 03 VIN/1
35 Adam Dunn 03 VIN 3D/7
36 Nomar Garciaparra 03 40M/2
37 Nomar Garciaparra 03 40M Flag/1
38 Nomar Garciaparra 03 GF/3
39 Nomar Garciaparra 03 MVP/1
40 Nomar Garciaparra 03 PB/7
41 Nomar Garciaparra 03 PB Red/2
42 Nomar Garciaparra 03 SPA/1
43 Nomar Garciaparra 03 UD/3
44 Nomar Garciaparra 03 UD MP/2
45 Nomar Garciaparra 03 UDA/2
46 Nomar Garciaparra 03 VIN/1
47 Tom Glavine 03 40M/1
48 Tom Glavine 03 40M Flag/3
49 Tom Glavine 03 GF/3
50 Tom Glavine 03 GF w/Vlad/2
51 Tom Glavine 03 MVP/1
52 Tom Glavine 03 PB/5
53 Tom Glavine 03 PB Red/3
54 Tom Glavine 03 SPA/7
55 Tom Glavine 03 UD/8
56 Tom Glavine 03 UD/5
57 Tom Glavine 03 UDA/5
58 Tom Glavine 03 VIN/7
59 Luis Gonzalez 03 40M/10
60 Luis Gonzalez 03 40M AS/15
61 Luis Gonzalez 03 40M HR/25 20.00 50.00
62 Luis Gonzalez 03 40M T40/15
63 Luis Gonzalez 03 40M Flag/5
64 Luis Gonzalez 03 GF/15
65 Luis Gonzalez 03 MVP/3
66 Luis Gonzalez 03 Patch/17 20.00 50.00
67 Luis Gonzalez 03 PB/15
68 Luis Gonzalez 03 SPA/25 20.00 50.00
69 Luis Gonzalez 03 SWS/15
70 Luis Gonzalez 03 UDA/15
71 Luis Gonzalez 03 VIN/25 20.00 50.00
72 K.Griffey Jr. 02-3 SUP/75 50.00 100.00
73 K.Griffey Jr. 02-3 SUP Spok/50 50.00 100.00
74 K.Griffey Jr. 03 40M/50 50.00 100.00
75 K.Griffey Jr. 03 40M HR824/50 50.00 100.00
76 K.Griffey Jr. 03 40M HR825/50 50.00 100.00
77 K.Griffey Jr. 03 40M HR829/50 50.00 100.00
78 K.Griffey Jr. 03 40M T40/50 50.00 100.00
79 K.Griffey Jr. 03 GF/50 50.00 100.00
80 K.Griffey Jr. 03 GF GF/3
81 K.Griffey Jr. 03 GF w/Oswalt/9
82 K.Griffey Jr. 03 HON/50 50.00 100.00
83 K.Griffey Jr. 03 HON SP/30 60.00 120.00
84 K.Griffey Jr. 03 Patch/75 50.00 100.00
85 K.Griffey Jr. 03 PB/75 50.00 100.00
86 K.Griffey Jr. 03 SPA/50 50.00 100.00
87 K.Griffey Jr. 03 SPA/75 50.00 100.00
88 K.Griffey Jr. 03 SPx/75 50.00 100.00
89 K.Griffey Jr. 03 SWS/75 50.00 100.00
90 K.Griffey Jr. 03 UD MP2/3
91 K.Griffey Jr. 03 UD MP4/3
92 K.Griffey Jr. 03 UD MP7/3
93 K.Griffey Jr. 03 UD MP26/3
94 K.Griffey Jr. 03 UDA/75 50.00 100.00
95 K.Griffey Jr. 03 VIN/50 50.00 100.00
96 Torii Hunter 03 40M/18 20.00 50.00
97 Torii Hunter 03 40M Flag/7
98 Torii Hunter 03 MVP/1
99 Torii Hunter 03 Patch/25 20.00 50.00
100 Torii Hunter 03 PB/50 15.00 40.00
101 Torii Hunter 03 PB Red/5
102 Torii Hunter 03 SPA/4
103 Torii Hunter 03 UD/10
104 Torii Hunter 03 UDA/5
105 Torii Hunter 03 VIN/25 20.00 50.00
106 Randy Johnson 03 40M/7
107 Randy Johnson 03 40M Flag/5
108 Randy Johnson 03 GF/10
109 Randy Johnson 03 MVP/1
110 Randy Johnson 03 PB/10
111 Randy Johnson 03 PB Red/5
112 Randy Johnson 03 SPA/1
113 Randy Johnson 03 UD/3
114 Randy Johnson 03 UDA/5
115 Randy Johnson 03 VIN/3
116 Austin Kearns 02-3 SUP/10
117 Austin Kearns 03 40M/8
118 Austin Kearns 03 40M/33 15.00 40.00
119 Austin Kearns 03 40M Flag/10
120 Austin Kearns 03 GF/10
121 Austin Kearns 03 MVP/3
122 Austin Kearns 03 Patch/10
123 Austin Kearns 03 SPA/9
124 Austin Kearns 03 UDA/5
125 Austin Kearns 03 VIN/10
126 Matsui 03 40M NR/20 250.00 400.00
127 H.Mat 03 40M FlagNR/20 250.00 400.00
128 H.Mat 03 GFw/Pedro/18 250.00 400.00
129 Hideki Matsui 03 MVP/12
130 Hideki Matsui 03 PB/17 250.00 400.00
131 Hideki Matsui 03 PB Red/6
132 Hideki Matsui 03 UD/25 250.00 400.00
133 Hideki Matsui 03 UD LS Jsy/4
134 Hideki Matsui 03 UD MP/3
135 Hideki Matsui 03 VIN/25 250.00 400.00
136 Stan Musial 99 CL/15
137 Stan Musial 99 HIT/25
138 Stan Musial 00 LG/5
139 Stan Musial 01 HF/10
140 Stan Musial 01 LG/10
141 Stan Musial 01 SPLC/15
142 Stan Musial 02 SPLC/1
143 Stan Musial 02 SPLC/30 40.00 80.00
144 Stan Musial 02 WSH/25
145 Stan Musial 03 PB/50 30.00 60.00
146 Stan Musial 03 PB Red/15
147 Stan Musial 03 SWSC/37 40.00 80.00
148 Stan Musial 03 UD MP/3
149 Stan Musial 03 UDA/9
150 Stan Musial 03 VIN/50 30.00 60.00
151 Mark Prior 03 40M/1
152 Mark Prior 03 40M Flag/5
153 Mark Prior 03 GF/5
154 Mark Prior 03 GF w/Berkman/7
155 Mark Prior 03 MVP/1
156 Mark Prior 03 Patch/3
157 Mark Prior 03 PB/10
158 Mark Prior 03 PB Red/1
159 Mark Prior 03 UD/7
160 Mark Prior 03 UDA/5
161 Mark Prior 03 VIN/5
162 Scott Rolen 03 40M/5
163 Scott Rolen 03 40M AS/7
164 Scott Rolen 03 40M Flag/1
165 Scott Rolen 03 GF/4
166 Scott Rolen 03 MVP/1
167 Scott Rolen 03 Patch/1
168 Scott Rolen 03 PB/5
169 Scott Rolen 03 PB Red/5
170 Scott Rolen 03 SPA/6
171 Scott Rolen 03 UD/5
172 Scott Rolen 03 UDA/5
173 Scott Rolen 03 VIN/4
174 Curt Schilling 02 SPA/1
175 Curt Schilling 03 40M/1
176 Curt Schilling 03 40M AS/1
177 Curt Schilling 03 GF/2
178 Curt Schilling 03 MVP/1
179 Curt Schilling 03 Patch/1
180 Curt Schilling 03 PB/6
181 Curt Schilling 03 PB Red/1
182 Curt Schilling 03 SPA/6
183 Curt Schilling 03 SWS/1
184 Curt Schilling 03 UDA/1
185 Curt Schilling 03 VIN/3
186 Sammy Sosa 02-3 SUP/25 50.00 100.00
187 Sammy Sosa 03 40M/13
188 Sammy Sosa 03 40M AS/1
189 Sammy Sosa 03 GF/10
190 Sammy Sosa 03 GF GF/10
191 S.Sosa 03 GF w/Mac/17
192 Sammy Sosa 03 MVP/7
193 Sammy Sosa 03 Patch/10
194 Sammy Sosa 03 PB/25 50.00 100.00
195 Sammy Sosa 03 SPA/25 50.00 100.00
196 Sammy Sosa 03 UD/7
197 Sammy Sosa 03 UD LS Jsy/5
198 Sammy Sosa 03 UD MP/3
199 Sammy Sosa 03 UDA/17 50.00 100.00
200 Sammy Sosa 03 UDA Blue/10
201 Sammy Sosa 03 UDA Red/10
202 Sammy Sosa 03 VIN/25 50.00 100.00
203 Mark Teixeira 03 40M/50 15.00 40.00
204 Mark Teixeira 03 40M Rain/15
205 Mark Teixeira 03 Patch/50 15.00 40.00
206 Mark Teixeira 03 SPA RA/25 20.00 50.00
207 Mark Teixeira 03 SWS/23 20.00 50.00
208 Mark Teixeira 03 UD/25 20.00 50.00
209 Mark Teixeira 03 UDA/15
210 Mark Teixeira 03 VIN/25 20.00 50.00
211 Kerry Wood 03 40M Flag/13
212 Kerry Wood 03 GF/7
213 Kerry Wood 03 GF w/Pujols/3
214 Kerry Wood 03 MVP/3
215 Kerry Wood 03 PB/10
216 Kerry Wood 03 PB Red/13
217 Kerry Wood 03 SPA/10
218 Kerry Wood 03 UD/7
219 Kerry Wood 03 UDA/5
220 Kerry Wood 03 VIN/4
221 Barry Zito 03 40M/2
222 Barry Zito 03 40M Flag/2
223 Barry Zito 03 GF/7
224 Barry Zito 03 MVP/2
225 Barry Zito 03 Patch/2
226 Barry Zito 03 PB/1
227 Barry Zito 03 PB Red/2
228 Barry Zito 03 SPA/7
229 Barry Zito 03 SPx/10
230 Barry Zito 03 UD/10
231 Barry Zito 03 UDA/5

2003 Ultimate Collection Double Barrel

RANDOM INSERTS IN PACKS
PRINT RUNS B/WN 1-3 COPIES PER
NO PRICING DUE TO SCARCITY
AB Roberto Alomar
Craig Biggio/3
AC Edgardo Alfonzo
Jose Cruz Jr./2
AE Garrett Anderson
Darin Erstad/3
AJ Bobby Abreu
Chipper Jones/1
BC Bret Boone
Mike Cameron/1
BH Rocco Baldelli
Torii Hunter/1
BK Sean Burroughs
Mark Kotsay/1
BL Kevin Brown
Paul Lo Duca/1
BR Pat Burrell
Jimmy Rollins/1
BS Carlos Beltran
Mike Sweeney/2
DP Carlos Delgado
Albert Pujols/1
DR Johnny Damon
Manny Ramirez/1
DT Adam Dunn
Jim Thome/1
EM Jim Edmonds
Stan Musial/2
FS Rafael Furcal
Gary Sheffield/3
GK Brian Giles
Jason Kendall/2
GM Ken Griffey Jr.
Fred McGriff/2
GS Tom Glavine
Tom Seaver/2
HL Mike Hampton
Javy Lopez/1
HP Rickey Henderson
Juan Pierre/1
HV Shea Hillenbrand
Jose Vidro/1
JB Jeff Bagwell
Barry Larkin/1
KN Ryan Klesko
Phil Nevin/1
KT Paul Konerko
Frank Thomas/1
LO Carlos Lee
Magglio Ordonez/1
LP Mike Lieberthal
Mike Piazza/2
LR Luis Gonzalez
Raul Mondesi/1
LV Al Leiter
Mo Vaughn/1
MN Hideki Matsui
Hideo Nomo/1
MO Edgar Martinez
John Olerud/1
MR Tino Martinez
Scott Rolen/1
PP Corey Patterson
Jay Payton/3
PR Jorge Posada
Mariano Rivera/1
TP Todd Helton
Preston Wilson/1

2003 Ultimate Collection Dual Jersey

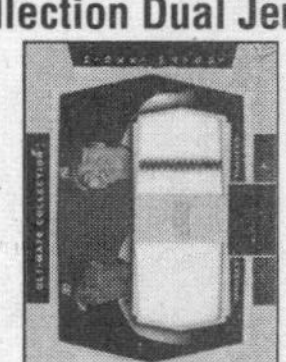

STATED PRINT RUN 50 SERIAL #'d SETS
*GOLD: .75X TO 1.5X BASIC
GOLD PRINT RUN 25 SERIAL #'d SETS
OVERALL GU ODDS 3:4
ALL ARE DUAL JSY UNLESS NOTED
AH Alfonso Soriano Jsy 20.00 50.00
Hideki Matsui Jsy
AI Albert Pujols Jsy 30.00 60.00
Ichiro Suzuki Jsy
BK Jeff Bagwell Jsy 10.00 25.00
Jeff Kent Jsy
CA Chipper Jones Jsy 10.00 25.00
Andruw Jones Jsy
CJ Carlos Delgado Jsy 6.00 15.00
Jason Giambi Jsy
DE J.D. Drew Jsy 6.00 15.00
Jim Edmonds Jsy
DG Carlos Delgado Jsy 10.00 25.00
Vladimir Guerrero Jsy
DM Joe DiMaggio Pants 175.00 300.00
Mickey Mantle Jsy/Pants
DP Carlos Delgado Jsy 10.00 25.00
Rafael Palmeiro Jsy
DW Joe DiMaggio Jsy/Pants 100.00 175.00
Ted Williams Jsy
GB Shawn Green Jsy 6.00 15.00
Kevin Brown Jsy
GD Ken Griffey Jr. Jsy 15.00 40.00
Adam Dunn Jsy
GE Troy Glaus Jsy 6.00 15.00
Darin Erstad Jsy
GP Ken Griffey Jr. Jsy 15.00 40.00
Rafael Palmeiro Jsy
GR Nomar Garciaparra Jsy 15.00 40.00
Alex Rodriguez Jsy
GS Vladimir Guerrero Jsy 10.00 25.00
Sammy Sosa Jsy
HJ Torii Hunter Jsy 6.00 15.00
Jacque Jones Jsy
HZ Roy Halladay Jsy 6.00 15.00
Barry Zito Jsy
IG Ichiro Suzuki Jsy 30.00 60.00
Ken Griffey Jr. Jsy
IN Ichiro Suzuki Jsy 40.00 80.00
Hideo Nomo Jsy
IS Ichiro Suzuki Jsy 30.00 60.00
Sammy Sosa Jsy
JF Andruw Jones Jsy 10.00 25.00
Rafael Furcal Jsy
JM Jorge Posada Jsy 15.00 40.00
Mike Piazza Jsy
MC Greg Maddux Jsy 15.00 40.00
Roger Clemens Jsy
MW Mickey Mantle Jsy/Pants 150.00 250.00
Ted Williams Jsy
NI Hideo Nomo Jsy 15.00 40.00
Kazuhisa Ishii Jsy
NM Hideo Nomo Jsy 30.00 60.00
Hideki Matsui Jsy
PC Pedro Martinez Jsy 15.00 40.00
Roger Clemens Jsy
PM Andy Pettitte Jsy 10.00 25.00
Mike Mussina Jsy
PS Mark Prior Jsy 10.00 25.00
Sammy Sosa Jsy
RM Manny Ramirez Jsy 10.00 25.00
Pedro Martinez Jsy
RP Alex Rodriguez Jsy 10.00 25.00
Rafael Palmeiro Jsy
SA Scott Rolen Jsy 20.00 50.00
Albert Pujols Jsy
SB Alfonso Soriano Jsy 10.00 25.00
Bernie Williams Jsy
SJ Curt Schilling Jsy 10.00 25.00
Randy Johnson Jsy
SM John Smoltz Jsy 15.00 40.00
Greg Maddux Jsy
TB Mark Teixeira Jsy 10.00 25.00
Hank Blalock Jsy
TH Jim Thome Jsy 10.00 25.00
Todd Helton Jsy
TR Miguel Tejada Jsy 10.00 25.00
Alex Rodriguez Jsy
WL Dontrelle Willis Jsy 10.00 25.00
Mike Lowell Jsy
YW Delmon Young Pants 15.00 40.00
Rickie Weeks Jsy

2003 Ultimate Collection Dual Patch

OVERALL GU ODDS 3:4
PRINT RUNS B/WN 14-99 COPIES PER
NO PRICING ON QTY OF 14 OR LESS
AI Albert Pujols 125.00 200.00
Ichiro Suzuki/99
AM Andy Pettitte 20.00 50.00
Mike Mussina/99
BK Jeff Bagwell 20.00 50.00
Jeff Kent/99
CA Chipper Jones 20.00 50.00
Andruw Jones/99
CV Carlos Delgado 20.00 50.00
Vladimir Guerrero/99
DE J.D. Drew 15.00 40.00
Jim Edmonds/99
DG Carlos Delgado 15.00 40.00
Jason Giambi/99
DP Carlos Delgado
Rafael Palmeiro/14
GB Shawn Green 15.00 40.00
Kevin Brown/99
GD Ken Griffey Jr. 30.00 60.00
Adam Dunn/99
GE Troy Glaus 15.00 40.00
Darin Erstad/99
GP Ken Griffey Jr.
Rafael Palmeiro/14
GR Nomar Garciaparra 50.00 100.00
Greg Maddux/99
GS Vladimir Guerrero 20.00 50.00
Sammy Sosa/99
HJ Torii Hunter 15.00 40.00
Jacque Jones/83
HZ Roy Halladay 15.00 40.00
Barry Zito/99
IG Ichiro Suzuki 60.00 120.00
Ken Griffey Jr./99
IN Ichiro Suzuki 75.00 150.00
Hideo Nomo/99
IS Ichiro Suzuki 60.00 120.00

Sammy Sosa/99
JF Andruw Jones 20.00 50.00
Rafael Furcal/99
JG John Smoltz 30.00 60.00
Greg Maddux/99
MC Greg Maddux 40.00 80.00
Roger Clemens/75
NI Hideo Nomo 50.00 100.00
Kazuhisa Ishii/63
PM Jorge Posada 30.00 60.00
Mike Piazza/73
PS Mark Prior 20.00 50.00
Sammy Sosa/99
RM Manny Ramirez 20.00 50.00
Pedro Martinez/99
SA Scott Rolen 50.00 100.00
Albert Pujols/99
SB Alfonso Soriano 40.00 80.00
Bernie Williams/21
SJ Curt Schilling 20.00 50.00
Randy Johnson/99
SM Alfonso Soriano 40.00 80.00
Hideki Matsui/99
TB Mark Teixeira 20.00 50.00
Hank Blalock/99
TH Jim Thome 20.00 50.00
Todd Helton/99
TR Miguel Tejada 30.00 60.00
Alex Rodriguez/99
WL Dontrelle Willis 20.00 50.00
Mike Lowell/85
YW Delmon Young 50.00 100.00
Rickie Weeks/28

2003 Ultimate Collection Dual Patch Gold

*GOLD: .6X TO 1.2X BASIC PATCH p/r 63-99
*GOLD: .5X TO 1X BASIC PATCH p/r 21-28
OVERALL GU ODDS 3:4
STATED PRINT RUN 35 SERIAL #'d SETS
DIMAGGIO/WILLIAMS PRINT RUN 1 #'d CARD
SORIANO/MATSUI PRINT RUN 15 #'d CARDS
NO PRICING ON QTY OF 15 OR LESS
DP Carlos Delgado 30.00 60.00
Rafael Palmeiro
DW Joe DiMaggio
Ted Williams/1
GP Ken Griffey Jr. 40.00 80.00
Rafael Palmeiro
NM Hideo Nomo 125.00 200.00
Hideki Matsui
PR Pedro Martinez 40.00 80.00
Roger Clemens
RP Alex Rodriguez 40.00 80.00
Rafael Palmeiro

2003 Ultimate Collection Signatures

ULT.SIG. & AU RC OVERALL ODDS 1:4
PRINT RUNS B/WN 30-350 COPIES PER
GRIFFEY/MATSUI PART LIVE/ PART EXCH.
EXCHANGE DEADLINE 12/17/06
AP1 Albert Pujols w/Glove/40 175.00 250.00
AP2 Albert Pujols w/Bat/35 175.00 250.00
AR1 Alex Rodriguez/75 75.00 150.00
AR2 Alex Rodriguez/60 75.00 150.00
BG1 Bob Gibson Arm Up/299 12.50 30.00
BG2 Bob Gibson Stance/199 12.50 30.00
CD1 Carlos Delgado Hitting/150 12.50 30.00
CR1 Cal Ripken w/Helmet/85 75.00 150.00
CR2 Cal Ripken Fielding/85 75.00 150.00
CY1 Carl Yastrzemski w/Bat/199 40.00 80.00
DY1 Delmon Young Run/300 50.00 100.00
DY2 Delmon Young w/Bat/300 50.00 100.00
EG1 Eric Gagne Arm Down/350 20.00 50.00
GC1 Gary Carter Hitting/199 8.00 20.00
GM1 Greg Maddux New Uni/250 40.00 80.00
GM2 G.Maddux Retro Uni/140 50.00 100.00
HM1 H.Matsui w/Glove/250 175.00 300.00
HM2 H.Matsui Throwing/240 175.00 300.00
IS1 I.Suzuki w/Shades/199 500.00 600.00
IS2 Ichiro Suzuki Running/99 500.00 600.00
JG1 Jason Giambi Torso/35 20.00 50.00
JG2 J.Giambi Open Swing/35 20.00 50.00
KG1 Ken Griffey Jr. Hitting/350 30.00 60.00
KG2 Ken Griffey Jr. w/Bat/350 30.00 60.00
KW1 K.Wood Black Glv/170 20.00 50.00
KW2 K.Wood Brown Glv/85 30.00 60.00
MP1 Mark Prior w/Glove/299 12.50 30.00
MP2 Mark Prior Arm Up/225 12.50 30.00
NG1 N.Garciaparra/125 50.00 100.00
NG2 N.Garciaparra Hitting/180 50.00 100.00
NR1 Nolan Ryan Blue Uni/85 75.00 150.00
NR2 Nolan Ryan White Uni/75 75.00 150.00
OS1 Ozzie Smith Hitting/199 30.00 60.00
RC1 R.Clemens Glove Out/70 75.00 150.00
RC2 R.Clemens Arm Up/30 100.00 175.00
RJ1 R.Johnson Stripe Uni/75 50.00 100.00
RJ2 R.Johnson Black Uni/50 60.00 120.00
RS1 R.Sandberg Blue Uni/240 30.00 60.00
RS2 R.Sandberg Stripe Uni/200 30.00 60.00
RW1 R.Weeks White Uni/300 20.00 50.00
RW2 R.Weeks Red Uni/300 20.00 50.00
TS1 Tom Seaver Arms Up/75 20.00 50.00
TS2 Tom Seaver Arm Down/60 20.00 50.00
VG1 V.Guerrero Smiling/75 30.00 60.00
VG2 V.Guerrero Hitting/50 40.00 80.00

2003 Ultimate Collection Signatures Gold

ULT.SIG. & AU RC OVERALL ODDS 1:4
STATED PRINT RUN 25 SERIAL #'d SETS
AP Albert Pujols w/Glove 175.00 250.00
AR Alex Rodriguez 150.00 250.00
BG Bob Gibson Arm Up 30.00 60.00
CD Carlos Delgado Hitting 30.00 60.00
CR Cal Ripken w/Helmet 175.00 300.00
CY Carl Yastrzemski w/Bat 75.00 150.00
DY Delmon Young Run
EG Eric Gagne Arm Down 50.00 100.00
GC Gary Carter Hitting 20.00 50.00
GM Greg Maddux New Uni 150.00 250.00
HM H.Matsui w/Glove 175.00 300.00
IS Ichiro Suzuki w/Shades 250.00 400.00
JG Jason Giambi Torso 30.00 60.00
KG Ken Griffey Jr. Hitting 60.00 120.00
KW K.Wood Black Glv 50.00 100.00
MP Mark Prior w/Glove 30.00 60.00
NG N.Garciaparra 60.00 120.00
NR Nolan Ryan Blue Uni 125.00 200.00
OS Ozzie Smith Hitting 75.00 150.00
RC R.Clemens Glove Out 150.00 250.00
RJ R.Johnson Stripe Uni 75.00 150.00
RS R.Sandberg Blue Uni 75.00 150.00
RW R.Weeks White Uni 60.00 120.00
TS Tom Seaver Arms Up 30.00 60.00
VG V.Guerrero Smiling 50.00 100.00

2003 Ultimate Collection Game Jersey Tier 1

STATED PRINT RUN 99 SERIAL #'d SETS
COPPER PRINT RUN 10 SERIAL #'d SETS
NO COPPER PRICING DUE TO SCARCITY
*GOLD p/r 75: .4X TO 1X BASIC
*GOLD MATSUI p/r 55: .6X TO 1.5X BASIC
*GOLD p/r 51: .6X TO 1.5X BASIC
*GOLD p/r 44-48: .75X TO 2X BASIC
*GOLD p/r 25-35: 1X TO 2.5X BASIC
*GOLD p/r 17-24: 1.25X TO 3X BASIC
GOLD PRINT RUNS B/WN 1-75 COPIES PER
NO GOLD PRICING ON QTY OF 15 OR LESS
OVERALL GU ODDS 3:4
AD Adam Dunn Red Jsy 4.00 10.00
AJ Andruw Jones w/Bat 6.00 15.00
AP Albert Pujols Running 10.00 25.00
AR Alex Rodriguez Throw 8.00 20.00
AS Alfonso Soriano No Glv 4.00 10.00
BW Bernie Williams White Jsy 6.00 15.00
BZ Barry Zito Green Jsy 4.00 10.00
CD Carlos Delgado Blue Jsy 4.00 10.00
CJ Chipper Jones No Bat 6.00 15.00
CS Curt Schilling Arm Up 4.00 10.00
DW Dontrelle Willis Black Jsy 6.00 15.00
DY Delmon Young Throw 6.00 15.00
FT Frank Thomas Black Jsy 6.00 15.00
GM Greg Maddux White Jsy 8.00 20.00
GS Gary Sheffield Throw 4.00 10.00
HM Hideki Matsui Ball Toss 20.00 50.00
HN Hideo Nomo Gray Jsy 10.00 25.00
IS Ichiro Suzuki Gray Jsy 30.00 60.00
JE Jim Edmonds White Jsy 4.00 10.00
JG Jason Giambi No Bat 4.00 10.00
JR Jose Reyes Throw 4.00 10.00
JT Jim Thome Red Jsy 6.00 15.00
KG Ken Griffey Jr. Gray Jsy 10.00 25.00
KI Kazuhisa Ishii Arms Up 4.00 10.00
KW Kerry Wood Pitching 4.00 10.00
MI Mike Piazza Mask On 8.00 20.00
MM Mike Mussina Blue Jsy 6.00 15.00
MP Mark Prior Pitching 6.00 15.00
MR Manny Ramirez Red Jsy 6.00 15.00
MT Miguel Tejada White Jsy 4.00 10.00
PB Pat Burrell Running 4.00 10.00
RB Rocco Baldelli Batting 4.00 10.00
RC Roger Clemens White Jsy 10.00 25.00
RF Rafael Furcal Fielding 4.00 10.00
RJ Randy Johnson White Jsy 6.00 15.00
RW Rickie Weeks Bat Up 5.00 12.00
SG Shawn Green White Jsy 4.00 10.00
SS Sammy Sosa Running 6.00 15.00
TG Tom Glavine Black Jsy 6.00 15.00
TH Torii Hunter Running 4.00 10.00
TR Troy Glaus Dirty Jsy 4.00 10.00
VG Vladimir Guerrero w/Bat 6.00 15.00

2003 Ultimate Collection Game Jersey Tier 2

STATED PRINT RUN 75 SERIAL #'d SETS
COPPER PRINT RUN 10 SERIAL #'d SETS

NO COPPER PRICING DUE TO SCARCITY
*GOLD p/r 75: .4X TO 1X BASIC
*GOLD MATSUI p/r 55: .6X TO 1.5X BASIC
*GOLD p/r 51: .6X TO 1.5X BASIC
*GOLD p/r 44-48: .75X TO 2X BASIC
*GOLD p/r 25-35: 1X TO 2.5X BASIC
*GOLD p/r 17-24: 1.25X TO 3X BASIC
GOLD PRINT RUNS B/WN 1-75 COPIES PER
NO GOLD PRICING ON QTY OF 15 OR LESS
OVERALL GU ODDS 3:4
AD2 Adam Dunn Swing 4.00 10.00
AJ2 Andruw Jones w/Glv 6.00 15.00
AP2 Albert Pujols Batting 10.00 25.00
AR2 Alex Rodriguez Running 8.00 20.00
AS2 Alfonso Soriano w/Glv 4.00 10.00
BW2 Bernie Williams Gray Jsy 6.00 15.00
BZ2 Barry Zito Gray Jsy 4.00 10.00
CD2 Carlos Delgado Gray Jsy 4.00 10.00
CJ2 Chipper Jones w/Bat 6.00 15.00
CS2 Curt Schilling Arm Down 4.00 10.00
DW Dontrelle Willis Gray Jsy 6.00 15.00
DY2 Delmon Young w/Ball 8.00 20.00
FT2 Frank Thomas White Jsy 6.00 15.00
GM2 Greg Maddux Blue Jsy 8.00 20.00
GS2 Gary Sheffield Batting 4.00 10.00
HM2 Hideki Matsui w/Bat 20.00 50.00
HN2 Hideo Nomo Blue Jsy 10.00 25.00
IS2 Ichiro Suzuki w/Bat 30.00 60.00
JE2 Jim Edmonds Gray Jsy 4.00 10.00
JG2 Jason Giambi w/Bat 4.00 10.00
JR2 Jose Reyes Walking 4.00 10.00
JT2 Jim Thome White Jsy 6.00 15.00
KG2 Ken Griffey Jr. Red Jsy 10.00 25.00
KI2 Kazuhisa Ishii Arms Down 4.00 10.00
KW2 Kerry Wood Standing 4.00 10.00
MI2 Mike Piazza w/Bat 8.00 20.00
MM2 Mike Mussina Gray Jsy 6.00 15.00
MP2 Mark Prior Hitting 6.00 15.00
MR2 Manny Ramirez Gray Jsy 6.00 15.00
MT2 Miguel Tejada Green Jsy 4.00 10.00
PB2 Pat Burrell Swinging 4.00 10.00
RB2 Rocco Baldelli Running 4.00 10.00
RC2 Roger Clemens Blue Jsy 10.00 25.00
RF2 Rafael Furcal Running 4.00 10.00
RJ2 Randy Johnson Black Jsy 6.00 15.00
RW2 Rickie Weeks Bat Forward 5.00 12.00
SG2 Shawn Green Gray Jsy 4.00 10.00
SS2 Sammy Sosa Batting 6.00 15.00
TG2 Tom Glavine Orange Jsy 6.00 15.00
TH2 Torii Hunter Swinging 4.00 10.00
TR2 Troy Glaus Clean Jsy 4.00 10.00
VG2 Vladimir Guerrero Point Up 6.00 15.00

2003 Ultimate Collection Game Patch

STATED PRINT RUN 99 SERIAL #'d SETS
SORIANO PRINT RUN 42 SERIAL #'d CARDS
*COPPER: .6X TO 1.2X BASIC p/r 99
*COPPER: .6X TO 1.2X BASIC p/r 42
COPPER PRINT RUN 35 SERIAL #'d SETS
*GOLD: .75X TO 1.5X BASIC p/r 99
*GOLD: .75X TO 1.5X BASIC p/r 42
GOLD PRINT RUN 25 SERIAL #'d SETS
OVERALL GU ODDS 3:4
AD Adam Dunn 10.00 25.00
AJ Andruw Jones 15.00 40.00
AP Albert Pujols 25.00 60.00
AR Alex Rodriguez 20.00 50.00
AS Alfonso Soriano/42 10.00 25.00
BW Bernie Williams 15.00 40.00
BZ Barry Zito 10.00 25.00
CD Carlos Delgado 10.00 25.00
CJ Chipper Jones 15.00 40.00
CS Curt Schilling 10.00 25.00
DW Dontrelle Willis 15.00 40.00
DY Delmon Young 30.00 60.00
FT Frank Thomas 15.00 40.00
GM Greg Maddux 20.00 50.00
HM Hideki Matsui 40.00 100.00
HN Hideo Nomo 20.00 50.00
IS Ichiro Suzuki 50.00 120.00
JE Jim Edmonds 10.00 25.00
JG Jason Giambi 10.00 25.00
JR Jose Reyes 10.00 25.00
JT Jim Thome 15.00 40.00
KG Ken Griffey Jr. 25.00 60.00
KI Kazuhisa Ishii 10.00 25.00
KW Kerry Wood 10.00 25.00
MI Mike Piazza 20.00 50.00
MM Mike Mussina 15.00 40.00
MP Mark Prior 15.00 40.00
MR Manny Ramirez 15.00 40.00
MT Miguel Tejada 10.00 25.00
PB Pat Burrell 10.00 25.00
RB Rocco Baldelli 10.00 25.00
RC Roger Clemens 25.00 60.00
RF Rafael Furcal 10.00 25.00
RH Roy Halladay 10.00 25.00
RJ Randy Johnson 15.00 40.00
RW Rickie Weeks 15.00 40.00
SG Shawn Green 10.00 25.00
SS Sammy Sosa 15.00 40.00
TG Tom Glavine 15.00 40.00
TH Torii Hunter 10.00 25.00
TR Troy Glaus 10.00 25.00
VG Vladimir Guerrero 15.00 40.00

2004 Ultimate Collection

This 222 card set was released in January, 2005. The set was issued in four card packs with an $100 SRP which came four packs to a box and four boxes to a case. Cards numbered 1-42 feature retired veterans while cards 43 through 126 feature active veterans. Cards numbered 127 through 222 feature rookies either grouped by tiers or signed cards. A few players did not return their autographs in time for insertion and those autographs had an exchange date of December 28, 2007.

COMMON CARD (1-42) 1.25 3.00
COMMON CARD (43-126) 1.25 3.00
1-126 STATED ODDS TWO PER PACK
1-126 PRINT RUN 675 SERIAL #'d CARDS
COMMON CARD (127-168) 2.00 5.00
127-209/222 STATED ODDS 3:4 PACKS
127-168 PRINT RUN 525 SERIAL #'d SETS
COMMON CARD (169-194) 2.50 6.00
169-194 PRINT RUN 299 SERIAL #'d SETS
COMMON (195-209/222) 3.00 8.00
195-209/222 PRINT RUN 199 SER.#'d SETS
210-221 STATED ODDS 1:10
210-221 PRINT RUN 75 SERIAL #'d SETS
EXCHANGE DEADLINE 12/28/07
1 Al Kaline 2.00 5.00
2 Billy Williams 1.25 3.00
3 Bob Feller 1.25 3.00
4 Bob Gibson 2.00 5.00
5 Bob Lemon 1.25 3.00
6 Bobby Doerr 1.25 3.00
7 Brooks Robinson 2.00 5.00
8 Cal Ripken 6.00 15.00
9 Catfish Hunter 2.00 5.00
10 Eddie Mathews 2.00 5.00
11 Enos Slaughter 1.25 3.00
12 Ernie Banks 2.00 5.00
13 Fergie Jenkins 1.25 3.00
14 Gaylord Perry 1.25 3.00
15 Harmon Killebrew 2.00 5.00
16 Jim Bunning 1.25 3.00
17 Joe DiMaggio 3.00 8.00
18 Joe Morgan 1.25 3.00
19 Juan Marichal 1.25 3.00
20 Lou Brock 2.00 5.00
21 Luis Aparicio 1.25 3.00
22 Mickey Mantle 6.00 15.00
23 Mike Schmidt 4.00 10.00
24 Monte Irvin 1.25 3.00
25 Nolan Ryan 5.00 12.00
26 Pee Wee Reese 2.00 5.00
27 Phil Niekro 1.25 3.00
28 Phil Rizzuto 2.00 5.00
29 Ralph Kiner 2.00 5.00
30 Richie Ashburn 2.00 5.00
31 Robin Roberts 1.25 3.00
32 Robin Yount 2.00 5.00
33 Rod Carew 2.00 5.00
34 Rollie Fingers 1.25 3.00
35 Stan Musial 3.00 8.00
36 Ted Williams 4.00 10.00
37 Tom Seaver 2.00 5.00
38 Warren Spahn 2.00 5.00
39 Whitey Ford 2.00 5.00
40 Willie McCovey 2.00 5.00
41 Willie Stargell 2.00 5.00
42 Yogi Berra 2.00 5.00
43 Adrian Beltre 1.25 3.00
44 Albert Pujols 4.00 10.00
45 Alex Rodriguez 3.00 8.00
46 Alfonso Soriano 1.25 3.00
47 Andruw Jones 2.00 5.00
48 Andy Pettitte 2.00 5.00
49 Aubrey Huff 1.25 3.00
50 Barry Larkin 2.00 5.00
51 Ben Sheets 1.25 3.00
52 Bernie Williams 2.00 5.00
53 Bobby Abreu 1.25 3.00
54 Brad Penny 1.25 3.00
55 Bret Boone 1.25 3.00
56 Brian Giles 1.25 3.00
57 Carlos Beltran 1.25 3.00
58 Carlos Delgado 1.25 3.00
59 Carlos Guillen 1.25 3.00
60 Carlos Lee 1.25 3.00
61 Carlos Zambrano 1.25 3.00
62 Chipper Jones 2.00 5.00
63 Craig Biggio 2.00 5.00
64 Craig Wilson 1.25 3.00
65 Curt Schilling 2.00 5.00
66 David Ortiz 2.00 5.00
67 Derek Jeter 4.00 10.00
68 Eric Chavez 1.25 3.00
69 Eric Gagne 1.25 3.00
70 Frank Thomas 2.00 5.00
71 Garret Anderson 1.25 3.00
72 Gary Sheffield 1.25 3.00
73 Greg Maddux 3.00 8.00
74 Hank Blalock 1.25 3.00
75 Hideki Matsui 3.00 8.00
76 Ichiro Suzuki 4.00 10.00
77 Ivan Rodriguez 2.00 5.00
78 J.D. Drew 1.25 3.00
79 Jake Peavy 1.25 3.00
80 Jason Schmidt 1.25 3.00
81 Jeff Bagwell 2.00 5.00
82 Jeff Kent 1.25 3.00
83 Jim Thome 2.00 5.00
84 Joe Mauer 2.00 5.00
85 Johan Santana 2.00 5.00
86 Jose Reyes 1.25 3.00
87 Jose Vidro 1.25 3.00
88 Ken Griffey Jr. 3.00 8.00
89 Kerry Wood 1.25 3.00
90 Larry Walker Cards 2.00 5.00
91 Luis Gonzalez 1.25 3.00
92 Lyle Overbay 1.25 3.00
93 Magglio Ordonez 1.25 3.00
94 Manny Ramirez 2.00 5.00
95 Mark Mulder 1.25 3.00
96 Mark Prior 2.00 5.00
97 Mark Teixeira 2.00 5.00
98 Melvin Mora 1.25 3.00
99 Michael Young 1.25 3.00
100 Miguel Cabrera 2.00 5.00
101 Miguel Tejada 1.25 3.00
102 Mike Lowell 1.25 3.00
103 Mike Piazza 3.00 8.00
104 Mike Sweeney 1.25 3.00
105 Nomar Garciaparra 3.00 8.00
106 Oliver Perez 1.25 3.00
107 Pedro Martinez 2.00 5.00
108 Preston Wilson 1.25 3.00
109 Rafael Palmeiro 2.00 5.00
110 Randy Johnson 2.00 5.00
111 Roger Clemens 4.00 10.00
112 Roy Halladay 1.25 3.00
113 Roy Oswalt 1.25 3.00
114 Sammy Sosa 2.00 5.00
115 Scott Podsednik 1.25 3.00
116 Scott Rolen 2.00 5.00
117 Shawn Green 1.25 3.00
118 Tim Hudson 1.25 3.00
119 Todd Helton 2.00 5.00
120 Tom Glavine 2.00 5.00
121 Torii Hunter 1.25 3.00
122 Travis Hafner 1.25 3.00
123 Troy Glaus 1.25 3.00
124 Vernon Wells 1.25 3.00
125 Victor Martinez 1.25 3.00
126 Vladimir Guerrero 2.00 5.00
127 Aarom Baldiris UR T1 RC 3.00 8.00
128 Alfredo Simon UR T1 RC 2.00 5.00
129 Andres Blanco UR T1 RC 2.00 5.00
130 Jeff Bajenaru UR T1 RC 2.00 5.00
131 Bart Fortunato UR T1 RC 2.00 5.00
132 B.Medders UR T1 RC 2.00 5.00
133 Brian Dallimore UR T1 RC 2.00 5.00
134 Carlos Hines UR T1 RC 2.00 5.00
135 Carlos Vasquez UR T1 RC 3.00 8.00
136 Casey Daigle UR T1 RC 2.00 5.00
137 Chad Bentz UR T1 RC 2.00 5.00
138 Chris Aguila UR T1 RC 2.00 5.00
139 Chris Saenz UR T1 RC 2.00 5.00
140 Chris Shelton UR T1 RC 5.00 12.00
141 Colby Miller UR T1 RC 2.00 5.00
142 Dave Crouthers UR T1 RC 2.00 5.00
143 David Aardsma UR T1 RC 3.00 8.00
144 Dennis Sarfate UR T1 RC 2.00 5.00
145 Donnie Kelly UR T1 RC 2.00 5.00
146 Eddy Rodriguez UR T1 RC 3.00 8.00
147 Eduardo Villacis UR T1 RC 2.00 5.00
148 Edwardo Sierra UR T1 RC 3.00 8.00
149 Edwin Moreno UR T1 RC 3.00 8.00
150 Kyle Denney UR T1 RC 2.00 5.00
151 Evan Rust UR T1 RC 2.00 5.00
152 Fernando Nieve UR T1 RC 3.00 8.00
153 Frank Francisco UR T1 RC 2.00 5.00
154 Frank Gracesqui UR T1 RC 2.00 5.00
155 Freddy Guzman UR T1 RC 2.00 5.00
156 Greg Dobbs UR T1 RC 2.00 5.00
157 Hector Gimenez UR T1 RC 2.00 5.00
158 Jason Alfaro UR T1 RC 2.00 5.00
159 Jake Woods UR T1 RC 2.00 5.00
160 Andy Green UR T1 RC 2.00 5.00
161 Jason Bartlett UR T1 RC 3.00 8.00
162 Jason Frasor UR T1 RC 2.00 5.00
163 Jeff Bennett UR T1 RC 2.00 5.00
164 Jerome Gamble UR T1 RC 2.00 5.00
165 Jerry Gil UR T1 RC 2.00 5.00
166 Joe Hietpas UR T1 RC 2.00 5.00
167 Jorge Sequea UR T1 RC 2.00 5.00
168 Jorge Vasquez UR T1 RC 2.00 5.00
169 Josh Labandeira UR T2 RC 2.50 6.00
170 Justin Germano UR T2 RC 2.50 6.00
171 Justin Hampson UR T2 RC 2.50 6.00
172 Chris Young UR T2 RC 20.00 50.00
173 Justin Knoedler UR T2 RC 2.50 6.00
174 Justin Lehr UR T2 RC 2.50 6.00
175 Justin Leone UR T2 RC 4.00 10.00
176 Kaz Tadano UR T2 RC 4.00 10.00
177 Kevin Cave UR T2 RC 2.50 6.00
178 Linc Holdzkom UR T2 RC 2.50 6.00
179 Mike Rose UR T2 RC 2.50 6.00
180 Luis Gonzalez UR T2 RC 2.50 6.00
181 Mariano Gomez UR T2 RC 2.50 6.00
182 Rene Rivera UR T2 RC 2.50 6.00
183 Michael Wuertz UR T2 RC 4.00 10.00
184 Mike Gosling UR T2 RC 2.50 6.00
185 Mike Johnston UR T2 RC 2.50 6.00
186 Mike Rouse UR T2 RC 2.50 6.00
187 Nick Regilio UR T2 RC 2.50 6.00
188 Onil Joseph UR T2 RC 2.50 6.00
189 Orl Rodriguez UR T2 RC 2.50 6.00
190 Phil Stockman UR T2 RC 2.50 6.00
191 Renyel Pinto UR T2 RC 4.00 10.00
192 Roberto Novoa UR T2 RC 4.00 10.00
193 Roman Colon UR T2 RC 2.50 6.00
194 Ronald Belisario UR T2 RC 2.50 6.00
195 Ronny Cedeno UR T3 RC 4.00 10.00
196 Ryan Meaux UR T3 RC 3.00 8.00
197 Ryan Wing UR T3 RC 3.00 8.00
198 Scott Dohmann UR T3 RC 3.00 8.00
199 Joey Gathright UR T3 RC 5.00 12.00
200 Shawn Camp UR T3 RC 3.00 8.00
201 Shawn Hill UR T3 RC 3.00 8.00
202 Steve Andrade UR T3 RC 3.00 8.00
203 Tim Bausher UR T3 RC 3.00 8.00
204 Tim Bittner UR T3 RC 3.00 8.00
205 Brad Halsey UR T3 RC 5.00 12.00
206 William Bergolla UR T3 RC 3.00 8.00
207 Kameron Loe UR T3 RC 8.00 20.00
208 Jesse Crain UR T3 RC 5.00 12.00
209 Scott Kazmir UR T3 RC 12.50 30.00
210 Akinori Otsuka AU RC 20.00 50.00
211 Chris Oxspring AU RC 10.00 25.00
212 Ian Snell AU RC 15.00 40.00
213 John Gall AU RC 15.00 40.00
214 Jose Capellan AU RC 10.00 25.00
215 Yadier Molina AU RC 50.00 80.00
216 Merkin Valdez AU RC 10.00 25.00
217 R.Ramirez AU RC EXCH 10.00 25.00
218 Rusty Tucker AU RC 15.00 40.00
219 Scott Proctor AU RC 15.00 40.00
220 Sean Henn AU RC 10.00 25.00
221 Shingo Takatsu AU RC 15.00 40.00
222 Kazuo Matsui UR T3 RC 4.00 10.00

2004 Ultimate Collection Gold

*GOLD 1-42: 1.25X TO 3X BASIC
*GOLD 43-126: 1.25X TO 3X BASIC
*GOLD 127-168: .75X TO 2X BASIC
*GOLD 169-194: .6X TO 1.5X BASIC
OVERALL PARALLEL ODDS 1:4
1-194 PRINT RUN 50 SERIAL #'d SETS
195-209/222 PRINT RUN 25 SER.#'d SETS
AU 210-221 PRINT RUN 15 SERIAL #'d SETS
195-222 NO PRICING DUE TO SCARCITY
EXCHANGE DEADLINE 12/28/07

2004 Ultimate Collection Platinum

OVERALL PARALLEL ODDS 1:4
1-126 PRINT RUN 10 SERIAL #'d SETS
AU 210-221 PRINT RUN 1 SERIAL #'d SET
NO PRICING DUE TO SCARCITY
EXCHANGE DEADLINE 12/28/07

2004 Ultimate Collection Rainbow

OVERALL PARALLEL ODDS 1:4
STATED PRINT RUN 1 SERIAL #'d SET
NO PRICING DUE TO SCARCITY

2004 Ultimate Collection Achievement Materials

OVERALL GAME-USED ODDS 1:4
PRINT RUNS B/WN 9-99 COPIES PER
NO PRICING ON QTY OF 9
BG Bob Gibson Jsy/68 6.00 15.00
BR Brooks Robinson Jsy/64 8.00 20.00
CA Roy Campanella Pants/51 10.00 25.00
CL Roger Clemens Jsy/63 12.50 30.00
CR Cal Ripken Pants/82 20.00 50.00
CY Carl Yastrzemski Jsy/67 12.50 30.00
DD Don Drysdale Pants/51 10.00 25.00
DJ Derek Jeter Jsy/96 12.50 30.00
DM Don Mattingly Jsy/85 10.00 25.00
EB Ernie Banks Jsy/58 10.00 25.00
EM Eddie Murray Jsy/77 6.00 15.00
FR Frank Robinson Pants/66 4.00 10.00
GB George Brett Jsy/80 10.00 25.00
GM Greg Maddux Jsy/92 10.00 25.00
HK Harmon Killebrew Jsy/69 6.00 15.00
JB Johnny Bench Jsy/68 6.00 15.00
JD Joe DiMaggio Pants/39 50.00 100.00
JP Jim Palmer Jsy/34 6.00 15.00
JR Jackie Robinson Jsy/47 30.00 60.00
KG Ken Griffey Jr. Jsy/97 10.00 25.00
MA Mickey Mantle Pants/56 125.00 200.00
MC Willie McCovey Jsy/59 8.00 20.00
MP Mike Piazza Jsy/93 10.00 25.00
MS Mike Schmidt Jsy/80 10.00 25.00
OC Orlando Cepeda Jsy/58 5.00 12.00
PM Pedro Martinez Jsy/87 6.00 15.00
RC Rob Clemente Pants/66 50.00 100.00
RJ Randy Johnson Jsy/57 6.00 15.00
RM Roger Maris Jsy/61 30.00 60.00
RO Rod Carew Jsy/49 8.00 20.00
RS Ryne Sandberg Jsy/84 15.00 40.00
RY Robin Yount Jsy/82 6.00 15.00
SC Steve Carlton Pants/72 4.00 10.00
SS Sammy Sosa Jsy/75 6.00 15.00
TC Ty Cobb Pants/9
TM Thurman Munson Pants/70 6.00 15.00
TS Tom Seaver Jsy/69 6.00 15.00

TW Ted Williams Jsy/42 40.00 80.00
WS Warren Spahn Jsy/9
YB Yogi Berra Jsy/51 10.00 25.00

2004 Ultimate Collection All-Stars Signatures

OVERALL AU ODDS 1:4
PRINT RUNS B/WN 1-24 COPIES PER
NO PRICING ON QTY OF 12 OR LESS
EXCHANGE DEADLINE 12/28/07
AK Al Kaline/15
BD Bobby Doerr/9
BF Bob Feller/8
BG Bob Gibson/8
BR Brooks Robinson/15 30.00 60.00
CB Carlos Beltran/1
CL Roger Clemens/10
CR Cal Ripken/19 150.00 250.00
CY Carl Yastrzemski/18 40.00 80.00
DJ Derek Jeter/6
DM Don Mattingly/6
DS Duke Snider/8
FT Frank Thomas/5
HB Hank Blalock/2
HK Harmon Killebrew/11
JB Jeff Bagwell/4
JC Joe Carter/5
JM Joe Morgan/10
JP Jim Palmer/6
KG Ken Griffey Jr./12
KW Kerry Wood/1
LA Luis Aparicio/10
LB Lou Brock/6 EXCH
MC Miguel Cabrera/1
MP Mark Prior/1
MR Manny Ramirez/8
MS Mike Schmidt/12
NG Nomar Garciaparra/5
NR Nolan Ryan/8
OS Ozzie Smith/15 40.00 80.00
RC Rod Carew/18 20.00 50.00
RP Rafael Palmeiro/4
RS Ryne Sandberg/10
SC Steve Carlton/10 EXCH
SM Stan Musial/24 40.00 80.00
SR Scott Rolen/3 EXCH
TH Todd Helton/5
VG Vladimir Guerrero/5
WC Will Clark/6
WF Whitey Ford/8
WM Willie McCovey/6

2004 Ultimate Collection Bat Barrel Signatures

OVERALL PREMIUM AU ODDS 1:20
PRINT RUNS B/WN 1-5 COPIES PER
NO PRICING DUE TO SCARCITY
AK Al Kaline/3
AS Alfonso Soriano/5
BE Johnny Bench/5
BG Brian Giles/5
BR Brooks Robinson/4
BW Billy Williams/4
CB Carlos Beltran/5
CF Carlton Fisk/4
CJ Chipper Jones/5
CP Corey Patterson/1
CR Cal Ripken/3
DJ Derek Jeter/5
DM Don Mattingly/5
DW Dave Winfield/5
EB Ernie Banks/2
EC Eric Chavez/5
FR Frank Robinson/2
FT Frank Thomas/4
GB George Brett/5
HB Hank Blalock/4
JB Jeff Bagwell/1
KG Ken Griffey Jr./5
KP Kirby Puckett/5
MC Miguel Cabrera/1
MO Joe Morgan/5
MP Mike Piazza/5
MR Manny Ramirez/3
MS Mike Schmidt/3
NG Nomar Garciaparra/2
PM Paul Molitor/3
RC Roger Clemens/1
RP Rafael Palmeiro/5
SC Sean Casey/3
SM Stan Musial/1
SR Scott Rolen/4
TE Miguel Tejada/5
TH Todd Helton/5
VG Vladimir Guerrero/5
WB Wade Boggs/4
WC Will Clark/1
YB Yogi Berra/1

2004 Ultimate Collection Dual Game Patch

*OVERALL 4-COLOR: ADD 20% PREMIUM
*OVERALL 5+ COLOR: ADD 50% PREMIUM
*LOGO PATCH: ADD 50% PREMIUM
OVERALL PATCH ODDS 1:4
STATED PRINT RUN 25 SERIAL #'d SETS
BB Carlos Beltran 20.00 50.00
Jeff Bagwell
BC Josh Beckett 20.00 50.00
Miguel Cabrera
BG Lou Brock 40.00 80.00
Tony Gwynn
BM Yogi Berra
Roger Maris
BS George Brett 60.00 120.00
Mike Schmidt
BT Hank Blalock 20.00 50.00
Mark Teixeira
CG Rod Carew 20.00 50.00
Tony Gwynn
CP Gary Carter 20.00 50.00
Mike Piazza
CR Eric Chavez 20.00 50.00
Scott Rolen
FB Carlton Fisk 20.00 50.00
Johnny Bench
FR Bob Feller 50.00 100.00
Nolan Ryan
GC Mark Grace 20.00 50.00
Will Clark
GG Ken Griffey Jr. 40.00 80.00
Ken Griffey Sr.
GM Bob Gibson 40.00 80.00
Stan Musial
GS Mark Grace 50.00 100.00
Ryne Sandberg
HF Catfish Hunter 20.00 50.00
Rollie Fingers
JC Randy Johnson 40.00 80.00
Roger Clemens
JJ Andruw Jones 20.00 50.00
Chipper Jones
JM Derek Jeter 75.00 150.00
Hideki Matsui
KC Harmon Killebrew 30.00 60.00
Rod Carew
KM Harmon Killebrew 30.00 60.00
Willie McCovey
KS Ken Griffey Jr. 40.00 80.00
Sammy Sosa
LS Fred Lynn 60.00 120.00
Ichiro Suzuki
MG Greg Maddux 20.00 50.00
Tom Glavine
MJ Eddie Mathews 40.00 80.00
Chipper Jones
MM Hideki Matsui
Kazuo Matsui
MY Paul Molitor 20.00 50.00
Robin Yount
PC Rafael Palmeiro 20.00 50.00
Will Clark
PR Albert Pujols 30.00 60.00
Scott Rolen
RC Nolan Ryan 50.00 100.00
Roger Clemens
RM Cal Ripken 125.00 200.00
Eddie Murray
RP Cal Ripken 75.00 150.00
Jim Palmer
RR Jackie Robinson 150.00 250.00
Pee Wee Reese
RS Nolan Ryan 50.00 100.00
Tom Seaver
RT Cal Ripken 40.00 80.00
Miguel Tejada
SB Jim Bunning 40.00 80.00
Mike Schmidt
SM Curt Schilling 30.00 60.00
Pedro Martinez
ST Mike Schmidt 40.00 80.00
Jim Thome
WM Dave Winfield 40.00 80.00
Don Mattingly
WP Kerry Wood 15.00 40.00
Mark Prior
WS Billy Williams 20.00 50.00
Sammy Sosa
YR Carl Yastrzemski 40.00 80.00
Jim Rice

2004 Ultimate Collection Dual Legendary Materials

OVERALL GAME-USED ODDS 1:4
STATED PRINT RUN 50 SERIAL #'d SETS
BM Ernie Banks Jsy 20.00 50.00
Willie McCovey Jsy
BR Babe Ruth Pants 250.00 400.00
Roger Maris Jsy
CB Roy Campanella Pants 20.00 50.00
Yogi Berra Jsy
CM Roberto Clemente Pants 60.00 120.00
Thurman Munson Pants
CS Roy Campanella Pants 20.00 50.00
Duke Snider Pants
DM Joe DiMaggio Pants 150.00 250.00
Mickey Mantle Pants
DW Joe DiMaggio Pants 90.00 180.00
Ted Williams Jsy
FD Bob Feller Jsy 20.00 50.00
Don Drysdale Pants
MB Thurman Munson Pants 20.00 50.00
Yogi Berra Jsy
MC Mickey Mantle Pants 125.00 200.00
Roberto Clemente Pants
MM Mickey Mantle Pants 150.00 250.00
Roger Maris Jsy
MW Mickey Mantle Pants 150.00 250.00
Ted Williams Jsy
RB Ernie Banks Jsy 40.00 80.00
Jackie Robinson Jsy
RC Jackie Robinson Jsy 40.00 80.00
Roy Campanella Pants
RD Babe Ruth Pants 250.00 400.00
Joe DiMaggio Pants
RM Babe Ruth Pants 300.00 500.00
Mickey Mantle Pants
RP Jackie Robinson Jsy 50.00 100.00
Satchel Paige Pants
RW Roberto Clemente Pants 60.00 120.00
Willie McCovey Jsy
WM Eddie Mathews Pants 75.00 150.00
Ted Williams Jsy

2004 Ultimate Collection Dual Materials

OVERALL GAME-USED ODDS 1:4
STATED PRINT RUN 60 SERIAL #'d SETS
BC Brooks Robinson Jsy 40.00 80.00
Cal Ripken Pants
BM Thurman Munson Jsy
Yogi Berra Jsy
BP Johnny Bench Jsy 15.00 40.00
Mike Piazza Jsy
BS George Brett Jsy 30.00 60.00
Mike Schmidt Jsy
CK Rod Carew Jsy 15.00 40.00
Harmon Killebrew Jsy
CM Will Clark Jsy 15.00 40.00
Willie McCovey Jsy
ER Ernie Banks Jsy 30.00 60.00
Ryne Sandberg Jsy
GS Sammy Sosa Jsy 15.00 40.00
Ken Griffey Jr. Jsy
JC Randy Johnson Jsy 20.00 50.00
Roger Clemens Jsy
JM Derek Jeter Jsy 30.00 60.00
Don Mattingly Jsy
MB Thurman Munson Pants
Johnny Bench Jsy
MC Don Mattingly Jsy 20.00 50.00
Will Clark Jsy
MP Joe Mauer Jsy 10.00 25.00
Mark Prior Jsy
MR Bill Mazeroski Jsy 40.00 80.00
Jackie Robinson Jsy
MT Kazuo Matsui Jsy 15.00 40.00
Shingo Takatsu Jsy
MY Paul Molitor Jsy 15.00 40.00
Robin Yount Jsy
PR Albert Pujols Jsy 20.00 50.00
Manny Ramirez Jsy
RC Nolan Ryan Jsy 30.00 60.00
Roger Clemens Jsy
RP Ivan Rodriguez Jsy 10.00 25.00
Mike Piazza Jsy
RR Brooks Robinson Jsy 15.00 40.00
Frank Robinson Jsy
RT Roy Campanella Pants 15.00 40.00
Thurman Munson Pants
SG Ichiro Suzuki Jsy 30.00 60.00
Ken Griffey Jr. Jsy
SP Ben Sheets Jsy 6.00 15.00
Mark Prior Jsy
SR Duke Snider Pants 15.00 40.00
Pee Wee Reese Jsy
SS Sammy Sosa Jsy 30.00 60.00
Ryne Sandberg Jsy
TS Jim Thome Jsy 20.00 50.00
Mike Schmidt Jsy
WM Dave Winfield Jsy 15.00 40.00
Don Mattingly Jsy
WP Kerry Wood Jsy 6.00 15.00
Mark Prior Jsy
WR Kerry Wood Jsy 20.00 50.00
Nolan Ryan Jsy
YR Carl Yastrzemski Jsy 20.00 50.00
Manny Ramirez Jsy

2004 Ultimate Collection Dual Materials Signature

STATED PRINT RUN 25 SERIAL #'d SETS
BANKS/SANTO PRINT RUN 12 #'d CARDS
NO BANKS/SANTO PRICING AVAILABLE
EXCHANGE DEADLINE 12/28/07
AB Luis Aparicio Jsy 50.00 100.00
Ernie Banks Jsy
BB Hank Blalock Jsy 40.00 80.00
Wade Boggs Jsy
BC Brooks Robinson Jsy 175.00 300.00
Cal Ripken Jsy

BF Carlton Fisk Jsy 50.00 100.00
Johnny Bench Jsy
BG Carlos Beltran Jsy 100.00 175.00
Ken Griffey Jr. Jsy
BJ Derek Jeter Jsy 175.00 300.00
Yogi Berra Jsy
BM Brian Giles Jsy 30.00 60.00
Marcus Giles Jsy
BP Johnny Bench Jsy 125.00 200.00
Mike Piazza Jsy
BR Jim Bunning Jsy 30.00 60.00
Robin Roberts Jsy
BS Brooks Robinson Jsy
Scott Rolen Jsy
BT Hank Blalock Jsy 40.00 80.00
Mark Teixeira Jsy
CB Eric Chavez Jsy 30.00 60.00
Hank Blalock Jsy
CC Roger Clemens Jsy 100.00 175.00
Steve Carlton Pants EXCH
CJ Randy Johnson Jsy 250.00 400.00
Roger Clemens Jsy
CK Rod Carew Jsy 50.00 100.00
Harmon Killebrew Jsy
CL Miguel Cabrera Jsy 40.00 80.00
Mike Lowell Jsy
CM Carlos Beltran Jsy 75.00 150.00
Miguel Cabrera Jsy
CR Eric Chavez Jsy
Scott Rolen Jsy EXCH
DD Derek Jeter Jsy 200.00 350.00
Don Mattingly Jsy
DG Don Sutton Jsy 30.00 60.00
Gaylord Perry Jsy
DJ Dave Parker Jsy 60.00 120.00
Jim Rice Jsy
DS Andre Dawson Jsy 60.00 120.00
Ryne Sandberg Jsy
DW Andre Dawson Pants 30.00 60.00
Billy Williams Jsy
ER Ernie Banks Jsy 125.00 200.00
Ryne Sandberg Jsy
FC Bob Feller Jsy 40.00 80.00
Rocky Colavito Jsy
FR Bob Feller Jsy 125.00 200.00
Nolan Ryan Jsy
GB Brooks Robinson Jsy 75.00 150.00
George Brett Jsy
GC Ron Guidry Jsy 30.00 60.00
Steve Carlton Pants EXCH
GG Ken Griffey Sr. Jsy 125.00 200.00
Ken Griffey Jr. Jsy
GM George Brett Jsy 125.00 200.00
Mike Schmidt Jsy
GP Ken Griffey Jr. Jsy 125.00 200.00
Rafael Palmeiro Jsy
GR Greg Maddux Jsy 200.00 350.00
Roger Clemens Jsy
GS Eric Gagne Jsy 40.00 80.00
John Smoltz Jsy
IJ Ivan Rodriguez Jsy
Joe Mauer Jsy EXCH
IM Ivan Rodriguez Jsy
Mike Piazza Jsy EXCH
IV Ivan Rodriguez Jsy 50.00 100.00
Victor Martinez Jsy EXCH
JB Fergie Jenkins Pants 60.00 120.00
Ernie Banks Pants
JC Randy Johnson Jsy 75.00 150.00
Steve Carlton Pants EXCH
JD Johnny Podres Jsy 30.00 60.00
Don Sutton Jsy
JG Randy Johnson Jsy 175.00 300.00
Ken Griffey Jr. Jsy
JM Chipper Jones Jsy 100.00 175.00
Dale Murphy Jsy
JP Fergie Jenkins Pants 30.00 60.00
Jim Palmer Jsy
JR Derek Jeter Jsy 350.00 600.00
Cal Ripken Jsy
KG Harmon Killebrew Jsy 100.00 175.00
Ken Griffey Jr. Jsy
KN Kerry Wood Jsy 125.00 200.00
Nolan Ryan Jsy
KT Scott Kazmir Jsy 40.00 80.00
Shingo Takatsu Jsy
LB Don Larsen Pants 150.00 250.00
Yogi Berra Pants
MB Joe Morgan Jsy 50.00 100.00
Johnny Bench Jsy
MC Don Mattingly Jsy 75.00 150.00
Will Clark Jsy
MH Mark Mulder Jsy 40.00 80.00
Tim Hudson Jsy
MP Joe Mauer Jsy 50.00 100.00
Mark Prior Jsy
MS Bill Mazeroski Jsy 75.00 150.00
Ryne Sandberg Jsy
MW Mark Grace Jsy 40.00 80.00
Will Clark Jsy
MY Paul Molitor Jsy 75.00 150.00
Robin Yount Jsy
NR Nolan Ryan Jsy 250.00 400.00
Roger Clemens Jsy
OR David Ortiz Jsy 125.00 200.00
Manny Ramirez Jsy
OS Ozzie Smith Jsy 100.00 175.00
Stan Musial Jsy
PC Rafael Palmeiro Jsy 50.00 100.00
Will Clark Jsy
PN Gaylord Perry Jsy 30.00 60.00
Phil Niekro Jsy
PS Duke Snider Pants 40.00 80.00
Johnny Podres Jsy
RB Bill Mazeroski Jsy 40.00 80.00
Rod Carew Jsy
RC Brooks Robinson Jsy 40.00 80.00
Eric Chavez Jsy
RM Cal Ripken Jsy 200.00 350.00
Eddie Murray Jsy
RP Brooks Robinson Jsy 40.00 80.00
Jim Palmer Jsy
RR Brooks Robinson Jsy 40.00 80.00
Frank Robinson Jsy
RS Robin Roberts Jsy 30.00 60.00
Steve Carlton Pants EXCH
RT Cal Ripken Pants 175.00 300.00
Miguel Tejada Jsy
RW Jose Reyes Jsy
David Wright Jsy EXCH
SB Ernie Banks Jsy
Ron Santo Jsy/12
SC Mike Schmidt Jsy 75.00 150.00
Steve Carlton Pants EXCH
SF Ben Sheets Jsy 30.00 60.00
Bob Feller Jsy
SG Bruce Sutter Jsy 40.00 80.00
Eric Gagne Jsy
SO Ben Sheets Jsy 30.00 60.00
Roy Oswalt Jsy
SP Ben Sheets Jsy 30.00 60.00
Mark Prior Jsy
SR Brooks Robinson Jsy 125.00 200.00
Mike Schmidt Jsy
SS Ben Sheets Jsy 50.00 100.00
Tom Seaver Jsy
TB Brian Giles Jsy 40.00 80.00
Tony Gwynn Jsy
TC Mark Teixeira Jsy 40.00 80.00
Miguel Cabrera Jsy
WM Dave Winfield Jsy 100.00 175.00
Don Mattingly Jsy
WO Willie McCovey Jsy 40.00 80.00
Orlando Cepeda Jsy
WP Kerry Wood Jsy
Mark Prior Jsy
WW Will Clark Jsy 40.00 80.00
Willie McCovey Jsy
YR Carl Yastrzemski Jsy 100.00 175.00
Manny Ramirez Jsy
YW Delmon Young Jsy
Rickie Weeks Jsy

2004 Ultimate Collection Game Materials

OVERALL GAME-USED ODDS 1:4
STATED PRINT RUN 99 SERIAL #'d SETS
AK Al Kaline Jsy 6.00 15.00
AP Albert Pujols Jsy 10.00 25.00
BF Bob Feller Jsy 4.00 10.00
BG Bob Gibson Jsy 6.00 15.00
BM Bill Mazeroski Jsy 6.00 15.00
BR Brooks Robinson Jsy 6.00 15.00
CF Carlton Fisk Pants 6.00 15.00
CL Roger Clemens Jsy 10.00 25.00
CR Cal Ripken Jsy 20.00 50.00
CY Carl Yastrzemski Jsy 10.00 25.00
DD Don Drysdale Pants 6.00 15.00
DJ Derek Jeter Jsy 12.50 30.00
DM Don Mattingly Jsy 10.00 25.00
DS Duke Snider Pants 6.00 15.00
DW Dave Winfield Jsy 4.00 10.00
EB Ernie Banks Jsy 6.00 15.00
ED Eddie Mathews Pants 6.00 15.00
EM Eddie Murray Jsy 6.00 15.00
FR Frank Robinson Pants 4.00 10.00
GB George Brett Jsy 10.00 25.00
HK Harmon Killebrew Jsy 6.00 15.00
IS Ichiro Suzuki Jsy 30.00 60.00
JB Johnny Bench Jsy 6.00 15.00
JP Jim Palmer Jsy 4.00 10.00
JR Jackie Robinson Jsy 20.00 50.00
KG Ken Griffey Jr. Jsy 10.00 25.00
KW Kerry Wood Jsy 4.00 10.00
LB Lou Brock Jsy 6.00 15.00
MA Juan Marichal Jsy 4.00 10.00
MP Mark Prior Jsy 6.00 15.00
MS Mike Schmidt Jsy 10.00 25.00
OS Ozzie Smith Jsy 10.00 25.00
PI Mike Piazza Jsy 10.00 25.00
PM Paul Molitor Jsy 4.00 10.00
RC Rod Carew Jsy 6.00 15.00
RJ Randy Johnson Jsy 6.00 15.00
RM Roger Maris Jsy 20.00 50.00
RS Ryne Sandberg Jsy 15.00 40.00
RY Robin Yount Jsy 6.00 15.00
SC Steve Carlton Pants 4.00 10.00
SM Stan Musial Jsy 10.00 25.00
TC Ty Cobb Pants 50.00 100.00
TG Tony Gwynn Jsy 10.00 25.00
TM Thurman Munson Pants 6.00 15.00
TS Tom Seaver Jsy 6.00 15.00
WB Wade Boggs Jsy 6.00 15.00
WC Will Clark Jsy 6.00 15.00
WM Willie McCovey Jsy 6.00 15.00
WS Warren Spahn Jsy 6.00 15.00
WS Willie Stargell Jsy 6.00 15.00

2004 Ultimate Collection Game Materials Signatures

OVERALL AUTO/GAME-USED ODDS 1:4
STATED PRINT RUN 50 SERIAL #'d SETS
TEJADA A's PRINT RUN 34 SER.#'d CARDS
EXCHANGE DEADLINE 12/28/07
AD Andre Dawson Cubs Jsy 15.00 40.00
AD1 Andre Dawson Expos Jsy 15.00 40.00
AK Al Kaline Jsy 30.00 60.00
AS Alfonso Soriano Jsy 20.00 50.00
BA Bobby Abreu Jsy EXCH 15.00 40.00
BE Josh Beckett Jsy 20.00 50.00

BF Bob Feller Jsy 15.00 40.00
BG Bob Gibson Jsy 20.00 50.00
BM Bill Mazeroski Jsy 20.00 50.00
BR Brooks Robinson Jsy 20.00 50.00
BS Ben Sheets Blue Jsy 15.00 40.00
BS1 Ben Sheets White Jsy 15.00 40.00
BU Jim Bunning Jsy 15.00 40.00
BW Billy Williams Jsy 15.00 40.00
CA Miguel Cabrera Jsy 20.00 50.00
CB Carlos Beltran Jsy 15.00 40.00
CF Carlton Fisk R.Sox Jsy 20.00 50.00
CF1 Carlton Fisk W.Sox Jsy 20.00 50.00
CJ Chipper Jones Jsy 30.00 60.00
CL R.Clemens Astros Jsy 60.00 120.00
CL1 R.Clemens Yanks Jsy 60.00 120.00
CL2 R.Clemens Sox Jsy 60.00 120.00
CO R.Colavito Tigers Jsy 40.00 80.00
CO1 R.Colavito Indians Jsy 40.00 80.00
CR Cal Ripken Jsy 125.00 200.00
CY Carl Yastrzemski Jsy 40.00 80.00
DE Dennis Eckersley Sox Jsy 15.00 40.00
DE1 Dennis Eckersley A's Jsy 15.00 40.00
DJ Derek Jeter Jsy 125.00 200.00
DL Don Larsen Pants EXCH * 15.00 40.00
DM Dale Murphy Jsy 20.00 50.00
DO Don Mattingly Jsy 40.00 80.00
DS Don Sutton Jsy 15.00 40.00
DW D.Winfield Yanks Jsy 20.00 50.00
DW1 D.Winfield Padres Jsy 20.00 50.00
DY Delmon Young D-Rays Jsy 20.00 50.00
DY1 Delmon Young USA Jsy 20.00 50.00
EB Ernie Banks Jsy 30.00 60.00
EC Eric Chavez Jsy 15.00 40.00
EG Eric Gagne Jsy 20.00 50.00
EM Eddie Murray O's Jsy 50.00 100.00
EM1 E.Murray Dgr Jsy EXCH * 50.00 100.00
FJ Fergie Jenkins Pants 15.00 40.00
FR Frank Robinson O's Jsy 20.00 50.00
FR1 Frank Robinson Reds Jsy 20.00 50.00
FT Frank Thomas Jsy 40.00 80.00
GB George Brett Jsy 50.00 100.00
GC Gary Carter Expos Jsy 15.00 40.00
GC1 Gary Carter Mets Jsy 15.00 40.00
GM Greg Maddux Cubs Jsy 75.00 150.00
GM1 Greg Maddux Braves Jsy 75.00 150.00
GP Gaylord Perry Indians Jsy 10.00 25.00
GP1 Gaylord Perry Giants Jsy 10.00 25.00
HB Hank Blalock Jsy 15.00 40.00
HE Todd Helton Jsy 20.00 50.00
HK Harmon Killebrew Jsy 30.00 60.00
IR Ivan Rodriguez Jsy EXCH 30.00 60.00
JB Johnny Bench Jsy 30.00 60.00
JC Joe Carter Pants 15.00 40.00
JE Jeff Bagwell Jsy 30.00 60.00
JM Joe Mauer Blue Jsy 20.00 50.00
JM1 Joe Mauer White Jsy 20.00 50.00
JP Jim Palmer Jsy 15.00 40.00
JR Jim Rice Jsy 15.00 40.00
JS John Smoltz Jsy 30.00 60.00
JU Juan Marichal Jsy 15.00 40.00
KG Ken Griffey Jr. Reds Jsy 60.00 120.00
KG1 Ken Griffey Jr. M's Jsy 60.00 120.00
KW Kerry Wood Jsy 20.00 50.00
LB Lou Brock Cards Jsy 20.00 50.00
LB1 Lou Brock Cubs Jsy 20.00 50.00
MC Willie McCovey Jsy 20.00 50.00
MG Mark Grace Jsy 20.00 50.00
ML Mike Lowell Jsy 10.00 25.00
MO Joe Morgan Jsy 15.00 40.00
MP Mark Prior Cubs Jsy 15.00 40.00
MP1 Mark Prior USA Jsy 15.00 40.00
MR Manny Ramirez Jsy 40.00 80.00
MS Mike Schmidt Jsy 50.00 100.00
MT Mark Teixeira Jsy 20.00 50.00
MU Mark Mulder Jsy 15.00 40.00
NG N.Garciaparra Cubs Jsy 60.00 120.00
NG1 N. Garciaparra Sox Jsy 60.00 120.00
NR Nolan Ryan Rgr Jsy 60.00 120.00
NR1 Nolan Ryan Angels Jsy 60.00 120.00
NR2 Nolan Ryan Astros Jsy 60.00 120.00
NR3 Nolan Ryan Mets Jsy 60.00 120.00
OC Orl Cepeda Giants Jsy 15.00 40.00
OC1 Orl Cepeda Cards Jsy 15.00 40.00
OS Ozzie Smith Jsy 30.00 60.00
PI Mike Piazza Mets Jsy 75.00 150.00
PI1 Mike Piazza Dodgers Jsy 75.00 150.00
PM Paul Molitor Brewers Jsy 15.00 40.00
PM1 Paul Molitor Twins Jsy 15.00 40.00
PM2 Paul Molitor Jays Jsy 15.00 40.00
PO Johnny Podres Jsy 15.00 40.00
RC Rod Carew Twins Jsy 20.00 50.00
RC1 Rod Carew Angels Pants 20.00 50.00
RF R.Fingers Brewers Pants 15.00 40.00
RF1 Rollie Fingers A's Pants 15.00 40.00
RG Ron Guidry Jsy 20.00 50.00
RJ R.Johnson D'backs Jsy 60.00 120.00
RJ1 Randy Johnson M's Jsy 60.00 120.00
RO Roy Oswalt Jsy 15.00 40.00
RP Rafael Palmeiro Jsy 30.00 60.00
RR Robin Roberts Jsy 15.00 40.00
RS Red Schoendienst Jsy 15.00 40.00
RW Rickie Weeks Brewers Jsy 15.00 40.00
RW1 Rickie Weeks USA Jsy 15.00 40.00
RY Robin Yount Jsy EXCH * 30.00 60.00
SA Ryne Sandberg Jsy 50.00 100.00
SC S.Carlt Phils Pants EXCH 15.00 40.00
SC1 S.Carlt Cards Pants EXCH 15.00 40.00
SN D.Snider Brooklyn Pants 20.00 50.00
SN1 Duke Snider L.A. Pants
SR Scott Rolen Jsy EXCH 20.00 50.00
TE Miguel Tejada O's Jsy
TE1 Miguel Tejada A's Jsy/34 20.00 50.00
TG Tony Gwynn Jsy 30.00 60.00
TH Tim Hudson Jsy 20.00 50.00
TP Tony Perez Jsy 20.00 50.00
TS Tom Seaver Mets Jsy 30.00 60.00
TS1 Tom Seaver Reds Jsy 30.00 60.00
VG Vladimir Guerrero Jsy 40.00 80.00

WB Wade Boggs Sox Jsy 30.00 60.00
WB1 Wade Boggs Yanks Jsy 30.00 60.00
WC Will Clark Giants Jsy 20.00 50.00
WC1 Will Clark Cards Jsy 20.00 50.00
WC2 Will Clark Rgr Jsy 20.00 50.00
WC3 Will Clark O's Jsy 20.00 50.00

2004 Ultimate Collection Game Patch

*3-COLOR PATCH: ADD 20% PREMIUM
*4-COLOR PATCH: ADD 50% PREMIUM
*5+ COLOR PATCH: ADD 100% PREMIUM
*LOGO PATCH: ADD 150% PREMIUM
OVERALL PATCH ODDS 1:4
PRINT RUNS B/WN 10-75 COPIES PER
NO PRICING ON QTY OF 10
AK Al Kaline/21 40.00 80.00
AP Albert Pujols/75 20.00 50.00
AS Alfonso Soriano/75 6.00 15.00
BA Jeff Bagwell/75 10.00 25.00
BE Josh Beckett/75 6.00 15.00
BF Bob Feller/75 15.00 40.00
BM Bill Mazeroski/55 20.00 50.00
BR Brooks Robinson/75 15.00 40.00
BS Ben Sheets/75 6.00 15.00
BU Jim Bunning/66 15.00 40.00
BW Bernie Williams/75 10.00 25.00
CA Miguel Cabrera/75 10.00 25.00
CB Carlos Beltran/75 6.00 15.00
CF Carlton Fisk R.Sox/18 30.00 60.00
CF1 Carlton Fisk W.Sox/10
CH Catfish Hunter/75 15.00 40.00
CJ Chipper Jones/75 10.00 25.00
CL Roger Clemens/75 15.00 40.00
CO1 Rocky Colavito/75 50.00 100.00
CR Cal Ripken/75 30.00 60.00
CS Curt Schilling/75 10.00 25.00
CY Carl Yastrzemski/75 15.00 40.00
DJ Derek Jeter/75 20.00 50.00
DM Don Mattingly/75 20.00 50.00
DW Dave Winfield/75 10.00 25.00
EC Eric Chavez/75 6.00 15.00
EM Eddie Mathews/17 40.00 80.00
GB George Brett/75 20.00 50.00
GC Gary Carter/75 10.00 25.00
GL Troy Glaus/75 6.00 15.00
GM Greg Maddux Cubs/75 12.50 30.00
GM1 Greg Maddux Braves/75 12.50 30.00
GS Gary Sheffield/75 6.00 15.00
HB Hank Blalock/75 6.00 15.00
HK Harmon Killebrew/75 15.00 40.00
HM Hideki Matsui/44 50.00 100.00
IR Ivan Rodriguez/75 10.00 25.00
IS Ichiro Suzuki/75 60.00 120.00
JB Johnny Bench/75 15.00 40.00
JD Joe DiMaggio/75 150.00 300.00
JM Joe Mauer/75 8.00 20.00
JP Jim Palmer/75 10.00 25.00
JT Jim Thome/75
KG Ken Griffey Jr./75 15.00 40.00
KM Kazuo Matsui/75 15.00 40.00
KW Kerry Wood/75 6.00 15.00
LB Lou Brock/75 15.00 40.00
MA Juan Marichal/75 10.00 25.00
MO Joe Morgan/75 10.00 25.00
MP Mark Prior/75 10.00 25.00
MR Manny Ramirez/75 10.00 25.00
MS Mike Schmidt/75 20.00 50.00
MT Mark Teixeira/75 10.00 25.00
MU Eddie Murray/75 15.00 40.00
NF Nellie Fox/55 60.00 120.00
NR Nolan Ryan Rgr/51 20.00 50.00
NR1 Nolan Ryan Astros/75 20.00 50.00
NR2 Nolan Ryan Angels/75 20.00 50.00
OS Ozzie Smith/75 15.00 40.00
PE Pedro Martinez/75 10.00 25.00
PI Mike Piazza/75 12.50 30.00
PM Paul Molitor/75 10.00 25.00
PO Johnny Podres/75 15.00 40.00
RB Roberto Clemente/75 125.00 200.00
RC Rod Carew Angels/75 15.00 40.00
RG Ron Guidry/75 15.00 40.00
RJ Randy Johnson D'backs/75 10.00 25.00
RJ1 Randy Johnson M's/75 10.00 25.00
RO Rod Carew Twins/75 15.00 40.00
RP Rafael Palmeiro/75 10.00 25.00
RS Ryne Sandberg/75 20.00 50.00
RY Robin Yount/75 10.00 25.00
SM Stan Musial/75 40.00 80.00
SP Warren Spahn/62 30.00 60.00
SR Scott Rolen/75 10.00 25.00
SS Sammy Sosa/75 10.00 25.00
TE Miguel Tejada/75 6.00 15.00
TG Tony Gwynn/75 12.50 30.00
TH Todd Helton/75 10.00 25.00
TM Thurman Munson/75 15.00 40.00
TS Tom Seaver/75 10.00 25.00
VG Vladimir Guerrero/75 10.00 25.00
WB Wade Boggs/75 10.00 25.00
WC Will Clark Giants/75 15.00 40.00
WC1 Will Clark Rgr/75 15.00 40.00
WI Billy Williams/75 10.00 25.00
WM Willie McCovey/75 15.00 40.00
WS Willie Stargell/75 15.00 40.00
YB Yogi Berra/75 15.00 40.00

2004 Ultimate Collection Game Patch Signature

*4-COLOR PATCH: ADD 20% PREMIUM
*5+ COLOR PATCH: ADD 50% PREMIUM
*LOGO PATCH: ADD 100% PREMIUM
OVERALL AUTO/GAME-USED ODDS 1:4
STATED PRINT RUN 30 SERIAL #'d SETS
C.FISK PRINT RUN 10 SERIAL #'d CARDS

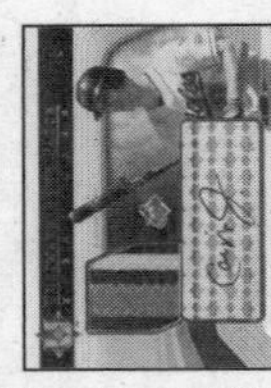

NO C.FISK PRICING DUE TO SCARCITY
EXCHANGE DEADLINE 12/28/07
AD Andre Dawson 20.00 50.00
AK Al Kaline 75.00 150.00
BG Bob Gibson 30.00 60.00
BR Brooks Robinson 30.00 60.00
BS Ben Sheets 20.00 50.00
CB Carlos Beltran 20.00 50.00
CF Carlton Fisk/10
CR Cal Ripken 150.00 250.00
CY Carl Yastrzemski 50.00 100.00
DJ Derek Jeter 150.00 250.00
DM Don Mattingly 50.00 100.00
EB Ernie Banks 40.00 80.00
EC Eric Chavez 20.00 50.00
EM Eddie Murray 40.00 80.00
FR Frank Robinson 60.00 120.00
GB George Brett 60.00 120.00
GM Greg Maddux 100.00 200.00
HB Hank Blalock 20.00 50.00
HK Harmon Killebrew 40.00 80.00
JB Johnny Bench 60.00 120.00
JM Joe Mauer 30.00 60.00
JP Jim Palmer 20.00 50.00
JR Jim Rice 20.00 50.00
KG Ken Griffey Jr. 100.00 200.00
KW Kerry Wood
MA Juan Marichal 20.00 50.00
MC Miguel Cabrera 30.00 60.00
MP Mark Prior 20.00 50.00
MS Mike Schmidt 60.00 120.00
MT Mark Teixeira 30.00 60.00
MU Mark Mulder 20.00 50.00
NR Nolan Ryan 100.00 200.00
OS Ozzie Smith 40.00 80.00
PI Mike Piazza 100.00 175.00
PM Paul Molitor 20.00 50.00
RC Rod Carew 30.00 60.00
RJ Randy Johnson 75.00 150.00
RO Roy Oswalt 20.00 50.00
RS Ryne Sandberg 75.00 150.00
RY Robin Yount 40.00 80.00
SC Red Schoendienst 20.00 50.00
SM Stan Musial 50.00 100.00
TG Tony Gwynn 40.00 80.00
TS Tom Seaver 40.00 80.00
WB Wade Boggs 40.00 80.00
WC Will Clark 30.00 60.00
WM Willie McCovey EXCH 30.00 60.00

2004 Ultimate Collection Gold Glove Signature Materials

OVERALL AUTO/GAME-USED ODDS 1:4
PRINT RUNS B/WN 1-16 COPIES PER
NO PRICING ON QTY OF 14 OR LESS
EXCHANGE DEADLINE 12/28/07
AD Andre Dawson Jsy/8
AK Al Kaline Jsy/10
BG Bob Gibson Jsy/9
BM Bill Mazeroski Jsy/8
BR Brooks Robinson Jsy/16
CY Carl Yastrzemski Jsy/7
DM Don Mattingly Jsy/9
DW Dave Winfield Jsy/7
GC Gary Carter Jsy/3
GM Greg Maddux Jsy/14
IR Ivan Rodriguez Jsy/11 EXCH
JB Johnny Bench Jsy/10
KG Ken Griffey Jr. Jsy/10
MS Mike Schmidt Jsy/10
OS Ozzie Smith Jsy/13
PN Phil Niekro Jsy/5
RG Ron Guidry Jsy/5
RS Ryne Sandberg Jsy/9
SR Scott Rolen Jsy/6 EXCH

2004 Ultimate Collection Legendary Materials

OVERALL GAME-USED ODDS 1:4
STATED PRINT RUN 50 SERIAL #'d SETS
BF Bob Feller Jsy 5.00 12.00
BR Babe Ruth Pants 175.00 300.00
CA Roy Campanella Pants 10.00 25.00
DD Don Drysdale Pants 10.00 25.00
DS Duke Snider Jsy 8.00 20.00
EB Ernie Banks Jsy 10.00 25.00
EM Eddie Mathews Pants 10.00 25.00
JD Joe DiMaggio Pants 50.00 100.00
JR Jackie Robinson Jsy 30.00 60.00
MM Mickey Mantle Pants 125.00 200.00
RC Roberto Clemente Jsy 50.00 100.00
RM Roger Maris Jsy 30.00 60.00
SM Stan Musial Jsy 15.00 40.00
SP Satchel Paige Pants 30.00 60.00
TC Ty Cobb Pants 60.00 120.00
TM Thurman Munson Pants 10.00 25.00
TW Ted Williams Jsy 40.00 80.00
WM Willie McCovey Jsy 8.00 20.00
YB Yogi Berra Jsy 10.00 25.00

2004 Ultimate Collection Logo Patch Signatures

OVERALL PREMIUM AUTO ODDS 1:20
STATED PRINT RUN 1 SERIAL #'d SET
NO PRICING DUE TO SCARCITY
EXCHANGE DEADLINE 12/28/07
AS Alfonso Soriano
BE Josh Beckett
BS Ben Sheets
CB Carlos Beltran
CJ Chipper Jones
CL Roger Clemens Astros
CL1 Roger Clemens Yanks
CR Cal Ripken
DJ Derek Jeter
EC Eric Chavez
GM Greg Maddux
HB Hank Blalock
IR Ivan Rodriguez EXCH
JB Jeff Bagwell
JM Joe Mauer
JS John Smoltz
KG Ken Griffey Jr.
KW Kerry Wood
MC Miguel Cabrera
MP Mark Prior
MR Manny Ramirez
MT Mark Teixeira
PI Mike Piazza
RJ Randy Johnson
RP Rafael Palmeiro
SR Scott Rolen EXCH
TE Miguel Tejada
TG Tony Gwynn
VG Vladimir Guerrero

2004 Ultimate Collection Loyalty Signature Materials

OVERALL AUTO/GAME-USED ODDS 1:4
PRINT RUNS B/WN 17-23 COPIES PER
BR Brooks Robinson Jsy/23 30.00 60.00
CR Cal Ripken Pants/21 150.00 250.00
CY Carl Yastrzemski Jsy/23 50.00 100.00
EB Ernie Banks Jsy/19 50.00 100.00
GB George Brett Jsy/21 60.00 120.00
HK Harmon Killebrew Jsy/21 40.00 80.00
JB Johnny Bench Jsy/17
MS Mike Schmidt Jsy/18 60.00 120.00
RY Robin Yount Jsy/20 40.00 80.00
TG Tony Gwynn Jsy/20 40.00 80.00

2004 Ultimate Collection Quadruple Materials

OVERALL GAME-USED ODDS 1:4
STATED PRINT RUN 15 SERIAL #'d SETS
J ='s JSY, P ='s PANTS
NO PRICING DUE TO SCARCITY
CCMM Orlando Cepeda Jsy
Will Clark Jsy
Willie McCovey Jsy
Juan Marichal Jsy
FWYR Carlton Fisk Jsy
Ted Williams Jsy
Carl Yastrzemski Jsy
Manny Ramirez Jsy
MPCS Bill Mazeroski Pants
Dave Parker Jsy
Roberto Clemente Pants
Willie Stargell Jsy
MSGP Stan Musial Jsy
Ozzie Smith Jsy
Bob Gibson Jsy
Albert Pujols Jsy
RGBP Frank Robinson Pants
Ken Griffey Sr. Jsy
Johnny Bench Jsy
Tony Perez Jsy
RMDM Babe Ruth Pants
Thurman Munson Pants
Joe DiMaggio Pants
Mickey Mantle Pants
RRMP Brooks Robinson Jsy
Cal Ripken Pants
Eddie Murray Jsy
Jim Palmer Jsy
SBRC Mike Schmidt Jsy
Jim Bunning Jsy
Robin Roberts Jsy
Steve Carlton Pants
SRCR Duke Snider Pants
Jackie Robinson Jsy
Roy Campanella Pants
Pee Wee Reese Jsy
WBSS Billy Williams Jsy
Ernie Banks Pants
Ryne Sandberg Jsy
Sammy Sosa Jsy

2004 Ultimate Collection Signature Numbers Patch

*4-COLOR PATCH: ADD 20% PREMIUM
*5+ COLOR PATCH: ADD 50% PREMIUM
*LOGO PATCH: ADD 100% PREMIUM
OVERALL AUTO/GAME-USED ODDS 1:4
PRINT RUNS B/WN 1-51 COPIES PER
NO PRICING ON QTY OF 14 OR LESS
EXCHANGE DEADLINE 12/28/07
BF Bob Feller/19 30.00 60.00
BM Bill Mazeroski/9
BU Jim Bunning/14
BW Billy Williams/26 20.00 50.00
CR Cal Ripken/8
CY Carl Yastrzemski/8
DJ Derek Jeter/2
DM Don Mattingly/23 60.00 120.00
DW Dave Winfield/31 30.00 60.00
EB Ernie Banks/14
EG Eric Gagne/38 20.00 50.00
GB George Brett/5
GM Greg Maddux/31
IR Ivan Rodriguez/7 EXCH
JB Johnny Bench/5
JP Jim Palmer/22 20.00 50.00
KG Ken Griffey Jr./30 75.00 150.00
LB Lou Brock/20 30.00 60.00
MA Juan Marichal/27
MC Miguel Cabrera/24 30.00 60.00
MG Mark Grace/17
MP Mark Prior/22 20.00 50.00
MS Mike Schmidt/20 60.00 120.00
MT Mark Teixeira/23 30.00 60.00
NR Nolan Ryan/30
OS Ozzie Smith/1
PI Mike Piazza/31 100.00 175.00
RC Rod Carew/29
RJ Randy Johnson/51 60.00 120.00
RO Roy Oswalt/44 15.00 40.00
RS Ryne Sandberg/23 75.00 150.00
RY Robin Yount/19 50.00 100.00
SM Stan Musial/6
SR Scott Rolen/27 EXCH
TE Miguel Tejada/10
TG Tony Gwynn/19
VG Vladimir Guerrero/27 50.00 100.00
WB Wade Boggs/26 40.00 80.00
WC Will Clark/22
WM Willie McCovey/44 20.00 50.00
YB Yogi Berra/8

2004 Ultimate Collection Signatures

PRINT RUNS B/WN 6-99 COPIES PER
NO PRICING ON QTY OF 6
*GOLD p/r 25: .6X TO 1.5X BASIC p/r 69-99
GOLD PRINT RUNS B/WN 10-25 PER
NO GOLD PRICING ON QTY OF 10
OVERALL AUTO ODDS 1:4
PLATINUM: PREMIUM AU ODDS 1:20
PLATINUM PRINT RUN 1 SERIAL #'d SET
NO PLATINUM PRICING DUE TO SCARCITY
EXCHANGE DEADLINE 12/28/07
AD Andre Dawson/25 10.00 25.00
AK Al Kaline/25 30.00 60.00
AK1 Al Kaline/25
AO Akinori Otsuka/99 15.00 40.00
AR Al Rosen/99 10.00 25.00
BA Bobby Abreu/25 EXCH 15.00 40.00
BB Bret Boone/25
BD Bobby Doerr/99 10.00 25.00
BE Johnny Bench/25
BF Bob Feller/25 15.00 40.00
BF1 Bob Feller/25
BG Brian Giles/99 6.00 15.00
BI Craig Biggio/25 20.00 50.00
BL Bert Blyleven/99 10.00 25.00
BM Bill Mazeroski/25 20.00 50.00
BR Brooks Robinson Btg/25 30.00 60.00
BR1 Brooks Robinson Fldg/25
BS Ben Sheets/99 10.00 25.00
BW Billy Williams/25 15.00 40.00
CA Steve Carlton Right/25
CA1 S.Carlton Ahead/25 EXCH
CB Carlos Beltran/25 15.00 40.00
CC Carl Crawford/99 6.00 15.00
CL Roger Clemens/25
CP Corey Patterson/99 6.00 15.00
CR Cal Ripken/25 125.00 200.00
CW Rod Carew/25 20.00 50.00
CY Carl Yastrzemski/25 40.00 80.00
CZ Carlos Zambrano/99
DC David Cone/99 10.00 25.00
DE Dennis Eckersley/25 15.00 40.00
DG Dwight Gooden/99 10.00 25.00
DJ Derek Jeter/25
DL Don Larsen/25 EXCH
DM Dale Murphy/99 12.50 30.00
DN Don Newcombe/25 10.00 25.00
DO Don Mattingly/25
DP Dave Parker/25 10.00 25.00
DS Don Sutton/25
DW Dave Winfield/25 15.00 40.00
DY Delmon Young/99 12.50 30.00
EC Eric Chavez/25 15.00 40.00
EG Eric Gagne/25 20.00 50.00
EM Eddie Murray/25 EXCH 50.00 100.00
FH Frank Howard/99 6.00 15.00
FL Fred Lynn/25 10.00 25.00
GB George Brett/25
GF George Foster/25 10.00 25.00
GG Goose Gossage/99 6.00 15.00
GI Bob Gibson/25 20.00 50.00
GK George Kell/99 10.00 25.00
GM Greg Maddux/25 75.00 150.00
GN Graig Nettles/99 10.00 25.00
GP Gaylord Perry/25 10.00 25.00
GR Mark Grace/99 15.00 40.00
HB Hank Blalock/25 15.00 40.00
HK H.Killebrew w/Bat/25 30.00 60.00
HK1 H.Killebrew Swing/25 30.00 60.00
HU Tim Hudson/25
JB Jim Bunning/99 10.00 25.00
JK Jim Kaat/99 10.00 25.00
JM Joe Mauer/99 12.50 30.00
JP Jim Palmer Knee Up/99 10.00 25.00
JP1 Jim Palmer Thigh Up/25 15.00 40.00
JR Jose Reyes/99
JS Jason Schmidt/99 10.00 25.00
KG Ken Griffey Sr./69 10.00 25.00
KG2 Ken Griffey Jr./25
KH Keith Hernandez/99 10.00 25.00
KP Kirby Puckett/25 50.00 100.00
LA Luis Aparicio R.Sox/25 10.00 25.00
LA1 Luis Aparicio W.Sox/25 10.00 25.00
LT Luis Tiant/99 6.00 15.00
MC M.Cabrera Swing/99 12.50 30.00
MC1 M.Cabrera Drop Bat/25 20.00 50.00
MG Marcus Giles/99 6.00 15.00
MI Monte Irvin/25 10.00 25.00
ML Mike Lowell/99 6.00 15.00
MM Mark Mulder/99 10.00 25.00
MO Joe Morgan/25 15.00 40.00
MP Mark Prior/25 15.00 40.00
MS Mike Schmidt/25
MT Mark Teixeira/25 20.00 50.00
MU Stan Musial/25 40.00 80.00
MW Maury Wills/25 10.00 25.00
NG Nomar Garciaparra/25 60.00 120.00
NR Nolan Ryan/6
OC Orlando Cepeda/25 10.00 25.00
OS Ozzie Smith/25 30.00 60.00
PI Mike Piazza/25 60.00 120.00
PN Phil Niekro/25
PO Johnny Podres/99 10.00 25.00
RC Rocky Colavito/99 20.00 50.00
RF Rollie Fingers Brewers/25 10.00 25.00
RF1 Rollie Fingers A's/25 10.00 25.00
RG Ron Guidry/25 20.00 50.00
RI Jim Rice/25
RJ Randy Johnson/25 60.00 120.00
RK Ralph Kiner B/W/25 20.00 50.00
RK1 Ralph Kiner Color/25 20.00 50.00
RO Roy Oswalt/99 10.00 25.00
RR Robin Roberts/25 15.00 40.00
RR1 Robin Roberts/25
RS Red Schoendienst/25 15.00 40.00
RW Rickie Weeks/99 10.00 25.00
RY Ryne Sandberg/25 50.00 100.00
SA Ron Santo/99 12.50 30.00
SC Sean Casey/99 10.00 25.00
SL Sparky Lyle/99 6.00 15.00
SM John Smoltz/25 30.00 60.00
SN Duke Snider/25 20.00 50.00
ST Shingo Takatsu/99 10.00 25.00
SU Bruce Sutter/99 12.50 30.00
TH Travis Hafner/99 10.00 25.00
TP Tony Perez/25 15.00 40.00
TS Tom Seaver/25 30.00 60.00
VG Vladimir Guerrero/25 30.00 60.00
VM Victor Martinez/99 10.00 25.00
WB Wade Boggs/25 30.00 60.00
WC Will Clark/25 20.00 50.00
WF Whitey Ford/25 20.00 50.00
WI Willie McCovey/25 EXCH * 20.00 50.00
YB Yogi Berra/25 30.00 60.00

2004 Ultimate Collection Signatures Dual

OVERALL AUTO ODDS 1:4
STATED PRINT RUN 25 SERIAL #'d SETS
EXCHANGE DEADLINE 12/28/07
BB Hank Blalock 40.00 80.00
Wade Boggs
BC Carlos Beltran 75.00 150.00
Miguel Cabrera
BG Carlos Beltran
Ken Griffey Jr.
BP Johnny Bench
Mike Piazza
BR Jim Bunning
Robin Roberts
BS George Brett 125.00 200.00
Mike Schmidt
BT Hank Blalock 40.00 80.00
Mark Teixeira
CB Eric Chavez 30.00 60.00
Hank Blalock
CG Ron Guidry
Steve Carlton EXCH
CJ Randy Johnson 250.00 400.00
Roger Clemens
CL Miguel Cabrera 40.00 80.00
Mike Lowell
CR Brooks Robinson 40.00 80.00
Eric Chavez
DW Andre Dawson 30.00 60.00
Billy Williams
EF Dennis Eckersley 30.00 60.00
Rollie Fingers
FR Bob Feller 125.00 200.00
Nolan Ryan
GC Mark Grace 40.00 80.00
Will Clark
GG Brian Giles 30.00 60.00
Marcus Giles
GK Harmon Killebrew 100.00 175.00
Ken Griffey Jr.
GS Eric Gagne 60.00 120.00
John Smoltz
IC Monte Irvin 30.00 60.00
Orlando Cepeda
JC Randy Johnson 75.00 150.00
Steve Carlton
JM Derek Jeter 250.00 400.00
Don Mattingly
JP Fergie Jenkins 30.00 60.00
Jim Palmer
JT Fergie Jenkins 30.00 60.00
Luis Tiant
KG Ken Griffey Sr. 125.00 200.00
Ken Griffey Jr.
KK Al Kaline 50.00 100.00
Harmon Killebrew
MC Don Mattingly 75.00 150.00
Will Clark
MH Mark Mulder 40.00 80.00
Tim Hudson
MK Bill Mazeroski
Ralph Kiner
MP Joe Mauer 50.00 100.00
Mark Prior
NR Nolan Ryan 300.00 500.00
Roger Clemens EXCH
NS Don Newcombe 30.00 60.00
Don Sutton
PC Rafael Palmeiro 75.00 150.00
Will Clark EXCH
PN Gaylord Perry 30.00 60.00
Phil Niekro
PR Dave Parker 40.00 80.00
Jim Rice
PS Ben Sheets 30.00 60.00
Mark Prior
RC Robin Roberts 30.00 60.00
Steve Carlton EXCH
RJ Cal Ripken 350.00 600.00
Derek Jeter EXCH
RM Cal Ripken
Eddie Murray
RP Brooks Robinson 50.00 100.00
Jim Palmer
SF Ben Sheets 30.00 60.00
Bob Feller
SG Bruce Sutter 40.00 80.00
Eric Gagne
SO Ben Sheets 30.00 60.00
Roy Oswalt
SP Don Sutton 30.00 60.00
Gaylord Perry
TC Mark Teixeira 40.00 80.00
Miguel Cabrera
VM Vladimir Guerrero 50.00 100.00
Miguel Cabrera
WS Billy Williams 40.00 80.00
Ron Santo
YW Delmon Young
Rickie Weeks EXCH *

2004 Ultimate Collection Signatures Triple

OVERALL AUTO ODDS 1:4
STATED PRINT RUN 20 SERIAL #'d SETS
EXCHANGE DEADLINE 12/28/07
NO PRICING DUE TO SCARCITY
BGP Carlos Beltran
Ken Griffey Jr.
Corey Patterson EXCH
BRC Jim Bunning
Robin Roberts
Steve Carlton EXCH
CBW Carl Crawford
Lou Brock
Maury Wills
CCM Will Clark
Orlando Cepeda
Willie McCovey
DMY Andre Dawson
Dale Murphy
Robin Yount
GJT Bob Gibson
Fergie Jenkins

Luis Tiant
MBG Joe Morgan
Johnny Bench
Ken Griffey Jr.
MDM Bill Mazeroski
Bobby Doerr
Joe Morgan
MPK Bill Mazeroski
Dave Parker
Ralph Kiner
NSP Don Newcombe
Don Sutton
Johnny Podres
OTT Akinori Otsuka
Kazuhito Tadano
Shingo Takatsu
RNS Brooks Robinson
Graig Nettles
Ron Santo
RRP Brooks Robinson
Cal Ripken
Jim Palmer
SBT Alfonso Soriano
Hank Blalock
Mark Teixeira
SGG Bruce Sutter
Eric Gagne
Goose Gossage
SKM Duke Snider
Ralph Kiner
Stan Musial
SOP Ben Sheets
Roy Oswalt
Mark Prior
SPN Don Sutton
Gaylord Perry
Phil Niekro
WBJ Billy Williams
Ernie Banks
Fergie Jenkins
WGG Billy Williams
Ken Griffey Jr.
Tony Gwynn
ZWP Carlos Zambrano
Kerry Wood
Mark Prior EXCH

2004 Ultimate Collection Signatures Quadruple

OVERALL AUTO ODDS 1:4
STATED PRINT RUN 10 SERIAL #'d SETS
NO PRICING DUE TO SCARCITY
EXCHANGE DEADLINE 12/28/07
AWSB Luis Aparicio
Maury Wills
Ozzie Smith
Ernie Banks
BGSS Ernie Banks
Mark Grace
Ron Santo
Ryne Sandberg
BJRG Carlos Beltran
Derek Jeter
Cal Ripken
Nomar Garciaparra
BMGG Johnny Bench
Joe Morgan
Ken Griffey Jr.
Ken Griffey Sr.
BSPJ Bret Boone
Tom Seaver
Mark Prior
Randy Johnson
CLJB David Cone
Don Larsen
Randy Johnson
Jim Bunning EXCH
DYBF Bobby Doerr
Carl Yastrzemski
Yogi Berra
Whitey Ford
ECHF Dennis Eckersley
Eric Chavez
Tim Hudson
Rollie Fingers
EGFL Dennis Eckersley
Eric Gagne
Rollie Fingers
Sparky Lyle
FPCS Bob Feller
Jim Palmer
Steve Carlton
Tom Seaver EXCH
JMSN Chipper Jones
Dale Murphy
John Smoltz
Phil Niekro
KKPC Harmon Killebrew
Jim Kaat
Kirby Puckett
Rod Carew
MDMS Bill Mazeroski
Bobby Doerr
Joe Morgan
Ryne Sandberg
MHGC Don Mattingly
Keith Hernandez
Mark Grace
Will Clark
RCBS Brooks Robinson
Eric Chavez
George Brett
Mike Schmidt
RJCC Nolan Ryan
Randy Johnson
Roger Clemens
Steve Carlton EXCH
SBTC Ben Sheets
Hank Blalock
Mark Teixeira
Miguel Cabrera
SKSM Duke Snider
Eric Gagne
Jason Schmidt
Willie McCovey
WBPR Kerry Wood
Jeff Bagwell
Mike Piazza

Scott Rolen EXCH
WBSM Billy Williams
Ernie Banks
Ozzie Smith
Stan Musial
YFLR Carl Yastrzemski
Carlton Fisk
Fred Lynn
Jim Rice

2004 Ultimate Collection Signatures Six

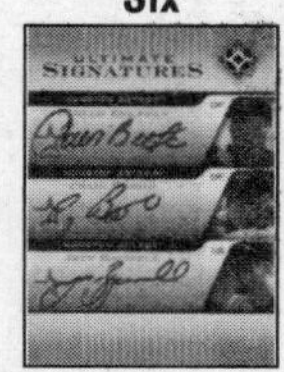

OVERALL AUTO ODDS 1:4
STATED PRINT RUN 5 SERIAL #'d SETS
NO PRICING DUE TO SCARCITY
EXCHANGE DEADLINE 12/28/07
BAL Brooks Robinson
Cal Ripken
Eddie Murray
Jim Palmer
Miguel Tejada
Rafael Palmeiro
BOS Bobby Doerr
Carl Yastrzemski
Carlton Fisk
Manny Ramirez
Nomar Garciaparra
Wade Boggs
CHC Andre Dawson
Billy Williams
Ernie Banks
Mark Grace
Ron Santo
Ryne Sandberg EXCH
GNTS Juan Marichal
Monte Irvin
Orlando Cepeda
Will Clark
Jason Schmidt
Willie McCovey EXCH
HOU Carlos Beltran
Craig Biggio
Jeff Bagwell
Lance Berkman
Roger Clemens
Roy Oswalt
LAD Don Newcombe
Don Sutton
Duke Snider
Johnny Podres
Maury Wills
Eric Gagne
NYM David Cone
Gary Carter
Keith Hernandez
Mike Piazza
Nolan Ryan
Tom Seaver
NYY Derek Jeter
Don Mattingly
Dave Winfield
Ron Guidry
Whitey Ford
Yogi Berra
PHL Bobby Abreu
Jim Bunning
Scott Rolen
Mike Schmidt
Robin Roberts
Steve Carlton
STL Lou Brock
Bob Gibson
Bruce Sutter
Ozzie Smith
Scott Rolen
Stan Musial EXCH

2004 Ultimate Collection Signatures Eight

OVERALL AUTO ODDS 1:4
STATED PRINT RUN 1 SERIAL #'d SET
NO PRICING DUE TO SCARCITY
EXCHANGE DEADLINE 12/28/07
300W Don Sutton
Gaylord Perry
Greg Maddux
Nolan Ryan
Phil Niekro
Roger Clemens
Steve Carlton
Tom Seaver EXCH
500HR Frank Robinson
Ernie Banks
Harmon Killebrew
Ken Griffey Jr.
Eddie Murray
Mike Schmidt
Rafael Palmeiro
Willie McCovey
3000H Al Kaline
Cal Ripken
George Brett
Paul Molitor
Robin Yount
Stan Musial
Tony Gwynn
Wade Boggs EXCH
ALCY David Cone
Gaylord Perry
Jim Palmer
Dennis Eckersley
Randy Johnson

Roger Clemens
Ron Guidry
Whitey Ford EXCH
CTRS Carlton Fisk
Gary Carter
Ivan Rodriguez
Joe Mauer
Johnny Bench
Mike Piazza
Victor Martinez
Yogi Berra EXCH
NLCY Bob Gibson
Don Newcombe
Eric Gagne
Greg Maddux
John Smoltz
Randy Johnson
Steve Carlton
Tom Seaver EXCH
OH Al Kaline
Billy Williams
Brooks Robinson
Don Mattingly
Duke Snider
Harmon Killebrew
Joe Morgan
Mike Schmidt
OSP Bob Feller
Bob Gibson
Jim Palmer
Juan Marichal
Nolan Ryan
Steve Carlton
Tom Seaver
Whitey Ford EXCH
YH Carlos Beltran
Corey Patterson
Hank Blalock
Jose Reyes
Marcus Giles
Mark Teixeira
Miguel Cabrera
Travis Hafner EXCH
YSP Ben Sheets
Carlos Zambrano
Jason Schmidt
Josh Beckett
Kerry Wood
Mark Mulder
Mark Prior
Roy Oswalt EXCH

2004 Ultimate Collection Stat Patch

*3-COLOR PATCH: ADD 20% PREMIUM
*4-COLOR PATCH: ADD 50% PREMIUM
*5+ COLOR PATCH: ADD 100% PREMIUM
*LOGO PATCH: ADD 150% PREMIUM
OVERALL PATCH ODDS 1:4
PRINT RUNS B/WN 4-66 COPIES PER
NO PRICING ON QTY OF 14 OR LESS

AP Albert Pujols/43	30.00	60.00
AP1 Albert Pujols/51	20.00	50.00
AS Alfonso Soriano/39	8.00	20.00
AS1 Alfonso Soriano/43	8.00	20.00
BE Johnny Bench/45	30.00	60.00
BG Bob Gibson/13		
BM Bill Mazeroski/11		
CB Carlos Beltran/29	10.00	25.00
CB1 Carlos Beltran/41	8.00	20.00
CF Carlton Fisk/17	15.00	40.00
CJ Chipper Jones/45	12.50	30.00
CL1 Roger Clemens Sox/24	20.00	50.00
CL2 Roger Clemens Yanks/7		
CR Cal Ripken/34	50.00	100.00
CR1 Cal Ripken/47	40.00	80.00
CY Carl Yastrzemski/44	20.00	50.00
DD Don Drysdale/25	40.00	80.00
DJ Derek Jeter/32	40.00	80.00
DJ1 Derek Jeter/24	40.00	80.00
DM Don Mattingly/35	40.00	80.00
DW Dave Winfield/37	12.50	30.00
EG Eric Gagne/55	8.00	20.00
EM Eddie Murray/19		
GB George Brett/20	40.00	80.00
GB1 George Brett/30		
GM Greg Maddux Braves/4		
GM1 Greg Maddux Cubs/20	20.00	50.00
GM2 Greg Maddux Cubs/49	15.00	40.00
HB Hank Blalock/29	10.00	25.00
HK Harmon Killebrew/49	30.00	60.00
HM Hideki Matsui/31	60.00	120.00
IR Ivan Rodriguez/35	15.00	40.00
IR1 Ivan Rodriguez/25	15.00	40.00
IS Ichiro Suzuki/56	60.00	120.00
IS1 Ichiro Suzuki/13		
JB Jeff Bagwell/47	12.50	30.00
JM Juan Marichal/26	15.00	40.00
JM1 Juan Marichal/10		
JP Jim Palmer/10		
JP1 Jim Palmer/23	15.00	40.00
JR Jim Rice/15	15.00	40.00
JR1 Jim Rice/46	12.50	30.00
JS John Smoltz/24	15.00	40.00
JS1 John Smoltz/55	12.50	30.00
JT Jim Thome/52	12.50	30.00
KG Ken Griffey Jr./56		
KG1 Ken Griffey Jr./10		
KW Kerry Wood/14		
KW1 Kerry Wood/20	10.00	25.00
MA Pedro Martinez/23	15.00	40.00
MP Mark Prior/18	20.00	50.00
MR Manny Ramirez/45	12.50	30.00
MS Mike Schmidt/48	30.00	60.00
MS1 Mike Schmidt/4		
MT Miguel Tejada/34	10.00	25.00
NR Nolan Ryan/9		
NR1 Nolan Ryan/22		
NR2 Nolan Ryan/7		
PI Mike Piazza/40	15.00	40.00
PM Paul Molitor/39	12.50	30.00
PN Phil Niekro Wins/23	15.00	40.00
PN1 Phil Niekro CG/23	15.00	40.00
RJ Randy Johnson/20	15.00	40.00
RO Jackie Robinson/19	150.00	250.00
RP Rafael Palmeiro/47	12.50	30.00
RS Ryne Sandberg/40	30.00	60.00
RS1 Ryne Sandberg/19	50.00	100.00
RY Robin Yount/49		
SP Warren Spahn/13		
SR Scott Rolen/31	15.00	40.00
SS Sammy Sosa/6		
SS1 Sammy Sosa/66	10.00	25.00
TG Tony Gwynn/56	15.00	40.00
TG1 Tony Gwynn/25	20.00	50.00
TM Thurman Munson/20	40.00	80.00
TS Tom Seaver/25	30.00	60.00
TS1 Tom Seaver/7		
VG Vladimir Guerrero/44	12.50	30.00
VG1 Vladimir Guerrero/40	12.50	30.00
WC Will Clark/35	30.00	60.00
WS Willie Stargell/48	20.00	50.00

2004 Ultimate Collection Super Patch

*3-COLOR PATCH: ADD 20% PREMIUM
*4-COLOR PATCH: ADD 50% PREMIUM
*5+ COLOR PATCH: ADD 100% PREMIUM
*LOGO PATCH: ADD 150% PREMIUM
OVERALL PATCH ODDS 1:4
PRINT RUNS B/WN 4-20 COPIES PER
NO PRICING ON QTY OF 4

AK Al Kaline/20		
AP Albert Pujols/20	60.00	120.00
CL Roger Clemens/20	30.00	60.00
CR Cal Ripken/20	75.00	150.00
CY Carl Yastrzemski/15	50.00	100.00
DJ Derek Jeter/20		
DM Don Mattingly/20	50.00	100.00
DW Dave Winfield/20	15.00	40.00
EM Eddie Murray/20	40.00	80.00
GB George Brett/20	50.00	100.00
GM Greg Maddux/20	40.00	80.00
HK Harmon Killebrew/20	40.00	80.00
HM Hideki Matsui/20	60.00	120.00
IS Ichiro Suzuki/20	125.00	200.00
JB Johnny Bench/20	40.00	80.00
JP Jim Palmer/20	15.00	40.00
KG Ken Griffey Jr./20	40.00	80.00
KW Kerry Wood/20	12.50	30.00
LB Lou Brock/20	30.00	60.00
MP Mark Prior/20	20.00	50.00
MR Manny Ramirez/20		
MS Mike Schmidt/20	50.00	100.00
NR Nolan Ryan/20	50.00	100.00
OS Ozzie Smith/20	40.00	80.00
PI Mike Piazza/20	40.00	80.00
PM Paul Molitor/20	15.00	40.00
RC Rod Carew/20	30.00	60.00
RS Ryne Sandberg/20	50.00	100.00
RY Robin Yount/20	40.00	80.00
SC Red Schoendienst/20	15.00	40.00
SS Sammy Sosa/20	20.00	50.00
TG Tony Gwynn/20	40.00	80.00
TS Tom Seaver/20	30.00	60.00
VG Vladimir Guerrero/20	30.00	60.00
WB Wade Boggs/20		
WC Will Clark Giants/20	30.00	60.00
WC1 Will Clark Rgr/4		

2005 Ultimate Collection

COMMON CARD (1-100)	1.25	3.00
1-100 APPX ODDS 3:2 PACKS		
1-100 PRINT RUN 475 SERIAL #'d SETS		
COMMON CARD (101-142)	2.00	5.00
101-142 APPX. ODDS 1:3		
101-142 PRINT RUN 275 SERIAL #'d SETS		
COMMON CARD (143-237)	2.00	5.00
COMMON RC (143-237)	2.00	5.00
143-237 STATED ODDS 3:4 PACKS		
143-237 PRINT RUN 275 SERIAL #'d SETS		
238-242 OVERALL AU ODDS 1:4		
238-242 PRINT RUN 99 SERIAL #'d SETS		
1 A.J. Burnett	1.25	3.00
2 Adam Dunn	1.25	3.00
3 Adrian Beltre	1.25	3.00
4 Albert Pujols	3.00	8.00
5 Alex Rodriguez	4.00	10.00
6 Alfonso Soriano	1.25	3.00
7 Andruw Jones	2.00	5.00
8 Andy Pettitte	2.00	5.00
9 Aramis Ramirez	1.25	3.00
10 Aubrey Huff	1.25	3.00
11 Ben Sheets	1.25	3.00
12 Bobby Abreu	1.25	3.00
13 Bobby Crosby	1.25	3.00
14 Chris Carpenter	1.25	3.00
15 Brian Giles	1.25	3.00
16 Brian Roberts	1.25	3.00
17 Carl Crawford	1.25	3.00
18 Carlos Beltran	1.25	3.00
19 Carlos Delgado	1.25	3.00
20 Carlos Zambrano	1.25	3.00
21 Chipper Jones	2.00	5.00
22 Corey Patterson	1.25	3.00
23 Craig Biggio	2.00	5.00
24 Curt Schilling	2.00	5.00
25 Dallas McPherson	1.25	3.00
26 David Ortiz	2.00	5.00
27 David Wright	3.00	8.00
28 Delmon Young	2.00	5.00
29 Derek Jeter	4.00	10.00
30 Derrek Lee	2.00	5.00
31 Dontrelle Willis	1.25	3.00
32 Eric Chavez	1.25	3.00
33 Eric Gagne	1.25	3.00
34 Francisco Rodriguez	1.25	3.00
35 Gary Sheffield	1.25	3.00
36 Greg Maddux	3.00	8.00
37 Hank Blalock	1.25	3.00
38 Hideki Matsui	2.50	6.00
39 Ichiro Suzuki	4.00	10.00
40 Ivan Rodriguez	2.00	5.00
41 J.D. Drew	1.25	3.00
42 Jake Peavy	1.25	3.00
43 Jason Bay	1.25	3.00
44 Jason Schmidt	1.25	3.00
45 Jeff Bagwell	2.00	5.00
46 Jeff Kent	1.25	3.00
47 Jeremy Bonderman	1.25	3.00
48 Jim Edmonds	1.25	3.00
49 Jim Thome	2.00	5.00
50 Joe Mauer	2.00	5.00
51 Johan Santana	2.00	5.00
52 John Smoltz	2.00	5.00
53 Johnny Damon	2.00	5.00
54 Jose Reyes	1.25	3.00
55 Jose Vidro	1.25	3.00
56 Josh Beckett	1.25	3.00
57 Justin Morneau	1.25	3.00
58 Ken Griffey Jr.	3.00	8.00
59 Kerry Wood	1.25	3.00
60 Khalil Greene	2.00	5.00
61 Lance Berkman	1.25	3.00
62 Larry Walker	2.00	5.00
63 Luis Gonzalez	1.25	3.00
64 Manny Ramirez	2.00	5.00
65 Mark Buehrle	1.25	3.00
66 Mark Mulder	1.25	3.00
67 Mark Prior	2.00	5.00
68 Mark Teixeira	2.00	5.00
69 Michael Young	1.25	3.00
70 Miguel Cabrera	2.00	5.00
71 Miguel Tejada	1.25	3.00
72 Mike Mussina	2.00	5.00
73 Mike Piazza	2.00	5.00
74 Moises Alou	1.25	3.00
75 Nomar Garciaparra	2.00	5.00
76 Oliver Perez	1.25	3.00
77 Pat Burrell	1.25	3.00
78 Paul Konerko	1.25	3.00
79 Pedro Feliz	1.25	3.00
80 Pedro Martinez	2.00	5.00
81 Randy Johnson	2.00	5.00
82 Richie Sexson	1.25	3.00
83 Rickie Weeks	1.25	3.00
84 Roger Clemens	3.00	8.00
85 Roy Halladay	1.25	3.00
86 Roy Oswalt	1.25	3.00
87 Sammy Sosa	2.00	5.00
88 Scott Kazmir	1.25	3.00
89 Scott Rolen	2.00	5.00
90 Shawn Green	1.25	3.00
91 Tim Hudson	1.25	3.00
92 Todd Helton	2.00	5.00
93 Tom Glavine	2.00	5.00
94 Torii Hunter	1.25	3.00
95 Travis Hafner	1.25	3.00
96 Troy Glaus	1.25	3.00
97 Vernon Wells	1.25	3.00
98 Victor Martinez	1.25	3.00
99 Vladimir Guerrero	2.00	5.00
100 Zack Greinke	1.25	3.00
101 Al Kaline RET	3.00	8.00
102 Babe Ruth RET	4.00	10.00
103 Bo Jackson RET	3.00	8.00
104 Bob Gibson RET	3.00	8.00
105 Brooks Robinson RET	3.00	8.00
106 Cal Ripken RET	8.00	20.00
107 Carl Yastrzemski RET	3.00	8.00
108 Carlton Fisk RET	3.00	8.00
109 Catfish Hunter RET	2.00	5.00
110 Christy Mathewson RET	3.00	8.00
111 Cy Young RET	3.00	8.00
112 Don Mattingly RET	4.00	10.00
113 Eddie Mathews RET	3.00	8.00
114 Eddie Murray RET	3.00	8.00
115 Gary Carter RET	2.00	5.00
116 Harmon Killebrew RET	3.00	8.00
117 Jim Palmer RET	2.00	5.00
118 Jimmie Foxx RET	3.00	8.00
119 Joe DiMaggio RET	3.00	8.00
120 Johnny Bench RET	3.00	8.00
121 Lefty Grove RET	3.00	8.00
122 Lou Gehrig RET	3.00	8.00
123 Mel Ott RET	3.00	8.00
124 Reggie Jackson RET	3.00	8.00
125 Mike Schmidt RET	4.00	10.00
126 Nolan Ryan RET	5.00	12.00
127 Ozzie Smith RET	3.00	8.00
128 Paul Molitor RET	2.00	5.00
129 Pee Wee Reese RET	3.00	8.00
130 Robin Yount RET	3.00	8.00
131 Ryne Sandberg RET	4.00	10.00
132 Ted Williams RET	3.00	8.00
133 Thurman Munson RET	3.00	8.00
134 Tom Seaver RET	3.00	8.00
135 Tony Gwynn RET	3.00	8.00
136 Wade Boggs RET	3.00	8.00
137 Walter Johnson RET	3.00	8.00
138 Warren Spahn RET	3.00	8.00
139 Will Clark RET	3.00	8.00
140 Willie McCovey RET	3.00	8.00
141 Willie Stargell RET	3.00	8.00
142 Yogi Berra RET	3.00	8.00
143 Ambiorix Burgos UP RC	2.00	5.00
144 Ambiorix Concepcion UP RC	2.00	5.00
145 Anibal Sanchez UP RC	6.00	15.00
146 Bill McCarthy UP RC	2.00	5.00
147 Brian Burres UP RC	2.00	5.00
148 Carlos Ruiz UP RC	2.00	5.00
149 Casey Rogowski UP RC	3.00	8.00
150 Chris Resop UP RC	2.00	5.00
151 Chris Roberson UP RC	2.00	5.00
152 Chris Seddon UP RC	2.00	5.00
153 Colter Bean UP RC	2.00	5.00
154 Dae-Sung Koo UP RC	2.00	5.00
155 Danny Rueckel UP RC	2.00	5.00
156 Dave Gassner UP RC	2.00	5.00
157 Ryan Howard UP	6.00	15.00
158 D.J. Houlton UP RC	2.00	5.00
159 Derek Wathan UP RC	2.00	5.00
160 Devon Lowery UP RC	2.00	5.00
161 Enrique Gonzalez UP RC	2.00	5.00
162 Erick Threets UP RC	2.00	5.00
163 Eude Brito UP RC	2.00	5.00
164 Francisco Butto UP RC	2.00	5.00
165 Franquelis Osoria UP RC	2.00	5.00
166 Garrett Jones UP RC	2.00	5.00
167 Geovany Soto UP RC	10.00	25.00
168 Ismael Ramirez UP RC	2.00	5.00
169 Jared Gothreaux UP RC	2.00	5.00
170 Jason Hammel UP RC	2.00	5.00
171 Jeff Housman UP RC	2.00	5.00
172 Jeff Miller UP RC	2.00	5.00
173 Jeff Francoeur UP	5.00	12.00
174 John Hattig UP RC	2.00	5.00
175 Jorge Campillo UP RC	2.00	5.00
176 Juan Morillo UP RC	2.00	5.00
177 Justin Wechsler UP RC	2.00	5.00
178 Keiichi Yabu UP RC	2.00	5.00
179 Kendry Morales UP RC	6.00	15.00
180 Luis Hernandez UP RC	2.00	5.00
181 Luis Mendoza UP RC	2.00	5.00
182 Luis Pena UP RC	2.00	5.00
183 Luis O.Rodriguez UP RC	2.00	5.00
184 Luke Scott UP RC	4.00	10.00
185 Marcos Carvajal UP RC	2.00	5.00
186 Mark Woodyard UP RC	2.00	5.00
187 Matt Smith UP RC	2.00	5.00
188 Matthew Lindstrom UP RC	2.00	5.00
189 Miguel Negron UP RC	3.00	8.00
190 Mike Morse UP RC	2.00	5.00
191 Nate McLouth UP RC	12.50	30.00
192 Nick Masset UP RC	2.00	5.00
193 Paulino Reynoso UP RC	2.00	5.00
194 Pedro Lopez UP RC	2.00	5.00
195 Pete Orr UP RC	2.00	5.00
196 Randy Messenger UP RC	2.00	5.00
197 Randy Williams UP RC	2.00	5.00
198 Raul Tablado UP RC	2.00	5.00
199 Ronny Paulino UP RC	2.50	6.00
200 Russ Rohlicek UP RC	2.00	5.00
201 Russell Martin UP RC	5.00	12.00
202 Scott Baker UP RC	3.00	8.00
203 Scott Munter UP RC	2.00	5.00
204 Sean Thompson UP RC	2.00	5.00
205 Sean Tracey UP RC	2.00	5.00
206 Steve Schmoll UP RC	2.00	5.00
207 Tony Pena UP RC	2.00	5.00
208 Travis Bowyer UP RC	2.00	5.00
209 Ubaldo Jimenez UP RC	4.00	10.00
210 Wladimir Balentien UP RC	4.00	10.00
211 Yorman Bazardo UP RC	2.00	5.00
212 Yuniesky Betancourt UP RC	4.00	10.00
213 Adam Shabala UP RC	2.00	5.00
214 Brandon McCarthy UP RC	4.00	10.00
215 Chad Orvella UP RC	2.00	5.00
216 Jermaine Van Buren UP	2.00	5.00
217 Anthony Reyes UP RC	10.00	25.00
218 Dana Eveland UP RC	2.00	5.00
219 Brian Anderson UP RC	3.00	8.00
220 Hayden Penn UP RC	3.00	8.00
221 Chris Denorfia UP RC	4.00	10.00
222 Joel Peralta UP RC	2.00	5.00
223 Ryan Garko UP RC	4.00	10.00
224 Felix Hernandez UP	4.00	10.00
225 Mark McLemore UP RC	2.00	5.00
226 Melky Cabrera UP RC	6.00	15.00
227 Nelson Cruz UP RC	4.00	10.00
228 Norihiro Nakamura UP RC	3.00	8.00
229 Oscar Robles UP RC	2.00	5.00
230 Rick Short UP RC	2.00	5.00
231 Ryan Zimmerman UP RC	12.50	30.00
232 Ryan Speier UP RC	2.00	5.00
233 Ryan Spilborghs UP RC	3.00	8.00
234 Shane Costa UP RC	2.00	5.00
235 Zach Duke UP	3.00	8.00
236 Tony Giarratano UP RC	2.00	5.00
237 Jeff Niemann UP RC	3.00	8.00
238 Stephen Drew AU RC	100.00	200.00
239 Justin Verlander AU RC	200.00	300.00
240 Prince Fielder AU RC	500.00	600.00
241 Philip Humber AU RC	40.00	80.00
242 Tadahito Iguchi AU RC	60.00	120.00

2005 Ultimate Collection Silver

*SILVER 1-100: .75X TO 2X BASIC
*SILVER 101-142: .75X TO 2X BASIC
*SILVER 143-237: .75X TO 2X BASIC
*SILVER 143-237: .75X TO 2X BASIC RC
APPROXIMATE ODDS 1:3 PACKS
STATED PRINT RUN 50 SERIAL #'d SETS

231 Ryan Zimmerman UP	40.00	80.00

2005 Ultimate Collection Baseball Stars Signatures

OVERALL AUTO ODDS 1:4
PRINT RUNS B/WN 5-25 COPIES PER
NO PRICING ON QTY OF 10 OR LESS
NO RC YR PRICING ON QTY OF 25 OR LESS
EXCHANGE DEADLINE 01/10/09

AB Adrian Beltre/15	12.50	30.00

AD Adam Dunn/10
AN Andruw Jones/10
AP Albert Pujols/5
AR Aramis Ramirez/20 10.00 25.00
BC Bobby Crosby/15 12.50 30.00
BE Johnny Bench/10
BG Brian Giles/15 12.50 30.00
BJ Bo Jackson/10
BL Barry Larkin/15 30.00 60.00
BO Jeremy Bonderman/25 10.00 25.00
BR Brian Roberts/25 10.00 25.00
BS Ben Sheets/15 12.50 30.00
BU B.J. Upton/25 10.00 25.00
CA Rod Carew/10
CB Craig Biggio/15 20.00 50.00
CC Carl Crawford/25 10.00 25.00
CF Carlton Fisk/10
CJ Chipper Jones/10
CO Coco Crisp/25 20.00 50.00
CR Cal Ripken/5 EXCH
CS Curt Schilling/5
CZ Carlos Zambrano/20 10.00 25.00
DA Andre Dawson/15 12.50 30.00
DG Dwight Gooden/25 10.00 25.00
DJ Derek Jeter/5
DO David Ortiz/10
DW Dontrelle Willis/15 20.00 50.00
EC Eric Chavez/15 12.50 30.00
EG Eric Gagne/10
FH Felix Hernandez/5
GC Gary Carter/10
GR Khalil Greene/15 20.00 50.00
HA Roy Halladay/10
HB Hank Blalock/15 12.50 30.00
HU Torii Hunter/15 12.50 30.00
JA Reggie Jackson/5
JB Jason Bay/25 10.00 25.00
JD J.D. Drew/10
JK Jeff Kent/10
JM Justin Morneau/25 10.00 25.00
JN Jeff Niemann/25
JO Joe Mauer/15 20.00 50.00
JP Jake Peavy/20 15.00 40.00
JR Jose Reyes/20 10.00 25.00
JV Jose Vidro/20 6.00 15.00
KG Ken Griffey Jr./25 50.00 100.00
KH Keith Hernandez/15 12.50 30.00
LE Derrek Lee/5
MA Don Mattingly/10
MC Miguel Cabrera/15 20.00 50.00
MM Mark Mulder/15 12.50 30.00
MP Mark Prior/10
MS Mike Schmidt/10
MT Mark Teixeira/15 20.00 50.00
MY Michael Young/20 10.00 25.00
NG Nomar Garciaparra/10
NR Nolan Ryan/5
OS Ozzie Smith/10
PF Prince Fielder/5
PH Philip Humber/25
PM Paul Molitor/15 12.50 30.00
RC Roger Clemens/5
RF Rafael Furcal/20 10.00 25.00
RH Rich Harden/25 10.00 25.00
RJ Randy Johnson/5
RO Roy Oswalt/15 12.50 30.00
RS Ryne Sandberg/10
RW Rickie Weeks/15 12.50 30.00
RY Robin Yount/10
SD Stephen Drew/15
SK Scott Kazmir/25 10.00 25.00
SM John Smoltz/15 40.00 80.00
SP Scott Podsednik/25 15.00 40.00
TE Miguel Tejada/5
TG Tony Gwynn/10
TH Tim Hudson/15 15.00 40.00
TI Tadahito Iguchi/20
TR Travis Hafner/25 10.00 25.00
VE Justin Verlander/25
VG Vladimir Guerrero/5
VM Victor Martinez/25 10.00 25.00
WB Wade Boggs/10
WC Will Clark/15 20.00 50.00
WP Wily Mo Pena/25 10.00 25.00
WR David Wright/15 50.00 100.00
ZG Zack Greinke/25 6.00 15.00

2005 Ultimate Collection Hurlers Materials

OVERALL GAME-USED ODDS 1:4
STATED PRINT RUN 20 SERIAL #'d SETS
*PATCH p/r 21-25: .6X TO 1.5X BASIC
OVERALL PATCH ODDS 1:4
PATCH PRINT RUN B/WN 2-25 PER
NO PATCH PRICING ON QTY OF 12 OR LESS
AB A.J. Burnett Jsy 4.00 10.00
BE Josh Beckett Jsy 4.00 10.00
BL Brad Lidge Jsy 4.00 10.00
BM Brett Myers Jsy 4.00 10.00
BO Jeremy Bonderman Jsy 4.00 10.00
BS Ben Sheets Jsy 4.00 10.00
CA Chris Carpenter Jsy 6.00 15.00
CC C.C. Sabathia Jsy 4.00 10.00
CP Carl Pavano Jsy 4.00 10.00
CS Curt Schilling Jsy 6.00 15.00
CZ Carlos Zambrano Jsy 4.00 10.00
DG Dwight Gooden Jsy 4.00 10.00
DH Danny Haren Jsy 4.00 10.00
DL Derek Lowe Jsy 4.00 10.00
DW Dontrelle Willis Jsy 4.00 10.00
EG Eric Gagne Jsy 4.00 10.00
FH Felix Hernandez Jsy 12.50 30.00
FR Francisco Rodriguez Jsy 4.00 10.00
GF Gavin Floyd Jsy 4.00 10.00
GM Greg Maddux Jsy 12.50 30.00
GP Gaylord Perry Jsy 4.00 10.00
HA Roy Halladay Jsy 4.00 10.00
HO Trevor Hoffman Jsy 6.00 15.00
JB Joe Blanton Jsy 4.00 10.00
JF Jeff Francis Jsy 4.00 10.00
JP Jake Peavy Jsy 4.00 10.00
JS Johan Santana Jsy 6.00 15.00
JW Jake Westbrook Jsy 4.00 10.00
KF Keith Foulke Jsy 4.00 10.00
KW Kerry Wood Jsy 4.00 10.00
LH Livan Hernandez Jsy 4.00 10.00
MA Matt Cain Jsy 15.00 40.00
MC Matt Clement Jsy 4.00 10.00
MM Mark Mulder Jsy 4.00 10.00
MP Mark Prior Jsy 6.00 15.00
MU Mike Mussina Jsy 6.00 15.00
NR1 Nolan Ryan Angels Jsy 15.00 40.00
NR2 Nolan Ryan Rgr Jsy 15.00 40.00
OP Odalis Perez Jsy 4.00 10.00
PE Oliver Perez Jsy 4.00 10.00
PM Pedro Martinez Jsy 6.00 15.00
RC Roger Clemens Jsy 12.50 30.00
RH Rich Harden Jsy 4.00 10.00
RJ Randy Johnson Jsy 8.00 20.00
RO Roy Oswalt Jsy 4.00 10.00
SK Scott Kazmir Jsy 4.00 10.00
SM John Smoltz Jsy 8.00 20.00
TG Tom Glavine Jsy 6.00 15.00
TH Tim Hudson Jsy 4.00 10.00
TW Tim Wakefield Jsy 10.00 25.00

2005 Ultimate Collection Hurlers Signature Materials

STATED PRINT RUN 20 SERIAL #'d SETS
PATCH PRINT RUN 10 SERIAL #'d SETS
NO PATCH PRICING DUE TO SCARCITY
OVERALL AU-GU ODDS 1:4
EXCHANGE DEADLINE 01/12/09
BE Josh Beckett Jsy 20.00 50.00
BL Brad Lidge Jsy 15.00 40.00
BM Brett Myers Jsy 6.00 15.00
BO Jeremy Bonderman Jsy 10.00 25.00
BS Ben Sheets Jsy 10.00 25.00
CA Chris Carpenter Jsy 20.00 50.00
CZ Carlos Zambrano Jsy 10.00 25.00
DG Dwight Gooden Jsy EXCH 10.00 25.00
DH Danny Haren Jsy 6.00 15.00
DW Dontrelle Willis Jsy 15.00 40.00
EG Eric Gagne Jsy 10.00 25.00
FH Felix Hernandez Jsy 60.00 120.00
FR Francisco Rodriguez Jsy 10.00 25.00
GF Gavin Floyd Jsy 6.00 15.00
GP Gaylord Perry Jsy 10.00 25.00
HA Roy Halladay Jsy 10.00 25.00
JB Joe Blanton Jsy 6.00 15.00
JF Jeff Francis Jsy 6.00 15.00
JP Jake Peavy Jsy 10.00 25.00
JW Jake Westbrook Jsy 6.00 15.00
KW Kerry Wood Jsy 15.00 40.00
LH Livan Hernandez Jsy 10.00 25.00
MC Matt Clement Jsy 10.00 25.00
MM Mark Mulder Jsy 10.00 25.00
MP Mark Prior Jsy 12.50 30.00
MU Mike Mussina Jsy 20.00 50.00
NR1 Nolan Ryan Angels Jsy 60.00 120.00
NR2 Nolan Ryan Rgr Jsy 60.00 120.00
RO Roy Oswalt Jsy 10.00 25.00
SK Scott Kazmir Jsy 10.00 25.00
SM John Smoltz Jsy 30.00 60.00
TH Tim Hudson Jsy 15.00 40.00
TW Tim Wakefield Jsy 50.00 100.00

2005 Ultimate Collection Materials

OVERALL GAME-USED ODDS 1:4
STATED PRINT RUN 25 SERIAL #'d SETS
*PATCH p/r 25: .6X TO 1.5X BASIC
*PATCH p/r 15: .75X TO 2X BASIC
OVERALL PATCH ODDS 1:4
PATCH PRINT RUN B/WN 5-25 PER
NO PATCH PRICING ON QTY OF 10 OR LESS
AB Adrian Beltre Jsy 4.00 10.00
AD Adam Dunn Jsy 4.00 10.00
AH Aubrey Huff Jsy 4.00 10.00
AJ Andruw Jones Jsy 6.00 15.00
AP Albert Pujols Jsy 12.50 30.00
AR Aaron Rowand Jsy 4.00 10.00
BA Bobby Abreu Jsy 4.00 10.00
BC Bobby Crosby Jsy 4.00 10.00
BE Josh Beckett Jsy 4.00 10.00
BG Brian Giles Jsy 4.00 10.00
BJ B.J. Upton Jsy 4.00 10.00
BL Brad Lidge Jsy 4.00 10.00
BO Jeremy Bonderman Jsy 4.00 10.00
BR Brian Roberts Jsy 4.00 10.00
BS Ben Sheets Jsy 4.00 10.00
BU A.J. Burnett Jsy 4.00 10.00
CA Miguel Cabrera Jsy 6.00 15.00
CB Craig Biggio Jsy 6.00 15.00
CC C.C. Sabathia Jsy 4.00 10.00
CO Coco Crisp Jsy 4.00 10.00
CP Carl Pavano Jsy 4.00 10.00
CR Carl Crawford Jsy 4.00 10.00
CS Curt Schilling Jsy 6.00 15.00
CU Chase Utley Jsy 10.00 25.00
CW Rod Carew Jsy 6.00 15.00
CZ Carlos Zambrano Jsy 4.00 10.00
DJ Derek Jeter Jsy 15.00 40.00
DL Derek Lowe Jsy 4.00 10.00
DO David Ortiz Jsy 6.00 15.00
DW Dontrelle Willis Jsy 4.00 10.00
EC Eric Chavez Jsy 4.00 10.00
EG Eric Gagne Jsy 4.00 10.00
ER Edgar Renteria Jsy 4.00 10.00
ES Johnny Estrada Jsy 4.00 10.00
FH Felix Hernandez Jsy 12.50 30.00
FR Francisco Rodriguez Jsy 4.00 10.00
GF Gavin Floyd Jsy 4.00 10.00
GM Greg Maddux Jsy 12.50 30.00
GR Khalil Greene Jsy 6.00 15.00
GS Gary Sheffield Jsy 4.00 10.00
HA Roy Halladay Jsy 4.00 10.00
HB Hank Blalock Jsy 4.00 10.00
HO Trevor Hoffman Jsy 6.00 15.00
HU Torii Hunter Jsy 4.00 10.00
JA Jason Bay Jsy 4.00 10.00
JB Jeff Bagwell Jsy 8.00 20.00
JD J.D. Drew Jsy 4.00 10.00
JF Jeff Francis Jsy 4.00 10.00
JK Jeff Kent Jsy 4.00 10.00
JM Joe Mauer Jsy 8.00 20.00
JP Jake Peavy Jsy 4.00 10.00
JR Jeremy Reed Jsy 4.00 10.00
JV Jose Vidro Jsy 4.00 10.00
JW Jake Westbrook Jsy 4.00 10.00
KF Keith Foulke Jsy 4.00 10.00
KG Ken Griffey Jr. Jsy 12.50 30.00
LE Derrek Lee Jsy 6.00 15.00
MA Matt Cain Jsy 15.00 40.00
MC Matt Clement Jsy 4.00 10.00
MG Marcus Giles Jsy 4.00 10.00
ML Mark Loretta Jsy 4.00 10.00
MM Mark Mulder Jsy 4.00 10.00
MO Justin Morneau Jsy 4.00 10.00
MP Mark Prior Jsy 6.00 15.00
MS Mike Schmidt Jsy 15.00 40.00
MT Mark Teixeira Jsy 6.00 15.00
MY Michael Young Jsy 4.00 10.00
NR Nolan Ryan Jsy 15.00 40.00
OP Oliver Perez Jsy 4.00 10.00
OS Roy Oswalt Jsy 4.00 10.00
PA Corey Patterson Jsy 4.00 10.00
PF Prince Fielder Jsy 15.00 40.00
PM Pedro Martinez Jsy 6.00 15.00
RA Aramis Ramirez Jsy 4.00 10.00
RC Roger Clemens Jsy 12.50 30.00
RE Jose Reyes Jsy 4.00 10.00
RF Rafael Furcal Jsy 4.00 10.00
RH Rich Harden Jsy 4.00 10.00
RI Cal Ripken Jsy 30.00 60.00
RJ Randy Johnson Jsy 8.00 20.00
RP Rafael Palmeiro Jsy 6.00 15.00
RS Ryne Sandberg Jsy 15.00 40.00
RW Rickie Weeks Jsy 4.00 10.00
SA Johan Santana Jsy 8.00 20.00
SC Sean Casey Jsy 4.00 10.00
SK Scott Kazmir Jsy 4.00 10.00
SM John Smoltz Jsy 8.00 20.00
SP Scott Podsednik Jsy 6.00 15.00
SR Scott Rolen Jsy 6.00 15.00
TE Miguel Tejada Jsy 4.00 10.00
TH Tim Hudson Jsy 4.00 10.00
TI Tadahito Iguchi Jsy 12.50 30.00
TR Travis Hafner Jsy 4.00 10.00
TW Tim Wakefield Jsy 10.00 25.00
VG Vladimir Guerrero Jsy 8.00 20.00
VM Victor Martinez Jsy 4.00 10.00
WP Wily Mo Pena Jsy 4.00 10.00
WR David Wright Jsy 12.50 30.00
ZG Zack Greinke Jsy 4.00 10.00

2005 Ultimate Collection Materials Signature

STATED PRINT RUN 25 SERIAL #'d SETS
NO RC YR PRICING DUE TO SCARCITY
PATCH PRINT RUN 10 SERIAL #'d SETS
NO PATCH PRICING DUE TO SCARCITY
OVERALL AU-GU ODDS 1:4
EXCHANGE DEADLINE 01/10/09
AB Adrian Beltre Jsy 10.00 25.00
AD Adam Dunn Jsy 10.00 25.00
AH Aubrey Huff Jsy 6.00 15.00
AJ Andruw Jones Jsy 20.00 50.00
BC Bobby Crosby Jsy 10.00 25.00
BE Josh Beckett Jsy 15.00 40.00
BG Brian Giles Jsy 10.00 25.00
BJ B.J. Upton Jsy 12.50 30.00
BL Brad Lidge Jsy 15.00 40.00
BO Jeremy Bonderman Jsy 10.00 25.00
BR Brian Roberts Jsy 10.00 25.00
BS Ben Sheets Jsy 10.00 25.00
CA Miguel Cabrera Jsy 15.00 40.00
CA Rod Carew Jsy 15.00 40.00
CB Craig Biggio Jsy 20.00 50.00
CR Carl Crawford Jsy 10.00 25.00
CU Chase Utley Jsy 30.00 60.00
CZ Carlos Zambrano Jsy 10.00 25.00
DJ Derek Jeter Jsy 150.00 250.00
DO David Ortiz Jsy 30.00 60.00
DW Dontrelle Willis Jsy 15.00 40.00
EG Eric Gagne Jsy 10.00 25.00
ES Johnny Estrada Jsy 6.00 15.00
FH Felix Hernandez Jsy 60.00 120.00
FR Francisco Rodriguez Jsy 10.00 25.00
GF Gavin Floyd Jsy 6.00 15.00
GR Khalil Greene Jsy 15.00 40.00
GS Gary Sheffield Jsy 15.00 40.00
HA Roy Halladay Jsy 10.00 25.00
HB Hank Blalock Jsy 10.00 25.00
HU Torii Hunter Jsy 10.00 25.00
JA Jason Bay Jsy 10.00 25.00
JB Jeff Bagwell Jsy 40.00 80.00
JD J.D. Drew Jsy 10.00 25.00
JF Jeff Francis Jsy 6.00 15.00
JM Joe Mauer Jsy 15.00 40.00
JP Jake Peavy Jsy 10.00 25.00
JR Jeremy Reed Jsy 6.00 15.00
JV Jose Vidro Jsy 6.00 15.00
JW Jake Westbrook Jsy 6.00 15.00
KG Ken Griffey Jr. Jsy 75.00 150.00
LA Barry Larkin Jsy 20.00 50.00
LE Derrek Lee Jsy 15.00 40.00
MC Matt Clement Jsy 10.00 25.00
ML Mark Loretta Jsy 6.00 15.00
MM Mark Mulder Jsy 10.00 25.00
MO Justin Morneau Jsy 10.00 25.00
MP Mark Prior Jsy 12.50 30.00
MS Mike Schmidt Jsy 30.00 60.00
MT Mark Teixeira Jsy 20.00 50.00
MY Michael Young Jsy 10.00 25.00
NR Nolan Ryan Jsy 60.00 120.00
OS Roy Oswalt Jsy 10.00 25.00
RA Aramis Ramirez Jsy 10.00 25.00
RE Jose Reyes Jsy 10.00 25.00
RF Rafael Furcal Jsy 10.00 25.00
RI Cal Ripken Jsy EXCH 125.00 200.00
RP Rafael Palmeiro Jsy 20.00 50.00
RS Ryne Sandberg Jsy 40.00 80.00
RW Rickie Weeks Jsy 10.00 25.00
SK Scott Kazmir Jsy 10.00 25.00
SM John Smoltz Jsy 30.00 60.00
SP Scott Podsednik Jsy 15.00 40.00
TE Miguel Tejada Jsy 20.00 50.00
TH Tim Hudson Jsy 15.00 40.00
TI Tadahito Iguchi Jsy
TR Travis Hafner Jsy 10.00 25.00
TW Tim Wakefield Jsy 50.00 100.00
VG Vladimir Guerrero Jsy 30.00 60.00
VM Victor Martinez Jsy 10.00 25.00
WP Wily Mo Pena Jsy 10.00 25.00
WR David Wright Jsy 50.00 100.00
ZG Zack Greinke Jsy 6.00 15.00

2005 Ultimate Collection Signatures

PRINT RUNS B/WN 10-99 COPIES PER
NO PRICING ON QTY OF 10
PLATINUM PRINT RUN 5 SERIAL #'d SETS
NO PLATINUM PRICING DUE TO SCARCITY
OVERALL AUTO ODDS 1:4
EXCHANGE DEADLINE 01/10/09
AB Adrian Beltre/69 10.00 25.00
AD Adam Dunn/35 10.00 25.00
AP Albert Pujols/10
AR Aramis Ramirez/69 10.00 25.00
BA Jason Bay/69 10.00 25.00
BC Bobby Crosby/69 10.00 25.00
BE Josh Beckett/35 15.00 40.00
BJ Bo Jackson/35 30.00 60.00
BL Barry Larkin/69 20.00 50.00
BR Brian Roberts/35 10.00 25.00
BS Ben Sheets/69 10.00 25.00
BU B.J. Upton/69 12.50 30.00
CB Craig Biggio/69 15.00 40.00
CF Carlton Fisk/15 20.00 50.00
CJ Chipper Jones/10
CO Coco Crisp/69 20.00 50.00
CR Cal Ripken EXCH/10
CS Curt Schilling/10
CU Chase Utley/TBD
CW Rod Carew/35 15.00 40.00
CY Carl Yastrzemski/10
CZ Carlos Zambrano/69 10.00 25.00
DJ Derek Jeter/10
DL Derrek Lee/10
DO David Ortiz/35 20.00 50.00
DW Dontrelle Willis/69 15.00 40.00
EC Eric Chavez/52 10.00 25.00
EG Eric Gagne/35 10.00 25.00
FH Felix Hernandez/69 50.00 100.00
GC Gary Carter/35 10.00 25.00
GM Greg Maddux/10
GR Khalil Greene/69 15.00 40.00
GS Gary Sheffield/25 15.00 40.00
GW Tony Gwynn/25 30.00 60.00
HA Roy Halladay/35 10.00 25.00
HB Hank Blalock/69 10.00 25.00
HU Torii Hunter/69 10.00 25.00
JA Reggie Jackson/10
JB Johnny Bench/15 30.00 60.00
JD J.D. Drew/29 10.00 25.00
JE Jeff Bagwell/15 40.00 80.00
JK Jeff Kent/TBD
JM Joe Mauer/69 15.00 40.00
JN Jeff Niemann/69 10.00 25.00
JO Andruw Jones/35 20.00 50.00
JP Jake Peavy/69 10.00 25.00
JR Jose Reyes/69 10.00 25.00
JV Justin Verlander/69 50.00 100.00
KG Ken Griffey Jr./69 40.00 80.00
KM Kendry Morales/69 40.00 80.00
KW Kerry Wood/15 20.00 50.00
MA Don Mattingly/25 50.00 100.00
MC Miguel Cabrera/69 15.00 40.00
MM Mark Mulder/69 10.00 25.00
MP Mark Prior/15 15.00 40.00
MS Mike Schmidt/25 30.00 60.00
MT Mark Teixeira/99 12.50 30.00
MU Mike Mussina/15 30.00 60.00
MY Michael Young/69 10.00 25.00
NG Nomar Garciaparra/10
NR Nolan Ryan/10
OS Ozzie Smith/35 20.00 50.00
PF Prince Fielder/35 75.00 150.00
PH Philip Humber/69 12.50 30.00
PI Mike Piazza/10
PM Paul Molitor/49 10.00 25.00
RC Roger Clemens/10
RH Rich Harden/69 10.00 25.00
RJ Randy Johnson/10
RO Roy Oswalt/69 10.00 25.00
RP Rafael Palmeiro/25 20.00 50.00
RS Ryne Sandberg/15 50.00 100.00
RW Rickie Weeks/30 10.00 25.00
RY Robin Yount/15 30.00 60.00
SD Stephen Drew/69
SK Scott Kazmir/69 10.00 25.00
SM John Smoltz/49 30.00 60.00
TE Miguel Tejada/10
TG Tom Glavine/10
TH Tim Hudson/69 15.00 40.00
TI Tadahito Iguchi/69 50.00 100.00
TR Travis Hafner/69 10.00 25.00
VG Vladimir Guerrero/10
VM Victor Martinez/69 10.00 25.00
WB Wade Boggs/15 20.00 50.00
WC Will Clark/69 15.00 40.00
WR David Wright/69 30.00 60.00
ZG Zack Greinke/69 6.00 15.00

2005 Ultimate Collection Sluggers Materials

OVERALL GAME-USED ODDS 1:4
STATED PRINT RUN 20 SERIAL #'d SETS
*PATCH p/r 25: .6X TO 1.5X BASIC
*PATCH p/r 19: .75X TO 2X BASIC
OVERALL PATCH ODDS 1:4
PATCH PRINT RUN B/WN 19-25 PER
AB Adrian Beltre Jsy 4.00 10.00
AD Adam Dunn Jsy 4.00 10.00
AH Aubrey Huff Jsy 4.00 10.00
AP Albert Pujols Jsy 12.50 30.00
AR Aramis Ramirez Jsy 4.00 10.00
BA Bobby Abreu Jsy 4.00 10.00
BC Bobby Crosby Jsy 4.00 10.00
BG Brian Giles Jsy 4.00 10.00
BR Brian Roberts Jsy 4.00 10.00
CA Rod Carew Jsy 6.00 15.00
CB Craig Biggio Jsy 6.00 15.00
CC Carl Crawford Jsy 4.00 10.00
CJ Chipper Jones Jsy 8.00 20.00
CO Coco Crisp Jsy 4.00 10.00
CP Corey Patterson Jsy 4.00 10.00
DJ Derek Jeter Jsy 15.00 40.00
DL Derrek Lee Jsy 6.00 15.00
DO David Ortiz Jsy 6.00 15.00
DW David Wright Jsy 12.50 30.00
EC Eric Chavez Jsy 4.00 10.00
ER Edgar Renteria Jsy 4.00 10.00
ES Johnny Estrada Jsy 4.00 10.00
GR Khalil Greene Jsy 6.00 15.00
GS Gary Sheffield Jsy 4.00 10.00
HA Travis Hafner Jsy 4.00 10.00
HB Hank Blalock Jsy 4.00 10.00
JA Jason Bay Jsy 4.00 10.00
JB Jeff Bagwell Jsy 8.00 20.00
JD J.D. Drew Jsy 4.00 10.00
JK Jeff Kent Jsy 4.00 10.00
JM Justin Morneau Jsy 4.00 10.00
JR Jose Reyes Jsy 4.00 10.00
JV Jose Vidro Jsy 4.00 10.00
KG Ken Griffey Jr. Jsy 12.50 30.00
MA Joe Mauer Jsy 8.00 20.00
MC Miguel Cabrera Jsy 6.00 15.00
MG Marcus Giles Jsy 4.00 10.00
ML Mark Loretta Jsy 4.00 10.00
MT Mark Teixeira Jsy 6.00 15.00
MY Michael Young Jsy 4.00 10.00
RF Rafael Furcal Jsy 4.00 10.00
RH Ryan Howard Jsy 15.00 40.00
RP Rafael Palmeiro Jsy 6.00 15.00
SC Sean Casey Jsy 4.00 10.00
SR Scott Rolen Jsy 6.00 15.00
TH Torii Hunter Jsy 4.00 10.00
VG Vladimir Guerrero Jsy 8.00 20.00
VM Victor Martinez Jsy 4.00 10.00
WP Wily Mo Pena Jsy 4.00 10.00

2005 Ultimate Collection Sluggers Signature Materials

STATED PRINT RUN 20 SERIAL #'d SETS
PATCH PRINT RUN B/WN 3-10 COPIES PER
NO PATCH PRICING DUE TO SCARCITY
OVERALL AU-GU ODDS 1:4
AB Adrian Beltre Jsy 10.00 25.00
AD Adam Dunn Jsy 10.00 25.00
AH Aubrey Huff Jsy 6.00 15.00
AR Aramis Ramirez Jsy 10.00 25.00
BC Bobby Crosby Jsy 10.00 25.00
BG Brian Giles Jsy 10.00 25.00
BR Brian Roberts Jsy 10.00 25.00
CA Rod Carew Jsy 15.00 40.00
CB Craig Biggio Jsy 20.00 50.00
CJ Chipper Jones Jsy 30.00 60.00
DJ Derek Jeter Jsy 150.00 250.00
DL Derrek Lee Jsy 15.00 40.00
DO David Ortiz Jsy 30.00 60.00
DW David Wright Jsy 50.00 100.00
EC Eric Chavez Jsy 10.00 25.00
ES Johnny Estrada Jsy 6.00 15.00
GR Khalil Greene Jsy 15.00 40.00
GS Gary Sheffield Jsy 15.00 40.00
HA Travis Hafner Jsy 10.00 25.00
HB Hank Blalock Jsy 10.00 25.00
JA Jason Bay Jsy 10.00 25.00
JB Jeff Bagwell Jsy 40.00 80.00
JD J.D. Drew Jsy 10.00 25.00
JM Justin Morneau Jsy 10.00 25.00
JR Jose Reyes Jsy 10.00 25.00
JV Jose Vidro Jsy 6.00 15.00
KG Ken Griffey Jr. Jsy 75.00 150.00
MA Joe Mauer Jsy 15.00 40.00
MC Miguel Cabrera Jsy 15.00 40.00
ML Mark Loretta Jsy 6.00 15.00
MT Mark Teixeira Jsy 20.00 50.00
MY Michael Young Jsy 10.00 25.00
RF Rafael Furcal Jsy 10.00 25.00
RH Ryan Howard Jsy 50.00 100.00
RP Rafael Palmeiro Jsy 20.00 50.00
TH Torii Hunter Jsy 10.00 25.00
VM Victor Martinez Jsy 10.00 25.00
WP Wily Mo Pena Jsy 10.00 25.00

2005 Ultimate Collection Veteran Materials

OVERALL GAME-USED ODDS 1:4
STATED PRINT RUN 20 SERIAL #'d SETS
*PATCH p/r 30: .6X TO 1.5X BASIC
*PATCH p/r 15-16: .75X TO 2X BASIC
OVERALL PATCH ODDS 1:4
PATCH PRINT RUN B/WN 7-30 PER
NO PATCH PRICING ON QTY OF 7
AB Adrian Beltre Jsy 4.00 10.00
AD Adam Dunn Jsy 4.00 10.00
AH Aubrey Huff Jsy 4.00 10.00
AJ Andruw Jones Jsy 6.00 15.00
AR Aramis Ramirez Jsy 4.00 10.00
AS Alfonso Soriano Jsy 4.00 10.00
BA Bobby Abreu Jsy 4.00 10.00
BE Josh Beckett Jsy 4.00 10.00
BG Brian Giles Jsy 4.00 10.00
BM Brett Myers Jsy 4.00 10.00
CA Rod Carew Jsy 6.00 15.00
CB Craig Biggio Jsy 6.00 15.00
CR Cal Ripken Jsy 30.00 60.00
CS C.C. Sabathia Jsy 4.00 10.00
DJ Derek Jeter Jsy 15.00 40.00
DL Derek Lowe Jsy 4.00 10.00
DO David Ortiz Jsy 6.00 15.00
DW Dontrelle Willis Jsy 4.00 10.00
EC Eric Chavez Jsy 4.00 10.00
EG Eric Gagne Jsy 4.00 10.00
ER Edgar Renteria Jsy 4.00 10.00
GM Greg Maddux Jsy 12.50 30.00
HB Hank Blalock Jsy 4.00 10.00
HO Trevor Hoffman Jsy 6.00 15.00
HU Torii Hunter Jsy 4.00 10.00
JB Jeff Bagwell Jsy 8.00 20.00
JD J.D. Drew Jsy 4.00 10.00
JK Jeff Kent Jsy 4.00 10.00
JV Jose Vidro Jsy 4.00 10.00
KF Keith Foulke Jsy 4.00 10.00
KG Ken Griffey Jr. Jsy 12.50 30.00
LE Derrek Lee Jsy 6.00 15.00
LH Livan Hernandez Jsy 4.00 10.00
MC Matt Clement Jsy 4.00 10.00
ML Mark Loretta Jsy 4.00 10.00
MM Mark Mulder Jsy 4.00 10.00
MP Mark Prior Jsy 6.00 15.00
MT Miguel Tejada Jsy 4.00 10.00
NR Nolan Ryan Jsy 15.00 40.00
OP Odalis Perez Jsy 4.00 10.00
RC Roger Clemens Jsy 12.50 30.00
RH Roy Halladay Jsy 4.00 10.00
RJ Randy Johnson Jsy 8.00 20.00
RO Roy Oswalt Jsy 4.00 10.00
SC Sean Casey Jsy 4.00 10.00
SM John Smoltz Jsy 8.00 20.00
SR Scott Rolen Jsy 6.00 15.00
TH Tim Hudson Jsy 4.00 10.00
TW Tim Wakefield Jsy 10.00 25.00
VG Vladimir Guerrero Jsy 8.00 20.00

2005 Ultimate Collection Veteran Materials Signature

STATED PRINT RUN 20 SERIAL #'d SETS
PATCH PRINT RUN 10 SERIAL #'d SETS
NO PATCH PRICING DUE TO SCARCITY
OVERALL AU-GU ODDS 1:4
EXCHANGE DEADLINE 01/10/09
AB Adrian Beltre Jsy 10.00 25.00
AD Adam Dunn Jsy 10.00 25.00
AH Aubrey Huff Jsy 6.00 15.00

AJ Andruw Jones Jsy 20.00 50.00
AR Aramis Ramirez Jsy 10.00 25.00
BE Josh Beckett Jsy 15.00 40.00
BG Brian Giles Jsy 10.00 25.00
BM Brett Myers Jsy 6.00 15.00
CA Rod Carew Jsy 15.00 40.00
CB Craig Biggio Jsy 20.00 50.00
CR Cal Ripken Jsy EXCH 125.00 200.00
DJ Derek Jeter Jsy 150.00 250.00
DO David Ortiz Jsy 30.00 60.00
DW Dontrelle Willis Jsy 15.00 40.00
EC Eric Chavez Jsy 10.00 25.00
EG Eric Gagne Jsy 10.00 25.00
HB Hank Blalock Jsy 10.00 25.00
HU Torii Hunter Jsy 10.00 25.00
JB Jeff Bagwell Jsy 40.00 80.00
JD J.D. Drew Jsy 10.00 25.00
JV Jose Vidro Jsy 6.00 15.00
KG Ken Griffey Jr. Jsy 75.00 150.00
LE Derrek Lee Jsy 15.00 40.00
LH Livan Hernandez Jsy 10.00 25.00
MC Matt Clement Jsy 10.00 25.00
ML Mark Loretta Jsy 6.00 15.00
MM Mark Mulder Jsy 10.00 25.00
MP Mark Prior Jsy 12.50 30.00
MT Miguel Tejada Jsy 20.00 50.00
NR Nolan Ryan Jsy 60.00 120.00
RH Roy Halladay Jsy 10.00 25.00
RO Roy Oswalt Jsy 10.00 25.00
SM John Smoltz Jsy 30.00 60.00
TH Tim Hudson Jsy 15.00 40.00
TW Tim Wakefield Jsy 50.00 100.00
VG Vladimir Guerrero Jsy 30.00 60.00

2005 Ultimate Collection Young Stars Materials

OVERALL GAME-USED ODDS 1:4
STATED PRINT RUN 20 SERIAL #'d SETS
*PATCH p/r 30: .6X TO 1.5X BASIC
*PATCH p/r 15: .75X TO 2X BASIC
OVERALL PATCH ODDS 1:4
PATCH PRINT RUN B/WN 6-30 PER
NO PATCH PRICING ON QTY OF 6

AB A.J. Burnett Jsy 4.00 10.00
AR Aaron Rowand Jsy 4.00 10.00
BA Jason Bay Jsy 4.00 10.00
BC Bobby Crosby Jsy 4.00 10.00
BL Brad Lidge Jsy 4.00 10.00
BO Jeremy Bonderman Jsy 4.00 10.00
BR Brian Roberts Jsy 4.00 10.00
BS Ben Sheets Jsy 4.00 10.00
BU B.J. Upton Jsy 4.00 10.00
CC Carl Crawford Jsy 4.00 10.00
CO Coco Crisp Jsy 4.00 10.00
CP Carl Pavano Jsy 4.00 10.00
CU Chase Utley Jsy 10.00 25.00
CZ Carlos Zambrano Jsy 4.00 10.00
DH Danny Haren Jsy 4.00 10.00
DW David Wright Jsy 12.50 30.00
FH Felix Hernandez Jsy 12.50 30.00
FR Francisco Rodriguez Jsy 4.00 10.00
GF Gavin Floyd Jsy 4.00 10.00
HO Ryan Howard Jsy 15.00 40.00
JB Joe Blanton Jsy 4.00 10.00
JE Johnny Estrada Jsy 4.00 10.00
JF Jeff Francis Jsy 4.00 10.00
JM Joe Mauer Jsy 6.00 15.00
JP Jake Peavy Jsy 4.00 10.00
JR Jeremy Reed Jsy 4.00 10.00
JS Johan Santana Jsy 6.00 15.00
JW Jake Westbrook Jsy 4.00 10.00
KG Khalil Greene Jsy 6.00 15.00
MA Matt Cain Jsy 15.00 40.00
MC Miguel Cabrera Jsy 6.00 15.00
MG Marcus Giles Jsy 4.00 10.00
MO Justin Morneau Jsy 4.00 10.00
MT Mark Teixeira Jsy 6.00 15.00
MY Michael Young Jsy 4.00 10.00
OP Oliver Perez Jsy 4.00 10.00
PA Corey Patterson Jsy 4.00 10.00
PF Prince Fielder Jsy 15.00 40.00
RE Jose Reyes Jsy 4.00 10.00
RF Rafael Furcal Jsy 4.00 10.00
RH Rich Harden Jsy 4.00 10.00
RW Rickie Weeks Jsy 4.00 10.00
SK Scott Kazmir Jsy 4.00 10.00
SP Scott Podsednik Jsy 6.00 15.00
TH Travis Hafner Jsy 4.00 10.00
TI Tadahito Iguchi Jsy 12.50 30.00
VM Victor Martinez Jsy 4.00 10.00
WP Wily Mo Pena Jsy 4.00 10.00
ZG Zack Greinke Jsy 4.00 10.00

2005 Ultimate Collection Young Stars Signature Materials

STATED PRINT RUN 20 SERIAL #'d SETS
NO RC YR PRICING DUE TO SCARCITY
PATCH PRINT RUN 10 SERIAL #'d SETS
NO PATCH PRICING DUE TO SCARCITY
OVERALL AU-GU ODDS 1:4

AR Aaron Rowand Jsy 10.00 25.00
BA Jason Bay Jsy 10.00 25.00
BC Bobby Crosby Jsy 10.00 25.00
BL Brad Lidge Jsy 15.00 40.00
BO Jeremy Bonderman Jsy 10.00 25.00
BR Brian Roberts Jsy 10.00 25.00
BS Ben Sheets Jsy 10.00 25.00
BU B.J. Upton Jsy 10.00 25.00
CC Carl Crawford Jsy 10.00 25.00
CZ Carlos Zambrano Jsy 10.00 25.00
DH Danny Haren Jsy 6.00 15.00
DW David Wright Jsy 50.00 100.00
FR Francisco Rodriguez Jsy 10.00 25.00
GF Gavin Floyd Jsy 6.00 15.00
JB Joe Blanton Jsy 6.00 15.00
JE Johnny Estrada Jsy 6.00 15.00
JF Jeff Francis Jsy 6.00 15.00
JM Joe Mauer Jsy 15.00 40.00
JP Jake Peavy Jsy 10.00 25.00
JR Jeremy Reed Jsy 6.00 15.00
JW Jake Westbrook Jsy 6.00 15.00
KG Khalil Greene Jsy 15.00 40.00
MA Matt Cain Jsy 75.00 150.00
MG Marcus Giles Jsy 10.00 25.00
MT Mark Teixeira Jsy 20.00 50.00
MY Michael Young Jsy 10.00 25.00
OP Oliver Perez Jsy 6.00 15.00
RE Jose Reyes Jsy 10.00 25.00
RF Rafael Furcal Jsy 10.00 25.00
RW Rickie Weeks Jsy 10.00 25.00
SK Scott Kazmir Jsy 10.00 25.00
SP Scott Podsednik Jsy 15.00 40.00
TH Travis Hafner Jsy 10.00 25.00
TI Tadahito Iguchi Jsy
VM Victor Martinez Jsy 10.00 25.00
WP Wily Mo Pena Jsy 10.00 25.00
ZG Zack Greinke Jsy 6.00 15.00

2005 Ultimate Collection Dual Materials

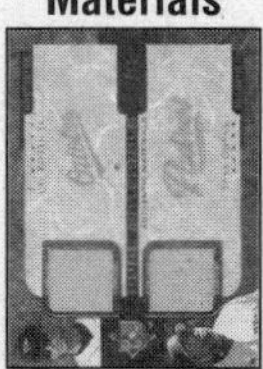

OVERALL GAME-USED ODDS 1:4
STATED PRINT RUN 15 SERIAL #'d SETS
NO RC YR PRICING DUE TO SCARCITY
OVERALL PATCH ODDS 1:4
PATCH PRINT RUN 10 SERIAL #'d SETS
NO PATCH PRICING DUE TO SCARCITY

AC Andruw Jones Jsy 12.50 30.00
Chipper Jones Jsy
AE Adrian Beltre Jsy 6.00 15.00
Eric Chavez Jsy
AH Adrian Beltre Jsy 6.00 15.00
Hank Blalock Jsy
AJ A.J. Burnett Jsy 6.00 15.00
Josh Beckett Jsy
AM Albert Pujols Jsy 20.00 50.00
Miguel Cabrera Jsy
AP Bobby Abreu Jsy 6.00 15.00
Corey Patterson Jsy
AU Bobby Abreu Jsy 15.00 40.00
Chase Utley Jsy
BC Josh Beckett Jsy 10.00 25.00
Miguel Cabrera Jsy
BG Jason Bay Jsy 12.50 30.00
Vladimir Guerrero Jsy
BH Adrian Beltre Jsy 15.00 40.00
Felix Hernandez Jsy
BJ Ben Sheets Jsy 6.00 15.00
Jake Peavy Jsy
BK Bobby Crosby Jsy 10.00 25.00
Khalil Greene Jsy
BM Jeremy Bonderman Jsy 30.00 60.00
Matt Cain Jsy
BS Ryne Sandberg Jsy 20.00 50.00
Wade Boggs Jsy
BT Hank Blalock Jsy 10.00 25.00
Mark Teixeira Jsy
BY Hank Blalock Jsy 6.00 15.00
Michael Young Jsy
CB Bobby Crosby Jsy 6.00 15.00
Jason Bay Jsy
CC Bobby Crosby Jsy 6.00 15.00
Eric Chavez Jsy
CG Miguel Cabrera Jsy 12.50 30.00
Vladimir Guerrero Jsy
CJ Craig Biggio Jsy 12.50 30.00
Jeff Bagwell Jsy
CO Roger Clemens Jsy 15.00 40.00
Roy Oswalt Jsy
CP Carl Crawford Jsy 10.00 25.00
Scott Podsednik Jsy
CR Eric Chavez Jsy 10.00 25.00
Scott Rolen Jsy
CT Cal Ripken Jsy 50.00 100.00
Tony Gwynn Jsy
CW Eric Chavez Jsy 15.00 40.00
David Wright Jsy
DG Adam Dunn Jsy 15.00 40.00
Ken Griffey Jr. Jsy
DJ David Wright Jsy 15.00 40.00
Jose Reyes Jsy
DP Adam Dunn Jsy 6.00 15.00
Wily Mo Pena Jsy
DR Derek Jeter Jsy 30.00 60.00
Randy Johnson Jsy
FW Prince Fielder Jsy
Rickie Weeks Jsy
GC Ken Griffey Jr. Jsy 15.00 40.00
Miguel Cabrera Jsy
GF Marcus Giles Jsy 6.00 15.00
Rafael Furcal Jsy
GG Brian Giles Jsy 6.00 15.00
Marcus Giles Jsy
GH Ken Griffey Jr. Jsy 15.00 40.00
Torii Hunter Jsy
GJ Derek Jeter Jsy 30.00 60.00
Ken Griffey Jr. Jsy
GL Khalil Greene Jsy 10.00 25.00
Mark Loretta Jsy
GP Ken Griffey Jr. Jsy 15.00 40.00
Wily Mo Pena Jsy
GR Eric Gagne Jsy 6.00 15.00
Francisco Rodriguez Jsy
HC Felix Hernandez Jsy 40.00 80.00
Matt Cain Jsy
HH Danny Haren Jsy 6.00 15.00
Rich Harden Jsy
HM Travis Hafner Jsy 6.00 15.00
Victor Martinez Jsy
HO Rich Harden Jsy 6.00 15.00
Roy Oswalt Jsy
HS Ben Sheets Jsy 6.00 15.00
Rich Harden Jsy
JC Randy Johnson Jsy 20.00 50.00
Roger Clemens Jsy
JF Johan Santana Jsy 15.00 40.00
Felix Hernandez Jsy
JG Andruw Jones Jsy 15.00 40.00
Ken Griffey Jr. Jsy
JH Andruw Jones Jsy 10.00 25.00
Torii Hunter Jsy
JJ Derek Jeter Jsy 30.00 60.00
Reggie Jackson Jsy
JL Derek Jeter Jsy 30.00 60.00
Barry Larkin Jsy
JO Johan Santana Jsy 10.00 25.00
Oliver Perez Jsy
JR Derek Jeter Jsy 30.00 60.00
Jose Reyes Jsy
JV Joe Mauer Jsy 10.00 25.00
Victor Martinez Jsy
LG Brad Lidge Jsy 6.00 15.00
Eric Gagne Jsy
LO Brad Lidge Jsy 6.00 15.00
Roy Oswalt Jsy
LR Brad Lidge Jsy 6.00 15.00
Francisco Rodriguez Jsy
ME Joe Mauer Jsy 10.00 25.00
Johnny Estrada Jsy
MG Greg Maddux Jsy 15.00 40.00
Mark Prior Jsy
MH Mark Mulder Jsy 6.00 15.00
Tim Hudson Jsy
MJ Pedro Martinez Jsy 12.50 30.00
Randy Johnson Jsy
MM Joe Mauer Jsy 10.00 25.00
Justin Morneau Jsy
MP Joe Mauer Jsy 10.00 25.00
Mark Prior Jsy
MR Mike Mussina Jsy 12.50 30.00
Randy Johnson Jsy
NR Nolan Ryan Jsy 30.00 60.00
Randy Johnson Jsy
OF David Ortiz Jsy
Prince Fielder Jsy
PC Mark Prior Jsy 15.00 40.00
Roger Clemens Jsy
PD Dwight Gooden Jsy 10.00 25.00
Pedro Martinez Jsy
PG Albert Pujols Jsy 30.00 60.00
Ken Griffey Jr. Jsy
PH Jake Peavy Jsy 6.00 15.00
Rich Harden Jsy
PJ Albert Pujols Jsy 30.00 60.00
Derek Jeter Jsy
PL Albert Pujols Jsy 20.00 50.00
Derrek Lee Jsy
PM Mike Piazza Jsy 12.50 30.00
Pedro Martinez Jsy
PS Ben Sheets Jsy 10.00 25.00
Mark Prior Jsy
RB Aramis Ramirez Jsy 6.00 15.00
Hank Blalock Jsy
RC Nolan Ryan Jsy 30.00 60.00
Roger Clemens Jsy
RE Aramis Ramirez Jsy 6.00 15.00
Eric Chavez Jsy
RF Jose Reyes Jsy 6.00 15.00
Rafael Furcal Jsy
RG Brian Roberts Jsy 6.00 15.00
Marcus Giles Jsy
RJ Cal Ripken Jsy 60.00 120.00
Derek Jeter Jsy
RL Aramis Ramirez Jsy 10.00 25.00
Derrek Lee Jsy
RP Aaron Rowand Jsy 10.00 25.00
Scott Podsednik Jsy
RR Aaron Rowand Jsy 6.00 15.00
Jeremy Reed Jsy
RS Mike Schmidt Jsy 50.00 100.00
Cal Ripken Jsy
RT Cal Ripken Jsy 40.00 80.00
Miguel Tejada Jsy
RU Jose Reyes Jsy 6.00 15.00
B.J. Upton Jsy
RW Aramis Ramirez Jsy 15.00 40.00
David Wright Jsy
SB Mike Schmidt Jsy 20.00 50.00
Wade Boggs Jsy
SC Johan Santana Jsy 15.00 40.00
Roger Clemens Jsy
SH John Smoltz Jsy 12.50 30.00
Tim Hudson Jsy
SJ Curt Schilling Jsy 12.50 30.00
Randy Johnson Jsy
SM Joe Mauer Jsy 10.00 25.00
Johan Santana Jsy
SO Curt Schilling Jsy 10.00 25.00
David Ortiz Jsy
SP Johan Santana Jsy 10.00 25.00
Mark Prior Jsy
SR Mike Schmidt Jsy 20.00 50.00
Scott Rolen Jsy
TC Mark Teixeira Jsy 10.00 25.00
Miguel Cabrera Jsy
UJ B.J. Upton Jsy 30.00 60.00
Derek Jeter Jsy
WR David Wright Jsy 15.00 40.00
Scott Rolen Jsy
ZH Carlos Zambrano Jsy 6.00 15.00
Rich Harden Jsy
ZO Carlos Zambrano Jsy 6.00 15.00
Roy Oswalt Jsy
ZP Carlos Zambrano Jsy 6.00 15.00
Oliver Perez Jsy

2005 Ultimate Collection Dual Materials Signature

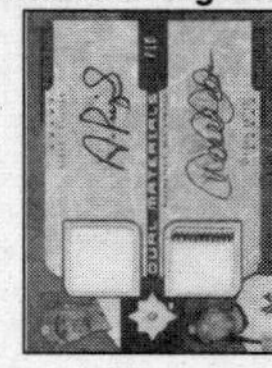

STATED PRINT RUN 10 SERIAL #'d SETS
PATCH PRINT RUN 5 SERIAL #'d SETS
OVERALL AU-GU ODDS 1:4
NO PRICING DUE TO SCARCITY
EXCHANGE DEADLINE 01/10/09

2005 Ultimate Collection Triple Materials

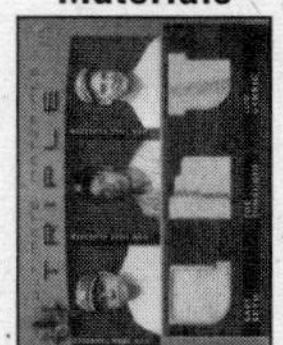

OVERALL GAME-USED ODDS 1:4
STATED PRINT RUN 15 SERIAL #'d SETS
ALL ARE TRIPLE JSY UNLESS NOTED
OVERALL PATCH ODDS 1:4
PATCH PRINT RUN 10 SERIAL #'d SETS
NO PRICING DUE TO SCARCITY

ATB Bobby Abreu Jsy
Jim Thome Jsy
Pat Burrell Jsy
BBB Craig Biggio Jsy
Jeff Bagwell Jsy
Lance Berkman Jsy
DRW Joe DiMaggio Jsy
Babe Ruth Bat
Ted Williams Jsy
FBM Carlton Fisk Jsy
Johnny Bench Jsy
Thurman Munson Jsy
GSP Ken Griffey Jr. Jsy
Sammy Sosa Jsy
Rafael Palmeiro Jsy
JMJ Derek Jeter Jsy
Don Mattingly Jsy
Reggie Jackson Jsy
JMM Derek Jeter Jsy
Don Mattingly Jsy
Thurman Munson Jsy
JSJ Derek Jeter Jsy
Gary Sheffield Jsy
Randy Johnson Jsy
LRJ Barry Larkin Jsy
Cal Ripken Jsy
Derek Jeter Jsy
MSG Greg Maddux Jsy
John Smoltz Jsy
Tom Glavine Jsy
PCO Andy Pettitte Jsy
Roger Clemens Jsy
Roy Oswalt Jsy
PMJ Carl Pavano Jsy
Mike Mussina Jsy
Randy Johnson Jsy
RDG Babe Ruth Bat
Joe DiMaggio Jsy
Lou Gehrig Pants
RFW Babe Ruth Bat
Jimmie Foxx Bat
Ted Williams Jsy
RJC Nolan Ryan Jsy
Randy Johnson Jsy
Roger Clemens Jsy
RSB Cal Ripken Jsy
Mike Schmidt Jsy
Wade Boggs Jsy
SCW Curt Schilling Jsy
Matt Clement Jsy
Tim Wakefield Jsy
SPO Ben Sheets Jsy
Mark Prior Jsy
Roy Oswalt Jsy
WRC Kerry Wood Jsy
Nolan Ryan Jsy
Roger Clemens Jsy
WRM David Wright Jsy
Jose Reyes Jsy
Kazuo Matsui Jsy
WSB David Wright Jsy
Mike Schmidt Jsy
Wade Boggs Jsy

2005 Ultimate Collection Quad Materials

OVERALL GAME-USED ODDS 1:4
STATED PRINT RUN 10 SERIAL #'d SETS
ALL ARE QUAD JSY UNLESS NOTED

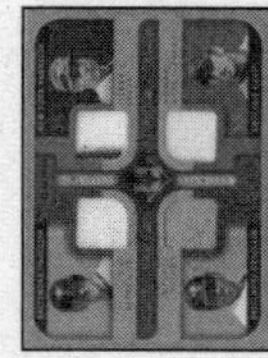

OVERALL PATCH ODDS 1:4
PATCH PRINT RUN 5 SERIAL #'d SETS
NO PRICING DUE TO SCARCITY

BMCB Adrian Beltre Jsy
Dallas McPherson Jsy
Eric Chavez Jsy
Hank Blalock Jsy
DWBC Carlos Delgado Jsy
Dontrelle Willis Jsy
Josh Beckett Jsy
Miguel Cabrera Jsy
GMMJ Lou Gehrig Pants
Thurman Munson Jsy
Don Mattingly Jsy
Derek Jeter Jsy
GSJS Ken Griffey Jr. Jsy
Mike Schmidt Jsy
Reggie Jackson Jsy
Sammy Sosa Jsy
JJSH Andruw Jones Jsy
Chipper Jones Jsy
John Smoltz Jsy
Tim Hudson Jsy
JTRG Derek Jeter Jsy
Miguel Tejada Jsy
Manny Ramirez Jsy
Vladimir Guerrero Jsy
MSMH Joe Mauer Jsy
Johan Santana Jsy
Justin Morneau Jsy
Torii Hunter Jsy
PBGC Albert Pujols Jsy
Carlos Beltran Jsy
Ken Griffey Jr. Jsy
Miguel Cabrera Jsy
PEWR Albert Pujols Jsy
Jim Edmonds Jsy
Larry Walker Jsy
Scott Rolen Jsy
PLGC Albert Pujols Jsy
Derrek Lee Jsy
Ken Griffey Jr. Jsy
Miguel Cabrera Jsy
POTK Albert Pujols Jsy
David Ortiz Jsy
Mark Teixeira Jsy
Paul Konerko Jsy
PSPT Albert Pujols Jsy
David Wright Jsy
Miguel Cabrera Jsy
Mark Teixeira Jsy
RDGB Babe Ruth Bat
Joe DiMaggio Jsy
Lou Gehrig Pants
Yogi Berra Pants
RJTG Cal Ripken Jsy
Derek Jeter Jsy
Miguel Tejada Jsy
Nomar Garciaparra Jsy
RMJC Nolan Ryan Jsy
Pedro Martinez Jsy
Randy Johnson Jsy
Roger Clemens Jsy
SBTY Alfonso Soriano Jsy
Hank Blalock Jsy
Mark Teixeira Jsy
Michael Young Jsy
SMJC Curt Schilling Jsy
Pedro Martinez Jsy
Randy Johnson Jsy
Roger Clemens Jsy
SODR Curt Schilling Jsy
David Ortiz Jsy
Johnny Damon Jsy
Manny Ramirez Jsy
WRPM David Wright Jsy
Jose Reyes Jsy
Mike Piazza Jsy
Pedro Martinez Jsy
ZHBH Barry Zito Jsy
Dan Haren Jsy
Joe Blanton Jsy
Rich Harden Jsy
ZMWP Carlos Zambrano Jsy
Greg Maddux Jsy
Kerry Wood Jsy
Mark Prior Jsy

2005 Ultimate Collection Dual Signatures

OVERALL AUTO ODDS 1:4
STATED PRINT RUN 25 SERIAL #'d SETS
NO RC YR PRICING DUE TO SCARCITY
EXCHANGE DEADLINE 01/10/09

BB Craig Biggio 60.00 120.00
Jeff Bagwell
BC Adrian Beltre 15.00 40.00
Eric Chavez
BH Adrian Beltre 75.00 150.00
Felix Hernandez
BJ Bobby Crosby 15.00 40.00
Jason Bay
BT Hank Blalock 30.00 60.00
Mark Teixeira
BV Jeremy Bonderman
Justin Verlander
BY Hank Blalock 15.00 40.00
Michael Young
CC Bobby Crosby 15.00 40.00
Eric Chavez
CG Bobby Crosby 30.00 60.00
Khalil Greene
CP Carl Crawford 30.00 60.00
Scott Podsednik
CT Cal Ripken 125.00 200.00
Tony Gwynn EXCH
CY Carl Crawford 30.00 60.00
Delmon Young
DD J.D. Drew
Stephen Drew
DG Adam Dunn 60.00 120.00
Ken Griffey Jr.
DJ Derek Jeter 100.00 175.00
Jose Reyes
DK Derek Jeter 150.00 250.00
Ken Griffey Jr.
DM David Wright 60.00 120.00
Mike Schmidt
DP Andre Dawson 15.00 40.00
Corey Patterson
FF Gavin Floyd 10.00 25.00
Jeff Francis
FW Prince Fielder
Rickie Weeks
GC Ken Griffey Jr. 75.00 150.00
Miguel Cabrera
GH Ken Griffey Jr. 60.00 120.00
Torii Hunter
GJ Andruw Jones 75.00 150.00
Ken Griffey Jr.
GL Khalil Greene 30.00 60.00
Mark Loretta
GP Ken Griffey Jr. 60.00 120.00
Wily Mo Pena
GR Eric Gagne 30.00 60.00
Francisco Rodriguez
HH Danny Haren 15.00 40.00
Rich Harden
HM Travis Hafner 15.00 40.00
Victor Martinez
HO Rich Harden 15.00 40.00
Roy Oswalt
HS Ben Sheets 15.00 40.00
Rich Harden
JB Ben Sheets 15.00 40.00
Jake Peavy
JG Derek Jeter 125.00 200.00
Nomar Garciaparra
JH Andruw Jones 30.00 60.00
Torii Hunter
JJ Andruw Jones 75.00 150.00
Chipper Jones
JM Derek Jeter 200.00 300.00
Don Mattingly
JV Joe Mauer 30.00 60.00
Victor Martinez
KH Scott Kazmir 75.00 150.00
Felix Hernandez
LO Brad Lidge 30.00 60.00
Roy Oswalt
LR Brad Lidge 30.00 60.00
Francisco Rodriguez
MC Don Mattingly 50.00 100.00
Will Clark
MG Greg Maddux 125.00 200.00
Tom Glavine
MH Justin Morneau 15.00 40.00
Travis Hafner
MM Joe Mauer 30.00 60.00
Justin Morneau
MP Joe Mauer 30.00 60.00
Mark Prior
MT Mark Mulder 30.00 60.00
Tim Hudson
NH Jeff Niemann
Philip Humber
NK Jeff Niemann
Scott Kazmir
NV Jeff Niemann
Justin Verlander
PH Jake Peavy 15.00 40.00
Rich Harden
PJ Albert Pujols 500.00 700.00
Derek Jeter
PP Gaylord Perry 15.00 40.00
Jake Peavy
RB Aramis Ramirez 15.00 40.00
Hank Blalock
RC Nolan Ryan 150.00 250.00
Roger Clemens
RE Aramis Ramirez 15.00 40.00
Eric Chavez
RF Jose Reyes 15.00 40.00
Rafael Furcal
RJ Cal Ripken 250.00 400.00
Derek Jeter EXCH
RL Aramis Ramirez 30.00 60.00
Derrek Lee
RP Aaron Rowand 15.00 40.00
Corey Patterson
RP Aaron Rowand 30.00 60.00
Scott Podsednik
RR Aaron Rowand 15.00 40.00
Jeremy Reed
RW Ryne Sandberg 60.00 120.00
Wade Boggs
RW Aramis Ramirez 50.00 100.00
David Wright
SH John Smoltz 40.00 80.00
Tim Hudson
SJ Curt Schilling 60.00 120.00
Randy Johnson EXCH
SO Curt Schilling 50.00 100.00
David Ortiz EXCH
SP Ben Sheets 15.00 40.00
Mark Prior
SW Ben Sheets 15.00 40.00
Rickie Weeks
TC Mark Teixeira 40.00 80.00
Miguel Cabrera
UJ B.J. Upton 100.00 175.00
Derek Jeter
UW B.J. Upton 15.00 40.00

Rickie Weeks
WR David Wright 60.00 120.00
Jose Reyes
YU Delmon Young 30.00 60.00
B.J. Upton
YW Delmon Young 30.00 60.00
Rickie Weeks
ZH Carlos Zambrano 15.00 40.00
Rich Harden
ZO Carlos Zambrano 15.00 40.00
Roy Oswalt

2005 Ultimate Collection Three Star Signatures

OVERALL AUTO ODDS 1:4
STATED PRINT RUN 20 SERIAL #'d SETS
NO PRICING DUE TO SCARCITY
EXCHANGE DEADLINE 01/10/09
BBB Craig Biggio
Jeff Bagwell
Lance Berkman
BCR Adrian Beltre
Eric Chavez
Scott Rolen
DGP Adam Dunn
Ken Griffey Jr.
Wily Mo Pena
HBH Danny Haren
Joe Blanton
Rich Harden
JMJ Derek Jeter
Don Mattingly
Reggie Jackson
MEM Joe Mauer
Johnny Estrada
Victor Martinez
MHP Justin Morneau
Ryan Howard
Wily Mo Pena
MSG Greg Maddux
John Smoltz
Tom Glavine
NVH Jeff Niemann
Justin Verlander
Philip Humber
PMR Albert Pujols
Mark Mulder
Scott Rolen
RCP Brian Roberts
Carl Crawford
Scott Podsednik
RPW Jose Reyes
Mike Piazza
David Wright
RSB Cal Ripken
Mike Schmidt
Wade Boggs EXCH
SCW Curt Schilling
Matt Clement
Tim Wakefield
SPO Ben Sheets
Mark Prior
Roy Oswalt
UYK B.J. Upton
Delmon Young
Scott Kazmir
ZWP Carlos Zambrano
Kerry Wood
Mark Prior

2005 Ultimate Collection Four Star Signatures

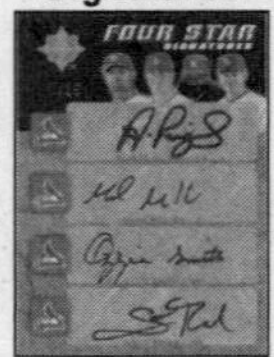

OVERALL AUTO ODDS 1:4
STATED PRINT RUN 15 SERIAL #'d SETS
NO PRICING DUE TO SCARCITY
EXCHANGE DEADLINE 01/10/09
BRCB Adrian Beltre
Aramis Ramirez
Eric Chavez
Hank Blalock
DCCB Adam Dunn
Carl Crawford
Miguel Cabrera
Jason Bay
FCBP Carlton Fisk
Gary Carter
Johnny Bench
Mike Piazza
GSPJ Ken Griffey Jr.
Mike Schmidt
Rafael Palmeiro
Reggie Jackson
HLGR Trevor Hoffman
Brad Lidge
Eric Gagne
Francisco Rodriguez
JPGH Andruw Jones
Corey Patterson
Ken Griffey Jr.
Torii Hunter
MSMH Joe Mauer
Johan Santana
Justin Morneau
Torii Hunter
PMSR Albert Pujols
Mark Mulder
Ozzie Smith
Scott Rolen
POTC Albert Pujols
David Ortiz
Mark Teixeira
Sean Casey
RJTG Cal Ripken
Derek Jeter
Miguel Tejada
Nomar Garciaparra EXCH
RRTP Brian Roberts
Cal Ripken
Miguel Tejada
Rafael Palmeiro EXCH
RWCR Aramis Ramirez
David Wright
Eric Chavez
Scott Rolen
SMWY Ben Sheets
Paul Molitor
Rickie Weeks
Robin Yount
SPPO Ben Sheets
Mark Prior
Oliver Perez
Roy Oswalt
SWHM C.C. Sabathia
Jake Westbrook
Travis Hafner
Victor Martinez
ZMWP Carlos Zambrano
Greg Maddux
Kerry Wood
Mark Prior

2005 Ultimate Collection Six Star Signatures

OVERALL AUTO ODDS 1:4
STATED PRINT RUN 10 SERIAL #'d SETS
NO PRICING DUE TO SCARCITY
AB Andruw Jones
Chipper Jones
John Smoltz
Marcus Giles
Rafael Furcal
Tim Hudson
CA Carlton Fisk
Gary Carter
Joe Mauer
Johnny Bench
Mike Piazza
Victor Martinez
CC Aramis Ramirez
Carlos Zambrano
Corey Patterson
Kerry Wood
Mark Prior
Nomar Garciaparra
CL Trevor Hoffman
Brad Lidge
Eric Gagne
Francisco Rodriguez
Keith Foulke
Huston Street
CR Adam Dunn
Barry Larkin
Johnny Bench
Ken Griffey Jr.
Sean Casey
Wily Mo Pena
CW Aaron Rowand
Luis Aparicio
Frank Thomas
Harold Baines
Scott Podsednik
Tadahito Iguchi
GR Cal Ripken
Ryne Sandberg
Mike Schmidt
Robin Yount
Tony Gwynn
Wade Boggs
HA Brad Lidge
Craig Biggio
Jeff Bagwell
Lance Berkman
Roger Clemens
Roy Oswalt
LD Derek Lowe
Eric Gagne
J.D. Drew
Jeff Kent
Brad Penny
Odalis Perez
LP Johan Santana
Mark Mulder
Oliver Perez
Randy Johnson
Scott Kazmir
Tom Glavine
PP Eude Brito
Bobby Abreu
Gavin Floyd
Brett Myers
Chase Utley
Ryan Howard EXCH
PR Jeff Niemann
Justin Verlander
Kendry Morales
Philip Humber
Prince Fielder
Stephen Drew
SP Brian Giles
Gaylord Perry
Jake Peavy
Khalil Greene
Mark Loretta
Tony Gwynn
SS B.J. Upton
Bobby Crosby
Jose Reyes
Khalil Greene
Michael Young
Rafael Furcal
TB Aubrey Huff
B.J. Upton
Carl Crawford
Delmon Young
Jonny Gomes
Scott Kazmir

2005 Ultimate Collection Eight Star Signatures

OVERALL AUTO ODDS 1:4
STATED PRINT RUN 5 SERIAL #'d SETS
NO PRICING DUE TO SCARCITY
EXCHANGE DEADLINE 01/10/09
1B Albert Pujols
David Ortiz
Don Mattingly
Jeff Bagwell
Mark Teixeira
Sean Casey
Rafael Palmeiro
Will Clark
3B Adrian Beltre
Chipper Jones
Eric Chavez
David Wright
Hank Blalock
Mike Schmidt
Scott Rolen
Wade Boggs
3000 Cal Ripken
Carl Yastrzemski
Rod Carew
Paul Molitor
Rafael Palmeiro
Robin Yount
Tony Gwynn
Wade Boggs EXCH
SS Barry Larkin
Cal Ripken
Derek Jeter
Michael Young
Miguel Tejada
Nomar Garciaparra
Ozzie Smith
Robin Yount
YSP Ben Sheets
Jake Peavy
Johan Santana
Josh Beckett
Mark Prior
Rich Harden
Roy Halladay
Roy Oswalt

2005 Ultimate Collection Eight Star Choice Signatures

OVERALL AUTO ODDS 1:4
AUTO PRINT RUN 1 SERIAL #'d SET
STATED PRINTEXCH STATED PRINT RUN 5
CARDS RUN 5 CARDS
NO PRICING DUE TO SCARCITY
EXCHANGE DEADLINE 01/10/09
GMRCJRPW Derek Jeter
Albert Pujols
Cal Ripken Jr.
Don Mattingly
Ken Griffey Jr.
David Wright
Roger Clemens
Nolan Ryan
MGJRCJRP Albert Pujols
Derek Jeter
Cal Ripken Jr.
Ken Griffey Jr.
Nolan Ryan
Roger Clemens
Greg Maddux
Randy Johnson
GPJRCRBS Ken Griffey Jr
Albert Pujols
Derek Jeter
Cal Ripken Jr.
Roger Clemens
Nolan Ryan
Johnny Bench
Ozzie Smith
UCS Exchange Card/5

2006 Ultimate Collection

This 274-card set was released in December, 2006. The base cards in this set were issued to a stated print run of 799 serial numbered sets while the signed Rookie Card subset (101-175) were issued to stated print runs between 150-180 serial numbered cards. The overall odds of recieving an autograph card from these packs were stated as one in two. Some players did not return their autographs in time for a pack out and those cards could be redeemed until December 20, 2009. No cards numbered 176-190 were issued as part of this product. Although a few retired greats were scattered throughout the set, there was also a subset which consisted of cards 191-219.

COMMON CARD (1-274) 1.00 2.50
VETERAN PRINT RUN 799 SER.#'d SETS
COMMON RC (1-274) 1.00 2.50
RC PRINT RUN 799 SERIAL #'d SETS
COMMON AU RC (101-175) 4.00 10.00
AU RC MINORS 4.00 10.00
OVERALL AU ODDS 1:2
AU RC PRINT RUNS B/WN 150-180
EXCHANGE DEADLINE 12/20/09
PLATE ODDS APPX. 7:10 BONUS PACKS
PLATE PRINT RUN 1 SET PER COLOR
BLACK-CYAN-MAGENTA-YELLOW ISSUED
NO PLATE PRICING DUE TO SCARCITY
1 Babe Ruth 4.00 10.00
2 Chad Tracy 1.00 2.50
3 Brandon Webb 1.00 2.50
4 Andruw Jones 1.50 4.00
5 Chipper Jones 2.00 5.00
6 John Smoltz 1.50 4.00
7 Eddie Mathews 2.00 5.00
8 Miguel Tejada 1.00 2.50
9 Brian Roberts 1.00 2.50
10 Mickey Cochrane 1.00 2.50
11 Curt Schilling 1.50 4.00
12 David Ortiz 2.00 5.00
13 Manny Ramirez 1.50 4.00
14 Johnny Bench 2.00 5.00
15 Cy Young 2.00 5.00
16 Greg Maddux 2.50 6.00
17 Derrek Lee 1.00 2.50
18 Yogi Berra 2.00 5.00
19 Walter Johnson 2.00 5.00
20 Jim Thome 1.50 4.00
21 Paul Konerko 1.00 2.50
22 Lou Gehrig 3.00 8.00
23 Jose Contreras 1.00 2.50
24 Ken Griffey Jr. 2.50 6.00
25 Adam Dunn 1.00 2.50
26 Reggie Jackson 1.50 4.00
27 Travis Hafner 1.00 2.50
28 Victor Martinez 1.00 2.50
29 Grady Sizemore 1.50 4.00
30 Casey Stengel 1.00 2.50
31 Todd Helton 1.50 4.00
32 Nolan Ryan 4.00 10.00
33 Clint Barmes 1.00 2.50
34 Ivan Rodriguez 1.50 4.00
35 Chris Shelton 1.00 2.50
36 Ty Cobb 3.00 8.00
37 Miguel Cabrera 1.50 4.00
38 Dontrelle Willis 1.00 2.50
39 Lance Berkman 1.00 2.50
40 Tom Seaver 1.50 4.00
41 Roy Oswalt 1.00 2.50
42 Christy Mathewson 2.00 5.00
43 Luis Aparicio 1.00 2.50
44 Vladimir Guerrero 2.00 5.00
45 Bartolo Colon 1.00 2.50
46 Roy Campanella 2.00 5.00
47 George Sisler 1.00 2.50
48 Jeff Kent 1.00 2.50
49 J.D. Drew 1.00 2.50
50 Carlos Lee 1.00 2.50
51 Willie Stargell 1.50 4.00
52 Rickie Weeks 1.00 2.50
53 Johan Santana 1.50 4.00
54 Torii Hunter 1.00 2.50
55 Joe Mauer 1.50 4.00
56 Pedro Martinez 1.50 4.00
57 David Wright 3.00 8.00
58 Carlos Beltran 1.00 2.50
59 Jimmie Foxx 2.00 5.00
60 Jose Reyes 1.00 2.50
61 Derek Jeter 4.00 10.00
62 Alex Rodriguez 3.00 8.00
63 Randy Johnson 2.00 5.00
64 Hideki Matsui 2.00 5.00
65 Thurman Munson 2.00 5.00
66 Rich Harden 1.00 2.50
67 Eric Chavez 1.00 2.50
68 Don Drysdale 1.50 4.00
69 Bobby Crosby 1.00 2.50
70 Pee Wee Reese 1.50 4.00
71 Ryan Howard 3.00 8.00
72 Chase Utley 2.00 5.00
73 Jackie Robinson 2.00 5.00
74 Jason Bay 1.00 2.50
75 Honus Wagner 2.00 5.00
76 Lefty Grove 1.00 2.50
77 Jake Peavy 1.00 2.50
78 Brian Giles 1.00 2.50
79 Eddie Murray 2.00 5.00
80 Omar Vizquel 1.50 4.00
81 Jason Schmidt 1.00 2.50
82 Ichiro Suzuki 2.50 6.00
83 Felix Hernandez 1.50 4.00
84 Kenji Johjima RC 3.00 8.00
85 Albert Pujols 3.00 8.00
86 Chris Carpenter 1.00 2.50
87 Brooks Robinson 1.50 4.00
88 Dizzy Dean 1.50 4.00
89 Carl Crawford 1.00 2.50
90 Rogers Hornsby 1.50 4.00
91 Scott Kazmir 1.50 4.00
92 Mark Teixeira 1.50 4.00
93 Michael Young 1.00 2.50
94 Johnny Mize 1.00 2.50
95 Vernon Wells 1.00 2.50
96 Roy Halladay 1.00 2.50
97 Mel Ott 1.00 2.50
98 Alfonso Soriano 1.00 2.50
99 Joe Morgan 1.00 2.50
100 Satchel Paige 2.00 5.00
101 Adam Wainwright AU/180 (RC) 10.00 25.00
102 Anderson Hernandez AU/180 (RC) 4.00 10.00
103 Andre Ethier AU/180 (RC) 12.50 30.00
104 Ben Johnson AU/180 (RC) 4.00 10.00
105 Boof Bonser AU/180 (RC) 6.00 15.00
106 Boone Logan AU/180 RC 4.00 10.00
107 Brian Anderson AU/180 (RC) 4.00 10.00
108 Brian Bannister AU/180 (RC) 20.00 50.00
109 Chris Demaria AU/180 RC 4.00 10.00
110 Chris Denorfia AU/180 (RC) 4.00 10.00
111 Cody Ross AU/180 (RC) 4.00 10.00
112 Cole Hamels AU/180 (RC) 30.00 60.00
113 Conor Jackson AU/180 (RC) 6.00 15.00
114 Dan Uggla AU/180 (RC) EXCH 12.50 30.00
115 Dave Gassner AU/180 (RC) 4.00 10.00
116 Eric Reed AU/180 (RC) 4.00 10.00
117 Fausto Carmona AU/180 (RC) 20.00 50.00
118 Fernando Nieve AU/180 (RC) 4.00 10.00
119 Francisco Liriano AU/180 (RC) 30.00 60.00
120 Freddie Bynum AU/180 (RC) 4.00 10.00
121 Hanley Ramirez AU/180 (RC) 15.00 40.00
122 Hong-Chih Kuo AU/180 (RC) EXCH 40.00 80.00
123 Ian Kinsler AU/180 (RC) 12.50 30.00
124 Jason Hammel AU/180 (RC) 4.00 10.00
125 Jason Kubel AU/180 (RC) 4.00 10.00
126 Jeff Harris AU/180 RC 4.00 10.00
127 Jered Weaver AU/150 (RC) 20.00 50.00
128 Jeremy Accardo AU/180 (RC) 4.00 10.00
129 Jeremy Hermida AU/180 (RC) 6.00 15.00
130 Joel Zumaya AU/180 (RC) 15.00 40.00
131 Joey Devine AU/180 RC 4.00 10.00
132 John Koronka AU/180 (RC) 4.00 10.00
133 John Van Benschoten AU/180 (RC) 4.0010.00
134 Jonathan Papelbon AU/180 (RC) 20.00 50.00
135 Jose Capellan AU/180 (RC) 4.00 10.00
136 Josh Johnson AU/180 (RC) 6.00 15.00
137 Josh Rupe AU/180 (RC) 4.00 10.00
138 Josh Willingham AU/180 (RC) 4.00 10.00
139 Josh Wilson AU/180 (RC) 4.00 10.00
140 Justin Verlander AU/180 (RC) 20.00 50.00
141 Kelly Shoppach AU/180 (RC) 4.00 10.00
142 Kendry Morales AU/180 (RC) 6.00 15.00
143 Macay McBride AU/180 (RC) 4.00 10.00
144 Martin Prado AU/180 (RC) 4.00 10.00
145 Matt Cain AU/180 (RC) 10.00 25.00
146 Mike Jacobs AU/180 (RC) 4.00 10.00
147 Mike Thompson AU/180 RC 4.00 10.00
148 Nate McLouth AU/180 (RC) 8.00 20.00
149 Paul Maholm AU/180 (RC) 4.00 10.00
150 Prince Fielder AU/180 (RC) EXCH 60.00 120.00
151 Reggie Abercrombie AU/180 (RC) 4.00 10.00
152 Rich Hill AU/180 (RC) 15.00 40.00
153 Ron Flores AU/180 RC 4.00 10.00
154 Ruddy Lugo AU/180 (RC) 4.00 10.00
155 Ryan Zimmerman AU/180 (RC) 30.00 60.00
156 Sean Marshall AU/180 (RC) 10.00 25.00
157 Takashi Saito AU/180 RC 10.00 25.00
158 Taylor Buchholz AU/180 (RC) 4.00 10.00
159 Tony Pena Jr. AU/180 (RC) 4.00 10.00
160 Wil Nieves AU/180 (RC) 4.00 10.00
161 Jamie Shields AU/180 RC 4.00 10.00
162 Jon Lester AU/180 RC 30.00 60.00
163 Craig Hansen AU/180 RC 15.00 40.00
164 Aaron Rakers AU/180 (RC) 4.00 10.00
165 Yusmeiro Petit AU/180 (RC) EXCH 4.0010.00
166 Bobby Livingston AU/180 (RC) 4.00 10.00
167 Brendan Harris AU/180 (RC) 4.00 10.00
169 Carlos Ruiz AU/180 (RC) 4.00 10.00
170 Chris Britton AU/180 RC 4.00 10.00
171 Howie Kendrick AU/180 (RC) 15.00 40.00
172 Jermaine Van Buren AU/180 (RC) 4.00 10.00
173 Kevin Frandsen AU/180 (RC) 6.00 15.00
174 Matt Capps AU/180 (RC) 4.00 10.00
175 Peter Moylan AU/180 RC 4.00 10.00
191 Richie Ashburn 1.50 4.00
192 Lou Brock 1.50 4.00
193 Lou Boudreau 1.00 2.50
194 Orlando Cepeda 1.00 2.50
195 Bobby Doerr 1.00 2.50
196 Dennis Eckersley 1.00 2.50
197 Bob Feller 1.00 2.50
198 Rollie Fingers 1.00 2.50
199 Carlton Fisk 1.50 4.00
200 Bob Gibson 1.50 4.00
201 Catfish Hunter 1.00 2.50
202 Fergie Jenkins 1.00 2.50
203 Al Kaline 2.00 5.00
204 Harmon Killebrew 2.00 5.00
205 Ralph Kiner 1.50 4.00
206 Buck Leonard 1.00 2.50
207 Juan Marichal 1.00 2.50
208 Bill Mazeroski 1.50 4.00
209 Willie McCovey 1.50 4.00
210 Jim Palmer 1.00 2.50
211 Tony Perez 1.00 2.50
212 Gaylord Perry 1.00 2.50
213 Phil Rizzuto 1.50 4.00
214 Robin Roberts 1.00 2.50
215 Mike Schmidt 2.50 6.00
216 Enos Slaughter 1.00 2.50
217 Ozzie Smith 2.50 6.00
218 Billy Williams 1.00 2.50
219 Robin Yount 2.00 5.00
220 Carlos Quentin (RC) 1.50 4.00
221 Jeff Francoeur 2.00 5.00
222 Brian McCann 1.00 2.50
223 Nick Markakis (RC) 1.50 4.00
224 Josh Beckett 1.00 2.50
225 Jason Varitek 2.00 5.00
226 Mark Prior 1.50 4.00
227 Aramis Ramirez 1.00 2.50
228 Jermaine Dye 1.00 2.50
229 Tadahito Iguchi 1.00 2.50
230 Bobby Jenks 1.00 2.50
231 C.C. Sabathia 1.00 2.50
232 Jeff Francis 1.00 2.50
233 Matt Holliday 1.25 3.00
234 Magglio Ordonez 1.00 2.50
235 Kenny Rogers 1.00 2.50
236 Roger Clemens 3.00 8.00
237 Andy Pettitte 1,00 2.50
238 Craig Biggio 1.50 4.00
239 Chone Figgins 1.00 2.50
240 John Lackey 1.00 2.50
241 Nomar Garciaparra 2.00 5.00
242 Prince Fielder 2,50 6.00
243 Ben Sheets 1.00 2.50
244 Bill Hall 1.00 2.50
245 Justin Morneau 1.00 2.50
246 Joe Nathan 1.00 2.50
247 Carlos Delgado 1.00 2.50
248 Shawn Green 1.00 2.50
249 Billy Wagner 1.00 2.50
250 Jason Giambi 1.00 2.50
251 Mike Mussina 1.50 4.00
252 Mariano Rivera 2.00 5.00
253 Robinson Cano 1.50 4.00
254 Bobby Abreu 1.00 2.50
255 Huston Street 1.00 2.50
256 Frank Thomas 2.00 5.00
257 Danny Haren 1.00 2.50
258 Jason Kendall 1.00 2.50
259 Nick Swisher 1.00 2.50
260 Pat Burrell 1.00 2.50
261 Tom Gordon 1.00 2.50
262 Freddy Sanchez 1.00 2.50
263 Trevor Hoffman 1.00 2.50
264 Khalil Greene 1.50 4.00
265 Adrian Gonzalez 1.00 2.50
266 Moises Alou 1.00 2.50
267 Matt Morris 1.00 2.50
268 Pedro Feliz 1.00 2.50
269 Richie Sexson 1.00 2.50
270 Hoyt Wilhelm 1.00 2.50
271 Adrian Beltre 1.00 2.50
272 Jim Edmonds 1.50 4.00
273 Scott Rolen 1.50 4.00
274 Jason Isringhausen 1.00 2.50
275 Jorge Cantu 1.00 2.50
276 Hank Blalock 1.00 2.50
277 Kevin Millwood 1.00 2.50
278 Alex Rios 1.00 2.50
279 Troy Glaus 1.00 2.50
280 B.J. Ryan 1.00 2.50
281 Nick Johnson 1.00 2.50
282 Chad Cordero 1.00 2.50
283 Austin Kearns 1.00 2.50
284 Ricky Nolasco (RC) 1.00 2.50
285 Travis Ishikawa (RC) 1.00 2.50
286 Lastings Milledge (RC) 1.50 4.00
287 James Loney (RC) 1.50 4.00
288 Red Schoendienst 1.00 2.50
289 Warren Spahn 1.50 4.00
290 Early Wynn 1.00 2.50

2006 Ultimate Collection Ensemble Materials Triple

OVERALL GAME-USED ODDS 1:2
STATED PRINT RUN 25 SER.#'d SETS
NO PRICING DUE TO SCARCITY
PATCH PRINT RUN 20 SER. #'d SETS
NO PATCH PRICING DUE TO SCARCITY
CCP Carl Crawford Jsy
Coco Crisp Jsy
Scott Podsednik Jsy
COP Chris Carpenter Jsy
Roy Oswalt Jsy
Jake Peavy Jsy
CRC Roger Clemens Jsy
Nolan Ryan Jsy
Steve Carlton Bat
CSG Roger Clemens Jsy
Tom Glavine Jsy
Curt Schilling Jsy
CZA Miguel Cabrera Jsy
Garrett Atkins Jsy
Ryan Zimmerman Jsy
FLW Carlos Lee Jsy
Rickie Weeks Jsy
Prince Fielder Jsy
FOH David Ortiz Jsy
Ryan Howard Jsy
Prince Fielder
GDK Ken Griffey Jr. Jsy
Austin Kearns Jsy
Adam Dunn Jsy
GJP Ken Griffey Jr. Jsy
Derek Jeter Jsy
Albert Pujols Jsy
GMW Tom Glavine Jsy
Pedro Martinez Jsy
Billy Wagner Jsy
HCW Chris Carpenter Jsy
Roy Halladay Jsy
Brandon Webb Jsy
HKL Francisco Liriano Jsy
Scott Kazmir Jsy
Cole Hamels Jsy
HOF Travis Hafner Jsy
David Ortiz Jsy
Prince Fielder Jsy
HWR Josh Willingham Jsy
Hanley Ramirez Jsy
Jeremy Hermida Jsy
JBM Johnny Bench Jsy
Victor Martinez Jsy
Kenji Johjima Jsy
JCZ Chipper Jones Jsy
Miguel Cabrera Jsy
Ryan Zimmerman Jsy
JFJ Andruw Jones Jsy
Chipper Jones Jsy
Jeff Francoeur Jsy
JMJ Don Mattingly Jsy
Derek Jeter Jsy
Reggie Jackson Jsy
KUU Chase Utley Jsy
Ian Kinsler Jsy
Dan Uggla Jsy
MGS Greg Maddux Jsy
Tom Glavine Jsy
John Smoltz Jsy
MLS Johan Santana Jsy
Joe Mauer Jsy
Francisco Liriano Jsy
PBL Derrek Lee Jsy
Albert Pujols Jsy
Jason Bay Jsy
PHN Trevor Hoffman Jsy
Joe Nathan Jsy
Jonathan Papelbon Jsy
RJT Cal Ripken Jsy
Derek Jeter Jsy
Miguel Tejada Jsy
RLO Manny Ramirez Jsy
Mark Loretta Jsy

David Ortiz Jsy
RUC Miguel Cabrera Jsy
Hanley Ramirez Jsy
Dan Uggla Jsy
SDC Johnny Damon Jsy
Gary Sheffield Jsy
Melky Cabrera Jsy
SHM Travis Hafner Jsy
Victor Martinez Jsy
Grady Sizemore Jsy
SHP Curt Schilling Jsy
Jonathan Papelbon Jsy
Craig Hansen Jsy
SJK Randy Johnson Jsy
Johan Santana Jsy
Scott Kazmir Jsy
SJR Chipper Jones Jsy
Cal Ripken Jsy
Mike Schmidt Jsy
TKD Jim Thome Jsy
Paul Konerko Jsy
Jermaine Dye Jsy
TYB Michael Young Jsy
Mark Teixeira Jsy
Hank Blalock Jsy
UIR Brian Roberts Jsy
Chase Utley Jsy
Tadahito Iguchi Jsy
VBZ Jeremy Bonderman Jsy
Justin Verlander Jsy
Joel Zumaya Jsy
VWK Scott Kazmir Jsy
Justin Verlander Jsy
Jered Weaver Jsy
WBD Carlos Delgado Jsy
Carlos Beltran Jsy
Jose Reyes Jsy
WKJ Randy Johnson Jsy
Scott Kazmir Jsy
Dontrelle Willis Jsy
ZSJ Nick Johnson Jsy
Alfonso Soriano Jsy
Ryan Zimmerman Jsy

2006 Ultimate Collection Ensemble Materials Quad

OVERALL GAME-USED ODDS 1:2
STATED PRINT RUN 20 SER.#'d SETS
NO PRICING DUE TO SCARCITY
PATCH PRINT RUN 15 SER. #'d SETS
NO PATCH PRICING DUE TO SCARCITY
BRMD Carlos Delgado Jsy
Carlos Beltran Jsy
Pedro Martinez Jsy
Jose Reyes Jsy
CMHK Lastings Milledge Jsy
Jason Kubel Jsy
Melky Cabrera Jsy
Jeremy Hermida J
CPOM Pedro Martinez Jsy
Chris Carpenter Jsy
Roy Oswalt Jsy
Jake Peavy Jsy
FBBB Lance Berkman Jsy
Pat Burrell Jsy
Jeff Francoeur Jsy
Jason Bay Jsy
GJPO Ken Griffey Jr. Jsy
Derek Jeter Jsy
David Ortiz Jsy
Albert Pujols Jsy
GSJZ Chipper Jones Jsy
Mike Schmidt Jsy
Troy Glaus Jsy
Ryan Zimmerman Jsy
GWRO Vernon Wells Jsy
Manny Ramirez Jsy
Vladimir Guerrero Jsy
Magglio Ordonez
HMSP Travis Hafner Jsy
Victor Martinez Jsy
Grady Sizemore Jsy
Jhonny Peralta
HRWU Josh Willingham Jsy
Hanley Ramirez Jsy
Jeremy Hermida Jsy
Dan Uggla Jsy
JGDS Derek Jeter Jsy
Jason Giambi Jsy
Johnny Damon Jsy
Gary Sheffield Jsy
JRMM Ivan Rodriguez Jsy
Victor Martinez Jsy
Joe Mauer Jsy
Kenji Johjima Jsy
JZCR Chipper Jones Jsy
Scott Rolen Jsy
Miguel Cabrera Jsy
Ryan Zimmerman Jsy
MCHW Josh Willingham Jsy
Lastings Milledge Jsy
Melky Cabrera Jsy
Jeremy Hermi
MFHJ Ryan Howard Jsy
Conor Jackson Jsy
Prince Fielder Jsy
Kendry Morales Jsy
NSLM Joe Nathan Jsy
Johan Santana Jsy
Joe Mauer Jsy
Francisco Liriano Jsy
PJLR Brad Lidge Jsy
Bobby Jenks Jsy
BJ Ryan Jsy
Jonathan Papelbon Jsy
SRBJ Andruw Jones Jsy
Alfonso Soriano Jsy
Jason Bay Jsy
Alex Rios Jsy
THOT Frank Thomas Jsy
Jim Thome Jsy
Travis Hafner Jsy
David Ortiz Jsy
TJRR Derek Jeter Jsy
Miguel Tejada Jsy
Jose Reyes Jsy
Hanley Ramirez Jsy
TODT Jim Thome Jsy
Carlos Delgado Jsy
David Ortiz Jsy
Mark Teixeira Jsy
UIRK Brian Roberts Jsy
Chase Utley Jsy
Tadahito Iguchi Jsy
Ian Kinsler Jsy
VHWH Justin Verlander Jsy
Felix Hernandez Jsy
Cole Hamels Jsy
Jered Weaver Js
VZWC Justin Verlander Jsy
Matt Cain Jsy
Joel Zumaya Jsy
Jered Weaver Jsy
WKGJ Randy Johnson Jsy
Tom Glavine Jsy
Scott Kazmir Jsy
Dontrelle Willis Jsy

2006 Ultimate Collection Ensemble Signatures Triple

OVERALL AU ODDS 1:2
STATED PRINT RUN 50 SER.#'d SETS
TRIPLE 15 PRINT RUN 15 SER.#'d SETS
NO TRI 15 PRICING DUE TO SCARCITY
TRIPLE 1 PRINT RUN 1 SER.#'d SET
NO TRI 1 PRICING DUE TO SCARCITY
EXCHANGE DEADLINE 12/20/09
AHW Josh Willingham 15.00 40.00
Reggie Abercrombie
Jeremy Hermida
BBB Jeff Bagwell 60.00 120.00
Craig Biggio
Lance Berkman EXCH
BBW Taylor Buchholz 15.00 40.00
Adam Wainwright
Brian Bannister
BDD Andre Dawson 30.00 60.00
Eric Davis
George Bell
BHR Roy Halladay 20.00 50.00
Alex Rios
AJ Burnett EXCH
BKM Bill Mazeroski 50.00 100.00
Ralph Kiner
Jason Bay
BNO Roy Oswalt 15.00 40.00
Taylor Buchholz
Fernando Nieve
BSH Ben Sheets 20.00 50.00
Rich Harden
AJ Burnett
BUK Craig Biggio 40.00 80.00
Chase Utley
Ian Kinsler
BWC Adam Wainwright 15.00 40.00
Matt Cain
Brian Bannister
BWV Boof Bonser 40.00 80.00
Justin Verlander
Jered Weaver
CBP Sean Casey 15.00 40.00
Oliver Perez
Jason Bay
CBS Ron Cey 30.00 60.00
Don Sutton
Dusty Baker
CBZ Boof Bonser 20.00 50.00
Matt Cain
Joel Zumaya
CDV Andy Van Slyke 15.00 40.00
Eric Davis
Jack Clark
CHK Jason Kubel 20.00 50.00
Melky Cabrera
Jeremy Hermida
CHO Chris Carpenter 30.00 60.00
Roy Oswalt
Rich Harden
CKH Jason Kendall 15.00 40.00
Bobby Crosby
Rich Harden
CKS Carl Crawford 20.00 50.00
Scott Kazmir
Jamie Shields
CLH Francisco Liriano 40.00 80.00
Fausto Carmona
Cole Hamels
CMH Travis Hafner 30.00 60.00
Victor Martinez
Fausto Carmona
CNS Ron Santo 30.00 60.00
Graig Nettles
Ron Cey
CPC Carl Crawford 15.00 40.00
Coco Crisp
Scott Podsednik
CSS Roger Clemens 100.00 200.00
John Smoltz
Curt Schilling
CWW Miguel Cabrera 30.00 60.00
Josh Willingham
Dontrelle Willis
CZC Eric Chavez 40.00 80.00
Miguel Cabrera
Ryan Zimmerman
DJH Derek Jeter 150.00 250.00
Jose Reyes
Hanley Ramirez
DPA Jermaine Dye 20.00 50.00
Brian Anderson
Scott Podsednik
DPI Jermaine Dye 30.00 60.00
Scott Podsednik
Tadahito Iguchi
FGC David Cone 40.00 80.00
Dwight Gooden
Sid Fernandez
FJM Conor Jackson 30.00 60.00
Prince Fielder
Kendry Morales
FWL Carlos Lee 30.00 60.00
Rickie Weeks
Prince Fielder
GCN Goose Gossage 30.00 60.00
Graig Nettles
Chris Chambliss
GCS David Cone 15.00 40.00
Dwight Gooden
Bret Saberhagen
GJB Ken Griffey Jr. 125.00 250.00
Derek Jeter
Jason Bay
GJP Ken Griffey Jr. 400.00 500.00
Derek Jeter
Albert Pujols
GLK Francisco Liriano 20.00 50.00
Jason Kubel
Dave Gassner
GPN Eric Gagne 20.00 50.00
Joe Nathan
Jonathan Papelbon
GRS Vladimir Guerrero 30.00 60.00
Alfonso Soriano
Alex Rios
HBS Nick Swisher 20.00 50.00
Rich Harden
Joe Blanton
HKP John Kruk 20.00 50.00
Kent Hrbek
Boog Powell
HMK Mark Mulder 30.00 60.00
Scott Kazmir
Cole Hamels
HNP Trevor Hoffman 40.00 80.00
Joe Nathan
Jonathan Papelbon
HOT Travis Hafner 40.00 80.00
David Ortiz
Mark Teixeira
HWU Josh Willingham 15.00 40.00
Jeremy Hermida
Dan Uggla
IKU Tadahito Iguchi 30.00 60.00
Ian Kinsler
Dan Uggla
JCN Derek Jeter 150.00 200.00
Wil Nieves
Melky Cabrera
JGS Ken Griffey Jr. 60.00 120.00
Andruw Jones
Alfonso Soriano
JRR Derek Jeter 125.00 200.00
Jose Reyes
Hanley Ramirez
JWV Josh Johnson 40.00 80.00
Justin Verlander
Jered Weaver
KGJ Wally Joyner 50.00 100.00
Mark Grace
John Kruk
KLB Boof Bonser 20.00 50.00
Francisco Liriano
Jason Kubel
KUU Chase Utley 30.00 60.00
Ian Kinsler
Dan Uggla
KWM Jason Kendall 15.00 40.00
Victor Martinez
Josh Willingham
LGB Boof Bonser 20.00 50.00
Francisco Liriano
Dave Gassner
LHC Francisco Liriano 20.00 50.00
Fausto Carmona
Felix Hernandez
LPO Derrek Lee 150.00 250.00
David Ortiz
Albert Pujols
MCN Graig Nettles 20.00 50.00
Bill Madlock
Ron Cey
MMK Jason Kendall 20.00 50.00
Victor Martinez
Joe Mauer
MNL Joe Nathan 30.00 60.00
Joe Mauer
Francisco Liriano
MWC Mark Mulder 40.00 80.00
Chris Carpenter
Adam Wainwright
MWP Josh Willingham 15.00 40.00
Russell Martin
Ronny Paulino
NLP Joe Nathan 20.00 50.00
Brad Lidge
Jonathan Papelbon
OBL Roy Oswalt 15.00 40.00
Brad Lidge
Taylor Buchholz
PCL Oliver Perez 30.00 60.00
Francisco Liriano
Fausto Carmona
PHL Oliver Perez 40.00 80.00
Francisco Liriano
Cole Hamels
PSO Ben Sheets 20.00 50.00
Roy Oswalt
Jake Peavy
PVW Justin Verlander 40.00 80.00
Jonathan Papelbon
Jered Weaver
RHW Cody Ross 15.00 40.00
Josh Willingham
Jeremy Hermida
RMM Ivan Rodriguez 40.00 80.00
Victor Martinez
Joe Mauer
RRB Jose Reyes 30.00 60.00
Hanley Ramirez
Yuniesky Betancourt
SGM Greg Maddux 125.00 200.00
Tom Glavine
John Smoltz
SJF Prince Fielder 20.00 50.00
Chris Shelton
Mike Jacobs
SKM Hong-Chih Kuo 100.00 200.00
Russell Martin
Takashi Saito
SWB Taylor Buchholz 30.00 60.00
Jered Weaver
Jamie Shields
TGB Ken Griffey Jr. 150.00 250.00
Jeff Bagwell
Frank Thomas
TKY Michael Young 40.00 80.00
Mark Teixeira
Ian Kinsler
UHC Miguel Cabrera 30.00 60.00
Jeremy Hermida
Dan Uggla
URC Miguel Cabrera 20.00 50.00
Hanley Ramirez
Dan Uggla
URW Josh Willingham 20.00 50.00
Hanley Ramirez
Dan Uggla
VBZ Jeremy Bonderman 60.00 120.00
Justin Verlander
Joel Zumaya
VWL Francisco Liriano 50.00 100.00
Justin Verlander
Jered Weaver
WJC Josh Johnson 30.00 60.00
Matt Cain
Jered Weaver
WJO Josh Johnson 30.00 60.00
Dontrelle Willis
Scott Olsen
WSV Justin Verlander 30.00 60.00
Jered Weaver
Jamie Shields
ZBC Boof Bonser 30.00 60.00
Matt Cain
Joel Zumaya
ZHZ Carlos Zambrano 30.00 60.00
Felix Hernandez
Joel Zumaya

2006 Ultimate Collection Ensemble Signatures Quad

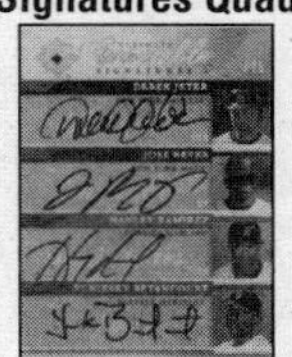

OVERALL AU ODDS 1:2
STATED PRINT RUN 25 SER.#'d SETS
NO PRICING DUE TO SCARCITY
EXCHANGE DEADLINE 12/20/09
1 Josh Willingham
Hanley Ramirez
Jeremy Hermida
Dan Uggla
2 Boof Bonser
Francisco Liriano
Justin Verlander
Jered Weaver
3 Ken Griffey Jr.
Derek Jeter
David Ortiz
Albert Pujols
5 Justin Verlander
Jonathan Papelbon
Joel Zumaya
Jered Weaver
6 Jason Kendall
Victor Martinez
Joe Mauer
Josh Willingham
8 Conor Jackson
Prince Fielder
Mike Jacobs
Kendry Morales
9 Derek Jeter
Jose Reyes
Ronny Cedeno
Hanley Ramirez
10 Miguel Cabrera
Josh Johnson
Hanley Ramirez
Dan Uggla
11 Boof Bonser
Francisco Liriano
Jason Kubel
Dave Gassner
12 Roger Clemens
Roy Oswalt
Brad Lidge
Taylor Buchholz
14 Josh Johnson
Adam Wainwright
Matt Cain
Jered Weaver
15 Jeremy Bonderman
Justin Verlander
Chris Shelton
Joel Zumaya
16 Jermaine Dye
Brian Anderson
Scott Podsednik
Tadahito Iguchi
17 Ben Sheets
Roy Oswalt
Jake Peavy
Rich Harden
18 Chase Utley
Tadahito Iguchi
Ian Kinsler
Dan Uggla
19 Travis Hafner
David Ortiz
Mark Teixeira
Prince Fielder
20 Justin Verlander
Matt Cain
Jered Weaver
Jamie Shields
22 Trevor Hoffman
Joe Nathan
Brad Lidge
Jonathan Papelbon
23 Carl Crawford
Coco Crisp
Scott Podsednik
Alex Rios
24 Francisco Liriano
Fausto Carmona
Felix Hernandez
Fernando Nieve
25 Taylor Buchholz
Adam Wainwright
Matt Cain
Brian Bannister
26 Sean Casey
Oliver Perez
Jason Bay
Ronny Paulino
27 Dave Parker
Bill Mazeroski
Ralph Kiner
Jason Bay
28 Boof Bonser
Joe Mauer
Francisco Liriano
Jason Kubel
29 Jason Kendall
Victor Martinez
Wil Nieves
Josh Willingham
30 Chris Carpenter
Roy Halladay
Roy Oswalt
Rich Harden
31 Derrek Lee
David Ortiz
Albert Pujols
Mark Teixeira
32 Jason Kendall
Bobby Crosby
Rich Harden
Joe Blanton
33 Steve Garvey
Ron Cey
Don Sutton
Dusty Baker
34 Wally Joyner
Mark Grace
John Kruk
Kent Hrbek
36 Derek Jeter
Jose Reyes
Hanley Ramirez
Yuniesky Betancourt
37 Carlos Lee
Ben Sheets
Rickie Weeks
Prince Fielder
38 Jeff Bagwell
Craig Biggio
Lance Berkman
Taylor Buchholz
39 Craig Biggio
Rickie Weeks
Chase Utley
Ian Kinsler
41 Mark Mulder
Scott Kazmir
Dontrelle Willis
Cole Hamels
42 Josh Johnson
Taylor Buchholz
Adam Wainwright
Brian Bannister
45 Michael Young
Mark Teixeira
Hank Blalock
Ian Kinsler
46 Marcus Giles
Tadahito Iguchi
Ian Kinsler
Dan Uggla
48 David Cone
Dwight Gooden
Bret Saberhagen
Sid Fernandez
49 Ron Santo
Graig Nettles
Bill Madlock
Ron Cey
50 Huston Street
Nick Swisher
Rich Harden
Joe Blanton

2006 Ultimate Collection Ensemble Signatures Five

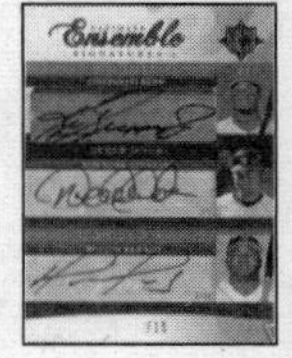

OVERALL AU ODDS 1:2
STATED PRINT RUN 15 SER.#'d SETS
NO PRICING DUE TO SCARCITY
EXCHANGE DEADLINE 12/20/09
1 Josh Johnson
Josh Willingham
Hanley Ramirez
Jeremy Hermida
Dan Uggla
2 Boof Bonser
Francisco Liriano
Justin Verlander
Jonathan Papelbon
Jered
3 Ken Griffey Jr.
Derek Jeter
David Ortiz
Albert Pujols
Miguel Cabrera
5 Jon Lester
Justin Verlander
Jonathan Papelbon
Joel Zumaya
Jered Weaver
6 Jason Kendall
Victor Martinez
Joe Mauer
Wil Nieves
Josh Willingham
9 Derek Jeter
Josh Wilson
Jose Reyes
Ronny Cedeno
Hanley Ramirez
10 Miguel Cabrera
Josh Johnson
Dontrelle Willis
Hanley Ramirez
Dan Uggla
11 Roger Clemens
Roy Oswalt
Brad Lidge
Taylor Buchholz
Fernando Nieve
13 Josh Johnson
Adam Wainwright
Justin Verlander
Matt Cain
Jered Weaver
14 Ben Sheets
Roy Oswalt
Jake Peavy
Rich Harden
Justin Verlander
15 Travis Hafner
David Ortiz
Mark Teixeira
Prince Fielder
Kendry Morales
17 Corey Patterson
Carl Crawford
Coco Crisp
Scott Podsednik
Alex Rios
20 Sean Casey
Oliver Perez
Jason Bay
Ronny Paulino
Nate McLouth
21 Dave Parker
Bill Mazeroski
Bill Madlock
Ralph Kiner
Jason Bay
22 Torii Hunter
Boof Bonser
Joe Mauer
Francisco Liriano
Jason Kubel
23 Jason Kendall
Victor Martinez
Wil Nieves
Josh Willingham
Ronny Paulino
24 Chris Carpenter
Roy Halladay
Roy Oswalt
Jake Peavy
Rich Harden
25 Derrek Lee
David Ortiz
Albert Pujols
Mark Teixeira
Prince Fielder EXCH
26 Jason Kendall
Bobby Crosby
Nick Swisher
Rich Harden
Joe Blanton
27 Steve Garvey
Ron Cey
Maury Wills
Don Sutton
Dusty Baker
29 Ron Santo
Mike Schmidt
Graig Nettles
Bill Madlock
Ron Cey

2006 Ultimate Collection Ensemble Signatures Six

OVERALL AU ODDS 1:2
STATED PRINT RUN 10 SER.#'d SETS
NO PRICING DUE TO SCARCITY
EXCHANGE DEADLINE 12/20/09
2 Taylor Buchholz
Justin Verlander
Jonathan Papelbon
Cole Hamels
Jered We
3 Ken Griffey Jr.
Alfonso Soriano
Carl Crawford
Coco Crisp
Scott Podsedni
4 Craig Biggio
Marcus Giles

Chase Utley		
Tadahito Iguchi		
Ian Kinsler		
Dan		
6 Jason Kendall		
Bobby Crosby		
Huston Street		
Nick Swisher		
Rich Harden		
Joe		
9 Jon Lester		
Josh Johnson		
Fausto Carmona		
Jonathan Papelbon		
Cole Hamels		
J		
12 Ken Griffey Jr.		
Derek Jeter		
Vladimir Guerrero		
Albert Pujols		
Mark Teixei		
15 Francisco Liriano		
Josh Johnson		
Justin Verlander		
Jonathan Papelbon		
Cole		

2006 Ultimate Collection Ensemble Signatures Eight

OVERALL AU ODDS 1:2
STATED PRINT RUN 10 SER.#'d SETS
NO PRICING DUE TO SCARCITY
EXCHANGE DEADLINE 12/20/09

2 Josh Johnson		
Taylor Buchholz		
Justin Verlander		
Matt Cain		
Jonathan Papelb		
3 Craig Biggio		
Brian Roberts		
Marcus Giles		
Rickie Weeks		
Chase Utley		
Tadah		
6 Ken Griffey Jr.		
Derek Jeter		
Derrek Lee		
Vladimir Guerrero		
David Ortiz		
A		
12 Tom Seaver		
Bob Feller		
Nolan Ryan		
Roy Oswalt		
Jim Palmer		
Jake Peavy		
Jus		

2006 Ultimate Collection Game Materials

OVERALL GAME-USED ODDS 1:2
STATED PRINT RUN 50 SERIAL #'d SETS
PLATE ODDS APPX. 7:10 BONUS PACKS
PLATE PRINT RUN 1 SET PER COLOR
BLACK-CYAN-MAGENTA-YELLOW ISSUED
NO PLATE PRICING DUE TO SCARCITY

AB A.J. Burnett Jsy	4.00	10.00
AD Adam Dunn Jsy	4.00	10.00
AJ Andruw Jones Jsy	5.00	12.00
AP Albert Pujols Jsy	12.50	30.00
AR Alex Rios Jsy	4.00	10.00
AS Alfonso Soriano Jsy	4.00	10.00
BA Brian Bannister Jsy	4.00	10.00
BG Brian Giles Jsy	4.00	10.00
BM Bill Mazeroski Bat	5.00	12.00
BO Jeremy Bonderman Jsy	4.00	10.00
BR Brian Roberts Jsy	4.00	10.00
CA Melky Cabrera Jsy	6.00	15.00
CC Carl Crawford Jsy	4.00	10.00
CH Chris Carpenter Jsy	4.00	10.00
CJ Conor Jackson Jsy	5.00	12.00
CL Carlos Lee Jsy	4.00	10.00
CR Coco Crisp Jsy	4.00	10.00
CS Chris Shelton Jsy	4.00	10.00
CU Chase Utley Jsy	6.00	15.00
CZ Carlos Zambrano Jsy	4.00	10.00
DJ Derek Jeter Jsy	12.50	30.00
DJ2 Derek Jeter Jsy	12.50	30.00
DL Derrek Lee Jsy	4.00	10.00
DU Dan Uggla Jsy	6.00	15.00
DW Dontrelle Willis Jsy	4.00	10.00
FH Felix Hernandez Jsy	5.00	12.00
FL Francisco Liriano Jsy	6.00	15.00
GA Garrett Atkins Jsy	4.00	10.00
GP Gaylord Perry Jsy	5.00	12.00
HA Cole Hamels Jsy	6.00	15.00
HB Hank Blalock Jsy	4.00	10.00
HC Craig Hansen Jsy	6.00	15.00
HO Trevor Hoffman Jsy	4.00	10.00
HR Hanley Ramirez Jsy	6.00	15.00
HT Tim Hudson Jsy	4.00	10.00
HU Torii Hunter Jsy	4.00	10.00
HY Roy Halladay Jsy	4.00	10.00
IK Ian Kinsler Jsy	5.00	12.00
IR Ivan Rodriguez Jsy	5.00	12.00
JB Jason Bay Jsy	4.00	10.00
JD Jermaine Dye Jsy	4.00	10.00
JH Jeremy Hermida Jsy	4.00	10.00
JJ Josh Johnson Jsy	5.00	12.00
JK Jason Kendall Jsy	4.00	10.00
JM Joe Mauer Jsy	5.00	12.00
JN Joe Nathan Jsy	4.00	10.00
JP Jake Peavy Jsy	4.00	10.00
JR Jose Reyes Jsy	4.00	10.00
JS Johan Santana Jsy	5.00	12.00
JV Justin Verlander Jsy	6.00	15.00
JW Jered Weaver Jsy	6.00	15.00
JZ Joel Zumaya Jsy	6.00	15.00
KG Ken Griffey Jr. Jsy	10.00	25.00
KG2 Ken Griffey Jr. Jsy	10.00	25.00
KH Khalil Greene Jsy	5.00	12.00
KJ Kenji Johjima Jsy	8.00	20.00
KM Kendry Morales Jsy	5.00	12.00
KU Jason Kubel Jsy	4.00	10.00
KY Kevin Youkilis Jsy	4.00	10.00
LA Luis Aparicio Jsy	5.00	12.00
LM Lastings Milledge Jsy	5.00	12.00
LY Fred Lynn Jsy	5.00	12.00
MA Matt Cain Jsy	5.00	12.00
MC Miguel Cabrera Jsy	5.00	12.00
MG Marcus Giles Jsy	4.00	10.00
MH Matt Holliday Jsy	8.00	20.00
ML Mark Loretta Jsy	4.00	10.00
MM Melvin Mora Jsy	4.00	10.00
MO Justin Morneau Jsy	5.00	12.00
MS Mike Schmidt Jsy	8.00	20.00
MT Mark Teixeira Jsy	5.00	12.00
MU Mark Mulder Jsy	4.00	10.00
MY Michael Young Jsy	4.00	10.00
NS Nick Swisher Jsy	4.00	10.00
PA Jonathan Papelbon Jsy	8.00	20.00
PF Prince Fielder Jsy	6.00	15.00
PM Paul Molitor Jsy	5.00	12.00
RC Cal Ripken Jsy	20.00	50.00
RH Rich Harden Jsy	4.00	10.00
RI Jim Rice Jsy	5.00	12.00
RO Roy Oswalt Jsy	4.00	10.00
RW Rickie Weeks Jsy	4.00	10.00
RZ Ryan Zimmerman Jsy	8.00	20.00
SK Scott Kazmir Jsy	5.00	12.00
SP Scott Podsednik Jsy	4.00	10.00
TE Miguel Tejada Jsy	4.00	10.00
TG Tony Gwynn Jsy	6.00	15.00
TH Travis Hafner Jsy	4.00	10.00
TI Tadahito Iguchi Jsy	4.00	10.00
TP Tony Perez Jsy	5.00	12.00
VM Victor Martinez Jsy	4.00	10.00
WC Will Clark Pants	5.00	12.00
WI Josh Willingham Jsy	4.00	10.00
YB Yuniesky Betancourt Jsy	4.00	10.00

2006 Ultimate Collection Game Materials Signatures

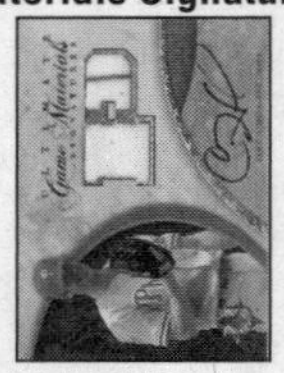

STATED PRINT RUN 35 SERIAL #'d SETS
EXCHANGE DEADLINE 12/20/09

AB A.J. Burnett Jsy	10.00	25.00
AD Adam Dunn Jsy	10.00	25.00
AJ Andruw Jones Jsy	20.00	50.00
AP Albert Pujols Jsy EXCH	150.00	250.00
AR Alex Rios Jsy	10.00	25.00
AS Alfonso Soriano Jsy	30.00	60.00
BA Brian Bannister Jsy	10.00	25.00
BG Brian Giles Jsy	10.00	25.00
BM Bill Mazeroski Jsy	20.00	50.00
BO Jeremy Bonderman Jsy	15.00	40.00
BR Brian Roberts Jsy	10.00	25.00
CA Melky Cabrera Jsy	15.00	40.00
CC Carl Crawford Jsy	10.00	25.00
CH Chris Carpenter Jsy	10.00	25.00
CJ Conor Jackson Jsy	15.00	40.00
CL Carlos Lee Jsy	10.00	25.00
CR Coco Crisp Jsy	12.50	30.00
CS Chris Shelton Jsy	10.00	25.00
CU Chase Utley Jsy	30.00	60.00
CZ Carlos Zambrano Jsy	15.00	40.00
DJ Derek Jeter Jsy	200.00	300.00
DJ2 Derek Jeter Jsy	200.00	300.00
DL Derrek Lee Jsy	12.50	30.00
DU Dan Uggla Jsy	30.00	60.00
DW Dontrelle Willis Jsy	12.50	30.00
FH Felix Hernandez Jsy	15.00	40.00
FL Francisco Liriano Jsy	30.00	60.00
GA Garrett Atkins Jsy	10.00	25.00
GP Gaylord Perry Pants	10.00	25.00
HA Cole Hamels Jsy	30.00	60.00
HB Hank Blalock Jsy	10.00	25.00
HC Craig Hansen Jsy	15.00	40.00
HO Trevor Hoffman Jsy	15.00	40.00
HR Hanley Ramirez Jsy	30.00	60.00
HT Tim Hudson Jsy	10.00	25.00
HU Torii Hunter Jsy	10.00	25.00
HY Roy Halladay Jsy	10.00	25.00
IK Ian Kinsler Jsy	15.00	40.00
IR Ivan Rodriguez Jsy	15.00	40.00
JB Jason Bay Jsy	10.00	25.00
JD Jermaine Dye Jsy	10.00	25.00
JH Jeremy Hermida Jsy	10.00	25.00
JJ Josh Johnson Jsy	15.00	40.00
JK Jason Kendall Jsy	10.00	25.00
JM Joe Mauer Jsy	15.00	40.00
JN Joe Nathan Jsy	10.00	25.00
JP Jake Peavy Jsy	10.00	25.00
JR Jose Reyes Jsy	15.00	40.00
JS Johan Santana Jsy	15.00	40.00
JV Justin Verlander Jsy	30.00	60.00
JW Jered Weaver Jsy	15.00	40.00
JZ Joel Zumaya Jsy	30.00	60.00
KG Ken Griffey Jr. Jsy	60.00	120.00
KG2 Ken Griffey Jr. Jsy	60.00	120.00
KH Khalil Greene Jsy	12.50	30.00
KM Kendry Morales Jsy	15.00	40.00
KU Jason Kubel Jsy	10.00	25.00
KY Kevin Youkilis Jsy	10.00	25.00
LA Luis Aparicio Jsy	10.00	25.00
LY Fred Lynn Jsy	10.00	25.00
MA Matt Cain Jsy	15.00	40.00
MC Miguel Cabrera Jsy	30.00	60.00
MG Marcus Giles Jsy	10.00	25.00
MH Matt Holliday Jsy	15.00	40.00
ML Mark Loretta Jsy	10.00	25.00
MM Melvin Mora Jsy	10.00	25.00
MO Justin Morneau Jsy	15.00	40.00
MS Mike Schmidt Jsy	30.00	60.00
MU Mark Mulder Jsy	10.00	25.00
MY Michael Young Jsy	10.00	25.00
NS Nick Swisher Jsy	10.00	25.00
PA Jonathan Papelbon Jsy	30.00	60.00
PM Paul Molitor Jsy	12.50	30.00
RC Cal Ripken Jsy	40.00	80.00
RH Rich Harden Jsy	12.50	30.00
RI Jim Rice Jsy	12.50	30.00
RO Roy Oswalt Jsy	10.00	25.00
RW Rickie Weeks Jsy	10.00	25.00
RZ Ryan Zimmerman Jsy	40.00	80.00
SK Scott Kazmir Jsy	15.00	40.00
SP Scott Podsednik Jsy	10.00	25.00
TE Miguel Tejada Jsy	10.00	25.00
TG Tony Gwynn Jsy	30.00	60.00
TH Travis Hafner Jsy	10.00	25.00
TI Tadahito Iguchi Jsy	15.00	40.00
TP Tony Perez Jsy	10.00	25.00
VM Victor Martinez Jsy	10.00	25.00
WC Will Clark Pants	15.00	40.00
WI Josh Willingham Jsy	10.00	25.00
YB Yuniesky Betancourt Jsy	10.00	25.00

2006 Ultimate Collection Game Patches

*PATCH p/r 40-50: .6X TO 1.5X BASIC
*PATCH p/r 27-31: .6X TO 1.5X BASIC
OVERALL GAME-USED ODDS 1:2
PATCH PRINT RUN B/WN 3-50 PER
NO PRICING ON QTY 25 OR LESS
OVERALL AU-GU ODDS 1:4
PATCH SIG PRINT RUN 10 SER.#'d SETS
NO PATCH SIG PRICING
EXCHANGE DEADLINE 12/20/09
PLATE ODDS APPX. 7:10 BONUS PACKS
PLATE PRINT RUN 1 SET PER COLOR
BLACK-CYAN-MAGENTA-YELLOW ISSUED
NO PLATE PRICING DUE TO SCARCITY

AP Albert Pujols	30.00	60.00
AS Alfonso Soriano	12.50	30.00
BO Jeremy Bonderman	10.00	25.00
CU Chase Utley	15.00	40.00
JR Jose Reyes	12.50	30.00
JV Justin Verlander	20.00	50.00
KG Ken Griffey Jr.	20.00	50.00
KG2 Ken Griffey Jr.	20.00	50.00
KJ Kenji Johjima	20.00	50.00
MA Matt Cain	10.00	25.00
MC Miguel Cabrera	12.50	30.00
MO Justin Morneau	10.00	25.00
RZ Ryan Zimmerman	20.00	50.00
TI Tadahito Iguchi	10.00	25.00

2006 Ultimate Collection Ken Griffey Jr. 1989 Autograph Buyback

RANDOM INSERT IN BONUS PACKS
STATED PRINT RUN 15 CARDS
CARD IS NOT SERIAL-NUMBERED
PRINT RUN PROVIDED BY UPPER DECK
NO PRICING DUE TO SCARCITY
1 Ken Griffey Jr./15 *

2006 Ultimate Collection Legendary Ensemble Signatures

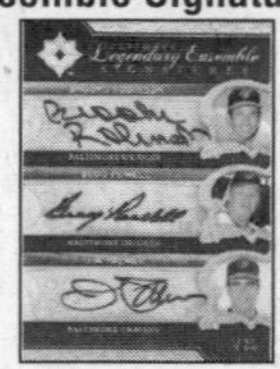

OVERALL AU ODDS 1:2
STATED PRINT RUN 25 SER.#'d SETS
NO PRICING DUE TO SCARCITY
EXCHANGE DEADLINE 12/20/09

BFR Bob Feller		
Robin Roberts		
Jim Bunning		
CHO Tony Oliva		
Kent Hrbek		
Rod Carew		
FBB Carlton Fisk		
Yogi Berra		
Johnny Bench		
FDJ Andre Dawson		
Bo Jackson		
George Foster		
GMW Tony Gwynn		
Stan Musial		
Billy Williams		
LRB Wade Boggs		
Jim Rice		
Fred Lynn		
MSM Ryne Sandberg		
Bill Mazeroski		
Joe Morgan		
PST Luis Tiant		
Gaylord Perry		
Don Sutton		
RBY Cal Ripken		
Ernie Banks		
Robin Yount		
RPP Brooks Robinson		
Boog Powell		
Jim Palmer		
RSP Tom Seaver		
Nolan Ryan		
Jim Palmer		
SAW Ozzie Smith		
Luis Aparicio		
Maury Wills		
SGF Rollie Fingers		
Bruce Sutter		
Goose Gossage		
WMY Stan Musial		
Carl Yastrzemski		
Billy Williams		

2006 Ultimate Collection Legendary Materials

ODDS APPX. 3:10 BONUS PACKS
PRINT RUNS B/WN 5-55 PER
NO PRICING ON QTY 25 OR LESS
PLATE ODDS APPX. 7:10 BONUS PACKS
PLATE PRINT RUN 1 SET PER COLOR
BLACK-CYAN-MAGENTA-YELLOW ISSUED
NO PLATE PRICING DUE TO SCARCITY

AK Al Kaline Bat/15		
AR Al Rosen Pants/55	6.00	15.00
BD Bill Dickey Jsy/55	12.50	30.00
BD2 Bill Dickey Jsy/55	12.50	30.00
BF Bob Feller Jsy/15		
BG Bob Gibson Jsy/25		
BM Bill Mazeroski Bat/25		
BO Bo Jackson Bat/55	8.00	20.00
BO2 Bo Jackson Bat/55	8.00	20.00
BR Babe Ruth Pants/25		
BR2 Babe Ruth Pants/25		
BS Bruce Sutter Pants/25		
BW Billy Williams Bat/25		
CF Carlton Fisk Pants/55	4.00	10.00
CF2 Carlton Fisk Pants/55	4.00	10.00
CR Cal Ripken Pants/15		
CR2 Cal Ripken Pants/15		
CW Rod Carew Jsy/55	4.00	10.00
CW2 Rod Carew Jsy/55	4.00	10.00
CY Carl Yastrzemski Bat/25		
CY2 Carl Yastrzemski Bat/25		
DE Dennis Eckersley Jsy/25		
DE2 Dennis Eckersley Jsy/25		
DL Don Larsen Pants/15		
DL2 Don Larsen Pants/15		
DW Dave Winfield Bat/10		
EB Ernie Banks Jsy/10		
EM Eddie Murray Jsy/25		
EM2 Eddie Murray Jsy/25		
FJ Fergie Jenkins Jsy/10		
FJ2 Fergie Jenkins Jsy/10		
FR Frank Robinson Jsy/5		
FR2 Frank Robinson Bat/25		
GP Gaylord Perry Jsy/55	4.00	10.00
GP2 Gaylord Perry Jsy/55	4.00	10.00
JB Johnny Bench Jsy/55	8.00	20.00
JD Joe DiMaggio Jsy/15		
JD2 Joe DiMaggio Jsy/15		
JO Joe Morgan Jsy/55	4.00	10.00
JO2 Joe Morgan Jsy/55	4.00	10.00
JP Jim Palmer Jsy/25		
JP2 Jim Palmer Jsy/25		
JU Juan Marichal Jsy/55	4.00	10.00
KI Kirk Gibson Jsy/55	4.00	10.00
KP Kirby Puckett Jsy/55	8.00	20.00
KP2 Kirby Puckett Jsy/55	8.00	20.00
LB Lou Brock Jsy/25		
LB2 Lou Brock Pants/25		
MA Don Mattingly Pants/55	10.00	25.00
MA2 Don Mattingly Jsy/55	10.00	25.00
MS Mike Schmidt Jsy/25		
MS2 Mike Schmidt Jsy/25		
MW Maury Wills Bat/41	4.00	10.00
NR Nolan Ryan Jkt/55	15.00	40.00
NR2 Nolan Ryan Jsy/25		
NR3 Nolan Ryan Jsy/25		
OS Ozzie Smith Jsy/55	10.00	25.00
OS2 Ozzie Smith Jsy/55	10.00	25.00
PM Paul Molitor Bat/55	4.00	10.00
PM2 Paul Molitor Bat/55	4.00	10.00
PN Phil Niekro Jsy/55	4.00	10.00
PN2 Phil Niekro Jsy/55	4.00	10.00
PR Phil Rizzuto Pants/15		
PR2 Phil Rizzuto Pants/15		
RC Rocky Colavito Bat/15		
RC2 Rocky Colavito Bat/15		
RE Red Schoendienst Jsy/15		
RF Rollie Fingers Jsy/25		
RJ Reggie Jackson Bat/25		
RJ2 Reggie Jackson Jsy/35	6.00	15.00
RK Ralph Kiner Bat/25		
RO Brooks Robinson Pants/35	6.00	15.00
RO2 Brooks Robinson Jsy/35	6.00	15.00
RR Robin Roberts Pants/15		
RS Ryne Sandberg Bat/35	10.00	25.00
RY Robin Yount Bat/25		
RY2 Robin Yount Bat/25		
SC Steve Carlton Bat/55	4.00	10.00
SC2 Steve Carlton Bat/47	4.00	10.00
SM Stan Musial Bat/25		
SM2 Stan Musial Bat/25		
SU Don Sutton Jsy/55	4.00	10.00
SU2 Don Sutton Jsy/55	4.00	10.00
TC Ty Cobb Pants/5		
TG Tony Gwynn Jsy/55	10.00	25.00
TG2 Tony Gwynn Jsy/55	10.00	25.00
TL Tony Lazzeri Bat/15		
TM Thurman Munson Pants/15		
TP Tony Perez Pants/55	4.00	10.00
TP2 Tony Perez Jsy/55	4.00	10.00
TS Tom Seaver Pants/15		
WB Wade Boggs Jsy/55	4.00	10.00
WB2 Wade Boggs Pants/55	4.00	10.00
WC Will Clark Pants/45	6.00	15.00
WC2 Will Clark Pants/45	6.00	15.00
WM Willie McCovey Pants/25		
WM2 Willie McCovey Pants/25		
YB Yogi Berra Pants/15		
YB2 Yogi Berra Pants/15		

2006 Ultimate Collection Maximum Materials

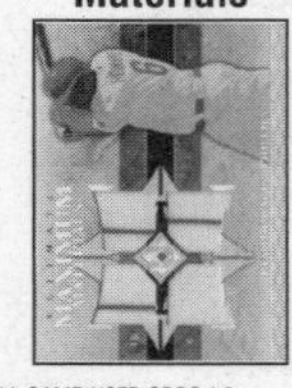

OVERALL GAME-USED ODDS 1:2
STATED PRINT RUN 25 SER.#'d SETS
NO PRICING DUE TO SCARCITY
PATCH PRINT RUN 15 SER.#'d SETS

AP Albert Pujols Jsy		
AR Alex Rios Jsy		
AS Alfonso Soriano Jsy		
CA Melky Cabrera Jsy		
CC Carl Crawford Jsy		
CH Craig Hansen Jsy		
CR Cal Ripken Jsy		
CU Chase Utley Jsy		
DJ Derek Jeter Jsy		
DO David Ortiz Jsy		
FL Francisco Liriano Jsy		
GS Grady Sizemore Jsy		
HR Hanley Ramirez Jsy		
IK Ian Kinsler Jsy		
JH Jeremy Hermida Jsy		
JM Joe Mauer Jsy		
JP Jonathan Papelbon Jsy		
JV Justin Verlander Jsy		
JW Jered Weaver Jsy		
KG Ken Griffey Jr. Jsy		
KJ Kenji Johjima Jsy		
KM Kendry Morales Jsy		
LM Lastings Milledge Jsy		
MC Miguel Cabrera Jsy		
MT Mark Teixeira Jsy		
PF Prince Fielder Jsy		
RC Roger Clemens Jsy		
RH Ryan Howard Jsy		
RZ Ryan Zimmerman Jsy		
TG Tony Gwynn Jsy		
TH Travis Hafner Jsy		
VG Vladimir Guerrero Jsy		
VM Victor Martinez Jsy		
WC Will Clark Jsy		
WI Josh Willingham Jsy		

2006 Ultimate Collection Ultimate Numbers Materials

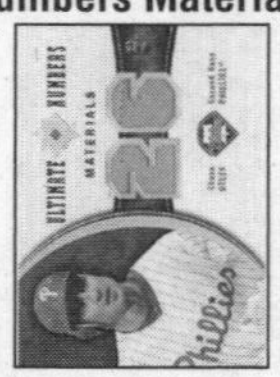

OVERALL GAME-USED ODDS 1:2
STATED PRINT RUN 35 SER.#'d SETS
PLATE ODDS APPX. 7:10 BONUS PACKS
PLATE PRINT RUN 1 SET PER COLOR
BLACK-CYAN-MAGENTA-YELLOW ISSUED
NO PLATE PRICING DUE TO SCARCITY

AB A.J. Burnett Jsy	5.00	12.00
AD Adam Dunn Jsy	5.00	12.00
AJ Andruw Jones Jsy	6.00	15.00
AP Albert Pujols Jsy	20.00	50.00
AR Alex Rios Jsy	5.00	12.00
AS Alfonso Soriano Jsy	5.00	12.00
BA Brian Bannister Jsy	6.00	15.00
BG Brian Giles Jsy	5.00	12.00
BM Bill Mazeroski Bat	6.00	15.00
BO Jeremy Bonderman Jsy	5.00	12.00
BR Brian Roberts Jsy	5.00	12.00
CA Melky Cabrera Jsy	8.00	20.00
CC Carl Crawford Jsy	5.00	12.00
CH Chris Carpenter Jsy	5.00	12.00
CJ Conor Jackson Jsy	6.00	15.00
CL Carlos Lee Jsy	5.00	12.00
CR Coco Crisp Jsy	5.00	12.00
CS Chris Shelton Jsy	5.00	12.00
CU Chase Utley Jsy	8.00	20.00
CZ Carlos Zambrano Jsy	5.00	12.00
DJ Derek Jeter Jsy	20.00	50.00
DJ2 Derek Jeter Jsy	20.00	50.00
DL Derrek Lee Jsy	5.00	12.00
DU Dan Uggla Jsy	8.00	20.00
DW Dontrelle Willis Jsy	5.00	12.00
FH Felix Hernandez Jsy	6.00	15.00
FL Francisco Liriano Jsy	8.00	20.00
GA Garrett Atkins Jsy	5.00	12.00
GP Gaylord Perry Pants	6.00	15.00
HA Cole Hamels Jsy	8.00	20.00
HB Hank Blalock Jsy	5.00	12.00
HC Craig Hansen Jsy	8.00	20.00
HO Trevor Hoffman Jsy	5.00	12.00
HR Hanley Ramirez Jsy	8.00	20.00
HT Tim Hudson Jsy	5.00	12.00
HU Torii Hunter Jsy	5.00	12.00
HY Roy Halladay Jsy	5.00	12.00
IK Ian Kinsler Jsy	5.00	12.00
IR Ivan Rodriguez Jsy	6.00	15.00
JB Jason Bay Jsy	5.00	12.00
JD Jermaine Dye Jsy	5.00	12.00
JH Jeremy Hermida Jsy	5.00	12.00
JJ Josh Johnson Jsy	6.00	15.00
JK Jason Kendall Jsy	5.00	12.00
JM Joe Mauer Jsy	6.00	15.00
JN Joe Nathan Jsy	5.00	12.00
JP Jake Peavy Jsy	5.00	12.00
JR Jose Reyes Jsy	5.00	12.00
JS Johan Santana Jsy	6.00	15.00
JV Justin Verlander Jsy	8.00	20.00
JW Jered Weaver Jsy	8.00	20.00
JZ Joel Zumaya Jsy	8.00	20.00
KG Ken Griffey Jr. Jsy	15.00	40.00
KG2 Ken Griffey Jr. Jsy	15.00	40.00
KH Khalil Greene Jsy	6.00	15.00
KJ Kenji Johjima Jsy	12.50	30.00
KM Kendry Morales Jsy	6.00	15.00
KU Jason Kubel Jsy	5.00	12.00
KY Kevin Youkilis Jsy	5.00	12.00
LA Luis Aparicio Jsy	6.00	15.00
LM Lastings Milledge Jsy	6.00	15.00
LY Fred Lynn Jsy	6.00	15.00
MA Matt Cain Jsy	6.00	15.00
MC Miguel Cabrera Jsy	6.00	15.00
MG Marcus Giles Jsy	5.00	12.00
MH Matt Holliday Jsy	6.00	15.00
ML Mark Loretta Jsy	5.00	12.00
MM Melvin Mora Jsy	5.00	12.00
MO Justin Morneau Jsy	6.00	15.00
MS Mike Schmidt Jsy	12.50	30.00
MT Mark Teixeira Jsy	6.00	15.00
MU Mark Mulder Jsy	5.00	12.00
MY Michael Young Jsy	5.00	12.00
NS Nick Swisher Jsy	5.00	12.00
PA Jonathan Papelbon Jsy	12.50	30.00
PF Prince Fielder Jsy	8.00	20.00
PM Paul Molitor Jsy	6.00	15.00
RC Cal Ripken Jsy	50.00	100.00
RH Rich Harden Jsy	5.00	12.00
RI Jim Rice Jsy	6.00	15.00
RO Roy Oswalt Jsy	5.00	12.00
RW Rickie Weeks Jsy	5.00	12.00
RZ Ryan Zimmerman Jsy	12.50	30.00
SK Scott Kazmir Jsy	6.00	15.00
SP Scott Podsednik Jsy	5.00	12.00
TE Miguel Tejada Jsy	5.00	12.00
TG Tony Gwynn Jsy	8.00	20.00
TH Travis Hafner Jsy	5.00	12.00
TI Tadahito Iguchi Jsy	5.00	12.00
TP Tony Perez Jsy	6.00	15.00
VM Victor Martinez Jsy	5.00	12.00
WC Will Clark Jsy	6.00	15.00
WI Josh Willingham Jsy	5.00	12.00
YB Yuniesky Betancourt Jsy	5.00	12.00

2006 Ultimate Collection Ultimate Numbers Patches

*PATCH p/r 35: .6X TO 1.5X BASIC
OVERALL GAME-USED ODDS 1:2
PATCH PRINT RUN B/WN 5-35 PER
NO PRICING ON QTY 25 OR LESS

AP Albert Pujols/35	50.00	100.00
AS Alfonso Soriano/35	10.00	25.00
BO Jeremy Bonderman/35	10.00	25.00
CU Chase Utley/35	15.00	40.00
DJ Derek Jeter/35	30.00	60.00
DJ2 Derek Jeter/35	30.00	60.00
IK Ian Kinsler/35	8.00	20.00
JV Justin Verlander/35	15.00	40.00
KG Ken Griffey Jr./35	20.00	50.00
KG2 Ken Griffey Jr./35	20.00	50.00
KJ Kenji Johjima/35	20.00	50.00
KY Kevin Youkilis/35	8.00	20.00
RC Cal Ripken/35	60.00	120.00
RZ Ryan Zimmerman/35	15.00	40.00
TI Tadahito Iguchi/35	10.00	25.00

2006 Ultimate Collection Tandem Materials

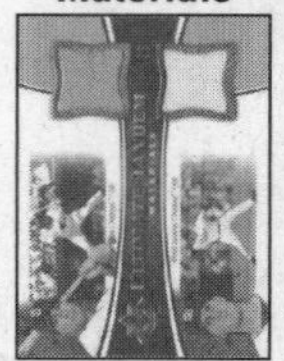

OVERALL GAME-USED ODDS 1:2
STATED PRINT RUN 25 SER.#'d SETS
NO PRICING DUE TO SCARCITY
OVERALL AU-GU ODDS 1:4
MAT.SIG. PRINT RUN 15 SER.#'d SETS
NO MAT.SIG.PRICING
SIG.PATCH PRINT RUN 5 SER.#'d SETS
NO SIG.PATCH PRICING
SIG.LOGO PRINT RUN 1 SER.#'d SET
NO SIG.LOGO PRICING
EXCHANGE DEADLINE 12/20/09

AA Alfonso Soriano Jsy		
Alex Rios Jsy		
AH Garrett Atkins Jsy		
Matt Holliday Jsy		
AJ Derek Jeter Jsy		

Luis Aparicio Jsy
BH Felix Hernandez Jsy
Yuniesky Betancourt Jsy
BM Lastings Milledge Jsy
Brian Bannister Jsy
BR Hanley Ramirez Jsy
Yuniesky Betancourt Jsy
BV Jeremy Bonderman Jsy
Justin Verlander Jsy
CH Melky Cabrera Jsy
Jeremy Hermida Jsy
CL Mark Loretta Jsy
Coco Crisp Jsy
CM Lastings Milledge Jsy
Melky Cabrera Jsy
CO Roger Clemens Jsy
Roy Oswalt Jsy
CP Carl Crawford Jsy
Scott Podsednik Jsy
CR Miguel Cabrera Jsy
Hanley Ramirez Jsy
CS Scott Kazmir Jsy
Cole Hamels Jsy
CV Justin Verlander Jsy
Matt Cain Jsy
CW Chris Carpenter Jsy
Dontrelle Willis Jsy
CZ Miguel Cabrera Jsy
Ryan Zimmerman Jsy
DH Derek Jeter Jsy
Hanley Ramirez Jsy
FP Tony Perez Jsy
Prince Fielder Jsy
FW Rickie Weeks Jsy
Prince Fielder Jsy
GD Ken Griffey Jr. Jsy
Adam Dunn Jsy
GG Tony Gwynn Jsy
Brian Giles Jsy
GP Ken Griffey Jr. Jsy
Albert Pujols Jsy
GR Ken Griffey Jr. Jsy
Alex Rios Jsy
GT Ken Griffey Jr. Jsy
Frank Thomas Jsy
HB Matt Holliday Jsy
Jason Bay Jsy
HC Steve Carlton Jsy
Cole Hamels Jsy
HF Travis Hafner Jsy
Prince Fielder Jsy
HG Brian Giles Jsy
Trevor Hoffman Jsy
HJ Andruw Jones Jsy
Torii Hunter Jsy
HK Jason Kubel Jsy
Jeremy Hermida Jsy
HM Travis Hafner Jsy
Victor Martinez Jsy
HN Trevor Hoffman Jsy
Joe Nathan Jsy
HO Roy Oswalt Jsy
Rich Harden Jsy
HP Trevor Hoffman Jsy
Jonathan Papelbon Jsy
HR Hanley Ramirez Jsy
Jeremy Hermida Jsy
HW Josh Willingham Jsy
Jeremy Hermida Jsy
ID Jermaine Dye Jsy
Tadahito Iguchi Jsy
JB Bill Mazeroski Jsy
Jason Bay Jsy
JC Derek Jeter Jsy
Melky Cabrera Jsy
JG Ken Griffey Jr. Jsy
Derek Jeter Jsy
JJ Derek Jeter Jsy
Reggie Jackson Jsy
JK Kendry Morales Jsy
Jered Weaver Jsy
JM Victor Martinez Jsy
Kenji Johjima Jsy
JR Cal Ripken Jsy
Derek Jeter Jsy
KB Brian Giles Jsy
Khalil Greene Jsy
KC Carl Crawford Jsy
Scott Kazmir Jsy
KM Jason Kendall Jsy
Joe Mauer Jsy
KU Ian Kinsler Jsy
Dan Uggla Jsy
KY Michael Young Jsy
Ian Kinsler Jsy
LC Fred Lynn Jsy
Coco Crisp Jsy
LF Carlos Lee Jsy
Prince Fielder Jsy
LH Francisco Liriano Jsy
Cole Hamels Jsy
MF Prince Fielder Jsy
Kendry Morales Jsy
MH Livan Hernandez Jsy
Kendry Morales Jsy
ML Joe Mauer Jsy
Francisco Liriano Jsy
MM Victor Martinez Jsy
Joe Mauer Jsy
MP Tony Perez Jsy
Kendry Morales Jsy
MR Melvin Mora Jsy
Brian Roberts Jsy
MW Paul Molitor Jsy
Rickie Weeks Jsy
NJ Joe Nathan Jsy
Joe Mauer Jsy
NL Joe Nathan Jsy
Francisco Liriano Jsy
NM Joe Nathan Jsy
Joe Mauer Jsy
NP Joe Nathan Jsy
Jonathan Papelbon Jsy
PC Gaylord Perry Jsy
Matt Cain Jsy
PH Jonathan Papelbon Jsy
Craig Hansen Jsy
PO Roy Oswalt Jsy
Jake Peavy Jsy
PP Gaylord Perry Jsy
Jake Peavy Jsy

RC Coco Crisp Jsy
Alex Rios Jsy
RM Jose Reyes Jsy
Lastings Milledge Jsy
RR Jose Reyes Jsy
Hanley Ramirez Jsy
RS Cal Ripken Jsy
Mike Schmidt Jsy
RU Hanley Ramirez Jsy
Dan Uggla Jsy
RV Ivan Rodriguez Jsy
Justin Verlander Jsy
RW Nolan Ryan Jsy
Jered Weaver Jsy
SH Nick Swisher Jsy
Rich Harden Jsy
SJ Conor Jackson Jsy
Chris Shelton Jsy
SZ Mike Schmidt Jsy
Ryan Zimmerman Jsy
TY Michael Young Jsy
Mark Teixeira Jsy
UK Chase Utley Jsy
Ian Kinsler Jsy
UM Joe Morgan Jsy
Chase Utley Jsy
UR Brian Roberts Jsy
Dan Uggla Jsy
VM Jack Morris Jsy
Justin Verlander Jsy
VZ Justin Verlander Jsy
Joel Zumaya Jsy
WM Joe Mauer Jsy
Josh Willingham Jsy
WP Jonathan Papelbon Jsy
Jered Weaver Jsy
WR Josh Willingham Jsy
Hanley Ramirez Jsy
WV Justin Verlander Jsy
Jered Weaver Jsy
YL Mark Loretta Jsy
Kevin Youkilis Jsy
ZA Garrett Atkins Jsy
Ryan Zimmerman Jsy
ZC Miguel Cabrera Jsy
Ryan Zimmerman Jsy
ZJ Josh Johnson Jsy
Joel Zumaya Jsy
ZZ Carlos Zambrano Jsy
Joel Zumaya Jsy

2006 Ultimate Collection Tandem Materials Patch

OVERALL GAME-USED ODDS 1:2
STATED PRINT RUN 35 SERIAL #'d SETS

AA Alfonso Soriano / Alex Rios	6.00	15.00
AH Garrett Atkins / Matt Holliday	8.00	20.00
AJ Derek Jeter / Luis Aparicio	15.00	40.00
BH Felix Hernandez / Yuniesky Betancourt	8.00	20.00
BM Lastings Milledge / Brian Bannister	8.00	20.00
BR Hanley Ramirez / Yuniesky Betancourt	6.00	15.00
BV Jeremy Bonderman / Justin Verlander	15.00	40.00
CH Melky Cabrera / Jeremy Hermida	8.00	20.00
CL Mark Loretta / Coco Crisp	6.00	15.00
CM Lastings Milledge / Melky Cabrera	10.00	25.00
CO Roger Clemens / Roy Oswalt	20.00	50.00
CP Carl Crawford / Scott Podsednik	6.00	15.00
CR Miguel Cabrera / Hanley Ramirez	8.00	20.00
CS Scott Kazmir / Cole Hamels	20.00	50.00
CV Justin Verlander / Matt Cain	15.00	40.00
CW Chris Carpenter / Dontrelle Willis	15.00	40.00
CZ Miguel Cabrera / Ryan Zimmerman	15.00	40.00
DH Derek Jeter / Hanley Ramirez	20.00	50.00
FW Rickie Weeks / Prince Fielder	12.50	30.00
GD Ken Griffey Jr. / Adam Dunn	15.00	40.00
GG Tony Gwynn / Brian Giles	15.00	40.00
GP Ken Griffey Jr. / Albert Pujols	40.00	80.00
GR Ken Griffey Jr. / Alex Rios	15.00	40.00
GT Ken Griffey Jr. / Frank Thomas	20.00	50.00
HB Matt Holliday / Jason Bay	10.00	25.00
HF Travis Hafner / Prince Fielder	12.50	30.00
HG Brian Giles / Trevor Hoffman	6.00	15.00
HJ Andruw Jones / Torii Hunter	12.50	30.00
HK Jason Kubel / Jeremy Hermida	6.00	15.00
HM Travis Hafner / Victor Martinez	8.00	20.00
HN Trevor Hoffman / Joe Nathan	6.00	15.00
HO Roy Oswalt / Rich Harden	6.00	15.00
HP Trevor Hoffman / Jonathan Papelbon	12.50	30.00
HR Hanley Ramirez / Jeremy Hermida	10.00	25.00
HW Josh Willingham / Jeremy Hermida	6.00	15.00
ID Jermaine Dye / Tadahito Iguchi	12.50	30.00
JC Derek Jeter / Melky Cabrera	30.00	60.00
JG Ken Griffey Jr. / Derek Jeter	40.00	80.00
JJ Derek Jeter / Reggie Jackson	30.00	60.00
JK Kendry Morales / Jered Weaver	10.00	25.00
JM Victor Martinez / Kenji Johjima	12.50	30.00
JR Cal Ripken / Derek Jeter	50.00	100.00
KB Brian Giles / Khalil Greene	12.50	30.00
KC Carl Crawford / Scott Kazmir	6.00	15.00
KM Jason Kendall / Joe Mauer	10.00	25.00
KU Ian Kinsler / Dan Uggla	10.00	25.00
KY Michael Young / Ian Kinsler	8.00	20.00
LC Fred Lynn / Coco Crisp	6.00	15.00
LF Carlos Lee / Prince Fielder	8.00	20.00
LH Francisco Liriano / Cole Hamels	12.50	30.00
MF Prince Fielder / Kendry Morales	10.00	25.00
MH Livan Hernandez / Kendry Morales	8.00	20.00
ML Joe Mauer / Francisco Liriano	15.00	40.00
MM Victor Martinez / Joe Mauer	10.00	25.00
MR Melvin Mora / Brian Roberts	6.00	15.00
MW Paul Molitor / Rickie Weeks	8.00	20.00
NJ Joe Nathan / Joe Mauer	8.00	20.00
NL Joe Nathan / Francisco Liriano	12.50	30.00
NM Joe Nathan / Joe Mauer	12.50	30.00
NP Joe Nathan / Jonathan Papelbon	12.50	30.00
PC Gaylord Perry / Matt Cain	12.50	30.00
PH Jonathan Papelbon / Craig Hansen	20.00	50.00
PO Roy Oswalt / Jake Peavy	6.00	15.00
PP Gaylord Perry / Jake Peavy	10.00	25.00
RC Coco Crisp / Alex Rios	6.00	15.00
RM Jose Reyes / Lastings Milledge	10.00	25.00
RR Jose Reyes / Hanley Ramirez	12.50	30.00
RS Cal Ripken / Mike Schmidt	40.00	80.00
RU Hanley Ramirez / Dan Uggla	15.00	40.00
RV Ivan Rodriguez / Justin Verlander	15.00	40.00
SH Nick Swisher / Rich Harden	6.00	15.00
SJ Conor Jackson / Chris Shelton	12.50	30.00
SZ Mike Schmidt / Ryan Zimmerman	20.00	50.00
TY Michael Young / Mark Teixeira	8.00	20.00
UK Chase Utley / Ian Kinsler	20.00	50.00
UM Joe Morgan / Chase Utley	20.00	50.00
UR Brian Roberts / Dan Uggla	6.00	15.00
VM Jack Morris / Justin Verlander	30.00	60.00
VZ Justin Verlander / Joel Zumaya	15.00	40.00
WM Joe Mauer / Josh Willingham	12.50	30.00
WR Josh Willingham / Hanley Ramirez	6.00	15.00
WV Justin Verlander / Jered Weaver	15.00	40.00
YL Mark Loretta / Kevin Youkilis	6.00	15.00
ZA Garrett Atkins / Ryan Zimmerman	15.00	40.00
ZC Miguel Cabrera / Ryan Zimmerman	15.00	40.00
ZJ Josh Johnson / Joel Zumaya	8.00	20.00
ZZ Carlos Zambrano / Joel Zumaya	10.00	25.00

2006 Ultimate Collection Tri-Marks Signatures

OVERALL AU ODDS 1:2
STATED PRINT RUN 15 SER.#'d SETS
NO PRICING DUE TO SCARCITY
EXCHANGE DEADLINE 12/20/09

BGL Boof Bonser
Francisco Liriano
Dave Gassner
BMP Dave Parker
Bill Mazeroski
Jason Bay
BSL Ryne Sandberg

Ernie Banks
Derrek Lee
BWH Jason Bay
Josh Willingham
Jeremy Hermida
CHR Robin Roberts
Steve Carlton
Cole Hamels
CSB Chris Carpenter
Boof Bonser
Jamie Shields
CTF Rod Carew
Mark Teixeira
Prince Fielder
FPH Trevor Hoffman
Rollie Fingers
Jonathan Papelbon
FVW Bob Feller
Justin Verlander
Jered Weaver
FWM Carlton Fisk
Victor Martinez
Josh Willingham
GHK Ken Griffey Jr.
Jason Kubel
Jeremy Hermida
GJC Ken Griffey Jr.
Derek Jeter
Miguel Cabrera
HWV Justin Verlander
Felix Hernandez
Jered Weaver EXCH
IKW Rickie Weeks
Tadahito Iguchi
Ian Kinsler
JCN Derek Jeter
Wil Nieves
Melky Cabrera
JMT Mark Teixeira
Conor Jackson
Kendry Morales
JSR Ozzie Smith
Derek Jeter
Hanley Ramirez
KMH Torii Hunter
Joe Mauer
Jason Kubel
LCK Francisco Liriano
Scott Kazmir
Steve Carlton
MMP Victor Martinez
Joe Mauer
Ronny Paulino
MUU Joe Morgan
Chase Utley
Dan Uggla
NPH Trevor Hoffman
Joe Nathan
Jonathan Papelbon
OBN Roy Oswalt
Taylor Buchholz
Fernando Nieve
PHY Kevin Youkilis
Jonathan Papelbon
Craig Hansen
PVO Roy Oswalt
Jim Palmer
Justin Verlander
SKC Jason Kendall
Bobby Crosby
Nick Swisher
ZCS Mike Schmidt
Miguel Cabrera
Ryan Zimmerman

2007 Ultimate Collection

This 141-card set was released in October, 2007. The set was issued in four-card packs, which came four packs to a box and four boxes to a case. Cards numbered 1-100 feature veteran players in team alphabetical order which is broken into National League (1-52) and American League (53-100). Those first 100 cards were issued to a stated print run of 450 serial numbered sets. Cards numbered 101-141 feature signed 2007 rookies and those cards were issued to stated print runs of between 289 and 299 serial numbered sets. A few players did not return their signatures in time for pack out and those cards could be redeemed until September 24, 2009.

COMMON CARD (1-100) .75 2.00
1-100 PRINT RUN 450 SER.#'d SETS
COMMON AU RC (101-141) 4.00 10.00
OVERALL AU ODDS ONE PER PACK
AU RC PRINT RUNS B/WN 289-299 COPIES PER
EXCHANGE DEADLINE 9/24/2009

1 Chipper Jones	2.00	5.00
2 Andruw Jones	1.25	3.00
3 Tim Hudson	.75	2.00
4 Stephen Drew	1.25	3.00
5 Randy Johnson	2.00	5.00
6 Brandon Webb	.75	2.00
7 Alfonso Soriano	.75	2.00
8 Derrek Lee	.75	2.00
9 Aramis Ramirez	.75	2.00
10 Carlos Zambrano	.75	2.00
11 Ken Griffey Jr.	3.00	8.00
12 Adam Dunn	.75	2.00
13 Ryan Freel	.75	2.00
14 Todd Helton	1.25	3.00
15 Garrett Atkins	.75	2.00
16 Matt Holliday	2.00	5.00
17 Hanley Ramirez	1.25	3.00
18 Dontrelle Willis	.75	2.00
19 Miguel Cabrera	1.25	3.00
20 Lance Berkman	.75	2.00
21 Roy Oswalt	.75	2.00
22 Carlos Lee	.75	2.00
23 Nomar Garciaparra	2.00	5.00
24 Jason Schmidt	.75	2.00
25 Juan Pierre	.75	2.00
26 Russell Martin	.75	2.00
27 Rickie Weeks	.75	2.00
28 Prince Fielder	2.00	5.00
29 Ben Sheets	.75	2.00
30 David Wright	3.00	8.00
31 Jose Reyes	2.00	5.00
32 Pedro Martinez	1.25	3.00
33 Carlos Beltran	.75	2.00
34 Brett Myers	.75	2.00
35 Jimmy Rollins	.75	2.00
36 Ryan Howard	3.00	8.00
37 Jason Bay	.75	2.00
38 Freddy Sanchez	.75	2.00
39 Ian Snell	.75	2.00
40 Jake Peavy	.75	2.00
41 Greg Maddux	3.00	8.00
42 Brian Giles	.75	2.00
43 Matt Cain	1.25	3.00
44 Barry Zito	.75	2.00
45 Ray Durham	.75	2.00
46 Albert Pujols	4.00	10.00
47 Chris Carpenter	.75	2.00
48 Chris Duncan	.75	2.00
49 Scott Rolen	1.25	3.00
50 Ryan Zimmerman	2.00	5.00
51 Chad Cordero	.75	2.00
52 Ryan Church	.75	2.00
53 Miguel Tejada	.75	2.00
54 Erik Bedard	.75	2.00
55 Brian Roberts	.75	2.00
56 David Ortiz	2.00	5.00
57 Josh Beckett	1.25	3.00
58 Manny Ramirez	1.25	3.00
59 Daisuke Matsuzaka RC	12.50	30.00
60 Jim Thome	1.25	3.00
61 Paul Konerko	.75	2.00
62 Jermaine Dye	.75	2.00
63 Grady Sizemore	1.25	3.00
64 Victor Martinez	.75	2.00
65 C.C. Sabathia	.75	2.00
66 Ivan Rodriguez	1.25	3.00
67 Justin Verlander	2.00	5.00
68 Gary Sheffield	.75	2.00
69 Jeremy Bonderman	.75	2.00
70 Gil Meche	.75	2.00
71 Mike Sweeney	.75	2.00
72 Mark Teahen	.75	2.00
73 Vladimir Guerrero	2.00	5.00
74 Howie Kendrick	.75	2.00
75 Francisco Rodriguez	.75	2.00
76 Johan Santana	1.25	3.00
77 Justin Morneau	.75	2.00
78 Joe Mauer	1.25	3.00
79 Michael Cuddyer	.75	2.00
80 Alex Rodriguez	3.00	8.00
81 Derek Jeter	5.00	12.00
82 Johnny Damon	1.25	3.00
83 Roger Clemens	3.00	8.00
84 Rich Harden	.75	2.00
85 Mike Piazza	2.00	5.00
86 Huston Street	.75	2.00
87 Ichiro Suzuki	3.00	8.00
88 Felix Hernandez	1.25	3.00
89 Kenji Johjima	2.00	5.00
90 Adrian Beltre	.75	2.00
91 Carl Crawford	.75	2.00
92 Scott Kazmir	1.25	3.00
93 B.J. Upton	.75	2.00
94 Michael Young	.75	2.00
95 Mark Teixeira	1.25	3.00
96 Sammy Sosa	2.00	5.00
97 Hank Blalock	.75	2.00
98 Vernon Wells	.75	2.00
99 Roy Halladay	.75	2.00
100 Frank Thomas	2.00	5.00
101 Adam Lind AU (RC)	4.00	10.00
102 Akinori Iwamura AU RC	12.50	30.00
103 Andrew Miller AU RC	20.00	50.00
104 Michael Bourn AU (RC)	4.00	10.00
105 Kory Casto AU (RC)	4.00	10.00
106 Ryan Braun AU (RC)	40.00	80.00
107 Sean Gallagher AU (RC)	4.00	10.00
108 Billy Butler AU (RC)	15.00	40.00
109 Alexi Casilla AU RC	4.00	10.00
110 Chris Stewart AU RC	4.00	10.00
111 Matt DeSalvo AU (RC)	6.00	15.00
112 Chase Headley AU (RC)	6.00	15.00
113 Delmon Young AU/292 (RC)	12.50	30.00
114 Homer Bailey AU (RC)	6.00	15.00
115 Kurt Suzuki AU (RC)	6.00	15.00
116 Alex Gordon AU/297 RC	30.00	60.00
117 Josh Hamilton AU (RC)	20.00	50.00
118 Fred Lewis AU (RC)	4.00	10.00
119 Glen Perkins AU (RC)	4.00	10.00
120 Hector Gimenez AU (RC)	4.00	10.00
121 Phil Hughes AU (RC)	30.00	60.00
122 Jeff Baker AU (RC)	4.00	10.00
123 Andy LaRoche AU (RC)	4.00	10.00
124 Tim Lincecum AU RC	50.00	100.00
125 Joaquin Arias AU (RC)	4.00	10.00
126 Daisuke Matsuzaka AU	100.00	200.00
127 Micah Owings AU (RC)	6.00	15.00
128 Hunter Pence AU/297 (RC)	30.00	60.00
129 Matt Chico AU (RC)	4.00	10.00
130 Kei Igawa AU RC	12.50	30.00
131 Kevin Kouzmanoff AU (RC)	4.00	10.00
132 Miguel Montero AU/289 (RC)	4.00	10.00
133 Mike Rabelo AU RC	6.00	15.00
134 Felix Pie AU (RC)	4.00	10.00
135 Curtis Thigpen AU (RC)	4.00	10.00
136 Ryan Z. Braun AU RC	6.00	15.00
137 Ryan Sweeney AU (RC)	4.00	10.00
138 Brandon Wood AU (RC)	6.00	15.00
139 Troy Tulowitzki AU (RC)	15.00	40.00
140 Justin Upton AU RC	50.00	100.00
141 Joba Chamberlain AU RC EXCH	100.00	200.00

2007 Ultimate Collection Jerseys

OVERALL GU ODDS TWO PER PACK
STATED PRINT RUN 50 SER.#'d SETS

1 Chipper Jones/50	4.00	10.00
2 Andruw Jones/50	4.00	10.00
3 Tim Hudson/50	3.00	8.00
4 Stephen Drew/50	4.00	10.00
5 Randy Johnson/50	4.00	10.00
6 Brandon Webb/50	4.00	10.00
7 Alfonso Soriano/50	3.00	8.00
8 Derrek Lee/50	3.00	8.00
9 Aramis Ramirez/50	3.00	8.00
10 Carlos Zambrano/50	3.00	8.00
11 Ken Griffey Jr./50	6.00	15.00
12 Adam Dunn/50	3.00	8.00
13 Ryan Freel/50	3.00	8.00
14 Todd Helton/50	4.00	10.00
15 Garrett Atkins/50	3.00	8.00
16 Matt Holliday/50	4.00	10.00
17 Hanley Ramirez/50	4.00	10.00
18 Dontrelle Willis/50	3.00	8.00
19 Miguel Cabrera/50	4.00	10.00
20 Lance Berkman/50	3.00	8.00
21 Roy Oswalt/50	3.00	8.00
22 Carlos Lee/50	3.00	8.00
24 Jason Schmidt/50	3.00	8.00
25 Juan Pierre/50	3.00	8.00
26 Russell Martin/50	3.00	8.00
27 Rickie Weeks/50	3.00	8.00
28 Prince Fielder/50	4.00	10.00
29 Ben Sheets/50	3.00	8.00
31 Jose Reyes/50	4.00	10.00
32 Pedro Martinez/50	4.00	10.00
33 Carlos Beltran/50	3.00	8.00
34 Brett Myers/50	3.00	8.00
35 Jimmy Rollins/50	6.00	15.00
37 Jason Bay/50	3.00	8.00
38 Freddy Sanchez/50	3.00	8.00
39 Ian Snell/50	3.00	8.00
40 Jake Peavy/50	3.00	8.00
41 Greg Maddux/50	6.00	15.00
42 Brian Giles/50	3.00	8.00
43 Matt Cain/50	4.00	10.00
44 Barry Zito/50	3.00	8.00
45 Ray Durham/50	3.00	8.00
46 Albert Pujols/50	8.00	20.00
47 Chris Carpenter/50	3.00	8.00
48 Chris Duncan/50	4.00	10.00
49 Scott Rolen/50	4.00	10.00
50 Ryan Zimmerman/50	4.00	10.00
51 Chad Cordero/50	3.00	8.00
52 Ryan Church/50	3.00	8.00
53 Miguel Tejada/50	3.00	8.00
54 Erik Bedard/50	3.00	8.00
55 Brian Roberts/50	3.00	8.00
56 David Ortiz/50	4.00	10.00
57 Josh Beckett/50	4.00	10.00
58 Manny Ramirez/50	4.00	10.00
59 Daisuke Matsuzaka/50	20.00	50.00
60 Jim Thome/50	4.00	10.00
61 Paul Konerko/50	3.00	8.00
62 Jermaine Dye/50	3.00	8.00
63 Grady Sizemore/50	4.00	10.00
64 Victor Martinez/50	3.00	8.00
65 C.C. Sabathia/50	3.00	8.00
66 Ivan Rodriguez/50	4.00	10.00
67 Justin Verlander/50	4.00	10.00
68 Gary Sheffield/50	3.00	8.00
69 Jeremy Bonderman/50	3.00	8.00
70 Gil Meche/50	3.00	8.00
71 Mike Sweeney/50	3.00	8.00
72 Mark Teahen/50	3.00	8.00
73 Vladimir Guerrero/50	4.00	10.00
74 Howie Kendrick/50	3.00	8.00
75 Francisco Rodriguez/50	3.00	8.00
76 Johan Santana/50	4.00	10.00
77 Justin Morneau/50	3.00	8.00
78 Joe Mauer/50	4.00	10.00
79 Michael Cuddyer/50	3.00	8.00
81 Derek Jeter/50	10.00	25.00
83 Roger Clemens/50	6.00	15.00
84 Rich Harden/50	3.00	8.00
85 Mike Piazza/50	6.00	15.00
86 Huston Street/50	3.00	8.00
88 Felix Hernandez/50	4.00	10.00
89 Kenji Johjima/50	4.00	10.00
90 Adrian Beltre/50	3.00	8.00
91 Carl Crawford/50	3.00	8.00
92 Scott Kazmir/50	4.00	10.00
93 B.J. Upton/50	3.00	8.00
94 Michael Young/50	3.00	8.00
95 Mark Teixeira/50	4.00	10.00
97 Hank Blalock/50	3.00	8.00
98 Vernon Wells/50	3.00	8.00
99 Roy Halladay/50	3.00	8.00
100 Frank Thomas/50	6.00	15.00

2007 Ultimate Collection Patches

OVERALL GU ODDS TWO PER PACK
STATED PRINT RUN 25 SER.#'d SETS
NO PRICING DUE TO SCARCITY

2007 Ultimate Collection America's Pastime Memorabilia

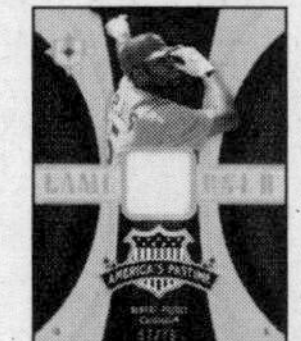

OVERALL GU ODDS TWO PER PACK
PRINT RUNS B/WN 25-75 COPIES PER
NO PRICING ON QTY 25 OR LESS

AB Adrian Beltre/75 3.00 8.00
AJ Andruw Jones/75 4.00 10.00
AP Andy Pettitte/75 4.00 10.00
AS Alfonso Soriano/75 3.00 8.00
BA Bobby Abreu/75 3.00 8.00
BE Josh Beckett/75 4.00 10.00
BG Brian Giles/75 3.00 8.00
BJ Jeff Bagwell/75 4.00 10.00
BR Brian Roberts/75 3.00 8.00
BS Ben Sheets/75 3.00 8.00
BW Brandon Webb/75 4.00 10.00
CA Chris Carpenter/75 3.00 8.00
CB Carlos Beltran/75 3.00 8.00
CC Carl Crawford/75 3.00 8.00
CF Carlton Fisk/75 4.00 10.00
CF2 Carlton Fisk/75 4.00 10.00
CJ Chipper Jones/75 4.00 10.00
CL Carlos Lee/75 3.00 8.00
CR Cal Ripken Jr./75 15.00 40.00
CS Curt Schilling/75 4.00 10.00
CU Chase Utley/75 4.00 10.00
DJ Derek Jeter/75 10.00 25.00
DL Derrek Lee/75 3.00 8.00
DO David Ortiz/75 4.00 10.00
DW Dontrelle Willis/75 3.00 8.00
FH Felix Hernandez/75 4.00 10.00
FL Francisco Liriano/75 4.00 10.00
FR Francisco Rodriguez/64 3.00 8.00
GA Garrett Atkins/75 3.00 8.00
GM Greg Maddux/75 6.00 15.00
GS Gary Sheffield/75 3.00 8.00
GW Tony Gwynn/75 4.00 10.00
GW2 Tony Gwynn/75 4.00 10.00
HA Rich Harden/75 3.00 8.00
HB Hank Blalock/75 3.00 8.00
HR Hanley Ramirez/75 4.00 10.00
JA Jason Bay/75 3.00 8.00
JB Jeremy Bonderman/75 3.00 8.00
JE Jim Edmonds/75 4.00 10.00
JG Jason Giambi/75 3.00 8.00
JM Justin Morneau/75 3.00 8.00
JN Joe Nathan/75 3.00 8.00
JO Randy Johnson/75 4.00 10.00
JP Jonathan Papelbon/75 4.00 10.00
JR Jim Rice/75 3.00 8.00
JS Johan Santana/75 4.00 10.00
JT Jim Thome/75 4.00 10.00
JV Justin Verlander/75 4.00 10.00
JW Josh Willingham/75 3.00 8.00
KG Ken Griffey Jr./75 6.00 15.00
KP Kirby Puckett/75 15.00 40.00
KY Kevin Youkilis/75 4.00 10.00
LB Lance Berkman/75 3.00 8.00
LO Lou Brock/25
MA Joe Mauer/75 4.00 10.00
MC Matt Cain/75 4.00 10.00
MH Matt Holliday/75 4.00 10.00
MI Miguel Cabrera/75 4.00 10.00
MM Mike Mussina/75 4.00 10.00
MR Manny Ramirez/75 4.00 10.00
MR2 Manny Ramirez/75 4.00 10.00
MS Mike Schmidt/75 6.00 15.00
MT Miguel Tejada/75 3.00 8.00
MY Michael Young/75 3.00 8.00
MZ Pedro Martinez/75 4.00 10.00
NR Nolan Ryan/75 12.50 30.00
OR Magglio Ordonez/75 3.00 8.00
OS Ozzie Smith/75 10.00 25.00
PE Jake Peavy/75 3.00 8.00
PF Prince Fielder/75 4.00 10.00
PM Paul Molitor/75 3.00 8.00
PU Albert Pujols/75 8.00 20.00
RB Rocco Baldelli/75 3.00 8.00
RC Roger Clemens/75 6.00 15.00
RE Jose Reyes/75 4.00 10.00
RE2 Jose Reyes/75 4.00 10.00
RH Roy Halladay/75 3.00 8.00
RJ Reggie Jackson/75 6.00 15.00
RO Roy Oswalt/75 3.00 8.00
RS Ryne Sandberg/75 6.00 15.00
RW Rickie Weeks/75 3.00 8.00
RZ Ryan Zimmerman/75 4.00 10.00
SC Steve Carlton/75 3.00 8.00
SE Richie Sexson/75 3.00 8.00
SI Grady Sizemore/75 4.00 10.00
SI2 Grady Sizemore/75 4.00 10.00
SK Scott Kazmir/75 4.00 10.00
SM John Smoltz/75 4.00 10.00
TE Mark Teixeira/75 4.00 10.00
TG Troy Glaus/75 3.00 8.00
TH Todd Helton/75 4.00 10.00
TR Travis Hafner/75 3.00 8.00
TR2 Travis Hafner/75 3.00 8.00
VA Jason Varitek/75 4.00 10.00
VG Vladimir Guerrero/75 4.00 10.00
VG2 Vladimir Guerrero/75 4.00 10.00
VM Victor Martinez/75 3.00 8.00
WC Will Clark/75 4.00 10.00

2007 Ultimate Collection America's Pastime Memorabilia Gold

OVERALL GU ODDS TWO PER PACK
STATED PRINT RUN 25 SER.#'d SETS
NO PRICING DUE TO SCARCITY

2007 Ultimate Collection America's Pastime Memorabilia Patches

OVERALL GU ODDS TWO PER PACK
PRINT RUNS B/WN 5-50 COPIES PER
NO PRICING ON QTY 25 OR LESS
AB Adrian Beltre/50 5.00 12.00
AJ Andruw Jones/50 6.00 15.00
AP Andy Pettitte/50 6.00 15.00
AS Alfonso Soriano/50 6.00 15.00
BA Bobby Abreu/50 5.00 12.00
BE Josh Beckett/50 10.00 25.00
BG Brian Giles/50 5.00 12.00
BJ Jeff Bagwell/50 10.00 25.00
BR Brian Roberts/50 6.00 15.00
BS Ben Sheets/50 5.00 12.00
BW Brandon Webb/50 6.00 15.00
CA Chris Carpenter/50 5.00 12.00
CB Carlos Beltran/50 6.00 15.00
CC Carl Crawford/50 6.00 15.00
CF Carlton Fisk/50 5.00 12.00
CF2 Carlton Fisk/50 5.00 12.00
CJ Chipper Jones/50 12.50 30.00
CL Carlos Lee/50 5.00 12.00
CR Cal Ripken Jr./32 30.00 60.00
CS Curt Schilling/50 6.00 15.00
CU Chase Utley/50 6.00 15.00
DL Derrek Lee/50 5.00 12.00
DO David Ortiz/50 10.00 25.00
DW Dontrelle Willis/50 5.00 12.00
FH Felix Hernandez/50 6.00 15.00
FL Francisco Liriano/50 6.00 15.00
FR Francisco Rodriguez/50 5.00 12.00
GA Garrett Atkins/50 5.00 12.00
GM Greg Maddux/20
GS Gary Sheffield/50 5.00 12.00
GW Tony Gwynn/50 10.00 25.00
GW2 Tony Gwynn/50 10.00 25.00
HA Rich Harden/50 5.00 12.00
HB Hank Blalock/50 5.00 12.00
HR Hanley Ramirez/50 6.00 15.00
JA Jason Bay/50 5.00 12.00
JB Jeremy Bonderman/50 5.00 12.00
JE Jim Edmonds/50 6.00 15.00
JG Jason Giambi/50 5.00 12.00
JM Justin Morneau/50 6.00 15.00
JN Joe Nathan/50 5.00 12.00
JO Randy Johnson/50 6.00 15.00
JP Jonathan Papelbon/50 10.00 25.00
JS Johan Santana/50 6.00 15.00
JT Jim Thome/50 5.00 12.00
JW Josh Willingham/50 5.00 12.00
KG Ken Griffey Jr./50 15.00 40.00
KP Kirby Puckett/50 30.00 60.00
KY Kevin Youkilis/50 10.00 25.00
LB Lance Berkman/50 6.00 15.00
LO Lou Brock/50 10.00 25.00
MA Joe Mauer/40 6.00 15.00
MC Matt Cain/50 5.00 12.00
MH Matt Holliday/50 10.00 25.00
MI Miguel Cabrera/50 5.00 12.00
MM Mike Mussina/50 10.00 25.00
MP Mike Piazza/50 15.00 40.00
MR Manny Ramirez/30 6.00 15.00
MR2 Manny Ramirez/28 6.00 15.00
MS Mike Schmidt/50 15.00 40.00
MT Miguel Tejada/50 5.00 12.00
MY Michael Young/50 5.00 12.00
MZ Pedro Martinez/50 6.00 15.00
NR Nolan Ryan/50 20.00 50.00
OR Magglio Ordonez/50 6.00 15.00
PE Jake Peavy/50 5.00 12.00
PF Prince Fielder/50 10.00 25.00
PM Paul Molitor/50 10.00 25.00
PU Albert Pujols/25
RB Rocco Baldelli/50 5.00 12.00
RC Roger Clemens/50 10.00 25.00
RE Jose Reyes/50 10.00 25.00
RE2 Jose Reyes/50 10.00 25.00
RH Roy Halladay/50 5.00 12.00
RJ Reggie Jackson/50 10.00 25.00
RO Roy Oswalt/50 5.00 12.00
RS Ryne Sandberg/50 15.00 40.00
RW Rickie Weeks/9
RY Robin Yount/50 15.00 40.00
RZ Ryan Zimmerman/50 10.00 25.00
SC Steve Carlton/50 5.00 12.00
SE Richie Sexson/50 5.00 12.00
SI Grady Sizemore/50 10.00 25.00
SI2 Grady Sizemore/50 10.00 25.00
SK Scott Kazmir/50 6.00 15.00
SM John Smoltz/50 6.00 15.00
TE Mark Teixeira/50 6.00 15.00
TG Troy Glaus/50 6.00 15.00
TH Todd Helton/50 6.00 15.00
TR Travis Hafner/50 5.00 12.00
TR2 Travis Hafner/50 5.00 12.00
VA Jason Varitek/50 10.00 25.00
VG Vladimir Guerrero/5
VG2 Vladimir Guerrero/5
VM Victor Martinez/50 5.00 12.00
WC Will Clark/50 6.00 15.00

2007 Ultimate Collection America's Pastime Signatures

OVERALL AU ODDS ONE PER PACK
EXCHANGE DEADLINE 9/24/2009
AD Adam Dunn 4.00 10.00
AE Andre Ethier 4.00 10.00
AG Adrian Gonzalez 4.00 10.00
AJ A.J. Burnett 4.00 10.00
AK Al Kaline EXCH 10.00 25.00
AL Adam LaRoche 4.00 10.00
AP Albert Pujols 100.00 150.00
AV Andy Van Slyke 4.00 10.00
BB Boof Bonser 4.00 10.00
BE Johnny Bench 10.00 25.00
BJ B.J. Upton 6.00 15.00
BM Bill Mazeroski 10.00 25.00
CB Chad Billingsley 6.00 15.00
CC Chad Cordero 4.00 10.00
CH Cole Hamels 10.00 25.00
CK Casey Kotchman EXCH 4.00 10.00
CQ Carlos Quentin 6.00 15.00
CR Craig Biggio 20.00 50.00
CT Curtis Thigpen 4.00 10.00
CW Chien-Ming Wang 75.00 150.00
CY Chris Young 4.00 10.00
DH Dan Haren 4.00 10.00
DJ Derek Jeter 60.00 120.00
DM Don Mattingly 30.00 60.00
DS Don Sutton 6.00 15.00
DU Dan Uggla 6.00 15.00
DY Delmon Young 6.00 15.00
EB Ernie Banks EXCH 30.00 60.00
FH Felix Hernandez 10.00 25.00
FR Frank Robinson 10.00 25.00
GA Garrett Atkins 4.00 10.00
GP Gaylord Perry 4.00 10.00
GR Khalil Greene 6.00 15.00
GW Tony Gwynn 30.00 60.00
HA Travis Hafner 4.00 10.00
HB Homer Bailey 6.00 15.00
HE Chase Headley 4.00 10.00
HO Howie Kendrick 4.00 10.00
HR Hanley Ramirez 6.00 15.00
HS Huston Street 4.00 10.00
HU Torii Hunter 6.00 15.00
IK Ian Kinsler 4.00 10.00
JB Jason Bay 4.00 10.00
JE Jeremy Bonderman 4.00 10.00
JI Jim Rice 4.00 10.00
JL James Loney 6.00 15.00
JM Jack Morris 4.00 10.00
JN Joe Nathan 4.00 10.00
JO Joe Blanton 4.00 10.00
JT Jim Thome 12.50 30.00
JV Justin Verlander 10.00 25.00
JZ Joel Zumaya 6.00 15.00
KI Kei Igawa 10.00 25.00
KJ Kelly Johnson 4.00 10.00
KM Kendry Morales 4.00 10.00
LA Andy LaRoche 4.00 10.00
LE Jon Lester 6.00 15.00
LY John Lackey 6.00 15.00
MA Daisuke Matsuzaka 125.00 250.00
MB Matt Brown 4.00 10.00
MC Matt Cain 6.00 15.00
MH Matt Holliday 8.00 20.00
MM Melvin Mora 4.00 10.00
MS Mike Schmidt 20.00 50.00
MT Mark Teixeira 6.00 15.00
NM Nick Markakis 6.00 15.00
NW Nick Swisher 4.00 10.00
OS Ozzie Smith 20.00 50.00
PA Jim Palmer 6.00 15.00
PB Jonathan Papelbon 15.00 40.00
PK Paul Konerko 4.00 10.00
RA Aramis Ramirez 6.00 15.00
RB Ryan Braun 20.00 50.00
RF Rafael Furcal 4.00 10.00
RG Ryan Garko 4.00 10.00
RH Rich Harden 4.00 10.00
RI Rich Hill 4.00 10.00
RT Ryan Theriot 6.00 15.00
RW Rickie Weeks 4.00 10.00
RZ Ryan Zimmerman 10.00 25.00
SD Stephen Drew 10.00 25.00
SG Sean Gallagher 4.00 10.00
SK Scott Kazmir 8.00 20.00
SM Stan Musial 30.00 60.00
SO Joakim Soria 10.00 25.00
TG Tom Glavine 20.00 50.00
TP Tony Perez 6.00 15.00
TR Tim Raines 4.00 10.00
TT Troy Tulowitzki 20.00 50.00
VM Victor Martinez 6.00 15.00
VW Vernon Wells 4.00 10.00
WC Will Clark 6.00 15.00
WI Josh Willingham 4.00 10.00
WM Willie McCovey
XN Xavier Nady 4.00 10.00

2007 Ultimate Collection The Ultimate Card

OVERALL AU ODDS ONE PER PACK
STATED PRINT RUN 1 SER.#'D SET
NO PRICING DUE TO SCARCITY

2007 Ultimate Collection The Ultimate Logo

OVERALL AU ODDS ONE PER PACK
STATED PRINT RUN 1 SER.#'D SET
NO PRICING DUE TO SCARCITY

2007 Ultimate Collection The Ultimate Patch

OVERALL AU ODDS ONE PER PACK
PRINT RUNS B/WN 5-25 COPIES PER
NO PRICING DUE TO SCARCITY

2007 Ultimate Collection The Ultimate Six Signatures

OVERALL AU ODDS ONE PER PACK
STATED PRINT RUN 10 SER.#'d SETS
NO PRICING DUE TO SCARCITY

2007 Ultimate Collection Ultimate Champions Signatures

OVERALL AU ODDS ONE PER PACK
PRINT RUNS B/WN 4-10 COPIES PER
NO PRICING DUE TO SCARCITY
EXCHANGE DEADLINE 9/24/2009

2007 Ultimate Collection Ultimate Ensemble Dual Swatches

OVERALL GU ODDS TWO PER PACK
PRINT RUNS B/WN 52-75 COPIES PER
BD Jason Bay 4.00 10.00
J.D. Drew/75
BH Jeremy Bonderman 4.00 10.00
Rich Harden/75
BZ Wade Boggs 5.00 12.00
Ryan Zimmerman/75
CG Miguel Cabrera 5.00 12.00
Vladimir Guerrero/75
CJ Curt Schilling 6.00 15.00
Josh Beckett/75
CR Roger Clemens 12.50 30.00
Nolan Ryan/75
CW Matt Cain 4.00 10.00
Jered Weaver/75
FT Prince Fielder 5.00 12.00
Mark Teixeira/75
GD Ken Griffey Jr. 8.00 20.00
Adam Dunn/75
GM Tom Glavine 4.00 10.00
Pedro Martinez/75
GP Tony Gwynn 10.00 25.00
Jake Peavy/75
GR Tony Gwynn 15.00 40.00
Cal Ripken Jr./75
HH Todd Helton 5.00 12.00
Matt Holliday/75
HJ Felix Hernandez 5.00 12.00
Kenji Johjima/75
HR J.J. Hardy 5.00 12.00
Jose Reyes/75
HW Roy Halladay 4.00 10.00
Vernon Wells/75
IK Tadahito Iguchi 4.00 10.00
Paul Konerko/75
JJ Chipper Jones 5.00 12.00
Andruw Jones/75
JR Derek Jeter 20.00 50.00
Mariano Rivera/75
JV Joe Mauer 4.00 10.00
Victor Martinez/75
KY Scott Kazmir 4.00 10.00
Delmon Young/75
LS Derrek Lee 4.00 10.00
Alfonso Soriano/75
MB Mike Schmidt 12.50 30.00
Brooks Robinson/75
MC Justin Morneau 4.00 10.00
Michael Cuddyer/75
MM Justin Morneau 5.00 12.00
Joe Mauer/75
NR Joe Nathan 5.00 12.00
Mariano Rivera/75
OB Roy Oswalt 5.00 12.00
Lance Berkman/75
PC Albert Pujols 8.00 20.00
Chris Carpenter/75
PO Albert Pujols 8.00 20.00
David Ortiz/75
RB Ivan Rodriguez 5.00 12.00
Johnny Bench/75
SB Grady Sizemore 5.00 12.00
Carlos Beltran/75
SC Alfonso Soriano 5.00 12.00
Carl Crawford/52
SL Johan Santana 6.00 15.00
Francisco Liriano/75
SP John Smoltz 5.00 12.00
Jake Peavy/75
SR Ryne Sandberg 30.00 60.00
Cal Ripken Jr./63
SW Johan Santana 5.00 12.00
Brandon Webb/75
TR Miguel Tejada 6.00 15.00
Cal Ripken Jr./75
WU Rickie Weeks 5.00 12.00
Chase Utley/75
YR Michael Young 5.00 12.00
Jose Reyes/75

2007 Ultimate Collection Ultimate Ensemble Dual Patches

OVERALL GU ODDS TWO PER PACK
STATED PRINT RUN 25 SER.#'d SETS
NO PRICING DUE TO SCARCITY
BC Carl Crawford
Rocco Baldelli/25
CG Miguel Cabrera
Vladimir Guerrero/25
CJ Curt Schilling
Josh Beckett/25
CR Roger Clemens
Nolan Ryan/25
CW Matt Cain
Jered Weaver/25
DR Rich Harden
Dan Haren/25
FT Prince Fielder
Mark Teixeira/25
GD Ken Griffey Jr.
Adam Dunn/25
GM Tom Glavine
Pedro Martinez/25
GP Tony Gwynn
Jake Peavy/25
GR Tony Gwynn
Cal Ripken Jr./25
HH Todd Helton
Matt Holliday/25
HJ Felix Hernandez
Kenji Johjima/25
HR J.J. Hardy
Jose Reyes/25
HW Roy Halladay
Vernon Wells/25
IK Tadahito Iguchi
Paul Konerko/25
JJ Andruw Jones
Chipper Jones/25
JV Joe Mauer
Victor Martinez/25
KC Carl Crawford
Scott Kazmir/25
MB Mike Schmidt
Brooks Robinson/25
MC Justin Morneau
Michael Cuddyer/25
MM Justin Morneau
Joe Mauer/25
NR Joe Nathan
Mariano Rivera/25
OB Roy Oswalt
Lance Berkman/25
RB Ivan Rodriguez
Johnny Bench/25
RD Manny Ramirez
J.D. Drew/25
RG Mariano Rivera
Jason Giambi/25
SH Grady Sizemore
Travis Hafner/25
SM Johan Santana
Daisuke Matsuzaka/25
SP John Smoltz
Jake Peavy/25
SR Ryne Sandberg
Cal Ripken Jr./25
SW Johan Santana
Brandon Webb/25
WU Rickie Weeks
Chase Utley/25
YM Robin Yount
Paul Molitor/25
YR Michael Young
Jose Reyes/25

2007 Ultimate Collection Ultimate Ensemble Triple Swatches

OVERALL GU ODDS TWO PER PACK
STATED PRINT RUN 50 SER.#'d SETS
BCG Hank Blalock 6.00 15.00
Eric Chavez
Troy Glaus/50
CBG Will Clark 10.00 25.00
Wade Boggs
Tony Gwynn/50
CRS Steve Carlton 10.00 25.00
Nolan Ryan
Don Sutton/50
CSK Steve Carlton 6.00 15.00
Johan Santana
Scott Kazmir/50
FHS Prince Fielder 6.00 15.00
J.J. Hardy
Ben Sheets/50
GRR Khalil Greene 10.00 25.00
Jose Reyes
Hanley Ramirez/50
HTP Travis Hafner 6.00 15.00
Frank Thomas
Mike Piazza/50
LPD Barry Larkin 6.00 15.00
Tony Perez
Adam Dunn/50
LRS Barry Larkin 12.50 30.00
Cal Ripken
Jr.
Ozzie Smith/50
MCS Pedro Martinez 10.00 25.00
Roger Clemens
Don Sutton/50
MJG Joe Mauer 12.50 30.00
Chipper Jones
Ken Griffey Jr./50
MMP Joe Mauer 6.00 15.00
Victor Martinez
Jorge Posada/50
MSB Daisuke Matsuzaka 40.00 80.00
Curt Schilling
Josh Beckett/50
MSU Bill Mazeroski 10.00 25.00
Ryne Sandberg
Chase Utley/50
OCZ Roy Oswalt 6.00 15.00
Chris Carpenter
Carlos Zambrano/50
ODH David Ortiz 6.00 15.00
Jermaine Dye
Travis Hafner/50
OMT David Ortiz 6.00 15.00
Justin Morneau
Mark Teixeira/50
OPR David Ortiz 10.00 25.00
Albert Pujols
Jose Reyes/50
PJL Albert Pujols 10.00 25.00
Andruw Jones
Derrek Lee/50
RDB Ivan Rodriguez 6.00 15.00
Carlos Delgado
Carlos Beltran/50
RJG Cal Ripken 20.00 50.00
Jr.
Derek Jeter
Ken Griffey Jr./50
RPJ Jim Rice 40.00 80.00
Kirby Puckett
Reggie Jackson/50
RPS Manny Ramirez 10.00 25.00
Albert Pujols
Alfonso Soriano/50
RSB Brooks Robinson 15.00 40.00
Mike Schmidt
Wade Boggs/50
SHS Johan Santana 6.00 15.00
Roy Halladay
Josh Beckett/50
UWG Chase Utley 10.00 25.00
Rickie Weeks
Marcus Giles/50
YBO Carl Yastrzemski 10.00 25.00
Wade Boggs
David Ortiz/50
YJT Michael Young 10.00 25.00
Derek Jeter
Miguel Tejada/50
YTS Michael Young 10.00 25.00
Mark Teixeira
Sammy Sosa/50
ZAJ Ryan Zimmerman 6.00 15.00
Garrett Atkins
Chipper Jones/50

2007 Ultimate Collection Ultimate Ensemble Triple Patches

OVERALL GU ODDS TWO PER PACK
PRINT RUNS B/WN 7-15 COPIES PER
NO PRICING DUE TO SCARCITY

2007 Ultimate Collection Ultimate Ensemble Quad Swatches

OVERALL GU ODDS TWO PER PACK
PRINT RUNS B/WN 5-25 COPIES PER
NO PRICING DUE TO SCARCITY

2007 Ultimate Collection Ultimate Ensemble Quad Patches

OVERALL GU ODDS TWO PER PACK
STATED PRINT RUN 10 SER.#'d SETS
NO PRICING DUE TO SCARCITY

2007 Ultimate Collection Ultimate Futures Signatures

OVERALL AU ODDS ONE PER PACK
PRINT RUNS B/WN 8-25 COPIES PER
NO PRICING DUE TO SCARCITY
EXCHANGE DEADLINE 9/24/2009

2007 Ultimate Collection Ultimate Iron Man Signatures

COMMON CARD 125.00 250.00
OVERALL AU ODDS ONE PER PACK
STATED PRINT RUN 8 SER.#'d SETS

2007 Ultimate Collection Ultimate Legendary Signatures

OVERALL AU ODDS ONE PER PACK
PRINT RUNS B/WN 15-25 COPIES PER
NO PRICING DUE TO SCARCITY
EXCHANGE DEADLINE 9/24/2009

2007 Ultimate Collection Ultimate Numbers Match Signatures

OVERALL AU ODDS ONE PER PACK
PRINT RUNS B/WN 2-48 COPIES PER
NO PRICING ON QTY 25 OR LESS
EXCHANGE DEADLINE 9/24/2009
AR Garrett Atkins 6.00 15.00
Mark Reynolds/27
BG Craig Biggio
Alex Gordon/7
BP Johnny Bench
Albert Pujols/5
BR Yogi Berra
Cal Ripken Jr./8
BW Jeremy Bonderman 6.00 15.00
Chase Wright/38
BZ Jason Bay 10.00 25.00
Carlos Zambrano/38
CP Roger Clemens
Jim Palmer/22
FG Carlton Fisk 40.00 80.00
Vladimir Guerrero/27
GF Tony Gwynn
Bob Feller/19
HH Travis Hafner 12.50 30.00
Torii Hunter/48
HR Felix Hernandez 50.00 100.00
Nolan Ryan/34
HV Cole Hamels 20.00 50.00
Justin Verlander/35
HW Rich Harden 150.00 200.00
Chien-Ming Wang/40
JD Reggie Jackson 30.00 60.00
Adam Dunn/44
JT Derek Jeter
Troy Tulowitzki/2
KC Scott Kazmir
Tyler Clippard/19
KM Al Kaline
Stan Musial/6
LL Derrek Lee
Adam LaRoche/25
MB Nick Markakis
Billy Butler/21
MS Don Mattingly
Ryne Sandberg/23
PB Hunter Pence
Michael Bourn/9
RB Brooks Robinson
Johnny Bench/5
RU Hanley Ramirez
B.J. Upton/2
SH Ben Sheets
Tim Hudson/15
TW Mark Teixeira
Rickie Weeks/23
UD Dan Uggla
Stephen Drew/6
WH Dontrelle Willis 30.00 60.00
Cole Hamels/35
YR Carl Yastrzemski
Cal Ripken Jr./8

2007 Ultimate Collection Ultimate Numbers Materials

OVERALL GU ODDS TWO PER PACK
PRINT RUNS B/WN 1-75 COPIES PER
NO PRICING ON QTY 25 OR LESS
AB A.J. Burnett/34 4.00 10.00
AD Adam Dunn/44 4.00 10.00
AG Alex Gordon/7
AJ Andruw Jones/25
AN Andy Pettitte/46 5.00 12.00
AS Alfonso Soriano/12
BA Bobby Abreu/53 4.00 10.00
BE Adrian Beltre/29 4.00 10.00

BG Brian Giles/24
BI Craig Biggio/7
BK Brooks Robinson/5
BR Brian Roberts/1
BS Ben Sheets/15
BT Carlos Beltran/15
BU B.J. Upton/2
BZ Barry Zito/75 4.00 10.00
CA Carl Crawford/13
CC Chris Carpenter/29 4.00 10.00
CF Carlton Fisk/27 5.00 12.00
CF2 Carlton Fisk/72 5.00 12.00
CJ Chipper Jones/10
CL Carlos Lee/45 4.00 10.00
CS Curt Schilling/38 5.00 12.00
CU Chase Utley/26 5.00 12.00
CY Carl Yastrzemski/8
DJ Derek Jeter/2
DJ2 Derek Jeter/2
DL Derrek Lee/25
DL2 Derrek Lee/25
DM Don Mattingly/23
DO David Ortiz/34 6.00 15.00
DO2 David Ortiz/25
DY Delmon Young/26 5.00 12.00
EC Eric Chavez/3
FH Felix Hernandez/34 6.00 15.00
FL Francisco Liriano/47 5.00 12.00
GA Garrett Atkins/27 4.00 10.00
GJ Geoff Jenkins/5
GL Troy Glaus/25
GP Gaylord Perry/36 4.00 10.00
GR Grady Sizemore/24
GW Tony Gwynn/19
HA Roy Halladay/32 4.00 10.00
HE Todd Helton/17
HF Travis Hafner/48 4.00 10.00
HP Hunter Pence/9
HU Torii Hunter/48 4.00 10.00
JB Jeff Bagwell/5
JE Jeremy Bonderman/38 4.00 10.00
JH Josh Hamilton/33 20.00 50.00
JJ J.J. Hardy/7
JM Joe Mauer/7
JR Jim Rice/14
JS Johan Santana/57 5.00 12.00
JT Jim Thome/25
JV Jason Varitek/33 12.50 30.00
KG Ken Griffey Jr./3
KG2 Ken Griffey Jr./3
KI Kirk Gibson/23
KJ Kenji Johjima/2
LD Lenny Dykstra/4
MA Daisuke Matsuzaka/18
MA2 Daisuke Matsuzaka/18
MO Magglio Ordonez/30 4.00 10.00
MR Manny Ramirez/24
MR2 Manny Ramirez/24
NR Nolan Ryan/34 20.00 50.00
OS Roy Oswalt/44 4.00 10.00
PF Prince Fielder/28 5.00 12.00
PU Albert Pujols/5
PU2 Albert Pujols/5
RC Rod Carew/29 6.00 15.00
RH Rich Harden/40 4.00 10.00
RI Cal Ripken Jr./8
RJ Randy Johnson/51 5.00 12.00
RO Roger Clemens/22
RS Ryne Sandberg/23
RW Rickie Weeks/23
RY Robin Yount/19
SA C.C. Sabathia/52 4.00 10.00
SC Steve Carlton/32 4.00 10.00
SK Scott Kazmir/19
SR Scott Rolen/27 5.00 12.00
TG Tom Glavine/47 6.00 15.00
TP Tony Perez/24
TR Tim Raines/30 4.00 10.00
TV Trevor Hoffman/51 4.00 10.00
VG Vladimir Guerrero/27 6.00 15.00
VM Victor Martinez/41 4.00 10.00
WB Wade Boggs/12
WB2 Wade Boggs/12
WC Will Clark/22
WI Dontrelle Willis/35 4.00 10.00

2007 Ultimate Collection Ultimate Star Materials

OVERALL GU ODDS TWO PER PACK
AD Adam Dunn 3.00 8.00
AG Alex Gordon 6.00 15.00
AG2 Alex Gordon 6.00 15.00
AK Austin Kearns 3.00 8.00
AK2 Austin Kearns 3.00 8.00
AP Albert Pujols 6.00 15.00
BG Brian Giles 3.00 8.00
BI Craig Biggio 4.00 10.00
BO Jeremy Bonderman 3.00 8.00
BS Ben Sheets 3.00 8.00
BU B.J. Upton 3.00 8.00
CA Chris Carpenter 3.00 8.00
CF Carlton Fisk 4.00 10.00
CL Carlos Lee 3.00 8.00
CL2 Carlos Lee 3.00 8.00
CR Cal Ripken Jr. 8.00 20.00
CR2 Cal Ripken Jr. 8.00 20.00
CY Carl Yastrzemski 4.00 10.00
CZ Carlos Zambrano 3.00 8.00
DH Dan Haren 3.00 8.00
DJ Derek Jeter 8.00 20.00
DJ2 Derek Jeter 8.00 20.00
DL Derrek Lee 3.00 8.00
DM Don Mattingly 5.00 12.00
DO David Ortiz 4.00 10.00
DW Dontrelle Willis 3.00 8.00
DW2 Dontrelle Willis 3.00 8.00
EC Eric Chavez 3.00 8.00
FH Felix Hernandez 4.00 10.00
FH2 Felix Hernandez 4.00 10.00
FL Francisco Liriano 4.00 10.00
FR Francisco Rodriguez 3.00 8.00
FT Frank Thomas 5.00 12.00
GA Garrett Atkins 3.00 8.00
GA2 Garrett Atkins 3.00 8.00
GR Khalil Greene 4.00 10.00
GW Tony Gwynn 4.00 10.00
HA Roy Halladay 3.00 8.00
HP Hunter Pence 5.00 12.00
HR Hanley Ramirez 4.00 10.00
HS Huston Street 3.00 8.00
HU Torii Hunter 3.00 8.00
JA Jason Bay 3.00 8.00
JB Josh Beckett 5.00 12.00
JH Jeremy Hermida 3.00 8.00
JL John Lackey 3.00 8.00
JM Joe Mauer 4.00 10.00
JN Joe Nathan 3.00 8.00
JP Jonathan Papelbon 4.00 10.00
JR Jim Rice 3.00 8.00
JS John Smoltz 4.00 10.00
JT Jim Thome 4.00 10.00
JT2 Jim Thome 4.00 10.00
JU Justin Morneau 3.00 8.00
JU2 Justin Morneau 3.00 8.00
KG Ken Griffey Jr. 6.00 15.00
MA Matt Cain 3.00 8.00
MA2 Matt Cain 3.00 8.00
MC Miguel Cabrera 4.00 10.00
MH Matt Holliday 4.00 10.00
MH2 Matt Holliday 4.00 10.00
MS Mike Schmidt 5.00 12.00
MT Mark Teixeira 4.00 10.00
MT2 Mark Teixeira 4.00 10.00
MY Michael Young 3.00 8.00
MY2 Michael Young 3.00 8.00
NM Nick Markakis 4.00 10.00
NR Nolan Ryan 6.00 15.00
NS Nick Swisher 3.00 8.00
OR Roy Oswalt 3.00 8.00
OS Ozzie Smith 5.00 12.00
PA Jim Palmer 3.00 8.00
PE Jake Peavy 3.00 8.00
PE2 Jake Peavy 3.00 8.00
PF Prince Fielder 4.00 10.00
PK Paul Konerko 3.00 8.00
PM Paul Molitor 3.00 8.00
PM2 Paul Molitor 3.00 8.00
RA Roberto Alomar 4.00 10.00
RC Roger Clemens 5.00 12.00
RF Rollie Fingers 3.00 8.00
RH Rich Harden 3.00 8.00
RJ Randy Johnson 4.00 10.00
RO Rod Carew 4.00 10.00
RW Rickie Weeks 3.00 8.00
RY Robin Yount 4.00 10.00
RZ Ryan Zimmerman 4.00 10.00
RZ2 Ryan Zimmerman 4.00 10.00
SK Scott Kazmir 4.00 10.00
TG Tom Glavine 4.00 10.00
TH Travis Hafner 3.00 8.00
TH2 Travis Hafner 3.00 8.00
TI Tim Hudson 3.00 8.00
TT Troy Tulowitzki 4.00 10.00
VM Victor Martinez 3.00 8.00
VW Vernon Wells 3.00 8.00
WB Wade Boggs 4.00 10.00
WI Josh Willingham 3.00 8.00

2007 Ultimate Collection Ultimate Star Materials Autograph

OVERALL AU ODDS ONE PER PACK
PRINT RUNS B/WN 3-15 COPIES PER
NO PRICING DUE TO SCARCITY
EXCHANGE DEADLINE 9/24/2009

2007 Ultimate Collection Ultimate Star Materials Autograph Patch

OVERALL AU ODDS ONE PER PACK
STATED PRINT RUN 5 SER.#'d SETS
NO PRICING DUE TO SCARCITY
EXCHANGE DEADLINE 9/24/2009

2007 Ultimate Collection Ultimate Team Marks

OVERALL AU ODDS ONE PER PACK
PRINT RUNS B/WN 56-60 COPIES PER
EXCHANGE DEADLINE 9/24/2009
AP Albert Pujols/60
BG Bob Gibson/60 15.00 40.00
CC Carl Crawford/60 6.00 15.00
CL Carlos Lee/57 10.00 25.00
CY Carl Yastrzemski/58 30.00 60.00
DJ Derek Jeter/60 100.00 150.00
DL Derrek Lee/58 10.00 25.00
DO David Ortiz/60 40.00 80.00
DW Dontrelle Willis/56 4.00 10.00
FH Felix Hernandez/60 12.50 30.00
JM Joe Mauer/60 10.00 25.00
MO Justin Morneau/60 10.00 25.00
MT Mark Teixeira/60 6.00 15.00
PF Prince Fielder/60 30.00 60.00
VM Victor Martinez/60 4.00 10.00
VW Vernon Wells/60 4.00 10.00

2007 Ultimate Collection Ultimate Team Materials

OVERALL GU ODDS TWO PER PACK
PRINT RUNS B/WN 25-50 COPIES PER
NO PRICING ON QTY 25 OR LESS
AD Adam Dunn/50 3.00 8.00
AK Austin Kearns/50 3.00 8.00
AN Garret Anderson/50 3.00 8.00
AP Albert Pujols/50 8.00 20.00
BE Josh Beckett/50 4.00 10.00
BG Brian Giles/50 3.00 8.00
BS Ben Sheets/50 3.00 8.00
BU B.J. Upton/50 3.00 8.00
CA Rod Carew/50 4.00 10.00
CF Carlton Fisk/50 4.00 10.00
CH Chris Carpenter/50 3.00 8.00
CL Carlos Lee/50 3.00 8.00
CR Bobby Crosby/50 3.00 8.00
CY Carl Yastrzemski/50 6.00 15.00
DH Dan Haren/50 3.00 8.00
DJ Derek Jeter/50 10.00 25.00
DL Derrek Lee/50 3.00 8.00
DM Don Mattingly/50 6.00 15.00
DO David Ortiz/50 4.00 10.00
DW Dontrelle Willis/50 3.00 8.00
DW2 Dontrelle Willis/50 3.00 8.00
EC Eric Chavez/50 3.00 8.00
EC2 Eric Chavez/50 3.00 8.00
FH Felix Hernandez/50 4.00 10.00
FJ Fergie Jenkins/50 3.00 8.00
FL Francisco Liriano/50 4.00 10.00
FR Francisco Rodriguez/50 3.00 8.00
FT Frank Thomas/50 6.00 15.00
GA Garrett Atkins/50 3.00 8.00
GA2 Garrett Atkins/50 3.00 8.00
GR Khalil Greene/50 4.00 10.00
GW Tony Gwynn/50 4.00 10.00
HA Rich Harden/50 3.00 8.00
HP Hunter Pence/50 6.00 15.00
HR Hanley Ramirez/50 4.00 10.00
HS Huston Street/50 3.00 8.00
HS2 Huston Street/50 3.00 8.00
HU Tim Hudson/50 3.00 8.00
JA Jason Bay/50 3.00 8.00
JE Jeremy Bonderman/50 3.00 8.00
JG Jonny Gomes/50 3.00 8.00
JH Jeremy Hermida/50 3.00 8.00
JI Jim Palmer/50 4.00 10.00
JL John Lackey/50 3.00 8.00
JM Joe Mauer/50 4.00 10.00
JN Joe Nathan/50 3.00 8.00
JP Jake Peavy/50 3.00 8.00
JR Jim Rice/50 3.00 8.00
JS John Smoltz/50 4.00 10.00
JT Jim Thome/50 4.00 10.00
KG Ken Griffey Jr./50 6.00 15.00
KG2 Ken Griffey Jr./50 6.00 15.00
KM Kendry Morales/50 4.00 10.00
MA Daisuke Matsuzaka/50 30.00 60.00
MC Matt Cain/50 4.00 10.00
MH Matt Holliday/50 4.00 10.00
MH2 Matt Holliday/50 4.00 10.00
MI Miguel Cabrera/50 4.00 10.00
MI2 Miguel Cabrera/50 4.00 10.00
MO Justin Morneau/50 3.00 8.00
MO2 Justin Morneau/50 3.00 8.00
MS Mike Schmidt/50 6.00 15.00
MT Mark Teixeira/50 4.00 10.00
MY Michael Young/50 3.00 8.00
NM Nick Markakis/50 4.00 10.00
NR Nolan Ryan/50 12.50 30.00
OS Ozzie Smith/50 10.00 25.00
OS2 Ozzie Smith/50 10.00 25.00
PA Jonathan Papelbon/50 4.00 10.00
PF Prince Fielder/50 4.00 10.00
PK Paul Konerko/50 3.00 8.00
PM Paul Molitor/50 3.00 8.00
PN Phil Niekro/50 3.00 8.00
RA Roberto Alomar/50 6.00 15.00
RC Roger Clemens/50 6.00 15.00
RF Rollie Fingers/50 3.00 8.00
RH Roy Halladay/50 3.00 8.00
RI Cal Ripken Jr./50 15.00 40.00
RI2 Cal Ripken Jr./50 15.00 40.00
RJ Randy Johnson/50 4.00 10.00
RO Roy Oswalt/50 3.00 8.00
RS Ryne Sandberg/50 6.00 15.00
RW Rickie Weeks/50 3.00 8.00
RY Robin Yount/25
RZ Ryan Zimmerman/50 4.00 10.00
RZ2 Ryan Zimmerman/50 4.00 10.00
SK Scott Kazmir/50 4.00 10.00
SK2 Scott Kazmir/50 4.00 10.00
TG Tom Glavine/50 4.00 10.00
TH Torii Hunter/50 3.00 8.00
TR Travis Hafner/50 3.00 8.00
TR2 Travis Hafner/50 3.00 8.00
TT Troy Tulowitzki/50 4.00 10.00
VM Victor Martinez/50 3.00 8.00
WI Josh Willingham/50 3.00 8.00
WI2 Josh Willingham/50 3.00 8.00

2007 Ultimate Collection Ultimate Team Materials Patch

OVERALL GU ODDS ONE PER PACK
PRINT RUNS B/WN 19-25 COPIES PER
NO PRICING DUE TO SCARCITY

2007 Ultimate Collection Ultimate Team Materials Signatures

OVERALL AU ODDS ONE PER PACK
PRINT RUNS B/WN 1-10 COPIES PER
NO PRICING DUE TO SCARCITY
EXCHANGE DEADLINE 9/24/2009

2007 Ultimate Collection Ultimate Write of Passage

OVERALL AU ODDS ONE PER PACK
STATED PRINT RUN 60 SER.#'d SETS
NO PRICING DUE TO SCARCITY
EXCHANGE DEADLINE 9/24/2009
BH Jeff Baker AU 4.00 10.00
Matt Holliday/60
BR Ryan Braun AU 20.00 50.00
Scott Rolen/60
GR Alex Gordon AU 30.00 60.00
Alex Rodriguez/60
HS Cole Hamels AU 15.00 40.00
Johan Santana/60
IC Kei Igawa AU/60 15.00 40.00
IR Akinori Iwamura AU 15.00 40.00
Aramis Ramirez/60
KB Howie Kendrick AU 4.00 10.00
Craig Biggio/60
KJ Kevin Kouzmanoff AU 4.00 10.00
Chipper Jones/60
LZ Tim Lincecum AU 20.00 50.00
Barry Zito/60
MS Andrew Miller AU 12.50 30.00
C.C. Sabathia/60
PG Hunter Pence AU 30.00 60.00
Ken Griffey Jr./60
PK Glen Perkins AU 4.00 10.00
Scott Kazmir/60
QC Carlos Quentin AU 4.00 10.00
Carl Crawford/60
RF Hanley Ramirez AU 10.00 25.00
Rafael Furcal/60
SD Ryan Sweeney AU 4.00 10.00
Jermaine Dye/60
SS Jeremy Sowers AU 4.00 10.00
C.C. Sabathia/60
TD Curtis Thigpen AU 4.00 10.00
Carlos Delgado/60
TJ Troy Tulowitzki AU 15.00 40.00
Derek Jeter/60
UU B.J. Upton AU 4.00 10.00
Chase Utley/60
YG Delmon Young AU 6.00 15.00
Vladimir Guerrero/60

2005 Ultimate Signature

This 110-card set is composed of retired stars (1-50), active stars (51-100) and prospect autographs (101-110). Cards 1-100 are serial numbered to 825 copies and 101-110 are numbered to a mere 225 copies. The product was issued in three-card tin boxes of which carried a suggested retail price of $99.99. Each sealed hobby case contained 20 tins. The product went live at hobby shops nationwide on June 1st, 2005. Cards 101-193 were issued in February, 2006 within Upper Deck Update packs. Each of these Update cards is signed by the featured athlete and serial-numbered to 125 copies. Of note, the following cards do not exist: 113, 123, 126-127, 150, 163, 170 and 189.

COMMON CARD (1-50) 1.25 3.00
COMMON CARD (51-100) 1.25 3.00
1-100 PRINT RUN 825 SERIAL #'d SETS
COMMON AUTO (101-110) 4.00 10.00
AU MINORS 101-110 6.00 15.00
AU SEMIS101-110 10.00 25.00
AU UNLISTED 101-110 15.00 40.00
101-110 STATED ODDS 1:20
101-110 PRINT RUN 225 SERIAL #'d SETS
COMMON AUTO (111-193) 4.00 10.00
111-193 ODDS APPX 1:8 '05 UD UPDATE
111-193 PRINT RUN 125 SERIAL #'d SETS
113, 123, 126-127, 150, 163 DO NOT EXIST
170, 189 DO NOT EXIST
1 Al Kaline 2.00 5.00
2 Babe Ruth 4.00 10.00
3 Billy Williams 1.25 3.00
4 Bob Feller 2.00 5.00
5 Bob Gibson 2.00 5.00
6 Brooks Robinson 2.00 5.00
7 Carlton Fisk 2.00 5.00
8 Cy Young 2.00 5.00
9 Dizzy Dean 2.00 5.00
10 Don Drysdale 2.00 5.00
11 Eddie Mathews 2.00 5.00
12 Enos Slaughter 1.25 3.00
13 Ernie Banks 2.00 5.00
14 Fergie Jenkins 1.25 3.00
15 Eddie Murray 2.00 5.00
16 Harmon Killebrew 2.00 5.00
17 Honus Wagner 2.00 5.00
18 Jackie Robinson 2.00 5.00
19 Jimmie Foxx 2.00 5.00
20 Joe DiMaggio 3.00 8.00
21 Joe Morgan 1.25 3.00
22 Juan Marichal 1.25 3.00
23 Larry Doby 1.25 3.00
24 Jim Palmer 1.25 3.00
25 Johnny Bench 2.00 5.00
26 Lou Brock 2.00 5.00
27 Lou Gehrig 3.00 8.00
28 Mel Ott 2.00 5.00
29 Mickey Cochrane 1.25 3.00
30 Mickey Mantle 6.00 15.00
31 Mike Schmidt 4.00 10.00
32 Nolan Ryan 5.00 12.00
33 Pee Wee Reese 2.00 5.00
34 Phil Rizzuto 2.00 5.00
35 Ralph Kiner 1.25 3.00
36 Robin Yount 2.00 5.00
37 Ozzie Smith 3.00 8.00
38 Roy Campanella 2.00 5.00
39 Satchel Paige 2.00 5.00
40 Stan Musial 3.00 8.00
41 Ted Williams 3.00 8.00
42 Thurman Munson 2.00 5.00
43 Tom Seaver 2.00 5.00
44 Ty Cobb 3.00 8.00
45 Walter Johnson 2.00 5.00
46 Warren Spahn 2.00 5.00
47 Whitey Ford 2.00 5.00
48 Willie McCovey 2.00 5.00
49 Willie Stargell 2.00 5.00
50 Yogi Berra 2.00 5.00
51 Adrian Beltre 1.25 3.00
52 Albert Pujols 4.00 10.00
53 Alex Rodriguez 3.00 8.00
54 Alfonso Soriano 1.25 3.00
55 Andruw Jones 2.00 5.00
56 B.J. Upton 1.25 3.00
57 Ben Sheets 1.25 3.00
58 Bret Boone 1.25 3.00
59 Brian Giles 1.25 3.00
60 Carlos Beltran 1.25 3.00
61 Carlos Delgado 1.25 3.00
62 Chipper Jones 2.00 5.00
63 Curt Schilling 2.00 5.00
64 David Ortiz 2.00 5.00
65 Derek Jeter 4.00 10.00
66 Eric Chavez 1.25 3.00
67 Frank Thomas 2.00 5.00
68 Gary Sheffield 1.25 3.00
69 Greg Maddux 3.00 8.00
70 Hank Blalock 1.25 3.00
71 Hideki Matsui 3.00 8.00
72 Ichiro Suzuki 4.00 10.00
73 Ivan Rodriguez 2.00 5.00
74 Jason Schmidt 1.25 3.00
75 Jeff Bagwell 2.00 5.00
76 Jim Thome 2.00 5.00
77 Johnny Damon 2.00 5.00
78 Jose Vidro 1.25 3.00
79 Ken Griffey Jr. 3.00 8.00
80 Kerry Wood 1.25 3.00
81 Manny Ramirez 2.00 5.00
82 Mark Prior 2.00 5.00
83 Mark Teixeira 2.00 5.00
84 Miguel Cabrera 2.00 5.00
85 Miguel Tejada 1.25 3.00
86 Mike Mussina 2.00 5.00
87 Mike Piazza 2.00 5.00
88 Mike Sweeney 1.25 3.00
89 Oliver Perez 1.25 3.00
90 Pedro Martinez 2.00 5.00
91 Rafael Palmeiro 2.00 5.00
92 Randy Johnson 2.00 5.00
93 Roger Clemens 3.00 8.00
94 Sammy Sosa 2.00 5.00
95 Scott Rolen 2.00 5.00
96 Tim Hudson 1.25 3.00
97 Todd Helton 2.00 5.00
98 Torii Hunter 1.25 3.00
99 Victor Martinez 1.25 3.00
100 Vladimir Guerrero 2.00 5.00
101 Adrian Gonzalez AU 4.00 10.00
102 Ambiorix Burgos AU RC 4.00 10.00
103 Ambiorix Concepcion AU RC 4.00 10.00
104 Dan Meyer AU 4.00 10.00
105 Ervin Santana AU 6.00 15.00
106 Gavin Floyd AU 4.00 10.00
107 Joe Blanton AU 4.00 10.00
108 Eric Crozier AU 4.00 10.00
109 Mark Teahen AU 4.00 10.00
110 Ryan Howard AU 30.00 60.00
111 Adam Shabala AU RC 4.00 10.00
112 Anibal Sanchez AU RC 30.00 60.00
114 Brandon McCarthy AU RC 12.50 30.00
115 Brian Burres AU RC 4.00 10.00
116 Carlos Ruiz AU RC 6.00 15.00
117 Casey Rogowski AU RC 6.00 15.00
118 Chad Orvella AU RC 4.00 10.00
119 Chris Resop AU RC 6.00 15.00
120 Chris Roberson AU RC 4.00 10.00
121 Chris Seddon AU RC 4.00 10.00
122 Colter Bean AU RC 6.00 15.00
124 Dave Gassner AU RC 4.00 10.00
125 Brian Anderson AU RC 15.00 40.00
128 Devon Lowery AU RC 4.00 10.00
129 Enrique Gonzalez AU RC 6.00 15.00
130 Eude Brito AU RC 4.00 10.00
131 Francisco Butto AU RC 4.00 10.00
132 Franquelis Osoria AU RC 4.00 10.00
133 Garrett Jones AU RC 4.00 10.00
134 Geovany Soto AU RC 100.00 175.00
135 Hayden Penn AU RC 8.00 20.00
136 Ismael Ramirez AU RC 4.00 10.00
137 Jared Gothreaux AU RC 4.00 10.00
138 Jason Hammel AU RC 4.00 10.00
139 Jeff Miller AU RC 4.00 10.00
140 Jeff Niemann AU RC 8.00 20.00
141 Joel Peralta AU RC 4.00 10.00
142 John Hattig AU RC 4.00 10.00
143 Jorge Campillo AU RC 4.00 10.00
144 Juan Morillo AU RC 4.00 10.00
145 Justin Verlander AU RC 75.00 125.00
146 Ryan Garko AU RC 12.50 30.00
147 Keiichi Yabu AU RC 6.00 15.00
148 Kendry Morales AU RC 30.00 60.00
149 Luis Hernandez AU RC 4.00 10.00
151 Luis O.Rodriguez AU RC 4.00 10.00
152 Luke Scott AU RC 12.50 30.00
153 Marcos Carvajal AU RC 4.00 10.00
154 Mark Woodyard AU RC 4.00 10.00
155 Matt A.Smith AU RC 4.00 10.00
156 Matthew Lindstrom AU RC 4.00 10.00
157 Miguel Negron AU RC 6.00 15.00
158 Mike Morse AU RC 6.00 15.00
159 Nate McLouth AU RC 20.00 50.00
160 Nelson Cruz AU RC 12.50 30.00
161 Nick Masset AU RC 4.00 10.00
162 Mark McLemore AU RC 4.00 10.00
164 Paulino Reynoso AU RC 4.00 10.00
165 Pedro Lopez AU RC 4.00 10.00
166 Pete Orr AU RC 4.00 10.00
167 Philip Humber AU RC 12.50 30.00
168 Prince Fielder AU RC 100.00 200.00
169 Randy Messenger AU RC 4.00 10.00
171 Raul Tablado AU RC 4.00 10.00
172 Ronny Paulino AU RC 6.00 15.00
173 Russ Rohlicek AU RC 4.00 10.00
174 Russell Martin AU RC 30.00 60.00
175 Scott Baker AU RC 6.00 15.00
176 Scott Munter AU RC 4.00 10.00
177 Sean Thompson AU RC 4.00 10.00
178 Sean Tracey AU RC 4.00 10.00
179 Shane Costa AU RC 4.00 10.00
180 Stephen Drew AU RC 40.00 80.00
181 Steve Schmoll AU RC 4.00 10.00
182 Tadahito Iguchi AU RC 30.00 60.00
183 Tony Giarratano AU RC 4.00 10.00
184 Tony Pena AU RC 4.00 10.00
185 Travis Bowyer AU RC 4.00 10.00
186 Ubaldo Jimenez AU RC 15.00 40.00
187 Wladimir Balentien AU RC 8.00 20.00
188 Yorman Bazardo AU RC 4.00 10.00
190 Ryan Zimmerman AU RC 90.00 150.00
191 Chris Denorfia AU RC 6.00 15.00
192 Ryan Speier AU RC 4.00 10.00
193 Jermaine Van Buren AU 4.00 10.00

2005 Ultimate Signature Platinum

101-110 OVERALL AU ODDS 1:20
111-APPX AU ODDS 1:8 '05 UD UPDATE
STATED PRINT RUN 1 SERIAL #'d SET
NO PRICING DUE TO SCARCITY

2005 Ultimate Signature Cuts

OVERALL RARE CUT AU ODDS 1:644
STATED PRINT RUN 1 SERIAL #'d SET
NO PRICING DUE TO SCARCITY
BR Babe Ruth
SP Satchel Paige
TC Ty Cobb
WJ Walter Johnson

2005 Ultimate Signature Cy Young Dual Autograph

OVERALL DUAL AU ODDS 1:4
PRINT RUNS B/WN 15-250 COPIES PER
NO PRICING ON QTY OF 25 OR LESS
EXCHANGE DEADLINE 06/07/08
CG Roger Clemens
Tom Glavine/15
CM David Cone 125.00 200.00
Greg Maddux/35 EXCH
EG Dennis Eckersley 15.00 40.00
Eric Gagne/200
ES Dennis Eckersley 12.50 30.00
Bruce Sutter/250 EXCH
GF Ron Guidry 30.00 60.00
Whitey Ford/250
GM Bob Gibson 15.00 40.00
Denny McLain/175
JC Randy Johnson
Roger Clemens/15
JM Fergie Jenkins
Greg Maddux/25
LC Sparky Lyle 12.50 30.00
Steve Carlton/250
MJ Greg Maddux
Randy Johnson/15 EXCH
MS Denny McLain 30.00 60.00
Tom Seaver/100
NF Don Newcombe 20.00 50.00
Whitey Ford/125
PC Gaylord Perry 12.50 30.00
Steve Carlton/250
PS Jim Palmer 40.00 80.00
Tom Seaver/100
SM Greg Maddux
John Smoltz/25

2005 Ultimate Signature Cy Young Dual Autograph-Cut

OVERALL RARE CUT AU ODDS 1:644
PRINT RUNS B/WN 1-3 COPIES PER
NO PRICING DUE TO SCARCITY
CY Roger Clemens
Cy Young Cut/1
JD Randy Johnson
Don Drysdale Cut/3

2005 Ultimate Signature Cy Young Quad Autograph-Cut

OVERALL RARE CUT AU ODDS 1:644
STATED PRINT RUN 1 SERIAL #'d SET
NO PRICING DUE TO SCARCITY
CSSD Steve Carlton
Tom Seaver
Warren Spahn Cut
Don Drysdale Cut

2005 Ultimate Signature Cy Young Triple Autograph-Cut

OVERALL RARE CUT AU ODDS 1:644
STATED PRINT RUN 1 SERIAL #'d SET
NO PRICING DUE TO SCARCITY
JCY Randy Johnson
Roger Clemens
Cy Young Cut/1

2005 Ultimate Signature Decades

TIER 3 PRINT RUNS 350+ PER
TIER 2 PRINT RUNS B/WN 225-275 PER
TIER 1 PRINT RUNS B/WN 100-175 PER
SERIAL #'d PRINT RUNS B/WN 10-99 PER
NO PRICING ON QTY OF 25 OR LESS
TIER 1-3 PRINT RUN INFO PROVIDED BY UD

TIER 1-3 ARE NOT SERIAL-NUMBERED
STATED ODDS 3:5 TINS
PLATINUM OVERALL PREMIUM AU ODDS 1:5
PLATINUM PRINT RUN 1 SERIAL #'d SET
NO PLATINUM PRICING DUE TO SCARCITY
EXCHANGE DEADLINE 06/07/08

AD Andre Dawson T2 6.00 15.00
AK Al Kaline/99 20.00 50.00
AR Al Rosen T3 6.00 15.00
BD Bobby Doerr T3 6.00 15.00
BE Johnny Bench/15
BF Bob Feller T1 10.00 25.00
BG Bob Gibson/15
BJ Bo Jackson/50 40.00 80.00
BM Bill Mazeroski/99 15.00 40.00
BR Brooks Robinson T2 10.00 25.00
BS Ben Sheets T3 6.00 15.00
BU B.J. Upton T3 10.00 25.00
BW Billy Williams T2 6.00 15.00
CA Rod Carew/15
CB Carlos Beltran/99 EXCH 10.00 25.00
CF Carlton Fisk/15
CJ Chipper Jones/10
CL Roger Clemens/10
CR Cal Ripken/10 EXCH
CY Carl Yastrzemski/10
DE Dennis Eckersley T1 6.00 15.00
DJ Derek Jeter/99 100.00 175.00
DL Don Larsen/99 EXCH 10.00 25.00
DM Don Mattingly/25
DN Don Newcombe/99 10.00 25.00
DO David Ortiz T1 20.00 50.00
DS Duke Snider/10
EB Ernie Banks/10
FJ Fergie Jenkins/50 12.50 30.00
FL Fred Lynn T2 6.00 15.00
FR Frank Robinson/25
GB George Brett/10
GC Gary Carter/50 12.50 30.00
GK George Kell T3 6.00 15.00
GM Greg Maddux/10
GP Gaylord Perry Giants T3 6.00 15.00
GP1 Gaylord Perry Rgr T3 6.00 15.00
HK Harmon Killebrew/99 20.00 50.00
JB Jim Bunning T2 6.00 15.00
JC Jose Canseco/99 20.00 50.00
JM Juan Marichal/99 10.00 25.00
JP Jim Palmer T2 6.00 15.00
JR Jim Rice T2 6.00 15.00
JS Johan Santana T1 10.00 25.00
KG Ken Griffey Jr. T3 30.00 60.00
KH Keith Hernandez Cards T3 6.00 15.00
KH1 Keith Hernandez Mets T3 6.00 15.00
LA Luis Aparicio W.Sox T1 6.00 15.00
LA1 Luis Aparicio R.Sox T1 6.00 15.00
LB Lou Brock/50 20.00 50.00
LT Luis Tiant Twins T3 6.00 15.00
LT1 Luis Tiant Sox T3 6.00 15.00
MC Miguel Cabrera T2 10.00 25.00
MI Monte Irvin T3 6.00 15.00
MO Joe Morgan/50 12.50 30.00
MP Mike Piazza/10
MS Mike Schmidt/15
MT Mark Teixeira T3 10.00 25.00
MU Dale Murphy T3 10.00 25.00
MW Maury Wills T2 6.00 15.00
NG Nomar Garciaparra/10
NR Nolan Ryan Angels/10
NR1 Nolan Ryan Astros/10
OC Orlando Cepeda T2 6.00 15.00
PM Paul Molitor/99 10.00 25.00
PN Phil Niekro T2 6.00 15.00
RC Rocky Colavito Indians T1 30.00 60.00
RC1 Rocky Colavito Tigers T1 30.00 60.00
RF Rollie Fingers T2 6.00 15.00
RG Ron Guidry T3 10.00 25.00
RJ Randy Johnson/10
RK Ralph Kiner/99 15.00 40.00
RO Roy Oswalt T3 6.00 15.00
RS Ron Santo T2 10.00 25.00
RW Rickie Weeks T3 6.00 15.00
RY Robin Yount/25
SA Ryne Sandberg/15
SC Steve Carlton Cards T1 6.00 15.00
SC1 Steve Carlton Phils T1 6.00 15.00
SM Stan Musial/10
SU Don Sutton T1 6.00 15.00
TG Tony Gwynn/15
TP Tony Perez T2 6.00 15.00
TS Tom Seaver/10
WB Wade Boggs Sox/25
WB1 Wade Boggs Yanks/25
WC Will Clark/99 15.00 40.00
WF Whitey Ford/15
WM Willie McCovey/10
YB Yogi Berra/25

2005 Ultimate Signature Hits Dual Autograph

OVERALL DUAL AU ODDS 1:4
PRINT RUNS B/WN 15-125 COPIES PER
NO PRICING ON QTY OF 15
EXCHANGE DEADLINE 06/07/08

BM Lou Brock 60.00 120.00
Stan Musial/35
MY Paul Molitor 40.00 80.00
Robin Yount/125
RM Cal Ripken
Eddie Murray/15 EXCH
WG Dave Winfield 50.00 100.00
Tony Gwynn/35
YB Carl Yastrzemski 75.00 150.00
Wade Boggs/35

2005 Ultimate Signature Hits Dual Autograph-Cut

OVERALL RARE CUT AU ODDS 1:644
STATED PRINT RUN 1 SERIAL #'d SET
NO PRICING DUE TO SCARCITY

KC Al Kaline
Ty Cobb Cut/1
RW Cal Ripken
Honus Wagner Cut/1

2005 Ultimate Signature Hits Quad Autograph-Cut

OVERALL RARE CUT AU ODDS 1:644
STATED PRINT RUN 1 SERIAL #'d SET
NO PRICING DUE TO SCARCITY

RBCC Cal Ripken
George Brett
Roberto Clemente Cut
Ty Cobb Cut

2005 Ultimate Signature Hits Triple Autograph-Cut

OVERALL RARE CUT AU ODDS 1:644
STATED PRINT RUN 1 SERIAL #'d SET
NO PRICING DUE TO SCARCITY

GMW Tony Gwynn
Stan Musial
Honus Wagner Cut/1
YYC Robin Yount
Carl Yastrzemski
Roberto Clemente Cut/1

2005 Ultimate Signature Home Runs Dual Autograph

OVERALL DUAL AU ODDS 1:4
PRINT RUNS B/WN 15-250 COPIES PER
NO PRICING ON QTY OF 25 OR LESS
EXCHANGE DEADLINE 06/07/08

BS Ernie Banks
Mike Schmidt/25
GM Ken Griffey Jr. 50.00 100.00
Willie McCovey/250
KM Harmon Killebrew
Willie McCovey/35
MR Eddie Murray
Frank Robinson/15
RG Frank Robinson 50.00 100.00
Ken Griffey Jr./250 EXCH

2005 Ultimate Signature Home Runs Dual Autograph-Cut

OVERALL RARE CUT AU ODDS 1:644
STATED PRINT RUN 1 SERIAL #'d SET
NO PRICING DUE TO SCARCITY

GM Ken Griffey Jr.
Mickey Mantle Cut/1
MO Willie McCovey
Mel Ott Cut/1

2005 Ultimate Signature Home Runs Quad Autograph-Cut

OVERALL RARE CUT AU ODDS 1:644
STATED PRINT RUN 1 SERIAL #'d SET
NO PRICING DUE TO SCARCITY

GSWR Ken Griffey Jr.
Mike Schmidt
Ted Williams Cut
Babe Ruth Cut

2005 Ultimate Signature Home Runs Triple Autograph-Cut

OVERALL RARE CUT AU ODDS 1:644
PRINT RUNS B/WN 1-5 COPIES PER
NO PRICING DUE TO SCARCITY

KMM Ken Griffey Jr.
Willie McCovey
Eddie Mathews Cut/5
RKF Frank Robinson
Harmon Killebrew
Jimmie Foxx Cut/1

2005 Ultimate Signature Immortal Inscriptions

OVERALL PREMIUM SINGLE AU 1:5
PRINT RUNS B/WN 10-99 COPIES PER
NO PRICING ON QTY OF 25 OR LESS
PLATINUM OVERALL PREMIUM AU ODDS 1:5
PLATINUM PRINT RUN 1 SERIAL #'d SET
NO PLATINUM PRICING DUE TO SCARCITY

BR Brooks Robinson/99 40.00 80.00
Hoover
CR Cal Ripken/10
2632
DM D.Mattingly/75 150.00 250.00
Donnie Baseball
EG Eric Gagne/99 60.00 120.00
Game Over
FT Frank Thomas/50 100.00 200.00
Big Hurt
GC Gary Carter/15
The Kid
GM Greg Maddux/10
Mad Dog
JB Jim Bunning/99 40.00 80.00
Senator
KG Ken Griffey Jr./99 400.00 500.00
Junior
NR Nolan Ryan/10
The Ryan Express
OS Ozzie Smith/75 40.00 80.00
The Wizard
RC Roger Clemens/15
The Rocket
RJ Randy Johnson/10
Big Unit
SC Steve Carlton/99 20.00 50.00
Lefty
SM Stan Musial/25
HOF '69
TG Tony Gwynn/50 60.00 120.00
The Tiger
TS Tom Seaver/25
HOF 92
WB Wade Boggs/75 40.00 80.00
Chicken Man
WC Will Clark/99 40.00 80.00
The Thrill
WM Willie McCovey/15
HOF '86

2005 Ultimate Signature MVP's Dual Autograph

OVERALL DUAL AU ODDS 1:4
PRINT RUNS B/WN 15-250 COPIES PER
NO PRICING ON QTY OF 25 OR LESS
EXCHANGE DEADLINE 06/07/08

BM Don Mattingly 60.00 120.00
Yogi Berra/175
BS Ernie Banks
Ryne Sandberg/25
CM Orlando Cepeda 40.00 80.00
Stan Musial/100
DS Andre Dawson 40.00 80.00
Ryne Sandberg/175
EF Dennis Eckersley 12.50 30.00
Rollie Fingers/250
FC George Foster 20.00 50.00
Rod Carew/125 EXCH
GM Ken Griffey Jr. 50.00 100.00
Joe Morgan/250 EXCH
HY Keith Hernandez 20.00 50.00
Robin Yount/200
JR Chipper Jones 100.00 175.00
Ivan Rodriguez/35
KC Harmon Killebrew 40.00 80.00
Rod Carew/100
KM Harmon Killebrew
Willie McCovey/35
LM Fred Lynn 12.50 30.00
Joe Morgan/200
LW Barry Larkin 15.00 40.00
Maury Wills/250
MB Joe Morgan
Johnny Bench/100
MG Bob Gibson 15.00 40.00
Denny McLain/175
MY Dale Murphy 30.00 60.00
Robin Yount/175 EXCH
PR Dave Parker 15.00 40.00
Jim Rice/250
RM Cal Ripken
Dale Murphy/25
SB George Brett
Mike Schmidt/15
SF Mike Schmidt 30.00 60.00
Rollie Fingers/175
SS Mike Schmidt 100.00 175.00
Ryne Sandberg/75
TB Frank Thomas 60.00 120.00
Jeff Bagwell/50
YC Carl Yastrzemski 40.00 80.00
Orlando Cepeda/100
YS Carl Yastrzemski 40.00 80.00
Jim Rice/100

2005 Ultimate Signature MVP's Dual Autograph-Cut

OVERALL RARE CUT AU ODDS 1:644
PRINT RUNS B/WN 1-2 COPIES PER
NO PRICING DUE TO SCARCITY

MM Joe Morgan
Thurman Munson Cut/2
RG Cal Ripken
Lou Gehrig Cut/1

2005 Ultimate Signature MVPs Quad Autograph-Cut

OVERALL RARE CUT AU ODDS 1:644
STATED PRINT RUN 1 SERIAL #'d SET
NO PRICING DUE TO SCARCITY

JMMD Derek Jeter
Don Mattingly
Mickey Mantle Cut
Joe DiMaggio Cut

2005 Ultimate Signature MVPs Triple Autograph-Cut

OVERALL RARE CUT AU ODDS 1:644
STATED PRINT RUN 1 SERIAL #'d SET
NO PRICING DUE TO SCARCITY

RBC Ivan Rodriguez
Johnny Bench
Mickey Cochrane Cut/1
SMC Mike Schmidt
Stan Musial
Roy Campanella Cut/1

2005 Ultimate Signature No-Hitters Dual Autograph

OVERALL DUAL AU ODDS 1:4
PRINT RUNS B/WN 15-250 COPIES PER
NO PRICING ON QTY OF 25 OR LESS
EXCHANGE DEADLINE 06/07/08

BG Jim Bunning 20.00 50.00
Bob Gibson/125
CL David Cone 12.50 30.00
Don Larsen/250 EXCH
FR Bob Feller
Nolan Ryan/25
GP Bob Gibson 20.00 50.00
Jim Palmer/125
RJ Nolan Ryan
Randy Johnson/15

2005 Ultimate Signature No-Hitters Dual Autograph-Cut

OVERALL RARE CUT AU ODDS 1:644
PRINT RUNS B/WN 1-5 COPIES PER
NO PRICING DUE TO SCARCITY

FL Bob Feller
Bob Lemon Cut/5
RY Nolan Ryan
Cy Young Cut/1

2005 Ultimate Signature No-Hitters Quad Autograph-Cut

OVERALL RARE CUT AU ODDS 1:644
STATED PRINT RUN 1 SERIAL #'d SET
NO PRICING DUE TO SCARCITY

RJSJ Nolan Ryan
Randy Johnson
Warren Spahn Cut
Walter Johnson Cut

2005 Ultimate Signature No-Hitters Triple Autograph-Cut

OVERALL RARE CUT AU ODDS 1:644
STATED PRINT RUN 1 SERIAL #'d SET
NO PRICING DUE TO SCARCITY

PMH Gaylord Perry
Juan Marichal
Carl Hubbell Cut/1

2005 Ultimate Signature Numbers

OVERALL PREMIUM SINGLE AU 1:5
PRINT RUNS B/WN 1-49 COPIES PER
NO PRICING ON QTY OF 24 OR LESS
PLATINUM OVERALL PREMIUM AU ODDS 1:5
PLATINUM PRINT RUN 1 SERIAL #'d SET
NO PLATINUM PRICING DUE TO SCARCITY
EXCHANGE DEADLINE 06/07/08

AK Al Kaline/6
BE Johnny Bench/5
BF Bob Feller/19
BG Bob Gibson/45 20.00 50.00
BM Bill Mazeroski/9
BR Brooks Robinson/5
BS Ben Sheets/15
BW Billy Williams/26 12.50 30.00
CA Rod Carew/29 20.00 50.00
CB Carlos Beltran/15
CF Carlton Fisk/27 20.00 50.00
CJ Chipper Jones/10
CL Roger Clemens/22
CR Cal Ripken/8
CY Carl Yastrzemski/8
DJ Derek Jeter/2
DM Don Mattingly/23
DO David Ortiz/34 30.00 60.00
DS Duke Snider/4
DW Dave Winfield/31 20.00 50.00
EB Ernie Banks/14
EC Eric Chavez/3
EG Eric Gagne/38 EXCH 20.00 50.00
EM Eddie Murray/33 75.00 150.00
FJ Fergie Jenkins/31 12.50 30.00
FR Frank Robinson/20
FT Frank Thomas/35 40.00 80.00
GB George Brett/5
GC Gary Carter/8
GL Tom Glavine/47 20.00 50.00
GM Greg Maddux/31
HB Hank Blalock/9
HK Harmon Killebrew/3
IR Ivan Rodriguez/7
JB Jeff Bagwell/5
JC Jose Canseco/33 30.00 60.00
JM Joe Morgan/8
JP Jim Palmer/22
JR Jim Rice/14
JS John Smoltz/29 20.00 50.00
KG Ken Griffey Jr./30 75.00 150.00
KP Kirby Puckett/34 50.00 100.00
KW Kerry Wood/34 20.00 50.00
LA Luis Aparicio/11
LB Lou Brock/20
MA Juan Marichal/27 12.50 30.00
MC Miguel Cabrera/24
MI Monte Irvin/20
MM Mark Mulder/20
MP Mark Prior/22
MS Mike Schmidt/20
MT Mark Teixeira/23
NG Nomar Garciaparra/5
NR Nolan Ryan/34 75.00 150.00
OC Orlando Cepeda/30 12.50 30.00
OS Ozzie Smith/1
PI Mike Piazza/31 EXCH
PM Paul Molitor/4
RC Rocky Colavito/7
RF Rollie Fingers/34 12.50 30.00
RG Ron Guidry/49 20.00 50.00
RJ Randy Johnson/41 50.00 100.00
RK Ralph Kiner/4
RO Roy Oswalt/44 12.50 30.00
RS Ryne Sandberg/23
RY Robin Yount/19
SC Steve Carlton/32 12.50 30.00
SM Stan Musial/6
SR Scott Rolen/27 20.00 50.00
TE Miguel Tejada/10
TG Tony Gwynn/19
TH Tim Hudson/15
TP Tony Perez/24
TS Tom Seaver/41 30.00 60.00
VG Vladimir Guerrero/27 30.00 60.00
WB Wade Boggs/26 20.00 50.00
WC Will Clark/22
WF Whitey Ford/16
WM Willie McCovey/44 20.00 50.00
YB Yogi Berra/8

2005 Ultimate Signature ROY Dual Autograph

OVERALL DUAL AU ODDS 1:4
PRINT RUNS B/WN 15-250 COPIES PER
NO PRICING ON QTY OF 25 OR LESS
EXCHANGE DEADLINE 06/07/08

BP Johnny Bench
Mike Piazza/15
BR Jeff Bagwell
Scott Rolen/15
CM Orlando Cepeda 30.00 60.00
Willie McCovey/75
CS Rod Carew
Tom Seaver/25
DM Andre Dawson
Eddie Murray/25
FB Carlton Fisk 50.00 100.00
Johnny Bench/35
FL Carlton Fisk 20.00 50.00
Fred Lynn/125
GR Nomar Garciaparra 30.00 60.00
Scott Rolen/200 EXCH
GS Tom Seaver 30.00 60.00
Dwight Gooden/100 EXCH
JG Derek Jeter 200.00 300.00
Nomar Garciaparra/75
RA Frank Robinson 20.00 50.00
Luis Aparicio/125
RJ Cal Ripken 300.00 450.00
Derek Jeter/75
RR Cal Ripken
Frank Robinson/20 EXCH
SG Darryl Strawberry 15.00 40.00
Dwight Gooden/250
WD Billy Williams 15.00 40.00
Andre Dawson/250

2005 Ultimate Signature ROY Dual Autograph-Cut

OVERALL RARE CUT AU ODDS 1:644
STATED PRINT RUN 3 SERIAL #'d SETS
NO PRICING DUE TO SCARCITY

JM Derek Jeter
Thurman Munson Cut/3
RR Frank Robinson
Jackie Robinson Cut/3

2005 Ultimate Signature ROY Quad Autograph-Cut

OVERALL RARE CUT AU ODDS 1:644
STATED PRINT RUN 1 SERIAL #'d SET
NO PRICING DUE TO SCARCITY

JPMR Derek Jeter
Mike Piazza
Thurman Munson Cut
Jackie Robinson Cut

2005 Ultimate Signature ROY Triple Autograph-Cut

OVERALL RARE CUT AU ODDS 1:644
STATED PRINT RUN 3 SERIAL #'d SETS
NO PRICING DUE TO SCARCITY

PNR Mike Piazza
Don Newcombe
Jackie Robinson Cut/3

2005 Ultimate Signature Signs of October Dual Autograph

OVERALL DUAL AU ODDS 1:4
PRINT RUNS B/WN 15-250 COPIES PER
NO PRICING ON QTY OF 25 OR LESS
EXCHANGE DEADLINE 06/07/08

BS George Brett
Mike Schmidt/15
BW Bill Buckner 15.00 40.00
Mookie Wilson/250 EXCH
CS Joe Carter 15.00 40.00
John Smoltz/250 EXCH
EG Dennis Eckersley 30.00 60.00
Kirk Gibson/200
FM Carlton Fisk 20.00 50.00
Joe Morgan/100
GB Bob Gibson 30.00 60.00
Lou Brock/100
GG Steve Garvey 15.00 40.00
Ron Guidry/250
GL Bob Gibson 20.00 50.00
Mickey Lolich/100
JC Randy Johnson
Roger Clemens/15
JG Derek Jeter 125.00 200.00
Tony Gwynn/250
LB Don Larsen 50.00 100.00
Yogi Berra/250
MP Jack Morris 50.00 100.00
Kirby Puckett/100
PC Mike Piazza
Roger Clemens/15
PS Kirby Puckett 125.00 200.00
Ozzie Smith/35
RM Cal Ripken
Eddie Murray/15
RR Brooks Robinson 30.00 60.00
Frank Robinson/250
SB Ozzie Smith
George Brett/25
SY Ozzie Smith 40.00 80.00
Robin Yount/100
TG Alan Trammell 12.50 30.00
Kirk Gibson/250

2005 Ultimate Signature Signs of October Dual Autograph-Cut

OVERALL RARE CUT AU ODDS 1:644
PRINT RUNS B/WN 4-5 COPIES PER
NO PRICING DUE TO SCARCITY

DJ Derek Jeter
Joe DiMaggio Cut/5
SM Duke Snider
Mickey Mantle Cut/6

2005 Ultimate Signature Signs of October Quad Autograph-Cut

OVERALL RARE CUT AU ODDS 1:644
STATED PRINT RUN 1 SERIAL #'d SET
NO PRICING DUE TO SCARCITY

JMMR Derek Jeter
Don Mattingly
Mickey Mantle Cut
Babe Ruth Cut

2005 Ultimate Signature Signs of October Triple Autograph-Cut

OVERALL RARE CUT AU ODDS 1:644
STATED PRINT RUN 1 SERIAL #'d SET
NO PRICING DUE TO SCARCITY

GMD Bob Gibson
Stan Musial
Dizzy Dean Cut/1
MKC Bill Mazeroski
Ralph Kiner
Roberto Clemente Cut/1

2005 Ultimate Signature Supremacy

OVERALL PREMIUM SINGLE AU 1:5
PRINT RUNS B/WN 15-99 COPIES PER
NO PRICING ON QTY OF 25 OR LESS
EXCHANGE DEADLINE 06/07/08

AD Andre Dawson/99 10.00 25.00
AK Al Kaline/50 30.00 60.00
AR Al Rosen/99 10.00 25.00
AS Alfonso Soriano/25
BD Bobby Doerr/99 10.00 25.00
BE Johnny Bench/25
BF Bob Feller/99 15.00 40.00
BG Bob Gibson/25
BM Bill Mazeroski/50 20.00 50.00
BR Brooks Robinson/99 15.00 40.00
BS Ben Sheets/99 10.00 25.00
BU Jim Bunning/99 10.00 25.00
BW Billy Williams/99 10.00 25.00
CA Rod Carew/25
CB Carlos Beltran/50 EXCH 12.50 30.00
CF Carlton Fisk/25
CJ Chipper Jones/25
CL Roger Clemens/15
CR Cal Ripken/15 EXCH
CY Carl Yastrzemski/25
DJ Derek Jeter/50 150.00 250.00
DM Dale Murphy/99 15.00 40.00
DN Don Newcombe/99 10.00 25.00
DO David Ortiz/99 20.00 50.00
DS Duke Snider/20
DW Dave Winfield/25
EB Ernie Banks/20
EC Eric Chavez/99 10.00 25.00
EG Eric Gagne/50 20.00 50.00
EM Eddie Murray/15
FJ Fergie Jenkins/25
FR Frank Robinson/25
FT Frank Thomas/25
GB George Brett/15
GC Gary Carter/25
GK George Kell/99 10.00 25.00
GM Greg Maddux/15
HB Hank Blalock/50 12.50 30.00
HK Harmon Killebrew/50 30.00 60.00
IR Ivan Rodriguez/25
JB Jeff Bagwell/25
JC Jose Canseco/25
JM Joe Morgan/25
JP Jim Palmer/99 10.00 25.00
JR Jim Rice/99 10.00 25.00
JS Johan Santana/99 15.00 40.00
JU Juan Marichal/25
KG Ken Griffey Jr./99 50.00 100.00
KP Kirby Puckett/20
KW Kerry Wood/25
LA Luis Aparicio/50 12.50 30.00
LB Lou Brock/25
MA Don Mattingly/25

MC Miguel Cabrera/99 15.00 40.00
MI Monte Irvin/99 10.00 25.00
MM Mark Mulder/99 10.00 25.00
MP Mark Prior/25
MS Mike Schmidt/25
MT Mark Teixeira/99 15.00 40.00
MU Stan Musial/25
NG Nomar Garciaparra/15
NR Nolan Ryan/15
OC Orlando Cepeda/99 10.00 25.00
OS Ozzie Smith/25
PI Mike Piazza/15
PM Paul Molitor/50 12.50 30.00
RC Rocky Colavito/25
RF Rollie Fingers/99 10.00 25.00
RG Ron Guidry/99 15.00 40.00
RJ Randy Johnson/15
RK Ralph Kiner/25
RO Roy Oswalt/99 10.00 25.00
RR Robin Roberts/99 10.00 25.00
RS Ron Santo/99 15.00 40.00
RY Robin Yount/25 EXCH
SA Ryne Sandberg/25
SC Steve Carlton/99 10.00 25.00
SM John Smoltz/50 20.00 50.00
SR Scott Rolen/25
TE Miguel Tejada/25
TG Tony Gwynn/25
TH Tim Hudson/50 20.00 50.00
TP Tony Perez/99 10.00 25.00
TS Tom Seaver/25
VG Vladimir Guerrero/20 EXCH
WB Wade Boggs/25
WC Will Clark/50 20.00 50.00
WF Whitey Ford/25
WM Willie McCovey/20
YB Yogi Berra/25

1999 Ultimate Victory

The 1999 Upper Deck Ultimate Victory Product was issued late in 1999. The cards were distributed in five card packs with a SRP of $2.99 per pack and each box had 24 packs in it. The set, consisting of 180 cards has 120 cards printed in normal quantites and 60 short prints. The cards from 121 through 150 feature players in their rookie campaign and cards numbered 151 through 180 all feature Mark McGwire in a set entitled "McGwire's Magic". Cards 121-180 were all released at a rate of one in four. Rookie Cards of Rick Ankiel, Josh Beckett, Pat Burrell, Freddy Garcia, Tim Hudson, Eric Munson, and Alfonso Soriano are all included in this set.

COMPLETE SET (180) 90.00 150.00
COMP.SET w/o SP's (120) 10.00 25.00
COMMON CARD (1-120) .10 .30
COMMON SP (121-150) .75 2.00
COMMON (151-180) .75 2.00
1 Troy Glaus .20 .50
2 Tim Salmon .20 .50
3 Mo Vaughn .10 .30
4 Garret Anderson .10 .30
5 Darin Erstad .10 .30
6 Randy Johnson .30 .75
7 Matt Williams .10 .30
8 Travis Lee .10 .30
9 Jay Bell .10 .30
10 Steve Finley .10 .30
11 Luis Gonzalez .10 .30
12 Greg Maddux .50 1.25
13 Chipper Jones .30 .75
14 Javy Lopez .10 .30
15 Tom Glavine .20 .50
16 John Smoltz .20 .50
17 Cal Ripken 1.00 2.50
18 Charles Johnson .10 .30
19 Albert Belle .10 .30
20 Mike Mussina .20 .50
21 Pedro Martinez .20 .50
22 Nomar Garciaparra .50 1.25
23 Jose Offerman .10 .30
24 Sammy Sosa .30 .75
25 Mark Grace .20 .50
26 Kerry Wood .10 .30
27 Frank Thomas .30 .75
28 Ray Durham .10 .30
29 Paul Konerko .10 .30
30 Pete Harnisch .10 .30
31 Greg Vaughn .10 .30
32 Sean Casey .10 .30
33 Manny Ramirez .20 .50
34 Jim Thome .20 .50
35 Sandy Alomar Jr. .10 .30
36 Roberto Alomar .20 .50
37 Travis Fryman .10 .30
38 Kenny Lofton .10 .30
39 Omar Vizquel .20 .50
40 Larry Walker .10 .30
41 Todd Helton .20 .50
42 Vinny Castilla .10 .30
43 Tony Clark .10 .30
44 Juan Encarnacion .10 .30
45 Dean Palmer .10 .30
46 Damion Easley .10 .30
47 Mark Kotsay .10 .30
48 Cliff Floyd .10 .30
49 Jeff Bagwell .20 .50
50 Ken Caminiti .10 .30
51 Craig Biggio .20 .50
52 Moises Alou .10 .30
53 Johnny Damon .20 .50
54 Larry Sutton .10 .30
55 Kevin Brown .20 .50
56 Adrian Beltre .10 .30
57 Raul Mondesi .10 .30
58 Gary Sheffield .10 .30
59 Jeromy Burnitz .10 .30
60 Sean Berry .10 .30
61 Jeff Cirillo .10 .30
62 Brad Radke .10 .30
63 Todd Walker .10 .30
64 Matt Lawton .10 .30
65 Vladimir Guerrero .30 .75
66 Rondell White .10 .30
67 Dustin Hermanson .10 .30
68 Mike Piazza .50 1.25
69 Rickey Henderson .30 .75
70 Robin Ventura .10 .30
71 John Olerud .10 .30
72 Derek Jeter .75 2.00
73 Roger Clemens .60 1.50
74 Orlando Hernandez .10 .30
75 Paul O'Neill .20 .50
76 Bernie Williams .20 .50
77 Chuck Knoblauch .10 .30
78 Tino Martinez .20 .50
79 Jason Giambi .10 .30
80 Ben Grieve .10 .30
81 Matt Stairs .10 .30
82 Scott Rolen .20 .50
83 Ron Gant .10 .30
84 Bobby Abreu .10 .30
85 Curt Schilling .10 .30
86 Brian Giles .10 .30
87 Jason Kendall .10 .30
88 Kevin Young .10 .30
89 Mark McGwire .75 2.00
90 Fernando Tatis .10 .30
91 Ray Lankford .10 .30
92 Eric Davis .10 .30
93 Tony Gwynn .40 1.00
94 Reggie Sanders .10 .30
95 Wally Joyner .10 .30
96 Trevor Hoffman .10 .30
97 Robb Nen .10 .30
98 Barry Bonds .75 2.00
99 Jeff Kent .10 .30
100 J.T. Snow .10 .30
101 Ellis Burks .10 .30
102 Ken Griffey Jr. .50 1.25
103 Alex Rodriguez .50 1.25
104 Jay Buhner .10 .30
105 Edgar Martinez .20 .50
106 David Bell .10 .30
107 Bobby Smith .10 .30
108 Wade Boggs .20 .50
109 Fred McGriff .20 .50
110 Rolando Arrojo .10 .30
111 Jose Canseco .20 .50
112 Ivan Rodriguez .20 .50
113 Juan Gonzalez .10 .30
114 Rafael Palmeiro .20 .50
115 Rusty Greer .10 .30
116 Todd Zeile .10 .30
117 Jose Cruz Jr. .10 .30
118 Carlos Delgado .10 .30
119 Shawn Green .10 .30
120 David Wells .10 .30
121 Eric Munson SP RC 1.25 3.00
122 Lance Berkman SP 1.25 3.00
123 Ed Yarnall SP .75 2.00
124 Jacque Jones SP 1.25 3.00
125 K.Farnsworth SP RC 1.25 3.00
126 Ryan Rupe SP RC .75 2.00
127 Jeff Weaver SP RC 2.00 5.00
128 Gabe Kapler SP 1.25 3.00
129 Alex Gonzalez SP .75 2.00
130 Randy Wolf SP .75 2.00
131 Ben Davis SP .75 2.00
132 Carlos Beltran SP 2.00 5.00
133 Jim Morris SP RC 2.00 5.00
134 J.Zimmerman SP RC 1.25 3.00
135 Bruce Aven SP .75 2.00
136 A.Soriano SP RC 12.50 30.00
137 Tim Hudson SP RC 5.00 12.00
138 Josh Beckett SP RC 15.00 40.00
139 Michael Barrett SP .75 2.00
140 Eric Chavez SP 1.25 3.00
141 Pat Burrell SP RC 6.00 15.00
142 Kris Benson SP .75 2.00
143 J.D. Drew SP 1.25 3.00
144 Matt Clement SP 1.25 3.00
145 Rick Ankiel SP RC 12.50 30.00
146 Vernon Wells SP 1.25 3.00
147 Ruben Mateo SP UER .75 2.00
Card is misnumbered
148 Roy Halladay SP 1.25 3.00
149 Joe McEwing SP RC 1.25 3.00
150 Freddy Garcia SP RC 3.00 8.00
151 Mark McGwire MM .75 2.00
152 Mark McGwire MM .75 2.00
153 Mark McGwire MM .75 2.00
154 Mark McGwire MM .75 2.00
155 Mark McGwire MM .75 2.00
156 Mark McGwire MM .75 2.00
157 Mark McGwire MM .75 2.00
158 Mark McGwire MM .75 2.00
159 Mark McGwire MM .75 2.00
160 Mark McGwire MM .75 2.00
161 Mark McGwire MM .75 2.00
162 Mark McGwire MM .75 2.00
163 Mark McGwire MM .75 2.00
164 Mark McGwire MM .75 2.00
165 Mark McGwire MM .75 2.00
166 Mark McGwire MM .75 2.00
167 Mark McGwire MM .75 2.00
168 Mark McGwire MM .75 2.00
169 Mark McGwire MM .75 2.00
170 Mark McGwire MM .75 2.00
171 Mark McGwire MM .75 2.00
172 Mark McGwire MM .75 2.00
173 Mark McGwire MM .75 2.00
174 Mark McGwire MM .75 2.00
175 Mark McGwire MM .75 2.00
176 Mark McGwire MM .75 2.00
177 Mark McGwire MM .75 2.00
178 Mark McGwire MM .75 2.00
179 Mark McGwire MM .75 2.00
180 Mark McGwire MM .75 2.00

1999 Ultimate Victory Parallel

Inserted at a rate of one in 12, these card parallel the regular set. They can be differentiated from the regular cards with the addition of linear holographic foil on each card.

*STARS 1-120: 2X TO 5X BASIC CARDS
*PARALLEL 121-150: .6X TO 1.5X BASIC
*PARALLEL 121-150: .6X TO 1.5X BASIC RC
136 Alfonso Soriano 40.00 80.00
138 Josh Beckett 15.00 40.00
145 Rick Ankiel 100.00 200.00

1999 Ultimate Victory Parallel 100

Randomly inserted into packs, these cards parallel the regular Ultimate Victory set. They feature silver holographic foil in trippy circular patterns and are sequentially numbered to 100 on the front.

*PAR.100 1-120: 5X TO 12X BASIC
*PAR.100 121-150: 1.5X TO 4X BASIC
*PAR.100 121-150: 2X TO 4X BASIC RC
*MCGWIRE 151-180: 3X TO 8X BASIC
136 Alfonso Soriano 100.00 200.00
138 Josh Beckett 50.00 100.00
145 Rick Ankiel 200.00 300.00

1999 Ultimate Victory Bleacher Reachers

Inserted one every 23 packs, these horizontal cards feature 11 players who are among baseball's leading sluggers.

COMPLETE SET (11) 25.00 50.00
BR1 Ken Griffey Jr. 1.50 4.00
BR2 Mark McGwire 2.50 6.00
BR3 Sammy Sosa 1.00 2.50
BR4 Barry Bonds 2.50 6.00
BR5 Nomar Garciaparra 1.50 4.00
BR6 Juan Gonzalez .40 1.00
BR7 Jose Canseco .60 1.50
BR8 Manny Ramirez .60 1.50
BR9 Mike Piazza 1.50 4.00
BR10 Jeff Bagwell .60 1.50
BR11 Alex Rodriguez 1.50 4.00

1999 Ultimate Victory Fame-Used Memorabilia

Randomly inserted into packs, these cards feature pieces of bats used by the four inductees into the Hall of Fame in 1999. Similar to the other bat cards Upper Deck has produced, approximately 350 of each card were made. There was also a special card made with bat pieces of all four of these players. Ninety-nine copies of that combo card were produced.

GB George Brett 10.00 25.00
NR Nolan Ryan 15.00 40.00
OC Orlando Cepeda 4.00 10.00
RY Robin Yount 6.00 15.00
HOF Nolan Ryan 60.00 120.00
George Brett
Robin Yount
Orlando Cepeda

1999 Ultimate Victory Frozen Ropes

Inserted one every 23 packs, these 10 cards feature players who consistently are among the best in the majors.

COMPLETE SET (10) 25.00 50.00
F1 Ken Griffey Jr. 1.50 4.00
F2 Mark McGwire 2.50 6.00
F3 Sammy Sosa 1.00 2.50
F4 Derek Jeter 2.50 6.00
F5 Tony Gwynn 1.25 3.00
F6 Nomar Garciaparra 1.50 4.00
F7 Alex Rodriguez 1.50 4.00
F8 Mike Piazza 1.50 4.00
F9 Mo Vaughn .40 1.00
F10 Craig Biggio .60 1.50

1999 Ultimate Victory STATure

Inserted one every six packs, these fifteen cards featured players who are among the statistical leaders.

COMPLETE SET (15) 12.50 25.00
S1 Ken Griffey Jr. .50 1.25
S2 Mark McGwire .75 2.00
S3 Sammy Sosa .30 .75
S4 Nomar Garciaparra .50 1.25
S5 Roger Clemens .60 1.50
S6 Greg Maddux .50 1.25
S7 Alex Rodriguez .50 1.25
S8 Derek Jeter .75 2.00
S9 Juan Gonzalez .10 .30
S10 Manny Ramirez .20 .50
S11 Mike Piazza .50 1.25
S12 Tony Gwynn .40 1.00
S13 Chipper Jones .30 .75
S14 Pedro Martinez .20 .50
S15 Frank Thomas .30 .75

1999 Ultimate Victory Tribute 1999

Inserted one every 11 packs, this set honors the four inductees into the Hall of Fame in 1999. Card backs carry a "T" prefix.

COMPLETE SET (4) 7.50 15.00
T1 Nolan Ryan 2.50 6.00
T2 Robin Yount 1.50 4.00
T3 George Brett 2.50 6.00
T4 Orlando Cepeda .60 1.50

1999 Ultimate Victory Ultimate Competitors

Inserted one every 23 packs, this 12 card set highlights the players who bring an winning attitude to the ballpark every day.

COMPLETE SET (12) 30.00 60.00
U1 Ken Griffey Jr. 2.00 5.00
U2 Roger Clemens 2.50 6.00
U3 Scott Rolen .75 2.00
U4 Greg Maddux 2.00 5.00
U5 Mark McGwire 3.00 8.00
U6 Derek Jeter 3.00 8.00
U7 Randy Johnson 1.25 3.00
U8 Cal Ripken 4.00 10.00
U9 Craig Biggio .75 2.00
U10 Kevin Brown .75 2.00
U11 Chipper Jones 1.25 3.00
U12 Vladimir Guerrero 1.25 3.00

1999 Ultimate Victory Ultimate Hit Men

Inserted one every 23 packs, this eight card set features players who were among the leading contenders for the 1999 batting titles in their respective leagues.

COMPLETE SET (8) 15.00 30.00
H1 Tony Gwynn 1.00 2.50
H2 Cal Ripken 2.50 6.00
H3 Wade Boggs .50 1.25
H4 Larry Walker .30 .75
H5 Alex Rodriguez 1.25 3.00
H6 Derek Jeter 2.00 5.00
H7 Ivan Rodriguez .50 1.25
H8 Ken Griffey Jr. 1.25 3.00

2000 Ultimate Victory

The 2000 Upper Deck Ultimate Victory product was released in October, 2000. The set features 120 cards broken into tiers as follows: 90 veterans (1-90), 10 Rookies serial numbered to 3500, 10 Rookies serial numbered to 2500, and 10 Rookies serial numbered to 1000. Each pack contained five cards and carried a suggested retail price of $3.99.

COMP.SET w/o SP's (90) 10.00 25.00
COMMON CARD (1-90) .10 .30
1 Mo Vaughn .10 .30
2 Darin Erstad .10 .30
3 Troy Glaus .10 .30
4 Adam Kennedy .10 .30
5 Jason Giambi .10 .30
6 Ben Grieve .10 .30
7 Terrence Long .10 .30
8 Tim Hudson .10 .30
9 David Wells .10 .30
10 Carlos Delgado .10 .30
11 Shannon Stewart .10 .30
12 Greg Vaughn .10 .30
13 Gerald Williams .10 .30
14 Manny Ramirez .20 .50
15 Roberto Alomar .20 .50
16 Jim Thome .20 .50
17 Edgar Martinez .20 .50
18 Alex Rodriguez .50 1.25
19 Matt Riley .10 .30
20 Cal Ripken 1.00 2.50
21 Mike Mussina .20 .50
22 Albert Belle .10 .30
23 Ivan Rodriguez .20 .50
24 Rafael Palmeiro .20 .50
25 Nomar Garciaparra .50 1.25
26 Pedro Martinez .20 .50
27 Carl Everett .10 .30
28 Tomokazu Ohka RC .10 .30
29 Jermaine Dye .10 .30
30 Johnny Damon .20 .50
31 Dean Palmer .10 .30
32 Juan Gonzalez .10 .30
33 Eric Milton .10 .30
34 Matt Lawton .10 .30
35 Frank Thomas .30 .75
36 Paul Konerko .10 .30
37 Magglio Ordonez .10 .30
38 Jon Garland .10 .30
39 Derek Jeter .75 2.00
40 Roger Clemens .60 1.50
41 Bernie Williams .20 .50
42 Nick Johnson .10 .30
43 Julio Lugo .10 .30
44 Jeff Bagwell .20 .50
45 Richard Hidalgo .10 .30
46 Chipper Jones .30 .75
47 Greg Maddux .50 1.25
48 Andruw Jones .20 .50
49 Andres Galarraga .10 .30
50 Rafael Furcal .10 .30
51 Jeromy Burnitz .10 .30
52 Geoff Jenkins .10 .30
53 Mark McGwire .75 2.00
54 Jim Edmonds .10 .30
55 Rick Ankiel .10 .30
56 Sammy Sosa .30 .75
57 Julio Zuleta RC .10 .30
58 Kerry Wood .10 .30
59 Randy Johnson .30 .75
60 Matt Williams .10 .30
61 Steve Finley .10 .30
62 Gary Sheffield .10 .30
63 Kevin Brown .10 .30
64 Shawn Green .10 .30
65 Milton Bradley .10 .30
66 Vladimir Guerrero .30 .75
67 Jose Vidro .10 .30
68 Barry Bonds .75 2.00
69 Jeff Kent .10 .30
70 Preston Wilson .10 .30
71 Mike Lowell .10 .30
72 Mike Piazza .50 1.25
73 Robin Ventura .10 .30
74 Edgardo Alfonzo .10 .30
75 Jay Payton .10 .30
76 Tony Gwynn .40 1.00
77 Adam Eaton .10 .30
78 Phil Nevin .10 .30
79 Scott Rolen .20 .50
80 Bob Abreu .10 .30
81 Pat Burrell .10 .30
82 Brian Giles .10 .30
83 Jason Kendall .10 .30
84 Kris Benson .10 .30
85 Gookie Dawkins .10 .30
86 Ken Griffey Jr. .50 1.25
87 Barry Larkin .20 .50
88 Larry Walker .10 .30
89 Todd Helton .20 .50
90 Ben Petrick .10 .30
91 Alex Cabrera/3500 RC 1.50 4.00
92 M.Wheatland/1000 RC 4.00 10.00
93 Joe Torres/1000 RC 4.00 10.00
94 Xavier Nady/1000 RC 5.00 12.00
95 Kenny Kelly/3500 RC 1.50 4.00
96 Matt Ginter/3500 RC 1.50 4.00
97 Ben Diggins/1000 RC 4.00 10.00
98 Danys Baez/3500 RC 1.50 4.00
99 Daylan Holt/2500 RC 2.00 5.00
100 K.Sasaki/3500 RC 2.00 5.00
101 D.Artman/2500 RC 2.00 5.00
102 Mike Tonis/1000 RC 4.00 10.00
103 Timo Perez/2500 RC 2.00 5.00
104 Barry Zito/2500 RC 5.00 12.00
105 Koyie Hill/2500 RC 2.00 5.00
106 B.Wilkerson/2500 RC 3.00 8.00
107 Juan Pierre/3500 RC 2.00 5.00
108 A.McNeal/3500 RC 1.50 4.00
109 J.Spurgeon/3500 RC 1.50 4.00
110 Sean Burnett/1000 RC 4.00 10.00
111 Luis Matos/3500 RC 1.50 4.00
112 Dave Krynzel/1000 RC 4.00 10.00
113 Scott Heard/1000 RC 4.00 10.00
114 Ben Sheets/2500 RC 3.00 8.00
115 D.Sardinha/1000 RC 4.00 10.00
116 D.Espinosa/1000 RC 4.00 10.00
117 Leo Estrella/3500 RC 1.50 4.00
118 K.Ainsworth/2500 RC 2.00 5.00
119 Jon Rauch/2500 RC 2.00 5.00
120 R.Franklin/2500 RC 2.00 5.00

2000 Ultimate Victory Parallel 25

Randomly inserted into packs, this 120-card insert is a complete parallel of the base set. They can be differentiated from the regular cards with the addition of gold foil on each card. Each card is serial numbered to 25. Pricing for the rookie subset cards 91-120 is not provided due to volatility.

*STARS 1-90: 15X TO 40X BASIC 1-90

2000 Ultimate Victory Parallel 100

Randomly inserted into packs, this 120-card insert is a complete parallel of the base set. They can be differentiated from the regular cards with the addition of red foil on each card. Each card is serial numbered to 100.

*STARS 1-90: 8X TO 20X BASIC 1-90
*ROOKIES 1-90: 10X TO 25X BASIC 1-90
*TIER 1 91-120: .4X TO 1X BASIC RC 1000
*TIER 2 91-120: .75X TO 2X BASIC 2500
*TIER 3 91-120: 1X TO 2.5X BASIC 3500

2000 Ultimate Victory Parallel 250

Randomly inserted into packs, this 120-card insert is a complete parallel of the base set. They can be differentiated from the regular cards with the addition of silver foil on each card. Each card is serial numbered to 250.

*STARS 1-90: 3X TO 8X BASIC 1-90
*ROOKIES 1-90: 6X TO 15X BASIC 1-90
*TIER 1 91-120: .2X TO .5X BASIC 1000
*TIER 2 91-120: .4X TO 1X BASIC 2500
*TIER 3 91-120: .6X TO 1.5X BASIC 3500

2000 Ultimate Victory Diamond Dignitaries

Randomly inserted into packs at one in 23, this 10-card insert set features players that are leaders on the playing field. Card backs carry a "D" prefix.

COMPLETE SET (10) 25.00 60.00
D1 Ken Griffey Jr. 2.50 6.00
D2 Nomar Garciaparra 2.50 6.00
D3 Chipper Jones 1.50 4.00
D4 Ivan Rodriguez 1.00 2.50
D5 Mark McGwire 4.00 10.00

D6 Cal Ripken 5.00 12.00
D7 Vladimir Guerrero 1.50 4.00
D8 Alex Rodriguez 2.50 6.00
D9 Sammy Sosa 1.50 4.00
D10 Derek Jeter 4.00 10.00

2000 Ultimate Victory Hall of Fame Game Jersey

Randomly inserted into packs, this four-card insert set features jersey cards of players that were inducted into the Hall of Fame in 2000. Each "single-player" card has an announced print run of 500 copies, and the card backs carry the player's initials as numbering. Please note that the combo card of Fisk/Anderson/Perez was serial numbered to 100.

CF Carlton Fisk 6.00 15.00
SA Sparky Anderson 6.00 15.00
TP Tony Perez 6.00 15.00
HOF Carlton Fisk 30.00 60.00
Sparky Anderson
Tony Perez/100

2000 Ultimate Victory Lasting Impressions

Randomly inserted into packs at one in 11, this 10-card insert set features players that leave a lasting impression on those who watch them perform. Card backs carry a "L" prefix.

COMPLETE SET (10) 12.50 30.00
L1 Barry Bonds 2.00 5.00
L2 Mike Piazza 1.25 3.00
L3 Manny Ramirez .50 1.25
L4 Pedro Martinez .50 1.25
L5 Mark McGwire 2.00 5.00
L6 Ken Griffey Jr. 1.25 3.00
L7 Ivan Rodriguez .50 1.25
L8 Jeff Bagwell .50 1.25
L9 Randy Johnson .75 2.00
L10 Alex Rodriguez 1.25 3.00

2000 Ultimate Victory Starstruck

Randomly inserted into packs at one in 11, this 10-card insert set features players that have been starstruck. Card backs carry a "S" prefix.

COMPLETE SET (10) 12.50 30.00
S1 Alex Rodriguez 1.25 3.00
S2 Frank Thomas .75 2.00
S3 Derek Jeter 2.00 5.00
S4 Mark McGwire 2.00 5.00
S5 Nomar Garciaparra 1.25 3.00
S6 Chipper Jones .75 2.00
S7 Cal Ripken 2.50 6.00
S8 Sammy Sosa .75 2.00
S9 Vladimir Guerrero .75 2.00
S10 Ken Griffey Jr. 1.25 3.00

1991 Ultra

This 400-card standard-size set marked Fleer's first entry into the premium card market. The cards were distributed exclusively in foil-wrapped packs. Fleer claimed in their original press release that there would only be 15 percent the amount of Ultra issued as there was of the regular 1991 Fleer issue. The cards feature full color action photography on the fronts and three full-color photos on the backs. Fleer also issued the sets in their now traditional alphabetical order as well as the teams in alphabetical order. Subsets include Major League Prospects (373-390), Elite Performance (391-396), and Checklists (397-400). Rookie Cards include Eric Karros and Denny Neagle.

COMPLETE SET (400) 8.00 20.00
1 Steve Avery .02 .10
2 Jeff Blauser .02 .10
3 Francisco Cabrera .02 .10
4 Ron Gant .07 .20
5 Tom Glavine .10 .30
6 Tommy Gregg .02 .10
7 Dave Justice .07 .20
8 Oddibe McDowell .02 .10
9 Greg Olson .02 .10
10 Terry Pendleton .07 .20
11 Lonnie Smith .02 .10
12 John Smoltz .10 .30
13 Jeff Treadway .02 .10
14 Glenn Davis .02 .10
15 Mike Devereaux .02 .10
16 Leo Gomez .02 .10
17 Chris Hoiles .02 .10
18 Dave Johnson .02 .10
19 Ben McDonald .02 .10
20 Randy Milligan .02 .10
21 Gregg Olson .02 .10
22 Joe Orsulak .02 .10
23 Bill Ripken .02 .10
24 Cal Ripken .60 1.50
25 David Segui .02 .10
26 Craig Worthington .02 .10
27 Wade Boggs .10 .30
28 Tom Bolton .02 .10
29 Tom Brunansky .02 .10
30 Ellis Burks .07 .20
31 Roger Clemens .60 1.50
32 Mike Greenwell .02 .10
33 Greg A. Harris .02 .10
34 Daryl Irvine RC .02 .10
35 Mike Marshall UER .02 .10
(1990 in stats is shown as 990)
36 Tim Naehring .02 .10
37 Tony Pena .02 .10
38 Phil Plantier RC .05 .15
39 Carlos Quintana .02 .10
40 Jeff Reardon .07 .20
41 Jody Reed .02 .10
42 Luis Rivera .02 .10
43 Jim Abbott .10 .30
44 Chuck Finley .07 .20
45 Bryan Harvey .02 .10
46 Donnie Hill .02 .10
47 Jack Howell .02 .10
48 Wally Joyner .07 .20
49 Mark Langston .02 .10
50 Kirk McCaskill .02 .10
51 Lance Parrish .07 .20
52 Dick Schofield .02 .10
53 Lee Stevens .02 .10
54 Dave Winfield .07 .20
55 George Bell .02 .10
56 Damon Berryhill .02 .10
57 Mike Bielecki .02 .10
58 Andre Dawson .07 .20
59 Shawon Dunston .02 .10
60 Joe Girardi UER .02 .10
(Bats right, LH hitter shown is Doug Dascenzo)
61 Mark Grace .10 .30
62 Mike Harkey .02 .10
63 Les Lancaster .02 .10
64 Greg Maddux .30 .75
65 Derrick May .02 .10
66 Ryne Sandberg .30 .75
67 Luis Salazar .02 .10
68 Dwight Smith .02 .10
69 Hector Villanueva .02 .10
70 Jerome Walton .02 .10
71 Mitch Williams .02 .10
72 Carlton Fisk .10 .30
73 Scott Fletcher .02 .10
74 Ozzie Guillen .07 .20
75 Greg Hibbard .02 .10
76 Lance Johnson .02 .10
77 Steve Lyons .02 .10
78 Jack McDowell .02 .10
79 Dan Pasqua .02 .10
80 Melido Perez .02 .10
81 Tim Raines .07 .20
82 Sammy Sosa .20 .50
83 Cory Snyder .02 .10
84 Bobby Thigpen .02 .10
85 Frank Thomas .20 .50
(Card says he is an outfielder)
86 Robin Ventura .07 .20
87 Todd Benzinger .02 .10
88 Glenn Braggs .02 .10
89 Tom Browning UER .02 .10
(Front photo actually Norm Charlton)
90 Norm Charlton .02 .10
91 Eric Davis .07 .20
92 Rob Dibble .07 .20
93 Bill Doran .02 .10
94 Mariano Duncan UER .02 .10
(Right back photo is Billy Hatcher)
95 Billy Hatcher .02 .10
96 Barry Larkin .10 .30
97 Randy Myers .02 .10
98 Hal Morris .02 .10
99 Joe Oliver .02 .10
100 Paul O'Neill .10 .30
101 Jeff Reed .02 .10
(See also 104)
102 Jose Rijo .02 .10
103 Chris Sabo .02 .10
(See also 106)
104 Beau Allred UER .02 .10
(Card number is 101)
105 Sandy Alomar Jr. .02 .10
106 Carlos Baerga UER .02 .10
(Card number is 103)
107 Albert Belle .07 .20
108 Jerry Browne .02 .10
109 Tom Candiotti .02 .10
110 Alex Cole .02 .10
111 John Farrell .02 .10
(See also 114)
112 Felix Fermin .02 .10
113 Brook Jacoby .02 .10
114 Chris James UER .02 .10
(Card number is 111)
115 Doug Jones .02 .10
116 Steve Olin .02 .10
(See also 119)
117 Greg Swindell .02 .10
118 Turner Ward RC .05 .15
119 Mitch Webster UER .02 .10
(Card number is 116)
120 Dave Bergman .02 .10
121 Cecil Fielder .07 .20
122 Travis Fryman .07 .20
123 Mike Henneman .02 .10
124 Lloyd Moseby .02 .10
125 Dan Petry .02 .10
126 Tony Phillips .02 .10
127 Mark Salas .02 .10
128 Frank Tanana .02 .10
129 Alan Trammell .07 .20
130 Lou Whitaker .07 .20
131 Eric Anthony .02 .10
132 Craig Biggio .10 .30
133 Ken Caminiti .07 .20
134 Casey Candaele .02 .10
135 Andujar Cedeno .02 .10
136 Mark Davidson .02 .10
137 Jim Deshaies .02 .10
138 Mark Portugal .02 .10
139 Rafael Ramirez .02 .10
140 Mike Scott .02 .10
141 Eric Yelding .02 .10
142 Gerald Young .02 .10
143 Kevin Appier .07 .20
144 George Brett .50 1.25
145 Jeff Conine RC .20 .50
146 Jim Eisenreich .02 .10
147 Tom Gordon .02 .10
148 Mark Gubicza .02 .10
149 Bo Jackson .20 .50
150 Brent Mayne .02 .10
151 Mike Macfarlane .02 .10
152 Brian McRae RC .15 .40
153 Jeff Montgomery .02 .10
154 Bret Saberhagen .07 .20
155 Kevin Seitzer .02 .10
156 Terry Shumpert .02 .10
157 Kurt Stillwell .02 .10
158 Danny Tartabull .02 .10
159 Tim Belcher .02 .10
160 Kal Daniels .02 .10
161 Alfredo Griffin .02 .10
162 Lenny Harris .02 .10
163 Jay Howell .02 .10
164 Ramon Martinez .02 .10
165 Mike Morgan .02 .10
166 Eddie Murray .20 .50
167 Jose Offerman .02 .10
168 Juan Samuel .02 .10
169 Mike Scioscia .02 .10
170 Mike Sharperson .02 .10
171 Darryl Strawberry .07 .20
172 Greg Brock .02 .10
173 Chuck Crim .02 .10
174 Jim Gantner .02 .10
175 Ted Higuera .02 .10
176 Mark Knudson .02 .10
177 Tim McIntosh .02 .10
178 Paul Molitor .07 .20
179 Dan Plesac .02 .10
180 Gary Sheffield .07 .20
181 Bill Spiers .02 .10
182 B.J. Surhoff .07 .20
183 Greg Vaughn .02 .10
184 Robin Yount .30 .75
185 Rick Aguilera .07 .20
186 Greg Gagne .02 .10
187 Dan Gladden .02 .10
188 Brian Harper .02 .10
189 Kent Hrbek .07 .20
190 Gene Larkin .02 .10
191 Shane Mack .02 .10
192 Pedro Munoz RC .05 .15
193 Al Newman .02 .10
194 Junior Ortiz .02 .10
195 Kirby Puckett .20 .50
196 Kevin Tapani .02 .10
197 Dennis Boyd .02 .10
198 Tim Burke .02 .10
199 Ivan Calderon .02 .10
200 Delino DeShields .07 .20
201 Mike Fitzgerald .02 .10
202 Steve Frey .02 .10
203 Andres Galarraga .07 .20
204 Marquis Grissom .07 .20
205 Dave Martinez .02 .10
206 Dennis Martinez .07 .20
207 Junior Noboa .02 .10
208 Spike Owen .02 .10
209 Scott Ruskin .02 .10
210 Tim Wallach .02 .10
211 Daryl Boston .02 .10
212 Vince Coleman .02 .10
213 David Cone .07 .20
214 Ron Darling .02 .10
215 Kevin Elster .02 .10
216 Sid Fernandez .02 .10
217 John Franco .07 .20
218 Dwight Gooden .07 .20
219 Tom Herr .02 .10
220 Todd Hundley .02 .10
221 Gregg Jefferies .02 .10
222 Howard Johnson .02 .10
223 Dave Magadan .02 .10
224 Kevin McReynolds .02 .10
225 Keith Miller .02 .10
226 Mackey Sasser .02 .10
227 Frank Viola .07 .20
228 Jesse Barfield .02 .10
229 Greg Cadaret .02 .10
230 Alvaro Espinoza .02 .10
231 Bob Geren .02 .10
232 Lee Guetterman .02 .10
233 Mel Hall .02 .10
234 Andy Hawkins UER .02 .10
(Back center photo is not him)
235 Roberto Kelly .02 .10
236 Tim Leary .02 .10
237 Jim Leyritz .02 .10
238 Kevin Maas .02 .10
239 Don Mattingly .50 1.25
240 Hensley Meulens .02 .10
241 Eric Plunk .02 .10
242 Steve Sax .02 .10
243 Todd Burns .02 .10
244 Jose Canseco .10 .30
245 Dennis Eckersley .07 .20
246 Mike Gallego .02 .10
247 Dave Henderson .02 .10
248 Rickey Henderson .20 .50
249 Rick Honeycutt .02 .10
250 Carney Lansford .07 .20
251 Mark McGwire .60 1.50
252 Mike Moore .02 .10
253 Terry Steinbach .02 .10
254 Dave Stewart .07 .20
255 Walt Weiss .02 .10
256 Bob Welch .02 .10
257 Curt Young .02 .10
258 Wes Chamberlain RC .15 .40
259 Pat Combs .02 .10
260 Darren Daulton .07 .20
261 Jose DeJesus .02 .10
262 Len Dykstra .07 .20
263 Charlie Hayes .02 .10
264 Von Hayes .02 .10
265 Ken Howell .02 .10
266 John Kruk .07 .20
267 Roger McDowell .02 .10
268 Mickey Morandini .02 .10
269 Terry Mulholland .02 .10
270 Dale Murphy .10 .30
271 Randy Ready .02 .10
272 Dickie Thon .02 .10
273 Stan Belinda .02 .10
274 Jay Bell .07 .20
275 Barry Bonds .60 1.50
276 Bobby Bonilla .07 .20
277 Doug Drabek .02 .10
278 Carlos Garcia RC .05 .15
279 Neal Heaton .02 .10
280 Jeff King .02 .10
281 Bill Landrum .02 .10
282 Mike LaValliere .02 .10
283 Jose Lind .02 .10
284 Orlando Merced RC .05 .15
285 Gary Redus .02 .10
286 Don Slaught .02 .10
287 Andy Van Slyke .10 .30
288 Jose DeLeon .02 .10
289 Pedro Guerrero .07 .20
290 Ray Lankford .07 .20
291 Joe Magrane .02 .10
292 Jose Oquendo .02 .10
293 Tom Pagnozzi .02 .10
294 Bryn Smith .02 .10
295 Lee Smith .07 .20
296 Ozzie Smith UER .30 .75
(Born 12-26, 54, should have hyphen)
297 Milt Thompson .02 .10
298 Craig Wilson RC .02 .10
299 Todd Zeile .02 .10
300 Shawn Abner .02 .10
301 Andy Benes .02 .10
302 Paul Faries RC .02 .10
303 Tony Gwynn .25 .60
304 Greg W. Harris .02 .10
305 Thomas Howard .02 .10
306 Bruce Hurst .02 .10
307 Craig Lefferts .02 .10
308 Fred McGriff .10 .30
309 Dennis Rasmussen .02 .10
310 Bip Roberts .02 .10
311 Benito Santiago .07 .20
312 Garry Templeton .02 .10
313 Ed Whitson .02 .10
314 Dave Anderson .02 .10
315 Kevin Bass .02 .10
316 Jeff Brantley .02 .10
317 John Burkett .02 .10
318 Will Clark .10 .30
319 Steve Decker RC .05 .15
320 Scott Garrelts .02 .10
321 Terry Kennedy .02 .10
322 Mark Leonard RC .02 .10
323 Darren Lewis .02 .10
324 Greg Litton .02 .10
325 Willie McGee .07 .20
326 Kevin Mitchell .02 .10
327 Don Robinson .02 .10
328 Andres Santana .02 .10
329 Robby Thompson .02 .10
330 Jose Uribe .02 .10
331 Matt Williams .07 .20
332 Scott Bradley .02 .10
333 Henry Cotto .02 .10
334 Alvin Davis .02 .10
335 Ken Griffey Sr. .07 .20
336 Ken Griffey Jr. .40 1.00
337 Erik Hanson .02 .10
338 Brian Holman .02 .10
339 Randy Johnson .25 .60
340 Edgar Martinez UER .10 .30
(Listed as playing SS)
341 Tino Martinez .20 .50
342 Pete O'Brien .02 .10
343 Harold Reynolds .07 .20
344 Dave Valle .02 .10
345 Omar Vizquel .10 .30
346 Brad Arnsberg .02 .10
347 Kevin Brown .07 .20
348 Julio Franco .07 .20
349 Jeff Huson .02 .10
350 Rafael Palmeiro .10 .30
351 Geno Petralli .02 .10
352 Gary Pettis .02 .10
353 Kenny Rogers .07 .20
354 Jeff Russell .02 .10
355 Nolan Ryan .75 2.00
356 Ruben Sierra .07 .20
357 Bobby Witt .02 .10
358 Roberto Alomar .10 .30
359 Pat Borders .02 .10
360 Joe Carter UER .07 .20
(Reverse negative on back photo)
361 Kelly Gruber .02 .10
362 Tom Henke .02 .10
363 Glenallen Hill .02 .10
364 Jimmy Key .07 .20
365 Manny Lee .02 .10
366 Rance Mulliniks .02 .10
367 John Olerud UER .07 .20
(Throwing left on card; back has throws right; he does throw lefty)
368 Dave Stieb .02 .10
369 Duane Ward .02 .10
370 David Wells .07 .20
371 Mark Whiten .02 .10
372 Mookie Wilson .07 .20
373 Willie Banks MLP .02 .10
374 Steve Carter MLP .02 .10
375 S.Chiamparino MLP .02 .10
376 Steve Chitren MLP RC .02 .10
377 Darrin Fletcher MLP .02 .10
378 Rich Garces MLP RC .05 .15
379 Reggie Jefferson MLP .02 .10
380 Eric Karros MLP RC .30 .75
381 Pat Kelly MLP RC .05 .15
382 C.Knoblauch MLP .07 .20
383 Denny Neagle MLP RC .15 .40
384 Dan Opperman MLP RC .02 .10
385 John Ramos MLP RC .02 .10
386 Henry Rodriguez MLP RC .15 .40
387 Mo Vaughn MLP .07 .20
388 Gerald Williams MLP RC .15 .40
389 Mike York MLP RC .02 .10
390 Eddie Zosky MLP .02 .10
391 Barry Bonds EP .30 .75
392 Cecil Fielder EP .02 .10
393 Rickey Henderson EP .10 .30
394 Dave Justice EP .02 .10
395 Nolan Ryan EP .40 1.00
396 Bobby Thigpen EP .02 .10
397 Gregg Jefferies CL .02 .10
398 Von Hayes CL .02 .10
399 Terry Kennedy CL .02 .10
400 Nolan Ryan CL .20 .50

1991 Ultra Gold

This ten-card standard-size set presents Fleer's 1991 Ultra Team. These cards were randomly inserted into Ultra packs. The set is sequenced in alphabetical order.

COMPLETE SET (10) 5.00 10.00
1 Barry Bonds 1.25 3.00
2 Will Clark .25 .60
3 Doug Drabek .07 .20
4 Ken Griffey Jr. .75 2.00
5 Rickey Henderson .40 1.00
6 Bo Jackson .40 1.00
7 Ramon Martinez .07 .20
8 Kirby Puckett UER .40 1.00
(Boggs won 1988 batting title, so Puckett didn't win consecutive titles)
9 Chris Sabo .07 .20
10 Ryne Sandberg UER .60 1.50
(Johnson and Hornsby didn't hit 40 homers in 1990, Fielder did hit 51 in '90)

1991 Ultra Update

The 120-card set was distributed exclusively in factory set form along with 20 team logo stickers through hobby dealers. The set includes the year's hottest rookies and important veteran players traded after the original Ultra series was produced. Card design is identical to regular issue 1991 cards except for the U-prefixed numbering on back. Cards are ordered alphabetically within and according to teams for each league. Rookie Cards in this set include Jeff Bagwell, Mike Mussina, and Ivan Rodriguez.

COMP.FACT.SET (120) 10.00 25.00
1 Dwight Evans .30 .75
2 Chito Martinez RC .08 .25
3 Bob Melvin .08 .25
4 Mike Mussina RC 2.00 5.00
5 Jack Clark .20 .50
6 Dana Kiecker .08 .25
7 Steve Lyons .08 .25
8 Gary Gaetti .20 .50
9 Dave Gallagher .08 .25
10 Dave Parker .20 .50
11 Luis Polonia .08 .25
12 Luis Sojo .08 .25
13 Wilson Alvarez .20 .50
14 Alex Fernandez .08 .25
15 Craig Grebeck .08 .25
16 Ron Karkovice .08 .25
17 Warren Newson RC .08 .25
18 Scott Radinsky .08 .25
19 Glenallen Hill .08 .25
20 Charles Nagy .08 .25
21 Mark Whiten .08 .25
22 Milt Cuyler .08 .25
23 Paul Gibson .08 .25
24 Mickey Tettleton .08 .25
25 Todd Benzinger .08 .25
26 Storm Davis .08 .25
27 Kirk Gibson .20 .50
28 Bill Pecota .08 .25
29 Gary Thurman .08 .25
30 Darryl Hamilton .08 .25
31 Jaime Navarro .08 .25
32 Willie Randolph .20 .50
33 Bill Wegman .08 .25
34 Randy Bush .08 .25
35 Chili Davis .20 .50
36 Scott Erickson .08 .25
37 Chuck Knoblauch .20 .50
38 Scott Leius .08 .25
39 Jack Morris .20 .50
40 John Habyan .08 .25
41 Pat Kelly .08 .25
42 Matt Nokes .08 .25
43 Scott Sanderson .08 .25
44 Bernie Williams .75 2.00
45 Harold Baines .20 .50
46 Brook Jacoby .08 .25
47 Earnest Riles .08 .25
48 Willie Wilson .08 .25
49 Jay Buhner .20 .50
50 Rich DeLucia RC .08 .25
51 Mike Jackson .08 .25
52 Bill Krueger .08 .25
53 Bill Swift .08 .25
54 Brian Downing .08 .25
55 Juan Gonzalez .60 1.50
56 Dean Palmer .20 .50
57 Kevin Reimer .08 .25
58 Ivan Rodriguez RC 3.00 8.00
59 Tom Candiotti .08 .25
60 Juan Guzman RC .20 .50
61 Bob MacDonald RC .08 .25
62 Greg Myers .08 .25
63 Ed Sprague .08 .25
64 Devon White .20 .50
65 Rafael Belliard .08 .25
66 Juan Berenguer .08 .25
67 Brian R. Hunter RC .20 .50
68 Kent Mercker .08 .25
69 Otis Nixon .08 .25
70 Danny Jackson .08 .25
71 Chuck McElroy .08 .25
72 Gary Scott RC .08 .25
73 Heathcliff Slocumb RC .08 .25
74 Chico Walker .08 .25
75 Rick Wilkins RC .08 .25
76 Chris Hammond .08 .25
77 Luis Quinones .08 .25
78 Herm Winningham .08 .25
79 Jeff Bagwell RC 2.50 6.00
80 Jim Corsi .08 .25
81 Steve Finley .20 .50
82 Luis Gonzalez RC .60 1.50
83 Pete Harnisch .08 .25
84 Darryl Kile .20 .50
85 Brett Butler .20 .50
86 Gary Carter .20 .50
87 Tim Crews .08 .25
88 Orel Hershiser .20 .50
89 Bob Ojeda .08 .25
90 Bret Barberie RC .08 .25
91 Barry Jones .08 .25
92 Gilberto Reyes .08 .25
93 Larry Walker .60 1.50
94 Hubie Brooks .08 .25
95 Tim Burke .08 .25
96 Rick Cerone .08 .25
97 Jeff Innis .08 .25
98 Wally Backman .08 .25
99 Tommy Greene .08 .25
100 Ricky Jordan .08 .25
101 Mitch Williams .08 .25
102 John Smiley .08 .25
103 Randy Tomlin RC .08 .25
104 Gary Varsho .08 .25
105 Cris Carpenter .08 .25
106 Ken Hill .08 .25
107 Felix Jose .08 .25
108 Omar Olivares RC .08 .25
109 Gerald Perry .08 .25
110 Jerald Clark .08 .25
111 Tony Fernandez .08 .25
112 Darrin Jackson .08 .25
113 Mike Maddux .08 .25
114 Tim Teufel .08 .25
115 Bud Black .08 .25
116 Kelly Downs .08 .25
117 Mike Felder .08 .25
118 Willie McGee .20 .50
119 Trevor Wilson .08 .25
120 Checklist 1-120 .08 .25

1992 Ultra

Consisting of 600 standard-size cards, the 1992 Ultra set was issued in two series of 300 cards each. Cards were distributed exclusively in foil packs. The cards are numbered on the back and ordered below alphabetically within and according to teams for each league with AL preceding NL. Some cards have been found without the word Fleer on the front.

COMPLETE SET (600) 12.00 30.00
COMP. SERIES 1 (300) 8.00 20.00
COMP. SERIES 2 (300) 4.00 10.00
1 Glenn Davis .02 .10
2 Mike Devereaux .02 .10
3 Dwight Evans .10 .30
4 Leo Gomez .02 .10
5 Chris Hoiles .02 .10
6 Sam Horn .02 .10
7 Chito Martinez .02 .10
8 Randy Milligan .02 .10
9 Mike Mussina .20 .50
10 Billy Ripken .02 .10
11 Cal Ripken .60 1.50
12 Tom Brunansky .02 .10
13 Ellis Burks .07 .20
14 Jack Clark .07 .20
15 Roger Clemens .40 1.00
16 Mike Greenwell .02 .10
17 Joe Hesketh .02 .10
18 Tony Pena .02 .10
19 Carlos Quintana .02 .10
20 Jeff Reardon .07 .20
21 Jody Reed .02 .10
22 Luis Rivera .02 .10
23 Mo Vaughn .07 .20
24 Gary DiSarcina .02 .10
25 Chuck Finley .07 .20
26 Gary Gaetti .07 .20
27 Bryan Harvey .02 .10
28 Lance Parrish .07 .20
29 Luis Polonia .02 .10
30 Dick Schofield .02 .10
31 Luis Sojo .02 .10
32 Wilson Alvarez .02 .10
33 Carlton Fisk .10 .30
34 Craig Grebeck .02 .10
35 Ozzie Guillen .07 .20
36 Greg Hibbard .02 .10
37 Charlie Hough .07 .20
38 Lance Johnson .02 .10
39 Ron Karkovice .02 .10
40 Jack McDowell .02 .10
41 Donn Pall .02 .10
42 Melido Perez .02 .10
43 Tim Raines .07 .20
44 Frank Thomas .20 .50
45 Sandy Alomar Jr. .02 .10
46 Carlos Baerga .02 .10
47 Albert Belle .07 .20
48 Jerry Browne UER .02 .10
(Reversed negative on card back)
49 Felix Fermin .02 .10
50 Reggie Jefferson UER .02 .10
(Born 1968, not 1966)
51 Mark Lewis .02 .10
52 Carlos Martinez .02 .10
53 Steve Olin .02 .10
54 Jim Thome .20 .50
55 Mark Whiten .02 .10
56 Dave Bergman .02 .10
57 Milt Cuyler .02 .10
58 Rob Deer .02 .10
59 Cecil Fielder .07 .20
60 Travis Fryman .07 .20
61 Scott Livingstone .02 .10
62 Tony Phillips .02 .10
63 Mickey Tettleton .02 .10
64 Alan Trammell .07 .20
65 Lou Whitaker .07 .20
66 Kevin Appier .07 .20
67 Mike Boddicker .02 .10
68 George Brett .50 1.25
69 Jim Eisenreich .02 .10
70 Mark Gubicza .02 .10
71 David Howard .02 .10
72 Joel Johnson .02 .10
73 Mike Macfarlane .02 .10
74 Brent Mayne .02 .10
75 Brian McRae .02 .10
76 Jeff Montgomery .02 .10
77 Terry Shumpert .02 .10
78 Don August .02 .10
79 Dante Bichette .07 .20
80 Ted Higuera .02 .10
81 Paul Molitor .07 .20
82 Jaime Navarro .02 .10
83 Gary Sheffield .07 .20
84 Bill Spiers .02 .10
85 B.J. Surhoff .07 .20
86 Greg Vaughn .02 .10
87 Robin Yount .30 .75
88 Rick Aguilera .07 .20
89 Chili Davis .07 .20
90 Scott Erickson .02 .10
91 Brian Harper .02 .10
92 Kent Hrbek .07 .20
93 Chuck Knoblauch .07 .20
94 Scott Leius .02 .10
95 Shane Mack .02 .10
96 Mike Pagliarulo .02 .10
97 Kirby Puckett .20 .50
98 Kevin Tapani .02 .10
99 Jesse Barfield .02 .10
100 Alvaro Espinoza .02 .10
101 Mel Hall .02 .10
102 Pat Kelly .02 .10
103 Roberto Kelly .02 .10
104 Kevin Maas .02 .10
105 Don Mattingly .50 1.25
106 Hensley Meulens .02 .10
107 Matt Nokes .02 .10
108 Steve Sax .02 .10
109 Harold Baines .07 .20
110 Jose Canseco .10 .30
111 Ron Darling .02 .10
112 Mike Gallego .02 .10
113 Dave Henderson .02 .10
114 Rickey Henderson .20 .50
115 Mark McGwire .50 1.25
116 Terry Steinbach .02 .10
117 Dave Stewart .07 .20
118 Todd Van Poppel .02 .10
119 Bob Welch .02 .10
120 Greg Briley .02 .10
121 Jay Buhner .07 .20
122 Rick DeLucia .02 .10
123 Ken Griffey Jr. .30 .75
124 Erik Hanson .02 .10
125 Randy Johnson .20 .50
126 Edgar Martinez .10 .30
127 Tino Martinez .10 .30
128 Pete O'Brien .02 .10

129 Harold Reynolds .07 .20
130 Dave Valle .02 .10
131 Julio Franco .07 .20
132 Juan Gonzalez .10 .30
133 Jeff Huson .07 .20
134 Mike Jeffcoat .02 .10
135 Terry Mathews .02 .10
136 Rafael Palmeiro .10 .30
137 Dean Palmer .07 .20
138 Geno Petralli .02 .10
139 Ivan Rodriguez .20 .50
140 Jeff Russell .02 .10
141 Nolan Ryan .75 2.00
142 Ruben Sierra .07 .20
143 Roberto Alomar .10 .30
144 Pat Borders .02 .10
145 Joe Carter .07 .20
146 Kelly Gruber .02 .10
147 Jimmy Key .07 .20
148 Manny Lee .02 .10
149 Rance Mulliniks .02 .10
150 Greg Myers .02 .10
151 John Olerud .07 .20
152 Dave Stieb .02 .10
153 Todd Stottlemyre .02 .10
154 Duane Ward .02 .10
155 Devon White .07 .20
156 Eddie Zosky .02 .10
157 Steve Avery .02 .10
158 Rafael Belliard .02 .10
159 Jeff Blauser .02 .10
160 Sid Bream .02 .10
161 Ron Gant .07 .20
162 Tom Glavine .10 .30
163 Brian Hunter .02 .10
164 Dave Justice .07 .20
165 Mark Lemke .02 .10
166 Greg Olson .02 .10
167 Terry Pendleton .07 .20
168 Lonnie Smith .02 .10
169 John Smoltz .10 .30
170 Mike Stanton .02 .10
171 Jeff Treadway .02 .10
172 Paul Assenmacher .02 .10
173 George Bell .02 .10
174 Shawon Dunston .02 .10
175 Mark Grace .10 .30
176 Danny Jackson .02 .10
177 Les Lancaster .02 .10
178 Greg Maddux .30 .75
179 Luis Salazar .02 .10
180 Rey Sanchez RC .08 .25
181 Ryne Sandberg .30 .75
182 Jose Vizcaino .02 .10
183 Chico Walker .02 .10
184 Jerome Walton .02 .10
185 Glenn Braggs .02 .10
186 Tom Browning .02 .10
187 Rob Dibble .07 .20
188 Bill Doran .02 .10
189 Chris Hammond .02 .10
190 Billy Hatcher .02 .10
191 Barry Larkin .10 .30
192 Hal Morris .02 .10
193 Joe Oliver .02 .10
194 Paul O'Neill .10 .30
195 Jeff Reed .02 .10
196 Jose Rijo .02 .10
197 Chris Sabo .02 .10
198 Jeff Bagwell .20 .50
199 Craig Biggio .10 .30
200 Ken Caminiti .07 .20
201 Andujar Cedeno .02 .10
202 Steve Finley .07 .20
203 Luis Gonzalez .07 .20
204 Pete Harnisch .02 .10
205 Xavier Hernandez .02 .10
206 Darryl Kile .07 .20
207 Al Osuna .02 .10
208 Curt Schilling .10 .30
209 Brett Butler .07 .20
210 Kal Daniels .02 .10
211 Lenny Harris .02 .10
212 Stan Javier .02 .10
213 Ramon Martinez .02 .10
214 Roger McDowell .02 .10
215 Jose Offerman .02 .10
216 Juan Samuel .02 .10
217 Mike Scioscia .02 .10
218 Mike Sharperson .02 .10
219 Darryl Strawberry .07 .20
220 Delino DeShields .02 .10
221 Tom Foley .02 .10
222 Steve Frey .02 .10
223 Dennis Martinez .07 .20
224 Spike Owen .02 .10
225 Gilberto Reyes .02 .10
226 Tim Wallach .02 .10
227 Daryl Boston .02 .10
228 Tim Burke .02 .10
229 Vince Coleman .02 .10
230 David Cone .07 .20
231 Kevin Elster .02 .10
232 Dwight Gooden .07 .20
233 Todd Hundley .02 .10
234 Jeff Innis .02 .10
235 Howard Johnson .02 .10
236 Dave Magadan .02 .10
237 Mackey Sasser .02 .10
238 Anthony Young .02 .10
239 Wes Chamberlain .02 .10
240 Darren Daulton .07 .20
241 Len Dykstra .07 .20
242 Tommy Greene .02 .10
243 Charlie Hayes .02 .10
244 Dave Hollins .02 .10
245 Ricky Jordan .02 .10
246 John Kruk .07 .20
247 Mickey Morandini .02 .10
248 Terry Mulholland .02 .10
249 Dale Murphy .10 .30
250 Jay Bell .07 .20
251 Barry Bonds .60 1.50
252 Steve Buechele .02 .10
253 Doug Drabek .02 .10
254 Mike LaValliere .02 .10
255 Jose Lind .02 .10
256 Lloyd McClendon .02 .10
257 Orlando Merced .02 .10
258 Don Slaught .02 .10
259 John Smiley .02 .10
260 Zane Smith .02 .10
261 Randy Tomlin .02 .10
262 Andy Van Slyke .10 .30
263 Pedro Guerrero .07 .20
264 Felix Jose .02 .10
265 Ray Lankford .07 .20
266 Omar Olivares .02 .10
267 Jose Oquendo .02 .10
268 Tom Pagnozzi .02 .10
269 Bryn Smith .02 .10
270 Lee Smith UER .07 .20
(1991 record listed
as 61-61)
271 Ozzie Smith UER .30 .75
(Comma before year of
birth on card back)
272 Milt Thompson .02 .10
273 Todd Zeile .02 .10
274 Andy Benes .02 .10
275 Jerald Clark .02 .10
276 Tony Fernandez .02 .10
277 Tony Gwynn .25 .60
278 Greg W. Harris .02 .10
279 Thomas Howard .02 .10
280 Bruce Hurst .02 .10
281 Mike Maddux .02 .10
282 Fred McGriff .10 .30
283 Benito Santiago .07 .20
284 Kevin Bass .02 .10
285 Jeff Brantley .02 .10
286 John Burkett .02 .10
287 Will Clark .10 .30
288 Royce Clayton .02 .10
289 Steve Decker .02 .10
290 Kelly Downs .02 .10
291 Mike Felder .02 .10
292 Darren Lewis .02 .10
293 Kirt Manwaring .02 .10
294 Willie McGee .07 .20
295 Robby Thompson .02 .10
296 Matt Williams .07 .20
297 Trevor Wilson .02 .10
298 Checklist 1-100 .02 .10
299 Checklist 101-200 .02 .10
300 Checklist 201-300 .02 .10
301 Brady Anderson .07 .20
302 Todd Frohwirth .02 .10
303 Ben McDonald .02 .10
304 Mark McLemore .02 .10
305 Jose Mesa .02 .10
306 Bob Milacki .02 .10
307 Gregg Olson .02 .10
308 David Segui .02 .10
309 Rick Sutcliffe .07 .20
310 Jeff Tackett .02 .10
311 Wade Boggs .10 .30
312 Scott Cooper .02 .10
313 John Flaherty .02 .10
314 Wayne Housie .02 .10
315 Peter Hoy .02 .10
316 John Marzano .02 .10
317 Tim Naehring .02 .10
318 Phil Plantier .02 .10
319 Frank Viola .07 .20
320 Matt Young .02 .10
321 Jim Abbott .10 .30
322 Hubie Brooks .02 .10
323 Chad Curtis RC .08 .25
324 Alvin Davis .02 .10
325 Junior Felix .02 .10
326 Von Hayes .02 .10
327 Mark Langston .02 .10
328 Scott Lewis .02 .10
329 Don Robinson .02 .10
330 Bobby Rose .02 .10
331 Lee Stevens .02 .10
332 George Bell .02 .10
333 Esteban Beltre .02 .10
334 Joey Cora .02 .10
335 Alex Fernandez .02 .10
336 Roberto Hernandez .02 .10
337 Mike Huff .02 .10
338 Kirk McCaskill .02 .10
339 Dan Pasqua .02 .10
340 Scott Radinsky .02 .10
341 Steve Sax .02 .10
342 Bobby Thigpen .02 .10
343 Robin Ventura .07 .20
344 Jack Armstrong .02 .10
345 Alex Cole .02 .10
346 Dennis Cook .02 .10
347 Glenallen Hill .02 .10
348 Thomas Howard .02 .10
349 Brook Jacoby .02 .10
350 Kenny Lofton .10 .30
351 Charles Nagy .02 .10
352 Rod Nichols .02 .10
353 Junior Ortiz .02 .10
354 Dave Otto .02 .10
355 Tony Perezchica .02 .10
356 Scott Scudder .02 .10
357 Paul Sorrento .02 .10
358 Skeeter Barnes .02 .10
359 Mark Carreon .02 .10
360 John Doherty RC .02 .10
361 Dan Gladden .02 .10
362 Bill Gullickson .02 .10
363 Shawn Hare RC .02 .10
364 Mike Henneman .02 .10
365 Chad Kreuter .02 .10
366 Mark Leiter .02 .10
367 Mike Munoz .02 .10
368 Kevin Ritz .02 .10
369 Mark Davis .02 .10
370 Tom Gordon .02 .10
371 Chris Gwynn .02 .10
372 Gregg Jefferies .02 .10
373 Wally Joyner .07 .20
374 Kevin McReynolds .02 .10
375 Keith Miller .02 .10
376 Rico Rossy .02 .10
377 Curtis Wilkerson .02 .10
378 Ricky Bones .02 .10
379 Chris Bosio .02 .10
380 Cal Eldred .02 .10
381 Scott Fletcher .02 .10
382 Jim Gantner .02 .10
383 Darryl Hamilton .02 .10
384 Doug Henry RC .08 .25
385 Pat Listach RC .08 .25
386 Tim McIntosh .02 .10
387 Edwin Nunez .02 .10
388 Dan Plesac .02 .10
389 Kevin Seitzer .02 .10
390 Franklin Stubbs .02 .10
391 William Suero .02 .10
392 Bill Wegman .02 .10
393 Willie Banks .02 .10
394 Jarvis Brown .02 .10
395 Greg Gagne .02 .10
396 Mark Guthrie .02 .10
397 Bill Krueger .02 .10
398 Pat Mahomes RC .08 .25
399 Pedro Munoz .02 .10
400 John Smiley .02 .10
401 Gary Wayne .02 .10
402 Lenny Webster .02 .10
403 Carl Willis .02 .10
404 Greg Cadaret .02 .10
405 Steve Farr .02 .10
406 Mike Gallego .02 .10
407 Charlie Hayes .02 .10
408 Steve Howe .02 .10
409 Dion James .02 .10
410 Jeff Johnson .02 .10
411 Tim Leary .02 .10
412 Jim Leyritz .02 .10
413 Melido Perez .02 .10
414 Scott Sanderson .02 .10
415 Andy Stankiewicz .02 .10
416 Mike Stanley .02 .10
417 Danny Tartabull .02 .10
418 Lance Blankenship .02 .10
419 Mike Bordick .02 .10
420 Scott Brosius RC .15 .40
421 Dennis Eckersley .07 .20
422 Scott Hemond .02 .10
423 Carney Lansford .07 .20
424 Henry Mercedes .02 .10
425 Mike Moore .02 .10
426 Gene Nelson .02 .10
427 Randy Ready .02 .10
428 Bruce Walton .02 .10
429 Willie Wilson .02 .10
430 Rich Amaral .02 .10
431 Dave Cochrane .02 .10
432 Henry Cotto .02 .10
433 Calvin Jones .02 .10
434 Kevin Mitchell .02 .10
435 Clay Parker .02 .10
436 Omar Vizquel .10 .30
437 Floyd Bannister .02 .10
438 Kevin Brown .07 .20
439 John Cangelosi .02 .10
440 Brian Downing .02 .10
441 Monty Fariss .02 .10
442 Jose Guzman .02 .10
443 Donald Harris .02 .10
444 Kevin Reimer .02 .10
445 Kenny Rogers .07 .20
446 Wayne Rosenthal .02 .10
447 Dickie Thon .02 .10
448 Derek Bell .07 .20
449 Juan Guzman .02 .10
450 Tom Henke .02 .10
451 Candy Maldonado .02 .10
452 Jack Morris .07 .20
453 David Wells .07 .20
454 Dave Winfield .07 .20
455 Juan Berenguer .02 .10
456 Damon Berryhill .02 .10
457 Mike Bielecki .02 .10
458 Marvin Freeman .02 .10
459 Charlie Leibrandt .02 .10
460 Kent Mercker .02 .10
461 Otis Nixon .02 .10
462 Alejandro Pena .02 .10
463 Ben Rivera .02 .10
464 Deion Sanders .10 .30
465 Mark Wohlers .02 .10
466 Shawn Boskie .02 .10
467 Frank Castillo .02 .10
468 Andre Dawson .07 .20
469 Joe Girardi .02 .10
470 Chuck McElroy .02 .10
471 Mike Morgan .02 .10
472 Ken Patterson .02 .10
473 Bob Scanlan .02 .10
474 Gary Scott .02 .10
475 Dave Smith .02 .10
476 Sammy Sosa .20 .50
477 Hector Villanueva .02 .10
478 Scott Bankhead .02 .10
479 Tim Belcher .02 .10
480 Freddie Benavides .02 .10
481 Jacob Brumfield .02 .10
482 Norm Charlton .02 .10
483 Dwayne Henry .02 .10
484 Dave Martinez .02 .10
485 Bip Roberts .02 .10
486 Reggie Sanders .07 .20
487 Greg Swindell .02 .10
488 Ryan Bowen .02 .10
489 Casey Candaele .02 .10
490 Juan Guerrero UER .02 .10
(photo on front is Andujar Cedeno
491 Pete Incaviglia .02 .10
492 Jeff Juden .02 .10
493 Rob Murphy .02 .10
494 Mark Portugal .02 .10
495 Rafael Ramirez .02 .10
496 Scott Servais .02 .10
497 Ed Taubensee RC .08 .25
498 Brian Williams RC .02 .10
499 Todd Benzinger .02 .10
500 John Candelaria .02 .10
501 Tom Candiotti .02 .10
502 Tim Crews .02 .10
503 Eric Davis .07 .20
504 Jim Gott .02 .10
505 Dave Hansen .02 .10
506 Carlos Hernandez .02 .10
507 Orel Hershiser .07 .20
508 Eric Karros .07 .20
509 Bob Ojeda .02 .10
510 Steve Wilson .02 .10
511 Moises Alou .07 .20
512 Bret Barberie .02 .10
513 Ivan Calderon .02 .10
514 Gary Carter .07 .20
515 Archi Cianfrocco RC .02 .10
516 Jeff Fassero .02 .10
517 Darrin Fletcher .02 .10
518 Marquis Grissom .07 .20
519 Chris Haney .02 .10
520 Ken Hill .02 .10
521 Chris Nabholz .02 .10
522 Bill Sampen .02 .10
523 John Vander Wal .02 .10
524 Dave Wainhouse .02 .10
525 Larry Walker .10 .30
526 John Wetteland .07 .20
527 Bobby Bonilla .07 .20
528 Sid Fernandez .02 .10
529 John Franco .07 .20
530 Dave Gallagher .02 .10
531 Paul Gibson .02 .10
532 Eddie Murray .20 .50
533 Junior Noboa .02 .10
534 Charlie O'Brien .02 .10
535 Bill Pecota .02 .10
536 Willie Randolph .07 .20
537 Bret Saberhagen .07 .20
538 Dick Schofield .02 .10
539 Pete Schourek .02 .10
540 Ruben Amaro .02 .10
541 Andy Ashby .02 .10
542 Kim Batiste .02 .10
543 Cliff Brantley .02 .10
544 Mariano Duncan .02 .10
545 Jeff Grotewold .02 .10
546 Barry Jones .02 .10
547 Julio Peguero .02 .10
548 Curt Schilling .10 .30
549 Mitch Williams .02 .10
550 Stan Belinda .02 .10
551 Scott Bullett RC .02 .10
552 Cecil Espy .02 .10
553 Jeff King .02 .10
554 Roger Mason .02 .10
555 Paul Miller .02 .10
556 Denny Neagle .07 .20
557 Vicente Palacios .02 .10
558 Bob Patterson .02 .10
559 Tom Prince .02 .10
560 Gary Redus .02 .10
561 Gary Varsho .02 .10
562 Juan Agosto .02 .10
563 Cris Carpenter .02 .10
564 Mark Clark RC .08 .25
565 Jose DeLeon .02 .10
566 Rich Gedman .02 .10
567 Bernard Gilkey .02 .10
568 Rex Hudler .02 .10
569 Tim Jones .02 .10
570 Donovan Osborne .02 .10
571 Mike Perez .02 .10
572 Gerald Perry .02 .10
573 Bob Tewksbury .02 .10
574 Todd Worrell .02 .10
575 Dave Eiland .02 .10
576 Jeremy Hernandez RC .02 .10
577 Craig Lefferts .02 .10
578 Jose Melendez .02 .10
579 Randy Myers .02 .10
580 Gary Pettis .02 .10
581 Rich Rodriguez .02 .10
582 Gary Sheffield .07 .20
583 Craig Shipley .02 .10
584 Kurt Stillwell .02 .10
585 Tim Teufel .02 .10
586 Rod Beck RC .15 .40
587 Dave Burba .02 .10
588 Craig Colbert .02 .10
589 Bryan Hickerson RC .02 .10
590 Mike Jackson .02 .10
591 Mark Leonard .02 .10
592 Jim McNamara .02 .10
593 John Patterson RC .02 .10
594 Dave Righetti .07 .20
595 Cory Snyder .02 .10
596 Bill Swift .02 .10
597 Ted Wood .02 .10
598 Checklist 301-400 .02 .10
599 Checklist 401-500 .02 .10
600 Checklist 501-600 .02 .10

1992 Ultra All-Rookies

Cards from this ten-card standard-size set highlighting a selection of top rookies were randomly inserted in 1992 Ultra II foil packs.

COMPLETE SET (10) 2.50 6.00
1 Eric Karros .40 1.00
2 Andy Stankiewicz .20 .50
3 Gary DiSarcina .20 .50
4 Archi Cianfrocco .20 .50
5 Jim McNamara .20 .50
6 Chad Curtis .50 1.25
7 Kenny Lofton .60 1.50
8 Reggie Sanders .40 1.00
9 Pat Mahomes .50 1.25
10 Donovan Osborne .20 .50

1992 Ultra All-Stars

Featuring many of the 1992 season's stars, cards from this 20-card standard-size set were randomly inserted in 1992 Ultra II foil packs.

COMPLETE SET (20) 10.00 25.00
1 Mark McGwire 1.50 4.00
2 Roberto Alomar .40 1.00
3 Cal Ripken Jr. 2.00 5.00
4 Wade Boggs .40 1.00
5 Mickey Tettleton .10 .30
6 Ken Griffey Jr. 1.00 2.50
7 Roberto Kelly .10 .30
8 Kirby Puckett .60 1.50
9 Frank Thomas .60 1.50
10 Jack McDowell .10 .30
11 Will Clark .40 1.00
12 Ryne Sandberg 1.00 2.50
13 Barry Larkin .40 1.00
14 Gary Sheffield .25 .60
15 Tom Pagnozzi .10 .30
16 Barry Bonds 2.00 5.00
17 Deion Sanders .40 1.00
18 Darryl Strawberry .25 .60
19 David Cone .25 .60
20 Tom Glavine .40 1.00

1992 Ultra Award Winners

This 25-card standard-size set features 18 Gold Glove winners, both Cy Young Award winners, both Rookies of the Year, both league MVP's, and the World Series MVP. The cards were randomly inserted in 1992 Fleer Ultra I packs.

COMPLETE SET (25) 15.00 40.00
1 Jack Morris .40 1.00
2 Chuck Knoblauch .40 1.00
3 Jeff Bagwell 1.00 2.50
4 Terry Pendleton .40 1.00
5 Cal Ripken 3.00 8.00
6 Roger Clemens 2.00 5.00
7 Tom Glavine .60 1.50
8 Tom Pagnozzi .20 .50
9 Ozzie Smith 1.50 4.00
10 Andy Van Slyke .60 1.50
11 Barry Bonds 3.00 8.00
12 Tony Gwynn 1.25 3.00
13 Matt Williams .40 1.00
14 Will Clark .60 1.50
15 Robin Ventura .40 1.00
16 Mark Langston .20 .50
17 Tony Pena .20 .50
18 Devon White .40 1.00
19 Don Mattingly 2.50 6.00
20 Roberto Alomar .60 1.50
21A Cal Ripken ERR 3.00 8.00
(Reversed negative
on card back)
21B Cal Ripken COR 3.00 8.00
22 Ken Griffey Jr. 1.50 4.00
23 Kirby Puckett 1.00 2.50
24 Greg Maddux 1.50 4.00
25 Ryne Sandberg 1.50 4.00

1992 Ultra Gwynn

Tony Gwynn served as a spokesperson for Ultra during 1992 and was the exclusive subject of this 12-card standard-size set. The first ten cards of this set were randomly inserted in 1992 Ultra one packs. More than 2,000 of these cards were personally autographed by Gwynn. These cards are numbered on the back as " X of 10." An additional special two-card subset was available through a mail-in offer for ten 1992 Ultra baseball wrappers plus 1.00 for shipping and handling. This offer was good through October 31st and, according to Fleer, over 100,000 sets were produced. The standard-size cards display action shots of Gwynn framed by green marbled borders. The player's name and the words "Commemorative Series" appear in gold-foil lettering in the bottom border. On a green marbled background, the backs features a color head shot and either a player profile (Special No. 1 on the card back) or Gwynn's comments about other players or the game itself (Special No. 2 on the card back).

COMPLETE SET (10) 4.00 10.00
COMMON GWYNN (1-10) .40 1.00
COMMON MAIL(S1-S2) .40 1.00
1AU Tony Gwynn AU 20.00 50.00

1993 Ultra

The 1993 Ultra baseball set was issued in two series and totaled 650 standard-size cards. The cards are numbered on the back, grouped alphabetically within teams, with NL teams preceding AL. The first series closes with checklist cards (298-300). The second series features 83 Ultra Rookies, 51 Rockies and Marlins, traded veteran players, and other major league veterans not included in the first series. The Rookie cards show a gold foil stamped Rookie "flag" as part of the card design. The key Rookie Card in this set is Jim Edmonds.

COMPLETE SET (650) 12.00 30.00
COMP. SERIES 1 (300) 6.00 15.00
COMP. SERIES 2 (350) 6.00 15.00
1 Steve Avery .05 .15
2 Rafael Belliard .05 .15
3 Damon Berryhill .05 .15
4 Sid Bream .05 .15
5 Ron Gant .10 .30
6 Tom Glavine .20 .50
7 Ryan Klesko .10 .30
8 Mark Lemke .05 .15
9 Javier Lopez .20 .50
10 Greg Olson .05 .15
11 Terry Pendleton .10 .30
12 Deion Sanders .20 .50
13 Mike Stanton .05 .15
14 Paul Assenmacher .05 .15
15 Steve Buechele .05 .15
16 Frank Castillo .05 .15
17 Shawon Dunston .05 .15
18 Mark Grace .20 .50
19 Derrick May .05 .15
20 Chuck McElroy .05 .15
21 Mike Morgan .05 .15
22 Bob Scanlan .05 .15
23 Dwight Smith .05 .15
24 Sammy Sosa .30 .75
25 Rick Wilkins .05 .15
26 Tim Belcher .05 .15
27 Jeff Branson .05 .15
28 Bill Doran .05 .15
29 Chris Hammond .05 .15
30 Barry Larkin .20 .50
31 Hal Morris .05 .15
32 Joe Oliver .05 .15
33 Jose Rijo .05 .15
34 Bip Roberts .05 .15
35 Chris Sabo .05 .15
36 Reggie Sanders .10 .30
37 Craig Biggio .20 .50
38 Ken Caminiti .10 .30
39 Steve Finley .10 .30
40 Luis Gonzalez .10 .30
41 Juan Guerrero .05 .15
42 Pete Harnisch .05 .15
43 Xavier Hernandez .05 .15
44 Doug Jones .05 .15
45 Al Osuna .05 .15
46 Eddie Taubensee .05 .15
47 Scooter Tucker .05 .15
48 Brian Williams .05 .15
49 Pedro Astacio .05 .15
50 Rafael Bournigal .05 .15
51 Brett Butler .10 .30
52 Tom Candiotti .05 .15
53 Eric Davis .10 .30
54 Lenny Harris .05 .15
55 Orel Hershiser .10 .30
56 Eric Karros .10 .30
57 Pedro Martinez .60 1.50
58 Roger McDowell .05 .15
59 Jose Offerman .05 .15
60 Mike Piazza 1.25 3.00
61 Moises Alou .10 .30
62 Kent Bottenfield .05 .15
63 Archi Cianfrocco .05 .15
64 Greg Colbrunn .05 .15
65 Wil Cordero .05 .15
66 Delino DeShields .05 .15
67 Darrin Fletcher .05 .15
68 Ken Hill .05 .15
69 Chris Nabholz .05 .15
70 Mel Rojas .05 .15
71 Larry Walker .10 .30
72 Sid Fernandez .05 .15
73 John Franco .10 .30
74 Dave Gallagher .05 .15
75 Todd Hundley .05 .15
76 Howard Johnson .05 .15
77 Jeff Kent .30 .75
78 Eddie Murray .30 .75
79 Bret Saberhagen .10 .30
80 Chico Walker .05 .15
81 Anthony Young .05 .15
82 Kyle Abbott .05 .15
83 Ruben Amaro .05 .15
84 Juan Bell .05 .15
85 Wes Chamberlain .05 .15
86 Darren Daulton .10 .30
87 Mariano Duncan .05 .15
88 Dave Hollins .05 .15
89 Ricky Jordan .05 .15
90 John Kruk .10 .30
91 Mickey Morandini .05 .15
92 Terry Mulholland .05 .15
93 Ben Rivera .05 .15
94 Mike Williams .05 .15
95 Stan Belinda .05 .15
96 Jay Bell .10 .30
97 Jeff King .05 .15
98 Mike LaValliere .05 .15
99 Lloyd McClendon .05 .15
100 Orlando Merced .05 .15
101 Zane Smith .05 .15
102 Randy Tomlin .05 .15
103 Andy Van Slyke .20 .50
104 Tim Wakefield .30 .75
105 John Wehner .05 .15
106 Bernard Gilkey .05 .15
107 Brian Jordan .10 .30
108 Ray Lankford .10 .30
109 Donovan Osborne .05 .15
110 Tom Pagnozzi .05 .15
111 Mike Perez .05 .15
112 Lee Smith .10 .30
113 Ozzie Smith .50 1.25
114 Bob Tewksbury .05 .15
115 Todd Zeile .05 .15
116 Andy Benes .05 .15
117 Greg W. Harris .05 .15
118 Darrin Jackson .05 .15
119 Fred McGriff .20 .50
120 Rich Rodriguez .05 .15
121 Frank Seminara .05 .15
122 Gary Sheffield .10 .30
123 Craig Shipley .05 .15
124 Kurt Stillwell .05 .15
125 Dan Walters .05 .15
126 Rod Beck .05 .15
127 Mike Benjamin .05 .15
128 Jeff Brantley .05 .15
129 John Burkett .05 .15
130 Will Clark .20 .50
131 Royce Clayton .05 .15

132 Steve Hosey	.05	.15
133 Mike Jackson	.05	.15
134 Darren Lewis	.05	.15
135 Kirt Manwaring	.05	.15
136 Bill Swift	.05	.15
137 Robby Thompson	.05	.15
138 Brady Anderson	.10	.30
139 Glenn Davis	.05	.15
140 Leo Gomez	.05	.15
141 Chito Martinez	.05	.15
142 Ben McDonald	.05	.15
143 Alan Mills	.05	.15
144 Mike Mussina	.20	.50
145 Gregg Olson	.05	.15
146 David Segui	.05	.15
147 Jeff Tackett	.05	.15
148 Jack Clark	.10	.30
149 Scott Cooper	.05	.15
150 Danny Darwin	.05	.15
151 John Dopson	.05	.15
152 Mike Greenwell	.05	.15
153 Tim Naehring	.05	.15
154 Tony Pena	.05	.15
155 Paul Quantrill	.05	.15
156 Mo Vaughn	.10	.30
157 Frank Viola	.10	.30
158 Bob Zupcic	.05	.15
159 Chad Curtis	.05	.15
160 Gary DiSarcina	.05	.15
161 Damion Easley	.05	.15
162 Chuck Finley	.10	.30
163 Tim Fortugno	.05	.15
164 Rene Gonzales	.05	.15
165 Joe Grahe	.05	.15
166 Mark Langston	.05	.15
167 John Orton	.05	.15
168 Luis Polonia	.05	.15
169 Julio Valera	.05	.15
170 Wilson Alvarez	.05	.15
171 George Bell	.05	.15
172 Joey Cora	.05	.15
173 Alex Fernandez	.05	.15
174 Lance Johnson	.05	.15
175 Ron Karkovice	.05	.15
176 Jack McDowell	.05	.15
177 Scott Radinsky	.05	.15
178 Tim Raines	.10	.30
179 Steve Sax	.05	.15
180 Bobby Thigpen	.05	.15
181 Frank Thomas	.30	.75
182 Sandy Alomar Jr.	.05	.15
183 Carlos Baerga	.05	.15
184 Felix Fermin	.05	.15
185 Thomas Howard	.05	.15
186 Mark Lewis	.05	.15
187 Derek Lilliquist	.05	.15
188 Carlos Martinez	.05	.15
189 Charles Nagy	.05	.15
190 Scott Scudder	.05	.15
191 Paul Sorrento	.05	.15
192 Jim Thome	.20	.50
193 Mark Whiten	.05	.15
194 Milt Cuyler UER (Reversed negative on card front)	.05	.15
195 Rob Deer	.05	.15
196 John Doherty	.05	.15
197 Travis Fryman	.10	.30
198 Dan Gladden	.05	.15
199 Mike Henneman	.05	.15
200 John Kiely	.05	.15
201 Chad Kreuter	.05	.15
202 Scott Livingstone	.05	.15
203 Tony Phillips	.05	.15
204 Alan Trammell	.10	.30
205 Mike Boddicker	.05	.15
206 George Brett	.75	2.00
207 Tom Gordon	.05	.15
208 Mark Gubicza	.05	.15
209 Gregg Jefferies	.05	.15
210 Wally Joyner	.10	.30
211 Kevin Koslofski	.05	.15
212 Brent Mayne	.05	.15
213 Brian McRae	.05	.15
214 Kevin McReynolds	.05	.15
215 Rusty Meacham	.05	.15
216 Steve Shifflett	.05	.15
217 Jim Austin	.05	.15
218 Cal Eldred	.05	.15
219 Darryl Hamilton	.05	.15
220 Doug Henry	.05	.15
221 John Jaha	.05	.15
222 Dave Nilsson	.05	.15
223 Jesse Orosco	.05	.15
224 B.J. Surhoff	.10	.30
225 Greg Vaughn	.05	.15
226 Bill Wegman	.05	.15
227 Robin Yount UER Born in Illinois, not in Virginia	.50	1.25
228 Rick Aguilera	.05	.15
229 J.T. Bruett	.05	.15
230 Scott Erickson	.05	.15
231 Kent Hrbek	.10	.30
232 Terry Jorgensen	.05	.15
233 Scott Leius	.05	.15
234 Pat Mahomes	.05	.15
235 Pedro Munoz	.05	.15
236 Kirby Puckett	.30	.75
237 Kevin Tapani	.05	.15
238 Lenny Webster	.05	.15
239 Carl Willis	.05	.15
240 Mike Gallego	.05	.15
241 John Habyan	.05	.15
242 Pat Kelly	.05	.15
243 Kevin Maas	.05	.15
244 Don Mattingly	.75	2.00
245 Hensley Meulens	.05	.15
246 Sam Militello	.05	.15
247 Matt Nokes	.05	.15
248 Melido Perez	.05	.15
249 Andy Stankiewicz	.05	.15
250 Randy Velarde	.05	.15
251 Bob Wickman	.05	.15
252 Bernie Williams	.20	.50
253 Lance Blankenship	.05	.15
254 Mike Bordick	.05	.15
255 Jerry Browne	.05	.15
256 Ron Darling	.05	.15
257 Dennis Eckersley	.10	.30
258 Rickey Henderson	.30	.75
259 Vince Horsman	.05	.15
260 Troy Neel	.05	.15
261 Jeff Parrett	.05	.15
262 Terry Steinbach	.05	.15
263 Bob Welch	.05	.15
264 Bobby Witt	.05	.15
265 Rich Amaral	.05	.15
266 Bret Boone	.10	.30
267 Jay Buhner	.10	.30
268 Dave Fleming	.05	.15
269 Randy Johnson	.30	.75
270 Edgar Martinez	.20	.50
271 Mike Schooler	.05	.15
272 Russ Swan	.05	.15
273 Dave Valle	.05	.15
274 Omar Vizquel	.20	.50
275 Kerry Woodson	.05	.15
276 Kevin Brown	.10	.30
277 Julio Franco	.10	.30
278 Jeff Frye	.05	.15
279 Juan Gonzalez	.10	.30
280 Jeff Huson	.05	.15
281 Rafael Palmeiro	.20	.50
282 Dean Palmer	.10	.30
283 Roger Pavlik	.05	.15
284 Ivan Rodriguez	.20	.50
285 Kenny Rogers	.10	.30
286 Derek Bell	.05	.15
287 Pat Borders	.05	.15
288 Joe Carter	.10	.30
289 Bob MacDonald	.05	.15
290 Jack Morris	.10	.30
291 John Olerud	.10	.30
292 Ed Sprague	.05	.15
293 Todd Stottlemyre	.05	.15
294 Mike Timlin	.05	.15
295 Duane Ward	.05	.15
296 David Wells	.10	.30
297 Devon White	.10	.30
298 Ray Lankford CL	.05	.15
299 Bobby Witt CL	.05	.15
300 Mike Piazza CL	.30	.75
301 Steve Bedrosian	.05	.15
302 Jeff Blauser	.05	.15
303 Francisco Cabrera	.05	.15
304 Marvin Freeman	.05	.15
305 Brian Hunter	.05	.15
306 David Justice	.10	.30
307 Greg Maddux	.50	1.25
308 Greg McMichael RC	.10	.30
309 Kent Mercker	.05	.15
310 Otis Nixon	.05	.15
311 Pete Smith	.05	.15
312 John Smoltz	.20	.50
313 Jose Guzman	.05	.15
314 Mike Harkey	.05	.15
315 Greg Hibbard	.05	.15
316 Candy Maldonado	.05	.15
317 Randy Myers	.05	.15
318 Dan Plesac	.05	.15
319 Rey Sanchez	.05	.15
320 Ryne Sandberg	.50	1.25
321 Tommy Shields	.05	.15
322 Jose Vizcaino	.05	.15
323 Matt Walbeck RC	.10	.30
324 Willie Wilson	.05	.15
325 Tom Browning	.05	.15
326 Tim Costo	.05	.15
327 Rob Dibble	.10	.30
328 Steve Foster	.05	.15
329 Roberto Kelly	.05	.15
330 Randy Milligan	.05	.15
331 Kevin Mitchell	.05	.15
332 Tim Pugh RC	.10	.30
333 Jeff Reardon	.10	.30
334 John Roper	.05	.15
335 Juan Samuel	.05	.15
336 John Smiley	.05	.15
337 Dan Wilson	.10	.30
338 Scott Aldred	.05	.15
339 Andy Ashby	.05	.15
340 Freddie Benavides	.05	.15
341 Dante Bichette	.10	.30
342 Willie Blair	.05	.15
343 Daryl Boston	.05	.15
344 Vinny Castilla	.30	.75
345 Jerald Clark	.05	.15
346 Alex Cole	.05	.15
347 Andres Galarraga	.10	.30
348 Joe Girardi	.05	.15
349 Ryan Hawblitzel	.05	.15
350 Charlie Hayes	.05	.15
351 Butch Henry	.05	.15
352 Darren Holmes	.05	.15
353 Dale Murphy	.20	.50
354 David Nied	.05	.15
355 Jeff Parrett	.05	.15
356 Steve Reed RC	.10	.30
357 Bruce Ruffin	.05	.15
358 Danny Sheaffer RC	.10	.30
359 Bryn Smith	.05	.15
360 Jim Tatum RC	.10	.30
361 Eric Young	.05	.15
362 Gerald Young	.05	.15
363 Luis Aquino	.05	.15
364 Alex Arias	.05	.15
365 Jack Armstrong	.05	.15
366 Bret Barberie	.05	.15
367 Ryan Bowen	.05	.15
368 Greg Briley	.05	.15
369 Cris Carpenter	.05	.15
370 Chuck Carr	.05	.15
371 Jeff Conine	.10	.30
372 Steve Decker	.05	.15
373 Orestes Destrade	.05	.15
374 Monty Fariss	.05	.15
375 Junior Felix	.05	.15
376 Chris Hammond	.05	.15
377 Bryan Harvey	.05	.15
378 Trevor Hoffman	.30	.75
379 Charlie Hough	.10	.30
380 Joe Klink	.05	.15
381 Richie Lewis RC	.10	.30
382 Dave Magadan	.05	.15
383 Bob McClure	.05	.15
384 Scott Pose RC	.10	.30
385 Rich Renteria	.05	.15
386 Benito Santiago	.10	.30
387 Walt Weiss	.05	.15
388 Nigel Wilson	.05	.15
389 Eric Anthony	.05	.15
390 Jeff Bagwell	.20	.50
391 Andujar Cedeno	.05	.15
392 Doug Drabek	.05	.15
393 Darryl Kile	.10	.30
394 Mark Portugal	.05	.15
395 Karl Rhodes	.05	.15
396 Scott Servais	.05	.15
397 Greg Swindell	.05	.15
398 Tom Goodwin	.05	.15
399 Kevin Gross	.05	.15
400 Carlos Hernandez	.05	.15
401 Ramon Martinez	.05	.15
402 Raul Mondesi	.10	.30
403 Jody Reed	.05	.15
404 Mike Sharperson	.05	.15
405 Cory Snyder	.05	.15
406 Darryl Strawberry	.10	.30
407 Rick Trlicek	.05	.15
408 Tim Wallach	.05	.15
409 Todd Worrell	.05	.15
410 Tavo Alvarez	.05	.15
411 Sean Berry	.05	.15
412 Frank Bolick	.05	.15
413 Cliff Floyd	.10	.30
414 Mike Gardiner	.05	.15
415 Marquis Grissom	.10	.30
416 Tim Laker RC	.10	.30
417 Mike Lansing RC	.20	.50
418 Dennis Martinez	.10	.30
419 John Vander Wal	.05	.15
420 John Wetteland	.10	.30
421 Rondell White	.10	.30
422 Bobby Bonilla	.10	.30
423 Jeromy Burnitz	.10	.30
424 Vince Coleman	.05	.15
425 Mike Draper	.05	.15
426 Tony Fernandez	.05	.15
427 Dwight Gooden	.10	.30
428 Jeff Innis	.05	.15
429 Bobby Jones	.10	.30
430 Mike Maddux	.05	.15
431 Charlie O'Brien	.05	.15
432 Joe Orsulak	.05	.15
433 Pete Schourek	.05	.15
434 Frank Tanana	.05	.15
435 Ryan Thompson	.05	.15
436 Kim Batiste	.05	.15
437 Mark Davis	.05	.15
438 Jose DeLeon	.05	.15
439 Len Dykstra	.10	.30
440 Jim Eisenreich	.05	.15
441 Tommy Greene	.05	.15
442 Pete Incaviglia	.05	.15
443 Danny Jackson	.05	.15
444 Todd Pratt RC	.20	.50
445 Curt Schilling	.10	.30
446 Milt Thompson	.05	.15
447 David West	.05	.15
448 Mitch Williams	.05	.15
449 Steve Cooke	.05	.15
450 Carlos Garcia	.05	.15
451 Al Martin	.05	.15
452 Blas Minor	.05	.15
453 Dennis Moeller	.05	.15
454 Denny Neagle	.10	.30
455 Don Slaught	.05	.15
456 Lonnie Smith	.05	.15
457 Paul Wagner	.05	.15
458 Bob Walk	.05	.15
459 Kevin Young	.10	.30
460 Rene Arocha RC	.20	.50
461 Brian Barber	.05	.15
462 Rheal Cormier	.05	.15
463 Gregg Jefferies	.05	.15
464 Joe Magrane	.05	.15
465 Omar Olivares	.05	.15
466 Geronimo Pena	.05	.15
467 Allen Watson	.05	.15
468 Mark Whiten	.05	.15
469 Derek Bell	.05	.15
470 Phil Clark	.05	.15
471 Pat Gomez RC	.10	.30
472 Tony Gwynn	.40	1.00
473 Jeremy Hernandez	.05	.15
474 Bruce Hurst	.05	.15
475 Phil Plantier	.05	.15
476 Scott Sanders RC	.10	.30
477 Tim Scott	.05	.15
478 Darrell Sherman RC	.10	.30
479 Guillermo Velasquez	.05	.15
480 Tim Worrell RC	.10	.30
481 Todd Benzinger	.05	.15
482 Bud Black	.05	.15
483 Barry Bonds	.75	2.00
484 Dave Burba	.05	.15
485 Bryan Hickerson	.05	.15
486 Dave Martinez	.05	.15
487 Willie McGee	.10	.30
488 Jeff Reed	.05	.15
489 Kevin Rogers	.05	.15
490 Matt Williams	.10	.30
491 Trevor Wilson	.05	.15
492 Harold Baines	.10	.30
493 Mike Devereaux	.05	.15
494 Todd Frohwirth	.05	.15
495 Chris Hoiles	.05	.15
496 Luis Mercedes	.05	.15
497 Sherman Obando RC	.10	.30
498 Brad Pennington	.05	.15
499 Harold Reynolds	.10	.30
500 Arthur Rhodes	.05	.15
501 Cal Ripken	1.00	2.50
502 Rick Sutcliffe	.10	.30
503 Fernando Valenzuela	.10	.30
504 Mark Williamson	.05	.15
505 Scott Bankhead	.05	.15
506 Greg Blosser	.05	.15
507 Ivan Calderon	.05	.15
508 Roger Clemens	.60	1.50
509 Andre Dawson	.10	.30
510 Scott Fletcher	.05	.15
511 Greg A. Harris	.05	.15
512 Billy Hatcher	.05	.15
513 Bob Melvin	.05	.15
514 Carlos Quintana	.05	.15
515 Luis Rivera	.05	.15
516 Jeff Russell	.05	.15
517 Ken Ryan RC	.10	.30
518 Chili Davis	.10	.30
519 Jim Edmonds RC	2.00	5.00
520 Gary Gaetti	.10	.30
521 Torey Lovullo	.05	.15
522 Troy Percival	.20	.50
523 Tim Salmon	.20	.50
524 Scott Sanderson	.05	.15
525 J.T. Snow RC	.30	.75
526 Jerome Walton	.05	.15
527 Jason Bere	.05	.15
528 Rod Bolton	.05	.15
529 Ellis Burks	.10	.30
530 Carlton Fisk	.20	.50
531 Craig Grebeck	.05	.15
532 Ozzie Guillen	.10	.30
533 Roberto Hernandez	.05	.15
534 Bo Jackson	.30	.75
535 Kirk McCaskill	.05	.15
536 Dave Stieb	.05	.15
537 Robin Ventura	.10	.30
538 Albert Belle	.10	.30
539 Mike Bielecki	.05	.15
540 Glenallen Hill	.05	.15
541 Reggie Jefferson	.05	.15
542 Kenny Lofton	.10	.30
543 Jeff Mutis	.05	.15
544 Junior Ortiz	.05	.15
545 Manny Ramirez	.50	1.25
546 Jeff Treadway	.05	.15
547 Kevin Wickander	.05	.15
548 Cecil Fielder	.10	.30
549 Kirk Gibson	.10	.30
550 Greg Gohr	.05	.15
551 David Haas	.05	.15
552 Bill Krueger	.05	.15
553 Mike Moore	.05	.15
554 Mickey Tettleton	.05	.15
555 Lou Whitaker	.10	.30
556 Kevin Appier	.10	.30
557 Billy Brewer	.05	.15
558 David Cone	.10	.30
559 Greg Gagne	.05	.15
560 Mark Gardner	.05	.15
561 Phil Hiatt	.05	.15
562 Felix Jose	.05	.15
563 Jose Lind	.05	.15
564 Mike Macfarlane	.05	.15
565 Keith Miller	.05	.15
566 Jeff Montgomery	.05	.15
567 Hipolito Pichardo	.05	.15
568 Ricky Bones	.05	.15
569 Tom Brunansky	.05	.15
570 Joe Kmak	.05	.15
571 Pat Listach	.05	.15
572 Graeme Lloyd RC	.20	.50
573 Carlos Maldonado	.05	.15
574 Josias Manzanillo	.05	.15
575 Matt Mieske	.05	.15
576 Kevin Reimer	.05	.15
577 Bill Spiers	.05	.15
578 Dickie Thon	.05	.15
579 Willie Banks	.05	.15
580 Jim Deshaies	.05	.15
581 Mark Guthrie	.05	.15
582 Brian Harper	.05	.15
583 Chuck Knoblauch	.10	.30
584 Gene Larkin	.05	.15
585 Shane Mack	.05	.15
586 David McCarty	.05	.15
587 Mike Pagliarulo	.05	.15
588 Mike Trombley	.05	.15
589 Dave Winfield	.10	.30
590 Jim Abbott	.20	.50
591 Wade Boggs	.20	.50
592 Russ Davis RC	.10	.30
593 Steve Farr	.05	.15
594 Steve Howe	.05	.15
595 Mike Humphreys	.05	.15
596 Jimmy Key	.10	.30
597 Jim Leyritz	.05	.15
598 Bobby Munoz	.05	.15
599 Paul O'Neill	.20	.50
600 Spike Owen	.05	.15
601 Mike Stanley	.05	.15
602 Danny Tartabull	.05	.15
603 Scott Brosius	.10	.30
604 Storm Davis	.05	.15
605 Eric Fox	.05	.15
606 Rich Gossage	.10	.30
607 Scott Hemond	.05	.15
608 Dave Henderson	.05	.15
609 Mark McGwire	.75	2.00
610 Mike Mohler RC	.10	.30
611 Edwin Nunez	.05	.15
612 Kevin Seitzer	.05	.15
613 Ruben Sierra	.10	.30
614 Chris Bosio	.05	.15
615 Norm Charlton	.05	.15
616 Jim Converse RC	.10	.30
617 John Cummings RC	.10	.30
618 Mike Felder	.05	.15
619 Ken Griffey Jr.	.50	1.25
620 Mike Hampton	.10	.30
621 Erik Hanson	.05	.15
622 Bill Haselman	.05	.15
623 Tino Martinez	.20	.50
624 Lee Tinsley	.05	.15
625 Fernando Vina RC	.20	.50
626 David Wainhouse	.05	.15
627 Jose Canseco	.20	.50
628 Benji Gil	.05	.15
629 Tom Henke	.05	.15
630 David Hulse RC	.10	.30
631 Manuel Lee	.05	.15
632 Craig Lefferts	.05	.15
633 Robb Nen	.10	.30
634 Gary Redus	.05	.15
635 Bill Ripken	.05	.15
636 Nolan Ryan	1.25	3.00
637 Dan Smith	.05	.15
638 Matt Whiteside RC	.10	.30
639 Roberto Alomar	.20	.50
640 Juan Guzman	.05	.15
641 Pat Hentgen	.05	.15
642 Darrin Jackson	.05	.15
643 Randy Knorr	.05	.15
644 Domingo Martinez RC	.10	.30
645 Paul Molitor	.10	.30
646 Dick Schofield	.05	.15
647 Dave Stewart	.10	.30
648 Rey Sanchez CL	.05	.15
649 Jeremy Hernandez CL	.05	.15
650 Junior Ortiz CL	.05	.15

1993 Ultra All-Rookies

Inserted into series II packs at a rate of one in 18, this ten-card standard-size set features cutout color player action shots that are superposed upon a black background, which carries the player's uniform number, position, team name, and the set's title in multicolored lettering. The set is sequenced in alphabetical order. The key cards in this set are Mike Piazza and Tim Salmon.

COMPLETE SET (10)	6.00	15.00
1 Rene Arocha	.75	2.00
2 Jeff Conine	.50	1.25
3 Phil Hiatt	.25	.60
4 Mike Lansing	.75	2.00
5 Al Martin	.25	.60
6 David Nied	.25	.60
7 Mike Piazza	5.00	12.00
8 Tim Salmon	.75	2.00
9 J.T. Snow	1.25	3.00
10 Kevin Young	.50	1.25

1993 Ultra All-Stars

Inserted into series II packs at a rate of one in nine, this 20-card standard-size set features National League (1-10) and American League (11-20) All-Stars.

COMPLETE SET (20)	15.00	40.00
1 Darren Daulton	.50	1.25
2 Will Clark	.75	2.00
3 Ryne Sandberg	2.00	5.00
4 Barry Larkin	.75	2.00
5 Gary Sheffield	.50	1.25
6 Barry Bonds	3.00	8.00
7 Ray Lankford	.50	1.25
8 Larry Walker	.50	1.25
9 Greg Maddux	2.00	5.00
10 Lee Smith	.50	1.25
11 Ivan Rodriguez	.75	2.00
12 Mark McGwire	3.00	8.00
13 Carlos Baerga	.25	.60
14 Cal Ripken	4.00	10.00
15 Edgar Martinez	.75	2.00
16 Juan Gonzalez	.50	1.25
17 Ken Griffey Jr.	2.00	5.00
18 Kirby Puckett	1.25	3.00
19 Frank Thomas	1.25	3.00
20 Mike Mussina	.75	2.00

1993 Ultra Award Winners

Randomly inserted in first series packs, this 25-card standard-size insert set of 1993 Ultra Award Winners honors the Top Glove for the National (1-9) and American (10-18) Leagues and other major award winners (19-25).

COMPLETE SET (25)	15.00	40.00
1 Greg Maddux	2.00	5.00
2 Tom Pagnozzi	.25	.60
3 Mark Grace	.75	2.00
4 Jose Lind	.25	.60
5 Terry Pendleton	.50	1.25
6 Ozzie Smith	2.00	5.00
7 Barry Bonds	3.00	8.00
8 Andy Van Slyke	.75	2.00
9 Larry Walker	.50	1.25
10 Mark Langston	.25	.60
11 Ivan Rodriguez	.75	2.00
12 Don Mattingly	3.00	8.00
13 Roberto Alomar	.75	2.00
14 Robin Ventura	.50	1.25
15 Cal Ripken	4.00	10.00
16 Ken Griffey	2.00	5.00
17 Kirby Puckett	1.25	3.00
18 Devon White	.50	1.25
19 Pat Listach	.25	.60
20 Eric Karros	.50	1.25
21 Pat Borders	.25	.60
22 Greg Maddux	2.00	5.00
23 Dennis Eckersley	.50	1.25
24 Barry Bonds	3.00	8.00
25 Gary Sheffield	.50	1.25

1993 Ultra Eckersley

Randomly inserted in first series foil packs, this 10-card (cards 11 and 12 were mail-aways) standard-size set salutes one of baseball's greatest relief pitchers, Dennis Eckersley. Two additional cards (11 and 12) were available through a mail-in offer

for ten,1993 Fleer Ultra baseball wrappers plus 1.00 for postage and handling. The expiration for this offer was September 30, 1993. Eckersley personally autographed more than 2,000 of these cards. The cards feature silver foil stamping on both sides.

COMPLETE SET (10)	1.50	4.00
COMMON CARD (1-10)	.20	.50
COMMON MAIL (11-12)	.40	1.00
P1 Dennis Eckersley Paul Mullan Promo	1.50	4.00
AU Dennis Eckersley AU	20.00	50.00

1993 Ultra Home Run Kings

Randomly inserted into all 1993 Ultra packs, this ten-card standard-size set features the best long ball hitters in baseball.

COMPLETE SET (10)	8.00	20.00
1 Juan Gonzalez	.60	1.50
2 Mark McGwire	4.00	10.00
3 Cecil Fielder	.60	1.50
4 Fred McGriff	1.00	2.50
5 Albert Belle	.60	1.50
6 Barry Bonds	4.00	10.00
7 Joe Carter	.60	1.50
8 Gary Sheffield	.60	1.50
9 Darren Daulton	.60	1.50
10 Dave Hollins	.30	.75

1993 Ultra Performers

This ten-card standard-size set could only be ordered directly from Fleer by sending in 9.95, five Fleer/Ultra baseball wrappers, and an order blank found in hobby and sports periodicals.

COMPLETE SET (10)	8.00	20.00
1 Barry Bonds	2.00	5.00
2 Juan Gonzalez	.30	.75
3 Ken Griffey Jr.	1.25	3.00
4 Eric Karros	.30	.75
5 Pat Listach	.15	.40
6 Greg Maddux	1.25	3.00
7 David Nied	.15	.40
8 Gary Sheffield	.30	.75
9 J.T. Snow	.75	2.00
10 Frank Thomas	.75	2.00

1993 Ultra Strikeout Kings

Inserted into series II packs at a rate of one in 37, this five-card standard-size showcases outstanding pitchers from both leagues.

COMPLETE SET (5)	12.50	25.00
1 Roger Clemens	4.00	10.00
2 Juan Guzman	.40	1.00
3 Randy Johnson	2.00	5.00
4 Nolan Ryan	8.00	20.00
5 John Smoltz	1.25	3.00

1994 Ultra

The 1994 Ultra baseball set consists of 600 standard-size cards that were issued in two series of 300. Each pack contains at least one insert card, while "Hot Packs" have nothing but insert cards in them. The cards are numbered on the back, grouped alphabetically within teams, and checklisted below alphabetically according to teams for each league with AL preceding NL. Rookie Cards include Ray Durham and Chan Ho Park.

COMPLETE SET (600)	12.00	30.00
COMP. SERIES 1 (300)	6.00	15.00
COMP. SERIES 2 (300)	6.00	15.00
1 Jeffrey Hammonds	.05	.15
2 Chris Hoiles	.05	.15
3 Ben McDonald	.05	.15

Card	Low	High
4 Mark McLemore	.05	.15
5 Alan Mills	.05	.15
6 Jamie Moyer	.10	.30
7 Brad Pennington	.05	.15
8 Jim Poole	.05	.15
9 Cal Ripken Jr.	1.00	2.50
10 Jack Voigt	.05	.15
11 Roger Clemens	.60	1.50
12 Danny Darwin	.05	.15
13 Andre Dawson	.10	.30
14 Scott Fletcher	.05	.15
15 Greg A. Harris	.05	.15
16 Billy Hatcher	.05	.15
17 Jeff Russell	.05	.15
18 Aaron Sele	.05	.15
19 Mo Vaughn	.10	.30
20 Mike Butcher	.05	.15
21 Rod Correia	.05	.15
22 Steve Frey	.05	.15
23 Phil Leftwich RC	.05	.15
24 Torey Lovullo	.05	.15
25 Ken Patterson	.05	.15
26 Eduardo Perez UER (listed as a Twin instead of Angel)	.05	.15
27 Tim Salmon	.20	.50
28 J.T. Snow	.10	.30
29 Chris Turner	.05	.15
30 Wilson Alvarez	.05	.15
31 Jason Bere	.05	.15
32 Joey Cora	.05	.15
33 Alex Fernandez	.05	.15
34 Roberto Hernandez	.05	.15
35 Lance Johnson	.05	.15
36 Ron Karkovice	.05	.15
37 Kirk McCaskill	.05	.15
38 Jeff Schwarz	.05	.15
39 Frank Thomas	.30	.75
40 Sandy Alomar Jr.	.05	.15
41 Albert Belle	.10	.30
42 Felix Fermin	.05	.15
43 Wayne Kirby	.05	.15
44 Tom Kramer	.05	.15
45 Kenny Lofton	.10	.30
46 Jose Mesa	.05	.15
47 Eric Plunk	.05	.15
48 Paul Sorrento	.05	.15
49 Jim Thome	.20	.50
50 Bill Wertz	.05	.15
51 John Doherty	.05	.15
52 Cecil Fielder	.10	.30
53 Travis Fryman	.10	.30
54 Chris Gomez	.05	.15
55 Mike Henneman	.05	.15
56 Chad Kreuter	.05	.15
57 Bob MacDonald	.05	.15
58 Mike Moore	.05	.15
59 Tony Phillips	.05	.15
60 Lou Whitaker	.10	.30
61 Kevin Appier	.10	.30
62 Greg Gagne	.05	.15
63 Chris Gwynn	.05	.15
64 Bob Hamelin	.05	.15
65 Chris Haney	.05	.15
66 Phil Hiatt	.05	.15
67 Felix Jose	.05	.15
68 Jose Lind	.05	.15
69 Mike Macfarlane	.05	.15
70 Jeff Montgomery	.05	.15
71 Hipolito Pichardo	.05	.15
72 Juan Bell	.05	.15
73 Cal Eldred	.05	.15
74 Darryl Hamilton	.05	.15
75 Doug Henry	.05	.15
76 Mike Ignasiak	.05	.15
77 John Jaha	.05	.15
78 Graeme Lloyd	.05	.15
79 Angel Miranda	.05	.15
80 Dave Nilsson	.05	.15
81 Troy O'Leary	.05	.15
82 Kevin Reimer	.05	.15
83 Willie Banks	.05	.15
84 Larry Casian	.05	.15
85 Scott Erickson	.05	.15
86 Eddie Guardado	.10	.30
87 Kent Hrbek	.10	.30
88 Terry Jorgensen	.05	.15
89 Chuck Knoblauch	.10	.30
90 Pat Meares	.05	.15
91 Mike Trombley	.05	.15
92 Dave Winfield	.10	.30
93 Wade Boggs	.20	.50
94 Scott Kamieniecki	.05	.15
95 Pat Kelly	.05	.15
96 Jimmy Key	.10	.30
97 Jim Leyritz	.05	.15
98 Bobby Munoz	.05	.15
99 Paul O'Neill	.20	.50
100 Melido Perez	.05	.15
101 Mike Stanley	.05	.15
102 Danny Tartabull	.05	.15
103 Bernie Williams	.20	.50
104 Kurt Abbott RC	.05	.15
105 Mike Bordick	.05	.15
106 Ron Darling	.05	.15
107 Brent Gates	.05	.15
108 Miguel Jimenez	.05	.15
109 Steve Karsay	.05	.15
110 Scott Lydy	.05	.15
111 Mark McGwire	.75	2.00
112 Troy Neel	.05	.15
113 Craig Paquette	.05	.15
114 Bob Welch	.05	.15
115 Bobby Witt	.05	.15
116 Rich Amaral	.05	.15
117 Mike Blowers	.05	.15
118 Jay Buhner	.10	.30
119 Dave Fleming	.05	.15
120 Ken Griffey Jr.	.50	1.25
121 Tino Martinez	.20	.50
122 Marc Newfield	.05	.15
123 Ted Power	.05	.15
124 Mackey Sasser	.05	.15
125 Omar Vizquel	.20	.50
126 Kevin Brown	.10	.30
127 Juan Gonzalez	.10	.30
128 Tom Henke	.05	.15
129 David Hulse	.05	.15
130 Dean Palmer	.10	.30
131 Roger Pavlik	.05	.15
132 Ivan Rodriguez	.20	.50
133 Kenny Rogers	.10	.30
134 Doug Strange	.05	.15
135 Pat Borders	.05	.15
136 Joe Carter	.10	.30
137 Darnell Coles	.05	.15
138 Pat Hentgen	.05	.15
139 Al Leiter	.10	.30
140 Paul Molitor	.10	.30
141 John Olerud	.10	.30
142 Ed Sprague	.05	.15
143 Dave Stewart	.10	.30
144 Mike Timlin	.05	.15
145 Duane Ward	.05	.15
146 Devon White	.10	.30
147 Steve Avery	.05	.15
148 Steve Bedrosian	.05	.15
149 Damon Berryhill	.05	.15
150 Jeff Blauser	.05	.15
151 Tom Glavine	.20	.50
152 Chipper Jones	.30	.75
153 Mark Lemke	.05	.15
154 Fred McGriff	.20	.50
155 Greg McMichael	.05	.15
156 Deion Sanders	.20	.50
157 John Smoltz	.20	.50
158 Mark Wohlers	.05	.15
159 Jose Bautista	.05	.15
160 Steve Buechele	.05	.15
161 Mike Harkey	.05	.15
162 Greg Hibbard	.05	.15
163 Chuck McElroy	.05	.15
164 Mike Morgan	.05	.15
165 Kevin Roberson	.05	.15
166 Ryne Sandberg	.50	1.25
167 Jose Vizcaino	.05	.15
168 Rick Wilkins	.05	.15
169 Willie Wilson	.05	.15
170 Willie Greene	.05	.15
171 Roberto Kelly	.05	.15
172 Larry Luebbers RC	.05	.15
173 Kevin Mitchell	.05	.15
174 Joe Oliver	.05	.15
175 John Roper	.05	.15
176 Johnny Ruffin	.05	.15
177 Reggie Sanders	.10	.30
178 John Smiley	.05	.15
179 Jerry Spradlin RC	.05	.15
180 Freddie Benavides	.05	.15
181 Dante Bichette	.10	.30
182 Willie Blair	.05	.15
183 Kent Bottenfield	.05	.15
184 Jerald Clark	.05	.15
185 Joe Girardi	.05	.15
186 Roberto Mejia	.05	.15
187 Steve Reed	.05	.15
188 Armando Reynoso	.05	.15
189 Bruce Ruffin	.05	.15
190 Eric Young	.05	.15
191 Luis Aquino	.05	.15
192 Bret Barberie	.05	.15
193 Ryan Bowen	.05	.15
194 Chuck Carr	.05	.15
195 Orestes Destrade	.05	.15
196 Richie Lewis	.05	.15
197 Dave Magadan	.05	.15
198 Bob Natal	.05	.15
199 Gary Sheffield	.10	.30
200 Matt Turner	.05	.15
201 Darrell Whitmore	.05	.15
202 Eric Anthony	.05	.15
203 Jeff Bagwell	.20	.50
204 Andujar Cedeno	.05	.15
205 Luis Gonzalez	.10	.30
206 Xavier Hernandez	.05	.15
207 Doug Jones	.05	.15
208 Darryl Kile	.10	.30
209 Scott Servais	.05	.15
210 Greg Swindell	.05	.15
211 Brian Williams	.05	.15
212 Pedro Astacio	.05	.15
213 Brett Butler	.10	.30
214 Omar Daal	.05	.15
215 Jim Gott	.05	.15
216 Raul Mondesi	.10	.30
217 Jose Offerman	.05	.15
218 Mike Piazza	.60	1.50
219 Cory Snyder	.05	.15
220 Tim Wallach	.05	.15
221 Todd Worrell	.05	.15
222 Moises Alou	.10	.30
223 Sean Berry	.05	.15
224 Wil Cordero	.05	.15
225 Jeff Fassero	.05	.15
226 Darrin Fletcher	.05	.15
227 Cliff Floyd	.10	.30
228 Marquis Grissom	.10	.30
229 Ken Hill	.05	.15
230 Mike Lansing	.05	.15
231 Kirk Rueter	.05	.15
232 John Wetteland	.10	.30
233 Rondell White	.10	.30
234 Tim Bogar	.05	.15
235 Jeromy Burnitz	.10	.30
236 Dwight Gooden	.10	.30
237 Todd Hundley	.05	.15
238 Jeff Kent	.20	.50
239 Josias Manzanillo	.05	.15
240 Joe Orsulak	.05	.15
241 Ryan Thompson	.05	.15
242 Kim Batiste	.05	.15
243 Darren Daulton	.10	.30
244 Tommy Greene	.05	.15
245 Dave Hollins	.05	.15
246 Pete Incaviglia	.05	.15
247 Danny Jackson	.05	.15
248 Ricky Jordan	.05	.15
249 John Kruk	.10	.30
250 Mickey Morandini	.05	.15
251 Terry Mulholland	.05	.15
252 Ben Rivera	.05	.15
253 Kevin Stocker	.05	.15
254 Jay Bell	.10	.30
255 Steve Cooke	.05	.15
256 Jeff King	.05	.15
257 Al Martin	.05	.15
258 Danny Miceli	.05	.15
259 Blas Minor	.05	.15
260 Don Slaught	.05	.15
261 Paul Wagner	.05	.15
262 Tim Wakefield	.20	.50
263 Kevin Young	.05	.15
264 Rene Arocha	.05	.15
265 Richard Batchelor RC	.05	.15
266 Gregg Jefferies	.05	.15
267 Brian Jordan	.10	.30
268 Jose Oquendo	.05	.15
269 Donovan Osborne	.05	.15
270 Erik Pappas	.05	.15
271 Mike Perez	.05	.15
272 Bob Tewksbury	.05	.15
273 Mark Whiten	.05	.15
274 Todd Zeile	.05	.15
275 Andy Ashby	.05	.15
276 Brad Ausmus	.20	.50
277 Phil Clark	.05	.15
278 Jeff Gardner	.05	.15
279 Ricky Gutierrez	.05	.15
280 Tony Gwynn	.40	1.00
281 Tim Mauser	.05	.15
282 Scott Sanders	.05	.15
283 Frank Seminara	.05	.15
284 Wally Whitehurst	.05	.15
285 Rod Beck	.05	.15
286 Barry Bonds	.75	2.00
287 Dave Burba	.05	.15
288 Mark Carreon	.05	.15
289 Royce Clayton	.05	.15
290 Mike Jackson	.05	.15
291 Darren Lewis	.05	.15
292 Kirt Manwaring	.05	.15
293 Dave Martinez	.05	.15
294 Billy Swift	.05	.15
295 Salomon Torres	.05	.15
296 Matt Williams	.10	.30
297 Checklist 1-75	.05	.15
298 Checklist 76-150	.05	.15
299 Checklist 151-225	.05	.15
300 Checklist 226-300	.05	.15
301 Brady Anderson	.10	.30
302 Harold Baines	.10	.30
303 Damon Buford	.05	.15
304 Mike Devereaux	.05	.15
305 Sid Fernandez	.05	.15
306 Rick Krivda RC	.05	.15
307 Mike Mussina	.20	.50
308 Rafael Palmeiro	.20	.50
309 Arthur Rhodes	.05	.15
310 Chris Sabo	.05	.15
311 Lee Smith	.10	.30
312 Gregg Zaun RC	.08	.25
313 Scott Cooper	.05	.15
314 Mike Greenwell	.05	.15
315 Tim Naehring	.05	.15
316 Otis Nixon	.05	.15
317 Paul Quantrill	.05	.15
318 John Valentin	.05	.15
319 Dave Valle	.05	.15
320 Frank Viola	.10	.30
321 Brian Anderson RC	.15	.40
322 Garret Anderson	.30	.75
323 Chad Curtis	.05	.15
324 Chili Davis	.10	.30
325 Gary DiSarcina	.05	.15
326 Damion Easley	.05	.15
327 Jim Edmonds	.30	.75
328 Chuck Finley	.10	.30
329 Joe Grahe	.05	.15
330 Bo Jackson	.30	.75
331 Mark Langston	.05	.15
332 Harold Reynolds	.10	.30
333 James Baldwin	.05	.15
334 Ray Durham RC	.40	1.00
335 Julio Franco	.10	.30
336 Craig Grebeck	.05	.15
337 Ozzie Guillen	.10	.30
338 Joe Hall RC	.05	.15
339 Darrin Jackson	.05	.15
340 Jack McDowell	.05	.15
341 Tim Raines	.10	.30
342 Robin Ventura	.10	.30
343 Carlos Baerga	.05	.15
344 Derek Lilliquist	.05	.15
345 Dennis Martinez	.10	.30
346 Jack Morris	.10	.30
347 Eddie Murray	.30	.75
348 Chris Nabholz	.05	.15
349 Charles Nagy	.05	.15
350 Chad Ogea	.05	.15
351 Manny Ramirez	.30	.75
352 Omar Vizquel	.20	.50
353 Tim Belcher	.05	.15
354 Eric Davis	.10	.30
355 Kirk Gibson	.10	.30
356 Rick Greene	.05	.15
357 Mickey Tettleton	.05	.15
358 Alan Trammell	.10	.30
359 David Wells	.10	.30
360 Stan Belinda	.05	.15
361 Vince Coleman	.05	.15
362 David Cone	.10	.30
363 Gary Gaetti	.10	.30
364 Tom Gordon	.05	.15
365 Dave Henderson	.05	.15
366 Wally Joyner	.10	.30
367 Brent Mayne	.05	.15
368 Brian McRae	.05	.15
369 Michael Tucker	.05	.15
370 Ricky Bones	.05	.15
371 Brian Harper	.05	.15
372 Tyrone Hill	.05	.15
373 Mark Kiefer	.05	.15
374 Pat Listach	.05	.15
375 Mike Matheny RC	.30	.75
376 Jose Mercedes RC	.05	.15
377 Jody Reed	.05	.15
378 Kevin Seitzer	.05	.15
379 B.J. Surhoff	.10	.30
380 Greg Vaughn	.05	.15
381 Turner Ward	.05	.15
382 Wes Weger RC	.05	.15
383 Bill Wegman	.05	.15
384 Rick Aguilera	.05	.15
385 Rich Becker	.05	.15
386 Alex Cole	.05	.15
387 Steve Dunn	.05	.15
388 Keith Garagozzo RC	.05	.15
389 LaTroy Hawkins RC	.15	.40
390 Shane Mack	.05	.15
391 David McCarty	.05	.15
392 Pedro Munoz	.05	.15
393 Derek Parks	.05	.15
394 Kirby Puckett	.30	.75
395 Kevin Tapani	.05	.15
396 Matt Walbeck	.05	.15
397 Jim Abbott	.20	.50
398 Mike Gallego	.05	.15
399 Xavier Hernandez	.05	.15
400 Don Mattingly	.75	2.00
401 Terry Mulholland	.05	.15
402 Matt Nokes	.05	.15
403 Luis Polonia	.05	.15
404 Bob Wickman	.05	.15
405 Mark Acre RC	.05	.15
406 Fausto Cruz RC	.05	.15
407 Dennis Eckersley	.10	.30
408 Rickey Henderson	.30	.75
409 Stan Javier	.05	.15
410 Carlos Reyes RC	.05	.15
411 Ruben Sierra	.10	.30
412 Terry Steinbach	.05	.15
413 Bill Taylor RC	.05	.15
414 Todd Van Poppel	.05	.15
415 Eric Anthony	.05	.15
416 Bobby Ayala	.05	.15
417 Chris Bosio	.05	.15
418 Tim Davis	.05	.15
419 Randy Johnson	.30	.75
420 Kevin King RC	.05	.15
421 Anthony Manahan RC	.05	.15
422 Edgar Martinez	.20	.50
423 Keith Mitchell	.05	.15
424 Roger Salkeld	.05	.15
425 Mac Suzuki RC	.15	.40
426 Dan Wilson	.05	.15
427 Duff Brumley RC	.05	.15
428 Jose Canseco	.20	.50
429 Will Clark	.20	.50
430 Steve Dreyer RC	.05	.15
431 Rick Helling	.05	.15
432 Chris James	.05	.15
433 Matt Whiteside	.05	.15
434 Roberto Alomar	.20	.50
435 Scott Brow	.05	.15
436 Domingo Cedeno	.05	.15
437 Carlos Delgado	.20	.50
438 Juan Guzman	.05	.15
439 Paul Spoljaric	.05	.15
440 Todd Stottlemyre	.05	.15
441 Woody Williams	.05	.15
442 David Justice	.10	.30
443 Mike Kelly	.05	.15
444 Ryan Klesko	.10	.30
445 Javier Lopez	.10	.30
446 Greg Maddux	.50	1.25
447 Kent Mercker	.05	.15
448 Charlie O'Brien	.05	.15
449 Terry Pendleton	.10	.30
450 Mike Stanton	.05	.15
451 Tony Tarasco	.05	.15
452 Terrell Wade RC	.05	.15
453 Willie Banks	.05	.15
454 Shawon Dunston	.05	.15
455 Mark Grace	.20	.50
456 Jose Guzman	.05	.15
457 Jose Hernandez	.05	.15
458 Glenallen Hill	.05	.15
459 Blaise Ilsley RC	.05	.15
460 Brooks Kieschnick RC	.05	.15
461 Derrick May	.05	.15
462 Randy Myers	.05	.15
463 Karl Rhodes	.05	.15
464 Sammy Sosa	.30	.75
465 Steve Trachsel	.05	.15
466 Anthony Young	.05	.15
467 Eddie Zambrano RC	.05	.15
468 Bret Boone	.10	.30
469 Tom Browning	.05	.15
470 Hector Carrasco	.05	.15
471 Rob Dibble	.10	.30
472 Erik Hanson	.05	.15
473 Thomas Howard	.05	.15
474 Barry Larkin	.20	.50
475 Hal Morris	.05	.15
476 Jose Rijo	.05	.15
477 John Burke	.05	.15
478 Ellis Burks	.10	.30
479 Marvin Freeman	.05	.15
480 Andres Galarraga	.10	.30
481 Greg W. Harris	.05	.15
482 Charlie Hayes	.05	.15
483 Darren Holmes	.05	.15
484 Howard Johnson	.05	.15
485 Marcus Moore	.05	.15
486 David Nied	.05	.15
487 Mark Thompson	.05	.15
488 Walt Weiss	.05	.15
489 Kurt Abbott	.05	.15
490 Matias Carrillo RC	.05	.15
491 Jeff Conine	.10	.30
492 Chris Hammond	.05	.15
493 Bryan Harvey	.05	.15
494 Charlie Hough	.10	.30
495 Yorkis Perez	.05	.15
496 Pat Rapp	.05	.15
497 Benito Santiago	.10	.30
498 David Weathers	.05	.15
499 Craig Biggio	.20	.50
500 Ken Caminiti	.10	.30
501 Doug Drabek	.05	.15
502 Tony Eusebio	.05	.15
503 Steve Finley	.10	.30
504 Pete Harnisch	.05	.15
505 Brian L. Hunter	.05	.15
506 Domingo Jean	.05	.15
507 Todd Jones	.05	.15
508 Orlando Miller	.05	.15
509 James Mouton	.05	.15
510 Roberto Petagine	.05	.15
511 Shane Reynolds	.05	.15
512 Mitch Williams	.05	.15
513 Billy Ashley	.05	.15
514 Tom Candiotti	.05	.15
515 Delino DeShields	.05	.15
516 Kevin Gross	.05	.15
517 Orel Hershiser	.10	.30
518 Eric Karros	.10	.30
519 Ramon Martinez	.05	.15
520 Chan Ho Park RC	.30	.75
521 Henry Rodriguez	.05	.15
522 Joey Eischen	.05	.15
523 Rod Henderson	.05	.15
524 Pedro Martinez	.30	.75
525 Mel Rojas	.05	.15
526 Larry Walker	.10	.30
527 Gabe White	.05	.15
528 Bobby Bonilla	.10	.30
529 Jonathan Hurst	.05	.15
530 Bobby Jones	.05	.15
531 Kevin McReynolds	.05	.15
532 Bill Pulsipher	.10	.30
533 Bret Saberhagen	.10	.30
534 David Segui	.05	.15
535 Pete Smith	.05	.15
536 Kelly Stinnett RC	.15	.40
537 Dave Telgheder	.05	.15
538 Quilvio Veras	.05	.15
539 Jose Vizcaino	.05	.15
540 Pete Walker RC	.05	.15
541 Ricky Bottalico RC	.05	.15
542 Wes Chamberlain	.05	.15
543 Mariano Duncan	.05	.15
544 Lenny Dykstra	.10	.30
545 Jim Eisenreich	.05	.15
546 Phil Geisler RC	.05	.15
547 Wayne Gomes RC	.15	.40
548 Doug Jones	.05	.15
549 Jeff Juden	.05	.15
550 Mike Lieberthal	.10	.30
551 Tony Longmire	.05	.15
552 Tom Marsh	.05	.15
553 Bobby Munoz	.05	.15
554 Curt Schilling	.10	.30
555 Carlos Garcia	.05	.15
556 Ravelo Manzanillo RC	.05	.15
557 Orlando Merced	.05	.15
558 Will Pennyfeather	.05	.15
559 Zane Smith	.05	.15
560 Andy Van Slyke	.20	.50
561 Rick White	.05	.15
562 Luis Alicea	.05	.15
563 Brian Barber	.05	.15
564 Clint Davis RC	.05	.15
565 Bernard Gilkey	.05	.15
566 Ray Lankford	.10	.30
567 Tom Pagnozzi	.05	.15
568 Ozzie Smith	.50	1.25
569 Rick Sutcliffe	.10	.30
570 Allen Watson	.05	.15
571 Dmitri Young	.10	.30
572 Derek Bell	.05	.15
573 Andy Benes	.05	.15
574 Archi Cianfrocco	.05	.15
575 Joey Hamilton	.05	.15
576 Gene Harris	.05	.15
577 Trevor Hoffman	.20	.50
578 Tim Hyers RC	.05	.15
579 Brian Johnson RC	.05	.15
580 Keith Lockhart RC	.15	.40
581 Pedro A. Martinez RC	.05	.15
582 Ray McDavid	.05	.15
583 Phil Plantier	.05	.15
584 Bip Roberts	.05	.15
585 Dave Staton	.05	.15
586 Todd Benzinger	.05	.15
587 John Burkett	.05	.15
588 Bryan Hickerson	.05	.15
589 Willie McGee	.10	.30
590 John Patterson	.05	.15
591 Mark Portugal	.05	.15
592 Kevin Rogers	.05	.15
593 Joe Rosselli	.05	.15
594 Steve Soderstrom RC	.05	.15
595 Robby Thompson	.05	.15
596 125th Anniversary	.05	.15
597 Jaime Navarro CL	.05	.15
598 Andy Van Slyke CL	.10	.30
599 Checklist	.05	.15
600 Bryan Harvey CL	.05	.15
P243 D.Daulton Promo	.75	2.00
P249 John Kruk Promo	.75	2.00

1994 Ultra All-Rookies

This 10-card standard-size set features top rookies of 1994 and were randomly inserted in second series jumbo and foil packs at a rate of one in 10.

Card	Low	High
COMPLETE SET (10)	3.00	8.00
*JUMBOS: .75X TO 2X BASIC CARDS		
ONE JUMBO SET PER 2ND SERIES HOBBY CASE		
1 Kurt Abbott	.20	.50
2 Carlos Delgado	.40	1.00
3 Cliff Floyd	.40	1.00
4 Jeffrey Hammonds	.20	.50
5 Ryan Klesko	.40	1.00
6 Javier Lopez	.40	1.00
7 Raul Mondesi	.40	1.00
8 James Mouton	.20	.50
9 Chan Ho Park	.40	1.00
10 Dave Staton	.20	.50

1994 Ultra All-Stars

Randomly inserted in second series foil and jumbo packs at a rate of one in three, this 20-card standard-size set contains top major league stars.

Card	Low	High
COMPLETE SET (20)	6.00	15.00
1 Chris Hoiles	.08	.25
2 Frank Thomas	.50	1.25
3 Roberto Alomar	.30	.75
4 Cal Ripken Jr.	1.50	4.00
5 Robin Ventura	.20	.50
6 Albert Belle	.20	.50
7 Juan Gonzalez	.20	.50
8 Ken Griffey Jr.	.75	2.00
9 John Olerud	.20	.50
10 Jack McDowell	.08	.25
11 Mike Piazza	1.00	2.50
12 Fred McGriff	.30	.75
13 Ryne Sandberg	.75	2.00
14 Jay Bell	.20	.50
15 Matt Williams	.20	.50
16 Barry Bonds	1.25	3.00
17 Lenny Dykstra	.20	.50
18 David Justice	.20	.50
19 Tom Glavine	.30	.75
20 Greg Maddux	.75	2.00

1994 Ultra Award Winners

Randomly inserted in all first series packs at a rate of one in three, this 25-card standard-size set features three MVP's, two Rookies of the Year, and 18 Top Glove defensive standouts. The set is divided into American League Top Gloves (1-9), National League Top Gloves (10-18), and Award Winners (19-25).

Card	Low	High
COMPLETE SET (25)	6.00	15.00
1 Ivan Rodriguez	.30	.75
2 Don Mattingly	1.25	3.00
3 Roberto Alomar	.30	.75
4 Robin Ventura	.20	.50
5 Omar Vizquel	.30	.75
6 Ken Griffey Jr.	.75	2.00
7 Kenny Lofton	.20	.50
8 Devon White	.20	.50
9 Mark Langston	.08	.25
10 Kirt Manwaring	.08	.25
11 Mark Grace	.30	.75
12 Robby Thompson	.08	.25
13 Matt Williams	.20	.50
14 Jay Bell	.20	.50
15 Barry Bonds	1.25	3.00
16 Marquis Grissom	.20	.50
17 Larry Walker	.20	.50
18 Greg Maddux	.75	2.00
19 Frank Thomas	.50	1.25
20 Barry Bonds	1.25	3.00
21 Paul Molitor	.20	.50
22 Jack McDowell	.08	.25
23 Greg Maddux	.75	2.00
24 Tim Salmon	.30	.75
25 Mike Piazza	1.00	2.50

1994 Ultra Career Achievement

Randomly inserted in all second series packs at a rate of one in 21, this five card standard-size set highlights veteran stars and milestones they have reached during their brilliant careers.

Card	Low	High
COMPLETE SET (5)	4.00	10.00
1 Joe Carter	.40	1.00
2 Paul Molitor	.40	1.00
3 Cal Ripken Jr.	3.00	8.00
4 Ryne Sandberg	1.50	4.00
5 Dave Winfield	.40	1.00

1994 Ultra Firemen

Randomly inserted in all first series packs at a rate of one in 11, this ten-card standard-size set features ten of baseball's top relief pitchers. The set is arranged according to American League (1-5) and National League (6-10) players.

Card	Low	High
COMPLETE SET (10)	2.00	5.00
1 Jeff Montgomery	.20	.50
2 Duane Ward	.20	.50
3 Tom Henke	.20	.50
4 Roberto Hernandez	.20	.50
5 Dennis Eckersley	.40	1.00
6 Randy Myers	.20	.50
7 Rod Beck	.20	.50
8 Bryan Harvey	.20	.50
9 John Wetteland	.40	1.00
10 Mitch Williams	.20	.50

1994 Ultra Hitting Machines

Randomly inserted in all second series packs at a rate of one in five, this 10-card horizontally designed standard-size set features top hitters from 1993.

COMPLETE SET (10)	4.00	10.00
1 Roberto Alomar	.30	.75
2 Carlos Baerga	.08	.25
3 Barry Bonds	1.25	3.00
4 Andres Galarraga	.20	.50
5 Juan Gonzalez	.20	.50
6 Tony Gwynn	.60	1.50
7 Paul Molitor	.20	.50
8 John Olerud	.20	.50
9 Mike Piazza	1.00	2.50
10 Frank Thomas	.50	1.25

1994 Ultra Home Run Kings

Randomly inserted exclusively in first series foil packs at a rate of one in 36, these 12 standard-size cards highlight home run hitters by an etched metalized look. Cards 1-6 feature American League Home Run Kings while cards 7-12 present National League Home Run Kings.

COMPLETE SET (12)	25.00	60.00
1 Juan Gonzalez	1.00	2.50
2 Ken Griffey Jr.	4.00	10.00
3 Frank Thomas	2.50	6.00
4 Albert Belle	1.00	2.50
5 Rafael Palmeiro	1.50	4.00
6 Joe Carter	1.00	2.50
7 Barry Bonds	6.00	15.00
8 David Justice	1.00	2.50
9 Matt Williams	1.00	2.50
10 Fred McGriff	1.50	4.00
11 Ron Gant	.50	1.25
12 Mike Piazza	5.00	12.00

1994 Ultra League Leaders

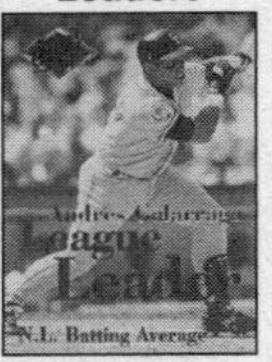

Randomly inserted in all first series packs at a rate of one in 11, this ten-card standard-size set features ten of 1993's leading players. The set is arranged according to American League (1-5) and National League (6-10) players.

COMPLETE SET (10)	2.00	5.00
1 John Olerud	.30	.75
2 Rafael Palmeiro	.50	1.25
3 Kenny Lofton	.30	.75
4 Jack McDowell	.15	.40
5 Randy Johnson	.75	2.00
6 Andres Galarraga	.30	.75
7 Lenny Dykstra	.30	.75
8 Chuck Carr	.15	.40
9 Tom Glavine	.50	1.25
10 Jose Rijo	.15	.40

1994 Ultra On-Base Leaders

Randomly inserted in second series jumbo packs at a rate of one in 36, this 12-card standard-size set features those that were among the Major League leaders in on-base percentage.

COMPLETE SET (12)	40.00	100.00
1 Roberto Alomar	3.00	8.00
2 Barry Bonds	12.50	30.00
3 Lenny Dykstra	2.00	5.00
4 Andres Galarraga	2.00	5.00
5 Mark Grace	3.00	8.00
6 Ken Griffey Jr.	8.00	20.00
7 Gregg Jefferies	1.00	2.50
8 Orlando Merced	1.00	2.50
9 Paul Molitor	2.00	5.00
10 John Olerud	2.00	5.00
11 Tony Phillips	1.00	2.50
12 Frank Thomas	5.00	12.00

1994 Ultra Phillies Finest

As the "Highlight Series" insert set, this 20-card standard-size set features Darren Daulton and John Kruk of the 1993 National League champion Philadelphia Phillies. The cards were inserted at a rate of one in six first series and one in 10 second series packs. Ten cards spotlight each player's career. Daulton and Kruk each signed more than 1,000 of their cards for random insertion. Moreover, the collector could receive four more cards (two of each player) through a mail-in offer by sending in ten 1994 series I wrappers plus 1.50 for postage and handling. The expiration for this redemption was September 30, 1994.

COMPLETE SET (20)	4.00	10.00
COMPLETE SERIES 1 (10)	2.00	5.00
COMPLETE SERIES 2 (10)	2.00	5.00
COMMON (1-5/11-15)	.20	.50
COMMON (6-10/16-20)	.20	.50
COMMON MAIL-IN (M1-M4)	.40	1.00
AU1 Darren Daulton Certified Autograph	30.00	60.00
AU2 John Kruk Certified Autograph	30.00	60.00

1994 Ultra RBI Kings

Randomly inserted in first series jumbo packs at a rate of one in 36, this 12-card standard-size set features RBI leaders. These horizontal, metallized cards have a color player photo on front that superimposes a player image.The backs have a write-up and a small color player photo. Cards 1-6 feature American League RBI Kings while cards 7-12 present National League RBI Kings.

COMPLETE SET (12)	25.00	60.00
1 Albert Belle	1.25	3.00
2 Frank Thomas	3.00	8.00
3 Joe Carter	1.25	3.00
4 Juan Gonzalez	1.25	3.00
5 Cecil Fielder	1.25	3.00
6 Carlos Baerga	.60	1.50
7 Barry Bonds	8.00	20.00
8 David Justice	1.25	3.00
9 Ron Gant	.60	1.50
10 Mike Piazza	6.00	15.00
11 Matt Williams	1.25	3.00
12 Darren Daulton	1.25	3.00

1994 Ultra Rising Stars

Randomly inserted in second series foil packs and jumbo packs at a rate of one in 36, this 12-card set spotlights top young major league stars.

COMPLETE SET (12)	25.00	60.00
1 Carlos Baerga	.75	2.00
2 Jeff Bagwell	2.50	6.00
3 Albert Belle	1.50	4.00
4 Cliff Floyd	1.50	4.00
5 Travis Fryman	1.50	4.00
6 Marquis Grissom	1.50	4.00
7 Kenny Lofton	1.50	4.00
8 John Olerud	1.50	4.00
9 Mike Piazza	8.00	20.00
10 Kirk Rueter	.75	2.00
11 Tim Salmon	2.50	6.00
12 Aaron Sele	.75	2.00

1994 Ultra Second Year Standouts

Randomly inserted in all first series packs at a rate of one in 11, this 10-card standard-size set included 10 1993 outstanding rookies who are destined to become future stars. The set is arranged in alphabetical order according to American League (1-5) and National League (6-10) players.

COMPLETE SET (10)	4.00	10.00
1 Jason Bere	.25	.60
2 Brent Gates	.25	.60
3 Jeffrey Hammonds	.25	.60
4 Tim Salmon	.75	2.00
5 Aaron Sele	.25	.60
6 Chuck Carr	.25	.60
7 Jeff Conine	.50	1.25
8 Greg McMichael	.25	.60
9 Mike Piazza	2.50	6.00
10 Kevin Stocker	.25	.60

1994 Ultra Strikeout Kings

Randomly inserted in all second series packs at a rate of one in seven, this five-card standard-size set features top strikeout artists.

COMPLETE SET (5)	1.50	4.00
1 Randy Johnson	.50	1.25
2 Mark Langston	.08	.25
3 Greg Maddux	.75	2.00
4 Jose Rijo	.08	.25
5 John Smoltz	.30	.75

1995 Ultra

This 450-card standard-size set was issued in two series. The first series contained 250 cards while the second series consisted of 200 cards. They were issued in 12-card packs (either hobby or retail) with a suggested retail price of $1.99. Also, 15-card pre-priced packs with a suggested retail of $2.69. Each pack contained two inserts: one is a Gold Medallion parallel while the other is from one of Ultra's many insert sets. "Hot Packs" contained nothing but insert cards. The full-bleed fronts feature the player's photo with the team name and player's name at the bottom. The "95 Fleer Ultra" logo is in the upper right corner. The backs have a two-photo design; one of which is a full-size duotone shot with the other being a full-color action shot. In each series the cards were grouped alphabetically within teams and checklisted alphabetically according to teams for each league with AL preceding NL.

COMPLETE SET (450)	12.00	30.00
COMP. SERIES 1 (250)	7.00	18.00
COMP.SERIES 2 (200)	5.00	12.00
1 Brady Anderson	.10	.30
2 Sid Fernandez	.05	.15
3 Jeffrey Hammonds	.05	.15
4 Chris Hoiles	.05	.15
5 Ben McDonald	.05	.15
6 Mike Mussina	.20	.50
7 Rafael Palmeiro	.20	.50
8 Jack Voigt	.05	.15
9 Wes Chamberlain	.05	.15
10 Roger Clemens	.60	1.50
11 Chris Howard	.05	.15
12 Tim Naehring	.05	.15
13 Otis Nixon	.05	.15
14 Rich Rowland	.05	.15
15 Ken Ryan	.05	.15
16 John Valentin	.05	.15
17 Mo Vaughn	.10	.30
18 Brian Anderson	.05	.15
19 Chili Davis	.10	.30
20 Damion Easley	.05	.15
21 Jim Edmonds	.20	.50
22 Mark Langston	.05	.15
23 Tim Salmon	.20	.50
24 J.T. Snow	.10	.30
25 Chris Turner	.05	.15
26 Wilson Alvarez	.05	.15
27 Joey Cora	.05	.15
28 Alex Fernandez	.05	.15
29 Roberto Hernandez	.05	.15
30 Lance Johnson	.05	.15
31 Ron Karkovice	.05	.15
32 Kirk McCaskill	.05	.15
33 Tim Raines	.10	.30
34 Frank Thomas	.30	.75
35 Sandy Alomar Jr.	.05	.15
36 Albert Belle	.10	.30
37 Mark Clark	.05	.15
38 Kenny Lofton	.10	.30
39 Eddie Murray	.30	.75
40 Eric Plunk	.05	.15
41 Manny Ramirez	.20	.50
42 Jim Thome	.20	.50
43 Omar Vizquel	.20	.50
44 Danny Bautista	.05	.15
45 Junior Felix	.05	.15
46 Cecil Fielder	.10	.30
47 Chris Gomez	.05	.15
48 Chad Kreuter	.05	.15
49 Mike Moore	.05	.15
50 Tony Phillips	.05	.15
51 Alan Trammell	.10	.30
52 David Wells	.10	.30
53 Kevin Appier	.10	.30
54 Billy Brewer	.05	.15
55 David Cone	.10	.30
56 Greg Gagne	.05	.15
57 Bob Hamelin	.05	.15
58 Jose Lind	.05	.15
59 Brent Mayne	.05	.15
60 Brian McRae	.05	.15
61 Terry Shumpert	.05	.15
62 Ricky Bones	.05	.15
63 Mike Fetters	.05	.15
64 Darryl Hamilton	.05	.15
65 John Jaha	.05	.15
66 Graeme Lloyd	.05	.15
67 Matt Mieske	.05	.15
68 Kevin Seitzer	.05	.15
69 Jose Valentin	.05	.15
70 Turner Ward	.05	.15
71 Rick Aguilera	.05	.15
72 Rich Becker	.05	.15
73 Alex Cole	.05	.15
74 Scott Leius	.05	.15
75 Pat Meares	.05	.15
76 Kirby Puckett	.30	.75
77 Dave Stevens	.05	.15
78 Kevin Tapani	.05	.15
79 Matt Walbeck	.05	.15
80 Wade Boggs	.20	.50
81 Scott Kamieniecki	.05	.15
82 Pat Kelly	.05	.15
83 Jimmy Key	.10	.30
84 Paul O'Neill	.20	.50
85 Luis Polonia	.05	.15
86 Mike Stanley	.05	.15
87 Danny Tartabull	.05	.15
88 Bob Wickman	.05	.15
89 Mark Acre	.05	.15
90 Geronimo Berroa	.05	.15
91 Mike Bordick	.05	.15
92 Ron Darling	.05	.15
93 Stan Javier	.05	.15
94 Mark McGwire	.75	2.00
95 Troy Neel	.05	.15
96 Ruben Sierra	.10	.30
97 Terry Steinbach	.05	.15
98 Eric Anthony	.05	.15
99 Chris Bosio	.05	.15
100 Dave Fleming	.05	.15
101 Ken Griffey Jr.	.50	1.25
102 Reggie Jefferson	.05	.15
103 Randy Johnson	.30	.75
104 Edgar Martinez	.20	.50
105 Bill Risley	.05	.15
106 Dan Wilson	.05	.15
107 Cris Carpenter	.05	.15
108 Will Clark	.20	.50
109 Juan Gonzalez	.10	.30
110 Rusty Greer	.10	.30
111 David Hulse	.05	.15
112 Roger Pavlik	.05	.15
113 Ivan Rodriguez	.20	.50
114 Doug Strange	.05	.15
115 Matt Whiteside	.05	.15
116 Roberto Alomar	.20	.50
117 Brad Cornett	.05	.15
118 Carlos Delgado	.10	.30
119 Alex Gonzalez	.05	.15
120 Darren Hall	.05	.15
121 Pat Hentgen	.05	.15
122 Paul Molitor	.10	.30
123 Ed Sprague	.05	.15
124 Devon White	.10	.30
125 Tom Glavine	.20	.50
126 David Justice	.10	.30
127 Roberto Kelly	.05	.15
128 Mark Lemke	.05	.15
129 Greg Maddux	.50	1.25
130 Greg McMichael	.05	.15
131 Kent Mercker	.05	.15
132 Charlie O'Brien	.05	.15
133 John Smoltz	.20	.50
134 Willie Banks	.05	.15
135 Steve Buechele	.05	.15
136 Kevin Foster	.05	.15
137 Glenallen Hill	.05	.15
138 Rey Sanchez	.05	.15
139 Sammy Sosa	.30	.75
140 Steve Trachsel	.05	.15
141 Rick Wilkins	.05	.15
142 Jeff Brantley	.05	.15
143 Hector Carrasco	.05	.15
144 Kevin Jarvis	.05	.15
145 Barry Larkin	.20	.50
146 Chuck McElroy	.05	.15
147 Jose Rijo	.05	.15
148 Johnny Ruffin	.05	.15
149 Deion Sanders	.20	.50
150 Eddie Taubensee	.05	.15
151 Dante Bichette	.10	.30
152 Ellis Burks	.10	.30
153 Joe Girardi	.05	.15
154 Charlie Hayes	.05	.15
155 Mike Kingery	.05	.15
156 Steve Reed	.05	.15
157 Kevin Ritz	.05	.15
158 Bruce Ruffin	.05	.15
159 Eric Young	.05	.15
160 Kurt Abbott	.05	.15
161 Chuck Carr	.05	.15
162 Chris Hammond	.05	.15
163 Bryan Harvey	.05	.15
164 Terry Mathews	.05	.15
165 Yorkis Perez	.05	.15
166 Pat Rapp	.05	.15
167 Gary Sheffield	.10	.30
168 Dave Weathers	.05	.15
169 Jeff Bagwell	.20	.50
170 Ken Caminiti	.10	.30
171 Doug Drabek	.05	.15
172 Steve Finley	.10	.30
173 John Hudek	.05	.15
174 Todd Jones	.05	.15
175 James Mouton	.05	.15
176 Shane Reynolds	.05	.15
177 Scott Servais	.05	.15
178 Tom Candiotti	.05	.15
179 Omar Daal	.05	.15
180 Darren Dreifort	.05	.15
181 Eric Karros	.10	.30
182 Ramon J.Martinez	.05	.15
183 Raul Mondesi	.10	.30
184 Henry Rodriguez	.05	.15
185 Todd Worrell	.05	.15
186 Moises Alou	.10	.30
187 Sean Berry	.05	.15
188 Wil Cordero	.05	.15
189 Jeff Fassero	.05	.15
190 Darrin Fletcher	.05	.15
191 Butch Henry	.05	.15
192 Ken Hill	.05	.15
193 Mel Rojas	.05	.15
194 John Wetteland	.10	.30
195 Bobby Bonilla	.10	.30
196 Rico Brogna	.05	.15
197 Bobby Jones	.05	.15
198 Jeff Kent	.10	.30
199 Josias Manzanillo	.05	.15
200 Kelly Stinnett	.05	.15
201 Ryan Thompson	.05	.15
202 Jose Vizcaino	.05	.15
203 Lenny Dykstra	.10	.30
204 Jim Eisenreich	.05	.15
205 Dave Hollins	.05	.15
206 Mike Lieberthal	.10	.30
207 Mickey Morandini	.05	.15
208 Bobby Munoz	.05	.15
209 Curt Schilling	.10	.30
210 Heathcliff Slocumb	.05	.15
211 David West	.05	.15
212 Dave Clark	.05	.15
213 Steve Cooke	.05	.15
214 Midre Cummings	.05	.15
215 Carlos Garcia	.05	.15
216 Jeff King	.05	.15
217 Jon Lieber	.05	.15
218 Orlando Merced	.05	.15
219 Don Slaught	.05	.15
220 Rick White	.05	.15
221 Rene Arocha	.05	.15
222 Bernard Gilkey	.05	.15
223 Brian Jordan	.10	.30
224 Tom Pagnozzi	.05	.15
225 Vicente Palacios	.05	.15
226 Geronimo Pena	.05	.15
227 Ozzie Smith	.50	1.25
228 Allen Watson	.05	.15
229 Mark Whiten	.05	.15
230 Brad Ausmus	.10	.30
231 Derek Bell	.05	.15
232 Andy Benes	.05	.15
233 Tony Gwynn	.40	1.00
234 Joey Hamilton	.05	.15
235 Luis Lopez	.05	.15
236 Pedro A.Martinez	.05	.15
237 Scott Sanders	.05	.15
238 Eddie Williams	.05	.15
239 Rod Beck	.05	.15
240 Dave Burba	.05	.15
241 Darren Lewis	.05	.15
242 Kirt Manwaring	.05	.15
243 Mark Portugal	.05	.15
244 Darryl Strawberry	.10	.30
245 Robby Thompson	.05	.15
246 Wm.VanLandingham	.05	.15
247 Matt Williams	.10	.30
248 Checklist	.05	.15
249 Checklist	.05	.15
250 Checklist	.05	.15
251 Harold Baines	.10	.30
252 Bret Barberie	.05	.15
253 Armando Benitez	.05	.15
254 Mike Devereaux	.05	.15
255 Leo Gomez	.05	.15
256 Jamie Moyer	.10	.30
257 Arthur Rhodes	.05	.15
258 Cal Ripken	1.00	2.50
259 Luis Alicea	.05	.15
260 Jose Canseco	.20	.50
261 Scott Cooper	.05	.15
262 Andre Dawson	.10	.30
263 Mike Greenwell	.05	.15
264 Aaron Sele	.05	.15
265 Garret Anderson	.10	.30
266 Chad Curtis	.05	.15
267 Gary DiSarcina	.05	.15
268 Chuck Finley	.10	.30
269 Rex Hudler	.05	.15
270 Andrew Lorraine	.05	.15
271 Spike Owen	.05	.15
272 Lee Smith	.10	.30
273 Jason Bere	.05	.15
274 Ozzie Guillen	.10	.30
275 Norberto Martin	.05	.15
276 Scott Ruffcorn	.05	.15
277 Robin Ventura	.10	.30
278 Carlos Baerga	.05	.15
279 Jason Grimsley	.05	.15
280 Dennis Martinez	.10	.30
281 Charles Nagy	.05	.15
282 Paul Sorrento	.05	.15
283 Dave Winfield	.10	.30
284 John Doherty	.05	.15
285 Travis Fryman	.10	.30
286 Kirk Gibson	.10	.30
287 Lou Whitaker	.10	.30
288 Gary Gaetti	.10	.30
289 Tom Gordon	.05	.15
290 Mark Gubicza	.05	.15
291 Wally Joyner	.10	.30
292 Mike Macfarlane	.05	.15
293 Jeff Montgomery	.05	.15
294 Jeff Cirillo	.05	.15
295 Cal Eldred	.05	.15
296 Pat Listach	.05	.15
297 Jose Mercedes	.05	.15
298 Dave Nilsson	.05	.15
299 Duane Singleton	.05	.15
300 Greg Vaughn	.05	.15
301 Scott Erickson	.05	.15
302 Denny Hocking	.05	.15
303 Chuck Knoblauch	.10	.30
304 Pat Mahomes	.05	.15
305 Pedro Munoz	.05	.15
306 Erik Schullstrom	.05	.15
307 Jim Abbott	.20	.50
308 Tony Fernandez	.05	.15
309 Sterling Hitchcock	.05	.15
310 Jim Leyritz	.05	.15
311 Don Mattingly	.75	2.00
312 Jack McDowell	.05	.15
313 Melido Perez	.05	.15
314 Bernie Williams	.20	.50
315 Scott Brosius	.10	.30
316 Dennis Eckersley	.10	.30
317 Brent Gates	.05	.15
318 Rickey Henderson	.30	.75
319 Steve Karsay	.05	.15
320 Steve Ontiveros	.05	.15
321 Bill Taylor	.05	.15
322 Todd Van Poppel	.05	.15
323 Bob Welch	.05	.15
324 Bobby Ayala	.05	.15
325 Mike Blowers	.05	.15
326 Jay Buhner	.10	.30
327 Felix Fermin	.05	.15
328 Tino Martinez	.20	.50
329 Marc Newfield	.05	.15
330 Greg Pirkl	.05	.15
331 Alex Rodriguez	.75	2.00
332 Kevin Brown	.10	.30
333 John Burkett	.05	.15
334 Jeff Frye	.05	.15
335 Kevin Gross	.05	.15
336 Dean Palmer	.10	.30
337 Joe Carter	.10	.30
338 Shawn Green	.10	.30
339 Juan Guzman	.05	.15
340 Mike Huff	.05	.15
341 Al Leiter	.10	.30
342 John Olerud	.10	.30
343 Dave Stewart	.10	.30
344 Todd Stottlemyre	.05	.15
345 Steve Avery	.05	.15
346 Jeff Blauser	.05	.15
347 Chipper Jones	.30	.75
348 Mike Kelly	.05	.15
349 Ryan Klesko	.10	.30
350 Javier Lopez	.10	.30
351 Fred McGriff	.20	.50
352 Jose Oliva	.05	.15
353 Terry Pendleton	.10	.30
354 Mike Stanton	.05	.15
355 Tony Tarasco	.05	.15
356 Mark Wohlers	.05	.15
357 Jim Bullinger	.05	.15
358 Shawon Dunston	.05	.15
359 Mark Grace	.20	.50
360 Derrick May	.05	.15
361 Randy Myers	.05	.15
362 Karl Rhodes	.05	.15
363 Bret Boone	.10	.30
364 Brian Dorsett	.05	.15
365 Ron Gant	.10	.30
366 Brian R.Hunter	.05	.15
367 Hal Morris	.05	.15
368 Jack Morris	.10	.30
369 John Roper	.05	.15
370 Reggie Sanders	.10	.30
371 Pete Schourek	.05	.15
372 John Smiley	.05	.15
373 Marvin Freeman	.05	.15
374 Andres Galarraga	.10	.30
375 Mike Munoz	.05	.15
376 David Nied	.05	.15
377 Walt Weiss	.05	.15
378 Greg Colbrunn	.05	.15
379 Jeff Conine	.10	.30
380 Charles Johnson	.10	.30
381 Kurt Miller	.05	.15
382 Robb Nen	.10	.30
383 Benito Santiago	.10	.30
384 Craig Biggio	.20	.50
385 Tony Eusebio	.05	.15
386 Luis Gonzalez	.10	.30
387 Brian L.Hunter	.05	.15
388 Darryl Kile	.10	.30
389 Orlando Miller	.05	.15
390 Phil Plantier	.05	.15
391 Greg Swindell	.05	.15
392 Billy Ashley	.05	.15
393 Pedro Astacio	.05	.15
394 Brett Butler	.10	.30
395 Delino DeShields	.05	.15
396 Orel Hershiser	.10	.30
397 Garey Ingram	.05	.15
398 Chan Ho Park	.10	.30
399 Mike Piazza	.50	1.25
400 Ismael Valdes	.05	.15
401 Tim Wallach	.05	.15
402 Cliff Floyd	.10	.30
403 Marquis Grissom	.10	.30
404 Mike Lansing	.05	.15
405 Pedro Martinez	.20	.50
406 Kirk Rueter	.05	.15
407 Tim Scott	.05	.15
408 Jeff Shaw	.05	.15
409 Larry Walker	.10	.30
410 Rondell White	.10	.30
411 John Franco	.10	.30
412 Todd Hundley	.05	.15
413 Jason Jacome	.05	.15
414 Joe Orsulak	.05	.15
415 Bret Saberhagen	.10	.30
416 David Segui	.05	.15
417 Darren Daulton	.10	.30
418 Mariano Duncan	.05	.15
419 Tommy Greene	.05	.15
420 Gregg Jefferies	.05	.15
421 John Kruk	.10	.30
422 Kevin Stocker	.05	.15
423 Jay Bell	.10	.30
424 Al Martin	.05	.15
425 Denny Neagle	.10	.30
426 Zane Smith	.05	.15
427 Andy Van Slyke	.20	.50
428 Paul Wagner	.05	.15
429 Tom Henke	.05	.15
430 Danny Jackson	.05	.15
431 Ray Lankford	.10	.30
432 John Mabry	.05	.15
433 Bob Tewksbury	.05	.15
434 Todd Zeile	.05	.15
435 Andy Ashby	.05	.15
436 Andujar Cedeno	.05	.15
437 Donnie Elliott	.05	.15
438 Bryce Florie	.05	.15
439 Trevor Hoffman	.10	.30
440 Melvin Nieves	.05	.15
441 Bip Roberts	.05	.15
442 Barry Bonds	.75	2.00
443 Royce Clayton	.05	.15
444 Mike Jackson	.05	.15
445 John Patterson	.05	.15
446 J.R. Phillips	.05	.15
447 Bill Swift	.05	.15
448 Checklist	.05	.15
449 Checklist	.05	.15
450 Checklist	.05	.15

1995 Ultra Gold Medallion

This 450-card parallels the regular Ultra issue. These cards were issued one per pack and are differentiated from the regular cards by the Ultra logo being replaced by the "Ultra Gold Medallion Edition logo."

COMPLETE SET (450) 55.00 110.00
COMP. SERIES 1 (250) 30.00 60.00
COMP. SERIES 2 (200) 25.00 50.00
*STARS: 1.25X TO 3X BASIC CARDS

1995 Ultra All-Rookies

This 10-card standard-size set features rookies who emerged with an impact in 1994. These cards were inserted one in every five second series packs. The cards are numbered in the lower left as "X" of 10 and are sequenced in alphabetical order.

COMPLETE SET (10) 2.00 5.00
*GOLD MEDAL: .75X TO 2X BASIC AR
GM SER.2 STATED ODDS 1:50
1 Cliff Floyd .30 .75
2 Chris Gomez .15 .40
3 Rusty Greer .30 .75
4 Bob Hamelin .15 .40
5 Joey Hamilton .15 .40
6 John Hudek .15 .40
7 Ryan Klesko .30 .75
8 Raul Mondesi .30 .75
9 Manny Ramirez .50 1.25
10 Steve Trachsel .15 .40

1995 Ultra All-Stars

This 20-card standard-size set feature players who are considered to be the top players in the game. Cards were inserted one in every four second series packs. The fronts feature two photos. The cards are numbered in the bottom left as "X" of 20 and are sequenced in alphabetical order.

COMPLETE SET (20) 6.00 15.00
*GOLD MEDAL: .75X TO 2X BASIC ALL-STARS
GM SER.2 STATED ODDS 1:40
1 Moises Alou .20 .50
2 Albert Belle .20 .50
3 Craig Biggio .30 .75
4 Wade Boggs .30 .75
5 Barry Bonds 1.25 3.00
6 David Cone .20 .50
7 Ken Griffey Jr. .75 2.00
8 Tony Gwynn .60 1.50
9 Chuck Knoblauch .20 .50
10 Barry Larkin .30 .75
11 Kenny Lofton .20 .50
12 Greg Maddux .75 2.00
13 Fred McGriff .30 .75
14 Paul O'Neill .30 .75
15 Mike Piazza .75 2.00
16 Kirby Puckett .50 1.25
17 Cal Ripken 1.50 4.00
18 Ivan Rodriguez .30 .75
19 Frank Thomas .50 1.25
20 Matt Williams .20 .50

1995 Ultra Award Winners

Featuring players who won major awards in 1994, this 25-card standard-size set was inserted one in every four first series packs. The cards are numbered as "X" of 25.

COMPLETE SET (25) 8.00 20.00
*GOLD MEDAL: .75X TO 2X BASIC BASIC AW
GM SER.1 STATED ODDS 1:40
1 Ivan Rodriguez .30 .75
2 Don Mattingly 1.25 3.00
3 Roberto Alomar .30 .75
4 Wade Boggs .30 .75
5 Omar Vizquel .30 .75
6 Ken Griffey Jr. .75 2.00
7 Kenny Lofton .20 .50
8 Devon White .20 .50
9 Mark Langston .08 .25
10 Tom Pagnozzi .08 .25
11 Jeff Bagwell .30 .75
12 Craig Biggio .30 .75
13 Matt Williams .20 .50
14 Barry Larkin .30 .75
15 Barry Bonds 1.25 3.00
16 Marquis Grissom .20 .50
17 Darren Lewis .08 .25
18 Greg Maddux .75 2.00
19 Frank Thomas .50 1.25
20 Jeff Bagwell .30 .75
21 David Cone .20 .50
22 Greg Maddux .75 2.00
23 Bob Hamelin .08 .25
24 Raul Mondesi .30 .75
25 Moises Alou .20 .50

1995 Ultra Gold Medallion Rookies

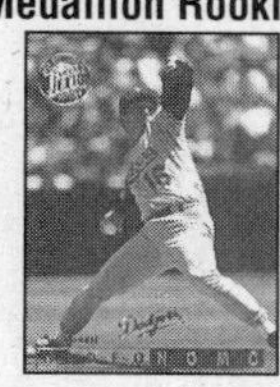

This 20-card standard-size set was available through a mail-in wrapper offer that expired 9/30/95. These players featured were all rookies in 1995 and were not included in the regular Ultra set. The design is essentially the same as the corresponding basic cards save for the medallion in the upper left-hand corner. The cards are numbered with an "M" prefix. The set is sequenced in alphabetical order.

COMPLETE SET (20) 3.00 8.00
M1 Manny Alexander .08 .25
M2 Edgardo Alfonzo .08 .25
M3 Jason Bates .08 .25
M4 Andres Berumen .08 .25
M5 Darren Bragg .08 .25
M6 Jamie Brewington .08 .25
M7 Jason Christiansen .08 .25
M8 Brad Clontz .08 .25
M9 Marty Cordova .08 .25
M10 Johnny Damon .30 .75
M11 Vaughn Eshelman .08 .25
M12 Chad Fonville .08 .25
M13 Curtis Goodwin .08 .25
M14 Tyler Green .08 .25
M15 Bobby Higginson .30 .75
M16 Jason Isringhausen .20 .50
M17 Hideo Nomo 1.00 2.50
M18 Jon Nunnally .08 .25
M19 Carlos Perez .20 .50
M20 Julian Tavarez .08 .25

1995 Ultra Golden Prospects

Inserted one every eight first series hobby packs, this 10-card standard-size set features potential impact players. The cards are numbered as "X" of 10 and are sequenced alphabetically.

COMPLETE SET (10) 5.00 10.00
*GOLD MEDAL: .75X TO 2X BASIC PROSPECTS
GM SER.1 STATED ODDS 1:80
1 James Baldwin .20 .50
2 Alan Benes .20 .50
3 Armando Benitez .20 .50
4 Ray Durham .40 1.00
5 LaTroy Hawkins .20 .50
6 Brian L.Hunter .20 .50
7 Derek Jeter 1.50 4.00
8 Charles Johnson .40 1.00
9 Alex Rodriguez 1.50 4.00
10 Michael Tucker .20 .50

1995 Ultra Hitting Machines

This 10-card standard-size set features some of baseball's leading batters. Inserted one in every eight second-series retail packs, these horizontal cards have the player's photo against a background of the words "Hitting Machine." The cards are numbered as "X" of 10 in the upper right and are sequenced in alphabetical order.

COMPLETE SET (10) 5.00 12.00
*GOLD MEDAL: .75X TO 2X BASIC HIT.MACH.
GM SER.2 STATED ODDS 1:80 RETAIL
1 Jeff Bagwell .30 .75
2 Albert Belle .20 .50
3 Dante Bichette .20 .50
4 Barry Bonds 1.25 3.00
5 Jose Canseco .30 .75
6 Ken Griffey Jr. .75 2.00
7 Tony Gwynn .60 1.50
8 Fred McGriff .30 .75
9 Mike Piazza .75 2.00
10 Frank Thomas .50 1.25

1995 Ultra Home Run Kings

This 10-card standard-size set featured the five leading home run hitters in each league. These cards were issued one every eight first series retail packs. The cards are numbered as "X" of 10 and are sequenced by league according to 1994's home rum standings. A Barry Bonds sample card was issued to dealers to prior to the release of 1995 Ultra.

COMPLETE SET (10) 12.50 30.00
*GOLD MEDAL: .75X TO 2X BASIC HR KINGS
GM SER.1 STATED ODDS 1:80 RETAIL
1 Ken Griffey Jr. 2.00 5.00
2 Frank Thomas 1.25 3.00
3 Albert Belle .50 1.25
4 Jose Canseco .75 2.00
5 Cecil Fielder .50 1.25
6 Matt Williams .50 1.25
7 Jeff Bagwell .75 2.00
8 Barry Bonds 3.00 8.00
9 Fred McGriff .75 2.00
10 Andres Galarraga .50 1.25
S8 Barry Bonds Sample .75 2.00

1995 Ultra League Leaders

This 10-card standard-size set was inserted one every three first series packs.

COMPLETE SET (10) 2.50 6.00
*GOLD MEDAL: .75X TO 2X BASIC LL
GM SER.1 STATED ODDS 1:30
1 Paul O'Neill .30 .75
2 Kenny Lofton .20 .50
3 Jimmy Key .20 .50
4 Randy Johnson .50 1.25
5 Lee Smith .20 .50
6 Tony Gwynn .60 1.50
7 Craig Biggio .30 .75
8 Greg Maddux .75 2.00
9 Andy Benes .08 .25
10 John Franco .20 .50

1995 Ultra On-Base Leaders

This 10-card standard-size set features ten players who are constantly reaching base safely. These cards were inserted one in every eight pre-priced second series jumbo packs. The cards are numbered in the upper right corner as "X" of 10 and are sequenced in alphabetical order.

COMPLETE SET (10) 15.00 40.00
*GOLD MEDAL: .75X TO 2X BASIC OBL
GM SER.2 STATED ODDS 1:80 JUMBO
1 Jeff Bagwell 1.25 3.00
2 Albert Belle .75 2.00
3 Craig Biggio 1.25 3.00
4 Wade Boggs 1.25 3.00
5 Barry Bonds 5.00 12.00
6 Will Clark 1.25 3.00
7 Tony Gwynn 2.50 6.00
8 David Justice .75 2.00
9 Paul O'Neill 1.25 3.00
10 Frank Thomas 2.00 5.00

1995 Ultra Power Plus

This six-card standard-size set was inserted one in every 37 first series packs. The six players portrayed are not only sluggers, but also excel at another part of the game. Unlike the 1995 Ultra cards and the other insert sets, these cards are 100 percent foil. The cards are numbered on the bottom right as "X" of 6 and are sequenced in alphabetical order by league.

COMPLETE SET (6) 10.00 25.00
*GOLD MEDAL: .75X TO 2X BASIC PLUS
GM SER.1 STATED ODDS 1:370
1 Albert Belle .60 1.50
2 Ken Griffey Jr. 2.50 6.00
3 Frank Thomas 1.50 4.00
4 Jeff Bagwell 1.00 2.50
5 Barry Bonds 4.00 10.00
6 Matt Williams .60 1.50

1995 Ultra RBI Kings

This 10-card standard-size set was inserted into series one jumbo packs at a rate of one every 11. The cards are numbered in the upper left as "X" of 10 and are sequenced in order by league.

COMPLETE SET (10) 12.50 30.00
*GOLD MEDAL: .75X TO 2X BASIC RBI KINGS
GM SER.1 STATED ODDS 1:110 JUMBO
1 Kirby Puckett 2.00 5.00
2 Joe Carter .75 2.00
3 Albert Belle .75 2.00
4 Frank Thomas 2.00 5.00
5 Julio Franco .40 1.00
6 Jeff Bagwell 1.25 3.00
7 Matt Williams .75 2.00
8 Dante Bichette .75 2.00
9 Fred McGriff 1.25 3.00
10 Mike Piazza 3.00 8.00

1995 Ultra Rising Stars

This nine-card standard-size set was inserted one every 37 second series packs. The cards are numbered "X" of 9 and are sequenced in alphabetical order.

COMPLETE SET (9) 15.00 40.00
*GOLD MEDAL: .75X TO 2X BASIC RISING
GM SER.2 STATED ODDS 1:370

1 Moises Alou 1.25 3.00
2 Jeff Bagwell 2.00 5.00
3 Albert Belle 1.25 3.00
4 Juan Gonzalez 1.25 3.00
5 Chuck Knoblauch 1.25 3.00
6 Kenny Lofton 1.25 3.00
7 Raul Mondesi 1.25 3.00
8 Mike Piazza 5.00 12.00
9 Frank Thomas 3.00 8.00

1995 Ultra Second Year Standouts

This 15-card standard-size set was inserted into first series packs at a rate of not greater than one in six packs. The players in this set were all rookies in 1994 whom big things were expected from in 1995. The cards are numbered in the lower right as "X" of 15 and are sequenced in alphabetical order.

COMPLETE SET (15) 3.00 8.00
*GOLD MEDAL: .75X TO 2X BASIC 2YS
GM SER.1 STATED ODDS 1:60
1 Cliff Floyd .50 1.25
2 Chris Gomez .25 .60
3 Rusty Greer .50 1.25
4 Darren Hall .25 .60
5 Bob Hamelin .25 .60
6 Joey Hamilton .25 .60
7 Jeffrey Hammonds .25 .60
8 John Hudek .25 .60
9 Ryan Klesko .50 1.25
10 Raul Mondesi .50 1.25
11 Manny Ramirez .75 2.00
12 Bill Risley .25 .60
13 Steve Trachsel .25 .60
14 W.VanLandingham .25 .60
15 Rondell White .50 1.25

1995 Ultra Strikeout Kings

This six-card standard-size set was inserted one every five second series packs. The cards are numbered as "X" of 6 and are sequenced in alphabetical order.

COMPLETE SET (6) 2.00 5.00
*GOLD MEDAL: .75X TO 2X BASIC K KINGS
GM SER.2 STATED ODDS 1:50
1 Andy Benes .08 .25
2 Roger Clemens 1.00 2.50
3 Randy Johnson .50 1.25
4 Greg Maddux .75 2.00
5 Pedro Martinez .30 .75
6 Jose Rijo .08 .25

1996 Ultra Promos

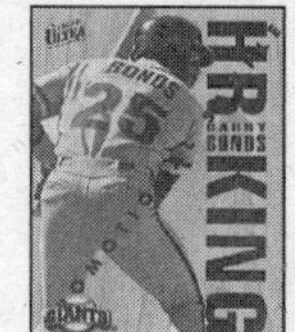

This six card standard-size set previews the 1996 Ultra series. The Griffey card represents the basic set and has the same front and back as its regular issue counterpart. The Bonds and Ripken cards are from insert series and carry advertisements on their backs. The Gwynn and Lofton cards hail from the Season Crowns insert. Each card has the disclaimer "PROMOTIONAL SAMPLE" stamped diagonally across it.

COMPLETE SET (6) 3.20 8.00
SC2 Tony Gwynn .60 1.50
Season Crown
SC4 Kenny Lofton .30 .75
Season Crown
NNO Roberto Alomar .30 .75
Prime Leather
NNO Ken Griffey Jr. .60 1.50
NNO Cal Ripken 1.25 3.00
Prime Leather
NNO Barry Bonds .50 1.25
HR King

1996 Ultra

The 1996 Ultra set, produced by Fleer, contains 600 standard-size cards. The cards were distributed in packs that included two inserts. One insert is a Gold Medallion parallel while the other insert comes from one of the many Ultra insert sets. The cards are thicker than their 1995 counterparts and the fronts feature the player in an action shot in full-bleed color. The cards are sequenced in alphabetical order within league and team order.

COMPLETE SET (600) 20.00 50.00
COMP.SERIES 1 (300) 10.00 25.00
COMP.SERIES 2 (300) 10.00 25.00
RIPKEN DUST AVAIL.VIA MAIL EXCHANGE
1 Manny Alexander .10 .30
2 Brady Anderson .10 .30
3 Bobby Bonilla .10 .30
4 Scott Erickson .10 .30
5 Curtis Goodwin .10 .30
6 Chris Hoiles .10 .30
7 Doug Jones .10 .30
8 Jeff Manto .10 .30
9 Mike Mussina .20 .50
10 Rafael Palmeiro .20 .50
11 Cal Ripken 1.00 2.50
12 Rick Aguilera .10 .30
13 Luis Alicea .10 .30
14 Stan Belinda .10 .30
15 Jose Canseco .20 .50
16 Roger Clemens .60 1.50
17 Mike Greenwell .10 .30
18 Mike Macfarlane .10 .30
19 Tim Naehring .10 .30
20 Troy O'Leary .10 .30
21 John Valentin .10 .30
22 Mo Vaughn .10 .30
23 Tim Wakefield .10 .30
24 Brian Anderson .10 .30
25 Garret Anderson .10 .30
26 Chili Davis .10 .30
27 Gary DiSarcina .10 .30
28 Jim Edmonds .10 .30
29 Jorge Fabregas .10 .30
30 Chuck Finley .10 .30
31 Mark Langston .10 .30
32 Troy Percival .10 .30
33 Tim Salmon .20 .50
34 Lee Smith .10 .30
35 Wilson Alvarez .10 .30
36 Ray Durham .10 .30
37 Alex Fernandez .10 .30
38 Ozzie Guillen .10 .30
39 Roberto Hernandez .10 .30
40 Lance Johnson .10 .30
41 Ron Karkovice .10 .30
42 Lyle Mouton .10 .30
43 Tim Raines .10 .30
44 Frank Thomas .30 .75
45 Carlos Baerga .10 .30
46 Albert Belle .10 .30
47 Orel Hershiser .10 .30
48 Kenny Lofton .10 .30
49 Dennis Martinez .10 .30
50 Jose Mesa .10 .30
51 Eddie Murray .30 .75
52 Chad Ogea .10 .30
53 Manny Ramirez .20 .50
54 Jim Thome .20 .50
55 Omar Vizquel .20 .50
56 Dave Winfield .10 .30
57 Chad Curtis .10 .30
58 Cecil Fielder .10 .30
59 John Flaherty .10 .30
60 Travis Fryman .10 .30
61 Chris Gomez .10 .30
62 Bob Higginson .10 .30
63 Felipe Lira .10 .30
64 Brian Maxcy .10 .30
65 Alan Trammell .10 .30
66 Lou Whitaker .10 .30
67 Kevin Appier .10 .30
68 Gary Gaetti .10 .30
69 Tom Goodwin .10 .30
70 Tom Gordon .10 .30
71 Jason Jacome .10 .30
72 Wally Joyner .10 .30
73 Brent Mayne .10 .30
74 Jeff Montgomery .10 .30
75 Jon Nunnally .10 .30
76 Joe Vitiello .10 .30
77 Ricky Bones .10 .30
78 Jeff Cirillo .10 .30
79 Mike Fetters .10 .30
80 Darryl Hamilton .10 .30
81 David Hulse .10 .30
82 Dave Nilsson .10 .30
83 Kevin Seitzer .10 .30
84 Steve Sparks .10 .30
85 B.J. Surhoff .10 .30
86 Jose Valentin .10 .30
87 Greg Vaughn .10 .30
88 Marty Cordova .10 .30
89 Chuck Knoblauch .10 .30
90 Pat Meares .10 .30
91 Pedro Munoz .10 .30
92 Kirby Puckett .30 .75
93 Brad Radke .10 .30
94 Scott Stahoviak .10 .30
95 Dave Stevens .10 .30
96 Mike Trombley .10 .30
97 Matt Walbeck .10 .30
98 Wade Boggs .20 .50
99 Russ Davis .10 .30
100 Jim Leyritz .10 .30
101 Don Mattingly .75 2.00
102 Jack McDowell .10 .30
103 Paul O'Neill .20 .50
104 Andy Pettitte .20 .50
105 Mariano Rivera .30 .75
106 Ruben Sierra .10 .30
107 Darryl Strawberry .10 .30
108 John Wetteland .10 .30
109 Bernie Williams .20 .50
110 Geronimo Berroa .10 .30
111 Scott Brosius .10 .30
112 Dennis Eckersley .10 .30
113 Brent Gates .10 .30
114 Rickey Henderson .30 .75
115 Mark McGwire .75 2.00
116 Ariel Prieto .10 .30
117 Terry Steinbach .10 .30
118 Todd Stottlemyre .10 .30
119 Todd Van Poppel .10 .30
120 Steve Wojciechowski .10 .30
121 Rich Amaral .10 .30
122 Bobby Ayala .10 .30
123 Mike Blowers .10 .30
124 Chris Bosio .10 .30
125 Joey Cora .10 .30
126 Ken Griffey Jr. .50 1.25
127 Randy Johnson .30 .75
128 Edgar Martinez .20 .50
129 Tino Martinez .20 .50
130 Alex Rodriguez .60 1.50
131 Dan Wilson .10 .30
132 Will Clark .20 .50
133 Jeff Frye .10 .30
134 Benji Gil .10 .30
135 Juan Gonzalez .10 .30
136 Rusty Greer .10 .30
137 Mark McLemore .10 .30
138 Roger Pavlik .10 .30
139 Ivan Rodriguez .20 .50
140 Kenny Rogers .10 .30
141 Mickey Tettleton .10 .30
142 Roberto Alomar .20 .50
143 Joe Carter .10 .30
144 Tony Castillo .10 .30
145 Alex Gonzalez .10 .30
146 Shawn Green .10 .30
147 Pat Hentgen .10 .30
148 Sandy Martinez .10 .30
149 Paul Molitor .10 .30
150 John Olerud .10 .30
151 Ed Sprague .10 .30
152 Jeff Blauser .10 .30
153 Brad Clontz .10 .30
154 Tom Glavine .20 .50
155 Marquis Grissom .10 .30
156 Chipper Jones .30 .75
157 David Justice .10 .30
158 Ryan Klesko .10 .30
159 Javier Lopez .10 .30
160 Greg Maddux .50 1.25
161 John Smoltz .20 .50
162 Mark Wohlers .10 .30
163 Jim Bullinger .10 .30
164 Frank Castillo .10 .30
165 Shawon Dunston .10 .30
166 Kevin Foster .10 .30
167 Luis Gonzalez .10 .30
168 Mark Grace .20 .50
169 Rey Sanchez .10 .30
170 Scott Servais .10 .30
171 Sammy Sosa .30 .75
172 Ozzie Timmons .10 .30
173 Steve Trachsel .10 .30
174 Bret Boone .10 .30
175 Jeff Branson .10 .30
176 Jeff Brantley .10 .30
177 Dave Burba .10 .30
178 Ron Gant .10 .30
179 Barry Larkin .20 .50
180 Darren Lewis .10 .30
181 Mark Portugal .10 .30
182 Reggie Sanders .10 .30
183 Pete Schourek .10 .30
184 John Smiley .10 .30
185 Jason Bates .10 .30
186 Dante Bichette .10 .30
187 Ellis Burks .10 .30
188 Vinny Castilla .10 .30
189 Andres Galarraga .10 .30
190 Darren Holmes .10 .30
191 Armando Reynoso .10 .30
192 Kevin Ritz .10 .30
193 Bill Swift .10 .30
194 Larry Walker .10 .30
195 Kurt Abbott .10 .30
196 John Burkett .10 .30
197 Greg Colbrunn .10 .30
198 Jeff Conine .10 .30
199 Andre Dawson .10 .30
200 Chris Hammond .10 .30
201 Charles Johnson .10 .30
202 Robb Nen .10 .30
203 Terry Pendleton .10 .30
204 Quilvio Veras .10 .30
205 Jeff Bagwell .20 .50
206 Derek Bell .10 .30
207 Doug Drabek .10 .30
208 Tony Eusebio .10 .30
209 Mike Hampton .10 .30
210 Brian L. Hunter .10 .30
211 Todd Jones .10 .30
212 Orlando Miller .10 .30
213 James Mouton .10 .30
214 Shane Reynolds .10 .30
215 Dave Veres .10 .30
216 Billy Ashley .10 .30
217 Brett Butler .10 .30
218 Chad Fonville .10 .30
219 Todd Hollandsworth .10 .30
220 Eric Karros .10 .30
221 Ramon Martinez .10 .30
222 Raul Mondesi .10 .30
223 Hideo Nomo .30 .75
224 Mike Piazza .50 1.25
225 Kevin Tapani .10 .30
226 Ismael Valdes .10 .30
227 Todd Worrell .10 .30
228 Moises Alou .10 .30
229 Wil Cordero .10 .30
230 Jeff Fassero .10 .30
231 Darrin Fletcher .10 .30
232 Mike Lansing .10 .30
233 Pedro Martinez .20 .50
234 Carlos Perez .10 .30

Card	Low	High
235 Mel Rojas	.10	.30
236 David Segui	.10	.30
237 Tony Tarasco	.10	.30
238 Rondell White	.10	.30
239 Edgardo Alfonzo	.10	.30
240 Rico Brogna	.10	.30
241 Carl Everett	.10	.30
242 Todd Hundley	.10	.30
243 Butch Huskey	.10	.30
244 Jason Isringhausen	.10	.30
245 Bobby Jones	.10	.30
246 Jeff Kent	.10	.30
247 Bill Pulsipher	.10	.30
248 Jose Vizcaino	.10	.30
249 Ricky Bottalico	.10	.30
250 Darren Daulton	.10	.30
251 Jim Eisenreich	.10	.30
252 Tyler Green	.10	.30
253 Charlie Hayes	.10	.30
254 Gregg Jefferies	.10	.30
255 Tony Longmire	.10	.30
256 Michael Mimbs	.10	.30
257 Mickey Morandini	.10	.30
258 Paul Quantrill	.10	.30
259 Heathcliff Slocumb	.10	.30
260 Jay Bell	.10	.30
261 Jacob Brumfield	.10	.30
262 A.Encarnacion RC	.10	.30
263 John Ericks	.10	.30
264 Mark Johnson	.10	.30
265 Esteban Loaiza	.10	.30
266 Al Martin	.10	.30
267 Orlando Merced	.10	.30
268 Dan Miceli	.10	.30
269 Denny Neagle	.10	.30
270 Brian Barber	.10	.30
271 Scott Cooper	.10	.30
272 Tripp Cromer	.10	.30
273 Bernard Gilkey	.10	.30
274 Tom Henke	.10	.30
275 Brian Jordan	.10	.30
276 John Mabry	.10	.30
277 Tom Pagnozzi	.10	.30
278 Mark Petkovsek	.10	.30
279 Ozzie Smith	.50	1.25
280 Andy Ashby	.10	.30
281 Brad Ausmus	.10	.30
282 Ken Caminiti	.10	.30
283 Glenn Dishman	.10	.30
284 Tony Gwynn	.40	1.00
285 Joey Hamilton	.10	.30
286 Trevor Hoffman	.10	.30
287 Phil Plantier	.10	.30
288 Jody Reed	.10	.30
289 Eddie Williams	.10	.30
290 Barry Bonds	.75	2.00
291 Jamie Brewington RC	.10	.30
292 Mark Carreon	.10	.30
293 Royce Clayton	.10	.30
294 Glenallen Hill	.10	.30
295 Mark Leiter	.10	.30
296 Kirt Manwaring	.10	.30
297 J.R. Phillips	.10	.30
298 Deion Sanders	.20	.50
299 Wm. VanLandingham	.10	.30
300 Matt Williams	.10	.30
301 Roberto Alomar	.20	.50
302 Armando Benitez	.10	.30
303 Mike Devereaux	.10	.30
304 Jeffrey Hammonds	.10	.30
305 Jimmy Haynes	.10	.30
306 Scott McClain	.10	.30
307 Kent Mercker	.10	.30
308 Randy Myers	.10	.30
309 B.J. Surhoff	.10	.30
310 Tony Tarasco	.10	.30
311 David Wells	.10	.30
312 Wil Cordero	.10	.30
313 Alex Delgado	.10	.30
314 Tom Gordon	.10	.30
315 Dwayne Hosey	.10	.30
316 Jose Malave	.10	.30
317 Kevin Mitchell	.10	.30
318 Jamie Moyer	.10	.30
319 Aaron Sele	.10	.30
320 Heathcliff Slocumb	.10	.30
321 Mike Stanley	.10	.30
322 Jeff Suppan	.10	.30
323 Jim Abbott	.20	.50
324 George Arias	.10	.30
325 Todd Greene	.10	.30
326 Bryan Harvey	.10	.30
327 J.T. Snow	.10	.30
328 Randy Velarde	.10	.30
329 Tim Wallach	.10	.30
330 Harold Baines	.10	.30
331 Jason Bere	.10	.30
332 Darren Lewis	.10	.30
333 Norberto Martin	.10	.30
334 Tony Phillips	.10	.30
335 Bill Simas	.10	.30
336 Chris Snopek	.10	.30
337 Kevin Tapani	.10	.30
338 Danny Tartabull	.10	.30
339 Robin Ventura	.10	.30
340 Sandy Alomar Jr.	.10	.30
341 Julio Franco	.10	.30
342 Jack McDowell	.10	.30
343 Charles Nagy	.10	.30
344 Julian Tavarez	.10	.30
345 Kimera Bartee	.10	.30
346 Greg Keagle	.10	.30
347 Mark Lewis	.10	.30
348 Jose Lima	.10	.30
349 Melvin Nieves	.10	.30
350 Mark Parent	.10	.30
351 Eddie Williams	.10	.30
352 Johnny Damon	.20	.50
353 Sal Fasano	.10	.30
354 Mark Gubicza	.10	.30
355 Bob Hamelin	.10	.30
356 Chris Haney	.10	.30
357 Keith Lockhart	.10	.30
358 Mike Macfarlane	.10	.30
359 Jose Offerman	.10	.30
360 Bip Roberts	.10	.30
361 Michael Tucker	.10	.30
362 Chuck Carr	.10	.30
363 Bobby Hughes	.10	.30
364 John Jaha	.10	.30
365 Mark Loretta	.10	.30
366 Mike Matheny	.10	.30
367 Ben McDonald	.10	.30
368 Matt Mieske	.10	.30
369 Angel Miranda	.10	.30
370 Fernando Vina	.10	.30
371 Rick Aguilera	.10	.30
372 Rich Becker	.10	.30
373 LaTroy Hawkins	.10	.30
374 Dave Hollins	.10	.30
375 Roberto Kelly	.10	.30
376 Matt Lawton RC	.15	.40
377 Paul Molitor	.10	.30
378 Dan Naulty	.10	.30
379 Rich Robertson	.10	.30
380 Frank Rodriguez	.10	.30
381 David Cone	.10	.30
382 Mariano Duncan	.10	.30
383 Andy Fox	.10	.30
384 Joe Girardi	.10	.30
385 Dwight Gooden	.10	.30
386 Derek Jeter	.75	2.00
387 Pat Kelly	.10	.30
388 Jimmy Key	.10	.30
389 Matt Luke	.10	.30
390 Tino Martinez	.20	.50
391 Jeff Nelson	.10	.30
392 Melido Perez	.10	.30
393 Tim Raines	.10	.30
394 Ruben Rivera	.10	.30
395 Kenny Rogers	.10	.30
396 Tony Batista RC	.25	.60
397 Allen Battle	.10	.30
398 Mike Bordick	.10	.30
399 Steve Cox	.10	.30
400 Jason Giambi	.10	.30
401 Doug Johns	.10	.30
402 Pedro Munoz	.10	.30
403 Phil Plantier	.10	.30
404 Scott Spiezio	.10	.30
405 George Williams	.10	.30
406 Ernie Young	.10	.30
407 Darren Bragg	.10	.30
408 Jay Buhner	.10	.30
409 Norm Charlton	.10	.30
410 Russ Davis	.10	.30
411 Sterling Hitchcock	.10	.30
412 Edwin Hurtado	.10	.30
413 Raul Ibanez RC	.30	.75
414 Mike Jackson	.10	.30
415 Luis Sojo	.10	.30
416 Paul Sorrento	.10	.30
417 Bob Wolcott	.10	.30
418 Damon Buford	.10	.30
419 Kevin Gross	.10	.30
420 Darryl Hamilton UER	.10	.30
421 Mike Henneman	.10	.30
422 Ken Hill	.10	.30
423 Dean Palmer	.10	.30
424 Bobby Witt	.10	.30
425 Tilson Brito RC	.10	.30
426 Giovanni Carrara RC	.10	.30
427 Domingo Cedeno	.10	.30
428 Felipe Crespo	.10	.30
429 Carlos Delgado	.10	.30
430 Juan Guzman	.10	.30
431 Erik Hanson	.10	.30
432 Marty Janzen	.10	.30
433 Otis Nixon	.10	.30
434 Robert Perez	.10	.30
435 Paul Quantrill	.10	.30
436 Bill Risley	.10	.30
437 Steve Avery	.10	.30
438 Jermaine Dye	.10	.30
439 Mark Lemke	.10	.30
440 Marty Malloy RC	.10	.30
441 Fred McGriff	.20	.50
442 Greg McMichael	.10	.30
443 Wonderful Monds RC	.10	.30
444 Eddie Perez	.10	.30
445 Jason Schmidt	.20	.50
446 Terrell Wade	.10	.30
447 Terry Adams	.10	.30
448 Scott Bullett	.10	.30
449 Robin Jennings	.10	.30
450 Doug Jones	.10	.30
451 Brooks Kieschnick	.10	.30
452 Dave Magadan	.10	.30
453 Jason Maxwell RC	.10	.30
454 Brian McRae	.10	.30
455 Rodney Myers RC	.10	.30
456 Jaime Navarro	.10	.30
457 Ryne Sandberg	.50	1.25
458 Vince Coleman	.10	.30
459 Eric Davis	.10	.30
460 Steve Gibralter	.10	.30
461 Thomas Howard	.10	.30
462 Mike Kelly	.10	.30
463 Hal Morris	.10	.30
464 Eric Owens	.10	.30
465 Jose Rijo	.10	.30
466 Chris Sabo	.10	.30
467 Eddie Taubensee	.10	.30
468 Trenidad Hubbard	.10	.30
469 Curt Leskanic	.10	.30
470 Quinton McCracken	.10	.30
471 Jayhawk Owens	.10	.30
472 Steve Reed	.10	.30
473 Bryan Rekar	.10	.30
474 Bruce Ruffin	.10	.30
475 Bret Saberhagen	.10	.30
476 Walt Weiss	.10	.30
477 Eric Young	.10	.30
478 Kevin Brown	.10	.30
479 Al Leiter	.10	.30
480 Pat Rapp	.10	.30
481 Gary Sheffield	.10	.30
482 Devon White	.10	.30
483 Bob Abreu	.30	.75
484 Sean Berry	.10	.30
485 Craig Biggio	.20	.50
486 Jim Dougherty	.10	.30
487 Richard Hidalgo	.10	.30
488 Darryl Kile	.10	.30
489 Derrick May	.10	.30
490 Greg Swindell	.10	.30
491 Rick Wilkins	.10	.30
492 Mike Blowers	.10	.30
493 Tom Candiotti	.10	.30
494 Roger Cedeno	.10	.30
495 Delino DeShields	.10	.30
496 Greg Gagne	.10	.30
497 Karim Garcia	.10	.30
498 Wilton Guerrero RC	.10	.30
499 Chan Ho Park	.10	.30
500 Israel Alcantara	.10	.30
501 Shane Andrews	.10	.30
502 Yamil Benitez	.10	.30
503 Cliff Floyd	.10	.30
504 Mark Grudzielanek	.10	.30
505 Ryan McGuire	.10	.30
506 Sherman Obando	.10	.30
507 Jose Paniagua	.10	.30
508 Henry Rodriguez	.10	.30
509 Kirk Rueter	.10	.30
510 Juan Acevedo	.10	.30
511 John Franco	.10	.30
512 Bernard Gilkey	.10	.30
513 Lance Johnson	.10	.30
514 Rey Ordonez	.10	.30
515 Robert Person	.10	.30
516 Paul Wilson	.10	.30
517 Toby Borland	.10	.30
518 David Doster RC	.10	.30
519 Lenny Dykstra	.10	.30
520 Sid Fernandez	.10	.30
521 Mike Grace RC	.10	.30
522 Rich Hunter	.10	.30
523 Benito Santiago	.10	.30
524 Gene Schall	.10	.30
525 Curt Schilling	.10	.30
526 Kevin Sefcik RC	.10	.30
527 Lee Tinsley	.10	.30
528 David West	.10	.30
529 Mark Whiten	.10	.30
530 Todd Zeile	.10	.30
531 Carlos Garcia	.10	.30
532 Charlie Hayes	.10	.30
533 Jason Kendall	.10	.30
534 Jeff King	.10	.30
535 Mike Kingery	.10	.30
536 Nelson Liriano	.10	.30
537 Dan Plesac	.10	.30
538 Paul Wagner	.10	.30
539 Luis Alicea	.10	.30
540 David Bell	.10	.30
541 Alan Benes	.10	.30
542 Andy Benes	.10	.30
543 Mike Busby RC	.10	.30
544 Royce Clayton	.10	.30
545 Dennis Eckersley	.10	.30
546 Gary Gaetti	.10	.30
547 Ron Gant	.10	.30
548 Aaron Holbert	.10	.30
549 Ray Lankford	.10	.30
550 T.J. Mathews	.10	.30
551 Willie McGee	.10	.30
552 Miguel Mejia	.10	.30
553 Todd Stottlemyre	.10	.30
554 Sean Bergman	.10	.30
555 Willie Blair	.10	.30
556 Andujar Cedeno	.10	.30
557 Steve Finley	.10	.30
558 Rickey Henderson	.30	.75
559 Wally Joyner	.10	.30
560 Scott Livingstone	.10	.30
561 Marc Newfield	.10	.30
562 Bob Tewksbury	.10	.30
563 Fernando Valenzuela	.10	.30
564 Rod Beck	.10	.30
565 Doug Creek	.10	.30
566 Shawon Dunston	.10	.30
567 O.Fernandez RC	.10	.30
568 Stan Javier	.10	.30
569 Marcus Jensen	.10	.30
570 Steve Scarsone	.10	.30
571 Robby Thompson	.10	.30
572 Allen Watson	.10	.30
573 Roberto Alomar STA	.10	.30
574 Jeff Bagwell STA	.10	.30
575 Albert Belle STA	.10	.30
576 Wade Boggs STA	.10	.30
577 Barry Bonds STA	.40	1.00
578 Juan Gonzalez STA	.10	.30
579 Ken Griffey Jr. STA	.30	.75
580 Tony Gwynn STA	.20	.50
581 Randy Johnson STA	.20	.50
582 Chipper Jones STA	.20	.50
583 Barry Larkin STA	.10	.30
584 Kenny Lofton STA	.10	.30
585 Greg Maddux STA	.30	.75
586 Raul Mondesi STA	.10	.30
587 Mike Piazza STA	.30	.75
588 Cal Ripken STA	.50	1.25
589 Tim Salmon STA	.10	.30
590 Frank Thomas STA	.20	.50
591 Mo Vaughn STA	.10	.30
592 Matt Williams STA	.10	.30
593 Marty Cordova RAW	.10	.30
594 Jim Edmonds RAW	.10	.30
595 Cliff Floyd RAW	.10	.30
596 Chipper Jones RAW	.20	.50
597 Ryan Klesko RAW	.10	.30
598 Raul Mondesi RAW	.10	.30
599 Manny Ramirez RAW	.10	.30
600 Ruben Rivera RAW	.10	.30
DD1 C. Ripken DD Issued through dealers Serial numbered to 2131	20.00	50.00
DD2 Cal Ripken DD Issued through a wrapper redemption	10.00	25.00

1996 Ultra Gold Medallion

The 1996 Ultra Gold Medallion is a parallel to the regular Ultra issue. The cards were inserted one per pack in both first and second series. The card consists of a full gold foil paper with a full-color player cut out on top. Backs are identical to the regular cards.

COMPLETE SET (600) 80.00 200.00
COMP.SERIES 1 (300) 40.00 100.00
COMP.SERIES 2 (300) 40.00 100.00
*STARS: 1.25X TO 3X BASIC CARDS
*ROOKIES: 1.25X TO 3X BASIC CARDS

1996 Ultra Call to the Hall

Randomly inserted in second series packs at a rate of one in 24, this ten-card set features original illustrations of possible future Hall of Famers. The backs state why the player is a possible HOF.

COMPLETE SET (10) 25.00 60.00
*GOLD MEDAL: .75X TO 2X BASIC CALL
GM SER.2 STATED ODDS 1:240

Card	Low	High
1 Barry Bonds	5.00	12.00
2 Ken Griffey Jr.	3.00	8.00
3 Tony Gwynn	2.50	6.00
4 Rickey Henderson	2.00	5.00
5 Greg Maddux	3.00	8.00
6 Eddie Murray	2.00	5.00
7 Cal Ripken	6.00	15.00
8 Ryne Sandberg	3.00	8.00
9 Ozzie Smith	3.00	8.00
10 Frank Thomas	2.00	5.00

1996 Ultra Checklists

Randomly inserted in packs at a rate of one every four packs, this set of 20 standard-size cards features superstars of the game. Fronts are full-bleed color action photos of players with "Checklist" written in gold foil across the card. The horizontal backs are numbered and show the different card sets that are included in the Ultra line. The cards are sequenced in alphabetical order. A gold medallion parallel version of each card was issued.

COMPLETE SERIES 1 (10) 4.00 10.00
COMPLETE SERIES 2 (10) 3.00 8.00
*GOLD MEDAL: .75X TO 2X BASIC CL
GM STATED ODDS 1:40

Card	Low	High
A1 Jeff Bagwell	.25	.60
A2 Barry Bonds	1.00	2.50
A3 Juan Gonzalez	.15	.40
A4 Ken Griffey Jr.	.60	1.50
A5 Chipper Jones	.40	1.00
A6 Mike Piazza	.60	1.50
A7 Manny Ramirez	.25	.60
A8 Cal Ripken	1.25	3.00
A9 Frank Thomas	.40	1.00
A10 Matt Williams	.15	.40
B1 Albert Belle	.15	.40
B2 Cecil Fielder	.15	.40
B3 Ken Griffey Jr.	.60	1.50
B4 Tony Gwynn	.50	1.25
B5 Derek Jeter	1.00	2.50
B6 Jason Kendall	.15	.40
B7 Ryan Klesko	.15	.40
B8 Greg Maddux	.60	1.50
B9 Cal Ripken	1.25	3.00
B10 Frank Thomas	.40	1.00

1996 Ultra Diamond Producers

This 12-card standard-size set highlights the achievements of Major League stars. The cards were randomly inserted at a rate of one in 20. The cards are sequenced in alphabetical order and there are also gold medallion versions of these cards.

COMPLETE SET (12) 25.00 60.00
*GOLD MEDAL: .75X TO 2X BASIC DIAMOND
GM SER.1 STATED ODDS 1:200

Card	Low	High
1 Albert Belle	.60	1.50
2 Barry Bonds	4.00	10.00
3 Ken Griffey Jr.	2.50	6.00
4 Tony Gwynn	2.00	5.00
5 Greg Maddux	2.50	6.00
6 Hideo Nomo	1.50	4.00
7 Mike Piazza	2.50	6.00
8 Kirby Puckett	1.50	4.00
9 Cal Ripken	5.00	12.00
10 Frank Thomas	1.50	4.00
11 Mo Vaughn	.60	1.50
12 Matt Williams	.60	1.50

1996 Ultra Fresh Foundations

Randomly inserted one every three packs, this 10-card standard-size set highlights the play of hot young players. The cards are sequenced in alphabetical order and there are also gold medallion versions of these cards.

COMPLETE SET (10) 1.25 3.00
*GOLD MEDAL: .75X TO 2X BASIC FRESH
GM SER.1 STATED ODDS 1:30

Card	Low	High
1 Garret Anderson	.10	.30
2 Marty Cordova	.10	.30
3 Jim Edmonds	.10	.30
4 Brian L.Hunter	.10	.30
5 Chipper Jones	.30	.75
6 Ryan Klesko	.10	.30
7 Raul Mondesi	.10	.30
8 Hideo Nomo	.30	.75
9 Manny Ramirez	.20	.50
10 Rondell White	.10	.30

1996 Ultra Golden Prospects

Randomly inserted at a rate of one in five hobby packs, this 10-card standard-size set features players who are likely to make it as major leaguers. The cards are sequenced in alphabetical order and there are also gold medallion versions of these cards.

COMPLETE SET (10) 2.00 5.00
*GOLD MEDAL: .75X TO 2X BASIC GOLDEN
GM SER.1 STATED ODDS 1:50 HOBBY

Card	Low	High
1 Yamil Benitez	.25	.60
2 Alberto Castillo	.25	.60
3 Roger Cedeno	.25	.60
4 Johnny Damon	.40	1.00
5 Micah Franklin	.25	.60
6 Jason Giambi	.25	.60
7 Jose Herrera	.25	.60
8 Derek Jeter	1.50	4.00
9 Kevin Jordan	.25	.60
10 Ruben Rivera	.25	.60

1996 Ultra Golden Prospects Hobby

Randomly inserted in hobby packs only at a rate of one in 72, this 15-card set is printed on crystal card stock and showcases players awaiting their Major League debut. The backs carry some information about their accomplishments in the Minor Leagues. A first year card of Tony Batista is featured within this set.

COMPLETE SET (15) 50.00 100.00
*GOLD MED: .75X TO 2X BASIC GOLD.HOB
GM SER.2 STATED ODDS 1:720 HOBBY

Card	Low	High
1 Bob Abreu	3.00	8.00
2 Israel Alcantara	1.50	4.00
3 Tony Batista	2.00	5.00
4 Mike Cameron	2.00	5.00
5 Steve Cox	1.50	4.00
6 Jermaine Dye	1.50	4.00
7 Wilton Guerrero	1.50	4.00
8 Richard Hidalgo	1.50	4.00
9 Raul Ibanez	2.00	5.00
10 Marty Janzen	1.50	4.00
11 Robin Jennings	1.50	4.00
12 Jason Maxwell	1.50	4.00
13 Scott McClain	1.50	4.00
14 Wonderful Monds	1.50	4.00
15 Chris Singleton	1.50	4.00

1996 Ultra Hitting Machines

Randomly inserted in second series packs at a rate of one in 288, this 10-card set features players who hit the ball hard and often.

COMPLETE SET (10) 40.00 100.00
*GOLD MEDAL: 1.25 TO 3X BASIC HIT.MACH.
GM SER.2 STATED ODDS 1:2880

Card	Low	High
1 Albert Belle	2.50	6.00
2 Barry Bonds	15.00	40.00
3 Juan Gonzalez	2.50	6.00
4 Ken Griffey Jr.	10.00	25.00
5 Edgar Martinez	4.00	10.00
6 Rafael Palmeiro	4.00	10.00
7 Mike Piazza	10.00	25.00
8 Tim Salmon	4.00	10.00
9 Frank Thomas	6.00	15.00
10 Matt Williams	2.50	6.00

1996 Ultra Home Run Kings

This 12-card standard-size set features leading power hitters. These cards were randomly inserted at a rate of one in 75 packs. The card fronts are thin wood with a color cut out of the player and HR KING printed diagonally in copper foil down the left side. The Fleer company was not happy with the final look of the card because of the transfer of the copper foil. Therefore all cards were made redemption cards. Backs of the cards have information about how to redeem the cards for replacement. The exchange offer expired on December 1, 1996. The cards are sequenced in alphabetical order.

COMPLETE SET (12) 20.00 50.00
*GOLD MEDAL: 4X TO 10X BASIC HR KINGS
GM SER.1 STATED ODDS 1:750
*REDEMPTION: .6X TO 1.5X BASIC HR KINGS
ONE RDMP.CARD VIA MAIL PER HR CARD

Card	Low	High
1 Albert Belle	.75	2.00
2 Dante Bichette	.75	2.00
3 Barry Bonds	5.00	12.00
4 Jose Canseco	1.25	3.00
5 Juan Gonzalez	.75	2.00
6 Ken Griffey Jr.	3.00	8.00
7 Mark McGwire	5.00	12.00
8 Manny Ramirez	1.25	3.00
9 Tim Salmon	1.25	3.00
10 Frank Thomas	2.00	5.00
11 Mo Vaughn	.75	2.00
12 Matt Williams	.75	2.00

1996 Ultra Home Run Kings Redemption Gold Medallion

These cards are parallel to the regular Home Run Kings Redemption cards. They are differentiated from the regular Home Run Kings Redemption cards by the Gold Medallion logo on the front of the cards.

*GM REDEMPTION CARDS: 4X TO 10X BASIC HOME RUN KINGS

1996 Ultra On-Base Leaders

Randomly inserted in second series packs at a rate of one in four, this 10-card set features players with consistently high on-base percentage.

COMPLETE SET (10) 2.00 5.00
*GOLD MEDAL: .75X TO 2X BASIC OBL
GM SER.2 STATED ODDS 1:40

Card	Low	High
1 Wade Boggs	.25	.60
2 Barry Bonds	1.00	2.50
3 Tony Gwynn	.50	1.25
4 Rickey Henderson	.40	1.00
5 Chuck Knoblauch	.15	.40
6 Edgar Martinez	.25	.60
7 Mike Piazza	.60	1.50
8 Tim Salmon	.25	.60
9 Frank Thomas	.40	1.00
10 Jim Thome	.25	.60

1996 Ultra Power Plus

Randomly inserted at a rate of one in ten packs, this 12-card standard-size set features top all-around players. The cards are sequenced in alphabetical order and gold medallion versions of these cards were also issued.

COMPLETE SET (12) 10.00 25.00
*GOLD MEDAL: .75X TO 2X BASIC PLUS
GM SER.1 STATED ODDS 1:100

Card	Low	High
1 Jeff Bagwell	.60	1.50
2 Barry Bonds	2.50	6.00
3 Ken Griffey Jr.	1.50	4.00
4 Raul Mondesi	.40	1.00
5 Rafael Palmeiro	.60	1.50
6 Mike Piazza	1.50	4.00
7 Manny Ramirez	.60	1.50
8 Tim Salmon	.60	1.50
9 Reggie Sanders	.40	1.00
10 Frank Thomas	1.00	2.50
11 Larry Walker	.40	1.00
12 Matt Williams	.40	1.00

1996 Ultra Prime Leather

Eighteen outstanding defensive players are featured in this standard-size set which is inserted approximately one in every eight packs. The cards are sequenced in alphabetical order and gold medallion versions of these cards were also issued.

COMPLETE SET (18) 10.00 25.00
*GOLD MEDAL: .75X TO 2X BASIC LEATHER
GM SER.1 STATED ODDS 1:80

Card	Low	High
1 Ivan Rodriguez	.60	1.50
2 Will Clark	.60	1.50
3 Roberto Alomar	.60	1.50
4 Cal Ripken	3.00	8.00
5 Wade Boggs	.60	1.50
6 Ken Griffey Jr.	1.50	4.00
7 Kenny Lofton	.40	1.00
8 Kirby Puckett	1.00	2.50
9 Tim Salmon	.60	1.50
10 Mike Piazza	1.50	4.00
11 Mark Grace	.60	1.50
12 Craig Biggio	.60	1.50
13 Barry Larkin	.60	1.50
14 Matt Williams	.40	1.00
15 Barry Bonds	2.50	6.00
16 Tony Gwynn	1.25	3.00

17 Brian McRae .40 1.00
18 Raul Mondesi .40 1.00
S4 Cal Ripken Jr Promo 3.00 8.00

1996 Ultra Rawhide

Randomly inserted in second series packs at a rate of one in eight, this 10-card set features leading defensive players.

COMPLETE SET (10) 6.00 15.00
*GOLD MEDAL: .75X TO 2X BASIC RAWHIDE
GM SER.2 STATED ODDS 1:80
1 Roberto Alomar .40 1.00
2 Barry Bonds 1.50 4.00
3 Mark Grace .40 1.00
4 Ken Griffey Jr. 1.00 2.50
5 Kenny Lofton .25 .60
6 Greg Maddux 1.00 2.50
7 Raul Mondesi .25 .60
8 Mike Piazza 1.00 2.50
9 Cal Ripken 2.00 5.00
10 Matt Williams .25 .60

1996 Ultra RBI Kings

This 10-card standard-size set was randomly inserted at a rate of one in five retail packs. The cards are sequenced in alphabetical order and gold medallion versions of these cards were also issued.

COMPLETE SET (10) 12.50 30.00
*GOLD MEDAL: .75X TO 2X BASIC RBI KINGS
GM SER.1 STATED ODDS 1:50 RETAIL
1 Derek Bell .75 2.00
2 Albert Belle .75 2.00
3 Dante Bichette .75 2.00
4 Barry Bonds 5.00 12.00
5 Jim Edmonds .75 2.00
6 Manny Ramirez 1.25 3.00
7 Reggie Sanders .75 2.00
8 Sammy Sosa 2.00 5.00
9 Frank Thomas 2.00 5.00
10 Mo Vaughn .75 2.00

1996 Ultra Respect

Randomly inserted in second series packs at a rate of one in 18, this 10-card set features players who are well regarded by their peers for both on and off field activies.

COMPLETE SET (10) 20.00 50.00
*GOLD MEDAL: .75X TO 2X BASIC RESPECT
GM SER.2 STATED ODDS 1:180
1 Joe Carter .60 1.50
2 Ken Griffey Jr. 2.50 6.00
3 Tony Gwynn 2.00 5.00
4 Greg Maddux 2.50 6.00
5 Eddie Murray 1.50 4.00
6 Kirby Puckett 1.50 4.00
7 Cal Ripken 5.00 12.00
8 Ryne Sandberg 2.50 6.00
9 Frank Thomas 1.50 4.00
10 Mo Vaughn .60 1.50

1996 Ultra Rising Stars

Randomly inserted in second series packs at a rate of one in four, this 10-card set features leading players of tomorrow.

COMPLETE SET (10) 1.50 4.00
*GOLD MEDAL: .75X TO 2X BASIC RISING
GM SER.2 STATED ODDS 1:40
1 Garret Anderson .10 .30
2 Marty Cordova .10 .30
3 Jim Edmonds .10 .30
4 Cliff Floyd .10 .30
5 Brian L.Hunter .10 .30
6 Chipper Jones .30 .75
7 Ryan Klesko .10 .30
8 Hideo Nomo .30 .75
9 Manny Ramirez .20 .50
10 Rondell White .10 .30

1996 Ultra Season Crowns

This set features ten award winners and stat leaders. The cards were randomly inserted at a rate of one in ten. The clear acetate cards feature a full-color player cutout against a background of colored foliage and laurels.

COMPLETE SET (10) 12.50 30.00
*GOLD MEDAL: .75X TO 2X BASIC CROWNS
GM SER.1 STATED ODDS 1:100
1 Barry Bonds 2.50 6.00
2 Tony Gwynn 1.25 3.00
3 Randy Johnson 1.00 2.50
4 Kenny Lofton .40 1.00
5 Greg Maddux 1.50 4.00
6 Edgar Martinez .60 1.50
7 Hideo Nomo 1.00 2.50
8 Cal Ripken 3.00 8.00
9 Frank Thomas 1.00 2.50
10 Tim Wakefield .40 1.00

1996 Ultra Thunderclap

Randomly inserted one in 72 retail packs, these cards feature the leading power hitters.

COMPLETE SET (20) 40.00 100.00
*GOLD MEDAL: 1.25X TO 3X BASIC THUNDER
GM SER.2 STATED ODDS 1:720 RETAIL
1 Albert Belle 2.00 5.00
2 Barry Bonds 12.50 30.00
3 Bobby Bonilla 2.00 5.00
4 Jose Canseco 3.00 8.00
5 Joe Carter 2.00 5.00
6 Will Clark 3.00 8.00
7 Andre Dawson 2.00 5.00
8 Cecil Fielder 2.00 5.00
9 Andres Galarraga 2.00 5.00
10 Juan Gonzalez 2.00 5.00
11 Ken Griffey Jr. 8.00 20.00
12 Fred McGriff 3.00 8.00
13 Mark McGwire 12.50 30.00
14 Eddie Murray 5.00 12.00
15 Rafael Palmeiro 3.00 8.00
16 Kirby Puckett 5.00 12.00
17 Cal Ripken 15.00 40.00
18 Ryne Sandberg 10.00 25.00
19 Frank Thomas 5.00 12.00
20 Matt Williams 2.00 5.00

1997 Ultra

The 1997 Ultra was issued in two series totalling 553 cards. The first series consisted of 300 cards with the second containing 253. The 10-card packs had a suggested retail price of 2.49 each. Each pack had two insert cards, with one insert being a gold medallion parallel and the other insert being from one of serveral other insert sets. The fronts features borderless color action player photos with career statistics on the backs. As in most Fleer produced sets, the cards are arranged in alphabetical order by league, player and team. Second series retail packs contained only cards 301-450 while second series hobby packs contained all cards from 301-553. Rookie Cards include Jose Cruz Jr., Brian Giles and Fernando Tatis.

COMPLETE SET (553) 55.00 110.00
COMP.SERIES 1 (300) 15.00 30.00
COMP.SERIES 2 (253) 40.00 80.00
COMMON CARD (1-553) .10 .30
COMMON RC .15 .40
1 Roberto Alomar .20 .50
2 Brady Anderson .10 .30
3 Rocky Coppinger .10 .30
4 Jeffrey Hammonds .10 .30
5 Chris Hoiles .10 .30
6 Eddie Murray .30 .75
7 Mike Mussina .20 .50
8 Jimmy Myers .10 .30
9 Randy Myers .10 .30
10 Arthur Rhodes .10 .30
11 Cal Ripken 1.00 2.50
12 Jose Canseco .20 .50
13 Roger Clemens .60 1.50
14 Tom Gordon .10 .30
15 Jose Malave .10 .30
16 Tim Naehring .10 .30
17 Troy O'Leary .10 .30
18 Bill Selby .10 .30
19 Heathcliff Slocumb .10 .30
20 Mike Stanley .10 .30
21 Mo Vaughn .10 .30
22 Garret Anderson .10 .30
23 George Arias .10 .30
24 Chili Davis .10 .30
25 Jim Edmonds .10 .30
26 Darin Erstad .10 .30
27 Chuck Finley .10 .30
28 Todd Greene .10 .30
29 Troy Percival .10 .30
30 Tim Salmon .20 .50
31 Jeff Schmidt .10 .30
32 Randy Velarde .10 .30
33 Shad Williams .10 .30
34 Wilson Alvarez .10 .30
35 Harold Baines .10 .30
36 James Baldwin .10 .30
37 Mike Cameron .10 .30
38 Ray Durham .10 .30
39 Ozzie Guillen .10 .30
40 Roberto Hernandez .10 .30
41 Darren Lewis .10 .30
42 Jose Munoz .10 .30
43 Tony Phillips .10 .30
44 Frank Thomas .30 .75
45 Sandy Alomar Jr. .10 .30
46 Albert Belle .10 .30
47 Mark Carreon .10 .30
48 Julio Franco .10 .30
49 Orel Hershiser .10 .30
50 Kenny Lofton .10 .30
51 Jack McDowell .10 .30
52 Jose Mesa .10 .30
53 Charles Nagy .10 .30
54 Manny Ramirez .20 .50
55 Julian Tavarez .10 .30
56 Omar Vizquel .20 .50
57 Raul Casanova .10 .30
58 Tony Clark .10 .30
59 Travis Fryman .10 .30
60 Bob Higginson .10 .30
61 Melvin Nieves .10 .30
62 Curtis Pride .10 .30
63 Justin Thompson .10 .30
64 Alan Trammell .10 .30
65 Kevin Appier .10 .30
66 Johnny Damon .20 .50
67 Keith Lockhart .10 .30
68 Jeff Montgomery .10 .30
69 Jose Offerman .10 .30
70 Bip Roberts .10 .30
71 Jose Rosado .10 .30
72 Chris Stynes .10 .30
73 Mike Sweeney .10 .30
74 Jeff Cirillo .10 .30
75 Jeff D'Amico .10 .30
76 John Jaha .10 .30
77 Scott Karl .10 .30
78 Mike Matheny .10 .30
79 Ben McDonald .10 .30
80 Matt Mieske .10 .30
81 Marc Newfield .10 .30
82 Dave Nilsson .10 .30
83 Jose Valentin .10 .30
84 Fernando Vina .10 .30
85 Rick Aguilera .10 .30
86 Marty Cordova .10 .30
87 Chuck Knoblauch .10 .30
88 Matt Lawton .10 .30
89 Pat Meares .10 .30
90 Paul Molitor .10 .30
91 Greg Myers .10 .30
92 Dan Naulty .10 .30
93 Kirby Puckett .30 .75
94 Frank Rodriguez .10 .30
95 Wade Boggs .20 .50
96 Cecil Fielder .10 .30
97 Joe Girardi .10 .30
98 Dwight Gooden .10 .30
99 Derek Jeter .75 2.00
100 Tino Martinez .20 .50
101 Ramiro Mendoza RC .10 .30
102 Andy Pettitte .20 .50
103 Mariano Rivera .30 .75
104 Ruben Rivera .10 .30
105 Kenny Rogers .10 .30
106 Darryl Strawberry .10 .30
107 Bernie Williams .20 .50
108 Tony Batista .10 .30
109 Geronimo Berroa .10 .30
110 Bobby Chouinard .10 .30
111 Brent Gates .10 .30
112 Jason Giambi .10 .30
113 Damon Mashore .10 .30
114 Mark McGwire .75 2.00
115 Scott Spiezio .10 .30
116 John Wasdin .10 .30
117 Steve Wojciechowski .10 .30
118 Ernie Young .10 .30
119 Norm Charlton .10 .30
120 Joey Cora .10 .30
121 Ken Griffey Jr. .50 1.25
122 Sterling Hitchcock .10 .30
123 Raul Ibanez .10 .30
124 Randy Johnson .30 .75
125 Edgar Martinez .20 .50
126 Alex Rodriguez .50 1.25
127 Matt Wagner .10 .30
128 Bob Wells .10 .30
129 Dan Wilson .10 .30
130 Will Clark .20 .50
131 Kevin Elster .10 .30
132 Juan Gonzalez .10 .30
133 Rusty Greer .10 .30
134 Darryl Hamilton .10 .30
135 Mike Henneman .10 .30
136 Ken Hill .10 .30
137 Mark McLemore .10 .30
138 Dean Palmer .10 .30
139 Roger Pavlik .10 .30
140 Ivan Rodriguez .20 .50
141 Joe Carter .10 .30
142 Carlos Delgado .10 .30
143 Alex Gonzalez .10 .30
144 Juan Guzman .10 .30
145 Pat Hentgen .10 .30
146 Marty Janzen .10 .30
147 Otis Nixon .10 .30
148 Charlie O'Brien .10 .30
149 John Olerud .10 .30
150 Robert Perez .10 .30
151 Jermaine Dye .10 .30
152 Tom Glavine .20 .50
153 Andruw Jones .20 .50
154 Chipper Jones .30 .75
155 Ryan Klesko .10 .30
156 Javier Lopez .10 .30
157 Greg Maddux .50 1.25
158 Fred McGriff .20 .50
159 Wonderful Monds .10 .30
160 John Smoltz .20 .50
161 Terrell Wade .10 .30
162 Mark Wohlers .10 .30
163 Brant Brown .10 .30
164 Mark Grace .20 .50
165 Tyler Houston .10 .30
166 Robin Jennings .10 .30
167 Jason Maxwell .10 .30
168 Ryne Sandberg .50 1.25
169 Sammy Sosa .30 .75
170 Amaury Telemaco .10 .30
171 Steve Trachsel .10 .30
172 Pedro Valdes RC .10 .30
173 Tim Belk .10 .30
174 Bret Boone .10 .30
175 Jeff Brantley .10 .30
176 Eric Davis .10 .30
177 Barry Larkin .20 .50
178 Chad Mottola .10 .30
179 Mark Portugal .10 .30
180 Reggie Sanders .10 .30
181 John Smiley .10 .30
182 Eddie Taubensee .10 .30
183 Dante Bichette .10 .30
184 Ellis Burks .10 .30
185 Andres Galarraga .10 .30
186 Curt Leskanic .10 .30
187 Quinton McCracken .10 .30
188 Jeff Reed .10 .30
189 Kevin Ritz .10 .30
190 Walt Weiss .10 .30
191 Jamey Wright .10 .30
192 Eric Young .10 .30
193 Kevin Brown .10 .30
194 Luis Castillo .10 .30
195 Jeff Conine .10 .30
196 Andre Dawson .10 .30
197 Charles Johnson .10 .30
198 Al Leiter .10 .30
199 Ralph Milliard .10 .30
200 Robb Nen .10 .30
201 Edgar Renteria .10 .30
202 Gary Sheffield .10 .30
203 Bob Abreu .20 .50
204 Jeff Bagwell .20 .50
205 Derek Bell .10 .30
206 Sean Berry .10 .30
207 Richard Hidalgo .10 .30
208 Todd Jones .10 .30
209 Darryl Kile .10 .30
210 Orlando Miller .10 .30
211 Shane Reynolds .10 .30
212 Billy Wagner .10 .30
213 Donne Wall .10 .30
214 Roger Cedeno .10 .30
215 Greg Gagne .10 .30
216 Karim Garcia .10 .30
217 Wilton Guerrero .10 .30
218 Todd Hollandsworth .10 .30
219 Ramon Martinez .10 .30
220 Raul Mondesi .10 .30
221 Hideo Nomo .30 .75
222 Chan Ho Park .10 .30
223 Mike Piazza .50 1.25
224 Ismael Valdes .10 .30
225 Moises Alou .10 .30
226 Derek Aucoin .10 .30
227 Yamil Benitez .10 .30
228 Jeff Fassero .10 .30
229 Darrin Fletcher .10 .30
230 Mark Grudzielanek .10 .30
231 Barry Manuel .10 .30
232 Pedro Martinez .20 .50
233 Henry Rodriguez .10 .30
234 Ugueth Urbina .10 .30
235 Rondell White .10 .30
236 Carlos Baerga .10 .30
237 John Franco .10 .30
238 Bernard Gilkey .10 .30
239 Todd Hundley .10 .30
240 Butch Huskey .10 .30
241 Jason Isringhausen .10 .30
242 Lance Johnson .10 .30
243 Bobby Jones .10 .30
244 Alex Ochoa .10 .30
245 Rey Ordonez .10 .30
246 Paul Wilson .10 .30
247 Ron Blazier .10 .30
248 David Doster .10 .30
249 Jim Eisenreich .10 .30
250 Mike Grace .10 .30
251 Mike Lieberthal .10 .30
252 Wendell Magee .10 .30
253 Mickey Morandini .10 .30
254 Ricky Otero .10 .30
255 Scott Rolen .20 .50
256 Curt Schilling .10 .30
257 Todd Zeile .10 .30
258 Jermaine Allensworth .10 .30
259 Trey Beamon .10 .30
260 Carlos Garcia .10 .30
261 Mark Johnson .10 .30
262 Jason Kendall .10 .30
263 Jeff King .10 .30
264 Al Martin .10 .30
265 Denny Neagle .10 .30
266 Matt Ruebel .10 .30
267 Marc Wilkins .10 .30
268 Alan Benes .10 .30
269 Dennis Eckersley .10 .30
270 Ron Gant .10 .30
271 Aaron Holbert .10 .30
272 Brian Jordan .10 .30
273 Ray Lankford .10 .30
274 John Mabry .10 .30
275 T.J. Mathews .10 .30
276 Ozzie Smith .50 1.25
277 Todd Stottlemyre .10 .30
278 Mark Sweeney .10 .30
279 Andy Ashby .10 .30
280 Steve Finley .10 .30
281 John Flaherty .10 .30
282 Chris Gomez .10 .30
283 Tony Gwynn .40 1.00
284 Joey Hamilton .10 .30
285 Rickey Henderson .30 .75
286 Trevor Hoffman .10 .30
287 Jason Thompson .10 .30
288 Fernando Valenzuela .10 .30
289 Greg Vaughn .10 .30
290 Barry Bonds .75 2.00
291 Jay Canizaro .10 .30
292 Jacob Cruz .10 .30
293 Shawon Dunston .10 .30
294 Shawn Estes .10 .30
295 Mark Gardner .10 .30
296 Marcus Jensen .10 .30
297 Bill Mueller RC .50 1.25
298 Chris Singleton .10 .30
299 Allen Watson .10 .30
300 Matt Williams .10 .30
301 Rod Beck .10 .30
302 Jay Bell .10 .30
303 Shawon Dunston .10 .30
304 Reggie Jefferson .10 .30
305 Darren Oliver .10 .30
306 Benito Santiago .10 .30
307 Gerald Williams .10 .30
308 Damon Buford .10 .30
309 Jeromy Burnitz .10 .30
310 Sterling Hitchcock .10 .30
311 Dave Hollins .10 .30
312 Mel Rojas .10 .30
313 Robin Ventura .10 .30
314 David Wells .10 .30
315 Cal Eldred .10 .30
316 Gary Gaetti .10 .30
317 John Hudek .10 .30
318 Brian Johnson .10 .30
319 Denny Neagle .10 .30
320 Larry Walker .10 .30
321 Russ Davis .10 .30
322 Delino DeShields .10 .30
323 Charlie Hayes .10 .30
324 Jermaine Dye .10 .30
325 John Ericks .10 .30
326 Jeff Fassero .10 .30
327 Nomar Garciaparra .50 1.25
328 Willie Greene .10 .30
329 Greg McMichael .10 .30
330 Damion Easley .10 .30
331 Ricky Bones .10 .30
332 John Burkett .10 .30
333 Royce Clayton .10 .30
334 Greg Colbrunn .10 .30
335 Tony Eusebio .10 .30
336 Gregg Jefferies .10 .30
337 Wally Joyner .10 .30
338 Jim Leyritz .10 .30
339 Paul O'Neill .20 .50
340 Bruce Ruffin .10 .30
341 Michael Tucker .10 .30
342 Andy Benes .10 .30
343 Craig Biggio .20 .50
344 Rex Hudler .10 .30
345 Brad Radke .10 .30
346 Deion Sanders .20 .50
347 Moises Alou .10 .30
348 Brad Ausmus .10 .30
349 Armando Benitez .10 .30
350 Mark Gubicza .10 .30
351 Terry Steinbach .10 .30
352 Mark Whiten .10 .30
353 Ricky Bottalico .10 .30
354 Brian Giles RC .60 1.50
355 Eric Karros .10 .30
356 Jimmy Key .10 .30
357 Carlos Perez .10 .30
358 Alex Fernandez .10 .30
359 J.T. Snow .10 .30
360 Bobby Bonilla .10 .30
361 Scott Brosius .10 .30
362 Greg Swindell .10 .30
363 Jose Vizcaino .10 .30
364 Matt Williams .10 .30
365 Darren Daulton .10 .30
366 Shane Andrews .10 .30
367 Jim Eisenreich .10 .30
368 Ariel Prieto .10 .30
369 Bob Tewksbury .10 .30
370 Mike Bordick .10 .30
371 Rheal Cormier .10 .30
372 Cliff Floyd .10 .30
373 David Justice .10 .30
374 John Wetteland .10 .30
375 Mike Blowers .10 .30
376 Jose Canseco .20 .50
377 Roger Clemens .60 1.50
378 Kevin Mitchell .10 .30
379 Todd Zeile .10 .30
380 Jim Thome .20 .50
381 Turk Wendell .10 .30
382 Rico Brogna .10 .30
383 Eric Davis .10 .30
384 Mike Lansing .10 .30
385 Devon White .10 .30
386 Marquis Grissom .10 .30
387 Todd Worrell .10 .30
388 Jeff Kent .10 .30
389 Mickey Tettleton .10 .30
390 Steve Avery .10 .30
391 David Cone .10 .30
392 Scott Cooper .10 .30
393 Lee Stevens .10 .30
394 Kevin Elster .10 .30
395 Tom Goodwin .10 .30
396 Shawn Green .10 .30
397 Pete Harnisch .10 .30
398 Eddie Murray .30 .75
399 Joe Randa .10 .30
400 Scott Sanders .10 .30
401 John Valentin .10 .30
402 Todd Jones .10 .30
403 Terry Adams .10 .30
404 Brian Hunter .10 .30
405 Pat Listach .10 .30
406 Kenny Lofton .10 .30
407 Hal Morris .10 .30
408 Ed Sprague .10 .30
409 Rich Becker .10 .30
410 Edgardo Alfonzo .10 .30
411 Albert Belle .10 .30
412 Jeff King .10 .30
413 Kirt Manwaring .10 .30
414 Jason Schmidt .10 .30
415 Allen Watson .10 .30
416 Lee Tinsley .10 .30
417 Brett Butler .10 .30
418 Carlos Garcia .10 .30
419 Mark Lemke .10 .30
420 Jaime Navarro .10 .30
421 David Segui .10 .30
422 Ruben Sierra .10 .30
423 B.J. Surhoff .10 .30
424 Julian Tavarez .10 .30
425 Billy Taylor .10 .30
426 Ken Caminiti .10 .30
427 Chuck Carr .10 .30
428 Benji Gil .10 .30
429 Terry Mulholland .10 .30
430 Mike Stanton .10 .30
431 Wil Cordero .10 .30
432 Chili Davis .10 .30
433 Mariano Duncan .10 .30
434 Orlando Merced .10 .30
435 Kent Mercker .10 .30
436 John Olerud .10 .30
437 Quilvio Veras .10 .30
438 Mike Fetters .10 .30
439 Glenallen Hill .10 .30
440 Bill Swift .10 .30
441 Tim Wakefield .10 .30
442 Pedro Astacio .10 .30
443 Vinny Castilla .10 .30
444 Doug Drabek .10 .30
445 Alan Embree .10 .30
446 Lee Smith .10 .30
447 Darryl Hamilton .10 .30
448 Brian McRae .10 .30
449 Mike Timlin .10 .30
450 Bob Wickman .10 .30
451 Jason Dickson .10 .30
452 Chad Curtis .10 .30
453 Mark Leiter .10 .30
454 Damon Berryhill .10 .30
455 Kevin Orie .10 .30
456 Dave Burba .10 .30
457 Chris Holt .10 .30
458 Ricky Ledee RC .15 .40
459 Mike Devereaux .10 .30
460 Pokey Reese .10 .30
461 Tim Raines .10 .30
462 Ryan Jones .10 .30
463 Shane Mack .10 .30
464 Darren Dreifort .10 .30
465 Mark Parent .10 .30
466 Mark Portugal .10 .30
467 Dante Powell .10 .30
468 Craig Grebeck .10 .30
469 Ron Villone .10 .30
470 Dmitri Young .10 .30
471 Shannon Stewart .10 .30
472 Rick Helling .10 .30
473 Bill Haselman .10 .30
474 Albie Lopez .10 .30
475 Glendon Rusch .10 .30
476 Derrick May .10 .30
477 Chad Ogea .10 .30
478 Kirk Rueter .10 .30
479 Chris Hammond .10 .30
480 Russ Johnson .10 .30
481 James Mouton .10 .30
482 Mike Macfarlane .10 .30
483 Scott Ruffcorn .10 .30
484 Jeff Frye .10 .30
485 Richie Sexson .15 .40
486 Emil Brown RC .15 .40
487 Desi Wilson .10 .30
488 Brent Gates .10 .30
489 Tony Graffanino .10 .30
490 Dan Miceli .10 .30
491 Orlando Cabrera RC .40 1.00
492 Tony Womack RC .15 .40
493 Jerome Walton .10 .30
494 Mark Thompson .10 .30
495 Jose Guillen .10 .30
496 Willie Blair .10 .30
497 T.J. Staton RC .15 .40
498 Scott Kamieniecki .10 .30
499 Vince Coleman .10 .30
500 Jeff Abbott .10 .30
501 Chris Widger .10 .30
502 Kevin Tapani .10 .30
503 Carlos Castillo RC .15 .40
504 Luis Gonzalez .10 .30
505 Tim Belcher .10 .30
506 Armando Reynoso .10 .30
507 Jamie Moyer .10 .30
508 Randall Simon RC .15 .40
509 Vladimir Guerrero .30 .75
510 Wady Almonte RC .15 .40
511 Dustin Hermanson .10 .30
512 Deivi Cruz RC .15 .40
513 Luis Alicea .10 .30
514 Felix Heredia RC .15 .40
515 Don Slaught .10 .30
516 S.Hasegawa RC .25 .60
517 Matt Walbeck .10 .30
518 David Arias-Ortiz RC 20.00 50.00
519 Brady Raggio RC .15 .40
520 Rudy Pemberton .10 .30
521 Wayne Kirby .10 .30
522 Calvin Maduro .10 .30
523 Mark Lewis .10 .30
524 Mike Jackson .10 .30
525 Sid Fernandez .10 .30
526 Mike Bielecki .10 .30
527 Bubba Trammell RC .15 .40
528 Brent Brede RC .15 .40
529 Matt Morris .10 .30
530 Joe Borowski RC .15 .40
531 Orlando Miller .10 .30
532 Jim Bullinger .10 .30
533 Robert Person .10 .30
534 Doug Glanville .10 .30
535 Terry Pendleton .10 .30
536 Jorge Posada .20 .50
537 Marc Sagmoen RC .15 .40
538 Fernando Tatis RC .15 .40
539 Aaron Sele .10 .30
540 Brian Banks .10 .30
541 Derrek Lee .20 .50
542 John Wasdin .10 .30
543 Justin Towle RC .15 .40
544 Pat Cline .10 .30

545 Dave Magadan	.10	.30
546 Jeff Blauser	.10	.30
547 Phil Nevin	.10	.30
548 Todd Walker	.10	.30
549 Eli Marrero	.10	.30
550 Bartolo Colon	.10	.30
551 Jose Cruz Jr. RC	.15	.40
552 Todd Dunwoody	.10	.30
553 Hideki Irabu RC	.15	.40
P11 Cal Ripken Promo Three Card Strip	.75	2.00

1997 Ultra Gold Medallion

This 553-card set is a gold-holofoil-stamped parallel version of the regular Ultra set and was inserted one per pack of both series one and series two cards. Unlike previous Gold Medallion sets, the 1997 edition features different photos than the corresponding regular cards.

COMPLETE SET (553)	110.00	270.00
COMP. SERIES 1 (300)	60.00	150.00
COMP. SERIES 2 (253)	50.00	120.00
*STARS: 1.25X TO 3X BASIC CARDS		
*ROOKIES: .75X TO 2X BASIC		
518 David Arias-Ortiz	20.00	50.00

1997 Ultra Platinum Medallion

This 553-card set is a parallel to the regular Ultra and was inserted one per 100 packs of both series 1 and series 2 cards. Sparkling platinum lettering on front differentiates these cards from their far more common regular issue brethren. No set price is provided due to scarcity. As with the 1997 Gold Medallion set, the Platinum Medallion set features different photos than the corresponding regular cards.

*STARS 1-450: 12.5X TO 30X BASIC CARDS		
*STARS 451-553: 10X TO 25X BASIC CARDS		
*ROOKIES 1-450: 6X TO 15X BASIC		
*ROOKIES: 451-553: 5X TO 12X BASIC		
518 David Arias-Ortiz	175.00	300.00

1997 Ultra Autographstix Emeralds

This six-card hobby exclusive Series two insert set consists of individually numbered Redemption cards for autographed bats from the players checklisted below. Only 25 of each card was produced. The deadline to exchange cards was July 1st, 1998. The bat a collector received for these cards was not easily identifiable as a special bat. Prices listed refer to the exchange cards.

EXCHANGE DEADLINE: 07/01/98
1 Alex Ochoa
2 Todd Walker
3 Scott Rolen
4 Darin Erstad
5 Alex Rodriguez
6 Todd Hollandsworth

1997 Ultra Baseball Rules

Randomly inserted into first series retail packs of 1997 Ultra at a rate of 1:36, cards from this 10-card set feature a selection of baseball's top performers from the 1996 season. The die cut cards feature a player photo surrounded by a group of baseballs. The back explains some of the rules involved in making various awards.

COMPLETE SET (10)	50.00	120.00
1 Barry Bonds	6.00	15.00
2 Ken Griffey Jr.	4.00	10.00
3 Derek Jeter	6.00	15.00
4 Chipper Jones	2.50	6.00
5 Greg Maddux	4.00	10.00
6 Mark McGwire	6.00	15.00
7 Troy Percival	1.00	2.50
8 Mike Piazza	4.00	10.00
9 Cal Ripken	8.00	20.00
10 Frank Thomas	2.50	6.00

1997 Ultra Checklists

Randomly inserted in all first and second series packs at a rate of one in four, this 20-card set features borderless player photos on the front along with the word "Checklist", the player's name as well as the "ultra" logo at the bottom. The backs are checklists. The checklists for Series 1 are listed below with an "A" prefix and for Series 2 with a "B" prefix.

COMPLETE SERIES 1 (10)	3.00	8.00
COMPLETE SERIES 2 (10)	5.00	12.00
A1 Dante Bichette	.10	.30
A2 Barry Bonds	.75	2.00
A3 Ken Griffey Jr.	.50	1.25
A4 Greg Maddux	.50	1.25
A5 Mark McGwire	.75	2.00
A6 Mike Piazza	.50	1.25
A7 Cal Ripken	1.00	2.50
A8 John Smoltz	.20	.50
A9 Sammy Sosa	.30	.75
A10 Frank Thomas	.30	.75
B1 Andruw Jones	.20	.50
B2 Ken Griffey Jr.	.50	1.25
B3 Frank Thomas	.30	.75
B4 Alex Rodriguez	.50	1.25
B5 Cal Ripken	1.00	2.50
B6 Mike Piazza	.50	1.25
B7 Greg Maddux	.50	1.25
B8 Chipper Jones	.30	.75
B9 Derek Jeter	.75	2.00
B10 Juan Gonzalez	.10	.30

1997 Ultra Diamond Producers

Randomly inserted in all first series packs at a rate of one in 288, this 12-card set features "flannel" material mounted on card stock and attempt to look and feel like actual uniforms.

COMPLETE SET (12)	100.00	250.00
1 Jeff Bagwell	4.00	10.00
2 Barry Bonds	15.00	40.00
3 Ken Griffey Jr.	10.00	25.00
4 Chipper Jones	6.00	15.00
5 Kenny Lofton	2.50	6.00
6 Greg Maddux	10.00	25.00
7 Mark McGwire	15.00	40.00
8 Mike Piazza	10.00	25.00
9 Cal Ripken	20.00	50.00
10 Alex Rodriguez	10.00	25.00
11 Frank Thomas	6.00	15.00
12 Matt Williams	2.50	6.00

1997 Ultra Double Trouble

Randomly inserted in series one packs at a rate of one in four, this 20-card set features two players from each team. The horizontal cards feature players photos with their names in silver foil on the bottom and the words "double trouble" on the top. The backs feature information on what the players contributed to their team in 1996

COMPLETE SET (20)	4.00	10.00
1 Roberto Alomar / Cal Ripken	1.00	2.50
2 Mo Vaughn / Jose Canseco	.10	.30
3 Jim Edmonds / Tim Salmon	.10	.30
4 Harold Baines / Frank Thomas	.30	.75
5 Albert Belle / Kenny Lofton	.10	.30
6 Marty Cordova / Chuck Knoblauch	.10	.30
7 Derek Jeter / Andy Pettitte	.75	2.00
8 Jason Giambi / Mark McGwire	.75	2.00
9 Ken Griffey Jr. / Alex Rodriguez	.50	1.25
10 Juan Gonzalez / Will Clark	.10	.30
11 Greg Maddux / Chipper Jones	.50	1.25
12 Mark Grace / Sammy Sosa	.30	.75
13 Dante Bichette / Andres Galarraga	.10	.30
14 Jeff Bagwell / Derek Bell	.20	.50
15 Hideo Nomo / Mike Piazza	.50	1.25
16 Henry Rodriguez / Moises Alou	.10	.30
17 Rey Ordonez / Alex Ochoa	.10	.30
18 Ray Lankford / Ron Gant	.10	.30
19 Tony Gwynn / Rickey Henderson	.40	1.00
20 Barry Bonds / Matt Williams	.75	2.00

1997 Ultra Fame Game

Randomly inserted in series two hobby packs only at a rate of one in eight, this 18-card set features color photos of players who have displayed Hall of Fame potential on an elegant card design.

COMPLETE SET (18)	25.00	60.00
1 Ken Griffey Jr.	2.00	5.00
2 Frank Thomas	1.25	3.00
3 Alex Rodriguez	2.00	5.00
4 Cal Ripken	4.00	10.00
5 Mike Piazza	2.00	5.00
6 Greg Maddux	2.00	5.00
7 Derek Jeter	3.00	8.00
8 Jeff Bagwell	.75	2.00
9 Juan Gonzalez	.50	1.25
10 Albert Belle	.50	1.25
11 Tony Gwynn	1.50	4.00
12 Mark McGwire	3.00	8.00
13 Andy Pettitte	.75	2.00
14 Kenny Lofton	.50	1.25
15 Roberto Alomar	.75	2.00
16 Ryne Sandberg	2.00	5.00
17 Barry Bonds	3.00	8.00
18 Eddie Murray	1.25	3.00

1997 Ultra Fielder's Choice

Randomly inserted in series one packs at a rate of one in 144, this 18-card set uses leather and gold foil to honor leading defensive players. The horizontal cards also include a player photo on the front as well as the big bold words "97 Fleer Ultra", "Fielder's Choice" and the player's name. The horizontal backs have another player photo as well as information about their defensive prowess.

COMPLETE SET (18)	80.00	200.00
1 Roberto Alomar	3.00	8.00
2 Jeff Bagwell	3.00	8.00
3 Wade Boggs	3.00	8.00
4 Barry Bonds	12.50	30.00
5 Mark Grace	3.00	8.00
6 Ken Griffey Jr.	8.00	20.00
7 Marquis Grissom	2.00	5.00
8 Charles Johnson	2.00	5.00
9 Chuck Knoblauch	2.00	5.00
10 Barry Larkin	3.00	8.00
11 Kenny Lofton	2.00	5.00
12 Greg Maddux	8.00	20.00
13 Raul Mondesi	2.00	5.00
14 Rey Ordonez	2.00	5.00
15 Cal Ripken	15.00	40.00
16 Alex Rodriguez	8.00	20.00
17 Ivan Rodriguez	3.00	8.00
18 Matt Williams	2.00	5.00

1997 Ultra Golden Prospects

Randomly inserted in series two hobby packs only at a rate of one in four, this 10-card set features color action player images on a gold baseball background with commentary on what makes these players so promising..

COMPLETE SET (10)	2.00	5.00
1 Andruw Jones	.20	.50
2 Vladimir Guerrero	.30	.75
3 Todd Walker	.10	.30
4 Karim Garcia	.10	.30
5 Kevin Orie	.10	.30
6 Brian Giles	.60	1.50
7 Jason Dickson	.10	.30
8 Jose Guillen	.10	.30
9 Ruben Rivera	.10	.30
10 Derrek Lee	.20	.50

1997 Ultra Hitting Machines

Randomly inserted in series two hobby packs only at a rate of one in 36, this 18-card set features color action player images of the MLB's most productive hitters in "machine-style" die-cut settings.

COMPLETE SET (18)	50.00	120.00
1 Andruw Jones	1.50	4.00
2 Ken Griffey Jr.	4.00	10.00
3 Frank Thomas	2.50	6.00
4 Alex Rodriguez	4.00	10.00
5 Cal Ripken	8.00	20.00
6 Mike Piazza	4.00	10.00
7 Derek Jeter	6.00	15.00
8 Albert Belle	1.00	2.50
9 Tony Gwynn	3.00	8.00
10 Jeff Bagwell	1.50	4.00
11 Mark McGwire	6.00	15.00
12 Kenny Lofton	1.00	2.50
13 Manny Ramirez	1.50	4.00
14 Roberto Alomar	1.50	4.00
15 Ryne Sandberg	4.00	10.00
16 Eddie Murray	2.50	6.00
17 Sammy Sosa	2.50	6.00
18 Ken Caminiti	1.00	2.50

1997 Ultra Home Run Kings

Randomly inserted in series one hobby packs only at a rate of one in 36, this 12-card set features ultra crystal cards with transparent refractive holo-foil technology. The players pictured are all leading power hitters.

COMPLETE SET (12)	30.00	80.00
1 Albert Belle	1.00	2.50
2 Barry Bonds	6.00	15.00
3 Juan Gonzalez	1.00	2.50
4 Ken Griffey Jr.	4.00	10.00
5 Todd Hundley	1.00	2.50
6 Ryan Klesko	1.00	2.50
7 Mark McGwire	6.00	15.00
8 Mike Piazza	4.00	10.00
9 Sammy Sosa	2.50	6.00
10 Frank Thomas	2.50	6.00
11 Mo Vaughn	1.00	2.50
12 Matt Williams	1.00	2.50

1997 Ultra Irabu Commemorative

These seven Irabu cards were distributed exclusively in 1997 Ultra series two international hobby boxes. Three of the seven cards are over-sized 5 x 7 issues, placed in each box as a chiptopper (within the sealed box, but laying on top of the packs). These three cards are serial numbered "of 2750" in silver foil on back. Due to poor sales overseas a number of these boxes made their way back to America but are still considered quite tricky to find.

COMPLETE SET (7)	6.00	15.00
COMMON 5 x 7 (C1-C3)	.80	2.00
COMMON CARD (C4-C7)	1.20	3.00

1997 Ultra Leather Shop

Randomly inserted in series two hobby packs only at a rate of one in six, this 12-card set features color player images of some of the best fielders in the game highlighted by simulated leather backgrounds.

COMPLETE SET (12)	6.00	15.00
1 Ken Griffey Jr.	.60	1.50
2 Alex Rodriguez	.60	1.50
3 Cal Ripken	1.25	3.00
4 Derek Jeter	1.00	2.50
5 Juan Gonzalez	.15	.40
6 Tony Gwynn	.50	1.25
7 Jeff Bagwell	.25	.60
8 Roberto Alomar	.25	.60
9 Ryne Sandberg	.60	1.50
10 Ken Caminiti	.15	.40
11 Kenny Lofton	.15	.40
12 John Smoltz	.25	.60

1997 Ultra Power Plus

Randomly inserted in series one packs at a rate of one in 24 and Series two hobby only packs at the rate of one in eight, this 12-card set utilizes silver rainbow holo-foil and features players who not only hit with power but also excel at other parts of the game. The cards in the Series one insert set have an "A" prefix while the cards in the Series two insert set carry a "B" prefix in the checklist below.

COMPLETE SERIES 1 (12)	30.00	80.00
COMPLETE SERIES 2 (12)	1.50	4.00
A1 Jeff Bagwell	1.00	2.50
A2 Barry Bonds	4.00	10.00
A3 Juan Gonzalez	.60	1.50
A4 Ken Griffey Jr.	2.50	6.00
A5 Chipper Jones	1.50	4.00
A6 Mark McGwire	4.00	10.00
A7 Mike Piazza	2.50	6.00
A8 Cal Ripken	5.00	12.00
A9 Alex Rodriguez	2.50	6.00
A10 Sammy Sosa	1.50	4.00
A11 Frank Thomas	1.50	4.00
A12 Matt Williams	.60	1.50
B1 Ken Griffey Jr.	1.00	2.50
B2 Frank Thomas	.60	1.50
B3 Alex Rodriguez	1.00	2.50
B4 Cal Ripken	2.00	5.00
B5 Mike Piazza	1.00	2.50
B6 Chipper Jones	.60	1.50
B7 Albert Belle	.25	.60
B8 Juan Gonzalez	.25	.60
B9 Jeff Bagwell	.40	1.00
B10 Mark McGwire	1.50	4.00
B11 Mo Vaughn	.25	.60
B12 Barry Bonds	1.50	4.00

1997 Ultra RBI Kings

Randomly inserted in series one packs at a rate of one in 18, this 10-card set features 100 percent etched-foil cards. The cards feature players who drive in many runs. The horizontal backs contain player information and another player photo.

COMPLETE SET (10)	12.50	30.00
1 Jeff Bagwell	1.00	2.50
2 Albert Belle	.60	1.50
3 Dante Bichette	.60	1.50
4 Barry Bonds	4.00	10.00
5 Jay Buhner	.60	1.50
6 Juan Gonzalez	.60	1.50
7 Ken Griffey Jr.	2.50	6.00
8 Sammy Sosa	1.50	4.00
9 Frank Thomas	1.50	4.00
10 Mo Vaughn	.60	1.50

1997 Ultra Rookie Reflections

Randomly inserted in series one packs at a rate of one in four, this 10-card set uses a silver foil design to feature young players. The horizontal backs contain player information as well as another player photo.

COMPLETE SET (10)	1.50	4.00
1 James Baldwin	.15	.40
2 Jermaine Dye	.15	.40
3 Darin Erstad	.15	.40
4 Todd Hollandsworth	.15	.40
5 Derek Jeter	1.00	2.50
6 Jason Kendall	.15	.40
7 Alex Ochoa	.15	.40
8 Rey Ordonez	.15	.40
9 Edgar Renteria	.15	.40
10 Scott Rolen	.25	.60

1997 Ultra Season Crowns

Randomly inserted in series one packs at a rate of one in eight, this 12-card set features color photos of baseball's top stars with etched foil backgrounds.

COMPLETE SET (12)	4.00	10.00
1 Albert Belle	.15	.40
2 Dante Bichette	.15	.40
3 Barry Bonds	1.00	2.50
4 Kenny Lofton	.15	.40
5 Edgar Martinez	.25	.60
6 Mark McGwire	1.00	2.50
7 Andy Pettitte	.25	.60
8 Mike Piazza	.60	1.50
9 Alex Rodriguez	.60	1.50
10 John Smoltz	.25	.60
11 Sammy Sosa	.40	1.00
12 Frank Thomas	.40	1.00

1997 Ultra Starring Role

Randomly inserted in series two hobby packs only at a rate of one in 288, this 12-card set featues color photos of tried-and-true clutch performers on die-cut plastic cards with foil stamping.

COMPLETE SET (12)	100.00	250.00
1 Andruw Jones	4.00	10.00
2 Ken Griffey Jr.	10.00	25.00
3 Frank Thomas	6.00	15.00
4 Alex Rodriguez	10.00	25.00
5 Cal Ripken	20.00	50.00
6 Mike Piazza	10.00	25.00
7 Greg Maddux	10.00	25.00
8 Chipper Jones	6.00	15.00
9 Derek Jeter	15.00	40.00
10 Juan Gonzalez	2.50	6.00
11 Albert Belle	2.50	6.00
12 Tony Gwynn	8.00	20.00

1997 Ultra Thunderclap

Randomly inserted in series two hobby packs only at a rate of one in 18, this 10-card set features color images of superstars who are feared by opponents for their ability to totally dominate a game on a background displaying lightning from a thunderstorm.

COMPLETE SET (10)	25.00	60.00
1 Barry Bonds	4.00	10.00
2 Mo Vaughn	.60	1.50
3 Mark McGwire	4.00	10.00
4 Jeff Bagwell	1.00	2.50
5 Juan Gonzalez	.60	1.50
6 Alex Rodriguez	2.50	6.00
7 Chipper Jones	1.50	4.00
8 Ken Griffey Jr.	2.50	6.00
9 Mike Piazza	2.50	6.00
10 Frank Thomas	1.50	4.00

1997 Ultra Top 30

Randomly inserted one in every Ultra series two retail packs only, this 30-card set features color action player images of top stars with a "Top 30" circle in the team-colored background. The backs carry another player image with his team logo the background circle.

COMPLETE SET (30)	15.00	40.00
*GOLD MED: 2.5X TO 6X BASIC TOP 30		1.25
G.MED SER.2 STATED ODDS 1:18 RETAIL		
1 Andruw Jones	.30	.75
2 Ken Griffey	.75	2.00
3 Frank Thomas	.50	1.25
4 Alex Rodriguez	.75	2.00
5 Cal Ripken	1.50	4.00
6 Mike Piazza	.75	2.00
7 Greg Maddux	.75	2.00
8 Chipper Jones	.50	1.25
9 Derek Jeter	1.25	3.00
10 Juan Gonzalez	.20	.50
11 Albert Belle	.20	.50
12 Tony Gwynn	.60	1.50
13 Jeff Bagwell	.30	.75
14 Mark McGwire	1.25	3.00
15 Andy Pettitte	.30	.75
16 Mo Vaughn	.20	.50
17 Kenny Lofton	.20	.50
18 Manny Ramirez	.30	.75
19 Roberto Alomar	.30	.75
20 Ryne Sandberg	.75	2.00
21 Hideo Nomo	.50	1.25
22 Barry Bonds	1.25	3.00
23 Eddie Murray	.50	1.25
24 Ken Caminiti	.20	.50
25 John Smoltz	.30	.75
26 Pat Hentgen	.20	.50
27 Todd Hollandsworth	.20	.50
28 Matt Williams	.20	.50
29 Bernie Williams	.30	.75
30 Brady Anderson	.20	.50

1998 Ultra

The complete 1998 Ultra set features 501 cards and was distributed in 10-card first and second series packs with a suggested retail price of $2.59. The fronts carry UV coated color action player photos printed on 20 pt. card stock. The backs display another player photo with player information and career statistics. The set contains the following subsets: Season's Crown (211-220) seeded 1:12 packs, Prospects (221-245) seeded 1:4 packs, Checklists (246-250), and Checklists (473-475) seeded 1:4 packs and Pizzazz (476-500) seeded 1:4 packs. Rookie Cards include Kevin Millwood and Magglio Ordonez. Though not confirmed by the manufacturer, it's believed that several cards within the Prospects subset are in shorter supply than others - most notably number 238 Ricky Ledee and number 243 Jorge Velandia. Also, seeded one in every pack, was one of 50 Million Dollar Moment cards which pictured some of the greatest moments in baseball histroy and gave the collector a chance to win a million dollars. As a special last minute promotion, Fleer/SkyBox got Alex Rodriguez to autograph 750 of his 1998 Fleer Promo cards. Each card is serial-numbered by hand on the card front. The signed cards were randomly seeded into Ultra Series two hobby packs.

COMPLETE SET (501)	65.00	160.00
COMP.SERIES 1 (250)	40.00	100.00
COMP.SERIES 2 (251)	25.00	60.00
COMP.SER.1 w/o SP's (210)	6.00	15.00
COMP.SER.2 w/o SP's (226)	6.00	15.00
COMMON (1-220/246-250)	.10	.30
COMMON (251-475/501)	.10	.30
COMMON SC (211-220)	.75	2.00
COMMON (221-245)	1.25	3.00
COMMON PZ (476-500)	.40	1.00
1 Ken Griffey Jr.	.50	1.25
2 Matt Morris	.10	.30
3 Roger Clemens	.60	1.50
4 Matt Williams	.10	.30
5 Roberto Hernandez	.10	.30
6 Rondell White	.10	.30
7 Tim Salmon	.20	.50
8 Brad Radke	.10	.30
9 Brett Butler	.10	.30
10 Carl Everett	.10	.30
11 Chili Davis	.10	.30
12 Chuck Finley	.10	.30
13 Darryl Kile	.10	.30
14 Deivi Cruz	.10	.30
15 Gary Gaetti	.10	.30
16 Matt Stairs	.10	.30
17 Pat Meares	.10	.30
18 Will Cunnane	.10	.30
19 Steve Woodard	.10	.30
20 Andy Ashby	.10	.30
21 Bobby Higginson	.10	.30
22 Brian Jordan	.10	.30
23 Craig Biggio	.20	.50
24 Jim Edmonds	.10	.30
25 Ryan McGuire	.10	.30

Card	Low	High
26 Scott Hatteberg	.10	.30
27 Willie Greene	.10	.30
28 Albert Belle	.10	.30
29 Ellis Burks	.10	.30
30 Hideo Nomo	.30	.75
31 Jeff Bagwell	.20	.50
32 Kevin Brown	.20	.50
33 Nomar Garciaparra	.50	1.25
34 Pedro Martinez	.20	.50
35 Raul Mondesi	.10	.30
36 Ricky Bottalico	.10	.30
37 Shawn Estes	.10	.30
38 Otis Nixon	.10	.30
39 Terry Steinbach	.10	.30
40 Tom Glavine	.20	.50
41 Todd Dunwoody	.10	.30
42 Deion Sanders	.20	.50
43 Gary Sheffield	.10	.30
44 Mike Lansing	.10	.30
45 Mike Lieberthal	.10	.30
46 Paul Sorrento	.10	.30
47 Paul O'Neill	.20	.50
48 Tom Goodwin	.10	.30
49 Andruw Jones	.20	.50
50 Barry Bonds	.75	2.00
51 Bernie Williams	.20	.50
52 Jeremi Gonzalez	.10	.30
53 Mike Piazza	.50	1.25
54 Russ Davis	.10	.30
55 Vinny Castilla	.10	.30
56 Rod Beck	.10	.30
57 Andres Galarraga	.10	.30
58 Ben McDonald	.10	.30
59 Billy Wagner	.10	.30
60 Charles Johnson	.10	.30
61 Fred McGriff	.20	.50
62 Dean Palmer	.10	.30
63 Frank Thomas	.30	.75
64 Ismael Valdes	.10	.30
65 Mark Bellhorn	.10	.30
66 Jeff King	.10	.30
67 John Wetteland	.10	.30
68 Mark Grace	.20	.50
69 Mark Kotsay	.10	.30
70 Scott Rolen	.20	.50
71 Todd Hundley	.10	.30
72 Todd Worrell	.10	.30
73 Wilson Alvarez	.10	.30
74 Bobby Jones	.10	.30
75 Jose Canseco	.20	.50
76 Kevin Appier	.10	.30
77 Neifi Perez	.10	.30
78 Paul Molitor	.10	.30
79 Quilvio Veras	.10	.30
80 Randy Johnson	.30	.75
81 Glendon Rusch	.10	.30
82 Curt Schilling	.10	.30
83 Alex Rodriguez	.50	1.25
84 Rey Ordonez	.10	.30
85 Jeff Juden	.10	.30
86 Mike Cameron	.10	.30
87 Ryan Klesko	.10	.30
88 Trevor Hoffman	.10	.30
89 Chuck Knoblauch	.10	.30
90 Larry Walker	.10	.30
91 Mark McLemore	.10	.30
92 B.J. Surhoff	.10	.30
93 Darren Daulton	.10	.30
94 Ray Durham	.10	.30
95 Sammy Sosa	.30	.75
96 Eric Young	.10	.30
97 Gerald Williams	.10	.30
98 Javy Lopez	.10	.30
99 John Smiley	.10	.30
100 Juan Gonzalez	.10	.30
101 Shawn Green	.10	.30
102 Charles Nagy	.10	.30
103 David Justice	.10	.30
104 Joey Hamilton	.10	.30
105 Pat Hentgen	.10	.30
106 Raul Casanova	.10	.30
107 Tony Phillips	.10	.30
108 Tony Gwynn	.40	1.00
109 Will Clark	.20	.50
110 Jason Giambi	.10	.30
111 Jay Bell	.10	.30
112 Johnny Damon	.20	.50
113 Alan Benes	.10	.30
114 Jeff Suppan	.10	.30
115 Kevin Polcovich	.10	.30
116 Shigetoshi Hasegawa	.10	.30
117 Steve Finley	.10	.30
118 Tony Clark	.10	.30
119 David Cone	.10	.30
120 Jose Guillen	.10	.30
121 Kevin Millwood RC	.40	1.00
122 Greg Maddux	.50	1.25
123 Dave Nilsson	.10	.30
124 Hideki Irabu	.10	.30
125 Jason Kendall	.10	.30
126 Jim Thome	.20	.50
127 Delino DeShields	.10	.30
128 Edgar Renteria	.10	.30
129 Edgardo Alfonzo	.10	.30
130 J.T. Snow	.10	.30
131 Jeff Abbott	.10	.30
132 Jeffrey Hammonds	.10	.30
133 Todd Greene	.10	.30
134 Vladimir Guerrero	.30	.75
135 Jay Buhner	.10	.30
136 Jeff Cirillo	.10	.30
137 Jeromy Burnitz	.10	.30
138 Mickey Morandini	.10	.30
139 Tino Martinez	.20	.50
140 Jeff Shaw	.10	.30
141 Rafael Palmeiro	.20	.50
142 Bobby Bonilla	.10	.30
143 Cal Ripken	1.00	2.50
144 Chad Fox RC	.10	.30
145 Dante Bichette	.10	.30
146 Dennis Eckersley	.10	.30
147 Mariano Rivera	.30	.75
148 Mo Vaughn	.10	.30
149 Reggie Sanders	.10	.30
150 Derek Jeter	.75	2.00
151 Rusty Greer	.10	.30
152 Brady Anderson	.10	.30
153 Brett Tomko	.10	.30
154 Jaime Navarro	.10	.30
155 Kevin Orie	.10	.30
156 Roberto Alomar	.20	.50
157 Edgar Martinez	.20	.50
158 John Olerud	.10	.30
159 John Smoltz	.20	.50
160 Ryne Sandberg	.50	1.25
161 Billy Taylor	.10	.30
162 Chris Holt	.10	.30
163 Damion Easley	.10	.30
164 Darin Erstad	.10	.30
165 Joe Carter	.10	.30
166 Kelvim Escobar	.10	.30
167 Ken Caminiti	.10	.30
168 Pokey Reese	.10	.30
169 Ray Lankford	.10	.30
170 Livan Hernandez	.10	.30
171 Steve Kline	.10	.30
172 Tom Gordon	.10	.30
173 Travis Fryman	.10	.30
174 Al Martin	.10	.30
175 Andy Pettitte	.20	.50
176 Jeff Kent	.10	.30
177 Jimmy Key	.10	.30
178 Mark Grudzielanek	.10	.30
179 Tony Saunders	.10	.30
180 Barry Larkin	.20	.50
181 Bubba Trammell	.10	.30
182 Carlos Delgado	.10	.30
183 Carlos Baerga	.10	.30
184 Derek Bell	.10	.30
185 Henry Rodriguez	.10	.30
186 Jason Dickson	.10	.30
187 Ron Gant	.10	.30
188 Tony Womack	.10	.30
189 Justin Thompson	.10	.30
190 Fernando Tatis	.10	.30
191 Mark Wohlers	.10	.30
192 Takashi Kashiwada	.10	.30
193 Garret Anderson	.10	.30
194 Jose Cruz Jr.	.10	.30
195 Ricardo Rincon	.10	.30
196 Tim Naehring	.10	.30
197 Moises Alou	.10	.30
198 Eric Karros	.10	.30
199 John Jaha	.10	.30
200 Marty Cordova	.10	.30
201 Ken Hill	.10	.30
202 Chipper Jones	.30	.75
203 Kenny Lofton	.10	.30
204 Mike Mussina	.20	.50
205 Manny Ramirez	.20	.50
206 Todd Hollandsworth	.10	.30
207 Cecil Fielder	.10	.30
208 Mark McGwire	.75	2.00
209 Jim Leyritz	.10	.30
210 Ivan Rodriguez	.20	.50
211 Jeff Bagwell SC	.75	2.00
212 Barry Bonds SC	3.00	8.00
213 Roger Clemens SC	2.50	6.00
214 N.Garciaparra SC	2.00	5.00
215 Ken Griffey Jr. SC	2.00	5.00
216 Tony Gwynn SC	1.50	4.00
217 Randy Johnson SC	1.25	3.00
218 Mark McGwire SC	3.00	8.00
219 Scott Rolen SC	.75	2.00
220 Frank Thomas SC	1.25	3.00
221 Matt Perisho PROS	1.25	3.00
222 Wes Helms PROS	1.25	3.00
223 D.Dellucci PROS RC	1.25	3.00
224 Todd Helton PROS	1.25	3.00
225 Brian Rose PROS	1.25	3.00
226 Aaron Boone PROS	1.25	3.00
227 Keith Foulke PROS	1.25	3.00
228 Homer Bush PROS	1.25	3.00
229 S.Stewart PROS	1.25	3.00
230 R.Hidalgo PROS	1.25	3.00
231 Russ Johnson PROS	1.25	3.00
232 H.Blanco PROS RC	1.25	3.00
233 Paul Konerko PROS	1.25	3.00
234 A.Williamson PROS	1.25	3.00
235 S.Bowers PROS RC	1.25	3.00
236 Jose Vidro PROS	1.25	3.00
237 Derek Wallace PROS	1.25	3.00
238 Ricky Ledee PROS SP	2.00	5.00
239 Ben Grieve PROS	1.25	3.00
240 Lou Collier PROS	1.25	3.00
241 Derrek Lee PROS	1.25	3.00
242 Ruben Rivera PROS	1.25	3.00
243 J.Velandia PROS SP	2.00	5.00
244 Andrew Vessel PROS	1.25	3.00
245 Chris Carpenter PROS	1.25	3.00
246 Ken Griffey Jr. CL	.30	.75
247 Alex Rodriguez CL	.30	.75
248 Diamond Ink CL	.10	.30
249 Frank Thomas CL	.20	.50
250 Cal Ripken CL	.50	1.25
251 Carlos Perez	.10	.30
252 Larry Sutton	.10	.30
253 Gary Sheffield	.10	.30
254 Wally Joyner	.10	.30
255 Todd Stottlemyre	.10	.30
256 Nerio Rodriguez	.10	.30
257 Charles Johnson	.10	.30
258 Pedro Astacio	.10	.30
259 Cal Eldred	.10	.30
260 Chili Davis	.10	.30
261 Freddy Garcia	.10	.30
262 Bobby Witt	.10	.30
263 Michael Coleman	.10	.30
264 Mike Caruso	.10	.30
265 Mike Lansing	.10	.30
266 Dennis Reyes	.10	.30
267 F.P. Santangelo	.10	.30
268 Darryl Hamilton	.10	.30
269 Mike Fetters	.10	.30
270 Charlie Hayes	.10	.30
271 Royce Clayton	.10	.30
272 Doug Drabek	.10	.30
273 James Baldwin	.10	.30
274 Brian Hunter	.10	.30
275 Chan Ho Park	.10	.30
276 John Franco	.10	.30
277 David Wells	.10	.30
278 Eli Marrero	.10	.30
279 Kerry Wood	.15	.40
280 Donnie Sadler	.10	.30
281 Scott Winchester RC	.10	.30
282 Hal Morris	.10	.30
283 [illegible]	.10	.30
284 Bernard Gilkey	.10	.30
285 Ramiro Mendoza	.10	.30
286 Kevin Brown	.20	.50
287 David Segui	.10	.30
288 Willie McGee	.10	.30
289 Darren Oliver	.10	.30
290 Antonio Alfonseca	.10	.30
291 Eric Davis	.10	.30
292 Mickey Morandini	.10	.30
293 Frank Catalanotto RC	.25	.60
294 Derrek Lee	.20	.50
295 Todd Zeile	.10	.30
296 Chuck Knoblauch	.10	.30
297 Wilson Delgado	.10	.30
298 Bobby Bonilla	.10	.30
299 Orel Hershiser	.10	.30
300 Ozzie Guillen	.10	.30
301 Aaron Sele	.10	.30
302 Joe Carter	.10	.30
303 Darryl Kile	.10	.30
304 Shane Reynolds	.10	.30
305 Todd Dunn	.10	.30
306 Bob Abreu	.10	.30
307 Doug Strange	.10	.30
308 Jose Canseco	.20	.50
309 Lance Johnson	.10	.30
310 Harold Baines	.10	.30
311 Todd Pratt	.10	.30
312 Greg Colbrunn	.10	.30
313 Masato Yoshii RC	.15	.40
314 Felix Heredia	.10	.30
315 Dennis Martinez	.10	.30
316 Geronimo Berroa	.10	.30
317 Darren Lewis	.10	.30
318 Bill Ripken	.10	.30
319 Enrique Wilson	.10	.30
320 Alex Ochoa	.10	.30
321 Doug Glanville	.10	.30
322 Mike Stanley	.10	.30
323 Gerald Williams	.10	.30
324 Pedro Martinez	.20	.50
325 Jaret Wright	.10	.30
326 Terry Pendleton	.10	.30
327 LaTroy Hawkins	.10	.30
328 Emil Brown	.10	.30
329 Walt Weiss	.10	.30
330 Omar Vizquel	.20	.50
331 Carl Everett	.10	.30
332 Fernando Vina	.10	.30
333 Mike Blowers	.10	.30
334 Dwight Gooden	.10	.30
335 Mark Lewis	.10	.30
336 Jim Leyritz	.10	.30
337 Kenny Lofton	.10	.30
338 John Halama RC	.15	.40
339 Jose Valentin	.10	.30
340 Desi Relaford	.10	.30
341 Dante Powell	.10	.30
342 Ed Sprague	.10	.30
343 Reggie Jefferson	.10	.30
344 Mike Hampton	.10	.30
345 Marquis Grissom	.10	.30
346 Heathcliff Slocumb	.10	.30
347 Francisco Cordova	.10	.30
348 Ken Cloude	.10	.30
349 Benito Santiago	.10	.30
350 Denny Neagle	.10	.30
351 Sean Casey	.10	.30
352 Robb Nen	.10	.30
353 Orlando Merced	.10	.30
354 Adrian Brown	.10	.30
355 Gregg Jefferies	.10	.30
356 Otis Nixon	.10	.30
357 Michael Tucker	.10	.30
358 Eric Milton	.10	.30
359 Travis Fryman	.10	.30
360 Gary DiSarcina	.10	.30
361 Mario Valdez	.10	.30
362 Craig Counsell	.10	.30
363 Jose Offerman	.10	.30
364 Tony Fernandez	.10	.30
365 Jason McDonald	.10	.30
366 Sterling Hitchcock	.10	.30
367 Donovan Osborne	.10	.30
368 Troy Percival	.10	.30
369 Henry Rodriguez	.10	.30
370 Dmitri Young	.10	.30
371 Jay Powell	.10	.30
372 Jeff Conine	.10	.30
373 Orlando Cabrera	.10	.30
374 Butch Huskey	.10	.30
375 Mike Lowell RC	.60	1.50
376 Kevin Young	.10	.30
377 Jamie Moyer	.10	.30
378 Jeff D'Amico	.10	.30
379 Scott Erickson	.10	.30
380 Magglio Ordonez RC	1.25	3.00
381 Melvin Nieves	.10	.30
382 Ramon Martinez	.10	.30
383 A.J. Hinch	.10	.30
384 Jeff Brantley	.10	.30
385 Kevin Elster	.10	.30
386 Allen Watson	.10	.30
387 Moises Alou	.10	.30
388 Jeff Blauser	.10	.30
389 Pete Harnisch	.10	.30
390 Shane Andrews	.10	.30
391 Rico Brogna	.10	.30
392 Stan Javier	.10	.30
393 David Howard	.10	.30
394 Darryl Strawberry	.10	.30
395 Kent Mercker	.10	.30
396 Juan Encarnacion	.10	.30
397 Sandy Alomar Jr.	.10	.30
398 Al Leiter	.10	.30
399 Tony Graffanino	.10	.30
400 Terry Adams	.10	.30
401 Bruce Aven	.10	.30
402 Derrick Gibson	.10	.30
403 Jose Cabrera RC	.10	.30
404 Rich Becker	.10	.30
405 David Ortiz	.40	1.00
406 Brian McRae	.10	.30
407 Bobby Estalella	.10	.30
408 Bill Mueller	.10	.30
409 Dennis Eckersley	.10	.30
410 Sandy Martinez	.10	.30
411 Jose Vizcaino	.10	.30
412 Jermaine Allensworth	.10	.30
413 Miguel Tejada	.30	.75
414 Turner Ward	.10	.30
415 Glenallen Hill	.10	.30
416 Lee Stevens	.10	.30
417 Cecil Fielder	.10	.30
418 Ruben Sierra	.10	.30
419 Jon Nunnally	.10	.30
420 Rod Myers	.10	.30
421 Dustin Hermanson	.10	.30
422 James Mouton	.10	.30
423 Dan Wilson	.10	.30
424 Roberto Kelly	.10	.30
425 Antonio Osuna	.10	.30
426 Jacob Cruz	.10	.30
427 Brent Mayne	.10	.30
428 Matt Karchner	.10	.30
429 Damian Jackson	.10	.30
430 Roger Cedeno	.10	.30
431 Rickey Henderson	.30	.75
432 Joe Randa	.10	.30
433 Greg Vaughn	.10	.30
434 Andres Galarraga	.10	.30
435 Rod Beck	.10	.30
436 Curtis Goodwin	.10	.30
437 Brad Ausmus	.10	.30
438 Bob Hamelin	.10	.30
439 Todd Walker	.10	.30
440 Scott Brosius	.10	.30
441 Len Dykstra	.10	.30
442 Abraham Nunez	.10	.30
443 Brian Johnson	.10	.30
444 Randy Myers	.10	.30
445 Bret Boone	.10	.30
446 Oscar Henriquez	.10	.30
447 Mike Sweeney	.10	.30
448 Kenny Rogers	.10	.30
449 Mark Langston	.10	.30
450 Luis Gonzalez	.10	.30
451 John Burkett	.10	.30
452 Bip Roberts	.10	.30
453 Travis Lee	.10	.30
454 Felix Rodriguez	.10	.30
455 Andy Benes	.10	.30
456 Willie Blair	.10	.30
457 Brian Anderson	.10	.30
458 Jay Bell	.10	.30
459 Matt Williams	.10	.30
460 Devon White	.10	.30
461 Karim Garcia	.10	.30
462 Jorge Fabregas	.10	.30
463 Wilson Alvarez	.10	.30
464 Roberto Hernandez	.10	.30
465 Tony Saunders	.10	.30
466 Rolando Arrojo RC	.15	.40
467 Wade Boggs	.30	.75
468 Fred McGriff	.20	.50
469 Paul Sorrento	.10	.30
470 Kevin Stocker	.10	.30
471 Bubba Trammell	.10	.30
472 Quinton McCracken	.10	.30
473 Ken Griffey Jr. CL	.30	.75
474 Cal Ripken CL	.50	1.25
475 Frank Thomas CL	.20	.50
476 Ken Griffey Jr. PZ	1.50	4.00
477 Cal Ripken PZ	3.00	8.00
478 Frank Thomas PZ	1.00	2.50
479 Alex Rodriguez PZ	1.50	4.00
480 Nomar Garciaparra PZ	1.50	4.00
481 Derek Jeter PZ	2.50	6.00
482 Andruw Jones PZ	.60	1.50
483 Chipper Jones PZ	1.00	2.50
484 Greg Maddux PZ	1.50	4.00
485 Mike Piazza PZ	1.50	4.00
486 Juan Gonzalez PZ	.40	1.00
487 Jose Cruz Jr. PZ	.40	1.00
488 Jaret Wright PZ	.40	1.00
489 Hideo Nomo PZ	1.00	2.50
490 Scott Rolen PZ	.60	1.50
491 Tony Gwynn PZ	1.25	3.00
492 Roger Clemens PZ	2.00	5.00
493 Darin Erstad PZ	.40	1.00
494 Mark McGwire PZ	2.50	6.00
495 Jeff Bagwell PZ	.60	1.50
496 Mo Vaughn PZ	.40	1.00
497 Albert Belle PZ	.40	1.00
498 Kenny Lofton PZ	.40	1.00
499 Ben Grieve PZ	.40	1.00
500 Barry Bonds PZ	2.50	6.00
501 Mike Piazza	.50	1.25
S100 A.Rodriguez AU/750	60.00	120.00

1998 Ultra Gold Medallion

Randomly inserted one in every first and second series hobby pack, this 501-card set is parallel to the base set and features a gold metallic foil background.

COMPLETE SET (501)	80.00	200.00
COMP.SERIES 1 (250)	40.00	100.00
COMP.SERIES 2 (251)	40.00	100.00

*STARS: 1.25X TO 3X BASIC CARDS
*ROOKIES: .75X TO 2X BASIC CARDS
*SEASON CROWNS: .3X TO .8X BASIC SC
*PROSPECTS: .25X TO .6X BASIC PROS.
*CHECKLISTS: 1.25X TO 3X BASIC CL'S
*PIZZAZZ: .4X TO 1.X BASIC PIZZAZZ

1998 Ultra Platinum Medallion

Randomly inserted in first and second series hobby packs, this 498-card set is parallel to the base set. Only 100 first series sets and 98 second series sets were produced and each card is serially numbered in gold foil on back. Ten Platinum exchange cards good for a complete Platinum series one set were inserted into first series hobby packs. Another ten Platinum exchange cards good for a complete series two set were inserted in second series hobby packs. The three basic-issue checklist cards (473,474 and 475) were never printed in platinum form.

*STARS: 10X TO 25X BASIC CARDS
*ROOKIES: 10X TO 25X BASIC CARDS
*SEASON CROWNS: 1.5X TO 4X BASIC SC
*PROSPECTS: 2.5X TO 6X BASIC PROSP.
*CHECKLISTS: 12.5X TO 30X BASIC CL'S
*PIZZAZZ: 2X TO 5X BASIC PIZZAZZ

1998 Ultra Artistic Talents

Randomly inserted in Series one packs at the rate of one in eight, this 18-card set features color pictures of top players on art enhanced cards.

COMPLETE SET (18)	20.00	50.00
1 Ken Griffey Jr.	1.50	4.00
2 Andruw Jones	.60	1.50
3 Alex Rodriguez	1.50	4.00
4 Frank Thomas	1.00	2.50
5 Cal Ripken	3.00	8.00
6 Derek Jeter	2.50	6.00
7 Chipper Jones	1.00	2.50
8 Greg Maddux	1.50	4.00
9 Mike Piazza	1.50	4.00
10 Albert Belle	.40	1.00
11 Darin Erstad	.40	1.00
12 Juan Gonzalez	.40	1.00
13 Jeff Bagwell	.60	1.50
14 Tony Gwynn	1.25	3.00
15 Mark McGwire	2.50	6.00
16 Scott Rolen	.60	1.50
17 Barry Bonds	2.50	6.00
18 Kenny Lofton	.40	1.00

1998 Ultra Back to the Future

Randomly inserted in Series one packs at the rate of one in six, this 15-card set features color photos of top Rookies. The backs carry player information.

COMPLETE SET (15)	5.00	12.00
1 Andruw Jones	.30	.75
2 Alex Rodriguez	.75	2.00
3 Derek Jeter	1.25	3.00
4 Darin Erstad	.20	.50
5 Mike Cameron	.20	.50
6 Scott Rolen	.30	.75
7 Nomar Garciaparra	.75	2.00
8 Hideki Irabu	.20	.50
9 Jose Cruz Jr.	.20	.50
10 Vladimir Guerrero	.50	1.25
11 Mark Kotsay	.20	.50
12 Tony Womack	.20	.50
13 Jason Dickson	.20	.50
14 Jose Guillen	.20	.50
15 Tony Clark	.20	.50

1998 Ultra Big Shots

Randomly inserted in Series one packs at the rate of one in four, this 15-card set features color photos of players who hit the longest home runs in the 1997 season.

COMPLETE SET (15)	4.00	10.00
1 Ken Griffey Jr.	.60	1.50
2 Frank Thomas	.40	1.00
3 Chipper Jones	.40	1.00
4 Albert Belle	.15	.40
5 Juan Gonzalez	.15	.40
6 Jeff Bagwell	.25	.60
7 Mark McGwire	1.00	2.50
8 Barry Bonds	1.00	2.50
9 Manny Ramirez	.25	.60
10 Mo Vaughn	.15	.40
11 Matt Williams	.15	.40
12 Jim Thome	.25	.60
13 Tino Martinez	.25	.60
14 Mike Piazza	.60	1.50
15 Tony Clark	.15	.40

1998 Ultra Diamond Immortals

Randomly inserted in packs at a rate of one in 288, this 15-card insert set highlights color action photos of future Hall of Famers on die-cut cards with full silver holofoil backgrounds.

COMPLETE SET (15)	150.00	400.00
1 Ken Griffey Jr.	15.00	40.00
2 Frank Thomas	10.00	25.00
3 Alex Rodriguez	15.00	40.00
4 Cal Ripken	30.00	80.00
5 Mike Piazza	15.00	40.00
6 Mark McGwire	25.00	60.00
7 Greg Maddux	15.00	40.00
8 Andruw Jones	6.00	15.00
9 Chipper Jones	10.00	25.00
10 Derek Jeter	25.00	60.00
11 Tony Gwynn	12.50	30.00
12 Juan Gonzalez	4.00	10.00
13 Jose Cruz Jr.	4.00	10.00
14 Roger Clemens	20.00	50.00
15 Barry Bonds	25.00	60.00

1998 Ultra Diamond Producers

Randomly inserted in Series one packs at the rate of one in 288, this 15-card set features color photos of Major League Baseball's top players.

COMPLETE SET (15)	150.00	400.00
1 Ken Griffey Jr.	12.50	30.00
2 Andruw Jones	5.00	12.00
3 Alex Rodriguez	12.50	30.00
4 Frank Thomas	8.00	20.00
5 Cal Ripken	25.00	60.00
6 Derek Jeter	20.00	50.00
7 Chipper Jones	8.00	20.00
8 Greg Maddux	12.50	30.00
9 Mike Piazza	12.50	30.00
10 Juan Gonzalez	3.00	8.00
11 Jeff Bagwell	5.00	12.00
12 Tony Gwynn	10.00	25.00
13 Mark McGwire	20.00	50.00
14 Barry Bonds	20.00	50.00
15 Jose Cruz Jr.	3.00	8.00

1998 Ultra Double Trouble

Randomly inserted in series one packs at the rate of one in four, this 20-card set features color photos of two star players per card.

COMPLETE SET (20)	6.00	15.00
1 Ken Griffey Jr.	.60	1.50
Alex Rodriguez		
2 Vladimir Guerrero	.40	1.00
Pedro Martinez		
3 Andruw Jones	.40	1.00
Kenny Lofton		
4 Chipper Jones	.60	1.50
Greg Maddux		
5 Derek Jeter	.75	2.00
Tino Martinez		
6 Frank Thomas	.40	1.00
Albert Belle		
7 Cal Ripken	1.25	3.00
Roberto Alomar		
8 Mike Piazza	.60	1.50
Hideo Nomo		
9 Darin Erstad	.30	.75
Jason Dickson		
10 Juan Gonzalez	.40	1.00
Ivan Rodriguez		
11 Jeff Bagwell	.40	1.00
Darryl Kile		
UER front Kyle		
12 Tony Gwynn	.50	1.25
Steve Finley		
13 Mark McGwire	1.00	2.50
Ray Lankford		
14 Barry Bonds	1.00	2.50
Jeff Kent		
15 Andy Pettitte	.40	1.00
Bernie Williams		
16 Mo Vaughn	.60	1.50
Nomar Garciaparra		
17 Matt Williams	.40	1.00
Jim Thome		
18 Hideki Irabu	.40	1.00
Mariano Rivera		
19 Roger Clemens	.75	2.00
Jose Cruz Jr.		
20 Manny Ramirez	.40	1.00
David Justice		

1998 Ultra Fall Classics

Randomly inserted in Series one packs at the rate of one in 18, this 15-card set features color photos of the top potential postseason heroes. The backs carry player information.

COMPLETE SET (15)	40.00	100.00
1 Ken Griffey Jr.	3.00	8.00
2 Andruw Jones	1.25	3.00
3 Alex Rodriguez	3.00	8.00
4 Frank Thomas	2.00	5.00
5 Cal Ripken	6.00	15.00
6 Derek Jeter	5.00	12.00
7 Chipper Jones	2.00	5.00
8 Greg Maddux	3.00	8.00
9 Mike Piazza	3.00	8.00
10 Albert Belle	.75	2.00
11 Juan Gonzalez	.75	2.00
12 Jeff Bagwell	1.25	3.00
13 Tony Gwynn	2.50	6.00
14 Mark McGwire	5.00	12.00
15 Barry Bonds	5.00	12.00

1998 Ultra Kid Gloves

Randomly inserted in Series one packs at the rate of one in eight, this 12-card set features color photos of top young defensive players. The backs carry player information.

COMPLETE SET (12)	6.00	15.00
1 Andruw Jones	.40	1.00
2 Alex Rodriguez	1.00	2.50
3 Derek Jeter	1.50	4.00
4 Chipper Jones	.60	1.50
5 Darin Erstad	.25	.60
6 Todd Walker	.25	.60
7 Scott Rolen	.40	1.00
8 Nomar Garciaparra	1.00	2.50
9 Jose Cruz Jr.	.25	.60
10 Charles Johnson	.25	.60
11 Rey Ordonez	.25	.60
12 Vladimir Guerrero	.60	1.50

1998 Ultra Millennium Men

Randomly inserted in hobby only packs at a rate of one in 35, this 15-card insert set features a player action photo on an irridescent silver foil underlay that opens to reveal a second photo with a personal profile. For an added touch, a foil stamp embossed in the center gives the feel of a wax seal.

COMPLETE SET (15)	50.00	120.00
1 Jose Cruz Jr.	1.00	2.50
2 Ken Griffey Jr.	4.00	10.00
3 Cal Ripken	8.00	20.00
4 Derek Jeter	6.00	15.00
5 Andruw Jones	1.50	4.00
6 Alex Rodriguez	4.00	10.00
7 Chipper Jones	2.50	6.00
8 Scott Rolen	1.50	4.00
9 Nomar Garciaparra	4.00	10.00
10 Frank Thomas	2.50	6.00
11 Mike Piazza	4.00	10.00
12 Greg Maddux	4.00	10.00
13 Juan Gonzalez	1.00	2.50
14 Ben Grieve	10.00	25.00
15 Jaret Wright	1.00	2.50

1998 Ultra Notables

Randomly inserted in packs at a rate of one in four, this 20-card insert set features a color action player photo on a borderless UV coated front with a design of the American Eagle in the background.

COMPLETE SET (20) 10.00 25.00
1 Frank Thomas .50 1.25
2 Ken Griffey Jr. .75 2.00
3 Edgar Renteria .20 .50
4 Albert Belle .20 .50
5 Juan Gonzalez .20 .50
6 Jeff Bagwell .30 .75
7 Mark McGwire 1.25 3.00
8 Barry Bonds 1.25 3.00
9 Scott Rolen .30 .75
10 Mo Vaughn .20 .50
11 Andruw Jones .30 .75
12 Chipper Jones .50 1.25
13 Tino Martinez .30 .75
14 Mike Piazza .75 2.00
15 Tony Clark .20 .50
16 Jose Cruz Jr. .20 .50
17 Nomar Garciaparra .75 2.00
18 Cal Ripken 1.50 4.00
19 Alex Rodriguez .75 2.00
20 Derek Jeter 1.25 3.00

1998 Ultra Power Plus

Randomly inserted in Series one packs at the rate of one in 36, this 10-card set features color action photos of top young and veteran players. The backs carry player information.

COMPLETE SET (10) 25.00 60.00
1 Ken Griffey Jr. 5.00 12.00
2 Andruw Jones 2.00 5.00
3 Alex Rodriguez 5.00 12.00
4 Frank Thomas 3.00 8.00
5 Mike Piazza 5.00 12.00
6 Albert Belle 1.25 3.00
7 Juan Gonzalez 1.25 3.00
8 Jeff Bagwell 2.00 5.00
9 Barry Bonds 8.00 20.00
10 Jose Cruz Jr. 1.25 3.00

1998 Ultra Prime Leather

Randomly inserted in Series one packs at the rate of one in 144, this 18-card set features color photos of young and veteran players considered to be good glove men. The backs carry player information.

1 Ken Griffey Jr. 10.00 25.00
2 Andruw Jones 4.00 10.00
3 Alex Rodriguez 10.00 25.00
4 Frank Thomas 6.00 15.00
5 Cal Ripken 20.00 50.00
6 Derek Jeter 15.00 40.00
7 Chipper Jones 6.00 15.00
8 Greg Maddux 10.00 25.00
9 Mike Piazza 10.00 25.00
10 Albert Belle 2.50 6.00
11 Darin Erstad 2.50 6.00
12 Juan Gonzalez 2.50 6.00
13 Jeff Bagwell 4.00 10.00
14 Tony Gwynn 8.00 20.00
15 Roberto Alomar 4.00 10.00
16 Barry Bonds 15.00 40.00
17 Kenny Lofton 2.50 6.00
18 Jose Cruz Jr. 2.50 6.00

1998 Ultra Rocket to Stardom

Randomly inserted in packs at a rate of one in 20, this 15-card insert set showcases rookies on a sculpted embossed and die-cut card designed to resemble a cloud of smoke.

COMPLETE SET (15) 12.50 30.00
1 Ben Grieve .75 2.00
2 Magglio Ordonez 2.50 6.00
3 Travis Lee .75 2.00
4 Mike Caruso .75 2.00
5 Brian Rose .75 2.00
6 Brad Fullmer .75 2.00
7 Michael Coleman .75 2.00
8 Juan Encarnacion .75 2.00
9 Karim Garcia .75 2.00
10 Todd Helton 1.25 3.00
11 Richard Hidalgo .75 2.00
12 Paul Konerko .75 2.00
13 Rod Myers .75 2.00
14 Jaret Wright .75 2.00
15 Miguel Tejada 2.00 5.00

1998 Ultra Ticket Studs

Randomly inserted in packs at a rate of one in 144, this 15-card insert set features color action player photos on sculpture embossed ticket-like designed cards. The cards open up to give details on what makes fans so crazy about their favorite players.

COMPLETE SET (15) 100.00 250.00
1 Travis Lee 2.50 6.00
2 Tony Gwynn 10.00 20.00
3 Scott Rolen 4.00 10.00
4 Nomar Garciaparra 12.50 25.00
5 Mike Piazza 12.50 25.00
6 Mark McGwire 20.00 40.00
7 Ken Griffey Jr. 12.50 25.00
8 Juan Gonzalez 2.50 6.00
9 Jose Cruz Jr. 2.50 6.00
10 Frank Thomas 6.00 15.00
11 Derek Jeter 20.00 40.00
12 Chipper Jones 6.00 15.00
13 Cal Ripken 25.00 50.00
14 Andruw Jones 4.00 10.00
15 Alex Rodriguez 12.50 25.00

1998 Ultra Top 30

These cards which feature 30 of the leading baseball players were issued one per retail series two pack.

COMPLETE SET (30) 10.00 25.00
1 Barry Bonds 1.00 2.50
2 Ivan Rodriguez .25 .60
3 Kenny Lofton .15 .40
4 Albert Belle .15 .40
5 Mo Vaughn .15 .40
6 Jeff Bagwell .25 .60
7 Mark McGwire 1.00 2.50
8 Darin Erstad .15 .40
9 Roger Clemens .75 2.00
10 Tony Gwynn .50 1.25
11 Scott Rolen .25 .60
12 Hideo Nomo .40 1.00
13 Juan Gonzalez .15 .40
14 Mike Piazza .60 1.50
15 Greg Maddux .60 1.50
16 Chipper Jones .40 1.00
17 Andruw Jones .25 .60
18 Derek Jeter 1.00 2.50
19 Nomar Garciaparra .60 1.50
20 Alex Rodriguez .60 1.50
21 Frank Thomas .40 1.00
22 Cal Ripken 1.25 3.00
23 Ken Griffey Jr. .60 1.50
24 Jose Cruz Jr. .15 .40
25 Jaret Wright .15 .40
26 Travis Lee .15 .40
27 Wade Boggs .40 1.00
28 Chuck Knoblauch .15 .40
29 Joe Carter .15 .40
30 Ben Grieve .15 .40

1998 Ultra Win Now

Randomly inserted in packs at a rate of one in 72, this 20-card insert set features color action photos on plastic cards. A transparent section of the front allows you to see the player image in reverse from the back.

COMPLETE SET (20) 100.00 250.00
1 Alex Rodriguez 8.00 20.00
2 Andruw Jones 3.00 8.00
3 Cal Ripken 15.00 40.00
4 Chipper Jones 5.00 12.00
5 Darin Erstad 2.00 5.00
6 Derek Jeter 12.50 30.00
7 Frank Thomas 5.00 12.00
8 Greg Maddux 8.00 20.00
9 Hideo Nomo 5.00 12.00
10 Jeff Bagwell 3.00 8.00
11 Jose Cruz Jr. 2.00 5.00
12 Juan Gonzalez 2.00 5.00
13 Ken Griffey Jr. 8.00 20.00
14 Mark McGwire 12.50 30.00
15 Mike Piazza 8.00 20.00
16 Mo Vaughn 2.00 5.00
17 Nomar Garciaparra 8.00 20.00
18 Roger Clemens 10.00 25.00
19 Scott Rolen 3.00 8.00
20 Tony Gwynn 6.00 15.00

1999 Ultra Promo Sheet

This six card uncut sheet was distributed in dealer wholesale order forms and hobby media releases in late October, several weeks prior to the release of 1999 Ultra 1 baseball. The sheet is made up of six player cards, each of which parallel the player's regular issue Ultra card, except of course, for bold diagonal text stating "PROMOTIONAL SAMPLE" on the front and back of the cards.

NNO 99 Ultra 1 Sheet 2.00 5.00
Nomar Garciaparra
Andruw Jones
Kenny Lofton
Mark McGwire
Alex Rodriguez
Kerry Wood

1999 Ultra

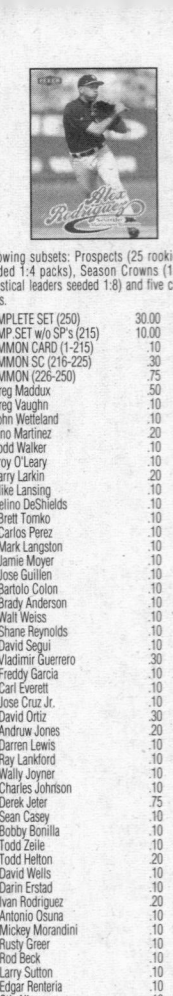

This 250-card single-series set was distributed in 10-card packs with a suggested retail price of $2.69 and features color player photos on the fronts with stats by year in 15 categories and career highlights on the backs for 210 veterans. The set contains the

following subsets: Prospects (25 rookie cards seeded 1:4 packs), Season Crowns (10 1998 statistical leaders seeded 1:8) and five checklist cards.

COMPLETE SET (250) 30.00 80.00
COMP.SET w/o SP's (215) 10.00 25.00
COMMON CARD (1-215) .10 .30
COMMON SC (216-225) .30 .75
COMMON (226-250) .75 2.00
1 Greg Maddux .50 1.25
2 Greg Vaughn .10 .30
3 John Wetteland .10 .30
4 Tino Martinez .20 .50
5 Todd Walker .10 .30
6 Troy O'Leary .10 .30
7 Barry Larkin .20 .50
8 Mike Lansing .10 .30
9 Delino DeShields .10 .30
10 Brett Tomko .10 .30
11 Carlos Perez .10 .30
12 Mark Langston .10 .30
13 Jamie Moyer .10 .30
14 Jose Guillen .10 .30
15 Bartolo Colon .10 .30
16 Brady Anderson .10 .30
17 Walt Weiss .10 .30
18 Shane Reynolds .10 .30
19 David Segui .10 .30
20 Vladimir Guerrero .30 .75
21 Freddy Garcia .10 .30
22 Carl Everett .10 .30
23 Jose Cruz Jr. .10 .30
24 David Ortiz .30 .75
25 Andruw Jones .20 .50
26 Darren Lewis .10 .30
27 Ray Lankford .10 .30
28 Wally Joyner .10 .30
29 Charles Johnson .10 .30
30 Derek Jeter .75 2.00
31 Sean Casey .10 .30
32 Bobby Bonilla .10 .30
33 Todd Zeile .10 .30
34 Todd Helton .20 .50
35 David Wells .10 .30
36 Darin Erstad .10 .30
37 Ivan Rodriguez .20 .50
38 Antonio Osuna .10 .30
39 Mickey Morandini .10 .30
40 Rusty Greer .10 .30
41 Rod Beck .10 .30
42 Larry Sutton .10 .30
43 Edgar Renteria .10 .30
44 Otis Nixon .10 .30
45 Eli Marrero .10 .30
46 Reggie Jefferson .10 .30
47 Trevor Hoffman .10 .30
48 Andres Galarraga .10 .30
49 Scott Brosius .10 .30
50 Vinny Castilla .10 .30
51 Bret Boone .10 .30
52 Masato Yoshii .10 .30
53 Matt Williams .10 .30
54 Robin Ventura .10 .30
55 Jay Powell .10 .30
56 Dean Palmer .10 .30
57 Eric Milton .10 .30
58 Willie McGee .10 .30
59 Tony Gwynn .40 1.00
60 Tom Gordon .10 .30
61 Dante Bichette .10 .30
62 Jaret Wright .10 .30
63 Devon White .10 .30
64 Frank Thomas .30 .75
65 Mike Piazza .50 1.25
66 Jose Offerman .10 .30
67 Pat Meares .10 .30
68 Brian Meadows .10 .30
69 Nomar Garciaparra .50 1.25
70 Mark McGwire .75 2.00
71 Tony Graffanino .10 .30
72 Ken Griffey Jr. .50 1.25
73 Ken Caminiti .10 .30
74 Todd Jones .10 .30
75 A.J. Hinch .10 .30
76 Marquis Grissom .10 .30
77 Jay Buhner .10 .30
78 Albert Belle .10 .30
79 Brian Anderson .10 .30
80 Quinton McCracken .10 .30
81 Omar Vizquel .20 .50
82 Todd Stottlemyre .10 .30
83 Cal Ripken 1.00 2.50
84 Magglio Ordonez .10 .30
85 John Olerud .10 .30
86 Hal Morris .10 .30
87 Derrek Lee .20 .50
88 Doug Glanville .10 .30
89 Marty Cordova .10 .30
90 Kevin Brown .10 .30
91 Kevin Young .10 .30
92 Rico Brogna .10 .30
93 Wilson Alvarez .10 .30
94 Bob Wickman .10 .30
95 Jim Thome .20 .50
96 Mike Mussina .20 .50
97 Al Leiter .10 .30
98 Travis Lee .10 .30
99 Jeff King .10 .30
100 Kerry Wood .10 .30
101 Cliff Floyd .10 .30
102 Jose Valentin .10 .30
103 Manny Ramirez .20 .50
104 Butch Huskey .10 .30
105 Scott Erickson .10 .30
106 Ray Durham .10 .30
107 Johnny Damon .20 .50
108 Craig Counsell .10 .30
109 Rolando Arrojo .10 .30
110 Bob Abreu .10 .30
111 Tony Womack .10 .30
112 Mike Stanley .10 .30
113 Kenny Lofton .10 .30
114 Eric Davis .10 .30
115 Jeff Conine .10 .30
116 Carlos Baerga .10 .30
117 Rondell White .10 .30
118 Billy Wagner .10 .30
119 Ed Sprague .10 .30
120 Jason Schmidt .10 .30
121 Edgar Martinez .20 .50
122 Travis Fryman .10 .30
123 Armando Benitez .10 .30
124 Matt Stairs .10 .30
125 Roberto Hernandez .10 .30
126 Jay Bell .10 .30
127 Justin Thompson .10 .30
128 John Jaha .10 .30
129 Mike Caruso .10 .30
130 Miguel Tejada .10 .30
131 Geoff Jenkins .10 .30
132 Wade Boggs .20 .50
133 Andy Benes .10 .30
134 Aaron Sele .10 .30
135 Bret Saberhagen .10 .30
136 Mariano Rivera .30 .75
137 Neifi Perez .10 .30
138 Paul Konerko .10 .30
139 Barry Bonds .75 2.00
140 Garret Anderson .10 .30
141 Bernie Williams .20 .50
142 Gary Sheffield .10 .30
143 Rafael Palmeiro .20 .50
144 Orel Hershiser .10 .30
145 Craig Biggio .20 .50
146 Dmitri Young .10 .30
147 Damion Easley .10 .30
148 Henry Rodriguez .10 .30
149 Brad Radke .10 .30
150 Pedro Martinez .20 .50
151 Mike Lieberthal .10 .30
152 Jim Leyritz .10 .30
153 Chuck Knoblauch .10 .30
154 Darryl Kile .10 .30
155 Brian Jordan .10 .30
156 Chipper Jones .30 .75
157 Pete Harnisch .10 .30
158 Moises Alou .10 .30
159 Ismael Valdes .10 .30
160 Stan Javier .10 .30
161 Mark Grace .20 .50
162 Jason Giambi .10 .30
163 Chuck Finley .10 .30
164 Juan Encarnacion .10 .30
165 Chan Ho Park .10 .30
166 Randy Johnson .30 .75
167 J.T. Snow .10 .30
168 Tim Salmon .20 .50
169 Brian L.Hunter .10 .30
170 Rickey Henderson .30 .75
171 Cal Eldred .10 .30
172 Curt Schilling .10 .30
173 Alex Rodriguez .50 1.25
174 Dustin Hermanson .10 .30
175 Mike Hampton .10 .30
176 Shawn Green .10 .30
177 Roberto Alomar .20 .50
178 Sandy Alomar Jr. .10 .30
179 Larry Walker .10 .30
180 Mo Vaughn .10 .30
181 Raul Mondesi .10 .30
182 Hideki Irabu .10 .30
183 Jim Edmonds .10 .30
184 Shawn Estes .10 .30
185 Tony Clark .10 .30
186 Dan Wilson .10 .30
187 Michael Tucker .10 .30
188 Jeff Shaw .10 .30
189 Mark Grudzielanek .10 .30
190 Roger Clemens .60 1.50
191 Juan Gonzalez .10 .30
192 Sammy Sosa .30 .75
193 Troy Percival .10 .30
194 Robb Nen .10 .30
195 Bill Mueller .10 .30
196 Ben Grieve .10 .30
197 Luis Gonzalez .10 .30
198 Will Clark .20 .50
199 Jeff Cirillo .10 .30
200 Scott Rolen .20 .50
201 Reggie Sanders .10 .30
202 Fred McGriff .20 .50
203 Denny Neagle .10 .30
204 Brad Fullmer .10 .30
205 Royce Clayton .10 .30
206 Jose Canseco .20 .50
207 Jeff Bagwell .20 .50
208 Hideo Nomo .30 .75
209 Karim Garcia .10 .30
210 Kenny Rogers .10 .30
211 Kerry Wood CL .10 .30
212 Alex Rodriguez CL .30 .75
213 Cal Ripken CL .50 1.25
214 Frank Thomas CL .20 .50
215 Ken Griffey Jr. CL .30 .75
216 Alex Rodriguez SC 1.25 3.00
217 Greg Maddux SC 1.25 3.00
218 Juan Gonzalez SC .30 .75
219 Ken Griffey Jr. SC 1.25 3.00
220 Kerry Wood SC .30 .75
221 Mark McGwire SC 2.00 5.00
222 Mike Piazza SC 1.25 3.00
223 Rickey Henderson SC .75 2.00
224 Sammy Sosa SC .75 2.00
225 Travis Lee SC .30 .75
226 Gabe Alvarez PROS .75 2.00
227 Matt Anderson PROS .75 2.00
228 Adrian Beltre PROS .75 2.00
229 O.Cabrera PROS .75 2.00
230 Orl. Hernandez PROS .75 2.00
231 A.Ramirez PROS .75 2.00
232 Troy Glaus PROS 1.25 3.00
233 Gabe Kapler PROS .75 2.00
234 Jeremy Giambi PROS .75 2.00
235 Derrick Gibson PROS .75 2.00
236 Carlton Loewer PROS .75 2.00
237 Mike Frank PROS .75 2.00
238 Carlos Guillen PROS .75 2.00
239 Alex Gonzalez PROS .75 2.00
240 Enrique Wilson PROS .75 2.00
241 J.D. Drew PROS .75 2.00
242 Bruce Chen PROS .75 2.00
243 Ryan Minor PROS .75 2.00
244 Preston Wilson PROS .75 2.00
245 Josh Booty PROS .75 2.00
246 Luis Ordaz PROS .75 2.00
247 G.Lombard PROS .75 2.00
248 Matt Clement PROS .75 2.00
249 Eric Chavez PROS .75 2.00
250 Corey Koskie PROS .75 2.00

1999 Ultra Gold Medallion

Randomly inserted one in every hobby only pack for regular cards, one in 40 for Prospects, and one in 80 for Season Crowns, this 250-card set is a gold parallel version of the base set.

*GOLD: 1.25X TO 3X BASIC CARDS
*GOLD SC: 2X TO 5X BASIC SC
*GOLD PROS: 1X TO 2.5X BASIC PROS

1999 Ultra Platinum Medallion

Randomly inserted in hobby packs only, this 250-card set is a parallel version of the base set. Only 99 of the 215 veteran cards were produced and numbered. Only 65 of the Prospects (cards numbered from 226 through 250) subset was produced and serially numbered. Only 50 of the Season Crowns (cards numbered from 216 through 225) subset was produced and serially numbered.

*PLAT: 15X TO 40X BASIC CARDS
*PLAT SC: 12.5X TO 30X BASIC SC
*PLAT PROS: 2.5X TO 6X BASIC PROS

1999 Ultra The Book On

Randomly inserted in packs at the rate of one in six, this 20-card set features action color photos of top players with a detailed analysis of why they are so good printed on the backs.

COMPLETE SET (20) 20.00 50.00
1 Kerry Wood .30 .75
2 Ken Griffey Jr. 1.25 3.00
3 Frank Thomas .75 2.00
4 Albert Belle .30 .75
5 Juan Gonzalez .30 .75
6 Jeff Bagwell .50 1.25
7 Mark McGwire 2.00 5.00
8 Barry Bonds 2.00 5.00
9 Andruw Jones .50 1.25
10 Mo Vaughn .30 .75
11 Scott Rolen .50 1.25
12 Travis Lee .30 .75
13 Tony Gwynn 1.00 2.50
14 Greg Maddux 1.25 3.00
15 Mike Piazza 1.25 3.00
16 Chipper Jones .75 2.00
17 Nomar Garciaparra 1.25 3.00
18 Cal Ripken 2.50 6.00
19 Derek Jeter 2.00 5.00
20 Alex Rodriguez 1.25 3.00

1999 Ultra Damage Inc.

Randomly inserted in packs at the rate of one in 72, this 15-card set features color images of top players printed on a business card design.

COMPLETE SET (15) 100.00 200.00
1 Alex Rodriguez 6.00 15.00
2 Greg Maddux 6.00 15.00
3 Cal Ripken 12.50 30.00
4 Chipper Jones 4.00 10.00
5 Derek Jeter 10.00 25.00
6 Frank Thomas 4.00 10.00
7 Juan Gonzalez 1.50 4.00
8 Ken Griffey Jr. 6.00 15.00
9 Kerry Wood 1.50 4.00
10 Mark McGwire 10.00 25.00
11 Mike Piazza 6.00 15.00
12 Nomar Garciaparra 6.00 15.00
13 Scott Rolen 2.50 6.00
14 Tony Gwynn 5.00 12.00
15 Travis Lee 1.50 4.00

1999 Ultra Diamond Producers

Randomly inserted in packs at the rate of one in 288, this 10-card set features action color player photos printed on full foil plastic die-cut cards with custom embossing.

COMPLETE SET (10) 125.00 300.00
1 Ken Griffey Jr. 8.00 20.00
2 Frank Thomas 5.00 12.00
3 Alex Rodriguez 8.00 20.00
4 Cal Ripken 15.00 40.00
5 Mike Piazza 8.00 20.00
6 Mark McGwire 12.50 30.00
7 Greg Maddux 8.00 20.00
8 Kerry Wood 2.00 5.00
9 Chipper Jones 5.00 12.00
10 Derek Jeter 12.50 30.00

1999 Ultra RBI Kings

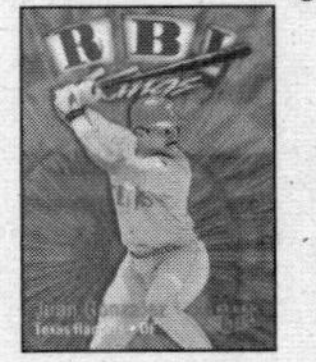

Randomly inserted one in every retail pack only, this 30-card set features action color photos of top run producing players.

COMPLETE SET (30) 12.50 30.00
1 Rafael Palmeiro .25 .60
2 Mo Vaughn .15 .40
3 Ivan Rodriguez .25 .60
4 Barry Bonds 1.00 2.50
5 Albert Belle .15 .40
6 Jeff Bagwell .25 .60
7 Mark McGwire 1.00 2.50
8 Darin Erstad .15 .40
9 Manny Ramirez .25 .60
10 Chipper Jones .40 1.00
11 Jim Thome .25 .60
12 Scott Rolen .25 .60
13 Tony Gwynn .50 1.25
14 Juan Gonzalez .15 .40
15 Mike Piazza .60 1.50
16 Sammy Sosa .40 1.00
17 Andruw Jones .25 .60
18 Derek Jeter 1.00 2.50
19 Nomar Garciaparra .60 1.50
20 Alex Rodriguez .60 1.50
21 Frank Thomas .40 1.00
22 Cal Ripken 1.25 3.00
23 Ken Griffey Jr. .60 1.50
24 Travis Lee .15 .40
25 Paul O'Neill .15 .40
26 Greg Vaughn .15 .40
27 Andres Galarraga .15 .40
28 Tino Martinez .25 .60
29 Jose Canseco .25 .60
30 Ben Grieve .15 .40

1999 Ultra Thunderclap

Randomly inserted in packs at the rate of one in 36, this 15-card set features color player photos printed on embossed cards with silver pattern holofoil.

COMPLETE SET (15) 40.00 100.00
1 Alex Rodriguez 3.00 8.00
2 Andruw Jones 1.25 3.00
3 Cal Ripken 6.00 15.00
4 Chipper Jones 2.00 5.00
5 Darin Erstad .75 2.00
6 Derek Jeter 5.00 12.00
7 Frank Thomas 2.00 5.00
8 Jeff Bagwell 1.25 3.00
9 Juan Gonzalez .75 2.00
10 Ken Griffey Jr. 3.00 8.00
11 Mark McGwire 5.00 12.00
12 Mike Piazza 3.00 8.00
13 Travis Lee .75 2.00
14 Nomar Garciaparra 3.00 8.00
15 Scott Rolen 1.25 3.00

1999 Ultra World Premiere

Randomly inserted in packs at the rate of one in 18, this 15-card set features action color photos of top

1998 rookies printed on sculpture embossed silver holofoil cards.

COMPLETE SET (15) 8.00 20.00
1 Gabe Alvarez .50 1.25
2 Kerry Wood .75 2.00
3 Orlando Hernandez .50 1.25
4 Mike Caruso .75 2.00
5 Matt Anderson .50 1.25
6 Randall Simon .75 2.00
7 Adrian Beltre .50 1.25
8 Scott Elarton .75 2.00
9 Karim Garcia .75 2.00
10 Mike Frank .50 1.25
11 Richard Hidalgo .75 2.00
12 Paul Konerko .75 2.00
13 Travis Lee .75 2.00
14 J.D. Drew .75 2.00
15 Miguel Tejada .75 2.00

2000 Ultra

This 300 card set was issued late in 1999. The cards were distributed in 10 card packs with an SRP of $2.69. The product was issued in either 8, 12 or 30 box cases. The prospect subset were numbered from 251 through 300 and were printed in shorter quantity than the regular cards and inserted one every four packs. Two separate Alex Rodriguez Promo cards were distributed to dealers and hobby media several weeks prior to the product's release. The first card features identical glossy card front stock as the basic Ultra 2000 product and has the words "PROMOTIONAL SAMPLE" running diagonally across the back of the card. The second, more scarce, card features a lenticular ribbed plastic card front (creating a primitive 3-D effect). Both promos share the same photo of Rodriguez as is used on the basic issue A-Rod 2000 Ultra card.

COMPLETE SET (300) 40.00 100.00
COMP.SET w/o SP's (250) 10.00 25.00
COMMON CARD (1-250) .10 .30
COMMON (251-300) 1.50 4.00
1 Alex Rodriguez .50 1.25
2 Shawn Green .10 .30
3 Magglio Ordonez .10 .30
4 Tony Gwynn .40 1.00
5 Joe McEwing .10 .30
6 Jose Rosado .10 .30
7 Sammy Sosa .30 .75
8 Gary Sheffield .10 .30
9 Mickey Morandini .10 .30
10 Mo Vaughn .10 .30
11 Todd Hollandsworth .10 .30
12 Tom Gordon .10 .30
13 Charles Johnson .10 .30
14 Derek Bell .10 .30
15 Kevin Young .10 .30
16 Jay Buhner .10 .30
17 J.T. Snow .10 .30
18 Jay Bell .10 .30
19 John Rocker .10 .30
20 Ivan Rodriguez .20 .50
21 Pokey Reese .10 .30
22 Paul O'Neill .20 .50
23 Ronnie Belliard .10 .30
24 Ryan Rupe .10 .30
25 Travis Fryman .10 .30
26 Trot Nixon .10 .30
27 Wally Joyner .10 .30
28 Andy Pettitte .20 .50
29 Dan Wilson .10 .30
30 Orlando Hernandez .10 .30
31 Dmitri Young .10 .30
32 Edgar Renteria .10 .30
33 Eric Karros .10 .30
34 Fernando Seguignol .10 .30
35 Jason Kendall .10 .30
36 Jeff Shaw .10 .30
37 Matt Lawton .10 .30
38 Robin Ventura .20 .50
39 Scott Williamson .10 .30
40 Ben Grieve .10 .30
41 Billy Wagner .10 .30
42 Javy Lopez .10 .30
43 Joe Randa .10 .30
44 Neifi Perez .10 .30
45 David Justice .10 .30
46 Ray Durham .10 .30
47 Dustin Hermanson .10 .30
48 Andres Galarraga .10 .30
49 Brad Fullmer .10 .30
50 Nomar Garciaparra .50 1.25
51 David Cone .10 .30
52 David Nilsson .10 .30
53 David Wells .10 .30
54 Miguel Tejada .10 .30
55 Ismael Valdes .10 .30
56 Jose Lima .10 .30
57 Juan Encarnacion .10 .30
58 Fred McGriff .20 .50
59 Kenny Rogers .10 .30
60 Vladimir Guerrero .30 .75
61 Benito Santiago .10 .30
62 Chris Singleton .10 .30
63 Carlos Lee .10 .30
64 Sean Casey .10 .30
65 Tom Goodwin .10 .30
66 Todd Hundley .10 .30
67 Ellis Burks .10 .30
68 Tim Hudson .10 .30
69 Matt Stairs .10 .30
70 Chipper Jones UER .30 .75
Dodgers logo on the back
71 Craig Biggio .20 .50
72 Brian Rose .10 .30
73 Carlos Delgado .10 .30
74 Eddie Taubensee .10 .30
75 John Smoltz .20 .50
76 Ken Caminiti .10 .30
77 Rafael Palmeiro .20 .50
78 Sidney Ponson .10 .30
79 Todd Helton .20 .50
80 Juan Gonzalez .10 .30
81 Bruce Aven .10 .30
82 Desi Relaford .10 .30
83 Johnny Damon .20 .50
84 Albert Belle .10 .30
85 Mark McGwire .75 2.00
86 Rico Brogna .10 .30
87 Tom Glavine .20 .50
88 Harold Baines .10 .30
89 Chad Allen .10 .30
90 Barry Bonds .75 2.00
91 Mark Grace .20 .50
92 Paul Byrd .10 .30
93 Roberto Alomar .20 .50
94 Roberto Hernandez .10 .30
95 Steve Finley .10 .30
96 Bret Boone .10 .30
97 Charles Nagy .10 .30
98 Eric Chavez .10 .30
99 Jamie Moyer .10 .30
100 Ken Griffey Jr. .50 1.25
101 J.D. Drew .10 .30
102 Todd Stottlemyre .10 .30
103 Tony Fernandez .10 .30
104 Jeromy Burnitz .10 .30
105 Jeremy Giambi .10 .30
106 Livan Hernandez .10 .30
107 Marlon Anderson .10 .30
108 Troy Glaus .10 .30
109 Troy O'Leary .10 .30
110 Scott Rolen .20 .50
111 Bernard Gilkey .10 .30
112 Brady Anderson .10 .30
113 Chuck Knoblauch .10 .30
114 Jeff Weaver .10 .30
115 B.J. Surhoff .10 .30
116 Alex Gonzalez .10 .30
117 Vinny Castilla .10 .30
118 Tim Salmon .20 .50
119 Brian Jordan .10 .30
120 Corey Koskie .10 .30
121 Dean Palmer .10 .30
122 Gabe Kapler .10 .30
123 Jim Edmonds .10 .30
124 John Jaha .10 .30
125 Mark Grudzielanek .10 .30
126 Mike Bordick .10 .30
127 Mike Lieberthal .10 .30
128 Pete Harnisch .10 .30
129 Russ Ortiz .10 .30
130 Kevin Brown .20 .50
131 Troy Percival .10 .30
132 Alex Gonzalez .10 .30
133 Bartolo Colon .10 .30
134 John Valentin .10 .30
135 Jose Hernandez .10 .30
136 Marquis Grissom .10 .30
137 Wade Boggs .20 .50
138 Dante Bichette .10 .30
139 Bobby Higginson .10 .30
140 Frank Thomas .30 .75
141 Geoff Jenkins .10 .30
142 Justin Giambi .10 .30
143 Jeff Cirillo .10 .30
144 Sandy Alomar Jr. .10 .30
145 Luis Gonzalez .10 .30
146 Preston Wilson .10 .30
147 Carlos Beltran .10 .30
148 Greg Vaughn .10 .30
149 Carlos Febles .10 .30
150 Jose Canseco .20 .50
151 Kris Benson .10 .30
152 Chuck Finley .10 .30
153 Michael Barrett .10 .30
154 Rey Ordonez .10 .30
155 Adrian Beltre .10 .30
156 Andruw Jones .20 .50
157 Barry Larkin .20 .50
158 Brian Giles .10 .30
159 Carl Everett .10 .30
160 Manny Ramirez .20 .50
161 Darryl Kile .10 .30
162 Edgar Martinez .20 .50
163 Jeff Kent .10 .30
164 Matt Williams .10 .30
165 Mike Piazza .50 1.25
166 Pedro Martinez .20 .50
167 Ray Lankford .10 .30
168 Roger Cedeno .10 .30
169 Ron Coomer .10 .30
170 Cal Ripken 1.00 2.50
171 Jose Offerman .10 .30
172 Kenny Lofton .10 .30
173 Kent Bottenfield .10 .30
174 Kevin Millwood .10 .30
175 Omar Daal .10 .30
176 Orlando Cabrera .10 .30
177 Pat Hentgen .10 .30
178 Tino Martinez .20 .50
179 Tony Clark .10 .30
180 Roger Clemens .60 1.50
181 Brad Radke .10 .30
182 Darin Erstad .10 .30
183 Jose Jimenez .10 .30
184 Jim Thome .20 .50
185 John Wetteland .10 .30
186 Justin Thompson .10 .30
187 John Halama .10 .30
188 Lee Stevens .10 .30
189 Miguel Cairo .10 .30
190 Mike Mussina .20 .50
191 Raul Mondesi .10 .30
192 Armando Rios .10 .30
193 Trevor Hoffman .10 .30
194 Tony Batista .10 .30
195 Will Clark .20 .50
196 Brad Ausmus .10 .30
197 Chili Davis .10 .30
198 Cliff Floyd .10 .30
199 Curt Schilling .10 .30
200 Derek Jeter .75 2.00
201 Henry Rodriguez .10 .30
202 Jose Cruz Jr. .10 .30
203 Omar Vizquel .20 .50
204 Randy Johnson .30 .75
205 Reggie Sanders .10 .30
206 Al Leiter .10 .30
207 Damion Easley .10 .30
208 David Bell .10 .30
209 Fernando Tatis .10 .30
210 Kerry Wood .10 .30
211 Kevin Appier .10 .30
212 Mariano Rivera .30 .75
213 Mike Caruso .10 .30
214 Moises Alou .10 .30
215 Randy Winn .10 .30
216 Roy Halladay .10 .30
217 Shannon Stewart .10 .30
218 Todd Walker .10 .30
219 Jim Parque .10 .30
220 Travis Lee .10 .30
221 Andy Ashby .10 .30
222 Ed Sprague .10 .30
223 Larry Walker .10 .30
224 Rick Helling .10 .30
225 Rusty Greer .10 .30
226 Todd Zeile .10 .30
227 Freddy Garcia .10 .30
228 Hideo Nomo .30 .75
229 Marty Cordova .10 .30
230 Greg Maddux .50 1.25
231 Rondell White .10 .30
232 Paul Konerko .10 .30
233 Warren Morris .10 .30
234 Bernie Williams .20 .50
235 Bob Abreu .10 .30
236 John Olerud .10 .30
237 Doug Glanville .10 .30
238 Eric Young .10 .30
239 Robb Nen .10 .30
240 Jeff Bagwell .20 .50
241 Sterling Hitchcock .10 .30
242 Todd Greene .10 .30
243 Bill Mueller .10 .30
244 Rickey Henderson .30 .75
245 Chan Ho Park .10 .30
246 Jason Schmidt .10 .30
247 Jeff Zimmerman .10 .30
248 Jermaine Dye .10 .30
249 Randall Simon .10 .30
250 Richie Sexson .10 .30
251 Micah Bowie PROS 1.50 4.00
252 Joe Nathan PROS 1.50 4.00
253 C.Woodward PROS 1.50 4.00
254 Lance Berkman PROS 1.50 4.00
255 Ruben Mateo PROS 1.50 4.00
256 R.Branyan PROS 1.50 4.00
257 Randy Wolf PROS 1.50 4.00
258 A.J. Burnett PROS 1.50 4.00
259 Mark Quinn PROS 1.50 4.00
260 Buddy Carlyle PROS 1.50 4.00
261 Ben Davis PROS 1.50 4.00
262 Yamid Haad PROS 1.50 4.00
263 Mike Colangelo PROS 1.50 4.00
264 Rick Ankiel PROS 1.50 4.00
265 Jacque Jones PROS 1.50 4.00
266 Kelly Dransfeldt PROS 1.50 4.00
267 Matt Riley PROS 1.50 4.00
268 Adam Kennedy PROS 1.50 4.00
269 Octavio Dotel PROS 1.50 4.00
270 F.Cordero PROS 1.50 4.00
271 Wilton Veras PROS 1.50 4.00
272 C.Pickering PROS 1.50 4.00
273 Alex Sanchez PROS 1.50 4.00
274 Tony Armas Jr. PROS 1.50 4.00
275 Pat Burrell PROS 1.50 4.00
276 Chad Meyers PROS 1.50 4.00
277 Ben Petrick PROS 1.50 4.00
278 R.Hernandez PROS 1.50 4.00
279 Ed Yarnall PROS 1.50 4.00
280 Erubiel Durazo PROS 1.50 4.00
281 Vernon Wells PROS 1.50 4.00
282 G.Matthews Jr. PROS 1.50 4.00
283 Kip Wells PROS 1.50 4.00
284 Peter Bergeron PROS 1.50 4.00
285 Travis Dawkins PROS 1.50 4.00
286 Jorge Toca PROS 1.50 4.00
287 Cole Liniak PROS 1.50 4.00
288 C.Hermansen PROS 1.50 4.00
289 Eric Gagne PROS 2.00 5.00
290 C.Hutchinson PROS 1.50 4.00
291 Eric Munson PROS 1.50 4.00
292 Wiki Gonzalez PROS 1.50 4.00
293 A.Soriano PROS 2.00 5.00
294 T.Durrington PROS 1.50 4.00
295 Ben Molina PROS 1.50 4.00
296 Aaron Myette PROS 1.50 4.00
297 Wily Pena PROS 1.50 4.00
298 Kevin Barker PROS 1.50 4.00
299 Geoff Blum PROS 1.50 4.00
300 Josh Beckett PROS 2.00 5.00
P1 Alex Rodriguez Promo .60 1.50
P2 A.Rodriguez Promo 3-D 2.00 5.00

2000 Ultra Gold Medallion

This set is a parallel to the regular Ultra set. The regular cards from 1 through 250 were issued one per hobby pack and the prospect cards were issued one every 24 hobby packs. These cards have special die-cutting and have gold coating and gold foil stamping.

*GOLD 1-250: 1.25X TO 3X BASIC CARDS
*GOLD PROS: .75X TO 2X BASIC CARDS

2000 Ultra Platinum Medallion

Randomly inserted into hobby packs, these cards parallel the regular Ultra set. These cards are serial numbered to 50 for the veterans and 25 for the prospects (251-300). These die cut cards have silver coating and silver foil. Pricing is unavaiable due to scarcity on cards 251-300.

*PLAT 1-250: 15X TO 40X BASIC CARDS
*PROSPECTS: 4X TO 10X BASIC CARDS
251-300 NO PRICING DUE TO SCARCITY

2000 Ultra Crunch Time

Inserted one every 72 packs, these 15 cards feature players who are among those players known for their clutch performances. The horizontal cards are printed on suede stock and then are gold foil stamped.

COMPLETE SET (15) 100.00 200.00
1 Nomar Garciaparra 5.00 12.00
2 Ken Griffey Jr. 5.00 12.00
3 Mark McGwire 8.00 20.00
4 Alex Rodriguez 5.00 12.00
5 Derek Jeter 8.00 20.00
6 Sammy Sosa 3.00 8.00
7 Mike Piazza 5.00 12.00
8 Cal Ripken 10.00 25.00
9 Frank Thomas 3.00 8.00
10 Juan Gonzalez 1.25 3.00
11 J.D. Drew 1.25 3.00
12 Greg Maddux 5.00 12.00
13 Tony Gwynn 4.00 10.00
14 Vladimir Guerrero 3.00 8.00
15 Ben Grieve 1.25 3.00

2000 Ultra Diamond Mine

Inserted one every six packs, these 15 cards feature some of the brightest stars of the baseball diamond. The cards are printed on silver metallic ink and have silver foil stamping.

COMPLETE SET (15) 15.00 30.00
1 Greg Maddux .75 2.00
2 Mark McGwire 1.25 3.00
3 Ken Griffey Jr. .75 2.00
4 Cal Ripken 1.50 4.00
5 Nomar Garciaparra .75 2.00
6 Mike Piazza .75 2.00
7 Alex Rodriguez .75 2.00
8 Frank Thomas .50 1.25
9 Juan Gonzalez .20 .50
10 Derek Jeter 1.25 3.00
11 Tony Gwynn .60 1.50
12 Chipper Jones .50 1.25
13 Sammy Sosa .50 1.25
14 Roger Clemens 1.00 2.50
15 Vladimir Guerrero .50 1.25

2000 Ultra Feel the Game

Inserted at a rate of one in 168, these cards feature pieces of game used memorabilia of some of today's stars. There is a player photo to go with the swatch of material used (either jersey or batting gloves). It is widely believed that the Frank Thomas is the toughest card to find in the set.

1 Alex Rodriguez Jsy 10.00 25.00
2 Chipper Jones Jsy 6.00 15.00
3 Rob Alomar Btg Glv SP 20.00 50.00
4 Greg Maddux Jsy 6.00 15.00
5 Pedro Martinez Jsy 6.00 15.00
6 Cal Ripken Jsy 20.00 50.00
7 Robin Ventura Jsy 4.00 10.00
8 J.D. Drew Jsy 4.00 10.00
9 Randy Johnson Jsy 6.00 15.00
10 Scott Rolen Jsy 6.00 15.00
11 Kevin Millwood Jsy 4.00 10.00
12 Frank Thomas Btg Glv SP 40.00 80.00
13 Tony Gwynn Btg Glv SP 40.00 80.00
14 Curt Schilling Jsy 4.00 10.00
15 Edgar Martinez Btg Glv 6.00 15.00

2000 Ultra Fresh Ink

Randomly inserted into packs, these cards feature signed cards of either young players or veteran stars. One card in this set is a combo signature card of the three players used in the Club 3000 series. After each player name in our checklist is a number indicating how many cards they signed for this promotion.

1 Bob Abreu/200 10.00 25.00
2 Chad Allen/975 4.00 10.00
3 Marlon Anderson/975 4.00 10.00
4 Rick Ankiel/500 10.00 25.00
5 Glen Barker/975 4.00 10.00
6 Michael Barrett/975 4.00 10.00
7 Carlos Beltran/975 6.00 15.00
8 Adrian Beltre/900 6.00 15.00
9 Peter Bergeron/1000 4.00 10.00
10 Wade Boggs/250 15.00 40.00
11 Barry Bonds/250 100.00 175.00
12 Pat Burrell/600 6.00 15.00
13 Roger Cedeno/500 6.00 15.00
14 Eric Chavez/800 6.00 15.00
15 Bruce Chen/600 4.00 10.00
16 Johnny Damon/750 15.00 40.00
17 Ben Davis/1000 4.00 10.00
18 Carlos Delgado/275 10.00 25.00
19 Einar Diaz/975 4.00 10.00
20 Octavio Dotel/950 4.00 10.00
21 J.D. Drew/600 6.00 15.00
22 Scott Elarton/1000 4.00 10.00
23 Freddy Garcia/500 6.00 15.00
24 Jeremy Giambi/975 4.00 10.00
25 Troy Glaus/500 10.00 25.00
26 Shawn Green/350 15.00 40.00
27 Tony Gwynn/250 30.00 60.00
28 Richard Hidalgo/500 4.00 10.00
29 Bobby Higginson/975 4.00 10.00
30 Tim Hudson/975 10.00 25.00
31 Norm Hutchins/1000 4.00 10.00
32 Derek Jeter/95 200.00 300.00
33 Randy Johnson/240 40.00 80.00
34 Gabe Kapler/725 6.00 15.00
35 Jason Kendall/375 10.00 25.00
36 Paul Konerko/500 10.00 25.00
37 Matt Lawton/1000 4.00 10.00
38 Carlos Lee/900 6.00 15.00
39 Jose Macias/1000 4.00 10.00
40 Greg Maddux/225 60.00 120.00
41 Kevin Millwood/500 6.00 15.00
42 Warren Morris/1000 4.00 10.00
43 Eric Munson/900 4.00 10.00
44 Heath Murray/925 4.00 10.00
45 Joe Nathan/1000 10.00 25.00
46 Magglio Ordonez/335 10.00 25.00
47 Angel Pena/1000 4.00 10.00
48 Cal Ripken/350 60.00 120.00
49 Alex Rodriguez/350 60.00 120.00
50 Scott Rolen/250 15.00 40.00
51 Ryan Rupe/1000 4.00 10.00
52 Curt Schilling/375 20.00 50.00
53 Randall Simon/1000 4.00 10.00
54 Alfonso Soriano/975 15.00 40.00
55 Shannon Stewart/275 10.00 25.00
56 Miguel Tejada/1000 10.00 25.00
57 Frank Thomas/150 50.00 100.00
58 Jeff Weaver/1000 6.00 15.00
59 Randy Wolf/1000 6.00 15.00
60 Ed Yarnall/1000 4.00 10.00
61 Kevin Young/1000 4.00 10.00
62 Wade Boggs 250.00 450.00
Tony Gwynn
Nolan Ryan 100

2000 Ultra Fresh Ink Gold

These cards were actually distributed in 2001 Fleer Platinum Rack Packs, but are catalogued here for easier reference. According to representatives at Fleer, twenty-five different cards were featured in this set. All of the cards are hand-numbered "1 of 1's" and feature a gold (rather than silver) foil signed sticker on front. Our checklist is incomplete at this time due to lack of information.

1 Lance Berkman
2 Roger Cedeno
3 Troy Glaus
4 Richard Hidalgo
5 Derek Jeter
6 Jose Macias
7 Cal Ripken
8 Alfonso Soriano
9 Miguel Tejada

2000 Ultra Swing Kings

Inserted one every 24 packs, these 10 cards feature some of the leading power hitters in baseball. These cards are made of contemporary plastice with glittering silver foil highlights.

COMPLETE SET (10) 20.00 50.00
1 Cal Ripken 3.00 8.00
2 Nomar Garciaparra 1.50 4.00
3 Frank Thomas 1.00 2.50
4 Tony Gwynn 1.25 3.00
5 Ken Griffey Jr. 1.50 4.00
6 Chipper Jones 1.00 2.50
7 Mark McGwire 2.50 6.00
8 Sammy Sosa 1.00 2.50
9 Derek Jeter 2.50 6.00
10 Alex Rodriguez 1.50 4.00

2000 Ultra Talented

Randomly inserted into hobby packs, these 10 cards feature multi-talented players. These cards feature metallic ink on holofoil background with gold foil stamped accents. 100 serial-numbered sets were produced.

1 Sammy Sosa 12.50 30.00
2 Derek Jeter 30.00 80.00
3 Alex Rodriguez 20.00 50.00
4 Mike Piazza 20.00 50.00
5 Ken Griffey Jr. 20.00 50.00
6 Nomar Garciaparra 20.00 50.00
7 Mark McGwire 30.00 80.00
8 Cal Ripken 40.00 100.00
9 Frank Thomas 12.50 30.00
10 J.D. Drew 5.00 12.00

2000 Ultra World Premiere

Inserted one every 12 packs, these 10 cards feature 12 of the leading prospects in baseball. The die cut cards are printed with etched foil.

COMPLETE SET (10) 5.00 12.00
1 Ruben Mateo .40 1.00
2 Lance Berkman .50 1.25
3 Octavio Dotel .40 1.00
4 Ben Davis .40 1.00
5 Warren Morris .40 1.00
6 Carlos Beltran .50 1.25
7 Rick Ankiel .40 1.00
8 Adam Kennedy .40 1.00
9 Tim Hudson .50 1.25
10 Jorge Toca .40 1.00

2001 Ultra

The 2001 Ultra product was released in December, 2000 and features a 275-card base set. The base set is broken into tiers as follows: 250 Base Veterans, and 25 Prospects (1:4). Each pack contained 10-cards, and carried a suggested retail price of $2.99.

COMPLETE SET (275) 60.00 120.00
COMP.SET w/o SP's (250) 10.00 25.00
COMMON CARD (1-250) .10 .30
COMMON (251-275) 1.25 3.00
COMMON (276-280) 2.00 5.00
1 Pedro Martinez .20 .50
2 Derek Jeter .75 2.00
3 Cal Ripken 1.00 2.50
4 Alex Rodriguez .50 1.25
5 Vladimir Guerrero .30 .75
6 Troy Glaus .10 .30
7 Sammy Sosa .30 .75
8 Mike Piazza .50 1.25
9 Tony Gwynn .40 1.00
10 Tim Hudson .10 .30
11 John Flaherty .10 .30
12 Jeff Cirillo .10 .30
13 Ellis Burks .10 .30
14 Carlos Lee .10 .30
15 Carlos Beltran .10 .30
16 Ruben Rivera .10 .30
17 Richard Hidalgo .10 .30
18 Omar Vizquel .20 .50
19 Michael Barrett .10 .30
20 Jose Canseco .20 .50
21 Jason Giambi .10 .30
22 Greg Maddux .50 1.25
23 Charles Johnson .10 .30
24 Sandy Alomar Jr. .10 .30
25 Rick Ankiel .10 .30
26 Richie Sexson .10 .30
27 Matt Williams .10 .30
28 Joe Girardi .10 .30
29 Jason Kendall .10 .30
30 Brad Fullmer .10 .30
31 Alex Gonzalez .10 .30
32 Rick Helling .10 .30
33 Mike Mussina .20 .50
34 Joe Randa .10 .30
35 J.T. Snow .10 .30
36 Edgardo Alfonzo .10 .30
37 Dante Bichette .10 .30
38 Brad Ausmus .10 .30
39 Bobby Abreu .10 .30
40 Warren Morris .10 .30
41 Tony Womack .10 .30
42 Russell Branyan .10 .30
43 Mike Lowell .10 .30
44 Mark Grace .20 .50
45 Jeromy Burnitz .10 .30
46 J.D. Drew .10 .30
47 David Justice .10 .30
48 Alex Gonzalez .10 .30
49 Tino Martinez .20 .50
50 Raul Mondesi .10 .30
51 Rafael Furcal .10 .30
52 Marquis Grissom .10 .30
53 Kevin Young .10 .30
54 Jon Lieber .10 .30
55 Henry Rodriguez .10 .30
56 Dave Burba .10 .30
57 Shannon Stewart .10 .30
58 Preston Wilson .10 .30
59 Paul O'Neill .20 .50
60 Jimmy Haynes .10 .30
61 Darryl Kile .10 .30
62 Bret Boone .10 .30
63 Bartolo Colon .10 .30
64 Andres Galarraga .10 .30
65 Trot Nixon .10 .30
66 Steve Finley .10 .30
67 Shawn Green .10 .30
68 Robert Person .10 .30
69 Kenny Rogers .10 .30
70 Bobby Higginson .10 .30
71 Barry Larkin .20 .50
72 Al Martin .10 .30
73 Tom Glavine .20 .50
74 Rondell White .10 .30
75 Ray Lankford .10 .30
76 Moises Alou .10 .30
77 Matt Clement .10 .30
78 Geoff Jenkins .10 .30
79 David Wells .10 .30
80 Chuck Finley .10 .30
81 Andy Pettitte .20 .50
82 Travis Fryman .10 .30
83 Ron Coomer .10 .30
84 Mark McGwire .75 2.00
85 Kerry Wood .10 .30
86 Jorge Posada .20 .50
87 Jeff Bagwell .20 .50
88 Andruw Jones .20 .50
89 Ryan Klesko .10 .30
90 Mariano Rivera .30 .75
91 Lance Berkman .10 .30
92 Kenny Lofton .10 .30
93 Jacque Jones .10 .30
94 Eric Young .10 .30
95 Edgar Renteria .10 .30
96 Chipper Jones .30 .75
97 Todd Helton .20 .50
98 Shawn Estes .10 .30
99 Mark Mulder .10 .30
100 Lee Stevens .10 .30
101 Jermaine Dye .10 .30
102 Greg Vaughn .10 .30
103 Chris Singleton .10 .30
104 Brady Anderson .10 .30
105 Terrence Long .10 .30
106 Quilvio Veras .10 .30
107 Magglio Ordonez .10 .30
108 Johnny Damon .20 .50
109 Jeffrey Hammonds .10 .30
110 Fred McGriff .20 .50
111 Carl Pavano .10 .30
112 Bobby Estalella .10 .30
113 Todd Hundley .10 .30
114 Scott Rolen .20 .50
115 Robin Ventura .10 .30
116 Pokey Reese .10 .30
117 Luis Gonzalez .10 .30
118 Jose Offerman .10 .30
119 Edgar Martinez .20 .50
120 Dean Palmer .10 .30
121 David Segui .10 .30
122 Troy O'Leary .10 .30
123 Tony Batista .10 .30
124 Todd Zeile .10 .30
125 Randy Johnson .30 .75
126 Luis Castillo .10 .30

127 Kris Benson .10 .30
128 John Olerud .10 .30
129 Eric Karros .10 .30
130 Eddie Taubensee .10 .30
131 Neifi Perez .10 .30
132 Matt Stairs .10 .30
133 Luis Alicea .10 .30
134 Jeff Kent .10 .30
135 Javier Vazquez .10 .30
136 Garret Anderson .10 .30
137 Frank Thomas .30 .75
138 Carlos Febles .10 .30
139 Albert Belle .10 .30
140 Tony Clark .10 .30
141 Pat Burrell .10 .30
142 Mike Sweeney .10 .30
143 Jay Buhner .10 .30
144 Gabe Kapler .10 .30
145 Derek Bell .10 .30
146 B.J. Surhoff .10 .30
147 Adam Kennedy .10 .30
148 Aaron Boone .10 .30
149 Todd Stottlemyre .10 .30
150 Roberto Alomar .20 .50
151 Orlando Hernandez .10 .30
152 Jason Varitek .30 .75
153 Gary Sheffield .10 .30
154 Cliff Floyd .10 .30
155 Chad Hermansen .10 .30
156 Carlos Delgado .10 .30
157 Aaron Sele .10 .30
158 Sean Casey .10 .30
159 Ruben Mateo .10 .30
160 Mike Bordick .10 .30
161 Mike Cameron .10 .30
162 Doug Glanville .10 .30
163 Damion Easley .10 .30
164 Carl Everett .10 .30
165 Bengie Molina .10 .30
166 Adrian Beltre .10 .30
167 Tom Goodwin .10 .30
168 Rickey Henderson .30 .75
169 Mo Vaughn .10 .30
170 Mike Lieberthal .10 .30
171 Ken Griffey Jr. .50 1.25
172 Juan Gonzalez .10 .30
173 Ivan Rodriguez .20 .50
174 Al Leiter .10 .30
175 Vinny Castilla .10 .30
176 Peter Bergeron .10 .30
177 Pedro Astacio .10 .30
178 Paul Konerko .10 .30
179 Mitch Meluskey .10 .30
180 Kevin Millwood .10 .30
181 Ben Grieve .10 .30
182 Barry Bonds .75 2.00
183 Rusty Greer .10 .30
184 Miguel Tejada .10 .30
185 Mark Quinn .10 .30
186 Larry Walker .10 .30
187 Jose Valentin .10 .30
188 Jose Vidro .10 .30
189 Delino DeShields .10 .30
190 Darin Erstad .10 .30
191 Bill Mueller .10 .30
192 Ray Durham .10 .30
193 Ken Caminiti .10 .30
194 Jim Thome .20 .50
195 Javy Lopez .10 .30
196 Fernando Vina .10 .30
197 Eric Chavez .10 .30
198 Eric Owens .10 .30
199 Brad Radke .10 .30
200 Travis Lee .10 .30
201 Tim Salmon .20 .50
202 Rafael Palmeiro .20 .50
203 Nomar Garciaparra .50 1.25
204 Mike Hampton .10 .30
205 Kevin Brown .10 .30
206 Juan Encarnacion .10 .30
207 Danny Graves .10 .30
208 Carlos Guillen .10 .30
209 Phil Nevin .10 .30
210 Matt Lawton .10 .30
211 Manny Ramirez .20 .50
212 James Baldwin .10 .30
213 Fernando Tatis .10 .30
214 Craig Biggio .20 .50
215 Brian Jordan .10 .30
216 Bernie Williams .20 .50
217 Ryan Dempster .10 .30
218 Roger Clemens .60 1.50
219 Jose Cruz Jr. .10 .30
220 John Valentin .10 .30
221 Dmitri Young .10 .30
222 Curt Schilling .10 .30
223 Jim Edmonds .10 .30
224 Chan Ho Park .10 .30
225 Brian Giles .10 .30
226 Jimmy Anderson .10 .30
Tike Redman
227 Adam Piatt .10 .30
Jose Ortiz
228 Kenny Kelly .10 .30
Aubrey Huff
229 Randy Choate .10 .30
Craig Dingman
230 Eric Cammack .10 .30
Grant Roberts
231 Yovanny Lara .10 .30
Andy Tracy
232 Wayne Franklin .10 .30
Scott Linebrink
233 Cameron Cairncross .10 .30
Chan Perry
234 J.C. Romero .10 .30
Matt LeCroy
235 Geraldo Guzman .10 .30
Jason Conti
236 Morgan Burkhart .10 .30
Paxton Crawford
237 Pasqual Coco .10 .30
Leo Estrella
238 John Parrish .10 .30
Fernando Lunar
239 Keith McDonald .10 .30
Justin Brunette
240 Carlos Casimiro .10 .30
Ivanon Coffie
241 Daniel Garibay .10 .30
Ruben Quevedo
242 Sang-Hoon Lee .10 .30
Tomo Ohka
243 Hector Ortiz .10 .30
Jeff D'Amico
244 Jeff Sparks .10 .30
Travis Harper
245 Jason Boyd .10 .30
David Coggin
246 Mark Buehrle .20 .50
Lorenzo Barcelo
247 Adam Melhuse .10 .30
Ben Petrick
248 Kane Davis .10 .30
Paul Rigdon
249 Mike Darr .10 .30
Kory DeHaan
250 Vicente Padilla 1.25 3.00
Mark Brownson
251 Barry Zito PROS 2.00 5.00
252 Tim Drew PROS 1.25 3.00
253 Luis Matos PROS 1.25 3.00
254 Alex Cabrera PROS 1.25 3.00
255 Jon Garland PROS 1.25 3.00
256 Milton Bradley PROS 1.25 3.00
257 Juan Pierre PROS 1.25 3.00
258 Ismael Villegas PROS 1.25 3.00
259 Eric Munson PROS 1.25 3.00
260 T.De la Rosa PROS 1.25 3.00
261 Chris Richard PROS 1.25 3.00
262 Jason Tyner PROS 1.25 3.00
263 B.J. Waszgis PROS 1.25 3.00
264 Jason Marquis PROS 1.25 3.00
265 Dusty Allen PROS 1.25 3.00
266 C.Patterson PROS 1.25 3.00
267 Eric Byrnes PROS 1.25 3.00
268 Xavier Nady PROS 1.25 3.00
269 G.Lombard PROS 1.25 3.00
270 Timo Perez PROS 1.25 3.00
271 G.Matthews Jr. PROS 1.25 3.00
272 Chad Durbin PROS 1.25 3.00
273 Tony Armas Jr. PROS 1.25 3.00
274 F.Cordero PROS 1.25 3.00
275 A.Soriano PROS 2.00 5.00
276 Junior Spivey RC 3.00 8.00
Juan Uribe RC
277 Albert Pujols RC 40.00 80.00
Bud Smith RC
278 Ichiro Suzuki RC 12.50 30.00
Tsuyoshi Shinjo RC
279 Drew Henson RC 3.00 8.00
Jackson Melian RC
280 Matt White RC 2.00 5.00
Adrian Hernandez RC

2001 Ultra Gold Medallion

Inserted into packs at a rate of one per pack (251-275 were inserted at 1:24), this 275-card set is a complete parallel of the Ultra base set. Please note that these cards were produced with gold coating and gold foil stamping.

*STARS 1-225: 1.25X TO 3X BASIC CARDS
*PROSPECTS 226-250: 1.25X TO 3X BASIC
*PROSPECTS 251-275: .75X TO 2X BASIC

2001 Ultra Platinum Medallion

Randomly inserted into packs, this 275-card set is a complete parallel of the Ultra base set. Cards 1-250 were individually serial numbered to 50, and cards 251-275 were individually serial numbered to 25. Please note that these cards were produced with a silver coating and silver foil stamping.

*PLATINUM 1-225: 15X TO 40X BASIC
*PLATINUM 251-275: 3X TO 8X BASIC

2001 Ultra Decade of Dominance

Randomly inserted into packs at one in eight, this 15-card insert set features players that dominated Major League Baseball in the 1990's. Card backs carry a "DD" prefix.

COMPLETE SET (15) 12.50 30.00
PLATINUM RANDOM INSERTS IN PACKS
PLATINUM PRINT RUN 10 SERIAL #'d SETS
PLATINUM NO PRICING DUE TO SCARCITY
DD1 Barry Bonds 1.50 4.00
DD2 Mark McGwire 1.50 4.00
DD3 Sammy Sosa .60 1.50
DD4 Ken Griffey Jr. 1.00 2.50
DD5 Cal Ripken 2.00 5.00
DD6 Tony Gwynn .75 2.00
DD7 Albert Belle .30 .75
DD8 Frank Thomas .60 1.50
DD9 Randy Johnson .60 1.50
DD10 Juan Gonzalez .30 .75
DD11 Greg Maddux 1.00 2.50
DD12 Craig Biggio .40 1.00
DD13 Edgar Martinez .40 1.00
DD14 Roger Clemens 1.25 3.00
DD15 Andres Galarraga .30 .75

2001 Ultra Fall Classics

Inserted into packs at one in 20, this 37-card insert set features some of the most legendary players of all time. Card backs carry a "FC" prefix.

FC1 Jackie Robinson 2.00 5.00
FC2 Enos Slaughter 1.25 3.00
FC3 Mariano Rivera 2.00 5.00
FC4 Hank Bauer 1.25 3.00
FC5 Cal Ripken 6.00 15.00
FC6 Babe Ruth 6.00 15.00
FC7 Thurman Munson 2.00 5.00
FC8 Tom Glavine 1.25 3.00
FC9 Fred Lynn 1.25 3.00
FC10 Johnny Bench 2.00 5.00
FC11 Tony Lazzeri 1.25 3.00
FC12 Al Kaline 2.00 5.00
FC13 Reggie Jackson 1.25 3.00
FC14 Derek Jeter 5.00 12.00
FC15 Willie Stargell 1.25 3.00
FC16 Roy Campanella 2.00 5.00
FC17 Phil Rizzuto 2.00 5.00
FC18 Roberto Clemente 6.00 15.00
FC19 Carlton Fisk 1.25 3.00
FC20 Duke Snider 1.25 3.00
FC21 Ted Williams 5.00 12.00
FC22 Bill Skowron 1.25 3.00
FC23 Bucky Dent 1.25 3.00
FC24 Mike Schmidt 4.00 10.00
FC25 Lou Brock 1.25 3.00
FC26 Whitey Ford 1.25 3.00
FC27 Brooks Robinson 1.25 3.00
FC28 Roberto Alomar 1.25 3.00
FC29 Yogi Berra 2.00 5.00
FC30 Joe Carter 1.25 3.00
FC31 Bill Mazeroski 1.25 3.00
FC32 Bob Gibson 1.25 3.00
FC33 Hank Greenberg 2.50 6.00
FC34 Andruw Jones 1.25 3.00
FC35 Bernie Williams 1.25 3.00
FC36 Don Larsen 1.25 3.00
FC37 Billy Martin 1.25 3.00

2001 Ultra Fall Classics Memorabilia

Randomly inserted into packs, this 26-card insert features game-used memorabilia from players like Derek Jeter, Al Kaline, and Cal Ripken. Please note that the cards a checklisted below in alphabetical order for convience.

1 Hank Bauer Bat 6.00 15.00
2 Johnny Bench Jsy 10.00 25.00
3 Lou Brock Jsy 10.00 25.00
4 Roy Campanella Bat 20.00 50.00
5 Roberto Clemente Bat 50.00 100.00
6 Bucky Dent Bat 6.00 15.00
7 Carlton Fisk Jsy 10.00 25.00
8 Tom Glavine Jsy 10.00 25.00
9 Reggie Jackson Jsy 10.00 25.00
10 Derek Jeter Jsy 15.00 40.00
11 Al Kaline Jsy 10.00 25.00
12 Tony Lazzeri Bat 6.00 15.00
13 Fred Lynn Bat 6.00 15.00
14 Thurman Munson Bat 15.00 40.00
15 Cal Ripken Jsy 15.00 40.00
16 Mariano Rivera Jsy 10.00 25.00
17 Phil Rizzuto Bat 10.00 25.00
18 Brooks Robinson Bat 10.00 25.00
19 Jackie Robinson Pants 30.00 60.00
20 Babe Ruth Bat 125.00 200.00
21 Mike Schmidt Jsy 10.00 25.00
22 Bill Skowron Bat 6.00 15.00
23 Enos Slaughter Bat 6.00 15.00
24 Duke Snider Bat 10.00 25.00
25 Willie Stargell Bat 10.00 25.00
26 Ted Williams Bat 50.00 100.00

2001 Ultra Fall Classics Memorabilia Autograph

Randomly inserted into packs, this nine-card insert features game-used memorabilia and autographs of legendary players. Due to market scarcity, not all cards are priced. All are listed for checklisting purposes. Please note that the Al Kaline jersey/autograph card contained an error, Kaline actually wore jersey number 6. However, Fleer produced seven of these cards. Reggie Jackson's card was distributed as an exchange card in packs. The exchange deadline was January 2nd, 2002.

1 Lou Brock Jsy AU/20
2 Carlton Fisk Jsy AU/27
3 Reggie Jackson 60.00 120.00
Bat-Jsy/44
4 Derek Jeter Jsy AU/2
5 Al Kaline Jsy AU/7 UER
Kaline wore Jersey number 6
6 Cal Ripken Jsy AU/8
7 Mike Schmidt Jsy AU/20
8 Enos Slaughter Jsy AU/9
9 Willie Stargell Jsy AU/8

2001 Ultra Greatest Hits

Randomly inserted into packs at one in 12, this 10-card insert set features players that dominante the Major Leagues. Card backs carry a "GH" prefix.

COMPLETE SET (10) 10.00 25.00
PLATINUM RANDOM INSERTS IN PACKS
PLATINUM PRINT RUN 10 SERIAL #'d SETS
PLATINUM NO PRICING DUE TO SCARCITY
GH1 Mark McGwire 1.50 4.00
GH2 Alex Rodriguez 1.00 2.50
GH3 Ken Griffey Jr. 1.00 2.50
GH4 Ivan Rodriguez .40 1.00
GH5 Cal Ripken 2.00 5.00
GH6 Todd Helton .40 1.00
GH7 Derek Jeter 1.50 4.00
GH8 Pedro Martinez .40 1.00
GH9 Tony Gwynn .75 2.00
GH10 Jim Edmonds .40 1.00

2001 Ultra Power Plus

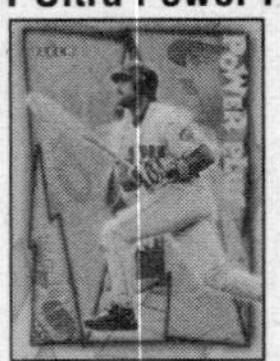

Randomly inserted into packs at one in 24, this 10-card insert set features players that are among the league leaders in homeruns every year. Card backs carry a "PP" prefix.

COMPLETE SET (10) 15.00 40.00
PLATINUM RANDOM INSERTS IN PACKS
PLATINUM PRINT RUN 10 SERIAL #'d SETS
PLATINUM NO PRICING DUE TO SCARCITY
PP1 Vladimir Guerrero 1.00 2.50
PP2 Mark McGwire 2.50 6.00
PP3 Mike Piazza 1.50 4.00
PP4 Derek Jeter 2.50 6.00
PP5 Chipper Jones 1.00 2.50
PP6 Carlos Delgado .60 1.50
PP7 Sammy Sosa 1.00 2.50
PP8 Ken Griffey Jr. 1.50 4.00
PP9 Nomar Garciaparra 1.50 4.00
PP10 Alex Rodriguez 1.50 4.00

2001 Ultra Tomorrow's Legends

Randomly inserted into packs at one in 4, this 15-card insert set features players that will most likely make the Hall of Fame when their careers are through. Card backs carry a "TL" prefix.

COMPLETE SET (15) 6.00 15.00
PLATINUM RANDOM INSERTS IN PACKS
PLATINUM PRINT RUN 10 SERIAL #'d SETS
PLATINUM NO PRICING DUE TO SCARCITY
TL1 Rick Ankiel .20 .50
TL2 J.D. Drew .20 .50
TL3 Carlos Delgado .20 .50
TL4 Todd Helton .30 .75
TL5 Andruw Jones .30 .75
TL6 Troy Glaus .20 .50
TL7 Jermaine Dye .20 .50
TL8 Vladimir Guerrero .50 1.25
TL9 Brian Giles .20 .50
TL10 Scott Rolen .30 .75
TL11 Darin Erstad .20 .50
TL12 Derek Jeter 1.25 3.00
TL13 Alex Rodriguez .75 2.00
TL14 Pat Burrell .20 .50
TL15 Nomar Garciaparra .75 2.00

2002 Ultra

This 285 card set was issued in November, 2001. The following subsets were issued for this set: All-Stars (cards numbered 201-220), Teammates (a veteran and prospect from each team, numbered 221-250), and Prospects (cards numbered 251-285). All three of these subsets were issued at a rate of one in four packs.

COMPLETE SET (285) 80.00 200.00
COMP.SET w/o SP's (200) 10.00 25.00
COMMON CARD (1-200) .10 .30

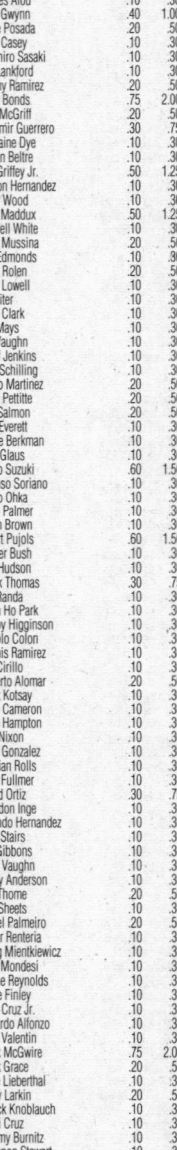

COMMON (201-220) .40 1.00
COMMON (221-250) .40 1.00
COMMON (251-285) 1.25 3.00
1 Jeff Bagwell .20 .50
2 Derek Jeter .75 2.00
3 Alex Rodriguez .50 1.25
4 Eric Chavez .10 .30
5 Tsuyoshi Shinjo .10 .30
6 Chris Stynes .10 .30
7 Ivan Rodriguez .20 .50
8 Cal Ripken 1.00 2.50
9 Freddy Garcia .10 .30
10 Chipper Jones .30 .75
11 Hideo Nomo .30 .75
12 Rafael Furcal .10 .30
13 Preston Wilson .10 .30
14 Jimmy Rollins .10 .30
15 Cristian Guzman .10 .30
16 Garret Anderson .10 .30
17 Todd Helton .20 .50
18 Moises Alou .10 .30
19 Tony Gwynn .40 1.00
20 Jorge Posada .20 .50
21 Sean Casey .10 .30
22 Kazuhiro Sasaki .10 .30
23 Ray Lankford .10 .30
24 Manny Ramirez .20 .50
25 Barry Bonds .75 2.00
26 Fred McGriff .20 .50
27 Vladimir Guerrero .30 .75
28 Jermaine Dye .10 .30
29 Adrian Beltre .10 .30
30 Ken Griffey Jr. .50 1.25
31 Ramon Hernandez .10 .30
32 Kerry Wood .10 .30
33 Greg Maddux .50 1.25
34 Rondell White .10 .30
35 Mike Mussina .20 .50
36 Jim Edmonds .10 .30
37 Scott Rolen .20 .50
38 Mike Lowell .10 .30
39 Al Leiter .10 .30
40 Tony Clark .10 .30
41 Joe Mays .10 .30
42 Mo Vaughn .10 .30
43 Geoff Jenkins .10 .30
44 Curt Schilling .10 .30
45 Pedro Martinez .20 .50
46 Andy Pettitte .20 .50
47 Tim Salmon .20 .50
48 Carl Everett .10 .30
49 Lance Berkman .10 .30
50 Troy Glaus .10 .30
51 Ichiro Suzuki .60 1.50
52 Alfonso Soriano .10 .30
53 Tomo Ohka .10 .30
54 Dean Palmer .10 .30
55 Kevin Brown .10 .30
56 Albert Pujols .60 1.50
57 Homer Bush .10 .30
58 Tim Hudson .10 .30
59 Frank Thomas .30 .75
60 Joe Randa .10 .30
61 Chan Ho Park .10 .30
62 Bobby Higginson .10 .30
63 Bartolo Colon .10 .30
64 Aramis Ramirez .10 .30
65 Jeff Cirillo .10 .30
66 Roberto Alomar .20 .50
67 Mark Kotsay .10 .30
68 Mike Cameron .10 .30
69 Mike Hampton .10 .30
70 Trot Nixon .10 .30
71 Juan Gonzalez .10 .30
72 Damian Rolls .10 .30
73 Brad Fullmer .10 .30
74 David Ortiz .30 .75
75 Brandon Inge .10 .30
76 Orlando Hernandez .10 .30
77 Matt Stairs .10 .30
78 Jay Gibbons .10 .30
79 Greg Vaughn .10 .30
80 Brady Anderson .10 .30
81 Jim Thome .20 .50
82 Ben Sheets .10 .30
83 Rafael Palmeiro .20 .50
84 Edgar Renteria .10 .30
85 Doug Mientkiewicz .10 .30
86 Raul Mondesi .10 .30
87 Shane Reynolds .10 .30
88 Steve Finley .10 .30
89 Jose Cruz Jr. .10 .30
90 Edgardo Alfonzo .10 .30
91 Jose Valentin .10 .30
92 Mark McGwire .75 2.00
93 Mark Grace .20 .50
94 Mike Lieberthal .10 .30
95 Barry Larkin .20 .50
96 Chuck Knoblauch .10 .30
97 Deivi Cruz .10 .30
98 Jeromy Burnitz .10 .30
99 Shannon Stewart .10 .30
100 David Wells .10 .30
101 Brook Fordyce .10 .30
102 Rusty Greer .10 .30
103 Andruw Jones .20 .50
104 Jason Kendall .10 .30
105 Nomar Garciaparra .50 1.25
106 Shawn Green .10 .30
107 Craig Biggio .20 .50
108 Masato Yoshii .10 .30
109 Ben Petrick .10 .30
110 Gary Sheffield .10 .30
111 Travis Lee .10 .30
112 Matt Williams .10 .30
113 Billy Wagner .10 .30
114 Robin Ventura .10 .30
115 Jerry Hairston .10 .30
116 Paul LoDuca .10 .30
117 Darin Erstad .10 .30
118 Ruben Sierra .10 .30
119 Ricky Gutierrez .10 .30
120 Bret Boone .10 .30
121 John Rocker .10 .30
122 Roger Clemens .60 1.50
123 Eric Karros .10 .30
124 J.D. Drew .10 .30
125 Carlos Delgado .10 .30
126 Jeffrey Hammonds .10 .30
127 Jeff Kent .10 .30
128 David Justice .10 .30
129 Cliff Floyd .10 .30
130 Omar Vizquel .20 .50
131 Matt Morris .10 .30
132 Rich Aurilia .10 .30
133 Larry Walker .10 .30
134 Miguel Tejada .10 .30
135 Eric Young .10 .30
136 Aaron Sele .10 .30
137 Eric Milton .10 .30
138 Travis Fryman .10 .30
139 Magglio Ordonez .10 .30
140 Sammy Sosa .30 .75
141 Pokey Reese .10 .30
142 Adam Eaton .10 .30
143 Adam Kennedy .10 .30
144 Mike Piazza .50 1.25
145 Larry Barnes .10 .30
146 Darryl Kile .10 .30
147 Tom Glavine .20 .50
148 Ryan Klesko .10 .30
149 Jose Vidro .10 .30
150 Joe Kennedy .10 .30
151 Bernie Williams .20 .50
152 C.C. Sabathia .10 .30
153 Alex Ochoa .10 .30
154 A.J. Pierzynski .10 .30
155 Johnny Damon .20 .50
156 Omar Daal .10 .30
157 A.J. Burnett .10 .30
158 Eric Munson .10 .30
159 Fernando Vina .10 .30
160 Chris Singleton .10 .30
161 Juan Pierre .10 .30
162 John Olerud .10 .30
163 Randy Johnson .30 .75
164 Paul Konerko .10 .30
165 Tino Martinez .20 .50
166 Richard Hidalgo .10 .30
167 Luis Gonzalez .10 .30
168 Ben Grieve .10 .30
169 Matt Lawton .10 .30
170 Gabe Kapler .10 .30
171 Mariano Rivera .30 .75
172 Kenny Lofton .10 .30
173 Brian Jordan .10 .30
174 Brian Giles .10 .30
175 Mark Quinn .10 .30
176 Neifi Perez .10 .30
177 Ellis Burks .10 .30
178 Bobby Abreu .10 .30
179 Jeff Weaver .10 .30
180 Andres Galarraga .10 .30
181 Javy Lopez .10 .30
182 Todd Walker .10 .30
183 Fernando Tatis .10 .30
184 Charles Johnson .10 .30
185 Pat Burrell .10 .30
186 Jay Bell .10 .30
187 Aaron Boone .10 .30
188 Jason Giambi .10 .30
189 Jay Payton .10 .30
190 Carlos Lee .10 .30
191 Phil Nevin .10 .30
192 Mike Sweeney .10 .30
193 J.T. Snow .10 .30
194 Dmitri Young .10 .30
195 Richie Sexson .10 .30
196 Derrek Lee .20 .50
197 Corey Koskie .10 .30
198 Edgar Martinez .20 .50
199 Wade Miller .10 .30
200 Tony Batista .10 .30
201 John Olerud AS .40 1.00
202 Bret Boone AS .40 1.00
203 Cal Ripken AS 2.00 5.00
204 Alex Rodriguez AS 1.00 2.50
205 Ichiro Suzuki AS 1.25 3.00
206 Manny Ramirez AS .20 .50
207 Juan Gonzalez AS .40 1.00
208 Ivan Rodriguez AS .60 1.50
209 Roger Clemens AS 1.25 3.00
210 Edgar Martinez AS .60 1.50
211 Todd Helton AS .60 1.50
212 Jeff Kent AS .40 1.00
213 Chipper Jones AS .60 1.50
214 Rich Aurilia AS .40 1.00
215 Barry Bonds AS 1.50 4.00
216 Sammy Sosa AS .60 1.50
217 Luis Gonzalez AS .40 1.00
218 Mike Piazza AS 1.00 2.50
219 Randy Johnson AS .60 1.50
220 Larry Walker AS .40 1.00
221 Todd Helton .40 1.00
Juan Uribe
All team players subset cards are noted to be 2001
222 Pat Burrell .40 1.00
Eric Valent
223 Edgar Martinez 1.25 3.00
Ichiro Suzuki
224 Ben Grieve .40 1.00
Jason Tyner
225 Mark Quinn .40 1.00
Dee Brown
226 Cal Ripken 2.00 5.00
Brian Roberts
227 Cliff Floyd .40 1.00
Abraham Nunez
228 Jeff Bagwell .40 1.00
Adam Everett
229 Mark McGwire 1.50 4.00
Albert Pujols
230 Doug Mientkiewicz .40 1.00
Luis Rivas
231 Juan Gonzalez .40 1.00
Danny Peoples
232 Kevin Brown .40 1.00
Luke Prokopec

233 Richie Sexson Ben Sheets	.40	1.00
234 Jason Giambi Jason Hart	.40	1.00
235 Barry Bonds Carlos Valderrama	1.50	4.00
236 Tony Gwynn Cesar Crespo	.75	2.00
237 Ken Griffey Jr. Adam Dunn	1.00	2.50
238 Frank Thomas Joe Crede	.60	1.50
239 Derek Jeter Drew Henson	1.50	4.00
240 Chipper Jones Wilson Betemit	.60	1.50
241 Luis Gonzalez Junior Spivey	.40	1.00
242 Bobby Higginson Andres Torres	.40	1.00
243 Carlos Delgado Vernon Wells	.40	1.00
244 Sammy Sosa Corey Patterson	.60	1.50
245 Nomar Garciaparra Shea Hillenbrand	1.00	2.50
246 Alex Rodriguez Jason Romano	1.00	2.50
247 Troy Glaus David Eckstein	.40	1.00
248 Mike Piazza Alex Escobar	1.00	2.50
249 Brian Giles Jack Wilson	.40	1.00
250 Vladimir Guerrero Scott Hodges	.60	1.50
251 Bud Smith PROS	1.25	3.00
252 Juan Diaz PROS	1.25	3.00
253 Wilkin Ruan PROS	1.25	3.00
254 C. Spurling PROS RC	1.25	3.00
255 Toby Hall PROS	1.25	3.00
256 Jason Jennings PROS	1.25	3.00
257 George Perez PROS	1.25	3.00
258 D. Jimenez PROS	1.25	3.00
259 Jose Acevedo PROS	1.25	3.00
260 Josue Perez PROS	1.25	3.00
261 Brian Rogers PROS	1.25	3.00
262 C. Maldonado PROS RC	1.25	3.00
263 Travis Phelps PROS	1.25	3.00
264 R. Mackowiak PROS	1.25	3.00
265 Ryan Drese PROS	1.25	3.00
266 Carlos Garcia PROS	1.25	3.00
267 Alexis Gomez PROS	1.25	3.00
268 Jeremy Affeldt PROS	1.25	3.00
269 S. Podsednik PROS	1.50	4.00
270 Adam Johnson PROS	1.25	3.00
271 Pedro Santana PROS	1.25	3.00
272 Les Walrond PROS	1.25	3.00
273 Jackson Melian PROS	1.25	3.00
274 C. Hernandez PROS	1.25	3.00
275 M. Nussbeck PROS RC	1.25	3.00
276 Cory Aldridge PROS	1.25	3.00
277 Troy Mattes PROS	1.25	3.00
278 B. Abernathy PROS	1.25	3.00
279 J.J. Davis PROS	1.25	3.00
280 B. Duckworth PROS	1.25	3.00
281 Kyle Lohse PROS	1.25	3.00
282 Justin Kaye PROS	1.25	3.00
283 Cody Ransom PROS	1.25	3.00
284 Dave Williams PROS	1.25	3.00
285 Luis Lopez PROS	1.25	3.00

2002 Ultra Gold Medallion

Issued at packs at different rates, this is a parallel to the Ultra set. Cards numbered 1-200 were issued at a rate of one per pack, cards numbered 201-250 were issued at a rate of one in 24 packs and cards numbered 251-285 were randomly inserted in packs. Cards numbered 251-285 were issued to 100 serial numbered sets.

COMP.SET w/o SP's (200)	60.00	150.00

*GOLD 1-200: 1.25X TO 3X BASIC
*GOLD 201-220: .75X TO 2X BASIC
*GOLD 221-250: 1X TO 2.5X BASIC
*GOLD 251-285: 3X TO 8X BASIC

2002 Ultra Fall Classic

Issued at a rate of one in 20 hobby packs, these 36 cards feature players who participated in the World Series.

COMPLETE SET (36)	100.00	200.00
1 Ty Cobb	4.00	10.00
2 Lou Gehrig	4.00	10.00
3 Babe Ruth	8.00	20.00
4 Stan Musial	4.00	10.00
5 Ted Williams	5.00	12.00
6 Dizzy Dean	3.00	8.00
7 Mickey Cochrane	2.00	5.00
8 Jimmie Foxx	3.00	8.00
9 Mel Ott	3.00	8.00
10 Rogers Hornsby	3.00	8.00
12 Clete Boyer	2.00	5.00
13 George Brett	6.00	15.00
14 Bob Gibson	3.00	8.00
15 Carlton Fisk	3.00	8.00
16 Johnny Bench	3.00	8.00
18 Willie McCovey	2.00	5.00
19 Paul Molitor	2.00	5.00
20 Jim Palmer	2.00	5.00
21 Frank Robinson	3.00	8.00
22 Derek Jeter	5.00	12.00
23 Earl Weaver	2.00	5.00
24 Lefty Grove	2.00	5.00
25 Tony Perez	2.00	5.00
26 Reggie Jackson	3.00	8.00
27 Sparky Anderson	2.00	5.00
28 Casey Stengel	2.00	5.00
29 Roy Campanella	3.00	8.00
31 Don Drysdale	3.00	8.00
32 Joe Morgan	2.00	5.00
33 Eddie Murray	3.00	8.00
34 Nolan Ryan	6.00	15.00
35 Tom Seaver	3.00	8.00
36 Bill Mazeroski	2.00	5.00
37 Jackie Robinson	3.00	8.00
38 Kirk Gibson	2.00	5.00
39 Robin Yount	3.00	8.00

2002 Ultra Fall Classic Autographs

This partial parallel to the Fall Classic set features authentic autographs from the featured players. All of the players except for Sparky Anderson and Earl Weaver were exchange cards. A few players were produced in lower quantities and those have been notated with SP's in our checklist.

1 Sparky Anderson	6.00	15.00
2 Johnny Bench SP	20.00	50.00
3 George Brett SP	50.00	100.00
4 Carlton Fisk	10.00	25.00
5 Bob Gibson	10.00	25.00
6 Kirk Gibson	6.00	15.00
7 Reggie Jackson SP	20.00	50.00
8 Derek Jeter SP		
9 Bill Mazeroski	10.00	25.00
10 Willie McCovey SP	15.00	40.00
11 Joe Morgan	6.00	15.00
12 Eddie Murray SP	20.00	50.00
13 Stan Musial SP		
14 Jim Palmer	6.00	15.00
15 Tony Perez	6.00	15.00
16 Frank Robinson	10.00	25.00
17 Nolan Ryan SP	125.00	250.00
18 Tom Seaver SP	15.00	40.00
19 Earl Weaver	6.00	15.00
20 Robin Yount SP	30.00	60.00

2002 Ultra Fall Classic Memorabilia

Inserted at a rate of one in 113, these 37 cards feature memorabilia from players who participated in World Series. A few cards were printed in lesser quantities and those have been notated with print runs as provided by Fleer.

1 Sparky Anderson Pants	4.00	10.00
2 Johnny Bench Pants	6.00	15.00
3 Johnny Bench Jsy	6.00	15.00
4 George Brett White Jsy	10.00	25.00
5 George Brett Bat	10.00	25.00
6 George Brett Blue Jsy/65 *		
7 Roy Campanella Bat/21 *		
8 Carlton Fisk Jsy	6.00	15.00
9 Carlton Fisk Bat/42 *	20.00	50.00
10 Jimmie Foxx Bat	20.00	50.00
11 Bob Gibson Jsy	6.00	15.00
12 Kirk Gibson Bat	4.00	10.00
13 Reggie Jackson Bat	6.00	15.00
14 Reggie Jackson Bat		
15 Reggie Jackson Jsy/73 *		
16 Derek Jeter Pants	15.00	40.00
17 Willie McCovey Jsy	4.00	10.00
18 Paul Molitor Bat	4.00	10.00
19 Paul Molitor Jsy		
20 Joe Morgan Bat	4.00	10.00
21 Joe Morgan Jsy		
22 Eddie Murray Bat	6.00	15.00
23 Eddie Murray Jsy/91 *	20.00	50.00
24 Jim Palmer White Jsy	4.00	10.00
25 J.Palmer Gray Jsy/85 *	15.00	40.00
26 Tony Perez Bat	4.00	10.00
27 Frank Robinson Bat/40 *	15.00	40.00
28 Jackie Robinson Pants	30.00	60.00
29 Babe Ruth Bat/44 *	100.00	200.00
30 Nolan Ryan Pants	20.00	50.00
31 Tom Seaver Jsy	6.00	15.00
32 Earl Weaver Jsy	4.00	10.00
33 Ted Williams Jsy	50.00	100.00
34 Ted Williams Bat/30 *		
35 Robin Yount Gray Jsy		
36 Robin Yount White Jsy/30 *		
37 Robin Yount Bat	6.00	15.00

2002 Ultra Glove Works

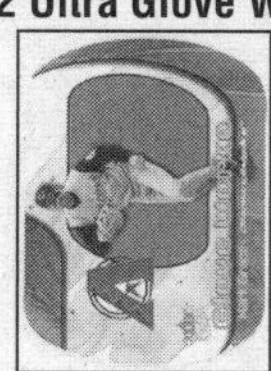

Inserted at a rate of one in 20, these 15 cards feature some of the leading fielders in the game.

COMPLETE SET (15)	20.00	50.00
1 Andruw Jones	1.25	3.00
2 Derek Jeter	3.00	8.00
3 Cal Ripken	4.00	10.00
4 Larry Walker	1.25	3.00
5 Chipper Jones	1.50	4.00
6 Barry Bonds	3.00	8.00
7 Scott Rolen	1.25	3.00
8 Jim Edmonds	1.25	3.00
9 Robin Ventura	1.25	3.00
10 Darin Erstad	1.25	3.00
11 Barry Larkin	1.25	3.00
12 Raul Mondesi	1.25	3.00
13 Mark Grace	1.25	3.00
14 Bernie Williams	1.25	3.00
15 Ivan Rodriguez	1.25	3.00

2002 Ultra Glove Works Memorabilia

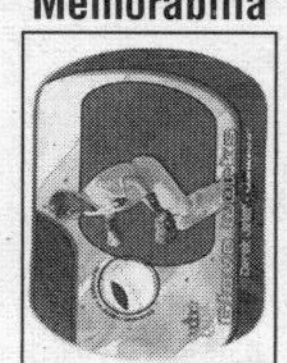

This 11-card insert set features game-used fielding mitts and batting gloves incorporated into the actual card. Each card is serial numbered to 450 copies - except for Barry Larkin (375 cards), Andruw Jones (100 cards) and Chipper Jones (100 cards). The first 75 serial numbered copies of the Cal Ripken, Barry Bonds and Ivan Rodriguez cards feature batting glove patches and cards serial numbered 76-450 for these players feature fielding mitt patches. The short-printed Andruw and Chipper Jones cards feature batting glove patches.

PLATINUM RANDOM INSERTS IN PACKS
PLATINUM PRINT RUN 25 SERIAL #'d SETS
PLATINUM: NO PRICING DUE TO SCARCITY

1 Derek Jeter/450	15.00	40.00
2 Andruw Jones/100		
3 Cal Ripken/450	25.00	60.00
5 Chipper Jones/100		
6 Barry Bonds/450	15.00	40.00
8 Robin Ventura/450	6.00	15.00
9 Barry Larkin/375	6.00	15.00
10 Raul Mondesi/450	6.00	15.00
11 Ivan Rodriguez/450	6.00	15.00

2002 Ultra Hitting Machines

Inserted at a rate of one in 20 retail packs, these 25 cards feature some of baseball's leading hitters.

COMPLETE SET (25)	60.00	120.00
1 Frank Thomas	2.00	5.00
2 Derek Jeter	5.00	12.00
3 Vladimir Guerrero	2.00	5.00
4 Jim Edmonds	1.00	2.50
5 Mike Piazza	3.00	8.00
6 Ivan Rodriguez	1.25	3.00
7 Chipper Jones	2.00	5.00
8 Tony Gwynn	2.50	6.00
9 Manny Ramirez	1.25	3.00
10 Andruw Jones	1.25	3.00
11 Carlos Delgado	1.00	2.50
12 Bernie Williams	1.25	3.00
13 Larry Walker	1.00	2.50
14 Juan Gonzalez	1.00	2.50
15 Ichiro Suzuki	4.00	10.00
16 Albert Pujols	4.00	10.00
17 Barry Bonds	5.00	12.00
18 Cal Ripken	6.00	15.00
19 Edgar Martinez	1.25	3.00
20 Luis Gonzalez	1.00	2.50
21 Moises Alou	1.00	2.50
22 Roberto Alomar	1.25	3.00
23 Todd Helton	1.25	3.00
24 Rafael Palmeiro	1.25	3.00
25 Bobby Abreu	1.00	2.50

2002 Ultra Hitting Machines Game Bat

Issued at a rate of one in 81 packs, these cards feature not only some of the leading hitters but also a slice of a game-used bat.

PLATINUM RANDOM INSERTS IN PACKS
PLATINUM PRINT RUN 25 SERIAL #'d SETS
PLATINUM: NO PRICING DUE TO SCARCITY

1 Bobby Abreu	4.00	10.00
2 Roberto Alomar	6.00	15.00
3 Moises Alou	4.00	10.00
4 Barry Bonds	12.50	30.00
5 Carlos Delgado	4.00	10.00
6 Jim Edmonds	4.00	10.00
7 Juan Gonzalez	4.00	10.00
8 Luis Gonzalez	4.00	10.00
9 Tony Gwynn	6.00	15.00
10 Todd Helton	6.00	15.00
11 Derek Jeter	12.50	30.00
12 Andruw Jones	6.00	15.00
13 Chipper Jones	6.00	15.00
14 Edgar Martinez	6.00	15.00
15 Rafael Palmeiro	6.00	15.00
16 Mike Piazza	6.00	15.00
17 Albert Pujols	15.00	40.00
18 Manny Ramirez	6.00	15.00
19 Cal Ripken	20.00	50.00
20 Ivan Rodriguez	6.00	15.00
21 Frank Thomas	6.00	15.00
22 Larry Walker	4.00	10.00
23 Bernie Williams	6.00	15.00

2002 Ultra On the Road Game Jersey

Inserted at a rate of one in 93, these 14 cards feature swatches of away uniforms used by the featured players.

PLATINUM RANDOM INSERTS IN PACKS
PLATINUM PRINT RUN 25 SERIAL #'d SETS
PLATINUM: NO PRICING DUE TO SCARCITY

1 Derek Jeter	15.00	40.00
2 Ivan Rodriguez	8.00	20.00
3 Carlos Delgado	6.00	15.00
4 Larry Walker	6.00	15.00
5 Roberto Alomar	8.00	20.00
6 Tony Gwynn	8.00	20.00
7 Greg Maddux	8.00	20.00
8 Barry Bonds	15.00	40.00
9 Todd Helton	8.00	20.00
10 Kazuhiro Sasaki	6.00	15.00
11 Jeff Bagwell	8.00	20.00
12 Omar Vizquel	8.00	20.00
13 Chan Ho Park	6.00	15.00
14 Tom Glavine	8.00	20.00

2002 Ultra Rising Stars

Issued at a rate of one in 12 packs, these 15 cards feature some of the leading young players in baseball.

COMPLETE SET (15)	12.50	30.00
1 Ichiro Suzuki	2.00	5.00
2 Derek Jeter	2.50	6.00
3 Albert Pujols	2.00	5.00
4 Jimmy Rollins	.75	2.00
5 Adam Dunn	.75	2.00
6 Sean Casey	.75	2.00
7 Kerry Wood	.75	2.00
8 Tsuyoshi Shinjo	.75	2.00
9 Shea Hillenbrand	.75	2.00
10 Pat Burrell	.75	2.00
11 Ben Sheets	.75	2.00
12 Alfonso Soriano	.75	2.00
13 J.D. Drew	.75	2.00
14 Kazuhiro Sasaki	.75	2.00
15 Corey Patterson	.75	2.00

2002 Ultra Rising Stars Game Hat

Randomly inserted in packs, these six cards feature not only some of the best young players in baseball but also a sliver of a cap they wore while playing.

PLATINUM RANDOM IN HOBBY PACKS
PLATINUM PRINT RUN 25 SERIAL #'d SETS
PLATINUM NO PRICING DUE TO SCARCITY

1 Derek Jeter	40.00	80.00
2 Albert Pujols	20.00	50.00
3 Tsuyoshi Shinjo	15.00	40.00
4 Alfonso Soriano	15.00	40.00
5 J.D. Drew	15.00	40.00
6 Kazuhiro Sasaki	15.00	40.00

2003 Ultra

This 265-card set was issued in two separate series. The primary Ultra product - containing the first 250 cards from the basic set - was released in November, 2002. It was issued in 10 card packs which were packed 24 packs to a box and 16 boxes to a case. Cards numbered 1 through 200 featured veterans while cards numbered 201 through 220 featured All-Stars, cards numbered 221 through 240 featured rookies of 2002 and cards numbered 241 through 250 featured rookies of 2003. Cards numbered 201 through 220 were inserted at a stated rate of one in four while cards numbered 221 through 250 were inserted at a stated rate of one in two. Cards 251-265 were randomly seeded within Fleer Rookies and Greats packs of which was distributed in December, 2003. Each of these 15 update cards features a top prospect and is serial numbered to 1,500 copies.

COMP.LO SET (250)	40.00	100.00
COMP.LO SET w/o SP's (200)	10.00	25.00
COMMON CARD (201-220)	.60	1.50
COMMON CARD (221-250)	.75	2.00
COMMON CARD (251-265)	1.25	3.00
1 Barry Bonds	.75	2.00
2 Derek Jeter	.75	2.00
3 Ichiro Suzuki	.60	1.50
4 Mike Lowell	.10	.30
5 Hideo Nomo	.30	.75
6 Javier Vazquez	.10	.30
7 Jeremy Giambi	.10	.30
8 Jamie Moyer	.10	.30
9 Rafael Palmeiro	.20	.50
10 Magglio Ordonez	.10	.30
11 Trot Nixon	.10	.30
12 Luis Castillo	.10	.30
13 Paul Byrd	.10	.30
14 Adam Kennedy	.10	.30
15 Trevor Hoffman	.10	.30
16 Matt Morris	.10	.30
17 Nomar Garciaparra	.50	1.25
18 Matt Lawton	.10	.30
19 Carlos Beltran	.10	.30
20 Jason Giambi	.10	.30
21 Brian Giles	.10	.30
22 Jim Edmonds	.10	.30
23 Garret Anderson	.10	.30
24 Tony Batista	.10	.30
25 Aaron Boone	.10	.30
26 Mike Hampton	.10	.30
27 Billy Wagner	.10	.30
28 Kazuhisa Ishii	.10	.30
29 Al Leiter	.10	.30
30 Pat Burrell	.10	.30
31 Jeff Kent	.10	.30
32 Randy Johnson	.30	.75
33 Ray Durham	.10	.30
34 Josh Beckett	.10	.30
35 Cristian Guzman	.10	.30
36 Roger Clemens	.60	1.50
37 Freddy Garcia	.10	.30
38 Roy Halladay	.10	.30
39 David Eckstein	.10	.30
40 Jerry Hairston	.10	.30
41 Barry Larkin	.20	.50
42 Larry Walker	.10	.30
43 Craig Biggio	.20	.50
44 Edgardo Alfonzo	.10	.30
45 Marlon Byrd	.10	.30
46 J.T. Snow	.10	.30
47 Juan Gonzalez	.10	.30
48 Ramon Ortiz	.10	.30
49 Jay Gibbons	.10	.30
50 Adam Dunn	.10	.30
51 Juan Pierre	.10	.30
52 Jeff Bagwell	.20	.50
53 Kevin Brown	.10	.30
54 Pedro Astacio	.10	.30
55 Mike Lieberthal	.10	.30
56 Johnny Damon	.20	.50
57 Tim Salmon	.20	.50
58 Mike Bordick	.10	.30
59 Ken Griffey Jr.	.50	1.25
60 Jason Jennings	.10	.30
61 Lance Berkman	.10	.30
62 Jeromy Burnitz	.10	.30
63 Jimmy Rollins	.10	.30
64 Tsuyoshi Shinjo	.10	.30
65 Alex Rodriguez	.50	1.25
66 Greg Maddux	.50	1.25
67 Mark Prior	.20	.50
68 Mike Maroth	.10	.30
69 Geoff Jenkins	.10	.30
70 Tony Armas Jr.	.10	.30
71 Jermaine Dye	.10	.30
72 Albert Pujols	.60	1.50
73 Shannon Stewart	.10	.30
74 Troy Glaus	.10	.30
75 Brook Fordyce	.10	.30
76 Juan Encarnacion	.10	.30
77 Todd Hollandsworth	.10	.30
78 Roy Oswalt	.10	.30
79 Paul Lo Duca	.10	.30
80 Mike Piazza	.50	1.25
81 Bobby Abreu	.10	.30
82 Sean Burroughs	.10	.30
83 Randy Winn	.10	.30
84 Curt Schilling	.10	.30
85 Chris Singleton	.10	.30
86 Sean Casey	.10	.30
87 Todd Zeile	.10	.30
88 Richard Hidalgo	.10	.30
89 Roberto Alomar	.20	.50
90 Tim Hudson	.10	.30
91 Ryan Klesko	.10	.30
92 Greg Vaughn	.10	.30
93 Tony Womack	.10	.30
94 Fred McGriff	.20	.50
95 Tom Glavine	.20	.50
96 Todd Walker	.10	.30
97 Travis Fryman	.10	.30
98 Shane Reynolds	.10	.30
99 Shawn Green	.10	.30
100 Mo Vaughn	.10	.30
101 Adam Piatt	.10	.30
102 Deivi Cruz	.10	.30
103 Steve Cox	.10	.30
104 Luis Gonzalez	.10	.30
105 Russell Branyan	.10	.30
106 Daryle Ward	.10	.30
107 Mariano Rivera	.30	.75
108 Phil Nevin	.10	.30
109 Ben Grieve	.10	.30
110 Moises Alou	.10	.30
111 Omar Vizquel	.20	.50
112 Joe Randa	.10	.30
113 Jorge Posada	.20	.50
114 Mark Kotsay	.10	.30
115 Ryan Rupe	.10	.30
116 Javy Lopez	.10	.30
117 Corey Patterson	.10	.30
118 Bobby Higginson	.10	.30
119 Jose Vidro	.10	.30
120 Barry Zito	.10	.30
121 Scott Rolen	.20	.50
122 Gary Sheffield	.10	.30
123 Kerry Wood	.10	.30
124 Brandon Inge	.10	.30
125 Jose Hernandez	.10	.30
126 Michael Barrett	.10	.30
127 Miguel Tejada	.10	.30
128 Edgar Renteria	.10	.30
129 Junior Spivey	.10	.30
130 Jose Valentin	.10	.30
131 Derrek Lee	.20	.50
132 A.J. Pierzynski	.10	.30
133 Mike Mussina	.20	.50
134 Bret Boone	.10	.30
135 Chan Ho Park	.10	.30
136 Steve Finley	.10	.30
137 Mark Buehrle	.10	.30
138 A.J. Burnett	.10	.30
139 Ben Sheets	.10	.30
140 David Ortiz	.30	.75
141 Nick Johnson	.10	.30
142 Randall Simon	.10	.30
143 Carlos Delgado	.10	.30
144 Darin Erstad	.10	.30
145 Shea Hillenbrand	.10	.30
146 Todd Helton	.20	.50
147 Preston Wilson	.10	.30
148 Eric Gagne	.10	.30
149 Vladimir Guerrero	.30	.75
150 Brandon Duckworth	.10	.30
151 Rich Aurilia	.10	.30
152 Ivan Rodriguez	.20	.50
153 Andruw Jones	.20	.50
154 Carlos Lee	.10	.30
155 Robert Fick	.10	.30
156 Jacque Jones	.10	.30
157 Bernie Williams	.20	.50
158 John Olerud	.10	.30
159 Eric Hinske	.10	.30
160 Matt Clement	.10	.30
161 Dmitri Young	.10	.30
162 Torii Hunter	.10	.30
163 Carlos Pena	.10	.30
164 Mike Cameron	.10	.30
165 Raul Mondesi	.10	.30
166 Pedro Martinez	.20	.50
167 Bob Wickman	.10	.30
168 Mike Sweeney	.10	.30
169 David Wells	.10	.30
170 Jason Kendall	.10	.30
171 Tino Martinez	.20	.50
172 Matt Williams	.10	.30
173 Frank Thomas	.30	.75
174 Cliff Floyd	.10	.30
175 Corey Koskie	.10	.30
176 Orlando Hernandez	.10	.30
177 Edgar Martinez	.20	.50
178 Richie Sexson	.10	.30
179 Manny Ramirez	.20	.50
180 Jim Thome	.20	.50
181 Andy Pettitte	.20	.50
182 Aramis Ramirez	.10	.30
183 J.D. Drew	.10	.30
184 Brian Jordan	.10	.30
185 Sammy Sosa	.30	.75
186 Jeff Weaver	.10	.30
187 Jeffrey Hammonds	.10	.30
188 Eric Milton	.10	.30
189 Eric Chavez	.10	.30
190 Kazuhiro Sasaki	.10	.30
191 Jose Cruz Jr.	.10	.30
192 Derek Lowe	.10	.30
193 C.C. Sabathia	.10	.30
194 Adrian Beltre	.10	.30
195 Alfonso Soriano	.10	.30
196 Jack Wilson	.10	.30
197 Fernando Vina	.10	.30
198 Chipper Jones	.30	.75
199 Paul Konerko	.10	.30
200 Rusty Greer	.10	.30
201 Jason Giambi AS	.60	1.50
202 Alfonso Soriano AS	.60	1.50
203 Shea Hillenbrand AS	.60	1.50
204 Alex Rodriguez AS	1.00	2.50
205 Jorge Posada AS	.60	1.50
206 Ichiro Suzuki AS	1.25	3.00
207 Manny Ramirez AS	.60	1.50
208 Torii Hunter AS	.60	1.50
209 Todd Helton AS	.60	1.50
210 Jose Vidro AS	.60	1.50
211 Scott Rolen AS	.60	1.50
212 Jimmy Rollins AS	.60	1.50
213 Mike Piazza AS	1.00	2.50
214 Barry Bonds AS	1.50	4.00
215 Sammy Sosa AS	.60	1.50
216 Vladimir Guerrero AS	.60	1.50
217 Lance Berkman AS	.60	1.50
218 Derek Jeter AS	1.50	4.00
219 Nomar Garciaparra AS	1.00	2.50

220 Luis Gonzalez AS .60 1.50
221 Kazuhisa Ishii 02R .75 2.00
222 Satoru Komiyama 02R .75 2.00
223 So Taguchi 02R .75 2.00
224 Jorge Padilla 02R .75 2.00
225 Ben Howard 02R .75 2.00
226 Jason Simontacchi 02R .75 2.00
227 Barry Wesson 02R .75 2.00
228 Howie Clark 02R .75 2.00
229 Aaron Guiel 02R .75 2.00
230 Oliver Perez 02R .75 2.00
231 David Ross 02R .75 2.00
232 Julius Matos 02R .75 2.00
233 Chris Snelling 02R .75 2.00
234 Rodrigo Lopez 02R .75 2.00
235 Will Nieves 02R .75 2.00
236 Joe Borchard 02R .75 2.00
237 Aaron Cook 02R .75 2.00
238 Anderson Machado 02R .75 2.00
239 Corey Thurman 02R .75 2.00
240 Tyler Yates 02R .75 2.00
241 Coco Crisp 03R 1.25 3.00
242 Andy Van Hekken 03R .75 2.00
243 Jim Rushford 03R .75 2.00
244 Jeriome Robertson 03R .75 2.00
245 Shane Nance 03R .75 2.00
246 Kevin Cash 03R .75 2.00
247 Kirk Saarloos 03R .75 2.00
248 Josh Bard 03R .75 2.00
249 Dave Pember 03R RC .75 2.00
250 Freddy Sanchez 03R .75 2.00
251 Chien-Ming Wang PROS RC 8.00 20.00
252 Rickie Weeks PROS RC 2.50 6.00
253 Brandon Webb PROS RC 3.00 8.00
254 Hideki Matsui PROS RC 4.00 10.00
255 Michael Hessman PROS RC 1.25 3.00
256 Ryan Wagner PROS RC 1.25 3.00
257 Matt Kata PROS RC 1.25 3.00
258 Edwin Jackson PROS RC 1.50 4.00
259 Jose Contreras PROS RC 1.50 4.00
260 Delmon Young PROS RC 4.00 10.00
261 Bo Hart PROS RC 1.25 3.00
262 Jeff Duncan PROS RC 1.25 3.00
263 Robby Hammock PROS RC 1.25 3.00
264 Jeremy Bonderman PROS RC 4.00 10.00
265 Clint Barmes PROS RC 1.00 2.50

2003 Ultra Gold Medallion

This 250 card set is a parallel to the 2003 Ultra set. The first 200 cards were inserted at a stated rate of one per pack while cards numbered 221 through 250 were issued at a stated rate of one per 24 packs.

*GOLD MED 1-200: 1.25X TO 3X BASIC
*GOLD MED 201-220: 1X TO 2.5X BASIC
*GOLD MED 221-250: 1X TO 2.5X BASIC

2003 Ultra Back 2 Back

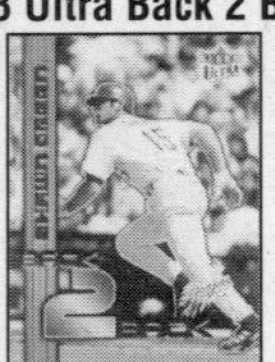

Randomly inserted into packs, these 17 cards feature some of the leading players in baseball. Each of these cards were printed to a stated print run of 1000 serial numbered sets.

1 Derek Jeter 6.00 15.00
2 Barry Bonds 6.00 15.00
3 Mike Piazza 4.00 10.00
4 Alex Rodriguez 4.00 10.00
5 Todd Helton 2.50 6.00
6 Edgar Martinez 2.50 6.00
7 Chipper Jones 2.50 6.00
8 Shawn Green 2.50 6.00
9 Chan Ho Park 2.50 6.00
10 Preston Wilson 2.50 6.00
11 Manny Ramirez 2.50 6.00
12 Aramis Ramirez 2.50 6.00
13 Pedro Martinez 2.50 6.00
14 Ivan Rodriguez 2.50 6.00
15 Ichiro Suzuki 5.00 12.00
16 Sammy Sosa 2.50 6.00
17 Jason Giambi 2.50 6.00

2003 Ultra Back 2 Back Memorabilia

Randomly inserted into packs, this is a parallel of the Ultra Back 2 Back insert set. Each of these cards feature a game-used memorabilia piece of the featured player and is issued to a stated print run of 500 serial numbered sets.

*GOLD: 1.25X TO 3X BASIC B2B MEMORABILIA
GOLD PRINT RUN 50 SERIAL #'d SETS

AR Aramis Ramirez Pants 4.00 10.00
AR1 Alex Rodriguez Jsy 8.00 20.00
BB Barry Bonds Bat 10.00 25.00
CJ Chipper Jones Jsy 6.00 15.00
CP Chan Ho Park Bat 4.00 10.00
DJ Derek Jeter Jsy 10.00 25.00
EM Edgar Martinez Jsy 6.00 15.00
IR Ivan Rodriguez Jsy 6.00 15.00
IS Ichiro Suzuki Base 8.00 20.00
JG Jason Giambi Base 4.00 10.00
MP Mike Piazza Jsy 6.00 15.00
MR Manny Ramirez Jsy 6.00 15.00
PM Pedro Martinez Jsy 6.00 15.00
PW Preston Wilson Jsy 4.00 10.00
SG Shawn Green Jsy 4.00 10.00
SS Sammy Sosa Base 6.00 15.00
TH Todd Helton Jsy 6.00 15.00

2003 Ultra Double Up

Inserted into packs at a stated rate of one in eight, each of these 16 cards feature two players with something in common. Among the common threads are teammates, nationality and position played.

COMPLETE SET (16) 15.00 40.00
1 Derek Jeter / Mike Piazza 2.50 6.00
2 Alex Rodriguez / Rafael Palmeiro 1.50 4.00
3 Chipper Jones / Andruw Jones 1.00 2.50
4 Derek Jeter / Alex Rodriguez 2.50 6.00
5 Nomar Garciaparra / Derek Jeter 2.50 6.00
6 Barry Bonds / Jason Giambi 2.50 6.00
7 Ichiro Suzuki / Hideo Nomo 2.00 5.00
8 Randy Johnson / Curt Schilling 1.00 2.50
9 Pedro Martinez / Nomar Garciaparra 1.50 4.00
10 Roger Clemens / Kevin Brown 2.00 5.00
11 Nomar Garciaparra / Manny Ramirez 1.50 4.00
12 Kazuhiro Sasaki / Hideo Nomo 1.00 2.50
13 Mike Piazza / Ivan Rodriguez 1.50 4.00
14 Ichiro Suzuki / Ken Griffey Jr. 2.00 5.00
15 Barry Bonds / Sammy Sosa 2.50 6.00
16 Alfonso Soriano / Roberto Alomar 1.00 2.50

2003 Ultra Double Up Memorabilia

Randomly inserted into packs, this is a parallel to the Double Up insert set. Each of these cards feature a piece of memorabilia from each of the players featured.

1 Derek Jeter Jsy / Mike Piazza Jsy 25.00 60.00
2 Alex Rodriguez Jsy / {Rafael Palmeiro Jsy 15.00 40.00
3 Chipper Jones Bat / Andruw Jones Jsy 10.00 25.00
4 Derek Jeter Jsy / Alex Rodriguez Jsy 25.00 60.00
5 Nomar Garciaparra Jsy / Derek Jeter Jsy 25.00 60.00
6 Barry Bonds Bat / Jason Giambi Base 15.00 40.00
7 Ichiro Suzuki Base / Hideo Nomo Jsy 50.00 120.00
8 Randy Johnson Jsy / Curt Schilling Jsy 10.00 25.00
9 Pedro Martinez Jsy / Nomar Garciaparra Jsy 15.00 40.00
10 Roger Clemens Jsy / Kevin Brown Jsy 15.00 40.00
11 Nomar Garciaparra Jsy / Manny Ramirez Jsy 15.00 40.00
12 Kazuhiro Sasaki Jsy / Hideo Nomo Jsy 25.00 60.00
13 Mike Piazza Jsy / Ivan Rodriguez Jsy 15.00 40.00
14 Ichiro Suzuki Base / Ken Griffey Jr. Base 30.00 80.00
15 Barry Bonds Bat / Sammy Sosa Base 25.00 60.00
16 Alfonso Soriano Pants / Roberto Alomar Jsy 10.00 25.00

2003 Ultra Moonshots

Inserted into packs at a stated rate of one in 12, these 20 cards feature some of the leading power hitters in baseball.

1 Mike Piazza 1.50 4.00
2 Alex Rodriguez 1.50 4.00

3 Manny Ramirez .75 2.00
4 Ivan Rodriguez .75 2.00
5 Luis Gonzalez .75 2.00
6 Shawn Green .75 2.00
7 Barry Bonds 2.50 6.00
8 Jason Giambi .75 2.00
9 Nomar Garciaparra 1.50 4.00
10 Edgar Martinez .75 2.00
11 Mo Vaughn .75 2.00
12 Chipper Jones 1.00 2.50
13 Todd Helton .75 2.00
14 Raul Mondesi .75 2.00
15 Preston Wilson .75 2.00
16 Rafael Palmeiro .75 2.00
17 Jim Edmonds .75 2.00
18 Bernie Williams .75 2.00
19 Vladimir Guerrero 1.00 2.50
20 Alfonso Soriano .75 2.00

2003 Ultra Moonshots Memorabilia

Inserted into packs at a stated rate of one in 20, this set parallels the Moonshot insert set except a game-used memorabilia piece is used on each of these cards.

AR Alex Rodriguez Jsy 6.00 15.00
AS Alfonso Soriano Pants 3.00 8.00
BB Barry Bonds Jsy 6.00 15.00
BW Bernie Williams Jsy 4.00 10.00
CG Vladimir Guerrero Base 4.00 10.00
CJ Chipper Jones Jsy 4.00 10.00
EM Edgar Martinez Jsy 4.00 10.00
IR Ivan Rodriguez Jsy 4.00 10.00
JE Jim Edmonds Jsy 3.00 8.00
JG Jason Giambi Base 3.00 8.00
LG Luis Gonzalez Jsy 3.00 8.00
MP Mike Piazza Jsy 6.00 15.00
MR Manny Ramirez Jsy 4.00 10.00
MV Mo Vaughn Jsy 3.00 8.00
NG Nomar Garciaparra Jsy 6.00 15.00
PW Preston Wilson Jsy 3.00 8.00
RM Raul Mondesi Jsy 3.00 8.00
RP Rafael Palmeiro Jsy 4.00 10.00
SG Shawn Green Jsy 3.00 8.00
TH Todd Helton Jsy 4.00 10.00

2003 Ultra Photo Effex

Inserted into packs at a stated rate of one in 12, these 20 cards feature intriguing photos of some of the leading players in the game.

GOLD RANDOM INSERTS IN PACKS
GOLD PRINT RUN 25 SERIAL #'d SETS
GOLD NO PRICING DUE TO SCARCITY
1 Derek Jeter 2.50 6.00
2 Barry Bonds 2.50 6.00
3 Sammy Sosa 1.00 2.50
4 Troy Glaus .75 2.00
5 Albert Pujols 2.00 5.00
6 Alex Rodriguez 1.50 4.00
7 Ichiro Suzuki 2.00 5.00
8 Greg Maddux 1.50 4.00
9 Nomar Garciaparra 1.50 4.00
10 Jeff Bagwell .75 2.00
11 Chipper Jones 1.00 2.50
12 Mike Piazza 1.50 4.00
13 Randy Johnson 1.00 2.50
14 Vladimir Guerrero 1.00 2.50
15 Alfonso Soriano .75 2.00
16 Lance Berkman .75 2.00
17 Todd Helton .75 2.00
18 Mike Lowell .75 2.00
19 Carlos Delgado .75 2.00
20 Jason Giambi .75 2.00

2003 Ultra When It Was A Game

Inserted into packs at a stated rate of one in 20, these 40 cards basically feature retired stars from baseball's past. Other than Derek Jeter and Barry Bonds, all the players in this set were retired at the time of issue.

1 Derek Jeter 5.00 12.00
2 Barry Bonds 5.00 12.00
3 Luis Aparicio 2.00 5.00
4 Richie Ashburn 3.00 8.00
5 Ernie Banks 3.00 8.00
6 Enos Slaughter 2.00 5.00
7 Yogi Berra 3.00 8.00
8 Lou Boudreau 2.00 5.00
9 Lou Brock 3.00 8.00
10 Jim Bunning 2.00 5.00
11 Rod Carew 3.00 8.00
12 Orlando Cepeda 2.00 5.00
13 Larry Doby 2.00 5.00
14 Bobby Doerr 2.00 5.00
15 Bob Feller 2.00 5.00
16 Brooks Robinson 3.00 8.00
17 Rollie Fingers 2.00 5.00
18 Whitey Ford 3.00 8.00
19 Bob Gibson 3.00 8.00
20 Catfish Hunter 3.00 8.00
21 Nolan Ryan 6.00 15.00
22 Reggie Jackson 3.00 8.00
23 Fergie Jenkins 2.00 5.00
24 Al Kaline 3.00 8.00
25 Mike Schmidt 6.00 15.00
26 Harmon Killebrew 3.00 8.00
27 Ralph Kiner 2.00 5.00
28 Willie Stargell 3.00 8.00
29 Billy Williams 2.00 5.00
30 Tom Seaver 3.00 8.00
31 Juan Marichal 2.00 5.00
32 Eddie Mathews 3.00 8.00
33 Willie McCovey 2.00 5.00
34 Joe Morgan 2.00 5.00
35 Stan Musial 4.00 10.00
36 Robin Roberts 2.00 5.00
37 Robin Yount 3.00 8.00
38 Jim Palmer 2.00 5.00
39 Phil Rizzuto 3.00 8.00
40 Pee Wee Reese 3.00 8.00

2003 Ultra When It Was A Game Used

Randomly inserted into packs, these 12 cards form a partial parallel to the When it was a Game Insert set. Since several different print runs were used, we have notated that print run information next to the player's name in our checklist.

1 Yogi Berra Pants/100 20.00 50.00
2 Barry Bonds Bat/200 15.00 40.00
3 Larry Doby Bat/150 8.00 20.00
4 Catfish Hunter Jsy/200 8.00 20.00
5 Reggie Jackson Bat/300 8.00 20.00
6 Derek Jeter Jsy/200 15.00 40.00
7 Juan Marichal Jsy/300 6.00 15.00
8 Eddie Mathews Bat/300 10.00 25.00
9 Willie McCovey Jsy/150 8.00 20.00
10 Joe Morgan Pants/200 6.00 15.00
11 Jim Palmer Pants/300 6.00 15.00
12 Tom Seaver Pants/100 10.00 25.00

2004 Ultra

This 220-card set was released in November, 2003. This set was issued in eight-card packs with an $2.99 SRP which came 24 packs to a box and 16 boxes to a case. Please note that cards 201-220 feature leading prospects and were randomly inserted into packs. An 170-card update set was released in October, 2004. The set was issued in five card hobby packs with an $6 SRP which came 12 packs to a box and 16 boxes to a case and in eight-card retail packs with an $3 SRP which came 24 packs to a box and 20 boxes to a case. Cards numbered 221 through 295 feature players who switched teams in the off-season while cards numbered 296 through 382 featured Rookie Cards. Cards numbered 383 through 395 feature 13 of the Leading rookies and the reason they are the lucky 13 is that they are the final 13 cards in the set and the platinum parallel of these cards were printed to a stated print run of 13 serial numbered sets.

COMPLETE SERIES 1 (220) 30.00 60.00
COMP.SERIES 1 w/o SP's (200) 10.00 25.00
COMP.SERIES 2 w/o SP's (75) 10.00 25.00
COMP.SERIES 2 w/o L13 (162) 50.00 100.00
COMMON CARD (1-200) .10 .30
COMMON CARD (201-220) .50 1.25
201-220 APPROXIMATE ODDS 1:2 HOBBY
201-220 RANDOM IN RETAIL PACKS
COMMON CARD (296-382) .75 2.00
296-382 ODDS TWO PER HOBBY/RETAIL
COMMON CARD (383-395) 5.00 12.00
383-395 ODDS 1:28 HOBBY, 1:2000 RETAIL
383-395 PRINT RUN 500 SERIAL #'d SETS
1 Magglio Ordonez .10 .30
2 Bobby Abreu .10 .30
3 Eric Munson .10 .30
4 Eric Byrnes .10 .30
5 Bartolo Colon .10 .30
6 Juan Encarnacion .10 .30
7 Jody Gerut .10 .30
8 Eddie Guardado .10 .30
9 Shea Hillenbrand .10 .30
10 Andruw Jones .20 .50
11 Carlos Lee .10 .30
12 Pedro Martinez .20 .50
13 Barry Larkin .20 .50
14 Angel Berroa .10 .30
15 Edgar Martinez .20 .50
16 Sidney Ponson .10 .30
17 Mariano Rivera .30 .75
18 Richie Sexson .10 .30
19 Frank Thomas .30 .75
20 Jerome Williams .10 .30
21 Barry Zito .10 .30
22 Roberto Alomar .20 .50
23 Rocky Biddle .10 .30
24 Orlando Cabrera .10 .30
25 Placido Polanco .10 .30
26 Morgan Ensberg .10 .30
27 Jason Giambi .10 .30
28 Jim Thome .20 .50
29 Vladimir Guerrero .30 .75
30 Tim Hudson .10 .30
31 Jacque Jones .10 .30
32 Derrek Lee .20 .50
33 Rafael Palmeiro .20 .50
34 Mike Mussina .20 .50
35 Corey Patterson .10 .30
36 Mike Cameron .10 .30
37 Ivan Rodriguez .20 .50
38 Ben Sheets .10 .30
39 Woody Williams .10 .30
40 Ichiro Suzuki .60 1.50
41 Moises Alou .10 .30
42 Craig Biggio .20 .50
43 Jorge Posada .20 .50
44 Craig Monroe .10 .30
45 Darin Erstad .10 .30
46 Jay Gibbons .10 .30
47 Aaron Guiel .10 .30
48 Travis Lee .10 .30
49 Jorge Julio .10 .30
50 Torii Hunter .10 .30
51 Luis Matos .10 .30
52 Brett Myers .10 .30
53 Sean Casey .10 .30
54 Mark Prior .20 .50
55 Alex Rodriguez .50 1.25
56 Gary Sheffield .10 .30
57 Jason Varitek .30 .75
58 Dontrelle Willis .20 .50
59 Garret Anderson .10 .30
60 Casey Blake .10 .30
61 Jay Payton .10 .30
62 Carl Crawford .10 .30
63 Carl Everett .10 .30
64 Marcus Giles .10 .30
65 Jose Guillen .10 .30
66 Eric Karros .10 .30
67 Mike Lieberthal .10 .30
68 Hideki Matsui .50 1.25
69 Xavier Nady .10 .30
70 Hank Blalock .10 .30
71 Albert Pujols .60 1.50
72 Jose Cruz Jr. .10 .30
73 Randall Simon .10 .30
74 Javier Vazquez .10 .30
75 Preston Wilson .10 .30
76 Danys Baez .10 .30
77 Alex Cintron .10 .30
78 Jake Peavy .10 .30
79 Scott Rolen .20 .50
80 Robert Fick .10 .30
81 Brian Giles .10 .30
82 Roy Halladay .10 .30
83 Kazuhisa Ishii .10 .30
84 Austin Kearns .10 .30
85 Paul Lo Duca .10 .30
86 Darrell May .10 .30
87 Phil Nevin .10 .30
88 Carlos Pena .10 .30
89 Manny Ramirez .20 .50
90 C.C. Sabathia .10 .30
91 John Smoltz .20 .50
92 Jose Vidro .10 .30
93 Randy Wolf .10 .30
94 Jeff Bagwell .20 .50
95 Barry Bonds .75 2.00
96 Frank Catalanotto .10 .30
97 Zach Day .10 .30
98 David Ortiz .30 .75
99 Troy Glaus .10 .30
100 Bo Hart .10 .30
101 Geoff Jenkins .10 .30
102 Jason Kendall .10 .30
103 Esteban Loaiza .10 .30
104 Doug Mientkiewicz .10 .30
105 Trot Nixon .10 .30
106 Troy Percival .10 .30
107 Aramis Ramirez .10 .30
108 Alex Sanchez .10 .30
109 Alfonso Soriano .10 .30
110 Omar Vizquel .20 .50
111 Kerry Wood .10 .30
112 Rocco Baldelli .10 .30
113 Bret Boone .10 .30
114 Shawn Chacon .10 .30
115 Carlos Delgado .10 .30
116 Shawn Green .10 .30
117 Tim Worrell .10 .30
118 Tom Glavine .20 .50
119 Shigetoshi Hasegawa .10 .30
120 Derek Jeter .60 1.50
121 Jeff Kent .10 .30
122 Braden Looper .10 .30
123 Kevin Millwood .10 .30
124 Hideo Nomo .30 .75
125 Jason Phillips .10 .30
126 Tim Redding .10 .30
127 Reggie Sanders .10 .30
128 Sammy Sosa .30 .75
129 Billy Wagner .10 .30
130 Miguel Batista .10 .30
131 Milton Bradley .10 .30
132 Eric Chavez .10 .30
133 J.D. Drew .10 .30
134 Keith Foulke .10 .30
135 Luis Gonzalez .10 .30
136 LaTroy Hawkins .10 .30
137 Randy Johnson .30 .75
138 Byung-Hyun Kim .10 .30
139 Javy Lopez .10 .30
140 Melvin Mora .10 .30
141 Aubrey Huff .10 .30
142 Mike Piazza .50 1.25
143 Mark Redman .10 .30
144 Kazuhiro Sasaki .10 .30
145 Shannon Stewart .10 .30
146 Larry Walker .10 .30
147 Dmitri Young .10 .30
148 Josh Beckett .10 .30
149 Jae Weong Seo .10 .30
150 Hee Seop Choi .10 .30
151 Adam Dunn .10 .30
152 Rafael Furcal .10 .30
153 Juan Gonzalez .10 .30
154 Todd Helton .20 .50
155 Carlos Zambrano .10 .30
156 Ryan Klesko .10 .30
157 Mike Lowell .10 .30
158 Jamie Moyer .10 .30
159 Russ Ortiz .10 .30
160 Juan Pierre .10 .30
161 Edgar Renteria .10 .30
162 Curt Schilling .10 .30
163 Mike Sweeney .10 .30
164 Brandon Webb .10 .30
165 Michael Young .10 .30
166 Carlos Beltran .10 .30
167 Sean Burroughs .10 .30
168 Luis Castillo .10 .30
169 David Eckstein .10 .30
170 Eric Gagne .10 .30
171 Chipper Jones .30 .75
172 Livan Hernandez .10 .30
173 Nick Johnson .10 .30
174 Corey Koskie .10 .30
175 Jason Schmidt .10 .30
176 Bill Mueller .10 .30
177 Steve Finley .10 .30
178 A.J. Pierzynski .10 .30
179 Rene Reyes .10 .30
180 Jason Johnson .10 .30
181 Mark Teixeira .20 .50
182 Kip Wells .10 .30
183 Mike MacDougal .10 .30
184 Lance Berkman .10 .30
185 Victor Zambrano .10 .30
186 Roger Clemens .60 1.50
187 Jim Edmonds .10 .30
188 Nomar Garciaparra .50 1.25
189 Ken Griffey Jr. .50 1.25
190 Richard Hidalgo .10 .30
191 Cliff Floyd .10 .30
192 Greg Maddux .50 1.25
193 Mark Mulder .10 .30
194 Roy Oswalt .10 .30
195 Marlon Byrd .10 .30
196 Jose Reyes .10 .30
197 Kevin Brown .10 .30
198 Miguel Tejada .10 .30
199 Vernon Wells .10 .30
200 Joel Pineiro .10 .30
201 Rickie Weeks AR .75 2.00
202 Chad Gaudin AR .50 1.25
203 Ryan Wagner AR .50 1.25
204 Chris Bootcheck AR .50 1.25
205 Koyie Hill AR .50 1.25
206 Jeff Duncan AR .50 1.25
207 Rich Harden AR .75 2.00
208 Edwin Jackson AR .50 1.25
209 Robby Hammock AR .50 1.25
210 Khalil Greene AR 1.25 3.00
211 Chien-Ming Wang AR 2.00 5.00
212 Prentice Redman AR .50 1.25
213 Todd Wellemeyer AR .50 1.25
214 Clint Barmes AR .75 2.00
215 Matt Kata AR .50 1.25
216 Jon Leicester AR .50 1.25
217 Jeremy Guthrie AR .50 1.25
218 Chin-Hui Tsao AR .75 2.00
219 Dan Haren AR .50 1.25
220 Delmon Young AR 1.25 3.00
221 Vladimir Guerrero .50 1.25
222 Andy Pettitte .30 .75
223 Gary Sheffield .20 .50
224 Javier Vazquez .20 .50
225 Alex Rodriguez .75 2.00
226 Billy Wagner .20 .50
227 Miguel Tejada .20 .50
228 Greg Maddux .75 2.00
229 Ivan Rodriguez .30 .75
230 Roger Clemens 1.00 2.50
231 Alfonso Soriano .20 .50
232 Miguel Cabrera .30 .75
233 Javy Lopez .20 .50
234 David Wells .20 .50
235 Eric Milton .20 .50
236 Armando Benitez .20 .50
237 Mike Cameron .20 .50
238 J.D. Drew .20 .50
239 Carlos Beltran .20 .50
240 Bartolo Colon .20 .50
241 Jose Guillen .20 .50
242 Kevin Brown .20 .50
243 Carlos Guillen .20 .50
244 Kenny Lofton .20 .50
245 Pokey Reese .20 .50
246 Rafael Palmeiro .30 .75
247 Nomar Garciaparra .75 2.00
248 Hee Seop Choi .20 .50
249 Juan Uribe .20 .50
250 Nick Johnson .20 .50
251 Scott Podsednik .20 .50
252 Richie Sexson .20 .50
253 Keith Foulke Sox .20 .50
254 Jaret Wright .20 .50
255 Johnny Estrada .20 .50
256 Michael Barrett .20 .50
257 Bernie Williams .30 .75
258 Octavio Dotel .20 .50
259 Jeromy Burnitz .20 .50
260 Kevin Youkilis .20 .50
261 Derrek Lee .30 .75
262 Jack Wilson .20 .50
263 Craig Wilson .20 .50
264 Richard Hidalgo .20 .50
265 Royce Clayton .20 .50

#	Player	Low	High
266	Curt Schilling	.30	.75
267	Joe Mauer	.30	.75
268	Bobby Crosby	.20	.50
269	Zack Greinke	.20	.50
270	Victor Martinez	.20	.50
271	Pedro Feliz	.20	.50
272	Tony Batista	.20	.50
273	Casey Kotchman	.20	.50
274	Freddy Garcia	.20	.50
275	Adam Everett	.20	.50
276	Alexis Rios	.20	.50
277	Lew Ford	.20	.50
278	Adam LaRoche	.20	.50
279	Lyle Overbay	.20	.50
280	Juan Gonzalez	.20	.50
281	A.J. Pierzynski	.20	.50
282	Scott Hairston	.20	.50
283	Danny Bautista	.20	.50
284	Brad Penny	.20	.50
285	Paul Konerko	.20	.50
286	Matt Lawton	.20	.50
287	Carl Pavano	.20	.50
288	Pat Burrell	.20	.50
289	Kenny Rogers	.20	.50
290	Laynce Nix	.20	.50
291	Johnny Damon	.30	.75
292	Paul Wilson	.20	.50
293	Vinny Castilla	.20	.50
294	Aaron Miles	.20	.50
295	Ken Harvey	.20	.50
296	Onil Joseph RC	.75	2.00
297	Kazuhito Tadano RC	1.25	3.00
298	Jeff Bennett RC	.75	2.00
299	Chad Bentz RC	.75	2.00
300	Akinori Otsuka RC	.75	2.00
301	Jon Knott RC	.75	2.00
302	Ian Snell RC	1.25	3.00
303	Fernando Nieve RC	1.25	3.00
304	Mike Rouse RC	.75	2.00
305	Dennis Sarfate RC	.75	2.00
306	Josh Labandeira RC	.75	2.00
307	Chris Oxspring RC	.75	2.00
308	Alfredo Simon RC	.75	2.00
309	Rusty Tucker RC	1.25	3.00
310	Lincoln Holdzkom RC	.75	2.00
311	Justin Leone RC	1.25	3.00
312	Jorge Sequea RC	.75	2.00
313	Brian Dallimore RC	.75	2.00
314	Tim Bittner RC	.75	2.00
315	Ronny Cedeno RC	1.25	3.00
316	Justin Hampson RC	.75	2.00
317	Ryan Wing RC	.75	2.00
318	Mariano Gomez RC	.75	2.00
319	Carlos Vasquez RC	1.25	3.00
320	Casey Daigle RC	.75	2.00
321	Renyel Pinto RC	1.25	3.00
322	Chris Shelton RC	1.25	3.00
323	Mike Gosling RC	.75	2.00
324	Aarom Baldiris RC	1.25	3.00
325	Ramon Ramirez RC	.75	2.00
326	Roberto Novoa RC	1.25	3.00
327	Sean Henn RC	.75	2.00
328	Nick Regilio RC	.75	2.00
329	Dave Crouthers RC	.75	2.00
330	Greg Dobbs RC	.75	2.00
331	Angel Chavez RC	.75	2.00
332	Luis A. Gonzalez RC	.75	2.00
333	Justin Knoedler RC	.75	2.00
334	Jason Frasor RC	.75	2.00
335	Jerry Gil RC	.75	2.00
336	Carlos Hines RC	.75	2.00
337	Ivan Ochoa RC	.75	2.00
338	Jose Capellan RC	1.25	3.00
339	Hector Gimenez RC	.75	2.00
340	Shawn Hill RC	.75	2.00
341	Freddy Guzman RC	.75	2.00
342	Scott Proctor RC	1.25	3.00
343	Frank Francisco RC	.75	2.00
344	Brandon Medders RC	.75	2.00
345	Andy Green RC	.75	2.00
346	Eddy Rodriguez RC	1.25	3.00
347	Tim Hamulack RC	.75	2.00
348	Michael Wuertz RC	1.25	3.00
349	Arnie Munoz	.75	2.00
350	Enemencio Pacheco RC	.75	2.00
351	Dusty Bergman RC	.75	2.00
352	Charles Thomas RC	.75	2.00
353	William Bergolla RC	.75	2.00
354	Ramon Castro RC	.75	2.00
355	Justin Lehr RC	.75	2.00
356	Lino Urdaneta RC	.75	2.00
357	Donnie Kelly RC	.75	2.00
358	Kevin Cave RC	.75	2.00
359	Franklyn Gracesqui RC	.75	2.00
360	Chris Aguila RC	.75	2.00
361	Jorge Vasquez RC	.75	2.00
362	Andres Blanco RC	.75	2.00
363	Orlando Rodriguez RC	.75	2.00
364	Colby Miller RC	.75	2.00
365	Shawn Camp RC	.75	2.00
366	Jake Woods RC	.75	2.00
367	George Sherrill RC	.75	2.00
368	Justin Hujsman RC	.75	2.00
369	Jimmy Serrano RC	.75	2.00
370	Mike Johnston RC	.75	2.00
371	Ryan Meaux RC	.75	2.00
372	Scott Dohmann RC	.75	2.00
373	Brad Halsey RC	1.25	3.00
374	Joey Gathright RC	1.50	4.00
375	Yadier Molina RC	2.00	5.00
376	Travis Blackley RC	.75	2.00
377	Steve Andrade RC	.75	2.00
378	Phil Stockman RC	.75	2.00
379	Roman Colon RC	.75	2.00
380	Jesse Crain RC	1.25	3.00
381	Edwardo Sierra RC	1.25	3.00
382	Justin Germano RC	.75	2.00
383	Kaz Matsui L13 RC	4.00	10.00
384	Shingo Takatsu L13 RC	4.00	10.00
385	John Gall L13 RC	5.00	12.00
386	Chris Saenz L13 RC	5.00	12.00
387	Merkin Valdez L13 RC	4.00	10.00
388	Jamie Brown L13 RC	5.00	12.00
389	Jason Bartlett L13 RC	5.00	12.00
390	David Aardsma L13 RC	5.00	12.00
391	Scott Kazmir L13 RC	12.50	30.00
392	David Wright L13	12.50	30.00
393	Dioner Navarro L13 RC	4.00	10.00
394	B.J. Upton L13	5.00	12.00
395	Gavin Floyd L13	5.00	12.00

2004 Ultra Gold Medallion

*GOLD 1-200: 1.25X TO 3X BASIC
1-200 SERIES 1 ODDS 1:1
*GOLD 201-220: 1X TO 2.5X BASIC
201-220 SERIES 1 ODDS 1:8
*GOLD 221-295: .75X TO 2X BASIC
221-295 SERIES 2 ODDS 1:1 H, 1:3 R
*GOLD 296-382: .6X TO 1.5X BASIC
*GOLD 383-395: .15X TO .4X BASIC
296-395 SERIES 2 ODDS 1:4 H, 1:12 R

#	Player	Low	High
391	Scott Kazmir L13	5.00	12.00
392	David Wright L13	8.00	20.00

2004 Ultra Platinum Medallion

*PLATINUM 1-200: 8X TO 20X BASIC
*PLATINUM 201-220: 3X TO 8X BASIC
1-220 SERIES 1 ODDS 1:36
1-220 PRINT RUN 66 SERIAL #'d SETS
*PLATINUM 221-295: 4X TO 10X BASIC
*PLATINUM 296-382: 1.5X TO 4X BASIC
221-382 PRINT RUN 100 SERIAL #'d SETS
383-395 PRINT RUN 13 SERIAL #'d SETS
383-395 NO PRICING DUE TO SCARCITY
221-395 SER.2 ODDS 1:12 HOB, 1:145 RET

2004 Ultra Season Crowns Autograph

Rickie Weeks did not return his autographs in time for pack-out, thus those cards were issued as exchange cards. There is no expiration date for those redemptions.

STATED PRINT RUN 150 SERIAL #'d SETS
GOLD PRINT RUN 25 SERIAL #'d SETS
NO GOLD PRICING DUE TO SCARCITY
SERIES 1 AUTO PARALLEL ODDS 1:192
EXCHANGE DEADLINE INDEFINITE

#	Player	Low	High
35	Corey Patterson	5.00	12.00
58	Dontrelle Willis	12.50	30.00
70	Hank Blalock	8.00	20.00
79	Scott Rolen	12.50	30.00
84	Austin Kearns	5.00	12.00
88	Carlos Pena	5.00	12.00
100	Bo Hart	5.00	12.00
112	Rocco Baldelli	8.00	20.00
141	Aubrey Huff	8.00	20.00
151	Mike Lowell	8.00	20.00
164	Brandon Webb	5.00	12.00
171	Chipper Jones	30.00	60.00
196	Jose Reyes	8.00	20.00
198	Miguel Tejada	12.50	30.00
201	Rickie Weeks EXCH		

2004 Ultra Season Crowns Game Used

STATED PRINT RUN 399 SERIAL #'d SETS
*GOLD: .5X TO 1.2X BASIC
GOLD PRINT RUN 99 SERIAL #'d SETS
*PLATINUM: .75X TO 2X BASIC
PLATINUM PRINT RUN 25 SERIAL #'d SETS
SERIES 1 GU PARALLEL ODDS 1:24

#	Player	Low	High
10	Andruw Jones Bat	4.00	10.00
12	Pedro Martinez Jsy	4.00	10.00
14	Angel Berroa Jsy	3.00	8.00
19	Frank Thomas Jsy	4.00	10.00
22	Roberto Alomar Bat	4.00	10.00
27	Jason Giambi Jsy	3.00	8.00
28	Jim Thome Jsy	4.00	10.00
29	Vladimir Guerrero Jsy	4.00	10.00
30	Tim Hudson Jsy	3.00	8.00
40	Ichiro Suzuki Base	10.00	25.00
50	Torii Hunter Bat	3.00	8.00
53	Sean Casey Bat	3.00	8.00
55	Alex Rodriguez Jsy	6.00	15.00
56	Gary Sheffield Bat	3.00	8.00
58	Dontrelle Willis Jsy	4.00	10.00
68	Hideki Matsui Base	10.00	25.00
70	Hank Blalock Bat	3.00	8.00
71	Albert Pujols Jsy	8.00	20.00
79	Scott Rolen Bat	4.00	10.00
84	Austin Kearns Bat	3.00	8.00
88	Carlos Pena Bat	3.00	8.00
89	Manny Ramirez Jsy	4.00	10.00
94	Jeff Bagwell Pants	4.00	10.00
95	Barry Bonds Base	8.00	20.00
99	Troy Glaus Jsy	3.00	8.00
102	Jason Kendall Jsy	3.00	8.00
109	Alfonso Soriano Bat	3.00	8.00
110	Omar Vizquel Jsy	4.00	10.00
112	Rocco Baldelli Jsy	3.00	8.00
115	Carlos Delgado Jsy	3.00	8.00
116	Shawn Green Jsy	3.00	8.00
118	Tom Glavine Bat	4.00	10.00
120	Derek Jeter Jsy	10.00	25.00
124	Hideo Nomo Jsy	4.00	10.00
128	Sammy Sosa Jsy	4.00	10.00
137	Randy Johnson Jsy	4.00	10.00
142	Mike Piazza Bat	6.00	15.00
144	Kazuhiro Sasaki Jsy	3.00	8.00
146	Larry Walker Jsy	3.00	8.00
151	Adam Dunn Bat	3.00	8.00
154	Todd Helton Jsy	4.00	10.00
164	Brandon Webb Jsy	3.00	8.00
166	Carlos Beltran Jsy	3.00	8.00
167	Sean Burroughs Jsy	3.00	8.00
171	Chipper Jones Jsy	4.00	10.00
184	Lance Berkman Bat	3.00	8.00
186	Roger Clemens Jsy	6.00	15.00
192	Greg Maddux Jsy	6.00	15.00
193	Mark Mulder Jsy	3.00	8.00
196	Jose Reyes Jsy	3.00	8.00

2004 Ultra Diamond Producers

SERIES 1 STATED ODDS 1:144

#	Player	Low	High
1	Greg Maddux	8.00	20.00
2	Dontrelle Willis	8.00	20.00
3	Jim Thome	8.00	20.00
4	Alfonso Soriano	8.00	20.00
5	Alex Rodriguez	8.00	20.00
6	Sammy Sosa	8.00	20.00
7	Nomar Garciaparra	8.00	20.00
8	Derek Jeter	10.00	25.00
9	Adam Dunn	8.00	20.00
10	Mark Prior	8.00	20.00

2004 Ultra Diamond Producers Game Used

SERIES 1 GU INSERT ODDS 1:12
STATED PRINT RUN 1000 SERIAL #'d SETS

#	Player	Low	High
1	Greg Maddux Jsy	4.00	10.00
2	Dontrelle Willis Jsy	4.00	10.00
3	Jim Thome Jsy	4.00	10.00
4	Alfonso Soriano Bat	3.00	8.00
5	Alex Rodriguez Jsy	6.00	15.00
6	Sammy Sosa Jsy	4.00	10.00
7	Nomar Garciaparra Jsy	6.00	15.00
8	Derek Jeter Jsy	10.00	25.00
9	Adam Dunn Bat	3.00	8.00
10	Mark Prior Jsy	4.00	10.00

2004 Ultra Diamond Producers Game Used UltraSwatch

SERIES 1 GU INSERT ODDS 1:12
PRINT RUNS B/WN 2-44 COPIES PER
NO PRICING DUE TO SCARCITY
1 Greg Maddux Jsy/31
2 Dontrelle Willis Jsy/35
3 Jim Thome Jsy/25
4 Alfonso Soriano Bat/12
5 Alex Rodriguez Jsy/3
6 Sammy Sosa Jsy/21
7 Nomar Garciaparra Jsy/5
8 Derek Jeter Jsy/2
9 Adam Dunn Bat/44
10 Mark Prior Jsy/22

2004 Ultra Hitting Machines

SERIES 2 ODDS 1:12 HOBBY, 1:24 RETAIL
*DIE CUT: .75X TO 2X BASIC

DC RANDOM IN SER.2 VINTAGE/MVP RETAIL

#	Player	Low	High
1	Albert Pujols	2.50	6.00
2	Ken Griffey Jr.	2.00	5.00
3	Vladimir Guerrero	1.25	3.00
4	Mike Piazza	2.00	5.00
5	Ichiro Suzuki	2.50	6.00
6	Miguel Cabrera	.75	2.00
7	Hideki Matsui	2.00	5.00
8	Nomar Garciaparra	2.00	5.00
9	Derek Jeter	2.50	6.00
10	Chipper Jones	1.25	3.00

2004 Ultra Hitting Machines Jersey Silver

*GOLD: 1.25X TO 3X SILVER
GOLD PRINT RUN 50 SERIAL #'d SETS
PLATINUM PRINT RUN 10 SERIAL #'d SETS
NO PLATINUM PRICING DUE TO SCARCITY
SER.2 OVERALL GU ODDS 1:6 H, 1:48 R

#	Player	Low	High
AD	Adam Dunn	2.00	5.00
AP	Albert Pujols	6.00	15.00
CJ	Chipper Jones	3.00	8.00
FT	Frank Thomas	3.00	8.00
HM	Hideki Matsui	8.00	20.00
JB	Jeff Bagwell	3.00	8.00
MC	Miguel Cabrera	3.00	8.00
MP	Mike Piazza	4.00	10.00
TH	Todd Helton	3.00	8.00
VG	Vladimir Guerrero	3.00	8.00

2004 Ultra HR Kings

SERIES 1 HR/K/RBI KING ODDS 1:12
*GOLD: 2X TO 5X BASIC
GOLD SER.1 HR/K/RBI KING ODDS 1:350
GOLD PRINT RUN 50 SERIAL #'d SETS

#	Player	Low	High
1	Barry Bonds	2.50	6.00
2	Albert Pujols	2.00	5.00
3	Jason Giambi	1.00	2.50
4	Jeff Bagwell	1.00	2.50
5	Ken Griffey Jr.	1.50	4.00
6	Alex Rodriguez	1.50	4.00
7	Sammy Sosa	1.00	2.50
8	Alfonso Soriano	1.00	2.50
9	Chipper Jones	1.00	2.50
10	Mike Piazza	1.50	4.00

2004 Ultra K Kings

SERIES 1 HR/K/RBI KING ODDS 1:12
*GOLD: 2X TO 5X BASIC
GOLD SER.1 HR/K/RBI KING ODDS 1:350
GOLD PRINT RUN 50 SERIAL #'d SETS

#	Player	Low	High
1	Randy Johnson	1.00	2.50
2	Pedro Martinez	1.00	2.50
3	Curt Schilling	1.00	2.50
4	Roger Clemens	2.00	5.00
5	Mike Mussina	1.00	2.50
6	Roy Halladay	1.00	2.50
7	Kerry Wood	1.00	2.50
8	Dontrelle Willis	1.00	2.50
9	Greg Maddux	1.50	4.00
10	Mark Prior	1.00	2.50

2004 Ultra Kings Triple Swatch

SERIES 1 GU INSERT ODDS 1:12
STATED PRINT RUN 33 SERIAL #'d SETS
NO PRICING DUE TO SCARCITY
1 Mike Piazza Bat
Roger Clemens Jsy
Alex Rodriguez Jsy
2 Albert Pujols Jsy
Mark Prior Jsy
Todd Helton Jsy
3 Alfonso Soriano Bat
Dontrelle Willis Jsy
Albert Pujols Jsy
4 Pedro Martinez Jsy
Sammy Sosa Jsy
Albert Pujols Jsy
5 Greg Maddux Jsy
Chipper Jones Jsy
Vladimir Guerrero Jsy
6 Randy Johnson Jsy
Albert Pujols Jsy
Todd Helton Jsy
7 Dontrelle Willis Jsy
Chipper Jones Jsy
Albert Pujols Jsy
8 Kerry Wood Jsy
Sammy Sosa Jsy
Nomar Garciaparra Jsy
9 Dontrelle Willis Jsy
Jeff Bagwell Pants
Jim Thome Jsy
10 Greg Maddux Jsy
Jason Giambi Jsy
Manny Ramirez Jsy

2004 Ultra Legendary 13 Collection Game Used

STATED PRINT RUN 13 SERIAL #'d SETS
KEY PLAYER HAS OVERSIZED SWATCH
AUTO MASTERPIECE PRINT RUN 1 #'d SET
AUTO MP KEY PLAYER HAS AUTOGRAPH
SER.2 OVERALL LGD 13 ODDS 1:192 HOBBY
EACH CARD FEATURES 13 JSY SWATCHES
NO PRICING DUE TO SCARCITY
AP Albert Pujols Oversized Jsy
Nolan Ryan Jsy
Roger Clemens Jsy
Cal Ripken Jsy
Mike Schmidt Jsy
Carlton Fisk Jsy
Carl Yastrzemski Jsy
Ted Williams Jsy
Stan Musial Jsy
Mark Prior Jsy
Yogi Berra Jsy
Johnny Bench Jsy
Don Mattingly Jsy
CF Carlton Fisk Oversized Jsy
Carl Yastrzemski Jsy
Ted Williams Jsy
Stan Musial Jsy
Mark Prior Jsy
Yogi Berra Jsy
Johnny Bench Jsy
Don Mattingly Jsy
Albert Pujols Jsy
Nolan Ryan Jsy
Roger Clemens Jsy
Cal Ripken Jsy
Mike Schmidt Jsy
CR Cal Ripken Oversized Jsy
Mike Schmidt Jsy
Carlton Fisk Jsy
Carl Yastrzemski Jsy
Ted Williams Jsy
Stan Musial Jsy
Mark Prior Jsy
Yogi Berra Jsy
Johnny Bench Jsy
Don Mattingly Jsy
Albert Pujols Jsy
Nolan Ryan Jsy
Roger Clemens Jsy
CY Carl Yastrzemski Oversized Jsy
Ted Williams Jsy
Stan Musial Jsy
Mark Prior Jsy
Yogi Berra Jsy
Johnny Bench Jsy
Don Mattingly Jsy
Albert Pujols Jsy
Nolan Ryan Jsy
Roger Clemens Jsy
Cal Ripken Jsy
Mike Schmidt Jsy
Carlton Fisk Jsy
DM Don Mattingly Oversized Jsy
Albert Pujols Jsy
Nolan Ryan Jsy
Roger Clemens Jsy
Cal Ripken Jsy
Mike Schmidt Jsy
Carlton Fisk Jsy
Carl Yastrzemski Jsy
Ted Williams Jsy
Stan Musial Jsy
Mark Prior Jsy
Yogi Berra Jsy
Johnny Bench Jsy
JB Johnny Bench Oversized Jsy
Don Mattingly Jsy
Albert Pujols Jsy
Nolan Ryan Jsy
Roger Clemens Jsy
Cal Ripken Jsy
Mike Schmidt Jsy
Carlton Fisk Jsy
Carl Yastrzemski Jsy
Ted Williams Jsy
Stan Musial Jsy
Mark Prior Jsy
Yogi Berra Jsy
MP Mark Prior Oversized Jsy
Yogi Berra Jsy
Johnny Bench Jsy
Don Mattingly Jsy
Albert Pujols Jsy
Nolan Ryan Jsy
Roger Clemens Jsy
Cal Ripken Jsy
Mike Schmidt Jsy
Carlton Fisk Jsy
Carl Yastrzemski Jsy
Ted Williams Jsy
Stan Musial Jsy
MS Mike Schmidt Oversized Jsy
Carlton Fisk Jsy
Carl Yastrzemski Jsy
Ted Williams Jsy
Stan Musial Jsy
Mark Prior Jsy
Yogi Berra Jsy
Johnny Bench Jsy
Don Mattingly Jsy
Albert Pujols Jsy
Nolan Ryan Jsy
Roger Clemens Jsy
Cal Ripken Jsy
NR Nolan Ryan Oversized Jsy
Roger Clemens Jsy
Cal Ripken Jsy
Mike Schmidt Jsy
Carlton Fisk Jsy
Carl Yastrzemski Jsy
Ted Williams Jsy
Stan Musial Jsy
Mark Prior Jsy
Yogi Berra Jsy
Johnny Bench Jsy
Don Mattingly Jsy
Albert Pujols Jsy
RC Roger Clemens Oversized Jsy
Cal Ripken Jsy
Mike Schmidt Jsy
Carlton Fisk Jsy
Carl Yastrzemski Jsy
Ted Williams Jsy
Stan Musial Jsy
Mark Prior Jsy
Yogi Berra Jsy
Johnny Bench Jsy
Don Mattingly Jsy
Albert Pujols Jsy
Nolan Ryan Jsy
SM Stan Musial Oversized Jsy
Mark Prior Jsy
Yogi Berra Jsy
Johnny Bench Jsy
Don Mattingly Jsy
Albert Pujols Jsy
Nolan Ryan Jsy
Roger Clemens Jsy
Cal Ripken Jsy
Mike Schmidt Jsy
Carlton Fisk Jsy
Carl Yastrzemski Jsy
Ted Williams Jsy
TW Ted Williams Oversized Jsy
Stan Musial Jsy
Mark Prior Jsy
Yogi Berra Jsy
Johnny Bench Jsy
Don Mattingly Jsy
Albert Pujols Jsy
Nolan Ryan Jsy
Roger Clemens Jsy
Cal Ripken Jsy
Mike Schmidt Jsy
Carlton Fisk Jsy
Carl Yastrzemski Jsy
YB Yogi Berra Oversized Jsy
Johnny Bench Jsy
Don Mattingly Jsy
Albert Pujols Jsy
Nolan Ryan Jsy
Roger Clemens Jsy
Cal Ripken Jsy
Mike Schmidt Jsy
Carlton Fisk Jsy
Carl Yastrzemski Jsy
Ted Williams Jsy
Stan Musial Jsy
Mark Prior Jsy

2004 Ultra Legendary 13 Dual Game Used Gold

STATED PRINT RUN 22 SERIAL #'d SETS
MASTERPIECE PRINT RUN 1 #'d SET
NO M'PIECE PRICING DUE TO SCARCITY
PLATINUM PRINT RUN 10 #'d SETS
NO PLATINUM PRICING DUE TO SCARCITY
SER.2 OVERALL LGD 13 ODDS 1:192 HOBBY
APCF Albert Pujols Patch
Carlton Fisk Patch
APCY Albert Pujols Patch
Carl Yastrzemski Jsy
CFMP Carlton Fisk Patch
Mark Prior Patch
CRMS Cal Ripken Patch
Mike Schmidt Patch
CYTW Carl Yastrzemski Jsy
Ted Williams Bat
DMAP Don Mattingly Patch
Albert Pujols Patch
DMCR Don Mattingly Patch

Cal Ripken Patch
MSSM Mike Schmidt Patch
Stan Musial Jsy
NRMP Nolan Ryan Patch
Mark Prior Patch
NRRC Nolan Ryan Jsy
Roger Clemens Patch
RCMP Roger Clemens Patch
Mark Prior Patch
YBDM Yogi Berra Bat
Don Mattingly Patch
YBJB Yogi Berra Bat
Johnny Bench Patch

2004 Ultra Legendary 13 Dual Game Used Autograph Platinum

STATED PRINT RUN 3 SERIAL #'d SETS
MASTERPIECE PRINT RUN 1 #'d SET
SER.2 OVERALL LGD 13 ODDS 1:192 HOBBY
NO PRICING DUE TO SCARCITY

2004 Ultra Legendary 13 Single Game Used Gold

PRINT RUNS B/WN 5-72 COPIES PER
NO PRICING ON QTY OF 9 OR LESS
MASTERPIECE PRINT RUN 1 #'d SET
NO M'PIECE PRICING DUE TO SCARCITY
SER.2 OVERALL LGD 13 ODDS 1:192 HOBBY
AP Albert Pujols Patch/5
CF Carlton Fisk Jsy/72 6.00 15.00
CR Cal Ripken Patch/8
CY Carl Yastrzemski Jsy/8
DM Don Mattingly Patch/23 40.00 80.00
JB Johnny Bench Patch/5
MP Mark Prior Patch/22 10.00 25.00
MS Mike Schmidt Patch/20 50.00 100.00
NR Nolan Ryan Jsy/34 15.00 40.00
RC Roger Clemens Patch/22 20.00 50.00
SM Stan Musial Jsy/6
TW Ted Williams Bat/9
YB Yogi Berra Bat/8

2004 Ultra Legendary 13 Single Game Used Autograph Platinum

STATED PRINT RUN 5 SERIAL #'d SETS
MASTERPIECE PRINT RUN 1 #'d SET
SER.2 OVERALL LGD 13 ODDS 1:192 HOBBY
NO PRICING DUE TO SCARCITY

2004 Ultra Performers

COMPLETE SET (15) 10.00 25.00
SERIES 1 STATED ODDS 1:6
1 Ichiro Suzuki 1.50 4.00
2 Albert Pujols 1.50 4.00
3 Barry Bonds 2.00 5.00
4 Hideki Matsui 1.25 3.00
5 Randy Johnson .75 2.00
6 Jason Giambi .75 2.00
7 Pedro Martinez .75 2.00
8 Hank Blalock .75 2.00
9 Chipper Jones .75 2.00
10 Mike Piazza 1.25 3.00
11 Derek Jeter 1.50 4.00
12 Vladimir Guerrero .75 2.00
13 Barry Zito .75 2.00
14 Rocco Baldelli .75 2.00
15 Hideo Nomo .75 2.00

2004 Ultra Performers Game Used

SERIES 1 GU INSERT ODDS 1:12
STATED PRINT RUN 500 SERIAL #'d SETS

1 Albert Pujols Jsy 8.00 20.00
2 Barry Bonds Base 8.00 20.00
3 Randy Johnson Jsy 4.00 10.00
4 Jason Giambi Jsy 3.00 8.00
5 Pedro Martinez Jsy 4.00 10.00
6 Hank Blalock Bat 3.00 8.00
7 Chipper Jones Jsy 4.00 10.00
8 Mike Piazza Bat 4.00 10.00
9 Derek Jeter Jsy 10.00 25.00
10 Vladimir Guerrero Jsy 4.00 10.00
11 Rocco Baldelli Jsy 3.00 8.00
12 Hideo Nomo Jsy 4.00 10.00

2004 Ultra Performers Game Used UltraSwatch

SERIES 1 GU INSERT ODDS 1:12
PRINT RUNS B/WN 2-51 COPIES PER
NO PRICING DUE TO SCARCITY
1 Albert Pujols Jsy/5
2 Barry Bonds Base/25
3 Randy Johnson Jsy/51
4 Jason Giambi Jsy/25
5 Pedro Martinez Jsy/45
6 Hank Blalock Bat/9
7 Chipper Jones Jsy/10
8 Mike Piazza Bat/31
9 Derek Jeter Jsy/2
10 Vladimir Guerrero Jsy/27
11 Rocco Baldelli Jsy/5
12 Hideo Nomo Jsy/10

2004 Ultra RBI Kings

OVERALL HR/K/RBI KING ODDS 1:12
*GOLD: 2X TO 5X BASIC
GOLD SER.1 HR/K/RBI KING ODDS 1:350
GOLD PRINT RUN 50 SERIAL #'d SETS
1 Hideki Matsui 1.50 4.00
2 Albert Pujols 2.00 5.00
3 Todd Helton 1.00 2.50
4 Jim Thome 1.00 2.50
5 Carlos Delgado 1.00 2.50
6 Alex Rodriguez 1.50 4.00
7 Barry Bonds 2.50 6.00
8 Manny Ramirez 1.00 2.50
9 Vladimir Guerrero 1.00 2.50
10 Nomar Garciaparra 1.50 4.00

2004 Ultra Turn Back the Clock

SERIES 2 ODDS 1:6 HOBBY, 1:12 RETAIL
1 Roger Clemens Sox 2.50 6.00
2 Alex Rodriguez Rgr 2.00 5.00
3 Randy Johnson M's 1.25 3.00
4 Pedro Martinez Expos .75 2.00
5 Alfonso Soriano Yanks .75 2.00
6 Curt Schilling Phils .75 2.00
7 Miguel Tejada A's .75 2.00
8 Scott Rolen Phils .75 2.00
9 Jim Thome Indians .75 2.00
10 Manny Ramirez Indians .75 2.00
11 Vladimir Guerrero Expos 1.25 3.00
12 Tom Glavine Braves .75 2.00
13 Andy Pettitte Yanks .75 2.00
14 Ivan Rodriguez Marlins .75 2.00
15 Jason Giambi A's .75 2.00
16 Rafael Palmeiro Rgr .75 2.00
17 Greg Maddux Braves 2.00 5.00
18 Hideo Nomo Sox 1.25 3.00
19 Mike Mussina O's .75 2.00
20 Sammy Sosa Sox 1.25 3.00

2004 Ultra Turn Back the Clock Jersey Copper

STATED PRINT RUN 399 SERIAL #'d SETS
*GOLD: .6X TO 1.5X COPPER
GOLD PRINT RUN 99 SERIAL #'d SETS
*SILVER: .5X TO 1.2X COPPER
SILVER PRINT RUN 199 SERIAL #'d SETS

*PATCH PLAT: 1.5X TO 4X COPPER
PATCH PLATINUM PRINT RUN 29 #'d SETS
SER.2 OVERALL GU ODDS 1:6 H, 1:48 R
AP Andy Pettitte Yanks 4.00 10.00
AR Alex Rodriguez Rgr 5.00 12.00
AS Alfonso Soriano Yanks 3.00 8.00
CS Curt Schilling Phils 3.00 8.00
GM Greg Maddux Braves 5.00 12.00
HM Hideo Nomo Sox 4.00 10.00
IR Ivan Rodriguez Marlins 4.00 10.00
JG Jason Giambi A's 3.00 8.00
JT Jim Thome Indians 4.00 10.00
MM Mike Mussina O's 4.00 10.00
MR Manny Ramirez Indians 4.00 10.00
MT Miguel Tejada A's 3.00 8.00
PR Pedro Martinez Expos 4.00 10.00
RC Roger Clemens Sox 5.00 12.00
RJ Randy Johnson M's 4.00 10.00
RP Rafael Palmeiro Rgr 4.00 10.00
SR Scott Rolen Phils 4.00 10.00
SS Sammy Sosa Sox 4.00 10.00
TG Tom Glavine Braves 4.00 10.00
VG Vladimir Guerrero Expos 4.00 10.00

2005 Ultra

This 220-card set, the first of the 2005 sets to hit the market, was released in November, 2004. Both the eight-card hobby and retail packs were issued with an $3 SRP although the insert ratios were far different between the two classes of packs. The hobby packs were issued 24 packs to a box and 16 boxes to a case while the hobby packs were issued 24 packs to a box and 20 boxes to a case. The first 200 cards of the set featured veterans while cards 201 through 220, which were issued at a stated rate of one in four hobby and one in five retail, feature leading prospects.

COMPLETE SET (220) 40.00 100.00
COMP.SET w/o SP's (200) 15.00 40.00
COMMON CARD (1-200) .10 .30
COMMON CARD (201-220) .75 2.00
201-220 ODDS 1:4 HOBBY, 1:5 RETAIL
1 Andy Pettitte .20 .50
2 Jose Cruz Jr. .10 .30
3 Cliff Floyd .10 .30
4 Paul Konerko .10 .30
5 Joe Mauer .30 .75
6 Scott Spiezio .10 .30
7 Ben Sheets .10 .30
8 Kerry Wood .10 .30
9 Carl Pavano .10 .30
10 Matt Morris .10 .30
11 Kaz Matsui .10 .30
12 Ivan Rodriguez .20 .50
13 Victor Martinez .10 .30
14 Justin Morneau .10 .30
15 Adam Everett .10 .30
16 Carl Crawford .10 .30
17 David Ortiz .30 .75
18 Jason Giambi .10 .30
19 Derrek Lee .20 .50
20 Magglio Ordonez .10 .30
21 Bobby Abreu .10 .30
22 Milton Bradley .10 .30
23 Jeff Bagwell .20 .50
24 Jim Edmonds .10 .30
25 Garret Anderson .10 .30
26 Jacque Jones .10 .30
27 Ted Lilly .10 .30
28 Greg Maddux .50 1.25
29 Jermaine Dye .10 .30
30 Bill Mueller .10 .30
31 Roy Oswalt .10 .30
32 Tony Womack .10 .30
33 Andruw Jones .20 .50
34 Tom Glavine .20 .50
35 Mariano Rivera .30 .75
36 Sean Casey .10 .30
37 Edgardo Alfonzo .10 .30
38 Brad Penny .10 .30
39 Johan Santana .30 .75
40 Mark Teixeira .20 .50
41 Manny Ramirez .20 .50
42 Gary Sheffield .10 .30
43 Matt Lawton .10 .30
44 Troy Percival .10 .30
45 Rocco Baldelli .10 .30
46 Doug Mientkiewicz .10 .30
47 Corey Patterson .10 .30
48 Austin Kearns .10 .30
49 Edgar Martinez .20 .50
50 Brad Radke .10 .30
51 Barry Larkin .20 .50
52 Chone Figgins .10 .30
53 Alexis Rios .10 .30
54 Alex Rodriguez .50 1.25
55 Vinny Castilla .10 .30
56 Javier Vazquez .10 .30
57 Javy Lopez .10 .30
58 Mike Cameron .10 .30
59 Brian Giles .10 .30
60 Dontrelle Willis .10 .30
61 Rafael Furcal .10 .30
62 Trot Nixon .10 .30
63 Mark Mulder .10 .30
64 Josh Beckett .10 .30
65 J.D. Drew .10 .30
66 Brandon Webb .10 .30
67 Wade Miller .10 .30
68 Lyle Overbay .10 .30
69 Pedro Martinez .20 .50
70 Rich Harden .10 .30
71 Al Leiter .10 .30
72 Adam Eaton .10 .30
73 Mike Sweeney .10 .30
74 Steve Finley .10 .30
75 Kris Benson .10 .30
76 Jim Thome .20 .50
77 Juan Pierre .10 .30
78 Bartolo Colon .10 .30
79 Carlos Delgado .10 .30
80 Jack Wilson .10 .30
81 Ken Harvey .10 .30
82 Nomar Garciaparra .30 .75
83 Paul Lo Duca .10 .30
84 Cesar Izturis .10 .30
85 Adrian Beltre .10 .30
86 Brian Roberts .10 .30
87 David Eckstein .10 .30
88 Jimmy Rollins .10 .30
89 Roger Clemens .50 1.25
90 Randy Johnson .30 .75
91 Orlando Hudson .10 .30
92 Tim Hudson .10 .30
93 Dmitri Young .10 .30
94 Chipper Jones .30 .75
95 John Smoltz .20 .50
96 Billy Wagner .10 .30
97 Hideo Nomo .30 .75
98 Sammy Sosa .30 .75
99 Darin Erstad .10 .30
100 Todd Helton .20 .50
101 Aubrey Huff .10 .30
102 Alfonso Soriano .10 .30
103 Jose Vidro .10 .30
104 Carlos Lee .10 .30
105 Corey Koskie .10 .30
106 Bret Boone .10 .30
107 Torii Hunter .10 .30
108 Aramis Ramirez .10 .30
109 Chase Utley .20 .50
110 Reggie Sanders .10 .30
111 Livan Hernandez .10 .30
112 Jeromy Burnitz .10 .30
113 Carlos Zambrano .10 .30
114 Hank Blalock .10 .30
115 Sidney Ponson .10 .30
116 Zack Greinke .10 .30
117 Trevor Hoffman .10 .30
118 Jeff Kent .10 .30
119 Richie Sexson .10 .30
120 Melvin Mora .10 .30
121 Eric Chavez .10 .30
122 Miguel Cabrera .20 .50
123 Ryan Freel .10 .30
124 Russ Ortiz .10 .30
125 Craig Wilson .10 .30
126 Craig Biggio .20 .50
127 Curt Schilling .20 .50
128 Kaz Ishii .10 .30
129 Marquis Grissom .10 .30
130 Bernie Williams .20 .50
131 Travis Hafner .10 .30
132 Hee Seop Choi .10 .30
133 Scott Rolen .20 .50
134 Tony Batista .10 .30
135 Frank Thomas .30 .75
136 Jason Varitek .30 .75
137 Ichiro Suzuki .60 1.50
138 Junior Spivey .10 .30
139 Adam Dunn .10 .30
140 Jorge Posada .20 .50
141 Edgar Renteria .10 .30
142 Hideki Matsui .50 1.25
143 Carlos Guillen .10 .30
144 Jody Gerut .10 .30
145 Wily Mo Pena .10 .30
146 Derek Jeter .60 1.50
147 C.C. Sabathia .10 .30
148 Geoff Jenkins .10 .30
149 Albert Pujols .60 1.50
150 Eric Munson .10 .30
151 Moises Alou .10 .30
152 Jerry Hairston .10 .30
153 Ray Durham .10 .30
154 Mike Piazza .30 .75
155 Omar Vizquel .10 .30
156 A.J. Pierzynski .10 .30
157 Michael Young .10 .30
158 Jason Bay .10 .30
159 Mark Loretta .10 .30
160 Shawn Green .10 .30
161 Luis Gonzalez .10 .30
162 Johnny Damon .20 .50
163 Eric Milton .10 .30
164 Mike Lowell .10 .30
165 Jose Guillen .10 .30
166 Eric Hinske .10 .30
167 Jason Kendall .10 .30
168 Carlos Beltran .10 .30
169 Johnny Estrada .10 .30
170 Scott Hatteberg .10 .30
171 Laynce Nix .10 .30
172 Eric Gagne .10 .30
173 Richard Hidalgo .10 .30
174 Bobby Crosby .10 .30
175 Woody Williams .10 .30
176 Justin Leone .10 .30
177 Orlando Cabrera .10 .30
178 Mark Prior .20 .50
179 Jorge Julio .10 .30
180 Jamie Moyer .10 .30
181 Jose Reyes .10 .30
182 Ken Griffey Jr. .50 1.25
183 Mike Lieberthal .10 .30
184 Kenny Rogers .10 .30
185 Mike Mussina .20 .50
186 Preston Wilson .10 .30
187 Khalil Greene .20 .50
188 Angel Berroa .10 .30
189 Miguel Tejada .10 .30
190 Freddy Garcia .10 .30
191 Pat Burrell .10 .30
192 Luis Castillo .10 .30
193 Vladimir Guerrero .30 .75
194 Roy Halladay .10 .30
195 Barry Zito .10 .30
196 Lance Berkman .10 .30
197 Rafael Palmeiro .20 .50
198 Nate Robertson .10 .30
199 Jason Schmidt .10 .30
200 Scott Podsednik .10 .30
201 Casey Kotchman AR 1.25 3.00
202 Scott Kazmir AR 2.00 5.00
203 Bucky Jacobsen AR .75 2.00
204 Jeff Keppinger AR .75 2.00
205 Dave Bush AR .75 2.00
206 Gavin Floyd AR .75 2.00
207 David Wright AR 3.00 8.00
208 B.J. Upton AR 2.00 5.00
209 David Aardsma AR .75 2.00
210 Jason Bartlett AR .75 2.00
211 Dioner Navarro AR 1.25 3.00
212 Jason Kubel AR .75 2.00
213 Ryan Howard AR 3.00 8.00
214 Charles Thomas AR .75 2.00
215 Freddy Guzman AR .75 2.00
216 Brad Halsey AR .75 2.00
217 Joey Gathright AR 1.25 3.00
218 Jeff Francis AR .75 2.00
219 Terry Tiffee AR .75 2.00
220 Nick Swisher AR 2.00 5.00

2005 Ultra Gold Medallion

*GOLD 1-200: 1.25X TO 3X BASIC
*GOLD 201-220: .6X TO 1.5X BASIC
STATED ODDS 1:1 HOBBY, 1:3 RETAIL

2005 Ultra Platinum Medallion

*PLATINUM 1-200: 8X TO 20X BASIC
*PLATINUM 201-220: 2X TO 5X BASIC
RANDOM INSERTS IN HOBBY PACKS
STATED PRINT RUN 50 SERIAL #'d SETS

2005 Ultra Season Crown Autographs Copper

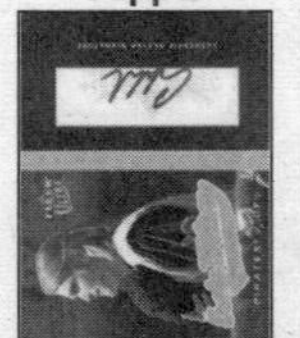

OVERALL SC AU ODDS 1:192 HOBBY
STATED PRINT RUN 199 SERIAL #'d SETS
UER'S #'d OF 199 BUT 22-199 PER MADE
ACTUAL UER QTY PROVIDED BY FLEER
31 Roy Oswalt/50 UER 10.00 25.00
80 Jack Wilson/199 8.00 20.00
125 Craig Wilson/130 UER 5.00 12.00
157 Michael Young/150 UER 8.00 20.00
200 Scott Podsednik/22 UER 20.00 50.00

2005 Ultra Season Crown Autographs Gold

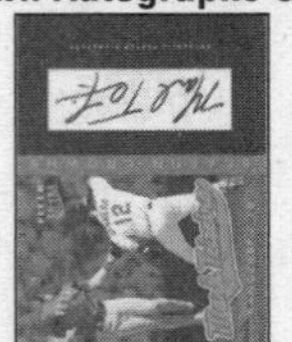

OVERALL SC AU ODDS 1:192 HOBBY
STATED PRINT RUN 99 SERIAL #'d SETS
UER'S ARE #'d OF 99 BUT 13-99 PER MADE
ACTUAL UER QTY PROVIDED BY FLEER
NO PRICING ON QTY OF 13 OR LESS
20 Magglio Ordonez/13 UER
31 Roy Oswalt/99 8.00 20.00
40 Mark Teixeira/25 UER 20.00 50.00
50 Brad Radke/89 UER 8.00 20.00
51 Barry Larkin/99 12.50 30.00
62 Trot Nixon/37 UER 10.00 25.00
70 Rich Harden/41 UER 10.00 25.00
80 Jack Wilson/99 8.00 20.00
88 Jimmy Rollins/45 UER 15.00 40.00
121 Eric Chavez/69 UER 8.00 20.00
125 Craig Wilson/99 5.00 12.00
157 Michael Young/99 8.00 20.00
200 Scott Podsednik/99 12.50 30.00
201 Casey Kotchman AR/21 UER 12.50 30.00

2005 Ultra Season Crown Autographs Masterpiece

OVERALL SC AU ODDS 1:192 HOBBY
STATED PRINT RUN 1 SERIAL #'d SET
NO PRICING DUE TO SCARCITY

2005 Ultra Season Crown Autographs Platinum

OVERALL SC AU ODDS 1:192 HOBBY
STATED PRINT RUN 50 SERIAL #'d SETS
UER'S ARE #'d OF 50 BUT 7-50 PER MADE
ACTUAL UER QTY PROVIDED BY FLEER
NO PRICING ON QTY OF 10 OR LESS
8 Kerry Wood/7 UER
12 Ivan Rodriguez/25 UER 30.00 60.00
20 Magglio Ordonez/50 10.00 25.00
25 Garret Anderson/50 10.00 25.00
31 Roy Oswalt/50 10.00 25.00
35 Mariano Rivera/25 UER 30.00 60.00
40 Mark Teixeira/50 15.00 40.00
41 Manny Ramirez/25 UER 30.00 60.00
50 Brad Radke/50 10.00 25.00
51 Barry Larkin/50 15.00 40.00
62 Trot Nixon/50 10.00 25.00
65 J.D. Drew/19 UER 15.00 40.00
70 Rich Harden/50 10.00 25.00
80 Jack Wilson/50 10.00 25.00
87 David Eckstein/45 UER 20.00 50.00
88 Jimmy Rollins/50 15.00 40.00
90 Randy Johnson/10 UER
94 Chipper Jones/19 UER 40.00 80.00
95 John Smoltz/23 UER 30.00 60.00
96 Billy Wagner/50 15.00 40.00
116 Zack Greinke/49 UER 6.00 15.00
121 Eric Chavez/50 10.00 25.00
125 Craig Wilson/50 6.00 15.00
130 Bernie Williams/15 UER 40.00 80.00
136 Jason Varitek/19 UER 40.00 80.00
149 Albett Pujols/10 UER
154 Mike Piazza/10 UER
157 Michael Young/50 10.00 25.00
161 Luis Gonzalez/50 10.00 25.00
185 Mike Mussina/50 15.00 40.00
195 Barry Zito/50 10.00 25.00
199 Jason Schmidt/50 10.00 25.00
200 Scott Podsednik/50 15.00 40.00
201 Casey Kotchman AR/50 10.00 25.00

2005 Ultra Season Crowns Game Used Copper

STATED PRINT RUN 399 SERIAL #'d SETS
*GOLD: .5X TO 1.2X COPPER
GOLD PRINT RUN 99 SERIAL #'d SETS
*PLATINUM: .75X TO 2X COPPER
*PLATINUM PATCH: ADD 100% PREMIUM
PLATINUM PRINT RUN 25 SERIAL #'d SETS
OVERALL SC GU 1:24 HOBBY
1 Andy Pettitte Jsy 4.00 10.00
3 Cliff Floyd Jsy 3.00 8.00
7 Ben Sheets Jsy 3.00 8.00
8 Kerry Wood Jsy 3.00 8.00
11 Kaz Matsui Bat 6.00 15.00
13 Victor Martinez Jsy 3.00 8.00
17 David Ortiz Jsy 4.00 10.00
20 Magglio Ordonez Bat 3.00 8.00
21 Bobby Abreu Bat 3.00 8.00
24 Jim Edmonds Jsy 3.00 8.00
31 Roy Oswalt Jsy 3.00 8.00
33 Andruw Jones Jsy 4.00 10.00
34 Tom Glavine Bat 4.00 10.00
36 Sean Casey Jsy 3.00 8.00
37 Edgardo Alfonzo Bat 3.00 8.00
41 Manny Ramirez Bat 4.00 10.00
42 Gary Sheffield Bat 3.00 8.00
45 Rocco Baldelli Jsy 3.00 8.00
48 Austin Kearns Jsy 3.00 8.00
49 Edgar Martinez Jsy 4.00 10.00
60 Dontrelle Willis Jsy 3.00 8.00
65 J.D. Drew Jsy 3.00 8.00
70 Rich Harden Jsy 3.00 8.00
71 Al Leiter Jsy 3.00 8.00
80 Jack Wilson Bat 3.00 8.00
93 Dmitri Young Bat 3.00 8.00
94 Chipper Jones Bat 4.00 10.00

97 Hideo Nomo Jsy 4.00 10.00
98 Sammy Sosa Bat 4.00 10.00
100 Todd Helton Bat 4.00 10.00
102 Alfonso Soriano Bat 3.00 8.00
107 Torii Hunter Jsy 3.00 8.00
114 Hank Blalock Bat 3.00 8.00
119 Richie Sexson Jsy 3.00 8.00
121 Eric Chavez Jsy 3.00 8.00
130 Bernie Williams Bat 4.00 10.00
135 Frank Thomas Bat 4.00 10.00
139 Adam Dunn Bat 3.00 8.00
142 Hideki Matsui Bat 10.00 25.00
144 Jody Gerut Bat 3.00 8.00
154 Mike Piazza Bat 4.00 10.00
158 Jason Bay Bat 3.00 8.00
162 Johnny Damon Jsy 4.00 10.00
168 Carlos Beltran Bat 3.00 8.00
173 Richard Hidalgo Jsy 3.00 8.00
181 Jose Reyes Bat 3.00 8.00
187 Khalil Greene Jsy 4.00 10.00
191 Pat Burrell Bat 3.00 8.00
193 Vladimir Guerrero Bat 4.00 10.00
197 Rafael Palmeiro Jsy 4.00 10.00

2005 Ultra 3 Kings Jersey Triple Swatch

BCB Jeff Bagwell 20.00 50.00
Roger Clemens
Lance Berkman
BCR Josh Beckett 15.00 40.00
Miguel Cabrera
Ivan Rodriguez
JMM Randy Johnson 15.00 40.00
Greg Maddux
Pedro Martinez
MPW Greg Maddux 20.00 50.00
Mark Prior
Kerry Wood
PDC Albert Pujols 20.00 50.00
Adam Dunn
Miguel Cabrera
RJB Scott Rolen 15.00 40.00
Chipper Jones
Adrian Beltre
SMP Gary Sheffield 20.00 50.00
Hideki Matsui
Mike Piazza
SMR Curt Schilling 30.00 60.00
Pedro Martinez
Manny Ramirez
TBS Mark Teixeira 15.00 40.00
Hank Blalock
Alfonso Soriano
TBW Jim Thome 15.00 40.00
Pat Burrell
Billy Wagner

2005 Ultra Follow the Leader

COMPLETE SET (15) 10.00 25.00
STATED ODDS 1:6 HOBBY, 1:8 RETAIL
*DIE CUT: .6X TO 1.5X BASIC
DIE CUT RANDOM IN EXCEL/MVP RETAIL
1 Roger Clemens 1.25 3.00
2 Albert Pujols 1.50 4.00
3 Sammy Sosa .75 2.00
4 Manny Ramirez .75 2.00
5 Vladimir Guerrero .75 2.00
6 Ivan Rodriguez .75 2.00
7 Mike Piazza .75 2.00
8 Scott Rolen .75 2.00
9 Ichiro Suzuki 1.50 4.00
10 Randy Johnson .75 2.00
11 Mark Prior .75 2.00
12 Jim Thome .75 2.00
13 Greg Maddux 1.25 3.00
14 Pedro Martinez .75 2.00
15 Miguel Cabrera .75 2.00

2005 Ultra Follow the Leader Jersey Copper

COPPER ISSUED ONLY IN HOBBY PACKS
*GOLD: .4X TO 1X COPPER
GOLD PRINT RUN 250 SERIAL #'d SETS
*PLATINUM: .5X TO 1.2X COPPER
*PLATINUM PATCH: ADD 100% PREMIUM
PLATINUM PRINT RUN 99 SERIAL #'d SETS
PLATINUM ISSUED ONLY IN HOBBY PACKS
*RED: .4X TO 1X COPPER
RED STATED ODDS 1:48 RETAIL
RED RANDOM IN HOBBY HOT PACKS
*ULTRA p/r 45-51: .75X TO 2X COPPER
*ULTRA p/r 21-31: 1X TO 2.5X COPPER
ULTRA PRINT RUNS B/WN 5-51 PER
NO ULTRA PRICING ON QTY OF 7 OR LESS
OVERALL GU ODDS 1:12 HOB, 1:48 RET
AP Albert Pujols 6.00 15.00
GM Greg Maddux 6.00 15.00
IR Ivan Rodriguez 4.00 10.00
JT Jim Thome 4.00 10.00
MC Miguel Cabrera 4.00 10.00
MPI Mike Piazza 4.00 10.00
MPR Mark Prior 4.00 10.00
MR Manny Ramirez 4.00 10.00
PM Pedro Martinez 4.00 10.00
RC Roger Clemens 6.00 15.00
RJ Randy Johnson 4.00 10.00
SR Scott Rolen 3.00 8.00
SS Sammy Sosa 4.00 10.00
VG Vladimir Guerrero 4.00 10.00

2005 Ultra Kings

OVERALL KINGS ODDS 1:12 HOB, 1:24 RET
K PERCEIVED 3X TOUGHER THAN HR-RBI
*GOLD: 2X TO 5X BASIC HR-RBI
*GOLD: 1.25X TO 3X BASIC K
GOLD RANDOM INSERTS IN HOBBY PACKS
GOLD PRINT RUN 50 SERIAL #'d SETS
H1 Jim Thome HR 1.00 2.50
H2 David Ortiz HR 1.00 2.50
H3 Adam Dunn HR 1.00 2.50
H4 Albert Pujols HR 2.00 5.00
H5 Manny Ramirez HR 1.00 2.50
H6 Vladimir Guerrero HR 1.00 2.50
H7 Miguel Tejada HR 1.00 2.50
H8 Rafael Palmeiro HR 1.00 2.50
H9 Mark Teixeira HR 1.00 2.50
H10 Sammy Sosa HR 1.00 2.50
H11 Frank Thomas HR 1.00 2.50
H12 Pat Burrell HR 1.00 2.50
H13 Adrian Beltre HR 1.00 2.50
H14 Miguel Cabrera HR 1.00 2.50
H15 Gary Sheffield HR 1.00 2.50
K1 Pedro Martinez K 1.50 4.00
K2 Randy Johnson K 1.50 4.00
K3 Mark Mulder K 1.50 4.00
K4 Barry Zito K 1.50 4.00
K5 Roger Clemens K 2.50 6.00
K6 Mark Prior K 1.50 4.00
K7 Ben Sheets K 1.50 4.00
K8 Curt Schilling K 1.50 4.00
K9 Billy Wagner K 1.50 4.00
K10 Eric Gagne K 1.50 4.00
K11 Josh Beckett K 1.50 4.00
K12 Kerry Wood K 1.50 4.00
K13 Jason Schmidt K 1.50 4.00
K14 Roy Halladay K 1.50 4.00
K15 Greg Maddux K 2.50 6.00
R1 Sean Casey RBI 1.00 2.50
R2 Ivan Rodriguez RBI 1.00 2.50
R3 Mike Piazza RBI 1.00 2.50
R4 Todd Helton RBI 1.00 2.50
R5 Scott Rolen RBI 1.00 2.50
R6 Hideki Matsui RBI 1.50 4.00
R7 Gary Sheffield RBI 1.00 2.50
R8 Alfonso Soriano RBI 1.00 2.50
R9 Bobby Abreu RBI 1.00 2.50
R10 Lance Berkman RBI 1.00 2.50
R11 Miguel Tejada RBI 1.00 2.50
R12 Travis Hafner RBI 1.00 2.50
R13 Hank Blalock RBI 1.00 2.50
R14 Jeff Bagwell RBI 1.00 2.50
R15 Chipper Jones RBI 1.00 2.50

2005 Ultra Kings Jersey Gold

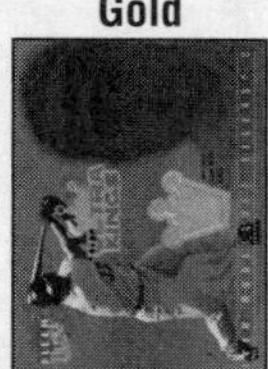

STATED PRINT RUN 150 SERIAL #'d SETS
*ULTRA p/r 75: .5X TO 1.2X GOLD
*ULTRA p/r 38-55: .6X TO 1.5X GOLD
*ULTRA p/r 20-34: .75X TO 2X GOLD
*ULTRA p/r 15-17: 1X TO 2.5X GOLD
ULTRA PRINT RUN B/WN 5-75 #'d PER
NO ULTRA PRICING ON QTY 13 OR LESS
*PLATINUM: .6X TO 1.5X COPPER
*PLATINUM PATCH: ADD 100% PREMIUM
PLATINUM PRINT RUN 25 SERIAL #'d SETS
PLATINUM ISSUED ONLY IN HOBBY PACKS
OVERALL GU ODDS 1:12 HOB, 1:48 RET
AB Adrian Beltre HR 4.00 10.00
AD Adam Dunn HR 4.00 10.00
AP Albert Pujols HR 8.00 20.00
AS Alfonso Soriano RBI 4.00 10.00
BA Bobby Abreu RBI 4.00 10.00
BS Ben Sheets K 4.00 10.00
BW Billy Wagner K 4.00 10.00
BZ Barry Zito K 4.00 10.00
CJ Chipper Jones RBI 5.00 12.00
CS Curt Schilling K 5.00 12.00
DO David Ortiz HR 5.00 12.00
EG Eric Gagne K 4.00 10.00
FT Frank Thomas HR 5.00 12.00
GM Greg Maddux K 8.00 20.00
GSH Gary Sheffield HR 4.00 10.00
GSR Gary Sheffield RBI 4.00 10.00
HB Hank Blalock RBI 4.00 10.00
HM Hideki Matsui RBI 12.50 30.00
IR Ivan Rodriguez RBI 5.00 12.00
JBA Jeff Bagwell RBI 5.00 12.00
JBE Josh Beckett K 4.00 10.00
JS Jason Schmidt K 4.00 10.00
JT Jim Thome HR 5.00 12.00
KW Kerry Wood K 4.00 10.00
LB Lance Berkman RBI 4.00 10.00
MC Miguel Cabrera HR 5.00 12.00
MM Mark Mulder K 4.00 10.00
MPI Mike Piazza RBI 5.00 12.00
MPR Mark Prior K 5.00 12.00
MR Manny Ramirez HR 5.00 12.00
MTH Miguel Tejada HR 4.00 10.00
MTR Miguel Tejada RBI 4.00 10.00
MTX Mark Teixeira HR 5.00 12.00
PB Pat Burrell HR 4.00 10.00
PM Pedro Martinez K 5.00 12.00
RC Roger Clemens K 8.00 20.00
RH Roy Halladay K 4.00 10.00
RJ Randy Johnson K 5.00 12.00
RP Rafael Palmeiro HR 5.00 12.00
SC Sean Casey RBI 4.00 10.00
SR Scott Rolen RBI 5.00 12.00
SS Sammy Sosa HR 5.00 12.00
THA Travis Hafner RBI 4.00 10.00
THE Todd Helton RBI 5.00 12.00
VG Vladimir Guerrero HR 5.00 12.00

2006 Ultra

This 251-card set was released in June, 2006. The set was issued in eight-card hobby and retail packs, both of which had an $2.99 SRP and both came 24 packs to a box and 12 boxes to a case. Cards numbered 1-180 feature veterans while cards 181-200 feature 2006 rookies and cards 201-250 were a Retro Lucky 13 subset. Those Retro Lucky subset cards were inserted at a stated rate of one in four hobby or retail packs. Card number 251 was an exchange for Kenji Johjima, and that card was announced to have a print run of 5000 cards. The Johjima card was issued as an exchange and that card could be redeemed until May 25, 2008.

COMP.SET w/o RL13 (200) 15.00 40.00
COMMON CARD (1-180) .15 .40
RL13 201-250 ODDS 1:4 HOBBY, 1:4 RETAIL
251 PRINT RUN 5000 CARDS
251 JOHJIMA IS NOT SERIAL NUMBERED
251 PRINT RUN INFO PROVIDED BY UD
251 JOHJIMA EXCH. DEADLINE 05/25/08
1 Vladimir Guerrero .40 1.00
2 Bartolo Colon .15 .40
3 Francisco Rodriguez .15 .40
4 Darin Erstad .15 .40
5 Chone Figgins .15 .40
6 Bengie Molina .15 .40
7 Roger Clemens .75 2.00
8 Lance Berkman .15 .40
9 Morgan Ensberg .15 .40
10 Roy Oswalt .15 .40
11 Andy Pettitte .25 .60
12 Craig Biggio .25 .60
13 Eric Chavez .15 .40
14 Barry Zito .15 .40
15 Huston Street .15 .40
16 Bobby Crosby .15 .40
17 Nick Swisher .15 .40
18 Rich Harden .15 .40
19 Vernon Wells .15 .40
20 Roy Halladay .15 .40
21 Alex Rios .15 .40
22 Orlando Hudson .15 .40
23 Shea Hillenbrand .15 .40
24 Gustavo Chacin .15 .40
25 Chipper Jones .40 1.00
26 Andruw Jones .25 .60
27 Jeff Francoeur .40 1.00
28 John Smoltz .25 .60
29 Tim Hudson .15 .40
30 Marcus Giles .15 .40
31 Carlos Lee .15 .40
32 Ben Sheets .15 .40
33 Rickie Weeks .15 .40
34 Chris Capuano .15 .40
35 Geoff Jenkins .15 .40
36 Brady Clark .15 .40
37 Albert Pujols .75 2.00
38 Jim Edmonds .25 .60
39 Chris Carpenter .15 .40
40 Mark Mulder .15 .40
41 Yadier Molina .15 .40
42 Scott Rolen .25 .60
43 Derrek Lee .15 .40
44 Mark Prior .25 .60
45 Aramis Ramirez .15 .40
46 Carlos Zambrano .15 .40
47 Greg Maddux .60 1.50
48 Nomar Garciaparra .40 1.00
49 Jonny Gomes .15 .40
50 Carl Crawford .15 .40
51 Scott Kazmir .25 .60
52 Jorge Cantu .15 .40
53 Julio Lugo .15 .40
54 Aubrey Huff .15 .40
55 Luis Gonzalez .15 .40
56 Brandon Webb .15 .40
57 Troy Glaus .15 .40
58 Shawn Green .15 .40
59 Craig Counsell .15 .40
60 Conor Jackson (RC) .60 1.50
61 Jeff Kent .15 .40
62 Eric Gagne .15 .40
63 J.D. Drew .15 .40
64 Milton Bradley .15 .40
65 Jeff Weaver .15 .40
66 Cesar Izturis .15 .40
67 Jason Schmidt .15 .40
68 Moises Alou .15 .40
69 Pedro Feliz .15 .40
70 Randy Winn .15 .40
71 Omar Vizquel .25 .60
72 Noah Lowry .15 .40
73 Travis Hafner .15 .40
74 Victor Martinez .15 .40
75 C.C. Sabathia .15 .40
76 Grady Sizemore .25 .60
77 Coco Crisp .15 .40
78 Cliff Lee .15 .40
79 Raul IbaÃ±ez .15 .40
80 Ichiro Suzuki .60 1.50
81 Richie Sexson .15 .40
82 Felix Hernandez .25 .60
83 Adrian Beltre .15 .40
84 Jamie Moyer .15 .40
85 Miguel Cabrera .25 .60
86 A.J. Burnett .15 .40
87 Juan Pierre .15 .40
88 Carlos Delgado .15 .40
89 Dontrelle Willis .15 .40
90 Juan Encarnacion .15 .40
91 Carlos Beltran .15 .40
92 Jose Reyes .40 1.00
93 David Wright .60 1.50
94 Tom Glavine .25 .60
95 Mike Piazza .40 1.00
96 Pedro Martinez .25 .60
97 Ryan Zimmerman (RC) 1.25 3.00
98 Nick Johnson .15 .40
99 Jose Vidro .15 .40
100 Jose Guillen .15 .40
101 Livan Hernandez .15 .40
102 John Patterson .15 .40
103 Miguel Tejada .15 .40
104 Melvin Mora .15 .40
105 Brian Roberts .15 .40
106 Erik Bedard .15 .40
107 Javy Lopez .15 .40
108 Rodrigo Lopez .15 .40
109 Jake Peavy .15 .40
110 Mike Cameron .15 .40
111 Mark Loretta .15 .40
112 Brian Giles .15 .40
113 Trevor Hoffman .15 .40
114 Ramon Hernandez .15 .40
115 Bobby Abreu .15 .40
116 Chase Utley .40 1.00
117 Pat Burrell .15 .40
118 Jimmy Rollins .15 .40
119 Ryan Howard .60 1.50
120 Billy Wagner .15 .40
121 Jason Bay .15 .40
122 Oliver Perez .15 .40
123 Jack Wilson .15 .40
124 Zach Duke .15 .40
125 Rob Mackowiak .15 .40
126 Freddy Sanchez .15 .40
127 Mark Teixeira .25 .60
128 Michael Young .15 .40
129 Alfonso Soriano .15 .40
130 Hank Blalock .15 .40
131 Kenny Rogers .15 .40
132 Kevin Mench .15 .40
133 Manny Ramirez .25 .60
134 Josh Beckett .15 .40
135 David Ortiz .40 1.00
136 Johnny Damon .25 .60
137 Edgar Renteria .15 .40
138 Curt Schilling .25 .60
139 Ken Griffey Jr. .60 1.50
140 Adam Dunn .15 .40
141 Felipe Lopez .15 .40
142 Wily Mo Pena .15 .40
143 Aaron Harang .15 .40
144 Sean Casey .15 .40
145 Todd Helton .25 .60
146 Garrett Atkins .15 .40
147 Matt Holliday .40 1.00
148 Jeff Francis .15 .40
149 Clint Barmes .15 .40
150 Luis Gonzalez .15 .40
151 Mike Sweeney .15 .40
152 Zack Greinke .15 .40
153 Angel Berroa .15 .40
154 Emil Brown .15 .40
155 David DeJesus .15 .40
156 Ivan Rodriguez .25 .60
157 Jeremy Bonderman .15 .40
158 Brandon Inge .15 .40
159 Craig Monroe .15 .40
160 Chris Shelton .15 .40
161 Dmitri Young .15 .40
162 Johan Santana .25 .60
163 Joe Mauer .25 .60
164 Torii Hunter .15 .40
165 Shannon Stewart .15 .40
166 Scott Baker .15 .40
167 Brad Radke .15 .40
168 Jon Garland .15 .40
169 Tadahito Iguchi .15 .40
170 Paul Konerko .15 .40
171 Scott Podsednik .15 .40
172 Mark Buehrle .15 .40
173 Joe Crede .15 .40
174 Derek Jeter 1.00 2.50
175 Alex Rodriguez .60 1.50
176 Hideki Matsui .60 1.50
177 Randy Johnson .40 1.00
178 Gary Sheffield .15 .40
179 Mariano Rivera .40 1.00
180 Jason Giambi .15 .40
181 Joey Devine RC .40 1.00
182 Alejandro Freire RC .40 1.00
183 Craig Hansen RC .75 2.00
184 Robert Andino RC .40 1.00
185 Ryan Jorgensen RC .40 1.00
186 Chris Demaria RC .40 1.00
187 Jonah Bayliss RC .40 1.00
188 Ryan Theriot RC .30 .75
189 Steve Stemle RC .40 1.00
190 Brian Myrow RC .40 1.00
191 Chris Heintz RC .40 1.00
192 Ron Flores RC .40 1.00
193 Danny Sandoval RC .40 1.00
194 Craig Breslow RC .40 1.00
195 Jeremy Accardo RC .40 1.00
196 Jeff Harris RC .40 1.00
197 Tim Corcoran RC .40 1.00
198 Scott Feldman RC .40 1.00
199 Robinson Cano .25 .60
200 Jason Bergmann RC .75 2.00
201 Ken Griffey Jr. RL13 3.00 8.00
202 Frank Thomas RL13 2.00 5.00
203 Chipper Jones RL13 2.00 5.00
204 Tony Clark RL13 .75 2.00
205 Mike Lieberthal RL13 .75 2.00
206 Manny Ramirez RL13 1.25 3.00
207 Phil Nevin RL13 .75 2.00
208 Derek Jeter RL13 4.00 10.00
209 Preston Wilson RL13 .75 2.00
210 Billy Wagner RL13 .75 2.00
211 Alex Rodriguez RL13 3.00 8.00
212 Trot Nixon RL13 .75 2.00
213 Jaret Wright RL13 .75 2.00
214 Nomar Garciaparra RL13 2.00 5.00
215 Paul Konerko RL13 .75 2.00
216 Paul Wilson RL13 .75 2.00
217 Dustin Hermanson RL13 .75 2.00
218 Todd Walker RL13 .75 2.00
219 Matt Morris RL13 .75 2.00
220 Darin Erstad RL13 .75 2.00
221 Todd Helton RL13 1.25 3.00
222 Geoff Jenkins RL13 .75 2.00
223 Eric Chavez RL13 .75 2.00
224 Kris Benson RL13 .75 2.00
225 Jon Garland RL13 .75 2.00
226 Troy Glaus RL13 .75 2.00
227 Vernon Wells RL13 .75 2.00
228 Michael Cuddyer RL13 .75 2.00
229 Justin Verlander RL13 3.00 8.00
230 Pat Burrell RL13 .75 2.00
231 Mark Mulder RL13 .75 2.00
232 Corey Patterson RL13 .75 2.00
233 J.D. Drew RL13 .75 2.00
234 Austin Kearns RL13 .75 2.00
235 Felipe Lopez RL13 .75 2.00
236 Sean Burroughs RL13 .75 2.00
237 Ben Sheets RL13 .75 2.00
238 Brett Myers RL13 .75 2.00
239 Josh Beckett RL13 .75 2.00
240 Barry Zito RL13 .75 2.00
241 Adrian Gonzalez RL13 .75 2.00
242 Rocco Baldelli RL13 .75 2.00
243 Chris Burke RL13 .75 2.00
244 Joe Mauer RL13 1.25 3.00
245 Mark Prior RL13 1.25 3.00
246 Mark Teixeira RL13 1.25 3.00
247 Khalil Greene RL13 1.25 3.00
248 Zack Greinke RL13 .75 2.00
249 Prince Fielder RL13 3.00 8.00
250 Rickie Weeks RL13 .75 2.00
251 Kenji Johjima 6.00 15.00

2006 Ultra Gold Medallion

COMP.SET w/o RL13 (200) 60.00 120.00
*GOLD 1-180: 1X TO 2.5X BASIC
*GOLD 60/97/181-198/200: .6X TO 1.5X BASIC
GOLD 1-200 ODDS 1:1 HOBBY/RETAIL
*GOLD 201-250: .5X TO 1.2X BASIC
GOLD 201-250 ODDS 1:24 HOB, 1:72 RET

2006 Ultra Autographics

STATED ODDS 1:576 HOBBY, 1:1920 RETAIL
NO PRICING DUE TO SCARCITY
AF Alejandro Freire
AS Alfonso Soriano SP
BR Brian Roberts
CA Chris Carpenter
CC Carl Crawford
CK Casey Kotchman
DL Derrek Lee
DS Danny Sandoval
DW Dontrelle Willis
FH Felix Hernandez
JA Jason Bay
JG Jonny Gomes
JH Jeff Harris
JM Joe Mauer
JO Joe Blanton
JR Jose Reyes
JV Justin Verlander
KG Ken Griffey Jr.
KW Kerry Wood SP
MC Matt Cain
MG Marcus Giles
MY Michael Young
NS Nick Swisher
PF Prince Fielder
PM Pedro Martinez
RC Roger Clemens
RO Roy Oswalt
RZ Ryan Zimmerman
SR Scott Rolen
SS Steve Stemle
TH Travis Hafner
TI Tadahito Iguchi
VG Vladimir Guerrero SP
VM Victor Martinez
YM Yadier Molina

2006 Ultra Diamond Producers

COMPLETE SET (25) 10.00 25.00
OVERALL INSERT ODDS 1:1 HOBBY/RETAIL
DP1 Derek Jeter 2.50 6.00
DP2 Chipper Jones 1.00 2.50
DP3 Jim Edmonds .60 1.50
DP4 Ken Griffey Jr. 1.50 4.00
DP5 David Ortiz 1.00 2.50
DP6 Manny Ramirez .60 1.50
DP7 Mark Teixeira .60 1.50
DP8 Alex Rodriguez 1.50 4.00
DP9 Jeff Kent .40 1.00
DP10 Albert Pujols 2.00 5.00
DP11 Todd Helton .60 1.50
DP12 Miguel Cabrera .60 1.50
DP13 Hideki Matsui 1.50 4.00
DP14 Derrek Lee .40 1.00
DP15 Vladimir Guerrero 1.00 2.50
DP16 Miguel Tejada .40 1.00
DP17 Jorge Cantu .40 1.00
DP18 Travis Hafner .40 1.00
DP19 Pat Burrell .40 1.00
DP20 Bobby Abreu .40 1.00
DP21 David Wright 1.50 4.00
DP22 Jason Bay .40 1.00
DP23 Adam Dunn .40 1.00
DP24 Eric Chavez .40 1.00
DP25 Paul Konerko .40 1.00

2006 Ultra Feel the Game

STATED ODDS 1:36 HOBBY, 1:72 RETAIL
AB Adrian Beltre Jsy 3.00 8.00
AJ Andruw Jones Jsy 4.00 10.00
AP Albert Pujols Jsy 8.00 20.00
AS Alfonso Soriano Jsy 3.00 8.00
BA Bobby Abreu Jsy 3.00 8.00
BG Brian Giles Jsy 3.00 8.00
CB Carlos Beltran Jsy 3.00 8.00
CD Carlos Delgado Jsy 3.00 8.00
CJ Chipper Jones Jsy 4.00 10.00
DJ Derek Jeter Jsy 10.00 25.00
DW David Wright Jsy 4.00 10.00
EC Eric Chavez Jsy 3.00 8.00
FH Felix Hernandez Jsy 4.00 10.00
FT Frank Thomas Jsy SP 4.00 10.00
GM Greg Maddux Jsy 4.00 10.00
IR Ivan Rodriguez Jsy 4.00 10.00
JB Josh Beckett Jsy 3.00 8.00
JR Jose Reyes Jsy SP 3.00 8.00
KG Ken Griffey Jr. Jsy 8.00 20.00
MC Matt Clement Jsy SP 3.00 8.00
MO Magglio Ordonez Jsy 3.00 8.00
MP Mike Piazza Jsy 4.00 10.00
MR Manny Ramirez Jsy 4.00 10.00
MT Miguel Tejada Jsy 3.00 8.00
PW Preston Wilson Jsy 3.00 8.00
RJ Randy Johnson Pants SP 4.00 10.00
RS Richie Sexson Jsy 3.00 8.00
SG Shawn Green Jsy 3.00 8.00
TG Troy Glaus Jsy 3.00 8.00
VG Vladimir Guerrero Jsy 4.00 10.00

2006 Ultra Fine Fabrics

STATED ODDS 1:18 HOBBY, 1:36 RETAIL
AB Adrian Beltre Jsy 3.00 8.00
AD Adam Dunn Jsy 3.00 8.00
AJ Andruw Jones Jsy 4.00 10.00
AP Albert Pujols Jsy 8.00 20.00
AS Alfonso Soriano Jsy 3.00 8.00
BA Bobby Abreu Jsy 3.00 8.00
BC Bobby Crosby Jsy 3.00 8.00
BG Brian Giles Jsy 3.00 8.00
BR Brian Roberts Jsy 3.00 8.00
BW Bernie Williams Jsy 4.00 10.00
BZ Barry Zito Jsy 3.00 8.00
CB Carlos Beltran Jsy 3.00 8.00
CD Carlos Delgado Jsy 3.00 8.00
CJ Chipper Jones Jsy 4.00 10.00
CP Corey Patterson Jsy 3.00 8.00
CU Chase Utley Jsy 4.00 10.00
DJ Derek Jeter Jsy 10.00 25.00
DL Derrek Lee Jsy 3.00 8.00
DO David Ortiz Jsy 4.00 10.00
DW David Wright Jsy 4.00 10.00
EC Eric Chavez Jsy 3.00 8.00
FH Felix Hernandez Jsy 4.00 10.00
FT Frank Thomas Jsy 4.00 10.00
GM Greg Maddux Jsy 4.00 10.00

HB Hank Blalock Jsy 3.00 8.00
HS Huston Street Jsy 3.00 8.00
IR Ivan Rodriguez Jsy 4.00 10.00
JB Josh Beckett Jsy 3.00 8.00
JD J.D. Drew Jsy 3.00 8.00
JG Jason Giambi Jsy 3.00 8.00
JK Jeff Kent Jsy 3.00 8.00
JP Jorge Posada Jsy 4.00 10.00
JR Jose Reyes Jsy 3.00 8.00
JS John Smoltz Jsy 4.00 10.00
KG Ken Griffey Jr. Jsy 8.00 20.00
KH Khalil Greene Jsy SP 4.00 10.00
KW Kerry Wood Jsy 3.00 8.00
MC Matt Clement Jsy 3.00 8.00
MO Magglio Ordonez Jsy 3.00 8.00
MP Mike Piazza Jsy 4.00 10.00
MR Manny Ramirez Jsy 4.00 10.00
MT Miguel Tejada Jsy 3.00 8.00
PW Preston Wilson Jsy 3.00 8.00
RC Roger Clemens Jsy SP 6.00 15.00
RH Ramon Hernandez Jsy 3.00 8.00
RJ Randy Johnson Pants SP 4.00 10.00
RK Ryan Klesko Jsy 3.00 8.00
RS Richie Sexson Jsy 3.00 8.00
RY Ryan Howard Jsy 6.00 15.00
SB Sean Burroughs Jsy 3.00 8.00
SF Steve Finley Jsy 3.00 8.00
SG Shawn Green Jsy 3.00 8.00
SR Scott Rolen Jsy 4.00 10.00
SS Sammy Sosa Jsy 4.00 10.00
TG Troy Glaus Jsy 3.00 8.00
TH Travis Hafner Jsy 3.00 8.00
TX Mark Teixeira Jsy 4.00 10.00
VG Vladimir Guerrero Jsy 4.00 10.00
VW Vernon Wells Jsy 3.00 8.00
WI Dontrelle Willis Jsy 3.00 8.00

2006 Ultra Home Run Kings

COMPLETE SET (15) 8.00 20.00
OVERALL INSERT ODDS 1:1 HOBBY/RETAIL
HRK1 Albert Pujols 2.00 5.00
HRK2 Ken Griffey Jr. 1.50 4.00
HRK3 Andruw Jones .60 1.50
HRK4 Alex Rodriguez 1.50 4.00
HRK5 David Ortiz 1.00 2.50
HRK6 Manny Ramirez .60 1.50
HRK7 Derrek Lee .40 1.00
HRK8 Mark Teixeira .60 1.50
HRK9 Adam Dunn .40 1.00
HRK10 Paul Konerko .40 1.00
HRK11 Richie Sexson .40 1.00
HRK12 Alfonso Soriano .40 1.00
HRK13 Vladimir Guerrero 1.00 2.50
HRK14 Gary Sheffield .40 1.00
HRK15 Mike Piazza 1.00 2.50

2006 Ultra Midsummer Classic Kings

COMPLETE SET (10) 6.00 15.00
OVERALL INSERT ODDS 1:1 HOBBY/RETAIL
MCK1 Ken Griffey Jr. 1.50 4.00
MCK2 Mike Piazza 1.00 2.50
MCK3 Derek Jeter 2.50 6.00
MCK4 Roger Clemens 2.00 5.00
MCK5 Randy Johnson 1.00 2.50
MCK6 Miguel Tejada .40 1.00
MCK7 Alfonso Soriano .40 1.00
MCK8 Garret Anderson .40 1.00
MCK9 Pedro Martinez .60 1.50
MCK10 Ivan Rodriguez .60 1.50

2006 Ultra RBI Kings

COMPLETE SET (20) 8.00 20.00
OVERALL INSERT ODDS 1:1 HOBBY/RETAIL
RBI1 Ken Griffey Jr. 1.50 4.00
RBI2 David Ortiz 1.00 2.50
RBI3 Manny Ramirez .60 1.50
RBI4 Mark Teixeira .60 1.50
RBI5 Alex Rodriguez 1.50 4.00
RBI6 Andruw Jones .60 1.50
RBI7 Jeff Bagwell .60 1.50
RBI8 Gary Sheffield .40 1.00
RBI9 Richie Sexson .40 1.00
RBI10 Jeff Kent .40 1.00
RBI11 Albert Pujols 2.00 5.00
RBI12 Todd Helton .60 1.50
RBI13 Miguel Cabrera .60 1.50
RBI14 Hideki Matsui 1.50 4.00
RBI15 Carlos Delgado .40 1.00
RBI16 Carlos Lee .40 1.00
RBI17 Derrek Lee .40 1.00
RBI18 Vladimir Guerrero 1.00 2.50
RBI19 Luis Gonzalez .40 1.00
RBI20 Mike Piazza 1.00 2.50

2006 Ultra Rising Stars

COMPLETE SET (10) 6.00 15.00
OVERALL INSERT ODDS 1:1 HOBBY/RETAIL
URS1 Ryan Howard 2.00 5.00
URS2 Huston Street .40 1.00
URS3 Jeff Francoeur 1.50 4.00
URS4 Felix Hernandez .60 1.50
URS5 Chase Utley 1.25 3.00
URS6 Robinson Cano .60 1.50
URS7 Zach Duke .40 1.00
URS8 Scott Kazmir .60 1.50
URS9 Willy Taveras .40 1.00
URS10 Tadahito Iguchi .40 1.00

2006 Ultra Star

OVERALL ODDS 2:1 FAT PACKS
1 Ken Griffey Jr. 1.50 4.00
2 Derek Jeter 2.50 6.00
3 Albert Pujols 2.00 5.00
4 Alex Rodriguez 1.50 4.00
5 Vladimir Guerrero 1.00 2.50
6 Roger Clemens 2.00 5.00
7 Derrek Lee .40 1.00
8 David Ortiz 1.00 2.50
9 Miguel Cabrera .60 1.50
10 Bobby Abreu .40 1.00
11 Mark Teixeira .60 1.50
12 Johan Santana 1.00 2.50
13 Hideki Matsui 1.00 2.50
14 Ichiro Suzuki 1.50 4.00
15 Andruw Jones .60 1.50
16 Eric Chavez .40 1.00
17 Roy Oswalt .40 1.00
18 Curt Schilling .60 1.50
19 Randy Johnson 1.00 2.50
20 Ivan Rodriguez .60 1.50
21 Chipper Jones 1.00 2.50
22 Mark Prior .60 1.50
23 Jason Bay .40 1.00
24 Pedro Martinez .60 1.50
25 David Wright 1.50 4.00
26 Carlos Beltran .40 1.00
27 Jim Edmonds .60 1.50
28 Chris Carpenter .40 1.00
29 Roy Halladay .40 1.00
30 Jake Peavy .40 1.00
31 Paul Konerko .40 1.00
32 Travis Hafner .40 1.00
33 Barry Zito .40 1.00
34 Miguel Tejada .40 1.00
35 Josh Beckett .40 1.00
36 Todd Helton .60 1.50
37 Dontrelle Willis .40 1.00
38 Manny Ramirez .60 1.50
39 Mariano Rivera 1.00 2.50
40 Jeff Kent .40 1.00

2006 Ultra Strikeout Kings

COMPLETE SET (10) 6.00 15.00
OVERALL INSERT ODDS 1:1 HOBBY/RETAIL
SOK1 Roger Clemens 2.00 5.00
SOK2 Johan Santana .60 1.50
SOK3 Jake Peavy .40 1.00
SOK4 Randy Johnson 1.00 2.50
SOK5 Curt Schilling .60 1.50
SOK6 Chris Carpenter .40 1.00
SOK7 Pedro Martinez .60 1.50
SOK8 Mark Prior .60 1.50
SOK9 Carlos Zambrano .40 1.00
SOK10 John Smoltz .60 1.50

2007 Ultra

This 250-card set was released in July, 2007. This set was issued both in hobby and retail versions. The hobby version came five cards to a pack which came five packs to a box and 16 boxes to a case. Cards numbered 1-200 featured veterans sequenced in team alphabetical order while cards 201-250 featured rookies with the final 13 cards of the set being Lucky 13 rookies.

COMP.SET w/o RC's (200) 20.00 50.00
COMMON CARD .20 .50
COMMON ROOKIE 1.00 2.50
COMMON L13 1.00 2.50
PRINTING PLATE ODDS 1:1252 HOB/RET
PLATE PRINT RUN 1 SET PER COLOR
BLACK-CYAN-MAGENTA-YELLOW ISSUED
NO PLATE PRICING DUE TO SCARCITY
1 Brandon Webb .20 .50
2 Randy Johnson .50 1.25
3 Conor Jackson .20 .50
4 Stephen Drew .30 .75
5 Eric Byrnes .20 .50
6 Carlos Quentin .20 .50
7 Andruw Jones .30 .75
8 Chipper Jones .50 1.25
9 Jeff Francoeur .50 1.25
10 Tim Hudson .20 .50
11 John Smoltz .30 .75
12 Edgar Renteria .20 .50
13 Erik Bedard .20 .50
14 Kris Benson .20 .50
15 Miguel Tejada .20 .50
16 Nick Markakis .30 .75
17 Brian Roberts .20 .50
18 Melvin Mora .20 .50
19 Aubrey Huff .20 .50
20 Curt Schilling .30 .75
21 Jonathan Papelbon .50 1.25
22 Josh Beckett .30 .75
23 Jason Varitek .50 1.25
24 David Ortiz .50 1.25
25 Manny Ramirez .30 .75
26 J.D. Drew .20 .50
27 Carlos Zambrano .20 .50
28 Derrek Lee .20 .50
29 Aramis Ramirez .20 .50
30 Alfonso Soriano .20 .50
31 Rich Hill .20 .50
32 Jacque Jones .20 .50
33 A.J. Pierzynski .20 .50
34 Jermaine Dye .20 .50
35 Paul Konerko .20 .50
36 Bobby Jenks .20 .50
37 Jon Garland .20 .50
38 Mark Buehrle .20 .50
39 Tadahito Iguchi .20 .50
40 Adam Dunn .20 .50
41 Ken Griffey Jr. .75 2.00
42 Aaron Harang .20 .50
43 Bronson Arroyo .20 .50
44 Ryan Freel .20 .50
45 Brandon Phillips .20 .50
46 Grady Sizemore .30 .75
47 Travis Hafner .20 .50
48 Victor Martinez .20 .50
49 Jhonny Peralta .20 .50
50 C.C. Sabathia .20 .50
51 Jeremy Sowers .20 .50
52 Ryan Garko .20 .50
53 Garrett Atkins .20 .50
54 Willy Taveras .20 .50
55 Todd Helton .30 .75
56 Jeff Francis .20 .50
57 Brad Hawpe .20 .50
58 Matt Holliday .50 1.25
59 Justin Verlander .50 1.25
60 Jeremy Bonderman .20 .50
61 Magglio Ordonez .20 .50
62 Ivan Rodriguez .30 .75
63 Gary Sheffield .20 .50
64 Kenny Rogers .20 .50
65 Brandon Inge .20 .50
66 Anibal Sanchez .20 .50
67 Scott Olsen .20 .50
68 Dontrelle Willis .20 .50
69 Dan Uggla .30 .75
70 Hanley Ramirez .30 .75
71 Miguel Cabrera .30 .75
72 Jeremy Hermida .20 .50
73 Roy Oswalt .20 .50
74 Brad Lidge .20 .50
75 Lance Berkman .20 .50
76 Carlos Lee .20 .50
77 Morgan Ensberg .20 .50
78 Craig Biggio .30 .75
79 Reggie Sanders .20 .50
80 Mike Sweeney .20 .50
81 Mark Teahen .20 .50
82 John Buck .20 .50
83 Mark Grudzielanek .20 .50
84 Gary Matthews .20 .50
85 Vladimir Guerrero .50 1.25
86 Garret Anderson .20 .50
87 Howie Kendrick .20 .50
88 Jered Weaver .30 .75
89 Chone Figgins .20 .50
90 Bartolo Colon .20 .50
91 Francisco Rodriguez .20 .50
92 Nomar Garciaparra .50 1.25
93 Andre Ethier .30 .75
94 Rafael Furcal .20 .50
95 Jeff Kent .20 .50
96 Derek Lowe .20 .50
97 Jason Schmidt .20 .50
98 Takashi Saito .20 .50
99 Ben Sheets .20 .50
100 Prince Fielder .50 1.25
101 Bill Hall .20 .50
102 Rickie Weeks .20 .50
103 Francisco Cordero .20 .50
104 J.J. Hardy .20 .50
105 Johan Santana .30 .75
106 Justin Morneau .20 .50
107 Joe Mauer .30 .75
108 Joe Nathan .20 .50
109 Torii Hunter .20 .50
110 Michael Cuddyer .20 .50
111 Boof Bonser .20 .50
112 Tom Glavine .30 .75
113 Pedro Martinez .30 .75
114 Billy Wagner .20 .50
115 Jose Reyes .50 1.25
116 David Wright .75 2.00
117 Carlos Delgado .20 .50
118 Carlos Beltran .20 .50
119 Alex Rodriguez .75 2.00
120 Chien-Ming Wang .75 2.00
121 Mariano Rivera .50 1.25
122 Bobby Abreu .20 .50
123 Hideki Matsui .50 1.25
124 Johnny Damon .30 .75
125 Robinson Cano .30 .75
126 Derek Jeter 1.25 3.00
127 Nick Swisher .20 .50
128 Eric Chavez .20 .50
129 Jason Kendall .20 .50
130 Bobby Crosby .20 .50
131 Huston Street .20 .50
132 Dan Haren .20 .50
133 Rich Harden .20 .50
134 Mike Piazza .50 1.25
135 Chase Utley .50 1.25
136 Jimmy Rollins .20 .50
137 Aaron Rowand .20 .50
138 Jamie Moyer .20 .50
139 Cole Hamels .50 1.25
140 Pat Burrell .20 .50
141 Ryan Howard .75 2.00
142 Freddy Sanchez .20 .50
143 Zach Duke .20 .50
144 Ian Snell .20 .50
145 Jack Wilson .20 .50
146 Jason Bay .20 .50
147 Albert Pujols 1.00 2.50
148 Scott Rolen .30 .75
149 Jim Edmonds .30 .75
150 Chris Carpenter .20 .50
151 Yadier Molina .20 .50
152 Adam Wainwright .20 .50
153 David Eckstein .20 .50
154 Trevor Hoffman .20 .50
155 Brian Giles .20 .50
156 Adrian Gonzalez .20 .50
157 Jake Peavy .20 .50
158 Khalil Greene .30 .75
159 Chris Young .20 .50
160 Greg Maddux .75 2.00
161 Mike Cameron .20 .50
162 Matt Cain .30 .75
163 Matt Morris .20 .50
164 Pedro Feliz .20 .50
165 Omar Vizquel .30 .75
166 Randy Winn .20 .50
167 Barry Zito .30 .75
168 Adrian Beltre .20 .50
169 Yuniesky Betancourt .20 .50
170 Richie Sexson .20 .50
171 Raul Ibanez .20 .50
172 Kenji Johjima .50 1.25
173 Ichiro Suzuki .75 2.00
174 Felix Hernandez .30 .75
175 Scott Kazmir .30 .75
176 Carl Crawford .20 .50
177 B.J. Upton .20 .50
178 James Shields .20 .50
179 Rocco Baldelli .20 .50
180 Jorge Cantu .20 .50
181 Ty Wigginton .20 .50
182 Mark Teixeira .30 .75
183 Hank Blalock .20 .50
184 Ian Kinsler .20 .50
185 Michael Young .20 .50
186 Vicente Padilla .20 .50
187 Akinori Otsuka .20 .50
188 Kenny Lofton .20 .50
189 A.J. Burnett .20 .50
190 Roy Halladay .20 .50
191 B.J. Ryan .20 .50
192 Vernon Wells .20 .50
193 Alex Rios .20 .50
194 Troy Glaus .20 .50
195 Frank Thomas .50 1.25
196 Ryan Zimmerman .50 1.25
197 Michael O'Connor .20 .50
198 Chad Cordero .20 .50
199 Nick Johnson .20 .50
200 Felipe Lopez .20 .50
201 Miguel Montero (RC) 1.00 2.50
202 Doug Slaten RC 1.00 2.50
203 Joseph Bisenius RC 1.00 2.50
204 Jared Burton RC 1.00 2.50
205 Kevin Cameron RC 1.00 2.50
206 Matt Chico (RC) 1.00 2.50
207 Chris Stewart RC 1.00 2.50
208 Joe Smith RC 1.00 2.50
209 Zack Segovia (RC) 1.00 2.50
210 John Danks RC 1.00 2.50
211 Lee Gardner (RC) 1.00 2.50
212 Jeff Baker (RC) 1.00 2.50
213 Jamie Burke (RC) 1.00 2.50
214 Phil Hughes (RC) 5.00 12.00
215 Mike Rabelo RC 1.00 2.50
216 Jose Garcia RC 1.00 2.50
217 Hector Gimenez (RC) 1.00 2.50
218 Jesus Flores RC 1.00 2.50
219 Brandon Morrow RC 2.50 6.00
220 Hideki Okajima RC 5.00 12.00
221 Jay Marshall RC 1.00 2.50
222 Matt Lindstrom (RC) 1.00 2.50
223 Juan Salas (RC) 1.00 2.50
224 Juan Perez RC 1.00 2.50
225 Sean Henn (RC) 1.00 2.50
226 Travis Buck (RC) 1.00 2.50
227 Gustavo Molina RC 1.00 2.50
228 Hunter Pence (RC) 5.00 12.00
229 Michael Bourn (RC) 1.00 2.50
230 Brian Barden RC 1.00 2.50
231 Don Kelly (RC) 1.00 2.50
232 Joakim Soria RC 1.00 2.50
233 Cesar Jimenez RC 1.00 2.50
234 Levale Speigner RC 1.00 2.50
235 Micah Owings (RC) 1.00 2.50
236 Brian Stokes (RC) 1.00 2.50
237 Joaquin Arias (RC) 1.00 2.50
238 Josh Hamilton L13 (RC) 2.50 6.00
239 Daisuke Matsuzaka L13 RC 6.00 15.00
240 Alejandro De Aza L13 RC 1.50 4.00
241 Kory Casto L13 (RC) 1.00 2.50
242 Troy Tulowitzki L13 (RC) 2.50 6.00
243 Akinori Iwamura L13 RC 2.50 6.00
244 Angel Sanchez L13 RC 1.00 2.50
245 Ryan Braun L13 (RC) 6.00 15.00
246 Alex Gordon L13 RC 5.00 12.00
247 Elijah Dukes L13 RC 1.50 4.00
248 Kei Igawa L13 RC 2.50 6.00
249 Kevin Kouzmanoff L13 (RC) 1.00 2.50
250 Delmon Young L13 (RC) 1.50 4.00

2007 Ultra Gold

*GOLD 1-200: 1.5X TO 3X BASIC
*GOLD RC 201-237: .5X TO 1.2X BASIC RC
*GOLD L13 238-250: .5X TO 1.2X BASIC L13

STATED ODDS 1:10 HOBBY
239 Daisuke Matsuzaka L13 5.00 12.00
245 Ryan Braun L13 5.00 12.00

2007 Ultra Retail

*RETAIL 1-200: .25X TO .6X BASIC
*RETAIL RC 201-237: .3X TO .8X BASIC RC
*RETAIL L13 238-250: .3X TO .8X BASIC L13

2007 Ultra Retail Gold

*RETAIL GLD 1-200: 1.5X TO 4X BASIC
*RETAIL RC GLD 201-237: .6X TO 1.5X BASIC RC
*RETAIL L13 GLD 238-250: .6X TO 1.5X BASIC L13
STATED ODDS 2:1 FAT PACK
STATED PRINT RUN 999 SER.#'d SETS
239 Daisuke Matsuzaka L13 6.00 15.00
245 Ryan Braun L13 5.00 12.00
246 Alex Gordon L13 5.00 12.00

2007 Ultra Autographics

RANDOM INSERTS IN PACKS
PRINT RUNS B/WN 49-499 COPIES PER
AG Alex Gordon/499 15.00 40.00
AH Aaron Harang/499 4.00 10.00
BA Bronson Arroyo/49
BM Brandon McCarthy/499 3.00 8.00
CC Chad Cordero/499 3.00 8.00
CH Clay Hensley/499 3.00 8.00
CI Cesar Izturis/122 4.00 10.00
JA Jason Bay/499 4.00 10.00
JB Joe Blanton/299 3.00 8.00
JE Johnny Estrada/132 6.00 15.00
JS Johan Santana/173 15.00 40.00
KG Khalil Greene/299 6.00 15.00
KI Kei Igawa/199 15.00 40.00

2007 Ultra Autographics Retail

STATED ODDS 1:1440 RETAIL
NO PRICING DUE TO SCARCITY
AG Alex Gordon
AH Aaron Harang
BM Brandon McCarthy
CH Clay Hensley
JB Joe Blanton
JS Johan Santana
KG Khalil Greene
KI Kei Igawa

2007 Ultra Dual Materials

RANDOM INSERTS IN PACKS
PRINT RUNS B/WN 81-160 COPIES PER
GOLD p/r 39-75: .5X TO 1.2X BASIC
GOLD p/r 20-25: .6X TO 1.5X BASIC
GOLD RANDOMLY INSERTED
GOLD PRINT RUN B/WN 20-75 PER
PATCH: .75X TO 2X BASIC
PATCHES RANDOMLY INSERTED
PATCH PRINT RUN B/WN 1-25 PER
NO PATCH PRICING ON QTY 16 OR LESS
AB A.J. Burnett 3.00 8.00
AE Andre Ethier 3.00 8.00
AJ Andruw Jones 3.00 8.00
AK Austin Kearns 3.00 8.00
AL Adam LaRoche 3.00 8.00
AN Garret Anderson 3.00 8.00
AP Albert Pujols 6.00 15.00
AS Anibal Sanchez 3.00 8.00
BA Bobby Abreu 3.00 8.00
BC Bobby Crosby 3.00 8.00
BE Adrian Beltre 3.00 8.00
BG Brian Giles 3.00 8.00
BI Craig Biggio 3.00 8.00
BJ Bobby Jenks 3.00 8.00
BL Brad Lidge 3.00 8.00
BM Brandon McCarthy 3.00 8.00
BR Brian Roberts 3.00 8.00
BS Ben Sheets 3.00 8.00
BW Brandon Webb 3.00 8.00
CA Carlos Beltran 3.00 8.00
CB Chris Burke 3.00 8.00
CC Carl Crawford 3.00 8.00
CF Chone Figgins 3.00 8.00
CH Chris Carpenter/81 4.00 10.00
CJ Conor Jackson 3.00 8.00
CK Casey Kotchman 3.00 8.00
CL Carlos Lee 3.00 8.00
CP Corey Patterson 3.00 8.00
CR Coco Crisp 3.00 8.00
CS C.C. Sabathia/154 3.00 8.00
CU Curt Schilling 3.00 8.00
DJ Derek Jeter 8.00 20.00
DL Derek Lowe 3.00 8.00
DO David Ortiz 4.00 10.00
DR J.D. Drew 3.00 8.00
DU Dan Uggla 3.00 8.00
DW David Wells 3.00 8.00
ED Jim Edmonds 3.00 8.00
ES Ervin Santana 3.00 8.00
FG Freddy Garcia 3.00 8.00
FH Felix Hernandez 3.00 8.00
GA Garrett Atkins 3.00 8.00
GJ Geoff Jenkins 3.00 8.00
GM Greg Maddux 4.00 10.00
GS Gary Sheffield 3.00 8.00
HE Todd Helton 3.00 8.00
HO Trevor Hoffman 3.00 8.00
HR Hanley Ramirez 3.00 8.00
HU Torii Hunter 3.00 8.00
IS Ian Snell 3.00 8.00
JB Jeremy Bonderman 3.00 8.00
JC Chipper Jones 4.00 10.00
JD Jermaine Dye 3.00 8.00
JG Jonny Gomes 3.00 8.00
JH J.J. Hardy 4.00 10.00
JJ Josh Johnson 3.00 8.00
JK Jeff Kent 3.00 8.00
JM Justin Morneau 3.00 8.00
JN Joe Nathan 3.00 8.00
JO Josh Beckett 3.00 8.00
JP Jorge Posada 3.00 8.00
JS James Shields 3.00 8.00
JV Jason Varitek 4.00 10.00
JW Josh Willingham 3.00 8.00
KG Kahlil Greene 3.00 8.00
KW Kerry Wood 3.00 8.00
LB Lance Berkman 3.00 8.00
LE Derrek Lee 3.00 8.00
LG Luis Gonzalez 3.00 8.00
LM Lastings Milledge 3.00 8.00
LS Luke Scott 3.00 8.00
MC Matt Cain 3.00 8.00
ME Melky Cabrera 3.00 8.00
MH Matt Holliday 4.00 10.00
MI Mike Mussina 3.00 8.00
MM Melvin Mora 3.00 8.00
MO Magglio Ordonez 3.00 8.00
MR Manny Ramirez 3.00 8.00
MS Mike Sweeney 3.00 8.00
MT Miguel Tejada 3.00 8.00
MU Mark Mulder 3.00 8.00
PE Andy Pettitte 3.00 8.00
PF Prince Fielder 4.00 10.00
PJ Jhonny Peralta 3.00 8.00
RH Rich Harden 3.00 8.00
SC Jason Schmidt 3.00 8.00
SI Grady Sizemore 3.00 8.00
SO Scott Olsen 3.00 8.00
TE Mark Teixeira 3.00 8.00
TH Travis Hafner 3.00 8.00
TW Tim Wakefield 3.00 8.00
VG Vladimir Guerrero 3.00 8.00
VM Victor Martinez 3.00 8.00
VW Vernon Wells 3.00 8.00
WI Dontrelle Willis 3.00 8.00
ZD Zach Duke 3.00 8.00

2007 Ultra Faces of the Game

STATED ODDS 1:10 HOBBY/RETAIL
PRINTING PLATE ODDS 1:1252 HOB/RET
PLATE PRINT RUN 1 SET PER COLOR
BLACK-CYAN-MAGENTA-YELLOW ISSUED
NO PLATE PRICING DUE TO SCARCITY
AB Adrian Beltre .50 1.25
AJ Andruw Jones .75 2.00
BS Ben Sheets .50 1.25
CJ Chipper Jones 1.25 3.00
CS C.C. Sabathia .50 1.25
CU Chase Utley 1.25 3.00
DJ Derek Jeter 3.00 8.00
FR Francisco Rodriguez .50 1.25
GM Greg Maddux 2.00 5.00
HU Torii Hunter .50 1.25
JB Jason Bay .50 1.25
JG Jason Giambi .50 1.25
KG Ken Griffey Jr. 2.00 5.00
LG Luis Gonzalez .50 1.25
MC Miguel Cabrera .75 2.00
MP Mike Piazza 1.25 3.00
MR Mariano Rivera 1.25 3.00
OV Omar Vizquel .75 2.00
TG Tom Glavine .75 2.00
TH Trevor Hoffman .50 1.25

2007 Ultra Faces of the Game Materials

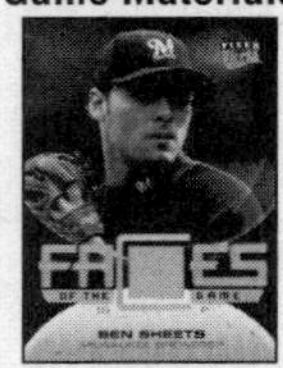

APPX.ODDS 1:8 HOBBY/RETAIL
AB Adrian Beltre 2.50 6.00
AJ Andruw Jones 3.00 8.00

BS Ben Sheets 2.50 6.00
CJ Chipper Jones 3.00 8.00
CS C.C. Sabathia 2.50 6.00
CU Chase Utley 4.00 10.00
DJ Derek Jeter 8.00 20.00
FR Francisco Rodriguez 2.50 6.00
GM Greg Maddux 4.00 10.00
HU Trevor Hoffman 2.50 6.00
JB Jason Bay 2.50 6.00
JG Jason Giambi 2.50 6.00
KG Ken Griffey Jr. 6.00 15.00
LG Luis Gonzalez 2.50 6.00
MC Miguel Cabrera 3.00 8.00
MP Mike Piazza 4.00 10.00
MR Mariano Rivera 4.00 10.00
OV Omar Vizquel 3.00 8.00
TG Tom Glavine 3.00 8.00
TH Torii Hunter 2.50 6.00

2007 Ultra Feel the Game

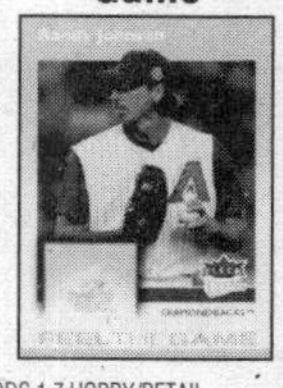

APPX.ODDS 1:7 HOBBY/RETAIL
PRINTING PLATE ODDS 1:1252 HOB/RET
PLATE PRINT RUN 1 SET PER COLOR
BLACK-CYAN-MAGENTA-YELLOW ISSUED
NO PLATE PRICING DUE TO SCARCITY
AP Albert Pujols 2.50 6.00
BA Bobby Abreu .50 1.25
BR Brian Roberts .50 1.25
BW Brandon Webb .50 1.25
CC Chris Carpenter .50 1.25
CJ Chipper Jones 1.25 3.00
CR Carl Crawford .50 1.25
CS Curt Schilling .75 2.00
CU Chase Utley 1.25 3.00
CZ Carlos Zambrano .50 1.25
DJ Derek Jeter 3.00 8.00
DW Dontrelle Willis .50 1.25
EC Eric Chavez .50 1.25
GS Grady Sizemore .75 2.00
HR Hanley Ramirez .75 2.00
IR Ivan Rodriguez .75 2.00
JM Justin Morneau .50 1.25
JP Jonathan Papelbon 1.25 3.00
JR Jose Reyes 1.25 3.00
JS John Smoltz .75 2.00
KG Ken Griffey Jr. 2.00 5.00
KJ Kenji Johjima 1.25 3.00
LB Lance Berkman .50 1.25
LG Luis Gonzalez .50 1.25
MC Miguel Cabrera .75 2.00
RC Robinson Cano .75 2.00
RJ Randy Johnson 1.25 3.00
SA Johan Santana .75 2.00
SC Jason Schmidt .50 1.25
VG Vladimir Guerrero 1.25 3.00

2007 Ultra Feel the Game Materials

APPX.ODDS 1:7 HOBBY/RETAIL
AP Albert Pujols 6.00 15.00
BA Bobby Abreu 2.50 6.00
BR Brian Roberts 3.00 8.00
BW Brandon Webb 2.50 6.00
CC Chris Carpenter 2.50 6.00
CJ Chipper Jones 3.00 8.00
CR Carl Crawford 2.50 6.00
CS Curt Schilling 3.00 8.00
CZ Carlos Zambrano 2.50 6.00
DJ Derek Jeter 8.00 20.00
DW Dontrelle Willis 2.50 6.00
EC Eric Chavez 2.50 6.00
GS Grady Sizemore 3.00 8.00
HR Hanley Ramirez 3.00 8.00
IR Ivan Rodriguez 3.00 8.00
JM Justin Morneau 2.50 6.00
JP Jonathan Papelbon 4.00 10.00
JR Jose Reyes 4.00 10.00
JS John Smoltz 3.00 8.00
KG Ken Griffey Jr. 6.00 15.00
KJ Kenji Johjima 4.00 10.00
LB Lance Berkman 2.50 6.00
LG Luis Gonzalez 2.50 6.00
MC Miguel Cabrera 3.00 8.00
RC Robinson Cano 4.00 10.00
RJ Randy Johnson 4.00 10.00
SA Johan Santana 3.00 8.00
SC Jason Schmidt 2.50 6.00
VG Vladimir Guerrero 3.00 8.00

2007 Ultra Hitting Machines

APPX.ODDS 1:13 HOBBY/RETAIL
PRINTING PLATE ODDS 1:1252 HOB/RET
PLATE PRINT RUN 1 SET PER COLOR
BLACK-CYAN-MAGENTA-YELLOW ISSUED
NO PLATE PRICING DUE TO SCARCITY
AR Aramis Ramirez .50 1.25
AS Alfonso Soriano .50 1.25
BI Craig Biggio .75 2.00
CB Carlos Beltran .50 1.25
DO David Ortiz 1.25 3.00

FS Freddy Sanchez .50 1.25
FT Frank Thomas 1.25 3.00
JK Jeff Kent .50 1.25
JM Joe Mauer .75 2.00
JT Jim Thome .75 2.00
MT Mark Teixeira .75 2.00
NS Nick Swisher .50 1.25
TE Miguel Tejada .50 1.25
TG Troy Glaus .50 1.25
TH Todd Helton .75 2.00

2007 Ultra Hitting Machines Materials

APPX.ODDS 1:12 HOBBY/RETAIL
AR Aramis Ramirez 2.50 6.00
AS Alfonso Soriano 2.50 6.00
BI Craig Biggio 3.00 8.00
CB Carlos Beltran 2.50 6.00
DO David Ortiz 4.00 10.00
FS Freddy Sanchez 2.50 6.00
FT Frank Thomas 4.00 10.00
JK Jeff Kent 2.50 6.00
JM Joe Mauer 3.00 8.00
JT Jim Thome 3.00 8.00
MT Mark Teixeira 3.00 8.00
NS Nick Swisher 2.50 6.00
TE Miguel Tejada 2.50 6.00
TG Troy Glaus 2.50 6.00
TH Todd Helton 3.00 8.00

2007 Ultra Iron Man

COMMON CARD 1.25 3.00
APPX.ODDS 1:3 HOBBY/RETAIL

2007 Ultra Iron Man Signatures

COMMON CARD 75.00 150.00
RANDOM INSERTS IN PACKS
STATED PRINT RUN 10 SER.#'d SETS

2007 Ultra Rookie Autographs

RANDOM INSERTS IN PACKS
PRINT RUNS B/WN 23-499 COPIES PER
NO PRICING ON QTY 38 OR LESS
201a Miguel Montero/299 3.00 8.00
201b Miguel Montero/149 4.00 10.00
202a Doug Slaten/299 3.00 8.00
202b Doug Slaten/349 3.00 8.00
203a Joseph Bisenius/299 3.00 8.00
203b Joseph Bisenius/349 3.00 8.00
204a Jared Burton/299 5.00 12.00
204b Jared Burton/349 5.00 12.00
205a Kevin Cameron/299 3.00 8.00
205b Kevin Cameron/349 3.00 8.00
206a Matt Chico/299 3.00 8.00
206b Matt Chico/349 3.00 8.00
207a Chris Stewart/299 3.00 8.00
207b Chris Stewart/349 3.00 8.00
209a Zack Segovia/299 4.00 10.00
209b Zack Segovia/149 5.00 12.00
210 John Danks/299 3.00 8.00
213a Jamie Burke/299 5.00 12.00
213b Jamie Burke/349 5.00 12.00
215a Mike Rabelo/299 3.00 8.00
215b Mike Rabelo/349 3.00 8.00
217a Hector Gimenez/299 3.00 8.00
217b Hector Gimenez/349 3.00 8.00
219a Brandon Morrow/299 10.00 25.00
219b Brandon Morrow/349 10.00 25.00
221a Jay Marshall/299 6.00 15.00
221b Jay Marshall/349 6.00 15.00
223 Juan Salas/23
225a Sean Henn/299 3.00 8.00
225b Sean Henn/349 3.00 8.00
226a Travis Buck/299 4.00 10.00
226b Travis Buck/99 6.00 15.00
227a Gustavo Molina/299 4.00 10.00
227b Gustavo Molina/349 4.00 10.00
229a Michael Bourn/299 4.00 10.00
229b Michael Bourn/349 4.00 10.00
232a Joakim Soria/299 4.00 10.00
232b Joakim Soria/349 4.00 10.00
233 Cesar Jimenez/38
234a Levale Speigner/299 3.00 8.00
234b Levale Speigner/349 3.00 8.00
236a Brian Stokes/299 3.00 8.00
236b Brian Stokes/349 3.00 8.00
237a Joaquin Arias/299 3.00 8.00
237b Joaquin Arias/349 3.00 8.00
238a Josh Hamilton L13/499 15.00 40.00
238b Josh Hamilton L13/99 30.00 60.00
241 Kory Casto L13/499 5.00 12.00
242 Troy Tulowitzki L13/499 30.00 60.00
243 Akinori Iwamura L13/99 30.00 60.00
245 Ryan Braun L13/499 40.00 80.00
246a Alex Gordon L13/499 20.00 50.00
246b Alex Gordon L13/99 40.00 80.00
248a Kei Igawa L13/299 12.50 30.00
248b Kei Igawa L13/99 20.00 50.00
249a Kevin Kouzmanoff L13/499 4.00 10.00
249b Kevin Kouzmanoff L13/199 5.00 12.00

2007 Ultra Rookie Autographs Retail

STATED ODDS 1:1440 RETAIL
NO PRICING DUE TO SCARCITY
201 Miguel Montero
202 Doug Slaten
204 Jared Burton SP
205 Kevin Cameron SP
206 Matt Chico
207 Chris Stewart
209 Zack Segovia
212 Jeff Baker
215 Mike Rabelo
217 Hector Gimenez
223 Juan Salas
225 Sean Henn
229 Michael Bourn SP
234 Levale Speigner
236 Brian Stokes
237 Joaquin Arias
238 Josh Hamilton L13
241 Kory Casto L13
242 Troy Tulowitzki L13
243 Akinori Iwamura L13
246 Alex Gordon L13 SP
248 Kei Igawa L13 SP
249 Kevin Kouzmanoff L13
250 Delmon Young L13

2007 Ultra Strike Zone

STATED ODDS 1:20 HOBBY/RETAIL
PRINTING PLATE ODDS 1:1252 HOB/RET
PLATE PRINT RUN 1 SET PER COLOR
BLACK-CYAN-MAGENTA-YELLOW ISSUED
NO PLATE PRICING DUE TO SCARCITY
BZ Barry Zito .50 1.25
CC C.C. Sabathia .50 1.25
CZ Carlos Zambrano .50 1.25
DW Dontrelle Willis .50 1.25
JS Johan Santana .75 2.00
JV Justin Verlander 1.25 3.00
MM Mike Mussina .75 2.00
PM Pedro Martinez .75 2.00
RH Roy Halladay .50 1.25
RO Roy Oswalt .50 1.25

2007 Ultra Strike Zone Materials

APPX.ODDS 1:14 HOBBY/RETAIL
BZ Barry Zito 2.50 6.00
CC C.C. Sabathia 2.50 6.00
CZ Carlos Zambrano 2.50 6.00
DW Dontrelle Willis 2.50 6.00
JS Johan Santana 3.00 8.00
JV Justin Verlander 4.00 10.00
MM Mike Mussina 3.00 8.00
PM Pedro Martinez 3.00 8.00
RH Roy Halladay 2.50 6.00
RO Roy Oswalt 2.50 6.00

2007 Ultra Swing Kings

STATED ODDS 1:8 HOBBY/RETAIL
PRINTING PLATE ODDS 1:1252 HOB/RET
PLATE PRINT RUN 1 SET PER COLOR
BLACK-CYAN-MAGENTA-YELLOW ISSUED
NO PLATE PRICING DUE TO SCARCITY
AD Adam Dunn .50 1.25
AJ Andruw Jones .75 2.00
AP Albert Pujols 2.50 6.00
AR Aramis Ramirez .50 1.25
AS Alfonso Soriano .50 1.25
CB Carlos Beltran .50 1.25
CL Carlos Lee .50 1.25
DJ Derek Jeter 3.00 8.00
DO David Ortiz 1.25 3.00
FT Frank Thomas 1.25 3.00
GS Gary Sheffield .50 1.25
HE Todd Helton .75 2.00
JM Joe Mauer .75 2.00
JR Jose Reyes 1.25 3.00
JT Jim Thome .75 2.00
KG Ken Griffey Jr. 2.00 5.00
MC Miguel Cabrera .75 2.00
MR Manny Ramirez .75 2.00
MT Miguel Tejada .50 1.25
NG Nomar Garciaparra 1.25 3.00
PB Pat Burrell .50 1.25
TE Mark Teixeira .75 2.00
TH Travis Hafner .50 1.25
VG Vladimir Guerrero 1.25 3.00
VW Vernon Wells .50 1.25

2007 Ultra Swing Kings Materials

APPX ODDS 1:7 HOBBY/RETAIL
AD Adam Dunn 2.50 6.00
AJ Andruw Jones 3.00 8.00
AP Albert Pujols 6.00 15.00
AR Aramis Ramirez 2.50 6.00
AS Alfonso Soriano 2.50 6.00
CB Carlos Beltran 2.50 6.00
CL Carlos Lee 2.50 6.00
DJ Derek Jeter 8.00 20.00
DO David Ortiz 4.00 10.00
FT Frank Thomas 4.00 10.00
GS Gary Sheffield 2.50 6.00
HE Todd Helton 3.00 8.00
JM Joe Mauer 3.00 8.00
JR Jose Reyes 4.00 10.00
JT Jim Thome 3.00 8.00
KG Ken Griffey Jr. 6.00 15.00
MC Miguel Cabrera 3.00 8.00
MR Manny Ramirez 3.00 8.00
MT Miguel Tejada 2.50 6.00
NG Nomar Garciaparra 4.00 10.00
PB Pat Burrell 2.50 6.00
TE Mark Teixeira 3.00 8.00
TH Travis Hafner 2.50 6.00
VG Vladimir Guerrero 4.00 10.00
VW Vernon Wells 2.50 6.00

2007 Ultra Ultragraphs

RANDOM INSERTS IN PACKS
PRINT RUNS B/WN 49-499 COPIES PER
AI Akinori Iwamura/49
AK Austin Kearns/399 3.00 8.00
AL Adam LaRoche/499 3.00 8.00
AN Garret Anderson/499 3.00 8.00
BB Boof Bonser/499 3.00 8.00
GA Garrett Atkins/499 3.00 8.00
JJ Jorge Julio/499 3.00 8.00
JN Joe Nathan/299 4.00 10.00
JW Jered Weaver/150 6.00 15.00
MM Mark Mulder/319 3.00 8.00
RW Rickie Weeks/68 6.00 15.00
TH Travis Hafner/499 4.00 10.00
ZG Zack Greinke/199 3.00 8.00

2007 Ultra Ultragraphs Retail

STATED ODDS 1:1440 RETAIL
NO PRICING DUE TO SCARCITY
AI Akinori Iwamura
AK Austin Kearns
AL Adam LaRoche
AN Garret Anderson
BB Boof Bonser
GA Garrett Atkins
JN Joe Nathan
MM Mark Mulder
TH Travis Hafner

1989 Upper Deck

This attractive 800-card standard-size set was introduced in 1989 as the premier issue by the then-fledgling Upper Deck company. Unlike other 1989 major releases, this set was issued in two separate series - a low series numbered 1-700 and a high series numbered 701-800. Cards were primarily issued in fin-wrapped low and high series foil packs, complete 800-card factory sets and 100-card high series factory sets. High series packs contained a mixture of both low and high series cards. Collectors should also note that many dealers consider that Upper Deck's "planned" production of 1,000,000 of each player was increased (perhaps even doubled) later in the year due to the explosion in popularity of the product. The cards feature slick paper stock, full color on both the front and the back and carry a hologram on the reverse to protect against counterfeiting. Subsets include Rookie Stars (1-26) and Collector's Choice art cards (668-693). The more significant variations involving changed photos or changed type are listed below. According to the company, the Murphy and Sheridan cards were corrected very early, after only two percent of the cards had been produced. Similarly, the Sheffield was corrected after 15 percent had been printed; Varsho, Gallego, and Schroeder were corrected after 20 percent; and Holton, Manrique, and Winningham were corrected 30 percent of the way through. Rookie Cards in the set include Jim Abbott, Sandy Alomar Jr., Dante Bichette, Craig Biggio, Steve Finley, Ken Griffey Jr., Randy Johnson, Gary Sheffield, John Smoltz and Todd Zeile. Cards with missing or duplicate holograms appear to be relatively common and are generally considered to be flawed copies that sell for substantial discounts.

COMPLETE SET (800) 40.00 80.00
COMP.FACT.SET (800) 50.00 100.00
COMP.HI FACT.SET (100) 4.00 10.00
1 Ken Griffey Jr. RC 15.00 40.00
2 Luis Medina RC .08 .25
3 Tony Chance RC .08 .25
4 Dave Otto .08 .25
5 S.Alomar Jr. RC UER .40 1.00
Born 6/16/66, should be 6/18/66
6 Rolando Roomes RC .08 .25
7 Dave West RC .08 .25
8 Cris Carpenter RC .08 .25
9 Gregg Jefferies .08 .25
10 Doug Dascenzo RC .08 .25
11 Ron Jones RC .08 .25
12 Luis DeLosSantos RC .08 .25
13 Gary Sheffield COR RC 2.00 5.00
13A G.Sheffield ERR 2.00 5.00
SS upside down on card front
14 Mike Harkey RC .08 .25
15 Lance Blankenship RC .08 .25
16 William Brennan RC .08 .25
17 John Smoltz RC 2.00 5.00
18 Ramon Martinez RC .20 .50
19 Mark Lemke RC .40 1.00
20 Juan Bell RC .08 .25
21 Rey Palacios RC .08 .25
22 Felix Jose RC .08 .25
23 Van Snider RC .08 .25
24 Dante Bichette RC .40 1.00
25 Randy Johnson RC 3.00 8.00
26 Carlos Quintana RC .08 .25
27 Star Rookie CL .08 .25
28 Mike Schooler .08 .25
29 Randy St.Claire .08 .25
30 Jerald Clark RC .08 .25
31 Kevin Gross .08 .25
32 Dan Firova .08 .25
33 Jeff Calhoun .08 .25
34 Tommy Hinzo .08 .25
35 Ricky Jordan RC .20 .50
36 Larry Parrish .08 .25
37 Bret Saberhagen UER .15 .40
Hit total 931, should be 1031
38 Mike Smithson .08 .25
39 Dave Dravecky .08 .25
40 Ed Romero .08 .25
41 Jeff Musselman .08 .25
42 Ed Hearn .08 .25
43 Rance Mulliniks .08 .25
44 Jim Eisenreich .08 .25
45 Sil Campusano .08 .25
46 Mike Krukow .08 .25
47 Paul Gibson .08 .25
48 Mike LaCoss .08 .25
49 Larry Herndon .08 .25
50 Scott Garrelts .08 .25
51 Dwayne Henry .08 .25
52 Jim Acker .08 .25
53 Steve Sax .08 .25
54 Pete O'Brien .08 .25
55 Paul Runge .08 .25
56 Rick Rhoden .08 .25
57 John Dopson .08 .25
58 Casey Candaele UER .08 .25
(No stats for Astros for '88 season)
59 Dave Righetti .15 .40
60 Joe Hesketh .08 .25
61 Frank DiPino .08 .25
62 Tim Laudner .08 .25
63 Jamie Moyer .15 .40
64 Fred Toliver .08 .25
65 Mitch Webster .08 .25
66 John Tudor .15 .40
67 John Cangelosi .08 .25
68 Mike Devereaux .08 .25
69 Brian Fisher .08 .25
70 Mike Marshall .08 .25
71 Zane Smith .08 .25
72A Brian Holton ERR .40 1.00
(Photo actually Shawn Hillegas)
72B Brian Holton COR .15 .40
73 Jose Guzman .08 .25
74 Rick Mahler .08 .25
75 John Shelby .08 .25
76 Jim Deshaies .08 .25
77 Bobby Meacham .08 .25
78 Bryn Smith .08 .25
79 Joaquin Andujar .15 .40
80 Richard Dotson .08 .25
81 Charlie Lea .08 .25
82 Calvin Schiraldi .08 .25
83 Les Straker .08 .25
84 Les Lancaster .08 .25
85 Allan Anderson .08 .25
86 Junior Ortiz .08 .25
87 Jesse Orosco .08 .25
88 Felix Fermin .08 .25
89 Dave Anderson .08 .25
90 Rafael Belliard UER .08 .25
(Born '61, not '51)
91 Franklin Stubbs .08 .25
92 Cecil Espy .08 .25
93 Albert Hall .08 .25
94 Tim Leary .08 .25
95 Mitch Williams .08 .25
96 Tracy Jones .08 .25
97 Danny Darwin .08 .25
98 Gary Ward .08 .25
99 Neal Heaton .08 .25
100 Jim Pankovits .08 .25
101 Bill Doran .08 .25
102 Tim Wallach .08 .25
103 Joe Magrane .08 .25
104 Ozzie Virgil .08 .25
105 Alvin Davis .08 .25
106 Tom Brookens .08 .25
107 Shawon Dunston .08 .25
108 Tracy Woodson .08 .25
109 Nelson Liriano .08 .25
110 Devon White UER .15 .40
(Doubles total 46, should be 56)
111 Steve Balboni .08 .25
112 Buddy Bell .15 .40
113 German Jimenez .08 .25
114 Ken Dayley .08 .25
115 Andres Galarraga .15 .40
116 Mike Scioscia .15 .40
117 Gary Pettis .08 .25
118 Ernie Whitt .08 .25
119 Bob Boone .15 .40
120 Ryne Sandberg .60 1.50
121 Bruce Benedict .08 .25
122 Hubie Brooks .08 .25
123 Mike Moore .08 .25
124 Wallace Johnson .08 .25
125 Bob Horner .15 .40
126 Chili Davis .15 .40
127 Manny Trillo .08 .25
128 Chet Lemon .15 .40
129 John Cerutti .08 .25
130 Orel Hershiser .15 .40
131 Terry Pendleton .15 .40
132 Jeff Blauser .08 .25
133 Mike Fitzgerald .08 .25
134 Henry Cotto .08 .25
135 Gerald Young .08 .25
136 Luis Salazar .08 .25
137 Alejandro Pena .08 .25
138 Jack Howell .08 .25
139 Tony Fernandez .08 .25
140 Mark Grace .40 1.00
141 Ken Caminiti .25 .60
142 Mike Jackson .08 .25
143 Larry McWilliams .08 .25
144 Andres Thomas .08 .25
145 Nolan Ryan 3X 1.50 4.00
146 Mike Davis .08 .25
147 DeWayne Buice .08 .25
148 Jody Davis .08 .25
149 Jesse Barfield .15 .40
150 Matt Nokes .08 .25
151 Jerry Reuss .08 .25
152 Rick Cerone .08 .25
153 Storm Davis .08 .25
154 Marvell Wynne .08 .25
155 Will Clark .25 .60
156 Luis Aguayo .08 .25
157 Willie Upshaw .08 .25
158 Randy Bush .08 .25
159 Ron Darling .15 .40
160 Kal Daniels .08 .25
161 Spike Owen .08 .25
162 Luis Polonia .08 .25
163 Kevin Mitchell UER .15 .40
('88/total HR's 18/52, should be 19/53)
164 Dave Gallagher .08 .25
165 Benito Santiago .15 .40
166 Greg Gagne .08 .25
167 Ken Phelps .08 .25
168 Sid Fernandez .08 .25
169 Bo Diaz .08 .25
170 Cory Snyder .08 .25
171 Eric Show .08 .25
172 Robby Thompson .08 .25
173 Marty Barrett .08 .25
174 Dave Henderson .08 .25
175 Ozzie Guillen .15 .40
176 Barry Lyons .08 .25
177 Kelvin Torve .08 .25
178 Don Slaught .08 .25
179 Steve Lombardozzi .08 .25
180 Chris Sabo RC .40 1.00
181 Jose Uribe .08 .25
182 Shane Mack .08 .25
183 Ron Karkovice .08 .25
184 Todd Benzinger .08 .25
185 Dave Stewart .15 .40
186 Julio Franco .15 .40
187 Ron Robinson .08 .25
188 Wally Backman .08 .25
189 Randy Velarde .08 .25
190 Joe Carter .15 .40
191 Bob Welch .15 .40
192 Kelly Paris .08 .25
193 Chris Brown .08 .25
194 Rick Reuschel .15 .40
195 Roger Clemens .75 2.00
196 Dave Concepcion .15 .40
197 Al Newman .08 .25
198 Brook Jacoby .08 .25
199 Mookie Wilson .15 .40
200 Don Mattingly 1.00 2.50
201 Dick Schofield .08 .25
202 Mark Gubicza .08 .25
203 Gary Gaetti .15 .40
204 Dan Pasqua .08 .25
205 Andre Dawson .15 .40
206 Chris Speier .08 .25
207 Kent Tekulve .08 .25
208 Rod Scurry .08 .25
209 Scott Bailes .08 .25
210 R.Henderson UER .40 1.00
Throws Right
211 Harold Baines .15 .40
212 Tony Armas .15 .40
213 Kent Hrbek .15 .40
214 Darrin Jackson .08 .25
215 George Brett 1.00 2.50

216 Rafael Santana .08 .25
217 Andy Allanson .08 .25
218 Brett Butler .15 .40
219 Steve Jeltz .08 .25
220 Jay Buhner .15 .40
221 Bo Jackson .40 1.00
222 Angel Salazar .08 .25
223 Kirk McCaskill .08 .25
224 Steve Lyons .08 .25
225 Bert Blyleven .15 .40
226 Scott Bradley .08 .25
227 Bob Melvin .08 .25
228 Ron Kittle .08 .25
229 Phil Bradley .08 .25
230 Tommy John .15 .40
231 Greg Walker .08 .25
232 Juan Berenguer .08 .25
233 Pat Tabler .08 .25
234 Terry Clark .08 .25
235 Rafael Palmeiro .40 1.00
236 Paul Zuvella .08 .25
237 Willie Randolph .15 .40
238 Bruce Fields .08 .25
239 Mike Aldrete .08 .25
240 Lance Parrish .15 .40
241 Greg Maddux 1.00 2.50
242 John Moses .08 .25
243 Melido Perez .08 .25
244 Willie Wilson .15 .40
245 Mark McLemore .08 .25
246 Von Hayes .08 .25
247 Matt Williams .40 1.00
248 John Candelaria UER .08 .25
Listed as Yankee for part of '87, should be Mets
249 Harold Reynolds .15 .40
250 Greg Swindell .08 .25
251 Juan Agosto .08 .25
252 Mike Felder .08 .25
253 Vince Coleman .08 .25
254 Larry Sheets .08 .25
255 George Bell .15 .40
256 Terry Steinbach .15 .40
257 Jack Armstrong RC .20 .50
258 Dickie Thon .08 .25
259 Ray Knight .15 .40
260 Darryl Strawberry .15 .40
261 Doug Sisk .08 .25
262 Alex Trevino .08 .25
263 Jeffrey Leonard .08 .25
264 Tom Henke .08 .25
265 Ozzie Smith .60 1.50
266 Dave Bergman .08 .25
267 Tony Phillips .08 .25
268 Mark Davis .08 .25
269 Kevin Elster .08 .25
270 Barry Larkin .25 .60
271 Manny Lee .08 .25
272 Tom Brunansky .08 .25
273 Craig Biggio RC 2.50 6.00
274 Jim Gantner .08 .25
275 Eddie Murray .40 1.00
276 Jeff Reed .08 .25
277 Tim Teufel .08 .25
278 Rick Honeycutt .08 .25
279 Guillermo Hernandez .08 .25
280 John Kruk .15 .40
281 Luis Alicea RC .20 .50
282 Jim Clancy .08 .25
283 Billy Ripken .08 .25
284 Craig Reynolds .08 .25
285 Robin Yount .60 1.50
286 Jimmy Jones .08 .25
287 Ron Oester .08 .25
288 Terry Leach .08 .25
289 Dennis Eckersley .25 .60
290 Alan Trammell .15 .40
291 Jimmy Key .15 .40
292 Chris Bosio .08 .25
293 Jose DeLeon .08 .25
294 Jim Traber .08 .25
295 Mike Scott .15 .40
296 Roger McDowell .08 .25
297 Garry Templeton .15 .40
298 Doyle Alexander .08 .25
299 Nick Esasky .08 .25
300 Mark McGwire UER 2.00 5.00
(Doubles total 52, should be 51)
301 Darryl Hamilton RC .20 .50
302 Dave Smith .08 .25
303 Rick Sutcliffe .15 .40
304 Dave Stapleton .08 .25
305 Alan Ashby .08 .25
306 Pedro Guerrero .15 .40
307 Ron Guidry .15 .40
308 Steve Farr .08 .25
309 Curt Ford .08 .25
310 Claudell Washington .08 .25
311 Tom Prince .08 .25
312 Chad Kreuter RC .20 .50
313 Ken Oberkfell .08 .25
314 Jerry Browne .08 .25
315 R.J. Reynolds .08 .25
316 Scott Bankhead .08 .25
317 Milt Thompson .08 .25
318 Mario Diaz .08 .25
319 Bruce Ruffin .08 .25
320 Dave Valle .08 .25
321A Gary Varsho ERR .75 2.00
(Back photo actually Mike Bielecki bunting)
321B Gary Varsho COR .08 .25
(In road uniform)
322 Paul Mirabella .08 .25
323 Chuck Jackson .08 .25
324 Drew Hall .08 .25
325 Don August .08 .25
326 Israel Sanchez .08 .25
327 Denny Walling .08 .25
328 Joel Skinner .08 .25
329 Danny Tartabull .08 .25
330 Tony Pena .08 .25
331 Jim Sundberg .15 .40
332 Jeff D. Robinson .08 .25
333 Oddibe McDowell .08 .25
334 Jose Lind .08 .25
335 Paul Kilgus .08 .25
336 Juan Samuel .08 .25
337 Mike Campbell .08 .25
338 Mike Maddux .08 .25
339 Darnell Coles .08 .25
340 Bob Dernier .08 .25
341 Rafael Ramirez .08 .25
342 Scott Sanderson .08 .25
343 B.J. Surhoff .15 .40
344 Billy Hatcher .08 .25
345 Pat Perry .08 .25
346 Jack Clark .15 .40
347 Gary Thurman .08 .25
348 Tim Jones .08 .25
349 Dave Winfield .15 .40
350 Frank White .15 .40
351 Dave Collins .08 .25
352 Jack Morris .15 .40
353 Eric Plunk .08 .25
354 Leon Durham .08 .25
355 Ivan DeJesus .08 .25
356 Brian Holman RC .08 .25
357A Dale Murphy ERR 12.50 30.00
(Front has reverse negative)
357B Dale Murphy COR .25 .60
358 Mark Portugal .08 .25
359 Andy McGaffigan .08 .25
360 Tom Glavine .40 1.00
361 Keith Moreland .08 .25
362 Todd Stottlemyre .08 .25
363 Dave Leiper .08 .25
364 Cecil Fielder .15 .40
365 Carmelo Martinez .08 .25
366 Dwight Evans .25 .60
367 Kevin McReynolds .08 .25
368 Rich Gedman .08 .25
369 Len Dykstra .15 .40
370 Jody Reed .08 .25
371 Jose Canseco UER .40 1.00
(Strikeout total 391, should be 491)
372 Rob Murphy .08 .25
373 Mike Henneman .08 .25
374 Walt Weiss .08 .25
375 Rob Dibble RC .40 1.00
376 Kirby Puckett .40 1.00
(Mark McGwire in background)
377 Dennis Martinez .15 .40
378 Ron Gant .15 .40
379 Brian Harper .08 .25
380 Nelson Santovenia .08 .25
381 Lloyd Moseby .08 .25
382 Lance McCullers .08 .25
383 Dave Stieb .15 .40
384 Tony Gwynn .50 1.25
385 Mike Flanagan .08 .25
386 Bob Ojeda .08 .25
387 Bruce Hurst .08 .25
388 Dave Magadan .08 .25
389 Wade Boggs .25 .60
390 Gary Carter .15 .40
391 Frank Tanana .15 .40
392 Curt Young .08 .25
393 Jeff Treadway .08 .25
394 Darrell Evans .15 .40
395 Glenn Hubbard .08 .25
396 Chuck Cary .08 .25
397 Frank Viola .15 .40
398 Jeff Parrett .08 .25
399 Terry Blocker .08 .25
400 Dan Gladden .08 .25
401 Louie Meadows .08 .25
402 Tim Raines .15 .40
403 Joey Meyer .08 .25
404 Larry Andersen .08 .25
405 Rex Hudler .08 .25
406 Mike Schmidt .75 2.00
407 John Franco .15 .40
408 Brady Anderson RC .40 1.00
409 Don Carman .08 .25
410 Eric Davis .15 .40
411 Bob Stanley .08 .25
412 Pete Smith .08 .25
413 Jim Rice .15 .40
414 Bruce Sutter .15 .40
415 Oil Can Boyd .08 .25
416 Ruben Sierra .15 .40
417 Mike LaValliere .08 .25
418 Steve Buechele .08 .25
419 Gary Redus .08 .25
420 Scott Fletcher .08 .25
421 Dale Sveum .08 .25
422 Bob Knepper .08 .25
423 Luis Rivera .08 .25
424 Ted Higuera .08 .25
425 Kevin Bass .08 .25
426 Ken Gerhart .08 .25
427 Shane Rawley .08 .25
428 Paul O'Neill .25 .60
429 Joe Orsulak .08 .25
430 Jackie Gutierrez .08 .25
431 Gerald Perry .08 .25
432 Mike Greenwell .08 .25
433 Jerry Royster .08 .25
434 Ellis Burks .15 .40
435 Ed Olwine .08 .25
436 Dave Rucker .08 .25
437 Charlie Hough .15 .40
438 Bob Walk .08 .25
439 Bob Brower .08 .25
440 Barry Bonds 2.00 5.00
441 Tom Foley .08 .25
442 Rob Deer .08 .25
443 Glenn Davis .08 .25
444 Dave Martinez .08 .25
445 Bill Wegman .08 .25
446 Lloyd McClendon .08 .25
447 Dave Schmidt .08 .25
448 Darren Daulton .15 .40
449 Frank Williams .08 .25
450 Don Aase .08 .25
451 Lou Whitaker .15 .40
452 Rich Gossage .15 .40
453 Ed Whitson .08 .25
454 Jim Walewander .08 .25
455 Damon Berryhill .08 .25
456 Tim Burke .08 .25
457 Barry Jones .08 .25
458 Joel Youngblood .08 .25
459 Floyd Youmans .08 .25
460 Mark Salas .08 .25
461 Jeff Russell .08 .25
462 Darrell Miller .08 .25
463 Jeff Kunkel .08 .25
464 Sherman Corbett .08 .25
465 Curtis Wilkerson .08 .25
466 Bud Black .08 .25
467 Cal Ripken 1.25 3.00
468 John Farrell .08 .25
469 Terry Kennedy .08 .25
470 Tom Candiotti .08 .25
471 Roberto Alomar .40 1.00
472 Jeff M. Robinson .08 .25
473 Vance Law .08 .25
474 Randy Ready UER .08 .25
(Strikeout total 136, should be 115)
475 Walt Terrell .08 .25
476 Kelly Downs .08 .25
477 Johnny Paredes .08 .25
478 Shawn Hillegas .08 .25
479 Bob Brenly .08 .25
480 Otis Nixon .08 .25
481 Johnny Ray .08 .25
482 Geno Petralli .08 .25
483 Stu Cliburn .08 .25
484 Pete Incaviglia .08 .25
485 Brian Downing .15 .40
486 Jeff Stone .08 .25
487 Carmen Castillo .08 .25
488 Tom Niedenfuer .08 .25
489 Jay Bell .15 .40
490 Rick Schu .08 .25
491 Jeff Pico .08 .25
492 Mark Parent .08 .25
493 Eric King .08 .25
494 Al Nipper .08 .25
495 Andy Hawkins .08 .25
496 Daryl Boston .08 .25
497 Ernie Riles .08 .25
498 Pascual Perez .08 .25
499 Bill Long UER .08 .25
(Games started total 70, should be 44)
500 Kirt Manwaring .08 .25
501 Chuck Crim .08 .25
502 Candy Maldonado .08 .25
503 Dennis Lamp .08 .25
504 Glenn Braggs .08 .25
505 Joe Price .08 .25
506 Ken Williams .08 .25
507 Bill Pecota .08 .25
508 Rey Quinones .08 .25
509 Jeff Bittiger .08 .25
510 Kevin Seitzer .15 .40
511 Steve Bedrosian .08 .25
512 Todd Worrell .08 .25
513 Chris James .08 .25
514 Jose Oquendo .08 .25
515 David Palmer .08 .25
516 John Smiley .08 .25
517 Dave Clark .08 .25
518 Mike Dunne .08 .25
519 Ron Washington .08 .25
520 Bob Kipper .08 .25
521 Lee Smith .15 .40
522 Juan Castillo .08 .25
523 Don Robinson .08 .25
524 Kevin Romine .08 .25
525 Paul Molitor .15 .40
526 Mark Langston .08 .25
527 Donnie Hill .08 .25
528 Larry Owen .08 .25
529 Jerry Reed .08 .25
530 Jack McDowell .15 .40
531 Greg Mathews .08 .25
532 John Russell .08 .25
533 Dan Quisenberry .08 .25
534 Greg Gross .08 .25
535 Danny Cox .08 .25
536 Terry Francona .15 .40
537 Andy Van Slyke .25 .60
538 Mel Hall .08 .25
539 Jim Gott .08 .25
540 Doug Jones .08 .25
541 Craig Lefferts .08 .25
542 Mike Boddicker .08 .25
543 Greg Brock .08 .25
544 Atlee Hammaker .08 .25
545 Tom Bolton .08 .25
546 Mike Macfarlane RC .20 .50
547 Rich Renteria .08 .25
548 John Davis .08 .25
549 Floyd Bannister .08 .25
550 Mickey Brantley .08 .25
551 Duane Ward .08 .25
552 Dan Petry .08 .25
553 Mickey Tettleton UER .08 .25
(Walks total 175, should be 136)
554 Rick Leach .08 .25
555 Mike Witt .08 .25
556 Sid Bream .08 .25
557 Bobby Witt .08 .25
558 Tommy Herr .08 .25
559 Randy Milligan .08 .25
560 Jose Cecena .08 .25
561 Mackey Sasser .08 .25
562 Carney Lansford .15 .40
563 Rick Aguilera .08 .25
564 Ron Hassey .08 .25
565 Dwight Gooden .15 .40
566 Paul Assenmacher .08 .25
567 Neil Allen .08 .25
568 Jim Morrison .08 .25
569 Mike Pagliarulo .08 .25
570 Ted Simmons .15 .40
571 Mark Thurmond .08 .25
572 Fred McGriff .25 .60
573 Wally Joyner .15 .40
574 Jose Bautista RC .08 .25
575 Kelly Gruber .08 .25
576 Cecilio Guante .08 .25
577 Mark Davidson .08 .25
578 Bobby Bonilla UER .15 .40
(Total steals 2 in '87, should be 3)
579 Mike Stanley .08 .25
580 Gene Larkin .08 .25
581 Stan Javier .08 .25
582 Howard Johnson .15 .40
583A Mike Gallego ERR .40 1.00
(Front reversed negative)
583B Mike Gallego COR .40 1.00
584 David Cone .15 .40
585 Doug Jennings .08 .25
586 Charles Hudson .08 .25
587 Dion James .08 .25
588 Al Leiter .40 1.00
589 Charlie Puleo .08 .25
590 Roberto Kelly .08 .25
591 Thad Bosley .08 .25
592 Pete Stanicek .08 .25
593 Pat Borders RC .20 .50
594 Bryan Harvey RC .20 .50
595 Jeff Ballard .08 .25
596 Jeff Reardon .15 .40
597 Doug Drabek .08 .25
598 Edwin Correa .08 .25
599 Keith Atherton .08 .25
600 Dave LaPoint .08 .25
601 Don Baylor .15 .40
602 Tom Pagnozzi .08 .25
603 Tim Flannery .08 .25
604 Gene Walter .08 .25
605 Dave Parker .15 .40
606 Mike Diaz .08 .25
607 Chris Gwynn .08 .25
608 Odell Jones .08 .25
609 Carlton Fisk .25 .60
610 Jay Howell .08 .25
611 Tim Crews .08 .25
612 Keith Hernandez .15 .40
613 Willie Fraser .08 .25
614 Jim Eppard .08 .25
615 Jeff Hamilton .08 .25
616 Kurt Stillwell .08 .25
617 Tom Browning .08 .25
618 Jeff Montgomery .08 .25
619 Jose Rijo .15 .40
620 Jamie Quirk .08 .25
621 Willie McGee .15 .40
622 Mark Grant UER .08 .25
(Glove on wrong hand)
623 Bill Swift .08 .25
624 Orlando Mercado .08 .25
625 John Costello .08 .25
626 Jose Gonzalez .08 .25
627A Bill Schroeder ERR .25 .60
(Back photo actually Ronn Reynolds buckling shin guards)
627B Bill Schroeder COR .25 .60
628A Fred Manrique ERR .25 .60
(Back photo actually Ozzie Guillen throwing)
628B Fred Manrique COR .08 .25
(Swinging bat on back)
629 Ricky Horton .08 .25
630 Dan Plesac .08 .25
631 Alfredo Griffin .08 .25
632 Chuck Finley .15 .40
633 Kirk Gibson .15 .40
634 Randy Myers .15 .40
635 Greg Minton .08 .25
636A Herm Winningham ERR .40 1.00
(W1nningham on back)
636B H.Winningham COR .08 .25
637 Charlie Leibrandt .08 .25
638 Tim Birtsas .08 .25
639 Bill Buckner .15 .40
640 Danny Jackson .08 .25
641 Greg Booker .08 .25
642 Jim Presley .08 .25
643 Gene Nelson .08 .25
644 Rod Booker .08 .25
645 Dennis Rasmussen .08 .25
646 Juan Nieves .08 .25
647 Bobby Thigpen .08 .25
648 Tim Belcher .08 .25
649 Mike Young .08 .25
650 Ivan Calderon .08 .25
651 Oswald Peraza .08 .25
652A Pat Sheridan ERR 6.00 15.00
(No position on front)
652B Pat Sheridan COR .08 .25
653 Mike Morgan .08 .25
654 Mike Heath .08 .25
655 Jay Tibbs .08 .25
656 Fernando Valenzuela .15 .40
657 Lee Mazzilli .15 .40
658 Frank Viola AL CY .08 .25
659A J.Canseco AL MVP .25 .60
Eagle logo in black
659B J.Canseco AL MVP .25 .60
Eagle logo in blue
660 Walt Weiss AL ROY .08 .25
661 Orel Hershiser NL CY .08 .25
662 Kirk Gibson NL MVP .15 .40
663 Chris Sabo NL ROY .15 .40
664 Dennis Eckersley .15 .40
ALCS MVP
665 Orel Hershiser .15 .40
NLCS MVP
666 Kirk Gibson WS .40 1.00
667 O.Hershiser WS MVP .08 .25
668 Wally Joyner TC .08 .25
669 Nolan Ryan TC .50 1.25
670 Jose Canseco TC .25 .60
671 Fred McGriff TC .15 .40
672 Dale Murphy TC .15 .40
673 Paul Molitor TC .15 .40
674 Ozzie Smith TC .40 1.00
675 Ryne Sandberg TC .40 1.00
676 Kirk Gibson TC .15 .40
677 Andres Galarraga TC .15 .40
678 Will Clark TC .15 .40
679 Cory Snyder TC .08 .25
680 Alvin Davis TC .08 .25
681 Darryl Strawberry TC .08 .25
682 Cal Ripken TC .40 1.00
683 Tony Gwynn TC .25 .60
684 Mike Schmidt TC .40 1.00
685 A.Van Slyke TC UER .15 .40
96 Junior Ortiz
686 Ruben Sierra TC .08 .25
687 Wade Boggs TC .15 .40
688 Eric Davis TC .15 .40
689 George Brett TC .40 1.00
690 Alan Trammell TC .15 .40
691 Frank Viola TC .08 .25
692 Harold Baines TC .08 .25
693 Don Mattingly TC .40 1.00
694 Checklist 1-100 .08 .25
695 Checklist 101-200 .08 .25
696 Checklist 201-300 .08 .25
697 Checklist 301-400 .08 .25
698 CL 401-500 UER .08 .25
467 Cal Ripkin Jr.
699 CL 501-600 UER .08 .25
543 Greg Booker
700 Checklist 601-700 .08 .25
701 Checklist 701-800 .08 .25
702 Jesse Barfield .15 .40
703 Walt Terrell .08 .25
704 Dickie Thon .08 .25
705 Al Leiter .40 1.00
706 Dave LaPoint .08 .25
707 Charlie Hayes RC .20 .50
708 Andy Hawkins .08 .25
709 Mickey Hatcher .08 .25
710 Lance McCullers .08 .25
711 Ron Kittle .08 .25
712 Bert Blyleven .15 .40
713 Rick Dempsey .08 .25
714 Ken Williams .08 .25
715 Steve Rosenberg .08 .25
716 Joe Skalski .08 .25
717 Spike Owen .08 .25
718 Todd Burns .08 .25
719 Kevin Gross .08 .25
720 Tommy Herr .08 .25
721 Rob Ducey .08 .25
722 Gary Green .08 .25
723 Gregg Olson RC .20 .50
724 Greg W. Harris RC .08 .25
725 Craig Worthington .08 .25
726 Tom Howard RC .08 .25
727 Dale Mohorcic .08 .25
728 Rich Yett .08 .25
729 Mel Hall .08 .25
730 Floyd Youmans .08 .25
731 Lonnie Smith .08 .25
732 Wally Backman .08 .25
733 Trevor Wilson RC .08 .25
734 Jose Alvarez RC .08 .25
735 Bob Milacki .08 .25
736 Tom Gordon RC .60 1.50
737 Wally Whitehurst RC .08 .25
738 Mike Aldrete .08 .25
739 Keith Miller .08 .25
740 Randy Milligan .08 .25
741 Jeff Parrett .08 .25
742 Steve Finley RC .75 2.00
743 Junior Felix RC .08 .25
744 Pete Harnisch RC .20 .50
745 Bill Spiers RC .20 .50
746 Hensley Meulens RC .08 .25
747 Juan Bell RC .08 .25
748 Steve Sax .08 .25
749 Phil Bradley .08 .25
750 Rey Quinones .08 .25
751 Tommy Gregg .08 .25
752 Kevin Brown .40 1.00
753 Derek Lilliquist RC .08 .25
754 Todd Zeile RC .40 1.00
755 Jim Abbott RC .75 2.00
Triple exposure
756 Ozzie Canseco .08 .25
757 Nick Esasky .08 .25
758 Mike Moore .08 .25
759 Rob Murphy .08 .25
760 Rick Mahler .08 .25
761 Fred Lynn .15 .40
762 Kevin Blankenship .08 .25
763 Eddie Murray .40 1.00
764 Steve Searcy .08 .25
765 Jerome Walton RC .20 .50
766 Erik Hanson RC .20 .50
767 Bob Boone .15 .40
768 Edgar Martinez .40 1.00
769 Jose DeJesus .08 .25
770 Greg Briley .08 .25
771 Steve Peters .08 .25
772 Rafael Palmeiro .40 1.00
773 Jack Clark .15 .40
774 Nolan Ryan 1.50 4.00
(Throwing football)
775 Lance Parrish .15 .40
776 Joe Girardi RC .40 1.00
777 Willie Randolph .15 .40
778 Mitch Williams .15 .40
779 Dennis Cook RC .20 .50
780 Dwight Smith RC .20 .50
781 Lenny Harris RC .20 .50
782 Torey Lovullo RC .08 .25
783 Norm Charlton RC .20 .50
784 Chris Brown .08 .25
785 Todd Benzinger .08 .25
786 Shane Rawley .08 .25
787 Omar Vizquel RC 1.25 3.00
788 LaVel Freeman .08 .25
789 Jeffrey Leonard .08 .25
790 Eddie Williams .08 .25
791 Jamie Moyer .15 .40
792 Bruce Hurst UER .08 .25
(World Series)
793 Julio Franco .15 .40
794 Claudell Washington .08 .25
795 Jody Davis .08 .25
796 Oddibe McDowell .08 .25
797 Paul Kilgus .08 .25
798 Tracy Jones .08 .25
799 Steve Wilson .08 .25
800 Pete O'Brien .08 .25

1990 Upper Deck

The 1990 Upper Deck set contains 800 standard-size cards issued in two series, low numbers (1-700) and high numbers (701-800). Cards were distributed in fin-wrapped low and high series foil packs, complete 800-card factory sets and 100-card high series factory sets. High series foil packs contained a mixture of low and high series cards. The front and back borders are white, and both sides feature full-color photos. The horizontally oriented backs have recent stats and anti-counterfeiting holograms. Team checklist cards are mixed in with the first 100 cards of the set. Rookie Cards in the set include Juan Gonzalez, David Justice, Ray Lankford, Dean Palmer, Sammy Sosa and Larry Walker. The high series contains a Nolan Ryan variation; all cards produced before August 12th only discuss Ryan's sixth no-hitter while the later-issue cards include a stripe honoring Ryan's 300th victory. Card 702 (Rookie Threats) was originally scheduled to be Mike Witt. A few Witt cards with 702 on back and checklist cards showing Witt as 702 escaped into early packs; they are characterized by a black rectangle covering much of the card's back.

COMPLETE SET (800) 10.00 25.00
COMP.FACT.SET (800) 10.00 25.00
COMPLETE LO SET (700) 15.00 25.00
COMPLETE HI SET (100) 2.00 5.00
COMP.HI FACT.SET (100) 2.00 4.00
1 Star Rookie Checklist .02 .10
2 Randy Nosek RC .02 .10
3 Tom Drees UER RC .02 .10
(11th line, hulred, should be hurled
4 Curt Young .02 .10
5 Devon White TC .02 .10
6 Luis Salazar .02 .10
7 Von Hayes TC .02 .10
8 Jose Bautista .02 .10
9 Marquis Grissom RC .20 .50
10 Orel Hershiser TC .02 .10
11 Rick Aguilera .07 .20
12 Benito Santiago TC .02 .10
13 Deion Sanders .20 .50
14 Marvell Wynne .02 .10
15 Dave West .02 .10
16 Bobby Bonilla TC .02 .10
17 Sammy Sosa RC 1.25 3.00
18 Steve Sax TC .02 .10
19 Jack Howell .02 .10
20 Mike Schmidt Special .40 1.00
UER (Suprising, should be surprising)
21 Robin Ventura UER .20 .50
(Samta Maria)
22 Brian Meyer .02 .10
23 Blaine Beatty RC .02 .10
24 Ken Griffey Jr. TC .25 .60
25 Greg Vaughn UER .02 .10
(Association misspelled as assiocation)
26 Xavier Hernandez RC .02 .10
27 Jason Grimsley RC .02 .10
28 Eric Anthony UER RC .02 .10
(Ashville, should be Asheville)
29 Tim Raines TC UER .02 .10
(Wallach listed before Walker)
30 David Wells .07 .20
31 Hal Morris .07 .20
32 Bo Jackson TC .07 .20
33 Kelly Mann RC .02 .10
34 Nolan Ryan Special .40 1.00
35 Scott Service UER .02 .10
(Born Cincinati on 7/27/67, should be Cincinnati 2/27)
36 Mark McGwire TC .30 .75
37 Tino Martinez .40 1.00
38 Chili Davis .07 .20
39 Scott Sanderson .02 .10
40 Kevin Mitchell TC .02 .10
41 Lou Whitaker TC .02 .10
42 Scott Coolbaugh UER .02 .10
(Definately) RC
43 Jose Cano UER RC .02 .10
(Born 9/7/62, should be 3/7/62)
44 Jose Vizcaino RC .08 .25
45 Bob Hamelin RC .08 .25
46 Jose Offerman UER RC .08 .25
(Posesses)
47 Kevin Blankenship .02 .10
48 Kirby Puckett TC .10 .30
49 Tommy Greene RC UER .02 .10
(Livest, should be liveliest)
50 Will Clark Special .07 .20
UER (Perenial, should be perennial)
51 Rob Nelson .02 .10
52 C.Hammond UER RC .02 .10
Chatanooga)
53 Joe Carter TC .02 .10
54A B.McDonald ERR .75 2.00
No Rookie designation on card front
54B B.McDonald COR RC .08 .25
55 Andy Benes UER .07 .20
(Whichita)
56 John Olerud RC .30 .75
57 Roger Clemens TC .30 .75
58 Tony Armas .02 .10
59 George Canale RC .02 .10
60A Mickey Tettleton TC .75 2.00
ERR (683 Jamie Weston)
60B Mickey Tettleton TC .02 .10
COR (683 Mickey Weston)
61 Mike Stanton RC .08 .25
62 Dwight Gooden TC .02 .10
63 Kent Mercker RC UER .08 .25
(Albuguerque)
64 Francisco Cabrera .02 .10
65 Steve Avery UER .02 .10
(Born NJ, should be MI, Merker should be Mercker
66 Jose Canseco .10 .30
67 Matt Merullo .02 .10
68 Vince Coleman TC UER .02 .10
(Guerrero)
69 Ron Karkovice .02 .10
70 Kevin Maas RC .08 .25

71 Dennis Cook UER .02 .10
(Shown with righty
glove on card back)
72 Juan Gonzalez UER RC .60 1.50
(135 games for Tulsa
in '89, should be 133)
73 Andre Dawson TC .02 .10
74 Dean Palmer UER RC .08 .25
(Permanent misspelled
as perminant)
75 Bo Jackson Special .07 .20
UER (Monsterous,
should be monstrous)
76 Rob Richie RC .02 .10
77 Bobby Rose UER .02 .10
(Pickin, should
be pick in)
78 Brian DuBois UER RC .02 .10
(Commiting)
79 Ozzie Guillen TC .02 .10
80 Gene Nelson .02 .10
81 Bob McClure .02 .10
82 Julio Franco TC .02 .10
83 Greg Minton .02 .10
84 John Smoltz TC UER .10 .30
(Oddibe not Odibbe)
85 Willie Fraser .02 .10
86 Neal Heaton .02 .10
87 Kevin Tapan UER RC .08 .25
(24th line has excpet,
should be except)
88 Mike Scott TC .02 .10
89A Jim Gott ERR .75 2.00
(Photo actually
Rick Reed)
89B Jim Gott COR .02 .10
90 Lance Johnson .02 .10
91 Robin Yount TC UER .20 .50
(Checklist on back has
178 Rob Deer and
176 Mike Felder)
92 Jeff Parrett .02 .10
93 Julio Machado UER RC .02 .10
(Valenzuelan, should
be Venezuelan)
94 Ron Jones .02 .10
95 George Bell TC .02 .10
96 Jerry Reuss .02 .10
97 Brian Fisher .02 .10
98 Kevin Ritz UER RC .02 .10
(Amercian)
99 Barry Larkin TC .07 .20
100 Checklist 1-100 .02 .10
101 Gerald Perry .02 .10
102 Kevin Appier .07 .20
103 Julio Franco .07 .20
104 Craig Biggio .20 .50
105 Bo Jackson UER .20 .50
('89 BA wrong,
should be .256)
106 Junior Felix .02 .10
107 Mike Harkey .02 .10
108 Fred McGriff .20 .50
109 Rick Sutcliffe .07 .20
110 Pete O'Brien .02 .10
111 Kelly Gruber .02 .10
112 Dwight Evans .10 .30
113 Pat Borders .02 .10
114 Dwight Gooden .07 .20
115 Kevin Batiste RC .02 .10
116 Eric Davis .07 .20
117 Kevin Mitchell UER .07 .20
(Career HR total 99,
should be 100)
118 Ron Oester .02 .10
119 Brett Butler .07 .20
120 Danny Jackson .02 .10
121 Tommy Gregg .02 .10
122 Ken Caminiti .07 .20
123 Kevin Brown .07 .20
124 George Brett UER .50 1.25
(133 runs, should
be 1300)
125 Mike Scott .02 .10
126 Cory Snyder .02 .10
127 George Bell .02 .10
128 Mark Grace .10 .30
129 Devon White .07 .20
130 Tony Fernandez .02 .10
131 Don Aase .02 .10
132 Rance Mulliniks .02 .10
133 Marty Barrett .02 .10
134 Nelson Liriano .02 .10
135 Mark Carreon .02 .10
136 Candy Maldonado .02 .10
137 Tim Birtsas .02 .10
138 Tom Brookens .02 .10
139 John Franco .07 .20
140 Mike LaCoss .02 .10
141 Jeff Treadway .02 .10
142 Pat Tabler .02 .10
143 Darrell Evans .07 .20
144 Rafael Ramirez .02 .10
145 O.McDowell UER .02 .10
Misspelled Odibbe
146 Brian Downing .02 .10
147 Curt Wilkerson .02 .10
148 Ernie Whitt .02 .10
149 Bill Schroeder .02 .10
150 Domingo Ramos UER .02 .10
(Says throws right,
but shows him
throwing lefty)
151 Rick Honeycutt .02 .10
152 Don Slaught .02 .10
153 Mitch Webster .02 .10
154 Tony Phillips .02 .10
155 Paul Kilgus .02 .10
156 Ken Griffey Jr. UER .60 1.50
(Simultaniously)
157 Gary Sheffield .20 .50
158 Wally Backman .02 .10
159 B.J. Surhoff .07 .20
160 Louie Meadows .02 .10
161 Paul O'Neill .10 .30
162 Jeff McKnight RC .02 .10
163 Alvaro Espinoza .02 .10
164 Scott Scudder .02 .10
165 Jeff Reed .02 .10
166 Gregg Jefferies .07 .20
167 Barry Larkin .10 .30
168 Gary Carter .07 .20
169 Robby Thompson .02 .10
170 Rolando Roomes .02 .10
171 Mark McGwire UER .60 1.50
(Total games 427 and
hits 479, should be
467 and 427)
172 Steve Sax .02 .10
173 Mark Williamson .02 .10
174 Mitch Williams .02 .10
175 Brian Holton .02 .10
176 Rob Deer .02 .10
177 Tim Raines .07 .20
178 Mike Felder .02 .10
179 Harold Reynolds .07 .20
180 Terry Francona .07 .20
181 Chris Sabo .02 .10
182 Darryl Strawberry .07 .20
183 Willie Randolph .07 .20
184 Bill Ripken .02 .10
185 Mackey Sasser .02 .10
186 Todd Benzinger .02 .10
187 Kevin Elster UER .02 .10
(16 homers in 1989,
should be 10)
188 Jose Uribe .02 .10
189 Tom Browning .02 .10
190 Keith Miller .02 .10
191 Don Mattingly .50 1.25
192 Dave Parker .07 .20
193 Roberto Kelly UER .02 .10
(96 RBI, should be 62)
194 Phil Bradley .02 .10
195 Ron Hassey .02 .10
196 Gerald Young .02 .10
197 Hubie Brooks .02 .10
198 Bill Doran .02 .10
199 Al Newman .02 .10
200 Checklist 101-200 .02 .10
201 Terry Puhl .02 .10
202 Frank DiPino .02 .10
203 Jim Clancy .02 .10
204 Bob Ojeda .02 .10
205 Alex Trevino .02 .10
206 Dave Henderson .02 .10
207 Henry Cotto .02 .10
208 Rafael Belliard UER .02 .10
(Born 1961, not 1951)
209 Stan Javier .02 .10
210 Jerry Reed .02 .10
211 Doug Dascenzo .02 .10
212 Andres Thomas .02 .10
213 Greg Maddux .30 .75
214 Mike Schooler .02 .10
215 Lonnie Smith .02 .10
216 Jose Rijo .02 .10
217 Greg Gagne .02 .10
218 Jim Gantner .02 .10
219 Allan Anderson .02 .10
220 Rick Mahler .02 .10
221 Jim Deshaies .02 .10
222 Keith Hernandez .07 .20
223 Vince Coleman .02 .10
224 David Cone .07 .20
225 Ozzie Smith .30 .75
226 Matt Nokes .02 .10
227 Barry Bonds .60 1.50
228 Felix Jose .02 .10
229 Dennis Powell .02 .10
230 Mike Gallego .02 .10
231 Shawon Dunston UER .02 .10
('89 stats are
Andre Dawson's)
232 Ron Gant .07 .20
233 Omar Vizquel .20 .50
234 Derek Lilliquist .02 .10
235 Erik Hanson .02 .10
236 Kirby Puckett UER .20 .50
(824 games, should
be 924)
237 Bill Spiers .02 .10
238 Dan Gladden .02 .10
239 Bryan Clutterbuck .02 .10
240 John Moses .02 .10
241 Ron Darling .02 .10
242 Joe Magrane .02 .10
243 Dave Magadan .02 .10
244 Pedro Guerrero UER .02 .10
(Misspelled Guerrero)
245 Glenn Davis .02 .10
246 Terry Steinbach .02 .10
247 Fred Lynn .02 .10
248 Gary Redus .02 .10
249 Ken Williams .02 .10
250 Sid Bream .02 .10
251 Bob Welch UER .02 .10
(2587 career strike-
outs, should be 1587)
252 Bill Buckner .02 .10
253 Carney Lansford .07 .20
254 Paul Molitor .07 .20
255 Jose DeJesus .02 .10
256 Orel Hershiser .07 .20
257 Tom Brunansky .02 .10
258 Mike Davis .02 .10
259 Jeff Ballard .02 .10
260 Scott Terry .02 .10
261 Sid Fernandez .02 .10
262 Mike Marshall .02 .10
263 Howard Johnson UER .02 .10
(192 SO, should be 592)
264 Kirk Gibson UER .07 .20
(659 runs, should
be 669)
265 Kevin McReynolds .02 .10
266 Cal Ripken .60 1.50
267 Ozzie Guillen UER .07 .20
(Career triples 27,
should be 29)
268 Jim Traber .02 .10
269 Bobby Thigpen UER .02 .10
(31 saves in 1989,
should be 34)
270 Joe Orsulak .02 .10
271 Bob Boone .07 .20
272 Dave Stewart UER .07 .20
(Totals wrong due to
omission of '86 stats)
273 Tim Wallach .02 .10
274 Luis Aquino UER .02 .10
(Says throws lefty,
but shows him
throwing righty)
275 Mike Moore .02 .10
276 Tony Pena .02 .10
277 Eddie Murray UER .20 .50
(Several typos in
career total stats)
278 Milt Thompson .02 .10
279 Alejandro Pena .02 .10
280 Ken Dayley .02 .10
281 Carmelo Castillo .02 .10
282 Tom Henke .02 .10
283 Mickey Hatcher .02 .10
284 Roy Smith .02 .10
285 Manny Lee .02 .10
286 Dan Pasqua .02 .10
287 Larry Sheets .02 .10
288 Garry Templeton .02 .10
289 Eddie Williams .02 .10
290 Brady Anderson UER .07 .20
(Home: Silver Springs,
not Siver Springs)
291 Spike Owen .02 .10
292 Storm Davis .02 .10
293 Chris Bosio .02 .10
294 Jim Eisenreich .02 .10
295 Don August .02 .10
296 Jeff Hamilton .02 .10
297 Mickey Tettleton .02 .10
298 Mike Scioscia .02 .10
299 Kevin Hickey .02 .10
300 Checklist 201-300 .02 .10
301 Shawn Abner .02 .10
302 Kevin Bass .02 .10
303 Bip Roberts .02 .10
304 Joe Girardi .10 .30
305 Danny Darwin .02 .10
306 Mike Heath .02 .10
307 Mike Macfarlane .02 .10
308 Ed Whitson .02 .10
309 Tracy Jones .02 .10
310 Scott Fletcher .02 .10
311 Darnell Coles .02 .10
312 Mike Brumley .02 .10
313 Bill Swift .02 .10
314 Charlie Hough .07 .20
315 Jim Presley .02 .10
316 Luis Polonia .02 .10
317 Mike Morgan .02 .10
318 Lee Guetterman .02 .10
319 Jose Oquendo .02 .10
320 Wayne Tolleson .02 .10
321 Jody Reed .02 .10
322 Damon Berryhill .02 .10
323 Roger Clemens .60 1.50
324 Ryne Sandberg .30 .75
325 Benito Santiago UER .07 .20
(Misspelled Santago
on card back)
326 Bret Saberhagen UER .07 .20
(1140 hits, should be
1240; 56 CG, should
be 52)
327 Lou Whitaker .07 .20
328 Dave Gallagher .02 .10
329 Mike Pagliarulo .02 .10
330 Doyle Alexander .02 .10
331 Jeffrey Leonard .02 .10
332 Torey Lovullo .02 .10
333 Pete Incaviglia .02 .10
334 Rickey Henderson .20 .50
335 Rafael Palmeiro .10 .30
336 Ken Hill .07 .20
337 Dave Winfield UER .07 .20
(1418 RBI, should
be 1438)
338 Alfredo Griffin .02 .10
339 Andy Hawkins .02 .10
340 Ted Power .02 .10
341 Steve Wilson .02 .10
342 Jack Clark UER .07 .20
(916 BB, should be
1006; 1142 SO,
should be 1130)
343 Ellis Burks .10 .30
344 Tony Gwynn UER .25 .60
(Doubles stats on
card back are wrong)
345 Jerome Walton UER .02 .10
(Total At Bats 476,
should be 475)
346 Roberto Alomar UER .10 .30
(61 doubles, should
be 51)
347 Carlos Martinez UER .02 .10
(Born 8/11/64, should
be 8/11/65)
348 Chet Lemon .02 .10
349 Willie Wilson .02 .10
350 Greg Walker .02 .10
351 Tom Bolton .02 .10
352 German Gonzalez .02 .10
353 Harold Baines .07 .20
354 Mike Greenwell .02 .10
355 Ruben Sierra .07 .20
356 Andres Galarraga .07 .20
357 Andre Dawson .07 .20
358 Jeff Brantley .02 .10
359 Mike Bielecki .02 .10
360 Ken Oberkfell .02 .10
361 Kurt Stillwell .02 .10
362 Brian Holman .02 .10
363 Kevin Seitzer UER .02 .10
(Career triples total
does not add up)
364 Alvin Davis .02 .10
365 Tom Gordon .07 .20
366 Bobby Bonilla UER .07 .20
(Two steals in 1987,
should be 3)
367 Carlton Fisk .10 .30
368 Steve Carter UER .02 .10
(Charlotesville)
369 Joel Skinner .02 .10
370 John Cangelosi .02 .10
371 Cecil Espy .02 .10
372 Gary Wayne .02 .10
373 Jim Rice .07 .20
374 Mike Dyer RC .02 .10
375 Joe Carter .07 .20
376 Dwight Smith .02 .10
377 John Wetteland .20 .50
378 Earnie Riles .02 .10
379 Otis Nixon .02 .10
380 Vance Law .02 .10
381 Dave Bergman .02 .10
382 Frank White .07 .20
383 Scott Bradley .02 .10
384 Israel Sanchez UER .02 .10
(Totals don't in-
clude '89 stats)
385 Gary Pettis .02 .10
386 Donn Pall .02 .10
387 John Smiley .02 .10
388 Tom Candiotti .02 .10
389 Junior Ortiz .02 .10
390 Steve Lyons .02 .10
391 Brian Harper .02 .10
392 Fred Manrique .02 .10
393 Lee Smith .07 .20
394 Jeff Kunkel .02 .10
395 Claudell Washington .02 .10
396 John Tudor .02 .10
397 Terry Kennedy UER .02 .10
(Career totals all
wrong)
398 Lloyd McClendon .02 .10
399 Craig Lefferts .02 .10
400 Checklist 301-400 .02 .10
401 Keith Moreland .02 .10
402 Rich Gedman .02 .10
403 Jeff D. Robinson .02 .10
404 Randy Ready .02 .10
405 Rick Cerone .02 .10
406 Jeff Blauser .02 .10
407 Larry Andersen .02 .10
408 Joe Boever .02 .10
409 Felix Fermin .02 .10
410 Glenn Wilson .02 .10
411 Rex Hudler .02 .10
412 Mark Grant .02 .10
413 Dennis Martinez .07 .20
414 Darrin Jackson .02 .10
415 Mike Aldrete .02 .10
416 Roger McDowell .02 .10
417 Jeff Reardon .07 .20
418 Darren Daulton .07 .20
419 Tim Laudner .02 .10
420 Don Carman .02 .10
421 Lloyd Moseby .02 .10
422 Doug Drabek .02 .10
423 Lenny Harris UER .02 .10
(Walks 2 in '89,
should be 20)
424 Jose Lind .02 .10
425 Dave Wayne Johnson RC .02 .10
426 Jerry Browne .02 .10
427 Eric Yelding RC .02 .10
428 Brad Komminsk .02 .10
429 Jody Davis .02 .10
430 Mariano Duncan .02 .10
431 Mark Davis .02 .10
432 Nelson Santovenia .02 .10
433 Bruce Hurst .02 .10
434 Jeff Huson RC .02 .10
435 Chris James .02 .10
436 Mark Guthrie RC .02 .10
437 Charlie Hayes .02 .10
438 Shane Rawley .02 .10
439 Dickie Thon .02 .10
440 Juan Berenguer .02 .10
441 Kevin Romine .02 .10
442 Bill Landrum .02 .10
443 Todd Frohwirth .02 .10
444 Craig Worthington .02 .10
445 Fernando Valenzuela .07 .20
446 Joey Belle .20 .50
447 Ed Whited UER RC .02 .10
(Ashville, should
be Asheville)
448 Dave Smith .02 .10
449 Dave Clark .02 .10
450 Juan Agosto .02 .10
451 Dave Valle .02 .10
452 Kent Hrbek .07 .20
453 Von Hayes .02 .10
454 Gary Gaetti .07 .20
455 Greg Briley .02 .10
456 Glenn Braggs .02 .10
457 Kirt Manwaring .02 .10
458 Mel Hall .02 .10
459 Brook Jacoby .02 .10
460 Pat Sheridan .02 .10
461 Rob Murphy .02 .10
462 Jimmy Key .07 .20
463 Nick Esasky .02 .10
464 Rob Ducey .02 .10
465 Carlos Quintana UER .02 .10
(Internatinoal)
466 Larry Walker RC .60 1.50
467 Todd Worrell .02 .10
468 Kevin Gross .02 .10
469 Terry Pendleton .07 .20
470 Dave Martinez .02 .10
471 Gene Larkin .02 .10
472 Len Dykstra UER .07 .20
('89 and total runs
understated by 10)
473 Barry Lyons .02 .10
474 Terry Mulholland .02 .10
475 Chip Hale RC .02 .10
476 Jesse Barfield .02 .10
477 Dan Plesac .02 .10
478A Scott Garrelts ERR .75 2.00
(Photo actually
Bill Bathe)
478B Scott Garrelts COR .02 .10
479 Dave Righetti .02 .10
480 Gus Polidor UER .02 .10
Wearing 14 on front,
but 10 on back
481 Mookie Wilson .07 .20
482 Luis Rivera .02 .10
483 Mike Flanagan .02 .10
484 Dennis Boyd .02 .10
485 John Cerutti .02 .10
486 John Costello .02 .10
487 Pascual Perez .02 .10
488 Tommy Herr .02 .10
489 Tom Foley .02 .10
490 Curt Ford .02 .10
491 Steve Lake .02 .10
492 Tim Teufel .02 .10
493 Randy Bush .02 .10
494 Mike Jackson .02 .10
495 Steve Jeltz .02 .10
496 Paul Gibson .02 .10
497 Steve Balboni .02 .10
498 Bud Black .02 .10
499 Dale Sveum .02 .10
500 Checklist 401-500 .02 .10
501 Tim Jones .02 .10
502 Mark Portugal .02 .10
503 Ivan Calderon .02 .10
504 Rick Rhoden .02 .10
505 Willie McGee .07 .20
506 Kirk McCaskill .02 .10
507 Dave LaPoint .02 .10
508 Jay Howell .02 .10
509 Johnny Ray .02 .10
510 Dave Anderson .02 .10
511 Chuck Crim .02 .10
512 Joe Hesketh .02 .10
513 Dennis Eckersley .07 .20
514 Greg Brock .02 .10
515 Tim Burke .02 .10
516 Frank Tanana .02 .10
517 Jay Bell .07 .20
518 Guillermo Hernandez .02 .10
519 Randy Kramer UER .02 .10
(Codiroli misspelled
as Codoroli)
520 Charles Hudson .02 .10
521 Jim Corsi .02 .10
Word 'originally' is
misspelled on back
522 Steve Rosenberg .02 .10
523 Cris Carpenter .02 .10
524 Matt Winters RC .02 .10
525 Melido Perez .02 .10
526 Chris Gwynn UER .02 .10
(Albeguergue)
527 Bert Blyleven UER .07 .20
(Games career total is
wrong, should be 644)
528 Chuck Cary .02 .10
529 Daryl Boston .02 .10
530 Dale Mohorcic .02 .10
531 Geronimo Berroa .02 .10
532 Edgar Martinez .10 .30
533 Dale Murphy .10 .30
534 Jay Buhner .07 .20
535 John Smoltz UER .20 .50
(HEA Stadium)
536 Andy Van Slyke .10 .30
537 Mike Henneman .02 .10
538 Miguel Garcia .02 .10
539 Frank Williams .02 .10
540 R.J. Reynolds .02 .10
541 Shawn Hillegas .02 .10
542 Walt Weiss .02 .10
543 Greg Hibbard RC .02 .10
544 Nolan Ryan .75 2.00
545 Todd Zeile .07 .20
546 Hensley Meulens .02 .10
547 Tim Belcher .02 .10
548 Mike Witt .02 .10
549 Greg Cadaret UER .02 .10
(Aquiring, should
be Acquiring)
550 Franklin Stubbs .02 .10
551 Tony Castillo .02 .10
552 Jeff M. Robinson .02 .10
553 Steve Olin RC .08 .25
554 Alan Trammell .07 .20
555 Wade Boggs 4X .10 .30
556 Will Clark .10 .30
557 Jeff King .02 .10
558 Mike Fitzgerald .02 .10
559 Ken Howell .02 .10
560 Bob Kipper .02 .10
561 Scott Bankhead .02 .10
562A Jeff Innis ERR .75 2.00
(Photo actually
David West)
562B Jeff Innis COR RC .02 .10
563 Randy Johnson .40 1.00
564 Wally Whitehurst .02 .10
565 Gene Harris .02 .10
566 Norm Charlton .02 .10
567 Robin Yount UER .30 .75
(7602 career hits,
should be 2606)
In addition, the career doubles are incorrect
568 Joe Oliver UER .02 .10
(Fl.orida)
569 Mark Parent .02 .10
570 John Farrell UER .02 .10
(Loss total added wrong)
571 Tom Glavine .10 .30
572 Rod Nichols .02 .10
573 Jack Morris .07 .20
574 Greg Swindell .02 .10
575 Steve Searcy .02 .10
576 Ricky Jordan .02 .10
577 Matt Williams .07 .20
578 Mike LaValliere .02 .10
579 Bryn Smith .02 .10
580 Bruce Ruffin .02 .10
581 Randy Myers .07 .20
582 Rick Wrona .02 .10
583 Juan Samuel .02 .10
584 Les Lancaster .02 .10
585 Jeff Musselman .02 .10
586 Rob Dibble .07 .20
587 Eric Show .02 .10
588 Jesse Orosco .02 .10
589 Herm Winningham .02 .10
590 Andy Allanson .02 .10
591 Dion James .02 .10
592 Carmelo Martinez .02 .10
593 Luis Quinones .02 .10
594 Dennis Rasmussen .02 .10
595 Rich Yett .02 .10
596 Bob Walk .02 .10
597A A.McGaffigan ERR .75 2.00
Photo actually
Rich Thompson
597B A.McGaffigan COR .02 .10
598 Billy Hatcher .02 .10
599 Bob Knepper .02 .10
600 CL 501-600 UER .02 .10
599 Bob Kneppers
601 Joey Cora .07 .20
602 Steve Finley .07 .20
603 Kal Daniels UER .02 .10
(12 hits in '87, should
be 123; 335 runs,
should be 235)
604 Gregg Olson .07 .20
605 Dave Stieb .07 .20
606 Kenny Rogers .07 .20
(Shown catching
football)
607 Zane Smith .02 .10
608 Bob Geren UER .02 .10
(Origionally)
609 Chad Kreuter .02 .10
610 Mike Smithson .02 .10
611 Jeff Wetherby RC .02 .10
612 Gary Mielke RC .02 .10
613 Pete Smith .02 .10
614 Jack Daugherty UER RC .02 .10
(Born 7/30/60, should
be 7/3/60)
615 Lance McCullers .02 .10
616 Don Robinson .02 .10
617 Jose Guzman .02 .10
618 Steve Bedrosian .02 .10
619 Jamie Moyer .07 .20
620 Atlee Hammaker .02 .10
621 Rick Luecken UER RC .02 .10
(Innings pitched wrong)
622 Greg W. Harris .02 .10
623 Pete Harnisch .02 .10
624 Jerald Clark .02 .10
625 Jack McDowell UER .02 .10
(Career totals for Games
and GS don't include
1987 season)
626 Frank Viola .02 .10
627 Teddy Higuera .02 .10
628 Marty Pevey RC .02 .10
629 Bill Wegman .02 .10
630 Eric Plunk .02 .10
631 Drew Hall .02 .10
632 Doug Jones .02 .10
633 Geno Petralli UER .02 .10
(Sacremento)
634 Jose Alvarez .02 .10
635 Bob Milacki .02 .10
636 Bobby Witt .02 .10
637 Trevor Wilson .02 .10
638 Jeff Russell UER .02 .10
(Shutout stats wrong)
639 Mike Krukow .02 .10
640 Rick Leach .02 .10
641 Dave Schmidt .02 .10
642 Terry Leach .02 .10
643 Calvin Schiraldi .02 .10
644 Bob Melvin .02 .10
645 Jim Abbott .10 .30
646 Jaime Navarro .02 .10
647 Mark Langston UER .02 .10
(Several errors in
stats totals)
648 Juan Nieves .02 .10
649 Damaso Garcia .02 .10
650 Charlie O'Brien .02 .10
651 Eric King .02 .10
652 Mike Boddicker .02 .10
653 Duane Ward .02 .10
654 Bob Stanley .02 .10
655 Sandy Alomar Jr. .07 .20
656 Danny Tartabull UER .02 .10
(395 BB, should be 295)
657 Randy McCament RC .02 .10
658 Charlie Leibrandt .02 .10
659 Dan Quisenberry .02 .10
660 Paul Assenmacher .02 .10
661 Walt Terrell .02 .10
662 Tim Leary .02 .10
663 Randy Milligan .02 .10
664 Bo Diaz .02 .10
665 Mark Lemke UER .02 .10
(Richmond misspelled
as Richomond)
666 Jose Gonzalez .02 .10
667 Chuck Finley UER .07 .20
(Born 11/16/62, should
be 11/26/62)
668 John Kruk .07 .20
669 Dick Schofield .02 .10
670 Tim Crews .02 .10
671 John Dopson .02 .10
672 John Orton RC .02 .10
673 Eric Hetzel .02 .10
674 Lance Parrish .02 .10
675 Ramon Martinez .02 .10
676 Mark Gubicza .02 .10
677 Greg Litton .02 .10
678 Greg Mathews .02 .10
679 Dave Dravecky .07 .20
680 Steve Farr .02 .10
681 Mike Devereaux .02 .10
682 Ken Griffey Sr. .07 .20
683A Mickey Weston ERR .75 2.00
(Listed as Jamie
on card)
683B Mickey Weston COR RC .02 .10
(Technically still an
error as birthdate is
listed as 3/26/81)
684 Jack Armstrong .02 .10
685 Steve Buechele .02 .10
686 Bryan Harvey .02 .10
687 Lance Blankenship .02 .10
688 Dante Bichette .07 .20
689 Todd Burns .02 .10
690 Dan Petry .02 .10
691 Kent Anderson .02 .10
692 Todd Stottlemyre .07 .20
693 Wally Joyner UER .07 .20
(Several stats errors)
694 Mike Rochford .02 .10
695 Floyd Bannister .02 .10
696 Rick Reuschel .02 .10
697 Jose DeLeon .02 .10
698 Jeff Montgomery .07 .20
699 Kelly Downs .02 .10
700A Checklist 601-700 .75 2.00
(683 Jamie Weston)
700B Checklist 601-700 .02 .10
(683 Mickey Weston)

Card	Low	High
701 Jim Gott	.02	.10
702 Delino DeShields	.20	.50
Marquis Grissom		
Larry Walker		
702A Mike Witt	4.00	10.00
Black rectangle covers much of back		
703 Alejandro Pena	.02	.10
704 Willie Randolph	.07	.20
705 Tim Leary	.02	.10
706 Chuck McElroy RC	.02	.10
707 Gerald Perry	.02	.10
708 Tom Brunansky	.02	.10
709 John Franco	.07	.20
710 Mark Davis	.02	.10
711 David Justice RC	.30	.75
712 Storm Davis	.02	.10
713 Scott Ruskin RC	.02	.10
714 Glenn Braggs	.02	.10
715 Kevin Bearse RC	.02	.10
716 Jose Nunez	.02	.10
717 Tim Layana RC	.02	.10
718 Greg Myers	.02	.10
719 Pete O'Brien	.02	.10
720 John Candelaria	.02	.10
721 Craig Grebeck RC	.02	.10
722 Shawn Boskie RC	.02	.10
723 Jim Leyritz RC	.08	.25
724 Bill Sampen RC	.02	.10
725 Scott Radinsky RC	.02	.10
726 Todd Hundley RC	.08	.25
727 Scott Hemond RC	.02	.10
728 Lenny Webster RC	.02	.10
729 Jeff Reardon	.07	.20
730 Mitch Webster	.02	.10
731 Brian Bohanon RC	.02	.10
732 Rick Parker RC	.02	.10
733 Terry Shumpert RC	.02	.10
734A Nolan Ryan	1.25	3.00
6th No-Hitter		
(No stripe on front)		
734B Nolan Ryan	.40	1.00
6th No-Hitter		
(stripe added on card front for 300th win)		
735 John Burkett	.02	.10
736 Derrick May RC	.02	.10
737 Carlos Baerga RC	.08	.25
738 Greg Smith RC	.02	.10
739 Scott Sanderson	.02	.10
740 Joe Kraemer RC	.02	.10
741 Hector Villanueva RC	.02	.10
742 Mike Fetters RC	.08	.25
743 Mark Gardner RC	.02	.10
744 Matt Nokes	.02	.10
745 Dave Winfield	.07	.20
746 Delino DeShields RC	.08	.25
747 Dann Howitt RC	.02	.10
748 Tony Pena	.02	.10
749 Oil Can Boyd	.02	.10
750 Mike Benjamin RC	.02	.10
751 Alex Cole RC	.02	.10
752 Eric Gunderson RC	.02	.10
753 Howard Farmer RC	.02	.10
754 Joe Carter	.07	.20
755 Ray Lankford RC	.20	.50
756 Sandy Alomar Jr.	.07	.20
757 Alex Sanchez	.02	.10
758 Nick Esasky	.02	.10
759 Stan Belinda RC	.02	.10
760 Jim Presley	.02	.10
761 Gary DiSarcina RC	.08	.25
762 Wayne Edwards RC	.02	.10
763 Pat Combs	.02	.10
764 Mickey Pina RC	.02	.10
765 Wilson Alvarez RC	.08	.25
766 Dave Parker	.07	.20
767 Mike Blowers RC	.02	.10
768 Tony Phillips	.02	.10
769 Pascual Perez	.02	.10
770 Gary Pettis	.02	.10
771 Fred Lynn	.02	.10
772 Mel Rojas RC	.02	.10
773 David Segui RC	.20	.50
774 Gary Carter	.07	.20
775 Rafael Valdez RC	.02	.10
776 Glenallen Hill	.02	.10
777 Keith Hernandez	.07	.20
778 Billy Hatcher	.02	.10
779 Marty Clary	.02	.10
780 Candy Maldonado	.02	.10
781 Mike Marshall	.02	.10
782 Billy Joe Robidoux	.02	.10
783 Mark Langston	.02	.10
784 Paul Sorrento RC	.08	.25
785 Dave Hollins RC	.08	.25
786 Cecil Fielder	.07	.20
787 Matt Young	.02	.10
788 Jeff Huson	.02	.10
789 Lloyd Moseby	.02	.10
790 Ron Kittle	.02	.10
791 Hubie Brooks	.02	.10
792 Craig Lefferts	.02	.10
793 Kevin Bass	.02	.10
794 Bryn Smith	.02	.10
795 Juan Samuel	.02	.10
796 Sam Horn	.02	.10
797 Randy Myers	.07	.20
798 Chris James	.02	.10
799 Bill Gullickson	.02	.10
800 Checklist 701-800	.02	.10

1990 Upper Deck Jackson Heroes

This ten-card standard-size set was issued as an insert in 1990 Upper Deck High Number packs as part of the Upper Deck promotional giveaway of 2,500 officially signed and personally numbered Reggie Jackson cards. Signed cards ending with 00 have the words "Mr. October" added to the autograph. These cards cover Jackson's major league career. The complete set price refers only to the unautographed card set of ten. One-card packs of over-sized (3 1/2" by 5") versions of these cards were later inserted into retail blister repacks containing one foil pack each of 1993 Upper Deck Series I and II. These cards were later inserted into various forms of repackaging. The larger cards are also distinguishable by the Upper Deck Fifth Anniversary logo and "1993 Hall of Fame Inductee" logo on the front of the card. These over-sized cards were a limited edition of 10,000 numbered cards and have no extra value than the basic cards.

Card	Low	High
COMPLETE SET (10)	6.00	15.00
COMMON REGGIE (1-9)	.60	1.50
NNO Reggie Jackson	1.25	3.00
Header Card		
AU1 Reggie Jackson AU	75.00	150.00
(Signed and Numbered out of 2500)		

1991 Upper Deck

This set marked the third year Upper Deck issued a 800-card standard-size set in two separate series of 700 and 100 cards respectively. Cards were distributed in low and high series foil packs and factory sets. The 100-card extended or high-number series was issued by Upper Deck several months after the release of their first series. For the first time in Upper Deck's three-year history, they did not issue a factory Extended set. The basic cards are made on the typical Upper Deck slick, white card stock and features full-color photos on both the front and the back. Subsets include Star Rookies (1-26), Team Cards (28-34, 43-49, 77-82, 95-99) and Top Prospects (50-76). Several other special achievement cards are seeded throughout the set. The team checklist (TC) cards in the set feature an attractive Vernon Wells drawing of a featured player for that particular team. Rookie Cards in this set include Jeff Bagwell, Luis Gonzalez, Chipper Jones, Eric Karros, and Mike Mussina. A special Michael Jordan card (numbered SP1) was randomly included in packs on a somewhat limited basis. The Hank Aaron hologram card was randomly inserted in the 1991 Upper Deck high number foil packs. Neither card is included in the price of the regular issue set though both are listed at the end of our checklist.

Card	Low	High
COMPLETE SET (800)	6.00	15.00
COMP.FACT.SET (800)	8.00	20.00
COMPLETE LO SET (700)	6.00	15.00
COMPLETE HI SET (100)	2.00	5.00
1 Star Rookie Checklist	.01	.05
2 Phil Plantier RC	.02	.10
3 D.J. Dozier	.01	.05
4 Dave Hansen	.01	.05
5 Maurice Vaughn	.02	.10
6 Leo Gomez	.01	.05
7 Scott Aldred	.01	.05
8 Scott Chiamparino	.01	.05
9 Lance Dickson RC	.02	.10
10 Sean Berry RC	.02	.10
11 Bernie Williams	.08	.25
12 Brian Barnes UER	.02	.10
(Photo either not him or in wrong jersey)		
13 Narciso Elvira RC	.01	.05
14 Mike Gardiner RC	.01	.05
15 Greg Colbrunn RC	.08	.25
16 Bernard Gilkey	.01	.05
17 Mark Lewis	.01	.05
18 Mickey Morandini	.01	.05
19 Charles Nagy	.01	.05
20 Geronimo Pena	.01	.05
21 Henry Rodriguez RC	.08	.25
22 Scott Cooper	.01	.05
23 Andujar Cedeno UER	.01	.05
(Shown batting left, back says right)		
24 Eric Karros RC	.30	.75
25 Steve Decker UER RC	.01	.05
Lewis-Clark State College, not Lewis and Clark)		
26 Kevin Belcher RC	.01	.05
27 Jeff Conine RC	.20	.50
28 Dave Stewart TC	.01	.05
29 Carlton Fisk TC	.02	.10
30 Rafael Palmeiro TC	.02	.10
31 Chuck Finley TC	.01	.05
32 Harold Reynolds TC	.01	.05
33 Bret Saberhagen TC	.01	.05
34 Gary Gaetti TC	.01	.05
35 Scott Leius	.01	.05
36 Neal Heaton	.01	.05
37 Terry Lee RC	.01	.05
38 Gary Redus	.01	.05
39 Barry Jones	.01	.05
40 Chuck Knoblauch	.02	.10
41 Larry Andersen	.01	.05
42 Darryl Hamilton	.01	.05
43 Mike Greenwell TC	.01	.05
44 Kelly Gruber TC	.01	.05
45 Jack Morris TC	.01	.05
46 Sandy Alomar Jr. TC	.01	.05
47 Gregg Olson TC	.01	.05
48 Dave Parker TC	.01	.05
49 Roberto Kelly TC	.01	.05
50 Top Prospect Checklist	.01	.05
51 Kyle Abbott	.01	.05
52 Jeff Juden	.01	.05
53 Todd Van Poppel UER RC	.08	.25
Born Arlington and attended John Martin HS, should say Hinsdale and James Martin HS		
54 Steve Karsay RC	.08	.25
55 Chipper Jones RC	1.50	4.00
56 Chris Johnson UER RC	.02	.10
(Called Tim on back)		
57 John Ericks	.01	.05
58 Gary Scott RC	.01	.05
59 Kiki Jones	.01	.05
60 Wil Cordero RC	.02	.10
61 Royce Clayton	.01	.05
62 Tim Costo RC	.02	.10
63 Roger Salkeld	.01	.05
64 Brook Fordyce RC	.08	.25
65 Mike Mussina RC	.75	2.00
66 Dave Staton RC	.02	.10
67 Mike Lieberthal RC	.20	.50
68 Kurt Miller RC	.01	.05
69 Dan Peltier RC	.02	.10
70 Greg Blosser	.01	.05
71 Reggie Sanders RC	.30	.75
72 Brent Mayne	.01	.05
73 Rico Brogna	.01	.05
74 Willie Banks	.01	.05
75 Len Brutcher RC	.01	.05
76 Pat Kelly RC	.02	.10
77 Chris Sabo TC	.01	.05
78 Ramon Martinez TC	.01	.05
79 Matt Williams TC	.01	.05
80 Roberto Alomar TC	.02	.10
81 Glenn Davis TC	.01	.05
82 Ron Gant TC	.01	.05
83 Cecil Fielder FEAT	.01	.05
84 Orlando Merced RC	.02	.10
85 Domingo Ramos	.01	.05
86 Tom Bolton	.01	.05
87 Andres Santana	.01	.05
88 John Dopson	.01	.05
89 Kenny Williams	.01	.05
90 Marty Barrett	.01	.05
91 Tom Pagnozzi	.01	.05
92 Carmelo Martinez	.01	.05
93 Bobby Thigpen SAVE	.01	.05
94 Barry Bonds TC	.20	.50
95 Gregg Jefferies TC	.01	.05
96 Tim Wallach TC	.01	.05
97 Len Dykstra TC	.01	.05
98 Pedro Guerrero TC	.01	.05
99 Mark Grace TC	.02	.10
100 Checklist 1-100	.01	.05
101 Kevin Elster	.01	.05
102 Tom Brookens	.01	.05
103 Mackey Sasser	.01	.05
104 Felix Fermin	.01	.05
105 Kevin McReynolds	.01	.05
106 Dave Stieb	.01	.05
107 Jeffrey Leonard	.01	.05
108 Dave Henderson	.01	.05
109 Sid Bream	.01	.05
110 Henry Cotto	.01	.05
111 Shawon Dunston	.01	.05
112 Mariano Duncan	.01	.05
113 Joe Girardi	.01	.05
114 Billy Hatcher	.01	.05
115 Greg Maddux	.15	.40
116 Jerry Browne	.01	.05
117 Juan Samuel	.01	.05
118 Steve Olin	.01	.05
119 Alfredo Griffin	.01	.05
120 Mitch Webster	.01	.05
121 Joel Skinner	.01	.05
122 Frank Viola	.02	.10
123 Cory Snyder	.01	.05
124 Howard Johnson	.01	.05
125 Carlos Baerga	.01	.05
126 Tony Fernandez	.01	.05
127 Dave Stewart	.02	.10
128 Jay Buhner	.02	.10
129 Mike LaValliere	.01	.05
130 Scott Bradley	.01	.05
131 Tony Phillips	.01	.05
132 Ryne Sandberg	.15	.40
133 Paul O'Neill	.05	.15
134 Mark Grace	.05	.15
135 Chris Sabo	.01	.05
136 Ramon Martinez	.01	.05
137 Brook Jacoby	.01	.05
138 Candy Maldonado	.01	.05
139 Mike Scioscia	.01	.05
140 Chris James	.01	.05
141 Craig Worthington	.01	.05
142 Manny Lee	.01	.05
143 Tim Raines	.02	.10
144 Sandy Alomar Jr.	.02	.10
145 John Olerud	.02	.10
146 Ozzie Canseco	.02	.10
(With Jose)		
147 Pat Borders	.01	.05
148 Harold Reynolds	.02	.10
149 Tom Henke	.01	.05
150 R.J. Reynolds	.01	.05
151 Mike Gallego	.01	.05
152 Bobby Bonilla	.02	.10
153 Terry Steinbach	.01	.05
154 Barry Bonds	.40	1.00
155 Jose Canseco	.05	.15
156 Gregg Jefferies	.01	.05
157 Matt Williams	.02	.10
158 Craig Biggio	.05	.15
159 Daryl Boston	.01	.05
160 Ricky Jordan	.01	.05
161 Stan Belinda	.01	.05
162 Ozzie Smith	.15	.40
163 Tom Brunansky	.01	.05
164 Todd Zeile	.01	.05
165 Mike Greenwell	.01	.05
166 Kal Daniels	.01	.05
167 Kent Hrbek	.02	.10
168 Franklin Stubbs	.01	.05
169 Dick Schofield	.01	.05
170 Junior Ortiz	.01	.05
171 Hector Villanueva	.01	.05
172 Dennis Eckersley	.02	.10
173 Mitch Williams	.01	.05
174 Mark McGwire	.30	.75
175 F.Valenzuela 3X	.02	.10
176 Gary Carter	.02	.10
177 Dave Magadan	.01	.05
178 Robby Thompson	.01	.05
179 Bob Ojeda	.01	.05
180 Ken Caminiti	.02	.10
181 Don Slaught	.01	.05
182 Luis Rivera	.01	.05
183 Jay Bell	.02	.10
184 Jody Reed	.01	.05
185 Wally Backman	.01	.05
186 Dave Martinez	.01	.05
187 Luis Polonia	.01	.05
188 Shane Mack	.01	.05
189 Spike Owen	.01	.05
190 Scott Bailes	.01	.05
191 John Russell	.01	.05
192 Walt Weiss	.01	.05
193 Jose Oquendo	.01	.05
194 Carney Lansford	.02	.10
195 Jeff Huson	.01	.05
196 Keith Miller	.01	.05
197 Eric Yelding	.01	.05
198 Ron Darling	.01	.05
199 John Kruk	.02	.10
200 Checklist 101-200	.01	.05
201 John Shelby	.01	.05
202 Bob Geren	.01	.05
203 Lance McCullers	.01	.05
204 Alvaro Espinoza	.01	.05
205 Mark Salas	.01	.05
206 Mike Pagliarulo	.01	.05
207 Jose Uribe	.01	.05
208 Jim Deshaies	.01	.05
209 Ron Karkovice	.01	.05
210 Rafael Ramirez	.01	.05
211 Donnie Hill	.01	.05
212 Brian Harper	.01	.05
213 Jack Howell	.01	.05
214 Wes Gardner	.01	.05
215 Tim Burke	.01	.05
216 Doug Jones	.01	.05
217 Hubie Brooks	.01	.05
218 Tom Candiotti	.01	.05
219 Gerald Perry	.01	.05
220 Jose DeLeon	.01	.05
221 Wally Whitehurst	.01	.05
222 Alan Mills	.01	.05
223 Alan Trammell	.02	.10
224 Dwight Gooden	.02	.10
225 Travis Fryman	.02	.10
226 Joe Carter	.02	.10
227 Julio Franco	.02	.10
228 Craig Lefferts	.01	.05
229 Gary Pettis	.01	.05
230 Dennis Rasmussen	.01	.05
231A Brian Downing ERR	.01	.05
(No position on front)		
231B Brian Downing COR	.08	.25
(DH on front)		
232 Carlos Quintana	.01	.05
233 Gary Gaetti	.02	.10
234 Mark Langston	.01	.05
235 Tim Wallach	.01	.05
236 Greg Swindell	.01	.05
237 Eddie Murray	.08	.25
238 Jeff Manto	.01	.05
239 Lenny Harris	.01	.05
240 Jesse Orosco	.01	.05
241 Scott Lusader	.01	.05
242 Sid Fernandez	.01	.05
243 Jim Leyritz	.01	.05
244 Cecil Fielder	.02	.10
245 Darryl Strawberry	.02	.10
246 Frank Thomas UER	.08	.25
(Comiskey Park misspelled Comisky)		
247 Kevin Mitchell	.01	.05
248 Lance Johnson	.01	.05
249 Rick Reuschel	.01	.05
250 Mark Portugal	.01	.05
251 Derek Lilliquist	.01	.05
252 Brian Holman	.01	.05
253 Rafael Valdez UER	.01	.05
(Born 4/17/68, should be 12/17/67)		
254 B.J. Surhoff	.02	.10
255 Tony Gwynn	.10	.30
256 Andy Van Slyke	.05	.15
257 Todd Stottlemyre	.01	.05
258 Jose Lind	.01	.05
259 Greg Myers	.01	.05
260 Jeff Ballard	.01	.05
261 Bobby Thigpen	.01	.05
262 Jimmy Kremers	.01	.05
263 Robin Ventura	.02	.10
264 John Smoltz	.05	.15
265 Sammy Sosa	.08	.25
266 Gary Sheffield	.02	.10
267 Len Dykstra	.02	.10
268 Bill Spiers	.01	.05
269 Charlie Hayes	.01	.05
270 Brett Butler	.02	.10
271 Bip Roberts	.01	.05
272 Rob Deer	.01	.05
273 Fred Lynn	.01	.05
274 Dave Parker	.02	.10
275 Andy Benes	.01	.05
276 Glenallen Hill	.01	.05
277 Steve Howard	.01	.05
278 Doug Drabek	.01	.05
279 Joe Oliver	.01	.05
280 Todd Benzinger	.01	.05
281 Eric King	.01	.05
282 Jim Presley	.01	.05
283 Ken Patterson	.01	.05
284 Jack Daugherty	.01	.05
285 Ivan Calderon	.01	.05
286 Edgar Diaz	.01	.05
287 Kevin Bass	.01	.05
288 Don Carman	.01	.05
289 Greg Brock	.01	.05
290 John Franco	.02	.10
291 Joey Cora	.01	.05
292 Bill Wegman	.01	.05
293 Eric Show	.01	.05
294 Scott Bankhead	.01	.05
295 Garry Templeton	.01	.05
296 Mickey Tettleton	.01	.05
297 Luis Sojo	.01	.05
298 Jose Rijo	.01	.05
299 Dave Johnson	.01	.05
300 Checklist 201-300	.01	.05
301 Mark Grant	.01	.05
302 Pete Harnisch	.01	.05
303 Greg Olson	.01	.05
304 Anthony Telford RC	.01	.05
305 Lonnie Smith	.01	.05
306 Chris Hoiles	.01	.05
307 Bryn Smith	.01	.05
308 Mike Devereaux	.01	.05
309A Milt Thompson ERR	.08	.25
(Under yr information has print dot)		
309B Milt Thompson COR	.01	.05
(Under yr information says 86)		
310 Bob Melvin	.01	.05
311 Luis Salazar	.01	.05
312 Ed Whitson	.01	.05
313 Charlie Hough	.02	.10
314 Dave Clark	.01	.05
315 Eric Gunderson	.01	.05
316 Dan Petry	.01	.05
317 Dante Bichette UER	.02	.10
(Assists misspelled as assissts)		
318 Mike Heath	.01	.05
319 Damon Berryhill	.01	.05
320 Walt Terrell	.01	.05
321 Scott Fletcher	.01	.05
322 Dan Plesac	.01	.05
323 Jack McDowell	.01	.05
324 Paul Molitor	.02	.10
325 Ozzie Guillen	.02	.10
326 Gregg Olson	.01	.05
327 Pedro Guerrero	.02	.10
328 Bob Milacki	.01	.05
329 John Tudor UER	.01	.05
('90 Cardinals, should be '90 Dodgers)		
330 Steve Finley UER	.02	.10
(Born 3/12/65, should be 5/12)		
331 Jack Clark	.02	.10
332 Jerome Walton	.01	.05
333 Andy Hawkins	.01	.05
334 Derrick May	.01	.05
335 Roberto Alomar	.05	.15
336 Jack Morris	.02	.10
337 Dave Winfield	.02	.10
338 Steve Searcy	.01	.05
339 Chili Davis	.02	.10
340 Larry Sheets	.01	.05
341 Ted Higuera	.01	.05
342 David Segui	.01	.05
343 Greg Cadaret	.01	.05
344 Robin Yount	.15	.40
345 Nolan Ryan	.40	1.00
346 Ray Lankford	.02	.10
347 Cal Ripken	.30	.75
348 Lee Smith	.02	.10
349 Brady Anderson	.02	.10
350 Frank DiPino	.01	.05
351 Hal Morris	.01	.05
352 Deion Sanders	.05	.15
353 Barry Larkin	.05	.15
354 Don Mattingly	.25	.60
355 Eric Davis	.02	.10
356 Jose Offerman	.01	.05
357 Mel Rojas	.01	.05
358 Rudy Seanez	.01	.05
359 Oil Can Boyd	.01	.05
360 Nelson Liriano	.01	.05
361 Ron Gant	.02	.10
362 Howard Farmer	.01	.05
363 David Justice	.02	.10
364 Delino DeShields	.02	.10
365 Steve Avery	.01	.05
366 David Cone	.02	.10
367 Lou Whitaker	.02	.10
368 Von Hayes	.01	.05
369 Frank Tanana	.01	.05
370 Tim Teufel	.01	.05
371 Randy Myers	.01	.05
372 Roberto Kelly	.01	.05
373 Jack Armstrong	.01	.05
374 Kelly Gruber	.01	.05
375 Kevin Maas	.01	.05
376 Randy Johnson	.10	.30
377 David West	.01	.05
378 Brent Knackert	.01	.05
379 Rick Honeycutt	.01	.05
380 Kevin Gross	.01	.05
381 Tom Foley	.01	.05
382 Jeff Blauser	.01	.05
383 Scott Ruskin	.01	.05
384 Andres Thomas	.01	.05
385 Dennis Martinez	.02	.10
386 Mike Henneman	.01	.05
387 Felix Jose	.01	.05
388 Alejandro Pena	.01	.05
389 Chet Lemon	.01	.05
390 Craig Wilson RC	.01	.05
391 Chuck Crim	.01	.05
392 Mel Hall	.01	.05
393 Mark Knudson	.01	.05
394 Norm Charlton	.01	.05
395 Mike Felder	.01	.05
396 Tim Layana	.01	.05
397 Steve Frey	.01	.05
398 Bill Doran	.01	.05
399 Dion James	.01	.05
400 Checklist 301-400	.01	.05
401 Ron Hassey	.01	.05
402 Don Robinson	.01	.05
403 Gene Nelson	.01	.05
404 Terry Kennedy	.01	.05
405 Todd Burns	.01	.05
406 Roger McDowell	.01	.05
407 Bob Kipper	.01	.05
408 Darren Daulton	.02	.10
409 Chuck Cary	.01	.05
410 Bruce Ruffin	.01	.05
411 Juan Berenguer	.01	.05
412 Gary Ward	.01	.05
413 Al Newman	.01	.05
414 Danny Jackson	.01	.05
415 Greg Gagne	.01	.05
416 Tom Herr	.01	.05
417 Jeff Parrett	.01	.05
418 Jeff Reardon	.02	.10
419 Mark Lemke	.01	.05
420 Charlie O'Brien	.01	.05
421 Willie Randolph	.02	.10
422 Steve Bedrosian	.01	.05
423 Mike Moore	.01	.05
424 Jeff Brantley	.01	.05
425 Bob Welch	.01	.05
426 Terry Mulholland	.01	.05
427 Willie Blair	.01	.05
428 Darrin Fletcher	.01	.05
429 Mike Witt	.01	.05
430 Joe Boever	.01	.05
431 Tom Gordon	.01	.05
432 Pedro Munoz RC	.02	.10
433 Kevin Seitzer	.01	.05
434 Kevin Tapani	.01	.05
435 Bret Saberhagen	.02	.10
436 Ellis Burks	.02	.10
437 Chuck Finley	.02	.10
438 Mike Boddicker	.01	.05
439 Francisco Cabrera	.01	.05
440 Todd Hundley	.01	.05
441 Kelly Downs	.01	.05
442 Dann Howitt	.01	.05
443 Scott Garrelts	.01	.05
444 Rickey Henderson 3X	.08	.25
445 Will Clark	.05	.15
446 Ben McDonald	.01	.05
447 Dale Murphy	.05	.15
448 Dave Righetti	.02	.10
449 Dickie Thon	.01	.05
450 Ted Power	.01	.05
451 Scott Coolbaugh	.01	.05
452 Dwight Smith	.01	.05
453 Pete Incaviglia	.01	.05
454 Andre Dawson	.02	.10
455 Ruben Sierra	.02	.10
456 Andres Galarraga	.02	.10
457 Alvin Davis	.01	.05
458 Tony Castillo	.01	.05
459 Pete O'Brien	.01	.05
460 Charlie Leibrandt	.01	.05
461 Vince Coleman	.01	.05
462 Steve Sax	.01	.05
463 Omar Olivares RC	.02	.10
464 Oscar Azocar	.01	.05
465 Joe Magrane	.01	.05
466 Karl Rhodes	.01	.05
467 Benito Santiago	.02	.10
468 Joe Klink	.01	.05
469 Sil Campusano	.01	.05
470 Mark Parent	.01	.05
471 Shawn Boskie UER	.01	.05
(Depleted misspelled as depleated)		
472 Kevin Brown	.02	.10
473 Rick Sutcliffe	.02	.10
474 Rafael Palmeiro	.05	.15
475 Mike Harkey	.01	.05
476 Jaime Navarro	.01	.05
477 Marquis Grissom UER	.02	.10
(DeShields misspelled as DeSheilds)		
478 Marty Clary	.01	.05
479 Greg Briley	.01	.05
480 Tom Glavine	.05	.15
481 Lee Guetterman	.01	.05
482 Rex Hudler	.01	.05
483 Dave LaPoint	.01	.05
484 Terry Pendleton	.02	.10
485 Jesse Barfield	.01	.05
486 Jose DeJesus	.01	.05
487 Paul Abbott RC	.02	.10
488 Ken Howell	.01	.05
489 Greg W. Harris	.01	.05
490 Roy Smith	.01	.05
491 Paul Assenmacher	.01	.05
492 Geno Petralli	.01	.05
493 Steve Wilson	.01	.05
494 Kevin Reimer	.01	.05
495 Bill Long	.01	.05
496 Mike Jackson	.01	.05
497 Oddibe McDowell	.01	.05
498 Bill Swift	.01	.05
499 Jeff Treadway	.01	.05
500 Checklist 401-500	.01	.05
501 Gene Larkin	.01	.05
502 Bob Boone	.02	.10
503 Allan Anderson	.01	.05
504 Luis Aquino	.01	.05
505 Mark Guthrie	.01	.05
506 Joe Orsulak	.01	.05
507 Dana Kiecker	.01	.05
508 Dave Gallagher	.01	.05
509 Greg A. Harris	.01	.05
510 Mark Williamson	.01	.05
511 Casey Candaele	.01	.05
512 Mookie Wilson	.02	.10
513 Dave Smith	.01	.05
514 Chuck Carr	.01	.05
515 Glenn Wilson	.01	.05
516 Mike Fitzgerald	.01	.05
517 Devon White	.02	.10
518 Dave Hollins	.01	.05
519 Mark Eichhorn	.01	.05
520 Otis Nixon	.01	.05
521 Terry Shumpert	.01	.05
522 Scott Erickson	.01	.05
523 Danny Tartabull	.01	.05
524 Orel Hershiser	.02	.10
525 George Brett	.25	.60
526 Greg Vaughn	.01	.05
527 Tim Naehring	.01	.05
528 Curt Schilling	.08	.25
529 Chris Bosio	.01	.05
530 Sam Horn	.01	.05
531 Mike Scott	.01	.05
532 George Bell	.01	.05
533 Eric Anthony	.01	.05
534 Julio Valera	.01	.05
535 Glenn Davis	.01	.05
536 Larry Walker UER	.08	.25
(Should have comma after Expos in text)		
537 Pat Combs	.01	.05
538 Chris Nabholz	.01	.05
539 Kirk McCaskill	.01	.05
540 Randy Ready	.01	.05
541 Mark Gubicza	.01	.05
542 Rick Aguilera	.02	.10
543 Brian McRae RC	.08	.25
544 Kirby Puckett	.08	.25
545 Bo Jackson	.08	.25
546 Wade Boggs	.05	.15
547 Tim McIntosh	.01	.05
548 Randy Milligan	.01	.05
549 Dwight Evans	.05	.15

550 Billy Ripken .01 .05
551 Erik Hanson .01 .05
552 Lance Parrish .02 .10
553 Tino Martinez .08 .25
554 Jim Abbott .05 .15
555 Ken Griffey Jr. UER .20 .50
(Second most votes for
1991 All-Star Game)
556 Milt Cuyler .01 .05
557 Mark Leonard RC .01 .05
558 Jay Howell .01 .05
559 Lloyd Moseby .01 .05
560 Chris Gwynn .01 .05
561 Mark Whiten .01 .05
562 Harold Baines .02 .10
563 Junior Felix .01 .05
564 Darren Lewis .01 .05
565 Fred McGriff .05 .15
566 Kevin Appier .02 .10
567 Luis Gonzalez RC .30 .75
568 Frank White .02 .10
569 Juan Agosto .01 .05
570 Mike Macfarlane .01 .05
571 Bert Blyleven .02 .10
572 Ken Griffey Sr. .08 .25
Ken Griffey Jr.
573 Lee Stevens .01 .05
574 Edgar Martinez .05 .15
575 Wally Joyner .02 .10
576 Tim Belcher .01 .05
577 John Burkett .01 .05
578 Mike Morgan .01 .05
579 Paul Gibson .01 .05
580 Jose Vizcaino .01 .05
581 Duane Ward .01 .05
582 Scott Sanderson .01 .05
583 David Wells .02 .10
584 Willie McGee .02 .10
585 John Cerutti .01 .05
586 Danny Darwin .01 .05
587 Kurt Stillwell .01 .05
588 Rich Gedman .01 .05
589 Mark Davis .01 .05
590 Bill Gullickson .01 .05
591 Matt Young .01 .05
592 Bryan Harvey .01 .05
593 Omar Vizquel .05 .15
594 Scott Lewis RC .02 .10
595 Dave Valle .01 .05
596 Tim Crews .01 .05
597 Mike Bielecki .01 .05
598 Mike Sharperson .01 .05
599 Dave Bergman .01 .05
600 Checklist 501-600 .01 .05
601 Steve Lyons .01 .05
602 Bruce Hurst .01 .05
603 Donn Pall .01 .05
604 Jim Vatcher RC .01 .05
605 Dan Pasqua .01 .05
606 Kenny Rogers .02 .10
607 Jeff Schulz RC .01 .05
608 Brad Arnsberg .01 .05
609 Willie Wilson .01 .05
610 Jamie Moyer .02 .10
611 Ron Oester .01 .05
612 Dennis Cook .01 .05
613 Rick Mahler .01 .05
614 Bill Landrum .01 .05
615 Scott Scudder .01 .05
616 Tom Edens RC .01 .05
617 1917 Revisited .02 .10
(White Sox vintage uniforms)
618 Jim Gantner .01 .05
619 Darrel Akerfelds .01 .05
620 Ron Robinson .01 .05
621 Scott Radinsky .01 .05
622 Pete Smith .01 .05
623 Melido Perez .01 .05
624 Jerald Clark .01 .05
625 Carlos Martinez .01 .05
626 Wes Chamberlain RC .08 .25
627 Bobby Witt .01 .05
628 Ken Dayley .01 .05
629 John Barfield .01 .05
630 Bob Tewksbury .01 .05
631 Glenn Braggs .01 .05
632 Jim Neidlinger RC .01 .05
633 Tom Browning .01 .05
634 Kirk Gibson .02 .10
635 Rob Dibble .02 .10
636 Rickey Henderson SB .08 .25
Lou Brock
May 1, 1991 on front
636A R.Henderson SB .08 .25
Lou Brock
no date on card
637 Jeff Montgomery .01 .05
638 Mike Schooler .01 .05
639 Storm Davis .01 .05
640 Rich Rodriguez RC .01 .05
641 Phil Bradley .01 .05
642 Kent Mercker .01 .05
643 Carlton Fisk .05 .15
644 Mike Bell RC .01 .05
645 Alex Fernandez .01 .05
646 Juan Gonzalez .08 .25
647 Ken Hill .01 .05
648 Jeff Russell .01 .05
649 Chuck Malone .01 .05
650 Steve Buechele .01 .05
651 Mike Benjamin .01 .05
652 Tony Pena .01 .05
653 Trevor Wilson .01 .05
654 Alex Cole .01 .05
655 Roger Clemens .30 .75
656 Mark McGwire BASH .15 .40
657 Joe Grahe RC .02 .10
658 Jim Eisenreich .01 .05
659 Dan Gladden .01 .05
660 Steve Farr .01 .05
661 Bill Sampen .01 .05
662 Dave Rohde .01 .05
663 Mark Gardner .01 .05
664 Mike Simms RC .01 .05
665 Moises Alou .02 .10
666 Mickey Hatcher .01 .05
667 Jimmy Key .02 .10
668 John Wetteland .02 .10
669 John Smiley .01 .05
670 Jim Acker .01 .05
671 Pascual Perez .01 .05
672 Reggie Harris UER .01 .05
(Opportunity misspelled
as oppurtinity)
673 Matt Nokes .01 .05
674 Rafael Novoa RC .01 .05
675 Hensley Meulens .01 .05
676 Jeff M. Robinson .01 .05
677 Ground Breaking .02 .10
(New Comiskey Park;
Carlton Fisk and
Robin Ventura)
678 Johnny Ray .01 .05
679 Greg Hibbard .01 .05
680 Paul Sorrento .01 .05
681 Mike Marshall .01 .05
682 Jim Clancy .01 .05
683 Rob Murphy .01 .05
684 Dave Schmidt .01 .05
685 Jeff Gray RC .01 .05
686 Mike Hartley .01 .05
687 Jeff King .01 .05
688 Stan Javier .01 .05
689 Bob Walk .01 .05
690 Jim Gott .01 .05
691 Mike LaCoss .01 .05
692 John Farrell .01 .05
693 Tim Leary .01 .05
694 Mike Walker .01 .05
695 Eric Plunk .01 .05
696 Mike Fetters .01 .05
697 Wayne Edwards .01 .05
698 Tim Drummond .01 .05
699 Willie Fraser .01 .05
700 Checklist 601-700 .01 .05
701 Mike Heath .01 .05
702 Luis Gonzalez .40 1.00
Karl Rhodes
Jeff Bagwell
703 Jose Mesa .01 .05
704 Dave Smith .01 .05
705 Danny Darwin .01 .05
706 Rafael Belliard .01 .05
707 Rob Murphy .01 .05
708 Terry Pendleton .02 .10
709 Mike Pagliarulo .01 .05
710 Sid Bream .01 .05
711 Junior Felix .01 .05
712 Dante Bichette .02 .10
713 Kevin Gross .01 .05
714 Luis Sojo .01 .05
715 Bob Ojeda .01 .05
716 Julio Machado .01 .05
717 Steve Farr .01 .05
718 Franklin Stubbs .01 .05
719 Mike Boddicker .01 .05
720 Willie Randolph .02 .10
721 Willie McGee .02 .10
722 Chili Davis .02 .10
723 Danny Jackson .01 .05
724 Cory Snyder .01 .05
725 Andre Dawson .08 .25
George Bell
Ryne Sandberg
726 Rob Deer .01 .05
727 Rich DeLucia RC .01 .05
728 Mike Perez RC .02 .10
729 Mickey Tettleton .01 .05
730 Mike Blowers .01 .05
731 Gary Gaetti .02 .10
732 Brett Butler .02 .10
733 Dave Parker .02 .10
734 Eddie Zosky .01 .05
735 Jack Clark .02 .10
736 Jack Morris .02 .10
737 Kirk Gibson .02 .10
738 Steve Bedrosian .01 .05
739 Candy Maldonado .01 .05
740 Matt Young .01 .05
741 Rich Garces RC .02 .10
742 George Bell .01 .05
743 Deion Sanders .05 .15
744 Bo Jackson .08 .25
745 Luis Mercedes RC .02 .10
746 Reggie Jefferson UER .01 .05
(Throwing left on card;
back has throws right)
747 Pete Incaviglia .01 .05
748 Chris Hammond .01 .05
749 Mike Stanton .01 .05
750 Scott Sanderson .01 .05
751 Paul Faries RC .01 .05
752 Al Osuna RC .01 .05
753 Steve Chitren RC .01 .05
754 Tony Fernandez .01 .05
755 Jeff Bagwell UER RC .60 1.50
(Strikeout and walk
totals reversed)
756 Kirk Dressendorfer RC .02 .10
757 Glenn Davis .01 .05
758 Gary Carter .02 .10
759 Zane Smith .01 .05
760 Vance Law .01 .05
761 Denis Boucher RC .02 .10
762 Turner Ward RC .02 .10
763 Roberto Alomar .05 .15
764 Albert Belle .02 .10
765 Joe Carter .02 .10
766 Pete Schourek RC .02 .10
767 Heathcliff Slocumb RC .02 .10
768 Vince Coleman .01 .05
769 Mitch Williams .01 .05
770 Brian Downing .01 .05
771 Dana Allison RC .01 .05
772 Pete Harnisch .01 .05
773 Tim Raines .02 .10
774 Darryl Kile .02 .10
775 Fred McGriff .05 .15
776 Dwight Evans .05 .15
777 Joe Slusarski RC .01 .05
778 Dave Righetti .02 .10
779 Jeff Hamilton .01 .05
780 Ernest Riles .01 .05
781 Ken Dayley .01 .05
782 Eric King .01 .05
783 Devon White .02 .10
784 Beau Allred .01 .05
785 Mike Timlin RC .08 .25
786 Ivan Calderon .01 .05
787 Hubie Brooks .01 .05
788 Juan Agosto .01 .05
789 Barry Jones .01 .05
790 Wally Backman .01 .05
791 Jim Presley .01 .05
792 Charlie Hough .02 .10
793 Larry Andersen .01 .05
794 Steve Finley .02 .10
795 Shawn Abner .01 .05
796 Jeff M. Robinson .01 .05
797 Joe Bitker RC .01 .05
798 Eric Show .01 .05
799 Bud Black .01 .05
800 Checklist 701-800 .01 .05
HH1 H.Aaron Hologram .60 1.50
SP1 Michael Jordan SP 3.00 8.00
(Shown batting in
White Sox uniform)
SP2 Rickey Henderson .75 2.00
Nolan Ryan
May 1, 1991 Records

1991 Upper Deck Aaron Heroes

These standard-size cards were issued in honor of Hall of Famer Hank Aaron and inserted in Upper Deck high number wax packs. Aaron autographed 2,500 of card number 27, which featured his portrait by noted sports artist Vernon Wells. The cards are numbered on the back in continuation of the Baseball Heroes set.

COMPLETE SET (10) 2.00 5.00
COMMON AARON (19-27) .20 .50
NNO Title/Header card SP .40 1.00
AU3 Hank Aaron AU/2500 100.00 200.00

1991 Upper Deck Heroes of Baseball

These standard-size cards were randomly inserted in Upper Deck Baseball Heroes wax packs. The fourth card features a color portrait of the three players by noted sports artist Vernon Wells. Each of the features heroes also signed 3,000 of each card for inclusion in this product.

COMPLETE SET (4) 12.50 25.00
H1 Harmon Killebrew 3.00 8.00
H2 Gaylord Perry 2.00 5.00
H3 Ferguson Jenkins 2.00 5.00
H4 Harmon Killebrew ART 3.00 8.00
Ferguson Jenkins
Gaylord Perry
AU1 Harmon Killebrew AU/3000 15.00 40.00
AU2 Gaylord Perry AU/3000 10.00 25.00
AU3 Fergie Jenkins AU/3000 10.00 25.00

1991 Upper Deck Ryan Heroes

This nine-card standard-size set was included in first series 1991 Upper Deck packs. The set which honors Nolan Ryan and is numbered as a continuation of the Baseball Heroes set which began with Reggie Jackson in 1990. This set honors Ryan's long career and his place in Baseball History. Card number 18 features the artwork of Vernon Wells while the other cards are photos. The complete set price below does not include the signed Ryan card of which only 2500 were made. Signed cards ending with 00 have the expression "Strikeout King" added. These Ryan cards were apparently issued on 100-card sheets with the following configuration: ten each of the nine Ryan Baseball Heroes cards, five Michael Jordan cards and five Baseball Heroes header cards. The Baseball Heroes header card is a standard size card which explains the continuation of the Baseball Heroes series on the back while the front just says Baseball Heroes.

COMPLETE SET (10) 2.00 5.00
COMMON RYAN (10-18) .20 .50
NNO Baseball Heroes SP .40 1.00
(Header card)
AU2 Nolan Ryan AU/2500 125.00 200.00

1991 Upper Deck Silver Sluggers

The Upper Deck Silver Slugger set features nine players from each league, representing the nine batting positions on the team. The cards were issued one per 1991 Upper Deck jumbo pack. The cards measure the standard size. The cards are numbered on the back with an "SS" prefix.

COMPLETE SET (18) 7.50 15.00
SS1 Julio Franco .30 .75
SS2 Alan Trammell .30 .75
SS3 Rickey Henderson .75 2.00
SS4 Jose Canseco .50 1.25
SS5 Barry Bonds 3.00 8.00
SS6 Eddie Murray .75 2.00
SS7 Kelly Gruber .15 .40
SS8 Ryne Sandberg 1.25 3.00
SS9 Darryl Strawberry .30 .75
SS10 Ellis Burks .30 .75
SS11 Lance Parrish .30 .75
SS12 Cecil Fielder .30 .75
SS13 Matt Williams .30 .75
SS14 Dave Parker .30 .75
SS15 Bobby Bonilla .30 .75
SS16 Don Robinson .15 .40
SS17 Benito Santiago .30 .75
SS18 Barry Larkin .50 1.25

1991 Upper Deck Final Edition

The 1991 Upper Deck Final Edition boxed set contains 100 standard-size cards and showcases players who made major contributions during their team's late-season pennant drive. In addition to the late season traded and impact rookie cards (22-78), the set includes two special subsets: Diamond Skills cards (1-21), depicting the best Minor League prospects, and All-Star cards (80-99). Six assorted team logo hologram cards were issued with each set. The cards are numbered on the back with an F suffix. Among the outstanding Rookie Cards in this set are Ryan Klesko, Kenny Lofton, Pedro Martinez, Ivan Rodriguez, Jim Thome, Rondell White, and Dmitri Young.

COMP.FACT.SET (100) 3.00 8.00
1F Ryan Klesko CL .08 .25
Reggie Sanders
2F Pedro Martinez RC 3.00 8.00
3F Lance Dickson .01 .05
4F Royce Clayton .01 .05
5F Scott Bryant .01 .05
6F Dan Wilson RC .08 .25
7F Dmitri Young RC .30 .75
8F Ryan Klesko RC .20 .50
9F Tom Goodwin .01 .05
10F Rondell White RC .20 .50
11F Reggie Sanders .20 .50
12F Todd Van Poppel .01 .05
13F Arthur Rhodes RC .08 .25
14F Eddie Zosky .01 .05
15F Gerald Williams RC .08 .25
16F Robert Eenhoorn RC .02 .10
17F Jim Thome RC 1.50 4.00
18F Marc Newfield RC .02 .10
19F Kerwin Moore RC .02 .10
20F Jeff McNeely RC .02 .10
21F Frankie Rodriguez RC .02 .10
22F Andy Mota RC .01 .05
23F Chris Haney RC .02 .10
24F Kenny Lofton RC .30 .75
25F Dave Nilsson RC .08 .25
26F Derek Bell .02 .10
27F Frank Castillo RC .08 .25
28F Candy Maldonado .01 .05
29F Chuck McElroy .01 .05
30F Chito Martinez RC .01 .05
31F Steve Howe .01 .05
32F Freddie Benavides RC .01 .05
33F Scott Kamieniecki RC .02 .10
34F Denny Neagle RC .08 .25
35F Mike Humphreys RC .02 .10
36F Mike Remlinger .01 .05
37F Scott Coolbaugh .01 .05
38F Darren Lewis .01 .05
39F Thomas Howard .01 .05
40F John Candelaria .01 .05
41F Todd Benzinger .01 .05
42F Wilson Alvarez .01 .05
43F Patrick Lennon RC .02 .10
44F Rusty Meacham RC .02 .10
45F Ryan Bowen RC .02 .10
46F Rick Wilkins RC .02 .10
47F Ed Sprague .01 .05
48F Bob Scanlan RC .01 .05
49F Tom Candiotti .01 .05
50F Dennis Martinez .02 .10
(Perfecto)
51F Oil Can Boyd .01 .05
52F Glenallen Hill .01 .05
53F Scott Livingstone RC .02 .10
54F Brian R. Hunter RC .08 .25
55F Ivan Rodriguez RC .75 2.00
56F Keith Mitchell RC .02 .10
57F Roger McDowell .01 .05
58F Otis Nixon .01 .05
59F Juan Bell .01 .05
60F Bill Krueger .01 .05
61F Chris Donnels RC .01 .05
62F Tommy Greene .01 .05
63F Doug Simons RC .01 .05
64F Andy Ashby RC .08 .25
65F Anthony Young RC .02 .10
66F Kevin Morton RC .01 .05
67F Bret Barberie RC .02 .10
68F Scott Servais RC .08 .25
69F Ron Darling .01 .05
70F Tim Burke .01 .05
71F Vicente Palacios .01 .05
72F Gerald Alexander RC .01 .05
73F Reggie Jefferson .01 .05
74F Dean Palmer .02 .10
75F Mark Whiten .01 .05
76F Randy Tomlin RC .02 .10
77F Mark Wohlers RC .08 .25
78F Brook Jacoby .01 .05
79F Ken Griffey Jr. CL .15 .40
Ryne Sandberg
80F Jack Morris AS .01 .05
81F Sandy Alomar Jr. AS .01 .05
82F Cecil Fielder AS .01 .05
83F Roberto Alomar AS .02 .10
84F Wade Boggs AS .02 .10
85F Cal Ripken AS .15 .40
86F Rickey Henderson AS .05 .15
87F Ken Griffey Jr. AS .08 .25
88F Dave Henderson AS .01 .05
89F Danny Tartabull AS .01 .05
90F Tom Glavine AS .02 .10
91F Benito Santiago AS .01 .05
92F Will Clark AS .02 .10
93F Ryne Sandberg AS .08 .25
94F Chris Sabo AS .01 .05
95F Ozzie Smith AS .08 .25
96F Ivan Calderon AS .01 .05
97F Tony Gwynn AS .05 .15
98F Andre Dawson AS .01 .05
99F Bobby Bonilla AS .01 .05
100F Checklist 1-100 .01 .05

1992 Upper Deck

The 1992 Upper Deck set contains 800 standard-size cards issued in two separate series of 700 and 100 cards respectively. The cards were distributed in low and high series foil packs in addition to factory sets. Factory sets feature a unique gold-foil hologram on the card backs (in contrast to the silver hologram on foil pack cards). Special subsets included in the set are Star Rookies (1-27), Team Checklists (29-40/86-99), with player portraits by Vernon Wells Sr.; Top Prospects (52-77); Bloodlines (79-85), Diamond Skills (640-650/711-721) and Diamond Debuts (771-780). Rookie Cards in the set include Shawn Green, Brian Jordan and Manny Ramirez. A special card picturing Tom Selleck and Frank Thomas, commemorating the forgettable movie "Mr. Baseball", was randomly inserted into high series packs. A standard-size Ted Williams hologram card was randomly inserted into low series packs. By mailing in 15 low series foil wrappers, a completed order form, and a handling fee, the collector could receive an 8 1/2" by 11" numbered, black and white lithograph picturing Ted Williams in his batting swing.

COMPLETE SET (800) 10.00 25.00
COMPLETE LO SET (700) 8.00 20.00
COMPLETE HI SET (100) 2.00 5.00
1 Ryan Klesko CL .08 .25
Jim Thome
2 Royce Clayton SR .01 .05
3 Brian Jordan RC .20 .50
4 Dave Fleming SR .01 .05
5 Jim Thome SR .08 .25
6 Jeff Juden SR .01 .05
7 Roberto Hernandez SR .01 .05
8 Kyle Abbott SR .01 .05
9 Chris George SR .01 .05
10 Rob Maurer SR .01 .05
11 Donald Harris SR .01 .05
12 Ted Wood SR .01 .05
13 Patrick Lennon SR .01 .05
14 Willie Banks SR .01 .05
15 Roger Salkeld SR UER .01 .05
(Bill was his grand-
father, not his father)
16 Wil Cordero SR .01 .05
17 Arthur Rhodes SR .01 .05
18 Pedro Martinez SR .40 1.00
19 Andy Ashby SR .01 .05
20 Tom Goodwin SR .01 .05
21 Braulio Castillo SR .01 .05
22 Todd Van Poppel SR .01 .05
23 Brian Williams RC .01 .05
24 Ryan Klesko SR .02 .10
25 Kenny Lofton SR .05 .15
26 Derek Bell SR .02 .10
27 Reggie Sanders SR .02 .10
28 Dave Winfield's 400th .01 .05
29 David Justice TC .01 .05
30 Rob Dibble TC .01 .05
31 Craig Biggio TC .02 .10
32 Eddie Murray TC .05 .15
33 Fred McGriff TC .02 .10
34 Willie McGee TC .01 .05
35 Shawon Dunston TC .01 .05
36 Delino DeShields TC .01 .05
37 Howard Johnson TC .01 .05
38 John Kruk TC .01 .05
39 Doug Drabek TC .01 .05
40 Todd Zeile TC .01 .05
41 Steve Avery .01 .05
Playoff Perfection
42 Jeremy Hernandez RC .01 .05
43 Doug Henry RC .02 .10
44 Chris Donnels .01 .05
45 Mo Sanford .01 .05
46 Scott Kamieniecki .01 .05
47 Mark Lemke .01 .05
48 Steve Farr .01 .05
49 Francisco Oliveras .01 .05
50 Ced Landrum .01 .05
51 Rondell White CL .02 .10
Mark Newfield
52 Eduardo Perez RC .08 .25
53 Tom Nevers TP .01 .05
54 David Zancanaro TP .01 .05
55 Shawn Green RC .40 1.00
56 Mark Wohlers TP .01 .05
57 Dave Nilsson TP .01 .05
58 Dmitri Young TP .02 .10
59 Ryan Hawblitzel RC .02 .10
60 Raul Mondesi TP .02 .10
61 Rondell White TP .02 .10
62 Steve Hosey TP .01 .05
63 Manny Ramirez RC 2.00 5.00
64 Marc Newfield TP .01 .05
65 Jeromy Burnitz TP .02 .10
66 Mark Smith RC .02 .10
67 Joey Hamilton RC .02 .10
68 Tyler Green RC .02 .10
69 Jon Farrell RC .02 .10
70 Kurt Miller TP .01 .05
71 Jeff Plympton TP .01 .05
72 Dan Wilson TP .01 .05
73 Joe Vitiello RC .02 .10
74 Rico Brogna TP .01 .05
75 David McCarty TP RC .08 .25
76 Bob Wickman TP .08 .25
77 Carlos Rodriguez TP .01 .05
78 Jim Abbott .02 .10
Stay In School
79 Ramon Martinez .08 .25
Pedro Martinez
80 Kevin Mitchell .01 .05
Keith Mitchell
81 Sandy Alomar Jr. .02 .10
Roberto Alomar
82 Cal Ripken .20 .50
Billy Ripken
83 Tony Gwynn .05 .15
Chris Gwynn
84 Dwight Gooden .02 .10
Gary Sheffield
85 Ken Griffey Sr. .08 .25
Ken Griffey Jr.
Craig Griffey
86 Jim Abbott TC .02 .10
87 Frank Thomas TC .05 .15
88 Danny Tartabull TC .01 .05
89 Scott Erickson TC .01 .05
90 Rickey Henderson TC .05 .15
91 Edgar Martinez TC .02 .10
92 Nolan Ryan TC .20 .50
93 Ben McDonald TC .01 .05
94 Ellis Burks TC .01 .05
95 Greg Swindell TC .01 .05
96 Cecil Fielder TC .01 .05
97 Greg Vaughn TC .01 .05
98 Kevin Maas TC .01 .05
99 Dave Stieb TC .01 .05
100 Checklist 1-100 .01 .05
101 Joe Oliver .01 .05
102 Hector Villanueva .01 .05
103 Ed Whitson .01 .05
104 Danny Jackson .01 .05
105 Chris Hammond .01 .05
106 Ricky Jordan .01 .05
107 Kevin Bass .01 .05
108 Darrin Fletcher .01 .05
109 Junior Ortiz .01 .05
110 Tom Bolton .01 .05
111 Jeff King .01 .05
112 Dave Magadan .01 .05
113 Mike LaValliere .01 .05
114 Hubie Brooks .01 .05
115 Jay Bell .02 .10
116 David Wells .02 .10
117 Jim Leyritz .01 .05
118 Manuel Lee .01 .05
119 Alvaro Espinoza .01 .05
120 B.J. Surhoff .02 .10
121 Hal Morris .01 .05
122 Shawon Dawson .01 .05
123 Chris Sabo .01 .05
124 Andre Dawson .02 .10
125 Eric Davis .02 .10
126 Chili Davis .02 .10
127 Dale Murphy .05 .15
128 Kirk McCaskill .01 .05
129 Terry Mulholland .01 .05
130 Rick Aguilera .02 .10
131 Vince Coleman .01 .05
132 Andy Van Slyke .05 .15
133 Gregg Jefferies .01 .05
134 Barry Bonds .40 1.00
135 Dwight Gooden .02 .10
136 Dave Stieb .01 .05
137 Albert Belle .02 .10
138 Teddy Higuera .01 .05
139 Jesse Barfield .01 .05
140 Pat Borders .01 .05
141 Bip Roberts .01 .05
142 Rob Dibble .02 .10
143 Mark Grace .05 .15
144 Barry Larkin .05 .15
145 Ryne Sandberg .15 .40
146 Scott Erickson .01 .05
147 Luis Polonia .01 .05
148 John Burkett .01 .05
149 Luis Sojo .01 .05
150 Dickie Thon .01 .05
151 Walt Weiss .01 .05
152 Mike Scioscia .01 .05
153 Mark McGwire .25 .60
154 Matt Williams .02 .10
155 Rickey Henderson .08 .25
156 Sandy Alomar Jr. .01 .05
157 Brian McRae .01 .05
158 Harold Baines .02 .10
159 Kevin Appier .02 .10
160 Felix Fermin .01 .05
161 Leo Gomez .01 .05
162 Craig Biggio .05 .15
163 Ben McDonald .01 .05
164 Randy Johnson .08 .25
165 Cal Ripken .30 .75
166 Frank Thomas .08 .25
167 Delino DeShields .01 .05
168 Greg Gagne .01 .05
169 Ron Karkovice .01 .05
170 Charlie Leibrandt .01 .05

171 Dave Righetti .02 .10
172 Dave Henderson .01 .05
173 Steve Decker .01 .05
174 Darryl Strawberry .02 .10
175 Will Clark .05 .15
176 Ruben Sierra .02 .10
177 Ozzie Smith .15 .40
178 Charles Nagy .01 .05
179 Gary Pettis .01 .05
180 Kirk Gibson .02 .10
181 Randy Milligan .01 .05
182 Dave Valle .01 .05
183 Chris Hoiles .01 .05
184 Tony Phillips .01 .05
185 Brady Anderson .02 .10
186 Scott Fletcher .01 .05
187 Gene Larkin .01 .05
188 Lance Johnson .01 .05
189 Greg Olson .01 .05
190 Melido Perez .01 .05
191 Lenny Harris .01 .05
192 Terry Kennedy .01 .05
193 Mike Gallego .01 .05
194 Willie McGee .02 .10
195 Juan Samuel .01 .05
196 Jeff Huson .02 .10
197 Alex Cole .01 .05
198 Ron Robinson .01 .05
199 Joel Skinner .01 .05
200 Checklist 101-200 .01 .05
201 Kevin Reimer .01 .05
202 Stan Belinda .01 .05
203 Pat Tabler .01 .05
204 Jose Guzman .01 .05
205 Jose Lind .01 .05
206 Spike Owen .01 .05
207 Joe Orsulak .01 .05
208 Charlie Hayes .01 .05
209 Mike Devereaux .01 .05
210 Mike Fitzgerald .01 .05
211 Willie Randolph .02 .10
212 Rod Nichols .01 .05
213 Mike Boddicker .01 .05
214 Bill Spiers .01 .05
215 Steve Olin .01 .05
216 David Howard .01 .05
217 Gary Varsho .01 .05
218 Mike Harkey .01 .05
219 Luis Aquino .01 .05
220 Chuck McElroy .01 .05
221 Doug Drabek .01 .05
222 Dave Winfield .02 .10
223 Rafael Palmeiro .05 .15
224 Joe Carter .02 .10
225 Bobby Bonilla .02 .10
226 Ivan Calderon .01 .05
227 Gregg Olson .01 .05
228 Tim Wallach .01 .05
229 Terry Pendleton .02 .10
230 Gilberto Reyes .01 .05
231 Carlos Baerga .01 .05
232 Greg Vaughn .01 .05
233 Bret Saberhagen .02 .10
234 Gary Sheffield .02 .10
235 Mark Lewis .01 .05
236 George Bell .01 .05
237 Danny Tartabull .01 .05
238 Willie Wilson .01 .05
239 Doug Dascenzo .01 .05
240 Bill Pecota .01 .05
241 Julio Franco .02 .10
242 Ed Sprague .01 .05
243 Juan Gonzalez .05 .15
244 Chuck Finley .02 .10
245 Ivan Rodriguez .08 .25
246 Len Dykstra .02 .10
247 Deion Sanders .05 .15
248 Dwight Evans .05 .15
249 Larry Walker .05 .15
250 Billy Ripken .01 .05
251 Mickey Tettleton .01 .05
252 Tony Pena .01 .05
253 Benito Santiago .02 .10
254 Kirby Puckett .08 .25
255 Cecil Fielder .02 .10
256 Howard Johnson .01 .05
257 Andujar Cedeno .01 .05
258 Jose Rijo .01 .05
259 Al Osuna .01 .05
260 Todd Hundley .01 .05
261 Orel Hershiser .02 .10
262 Ray Lankford .02 .10
263 Robin Ventura .02 .10
264 Felix Jose .01 .05
265 Eddie Murray .08 .25
266 Kevin Mitchell .01 .05
267 Gary Carter .02 .10
268 Mike Benjamin .01 .05
269 Dick Schofield .01 .05
270 Jose Uribe .01 .05
271 Pete Incaviglia .01 .05
272 Tony Fernandez .01 .05
273 Alan Trammell .02 .10
274 Tony Gwynn .10 .30
275 Mike Greenwell .01 .05
276 Jeff Bagwell .08 .25
277 Frank Viola .01 .05
278 Randy Myers .01 .05
279 Ken Caminiti .02 .10
280 Bill Doran .01 .05
281 Dan Pasqua .01 .05
282 Alfredo Griffin .01 .05
283 Jose Oquendo .01 .05
284 Kal Daniels .01 .05
285 Bobby Thigpen .01 .05
286 Robby Thompson .01 .05
287 Mark Eichhorn .01 .05
288 Mike Felder .01 .05
289 Dave Gallagher .01 .05
290 Dave Anderson .01 .05
291 Mel Hall .01 .05
292 Jerald Clark .01 .05
293 Al Newman .01 .05
294 Rob Deer .01 .05
295 Matt Nokes .01 .05
296 Jack Armstrong .01 .05
297 Jim Deshaies .01 .05
298 Jeff Innis .01 .05
299 Jeff Reed .01 .05
300 Checklist 201-300 .01 .05
301 Lonnie Smith .01 .05
302 Jimmy Key .02 .10
303 Junior Felix .01 .05
304 Mike Heath .01 .05
305 Mark Langston .01 .05
306 Greg W. Harris .01 .05
307 Brett Butler .02 .10
308 Luis Rivera .01 .05
309 Bruce Ruffin .01 .05
310 Paul Faries .01 .05
311 Terry Leach .01 .05
312 Scott Brosius RC .20 .50
313 Scott Leius .01 .05
314 Harold Reynolds .02 .10
315 Jack Morris .02 .10
316 David Segui .01 .05
317 Bill Gullickson .01 .05
318 Todd Frohwirth .01 .05
319 Mark Leiter .01 .05
320 Jeff M. Robinson .01 .05
321 Gary Gaetti .02 .10
322 John Smoltz .05 .15
323 Andy Benes .01 .05
324 Kelly Gruber .01 .05
325 Jim Abbott .05 .15
326 John Kruk .02 .10
327 Kevin Seitzer .01 .05
328 Darrin Jackson .01 .05
329 Kurt Stillwell .01 .05
330 Mike Maddux .01 .05
331 Dennis Eckersley .02 .10
332 Dan Gladden .01 .05
333 Jose Canseco .05 .15
334 Kent Hrbek .02 .10
335 Ken Griffey Sr. .02 .10
336 Greg Swindell .01 .05
337 Trevor Wilson .01 .05
338 Sam Horn .01 .05
339 Mike Henneman .01 .05
340 Jerry Browne .01 .05
341 Glenn Braggs .01 .05
342 Tom Glavine .05 .15
343 Wally Joyner .02 .10
344 Fred McGriff .05 .15
345 Ron Gant .02 .10
346 Ramon Martinez .01 .05
347 Wes Chamberlain .01 .05
348 Terry Shumpert .01 .05
349 Tim Teufel .01 .05
350 Wally Backman .01 .05
351 Joe Girardi .01 .05
352 Devon White .02 .10
353 Greg Maddux .15 .40
354 Ryan Bowen .01 .05
355 Roberto Alomar .05 .15
356 Don Mattingly .25 .60
357 Pedro Guerrero .02 .10
358 Steve Sax .01 .05
359 Joey Cora .01 .05
360 Jim Gantner .01 .05
361 Brian Barnes .01 .05
362 Kevin McReynolds .01 .05
363 Bret Barberie .01 .05
364 David Cone .02 .10
365 Dennis Martinez .02 .10
366 Brian Hunter .01 .05
367 Edgar Martinez .05 .15
368 Steve Finley .02 .10
369 Greg Briley .01 .05
370 Jeff Blauser .01 .05
371 Todd Stottlemyre .01 .05
372 Luis Gonzalez .02 .10
373 Rick Wilkins .01 .05
374 Darryl Kile .02 .10
375 John Olerud .02 .10
376 Lee Smith .02 .10
377 Kevin Maas .01 .05
378 Dante Bichette .02 .10
379 Tom Pagnozzi .01 .05
380 Mike Flanagan .01 .05
381 Charlie O'Brien .01 .05
382 Dave Martinez .01 .05
383 Keith Miller .01 .05
384 Scott Ruskin .01 .05
385 Kevin Elster .01 .05
386 Alvin Davis .01 .05
387 Casey Candaele .01 .05
388 Pete O'Brien .01 .05
389 Jeff Treadway .01 .05
390 Scott Bradley .01 .05
391 Mookie Wilson .02 .10
392 Jimmy Jones .01 .05
393 Candy Maldonado .01 .05
394 Eric Yelding .01 .05
395 Tom Henke .01 .05
396 Franklin Stubbs .01 .05
397 Milt Thompson .01 .05
398 Mark Carreon .01 .05
399 Randy Velarde .01 .05
400 Checklist 301-400 .01 .05
401 Omar Vizquel .05 .15
402 Joe Boever .01 .05
403 Bill Krueger .01 .05
404 Jody Reed .01 .05
405 Mike Schooler .01 .05
406 Jason Grimsley .01 .05
407 Greg Myers .01 .05
408 Randy Ready .01 .05
409 Mike Timlin .01 .05
410 Mitch Williams .01 .05
411 Garry Templeton .01 .05
412 Greg Cadaret .01 .05
413 Donnie Hill .01 .05
414 Wally Whitehurst .01 .05
415 Scott Sanderson .01 .05
416 Thomas Howard .01 .05
417 Neal Heaton .01 .05
418 Charlie Hough .02 .10
419 Jack Howell .01 .05
420 Greg Hibbard .01 .05
421 Carlos Quintana .01 .05
422 Kim Batiste .01 .05
423 Paul Molitor .02 .10
424 Ken Griffey Jr. .15 .40
425 Phil Plantier .01 .05
426 Denny Neagle .02 .10
427 Von Hayes .01 .05
428 Shane Mack .01 .05
429 Darren Daulton .02 .10
430 Dwayne Henry .01 .05
431 Lance Parrish .02 .10
432 Mike Humphreys .01 .05
433 Tim Burke .01 .05
434 Bryan Harvey .01 .05
435 Pat Kelly .01 .05
436 Ozzie Guillen .02 .10
437 Bruce Hurst .01 .05
438 Sammy Sosa .08 .25
439 Dennis Rasmussen .01 .05
440 Ken Patterson .01 .05
441 Jay Buhner .02 .10
442 Pat Combs .01 .05
443 Wade Boggs .05 .15
444 George Brett .25 .60
445 Mo Vaughn .02 .10
446 Chuck Knoblauch .02 .10
447 Tom Candiotti .01 .05
448 Mark Portugal .01 .05
449 Mickey Morandini .01 .05
450 Duane Ward .01 .05
451 Otis Nixon .01 .05
452 Bob Welch .01 .05
453 Rusty Meacham .01 .05
454 Keith Mitchell .01 .05
455 Marquis Grissom .02 .10
456 Robin Yount .15 .40
457 Harvey Pulliam .01 .05
458 Jose DeLeon .01 .05
459 Mark Gubicza .01 .05
460 Darryl Hamilton .01 .05
461 Tom Browning .01 .05
462 Monty Fariss .01 .05
463 Jerome Walton .01 .05
464 Paul O'Neill .05 .15
465 Dean Palmer .02 .10
466 Travis Fryman .02 .10
467 John Smiley .01 .05
468 Lloyd Moseby .01 .05
469 John Wehner .01 .05
470 Skeeter Barnes .01 .05
471 Steve Chitren .01 .05
472 Kent Mercker .01 .05
473 Terry Steinbach .01 .05
474 Andres Galarraga .02 .10
475 Steve Avery .01 .05
476 Tom Gordon .01 .05
477 Cal Eldred .01 .05
478 Omar Olivares .01 .05
479 Julio Machado .01 .05
480 Bob Milacki .01 .05
481 Les Lancaster .01 .05
482 John Candelaria .01 .05
483 Brian Downing .01 .05
484 Roger McDowell .01 .05
485 Scott Scudder .01 .05
486 Zane Smith .01 .05
487 John Cerutti .01 .05
488 Steve Buechele .01 .05
489 Paul Gibson .01 .05
490 Curtis Wilkerson .01 .05
491 Marvin Freeman .01 .05
492 Tom Foley .01 .05
493 Juan Berenguer .01 .05
494 Ernest Riles .01 .05
495 Sid Bream .01 .05
496 Chuck Crim .01 .05
497 Mike Macfarlane .01 .05
498 Dale Sveum .01 .05
499 Storm Davis .01 .05
500 Checklist 401-500 .01 .05
501 Jeff Reardon .02 .10
502 Shawn Abner .01 .05
503 Tony Fossas .01 .05
504 Cory Snyder .01 .05
505 Matt Young .01 .05
506 Allan Anderson .01 .05
507 Mark Lee .01 .05
508 Gene Nelson .01 .05
509 Mike Pagliarulo .01 .05
510 Rafael Belliard .01 .05
511 Jay Howell .01 .05
512 Bob Tewksbury .01 .05
513 Mike Morgan .01 .05
514 John Franco .02 .10
515 Kevin Gross .01 .05
516 Lou Whitaker .02 .10
517 Orlando Merced .01 .05
518 Todd Benzinger .01 .05
519 Gary Redus .01 .05
520 Walt Terrell .01 .05
521 Jack Clark .02 .10
522 Dave Parker .02 .10
523 Tim Naehring .01 .05
524 Mark Whiten .01 .05
525 Ellis Burks .02 .10
526 Frank Castillo .01 .05
527 Brian Harper .01 .05
528 Brook Jacoby .01 .05
529 Rick Sutcliffe .02 .10
530 Joe Klink .01 .05
531 Terry Bross .01 .05
532 Jose Offerman .01 .05
533 Todd Zeile .01 .05
534 Eric Karros .02 .10
535 Anthony Young .01 .05
536 Milt Cuyler .01 .05
537 Randy Tomlin .01 .05
538 Scott Livingstone .01 .05
539 Jim Eisenreich .01 .05
540 Don Slaught .01 .05
541 Scott Cooper .01 .05
542 Joe Grahe .01 .05
543 Tom Brunansky .01 .05
544 Eddie Zosky .01 .05
545 Roger Clemens .20 .50
546 David Justice .02 .10
547 Dave Stewart .02 .10
548 David West .01 .05
549 Dave Smith .01 .05
550 Dan Plesac .01 .05
551 Alex Fernandez .01 .05
552 Bernard Gilkey .01 .05
553 Jack McDowell .01 .05
554 Tino Martinez .05 .15
555 Bo Jackson .08 .25
556 Bernie Williams .05 .15
557 Mark Gardner .01 .05
558 Glenallen Hill .01 .05
559 Oil Can Boyd .01 .05
560 Chris James .01 .05
561 Scott Servais .01 .05
562 Rey Sanchez RC .08 .25
563 Paul McClellan .01 .05
564 Andy Mota .01 .05
565 Darren Lewis .01 .05
566 Jose Melendez .01 .05
567 Tommy Greene .01 .05
568 Rich Rodriguez .01 .05
569 Heathcliff Slocumb .01 .05
570 Joe Hesketh .01 .05
571 Carlton Fisk .05 .15
572 Erik Hanson .01 .05
573 Wilson Alvarez .01 .05
574 Rheal Cormier .01 .05
575 Tim Raines .02 .10
576 Bobby Witt .01 .05
577 Roberto Kelly .01 .05
578 Kevin Brown .02 .10
579 Chris Nabholz .01 .05
580 Jesse Orosco .01 .05
581 Jeff Brantley .01 .05
582 Rafael Ramirez .01 .05
583 Kelly Downs .01 .05
584 Mike Simms .01 .05
585 Mike Remlinger .01 .05
586 Dave Hollins .01 .05
587 Larry Andersen .01 .05
588 Mike Gardiner .01 .05
589 Craig Lefferts .01 .05
590 Paul Assenmacher .01 .05
591 Bryn Smith .01 .05
592 Donn Pall .01 .05
593 Mike Jackson .01 .05
594 Scott Radinsky .01 .05
595 Brian Holman .01 .05
596 Geronimo Pena .01 .05
597 Mike Jeffcoat .01 .05
598 Carlos Martinez .01 .05
599 Geno Petralli .01 .05
600 Checklist 501-600 .01 .05
601 Jerry Don Gleaton .01 .05
602 Adam Peterson .01 .05
603 Craig Grebeck .01 .05
604 Mark Guthrie .01 .05
605 Frank Tanana .01 .05
606 Hensley Meulens .01 .05
607 Mark Davis .01 .05
608 Eric Plunk .01 .05
609 Mark Williamson .01 .05
610 Lee Guetterman .01 .05
611 Bobby Rose .01 .05
612 Bill Wegman .01 .05
613 Mike Hartley .01 .05
614 Chris Beasley .01 .05
615 Chris Bosio .01 .05
616 Henry Cotto .01 .05
617 Chico Walker .01 .05
618 Russ Swan .01 .05
619 Bob Walk .01 .05
620 Bill Swift .01 .05
621 Warren Newson .01 .05
622 Steve Bedrosian .01 .05
623 Ricky Bones .01 .05
624 Kevin Tapani .01 .05
625 Juan Guzman .01 .05
626 Jeff Johnson .01 .05
627 Jeff Montgomery .01 .05
628 Ken Hill .01 .05
629 Gary Thurman .01 .05
630 Steve Howe .01 .05
631 Jose DeJesus .01 .05
632 Kirk Dressendorfer .01 .05
633 Jaime Navarro .01 .05
634 Lee Stevens .01 .05
635 Pete Harnisch .01 .05
636 Bill Landrum .01 .05
637 Rich DeLucia .01 .05
638 Luis Salazar .01 .05
639 Rob Murphy .01 .05
640 Jose Canseco CL .05 .15
Rickey Henderson
641 Roger Clemens DS .08 .25
642 Jim Abbott DS .02 .10
643 Travis Fryman DS .01 .05
644 Jesse Barfield DS .01 .05
645 Cal Ripken DS .15 .40
646 Wade Boggs DS .02 .10
647 Cecil Fielder DS .01 .05
648 Rickey Henderson DS .05 .15
649 Jose Canseco DS .02 .10
650 Ken Griffey Jr. DS .08 .25
651 Kenny Rogers .02 .10
652 Luis Mercedes .01 .05
653 Mike Stanton .01 .05
654 Glenn Davis .01 .05
655 Nolan Ryan .40 1.00
656 Reggie Jefferson .01 .05
657 Javier Ortiz .01 .05
658 Greg A. Harris .01 .05
659 Mariano Duncan .01 .05
660 Jeff Shaw .01 .05
661 Mike Moore .01 .05
662 Chris Haney .01 .05
663 Joe Slusarski .01 .05
664 Wayne Housie .01 .05
665 Carlos Garcia .01 .05
666 Bob Ojeda .01 .05
667 Bryan Hickerson RC .02 .10
668 Tim Belcher .01 .05
669 Ron Darling .01 .05
670 Rex Hudler .01 .05
671 Sid Fernandez .01 .05
672 Chito Martinez .01 .05
673 Pete Schourek .01 .05
674 Armando Reynoso RC .08 .25
675 Mike Mussina .08 .25
676 Kevin Morton .01 .05
677 Norm Charlton .01 .05
678 Danny Darwin .01 .05
679 Eric King .01 .05
680 Ted Power .01 .05
681 Barry Jones .01 .05
682 Carney Lansford .02 .10
683 Mel Rojas .01 .05
684 Rick Honeycutt .01 .05
685 Jeff Fassero .01 .05
686 Cris Carpenter .01 .05
687 Tim Crews .01 .05
688 Scott Terry .01 .05
689 Chris Gwynn .01 .05
690 Gerald Perry .01 .05
691 John Barfield .01 .05
692 Bob Melvin .01 .05
693 Juan Agosto .01 .05
694 Alejandro Pena .01 .05
695 Jeff Russell .01 .05
696 Carmelo Martinez .01 .05
697 Bud Black .01 .05
698 Dave Otto .01 .05
699 Billy Hatcher .01 .05
700 Checklist 601-700 .01 .05
701 Clemente Nunez RC .01 .05
702 Mark Clark .01 .05
Donovan Osborne
Brian Jordan
703 Mike Morgan .01 .05
704 Keith Miller .01 .05
705 Kurt Stillwell .01 .05
706 Damon Berryhill .01 .05
707 Von Hayes .01 .05
708 Rick Sutcliffe .02 .10
709 Hubie Brooks .01 .05
710 Ryan Turner RC .02 .10
711 Barry Bonds CL .20 .50
Andy Van Slyke
712 Jose Rijo DS .01 .05
713 Tom Glavine DS .02 .10
714 Shawon Dunston DS .01 .05
715 Andy Van Slyke DS .02 .10
716 Ozzie Smith DS .08 .25
717 Tony Gwynn DS .05 .15
718 Will Clark DS .02 .10
719 Marquis Grissom DS .01 .05
720 Howard Johnson DS .01 .05
721 Barry Bonds DS .20 .50
722 Kirk McCaskill .01 .05
723 Sammy Sosa .30 .75
724 George Bell .01 .05
725 Gregg Jefferies .01 .05
726 Gary DiSarcina .01 .05
727 Mike Bordick .01 .05
728 Eddie Murray 400 HR .05 .15
729 Rene Gonzales .01 .05
730 Mike Bielecki .01 .05
731 Calvin Jones .01 .05
732 Jack Morris .02 .10
733 Frank Viola .02 .10
734 Dave Winfield .02 .10
735 Kevin Mitchell .02 .10
736 Bill Swift .01 .05
737 Dan Gladden .01 .05
738 Mike Jackson .01 .05
739 Mark Carreon .01 .05
740 Kirt Manwaring .01 .05
741 Randy Myers .01 .05
742 Kevin McReynolds .01 .05
743 Steve Sax .01 .05
744 Wally Joyner .02 .10
745 Gary Sheffield .02 .10
746 Danny Tartabull .01 .05
747 Julio Valera .01 .05
748 Denny Neagle .02 .10
749 Lance Blankenship .01 .05
750 Mike Gallego .01 .05
751 Bret Saberhagen .02 .10
752 Ruben Amaro .01 .05
753 Eddie Murray .08 .25
754 Kyle Abbott .01 .05
755 Bobby Bonilla .02 .10
756 Eric Davis .02 .10
757 Eddie Taubensee RC .08 .25
758 Andres Galarraga .02 .10
759 Pete Incaviglia .01 .05
760 Tom Candiotti .01 .05
761 Tim Belcher .01 .05
762 Ricky Bones .01 .05
763 Bip Roberts .01 .05
764 Pedro Munoz .01 .05
765 Greg Swindell .01 .05
766 Kenny Lofton .05 .15
767 Gary Carter .02 .10
768 Charlie Hayes .01 .05
769 Dickie Thon .01 .05
770 D. Osborne DD CL .01 .05
771 Bret Boone DD .05 .15
772 Archi Cianfrocco RC .02 .10
773 Mark Clark RC .02 .10
774 Chad Curtis RC .08 .25
775 Pat Listach RC .08 .25
776 Pat Mahomes RC .08 .25
777 Donovan Osborne DD .01 .05
778 John Patterson RC .02 .10
779 Andy Stankiewicz DD .01 .05
780 Turk Wendell RC .08 .25
781 Bill Krueger .01 .05
782 Rickey Henderson 1000 .05 .15
783 Kevin Seitzer .01 .05
784 Dave Martinez .01 .05
785 John Smiley .01 .05
786 Matt Stairs RC .08 .25
787 Scott Scudder .01 .05
788 John Wetteland .02 .10
789 Jack Armstrong .01 .05
790 Ken Hill .01 .05
791 Dick Schofield .01 .05
792 Mariano Duncan .01 .05
793 Bill Pecota .01 .05
794 Mike Kelly RC .02 .10
795 Willie Randolph .02 .10
796 Butch Henry .01 .05
797 Carlos Hernandez .01 .05
798 Doug Jones .01 .05
799 Melido Perez .01 .05
800 Checklist 701-800 .01 .05
HH2 T.Williams Hologram .75 2.00
Top left corner says
91 Upper Deck 92
SP3 Deion Sanders FB/BB .40 1.00
SP4 Tom Selleck .40 1.00
Frank Thomas SP
(Mr. Baseball)

1992 Upper Deck Gold Hologram

All cards issued in 1992 Upper Deck factory sets have a gold hologram on the back.

COMP.FACT.SET (800) 10.00 25.00
*STARS: .4X TO 1X BASIC CARDS
*ROOKIES: .4X TO 1X BASIC

1992 Upper Deck Bench/Morgan Heroes

This standard size 10-card set was randomly inserted in 1992 Upper Deck high number packs. Both Bench and Morgan autographed 2,500 of card number 45, which displays a portrait by sports artist Vernon Wells. The fronts feature color photos of Bench (37-39), Morgan (40-42), or both (43-44) at various stages of their baseball careers.

COMPLETE SET (10) 7.50 15.00
COMMON CARD (37-45) .60 1.50
NNO Baseball Heroes SP 1.00 2.50
(Header card)
AU5 J.Bench/J.Morgan 100.00 175.00
AU/2500

1992 Upper Deck College POY Holograms

This three-card standard-size set was randomly inserted in 1992 Upper Deck high series foil packs. This set features College Player of the Year winners for 1989 through 1991. The cards are numbered on the back with the prefix "CP".

COMPLETE SET (3) .75 2.00
CP1 David McCarty .40 1.00
CP2 Mike Kelly .40 1.00
CP3 Ben McDonald .40 1.00

1992 Upper Deck Heroes of Baseball

Continuing a popular insert set introduced the previous year, Upper Deck produced four new commemorative cards, including three player cards and one portrait card by sports artist Vernon Wells. These cards were randomly inserted in 1992 Upper Deck baseball low number foil packs. Three thousand of each card were personally numbered and autographed by each player.

H5 Vida Blue .75 2.00
H6 Lou Brock .75 2.00
H7 Rollie Fingers .75 2.00
H8 Vida Blue ART .75 2.00
Lou Brock
Rollie Fingers
AU5 Vida Blue AU/3000 6.00 15.00
AU6 Lou Brock AU/3000 10.00 25.00
AU7 R.Fingers AU/3000 6.00 15.00

1992 Upper Deck Heroes Highlights

To dealers participating in Heroes of Baseball Collectors shows, Upper Deck made available this ten-card insert standard-size set, which commemorates one of the greatest moments in the careers of ten of baseball's all-time players. The cards were primarily randomly inserted in high number packs sold at these shows. However at the first Heroes show in Anaheim, the cards were inserted into low number packs. The fronts feature color player photos with a shadowed strip for a three-dimensional effect. The player's name and the date of the great moment in the hero's career appear with a "Heroes Highlights" logo in a bottom border of varying shades of brown and blue-green. The backs have white borders and display a blue-green and brown bordered monument design accented with baseballs. The major portion of the design is parchment-textured and contains text highlighting a special moment in the player's career. The cards are numbered on the back with an "HI" prefix. The card numbering follows alphabetical order by player's name.

COMPLETE SET (10) 6.00 15.00
HI1 Bobby Bonds .20 .50
HI2 Lou Brock 1.25 3.00
HI3 Rollie Fingers .75 2.00
HI4 Bob Gibson 1.25 3.00
HI5 Reggie Jackson 1.50 4.00
HI6 Gaylord Perry .75 2.00
HI7 Robin Roberts .75 2.00
HI8 Brooks Robinson 1.50 4.00
HI9 Billy Williams .75 2.00
HI10 Ted Williams 2.50 6.00

1992 Upper Deck Home Run Heroes

This 26-card standard-size set was inserted one per pack into 1992 Upper Deck low series jumbo packs. The set spotlights the 1991 home run leaders from each of the 26 Major League teams.

COMPLETE SET (26)	5.00	12.00
HR1 Jose Canseco	.20	.50
HR2 Cecil Fielder	.10	.30
HR3 Howard Johnson	.05	.15
HR4 Cal Ripken	1.00	2.50
HR5 Matt Williams	.10	.30
HR6 Joe Carter	.10	.30
HR7 Ron Gant	.10	.30
HR8 Frank Thomas	.30	.75
HR9 Andre Dawson	.10	.30
HR10 Fred McGriff	.20	.50
HR11 Danny Tartabull	.05	.15
HR12 Chili Davis	.10	.30
HR13 Albert Belle	.10	.30
HR14 Jack Clark	.10	.30
HR15 Paul O'Neill	.20	.50
HR16 Darryl Strawberry	.10	.30
HR17 Dave Winfield	.10	.30
HR18 Jay Buhner	.10	.30
HR19 Juan Gonzalez	.20	.50
HR20 Greg Vaughn	.05	.15
HR21 Barry Bonds	1.25	3.00
HR22 Matt Nokes	.05	.15
HR23 John Kruk	.10	.30
HR24 Ivan Calderon	.05	.15
HR25 Jeff Bagwell	.30	.75
HR26 Todd Zeile	.05	.15

1992 Upper Deck Scouting Report

Inserted one per high series jumbo pack, cards from this 25-card standard-size set feature outstanding prospects in baseball. Please note these cards are highly condition sensitive and are priced below in NmMt condition. Mint copies trade for premiums.

COMPLETE SET (25)	10.00	20.00
SR1 Andy Ashby	.40	1.00
SR2 Willie Banks	.40	1.00
SR3 Kim Batiste	.40	1.00
SR4 Derek Bell	.40	1.00
SR5 Archi Cianfrocco	.40	1.00
SR6 Royce Clayton	.40	1.00
SR7 Gary DiSarcina	.40	1.00
SR8 Dave Fleming	.40	1.00
SR9 Butch Henry	.40	1.00
SR10 Todd Hundley	.40	1.00
SR11 Brian Jordan	.40	1.00
SR12 Eric Karros	.40	1.00
SR13 Pat Listach	.40	1.00
SR14 Scott Livingstone	.40	1.00
SR15 Kenny Lofton	.40	1.00
SR16 Pat Mahomes	.40	1.00
SR17 Denny Neagle	.40	1.00
SR18 Dave Nilsson	.40	1.00
SR19 Donovan Osborne	.40	1.00
SR20 Reggie Sanders	.40	1.00
SR21 Andy Stankiewicz	.40	1.00
SR22 Jim Thome	.75	2.00
SR23 Julio Valera	.40	1.00
SR24 Mark Wohlers	.40	1.00
SR25 Anthony Young	.40	1.00

1992 Upper Deck Williams Best

This 20-card standard-size set contains Ted Williams' choices of best current and future hitters in the game. The cards were randomly inserted in Upper Deck high number foil packs. These cards are condition sensitive and priced below in NmMt condition. True mint condition copies do sell for more than these listed prices.

COMPLETE SET (20)	8.00	20.00
T1 Wade Boggs	.30	.75
T2 Barry Bonds	2.00	5.00
T3 Jose Canseco	.30	.75
T4 Will Clark	.30	.75
T5 Cecil Fielder	.20	.50
T6 Tony Gwynn	.60	1.50
T7 Rickey Henderson	.50	1.25
T8 Fred McGriff	.30	.75
T9 Kirby Puckett	.50	1.25
T10 Ruben Sierra	.20	.50
T11 Roberto Alomar	.30	.75
T12 Jeff Bagwell	.50	1.25
T13 Albert Belle	.20	.50
T14 Juan Gonzalez	.30	.75
T15 Ken Griffey Jr.	.75	2.00
T16 Chris Hoiles	.08	.25
T17 David Justice	.20	.50
T18 Phil Plantier	.08	.25
T19 Frank Thomas	.50	1.25
T20 Robin Ventura	.20	.50

1992 Upper Deck Williams Heroes

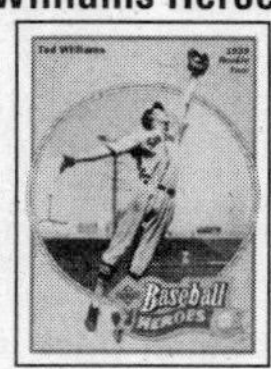

This standard-size ten-card set was randomly inserted in 1992 Upper Deck low number foil packs. Williams autographed 2,500 of card 36, which displays his portrait by sports artist Vernon Wells. The cards are numbered on the back in continuation of the Upper Deck heroes series.

COMPLETE SET (10)	3.00	6.00
COMMON (28-36)	.20	.50
NNO Baseball Heroes SP (Header card)	.75	2.00
AU4 Ted Williams AU/2500	300.00	500.00

1992 Upper Deck Williams Wax Boxes

These eight oversized blank-backed "cards," measuring approximately 5 1/4" by 7 1/4", were featured on the bottom panels of 1992 Upper Deck low series wax boxes. They are identical in design to the Williams Heroes insert cards, displaying color player photos in an oval frame. These boxes are unnumbered. We have checklisted them below according to the numbering of the Heroes cards.

COMMON CARD (28-35)	.20	.50

1993 Upper Deck

The 1993 Upper Deck set consists of two series of 420 standard-size cards. Special subsets featured include Star Rookies (1-29), Community Heroes (30-40), and American League Teammates (41-55), Top Prospects (421-449), Inside the Numbers (450-470), Team Stars (471-485), Award Winners (486-499), and Diamond Debuts (500-510). Derek Jeter is the only notable Rookie Card in this set. A special card (SP5) was randomly inserted in first series packs to commemorate the 3,000th hit of George Brett and Robin Yount. A special card (SP6) commemorating Nolan Ryan's last season was randomly inserted into second series packs. Both SP cards were inserted at a rate of one every 72 packs

COMPLETE SET (840)	15.00	40.00
COMP.FACT.SET (840)	20.00	50.00
COMP. SERIES 1 (420)	6.00	15.00
COMP. SERIES 2 (420)	10.00	25.00
1 Tim Salmon CL	.07	.20
2 Mike Piazza SR	1.25	3.00
3 Rene Arocha SR RC	.20	.50
4 Willie Greene SR	.02	.10
5 Manny Alexander	.02	.10
6 Dan Wilson	.07	.20
7 Dan Smith	.02	.10
8 Kevin Rogers	.02	.10
9 Kurt Miller SR	.02	.10
10 Joe Vitko	.02	.10
11 Tim Costo	.02	.10
12 Alan Embree SR	.02	.10
13 Jim Tatum SR RC	.05	.15
14 Cris Colon	.02	.10
15 Steve Hosey	.02	.10
16 S. Hitchcock SR RC	.20	.50
17 Dave Mlicki	.02	.10
18 Jessie Hollins	.02	.10
19 Bobby Jones SR	.07	.20
20 Kurt Miller	.02	.10
21 Melvin Nieves SR	.02	.10
22 Billy Ashley SR	.02	.10
23 J.T. Snow SR RC	.30	.75
24 Chipper Jones SR	.20	.50
25 Tim Salmon SR	.10	.30
26 Tim Pugh SR RC	.05	.15
27 David Nied SR	.02	.10
28 Mike Trombley	.02	.10
29 Javier Lopez SR	.10	.30
30 Jim Abbott CH CL	.07	.20
31 Jim Abbott CH	.02	.10
32 Dale Murphy CH	.10	.30
33 Tony Pena CH	.02	.10
34 Kirby Puckett CH	.10	.30
35 Harold Reynolds CH	.02	.10
36 Cal Ripken CH	.30	.75
37 Nolan Ryan CH	.40	1.00
38 Ryne Sandberg CH	.20	.50
39 Dave Stewart CH	.02	.10
40 Dave Winfield CH	.02	.10
41 Joe Carter CL	.20	.50
Mark McGwire		
42 Joe Carter	.07	.20
Roberto Alomar		
43 Paul Molitor	.20	.50
Pat Listach		
Robin Yount		
44 Cal Ripken	.20	.50
Brady Anderson		
45 Albert Belle	.07	.20
Sandy Alomar Jr.		
Jim Thome		
Carlos Baerga		
Kenny Lofton		
46 Cecil Fielder	.02	.10
Mickey Tettleton		
47 Roberto Kelly	.25	.60
Don Mattingly		
48 Frank Viola	.20	.50
Roger Clemens		
49 Ruben Sierra	.20	.50
Mark McGwire		
50 Kent Hrbek	.10	.30
Kirby Puckett		
51 Robin Ventura	.10	.30
Frank Thomas		
52 Juan Gonzalez	.10	.30
Jose Canseco		
Ivan Rodriguez		
Rafael Palmeiro		
53 Mark Langston	.07	.20
Jim Abbott		
Chuck Finley		
54 Wally Joyner	.20	.50
Gregg Jefferies		
George Brett		
55 Kevin Mitchell	.20	.50
Ken Griffey Jr.		
Jay Buhner		
56 George Brett	.50	1.25
57 Scott Cooper	.02	.10
58 Mike Maddux	.02	.10
59 Rusty Meacham	.02	.10
60 Wil Cordero	.02	.10
61 Tim Teufel	.02	.10
62 Jeff Montgomery	.02	.10
63 Scott Livingstone	.02	.10
64 Doug Dascenzo	.02	.10
65 Bret Boone	.07	.20
66 Tim Wakefield	.20	.50
67 Curt Schilling	.07	.20
68 Frank Tanana	.02	.10
69 Len Dykstra	.07	.20
70 Derek Lilliquist	.02	.10
71 Anthony Young	.02	.10
72 Hipolito Pichardo	.02	.10
73 Rod Beck	.02	.10
74 Kent Hrbek	.07	.20
75 Tom Glavine	.10	.30
76 Kevin Brown	.07	.20
77 Chuck Finley	.07	.20
78 Bob Walk	.02	.10
79 Rheal Cormier UER (Born in New Brunswick, not British Columbia)	.02	.10
80 Rick Sutcliffe	.07	.20
81 Harold Baines	.07	.20
82 Lee Smith	.07	.20
83 Geno Petralli	.02	.10
84 Jose Oquendo	.02	.10
85 Mark Gubicza	.02	.10
86 Mickey Tettleton	.02	.10
87 Bobby Witt	.02	.10
88 Mark Lewis	.02	.10
89 Kevin Appier	.07	.20
90 Mike Stanton	.02	.10
91 Rafael Belliard	.02	.10
92 Kenny Rogers	.07	.20
93 Randy Velarde	.02	.10
94 Luis Sojo	.02	.10
95 Mark Leiter	.02	.10
96 Jody Reed	.02	.10
97 Pete Harnisch	.02	.10
98 Tom Candiotti	.02	.10
99 Mark Portugal	.02	.10
100 Dave Valle	.02	.10
101 Shawon Dunston	.02	.10
102 B.J. Surhoff	.07	.20
103 Jay Bell	.07	.20
104 Sid Bream	.02	.10
105 Frank Thomas CL	.10	.30
106 Mike Morgan	.02	.10
107 Bill Doran	.02	.10
108 Lance Blankenship	.02	.10
109 Mark Lemke	.02	.10
110 Brian Harper	.02	.10
111 Brady Anderson	.07	.20
112 Bip Roberts	.02	.10
113 Mitch Williams	.02	.10
114 Craig Biggio	.10	.30
115 Eddie Murray	.20	.50
116 Matt Nokes	.02	.10
117 Lance Parrish	.07	.20
118 Bill Swift	.02	.10
119 Jeff Innis	.02	.10
120 Mike LaValliere	.02	.10
121 Hal Morris	.02	.10
122 Walt Weiss	.02	.10
123 Ivan Rodriguez	.10	.30
124 Andy Van Slyke	.10	.30
125 Roberto Alomar	.10	.30
126 Robby Thompson	.02	.10
127 Sammy Sosa	.20	.50
128 Mark Langston	.02	.10
129 Jerry Browne	.02	.10
130 Chuck McElroy	.02	.10
131 Frank Viola	.07	.20
132 Leo Gomez	.02	.10
133 Ramon Martinez	.02	.10
134 Don Mattingly	.50	1.25
135 Roger Clemens	.40	1.00
136 Rickey Henderson	.20	.50
137 Darren Daulton	.07	.20
138 Ken Hill	.02	.10
139 Ozzie Guillen	.07	.20
140 Jerald Clark	.02	.10
141 Dave Fleming	.02	.10
142 Delino DeShields	.02	.10
143 Matt Williams	.07	.20
144 Larry Walker	.07	.20
145 Ruben Sierra	.07	.20
146 Ozzie Smith	.30	.75
147 Chris Sabo	.02	.10
148 Carlos Hernandez	.02	.10
149 Pat Borders	.02	.10
150 Orlando Merced	.02	.10
151 Royce Clayton	.02	.10
152 Kurt Stillwell	.02	.10
153 Dave Hollins	.02	.10
154 Mike Greenwell	.02	.10
155 Nolan Ryan	.75	2.00
156 Felix Jose	.02	.10
157 Junior Felix	.02	.10
158 Derek Bell	.02	.10
159 Steve Buechele	.02	.10
160 John Burkett	.02	.10
161 Pat Howell	.02	.10
162 Milt Cuyler	.02	.10
163 Terry Pendleton	.07	.20
164 Jack Morris	.07	.20
165 Tony Gwynn	.25	.60
166 Deion Sanders	.10	.30
167 Mike Devereaux	.02	.10
168 Ron Darling	.02	.10
169 Orel Hershiser	.07	.20
170 Mike Jackson	.02	.10
171 Doug Jones	.02	.10
172 Dan Walters	.02	.10
173 Darren Lewis	.02	.10
174 Carlos Baerga	.02	.10
175 Ryne Sandberg	.30	.75
176 Gregg Jefferies	.02	.10
177 John Jaha	.02	.10
178 Luis Polonia	.02	.10
179 Kirt Manwaring	.02	.10
180 Mike Magnante	.02	.10
181 Billy Ripken	.02	.10
182 Mike Moore	.02	.10
183 Eric Anthony	.02	.10
184 Lenny Harris	.02	.10
185 Tony Pena	.02	.10
186 Mike Felder	.02	.10
187 Greg Olson	.02	.10
188 Rene Gonzales	.02	.10
189 Mike Bordick	.02	.10
190 Mel Rojas	.02	.10
191 Todd Frohwirth	.02	.10
192 Darryl Hamilton	.02	.10
193 Mike Fetters	.02	.10
194 Omar Olivares	.02	.10
195 Tony Phillips	.02	.10
196 Paul Sorrento	.02	.10
197 Trevor Wilson	.02	.10
198 Kevin Gross	.02	.10
199 Ron Karkovice	.02	.10
200 Brook Jacoby	.02	.10
201 Mariano Duncan	.02	.10
202 Dennis Cook	.02	.10
203 Daryl Boston	.02	.10
204 Mike Perez	.02	.10
205 Manuel Lee	.02	.10
206 Steve Olin	.02	.10
207 Charlie Hough	.07	.20
208 Scott Scudder	.02	.10
209 Charlie O'Brien	.02	.10
210 Barry Bonds CL	.30	.75
211 Jose Vizcaino	.02	.10
212 Scott Leius	.02	.10
213 Kevin Mitchell	.02	.10
214 Brian Barnes	.02	.10
215 Pat Kelly	.02	.10
216 Chris Hammond	.02	.10
217 Rob Deer	.02	.10
218 Cory Snyder	.02	.10
219 Gary Carter	.07	.20
220 Danny Darwin	.02	.10
221 Tom Gordon	.02	.10
222 Gary Sheffield	.07	.20
223 Joe Carter	.07	.20
224 Jay Buhner	.07	.20
225 Jose Offerman	.02	.10
226 Jose Rijo	.02	.10
227 Mark Whiten	.02	.10
228 Randy Milligan	.02	.10
229 Bud Black	.02	.10
230 Gary DiSarcina	.02	.10
231 Steve Finley	.07	.20
232 Dennis Martinez	.07	.20
233 Mike Mussina	.10	.30
234 Joe Oliver	.02	.10
235 Chad Curtis	.02	.10
236 Shane Mack	.02	.10
237 Jaime Navarro	.02	.10
238 Brian McRae	.02	.10
239 Chili Davis	.07	.20
240 Jeff King	.02	.10
241 Dean Palmer	.07	.20
242 Danny Tartabull	.02	.10
243 Charles Nagy	.02	.10
244 Ray Lankford	.07	.20
245 Barry Larkin	.10	.30
246 Steve Avery	.02	.10
247 John Kruk	.07	.20
248 Derrick May	.02	.10
249 Stan Javier	.02	.10
250 Roger McDowell	.02	.10
251 Dan Gladden	.02	.10
252 Wally Joyner	.07	.20
253 Pat Listach	.02	.10
254 Chuck Knoblauch	.07	.20
255 Sandy Alomar Jr.	.02	.10
256 Jeff Bagwell	.10	.30
257 Andy Stankiewicz	.02	.10
258 Darrin Jackson	.02	.10
259 Brett Butler	.07	.20
260 Joe Orsulak	.02	.10
261 Andy Benes	.02	.10
262 Kenny Lofton	.07	.20
263 Robin Ventura	.07	.20
264 Ron Gant	.07	.20
265 Ellis Burks	.07	.20
266 Juan Guzman	.02	.10
267 Wes Chamberlain	.02	.10
268 John Smiley	.02	.10
269 Franklin Stubbs	.02	.10
270 Tom Browning	.02	.10
271 Dennis Eckersley	.07	.20
272 Carlton Fisk	.10	.30
273 Lou Whitaker	.07	.20
274 Phil Plantier	.02	.10
275 Bobby Bonilla	.07	.20
276 Ben McDonald	.02	.10
277 Bob Zupcic	.02	.10
278 Terry Steinbach	.02	.10
279 Terry Mulholland	.02	.10
280 Lance Johnson	.02	.10
281 Willie McGee	.07	.20
282 Bret Saberhagen	.07	.20
283 Randy Myers	.02	.10
284 Randy Tomlin	.02	.10
285 Mickey Morandini	.02	.10
286 Brian Williams	.02	.10
287 Tino Martinez	.10	.30
288 Jose Melendez	.02	.10
289 Jeff Huson	.02	.10
290 Joe Grahe	.02	.10
291 Mel Hall	.02	.10
292 Otis Nixon	.02	.10
293 Todd Hundley	.02	.10
294 Casey Candaele	.02	.10
295 Kevin Seitzer	.02	.10
296 Eddie Taubensee	.02	.10
297 Moises Alou	.07	.20
298 Scott Radinsky	.02	.10
299 Thomas Howard	.02	.10
300 Kyle Abbott	.02	.10
301 Omar Vizquel	.10	.30
302 Keith Miller	.02	.10
303 Rick Aguilera	.02	.10
304 Bruce Hurst	.02	.10
305 Ken Caminiti	.07	.20
306 Mike Pagliarulo	.02	.10
307 Frank Seminara	.02	.10
308 Andre Dawson	.07	.20
309 Jose Lind	.02	.10
310 Joe Boever	.02	.10
311 Jeff Parrett	.02	.10
312 Alan Mills	.02	.10
313 Kevin Tapani	.02	.10
314 Darryl Kile	.07	.20
315 Will Clark CL	.07	.20
316 Mike Sharperson	.02	.10
317 John Orton	.02	.10
318 Bob Tewksbury	.02	.10
319 Xavier Hernandez	.02	.10
320 Paul Assenmacher	.02	.10
321 John Franco	.07	.20
322 Mike Timlin	.02	.10
323 Jose Guzman	.02	.10
324 Pedro Martinez	.40	1.00
325 Bill Spiers	.02	.10
326 Melido Perez	.02	.10
327 Mike Macfarlane	.02	.10
328 Ricky Bones	.02	.10
329 Scott Bankhead	.02	.10
330 Rich Rodriguez	.02	.10
331 Geronimo Pena	.02	.10
332 Bernie Williams	.10	.30
333 Paul Molitor	.07	.20
334 Carlos Garcia	.02	.10
335 David Cone	.07	.20
336 Randy Johnson	.20	.50
337 Pat Mahomes	.02	.10
338 Erik Hanson	.02	.10
339 Duane Ward	.02	.10
340 Al Martin	.02	.10
341 Pedro Munoz	.02	.10
342 Greg Colbrunn	.02	.10
343 Julio Valera	.02	.10
344 John Olerud	.07	.20
345 George Bell	.02	.10
346 Devon White	.07	.20
347 Donovan Osborne	.02	.10
348 Mark Gardner	.02	.10
349 Zane Smith	.02	.10
350 Wilson Alvarez	.02	.10
351 Kevin Koslofski	.02	.10
352 Roberto Hernandez	.02	.10
353 Glenn Davis	.02	.10
354 Reggie Sanders	.07	.20
355 Ken Griffey Jr.	.30	.75
356 Marquis Grissom	.07	.20
357 Jack McDowell	.02	.10
358 Jimmy Key	.07	.20
359 Stan Belinda	.02	.10
360 Gerald Williams	.02	.10
361 Sid Fernandez	.02	.10
362 Alex Fernandez	.02	.10
363 John Smoltz	.10	.30
364 Travis Fryman	.07	.20
365 Jose Canseco	.10	.30
366 David Justice	.07	.20
367 Pedro Astacio	.02	.10
368 Tim Belcher	.02	.10
369 Steve Sax	.02	.10
370 Gary Gaetti	.07	.20
371 Jeff Frye	.02	.10
372 Bob Wickman	.02	.10
373 Ryan Thompson	.02	.10
374 David Hulse RC	.05	.15
375 Cal Eldred	.02	.10
376 Ryan Klesko	.07	.20
377 Damion Easley	.02	.10
378 John Kiely	.02	.10
379 Jim Bullinger	.02	.10
380 Brian Bohanon	.02	.10
381 Rod Brewer	.02	.10
382 Fernando Ramsey RC	.05	.15
383 Sam Militello	.02	.10
384 Arthur Rhodes	.02	.10
385 Eric Karros	.07	.20
386 Rico Brogna	.02	.10
387 John Valentin	.02	.10
388 Kerry Woodson	.02	.10
389 Ben Rivera	.02	.10
390 Matt Whiteside RC	.05	.15
391 Henry Rodriguez	.02	.10
392 John Wetteland	.07	.20
393 Kent Mercker	.02	.10
394 Bernard Gilkey	.02	.10
395 Doug Henry	.02	.10
396 Mo Vaughn	.07	.20
397 Scott Erickson	.02	.10
398 Bill Gullickson	.02	.10
399 Mark Guthrie	.02	.10
400 Dave Martinez	.02	.10
401 Jeff Kent	.20	.50
402 Chris Hoiles	.02	.10
403 Mike Henneman	.02	.10
404 Chris Nabholz	.02	.10
405 Tom Pagnozzi	.02	.10
406 Kelly Gruber	.02	.10
407 Bob Welch	.02	.10
408 Frank Castillo	.02	.10
409 John Dopson	.02	.10
410 Steve Farr	.02	.10
411 Henry Cotto	.02	.10
412 Bob Patterson	.02	.10
413 Todd Stottlemyre	.02	.10
414 Greg A. Harris	.02	.10
415 Denny Neagle	.07	.20
416 Bill Wegman	.02	.10
417 Willie Wilson	.02	.10
418 Terry Leach	.02	.10
419 Willie Randolph	.07	.20
420 Mark McGwire CL	.10	.30
421 Calvin Murray CL	.02	.10
422 Pete Janicki TP RC	.05	.15
423 Todd Jones TP	.07	.20
424 Mike Neill TP	.02	.10
425 Carlos Delgado TP	.20	.50
426 Jose Oliva TP	.02	.10
427 Tyrone Hill TP	.02	.10
428 Dmitri Young TP	.07	.20
429 Derek Wallace TP RC	.05	.15
430 Michael Moore TP RC	.05	.15
431 Cliff Floyd TP	.07	.20
432 Calvin Murray TP	.02	.10
433 Manny Ramirez TP	.30	.75
434 Marc Newfield TP	.02	.10
435 Charles Johnson TP	.07	.20
436 Butch Huskey TP	.02	.10
437 Brad Pennington TP	.02	.10
438 Ray McDavid TP RC	.05	.15
439 Chad McConnell TP	.02	.10
440 M.Cummings TP RC	.05	.15
441 Benji Gil TP	.02	.10
442 Frankie Rodriguez TP	.02	.10
443 Chad Mottola TP RC	.05	.15
444 John Burke TP RC	.05	.15
445 Michael Tucker TP	.02	.10
446 Rick Greene TP	.02	.10
447 Rich Becker TP	.02	.10
448 Mike Robertson TP	.02	.10
449 Derek Jeter TP RC	4.00	10.00
450 Ivan Rodriguez CL	.10	.30
David McCarty		
451 Jim Abbott IN	.07	.20
452 Jeff Bagwell IN	.07	.20
453 Jason Bere IN	.02	.10
454 Delino DeShields IN	.02	.10
455 Travis Fryman IN	.02	.10
456 Alex Gonzalez IN	.02	.10
457 Phil Hiatt IN	.02	.10
458 Dave Hollins IN	.02	.10
459 Chipper Jones IN	.10	.30
460 David Justice IN	.02	.10
461 Ray Lankford IN	.02	.10
462 David McCarty IN	.02	.10
463 Mike Mussina IN	.07	.20
464 Jose Offerman IN	.02	.10
465 Dean Palmer IN	.02	.10
466 Geronimo Pena IN	.02	.10
467 Eduardo Perez IN	.02	.10
468 Ivan Rodriguez IN	.07	.20
469 Reggie Sanders IN	.02	.10
470 Bernie Williams IN	.07	.20
471 Barry Bonds CL	.30	.75
Matt Williams		
Will Clark		
472 Greg Maddux	.20	.50
Steve Avery		
John Smoltz		
Tom Glavine		
473 Jose Rijo	.07	.20
Rob Dibble		
Roberto Kelly		
Reggie Sanders		
Barry Larkin		
474 Gary Sheffield	.07	.20
Phil Plantier		
Tony Gwynn		
Fred McGriff		
475 Doug Drabek	.07	.20
Craig Biggio		
Jeff Bagwell		
476 Will Clark	.30	.75
Barry Bonds		
Matt Williams		
477 Eric Davis	.07	.20
Darryl Strawberry		
478 Dante Bichette	.07	.20
David Nied		
Andres Galarraga		
479 Dave Magadan	.02	.10
Orestes Destrade		
Bret Barberie		
Jeff Conine		
480 Tim Wakefield	.07	.20
Andy Van Slyke		
Jay Bell		
481 Marquis Grissom	.10	.30
Delino DeShields		
Dennis Martinez		
Larry Walker		
482 Geronimo Pena	.20	.50
Ray Lankford		
Ozzie Smith		
Bernard Gilkey		
483 Randy Myers	.20	.50
Ryne Sandberg		
Mark Grace		
484 Eddie Murray	.10	.30
Howard Johnson		
Bobby Bonilla		
485 John Kruk	.02	.10
Dave Hollins		
Darren Daulton		
Len Dykstra		
486 Barry Bonds AW	.30	.75
487 Dennis Eckersley AW	.07	.20
488 Greg Maddux AW	.20	.50
489 Dennis Eckersley AW	.07	.20
490 Eric Karros AW	.02	.10
491 Pat Listach AW	.02	.10
492 Gary Sheffield AW	.02	.10

493 Mark McGwire AW .25 .60
494 Gary Sheffield AW .02 .10
495 Edgar Martinez AW .07 .20
496 Fred McGriff AW .07 .20
497 Juan Gonzalez AW .02 .10
498 Darren Daulton AW .02 .10
499 Cecil Fielder AW .02 .10
500 Brent Gates CL .02 .10
501 Tavo Alvarez DD .02 .10
502 Rod Bolton .02 .10
503 J.Cummings DD RC .05 .15
504 Brent Gates DD .02 .10
505 Tyler Green .02 .10
506 Jose Martinez DD RC .05 .15
507 Troy Percival .10 .30
508 Kevin Stocker DD .02 .10
509 Matt Walbeck DD RC .05 .15
510 Rondell White DD .07 .20
511 Billy Ripken .02 .10
512 Mike Moore .02 .10
513 Jose Lind .02 .10
514 Chito Martinez .02 .10
515 Jose Guzman .02 .10
516 Kim Batiste .02 .10
517 Jeff Tackett .02 .10
518 Charlie Hough .07 .20
519 Marvin Freeman .02 .10
520 Carlos Martinez .02 .10
521 Eric Young .02 .10
522 Pete Incaviglia .02 .10
523 Scott Fletcher .02 .10
524 Orestes Destrade .02 .10
525 Ken Griffey Jr. CL .20 .50
526 Ellis Burks .07 .20
527 Juan Samuel .02 .10
528 Dave Magadan .02 .10
529 Jeff Parrett .02 .10
530 Bill Krueger .02 .10
531 Frank Bolick .02 .10
532 Alan Trammell .07 .20
533 Walt Weiss .02 .10
534 David Cone .07 .20
535 Greg Maddux .30 .75
536 Kevin Young .07 .20
537 Dave Hansen .02 .10
538 Alex Cole .02 .10
539 Greg Hibbard .02 .10
540 Gene Larkin .02 .10
541 Jeff Reardon .07 .20
542 Felix Jose .02 .10
543 Jimmy Key .07 .20
544 Reggie Jefferson .02 .10
545 Gregg Jefferies .02 .10
546 Dave Stewart .07 .20
547 Tim Wallach .02 .10
548 Spike Owen .02 .10
549 Tommy Greene .02 .10
550 Fernando Valenzuela .07 .20
551 Rich Amaral .02 .10
552 Bret Barberie .02 .10
553 Edgar Martinez .10 .30
554 Jim Abbott .10 .30
555 Frank Thomas .20 .50
556 Wade Boggs .10 .30
557 Tom Henke .02 .10
558 Milt Thompson .02 .10
559 Lloyd McClendon .02 .10
560 Vinny Castilla .20 .50
561 Ricky Jordan .02 .10
562 Andujar Cedeno .02 .10
563 Greg Vaughn .02 .10
564 Cecil Fielder .07 .20
565 Kirby Puckett .20 .50
566 Mark McGwire .50 1.25
567 Barry Bonds .60 1.50
568 Jody Reed .02 .10
569 Todd Zeile .02 .10
570 Mark Carreon .02 .10
571 Joe Girardi .02 .10
572 Luis Gonzalez .07 .20
573 Mark Grace .10 .30
574 Rafael Palmeiro .10 .30
575 Darryl Strawberry .07 .20
576 Will Clark .10 .30
577 Fred McGriff .10 .30
578 Kevin Reimer .02 .10
579 Dave Righetti .07 .20
580 Juan Bell .02 .10
581 Jeff Brantley .02 .10
582 Brian Hunter .02 .10
583 Tim Naehring .02 .10
584 Glenallen Hill .02 .10
585 Cal Ripken .60 1.50
586 Albert Belle .07 .20
587 Robin Yount .30 .75
588 Chris Bosio .02 .10
589 Pete Smith .02 .10
590 Chuck Carr .02 .10
591 Jeff Blauser .02 .10
592 Kevin McReynolds .02 .10
593 Andres Galarraga .07 .20
594 Kevin Maas .02 .10
595 Eric Davis .07 .20
596 Brian Jordan .07 .20
597 Tim Raines .07 .20
598 Rick Wilkins .02 .10
599 Steve Cooke .02 .10
600 Mike Gallego .02 .10
601 Mike Munoz .02 .10
602 Luis Rivera .02 .10
603 Junior Ortiz .02 .10
604 Brent Mayne .02 .10
605 Luis Alicea .02 .10
606 Damon Berryhill .02 .10
607 Dave Henderson .02 .10
608 Kirk McCaskill .02 .10
609 Jeff Fassero .02 .10
610 Mike Harkey .02 .10
611 Francisco Cabrera .02 .10
612 Rey Sanchez .02 .10
613 Scott Servais .02 .10
614 Darrin Fletcher .02 .10
615 Felix Fermin .02 .10
616 Kevin Seitzer .02 .10
617 Bob Scanlan .02 .10
618 Billy Hatcher .02 .10
619 John Vander Wal .02 .10
620 Joe Hesketh .02 .10
621 Hector Villanueva .02 .10
622 Randy Milligan .02 .10
623 Tony Tarasco RC .05 .15
624 Russ Swan .02 .10
625 Willie Wilson .02 .10
626 Frank Tanana .02 .10
627 Pete O'Brien .02 .10
628 Lenny Webster .02 .10
629 Mark Clark .02 .10
630 Roger Clemens CL .20 .50
631 Alex Arias .02 .10
632 Chris Gwynn .02 .10
633 Tom Bolton .02 .10
634 Greg Briley .02 .10
635 Kent Bottenfield .02 .10
636 Kelly Downs .02 .10
637 Manuel Lee .02 .10
638 Al Leiter .07 .20
639 Jeff Gardner .02 .10
640 Mike Gardiner .02 .10
641 Mark Gardner .02 .10
642 Jeff Branson .02 .10
643 Paul Wagner .02 .10
644 Sean Berry .02 .10
645 Phil Hiatt .02 .10
646 Kevin Mitchell .02 .10
647 Charlie Hayes .02 .10
648 Jim Deshaies .02 .10
649 Dan Pasqua .02 .10
650 Mike Maddux .02 .10
651 Domingo Martinez RC .05 .15
652 Greg McMichael RC .05 .15
653 Eric Wedge RC .20 .50
654 Mark Whiten .02 .10
655 Roberto Kelly .02 .10
656 Julio Franco .07 .20
657 Gene Harris .02 .10
658 Pete Schourek .02 .10
659 Mike Bielecki .02 .10
660 Ricky Gutierrez .02 .10
661 Chris Hammond .02 .10
662 Tim Scott .02 .10
663 Norm Charlton .02 .10
664 Doug Drabek .02 .10
665 Dwight Gooden .07 .20
666 Jim Gott .02 .10
667 Randy Myers .02 .10
668 Darren Holmes .02 .10
669 Tim Spehr .02 .10
670 Bruce Ruffin .02 .10
671 Bobby Thigpen .02 .10
672 Tony Fernandez .02 .10
673 Darrin Jackson .02 .10
674 Gregg Olson .02 .10
675 Rob Dibble .07 .20
676 Howard Johnson .02 .10
677 Mike Lansing RC .20 .50
678 Charlie Leibrandt .02 .10
679 Kevin Bass .02 .10
680 Hubie Brooks .02 .10
681 Scott Brosius .07 .20
682 Randy Knorr .02 .10
683 Dante Bichette .07 .20
684 Bryan Harvey .02 .10
685 Greg Gohr .02 .10
686 Willie Banks .02 .10
687 Robb Nen .07 .20
688 Mike Scioscia .02 .10
689 John Farrell .02 .10
690 John Candelaria .02 .10
691 Damon Buford .02 .10
692 Todd Worrell .02 .10
693 Pat Hentgen .02 .10
694 John Smiley .02 .10
695 Greg Swindell .02 .10
696 Derek Bell .02 .10
697 Terry Jorgensen .02 .10
698 Jimmy Jones .02 .10
699 David Wells .07 .20
700 Dave Martinez .02 .10
701 Steve Bedrosian .02 .10
702 Jeff Russell .02 .10
703 Joe Magrane .02 .10
704 Matt Mieske .02 .10
705 Paul Molitor .07 .20
706 Dale Murphy .10 .30
707 Steve Howe .02 .10
708 Greg Gagne .02 .10
709 Dave Eiland .02 .10
710 David West .02 .10
711 Luis Aquino .02 .10
712 Joe Orsulak .02 .10
713 Eric Plunk .02 .10
714 Mike Felder .02 .10
715 Joe Klink .02 .10
716 Lonnie Smith .02 .10
717 Monty Fariss .02 .10
718 Craig Lefferts .02 .10
719 John Habyan .02 .10
720 Willie Blair .02 .10
721 Darnell Coles .02 .10
722 Mark Williamson .02 .10
723 Bryn Smith .02 .10
724 Greg W. Harris .02 .10
725 Graeme Lloyd RC .20 .50
726 Cris Carpenter .02 .10
727 Chico Walker .02 .10
728 Tracy Woodson .02 .10
729 Jose Uribe .02 .10
730 Stan Javier .02 .10
731 Jay Howell .02 .10
732 Freddie Benavides .02 .10
733 Jeff Reboulet .02 .10
734 Scott Sanderson .02 .10
735 Ryne Sandberg CL .20 .50
736 Archi Cianfrocco .02 .10
737 Daryl Boston .02 .10
738 Craig Grebeck .02 .10
739 Doug Dascenzo .02 .10
740 Gerald Young .02 .10
741 Candy Maldonado .02 .10
742 Joey Cora .02 .10
743 Don Slaught .02 .10
744 Steve Decker .02 .10
745 Blas Minor .02 .10
746 Storm Davis .02 .10
747 Carlos Quintana .02 .10
748 Vince Coleman .02 .10
749 Todd Burns .02 .10
750 Steve Frey .02 .10
751 Ivan Calderon .02 .10
752 Steve Reed RC .05 .15
753 Danny Jackson .02 .10
754 Jeff Conine .07 .20
755 Juan Gonzalez .07 .20
756 Mike Kelly .02 .10
757 John Doherty .02 .10
758 Jack Armstrong .02 .10
759 John Wehner .02 .10
760 Scott Bankhead .02 .10
761 Jim Tatum .02 .10
762 Scott Pose RC .05 .15
763 Andy Ashby .02 .10
764 Ed Sprague .02 .10
765 Harold Baines .07 .20
766 Kirk Gibson .07 .20
767 Troy Neel .02 .10
768 Dick Schofield .02 .10
769 Dickie Thon .02 .10
770 Butch Henry .02 .10
771 Junior Felix .02 .10
772 Ken Ryan RC .05 .15
773 Trevor Hoffman .20 .50
774 Phil Plantier .02 .10
775 Bo Jackson .20 .50
776 Benito Santiago .07 .20
777 Andre Dawson .07 .20
778 Bryan Hickerson .02 .10
779 Dennis Moeller .02 .10
780 Ryan Bowen .02 .10
781 Eric Fox .02 .10
782 Joe Kmak .02 .10
783 Mike Hampton .07 .20
784 Darrell Sherman RC .05 .15
785 J.T. Snow .10 .30
786 Dave Winfield .07 .20
787 Jim Austin .02 .10
788 Craig Shipley .02 .10
789 Greg Myers .02 .10
790 Todd Benzinger .02 .10
791 Cory Snyder .02 .10
792 David Segui .02 .10
793 Armando Reynoso .02 .10
794 Chili Davis .07 .20
795 Dave Nilsson .02 .10
796 Paul O'Neill .10 .30
797 Jerald Clark .02 .10
798 Jose Mesa .02 .10
799 Brain Holman .02 .10
800 Jim Eisenreich .02 .10
801 Mark McLemore .02 .10
802 Luis Sojo .02 .10
803 Harold Reynolds .07 .20
804 Dan Plesac .02 .10
805 Dave Stieb .02 .10
806 Tom Brunansky .07 .20
807 Kelly Gruber .02 .10
808 Bob Ojeda .02 .10
809 Dave Burba .02 .10
810 Joe Boever .02 .10
811 Jeremy Hernandez .02 .10
812 Tim Salmon TC .07 .20
813 Jeff Bagwell TC .07 .20
814 Dennis Eckersley TC .07 .20
815 Roberto Alomar TC .07 .20
816 Steve Avery TC .02 .10
817 Pat Listach TC .02 .10
818 Gregg Jefferies TC .07 .20
819 Sammy Sosa TC .20 .50
820 Darryl Strawberry TC .02 .10
821 Dennis Martinez TC .02 .10
822 Robby Thompson TC .02 .10
823 Albert Belle TC .07 .20
824 Randy Johnson TC .10 .30
825 Nigel Wilson TC .02 .10
826 Bobby Bonilla TC .02 .10
827 Glenn Davis TC .02 .10
828 Gary Sheffield TC .02 .10
829 Darren Daulton TC .02 .10
830 Jay Bell TC .02 .10
831 Juan Gonzalez TC .02 .10
832 Andre Dawson TC .02 .10
833 Hal Morris TC .02 .10
834 David Nied TC .02 .10
835 Felix Jose TC .02 .10
836 Travis Fryman TC .02 .10
837 Shane Mack TC .02 .10
838 Robin Ventura TC .02 .10
839 Danny Tartabull TC .02 .10
840 Roberto Alomar CL .07 .20
SP5 George Brett .40 1.00
Robin Yount
SP6 Nolan Ryan .75 2.00

1993 Upper Deck Gold Hologram

These gold parallel cards were made available exclusively in factory set form. One set in every 15 ct. case of factory sets featured cards with gold foil holograms on the card backs, rather than the traditional silver foil holograms. The factory boxes for the basic sets and the much scarcer Gold Hologram sets are identical, thus all Gold Hologram sets offered for sale are for opened factory sets. Please refer to the multipliers provided below for values on single cards.

COMP.FACT.SET (840) 75.00 150.00
*STARS: 3X TO 8X BASIC CARDS
*ROOKIES: 3X TO 8X BASIC CARDS

1993 Upper Deck Clutch Performers

These 20 standard-size cards were inserted one every nine series II retail foil packs, as well as inserted one per series II retail jumbo packs. The cards are numbered on the back with an "R" prefix and appear in alphabetical order. These 20 cards represent Reggie Jackson's selection of players who have come through under pressure. Please note these cards are condition sensitive and trade for premium values if found in Mint.

COMPLETE SET (20) 8.00 20.00
R1 Roberto Alomar .30 .75
R2 Wade Boggs .30 .75
R3 Barry Bonds 1.50 4.00
R4 Jose Canseco .30 .75
R5 Joe Carter .20 .50
R6 Will Clark .30 .75
R7 Roger Clemens 1.00 2.50
R8 Dennis Eckersley .20 .50
R9 Cecil Fielder .20 .50
R10 Juan Gonzalez .20 .50
R11 Ken Griffey Jr. .75 2.00
R12 Rickey Henderson .50 1.25
R13 Barry Larkin .30 .75
R14 Don Mattingly 1.25 3.00
R15 Fred McGriff .30 .75
R16 Terry Pendleton .20 .50
R17 Kirby Puckett .50 1.25
R18 Ryne Sandberg .75 2.00
R19 John Smoltz .30 .75
R20 Frank Thomas .50 1.25

1993 Upper Deck Fifth Anniversary

This 15-card standard-size set celebrates Upper Deck's five years in the sports card business. The cards are essentially reprinted versions of some of Upper Deck's most popular cards in the last five years. These cards were inserted one every nine second series hobby packs. The black-bordered fronts feature player photos that previously appeared on an Upper Deck card. The cards are numbered on the back with an "A" prefix. These cards are condition sensitive and trade for premium values in Mint.

COMPLETE SET (15) 6.00 15.00
A1 Ken Griffey Jr. .75 2.00
A2 Gary Sheffield .20 .50
A3 Roberto Alomar .30 .75
A4 Jim Abbott .30 .75
A5 Nolan Ryan 2.00 5.00
A6 Juan Gonzalez .20 .50
A7 David Justice .20 .50
A8 Carlos Baerga .08 .25
A9 Reggie Jackson .30 .75
A10 Eric Karros .20 .50
A11 Chipper Jones .50 1.25
A12 Ivan Rodriguez .30 .75
A13 Pat Listach .08 .25
A14 Frank Thomas .50 1.25
A15 Tim Salmon .30 .75

1993 Upper Deck Future Heroes

Inserted in second series foil packs at a rate of one every nine pack; this set continues the Heroes insert set begun in the 1990 Upper Deck high-number set, this ten-card standard-size set features eight different "Future Heroes" along with a checklist and header card.

COMPLETE SET (10) 5.00 12.00
55 Roberto Alomar .30 .75
56 Barry Bonds 1.50 4.00
57 Roger Clemens 1.00 2.50
58 Juan Gonzalez .20 .50
59 Ken Griffey Jr. .75 2.00
60 Mark McGwire 1.25 3.00
61 Kirby Puckett .50 1.25
62 Frank Thomas .50 1.25
63 Checklist .20 .50
NNO Header Card SP .08 .25

1993 Upper Deck Home Run Heroes

This 28-card standard-size set features the home run leader from each Major League team. Each 1993 first series 27-card jumbo pack contained one of these cards. The cards are numbered on the back with an "HR" prefix and the set is arranged in descending order according to the number of home runs.

COMPLETE SET (28) 6.00 15.00
HR1 Juan Gonzalez .20 .50
HR2 Mark McGwire 1.25 3.00
HR3 Cecil Fielder .20 .50
HR4 Fred McGriff .30 .75
HR5 Albert Belle .20 .50
HR6 Barry Bonds 1.50 4.00
HR7 Joe Carter .20 .50
HR8 Darren Daulton .20 .50
HR9 Ken Griffey Jr. .75 2.00
HR10 Dave Hollins .08 .25
HR11 Ryne Sandberg .75 2.00
HR12 George Bell .08 .25
HR13 Danny Tartabull .08 .25
HR14 Mike Devereaux .08 .25
HR15 Greg Vaughn .08 .25
HR16 Larry Walker .20 .50
HR17 David Justice .20 .50
HR18 Terry Pendleton .20 .50
HR19 Eric Karros .20 .50
HR20 Ray Lankford .20 .50
HR21 Matt Williams .20 .50
HR22 Eric Anthony .08 .25
HR23 Bobby Bonilla .20 .50
HR24 Kirby Puckett .50 1.25
HR25 Mike Macfarlane .08 .25
HR26 Tom Brunansky .08 .25
HR27 Paul O'Neill .30 .75
HR28 Gary Gaetti .20 .50

1993 Upper Deck Iooss Collection

This 27-card standard-size set spotlights the work of famous sports photographer Walter Iooss Jr. by presenting 26 of the game's current greats in a candid photo set. The cards were inserted in series I retail foil packs at a rate of one every nine packs. They were also in retail jumbo packs at a rate of one in five packs. The cards are numbered on the back with a "WI" prefix. Please note these cards are condition sensitive and trade for premium values in Mint.

COMPLETE SET (27) 12.50 30.00
*JUMBO CARDS: 2X TO 5X BASIC IOOSS
JUMBOS DISTRIBUTED IN RETAIL PACKS
WI1 Tim Salmon .40 1.00
WI2 Jeff Bagwell .40 1.00
WI3 Mark McGwire 1.50 4.00
WI4 Roberto Alomar .40 1.00
WI5 Steve Avery .10 .30
WI6 Paul Molitor .25 .60
WI7 Ozzie Smith 1.00 2.50
WI8 Mark Grace .40 1.00
WI9 Eric Karros .25 .60
WI10 Delino DeShields .10 .30
WI11 Will Clark .40 1.00
WI12 Albert Belle .25 .60
WI13 Ken Griffey Jr. 1.00 2.50
WI14 Howard Johnson .10 .30
WI15 Cal Ripken Jr. 2.00 5.00
WI16 Fred McGriff .40 1.00
WI17 Darren Daulton .25 .60
WI18 Andy Van Slyke .40 1.00
WI19 Nolan Ryan 2.50 6.00
WI20 Wade Boggs .40 1.00
WI21 Barry Larkin .40 1.00
WI22 George Brett 1.50 4.00
WI23 Cecil Fielder .25 .60
WI24 Kirby Puckett .60 1.50
WI25 Frank Thomas .60 1.50
WI26 Don Mattingly 1.50 4.00
NNO Title Card .10 .30
Iooss Header

1993 Upper Deck Mays Heroes

This standard-size ten-card set was randomly inserted in 1993 Upper Deck first series foil packs. The fronts feature color photos of Mays at various stages of his career that are partially contained within a black bordered circle. The cards are numbered in continuation of Upper Deck's Heroes series.

COMPLETE SET (10) 1.50 3.00
COMMON (46-54/HDR) .20 .50

1993 Upper Deck On Deck

Inserted one per series II jumbo packs, these 25 standard-size cards profile baseball's top players. The cards are numbered on the back with a "D" prefix in alphabetical order by name.

COMPLETE SET (25) 8.00 20.00
D1 Jim Abbott .30 .75
D2 Roberto Alomar .30 .75
D3 Carlos Baerga .08 .25
D4 Albert Belle .20 .50
D5 Wade Boggs .30 .75
D6 George Brett 1.25 3.00
D7 Jose Canseco .30 .75
D8 Will Clark .30 .75
D9 Roger Clemens 1.00 2.50
D10 Dennis Eckersley .20 .50
D11 Cecil Fielder .20 .50
D12 Juan Gonzalez .20 .50
D13 Ken Griffey Jr. .75 2.00
D14 Tony Gwynn .60 1.50
D15 Bo Jackson .50 1.25
D16 Chipper Jones .50 1.25
D17 Eric Karros .20 .50
D18 Mark McGwire 1.25 3.00
D19 Kirby Puckett .50 1.25
D20 Nolan Ryan 2.00 5.00
D21 Tim Salmon .30 .75
D22 Ryne Sandberg .75 2.00
D23 Darryl Strawberry .20 .50
D24 Frank Thomas .50 1.25
D25 Andy Van Slyke .30 .75

1993 Upper Deck Season Highlights

This 20-card standard-size insert set captures great moments of the 1992 Major League Baseball season. The cards were exclusively distributed in specially marked cases that were available only at Upper Deck Heroes of Baseball Card Shows and through the purchase of a specified quantity of second series cases. In these packs, the cards were inserted at a rate of one every nine. The cards are numbered on the back with an "HI" prefix in alphabetical order by player's name.

COMPLETE SET (20) 50.00 120.00
HI1 Roberto Alomar 2.00 5.00
HI2 Steve Avery .60 1.50
HI3 Harold Baines 1.25 3.00
HI4 Damon Berryhill .60 1.50
HI5 Barry Bonds 10.00 25.00
HI6 Bret Boone 1.25 3.00
HI7 George Brett 8.00 20.00
HI8 Francisco Cabrera .60 1.50
HI9 Ken Griffey Jr. 5.00 12.00
HI10 Rickey Henderson 3.00 8.00
HI11 Kenny Lofton 1.25 3.00
HI12 Mickey Morandini .60 1.50
HI13 Eddie Murray 3.00 8.00
HI14 David Nied .60 1.50
HI15 Jeff Reardon 1.25 3.00
HI16 Bip Roberts .60 1.50
HI17 Nolan Ryan 12.50 30.00
HI18 Ed Sprague .60 1.50
HI19 Dave Winfield 1.25 3.00
HI20 Robin Yount 5.00 12.00

1993 Upper Deck Then And Now

This 18-card, standard-size hologram set highlights veteran stars in their rookie year and today, reflecting on how they and the game have changed. Cards 1-9 were randomly inserted in series I foil packs; cards 10-18 were randomly inserted in series II foil packs. In either series, the cards were inserted one every 27 packs. The nine lithogram cards in the second series feature one card each of Hall of Famers Reggie Jackson, Mickey Mantle, and Willie Mays, as well as six active players. The cards are numbered on the back with a "TN" prefix and arranged alphabetically within subgroup according to player's last name.

COMPLETE SET (18) 15.00 40.00
COMPLETE SERIES 1 (9) 6.00 15.00
COMPLETE SERIES 2 (9) 10.00 25.00
TN1 Wade Boggs .50 1.25
TN2 George Brett 2.00 5.00
TN3 Rickey Henderson .75 2.00
TN4 Cal Ripken 2.50 6.00
TN5 Nolan Ryan 3.00 8.00
TN6 Ryne Sandberg 1.25 3.00
TN7 Ozzie Smith 1.25 3.00
TN8 Darryl Strawberry .30 .75
TN9 Dave Winfield .30 .75
TN10 Dennis Eckersley .30 .75
TN11 Tony Gwynn 1.00 2.50
TN12 Howard Johnson .15 .40
TN13 Don Mattingly 2.00 5.00
TN14 Eddie Murray .75 2.00
TN15 Robin Yount 1.25 3.00
TN16 Reggie Jackson 1.00 2.50
TN17 Mickey Mantle 5.00 12.00
TN18 Willie Mays 2.50 6.00

1993 Upper Deck Triple Crown

This ten-card, standard-size insert set highlights ten players who were selected by Upper Deck as having

the best shot at winning Major League Baseball's Triple Crown. The cards were randomly inserted in series I hobby foil packs at a rate of one in 15. The cards are numbered on the back with a "TC" prefix and arranged alphabetically by player's last name.

COMPLETE SET (10) 5.00 12.00
TC1 Barry Bonds 1.50 4.00
TC2 Jose Canseco .30 .75
TC3 Will Clark .30 .75
TC4 Ken Griffey Jr. .75 2.00
TC5 Fred McGriff .30 .75
TC6 Kirby Puckett .50 1.25
TC7 Cal Ripken Jr. 1.50 4.00
TC8 Gary Sheffield .20 .50
TC9 Frank Thomas .50 1.25
TC10 Larry Walker .20 .50

1994 Upper Deck

The 1994 Upper Deck set was issued in two series of 280 and 270 standard-size cards for a total of 550. There are number of topical subsets including Star Rookies (1-30), Fantasy Team (31-40), The Future is Now (41-55), Home Field Advantage (267-294), Upper Deck Classic Alumni (295-299), Diamond Debuts (511-522) and Top Prospects (523-550). Three autograph cards were randomly inserted into first series retail packs. They are Ken Griffey Jr. (KG), Mickey Mantle (MM) and a combo card with Griffey and Mantle (GM). Though they lack serial-numbering, all three cards have an announced print run of 1,000 copies per. An Alex Rodriguez (298A) autograph card was randomly inserted into second series retail packs but production quantities were never divulged by the manufacturer. Rookie Cards include Michael Jordan (as an baseball player), Chan Ho Park, Alex Rodriguez and Billy Wagner. Many cards have been found with a significant variation on the back. The player's name, the horizontal bar containing the biographical information and the vertical bar containing the stats header are normally printed in copper-gold color. On the variation cards, these areas are printed in silver. It is not known exactly how many of the 550 cards have silver versions, nor has any premium been established for them. Also, all of the American League Home Field Advantage subset cards (numbers 281-294) are minor uncorrected errors because the Upper Deck logos on the front are missing the year "1994".

COMPLETE SET (550) 15.00 40.00
COMP. SERIES 1 (280) 12.50 25.00
COMP. SERIES 2 (270) 7.50 15.00
1 Brian Anderson RC .15 .40
2 Shane Andrews .05 .15
3 James Baldwin .05 .15
4 Rich Becker .05 .15
5 Greg Blosser .05 .15
6 Ricky Bottalico RC .05 .15
7 Midre Cummings .05 .15
8 Carlos Delgado .20 .50
9 Steve Dreyer RC .05 .15
10 Joey Eischen .05 .15
11 Carl Everett .10 .30
12 Cliff Floyd UER .10 .30
(text indicates he throws left; should be right)
13 Alex Gonzalez .05 .15
14 Jeff Granger .05 .15
15 Shawn Green .30 .75
16 Brian L. Hunter .05 .15
17 Butch Huskey .05 .15
18 Mark Hutton .05 .15
19 Michael Jordan RC 3.00 8.00
20 Steve Karsay .05 .15
21 Jeff McNeely .05 .15
22 Marc Newfield .05 .15
23 Manny Ramirez .30 .75
24 Alex Rodriguez RC 10.00 25.00
25 Scott Ruffcorn UER .05 .15
(photo on back is Robert Ellis)
26 Paul Spoljaric UER .05 .15
(Expos logo on back)
27 Salomon Torres .05 .15
28 Steve Trachsel .05 .15
29 Chris Turner .05 .15
30 Gabe White .05 .15
31 Randy Johnson FT .20 .50
32 John Wetteland FT .05 .15
33 Mike Piazza FT .30 .75
34 Rafael Palmeiro FT .10 .30
35 Roberto Alomar FT .10 .30
36 Matt Williams FT .05 .15
37 Travis Fryman FT .05 .15
38 Barry Bonds FT .40 1.00
39 Marquis Grissom FT .05 .15
40 Albert Belle FT .10 .30
41 Steve Avery FUT .05 .15
42 Jason Bere FUT .05 .15
43 Alex Fernandez FUT .05 .15
44 Mike Mussina FUT .10 .30
45 Aaron Sele FUT .05 .15
46 Rod Beck FUT .05 .15
47 Mike Piazza FUT .30 .75
48 John Olerud FUT .05 .15
49 Carlos Baerga FUT .05 .15
50 Gary Sheffield FUT .05 .15
51 Travis Fryman FUT .05 .15
52 Juan Gonzalez FUT .05 .15
53 Ken Griffey Jr. FUT .30 .75
54 Tim Salmon FUT .10 .30
55 Frank Thomas FUT .20 .50
56 Tony Phillips .05 .15
57 Julio Franco .10 .30
58 Kevin Mitchell .05 .15
59 Raul Mondesi .10 .30
60 Rickey Henderson .30 .75
61 Jay Buhner .10 .30
62 Bill Swift .05 .15
63 Brady Anderson .10 .30
64 Ryan Klesko .10 .30
65 Darren Daulton .10 .30
66 Damion Easley .05 .15
67 Mark McGwire .75 2.00
68 John Roper .05 .15
69 Dave Telgheder .05 .15
70 David Nied .05 .15
71 Mo Vaughn .10 .30
72 Tyler Green .05 .15
73 Dave Magadan .05 .15
74 Chili Davis .10 .30
75 Archi Cianfrocco .05 .15
76 Joe Girardi .05 .15
77 Chris Hoiles .05 .15
78 Ryan Bowen .05 .15
79 Greg Gagne .05 .15
80 Aaron Sele .05 .15
81 Dave Winfield .10 .30
82 Chad Curtis .05 .15
83 Andy Van Slyke .20 .50
84 Kevin Stocker .05 .15
85 Deion Sanders .20 .50
86 Bernie Williams .20 .50
87 John Smoltz .20 .50
88 Ruben Santana .05 .15
89 Dave Stewart .10 .30
90 Don Mattingly .75 2.00
91 Joe Carter .10 .30
92 Ryne Sandberg .50 1.25
93 Chris Gomez .05 .15
94 Tino Martinez .20 .50
95 Terry Pendleton .10 .30
96 Andre Dawson .10 .30
97 Wil Cordero .05 .15
98 Kent Hrbek .10 .30
99 John Olerud .10 .30
100 Kirt Manwaring .05 .15
101 Tim Bogar .05 .15
102 Mike Mussina .20 .50
103 Nigel Wilson .05 .15
104 Ricky Gutierrez .05 .15
105 Roberto Mejia .05 .15
106 Tom Pagnozzi .05 .15
107 Mike Macfarlane .05 .15
108 Jose Bautista .05 .15
109 Luis Ortiz .05 .15
110 Brent Gates .05 .15
111 Tim Salmon .20 .50
112 Wade Boggs .20 .50
113 Tripp Cromer .05 .15
114 Denny Hocking .05 .15
115 Carlos Baerga .05 .15
116 J.R. Phillips .05 .15
117 Bo Jackson .30 .75
118 Lance Johnson .05 .15
119 Bobby Jones .05 .15
120 Bobby Witt .05 .15
121 Ron Karkovice .05 .15
122 Jose Vizcaino .05 .15
123 Danny Darwin .05 .15
124 Eduardo Perez .05 .15
125 Brian Looney RC .05 .15
126 Pat Hentgen .05 .15
127 Frank Viola .10 .30
128 Darren Holmes .05 .15
129 Wally Whitehurst .05 .15
130 Matt Walbeck .05 .15
131 Albert Belle .10 .30
132 Steve Cooke .05 .15
133 Kevin Appier .10 .30
134 Joe Oliver .05 .15
135 Benji Gil .05 .15
136 Steve Buechele .05 .15
137 Devon White .10 .30
138 S.Hitchcock UER .05 .15
two losses for career; should be four
139 Phil Leftwich RC .05 .15
140 Jose Canseco .20 .50
141 Rick Aguilera .05 .15
142 Rod Beck .05 .15
143 Jose Rijo .05 .15
144 Tom Glavine .20 .50
145 Phil Plantier .05 .15
146 Jason Bere .05 .15
147 Jamie Moyer .10 .30
148 Wes Chamberlain .05 .15
149 Glenallen Hill .05 .15
150 Mark Whiten .05 .15
151 Bret Barberie .05 .15
152 Chuck Knoblauch .10 .30
153 Trevor Hoffman .20 .50
154 Rick Wilkins .05 .15
155 Juan Gonzalez .10 .30
156 Ozzie Guillen .10 .30
157 Jim Eisenreich .05 .15
158 Pedro Astacio .05 .15
159 Joe Magrane .05 .15
160 Ryan Thompson .05 .15
161 Jose Lind .05 .15
162 Jeff Conine .10 .30
163 Todd Benzinger .05 .15
164 Roger Salkeld .05 .15
165 Gary DiSarcina .05 .15
166 Kevin Gross .05 .15
167 Charlie Hayes .05 .15
168 Tim Costo .05 .15
169 Wally Joyner .10 .30
170 Johnny Ruffin .05 .15
171 Kirk Rueter .05 .15
172 Lenny Dykstra .10 .30
173 Ken Hill .05 .15
174 Mike Bordick .05 .15
175 Billy Hall .05 .15
176 Rob Butler .05 .15
177 Jay Bell .10 .30
178 Jeff Kent .20 .50
179 David Wells .10 .30
180 Dean Palmer .10 .30
181 Mariano Duncan .05 .15
182 Orlando Merced .05 .15
183 Brett Butler .10 .30
184 Milt Thompson .05 .15
185 Chipper Jones .30 .75
186 Paul O'Neill .20 .50
187 Mike Greenwell .05 .15
188 Harold Baines .10 .30
189 Todd Stottlemyre .05 .15
190 Jeromy Burnitz .10 .30
191 Rene Arocha .05 .15
192 Jeff Fassero .05 .15
193 Robby Thompson .05 .15
194 Greg W. Harris .05 .15
195 Todd Van Poppel .05 .15
196 Jose Guzman .05 .15
197 Shane Mack .05 .15
198 Carlos Garcia .05 .15
199 Kevin Roberson .05 .15
200 David McCarty .05 .15
201 Alan Trammell .10 .30
202 Chuck Carr .05 .15
203 Tommy Greene .05 .15
204 Wilson Alvarez .05 .15
205 Dwight Gooden .10 .30
206 Tony Tarasco .05 .15
207 Darren Lewis .05 .15
208 Eric Karros .10 .30
209 Chris Hammond .05 .15
210 Jeffrey Hammonds .05 .15
211 Rich Amaral .05 .15
212 Danny Tartabull .05 .15
213 Jeff Russell .05 .15
214 Dave Staton .05 .15
215 Kenny Lofton .10 .30
216 Manuel Lee .05 .15
217 Brian Koelling .05 .15
218 Scott Lydy .05 .15
219 Tony Gwynn .40 1.00
220 Cecil Fielder .10 .30
221 Royce Clayton .05 .15
222 Reggie Sanders .10 .30
223 Brian Jordan .10 .30
224 Ken Griffey Jr. .50 1.25
225 Fred McGriff .20 .50
226 Felix Jose .05 .15
227 Brad Pennington .05 .15
228 Chris Bosio .05 .15
229 Mike Stanley .05 .15
230 Willie Greene .05 .15
231 Alex Fernandez .05 .15
232 Brad Ausmus .20 .50
233 Darrell Whitmore .05 .15
234 Marcus Moore .05 .15
235 Allen Watson .05 .15
236 Jose Offerman .05 .15
237 Rondell White .10 .30
238 Jeff King .05 .15
239 Luis Alicea .05 .15
240 Dan Wilson .05 .15
241 Ed Sprague .05 .15
242 Todd Hundley .05 .15
243 Al Martin .05 .15
244 Mike Lansing .05 .15
245 Ivan Rodriguez .20 .50
246 Dave Fleming .05 .15
247 John Doherty .05 .15
248 Mark McLemore .05 .15
249 Bob Hamelin .05 .15
250 Curtis Pride RC .15 .40
251 Zane Smith .05 .15
252 Eric Young .05 .15
253 Brian McRae .05 .15
254 Tim Raines .10 .30
255 Javier Lopez .10 .30
256 Melvin Nieves .05 .15
257 Randy Myers .05 .15
258 Willie McGee .10 .30
259 Jimmy Key UER .10 .30
(birthdate missing on back)
260 Tom Candiotti .05 .15
261 Eric Davis .10 .30
262 Craig Paquette .05 .15
263 Robin Ventura .10 .30
264 Pat Kelly .05 .15
265 Gregg Jefferies .05 .15
266 Cory Snyder .05 .15
267 David Justice HFA .05 .15
268 Sammy Sosa HFA .30 .75
269 Barry Larkin HFA .10 .30
270 Andres Galarraga HFA .05 .15
271 Gary Sheffield HFA .05 .15
272 Jeff Bagwell HFA .10 .30
273 Mike Piazza HFA .30 .75
274 Larry Walker HFA .05 .15
275 Bobby Bonilla HFA .05 .15
276 John Kruk HFA .05 .15
277 Jay Bell HFA .05 .15
278 Ozzie Smith HFA .30 .75
279 Tony Gwynn HFA .30 .75
280 Barry Bonds HFA .40 1.00
281 Cal Ripken Jr. HFA .50 1.25
282 Mo Vaughn HFA .05 .15
283 Tim Salmon HFA .10 .30
284 Frank Thomas HFA .20 .50
285 Albert Belle HFA .05 .15
286 Cecil Fielder HFA .05 .15
287 Wally Joyner HFA .05 .15
288 Greg Vaughn HFA .05 .15
289 Kirby Puckett HFA .20 .50
290 Don Mattingly HFA .40 1.00
291 Terry Steinbach HFA .05 .15
292 Ken Griffey Jr. HFA .30 .75
293 Juan Gonzalez HFA .05 .15
294 Paul Molitor HFA .05 .15
295 Tavo Alvarez UDC .05 .15
296 Matt Brunson UDC .05 .15
297 Shawn Green UDC .20 .50
298 Alex Rodriguez UDC 2.50 6.00
299 S.Stewart UDC .30 .75
300 Frank Thomas .30 .75
301 Mickey Tettleton .05 .15
302 Pedro Munoz .05 .15
303 Jose Valentin .05 .15
304 Orestes Destrade .05 .15
305 Pat Listach .05 .15
306 Scott Brosius .10 .30
307 Kurt Miller .05 .15
308 Rob Dibble .10 .30
309 Mike Blowers .05 .15
310 Jim Abbott .20 .50
311 Mike Jackson .05 .15
312 Craig Biggio .20 .50
313 Kurt Abbott RC .05 .15
314 Chuck Finley .10 .30
315 Andres Galarraga .10 .30
316 Mike Moore .05 .15
317 Doug Strange .05 .15
318 Pedro Martinez .30 .75
319 Kevin McReynolds .05 .15
320 Greg Maddux .50 1.25
321 Mike Henneman .05 .15
322 Scott Leius .05 .15
323 John Franco .10 .30
324 Jeff Blauser .05 .15
325 Kirby Puckett .30 .75
326 Darryl Hamilton .05 .15
327 John Smiley .05 .15
328 Derrick May .05 .15
329 Jose Vizcaino .05 .15
330 Randy Johnson .30 .75
331 Jack Morris .10 .30
332 Graeme Lloyd .05 .15
333 Dave Valle .05 .15
334 Greg Myers .05 .15
335 John Wetteland .10 .30
336 Jim Gott .05 .15
337 Tim Naehring .05 .15
338 Mike Kelly .05 .15
339 Jeff Montgomery .05 .15
340 Rafael Palmeiro .20 .50
341 Eddie Murray .30 .75
342 Xavier Hernandez .05 .15
343 Bobby Munoz .05 .15
344 Bobby Bonilla .10 .30
345 Travis Fryman .10 .30
346 Steve Finley .10 .30
347 Chris Sabo .05 .15
348 Armando Reynoso .05 .15
349 Ramon Martinez .05 .15
350 Will Clark .20 .50
351 Moises Alou .10 .30
352 Jim Thome .20 .50
353 Bob Tewksbury .05 .15
354 Andujar Cedeno .05 .15
355 Orel Hershiser .10 .30
356 Mike Devereaux .05 .15
357 Mike Perez .05 .15
358 Dennis Martinez .10 .30
359 Dave Nilsson .05 .15
360 Ozzie Smith .50 1.25
361 Eric Anthony .05 .15
362 Scott Sanders .05 .15
363 Paul Sorrento .05 .15
364 Tim Belcher .05 .15
365 Dennis Eckersley .10 .30
366 Mel Rojas .05 .15
367 Tom Henke .05 .15
368 Randy Tomlin .05 .15
369 B.J. Surhoff .10 .30
370 Larry Walker .10 .30
371 Joey Cora .05 .15
372 Mike Harkey .05 .15
373 John Valentin .05 .15
374 Doug Jones .05 .15
375 David Justice .10 .30
376 Vince Coleman .05 .15
377 David Hulse .05 .15
378 Kevin Seitzer .05 .15
379 Pete Harnisch .05 .15
380 Ruben Sierra .10 .30
381 Mark Lewis .05 .15
382 Bip Roberts .05 .15
383 Paul Wagner .05 .15
384 Stan Javier .05 .15
385 Barry Larkin .20 .50
386 Mark Portugal .05 .15
387 Roberto Kelly .05 .15
388 Andy Benes .05 .15
389 Felix Fermin .05 .15
390 Marquis Grissom .10 .30
391 Troy Neel .05 .15
392 Chad Kreuter .05 .15
393 Gregg Olson .05 .15
394 Charles Nagy .05 .15
395 Jack McDowell .05 .15
396 Luis Gonzalez .10 .30
397 Benito Santiago .10 .30
398 Chris James .05 .15
399 Terry Mulholland .05 .15
400 Barry Bonds .75 2.00
401 Joe Grahe .05 .15
402 Duane Ward .05 .15
403 John Burkett .05 .15
404 Scott Servais .05 .15
405 Bryan Harvey .05 .15
406 Bernard Gilkey .05 .15
407 Greg McMichael .05 .15
408 Tim Wallach .05 .15
409 Ken Caminiti .10 .30
410 John Kruk .10 .30
411 Darrin Jackson .05 .15
412 Mike Gallego .05 .15
413 David Cone .10 .30
414 Lou Whitaker .10 .30
415 Sandy Alomar Jr. .05 .15
416 Bill Wegman .05 .15
417 Pat Borders .05 .15
418 Roger Pavlik .05 .15
419 Pete Smith .05 .15
420 Steve Avery .05 .15
421 David Segui .05 .15
422 Rheal Cormier .05 .15
423 Harold Reynolds .10 .30
424 Edgar Martinez .20 .50
425 Cal Ripken Jr. 1.00 2.50
426 Jaime Navarro .05 .15
427 Sean Berry .05 .15
428 Bret Saberhagen .10 .30
429 Bob Welch .05 .15
430 Juan Guzman .05 .15
431 Cal Eldred .05 .15
432 Dave Hollins .05 .15
433 Sid Fernandez .05 .15
434 Willie Banks .05 .15
435 Darryl Kile .10 .30
436 Henry Rodriguez .05 .15
437 Tony Fernandez .05 .15
438 Walt Weiss .05 .15
439 Kevin Tapani .05 .15
440 Mark Grace .20 .50
441 Brian Harper .05 .15
442 Kent Mercker .05 .15
443 Anthony Young .05 .15
444 Todd Zeile .05 .15
445 Greg Vaughn .05 .15
446 Ray Lankford .10 .30
447 Dave Weathers .05 .15
448 Bret Boone .10 .30
449 Charlie Hough .10 .30
450 Roger Clemens .60 1.50
451 Mike Morgan .05 .15
452 Doug Drabek .05 .15
453 Danny Jackson .05 .15
454 Dante Bichette .10 .30
455 Roberto Alomar .20 .50
456 Ben McDonald .05 .15
457 Kenny Rogers .10 .30
458 Bill Gullickson .05 .15
459 Darrin Fletcher .05 .15
460 Curt Schilling .10 .30
461 Billy Hatcher .05 .15
462 Howard Johnson .05 .15
463 Mickey Morandini .05 .15
464 Frank Castillo .05 .15
465 Delino DeShields .05 .15
466 Gary Gaetti .10 .30
467 Steve Farr .05 .15
468 Roberto Hernandez .05 .15
469 Jack Armstrong .05 .15
470 Paul Molitor .10 .30
471 Melido Perez .05 .15
472 Greg Hibbard .05 .15
473 Jody Reed .05 .15
474 Tom Gordon .05 .15
475 Gary Sheffield .10 .30
476 John Jaha .05 .15
477 Shawon Dunston .05 .15
478 Reggie Jefferson .05 .15
479 Don Slaught .05 .15
480 Jeff Bagwell .20 .50
481 Tim Pugh .05 .15
482 Kevin Young .05 .15
483 Ellis Burks .10 .30
484 Greg Swindell .05 .15
485 Mark Langston .05 .15
486 Omar Vizquel .20 .50
487 Kevin Brown .10 .30
488 Terry Steinbach .05 .15
489 Mark Lemke .05 .15
490 Matt Williams .10 .30
491 Pete Incaviglia .05 .15
492 Karl Rhodes .05 .15
493 Shawn Green .30 .75
494 Hal Morris .05 .15
495 Derek Bell .05 .15
496 Luis Polonia .05 .15
497 Otis Nixon .05 .15
498 Ron Darling .05 .15
499 Mitch Williams .05 .15
500 Mike Piazza .60 1.50
501 Pat Meares .05 .15
502 Scott Cooper .05 .15
503 Scott Erickson .05 .15
504 Jeff Juden .05 .15
505 Lee Smith .10 .30
506 Bobby Ayala .05 .15
507 Dave Henderson .05 .15
508 Erik Hanson .05 .15
509 Bob Wickman .05 .15
510 Sammy Sosa .30 .75
511 Hector Carrasco .05 .15
512 Tim Davis .05 .15
513 Joey Hamilton .05 .15
514 Robert Eenhoorn .05 .15
515 Jorge Fabregas .05 .15
516 Tim Hyers RC .05 .15
517 John Hudek RC .05 .15
518 James Mouton .05 .15
519 Herbert Perry RC .05 .15
520 Chan Ho Park RC .30 .75
521 W.Va Landingham RC .05 .15
522 Paul Shuey .05 .15
523 Ryan Hancock RC .05 .15
524 Billy Wagner RC .75 2.00
525 Jason Giambi .30 .75
526 Jose Silva RC .05 .15
527 Terrell Wade RC .05 .15
528 Todd Dunn .05 .15
529 Alan Benes RC .15 .40
530 B.Kieschnick RC .05 .15
531 T.Hollandsworth .05 .15
532 Brad Fullmer RC .15 .40
533 S.Soderstrom RC .05 .15
534 Daron Kirkreit .05 .15
535 Arquimedez Pozo RC .05 .15
536 Charles Johnson .10 .30
537 Preston Wilson .10 .30
538 Alex Ochoa .05 .15
539 Derrek Lee RC 1.50 4.00
540 Wayne Gomes RC .05 .15
541 J.Allensworth RC .05 .15
542 Mike Bell RC .05 .15
543 Trot Nixon RC .75 2.00
544 Pokey Reese .05 .15
545 Neifi Perez RC .15 .40
546 Johnny Damon .30 .75
547 Matt Brunson RC .05 .15
548 L.Hawkins RC .15 .40
549 Eddie Pearson RC .05 .15
550 Derek Jeter 1.00 2.50
A298 Alex Rodriguez AU 350.00 700.00
P224 K.Griffey Jr. Promo .75 2.00
GM1 Ken Griffey Jr. AU 700.00 900.00
Mickey Mantle AU/1000
KG1 K.Griffey Jr. AU/1000 150.00 300.00
MM1 M.Mantle AU/1000 300.00 600.00

1994 Upper Deck Electric Diamond

This 550-card set is a parallel issue to the basic 1994 Upper Deck cards. The cards were issued one per foil pack and two per mini jumbo. The only differences between these and the basic cards is the "Electric Diamond" in silver foil toward the bottom and the player's name is also in silver foil.

COMPLETE SET (550) 40.00 100.00
COMP.SERIES 1 (280) 25.00 60.00
COMP.SERIES 2 (270) 15.00 40.00
*STARS: .75X TO 2X BASIC CARDS
*ROOKIES: .6X TO 1.5X BASIC CARDS

1994 Upper Deck Diamond Collection

This 30-card standard-size set was inserted regionally in first series hobby packs at a rate of one in 18. The three regions are Central (C1-C10), East (E1-E10) and West (W1-W10). While each card has the same horizontal format, the color scheme differs by region. The Central cards have a blue background, the East green and the West a deep shade of red. Color player photos are superimposed over the backgrounds. Each card has, "The Upper Deck Diamond Collection" as part of the background. The backs have a small photo and career highlights.

COMPLETE SET (30) 70.00 180.00
COMPLETE CENTRAL (10) 30.00 80.00
COMPLETE EAST (10) 15.00 40.00
COMPLETE WEST (10) 25.00 60.00
C1 Jeff Bagwell 1.50 4.00
C2 Michael Jordan 6.00 15.00
C3 Barry Larkin 1.50 4.00
C4 Kirby Puckett 2.50 6.00
C5 Manny Ramirez 2.50 6.00
C6 Ryne Sandberg 4.00 10.00
C7 Ozzie Smith 4.00 10.00
C8 Frank Thomas 2.50 6.00
C9 Andy Van Slyke 1.50 4.00
C10 Robin Yount 2.50 6.00
E1 Roberto Alomar 1.50 4.00
E2 Roger Clemens 5.00 12.00
E3 Lenny Dykstra 1.00 2.50
E4 Cecil Fielder 1.00 2.50
E5 Cliff Floyd 1.00 2.50
E6 Dwight Gooden 1.00 2.50
E7 David Justice 1.00 2.50
E8 Don Mattingly 6.00 15.00
E9 Cal Ripken Jr. 8.00 20.00
E10 Gary Sheffield 1.00 2.50
W1 Barry Bonds 6.00 15.00
W2 Andres Galarraga 1.00 2.50
W3 Juan Gonzalez 1.00 2.50
W4 Ken Griffey Jr. 4.00 10.00
W5 Tony Gwynn 3.00 8.00
W6 Rickey Henderson 2.50 6.00
W7 Bo Jackson 2.50 6.00
W8 Mark McGwire 6.00 15.00
W9 Mike Piazza 5.00 12.00
W10 Tim Salmon 1.50 4.00

1994 Upper Deck Griffey Jumbos

Measuring 4 7/8" by 6 13/16", these four Griffey cards serve as checklists for first series Upper Deck issues. They were issued one per first series hobby foil box. Card fronts have a full color photo with a small Griffey hologram. The first three cards provide a numerical, alphabetical and team organized checklist for the basic set. The fourth card is a checklist of inserts. Each card was printed in different quantities with CL1 the most plentiful and CL4 the more scarce. The backs are numbered with a CL prefix.

COMMON GRIFFEY (CL1-CL4) 1.25 3.00

1994 Upper Deck Mantle Heroes

Randomly inserted in second series packs at a rate of one in 35, this 10-card standard-size set looks at various moments from The Mick's career. Metallic fronts feature a vintage photo with the card title at the bottom. The backs contain career highlights with a small scrapbook like photo. The numbering (64-72) is a continuation from previous Heroes sets.

COMPLETE SET (10) 30.00 80.00
COMMON (64-72/HDR) 4.00 10.00

1994 Upper Deck Mantle's Long Shots

Randomly inserted in first series retail packs at a rate of one in 18, this 21-card silver foil standard-size set features top longball hitters as selected by Mickey Mantle. The cards are numbered on the back with a "MM" prefix and sequenced in alphabetical order. Two trade cards, were also random inserts and were redeemable (expiration: December 31, 1994) for either the basic silver foil set version (Silver Trade card) or the Electric Diamond version (blue Trade card).

COMPLETE SET (21) 15.00 40.00
*ED: .5X TO 1.2X BASIC MANTLE LS
ONE ED SET VIA MAIL PER BLUE TRADE CARD
MANTLE TRADES: RANDOM IN SER.1 HOB
MM1 Jeff Bagwell .60 1.50
MM2 Albert Belle .40 1.00
MM3 Barry Bonds 2.50 6.00
MM4 Jose Canseco .60 1.50
MM5 Joe Carter .40 1.00
MM6 Carlos Delgado .60 1.50
MM7 Cecil Fielder .40 1.00
MM8 Cliff Floyd .40 1.00
MM9 Juan Gonzalez .40 1.00
MM10 Ken Griffey Jr. 1.50 4.00
MM11 David Justice .40 1.00
MM12 Fred McGriff .60 1.50
MM13 Mark McGwire 2.50 6.00
MM14 Dean Palmer .40 1.00
MM15 Mike Piazza 2.00 5.00
MM16 Manny Ramirez 1.00 2.50
MM17 Tim Salmon .60 1.50
MM18 Frank Thomas 1.00 2.50
MM19 Mo Vaughn .40 1.00
MM20 Matt Williams .40 1.00
MM21 Mickey Mantle 6.00 15.00
NNO Mickey Mantle 2.50 6.00
Silver Trade
NNO Mickey Mantle 6.00 15.00
Blue ED Trade

1994 Upper Deck Next Generation

Randomly inserted in second series retail packs at a rate of one in 20, this 18-card standard-size set spotlights young established stars and promising prospects. The set is sequenced in alphabetical order. A Next Generation Electric Diamond Trade Card and a Next Generation Trade Card were seeded randomly in second series hobby packs. Each card could be redeemed for that set. Expiration date for redemption was October 31, 1994.

COMPLETE SET (18) 40.00 100.00
1 Roberto Alomar 1.25 3.00
2 Carlos Delgado 1.25 3.00
3 Cliff Floyd .75 2.00
4 Alex Gonzalez .40 1.00
5 Juan Gonzalez .75 2.00
6 Ken Griffey Jr. 3.00 8.00
7 Jeffrey Hammonds .40 1.00
8 Michael Jordan 6.00 15.00
9 David Justice .75 2.00
10 Ryan Klesko .75 2.00
11 Javier Lopez .75 2.00
12 Raul Mondesi .75 2.00
13 Mike Piazza 4.00 10.00
14 Kirby Puckett 2.00 5.00
15 Manny Ramirez 2.00 5.00
16 Alex Rodriguez 30.00 60.00
17 Tim Salmon 1.25 3.00
18 Gary Sheffield .75 2.00
NNO Exp. NG Trade Card .40 1.00

1994 Upper Deck Next Generation Electric Diamond

This 18 card set parallels the regular Next Generation insert set. The cards are differentiated by an "Electric Diamond" logo on the bottom. These cards were sent if a collector received a ED trade card in a pack.

*ELEC.DIAM: .5X TO 1.2X BASIC NEXT.GEN.
8 Michael Jordan 10.00 25.00
16 Alex Rodriguez 35.00 60.00

1995 Upper Deck

COMPLETE SET (450) 20.00 50.00
COMP. SERIES 1 (225) 10.00 25.00
COMP. SERIES 2 (225) 10.00 25.00
COMMON CARD (1-450) .05 .15
COMP.TRADE SET (45) 30.00 60.00
COMMON (451T-495T) .40 1.00
1 Ruben Rivera .05 .15
2 Bill Pulsipher .05 .15
3 Ben Grieve .05 .15
4 Curtis Goodwin .05 .15
5 Damon Hollins .05 .15
6 Todd Greene .05 .15
7 Glenn Williams .05 .15
8 Bret Wagner .05 .15
9 Karim Garcia RC .10 .30
10 Nomar Garciaparra .75 2.00
11 Raul Casanova RC .05 .15
12 Matt Smith .05 .15
13 Paul Wilson .05 .15
14 Jason Isringhausen .10 .30
15 Reid Ryan .10 .30
16 Lee Smith .10 .30
17 Chili Davis .10 .30
18 Brian Anderson .05 .15
19 Gary DiSarcina .05 .15
20 Bo Jackson .30 .75
21 Chuck Finley .10 .30
22 Darryl Kile .10 .30
23 Shane Reynolds .05 .15
24 Tony Eusebio .05 .15
25 Craig Biggio .20 .50
26 Doug Drabek .05 .15
27 Brian L. Hunter .05 .15
28 James Mouton .05 .15
29 Geronimo Berroa .05 .15
30 Rickey Henderson .30 .75
31 Steve Karsay .05 .15
32 Steve Ontiveros .05 .15
33 Ernie Young .05 .15
34 Dennis Eckersley .10 .30
35 Mark McGwire .75 2.00
36 Dave Stewart .10 .30
37 Pat Hentgen .05 .15
38 Carlos Delgado .10 .30
39 Joe Carter .10 .30
40 Roberto Alomar .20 .50
41 John Olerud .10 .30
42 Devon White .10 .30
43 Roberto Kelly .05 .15
44 Jeff Blauser .05 .15
45 Fred McGriff .20 .50
46 Tom Glavine .20 .50
47 Mike Kelly .05 .15
48 Javier Lopez .10 .30
49 Greg Maddux .50 1.25
50 Matt Mieske .05 .15
51 Troy O'Leary .05 .15
52 Jeff Cirillo .05 .15
53 Cal Eldred .05 .15
54 Pat Listach .05 .15
55 Jose Valentin .05 .15
56 John Mabry .05 .15
57 Bob Tewksbury .05 .15
58 Brian Jordan .10 .30
59 Gregg Jefferies .05 .15
60 Ozzie Smith .50 1.25
61 Geronimo Pena .05 .15
62 Mark Whiten .05 .15
63 Rey Sanchez .05 .15
64 Willie Banks .05 .15
65 Mark Grace .20 .50
66 Randy Myers .05 .15
67 Steve Trachsel .05 .15
68 Derrick May .05 .15
69 Brett Butler .10 .30
70 Eric Karros .10 .30
71 Tim Wallach .05 .15
72 Delino DeShields .05 .15
73 Darren Dreifort .05 .15
74 Orel Hershiser .10 .30
75 Billy Ashley .05 .15
76 Sean Berry .05 .15
77 Ken Hill .05 .15
78 John Wetteland .10 .30
79 Moises Alou .10 .30
80 Cliff Floyd .10 .30
81 Marquis Grissom .10 .30
82 Larry Walker .10 .30
83 Rondell White .10 .30
84 W.VanLandingham .05 .15
85 Matt Williams .10 .30
86 Rod Beck .05 .15
87 Darren Lewis .05 .15
88 Robby Thompson .05 .15
89 Darryl Strawberry .10 .30
90 Kenny Lofton .10 .30
91 Charles Nagy .05 .15
92 Sandy Alomar Jr. .05 .15
93 Mark Clark .05 .15
94 Dennis Martinez .10 .30
95 Dave Winfield .10 .30
96 Jim Thome .20 .50
97 Manny Ramirez .20 .50
98 Goose Gossage .10 .30
99 Tino Martinez .20 .50
100 Ken Griffey Jr. .50 1.25
101 Greg Maddux ANA .30 .75
102 Randy Johnson ANA .20 .50
103 Barry Bonds ANA .40 1.00
104 Juan Gonzalez ANA .05 .15
105 Frank Thomas ANA .20 .50
106 Matt Williams ANA .05 .15
107 Paul Molitor ANA .05 .15
108 Fred McGriff ANA .10 .30
109 Carlos Baerga ANA .05 .15
110 Ken Griffey Jr. ANA .30 .75
111 Reggie Jefferson .05 .15
112 Randy Johnson .30 .75
113 Marc Newfield .05 .15
114 Robb Nen .10 .30
115 Jeff Conine .10 .30
116 Kurt Abbott .05 .15
117 Charlie Hough .10 .30
118 Dave Weathers .05 .15
119 Juan Castillo .05 .15
120 Bret Saberhagen .10 .30
121 Rico Brogna .05 .15
122 John Franco .10 .30
123 Todd Hundley .05 .15
124 Jason Jacome .05 .15
125 Bobby Jones .05 .15
126 Bret Barberie .05 .15
127 Ben McDonald .05 .15
128 Harold Baines .10 .30
129 Jeffrey Hammonds .05 .15
130 Mike Mussina .20 .50
131 Chris Hoiles .05 .15
132 Brady Anderson .10 .30
133 Eddie Williams .05 .15
134 Andy Benes .05 .15
135 Tony Gwynn .40 1.00
136 Bip Roberts .05 .15
137 Joey Hamilton .05 .15
138 Luis Lopez .05 .15
139 Ray McDavid .05 .15
140 Lenny Dykstra .10 .30
141 Mariano Duncan .05 .15
142 Fernando Valenzuela .10 .30
143 Bobby Munoz .05 .15
144 Kevin Stocker .05 .15
145 John Kruk .10 .30
146 Jon Lieber .05 .15
147 Zane Smith .05 .15
148 Steve Cooke .05 .15
149 Andy Van Slyke .20 .50
150 Jay Bell .10 .30
151 Carlos Garcia .05 .15
152 John Dettmer .05 .15
153 Darren Oliver .05 .15
154 Dean Palmer .10 .30
155 Otis Nixon .05 .15
156 Rusty Greer .10 .30
157 Rick Helling .05 .15
158 Jose Canseco .20 .50
159 Roger Clemens .60 1.50
160 Andre Dawson .10 .30
161 Mo Vaughn .10 .30
162 Aaron Sele .05 .15
163 John Valentin .05 .15
164 Brian R. Hunter .05 .15
165 Bret Boone .10 .30
166 Hector Carrasco .05 .15
167 Pete Schourek .05 .15
168 Willie Greene .05 .15
169 Kevin Mitchell .05 .15
170 Deion Sanders .20 .50
171 John Roper .05 .15
172 Charlie Hayes .05 .15
173 David Nied .05 .15
174 Ellis Burks .10 .30
175 Dante Bichette .10 .30
176 Marvin Freeman .05 .15
177 Eric Young .05 .15
178 David Cone .10 .30
179 Greg Gagne .05 .15
180 Bob Hamelin .05 .15
181 Wally Joyner .10 .30
182 Jeff Montgomery .05 .15
183 Jose Lind .05 .15
184 Chris Gomez .05 .15
185 Travis Fryman .10 .30
186 Kirk Gibson .10 .30
187 Mike Moore .05 .15
188 Lou Whitaker .10 .30
189 Sean Bergman .05 .15
190 Shane Mack .05 .15
191 Rick Aguilera .05 .15
192 Denny Hocking .05 .15
193 Chuck Knoblauch .10 .30
194 Kevin Tapani .05 .15
195 Kent Hrbek .10 .30
196 Ozzie Guillen .10 .30
197 Wilson Alvarez .05 .15
198 Tim Raines .10 .30
199 Scott Ruffcorn .05 .15
200 Michael Jordan 1.00 2.50
Interviewed by famed annoucer Harry Caray
201 Robin Ventura .10 .30
202 Jason Bere .05 .15
203 Darrin Jackson .05 .15
204 Russ Davis .05 .15
205 Jimmy Key .10 .30
206 Jack McDowell .05 .15
207 Jim Abbott .20 .50
208 Paul O'Neill .20 .50
209 Bernie Williams .20 .50
210 Don Mattingly .75 2.00
211 Orlando Miller .05 .15
212 Alex Gonzalez .05 .15
213 Terrell Wade .05 .15
214 Jose Oliva .05 .15
215 Alex Rodriguez .75 2.00
216 Garret Anderson .10 .30
217 Alan Benes .05 .15
218 Armando Benitez .05 .15
219 Dustin Hermanson .05 .15
220 Charles Johnson .10 .30
221 Julian Tavarez .05 .15
222 Jason Giambi .20 .50
223 LaTroy Hawkins .05 .15
224 Todd Hollandsworth .05 .15
225 Derek Jeter .75 2.00
226 Hideo Nomo RC 1.00 2.50
227 Tony Clark .05 .15
228 Roger Cedeno .05 .15
229 Scott Stahoviak .05 .15
230 Michael Tucker .05 .15
231 Joe Rosselli .05 .15
232 Antonio Osuna .05 .15
233 Bobby Higginson RC .30 .75
234 Mark Grudzielanek RC .30 .75
235 Ray Durham .10 .30
236 Frank Rodriguez .05 .15
237 Quilvio Veras .05 .15
238 Darren Bragg .05 .15
239 Ugueth Urbina .05 .15
240 Jason Bates .05 .15
241 David Bell .05 .15
242 Ron Villone .05 .15
243 Joe Randa .10 .30
244 Carlos Perez RC .15 .40
245 Brad Clontz .05 .15
246 Steve Rodriguez .05 .15
247 Joe Vitiello .05 .15
248 Ozzie Timmons .05 .15
249 Rudy Pemberton .05 .15
250 Marty Cordova .05 .15
251 Tony Graffanino .05 .15
252 Mark Johnson RC .15 .40
253 Tomas Perez RC .05 .15
254 Jimmy Hurst .05 .15
255 Edgardo Alfonzo .05 .15
256 Jose Malave .05 .15
257 Brad Radke RC .30 .75
258 Jon Nunnally .05 .15
259 Dilson Torres RC .05 .15
260 Esteban Loaiza .05 .15
261 Freddy Adrian Garcia RC .05 .15
262 Don Wengert .05 .15
263 Robert Person RC .15 .40
264 Tim Unroe RC .05 .15
265 Juan Acevedo RC .05 .15
266 Eduardo Perez .05 .15
267 Tony Phillips .05 .15
268 Jim Edmonds .20 .50
269 Jorge Fabregas .05 .15
270 Tim Salmon .20 .50
271 Mark Langston .05 .15
272 J.T. Snow .10 .30
273 Phil Plantier .05 .15
274 Derek Bell .05 .15
275 Jeff Bagwell .20 .50
276 Luis Gonzalez .10 .30
277 John Hudek .05 .15
278 Todd Stottlemyre .05 .15
279 Mark Acre .05 .15
280 Ruben Sierra .10 .30
281 Mike Bordick .05 .15
282 Ron Darling .05 .15
283 Brent Gates .05 .15
284 Todd Van Poppel .05 .15
285 Paul Molitor .10 .30
286 Ed Sprague .05 .15
287 Juan Guzman .05 .15
288 David Cone .10 .30
289 Shawn Green .10 .30
290 Marquis Grissom .10 .30
291 Kent Mercker .05 .15
292 Steve Avery .05 .15
293 Chipper Jones .30 .75
294 John Smoltz .20 .50
295 David Justice .10 .30
296 Ryan Klesko .10 .30
297 Joe Oliver .05 .15
298 Ricky Bones .05 .15
299 John Jaha .05 .15
300 Greg Vaughn .05 .15
301 Dave Nilsson .05 .15
302 Kevin Seitzer .05 .15
303 Bernard Gilkey .05 .15
304 Allen Battle .05 .15
305 Ray Lankford .10 .30
306 Tom Pagnozzi .05 .15
307 Allen Watson .05 .15
308 Danny Jackson .05 .15
309 Ken Hill .05 .15
310 Todd Zeile .05 .15
311 Kevin Roberson .05 .15
312 Steve Buechele .05 .15
313 Rick Wilkins .05 .15
314 Kevin Foster .05 .15
315 Sammy Sosa .30 .75
316 Howard Johnson .05 .15
317 Greg Hansell .05 .15
318 Pedro Astacio .05 .15
319 Rafael Bournigal .05 .15
320 Mike Piazza .50 1.25
321 Ramon Martinez .05 .15
322 Raul Mondesi .10 .30
323 Ismael Valdes .05 .15
324 Wil Cordero .05 .15
325 Tony Tarasco .05 .15
326 Roberto Kelly .05 .15
327 Jeff Fassero .05 .15
328 Mike Lansing .05 .15
329 Pedro Martinez .20 .50
330 Kirk Rueter .05 .15
331 Glenallen Hill .05 .15
332 Kirt Manwaring .05 .15
333 Royce Clayton .05 .15
334 J.R. Phillips .05 .15
335 Barry Bonds .75 2.00
336 Mark Portugal .05 .15
337 Terry Mulholland .05 .15
338 Omar Vizquel .20 .50
339 Carlos Baerga .05 .15
340 Albert Belle .10 .30
341 Eddie Murray .30 .75
342 Wayne Kirby .05 .15
343 Chad Ogea .05 .15
344 Tim Davis .05 .15
345 Jay Buhner .10 .30
346 Bobby Ayala .05 .15
347 Mike Blowers .05 .15
348 Dave Fleming .05 .15
349 Edgar Martinez .20 .50
350 Andre Dawson .10 .30
351 Darrell Whitmore .05 .15
352 Chuck Carr .05 .15
353 John Burkett .05 .15
354 Chris Hammond .05 .15
355 Gary Sheffield .10 .30
356 Pat Rapp .05 .15
357 Greg Colbrunn .05 .15
358 David Segui .05 .15
359 Jeff Kent .10 .30
360 Bobby Bonilla .10 .30
361 Pete Harnisch .05 .15
362 Ryan Thompson .05 .15
363 Jose Vizcaino .05 .15
364 Brett Butler .10 .30
365 Cal Ripken Jr. 1.00 2.50
366 Rafael Palmeiro .20 .50
367 Leo Gomez .05 .15
368 Andy Van Slyke .20 .50
369 Arthur Rhodes .05 .15
370 Ken Caminiti .10 .30
371 Steve Finley .10 .30
372 Melvin Nieves .05 .15
373 Andujar Cedeno .05 .15
374 Trevor Hoffman .10 .30
375 Fernando Valenzuela .10 .30
376 Ricky Bottalico .05 .15
377 Dave Hollins .05 .15
378 Charlie Hayes .05 .15
379 Tommy Greene .05 .15
380 Darren Daulton .10 .30
381 Curt Schilling .10 .30
382 Midre Cummings .05 .15
383 Al Martin .05 .15
384 Jeff King .05 .15
385 Orlando Merced .05 .15
386 Denny Neagle .10 .30
387 Don Slaught .05 .15
388 Dave Clark .05 .15
389 Kevin Gross .05 .15
390 Will Clark .20 .50
391 Ivan Rodriguez .20 .50
392 Benji Gil .05 .15
393 Jeff Frye .05 .15
394 Kenny Rogers .10 .30
395 Juan Gonzalez .10 .30
396 Mike Macfarlane .05 .15
397 Lee Tinsley .05 .15
398 Tim Naehring .05 .15
399 Tim Vanegmond .05 .15
400 Mike Greenwell .05 .15
401 Ken Ryan .05 .15
402 John Smiley .05 .15
403 Tim Pugh .05 .15
404 Reggie Sanders .10 .30
405 Barry Larkin .20 .50
406 Hal Morris .05 .15
407 Jose Rijo .05 .15
408 Lance Painter .05 .15
409 Joe Girardi .05 .15
410 Andres Galarraga .10 .30
411 Mike Kingery .05 .15
412 Roberto Mejia .05 .15
413 Walt Weiss .05 .15
414 Bill Swift .05 .15
415 Larry Walker .10 .30
416 Billy Brewer .05 .15
417 Pat Borders .05 .15
418 Tom Gordon .05 .15
419 Kevin Appier .10 .30
420 Gary Gaetti .10 .30
421 Greg Gohr .05 .15
422 Felipe Lira .05 .15
423 John Doherty .05 .15
424 Chad Curtis .05 .15
425 Cecil Fielder .10 .30
426 Alan Trammell .10 .30
427 David McCarty .05 .15
428 Scott Erickson .05 .15
429 Pat Mahomes .05 .15
430 Kirby Puckett .30 .75
431 Dave Stevens .05 .15
432 Pedro Munoz .05 .15
433 Chris Sabo .05 .15
434 Alex Fernandez .05 .15
435 Frank Thomas .30 .75
436 Roberto Hernandez .05 .15
437 Lance Johnson .05 .15
438 Jim Abbott .20 .50
439 John Wetteland .10 .30
440 Melido Perez .05 .15
441 Tony Fernandez .05 .15
442 Pat Kelly .05 .15
443 Mike Stanley .05 .15
444 Danny Tartabull .05 .15
445 Wade Boggs .20 .50
446 Robin Yount .50 1.25
447 Ryne Sandberg .50 1.25
448 Nolan Ryan 1.25 3.00
449 George Brett .75 2.00
450 Mike Schmidt .50 1.25
451 Jim Abbott TRADE .75 2.00
452 D.Tartabull TRADE .40 1.00
453 Ariel Prieto TRADE .40 1.00
454 Scott Cooper TRADE .40 1.00
455 Tom Henke TRADE .40 1.00
456 Todd Zeile TRADE .40 1.00
457 Brian McRae TRADE .40 1.00
458 Luis Gonzalez TRADE .60 1.50
459 Jaime Navarro TRADE .40 1.00
460 Todd Worrell TRADE .40 1.00
461 Roberto Kelly TRADE .40 1.00
462 Chad Fonville TRADE .40 1.00
463 S.Andrews TRADE .40 1.00
464 David Segui TRADE .40 1.00
465 Deion Sanders TRADE .75 2.00
466 Orel Hershiser TRADE .60 1.50
467 Ken Hill TRADE .40 1.00
468 Andy Benes TRADE .40 1.00
469 T.Pendleton TRADE .60 1.50
470 Bobby Bonilla TRADE .60 1.50
471 Scott Erickson TRADE .40 1.00
472 Kevin Brown TRADE .60 1.50
473 G.Dishman TRADE .40 1.00
474 Phil Plantier TRADE .40 1.00
475 G.Jefferies TRADE .40 1.00
476 Tyler Green TRADE .40 1.00
477 H. Slocumb TRADE .40 1.00
478 Mark Whiten TRADE .40 1.00
479 M.Tettleton TRADE .40 1.00
480 Tim Wakefield TRADE .60 1.50
481 V. Eshelman TRADE .40 1.00
482 Rick Aguilera TRADE .40 1.00
483 Erik Hanson TRADE .40 1.00
484 Willie McGee TRADE .60 1.50
485 Troy O'Leary TRADE .40 1.00
486 B.Santiago TRADE .60 1.50
487 Darren Lewis TRADE .40 1.00
488 Dave Burba TRADE .40 1.00
489 Ron Gant TRADE .60 1.50
490 B.Saberhagen TRADE .60 1.50
491 Vinny Castilla TRADE .60 1.50
492 F.Rodriguez TRADE .40 1.00
493 Andy Pettitte TRADE .75 2.00
494 Ruben Sierra TRADE .60 1.50
495 David Cone TRADE .60 1.50
J159 R. Clemens Jumbo AU 40.00 80.00
J215 A. Rodriguez Jumbo AU 75.00 150.00
P100 K.Griffey Jr. Promo .75 2.00

1995 Upper Deck Electric Diamond

This 450-card parallel set was inserted one per retail pack or two per mini-jumbo pack. These issue cards are distinguished from their regular issue counterparts in that they are printed on a heavier cardstock and use a special foil treatment.

COMPLETE SET (450) 50.00 100.00
COMP. SERIES 1 (225) 25.00 50.00
COMP. SERIES 2 (225) 30.00 60.00
*STARS: 1.25X to 3X BASIC CARDS
*ROOKIES: 1X TO 2.5X BASIC CARDS

1995 Upper Deck Autographs

Trade cards to redeem these autographed issues were randomly seeded into second series packs. The actual signed cards share the same front design as the basic issue 1995 Upper Deck cards. The cards were issued along with a card signed in facsimile by Brain Burr of Upper Deck along with instructions on how to register these cards.

AC1 Reggie Jackson 15.00 40.00
AC2 Willie Mays 60.00 120.00
AC3 Frank Robinson 15.00 40.00
AC4 Roger Clemens 30.00 60.00
AC5 Raul Mondesi 10.00 25.00

1995 Upper Deck Checklists

Each of these 10 cards features a star player(s) on the front and a checklist on the back. The cards were randomly inserted in hobby and retail packs at a rate of one in 17. The horizontal fronts feature a player photo along with a sentence about the 1994 highlight. The cards are numbered as "X" of 5 in the upper left.

COMPLETE SET (5) 4.50 12.00
COMPLETE SERIES 1 (5) 1.50 4.00
COMPLETE SERIES 2 (5) 3.00 8.00
1A Montreal Expos .10 .30
2A Fred McGriff .40 1.00
3A John Valentin .10 .30
4A Kenny Rogers .25 .60
5A Greg Maddux 1.00 2.50
1B Cecil Fielder .25 .60
2B Tony Gwynn .75 2.00
3B Greg Maddux 1.00 2.50
4B Randy Johnson .60 1.50
5B Mike Schmidt 1.00 2.50

1995 Upper Deck Predictor Award Winners

Cards from this set were inserted in hobby packs at a rate of approximately one in 30. This 40-card standard-size set features nine players and a Long Shot in each league for each of two categories -- MVP and Rookie of the Year. If the player pictured on the card won his category, the card was redeemable for a special foil version of all 20 Hobby Predictor cards. Winning cards are marked with a "W" in the checklist below. Both MVP winners for the season (Barry Larkin in the NL and Mo Vaughn in the AL) were not featured on their own Predictor cards and thus the Longshot card became the winner. Fronts are full-color player action photos. Backs include the rules of the contest. These cards were redeemable until December 31, 1995.

COMPLETE SERIES 1 (20) 15.00 40.00
COMPLETE SERIES 2 (20) 15.00 40.00
*AW EXCH: .4X TO 1X BASIC PRED.AW
ONE EXCH.SET VIA MAIL PER PRED.WINNER
H1 Albert Belle MVP .50 1.25
H2 Juan Gonzalez MVP .50 1.25
H3 Ken Griffey Jr. MVP 2.00 5.00
H4 Kirby Puckett MVP 1.25 3.00
H5 Frank Thomas MVP 1.25 3.00
H6 Jeff Bagwell MVP .75 2.00
H7 Barry Bonds MVP 3.00 8.00
H8 Mike Piazza MVP 2.00 5.00
H9 Matt Williams MVP .50 1.25
H10 MVP Wild Card W .25 .60
Mo Vaughn, Barry Larkin
H11 A.Benitez ROY .25 .60
H12 Alex Gonzalez ROY .25 .60
H13 Shawn Green ROY .50 1.25
H14 Derek Jeter ROY 3.00 8.00
H15 Alex Rodriguez ROY 3.00 8.00
H16 Alan Benes ROY .25 .60
H17 Brian L.Hunter ROY .25 .60
H18 Charles Johnson ROY .50 1.25
H19 Jose Oliva ROY .25 .60
H20 ROY Wild Card .25 .60
H21 Cal Ripken MVP 4.00 10.00
H22 Don Mattingly MVP 3.00 8.00
H23 Roberto Alomar MVP .75 2.00
H24 Kenny Lofton MVP .50 1.25
H25 Will Clark MVP .75 2.00
H26 Mark McGwire MVP 3.00 8.00
H27 Greg Maddux MVP 2.00 5.00
H28 Fred McGriff MVP .75 2.00
H29 A.Galarraga MVP .50 1.25
H30 Jose Canseco MVP .75 2.00
H31 Ray Durham ROY .50 1.25
H32 M.Grudzielanek ROY 1.25 3.00
H33 Scott Ruffcorn ROY .25 .60
H34 Michael Tucker ROY .25 .60
H35 Garret Anderson ROY .50 1.25
H36 Darren Bragg ROY .25 .60
H37 Quilvio Veras ROY .25 .60
H38 Hideo Nomo ROY W 4.00 10.00
H39 Chipper Jones ROY 1.25 3.00
H40 M.Cordova ROY W .25 .60

1995 Upper Deck Predictor League Leaders

Cards from this 60-card standard size set were seeded exclusively in first and second series retail packs at a rate of 1:30 and ANCO packs at 1:17. Cards 1-30 were distributed in series one packs and

cards 31-60 in series two packs. The set includes nine players and a Long Shot in each league for each of three categories -- Batting Average Leader, Home Run Leader and Runs Batted In Leader. If the player pictured on the card won his category, the card was redeemable for a special foil version of 30 Retail Predictor cards (based upon the first or second series that it was associated with). These cards were redeemable until December 31, 1995. Card fronts are full-color action photos of the player emerging from a marble diamond. Backs list the rules of the game. Winning cards are designated with a W in our listings and are in noticeably shorter supply than other cards from this set as the bulk of them were mailed in to Upper Deck (and destroyed) in exchange for the parallel card prizes.

COMPLETE SERIES 1 (30) 25.00 60.00
COMPLETE SERIES 2 (30) 15.00 40.00
*EXCH: .5X TO 1.2X BASIC PREDICTOR LL
ONE EXCH.SET VIA MAIL PER PRED.WINNER
R1 Albert Belle HR W .50 1.25
R2 Jose Canseco HR .75 2.00
R3 Juan Gonzalez HR .50 1.25
R4 Ken Griffey Jr. HR 2.00 5.00
R5 Frank Thomas HR 1.25 3.00
R6 Jeff Bagwell HR .75 2.00
R7 Barry Bonds HR 3.00 8.00
R8 Fred McGriff HR .75 2.00
R9 Matt Williams HR .50 1.25
R10 HR Wild Card W .25 .60
Dante Bichette
R11 Albert Belle RBI W .50 1.25
R12 Joe Carter RBI .50 1.25
R13 Cecil Fielder RBI .50 1.25
R14 Kirby Puckett RBI 1.25 3.00
R15 Frank Thomas RBI 1.25 3.00
R16 Jeff Bagwell RBI .75 2.00
R17 Barry Bonds RBI 3.00 8.00
R18 Mike Piazza RBI 2.00 5.00
R19 Matt Williams RBI .50 1.25
R20 RBI Wild Card W .25 .60
Mo Vaughn
R21 Wade Boggs BAT .75 2.00
R22 Kenny Lofton BAT .50 1.25
R23 Paul Molitor BAT .50 1.25
R24 Paul O'Neill BAT .75 2.00
R25 Frank Thomas BAT 1.25 3.00
R26 Jeff Bagwell BAT .75 2.00
R27 Tony Gwynn BAT W 1.50 4.00
R28 Gregg Jefferies BAT .25 .60
R29 Hal Morris BAT .25 .60
R30 Batting WC W .25 .60
Edgar Martinez
R31 Joe Carter HR .50 1.25
R32 Cecil Fielder HR .50 1.25
R33 Rafael Palmeiro HR .75 2.00
R34 Larry Walker HR .50 1.25
R35 Manny Ramirez HR .75 2.00
R36 Tim Salmon HR .75 2.00
R37 Mike Piazza HR 2.00 5.00
R38 Andres Galarraga HR .50 1.25
R39 David Justice HR .50 1.25
R40 Gary Sheffield HR .50 1.25
R41 Juan Gonzalez RBI .50 1.25
R42 Jose Canseco RBI .75 2.00
R43 Will Clark RBI .75 2.00
R44 Rafael Palmeiro RBI .75 2.00
R45 Ken Griffey Jr. RBI 2.00 5.00
R46 Ruben Sierra RBI .50 1.25
R47 Larry Walker RBI .50 1.25
R48 Fred McGriff RBI .75 2.00
R49 Dante Bichette RBI W .50 1.25
R50 Darren Daulton RBI .50 1.25
R51 Will Clark BAT .75 2.00
R52 Ken Griffey Jr. BAT 2.00 5.00
R53 Don Mattingly BAT 3.00 8.00
R54 John Olerud BAT .50 1.25
R55 Kirby Puckett BAT 1.25 3.00
R56 Raul Mondesi BAT .50 1.25
R57 Moises Alou BAT .50 1.25
R58 Bret Boone BAT .50 1.25
R59 Albert Belle BAT .50 1.25
R60 Mike Piazza BAT 2.00 5.00

1995 Upper Deck Ruth Heroes

Randomly inserted in second series hobby and retail packs at a rate of 1:34, this set of 10 standard-size cards celebrates the achievements of one of baseball's all-time greats. The set was issued on the Centennial of Ruth's birth. The numbering (73-81) is a continuation from previous Heroes sets.

COMPLETE SET (10) 50.00 100.00
COMMON (73-81/HDR) 6.00 15.00

1995 Upper Deck Special Edition

Inserted at a rate of one per pack, this 270 standard-size card set features full color action shots of players on a silver foil background. The back highlights the player's previous performance, including 1994 and career statistics. Another player photo is also featured on the back.

COMPLETE SET (270) 40.00 100.00
COMP. SERIES 1 (135) 20.00 50.00
COMP. SERIES 2 (135) 20.00 50.00
*SE GOLD: 2.5X TO 6X BASIC SE
*SE GOLD RC's: 2.5X TO 6X BASIC SE
SE GOLD ODDS 1:35 HOBBY
1 Cliff Floyd .30 .75
2 Wil Cordero .15 .40
3 Pedro Martinez .50 1.25
4 Larry Walker .30 .75
5 Derek Jeter 2.00 5.00
6 Mike Stanley .15 .40
7 Melido Perez .15 .40
8 Jim Leyritz .15 .40
9 Danny Tartabull .15 .40
10 Wade Boggs .50 1.25
11 Ryan Klesko .30 .75
12 Steve Avery .15 .40
13 Damon Hollins .15 .40
14 Chipper Jones .75 2.00
15 David Justice .30 .75
16 Glenn Williams .15 .40
17 Jose Oliva .15 .40
18 Terrell Wade .15 .40
19 Alex Fernandez .15 .40
20 Frank Thomas .75 2.00
21 Ozzie Guillen .30 .75
22 Roberto Hernandez .15 .40
23 Albie Lopez .15 .40
24 Eddie Murray .75 2.00
25 Albert Belle .30 .75
26 Omar Vizquel .50 1.25
27 Carlos Baerga .15 .40
28 Jose Rijo .15 .40
29 Hal Morris .15 .40
30 Reggie Sanders .30 .75
31 Jack Morris .30 .75
32 Raul Mondesi .30 .75
33 Karim Garcia .15 .40
34 Todd Hollandsworth .15 .40
35 Mike Piazza 1.25 3.00
36 Chan Ho Park .30 .75
37 Ramon Martinez .30 .75
38 Kenny Rogers .30 .75
39 Will Clark .50 1.25
40 Juan Gonzalez .30 .75
41 Ivan Rodriguez .50 1.25
42 Orlando Miller .15 .40
43 John Hudek .15 .40
44 Luis Gonzalez .30 .75
45 Jeff Bagwell .50 1.25
46 Cal Ripken 2.50 6.00
47 Mike Oquist .15 .40
48 Armando Benitez .15 .40
49 Ben McDonald .15 .40
50 Rafael Palmeiro .50 1.25
51 Curtis Goodwin .15 .40
52 Vince Coleman .15 .40
53 Tom Gordon .15 .40
54 Mike Macfarlane .15 .40
55 Brian McRae .15 .40
56 Matt Smith .15 .40
57 David Segui .15 .40
58 Paul Wilson .15 .40
59 Bill Pulsipher .15 .40
60 Bobby Bonilla .30 .75
61 Jeff Kent .30 .75
62 Ryan Thompson .15 .40
63 Jason Isringhausen .30 .75
64 Ed Sprague .15 .40
65 Paul Molitor .30 .75
66 Juan Guzman .15 .40
67 Alex Gonzalez .15 .40
68 Shawn Green .30 .75
69 Mark Portugal .15 .40
70 Barry Bonds 2.00 5.00
71 Robby Thompson .15 .40
72 Royce Clayton .15 .40
73 Ricky Bottalico .15 .40
74 Doug Jones .15 .40
75 Darren Daulton .30 .75
76 Gregg Jefferies .15 .40
77 Scott Cooper .15 .40
78 Nomar Garciaparra 1.25 3.00
79 Ken Ryan .15 .40
80 Mike Greenwell .15 .40
81 LaTroy Hawkins .15 .40
82 Rich Becker .15 .40
83 Scott Erickson .15 .40
84 Pedro Munoz .15 .40
85 Kirby Puckett .75 2.00
86 Orlando Merced .15 .40
87 Jeff King .15 .40
88 Midre Cummings .15 .40
89 Bernard Gilkey .15 .40
90 Ray Lankford .30 .75
91 Todd Zeile .15 .40
92 Alan Benes .15 .40
93 Bret Wagner .15 .40
94 Rene Arocha .15 .40
95 Cecil Fielder .30 .75
96 Alan Trammell .30 .75
97 Tony Phillips .15 .40
98 Junior Felix .15 .40
99 Brian Harper .15 .40
100 Greg Vaughn .15 .40
101 Ricky Bones .15 .40
102 Walt Weiss .15 .40
103 Lance Painter .15 .40
104 Roberto Mejia .15 .40
105 Andres Galarraga .30 .75
106 Todd Van Poppel .15 .40
107 Ben Grieve .15 .40
108 Brent Gates .15 .40
109 Jason Giambi .50 1.25
110 Ruben Sierra .30 .75
111 Terry Steinbach .15 .40
112 Chris Hammond .15 .40
113 Charles Johnson .30 .75
114 Jesus Tavarez .15 .40
115 Gary Sheffield .30 .75
116 Chuck Carr .15 .40
117 Bobby Ayala .15 .40
118 Randy Johnson .75 2.00
119 Edgar Martinez .50 1.25
120 Alex Rodriguez 2.00 5.00
121 Kevin Foster .15 .40
122 Kevin Roberson .15 .40
123 Sammy Sosa .75 2.00
124 Steve Trachsel .15 .40
125 Eduardo Perez .15 .40
126 Tim Salmon .50 1.25
127 Todd Greene .15 .40
128 Jorge Fabregas .15 .40
129 Mark Langston .15 .40
130 Mitch Williams .15 .40
131 Raul Casanova .15 .40
132 Mel Nieves .15 .40
133 Andy Benes .15 .40
134 Dustin Hermanson .15 .40
135 Trevor Hoffman .30 .75
136 Mark Grudzielanek .50 1.25
137 Ugueth Urbina .15 .40
138 Moises Alou .30 .75
139 Roberto Kelly .15 .40
140 Rondell White .30 .75
141 Paul O'Neill .50 1.25
142 Jimmy Key .30 .75
143 Jack McDowell .15 .40
144 Ruben Rivera .15 .40
145 Don Mattingly 2.00 5.00
146 John Wetteland .30 .75
147 Tom Glavine .50 1.25
148 Marquis Grissom .30 .75
149 Javier Lopez .30 .75
150 Fred McGriff .50 1.25
151 Greg Maddux 1.25 3.00
152 Chris Sabo .15 .40
153 Ray Durham .30 .75
154 Robin Ventura .30 .75
155 Jim Abbott .50 1.25
156 Jimmy Hurst .15 .40
157 Tim Raines .30 .75
158 Dennis Martinez .30 .75
159 Kenny Lofton .30 .75
160 Dave Winfield .30 .75
161 Manny Ramirez .50 1.25
162 Jim Thome .50 1.25
163 Barry Larkin .50 1.25
164 Bret Boone .30 .75
165 Deion Sanders .50 1.25
166 Ron Gant .30 .75
167 Benito Santiago .30 .75
168 Hideo Nomo 2.00 5.00
169 Billy Ashley .15 .40
170 Roger Cedeno .15 .40
171 Ismael Valdes .15 .40
172 Eric Karros .30 .75
173 Rusty Greer .30 .75
174 Rick Helling .15 .40
175 Nolan Ryan 3.00 8.00
176 Dean Palmer .30 .75
177 Phil Plantier .15 .40
178 Darryl Kile .30 .75
179 Derek Bell .15 .40
180 Doug Drabek .15 .40
181 Craig Biggio .50 1.25
182 Kevin Brown .30 .75
183 Harold Baines .30 .75
184 Jeffrey Hammonds .15 .40
185 Chris Hoiles .15 .40
186 Mike Mussina .50 1.25
187 Bob Hamelin .15 .40
188 Jeff Montgomery .15 .40
189 Michael Tucker .15 .40
190 George Brett 2.00 5.00
191 Edgardo Alfonzo .30 .75
192 Brett Butler .30 .75
193 Bobby Jones .15 .40
194 Todd Hundley .15 .40
195 Bret Saberhagen .30 .75
196 Pat Hentgen .30 .75
197 Roberto Alomar .50 1.25
198 David Cone .30 .75
199 Carlos Delgado .30 .75
200 Joe Carter .30 .75
201 Wm. VanLandingham .15 .40
202 Rod Beck .15 .40
203 J.R. Phillips .15 .40
204 Darren Lewis .15 .40
205 Matt Williams .30 .75
206 Lenny Dykstra .30 .75
207 Dave Hollins .15 .40
208 Mike Schmidt 1.25 3.00
209 Charlie Hayes .15 .40
210 Mo Vaughn .30 .75
211 Jose Malave .15 .40
212 Roger Clemens 1.50 4.00
213 Jose Canseco .50 1.25
214 Mark Whiten .15 .40
215 Marty Cordova .15 .40
216 Rick Aguilera .15 .40
217 Kevin Tapani .15 .40
218 Chuck Knoblauch .30 .75
219 Al Martin .15 .40
220 Jay Bell .30 .75
221 Carlos Garcia .15 .40
222 Freddy Adrian Garcia .15 .40
223 Jon Lieber .15 .40
224 Danny Jackson .15 .40
225 Ozzie Smith 1.25 3.00
226 Brian Jordan .30 .75
227 Ken Hill .15 .40
228 Scott Cooper .15 .40
229 Chad Curtis .15 .40
230 Lou Whitaker .30 .75
231 Kirk Gibson .30 .75
232 Travis Fryman .30 .75
233 Jose Valentin .15 .40
234 Dave Nilsson .15 .40
235 Cal Eldred .15 .40
236 Matt Mieske .15 .40
237 Bill Swift .15 .40
238 Marvin Freeman .15 .40
239 Jason Bates .15 .40
240 Larry Walker .30 .75
241 Dave Nied .15 .40
242 Dante Bichette .30 .75
243 Dennis Eckersley .30 .75
244 Todd Stottlemyre .15 .40
245 Rickey Henderson .75 2.00
246 Geronimo Berroa .15 .40
247 Mark McGwire 2.00 5.00
248 Quilvio Veras .15 .40
249 Terry Pendleton .30 .75
250 Andre Dawson .30 .75
251 Jeff Conine .30 .75
252 Kurt Abbott .15 .40
253 Jay Buhner .30 .75
254 Darren Bragg .15 .40
255 Ken Griffey Jr. 1.25 3.00
256 Tino Martinez .50 1.25
257 Mark Grace .50 1.25
258 Ryne Sandberg 1.25 3.00
259 Randy Myers .15 .40
260 Howard Johnson .15 .40
261 Lee Smith .30 .75
262 J.T. Snow .30 .75
263 Chili Davis .30 .75
264 Chuck Finley .30 .75
265 Eddie Williams .15 .40
266 Joey Hamilton .15 .40
267 Ken Caminiti .30 .75
268 Andujar Cedeno .15 .40
269 Steve Finley .30 .75
270 Tony Gwynn 1.00 2.50

1995 Upper Deck Steal of a Deal

This set was inserted in hobby and retail packs at a rate of approximately one in 34. This 15-card standard-size set focuses on players who were acquired through, according to Upper Deck, "astute trades" or low round draft picks. The cards are numbered in the upper left with an "SD" prefix.

COMPLETE SET (15) 30.00 80.00
SD1 Mike Piazza 5.00 12.00
SD2 Fred McGriff 2.00 5.00
SD3 Kenny Lofton 1.25 3.00
SD4 Jose Oliva .60 1.50
SD5 Jeff Bagwell 2.00 5.00
SD6 Roberto Alomar 2.00 5.00
Joe Carter
SD7 Steve Karsay .60 1.50
SD8 Ozzie Smith 5.00 12.00
SD9 Dennis Eckersley 1.25 3.00
SD10 Jose Canseco 2.00 5.00
SD11 Carlos Baerga .60 1.50
SD12 Cecil Fielder 1.25 3.00
SD13 Don Mattingly 8.00 20.00
SD14 Bret Boone 1.25 3.00
SD15 Michael Jordan 10.00 25.00

1995 Upper Deck Trade Exchange

These five cards were randomly inserted into second series Upper Deck packs. A collector could send in these cards and receive nine cards from the trade set for the base 1995 Upper Deck set (numbers 451-495). These cards were redeemable until February 1, 1996.

COMPLETE SET (5) 2.50 5.00
TC1 Orel Hershiser .60 1.50
TC2 Terry Pendleton .40 1.00
TC3 Benito Santiago .60 1.50
TC4 Kevin Brown .75 2.00
TC5 Gregg Jefferies .40 1.00

1996 Upper Deck

The 1996 Upper Deck set was issued in two series of 240 cards, and a 30 card update set, for a total of 510 cards. The cards were distributed in 10-card packs with a suggested retail price of $1.99, and 28 packs were contained in each box. Upper Deck issued 15,000 factory sets (containing all 510 cards) at season's end. In addition to being included in factory sets, the 30-card Update sets (U481-U510) were also available via mail through a wrapper exchange program. The attractive fronts of each basic card feature a full-bleed photo above a bronze foil bar that includes the player's name, team and position in a white oval. Subsets include Young at Heart (100-117), Beat the Odds (145-153), Postseason Checklist (218-222), Best of a Generation (370-387), Strange But True (415-423) and Managerial Salute Checklists (476-480). The only Rookie Card of note is Livan Hernandez.

COMPLETE SET (480) 20.00 50.00
COMP.FACT.SET (510) 50.00 100.00
COMP. SERIES 1 (240) 10.00 25.00
COMP. SERIES 2 (240) 10.00 25.00
COMMON CARD (1-480) .10 .30
COMP.UPDATE SET (30) 10.00 20.00
COMMON (481U-510U) .20 .50
1 Cal Ripken 2131 1.50 4.00
2 Eddie Murray 3000 Hits .20 .50
3 Mark Wohlers .10 .30
4 David Justice .10 .30
5 Chipper Jones .30 .75
6 Javier Lopez .10 .30
7 Mark Lemke .10 .30
8 Marquis Grissom .10 .30
9 Tom Glavine .20 .50
10 Greg Maddux .50 1.25
11 Manny Alexander .10 .30
12 Curtis Goodwin .10 .30
13 Scott Erickson .10 .30
14 Chris Hoiles .10 .30
15 Rafael Palmeiro .20 .50
16 Rick Krivda .10 .30
17 Jeff Manto .10 .30
18 Mo Vaughn .10 .30
19 Tim Wakefield .10 .30
20 Roger Clemens .60 1.50
21 Tim Naehring .10 .30
22 Troy O'Leary .10 .30
23 Mike Greenwell .10 .30
24 Stan Belinda .10 .30
25 John Valentin .10 .30
26 J.T. Snow .10 .30
27 Gary DiSarcina .10 .30
28 Mark Langston .10 .30
29 Brian Anderson .10 .30
30 Jim Edmonds .10 .30
31 Garret Anderson .10 .30
32 Orlando Palmeiro .10 .30
33 Brian McRae .10 .30
34 Kevin Foster .10 .30
35 Sammy Sosa .30 .75
36 Todd Zeile .10 .30
37 Jim Bullinger .10 .30
38 Luis Gonzalez .10 .30
39 Lyle Mouton .10 .30
40 Ray Durham .10 .30
41 Ozzie Guillen .10 .30
42 Alex Fernandez .10 .30
43 Brian Keyser .10 .30
44 Robin Ventura .10 .30
45 Reggie Sanders .10 .30
46 Pete Schourek .10 .30
47 John Smiley .10 .30
48 Jeff Brantley .10 .30
49 Thomas Howard .10 .30
50 Bret Boone .10 .30
51 Kevin Jarvis .10 .30
52 Jeff Branson .10 .30
53 Carlos Baerga .10 .30
54 Jim Thome .20 .50
55 Manny Ramirez .20 .50
56 Omar Vizquel .20 .50
57 Jose Mesa .10 .30
58 Julian Tavarez UER .10 .30
59 Orel Hershiser .10 .30
60 Larry Walker .10 .30
61 Bret Saberhagen .10 .30
62 Vinny Castilla .10 .30
63 Eric Young .10 .30
64 Bryan Rekar .10 .30
65 Andres Galarraga .10 .30
66 Steve Reed .10 .30
67 Chad Curtis .10 .30
68 Bobby Higginson .10 .30
69 Phil Nevin .10 .30
70 Cecil Fielder .10 .30
71 Felipe Lira .10 .30
72 Chris Gomez .10 .30
73 Charles Johnson .10 .30
74 Quilvio Veras .10 .30
75 Jeff Conine .10 .30
76 John Burkett .10 .30
77 Greg Colbrunn .10 .30
78 Terry Pendleton .10 .30
79 Shane Reynolds .10 .30
80 Jeff Bagwell .20 .50
81 Orlando Miller .10 .30
82 Mike Hampton .10 .30
83 James Mouton .10 .30
84 Brian L. Hunter .10 .30
85 Derek Bell .10 .30
86 Kevin Appier .10 .30
87 Joe Vitiello .10 .30
88 Wally Joyner .10 .30
89 Michael Tucker .10 .30
90 Johnny Damon .20 .50
91 Jon Nunnally .10 .30
92 Jason Jacome .10 .30
93 Chad Fonville .10 .30
94 Chan Ho Park .10 .30
95 Hideo Nomo .30 .75
96 Ismael Valdes .10 .30
97 Greg Gagne .10 .30
98 Arizona Diamondbacks .30 .75
Tampa Bay Devil Rays
99 Raul Mondesi .10 .30
100 Dave Winfield YH .10 .30
101 Dennis Eckersley YH .10 .30
102 Andre Dawson YH .10 .30
103 Dennis Martinez YH .10 .30
104 Lance Parrish YH .10 .30
105 Eddie Murray YH .20 .50
106 Alan Trammell YH .10 .30
107 Lou Whitaker YH .10 .30
108 Ozzie Smith YH .30 .75
109 Paul Molitor YH .10 .30
110 Rickey Henderson YH .20 .50
111 Tim Raines YH .10 .30
112 Harold Baines YH .10 .30
113 Lee Smith YH .10 .30
114 F.Valenzuela YH .10 .30
115 Cal Ripken YH .50 1.25
116 Tony Gwynn YH .20 .50
117 Wade Boggs .20 .50
118 Todd Hollandsworth .10 .30
119 Dave Nilsson .10 .30
120 Jose Valentin .10 .30
121 Steve Sparks .10 .30
122 Chuck Carr .10 .30
123 John Jaha .10 .30
124 Scott Karl .10 .30
125 Chuck Knoblauch .10 .30
126 Brad Radke .10 .30
127 Pat Meares .10 .30
128 Ron Coomer .10 .30
129 Pedro Munoz .10 .30
130 Kirby Puckett .30 .75
131 David Segui .10 .30
132 Mark Grudzielanek .10 .30
133 Mike Lansing .10 .30
134 Sean Berry .10 .30
135 Rondell White .10 .30
136 Pedro Martinez .20 .50
137 Carl Everett .10 .30
138 Dave Mlicki .10 .30
139 Bill Pulsipher .10 .30
140 Jason Isringhausen .10 .30
141 Rico Brogna .10 .30
142 Edgardo Alfonzo .10 .30
143 Jeff Kent .10 .30
144 Andy Pettitte .20 .50
145 Mike Piazza BO .30 .75
146 Cliff Floyd BO .10 .30
147 J.Isringhausen BO .10 .30
148 Tim Wakefield BO .10 .30
149 Chipper Jones BO .20 .50
150 Hideo Nomo BO .20 .50
151 Mark McGwire BO .40 1.00
152 Ron Gant BO .10 .30
153 Gary Gaetti BO .10 .30
154 Don Mattingly .75 2.00
155 Paul O'Neill .20 .50
156 Derek Jeter .75 2.00
157 Joe Girardi .10 .30
158 Ruben Sierra .10 .30
159 Jorge Posada .20 .50
160 Geronimo Berroa .10 .30
161 Steve Ontiveros .10 .30
162 George Williams .10 .30
163 Doug Johns .10 .30
164 Ariel Prieto .10 .30
165 Scott Brosius .10 .30
166 Mike Bordick .10 .30
167 Tyler Green .10 .30
168 Mickey Morandini .10 .30
169 Darren Daulton .10 .30
170 Gregg Jefferies .10 .30
171 Jim Eisenreich .10 .30
172 Heathcliff Slocumb .10 .30
173 Kevin Stocker .10 .30
174 Esteban Loaiza .10 .30
175 Jeff King .10 .30
176 Mark Johnson .10 .30
177 Denny Neagle .10 .30
178 Orlando Merced .10 .30
179 Carlos Garcia .10 .30
180 Brian Jordan .10 .30
181 Mike Morgan .10 .30
182 Mark Petkovsek .10 .30
183 Bernard Gilkey .10 .30
184 John Mabry .10 .30
185 Tom Henke .10 .30
186 Glenn Dishman .10 .30
187 Andy Ashby .10 .30
188 Bip Roberts .10 .30
189 Melvin Nieves .10 .30
190 Ken Caminiti .10 .30
191 Brad Ausmus .10 .30
192 Deion Sanders .20 .50
193 Jamie Brewington RC .10 .30
194 Glenallen Hill .10 .30
195 Barry Bonds .75 2.00
196 Wm. Van Landingham .10 .30
197 Mark Carreon .10 .30
198 Royce Clayton .10 .30
199 Joey Cora .10 .30
200 Ken Griffey Jr. .50 1.25
201 Jay Buhner .10 .30
202 Alex Rodriguez .60 1.50
203 Norm Charlton .10 .30
204 Andy Benes .10 .30
205 Edgar Martinez .20 .50
206 Juan Gonzalez .10 .30
207 Will Clark .20 .50
208 Kevin Gross .10 .30
209 Roger Pavlik .10 .30
210 Ivan Rodriguez .20 .50
211 Rusty Greer .10 .30
212 Angel Martinez .10 .30
213 Tomas Perez .10 .30
214 Alex Gonzalez .10 .30
215 Joe Carter .10 .30
216 Shawn Green .10 .30
217 Edwin Hurtado .10 .30
218 Edgar Martinez .10 .30
Tony Pena CL
219 Chipper Jones .20 .50
Barry Larkin CL
220 Orel Hershiser CL .10 .30
221 Mike Devereaux CL .10 .30
222 Tom Glavine CL .10 .30
223 Karim Garcia .10 .30
224 Arquimedez Pozo .10 .30
225 Billy Wagner .10 .30
226 John Wasdin .10 .30
227 Jeff Suppan .10 .30
228 Steve Gibralter .10 .30
229 Jimmy Haynes .10 .30
230 Ruben Rivera .10 .30
231 Chris Snopek .10 .30
232 Alex Ochoa .10 .30
233 Shannon Stewart .10 .30
234 Quinton McCracken .10 .30
235 Trey Beamon .10 .30
236 Billy McMillon .10 .30
237 Steve Cox .10 .30
238 George Arias .10 .30
239 Yamil Benitez .10 .30
240 Todd Greene .10 .30
241 Jason Kendall .10 .30
242 Brooks Kieschnick .10 .30
243 O. Fernandez RC .10 .30
244 Livan Hernandez RC .40 1.00
245 Rey Ordonez .10 .30
246 Mike Grace RC .10 .30
247 Jay Canizaro .10 .30
248 Bob Wolcott .10 .30
249 Jermaine Dye .10 .30
250 Jason Schmidt .20 .50
251 Mike Sweeney RC .40 1.00
252 Marcus Jensen .10 .30
253 Mendy Lopez .10 .30
254 Wilton Guerrero RC .10 .30
255 Paul Wilson .10 .30
256 Edgar Renteria .10 .30
257 Richard Hidalgo .10 .30
258 Bob Abreu .30 .75
259 Robert Smith RC .10 .30
260 Sal Fasano .10 .30
261 Enrique Wilson .10 .30
262 Rich Hunter RC .10 .30
263 Sergio Nunez .10 .30
264 Dan Serafini .10 .30
265 David Doster .10 .30
266 Ryan McGuire .10 .30
267 Scott Spiezio .10 .30
268 Rafael Orellano .10 .30
269 Steve Avery .10 .30
270 Fred McGriff .20 .50
271 John Smoltz .20 .50
272 Ryan Klesko .10 .30
273 Jeff Blauser .10 .30
274 Brad Clontz .10 .30
275 Roberto Alomar .20 .50
276 B.J. Surhoff .10 .30
277 Jeffrey Hammonds .10 .30
278 Brady Anderson .10 .30
279 Bobby Bonilla .10 .30
280 Cal Ripken 1.00 2.50
281 Mike Mussina .20 .50
282 Wil Cordero .10 .30
283 Mike Stanley .10 .30
284 Aaron Sele .10 .30
285 Jose Canseco .20 .50
286 Tom Gordon .10 .30
287 Heathcliff Slocumb .10 .30
288 Lee Smith .10 .30

289 Troy Percival .10 .30
290 Tim Salmon .20 .50
291 Chuck Finley .10 .30
292 Jim Abbott .20 .50
293 Chili Davis .10 .30
294 Steve Trachsel .10 .30
295 Mark Grace .20 .50
296 Rey Sanchez .10 .30
297 Scott Servais .10 .30
298 Jaime Navarro .10 .30
299 Frank Castillo .10 .30
300 Frank Thomas .30 .75
301 Jason Bere .10 .30
302 Danny Tartabull .10 .30
303 Darren Lewis .10 .30
304 Roberto Hernandez .10 .30
305 Tony Phillips .10 .30
306 Wilson Alvarez .10 .30
307 Jose Rijo .10 .30
308 Hal Morris .10 .30
309 Mark Portugal .10 .30
310 Barry Larkin .20 .50
311 Dave Burba .10 .30
312 Eddie Taubensee .10 .30
313 Sandy Alomar Jr. .10 .30
314 Dennis Martinez .10 .30
315 Albert Belle .10 .30
316 Eddie Murray .30 .75
317 Charles Nagy .10 .30
318 Chad Ogea .10 .30
319 Kenny Lofton .10 .30
320 Dante Bichette .10 .30
321 Armando Reynoso .10 .30
322 Walt Weiss .10 .30
323 Ellis Burks .10 .30
324 Kevin Ritz .10 .30
325 Bill Swift .10 .30
326 Jason Bates .10 .30
327 Tony Clark .10 .30
328 Travis Fryman .10 .30
329 Mark Parent .10 .30
330 Alan Trammell .10 .30
331 C.J. Nitkowski .10 .30
332 Jose Lima .10 .30
333 Phil Plantier .10 .30
334 Kurt Abbott .10 .30
335 Andre Dawson .10 .30
336 Chris Hammond .10 .30
337 Robb Nen .10 .30
338 Pat Rapp .10 .30
339 Al Leiter .10 .30
340 Gary Sheffield UER .10 .30
(HR total says 17
341 Todd Jones .10 .30
342 Doug Drabek .10 .30
343 Greg Swindell .10 .30
344 Tony Eusebio .10 .30
345 Craig Biggio .20 .50
346 Darryl Kile .10 .30
347 Mike Macfarlane .10 .30
348 Jeff Montgomery .10 .30
349 Chris Haney .10 .30
350 Bip Roberts .10 .30
351 Tom Goodwin .10 .30
352 Mark Gubicza .10 .30
353 Joe Randa .10 .30
354 Ramon Martinez .10 .30
355 Eric Karros .10 .30
356 Delino DeShields .10 .30
357 Brett Butler .10 .30
358 Todd Worrell .10 .30
359 Mike Blowers .10 .30
360 Mike Piazza .50 1.25
361 Ben McDonald .10 .30
362 Ricky Bones .10 .30
363 Greg Vaughn .10 .30
364 Matt Mieske .10 .30
365 Kevin Seitzer .10 .30
366 Jeff Cirillo .10 .30
367 LaTroy Hawkins .10 .30
368 Frank Rodriguez .10 .30
369 Rick Aguilera .10 .30
370 Roberto Alomar BG .10 .30
371 Albert Belle BG .10 .30
372 Wade Boggs BG .10 .30
373 Barry Bonds BG .40 1.00
374 Roger Clemens BG .30 .75
375 Dennis Eckersley BG .10 .30
376 Ken Griffey Jr. BG .30 .75
377 Tony Gwynn BG .20 .50
378 Rickey Henderson BG .20 .50
379 Greg Maddux BG .30 .75
380 Fred McGriff BG .10 .30
381 Paul Molitor BG .10 .30
382 Eddie Murray BG .20 .50
383 Mike Piazza BG .30 .75
384 Kirby Puckett BG .20 .50
385 Cal Ripken BG .50 1.25
386 Ozzie Smith BG .30 .75
387 Frank Thomas BG .20 .50
388 Matt Walbeck .10 .30
389 Dave Stevens .10 .30
390 Marty Cordova .10 .30
391 Darrin Fletcher .10 .30
392 Cliff Floyd .10 .30
393 Mel Rojas .10 .30
394 Shane Andrews .10 .30
395 Moises Alou .10 .30
396 Carlos Perez .10 .30
397 Jeff Fassero .10 .30
398 Bobby Jones .10 .30
399 Todd Hundley .10 .30
400 John Franco .10 .30
401 Jose Vizcaino .10 .30
402 Bernard Gilkey .10 .30
403 Pete Harnisch .10 .30
404 Pat Kelly .10 .30
405 David Cone .10 .30
406 Bernie Williams .20 .50
407 John Wetteland .10 .30
408 Scott Kamieniecki .10 .30
409 Tim Raines .10 .30
410 Wade Boggs .20 .50
411 Terry Steinbach .10 .30
412 Jason Giambi .10 .30
413 Todd Van Poppel .10 .30
414 Pedro Munoz .10 .30
415 Eddie Murray SBT .20 .50
416 Dennis Eckersley SBT .10 .30
417 Bip Roberts SBT .10 .30
418 Glenallen Hill SBT .10 .30
419 John Hudek SBT .10 .30
420 Derek Bell SBT .10 .30
421 Larry Walker SBT .10 .30
422 Greg Maddux SBT .30 .75
423 Ken Caminiti SBT .10 .30
424 Brent Gates .10 .30
425 Mark McGwire .75 2.00
426 Mark Whiten .10 .30
427 Sid Fernandez .10 .30
428 Ricky Bottalico .10 .30
429 Mike Mimbs .10 .30
430 Lenny Dykstra .10 .30
431 Todd Zeile .10 .30
432 Benito Santiago .10 .30
433 Danny Miceli .10 .30
434 Al Martin .10 .30
435 Jay Bell .10 .30
436 Charlie Hayes .10 .30
437 Mike Kingery .10 .30
438 Paul Wagner .10 .30
439 Tom Pagnozzi .10 .30
440 Ozzie Smith .50 1.25
441 Ray Lankford .10 .30
442 Dennis Eckersley .10 .30
443 Ron Gant .10 .30
444 Alan Benes .10 .30
445 Rickey Henderson .30 .75
446 Jody Reed .10 .30
447 Trevor Hoffman .10 .30
448 Andujar Cedeno .10 .30
449 Steve Finley .10 .30
450 Tony Gwynn .40 1.00
451 Joey Hamilton .10 .30
452 Mark Leiter .10 .30
453 Rod Beck .10 .30
454 Kirt Manwaring .10 .30
455 Matt Williams .10 .30
456 Robby Thompson .10 .30
457 Shawon Dunston .10 .30
458 Russ Davis .10 .30
459 Paul Sorrento .10 .30
460 Randy Johnson .30 .75
461 Chris Bosio .10 .30
462 Luis Sojo .10 .30
463 Sterling Hitchcock .10 .30
464 Benji Gil .10 .30
465 Mickey Tettleton .10 .30
466 Mark McLemore .10 .30
467 Darryl Hamilton .10 .30
468 Ken Hill .10 .30
469 Dean Palmer .10 .30
470 Carlos Delgado .10 .30
471 Ed Sprague .10 .30
472 Otis Nixon .10 .30
473 Pat Hentgen .10 .30
474 Juan Guzman .10 .30
475 John Olerud .10 .30
476 Buck Showalter CL .10 .30
477 Bobby Cox CL .10 .30
478 Tommy Lasorda CL .10 .30
479 Buck Showalter CL .10 .30
480 Sparky Anderson CL .10 .30
481U Randy Myers .20 .50
482U Kent Mercker .20 .50
483U David Wells .30 .75
484U Kevin Mitchell .20 .50
485U Randy Velarde .20 .50
486U Ryne Sandberg 1.50 4.00
487U Doug Jones .20 .50
488U Terry Adams .20 .50
489U Kevin Tapani .20 .50
490U Harold Baines .30 .75
491U Eric Davis .30 .75
492U Julio Franco .30 .75
493U Jack McDowell .20 .50
494U Devon White .30 .75
495U Kevin Brown .30 .75
496U Rick Wilkins .20 .50
497U Sean Berry .20 .50
498U Keith Lockhart .20 .50
499U Mark Loretta .20 .50
500U Paul Molitor .30 .75
501U Roberto Kelly .20 .50
502U Lance Johnson .20 .50
503U Tino Martinez .50 1.25
504U Kenny Rogers .30 .75
505U Todd Stottlemyre .20 .50
506U Gary Gaetti .30 .75
507U Royce Clayton .20 .50
508U Andy Benes .20 .50
509U Wally Joyner .30 .75
510U Erik Hanson .20 .50
P100 Ken Griffey Jr Promo 1.25 3.00

1996 Upper Deck Blue Chip Prospects

Randomly inserted in first series retail packs at a rate of one in 72, this 20-card set, diecut on the top and bottom, features some of the best young stars in the majors against a bluish background.

COMPLETE SET (20) 40.00 100.00
BC1 Hideo Nomo 4.00 10.00
BC2 Johnny Damon 2.50 6.00
BC3 Jason Isringhausen 1.50 4.00
BC4 Bill Pulsipher 1.50 4.00
BC5 Marty Cordova 1.50 4.00
BC6 Michael Tucker 1.50 4.00
BC7 John Wasdin 1.50 4.00
BC8 Karim Garcia 1.50 4.00
BC9 Ruben Rivera 1.50 4.00
BC10 Chipper Jones 4.00 10.00
BC11 Billy Wagner 1.50 4.00
BC12 Brooks Kieschnick 1.50 4.00
BC13 Alan Benes 1.50 4.00
BC14 Roger Cedeno 1.50 4.00
BC15 Alex Rodriguez 8.00 20.00
BC16 Jason Schmidt 2.50 6.00
BC17 Derek Jeter 10.00 25.00
BC18 Brian L.Hunter 1.50 4.00
BC19 Garret Anderson 1.50 4.00
BC20 Manny Ramirez 2.50 6.00

1996 Upper Deck Diamond Destiny

Issued one per Wal Mart pack, these 40 cards feature leading players of baseball. The cards have two photos on the front with the player's name listed on the bottom. The backs have another photo along with biographical information.

COMPLETE SET (40) 30.00 80.00
*GOLD: 5X TO 12 X BASIC DESTINY
GOLD ODDS 1:143 UD TECH RETAIL PACKS
*SILVER: 1.5X TO 4X BASIC DESTINY
SILVER ODDS 1:35 UD TECH RETAIL PACKS
DD1 Chipper Jones 1.00 2.50
DD2 Fred McGriff .60 1.50
DD3 John Smoltz .60 1.50
DD4 Ryan Klesko .40 1.00
DD5 Greg Maddux 1.50 4.00
DD6 Cal Ripken 3.00 8.00
DD7 Roberto Alomar .60 1.50
DD8 Eddie Murray 1.00 2.50
DD9 Brady Anderson .40 1.00
DD10 Mo Vaughn .40 1.00
DD11 Roger Clemens 2.00 5.00
DD12 Darin Erstad .75 2.00
DD13 Sammy Sosa 1.00 2.50
DD14 Frank Thomas 1.00 2.50
DD15 Barry Larkin .60 1.50
DD16 Albert Belle .40 1.00
DD17 Manny Ramirez .60 1.50
DD18 Kenny Lofton .40 1.00
DD19 Dante Bichette .40 1.00
DD20 Gary Sheffield .40 1.00
DD21 Jeff Bagwell .60 1.50
DD22 Hideo Nomo 1.00 2.50
DD23 Mike Piazza 1.50 4.00
DD24 Kirby Puckett 1.00 2.50
DD25 Paul Molitor 1.00 2.50
DD26 Chuck Knoblauch .40 1.00
DD27 Wade Boggs .60 1.50
DD28 Derek Jeter 2.50 6.00
DD29 Rey Ordonez .40 1.00
DD30 Mark McGwire 2.50 6.00
DD31 Ozzie Smith 1.50 4.00
DD32 Tony Gwynn 1.25 3.00
DD33 Barry Bonds 2.50 6.00
DD34 Matt Williams .40 1.00
DD35 Ken Griffey Jr. 1.50 4.00
DD36 Jay Buhner .40 1.00
DD37 Randy Johnson 1.00 2.50
DD38 Alex Rodriguez 2.00 5.00
DD39 Juan Gonzalez .40 1.00
DD40 Joe Carter .40 1.00

1996 Upper Deck Future Stock Prospects

Randomly inserted in packs at a rate of one in 6, this 20-card set highlights the top prospects who made their major league debuts in 1995. The cards are diecut at the top and feature a purple border surrounding the player's picture.

COMPLETE SET (20) 3.00 8.00
FS1 George Arias .40 1.00
FS2 Brian Barber .40 1.00
FS3 Trey Beamon .40 1.00
FS4 Yamil Benitez .40 1.00
FS5 Jamie Brewington .40 1.00
FS6 Tony Clark .40 1.00
FS7 Steve Cox .40 1.00
FS8 Carlos Delgado .40 1.00
FS9 Chad Fonville .40 1.00
FS10 Alex Ochoa .40 1.00
FS11 Curtis Goodwin .40 1.00
FS12 Todd Greene .40 1.00
FS13 Jimmy Haynes .40 1.00
FS14 Quinton McCracken .40 1.00
FS15 Billy McMillon .40 1.00
FS16 Chan Ho Park .40 1.00
FS17 Arquimedez Pozo .40 1.00
FS18 Chris Snopek .40 1.00
FS19 Shannon Stewart .40 1.00
FS20 Jeff Suppan .40 1.00

1996 Upper Deck Gameface

These Gameface cards were seeded at a rate of one per Upper Deck and Collector's Choice Wal Mart retail pack. The Upper Deck packs contained eight cards and the Collector's Choice packs contained sixteen cards. Both packs carried a suggested retail price of $1.50. The card fronts feature the player's photo surrounded by a "cloudy" white border along with a Gameface logo at the bottom.

COMPLETE SET (10) 5.00 12.00
GF1 Ken Griffey Jr. .50 1.25
GF2 Frank Thomas .30 .75
GF3 Barry Bonds .75 2.00
GF4 Albert Belle .10 .30
GF5 Cal Ripken 1.00 2.50
GF6 Mike Piazza .50 1.25
GF7 Chipper Jones .30 .75
GF8 Matt Williams .10 .30
GF9 Hideo Nomo .30 .75
GF10 Greg Maddux .50 1.25

1996 Upper Deck Hot Commodities

Cards from this 20 card set double die-cut set were randomly inserted into series two Upper Deck packs at a rate of one in 37. The set features some of baseball's most popular players.

COMPLETE SET (20) 60.00 150.00
HC1 Ken Griffey Jr. 5.00 12.00
HC2 Hideo Nomo 3.00 8.00
HC3 Roberto Alomar 2.00 5.00
HC4 Paul Wilson 1.25 3.00
HC5 Albert Belle 1.25 3.00
HC6 Manny Ramirez 2.00 5.00
HC7 Kirby Puckett 3.00 8.00
HC8 Johnny Damon 2.00 5.00
HC9 Randy Johnson 3.00 8.00
HC10 Greg Maddux 5.00 12.00
HC11 Chipper Jones 3.00 8.00
HC12 Barry Bonds 8.00 20.00
HC13 Mo Vaughn 1.25 3.00
HC14 Mike Piazza 5.00 12.00
HC15 Cal Ripken 10.00 25.00
HC16 Tim Salmon 2.00 5.00
HC17 Sammy Sosa 3.00 8.00
HC18 Kenny Lofton 1.25 3.00
HC19 Tony Gwynn 4.00 10.00
HC20 Frank Thomas 3.00 8.00

1996 Upper Deck V.J. Lovero Showcase

Upper Deck utilized photos from the files of V.J. Lovero to produce this set. The cards feature the photos along with a story of how Lovero took the photos. The cards are numbered with a "VJ" prefix. These cards were inserted at a rate of one every six packs.

COMPLETE SET (19) 10.00 25.00
VJ1 Jim Abbott .50 1.25
VJ2 Hideo Nomo .75 2.00
VJ3 Derek Jeter 2.00 5.00
VJ4 Barry Bonds 2.00 5.00
VJ5 Greg Maddux 1.25 3.00
VJ6 Mark McGwire 2.00 5.00
VJ7 Jose Canseco .50 1.25
VJ8 Ken Caminiti .30 .75
VJ9 Raul Mondesi .30 .75
VJ10 Ken Griffey Jr. 1.25 3.00
VJ11 Jay Buhner .30 .75
VJ12 Randy Johnson .75 2.00
VJ13 Roger Clemens 1.50 4.00
VJ14 Brady Anderson .30 .75
VJ15 Frank Thomas .75 2.00
VJ16 Garret Anderson .30 .75
Jim Edmonds
Tim Salmon
VJ17 Mike Piazza 1.25 3.00
VJ18 Dante Bichette .30 .75
VJ19 Tony Gwynn 1.00 2.50

1996 Upper Deck Nomo Highlights

Los Angeles Dodgers star pitcher and Upper Deck spokesperson Hideo Nomo was featured in this special five card set. The cards were randomly seeded into second series packs at a rate of one in 24 and feature game action as well as descriptions of some of Nomo's key 1995 games.

COMPLETE SET (5) 8.00 20.00
COMMON CARD (1-5) 2.00 5.00

1996 Upper Deck Power Driven

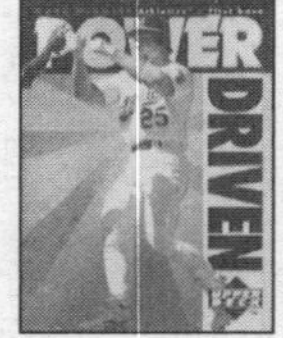

Randomly inserted in first series packs at a rate of one in 36, this 20-card set consists of embossed rainbow foil inserts of baseball's top power hitters.

COMPLETE SET (20) 50.00 120.00
PD1 Albert Belle 1.25 3.00
PD2 Barry Bonds 8.00 20.00
PD3 Jay Buhner 1.25 3.00
PD4 Jose Canseco 2.00 5.00
PD5 Cecil Fielder 1.25 3.00
PD6 Juan Gonzalez 1.25 3.00
PD7 Ken Griffey Jr. 5.00 12.00
PD8 Todd Hundley 1.25 3.00
PD9 Fred McGriff 2.00 5.00
PD10 Mark McGwire 8.00 20.00
PD11 Rafael Palmeiro 2.00 5.00
PD12 Mike Piazza 5.00 12.00
PD13 Manny Ramirez 2.00 5.00
PD14 Tim Salmon 2.00 5.00
PD15 Reggie Sanders 1.25 3.00
PD16 Sammy Sosa 3.00 8.00
PD17 Frank Thomas 3.00 8.00
PD18 Mo Vaughn 1.25 3.00
PD19 Larry Walker 1.25 3.00
PD20 Matt Williams 1.25 3.00

1996 Upper Deck Predictor Hobby

Randomly inserted in both series hobby packs at a rate of one in 12, this 60-card predictor set offered six different 10-card parallel exchange sets for players as featured players competed for monthly milestones and awards. The fronts feature a cutout player photo against a pinstriped background surrounded by a gray marble border. Card backs feature game rules and guidelines. Winner cards are signified with a W in our listings and are in noticeably shorter supply since they had to be mailed in to Upper Deck (where they were destroyed) to claim your exchange cards. The deadline to mail in winning cards was November 18th, 1996.

COMPLETE SERIES 1 (30) 12.50 30.00
COMPLETE SERIES 2 (30) 12.50 30.00
*EXCHANGE: .4X TO 1X BASIC PREDICTOR
ONE EXCH.SET VIA MAIL PER PRED.WINNER
H1 Albert Belle .25 .60
H2 Kenny Lofton .25 .60
H3 Rafael Palmeiro .40 1.00
H4 Ken Griffey Jr. 1.00 2.50
H5 Tim Salmon .40 1.00
H6 Cal Ripken 2.00 5.00
H7 Mark McGwire W 1.50 4.00
H8 Frank Thomas W .60 1.50
H9 Mo Vaughn W .25 .60
H10 Player of Month LS W .25 .60
H11 Roger Clemens 1.25 3.00
H12 David Cone .25 .60
H13 Jose Mesa .25 .60
H14 Randy Johnson .60 1.50
H15 Chuck Finley .25 .60
H16 Mike Mussina .40 1.00
H17 Kevin Appier .25 .60
H18 Kenny Rogers .60 1.50
H19 Lee Smith .25 .60
H20 Pitcher of Month LS W .25 .60
H21 George Arias .25 .60
H22 Jose Herrera .25 .60
H23 Tony Clark .25 .60
H24 Todd Greene .25 .60
H25 Derek Jeter W 1.50 4.00
H26 Arquimedez Pozo .25 .60
H27 Matt Lawton .25 .60
H28 Shannon Stewart .25 .60
H29 Chris Snopek .25 .60
H30 Most Rookie Hits LS .25 .60
H31 Jeff Bagwell W .40 1.00
H32 Dante Bichette .25 .60
H33 Barry Bonds W 1.50 4.00
H34 Tony Gwynn .75 2.00
H35 Chipper Jones .60 1.50
H36 Eric Karros .25 .60
H37 Barry Larkin .40 1.00
H38 Mike Piazza 1.00 2.50
H39 Matt Williams .25 .60
H40 Long Shot Card .25 .60
H41 Osvaldo Fernandez .25 .60
H42 Tom Glavine .40 1.00
H43 Jason Isringhausen .25 .60
H44 Greg Maddux 1.00 2.50
H45 Pedro Martinez .40 1.00
H46 Hideo Nomo .60 1.50
H47 Pete Schourek .25 .60
H48 Paul Wilson .25 .60
H49 Mark Wohlers .25 .60
H50 Long Shot Card .25 .60
H51 Bob Abreu .60 1.50
H52 Trey Beamon .25 .60
H53 Yamil Benitez .25 .60
H54 Roger Cedeno .25 .60
H55 Todd Hollandsworth .25 .60
H56 Marvin Benard .25 .60
H57 Jason Kendall .25 .60
H58 Brooks Kieschnick .25 .60
H59 Rey Ordonez W .25 .60
H60 Long Shot Card .25 .60

1996 Upper Deck Predictor Retail

Randomly inserted in both series retail packs at a rate of one in 12, this 60-card Predictor set offered six different 10-card parallel exchange sets as featured players competed for "monthly milestones and awards." The fronts feature a "cutout" player photo against a pinstriped background surrounded by a gray marble border. Card backs feature game rules and guidelines. Winner cards are signified with a W in our listings and are in noticeably shorter supply since they had to be mailed in to Upper Deck (where they were destroyed) to claim your exchange cards. The expiration date to send in cards was November 18th, 1996.

COMPLETE SERIES 1 (30) 15.00 40.00
COMPLETE SERIES 2 (30) 15.00 40.00
*EXCHANGE: .4X TO 1X BASIC PREDICTOR
ONE EXCH.SET VIA MAIL PER PRED.WINNER
R1 Albert Belle W .25 .60
R2 Jay Buhner W .25 .60
R3 Juan Gonzalez .25 .60
R4 Ken Griffey Jr. 1.00 2.50
R5 Mark McGwire W 1.50 4.00
R6 Rafael Palmeiro .40 1.00
R7 Tim Salmon .40 1.00
R8 Frank Thomas .60 1.50
R9 Mo Vaughn W .25 .60
R10 Monthly HR Ldr LS W .25 .60
R11 Albert Belle W .25 .60
R12 Jay Buhner .25 .60
R13 Jim Edmonds .25 .60
R14 Cecil Fielder .25 .60
R15 Ken Griffey Jr. 1.00 2.50
R16 Edgar Martinez .40 1.00
R17 Manny Ramirez .40 1.00
R18 Frank Thomas .60 1.50
R19 Mo Vaughn W .25 .60
R20 Monthly RBI Ldr LS W .25 .60
R21 Roberto Alomar W .40 1.00
R22 Carlos Baerga .25 .60
R23 Wade Boggs .40 1.00
R24 Ken Griffey Jr. 1.00 2.50
R25 Chuck Knoblauch .25 .60
R26 Kenny Lofton .25 .60
R27 Edgar Martinez .40 1.00
R28 Tim Salmon .40 1.00
R29 Frank Thomas .60 1.50
R30 Monthly Hits Ldr Longshot W .25 .60
R31 Dante Bichette .25 .60
R32 Barry Bonds W 1.50 4.00
R33 Ron Gant .25 .60
R34 Chipper Jones .60 1.50
R35 Fred McGriff .40 1.00
R36 Mike Piazza 1.00 2.50
R37 Sammy Sosa .60 1.50
R38 Larry Walker .25 .60
R39 Matt Williams .25 .60
R40 Long Shot Card .25 .60
R41 Jeff Bagwell W .40 1.00
R42 Dante Bichette .25 .60
R43 Barry Bonds W 1.50 4.00
R44 Jeff Conine .25 .60
R45 Andres Galarraga .25 .60
R46 Mike Piazza 1.00 2.50
R47 Reggie Sanders .25 .60
R48 Sammy Sosa .60 1.50
R49 Matt Williams .25 .60
R50 Long Shot Card .25 .60
R51 Jeff Bagwell .40 1.00
R52 Derek Bell .25 .60
R53 Dante Bichette .25 .60
R54 Craig Biggio .40 1.00
R55 Barry Bonds 1.50 4.00
R56 Bret Boone .25 .60
R57 Tony Gwynn .75 2.00
R58 Barry Larkin .40 1.00
R59 Mike Piazza W 1.00 2.50
R60 Long Shot Card .25 .60

1996 Upper Deck Ripken Collection

This 23 card set was issued across all the various Upper Deck brands. The cards were issued to commemorate Cal Ripken's career, which had been capped the previous season by the breaking of the consecutive game streak long held by Lou Gehrig. The cards were inserted at the following ratios: Cards 1-4 were in Collector Choice first series packs at a rate of one in 12. Cards 5-8 were inserted into Upper Deck series one packs at a rate of one in 24. Cards 9-12 were placed into second series Collector Choice packs at a rate of one in 12. Cards 13-17 were in second series Upper Deck packs at a rate of one in 24. And Cards 18-22 were in SP Packs at a rate of one in 45. The header card (number 23) was also inserted into only Collector Choice packs.

COMMON COLC (1-4/9-12) 1.25 3.00
COMMON UD (5-8/13-17) 2.50 6.00
COMMON SP (18-22) 6.00 15.00
NNO C.Ripken Header COLC 1.25 3.00

1996 Upper Deck Ripken Collection Jumbos

With a suggested retail price of $19.95, cards from this 22-card boxed set measures approximately 3 1/2" by 5" and features color borderless photos of Cal Ripken Jr. with a gold foil facsimile autograph. The cards parallel the standard Ripken Collection inserted into various 1996 Upper Deck Baseball products. The backs carry information about the player.

COMP.FACT SET 8.00 20.00
COMMON CARD .40 1.00
1 Cal Ripken COLC .75 2.00
after playing in 2131 consecutive games
2 Cal Ripken COLC 1.00 2.50
Barry Bonds
1995 All-Star Game
6 Cal Ripken UD. .60 1.50
Brian McRae sliding into second
1992
22 Cal Ripken SP 1.00 2.50
Eddie Murray
1981

1996 Upper Deck Run Producers

This 20 card set was randomly inserted into series two packs at a rate of one every 71 packs. The cards are thermographically printed, which gives the card a rubber surface texture. The cards are double die-cut and are foil stamped. These cards are highly condition sensitive, often found with noticable chipping on the edges.

COMPLETE SET (20) 60.00 150.00
RP1 Albert Belle 1.50 4.00
RP2 Dante Bichette 1.50 4.00
RP3 Barry Bonds 10.00 25.00
RP4 Jay Buhner 1.50 4.00
RP5 Jose Canseco 2.50 6.00
RP6 Juan Gonzalez 1.50 4.00
RP7 Ken Griffey Jr. 6.00 15.00
RP8 Tony Gwynn 5.00 12.00
RP9 Kenny Lofton 1.50 4.00
RP10 Edgar Martinez 2.50 6.00
RP11 Fred McGriff 2.50 6.00
RP12 Mark McGwire 10.00 25.00
RP13 Rafael Palmeiro 2.50 6.00
RP14 Mike Piazza 6.00 15.00
RP15 Manny Ramirez 2.50 6.00
RP16 Tim Salmon 2.50 6.00
RP17 Sammy Sosa 4.00 10.00
RP18 Frank Thomas 4.00 10.00
RP19 Mo Vaughn 1.50 4.00
RP20 Matt Williams 1.50 4.00

1997 Upper Deck

The 1997 Upper Deck set was issued in two series (series one 1-240, series two 271-520). The 12-card packs retailed for $2.49 each. Many cards have dates on the front to identify when, and when possible, what significant event is pictured. The backs include a player photo, stats and a brief blurb to go with vital statistics. Subsets include Jackie Robinson Tribute (1-9), Strike Force (64-72), Defensive Gems (136-153), Global Impact (181-207), Season Highlight Checklists (214-222/316-324), Star Rookies (223-240/271-288), Capture the Flag (370-387), Griffey's Hot List (415-424) and Diamond Debuts (470-483). It's critical to note that the Griffey's Hot List subset cards (in an unannounced move by the manufacturer) were shortprinted (about 1:7 packs) in relation to other cards in the series two set. The comparatively low print run on these cards created a dramatic surge in demand amongst set collectors and the cards soared in value on the secondary market. A 30-card first series Update set (numbered 241-270) was available to collectors that mailed in 10 series one wrappers along with $3 for postage and handling. The Series One Update set is composed primarily of 1996 post-season highlights. An additional 30-card series two Trade set (numbered 521-550) was also released around the end of the season. It too was available to collectors that mailed in ten series two wrappers along with $3 for postage and handling. The Series Two Trade set is composed primarily of traded players pictured in their new uniforms and a selection of rookies and prospects highlighted by the inclusion of Jose Cruz Jr. and Hideki Irabu.

COMP.MASTER SET (550) 80.00 200.00
COMPLETE SET (490) 50.00 100.00
COMP. SERIES 1 (240) 20.00 40.00
COMP. SERIES 2 (250) 30.00 60.00
COMP.SER.2 w/o GHL (240) 10.00 25.00
COMMON (1-240/271-520) .10 .30
COMP.UPDATE SET (30) 40.00 80.00
COMMON (241-270) .40 1.00
ONE UPD.SET VIA MAIL PER 10 SER.1 WRAPPERS

COMMON GHL (415-424) .60 1.50
COMP.TRADE SET (30) 8.00 20.00
COMMON (521-550) .20 .50
1 Jackie Robinson .20 .50
The Beginnings
2 Jackie Robinson .20 .50
Breaking the Barrier
3 Jackie Robinson .20 .50
The MVP Season, 1949
4 Jackie Robinson .20 .50
1951 season
5 Jackie Robinson .20 .50
1952 and 1953 seasons
6 Jackie Robinson .20 .50
1954 season
7 Jackie Robinson .20 .50
1955 season
8 Jackie Robinson .20 .50
1956 season
9 Jackie Robinson HOF .20 .50
10 Chipper Jones .30 .75
11 Marquis Grissom .10 .30
12 Jermaine Dye .10 .30
13 Mark Lemke .10 .30
14 Terrell Wade .10 .30
15 Fred McGriff .20 .50
16 Tom Glavine .20 .50
17 Mark Wohlers .10 .30
18 Randy Myers .10 .30
19 Roberto Alomar .20 .50
20 Cal Ripken 1.00 2.50
21 Rafael Palmeiro .20 .50
22 Mike Mussina .20 .50
23 Brady Anderson .10 .30
24 Jose Canseco .20 .50
25 Mo Vaughn .10 .30
26 Roger Clemens .60 1.50
27 Tim Naehring .10 .30
28 Jeff Suppan .10 .30
29 Troy Percival .10 .30
30 Sammy Sosa .30 .75
31 Amaury Telemaco .10 .30
32 Rey Sanchez .10 .30
33 Scott Servais .10 .30
34 Steve Trachsel .10 .30
35 Mark Grace .20 .50
36 Wilson Alvarez .10 .30
37 Harold Baines .10 .30
38 Tony Phillips .10 .30
39 James Baldwin .10 .30
40 Frank Thomas UER .30 .75
Bio information is Ken Griffey Jr.'s
41 Lyle Mouton .10 .30
42 Chris Snopek .10 .30
43 Hal Morris .10 .30
44 Eric Davis .10 .30
45 Barry Larkin .20 .50
46 Reggie Sanders .10 .30
47 Pete Schourek .10 .30
48 Lee Smith .10 .30
49 Charles Nagy .10 .30
50 Albert Belle .10 .30
51 Julio Franco .10 .30
52 Kenny Lofton .10 .30
53 Orel Hershiser .10 .30
54 Omar Vizquel .20 .50
55 Eric Young .10 .30
56 Curtis Leskanic .10 .30
57 Quinton McCracken .10 .30
58 Kevin Ritz .10 .30
59 Walt Weiss .10 .30
60 Dante Bichette .10 .30
61 Mark Lewis .10 .30
62 Tony Clark .10 .30
63 Travis Fryman .10 .30
64 John Smoltz SF .10 .30
65 Greg Maddux SF .30 .75
66 Tom Glavine SF .10 .30
67 Mike Mussina SF .10 .30
68 Andy Pettitte SF .10 .30
69 Mariano Rivera SF .20 .50
70 Hideo Nomo SF .10 .30
71 Kevin Brown SF .10 .30
72 Randy Johnson SF .20 .50
73 Felipe Lira .10 .30
74 Kimera Bartee .10 .30
75 Alan Trammell .10 .30
76 Kevin Brown .10 .30
77 Edgar Renteria .10 .30
78 Al Leiter .10 .30
79 Charles Johnson .10 .30
80 Andre Dawson .10 .30
81 Billy Wagner .10 .30
82 Donne Wall .10 .30
83 Jeff Bagwell .20 .50
84 Keith Lockhart .10 .30
85 Jeff Montgomery .10 .30
86 Tom Goodwin .10 .30
87 Tim Belcher .10 .30
88 Mike Macfarlane .10 .30
89 Joe Randa .10 .30
90 Brett Butler .10 .30
91 Todd Worrell .10 .30
92 Todd Hollandsworth .10 .30
93 Ismael Valdes .10 .30
94 Hideo Nomo .30 .75
95 Mike Piazza .50 1.25
96 Jeff Cirillo .10 .30
97 Ricky Bones .10 .30
98 Fernando Vina .10 .30
99 Ben McDonald .10 .30
100 John Jaha .10 .30
101 Mark Loretta .10 .30
102 Paul Molitor .10 .30
103 Rick Aguilera .10 .30
104 Marty Cordova .10 .30
105 Kirby Puckett .30 .75
106 Dan Naulty .10 .30
107 Frank Rodriguez .10 .30
108 Shane Andrews .10 .30
109 Henry Rodriguez .10 .30
110 Mark Grudzielanek .10 .30
111 Pedro Martinez .20 .50
112 Ugueth Urbina .10 .30
113 David Segui .10 .30
114 Rey Ordonez .10 .30
115 Bernard Gilkey .10 .30
116 Butch Huskey .10 .30
117 Paul Wilson .10 .30
118 Alex Ochoa .10 .30
119 John Franco .10 .30
120 Dwight Gooden .10 .30
121 Ruben Rivera .10 .30
122 Andy Pettitte .20 .50
123 Tino Martinez .20 .50
124 Bernie Williams .20 .50
125 Wade Boggs .20 .50
126 Paul O'Neill .20 .50
127 Scott Brosius .10 .30
128 Ernie Young .10 .30
129 Doug Johns .10 .30
130 Geronimo Berroa .10 .30
131 Jason Giambi .10 .30
132 John Wasdin .10 .30
133 Jim Eisenreich .10 .30
134 Ricky Otero .10 .30
135 Ricky Bottalico .10 .30
136 Mark Langston DG .10 .30
137 Greg Maddux DG .30 .75
138 Ivan Rodriguez DG .10 .30
139 Charles Johnson DG .10 .30
140 J.T. Snow DG .10 .30
141 Mark Grace DG .10 .30
142 Roberto Alomar DG .10 .30
143 Craig Biggio DG .10 .30
144 Ken Caminiti DG .10 .30
145 Matt Williams DG .10 .30
146 Omar Vizquel DG .10 .30
147 Cal Ripken DG .50 1.25
148 Ozzie Smith DG .30 .75
149 Rey Ordonez DG .10 .30
150 Ken Griffey Jr. DG .30 .75
151 Devon White DG .10 .30
152 Barry Bonds DG .40 1.00
153 Kenny Lofton DG .10 .30
154 Mickey Morandini .10 .30
155 Gregg Jefferies .10 .30
156 Curt Schilling .10 .30
157 Jason Kendall .10 .30
158 Francisco Cordova .10 .30
159 Dennis Eckersley .10 .30
160 Ron Gant .10 .30
161 Ozzie Smith .50 1.25
162 Brian Jordan .10 .30
163 John Mabry .10 .30
164 Andy Ashby .10 .30
165 Steve Finley .10 .30
166 Fernando Valenzuela .10 .30
167 Archi Cianfrocco .10 .30
168 Wally Joyner .10 .30
169 Greg Vaughn .10 .30
170 Barry Bonds .75 2.00
171 W.VanLandingham .10 .30
172 Marvin Benard .10 .30
173 Rich Aurilia .10 .30
174 Jay Canizaro .10 .30
175 Ken Griffey Jr. .50 1.25
176 Bob Wells .10 .30
177 Jay Buhner .10 .30
178 Sterling Hitchcock .10 .30
179 Edgar Martinez .20 .50
180 Rusty Greer .10 .30
181 Dave Nilsson GI .10 .30
182 Larry Walker GI .10 .30
183 Edgar Renteria GI .10 .30
184 Rey Ordonez GI .10 .30
185 Rafael Palmeiro GI .10 .30
186 Osvaldo Fernandez GI .10 .30
187 Raul Mondesi GI .10 .30
188 Manny Ramirez GI .10 .30
189 Sammy Sosa GI UER .20 .50
The flag pictured is wrong
190 Robert Eenhoorn GI .10 .30
191 Devon White GI .10 .30
192 Hideo Nomo GI .10 .30
193 Mac Suzuki GI .10 .30
194 Chan Ho Park GI .10 .30
195 F.Valenzuela GI .10 .30
196 Andruw Jones GI .10 .30
197 Vinny Castilla GI .10 .30
198 Dennis Martinez GI .10 .30
199 Ruben Rivera GI .10 .30
200 Juan Gonzalez GI .10 .30
201 Roberto Alomar GI .10 .30
202 Edgar Martinez GI .10 .30
203 Ivan Rodriguez GI .10 .30
204 Carlos Delgado GI .10 .30
205 Andres Galarraga GI .10 .30
206 Ozzie Guillen GI .10 .30
207 Midre Cummings GI .10 .30
208 Roger Pavlik .10 .30
209 Darren Oliver .10 .30
210 Dean Palmer .10 .30
211 Ivan Rodriguez .20 .50
212 Otis Nixon .10 .30
213 Pat Hentgen .10 .30
214 Ozzie Smith .20 .50
Andre Dawson
Kirby Pucket HL CL
215 Barry Bonds .40 1.00
Gary Sheffield
Brady Anderson HL CL
216 Ken Caminiti SH CL .10 .30
217 John Smoltz SH CL .10 .30
218 Eric Young SH CL .10 .30
219 Juan Gonzalez SH CL .10 .30
220 Eddie Murray SH CL .20 .50
221 T. Lasorda SH CL .10 .30
222 Paul Molitor SH CL .10 .30
223 Luis Castillo .10 .30
224 Justin Thompson .10 .30
225 Rocky Coppinger .10 .30
226 Jermaine Allensworth .10 .30
227 Jeff D'Amico .10 .30
228 Jamey Wright .10 .30
229 Scott Rolen .20 .50
230 Darin Erstad .10 .30
231 Marty Janzen .10 .30
232 Jacob Cruz .10 .30
233 Raul Ibanez .10 .30
234 Nomar Garciaparra .50 1.25
235 Todd Walker .10 .30
236 Brian Giles RC .60 1.50
237 Matt Beech .10 .30
238 Mike Cameron .10 .30
239 Jose Paniagua .10 .30
240 Andruw Jones .20 .50
241 Brant Brown UPD .40 1.00
242 Robin Jennings UPD .40 1.00
243 Willie Adams UPD .40 1.00
244 Ken Caminiti UPD .60 1.50
245 Brian Jordan UPD .60 1.50
246 Chipper Jones UPD 1.50 4.00
247 Juan Gonzalez UPD .60 1.50
248 Bernie Williams UPD 1.00 2.50
249 Roberto Alomar UPD 1.00 2.50
250 Bernie Williams UPD 1.00 2.50
251 David Wells UPD .60 1.50
252 Cecil Fielder UPD .60 1.50
253 D.Strawberry UPD .60 1.50
254 Andy Pettitte UPD 1.00 2.50
255 Javier Lopez UPD .60 1.50
256 Gary Gaetti UPD .60 1.50
257 Ron Gant UPD .60 1.50
258 Brian Jordan UPD .60 1.50
259 John Smoltz UPD 1.00 2.50
260 Greg Maddux UPD 3.00 8.00
261 Tom Glavine UPD 1.00 2.50
262 Andruw Jones UPD 1.00 2.50
263 Greg Maddux UPD 3.00 8.00
264 David Cone UPD .60 1.50
265 Jim Leyritz UPD .40 1.00
266 Andy Pettitte UPD 1.00 2.50
267 John Wetteland UPD .60 1.50
268 Dario Veras UPD .40 1.00
269 Neifi Perez UPD .40 1.00
270 Bill Mueller UPD 1.50 4.00
271 Vladimir Guerrero .30 .75
272 Dmitri Young .10 .30
273 Nerio Rodriguez RC .10 .30
274 Kevin Orie .10 .30
275 Felipe Crespo .10 .30
276 Danny Graves .10 .30
277 Rod Myers .10 .30
278 Felix Heredia RC .10 .30
279 Ralph Milliard .10 .30
280 Greg Norton .10 .30
281 Derek Wallace .10 .30
282 Trot Nixon .10 .30
283 Bobby Chouinard .10 .30
284 Jay Witasick .10 .30
285 Travis Miller .10 .30
286 Brian Bevil .10 .30
287 Bobby Estalella .10 .30
288 Steve Soderstrom .10 .30
289 Mark Langston .10 .30
290 Tim Salmon .20 .50
291 Jim Edmonds .10 .30
292 Garret Anderson .10 .30
293 George Arias .10 .30
294 Gary DiSarcina .10 .30
295 Chuck Finley .10 .30
296 Todd Greene .10 .30
297 Randy Velarde .10 .30
298 David Justice .10 .30
299 Ryan Klesko .10 .30
300 John Smoltz .20 .50
301 Javier Lopez .10 .30
302 Greg Maddux .50 1.25
303 Denny Neagle .10 .30
304 B.J. Surhoff .10 .30
305 Chris Hoiles .10 .30
306 Eric Davis .10 .30
307 Scott Erickson .10 .30
308 Mike Bordick .10 .30
309 John Valentin .10 .30
310 Heathcliff Slocumb .10 .30
311 Tom Gordon .10 .30
312 Mike Stanley .10 .30
313 Reggie Jefferson .10 .30
314 Darren Bragg .10 .30
315 Troy O'Leary .10 .30
316 John Mabry SH CL .10 .30
317 Mark Whiten SH CL .10 .30
318 Edgar Martinez SH CL .10 .30
319 Alex Rodriguez SH CL .30 .75
320 Mark McGwire SH CL .40 1.00
321 Hideo Nomo SH CL .10 .30
322 Todd Hundley SH CL .10 .30
323 Barry Bonds SH CL .40 1.00
324 Andruw Jones SH CL .10 .30
325 Ryne Sandberg .50 1.25
326 Brian McRae .10 .30
327 Frank Castillo .10 .30
328 Shawon Dunston .10 .30
329 Ray Durham .10 .30
330 Robin Ventura .10 .30
331 Ozzie Guillen .10 .30
332 Roberto Hernandez .10 .30
333 Albert Belle .10 .30
334 Dave Martinez .10 .30
335 Willie Greene .10 .30
336 Jeff Brantley .10 .30
337 Kevin Jarvis .10 .30
338 John Smiley .10 .30
339 Eddie Taubensee .10 .30
340 Bret Boone .10 .30
341 Kevin Seitzer .10 .30
342 Jack McDowell .10 .30
343 Sandy Alomar Jr. .10 .30
344 Chad Curtis .10 .30
345 Manny Ramirez .20 .50
346 Chad Ogea .10 .30
347 Jim Thome .20 .50
348 Mark Thompson .10 .30
349 Ellis Burks .10 .30
350 Andres Galarraga .10 .30
351 Vinny Castilla .10 .30
352 Kirt Manwaring .10 .30
353 Larry Walker .10 .30
354 Omar Olivares .10 .30
355 Bobby Higginson .10 .30
356 Melvin Nieves .10 .30
357 Brian Johnson .10 .30
358 Devon White .10 .30
359 Jeff Conine .10 .30
360 Gary Sheffield .10 .30
361 Robb Nen .10 .30
362 Mike Hampton .10 .30
363 Bob Abreu .20 .50
364 Luis Gonzalez .10 .30
365 Derek Bell .10 .30
366 Sean Berry .10 .30
367 Craig Biggio .20 .50
368 Darryl Kile .10 .30
369 Shane Reynolds .10 .30
370 Jeff Bagwell CF .10 .30
371 Ron Gant CF .10 .30
372 Andy Benes CF .10 .30
373 Gary Gaetti CF .10 .30
374 Ramon Martinez CF .10 .30
375 Raul Mondesi CF .10 .30
376 Steve Finley CF .10 .30
377 Ken Caminiti CF .10 .30
378 Tony Gwynn CF .20 .50
379 Dario Veras RC .10 .30
380 Andy Pettitte CF .10 .30
381 Ruben Rivera CF .10 .30
382 David Cone CF .10 .30
383 Roberto Alomar CF .10 .30
384 Edgar Martinez CF .10 .30
385 Ken Griffey Jr. CF .30 .75
386 Mark McGwire CF .40 1.00
387 Rusty Greer CF .10 .30
388 Jose Rosado .10 .30
389 Kevin Appier .10 .30
390 Johnny Damon .20 .50
391 Jose Offerman .10 .30
392 Michael Tucker .10 .30
393 Craig Paquette .10 .30
394 Bip Roberts .10 .30
395 Ramon Martinez .10 .30
396 Greg Gagne .10 .30
397 Chan Ho Park .10 .30
398 Karim Garcia .10 .30
399 Wilton Guerrero .10 .30
400 Eric Karros .10 .30
401 Raul Mondesi .10 .30
402 Matt Mieske .10 .30
403 Mike Fetters .10 .30
404 Dave Nilsson .10 .30
405 Jose Valentin .10 .30
406 Scott Karl .10 .30
407 Marc Newfield .10 .30
408 Cal Eldred .10 .30
409 Rich Becker .10 .30
410 Terry Steinbach .10 .30
411 Chuck Knoblauch .10 .30
412 Pat Meares .10 .30
413 Brad Radke .10 .30
414 Kirby Puckett UER .30 .75
Card numbered 415
415 A.Jones GHL SP .60 1.50
416 C.Jones GHL SP 1.00 2.50
417 Mo Vaughn GHL SP .60 1.50
418 F.Thomas GHL SP 1.00 2.50
419 Albert Belle GHL SP .60 1.50
420 M.McGwire GHL SP 3.00 8.00
421 Derek Jeter GHL SP 3.00 8.00
422 A.Rodriguez GHL SP 2.00 5.00
423 J.Gonzalez GHL SP .60 1.50
424 K.Griffey Jr. GHL SP 2.00 5.00
425 Rondell White .10 .30
426 Darrin Fletcher .10 .30
427 Cliff Floyd .10 .30
428 Mike Lansing .10 .30
429 F.P. Santangelo .10 .30
430 Todd Hundley .10 .30
431 Mark Clark .10 .30
432 Pete Harnisch .10 .30
433 Jason Isringhausen .10 .30
434 Bobby Jones .10 .30
435 Lance Johnson .10 .30
436 Carlos Baerga .10 .30
437 Mariano Duncan .10 .30
438 David Cone .10 .30
439 Mariano Rivera .30 .75
440 Derek Jeter .75 2.00
441 Joe Girardi .10 .30
442 Charlie Hayes .10 .30
443 Tim Raines .10 .30
444 Darryl Strawberry .10 .30
445 Cecil Fielder .10 .30
446 Ariel Prieto .10 .30
447 Tony Batista .10 .30
448 Brent Gates .10 .30
449 Scott Spiezio .10 .30
450 Mark McGwire .75 2.00
451 Don Wengert .10 .30
452 Mike Lieberthal .10 .30
453 Lenny Dykstra .10 .30
454 Rex Hudler .10 .30
455 Darren Daulton .10 .30
456 Kevin Stocker .10 .30
457 Trey Beamon .10 .30
458 Midre Cummings .10 .30
459 Mark Johnson .10 .30
460 Al Martin .10 .30
461 Kevin Elster .10 .30
462 Jon Lieber .10 .30
463 Jason Schmidt .10 .30
464 Paul Wagner .10 .30
465 Andy Benes .10 .30
466 Alan Benes .10 .30
467 Royce Clayton .10 .30
468 Gary Gaetti .10 .30
469 Curt Lyons RC .10 .30
470 Eugene Kingsale DD .10 .30
471 Damian Jackson DD .10 .30
472 Wendell Magee DD .10 .30
473 Kevin L. Brown DD .10 .30
474 Raul Casanova DD .10 .30
475 R.Mendoza DD RC .10 .30
476 Todd Dunn DD .10 .30
477 Chad Mottola DD .10 .30
478 Andy Larkin DD .10 .30
479 Jaime Bluma DD .10 .30
480 Mac Suzuki DD .10 .30
481 Brian Banks DD .10 .30
482 Desi Wilson DD .10 .30
483 Einar Diaz DD .10 .30
484 Tom Pagnozzi .10 .30
485 Ray Lankford .10 .30
486 Todd Stottlemyre .10 .30
487 Donovan Osborne .10 .30
488 Trevor Hoffman .10 .30
489 Chris Gomez .10 .30
490 Ken Caminiti .10 .30
491 John Flaherty .10 .30
492 Tony Gwynn .40 1.00
493 Joey Hamilton .10 .30
494 Rickey Henderson .30 .75
495 Glenallen Hill .10 .30
496 Rod Beck .10 .30
497 Osvaldo Fernandez .10 .30
498 Rick Wilkins .10 .30
499 Joey Cora .10 .30
500 Alex Rodriguez .50 1.25
501 Randy Johnson .30 .75
502 Paul Sorrento .10 .30
503 Dan Wilson .10 .30
504 Jamie Moyer .10 .30
505 Will Clark .20 .50
506 Mickey Tettleton .10 .30
507 John Burkett .10 .30
508 Ken Hill .10 .30
509 Mark McLemore .10 .30
510 Juan Gonzalez .10 .30
511 Bobby Witt .10 .30
512 Carlos Delgado .10 .30
513 Alex Gonzalez .10 .30
514 Shawn Green .10 .30
515 Joe Carter .10 .30
516 Juan Guzman .10 .30
517 Charlie O'Brien .10 .30
518 Ed Sprague .10 .30
519 Mike Timlin .10 .30
520 Roger Clemens .60 1.50
521 Eddie Murray TRADE .75 2.00
522 Jason Dickson TRADE .20 .50
523 Jim Leyritz TRADE .20 .50
524 M.Tucker TRADE .20 .50
525 Kenny Lofton TRADE .30 .75
526 Jimmy Key TRADE .30 .75
527 Mel Rojas TRADE .20 .50
528 Deion Sanders TRADE .50 1.25
529 Bartolo Colon TRADE .30 .75
530 Matt Williams TRADE .30 .75
531 M.Grissom TRADE .30 .75
532 David Justice TRADE .30 .75
533 B.Trammell TRADE .30 .75
534 Moises Alou TRADE .30 .75
535 Bobby Bonilla TRADE .30 .75
536 A.Fernandez TRADE .20 .50
537 Jay Bell TRADE .30 .75
538 Chili Davis TRADE .30 .75
539 Jeff King TRADE .20 .50
540 Todd Zeile TRADE .20 .50
541 John Olerud TRADE .30 .75
542 Jose Guillen TRADE .30 .75
543 Derrek Lee TRADE .50 1.25
544 Dante Powell TRADE .20 .50
545 J.T. Snow TRADE .30 .75
546 Jeff Kent TRADE .30 .75
547 Jose Cruz Jr. TRADE .30 .75
548 J.Wetteland TRADE .30 .75
549 O.Merced TRADE .20 .50
550 Hideki Irabu TRADE .30 .75

1997 Upper Deck Amazing Greats

Randomly inserted in all first series packs at a rate of one in 69, this 20-card set features a horizontal design along with two player photos on the front. The cards feature translucent player images against a real wood grain stock.

AG1 Ken Griffey Jr. 8.00 20.00
AG2 Roberto Alomar 3.00 8.00
AG3 Alex Rodriguez 8.00 20.00
AG4 Paul Molitor 2.00 5.00
AG5 Chipper Jones 5.00 12.00
AG6 Tony Gwynn 6.00 15.00
AG7 Kenny Lofton 2.00 5.00
AG8 Albert Belle 2.00 5.00
AG9 Matt Williams 2.00 5.00
AG10 Frank Thomas 5.00 12.00
AG11 Greg Maddux 8.00 20.00
AG12 Sammy Sosa 5.00 12.00
AG13 Kirby Puckett 5.00 12.00
AG14 Jeff Bagwell 3.00 8.00
AG15 Cal Ripken 15.00 40.00
AG16 Manny Ramirez 3.00 8.00
AG17 Barry Bonds 12.50 30.00
AG18 Mo Vaughn 2.00 5.00
AG19 Eddie Murray 5.00 12.00
AG20 Mike Piazza 8.00 20.00

1997 Upper Deck Blue Chip Prospects

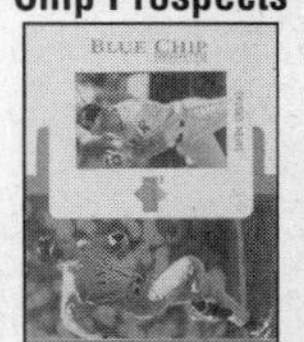

This rare 20-card set, randomly inserted into series two packs, features color photos of high expectation prospects who are likely to have a big impact on Major League Baseball. Only 500 of this crash numbered, limited edition set was produced.

BC1 Andruw Jones 15.00 40.00
BC2 Derek Jeter 40.00 80.00
BC3 Scott Rolen 15.00 40.00
BC4 Manny Ramirez 15.00 40.00
BC5 Todd Walker 10.00 25.00
BC6 Rocky Coppinger 6.00 15.00
BC7 Nomar Garciaparra 20.00 50.00
BC8 Darin Erstad 10.00 25.00
BC9 Jermaine Dye 10.00 25.00
BC10 Vladimir Guerrero 20.00 50.00
BC11 Edgar Renteria 10.00 25.00
BC12 Bob Abreu 15.00 40.00
BC13 Karim Garcia 6.00 15.00
BC14 Jeff D'Amico 6.00 15.00
BC15 Chipper Jones 20.00 50.00
BC16 Todd Hollandsworth 6.00 15.00
BC17 Andy Pettitte 15.00 40.00
BC18 Ruben Rivera 6.00 15.00
BC19 Jason Kendall 10.00 25.00
BC20 Alex Rodriguez 30.00 60.00

1997 Upper Deck Game Jersey

Randomly inserted in all first series packs at a rate of one in 800, this three-card set feaures swatches of real game-worn jerseys cut up and placed on the cards. These cards represent the first memorabilia insert cards to hit the baseball card market and thus carry a significant impact in the development of the hobby in the late 1990's.

GJ1 Ken Griffey Jr. 150.00 250.00
GJ2 Tony Gwynn 15.00 40.00
GJ3 Rey Ordonez 10.00 25.00

1997 Upper Deck Hot Commodities

Randomly inserted in series two packs at a rate of one in 13, this 20-card set features color player images on a flame background in a black border. The backs carry a player head photo, statistics, and a commentary by ESPN sportscaster Dan Patrick.

COMPLETE SET (20) 25.00 60.00
HC1 Alex Rodriguez 1.50 4.00
HC2 Andruw Jones .60 1.50
HC3 Derek Jeter 2.50 6.00
HC4 Frank Thomas 1.00 2.50
HC5 Ken Griffey Jr. 1.50 4.00
HC6 Chipper Jones 1.00 2.50
HC7 Juan Gonzalez .40 1.00
HC8 Cal Ripken 3.00 8.00
HC9 John Smoltz .60 1.50
HC10 Mark McGwire 2.50 6.00
HC11 Barry Bonds 2.50 6.00
HC12 Albert Belle .40 1.00
HC13 Mike Piazza 1.50 4.00
HC14 Manny Ramirez .60 1.50
HC15 Mo Vaughn .40 1.00
HC16 Tony Gwynn 1.25 3.00
HC17 Vladimir Guerrero 1.00 2.50
HC18 Hideo Nomo 1.00 2.50
HC19 Greg Maddux 1.50 4.00
HC20 Kirby Puckett 1.00 2.50

1997 Upper Deck Long Distance Connection

Randomly inserted in series two packs at a rate of one in 35, this 20-card set features color player images of some of the League's top power hitters on backgrounds utilizing Light/FX technology. The backs carry the pictured player's statistics.

COMPLETE SET (20) 60.00 150.00
LD1 Mark McGwire 6.00 15.00
LD2 Brady Anderson 1.00 2.50
LD3 Ken Griffey Jr. 4.00 10.00
LD4 Albert Belle 1.00 2.50
LD5 Juan Gonzalez 1.00 2.50
LD6 Andres Galarraga 1.00 2.50
LD7 Jay Buhner 1.00 2.50
LD8 Mo Vaughn 1.00 2.50
LD9 Barry Bonds 6.00 15.00
LD10 Gary Sheffield 1.00 2.50
LD11 Todd Hundley 1.00 2.50
LD12 Frank Thomas 2.50 6.00
LD13 Sammy Sosa 2.50 6.00
LD14 Rafael Palmeiro 1.50 4.00

LD15 Alex Rodriguez	4.00	10.00
LD16 Mike Piazza	4.00	10.00
LD17 Ken Caminiti	1.00	2.50
LD18 Chipper Jones	2.50	6.00
LD19 Manny Ramirez	1.50	4.00
LD20 Andruw Jones	1.50	4.00

1997 Upper Deck Memorable Moments

Cards from these sets were distributed exclusively in six-card retail Collector's Choice series one and two packs. Each pack contained one of ten different Memorable Moments inserts. Each set features a selection of top stars captured in highlights of season's gone by. Each card features wave-like die cut top and bottom borders wth gold foil.

COMPLETE SERIES 1 (10)	5.00	12.00
COMPLETE SERIES 2 (10)	5.00	12.00
A1 Andruw Jones	.20	.50
A2 Chipper Jones	.30	.75
A3 Cal Ripken	1.00	2.50
A4 Frank Thomas	.30	.75
A5 Manny Ramirez	.20	.50
A6 Mike Piazza	.50	1.25
A7 Mark McGwire	.75	2.00
A8 Barry Bonds	.75	2.00
A9 Ken Griffey Jr.	.50	1.25
A10 Alex Rodriguez	.50	1.25
B1 Ken Griffey Jr.	.50	1.25
B2 Albert Belle	.10	.30
B3 Derek Jeter	.75	2.00
B4 Greg Maddux	.50	1.25
B5 Tony Gwynn	.40	1.00
B6 Ryne Sandberg	.50	1.25
B7 Juan Gonzalez	.10	.30
B8 Roger Clemens	.60	1.50
B9 Jose Cruz Jr.	.10	.30
B10 Mo Vaughn	.10	.30

1997 Upper Deck Power Package

Randomly inserted in all first series packs at a rate of one in 24, this 20-card set features some of the best longball hitters. The die cut cards feature some of baseball's leading power hitters.

COMPLETE SET (20)	30.00	80.00
*JUMBOS: .2X TO .5X BASIC PP		
JUMBOS ONE PER RETAIL JUMBO PACK		
PP1 Ken Griffey Jr.	3.00	8.00
PP2 Joe Carter	.75	2.00
PP3 Rafael Palmeiro	1.25	3.00
PP4 Jay Buhner	.75	2.00
PP5 Sammy Sosa	2.00	5.00
PP6 Fred McGriff	1.25	3.00
PP7 Jeff Bagwell	1.25	3.00
PP8 Albert Belle	.75	2.00
PP9 Matt Williams	.75	2.00
PP10 Mark McGwire	5.00	12.00
PP11 Gary Sheffield	.75	2.00
PP12 Tim Salmon	1.25	3.00
PP13 Ryan Klesko	.75	2.00
PP14 Manny Ramirez	1.25	3.00
PP15 Mike Piazza	3.00	8.00
PP16 Barry Bonds	5.00	12.00
PP17 Mo Vaughn	.75	2.00
PP18 Jose Canseco	1.25	3.00
PP19 Juan Gonzalez	.75	2.00
PP20 Frank Thomas	2.00	5.00

1997 Upper Deck Predictor

Randomly inserted in series two packs at a rate of one in five, this 30-card set featues a color player photo alongside a series of bats. The collector could activate the card by scratching off one of the bats to predict the performance of the pictured player during a single game. If the player matches or exceeds the predicted performance, the card could be mailed in with $2 to receive a Totally Virtual high-tech cel-card of the player pictured on the front. The backs carry the rules of the game. The deadline to redeem these cards was November 22nd, 1997. Winners and Losers are specified in our checklist with a "W" or a "L" after the player's name.

COMPLETE SET (30)	12.50	30.00
*SCRATCH LOSER: .25X TO .6X UNSCRATCH		
*EXCH.WIN: 1X TO 2.5X BASIC PREDICTOR		
SER.2 STATED ODDS 1:5		
1 Andruw Jones L	.25	.60
2 Chipper Jones L	.40	1.00
3 Greg Maddux W Complete Game Shutout	.60	1.50
4 Fred McGriff W 4 Hits/2HR/3B	.25	.60
5 John Smoltz W Complete Game Shutout	.25	.60
6 Brady Anderson W Leadoff HR	.15	.40
7 Cal Ripken W Grand Slam	1.25	3.00
8 Mo Vaughn W 3HR/6RBI	.15	.40
9 Sammy Sosa L	.40	1.00
10 Albert Belle W Grand Slam/9th HR	.15	.40
11 Frank Thomas L	.40	1.00
12 Kenny Lofton W 5 Hits	.15	.40
13 Jim Thome L	.25	.60
14 Dante Bichette W 6RBI's	.15	.40
15 Andres Galarraga L	.15	.40
16 Gary Sheffield L	.15	.40
17 Hideo Nomo W Base Hit	.40	1.00
18 Mike Piazza W Steal/9th HR	.60	1.50
19 Derek Jeter W 2HR	1.00	2.50
20 Bernie Williams L	.25	.60
21 Mark McGwire W Grand Slam/4HR	1.00	2.50
22 Ken Caminiti W 5RBI's	.15	.40
23 Tony Gwynn W 2 2B/3RBI	.50	1.25
24 Barry Bonds W 5RBI's	1.00	2.50
25 Jay Buhner W 5RBI's	.15	.40
26 Ken Griffey Jr. W 3HR's	.60	1.50
27 Alex Rodriguez W Cycle	.60	1.50
28 Juan Gonzalez W 5RBI's/4 Hits	.15	.40
29 Dean Palmer W 2HR's/5RBI's	.15	.40
30 Roger Clemens W Complete Game Shutout	.75	2.00

1997 Upper Deck Rock Solid Foundation

Randomly inserted in all first series packs at a rate of one in seven, this 20-card set features players 25 and under who have made an impact in the majors. The fronts feature a player photo against a "silver" type background. The backs give player information as well as another player photo and are numbered with a "RS" prefix.

COMPLETE SET (20)	15.00	40.00
RS1 Alex Rodriguez	2.50	6.00
RS2 Rey Ordonez	.60	1.50
RS3 Derek Jeter	4.00	10.00
RS4 Darin Erstad	.60	1.50
RS5 Chipper Jones	1.50	4.00
RS6 Johnny Damon	1.00	2.50
RS7 Ryan Klesko	.60	1.50
RS8 Charles Johnson	.60	1.50
RS9 Andy Pettitte	1.00	2.50
RS10 Manny Ramirez	1.00	2.50
RS11 Ivan Rodriguez	1.00	2.50
RS12 Jason Kendall	.60	1.50
RS13 Rondell White	.60	1.50
RS14 Alex Ochoa	.60	1.50
RS15 Javier Lopez	.60	1.50
RS16 Pedro Martinez	1.00	2.50
RS17 Carlos Delgado	.60	1.50
RS18 Paul Wilson	.60	1.50
RS19 Alan Benes	.60	1.50
RS20 Raul Mondesi	.60	1.50

1997 Upper Deck Run Producers

Randomly inserted in series two packs at a rate of one in 69, this 24-card set features color player images on die-cut cards that actually look and feel like home plate. The backs carry player information and career statistics.

COMPLETE SET (24)	60.00	150.00
RP1 Ken Griffey Jr.	6.00	15.00
RP2 Barry Bonds	10.00	25.00
RP3 Albert Belle	1.50	4.00
RP4 Mark McGwire	10.00	25.00
RP5 Frank Thomas	4.00	10.00
RP6 Juan Gonzalez	1.50	4.00
RP7 Brady Anderson	1.50	4.00
RP8 Andres Galarraga	1.50	4.00
RP9 Rafael Palmeiro	2.50	6.00
RP10 Alex Rodriguez	6.00	15.00
RP11 Jay Buhner	1.50	4.00
RP12 Gary Sheffield	1.50	4.00
RP13 Sammy Sosa	4.00	10.00
RP14 Dante Bichette	1.50	4.00
RP15 Mike Piazza	6.00	15.00
RP16 Manny Ramirez	2.50	6.00
RP17 Kenny Lofton	1.50	4.00
RP18 Mo Vaughn	1.50	4.00
RP19 Tim Salmon	2.50	6.00
RP20 Chipper Jones	4.00	10.00
RP21 Jim Thome	2.50	6.00
RP22 Ken Caminiti	1.50	4.00
RP23 Jeff Bagwell	2.50	6.00
RP24 Paul Molitor	1.50	4.00

1997 Upper Deck Star Attractions

These 20 cards were issued one per pack in special Upper Deck Memorabilia Madness packs. The Memorabilia Madness packs included various redemptions for signed 8 by 10 photos with the grand prize being a grouping of Ken Griffey Jr. signed jersey, baseball and 8 by 10 photo. The die cut cards feature the words "Star Attraction" on the top with the player and team identification on the sides. The backs have a photo and a brief blurb on the player. Cards numbered 1-10 were inserted in Upper Deck packs while cards numbered 11-20 were in Collectors Choice packs.

COMPLETE SET (20)	10.00	25.00
*GOLD: 2X TO 5X BASE STAR ATT.		
GOLD INSERTS IN UD/CC MADNESS RETAIL		
1 Ken Griffey Jr.	.60	1.50
2 Barry Bonds	1.00	2.50
3 Jeff Bagwell	.25	.60
4 Nomar Garciaparra	.60	1.50
5 Tony Gwynn	.50	1.25
6 Roger Clemens	.75	2.00
7 Chipper Jones	.40	1.00
8 Tino Martinez	.25	.60
9 Albert Belle	.15	.40
10 Kenny Lofton	.15	.40
11 Alex Rodriguez	.60	1.50
12 Mark McGwire	1.00	2.50
13 Cal Ripken	1.25	3.00
14 Larry Walker	.15	.40
15 Mike Piazza	.60	1.50
16 Frank Thomas	.40	1.00
17 Juan Gonzalez	.15	.40
18 Greg Maddux	.60	1.50
19 Jose Cruz Jr.	.40	1.00
20 Mo Vaughn	.15	.40

1997 Upper Deck Ticket To Stardom

Randomly inserted in all first series packs at a rate of one in 34, this 20-card set is designed in the form of a ticket and are designed to be matched. The horizontal fronts feature two player photos as well as using "light f/x technology and embossed player images.

TS1 Chipper Jones	2.50	6.00
TS2 Jermaine Dye	1.00	2.50
TS3 Rey Ordonez	1.00	2.50
TS4 Alex Ochoa	1.00	2.50
TS5 Derek Jeter	6.00	15.00
TS6 Ruben Rivera	1.00	2.50
TS7 Billy Wagner	1.00	2.50
TS8 Jason Kendall	1.00	2.50
TS9 Darin Erstad	1.00	2.50
TS10 Alex Rodriguez	4.00	10.00
TS11 Bob Abreu	1.50	4.00
TS12 Richard Hidalgo	2.50	6.00
TS13 Karim Garcia	1.00	2.50
TS14 Andruw Jones	1.50	4.00
TS15 Carlos Delgado	1.00	2.50
TS16 Rocky Coppinger	1.00	2.50
TS17 Jeff D'Amico	1.00	2.50
TS18 Johnny Damon	1.50	4.00
TS19 John Wasdin	1.00	2.50
TS20 Manny Ramirez	1.50	4.00

1997 Upper Deck Ticket To Stardom Combos

These ten dual-player cards parallel a selection of cards from the Ticket to Stardom cards randomly seeded in basic 1997 UD packs. These "Combo" cards, however, measure twice as long as a standard size card (2 1/2" tall by 6 1/2 inches wide) and are essentially the mutated offspring of two standard size cards fused together side by side. Interestingly, these Combo cards were distributed one per Collector's Choice retail "Ticket to Stardom" box. Each of these boxes contained three packs of Collector's Choice series one packs plus the Ticket to Stardom Combo card (of which was clearly displayed through a viewing window on thje box front - thus one could select the exact Combo card they wanted).

COMPLETE SET (10)	10.00	25.00
TS1 Chipper Jones Andruw Jones	1.25	3.00
TS2 Rey Ordonez Kevin Orie	.75	2.00
TS3 Derek Jeter Nomar Garciaparra	2.00	5.00
TS4 Billy Wagner Jason Kendall	.75	2.00
TS5 Darin Erstad Alex Rodriguez	1.50	4.00
TS6 Bob Abreu Jose Guillen	1.00	2.50
TS7 Wilton Guerrero Vladimir Guerrero	1.00	2.50
TS8 Carlos Delgado Rocky Coppinger	1.00	2.50
TS9 Jason Dickson Johnny Damon	.75	2.00
TS10 Bartolo Colon Manny Ramirez	1.00	2.50

1998 Upper Deck

The 1998 Upper Deck set was issued in three series consisting of a 270-card first series, a 270-card second series and a 211-card third series. Each series was distributed in 12-card packs which carried a suggested retail price of $2.49. Card fronts feature game dated photographs of some of the season's most memorable moments. The following subsets are contained within the set: History in the Making (1-8/361-369), Griffey's Hot List (9-18), Define the Game (136-153), Season Highlights (244-252/532-540/748-750), Star Rookies (253-288/541-600), Postseason Headliners (415-432), Upper Echelon (451-459) and Eminent Prestige (601-630). The Eminent Prestige subset cards were slightly shortprinted (approximately 1:4 packs) and Upper Deck offered a free service to collectors trying to finish their Series three sets whereby Eminent Prestige cards were mailed to collectors who sent in proof of purchase of one-and-a-half boxes or more. The print run for Mike Piazza card number 681 was split exactly in half creating two shortprints: card number 681 (picturing Piazza as a New York Met) and card number 681A (picturing Piazza as a Florida Marlin). Both cards are exactly two times tougher to pull from packs than other regular issue Series three cards. The series three set is considered complete with both versions at 251 total cards. Notable Rookie Cards include Gabe Kapler and Magglio Ordonez.

COMPLETE SET (751)	80.00	200.00
COMP.SERIES 1 (270)	15.00	40.00
COMP.SERIES 2 (270)	15.00	40.00
COMP.SERIES 3 (211)	50.00	120.00
COMMON (1-600/631-750)	.10	.30
COMMON EP (601-630)	.75	2.00
EP SER.2 ODDS APPROXIMATELY 1:4		
1 Tino Martinez HIST	.10	.30
2 Jimmy Key HIST	.10	.30
3 Jay Buhner HIST	.10	.30
4 Mark Gardner HIST	.10	.30
5 Greg Maddux HIST	.30	.75
6 Pedro Martinez HIST	.20	.50
7 Hideo Nomo HIST	.20	.50
8 Sammy Sosa HIST	.20	.50
9 Mark McGwire GHL	.40	1.00
10 Ken Griffey Jr. GHL	.30	.75
11 Larry Walker GHL	.10	.30
12 Tino Martinez GHL	.10	.30
13 Mike Piazza GHL	.30	.75
14 Jose Cruz Jr. GHL	.10	.30
15 Tony Gwynn GHL	.20	.50
16 Greg Maddux GHL	.30	.75
17 Roger Clemens GHL	.30	.75
18 Alex Rodriguez GHL	.30	.75
19 Shigetoshi Hasegawa	.10	.30
20 Eddie Murray	.30	.75
21 Jason Dickson	.10	.30
22 Darin Erstad	.10	.30
23 Chuck Finley	.10	.30
24 Dave Hollins	.10	.30
25 Garret Anderson	.10	.30
26 Michael Tucker	.10	.30
27 Kenny Lofton	.10	.30
28 Javier Lopez	.10	.30
29 Fred McGriff	.20	.50
30 Greg Maddux	.50	1.25
31 Jeff Blauser	.10	.30
32 John Smoltz	.20	.50
33 Mark Wohlers	.10	.30
34 Scott Erickson	.10	.30
35 Jimmy Key	.10	.30
36 Harold Baines	.10	.30
37 Randy Myers	.10	.30
38 B.J. Surhoff	.10	.30
39 Eric Davis	.10	.30
40 Rafael Palmeiro	.20	.50
41 Jeffrey Hammonds	.10	.30
42 Mo Vaughn	.10	.30
43 Tom Gordon	.10	.30
44 Tim Naehring	.10	.30
45 Darren Bragg	.10	.30
46 Aaron Sele	.10	.30
47 Troy O'Leary	.10	.30
48 John Valentin	.10	.30
49 Doug Glanville	.10	.30
50 Ryne Sandberg	.50	1.25
51 Steve Trachsel	.10	.30
52 Mark Grace	.20	.50
53 Kevin Foster	.10	.30
54 Kevin Tapani	.10	.30
55 Kevin Orie	.10	.30
56 Lyle Mouton	.10	.30
57 Ray Durham	.10	.30
58 Jaime Navarro	.10	.30
59 Mike Cameron	.10	.30
60 Albert Belle	.10	.30
61 Doug Drabek	.10	.30
62 Chris Snopek	.10	.30
63 Eddie Taubensee	.10	.30
64 Terry Pendleton	.10	.30
65 Barry Larkin	.20	.50
66 Willie Greene	.10	.30
67 Deion Sanders	.20	.50
68 Pokey Reese	.10	.30
69 Jeff Shaw	.10	.30
70 Jim Thome	.20	.50
71 Orel Hershiser	.10	.30
72 Omar Vizquel	.20	.50
73 Brian Giles	.10	.30
74 David Justice	.10	.30
75 Bartolo Colon	.10	.30
76 Sandy Alomar Jr.	.10	.30
77 Neifi Perez	.10	.30
78 Dante Bichette	.10	.30
79 Vinny Castilla	.10	.30
80 Eric Young	.10	.30
81 Quinton McCracken	.10	.30
82 Jamey Wright	.10	.30
83 John Thomson	.10	.30
84 Damion Easley	.10	.30
85 Justin Thompson	.10	.30
86 Willie Blair	.10	.30
87 Raul Casanova	.10	.30
88 Bobby Higginson	.10	.30
89 Bubba Trammell	.10	.30
90 Tony Clark	.10	.30
91 Livan Hernandez	.10	.30
92 Charles Johnson	.10	.30
93 Edgar Renteria	.10	.30
94 Alex Fernandez	.10	.30
95 Gary Sheffield	.10	.30
96 Moises Alou	.10	.30
97 Tony Saunders	.10	.30
98 Robb Nen	.10	.30
99 Darryl Kile	.10	.30
100 Craig Biggio	.20	.50
101 Chris Holt	.10	.30
102 Bob Abreu	.10	.30
103 Luis Gonzalez	.10	.30
104 Billy Wagner	.10	.30
105 Brad Ausmus	.10	.30
106 Chili Davis	.10	.30
107 Tim Belcher	.10	.30
108 Dean Palmer	.10	.30
109 Jeff King	.10	.30
110 Jose Rosado	.10	.30
111 Mike Macfarlane	.10	.30
112 Jay Bell	.10	.30
113 Todd Worrell	.10	.30
114 Chan Ho Park	.10	.30
115 Raul Mondesi	.10	.30
116 Brett Butler	.10	.30
117 Greg Gagne	.10	.30
118 Hideo Nomo	.30	.75
119 Todd Zeile	.10	.30
120 Eric Karros	.10	.30
121 Cal Eldred	.10	.30
122 Jeff D'Amico	.10	.30
123 Antone Williamson	.10	.30
124 Doug Jones	.10	.30
125 Dave Nilsson	.10	.30
126 Gerald Williams	.10	.30
127 Fernando Vina	.10	.30
128 Ron Coomer	.10	.30
129 Matt Lawton	.10	.30
130 Paul Molitor	.10	.30
131 Todd Walker	.10	.30
132 Rick Aguilera	.10	.30
133 Brad Radke	.10	.30
134 Bob Tewksbury	.10	.30
135 Vladimir Guerrero	.30	.75
136 Tony Gwynn DG	.20	.50
137 Roger Clemens DG	.30	.75
138 Dennis Eckersley DG	.10	.30
139 Brady Anderson DG	.10	.30
140 Ken Griffey Jr. DG	.30	.75
141 Derek Jeter DG	.40	1.00
142 Ken Caminiti DG	.10	.30
143 Frank Thomas DG	.20	.50
144 Barry Bonds DG	.40	1.00
145 Cal Ripken DG	.50	1.25
146 Alex Rodriguez DG	.30	.75
147 Greg Maddux DG	.30	.75
148 Kenny Lofton DG	.10	.30
149 Mike Piazza DG	.30	.75
150 Mark McGwire DG	.40	1.00
151 Andruw Jones DG	.10	.30
152 Rusty Greer DG	.10	.30
153 F.P. Santangelo DG	.10	.30
154 Mike Lansing	.10	.30
155 Lee Smith	.10	.30
156 Carlos Perez	.10	.30
157 Pedro Martinez	.20	.50
158 Ryan McGuire	.10	.30
159 F.P. Santangelo	.10	.30
160 Rondell White	.10	.30
161 T.Kashiwada RC	.15	.40
162 Butch Huskey	.10	.30
163 Edgardo Alfonzo	.10	.30
164 John Franco	.10	.30
165 Todd Hundley	.10	.30
166 Rey Ordonez	.10	.30
167 Armando Reynoso	.10	.30
168 John Olerud	.10	.30
169 Bernie Williams	.20	.50
170 Andy Pettitte	.20	.50
171 Wade Boggs	.20	.50
172 Paul O'Neill	.20	.50
173 Cecil Fielder	.10	.30
174 Charlie Hayes	.10	.30
175 David Cone	.10	.30
176 Hideki Irabu	.10	.30
177 Mark Bellhorn	.10	.30
178 Steve Karsay	.10	.30
179 Damon Mashore	.10	.30
180 Jason McDonald	.10	.30
181 Scott Spiezio	.10	.30
182 Ariel Prieto	.10	.30
183 Jason Giambi	.10	.30
184 Wendell Magee	.10	.30
185 Rico Brogna	.10	.30
186 Garrett Stephenson	.10	.30
187 Wayne Gomes	.10	.30
188 Ricky Bottalico	.10	.30
189 Mickey Morandini	.10	.30
190 Mike Lieberthal	.10	.30
191 Kevin Polcovich	.10	.30
192 Francisco Cordova	.10	.30
193 Kevin Young	.10	.30
194 Jon Lieber	.10	.30
195 Kevin Elster	.10	.30
196 Tony Womack	.10	.30
197 Lou Collier	.10	.30
198 Mike Difelice RC	.15	.40
199 Gary Gaetti	.10	.30
200 Dennis Eckersley	.10	.30
201 Alan Benes	.10	.30
202 Willie McGee	.10	.30
203 Ron Gant	.10	.30
204 Fernando Valenzuela	.10	.30
205 Mark McGwire	.75	2.00
206 Archi Cianfrocco	.10	.30
207 Andy Ashby	.10	.30
208 Steve Finley	.10	.30
209 Quilvio Veras	.10	.30
210 Ken Caminiti	.10	.30
211 Rickey Henderson	.30	.75
212 Joey Hamilton	.10	.30
213 Derrek Lee	.20	.50
214 Bill Mueller	.10	.30
215 Shawn Estes	.10	.30
216 J.T. Snow	.10	.30
217 Mark Gardner	.10	.30
218 Terry Mulholland	.10	.30
219 Dante Powell	.10	.30
220 Jeff Kent	.10	.30
221 Jamie Moyer	.10	.30
222 Joey Cora	.10	.30
223 Jeff Fassero	.10	.30
224 Dennis Martinez	.10	.30
225 Ken Griffey Jr.	.50	1.25
226 Edgar Martinez	.20	.50
227 Russ Davis	.10	.30
228 Dan Wilson	.10	.30
229 Will Clark	.20	.50
230 Ivan Rodriguez	.20	.50
231 Benji Gil	.10	.30
232 Lee Stevens	.10	.30
233 Mickey Tettleton	.10	.30
234 Julio Santana	.10	.30
235 Rusty Greer	.10	.30
236 Bobby Witt	.10	.30
237 Ed Sprague	.10	.30
238 Pat Hentgen	.10	.30
239 Kelvim Escobar	.10	.30
240 Joe Carter	.10	.30
241 Carlos Delgado	.10	.30
242 Shannon Stewart	.10	.30
243 Benito Santiago	.10	.30
244 Tino Martinez SH	.10	.30
245 Ken Griffey Jr. SH	.30	.75
246 Kevin Brown SH	.10	.30
247 Ryne Sandberg SH	.20	.50
248 Mo Vaughn SH	.10	.30
249 Darryl Hamilton SH	.10	.30
250 Randy Johnson SH	.20	.50
251 Steve Finley SH	.10	.30
252 Bobby Higginson SH	.10	.30
253 Brett Tomko	.10	.30
254 Mark Kotsay	.10	.30
255 Jose Guillen	.10	.30
256 Eli Marrero	.10	.30
257 Dennis Reyes	.10	.30
258 Richie Sexson	.10	.30
259 Pat Cline	.10	.30
260 Todd Helton	.20	.50
261 Juan Melo	.10	.30
262 Matt Morris	.10	.30
263 Jeremi Gonzalez	.10	.30
264 Jeff Abbott	.10	.30
265 Aaron Boone	.10	.30
266 Todd Dunwoody	.10	.30
267 Jaret Wright	.10	.30
268 Derrick Gibson	.10	.30
269 Mario Valdez	.10	.30
270 Fernando Tatis	.10	.30
271 Craig Counsell	.10	.30
272 Brad Rigby	.10	.30
273 Danny Clyburn	.10	.30
274 Brian Rose	.10	.30
275 Miguel Tejada	.30	.75
276 Jason Varitek	.30	.75
277 Dave Dellucci RC	.25	.60
278 Michael Coleman	.10	.30
279 Adam Riggs	.10	.30
280 Ben Grieve	.10	.30
281 Brad Fullmer	.10	.30
282 Ken Cloude	.10	.30
283 Tom Evans	.10	.30
284 Kevin Millwood RC	.40	1.00
285 Paul Konerko	.10	.30
286 Juan Encarnacion	.10	.30
287 Chris Carpenter	.10	.30
288 Tom Fordham	.10	.30
289 Gary DiSarcina	.10	.30
290 Tim Salmon	.20	.50
291 Troy Percival	.10	.30
292 Todd Greene	.10	.30
293 Ken Hill	.10	.30
294 Dennis Springer	.10	.30
295 Jim Edmonds	.10	.30
296 Allen Watson	.10	.30
297 Brian Anderson	.10	.30
298 Keith Lockhart	.10	.30
299 Tom Glavine	.20	.50
300 Chipper Jones	.30	.75
301 Randall Simon	.10	.30
302 Mark Lemke	.10	.30
303 Ryan Klesko	.10	.30
304 Denny Neagle	.10	.30
305 Andruw Jones	.20	.50
306 Mike Mussina	.20	.50
307 Brady Anderson	.10	.30
308 Chris Hoiles	.10	.30
309 Mike Bordick	.10	.30
310 Cal Ripken	1.00	2.50
311 Geronimo Berroa	.10	.30
312 Armando Benitez	.10	.30
313 Roberto Alomar	.20	.50
314 Tim Wakefield	.10	.30
315 Reggie Jefferson	.10	.30
316 Jeff Frye	.10	.30
317 Scott Hatteberg	.10	.30
318 Steve Avery	.10	.30
319 Robinson Checo	.10	.30
320 Nomar Garciaparra	.50	1.25
321 Lance Johnson	.10	.30
322 Tyler Houston	.10	.30
323 Mark Clark	.10	.30
324 Terry Adams	.10	.30
325 Sammy Sosa	.30	.75
326 Scott Servais	.10	.30
327 Manny Alexander	.10	.30
328 Norberto Martin	.10	.30
329 Scott Eyre	.10	.30
330 Frank Thomas	.30	.75
331 Robin Ventura	.10	.30
332 Matt Karchner	.10	.30
333 Keith Foulke	.10	.30
334 James Baldwin	.10	.30
335 Chris Stynes	.10	.30

336 Bret Boone .10 .30
337 Jon Nunnally .10 .30
338 Dave Burba .10 .30
339 Eduardo Perez .10 .30
340 Reggie Sanders .10 .30
341 Mike Remlinger .10 .30
342 Pat Watkins .10 .30
343 Chad Ogea .10 .30
344 John Smiley .10 .30
345 Kenny Lofton .10 .30
346 Jose Mesa .10 .30
347 Charles Nagy .10 .30
348 Enrique Wilson .10 .30
349 Bruce Aven .10 .30
350 Manny Ramirez .20 .50
351 Jerry DiPoto .10 .30
352 Ellis Burks .10 .30
353 Kirt Manwaring .10 .30
354 Vinny Castilla .10 .30
355 Larry Walker .10 .30
356 Kevin Ritz .10 .30
357 Pedro Astacio .10 .30
358 Scott Sanders .10 .30
359 Deivi Cruz .10 .30
360 Brian L. Hunter .10 .30
361 Pedro Martinez HM .20 .50
362 Tom Glavine HM .10 .30
363 Willie McGee HM .10 .30
364 J.T. Snow HM .10 .30
365 Rusty Greer HM .10 .30
366 Mike Grace HM .10 .30
367 Tony Clark HM .10 .30
368 Ben Grieve HM .10 .30
369 Gary Sheffield HM .10 .30
370 Joe Oliver .10 .30
371 Todd Jones .10 .30
372 Frank Catalanotto RC .25 .60
373 Brian Moehler .10 .30
374 Cliff Floyd .10 .30
375 Bobby Bonilla .10 .30
376 Al Leiter .10 .30
377 Josh Booty .10 .30
378 Darren Daulton .10 .30
379 Jay Powell .10 .30
380 Felix Heredia .10 .30
381 Jim Eisenreich .10 .30
382 Richard Hidalgo .10 .30
383 Mike Hampton .10 .30
384 Shane Reynolds .10 .30
385 Jeff Bagwell .20 .50
386 Derek Bell .10 .30
387 Ricky Gutierrez .10 .30
388 Bill Spiers .10 .30
389 Jose Offerman .10 .30
390 Johnny Damon .20 .50
391 Jermaine Dye .10 .30
392 Jeff Montgomery .10 .30
393 Glendon Rusch .10 .30
394 Mike Sweeney .10 .30
395 Kevin Appier .10 .30
396 Joe Vitiello .10 .30
397 Ramon Martinez .10 .30
398 Darren Dreifort .10 .30
399 Wilton Guerrero .10 .30
400 Mike Piazza .50 1.25
401 Eddie Murray .30 .75
402 Ismael Valdes .10 .30
403 Todd Hollandsworth .10 .30
404 Mark Loretta .10 .30
405 Jeromy Burnitz .10 .30
406 Jeff Cirillo .10 .30
407 Scott Karl .10 .30
408 Mike Matheny .10 .30
409 Jose Valentin .10 .30
410 John Jaha .10 .30
411 Terry Steinbach .10 .30
412 Torii Hunter .10 .30
413 Pat Meares .10 .30
414 Marty Cordova .10 .30
415 Jaret Wright PH .10 .30
416 Mike Mussina PH .10 .30
417 John Smoltz PH .10 .30
418 Devon White PH .10 .30
419 Denny Neagle PH .10 .30
420 Livan Hernandez PH .10 .30
421 Kevin Brown PH .10 .30
422 Marquis Grissom PH .10 .30
423 Mike Mussina PH .10 .30
424 Eric Davis PH .10 .30
425 Tony Fernandez PH .10 .30
426 Moises Alou PH .10 .30
427 Sandy Alomar Jr. PH .10 .30
428 Gary Sheffield PH .10 .30
429 Jaret Wright PH .10 .30
430 Livan Hernandez PH .10 .30
431 Chad Ogea PH .10 .30
432 Edgar Renteria PH .10 .30
433 LaTroy Hawkins .10 .30
434 Rich Robertson .10 .30
435 Chuck Knoblauch .10 .30
436 Jose Vidro .10 .30
437 Dustin Hermanson .10 .30
438 Jim Bullinger .10 .30
439 Orlando Cabrera .10 .30
440 Vladimir Guerrero .30 .75
441 Ugueth Urbina .10 .30
442 Brian McRae .10 .30
443 Matt Franco .10 .30
444 Bobby Jones .10 .30
445 Bernard Gilkey .10 .30
446 Dave Mlicki .10 .30
447 Brian Bohanon .10 .30
448 Mel Rojas .10 .30
449 Tim Raines .10 .30
450 Derek Jeter .75 2.00
451 Roger Clemens UE .30 .75
452 N.Garciaparra UE .30 .75
453 Mike Piazza UE .30 .75
454 Mark McGwire UE .40 1.00
455 Ken Griffey Jr. UE .30 .75
456 Larry Walker UE .10 .30
457 Alex Rodriguez UE .30 .75
458 Tony Gwynn UE .20 .50
459 Frank Thomas UE .20 .50
460 Tino Martinez .20 .50
461 Chad Curtis .10 .30
462 Ramiro Mendoza .10 .30
463 Joe Girardi .10 .30
464 David Wells .10 .30
465 Mariano Rivera .30 .75
466 Willie Adams .10 .30
467 George Williams .10 .30
468 Dave Telgheder .10 .30
469 Dave Magadan .10 .30
470 Matt Stairs .10 .30
471 Bill Taylor .10 .30
472 Jimmy Haynes .10 .30
473 Gregg Jefferies .10 .30
474 Midre Cummings .10 .30
475 Curt Schilling .10 .30
476 Mike Grace .10 .30
477 Mark Leiter .10 .30
478 Matt Beech .10 .30
479 Scott Rolen .20 .50
480 Jason Kendall .10 .30
481 Esteban Loaiza .10 .30
482 Jermaine Allensworth .10 .30
483 Mark Smith .10 .30
484 Jason Schmidt .10 .30
485 Jose Guillen .10 .30
486 Al Martin .10 .30
487 Delino DeShields .10 .30
488 Todd Stottlemyre .10 .30
489 Brian Jordan .10 .30
490 Ray Lankford .10 .30
491 Matt Morris .10 .30
492 Royce Clayton .10 .30
493 John Mabry .10 .30
494 Wally Joyner .10 .30
495 Trevor Hoffman .10 .30
496 Chris Gomez .10 .30
497 Sterling Hitchcock .10 .30
498 Pete Smith .10 .30
499 Greg Vaughn .10 .30
500 Tony Gwynn .40 1.00
501 Will Cunnane .10 .30
502 Darryl Hamilton .10 .30
503 Brian Johnson .10 .30
504 Kirk Rueter .10 .30
505 Barry Bonds .75 2.00
506 Osvaldo Fernandez .10 .30
507 Stan Javier .10 .30
508 Julian Tavarez .10 .30
509 Rich Aurilia .10 .30
510 Alex Rodriguez .50 1.25
511 David Segui .10 .30
512 Rich Amaral .10 .30
513 Raul Ibanez .10 .30
514 Jay Buhner .10 .30
515 Randy Johnson .30 .75
516 Heathcliff Slocumb .10 .30
517 Tony Saunders .10 .30
518 Kevin Elster .10 .30
519 John Burkett .10 .30
520 Juan Gonzalez .10 .30
521 John Wetteland .10 .30
522 Domingo Cedeno .10 .30
523 Darren Oliver .10 .30
524 Roger Pavlik .10 .30
525 Jose Cruz Jr. .10 .30
526 Woody Williams .10 .30
527 Alex Gonzalez .10 .30
528 Robert Person .10 .30
529 Juan Guzman .10 .30
530 Roger Clemens .60 1.50
531 Shawn Green .10 .30
532 Francisco Cordova SH .10 .30
Ricardo Rincon
Mark Smith
533 N.Garciaparra SH .30 .75
534 Roger Clemens SH .30 .75
535 Mark McGwire SH .40 1.00
536 Larry Walker SH .10 .30
537 Mike Piazza SH .30 .75
538 Curt Schilling SH .10 .30
539 Tony Gwynn SH .20 .50
540 Ken Griffey Jr. SH .30 .75
541 Carl Pavano .10 .30
542 Shane Monahan .10 .30
543 Gabe Kapler RC .25 .60
544 Eric Milton .10 .30
545 Gary Matthews Jr. RC .25 .60
546 Mike Kinkade RC .10 .30
547 Ryan Christenson RC .10 .30
548 Corey Koskie RC .25 .60
549 Norm Hutchins .10 .30
550 Russell Branyan .10 .30
551 Masato Yoshii RC .15 .40
552 Jesus Sanchez RC .10 .30
553 Anthony Sanders .10 .30
554 Edwin Diaz .10 .30
555 Gabe Alvarez .10 .30
556 Carlos Lee RC .75 2.00
557 Mike Darr .10 .30
558 Kerry Wood .15 .40
559 Carlos Guillen .10 .30
560 Sean Casey .10 .30
561 Manny Aybar RC .10 .30
562 Octavio Dotel .10 .30
563 Jarrod Washburn .10 .30
564 Mark L. Johnson .10 .30
565 Ramon Hernandez .10 .30
566 Rich Butler RC .10 .30
567 Mike Caruso .10 .30
568 Cliff Politte .10 .30
569 Scott Elarton .30 .75
570 Magglio Ordonez RC 1.25 3.00
571 Adam Butler RC .10 .30
572 Marlon Anderson .10 .30
573 Julio Ramirez RC .10 .30
574 Darron Ingram RC .10 .30
575 Bruce Chen .10 .30
576 Steve Woodard .10 .30
577 Hiram Bocachica .10 .30
578 Kevin Witt .10 .30
579 Javier Vazquez .10 .30
580 Alex Gonzalez .10 .30
581 Brian Powell .10 .30
582 Wes Helms .10 .30
583 Ron Wright .10 .30
584 Rafael Medina .10 .30
585 Daryle Ward .10 .30
586 Geoff Jenkins .10 .30
587 Preston Wilson .10 .30
588 Jim Chamblee RC .10 .30
589 Mike Lowell RC .60 1.50
590 A.J. Hinch .10 .30
591 Francisco Cordero RC .25 .60
592 Rolando Arrojo RC .15 .40
593 Braden Looper .10 .30
594 Sidney Ponson .30 .75
595 Matt Clement .10 .30
596 Carlton Loewer .10 .30
597 Brian Meadows .10 .30
598 Danny Klassen .10 .30
599 Larry Sutton .10 .30
600 Travis Lee .10 .30
601 Randy Johnson EP 1.00 2.50
602 Greg Maddux EP 1.50 4.00
603 Roger Clemens EP 2.00 5.00
604 Jaret Wright EP .75 2.00
605 Mike Piazza EP 1.50 4.00
606 Tino Martinez EP .75 2.00
607 Frank Thomas EP 1.00 2.50
608 Mo Vaughn EP .75 2.00
609 Todd Helton EP .75 2.00
610 Mark McGwire EP 2.50 6.00
611 Jeff Bagwell EP .75 2.00
612 Travis Lee EP .75 2.00
613 Scott Rolen EP .75 2.00
614 Cal Ripken EP 3.00 8.00
615 Chipper Jones EP 1.00 2.50
616 Nomar Garciaparra EP 1.50 4.00
617 Alex Rodriguez EP 1.50 4.00
618 Derek Jeter EP 2.50 6.00
619 Tony Gwynn EP 1.25 3.00
620 Ken Griffey Jr. EP 1.50 4.00
621 Kenny Lofton EP .75 2.00
622 Juan Gonzalez EP .75 2.00
623 Jose Cruz Jr. EP .75 2.00
624 Larry Walker EP .75 2.00
625 Barry Bonds EP 2.50 6.00
626 Ben Grieve EP .75 2.00
627 Andruw Jones EP .75 2.00
628 Vladimir Guerrero EP 1.00 2.50
629 Paul Konerko EP .75 2.00
630 Paul Molitor EP .75 2.00
631 Cecil Fielder .10 .30
632 Jack McDowell .10 .30
633 Mike James .10 .30
634 Brian Anderson .10 .30
635 Jay Bell .10 .30
636 Devon White .10 .30
637 Andy Stankiewicz .10 .30
638 Tony Batista .10 .30
639 Omar Daal .10 .30
640 Matt Williams .10 .30
641 Brent Brede .10 .30
642 Jorge Fabregas .10 .30
643 Karim Garcia .10 .30
644 Felix Rodriguez .10 .30
645 Andy Benes .10 .30
646 Willie Blair .10 .30
647 Jeff Suppan .10 .30
648 Yamil Benitez .10 .30
649 Walt Weiss .10 .30
650 Andres Galarraga .10 .30
651 Doug Drabek .10 .30
652 Ozzie Guillen .10 .30
653 Joe Carter .10 .30
654 Dennis Eckersley .10 .30
655 Pedro Martinez .20 .50
656 Jim Leyritz .10 .30
657 Henry Rodriguez .10 .30
658 Rod Beck .10 .30
659 Mickey Morandini .10 .30
660 Jeff Blauser .10 .30
661 Ruben Sierra .10 .30
662 Mike Sirotka .10 .30
663 Pete Harnisch .10 .30
664 Damian Jackson .10 .30
665 Dmitri Young .10 .30
666 Steve Cooke .10 .30
667 Geronimo Berroa .10 .30
668 Shawon Dunston .10 .30
669 Mike Jackson .10 .30
670 Travis Fryman .10 .30
671 Dwight Gooden .10 .30
672 Paul Assenmacher .10 .30
673 Eric Plunk .10 .30
674 Mike Lansing .10 .30
675 Darryl Kile .10 .30
676 Luis Gonzalez .10 .30
677 Frank Castillo .10 .30
678 Joe Randa .10 .30
679 Bip Roberts .10 .30
680 Derrek Lee .20 .50
681 Mike Piazza SP 1.25 3.00
New York Mets
681A Mike Piazza SP 1.25 3.00
Florida Marlins
682 Sean Berry .10 .30
683 Ramon Garcia .10 .30
684 Carl Everett .10 .30
685 Moises Alou .10 .30
686 Hal Morris .10 .30
687 Jeff Conine .10 .30
688 Gary Sheffield .10 .30
689 Jose Vizcaino .10 .30
690 Charles Johnson .10 .30
691 Bobby Bonilla .10 .30
692 Marquis Grissom .10 .30
693 Alex Ochoa .10 .30
694 Mike Morgan .10 .30
695 Orlando Merced .10 .30
696 David Ortiz .40 1.00
697 Brent Gates .10 .30
698 Otis Nixon .10 .30
699 Trey Moore .10 .30
700 Derrick May .10 .30
701 Rich Becker .10 .30
702 Al Leiter .10 .30
703 Chili Davis .10 .30
704 Scott Brosius .10 .30
705 Chuck Knoblauch .10 .30
706 Kenny Rogers .10 .30
707 Mike Blowers .10 .30
708 Mike Fetters .10 .30
709 Tom Candiotti .10 .30
710 Rickey Henderson .30 .75
711 Bob Abreu .10 .30
712 Mark Lewis .10 .30
713 Doug Glanville .10 .30
714 Desi Relaford .10 .30
715 Kent Mercker .10 .30
716 Kevin Brown .20 .50
717 James Mouton .10 .30
718 Mark Langston .10 .30
719 Greg Myers .10 .30
720 Orel Hershiser .10 .30
721 Charlie Hayes .10 .30
722 Robb Nen .10 .30
723 Glenallen Hill .10 .30
724 Tony Saunders .10 .30
725 Wade Boggs .20 .50
726 Kevin Stocker .10 .30
727 Wilson Alvarez .10 .30
728 Albie Lopez .10 .30
729 Dave Martinez .10 .30
730 Fred McGriff .20 .50
731 Quinton McCracken .10 .30
732 Bryan Rekar .10 .30
733 Paul Sorrento .10 .30
734 Roberto Hernandez .10 .30
735 Bubba Trammell .10 .30
736 Miguel Cairo .10 .30
737 John Flaherty .10 .30
738 Terrell Wade .10 .30
739 Roberto Kelly .10 .30
740 Mark McLemore .10 .30
741 Danny Patterson .10 .30
742 Aaron Sele .10 .30
743 Tony Fernandez .10 .30
744 Randy Myers .10 .30
745 Jose Canseco .20 .50
746 Darrin Fletcher .10 .30
747 Mike Stanley .10 .30
748 M.Grissom SH CL .10 .30
749 Fred McGriff SH CL .10 .30
750 Travis Lee SH CL .10 .30

1998 Upper Deck 5 x 7 Blow Ups

These jumbo parallel cards capture a selection of players taken from each of the three basic series of the 1998 Upper Deck set. Besides the obvious difference in size, these 5" by 7" cards also lack the silver foil coating on front that the standard 2 1/2" by 3 1/2" cards have. The first fifteen cards checklisted below (skip-numbered between 30 and 230) comprise the first series 5 x 7 Blow Up set. These first series jumbo cards were available only via redemption from Upper Deck. Collector's had to send in ten first series wrappers plus $3 to the UD redemption center. The next ten cards checklisted below (skip-numbered between 310 and 530) comprise the second series 5 x 7 Blow Up set. These second series jumbo cards were available only in specially marked mass market retail series 2 boxes (carrying an $11.99 SRP). Each box contained five basic series 2 retail packs and one 5 x 7 Blow Up. The third series 5 x 7 Blow Ups (numbered between 605 and 620 in the listings below) are comprised of selected stars from the Eminent Prestige subset within the basic issue Series 3 set.

27 Kenny Lofton .40 1.00
30 Greg Maddux 1.25 3.00
40 Rafael Palmeiro .50 1.25
50 Ryne Sandberg 1.25 3.00
60 Albert Belle .30 .75
65 Barry Larkin .50 1.25
68 Deion Sanders .30 .75
95 Gary Sheffield .60 1.50
130 Paul Molitor .60 1.50
135 Vladimir Guerrero .60 1.50
176 Hideki Irabu .20 .50
205 Mark McGwire 1.50 4.00
211 Rickey Henderson .75 2.00
225 Ken Griffey Jr. 1.25 3.00
230 Ivan Rodriguez .60 1.50
310 Cal Ripken 2.50 6.00
320 Nomar Garciaparra 1.25 3.00
330 Frank Thomas .60 1.50
355 Larry Walker .50 1.25
385 Jeff Bagwell .60 1.50
400 Mike Piazza 1.50 4.00
450 Derek Jeter 2.50 6.00
500 Tony Gwynn 1.25 3.00
510 Alex Rodriguez 1.50 4.00
530 Roger Clemens 1.25 3.00
605 Mike Piazza EP 1.50 4.00
607 Frank Thomas EP .60 1.50
610 Mark McGwire EP 1.25 3.00
611 Jeff Bagwell EP .60 1.50
612 Travis Lee EP .30 .75
614 Cal Ripken EP 2.50 6.00
616 Nomar Garciaparra EP 1.25 3.00
617 Alex Rodriguez EP 1.50 4.00
619 Tony Gwynn EP 1.25 3.00
620 Ken Griffey Jr. EP 1.25 3.00

1998 Upper Deck 10th Anniversary Preview

Randomly inserted in Series one packs at the rate of one in five, this 60-card set features color player photos in a design similar to the inaugural 1989 Upper Deck series. The backs carry a photo of that player's previous Upper Deck card. A 10th Anniversary Ballot Card was inserted one in four packs which allowed the collector to vote for the players they wanted to see in the 1999 Upper Deck tenth anniversary series.

COMPLETE SET (60) 50.00 120.00
COMP.RETAIL SET (60) 8.00 20.00
*RETAIL: .08X TO .2X BASIC 10TH ANN
RETAIL DISTRIBUTED AS FACTORY SET
1 Greg Maddux 2.00 5.00
2 Mike Mussina .75 2.00
3 Roger Clemens 2.50 6.00
4 Hideo Nomo 1.25 3.00
5 David Cone .50 1.25
6 Tom Glavine .75 2.00
7 Andy Pettitte .75 2.00
8 Jimmy Key .50 1.25
9 Randy Johnson 1.25 3.00
10 Dennis Eckersley .50 1.25
11 Lee Smith .50 1.25
12 John Franco .50 1.25
13 Randy Myers .50 1.25
14 Mike Piazza 2.00 5.00
15 Ivan Rodriguez .75 2.00
16 Todd Hundley .50 1.25
17 Sandy Alomar Jr. .50 1.25
18 Frank Thomas 1.25 3.00
19 Rafael Palmeiro .75 2.00
20 Mark McGwire 3.00 8.00
21 Mo Vaughn .50 1.25
22 Fred McGriff .75 2.00
23 Andres Galarraga .50 1.25
24 Mark Grace .75 2.00
25 Jeff Bagwell .75 2.00
26 Roberto Alomar .75 2.00
27 Chuck Knoblauch .50 1.25
28 Ryne Sandberg 2.00 5.00
29 Eric Young .50 1.25
30 Craig Biggio .75 2.00
31 Carlos Baerga .50 1.25
32 Robin Ventura .50 1.25
33 Matt Williams .50 1.25
34 Wade Boggs .75 2.00
35 Dean Palmer .50 1.25
36 Chipper Jones 1.25 3.00
37 Vinny Castilla .50 1.25
38 Ken Caminiti .50 1.25
39 Omar Vizquel .75 2.00
40 Cal Ripken 4.00 10.00
41 Derek Jeter 3.00 8.00
42 Alex Rodriguez 2.00 5.00
43 Barry Larkin .75 2.00
44 Mark Grudzielanek .50 1.25
45 Albert Belle .50 1.25
46 Manny Ramirez .75 2.00
47 Jose Canseco .75 2.00
48 Ken Griffey Jr. 2.00 5.00
49 Juan Gonzalez .50 1.25
50 Kenny Lofton .50 1.25
51 Sammy Sosa 1.25 3.00
52 Larry Walker .50 1.25
53 Gary Sheffield .50 1.25
54 Rickey Henderson 1.25 3.00
55 Tony Gwynn 1.50 4.00
56 Barry Bonds 3.00 8.00
57 Paul Molitor .50 1.25
58 Edgar Martinez .75 2.00
59 Chili Davis .50 1.25
60 Eddie Murray 1.25 3.00

1998 Upper Deck 10th Anniversary Preview Retail

This 60 card set is a parallel to the 10th Anniversary Preview set inserted into 1998 Upper Deck Series 1. This set was only available as part of a retail package which also included 200 better 1997 Collectors Choice cards. The difference between these cards and the pack inserts are the gold foil printed on the card along with the words "Preview Edition" printed on the side. The box which contained all these cards had a SRP of $19.99.

COMPLETE SET (60) 8.00 20.00
*:STARS: .4X TO 1X BASIC CARDS

1998 Upper Deck A Piece of the Action 1

Randomly inserted in first series packs at the rate of one in 2,500, cards from this set feature color photos of top players with pieces of actual game worn jerseys and/or game used bats embedded in the cards.

1 Jay Buhner Bat 10.00 25.00
2 Tony Gwynn Bat 15.00 40.00
3 Tony Gwynn Jersey 15.00 40.00
4 Todd Hollandsworth Bat 6.00 15.00
5 T.Hollandsworth Jersey 6.00 15.00
6 Greg Maddux Jersey 30.00 60.00
7 Alex Rodriguez Bat 30.00 60.00
8 Alex Rodriguez Jersey 30.00 60.00
9 Gary Sheffield Bat 10.00 25.00
10 Gary Sheffield Jersey 10.00 25.00

1998 Upper Deck A Piece of the Action 2

Randomly seeded into second series packs at a rate of 1:2500, each of these four different cards features pieces of both game-used bats and jerseys incorporated into the design of the card. According to information provided on the media release, only 225 of each card was produced. The cards are numbered by the player's initials.

AJ Andruw Jones 30.00 60.00
GS Gary Sheffield 15.00 40.00
JB Jay Buhner 15.00 40.00
RA Roberto Alomar 30.00 60.00

1998 Upper Deck A Piece of the Action 3

Randomly seeded into third series packs, each of these cards featured a jersey swatch embedded on the card. The portion of the bat which was in series two is now just a design element. Ken Griffey, Jr. signed 24 of these cards and they were inserted into the packs as well.

GRIFFEY AU PRINT RUN 24 #'d CARDS
NO GRIFFEY AU PRICE DUE TO SCARCITY
BG Ben Grieve/200 10.00 25.00
JC Jose Cruz Jr./200 10.00 25.00
KG Ken Griffey Jr./300 60.00 120.00
TL Travis Lee/200 10.00 25.00
KGS Ken Griffey Jr. AU/24

1998 Upper Deck All-Star Credentials

Randomly inserted in packs at a rate of one in nine, this 30-card insert set features players who have the best chance of appearing in future All-Star games.

COMPLETE SET (30) 40.00 100.00
AS1 Ken Griffey Jr. 2.00 5.00
AS2 Travis Lee .50 1.25
AS3 Ben Grieve .50 1.25
AS4 Jose Cruz Jr. .50 1.25
AS5 Andruw Jones .75 2.00
AS6 Craig Biggio .75 2.00
AS7 Hideo Nomo 1.25 3.00
AS8 Cal Ripken 4.00 10.00
AS9 Jaret Wright .50 1.25
AS10 Mark McGwire 3.00 8.00
AS11 Derek Jeter 3.00 8.00
AS12 Scott Rolen .75 2.00
AS13 Jeff Bagwell .75 2.00
AS14 Manny Ramirez .75 2.00
AS15 Alex Rodriguez 2.00 5.00
AS16 Chipper Jones 1.25 3.00
AS17 Larry Walker .50 1.25
AS18 Barry Bonds 3.00 8.00
AS19 Tony Gwynn 1.50 4.00
AS20 Mike Piazza 2.00 5.00
AS21 Roger Clemens 2.50 6.00
AS22 Greg Maddux 2.00 5.00
AS23 Jim Thome .75 2.00
AS24 Tino Martinez .75 2.00
AS25 Nomar Garciaparra 2.00 5.00
AS26 Juan Gonzalez .50 1.25
AS27 Kenny Lofton .50 1.25
AS28 Randy Johnson 1.25 3.00
AS29 Todd Helton .75 2.00
AS30 Frank Thomas 1.25 3.00

1998 Upper Deck Amazing Greats

Randomly inserted in Series one packs, this 30-card set features color photos of amazing players printed on a hi-tech plastic card. Only 2000 of this set were produced and are sequentially numbered.

COMPLETE SET (30) 150.00 400.00
*DIE CUTS: 1X TO 2.5X BASIC AMAZING
DIE CUT PRINT RUN 250 SERIAL #'d SETS
RANDOM INSERTS IN SER.1 PACKS
AG1 Ken Griffey Jr. 5.00 12.00
AG2 Derek Jeter 8.00 20.00
AG3 Alex Rodriguez 5.00 12.00
AG4 Paul Molitor 1.25 3.00
AG5 Jeff Bagwell 2.00 5.00
AG6 Larry Walker 1.25 3.00
AG7 Kenny Lofton 1.25 3.00
AG8 Cal Ripken 10.00 25.00
AG9 Juan Gonzalez 1.25 3.00
AG10 Chipper Jones 3.00 8.00
AG11 Greg Maddux 5.00 12.00
AG12 Roberto Alomar 2.00 5.00
AG13 Mike Piazza 5.00 12.00
AG14 Andres Galarraga 1.25 3.00
AG15 Barry Bonds 8.00 20.00
AG16 Andy Pettitte 2.00 5.00

AG17 Nomar Garciaparra 5.00 12.00
AG18 Tino Martinez 2.00 5.00
AG19 Tony Gwynn 4.00 10.00
AG20 Frank Thomas 3.00 8.00
AG21 Roger Clemens 6.00 15.00
AG22 Sammy Sosa 3.00 8.00
AG23 Jose Cruz Jr. 1.25 3.00
AG24 Manny Ramirez 2.00 5.00
AG25 Mark McGwire 8.00 20.00
AG26 Randy Johnson 3.00 8.00
AG27 Mo Vaughn 1.25 3.00
AG28 Gary Sheffield 1.25 3.00
AG29 Andruw Jones 2.00 5.00
AG30 Albert Belle 1.25 3.00

1998 Upper Deck Blue Chip Prospects

Randomly inserted in Series two packs, this 30-card set features color photos of some of the league's most impressive prospects printed on die-cut acetate cards. Only 2,000 of each card were produced.

COMPLETE SET (30) 100.00 250.00
BC1 Nomar Garciaparra 10.00 25.00
BC2 Scott Rolen 4.00 10.00
BC3 Jason Dickson 1.50 4.00
BC4 Darin Erstad 2.50 6.00
BC5 Brad Fullmer 1.50 4.00
BC6 Jaret Wright 1.50 4.00
BC7 Justin Thompson 1.50 4.00
BC8 Matt Morris 2.50 6.00
BC9 Fernando Tatis 1.50 4.00
BC10 Alex Rodriguez 10.00 25.00
BC11 Todd Helton 4.00 10.00
BC12 Andy Pettitte 4.00 10.00
BC13 Jose Cruz Jr. 1.50 4.00
BC14 Mark Kotsay 2.50 6.00
BC15 Derek Jeter 15.00 40.00
BC16 Paul Konerko 2.50 6.00
BC17 Todd Dunwoody 1.50 4.00
BC18 Vladimir Guerrero 6.00 15.00
BC19 Miguel Tejada 6.00 15.00
BC20 Chipper Jones 6.00 15.00
BC21 Kevin Orie 1.50 4.00
BC22 Ramon Encarnacion 1.50 4.00
BC23 Brian Rose 1.50 4.00
BC24 Livan Hernandez 2.50 6.00
BC25 Andruw Jones 4.00 10.00
BC26 Brian Giles 2.50 6.00
BC27 Brett Tomko 1.50 4.00
BC28 Jose Guillen 2.50 6.00
BC29 Aaron Boone 2.50 6.00
BC30 Ben Grieve 1.50 4.00

1998 Upper Deck Clearly Dominant

Randomly inserted in Series two packs, this 30-card set features color head photos of top players with a black-and-white action shot in the background printed on Light F/X plastic stock. Only 250 sequentially numbered sets were produced.

CD1 Mark McGwire 15.00 40.00
CD2 Derek Jeter 15.00 40.00
CD3 Alex Rodriguez 10.00 25.00
CD4 Paul Molitor 2.50 6.00
CD5 Jeff Bagwell 4.00 10.00
CD6 Ivan Rodriguez 4.00 10.00
CD7 Kenny Lofton 2.50 6.00
CD8 Cal Ripken 20.00 50.00
CD9 Albert Belle 2.50 6.00
CD10 Chipper Jones 6.00 15.00
CD11 Gary Sheffield 2.50 6.00
CD12 Roberto Alomar 4.00 10.00
CD13 Mo Vaughn 2.50 6.00
CD14 Andres Galarraga 2.50 6.00
CD15 Nomar Garciaparra 10.00 25.00
CD16 Randy Johnson 6.00 15.00
CD17 Mike Mussina 4.00 10.00
CD18 Greg Maddux 10.00 25.00
CD19 Tony Gwynn 8.00 20.00
CD20 Frank Thomas 6.00 15.00
CD21 Roger Clemens 12.50 30.00
CD22 Dennis Eckersley 2.50 6.00
CD23 Juan Gonzalez 2.50 6.00
CD24 Tino Martinez 4.00 10.00
CD25 Andruw Jones 4.00 10.00
CD26 Larry Walker 2.50 6.00
CD27 Ken Caminiti 2.50 6.00
CD28 Mike Piazza 10.00 25.00
CD29 Barry Bonds 15.00 40.00
CD30 Ken Griffey Jr. 10.00 25.00

1998 Upper Deck Destination Stardom

Randomly inserted in packs at a rate of one in five, this 60-card insert set features color action photos of today's star potential placed in a diamond-cut center with four colored corners. The cards are foil enhanced and die-cut.

COMPLETE SET (60) 40.00 100.00
DS1 Travis Lee .40 1.00

DS2 Nomar Garciaparra 2.50 6.00
DS3 Alex Gonzalez .40 1.00
DS4 Richard Hidalgo .40 1.00
DS5 Jaret Wright .40 1.00
DS6 Mike Kinkade 1.25 3.00
DS7 Matt Morris .60 1.50
DS8 Gary Matthews Jr. 1.25 3.00
DS9 Brett Tomko .40 1.00
DS10 Todd Helton .75 2.00
DS11 Scott Elarton .40 1.00
DS12 Scott Rolen .75 2.00
DS13 Jose Cruz Jr. .40 1.00
DS14 Jarrod Washburn .40 1.00
DS15 Sean Casey .60 1.50
DS16 Magglio Ordonez 2.50 6.00
DS17 Gabe Alvarez .40 1.00
DS18 Todd Dunwoody .40 1.00
DS19 Kevin Witt .40 1.00
DS20 Ben Grieve .40 1.00
DS21 Daryle Ward .40 1.00
DS22 Matt Clement .60 1.50
DS23 Carlton Loewer .40 1.00
DS24 Javier Vazquez .60 1.50
DS25 Paul Konerko .60 1.50
DS26 Preston Wilson .60 1.50
DS27 Wes Helms .40 1.00
DS28 Derek Jeter 4.00 10.00
DS29 Corey Koskie 1.25 3.00
DS30 Russell Branyan .40 1.00
DS31 Vladimir Guerrero 1.25 3.00
DS32 Ryan Christenson .60 1.50
DS33 Carlos Lee 2.50 6.00
DS34 Dave Dellucci .75 2.00
DS35 Bruce Chen .40 1.00
DS36 Ricky Ledee .40 1.00
DS37 Ron Wright .40 1.00
DS38 Derrek Lee .75 2.00
DS39 Miguel Tejada 1.25 3.00
DS40 Brad Fullmer .40 1.00
DS41 Rich Butler .40 1.00
DS42 Chris Carpenter .60 1.50
DS43 Alex Rodriguez 2.50 6.00
DS44 Darron Ingram .60 1.50
DS45 Kerry Wood .60 1.50
DS46 Jason Varitek 1.25 3.00
DS47 Ramon Hernandez .40 1.00
DS48 Aaron Boone .60 1.50
DS49 Juan Encarnacion .40 1.00
DS50 A.J. Hinch .40 1.00
DS51 Mike Lowell 2.00 5.00
DS52 Fernando Tatis .40 1.00
DS53 Jose Guillen .60 1.50
DS54 Mike Caruso .40 1.00
DS55 Carl Pavano .60 1.50
DS56 Chris Clemons .40 1.00
DS57 Mark L. Johnson .40 1.00
DS58 Ken Cloude .40 1.00
DS59 Rolando Arrojo 1.25 3.00
DS60 Mark Kotsay .60 1.50

1998 Upper Deck Griffey Home Run Chronicles

Randomly inserted in first and second series packs at the rate of one in nine, this 56-card set features color photos of Ken Griffey Jr.'s 56 home runs of the 1997 season. The fronts of the Series one inserts have photos and a brief headline of each homer. The backs all have the same photo and more details about each homer. The cards are notated on the back with what date each homer was hit. Series two inserts feature game-dated photos from the actual games in which the homers were hit.

COMPLETE SET (56) 40.00 100.00
COMMON GRIFFEY (1-56) .75 2.00

1998 Upper Deck National Pride

Randomly inserted in Series one packs at the rate of one in 23, this 42-card set features color photos of some of the league's great players from countries other than the United States printed on die-cut ranbow foil cards. The backs carry player information.

NP1 Dave Nilsson 2.00 5.00
NP2 Larry Walker 2.00 5.00
NP3 Edgar Renteria 2.00 5.00
NP4 Jose Canseco 3.00 8.00
NP5 Rey Ordonez 2.00 5.00
NP6 Rafael Palmeiro 3.00 8.00
NP7 Livan Hernandez 2.00 5.00
NP8 Andruw Jones 3.00 8.00
NP9 Manny Ramirez 3.00 8.00
NP10 Sammy Sosa 5.00 12.00
NP11 Raul Mondesi 2.00 5.00
NP12 Moises Alou 2.00 5.00
NP13 Pedro Martinez 3.00 8.00
NP14 Vladimir Guerrero 5.00 12.00
NP15 Chili Davis 2.00 5.00
NP16 Hideo Nomo 5.00 12.00
NP17 Hideki Irabu 2.00 5.00
NP18 S.Hasegawa 2.00 5.00
NP19 Takashi Kashiwada 2.50 6.00
NP20 Chan Ho Park 2.00 5.00
NP21 Fernando Valenzuela 2.00 5.00
NP22 Vinny Castilla 2.00 5.00
NP23 Armando Reynoso 2.00 5.00
NP24 Karim Garcia 2.00 5.00
NP25 Marvin Benard 2.00 5.00
NP26 Mariano Rivera 5.00 12.00
NP27 Juan Gonzalez 2.00 5.00
NP28 Roberto Alomar 3.00 8.00
NP29 Ivan Rodriguez 3.00 8.00
NP30 Carlos Delgado 2.00 5.00
NP31 Bernie Williams 3.00 8.00
NP32 Edgar Martinez 3.00 8.00
NP33 Frank Thomas 5.00 12.00
NP34 Barry Bonds 12.50 30.00
NP35 Mike Piazza 8.00 20.00
NP36 Chipper Jones 5.00 12.00
NP37 Cal Ripken 15.00 40.00
NP38 Alex Rodriguez 8.00 20.00
NP39 Ken Griffey Jr. 8.00 20.00
NP40 Andres Galarraga 2.00 5.00
NP41 Omar Vizquel 3.00 8.00
NP42 Ozzie Guillen 2.00 5.00

1998 Upper Deck Power Deck Audio Griffey

In an effort to premier their new Power Deck Audio technology, Upper Deck created three special Ken Griffey Jr. cards (blue, green and silver backgrounds), each of which contained the same five minute interview with the Mariner's superstar. These cards were randomly seeded exclusively into test packs comprising only 10 percent of the total first series 1998 Upper Deck print run. The seeding ratios are as follows: blue 1:8, green 1:100 and silver 1:2400. Each test issue box contained a clear CD disc for which the card could be placed upon for playing on any common CD player. To play the card, the center hole had to be punched out. Prices below are for Mint unpunched cards. Punched out cards trade at twenty-five percent of the listed values.

1 Ken Griffey Jr. Blue .75 2.00
2 Ken Griffey Jr. Green 5.00 12.00
3 Ken Griffey Jr. Silver 15.00 40.00

1998 Upper Deck Prime Nine

Randomly inserted in Series two packs at the rate of one in five, this 60-card set features color photos of the current most popular players printed on premium silver card stock.

COMPLETE SET (60) 40.00 100.00
COMMON GRIFFEY (1-7) .75 2.00
COMMON PIAZZA (8-14) .75 2.00
COMMON THOMAS (15-21) .50 1.25
COMMON MCGWIRE (22-28) 1.25 3.00
COMMON RIPKEN (29-35) 1.50 4.00
COMMON GONZALEZ (36-42) .20 .50
COMMON GWYNN (43-49) .60 1.50
COMMON BONDS (50-55) 1.25 3.00
COMMON MADDUX (56-60) .75 2.00

1998 Upper Deck Retrospectives

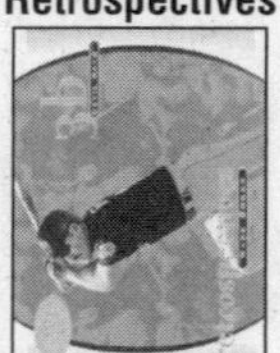

Randomly inserted in series three packs at a rate of one in 24, this 30-card insert set takes a look back at the unforgettable careers of some of baseball's most valuable contributors. The fronts feature a color action photo from each player's rookie season.

1 Dennis Eckersley 1.25 3.00
2 Rickey Henderson 3.00 8.00
3 Harold Baines 1.25 3.00
4 Cal Ripken 10.00 25.00
5 Tony Gwynn 4.00 10.00
6 Wade Boggs 2.00 5.00
7 Orel Hershiser 1.25 3.00
8 Joe Carter 1.25 3.00
9 Roger Clemens 6.00 15.00
10 Barry Bonds 8.00 20.00
11 Mark McGwire 8.00 20.00
12 Greg Maddux 5.00 12.00
13 Fred McGriff 2.00 5.00
14 Rafael Palmeiro 2.00 5.00
15 Craig Biggio 2.00 5.00
16 Brady Anderson 1.25 3.00
17 Randy Johnson 3.00 8.00
18 Gary Sheffield 1.25 3.00
19 Albert Belle 1.25 3.00
20 Ken Griffey Jr. 5.00 12.00
21 Juan Gonzalez 1.25 3.00
22 Larry Walker 1.25 3.00
23 Tino Martinez 2.00 5.00
24 Frank Thomas 3.00 8.00
25 Jeff Bagwell 2.00 5.00
26 Kenny Lofton 1.25 3.00
27 Mo Vaughn 1.25 3.00
28 Mike Piazza 5.00 12.00
29 Alex Rodriguez 5.00 12.00
30 Chipper Jones 3.00 8.00

1998 Upper Deck Rookie Edition Preview

Randomly inserted in Upper Deck Series two packs at an approximate rate of one in six, this 10-card set features color photos of players who were top rookies. The backs carry player information.

COMPLETE SET (10) 2.50 6.00
1 Nomar Garciaparra .75 2.00
2 Scott Rolen .30 .75
3 Mark Kotsay .20 .50
4 Todd Helton .30 .75
5 Paul Konerko .20 .50
6 Juan Encarnacion .20 .50
7 Brad Fullmer .20 .50
8 Miguel Tejada .50 1.25
9 Richard Hidalgo .20 .50
10 Ben Grieve .20 .50

1998 Upper Deck Tape Measure Titans

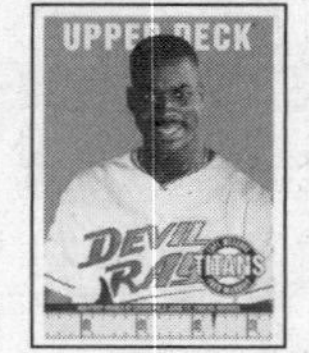

Randomly inserted in Series two packs at the rate of one in 23, this 30-card set features color photos of the league's most productive long-ball hitters printed on unique retro cards.

COMPLETE SET (30) 60.00 150.00
*GOLD: .4X TO 1X BASIC TITAN
GOLD: RANDOM IN RETAIL PACKS
GOLD PRINT RUN 2667 SERIAL #'d SETS
1 Mark McGwire 8.00 20.00
2 Andres Galarraga 1.25 3.00
3 Jeff Bagwell 2.00 5.00
4 Larry Walker 1.25 3.00
5 Frank Thomas 3.00 8.00
6 Rafael Palmeiro 2.00 5.00
7 Nomar Garciaparra 5.00 12.00
8 Mo Vaughn 1.25 3.00
9 Albert Belle 1.25 3.00
10 Ken Griffey Jr. 5.00 12.00
11 Manny Ramirez 2.00 5.00
12 Jim Thome 2.00 5.00
13 Tony Clark 1.25 3.00
14 Juan Gonzalez 1.25 3.00
15 Mike Piazza 5.00 12.00
16 Jose Canseco 2.00 5.00
17 Jay Buhner 1.25 3.00
18 Alex Rodriguez 5.00 12.00
19 Jose Cruz Jr. 1.25 3.00
20 Tino Martinez 2.00 5.00
21 Carlos Delgado 1.25 3.00
22 Andruw Jones 2.00 5.00
23 Chipper Jones 3.00 8.00
24 Fred McGriff 2.00 5.00
25 Matt Williams 1.25 3.00
26 Sammy Sosa 3.00 8.00
27 Vinny Castilla 1.25 3.00
28 Tim Salmon 2.00 5.00
29 Ken Caminiti 1.25 3.00
30 Barry Bonds 8.00 20.00

1998 Upper Deck Unparalleled

Randomly inserted in series three hobby packs only at a rate of one in 72, this 20-card insert set features color action photos on a high-tech designed card.

COMPLETE SET (20) 100.00 250.00
1 Ken Griffey Jr. 6.00 15.00
2 Travis Lee 1.50 4.00
3 Ben Grieve 1.50 4.00
4 Jose Cruz Jr. 1.50 4.00
5 Nomar Garciaparra 6.00 15.00
6 Hideo Nomo 4.00 10.00
7 Kenny Lofton 1.50 4.00
8 Cal Ripken 12.50 30.00
9 Roger Clemens 8.00 20.00
10 Mike Piazza 6.00 15.00
11 Jeff Bagwell 2.50 6.00
12 Chipper Jones 4.00 10.00
13 Greg Maddux 6.00 15.00
14 Randy Johnson 4.00 10.00
15 Alex Rodriguez 6.00 15.00
16 Barry Bonds 10.00 25.00
17 Frank Thomas 4.00 10.00
18 Juan Gonzalez 1.50 4.00
19 Tony Gwynn 5.00 12.00
20 Mark McGwire 10.00 25.00

1998 Upper Deck Griffey Most Memorable Home Runs

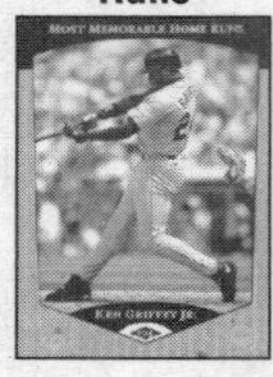

This 10-card set features color action photos of Ken Griffey Jr. hitting the most memorable home runs of his career printed on cards measuring approximately 3 1/2" by 5" with gold foil highlights. The backs carry another photo of the home run along with the date and why the home run was important in his career. Limited Edition Ken Griffey Jr. Autograph cards were randomly inserted in the set boxes. Also inserted was a special redemption card to be redeemed for an exclusive Ken Griffey Jr. 300th HR Commemorative Card or a special oversized card of equal or geater value.

COMMON CARD (1-10) .50 1.25

1998 Upper Deck Griffey Most Memorable Home Runs Autographed

Randomly inserted into boxes of Griffey Most Memorable Home Runs sets were these autographed cards. Ken Griffey Jr. signed 10 each of the cards in the set and the cards are all serial numbered on the front "x"/10. No pricing is available due to scarcity.

1 Ken Griffey Jr. 4/10/89
2 Ken Griffey Jr. 9/14/90
3 Ken Griffey Jr. 7/14/92
4 Ken Griffey Jr. 7/28/93
5 Ken Griffey Jr. 6/30/94
6 Ken Griffey Jr. 8/24/95
7 Ken Griffey Jr. 10/8/95
8 Ken Griffey Jr. 4/25/97
9 Ken Griffey Jr. 9/7/97
10 Ken Griffey Jr. 9/27/97

1999 Upper Deck

This 525-card set was distributed in two separate series. Series one packs contained cards 1-255 and series two contained 266-535. Cards 256-265 were never created. Subsets are as follows: Star Rookies (1-18, 266-292), Foreign Focus (229-246), Season Highlights Checklists (247-255, 527-535), and Arms Race '99 (518-526). The product was distributed in 10-card packs with a suggested retail price of $2.99. Though not confirmed by Upper Deck, it's widely believed by dealers that broke a good deal of product that these subset cards were slightly short-printed in comparison to other cards in the set. Notable Rookie Cards include Pat Burrell. 100 signed 1989 Upper Deck Ken Griffey Jr. RC's were randomly seeded into series one packs. These signed cards are real 89 RC's and they contain an additional diamond shaped hologram on back signifying that UD has verified Griffey's signature. Approximately 350 Babe Ruth A Piece of History cards were randomly seeded into all series one packs at a rate of one in 15,000. 50 Babe Ruth A Piece of History 500 Club bat cards were randomly seeded into second series packs. Pricing for these bat cards can be referenced under 1999 Upper Deck A Piece of History 500 Club.

COMPLETE SET (525) 50.00 100.00
COMP. SERIES 1 (255) 30.00 60.00
COMP. SERIES 2 (270) 20.00 40.00
COMMON (19-255/293-535) .10 .30
COMMON SER.1 SR (1-18) .20 .50
COMMON (266-292) .20 .50
1 Troy Glaus SR .40 1.00
2 Adrian Beltre SR .25 .60
3 Matt Anderson SR .20 .50
4 Eric Chavez SR .25 .60
5 Jin Ho Cho SR .20 .50
6 Robert Smith SR .20 .50
7 George Lombard SR .20 .50
8 Mike Kinkade SR .20 .50
9 Seth Greisinger SR .20 .50
10 J.D. Drew SR .25 .60
11 Aramis Ramirez SR .25 .60
12 Carlos Guillen SR .25 .60
13 Justin Baughman SR .20 .50
14 Jim Parque SR .20 .50
15 Ryan Jackson SR .20 .50
16 Ramon E.Martinez SR RC .20 .50
17 Orlando Hernandez SR .25 .60
18 Jeremy Giambi SR .20 .50
19 Gary DiSarcina .10 .30
20 Darin Erstad .10 .30
21 Troy Glaus .20 .50
22 Chuck Finley .10 .30
23 Dave Hollins .10 .30
24 Troy Percival .10 .30
25 Tim Salmon .20 .50
26 Brian Anderson .10 .30
27 Jay Bell .10 .30
28 Andy Benes .10 .30
29 Brent Brede .10 .30
30 David Dellucci .10 .30
31 Karim Garcia .10 .30
32 Travis Lee .10 .30
33 Andres Galarraga .10 .30
34 Ryan Klesko .10 .30
35 Keith Lockhart .10 .30
36 Kevin Millwood .10 .30
37 Denny Neagle .10 .30
38 John Smoltz .20 .50
39 Michael Tucker .10 .30
40 Walt Weiss .10 .30
41 Dennis Martinez .10 .30
42 Javy Lopez .10 .30
43 Brady Anderson .10 .30
44 Harold Baines .10 .30
45 Mike Bordick .10 .30
46 Roberto Alomar .20 .50
47 Scott Erickson .10 .30
48 Mike Mussina .20 .50
49 Cal Ripken 1.00 2.50
50 Darren Bragg .10 .30
51 Dennis Eckersley .10 .30
52 Nomar Garciaparra .50 1.25
53 Scott Hatteberg .10 .30
54 Troy O'Leary .10 .30
55 Bret Saberhagen .10 .30
56 John Valentin .10 .30
57 Rod Beck .10 .30
58 Jeff Blauser .10 .30
59 Brant Brown .10 .30
60 Mark Clark .10 .30
61 Mark Grace .20 .50
62 Kevin Tapani .10 .30
63 Henry Rodriguez .10 .30
64 Mike Cameron .10 .30
65 Mike Caruso .10 .30
66 Ray Durham .10 .30
67 Jaime Navarro .10 .30
68 Magglio Ordonez .10 .30
69 Mike Sirotka .10 .30
70 Sean Casey .10 .30
71 Barry Larkin .20 .50
72 Jon Nunnally .10 .30
73 Paul Konerko .10 .30
74 Chris Stynes .10 .30
75 Brett Tomko .10 .30
76 Dmitri Young .10 .30
77 Sandy Alomar Jr. .10 .30
78 Bartolo Colon .10 .30
79 Travis Fryman .10 .30
80 Brian Giles .10 .30
81 David Justice .10 .30
82 Omar Vizquel .20 .50
83 Jaret Wright .10 .30
84 Jim Thome .20 .50
85 Charles Nagy .10 .30
86 Pedro Astacio .10 .30
87 Todd Helton .20 .50
88 Darryl Kile .10 .30
89 Mike Lansing .10 .30
90 Neifi Perez .10 .30
91 John Thomson .10 .30
92 Larry Walker .10 .30
93 Tony Clark .10 .30
94 Deivi Cruz .10 .30
95 Damion Easley .10 .30
96 Brian L.Hunter .10 .30
97 Todd Jones .10 .30
98 Brian Moehler .10 .30
99 Gabe Alvarez .10 .30
100 Craig Counsell .10 .30
101 Cliff Floyd .10 .30
102 Livan Hernandez .10 .30
103 Andy Larkin .10 .30
104 Derrek Lee .20 .50
105 Brian Meadows .10 .30
106 Moises Alou .10 .30
107 Sean Berry .10 .30
108 Craig Biggio .20 .50
109 Ricky Gutierrez .10 .30
110 Mike Hampton .10 .30
111 Jose Lima .10 .30
112 Billy Wagner .10 .30
113 Hal Morris .10 .30
114 Johnny Damon .20 .50
115 Jeff King .10 .30
116 Jeff Montgomery .10 .30
117 Glendon Rusch .10 .30
118 Larry Sutton .10 .30
119 Bobby Bonilla .10 .30
120 Jim Eisenreich .10 .30
121 Eric Karros .10 .30
122 Matt Luke .10 .30
123 Ramon Martinez .10 .30
124 Gary Sheffield .10 .30
125 Eric Young .10 .30
126 Charles Johnson .10 .30
127 Jeff Cirillo .10 .30
128 Marquis Grissom .10 .30
129 Jeromy Burnitz .10 .30
130 Bob Wickman .10 .30
131 Scott Karl .10 .30

132 Mark Loretta .10 .30
133 Fernando Vina .10 .30
134 Matt Lawton .10 .30
135 Pat Meares .10 .30
136 Eric Milton .10 .30
137 Paul Molitor .10 .30
138 David Ortiz .30 .75
139 Todd Walker .10 .30
140 Shane Andrews .10 .30
141 Brad Fullmer .10 .30
142 Vladimir Guerrero .30 .75
143 Dustin Hermanson .10 .30
144 Ryan McGuire .10 .30
145 Ugueth Urbina .10 .30
146 John Franco .10 .30
147 Butch Huskey .10 .30
148 Bobby Jones .10 .30
149 John Olerud .10 .30
150 Rey Ordonez .10 .30
151 Mike Piazza .50 1.25
152 Hideo Nomo .30 .75
153 Masato Yoshii .10 .30
154 Derek Jeter .75 2.00
155 Chuck Knoblauch .10 .30
156 Paul O'Neill .20 .50
157 Andy Pettitte .20 .50
158 Mariano Rivera .30 .75
159 Darryl Strawberry .10 .30
160 David Wells .10 .30
161 Jorge Posada .20 .50
162 Ramiro Mendoza .10 .30
163 Miguel Tejada .10 .30
164 Ryan Christenson .10 .30
165 Rickey Henderson .30 .75
166 A.J. Hinch .10 .30
167 Ben Grieve .10 .30
168 Kenny Rogers .10 .30
169 Matt Stairs .10 .30
170 Bob Abreu .10 .30
171 Rico Brogna .10 .30
172 Doug Glanville .10 .30
173 Mike Grace .10 .30
174 Desi Relaford .10 .30
175 Scott Rolen .20 .50
176 Jose Guillen .10 .30
177 Francisco Cordova .10 .30
178 Al Martin .10 .30
179 Jason Schmidt .10 .30
180 Turner Ward .10 .30
181 Kevin Young .10 .30
182 Mark McGwire .75 2.00
183 Delino DeShields .10 .30
184 Eli Marrero .10 .30
185 Tom Lampkin .10 .30
186 Ray Lankford .10 .30
187 Willie McGee .10 .30
188 Matt Morris UER .10 .30
Career strikeout totals are wrong
189 Andy Ashby .10 .30
190 Kevin Brown .20 .50
191 Ken Caminiti .10 .30
192 Trevor Hoffman .10 .30
193 Wally Joyner .10 .30
194 Greg Vaughn .10 .30
195 Danny Darwin .10 .30
196 Shawn Estes .10 .30
197 Orel Hershiser .10 .30
198 Jeff Kent .10 .30
199 Bill Mueller .10 .30
200 Robb Nen .10 .30
201 J.T. Snow .10 .30
202 Ken Cloude .10 .30
203 Russ Davis .10 .30
204 Jeff Fassero .10 .30
205 Ken Griffey Jr. .50 1.25
206 Shane Monahan .10 .30
207 David Segui .10 .30
208 Dan Wilson .10 .30
209 Wilson Alvarez .10 .30
210 Wade Boggs .20 .50
211 Miguel Cairo .10 .30
212 Bubba Trammell .10 .30
213 Quinton McCracken .10 .30
214 Paul Sorrento .10 .30
215 Kevin Stocker .10 .30
216 Will Clark .20 .50
217 Rusty Greer .10 .30
218 Rick Helling .10 .30
219 Mark McLemore .10 .30
220 Ivan Rodriguez .20 .50
221 John Wetteland .10 .30
222 Jose Canseco .20 .50
223 Roger Clemens .60 1.50
224 Carlos Delgado .10 .30
225 Darrin Fletcher .10 .30
226 Alex Gonzalez .10 .30
227 Jose Cruz Jr. .10 .30
228 Shannon Stewart .10 .30
229 Rolando Arrojo FF .10 .30
230 Livan Hernandez FF .10 .30
231 Orlando Hernandez FF .10 .30
232 Raul Mondesi FF .10 .30
233 Moises Alou FF .10 .30
234 Pedro Martinez FF .20 .50
235 Sammy Sosa FF .20 .50
236 Vladimir Guerrero FF .30 .75
237 Bartolo Colon FF .10 .30
238 Miguel Tejada FF .10 .30
239 Ismael Valdes FF .10 .30
240 Mariano Rivera FF .20 .50
241 Jose Cruz Jr. FF .10 .30
242 Juan Gonzalez FF .10 .30
243 Ivan Rodriguez FF .20 .50
244 Sandy Alomar Jr. FF .10 .30
245 Roberto Alomar FF .20 .50
246 Magglio Ordonez FF .10 .30
247 Kerry Wood SH CL .10 .30
248 Mark McGwire SH CL .75 2.00
249 David Wells SH CL .10 .30
250 Rolando Arrojo SH CL .10 .30
251 Ken Griffey Jr. SH CL .50 1.25
252 T.Hoffman SH CL .10 .30
253 Travis Lee SH CL .10 .30
254 R.Alomar SH CL .10 .30
255 Sammy Sosa SH CL .20 .50
266 Pat Burrell SR RC 1.25 3.00
267 S.Hillenbrand SR RC .60 1.50
268 Robert Fick SR .20 .50
269 Roy Halladay SR .25 .60
270 Ruben Mateo SR .20 .50
271 Bruce Chen SR .20 .50
272 Angel Pena SR .20 .50
273 Michael Barrett SR .20 .50
274 Kevin Witt SR .20 .50
275 Damon Minor SR .20 .50
276 Ryan Minor SR .20 .50
277 A.J. Pierzynski SR .25 .60
278 A.J. Burnett SR RC .60 1.50
279 Dermal Brown SR .20 .50
280 Joe Lawrence SR .20 .50
281 Derrick Gibson SR .20 .50
282 Carlos Febles SR .20 .50
283 Chris Haas SR .20 .50
284 Cesar King SR .20 .50
285 Calvin Pickering SR .20 .50
286 Mitch Meluskey SR .20 .50
287 Carlos Beltran SR .40 1.00
288 Ron Belliard SR .20 .50
289 Jerry Hairston Jr. SR .20 .50
290 F.Seguignol SR .20 .50
291 Kris Benson SR .20 .50
292 C.Hutchinson SR RC .25 .60
293 Jarrod Washburn .10 .30
294 Jason Dickson .10 .30
295 Mo Vaughn .10 .30
296 Garret Anderson .10 .30
297 Jim Edmonds .10 .30
298 Ken Hill .10 .30
299 Shigetoshi Hasegawa .10 .30
300 Todd Stottlemyre .10 .30
301 Randy Johnson .30 .75
302 Omar Daal .10 .30
303 Steve Finley .10 .30
304 Matt Williams .10 .30
305 Danny Klassen .10 .30
306 Tony Batista .10 .30
307 Brian Jordan .10 .30
308 Greg Maddux .50 1.25
309 Chipper Jones .30 .75
310 Bret Boone .10 .30
311 Ozzie Guillen .10 .30
312 John Rocker .10 .30
313 Tom Glavine .20 .50
314 Andruw Jones .20 .50
315 Albert Belle .10 .30
316 Charles Johnson .10 .30
317 Will Clark .20 .50
318 B.J. Surhoff .10 .30
319 Delino DeShields .10 .30
320 Heathcliff Slocumb .10 .30
321 Sidney Ponson .10 .30
322 Juan Guzman .10 .30
323 Reggie Jefferson .10 .30
324 Mark Portugal .10 .30
325 Tim Wakefield .10 .30
326 Jason Varitek .30 .75
327 Jose Offerman .10 .30
328 Pedro Martinez .20 .50
329 Trot Nixon .10 .30
330 Kerry Wood .10 .30
331 Sammy Sosa .30 .75
332 Glenallen Hill .10 .30
333 Gary Gaetti .10 .30
334 Mickey Morandini .10 .30
335 Benito Santiago .10 .30
336 Jeff Blauser .10 .30
337 Frank Thomas .30 .75
338 Paul Konerko .10 .30
339 Jaime Navarro .10 .30
340 Carlos Lee .10 .30
341 Brian Simmons .10 .30
342 Mark Johnson .10 .30
343 Jeff Abbott .10 .30
344 Steve Avery .10 .30
345 Mike Cameron .10 .30
346 Michael Tucker .10 .30
347 Greg Vaughn .10 .30
348 Hal Morris .10 .30
349 Pete Harnisch .10 .30
350 Denny Neagle .10 .30
351 Manny Ramirez .20 .50
352 Roberto Alomar .20 .50
353 Dwight Gooden .10 .30
354 Kenny Lofton .10 .30
355 Mike Jackson .10 .30
356 Charles Nagy .10 .30
357 Enrique Wilson .10 .30
358 Russ Branyan .10 .30
359 Richie Sexson .10 .30
360 Vinny Castilla .10 .30
361 Dante Bichette .10 .30
362 Kirt Manwaring .10 .30
363 Darryl Hamilton .10 .30
364 Jamey Wright .10 .30
365 Curtis Leskanic .10 .30
366 Jeff Reed .10 .30
367 Bobby Higginson .10 .30
368 Justin Thompson .10 .30
369 Brad Ausmus .10 .30
370 Dean Palmer .10 .30
371 Gabe Kapler .10 .30
372 Juan Encarnacion .10 .30
373 Karim Garcia .10 .30
374 Alex Gonzalez .10 .30
375 Braden Looper .10 .30
376 Preston Wilson .10 .30
377 Todd Dunwoody .10 .30
378 Alex Fernandez .10 .30
379 Mark Kotsay .10 .30
380 Matt Mantei .10 .30
381 Ken Caminiti .10 .30
382 Scott Elarton .10 .30
383 Jeff Bagwell .20 .50
384 Derek Bell .10 .30
385 Ricky Gutierrez .10 .30
386 Richard Hidalgo .10 .30
387 Shane Reynolds .10 .30
388 Carl Everett .10 .30
389 Scott Service .10 .30
390 Jeff Suppan .10 .30
391 Joe Randa .10 .30
392 Kevin Appier .10 .30
393 Shane Halter .10 .30
394 Chad Kreuter .10 .30
395 Mike Sweeney .10 .30
396 Kevin Brown .20 .50
397 Devon White .10 .30
398 Todd Hollandsworth .10 .30
399 Todd Hundley .10 .30
400 Chan Ho Park .10 .30
401 Mark Grudzielanek .10 .30
402 Raul Mondesi .10 .30
403 Ismael Valdes .10 .30
404 Rafael Roque RC .10 .30
405 Sean Berry .10 .30
406 Kevin Barker .10 .30
407 Dave Nilsson .10 .30
408 Geoff Jenkins .10 .30
409 Jim Abbott .20 .50
410 Bobby Hughes .10 .30
411 Corey Koskie .10 .30
412 Rick Aguilera .10 .30
413 LaTroy Hawkins .10 .30
414 Ron Coomer .10 .30
415 Denny Hocking .10 .30
416 Marty Cordova .10 .30
417 Terry Steinbach .10 .30
418 Rondell White .10 .30
419 Wilton Guerrero .10 .30
420 Shane Andrews .10 .30
421 Orlando Cabrera .10 .30
422 Carl Pavano .10 .30
423 Javier Vazquez .10 .30
424 Chris Widger .10 .30
425 Robin Ventura .10 .30
426 Rickey Henderson .30 .75
427 Al Leiter .10 .30
428 Bobby Jones .10 .30
429 Brian McRae .10 .30
430 Roger Cedeno .10 .30
431 Bobby Bonilla .10 .30
432 Edgardo Alfonzo .10 .30
433 Bernie Williams .20 .50
434 Ricky Ledee .10 .30
435 Chili Davis .10 .30
436 Tino Martinez .20 .50
437 Scott Brosius .10 .30
438 David Cone .10 .30
439 Joe Girardi .10 .30
440 Roger Clemens .60 1.50
441 Chad Curtis .10 .30
442 Hideki Irabu .10 .30
443 Jason Giambi .10 .30
444 Scott Spiezio .10 .30
445 Tony Phillips .10 .30
446 Ramon Hernandez .10 .30
447 Mike Macfarlane .10 .30
448 Tom Candiotti .10 .30
449 Billy Taylor .10 .30
450 Bobby Estalella .10 .30
451 Curt Schilling .10 .30
452 Carlton Loewer .10 .30
453 Marlon Anderson .10 .30
454 Kevin Jordan .10 .30
455 Ron Gant .10 .30
456 Chad Ogea .10 .30
457 Abraham Nunez .10 .30
458 Jason Kendall .10 .30
459 Pat Meares .10 .30
460 Brant Brown .10 .30
461 Brian Giles .10 .30
462 Chad Hermansen .10 .30
463 Freddy Adrian Garcia .10 .30
464 Edgar Renteria .10 .30
465 Fernando Tatis .10 .30
466 Eric Davis .10 .30
467 Darren Bragg .10 .30
468 Donovan Osborne .10 .30
469 Manny Aybar .10 .30
470 Jose Jimenez .10 .30
471 Kent Mercker .10 .30
472 Reggie Sanders .10 .30
473 Ruben Rivera .10 .30
474 Tony Gwynn .40 1.00
475 Jim Leyritz .10 .30
476 Chris Gomez .10 .30
477 Matt Clement .10 .30
478 Carlos Hernandez .10 .30
479 Sterling Hitchcock .10 .30
480 Ellis Burks .10 .30
481 Barry Bonds .75 2.00
482 Marvin Benard .10 .30
483 Kirk Rueter .10 .30
484 F.P. Santangelo .10 .30
485 Stan Javier .10 .30
486 Jeff Kent .10 .30
487 Alex Rodriguez .50 1.25
488 Tom Lampkin .10 .30
489 Jose Mesa .10 .30
490 Jay Buhner .10 .30
491 Edgar Martinez .20 .50
492 Butch Huskey .10 .30
493 John Mabry .10 .30
494 Jamie Moyer .10 .30
495 Roberto Hernandez .10 .30
496 Tony Saunders .10 .30
497 Fred McGriff .20 .50
498 Dave Martinez .10 .30
499 Jose Canseco .20 .50
500 Rolando Arrojo .10 .30
501 Esteban Yan .10 .30
502 Juan Gonzalez .10 .30
503 Rafael Palmeiro .20 .50
504 Aaron Sele .10 .30
505 Royce Clayton .10 .30
506 Todd Zeile .10 .30
507 Tom Goodwin .10 .30
508 Lee Stevens .10 .30
509 Esteban Loaiza .10 .30
510 Joey Hamilton .10 .30
511 Homer Bush .10 .30
512 Willie Greene .10 .30
513 Shawn Green .10 .30
514 David Wells .10 .30
515 Kelvim Escobar .10 .30
516 Tony Fernandez .10 .30
517 Pat Hentgen .10 .30
518 Mark McGwire AR .40 1.00
519 Ken Griffey Jr. AR .30 .75
520 Sammy Sosa AR .20 .50
521 Juan Gonzalez AR .10 .30
522 J.D. Drew AR .10 .30
523 Chipper Jones AR .20 .50
524 Alex Rodriguez AR .30 .75
525 Mike Piazza AR .30 .75
526 N.Garciaparra AR .30 .75
527 Mark McGwire SH CL .40 1.00
528 Sammy Sosa SH CL .20 .50
529 Scott Brosius SH CL .10 .30
530 Cal Ripken SH CL .50 1.25
531 Barry Bonds SH CL .40 1.00
532 Roger Clemens SH CL .30 .75
533 Ken Griffey Jr. SH CL .30 .75
534 Alex Rodriguez SH CL .30 .75
535 Curt Schilling SH CL .10 .30
NNO Ken Griffey Jr. 1000.00 1250.00
1989 AU/100

1999 Upper Deck Exclusives Level 1

This 525-card set is a hobby only parallel version of the base set. Each card is sequentially numbered to 100 on back. In addition, Bronze foil fronts make them easy to differentiate from their silver foiled basic issue brethren. As is the case with the basic set, cards 256-265 were never printed due to a numbering error at the manufacturer.

*STARS: 10X TO 25X BASIC CARDS
*SER.1 STAR ROOK: 4X TO 10X BASIC SR
*SER.2 STAR ROOK: 6X TO 15X BASIC SR

1999 Upper Deck 10th Anniversary Team

Randomly inserted in first series packs at the rate of one in four, this 30-card set features color photos of collectors' favorite players selected for this special All-Star team.

COMPLETE SET (30) 20.00 50.00
*DOUBLES: 1.25X TO 3X BASIC 10TH ANN.
DOUBLES RANDOM INSERTS IN SER.1 PACKS
DOUBLES PRINT RUN 4000 SERIAL #'d SETS
*TRIPLES: 8X TO 20X BASIC 10TH ANN
TRIPLES RANDOM INSERTS IN SER.1 PACKS
TRIPLES PRINT RUN 100 SERIAL #'d SETS
HR'S RANDOM INSERTS IN SER.1 PACKS
HOME RUN PRINT RUN 1 SERIAL #'d SET
HR'S NOT PRICED DUE TO SCARCITY
X1 Mike Piazza 1.00 2.50
X2 Mark McGwire 1.50 4.00
X3 Roberto Alomar .40 1.00
X4 Chipper Jones .60 1.50
X5 Cal Ripken 2.00 5.00
X6 Ken Griffey Jr. 1.00 2.50
X7 Barry Bonds 1.50 4.00
X8 Tony Gwynn .75 2.00
X9 Nolan Ryan 2.50 6.00
X10 Randy Johnson .60 1.50
X11 Dennis Eckersley .25 .60
X12 Ivan Rodriguez .40 1.00
X13 Frank Thomas .60 1.50
X14 Craig Biggio .40 1.00
X15 Wade Boggs .40 1.00
X16 Alex Rodriguez 1.00 2.50
X17 Albert Belle .25 .60
X18 Juan Gonzalez .25 .60
X19 Rickey Henderson .60 1.50
X20 Greg Maddux 1.00 2.50
X21 Tom Glavine .40 1.00
X22 Randy Myers .25 .60
X23 Sandy Alomar Jr. .25 .60
X24 Jeff Bagwell .40 1.00
X25 Derek Jeter 1.50 4.00
X26 Matt Williams .25 .60
X27 Kenny Lofton .25 .60
X28 Sammy Sosa .60 1.50
X29 Larry Walker .25 .60
X30 Roger Clemens 1.25 3.00

1999 Upper Deck A Piece of History

This limited edition set features photos of Babe Ruth along with a bat chip from an actual game-used Louisville Slugger swung by him during the late 20's. Approximately 350 cards were made and seeded into packs at a rate of 1:15,000. Another insert card incorporates both a "cut" signature of Ruth along with a piece of his game-used bat. Only three of these cards were produced.

B.RUTH AU RANDOM IN SER.1 PACKS
B.RUTH AU PRINT RUN 3 #'d CARDS
PHLC Babe Ruth AU/3
PH Babe Ruth 750.00 1000.00

1999 Upper Deck A Piece of History 500 Club

During the 1999 season, Upper Deck inserted into various products these cards which are cut up bats from all except one of the members of the 500

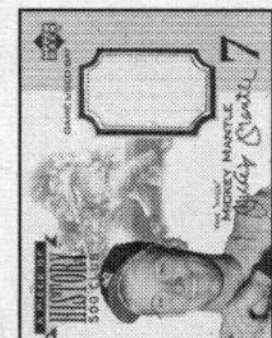

homer club. Mark McGwire asked that one of his bats not be included in this set, thus there was no Mark McGwire card in this grouping (until 2003 when McGwire signed a deal with Upper Deck). With the exception of Babe Ruth, approximately 350 of each card was produced. Only 50 Babe Ruth's were made. The cards were released in the following products: 1999 SP Authentic: Ernie Banks; 1999 SP Signature: Mel Ott; 1999 SPx: Willie Mays, 1999 UD Choice: Eddie Murray; 1999 UD Ionix: Frank Robinson; 1999 Upper Deck 2: Babe Ruth; 1999 Upper Deck Century Legends: Jimmie Foxx; 1999 Upper Deck Challengers for 70: Harmon Killebrew; 1999 Upper Deck HoloGrFx: Eddie Mathews and Willie McCovey; 1999 Upper Deck MVP: Mike Schmidt; 1999 Upper Deck Ovation: Mickey Mantle: 1999 Upper Deck Retro: Ted Williams; 2000 Black Diamond: Reggie Jackson; 2000 Upper Deck 1: Hank Aaron.

BR Babe Ruth/50
EB Ernie Banks 125.00 250.00
EM Eddie Mathews 150.00 300.00
EM Eddie Murray 100.00 200.00
FR Frank Robinson 75.00 150.00
HA Hank Aaron 150.00 300.00
HK Harmon Killebrew 100.00 200.00
JF Jimmie Foxx 100.00 200.00
MM Mickey Mantle 350.00 600.00
MO Mel Ott 100.00 200.00
MS Mike Schmidt 100.00 200.00
RJ Reggie Jackson 60.00 120.00
TW Ted Williams 150.00 300.00
WM Willie Mays 150.00 300.00
WM Willie McCovey 60.00 120.00
XX Instant Winner Card

1999 Upper Deck A Piece of History 500 Club Autographs

As part of the Upper Deck A Piece of History 500 Club Autograph promotion, Upper Deck had most of the living members of the 500 homer club sign a number of cards which matched their uniform number (except for Mantle of which is a true 1/1, features a cut signature and altered card front design from the other cards in the set). On some of the players, the cards are not priced due to scarcity. Each card is serial numbered on the front except Mantle. Each of these cards was issued in a separate UD brand from 1999.

536HR Mickey Mantle/1
EBAU Ernie Banks/14
EMAU Eddie Mathews/41 500.00 800.00
FRAU Frank Robinson/20
HAAU Hank Aaron/44 700.00 1200.00
HKAU Harmon Killebrew/3
MSAU Mike Schmidt/20
RJAU Reggie Jackson/44 350.00 600.00
TWAU Ted Williams/9
WMAU Willie Mays/24
WMAU Willie McCovey/44 500.00 800.00

1999 Upper Deck Crowning Glory

Randomly inserted in first series packs at the rate of one in 23, this three-card set features color photos of players who reached major milestones during the '98 MLB season and printed on double sided cards.

COMPLETE SET (3) 25.00 60.00
*DOUBLES: .6X TO 1.5X BASIC CROWN
DOUBLES RANDOM INSERTS IN SER.1 PACKS
DOUBLES PRINT RUN 1000 SERIAL #'d SETS
*TRIPLES: 4X TO 10X BASIC CROWN
TRIPLES RANDOM INSERTS IN SER.1 PACKS
TRIPLES PRINT RUN 25 SERIAL #'d SETS
HR'S RANDOM INSERTS IN SER.1 PACKS
HOME RUNS PRINT RUN 1 SERIAL #'d SET
HOME RUNS NOT PRICED DUE TO SCARCITY
CG1 Roger Clemens 6.00 15.00
Kerry Wood
CG2 Mark McGwire 8.00 20.00
Barry Bonds
CG3 Ken Griffey Jr. 6.00 15.00
Mark McGwire

1999 Upper Deck Forte

Randomly inserted in series two packs at the rate of one in 23, this 30-card set features color photos of

the most collectible superstars captured on super premium cards with extensive rainbow foil coverage. Three limited parallel sets were also produced and randomly inserted into Series two packs. Forte Doubles was serially numbered to 2000; Forte Triples, to 100; and Forte Quadruples, to 10.

COMPLETE SET (30) 80.00 200.00
*DOUBLES: .6X TO 1.5X BASIC FORTE
DOUBLES RANDOM INSERTS IN SER.2 PACKS
DOUBLES PRINT RUN 2000 SERIAL #'d SETS
*TRIPLES: 2X TO 5X BASIC FORTE
TRIPLES RANDOM INSERTS IN SER.2 PACKS
TRIPLES PRINT RUN 100 SERIAL #'d SETS
QUADS RANDOM INSERTS IN SER.2 PACKS
QUADRUPLES NOT PRICED DUE TO SCARCITY
F1 Darin Erstad 1.00 2.50
F2 Troy Glaus 1.50 4.00
F3 Mo Vaughn 1.00 2.50
F4 Greg Maddux 4.00 10.00
F5 Andres Galarraga 1.00 2.50
F6 Chipper Jones 2.50 6.00
F7 Cal Ripken 8.00 20.00
F8 Albert Belle 1.00 2.50
F9 Nomar Garciaparra 4.00 10.00
F10 Sammy Sosa 2.50 6.00
F11 Kerry Wood 1.00 2.50
F12 Frank Thomas 2.50 6.00
F13 Jim Thome 1.50 4.00
F14 Jeff Bagwell 1.50 4.00
F15 Vladimir Guerrero 2.50 6.00
F16 Mike Piazza 4.00 10.00
F17 Derek Jeter 6.00 15.00
F18 Ben Grieve 1.00 2.50
F19 Eric Chavez .60 1.50
F20 Scott Rolen 1.50 4.00
F21 Mark McGwire 6.00 15.00
F22 J.D. Drew .60 1.50
F23 Tony Gwynn 3.00 8.00
F24 Barry Bonds 6.00 15.00
F25 Alex Rodriguez 4.00 10.00
F26 Ken Griffey Jr. 4.00 10.00
F27 Ivan Rodriguez 1.50 4.00
F28 Juan Gonzalez 1.00 2.50
F29 Roger Clemens 5.00 12.00
F30 Andruw Jones 1.50 4.00

1999 Upper Deck Game Jersey

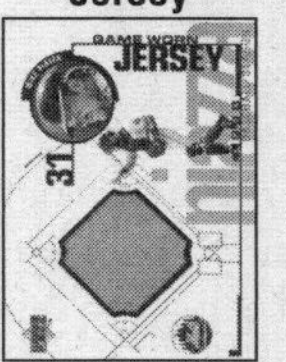

This set consists of 23 cards inserted in first and second series packs. Hobby packs contained Game Jersey hobby cards (signified in the listings with an H after the player's name) at a rate of 1:288. Hobby and retail packs contained much scarcer Game Jersey hobby/retail cards (signified with an H/R after the player's name in the listings below) at a rate of 1:2500. Each card features a piece of an actual game worn jersey. Five additional cards were signed by the athlete and serial numbered by hand to the player's respective jersey number. These rare signed Game Jersey cards are priced below but not considered part of the complete set.

AB Adrian Beltre H1 10.00 25.00
AR Alex Rodriguez HR1 12.50 30.00
BF Brad Fullmer H2 6.00 15.00
BG Ben Grieve H1 6.00 15.00
BT Bubba Trammell H2 6.00 15.00
CJ Charles Johnson HR1 10.00 25.00
CJ Chipper Jones H2 12.50 30.00
DE Darin Erstad H1 10.00 25.00
EC Eric Chavez H2 10.00 25.00
FT Frank Thomas HR2 15.00 40.00
GM Greg Maddux HR2 20.00 50.00
IR Ivan Rodriguez H1 15.00 40.00
JD J.D. Drew H2 10.00 25.00
JG Juan Gonzalez HR1 10.00 25.00
JR K.Griffey Jr. HR2 15.00 40.00
KG K.Griffey Jr. H1 15.00 40.00
KW Kerry Wood HR1 10.00 25.00
MP Mike Piazza HR1 20.00 50.00
MR Manny Ramirez H2 15.00 40.00
NRA Nolan Ryan 30.00 60.00
Astros H2
NRB Nolan Ryan 30.00 60.00
Rangers HR2
SS Sammy Sosa H2 15.00 40.00
TH Todd Helton H2 15.00 40.00
TGW Tony Gwynn H2 15.00 40.00
TL Travis Lee H1 6.00 15.00
JDS J.Drew AU/8 H2
JRS Ken Griffey Jr. AU/24 HR2
KGAU Ken Griffey Jr. AU/24 H1
KWAU Kerry Wood AU/34 150.00 250.00
HR1
NRAS Nolan Ryan Astros 500.00 800.00
AU/34, H2

1999 Upper Deck Ken Griffey Jr. Box Blasters

These ten 5" by 7" cards were inserted one per Upper Deck special retail boxes. The cards feature oversize reprints of the regular issue Ken Griffey Jr. Upper Deck cards during both his 10 year career

and the 10 seasons Upper Deck has made cards for. We have numbered the cards 1-10 based on the year of the card's original issue.

COMPLETE SET (1-10) 20.00 50.00
COMMON CARD (1-10) 2.00 5.00

1999 Upper Deck Ken Griffey Jr. Box Blasters Autographs

Randomly seeded into one in every 64 special retail boxes, each of these attractive cards was signed by Ken Griffey Jr. The cards are over-sized 5" by 7" replicas of each of Griffey's basic issue Upper Deck cards from 1989-1999. The backs of the cards provide a certificate of authenticity from UD Chairman and CEO Richard McWilliam.

COMMON CARD (90-99) 50.00 100.00
STATED ODDS 1:64 SPECIAL RETAIL BOXES
KG1989 Ken Griffey Jr. AU 89 150.00 250.00

1999 Upper Deck Immaculate Perception

Randomly inserted in Series one packs at the rate of one in 23, this 27-card set features top player photos printed on unique, foil-enhanced cards.

COMPLETE SET (27) 125.00 250.00
*DOUBLES: .75X TO 2X BASIC IMM.PERC.
DOUBLES RANDOM INSERTS IN SER.1 PACKS
DOUBLES PRINT RUN 1000 SERIAL #'d SETS
*TRIPLES: 5X TO 12X BASIC IMM.PERC.
TRIPLES RANDOM INSERTS IN SER.1 PACKS
TRIPLES PRINT RUN 25 SERIAL #'d SETS
HR'S RANDOM INSERTS IN SER.1 PACKS
HOME RUNS PRINT RUN 1 SERIAL #'d SET
HOME RUNS NOT PRICED DUE TO SCARCITY
I1 Jeff Bagwell 2.00 5.00
I2 Craig Biggio 2.00 5.00
I3 Barry Bonds 8.00 20.00
I4 Roger Clemens 6.00 15.00
I5 Jose Cruz Jr. 1.25 3.00
I6 Nomar Garciaparra 5.00 12.00
I7 Tony Clark 1.25 3.00
I8 Ben Grieve 1.25 3.00
I9 Ken Griffey Jr. 5.00 12.00
I10 Tony Gwynn 4.00 10.00
I11 Randy Johnson 3.00 8.00
I12 Chipper Jones 3.00 8.00
I13 Travis Lee 1.25 3.00
I14 Kenny Lofton 1.25 3.00
I15 Greg Maddux 5.00 12.00
I16 Mark McGwire 8.00 20.00
I17 Hideo Nomo 3.00 8.00
I18 Mike Piazza 5.00 12.00
I19 Manny Ramirez 2.00 5.00
I20 Cal Ripken 10.00 25.00
I21 Alex Rodriguez 5.00 12.00
I22 Scott Rolen 2.00 5.00
I23 Frank Thomas 3.00 8.00
I24 Kerry Wood 1.25 3.00
I25 Larry Walker 1.25 3.00
I26 Vinny Castilla 1.25 3.00
I27 Derek Jeter 8.00 20.00

1999 Upper Deck Textbook Excellence

Inserted one every 23 second series packs, these cards offer information on the skills of some of the game's most fundamentally sound performers.

COMPLETE SET (30) 20.00 50.00
*DOUBLES: 1.5X TO 4X BASIC TEXTBOOK
DOUBLES RANDOM INSERTS IN SER.2 PACKS
DOUBLES PRINT RUN 2000 SERIAL #'d SETS
*TRIPLES: 6X TO 15X BASIC TEXTBOOK
TRIPLES RANDOM INSERTS IN SER.2 PACKS
TRIPLES PRINT RUN 100 SERIAL #'d SETS
QUADS RANDOM INSERTS IN SER.2 PACKS
QUADRUPLES PRINT RUN 10 SERIAL #'d SETS
QUADRUPLES NOT PRICED DUE TO SCARCITY
T1 Mo Vaughn .30 .75
T2 Greg Maddux 1.25 3.00
T3 Chipper Jones .75 2.00
T4 Andruw Jones .50 1.25
T5 Cal Ripken 2.50 6.00
T6 Albert Belle .30 .75
T7 Roberto Alomar .50 1.25
T8 Nomar Garciaparra 1.25 3.00
T9 Kerry Wood .30 .75
T10 Sammy Sosa .75 2.00
T11 Greg Vaughn .30 .75
T12 Jeff Bagwell .50 1.25
T13 Kevin Brown .50 1.25
T14 Vladimir Guerrero .75 2.00
T15 Mike Piazza 1.25 3.00
T16 Bernie Williams .50 1.25
T17 Derek Jeter 2.00 5.00
T18 Ben Grieve .30 .75
T19 Eric Chavez .20 .50
T20 Scott Rolen .50 1.25
T21 Mark McGwire 2.00 5.00
T22 David Wells .30 .75
T23 J.D. Drew .20 .50
T24 Tony Gwynn 1.00 2.50
T25 Barry Bonds 2.00 5.00
T26 Alex Rodriguez 1.25 3.00
T27 Ken Griffey Jr. 1.25 3.00
T28 Juan Gonzalez .30 .75
T29 Ivan Rodriguez .50 1.25
T30 Roger Clemens 1.50 4.00

1999 Upper Deck View to a Thrill

These cards, inserted one every seven second series packs feature special die-cuts and embossing and takes a new look at 30 of the best overall athletes in baseball.

COMPLETE SET (30) 40.00 100.00
*DOUBLES: 1X TO 2.5X BASIC VIEW
DOUBLES RANDOM INSERTS IN SER.2 PACKS
DOUBLES PRINT RUN 2000 SERIAL #'d SETS
*TRIPLES: 4X TO 10X BASIC VIEW
TRIPLES RANDOM INSERTS IN SER.2 PACKS
TRIPLES PRINT RUN 100 SERIAL #'d SETS
QUADS RANDOM INSERTS IN SER.2 PACKS
QUADRUPLES PRINT RUN 10 SERIAL #'d SETS
QUADRUPLES NOT PRICED DUE TO SCARCITY
V1 Mo Vaughn .50 1.25
V2 Darin Erstad .50 1.25
V3 Travis Lee .50 1.25
V4 Chipper Jones 1.25 3.00
V5 Greg Maddux 2.00 5.00
V6 Gabe Kapler .50 1.25
V7 Cal Ripken 4.00 10.00
V8 Nomar Garciaparra 2.00 5.00
V9 Kerry Wood .50 1.25
V10 Frank Thomas 1.25 3.00
V11 Manny Ramirez .75 2.00
V12 Larry Walker .50 1.25
V13 Tony Clark .50 1.25
V14 Jeff Bagwell .75 2.00
V15 Craig Biggio .75 2.00
V16 Vladimir Guerrero 1.25 3.00
V17 Mike Piazza 2.00 5.00
V18 Bernie Williams .75 2.00
V19 Derek Jeter 3.00 8.00
V20 Ben Grieve .50 1.25
V21 Eric Chavez .30 .75
V22 Scott Rolen .75 2.00
V23 Mark McGwire 3.00 8.00
V24 Tony Gwynn 1.50 4.00
V25 Barry Bonds 3.00 8.00
V26 Ken Griffey Jr. 2.00 5.00
V27 Alex Rodriguez 2.00 5.00
V28 J.D. Drew .30 .75
V29 Juan Gonzalez .50 1.25
V30 Roger Clemens 2.50 6.00

1999 Upper Deck Wonder Years

Randomly inserted in Series one packs at the rate of one in seven, this 30-card set features color photos of top stars.

COMPLETE SET (30) 30.00 80.00
*DOUBLES: 1X TO 2.5X BASIC WONDER
DOUBLES RANDOM INSERTS IN SER.1 PACKS
DOUBLES PRINT RUN 2000 SERIAL #'d SETS
*TRIPLES: 8X TO 20X BASIC WONDER
TRIPLES RANDOM INSERTS IN SER.1 PACKS
TRIPLES PRINT RUN 50 SERIAL #'d SETS
HR'S RANDOM INSERTS IN SER.1 PACKS
HOME RUNS PRINT RUN 1 SERIAL #'d SET
HOME RUNS NOT PRICED DUE TO SCARCITY
W1 Kerry Wood .50 1.25
W2 Travis Lee .50 1.25
W3 Jeff Bagwell .75 2.00
W4 Barry Bonds 3.00 8.00
W5 Roger Clemens 2.50 6.00
W6 Jose Cruz Jr. .50 1.25
W7 Andres Galarraga .50 1.25
W8 Nomar Garciaparra 2.00 5.00
W9 Juan Gonzalez .50 1.25
W10 Ken Griffey Jr. 2.00 5.00
W11 Tony Gwynn 1.50 4.00
W12 Derek Jeter 3.00 8.00
W13 Randy Johnson 1.25 3.00
W14 Andruw Jones .75 2.00
W15 Chipper Jones 1.25 3.00
W16 Kenny Lofton .50 1.25
W17 Greg Maddux 2.00 5.00
W18 Tino Martinez .75 2.00
W19 Mark McGwire 3.00 8.00
W20 Paul Molitor .50 1.25
W21 Mike Piazza 2.00 5.00
W22 Manny Ramirez .75 2.00
W23 Cal Ripken 4.00 10.00
W24 Alex Rodriguez 2.00 5.00
W25 Sammy Sosa 1.25 3.00
W26 Frank Thomas 1.25 3.00
W27 Mo Vaughn .50 1.25
W28 Larry Walker .50 1.25
W29 Scott Rolen .75 2.00
W30 Ben Grieve .50 1.25

2000 Upper Deck

Upper Deck Series one was released in December, 1999 and offered 270 standard-size cards. The first series was distributed in 10 card packs with a SRP of $2.99 per pack. The second series was released in July, 2000 and offered 270 standard-size cards. The cards were issued in 24 pack boxes. Cards numbered 1-28 and 271-297 are Star Rookie subsets while cards numbered 262-270 and 532-540 feature 1999 season highlights and have checklists on back. Cards 523-531 feature the All-UD Team subset - a collection of top stars as selected by Upper Deck. Notable Rookie Cards include Kazuhiro Sasaki. Also, 350 1999 A Piece of History 500 Club Hank Aaron bat cards were randomly seeded into first series packs. In addition, Aaron signed and numbered 44 copies. Pricing for these bat cards can be referenced under 1999 Upper Deck A Piece of History 500 Club. Also, a selection of A Piece of History 3000 Club Hank Aaron memorabilia cards were randomly seeded into second series packs. 350 bat cards, 350 jersey cards, 100 hand-numbered, combination bat-jersey cards and forty-four hand-numbered, autographed, combination bat-jersey cards were produced. Pricing for these memorabilia cards can be referenced under 2000 Upper Deck A Piece of History 3000 Club.

COMPLETE SET (540) 40.00 100.00
COMP. SERIES 1 (270) 20.00 50.00
COMP. SERIES 2 (270) 20.00 50.00
COMMON (28-270/298-540) .10 .30
COMMON (1-28/271-297) .20 .50
1 Rick Ankiel SR .20 .50
2 Vernon Wells SR .30 .75
3 Ryan Anderson SR .20 .50
4 Ed Yarnall SR .20 .50
5 Brian McNichol SR .20 .50
6 Ben Petrick SR .20 .50
7 Kip Wells SR .20 .50
8 Eric Munson SR .20 .50
9 Matt Riley SR .20 .50
10 Peter Bergeron SR .20 .50
11 Eric Gagne SR .75 2.00
12 Ramon Ortiz SR .20 .50
13 Josh Beckett SR .75 2.00
14 Alfonso Soriano SR .75 2.00
15 Jorge Toca SR .20 .50
16 Buddy Carlyle SR .20 .50
17 Chad Hermansen SR .20 .50
18 Matt Perisho SR .20 .50
19 Tomokazu Ohka SR RC .30 .75
20 Jacque Jones SR .20 .50
21 Josh Paul SR .20 .50
22 Dermal Brown SR .20 .50
23 Adam Kennedy SR .20 .50
24 Chad Harville SR .20 .50
25 Calvin Murray SR .20 .50
26 Chad Meyers SR .20 .50
27 Brian Cooper SR .20 .50
28 Troy Glaus .10 .30
29 Ben Molina .10 .30
30 Troy Percival .10 .30
31 Ken Hill .10 .30
32 Chuck Finley .10 .30
33 Todd Greene .10 .30
34 Tim Salmon .20 .50
35 Gary DiSarcina .10 .30
36 Luis Gonzalez .10 .30
37 Tony Womack .10 .30
38 Omar Daal .10 .30
39 Randy Johnson .30 .75
40 Erubiel Durazo .10 .30
41 Jay Bell .10 .30
42 Steve Finley .10 .30
43 Travis Lee .10 .30
44 Greg Maddux .50 1.25
45 Bret Boone .10 .30
46 Brian Jordan .10 .30
47 Kevin Millwood .10 .30
48 Odalis Perez .10 .30
49 Javy Lopez .10 .30
50 John Smoltz .20 .50
51 Bruce Chen .10 .30
52 Albert Belle .10 .30
53 Jerry Hairston Jr. .10 .30
54 Will Clark .20 .50
55 Sidney Ponson .10 .30
56 Charles Johnson .10 .30
57 Cal Ripken 1.00 2.50
58 Ryan Minor .10 .30
59 Mike Mussina .20 .50
60 Tom Gordon .10 .30
61 Jose Offerman .10 .30
62 Trot Nixon .10 .30
63 Pedro Martinez .20 .50
64 John Valentin .10 .30
65 Jason Varitek .30 .75
66 Juan Pena .10 .30
67 Troy O'Leary .10 .30
68 Sammy Sosa .30 .75
69 Henry Rodriguez .10 .30
70 Kyle Farnsworth .10 .30
71 Glenallen Hill .10 .30
72 Lance Johnson .10 .30
73 Mickey Morandini .10 .30
74 Jon Lieber .10 .30
75 Kevin Tapani .10 .30
76 Carlos Lee .10 .30
77 Ray Durham .10 .30
78 Jim Parque .10 .30
79 Bob Howry .10 .30
80 Magglio Ordonez .10 .30
81 Paul Konerko .10 .30
82 Mike Caruso .10 .30
83 Chris Singleton .10 .30
84 Sean Casey .10 .30
85 Barry Larkin .20 .50
86 Pokey Reese .10 .30
87 Eddie Taubensee .10 .30
88 Scott Williamson .10 .30
89 Jason LaRue .10 .30
90 Aaron Boone .10 .30
91 Jeffrey Hammonds .10 .30
92 Omar Vizquel .20 .50
93 Manny Ramirez .20 .50
94 Kenny Lofton .10 .30
95 Jaret Wright .10 .30
96 Einar Diaz .10 .30
97 Charles Nagy .10 .30
98 David Justice .10 .30
99 Richie Sexson .10 .30
100 Steve Karsay .10 .30
101 Todd Helton .20 .50
102 Dante Bichette .10 .30
103 Larry Walker .10 .30
104 Pedro Astacio .10 .30
105 Neifi Perez .10 .30
106 Brian Bohanon .10 .30
107 Edgard Clemente .10 .30
108 Dave Veres .10 .30
109 Gabe Kapler .10 .30
110 Juan Encarnacion .10 .30
111 Jeff Weaver .10 .30
112 Damion Easley .10 .30
113 Justin Thompson .10 .30
114 Brad Ausmus .10 .30
115 Frank Catalanotto .10 .30
116 Todd Jones .10 .30
117 Preston Wilson .10 .30
118 Cliff Floyd .10 .30
119 Mike Lowell .10 .30
120 Antonio Alfonseca .10 .30
121 Alex Gonzalez .10 .30
122 Braden Looper .10 .30
123 Bruce Aven .10 .30
124 Richard Hidalgo .10 .30
125 Mitch Meluskey .10 .30
126 Jeff Bagwell .20 .50
127 Jose Lima .10 .30
128 Derek Bell .10 .30
129 Billy Wagner .10 .30
130 Shane Reynolds .10 .30
131 Moises Alou .10 .30
132 Carlos Beltran .10 .30
133 Carlos Febles .10 .30
134 Jermaine Dye .10 .30
135 Jeremy Giambi .10 .30
136 Joe Randa .10 .30
137 Jose Rosado .10 .30
138 Chad Kreuter .10 .30
139 Jose Vizcaino .10 .30
140 Adrian Beltre .10 .30
141 Kevin Brown .20 .50
142 Ismael Valdes .10 .30
143 Angel Pena .10 .30
144 Chan Ho Park .10 .30
145 Mark Grudzielanek .10 .30
146 Jeff Shaw .10 .30
147 Geoff Jenkins .10 .30
148 Jeromy Burnitz .10 .30
149 Hideo Nomo .30 .75
150 Ron Belliard .10 .30
151 Sean Berry .10 .30
152 Mark Loretta .10 .30
153 Steve Woodard .10 .30
154 Joe Mays .10 .30
155 Eric Milton .10 .30
156 Corey Koskie .10 .30
157 Ron Coomer .10 .30
158 Brad Radke .10 .30
159 Terry Steinbach .10 .30
160 Cristian Guzman .10 .30
161 Vladimir Guerrero .30 .75
162 Wilton Guerrero .10 .30
163 Michael Barrett .10 .30
164 Chris Widger .10 .30
165 Fernando Seguignol .10 .30
166 Ugueth Urbina .10 .30
167 Dustin Hermanson .10 .30
168 Kenny Rogers .10 .30
169 Edgardo Alfonzo .10 .30
170 Orel Hershiser .10 .30
171 Robin Ventura .10 .30
172 Octavio Dotel .10 .30
173 Rickey Henderson .30 .75
174 Roger Cedeno .10 .30
175 John Olerud .10 .30
176 Derek Jeter .75 2.00
177 Tino Martinez .20 .50
178 Orlando Hernandez .10 .30
179 Chuck Knoblauch .10 .30
180 Bernie Williams .20 .50
181 Chili Davis .10 .30
182 David Cone .10 .30
183 Ricky Ledee .10 .30
184 Paul O'Neill .20 .50
185 Jason Giambi .10 .30
186 Eric Chavez .10 .30
187 Matt Stairs .10 .30
188 Miguel Tejada .10 .30
189 Olmedo Saenz .10 .30
190 Tim Hudson .10 .30
191 John Jaha .10 .30
192 Randy Velarde .10 .30
193 Rico Brogna .10 .30
194 Mike Lieberthal .10 .30
195 Marlon Anderson .10 .30
196 Bob Abreu .10 .30
197 Ron Gant .10 .30
198 Randy Wolf .10 .30
199 Desi Relaford .10 .30
200 Doug Glanville .10 .30
201 Warren Morris .10 .30
202 Kris Benson .10 .30
203 Kevin Young .10 .30
204 Brian Giles .10 .30
205 Jason Schmidt .10 .30
206 Ed Sprague .10 .30
207 Francisco Cordova .10 .30
208 Mark McGwire .75 2.00
209 Jose Jimenez .10 .30
210 Fernando Tatis .10 .30
211 Kent Bottenfield .10 .30
212 Eli Marrero .10 .30
213 Edgar Renteria .10 .30
214 Joe McEwing .10 .30
215 J.D. Drew .10 .30
216 Tony Gwynn .40 1.00
217 Gary Matthews Jr. .10 .30
218 Eric Owens .10 .30
219 Damian Jackson .10 .30
220 Reggie Sanders .10 .30
221 Trevor Hoffman .10 .30
222 Ben Davis .10 .30
223 Shawn Estes .10 .30
224 F.P. Santangelo .10 .30
225 Livan Hernandez .10 .30
226 Ellis Burks .10 .30
227 J.T. Snow .10 .30
228 Jeff Kent .10 .30
229 Robb Nen .10 .30
230 Marvin Benard .10 .30
231 Ken Griffey Jr. .50 1.25
232 John Halama .10 .30
233 Gil Meche .10 .30
234 David Bell .10 .30
235 Brian Hunter .10 .30
236 Jay Buhner .10 .30
237 Edgar Martinez .20 .50
238 Jose Mesa .10 .30
239 Wilson Alvarez .10 .30
240 Wade Boggs .20 .50
241 Fred McGriff .20 .50
242 Jose Canseco .20 .50
243 Kevin Stocker .10 .30
244 Roberto Hernandez .10 .30
245 Bubba Trammell .10 .30
246 John Flaherty .10 .30
247 Ivan Rodriguez .20 .50
248 Rusty Greer .10 .30
249 Rafael Palmeiro .20 .50
250 Jeff Zimmerman .10 .30
251 Royce Clayton .10 .30
252 Todd Zeile .10 .30
253 John Wetteland .10 .30
254 Ruben Mateo .10 .30
255 Kelvim Escobar .10 .30
256 David Wells .10 .30
257 Shawn Green .10 .30
258 Homer Bush .10 .30
259 Shannon Stewart .10 .30
260 Carlos Delgado .10 .30
261 Roy Halladay .10 .30
262 Fernando Tatis SH CL .10 .30
263 Jose Jimenez SH CL .10 .30
264 Tony Gwynn SH CL .20 .50
265 Wade Boggs SH CL .10 .30
266 Cal Ripken SH CL .50 1.25
267 David Cone SH CL .10 .30
268 Mark McGwire SH CL .50 1.25
269 Pedro Martinez SH CL .20 .50
270 N. Garciaparra SH CL .30 .75
271 Nick Johnson SR .30 .75
272 Mark Quinn SR .20 .50
273 Roosevelt Brown SR .20 .50
274 Terrence Long SR .20 .50
275 Jason Marquis SR .20 .50
276 K.Sasaki SR RC .50 1.25
277 Aaron Myette SR .20 .50
278 Danys Baez SR RC .30 .75
279 Travis Dawkins SR .20 .50
280 Mark Mulder SR .30 .75
281 Chris Haas SR .20 .50
282 Milton Bradley SR .30 .75
283 Brad Penny SR .20 .50
284 Rafael Furcal SR .30 .75
285 Luis Matos SR RC .30 .75
286 Victor Santos SR RC .30 .75
287 R.Washington SR RC .20 .50
288 Rob Bell SR .20 .50
289 Joe Crede SR 1.00 2.50
290 Pablo Ozuna SR .20 .50
291 W.Serrano SR RC .20 .50
292 S-H. Lee SR RC .20 .50
293 C.Wakeland SR RC .20 .50
294 Luis Rivera SR RC .20 .50
295 Mike Lamb SR RC .50 1.25
296 Wily Mo Pena SR .30 .75
297 Mike Meyers SR RC .30 .75
298 Mo Vaughn .10 .30
299 Darin Erstad .10 .30
300 Garret Anderson .10 .30
301 Tim Belcher .10 .30
302 Scott Spiezio .10 .30
303 Kent Bottenfield .10 .30
304 Orlando Palmeiro .10 .30
305 Jason Dickson .10 .30
306 Matt Williams .10 .30
307 Brian Anderson .10 .30
308 Hanley Frias .10 .30
309 Todd Stottlemyre .10 .30
310 Matt Mantei .10 .30
311 David Dellucci .10 .30
312 Armando Reynoso .10 .30
313 Bernard Gilkey .10 .30
314 Chipper Jones .30 .75
315 Tom Glavine .20 .50
316 Quilvio Veras .10 .30
317 Andruw Jones .20 .50
318 Bobby Bonilla .10 .30
319 Reggie Sanders .10 .30
320 Andres Galarraga .10 .30
321 George Lombard .10 .30
322 John Rocker .10 .30
323 Wally Joyner .10 .30
324 B.J. Surhoff .10 .30
325 Scott Erickson .10 .30
326 Delino DeShields .10 .30
327 Jeff Conine .10 .30
328 Mike Timlin .10 .30
329 Brady Anderson .10 .30
330 Mike Bordick .10 .30
331 Harold Baines .10 .30
332 Nomar Garciaparra .50 1.25
333 Bret Saberhagen .10 .30
334 Ramon Martinez .10 .30
335 Donnie Sadler .10 .30
336 Wilton Veras .10 .30
337 Mike Stanley .10 .30
338 Brian Rose .10 .30
339 Carl Everett .10 .30
340 Tim Wakefield .10 .30
341 Mark Grace .20 .50
342 Kerry Wood .10 .30
343 Eric Young .10 .30
344 Jose Nieves .10 .30
345 Ismael Valdes .10 .30
346 Joe Girardi .10 .30
347 Damon Buford .10 .30
348 Ricky Gutierrez .10 .30
349 Frank Thomas .30 .75
350 Brian Simmons .10 .30
351 James Baldwin .10 .30
352 Brook Fordyce .10 .30
353 Jose Valentin .10 .30
354 Mike Sirotka .10 .30
355 Greg Norton .10 .30
356 Dante Bichette .10 .30
357 Deion Sanders .20 .50
358 Ken Griffey Jr. .50 1.25
359 Denny Neagle .10 .30
360 Dmitri Young .10 .30
361 Pete Harnisch .10 .30
362 Michael Tucker .10 .30
363 Roberto Alomar .20 .50
364 Dave Roberts .10 .30
365 Jim Thome .20 .50
366 Bartolo Colon .10 .30
367 Travis Fryman .10 .30
368 Chuck Finley .10 .30
369 Russell Branyan .10 .30
370 Alex Ramirez .10 .30
371 Jeff Cirillo .10 .30
372 Jeffrey Hammonds .10 .30
373 Scott Karl .10 .30
374 Brent Mayne .10 .30
375 Tom Goodwin .10 .30
376 Jose Jimenez .10 .30
377 Rolando Arrojo .10 .30
378 Terry Shumpert .10 .30
379 Juan Gonzalez .10 .30
380 Bobby Higginson .10 .30
381 Tony Clark .10 .30
382 Dave Mlicki .10 .30
383 Deivi Cruz .10 .30
384 Brian Moehler .10 .30
385 Dean Palmer .10 .30
386 Luis Castillo .10 .30
387 Mike Redmond .10 .30
388 Alex Fernandez .10 .30
389 Brant Brown .10 .30
390 Dave Berg .10 .30
391 A.J. Burnett .10 .30
392 Mark Kotsay .10 .30
393 Craig Biggio .20 .50
394 Daryle Ward .10 .30
395 Lance Berkman .10 .30
396 Roger Cedeno .10 .30
397 Scott Elarton .10 .30
398 Octavio Dotel .10 .30
399 Ken Caminiti .10 .30
400 Johnny Damon .20 .50
401 Mike Sweeney .10 .30
402 Jeff Suppan .10 .30
403 Rey Sanchez .10 .30
404 Blake Stein .10 .30
405 Ricky Bottalico .10 .30
406 Jay Witasick .10 .30
407 Shawn Green .10 .30
408 Orel Hershiser .10 .30
409 Gary Sheffield .10 .30
410 Todd Hollandsworth .10 .30
411 Terry Adams .10 .30
412 Todd Hundley .10 .30
413 Eric Karros .10 .30
414 F.P. Santangelo .10 .30
415 Alex Cora .10 .30
416 Marquis Grissom .10 .30
417 Henry Blanco .10 .30
418 Jose Hernandez .10 .30
419 Kyle Peterson .10 .30
420 John Snyder RC .10 .30
421 Bob Wickman .10 .30
422 Jamey Wright .10 .30
423 Chad Allen .10 .30
424 Todd Walker .10 .30
425 J.C. Romero RC .10 .30
426 Butch Huskey .10 .30
427 Jacque Jones .10 .30
428 Matt Lawton .10 .30
429 Rondell White .10 .30
430 Jose Vidro .10 .30
431 Hideki Irabu .10 .30
432 Javier Vazquez .10 .30
433 Lee Stevens .10 .30
434 Mike Thurman .10 .30
435 Geoff Blum .10 .30
436 Mike Hampton .10 .30
437 Mike Piazza .50 1.25
438 Al Leiter .10 .30
439 Derek Bell .10 .30
440 Armando Benitez .10 .30
441 Rey Ordonez .10 .30
442 Todd Zeile .10 .30
443 Roger Clemens .60 1.50
444 Ramiro Mendoza .10 .30
445 Andy Pettitte .20 .50
446 Scott Brosius .10 .30
447 Mariano Rivera .30 .75
448 Jim Leyritz .10 .30
449 Jorge Posada .20 .50
450 Omar Olivares .10 .30
451 Ben Grieve .10 .30

452 A.J. Hinch .10 .30
453 Gil Heredia .10 .30
454 Kevin Appier .10 .30
455 Ryan Christenson .10 .30
456 Ramon Hernandez .10 .30
457 Scott Rolen .20 .50
458 Alex Arias .10 .30
459 Andy Ashby .10 .30
460 K.Jordan UER 474 .10 .30
461 Robert Person .10 .30
462 Paul Byrd .10 .30
463 Curt Schilling .10 .30
464 Mike Jackson .10 .30
465 Jason Kendall .10 .30
466 Pat Meares .10 .30
467 Bruce Aven .10 .30
468 Todd Ritchie .10 .30
469 Wil Cordero .10 .30
470 Aramis Ramirez .10 .30
471 Andy Benes .10 .30
472 Ray Lankford .10 .30
473 Fernando Vina .10 .30
474 Jim Edmonds .10 .30
475 Craig Paquette .10 .30
476 Pat Hentgen .10 .30
477 Darryl Kile .10 .30
478 Sterling Hitchcock .10 .30
479 Ruben Rivera .10 .30
480 Ryan Klesko .10 .30
481 Phil Nevin .10 .30
482 Woody Williams .10 .30
483 Carlos Hernandez .10 .30
484 Brian Meadows .10 .30
485 Bret Boone .10 .30
486 Barry Bonds .75 2.00
487 Russ Ortiz .10 .30
488 Bobby Estalella .10 .30
489 Rich Aurilia .10 .30
490 Bill Mueller .10 .30
491 Joe Nathan .10 .30
492 Russ Davis .10 .30
493 John Olerud .10 .30
494 Alex Rodriguez .50 1.25
495 Freddy Garcia .10 .30
496 Carlos Guillen .10 .30
497 Aaron Sele .10 .30
498 Brett Tomko .10 .30
499 Jamie Moyer .10 .30
500 Mike Cameron .10 .30
501 Vinny Castilla .10 .30
502 Gerald Williams .10 .30
503 Mike DiFelice .10 .30
504 Ryan Rupe .10 .30
505 Greg Vaughn .10 .30
506 Miguel Cairo .10 .30
507 Juan Guzman .10 .30
508 Jose Guillen .10 .30
509 Gabe Kapler .10 .30
510 Rick Helling .10 .30
511 David Segui .10 .30
512 Doug Davis .10 .30
513 Justin Thompson .10 .30
514 Chad Curtis .10 .30
515 Tony Batista .10 .30
516 Billy Koch .10 .30
517 Raul Mondesi .10 .30
518 Joey Hamilton .10 .30
519 Darrin Fletcher .10 .30
520 Brad Fullmer .10 .30
521 Jose Cruz Jr. .10 .30
522 Kevin Witt .10 .30
523 Mark McGwire AUT .40 1.00
524 Roberto Alomar AUT .10 .30
525 Chipper Jones AUT .20 .50
526 Derek Jeter AUT .40 1.00
527 Ken Griffey Jr. AUT .30 .75
528 Sammy Sosa AUT .20 .50
529 Manny Ramirez AUT .20 .50
530 Ivan Rodriguez AUT .10 .30
531 Pedro Martinez AUT .20 .50
532 Mariano Rivera CL .20 .50
533 Sammy Sosa CL .20 .50
534 Cal Ripken CL .50 1.25
535 Vladimir Guerrero CL .20 .50
536 Tony Gwynn CL .20 .50
537 Mark McGwire CL .40 1.00
538 Bernie Williams CL .10 .30
539 Pedro Martinez CL .20 .50
540 Ken Griffey Jr. CL .30 .75

2000 Upper Deck Exclusives Silver

This set parallels the regular Upper Deck set and cards were randomly seeded into packs. The cards feature coral and red borders and utilize silver foil stamping on front (instead of blue borders and bronze foil in the base set). In addition, each Exclusive Silver parallel is machine serial numbered to 100 on front.

*STARS: 8X TO 20X BASIC CARDS
*SR NON-RC'S: 2.5X TO 6X BASIC SR
*SR RC'S: 4X TO 10X BASIC SR

2000 Upper Deck 2K Plus

Inserted one every 23 first series packs, these 12 cards feature some players who are expected to be stars in the beginning of the 21st century.

COMPLETE SET (12) 25.00 60.00
*DIE CUTS: 2.5X TO 6X BASIC 2K PLUS 1.504.00
DIE CUTS RANDOM INSERTS IN SER.1 HOBBY
DIE CUTS PRINT RUN 100 SERIAL #'d SETS
GOLD DIE CUTS RANDOM IN SER.1 HOBBY
GOLD DIE CUT PRINT RUN 1 SERIAL #'d SET
GOLD DC NOT PRICED DUE TO SCARCITY

2K1 Ken Griffey Jr. 2.50 6.00
2K2 J.D. Drew .60 1.50
2K3 Derek Jeter 4.00 10.00
2K4 Nomar Garciaparra 2.50 6.00
2K5 Pat Burrell 4.00 10.00
2K6 Ruben Mateo .60 1.50
2K7 Carlos Beltran .60 1.50
2K8 Vladimir Guerrero 1.50 4.00
2K9 Scott Rolen 1.00 2.50
2K10 Chipper Jones 1.50 4.00
2K11 Alex Rodriguez 2.50 6.00
2K12 Magglio Ordonez .60 1.50

2000 Upper Deck A Piece of History 3000 Club

During the 2000 and early 2001 season, Upper Deck inserted a selection of memorabilia cards celebrating members of the 3000 hit club. Approximately 350 of each bat or jersey card was produced. In addition, a wide array of scarce, hand-numbered, autographed cards and combination memorabilia cards were made available. Complete print run information for these cards is provided in our checklist. The cards were released in the following products: 2000 SP Authentic: Tris Speaker and Paul Waner; 2000 SPx: Ty Cobb; 2000 UD Ionix: Roberto Clemente; 2000 Upper Deck 2: Hank Aaron; 2000 Upper Deck Gold Reserve: Al Kaline; 2000 Upper Deck Hitter's Club: Wade Boggs and Tony Gwynn; 2000 Upper Deck HoloGrFx: George Brett and Robin Yount; 2000 Upper Deck Legends: Paul Molitor and Carl Yastrzemski; 2000 Upper Deck MVP: Stan Musial; 2000 Upper Deck Ovation: Willie Mays; 2000 Upper Deck Pros and Prospects: Lou Brock and Rod Carew; 2000 Upper Deck Yankees Legends: Dave Winfield; 2001 Upper Deck: Eddie Murray and Cal Ripken. Exchange cards were seeded into packs for the following cards: Al Kaline Bat AU, Eddie Murray Bat AU, Cal Ripken Bat and Cal Ripken Bat-Jsy. The deadline to exchange the Kaline card was April 10th, 2001 and the Murray/Ripken cards was August 22nd, 2001.

AKB Al Kaline Bat/400 15.00 40.00
AKBS Al Kaline Bat AU/6
BGB Wade Boggs 75.00 150.00
Tony Gwynn Bat/99
BYB George Brett 75.00 150.00
Robin Yount
Bat/99
BYBS George Brett
Robin Yount
Bat AU/10
BYJ George Brett 125.00 200.00
Robin Yount
Jersey/99
BYJS George Brett
Robin Yount
Jersey AU/10
CRB Cal Ripken 30.00 60.00
Bat/350
CRJ Cal Ripken 30.00 60.00
Jersey/350
CRJB Cal Ripken 75.00 150.00
Bat-Jsy/100
CRJBS Cal Ripken
Bat-Jsy AU/8
CYB Carl Yaz 15.00 40.00
Bat/350
CYJ Carl Yaz 15.00 40.00
Jersey/350
CYJB Carl Yaz 60.00 120.00
Bat-Jsy/100
CYJBS Carl Yaz
Bat-Jsy AU/8
DWB Dave Winf. 10.00 25.00
Bat/350
DWJ Dave Winf. 10.00 25.00
Jersey/350
DWJB Dave Winf. 15.00 40.00
Bat-Jsy/100
DWJBS Dave Winfield
Bat-Jsy AU/31
EMB Eddie Murray 15.00 40.00
Bat/350
EMJ Eddie Murray 15.00 40.00
Jersey/350
EMJB Eddie Murray 50.00 100.00
Bat-Jsy/100
EMJBS Eddie Murray
Bat-Jsy AU/33
GBB George Brett 20.00 50.00
Bat/350
GBJ George Brett 20.00 50.00
Jersey/350
HAB Hank Aaron 40.00 80.00
Bat/350
HABS Hank Aaron 700.00 1000.00
Bat-Jsy AU/44
HAJ Hank Aaron 40.00 80.00
Jersey/350
HAJB Hank Aaron 125.00 200.00
Bat-Jsy/100
LBB Lou Brock 15.00 40.00
Bat/350
LBJ Lou Brock 15.00 40.00
Jsy/350
LBJB Lou Brock 30.00 60.00
Bat-Jsy/100
LBJBS Lou Brock
Bat-Jsy AU/20
PMB Paul Molitor 10.00 25.00
Bat/350
PWB Paul Waner 40.00 80.00
Bat/350
PWBC Paul Waner
Bat-Cut AU/5
RCAB Rod Carew 15.00 40.00
Bat/350
RCAJ Rod Carew 15.00 40.00
Jsy/350
RCABJ Rod Carew 30.00 60.00
Bat-Jsy/100
RCAJS Rod Carew
Bat-Jsy AU/30
RCLB Roberto Clemente 75.00 150.00
Bat/350
RCLC Roberto Clemente
Cut AU/4
RCLBC Roberto Clemente
Bat-Cut AU/5
RYB Robin Yount 10.00 25.00
Bat/350
RYJ Robin Yount 10.00 25.00
Jersey/350
SMB Stan Musial 20.00 50.00
Bat/350
SMJ Stan Musial 20.00 50.00
Jersey/350
SMJB Stan Musial 75.00 150.00
Bat-Jsy/100
SMJBS Stan Musial
Bat-Jsy AU/6
TCB Ty Cobb 90.00 180.00
Bat/350
TCBC Ty Cobb
Bat-Cut AU/1
TCC Ty Cobb
Cut AU/3
TGB Tony Gwynn 15.00 40.00
Bat/350
TGBC Tony Gwynn 75.00 150.00
Bat-Cap/50
TGBS Tony Gwynn
Bat AU/19
TSB Tris Speaker 90.00 180.00
Bat/350
TSBC Tris Speaker
Bat-Cut AU/5
WBB Wade Boggs 15.00 40.00
Bat/350
WBBC Wade Boggs 50.00 100.00
Bat-Cap/50
WBBS Wade Boggs
Bat AU/12
WMB Willie Mays 40.00 80.00
Bat/300
WMJ Willie Mays 40.00 80.00
Jersey/350
WMJB Willie Mays 150.00 250.00
Bat-Jsy/50
WMJBS Willie Mays
Bat-Jsy AU/24

2000 Upper Deck Cooperstown Calling

Randomly inserted into Upper Deck Series two packs at one in 23, this 15-card insert features players that will be going to Cooperstown after they retire from baseball. Card backs carry a "CC" prefix.

COMPLETE SET (15) 40.00 100.00
CC1 Roger Clemens 3.00 8.00
CC2 Cal Ripken 5.00 12.00
CC3 Ken Griffey Jr. 2.50 6.00
CC4 Mike Piazza 2.50 6.00
CC5 Tony Gwynn 2.00 5.00
CC6 Sammy Sosa 1.50 4.00
CC7 Jose Canseco 1.00 2.50
CC8 Larry Walker .60 1.50
CC9 Barry Bonds 4.00 10.00
CC10 Greg Maddux 2.50 6.00
CC11 Derek Jeter 4.00 10.00
CC12 Mark McGwire 4.00 10.00
CC13 Randy Johnson 1.50 4.00
CC14 Frank Thomas 1.50 4.00
CC15 Jeff Bagwell 1.00 2.50

2000 Upper Deck e-Card

Inserted as a two-pack box-topper in Upper Deck Series two, this six-card insert features cards that can be viewed over the Upper Deck website. Cards feature a serial number that is to be typed in a the Upper Deck website to reveal that card. Card backs carry an "E" prefix.

COMPLETE SET (6) 3.00 8.00
E1 Ken Griffey Jr. .60 1.50
E2 Alex Rodriguez .60 1.50
E3 Cal Ripken Jr. 1.25 3.00
E4 Jeff Bagwell .25 .60
E5 Barry Bonds 1.00 2.50
E6 Manny Ramirez .25 .60

2000 Upper Deck eVolve Autograph

Lucky participants in Upper Deck's E-Card program received special upgraded E-Cards available by checking the UD website (www.upperdeck.com) and entering their basic E-Card serial code (printed on the front of each basic E-Card). When viewed on the Upper Deck website, if an autographed card of the depicted player appeared, the bearer of the base card could then exchange their basic E-Card and receive the signed upgrade via mail. Only 200 serial numbered E-Card Autograph sets were produced. Signed E-Cards all have an ES prefix on the card numbers.

ES1 Ken Griffey Jr. 50.00 100.00
ES2 Alex Rodriguez 60.00 120.00
ES3 Cal Ripken 75.00 150.00
ES4 Jeff Bagwell 20.00 50.00
ES5 Barry Bonds 100.00 175.00
ES6 Manny Ramirez 20.00 50.00

2000 Upper Deck eVolve Game Jersey

Lucky participants in Upper Deck's E-Card program received special upgraded E-Cards available by checking the UD website (www.upperdeck.com) and entering their basic E-Card serial code (printed on the front of each basic E-Card). When viewed on the Upper Deck website, if a jersey card of the depicted player appeared, the bearer of the base card could then exchange their basic E-Card and receive the Game Jersey upgrade via mail. The cards closely parallel basic 2000 Game Jerseys that were distributed in first and second series packs except for the gold foil "e-volve" logo on front. Only 300 serial numbered E-Card Jersey sets were produced with each card being serial -numbered by hand in blue ink sharpie at the bottom right front corner. Unsigned E-Card Game Jerseys all have an EJ prefix on the card numbers.

EJ1 Ken Griffey Jr. 15.00 40.00
EJ2 Alex Rodriguez 15.00 40.00
EJ3 Cal Ripken 25.00 60.00
EJ4 Jeff Bagwell 10.00 25.00
EJ5 Barry Bonds 20.00 50.00
EJ6 Manny Ramirez 10.00 25.00

2000 Upper Deck eVolve Game Jersey Autograph

Lucky participants in Upper Deck's E-Card program received special upgraded E-Cards available by checking the UD website (www.upperdeck.com) and entering their basic E-Card serial code (printed on the front of each basic E-Card). When viewed on the Upper Deck website, if an autographed card of the depicted player appeared, the bearer of the base card could then exchange their basic E-Card and receive the signed upgrade via mail. A mere 50 serial numbered sets were produced. Signed jersey E-Cards all have an ESJ prefix on the card numbers.

ESJ1 Ken Griffey Jr. 75.00 150.00
ESJ2 Alex Rodriguez 100.00 175.00
ESJ3 Cal Ripken 75.00 150.00
ESJ4 Jeff Bagwell 50.00 100.00
ESJ5 Barry Bonds 125.00 200.00
ESJ6 Manny Ramirez 50.00 100.00

2000 Upper Deck Faces of the Game

Inserted one every 11 first series packs, these 20 cards feature leading players captured by exceptional photography.

COMPLETE SET (20) 30.00 80.00
*DIE CUTS: 3X TO 8X BASIC FACES 1.25 3.00
DIE CUTS RANDOM INSERTS IN SER.1 HOBBY
DIE CUTS PRINT RUN 100 SERIAL #'d SETS
GOLD DIE CUTS RANDOM IN SER.1 HOBBY
GOLD DIE CUT PRINT RUN 1 SERIAL #'d SET
GOLD DC NOT PRICED DUE TO SCARCITY
F1 Ken Griffey Jr. 2.00 5.00
F2 Mark McGwire 3.00 8.00
F3 Sammy Sosa 1.25 3.00
F4 Alex Rodriguez 2.00 5.00
F5 Manny Ramirez .75 2.00
F6 Derek Jeter 3.00 8.00
F7 Jeff Bagwell .75 2.00
F8 Roger Clemens 2.50 6.00
F9 Scott Rolen .75 2.00
F10 Tony Gwynn 1.50 4.00
F11 Nomar Garciaparra 2.00 5.00
F12 Randy Johnson 1.25 3.00
F13 Greg Maddux 2.00 5.00
F14 Mike Piazza 2.00 5.00
F15 Frank Thomas 1.25 3.00
F16 Cal Ripken 4.00 10.00
F17 Ivan Rodriguez .75 2.00
F18 Mo Vaughn .50 1.25
F19 Chipper Jones 1.25 3.00
F20 Sean Casey .50 1.25

2000 Upper Deck Five-Tool Talents

Randomly inserted into packs at one in 11, this 15-card insert features players that possess all of the tools needed to succeed in the Major Leagues. Card backs carry a "FT" prefix.

COMPLETE SET (15) 12.50 30.00
FT1 Vladimir Guerrero .75 2.00
FT2 Barry Bonds 2.00 5.00
FT3 Jason Kendall .30 .75
FT4 Derek Jeter 2.00 5.00
FT5 Ken Griffey Jr. 1.25 3.00
FT6 Andruw Jones .50 1.25
FT7 Bernie Williams .50 1.25
FT8 Jose Canseco .50 1.25
FT9 Scott Rolen .50 1.25
FT10 Shawn Green .30 .75
FT11 Nomar Garciaparra 1.25 3.00
FT12 Jeff Bagwell .50 1.25
FT13 Larry Walker .30 .75
FT14 Chipper Jones .75 2.00
FT15 Alex Rodriguez 1.25 3.00

2000 Upper Deck Game Ball

Randomly inserted into packs at one in 287, this 10-card insert features game-used baseballs from the depicted players. Card backs carry a "B" prefix.

BAJ Andruw Jones 4.00 10.00
BAR Alex Rodriguez 6.00 15.00
BBW Bernie Williams 4.00 10.00
BDJ Derek Jeter 10.00 25.00
BJB Jeff Bagwell 4.00 10.00
BKG Ken Griffey Jr. 6.00 15.00
BMM Mark McGwire 20.00 50.00
BRC Roger Clemens 6.00 15.00
BTG Tony Gwynn 6.00 15.00
BVG Vladimir Guerrero 4.00 10.00

2000 Upper Deck Game Jersey

These cards feature swatches of jerseys of various major league stars. The cards with an "H" after the player names are available only in hobby packs at a rate of one every 288 first series and 1:287 second series. The cards which have an "HR" after the player names are available in either hobby or retail packs at a rate of one every 2500 packs.

AJ Andruw Jones HR2 10.00 25.00
AR Alex Rodriguez H1 20.00 50.00
AR Alex Rodriguez HR2 20.00 50.00
BG Ben Grieve HR2 6.00 15.00
CJ Chipper Jones HR1 15.00 40.00
CR Cal Ripken HR1 30.00 60.00
CY Tom Glavine H1 10.00 25.00
DC David Cone HR2 6.00 15.00
DJ Derek Jeter H1 30.00 60.00
EC Eric Chavez HR2 6.00 15.00
EM Edgar Martinez HR2 10.00 25.00
FT Frank Thomas H1 15.00 40.00
FT Frank Thomas HR2 15.00 40.00
GK Gabe Kapler HR1 6.00 15.00
GM Greg Maddux HR1 20.00 50.00
GM Greg Maddux HR2 20.00 50.00
GV Greg Vaughn HR1 6.00 15.00
JB Jeff Bagwell H1 10.00 25.00
JC Jose Canseco HR1 10.00 25.00
JR Ken Griffey Jr. H1 20.00 50.00
KG K.Griffey Jr. Reds HR2 20.00 50.00
KM Kevin Millwood HR2 6.00 15.00
MH Mike Hampton HR2 6.00 15.00
MP Mike Piazza H1 20.00 50.00
MR Manny Ramirez HR1 10.00 25.00
MV Mo Vaughn HR2 6.00 15.00
MW Matt Williams HR2 6.00 15.00
PM Pedro Martinez H1 10.00 25.00
RJ Randy Johnson HR2 15.00 40.00
RV Robin Ventura HR2 6.00 15.00
SA Sandy Alomar Jr. HR2 6.00 15.00
TG Tony Gwynn HR2 15.00 40.00
TH Todd Helton HR1 10.00 25.00
TH Todd Helton HR2 10.00 25.00
VG Vladimir Guerrero HR1 15.00 40.00
TGL Tom Glavine HR2 10.00 25.00
TRG Troy Glaus H1 6.00 15.00
TRG Troy Glaus HR2 6.00 15.00

2000 Upper Deck Game Jersey Autograph

Randomly inserted into Upper Deck Series two hobby packs, this insert set features autographed game-used jersey cards from some of the hottest players in major league baseball. Cards carry an "H" prefix. A few autographs were not available in packs and had to be exchanged for signed cards. These cards had to be returned to Upper Deck by March 6th, 2001.

HAR A.Rodriguez 125.00 200.00
HBB Barry Bonds 125.00 200.00
HCR Cal Ripken 75.00 150.00
HDJ Derek Jeter 150.00 250.00
HIR I.Rodriguez AU H2 40.00 80.00
HJB Jeff Bagwell 40.00 80.00
HJC Jose Canseco 20.00 50.00
HJK Jason Kendall 15.00 40.00
HKG K.Griffey Jr. Reds 75.00 150.00
HMR Manny Ramirez 40.00 80.00
HPO Paul O'Neill 20.00 50.00
HSR Scott Rolen 20.00 50.00
HVG Vladimir Guerrero 40.00 80.00

2000 Upper Deck Game Jersey Autograph Numbered

Randomly inserted into Upper Deck hobby packs, this insert set features autographed game-used jersey cards of the hottest players in baseball. Please note that these cards are hand-numbered on front in blue ink sharpie pen to the depicted players jersey number. Due to scarcity, some of these cards are not priced. A few cards were available via exchange: Series one exchange cards had to be redeemed by July 15th, 2000 while series two exchange cards were to be redeemed by March 6th, 2001. Cards tagged with an H1 or H2 suffix in the description were distributed exclusively in first and second series hobby packs. Cards tagged with an HR1 or HR2 suffix were distributed in hobby and retail packs. The "hobby-only" cards carry an "HN" prefix for the numbering on the back of each card (i.e. Scott Rolen is HN-SR). In addition, each of these cards features features a congratulations from UD President Richard McWilliams with the reference to the card being "crash numbered". These two differences make these scarce numbered inserts easy to legitimize against possible fakes whereby unscrupulous parties may have numbered the cards themselves on front (not very tough to do given the cards were hand-numbered by UD). Unfortunately, the hobby-retail cards do not carry these key differences in design. It's believed that these Numbered inserts feature a gold hologram on back (lower left corner) rather than the silver hologram featured on the more common non-Numbered Game Jersey Autograph cards. Nonetheless, buyers are encouraged to exercise extreme caution for fakes when purchasing the hobby-retail versions of these cards.

AJ Andruw Jones/25 H2
AR Alex Rodriguez/3 HR1
BB Barry Bonds/25 H2
BG Ben Grieve /14 HR2
CR Cal Ripken/8 H2
DJ Derek Jeter/2 HR1
EM Edgar Martinez /11 HR2
FT Frank Thomas/35 HR2 75.00 150.00
GM Greg Maddux/31 HR2 175.00 300.00
IR Ivan Rodriguez/7 H2
JB Jeff Bagwell/5 H2
JC Jose Canseco/33 H2 50.00 100.00
JK Jason Kendall/18 H2
JR K.Griffey Jr./24 H1 EX
KG K.Griffey Jr. Reds/30 H2 150.00 250.00
MH Mike Hampton/10 HR2
MR Manny Ramirez/24 H1
MR M.Ramirez/24 H2 EX
MV Mo Vaughn/42 HR2 30.00 60.00
MW Matt Williams/9 HR2
PO Paul O'Neill/21 H2
RJ R.Johnson/51 HR2 125.00 200.00
SR Scott Rolen/17 H2
TG Tony Gwynn/19 HR2
VG V.Guerrero/27 H2 150.00 250.00
TGl Tom Glavine/47 HR2 50.00 100.00
TRG Troy Glaus/14 HR2

2000 Upper Deck Game Jersey Patch

Randomly inserted into series one packs at one in 10,000 and series two packs at a rate of 1:7500, these cards feature game-worn uniform patches.

1 OF 1 PATCH RANDOM IN ALL PACKS
1 OF 1 PATCH PRINT RUN 1 SERIAL #'d SET
NO 1 OF 1 PATCH PRICING AVAILABLE
PAJ Andruw Jones 2 50.00 100.00
PAR Alex Rodriguez 1 75.00 150.00
PAR Alex Rodriguez 2 75.00 150.00
PBB Barry Bonds 2 100.00 200.00
PBG Ben Grieve 2 20.00 50.00
PCJ Chipper Jones 1 50.00 100.00
PCR Cal Ripken 1 75.00 150.00
PCR Cal Ripken 2 75.00 150.00
PCY Tom Glavine 1 50.00 100.00
PDC David Cone 30.00 60.00
PDJ Derek Jeter 1 75.00 150.00
PDJ Derek Jeter 2 75.00 150.00
PEC Eric Chavez 1 30.00 60.00
PFT Frank Thomas 1 50.00 100.00
PGK Gabe Kapler 1 30.00 60.00
PGM Greg Maddux 1 60.00 120.00
PGM Greg Maddux 2 60.00 120.00
PGV Greg Vaughn 1 20.00 50.00
PIR Ivan Rodriguez 2 50.00 100.00
PJB Jeff Bagwell 1 50.00 100.00
PJC Jose Canseco 1 50.00 100.00
PJR Ken Griffey Jr. 1 75.00 150.00
PKG K.Griffey Jr. Reds 2 75.00 150.00
PMP Mike Piazza 1 60.00 120.00
PMR Manny Ramirez 1 50.00 100.00
PMR Manny Ramirez 2 50.00 100.00
PMV Mo Vaughn 2 30.00 60.00
PMW Matt Williams 2 30.00 60.00
PPM Pedro Martinez 1 50.00 100.00
PRJ Randy Johnson 2 50.00 100.00
PSR Scott Rolen 2 50.00 100.00
PTG Tony Gwynn 2 50.00 100.00
PTH Todd Helton 1 50.00 100.00
PTRG Troy Glaus 1 30.00 60.00
PTRG Troy Glaus 2 30.00 60.00
PVG Vladimir Guerrero 1 60.00 120.00
PVG Vladimir Guerrero 2 60.00 120.00

2000 Upper Deck Hit Brigade

Inserted into first series packs at a rate of one in eight, these 15 cards feature some of the best hitters. These cards are printed in etched foil.

COMPLETE SET (15) 12.50 30.00
*DIE CUTS: 6X TO 15X BASIC HIT BRIGADE .60 1.50
DIE CUTS RANDOM INSERTS IN SER.1 PACKS
DIE CUTS PRINT RUN 100 SERIAL #'d SETS
GOLD DIE CUTS RANDOM IN SER.1 PACKS
GOLD DIE CUT PRINT RUN 1 SERIAL #'d SET
GOLD DC NOT PRICED DUE TO SCARCITY
H1 Ken Griffey Jr. 1.00 2.50
H2 Tony Gwynn .75 2.00
H3 Alex Rodriguez 1.00 2.50
H4 Derek Jeter 1.50 4.00
H5 Mike Piazza 1.00 2.50
H6 Sammy Sosa .60 1.50

H7 Juan Gonzalez .25 .60
H8 Scott Rolen .40 1.00
H9 Nomar Garciaparra 1.00 2.50
H10 Barry Bonds 1.50 4.00
H11 Craig Biggio .40 1.00
H12 Chipper Jones .60 1.50
H13 Frank Thomas .60 1.50
H14 Larry Walker .25 .60
H15 Mark McGwire 1.50 4.00

2000 Upper Deck Hot Properties

Randomly inserted into Upper Deck series two packs at one in 11, this 15-card insert features the major league's top prospects. Card backs carry a "HP" prefix.

COMPLETE SET (15) 5.00 12.00
HP1 Carlos Beltran .30 .75
HP2 Rick Ankiel .30 .75
HP3 Sean Casey .30 .75
HP4 Preston Wilson .30 .75
HP5 Vernon Wells .50 1.25
HP6 Pat Burrell .30 .75
HP7 Eric Chavez .30 .75
HP8 J.D. Drew .30 .75
HP9 Alfonso Soriano 1.25 3.00
HP10 Gabe Kapler .30 .75
HP11 Rafael Furcal .50 1.25
HP12 Ruben Mateo .30 .75
HP13 Corey Koskie .20 .50
HP14 Kip Wells .30 .75
HP15 Ramon Ortiz .30 .75

2000 Upper Deck Legendary Cuts

Randomly inserted into Upper Deck series two packs, this eight-card insert features cut-signatures from some of the all-time great players of the 20th Century. Please note that only one set was produced of this insert.

1 Cap Anson
2 Roberto Clemente
3 Ty Cobb
4 Eddie Collins
5 Nap Lajoie
6 Tris Speaker
7 Honus Wagner
8 Paul Waner

2000 Upper Deck Pennant Driven

Randomly inserted into packs at one in four, this 10-card insert features players that are driven to win the pennant. Card backs carry a "PD" prefix.

COMPLETE SET (10) 4.00 10.00
PD1 Derek Jeter .75 2.00
PD2 Roberto Alomar .20 .50
PD3 Chipper Jones .30 .75
PD4 Jeff Bagwell .20 .50
PD5 Roger Clemens .60 1.50
PD6 Nomar Garciaparra .50 1.25
PD7 Manny Ramirez .20 .50
PD8 Mike Piazza .50 1.25
PD9 Ivan Rodriguez .20 .50
PD10 Randy Johnson .30 .75

2000 Upper Deck People's Choice

Randomly inserted into second series packs at one in 23, this 15-card set features players that people have voted as their favorites to watch. Card backs carry a "PC" prefix.

COMPLETE SET (15) 40.00 100.00
PC1 Mark McGwire 4.00 10.00
PC2 Nomar Garciaparra 2.50 6.00
PC3 Derek Jeter 4.00 10.00
PC4 Shawn Green .60 1.50
PC5 Manny Ramirez 1.00 2.50
PC6 Pedro Martinez 1.00 2.50
PC7 Ivan Rodriguez 1.00 2.50
PC8 Alex Rodriguez 2.50 6.00
PC9 Juan Gonzalez .60 1.50
PC10 Ken Griffey Jr. 2.50 6.00
PC11 Sammy Sosa 1.50 4.00
PC12 Jeff Bagwell 1.00 2.50
PC13 Chipper Jones 1.50 4.00
PC14 Cal Ripken 5.00 12.00
PC15 Mike Piazza 2.50 6.00

2000 Upper Deck Power MARK

Inserted one every 23 first series packs, these 10 cards all feature Mark McGwire.

COMPLETE SET (10) 25.00 50.00
COMMON (MC1-MC10) 2.50 6.00
*DIE CUTS: 3X TO 8X BASIC POWER MARK
DIE CUTS RANDOM INSERTS IN SER.1 HOBBY
DIE CUTS PRINT RUN 100 SERIAL #'d SETS
GOLD DIE CUTS RANDOM IN SER.1 HOBBY
GOLD DIE CUT PRINT RUN 1 SERIAL #'d SET
GOLD DC NOT PRICED DUE TO SCARCITY

2000 Upper Deck Power Rally

Inserted one every 11 first series packs, these 15 cards feature baseball's leading power hitters.

COMPLETE SET (15) 15.00 40.00
*DIE CUTS: 5X TO 12X BASIC POWER RALLY
DIE CUTS RANDOM INSERTS IN SER.1 PACKS
DIE CUTS PRINT RUN 100 SERIAL #'d SETS
GOLD DIE CUTS RANDOM IN SER.1 PACKS
GOLD DIE CUT PRINT RUN 1 SERIAL #'d SET
GOLD DC NOT PRICED DUE TO SCARCITY
P1 Ken Griffey Jr. 1.25 3.00
P2 Mark McGwire 2.00 5.00
P3 Sammy Sosa .75 2.00
P4 Jose Canseco .50 1.25
P5 Juan Gonzalez .30 .75
P6 Bernie Williams .50 1.25
P7 Jeff Bagwell .50 1.25
P8 Chipper Jones .75 2.00
P9 Vladimir Guerrero .75 2.00
P10 Mo Vaughn .30 .75
P11 Derek Jeter 2.00 5.00
P12 Mike Piazza 1.25 3.00
P13 Barry Bonds 2.00 5.00
P14 Alex Rodriguez 1.25 3.00
P15 Nomar Garciaparra 1.25 3.00

2000 Upper Deck PowerDeck Inserts

These CD's were inserted into packs at two different rates. PD1 through PD 8 were inserted at a rate of one every 23 packs while PD9 through PD 11 were inserted at a rate of one every 287 packs. Due to problems at the manufacturer, the Alex Rodriguez CD was not inserted into the first series packs so a collector could acquire one of those by sending in a UPC code on the bottom of the 2000 Upper Deck first series boxes. Also, some of the 1999 Upper Deck PowerDeck CD's were mistakenly inserted into this product. Those CD's are priced under the 1999 Upper Deck PowerDeck listings. Finally, Ken Griffey Jr., Reggie Jackson and Mark McGwire have all been confirmed as short prints by representatives at Upper Deck.

COMPLETE SET (11) 60.00 120.00
PD1 Ken Griffey Jr. 2.50 6.00
PD2 Cal Ripken 5.00 12.00
PD3 Mark McGwire 4.00 10.00
PD4 Tony Gwynn 2.00 5.00
PD5 Roger Clemens 3.00 8.00
PD6 Alex Rodriguez 3.00 8.00
PD7 Sammy Sosa 1.50 4.00
PD8 Derek Jeter 4.00 10.00
PD9 Ken Griffey Jr. SP 6.00 15.00
PD10 Mark McGwire SP 10.00 25.00
PD11 Reggie Jackson SP 6.00 15.00

2000 Upper Deck Prime Performers

Randomly inserted into series two packs at one in eight, this 10-card insert features players that are prime performers. Card backs carry a "PP" prefix.

COMPLETE SET (10) 5.00 12.00
PP1 Manny Ramirez .25 .60
PP2 Pedro Martinez .25 .60
PP3 Carlos Delgado .15 .40
PP4 Ken Griffey Jr. .60 1.50
PP5 Derek Jeter 1.00 2.50
PP6 Chipper Jones .40 1.00
PP7 Sean Casey .15 .40
PP8 Shawn Green .15 .40
PP9 Sammy Sosa .40 1.00
PP10 Alex Rodriguez .60 1.50

2000 Upper Deck Statitude

Inserted one every four packs, these 30 cards feature some of the most statistically dominant players in baseball.

COMPLETE SET (30) 15.00 40.00
*DIE CUTS: 6X TO 15X BASIC STATITUDE
DIE CUTS RANDOM INSERTS IN SER.1 RETAIL
DIE CUTS PRINT RUN 100 SERIAL #'d SETS
GOLD DIE CUTS RANDOM IN SER.1 RETAIL
GOLD DIE CUT PRINT RUN 1 SERIAL #'d SET
GOLD DC NOT PRICED DUE TO SCARCITY
S1 Mo Vaughn .25 .60
S2 Matt Williams .25 .60
S3 Travis Lee .25 .60
S4 Chipper Jones .60 1.50
S5 Greg Maddux 1.00 2.50
S6 Gabe Kapler .25 .60
S7 Cal Ripken 2.00 5.00
S8 Nomar Garciaparra 1.00 2.50
S9 Sammy Sosa .60 1.50
S10 Frank Thomas .60 1.50
S11 Manny Ramirez .40 1.00
S12 Larry Walker .25 .60
S13 Ivan Rodriguez .40 1.00
S14 Jeff Bagwell .40 1.00
S15 Craig Biggio .40 1.00
S16 Vladimir Guerrero .60 1.50
S17 Mike Piazza 1.00 2.50
S18 Bernie Williams .40 1.00
S19 Derek Jeter 1.50 4.00
S20 Jose Canseco .40 1.00
S21 Eric Chavez .25 .60
S22 Scott Rolen .40 1.00
S23 Mark McGwire 1.50 4.00
S24 Tony Gwynn .75 2.00
S25 Barry Bonds 1.50 4.00
S26 Ken Griffey Jr. 1.00 2.50
S27 Alex Rodriguez 1.00 2.50
S28 J.D. Drew .25 .60
S29 Juan Gonzalez .25 .60
S30 Roger Clemens 1.25 3.00

2001 Upper Deck

The 2001 Upper Deck Series one product was released in November, 2000 and featured a 270-card base set. Series two (entitled Mid-Summer Classic) was released in June, 2001 and featured a 180-card base set. The complete set is broken into subsets as follows: Star Rookies (1-45/271-300), basic cards (46-261/301-444), and Season Highlight checklists (262-270/445-450). Each pack contained 8-cards and carried a suggested retail price of $2.99. Key Rookie Cards in the set include Albert Pujols and Ichiro Suzuki. Also, a selection of A Piece of History 3000 Club Eddie Murray and Cal Ripken memorabilia cards were randomly seeded into series one packs. 350 bat cards, 350 jersey cards and 100 hand-numbered, combination bat-jersey cards were produced for each player. In addition, thirty-three autographed, hand-numbered, combination bat-jersey Eddie Murray cards and eight autographed, hand-numbered, combination bat-jersey Cal Ripken cards were produced. The Ripken Bat, Ripken Bat-Jsy Combo and Murray Bat-Jsy Combo Autograph were all exchange cards. The deadline to send in the exchange cards was August 22nd, 2001. Pricing for these memorabilia cards can be referenced under 2000 Upper Deck A Piece of History 3000 Club.

COMPLETE SET (450) 90.00 150.00
COMP. SERIES 1 (270) 20.00 40.00
COMP. SERIES 2 (180) 60.00 100.00
COMMON (46-270/300-450) .10 .30
COMMON SR (1-45) .20 .50
1 Jeff DaVanon SR .20 .50
2 Aubrey Huff SR .20 .50
3 Pasqual Coco SR .20 .50
4 Barry Zito SR .25 .60
5 Augie Ojeda SR .20 .50
6 Chris Richard SR .20 .50
7 Josh Phelps SR .20 .50
8 Kevin Nicholson SR .20 .50
9 Juan Guzman SR .20 .50
10 Brandon Kolb SR .20 .50
11 Johan Santana SR 2.50 6.00
12 Josh Kalinowski SR .20 .50
13 Tike Redman SR .20 .50
14 Ivanon Coffie SR .20 .50
15 Chad Durbin SR .20 .50
16 Derrick Turnbow SR .20 .50
17 Scott Downs SR .20 .50
18 Jason Grilli SR .20 .50
19 Mark Buehrle SR .25 .60
20 Paxton Crawford SR .20 .50
21 Bronson Arroyo SR .40 1.00
22 Tomas De la Rosa SR .20 .50
23 Paul Rigdon SR .20 .50
24 Rob Ramsay SR .20 .50
25 Damian Rolls SR .20 .50
26 Jason Conti SR .20 .50
27 John Parrish SR .20 .50
28 Geraldo Guzman SR .20 .50
29 Tony Mota SR .20 .50
30 Luis Rivas SR .20 .50
31 Brian Tollberg SR .20 .50
32 Adam Bernero SR .20 .50
33 Michael Cuddyer SR .20 .50
34 Josue Espada SR .20 .50
35 Joe Lawrence SR .20 .50
36 Chad Moeller SR .20 .50
37 Nick Bierbrodt SR .20 .50
38 DeWayne Wise SR .20 .50
39 Javier Cardona SR .20 .50
40 Hiram Bocachica SR .20 .50
41 G.Chiaramonte SR .20 .50
42 Alex Cabrera SR .20 .50
43 Jimmy Rollins SR .20 .50
44 Pat Flury SR RC .20 .50
45 Leo Estrella SR .20 .50
46 Darin Erstad .10 .30
47 Seth Etherton .10 .30
48 Troy Glaus .10 .30
49 Brian Cooper .10 .30
50 Tim Salmon .20 .50
51 Adam Kennedy .10 .30
52 Bengie Molina .10 .30
53 Jason Giambi .10 .30
54 Miguel Tejada .10 .30
55 Tim Hudson .10 .30
56 Eric Chavez .10 .30
57 Terrence Long .10 .30
58 Jason Isringhausen .10 .30
59 Ramon Hernandez .10 .30
60 Raul Mondesi .10 .30
61 David Wells .10 .30
62 Shannon Stewart .10 .30
63 Tony Batista .10 .30
64 Brad Fullmer .10 .30
65 Chris Carpenter .10 .30
66 Homer Bush .10 .30
67 Gerald Williams .10 .30
68 Miguel Cairo .10 .30
69 Ryan Rupe .10 .30
70 Greg Vaughn .10 .30
71 John Flaherty .10 .30
72 Dan Wheeler .10 .30
73 Fred McGriff .20 .50
74 Roberto Alomar .20 .50
75 Bartolo Colon .10 .30
76 Kenny Lofton .10 .30
77 David Segui .10 .30
78 Omar Vizquel .20 .50
79 Russ Branyan .10 .30
80 Chuck Finley .10 .30
81 Manny Ramirez UER .20 .50
Back photo is of David Segui
82 Alex Rodriguez .50 1.25
83 John Halama .10 .30
84 Mike Cameron .10 .30
85 David Bell .10 .30
86 Jay Buhner .10 .30
87 Aaron Sele .10 .30
88 Rickey Henderson .30 .75
89 Brook Fordyce .10 .30
90 Cal Ripken 1.00 2.50
91 Mike Mussina .20 .50
92 Delino DeShields .10 .30
93 Melvin Mora .10 .30
94 Sidney Ponson .10 .30
95 Brady Anderson .10 .30
96 Ivan Rodriguez .20 .50
97 Ricky Ledee .10 .30
98 Rick Helling .10 .30
99 Ruben Mateo .10 .30
100 Luis Alicea .10 .30
101 John Wetteland .10 .30
102 Mike Lamb .10 .30
103 Carl Everett .10 .30
104 Troy O'Leary .10 .30
105 Wilton Veras .10 .30
106 Pedro Martinez UER .20 .50
Birthdate is incorrect
107 Rolando Arrojo .10 .30
108 Scott Hatteberg .10 .30
109 Jason Varitek .30 .75
110 Jose Offerman .10 .30
111 Carlos Beltran .10 .30
112 Johnny Damon .20 .50
113 Mark Quinn .10 .30
114 Rey Sanchez .10 .30
115 Mac Suzuki .10 .30
116 Jermaine Dye .10 .30
117 Chris Fussell .10 .30
118 Jeff Weaver .10 .30
119 Dean Palmer .10 .30
120 Robert Fick .10 .30
121 Brian Moehler .10 .30
122 Damion Easley .10 .30
123 Juan Encarnacion .10 .30
124 Tony Clark .10 .30
125 Cristian Guzman .10 .30
126 Matt LeCroy .10 .30
127 Eric Milton .10 .30
128 Jay Canizaro .10 .30
129 David Ortiz .30 .75
130 Brad Radke .10 .30
131 Jacque Jones .10 .30
132 Magglio Ordonez .10 .30
133 Carlos Lee .10 .30
134 Mike Sirotka .10 .30
135 Ray Durham .10 .30
136 Paul Konerko .10 .30
137 Charles Johnson .10 .30
138 James Baldwin .10 .30
139 Jeff Abbott .10 .30
140 Roger Clemens .60 1.50
141 Derek Jeter .75 2.00
142 David Justice .10 .30
143 Ramiro Mendoza .10 .30
144 Chuck Knoblauch .10 .30
145 Orlando Hernandez .10 .30
146 Alfonso Soriano .20 .50
147 Jeff Bagwell .20 .50
148 Julio Lugo .10 .30
149 Mitch Meluskey .10 .30
150 Jose Lima .10 .30
151 Richard Hidalgo .10 .30
152 Moises Alou .10 .30
153 Scott Elarton .10 .30
154 Andruw Jones .20 .50
155 Quilvio Veras .10 .30
156 Greg Maddux .50 1.25
157 Brian Jordan .10 .30
158 Andres Galarraga .10 .30
159 Kevin Millwood .10 .30
160 Rafael Furcal .10 .30
161 Jeromy Burnitz .10 .30
162 Jimmy Haynes .10 .30
163 Mark Loretta .10 .30
164 Ron Belliard .10 .30
165 Richie Sexson .10 .30
166 Kevin Barker .10 .30
167 Jeff D'Amico .10 .30
168 Rick Ankiel .10 .30
169 Mark McGwire .75 2.00
170 J.D. Drew .10 .30
171 Eli Marrero .10 .30
172 Darryl Kile .10 .30
173 Glenallen Hill .10 .30
174 Will Clark .20 .50
175 Eric Young .10 .30
176 Mark Grace .20 .50
177 Jon Lieber .10 .30
178 Damon Buford .10 .30
179 Kerry Wood .10 .30
180 Rondell White .10 .30
181 Joe Girardi .10 .30
182 Curt Schilling .10 .30
183 Randy Johnson .30 .75
184 Steve Finley .10 .30
185 Kelly Stinnett .10 .30
186 Jay Bell .10 .30
187 Matt Mantei .10 .30
188 Luis Gonzalez .10 .30
189 Shawn Green .10 .30
190 Todd Hundley .10 .30
191 Chan Ho Park .10 .30
192 Adrian Beltre .10 .30
193 Mark Grudzielanek .10 .30
194 Gary Sheffield .10 .30
195 Tom Goodwin .10 .30
196 Lee Stevens .10 .30
197 Javier Vazquez .10 .30
198 Milton Bradley .10 .30
199 Vladimir Guerrero .30 .75
200 Carl Pavano .10 .30
201 Orlando Cabrera .10 .30
202 Tony Armas Jr. .10 .30
203 Jeff Kent .10 .30
204 Calvin Murray .10 .30
205 Ellis Burks .10 .30
206 Barry Bonds .75 2.00
207 Russ Ortiz .10 .30
208 Marvin Benard .10 .30
209 Joe Nathan .10 .30
210 Preston Wilson .10 .30
211 Cliff Floyd .10 .30
212 Mike Lowell .10 .30
213 Ryan Dempster .10 .30
214 Brad Penny .10 .30
215 Mike Redmond .10 .30
216 Luis Castillo .10 .30
217 Derek Bell .10 .30
218 Mike Hampton .10 .30
219 Todd Zeile .10 .30
220 Robin Ventura .10 .30
221 Mike Piazza .50 1.25
222 Al Leiter .10 .30
223 Edgardo Alfonzo .10 .30
224 Mike Bordick .10 .30
225 Phil Nevin .10 .30
226 Ryan Klesko .10 .30
227 Adam Eaton .10 .30
228 Eric Owens .10 .30
229 Tony Gwynn .40 1.00
230 Matt Clement .10 .30
231 Wiki Gonzalez .10 .30
232 Robert Person .10 .30
233 Doug Glanville .10 .30
234 Scott Rolen .20 .50
235 Mike Lieberthal .10 .30
236 Randy Wolf .10 .30
237 Bob Abreu .10 .30
238 Pat Burrell .10 .30
239 Bruce Chen .10 .30
240 Kevin Young .10 .30
241 Todd Ritchie .10 .30
242 Adrian Brown .10 .30
243 Chad Hermansen .10 .30
244 Warren Morris .10 .30
245 Kris Benson .10 .30
246 Jason Kendall .10 .30
247 Pokey Reese .10 .30
248 Rob Bell .10 .30
249 Ken Griffey Jr. .50 1.25
250 Sean Casey .10 .30
251 Aaron Boone .10 .30
252 Pete Harnisch .10 .30
253 Barry Larkin .20 .50
254 Dmitri Young .10 .30
255 Todd Hollandsworth .10 .30
256 Pedro Astacio .10 .30
257 Todd Helton .20 .50
258 Terry Shumpert .10 .30
259 Neifi Perez .10 .30
260 Jeffrey Hammonds .10 .30
261 Ben Petrick .10 .30
262 Mark McGwire SH .40 1.00
263 Derek Jeter SH .40 1.00
264 Sammy Sosa SH .20 .50
265 Cal Ripken SH .50 1.25
266 Pedro Martinez SH .10 .30
267 Barry Bonds SH .40 1.00
268 Fred McGriff SH .10 .30
269 Randy Johnson SH .20 .50
270 Darin Erstad SH .10 .30
271 Ichiro Suzuki SR RC 6.00 15.00
272 W. Betemit SR RC .75 2.00
273 Corey Patterson SR .20 .50
274 Sean Douglass SR RC .20 .50
275 Mike Penney SR RC .20 .50
276 Nate Teut SR RC .20 .50
277 R. Rodriguez SR RC .20 .50
278 B. Duckworth SR RC .20 .50
279 Rafael Soriano SR RC .20 .50
280 Juan Diaz SR RC .20 .50
281 H. Ramirez SR RC .25 .60
282 T. Shinjo SR RC .25 .60
283 Keith Ginter SR .20 .50
284 Esix Snead SR RC .20 .50
285 Erick Almonte SR RC .20 .50
286 Travis Hafner SR RC 2.00 5.00
287 Jason Smith SR RC .20 .50
288 J. Melian SR RC .20 .50
289 Tyler Walker SR RC .20 .50
290 Jason Standridge SR .20 .50
291 Juan Uribe SR RC .25 .60
292 A. Hernandez SR RC .20 .50
293 J. Michaels SR RC .20 .50
294 Jason Hart SR .20 .50
295 Albert Pujols SR RC 15.00 40.00
296 M. Ensberg SR RC .75 2.00
297 Brandon Inge SR .20 .50
298 Jesus Colome SR .20 .50
299 K. Kessel SR RC UER .20 .50
L Missing from MLB experience
300 Timo Perez SR .20 .50
301 Mo Vaughn .10 .30
302 Ismael Valdes .10 .30
303 Glenallen Hill .10 .30
304 Garret Anderson .10 .30
305 Johnny Damon .20 .50
306 Jose Ortiz .10 .30
307 Mark Mulder .10 .30
308 Adam Piatt .10 .30
309 Gil Heredia .10 .30
310 Mike Sirotka .10 .30
311 Carlos Delgado .10 .30
312 Alex Gonzalez .10 .30
313 Jose Cruz Jr. .10 .30
314 Darrin Fletcher .10 .30
315 Ben Grieve .10 .30
316 Vinny Castilla .10 .30
317 Wilson Alvarez .10 .30
318 Brent Abernathy .10 .30
319 Ellis Burks .10 .30
320 Jim Thome .20 .50
321 Juan Gonzalez .10 .30
322 Ed Taubensee .10 .30
323 Travis Fryman .10 .30
324 John Olerud .10 .30
325 Edgar Martinez .20 .50
326 Freddy Garcia .10 .30
327 Bret Boone .20 .50
328 Kazuhiro Sasaki .10 .30
329 Albert Belle .10 .30
330 Mike Bordick .10 .30
331 David Segui .10 .30
332 Pat Hentgen .10 .30
333 Alex Rodriguez .50 1.25
334 Andres Galarraga .10 .30
335 Gabe Kapler .10 .30
336 Ken Caminiti .10 .30
337 Rafael Palmeiro .20 .50
338 Manny Ramirez Sox .20 .50
339 David Cone .10 .30
340 Nomar Garciaparra .50 1.25
341 Trot Nixon .10 .30
342 Derek Lowe .10 .30
343 Roberto Hernandez .10 .30
344 Mike Sweeney .10 .30
345 Carlos Febles .10 .30
346 Jeff Suppan .10 .30
347 Roger Cedeno .10 .30
348 Bobby Higginson .10 .30
349 Deivi Cruz .10 .30
350 Mitch Meluskey .10 .30
351 Matt Lawton .10 .30
352 Mark Redman .10 .30
353 Jay Canizaro .10 .30
354 Corey Koskie .10 .30
355 Matt Kinney .10 .30
356 Frank Thomas .30 .75
357 Sandy Alomar Jr. .10 .30
358 David Wells .10 .30
359 Jim Parque .10 .30
360 Chris Singleton .10 .30
361 Tino Martinez .20 .50
362 Paul O'Neill .20 .50
363 Mike Mussina .20 .50
364 Bernie Williams .20 .50
365 Andy Pettite .20 .50
366 Mariano Rivera .30 .75
367 Brad Ausmus .10 .30
368 Craig Biggio .20 .50
369 Lance Berkman .10 .30
370 Shane Reynolds .10 .30
371 Chipper Jones .30 .75
372 Tom Glavine .20 .50
373 B.J. Surhoff .10 .30
374 John Smoltz .20 .50
375 Rico Brogna .10 .30
376 Geoff Jenkins .10 .30
377 Jose Hernandez .10 .30
378 Tyler Houston .10 .30
379 Henry Blanco .10 .30
380 Jeffrey Hammonds .10 .30
381 Jim Edmonds .10 .30
382 Fernando Vina .10 .30
383 Andy Benes .10 .30
384 Ray Lankford .10 .30
385 Dustin Hermanson .10 .30
386 Todd Hundley .10 .30
387 Sammy Sosa .30 .75
388 Tom Gordon .10 .30
389 Bill Mueller .10 .30
390 Ron Coomer .10 .30
391 Matt Stairs .10 .30
392 Mark Grace .20 .50
393 Matt Williams .10 .30
394 Todd Stottlemyre .10 .30
395 Tony Womack .10 .30
396 Erubiel Durazo .10 .30
397 Reggie Sanders .10 .30
398 Andy Ashby .10 .30
399 Eric Karros .10 .30
400 Kevin Brown .10 .30
401 Darren Dreifort .10 .30
402 Fernando Tatis .10 .30
403 Jose Vidro .10 .30
404 Peter Bergeron .10 .30
405 Geoff Blum .10 .30
406 J.T. Snow .10 .30
407 Livan Hernandez .10 .30
408 Robb Nen .10 .30
409 Bobby Estalella .10 .30
410 Rich Aurilia .10 .30
411 Eric Davis .10 .30
412 Charles Johnson .10 .30
413 Alex Gonzalez .10 .30
414 A.J. Burnett .10 .30
415 Antonio Alfonseca .10 .30
416 Derrek Lee .20 .50
417 Jay Payton .10 .30
418 Kevin Appier .10 .30
419 Steve Trachsel .10 .30
420 Rey Ordonez .10 .30
421 Darryl Hamilton .10 .30
422 Ben Davis .10 .30
423 Damian Jackson .10 .30
424 Mark Kotsay .10 .30
425 Trevor Hoffman .10 .30
426 Travis Lee .10 .30
427 Omar Daal .10 .30
428 Paul Byrd .10 .30
429 Reggie Taylor .10 .30
430 Brian Giles .10 .30
431 Derek Bell .10 .30
432 Francisco Cordova .10 .30
433 Pat Meares .10 .30
434 Scott Williamson .10 .30
435 Jason LaRue .10 .30
436 Michael Tucker .10 .30
437 Wilton Guerrero .10 .30
438 Mike Hampton .10 .30
439 Ron Gant .10 .30
440 Jeff Cirillo .10 .30
441 Denny Neagle .10 .30
442 Larry Walker .10 .30
443 Juan Pierre .10 .30
444 Todd Walker .10 .30
445 Jason Giambi SH CL .10 .30
446 Jeff Kent SH CL .10 .30
447 Mariano Rivera SH CL .20 .50
448 Edgar Martinez SH CL .10 .30
449 Troy Glaus SH CL .10 .30
450 Alex Rodriguez SH CL .30 .75

2001 Upper Deck Exclusives Gold

Randomly inserted into series one packs, this 270-card set is a complete parallel of the 2001 Upper Deck series one base set. Please note that these cards were produced with gold lettering on the front and are individually serial numbered to 25. The words "Gold UD Exclusives" also run down the left side of each card front.

*STARS: 30X TO 80X BASIC CARDS
*SR STARS: 15X TO 40X BASIC SR
*SR ROOKIES: 15X TO 40X BASIC SR
11 Johan Santana SR 20.00 50.00

2001 Upper Deck Exclusives Silver

Randomly inserted into series one packs, this 270-card set is a complete parallel of the 2001 Upper Deck series one base set. Please note that these cards were produced with silver lettering on the front and are individually serial numbered to 100. The words "UD Exclusives" also run down the left side of each card front.

STARS: 12.5X TO 30X BASIC CARDS
*SR YNG.STARS: 6X TO 15X BASIC SR
*SR RC's: 6X TO 15X BASIC SR
11 Johan Santana SR 8.00 20.00

2001 Upper Deck 1971 All-Star Game Salute

Inserted in second series packs at a rate of one in 288, these 12 memorabilia cards feature players who participated in the 1971 All-Star Game which was highlighted by Reggie Jackson's home run off the light tower at Tiger Stadium.

ASBR B. Robinson Bat 8.00 20.00
ASFR Frank Robinson Jsy 6.00 15.00
ASHA Hank Aaron Bat 15.00 40.00
ASHA Hank Aaron Jsy 20.00 50.00
ASJB Johnny Bench Bat 8.00 20.00
ASJB Johnny Bench Jsy 8.00 20.00
ASLA Luis Aparicio Jsy 6.00 15.00
ASLB Lou Brock Bat 8.00 20.00
ASRC R. Clemente Jsy 50.00 100.00
ASRJ Reggie Jackson Jsy 8.00 20.00
ASTM T. Munson Jsy 15.00 40.00
ASTS Tom Seaver Jsy 8.00 20.00

2001 Upper Deck All-Star Heroes Memorabilia

Randomly inserted in second series packs, these 14 cards feature a mix of past and present players who have starred in All-Star Games. Since each player was issued to a different amount, we have notated that information in our checklist.

ASHAR Alex Rodriguez Bat/1998 6.00 15.00
ASHBR Babe Ruth Bat/1933 100.00 200.00
ASHCR Cal Ripken Bat/1991 15.00 40.00
ASHDJ Derek Jeter Base/2000 10.00 25.00
ASHJD Joe DiMaggio Jsy/36
ASHKG Ken Griffey Jr. Bat/1992 6.00 15.00
ASHMM Mickey Mantle Jsy/54 175.00 300.00
ASHMP Mike Piazza Base/1996 6.00 15.00
ASHRC Roger Clemens Jsy/1986 6.00 15.00
ASHRJ Randy Johnson Jsy/1993 6.00 15.00
ASHSS Sammy Sosa Jsy/2000 6.00 15.00
ASHTG Tony Gwynn Jsy/1994 6.00 15.00
ASHTP Tony Perez Bat 1967 4.00 10.00
ASHROC R.Clemente Bat/1961 40.00 80.00

2001 Upper Deck Big League Beat

Randomly inserted into packs at one in three, this 20-card insert features some of the most prolific players in the Major Leagues. Card backs carry a "BB" prefix.

COMPLETE SET (20) 8.00 20.00
BB1 Barry Bonds .75 2.00
BB2 Nomar Garciaparra .50 1.25
BB3 Mark McGwire .75 2.00
BB4 Roger Clemens .60 1.50
BB5 Chipper Jones .30 .75
BB6 Jeff Bagwell .20 .50
BB7 Sammy Sosa .30 .75
BB8 Cal Ripken 1.00 2.50
BB9 Randy Johnson .30 .75
BB10 Carlos Delgado .20 .50
BB11 Manny Ramirez .20 .50
BB12 Derek Jeter .75 2.00
BB13 Tony Gwynn .40 1.00
BB14 Pedro Martinez .20 .50
BB15 Jose Canseco .20 .50
BB16 Frank Thomas .30 .75
BB17 Alex Rodriguez .50 1.25
BB18 Bernie Williams .20 .50
BB19 Greg Maddux .50 1.25
BB20 Rafael Palmeiro .20 .50

2001 Upper Deck Big League Challenge Game Jerseys

Issued at a rate of one in 288 second series packs, these 11 cards feature jersey pieces from participants in the 2001 Big League Challenge home run hitting contest.

BLCBB Barry Bonds 15.00 40.00
BLCFT Frank Thomas 8.00 20.00
BLCGS Gary Sheffield 6.00 15.00
BLCJC Jose Canseco 8.00 20.00
BLCJE Jim Edmonds 6.00 15.00
BLCMP Mike Piazza 10.00 25.00
BLCRH Richard Hidalgo 6.00 15.00
BLCRP Rafael Palmeiro 8.00 20.00
BLCSF Steve Finley 6.00 15.00
BLCTG Troy Glaus 6.00 15.00
BLCTH Todd Helton 8.00 20.00

2001 Upper Deck e-Card

Inserted as a two-pack box-topper, this six-card insert features cards that can be viewed over the Upper Deck website. Cards feature a serial number that is to be typed in a the Upper Deck website to reveal that card. Card backs carry an "E" prefix.

COMPLETE SET (12) 7.50 15.00
COMPLETE SERIES 1 (6) 3.00 6.00
COMPLETE SERIES 2 (6) 5.00 10.00
E1 Andruw Jones .40 1.00
E2 Alex Rodriguez .60 1.50
E3 Frank Thomas .40 1.00
E4 Todd Helton .40 1.00
E5 Troy Glaus .40 1.00
E6 Barry Bonds 1.00 2.50
E7 Alex Rodriguez .60 1.50
E8 Ken Griffey Jr. .60 1.50
E9 Sammy Sosa .40 1.00
E10 Gary Sheffield .40 1.00
E11 Barry Bonds 1.00 2.50
E12 Andruw Jones .40 1.00

2001 Upper Deck eVolve Autograph

Lucky participants in Upper Deck's E-Card program received special upgraded E-Cards available by checking the UD website (www.upperdeck.com) and entering their basic E-Card serial code (printed on the front of each basic E-Card). When viewed on the Upper Deck website, if an autographed card of the depicted player appeared, the bearer of the base card could then exchange their basic E-Card and receive the signed upgrade via mail. Only 200 serial numbered E-Card Autograph sets were produced. Signed E-Cards all have an ES prefix on the card numbers.

ESAJ Andruw Jones S1 20.00 50.00
ESAJ Andruw Jones S2 20.00 50.00
ESAR Alex Rodriguez S1 60.00 120.00
ESAR Alex Rodriguez S2 60.00 120.00
ESBB Barry Bonds S1 125.00 200.00
ESBB Barry Bonds S2 125.00 200.00
ESFT Frank Thomas S1 30.00 60.00
ESGS Gary Sheffield S2 20.00 50.00
ESKG Ken Griffey Jr. S2 50.00 100.00
ESSS Sammy Sosa S2 50.00 100.00
ESTG Troy Glaus S1 20.00 50.00
ESTH Todd Helton S1 20.00 50.00

2001 Upper Deck eVolve Game Jersey

Lucky participants in Upper Deck's E-Card program received special upgraded E-Cards available by checking the UD website (www.upperdeck.com) and entering their basic E-Card serial code (printed on the front of each basic E-Card). When viewed on the Upper Deck website, if a jersey card of the depicted player appeared, the bearer of the base card could then exchange their basic E-Card and receive the Game Jersey upgrade via mail. The cards closely parallel basic 2000 Game Jerseys that were distributed in first and second series packs except for the gold foil "e-volve" logo on front. Only 300 serial numbered E-Card Jersey sets were produced with each card being serial -numbered by hand in blue ink sharpie at the bottom right front corner. Unsigned E-Card Game Jerseys all have an EJ prefix on the card numbers.

EJAJ Andruw Jones S1 6.00 15.00
EJAJ Andruw Jones S2 6.00 15.00
EJAR Alex Rodriguez S1 8.00 20.00
EJAR Alex Rodriguez S2 8.00 20.00
EJBB Barry Bonds S1 12.50 30.00
EJBB Barry Bonds S2 12.50 30.00
EJFT Frank Thomas S1 6.00 15.00
EJGS Gary Sheffield S2 4.00 10.00
EJKG Ken Griffey Jr. S2 10.00 25.00
EJSS Sammy Sosa S2 6.00 15.00
EJTG Troy Glaus S1 4.00 10.00
EJTH Todd Helton S1 6.00 15.00

2001 Upper Deck eVolve Game Jersey Autograph

Lucky participants in Upper Deck's E-Card program received special upgraded E-Cards available by checking the UD website (www.upperdeck.com) and entering their basic E-Card serial code (printed on the front of each basic E-Card). When viewed on the Upper Deck website, if an autographed card of the depicted player appeared, the bearer of the base card could then exchange their basic E-Card and receive the signed jersey upgrade via mail. A mere 50 serial numbered sets were produced. Signed jersey E-Cards all have an ESJ prefix on the card numbers.

ESJAJ Andruw Jones S1 30.00 60.00
ESJAJ Andruw Jones S2 30.00 60.00
ESJAR Alex Rodriguez S1 90.00 150.00
ESJAR Alex Rodriguez S2 90.00 150.00
ESJBB Barry Bonds S1 125.00 250.00
ESJBB Barry Bonds S2 125.00 250.00
ESJFT Frank Thomas S1 40.00 80.00
ESJGS Gary Sheffield S2 30.00 60.00
ESJKG Ken Griffey Jr. S2 60.00 120.00
ESJSS Sammy Sosa S2 50.00 100.00
ESJTG Troy Glaus S1 30.00 60.00
ESJTH Todd Helton S1 30.00 60.00

2001 Upper Deck Franchise

Inserted at a rate of one in 36 second series packs, these 10 cards feature players who are considered the money players for their franchise.

COMPLETE SET (10) 25.00 60.00
F1 Frank Thomas 1.50 4.00
F2 Mark McGwire 4.00 10.00
F3 Ken Griffey Jr. 2.50 6.00
F4 Manny Ramirez Sox 1.50 4.00
F5 Alex Rodriguez 2.50 6.00
F6 Greg Maddux 2.50 6.00
F7 Sammy Sosa 1.50 4.00
F8 Derek Jeter 4.00 10.00
F9 Mike Piazza 2.50 6.00
F10 Vladimir Guerrero 1.50 4.00

2001 Upper Deck Game Ball 1

Randomly inserted into packs, this 18-card insert features game-used baseballs from the depicted players. Card backs carry a "B" prefix. Please note that only 100 serial numbered sets were produced.

BAJ Andruw Jones 15.00 40.00
BAR A.Rodriguez Mariners 30.00 60.00
BBB Barry Bonds 40.00 80.00
BDJ Derek Jeter 40.00 80.00
BIR Ivan Rodriguez 15.00 40.00
BJG Jason Giambi 10.00 25.00
BJG Jeff Bagwell 15.00 40.00
BKG Ken Griffey Jr. 20.00 50.00
BMM Mark McGwire 75.00 150.00
BMP Mike Piazza 30.00 60.00
BRA Rick Ankiel 10.00 25.00
BRJ Randy Johnson 15.00 40.00
BSG Shawn Green 10.00 25.00
BSS Sammy Sosa 15.00 40.00
BTH Todd Helton 15.00 40.00
BTOG Tony Gwynn 15.00 40.00
BTRG Troy Glaus 10.00 25.00
BVG Vladimir Guerrero 15.00 40.00

2001 Upper Deck Game Ball 2

Inserted into second series packs at a rate of one in 288 , this 18-card insert features game-used baseballs from the depicted players. Card backs carry a "B" prefix. The Nomar Garciaparra card was short printed and has been notated as such in our checklist.

BAJ Andruw Jones 6.00 15.00
BAR A.Rodriguez Rangers 10.00 25.00
BBB Barry Bonds 15.00 40.00
BBW Bernie Williams 6.00 15.00
BCJ Chipper Jones 6.00 15.00
BCR Cal Ripken 15.00 40.00
BDJ Derek Jeter 15.00 40.00
BGS Gary Sheffield 4.00 10.00
BJB Jeff Bagwell 6.00 15.00
BJK Jeff Kent 4.00 10.00
BKG Ken Griffey Jr. 10.00 25.00
BMM Mark McGwire 20.00 50.00
BMP Mike Piazza 10.00 25.00
BMR Mariano Rivera 6.00 15.00
BNG N.Garciaparra SP 15.00 40.00
BRC Roger Clemens 10.00 25.00
BSS Sammy Sosa 6.00 15.00
BVG Vladimir Guerrero 6.00 15.00

2001 Upper Deck Game Ball Gold Autograph

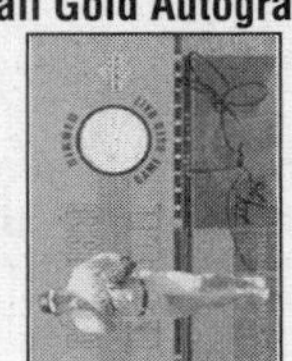

Randomly inserted into packs, this nine-card insert set features autographs and game-used baseball swatches from the depicted players below. Card backs carry a "SB" prefix. Please note that only 25 serial numbered sets were produced. The following cards packed out as exchange cards with a redmption deadline of August 7th, 2001: Alex Rodriguez, Jeff Bagwell, Ken Griffey Jr. and Rick Ankiel.

SBAR Alex Rodriguez
SBBB Barry Bonds
SBJB Jeff Bagwell
SBJG Jason Giambi
SBKG Ken Griffey Jr.
SBRA Rick Ankiel
SBRJ Randy Johnson
SBSG Shawn Green
SBTH Todd Helton

2001 Upper Deck Game Jersey

These cards feature swatches of jerseys of various major league stars. These cards were available in either series one hobby or retail packs at a rate of one every 288 packs. Card backs carry a "C" prefix.

CAJ A.Jones HR1 10.00 25.00
CAR Alex Rodriguez 10.00 25.00
CBW B.Williams HR1 10.00 25.00
CCR Cal Ripken 20.00 50.00
CDJ Derek Jeter 20.00 50.00
CFT Fernando Tatis 6.00 15.00
CIR Ivan Rodriguez 10.00 25.00
CKG Ken Griffey Jr. 15.00 40.00
CMR M.Ramirez HR1 10.00 25.00
CMW Matt Williams 6.00 15.00
CNRA Nolan Ryan Astros HR1 20.00 50.00
CNRR Nolan Ryan Rangers HR1 20.00 50.00
CPO Paul O'Neill 10.00 25.00
CRV Robin Ventura 6.00 15.00
CSK Sandy Koufax 75.00 150.00
CTG Tony Gwynn 10.00 25.00
CTH Todd Helton 10.00 25.00
CTIH Tim Hudson 6.00 15.00

2001 Upper Deck Game Jersey Autograph 1

These cards feature both autographs and swatches of jerseys from various major league stars. The cards which have an "H1" after the player names are available in series one hobby packs at a rate of one in every 288 packs. Card backs carry a "H" prefix. The following cards were distributed in packs as exchange cards: Alex Rodriguez, Jeff Bagwell, Ken Griffey Jr., Mike Hampton and Rick Ankiel. The deadline to exchange these cards was August 7th, 2001.

HAR A.Rodriguez H1 75.00 150.00
HBB Barry Bonds 125.00 200.00
HFT Frank Thomas 40.00 80.00
HGM Greg Maddux 75.00 150.00
HJB J.Bagwell H1 40.00 80.00
HJC Jose Canseco 20.00 50.00
HJD J.D. Drew 15.00 40.00
HJG Jason Giambi 15.00 40.00
HJL Javy Lopez 15.00 40.00
HKG K.Griffey Jr. H1 60.00 120.00
HMH M.Hampton H1 15.00 40.00
HNRA Nolan Ryan Angels 75.00 150.00
HNRM Nolan Ryan Mets 100.00 200.00
HRA R.Ankiel H1 12.50 30.00
HRJ Randy Johnson 50.00 100.00
HRP Rafael Palmeiro 40.00 80.00
HSC Sean Casey 15.00 40.00
HSG Shawn Green 20.00 50.00

2001 Upper Deck Game Jersey Autograph 2

These cards feature both autographs and swatches of jerseys from various major league stars. The cards which have an "H2" after the player names are available in series one hobby packs at a rate of one in every 288 packs. Card backs carry a "H" prefix. Please note a few of the players were issued in lesser quantiles and we have notated those as SP's. The following players packed out as exchange cards: Alex Rodriguez and Ken Griffey Jr. The deadline for exchange was June 26th, 2006.

AJ Andruw Jones 20.00 50.00
AR Alex Rodriguez 75.00 150.00
BB Barry Bonds 125.00 200.00
CJ Chipper Jones 40.00 80.00
CR Cal Ripken SP 75.00 150.00
GS Gary Sheffield 20.00 50.00
IR Ivan Rodriguez SP 50.00 100.00
JB Johnny Bench 40.00 80.00
JC Jose Canseco 20.00 50.00
KG Ken Griffey Jr. 60.00 120.00
NR Nolan Ryan 75.00 150.00
RC Roger Clemens 75.00 150.00
SS Sammy Sosa SP 50.00 100.00
TG Troy Glaus 20.00 50.00

2001 Upper Deck Game Jersey Autograph Numbered

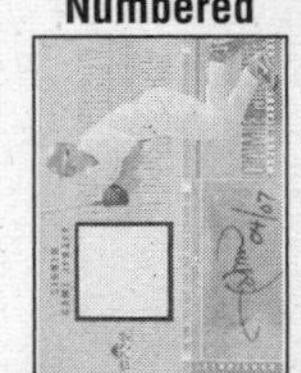

These cards feature both autographs and swatches of jerseys from various major league stars. The cards which have an "H" after the player names were only available in series one hobby packs, while the cards with a "C" can be found in either series one hobby or retail packs. Hobby cards feature gold backgrounds and say "Signed Game Jersey" on front. Hobby/Retail cards feature white backgrounds and simply say "Game Jersey" on front. These cards are individually serial numbered to the depicted player's jersey number. The following players packed out as exchange cards: Alex Rodriguez, Ken Griffey Jr., Jeff Bagwell, Mike Hampton and Rick Ankiel. The exchange deadline was August 7th, 2001.

CAJ Andruw Jones/25
CAR Alex Rodriguez/3
CFT Fernando Tatis/23
CIR Ivan Rodriguez/7
CJL Javy Lopez/8
CKG Ken Griffey Jr./30 HR1 125.00 250.00
CMW Matt Williams/9
CNRA Nolan Ryan Astros/34 HR1 175.00 300.00
CNRR Nolan Ryan Rangers 34 HR1 175.00 300.00
CPO Paul O'Neill/21
CRV Robin Ventura/4
CSK Sandy Koufax 32 HR1 600.00 1000.00
CTG Tony Gwynn/19
CTH Todd Helton/17
CTIH Tim Hudson/15
HAR Alex Rodriguez/3
HBB Barry Bonds/25
HFT Frank Thomas/35 75.00 150.00
HGM Greg Maddux/31 175.00 300.00
HJB Jeff Bagwell/5
HJC Jose Canseco/33 50.00 100.00
HJD J.D. Drew/7
HJG Jason Giambi/16
HKG Ken Griffey Jr. 30 H1 125.00 250.00
HMH Mike Hampton/32 30.00 60.00
HNRA Nolan Ryan 30/Angels H1 200.00 350.00
HNRM Nolan Ryan 30/Mets H1 250.00 400.00
HRA Rick Ankiel 66 H1 30.00 60.00
HRJ Randy Johnson 51 H1 125.00 200.00
HRP Rafael Palmeiro 25 H1
HSC Sean Casey/21
HSG Shawn Green/15

2001 Upper Deck Game Jersey Combo

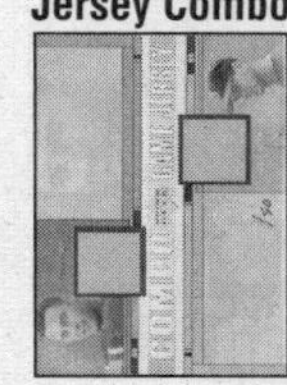

Randomly inserted into series one packs, these 13 cards feature dual player game-worn uniform patches. Card backs carry both players initials as numbering. Please note that there were only 50 serial numbered sets produced.

AJKG Andruw Jones Ken Griffey Jr. 40.00 80.00
BBJC Barry Bonds Jose Canseco 50.00 100.00
BBKG Barry Bonds Ken Griffey Jr. 50.00 100.00
DJAR Derek Jeter Alex Rodriguez 50.00 100.00
FTJB Frank Thomas Jeff Bagwell 20.00 50.00
IRRP Ivan Rodriguez Rafael Palmeiro 20.00 50.00
JDRA J.D. Drew Rick Ankiel 15.00 40.00
MMKG Mickey Mantle Ken Griffey Jr.
NRAR Nolan Rya Astros-Rangers 60.00 120.00
NRMA Nolan Ryan Mets-Angels 60.00 120.00
RATH Rick Ankiel Tim Hudson 15.00 40.00
RJGM Randy Johnson Greg Maddux 30.00 60.00
TGCR Tony Gwynn Cal Ripken 50.00 100.00
VGMR Vladimir Guerrero Manny Ramirez 20.00 50.00

2001 Upper Deck Game Jersey Combo Autograph

Randomly inserted into series one hobby packs, these seven cards feature autographed dual player game-worn uniform patches. Card backs carry both players initials as numbering with a "S" prefix. Please note that there were only 10 serial numbered sets produced. Cards SAJ-KG and SJD-RA both packed out as exchange cards with a redemption deadline of 8/07/01. Due to market scarcity, no pricing is provided.

SAJKG Andruw Jones Ken Griffey Jr. EXCH
SBBJC Barry Bonds Jose Canseco
SBBKG Barry Bonds Ken Griffey Jr.
SDJAR Derek Jeter Alex Rodriguez
SJDRA J.D. Drew Rick Ankiel
SNRAR Nolan Ryan Astros-Rangers
SNRMA Nolan Ryan Mets-Angels

2001 Upper Deck Game Jersey Patch

Randomly inserted into series one packs at one in 7500 and series 2 packs at 1:5000, these cards feature game-worn uniform patches. Card backs carry a "P" prefix.

PAR Alex Rodriguez S1	60.00	120.00
PAR Alex Rodriguez S2	60.00	120.00
PBB Barry Bonds S1	75.00	150.00
PBB Barry Bonds S2	75.00	150.00
PCJ Chipper Jones S2	50.00	100.00
PCR Cal Ripken S1	75.00	150.00
PCR Cal Ripken S2	75.00	150.00
PDJ Derek Jeter S1	75.00	150.00
PFT Frank Thomas S1	50.00	100.00
PIR Ivan Rodriguez S1	40.00	80.00
PIR Ivan Rodriguez S2	40.00	80.00
PJB Johnny Bench S2	50.00	100.00
PJB Jeff Bagwell S1	40.00	80.00
PJC Jose Canseco S1	40.00	80.00
PJG Jason Giambi S1	30.00	60.00
PKG Ken Griffey Jr. S1	60.00	120.00
PKG Ken Griffey Jr. S2	60.00	120.00
PNRA Nolan Ryan Astros	60.00	120.00
PNRR N.Ryan Rangers S1	60.00	120.00
PNRR N.Ryan Rangers S2	60.00	120.00
PRA Rick Ankiel S1	15.00	40.00
PRP Rafael Palmeiro S1	40.00	80.00
PSS Sammy Sosa S2	50.00	100.00
PTG Tony Gwynn S1	50.00	100.00

2001 Upper Deck Game Jersey Patch Autograph Numbered

Randomly inserted into series one hobby packs, these cards feature both autographs and game-worn uniform patches. Card backs carry a "SP" prefix. Please note that these cards are hand-numbered to the depicted players jersey number. All of these cards packed out as exchange cards with a redemption deadline of 8/07/01.

SPAR Alex Rodriguez/3		
SPKG K.Griffey Jr./30	250.00	400.00
SPRA Rick Ankiel/66	40.00	80.00

2001 Upper Deck Home Run Derby Heroes

Inserted in second series packs at a rate of one in 36, these 10 cards features a look back at some of the most explosive performances from past Home Run Derby competitions.

COMPLETE SET (10)	20.00	50.00
HD1 Mark McGwire 99	4.00	10.00
HD2 Sammy Sosa 00	1.50	4.00
HD3 Frank Thomas 96	1.50	4.00
HD4 Cal Ripken 91	5.00	12.00
HD5 Tino Martinez 97	1.00	2.50
HD6 Ken Griffey Jr. 99	2.50	6.00
HD7 Barry Bonds 96	4.00	10.00
HD8 Albert Belle 95	.75	2.00
HD9 Mark McGwire 92	4.00	10.00
HD10 Juan Gonzalez 93	.75	2.00

2001 Upper Deck Home Run Explosion

Randomly inserted into series one packs at one in 12, this 15-card insert features players that are among the league leaders in homeruns every year. Card backs carry a "HR" prefix.

COMPLETE SET (15)	15.00	40.00
HR1 Mark McGwire	2.00	5.00
HR2 Chipper Jones	.75	2.00
HR3 Jeff Bagwell	.50	1.25
HR4 Carlos Delgado	.40	1.00
HR5 Barry Bonds	2.00	5.00
HR6 Troy Glaus	.40	1.00
HR7 Sammy Sosa	.75	2.00
HR8 Alex Rodriguez	1.25	3.00
HR9 Mike Piazza	1.25	3.00
HR10 Vladimir Guerrero	.75	2.00
HR11 Ken Griffey Jr.	1.25	3.00
HR12 Frank Thomas	.75	2.00
HR13 Ivan Rodriguez	.50	1.25
HR14 Jason Giambi	.40	1.00
HR15 Carl Everett	.40	1.00

2001 Upper Deck Midseason Superstar Summit

Inserted in series two packs at a rate of one in 24, these 15 cards feature some of the most dominant players of the 2000 season.

COMPLETE SET (15)	25.00	60.00
MS1 Derek Jeter	4.00	10.00
MS2 Sammy Sosa	1.50	4.00
MS3 Jeff Bagwell	1.00	2.50
MS4 Tony Gwynn	2.00	5.00
MS5 Alex Rodriguez	2.50	6.00
MS6 Greg Maddux	2.50	6.00
MS7 Jason Giambi	.75	2.00
MS8 Mark McGwire	4.00	10.00
MS9 Barry Bonds	4.00	10.00
MS10 Ken Griffey Jr.	2.50	6.00
MS11 Carlos Delgado	.75	2.00
MS12 Troy Glaus	.75	2.00
MS13 Todd Helton	1.00	2.50
MS14 Manny Ramirez Sox	1.00	2.50
MS15 Jeff Kent	.75	2.00

2001 Upper Deck Midsummer Classic Moments

Inserted in series two packs at a rate of one in 12, these 20 cards feature some of the most memorable moments from All Star Game history.

COMPLETE SET (20)	15.00	40.00
CM1 Joe DiMaggio 36	1.25	3.00
CM2 Joe DiMaggio 51	1.25	3.00
CM3 Mickey Mantle 52	2.50	6.00
CM4 Mickey Mantle 68	2.50	6.00
CM5 Roger Clemens 86	1.50	4.00
CM6 Mark McGwire 87	2.00	5.00
CM7 Cal Ripken 91	2.50	6.00
CM8 Ken Griffey Jr. 92	1.25	3.00
CM9 Randy Johnson 93	.75	2.00
CM10 Tony Gwynn 94	1.00	2.50
CM11 Fred McGriff 94	.50	1.25
CM12 Hideo Nomo 95	.75	2.00
CM13 Jeff Conine 95	.40	1.00
CM14 Mike Piazza 96	1.25	3.00
CM15 Sandy Alomar Jr.	.40	1.00
CM16 Alex Rodriguez 98	1.00	2.50
CM17 Roberto Alomar 98	.50	1.25
CM18 Pedro Martinez 99	.50	1.25
CM19 Andres Galarraga	.40	1.00
CM20 Derek Jeter 00	1.50	4.00

2001 Upper Deck People's Choice

Inserted one per 24 series two packs, these 15 cards feature the players who fans want to see the most.

COMPLETE SET (15)	30.00	80.00
PC1 Alex Rodriguez	2.50	6.00
PC2 Ken Griffey Jr.	2.50	6.00
PC3 Mark McGwire	4.00	10.00
PC4 Todd Helton	1.00	2.50
PC5 Manny Ramirez	1.00	2.50
PC6 Mike Piazza	2.50	6.00
PC7 Vladimir Guerrero	1.50	4.00
PC8 Randy Johnson	1.50	4.00
PC9 Cal Ripken	5.00	12.00
PC10 Andruw Jones	1.00	2.50
PC11 Sammy Sosa	1.50	4.00
PC12 Derek Jeter	4.00	10.00
PC13 Pedro Martinez	1.00	2.50
PC14 Frank Thomas	1.50	4.00
PC15 Nomar Garciaparra	2.50	6.00

2001 Upper Deck Rookie Roundup

Randomly inserted into series one packs at one in six, this 10-card insert features some of the younger players in Major League baseball. Card backs carry a "RR" prefix.

COMPLETE SET (10)	2.00	5.00
RR1 Rick Ankiel	.20	.50
RR2 Adam Kennedy	.20	.50
RR3 Mike Lamb	.20	.50
RR4 Adam Eaton	.20	.50
RR5 Rafael Furcal	.30	.75
RR6 Pat Burrell	.30	.75
RR7 Adam Piatt	.20	.50
RR8 Eric Munson	.20	.50
RR9 Brad Penny	.20	.50
RR10 Mark Mulder	.30	.75

2001 Upper Deck Subway Series Game Jerseys

While the set name seemed to indicate that these cards were from jerseys worn during the 2000 World series, they were actually swatches from regular-season game jerseys.

SSAL Al Leiter	4.00	10.00
SSAP Andy Pettitte	10.00	25.00
SSBW Bernie Williams	10.00	25.00
SSEA Edgardo Alfonzo	3.00	8.00
SSJF John Franco	4.00	10.00
SSJP Jay Payton	3.00	8.00
SSOH Orlando Hernandez	8.00	20.00
SSPO Paul O'Neill	10.00	25.00
SSRC Roger Clemens	15.00	40.00
SSTP Timo Perez	3.00	8.00

2001 Upper Deck Superstar Summit

Randomly inserted into packs at one in 12, this 15-card insert features the Major League's top superstar caliber players. Card backs carry a "SS" prefix.

COMPLETE SET (15)	20.00	50.00
SS1 Derek Jeter	2.00	5.00
SS2 Randy Johnson	.75	2.00
SS3 Barry Bonds	2.00	5.00
SS4 Frank Thomas	.75	2.00
SS5 Cal Ripken	2.50	6.00
SS6 Pedro Martinez	.75	2.00
SS7 Ivan Rodriguez	.75	2.00
SS8 Mike Piazza	1.25	3.00
SS9 Mark McGwire	2.00	5.00
SS10 Manny Ramirez Sox	.75	2.00
SS11 Ken Griffey Jr.	1.25	3.00
SS12 Sammy Sosa	.75	2.00
SS13 Alex Rodriguez	1.25	3.00
SS14 Chipper Jones	.75	2.00
SS15 Nomar Garciaparra	1.25	3.00

2001 Upper Deck UD's Most Wanted

Randomly inserted into packs at one in 14, this 15-card insert features players that are in high demand on the collectibles market. Card backs carry a "MW" prefix.

COMPLETE SET (15)	25.00	60.00
MW1 Mark McGwire	2.50	6.00
MW2 Cal Ripken	3.00	8.00
MW3 Ivan Rodriguez	1.00	2.50
MW4 Pedro Martinez	1.00	2.50
MW5 Sammy Sosa	1.00	2.50
MW6 Tony Gwynn	1.25	3.00
MW7 Vladimir Guerrero	1.00	2.50
MW8 Derek Jeter	2.50	6.00
MW9 Mike Piazza	1.50	4.00
MW10 Chipper Jones	1.00	2.50
MW11 Alex Rodriguez	1.50	4.00
MW12 Barry Bonds	2.50	6.00
MW13 Jeff Bagwell	1.00	2.50
MW14 Frank Thomas	1.00	2.50
MW15 Nomar Garciaparra	1.50	4.00

2001 Upper Deck Pinstripe Exclusives DiMaggio

This 56-card set features a wide selection of cards focusing on Yankees legend Joe DiMaggio. The cards were distributed in special three-card foil wrapped packs, exclusively seeded into 2001 SP Game Bat Milestone, SP Game-Used, SPx, Upper Deck Decade 1970's, Upper Deck Gold Glove, Upper Deck Legends, Upper Deck Ovation and Upper Deck Sweet Spot hobby boxes at a rate of one pack per sealed box.

COMPLETE SET (56)	30.00	60.00
COMMON (JD1-JD56)	.60	1.50

2001 Upper Deck Pinstripe Exclusives DiMaggio Memorabilia

Randomly seeded into special three-card Pinstripe Exclusives DiMaggio foil packs (of which were distributed exclusively in 2001 SP Game Bat Milestone, SP Game-Used, SPx, Upper Deck Decade 1970's, Upper Deck Gold Glove, Upper Deck Legends, Upper Deck Ovation and Upper Deck Sweet Spot Sweet Spot hobby boxes) were a selection of scarce game-used memorabilia and autograph cut cards featuring Joe DiMaggio. Each card is serial-numbered and features either a game-used bat chip, jersey swatch or autograph cut.

COMMON BAT (B1-B9)	50.00	100.00
COMMON JERSEY (J1-J9)	50.00	100.00
SUFFIX 1 CARDS DIST.IN SWEET SPOT		
SUFFIX 2 CARDS DIST.IN OVATION		
SUFFIX 3 CARDS DIST.IN SPX		
SUFFIX 4 CARDS DIST.IN SP GAME USED		
SUFFIX 5 CARDS DIST.IN LEGENDS		
SUFFIX 6 CARDS DIST. IN DECADE 1970		
SUFFIX 7 CARDS DIST.IN SP BAT MILE		
SUFFIX 8 CARDS DIST.IN UD GOLD GLOVE		
BAT 1-9 PRINT RUN 100 SERIAL #'d SETS		
BAT-CUT 1-7 PRINT RUN 5 SERIAL #'d SETS		
COMBO 1-6 PRINT RUN 50 SERIAL #'D SETS		
CUT 1-8 PRINT RUN 5 SERIAL #'d SETS		
JERSEY 1-8 PRINT RUN 100 SERIAL #'d SETS		
CJ1 Joe DiMaggio Jsy Lou Gehrig Pants/50	300.00	600.00
CJ2 Joe DiMaggio Jsy Mickey Mantle Jsy/50	175.00	300.00
CJ3 Joe DiMaggio Jsy Ken Griffey Jr. Jsy/50	100.00	200.00
CJ4 Joe DiMaggio Jsy Dom DiMaggio Jsy/50	150.00	250.00
CJ5 Joe DiMaggio Jsy Mickey Mantle Jsy/50	175.00	300.00
CJ6 Joe DiMaggio Jsy Mickey Mantle Jsy/50	175.00	300.00

2001 Upper Deck Pinstripe Exclusives Mantle

This 56-card set features a wide selection of cards focusing on Yankees legend Mickey Mantle. The cards were distributed in special three-card foil wrapped packs, seeded into 2001 Upper Deck Series 2, Upper Deck Hall of Famers, Upper Deck MVP and Upper Deck Vintage hobby boxes at a rate of one pack per 24 ct. box.

COMPLETE SET (56)	50.00	100.00
COMMON (MM1-MM56)	1.00	2.50

2001 Upper Deck Pinstripe Exclusives Mantle Memorabilia

Randomly seeded into special three-card Pinstripe Exclusives Mantle foil packs (of which were distributed in hobby boxes of 2001 SP Authentic, 2001 SP Game Bat Milestone, 2001 Upper Deck series 2, 2001 Upper Deck Hall of Famers, 2001 Upper Deck Legends of New York, 2001 Upper Deck MVP and 2001 Upper Deck Vintage) were a selection of scarce game-used memorabilia and autograph cut cards featuring Mickey Mantle. Each card is serial-numbered and features either a game-used bat chip, jersey swatch or autograph cut.

COMMON BAT (B1-B4)	75.00	150.00
COMMON JERSEY (J1-J7)	100.00	200.00
COMMON BAT CUT (BC1-BC4)		
COMMON CUT (C1-C4)		
SUFFIX 1 CARDS DIST.IN UD VINTAGE		
SUFFIX 2 CARDS DIST.IN UD HOF'ers		
SUFFIX 3 CARDS DIST.IN UD MVP		
SUFFIX 4 CARDS DIST.IN UD SER.2		
SUFFIX 5 CARDS DIST. IN SP AUTH		
SUFFIX 6 CARDS DIST. IN SP GAME BAT MILE		
SUFFIX 7 CARDS DIST. IN UD LEG OF NY		
BAT 1-9 PRINT RUN 100 SERIAL #'d SETS		
BAT-CUT 1-4 PRINT RUN 7 SERIAL #'d SETS		
COMBO 1-6 PRINT RUN 50 SERIAL #'d SETS		
CUT 1-4 PRINT RUN 7 SERIAL #'d SETS		
JERSEY 1-7 PRINT RUN 100 SERIAL #'d SETS		
CJ1 Mickey Mantle Roger Maris Jsy/50	175.00	300.00
CJ2 Mickey Mantle Joe DiMag Jsy/50	150.00	250.00
CJ3 Mickey Mantle Ken Griffey Jsy/50	75.00	150.00
CJ4 Mickey Mantle Roger Maris Jsy/50	175.00	300.00
CJ5 Mickey Mantle Joe DiMaggio Jsy/50	150.00	250.00
CJ6 Mickey Mantle Joe DiMaggio Jsy/50	150.00	250.00
CJ7 Mickey Mantle Joe DiMaggio Jsy 50	150.00	250.00

2002 Upper Deck

The 500 card first series set was issued in November, 2001. The 245-card second series set was issued in May, 2002. The cards were issued in eight card packs with 24 packs to a box. Subsets include Star Rookies (cards numbered 1-50, 501-545), World Stage (cards numbered 461-480), Griffey Gallery (481-490) and Checklists (491-500, 736-745) and Year of the Record (726-735). Star Rookies were inserted at a rate of one per pack into second series packs, making them 1.75X times tougher to pull than veteran second series cards.

COMPLETE SET (745)	85.00	160.00
COMPLETE SERIES 1 (500)	60.00	110.00
COMPLETE SERIES 2 (245)	25.00	50.00
COMMON (51-500/546-745)	.10	.30
COMMON SR (1-50/501-545)	.40	1.00
1 Mark Prior SR	.75	2.00
2 Mark Teixeira SR	2.00	5.00
3 Brian Roberts SR	.75	2.00
4 Jason Romano SR	.40	1.00
5 Dennis Stark SR	.40	1.00
6 Oscar Salazar SR	.40	1.00
7 John Patterson SR	.40	1.00
8 Shane Loux SR	.40	1.00
9 Marcus Giles SR	.40	1.00
10 Juan Cruz SR	.40	1.00
11 Jorge Julio SR	.40	1.00
12 Adam Dunn SR	.40	1.00
13 Delvin James SR	.40	1.00
14 Jeremy Affeldt SR	.40	1.00
15 Tim Raines Jr. SR	.40	1.00
16 Luke Hudson SR	.40	1.00
17 Todd Sears SR	.40	1.00
18 George Perez SR	.40	1.00
19 Wilmy Caceres SR	.40	1.00
20 Abraham Nunez SR	.40	1.00
21 Mike Amrhein SR RC	.40	1.00
22 Carlos Hernandez SR	.40	1.00
23 Scott Hodges SR	.40	1.00
24 Brandon Knight SR	.40	1.00
25 Geoff Goetz SR	.40	1.00
26 Carlos Garcia SR	.40	1.00
27 Luis Pineda SR	.40	1.00
28 Chris Gissell SR	.40	1.00
29 Jae Weong Seo SR	.40	1.00
30 Paul Phillips SR	.40	1.00
31 Cory Aldridge SR	.40	1.00
32 Aaron Cook SR RC	.40	1.00
33 Rendy Espina SR RC	.40	1.00
34 Jason Phillips SR	.40	1.00
35 Carlos Silva SR	.40	1.00
36 Ryan Mills SR	.40	1.00
37 Pedro Santana SR	.40	1.00
38 John Grabow SR	.40	1.00
39 Cody Ransom SR	.40	1.00
40 Orlando Woodards SR	.40	1.00
41 Bud Smith SR	.40	1.00
42 Junior Guerrero SR	.40	1.00
43 David Brous SR	.40	1.00
44 Steve Green SR	.40	1.00
45 Brian Rogers SR	.40	1.00
46 Juan Figueroa SR RC	.40	1.00
47 Nick Punto SR	.40	1.00
48 Junior Herndon SR	.40	1.00
49 Justin Kaye SR	.40	1.00
50 Jason Karnuth SR	.40	1.00
51 Troy Glaus	.10	.30
52 Bengie Molina	.10	.30
53 Ramon Ortiz	.10	.30
54 Adam Kennedy	.10	.30
55 Jarrod Washburn	.10	.30
56 Troy Percival	.10	.30
57 David Eckstein	.10	.30
58 Ben Weber	.10	.30
59 Larry Barnes	.10	.30
60 Ismael Valdes	.10	.30
61 Benji Gil	.10	.30
62 Scott Schoeneweis	.10	.30
63 Pat Rapp	.10	.30
64 Jason Giambi	.10	.30
65 Mark Mulder	.10	.30
66 Ron Gant	.10	.30
67 Johnny Damon	.20	.50
68 Adam Piatt	.10	.30
69 Jermaine Dye	.10	.30
70 Jason Hart	.10	.30
71 Eric Chavez	.10	.30
72 Jim Mecir	.10	.30
73 Barry Zito	.10	.30
74 Jason Isringhausen	.10	.30
75 Jeremy Giambi	.10	.30
76 Olmedo Saenz	.10	.30
77 Terrence Long	.10	.30
78 Ramon Hernandez	.10	.30
79 Chris Carpenter	.10	.30
80 Raul Mondesi	.10	.30
81 Carlos Delgado	.10	.30
82 Billy Koch	.10	.30
83 Vernon Wells	.10	.30
84 Darrin Fletcher	.10	.30
85 Homer Bush	.10	.30
86 Pasqual Coco	.10	.30
87 Shannon Stewart	.10	.30
88 Chris Woodward	.10	.30
89 Joe Lawrence	.10	.30
90 Esteban Loaiza	.10	.30
91 Cesar Izturis	.10	.30
92 Kelvim Escobar	.10	.30
93 Greg Vaughn	.10	.30
94 Brent Abernathy	.10	.30
95 Tanyon Sturtze	.10	.30
96 Steve Cox	.10	.30
97 Aubrey Huff	.10	.30
98 Jesus Colome	.10	.30
99 Ben Grieve	.10	.30
100 Esteban Yan	.10	.30
101 Joe Kennedy	.10	.30
102 Felix Martinez	.10	.30
103 Nick Bierbrodt	.10	.30
104 Damian Rolls	.10	.30
105 Russ Johnson	.10	.30
106 Toby Hall	.10	.30
107 Roberto Alomar	.20	.50
108 Bartolo Colon	.10	.30
109 John Rocker	.10	.30
110 Juan Gonzalez	.10	.30
111 Einar Diaz	.10	.30
112 Chuck Finley	.10	.30
113 Kenny Lofton	.10	.30
114 Danys Baez	.10	.30
115 Travis Fryman	.10	.30
116 C.C. Sabathia	.10	.30
117 Paul Shuey	.10	.30
118 Marty Cordova	.10	.30
119 Ellis Burks	.10	.30
120 Bob Wickman	.10	.30
121 Edgar Martinez	.20	.50
122 Freddy Garcia	.10	.30
123 Ichiro Suzuki	.60	1.50
124 John Olerud	.10	.30
125 Gil Meche	.10	.30
126 Dan Wilson	.10	.30
127 Aaron Sele	.10	.30
128 Kazuhiro Sasaki	.10	.30
129 Mark McLemore	.10	.30
130 Carlos Guillen	.10	.30
131 Al Martin	.10	.30
132 David Bell	.10	.30
133 Jay Buhner	.10	.30
134 Stan Javier	.10	.30
135 Tony Batista	.10	.30
136 Jason Johnson	.10	.30
137 Brook Fordyce	.10	.30
138 Mike Kinkade	.10	.30
139 Willis Roberts	.10	.30
140 David Segui	.10	.30
141 Josh Towers	.10	.30
142 Jeff Conine	.10	.30
143 Chris Richard	.10	.30
144 Pat Hentgen	.10	.30
145 Melvin Mora	.10	.30
146 Jerry Hairston Jr.	.10	.30
147 Calvin Maduro	.10	.30
148 Brady Anderson	.10	.30
149 Alex Rodriguez	.50	1.25
150 Kenny Rogers	.10	.30
151 Chad Curtis	.10	.30
152 Ricky Ledee	.10	.30
153 Rafael Palmeiro	.20	.50
154 Rob Bell	.10	.30
155 Rick Helling	.10	.30
156 Doug Davis	.10	.30
157 Mike Lamb	.10	.30
158 Gabe Kapler	.10	.30
159 Jeff Zimmerman	.10	.30
160 Bill Haselman	.10	.30
161 Tim Crabtree	.10	.30
162 Carlos Pena	.10	.30
163 Nomar Garciaparra	.50	1.25
164 Shea Hillenbrand	.10	.30
165 Hideo Nomo	.30	.75
166 Manny Ramirez	.20	.50
167 Jose Offerman	.10	.30
168 Scott Hatteberg	.10	.30
169 Trot Nixon	.10	.30
170 Darren Lewis	.10	.30
171 Derek Lowe	.10	.30
172 Troy O'Leary	.10	.30
173 Tim Wakefield	.10	.30
174 Chris Stynes	.10	.30
175 John Valentin	.10	.30
176 David Cone	.10	.30
177 Neifi Perez	.10	.30
178 Brent Mayne	.10	.30
179 Dan Reichert	.10	.30
180 A.J. Hinch	.10	.30
181 Chris George	.10	.30
182 Mike Sweeney	.10	.30
183 Jeff Suppan	.10	.30
184 Roberto Hernandez	.10	.30
185 Joe Randa	.10	.30
186 Paul Byrd	.10	.30
187 Luis Ordaz	.10	.30
188 Kris Wilson	.10	.30
189 Dee Brown	.10	.30
190 Tony Clark	.10	.30
191 Matt Anderson	.10	.30
192 Robert Fick	.10	.30
193 Juan Encarnacion	.10	.30
194 Dean Palmer	.10	.30
195 Victor Santos	.10	.30
196 Damion Easley	.10	.30
197 Jose Lima	.10	.30
198 Deivi Cruz	.10	.30
199 Roger Cedeno	.10	.30
200 Jose Macias	.10	.30
201 Jeff Weaver	.10	.30
202 Brandon Inge	.10	.30
203 Brian Moehler	.10	.30
204 Brad Radke	.10	.30
205 Doug Mientkiewicz	.10	.30
206 Cristian Guzman	.10	.30
207 Corey Koskie	.10	.30
208 LaTroy Hawkins	.10	.30
209 J.C. Romero	.10	.30
210 Chad Allen	.10	.30
211 Torii Hunter	.10	.30
212 Travis Miller	.10	.30
213 Joe Mays	.10	.30
214 Todd Jones	.10	.30
215 David Ortiz	.30	.75
216 Brian Buchanan	.10	.30
217 A.J. Pierzynski	.10	.30
218 Carlos Lee	.10	.30
219 Gary Glover	.10	.30
220 Jose Valentin	.10	.30
221 Aaron Rowand	.10	.30
222 Sandy Alomar Jr.	.10	.30
223 Herbert Perry	.10	.30
224 Jon Garland	.10	.30
225 Mark Buehrle	.10	.30
226 Chris Singleton	.10	.30
227 Kip Wells	.10	.30
228 Ray Durham	.10	.30
229 Joe Crede	.10	.30
230 Keith Foulke	.10	.30
231 Royce Clayton	.10	.30

232 Andy Pettitte .20 .50
233 Derek Jeter .75 2.00
234 Jorge Posada .20 .50
235 Roger Clemens .60 1.50
236 Paul O'Neill .20 .50
237 Nick Johnson .10 .30
238 Gerald Williams .10 .30
239 Mariano Rivera .30 .75
240 Alfonso Soriano .10 .30
241 Ramiro Mendoza .10 .30
242 Mike Mussina .20 .50
243 Luis Sojo .10 .30
244 Scott Brosius .10 .30
245 David Justice .10 .30
246 Wade Miller .10 .30
247 Brad Ausmus .10 .30
248 Jeff Bagwell .20 .50
249 Daryle Ward .10 .30
250 Shane Reynolds .10 .30
251 Chris Truby .10 .30
252 Billy Wagner .10 .30
253 Craig Biggio .20 .50
254 Moises Alou .10 .30
255 Vinny Castilla .10 .30
256 Tim Redding .10 .30
257 Roy Oswalt .10 .30
258 Julio Lugo .10 .30
259 Chipper Jones .30 .75
260 Greg Maddux .50 1.25
261 Ken Caminiti .10 .30
262 Kevin Millwood .10 .30
263 Keith Lockhart .10 .30
264 Rey Sanchez .10 .30
265 Jason Marquis .10 .30
266 Brian Jordan .10 .30
267 Steve Karsay .10 .30
268 Wes Helms .10 .30
269 B.J. Surhoff .10 .30
270 Wilson Betemit .10 .30
271 John Smoltz .20 .50
272 Rafael Furcal .10 .30
273 Jeromy Burnitz .10 .30
274 Jimmy Haynes .10 .30
275 Mark Loretta .10 .30
276 Jose Hernandez .10 .30
277 Paul Rigdon .10 .30
278 Alex Sanchez .10 .30
279 Chad Fox .10 .30
280 Devon White .10 .30
281 Tyler Houston .10 .30
282 Ronnie Belliard .10 .30
283 Luis Lopez .10 .30
284 Ben Sheets .10 .30
285 Curtis Leskanic .10 .30
286 Henry Blanco .10 .30
287 Mark McGwire .75 2.00
288 Edgar Renteria .10 .30
289 Matt Morris .10 .30
290 Gene Stechschulte .10 .30
291 Dustin Hermanson .10 .30
292 Eli Marrero .10 .30
293 Albert Pujols .60 1.50
294 Luis Saturria .10 .30
295 Bobby Bonilla .10 .30
296 Garrett Stephenson .10 .30
297 Jim Edmonds .10 .30
298 Rick Ankiel .10 .30
299 Placido Polanco .10 .30
300 Dave Veres .10 .30
301 Sammy Sosa .30 .75
302 Eric Young .10 .30
303 Kerry Wood .10 .30
304 Jon Lieber .10 .30
305 Joe Girardi .10 .30
306 Fred McGriff .20 .50
307 Jeff Fassero .10 .30
308 Julio Zuleta .10 .30
309 Kevin Tapani .10 .30
310 Rondell White .10 .30
311 Julian Tavarez .10 .30
312 Tom Gordon .10 .30
313 Corey Patterson .10 .30
314 Bill Mueller .10 .30
315 Randy Johnson .30 .75
316 Chad Moeller .10 .30
317 Tony Womack .10 .30
318 Erubiel Durazo .10 .30
319 Luis Gonzalez .10 .30
320 Brian Anderson .10 .30
321 Reggie Sanders .10 .30
322 Greg Colbrunn .10 .30
323 Robert Ellis .10 .30
324 Jack Cust .10 .30
325 Bret Prinz .10 .30
326 Steve Finley .10 .30
327 Byung-Hyun Kim .10 .30
328 Albie Lopez .10 .30
329 Gary Sheffield .10 .30
330 Mark Grudzielanek .10 .30
331 Paul LoDuca .10 .30
332 Tom Goodwin .10 .30
333 Andy Ashby .10 .30
334 Hiram Bocachica .10 .30
335 Dave Hansen .10 .30
336 Kevin Brown .10 .30
337 Marquis Grissom .10 .30
338 Terry Adams .10 .30
339 Chan Ho Park .10 .30
340 Adrian Beltre .10 .30
341 Luke Prokopec .10 .30
342 Jeff Shaw .10 .30
343 Vladimir Guerrero .30 .75
344 Orlando Cabrera .10 .30
345 Tony Armas Jr. .10 .30
346 Michael Barrett .10 .30
347 Geoff Blum .10 .30
348 Ryan Minor .10 .30
349 Peter Bergeron .10 .30
350 Graeme Lloyd .10 .30
351 Jose Vidro .10 .30
352 Javier Vazquez .10 .30
353 Matt Blank .10 .30
354 Masato Yoshii .10 .30
355 Carl Pavano .10 .30
356 Barry Bonds .75 2.00
357 Shawon Dunston .10 .30
358 Livan Hernandez .10 .30
359 Felix Rodriguez .10 .30
360 Pedro Feliz .10 .30
361 Calvin Murray .10 .30
362 Robb Nen .10 .30
363 Marvin Benard .10 .30
364 Russ Ortiz .10 .30
365 Jason Schmidt .10 .30
366 Rich Aurilia .10 .30
367 John Vander Wal .10 .30
368 Benito Santiago .10 .30
369 Ryan Dempster .10 .30
370 Charles Johnson .10 .30
371 Alex Gonzalez .10 .30
372 Luis Castillo .10 .30
373 Mike Lowell .10 .30
374 Antonio Alfonseca .10 .30
375 A.J. Burnett .10 .30
376 Brad Penny .10 .30
377 Jason Grilli .10 .30
378 Derrek Lee .20 .50
379 Matt Clement .10 .30
380 Eric Owens .10 .30
381 Vladimir Nunez .10 .30
382 Cliff Floyd .10 .30
383 Mike Piazza .50 1.25
384 Lenny Harris .10 .30
385 Glendon Rusch .10 .30
386 Todd Zeile .10 .30
387 Al Leiter .10 .30
388 Armando Benitez .10 .30
389 Alex Escobar .10 .30
390 Kevin Appier .10 .30
391 Matt Lawton .10 .30
392 Bruce Chen .10 .30
393 John Franco .10 .30
394 Tsuyoshi Shinjo .10 .30
395 Rey Ordonez .10 .30
396 Joe McEwing .10 .30
397 Ryan Klesko .10 .30
398 Brian Lawrence .10 .30
399 Kevin Walker .10 .30
400 Phil Nevin .10 .30
401 Bubba Trammell .10 .30
402 Wiki Gonzalez .10 .30
403 D'Angelo Jimenez .10 .30
404 Rickey Henderson .30 .75
405 Mike Darr .10 .30
406 Trevor Hoffman .10 .30
407 Damian Jackson .10 .30
408 Santiago Perez .10 .30
409 Cesar Crespo .10 .30
410 Robert Person .10 .30
411 Travis Lee .10 .30
412 Scott Rolen .20 .50
413 Turk Wendell .10 .30
414 Randy Wolf .10 .30
415 Kevin Jordan .10 .30
416 Jose Mesa .10 .30
417 Mike Lieberthal .10 .30
418 Bobby Abreu .10 .30
419 Tomas Perez .10 .30
420 Doug Glanville .10 .30
421 Reggie Taylor .10 .30
422 Jimmy Rollins .10 .30
423 Brian Giles .10 .30
424 Rob Mackowiak .10 .30
425 Bronson Arroyo .10 .30
426 Kevin Young .10 .30
427 Jack Wilson .10 .30
428 Adrian Brown .10 .30
429 Chad Hermansen .10 .30
430 Jimmy Anderson .10 .30
431 Aramis Ramirez .10 .30
432 Todd Ritchie .10 .30
433 Pat Meares .10 .30
434 Warren Morris .10 .30
435 Derek Bell .10 .30
436 Ken Griffey Jr. .50 1.25
437 Elmer Dessens .10 .30
438 Ruben Rivera .10 .30
439 Jason LaRue .10 .30
440 Sean Casey .10 .30
441 Pete Harnisch .10 .30
442 Danny Graves .10 .30
443 Aaron Boone .10 .30
444 Dmitri Young .10 .30
445 Brandon Larson .10 .30
446 Pokey Reese .10 .30
447 Todd Walker .10 .30
448 Juan Castro .10 .30
449 Todd Helton .20 .50
450 Ben Petrick .10 .30
451 Juan Pierre .10 .30
452 Jeff Cirillo .10 .30
453 Juan Uribe .10 .30
454 Brian Bohanon .10 .30
455 Terry Shumpert .10 .30
456 Mike Hampton .10 .30
457 Shawn Chacon .10 .30
458 Adam Melhuse .10 .30
459 Greg Norton .10 .30
460 Gabe White .10 .30
461 Ichiro Suzuki WS .30 .75
462 Carlos Delgado WS .10 .30
463 Manny Ramirez WS .20 .50
464 Miguel Tejada WS .10 .30
465 Tsuyoshi Shinjo WS .10 .30
466 Bernie Williams WS .10 .30
467 Juan Gonzalez WS .10 .30
468 Andruw Jones WS .10 .30
469 Ivan Rodriguez WS .10 .30
470 Larry Walker WS .10 .30
471 Hideo Nomo WS .10 .30
472 Albert Pujols WS .30 .75
473 Pedro Martinez WS .20 .50
474 Vladimir Guerrero WS .20 .50
475 Tony Batista WS .10 .30
476 Kazuhiro Sasaki WS .10 .30
477 Richard Hidalgo WS .10 .30
478 Carlos Lee WS .10 .30
479 Roberto Alomar WS .10 .30
480 Rafael Palmeiro WS .10 .30
481 Ken Griffey Jr. GG .30 .75
482 Ken Griffey Jr. GG .30 .75
483 Ken Griffey Jr. GG .30 .75
484 Ken Griffey Jr. GG .30 .75
485 Ken Griffey Jr. GG .30 .75
486 Ken Griffey Jr. GG .30 .75
487 Ken Griffey Jr. GG .30 .75
488 Ken Griffey Jr. GG .30 .75
489 Ken Griffey Jr. GG .30 .75
490 Ken Griffey Jr. GG .30 .75
491 Barry Bonds CL .40 1.00
492 Hideo Nomo CL .10 .30
493 Ichiro Suzuki CL .30 .75
494 Cal Ripken CL .50 1.25
495 Tony Gwynn CL .20 .50
496 Randy Johnson CL .20 .50
497 A.J. Burnett CL .10 .30
498 Rickey Henderson CL .20 .50
499 Albert Pujols CL .30 .75
500 Luis Gonzalez CL .10 .30
501 Brandon Puffer SR RC .40 1.00
502 Rodrigo Rosario SR RC .40 1.00
503 Tom Shearn SR RC .40 1.00
504 Reed Johnson SR RC .60 1.50
505 Chris Baker SR RC .40 1.00
506 John Ennis SR RC .40 1.00
507 Luis Martinez SR RC .40 1.00
508 So Taguchi SR RC .60 1.50
509 Scotty Layfield SR RC .40 1.00
510 Francis Beltran SR RC .40 1.00
511 Brandon Backe SR RC .60 1.50
512 Doug Devore SR RC .40 1.00
513 Jeremy Ward SR RC .40 1.00
514 Jose Valverde SR RC .40 1.00
515 P.J. Bevis SR RC .40 1.00
516 Victor Alvarez SR RC .40 1.00
517 Kazuhisa Ishii SR RC .60 1.50
518 Jorge Nunez SR RC .40 1.00
519 Eric Good SR RC .40 1.00
520 Ron Calloway SR RC .40 1.00
521 Val Pascucci SR .40 1.00
522 Nelson Castro SR RC .40 1.00
523 Deivis Santos SR .40 1.00
524 Luis Ugueto SR RC .40 1.00
525 Matt Thornton SR RC .40 1.00
526 Hansel Izquierdo SR RC .40 1.00
527 Tyler Yates SR RC .40 1.00
528 Mark Corey SR RC .40 1.00
529 Jaime Cerda SR RC .40 1.00
530 Satoru Komiyama SR RC .40 1.00
531 Steve Bechler SR RC .40 1.00
532 Ben Howard SR RC .40 1.00
533 An. Machado SR RC .40 1.00
534 Jorge Padilla SR RC .40 1.00
535 Eric Junge SR RC .40 1.00
536 Adrian Burnside SR RC .40 1.00
537 Mike Gonzalez SR RC .40 1.00
538 Josh Hancock SR RC .50 1.25
539 Colin Young SR RC .40 1.00
540 Rene Reyes SR RC .40 1.00
541 Cam Esslinger SR RC .40 1.00
542 Tim Kalita SR RC .40 1.00
543 Kevin Frederick SR RC .40 1.00
544 Kyle Kane SR RC .40 1.00
545 Edwin Almonte SR RC .40 1.00
546 Aaron Sele .10 .30
547 Garret Anderson .10 .30
548 Darin Erstad .10 .30
549 Brad Fullmer .10 .30
550 Kevin Appier .10 .30
551 Tim Salmon .20 .50
552 David Justice .10 .30
553 Billy Koch .10 .30
554 Scott Hatteberg .10 .30
555 Tim Hudson .10 .30
556 Miguel Tejada .10 .30
557 Carlos Pena .10 .30
558 Mike Sirotka .10 .30
559 Jose Cruz Jr. .10 .30
560 Josh Phelps .10 .30
561 Brandon Lyon .10 .30
562 Luke Prokopec .10 .30
563 Felipe Lopez .10 .30
564 Jason Standridge .10 .30
565 Chris Gomez .10 .30
566 John Flaherty .10 .30
567 Jason Tyner .10 .30
568 Bobby Smith .10 .30
569 Wilson Alvarez .10 .30
570 Matt Lawton .10 .30
571 Omar Vizquel .20 .50
572 Jim Thome .20 .50
573 Brady Anderson .10 .30
574 Alex Escobar .10 .30
575 Russell Branyan .10 .30
576 Bret Boone .10 .30
577 Ben Davis .10 .30
578 Mike Cameron .10 .30
579 Jamie Moyer .10 .30
580 Ruben Sierra .10 .30
581 Jeff Cirillo .10 .30
582 Marty Cordova .10 .30
583 Mike Bordick .10 .30
584 Brian Roberts .10 .30
585 Luis Matos .10 .30
586 Geronimo Gil .10 .30
587 Jay Gibbons .10 .30
588 Carl Everett .10 .30
589 Ivan Rodriguez .20 .50
590 Chan Ho Park .10 .30
591 Juan Gonzalez .10 .30
592 Hank Blalock .20 .50
593 Todd Van Poppel .10 .30
594 Pedro Martinez .20 .50
595 Jason Varitek .30 .75
596 Tony Clark .10 .30
597 Johnny Damon Sox .20 .50
598 Dustin Hermanson .10 .30
599 John Burkett .10 .30
600 Carlos Beltran .10 .30
601 Mark Quinn .10 .30
602 Chuck Knoblauch .10 .30
603 Michael Tucker .10 .30
604 Carlos Febles .10 .30
605 Jose Rosado .10 .30
606 Dmitri Young .10 .30
607 Bobby Higginson .10 .30
608 Craig Paquette .10 .30
609 Mitch Meluskey .10 .30
610 Wendell Magee .10 .30
611 Mike Rivera .10 .30
612 Jacque Jones .10 .30
613 Luis Rivas .10 .30
614 Eric Milton .10 .30
615 Eddie Guardado .10 .30
616 Matt LeCroy .10 .30
617 Mike Jackson .10 .30
618 Magglio Ordonez .10 .30
619 Frank Thomas .30 .75
620 Rocky Biddle .10 .30
621 Paul Konerko .10 .30
622 Todd Ritchie .10 .30
623 Jon Rauch .10 .30
624 John Vander Wal .10 .30
625 Rondell White .10 .30
626 Jason Giambi .10 .30
627 Robin Ventura .10 .30
628 David Wells .10 .30
629 Bernie Williams .20 .50
630 Lance Berkman .10 .30
631 Richard Hidalgo .10 .30
632 Greg Zaun .10 .30
633 Jose Vizcaino .10 .30
634 Octavio Dotel .10 .30
635 Morgan Ensberg .10 .30
636 Andruw Jones .20 .50
637 Tom Glavine .20 .50
638 Gary Sheffield .10 .30
639 Vinny Castilla .10 .30
640 Javy Lopez .10 .30
641 Albie Lopez .10 .30
642 Geoff Jenkins .10 .30
643 Jeffrey Hammonds .10 .30
644 Alex Ochoa .10 .30
645 Richie Sexson .10 .30
646 Eric Young .10 .30
647 Glendon Rusch .10 .30
648 Tino Martinez .20 .50
649 Fernando Vina .10 .30
650 J.D. Drew .10 .30
651 Woody Williams .10 .30
652 Darryl Kile .10 .30
653 Jason Isringhausen .10 .30
654 Moises Alou .10 .30
655 Alex Gonzalez .10 .30
656 Delino DeShields .10 .30
657 Todd Hundley .10 .30
658 Chris Stynes .10 .30
659 Jason Bere .10 .30
660 Curt Schilling .10 .30
661 Craig Counsell .10 .30
662 Mark Grace .20 .50
663 Matt Williams .10 .30
664 Jay Bell .10 .30
665 Rick Helling .10 .30
666 Shawn Green .10 .30
667 Eric Karros .10 .30
668 Hideo Nomo .30 .75
669 Omar Daal .10 .30
670 Brian Jordan .10 .30
671 Cesar Izturis .10 .30
672 Fernando Tatis .10 .30
673 Lee Stevens .10 .30
674 Tomo Ohka .10 .30
675 Brian Schneider .10 .30
676 Brad Wilkerson .10 .30
677 Bruce Chen .10 .30
678 Tsuyoshi Shinjo .10 .30
679 Jeff Kent .10 .30
680 Kirk Rueter .10 .30
681 J.T. Snow .10 .30
682 David Bell .10 .30
683 Reggie Sanders .10 .30
684 Preston Wilson .10 .30
685 Vic Darensbourg .10 .30
686 Josh Beckett .10 .30
687 Pablo Ozuna .10 .30
688 Mike Redmond .10 .30
689 Scott Strickland .10 .30
690 Mo Vaughn .10 .30
691 Roberto Alomar .20 .50
692 Edgardo Alfonzo .10 .30
693 Shawn Estes .10 .30
694 Roger Cedeno .10 .30
695 Jeromy Burnitz .10 .30
696 Ray Lankford .10 .30
697 Mark Kotsay .10 .30
698 Kevin Jarvis .10 .30
699 Bobby Jones .10 .30
700 Sean Burroughs .10 .30
701 Ramon Vazquez .10 .30
702 Pat Burrell .10 .30
703 Marlon Byrd .10 .30
704 Brandon Duckworth .10 .30
705 Marlon Anderson .10 .30
706 Vicente Padilla .10 .30
707 Kip Wells .10 .30
708 Jason Kendall .10 .30
709 Pokey Reese .10 .30
710 Pat Meares .10 .30
711 Kris Benson .10 .30
712 Armando Rios .10 .30
713 Mike Williams .10 .30
714 Barry Larkin .20 .50
715 Adam Dunn .10 .30
716 Juan Encarnacion .10 .30
717 Scott Williamson .10 .30
718 Wilton Guerrero .10 .30
719 Chris Reitsma .10 .30
720 Larry Walker .10 .30
721 Denny Neagle .10 .30
722 Todd Zeile .10 .30
723 Jose Ortiz .10 .30
724 Jason Jennings .10 .30
725 Tony Eusebio .10 .30
726 Ichiro Suzuki YR .30 .75
727 Barry Bonds YR .40 1.00
728 Randy Johnson YR .20 .50
729 Albert Pujols YR .30 .75
730 Roger Clemens YR .30 .75
731 Sammy Sosa YR .20 .50
732 Alex Rodriguez YR .30 .75
733 Chipper Jones YR .20 .50
734 Rickey Henderson YR .20 .50
735 Ichiro Suzuki YR .30 .75
736 Luis Gonzalez SH CL .10 .30
737 Derek Jeter SH CL .40 1.00
738 Ichiro Suzuki SH CL .30 .75
739 Barry Bonds SH CL .40 1.00
740 Curt Schilling SH CL .10 .30
741 Shawn Green SH CL .10 .30
742 Jason Giambi SH CL .10 .30
743 Roberto Alomar SH CL .10 .30
744 Larry Walker SH CL .10 .30
745 Mark McGwire SH CL .40 1.00

2002 Upper Deck 2001 Greatest Hits

Issued into first series packs at a rate of one in 14, these 10 cards feature some of the leading hitters during the 2001 season.

COMPLETE SET (10) 15.00 40.00
GH1 Barry Bonds 2.50 6.00

GH2 Ichiro Suzuki 2.00 5.00
GH3 Albert Pujols 2.00 5.00
GH4 Mike Piazza 1.50 4.00
GH5 Alex Rodriguez 1.50 4.00
GH6 Mark McGwire 2.50 6.00
GH7 Manny Ramirez 1.00 2.50
GH8 Ken Griffey Jr. 1.50 4.00
GH9 Sammy Sosa 1.00 2.50
GH10 Derek Jeter 2.50 6.00

2002 Upper Deck A Piece of History 500 Club

Randomly inserted in 2002 Upper Deck second series packs, this card features a bat slice from Mark McGwire and continues the Upper Deck A Piece of History set begun in 1999. Though lacking actual serial-numbering, according to Upper Deck this card was printed to a stated print run of 350 copies.

MMC Mark McGwire 250.00 400.00

2002 Upper Deck A Piece of History 500 Club Autograph

Randomly inserted in 2002 Upper Deck second series packs, this card features a bat slice from Mark McGwire and an authentic autograph and continues the Upper Deck A Piece of History set begun in 1999. This card was printed to a stated print run of 25 serial numbered sets.

SMMC Mark McGwire/25

2002 Upper Deck AL Centennial Memorabilia

Inserted into first series packs at a rate of one in 144, these 10 cards feature memorabilia from some of the leading players in American League history. The bat jersey cards were produced in smaller quantites than the jersey cards and we have notated those cards with SP's in our checklist.

ALBBR Babe Ruth Bat SP 75.00 150.00
ALBJD Joe DiMaggio Bat SP 50.00 100.00
ALBMM M. Mantle Bat SP 75.00 150.00
ALJAR A. Rodriguez Jsy 6.00 15.00
ALJCR Cal Ripken Jsy 15.00 40.00
ALJFT Frank Thomas Jsy 6.00 15.00
ALJIR Ivan Rodriguez Jsy 6.00 15.00
ALJNR Nolan Ryan Jsy 15.00 40.00
ALJPM P. Martinez Jsy 6.00 15.00
ALJRA R. Alomar Jsy 6.00 15.00

2002 Upper Deck AL Centennial Memorabilia Autograph

Randomly inserted into first series packs, these four cards featured autographs of players whose memorabilia is featured in the Centennial Memorabilia set. These cards are serial numbered to 25. Due to market scarcity, no pricing is provided.

SALCR Cal Ripken Jsy
SALIR Ivan Rodriguez Jsy
SALNR Nolan Ryan Jsy
SALPM Pedro Martinez Jsy

2002 Upper Deck All-Star Home Run Derby Game Jersey

Inserted into first series packs at a rate of one in 288, these seven cards feature jersey swatches from these players who participated in the Home Run Derby. A couple of the jerseys were from regular use and we have notated that information in our checklist.

GOLD RANDOM INSERTS IN PACKS
GOLD PRINT RUN 25 SERIAL #'d SETS
NO GOLD PRICING DUE TO SCARCITY

ASAR Alex Rodriguez 10.00 25.00
ASBRB Bret Boone 6.00 15.00
ASJG1 Jason Giambi 6.00 15.00
ASJG2 Jason Giambi A's 6.00 15.00
ASSS1 Sammy Sosa 8.00 20.00
ASSS2 S. Sosa Cubs 8.00 20.00
ASTH Todd Helton 6.00 15.00

2002 Upper Deck All-Star Salute Game Jersey

Inserted into first series packs at a rate of one in 288, these nine cards feature game jersey swatches of some of the most exciting All-Star performers.

GOLD RANDOM INSERTS IN PACKS
GOLD PRINT RUN 25 SERIAL #'d SETS
NO GOLD PRICING DUE TO SCARCITY

SJAR1 A.Rodriguez Mariners 10.00 25.00
SJAR2 A.Rodriguez Rangers 10.00 25.00
SJDE Dennis Eckersley 6.00 15.00
SJDS Don Sutton 6.00 15.00
SJIS Ichiro Suzuki 20.00 50.00
SJKG Ken Griffey Jr. 12.50 30.00
SJLB Lou Boudreau 6.00 15.00
SJNF Nellie Fox 6.00 15.00
SJSA Sparky Anderson 6.00 15.00

2002 Upper Deck Authentic McGwire

Randomly inserted in second series packs, these two cards feature authentic memorabilia from Mark McGwire's career. These cards have a stated print run of 70 serial numbered sets.

AMB Mark McGwire Bat 50.00 100.00
AMJ Mark McGwire Jsy 50.00 100.00

2002 Upper Deck Big Fly Zone

Issued into first series packs at a rate of one in 14, these 10 cards feature some of the leading power hitters in the game.

COMPLETE SET (10) 12.50 30.00
Z1 Mark McGwire 2.50 6.00
Z2 Ken Griffey Jr. 1.50 4.00
Z3 Manny Ramirez .60 1.50
Z4 Sammy Sosa 1.00 2.50
Z5 Todd Helton .60 1.50
Z6 Barry Bonds 2.50 6.00
Z7 Luis Gonzalez .60 1.50
Z8 Alex Rodriguez 1.50 4.00
Z9 Carlos Delgado .60 1.50
Z10 Chipper Jones 1.00 2.50

2002 Upper Deck Breakout Performers

Issued into first series packs at a rate of one in 14, these 10 cards feature players who had breakout seasons in 2001.

COMPLETE SET (10) 10.00 25.00
BP1 Ichiro Suzuki 2.00 5.00
BP2 Albert Pujols 2.00 5.00
BP3 Doug Mientkiewicz .60 1.50
BP4 Lance Berkman .60 1.50
BP5 Tsuyoshi Shinjo .60 1.50
BP6 Ben Sheets .60 1.50
BP7 Jimmy Rollins .60 1.50
BP8 J.D. Drew .60 1.50
BP9 Bret Boone .60 1.50
BP10 Alfonso Soriano .60 1.50

2002 Upper Deck Championship Caliber

Inserted into first series packs at a rate of one in 23, these six cards feature players who have all earned World Series rings.

COMPLETE SET (6) 8.00 20.00
CC1 Derek Jeter 2.50 6.00
CC2 Roberto Alomar .60 1.50
CC3 Chipper Jones 1.00 2.50
CC4 Gary Sheffield .60 1.50
CC5 Roger Clemens 2.00 5.00
CC6 Greg Maddux 1.50 4.00

2002 Upper Deck Championship Caliber Swatch

Inserted in second series packs at a stated rate of one in 288, these 14 cards feature not only players who have been on World Champions but also a game-worn swatch. A few players were issued in shorter supply and we have notated that information in our checklist.

AP Andy Pettitte 6.00 15.00
BL Barry Larkin 6.00 15.00
BW Bernie Williams 6.00 15.00
CF Cliff Floyd 4.00 10.00
CHJ Charles Johnson 4.00 10.00
CJO Chipper Jones SP
CS Curt Schilling 4.00 10.00
GM Greg Maddux SP
JO John Olerud 4.00 10.00
JP Jorge Posada 6.00 15.00
KB Kevin Brown SP 6.00 15.00
RA Roberto Alomar SP
RJ Randy Johnson 6.00 15.00
TM Tino Martinez 6.00 15.00

2002 Upper Deck Chasing History

Inserted at stated odds of one in 11, these 15 cards feature players who are moving up in the record books.

COMPLETE SET (15) 15.00 40.00
CH1 Sammy Sosa 1.25 3.00
CH2 Ken Griffey Jr. 2.00 5.00
CH3 Roger Clemens 2.50 6.00
CH4 Barry Bonds 3.00 8.00
CH5 Rafael Palmeiro .75 2.00
CH6 Andres Galarraga .75 2.00
CH7 Juan Gonzalez .75 2.00
CH8 Roberto Alomar .75 2.00
CH9 Randy Johnson 1.25 3.00
CH10 Jeff Bagwell .75 2.00
CH11 Fred McGriff .75 2.00
CH12 Matt Williams .75 2.00
CH13 Greg Maddux 2.00 5.00
CH14 Robb Nen .75 2.00
CH15 Kenny Lofton .75 2.00

2002 Upper Deck Combo Memorabilia

Issued into first series packs at a rate of one in 288, these seven cards feature two pieces of game-used memorabilia from players who have something in common.

GOLD RANDOM INSERTS IN PACKS
GOLD PRINT RUN 25 SERIAL #'d SETS
NO GOLD PRICING DUE TO SCARCITY
BDM Joe DiMaggio Bat 100.00 200.00
Mickey Mantle Bat
BRG Alex Rodriguez Bat 15.00 40.00
Ken Griffey Jr. Bat
JBS Barry Bonds Jsy 20.00 50.00
Sammy Sosa Jsy
JHK S. Hasegawa Jsy 6.00 15.00
Byung-Hyun Kim Jsy
JRC Nolan Ryan Jsy 30.00 60.00
Roger Clemens Jsy
JRM Nolan Ryan Jsy 25.00 50.00
Pedro Martinez Jsy
JRS Alex Rodriguez Jsy 15.00 40.00
Sammy Sosa Jsy

2002 Upper Deck Double Game Worn Gems

Randomly inserted in second series retail packs, these 12 cards feature two teammates along with pieces of game used memorabilia. These cards have a stated print run of 450 serial numbered sets, except for the Martinez/Ichiro card of which only 150 #'d copies were issued.

DGAP Roberto Alomar 10.00 25.00
Mike Piazza
DGDF Carlos Delgado 6.00 15.00
Shannon Stewart
DGDH Jermaine Dye 6.00 15.00
Tim Hudson
DGGS Luis Gonzalez 6.00 15.00
Curt Schilling
DGKG Jason Kendall 6.00 15.00
Brian Giles
DGMI Edgar Martinez
Ichiro Suzuki SP/150
DGMM Kevin Millwood 10.00 25.00
Greg Maddux
DGNK Phil Nevin 6.00 15.00
Ryan Klesko
DGPL Robert Person 6.00 15.00
Mike Lieberthal
DGPN Chan Ho Park 20.00 50.00
Hideo Nomo
DGTO Frank Thomas 8.00 20.00
Magglio Ordonez
DGVB Omar Vizquel 6.00 15.00
Russell Branyan

2002 Upper Deck Double Game Worn Gems Gold

Randomly inserted in second series retail packs, these cards parallel the Double Game Worn Gem insert set. These cards have a stated print run of 100 serial numbered sets except for the Martinez/Ichiro card of which only 40 #'d copies were issued.

DGAP Roberto Alomar 20.00 50.00
Mike Piazza
DGDF Carlos Delgado 12.50 30.00
Shannon Stewart
DGDH Jermaine Dye 12.50 30.00
Tim Hudson
DGGS Luis Gonzalez 12.50 30.00
Curt Schilling
DGKG Jason Kendall 12.50 30.00
Brian Giles
DGMI Edgar Martinez 50.00 100.00
Ichiro Suzuki/40
DGMM Kevin Millwood 20.00 50.00
Greg Maddux
DGNK Phil Nevin 12.50 30.00
Ryan Klesko
DGPL Robert Person 12.50 30.00
Mike Lieberthal
DGPN Chan Ho Park 40.00 100.00
Hideo Nomo
DGTO Frank Thomas 15.00 40.00
Magglio Ordonez
DGVB Omar Vizquel 12.50 30.00
Russell Branyan

2002 Upper Deck First Timers Game Jersey

Inserted into first series hobby packs at a rate of one in 288 hobby packs, these nine cards feature players who have never before been featured on a Upper Deck game jersey card before.

FTAP Albert Pujols 20.00 50.00
FTCP Corey Patterson 4.00 10.00
FTEM Eric Milton 4.00 10.00
FTFG Freddy Garcia 4.00 10.00
FTJM Joe Mays 4.00 10.00
FTML Matt Lawton 4.00 10.00
FTOD Omar Daal 4.00 10.00
FTRB Russell Branyan 4.00 10.00
FTSS Shannon Stewart 4.00 10.00

2002 Upper Deck First Timers Game Jersey Autograph

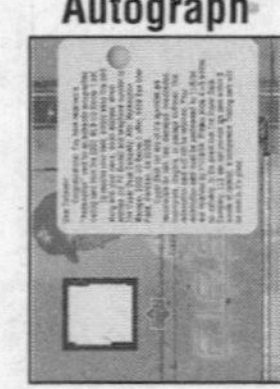

This parallel to the First Timers Game Jersey set features the players signing 25 copies of these cards. These cards were distributed exclusively in first series hobby packs. Freddy Garcia did not return his cards in time for packout and thus was available only in exchange format with a redemption deadline of 11/19/04. Due to market scarcity, no pricing is provided.

SFTAP Albert Pujols
SFTCP Corey Patterson
SFTFG Freddy Garcia
SFTJM Joe Mays
SFTSS Shannon Stewart

2002 Upper Deck Game Base

Inserted into first series packs at a rate of one in 288, these 22 cards feature authentic pieces of bases used in official Major League games.

BAJ Andruw Jones 6.00 15.00
BAR Alex Rodriguez 8.00 20.00
BBB Barry Bonds 12.50 30.00
BCD Carlos Delgado 4.00 10.00
BCJ Chipper Jones 6.00 15.00
BCR Cal Ripken 15.00 40.00
BDJ Derek Jeter 12.50 30.00
BIR Ivan Rodriguez 6.00 15.00
BIS Ichiro Suzuki 20.00 50.00
BJG Jason Giambi 4.00 10.00
BJG Juan Gonzalez 4.00 10.00
BKG Ken Griffey Jr. 8.00 20.00
BKS Kazuhiro Sasaki 4.00 10.00
BLG Luis Gonzalez 4.00 10.00
BMM Mark McGwire 20.00 50.00
BMP Mike Piazza 6.00 15.00
BRC Roger Clemens 10.00 25.00
BSG Shawn Green 4.00 10.00
BSS Sammy Sosa 6.00 15.00
BTG Troy Glaus 4.00 10.00
CBMJ Mark McGwire 30.00 60.00
Derek Jeter
CBRG Alex Rodriguez 15.00 40.00
Ken Griffey Jr.

2002 Upper Deck Game Base Autograph

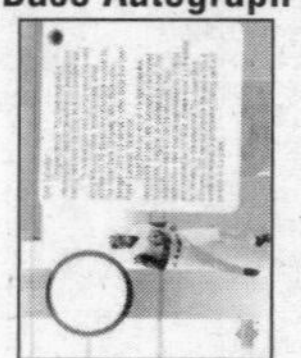

Randomly inserted into first series packs, Ken Griffey Jr. signed 25 cards for inclusion in this set. However, Griffey did not return his cards in time for inclusion in the packs and therefore these cards could be redeemed until November 5, 2004. Due to market scarcity, no pricing is provided.

SBKG Ken Griffey Jr.

2002 Upper Deck Game Jersey

Randomly inserted in packs, these 11 cards feature some of today's star players along with a game-worn swatch of the featured player.

AB Adrian Beltre 4.00 10.00
CS Curt Schilling 4.00 10.00
FT Frank Thomas 6.00 15.00
JC Jeff Cirillo Pants 4.00 10.00
KG Ken Griffey Jr. 10.00 25.00
MP Mike Piazza Pants 6.00 15.00
PW Preston Wilson 4.00 10.00
SR Scott Rolen 6.00 15.00
SS Sammy Sosa 6.00 15.00
TB Tony Batista 4.00 10.00
TH Tim Hudson 4.00 10.00

2002 Upper Deck Game Jersey Autograph

Randomly inserted into first series hobby packs, these 12 cards feature not only a game jersey swatch but also an authentic autograph of the player featured. These cards are serial numbered to 200. The following players did not return their signed cards in time for release in the packs and those cards had an exchange deadline of November 19, 2004: Andruw Jones, Albert Pujols and Ken Griffey Jr.

JAJ Andruw Jones 20.00 50.00
JAP Albert Pujols 150.00 250.00
JBB Barry Bonds 100.00 175.00
JCD Carlos Delgado 15.00 40.00
JCR Cal Ripken 75.00 150.00
JGS Gary Sheffield 20.00 50.00
JIS Ichiro Suzuki UER 250.00 400.00
Word Close repeated in ninth line of text
JJGI Jason Giambi 15.00 40.00
JKG Ken Griffey Jr. 60.00 120.00
JNR Nolan Ryan 75.00 150.00
JPW Preston Wilson 15.00 40.00
JRF Rafael Furcal 15.00 40.00

2002 Upper Deck Game Jersey Patch

Inserted at a rate of one in 2,500 first series packs, these cards feature a jersey patch from the star players featured.

PLAR Alex Rodriguez L 75.00 150.00
PLBB Barry Bonds L 75.00 150.00
PLCR Cal Ripken L 60.00 120.00
PLJG Jason Giambi L 20.00 50.00
PLKG Ken Griffey Jr. L 50.00 100.00
PLPM Pedro Martinez L 40.00 80.00
PLSS Sammy Sosa L 40.00 80.00
PNAR Alex Rodriguez N 50.00 100.00
PNBB Barry Bonds N 75.00 150.00
PNCR Cal Ripken N 60.00 120.00
PNJG Jason Giambi N 20.00 50.00
PNKG Ken Griffey Jr. N 50.00 100.00
PNPM Pedro Martinez N 40.00 80.00
PNSS Sammy Sosa N 40.00 80.00
PSAR Alex Rodriguez S 50.00 100.00
PSBB Barry Bonds S 75.00 150.00
PSCR Cal Ripken S 60.00 120.00
PSJG Jason Giambi S 20.00 50.00
PSKG Ken Griffey Jr. S 60.00 120.00
PSPM Pedro Martinez S 40.00 80.00
PSSS Sammy Sosa S 40.00 80.00

2002 Upper Deck Game Jersey Patch Autograph

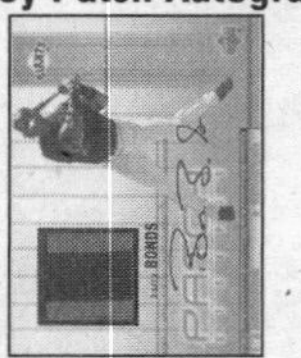

Randomly inserted into first series packs, these six cards feature not only a game jersey patch swatch but also an authentic autograph of the player featured. These cards are serial numbered to 25. Ken Griffey Jr. did not return his cards in time for pack out and those cards were issued as exchange cards with a redemption deadline of 11/5/04. Due to market scarcity, no pricing is provided.

SPNBB Barry Bonds N
SPNCR Cal Ripken N
SPNKG Ken Griffey Jr. N
SPNSS Sammy Sosa N
SPSBB Barry Bonds S
SPSCR Cal Ripken S

2002 Upper Deck Game Worn Gems

Inserted in second series retail packs at a stated rate of one in 48 retail packs, these 31 cards feature leading stars along a game-used memorabilia piece. A few cards were issued in shorter supply and those cards are notated in our checklist with an SP. Cards notated with an SP are not priced due to market scarcity.

GAS Aaron Sele 4.00 10.00
GCD Carlos Delgado 4.00 10.00
GCJ Chipper Jones 6.00 15.00
GCR Cal Ripken 20.00 50.00
GCS Curt Schilling 4.00 10.00
GDE Darin Erstad SP
GEC Eric Chavez 4.00 10.00
GEM Edgar Martinez 6.00 15.00
GEM Eric Milton 4.00 10.00
GFG Freddy Garcia SP
GFT Frank Thomas 6.00 15.00
GGM Greg Maddux 6.00 15.00
GGS Gary Sheffield SP
GHN Hideo Nomo SP
GIR Ivan Rodriguez 6.00 15.00
GJG Juan Gonzalez 4.00 10.00
GJK Jason Kendall 4.00 10.00
GJM Joe Mays 4.00 10.00
GJO John Olerud SP
GLG Luis Gonzalez SP
GMH Mike Hampton SP
GOV Omar Vizquel SP
GPM Pedro Martinez SP
GPN Phil Nevin 4.00 10.00
GRA Roberto Alomar 6.00 15.00
GRK Ryan Klesko SP
GRP Robert Person 4.00 10.00
GRY Robin Yount 6.00 15.00
GSR Scott Rolen 6.00 15.00
GTG Tom Glavine 6.00 15.00
GTM Tino Martinez 6.00 15.00

2002 Upper Deck Global Swatch Game Jersey

Issued at a rate of one in 144 first series packs, these 10 cards feature swatches of game jerseys worn by players who were born outside the continental United States.

GSBK Byung-Hyun Kim 4.00 10.00
GSCD Carlos Delgado 4.00 10.00
GSCP Chan Ho Park 4.00 10.00
GSHN Hideo Nomo 15.00 40.00
GSIS Ichiro Suzuki 20.00 50.00
GSKS Kazuhiro Sasaki 4.00 10.00
GSMR Manny Ramirez 6.00 15.00

GSMY Masato Yoshii 4.00 10.00
GSSH Shig Hasegawa 4.00 10.00
GSTS Tsuyoshi Shinjo 4.00 10.00

2002 Upper Deck Global Swatch Game Jersey Autograph

Randomly inserted into first series packs, these five cards feature not only a game-jersey swatch but also authentic autographs from the players. These cards are serial numbered to 25. Due to market scarcity, no pricing is provided.

SGSBK Byung-Hyun Kim
SGSCD Carlos Delgado
SGSCP Chan Ho Park
SGSHN Hideo Nomo
SGSTS Tsuyoshi Shinjo

2002 Upper Deck McGwire Combo Jersey

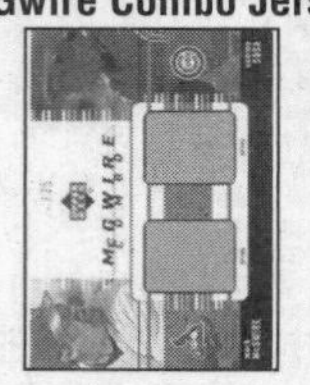

Randomly inserted in second series packs, these three cards feature swatches of Mark McGwire pictured alongside another active slugger. These cards were printed to a stated print run of 25 serial numbered sets and no pricing is available due to market scarcity.

MMJG Mark McGwire
Jason Giambi
MMKG Mark McGwire
Ken Griffey Jr.
MMSS Mark McGwire
Sammy Sosa

2002 Upper Deck Peoples Choice Game Jersey

Inserted in second series hobby packs at a stated rate of one in 24, these 39 cards feature some of the most popular player in baseball along with a game-worn memorabilia swatch. A few cards were in lesser quantity and we have notated those cards with an SP in our checklist.

PJAG Andres Galarraga SP 6.00 15.00
PJAP Andy Pettitte 6.00 15.00
PJAR Alex Rodriguez 6.00 15.00
PJBG Brian Giles 4.00 10.00
PJBW Bernie Williams 6.00 15.00
PJCD Carlos Delgado 4.00 10.00
PJCJ Charles Johnson 4.00 10.00
PJCS Curt Schilling 4.00 10.00
PJDL Derek Lowe 4.00 10.00
PJDW David Wells 4.00 10.00
PJEB Ellis Burks SP 6.00 15.00
PJFT Frank Thomas 6.00 15.00
PJGM Greg Maddux 6.00 15.00
PJHI Hideki Irabu 4.00 10.00
PJJG Juan Gonzalez 4.00 10.00
PJJN Jeff Nelson 4.00 10.00
PJJS J.T. Snow 4.00 10.00
PJJBA Jeff Bagwell 6.00 15.00
PJJBU Jeromy Burnitz 4.00 10.00
PJKG Ken Griffey Jr. 8.00 20.00
PJMP Mike Piazza 6.00 15.00
PJMS Mike Stanton 4.00 10.00
PJMW Matt Williams SP 6.00 15.00
PJMRA Manny Ramirez 6.00 15.00
PJMRI Mariano Rivera 6.00 15.00
PJOD Omar Daal 4.00 10.00
PJOV Omar Vizquel 6.00 15.00
PJRF Rafael Furcal 4.00 10.00
PJRO Rey Ordonez 4.00 10.00
PJRP Rafael Palmeiro SP 10.00 25.00
PJRP Robert Person SP 6.00 15.00
PJRV Robin Ventura 4.00 10.00
PJSH Sterling Hitchcock 4.00 10.00
PJSS Sammy Sosa 6.00 15.00
PJTG Tony Gwynn 6.00 15.00
PJTM Tino Martinez 6.00 15.00
PJTR Tim Raines Sr. 4.00 10.00
PJTS Tim Salmon 6.00 15.00
PJTSh Tsuyoshi Shinjo 4.00 10.00

2002 Upper Deck Return of the Ace

Inserted into second series packs at a stated rate of one in 11 packs, these 15 cards feature some of today's leading pitchers.

COMPLETE SET (15) 12.50 30.00
RA1 Randy Johnson 1.25 3.00
RA2 Greg Maddux 2.00 5.00
RA3 Pedro Martinez .75 2.00
RA4 Freddy Garcia .75 2.00
RA5 Matt Morris .75 2.00
RA6 Mark Mulder .75 2.00
RA7 Wade Miller .75 2.00
RA8 Kevin Brown .75 2.00
RA9 Roger Clemens 2.50 6.00
RA10 Jon Lieber .75 2.00
RA11 C.C. Sabathia .75 2.00
RA12 Tim Hudson .75 2.00
RA13 Curt Schilling .75 2.00
RA14 Al Leiter .75 2.00
RA15 Mike Mussina .75 2.00

2002 Upper Deck Sons of Summer Game Jersey

Inserted at a stated rate of one in 288 second series packs, these eight cards feature some of the best players in the game along with a game jersey swatch. According to Upper Deck, the Pedro Martinez card was issued in shorter supply.

SSAR Alex Rodriguez 8.00 20.00
SSGM Greg Maddux 8.00 20.00
SSJB Jeff Bagwell 8.00 20.00
SSJG Juan Gonzalez 6.00 15.00
SSMP Mike Piazza 8.00 20.00
SSPM Pedro Martinez SP 10.00 25.00
SSRA Roberto Alomar 8.00 20.00
SSRC Roger Clemens 12.50 30.00

2002 Upper Deck Superstar Summit I

Inserted into first series packs at a rate of one in 23, these six cards feature the most popular players in the game.

COMPLETE SET (6) 10.00 25.00
SS1 Sammy Sosa 1.50 4.00
SS2 Alex Rodriguez 1.50 4.00
SS3 Mark McGwire 2.50 6.00
SS4 Barry Bonds 2.50 6.00
SS5 Mike Piazza 1.50 4.00
SS6 Ken Griffey Jr. 1.50 4.00

2002 Upper Deck Superstar Summit II

Inserted into second series packs at a rate of one in 11, these fifteen cards feature the most popular players in the game.

COMPLETE SET (15) 25.00 60.00
SS1 Alex Rodriguez 2.00 5.00
SS2 Jason Giambi 1.25 3.00
SS3 Vladimir Guerrero 1.25 3.00
SS4 Randy Johnson 1.25 3.00
SS5 Chipper Jones 1.25 3.00
SS6 Ichiro Suzuki 2.50 6.00
SS7 Sammy Sosa 1.25 3.00
SS8 Greg Maddux 2.00 5.00
SS9 Ken Griffey Jr. 2.00 5.00

SS10 Todd Helton 1.25 3.00
SS11 Barry Bonds 3.00 8.00
SS12 Derek Jeter 3.00 8.00
SS13 Mike Piazza 2.00 5.00
SS14 Ivan Rodriguez 1.25 3.00
SS15 Frank Thomas 1.25 3.00

2002 Upper Deck UD Plus Hobby

Issued as a two-card box topper in second series Upper Deck packs, these 100 cards could be exchanged for Joe DiMaggio or Mickey Mantle jersey cards if a collector finished the entire set. These cards were numbered to a stated print run of 1125 serial numbered sets. Hobby cards feature silver foil accents on front (unlike the Retail UD Plus cards - of which feature bronze fronts and backs). These cards could be exchanged until May 16, 2003.

UD1 Darin Erstad 2.00 5.00
UD2 Troy Glaus 2.00 5.00
UD3 Tim Hudson 2.00 5.00
UD4 Jermaine Dye 2.00 5.00
UD5 Barry Zito 2.00 5.00
UD6 Carlos Delgado 2.00 5.00
UD7 Shannon Stewart 2.00 5.00
UD8 Greg Vaughn 2.00 5.00
UD9 Jim Thome 2.00 5.00
UD10 C.C. Sabathia 2.00 5.00
UD11 Ichiro Suzuki 5.00 12.00
UD12 Edgar Martinez 2.00 5.00
UD13 Bret Boone 2.00 5.00
UD14 Freddy Garcia 2.00 5.00
UD15 Matt Thornton 2.00 5.00
UD16 Jeff Conine 2.00 5.00
UD17 Steve Bechler 2.00 5.00
UD18 Rafael Palmeiro 2.00 5.00
UD19 Juan Gonzalez 2.00 5.00
UD20 Alex Rodriguez 4.00 10.00
UD21 Ivan Rodriguez 2.00 5.00
UD22 Carl Everett 2.00 5.00
UD23 Manny Ramirez 2.00 5.00
UD24 Nomar Garciaparra 4.00 10.00
UD25 Pedro Martinez 2.00 5.00
UD26 Mike Sweeney 2.00 5.00
UD27 Chuck Knoblauch 2.00 5.00
UD28 Dmitri Young 2.00 5.00
UD29 Bobby Higginson 2.00 5.00
UD30 Dean Palmer 2.00 5.00
UD31 Doug Mientkiewicz 2.00 5.00
UD32 Corey Koskie 2.00 5.00
UD33 Brad Radke 2.00 5.00
UD34 Cristian Guzman 2.00 5.00
UD35 Frank Thomas 2.50 6.00
UD36 Magglio Ordonez 2.00 5.00
UD37 Carlos Lee 2.00 5.00
UD38 Roger Clemens 5.00 12.00
UD39 Bernie Williams 2.00 5.00
UD40 Derek Jeter 6.00 15.00
UD41 Jason Giambi 2.00 5.00
UD42 Mike Mussina 2.00 5.00
UD43 Jeff Bagwell 2.00 5.00
UD44 Lance Berkman 2.00 5.00
UD45 Wade Miller 2.00 5.00
UD46 Greg Maddux 4.00 10.00
UD47 Chipper Jones 2.50 6.00
UD48 Andruw Jones 2.00 5.00
UD49 Gary Sheffield 2.00 5.00
UD50 Richie Sexson 2.00 5.00
UD51 Albert Pujols 5.00 12.00
UD52 J.D. Drew 2.00 5.00
UD53 Matt Morris 2.00 5.00
UD54 Jim Edmonds 2.00 5.00
UD55 So Taguchi 2.00 5.00
UD56 Sammy Sosa 2.50 6.00
UD57 Fred McGriff 2.00 5.00
UD58 Kerry Wood 2.00 5.00
UD59 Moises Alou 2.00 5.00
UD60 Randy Johnson 2.50 6.00
UD61 Luis Gonzalez 2.00 5.00
UD62 Mark Grace 2.00 5.00
UD63 Curt Schilling 2.00 5.00
UD64 Matt Williams 2.00 5.00
UD65 Kevin Brown 2.00 5.00
UD66 Brian Jordan 2.00 5.00
UD67 Shawn Green 2.00 5.00
UD68 Hideo Nomo 5.00 12.00
UD69 Kazuhisa Ishii 2.00 5.00
UD70 Vladimir Guerrero 2.50 6.00
UD71 Jose Vidro 2.00 5.00
UD72 Eric Good 2.00 5.00
UD73 Barry Bonds 6.00 15.00
UD74 Jeff Kent 2.00 5.00
UD75 Rich Aurilia 2.00 5.00
UD76 Deivis Santos 2.00 5.00
UD77 Preston Wilson 2.00 5.00
UD78 Cliff Floyd 2.00 5.00
UD79 Josh Beckett 2.00 5.00
UD80 Hansel Izquierdo 2.00 5.00
UD81 Mike Piazza 4.00 10.00
UD82 Roberto Alomar 2.00 5.00
UD83 Mo Vaughn 2.00 5.00
UD84 Jeromy Burnitz 2.00 5.00
UD85 Phil Nevin 2.00 5.00
UD86 Ryan Klesko 2.00 5.00
UD87 Bobby Abreu 2.00 5.00
UD88 Scott Rolen 2.00 5.00
UD89 Jimmy Rollins 2.00 5.00
UD90 Jason Kendall 2.00 5.00
UD91 Brian Giles 2.00 5.00
UD92 Aramis Ramirez 2.00 5.00
UD93 Ken Griffey Jr. 4.00 10.00
UD94 Sean Casey 2.00 5.00
UD95 Barry Larkin 2.00 5.00
UD96 Adam Dunn 2.00 5.00
UD97 Todd Helton 2.00 5.00
UD98 Larry Walker 2.00 5.00
UD99 Mike Hampton 2.00 5.00
UD100 Rene Reyes 2.00 5.00

2002 Upper Deck UD Plus Memorabilia Moments Game Uniform

These cards were available only through a mail exchange. Collectors who finished the UD Plus set earliest had an opportunity to receive cards with game-used jersey swatches of either Mickey Mantle or Joe DiMaggio. These cards were issued to a stated print run of 25 serial numbered sets. The deadline to redeem these cards was 5/16/03. Due to market scarcity, no pricing will be provided for these cards.

COMMON DIMAGGIO (1-5) 60.00 120.00
COMMON MANTLE (1-5) 150.00 250.00
AVAILABLE VIA MAIL EXCHANGE
STATED PRINT RUN 25 SERIAL #'d SETS

2002 Upper Deck World Series Heroes Memorabilia

Issued into first series packs at a rate of one in 288 hobby packs, these eight cards feature memorabilia from players who had star moments in the World Series.

BDJ Derek Jeter Base SP 15.00 40.00
BES E.Slaughter Bat 6.00 15.00
BJD Joe DiMaggio Bat SP 50.00 100.00
BKP Kirby Puckett Bat 10.00 25.00
BMM M.Mantle Bat 75.00 150.00
SBM B.Mazeroski Jsy 8.00 20.00
SCF Carlton Fisk Jsy 8.00 20.00
SDL Don Larsen Jsy 8.00 20.00
SJC Joe Carter Jsy 6.00 15.00

2002 Upper Deck World Series Heroes Memorabilia Autograph

Randomly inserted in first series hobby packs, these four cards feature not only a piece of memorabilia from a World Series hero but also were signed by the featured player. A stated print run of twenty-five serial numbered cards were produced. Due to market scarcity, no pricing is provided for these cards.

SBM Bill Mazeroski Jsy
SCF Carlton Fisk Jsy
SDL Don Larsen Jsy
SJC Joe Carter Jsy

2002 Upper Deck Yankee Dynasty Memorabilia

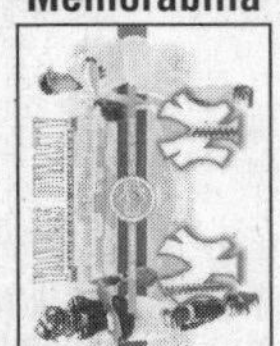

Issued into first series packs at a rate of one in 144, these 13 cards feature two pieces of game-worn memorabilia from various members of the Yankees Dynasty.

YBCJ Roger Clemens Base 75.00 150.00
Derek Jeter Base SP
YBJW Derek Jeter Base 50.00 100.00
Bernie Williams Base
YJBJ Scott Brosius Jsy 10.00 25.00
David Justice Jsy
YJBT Wade Bogg Jsys 10.00 25.00
Joe Torre Jsy
YJCP Roger Clemens Jsy 20.00 50.00
Jorge Posada Jsy
YJDM Joe DiMaggio Jsy 150.00 250.00
Mickey Mantle Jsy
YJGC Joe Girardi Jsy 10.00 25.00
David Cone Jsy
YJKR Chuck Knoblauch Jsy 10.00 25.00
Tim Raines Jsy
YJOM Paul O'Neill Jsy 10.00 25.00
Tino Martinez Jsy
YJPR Andy Pettitte Jsy 15.00 40.00
Mariano Rivera Jsy
YJRK Willie Randolph Jsy 10.00 25.00
Chuck Knoblauch Jsy
YJWG David Wells Jsy 10.00 25.00
Dwight Gooden Jsy
YJWO Bernie Williams Jsy 10.00 25.00
Paul O'Neill Jsy

2003 Upper Deck

The 270 card first series was released in November, 2002. The 270 card second series was released in June, 2003. The final 60 cards were released as part of an special boxed insert in the 2004 Upper Deck Series one product. The first tw series cards were issued in eight card packs which came 24 packs to a box and 12 boxes to a case with an SRP of $3 per pack. Cards numbered from 1 through 30 featured leading rookie prospects while cards numbered from 261 through 270 featured checklist cards honoring the leading events of the 2002 season. In the second series the following subsets were issued: Cards numbered 501 through 530 feature Star Rookies while cards numbered 531 through 540 feature Season Highlight fronts and checklist backs. Due to an error in printing, card 19 was originally intended to feature Marcos Scutaro but the card was erroneosuly numbered as card 96. Thus, the set features two card 96's (Scutaro and Nomar Garciaparra) and no card number 19.

COMPLETE SERIES 1 (270) 20.00 50.00
COMPLETE SERIES 2 (270) 20.00 50.00
COMP.UPDATE SET (60) 10.00 20.00
COMMON (31-500/531-600) .10 .30
COMMON (1-30/501-530) .40 1.00
COMMON RC (541-600) .20 .50
SR 1-30/501-530 ARE NOT SHORT PRINTS
CARD 19 DOES NOT EXIST
SCUTARO/NOMAR ARE BOTH CARD 96
541-600 ISSUED IN 04 UD1 HOBBY BOXES
UPDATE SET EXCH 1:240 '04 UD1 RETAIL
UPDATE SET EXCH.DEADLINE 11/10/06

1 John Lackey SR .40 1.00
2 Alex Cintron SR .40 1.00
3 Jose Leon SR .40 1.00
4 Bobby Hill SR .40 1.00
5 Brandon Larson SR .40 1.00
6 Raul Gonzalez SR .40 1.00
7 Ben Broussard SR .40 1.00
8 Earl Snyder SR .40 1.00
9 Ramon Santiago SR .40 1.00
10 Jason Lane SR .40 1.00
11 Keith Ginter SR .40 1.00
12 Kirk Saarloos SR .40 1.00
13 Juan Brito SR .40 1.00
14 Runelvys Hernandez SR .40 1.00
15 Shawn Sedlacek SR .40 1.00
16 Jayson Durocher SR .40 1.00
17 Kevin Frederick SR .40 1.00
18 Zach Day SR .40 1.00
19 Marcos Scutaro SR UER .40 1.00
Card number 96 on back
20 Marcus Thames SR .40 1.00
21 Esteban German SR .40 1.00
22 Brett Myers SR .40 1.00
23 Oliver Perez SR .40 1.00
24 Dennis Tankersley SR .40 1.00
25 Julius Matos SR .40 1.00
26 Jake Peavy SR .40 1.00
27 Eric Cyr SR .40 1.00
28 Mike Crudale SR .40 1.00
29 Josh Pearce SR .40 1.00
30 Carl Crawford SR .40 1.00
31 Tim Salmon .20 .50
32 Troy Glaus .10 .30
33 Adam Kennedy .10 .30
34 David Eckstein .10 .30
35 Ben Molina .10 .30
36 Jarrod Washburn .10 .30
37 Ramon Ortiz .10 .30
38 Eric Chavez .10 .30
39 Miguel Tejada .10 .30
40 Adam Piatt .10 .30
41 Jermaine Dye .10 .30
42 Olmedo Saenz .10 .30
43 Tim Hudson .10 .30
44 Barry Zito .10 .30
45 Billy Koch .10 .30
46 Shannon Stewart .10 .30
47 Kelvim Escobar .10 .30
48 Jose Cruz Jr. .10 .30
49 Vernon Wells .10 .30
50 Roy Halladay .10 .30
51 Esteban Loaiza .10 .30
52 Eric Hinske .10 .30
53 Steve Cox .10 .30
54 Brent Abernathy .10 .30
55 Ben Grieve .10 .30
56 Aubrey Huff .10 .30
57 Jared Sandberg .10 .30
58 Paul Wilson .10 .30
59 Tanyon Sturtze .10 .30
60 Jim Thome .20 .50
61 Omar Vizquel .20 .50
62 C.C. Sabathia .10 .30
63 Chris Magruder .10 .30
64 Ricky Gutierrez .10 .30
65 Einar Diaz .10 .30
66 Danys Baez .10 .30
67 Ichiro Suzuki .60 1.50
68 Ruben Sierra .10 .30
69 Carlos Guillen .10 .30
70 Mark McLemore .10 .30
71 Dan Wilson .10 .30
72 Jamie Moyer .10 .30
73 Joel Pineiro .10 .30
74 Edgar Martinez .20 .50
75 Tony Batista .10 .30
76 Jay Gibbons .10 .30
77 Chris Singleton .10 .30
78 Melvin Mora .10 .30
79 Geronimo Gil .10 .30
80 Rodrigo Lopez .10 .30
81 Jorge Julio .10 .30
82 Rafael Palmeiro .20 .50
83 Juan Gonzalez .10 .30
84 Mike Young .20 .50
85 Hideki Irabu .10 .30
86 Chan Ho Park .10 .30
87 Kevin Mench .10 .30
88 Doug Davis .10 .30
89 Pedro Martinez .20 .50
90 Shea Hillenbrand .10 .30
91 Derek Lowe .10 .30
92 Jason Varitek .30 .75
93 Tony Clark .10 .30
94 John Burkett .10 .30
95 Frank Castillo .10 .30
96 Nomar Garciaparra .50 1.25
97 Rickey Henderson .30 .75
98 Mike Sweeney .10 .30
99 Carlos Febles .10 .30
100 Mark Quinn .10 .30
101 Raul Ibanez .10 .30
102 A.J. Hinch .10 .30
103 Paul Byrd .10 .30
104 Chuck Knoblauch .10 .30
105 Dmitri Young .10 .30
106 Randall Simon .10 .30
107 Brandon Inge .10 .30
108 Damion Easley .10 .30
109 Carlos Pena .10 .30
110 George Lombard .10 .30
111 Juan Acevedo .10 .30
112 Torii Hunter .10 .30
113 Doug Mientkiewicz .10 .30
114 David Ortiz .20 .50
115 Eric Milton .10 .30
116 Eddie Guardado .10 .30
117 Cristian Guzman .10 .30
118 Corey Koskie .10 .30
119 Magglio Ordonez .10 .30
120 Mark Buehrle .10 .30
121 Todd Ritchie .10 .30
122 Jose Valentin .10 .30
123 Paul Konerko .10 .30
124 Carlos Lee .10 .30
125 Jon Garland .10 .30
126 Jason Giambi .10 .30
127 Derek Jeter .75 2.00
128 Roger Clemens .60 1.50
129 Raul Mondesi .10 .30
130 Jorge Posada .20 .50
131 Rondell White .10 .30
132 Robin Ventura .10 .30
133 Mike Mussina .20 .50
134 Jeff Bagwell .20 .50
135 Craig Biggio .20 .50
136 Morgan Ensberg .10 .30
137 Richard Hidalgo .10 .30
138 Brad Ausmus .10 .30
139 Roy Oswalt .10 .30
140 Carlos Hernandez .10 .30
141 Shane Reynolds .10 .30
142 Gary Sheffield .10 .30
143 Andruw Jones .20 .50
144 Tom Glavine .20 .50
145 Rafael Furcal .10 .30
146 Javy Lopez .10 .30
147 Vinny Castilla .10 .30
148 Marcus Giles .10 .30
149 Kevin Millwood .10 .30
150 Jason Marquis .10 .30
151 Ruben Quevedo .10 .30
152 Ben Sheets .10 .30
153 Geoff Jenkins .10 .30
154 Jose Hernandez .10 .30
155 Glendon Rusch .10 .30
156 Jeffrey Hammonds .10 .30
157 Alex Sanchez .10 .30
158 Jim Edmonds .10 .30
159 Tino Martinez .20 .50
160 Albert Pujols .60 1.50
161 Eli Marrero .10 .30
162 Woody Williams .10 .30
163 Fernando Vina .10 .30
164 Jason Isringhausen .10 .30
165 Jason Simontacchi .10 .30
166 Kerry Robinson .10 .30
167 Sammy Sosa .30 .75
168 Juan Cruz .10 .30
169 Fred McGriff .20 .50
170 Antonio Alfonseca .10 .30
171 Jon Lieber .10 .30
172 Mark Prior .20 .50
173 Moises Alou .10 .30
174 Matt Clement .10 .30
175 Mark Bellhorn .10 .30
176 Randy Johnson .30 .75
177 Luis Gonzalez .10 .30
178 Tony Womack .10 .30
179 Mark Grace .20 .50
180 Junior Spivey .10 .30
181 Byung Hyun Kim .10 .30
182 Danny Bautista .10 .30
183 Brian Anderson .10 .30
184 Shawn Green .10 .30
185 Brian Jordan .10 .30
186 Eric Karros .10 .30
187 Andy Ashby .10 .30
188 Cesar Izturis .10 .30
189 Dave Roberts .10 .30
190 Eric Gagne .10 .30
191 Kazuhisa Ishii .10 .30
192 Adrian Beltre .10 .30
193 Vladimir Guerrero .30 .75
194 Tony Armas Jr. .10 .30
195 Bartolo Colon .10 .30
196 Troy O'Leary .10 .30
197 Tomo Ohka .10 .30
198 Brad Wilkerson .10 .30
199 Orlando Cabrera .10 .30
200 Barry Bonds .75 2.00
201 David Bell .10 .30
202 Tsuyoshi Shinjo .10 .30
203 Benito Santiago .10 .30
204 Livan Hernandez .10 .30
205 Jason Schmidt .10 .30
206 Kirk Rueter .10 .30
207 Ramon E. Martinez .10 .30
208 Mike Lowell .10 .30
209 Luis Castillo .10 .30
210 Derrek Lee .20 .50
211 Andy Fox .10 .30
212 Eric Owens .10 .30
213 Charles Johnson .10 .30
214 Brad Penny .10 .30
215 A.J. Burnett .10 .30
216 Edgardo Alfonzo .10 .30
217 Roberto Alomar .20 .50
218 Rey Ordonez .10 .30
219 Al Leiter .10 .30
220 Roger Cedeno .10 .30
221 Timo Perez .10 .30
222 Jeromy Burnitz .10 .30
223 Pedro Astacio .10 .30
224 Joe McEwing .10 .30
225 Ryan Klesko .10 .30
226 Ramon Vazquez .10 .30
227 Mark Kotsay .10 .30
228 Bubba Trammell .10 .30
229 Wiki Gonzalez .10 .30
230 Trevor Hoffman .10 .30
231 Ron Gant .10 .30
232 Bob Abreu .10 .30
233 Marlon Anderson .10 .30
234 Jeremy Giambi .10 .30
235 Jimmy Rollins .10 .30
236 Mike Lieberthal .10 .30
237 Vicente Padilla .10 .30
238 Randy Wolf .10 .30
239 Pokey Reese .10 .30
240 Brian Giles .10 .30
241 Jack Wilson .10 .30
242 Mike Williams .10 .30
243 Kip Wells .10 .30
244 Rob Mackowiak .10 .30
245 Craig Wilson .10 .30
246 Adam Dunn .10 .30
247 Sean Casey .10 .30
248 Todd Walker .10 .30
249 Corky Miller .10 .30
250 Ryan Dempster .10 .30
251 Reggie Taylor .10 .30
252 Aaron Boone .10 .30
253 Larry Walker .10 .30
254 Jose Ortiz .10 .30
255 Todd Zeile .10 .30
256 Bobby Estalella .10 .30
257 Juan Pierre .10 .30
258 Terry Shumpert .10 .30
259 Mike Hampton .10 .30
260 Denny Stark .10 .30
261 Shawn Green SH CL .10 .30
262 Derek Lowe SH CL .10 .30
263 Barry Bonds SH CL .40 1.00
264 Mike Cameron SH CL .10 .30
265 Luis Castillo SH CL .10 .30
266 Vladimir Guerrero SH CL .20 .50
267 Jason Giambi SH CL .10 .30
268 Eric Gagne SH CL .10 .30
269 Magglio Ordonez SH CL .10 .30
270 Jim Thome SH CL .10 .30
271 Garret Anderson .10 .30
272 Troy Percival .10 .30
273 Brad Fullmer .10 .30
274 Scott Spiezio .10 .30
275 Darin Erstad .10 .30
276 Francisco Rodriguez .10 .30
277 Kevin Appier .10 .30
278 Shawn Wooten .10 .30
279 Eric Owens .10 .30
280 Scott Hatteberg .10 .30
281 Terrence Long .10 .30
282 Mark Mulder .10 .30
283 Ramon Hernandez .10 .30
284 Ted Lilly .10 .30
285 Erubiel Durazo .10 .30
286 Mark Ellis .10 .30
287 Carlos Delgado .10 .30
288 Orlando Hudson .10 .30
289 Chris Woodward .10 .30
290 Mark Hendrickson .10 .30
291 Josh Phelps .10 .30
292 Ken Huckaby .10 .30
293 Justin Miller .10 .30
294 Travis Lee .10 .30
295 Jorge Sosa .10 .30
296 Joe Kennedy .10 .30
297 Carl Crawford .10 .30
298 Toby Hall .10 .30
299 Rey Ordonez .10 .30
300 Brandon Phillips .10 .30
301 Matt Lawton .10 .30
302 Ellis Burks .10 .30
303 Bill Selby .10 .30
304 Travis Hafner .10 .30
305 Milton Bradley .10 .30
306 Karim Garcia .10 .30
307 Cliff Lee .10 .30
308 Jeff Cirillo .10 .30
309 John Olerud .10 .30
310 Kazuhiro Sasaki .10 .30
311 Freddy Garcia .10 .30
312 Bret Boone .10 .30
313 Mike Cameron .10 .30
314 Ben Davis .10 .30
315 Randy Winn .10 .30
316 Gary Matthews Jr. .10 .30
317 Jeff Conine .10 .30
318 Sidney Ponson .10 .30
319 Jerry Hairston .10 .30
320 David Segui .10 .30
321 Scott Erickson .10 .30
322 Marty Cordova .10 .30
323 Hank Blalock .10 .30
324 Herbert Perry .10 .30
325 Alex Rodriguez .50 1.25
326 Carl Everett .10 .30
327 Einar Diaz .10 .30
328 Ugueth Urbina .10 .30
329 Mark Teixeira .20 .50
330 Manny Ramirez .20 .50
331 Johnny Damon .20 .50
332 Trot Nixon .10 .30
333 Tim Wakefield .10 .30
334 Casey Fossum .10 .30
335 Todd Walker .10 .30
336 Jeremy Giambi .10 .30
337 Bill Mueller .10 .30
338 Ramiro Mendoza .10 .30
339 Carlos Beltran .10 .30
340 Jason Grimsley .10 .30
341 Brent Mayne .10 .30
342 Angel Berroa .10 .30
343 Albie Lopez .10 .30
344 Michael Tucker .10 .30
345 Bobby Higginson .10 .30
346 Shane Halter .10 .30
347 Jeremy Bonderman RC 1.50 4.00
348 Eric Munson .10 .30
349 Andy Van Hekken .10 .30
350 Matt Anderson .10 .30
351 Jacque Jones .10 .30
352 A.J. Pierzynski .10 .30
353 Joe Mays .10 .30
354 Brad Radke .10 .30
355 Dustan Mohr .10 .30
356 Bobby Kielty .10 .30
357 Michael Cuddyer .10 .30
358 Luis Rivas .10 .30
359 Frank Thomas .30 .75
360 Joe Borchard .10 .30
361 D'Angelo Jimenez .10 .30
362 Bartolo Colon .10 .30
363 Joe Crede .10 .30
364 Miguel Olivo .10 .30
365 Billy Koch .10 .30
366 Bernie Williams .20 .50
367 Nick Johnson .10 .30
368 Andy Pettitte .20 .50
369 Mariano Rivera .30 .75
370 Alfonso Soriano .10 .30
371 David Wells .10 .30
372 Drew Henson .10 .30
373 Juan Rivera .10 .30
374 Steve Karsay .10 .30
375 Jeff Kent .10 .30
376 Lance Berkman .10 .30
377 Octavio Dotel .10 .30
378 Julio Lugo .10 .30
379 Jason Lane .10 .30
380 Wade Miller .10 .30
381 Billy Wagner .10 .30
382 Brad Ausmus .10 .30
383 Mike Hampton .10 .30
384 Chipper Jones .30 .75
385 John Smoltz .20 .50
386 Greg Maddux .50 1.25
387 Javy Lopez .10 .30
388 Robert Fick .10 .30
389 Mark DeRosa .10 .30
390 Russ Ortiz .10 .30
391 Julio Franco .10 .30
392 Richie Sexson .10 .30
393 Eric Young .10 .30
394 Robert Machado .10 .30
395 Mike DeJean .10 .30
396 Todd Ritchie .10 .30
397 Royce Clayton .10 .30
398 Nick Neugebauer .10 .30
399 J.D. Drew .10 .30
400 Edgar Renteria .10 .30
401 Scott Rolen .20 .50
402 Matt Morris .10 .30
403 Garrett Stephenson .10 .30
404 Eduardo Perez .10 .30
405 Mike Matheny .10 .30
406 Miguel Cairo .10 .30
407 Brett Tomko .10 .30
408 Bobby Hill .10 .30
409 Troy O'Leary .10 .30
410 Corey Patterson .10 .30
411 Kerry Wood .10 .30
412 Eric Karros .10 .30
413 Hee Seop Choi .10 .30
414 Alex Gonzalez .10 .30
415 Matt Clement .10 .30
416 Mark Grudzielanek .10 .30
417 Curt Schilling .10 .30
418 Steve Finley .10 .30
419 Craig Counsell .10 .30
420 Matt Williams .10 .30
421 Quinton McCracken .10 .30
422 Chad Moeller .10 .30
423 Lyle Overbay .10 .30
424 Miguel Batista .10 .30
425 Paul Lo Duca .10 .30
426 Kevin Brown .10 .30
427 Hideo Nomo .30 .75
428 Fred McGriff .20 .50
429 Joe Thurston .10 .30
430 Odalis Perez .10 .30
431 Darren Dreifort .10 .30
432 Todd Hundley .10 .30
433 Dave Roberts .10 .30
434 Jose Vidro .10 .30
435 Javier Vazquez .10 .30
436 Michael Barrett .10 .30
437 Fernando Tatis .10 .30
438 Peter Bergeron .10 .30
439 Endy Chavez .10 .30
440 Orlando Hernandez .10 .30
441 Marvin Benard .10 .30
442 Rich Aurilia .10 .30
443 Pedro Feliz .10 .30
444 Robb Nen .10 .30
445 Ray Durham .10 .30
446 Marquis Grissom .10 .30
447 Damian Moss .10 .30
448 Edgardo Alfonzo .10 .30
449 Juan Pierre .10 .30
450 Braden Looper .10 .30
451 Alex Gonzalez .10 .30
452 Justin Wayne .10 .30
453 Josh Beckett .10 .30
454 Juan Encarnacion .10 .30
455 Ivan Rodriguez .20 .50
456 Todd Hollandsworth .10 .30
457 Cliff Floyd .10 .30
458 Rey Sanchez .10 .30
459 Mike Piazza .50 1.25
460 Mo Vaughn .10 .30
461 Armando Benitez .10 .30

462 Tsuyoshi Shinjo .10 .30
463 Tom Glavine .20 .50
464 David Cone .10 .30
465 Phil Nevin .10 .30
466 Sean Burroughs .10 .30
467 Jake Peavy .10 .30
468 Brian Lawrence .10 .30
469 Mark Loretta .10 .30
470 Dennis Tankersley .10 .30
471 Jesse Orosco .10 .30
472 Jim Thome .20 .50
473 Kevin Millwood .10 .30
474 David Bell .10 .30
475 Pat Burrell .10 .30
476 Brandon Duckworth .10 .30
477 Jose Mesa .10 .30
478 Marlon Byrd .10 .30
479 Reggie Sanders .10 .30
480 Jason Kendall .10 .30
481 Aramis Ramirez .10 .30
482 Kris Benson .10 .30
483 Matt Stairs .10 .30
484 Kevin Young .10 .30
485 Kenny Lofton .10 .30
486 Austin Kearns .10 .30
487 Barry Larkin .20 .50
488 Jason LaRue .10 .30
489 Ken Griffey Jr. .50 1.25
490 Danny Graves .10 .30
491 Russell Branyan .10 .30
492 Reggie Taylor .10 .30
493 Jimmy Haynes .10 .30
494 Charles Johnson .10 .30
495 Todd Helton .20 .50
496 Juan Uribe .10 .30
497 Preston Wilson .10 .30
498 Chris Stynes .10 .30
499 Jason Jennings .10 .30
500 Jay Payton .10 .30
501 Hideki Matsui SR RC 2.00 5.00
502 Jose Contreras SR RC .60 1.50
503 Brandon Webb SR RC 1.25 3.00
504 Robby Hammock SR RC .40 1.00
505 Matt Kata SR RC .40 1.00
506 Tim Olson SR RC .40 1.00
507 Michael Hessman SR RC .40 1.00
508 Jon Leicester SR RC .40 1.00
509 Todd Wellemeyer SR RC .40 1.00
510 David Sanders SR RC .40 1.00
511 Josh Stewart SR RC .40 1.00
512 Luis Ayala SR RC .40 1.00
513 Clint Barmes SR RC .50 1.25
514 Josh Willingham SR RC .75 2.00
515 Al. Machado SR RC .40 1.00
516 Felix Sanchez SR RC .40 1.00
517 Willie Eyre SR RC .40 1.00
518 Brent Hoard SR RC .40 1.00
519 Lew Ford SR RC .60 1.50
520 Termel Sledge SR RC .40 1.00
521 Jeremy Griffiths SR RC .40 1.00
522 Phil Seibel SR RC .40 1.00
523 Craig Brazell SR RC .40 1.00
524 Prentice Redman SR RC .40 1.00
525 Jeff Duncan SR RC .40 1.00
526 Shane Bazzell SR RC .40 1.00
527 Bernie Castro SR RC .40 1.00
528 Rett Johnson SR RC .40 1.00
529 Bobby Madritsch SR RC .40 1.00
530 Rocco Baldelli SR .40 1.00
531 Alex Rodriguez SH CL .30 .75
532 Eric Chavez SH CL .10 .30
533 Miguel Tejada SH CL .10 .30
534 Ichiro Suzuki SH CL .30 .75
535 Sammy Sosa SH CL .20 .50
536 Barry Zito SH CL .10 .30
537 Darin Erstad SH CL .10 .30
538 Alfonso Soriano SH CL .10 .30
539 Troy Glaus SH CL .10 .30
540 N.Garciaparra SH CL .30 .75
541 Bo Hart RC .20 .50
542 Dan Haren RC .30 .75
543 Ryan Wagner RC .20 .50
544 Rich Harden .20 .50
545 Dontrelle Willis .30 .75
546 Jerome Williams .10 .30
547 Bobby Crosby .10 .30
548 Greg Jones RC .20 .50
549 Todd Linden .10 .30
550 Byung-Hyun Kim .10 .30
551 Rickie Weeks RC 1.25 3.00
552 Jason Roach RC .20 .50
553 Oscar Villarreal RC .20 .50
554 Justin Duchscherer .10 .30
555 Chris Capuano RC .60 1.50
556 Josh Hall RC .20 .50
557 Luis Matos .10 .30
558 Miguel Ojeda RC .20 .50
559 Kevin Ohme RC .20 .50
560 Julio Manon RC .20 .50
561 Kevin Correia RC .20 .50
562 Delmon Young RC 2.00 5.00
563 Aaron Boone .10 .30
564 Aaron Looper RC .20 .50
565 Mike Neu RC .20 .50
566 Alfonso Lopez RC .20 .50
567 Jhonny Peralta .30 .75
568 Duaner Sanchez .10 .30
569 Stephen Randolph RC .20 .50
570 Nate Bland RC .20 .50
571 Chin-Hui Tsao .10 .30
572 Michel Hernandez RC .20 .50
573 Rocco Baldelli .10 .30
574 Robb Quinlan .10 .30
575 Aaron Heilman .10 .30
576 Jae Weong Seo .10 .30
577 Joe Borowski .10 .30
578 Chris Bootcheck .10 .30
579 Michael Ryan RC .20 .50
580 Mark Malaska RC .20 .50
581 Jose Guillen .10 .30
582 Josh Towers .10 .30
583 Tom Gregorio RC .20 .50
584 Edwin Jackson RC .20 .50
585 Jason Anderson .10 .30
586 Jose Reyes .10 .30
587 Miguel Cabrera .30 .75
588 Nate Bump .10 .30
589 Jeromy Burnitz .10 .30
590 David Ross .10 .30
591 Chase Utley .30 .75
592 Brandon Webb .60 1.50
593 Masao Kida .10 .30
594 Jimmy Journell .10 .30
595 Eric Young .10 .30
596 Tony Womack .10 .30
597 Amaury Telemaco .10 .30
598 Rickey Henderson .30 .75
599 Esteban Loaiza .10 .30
600 Sidney Ponson .10 .30
NNO Update Set Exchange Card

2003 Upper Deck Gold

COMP.FACT.SET (60) 15.00 40.00
*GOLD: 2X TO 5X BASIC
*GOLD: 1.25X TO 3X BASIC RC'S
ONE GOLD SET PER 12 CT HOBBY CASE

2003 Upper Deck A Piece of History 500 Club

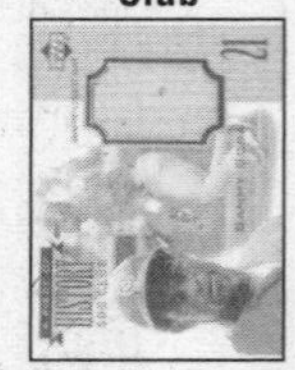

This card, which continues the Upper Deck A Piece of History 500 club set which began in 1999, was randomly inserted into second series packs. These cards were issued to a stated print run of 350 cards.

SS Sammy Sosa 75.00 150.00

2003 Upper Deck A Piece of History 500 Club Autograph

Randomly inserted into packs, this is a parallel to the Piece of History insert card of Sammy Sosa. Sosa signed 21 copies of this card but did not return them in time for pack-out. Please note that the exchange date for these cards are June 9th, 2006 and since only 21 cards were created there is no pricing due to market scarcity.

RANDOM INSERT IN SERIES 2 PACKS
STATED PRINT RUN 21 SERIAL #'d CARDS
NO PRICING DUE TO SCARCITY
EXCHANGE DEADLINE 06/09/06
SSAU Sammy Sosa AU/21

2003 Upper Deck AL All-Star Swatches

Inserted into first series retail packs at a stated rate of one in 144, these 13 cards feature game-used uniform swatches of players who had made the AL All-Star game during their career.

AP Andy Pettitte 6.00 15.00
AS Aaron Sele 4.00 10.00
CE Carl Everett 4.00 10.00
CF Chuck Finley 4.00 10.00
JG Juan Gonzalez 4.00 10.00
JM Joe Mays 4.00 10.00
JP Jorge Posada 6.00 15.00
MC Mike Cameron 4.00 10.00
MO Magglio Ordonez 4.00 10.00
MR Mariano Rivera 6.00 15.00
MS Mike Sweeney 4.00 10.00
RD Ray Durham 4.00 10.00
TF Travis Fryman 4.00 10.00

2003 Upper Deck Big League Breakdowns

Inserted into series one packs at a stated rate of one in eight, these 15 cards feature some of the leading hitters in the game.

COMPLETE SET (15) 15.00 40.00
BL1 Troy Glaus .75 2.00
BL2 Miguel Tejada .75 2.00
BL3 Chipper Jones 1.00 2.50
BL4 Torii Hunter .75 2.00
BL5 Nomar Garciaparra 1.50 4.00

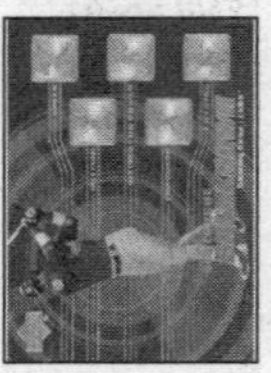

BL6 Sammy Sosa 1.00 2.50
BL7 Todd Helton .75 2.00
BL8 Lance Berkman .75 2.00
BL9 Shawn Green .75 2.00
BL10 Vladimir Guerrero 1.00 2.50
BL11 Jason Giambi .75 2.00
BL12 Derek Jeter 2.50 6.00
BL13 Barry Bonds 2.50 6.00
BL14 Ichiro Suzuki 2.00 5.00
BL15 Alex Rodriguez 1.50 4.00

2003 Upper Deck Chase for 755

Inserted into first series packs at a stated rate of one in eight, these 15 cards feature players who are considered to have some chance of surpassing Hank Aaron's career home run total.

COMPLETE SET (15) 12.50 30.00
C1 Troy Glaus .75 2.00
C2 Andruw Jones .75 2.00
C3 Manny Ramirez .75 2.00
C4 Sammy Sosa 1.00 2.50
C5 Ken Griffey Jr. 1.50 4.00
C6 Adam Dunn .75 2.00
C7 Todd Helton .75 2.00
C8 Lance Berkman .75 2.00
C9 Jeff Bagwell .75 2.00
C10 Shawn Green .75 2.00
C11 Vladimir Guerrero 1.00 2.50
C12 Barry Bonds 2.50 6.00
C13 Alex Rodriguez 1.50 4.00
C14 Juan Gonzalez .75 2.00
C15 Carlos Delgado .75 2.00

2003 Upper Deck Game Swatches

Inserted into first series packs at a stated rate of one in 72, these 25 cards feature game-used memorabilia swatches. A few cards were printed to a lesser quantity and we have notated those cards in our checklist.

HJAR Alex Rodriguez 6.00 15.00
HJBW Bernie Williams 4.00 10.00
HJCC C.C. Sabathia 3.00 8.00
HJCD Carlos Delgado SP 6.00 15.00
HJCP Carlos Pena 3.00 8.00
HJCS Curt Schilling SP/100 6.00 15.00
HJGM Greg Maddux 4.00 10.00
HJMM Mike Mussina 4.00 10.00
HJMO Magglio Ordonez 3.00 8.00
HJMP Mike Piazza SP 10.00 25.00
HJSB Sean Burroughs SP 6.00 15.00
HJSS Sammy Sosa 4.00 10.00
RJAD Adam Dunn 3.00 8.00
RJDE Darin Erstad 3.00 8.00
RJEM Edgar Martinez 4.00 10.00
RJFT Frank Thomas 4.00 10.00
RJIR Ivan Rodriguez 4.00 10.00
RJJD J.D. Drew 3.00 8.00
RJJE Jim Edmonds 3.00 8.00
RJJG Jason Giambi 3.00 8.00
RJJK Jeff Kent 3.00 8.00
RJKG Ken Griffey Jr. 6.00 15.00
RJRC Roger Clemens 8.00 20.00
RJRJ Randy Johnson 4.00 10.00
RJTH Tim Hudson 3.00 8.00

2003 Upper Deck Leading Swatches

SERIES 2 STATED ODDS 1:24 HOB/1:48 RET
SP INFO PROVIDED BY UPPER DECK
SP'S ARE NOT SERIAL-NUMBERED
*GOLD: .75X TO 2X BASIC SWATCHES
*GOLD: .6X TO 1.5X BASIC SP SWATCHES
*GOLD MATSUI HR: .75X TO 1.5X BASIC HR
*GOLD MATSUI RBI: .6X TO 1.2X BASIC RBI
GOLD RANDOM INSERTS IN SER.2 PACKS
GOLD PRINT RUN 100 SERIAL #'d SETS
AB Adrian Beltre GM 3.00 8.00
AD Adam Dunn RUN 3.00 8.00
AD1 Adam Dunn BB SP 4.00 10.00
AJ Andruw Jones HR 4.00 10.00
AJ1 Andruw Jones AB SP 6.00 15.00
AP Andy Pettitte WIN SP 6.00 15.00
AR Alex Rodriguez HR 6.00 15.00
AR1 Alex Rodriguez RBI 6.00 15.00
AS Alfonso Soriano SB 3.00 8.00
AS1 Alfonso Soriano RUN 3.00 8.00
AS2 Aaron Sele WIN 3.00 8.00
BA Bobby Abreu 2B 3.00 8.00
BG Brian Giles HR 3.00 8.00
BG1 Brian Giles OBP 3.00 8.00
BW Bernie Williams 333 AVG 4.00 10.00
BW1 Bernie Williams 339 AVG 4.00 10.00
BZ Barry Zito WIN 3.00 8.00
CD Carlos Delgado RBI 3.00 8.00
CJ Chipper Jones AVG-RBI 4.00 10.00
CP Corey Patterson HR 3.00 8.00
CS Curt Schilling WIN 3.00 8.00
EC Eric Chavez HR 3.00 8.00
GA Garret Anderson RBI 3.00 8.00
GM Greg Maddux 2.62 ERA 4.00 10.00
GM1 Greg Maddux 1.56 ERA SP 6.00 15.00
GO Juan Gonzalez RBI 3.00 8.00
HM Hideki Matsui HR 15.00 40.00
HM1 Hideki Matsui RBI SP 20.00 50.00
HN Hideo Nomo WIN 6.00 15.00
IR Ivan Rodriguez AVG 4.00 10.00
IS Ichiro Suzuki HIT 12.50 30.00
IS1 Ichiro Suzuki SB SP 15.00 40.00
JB Jeff Bagwell RBI 4.00 10.00
JB1 Jeff Bagwell SLG SP 6.00 15.00
JD J.D. Drew RBI 3.00 8.00
JE Jim Edmonds RUN 3.00 8.00
JG Jason Giambi HR 3.00 8.00
JG1 Jason Giambi SLG 3.00 8.00
JL Javy Lopez NLCS 3.00 8.00
JP Jay Payton 3B 3.00 8.00
JS J.T. Snow GLV 3.00 8.00
JT Jim Thome HR 4.00 10.00
JT1 Jim Thome SLG 4.00 10.00
KE Jason Kendall RUN 3.00 8.00
KG Ken Griffey Jr. 40 HR 6.00 15.00
KG1 Ken Griffey Jr. 56 HR SP 8.00 20.00
KI Kazuhisa Ishii K 3.00 8.00
KS Kazuhiro Sasaki SV 3.00 8.00
KW Kerry Wood K 3.00 8.00
LB Lance Berkman HR 3.00 8.00
LG Luis Gonzalez RUN 3.00 8.00
LW Larry Walker AVG 3.00 8.00
MP Mike Piazza HR 6.00 15.00
MP1 Mike Piazza SLG 6.00 15.00
MR Manny Ramirez AVG 4.00 10.00
MSL Mike Sweeney AVG 3.00 8.00
MSW Mike Stanton Pants GM 3.00 8.00
MT Miguel Tejada RBI 3.00 8.00
MT1 Miguel Tejada GM SP 4.00 10.00
OV Omar Vizquel SAC 4.00 10.00
PB Pat Burrell HR 3.00 8.00
PB1 Pat Burrell RBI 3.00 8.00
PM Pedro Martinez K 4.00 10.00
RC Roger Clemens K 6.00 15.00
RC1 Roger Clemens ERA 6.00 15.00
RJ Randy Johnson K 4.00 10.00
RJ1 Randy Johnson ERA 4.00 10.00
RO Roy Oswalt WIN 3.00 8.00
RO1 Roy Oswalt PCT SP 4.00 10.00
RP Rafael Palmeiro RBI 4.00 10.00
RP1 Rafael Palmeiro 2B 4.00 10.00
SG Shawn Green HR 3.00 8.00
SG1 Shawn Green TB 3.00 8.00
SR Scott Rolen HR 4.00 10.00
SS Sammy Sosa 49 HR 4.00 10.00
SS1 Sammy Sosa 50 HR SP/170 6.00 15.00
TB Tony Batista HR 3.00 8.00
TG Troy Glaus HR 3.00 8.00
THE Todd Helton RBI 4.00 10.00
THU Tim Hudson IP 3.00 8.00
THU1 Tim Hudson GM SP 4.00 10.00
TP Troy Percival SV 3.00 8.00
VG Vladimir Guerrero HIT 4.00 10.00

2003 Upper Deck Lineup Time Jerseys

Inserted into first series hobby packs at a stated rate of one in 96, these 10 cards feature game-used uniform swatches from some of the leading players in the game. A couple of cards were printed to a smaller quantity and we have notated those cards with an SP in our checklist.

BW Bernie Williams 4.00 10.00
CD Carlos Delgado 3.00 8.00
GM Greg Maddux 4.00 10.00
IS Ichiro Suzuki 15.00 40.00
JD J.D. Drew 3.00 8.00
JT Jim Thome 4.00 10.00
RC Roger Clemens SP 10.00 25.00
RJ Randy Johnson SP 8.00 20.00
SG Shawn Green 3.00 8.00
TH Todd Helton 4.00 10.00

2003 Upper Deck Magical Performances

*GOLD: 1X TO 2.5X BASIC MAGIC
GOLD RANDOM INSERTS IN SER.2 PACKS
GOLD PRINT RUN 50 SERIAL #'d SETS
DUPE STARS EQUALLY VALUED
MP1 Hideki Matsui 8.00 20.00
MP2 Ken Griffey Jr. 8.00 20.00
MP3 Ichiro Suzuki 8.00 20.00
MP4 Ken Griffey Jr. 8.00 20.00

MP5 Hideo Nomo 6.00 15.00
MP6 Mickey Mantle 20.00 50.00
MP7 Ken Griffey Jr. 8.00 20.00
MP8 Barry Bonds 10.00 25.00
MP9 Mickey Mantle 20.00 50.00
MP10 Tom Seaver 6.00 15.00
MP11 Mike Piazza 8.00 20.00
MP12 Roger Clemens 8.00 20.00
MP13 Nolan Ryan 15.00 40.00
MP14 Nomar Garciaparra 8.00 20.00
MP15 Ernie Banks 6.00 15.00
MP16 Stan Musial 10.00 25.00
MP17 Mickey Mantle 20.00 50.00
MP18 Nolan Ryan 15.00 40.00
MP19 Nolan Ryan 15.00 40.00
MP20 Mickey Mantle 20.00 50.00
MP21 Ichiro Suzuki 8.00 20.00
MP22 Nolan Ryan 15.00 40.00
MP23 Tom Seaver 6.00 15.00
MP24 Ken Griffey Jr. 8.00 20.00
MP25 Hideo Nomo 6.00 15.00
MP26 Ken Griffey Jr. 8.00 20.00
MP27 Mark McGwire 10.00 25.00
MP28 Barry Bonds 10.00 25.00
MP29 Alex Rodriguez 8.00 20.00
MP30 Nolan Ryan 15.00 40.00
MP31 Mark McGwire 10.00 25.00
MP32 Nolan Ryan 15.00 40.00
MP33 Sammy Sosa 6.00 15.00
MP34 Ichiro Suzuki 8.00 20.00
MP35 Barry Bonds 10.00 25.00
MP36 Derek Jeter 10.00 25.00
MP37 Roger Clemens 8.00 20.00
MP38 Jason Giambi 6.00 15.00
MP39 Mickey Mantle 20.00 50.00
MP40 Ted Williams 12.50 30.00
MP41 Ted Williams 12.50 30.00
MP42 Ted Williams 12.50 30.00

2003 Upper Deck Mark of Greatness Autograph Jerseys

Randomly inserted into first series packs, these three cards feature authentically signed Mark McGwire cards. There are three different versions of this card, which were all signed to a different print run, and we have notated that information in our checklist.

MOG M.McGwire/400 * 175.00 300.00
MOGG M.McGwire Gold/25
MOGS M.McGwire Silver/70 250.00 400.00

2003 Upper Deck Masters with the Leather

COMPLETE SET (12) 10.00 25.00
L1 Darin Erstad .75 2.00
L2 Andruw Jones .75 2.00
L3 Greg Maddux 1.50 4.00
L4 Nomar Garciaparra 1.50 4.00
L5 Torii Hunter .75 2.00
L6 Roberto Alomar .75 2.00
L7 Derek Jeter 2.50 6.00
L8 Eric Chavez .75 2.00
L9 Ichiro Suzuki 2.00 5.00
L10 Jim Edmonds .75 2.00
L11 Scott Rolen .75 2.00
L12 Alex Rodriguez 1.50 4.00

2003 Upper Deck Mid-Summer Stars Swatches

Inserted into first series packs at a stated rate of one in 72, these 23 cards feature a mix of players who shine all during the season. A few cards do not feature jersey swatches and we have notated that information in our checklist. In addition, a few cards were issued to a smaller quantity and we have notated those cards with an SP in our checklist.

AJ Andruw Jones 4.00 10.00
AR Alex Rodriguez 6.00 15.00
BZ Barry Zito 3.00 8.00
CD Carlos Delgado 3.00 8.00
CS Curt Schilling 3.00 8.00
DE Darin Erstad 3.00 8.00
DW David Wells 3.00 8.00
EM Edgar Martinez 4.00 10.00
FG Freddy Garcia 3.00 8.00
FT Frank Thomas 4.00 10.00
HN Hideo Nomo 8.00 20.00
IS Ichiro Suzuki Turtleneck SP 20.00 50.00
JE Jim Edmonds SP * 4.00 10.00
JG Juan Gonzalez Pants 3.00 8.00
KS Kazuhiro Sasaki 3.00 8.00
MP Mike Piazza 6.00 15.00
MR Manny Ramirez 4.00 10.00
RC Roger Clemens 6.00 15.00
RJ Randy Johnson Shirt 4.00 10.00
RV Robin Ventura 4.00 10.00
SG Shawn Green SP 4.00 10.00
SS Sammy Sosa 4.00 10.00
TG Tom Glavine 4.00 10.00

2003 Upper Deck NL All-Star Swatches

Inserted into first series hobby packs at a stated rate of one in 72, these 12 cards feature game-used memorabilia swatch of players who had participated in the All-Star game for the National League.

AL Al Leiter 3.00 8.00
CF Cliff Floyd 3.00 8.00
CS Curt Schilling 3.00 8.00
FM Fred McGriff 4.00 10.00
JV Jose Vidro 3.00 8.00
MH Mike Hampton 3.00 8.00
MM Matt Morris 3.00 8.00
RK Ryan Klesko 3.00 8.00
SC Sean Casey 3.00 8.00
TG Tom Glavine 4.00 10.00
TG Tony Gwynn 6.00 15.00
TH Trevor Hoffman 3.00 8.00

2003 Upper Deck National Pride Memorabilia

SERIES 2 ODDS 1:24 HOBBY/1:48 RETAIL
SP PRINT RUNS PROVIDED BY UPPER DECK
SP'S ARE NOT SERIAL-NUMBERED
ALL FEATURE PANTS UNLESS NOTED
AA Abe Alvarez 3.00 8.00
AH Aaron Hill 3.00 8.00
AJ A.J. Hinch Jsy 3.00 8.00
AK A.Kearns Right Jsy 3.00 8.00
AK1 A.Kearns Left Jsy SP/250 6.00 15.00
BH Bobby Hill Field Jsy 3.00 8.00
BH1 Bobby Hill Run Jsy SP/100 8.00 20.00
BS Brad Sullivan Wind Up 3.00 8.00
BS1 Brad Sullivan Throw SP/250 6.00 15.00
BZ Bob Zimmermann 2.00 5.00
CC Chad Cordero 3.00 8.00
CJ Conor Jackson 4.00 10.00
CQ Carlos Quentin 4.00 10.00
CS Clint Sammons 3.00 8.00
DP Dustin Pedroia 4.00 10.00
EM Eric Milton White Jsy 3.00 8.00
EM1 Eric Milton Blue Jsy SP/50 8.00 20.00
EP Eric Patterson 3.00 8.00
GJ Grant Johnson 3.00 8.00
HS Huston Street 3.00 8.00
JJ0 J.Jones White Jsy 3.00 8.00
JJ1 J.Jones Blue Jsy SP/250 6.00 15.00
JJE Jason Jennings Jsy 3.00 8.00
KB Kyle Bakker 2.00 5.00
KSA K.Saarloos Red Jsy 3.00 8.00
KSL Kyle Sleeth 3.00 8.00
KSA1 K.Saarloos Grey Jsy SP/250 6.00 15.00
LP Landon Powell 3.00 8.00
MA Michael Aubrey 3.00 8.00
MJ Mark Jurich 2.00 5.00
MP Mark Prior Pinstripes Jsy 4.00 10.00
MP1 Mark Prior Grey Jsy SP/100 10.00 25.00
PH Philip Humber 3.00 8.00
RF Robert Fick Jsy 3.00 8.00
RO R.Oswalt Behind Jsy 3.00 8.00
RO1 R.Oswalt Beside Jsy SP/100 8.00 20.00
RW R.Weeks Glove-Chest 5.00 12.00
RW1 R.Weeks Glove-Head SP/250
SB Sean Burroughs 3.00 8.00
SC Shane Costa 2.00 5.00
SF Sam Fuld 2.00 5.00
WL Wes Littleton 3.00 8.00

2003 Upper Deck Piece of the Action Game Ball

SERIES 2 ODDS 1:288 HOBBY/1:576 RETAIL
PRINT RUNS B/WN 10-175 COPIES PER
PRINT RUNS PROVIDED BY UPPER DECK

CARDS ARE NOT SERIAL-NUMBERED
NO PRICING ON QTY OF 25 OR LESS
AB Adrian Beltre/100 4.00 10.00
ARA Aramis Ramirez/100 4.00 10.00
ARO Alex Rodriguez/100 10.00 25.00
BA Bobby Abreu/125 4.00 10.00
BB Barry Bonds/125 15.00 40.00
BG Brian Giles/100 4.00 10.00
BW Bernie Williams/125 6.00 15.00
CJ Chipper Jones/62 10.00 25.00
CS Curt Schilling/100 4.00 10.00
DE Darin Erstad/125 4.00 10.00
DJ Derek Jeter/65 25.00 60.00
EM Edgar Martinez/125 6.00 15.00
FG Freddy Garcia/100 4.00 10.00
FT Frank Thomas/150 6.00 15.00
GA Garret Anderson/150 4.00 10.00
GS Gary Sheffield/100 4.00 10.00
HN Hideo Nomo/100 15.00 40.00
IR Ivan Rodriguez/10
IS Ichiro Suzuki/25
JG Juan Gonzalez/100 4.00 10.00
JK Jason Kendall/100 4.00 10.00
JT Jim Thome/125 6.00 15.00
JV Jose Vidro/100 4.00 10.00
KB Kevin Brown/100 4.00 10.00
KE Jeff Kent/150 4.00 10.00
KS Kazuhiro Sasaki/100 4.00 10.00
LG Luis Gonzalez/100 4.00 10.00
LW Larry Walker/150 4.00 10.00
MP Mike Piazza/150 10.00 25.00
PB Pat Burrell/150 4.00 10.00
PM Pedro Martinez/150 6.00 15.00
PN Phil Nevin/75 6.00 15.00
RJ Randy Johnson/100 6.00 15.00
RK Ryan Klesko/75 6.00 15.00
RP Rafael Palmeiro/150 6.00 15.00
RS Richie Sexson/160 4.00 10.00
SG Shawn Green/175 4.00 10.00
SS Sammy Sosa/85 10.00 25.00
TG Troy Glaus/150 4.00 10.00
THE Todd Helton/100 6.00 15.00
THO Trevor Hoffman/150 4.00 10.00
VG Vladimir Guerrero/50 10.00 25.00

2003 Upper Deck Piece of the Action Game Ball Gold

*GOLD: 1X TO 2.5X GAME BALL p/r 150-175
*GOLD: 1X TO 2.5X GAME BALL p/r 100-125
*GOLD: .6X TO 1.5X GAME BALL p/r 50-85
RANDOM INSERTS IN SERIES 2 PACKS
STATED PRINT RUN 50 SERIAL #'d SETS
IR Ivan Rodriguez 15.00 40.00
IS Ichiro Suzuki

2003 Upper Deck Signed Game Jerseys

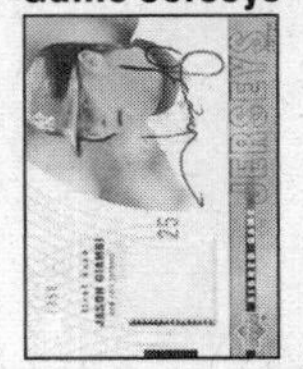

Randomly inserted into first series packs, these seven cards feature not only game-used memorabilia swatches but also an authentic autograph of the player. We have notated the print run for each card next to the player's name. In addition, Ken Griffey Jr. did not sign cards in time for inclusion into packs and those cards could be redeemed until February 11th, 2006.

RANDOM INSERTS IN SERIES 1 PACKS
PRINT RUNS B/WN 150-350 COPIES PER
AR Alex Rodriguez/350 75.00 150.00
CR Cal Ripken/350 75.00 150.00
JG Jason Giambi/350 20.00 50.00
KG Ken Griffey Jr./350 60.00 120.00
MM Mark McGwire/150 250.00 400.00
RC Roger Clemens/350 60.00 120.00
SS Sammy Sosa/150 50.00 100.00

2003 Upper Deck Signed Game Jerseys Gold

Randomly inserted into first series packs, this is a partial parallel to the Signed Game Jersey insert set. These three cards were issued to a stated print run of 25 serial numbered sets and no pricing is provided due to market scarcity. Please note that Ken Griffey Jr. did not return his cards in time for inclusion in packs and those cards could be redeemed until February 11th, 2006.

KG Ken Griffey Jr.

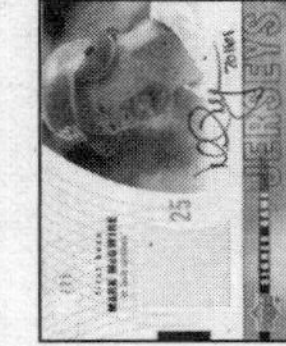

MM Mark McGwire
SS Sammy Sosa

2003 Upper Deck Signed Game Jerseys Silver

Randomly inserted into first series packs, this is a partial parallel to the Signed Game Jersey insert set. These five cards were issued to a stated print run of 75 serial numbered sets. Please note that Ken Griffey Jr. did not return his cards in time for inclusion in packs and those cards could be redeemed until February 11, 2006.

RANDOM INSERTS IN SER.1 HOBBY PACKS
STATED PRINT RUN 75 SERIAL #'d SETS
AR Alex Rodriguez
JG Jason Giambi 30.00 60.00
KG Ken Griffey Jr.
MM Mark McGwire
SS Sammy Sosa

2003 Upper Deck Slammin Sammy Autograph Jerseys

Randomly inserted into first series packs, these three cards feature authentically signed Sammy Sosa cards. Each of these cards also have a game-worn uniform swatch on them. There are three different versions of this card, which were all signed to a different print run, and we have notated that information in our checklist.

RANDOM INSERTS IN SERIES 1 PACKS
PRINT RUNS B/WN 25-384 COPIES PER
NO PRICING ON QTY OF 25 OR LESS
SST Sammy Sosa/384 75.00 150.00
SSTG Sammy Sosa Gold/25
SSTS Sammy Sosa Silver/66 125.00 200.00

2003 Upper Deck Star-Spangled Swatches

Inserted into first series packs at a stated rate of one in 72, these 16 cards feature game-worn uniform swatches of players who were on the USA National Team.

AH Aaron Hill H 3.00 8.00
BS Brad Sullivan H 3.00 8.00
CC Chad Cordero H 3.00 8.00
CJ Conor Jackson Pants R 4.00 10.00
CQ Carlos Quentin H 4.00 10.00
DP Dustin Pedroia R 8.00 20.00
EP Eric Patterson H 3.00 8.00
GJ Grant Johnson H 3.00 8.00
HS Huston Street R 3.00 8.00
KB Kyle Bakker R 2.00 5.00
KS Kyle Sleeth R 3.00 8.00
LP Landon Powell R 3.00 8.00
MA Michael Aubrey H 3.00 8.00
PH Philip Humber R 3.00 8.00
RW Rickie Weeks H 6.00 15.00
SC Shane Costa R 2.00 5.00

2003 Upper Deck Superior Sluggers

Inserted into second series packs at a stated rate of one in eight, these cards feature a mix of active and retired players known for their extra base power while batting.

COMPLETE SET (18) 15.00 40.00
S1 Troy Glaus .75 2.00
S2 Chipper Jones 1.00 2.50
S3 Manny Ramirez .75 2.00
S4 Ken Griffey Jr. 1.50 4.00
S5 Jim Thome .75 2.00
S6 Todd Helton .75 2.00

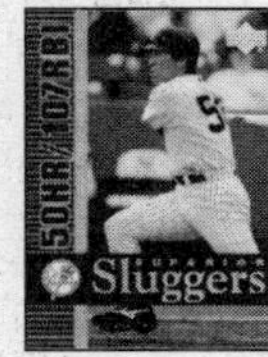

S7 Lance Berkman .75 2.00
S8 Derek Jeter 2.50 6.00
S9 Vladimir Guerrero 1.00 2.50
S10 Mike Piazza 1.50 4.00
S11 Hideki Matsui 2.00 5.00
S12 Barry Bonds 2.50 6.00
S13 Mickey Mantle 4.00 10.00
S14 Alex Rodriguez 1.50 4.00
S15 Ted Williams 2.50 6.00
S16 Carlos Delgado .75 2.00
S17 Frank Thomas 1.00 2.50
S18 Adam Dunn .75 2.00

2003 Upper Deck Superstar Scrapbooks

Randomly inserted into series one packs, these seven cards feature game-worn jersey swatches of some of baseball's major superstars. Each of these cards was issued to a stated print run of 24 serial numbered sets and there is no pricing due to market scarcity.

AR Alex Rodriguez
IS Ichiro Suzuki
JG Jason Giambi
KG Ken Griffey Jr.
MP Mike Piazza
RC Roger Clemens
SS Sammy Sosa

2003 Upper Deck Superstar Scrapbooks Gold

Randomly inserted into series one packs, these seven cards are a parallel of the Superstar Scrapbook set. Each of these cards feature game-worn jersey swatches of some of baseball's major superstars. Each of these cards was issued to a stated print run of one serial numbered set and there is no pricing due to market scarcity.

RANDOM INSERTS IN SERIES 1 PACKS
STATED PRINT RUN 1 SERIAL #'d SET
NO PRICING DUE TO SCARCITY
IS Ichiro Suzuki
KG Ken Griffey Jr.
SS Sammy Sosa

2003 Upper Deck Superstar Scrapbooks Silver

Randomly inserted into series one packs, these seven cards are a parallel of the Superstar Scrapbook set. Each of these cards feature game-worn jersey swatches of some of baseball's major superstars. Each of these cards was issued to a stated print run of six serial numbered set and there is no pricing due to market scarcity.

RANDOM INSERTS IN SERIES 1 PACKS
STATED PRINT RUN 6 SERIALS #'d SETS
NO PRICING DUE TO SCARCITY
AR Alex Rodriguez
IS Ichiro Suzuki
JG Jason Giambi
KG Ken Griffey Jr.
SS Sammy Sosa

2003 Upper Deck Triple Game Jersey

Randomly inserted into first series packs, these nine cards feature three game-worn uniform swatches of teammates. These cards were issued to a stated print run of anywhere from 25 to 150 serial numbered sets depending on which group the card belongs to. Please note the cards from group C are not priced due to market scarcity.

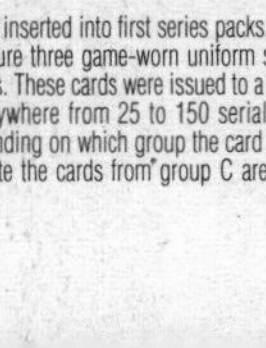

GROUP A 150 SERIAL #'d SETS
GROUP B 75 SERIAL #'d SETS
GROUP C 25 SERIAL #'d SETS
ARZ Randy Johnson 20.00 50.00
Curt Schilling
Luis Gonzalez A
ATL Chipper Jones 40.00 80.00
Greg Maddux
Gary Sheffield B
CHC Sammy Sosa 20.00 50.00
Moises Alou
Kerry Wood B
CIN Ken Griffey Jr. 15.00 40.00
Sean Casey
Adam Dunn A
HOU Jeff Bagwell 20.00 50.00
Lance Berkman
Craig Biggio A
NYM Mike Piazza Pants 20.00 50.00
Roberto Alomar
Mo Vaughn B
NYY Roger Clemens
Jason Giambi
Bernie Williams C
SEA Ichiro Suzuki 60.00 120.00
Freddy Garcia
Bret Boone B
TEX Rafael Palmeiro 20.00 50.00
Alex Rodriguez
Juan Gonzalez A

2003 Upper Deck Triple Game Jersey Gold

Randomly inserted in packs, this is a parallel to the Triple Game Jersey insert set. Depending on the group, each card is printed to a stated print run of between 10 and 50 serial numbered sets. Those cards in group B and C are not priced due to market scarcity.

GROUP A 50 SERIAL #'d SETS
GROUP B 25 SERIAL #'d SETS
GROUP C 10 SERIAL #'d SETS

2003 Upper Deck UD Bonus

Inserted into second series packs at a stated rate of one in 288, these are copies of various recent year Upper Deck cards which were repurchased for insertion in 2003 Upper Deck 2nd series. Please note that these cards were all stamped with a "UD Bonus" logo. Each of these cards were issued to differening print runs and we have notated the print runs next to the player's name in our checklist.

1 Jeff Bagwell 01 GG Glv/6
2 Josh Beckett 01 TP AU/55 12.50 30.00
3 C.Beltran 00 SPA AU/118 6.00 15.00
4 Barry Bonds 01 UD Ball/34
5 Barry Bonds 01 GG Glv/5
6 Barry Bonds 01 P/P Jsy/117 10.00 25.00
7 Lou Brock 00 LGD AU/198 10.00 25.00
8 Gary Carter 00 LGD AU/63 8.00 20.00
9 Sean Casey 00 SPA AU/11
10 Roger Clemens 00 HFX Base/12
11 Roger Clemens 00 LGD Jsy/12
12 Roger Clemens 01 P/P Jsy/117 6.00 15.00
13 A.Dawson 00 LGD AU/140 6.00 15.00
14 J.D. Drew 00 SPA AU/55 8.00 20.00
15 Rollie Fingers 00 LGD AU/116 6.00 15.00
16 Rafael Furcal 00 SPA AU/87 6.00 15.00
17 Rafael Furcal 00 SPA AU/39
18 Jason Giambi 00 SPA AU/106 6.00 15.00
19 Jason Giambi 01 UD Ball/35
20 Jason Giambi 01 P/P Jsy/97 4.00 10.00
21 Troy Glaus 00 SPA AU/110 10.00 25.00
22 Shawn Green 01 UD Ball/10
23 Ken Griffey Jr. 01 UD Ball/28
24 Ken Griffey Jr. 01 GG Glv/2
25 Vladimir Guerrero 00 SPA AU/8
26 Vladimir Guerrero 00 LGD AU/26
27 Vladimir Guerrero 00 OV Bat/16
28 Brandon Inge 01 TP AU/113 4.00 10.00
29 Derek Jeter 01 UD Ball/17
30 Randy Johnson 01 UD Ball/37
31 Andruw Jones 01 UD Ball/38
32 Chipper Jones 00 HFX AU/5
33 Chipper Jones 00 OV Bat/19
34 Harmon Killebrew 00 LGD AU/31
35 Roger Maris 00 YL Jsy/11
36 Eddie Mathews 00 LGD Jsy/12
37 Hideki Matsui 03 PB AU/31
38 Hideki Matsui 03 PB Red AU/20
39 Don Mattingly 00 YL Jsy/26
40 Don Mattingly 01 LGD NY Bat/20
41 Joe Mays 00 SPA AU/30
42 Mark McGwire 01 UD Ball/19
43 D.Mientkiewicz 00 BD Jsy/57 4.00 10.00
44 Dale Murphy 00 LGD AU/91 10.00 25.00
45 Stan Musial 00 LGD AU/5
46 Jim Palmer 00 LGD AU/121 6.00 15.00
47 P.Reese 01 HOF Jsy/46 6.00 15.00
48 Phil Rizzuto 00 YL Jsy/19
49 Ivan Rodriguez 00 SPA AU/27
50 Ivan Rodriguez 01 GG Glv/4
51 Nolan Ryan 01 HOF Bat/37
52 Nolan Ryan 01 HOF Jsy/76
53 C.C. Sabathia 01 TP AU/64 8.00 20.00
54 Tim Salmon 01 GG Glv/12
55 Tom Seaver 00 LGD Jsy/18
56 Ben Sheets 01 TP AU/60 8.00 20.00
57 Ozzie Smith 00 LGD Jsy/14
58 Alf Soriano 00 SPA AU/80 10.00 25.00
59 Sammy Sosa 01 P/P Jsy/77 6.00 15.00
60 Larry Walker 01 GG Glv/10
61 Bernie Williams 01 GG Glv/10
62 Maury Wills 00 LGD Jsy/22
63 Dave Winfield 00 YL Bat/53 4.00 10.00
64 Bernie Williams 20.00 50.00
Ichiro Suzuki 01 P/P Bat/87
65 Sammy Sosa 6.00 15.00
Luis Gonzalez 01 P/P Bat/61

2003 Upper Deck UD Patch Logos

Inserted into first series packs at a stated rate of one in 7500, these eight cards feature game-used patch pieces. Each card has a print run between 41 and 54 and we have notated that print run information next to the player's name in our checklist.

BW Bernie Williams/42
CJ Chipper Jones/52 60.00 120.00
FT Frank Thomas/52 60.00 120.00
GM Greg Maddux/50 75.00 150.00
JB Jeff Bagwell/41
KI Kazuhisa Ishii/54 50.00 100.00
RJ Randy Johnson/50 60.00 120.00
TH Todd Helton/41

2003 Upper Deck UD Patch Logos Exclusives

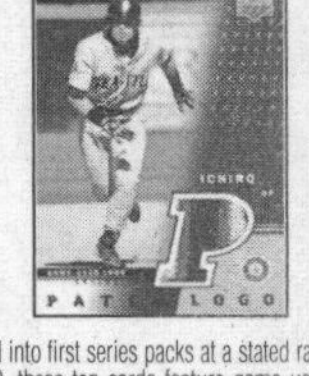

Inserted into first series packs at a stated rate of one in 7500, these ten cards feature game-used patch pieces. Each card has a print run between nine and 61 and we have notated that print run information next to the player's name in our checklist. The cards with a print run of 25 or fewer are not priced due to market scarcity.

AR Alex Rodriguez/34
IS Ichiro Suzuki/46
JD Joe DiMaggio/9
JG Jason Giambi/34
KG Ken Griffey Jr./50 75.00 150.00
MG Mark McGwire/43
MM Mickey Mantle/10
MP Mike Piazza/61 60.00 120.00
RC Roger Clemens/34
SS Sammy Sosa/60 40.00 80.00

2003 Upper Deck UD Patch Numbers

Inserted into first series packs at a stated rate of one in 7500, these six cards feature game-used patch number pieces. Each card has a print run between 27 and 90 and we have notated that print run information next to the player's name in our checklist.

BW Bernie Williams/66 40.00 80.00
CJ Chipper Jones/44
FT Frank Thomas/81 40.00 80.00
KI Kazuhisa Ishii/63 30.00 60.00
RJ Randy Johnson/90 40.00 80.00
TH Todd Helton/27

2003 Upper Deck UD Patch Numbers Exclusives

Inserted into first series packs at a stated rate of one in 7500, these six cards feature game-used patch number pieces. Each card has a print run between 56 and 100 and we have notated that print run information next to the player's name in our checklist.

AR Alex Rodriguez/56 75.00 150.00
JG Jason Giambi/68 30.00 60.00
KG Ken Griffey Jr./97 50.00 100.00
MG Mark McGwire/60 150.00 250.00
SS Sammy Sosa/100 40.00 80.00

2003 Upper Deck UD Patch Stripes

Inserted into first series packs at a stated rate of one in 7500, these seven cards feature game-used patch striped pieces. Each card has a print run between 43 and 73 and we have notated that print run information next to the player's name in our checklist.

BW Bernie Williams/58 40.00 80.00
CJ Chipper Jones/58 40.00 80.00
FT Frank Thomas/58 40.00 80.00
JB Jeff Bagwell/73 40.00 80.00
KI Kazuhisa Ishii/58 30.00 60.00
RJ Randy Johnson/58 40.00 80.00
TH Todd Helton/43

2003 Upper Deck UD Patch Stripes Exclusives

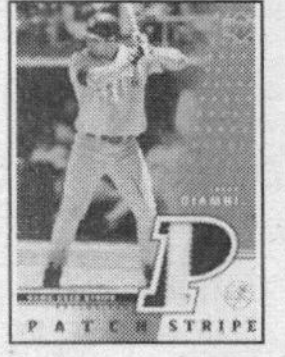

Inserted into first series packs at a stated rate of one in 7500, these seven cards feature game-used patch striped pieces. Each card has a print run between 63 and 66 and we have notated that print run information next to the player's name in our checklist.

AR Alex Rodriguez/63 60.00 120.00
IS Ichiro Suzuki/63 150.00 250.00
JG Jason Giambi/66 30.00 60.00
KG Ken Griffey Jr./63 60.00 120.00
MG Mark McGwire/63 150.00 250.00
SS Sammy Sosa/63 60.00 120.00

2003 Upper Deck UD Super Patch Logos

NO PRICING DUE TO VOLATILITY
AJ Andruw Jones/92
AR Alex Rodriguez/45
AS Alfonso Soriano/15
GM Greg Maddux/95
HM Hideki Matsui/8
IS Ichiro Suzuki/20
KG Ken Griffey Jr./22
MP Mike Piazza/30
MR Manny Ramirez/22
SS Sammy Sosa/21

2003 Upper Deck UD Super Patch Numbers

AP Albert Pujols/8
AR Alex Rodriguez/13
CJ Chipper Jones/11
CS Curt Schilling/18
IR Ivan Rodriguez/10
IS Ichiro Suzuki/14
JB Jeff Bagwell/8
JG Jason Giambi/40
RC Roger Clemens/12

2003 Upper Deck UD Super Patch Stripes

AD Adam Dunn/70
AS Alfonso Soriano/16
JG Jason Giambi/50

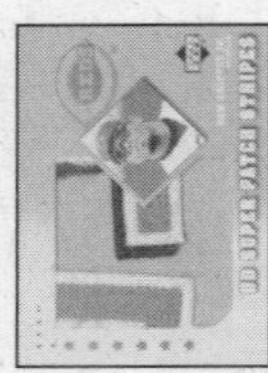

KG Ken Griffey Jr./12
LB Lance Berkman/30
MP Mike Piazza/10
RJ Randy Johnson/73
SS Sammy Sosa/70
TH Todd Helton/50
VG Vladimir Guerrero/75

2003 Upper Deck UD Superstar Slam Jerseys

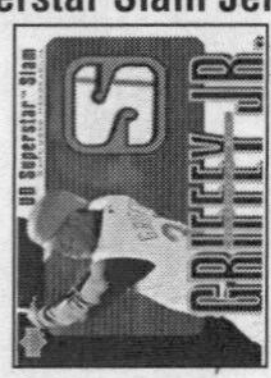

Inserted into first series hobby packs at a stated rate of one in 48, these 10 cards feature game-used jersey pieces of the featured players.

AR Alex Rodriguez 6.00 15.00
CJ Chipper Jones 4.00 10.00
FT Frank Thomas 4.00 10.00
JB Jeff Bagwell 4.00 10.00
JG Jason Giambi 3.00 8.00
KG Ken Griffey Jr. 6.00 15.00
LG Luis Gonzalez 3.00 8.00
MP Mike Piazza 6.00 15.00
SS Sammy Sosa 4.00 10.00
JGO Juan Gonzalez 3.00 8.00

2004 Upper Deck

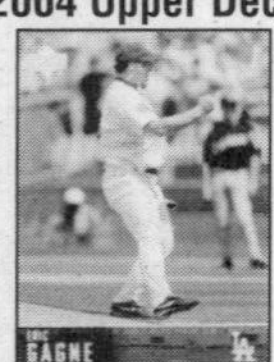

The 270-card first series was released in November, 2003. The cards were issued in eight-card hobby packs with an $3 SRP which came 24 packs to a box and 12 boxes to a case. These cards were also issued in nine-card retail packs also with a $3 SRP which came 24 packs to a box and 12 boxes to a case. Please note that insert cards were much more prevalent in the hobby packs. The following subsets were included in the first series: Super Rookies (1-30); Season Highlights Checklists (261-270). In addition, please note that the Super Rookie cards were not short printed. The second series, also of 270 cards, was released in June 2004. That series was highlighted by the following subsets: Season Highlights Checklists (471-480), Super Rookies (481-540). In addition, an update set was issued as a complete set with the 2005 Upper Deck I product. Those cards feature a mix of players who changed teams and Rookie Cards.

COMPLETE SERIES 1 (270) 20.00 50.00
COMPLETE SERIES 2 (270) 20.00 50.00
COMP.UPDATE SET (50) 7.50 15.00
COMMON (31-480/541-565) .10 .30
COMMON (1-30/481-540) .40 1.00
COMMON CARD (566-590) .20 .50
541-590 ONE SET PER '05 UD1 HOBBY BOX
UPDATE SET EXCH 1:480 '05 UD1 RETAIL
UPDATE SET EXCH.DEADLINE TBD
1 Dontrelle Willis SR .60 1.50
2 Edgar Gonzalez SR .40 1.00
3 Jose Reyes SR .40 1.00
4 Jae Weong Seo SR .40 1.00
5 Miguel Cabrera SR .60 1.50
6 Jesse Foppert SR .40 1.00
7 Mike Neu SR .40 1.00
8 Michael Nakamura SR .40 1.00
9 Luis Ayala SR .40 1.00
10 Jared Sandberg SR .40 1.00
11 Jhonny Peralta SR .40 1.00
12 Wil Ledezma SR .40 1.00
13 Jason Roach SR .40 1.00
14 Kirk Saarloos SR .40 1.00
15 Cliff Lee SR .40 1.00
16 Bobby Hill SR .40 1.00
17 Lyle Overbay SR .40 1.00
18 Josh Hall SR .40 1.00
19 Joe Thurston SR .40 1.00
20 Matt Kata SR .40 1.00
21 Jeremy Bonderman SR .40 1.00
22 Julio Manon SR .40 1.00
23 Rodrigo Rosario SR .40 1.00
24 Robby Hammock SR .40 1.00
25 David Sanders SR .40 1.00
26 Miguel Ojeda SR .40 1.00
27 Mark Teixeira SR .60 1.50
28 Franklyn German SR .40 1.00
29 Ken Harvey SR .40 1.00
30 Xavier Nady SR .40 1.00
31 Tim Salmon .20 .50
32 Troy Glaus .10 .30
33 Adam Kennedy .10 .30
34 David Eckstein .10 .30
35 Ben Molina .10 .30
36 Jarrod Washburn .10 .30
37 Ramon Ortiz .10 .30
38 Eric Chavez .10 .30
39 Miguel Tejada .10 .30
40 Chris Singleton .10 .30
41 Jermaine Dye .10 .30
42 John Halama .10 .30
43 Tim Hudson .10 .30
44 Barry Zito .10 .30
45 Ted Lilly .10 .30
46 Bobby Kielty .10 .30
47 Kelvim Escobar .10 .30
48 Josh Phelps .10 .30
49 Vernon Wells .10 .30
50 Roy Halladay .10 .30
51 Orlando Hudson .10 .30
52 Eric Hinske .10 .30
53 Brandon Backe .10 .30
54 Dewon Brazelton .10 .30
55 Ben Grieve .10 .30
56 Aubrey Huff .10 .30
57 Toby Hall .10 .30
58 Rocco Baldelli .10 .30
59 Al Martin .10 .30
60 Brandon Phillips .10 .30
61 Omar Vizquel .20 .50
62 C.C. Sabathia .10 .30
63 Milton Bradley .10 .30
64 Ricky Gutierrez .10 .30
65 Matt Lawton .10 .30
66 Danys Baez .10 .30
67 Ichiro Suzuki .60 1.50
68 Randy Winn .10 .30
69 Carlos Guillen .10 .30
70 Mark McLemore .10 .30
71 Dan Wilson .10 .30
72 Jamie Moyer .10 .30
73 Joel Pineiro .10 .30
74 Edgar Martinez .20 .50
75 Tony Batista .10 .30
76 Jay Gibbons .10 .30
77 Jeff Conine .10 .30
78 Melvin Mora .10 .30
79 Geronimo Gil .10 .30
80 Rodrigo Lopez .10 .30
81 Jorge Julio .10 .30
82 Rafael Palmeiro .20 .50
83 Juan Gonzalez .10 .30
84 Mike Young .10 .30
85 Alex Rodriguez .50 1.25
86 Einar Diaz .10 .30
87 Kevin Mench .10 .30
88 Hank Blalock .10 .30
89 Pedro Martinez .20 .50
90 Byung-Hyun Kim .10 .30
91 Derek Lowe .10 .30
92 Jason Varitek .30 .75
93 Manny Ramirez .20 .50
94 John Burkett .10 .30
95 Todd Walker .10 .30
96 Nomar Garciaparra .50 1.25
97 Trot Nixon .10 .30
98 Mike Sweeney .10 .30
99 Carlos Febles .10 .30
100 Mike MacDougal .10 .30
101 Raul Ibanez .10 .30
102 Jason Grimsley .10 .30
103 Chris George .10 .30
104 Brent Mayne .10 .30
105 Dmitri Young .10 .30
106 Eric Munson .10 .30
107 A.J. Hinch .10 .30
108 Andres Torres .10 .30
109 Bobby Higginson .10 .30
110 Shane Halter .10 .30
111 Matt Walbeck .10 .30
112 Torii Hunter .10 .30
113 Doug Mientkiewicz .10 .30
114 Lew Ford .10 .30
115 Eric Milton .10 .30
116 Eddie Guardado .10 .30
117 Cristian Guzman .10 .30
118 Corey Koskie .10 .30
119 Magglio Ordonez .10 .30
120 Mark Buehrle .10 .30
121 Billy Koch .10 .30
122 Jose Valentin .10 .30
123 Paul Konerko .10 .30
124 Carlos Lee .10 .30
125 Jon Garland .10 .30
126 Jason Giambi .10 .30
127 Derek Jeter .60 1.50
128 Roger Clemens .60 1.50
129 Andy Pettitte .20 .50
130 Jorge Posada .20 .50
131 David Wells .10 .30
132 Hideki Matsui .50 1.25
133 Mike Mussina .20 .50
134 Jeff Bagwell .20 .50
135 Craig Biggio .20 .50
136 Morgan Ensberg .10 .30
137 Richard Hidalgo .10 .30
138 Brad Ausmus .10 .30
139 Roy Oswalt .10 .30
140 Billy Wagner .10 .30
141 Octavio Dotel .10 .30
142 Gary Sheffield .10 .30
143 Andruw Jones .20 .50
144 John Smoltz .20 .50
145 Rafael Furcal .10 .30
146 Javy Lopez .10 .30
147 Shane Reynolds .10 .30
148 Horacio Ramirez .10 .30
149 Mike Hampton .10 .30
150 Jung Bong .10 .30
151 Ruben Quevedo .10 .30
152 Ben Sheets .10 .30
153 Geoff Jenkins .10 .30
154 Royce Clayton .10 .30
155 Glendon Rusch .10 .30
156 John Vander Wal .10 .30
157 Scott Podsednik .10 .30
158 Jim Edmonds .10 .30
159 Tino Martinez .20 .50
160 Albert Pujols .60 1.50
161 Matt Morris .10 .30
162 Woody Williams .10 .30
163 Edgar Renteria .10 .30
164 Jason Isringhausen .10 .30
165 Jason Simontacchi .10 .30
166 Kerry Robinson .10 .30
167 Sammy Sosa .30 .75
168 Joe Borowski .10 .30
169 Tony Womack .10 .30
170 Antonio Alfonseca .10 .30
171 Corey Patterson .10 .30
172 Mark Prior .20 .50
173 Moises Alou .10 .30
174 Matt Clement .10 .30
175 Randall Simon .10 .30
176 Randy Johnson .30 .75
177 Luis Gonzalez .10 .30
178 Craig Counsell .10 .30
179 Miguel Batista .10 .30
180 Steve Finley .10 .30
181 Brandon Webb .10 .30
182 Danny Bautista .10 .30
183 Oscar Villarreal .10 .30
184 Shawn Green .10 .30
185 Brian Jordan .10 .30
186 Fred McGriff .20 .50
187 Andy Ashby .10 .30
188 Rickey Henderson .30 .75
189 Dave Roberts .10 .30
190 Eric Gagne .10 .30
191 Kazuhisa Ishii .10 .30
192 Adrian Beltre .10 .30
193 Vladimir Guerrero .30 .75
194 Livan Hernandez .10 .30
195 Ron Calloway .10 .30
196 Sun Woo Kim .10 .30
197 Wil Cordero .10 .30
198 Brad Wilkerson .10 .30
199 Orlando Cabrera .10 .30
200 Barry Bonds .75 2.00
201 Ray Durham .10 .30
202 Andres Galarraga .10 .30
203 Benito Santiago .10 .30
204 Jose Cruz Jr. .10 .30
205 Jason Schmidt .10 .30
206 Kirk Rueter .10 .30
207 Felix Rodriguez .10 .30
208 Mike Lowell .10 .30
209 Luis Castillo .10 .30
210 Derrek Lee .20 .50
211 Andy Fox .10 .30
212 Tommy Phelps .10 .30
213 Todd Hollandsworth .10 .30
214 Brad Penny .10 .30
215 Juan Pierre .10 .30
216 Mike Piazza .50 1.25
217 Jae Weong Seo .10 .30
218 Ty Wigginton .10 .30
219 Al Leiter .10 .30
220 Roger Cedeno .10 .30
221 Timo Perez .10 .30
222 Aaron Heilman .10 .30
223 Pedro Astacio .10 .30
224 Joe McEwing .10 .30
225 Ryan Klesko .10 .30
226 Brian Giles .10 .30
227 Mark Kotsay .10 .30
228 Brian Lawrence .10 .30
229 Rod Beck .10 .30
230 Trevor Hoffman .10 .30
231 Sean Burroughs .10 .30
232 Bob Abreu .10 .30
233 Jim Thome .20 .50
234 David Bell .10 .30
235 Jimmy Rollins .10 .30
236 Mike Lieberthal .10 .30
237 Vicente Padilla .10 .30
238 Randy Wolf .10 .30
239 Reggie Sanders .10 .30
240 Jason Kendall .10 .30
241 Jack Wilson .10 .30
242 Jose Hernandez .10 .30
243 Kip Wells .10 .30
244 Carlos Rivera .10 .30
245 Craig Wilson .10 .30
246 Adam Dunn .10 .30
247 Sean Casey .10 .30
248 Danny Graves .10 .30
249 Ryan Dempster .10 .30
250 Barry Larkin .20 .50
251 Reggie Taylor .10 .30
252 Wily Mo Pena .10 .30
253 Larry Walker .10 .30
254 Mark Sweeney .10 .30
255 Preston Wilson .10 .30
256 Jason Jennings .10 .30
257 Charles Johnson .10 .30
258 Jay Payton .10 .30
259 Chris Stynes .10 .30
260 Juan Uribe .10 .30
261 Hideki Matsui SH CL .30 .75
262 Barry Bonds SH CL .40 1.00
263 Dontrelle Willis SH CL .10 .30
264 Kevin Millwood SH CL .10 .30
265 Billy Wagner SH CL .10 .30
266 Rocco Baldelli SH CL .10 .30
267 Roger Clemens SH CL .30 .75
268 Rafael Palmeiro SH CL .10 .30
269 Miguel Cabrera SH CL .20 .50
270 Jose Contreras SH CL .10 .30
271 Aaron Sele .10 .30
272 Bartolo Colon .10 .30
273 Darin Erstad .10 .30
274 Francisco Rodriguez .10 .30
275 Garret Anderson .10 .30
276 Jose Guillen .10 .30
277 Troy Percival .10 .30
278 Alex Cintron .10 .30
279 Casey Fossum .10 .30
280 Elmer Dessens .10 .30
281 Jose Valverde .10 .30
282 Matt Mantei .10 .30
283 Richie Sexson .10 .30
284 Roberto Alomar .20 .50
285 Shea Hillenbrand .10 .30
286 Chipper Jones .30 .75
287 Greg Maddux .50 1.25
288 J.D. Drew .10 .30
289 Marcus Giles .10 .30
290 Mike Hessman .10 .30
291 John Thomson .10 .30
292 Russ Ortiz .10 .30
293 Adam Loewen .10 .30
294 Jack Cust .10 .30
295 Jerry Hairston Jr. .10 .30
296 Kurt Ainsworth .10 .30
297 Luis Matos .10 .30
298 Marty Cordova .10 .30
299 Sidney Ponson .10 .30
300 Bill Mueller .10 .30
301 Curt Schilling .10 .30
302 David Ortiz .20 .50
303 Johnny Damon .20 .50
304 Keith Foulke Sox .10 .30
305 Pokey Reese .10 .30
306 Scott Williamson .10 .30
307 Tim Wakefield .10 .30
308 Alex S. Gonzalez .10 .30
309 Aramis Ramirez .10 .30
310 Carlos Zambrano .10 .30
311 Juan Cruz .10 .30
312 Kerry Wood .10 .30
313 Kyle Farnsworth .10 .30
314 Aaron Rowand .10 .30
315 Esteban Loaiza .10 .30
316 Frank Thomas .30 .75
317 Joe Borchard .10 .30
318 Joe Crede .10 .30
319 Miguel Olivo .10 .30
320 Willie Harris .10 .30
321 Aaron Harang .10 .30
322 Austin Kearns .10 .30
323 Brandon Claussen .10 .30
324 Brandon Larson .10 .30
325 Ryan Freel .10 .30
326 Ken Griffey Jr. .50 1.25
327 Ryan Wagner .10 .30
328 Alex Escobar .10 .30
329 Coco Crisp .10 .30
330 David Riske .10 .30
331 Jody Gerut .10 .30
332 Josh Bard .10 .30
333 Travis Hafner .10 .30
334 Chin-Hui Tsao .10 .30
335 Denny Stark .10 .30
336 Jeromy Burnitz .10 .30
337 Shawn Chacon .10 .30
338 Todd Helton .20 .50
339 Vinny Castilla .10 .30
340 Alex Sanchez .10 .30
341 Carlos Pena .10 .30
342 Fernando Vina .10 .30
343 Jason Johnson .10 .30
344 Matt Anderson .10 .30
345 Mike Maroth .10 .30
346 Rondell White .10 .30
347 A.J. Burnett .10 .30
348 Alex Gonzalez .10 .30
349 Armando Benitez .10 .30
350 Carl Pavano .10 .30
351 Hee Seop Choi .10 .30
352 Ivan Rodriguez .20 .50
353 Josh Beckett .10 .30
354 Josh Willingham .10 .30
355 Adam Everett .10 .30
356 Brandon Duckworth .10 .30
357 Jason Lane .10 .30
358 Jeff Kent .10 .30
359 Jeriome Robertson .10 .30
360 Lance Berkman .10 .30
361 Wade Miller .10 .30
362 Aaron Guiel .10 .30
363 Angel Berroa .10 .30
364 Carlos Beltran .10 .30
365 David DeJesus .10 .30
366 Desi Relaford .10 .30
367 Joe Randa .10 .30
368 Runelvys Hernandez .10 .30
369 Edwin Jackson .10 .30
370 Hideo Nomo .30 .75
371 Jeff Weaver .10 .30
372 Juan Encarnacion .10 .30
373 Odalis Perez .10 .30
374 Paul Lo Duca .10 .30
375 Robin Ventura .10 .30
376 Bill Hall .10 .30
377 Chad Moeller .10 .30
378 Chris Capuano .10 .30
379 Junior Spivey .10 .30
380 Rickie Weeks .10 .30
381 Wes Helms .10 .30
382 Brad Radke .10 .30
383 Jacque Jones .10 .30
384 Joe Mays .10 .30
385 Joe Nathan .10 .30
386 Johan Santana .30 .75
387 Nick Punto .10 .30
388 Shannon Stewart .10 .30
389 Carl Everett .10 .30
390 Claudio Vargas .10 .30
391 Jose Vidro .10 .30
392 Nick Johnson .10 .30
393 Rocky Biddle .10 .30
394 Tony Armas Jr. .10 .30
395 Braden Looper .10 .30
396 Cliff Floyd .10 .30
397 Jason Phillips .10 .30
398 Mike Cameron .10 .30
399 Tom Glavine .20 .50
400 Kenny Lofton .10 .30
401 Alfonso Soriano .10 .30
402 Bernie Williams .20 .50
403 Javier Vazquez .10 .30
404 Jon Lieber .10 .30
405 Jose Contreras .10 .30
406 Kevin Brown .10 .30
407 Mariano Rivera .30 .75
408 Arthur Rhodes .10 .30
409 Eric Byrnes .10 .30
410 Erubiel Durazo .10 .30
411 Graham Koonce .10 .30
412 Marco Scutaro .10 .30
413 Mark Mulder .10 .30
414 Mark Redman .10 .30
415 Rich Harden .10 .30
416 Brett Myers .10 .30
417 Chase Utley .20 .50
418 Kevin Millwood .10 .30
419 Marlon Byrd .10 .30
420 Pat Burrell .10 .30
421 Placido Polanco .10 .30
422 Tim Worrell .10 .30
423 Jason Bay .10 .30
424 Josh Fogg .10 .30
425 Kris Benson .10 .30
426 Mike Gonzalez .10 .30
427 Oliver Perez .10 .30
428 Tike Redman .10 .30
429 Adam Eaton .10 .30
430 Ismael Valdes .10 .30
431 Jake Peavy .10 .30
432 Khalil Greene .20 .50
433 Mark Loretta .10 .30
434 Phil Nevin .10 .30
435 Ramon Hernandez .10 .30
436 A.J. Pierzynski .10 .30
437 Edgardo Alfonzo .10 .30
438 J.T. Snow .10 .30
439 Jerome Williams .10 .30
440 Marquis Grissom .10 .30
441 Robb Nen .10 .30
442 Bret Boone .10 .30
443 Freddy Garcia .10 .30
444 Gil Meche .10 .30
445 John Olerud .10 .30
446 Rich Aurilia .10 .30
447 Shigetoshi Hasegawa .10 .30
448 Bo Hart .10 .30
449 Danny Haren .10 .30
450 Jason Marquis .10 .30
451 Marlon Anderson .10 .30
452 Scott Rolen .20 .50
453 So Taguchi .10 .30
454 Carl Crawford .10 .30
455 Delmon Young .20 .50
456 Geoff Blum .10 .30
457 Jesus Colome .10 .30
458 Jonny Gomes .10 .30
459 Lance Carter .10 .30
460 Robert Fick .10 .30
461 Chan Ho Park .10 .30
462 Francisco Cordero .10 .30
463 Jeff Nelson .10 .30
464 Jeff Zimmerman .10 .30
465 Kenny Rogers .10 .30
466 Aquilino Lopez .10 .30
467 Carlos Delgado .10 .30
468 Frank Catalanotto .10 .30
469 Reed Johnson .10 .30
470 Pat Hentgen .10 .30
471 Curt Schilling SH CL .10 .30
472 Gary Sheffield SH CL .10 .30
473 Javier Vazquez SH CL .10 .30
474 Kazuo Matsui SH CL .20 .50
475 Kevin Brown SH CL .10 .30
476 Rafael Palmeiro SH CL .10 .30
477 Richie Sexson SH CL .10 .30
478 Roger Clemens SH CL .30 .75
479 Vladimir Guerrero SH CL .20 .50
480 Alex Rodriguez SH CL .30 .75
481 Jake Woods SR RC .40 1.00
482 Tim Bittner SR RC .40 1.00
483 Brandon Medders SR RC .40 1.00
484 Casey Daigle SR RC .40 1.00
485 Jerry Gil SR RC .40 1.00
486 Mike Gosling SR RC .40 1.00
487 Jose Capellan SR RC .60 1.50
488 Onil Joseph SR RC .40 1.00
489 Roman Colon SR RC .40 1.00
490 Dave Crouthers SR RC .40 1.00
491 Eddy Rodriguez SR RC .60 1.50
492 Franklyn Gracesqui SR RC .40 1.00
493 Jamie Brown SR RC .40 1.00
494 Jerome Gamble SR RC .40 1.00
495 Tim Hamulack SR RC .40 1.00
496 Carlos Vasquez SR RC .60 1.50
497 Renyel Pinto SR RC .60 1.50
498 Ronny Cedeno SR RC .75 2.00
499 Enemencio Pacheco SR RC .40 1.00
500 Ryan Meaux SR RC .40 1.00
501 Ryan Wing SR RC .40 1.00
502 Shingo Takatsu SR RC .60 1.50
503 William Bergolla SR RC .40 1.00
504 Ivan Ochoa SR RC .40 1.00
505 Mariano Gomez SR RC .40 1.00
506 Justin Hampson SR RC .40 1.00
507 Justin Huisman SR RC .40 1.00
508 Scott Dohmann SR RC .40 1.00
509 Donnie Kelly SR RC .40 1.00
510 Chris Aguila SR RC .40 1.00
511 Lincoln Holdzkom SR RC .40 1.00
512 Freddy Guzman SR RC .40 1.00
513 Hector Gimenez SR RC .40 1.00
514 Jorge Vasquez SR RC .40 1.00
515 Jason Frasor SR RC .40 1.00
516 Chris Saenz SR RC .40 1.00
517 Dennis Sarfate SR RC .40 1.00
518 Colby Miller SR RC .40 1.00
519 Jason Bartlett SR RC .60 1.50
520 Chad Bentz SR RC .40 1.00
521 Josh Labandeira SR RC .40 1.00
522 Shawn Hill SR RC .40 1.00
523 Kazuo Matsui SR RC .60 1.50
524 Carlos Hines SR RC .40 1.00
525 Mike Vento SR RC .60 1.50
526 Scott Proctor SR RC .60 1.50
527 Sean Henn SR RC .40 1.00
528 David Aardsma SR RC .40 1.00
529 Ian Snell SR RC .75 2.00
530 Mike Johnston SR RC .40 1.00
531 Akinori Otsuka SR RC .40 1.00
532 Rusty Tucker SR RC .60 1.50
533 Justin Knoedler SR RC .40 1.00
534 Merkin Valdez SR RC .60 1.50
535 Greg Dobbs SR RC .60 1.50
536 Justin Leone SR RC .60 1.50
537 Shawn Camp SR RC .40 1.00
538 Edwin Moreno SR RC .40 1.00
539 Angel Chavez SR RC .40 1.00
540 Jesse Harper SR RC .40 1.00
541 Alex Rodriguez .50 1.25
542 Roger Clemens .50 1.25
543 Andy Pettitte .20 .50
544 Vladimir Guerrero .30 .75
545 David Wells .10 .30
546 Derrek Lee .20 .50
547 Carlos Beltran .10 .30
548 Orlando Cabrera Sox .10 .30
549 Paul Lo Duca .10 .30
550 Dave Roberts .10 .30
551 Guillermo Mota .10 .30
552 Steve Finley .10 .30
553 Juan Encarnacion .10 .30
554 Larry Walker .10 .30
555 Ty Wigginton .10 .30
556 Doug Mientkiewicz .10 .30
557 Roberto Alomar .20 .50
558 B.J. Upton .20 .50
559 Brad Penny .10 .30
560 Hee Seop Choi .10 .30
561 David Wright 1.25 3.00
562 Nomar Garciaparra .50 1.25
563 Felix Rodriguez .10 .30
564 Victor Zambrano .10 .30
565 Kris Benson .10 .30
566 Aarom Baldiris SR RC .20 .50
567 Joey Gathright SR RC .40 1.00
568 Charles Thomas SR RC .20 .50
569 Brian Dallimore SR RC .20 .50
570 Chris Oxspring SR RC .20 .50
571 Chris Shelton SR RC .75 2.00
572 Dioner Navarro SR RC .50 1.25
573 Edwardo Sierra SR RC .20 .50
574 Fernando Nieve SR RC .30 .75
575 Frank Francisco SR RC .20 .50
576 Jeff Bennett SR RC .20 .50
577 Justin Lehr SR RC .20 .50
578 John Gall SR RC .20 .50
579 Jorge Sequea SR RC .20 .50
580 Justin Germano SR RC .20 .50
581 Kazuhito Tadano SR RC .20 .50
582 Kevin Cave SR RC .20 .50
583 Jesse Crain SR RC .30 .75
584 Luis A. Gonzalez SR RC .20 .50
585 Michael Wuertz SR RC .20 .50
586 Orlando Rodriguez SR RC .20 .50
587 Phil Stockman SR RC .20 .50
588 Ramon Ramirez SR RC .20 .50
589 Roberto Novoa SR RC .20 .50
590 Scott Kazmir SR RC 1.50 4.00
NNO Update Set Exchange Card

2004 Upper Deck Glossy

COMP.FACT.SET (590) 70.00 100.00
*GLOSSY: .75X TO 2X BASIC
ISSUED ONLY IN FACTORY SET FORM

2004 Upper Deck A Piece of History 500 Club

SERIES 1 STATED ODDS 1:8700
STATED PRINT RUN 350 SERIAL #'D CARDS
504HR Rafael Palmeiro 100.00 200.00

2004 Upper Deck A Piece of History 500 Club Autograph

RANDOM INSERT IN SERIES 1 PACKS
STATED PRINT RUN 25 SERIAL #'d CARDS
NO PRICING DUE TO SCARCITY
RPAU0 Rafael Palmeiro AU/25

2004 Upper Deck Authentic Stars Jersey

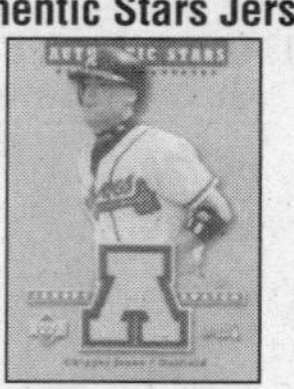

SERIES 1 ODDS 1:48 HOBBY, 1:96 RETAIL
*GOLD: .75X TO 2X BASIC AS JSY
GOLD RANDOM INSERTS IN SERIES 1 PACKS
GOLD PRINT RUN 100 SERIAL #'d SETS
AJ Andruw Jones 4.00 10.00
AP Albert Pujols 6.00 15.00
AR Alex Rodriguez 4.00 10.00
AS Alfonso Soriano 3.00 8.00
BA Bob Abreu 3.00 8.00
BW Bernie Williams 4.00 10.00
BZ Barry Zito 3.00 8.00
CD Carlos Delgado 3.00 8.00
CJ Chipper Jones 4.00 10.00
CS Curt Schilling 3.00 8.00
DE Darin Erstad 3.00 8.00
EC Eric Chavez 3.00 8.00
FT Frank Thomas 4.00 10.00
GM Greg Maddux 4.00 10.00
HB Hank Blalock 3.00 8.00
HM Hideki Matsui 15.00 40.00
IR Ivan Rodriguez 4.00 10.00
IS Ichiro Suzuki 10.00 25.00
JB Jeff Bagwell 4.00 10.00
JD J.D. Drew 3.00 8.00
JG Jason Giambi 3.00 8.00
JH Josh Beckett 3.00 8.00
JK Jeff Kent 3.00 8.00
KG Ken Griffey Jr. 6.00 15.00
LW Larry Walker 3.00 8.00
MI Mike Piazza 4.00 10.00
MP Mark Prior 4.00 10.00
MT Mark Teixeira 4.00 10.00
PM Pedro Martinez 4.00 10.00
PN Phil Nevin 3.00 8.00
RB Rocco Baldelli 3.00 8.00

RC Roger Clemens 6.00 15.00
RJ Randy Johnson 4.00 10.00
RO Roberto Alomar 4.00 10.00
SG Shawn Green 3.00 8.00
SS Sammy Sosa 4.00 10.00
TG Troy Glaus 3.00 8.00
TH Todd Helton 4.00 10.00
TL Tom Glavine 4.00 10.00
TM Tino Martinez 4.00 10.00
TO Torii Hunter 3.00 8.00
VG Vladimir Guerrero 4.00 10.00

2004 Upper Deck Authentic Stars Jersey Update

UPDATE GU ODDS 1:12 '04 UPDATE SETS
STATED PRINT RUN 75 SERIAL #'d SETS
AK Austin Kearns 4.00 10.00
CB Carlos Beltran 4.00 10.00
DJ Derek Jeter 15.00 40.00
HA Roy Halladay 4.00 10.00
HN Hideo Nomo 10.00 25.00
HU Tim Hudson 4.00 10.00
JE Jim Edmonds 4.00 10.00
JR Jose Reyes 4.00 10.00
JT Jim Thome 6.00 15.00
KW Kerry Wood 4.00 10.00
LB Lance Berkman 4.00 10.00
MO Magglio Ordonez 4.00 10.00
MR Manny Ramirez 6.00 15.00
OS Roy Oswalt 4.00 10.00
PW Preston Wilson 4.00 10.00
RF Rafael Furcal 4.00 10.00
RH Rich Harden 4.00 10.00
RP Rafael Palmeiro 6.00 15.00
SR Scott Rolen 6.00 15.00
TE Miguel Tejada 4.00 10.00
VW Vernon Wells 4.00 10.00
WE Brandon Webb 4.00 10.00

2004 Upper Deck Awesome Honors

COMPLETE SET (10) 8.00 20.00
SERIES 2 STATED ODDS 1:12 H/R
1 Albert Pujols 2.00 5.00
2 Alex Rodriguez 1.50 4.00
3 Angel Berroa .75 2.00
4 Dontrelle Willis .75 2.00
5 Eric Gagne .75 2.00
6 Garret Anderson .75 2.00
7 Ivan Rodriguez .75 2.00
8 Josh Beckett .75 2.00
9 Mariano Rivera 1.00 2.50
10 Roy Halladay .75 2.00

2004 Upper Deck Awesome Honors Jersey

*GOLD: .6X TO 1.5X BASIC
GOLD PRINT RUN 165 SERIAL #'d SETS
OVERALL SER.2 GU ODDS 1:12 H, 1:24 R
AJ Andruw Jones GG 3.00 8.00
AP Albert Pujols PC 6.00 15.00
AP1 Albert Pujols HA 6.00 15.00
AP2 Albert Pujols POM 6.00 15.00
AR Alex Rodriguez MVP 5.00 12.00
AR1 Alex Rodriguez GG 5.00 12.00
AR2 Alex Rodriguez HA 5.00 12.00
AR3 Alex Rodriguez POM 5.00 12.00
AS Alfonso Soriano POM 2.00 5.00
BB Bret Boone GG 2.00 5.00
BM Ben Molina GG 2.00 5.00
DL Derrek Lee GG 3.00 8.00
DW Dontrelle Willis ROY 3.00 8.00
EC Eric Chavez GG 2.00 5.00
EG Eric Gagne CY 2.00 5.00
EG1 Eric Gagne RA 2.00 5.00
EM Edgar Martinez POM 3.00 8.00
GA Garret Anderson AS MVP 2.00 5.00
HU Torii Hunter GG 2.00 5.00
IR Ivan Rodriguez NLCS MVP 3.00 8.00
IS Ichiro Suzuki GG 10.00 25.00
JB Josh Beckett WS MVP 2.00 5.00
JE Jim Edmonds GG 2.00 5.00
JG Jason Giambi POM 2.00 5.00
JM Jamie Moyer MAN 2.00 5.00
JO John Olerud GG 2.00 5.00
JS John Smoltz MAN 3.00 8.00
JT Jim Thome POM 3.00 8.00
LC Luis Castillo GG 2.00 5.00
MC Mike Cameron GG 2.00 5.00
MH Mike Hampton GG 2.00 5.00
MO Magglio Ordonez POM 2.00 5.00
MR Mariano Rivera ALCS MVP 3.00 8.00
MU Mike Mussina GG 3.00 8.00
RH Roy Halladay CY 2.00 5.00
SR Scott Rolen GG 3.00 8.00
TH Todd Helton POM 3.00 8.00
VG Vladimir Guerrero POM 3.00 8.00

2004 Upper Deck Awesome Honors Jersey Update

UPDATE GU ODDS 1:12 '04 UPDATE SETS
AB Angel Berroa 4.00 10.00
AP Albert Pujols 10.00 25.00
AS Alfonso Soriano 4.00 10.00
BE Adrian Beltre 4.00 10.00
BG Brian Giles 4.00 10.00
DL Derrek Lee 6.00 15.00
EG Eric Gagne 4.00 10.00
GS Gary Sheffield 4.00 10.00
IR Ivan Rodriguez 6.00 15.00
JM Joe Mauer 4.00 10.00
KB Kevin Brown 4.00 10.00
KM Kazuo Matsui 4.00 10.00
MC Miguel Cabrera 6.00 15.00
PE Andy Pettitte 6.00 15.00
RC Roger Clemens 10.00 25.00
RS Richie Sexson 4.00 10.00
SC Curt Schilling 6.00 15.00
SP Scott Podsednik 4.00 10.00
VA Javier Vazquez 4.00 10.00

2004 Upper Deck First Pitch Inserts

SERIES 1 STATED ODDS 1:72
CARD SP9 DOES NOT EXIST
SP7 LeBron James 6.00 15.00
SP8 Gordie Howe 4.00 10.00
SP10 Ernie Banks 4.00 10.00
SP11 General Tommy Franks 2.00 5.00
SP12 Ben Affleck 4.00 10.00
SP13 Halle Berry UER 4.00 10.00
Last name misspelled Barry
SP14 George H.W. Bush 2.00 5.00
SP15 George W. Bush 4.00 10.00

2004 Upper Deck Game Winners Bat

*GOLD: .6X TO 1.5X BASIC
GOLD PRINT RUN 50 SERIAL #'d SETS
OVERALL SER.2 GU ODDS 1:12 H, 1:24 R
AG Alex Gonzalez 3.00 8.00
AJ Andruw Jones 4.00 10.00
AP Albert Pujols 8.00 20.00
AS Alfonso Soriano 3.00 8.00
BA Bobby Abreu 3.00 8.00
BW Bernie Williams 4.00 10.00
CJ Chipper Jones 4.00 10.00
CP Corey Patterson 3.00 8.00
DE Darin Erstad 3.00 8.00
DJ Derek Jeter 10.00 25.00
GA Garret Anderson
GS Gary Sheffield 3.00 8.00
HB Hank Blalock 3.00 8.00
HM Hideki Matsui 12.50 30.00
HU Torii Hunter 3.00 8.00
IR Ivan Rodriguez 4.00 10.00
JB Jeff Bagwell 4.00 10.00
JE Jim Edmonds 3.00 8.00
JG Jason Giambi 3.00 8.00
JL Javy Lopez
JP Jorge Posada 4.00 10.00
JT Jim Thome 4.00 10.00
KG Ken Griffey Jr.
MC Miguel Cabrera 4.00 10.00
ML Mike Lowell 3.00 8.00
MO Magglio Ordonez 3.00 8.00
MP Mike Piazza 6.00 15.00
MT Mark Teixeira 4.00 10.00
RF Rafael Furcal 3.00 8.00
RH Ramon Hernandez 3.00 8.00
RK Ryan Klesko 3.00 8.00
SG Shawn Green 3.00 8.00
SR Scott Rolen 4.00 10.00
TE Miguel Tejada 3.00 8.00
TG Troy Glaus 3.00 8.00
TH Todd Helton 4.00 10.00
TN Trot Nixon 3.00 8.00
VG Vladimir Guerrero 4.00 10.00

2004 Upper Deck Going Deep Bat

SERIES 1 ODDS 1:288 HOB, 1:576 RET
SP PRINT RUNS B/WN 12-123 COPIES PER
SP PRINT RUNS PROVIDED BY UPPER DECK
NO PRICING ON QTY OF 41 OR LESS
GOLD RANDOM INSERTS IN PACKS
GOLD PRINT RUN 50 SERIAL #'d SETS
NO GOLD PRICING DUE TO SCARCITY
AJ Andruw Jones SP/12
AP Albert Pujols 10.00 25.00
AS Alfonso Soriano SP/53 4.00 10.00
BA Bob Abreu SP/110 4.00 10.00
BW Bernie Williams SP/56 6.00 15.00
CB Craig Biggio SP/89 6.00 15.00
CJ Chipper Jones SP/69 6.00 15.00
CP Corey Patterson SP/41
CS Curt Schilling SP/57 4.00 10.00
DE Darin Erstad 4.00 10.00
DM Doug Mientkiewicz SP/123 4.00 10.00
GA Garret Anderson 4.00 10.00
HM Hideki Matsui SP/70 15.00 40.00
HN Hideo Nomo 6.00 15.00
JB Jeff Bagwell SP/92 6.00 15.00
JE Jim Edmonds SP 4.00 10.00
JL Javy Lopez SP/77 4.00 10.00
JPA Jorge Posada 6.00 15.00
JPO Jay Payton SP/100 4.00 10.00
JT Jim Thome 6.00 15.00
KG Ken Griffey Jr. SP 15.00 40.00
KW Kerry Wood SP/108 4.00 10.00
MO Magglio Ordonez 4.00 10.00
MP Mike Piazza 6.00 15.00
MT Miguel Tejada SP/23
OV Omar Vizquel SP/115 6.00 15.00
RA Rich Aurilia SP/102 4.00 10.00
RB Rocco Baldelli SP 4.00 10.00
RF Rafael Furcal SP 4.00 10.00
RH Rickey Henderson SP/77 6.00 15.00
RO Roberto Alomar 6.00 15.00
SC Sandy Alomar Jr. SP/95 4.00 10.00
SG Shawn Green SP/100 4.00 10.00
SR Scott Rolen SP/77 6.00 15.00
TG Troy Glaus SP/113 4.00 10.00
TH Torii Hunter SP/115 4.00 10.00

2004 Upper Deck Headliners Jersey

SERIES 1 ODDS 1:48 HOBBY, 1:96 RETAIL
SP PRINT RUNS B/WN 97-153 COPIES PER
SP PRINT RUNS PROVIDED BY UPPER DECK
*GOLD: .75X TO 2X BASIC
GOLD RANDOM INSERTS IN SERIES 1 PACKS
GOLD PRINT RUN 100 SERIAL #'d SETS
AD Adam Dunn 3.00 8.00
BK Byung-Hyun Kim AS 3.00 8.00
BS Benito Santiago AS 3.00 8.00
CS Curt Schilling 3.00 8.00
GM Greg Maddux 4.00 10.00
HM Hideki Matsui 15.00 40.00
IS Ichiro Suzuki SP/153 15.00 40.00
JB Josh Beckett 3.00 8.00
JD Joe DiMaggio SP/153 50.00 100.00
JE Jim Edmonds 3.00 8.00
JH Jose Hernandez AS 3.00 8.00
JR Jimmy Rollins AS 3.00 8.00
JS Junior Spivey AS 3.00 8.00
JT Jim Thome 4.00 10.00
JV Jose Vidro AS 3.00 8.00
KG Ken Griffey Jr. 6.00 15.00
LB Lance Berkman 3.00 8.00
LC Luis Castillo AS 3.00 8.00
LG Luis Gonzalez 3.00 8.00
MA Mariano Rivera 4.00 10.00
MB Mark Buehrle AS 3.00 8.00
ML Mike Lowell AS 3.00 8.00
MM Mickey Mantle SP/97 75.00 150.00
MO Magglio Ordonez 3.00 8.00
MR Manny Ramirez 4.00 10.00
MS Matt Morris AS 3.00 8.00
MT Miguel Tejada 3.00 8.00
MU Mike Mussina 4.00 10.00
MY Mike Sweeney AS 3.00 8.00
PK Paul Konerko AS 3.00 8.00
PM Pedro Martinez 4.00 10.00
RF Robert Fick AS 3.00 8.00
RH Roy Halladay AS 3.00 8.00
RK Ryan Klesko 3.00 8.00
RO Roy Oswalt 3.00 8.00
SG Shawn Green 3.00 8.00
TB Tony Batista AS 3.00 8.00
TG Tom Glavine 4.00 10.00
TH Trevor Hoffman AS 3.00 8.00
TW Ted Williams SP/153 40.00 80.00
VG Vladimir Guerrero SP/153 6.00 15.00

2004 Upper Deck Derek Jeter Bonus

COMMON CARD (1-25) 2.00 5.00
1-25 THREE PER JETER BONUS PACK
COMMON JSY (26-32) 15.00 40.00
26-32 JSY PRINT RUN 99 #'d SETS
COMMON AU (33-37) 100.00 175.00
33-37 AU PRINT RUN 50 #'d SETS
38-42 AU JSY PRINT RUN 10 #'d SETS
AU JSY NO PRICING DUE TO SCARCITY
26-42 RANDOM IN JETER BONUS PACKS
ONE JETER BONUS PACK PER FACT.SET

2004 Upper Deck Magical Performances

SERIES 1 STATED ODDS 1:96 HOBBY
GOLD RANDOM INSERTS IN SER.1 HOBBY
GOLD STATED ODDS 1:1300 RETAIL
GOLD PRINT RUN 50 SERIAL #'d SETS
NO GOLD PRICING DUE TO SCARCITY
1 Mickey Mantle USC HR 20.00 50.00
2 Mickey Mantle 56 Triple Crown 20.00 50.00
3 Joe DiMaggio 56th Game 10.00 25.00
4 Joe DiMaggio Slides Home 10.00 25.00
5 Derek Jeter The Flip 10.00 25.00
6 Derek Jeter 00 AS/MVP 10.00 25.00
7 R.Clemens 300 Win/4000 K 10.00 25.00
8 Roger Clemens 20-1 10.00 25.00
9 Alfonso Soriano Walkoff 6.00 15.00
10 Andy Pettitte 96 8.00 20.00
11 Hideki Matsui Grand Slam 8.00 20.00
12 Mike Mussina 1-Hitter 8.00 20.00
13 Jorge Posada ALDS HR 8.00 20.00
14 Jason Giambi Grand Slam 6.00 15.00
15 David Wells Perfect 6.00 15.00
16 Mariano Rivera 99 WS MVP 8.00 20.00
17 Yogi Berra 12 K's 8.00 20.00
18 Phil Rizzuto 50 MVP 8.00 20.00
19 Whitey Ford 61 CY 8.00 20.00
20 Jose Contreras 1st Win 6.00 15.00
21 Catfish Hunter Free Agent 8.00 20.00
22 Mickey Mantle Cycle 20.00 50.00
23 M.Mantle HR's Both Sides 20.00 50.00
24 Joe DiMaggio 3-Time MVP 10.00 25.00
25 Joe DiMaggio Cycle 10.00 25.00
26 Derek Jeter 7 Seasons 10.00 25.00
27 Derek Jeter Mr. November 10.00 25.00
28 Roger Clemens 1-Hitter 10.00 25.00
29 Roger Clemens 01 CY 10.00 25.00
30 Alfonso Soriano HR Record 6.00 15.00
31 Andy Pettitte ALCS 8.00 20.00
32 Hideki Matsui 4 Hits 8.00 20.00
33 Mike Mussina 1st Postseason 8.00 20.00
34 Jorge Posada 40 Doubles 8.00 20.00
35 Jason Giambi 200th HR 6.00 15.00
36 David Wells 3-Hitter 6.00 15.00
37 Mariano Rivera Saves 3 8.00 20.00
38 Yogi Berra 3-Time MVP 8.00 20.00
39 Phil Rizzuto Broadcasting 8.00 20.00
40 Whitey Ford 10 WS Wins 8.00 20.00
41 Jose Contreras 2 Hits 6.00 15.00
42 Catfish Hunter 200th Win 8.00 20.00

2004 Upper Deck Matsui Chronicles

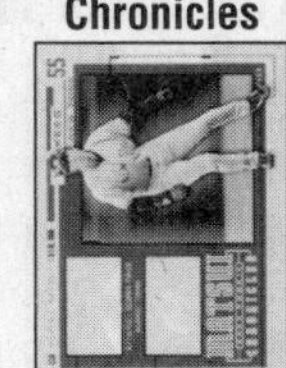

COMPLETE SET (60) 30.00 60.00
COMMON CARD (HM1-HM60) .75 2.00
ONE PER SERIES 1 RETAIL PACK

2004 Upper Deck National Pride

SERIES 1 STATED ODDS 1:6
1 Justin Orenduff .60 1.50
2 Micah Owings .60 1.50
3 Steven Register .60 1.50
4 Huston Street .75 2.00
5 Justin Verlander 1.25 3.00
6 Jered Weaver 1.25 3.00
7 Matt Campbell .60 1.50
8 Stephen Head .60 1.50
9 Mark Romanczuk .60 1.50
10 Jeff Clement 1.00 2.50
11 Mike Nickeas .60 1.50
12 Tyler Greene .60 1.50
13 Paul Janish .60 1.50
14 Jeff Larish .60 1.50
15 Eric Patterson .60 1.50
16 Dustin Pedroia .60 1.50
17 Michael Griffin .60 1.50
18 Brent Lillibridge .60 1.50
19 Danny Putnam .60 1.50
20 Seth Smith .60 1.50

2004 Upper Deck National Pride Jersey 1

SERIES 1 ODDS 1:24 HOBBY, 1:48 RETAIL
1 Justin Orenduff 2.00 5.00
2 Micah Owings 2.00 5.00
3 Steven Register 2.00 5.00
4 Huston Street 2.50 6.00
5 Justin Verlander 6.00 15.00
6 Jered Weaver 5.00 12.00
7 Matt Campbell 2.00 5.00
8 Stephen Head 2.00 5.00
9 Mark Romanczuk 2.00 5.00
10 Jeff Clement 4.00 10.00
11 Mike Nickeas 2.00 5.00
12 Tyler Greene 2.00 5.00
13 Paul Janish 2.00 5.00
14 Jeff Larish 2.00 5.00
15 Eric Patterson 2.00 5.00
16 Dustin Pedroia 2.00 5.00
17 Michael Griffin 2.00 5.00
18 Brent Lillibridge 2.00 5.00
19 Danny Putnam 2.00 5.00
20 Seth Smith 3.00 8.00
21 Justin Orenduff SP 3.00 8.00
22 Micah Owings SP 3.00 8.00
23 Steven Register SP 3.00 8.00
24 Huston Street SP 3.00 8.00
25 Justin Verlander SP 8.00 20.00
26 Jered Weaver SP 6.00 15.00
27 Matt Campbell SP 3.00 8.00
28 Stephen Head SP 3.00 8.00
29 Mark Romanczuk SP 3.00 8.00
30 Jeff Clement SP 5.00 12.00
31 Mike Nickeas SP 3.00 8.00
32 Tyler Greene SP 3.00 8.00
33 Paul Janish SP 3.00 8.00
34 Jeff Larish SP 3.00 8.00
35 Eric Patterson SP 3.00 8.00
36 Dustin Pedroia SP 3.00 8.00
37 Michael Griffin SP 3.00 8.00
38 Brent Lillibridge SP 3.00 8.00
39 Danny Putnam SP 3.00 8.00
40 Seth Smith SP 4.00 10.00
41 Delmon Young SP 6.00 15.00
42 Rickie Weeks SP 4.00 10.00

2004 Upper Deck National Pride Memorabilia 2

OVERALL SER.2 GU ODDS 1:12 H, 1:24 R
BBJ Brian Bruney Jsy 2.00 5.00
CBJ Chris Burke Jsy 2.00 5.00
CBP Chris Burke Pants 2.00 5.00
DUJ Justin Duchscherer Jsy 2.00 5.00
DUP Justin Duchscherer Pants 2.00 5.00
ERJ Eddie Rodriguez CO Jsy 2.00 5.00
ERP Eddie Rodriguez CO Pants 2.00 5.00
EYJ Ernie Young Jsy 2.00 5.00
GGJ Gabe Gross Jsy 2.00 5.00
GKJ Graham Koonce Jsy 2.00 5.00
GKP Graham Koonce Pants 2.00 5.00
GLJ Gerald Laird Jsy 2.00 5.00
GSJ Grady Sizemore Jsy 3.00 8.00
GSP Grady Sizemore Pants 3.00 8.00
HRJ Horacio Ramirez Jsy 2.00 5.00
HRP Horacio Ramirez Pants 2.00 5.00
JBJ John Van Benschoten Jsy 2.00 5.00
JBP John Van Benschoten Pants 2.00 5.00
JCJ Jesse Crain Jsy 3.00 8.00
JCP Jesse Crain Pants 3.00 8.00
JDJ J.D. Durbin Jsy 2.00 5.00
JGJ John Grabow Jsy 2.00 5.00
JHJ J.J. Hardy Jsy 2.00 5.00
JLJ Justin Leone Jsy 3.00 8.00
JLP Justin Leone Pants 3.00 8.00
JMJ Joe Mauer Jsy 6.00 15.00
JMP Joe Mauer Pants 6.00 15.00
JRJ Jeremy Reed Jsy 4.00 10.00
JSJ Jason Stanford Jsy 2.00 5.00
JSP Jason Stanford Pants 2.00 5.00
MLJ Mike Lamb Jsy 2.00 5.00
MRJ Mike Rouse Jsy 2.00 5.00
MRP Mike Rouse Pants 2.00 5.00
RMP Ryan Madson Pants 2.00 5.00
RRJ Royce Ring Jsy 2.00 5.00
RRP Royce Ring Pants 2.00 5.00
TBJ Thad Bosley CO Jsy 2.00 5.00
TWJ Todd Williams Jsy 2.00 5.00

2004 Upper Deck Peak Performers Jersey

*GOLD: .6X TO 1.5X BASIC
GOLD PRINT RUN 165 SERIAL #'d SETS
OVERALL SER.2 GU ODDS 1:12 H, 1:24 R
AP Albert Pujols 6.00 15.00
AS Alfonso Soriano 2.00 5.00
BE Josh Beckett 2.00 5.00
BP Brandon Phillips 2.00 5.00
CB Craig Biggio 3.00 8.00
CD Carlos Delgado 2.00 5.00
CS Curt Schilling 3.00 8.00
EG Eric Gagne 2.00 5.00
FT Frank Thomas 3.00 8.00
HB Hank Blalock 2.00 5.00
HM Hideki Matsui 10.00 25.00
HN Hideo Nomo 3.00 8.00
IR Ivan Rodriguez 3.00 8.00
IS Ichiro Suzuki 10.00 25.00
JB Jeff Bagwell 3.00 8.00
JR Jose Reyes 2.00 5.00
JT Jim Thome 3.00 8.00
KG Ken Griffey Jr. 6.00 15.00
KW Kerry Wood 2.00 5.00
LB Lance Berkman 2.00 5.00
LC Luis Castillo 2.00 5.00
MM Mike Mussina 3.00 8.00
MO Magglio Ordonez 2.00 5.00
MP Mark Prior 3.00 8.00
MT Miguel Tejada 2.00 5.00
OV Omar Vizquel 3.00 8.00
PB Pat Burrell 2.00 5.00
PE Andy Pettitte 3.00 8.00
PL Paul Lo Duca 2.00 5.00
PM Pedro Martinez 3.00 8.00
RF Rafael Furcal 2.00 5.00
RP Rafael Palmeiro 3.00 8.00
SA C.C. Sabathia 2.00 5.00
SG Shawn Green 2.00 5.00
SR Scott Rolen 3.00 8.00
TH Todd Helton 3.00 8.00
VG Vladimir Guerrero 3.00 8.00
VW Vernon Wells 2.00 5.00

2004 Upper Deck Famous Quotes

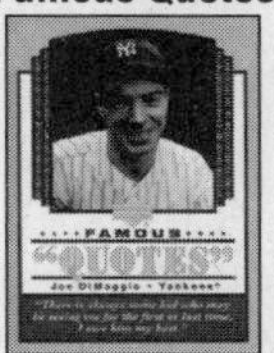

COMPLETE SET (20) 15.00 40.00
SERIES 2 STATED ODDS 1:6 H/R
1 Al Lopez .75 2.00
2 Bob Feller .75 2.00
3 Bob Gibson .75 2.00
4 Brooks Robinson .75 2.00
5 Cal Ripken 3.00 8.00
6 Carl Yastrzemski 1.50 4.00
7 Earl Weaver .75 2.00
8 Eddie Mathews 1.00 2.50
9 Ernie Banks 1.00 2.50
10 Greg Maddux 1.50 4.00
11 Joe DiMaggio 2.00 5.00
12 Mickey Mantle 3.00 8.00
13 Nolan Ryan 2.50 6.00
14 Stan Musial 1.50 4.00
15 Ted Williams 2.50 6.00
16 Tom Seaver .75 2.00
17 Tommy Lasorda .75 2.00
18 Warren Spahn .75 2.00
19 Whitey Ford .75 2.00
20 Yogi Berra 1.00 2.50

2004 Upper Deck Signature Stars Black Ink 1

Please note that Roger Clemens did not return his cards in time for pack-out and those cards could be redeemed until November 10, 2006.

SER.1 ODDS 1:288 H,1:24 UPD BOX, 1:1800 R
PRINT RUNS B/WN 18-479 COPIES PER
NO PRICING ON QTY OF 25 OR LESS
EXCHANGE DEADLINE 11/10/06
AG Andres Galarraga/248 6.00 15.00
AH Aaron Heilman/49 10.00 25.00
BG Bob Gibson/19
BK Billy Koch/429 4.00 10.00

CR Cal Ripken/69 125.00 200.00
DR1 Dave Roberts/278 4.00 10.00
HM Hideki Matsui/25
IS1 Ichiro Suzuki/19
JRA Joe Randa/271 6.00 15.00
KI Kazuhisa Ishii/58 10.00 25.00
MO Magglio Ordonez/377 6.00 15.00
MU Mike Mussina/68 15.00 40.00
NG Nomar Garciaparra/69 60.00 120.00
NR1 Nolan Ryan/69 75.00 150.00
RA Rich Aurilia/479 4.00 10.00
RC Roger Clemens/19 EXCH
RH1 Rich Harden/163 6.00 15.00
RP Rafael Palmeiro/18
TH Torii Hunter/374 6.00 15.00
VG Vladimir Guerrero/68 30.00 60.00

2004 Upper Deck Signature Stars Black Ink 2

OVERALL SER.2 SIG ODDS 1:288 H, 1:1500 R
PRINT RUNS B/WN 43-450 COPIES PER
BB Bret Boone/43 15.00 40.00
BW Brandon Webb/60 6.00 15.00
DB Dewon Brazelton/96 4.00 10.00
DR2 Dave Roberts/450 4.00 10.00
DS Darryl Strawberry/160 10.00 25.00
DW Dontrelle Willis/160 10.00 25.00
EC Eric Chavez/60 10.00 25.00
EG Eric Gagne/160 10.00 25.00
JC Jose Canseco/160 10.00 25.00
JV Javier Vazquez/60 10.00 25.00
KG Ken Griffey Jr./450 50.00 100.00
MT Mark Teixeira/200 10.00 25.00
RH2 Rich Harden/65 10.00 25.00
RW Rickie Weeks/65 10.00 25.00

2004 Upper Deck Signature Stars Blue Ink 1

SER.1 ODDS 1:288 H,1:24 UPD BOX, 1:1800 R
STATED PRINT RUN 25 SERIAL #'d SETS
MATSUI PRINT RUN 324 SERIAL #'d CARDS
NO PRICING ON QTY OF 25 OR LESS
EXCHANGE DEADLINE 11/10/06
HM Hideki Matsui/324 175.00 300.00

2004 Upper Deck Signature Stars Blue Ink 2

OVERALL SER.2 SIG ODDS 1:288 H, 1:1500 R
PRINT RUNS B/WN 20-95 COPIES PER
NO PRICING ON QTY OF 25 OR LESS
NR2 Nolan Ryan/95 75.00 150.00

2004 Upper Deck Signature Stars Red Ink 1

SER.1 ODDS 1:288 H,1:24 UPD BOX, 1:1800 R
STATED PRINT RUN 10 SERIAL #'d SETS
NO PRICING DUE TO SCARCITY
EXCHANGE DEADLINE 11/10/06

2004 Upper Deck Signature Stars Red Ink 2

OVERALL SER.2 SIG ODDS 1:288 H, 1:1500 R
PRINT RUNS B/WN 5-10 COPIES PER
NO PRICING DUE TO SCARCITY

2004 Upper Deck Signature Stars Gold

SER.1 ODDS 1:288 H, 1:24 MINI, 1:1800 R
STATED PRINT RUN 99 SERIAL #'d SETS
ALL EXCEPT MATSUI FEATURE BLUE INK
NO PRICING DUE TO SCARCITY
EXCHANGE DEADLINE 11/10/06

2004 Upper Deck Super Patch Logos 2

OVERALL SERIES 2 ODDS 1:2500 H/R
PRINT RUNS B/WN 8-34 COPIES PER
PRINT RUNS PROVIDED BY UPPER DECK
CARDS ARE NOT SERIAL-NUMBERED
NO PRICING DUE TO SCARCITY
HU Torii Hunter/32
MP Mike Piazza/22
PM Pedro Martinez/10
RJ Randy Johnson/20
RP Rafael Palmeiro/8
RS Richie Sexson/9
SS Sammy Sosa/16
TH Todd Helton/29
VG Vladimir Guerrero/34
VW Vernon Wells/13

2004 Upper Deck Super Patches Logos 1

OVERALL PATCH SERIES 1 ODDS 1:7500
PRINT RUNS B/WN 8-25 COPIES PER
PRINT RUNS PROVIDED BY UPPER DECK
NO PRICING DUE TO SCARCITY
AD Adam Dunn/8
AJ Andruw Jones/25
AP Albert Pujols/20
AR Alex Rodriguez/20
AS Alfonso Soriano/10
CJ Chipper Jones/25
CS Curt Schilling/20
GM Greg Maddux/25
HM Hideki Matsui /10
IS Ichiro Suzuki/20

2004 Upper Deck Super Patch Numbers 2

OVERALL SERIES 2 ODDS 1:2500 H/R
PRINT RUNS B/WN 2-45 COPIES PER
PRINT RUNS PROVIDED BY UPPER DECK
CARDS ARE NOT SERIAL-NUMBERED
NO PRICING DUE TO SCARCITY
BE Josh Beckett/17
IR Ivan Rodriguez/2
JB Jeff Bagwell/14
JK Jeff Kent/2
JT Jim Thome/21
KG Ken Griffey Jr./45
LB Lance Berkman/12
MR Manny Ramirez/10

2004 Upper Deck Super Patches Numbers 1

OVERALL PATCH SERIES 1 ODDS 1:7500
PRINT RUNS B/WN 10-25 COPIES PER
PRINT RUNS PROVIDED BY UPPER DECK
NO PRICING DUE TO SCARCITY
IR Ivan Rodriguez/14
JB Jeff Bagwell/16
JG Jason Giambi/10
JK Jeff Kent/20
JT Jim Thome/25
KG Ken Griffey Jr./15
LB Lance Berkman/10
MP Mark Prior/20
MR Manny Ramirez/18
SS Sammy Sosa/15

2004 Upper Deck Super Patch Stripes 2

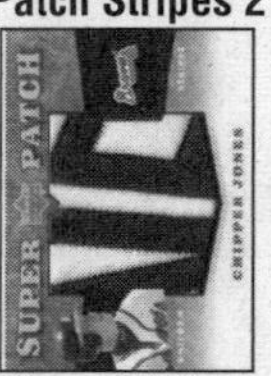

OVERALL SERIES 2 ODDS 1:2500 H/R
PRINT RUNS B/WN 6-65 COPIES PER
PRINT RUNS PROVIDED BY UPPER DECK
CARDS ARE NOT SERIAL-NUMBERED
NO PRICING DUE TO SCARCITY
AJ Andruw Jones/52
AP Albert Pujols/37
AR Alex Rodriguez/65
AS Alfonso Soriano/6
CJ Chipper Jones/37
CS Curt Schilling/14
GM Greg Maddux/19
HN Hideo Nomo/27
IS Ichiro Suzuki/29

2004 Upper Deck Super Patches Stripes 1

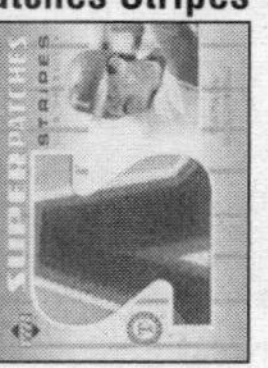

OVERALL PATCH SERIES 1 ODDS 1:7500
PRINT RUNS B/WN 25-40 COPIES PER
PRINT RUNS PROVIDED BY UPPER DECK
NO PRICING DUE TO SCARCITY
MP Mike Piazza/30
PM Pedro Martinez/25
RB Rocco Baldelli/30
RC Roger Clemens/30
RJ Randy Johnson/30
RP Rafael Palmeiro/40
SS Sammy Sosa/30
TH Todd Helton/30
TH Torii Hunter/30
VG Vladimir Guerrero/40

2004 Upper Deck Super Sluggers

COMPLETE SET (30) 10.00 25.00
ONE PER SERIES 2 RETAIL PACK
1 Albert Pujols 1.00 2.50
2 Alex Rodriguez .75 2.00
3 Alfonso Soriano .40 1.00
4 Andruw Jones .40 1.00
5 Bret Boone .40 1.00
6 Carlos Delgado .40 1.00
7 Edgar Renteria .40 1.00
8 Eric Chavez .40 1.00
9 Frank Thomas .50 1.25
10 Garret Anderson .40 1.00
11 Gary Sheffield .40 1.00
12 Jason Giambi .40 1.00
13 Javy Lopez .40 1.00
14 Jeff Bagwell .40 1.00
15 Jim Edmonds .40 1.00
16 Jim Thome .40 1.00
17 Jorge Posada .40 1.00
18 Lance Berkman .40 1.00
19 Magglio Ordonez .40 1.00
20 Manny Ramirez .40 1.00
21 Mike Lowell .40 1.00
22 Nomar Garciaparra .75 2.00
23 Preston Wilson .40 1.00
24 Rafael Palmeiro .40 1.00
25 Richie Sexson .40 1.00
26 Sammy Sosa .50 1.25
27 Shawn Green .40 1.00
28 Todd Helton .40 1.00
29 Vernon Wells .40 1.00
30 Vladimir Guerrero .50 1.25

2004 Upper Deck Twenty-Five Salute

COMPLETE SET (10) 8.00 20.00
SERIES 1 STATED ODDS 1:12
1 Barry Bonds 2.50 6.00
2 Troy Glaus .75 2.00
3 Andruw Jones .75 2.00
4 Jay Gibbons .75 2.00
5 Jeremy Giambi .75 2.00
6 Jason Giambi .75 2.00
7 Jim Thome .75 2.00
8 Rafael Palmeiro .75 2.00
9 Carlos Delgado .75 2.00
10 Dmitri Young .75 2.00

2005 Upper Deck

This 300-card first series was released in November, 2004.The set was issued in 10-card hobby packs with an $3 SRP which came 24 packs to a box and 12 boxes to a case. The set was also issued in 10-card retail packs which also had a $3 SRP and came 24 packs to a box and 12 boxes to a case. The hobby and retail packs are differentiated as there is different insert odds depending on which class of pack it is. Subsets include: Super Rookies (211-260); Team Leaders (261-290) and Pennant Race (291-300). The 200-card second series was released in June, 2004 and had the following subsets: Super Rookies (431-450); Bound for Glory (451-470) and Team Checklists (471-500).

COMPLETE SERIES 1 (300) 30.00 50.00
COMMON (1-210) .10 .30
COMMON (211-250) .40 1.00
OVERALL PLATES SER.1 ODDS 1:1080 H
PLATES PRINT RUN 1 #'d SET PER COLOR
BLACK-CYAN-MAGENTA-YELLOW ISSUED
NO PLATES PRICING DUE TO SCARCITY
1 Casey Kotchman .10 .30
2 Chone Figgins .10 .30
3 David Eckstein .10 .30
4 Jarrod Washburn .10 .30
5 Robb Quinlan .10 .30
6 Troy Glaus .10 .30
7 Vladimir Guerrero .30 .75
8 Brandon Webb .10 .30
9 Danny Bautista .10 .30
10 Luis Gonzalez .10 .30
11 Matt Kata .10 .30
12 Randy Johnson .30 .75
13 Robby Hammock .10 .30
14 Shea Hillenbrand .10 .30
15 Adam LaRoche .10 .30
16 Andruw Jones .20 .50
17 Horacio Ramirez .10 .30
18 John Smoltz .20 .50
19 Johnny Estrada .10 .30
20 Mike Hampton .10 .30
21 Rafael Furcal .10 .30
22 Brian Roberts .10 .30
23 Javy Lopez .10 .30
24 Jay Gibbons .10 .30
25 Jorge Julio .10 .30
26 Melvin Mora .10 .30
27 Miguel Tejada .10 .30
28 Rafael Palmeiro .20 .50
29 Derek Lowe .10 .30
30 Jason Varitek .30 .75
31 Kevin Youkilis .10 .30
32 Manny Ramirez .20 .50
33 Curt Schilling .20 .50
34 Pedro Martinez .20 .50
35 Trot Nixon .10 .30
36 Corey Patterson .10 .30
37 Derrek Lee .20 .50
38 LaTroy Hawkins .10 .30
39 Mark Prior .20 .50
40 Matt Clement .10 .30
41 Moises Alou .10 .30
42 Sammy Sosa .30 .75
43 Aaron Rowand .10 .30
44 Carlos Lee .10 .30
45 Jose Valentin .10 .30
46 Juan Uribe .10 .30
47 Magglio Ordonez .10 .30
48 Mark Buehrle .10 .30
49 Paul Konerko .10 .30
50 Adam Dunn .10 .30
51 Barry Larkin .20 .50
52 D'Angelo Jimenez .10 .30
53 Danny Graves .10 .30
54 Paul Wilson .10 .30
55 Sean Casey .10 .30
56 Wily Mo Pena .10 .30
57 Ben Broussard .10 .30
58 C.C. Sabathia .10 .30
59 Casey Blake .10 .30
60 Cliff Lee .10 .30
61 Matt Lawton .10 .30
62 Omar Vizquel .10 .30
63 Victor Martinez .10 .30
64 Charles Johnson .10 .30
65 Joe Kennedy .10 .30
66 Jeromy Burnitz .10 .30
67 Matt Holliday .15 .40
68 Preston Wilson .10 .30
69 Royce Clayton .10 .30
70 Shawn Estes .10 .30
71 Bobby Higginson .10 .30
72 Brandon Inge .10 .30
73 Carlos Guillen .10 .30
74 Dmitri Young .10 .30
75 Eric Munson .10 .30
76 Jeremy Bonderman .10 .30
77 Ugueth Urbina .10 .30
78 Josh Beckett .10 .30
79 Dontrelle Willis .10 .30
80 Jeff Conine .10 .30
81 Juan Pierre .10 .30
82 Luis Castillo .10 .30
83 Miguel Cabrera .20 .50
84 Mike Lowell .10 .30
85 Andy Pettitte .20 .50
86 Brad Lidge .10 .30
87 Carlos Beltran .10 .30
88 Craig Biggio .20 .50
89 Jeff Bagwell .20 .50
90 Roger Clemens .50 1.25
91 Roy Oswalt .10 .30
92 Benito Santiago .10 .30
93 Jeremy Affeldt .10 .30
94 Juan Gonzalez .10 .30
95 Ken Harvey .10 .30
96 Mike MacDougal .10 .30
97 Mike Sweeney .10 .30
98 Zack Greinke .10 .30
99 Adrian Beltre .10 .30
100 Alex Cora .10 .30
101 Cesar Izturis .10 .30
102 Eric Gagne .10 .30
103 Kazuhisa Ishii .10 .30
104 Milton Bradley .10 .30
105 Shawn Green .10 .30
106 Danny Kolb .10 .30
107 Ben Sheets .10 .30
108 Brooks Kieschnick .10 .30
109 Craig Counsell .10 .30
110 Geoff Jenkins .10 .30
111 Lyle Overbay .10 .30
112 Scott Podsednik .10 .30
113 Corey Koskie .10 .30
114 Johan Santana .30 .75
115 Joe Mauer .30 .75
116 Justin Morneau .10 .30
117 Lew Ford .10 .30
118 Matt LeCroy .10 .30
119 Torii Hunter .10 .30
120 Brad Wilkerson .10 .30
121 Chad Cordero .10 .30
122 Livan Hernandez .10 .30
123 Jose Vidro .10 .30
124 Termel Sledge .10 .30
125 Tony Batista .10 .30
126 Zach Day .10 .30
127 Al Leiter .10 .30
128 Jae Weong Seo .10 .30
129 Jose Reyes .10 .30
130 Kazuo Matsui .10 .30
131 Mike Piazza .30 .75
132 Todd Zeile .10 .30
133 Cliff Floyd .10 .30
134 Alex Rodriguez .50 1.25
135 Derek Jeter .60 1.50
136 Gary Sheffield .10 .30
137 Hideki Matsui .50 1.25
138 Jason Giambi .10 .30
139 Jorge Posada .20 .50
140 Mike Mussina .20 .50
141 Barry Zito .10 .30
142 Bobby Crosby .10 .30
143 Octavio Dotel .10 .30
144 Eric Chavez .10 .30
145 Jermaine Dye .10 .30
146 Mark Kotsay .10 .30
147 Tim Hudson .10 .30
148 Billy Wagner .10 .30
149 Bobby Abreu .10 .30
150 David Bell .10 .30
151 Jim Thome .20 .50
152 Jimmy Rollins .10 .30
153 Mike Lieberthal .10 .30
154 Randy Wolf .10 .30
155 Craig Wilson .10 .30
156 Daryle Ward .10 .30
157 Jack Wilson .10 .30
158 Jason Kendall .10 .30
159 Kip Wells .10 .30
160 Oliver Perez .10 .30
161 Rob Mackowiak .10 .30
162 Brian Giles .10 .30
163 Brian Lawrence .10 .30
164 David Wells .10 .30
165 Jay Payton .10 .30
166 Ryan Klesko .10 .30
167 Sean Burroughs .10 .30
168 Trevor Hoffman .10 .30
169 Brett Tomko .10 .30
170 J.T. Snow .10 .30
171 Jason Schmidt .10 .30
172 Kirk Rueter .10 .30
173 A.J. Pierzynski .10 .30
174 Pedro Feliz .10 .30
175 Ray Durham .10 .30
176 Eddie Guardado .10 .30
177 Edgar Martinez .20 .50
178 Ichiro Suzuki .60 1.50
179 Jamie Moyer .10 .30
180 Joel Pineiro .10 .30
181 Randy Winn .10 .30
182 Raul Ibanez .10 .30
183 Albert Pujols .60 1.50
184 Edgar Renteria .10 .30
185 Jason Isringhausen .10 .30
186 Jim Edmonds .10 .30
187 Matt Morris .10 .30
188 Reggie Sanders .10 .30
189 Tony Womack .10 .30
190 Aubrey Huff .10 .30
191 Danys Baez .10 .30
192 Carl Crawford .10 .30
193 Jose Cruz Jr. .10 .30
194 Rocco Baldelli .10 .30
195 Tino Martinez .20 .50
196 Dewon Brazelton .10 .30
197 Alfonso Soriano .10 .30
198 Brad Fullmer .10 .30
199 Gerald Laird .10 .30
200 Hank Blalock .10 .30
201 Laynce Nix .10 .30
202 Mark Teixeira .20 .50
203 Michael Young .10 .30
204 Alexis Rios .10 .30
205 Eric Hinske .10 .30
206 Miguel Batista .10 .30
207 Orlando Hudson .10 .30
208 Roy Halladay .10 .30
209 Ted Lilly .10 .30
210 Vernon Wells .10 .30
211 Aarom Baldiris SR .40 1.00
212 B.J. Upton SR .40 1.00
213 Dallas McPherson SR .40 1.00
214 Brian Dallimore SR .40 1.00
215 Chris Oxspring SR .40 1.00
216 Chris Shelton SR .60 1.50
217 David Wright SR .75 2.00
218 Edwardo Sierra SR .40 1.00
219 Fernando Nieve SR .40 1.00
220 Frank Francisco SR .40 1.00
221 Jeff Bennett SR .40 1.00
222 Justin Lehr SR .40 1.00
223 John Gall SR .40 1.00
224 Jorge Sequea SR .40 1.00
225 Justin Germano SR .40 1.00
226 Kazuhito Tadano SR .40 1.00
227 Kevin Cave SR .40 1.00
228 Joe Blanton SR .40 1.00
229 Luis A. Gonzalez SR .40 1.00
230 Michael Wuertz SR .40 1.00
231 Mike Rouse SR .40 1.00
232 Nick Regilio SR .40 1.00
233 Orlando Rodriguez SR .40 1.00
234 Phil Stockman SR .40 1.00
235 Ramon Ramirez SR .40 1.00
236 Roberto Novoa SR .40 1.00
237 Dioner Navarro SR .40 1.00
238 Tim Bausher SR .40 1.00
239 Logan Kensing SR .40 1.00
240 Andy Green SR .40 1.00
241 Brad Halsey SR .40 1.00
242 Charles Thomas SR .40 1.00
243 George Sherrill SR .40 1.00
244 Jesse Crain SR .40 1.00
245 Jimmy Serrano SR .40 1.00
246 Joe Horgan SR .40 1.00
247 Chris Young SR .40 1.00
248 Joey Gathright SR .40 1.00
249 Gavin Floyd SR .40 1.00
250 Ryan Howard SR 2.00 5.00
251 Lance Cormier SR .40 1.00
252 Matt Treanor SR .40 1.00
253 Jeff Francis SR .40 1.00
254 Nick Swisher SR .40 1.00
255 Scott Atchison SR .40 1.00
256 Travis Blackley SR .40 1.00
257 Travis Smith SR .40 1.00
258 Yadier Molina SR .40 1.00
259 Jeff Keppinger SR .40 1.00
260 Scott Kazmir SR .40 1.00
261 Garret Anderson .20 .50
Vladimir Guerrero TL
262 Luis Gonzalez .20 .50
Randy Johnson TL
263 Andruw Jones .20 .50
Chipper Jones TL
264 Miguel Tejada .10 .30
Rafael Palmeiro TL
265 Curt Schilling .20 .50
Manny Ramirez TL
266 Mark Prior .20 .50
Sammy Sosa TL
267 Frank Thomas .20 .50
Magglio Ordonez TL
268 Barry Larkin .30 .75
Ken Griffey Jr. TL
269 C.C. Sabathia .10 .30
Victor Martinez TL
270 Jeromy Burnitz .10 .30
Todd Helton TL
271 Dmitri Young .10 .30
Ivan Rodriguez TL
272 Josh Beckett .10 .30
Miguel Cabrera TL
273 Jeff Bagwell .30 .75
Roger Clemens TL
274 Ken Harvey .10 .30
Mike Sweeney TL
275 Adrian Beltre .10 .30
Eric Gagne TL
276 Ben Sheets .10 .30
Geoff Jenkins TL
277 Joe Mauer .20 .50
Torii Hunter TL
278 Jose Vidro .10 .30
Livan Hernandez TL
279 Kazuo Matsui .20 .50
Mike Piazza TL
280 Alex Rodriguez .60 1.50
Derek Jeter TL
281 Eric Chavez .10 .30
Tim Hudson TL
282 Bobby Abreu .10 .30
Jim Thome TL
283 Craig Wilson .10 .30
Jason Kendall TL
284 Brian Giles .10 .30
Phil Nevin TL
285 A.J. Pierzynski .10 .30
Jason Schmidt TL
286 Bret Boone .30 .75
Ichiro Suzuki TL
287 Albert Pujols .30 .75
Scott Rolen TL
288 Aubrey Huff .10 .30
Tino Martinez TL
289 Hank Blalock .10 .30

Mark Teixeira TL
290 Carlos Delgado .10 .30
Roy Halladay TL
291 Vladimir Guerrero PR .20 .50
292 Curt Schilling PR .10 .30
293 Mark Prior PR .20 .50
294 Josh Beckett PR .10 .30
295 Roger Clemens PR .30 .75
296 Derek Jeter PR .30 .75
297 Eric Chavez PR .10 .30
298 Jim Thome PR .10 .30
299 Albert Pujols PR .30 .75
300 Hank Blalock PR .10 .30
301 Bartolo Colon .10 .30
302 Darin Erstad .10 .30
303 Garret Anderson .10 .30
304 Orlando Cabrera .10 .30
305 Steve Finley .10 .30
306 Javier Vazquez .10 .30
307 Russ Ortiz .10 .30
308 Chipper Jones .30 .75
309 Marcus Giles .10 .30
310 Raul Mondesi .10 .30
311 B.J. Ryan .10 .30
312 Luis Matos .10 .30
313 Sidney Ponson .10 .30
314 Bill Mueller .10 .30
315 David Ortiz .30 .75
316 Johnny Damon .20 .50
317 Keith Foulke .10 .30
318 Mark Bellhorn .10 .30
319 Wade Miller .10 .30
320 Aramis Ramirez .10 .30
321 Carlos Zambrano .10 .30
322 Greg Maddux .50 1.25
323 Kerry Wood .10 .30
324 Nomar Garciaparra .30 .75
325 Todd Walker .10 .30
326 Frank Thomas .30 .75
327 Freddy Garcia .10 .30
328 Joe Crede .10 .30
329 Jose Contreras .10 .30
330 Orlando Hernandez .10 .30
331 Shingo Takatsu .10 .30
332 Austin Kearns .10 .30
333 Eric Milton .10 .30
334 Ken Griffey Jr. .50 1.25
335 Aaron Boone .10 .30
336 David Riske .10 .30
337 Jake Westbrook .10 .30
338 Kevin Millwood .10 .30
339 Travis Hafner .10 .30
340 Aaron Miles .10 .30
341 Jeff Baker .10 .30
342 Todd Helton .20 .50
343 Garrett Atkins .10 .30
344 Carlos Pena .10 .30
345 Ivan Rodriguez .20 .50
346 Rondell White .10 .30
347 Troy Percival .10 .30
348 A.J. Burnett .10 .30
349 Carlos Delgado .10 .30
350 Guillermo Mota .10 .30
351 Paul Lo Duca .10 .30
352 Jason Lane .10 .30
353 Lance Berkman .10 .30
354 Angel Berroa .10 .30
355 David DeJesus .10 .30
356 Ruben Gotay .10 .30
357 Jose Lima .10 .30
358 Brad Penny .10 .30
359 J.D. Drew .10 .30
360 Jayson Werth .10 .30
361 Jeff Kent .10 .30
362 Odalis Perez .10 .30
363 Brady Clark .10 .30
364 Junior Spivey .10 .30
365 Rickie Weeks .10 .30
366 Jacque Jones .10 .30
367 Joe Nathan .10 .30
368 Nick Punto .10 .30
369 Shannon Stewart .10 .30
370 Doug Mientkiewicz .10 .30
371 Kris Benson .10 .30
372 Tom Glavine .20 .50
373 Victor Zambrano .10 .30
374 Bernie Williams .20 .50
375 Carl Pavano .10 .30
376 Jaret Wright .10 .30
377 Kevin Brown .10 .30
378 Mariano Rivera .30 .75
379 Danny Haren .10 .30
380 Eric Byrnes .10 .30
381 Erubiel Durazo .10 .30
382 Rich Harden .10 .30
383 Brett Myers .10 .30
384 Chase Utley .20 .50
385 Marlon Byrd .10 .30
386 Pat Burrell .10 .30
387 Placido Polanco .10 .30
388 Freddy Sanchez .10 .30
389 Jason Bay .10 .30
390 Josh Fogg .10 .30
391 Adam Eaton .10 .30
392 Jake Peavy .10 .30
393 Khalil Greene .20 .50
394 Mark Loretta .10 .30
395 Phil Nevin .10 .30
396 Ramon Hernandez .10 .30
397 Woody Williams .10 .30
398 Armando Benitez .10 .30
399 Edgardo Alfonzo .10 .30
400 Marquis Grissom .10 .30
401 Mike Matheny .10 .30
402 Richie Sexson .10 .30
403 Bret Boone .10 .30
404 Gil Meche .10 .30
405 Chris Carpenter .10 .30
406 Jeff Suppan .10 .30
407 Larry Walker .20 .50
408 Mark Grudzielanek .10 .30
409 Mark Mulder .10 .30
410 Scott Rolen .20 .50
411 Josh Phelps .10 .30
412 Jonny Gomes .10 .30
413 Francisco Cordero .10 .30
414 Kenny Rogers .10 .30
415 Richard Hidalgo .10 .30
416 Dave Bush .10 .30
417 Frank Catalanotto .10 .30
418 Gabe Gross .10 .30
419 Guillermo Quiroz .10 .30
420 Reed Johnson .10 .30
421 Cristian Guzman .10 .30
422 Esteban Loaiza .10 .30
423 Jose Guillen .10 .30
424 Nick Johnson .10 .30
425 Vinny Castilla .10 .30
426 Pete Orr SR RC .40 1.00
427 Tadahito Iguchi SR RC 1.00 2.50
428 Jeff Baker SR .40 1.00
429 Marcos Carvajal SR RC .40 1.00
430 Justin Verlander SR RC 2.00 5.00
431 Luke Scott SR RC 1.25 3.00
432 Willy Taveras SR .40 1.00
433 Ambiorix Burgos SR RC .40 1.00
434 Andy Sisco SR .40 1.00
435 Denny Bautista SR .40 1.00
436 Mark Teahen SR .40 1.00
437 Ervin Santana SR .40 1.00
438 Dennis Houlton SR RC .40 1.00
439 Philip Humber SR RC .60 1.50
440 Steve Schmoll SR RC .40 1.00
441 J.J. Hardy SR .40 1.00
442 Ambiorix Concepcion SR RC .40 1.00
443 Dae-Sung Koo SR RC .40 1.00
444 Andy Phillips SR .40 1.00
445 Dan Meyer SR .40 1.00
446 Huston Street SR .60 1.50
447 Keiichi Yabu SR RC .40 1.00
448 Jeff Niemann SR RC .60 1.50
449 Jeremy Reed SR .40 1.00
450 Tony Blanco SR .40 1.00
451 Albert Pujols BG .30 .75
452 Alex Rodriguez BG .30 .75
453 Curt Schilling BG .10 .30
454 Derek Jeter BG .30 .75
455 Greg Maddux BG .30 .75
456 Ichiro Suzuki BG .30 .75
457 Ivan Rodriguez BG .10 .30
458 Jeff Bagwell BG .10 .30
459 Jim Thome BG .10 .30
460 Ken Griffey Jr. BG .30 .75
461 Manny Ramirez BG .20 .50
462 Mike Mussina BG .10 .30
463 Mike Piazza BG .20 .50
464 Pedro Martinez BG .10 .30
465 Rafael Palmeiro BG .10 .30
466 Randy Johnson BG .20 .50
467 Roger Clemens BG .30 .75
468 Sammy Sosa BG .20 .50
469 Todd Helton BG .10 .30
470 Vladimir Guerrero BG .20 .50
471 Vladimir Guerrero TC .20 .50
472 Shawn Green TC .10 .30
473 John Smoltz TC .10 .30
474 Miguel Tejada TC .10 .30
475 Curt Schilling TC .10 .30
476 Mark Prior TC .10 .30
477 Frank Thomas TC .20 .50
478 Ken Griffey Jr. TC .30 .75
479 C.C. Sabathia TC .10 .30
480 Todd Helton TC .10 .30
481 Ivan Rodriguez TC .10 .30
482 Miguel Cabrera TC .10 .30
483 Roger Clemens TC .30 .75
484 Mike Sweeney TC .10 .30
485 Eric Gagne TC .10 .30
486 Ben Sheets TC .10 .30
487 Johan Santana TC .10 .30
488 Mike Piazza TC .20 .50
489 Derek Jeter TC .30 .75
490 Eric Chavez TC .10 .30
491 Jim Thome TC .10 .30
492 Craig Wilson TC .10 .30
493 Jake Peavy TC .10 .30
494 Jason Schmidt TC .10 .30
495 Ichiro Suzuki TC .30 .75
496 Albert Pujols TC .30 .75
497 Carl Crawford TC .10 .30
498 Mark Teixeira TC .10 .30
499 Vernon Wells TC .10 .30
500 Jose Vidro TC .10 .30

2005 Upper Deck American Flag

SERIES 1 STATED ODDS 1:220 HOBBY
STATED PRINT RUN 15 SERIAL #'d SETS
NO PRICING DUE TO SCARCITY
OVERALL PLATES SER.1 ODDS 1:1080 H
PLATES PRINT RUN 1 #'d SET PER COLOR
BLACK-CYAN-MAGENTA-YELLOW ISSUED
NO PLATES PRICING DUE TO SCARCITY

2005 Upper Deck Blue

*BLUE 300-425/451-500: 4X TO 10X BASIC
*BLUE 426-450: 2.5X TO 6X BASIC
OVERALL SER.2 PARALLEL ODDS 1:12 H
STATED PRINT RUN 150 SERIAL #'d SETS

2005 Upper Deck Emerald

*EMER 300-425/451-500: 12.5X TO 30X BASIC
OVERALL SER.2 PARALLEL ODDS 1:12 H
STATED PRINT RUN 25 SERIAL #'d SETS
NO PRICING AVAILABLE ON 426-450

2005 Upper Deck Gold

*GOLD 300-425/451-500: 5X TO 12X BASIC
*GOLD 426-450: 3X TO 8X BASIC
OVERALL SER.2 PARALLEL ODDS 1:12 H
STATED PRINT RUN 99 SERIAL #'d SETS

2005 Upper Deck Platinum

OVERALL SER.2 PARALLEL ODDS 1:12 H
STATED PRINT RUN 5 SERIAL #'d SETS
NO PRICING DUE TO SCARCITY

2005 Upper Deck Retro

*RETRO: 1.25X TO 3X BASIC
ONE RETRO BOX PER SER.1 HOBBY CASE
SER.1 HOBBY CASES CONTAIN 12 BOXES
OVERALL PLATES SER.1 ODDS 1:1080 H
PLATES PRINT RUN 1 #'d SET PER COLOR
BLACK-CYAN-MAGENTA-YELLOW ISSUED
NO PLATES PRICING DUE TO SCARCITY

2005 Upper Deck 4000 Strikeout

RANDOM INSERTS IN SERIES 1 PACKS
STATED PRINT RUN 4000 SERIAL #'d SETS
CRCJ Steve Carlton 6.00 15.00
Nolan Ryan
Roger Clemens
Randy Johnson/4000

2005 Upper Deck 4000 Strikeout Autographs

RANDOM INSERTS IN SERIES 1 PACKS
STATED PRINT RUN 50 SERIAL #'d SETS
QUAD PRINT RUN 10 SERIAL #'d CARDS
NO PRICING DUE TO SCARCITY
ALL ARE EXCHANGE CARDS
EXCHANGE DEADLINE 11/16/07
NR Nolan Ryan AU/50
Steve Carlton
Roger Clemens
Randy Johnson
RC Roger Clemens AU/50
Steve Carlton
Nolan Ryan
Randy Johnson
RJ Randy Johnson AU/50
Steve Carlton
Nolan Ryan
Roger Clemens
SC Steve Carlton AU/50
Nolan Ryan
Roger Clemens
Randy Johnson
CRCJ Steve Carlton AU
Nolan Ryan AU
Roger Clemens AU
Randy Johnson AU/10

2005 Upper Deck Baseball Heroes Jeter

COMPLETE SET (10) 12.50 30.00
COMMON CARD (91-99) 1.50 4.00
SERIES 1 STATED ODDS 1:6 H/R

2005 Upper Deck Baseball Heroes Jeter Jersey

COMMON CARD (1-9)
SERIES 1 STATED ODDS 1:3500 H/R
STATED PRINT RUN 75 SERIAL #'d SETS
NO PRICING DUE TO LACK OF INFO

2005 Upper Deck Baseball Heroes Jeter Signature

SERIES 1 STATED ODDS 1:1,200,000 H/R
STATED PRINT RUN 2 SERIAL #'d SETS
NO PRICING DUE TO SCARCITY

2005 Upper Deck Flyball

ONE PER '05 PRO SIGS PACK
8 Mariano Rivera .20 .50
21 Adrian Beltre .08 .25
29 Jim Edmonds .08 .25
47 Armando Benitez .08 .25
59 Derrek Lee .15 .40
62 David Ortiz .25 .60

2005 Upper Deck Game Jersey

SERIES 2 OVERALL GU ODDS 1:8
SP INFO PROVIDED BY UPPER DECK
AB Adrian Beltre 3.00 8.00
AP Albert Pujols 6.00 15.00
AS Alfonso Soriano 3.00 8.00
CB Carlos Beltran SP 3.00 8.00
CJ Chipper Jones 4.00 10.00
CS Curt Schilling 4.00 10.00
DJ Derek Jeter 8.00 20.00
DO David Ortiz SP 4.00 10.00
DW David Wright 6.00 15.00
EC Eric Chavez 3.00 8.00
EG Eric Gagne 3.00 8.00
FT Frank Thomas 4.00 10.00
GM Greg Maddux SP 4.00 10.00
HB Hank Blalock 3.00 8.00
HE Todd Helton 4.00 10.00
HU Torii Hunter 3.00 8.00
IR Ivan Rodriguez 4.00 10.00
JB Jeff Bagwell SP 4.00 10.00
JK Jeff Kent 3.00 8.00
JS Johan Santana SP 4.00 10.00
JT Jim Thome SP 4.00 10.00
KG Ken Griffey Jr. SP 6.00 15.00
KW Kerry Wood 3.00 8.00
LB Lance Berkman 3.00 8.00
MC Miguel Cabrera 4.00 10.00
MM Mark Mulder 3.00 8.00
MP Mark Prior 4.00 10.00
MR Manny Ramirez SP 4.00 10.00
MT Mark Teixeira SP 4.00 10.00
PI Mike Piazza 4.00 10.00
PM Pedro Martinez 4.00 10.00
RJ Randy Johnson SP 4.00 10.00
SM John Smoltz 4.00 10.00
SR Scott Rolen 4.00 10.00
SS Sammy Sosa 4.00 10.00
TE Miguel Tejada 3.00 8.00
TG Troy Glaus 3.00 8.00
TH Tim Hudson 3.00 8.00
VG Vladimir Guerrero 4.00 10.00

2005 Upper Deck Game Patch

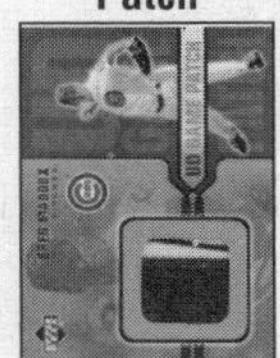

SERIES 2 STATED ODDS 1:288 H
STATED PRINT RUN 45 SETS
CARDS ARE NOT SERIAL-NUMBERED
PRINT RUN INFO PROVIDED BY UD
NO PRICING DUE TO SCARCITY

2005 Upper Deck Hall of Fame Plaques

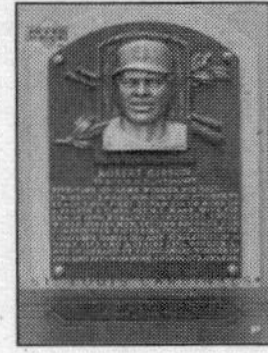

SERIES 1 STATED ODDS 1:36 H/R
16 Ernie Banks 3.00 8.00
17 Yogi Berra 3.00 8.00
18 Whitey Ford 3.00 8.00
19 Bob Gibson 3.00 8.00
20 Willie McCovey 3.00 8.00
21 Stan Musial 4.00 10.00
22 Nolan Ryan 6.00 15.00
23 Mike Schmidt 4.00 10.00
24 Tom Seaver 3.00 8.00
25 Robin Yount 3.00 8.00

2005 Upper Deck Marquee Attractions Jersey

SER.1 OVERALL GU ODDS 1:12 H
AD Adam Dunn 3.00 8.00
AJ Andruw Jones 4.00 10.00
AP Albert Pujols 6.00 15.00
BE Josh Beckett 3.00 8.00
BG Brian Giles 3.00 8.00
BW Billy Wagner 3.00 8.00
CD Carlos Delgado 3.00 8.00
CJ Chipper Jones 4.00 10.00
CS Curt Schilling 4.00 10.00
DJ Derek Jeter 8.00 20.00
DW Dontrelle Willis 3.00 8.00
EG Eric Gagne 3.00 8.00
GM Greg Maddux 5.00 12.00
HM Hideki Matsui 10.00 25.00
HN Hideo Nomo 4.00 10.00
HO Trevor Hoffman 3.00 8.00
IR Ivan Rodriguez 4.00 10.00
IS Ichiro Suzuki 10.00 25.00
JB Jeff Bagwell 4.00 10.00
JG Jason Giambi 3.00 8.00
JM Joe Mauer 4.00 10.00
JS Jason Schmidt 3.00 8.00
JT Jim Thome 4.00 10.00
KB Kevin Brown 3.00 8.00
KM Kazuo Matsui 3.00 8.00
KW Kerry Wood 3.00 8.00
MC Miguel Cabrera 4.00 10.00
MP Mark Prior 4.00 10.00
MT Miguel Tejada 3.00 8.00
PE Andy Pettitte 4.00 10.00
PI Mike Piazza 4.00 10.00
PM Pedro Martinez 4.00 10.00
PW Preston Wilson 3.00 8.00
RC Roger Clemens 5.00 12.00
RJ Randy Johnson 4.00 10.00
SG Shawn Green 3.00 8.00
SS Sammy Sosa 4.00 10.00
TH Todd Helton 4.00 10.00
VG Vladimir Guerrero 4.00 10.00

2005 Upper Deck Marquee Attractions Jersey Gold

*GOLD: .6X TO 1.5X BASIC
SER.1 OVERALL GU ODDS 1:12 H
GA Garret Anderson 5.00 12.00
KG Ken Griffey Jr.
RO Roy Oswalt 5.00 12.00

2005 Upper Deck Matinee Idols Jersey

SER.1 OVERALL GU ODDS 1:12 H, 1:24 R
SP INFO PROVIDED BY UPPER DECK
BB Bret Boone SP 4.00 10.00
BE Josh Beckett 3.00 8.00
BW Billy Wagner 3.00 8.00
BZ Barry Zito 3.00 8.00
CD Carlos Delgado 3.00 8.00
CJ Chipper Jones 4.00 10.00
CR Cal Ripken 15.00 40.00
CS Curt Schilling 4.00 10.00
DJ Derek Jeter 8.00 20.00
DW Dontrelle Willis 3.00 8.00
EC Eric Chavez 3.00 8.00
GS Gary Sheffield 3.00 8.00
HB Hank Blalock 3.00 8.00
HU Torii Hunter 3.00 8.00
JB Jeff Bagwell 4.00 10.00
JE Jim Edmonds 3.00 8.00
JG Jason Giambi 3.00 8.00
JT Jim Thome 4.00 10.00
KG Ken Griffey Jr. 6.00 15.00
KW Kerry Wood 3.00 8.00
ML Mike Lowell 4.00 10.00
MM Mike Mussina 4.00 10.00
MP Mark Prior 4.00 10.00
MT Mark Teixeira 4.00 10.00
NR Nolan Ryan 15.00 40.00
PB Pat Burrell 3.00 8.00
PI Mike Piazza 4.00 10.00
RB Rocco Baldelli 3.00 8.00
RC Roger Clemens 5.00 12.00
RH Roy Halladay 3.00 8.00
RJ Randy Johnson 4.00 10.00
RW Rickie Weeks 3.00 8.00
SG Shawn Green 3.00 8.00
SR Scott Rolen 4.00 10.00
SS Sammy Sosa 4.00 10.00
TG Troy Glaus 3.00 8.00
TH Todd Helton 4.00 10.00
TS Tom Seaver 6.00 15.00
VG Vladimir Guerrero 4.00 10.00
VW Vernon Wells 3.00 8.00

2005 Upper Deck Milestone Materials

SERIES 2 OVERALL GU ODDS 1:8
AP Albert Pujols 6.00 15.00
BA Jeff Bagwell 4.00 10.00
BC Bobby Crosby 3.00 8.00
CB Carlos Beltran 3.00 8.00
CS Curt Schilling 4.00 10.00
DO David Ortiz 4.00 10.00
EG Eric Gagne 3.00 8.00
GM Greg Maddux 4.00 10.00
JB Jason Bay 3.00 8.00
JP Jake Peavy 3.00 8.00
JS Johan Santana 4.00 10.00
JT Jim Thome 4.00 10.00
KG Ken Griffey Jr. 6.00 15.00
MR Manny Ramirez 4.00 10.00
MT Mark Teixeira 4.00 10.00
RJ Randy Johnson 4.00 10.00
RP Rafael Palmeiro 4.00 10.00
TE Miguel Tejada 3.00 8.00
VG Vladimir Guerrero 4.00 10.00

2005 Upper Deck Origins Jersey

SER.1 OVERALL GU ODDS 1:12 H, 1:24 R
AB Adrian Beltre 3.00 8.00
AJ Andruw Jones 4.00 10.00
AP Albert Pujols 6.00 15.00
AS Alfonso Soriano 3.00 8.00
BG Brian Giles 3.00 8.00
BU B.J. Upton 4.00 10.00
CB Carlos Beltran 3.00 8.00
EG Eric Gagne 3.00 8.00
GA Garret Anderson 3.00 8.00
GM Greg Maddux 5.00 12.00
HM Hideki Matsui 10.00 25.00
HN Hideo Nomo 4.00 10.00
IR Ivan Rodriguez 4.00 10.00
IS Ichiro Suzuki 10.00 25.00
JG Juan Gonzalez 3.00 8.00
JK Jeff Kent 3.00 8.00
JL Javy Lopez 3.00 8.00
JP Jorge Posada 4.00 10.00
JR Jose Reyes 3.00 8.00
JS Jason Schmidt 3.00 8.00
JV Javier Vazquez 3.00 8.00
KM Kazuo Matsui 3.00 8.00
LB Lance Berkman 3.00 8.00
LG Luis Gonzalez 3.00 8.00
MC Miguel Cabrera 4.00 10.00
MM Mark Mulder 3.00 8.00
MO Magglio Ordonez 3.00 8.00
MR Manny Ramirez 4.00 10.00
MT Miguel Tejada 3.00 8.00
PE Jake Peavy 3.00 8.00
PM Pedro Martinez 4.00 10.00
PW Preston Wilson 3.00 8.00
RF Rafael Furcal 3.00 8.00
RP Rafael Palmeiro 4.00 10.00
RS Richie Sexson 3.00 8.00
SS Sammy Sosa 4.00 10.00
TH Tim Hudson 3.00 8.00
VG Vladimir Guerrero 4.00 10.00

2005 Upper Deck Rewind to 1997 Jersey

SER.2 STATED ODDS 1:288 H, 1:480 R
PRINT RUNS B/WN 100-150 COPIES PER
CARDS ARE NOT SERIAL-NUMBERED
PRINT RUN INFO PROVIDED BY UD
AJ Andruw Jones 15.00 40.00
CJ Chipper Jones 15.00 40.00
CR Cal Ripken 20.00 50.00
CS Curt Schilling Phils 10.00 25.00
DJ Derek Jeter 20.00 50.00
FT Frank Thomas 15.00 40.00
GM Greg Maddux Braves 15.00 40.00
IR Ivan Rodriguez Rgr 15.00 40.00
JB Jeff Bagwell 15.00 40.00

JS John Smoltz 15.00 40.00
JT Jim Thome Indians 15.00 40.00
KG Ken Griffey Jr. M's 30.00 60.00
MP Mike Piazza Dgr 15.00 40.00
MR Manny Ramirez Indians 15.00 40.00
PM Pedro Martinez Expos 15.00 40.00
RJ Randy Johnson M's 15.00 40.00
SR Scott Rolen Phils Pants 15.00 40.00
TG Tony Gwynn 15.00 40.00
VG Vladimir Guerrero Expos 15.00 40.00
WC Will Clark Rgr 15.00 40.00

2005 Upper Deck Season Opener MLB Game-Worn Jersey Collection

STATED ODDS 1:8
AB Angel Berroa 2.00 5.00
AD Adam Dunn 2.00 5.00
AJ Andruw Jones 3.00 8.00
CD Carlos Delgado 2.00 5.00
CP Corey Patterson 2.00 5.00
DJ Derek Jeter 10.00 25.00
EB Eric Byrnes 2.00 5.00
EH Eric Hinske 2.00 5.00
JB Josh Beckett 2.00 5.00
JG Jody Gerut 2.00 5.00
JT Jim Thome 3.00 8.00
MO Magglio Ordonez 2.00 5.00
MT Michael Tucker 2.00 5.00
PM Pedro Martinez 3.00 8.00
RB Rocco Baldelli 2.00 5.00
RK Ryan Klesko 2.00 5.00
SG Shawn Green 2.00 5.00
SR Scott Rolen 3.00 8.00

2005 Upper Deck Signature Sensations

STATED PRINT RUN 15 SERIAL #'d SETS
DIE CUT PRINT RUN 10 SERIAL #'d SETS
SERIES 2 OVERALL AU ODDS 1:288 H
NO PRICING DUE TO SCARCITY

2005 Upper Deck Signature Stars Hobby

SERIES 1 STATED ODDS 1:288 HOBBY
SP INFO PROVIDED BY UPPER DECK
BB Bret Boone
BC Bobby Crosby 6.00 15.00
BS Ben Sheets 6.00 15.00
BZ Barry Zito
CB Carlos Beltran SP
CR Cal Ripken SP 125.00 200.00
DW Dontrelle Willis 6.00 15.00
DY Delmon Young 10.00 25.00
HB Hank Blalock 6.00 15.00
JB Josh Beckett SP
JL Javy Lopez 6.00 15.00
JM Joe Mauer 12.50 30.00
KG Ken Griffey Jr. 50.00 100.00
KW Kerry Wood 10.00 25.00
LB Lance Berkman SP
LF Lew Ford 4.00 10.00
MC Miguel Cabrera 10.00 25.00
MO Magglio Ordonez SP
MP Mark Prior
MT Mark Teixeira SP
NG Nomar Garciaparra SP
OP Odalis Perez
RO Roy Oswalt SP
RW Rickie Weeks SP

2005 Upper Deck Signature Stars Retail

NO PRICING DUE TO SCARCITY
SERIES 1 STATED ODDS 1:480 RETAIL
SP INFO PROVIDED BY UPPER DECK
BB1 Bret Boone
CB1 Carlos Beltran
JB1 Josh Beckett SP
KG1 Ken Griffey Jr.
KW1 Kerry Wood
MC1 Miguel Cabrera
MO1 Magglio Ordonez
MP1 Mark Prior SP
NG1 Nomar Garciaparra

2005 Upper Deck Super Patch Logo

SER.1 OVERALL GU ODDS 1:12 H, 1:24 R
PRINT RUNS B/WN 8-34 COPIES PER
CARDS ARE NOT SERIAL-NUMBERED
PRINT RUNS PROVIDED BY UPPER DECK
AP Albert Pujols/34 *
BZ Barry Zito/26 *
JT Jim Thome/28 *
KW Kerry Wood/24 *
MP Mike Piazza/24 *
MR Manny Ramirez/8 *
MT Miguel Tejada/24 *

RH Roy Halladay/24 *
RJ Randy Johnson/24 *
SG Shawn Green/24 *

2005 Upper Deck Super Patch Name

SER.1 OVERALL GU ODDS 1:12 H, 1:24 R
PRINT RUNS B/WN 10-78 COPIES PER
CARDS ARE NOT SERIAL-NUMBERED
PRINT RUNS PROVIDED BY UPPER DECK
CB Carlos Beltran/10 *
JR Jose Reyes/16 *
KG Ken Griffey Jr./78 *
MC Miguel Cabrera/27 *
RC Roger Clemens/31 *
RS Richie Sexson/23 *
SS Sammy Sosa/25 *
VG Vladimir Guerrero/27 *

2005 Upper Deck Super Patch Number

SER.1 OVERALL GU ODDS 1:12 H, 1:24 R
PRINT RUNS B/WN 8-34 COPIES PER
CARDS ARE NOT SERIAL-NUMBERED
PRINT RUNS PROVIDED BY UPPER DECK
BE Josh Beckett/28 *
CD Carlos Delgado/30 *
EC Eric Chavez/24 *
HN Hideo Nomo/29 *
IS Ichiro Suzuki/10 *
JB Jeff Bagwell/20 *
KM Kazuo Matsui/24 *
MP Mark Prior/24 *
MT Mark Teixeira/24 *
PM Pedro Martinez/31 *

2005 Upper Deck Wingfield Collection

COMPLETE SET (20) 30.00 60.00
SERIES 1 STATED ODDS 1:9 H/R
1 Eddie Mathews 1.25 3.00
2 Ernie Banks 1.25 3.00
3 Joe DiMaggio 1.50 4.00
4 Mickey Mantle 4.00 10.00
5 Pee Wee Reese 1.25 3.00
6 Phil Rizzuto 1.25 3.00
7 Stan Musial 1.50 4.00
8 Ted Williams 2.00 5.00
9 Bob Feller 1.25 3.00
10 Whitey Ford 1.25 3.00
11 Willie Stargell 1.25 3.00
12 Yogi Berra 1.25 3.00
13 Roy Campanella 1.25 3.00
14 Franklin D. Roosevelt 1.25 3.00
15 Harry Truman 1.25 3.00
16 Dwight D. Eisenhower 1.25 3.00
17 John F. Kennedy 2.00 5.00
18 Lyndon Johnson 1.25 3.00
19 Richard Nixon 1.25 3.00
20 Thurman Munson 1.25 3.00

2005 Upper Deck World Series Heroes

COMPLETE SET (45) 10.00 25.00
SERIES 1 STATED ODDS 1:1 RETAIL
1 Garret Anderson .20 .50
2 Troy Glaus .20 .50
3 Vladimir Guerrero .40 1.00
4 Andruw Jones .30 .75
5 Chipper Jones .40 1.00
6 Curt Schilling .30 .75
7 Keith Foulke .20 .50
8 Manny Ramirez .30 .75
9 Nomar Garciaparra .40 1.00
10 Pedro Martinez .30 .75
11 Kerry Wood .20 .50
12 Mark Prior .30 .75
13 Sammy Sosa .40 1.00
14 Frank Thomas .40 1.00
15 Magglio Ordonez .20 .50
16 Dontrelle Willis .20 .50
17 Josh Beckett .20 .50
18 Miguel Cabrera .30 .75
19 Jeff Bagwell .30 .75
20 Lance Berkman .20 .50
21 Roger Clemens .60 1.50
22 Eric Gagne .20 .50
23 Torii Hunter .20 .50
24 Mike Piazza .40 1.00
25 Alex Rodriguez .60 1.50
26 Derek Jeter .75 2.00
27 Gary Sheffield .20 .50
28 Hideki Matsui .60 1.50
29 Jason Giambi .20 .50
30 Jorge Posada .30 .75
31 Kevin Brown .20 .50
32 Mariano Rivera .40 1.00
33 Mike Mussina .30 .75
34 Eric Chavez .20 .50
35 Mark Mulder .20 .50
36 Tim Hudson .20 .50
37 Billy Wagner .20 .50
38 Jim Thome .30 .75
39 Brian Giles .20 .50
40 Jason Schmidt .20 .50
41 Albert Pujols .75 2.00
42 Scott Rolen .30 .75
43 Alfonso Soriano .20 .50
44 Hank Blalock .20 .50
45 Mark Teixeira .30 .75

2005 Upper Deck Chicago National

This six-card standard-size set was distributed as a give-away during the 2005 National Sports Collectors Convention. Each of these cards feature a current Chicago baseball player and were issued to a stated print run of 750 serial numbered sets.

COMPLETE SET (6)
DISTRIBUTED AT '05 CHICAGO NSCC
MLB1 Mark Prior .75 2.00
MLB2 Greg Maddux 1.00 2.50
MLB3 Derrek Lee .75 2.00
MLB4 Kerry Wood .50 1.25
MLB5 Tadahito Iguchi 1.25 3.00
MLB6 Paul Konerko .75 2.00

2005 Upper Deck Signature Cuts Hawaii

ISSUED AT 05 HAWAII TRADE SHOW
STATED PRINT RUN 1 SERIAL #'d SET
NO PRICING DUE TO SCARCITY
SCP1 Babe Ruth
SCP2 Lou Gehrig
SCP3 Don Drysdale
SCP4 George Sisler
SCP5 Satchel Paige
SCP6 Honus Wagner
SCP7 Jackie Robinson

2006 Upper Deck

This 1,252-card set was issued over three series in 2006. The first series was released in April, the second series in August, and the Update set in December. All three series were issued in eight-card packs with an $2.99 SRP. These cards came 24 packs to a box and 12 boxes to a case. The first two series were sequenced in alphabetical team order, with the players in first name alphabetical order in the first series as well. However, if the player was traded, he was still sequenced as if he were with his 2005 team. The second series was just sequenced in alpabetical team order. Cards 871-900 were checklists while cards 901-999 featured 2006 rookies. The final cards in this set feature a mix of players with new teams and more 2006 rookies. Cards numbered 1221--1250 were also checklist cards sequenced in alphabetical team order and were printed to stated odds of one in two update packs. Jason Repko card number 245 was not issued in packs; however, when the Upper Deck Fat Packs, which included series one and two cards that situation was rectified. However, the Repko card was issued as card number 283.

COMPLETE SET (1250) 375.00 600.00
COMPLETE SERIES 1 (500) 125.00 200.00
COMPLETE SERIES 2 (500) 125.00 200.00
COMPLETE UPDATE (250) 125.00 200.00
COMP.UPDATE w/o SP's (200) 30.00 50.00
COMMON CARD (1-1250) .15 .40
1-500 ISSUED IN SERIES 1 PACKS
501-1000 ISSUED IN SERIES 2 PACKS
1001-1250 ISSUED IN UPDATE PACKS
BAKER & REPKO BOTH CARD 283
1001-1250 SP STATED ODDS 1:2
SP: 1005/1013/1021/1037/1045/1061/1069
SP: 1077/1093/1101/1117/1125/1133/1149
SP: 1157/1173/1181/1189/1205/1213
SP: 1221-1250
4 MATCHED PLATES 1:2 SER.2 HOBBY CASES
PLATE PRINT RUN 1 SET PER COLOR
BLACK-CYAN-MAGENTA-YELLOW ISSUED
NO PLATE PRICING DUE TO SCARCITY
EXQUISITE EXCH 1 PER SER.2 HOBBY CASE
EXQUISITE EXCH RANDOM IN UPD.CASES
EXQUISITE EXCH DEADLINE 07/27/07
1 Adam Kennedy .15 .40
2 Bartolo Colon .15 .40
3 Bengie Molina .15 .40
4 Casey Kotchman .15 .40
5 Chone Figgins .15 .40
6 Dallas McPherson .15 .40
7 Darin Erstad .15 .40
8 Ervin Santana .15 .40
9 Francisco Rodriguez .15 .40
10 Garret Anderson .15 .40
11 Jarrod Washburn .15 .40
12 John Lackey .15 .40
13 Juan Rivera .15 .40
14 Orlando Cabrera .15 .40
15 Paul Byrd .15 .40
16 Steve Finley .15 .40
17 Vladimir Guerrero .40 1.00
18 Alex Cintron .15 .40
19 Brandon Lyon .15 .40
20 Brandon Webb .15 .40
21 Chad Tracy .15 .40
22 Chris Snyder .15 .40
23 Claudio Vargas .15 .40
24 Conor Jackson .25 .60
25 Craig Counsell .15 .40
26 Javier Vazquez .15 .40
27 Jose Valverde .15 .40
28 Luis Gonzalez .15 .40
29 Royce Clayton .15 .40
30 Russ Ortiz .15 .40
31 Shawn Green .15 .40
32 Dustin Nippert (RC) .30 .75
33 Tony Clark .15 .40
34 Troy Glaus .15 .40
35 Adam LaRoche .15 .40
36 Andruw Jones .25 .60
37 Craig Hansen RC 1.25 3.00
38 Chipper Jones .40 1.00
39 Horacio Ramirez .15 .40
40 Jeff Francoeur .40 1.00
41 John Smoltz .25 .60
42 Joey Devine RC .30 .75
43 Johnny Estrada .15 .40
44 Anthony Lerew (RC) .30 .75
45 Julio Franco .15 .40
46 Kyle Farnsworth .15 .40
47 Marcus Giles .15 .40
48 Mike Hampton .15 .40
49 Rafael Furcal .15 .40
50 Chuck James (RC) .50 1.25
51 Tim Hudson .15 .40
52 B.J. Ryan .15 .40
53 Bernie Castro (RC) .30 .75
54 Brian Roberts .15 .40
55 Walter Young (RC) .30 .75
56 Daniel Cabrera .15 .40
57 Eric Byrnes .15 .40
58 Alejandro Freire RC .30 .75
59 Erik Bedard .15 .40
60 Javy Lopez .15 .40
61 Jay Gibbons .15 .40
62 Jorge Julio .15 .40
63 Luis Matos .15 .40
64 Melvin Mora .15 .40
65 Miguel Tejada .15 .40
66 Rafael Palmeiro .25 .60
67 Rodrigo Lopez .15 .40
68 Sammy Sosa .40 1.00
69 Alejandro Machado (RC) .30 .75
70 Bill Mueller .15 .40
71 Bronson Arroyo .15 .40
72 Curt Schilling .25 .60
73 David Ortiz .40 1.00
74 David Wells .15 .40
75 Edgar Renteria .15 .40
76 Ryan Jorgensen RC .30 .75
77 Jason Varitek .40 1.00
78 Johnny Damon .25 .60
79 Keith Foulke .15 .40
80 Kevin Youkilis .15 .40
81 Manny Ramirez .25 .60
82 Matt Clement .15 .40
83 Hanley Ramirez (RC) .75 2.00
84 Tim Wakefield .15 .40
85 Trot Nixon .15 .40
86 Wade Miller .15 .40
87 Aramis Ramirez .15 .40
88 Carlos Zambrano .15 .40
89 Corey Patterson .15 .40
90 Derrek Lee .15 .40
91 Geovany Soto (RC) .75 2.00
92 Greg Maddux .60 1.50
93 Jeromy Burnitz .15 .40
94 Jerry Hairston .15 .40
95 Kerry Wood .15 .40
96 Mark Prior .25 .60
97 Matt Murton .15 .40
98 Michael Barrett .15 .40
99 Neifi Perez .15 .40
100 Nomar Garciaparra .40 1.00
101 Rich Hill .15 .40
102 Ryan Dempster .15 .40
103 Todd Walker .15 .40
104 A.J. Pierzynski .15 .40
105 Aaron Rowand .15 .40
106 Bobby Jenks .15 .40
107 Carl Everett .15 .40
108 Dustin Hermanson .15 .40
109 Frank Thomas UER .40 1.00
Card has wrong birthdate
110 Freddy Garcia .15 .40
111 Jermaine Dye .15 .40
112 Joe Crede .15 .40
113 Jon Garland .15 .40
114 Jose Contreras .15 .40
115 Juan Uribe .15 .40
116 Mark Buehrle .15 .40
117 Orlando Hernandez .15 .40
118 Paul Konerko .15 .40
119 Scott Podsednik .15 .40
120 Tadahito Iguchi .15 .40
121 Aaron Harang .15 .40
122 Adam Dunn .15 .40
123 Austin Kearns .15 .40
124 Brandon Claussen .15 .40
125 Chris Denorfia (RC) .30 .75
126 Edwin Encarnacion .15 .40
127 Miguel Perez (RC) .30 .75
128 Felipe Lopez .15 .40
129 Jason LaRue .15 .40
130 Ken Griffey Jr. .60 1.50
131 Chris Booker (RC) .30 .75
132 Luke Hudson .15 .40
133 Jason Bergmann RC .30 .75
134 Ryan Freel .15 .40
135 Sean Casey .15 .40
136 Wily Mo Pena .15 .40
137 Aaron Boone .15 .40
138 Ben Broussard .15 .40
139 Ryan Garko (RC) .30 .75
140 C.C. Sabathia .15 .40
141 Casey Blake .15 .40
142 Cliff Lee .15 .40
143 Coco Crisp .15 .40
144 David Riske .15 .40
145 Grady Sizemore .25 .60
146 Jake Westbrook .15 .40
147 Jhonny Peralta .15 .40
148 Josh Bard .15 .40
149 Kevin Millwood .15 .40
150 Ronnie Belliard .15 .40
151 Scott Elarton .15 .40
152 Travis Hafner .15 .40
153 Victor Martinez .15 .40
154 Aaron Cook .15 .40
155 Aaron Miles .15 .40
156 Brad Hawpe .15 .40
157 Mike Esposito (RC) .30 .75
158 Chin-Hui Tsao .15 .40
159 Clint Barmes .15 .40
160 Cory Sullivan .15 .40
161 Garrett Atkins .15 .40
162 J.D. Closser .15 .40
163 Jason Jennings .15 .40
164 Jeff Baker .15 .40
165 Jeff Francis .15 .40
166 Luis A. Gonzalez .15 .40
167 Matt Holliday .40 1.00
168 Todd Helton .25 .60
169 Bradon Inge .15 .40
170 Carlos Guillen .15 .40
171 Carlos Pena .15 .40
172 Chris Shelton .15 .40
173 Craig Monroe .15 .40
174 Curtis Granderson .15 .40
175 Dmitri Young .15 .40
176 Ivan Rodriguez .25 .60
177 Jason Johnson .15 .40
178 Jeremy Bonderman .15 .40
179 Magglio Ordonez .15 .40
180 Mark Woodyard (RC) .30 .75
181 Nook Logan .15 .40
182 Omar Infante .15 .40
183 Placido Polanco .15 .40
184 Chris Heintz RC .30 .75
185 A.J. Burnett .15 .40
186 Alex Gonzalez .15 .40
187 Josh Johnson (RC) .30 .75
188 Carlos Delgado .15 .40
189 Dontrelle Willis .15 .40
190 Josh Wilson (RC) .30 .75
191 Jason Vargas .15 .40
192 Jeff Conine .15 .40
193 Jeremy Hermida .15 .40
194 Josh Beckett .15 .40
195 Juan Encarnacion .15 .40
196 Juan Pierre .15 .40
197 Luis Castillo .15 .40
198 Miguel Cabrera .25 .60
199 Mike Lowell .15 .40
200 Paul Lo Duca .15 .40
201 Todd Jones .15 .40
202 Adam Everett .15 .40
203 Andy Pettitte .25 .60
204 Brad Ausmus .15 .40
205 Brad Lidge .15 .40
206 Brandon Backe .15 .40
207 Charlton Jimerson (RC) .30 .75
208 Chris Burke .15 .40
209 Craig Biggio .25 .60
210 Dan Wheeler .15 .40
211 Jason Lane .15 .40
212 Jeff Bagwell .25 .60
213 Lance Berkman .15 .40
214 Luke Scott .15 .40
215 Morgan Ensberg .15 .40
216 Roger Clemens .75 2.00
217 Roy Oswalt .15 .40
218 Willy Taveras .15 .40
219 Andres Blanco .15 .40
220 Angel Berroa .15 .40
221 Ruben Gotay .15 .40
222 David DeJesus .15 .40
223 Emil Brown .15 .40
224 J.P. Howell .15 .40
225 Jeremy Affeldt .15 .40
226 Jimmy Gobble .15 .40
227 John Buck .15 .40
228 Jose Lima .15 .40
229 Mark Teahen .15 .40
230 Matt Stairs .15 .40
231 Mike MacDougal .15 .40
232 Mike Sweeney .15 .40
233 Runelvys Hernandez .15 .40
234 Terrence Long .15 .40
235 Zack Greinke .15 .40
236 Ron Flores RC .30 .75
237 Brad Penny .15 .40
238 Cesar Izturis .15 .40
239 D.J. Houlton .15 .40
240 Derek Lowe .15 .40
241 Eric Gagne .15 .40
242 Hee Seop Choi .15 .40
243 J.D. Drew .15 .40
244 Jason Phillips .15 .40
245 Jason Repko .15 .40
246 Jayson Werth .15 .40
247 Jeff Kent .15 .40
248 Jeff Weaver .15 .40
249 Milton Bradley .15 .40
250 Odalis Perez .15 .40
251 Hong-Chih Kuo (RC) .75 2.00
252 Oscar Robles .15 .40
253 Ben Sheets .15 .40
254 Bill Hall .15 .40
255 Brady Clark .15 .40
256 Carlos Lee .15 .40
257 Chris Capuano .15 .40
258 Nelson Cruz (RC) .30 .75
259 Derrick Turnbow .15 .40
260 Doug Davis .15 .40
261 Geoff Jenkins .15 .40
262 J.J. Hardy .15 .40
263 Lyle Overbay .15 .40
264 Prince Fielder .60 1.50
265 Rickie Weeks .15 .40
266 Russell Branyan .15 .40
267 Tomo Ohka .15 .40
268 Jonah Bayliss (RC) .30 .75
269 Brad Radke .15 .40
270 Carlos Silva .15 .40
271 Francisco Liriano (RC) 1.50 4.00
272 Jacque Jones .15 .40
273 Joe Mauer .25 .60
274 Travis Bowyer (RC) .30 .75
275 Joe Nathan .15 .40
276 Johan Santana .25 .60
277 Justin Morneau .15 .40
278 Kyle Lohse .15 .40
279 Lew Ford .15 .40
280 Matt LeCroy .15 .40
281 Michael Cuddyer .15 .40
282 Nick Punto .15 .40
283a Scott Baker .15 .40
283b Jason Repko UER .15 .40
Intended as card 245
284 Shannon Stewart .15 .40
285 Torii Hunter .15 .40
286 Braden Looper .15 .40
287 Carlos Beltran .15 .40
288 Cliff Floyd .15 .40
289 David Wright .60 1.50
290 Doug Mientkiewicz .15 .40
291 Anderson Hernandez (RC) .30 .75
292 Jose Reyes .40 1.00
293 Kazuo Matsui .15 .40
294 Kris Benson .15 .40
295 Miguel Cairo .15 .40
296 Mike Cameron .15 .40
297 Robert Andino RC .30 .75
298 Mike Piazza .40 1.00
299 Pedro Martinez .25 .60
300 Tom Glavine .25 .60
301 Victor Diaz .15 .40
302 Tim Hamulack (RC) .30 .75
303 Alex Rodriguez .60 1.50
304 Bernie Williams .25 .60
305 Carl Pavano .15 .40
306 Chien-Ming Wang .60 1.50
307 Derek Jeter 1.00 2.50
308 Gary Sheffield .15 .40
309 Hideki Matsui .40 1.00
310 Jason Giambi .15 .40
311 Jorge Posada .25 .60
312 Kevin Brown .15 .40
313 Mariano Rivera .40 1.00
314 Matt Lawton .15 .40
315 Mike Mussina .25 .60
316 Randy Johnson .40 1.00
317 Robinson Cano .25 .60
318 Mike Vento (RC) .30 .75
319 Tino Martinez .15 .40
320 Tony Womack .15 .40
321 Barry Zito .15 .40
322 Bobby Crosby .15 .40
323 Bobby Kielty .15 .40
324 Dan Johnson .15 .40
325 Danny Haren .15 .40
326 Eric Chavez .15 .40
327 Erubiel Durazo .15 .40
328 Huston Street .15 .40
329 Jason Kendall .15 .40
330 Jay Payton .15 .40
331 Joe Blanton .15 .40
332 Joe Kennedy .15 .40
333 Kirk Saarloos .15 .40
334 Mark Kotsay .15 .40
335 Nick Swisher .15 .40
336 Rich Harden .15 .40
337 Scott Hatteberg .15 .40
338 Billy Wagner .15 .40
339 Bobby Abreu .15 .40
340 Brett Myers .15 .40
341 Chase Utley .40 1.00
342 Danny Sandoval RC .30 .75
343 David Bell .15 .40
344 Gavin Floyd .15 .40
345 Jim Thome .25 .60
346 Jimmy Rollins .15 .40
347 Jon Lieber .15 .40
348 Kenny Lofton .15 .40
349 Mike Lieberthal .15 .40
350 Pat Burrell .15 .40
351 Randy Wolf .15 .40
352 Ryan Howard .60 1.50
353 Vicente Padilla .15 .40
354 Bryan Bullington (RC) .30 .75
355 J.J. Furmaniak (RC) .30 .75
356 Craig Wilson .15 .40
357 Matt Capps (RC) .30 .75
358 Tom Gorzelanny (RC) .30 .75
359 Jack Wilson .15 .40
360 Jason Bay .15 .40
361 Jose Mesa .15 .40
362 Josh Fogg .15 .40
363 Kip Wells .15 .40
364 Steve Stemle RC .30 .75
365 Oliver Perez .15 .40
366 Rob Mackowiak .15 .40
367 Ronny Paulino (RC) .30 .75
368 Tike Redman .15 .40
369 Zach Duke .15 .40
370 Adam Eaton .15 .40
371 Scott Feldman RC .30 .75
372 Brian Giles .15 .40
373 Brian Lawrence .15 .40
374 Damian Jackson .15 .40
375 Dave Roberts .15 .40
376 Jake Peavy .15 .40
377 Joe Randa .15 .40
378 Khalil Greene .25 .60
379 Mark Loretta .15 .40
380 Ramon Hernandez .15 .40
381 Robert Fick .15 .40

Card	Low	High
382 Ryan Klesko	.15	.40
383 Trevor Hoffman	.15	.40
384 Woody Williams	.15	.40
385 Xavier Nady	.15	.40
386 Armando Benitez	.15	.40
387 Brad Hennessey	.15	.40
388 Brian Myrow RC	.30	.75
389 Edgardo Alfonzo	.15	.40
390 J.T. Snow	.15	.40
391 Jeremy Accardo RC	.30	.75
392 Jason Schmidt	.15	.40
393 Lance Niekro	.15	.40
394 Matt Cain	.25	.60
395 Dan Ortmeier (RC)	.30	.75
396 Moises Alou	.15	.40
397 Doug Clark (RC)	.30	.75
398 Omar Vizquel	.25	.60
399 Pedro Feliz	.15	.40
400 Randy Winn	.15	.40
401 Ray Durham	.15	.40
402 Adrian Beltre	.15	.40
403 Eddie Guardado	.15	.40
404 Felix Hernandez	.25	.60
405 Gil Meche	.15	.40
406 Ichiro Suzuki	.60	1.50
407 Jamie Moyer	.15	.40
408 Jeff Nelson	.15	.40
409 Jeremy Reed	.15	.40
410 Joel Pineiro	.15	.40
411 Jaime Bubela (RC)	.30	.75
412 Raul Ibanez	.15	.40
413 Rickie Sexson	.15	.40
414 Ryan Franklin	.15	.40
415 Willie Bloomquist	.15	.40
416 Yorvit Torrealba	.15	.40
417 Yuniesky Betancourt	.15	.40
418 Jeff Harris RC	.30	.75
419 Albert Pujols	.75	2.00
420 Chris Carpenter	.15	.40
421 David Eckstein	.15	.40
422 Jason Isringhausen	.15	.40
423 Jason Marquis	.15	.40
424 Adam Wainwright (RC)	.30	.75
425 Jim Edmonds	.25	.60
426 Ryan Theriot RC	.30	.75
427 Chris Duncan (RC)	.30	.75
428 Mark Grudzielanek	.15	.40
429 Mark Mulder	.15	.40
430 Matt Morris	.15	.40
431 Reggie Sanders	.15	.40
432 Scott Rolen	.25	.60
433 Tyler Johnson (RC)	.30	.75
434 Yadier Molina	.15	.40
435 Alex S. Gonzalez	.15	.40
436 Aubrey Huff	.15	.40
437 Tim Corcoran RC	.30	.75
438 Carl Crawford	.15	.40
439 Casey Fossum	.15	.40
440 Danys Baez	.15	.40
441 Edwin Jackson	.15	.40
442 Joey Gathright	.15	.40
443 Jonny Gomes	.15	.40
444 Jorge Cantu	.15	.40
445 Julio Lugo	.15	.40
446 Nick Green	.15	.40
447 Rocco Baldelli	.15	.40
448 Scott Kazmir	.25	.60
449 Seth McClung	.15	.40
450 Toby Hall	.15	.40
451 Travis Lee	.15	.40
452 Craig Breslow RC	.30	.75
453 Alfonso Soriano	.15	.40
454 Chris R. Young	.15	.40
455 David Dellucci	.15	.40
456 Francisco Cordero	.15	.40
457 Gary Matthews	.15	.40
458 Hank Blalock	.15	.40
459 Juan Dominguez	.15	.40
460 Josh Rupe (RC)	.30	.75
461 Kenny Rogers	.15	.40
462 Kevin Mench	.15	.40
463 Laynce Nix	.15	.40
464 Mark Teixeira	.25	.60
465 Michael Young	.15	.40
466 Richard Hidalgo	.15	.40
467 Jason Botts (RC)	.30	.75
468 Aaron Hill	.15	.40
469 Alex Rios	.15	.40
470 Corey Koskie	.15	.40
471 Chris Demaria RC	.30	.75
472 Eric Hinske	.15	.40
473 Frank Catalanotto	.15	.40
474 John-Ford Griffin (RC)	.30	.75
475 Gustavo Chacin	.15	.40
476 Josh Towers	.15	.40
477 Miguel Batista	.15	.40
478 Orlando Hudson	.15	.40
479 Reed Johnson	.15	.40
480 Roy Halladay	.15	.40
481 Shaun Marcum (RC)	.30	.75
482 Shea Hillenbrand	.15	.40
483 Ted Lilly	.15	.40
484 Vernon Wells	.15	.40
485 Brad Wilkerson	.15	.40
486 Darrell Rasner (RC)	.30	.75
487 Chad Cordero	.15	.40
488 Cristian Guzman	.15	.40
489 Esteban Loaiza	.15	.40
490 John Patterson	.15	.40
491 Jose Guillen	.15	.40
492 Jose Vidro	.15	.40
493 Livan Hernandez	.15	.40
494 Marlon Byrd	.15	.40
495 Nick Johnson	.15	.40
496 Preston Wilson	.15	.40
497 Ryan Church	.15	.40
498 Ryan Zimmerman (RC)	2.00	5.00
499 Tony Armas Jr.	.15	.40
500 Vinny Castilla	.15	.40
501 Andy Green	.15	.40
502 Damion Easley	.15	.40
503 Eric Byrnes	.15	.40
504 Jason Grimsley	.15	.40
505 Jeff DaVanon	.15	.40
506 Johnny Estrada	.15	.40
507 Luis Vizcaino	.15	.40
508 Miguel Batista	.15	.40
509 Orlando Hernandez	.15	.40
510 Orlando Hudson	.15	.40
511 Elmer Mulholland	.15	.40
512 Chris Reitsma	.15	.40
513 Edgar Renteria	.15	.40
514 John Thomson	.15	.40
515 Jorge Sosa	.15	.40
516 Oscar Villarreal	.15	.40
517 Pete Orr	.15	.40
518 Ryan Langerhans	.15	.40
519 Todd Pratt	.15	.40
520 Wilson Betemit	.15	.40
521 Brian Jordan	.15	.40
522 Lance Cormier	.15	.40
523 Matt Diaz	.15	.40
524 Mike Remlinger	.15	.40
525 Bruce Chen	.15	.40
526 Chris Gomez	.15	.40
527 Chris Ray	.15	.40
528 Corey Patterson	.15	.40
529 David Newhan	.15	.40
530 Ed Rogers (RC)	.30	.75
531 John Halama	.15	.40
532 Kris Benson	.15	.40
533 LaTroy Hawkins	.15	.40
534 Raul Chavez	.15	.40
535 Alex Cora	.15	.40
536 Alex Gonzalez	.15	.40
537 Coco Crisp	.15	.40
538 David Riske	.15	.40
539 Doug Mirabelli	.15	.40
540 Josh Beckett	.15	.40
541 J.T. Snow	.15	.40
542 Mike Timlin	.15	.40
543 Julian Tavarez	.15	.40
544 Rudy Seanez	.15	.40
545 Wily Mo Pena	.15	.40
546 Bob Howry	.15	.40
547 Glendon Rusch	.15	.40
548 Henry Blanco	.15	.40
549 Jacque Jones	.15	.40
550 Jerome Williams	.15	.40
551 John Mabry	.15	.40
552 Juan Pierre	.15	.40
553 Scott Eyre	.15	.40
554 Scott Williamson	.15	.40
555 Wade Miller	.15	.40
556 Will Ohman	.15	.40
557 Alex Cintron	.15	.40
558 Rob Mackowiak	.15	.40
559 Brandon McCarthy	.15	.40
560 Chris Widger	.15	.40
561 Cliff Politte	.15	.40
562 Javier Vazquez	.15	.40
563 Jim Thome	.25	.60
564 Matt Thornton	.15	.40
565 Neal Cotts	.15	.40
566 Pablo Ozuna	.15	.40
567 Ross Gload	.15	.40
568 Brandon Phillips	.15	.40
569 Bronson Arroyo	.15	.40
570 Dave Williams	.15	.40
571 David Ross	.15	.40
572 David Weathers	.15	.40
573 Eric Milton	.15	.40
574 Javier Valentin	.15	.40
575 Kent Mercker	.15	.40
576 Matt Belisle	.15	.40
577 Paul Wilson	.15	.40
578 Rich Aurilia	.15	.40
579 Rick White	.15	.40
580 Scott Hatteberg	.15	.40
581 Todd Coffey	.15	.40
582 Bob Wickman	.15	.40
583 Danny Graves	.15	.40
584 Eduardo Perez	.15	.40
585 Guillermo Mota	.15	.40
586 Jason Davis	.15	.40
587 Jason Johnson	.15	.40
588 Jason Michaels	.15	.40
589 Rafael Betancourt	.15	.40
590 Ramon Vazquez	.15	.40
591 Scott Sauerbeck	.15	.40
592 Todd Hollandsworth	.15	.40
593 Brian Fuentes	.15	.40
594 Danny Ardoin	.15	.40
595 David Cortes	.15	.40
596 Eli Marrero	.15	.40
597 Jamey Carroll	.15	.40
598 Jason Smith	.15	.40
599 Josh Fogg	.15	.40
600 Miguel Ojeda	.15	.40
601 Mike DeJean	.15	.40
602 Ray King	.15	.40
603 Omar Quintanilla (RC)	.30	.75
604 Zach Day	.15	.40
605 Fernando Rodney	.15	.40
606 Kenny Rogers	.15	.40
607 Mike Maroth	.15	.40
608 Nate Robertson	.15	.40
609 Todd Jones	.15	.40
610 Vance Wilson	.15	.40
611 Bobby Seay	.15	.40
612 Chris Spurling	.15	.40
613 Roman Colon	.15	.40
614 Jason Grilli	.15	.40
615 Marcus Thames	.15	.40
616 Ramon Santiago	.15	.40
617 Alfredo Amezaga	.15	.40
618 Brian Moehler	.15	.40
619 Chris Aguila	.15	.40
620 Franklyn German	.15	.40
621 Joe Borowski	.15	.40
622 Logan Kensing (RC)	.30	.75
623 Matt Treanor	.15	.40
624 Miguel Olivo	.15	.40
625 Sergio Mitre	.15	.40
626 Todd Wellemeyer	.15	.40
627 Wes Helms	.15	.40
628 Chad Qualls	.15	.40
629 Eric Bruntlett	.15	.40
630 Mike Gallo	.15	.40
631 Mike Lamb	.15	.40
632 Orlando Palmeiro	.15	.40
633 Russ Springer	.15	.40
634 Dan Wheeler	.15	.40
635 Eric Munson	.15	.40
636 Preston Wilson	.15	.40
637 Trever Miller	.15	.40
638 Ambiorix Burgos	.15	.40
639 Andy Sisco	.15	.40
640 Denny Bautista	.15	.40
641 Doug Mientkiewicz	.15	.40
642 Elmer Dessens	.15	.40
643 Esteban German	.15	.40
644 Joe Nelson (RC)	.30	.75
645 Mark Grudzielanek	.15	.40
646 Mark Redman	.15	.40
647 Mike Wood	.15	.40
648 Paul Bako	.15	.40
649 Reggie Sanders	.15	.40
650 Scott Elarton	.15	.40
651 Shane Costa	.15	.40
652 Tony Graffanino	.15	.40
653 Jason Bulger (RC)	.30	.75
654 Chris Bootcheck (RC)	.30	.75
655 Esteban Yan	.15	.40
656 Hector Carrasco	.15	.40
657 J.C. Romero	.15	.40
658 Jeff Weaver	.15	.40
659 Jose Molina	.15	.40
660 Kelvim Escobar	.15	.40
661 Maicer Izturis	.15	.40
662 Robb Quinlan	.15	.40
663 Scot Shields	.15	.40
664 Tim Salmon	.15	.40
665 Bill Mueller	.15	.40
666 Brett Tomko	.15	.40
667 Dioner Navarro	.15	.40
668 Jae Seo	.15	.40
669 Jose Cruz Jr.	.15	.40
670 Kenny Lofton	.15	.40
671 Lance Carter	.15	.40
672 Nomar Garciaparra	.40	1.00
673 Olmedo Saenz	.15	.40
674 Rafael Furcal	.15	.40
675 Ramon Martinez	.15	.40
676 Ricky Ledee	.15	.40
677 Sandy Alomar Jr.	.15	.40
678 Yhency Brazoban	.15	.40
679 Corey Koskie	.15	.40
680 Dan Kolb	.15	.40
681 Gabe Gross	.15	.40
682 Jeff Cirillo	.15	.40
683 Matt Wise	.15	.40
684 Rick Helling	.15	.40
685 Chad Moeller	.15	.40
686 Dave Bush	.15	.40
687 Jorge De La Rosa	.15	.40
688 Justin Lehr	.15	.40
689 Jason Bartlett	.15	.40
690 Jesse Crain	.15	.40
691 Juan Rincon	.15	.40
692 Luis Castillo	.15	.40
693 Mike Redmond	.15	.40
694 Rondell White	.15	.40
695 Tony Batista	.15	.40
696 Juan Castro	.15	.40
697 Luis Rodriguez	.15	.40
698 Matt Guerrier	.15	.40
699 Willie Eyre (RC)	.30	.75
700 Aaron Heilman	.15	.40
701 Billy Wagner	.15	.40
702 Carlos Delgado	.15	.40
703 Chad Bradford	.15	.40
704 Chris Woodward	.15	.40
705 Darren Oliver	.15	.40
706 Duaner Sanchez	.15	.40
707 Endy Chavez	.15	.40
708 Jorge Julio	.15	.40
709 Jose Valentin	.15	.40
710 Julio Franco	.15	.40
711 Paul Lo Duca	.15	.40
712 Ramon Castro	.15	.40
713 Steve Trachsel	.15	.40
714 Victor Zambrano	.15	.40
715 Xavier Nady	.15	.40
716 Andy Phillips	.15	.40
717 Bubba Crosby	.15	.40
718 Jaret Wright	.15	.40
719 Kelly Stinnett	.15	.40
720 Kyle Farnsworth	.15	.40
721 Mike Myers	.15	.40
722 Octavio Dotel	.15	.40
723 Ron Villone	.15	.40
724 Scott Proctor	.15	.40
725 Shawn Chacon	.15	.40
726 Tanyon Sturtze	.15	.40
727 Adam Melhuse	.15	.40
728 Brad Halsey	.15	.40
729 Esteban Loaiza	.15	.40
730 Frank Thomas	.40	1.00
731 Jay Witasick	.15	.40
732 Justin Duchscherer	.15	.40
733 Kiko Calero	.15	.40
734 Marco Scutaro	.15	.40
735 Mark Ellis	.15	.40
736 Milton Bradley	.15	.40
737 Aaron Fultz	.15	.40
738 Aaron Rowand	.15	.40
739 Geoff Geary	.15	.40
740 Arthur Rhodes	.15	.40
741 Chris Coste RC	.30	.75
742 Rheal Cormier	.15	.40
743 Ryan Franklin	.15	.40
744 Ryan Madson	.15	.40
745 Sal Fasano	.15	.40
746 Tom Gordon	.15	.40
747 Abraham Nunez	.15	.40
748 David Dellucci	.15	.40
749 Julio Santana	.15	.40
750 Shane Victorino	.15	.40
751 Damaso Marte	.15	.40
752 Freddy Sanchez	.15	.40
753 Humberto Cota	.30	.75
754 Jeromy Burnitz	.15	.40
755 Joe Randa	.15	.40
756 Jose Castillo	.15	.40
757 Mike Gonzalez	.15	.40
758 Ryan Doumit	.15	.40
759 Sean Burnett	.15	.40
760 Sean Casey	.15	.40
761 Ian Snell	.15	.40
762 John Grabow	.15	.40
763 Jose Hernandez	.15	.40
764 Roberto Hernandez	.15	.40
765 Ryan Vogelsong	.15	.40
766 Victor Santos	.15	.40
767 Adrian Gonzalez	.15	.40
768 Alan Embree	.15	.40
769 Brian Sweeney (RC)	.30	.75
770 Chan Ho Park	.15	.40
771 Clay Hensley	.15	.40
772 Dewon Brazelton	.15	.40
773 Doug Brocail	.15	.40
774 Eric Young	.15	.40
775 Geoff Blum	.15	.40
776 Josh Bard	.15	.40
777 Mark Bellhorn	.15	.40
778 Mike Cameron	.15	.40
779 Mike Piazza	.40	1.00
780 Rob Bowen	.15	.40
781 Scott Cassidy	.15	.40
782 Scott Linebrink	.15	.40
783 Shawn Estes	.15	.40
784 Termel Sledge	.15	.40
785 Vinny Castilla	.15	.40
786 Jeff Fassero	.15	.40
787 Jose Vizcaino	.15	.40
788 Mark Sweeney	.15	.40
789 Matt Morris	.15	.40
790 Steve Finley	.15	.40
791 Tim Worrell	.15	.40
792 Jamey Wright	.15	.40
793 Jason Ellison	.15	.40
794 Noah Lowry	.15	.40
795 Steve Kline	.15	.40
796 Todd Greene	.15	.40
797 Carl Everett	.15	.40
798 George Sherrill	.15	.40
799 J.J. Putz	.15	.40
800 Jake Woods	.15	.40
801 Jose Lopez	.15	.40
802 Julio Mateo	.15	.40
803 Mike Morse	.15	.40
804 Rafael Soriano	.15	.40
805 Roberto Petagine	.15	.40
806 Aaron Miles	.15	.40
807 Braden Looper	.15	.40
808 Gary Bennett	.15	.40
809 Hector Luna	.15	.40
810 Jeff Suppan	.15	.40
811 John Rodriguez	.15	.40
812 Josh Hancock	.15	.40
813 Juan Encarnacion	.15	.40
814 Larry Bigbie	.15	.40
815 Scott Spiezio	.15	.40
816 Sidney Ponson	.15	.40
817 So Taguchi	.15	.40
818 Brian Meadows	.15	.40
819 Damon Hollins	.15	.40
820 Dan Miceli	.15	.40
821 Doug Waechter	.15	.40
822 Jason Childers RC	.30	.75
823 Josh Paul	.15	.40
824 Julio Lugo	.15	.40
825 Mark Hendrickson	.15	.40
826 Sean Burroughs	.15	.40
827 Shawn Camp	.15	.40
828 Travis Harper	.15	.40
829 Ty Wigginton	.15	.40
830 Adam Eaton	.15	.40
831 Adrian Brown	.15	.40
832 Akinori Otsuka	.15	.40
833 Antonio Alfonseca	.15	.40
834 Brad Wilkerson	.15	.40
835 D'Angelo Jimenez	.15	.40
836 Gerald Laird	.15	.40
837 Joaquin Benoit	.15	.40
838 Kameron Loe	.15	.40
839 Kevin Millwood	.15	.40
840 Mark DeRosa	.15	.40
841 Phil Nevin	.15	.40
842 Rod Barajas	.15	.40
843 Vicente Padilla	.15	.40
844 A.J. Burnett	.15	.40
845 Bengie Molina	.15	.40
846 Gregg Zaun	.15	.40
847 John McDonald	.15	.40
848 Lyle Overbay	.15	.40
849 Russ Adams	.15	.40
850 Troy Glaus	.15	.40
851 Vinny Chulk	.15	.40
852 B.J. Ryan	.15	.40
853 Justin Speier	.15	.40
854 Pete Walker	.15	.40
855 Scott Downs	.15	.40
856 Scott Schoeneweis	.15	.40
857 Alfonso Soriano	.15	.40
858 Brian Schneider	.15	.40
859 Daryle Ward	.15	.40
860 Felix Rodriguez	.15	.40
861 Gary Majewski	.15	.40
862 Joey Eischen	.15	.40
863 Jon Rauch	.15	.40
864 Marlon Anderson	.15	.40
865 Matt LeCroy	.15	.40
866 Mike Stanton	.15	.40
867 Ramon Ortiz	.15	.40
868 Robert Fick	.15	.40
869 Royce Clayton	.15	.40
870 Ryan Drese	.15	.40
871 Vladimir Guerrero CL	.40	1.00
872 Craig Biggio CL	.25	.60
873 Barry Zito CL	.15	.40
874 Vernon Wells CL	.15	.40
875 Chipper Jones CL	.40	1.00
876 Prince Fielder CL	.60	1.50
877 Albert Pujols CL	.75	2.00
878 Greg Maddux CL	.60	1.50
879 Carl Crawford CL	.15	.40
880 Brandon Webb CL	.15	.40
881 J.D. Drew CL	.15	.40
882 Jason Schmidt CL	.15	.40
883 Victor Martinez CL	.15	.40
884 Ichiro Suzuki CL	.60	1.50
885 Miguel Cabrera CL	.25	.60
886 David Wright CL	.60	1.50
887 Alfonso Soriano CL	.15	.40
888 Miguel Tejada CL	.15	.40
889 Khalil Greene CL	.25	.60
890 Ryan Howard CL	.60	1.50
891 Jason Bay CL	.15	.40
892 Mark Teixeira CL	.25	.60
893 Manny Ramirez CL	.25	.60
894 Ken Griffey Jr. CL	.60	1.50
895 Todd Helton CL	.25	.60
896 Angel Berroa CL	.15	.40
897 Ivan Rodriguez CL	.25	.60
898 Johan Santana CL	.25	.60
899 Paul Konerko CL	.15	.40
900 Derek Jeter CL	1.00	2.50
901 Macay McBride (RC)	.30	.75
902 Tony Pena (RC)	.30	.75
903 Peter Moylan RC	.30	.75
904 Aaron Rakers (RC)	.30	.75
905 Chris Britton RC	.30	.75
906 Nick Markakis (RC)	.50	1.25
907 Sendy Rleal RC	.30	.75
908 Val Majewski (RC)	.30	.75
909 Jermaine Van Buren (RC)	.30	.75
910 Jonathan Papelbon (RC)	1.50	4.00
911 Angel Pagan (RC)	.30	.75
912 David Aardsma (RC)	.30	.75
913 Sean Marshall (RC)	.30	.75
914 Brian Anderson (RC)	.30	.75
915 Freddie Bynum (RC)	.30	.75
916 Fausto Carmona (RC)	.30	.75
917 Kelly Shoppach (RC)	.30	.75
918 Choo Freeman (RC)	.30	.75
919 Ryan Shealy (RC)	.30	.75
920 Joel Zumaya (RC)	.75	2.00
921 Jordan Tata RC	.30	.75
922 Justin Verlander (RC)	1.25	3.00
923 Carlos Martinez RC	.30	.75
924 Chris Resop (RC)	.30	.75
925 Dan Uggla (RC)	.75	2.00
926 Eric Reed (RC)	.30	.75
927 Hanley Ramirez (RC)	.75	2.00
928 Yusmeiro Petit (RC)	.30	.75
929 Josh Willingham (RC)	.30	.75
930 Mike Jacobs (RC)	.30	.75
931 Reggie Abercrombie (RC)	.30	.75
932 Ricky Nolasco (RC)	.30	.75
933 Scott Olsen (RC)	.30	.75
934 Fernando Nieve (RC)	.30	.75
935 Taylor Buchholz (RC)	.50	1.25
936 Cody Ross (RC)	.30	.75
937 James Loney (RC)	.50	1.25
938 Takashi Saito RC	.50	1.25
939 Tim Hamulack (RC)	.30	.75
940 Chris Demaria RC	.30	.75
941 Jose Capellan (RC)	.30	.75
942 David Gassner (RC)	.30	.75
943 Jason Kubel (RC)	.30	.75
944 Brian Bannister (RC)	.30	.75
945 Mike Thompson RC	.30	.75
946 Cole Hamels (RC)	1.25	3.00
947 Paul Maholm (RC)	.30	.75
948 John Van Benschoten (RC)	.30	.75
949 Nate McLouth (RC)	.30	.75
950 Ben Johnson (RC)	.30	.75
951 Josh Barfield (RC)	.30	.75
952 Travis Ishikawa (RC)	.30	.75
953 Jack Taschner (RC)	.30	.75
954 Kenji Johjima RC	1.50	4.00
955 Skip Schumaker (RC)	.30	.75
956 Ruddy Lugo (RC)	.30	.75
957 Jason Hammel (RC)	.30	.75
958 Chris Roberson (RC)	.30	.75
959 Fabio Castro RC	.30	.75
960 Ian Kinsler (RC)	.50	1.25
961 John Koronka (RC)	.30	.75
962 Brandon Watson (RC)	.30	.75
963 Jon Lester RC	2.00	5.00
964 Ben Hendrickson (RC)	.30	.75
965 Martin Prado (RC)	.30	.75
966 Erick Aybar (RC)	.30	.75
967 Bobby Livingston (RC)	.30	.75
968 Ryan Spilborghs (RC)	.50	1.25
969 Tommy Murphy (RC)	.30	.75
970 Howie Kendrick (RC)	1.50	4.00
971 Casey Janssen RC	.30	.75
972 Michael O'Connor RC	.30	.75
973 Conor Jackson (RC)	.50	1.25
974 Jeremy Hermida (RC)	.30	.75
975 Renyel Pinto (RC)	.30	.75
976 Prince Fielder (RC)	1.25	3.00
977 Kevin Frandsen (RC)	.50	1.25
978 Ty Taubenheim RC	.50	1.25
979 Rich Hill (RC)	.30	.75
980 Jonathan Broxton (RC)	.30	.75
981 Jamie Shields RC	.30	.75
982 Carlos Villanueva RC	.30	.75
983 Boone Logan RC	.30	.75
984 Brian Wilson RC	.30	.75
985 Andre Ethier (RC)	.75	2.00
986 Mike Napoli RC	.75	2.00
987 Agustin Montero (RC)	.30	.75
988 Jack Hannahan RC	.30	.75
989 Boof Bonser (RC)	.30	.75
990 Carlos Ruiz (RC)	.30	.75
991 Jason Botts (RC)	.30	.75
992 Kendry Morales (RC)	.75	2.00
993 Alay Soler RC	.30	.75
994 Santiago Ramirez (RC)	.30	.75
995 Saul Rivera (RC)	.30	.75
996 Anthony Reyes (RC)	.30	.75
997 Matt Kemp (RC)	.50	1.25
998 Jae Kuk Ryu RC	.30	.75
999 Lastings Milledge (RC)	.50	1.25
NNO Exquisite Redemption		
1000 Jered Weaver (RC)	1.50	4.00
1001 Stephen Drew (RC)	.75	2.00
1002 Carlos Quentin (RC)	.50	1.25
1003 Livan Hernandez	.15	.40
1004 Chris B. Young (RC)	.50	1.25
1005 Alberto Callaspo SP (RC)	3.00	8.00
1006 Enrique Gonzalez (RC)	.30	.75
1007 Tony Pena (RC)	.30	.75
1008 Bob Melvin MG	.15	.40
1009 Fernando Tatis	.15	.40
1010 Willy Aybar (RC)	.30	.75
1011 Ken Ray (RC)	.30	.75
1012 Scott Thorman (RC)	.30	.75
1013 Eric Hinske SP	3.00	8.00
1014 Kevin Barry (RC)	.30	.75
1015 Bobby Cox MG	.15	.40
1016 Phil Stockman (RC)	.30	.75
1017 Brayan Pena (RC)	.30	.75
1018 Adam Loewen (RC)	.50	1.25
1019 Brandon Fahey RC	.30	.75
1020 Jim Hoey RC	.30	.75
1021 Kurt Birkins SP RC	3.00	8.00
1022 Jim Johnson RC	.30	.75
1023 Sam Perlozzo MG	.15	.40
1024 Cory Morris RC	.30	.75
1025 Hayden Penn (RC)	.30	.75
1026 Javy Lopez	.15	.40
1027 Dustin Pedroia (RC)	4.00	10.00
1028 Kason Gabbard (RC)	.30	.75
1029 David Pauley (RC)	.30	.75
1030 Kyle Snyder	.15	.40
1031 Terry Francona MG	.15	.40
1032 Craig Breslow RC	.30	.75
1033 Bryan Corey (RC)	.30	.75
1034 Manny Delcarmen (RC)	.30	.75
1035 Carlos Marmol RC	.30	.75
1036 Buck Coats (RC)	.30	.75
1037 Ryan O'Malley SP RC	3.00	8.00
1038 Angel Guzman (RC)	.30	.75
1039 Ronny Cedeno	.15	.40
1040 Juan Mateo RC	.30	.75
1041 Cesar Izturis	.15	.40
1042 Les Walrond (RC)	.30	.75
1043 Geovany Soto (RC)	.75	2.00
1044 Sean Tracey (RC)	.30	.75
1045 Ozzie Guillen MG SP	3.00	8.00
1046 Royce Clayton	.15	.40
1047 Norris Hopper RC	.30	.75
1048 Bill Bray (RC)	.30	.75
1049 Jerry Narron MG	.15	.40
1050 Brendan Harris (RC)	.30	.75
1051 Brian Shackelford	.15	.40
1052 Jeremy Sowers (RC)	.30	.75
1053 Joe Inglett RC	.30	.75
1054 Brian Slocum (RC)	.30	.75
1055 Andrew Brown (RC)	.30	.75
1056 Rafael Perez RC	.30	.75
1057 Edward Mujica RC	.30	.75
1058 Andy Marte (RC)	.30	.75
1059 Shin-Soo Choo (RC)	.30	.75
1060 Jeremy Guthrie (RC)	.30	.75
1061 Franklin Gutierrez SP (RC)	3.00	8.00
1062 Kazuo Matsui	.15	.40
1063 Chris Iannetta RC	.30	.75
1064 Manny Corpas RC	.30	.75
1065 Clint Hurdle MG	.15	.40
1066 Ramon Ramirez (RC)	.30	.75
1067 Sean Casey	.15	.40
1068 Zach Miner (RC)	.30	.75
1069 Brent Clevlen SP (RC)	3.00	8.00
1070 Bob Wickman	.15	.40
1071 Jim Leyland MG	.15	.40
1072 Alexis Gomez (RC)	.30	.75
1073 Anibal Sanchez (RC)	.50	1.25
1074 Taylor Tankersley (RC)	.30	.75
1075 Eric Wedge MG	.15	.40
1076 Jonah Bayliss RC	.30	.75
1077 Paul Hoover SP (RC)	3.00	8.00
1078 Eddie Guardado	.15	.40
1079 Cody Ross (RC)	.30	.75
1080 Aubrey Huff	.15	.40
1081 Jason Hirsh (RC)	.30	.75
1082 Brandon League	.15	.40
1083 Matt Albers (RC)	.30	.75
1084 Chris Sampson RC	.30	.75
1085 Phil Garner MG	.15	.40
1086 J.R. House (RC)	.30	.75
1087 Ryan Shealy (RC)	.30	.75
1088 Stephen Andrade (RC)	.30	.75
1089 Bob Keppel (RC)	.30	.75
1090 Buddy Bell MG	.15	.40
1091 Justin Huber (RC)	.30	.75
1092 Paul Phillips (RC)	.30	.75
1093 Greg Jones SP (RC)	3.00	8.00
1094 Jeff Mathis (RC)	.30	.75
1095 Dustin Moseley (RC)	.30	.75
1096 Joe Saunders (RC)	.30	.75
1097 Reggie Willits RC	.50	1.25
1098 Mike Scioscia MG	.15	.40
1099 Greg Maddux	.60	1.50
1100 Wilson Betemit	.15	.40
1101 Chad Billingsley SP (RC)	3.00	8.00
1102 Russell Martin (RC)	.50	1.25
1103 Grady Little MG	.15	.40
1104 David Bell	.15	.40
1105 Kevin Mench	.15	.40
1106 Laynce Nix	.15	.40
1107 Chris Barnwell RC	.30	.75
1108 Tony Gwynn Jr. (RC)	.30	.75
1109 Corey Hart (RC)	.30	.75
1110 Zach Jackson (RC)	.30	.75
1111 Francisco Cordero	.15	.40
1112 Joe Winkelsas (RC)	.30	.75
1113 Ned Yost MG	.15	.40
1114 Matt Garza (RC)	.30	.75
1115 Chris Heintz	.15	.40
1116 Pat Neshek RC	3.00	8.00
1117 Josh Rabe SP RC	8.00	20.00
1118 Mike Rivera	.15	.40
1119 Ron Gardenhire MG	.15	.40
1120 Shawn Green	.15	.40
1121 Oliver Perez	.15	.40
1122 Heath Bell	.15	.40
1123 Bartolome Fortunato (RC)	.30	.75
1124 Anderson Garcia RC	.30	.75
1125 John Maine SP (RC)	3.00	8.00
1126 Henry Owens RC	.50	1.25
1127 Mike Pelfrey RC	1.25	3.00
1128 Royce Ring (RC)	.30	.75
1129 Willie Randolph MG	.15	.40
1130 Bobby Abreu	.15	.40
1131 Craig Wilson	.15	.40
1132 T.J. Beam (RC)	.30	.75
1133 Colter Bean SP (RC)	3.00	8.00
1134 Melky Cabrera (RC)	.50	1.25
1135 Mitch Jones (RC)	.30	.75
1136 Jeffrey Karstens RC	.75	2.00
1137 Wil Nieves (RC)	.30	.75
1138 Kevin Reese (RC)	.50	1.25
1139 Kevin Thompson (RC)	.30	.75
1140 Jose Veras RC	.30	.75
1141 Joe Torre MG	.25	.60
1142 Jeremy Brown (RC)	.30	.75
1143 Santiago Casilla (RC)	.30	.75
1144 Shane Komine RC	.50	1.25
1145 Mike Rouse (RC)	.30	.75
1146 Jason Windsor (RC)	.30	.75
1147 Ken Macha MG	.15	.40
1148 Jamie Moyer	.15	.40
1149 Phil Nevin SP	3.00	8.00
1150 Eude Brito (RC)	.30	.75
1151 Fabio Castro	.15	.40
1152 Jeff Conine	.15	.40
1153 Scott Mathieson (RC)	.30	.75
1154 Brian Sanches (RC)	.30	.75
1155 Matt Smith RC	.30	.75
1156 Joe Thurston (RC)	.30	.75
1157 Marlon Anderson SP	3.00	8.00
1158 Xavier Nady	.15	.40
1159 Shawn Chacon	.15	.40
1160 Rajai Davis (RC)	.30	.75
1161 Yurendell DeCaster (RC)	.30	.75
1162 Marty McLeary (RC)	.30	.75
1163 Chris Duffy	.15	.40
1164 Josh Sharpless RC	.30	.75
1165 Jim Tracy MG	.15	.40
1166 David Wells	.15	.40

1167 Russell Branyan .15 .40
1168 Todd Walker .15 .40
1169 Paul McAnulty (RC) .30 .75
1170 Bruce Bochy MG .15 .40
1171 Shea Hillenbrand .15 .40
1172 Eliezer Alfonzo RC .30 .75
1173 Justin Knoedler SP (RC) 3.00 8.00
1174 Jonathan Sanchez (RC) .30 .75
1175 Travis Smith (RC) .30 .75
1176 Cha-Seung Baek .15 .40
1177 T.J. Bohn (RC) .30 .75
1178 Emiliano Fruto RC .30 .75
1179 Sean Green RC .30 .75
1180 Jon Huber RC .30 .75
1181 Adam Jones SP RC 5.00 12.00
1182 Mark Lowe (RC) .30 .75
1183 Eric O'Flaherty RC .30 .75
1184 Preston Wilson .15 .40
1185 Mike Hargrove MG .15 .40
1186 Jeff Weaver .15 .40
1187 Ronnie Belliard .15 .40
1188 John Gall (RC) .30 .75
1189 Josh Kinney SP RC 3.00 8.00
1190 Tony LaRussa MG .15 .40
1191 Scott Dunn (RC) .30 .75
1192 B.J. Upton .15 .40
1193 Jon Switzer (RC) .30 .75
1194 Ben Zobrist (RC) .50 1.25
1195 Joe Maddon .15 .40
1196 Carlos Lee .15 .40
1197 Matt Stairs .15 .40
1198 Nick Masset (RC) .30 .75
1199 Nelson Cruz (RC) .30 .75
1200 Francisco Rosario (RC) .30 .75
1201 Wes Littleton (RC) .30 .75
1202 Drew Meyer (RC) .30 .75
1203 John Rheinecker (RC) .30 .75
1204 Robinson Tejeda .15 .40
1205 Jeremy Accardo SP 3.00 8.00
1206 Luis Figueroa RC .30 .75
1207 John Hattig (RC) .30 .75
1208 Dustin McGowan (RC) .30 .75
1209 Ryan Roberts RC .30 .75
1210 Davis Romero (RC) .30 .75
1211 Ty Taubenheim .50 1.25
1212 John Gibbons MG .15 .40
1213 Shawn Hill SP (RC) 3.00 8.00
1214 Brandon Harper RC .30 .75
1215 Travis Hughes (RC) .30 .75
1216 Chris Schroder RC .30 .75
1217 Austin Kearns .15 .40
1218 Felipe Lopez .15 .40
1219 Roy Corcoran RC .30 .75
1220 Melvin Dorta RC .30 .75
1221 Brandon Webb CL SP 2.00 5.00
1222 Andruw Jones CL SP 2.00 5.00
1223 Miguel Tejada CL SP 2.00 5.00
1224 David Ortiz CL SP 2.00 5.00
1225 Derrek Lee CL SP 2.00 5.00
1226 Jim Thome CL SP 2.00 5.00
1227 Ken Griffey Jr. CL SP UER 3.00 8.00
Royce Clayton card #1046 not listed on back
1228 Travis Hafner CL SP 2.00 5.00
1229 Todd Helton CL SP 2.00 5.00
1230 Magglio Ordonez CL SP 2.00 5.00
1231 Miguel Cabrera CL SP 2.00 5.00
1232 Lance Berkman CL SP 2.00 5.00
1233 Mike Sweeney CL SP 2.00 5.00
1234 Vladimir Guerrero CL SP 2.00 5.00
1235 Nomar Garciaparra CL SP 2.00 5.00
1236 Prince Fielder CL SP 2.00 5.00
1237 Johan Santana CL SP 2.00 5.00
1238 Pedro Martinez CL SP 2.00 5.00
1239 Derek Jeter CL SP 4.00 10.00
1240 Barry Zito CL SP 2.00 5.00
1241 Ryan Howard CL SP UER 3.00 8.00
Chris Coste is listed as card 1046
1242 Jason Bay CL SP 2.00 5.00
1243 Trevor Hoffman CL SP 2.00 5.00
1244 Jason Schmidt CL SP 2.00 5.00
1245 Ichiro Suzuki CL SP 3.00 8.00
1246 Albert Pujols CL SP 3.00 8.00
1247 Carl Crawford CL SP 2.00 5.00
1248 Mark Teixeira CL SP 2.00 5.00
1249 Vernon Wells CL SP 2.00 5.00
1250 Alfonso Soriano CL SP 2.00 5.00

2006 Upper Deck Gold

*GOLD 1-1000: 2X TO 5X BASIC
*GOLD 1-1000: 1X TO 2.5X BASIC RC's
*GOLD 1001-1250: 3X TO 8X BASIC
*GOLD 1001-1250: 1.5X TO 4X BASIC RC'S
*GOLD 1001-1220: .15X TO .4X BASIC SP
COMMON (1221-1250) 1.25 3.00
SEMIS 1221-1250 2.00 5.00
UNLISTED 1221-1250 3.00 8.00
1-500 FIVE #'d INSERTS PER SER.1 HOB.BOX
501-1000 SER.2 ODDS 1:8 H, RANDOM IN RET
1001-1250 UPDATE ODDS 1:24 RET
1-1000 PRINT RUN 299 SERIAL #'d SETS
1001-1250 PRINT RUN 99 SERIAL #'d SETS
1116 Pat Neshek 10.00 25.00
1227 Ken Griffey Jr. CL 5.00 12.00
1236 Prince Fielder CL 5.00 12.00
1239 Derek Jeter CL 8.00 20.00
1241 Ryan Howard CL 5.00 12.00
1245 Ichiro Suzuki CL 5.00 12.00
1246 Albert Pujols CL 6.00 15.00

2006 Upper Deck Silver Spectrum

*501-1000: 3X TO 8X BASIC
*501-1000: 1.5X TO 4X BASIC RC's
1-500 FIVE #'d INSERTS PER SER.1 HOB.BOX
501-1000 SER.2 ODDS1:24 H,RANDOM IN RET
1-500 PRINT RUN 25 SERIAL #'d SETS

501-1000 PRINT RUN 99 SERIAL #'d SETS
1-500 NO PRICING DUE TO SCARCITY

2006 Upper Deck Rookie Foil Silver

*SILVER: 1X TO 2.5X BASIC
2-3 PER SER.2 RC PACK
ONE RC PACK PER SER.2 HOBBY BOX
3-CARDS PER SEALED RC PACK
STATED PRINT RUN 399 SERIAL #'d SETS
*GOLD: 1.5X TO 4X BASIC
GOLD RANDOM IN SER.2 RC PACKS
GOLD PRINT RUN 99 SERIAL #'d SETS
PLAT.RANDOM IN SER.2 RC PACKS
PLATINUM PRINT RUN 15 #'d SETS
NO PLATINUM PRICING DUE TO SCARCITY
AU PLATES RANDOM IN RC PACKS
AU PLATE PRINT RUN 1 SET PER COLOR
BLACK-CYAN-MAGENTA-YELLOW ISSUED
NO AU PLATE PRICING DUE TO SCARCITY
AU PLATES ISSUED FOR 28 OF 100 FOILS
SEE BECKETT.COM FOR AU PLATE CL
954 Kenji Johjima 4.00 10.00

2006 Upper Deck All-Time Legends

TWO PER SERIES 2 FAT PACK
AT1 Ty Cobb 1.50 4.00
AT2 Lou Gehrig 2.00 5.00
AT3 Babe Ruth 3.00 8.00
AT4 Jimmie Foxx 1.00 2.50
AT5 Honus Wagner 1.00 2.50
AT6 Lou Brock .60 1.50
AT7 Joe Morgan .40 1.00
AT8 Christy Mathewson 1.00 2.50
AT9 Walter Johnson 1.00 2.50
AT10 Mike Schmidt 1.50 4.00
AT11 Al Kaline 1.00 2.50
AT12 Robin Yount 1.00 2.50
AT13 Johnny Bench 1.00 2.50
AT14 Yogi Berra 1.00 2.50
AT15 Rod Carew .60 1.50
AT16 Bob Feller .60 1.50
AT17 Carlton Fisk .60 1.50
AT18 Bob Gibson .60 1.50
AT19 Cy Young 1.00 2.50
AT20 Reggie Jackson .60 1.50
AT21 Jackie Robinson 1.00 2.50
AT22 Harmon Killebrew 1.00 2.50
AT23 Mickey Cochrane .60 1.50
AT24 Eddie Mathews 1.00 2.50
AT25 Bill Mazeroski .60 1.50
AT26 Willie McCovey .60 1.50
AT27 Eddie Murray 1.00 2.50
AT28 Lefty Grove .60 1.50
AT29 Jim Palmer .40 1.00
AT30 Pee Wee Reese .60 1.50
AT31 Phil Rizzuto .60 1.50
AT32 Brooks Robinson .60 1.50
AT33 Nolan Ryan 2.50 6.00
AT34 Tom Seaver .60 1.50
AT35 Ozzie Smith 1.50 4.00
AT36 Roy Campanella .60 1.50
AT37 Thurman Munson 1.00 2.50
AT38 Mel Ott .60 1.50
AT39 Satchel Paige 1.00 2.50
AT40 Rogers Hornsby .60 1.50

2006 Upper Deck All-Upper Deck Team

TWO PER SERIES 1 FAT PACK
UD1 Ken Griffey Jr. 1.50 4.00
UD2 Derek Jeter 2.50 6.00
UD3 Albert Pujols 2.00 5.00
UD4 Alex Rodriguez 1.50 4.00
UD5 Vladimir Guerrero 1.00 2.50
UD6 Roger Clemens 1.50 4.00
UD7 Derrek Lee .60 1.50
UD8 David Ortiz 1.00 2.50
UD9 Miguel Cabrera .60 1.50
UD10 Bobby Abreu .40 1.00
UD11 Mark Teixeira .40 1.00
UD12 Johan Santana .60 1.50
UD13 Hideki Matsui 1.00 2.50
UD14 Ichiro Suzuki 1.50 4.00
UD15 Andruw Jones .60 1.50
UD16 Eric Chavez .40 1.00
UD17 Roy Oswalt .40 1.00
UD18 Curt Schilling .60 1.50
UD19 Randy Johnson 1.00 2.50
UD20 Ivan Rodriguez .60 1.50
UD21 Chipper Jones 1.00 2.50
UD22 Mark Prior .40 1.00
UD23 Jason Bay .40 1.00
UD24 Pedro Martinez .60 1.50
UD25 David Wright 1.50 4.00
UD26 Carlos Beltran .40 1.00
UD27 Jim Edmonds .40 1.00
UD28 Chris Carpenter .40 1.00
UD29 Roy Halladay .40 1.00
UD30 Jake Peavy .40 1.00
UD31 Paul Konerko .40 1.00
UD32 Travis Hafner .40 1.00
UD33 Barry Zito .40 1.00
UD34 Miguel Tejada .40 1.00
UD35 Josh Beckett .40 1.00
UD36 Todd Helton .60 1.50
UD37 Dontrelle Willis .40 1.00
UD38 Manny Ramirez .60 1.50
UD39 Mariano Rivera 1.00 2.50
UD40 Jeff Kent .40 1.00

2006 Upper Deck Amazing Greats

SER.1 ODDS 1:6 HOBBY, 1:12 RETAIL
*GOLD: .6X TO 1.5X BASIC
FIVE #'d INSERTS PER SER.1 HOBBY BOX
GOLD STATED PRINT RUN 699 SERIAL #'d SETS
AB Adrian Beltre .50 1.25
AJ Andruw Jones .75 2.00
AP Albert Pujols 2.50 6.00
AS Alfonso Soriano .50 1.25
BA Bobby Abreu .50 1.25
CB Carlos Beltran .50 1.25
CC Carl Crawford .50 1.25
CJ Chipper Jones 1.25 3.00
CL Carlos Lee .50 1.25
CP Corey Patterson .50 1.25
CS Curt Schilling .75 2.00
DJ Derek Jeter 3.00 8.00
DO David Ortiz 1.25 3.00
DW Dontrelle Willis .50 1.25
EG Eric Gagne .50 1.25
FT Frank Thomas 1.25 3.00
GM Greg Maddux 2.00 5.00
GS Gary Sheffield .50 1.25
HE Todd Helton .75 2.00
IR Ivan Rodriguez .75 2.00
JB Jeff Bagwell .75 2.00
JD Johnny Damon .75 2.00
JE Jim Edmonds .75 2.00
JG Jason Giambi .75 2.00
JJ Jacque Jones .50 1.25
JL Javy Lopez .50 1.25
JR Jose Reyes 1.25 3.00
JS Johan Santana .75 2.00
JT Jim Thome .75 2.00
KG Ken Griffey Jr. 2.00 5.00
KW Kerry Wood .50 1.25
MC Miguel Cabrera .75 2.00
MP Mike Piazza 1.25 3.00
MR Manny Ramirez .75 2.00
MT Mark Teixeira .75 2.00
PK Paul Konerko .50 1.25
PM Pedro Martinez .75 2.00
PR Mark Prior .75 2.00
RC Roger Clemens 2.50 6.00
RF Rafael Furcal .50 1.25
RJ Randy Johnson 1.25 3.00
RO Roy Oswalt .50 1.25
RP Rafael Palmeiro .75 2.00
SM John Smoltz .75 2.00
SR Scott Rolen .75 2.00
SS Sammy Sosa 1.25 3.00
TE Miguel Tejada .50 1.25
TG Tom Glavine .75 2.00
TH Tim Hudson .50 1.25
WR David Wright 2.00 5.00

2006 Upper Deck Amazing Greats Materials

SER.1 ODDS 1:48 HOBBY, 1:288 RETAIL
AB Adrian Beltre Jsy 3.00 8.00
AJ Andruw Jones Jsy 4.00 10.00
AP Albert Pujols Jsy 6.00 15.00
AS Alfonso Soriano Jsy 3.00 8.00
BA Bobby Abreu Jsy 3.00 8.00
CB Carlos Beltran Jsy 3.00 8.00
CC Carl Crawford Jsy 3.00 8.00
CJ Chipper Jones Jsy 4.00 10.00
CL Carlos Lee Jsy 3.00 8.00
CP Corey Patterson Jsy 3.00 8.00
CS Curt Schilling Jsy 4.00 10.00
DJ Derek Jeter Jsy 10.00 25.00
DO David Ortiz Jsy 4.00 10.00
DW Dontrelle Willis Jsy 3.00 8.00
EG Eric Gagne Jsy 3.00 8.00
FT Frank Thomas Jsy 4.00 10.00
GM Greg Maddux Jsy 4.00 10.00
GS Gary Sheffield Jsy 3.00 8.00
HE Todd Helton Jsy 4.00 10.00
IR Ivan Rodriguez Jsy 4.00 10.00
JB Jeff Bagwell Jsy 4.00 10.00
JD Johnny Damon Jsy 4.00 10.00
JE Jim Edmonds Jsy 3.00 8.00
JG Jason Giambi Jsy 3.00 8.00
JJ Jacque Jones Jsy 3.00 8.00
JL Javy Lopez Jsy 3.00 8.00
JR Jose Reyes Jsy 3.00 8.00
JS Johan Santana Jsy 4.00 10.00
JT Jim Thome Jsy 4.00 10.00
KG Ken Griffey Jr. Jsy 6.00 15.00
KW Kerry Wood Jsy 3.00 8.00
MC Miguel Cabrera Jsy 4.00 10.00
MP Mike Piazza Jsy 4.00 10.00
MR Manny Ramirez Jsy 4.00 10.00
MT Mark Teixeira Jsy 4.00 10.00
PK Paul Konerko Jsy 3.00 8.00
PM Pedro Martinez Jsy 4.00 10.00
PR Mark Prior Jsy 3.00 8.00
RC Roger Clemens Jsy 6.00 15.00
RF Rafael Furcal Jsy 3.00 8.00
RJ Randy Johnson Pants 4.00 10.00
RO Roy Oswalt Jsy 3.00 8.00
RP Rafael Palmeiro Jsy 4.00 10.00
SM John Smoltz Jsy 4.00 10.00
SR Scott Rolen Jsy 4.00 10.00
SS Sammy Sosa Jsy 4.00 10.00
TE Miguel Tejada Jsy 3.00 8.00
TG Tom Glavine Jsy 4.00 10.00
TH Tim Hudson Jsy 3.00 8.00
WR David Wright Jsy 4.00 10.00

2006 Upper Deck Diamond Collection

SER.1 ODDS 1:6 HOBBY, 1:12 RETAIL
*GOLD: .6X TO 1.5X BASIC
FIVE #'d INSERTS PER SER.1 HOBBY BOX
GOLD PRINT RUN 699 SERIAL #'d SETS
AE Adam Eaton .50 1.25
AH Aubrey Huff .50 1.25
AK Adam Kennedy .50 1.25
AL Moises Alou .50 1.25
AO Akinori Otsuka .50 1.25
BC Bobby Crosby .50 1.25
BR Brad Radke .50 1.25
CC C.C. Sabathia .50 1.25
CK Casey Kotchman .50 1.25
CO Jose Contreras .50 1.25
CP Carl Pavano .50 1.25
CS Chris Shelton .50 1.25
DJ Derek Jeter 3.00 8.00
DO David Ortiz 1.25 3.00
EC Eric Chavez .50 1.25
EJ Edwin Jackson .50 1.25
FG Freddy Garcia .50 1.25
GM Greg Maddux 2.00 5.00
GO Juan Gonzalez .50 1.25
IR Ivan Rodriguez .75 2.00
JB Jeff Bagwell .75 2.00
JC Jesse Crain .50 1.25
JD Johnny Damon .75 2.00
JE Jim Edmonds .75 2.00
JG Jose Guillen .50 1.25
JJ Jacque Jones .50 1.25
JK Jason Kendall .50 1.25
JP Jorge Posada .75 2.00
JS John Smoltz .75 2.00
JT Jim Thome .75 2.00
JW Jayson Werth .50 1.25
KE Austin Kearns .50 1.25
KG Ken Griffey Jr. 2.00 5.00
KL Kenny Lofton .50 1.25
KM Kevin Millwood .50 1.25
LA Matt Lawton .50 1.25
LO Mike Lowell .50 1.25
MA Kazuo Matsui .50 1.25
MC Mike Cameron .50 1.25
MH Mike Hampton .50 1.25
ML Mike Lieberthal .50 1.25
NJ Nick Johnson .50 1.25
OC Orlando Cabrera .50 1.25
PL Paul Lo Duca .50 1.25
PW Preston Wilson .50 1.25
RB Rocco Baldelli .50 1.25
RJ Randy Johnson 1.25 3.00
SF Steve Finley .50 1.25
SK Scott Kazmir .75 2.00
SS Shannon Stewart .50 1.25

2006 Upper Deck Diamond Collection Materials

SER.1 ODDS 1:48 HOBBY, 1:288 RETAIL
AE Adam Eaton Jsy 3.00 8.00
AH Aubrey Huff Jsy 3.00 8.00
AK Adam Kennedy Jsy 3.00 8.00
AL Moises Alou Jsy 3.00 8.00
AO Akinori Otsuka Jsy 3.00 8.00
BC Bobby Crosby Jsy 3.00 8.00
BR Brad Radke Jsy 3.00 8.00
CC C.C. Sabathia Jsy 3.00 8.00
CK Casey Kotchman Jsy 3.00 8.00
CO Jose Contreras Jsy 3.00 8.00
CP Carl Pavano Jsy 3.00 8.00
CS Chris Shelton Jsy 4.00 10.00
DJ Derek Jeter Jsy 10.00 25.00
DO David Ortiz Jsy 4.00 10.00
EC Eric Chavez Jsy 3.00 8.00
EJ Edwin Jackson Jsy 3.00 8.00
FG Freddy Garcia Jsy 3.00 8.00
GM Greg Maddux Jsy 4.00 10.00
GO Juan Gonzalez Jsy 3.00 8.00
IR Ivan Rodriguez Jsy 4.00 10.00
JB Jeff Bagwell Jsy 4.00 10.00
JC Jesse Crain Jsy 3.00 8.00
JD Johnny Damon Jsy 4.00 10.00
JE Jim Edmonds Jsy 3.00 8.00
JG Jose Guillen Jsy 3.00 8.00
JJ Jacque Jones Jsy 3.00 8.00
JK Jason Kendall Jsy 3.00 8.00
JP Jorge Posada Jsy 4.00 10.00
JS John Smoltz Jsy 4.00 10.00
JT Jim Thome Jsy 4.00 10.00
JW Jayson Werth Jsy 3.00 8.00
KE Austin Kearns Jsy 3.00 8.00
KG Ken Griffey Jr. Jsy 6.00 15.00
KL Kenny Lofton Jsy 3.00 8.00
KM Kevin Millwood Jsy 3.00 8.00
LA Matt Lawton Jsy 3.00 8.00
LO Mike Lowell Jsy 3.00 8.00
MA Kazuo Matsui Jsy 3.00 8.00
MC Mike Cameron Jsy 3.00 8.00
MH Mike Hampton Jsy 3.00 8.00
ML Mike Lieberthal Jsy 3.00 8.00
NJ Nick Johnson Jsy 3.00 8.00
OC Orlando Cabrera Jsy 3.00 8.00
PL Paul Lo Duca Jsy 3.00 8.00
PW Preston Wilson Jsy 3.00 8.00
RB Rocco Baldelli Jsy 3.00 8.00
RJ Randy Johnson Pants 4.00 10.00
SF Steve Finley Jsy 3.00 8.00
SK Scott Kazmir Jsy 3.00 8.00
SS Shannon Stewart Jsy 3.00 8.00

2006 Upper Deck Diamond Debut

STATED ODDS 1:4 WAL MART PACKS
1-40 ISSUED IN SERIES 1 PACKS
41-82 ISSUED IN SERIES 2 PACKS
DD1 Tadahito Iguchi .75 2.00
DD2 Huston Street .75 2.00
DD3 Norihiro Nakamura .75 2.00
DD4 Chien-Ming Wang 2.00 5.00
DD5 Pedro Lopez .75 2.00
DD6 Robinson Cano 1.25 3.00
DD7 Tim Stauffer .75 2.00
DD8 Ervin Santana .75 2.00
DD9 Brandon McCarthy .75 2.00
DD10 Hayden Penn .75 2.00
DD11 Derek Jeter 3.00 8.00
DD12 Ken Griffey Jr. 2.00 5.00
DD13 Prince Fielder 1.50 4.00
DD14 Edwin Encarnacion .75 2.00
DD15 Scott Olsen .75 2.00
DD16 Chris Resop .75 2.00
DD17 Justin Verlander 1.50 4.00
DD18 Melky Cabrera .75 2.00
DD19 Jeff Francoeur 1.25 3.00
DD20 Yuniesky Betancourt .75 2.00
DD21 Conor Jackson .75 2.00
DD22 Felix Hernandez 1.25 3.00
DD23 Anthony Reyes .75 2.00
DD24 John-Ford Griffin .75 2.00
DD25 Adam Wainwright .75 2.00
DD26 Ryan Garko .75 2.00
DD27 Ryan Zimmerman 2.50 6.00
DD28 Tom Seaver 2.00 5.00
DD29 Johnny Bench 2.00 5.00
DD30 Reggie Jackson 2.00 5.00
DD31 Rod Carew 2.00 5.00
DD32 Nolan Ryan 4.00 10.00
DD33 Richie Ashburn 2.00 5.00
DD34 Yogi Berra 2.00 5.00
DD35 Lou Brock 2.00 5.00
DD36 Carlton Fisk 2.00 5.00
DD37 Joe Morgan 1.25 3.00
DD38 Bob Gibson 2.00 5.00
DD39 Willie McCovey 2.00 5.00
DD40 Harmon Killebrew 2.00 5.00
DD41 Takashi Saito .75 2.00
DD42 Kenji Johjima 2.00 5.00
DD43 Joel Zumaya 1.25 3.00
DD44 Dan Uggla 2.00 5.00
DD45 Taylor Buchholz .75 2.00
DD46 Josh Barfield .75 2.00
DD47 Brian Bannister .75 2.00
DD48 Nick Markakis .75 2.00
DD49 Carlos Martinez .75 2.00
DD50 Macay McBride .75 2.00
DD51 Brian Anderson .75 2.00
DD52 Freddie Bynum .75 2.00
DD53 Kelly Shoppach .75 2.00
DD54 Choo Freeman .75 2.00
DD55 Ryan Shealy .75 2.00
DD56 Chris Resop .75 2.00
DD57 Hanley Ramirez 1.00 2.50
DD58 Mike Jacobs .75 2.00
DD59 Cody Ross .75 2.00
DD60 Jose Capellan .75 2.00
DD61 David Gassner .75 2.00
DD62 Jason Kubel .75 2.00
DD63 Jered Weaver 2.00 5.00
DD64 Paul Maholm .75 2.00
DD65 Nate McLouth .75 2.00
DD66 Ben Johnson .75 2.00
DD67 Jack Taschner .75 2.00
DD68 Skip Schumaker .75 2.00
DD69 Brandon Watson .75 2.00
DD70 David Wright 2.00 5.00
DD71 David Ortiz 1.25 3.00
DD72 Alex Rodriguez 2.00 5.00
DD73 Johan Santana 1.25 3.00
DD74 Greg Maddux 2.00 5.00
DD75 Ichiro Suzuki 2.00 5.00
DD76 Albert Pujols 2.50 6.00
DD77 Hideki Matsui 1.25 3.00
DD78 Vladimir Guerrero 1.25 3.00
DD79 Pedro Martinez 1.25 3.00
DD80 Mike Schmidt 3.00 8.00
DD81 Al Kaline 2.00 5.00
DD82 Robin Yount 2.00 5.00

2006 Upper Deck First Class Cuts

RANDOM INSERTS IN SERIES 1 PACKS
STATED PRINT RUN 1 SERIAL #'d SET
NO PRICING DUE TO SCARCITY
BR Babe Ruth
HW Honus Wagner
TC Ty Cobb
WJ Walter Johnson

2006 Upper Deck First Class Legends

COMMON RUTH (1-20) 1.25 3.00
COMMON COBB (21-40) .75 2.00
COMMON WAGNER (41-60 .40 1.00
COMMON MATHEWSON (61-80) .40 1.00
COMMON W.JOHNSON (81-100) .40 1.00
SER.1 STATED ODDS: 1:6 HOBBY
SER.2 ODDS APPROX. 1:12 HOBBY
*GOLD: .75X TO 2X BASIC
GOLD PRINT RUN 699 SERIAL #'d SETS
*SILVER SPECTRUM: 1.25X TO 3X BASIC
SILVER SPEC. PRINT RUN 99 SERIAL #'d SETS
FIVE #'d INSERTS PER SER.1 HOBBY BOX
GOLD-SILVER AVAIL ONLY IN SER.1 PACKS

2006 Upper Deck Collect the Mascots

COMPLETE SET (3) .40 1.00
ISSUED IN 06 UD 1 AND 2 FAT PACKS
MLB1 Wally the Green Monster .20 .50
MLB2 Phillie Phanatic .20 .50
MLB3 Mr. Met .20 .50

2006 Upper Deck Inaugural Images

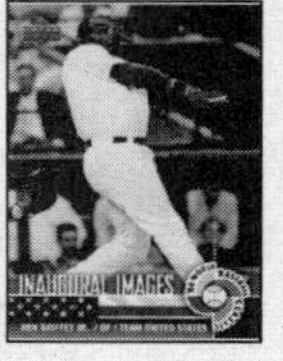

SER.2 ODDS 1:18 H, RANDOM IN RETAIL
II1 Sung-Heon Hong 1.25 3.00
II2 Yulieski Gourriel 1.25 3.00
II3 Tsuyoshi Nishioka 2.00 5.00
II4 Miguel Cabrera 1.25 3.00
II5 Yung Chi Chen 2.50 6.00
II6 Ormari Romero 1.25 3.00
II7 Ken Griffey Jr. 1.50 4.00
II8 Bernie Williams 1.25 3.00
II9 Daniel Cabrera .75 2.00
II10 David Ortiz 1.25 3.00
II11 Alex Rodriguez 1.50 4.00
II12 Frederich Cepeda 1.25 3.00
II13 Derek Jeter 2.50 6.00
II14 Jorge Cantu .75 2.00
II15 Alexi Ramirez 6.00 15.00
II16 Yoandy Garlobo 1.25 3.00
II17 Koji Uehara 2.00 5.00
II18 Nobuhiko Matsunaka 2.00 5.00
II19 Tomoya Satozaki 2.00 5.00
II20 Seung Yeop Lee 1.25 3.00
II21 Yulieski Gourriel 1.25 3.00
II22 Adrian Beltre .75 2.00
II23 Ken Griffey Jr. 1.50 4.00
II24 Jong Beom Lee 1.25 3.00
II25 Ichiro Suzuki 2.00 5.00
II26 Yoandy Garlobo 1.25 3.00
II27 Daisuke Matsuzaka 10.00 25.00
II28 Yadel Marti 1.25 3.00
II29 Chan Ho Park 1.25 3.00
II30 Daisuke Matsuzaka 10.00 25.00

2006 Upper Deck INKredible

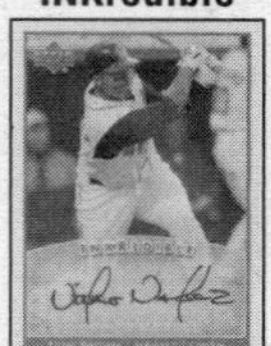

SER.2 ODDS 1:288 H, RANDOM IN RETAIL
UPDATE ODDS 1:24 RETAIL
SP INFO/PRINT RUNS PROVIDED BY UD
SP * INFO PROVIDED BY BECKETT
SP's ARE NOT SERIAL-NUMBERED
NO PRICING ON QTY OF 36 OR LESS
AB Ambiorix Burgos UPD SP * 6.00 15.00
AH Aaron Harang UPD 4.00 10.00
AJ Adam Jones UPD 20.00 50.00
AL Eliezer Alfonzo UPD SP *
AM Aaron Miles UPD SP
AP Angel Pagan UPD 6.00 15.00
AR2 Alex Rios UPD SP 15.00 40.00
AR Alexis Rios 6.00 15.00
BA Brandon Backe UPD 4.00 10.00
BB Ben Broussard UPD 6.00 15.00
BC Brandon Claussen UPD 4.00 10.00

BM Brandon McCarthy UPD SP 10.00 25.00
BM Brett Myers SP/72 * 6.00 15.00
BR Brian Roberts 6.00 15.00
BR2 Brian Roberts UPD 6.00 15.00
BW Brian Wilson UPD 4.00 10.00
CA Miguel Cabrera 15.00 40.00
CB Colter Bean UPD 4.00 10.00
CC Coco Crisp UPD 10.00 25.00
CC Carl Crawford 6.00 15.00
CC2 Carl Crawford UPD 6.00 15.00
CD Chris Duffy UPD 4.00 10.00
CI Cesar Izturis UPD SP * 6.00 15.00
CK Casey Kotchman 4.00 10.00
CK2 Casey Kotchman UPD 4.00 10.00
CL Cliff Lee UPD 4.00 10.00
CO Chad Cordero 6.00 15.00
CO2 Chad Cordero UPD SP 6.00 15.00
CW C.J. Wilson UPD 4.00 10.00
DJ Derek Jeter 60.00 120.00
DJ2 Derek Jeter UPD SP 125.00 200.00
DR Darrell Rasner UPD 4.00 10.00
DW David Wright SP/91 * 30.00 60.00
EA Erick Aybar UPD 4.00 10.00
EB Eude Brito UPD 6.00 15.00
EF Emiliano Fruto UPD SP *
EG Eric Gagne UPD SP 30.00 60.00
GC Gustavo Chacin UPD 4.00 10.00
GF Gavin Floyd UPD 4.00 10.00
JB Joe Blanton 6.00 15.00
JC Jesse Crain 4.00 10.00
JD Jermaine Dye UPD 6.00 15.00
JE Johnny Estrada UPD SP
JH John Hattig UPD 4.00 10.00
JH J.J. Hardy 4.00 10.00
JJ Jorge Julio UPD SP 6.00 15.00
JM Joe Mauer SP/91 * 15.00 40.00
JO Jacque Jones UPD 6.00 15.00
JP Jhonny Peralta UPD 4.00 10.00
JR Juan Rivera UPD SP 10.00 25.00
JR Jeremy Reed 4.00 10.00
JV Justin Verlander SP/91 * 15.00 40.00
KG Ken Griffey Jr. 60.00 120.00
KG2 Ken Griffey Jr. UPD SP 75.00 150.00
KR Ken Ray UPD 4.00 10.00
KY Kevin Youkilis 6.00 15.00
KY2 Kevin Youkilis UPD 6.00 15.00
LN Leo Nunez UPD 4.00 10.00
LO Lyle Overbay SP/91 * 6.00 15.00
MC Matt Clement SP/36 *
MH Matt Holliday UPD 8.00 20.00
MM Matt Murton UPD 10.00 25.00
MO Justin Morneau 10.00 25.00
MR Mike Rouse UPD 4.00 10.00
MT Mark Teahen UPD 6.00 15.00
MT Mark Teixeira 10.00 25.00
MV Mike Vento UPD 4.00 10.00
NG Nomar Garciaparra 30.00 60.00
NL Noah Lowry UPD 6.00 15.00
NS Nick Swisher UPD 6.00 15.00
PA John Patterson UPD 4.00 10.00
PE Joel Peralta UPD 4.00 10.00
PF Prince Fielder SP/10 *
PI Joel Pineiro UPD 6.00 15.00
RE Jose Reyes SP/91 * 15.00 40.00
RF Ryan Freel UPD 6.00 15.00
RG Ryan Garko UPD 4.00 10.00
RP Ronny Paulino UPD 10.00 25.00
RS Ryan Shealy UPD 6.00 15.00
RZ Ryan Zimmerman SP/91 * 20.00 50.00
SK Scott Kazmir 8.00 20.00
TH Travis Hafner 10.00 25.00
TI Tadahito Iguchi SP/91 * 20.00 50.00
TI2 Tadahito Iguchi UPD SP 30.00 60.00
VM Victor Martinez 6.00 15.00
WI Dontrelle Willis 10.00 25.00
YB Yuniesky Betancourt UPD 6.00 15.00
YM Yadier Molina UPD 6.00 15.00
ZM Zach Miner UPD 4.00 10.00

2006 Upper Deck Derek Jeter Spell and Win

COMPLETE SET (5) 6.00 15.00
COMMON CARD (1-5) 1.25 3.00
RANDOM IN SER.2 WAL-MART PACKS

2006 Upper Deck Player Highlights

SER.2 ODDS 1:6 H, RANDOM IN RETAIL
PH1 Andruw Jones .60 1.50
PH2 Manny Ramirez .60 1.50
PH3 Travis Hafner .40 1.00
PH4 Johnny Damon .60 1.50
PH5 Miguel Cabrera .60 1.50
PH6 Chris Carpenter .40 1.00
PH7 Derrek Lee .40 1.00
PH8 Jason Bay .40 1.00
PH9 Jason Varitek 1.00 2.50
PH10 Ryan Howard 1.25 3.00
PH11 Mark Teixeira .60 1.50
PH12 Carlos Delgado .40 1.00
PH13 Bartolo Colon .40 1.00
PH14 David Wright 1.25 3.00
PH15 Miguel Tejada .40 1.00
PH16 Mike Piazza 1.00 2.50
PH17 Paul Konerko .40 1.00
PH18 Jermaine Dye .40 1.00
PH19 Ichiro Suzuki 1.25 3.00
PH20 Brad Wilkerson .40 1.00
PH21 Hideki Matsui 1.00 2.50
PH22 Albert Pujols 1.50 4.00
PH23 Chris Burke .40 1.00
PH24 Derek Jeter 2.00 5.00
PH25 Brian Roberts .40 1.00
PH26 David Ortiz 1.00 2.50
PH27 Alex Rodriguez 1.25 3.00
PH28 Ken Griffey Jr. 1.25 3.00
PH29 Prince Fielder 1.25 3.00
PH30 Bobby Abreu .40 1.00
PH31 Vladimir Guerrero 1.00 2.50
PH32 Tadahito Iguchi .40 1.00
PH33 Jose Reyes .40 1.00
PH34 Scott Podsednik .40 1.00
PH35 Gary Sheffield .40 1.00

2006 Upper Deck Run Producers

SER.2 ODDS 1:8 H, RANDOM IN RETAIL
RP1 Ty Cobb 1.50 4.00
RP2 Derrek Lee .40 1.00
RP3 Andruw Jones .60 1.50
RP4 David Ortiz 1.00 2.50
RP5 Lou Gehrig 2.00 5.00
RP6 Ken Griffey Jr. 1.50 4.00
RP7 Albert Pujols 2.00 5.00
RP8 Derek Jeter 2.50 6.00
RP9 Manny Ramirez .60 1.50
RP10 Alex Rodriguez 1.50 4.00
RP11 Gary Sheffield .40 1.00
RP12 Miguel Cabrera .60 1.50
RP13 Hideki Matsui 1.00 2.50
RP14 Vladimir Guerrero 1.00 2.50
RP15 David Wright 1.50 4.00
RP16 Mike Schmidt 1.50 4.00
RP17 Mark Teixeira .40 1.00
RP18 Babe Ruth 3.00 8.00
RP19 Jimmie Foxx 1.00 2.50
RP20 Honus Wagner 1.00 2.50

2006 Upper Deck Season Highlights

COMPLETE SET (30)
ISSUED IN 06 UD 1 AND 2 FAT PACKS
SH1 Albert Pujols 2.00 5.00
SH2 Ken Griffey Jr. 1.50 4.00
SH3 Travis Hafner .40 1.00
SH4 David Ortiz 1.00 2.50
SH5 David Ortiz 1.00 2.50
SH6 Ryan Howard 1.50 4.00
SH7 Chase Utley 1.00 2.50
SH8 Manny Ramirez .60 1.50
SH9 Barry Zito .40 1.00
SH10 Roger Clemens 2.00 5.00
SH11 Francisco Liriano 1.00 2.50
SH12 Jered Weaver 1.25 3.00
SH13 Roy Halladay .40 1.00
SH14 Johan Santana .60 1.50
SH15 Tom Glavine .60 1.50
SH16 Pedro Martinez .60 1.50
SH17 Mike Piazza 1.00 2.50
SH18 Alfonso Soriano .40 1.00
SH19 Miguel Cabrera .60 1.50
SH20 Vladimir Guerrero 1.00 2.50
SH21 Joe Mauer .60 1.50
SH22 Ryan Zimmerman 2.50 6.00
SH23 Carlos Delgado .40 1.00
SH24 Jim Thome .60 1.50
SH25 Jermaine Dye .40 1.00
SH26 Derek Jeter 2.50 6.00
SH27 Ivan Rodriguez .60 1.50
SH28 Bobby Abreu .40 1.00
SH29 Greg Maddux 1.50 4.00
SH30 Alex Rodriguez 1.50 4.00

2006 Upper Deck Signature Sensations

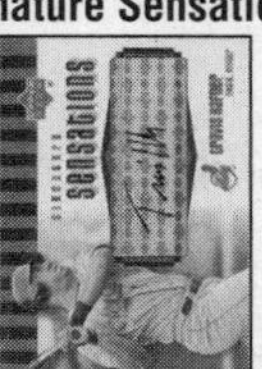

SER.1 ODDS 1:288 HOBBY, 1:1920 RETAIL
SP INFO PROVIDED BY UPPER DECK
AL Al Leiter 6.00 15.00
AM Aaron Miles 4.00 10.00
AO Akinori Otsuka SP
AR Aaron Rowand 6.00 15.00
BA Bronson Arroyo 6.00 15.00
BH Bobby Hill SP
CD Carlos Delgado SP
CS Cory Sullivan 4.00 10.00
DY Delmon Young SP
EG Eric Gagne SP
GA Garrett Atkins 4.00 10.00
HS Huston Street SP
JA Javier Vazquez SP
JE Johnny Estrada 4.00 10.00
JJ Josh Johnson 4.00 10.00
JK Jason Kendall SP
JS Jeff Suppan 4.00 10.00
JV Joe Valentine 4.00 10.00
KC Kiko Calero 4.00 10.00
KG Ken Griffey Jr. SP
MH Mike Hampton SP
MP Mark Prior SP
NP Nick Punto 4.00 10.00
SB Scott Baker 6.00 15.00
TH Trevor Hoffman SP
TR Travis Hafner 6.00 15.00
YM Yadier Molina 6.00 15.00

2006 Upper Deck Speed To Burn

SER.2 ODDS 1:12 H, RANDOM IN RETAIL
CARDS 2/10/13 DO NOT EXIST
SB1 Lou Brock 1.25 3.00
SB3 Alfonso Soriano .50 1.25
SB4 Carl Crawford .50 1.25
SB5 Chone Figgins .50 1.25
SB6 Ichiro Suzuki 2.00 5.00
SB7 Jose Reyes .50 1.25
SB8 Juan Pierre .50 1.25
SB9 Scott Podsednik .50 1.25
SB11 Alex Rodriguez 2.00 5.00
SB12 David Wright 2.00 5.00
SB14 Bobby Abreu .50 1.25
SB15 Brian Roberts .50 1.25

2006 Upper Deck Star Attractions

COMPLETE UPDATE (50) 20.00 50.00
SER.1 ODDS 1:6 HOBBY, 1:12 RETAIL
UPDATE ODDS 1:2 RETAIL
*GOLD: .6X TO 1.5X BASIC
FIVE #'d INSERTS PER SER.1 HOBBY BOX
GOLD PRINT RUN 699 SERIAL #'d SETS
*SILVER: 1.25X TO 3X BASIC
ONE #'d INSERT PER UPDATE BOX
SILVER PRINT RUN 99 SERIAL #'d SETS
AB Adrian Beltre .50 1.25
AE Andre Ethier UPD 1.00 2.50
AH Aubrey Huff .50 1.25
AJ Adam Jones UPD 1.25 3.00
AJ Andruw Jones .75 2.00
AL Adam Loewen UPD .40 1.00
AM Andy Marte UPD .40 1.00
AN Anibal Sanchez UPD .40 1.00
AP Andy Pettitte .75 2.00
AR Anthony Reyes UPD .40 1.00
AS Alfonso Soriano .50 1.25
AW Adam Wainwright UPD .40 1.00
BA Bobby Abreu .50 1.25
BI Chad Billingsley UPD .60 1.50
BR Brian Anderson UPD .40 1.00
BZ Barry Zito .50 1.25
CB Carlos Beltran .50 1.25
CD Carlos Delgado .50 1.25
CH Cole Hamels UPD 1.50 4.00
CJ Chipper Jones 1.25 3.00
CL Carlos Lee .50 1.25
CO Conor Jackson UPD .60 1.50
CQ Carlos Quentin UPD .60 1.50
CS Curt Schilling .75 2.00
CY Chris Young UPD .40 1.00
DJ Derek Jeter 3.00 8.00
DL Derrek Lee .50 1.25
DM Dustin McGowan UPD .40 1.00
DO David Ortiz 1.25 3.00
DP Dustin Pedroia UPD 1.00 2.50
DU Dan Uggla UPD 1.00 2.50
DW Dontrelle Willis .50 1.25
EA Erick Aybar UPD .40 1.00
EG Eric Gagne .50 1.25
FL Francisco Liriano UPD 1.00 2.50
FT Frank Thomas 1.25 3.00
GA Garret Anderson .50 1.25
GM Greg Maddux 2.00 5.00
GR Khalil Greene .75 2.00
GS Gary Sheffield .50 1.25
GU Jose Guillen .50 1.25
HI Jason Hirsh UPD .40 1.00
HK Howie Kendrick UPD 2.00 5.00
HP Hayden Penn UPD .40 1.00
HR Hanley Ramirez UPD 1.00 2.50
HU Justin Huber UPD .40 1.00
JA Chuck James UPD .60 1.50
JB Josh Beckett .50 1.25
JC Jose Contreras .50 1.25
JD Johnny Damon .75 2.00
JE Jim Edmonds .75 2.00
JG Jason Giambi .50 1.25
JH Jeremy Hermida UPD .40 1.00
JJ Josh Johnson UPD .60 1.50
JJ Jacque Jones .50 1.25
JK Jason Kubel UPD .40 1.00
JL Javy Lopez .50 1.25
JM Joe Mauer .75 2.00
JO Josh Barfield UPD .40 1.00
JP Jorge Posada .75 2.00
JR Jose Reyes 1.25 3.00
JS Jason Schmidt .50 1.25
JV Justin Verlander UPD 1.50 4.00
JW Jered Weaver UPD 2.00 5.00
JZ Joel Zumaya UPD 1.00 2.50
KG Ken Griffey Jr. 2.00 5.00
KJ Kenji Johjima UPD 2.00 5.00
KM Kendry Morales UPD 1.00 2.50
KW Kerry Wood .50 1.25
LB Lance Berkman .50 1.25
LE Jon Lester UPD 2.50 6.00
LM Lastings Milledge UPD .60 1.50
MA Jeff Mathis UPD .40 1.00
MC Matt Cain UPD .60 1.50
MK Matt Kemp UPD .60 1.50
MM Mark Mulder .50 1.25
MO Magglio Ordonez .50 1.25
MP Mark Prior .75 2.00
MR Manny Ramirez .75 2.00
MT Mark Teixeira .75 2.00
NM Nick Markakis UPD .60 1.50
PA Jonathan Papelbon UPD 2.00 5.00
PE Mike Pelfrey UPD 1.50 4.00
PF Prince Fielder UPD 1.50 4.00
PM Pedro Martinez .75 2.00
PU Albert Pujols 2.50 6.00
RC Ronny Cedeno UPD .40 1.00
RH Rich Harden .50 1.25
RM Russell Martin UPD .60 1.50
RZ Ryan Zimmerman UPD 2.50 6.00
SD Stephen Drew UPD 1.00 2.50
SG Shawn Green .50 1.25
SM John Smoltz .75 2.00
SO Scott Olsen UPD .40 1.00
SW Jeremy Sowers UPD .40 1.00
TG Tony Gwynn Jr. UPD .40 1.00
TH Torii Hunter .50 1.25
TI Tadahito Iguchi .50 1.25
WA Willy Aybar UPD .40 1.00
WR David Wright 2.00 5.00

2006 Upper Deck Star Attractions Swatches

SER.1 ODDS 1:48 HOBBY, 1:288 RETAIL
AB Adrian Beltre Jsy 3.00 8.00
AH Aubrey Huff Jsy 3.00 8.00
AJ Andruw Jones Jsy 4.00 10.00
AP Andy Pettitte Jsy 4.00 10.00
AS Alfonso Soriano Jsy 3.00 8.00
BA Bobby Abreu Jsy 3.00 8.00
BZ Barry Zito Jsy 3.00 8.00
CB Carlos Beltran Jsy 3.00 8.00
CD Carlos Delgado Jsy 3.00 8.00
CJ Chipper Jones Jsy 4.00 10.00
CL Carlos Lee Jsy 3.00 8.00
CS Curt Schilling Jsy 4.00 10.00
DJ Derek Jeter Jsy 10.00 25.00
DL Derrek Lee Jsy 4.00 10.00
DO David Ortiz Jsy 4.00 10.00
DW Dontrelle Willis Jsy 3.00 8.00
EG Eric Gagne Jsy 3.00 8.00
FT Frank Thomas Jsy 4.00 10.00
GA Garret Anderson Jsy 3.00 8.00
GM Greg Maddux Jsy 4.00 10.00
GR Khalil Greene Jsy 4.00 10.00
GS Gary Sheffield Jsy 3.00 8.00
GU Jose Guillen Jsy 3.00 8.00
JB Josh Beckett Jsy 3.00 8.00
JC Jose Contreras Jsy 3.00 8.00
JD Johnny Damon Jsy 4.00 10.00
JE Jim Edmonds Jsy 3.00 8.00
JG Jason Giambi Jsy 3.00 8.00
JJ Jacque Jones Jsy 3.00 8.00
JL Javy Lopez Jsy 3.00 8.00
JM Joe Mauer Jsy 4.00 10.00
JP Jorge Posada Jsy 4.00 10.00
JR Jose Reyes Jsy 3.00 8.00
JS Jason Schmidt Jsy 3.00 8.00
KG Ken Griffey Jr. Jsy 6.00 15.00
KW Kerry Wood Jsy 3.00 8.00
LB Lance Berkman Jsy 3.00 8.00
MM Mark Mulder Jsy 3.00 8.00
MO Magglio Ordonez Jsy 3.00 8.00
MP Mark Prior Jsy 3.00 8.00
MR Manny Ramirez Jsy 4.00 10.00
MT Mark Teixeira Jsy 4.00 10.00
PM Pedro Martinez Jsy 4.00 10.00
PU Albert Pujols Jsy 6.00 15.00
RH Rich Harden Jsy 3.00 8.00
SG Shawn Green Jsy 3.00 8.00
SM John Smoltz Jsy 4.00 10.00
TH Torii Hunter Jsy 3.00 8.00
TI Tadahito Iguchi Jsy 4.00 10.00
WR David Wright Jsy 4.00 10.00

2006 Upper Deck Team Pride

SER.1 ODDS 1:6 HOBBY, 1:12 RETAIL
*GOLD: .6X TO 1.5X BASIC
FIVE #'d INSERTS PER SER.1 HOBBY BOX
GOLD PRINT RUN 699 SERIAL #'d SETS
AH Aubrey Huff .50 1.25
AJ Andruw Jones .75 2.00
AP Albert Pujols 2.50 6.00
BA Bobby Abreu .50 1.25
BW Bernie Williams .75 2.00
BZ Barry Zito .50 1.25
CC C.C. Sabathia .50 1.25
CD Carlos Delgado .50 1.25
CJ Chipper Jones 1.25 3.00
CK Casey Kotchman .50 1.25
CS Curt Schilling .75 2.00
DJ Derek Jeter 3.00 8.00
DO David Ortiz 1.25 3.00
DW Dontrelle Willis .50 1.25
EC Eric Chavez .50 1.25
EG Eric Gagne .50 1.25
FT Frank Thomas 1.25 3.00
GA Garret Anderson .50 1.25
GM Greg Maddux 2.00 5.00
GR Khalil Greene .75 2.00
IR Ivan Rodriguez .75 2.00
JB Jeff Bagwell .75 2.00
JD Johnny Damon .75 2.00
JE Jim Edmonds .75 2.00
JM Jamie Moyer .50 1.25
JP Jorge Posada .75 2.00
JR Jose Reyes 1.25 3.00
JS John Smoltz .75 2.00
JT Jim Thome .75 2.00
JV Jose Vidro .50 1.25
KF Keith Foulke .50 1.25
KG Ken Griffey Jr. 2.00 5.00
KW Kerry Wood .50 1.25
LC Luis Castillo .50 1.25
LG Luis Gonzalez .50 1.25
LO Mike Lowell .50 1.25
MA Joe Mauer .75 2.00
ME Morgan Ensberg .50 1.25
ML Mike Lieberthal .50 1.25
MP Mark Prior .75 2.00
MS Mike Sweeney .50 1.25
MY Michael Young .50 1.25
NJ Nick Johnson .50 1.25
PE Andy Pettitte .75 2.00
RB Rocco Baldelli .50 1.25
RH Rich Harden .50 1.25
RK Ryan Klesko .50 1.25
SC Sean Casey .50 1.25
TH Trevor Hoffman .50 1.25
VA Jason Varitek 1.25 3.00

2006 Upper Deck Team Pride Materials

SER.1 ODDS 1:48 HOBBY, 1:288 RETAIL
AH Aubrey Huff Jsy 3.00 8.00
AJ Andruw Jones Jsy 4.00 10.00
AP Albert Pujols Jsy 6.00 15.00
BA Bobby Abreu Jsy 3.00 8.00
BW Bernie Williams Jsy 4.00 10.00
BZ Barry Zito Jsy 3.00 8.00
CC C.C. Sabathia Jsy 3.00 8.00
CD Carlos Delgado Jsy 3.00 8.00
CJ Chipper Jones Jsy 4.00 10.00
CK Casey Kotchman Jsy 3.00 8.00
CS Curt Schilling Jsy 4.00 10.00
DJ Derek Jeter Jsy 10.00 25.00
DO David Ortiz Jsy 4.00 10.00
DW Dontrelle Willis Jsy 3.00 8.00
EC Eric Chavez Jsy 3.00 8.00
EG Eric Gagne Jsy 3.00 8.00
FT Frank Thomas Jsy 4.00 10.00
GA Garret Anderson Jsy 3.00 8.00
GM Greg Maddux Jsy 4.00 10.00
GR Khalil Greene Jsy 4.00 10.00
IR Ivan Rodriguez Jsy 4.00 10.00
JB Jeff Bagwell Jsy 4.00 10.00
JD Johnny Damon Jsy 4.00 10.00
JE Jim Edmonds Jsy 3.00 8.00
JM Jamie Moyer Jsy 3.00 8.00
JP Jorge Posada Jsy 4.00 10.00
JR Jose Reyes Jsy 3.00 8.00
JS John Smoltz Jsy 4.00 10.00
JT Jim Thome Jsy 4.00 10.00
JV Jose Vidro Jsy 3.00 8.00
KF Keith Foulke Jsy 3.00 8.00
KG Ken Griffey Jr. Jsy 6.00 15.00
KW Kerry Wood Jsy 3.00 8.00
LC Luis Castillo Jsy 3.00 8.00
LG Luis Gonzalez Jsy 3.00 8.00
LO Mike Lowell Jsy 3.00 8.00
MA Joe Mauer Jsy 4.00 10.00
ME Morgan Ensberg Jsy 3.00 8.00
ML Mike Lieberthal Jsy 3.00 8.00
MP Mark Prior Jsy 3.00 8.00
MS Mike Sweeney Jsy 3.00 8.00
MY Michael Young Jsy 3.00 8.00
NJ Nick Johnson Jsy 3.00 8.00
PE Andy Pettitte Jsy 4.00 10.00
RB Rocco Baldelli Jsy 3.00 8.00
RH Rich Harden Jsy 3.00 8.00
RK Ryan Klesko Jsy 3.00 8.00
SC Sean Casey Jsy 3.00 8.00
TH Trevor Hoffman Jsy 3.00 8.00
VA Jason Varitek Jsy 4.00 10.00

2006 Upper Deck UD Game Materials

SER.1 ODDS 1:24 HOBBY, 1:24 RETAIL
SER.2 GU ODDS 1:24 H, RANDOM IN RETAIL
SP INFO PROVIDED BY UPPER DECK
SER.1 PATCH ODDS 1:288 H, 1:1500 R
SER.2 PATCH RANDOM IN HOBBY/RETAIL
SER.2 PATCH PRINT RUN 11 SETS
SER.2 PATCH PRINT RUN PROVIDED BY UD
NO PATCH PRICING DUE TO SCARCITY
AB Adrian Beltre Bat S2 3.00 8.00
AD Adam Dunn Jsy S2 3.00 8.00
AJ Andruw Jones Pants S1 4.00 10.00
AP1 Andy Pettitte Jsy S2 4.00 10.00
AP2 Albert Pujols Pants S1 6.00 15.00
AS Alfonso [illegible]
BA Bobby Ab[illegible]
BI Craig Biggio [illegible]
BR Brian Roberts [illegible]
BZ Barry Zito Jsy [illegible]
CB Carlos Beltran [illegible]
CD Carlos Delgado [illegible]
CJ Chipper Jones Pa[illegible]
CL Carlos Lee Jsy S2 [illegible]
CP Corey Patterson Jsy [illegible]
CS Curt Schilling Jsy S1 [illegible]
DJ1 Derek Jeter Jsy S1 [illegible]
DJ2 Derek Jeter Jsy S2 [illegible]
DL Derrek Lee Pants S1 [illegible]
DO David Ortiz Jsy S1 [illegible]
DW Dontrelle Willis Jsy S1 [illegible]
EC Eric Chavez Jsy S1 [illegible]
EG Eric Gagne Jsy S1 [illegible]
FT Frank Thomas Jsy S1 [illegible]
GA Garrett Atkins Jsy S2 3.[illegible]
GM Greg Maddux Jsy S1 4.0[illegible]
GR Khalil Greene Jsy S2 3.00 [illegible]
GS Gary Sheffield Jsy S2 3.00 [illegible]
HA Travis Hafner Jsy S2 3.00 [illegible]
HB Hank Blalock Jsy S2 3.00 [illegible]
IR Ivan Rodriguez Jsy S1 4.00 10[illegible]
JB1 Jeff Bagwell Pants S1 4.00 10.[illegible]
JB2 Josh Beckett Jsy S2 3.00 8.0[illegible]
JD1 Johnny Damon Jsy S1 4.00 10.00
JD2 Johnny Damon Jsy S2 4.00 10.00
JE Jim Edmonds Jsy S1 3.00 8.00
JG Jason Giambi Jsy S1 3.00 8.00
JJ Jacque Jones Jsy S1 3.00 8.00
JL Javy Lopez Jsy S2 3.00 8.00
JM Joe Mauer Jsy S2 4.00 10.00
JP Jake Peavy Jsy S1 3.00 8.00
JR Jose Reyes Jsy S2 3.00 8.00
JS Johan Santana Pants S1 4.00 10.00
JT Jim Thome Jsy S1 4.00 10.00
JV Jason Varitek Jsy S2 4.00 10.00
KG1 Ken Griffey Jr. Jsy S1 6.00 15.00
KG2 Ken Griffey Jr. Jsy S2 6.00 15.00
KW Kerry Wood Jsy S2 3.00 8.00
MC Miguel Cabrera Pants S1 4.00 10.00
MM Mike Mussina Pants S2 4.00 10.00
MO Magglio Ordonez Jsy S2 3.00 8.00
MP1 Mike Piazza Jsy S1 4.00 10.00
MP2 Mike Piazza Bat S2 4.00 10.00
MR Manny Ramirez Jsy S1 4.00 10.00
MT Mark Teixeira Jsy S1 4.00 10.00
MY Michael Young Jsy S2 3.00 8.00
PF Prince Fielder Jsy S2 4.00 10.00
PK Paul Konerko Jsy S2 3.00 8.00
PM Pedro Martinez Pants S1 4.00 10.00
PO Jorge Posada Jsy S1 4.00 10.00
PR Mark Prior Jsy S1 3.00 8.00
RC Roger Clemens Jsy S1 6.00 15.00
RF Rafael Furcal Jsy S1 3.00 8.00
RH1 Roy Halladay Jsy S1 3.00 8.00
RH2 Ryan Howard Jsy S2 10.00 25.00
RJ R.Johnson Jsy SP S1
RO Roy Oswalt Jsy S2 3.00 8.00
RP Rafael Palmeiro Jsy S1 4.00 10.00
RW Rickie Weeks Jsy S2 3.00 8.00
RZ Ryan Zimmerman Jsy S2 6.00 15.00
SC Sean Casey Jsy S2 3.00 8.00
SI Grady Sizemore Jsy S2 4.00 10.00
SM John Smoltz Jsy S1 4.00 10.00
SR Scott Rolen Jsy S1 4.00 10.00
TE Miguel Tejada Pants S1 4.00 10.00
TG Tom Glavine Jsy S2 4.00 10.00
TH Todd Helton Jsy S2 4.00 10.00
TI Tadahito Iguchi Jsy S2 3.00 8.00
VG Vladimir Guerrero Jsy S1 4.00 10.00
VM Victor Martinez Jsy S2 3.00 8.00
WR David Wright Pants S1 4.00 10.00

2006 Upper Deck WBC Collection Jersey

SER.2 GU ODDS 1:24 H, RANDOM IN RETAIL
SER.2 PATCH RANDOM IN HOBBY/RETAIL
PATCH PRINT RUN 8 SETS
PATCH PRINT RUN PROVIDED BY UD
NO PATCH PRICING DUE TO SCARCITY
AI Akinori Iwamura 20.00 50.00
AJ Andruw Jones 8.00 20.00
AP Albert Pujols 15.00 40.00
AR Alex Rodriguez 20.00 50.00
AS Alfonso Soriano 6.00 15.00
CB Carlos Beltran 6.00 15.00
CD Carlos Delgado 6.00 15.00
CH Chin-Lung Hu 50.00 100.00
CL Carlos Lee 4.00 10.00
DL Derrek Lee 6.00 15.00
DM Daisuke Matsuzaka 100.00 200.00
DO David Ortiz 10.00 25.00
EB Erik Bedard 6.00 15.00
EP Eduardo Paret 10.00 25.00
FC Frederich Cepeda 10.00 25.00
FG Freddy Garcia 6.00 15.00
FR Jeff Francoeur 15.00 40.00
GL Guangbiao Liu 6.00 15.00
GY Guogan Yang 6.00 15.00
HS Chia-Hsien Hseih 40.00 80.00
HT Hitoshi Tamura 30.00 60.00
IR Ivan Rodriguez 6.00 15.00
IS Ichiro Suzuki 175.00 225.00
JB Jason Bay 6.00 15.00
JD Johnny Damon 6.00 15.00
JF Jeff Francis 6.00 15.00
JG Jason Grilli 4.00 10.00
JH Justin Huber 6.00 15.00
JL Jong Beom Lee 6.00 15.00
JM Justin Morneau 8.00 20.00
JP Jin Man Park 6.00 15.00
JS Johan Santana 10.00 25.00
JV Jason Varitek 10.00 25.00

		...00
		15.00
		150.00
	...00	100.00
	6.00	15.00
	15.00	40.00
	10.00	25.00

...er Deck World ...all Classic Box Set

This 50-card set was issued only in factory set form and was available through the Upper Deck web site with an $9.99 SRP. This set included mainly major league players but a few players from foreign countries were also included in this set.

COMP.FACT.SET (50)	10.00	15.00
COMMON CARD (1-50)	.20	.50
UNLISTED STARS	.30	.75
ISSUED ONLY IN FACTORY SET FORMAT		
DISTRIBUTED IN U.S.A. AND ASIA		
1 Derek Jeter	.60	1.50
2 Ken Griffey Jr.	.50	1.25
3 Derrek Lee	.20	.50
4 Dontrelle Willis	.20	.50
5 Alex Rodriguez	.60	1.50
6 Jeff Francoeur	.50	1.25
7 Roger Clemens	.50	1.25
8 Johnny Damon	.20	.50
9 Chipper Jones	.30	.75
10 Mark Teixeira	.20	.50
11 Chase Utley	.40	1.00
12 Jake Peavy	.20	.50
13 Michael Collins	.20	.50
14 Justin Huber	.20	.50
15 Jason Bay	.20	.50
16 Jeff Francis	.20	.50
17 Justin Morneau	.20	.50
18 Guogang Yang	.20	.50
19 Wei Wang	.20	.50
20 Chia-Hsien Hseih	.75	2.00
21 Chin-Lung Hu	.75	2.00
22 Wei-Lun Pan	.75	2.00
23 Yung Chi Chen	.75	2.00
24 Mike Piazza	.30	.75
25 Albert Pujols	.75	2.00
26 David Ortiz	.30	.75
27 Jose Reyes	.20	.50
28 Miguel Tejada	.20	.50
29 Ichiro Suzuki	.75	2.00
30 Nobuhiko Matsunaka	.30	.75
31 Toshiaki Imae	.20	.50
32 Kazuhiro Wada	.20	.50
33 Shunsuke Watanabe	.20	.50
34 Jung Bong	.20	.50
35 Jong Beom Lee	.40	1.00
36 Seung-Yeop Lee	.60	1.50
37 Vinny Castilla	.20	.50
38 Oliver Perez	.20	.50
39 Jorge Cantu	.20	.50
40 Andruw Jones	.20	.50
41 Carlos Lee	.20	.50
42 Carlos Beltran	.20	.50
43 Carlos Delgado	.20	.50
44 Ivan Rodriguez	.20	.50
45 Bernie Williams	.20	.50
46 Bobby Abreu	.20	.50
47 Miguel Cabrera	.20	.50
48 Johan Santana	.20	.50
49 Victor Martinez	.20	.50
50 Omar Vizquel	.40	1.00

2007 Upper Deck

This 1024-card set was issued over two series. In addition, a 20-card Rookie Exchange set was also produced and numbered sequentially at the beginning of the second series. The first series was released in March, 2007 and the second series was released in June, 2007. The cards were released in both hobby and retail packs. The hobby packs contained 15 cards per pack which came 16 packs to a box and 12 boxes to a case. Cards numbered 1-50 and 501-520 are rookie subsets while cards ...bered 471-500 are checklist cards. There was a ... Exchange card for cards 501-520 which was ... until February 27, 2010. The rest of the ...ced alphabetically by what team the ...s playing for when the individual

	200.00	300.00
...000)	120.00	200.00
...0)	40.00	80.00
...500)	80.00	120.00
...)	.15	.40
	.30	.75
...(501-520)	1.00	2.50
...N SERIES 1 PACKS		
...SUED IN SERIES 2 PACKS		
...AKA JSY RANDOMLY INSERTED		
...ATSUZAKA JSY PRICING AVAILABLE		
...VERALL PLATE SER.1 ODDS 1:192 H		
OVERALL PLATE SER.2 ODDS 1:96 H		
PLATE PRINT RUN 1 SET PER COLOR		
BLACK-CYAN-MAGENTA-YELLOW ISSUED		
NO PLATE PRICING DUE TO SCARCITY		
ROOKIE EXCH APPX. 1-2 PER CASE		
ROOKIE EXCH DEADLINE 02/27/2010		
1 Doug Slaten RC	.30	.75
2 Miguel Montero (RC)	.30	.75
3 Brian Burres (RC)	.30	.75
4 Devern Hansack RC	.30	.75
5 David Murphy (RC)	.30	.75
6 Jose Reyes RC	.30	.75
7 Scott Moore (RC)	.30	.75
8 Josh Fields (RC)	.30	.75
9 Chris Stewart RC	.30	.75
10 Jerry Owens (RC)	.30	.75
11 Ryan Sweeney (RC)	.30	.75
12 Kevin Kouzmanoff (RC)	.30	.75
13 Jeff Baker (RC)	.30	.75
14 Justin Hampson (RC)	.30	.75
15 Jeff Salazar (RC)	.30	.75
16 Alvin Colina RC	.75	2.00
17 Troy Tulowitzki (RC)	.75	2.00
18 Andrew Miller RC	2.00	5.00
19 Mike Rabelo RC	.30	.75
20 Jose Diaz (RC)	.30	.75
21 Angel Sanchez RC	.30	.75
22 Ryan Braun RC	.30	.75
23 Delwyn Young (RC)	.30	.75
24 Drew Anderson RC	.30	.75
25 Dennis Sarfate (RC)	.30	.75
26 Vinny Rottino (RC)	.30	.75
27 Glen Perkins (RC)	.30	.75
28 Alexi Casilla RC	.50	1.25
29 Philip Humber (RC)	.30	.75
30 Andy Cannizaro RC	.30	.75
31 Jeremy Brown	.15	.40
32 Sean Henn (RC)	.30	.75
33 Brian Rogers	.15	.40
34 Carlos Maldonado (RC)	.30	.75
35 Juan Morillo (RC)	.30	.75
36 Fred Lewis (RC)	.30	.75
37 Patrick Misch (RC)	.30	.75
38 Billy Sadler (RC)	.30	.75
39 Ryan Feierabend (RC)	.30	.75
40 Cesar Jimenez RC	.30	.75
41 Oswaldo Navarro RC	.30	.75
42 Travis Chick (RC)	.30	.75
43 Delmon Young (RC)	.75	2.00
44 Shawn Riggans (RC)	.30	.75
45 Brian Stokes (RC)	.30	.75
46 Juan Salas (RC)	.30	.75
47 Joaquin Arias (RC)	.30	.75
48 Adam Lind (RC)	.30	.75
49 Beltran Perez (RC)	.30	.75
50 Brett Campbell RC	.30	.75
51 Brian Roberts	.15	.40
52 Miguel Tejada	.15	.40
53 Brandon Fahey	.15	.40
54 Jay Gibbons	.15	.40
55 Corey Patterson	.15	.40
56 Nick Markakis	.25	.60
57 Ramon Hernandez	.15	.40
58 Kris Benson	.15	.40
59 Adam Loewen	.15	.40
60 Erik Bedard	.15	.40
61 Chris Ray	.15	.40
62 Chris Britton	.15	.40
63 Daniel Cabrera	.15	.40
64 Sendy Rleal	.15	.40
65 Manny Ramirez	.25	.60
66 David Ortiz	.40	1.00
67 Gabe Kapler	.15	.40
68 Alex Cora	.15	.40
69 Dustin Pedroia	.60	1.50
70 Trot Nixon	.15	.40
71 Doug Mirabelli	.15	.40
72 Mark Loretta	.15	.40
73 Curt Schilling	.25	.60
74 Jonathan Papelbon	.40	1.00
75 Tim Wakefield	.15	.40
76 Jon Lester	.25	.60
77 Craig Hansen	.15	.40
78 Keith Foulke	.15	.40
79 Jermaine Dye	.15	.40
80 Jim Thome	.25	.60
81 Tadahito Iguchi	.15	.40
82 Rob Mackowiak	.15	.40
83 Brian Anderson	.15	.40
84 Juan Uribe	.15	.40
85 A.J. Pierzynski	.15	.40
86 Alex Cintron	.15	.40
87 Jon Garland	.15	.40
88 Jose Contreras	.15	.40
89 Neal Cotts	.15	.40
90 Bobby Jenks	.15	.40
91 Mike MacDougal	.15	.40
92 Javier Vazquez	.15	.40
93 Travis Hafner	.15	.40
94 Jhonny Peralta	.15	.40
95 Ryan Garko	.15	.40
96 Victor Martinez	.15	.40
97 Hector Luna	.15	.40
98 Casey Blake	.15	.40
99 Jason Michaels	.15	.40
100 Shin-Soo Choo	.25	.60
101 C.C. Sabathia	.15	.40
102 Paul Byrd	.15	.40
103 Jeremy Sowers	.15	.40
104 Cliff Lee	.15	.40
105 Rafael Betancourt	.15	.40
106 Francisco Cruceta	.15	.40
107 Sean Casey	.15	.40
108 Brandon Inge	.15	.40
109 Placido Polanco	.15	.40
110 Omar Infante	.15	.40
111 Ivan Rodriguez	.25	.60
112 Magglio Ordonez	.15	.40
113 Craig Monroe	.15	.40
114 Marcus Thames	.15	.40
115 Justin Verlander	.40	1.00
116 Todd Jones	.15	.40
117 Kenny Rogers	.15	.40
118 Joel Zumaya	.25	.60
119 Jeremy Bonderman	.15	.40
120 Nate Robertson	.15	.40
121 Mark Teahen	.15	.40
122 Ryan Shealy	.15	.40
123 Mitch Maier RC	.30	.75
124 Doug Mientkiewicz	.15	.40
125 Mark Grudzielanek	.15	.40
126 Shane Costa	.15	.40
127 John Buck	.15	.40
128 Reggie Sanders	.15	.40
129 Mike Sweeney	.15	.40
130 Mark Redman	.15	.40
131 Todd Wellemeyer	.15	.40
132 Scott Elarton	.15	.40
133 Ambiorix Burgos	.15	.40
134 Joe Nelson	.15	.40
135 Howie Kendrick	.15	.40
136 Chone Figgins	.15	.40
137 Orlando Cabrera	.15	.40
138 Maicer Izturis	.15	.40
139 Jose Molina	.15	.40
140 Vladimir Guerrero	.40	1.00
141 Darin Erstad	.15	.40
142 Juan Rivera	.15	.40
143 Jered Weaver	.25	.60
144 John Lackey	.15	.40
145 Joe Saunders	.15	.40
146 Bartolo Colon	.15	.40
147 Scot Shields	.15	.40
148 Francisco Rodriguez	.15	.40
149 Justin Morneau	.15	.40
150 Jason Bartlett	.15	.40
151 Luis Castillo	.15	.40
152 Nick Punto	.15	.40
153 Shannon Stewart	.15	.40
154 Michael Cuddyer	.15	.40
155 Jason Kubel	.15	.40
156 Joe Mauer	.25	.60
157 Francisco Liriano	.40	1.00
158 Joe Nathan	.15	.40
159 Dennys Reyes	.15	.40
160 Brad Radke	.15	.40
161 Boof Bonser	.15	.40
162 Juan Rincon	.15	.40
163 Derek Jeter	1.00	2.50
164 Jason Giambi	.15	.40
165 Robinson Cano	.25	.60
166 Andy Phillips	.15	.40
167 Bobby Abreu	.15	.40
168 Gary Sheffield	.15	.40
169 Bernie Williams	.25	.60
170 Melky Cabrera	.15	.40
171 Mike Mussina	.25	.60
172 Chien-Ming Wang	.60	1.50
173 Mariano Rivera	.40	1.00
174 Scott Proctor	.15	.40
175 Jaret Wright	.15	.40
176 Kyle Farnsworth	.15	.40
177 Eric Chavez	.15	.40
178 Bobby Crosby	.15	.40
179 Frank Thomas	.40	1.00
180 Dan Johnson	.15	.40
181 Marco Scutaro	.15	.40
182 Nick Swisher	.15	.40
183 Milton Bradley	.15	.40
184 Jay Payton	.15	.40
185 Joe Blanton	.15	.40
186 Barry Zito	.15	.40
187 Rich Harden	.15	.40
188 Esteban Loaiza	.15	.40
189 Huston Street	.15	.40
190 Chad Gaudin	.15	.40
191 Richie Sexson	.15	.40
192 Yuniesky Betancourt	.15	.40
193 Willie Bloomquist	.15	.40
194 Ben Broussard	.15	.40
195 Kenji Johjima	.40	1.00
196 Ichiro Suzuki	.60	1.50
197 Raul Ibanez	.15	.40
198 Chris Snelling	.15	.40
199 Felix Hernandez	.25	.60
200 Cha-Seung Baek	.15	.40
201 Joel Pineiro	.15	.40
202 Julio Mateo	.15	.40
203 J.J. Putz	.15	.40
204 Rafael Soriano	.15	.40
205 Jorge Cantu	.15	.40
206 B.J. Upton	.15	.40
207 Ty Wigginton	.15	.40
208 Greg Norton	.15	.40
209 Dioner Navarro	.15	.40
210 Carl Crawford	.15	.40
211 Jonny Gomes	.15	.40
212 Damon Hollins	.15	.40
213 Scott Kazmir	.25	.60
214 Casey Fossum	.15	.40
215 Ruddy Lugo	.15	.40
216 James Shields	.15	.40
217 Tyler Walker	.15	.40
218 Shawn Camp	.15	.40
219 Mark Teixeira	.25	.60
220 Hank Blalock	.15	.40
221 Ian Kinsler	.15	.40
222 Jerry Hairston Jr.	.15	.40
223 Gerald Laird	.15	.40
224 Carlos Lee	.15	.40
225 Gary Matthews	.15	.40
226 Mark DeRosa	.15	.40
227 Kip Wells	.15	.40
228 Akinori Otsuka	.15	.40
229 Vicente Padilla	.15	.40
230 John Koronka	.15	.40
231 Kevin Millwood	.15	.40
232 Wes Littleton	.15	.40
233 Troy Glaus	.15	.40
234 Lyle Overbay	.15	.40
235 Aaron Hill	.15	.40
236 John McDonald	.15	.40
237 Bengie Molina	.15	.40
238 Vernon Wells	.15	.40
239 Reed Johnson	.15	.40
240 Frank Catalanotto	.15	.40
241 Roy Halladay	.15	.40
242 B.J. Ryan	.15	.40
243 Gustavo Chacin	.15	.40
244 Scott Downs	.15	.40
245 Casey Janssen	.15	.40
246 Justin Speier	.15	.40
247 Stephen Drew	.25	.60
248 Conor Jackson	.15	.40
249 Orlando Hudson	.15	.40
250 Chad Tracy	.15	.40
251 Johnny Estrada	.15	.40
252 Luis Gonzalez	.15	.40
253 Eric Byrnes	.15	.40
254 Carlos Quentin	.15	.40
255 Brandon Webb	.15	.40
256 Claudio Vargas	.15	.40
257 Juan Cruz	.15	.40
258 Jorge Julio	.15	.40
259 Luis Vizcaino	.15	.40
260 Livan Hernandez	.15	.40
261 Chipper Jones	.40	1.00
262 Edgar Renteria	.15	.40
263 Adam LaRoche	.15	.40
264 Willy Aybar	.15	.40
265 Brian McCann	.15	.40
266 Ryan Langerhans	.15	.40
267 Jeff Francoeur	.40	1.00
268 Matt Diaz	.15	.40
269 Tim Hudson	.15	.40
270 John Smoltz	.25	.60
271 Oscar Villarreal	.15	.40
272 Horacio Ramirez	.15	.40
273 Bob Wickman	.15	.40
274 Chad Paronto	.15	.40
275 Derrek Lee	.15	.40
276 Ryan Theriot	.15	.40
277 Cesar Izturis	.15	.40
278 Ronny Cedeno	.15	.40
279 Michael Barrett	.15	.40
280 Juan Pierre	.15	.40
281 Jacque Jones	.15	.40
282 Matt Murton	.15	.40
283 Carlos Zambrano	.15	.40
284 Mark Prior	.25	.60
285 Rich Hill	.15	.40
286 Sean Marshall	.15	.40
287 Ryan Dempster	.15	.40
288 Ryan O'Malley	.15	.40
289 Scott Hatteberg	.15	.40
290 Brandon Phillips	.15	.40
291 Edwin Encarnacion	.15	.40
292 Rich Aurilia	.15	.40
293 David Ross	.15	.40
294 Ken Griffey Jr.	.60	1.50
295 Ryan Freel	.15	.40
296 Chris Denorfia	.15	.40
297 Bronson Arroyo	.15	.40
298 Aaron Harang	.15	.40
299 Brandon Claussen	.15	.40
300 Todd Coffey	.15	.40
301 David Weathers	.15	.40
302 Eric Milton	.15	.40
303 Todd Helton	.25	.60
304 Clint Barmes	.15	.40
305 Kazuo Matsui	.15	.40
306 Jamey Carroll	.15	.40
307 Yorvit Torrealba	.15	.40
308 Matt Holliday	.40	1.00
309 Choo Freeman	.15	.40
310 Brad Hawpe	.15	.40
311 Jason Jennings	.15	.40
312 Jeff Francis	.15	.40
313 Josh Fogg	.15	.40
314 Aaron Cook	.15	.40
315 Ubaldo Jimenez (RC)	.30	.75
316 Manny Corpas	.15	.40
317 Miguel Cabrera	.25	.60
318 Dan Uggla	.25	.60
319 Hanley Ramirez	.25	.60
320 Wes Helms	.15	.40
321 Miguel Olivo	.15	.40
322 Jeremy Hermida	.15	.40
323 Cody Ross	.15	.40
324 Josh Willingham	.15	.40
325 Dontrelle Willis	.15	.40
326 Anibal Sanchez	.15	.40
327 Josh Johnson	.15	.40
328 Jose Garcia RC	.30	.75
329 Joe Borowski	.15	.40
330 Taylor Tankersley	.15	.40
331 Lance Berkman	.15	.40
332 Craig Biggio	.25	.60
333 Aubrey Huff	.15	.40
334 Adam Everett	.15	.40
335 Brad Ausmus	.15	.40
336 Willy Taveras	.15	.40
337 Luke Scott	.15	.40
338 Chris Burke	.15	.40
339 Roger Clemens	.60	1.50
340 Andy Pettitte	.25	.60
341 Brandon Backe	.15	.40
342 Hector Gimenez (RC)	.30	.75
343 Brad Lidge	.15	.40
344 Dan Wheeler	.15	.40
345 Nomar Garciaparra	.40	1.00
346 Rafael Furcal	.15	.40
347 Wilson Betemit	.15	.40
348 Julio Lugo	.15	.40
349 Russell Martin	.15	.40
350 Andre Ethier	.25	.60
351 Matt Kemp	.15	.40
352 Kenny Lofton	.15	.40
353 Brad Penny	.15	.40
354 Derek Lowe	.15	.40
355 Chad Billingsley	.15	.40
356 Greg Maddux	.60	1.50
357 Takashi Saito	.15	.40
358 Jonathan Broxton	.15	.40
359 Prince Fielder	.40	1.00
360 Rickie Weeks	.15	.40
361 Bill Hall	.15	.40
362 J.J. Hardy	.15	.40
363 Jeff Cirillo	.15	.40
364 Tony Gwynn Jr.	.15	.40
365 Corey Hart	.15	.40
366 Laynce Nix	.15	.40
367 Doug Davis	.15	.40
368 Ben Sheets	.15	.40
369 Chris Capuano	.15	.40
370 Dave Bush	.15	.40
371 Derrick Turnbow	.15	.40
372 Francisco Cordero	.15	.40
373 Jose Reyes	.15	.40
374 Carlos Delgado	.15	.40
375 Julio Franco	.15	.40
376 Jose Valentin	.15	.40
377 Paul LoDuca	.15	.40
378 Carlos Beltran	.15	.40
379 Shawn Green	.15	.40
380 Lastings Milledge	.25	.60
381 Endy Chavez	.15	.40
382 Pedro Martinez	.25	.60
383 John Maine	.15	.40
384 Orlando Hernandez	.15	.40
385 Steve Trachsel	.15	.40
386 Billy Wagner	.15	.40
387 Ryan Howard	.60	1.50
388 Chase Utley	.40	1.00
389 Jimmy Rollins	.15	.40
390 Chris Coste	.15	.40
391 Jeff Conine	.15	.40
392 Aaron Rowand	.15	.40
393 Shane Victorino	.15	.40
394 David Dellucci	.15	.40
395 Cole Hamels	.40	1.00
396 Jamie Moyer	.15	.40
397 Ryan Madson	.15	.40
398 Brett Myers	.15	.40
399 Tom Gordon	.15	.40
400 Geoff Geary	.15	.40
401 Freddy Sanchez	.15	.40
402 Xavier Nady	.15	.40
403 Jose Castillo	.15	.40
404 Joe Randa	.15	.40
405 Jason Bay	.15	.40
406 Chris Duffy	.15	.40
407 Jose Bautista	.15	.40
408 Ronny Paulino	.15	.40
409 Ian Snell	.15	.40
410 Zach Duke	.15	.40
411 Tom Gorzelanny	.15	.40
412 Shane Youman RC	.30	.75
413 Mike Gonzalez	.15	.40
414 Matt Capps	.15	.40
415 Adrian Gonzalez	.15	.40
416 Josh Barfield	.15	.40
417 Todd Walker	.15	.40
418 Khalil Greene	.25	.60
419 Mike Piazza	.40	1.00
420 Dave Roberts	.15	.40
421 Mike Cameron	.15	.40
422 Geoff Blum	.15	.40
423 Jake Peavy	.15	.40
424 Chris R. Young	.15	.40
425 Woody Williams	.15	.40
426 Clay Hensley	.15	.40
427 Cla Meredith	.15	.40
428 Trevor Hoffman	.15	.40
429 Shea Hillenbrand	.15	.40
430 Pedro Feliz	.15	.40
431 Ray Durham	.15	.40
432 Mark Sweeney	.15	.40
433 Eliezer Alfonzo	.15	.40
434 Moises Alou	.15	.40
435 Steve Finley	.15	.40
436 Todd Linden	.15	.40
437 Jason Schmidt	.15	.40
438 Matt Cain	.25	.60
439 Noah Lowry	.15	.40
440 Brad Hennessey	.15	.40
441 Armando Benitez	.15	.40
442 Jonathan Sanchez	.15	.40
443 Albert Pujols	.75	2.00
444 Ronnie Belliard	.15	.40
445 David Eckstein	.15	.40
446 Aaron Miles	.15	.40
447 Yadier Molina	.15	.40
448 Jim Edmonds	.25	.60
449 Chris Duncan	.15	.40
450 Juan Encarnacion	.15	.40
451 Chris Carpenter	.15	.40
452 Jeff Suppan	.15	.40
453 Jason Marquis	.15	.40
454 Jeff Weaver	.15	.40
455 Jason Isringhausen	.15	.40
456 Braden Looper	.15	.40
457 Ryan Zimmerman	.40	1.00
458 Nick Johnson	.15	.40
459 Felipe Lopez	.15	.40
460 Brian Schneider	.15	.40
461 Alfonso Soriano	.15	.40
462 Austin Kearns	.15	.40
463 Ryan Church	.15	.40
464 Alex Escobar	.15	.40
465 Ramon Ortiz	.15	.40
466 Tony Armas	.15	.40
467 Michael O'Connor	.15	.40
468 Chad Cordero	.15	.40
469 Jon Rauch	.15	.40
470 Pedro Astacio	.15	.40
471 Miguel Tejada CL	.15	.40
472 David Ortiz CL	.40	1.00
473 Jermaine Dye CL	.15	.40
474 Travis Hafner CL	.15	.40
475 Magglio Ordonez CL	.15	.40
476 Mark Teahen CL	.15	.40
477 Vladimir Guerrero CL	.40	1.00
478 Justin Morneau CL	.15	.40
479 Derek Jeter CL	1.00	2.50
480 Nick Swisher CL	.15	.40
481 Ichiro Suzuki CL	.60	1.50
482 Scott Kazmir CL	.25	.60
483 Mark Teixeira CL	.25	.60
484 Vernon Wells CL	.15	.40
485 Brandon Webb CL	.15	.40
486 Andruw Jones CL	.25	.60
487 Carlos Zambrano CL	.15	.40
488 Adam Dunn CL	.15	.40
489 Matt Holliday CL	.40	1.00
490 Miguel Cabrera CL	.25	.60
491 Lance Berkman CL	.15	.40
492 Nomar Garciaparra CL	.40	1.00
493 Prince Fielder CL	.40	1.00
494 Carlos Beltran CL	.15	.40
495 Ryan Howard CL	.60	1.50
496 Jason Bay CL	.15	.40
497 Adrian Gonzalez CL	.15	.40
498 Matt Cain CL	.25	.60
499 Albert Pujols CL	.75	2.00
500 Ryan Zimmerman CL	.40	1.00
501a Daisuke Matsuzaka Suit RC	20.00	50.00
501b Daisuke Matsuzaka Throwing RC	6.00	15.00
501c Daisuke Matsuzaka Jsy/100		
501d Daisuke Matsuzaka Ball/150		
502 Kei Igawa RC	1.50	4.00
503 Akinori Iwamura RC	2.50	6.00
504 Alex Gordon RC	10.00	25.00
505 Matt Chico (RC)	1.00	2.50
506 John Danks RC	1.00	2.50
507 Elijah Dukes RC	1.00	2.50
508 Gustavo Molina RC	1.00	2.50
509 Joakim Soria RC	2.50	6.00
510 Jay Marshall RC	2.50	6.00
511 Travis Buck (RC)	1.00	2.50
512 Brandon Wood (RC)	1.00	2.50
513 Kevin Cameron RC	1.00	2.50
514 Jared Burton RC	2.50	6.00
515 Kory Casto (RC)	1.00	2.50
516 Joe Smith RC	1.00	2.50
517 Jose Garcia RC	1.00	2.50
518 Hunter Pence (RC)	6.00	15.00
519 Felix Pie (RC)	1.00	2.50
520 Zach Segovia (RC)	1.00	2.50
521 Randy Johnson	.40	1.00
522 Brandon Lyon	.15	.40
523 Robby Hammock	.15	.40
524 Micah Owings (RC)	.30	.75
525 Doug Davis	.15	.40
526 Brian Barden RC	.30	.75
527 Alberto Callaspo	.15	.40
528 Stephen Drew	.25	.60
529 Chris Young	.15	.40
530 Edgar Gonzalez	.15	.40
531 Brandon Medders	.15	.40
532 Tony Pena	.15	.40
533 Jose Valverde	.15	.40
534 Chris Snyder	.15	.40
535 Tony Clark	.15	.40
536 Scott Hairston	.15	.40
537 Jeff DaVanon	.15	.40
538 Randy Johnson CL	.40	1.00
539 Mark Redman	.15	.40
540 Andruw Jones	.25	.60
541 Rafael Soriano	.15	.40
542 Scott Thorman	.15	.40
543 Chipper Jones	.40	1.00
544 Mike Gonzalez	.15	.40
545 Lance Cormier	.15	.40
546 Kyle Davies	.15	.40
547 Mike Hampton	.15	.40
548 Chuck James	.15	.40
549 Macay McBride	.15	.40
550 Tanyon Sturtze	.15	.40
551 Tyler Yates	.15	.40
552 Pete Orr	.15	.40
553 Craig Wilson	.15	.40
554 Chris Woodward	.15	.40
555 Kelly Johnson	.15	.40
556 Chipper Jones CL	.40	1.00
557 Chad Bradford	.15	.40
558 John Parrish	.15	.40
559 Jeremy Guthrie	.15	.40
560 Steve Trachsel	.15	.40
561 Scott Williamson	.15	.40
562 Jaret Wright	.15	.40
563 Paul Bako	.15	.40
564 Chris Gomez	.15	.40
565 Melvin Mora	.15	.40
566 Freddie Bynum	.15	.40
567 Aubrey Huff	.15	.40
568 Jay Payton	.15	.40
569 Miguel Tejada	.15	.40
570 Kurt Birkins	.15	.40
571 Danys Baez	.15	.40
572 Brian Roberts CL	.15	.40
573 Josh Beckett	.25	.60
574 Matt Clement	.15	.40
575 Hideki Okajima RC	2.00	5.00
576 Javier Lopez	.15	.40
577 Joel Pineiro	.15	.40
578 J.C. Romero	.15	.40
579 Kyle Snyder	.15	.40
580 Julian Tavarez	.15	.40
581 Mike Timlin	.15	.40
582 Jason Varitek	.40	1.00
583 Mike Lowell	.15	.40
584 Kevin Youkilis	.15	.40
585 Coco Crisp	.15	.40
586 J.D. Drew	.15	.40
587 Eric Hinske	.15	.40
588 Wily Mo Pena	.15	.40
589 Julio Lugo	.15	.40
590 David Ortiz	.40	1.00
591 Manny Ramirez	.25	.60
592 Daisuke Matsuzaka CL	1.50	4.00
593 Scott Eyre	.15	.40
594 Angel Guzman	.15	.40
595 Bob Howry	.15	.40
596 Ted Lilly	.15	.40
597 Juan Mateo	.15	.40
598 Wade Miller	.15	.40
599 Carlos Zambrano	.15	.40
600 Will Ohman	.15	.40
601 Michael Wuertz	.15	.40
602 Henry Blanco	.15	.40
603 Aramis Ramirez	.15	.40
604 Cliff Floyd	.15	.40
605 Kerry Wood	.15	.40
606 Alfonso Soriano	.15	.40
607 Daryle Ward	.15	.40
608 Jason Marquis	.15	.40
609 Mark DeRosa	.15	.40
610 Neal Cotts	.15	.40
611 Derrek Lee	.15	.40
612 Aramis Ramirez CL	.15	.40
613 David Aardsma	.15	.40
614 Mark Buehrle	.15	.40
615 Nick Masset	.15	.40
616 Andrew Sisco	.15	.40
617 Matt Thornton	.15	.40
618 Toby Hall	.15	.40
619 Joe Crede	.15	.40
620 Paul Konerko	.15	.40
621 Darin Erstad	.15	.40
622 Pablo Ozuna	.15	.40
623 Scott Podsednik	.15	.40
624 Jim Thome	.25	.60
625 Jermaine Dye	.15	.40

Card	Low	High
626 Jim Thome CL	.25	.60
627 Adam Dunn	.15	.40
628 Bill Bray	.15	.40
629 Alex Gonzalez	.15	.40
630 Josh Hamilton (RC)	4.00	10.00
631 Matt Belisle	.15	.40
632 Rheal Cormier	.15	.40
633 Kyle Lohse	.15	.40
634 Eric Milton	.15	.40
635 Kirk Saarloos	.15	.40
636 Mike Stanton	.15	.40
637 Javier Valentin	.15	.40
638 Juan Castro	.15	.40
639 Jeff Conine	.15	.40
640 Jon Coutlangus (RC)	.30	.75
641 Ken Griffey Jr.	.60	1.50
642 Ken Griffey Jr. CL	.60	1.50
643 Fernando Cabrera	.15	.40
644 Fausto Carmona	.15	.40
645 Jason Davis	.15	.40
646 Aaron Fultz	.15	.40
647 Roberto Hernandez	.15	.40
648 Jake Westbrook	.15	.40
649 Kelly Shoppach	.15	.40
650 Josh Barfield	.15	.40
651 Andy Marte	.15	.40
652 Joe Inglett	.15	.40
653 David Dellucci	.15	.40
654 Joe Borowski	.15	.40
655 Franklin Gutierrez	.15	.40
656 Trot Nixon	.15	.40
657 Grady Sizemore	.25	.60
658 Mike Rouse	.15	.40
659 Travis Hafner	.15	.40
660 Victor Martinez	.15	.40
661 C.C. Sabathia	.15	.40
662 Grady Sizemore CL	.25	.60
663 Jeremy Affeldt	.15	.40
664 Taylor Buchholz	.15	.40
665 Brian Fuentes	.15	.40
666 Latroy Hawkins	.15	.40
667 Byung-Hyun Kim	.15	.40
668 Brian Lawrence	.15	.40
669 Rodrigo Lopez	.15	.40
670 Jeff Francis	.15	.40
671 Chris Ianetta	.15	.40
672 Garrett Atkins	.15	.40
673 Todd Helton	.25	.60
674 Steve Finley	.15	.40
675 John Mabry	.15	.40
676 Willy Taveras	.15	.40
677 Jason Hirsh	.15	.40
678 Ramon Ramirez	.15	.40
679 Matt Holliday	.40	1.00
680 Todd Helton CL	.25	.60
681 Roman Colon	.15	.40
682 Chad Durbin	.15	.40
683 Jason Grilli	.15	.40
684 Wilfredo Ledezma	.15	.40
685 Mike Maroth	.15	.40
686 Jose Mesa	.15	.40
687 Justin Verlander	.40	1.00
688 Fernando Rodney	.15	.40
689 Vance Wilson	.15	.40
690 Carlos Guillen	.15	.40
691 Neifi Perez	.15	.40
692 Curtis Granderson	.15	.40
693 Gary Sheffield	.15	.40
694 Justin Verlander CL	.40	1.00
695 Kevin Gregg	.15	.40
696 Logan Kensing	.15	.40
697 Randy Messenger	.15	.40
698 Sergio Mitre	.15	.40
699 Ricky Nolasco	.15	.40
700 Scott Olsen	.15	.40
701 Renyel Pinto	.15	.40
702 Matt Treanor	.15	.40
703 Alfredo Amezaga	.15	.40
704 Aaron Boone	.15	.40
705 Mike Jacobs	.15	.40
706 Miguel Cabrera	.25	.60
707 Joe Borchard	.15	.40
708 Jorge Julio	.15	.40
709 Rick Vanden Hurk RC	.50	1.25
710 Lee Gardner (RC)	.30	.75
711 Matt Lindstrom (RC)	.30	.75
712 Henry Owens	.15	.40
713 Hanley Ramirez	.25	.60
714 Alejandro De Aza RC	.30	.75
715 Hanley Ramirez CL	.25	.60
716 Dave Borkowski	.15	.40
717 Jason Jennings	.15	.40
718 Trever Miller	.15	.40
719 Roy Oswalt	.15	.40
720 Wandy Rodriguez	.15	.40
721 Humberto Quintero	.15	.40
722 Morgan Ensberg	.15	.40
723 Mike Lamb	.15	.40
724 Mark Loretta	.15	.40
725 Jason Lane	.15	.40
726 Carlos Lee	.15	.40
727 Orlando Palmeiro	.15	.40
728 Woody Williams	.15	.40
729 Chad Qualls	.15	.40
730 Lance Berkman	.15	.40
731 Rick White	.15	.40
732 Chris Sampson	.15	.40
733 Carlos Lee CL	.15	.40
734 Jorge De La Rosa	.15	.40
735 Octavio Dotel	.15	.40
736 Jimmy Gobble	.15	.40
737 Zack Greinke	.15	.40
738 Luke Hudson	.15	.40
739 Gil Meche	.15	.40
740 Joel Peralta	.15	.40
741 Odalis Perez	.15	.40
742 David Riske	.15	.40
743 Jason LaRue	.15	.40
744 Tony Pena	.15	.40
745 Esteban German	.15	.40
746 Ross Gload	.15	.40
747 Emil Brown	.15	.40
748 David DeJesus	.15	.40
749 Brandon Duckworth	.15	.40
750 Alex Gordon CL	1.00	2.50
751 Jered Weaver	.25	.60
752 Vladimir Guerrero	.40	1.00
753 Hector Carrasco	.15	.40
754 Kelvim Escobar	.15	.40
755 Darren Oliver	.15	.40
756 Dustin Moseley	.15	.40
757 Ervin Santana	.15	.40
758 Mike Napoli	.15	.40
759 Shea Hillenbrand	.15	.40
760 Casey Kotchman	.15	.40
761 Reggie Willits	.15	.40
762 Robb Quinlan	.15	.40
763 Garret Anderson	.15	.40
764 Gary Matthews	.15	.40
765 Justin Speier	.15	.40
766 Jered Weaver CL	.25	.60
767 Joe Beimel	.15	.40
768 Yhency Brazoban	.15	.40
769 Elmer Dessens	.15	.40
770 Mark Hendrickson	.15	.40
771 Hong-Chih Kuo	.15	.40
772 Jason Schmidt	.15	.40
773 Brett Tomko	.15	.40
774 Randy Wolf	.15	.40
775 Mike Lieberthal	.15	.40
776 Marlon Anderson	.15	.40
777 Jeff Kent	.15	.40
778 Ramon Martinez	.15	.40
779 Olmedo Saenz	.15	.40
780 Luis Gonzalez	.15	.40
781 Juan Pierre	.15	.40
782 Jason Repko	.15	.40
783 Nomar Garciaparra	.40	1.00
784 Wilson Valdez	.15	.40
785 Jason Schmidt CL	.15	.40
786 Greg Aquino	.15	.40
787 Brian Shouse	.15	.40
788 Jeff Suppan	.15	.40
789 Carlos Villanueva	.15	.40
790 Matt Wise	.15	.40
791 Johnny Estrada	.15	.40
792 Craig Counsell	.15	.40
793 Tony Graffanino	.15	.40
794 Corey Koskie	.15	.40
795 Claudio Vargas	.15	.40
796 Brady Clark	.15	.40
797 Gabe Gross	.15	.40
798 Geoff Jenkins	.15	.40
799 Kevin Mench	.15	.40
800 Bill Hall CL	.15	.40
801 Sidney Ponson	.15	.40
802 Jesse Crain	.15	.40
803 Matt Guerrier	.15	.40
804 Pat Neshek	.25	.60
805 Ramon Ortiz	.15	.40
806 Johan Santana	.25	.60
807 Carlos Silva	.15	.40
808 Mike Redmond	.15	.40
809 Jeff Cirillo	.15	.40
810 Luis Rodriguez	.15	.40
811 Lew Ford	.15	.40
812 Torii Hunter	.15	.40
813 Jason Tyner	.15	.40
814 Rondell White	.15	.40
815 Justin Morneau	.15	.40
816 Joe Mauer	.25	.60
817 Johan Santana CL	.25	.60
818 David Newhan	.15	.40
819 Aaron Sele	.15	.40
820 Ambiorix Burgos	.15	.40
821 Pedro Feliciano	.15	.40
822 Tom Glavine	.25	.60
823 Aaron Heilman	.15	.40
824 Guillermo Mota	.15	.40
825 Jose Reyes	.25	.60
826 Oliver Perez	.15	.40
827 Duaner Sanchez	.15	.40
828 Scott Schoeneweis	.15	.40
829 Ramon Castro	.15	.40
830 Damion Easley	.15	.40
831 David Wright	.60	1.50
832 Moises Alou	.15	.40
833 Carlos Beltran	.15	.40
834 Dave Williams	.15	.40
835 David Wright CL	.60	1.50
836 Brian Bruney	.15	.40
837 Mike Myers	.15	.40
838 Carl Pavano	.15	.40
839 Andy Pettitte	.25	.60
840 Luis Vizcaino	.15	.40
841 Jorge Posada	.25	.60
842 Miguel Cairo	.15	.40
843 Doug Mientkiewicz	.15	.40
844 Derek Jeter	1.00	2.50
845 Alex Rodriguez	.60	1.50
846 Johnny Damon	.25	.60
847 Hideki Matsui	.40	1.00
848 Josh Phelps	.15	.40
849 Phil Hughes (RC)	1.50	4.00
850 Roger Clemens	.60	1.50
851 Jason Giambi CL	.15	.40
852 Kiko Calero	.15	.40
853 Justin Duchscherer	.15	.40
854 Alan Embree	.15	.40
855 Todd Walker	.15	.40
856 Rich Harden	.15	.40
857 Dan Haren	.15	.40
858 Joe Kennedy	.15	.40
859 Jason Kendall	.15	.40
860 Adam Melhuse	.15	.40
861 Mark Ellis	.15	.40
862 Bobby Kielty	.15	.40
863 Mark Kotsay	.15	.40
864 Shannon Stewart	.15	.40
865 Mike Piazza	.40	1.00
866 Mike Piazza CL	.40	1.00
867 Antonio Alfonseca	.15	.40
868 Carlos Ruiz	.15	.40
869 Adam Eaton	.15	.40
870 Freddy Garcia	.15	.40
871 Jon Lieber	.15	.40
872 Matt Smith	.15	.40
873 Rod Barajas	.15	.40
874 Wes Helms	.15	.40
875 Abraham Nunez	.15	.40
876 Pat Burrell	.15	.40
877 Jayson Werth	.15	.40
878 Greg Dobbs	.15	.40
879 Joseph Bisenius RC	.30	.75
880 Michael Bourn (RC)	.30	.75
881 Chase Utley	.40	1.00
882 Ryan Howard	.60	1.50
883 Chase Utley CL	.40	1.00
884 Tony Armas	.15	.40
885 Shawn Chacon	.15	.40
886 John Grabow	.15	.40
887 Paul Maholm	.15	.40
888 Damaso Marte	.15	.40
889 Salomon Torres	.15	.40
890 Humberto Cota	.15	.40
891 Ryan Doumit	.15	.40
892 Adam LaRoche	.15	.40
893 Jack Wilson	.15	.40
894 Nate McLouth	.15	.40
895 Brad Eldred	.15	.40
896 Jonah Bayliss	.15	.40
897 Juan Perez RC	.30	.75
898 Jason Bay	.15	.40
899 Adam LaRoche CL	.15	.40
900 Doug Brocail	.15	.40
901 Scott Cassidy	.15	.40
902 Scott Linebrink	.15	.40
903 Greg Maddux	.60	1.50
904 Jake Peavy	.15	.40
905 Mike Thompson	.15	.40
906 David Wells	.15	.40
907 Josh Bard	.15	.40
908 Rob Bowen	.15	.40
909 Marcus Giles	.15	.40
910 Russell Branyan	.15	.40
911 Jose Cruz	.15	.40
912 Terrmel Sledge	.15	.40
913 Trevor Hoffman	.15	.40
914 Brian Giles	.15	.40
915 Trevor Hoffman CL	.15	.40
916 Vinnie Chulk	.15	.40
917 Kevin Correia	.15	.40
918 Tim Lincecum RC	8.00	20.00
919 Matt Morris	.15	.40
920 Russ Ortiz	.15	.40
921 Barry Zito	.15	.40
922 Bengie Molina	.15	.40
923 Rich Aurilia	.15	.40
924 Omar Vizquel	.25	.60
925 Jason Ellison	.15	.40
926 Ryan Klesko	.15	.40
927 Dave Roberts	.15	.40
928 Randy Winn	.15	.40
929 Barry Zito CL	.15	.40
930 Miguel Batista	.15	.40
931 Horacio Ramirez	.15	.40
932 Chris Reitsma	.15	.40
933 George Sherrill	.15	.40
934 Jarrod Washburn	.15	.40
935 Jeff Weaver	.15	.40
936 Jake Woods	.15	.40
937 Adrian Beltre	.25	.60
938 Jose Lopez	.15	.40
939 Ichiro Suzuki	.60	1.50
940 Jose Vidro	.15	.40
941 Jose Guillen	.15	.40
942 Sean White RC	.30	.75
943 Brandon Morrow RC	.75	2.00
944 Felix Hernandez	.25	.60
945 Felix Hernandez CL	.25	.60
946 Randy Flores	.15	.40
947 Ryan Franklin	.15	.40
948 Kelvin Jimenez RC	.30	.75
949 Tyler Johnson	.15	.40
950 Mark Mulder	.15	.40
951 Anthony Reyes	.15	.40
952 Russ Springer	.15	.40
953 Brad Thompson	.15	.40
954 Adam Wainwright	.15	.40
955 Kip Wells	.15	.40
956 Gary Bennett	.15	.40
957 Adam Kennedy	.15	.40
958 Scott Rolen	.25	.60
959 Scott Spiezio	.15	.40
960 So Taguchi	.15	.40
961 Preston Wilson	.15	.40
962 Skip Schumaker	.15	.40
963 Albert Pujols	.75	2.00
964 Chris Carpenter	.15	.40
965 Chris Carpenter CL	.15	.40
966 Edwin Jackson	.15	.40
967 Jae Kuk Ryu	.15	.40
968 Jae Seo	.15	.40
969 Jon Switzer	.15	.40
970 Josh Paul	.15	.40
971 Ben Zobrist	.15	.40
972 Rocco Baldelli	.15	.40
973 Scott Kazmir	.25	.60
974 Carl Crawford	.15	.40
975 Delmon Young CL	.25	.60
976 Bruce Chen	.15	.40
977 Joaquin Benoit	.15	.40
978 Scott Feldman	.15	.40
979 Eric Gagne	.15	.40
980 Kameron Loe	.15	.40
981 Brandon McCarthy	.15	.40
982 Robinson Tejeda	.15	.40
983 C.J. Wilson	.15	.40
984 Mark Teixeira	.25	.60
985 Michael Young	.15	.40
986 Kenny Lofton	.15	.40
987 Brad Wilkerson	.15	.40
988 Nelson Cruz	.15	.40
989 Sammy Sosa	.40	1.00
990 Michael Young CL	.15	.40
991 Vernon Wells	.15	.40
992 Matt Stairs	.15	.40
993 Jeremy Accardo	.15	.40
994 A.J. Burnett	.15	.40
995 Jason Frasor	.15	.40
996 Roy Halladay	.15	.40
997 Shaun Marcum	.15	.40
998 Tomo Ohka	.15	.40
999 Josh Towers	.15	.40
1000 Gregg Zaun	.15	.40
1001 Royce Clayton	.15	.40
1002 Jason Smith	.15	.40
1003 Alex Rios	.15	.40
1004 Frank Thomas	.40	1.00
1005 Roy Halladay CL	.15	.40
1006 Jesus Flores RC	.30	.75
1007 Dmitri Young	.15	.40
1008 Ray King	.15	.40
1009 Micah Bowie	.15	.40
1010 Shawn Hill	.15	.40
1011 John Patterson	.15	.40
1012 Levale Speigner RC	.30	.75
1013 Ryan Wagner	.15	.40
1014 Jerome Williams	.15	.40
1015 Ryan Zimmerman	.40	1.00
1016 Cristian Guzman	.15	.40
1017 Nook Logan	.15	.40
1018 Chris Snelling	.15	.40
1019 Ronnie Belliard	.15	.40
1020 Nick Johnson CL	.15	.40
NNO Rookie EXCH	30.00	60.00

2007 Upper Deck Gold

*GOLD: 3X TO 8X BASIC
*GOLD RC: 2.5X TO 6X BASIC RC
STATED ODDS 1:16 HOBBY
RANDOM INSERTS IN RETAIL PACKS
STATED PRINT RUN 75 SER.#'d SETS

Card	Low	High
18 Andrew Miller	10.00	25.00
163 Derek Jeter	10.00	25.00
172 Chien-Ming Wang	10.00	25.00
196 Ichiro Suzuki	6.00	15.00
443 Albert Pujols	10.00	25.00
479 Derek Jeter CL	10.00	25.00
481 Ichiro Suzuki CL	6.00	15.00
499 Albert Pujols CL	10.00	25.00

2007 Upper Deck 1989 Reprints

COMPLETE SET (26) 20.00 50.00
STATED ODDS 1:4 HOBBY

Card	Low	High
AK Al Kaline	1.25	3.00
BF Bob Feller	.75	2.00
BR Babe Ruth	3.00	8.00
CA Rod Carew	.75	2.00
CF Carlton Fisk	.75	2.00
CM Christy Mathewson	1.25	3.00
CS Casey Stengel	.75	2.00
CY Cy Young	1.25	3.00
DR Don Drysdale	.75	2.00
FR Frank Robinson	.75	2.00
GE Lou Gehrig	2.50	6.00
HW Honus Wagner	1.25	3.00
JB Johnny Bench	1.25	3.00
JF Jimmie Foxx	1.25	3.00
JR Jackie Robinson	1.25	3.00
LG Lefty Grove	.75	2.00
MO Mel Ott	.75	2.00
RC Roy Campanella	1.25	3.00
RH Rogers Hornsby	.75	2.00
RJ Reggie Jackson	.75	2.00
RO Brooks Robinson	.75	2.00
SM Stan Musial	2.00	5.00
SP Satchel Paige	1.25	3.00
TC Ty Cobb	2.00	5.00
TM Thurman Munson	1.25	3.00
WJ Walter Johnson	1.25	3.00

2007 Upper Deck 1989 Rookie Reprints

STATED ODDS 1:4 HOBBY
OVERALL PRINTING PLATE ODDS 1:96 H
PLATE PRINT RUN 1 SET PER COLOR
BLACK-CYAN-MAGENTA-YELLOW ISSUED
NO PLATE PRICING DUE TO SCARCITY

Card	Low	High
AD Alejandro De Aza	.75	2.00
AG Alex Gordon	5.00	12.00
AI Akinori Iwamura	2.00	5.00
AS Angel Sanchez	.75	2.00
BB Brian Barden	.75	2.00
BI Joseph Bisenius	.75	2.00
BM Brandon Morrow	.75	2.00
BN Jared Burton	.75	2.00
BU Jamie Burke	.75	2.00
CJ Cesar Jimenez	.75	2.00
CS Chris Stewart	.75	2.00
CW Chase Wright	.75	2.00
DK Don Kelly	.75	2.00
DM Daisuke Matsuzaka	8.00	20.00
DY Delmon Young	2.00	5.00
ED Elijah Dukes	2.00	5.00
FP Felix Pie	1.25	3.00
GM Gustavo Molina	.75	2.00
HG Hector Gimenez	.75	2.00
HO Hideki Okajima	6.00	15.00
JA Joaquin Arias	.75	2.00
JB Jeff Baker	.75	2.00
JD John Danks	1.25	3.00
JF Jesus Flores	.75	2.00
JG Jose Garcia	.75	2.00
JH Josh Hamilton	6.00	15.00
JM Jay Marshall	.75	2.00
JP Juan Perez	.75	2.00
JS Joe Smith	.75	2.00
KC Kevin Cameron	.75	2.00
KI Kei Igawa	2.00	5.00
KK Kevin Kouzmanoff	.75	2.00
KO Kory Casto	.75	2.00
LG Lee Gardner	.75	2.00
LS Levale Speigner	.75	2.00
MB Michael Bourn	.75	2.00
MC Matt Chico	.75	2.00
ML Matt Lindstrom	.75	2.00
MM Miguel Montero	.75	2.00
MO Micah Owings	1.25	3.00
MR Mike Rabelo	.75	2.00
RB Ryan Z. Braun	.75	2.00
SA Juan Salas	.75	2.00
SH Sean Henn	.75	2.00
SL Doug Slaten	.75	2.00
SO Joakim Soria	3.00	8.00
ST Brian Stokes	.75	2.00
TB Travis Buck	1.25	3.00
TT Troy Tulowitzki	1.25	3.00
ZS Zack Segovia	.75	2.00

2007 Upper Deck 1989 Rookie Reprints Signatures

RANDOM INSERTS IN PACKS
STATED PRINT RUN 5 SERIAL #'d SETS
NO PRICING DUE TO SCARCITY

AG Alex Gordon
AI Akinori Iwamura
AS Angel Sanchez
BN Jared Burton
CJ Cesar Jimenez
CS Chris Stewart
CW Chase Wright
DY Delmon Young
HG Hector Gimenez
JA Joaquin Arias
JB Jeff Baker
JD John Danks
JH Josh Hamilton
KI Kei Igawa
KK Kevin Kouzmanoff
LS Levale Speigner
MB Michael Bourn
MC Matt Chico
MM Miguel Montero
SA Juan Salas
SH Sean Henn
ST Brian Stokes
TT Troy Tulowitzki
ZS Zack Segovia

2007 Upper Deck Cal Ripken Jr. Chronicles

COMMON RIPKEN 2.50 6.00
STATED ODDS 1:8 H, 1:72 R
PRINTING PLATE ODDS 1:192 H
PLATE PRINT RUN 1 SET PER COLOR
BLACK-CYAN-MAGENTA-YELLOW ISSUED
NO PLATE PRICING DUE TO SCARCITY

2007 Upper Deck Cooperstown Calling

STATED ODDS 1:4 WAL MART PACKS
NO PRICING DUE TO LACK OF MARKET INFO
OVERALL PRINTING PLATE ODDS 1:96 H
PLATE PRINT RUN 1 SET PER COLOR
BLACK-CYAN-MAGENTA-YELLOW ISSUED
NO PLATE PRICING DUE TO SCARCITY

2007 Upper Deck Cooperstown Calling Signatures

STATED ODDS 1:1440 WAL-MART PACKS
NO PRICING DUE TO SCARCITY

AS Alfonso Soriano
CA Chris Carpenter
CC Carl Crawford
CR Cal Ripken Jr.
DJ Derek Jeter
JM Justin Morneau
JS Johan Santana
JT Jim Thome
SR Scott Rolen
TE Miguel Tejada
VG Vladimir Guerrero

2007 Upper Deck Ken Griffey Jr. Chronicles

COMMON GRIFFEY 2.00 5.00
STATED ODDS 1:8 H, 1:72 R
PRINTING PLATE ODDS 1:192 H
PLATE PRINT RUN 1 SET PER COLOR
BLACK-CYAN-MAGENTA-YELLOW ISSUED
NO PLATE PRICING DUE TO SCARCITY

2007 Upper Deck MVP Potential

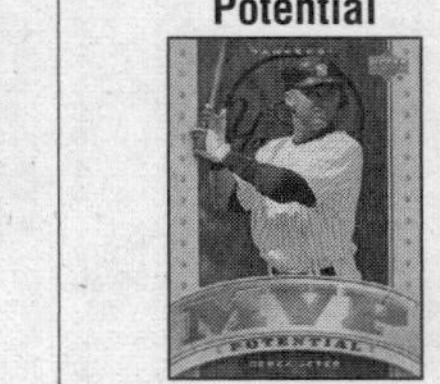

STATED ODDS 2:1 FAT PACKS
NO PRICING DUE TO LACK OF MARKET INFO

2007 Upper Deck MVP Predictors

STATED ODDS 1:16 H, 1:240 R

Card	Low	High
MVP1 Miguel Tejada	2.00	5.00
MVP2 David Ortiz	4.00	10.00
MVP3 Manny Ramirez	2.00	5.00
MVP4 Jermaine Dye	2.00	5.00
MVP5 Jim Thome	2.00	5.00
MVP6 Paul Konerko	2.00	5.00
MVP7 Travis Hafner	2.00	5.00
MVP8 Grady Sizemore	2.00	5.00
MVP9 Victor Martinez	2.00	5.00
MVP10 Magglio Ordonez	2.00	5.00
MVP11 Justin Verlander	2.00	5.00
MVP12 Vladimir Guerrero	4.00	10.00
MVP13 Jered Weaver	2.00	5.00
MVP14 Justin Morneau	2.00	5.00
MVP15 Joe Mauer	2.00	5.00
MVP16 Johan Santana	2.00	5.00
MVP17 Alex Rodriguez	6.00	15.00
MVP18 Derek Jeter	12.50	30.00
MVP19 Jason Giambi	2.00	5.00
MVP20 Johnny Damon	3.00	8.00
MVP21 Bobby Abreu	2.00	5.00
MVP22 American League Field	6.00	15.00
MVP23 Frank Thomas	3.00	8.00
MVP24 Eric Chavez	2.00	5.00
MVP25 Ichiro Suzuki	2.00	5.00
MVP26 Adrian Beltre	2.00	5.00
MVP27 Carl Crawford	2.00	5.00
MVP28 Scott Kazmir	2.00	5.00
MVP29 Mark Teixeira	2.00	5.00
MVP30 Michael Young	2.00	5.00
MVP31 Carlos Lee	2.00	5.00
MVP32 Vernon Wells	2.00	5.00
MVP33 Roy Halladay	2.00	5.00
MVP34 Troy Glaus	2.00	5.00
MVP35 Stephen Drew	2.00	5.00
MVP36 Chipper Jones	2.00	5.00
MVP37 Andruw Jones	2.00	5.00
MVP38 Adam LaRoche	2.00	5.00
MVP39 Derrek Lee	3.00	8.00
MVP40 Aramis Ramirez	2.00	5.00
MVP41 Adam Dunn	2.00	5.00
MVP42 Ken Griffey Jr.	12.50	30.00
MVP43 Matt Holliday	2.50	6.00
MVP44 Garrett Atkins	2.00	5.00
MVP45 Miguel Cabrera	2.00	5.00
MVP46 Hanley Ramirez	2.00	5.00
MVP47 Dan Uggla	2.00	5.00
MVP48 Lance Berkman	2.00	5.00
MVP49 Roy Oswalt	2.00	5.00
MVP50 Nomar Garciaparra	2.00	5.00
MVP51 J.D. Drew	2.00	5.00
MVP52 Rafael Furcal	2.00	5.00
MVP53 Prince Fielder	15.00	40.00
MVP54 Bill Hall	3.00	8.00
MVP55 Jose Reyes	4.00	10.00
MVP56 Carlos Beltran	2.00	5.00
MVP57 Carlos Delgado	2.00	5.00
MVP58 David Wright	4.00	10.00
MVP59 National League Field	6.00	15.00
MVP60 Chase Utley	3.00	8.00
MVP61 Ryan Howard	6.00	15.00
MVP62 Jimmy Rollins	2.00	5.00
MVP63 Jason Bay	2.00	5.00
MVP64 Freddy Sanchez	2.00	5.00
MVP65 Adrian Gonzalez	2.00	5.00
MVP66 Albert Pujols	10.00	25.00
MVP67 Scott Rolen	2.00	5.00
MVP68 Chris Carpenter	2.00	5.00
MVP69 Alfonso Soriano	4.00	10.00
MVP70 Ryan Zimmerman	2.00	5.00

2007 Upper Deck Postseason Predictors

STATED ODDS 1:16 H, 1:240 R
PP1 Arizona Diamondbacks 2.00 5.00
PP2 Atlanta Braves 4.00 10.00
PP3 Baltimore Orioles 2.00 5.00
PP4 Boston Red Sox 10.00 25.00
PP5 Chicago Cubs 6.00 15.00
PP6 Chicago White Sox 4.00 10.00
PP7 Cincinnati Reds 2.00 5.00
PP8 Cleveland Indians 4.00 10.00
PP9 Colorado Rockies 2.00 5.00
PP10 Detroit Tigers 6.00 15.00
PP11 Florida Marlins 2.00 5.00
PP12 Houston Astros 2.00 5.00
PP13 Kansas City Royals 2.00 5.00
PP14 Los Angeles Angels 6.00 15.00
PP15 Los Angeles Dodgers 4.00 10.00
PP16 Milwaukee Brewers 2.00 5.00
PP17 Minnesota Twins 6.00 15.00
PP18 New York Mets 10.00 25.00
PP19 New York Yankees 12.50 30.00
PP20 Oakland Athletics 4.00 10.00
PP21 Philadelphia Phillies 4.00 10.00
PP22 Pittsburgh Pirates 2.00 5.00
PP23 San Diego Padres 4.00 10.00
PP24 San Francisco Giants 4.00 10.00
PP25 Seattle Mariners 2.00 5.00
PP26 St. Louis Cardinals 6.00 15.00
PP27 Tampa Bay Devil Rays 2.00 5.00
PP28 Texas Rangers 2.00 5.00
PP29 Toronto Blue Jays 2.00 5.00
PP30 Washington Nationals 2.00 5.00

2007 Upper Deck Rookie of the Year Predictor

STATED ODDS 1:16 HOBBY, 1:96 RETAIL
OVERALL PRINTING PLATE ODDS 1:96 H
PLATE PRINT RUN 1 SET PER COLOR
BLACK-CYAN-MAGENTA-YELLOW ISSUED
NO PLATE PRICING DUE TO SCARCITY
ROY1 Doug Slaten 1.25 3.00
ROY2 Miguel Montero 1.25 3.00
ROY3 Joseph Bisenius 1.25 3.00
ROY4 Kory Casto 1.25 3.00
ROY5 Jesus Flores 1.25 3.00
ROY6 John Danks 1.25 3.00
ROY7 Daisuke Matsuzaka 12.50 30.00
ROY8 Matt Lindstrom 1.25 3.00
ROY9 Chris Stewart 1.25 3.00
ROY10 Kevin Cameron 1.25 3.00
ROY11 Hideki Okajima 6.00 15.00
ROY12 Levale Speigner 1.25 3.00
ROY13 Kevin Kouzmanoff 1.25 3.00
ROY14 Jeff Baker 1.25 3.00
ROY15 Don Kelly 1.25 3.00
ROY16 Troy Tulowitzki 4.00 10.00
ROY17 Felix Pie 4.00 10.00
ROY18 Cesar Jimenez 1.25 3.00
ROY19 Alejandro De Aza 1.25 3.00
ROY20 Jose Garcia 1.25 3.00
ROY21 Micah Owings 1.25 3.00
ROY22 Josh Hamilton 30.00 60.00
ROY23 Brian Barden 1.25 3.00
ROY24 Jamie Burke 1.25 3.00
ROY25 Mike Rabelo 1.25 3.00
ROY26 Elijah Dukes 2.00 5.00
ROY27 Travis Buck 1.25 3.00
ROY28 Kei Igawa 2.00 5.00
ROY29 Sean Henn 1.25 3.00
ROY30 American League Field 10.00 25.00
ROY31 National League Field 10.00 25.00
ROY32 Michael Bourn 1.25 3.00
ROY33 Alex Gordon 10.00 25.00
ROY34 Chase Wright 2.00 5.00
ROY35 Matt Chico 1.25 3.00
ROY36 Joe Smith 1.25 3.00
ROY37 Lee Gardner 1.25 3.00
ROY38 Gustavo Molina 1.25 3.00
ROY39 Jared Burton 1.25 3.00
ROY40 Jay Marshall 1.25 3.00
ROY41 Brandon Morrow 2.00 5.00
ROY42 Akinori Iwamura 4.00 10.00
ROY43 Delmon Young 2.00 5.00
ROY44 Juan Salas 1.25 3.00
ROY45 Zack Segovia 1.25 3.00
ROY46 Brian Stokes 1.25 3.00
ROY47 Joaquin Arias 1.25 3.00
ROY48 Hector Gimenez 1.25 3.00
ROY49 Ryan Z. Braun 1.25 3.00
ROY50 Juan Perez 1.25 3.00

2007 Upper Deck Star Power

COMMON CARD .40 1.00
SEMISTARS .60 1.50
UNLISTED STARS 1.00 2.50
STATED ODDS 2:1 FAT PACKS
AJ Andruw Jones .60 1.50
AP Albert Pujols 2.00 5.00
AR Alex Rodriguez 1.50 4.00
BR Brian Roberts .40 1.00
BZ Barry Zito .40 1.00
CA Chris Carpenter .40 1.00
CB Carlos Beltran .40 1.00
CC Carl Crawford .40 1.00
CJ Chipper Jones 1.00 2.50
CS Curt Schilling .60 1.50
CU Chase Utley 1.00 2.50
CZ Carlos Zambrano .40 1.00
DA Johnny Damon .60 1.50
DJ Derek Jeter 2.50 6.00
DO David Ortiz 1.00 2.50
DW Dontrelle Willis .40 1.00
FS Freddy Sanchez .40 1.00
FT Frank Thomas 1.00 2.50
HA Roy Halladay .40 1.00
HO Trevor Hoffman .40 1.00
IS Ichiro Suzuki 1.50 4.00
JB Jason Bay .40 1.00
JD Jermaine Dye .40 1.00
JM Joe Mauer .60 1.50
JP Jake Peavy .40 1.00
JR Jose Reyes .60 1.50
JS Johan Santana .60 1.50
JT Jim Thome .60 1.50
JU Justin Morneau .40 1.00
JV Justin Verlander 1.00 2.50
KG Ken Griffey Jr. 1.50 4.00
KR Kenny Rogers .40 1.00
LB Lance Berkman .60 1.50
MA Matt Cain .60 1.50
MC Miguel Cabrera .60 1.50
MH Matt Holliday .50 1.25
MO Magglio Ordonez .40 1.00
MR Manny Ramirez .60 1.50
MT Mark Teixeira .60 1.50
MY Michael Young .40 1.00
NG Nomar Garciaparra 1.00 2.50
NS Nick Swisher .40 1.00
PF Prince Fielder 1.00 2.50
RH Ryan Howard 1.50 4.00
RO Roy Oswalt .40 1.00
RZ Ryan Zimmerman 1.00 2.50
SM John Smoltz .60 1.50
TH Travis Hafner .40 1.00
VG Vladimir Guerrero 1.00 2.50
WR David Wright 1.50 4.00

2007 Upper Deck Star Rookies

SR1 Adam Lind .40 1.00
SR2 Akinori Iwamura 1.00 2.50
SR3 Alexi Casilla .60 1.50
SR4 Alex Gordon 2.00 5.00
SR5 Matt Chico .40 1.00
SR6 John Danks .40 1.00
SR7 Angel Sanchez .40 1.00
SR8 Elijah Dukes .60 1.50
SR9 Brian Burres .40 1.00
SR10 Gustavo Molina .40 1.00
SR11 Chris Stewart .40 1.00
SR12 Daisuke Matsuzaka 4.00 10.00
SR13 Joakim Soria .40 1.00
SR14 Delmon Young .60 1.50
SR15 Jay Marshall .40 1.00
SR16 Travis Buck .40 1.00
SR17 Doug Slaten .40 1.00
SR18 Don Kelly .40 1.00
SR19 Kevin Cameron .40 1.00
SR20 Glen Perkins .40 1.00
SR21 Hector Gimenez .40 1.00
SR22 Jeff Baker .40 1.00
SR23 Jared Burton .40 1.00
SR24 Kory Casto .40 1.00
SR25 Joe Smith .40 1.00
SR26 Joaquin Arias .40 1.00
SR27 Dallas Braden .60 1.50
SR28 Jon Knott .40 1.00
SR29 Jose Garcia .40 1.00
SR30 Jamie Burke .40 1.00
SR31 Zach Segovia .40 1.00
SR32 Felix Pie .40 1.00
SR33 Juan Salas .40 1.00
SR34 Kei Igawa 1.00 2.50
SR35 Philip Hughes 2.00 5.00
SR36 Kevin Kouzmanoff .40 1.00
SR37 Michael Bourn .40 1.00
SR38 Miguel Montero .40 1.00
SR39 Mike Rabelo .40 1.00
SR40 Josh Hamilton 1.00 2.50
SR41 Micah Owings .40 1.00
SR42 Alejandro De Aza .60 1.50
SR43 Brian Barden .40 1.00
SR44 Andy Gonzalez .40 1.00
SR45 Chase Wright 1.00 2.50
SR46 Sean Henn .40 1.00
SR47 Rick Vanden Hurk .60 1.50
SR48 Troy Tulowitzki 1.00 2.50
SR49 Rocky Cherry 1.00 2.50
SR50 Jesus Flores .40 1.00

2007 Upper Deck Star Signings

SER.1 ODDS 1:16 HOBBY, 1:960 RETAIL
SER.2 ODDS 1:16 HOBBY, 1:960 RETAIL
SP INFO PROVIDED BY UPPER DECK
EXCH DEADLINE 02/27/2010
AB Ambiorix Burgos EXCH 3.00 8.00
AB Adrian Beltre S2 SP 5.00 12.00
AC Aaron Cook EXCH 3.00 8.00
AC Alberto Callaspo S2 3.00 8.00
AG Alex Gordon S2 20.00 50.00
AH Aubrey Huff SP 5.00 12.00
AI Akinori Iwamura S2 SP EXCH 10.00 25.00
AP Albert Pujols S2 SP
AR Alex Rios 6.00 15.00
AS Angel Sanchez S2 3.00 8.00
BA Bobby Abreu 10.00 25.00
BA Jeff Baker S2 3.00 8.00
BB Brian Burres S2 3.00 8.00
BC Bobby Crosby S2 SP
BE Josh Beckett S2 SP 20.00 50.00
BL Joe Blanton 3.00 8.00
BO Jeremy Bonderman 15.00 40.00
BO Ben Broussard S2 4.00 10.00
BR Brandon Backe 3.00 8.00
BU B.J. Upton S2 SP 20.00 50.00
CB Craig Biggio S2 SP 15.00 40.00
CC Carl Crawford S2 SP 8.00 20.00
CJ Conor Jackson 6.00 15.00
CO Chad Cordero 3.00 8.00
CP Corey Patterson 3.00 8.00
CR Coco Crisp SP 5.00 12.00
CR Cal Ripken Jr. S2 SP 75.00 125.00
CS Chris Shelton 3.00 8.00
CY Chris Young SP 6.00 15.00
DC Daniel Cabrera SP 5.00 12.00
DH Danny Haren 4.00 10.00
DJ Derek Jeter 75.00 125.00
DJ Derek Jeter S2 75.00 125.00
DL Derrek Lee SP 6.00 15.00
DU Chris Duffy 3.00 8.00
DY Delmon Young S2 SP 6.00 15.00
ED Elijah Dukes S2 6.00 15.00
FH Felix Hernandez S2 10.00 25.00
GA Garrett Atkins 3.00 8.00
GC Gustavo Chacin 3.00 8.00
HS Huston Street 3.00 8.00
HU Torii Hunter 6.00 15.00
IK Ian Kinsler S2 SP 6.00 15.00
IS Ian Snell SP 5.00 12.00
IS Ian Snell S2 5.00 12.00
JA Jeremy Accardo 3.00 8.00
JB Jason Bergmann SP 5.00 12.00
JD Joey Devine 3.00 8.00
JD J.D. Drew S2 SP 8.00 20.00
JG Jonny Gomes 3.00 8.00
JJ Jorge Julio 3.00 8.00
JK Jason Kubel 3.00 8.00
JM Justin Morneau 10.00 25.00
JN Joe Nathan 6.00 15.00
JS Jason Bay 6.00 15.00
JT Jim Thome S2 SP
JW Jake Westbrook 3.00 8.00
KF Keith Foulke 4.00 10.00
KG Ken Griffey Jr. 40.00 80.00
KG Ken Griffey Jr. S2 SP
KI Kei Igawa S2 SP 15.00 40.00
KJ Kelly Johnson S2 6.00 15.00
KM Kevin Mench 3.00 8.00
KS Kirk Saarloos 3.00 8.00
KY Kevin Youkilis 10.00 25.00
LN Laynce Nix SP 5.00 12.00
LO Lyle Overbay 3.00 8.00
MA Matt Cain SP 6.00 15.00
MH Matt Holliday 8.00 20.00
MK Mark Kotsay 4.00 10.00
MM Melvin Mora 4.00 10.00
MT Mark Teahen SP 5.00 12.00
NC Nelson Cruz S2 4.00 10.00
NM Nate McLouth SP 5.00 12.00
OP Oliver Perez S2 SP 15.00 40.00
RA Chris Ray S2 4.00 10.00
RC Ryan Church 3.00 8.00
RC Roger Clemens S2 SP
RF Rafael Furcal SP 5.00 12.00
RG Ryan Garko 4.00 10.00
RI Juan Rivera SP 5.00 12.00
RJ Reed Johnson 3.00 8.00
RO Aaron Rowand SP 5.00 12.00
RU Carlos Ruiz 3.00 8.00
SA Juan Salas S2 3.00 8.00
SC Sean Casey SP 5.00 12.00
SD Stephen Drew 10.00 25.00
SH Sean Henn S2 3.00 8.00
SP Scott Podsednik SP 6.00 15.00
TI Tadahito Iguchi 8.00 20.00
VE Justin Verlander 10.00 25.00
WM Wily Mo Pena 6.00 15.00
XN Xavier Nady 4.00 10.00
YB Yuniesky Betancourt 4.00 10.00
YO Chris Young S2 10.00 25.00
ZS Zack Segovia S2 3.00 8.00

2007 Upper Deck Ticket to Stardom

STATED ODDS 1:4 TARGET PACKS
NO PRICING DUE TO LACK OF MARKET INFO
OVERALL PRINTING PLATE ODDS 1:96 HOBBY
PLATE PRINT RUN 1 SET PER COLOR
BLACK-CYAN-MAGENTA-YELLOW ISSUED
NO PLATE PRICING DUE TO SCARCITY

2007 Upper Deck Ticket to Stardom Signatures

STATED ODDS 1:1440 TARGET PACKS
NO PRICING DUE TO SCARCITY
CH Matt Chico
CJ Cesar Jimenez
CS Chris Stewart
DA John Danks
HG Hector Gimenez
KK Kevin Kouzmanoff
SA Juan Salas
ST Brian Stokes
TT Troy Tulowitzki
ZS Zack Segovia

2007 Upper Deck UD Game Materials

SER.1 STATED ODDS 1:8 H, 1:24 R
SER.2 STATED ODDS 1:8 H, 1:24 R

AB A.J. Burnett S2 3.00 8.00
AJ Andruw Jones Jsy S1 3.00 8.00
AP Albert Pujols Pants S1 6.00 15.00
AP Albert Pujols S2 6.00 15.00
AR Alex Rios S2 4.00 10.00
BA Bobby Abreu S2 3.00 8.00
BC Bartolo Colon S2 3.00 8.00
BE Josh Beckett Jsy S1 3.00 8.00
BJ Bobby Jenks S2 3.00 8.00
BR Brian Roberts Jsy S1 3.00 8.00
BS Ben Sheets Jsy S1 3.00 8.00
CA Chris Carpenter Jsy S1 3.00 8.00
CB Carlos Beltran Pants S1 4.00 10.00
CC Carl Crawford Pants S1 3.00 8.00
CC Carl Crawford S2 3.00 8.00
CD Carlos Delgado Jsy S1 3.00 8.00
CJ Chipper Jones S2 3.00 8.00
CL Carlos Lee Jsy S1 3.00 8.00
CP Corey Patterson Jsy S1 3.00 8.00
CS C.C. Sabathia Jsy S1 3.00 8.00
CS Curt Schilling S2 4.00 10.00
CU Chase Utley S2 4.00 10.00
DJ Derek Jeter Pants S1 8.00 20.00
DJ Derek Jeter S2 8.00 20.00
DO David Ortiz Jsy S1 4.00 10.00
DW Dontrelle Willis Jsy S1 3.00 8.00
EB Erik Bedard S2 4.00 10.00
EC Eric Chavez Jsy S1 3.00 8.00
EN Juan Encarnacion S2 3.00 8.00
FH Felix Hernandez Jsy S1 4.00 10.00
FR Jeff Francoeur S2 4.00 10.00
GS Gary Sheffield S2 3.00 8.00
HB Hank Blalock S2 3.00 8.00
HO Trevor Hoffman S2 3.00 8.00
HU Torii Hunter Jsy S1 3.00 8.00
IR Ivan Rodriguez Jsy S1 3.00 8.00
JB Jason Bay Jsy S1 3.00 8.00
JD Johnny Damon S2 3.00 8.00
JE Jim Edmonds S2 3.00 8.00
JF Jeff Francis S2 3.00 8.00
JG Jason Giambi Jsy S1 3.00 8.00
JM Joe Mauer Jsy S1 3.00 8.00
JR Jose Reyes Jsy S1 4.00 10.00
JS Johan Santana Jsy S1 3.00 8.00
JS John Smoltz S2 4.00 10.00
JT Jim Thome S2 3.00 8.00
JU Juan Uribe Jsy S1 3.00 8.00
JV Justin Verlander Jsy S1 4.00 10.00
JV Jose Vidro S2 3.00 8.00
KG Ken Griffey Jr. Pants S1 6.00 15.00
KG Ken Griffey Jr. S2 6.00 15.00
LB Lance Berkman S2 3.00 8.00
LG Luis Gonzalez S2 3.00 8.00
MC Miguel Cabrera Jsy S1 4.00 10.00
MH Matt Holliday Jsy S1 4.00 10.00
MM Melvin Mora Jsy S1 3.00 8.00
MO Justin Morneau Jsy S1 4.00 10.00
MR Manny Ramirez Jsy S1 4.00 10.00
MR Manny Ramirez S2 4.00 10.00
MS Mike Sweeney Jsy S1 3.00 8.00
MT Miguel Tejada Jsy S1 3.00 8.00
MT Mark Teixeira S2 3.00 8.00
MU Mike Mussina Jsy S1 4.00 10.00
OR Magglio Ordonez Jsy S1 3.00 8.00
PF Prince Fielder Jsy S1 4.00 10.00
RB Rocco Baldelli S2 3.00 8.00
RH Roy Halladay Jsy S1 3.00 8.00
RJ Randy Johnson S2 4.00 10.00
RN Ricky Nolasco S2 3.00 8.00
RO Roy Oswalt S2 3.00 8.00
RW Rickie Weeks S2 3.00 8.00
RZ Ryan Zimmerman Jsy S1 4.00 10.00
SD Stephen Drew S2 3.00 8.00
SK Scott Kazmir S2 3.00 8.00
SR Scott Rolen Jsy S1 4.00 10.00
SR Scott Rolen S2 3.00 8.00
TG Tom Glavine S2 4.00 10.00
TH Tim Hudson Jsy S1 3.00 8.00
TH Todd Helton S2 3.00 8.00
TN Trot Nixon S2 3.00 8.00
VG Vladimir Guerrero S2 4.00 10.00
VM Victor Martinez Jsy S1 3.00 8.00
ZD Zach Duke S2 3.00 8.00

2007 Upper Deck UD Game Patch

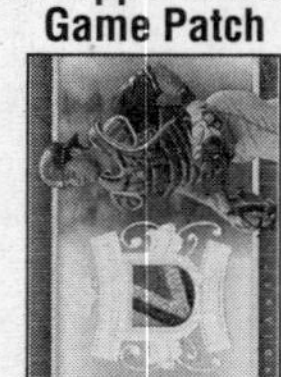

STATED ODDS 1:192 H, 1:2500 R
AJ Andruw Jones 15.00 40.00
AP Albert Pujols 40.00 80.00
BE Josh Beckett 10.00 25.00
BR Brian Roberts 10.00 25.00
BS Ben Sheets 10.00 25.00
CA Chris Carpenter 15.00 40.00
CB Carlos Beltran 15.00 40.00
CC Carl Crawford 10.00 25.00
CD Carlos Delgado 10.00 25.00
CL Carlos Lee 10.00 25.00
CP Corey Patterson 10.00 25.00
CS C.C. Sabathia 10.00 25.00
DJ Derek Jeter 40.00 80.00
DO David Ortiz 20.00 50.00
DW Dontrelle Willis 10.00 25.00
EC Eric Chavez 10.00 25.00
FH Felix Hernandez 15.00 40.00
HU Torii Hunter 15.00 40.00
IR Ivan Rodriguez 15.00 40.00
JB Jason Bay 15.00 40.00
JG Jason Giambi 15.00 40.00
JM Joe Mauer 15.00 40.00
JR Jose Reyes 20.00 50.00
JS Johan Santana 15.00 40.00
JU Juan Uribe 10.00 25.00
KG Ken Griffey Jr. 40.00 80.00
MC Miguel Cabrera 15.00 40.00
MH Matt Holliday 12.50 30.00
MM Melvin Mora 10.00 25.00
MO Justin Morneau 10.00 25.00
MR Manny Ramirez 20.00 50.00
MS Mike Sweeney 10.00 25.00
MT Miguel Tejada 10.00 25.00
MU Mike Mussina 10.00 25.00
OR Magglio Ordonez 10.00 25.00
PF Prince Fielder 15.00 40.00
RH Roy Halladay 10.00 25.00
RZ Ryan Zimmerman 20.00 50.00
SR Scott Rolen 20.00 50.00
TH Tim Hudson 10.00 25.00
VM Victor Martinez 15.00 40.00

2008 Upper Deck

This 400-card first series was released in February, 2008. The set was issued into the hobby in 20-card packs, with an $4.99 SRP, which came 16 packs to a box and 12 boxes to a case. Cards numbered 1-300 feature veterans in team nickname alphabetical order while cards numbered 301-350 feature 2007 rookies in alphabetical order. The first series concludes with team checklist cards (also in team nickname alphabetical order) from cards 351-380 and 20 highlight cards from 381-400.

COMPLETE SET (799) 50.00 100.00
COMP.SER.1 (1-400) 20.00 50.00
COMP.SER.2 (401-799) 20.00 50.00
COMMON CARD (1-799) .15 .40
COMMON ROOKIE (1-799) .40 1.00
1 Joe Saunders .15 .40
2 Kelvim Escobar .15 .40
3 Jered Weaver .15 .40
4 Justin Speier .15 .40
5 Scot Shields .15 .40
6 Mike Napoli .15 .40
7 Orlando Cabrera .15 .40
8 Casey Kotchman .15 .40
9 Vladimir Guerrero .40 1.00
10 Garret Anderson .15 .40
11 Roy Oswalt .15 .40
12 Wandy Rodriguez .15 .40
13 Woody Williams .15 .40
14 Chad Qualls .15 .40
15 Brian Moehler .15 .40
16 Mark Loretta .15 .40
17 Brad Ausmus .15 .40
18 Ty Wigginton .15 .40
19 Carlos Lee .15 .40
20 Hunter Pence .40 1.00
21 Dan Haren .15 .40
22 Lenny DiNardo .15 .40
23 Chad Gaudin .15 .40
24 Huston Street .15 .40
25 Andrew Brown .15 .40
26 Mike Piazza .40 1.00
27 Jack Cust .15 .40
28 Mark Ellis .15 .40
29 Shannon Stewart .15 .40
30 Travis Buck .15 .40
31 Shaun Marcum .15 .40
32 A.J. Burnett .15 .40
33 Jesse Litsch .15 .40
34 Casey Janssen .15 .40
35 Jeremy Accardo .15 .40
36 Gregg Zaun .15 .40
37 Aaron Hill .15 .40
38 Frank Thomas .40 1.00
39 Matt Stairs .15 .40
40 Vernon Wells .15 .40
41 Tim Hudson .15 .40
42 Chuck James .15 .40
43 Buddy Carlyle .15 .40
44 Rafael Soriano .15 .40
45 Peter Moylan .15 .40
46 Brian McCann .25 .60
47 Edgar Renteria .15 .40
48 Mark Teixeira .25 .60
49 Willie Harris .15 .40
50 Andruw Jones .15 .40
51 Ben Sheets .25 .60
52 Dave Bush .15 .40
53 Yovani Gallardo .15 .40
54 Francisco Cordero .15 .40
55 Matt Wise .15 .40
56 Johnny Estrada .15 .40
57 Prince Fielder .40 1.00
58 J.J. Hardy .15 .40
59 Corey Hart .15 .40
60 Geoff Jenkins .15 .40
61 Adam Wainwright .15 .40
62 Joel Pineiro .15 .40
63 Brad Thompson .15 .40
64 Jason Isringhausen .15 .40
65 Troy Percival .15 .40
66 Yadier Molina .25 .60
67 Albert Pujols .75 2.00
68 David Eckstein .15 .40
69 Jim Edmonds .25 .60
70 Rick Ankiel .15 .40
71 Ted Lilly .15 .40
72 Rich Hill .15 .40
73 Jason Marquis .15 .40
74 Carlos Marmol .15 .40
75 Ryan Dempster .15 .40
76 Jason Kendall .15 .40
77 Aramis Ramirez .15 .40
78 Ryan Theriot .15 .40
79 Alfonso Soriano .25 .60
80 Jacque Jones .15 .40
81 James Shields .15 .40
82 Andy Sonnanstine .15 .40
83 Scott Dohmann .15 .40
84 Al Reyes .15 .40
85 Dioner Navarro .15 .40
86 B.J. Upton .25 .60
87 Carlos Pena .40 1.00
88 Brendan Harris .15 .40
89 Josh Wilson .15 .40
90 Jonny Gomes .15 .40
91 Brandon Webb .25 .60
92 Micah Owings .15 .40
93 Livan Hernandez .15 .40
94 Doug Slaten .15 .40
95 Brandon Lyon .15 .40
96 Miguel Montero .15 .40
97 Stephen Drew .15 .40
98 Mark Reynolds .15 .40
99 Conor Jackson .15 .40
100 Chris B. Young .15 .40
101 Chad Billingsley .15 .40
102 Derek Lowe .15 .40
103 Mark Hendrickson .15 .40
104 Takashi Saito .15 .40
105 Rudy Seanez .15 .40
106 Russell Martin .15 .40
107 Jeff Kent .15 .40
108 Nomar Garciaparra .40 1.00
109 Matt Kemp .15 .40
110 Juan Pierre .15 .40
111 Matt Cain .15 .40
112 Barry Zito .15 .40
113 Kevin Correia .15 .40
114 Brad Hennessey .15 .40
115 Jack Taschner .15 .40
116 Bengie Molina .15 .40
117 Ryan Klesko .15 .40
118 Omar Vizquel .15 .40
119 Dave Roberts .15 .40
120 Rajai Davis .15 .40
121 Fausto Carmona .15 .40
122 Jake Westbrook .15 .40
123 Cliff Lee .15 .40
124 Rafael Betancourt .15 .40
125 Joe Borowski .15 .40
126 Victor Martinez .15 .40
127 Travis Hafner .15 .40
128 Ryan Garko .15 .40
129 Kenny Lofton .15 .40
130 Franklin Gutierrez .15 .40
131 Felix Hernandez .25 .60
132 Jeff Weaver .15 .40
133 J.J. Putz .15 .40
134 Brandon Morrow .15 .40
135 Sean Green .15 .40
136 Kenji Johjima .15 .40
137 Jose Vidro .15 .40
138 Richie Sexson .15 .40
139 Ichiro Suzuki .60 1.50
140 Ben Broussard .15 .40
141 Sergio Mitre .15 .40
142 Scott Olsen .15 .40
143 Rick Vanden Hurk .15 .40
144 Justin Miller .15 .40
145 Lee Gardner .15 .40
146 Miguel Olivo .15 .40
147 Hanley Ramirez .40 1.00
148 Mike Jacobs .15 .40
149 Josh Willingham .15 .40
150 Alfredo Amezaga .15 .40
151 John Maine .15 .40
152 Tom Glavine .25 .60
153 Orlando Hernandez .15 .40
154 Billy Wagner .15 .40
155 Aaron Heilman .15 .40
156 David Wright .50 1.25
157 Luis Castillo .15 .40
158 Shawn Green .15 .40
159 Damion Easley .15 .40
160 Carlos Delgado .15 .40
161 Shawn Hill .15 .40
162 Mike Bacsik .15 .40
163 John Lannan .15 .40
164 Chad Cordero .15 .40
165 Jon Rauch .15 .40
166 Jesus Flores .15 .40
167 Dmitri Young .15 .40
168 Cristian Guzman .15 .40
169 Austin Kearns .15 .40
170 Nook Logan .15 .40
171 Erik Bedard .15 .40
172 Daniel Cabrera .15 .40
173 Chris Ray .15 .40
174 Danys Baez .15 .40
175 Chad Bradford .15 .40
176 Ramon Hernandez .15 .40
177 Miguel Tejada .15 .40
178 Freddie Bynum .15 .40
179 Corey Patterson .15 .40
180 Aubrey Huff .15 .40
181 Chris Young .15 .40
182 Greg Maddux .50 1.25
183 Clay Hensley .15 .40
184 Kevin Cameron .15 .40
185 Doug Brocail .15 .40
186 Josh Bard .15 .40
187 Kevin Kouzmanoff .15 .40
188 Geoff Blum .15 .40
189 Milton Bradley .15 .40
190 Brian Giles .15 .40
191 Jamie Moyer .15 .40
192 Kyle Kendrick .15 .40
193 Kyle Lohse .15 .40
194 Antonio Alfonseca .15 .40
195 Ryan Madson .15 .40
196 Chris Coste .15 .40
197 Chase Utley .40 1.00
198 Tadahito Iguchi .15 .40
199 Aaron Rowand .15 .40
200 Shane Victorino .15 .40
201 Paul Maholm .15 .40
202 Ian Snell .15 .40
203 Shane Youman .15 .40
204 Damaso Marte .15 .40
205 Shawn Chacon .15 .40
206 Ronny Paulino .15 .40
207 Jack Wilson .15 .40

208 Adam LaRoche .15 .40
209 Ryan Doumit .15 .40
210 Xavier Nady .15 .40
211 Kevin Millwood .15 .40
212 Brandon McCarthy .15 .40
213 Joaquin Benoit .15 .40
214 Wes Littleton .15 .40
215 Mike Wood .15 .40
216 Gerald Laird .15 .40
217 Hank Blalock .15 .40
218 Ian Kinsler .25 .60
219 Marlon Byrd .15 .40
220 Brad Wilkerson .15 .40
221 Tim Wakefield .15 .40
222 Daisuke Matsuzaka .60 1.50
223 Julian Tavarez .15 .40
224 Hideki Okajima .15 .40
225 Manny Delcarmen .15 .40
226 Doug Mirabelli .15 .40
227 Dustin Pedroia .60 1.50
228 Mike Lowell .15 .40
229 Manny Ramirez .40 1.00
230 Coco Crisp .15 .40
231 Bronson Arroyo .15 .40
232 Matt Belisle .15 .40
233 Jared Burton .15 .40
234 David Weathers .15 .40
235 Mike Gosling .15 .40
236 David Ross .15 .40
237 Jeff Keppinger .15 .40
238 Edwin Encarnacion .15 .40
239 Ken Griffey Jr. .60 1.50
240 Adam Dunn .15 .40
241 Jeff Francis .15 .40
242 Jason Hirsh .15 .40
243 Josh Fogg .15 .40
244 Manny Corpas .15 .40
245 Jeremy Affeldt .15 .40
246 Yorvit Torrealba .15 .40
247 Todd Helton .25 .60
248 Kazuo Matsui .15 .40
249 Brad Hawpe .15 .40
250 Willy Taveras .15 .40
251 Brian Bannister .15 .40
252 Zack Greinke .15 .40
253 Kyle Davies .15 .40
254 David Riske .15 .40
255 Joel Peralta .15 .40
256 John Buck .15 .40
257 Mark Grudzielanek .15 .40
258 Ross Gload .15 .40
259 Billy Butler .15 .40
260 David DeJesus .15 .40
261 Jeremy Bonderman .15 .40
262 Chad Durbin .15 .40
263 Andrew Miller .25 .60
264 Bobby Seay .15 .40
265 Todd Jones .15 .40
266 Brandon Inge .15 .40
267 Sean Casey .15 .40
268 Placido Polanco .15 .40
269 Gary Sheffield .15 .40
270 Magglio Ordonez .25 .60
271 Matt Garza .15 .40
272 Boof Bonser .15 .40
273 Scott Baker .15 .40
274 Joe Nathan .15 .40
275 Dennys Reyes .15 .40
276 Joe Mauer .25 .60
277 Michael Cuddyer .15 .40
278 Jason Bartlett .15 .40
279 Torii Hunter .15 .40
280 Jason Tyner .15 .40
281 Mark Buehrle .15 .40
282 Jon Garland .15 .40
283 Jose Contreras .15 .40
284 Matt Thornton .15 .40
285 Ryan Bukvich .15 .40
286 Juan Uribe .15 .40
287 Jim Thome .25 .60
288 Scott Podsednik .15 .40
289 Jerry Owens .15 .40
290 Jermaine Dye .15 .40
291 Andy Pettitte .25 .60
292 Phil Hughes .40 1.00
293 Mike Mussina .25 .60
294 Joba Chamberlain .50 1.25
295 Brian Bruney .15 .40
296 Jorge Posada .25 .60
297 Derek Jeter 1.00 2.50
298 Jason Giambi .25 .60
299 Johnny Damon .25 .60
300 Melky Cabrera .15 .40
301 Jonathan Albaladejo RC .60 1.50
302 Josh Anderson (RC) .40 1.00
303 Wladimir Balentien (RC) .40 1.00
304 Josh Banks (RC) .40 1.00
305 Daric Barton (RC) .40 1.00
306 Jerry Blevins RC .60 1.50
307 Emilio Bonifacio RC .60 1.50
308 Lance Broadway (RC) .40 1.00
309 Clay Buchholz (RC) 1.00 2.50
310 Billy Buckner (RC) .40 1.00
311 Jeff Clement (RC) .40 1.00
312 Willie Collazo RC .60 1.50
313 Ross Detwiler RC 1.00 2.50
314 Sam Fuld RC .40 1.00
315 Harvey Garcia (RC) .40 1.00
316 Alberto Gonzalez RC .60 1.50
317 Ryan Hanigan RC .60 1.50
318 Kevin Hart (RC) .40 1.00
319 Luke Hochevar RC 1.00 2.50
320 Chin-Lung Hu (RC) .60 1.50
321 Rob Johnson (RC) .40 1.00
322 Radhames Liz RC .60 1.50
323 Ian Kennedy RC 1.00 2.50
324 Joe Koshansky (RC) .40 1.00
325 Donny Lucy (RC) .40 1.00
326 Justin Maxwell RC .60 1.50
327 Jonathan Meloan RC .60 1.50
328 Luis Mendoza (RC) .40 1.00
329 Jose Morales (RC) .40 1.00
330 Nyjer Morgan (RC) .40 1.00
331 Carlos Muniz RC .60 1.50
332 Bill Murphy (RC) .40 1.00
333 Josh Newman RC .60 1.50
334 Ross Ohlendorf RC .60 1.50
335 Troy Patton (RC) .40 1.00
336 Felipe Paulino RC .60 1.50
337 Steve Pearce RC .60 1.50
338 Heath Phillips RC .60 1.50
339 Justin Ruggiano RC .60 1.50
340 Clint Sammons (RC) .40 1.00
341 Bronson Sardinha (RC) .40 1.00
342 Chris Seddon (RC) .40 1.00
343 Seth Smith (RC) .40 1.00
344 Mitch Stetter RC .60 1.50
345 Dave Davidson RC .60 1.50
346 Rich Thompson RC .60 1.50
347 J.R. Towles RC 1.00 2.50
348 Eugenio Velez RC .40 1.00
349 Joey Votto (RC) 1.00 2.50
350 Bill White RC .40 1.00
351 Vladimir Guerrero CL .40 1.00
352 Lance Berkman CL .25 .60
353 Dan Haren CL .15 .40
354 Frank Thomas CL .40 1.00
355 Chipper Jones CL .50 1.25
356 Prince Fielder CL .40 1.00
357 Albert Pujols CL .75 2.00
358 Alfonso Soriano CL .25 .60
359 B.J. Upton CL .25 .60
360 Eric Byrnes CL .15 .40
361 Russell Martin CL .15 .40
362 Tim Lincecum CL .40 1.00
363 Grady Sizemore CL .25 .60
364 Ichiro Suzuki CL .60 1.50
365 Hanley Ramirez CL .40 1.00
366 David Wright CL .50 1.25
367 Ryan Zimmerman CL .25 .60
368 Nick Markakis CL .25 .60
369 Jake Peavy CL .25 .60
370 Ryan Howard CL .50 1.25
371 Freddy Sanchez CL .15 .40
372 Michael Young CL .15 .40
373 David Ortiz CL .40 1.00
374 Ken Griffey Jr. CL .60 1.50
375 Matt Holliday CL .25 .60
376 Brian Bannister CL .15 .40
377 Magglio Ordonez CL .25 .60
378 Johan Santana CL .25 .60
379 Jim Thome CL .25 .60
380 Alex Rodriguez CL .60 1.50
381 Alex Rodriguez HL .60 1.50
382 Brandon Webb HL .25 .60
383 Chone Figgins HL .15 .40
384 Clay Buchholz HL .40 1.00
385 Curtis Granderson HL .15 .40
386 Frank Thomas HL .40 1.00
387 Fred Lewis HL .15 .40
388 Garret Anderson HL .15 .40
389 J.R. Towles HL .40 1.00
390 Jake Peavy HL .25 .60
391 Jim Thome HL .25 .60
392 Jimmy Rollins HL .25 .60
393 Johan Santana HL .25 .60
394 Justin Verlander HL .25 .60
395 Mark Buehrle HL .15 .40
396 Matt Holliday HL .25 .60
397 Jarrod Saltalamacchia HL .15 .40
398 Sammy Sosa HL .25 .60
399 Tom Glavine HL .25 .60
400 Trevor Hoffman HL .15 .40
401 Dan Haren .15 .40
402 Randy Johnson .40 1.00
403 Chris Burke .15 .40
404 Orlando Hudson .15 .40
405 Justin Upton .40 1.00
406 Eric Byrnes .15 .40
407 Doug Davis .15 .40
408 Chad Tracy .15 .40
409 Tom Glavine .25 .60
410 Kelly Johnson .15 .40
411 Chipper Jones .50 1.25
412 Matt Diaz .15 .40
413 Jeff Francoeur .25 .60
414 Mark Kotsay .15 .40
415 John Smoltz .40 1.00
416 Tyler Yates .15 .40
417 Yunel Escobar .15 .40
418 Mike Hampton .15 .40
419 Luke Scott .15 .40
420 Adam Jones .15 .40
421 Jeremy Guthrie .15 .40
422 Nick Markakis .25 .60
423 Jay Payton .15 .40
424 Brian Roberts .25 .60
425 Melvin Mora .15 .40
426 Adam Loewen .15 .40
427 Luis Hernandez .15 .40
428 Steve Trachsel .15 .40
429 Josh Beckett .25 .60
430 Jon Lester .25 .60
431 Curt Schilling .25 .60
432 Jonathan Papelbon .25 .60
433 Jason Varitek .40 1.00
434 David Ortiz .40 1.00
435 Jacoby Ellsbury .60 1.50
436 Julio Lugo .15 .40
437 Sean Casey .15 .40
438 Kevin Youkilis .25 .60
439 J.D. Drew .15 .40
440 Alex Cora .15 .40
441 Derrek Lee .25 .60
442 Carlos Zambrano .15 .40
443 Sean Marshall .15 .40
444 Matt Murton .15 .40
445 Kerry Wood .15 .40
446 Felix Pie .15 .40
447 Mark DeRosa .15 .40
448 Ronny Cedeno .15 .40
449 Jon Lieber .15 .40
450 Geovany Soto .40 1.00
451 Gavin Floyd .15 .40
452 Bobby Jenks .15 .40
453 Scott Linebrink .15 .40
454 Javier Vazquez .15 .40
455 A.J. Pierzynski .15 .40
456 Orlando Cabrera .15 .40
457 Joe Crede .15 .40
458 Josh Fields .15 .40
459 Paul Konerko .15 .40
460 Brian Anderson .15 .40
461 Nick Swisher .15 .40
462 Carlos Quentin .15 .40
463 Jermaine Dye .15 .40
464 Francisco Cordero .15 .40
465 Aaron Harang .15 .40
466 Alex Gonzalez .15 .40
467 Brandon Phillips .15 .40
468 Ryan Freel .15 .40
469 Scott Hatteberg .15 .40
470 Juan Castro .15 .40
471 Norris Hopper .15 .40
472 Josh Barfield .15 .40
473 Casey Blake .15 .40
474 Paul Byrd .15 .40
475 Grady Sizemore .25 .60
476 Jason Michaels .15 .40
477 Jhonny Peralta .15 .40
478 Asdrubal Cabrera .15 .40
479 David Dellucci .15 .40
480 C.C. Sabathia .15 .40
481 Andy Marte .15 .40
482 Troy Tulowitzki .25 .60
483 Matt Holliday .25 .60
484 Garrett Atkins .15 .40
485 Aaron Cook .15 .40
486 Brian Fuentes .15 .40
487 Ryan Spilborghs .15 .40
488 Ubaldo Jimenez .15 .40
489 Jayson Nix .15 .40
490 Nate Robertson .15 .40
491 Kenny Rogers .15 .40
492 Justin Verlander .25 .60
493 Dontrelle Willis .15 .40
494 Joel Zumaya .15 .40
495 Ivan Rodriguez .25 .60
496 Miguel Cabrera .25 .60
497 Carlos Guillen .15 .40
498 Edgar Renteria .15 .40
499 Curtis Granderson .15 .40
500 Jacque Jones .15 .40
501 Marcus Thames .15 .40
502 Josh Johnson .15 .40
503 Jeremy Hermida .15 .40
504 Dan Uggla .25 .60
505 Mark Hendrickson .15 .40
506 Luis Gonzalez .15 .40
507 Dallas McPherson .15 .40
508 Cody Ross .15 .40
509 Matt Treanor .15 .40
510 Andrew Miller .25 .60
511 Jorge Cantu .15 .40
512 Kazuo Matsui .15 .40
513 Lance Berkman .25 .60
514 Darin Erstad .15 .40
515 Miguel Tejada .15 .40
516 Jose Valverde .15 .40
517 Geoff Blum .15 .40
518 Reggie Abercrombie .15 .40
519 Brandon Backe .15 .40
520 Michael Bourn .15 .40
521 Gil Meche .15 .40
522 Brett Tomko .15 .40
523 Miguel Olivo .15 .40
524 Shane Costa .15 .40
525 Joey Gathright .15 .40
526 Mark Teahen .15 .40
527 Alex Gordon .40 1.00
528 Tony Pena .15 .40
529 Jose Guillen .15 .40
530 Torii Hunter .15 .40
531 Ervin Santana .15 .40
532 Francisco Rodriguez .15 .40
533 Howie Kendrick .15 .40
534 Reggie Willits .15 .40
535 John Lackey .15 .40
536 Gary Matthews .15 .40
537 Jon Garland .15 .40
538 Kendry Morales .15 .40
539 Chone Figgins .15 .40
540 Andruw Jones .15 .40
541 Jason Schmidt .15 .40
542 James Loney .25 .60
543 Andre Ethier .25 .60
544 Rafael Furcal .15 .40
545 Brad Penny .15 .40
546 Hong-Chih Kuo .15 .40
547 Jonathan Broxton .15 .40
548 Esteban Loaiza .15 .40
549 Delwyn Young .15 .40
550 Mike Cameron .15 .40
551 Ryan Braun .50 1.25
552 Rickie Weeks .15 .40
553 Bill Hall .15 .40
554 Tony Gwynn Jr. .15 .40
555 Eric Gagne .15 .40
556 Jeff Suppan .15 .40
557 Chris Capuano .15 .40
558 Derrick Turnbow .15 .40
559 Jason Kendall .15 .40
560 Livan Hernandez .15 .40
561 Philip Humber .15 .40
562 Francisco Liriano .25 .60
563 Pat Neshek .15 .40
564 Adam Everett .15 .40
565 Brendan Harris .15 .40
566 Justin Morneau .25 .60
567 Craig Monroe .15 .40
568 Carlos Gomez .15 .40
569 Delmon Young .25 .60
570 Mike Lamb .15 .40
571 Oliver Perez .15 .40
572 Jose Reyes .25 .60
573 Moises Alou .15 .40
574 Carlos Beltran .15 .40
575 Endy Chavez .15 .40
576 Ryan Church .15 .40
577 Pedro Martinez .25 .60
578 Johan Santana .25 .60
579 Mike Pelfrey .15 .40
580 Brian Schneider .15 .40
581 Joe Smith .15 .40
582 Matt Wise .15 .40
583 Duaner Sanchez .15 .40
584 Ramon Castro .15 .40
585 Kei Igawa .15 .40
586 Mariano Rivera .40 1.00
587 Chien-Ming Wang .50 1.25
588 Wilson Betemit .15 .40
589 Robinson Cano .25 .60
590 Alex Rodriguez .60 1.50
591 Bobby Abreu .15 .40
592 Shelley Duncan .15 .40
593 Hideki Matsui .40 1.00
594 Kyle Farnsworth .15 .40
595 Joe Blanton .15 .40
596 Bobby Crosby .15 .40
597 Eric Chavez .15 .40
598 Dan Johnson .15 .40
599 Rich Harden .15 .40
600 Justin Duchscherer .15 .40
601 Kurt Suzuki .15 .40
602 Chris Denorfia .15 .40
603 Emil Brown .15 .40
604 Ryan Howard .50 1.25
605 Jimmy Rollins .25 .60
606 Pedro Feliz .15 .40
607 Adam Eaton .15 .40
608 Brad Lidge .15 .40
609 Brett Myers .15 .40
610 Pat Burrell .15 .40
611 So Taguchi .15 .40
612 Geoff Jenkins .15 .40
613 Tom Gordon .15 .40
614 Zach Duke .15 .40
615 Matt Morris .15 .40
616 Tom Gorzelanny .15 .40
617 Jason Bay .15 .40
618 Chris Duffy .15 .40
619 Freddy Sanchez .15 .40
620 Jose Bautista .15 .40
621 Nyjer Morgan .15 .40
622 Matt Capps .15 .40
623 Paul Maholm .15 .40
624 Tadahito Iguchi .15 .40
625 Adrian Gonzalez .25 .60
626 Jim Edmonds .25 .60
627 Jake Peavy .25 .60
628 Khalil Greene .25 .60
629 Trevor Hoffman .25 .60
630 Mark Prior .25 .60
631 Randy Wolf .15 .40
632 Michael Barrett .15 .40
633 Scott Hairston .15 .40
634 Tim Lincecum .40 1.00
635 Noah Lowry .15 .40
636 Rich Aurilia .15 .40
637 Aaron Rowand .15 .40
638 Randy Winn .15 .40
639 Daniel Ortmeier .15 .40
640 Ray Durham .15 .40
641 Brian Wilson .15 .40
642 Adrian Beltre .15 .40
643 Jeremy Reed .15 .40
644 Jarrod Washburn .15 .40
645 Yuniesky Betancourt .15 .40
646 Jose Lopez .15 .40
647 Raul Ibanez .15 .40
648 Mike Morse .15 .40
649 Erik Bedard .15 .40
650 Brad Wilkerson .15 .40
651 Chris Carpenter .15 .40
652 Mark Mulder .15 .40
653 Juan Encarnacion .15 .40
654 Skip Schumaker .15 .40
655 Troy Glaus .25 .60
656 Anthony Reyes .15 .40
657 Cesar Izturis .15 .40
658 Adam Kennedy .15 .40
659 Chris Duncan .15 .40
660 Matt Clement .15 .40
661 Scott Kazmir .25 .60
662 Troy Percival .15 .40
663 Akinori Iwamura .15 .40
664 Carl Crawford .15 .40
665 Cliff Floyd .15 .40
666 Jason Bartlett .15 .40
667 Rocco Baldelli .15 .40
668 Matt Garza .15 .40
669 Edwin Jackson .15 .40
670 Vicente Padilla .15 .40
671 Josh Hamilton .50 1.25
672 Jason Botts .15 .40
673 Milton Bradley .15 .40
674 Michael Young .15 .40
675 Eddie Guardado .15 .40
676 David Murphy .15 .40
677 Ramon Vazquez .15 .40
678 Ben Broussard .15 .40
679 C.J. Wilson .15 .40
680 Jason Jennings .15 .40
681 Gustavo Chacin .15 .40
682 BJ Ryan .15 .40
683 David Eckstein .15 .40
684 Alex Rios .15 .40
685 John McDonald .15 .40
686 Rod Barajas .15 .40
687 Lyle Overbay .15 .40
688 Scott Rolen .25 .60
689 Reed Johnson .15 .40
690 Marco Scutaro .15 .40
691 Lastings Milledge .15 .40
692 Johnny Estrada .15 .40
693 Paul Lo Duca .15 .40
694 Ryan Zimmerman .25 .60
695 Odalis Perez .15 .40
696 Wily Mo Pena .15 .40
697 Elijah Dukes .15 .40
698 Aaron Boone .15 .40
699 Ronnie Belliard .15 .40
700 Nick Johnson .15 .40
701 Randor Bierd RC .40 1.00
702 Brian Barton RC .60 1.50
703 Brian Bass (RC) .40 1.00
704 Brian Bocock RC .40 1.00
705 Gregor Blanco (RC) .40 1.00
706 Callix Crabbe (RC) .40 1.00
707 Johnny Cueto RC .60 1.50
708 Kosuke Fukudome RC 4.00 10.00
708b Kosuke Fukudome Japanese 40.00 80.00
709 Scott Kazmir SH .25 .60
710 Steve Holm RC .40 1.00
711 Fernando Hernandez RC .40 1.00
712 Elliot Johnson (RC) .40 1.00
713 Masahide Kobayashi RC .60 1.50
714 Hiroki Kuroda RC .60 1.50
715 Blake DeWitt (RC) 1.00 2.50
716 Kyle McClellan RC .40 1.00
717 Evan Meek RC .40 1.00
718 Denard Span (RC) .60 1.50
719 Darren O'Day RC .40 1.00
720 Alexei Ramirez RC 2.50 6.00
721 Alex Romero (RC) .60 1.50
722 Clete Thomas RC .60 1.50
723 Matt Tolbert RC .60 1.50
724 Ramon Troncoso RC .40 1.00
725 Matt Tupman RC .40 1.00
726 Rico Washington (RC) .40 1.00
727 Randy Wells RC .40 1.00
728 Wesley Wright RC .40 1.00
729 Yasuhiko Yabuta RC .60 1.50
730 Alex Rodriguez SH .60 1.50
731 Andruw Jones SH .15 .40
732 C.C. Sabathia SH .15 .40
733 Carlos Beltran SH .15 .40
734 David Wright SH .50 1.25
735 Derrek Lee SH .25 .60
736 Dustin Pedroia SH .60 1.50
737 Grady Sizemore SH .25 .60
738 Greg Maddux SH .50 1.25
739 Ichiro Suzuki SH .60 1.50
740 Ivan Rodriguez SH .25 .60
741 Jake Peavy SH .25 .60
742 Jimmy Rollins SH .25 .60
743 Johan Santana SH .25 .60
744 Josh Beckett SH .25 .60
745 Kevin Youkilis SH .25 .60
746 Matt Holliday SH .25 .60
747 Mike Lowell SH .15 .40
748 Ryan Braun SH .50 1.25
749 Torii Hunter SH .15 .40
750 Alex Rodriguez SH .60 1.50
751 Torii Hunter CL .15 .40
752 Miguel Tejada CL .15 .40
753 Huston Street CL .15 .40
754 Scott Rolen CL .25 .60
755 Tom Glavine CL .25 .60
756 Ryan Braun CL .50 1.25
757 Troy Glaus CL .25 .60
758 Carlos Zambrano CL .15 .40
759 Carl Crawford CL .15 .40
760 Dan Haren CL .15 .40
761 Andruw Jones CL .15 .40
762 Barry Zito CL .15 .40
763 Victor Martinez CL .15 .40
764 Erik Bedard CL .15 .40
765 Josh Willingham CL .15 .40
766 Johan Santana CL .25 .60
767 Dmitri Young CL .15 .40
768 Brian Roberts CL .25 .60
769 Jim Edmonds CL .25 .60
770 Jimmy Rollins CL .25 .60
771 Jason Bay CL .15 .40
772 Josh Hamilton CL .50 1.25
773 Josh Beckett CL .25 .60
774 Aaron Harang CL .15 .40
775 Troy Tulowitzki CL .25 .60
776 Jose Guillen CL .15 .40
777 Miguel Cabrera CL .25 .60
778 Joe Mauer CL .25 .60
779 Nick Swisher CL .15 .40
780 Derek Jeter CL 1.00 2.50
781 Brandon Webb SH .25 .60
782 Brian Roberts SH .25 .60
783 C.C. Sabathia SH .15 .40
784 Carl Crawford SH .15 .40
785 Curtis Granderson SH .15 .40
786 David Ortiz SH .40 1.00
787 Ichiro Suzuki SH .60 1.50
788 Jake Peavy SH .25 .60
789 Jimmy Rollins SH .25 .60
790 Joe Borowski SH .15 .40
791 Johan Santana SH .25 .60
792 John Lackey SH .15 .40
793 Jose Reyes SH .25 .60
794 Jose Valverde SH .15 .40
795 Josh Beckett SH .25 .60
796 Juan Pierre SH .15 .40
797 Magglio Ordonez SH .25 .60
798 Matt Holliday SH .25 .60
799 Prince Fielder SH .40 1.00

2008 Upper Deck Gold

*GOLD VET: 4X TO 10X BASIC
*GOLD RC: 3X TO 8X BASIC
RANDOM INSERTS IN PACKS
STATED PRINT RUN 99 SER.#'d SETS
708 Kosuke Fukudome 50.00 100.00

2008 Upper Deck A Piece of History 500 Club

STATED ODDS 1:192 HOBBY
EXCHANGE DEADLINE 1/14/2010
FT Frank Thomas 20.00 50.00
JT Jim Thome 20.00 50.00

2008 Upper Deck All Rookie Team Signatures

STATED ODDS 1:80 H, 1:7500 R
AI Akinori Iwamura 10.00 25.00
AL Adam Lind 3.00 8.00
AM Andrew Miller
BB Billy Butler 5.00 12.00
BU Brian Burres 3.00 8.00
DM Daisuke Matsuzaka EXCH
DY Delmon Young 6.00 15.00
HA Justin Hampson 3.00 8.00
HP Hunter Pence
JH Josh Hamilton 10.00 25.00
KC Kevin Cameron 3.00 8.00
KK Kyle Kendrick 6.00 15.00
MB Michael Bourn 3.00 8.00
MF Mike Fontenot 5.00 12.00
MO Micah Owings 5.00 12.00
RB Ryan Braun 20.00 50.00
SO Joakim Soria 3.00 8.00
TL Tim Lincecum
TT Troy Tulowitzki
YG Yovani Gallardo

2008 Upper Deck Derek Jeter Chronicles

STATED ODDS 1:6 TARGET
DJC1 Derek Jeter 1.50 4.00
DJC2 Derek Jeter 1.50 4.00
DJC3 Derek Jeter 1.50 4.00
DJC4 Derek Jeter 1.50 4.00
DJC5 Derek Jeter 1.50 4.00
DJC6 Derek Jeter 1.50 4.00
DJC7 Derek Jeter 1.50 4.00
DJC8 Derek Jeter 1.50 4.00
DJC9 Derek Jeter 1.50 4.00
DJC10 Derek Jeter 1.50 4.00
DJC11 Derek Jeter 1.50 4.00
DJC12 Derek Jeter 1.50 4.00
DJC13 Derek Jeter 1.50 4.00
DJC14 Derek Jeter 1.50 4.00
DJC15 Derek Jeter 1.50 4.00
DJC16 Derek Jeter 1.50 4.00
DJC17 Derek Jeter 1.50 4.00
DJC18 Derek Jeter 1.50 4.00
DJC19 Derek Jeter 1.50 4.00
DJC20 Derek Jeter 1.50 4.00

2008 Upper Deck Derek Jeter Chronicles Autographs

RANDOM INSERTS IN PACKS
STATED PRINT RUN 1 SER.#'d SET
NO PRICING DUE TO SCARCITY

2008 Upper Deck Derek Jeter O-Pee-Chee Reprints

STATED ODDS 1:6 TARGET
DJ1 Derek Jeter 1.50 4.00
DJ2 Derek Jeter 1.50 4.00
DJ3 Derek Jeter 1.50 4.00
DJ4 Derek Jeter 1.50 4.00
DJ5 Derek Jeter 1.50 4.00
DJ6 Derek Jeter 1.50 4.00
DJ7 Derek Jeter 1.50 4.00
DJ8 Derek Jeter 1.50 4.00
DJ9 Derek Jeter 1.50 4.00
DJ10 Derek Jeter 1.50 4.00
DJ11 Derek Jeter 1.50 4.00
DJ12 Derek Jeter 1.50 4.00
DJ13 Derek Jeter 1.50 4.00
DJ14 Derek Jeter 1.50 4.00
DJ15 Derek Jeter 1.50 4.00

2008 Upper Deck Diamond Collection

COMPLETE SET (20) 6.00 15.00
1 Adam LaRoche .40 1.00
2 Brian McCann .60 1.50
3 Bronson Arroyo .40 1.00
4 Chad Billingsley .60 1.50
5 Chin-Lung Hu .60 1.50
6 Felix Pie .40 1.00
7 Garrett Atkins .40 1.00
8 Homer Bailey .60 1.50
9 Ian Kennedy 1.00 2.50
10 James Shields .40 1.00
11 Jarrod Saltalamacchia .40 1.00
12 Manny Corpas .40 1.00
13 Mark Ellis .40 1.00
14 Micah Owings .40 1.00
15 Nick Swisher .40 1.00
16 Rich Hill .40 1.00
17 Russell Martin .40 1.00
18 Ryan Theriot .40 1.00
19 Steve Pearce .60 1.50
20 Victor Martinez .40 1.00

2008 Upper Deck Diamond Collection Autographs

STATED PRINT RUN 5 SER.#'d SETS
NO PRICING DUE TO SCARCITY

2008 Upper Deck Hit Brigade

HB1 Albert Pujols 2.00 5.00
HB2 Alex Rodriguez 1.50 4.00
HB3 David Ortiz 1.00 2.50
HB4 David Wright 1.25 3.00
HB5 Derek Jeter 2.50 6.00
HB6 Derrek Lee .60 1.50
HB7 Freddy Sanchez .40 1.00
HB8 Hanley Ramirez 1.00 2.50
HB9 Ichiro Suzuki 1.50 4.00
HB10 Joe Mauer .60 1.50
HB11 Magglio Ordonez .60 1.50
HB12 Matt Holliday .60 1.50
HB13 Miguel Cabrera .60 1.50
HB14 Todd Helton .60 1.50
HB15 Vladimir Guerrero 1.00 2.50

2008 Upper Deck Hit Brigade Autographs

STATED PRINT RUN 5 SER.#'d SETS
NO PRICING DUE TO SCARCITY
HB6 Derrek Lee
HB8 Hanley Ramirez
HB10 Joe Mauer
HB12 Matt Holliday
HB13 Miguel Cabrera

2008 Upper Deck Hot Commodities

COMPLETE SET (50) 30.00 60.00
STATED ODDS 2:1 WALMART/FAT PACKS
HC1 Miguel Tejada .40 1.00
HC2 Daisuke Matsuzaka 1.50 4.00
HC3 David Ortiz 1.00 2.50
HC4 Manny Ramirez 1.00 2.50
HC5 Alex Rodriguez 1.50 4.00
HC6 Derek Jeter 2.50 6.00
HC7 Carl Crawford .40 1.00
HC8 Alex Rios .40 1.00
HC9 Jim Thome .60 1.50
HC10 Grady Sizemore .60 1.50
HC11 Travis Hafner .40 1.00
HC12 Victor Martinez .40 1.00

HC13 Justin Verlander .60 1.50
HC14 Magglio Ordonez .60 1.50
HC15 Gary Sheffield .40 1.00
HC16 Alex Gordon 1.00 2.50
HC17 Justin Morneau .60 1.50
HC18 Johan Santana .60 1.50
HC19 Vladimir Guerrero 1.00 2.50
HC20 Dan Haren .40 1.00
HC21 Ichiro Suzuki 1.50 4.00
HC22 Mark Teixeira .60 1.50
HC23 Chipper Jones 1.25 3.00
HC24 John Smoltz 1.00 2.50
HC25 Miguel Cabrera .60 1.50
HC26 Hanley Ramirez 1.00 2.50
HC27 Jose Reyes .60 1.50
HC28 David Wright 1.25 3.00
HC29 Carlos Beltran .40 1.00
HC30 Ryan Howard 1.25 3.00
HC31 Chase Utley 1.00 2.50
HC32 Ryan Zimmerman .60 1.50
HC33 Aramis Ramirez .40 1.00
HC34 Derrek Lee .60 1.50
HC35 Alfonso Soriano .60 1.50
HC36 Ken Griffey Jr. 1.50 4.00
HC37 Adam Dunn .40 1.00
HC38 Carlos Lee .40 1.00
HC39 Lance Berkman .60 1.50
HC40 Prince Fielder 1.00 2.50
HC41 Ryan Braun 1.25 3.00
HC42 Jason Bay .40 1.00
HC43 Albert Pujols 2.00 5.00
HC44 Brandon Webb .60 1.50
HC45 Matt Holliday .60 1.50
HC46 Brad Penny .40 1.00
HC47 Russell Martin .40 1.00
HC48 Trevor Hoffman .40 1.00
HC49 Jake Peavy .60 1.50
HC50 Tim Lincecum 1.00 2.50

2008 Upper Deck Inkredible

STATED ODDS 1:80 H, 1:7500 R
AL Adam Lind 3.00 8.00
CC Chris Carpenter
CP Corey Patterson 3.00 8.00
CR Cody Ross 3.00 8.00
DL Derrek Lee 6.00 15.00
EA Erick Aybar 3.00 8.00
IK Ian Kinsler 5.00 12.00
IR Ivan Rodriguez 20.00 50.00
JB Josh Barfield 5.00 12.00
JH Jason Hammel 3.00 8.00
JS James Shields 3.00 8.00
KE Ian Kennedy
LS Luke Scott 3.00 8.00
MJ Mike Jacobs 5.00 12.00
RC Ryan Church 3.00 8.00
RL Ruddy Lugo 3.00 8.00
RS Ryan Shealy 3.00 8.00
RT Ryan Theriot 6.00 15.00
SO Jorge Sosa 5.00 12.00
TB Taylor Buchholz 3.00 8.00

2008 Upper Deck Milestone Memorabilia

STATED ODDS 1:192 HOBBY
GS Gary Sheffield 4.00 10.00
KG Ken Griffey Jr. 12.50 30.00
SS Sammy Sosa
TG Tom Glavine 8.00 20.00
TH Trevor Hoffman 4.00 10.00

2008 Upper Deck Mr. November

STATED ODDS 1:6 TARGET
1 Derek Jeter 1.50 4.00
2 Derek Jeter 1.50 4.00
3 Derek Jeter 1.50 4.00
4 Derek Jeter 1.50 4.00
5 Derek Jeter 1.50 4.00
6 Derek Jeter 1.50 4.00
7 Derek Jeter 1.50 4.00
8 Derek Jeter 1.50 4.00
9 Derek Jeter 1.50 4.00
10 Derek Jeter 1.50 4.00
11 Derek Jeter 1.50 4.00
12 Derek Jeter 1.50 4.00
13 Derek Jeter 1.50 4.00
14 Derek Jeter 1.50 4.00
15 Derek Jeter 1.50 4.00

2008 Upper Deck O-Pee-Chee

COMPLETE SET (50) 30.00 60.00
STATED ODDS 1:2 HOBBY
AG Alex Gordon 1.00 2.50
AP Albert Pujols 2.00 5.00
AR Alex Rodriguez 1.50 4.00
BP Brad Penny .40 1.00
BR Babe Ruth 2.50 6.00
BU B.J. Upton .60 1.50
BW Brandon Webb .60 1.50
CD Chris Duncan .40 1.00
CJ Chipper Jones 1.25 3.00
CL Carlos Lee .40 1.00
CP Carlos Pena 1.00 2.50
CU Chase Utley 1.00 2.50
CY Chris Young .40 1.00
DH Dan Haren .40 1.00
DJ Derek Jeter 2.50 6.00
DL Derrek Lee .60 1.50
DM Daisuke Matsuzaka 1.50 4.00
DO David Ortiz 1.00 2.50
DW David Wright 1.25 3.00
EB Erik Bedard .40 1.00
ER Edgar Renteria .40 1.00
GS Gary Sheffield .40 1.00
HP Hunter Pence 1.00 2.50
HR Hanley Ramirez 1.00 2.50
IS Ichiro Suzuki 1.50 4.00
JB Jason Bay .40 1.00
JJ J.J. Putz .40 1.00
JM Justin Morneau .60 1.50
JP Jake Peavy .60 1.50
JR Jose Reyes .60 1.50
JS Johan Santana .60 1.50
JT Jim Thome .60 1.50
JW Jered Weaver .40 1.00
KG Ken Griffey Jr. 1.50 4.00
MC Miguel Cabrera .60 1.50
MH Matt Holliday .60 1.50
MO Magglio Ordonez .60 1.50
MR Manny Ramirez 1.00 2.50
MT Mark Teixeira .60 1.50
NL Noah Lowry .40 1.00
PF Prince Fielder 1.00 2.50
PH Brandon Phillips .40 1.00
RA Aramis Ramirez .40 1.00
RB Ryan Braun 1.25 3.00
RH Ryan Howard 1.25 3.00
RM Russell Martin .40 1.00
RZ Ryan Zimmerman .60 1.50
TH Todd Helton .60 1.50
VG Vladimir Guerrero 1.00 2.50
VW Vernon Wells .40 1.00

2008 Upper Deck O-Pee-Chee Autographs

RANDOM INSERTS IN PACKS
STATED PRINT RUN 1 SER.#'d SET
NO PRICING DUE TO SCARCITY

2008 Upper Deck Presidential Predictors

COMP.SET w/o HILLARY (8) 15.00 40.00
STATED ODDS 1:6 H,1:6 R,1:10 WAL MART
PP1 Rudy Giuliani 2.00 5.00
PP2 John Edwards 2.00 5.00
PP3 John McCain 2.00 5.00
PP4 Barack Obama 5.00 12.00
PP5 Mitt Romney 2.00 5.00
PP6 Fred Thompson 2.00 5.00
PP7 Hillary Clinton SP 60.00 120.00
PP8 Al Gore 2.00 5.00
George Bush
PP9 Wild Card 2.00 5.00
PV1 Barack Obama Victor 6.00 15.00
PP15 Sarah Palin 60.00 120.00
PP16 Joe Biden 50.00 100.00

2008 Upper Deck Presidential Running Mate Predictors

PP7B Hillary Clinton 12.50 30.00
Barack Obama
PP7H Hillary Clinton 40.00 80.00
Barack Obama
PP10 Barack Obama 4.00 10.00
John McCain
PP10A John McCain 4.00 10.00
Hillary Clinton
PP11 Barack Obama 6.00 15.00
John McCain
PP11A John McCain 2.00 5.00
Hillary Clinton
PP12 Barack Obama 6.00 15.00
John McCain
PP12A John McCain 2.00 5.00
Hillary Clinton
PP13 Barack Obama 3.00 8.00
John McCain
PP13A John McCain 2.00 5.00
Hillary Clinton
PP14 Barack Obama 4.00 10.00
John McCain
PP14A John McCain 2.00 5.00
Hillary Clinton
PP15 Barack Obama
John McCain

2008 Upper Deck Season Highlights Signatures

STATED ODDS 1:80 H, 1:7500 R
BB Brian Bannister 6.00 15.00
BF Ben Francisco 3.00 8.00
CG Curtis Granderson 12.50 30.00
CS Curt Schilling 20.00 50.00
FL Fred Lewis 3.00 8.00
FT Frank Thomas
GA Garret Anderson
JS Jarrod Saltalamacchia 5.00 12.00
JV Justin Verlander
JW Josh Willingham 3.00 8.00
KK Kevin Kouzmanoff 3.00 8.00
MO Micah Owings 5.00 12.00
MR Mark Reynolds 6.00 15.00
MT Miguel Tejada 12.50 30.00
PF Prince Fielder
PM Pedro Martinez
RB Ryan Braun 20.00 50.00
RM Russell Martin
RS Ryan Spilborghs 6.00 15.00
TG Tom Glavine

2008 Upper Deck Signature Sensations

STATED ODDS 1:80 H, 1:7500 R
AE Andre Ethier 3.00 8.00
AK Austin Kearns 5.00 12.00
AM Aaron Miles 5.00 12.00
BB Boof Bonser 3.00 8.00
BH Brendan Harris 3.00 8.00
BM Brandon McCarthy 3.00 8.00
CB Cha-Seung Baek 3.00 8.00
CC Chris Carpenter
DL Derrek Lee 6.00 15.00
IR Ivan Rodriguez 20.00 50.00
JP Joel Peralta 3.00 8.00
JS James Shields 3.00 8.00
JV John Van Benschoten 3.00 8.00
KG Ken Griffey Jr.
LS Luke Scott 3.00 8.00
MC Matt Cain 5.00 12.00
NS Nick Swisher 5.00 12.00
RA Reggie Abercrombie 3.00 8.00
SM Sean Marshall 3.00 8.00
YP Yusmeiro Petit 3.00 8.00

2008 Upper Deck Signs of History Cut Signatures

AJ Andrew Johnson/5
BC Bill Clinton/12
BH Benjamin Harrison/30 700.00 1000.00
CC Calvin Coolidge/18
FP Franklin Pierce/8
FR Franklin D. Roosevelt/5
GB George H.W. Bush/18
GC Grover Cleveland/30 600.00 850.00
GF Gerald Ford/75
GW George Washington/1
HT Harry Truman/47 400.00 700.00
JC Jimmy Carter/49
JT John Tyler/8
RH Rutherford B. Hayes/75 400.00 650.00
RN Richard Nixon/19
RR Ronald Reagan/16
TR Theodore Roosevelt/3
WH William Henry Harrison/1
WM William McKinley/6
WT William H. Taft/50 500.00 750.00
WW Woodrow Wilson/22
NNO Exchange Card 700.00 1000.00

2008 Upper Deck Signs of History Cut Signatures Dual

BR George H. Bush
Ronald Reagan/3
CC Roselyn Carter
Jimmy Carter/3
CH Calvin Coolidge
Warren G. Harding/1
FN Gerald Ford
Richard Nixon/3
GA James Garfield
Chester Arthur/1
JJ Lyndon Johnson
Lady Bird Johnson/1
MR William McKinley
Theodore Roosevelt/1

2008 Upper Deck Signs of History Cut Signatures Quad

JJCC Lyndon B. Johnson
Lady Bird Johnson
Rosalynn Carter
Jimmy Carter/1
NRBB Richard Nixon
Ronald Reagan
George H Bush
George W. Bush/1
RBCB Ronald Reagan
George H Bush
Bill Clinton
George W. Bush/3
WLJR George Washington
Abraham Lincoln
Thomas Jefferson
Theodore Roosevelt/1

2008 Upper Deck Star Attractions

SA1 B.J. Upton .60 1.50
SA2 Carl Crawford .40 1.00
SA3 Chris B. Young .40 1.00
SA4 John Maine .40 1.00
SA5 Jonathan Papelbon .60 1.50
SA6 Nick Markakis .60 1.50
SA7 Prince Fielder 1.00 2.50
SA8 Takashi Saito .40 1.00
SA9 Tom Gorzelanny .40 1.00
SA10 Troy Tulowitzki .60 1.50

2008 Upper Deck Star Attractions Autographs

STATED PRINT RUN 5 SER.#'d SETS
NO PRICING DUE TO SCARCITY

2008 Upper Deck Star Quest

SER.1 ODDS 1:1 RETAIL/TARGET
SER.1 ODDS 1:1 WAL MART
*UNCOMMON: .4X TO 1X COMMON
SER.1 UNC ODDS 1:4 RETAIL/TARGET
SER.1 UNC ODDS 1:6 WAL MART
*RARE: .6X TO 1.5X COMMON
SER.1 RARE ODDS 1:8 RETAIL/TARGET
SER.1 RARE ODDS 1:12 WAL MART
*SUPER: 1X TO 2.5X COMMON
SER.1 SUPER ODDS 1:16 RETAIL/TARGET
SER.1 SUPER ODDS 1:24 WAL MART
*ULTRA: 1.5X TO 4X BASIC
SER.1 ULTRA ODDS 1:24 RETAIL/TARGET
SER.1 ULTRA ODDS 1:36 WAL MART
1 Ichiro Suzuki 1.50 4.00
2 Ryan Braun 1.25 3.00
3 Prince Fielder 1.00 2.50
4 Ken Griffey Jr. 1.50 4.00
5 Vladimir Guerrero 1.00 2.50
6 Travis Hafner .40 1.00
7 Matt Holliday .60 1.50
8 Ryan Howard 1.25 3.00
9 Derek Jeter 2.50 6.00
10 Chipper Jones 1.25 3.00
11 Carlos Lee .40 1.00
12 Justin Morneau .60 1.50
13 Magglio Ordonez .60 1.50
14 David Ortiz 1.00 2.50
15 Jake Peavy .60 1.50
16 Albert Pujols 2.00 5.00
17 Hanley Ramirez 1.00 2.50
18 Manny Ramirez 1.00 2.50
19 Jose Reyes .60 1.50
20 Alex Rodriguez 1.50 4.00
21 Johan Santana .60 1.50
22 Grady Sizemore .60 1.50
23 Alfonso Soriano .60 1.50
24 Mark Teixeira .60 1.50
25 Frank Thomas 1.00 2.50
26 Jim Thome .60 1.50
27 Chase Utley 1.00 2.50
28 Brandon Webb .60 1.50
29 David Wright 1.25 3.00
30 Michael Young .40 1.00
31 Adam Dunn .40 1.00
32 Albert Pujols 2.00 5.00
33 Alex Rodriguez 1.50 4.00
34 B.J. Upton .60 1.50
35 C.C. Sabathia .40 1.00
36 Carlos Beltran .40 1.00
37 Carlos Pena 1.00 2.50
38 Cole Hamels 1.00 2.50
39 Curtis Granderson 1.00 2.50
40 Daisuke Matsuzaka 1.50 4.00
41 David Ortiz 1.00 2.50
42 Derek Jeter 2.50 6.00
43 Derrek Lee .60 1.50
44 Eric Byrnes .40 1.00
45 Felix Hernandez .60 1.50
46 Ichiro Suzuki 1.50 4.00
47 Jeff Francoeur .60 1.50
48 Jimmy Rollins .60 1.50
49 Joe Mauer .60 1.50
50 John Smoltz 1.00 2.50
51 Ken Griffey Jr. 1.50 4.00
52 Lance Berkman .60 1.50
53 Miguel Cabrera .60 1.50
54 Paul Konerko .40 1.00
55 Pedro Martinez .60 1.50
56 Randy Johnson 1.00 2.50
57 Russell Martin .40 1.00
58 Troy Tulowitzki .60 1.50
59 Vernon Wells .40 1.00
60 Vladimir Guerrero 1.00 2.50

2008 Upper Deck Superstar Scrapbooks

SS1 Albert Pujols 2.00 5.00
SS2 Alex Rodriguez 1.50 4.00
SS3 Chase Utley 1.00 2.50
SS4 Chipper Jones 1.25 3.00
SS5 David Ortiz 1.00 2.50
SS6 Derek Jeter 2.50 6.00
SS7 Ichiro Suzuki 1.50 4.00
SS8 Johan Santana .60 1.50
SS9 Jose Reyes .60 1.50
SS10 Ken Griffey Jr. 1.50 4.00
SS11 Manny Ramirez 1.00 2.50
SS12 Prince Fielder 1.00 2.50
SS13 Randy Johnson 1.00 2.50
SS14 Ryan Howard 1.25 3.00
SS15 Vladimir Guerrero 1.00 2.50

2008 Upper Deck Superstar Scrapbooks Autographs

STATED PRINT RUN 5 SER.#'d SETS
NO PRICING DUE TO SCARCITY

2008 Upper Deck The House That Ruth Built

STATED ODDS 1:4 WAL MART BLISTER
STATED ODDS 1:6 WAL MART BLASTER
SILVER INSERTED IN WAL MART PACKS
SILVER PRINT RUN 1 SER.#'d SET
NO SILVER PRICING DUE TO SCARCITY
HRB1 Babe Ruth 1.50 4.00
HRB2 Babe Ruth 1.50 4.00
HRB3 Babe Ruth 1.50 4.00
HRB4 Babe Ruth 1.50 4.00
HRB5 Babe Ruth 1.50 4.00
HRB6 Babe Ruth 1.50 4.00
HRB7 Babe Ruth 1.50 4.00
HRB8 Babe Ruth 1.50 4.00
HRB9 Babe Ruth 1.50 4.00
HRB10 Babe Ruth 1.50 4.00
HRB11 Babe Ruth 1.50 4.00
HRB12 Babe Ruth 1.50 4.00
HRB13 Babe Ruth 1.50 4.00
HRB14 Babe Ruth 1.50 4.00
HRB15 Babe Ruth 1.50 4.00
HRB16 Babe Ruth 1.50 4.00
HRB17 Babe Ruth 1.50 4.00
HRB18 Babe Ruth 1.50 4.00
HRB19 Babe Ruth 1.50 4.00
HRB20 Babe Ruth 1.50 4.00
HRB21 Babe Ruth 1.50 4.00
HRB22 Babe Ruth 1.50 4.00
HRB23 Babe Ruth 1.50 4.00
HRB24 Babe Ruth 1.50 4.00
HRB25 Babe Ruth 1.50 4.00

2008 Upper Deck UD Autographs

STATED ODDS 1:80 H, 1:7500 R
CD Chris Duffy 3.00 8.00
CS Curt Schilling 20.00 50.00
JK Jeff Karstens 3.00 8.00
JP Joel Peralta 3.00 8.00
JS Jorge Sosa 5.00 12.00
JV John Van Benschoten 3.00 8.00
KI Kei Igawa 6.00 15.00
KS Kelly Shoppach 3.00 8.00
LS Luke Scott 3.00 8.00
MC Manny Corpas 6.00 15.00
MP Mike Pelfrey 5.00 12.00
MT Miguel Tejada 12.50 30.00
NM Nate McLouth 6.00 15.00
RH Ramon Hernandez 5.00 12.00
SA Kirk Saarloos 3.00 8.00
SF Scott Feldman 3.00 8.00
SH James Shields 3.00 8.00
SR Saul Rivera 3.00 8.00
SS Skip Schumaker 3.00 8.00
ZG Zack Greinke

2008 Upper Deck UD Game Materials

SER.1 ODDS 1:32 HOBBY,1:96 RETAIL
SER.1 ODDS 1:40 WAL MART BLASTER
SER.1 ODDS 1:96 TARGET/WM BLISTER
AJ Andruw Jones S2 3.00 8.00
AP Albert Pujols S2 6.00 15.00
BB Boof Bonser S2 3.00 8.00
BM Brandon McCarthy S2 3.00 8.00
BP Brandon Phillips S2 3.00 8.00
BR Brian Roberts 3.00 8.00
BU B.J. Upton S2 3.00 8.00
BZ Barry Zito S2 3.00 8.00
CA Matt Cain S2 3.00 8.00
CB Carlos Beltran 3.00 8.00
CB Chris Burke S2 3.00 8.00
CC Coco Crisp 3.00 8.00
CC Chris Carpenter S2 3.00 8.00
CD Chris Duncan S2 3.00 8.00
CG Carlos Guillen 3.00 8.00
CJ Conor Jackson S2 3.00 8.00
CL Cliff Lee S2 3.00 8.00
CQ Carlos Quentin S2 3.00 8.00
CU Michael Cuddyer S2 3.00 8.00
DC Daniel Cabrera 3.00 8.00
DJ Derek Jeter 8.00 20.00
DJ Derek Jeter S2 8.00 20.00
DL Derrek Lee S2 3.00 8.00
DO David Ortiz 4.00 10.00
DO David Ortiz S2 4.00 10.00
DW Dontrelle Willis 3.00 8.00
DW David Wells S2 3.00 8.00
EC Eric Chavez S2 3.00 8.00
EG Eric Gagne 3.00 8.00
ES Ervin Santana S2 3.00 8.00
FH Felix Hernandez S2 3.00 8.00
FL Francisco Liriano S2 3.00 8.00
FR Francisco Rodriguez S2 3.00 8.00
FS Freddy Sanchez S2 3.00 8.00
GA Garrett Atkins S2 3.00 8.00
GC Gustavo Chacin 3.00 8.00
GJ Geoff Jenkins 3.00 8.00
GL Troy Glaus S2 3.00 8.00
GM Gil Meche S2 3.00 8.00
GO Jonny Gomes S2 3.00 8.00
HR Hanley Ramirez S2 3.00 8.00
IR Ivan Rodriguez S2 3.00 8.00
JB Jason Bay 3.00 8.00
JB Jeremy Bonderman S2 3.00 8.00
JD Justin Duchscherer 3.00 8.00
JD Jermaine Dye S2 3.00 8.00
JG Jason Giambi S2 3.00 8.00
JH Jeremy Hermida S2 3.00 8.00
JJ Josh Johnson S2 3.00 8.00
JL James Loney S2 3.00 8.00
JP Jake Peavy 4.00 10.00
JP Jonathan Papelbon S2 4.00 10.00
JR Jeremy Reed S2 3.00 8.00
JS Jeremy Sowers 3.00 8.00
JS Jason Schmidt S2 3.00 8.00
JV Jason Varitek 4.00 10.00
JV Justin Verlander S2 3.00 8.00
JW Jered Weaver S2 3.00 8.00
KG Khalil Greene S2 3.00 8.00
KJ Kenji Johjima S2 3.00 8.00
KM Kazuo Matsui 3.00 8.00
KW Kerry Wood S2 3.00 8.00
MC Miguel Cabrera S2 4.00 10.00
ME Morgan Ensberg 3.00 8.00
ME Melky Cabrera S2 3.00 8.00
MG Marcus Giles S2 3.00 8.00
MJ Mike Jacobs S2 3.00 8.00
MK Masumi Kuwata 3.00 8.00
MM Melvin Mora 3.00 8.00
MN Mike Napoli S2 3.00 8.00
MP Mark Prior S2 3.00 8.00
MS Mike Sweeney 3.00 8.00
MY Michael Young 3.00 8.00
MY Brett Myers S2 3.00 8.00
OL Scott Olsen S2 3.00 8.00
PA Jonathan Papelbon 4.00 10.00
PE Mike Pelfrey S2 3.00 8.00
PF Prince Fielder S2 4.00 10.00
PK Paul Konerko S2 3.00 8.00
RC Ryan Church S2 3.00 8.00
RD Ray Durham S2 3.00 8.00
RF Ryan Freel S2 3.00 8.00
RH Roy Halladay 3.00 8.00
RJ Reed Johnson S2 3.00 8.00
RQ Robb Quinlan S2 3.00 8.00
RW Rickie Weeks S2 3.00 8.00
RZ Ryan Zimmerman S2 4.00 10.00
SK Scott Kazmir S2 3.00 8.00
SO Jeremy Sowers S2 3.00 8.00
TG Tom Glavine S2 3.00 8.00
TS Takashi Saito 3.00 8.00
VW Vernon Wells S2 3.00 8.00
WI Dontrelle Willis S2 3.00 8.00
YM Yadier Molina S2 3.00 8.00
ZD Zach Duke S2 3.00 8.00

2008 Upper Deck UD Game Patch

SER.1 ODDS 1:768 H,1:7500 R
AJ Andruw Jones S2 8.00 20.00
AP Albert Pujols S2 30.00 60.00
BB Boof Bonser S2 8.00 20.00
BM Brandon McCarthy S2 8.00 20.00
BP Brandon Phillips S2 8.00 20.00
BR Brian Roberts 8.00 20.00
BU B.J. Upton S2 8.00 20.00
BZ Barry Zito S2 8.00 20.00
CA Matt Cain S2 8.00 20.00
CB Carlos Beltran 8.00 20.00
CB Chris Burke S2 8.00 20.00
CC Coco Crisp 8.00 20.00
CC Chris Carpenter S2 8.00 20.00
CD Chris Duncan S2 8.00 20.00
CG Carlos Guillen 8.00 20.00
CJ Conor Jackson S2 8.00 20.00
CL Cliff Lee S2 8.00 20.00
CQ Carlos Quentin S2 8.00 20.00
CU Michael Cuddyer S2 8.00 20.00
DC Daniel Cabrera 8.00 20.00
DJ Derek Jeter 50.00 100.00
DJ Derek Jeter S2 50.00 100.00
DL Derrek Lee S2 8.00 20.00
DO David Ortiz 12.50 30.00
DO David Ortiz S2 12.50 30.00
DW Dontrelle Willis 8.00 20.00
DW David Wells S2 8.00 20.00
EC Eric Chavez S2 8.00 20.00
EG Eric Gagne 8.00 20.00
ES Ervin Santana S2 8.00 20.00
FH Felix Hernandez S2 8.00 20.00
FL Francisco Liriano S2 8.00 20.00
FR Francisco Rodriguez S2 8.00 20.00
FS Freddy Sanchez S2 8.00 20.00
GA Garrett Atkins S2 8.00 20.00
GC Gustavo Chacin 8.00 20.00
GJ Geoff Jenkins 8.00 20.00
GL Troy Glaus S2 8.00 20.00
GM Gil Meche S2 8.00 20.00
GO Jonny Gomes S2 8.00 20.00
HR Hanley Ramirez S2 8.00 20.00
IR Ivan Rodriguez S2 8.00 20.00
JB Jason Bay 8.00 20.00
JB Jeremy Bonderman S2 8.00 20.00
JD Justin Duchscherer 8.00 20.00
JD Jermaine Dye S2 8.00 20.00
JG Jason Giambi S2 8.00 20.00
JH Jeremy Hermida S2 8.00 20.00
JJ Josh Johnson S2 8.00 20.00
JL James Loney S2 8.00 20.00
JP Jake Peavy 12.50 30.00
JP Jonathan Papelbon S2 12.50 30.00
JR Jeremy Reed S2 8.00 20.00
JS Jeremy Sowers 8.00 20.00
JS Jason Schmidt S2 8.00 20.00
JV Jason Varitek 12.50 30.00
JV Justin Verlander S2 8.00 20.00
JW Jered Weaver S2 8.00 20.00
KG Khalil Greene S2 8.00 20.00
KJ Kenji Johjima S2 8.00 20.00
KM Kazuo Matsui 8.00 20.00
KW Kerry Wood S2 8.00 20.00
MC Miguel Cabrera S2 12.50 30.00
ME Morgan Ensberg 8.00 20.00
ME Melky Cabrera S2 8.00 20.00
MG Marcus Giles S2 8.00 20.00

MJ Mike Jacobs S2 8.00 20.00
MK Masumi Kuwata 8.00 20.00
MM Melvin Mora 8.00 20.00
MN Mike Napoli S2 8.00 20.00
MP Mark Prior S2 8.00 20.00
MS Mike Sweeney 8.00 20.00
MY Michael Young 8.00 20.00
MY Brett Myers S2 8.00 20.00
OL Scott Olsen S2 8.00 20.00
PA Jonathan Papelbon 12.50 30.00
PE Mike Pelfrey S2 8.00 20.00
PF Prince Fielder S2 12.50 30.00
PK Paul Konerko S2 8.00 20.00
RC Ryan Church S2 8.00 20.00
RD Ray Durham S2 8.00 20.00
RF Ryan Freel S2 8.00 20.00
RH Roy Halladay 8.00 20.00
RJ Reed Johnson S2 8.00 20.00
RQ Robb Quinlan S2 8.00 20.00
RW Rickie Weeks S2 8.00 20.00
RZ Ryan Zimmerman S2 12.50 30.00
SK Scott Kazmir S2 8.00 20.00
SO Jeremy Sowers S2 8.00 20.00
TG Tom Glavine S2 8.00 20.00
TS Takashi Saito 8.00 20.00
VW Vernon Wells S2 8.00 20.00
WI Dontrelle Willis S2 8.00 20.00
YM Yadier Molina S2 8.00 20.00
ZD Zach Duke S2 8.00 20.00

2008 Upper Deck UD Game Materials 1997

SER.1 ODDS 1:32 HOBBY,1:96 RETAIL
SER.1 ODDS 1:40 WAL MART BLASTER
SER.1 ODDS 1:96 TARGET/WM BLISTER
AP Albert Pujols 8.00 20.00
BC Bobby Crosby 3.00 8.00
BG Brian Giles 3.00 8.00
BR B.J. Ryan 3.00 8.00
BS Ben Sheets 3.00 8.00
CH Cole Hamels S2 3.00 8.00
CS Curt Schilling 4.00 10.00
DL Derek Lowe 3.00 8.00
DO David Ortiz 4.00 10.00
DO David Ortiz S2 4.00 10.00
DU Dan Uggla S2 3.00 8.00
GJ Geoff Jenkins 3.00 8.00
HK Hong-Chih Kuo 4.00 10.00
IR Ivan Rodriguez 4.00 10.00
JB Joe Blanton 3.00 8.00
JC Joe Crede 3.00 8.00
JJ Josh Johnson 3.00 8.00
JM Justin Morneau S2 3.00 8.00
JP Jonathan Papelbon S2 4.00 10.00
JS James Shields 3.00 8.00
JV Justin Verlander S2 3.00 8.00
JW Jake Westbrook 3.00 8.00
JZ Joel Zumaya S2 3.00 8.00
LM Lastings Milledge 3.00 8.00
MC Miguel Cabrera 4.00 10.00
MO Magglio Ordonez 4.00 10.00
NM Nick Markakis 4.00 10.00
PE Andy Pettitte 4.00 10.00
PF Prince Fielder S2 4.00 10.00
PO Jorge Posada S2 3.00 8.00
RB Rocco Baldelli 3.00 8.00
TH Todd Helton 4.00 10.00
VG Vladimir Guerrero S2 3.00 8.00
VM Victor Martinez 3.00 8.00
XN Xavier Nady 3.00 8.00

2008 Upper Deck UD Game Materials 1997 Patch

SER.1 ODDS 1:768 H,1:7500 R
AP Albert Pujols 15.00 40.00
BC Bobby Crosby 8.00 20.00
BG Brian Giles 8.00 20.00
BR BJ Ryan 8.00 20.00
BS Ben Sheets 8.00 20.00
CH Cole Hamels S2 8.00 20.00
CS Curt Schilling 12.50 30.00
DL Derek Lowe 8.00 20.00
DO David Ortiz 12.50 30.00
DO David Ortiz S2 12.50 30.00
DU Dan Uggla S2 8.00 20.00
GJ Geoff Jenkins 8.00 20.00
HK Hong-Chih Kuo 8.00 20.00
IR Ivan Rodriguez 12.50 30.00
JB Joe Blanton 8.00 20.00
JC Joe Crede 8.00 20.00
JJ Josh Johnson 8.00 20.00
JM Justin Morneau S2 8.00 20.00
JP Jonathan Papelbon S2 12.50 30.00
JS James Shields 8.00 20.00
JV Justin Verlander S2 8.00 20.00
JW Jake Westbrook 8.00 20.00
JZ Joel Zumaya S2 8.00 20.00
LM Lastings Milledge 8.00 20.00
MC Miguel Cabrera 12.50 30.00
MO Magglio Ordonez 12.50 30.00
NM Nick Markakis 12.50 30.00
PE Andy Pettitte 12.50 30.00
PF Prince Fielder S2 12.50 30.00
PO Jorge Posada S2 8.00 20.00
RB Rocco Baldelli 8.00 20.00
TH Todd Helton 12.50 30.00
VG Vladimir Guerrero S2 8.00 20.00
VM Victor Martinez 8.00 20.00
XN Xavier Nady 8.00 20.00

2008 Upper Deck UD Game Materials 1998

SER.1 ODDS 1:32 HOBBY,1:96 RETAIL
SER.1 ODDS 1:40 WAL MART BLASTER
SER.1 ODDS 1:96 TARGET/WM BLISTER
AJ Andruw Jones S2 3.00 8.00
BH Bill Hall 3.00 8.00
BS Ben Sheets 3.00 8.00
CD Chris Duncan S2 3.00 8.00
CF Chone Figgins 3.00 8.00
CZ Carlos Zambrano 3.00 8.00
DJ Derek Jeter S2 10.00 25.00
DL Derrek Lee S2 3.00 8.00
EG Eric Gagne 3.00 8.00
FC Fausto Carmona 3.00 8.00
FH Felix Hernandez 4.00 10.00
GM Greg Maddux S2 5.00 12.00
GS Grady Sizemore 4.00 10.00
HB Hank Blalock 3.00 8.00
IS Ian Snell 3.00 8.00
JE Johnny Estrada 3.00 8.00
JJ Jacque Jones 3.00 8.00
JK Jason Kendall 3.00 8.00
JS Johan Santana 4.00 10.00
KM Kevin Millwood 3.00 8.00
MB Mark Buehrle 3.00 8.00
MG Marcus Giles 3.00 8.00
NM Nick Markakis 4.00 10.00
PK Paul Konerko 3.00 8.00
RM Russell Martin S2 3.00 8.00
RO Roy Oswalt S2 3.00 8.00
TH Travis Hafner S2 3.00 8.00
VG Vladimir Guerrero S2 3.00 8.00
VM Victor Martinez 3.00 8.00
VM Victor Martinez S2 3.00 8.00

2008 Upper Deck UD Game Materials 1998 Patch

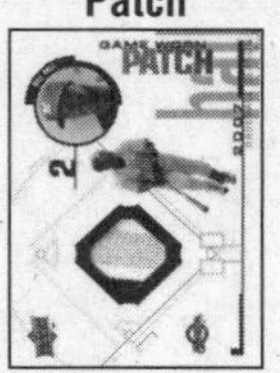

SER.1 ODDS 1:768 H,1:7500 R
AJ Andruw Jones S2 8.00 20.00
BH Bill Hall 8.00 20.00
BS Ben Sheets 8.00 20.00
CD Chris Duncan S2 8.00 20.00
CF Chone Figgins 8.00 20.00
CZ Carlos Zambrano 8.00 20.00
DJ Derek Jeter S2 20.00 50.00
DL Derrek Lee S2 8.00 20.00
EG Eric Gagne 8.00 20.00
FC Fausto Carmona 8.00 20.00
FH Felix Hernandez 12.50 30.00
GM Greg Maddux S2 12.50 30.00
GS Grady Sizemore 12.50 30.00
HB Hank Blalock 8.00 20.00
IS Ian Snell 8.00 20.00
JE Johnny Estrada 8.00 20.00
JJ Jacque Jones 8.00 20.00
JK Jason Kendall 8.00 20.00
JS Johan Santana 12.50 30.00
KM Kevin Millwood 8.00 20.00
MB Mark Buehrle 8.00 20.00
MG Marcus Giles 8.00 20.00
NM Nick Markakis 12.50 30.00
PK Paul Konerko 8.00 20.00
RM Russell Martin S2 8.00 20.00
RO Roy Oswalt S2 8.00 20.00
TH Travis Hafner S2 8.00 20.00
VG Vladimir Guerrero S2 8.00 20.00
VM Victor Martinez 8.00 20.00
VM Victor Martinez S2 8.00 20.00

2008 Upper Deck UD Game Materials 1999

SER.1 ODDS 1:32 HOBBY,1:96 RETAIL
SER.1 ODDS 1:40 WAL MART BLASTER
SER.1 ODDS 1:96 TARGET/WM BLISTER
BR Brian Roberts 3.00 8.00
BU B.J. Upton S2 3.00 8.00
BW Brandon Webb S2 3.00 8.00
CA Matt Cain S2 3.00 8.00
CD Chris Duffy 3.00 8.00
CJ Chipper Jones 4.00 10.00
CS C.C. Sabathia 3.00 8.00
DL Derrek Lee 3.00 8.00
DO David Ortiz S2 4.00 10.00
DW David Wells 3.00 8.00
EB Erik Bedard 3.00 8.00
FS Freddy Sanchez 3.00 8.00
HR Hanley Ramirez S2 3.00 8.00
JB Jason Bay 3.00 8.00
JD Johnny Damon 3.00 8.00
JG Jeremy Guthrie 3.00 8.00
JH J.J. Hardy 3.00 8.00
JK Jason Kubel 3.00 8.00
JM Joe Mauer S2 3.00 8.00
JP Jorge Posada 4.00 10.00
KG Khalil Greene S2 3.00 8.00
KJ Kenji Johjima 3.00 8.00
KM Kendry Morales 3.00 8.00
MC Miguel Cabrera S2 3.00 8.00
MT Mark Teixeira 4.00 10.00
NM Nick Markakis S2 3.00 8.00
RW Rickie Weeks 3.00 8.00
TE Miguel Tejada 3.00 8.00
TH Travis Hafner 3.00 8.00
TH Torii Hunter S2 3.00 8.00

2008 Upper Deck UD Game Materials 1999 Patch

SER.1 ODDS 1:768 H,1:7500 R
BR Brian Roberts 8.00 20.00
BU B.J. Upton S2 8.00 20.00
BW Brandon Webb S2 8.00 20.00
CA Matt Cain S2 8.00 20.00
CD Chris Duffy 8.00 20.00
CJ Chipper Jones 12.50 30.00
CS C.C. Sabathia 8.00 20.00
DL Derrek Lee 8.00 20.00
DO David Ortiz S2 12.50 30.00
DW David Wells 8.00 20.00
EB Erik Bedard 8.00 20.00
FS Freddy Sanchez 8.00 20.00
HR Hanley Ramirez S2 8.00 20.00
JB Jason Bay 8.00 20.00
JD Johnny Damon 8.00 20.00
JG Jeremy Guthrie 8.00 20.00
JH J.J. Hardy 8.00 20.00
JK Jason Kubel 8.00 20.00
JM Joe Mauer S2 8.00 20.00
JP Jorge Posada 12.50 30.00
KG Khalil Greene S2 8.00 20.00
KJ Kenji Johjima 8.00 20.00
KM Kendry Morales 8.00 20.00
MC Miguel Cabrera S2 8.00 20.00
MT Mark Teixeira 12.50 30.00
NM Nick Markakis S2 8.00 20.00
RW Rickie Weeks 8.00 20.00
TE Miguel Tejada 8.00 20.00
TH Travis Hafner 8.00 20.00
TH Torii Hunter S2 8.00 20.00

2008 Upper Deck Superstar

COMPLETE SET (10) 6.00 15.00
STATED ODDS 3:1 SUPER PACKS
9 Vladimir Guerrero .60 1.50
48 Mark Teixeira .40 1.00
57 Prince Fielder .60 1.50
67 Albert Pujols 1.25 3.00
139 Ichiro Suzuki 1.00 2.50
147 Hanley Ramirez .60 1.50
156 David Wright .75 2.00
239 Ken Griffey Jr. 1.00 2.50
270 Magglio Ordonez .40 1.00
297 Derek Jeter 1.50 4.00

2008 Upper Deck Superstar Autographs

RANDOM INSERTS IN PACKS
STATED PRINT RUN 5 SER.#'d SETS
NO PRICING DUE TO SCARCITY

2008 Upper Deck USA Junior National Team

USJR1 Eric Hosmer 4.00 10.00
USJR2 Garrison Lassiter 1.25 3.00
USJR3 Harold Martinez 1.25 3.00
USJR4 J.P. Ramirez 1.25 3.00
USJR5 Jeff Malm 2.00 5.00
USJR6 Jordan Swagerty 1.25 3.00
USJR7 Kyle Buchanan 1.25 3.00
USJR8 Kyle Skipworth 3.00 8.00
USJR9 L.J. Hoes 3.00 8.00
USJR10 Matthew Purke 1.25 3.00
USJR11 Mychal Givens 1.25 3.00
USJR12 Nick Maronde 1.25 3.00
USJR13 Riccio Torrez 1.25 3.00
USJR14 Robbie Grossman 2.00 5.00
USJR15 Ryan Weber 1.25 3.00
USJR16 T.J. House 1.25 3.00
USJR17 Tim Melville 1.25 3.00
USJR18 Tyler Hibbs 1.25 3.00
USJR19 Tyler Stovall 1.25 3.00
USJR20 Tyler Wilson 1.25 3.00

2008 Upper Deck USA Junior National Team Autographs

PRINT RUNS B/WN 133-500 COPIES PER
EH Eric Hosmer/238 6.00 15.00
GL Garrison Lassiter/375 4.00 10.00
HI Tyler Hibbs/375 4.00 10.00
HM Harold Martinez/237 4.00 10.00
JM Jeff Malm/375 4.00 10.00
JR J.P. Ramirez/239 4.00 10.00
JS Jordan Swagerty/350 4.00 10.00
KB Kyle Buchanan/375 4.00 10.00
KS Kyle Skipworth/177 6.00 15.00
LH L.J. Hoes/158 4.00 10.00
MG Mychal Givens/209 4.00 10.00
MP Matthew Purke/375 4.00 10.00
NM Nick Maronde/166 4.00 10.00
RG Robbie Grossman/155 4.00 10.00
RT Riccio Torrez/500 4.00 10.00
RW Ryan Weber/375 4.00 10.00
TH T.J. House/147 4.00 10.00
TM Tim Melville/133 4.00 10.00
TS Tyler Stovall/375 4.00 10.00
TW Tyler Wilson/375 4.00 10.00

2008 Upper Deck USA Junior National Team Autographs Blue

*BLUE AU: .4X TO 1X BASIC AU
PRINT RUNS B/WN 75-400 COPIES PER
EH Eric Hosmer/75 8.00 20.00
GL Garrison Lassiter/175 4.00 10.00
HI Tyler Hibbs/400 4.00 10.00
HM Harold Martinez/275 4.00 10.00
JM Jeff Malm/175 4.00 10.00
JR J.P. Ramirez/90 4.00 10.00
JS Jordan Swagerty/195 4.00 10.00
KB Kyle Buchanan/175 4.00 10.00
KS Kyle Skipworth/200 8.00 20.00
LH L.J. Hoes/300 4.00 10.00
MG Mychal Givens/309 4.00 10.00
MP Matthew Purke/390 4.00 10.00
NM Nick Maronde/100 4.00 10.00
RG Robbie Grossman/175 4.00 10.00
RT Riccio Torrez/400 4.00 10.00
RW Ryan Weber/392 4.00 10.00
TH T.J. House/75 4.00 10.00
TM Tim Melville/330 4.00 10.00
TS Tyler Stovall/186 4.00 10.00
TW Tyler Wilson/75 4.00 10.00

2008 Upper Deck USA Junior National Team Autographs Green

STATED PRINT RUN 10 SER.#'d SETS
NO PRICING DUE TO SCARCITY

2008 Upper Deck USA Junior National Team Autographs Red

*RED AU: .5X TO 1.2X BASIC AU
PRINT RUNS B/WN 50-150 COPIES PER
EH Eric Hosmer/50 10.00 25.00
KS Kyle Skipworth/50 10.00 25.00

2008 Upper Deck USA Junior National Team Jerseys

EH Eric Hosmer 4.00 10.00
GL Garrison Lassiter 3.00 8.00
HI Tyler Hibbs 3.00 8.00
HM Harold Martinez 3.00 8.00
JM Jeff Malm 3.00 8.00
JR J.P. Ramirez 3.00 8.00
JS Jordan Swagerty 3.00 8.00
KB Kyle Buchanan 3.00 8.00
KS Kyle Skipworth 4.00 10.00
LH L.J. Hoes 3.00 8.00
MG Mychal Givens 3.00 8.00
MP Matthew Purke 3.00 8.00
NM Nick Maronde 3.00 8.00
RG Robbie Grossman 3.00 8.00
RT Riccio Torrez 3.00 8.00
RW Ryan Weber 3.00 8.00
TH T.J. House 3.00 8.00
TM Tim Melville 3.00 8.00
TS Tyler Stovall 3.00 8.00
TW Tyler Wilson 3.00 8.00

2008 Upper Deck USA Junior National Team Jerseys Autographs Black

PRINT RUNS B/WN 99-400 COPIES PER
EH Eric Hosmer/170 10.00 25.00
GL Garrison Lassiter/226 4.00 10.00
HI Tyler Hibbs/222 4.00 10.00
HM Harold Martinez/99 4.00 10.00
JM Jeff Malm/258 4.00 10.00
JR J.P. Ramirez/99 4.00 10.00
JS Jordan Swagerty/199 4.00 10.00
KB Kyle Buchanan/205 4.00 10.00
KS Kyle Skipworth/99 10.00 25.00
LH L.J. Hoes/150 4.00 10.00
MG Mychal Givens/99 4.00 10.00
MP Matthew Purke/209 4.00 10.00
NM Nick Maronde/99 4.00 10.00
RG Robbie Grossman/150 4.00 10.00
RT Riccio Torrez/400 4.00 10.00
RW Ryan Weber/222 4.00 10.00
TH T.J. House/149 4.00 10.00
TM Tim Melville/175 4.00 10.00
TS Tyler Stovall/199 4.00 10.00
TW Tyler Wilson/199 4.00 10.00

2008 Upper Deck USA Junior National Team Jerseys Autographs Blue

*JSY BLUE: .4X TO 1X JSY BLACK
PRINT RUNS B/WN 50-400 COPIES PER
EH Eric Hosmer/121 10.00 25.00
GL Garrison Lassiter/172 4.00 10.00
HI Tyler Hibbs/392 4.00 10.00
HM Harold Martinez/375 4.00 10.00
JM Jeff Malm/107 4.00 10.00
JR J.P. Ramirez/200 4.00 10.00
JS Jordan Swagerty/173 4.00
KB Kyle Buchanan/131 4.00
KS Kyle Skipworth/300 6.00 15.00
LH L.J. Hoes/340 4.00
MG Mychal Givens/300 4.00
MP Matthew Purke/390 4.00
NM Nick Maronde/50 4.00
RG Robbie Grossman/100 4.00
RT Riccio Torrez/400 4.00
RW Ryan Weber/400 4.00 10.00
TH T.J. House/75 4.00
TM Tim Melville/350 4.00
TS Tyler Stovall/125 4.00
TW Tyler Wilson/235 4.00

2008 Upper Deck USA Junior National Team Jerseys Autographs Green

STATED PRINT RUN 10 SER.#'d SETS
NO PRICING DUE TO SCARCITY
EH Eric Hosmer
GL Garrison Lassiter
HI Tyler Hibbs
HM Harold Martinez
JM Jeff Malm
JR J.P. Ramirez
JS Jordan Swagerty
KB Kyle Buchanan
KS Kyle Skipworth
LH L.J. Hoes
MG Mychal Givens
MP Matthew Purke
NM Nick Maronde
RG Robbie Grossman
RT Riccio Torrez
RW Ryan Weber
TH T.J. House
TM Tim Melville
TS Tyler Stovall
TW Tyler Wilson

2008 Upper Deck USA Junior National Team Jerseys Autographs Red

*JSY RED: .5X TO 1.2X JSY BLACK
PRINT RUNS B/WN 25-150 COPIES PER
NO PRICING ON QTY 25 OR LESS
EH Eric Hosmer/50 12.50 30.00
GL Garrison Lassiter/50 5.00 12.00
HI Tyler Hibbs/75 5.00 12.00
HM Harold Martinez/50 5.00 12.00
JM Jeff Malm/75 5.00 12.00
JR J.P. Ramirez/50 5.00 12.00
JS Jordan Swagerty/60 5.00 12.00
KB Kyle Buchanan/85 5.00 21.00
KS Kyle Skipworth/56 12.50 30.00
LH L.J. Hoes/60 5.00 12.00
MG Mychal Givens/60 5.00 12.00
MP Matthew Purke/74 5.00 12.00
NM Nick Maronde/25
RG Robbie Grossman/50 5.00 12.00
RT Riccio Torrez/150 5.00 12.00
RW Ryan Weber/50 5.00 12.00
TH T.J. House/50 5.00 12.00
TM Tim Melville/50 5.00 12.00
TS Tyler Stovall/85 5.00 12.00
TW Tyler Wilson/85 5.00 12.00

2008 Upper Deck USA Junior National Team Patch

*PATCH 99: .5X TO 1.2X BASIC JSY
STATED PRINT RUN 99 SER.#'d SETS
EH Eric Hosmer 6.00 15.00
KS Kyle Skipworth 6.00 15.00

2008 Upper Deck USA Junior National Team Patch Autographs

STATED PRINT RUN 99 SER.#'d SETS
EH Eric Hosmer 10.00 25.00
GL Garrison Lassiter 6.00 15.00
HI Tyler Hibbs 6.00 15.00
HM Harold Martinez 6.00 15.00
JM Jeff Malm 6.00 15.00
JR J.P. Ramirez 6.00 15.00
JS Jordan Swagerty 6.00 15.00
KB Kyle Buchanan 6.00 15.00
KS Kyle Skipworth 10.00 25.00
LH L.J. Hoes 6.00 15.00
MG Mychal Givens 6.00 15.00
MP Matthew Purke 6.00 15.00
NM Nick Maronde 6.00 15.00
RG Robbie Grossman 6.00 15.00
RT Riccio Torrez 6.00 15.00
RW Ryan Weber 6.00 15.00
TH T.J. House 6.00 15.00
TM Tim Melville 6.00 15.00
TS Tyler Stovall 6.00 15.00
TW Tyler Wilson 6.00 15.00

2008 Upper Deck USA National Team

USA1 Brett Hunter 1.25 3.00
USA2 Brian Matusz 1.25 3.00
USA3 Brett Wallace 1.25 3.00
USA4 Cody Satterwhite 1.25 3.00
USA5 Danny Espinosa 1.25 3.00
USA6 Eric Surkamp 1.25 3.00
USA7 Jordan Danks 1.25 3.00
USA8 Jeremy Hamilton 1.25 3.00
USA9 Joe Kelly 1.25 3.00
USA10 Jordy Mercer 1.25 3.00
USA11 Josh Romanski 1.25 3.00
USA12 Justin Smoak 1.25 3.00
USA13 Jacob Thompson 1.25 3.00
USA14 Logan Forsythe 1.25 3.00
USA15 Lance Lynn 1.25 3.00
USA16 Mike Minor 1.25 3.00
USA17 Pedro Alvarez 1.25 3.00
USA18 Petey Paramore 1.25 3.00
USA19 Ryan Berry 1.25 3.00
USA20 Ryan Flaherty 1.25 3.00
USA21 Roger Kieschnick 1.25 3.00
USA22 Seth Frankoff 1.25 3.00
USA23 Scott Gorgen 1.25 3.00
USA24 Tommy Medica 1.25 3.00
USA25 Tyson Ross 1.25 3.00

2008 Upper Deck USA National Team Autographs

PRINT RUNS B/WN 183-500 COPIES PER
BH Brett Hunter/297 4.00 10.00
BM Brian Matusz/264 5.00 12.00
BW Brett Wallace/183 6.00 15.00
CS Cody Satterwhite/375 4.00 10.00
DE Danny Espinosa/311 4.00 10.00
ES Eric Surkamp/
JD Jordan Danks/311 4.00 10.00
JH Jeremy Hamilton/375 4.00 10.00
JK Joe Kelly/457 4.00 10.00
JM Jordy Mercer/375 4.00 10.00
JR Josh Romanski/375 4.00 10.00
JS Justin Smoak/345 8.00 20.00
JT Jacob Thompson/267 4.00 10.00
LF Logan Forsythe/201 5.00 12.00
LL Lance Lynn/425 4.00 10.00
MM Mike Minor/375 4.00 10.00
PA Pedro Alvarez/205 8.00 20.00
PP Petey Paramore/237 4.00 10.00
RB Ryan Berry/375 4.00 10.00
RF Ryan Flaherty/244 4.00 10.00
RK Roger Kieschnick/272 4.00 10.00
SF Seth Frankoff/
SG Scott Gorgen/
TM Tommy Medica/487 4.00 10.00
TR Tyson Ross/500 4.00 10.00

2008 Upper Deck USA National Team Autographs Blue

*BLUE AU: .4X TO 1X BASIC AU
PRINT RUNS B/WN 50-204 COPIES PER
BH Brett Hunter/129 4.00 10.00
BM Brian Matusz/50 15.00 40.00
BW Brett Wallace/75 6.00 15.00
CS Cody Satterwhite/131 4.00 10.00
DE Danny Espinosa/75 4.00 10.00
ES Eric Surkamp/117 4.00 10.00
JD Jordan Danks/75 6.00 15.00
JH Jeremy Hamilton/204 4.00 10.00
JK Joe Kelly/125 4.00 10.00
JM Jordy Mercer/175 4.00 10.00
JR Josh Romanski/175 4.00 10.00
JS Justin Smoak/60 15.00 40.00
JT Jacob Thompson/105 4.00 10.00
LF Logan Forsythe/75 5.00 12.00
LL Lance Lynn/
MM Mike Minor/175 4.00 10.00
PA Pedro Alvarez/75 15.00 40.00
PP Petey Paramore/175 4.00 10.00
RB Ryan Berry/175 4.00 10.00
RF Ryan Flaherty/75 4.00 10.00
RK Roger Kieschnick/113 5.00 12.00
SF Seth Frankoff/175 4.00 10.00
SG Scott Gorgen/175 4.00 10.00
TM Tommy Medica/175 4.00 10.00
TR Tyson Ross/75 4.00 10.00

2008 Upper Deck USA National Team Autographs Green

STATED PRINT RUN 10 SER.#'d SETS
NO PRICING DUE TO SCARCITY

2008 Upper Deck USA National Team Autographs Red

*RED AU: .5X TO 1.2X BASIC AU
STATED PRINT RUN 50 SER.#'d SETS
BM Brian Matusz 15.00 40.00
BW Brett Wallace 6.00 15.00
JD Jordan Danks 6.00 15.00
JS Justin Smoak 15.00 40.00
LF Logan Forsythe 5.00 12.00
LL Lance Lynn 4.00 10.00
RF Ryan Flaherty 4.00 10.00
TR Tyson Ross 4.00 10.00

2008 Upper Deck USA National Team Highlights

H1 Game 1 1.00 2.50
H2 Game 2 1.00 2.50
H3 Game 3 1.00 2.50
H4 Game 4 1.00 2.50
H5 Game 5 1.00 2.50

2008 Upper Deck USA National Team Jerseys

BH Brett Hunter 3.00 8.00
BM Brian Matusz 3.00 8.00
BW Brett Wallace 3.00 8.00
CS Cody Satterwhite 3.00 8.00
DE Danny Espinosa 3.00 8.00
ES Eric Surkamp 3.00 8.00
JD Jordan Danks 3.00 8.00
JH Jeremy Hamilton 3.00 8.00
JK Joe Kelly 3.00 8.00
JM Jordy Mercer 3.00 8.00
JR Josh Romanski 3.00 8.00
JS Justin Smoak 4.00 10.00
JT Jacob Thompson 3.00 8.00
LF Logan Forsythe 3.00 8.00
LL Lance Lynn 3.00 8.00
MM Mike Minor 3.00 8.00
PA Pedro Alvarez 4.00 10.00
PP Petey Paramore 3.00 8.00
RB Ryan Berry 3.00 8.00
RF Ryan Flaherty 3.00 8.00
RK Roger Kieschnick 3.00 8.00
SF Seth Frankoff 3.00 8.00
SG Scott Gorgen 3.00 8.00
TM Tommy Medica 3.00 8.00
TR Tyson Ross 3.00 8.00

2008 Upper Deck USA National Team Jerseys Autographs Black

PRINT RUNS B/WN 99-400 COPIES PER
BH Brett Hunter/99 4.00 10.00
BM Brian Matusz/181 8.00 20.00
BW Brett Wallace/199 4.00 10.00
CS Cody Satterwhite/273 6.00 15.00
DE Danny Espinosa/130 4.00 10.00
ES Eric Surkamp/
JD Jordan Danks/99 6.00 15.00
JH Jeremy Hamilton/271 4.00 10.00
JK Joe Kelly/300 4.00 10.00
JM Jordy Mercer/287 4.00 10.00
JR Josh Romanski/311 4.00 10.00
JS Justin Smoak/199 12.50 30.00
JT Jacob Thompson/199 4.00 10.00
LF Logan Forsythe/199 4.00 10.00
LL Lance Lynn/149 4.00 10.00
MM Mike Minor/359 4.00 10.00
PA Pedro Alvarez/275 10.00 25.00
PP Petey Paramore/199 4.00 10.00
RB Ryan Berry/284 4.00 10.00
RF Ryan Flaherty/149 6.00 15.00
RK Roger Kieschnick/199 4.00 10.00
SF Seth Frankoff/
SG Scott Gorgen/
TM Tommy Medica/400 4.00 10.00
TR Tyson Ross/400 4.00 10.00

2008 Upper Deck USA National Team Jerseys Autographs Blue

*BLUE JSY AU: .4X TO 1X BLACK JSY AU
PRINT RUNS B/WN 69-292 COPIES PER
ES Eric Surkamp/200 4.00 10.00
LL Lance Lynn/
SF Seth Frankoff/69 4.00 10.00
SG Scott Gorgen/247 4.00 10.00

2008 Upper Deck USA National Team Jerseys Autographs Green

STATED PRINT RUN 10 SER.#'d SETS
NO PRICING DUE TO SCARCITY

2008 Upper Deck USA National Team Jerseys Autographs Red

*RED JSY AU: .5X TO 1.2X BASIC JSY AU
PRINT RUNS B/WN 50-182 COPIES PER
ES Eric Surkamp/50 5.00 12.00
PA Pedro Alvarez/50 15.00 40.00
SF Seth Frankoff/50 5.00 12.00
SG Scott Gorgen/50 5.00 12.00

2008 Upper Deck USA National Team Patch

*PATCH: .5X TO 1.2X BASIC JSY
STATED PRINT RUN 99 SER.#'d SETS
JS Justin Smoak 10.00 25.00
PA Pedro Alvarez 10.00 25.00

2008 Upper Deck USA National Team Patch Autographs

STATED PRINT RUN 99 SER.#'d SETS
BH Brett Hunter 6.00 15.00
BM Brian Matusz 12.50 30.00
BW Brett Wallace 12.50 30.00
CS Cody Satterwhite 15.00 40.00
DE Danny Espinosa 10.00 25.00
ES Eric Surkamp 6.00 15.00
JD Jordan Danks 15.00 40.00
JH Jeremy Hamilton 6.00 15.00
JK Joe Kelly 6.00 15.00
JM Jordy Mercer 6.00 15.00
JR Josh Romanski 6.00 15.00
JS Justin Smoak 20.00 50.00
JT Jacob Thompson 6.00 15.00
LF Logan Forsythe 6.00 15.00
LL Lance Lynn 6.00 15.00
MM Mike Minor 6.00 15.00
PA Pedro Alvarez 30.00 60.00
PP Petey Paramore 6.00 15.00
RB Ryan Berry 6.00 15.00
RF Ryan Flaherty 6.00 15.00
RK Roger Kieschnick 6.00 15.00
SF Seth Frankoff 6.00 15.00
SG Scott Gorgen 6.00 15.00
TM Tommy Medica 6.00 15.00
TR Tyson Ross 10.00 25.00

2008 Upper Deck Yankee Stadium Legacy Collection

COMMON CARD 1.25 3.00
COMMON CLEMENS 2.00 5.00
COMMON DIMAGGIO 2.50 6.00
COMMON GEHRIG 2.50 6.00
COMMON JETER 3.00 8.00
COMMON MARIS 2.00 5.00
COMMON MATTINGLY 2.50 6.00
COMMON RODRIGUEZ 2.50 6.00
COMMON RUTH 3.00 8.00
1 Babe Ruth 40.00 80.00

2008 Upper Deck Yankee Stadium Legacy Collection Historical Moments

473 Notre Dame v. Army 3.00 8.00
1198 Joe Louis
1288 Joe DiMaggio 4.00 10.00
1939 All Star Game
2835 1958 NFL Championship 3.00 8.00
2946 Whitey Ford 3.00 8.00
1960 All Star Game
3407 Pope Paul VI 2.50 6.00
4131 Muhammad Ali v. Ken Norton 4.00 10.00
4181 Reggie Jackson 3.00 8.00
1977 All Star Game
5404 U2

2008 Upper Deck Yankee Stadium Legacy Collection Memorabilia

AP Andy Pettitte 12.50 30.00
BD Bill Dickey 40.00 80.00
BM Billy Martin 30.00 60.00
BR Babe Ruth 250.00 500.00
CL Roger Clemens 30.00 60.00
CS Casey Stengel 20.00 50.00
CW Chien-Ming Wang 20.00 50.00
DE Bucky Dent 15.00 40.00
DJ Derek Jeter 50.00 100.00
DM Don Mattingly 30.00 60.00
DW Dave Winfield 15.00 40.00
EH Elston Howard 15.00 40.00
FC Frankie Crosetti 20.00 50.00
GG Goose Gossage 10.00 25.00
GM Gil McDougald 50.00 100.00
GN Graig Nettles 15.00 40.00
GS Gary Sheffield 6.00 15.00
JA Reggie Jackson 12.50 30.00
JC Joba Chamberlain 20.00 50.00
JD Joe DiMaggio 100.00 200.00
JG Jason Giambi 6.00 15.00
JP Joe Pepitone 50.00 100.00
LG Lou Gehrig 150.00 250.00
LP Lou Piniella 60.00 120.00
MC Melky Cabrera 15.00 40.00
MM Mike Mussina 30.00 60.00
MU Bobby Murcer 6.00 15.00
ON Paul O'Neill 30.00 60.00
PN Phil Niekro 30.00 60.00
PO Jorge Posada 6.00 15.00
RC Robinson Cano 15.00 40.00
RE Allie Reynolds 20.00 50.00
RG Ron Guidry 20.00 50.00
RJ Randy Johnson 6.00 15.00
RM Roger Maris 50.00 100.00
SL Sparky Lyle 20.00 50.00
TH Tommy Henrich 20.00 50.00
TM Thurman Munson 20.00 50.00
WB Wade Boggs 15.00 40.00
WF Whitey Ford 20.00 50.00
WR Willie Randolph 20.00 50.00
YB Yogi Berra 30.00 60.00

2008 Upper Deck Ballpark Collection

This set was released on September 17, 2008. The base set consists of 340 cards.

COMMON CARD (1-100) .60 1.50
COMMON AU RC (101-150) 3.00 8.00
OVERALL AU ODDS 1:5 HOBBY
EXCHANGE DEADLINE 08/27/2010
COMMON 2X GU (151-200) 4.00 10.00
COMMON 4X GU (201-250) 4.00 10.00
COMMON 6X GU (251-295) 5.00 12.00
COMMON 8X GU (296-340) 6.00 15.00
OVERALL GU ODDS 2:1 HOBBY
1 Brandon Webb 1.00 2.50
2 Dan Haren .60 1.50
3 Chris B. Young .60 1.50
4 Randy Johnson 1.50 4.00
5 Mark Teixeira 1.00 2.50
6 John Smoltz 1.50 4.00
7 Tom Glavine 1.00 2.50
8 Brian McCann 1.00 2.50
9 Chipper Jones 2.00 5.00
10 Nick Markakis 1.00 2.50
11 Brian Roberts 1.00 2.50
12 Josh Beckett 1.00 2.50
13 David Ortiz 1.50 4.00
14 Manny Ramirez 1.50 4.00
15 Dustin Pedroia 2.50 6.00
16 Jonathan Papelbon 1.00 2.50
17 Daisuke Matsuzaka 2.50 6.00
18 Alfonso Soriano 1.00 2.50
19 Aramis Ramirez .60 1.50
20 Carlos Zambrano .60 1.50
21 Nick Swisher .60 1.50
22 Jim Thome 1.00 2.50
23 Ken Griffey Jr. 2.50 6.00
24 Adam Dunn .60 1.50
25 Grady Sizemore 1.00 2.50
26 Victor Martinez .60 1.50
27 Travis Hafner .60 1.50
28 C.C. Sabathia .60 1.50
29 Garrett Atkins .60 1.50
30 Matt Holliday 1.00 2.50
31 Troy Tulowitzki 1.00 2.50
32 Magglio Ordonez 1.00 2.50
33 Justin Verlander 1.00 2.50
34 Miguel Cabrera 1.00 2.50
35 Gary Sheffield .60 1.50
36 Ivan Rodriguez 1.00 2.50
37 Dontrelle Willis .60 1.50
38 Curtis Granderson .60 1.50
39 Hanley Ramirez 1.50 4.00
40 Dan Uggla 1.00 2.50
41 Lance Berkman 1.00 2.50
42 Roy Oswalt .60 1.50
43 Carlos Lee .60 1.50
44 Hunter Pence 1.50 4.00
45 Alex Gordon 1.50 4.00
46 Jose Guillen .60 1.50
47 Torii Hunter .60 1.50
48 Vladimir Guerrero 1.50 4.00
49 Andruw Jones .60 1.50
50 Matt Kemp .60 1.50
51 Russell Martin .60 1.50
52 Jeff Kent .60 1.50
53 Ryan Braun 2.00 5.00
54 Prince Fielder 1.50 4.00
55 Delmon Young 1.00 2.50
56 Joe Mauer 1.00 2.50
57 Justin Morneau 1.00 2.50
58 Jose Reyes 1.00 2.50
59 David Wright 2.00 5.00
60 Carlos Beltran .60 1.50
61 Johan Santana 1.00 2.50
62 Pedro Martinez 1.00 2.50
63 Alex Rodriguez 2.50 6.00
64 Derek Jeter 4.00 10.00
65 Hideki Matsui 1.50 4.00
66 Robinson Cano 1.00 2.50
67 Joba Chamberlain 2.00 5.00
68 Phil Hughes 1.50 4.00
69 Mariano Rivera 1.50 4.00
70 Eric Chavez .60 1.50
71 Bobby Crosby .60 1.50
72 Cole Hamels 1.50 4.00
73 Ryan Howard 2.00 5.00
74 Jimmy Rollins 1.00 2.50
75 Chase Utley 1.50 4.00
76 Jason Bay .60 1.50
77 Freddy Sanchez .60 1.50
78 Jake Peavy 1.00 2.50
79 Greg Maddux 2.00 5.00
80 Trevor Hoffman .60 1.50
81 Kosuke Fukudome RC 3.00 8.00
82 Barry Zito .60 1.50
83 Tim Lincecum 1.50 4.00
84 Erik Bedard .60 1.50
85 Felix Hernandez 1.00 2.50
86 Ichiro Suzuki 2.50 6.00
87 Troy Glaus 1.00 2.50
88 Albert Pujols 3.00 8.00
89 Chris Carpenter .60 1.50
90 Scott Kazmir 1.00 2.50
91 Carl Crawford .60 1.50
92 Michael Young .60 1.50
93 Hank Blalock .60 1.50
94 Roy Halladay .60 1.50
95 Vernon Wells .60 1.50
96 Alex Rios .60 1.50
97 Scott Rolen 1.00 2.50
98 Frank Thomas 1.50 4.00
99 Lastings Milledge .60 1.50
100 Ryan Zimmerman 1.00 2.50
101 Bobby Wilson AU RC 3.00 8.00
102 Alex Romero AU (RC) 4.00 10.00
103 Alexei Ramirez AU RC
104 Brandon Boggs AU (RC) 3.00 8.00
105 Brian Barton AU RC 4.00 10.00
106 Brian Bass AU (RC) 6.00 15.00
107 Brian Bixler AU (RC) 3.00 8.00
108 Brian Bocock AU RC 3.00 8.00
109 Burke Badenhop AU RC 3.00 8.00
110 Callix Crabbe AU (RC) 3.00 8.00
111 Clayton Kershaw AU RC 12.50 30.00
112 Chin-Lung Hu AU (RC) 10.00 25.00
113 Clay Buchholz AU (RC) 8.00 20.00
114 Eider Torres AU (RC) 5.00 12.00
115 Clete Thomas AU RC 3.00 8.00
116 Colt Morton AU RC 3.00 8.00
117 Daric Barton AU (RC) 3.00 8.00
118 Cory Wade AU (RC) 5.00 12.00
119 Elliot Johnson AU (RC) 3.00 8.00
120 Emmanuel Burriss AU RC
121 Evan Longoria AU RC 40.00 80.00
122 Evan Meek AU RC 3.00 8.00
123 German Duran AU RC 3.00 8.00
124 Fernando Hernandez AU RC 3.00 8.00
125 Greg Smith AU RC 3.00 8.00
126 Jay Bruce AU (RC) EXCH 20.00 50.00
127 Wladimir Balentien AU (RC) 4.00 10.00
128 Hernan Iribarren AU (RC) 3.00 8.00
129 Jed Lowrie AU (RC) 20.00 50.00
130 Ian Kennedy AU RC 6.00 15.00
131 Jeff Clement AU (RC) 8.00 20.00
132 Jesse Carlson AU RC 6.00 15.00
133 Jonathan Herrera AU RC 3.00 8.00
134 Johnny Cueto AU RC 6.00 15.00
135 Jonathan Albaladejo AU RC 4.00 10.00
136 Josh Newman AU RC 3.00 8.00
137 Kevin Hart AU (RC) 4.00 10.00
138 Justin Masterson AU RC 15.00 40.00
139 Luke Hochevar AU (RC)
140 Luis Mendoza AU (RC) 3.00 8.00
141 Matt Tupman AU RC 8.00 20.00
142 Max Scherzer AU RC EXCH 10.00 25.00
143 Nick Blackburn AU RC 12.50 30.00
144 Nick Adenhart AU (RC) 5.00 12.00
145 Ramon Troncoso AU RC 5.00 12.00
146 Paul Janish AU (RC) 4.00 10.00
147 Randor Bierd AU RC 15.00 40.00
148 Robinzon Diaz AU (RC) 3.00 8.00
149 Steve Holm AU RC 4.00 10.00
150 Wesley Wright AU RC 6.00 15.00
151 Jason Giambi 4.00 10.00
David Ortiz
152 Jonathan Papelbon 5.00 12.00
Mariano Rivera
153 Nolan Ryan 6.00 15.00
Johan Santana
154 Mike Mussina 5.00 12.00
Jorge Posada
155 Jonathan Papelbon 5.00 12.00
Jason Varitek
156 Dan Uggla 4.00 10.00
Howie Kendrick
157 Kenji Johjima 4.00 10.00
Jason Varitek
158 Carlos Lee 4.00 10.00
Roy Oswalt
159 Albert Pujols 5.00 12.00
Derrek Lee
160 Albert Pujols 8.00 20.00
Ozzie Smith
161 Alfonso Soriano 6.00 15.00
Carlos Zambrano
162 Tony Gwynn 4.00 10.00
Trevor Hoffman
163 Cole Hamels 4.00 10.00
Johan Santana
164 David Ortiz 4.00 10.00
Kendry Morales
165 Curt Schilling 4.00 10.00
Randy Johnson
166 Curtis Granderson 4.00 10.00
B.J. Upton
167 Chase Utley 12.50 30.00
Ryne Sandberg
168 Nick Markakis 4.00 10.00
Melvin Mora
169 Conor Jackson 4.00 10.00
Prince Fielder
170 Roy Halladay 4.00 10.00
Ben Sheets
171 Kerry Wood 4.00 10.00
Mark Mulder
172 Andruw Jones 5.00 12.00
Ken Griffey Jr.
173 Troy Tulowitzki 4.00 10.00
J.J. Hardy
174 Matt Cain 5.00 12.00
Tim Lincecum
175 Derek Jeter 5.00 12.00
Orlando Cabrera
176 Albert Pujols 5.00 12.00
Prince Fielder
177 Frank Thomas 5.00 12.00
Roy Halladay
178 Josh Beckett 4.00 10.00
Jason Varitek
179 Miguel Cabrera 5.00 12.00
Mike Schmidt
180 Albert Pujols 5.00 12.00
Chris Duncan
181 C.C. Sabathia 4.00 10.00
Dontrelle Willis
182 Matt Holliday 4.00 10.00
Manny Ramirez
183 Roy Halladay 4.00 10.00
Zack Greinke
184 Nick Markakis 4.00 10.00
Vladimir Guerrero
185 Ben Sheets 4.00 10.00
Roy Halladay
186 Albert Pujols 5.00 12.00
Vladimir Guerrero
187 Johnny Damon 4.00 10.00
Manny Ramirez
188 Johan Santana 4.00 10.00
Chris Carpenter
189 Ken Griffey Jr.
Frank Thomas
190 Tadahito Iguchi
Akinori Iwamura
191 Curt Schilling 5.00 12.00
Jonathan Papelbon
192 Derek Jeter 12.50 30.00
Cal Ripken Jr.
193 Jason Varitek 4.00 10.00
Wade Boggs
194 Derrek Lee 5.00 12.00
Alfonso Soriano
195 Vladimir Guerrero
Rod Carew
196 Hong-Chih Kuo 4.00 10.00
Kenji Johjima
197 Kerry Wood 4.00 10.00
Alfonso Soriano
198 Albert Pujols 5.00 12.00
Carlos Delgado
199 Don Mattingly 12.50 30.00
Derek Jeter
200 Derek Jeter 6.00 15.00
Johnny Damon
201 Prince Fielder 4.00 10.00
Ben Sheets
Matt Kemp
James Loney
202 David Ortiz 8.00 20.00
Kevin Youkilis
Jason Giambi
Derek Jeter
203 Cal Ripken Jr. 10.00 25.00
Derek Jeter
Khalil Greene
Troy Tulowitzki
204 Robin Yount 6.00 15.00
Prince Fielder
Rickie Weeks
J.J. Hardy
205 Vladimir Guerrero 4.00 10.00
Howie Kendrick
Casey Kotchman
Chone Figgins
206 Jason Varitek 4.00 10.00
Jorge Posada
Ivan Rodriguez
Kenji Johjima
207 Trevor Hoffman 4.00 10.00
Mariano Rivera
Eric Gagne
Joe Nathan
208 Carlos Guillen 4.00 10.00
Brandon Inge
Gary Sheffield
Ivan Rodriguez
209 Scott Kazmir 5.00 12.00
Randy Johnson
Francisco Liriano
Johan Santana
210 Johan Santana 5.00 12.00
Billy Wagner
John Maine
Pedro Martinez
211 Conor Jackson 6.00 15.00
Prince Fielder
Albert Pujols
Derrek Lee
212 Josh Beckett 4.00 10.00
Justin Verlander
Jered Weaver
Zack Greinke
213 Greg Maddux 5.00 12.00
Jake Peavy
Chris Young
Trevor Hoffman
214 Nolan Ryan
John Smoltz
Mike Mussina
Roy Halladay
215 Greg Maddux 6.00 15.00
Trevor Hoffman
Khalil Greene
Tony Gwynn
216 Ken Griffey Jr. 6.00 15.00
Aaron Harang
Alfonso Soriano
Carlos Zambrano
217 Greg Maddux 6.00 15.00
John Smoltz
Mike Mussina
Roy Halladay
218 Ken Griffey Jr. 6.00 15.00
Jim Thome
Frank Thomas
Manny Ramirez
219 Pat Burrell
Josh Willingham
Johnny Damon
Manny Ramirez
220 Vladimir Guerrero 6.00 15.00
Manny Ramirez
Albert Pujols
Carlos Lee
221 Ken Griffey Jr. 6.00 15.00
Alfonso Soriano
Carlos Lee
Jason Bay
222 Pat Burrell
Geoff Jenkins
Cole Hamels
Brad Lidge
223 Derrek Lee 6.00 15.00
Alfonso Soriano
Derek Jeter
Jason Giambi
224 Takashi Saito 5.00 12.00
Tadahito Iguchi
Akinori Iwamura
Kenji Johjima
225 C.C. Sabathia 4.00 10.00
Randy Johnson
Scott Kazmir
Cole Hamels
226 Albert Pujols 10.00 25.00
Rick Ankiel
Chris Carpenter
Ozzie Smith
227 Mike Schmidt 10.00 25.00
Albert Pujols
Ken Griffey Jr.
David Ortiz
228 Curtis Granderson 5.00 12.00
Rafael Furcal
Derek Jeter
Rickie Weeks
229 David Ortiz 6.00 15.00
Manny Ramirez
Jason Varitek
Wade Boggs
230 Andy Pettitte 6.00 15.00
Derek Jeter
Jake Peavy
Khalil Greene
231 Don Mattingly 12.50 30.00
Derek Jeter
Manny Ramirez
David Ortiz
232 John Smoltz 5.00 12.00
Chipper Jones
Johan Santana
Carlos Delgado
233 Derek Jeter 6.00 15.00
Jason Giambi
Melvin Mora
Brian Roberts
234 Derrek Lee 6.00 15.00
Aramis Ramirez
Albert Pujols
Chris Duncan
235 Mark Mulder 6.00 15.00
Albert Pujols
Ben Sheets
Prince Fielder
236 Ken Griffey Jr.
Derek Jeter
David Ortiz
Albert Pujols
237 Manny Ramirez 6.00 15.00
Vladimir Guerrero
Pat Burrell
Albert Pujols
238 Andy Pettitte 6.00 15.00
Derek Jeter
Ivan Rodriguez
Justin Verlander
239 Jason Varitek 5.00 12.00
Ivan Rodriguez
Jorge Posada
Kenji Johjima
240 Brian Roberts 4.00 10.00
Rickie Weeks
Chase Utley
Dan Uggla
241 Mark Mulder 6.00 15.00
Albert Pujols
Ivan Rodriguez
Magglio Ordonez
242 Ken Griffey Jr. 6.00 15.00
Prince Fielder
David Ortiz
Nick Markakis
243 Derek Jeter 6.00 15.00
Brian Roberts
Michael Young
Dan Uggla
244 Manny Ramirez 5.00 12.00
David Ortiz
Magglio Ordonez
Vladimir Guerrero
245 Randy Johnson 4.00 10.00
Conor Jackson
Chad Billingsley
James Loney
246 Manny Ramirez 4.00 10.00
Magglio Ordonez
Pat Burrell
Josh Willingham
247 Derek Jeter 12.50 30.00
Jason Giambi
Mariano Rivera
Chien-Ming Wang
248 Carl Crawford 4.00 10.00
B.J. Upton
Hanley Ramirez
Dan Uggla
249 Albert Pujols 6.00 15.00
Ken Griffey Jr.
Derrek Lee
Prince Fielder
250 Garret Anderson
Vladimir Guerrero
Chone Figgins
Rod Carew
251 Chris Carpenter 5.00 12.00
Ben Sheets
Dan Haren
Josh Johnson
Jake Peavy
Cole Hamels
252 Vladimir Guerrero 6.00 15.00
Manny Ramirez
Curtis Granderson
Mark Teahen
Rocco Baldelli
Nick Markakis
253 Randy Johnson 5.00 12.00
Barry Zito
Johan Santana
Francisco Liriano
Mark Mulder
Scott Kazmir
254 Derek Jeter
Jason Giambi
Mike Mussina
Manny Ramirez
David Ortiz
Jonathan Papelbon
255 Travis Hafner 10.00 25.00
Victor Martinez
C.C. Sabathia
Vladimir Guerrero
John Lackey
Howie Kendrick
256 Albert Pujols 10.00 25.00
Derrek Lee
Carlos Delgado
Adrian Gonzalez
Prince Fielder
Adam LaRoche
257 Ken Griffey Jr. 12.50 30.00
Carlos Lee
Matt Holliday
Jason Bay
Josh Willingham
Tony Gwynn

258 Johan Santana
Carlos Delgado
John Smoltz
Chipper Jones
Cole Hamels
Pat Burrell
259 Derek Jeter
Michael Young
Khalil Greene
Brian Roberts
Rickie Weeks
Ryne Sandberg
260 Derek Jeter 12.50 30.00
Andy Pettitte
Jason Giambi
Carlos Delgado
Johan Santana
Moises Alou
261 Frank Thomas
Jason Giambi
David Ortiz
Aubrey Huff
Casey Kotchman
Rod Carew
262 Jered Weaver 5.00 12.00
Rickie Weeks
Zack Greinke
Khalil Greene
Scott Kazmir
Howie Kendrick
263 Mike Mussina 6.00 15.00
Andy Pettitte
John Smoltz
Randy Johnson
Roy Halladay
Tom Glavine
264 Derek Jeter
Jason Giambi
Melvin Mora
Jorge Posada
Brian Roberts
Nick Markakis
265 Derrek Lee 10.00 25.00
Kerry Wood
Aramis Ramirez
Albert Pujols
Mark Mulder
Chris Duncan
266 Andruw Jones 5.00 12.00
Rafael Furcal
Takashi Saito
Vladimir Guerrero
Howie Kendrick
Jered Weaver
267 Albert Pujols 8.00 20.00
Mark Mulder
Derrek Lee
Kerry Wood
Prince Fielder
Ben Sheets
268 Ken Griffey Jr. 15.00 40.00
Derek Jeter
Manny Ramirez
Vladimir Guerrero
David Ortiz
Albert Pujols
269 Mark Teixeira 8.00 20.00
Chipper Jones
Carlos Delgado
Moises Alou
Josh Willingham
Dan Uggla
270 Frank Thomas 10.00 25.00
Manny Ramirez
Vladimir Guerrero
Carlos Lee
Mike Schmidt
Albert Pujols
271 Ivan Rodriguez 6.00 15.00
Jason Varitek
Jorge Posada
Joe Mauer
Brian McCann
Kenji Johjima
272 Manny Ramirez 5.00 12.00
Magglio Ordonez
Pat Burrell
Josh Willingham
Delmon Young
Nick Markakis
273 Miguel Tejada 6.00 15.00
Mark Loretta
Roy Oswalt
Kevin Millwood
Michael Young
Josh Hamilton
274 Johan Santana 10.00 25.00
Carlos Delgado
Moises Alou
Cole Hamels
Pat Burrell
Chase Utley
275 Chase Utley 5.00 12.00
Aaron Hill
Rickie Weeks
Chris Burke
Dan Uggla
Akinori Iwamura
276 Kerry Wood 10.00 25.00
Derrek Lee
Aramis Ramirez
Randy Johnson
Dan Haren
Chad Tracy
277 Ivan Rodriguez 8.00 20.00
Magglio Ordonez
Brandon Inge
Albert Pujols
Mark Mulder
Chris Duncan
278 Ken Griffey Jr. 8.00 20.00
Prince Fielder
Geoff Jenkins
David Ortiz
Garret Anderson
Nick Markakis
279 Derek Jeter
Michael Young
Troy Tulowitzki
Brian Roberts
Dan Uggla
Aaron Hill
280 Manny Ramirez 6.00 15.00
Vladimir Guerrero
Magglio Ordonez
David Ortiz
Aramis Ramirez
Kendry Morales
281 Jason Varitek 5.00 12.00
Jorge Posada
Kenji Johjima
Miguel Cabrera
Melvin Mora
Eric Chavez
282 Ken Griffey Jr. 6.00 15.00
Mike Cameron
Jason Bay
Grady Sizemore
Mark Teahen
Delmon Young
283 Mariano Rivera
Jorge Posada
Joe Nathan
Joe Mauer
Jonathan Papelbon
Jason Varitek
284 David Ortiz 6.00 15.00
Jonathan Papelbon
Josh Beckett
Magglio Ordonez
Dontrelle Willis
Joel Zumaya
285 Prince Fielder 6.00 15.00
Mike Cameron
Rickie Weeks
Justin Morneau
Delmon Young
Francisco Liriano
286 Carl Crawford 5.00 12.00
Scott Kazmir
Akinori Iwamura
Luis Gonzalez
Josh Johnson
Dan Uggla
287 Nick Markakis 8.00 20.00
Rick Ankiel
Josh Hamilton
Xavier Nady
J.D. Drew
Chris Duncan
288 Jake Peavy 5.00 12.00
Chris Young
Troy Tulowitzki
Jeff Francis
Matt Cain
Aaron Rowand
289 Ken Griffey Jr.
Andruw Jones
Carlos Beltran
Jim Edmonds
Mike Cameron
Coco Crisp
290 Derek Jeter 20.00 50.00
Jason Giambi
Mariano Rivera
Jorge Posada
Chien-Ming Wang
Don Mattingly
291 Manny Ramirez 10.00 25.00
Jason Varitek
Josh Beckett
J.D. Drew
Jonathan Papelbon
Wade Boggs
292 Dan Haren 5.00 12.00
Conor Jackson
Jeff Francis
Troy Tulowitzki
Rafael Furcal
Chad Billingsley
293 Ken Griffey Jr.
Aaron Harang
Albert Pujols
Mark Mulder
Derrek Lee
Carlos Zambrano
294 Gary Sheffield 10.00 25.00
Ivan Rodriguez
Carlos Guillen
Magglio Ordonez
Miguel Cabrera
Dontrelle Willis
295 Vladimir Guerrero 6.00 15.00
Garret Anderson
John Lackey
Chone Figgins
Jered Weaver
Casey Kotchman
296 Kerry Wood
Eric Gagne
Brad Lidge
Chad Cordero
Joe Nathan
Joel Zumaya
Jonathan Papelbon
Mariano Rivera
297 Manny Ramirez 20.00 50.00
David Ortiz
Jason Varitek
Jonathan Papelbon
Derek Jeter
Jason Giambi
Jorge Posada
Mariano Rivera
298 Vladimir Guerrero 8.00 20.00
John Lackey
Howie Kendrick
Kendry Morales
Travis Hafner
C.C. Sabathia
Victor Martinez
Grady Sizemore
299 Albert Pujols 12.50 30.00
Prince Fielder
Lance Berkman
Derrek Lee
Mark Teixeira
Carlos Delgado
Adrian Gonzalez
Adam LaRoche
300 Matt Holliday 8.00 20.00
Carlos Lee
Josh Willingham
Jason Bay
Ken Griffey Jr.
Carlos Beltran
Chris Duncan
Mike Cameron
301 Johan Santana 6.00 15.00
Carlos Delgado
Josh Johnson
Josh Willingham
John Smoltz
Chipper Jones
Cole Hamels
Pat Burrell
302 Ozzie Smith
Derek Jeter
Khalil Greene
Stephen Drew
Brian Roberts
Dan Uggla
Mark Loretta
Rickie Weeks
303 Johan Santana 15.00 40.00
Jose Reyes
Carlos Delgado
Moises Alou
Andy Pettitte
Derek Jeter
Jason Giambi
Johnny Damon
304 David Ortiz 15.00 40.00
Casey Kotchman
Jason Giambi
Frank Thomas
Richie Sexson
Aubrey Huff
Jim Thome
Justin Morneau
305 Jake Peavy
Matt Cain
Tim Lincecum
Dan Haren
Roy Halladay
Mike Mussina
Curt Schilling
John Smoltz
306 Ken Griffey Jr. 12.50 30.00
Albert Pujols
Carlos Lee
Derrek Lee
Prince Fielder
Chris Duncan
Lance Berkman
Alfonso Soriano
307 Randy Johnson
John Smoltz
Tom Glavine
Pedro Martinez
Mike Mussina
John Lackey
Andy Pettitte
Roy Halladay
308 Nick Markakis
Melvin Mora
Brian Roberts
Aubrey Huff
Johnny Damon
Derek Jeter
Jason Giambi
Jorge Posada
309 Alfonso Soriano
Derrek Lee
Aramis Ramirez
Ryne Sandberg
Albert Pujols
Chris Duncan
Mark Mulder
Chris Carpenter
310 Vladimir Guerrero
Howie Kendrick
Jered Weaver
John Lackey
Russell Martin
Rafael Furcal
Matt Kemp
Juan Pierre
311 Albert Pujols 10.00 25.00
Mark Mulder
Derrek Lee
Kerry Wood
Prince Fielder
Ben Sheets
Tom Gorzelanny
Xavier Nady
312 Cal Ripken Jr. 20.00 50.00
Derek Jeter
Albert Pujols
David Ortiz
Ken Griffey Jr.
Manny Ramirez
Mark Teixeira
Vladimir Guerrero
313 Moises Alou
Carlos Delgado
Luis Gonzalez
Dan Uggla
Mark Teixeira
Chipper Jones
Pat Burrell
Chase Utley
314 Albert Pujols 12.50 30.00
Vladimir Guerrero
Pat Burrell
Jason Giambi
Frank Thomas
Carlos Lee
Aramis Ramirez
Manny Ramirez
315 Gary Sheffield
Justin Verlander
Dontrelle Willis
Ivan Rodriguez
Derek Jeter
Mike Mussina
Andy Pettitte
Jorge Posada
316 Miguel Cabrera
Chad Tracy
Chone Figgins
Melvin Mora
Eric Chavez
Aramis Ramirez
Chipper Jones
Brandon Inge
317 Manny Ramirez 6.00 15.00
Magglio Ordonez
Nick Markakis
RoC.C.o Baldelli
Moises Alou
Pat Burrell
Josh Willingham
Delmon Young
318 Michael Young 8.00 20.00
Kevin Millwood
Hank Blalock
Josh Hamilton
Carlos Lee
Roy Oswalt
Miguel Tejada
Mark Loretta
319 Chase Utley 8.00 20.00
Cole Hamels
Pat Burrell
Brad Lidge
Carlos Delgado
Johan Santana
Moises Alou
Billy Wagner
320 Chase Utley 10.00 25.00
Robinson Cano
Rickie Weeks
Brian Roberts
Dan Uggla
Mark Loretta
Aaron Hill
Chris Burke
321 Randy Johnson 6.00 15.00
Chad Tracy
Chris Burke
Stephen Drew
Kerry Wood
Alfonso Soriano
Derrek Lee
Aramis Ramirez
322 Magglio Ordonez 12.50 30.00
Joel Zumaya
Brandon Inge
Ivan Rodriguez
Albert Pujols
Chris Carpenter
Chris Duncan
Mark Mulder
323 David Ortiz 8.00 20.00
Manny Ramirez
Jonathan Papelbon
Jason Varitek
Matt Holliday
Troy Tulowitzki
Jeff Francis
Garrett Atkins
324 Ken Griffey Jr. 15.00 40.00
Prince Fielder
Geoff Jenkins
Chad Tracy
David Ortiz
Nick Markakis
Garret Anderson
Eric Chavez
325 Lance Berkman
Casey Kotchman
Aubrey Huff
Justin Morneau
Carlos Delgado
Jason Giambi
Kevin Youkilis
James Loney
326 Michael Young
Chase Utley
Troy Tulowitzki
Akinori Iwamura
Aaron Hill
Khalil Greene
Dan Uggla
Derek Jeter
327 Johan Santana 6.00 15.00
Magglio Ordonez
Vladimir Guerrero
David Ortiz
Aramis Ramirez
Kendry Morales
Ivan Rodriguez
Manny Ramirez
328 Miguel Cabrera
Melvin Mora
Chone Figgins
Eric Chavez
Kenji Johjima
Jason Varitek
Jorge Posada
Victor Martinez
329 Ken Griffey Jr. 15.00 40.00
Mike Cameron
Chris Duncan
Jason Bay
Magglio Ordonez
Grady Sizemore
Delmon Young
Mark Teahen
330 James Loney 6.00 15.00
Adam LaRoche
Mark Teixeira
Aaron Boone
Casey Kotchman
Kevin Youkilis
Jason Giambi
Aubrey Huff
331 Miguel Cabrera 6.00 15.00
Magglio Ordonez
Dontrelle Willis
Joel Zumaya
Manny Ramirez
David Ortiz
Jonathan Papelbon
Josh Beckett
332 Robin Yount
Prince Fielder
Rickie Weeks
Ben Sheets
Francisco Liriano
Joe Nathan
Delmon Young
Justin Morneau
333 Carl Crawford 6.00 15.00
Scott Kazmir
RoC.C.o Baldelli
B.J. Upton
Hanley Ramirez
Josh Johnson
Josh Willingham
Dan Uggla
334 Pat Burrell 8.00 20.00
Nick Markakis
Josh Willingham
Xavier Nady
J.D. Drew
Chris Duncan
Rick Ankiel
Josh Hamilton
335 Jake Peavy 8.00 20.00
Chris Young
Jeff Francis
Troy Tulowitzki
Randy Johnson
Chad Tracy
Tim Lincecum
Matt Cain
336 Derek Jeter 30.00 60.00
Mike Mussina
Mariano Rivera
Chien-Ming Wang
Andy Pettitte
Jason Giambi
Don Mattingly
Jorge Posada
337 David Ortiz 12.50 30.00
Manny Ramirez
Jonathan Papelbon
Josh Beckett
J.D. Drew
Jason Varitek
Kevin Youkilis
Wade Boggs
338 Ken Griffey Jr. 10.00 25.00
Aaron Harang
Derrek Lee
Carlos Zambrano
Prince Fielder
Ben Sheets
Albert Pujols
Mark Mulder
339 Aaron Harang 6.00 15.00
Dan Haren
Roy Oswalt
Chad Billingsley
Josh Johnson
Zack Greinke
A.J. Burnett
Jered Weaver
340 Rod Carew
Vladimir Guerrero
Chone Figgins
Garret Anderson
Kendry Morales
John Lackey
Jered Weaver
Howie Kendrick

2008 Upper Deck Ballpark Collection Dual Memorabilia Autographs

OVERALL AU ODDS 1:5 HOBBY
NO PRICING DUE TO SCARCITY

2008 Upper Deck Ballpark Collection Jersey Autographs

OVERALL AU ODDS 1:5 HOBBY
1 Aaron Harang 4.00 10.00
2 Takashi Saito 10.00 25.00
3 Troy Tulowitzki 10.00 25.00
4 Adam LaRoche 5.00 12.00
5 Adrian Gonzalez 5.00 12.00
6 Albert Pujols
7 Andre Ethier 6.00 15.00
8 Joe Mauer 12.50 30.00
9 Justin Upton 12.50 30.00
10 Aramis Ramirez 6.00 15.00
11 Scott Baker 4.00 10.00
12 B.J. Upton 12.50 30.00
13 Bill Hall 5.00 12.00
14 Billy Wagner 30.00 60.00
15 Brandon Phillips 6.00 15.00
16 Brandon Webb 30.00 60.00
17 Sean Marshall
18 Brian McCann 8.00 20.00
19 Brian Roberts 10.00 25.00
20 Bronson Arroyo 5.00 12.00
21 Tim Lincecum 40.00 80.00
22 Mark Reynolds 5.00 12.00
23 Chad Billingsley 12.50 30.00
24 Chad Cordero 4.00 10.00
25 Chone Figgins 5.00 12.00
26 Chris Duffy
27 Chris B. Young 6.00 15.00
28 Tom Gorzelanny 4.00 10.00
29 Corey Hart 10.00 25.00
30 Dan Uggla 4.00 10.00
31 David Murphy
32 Derek Jeter EXCH 75.00 150.00
33 Edinson Volquez 8.00 20.00
34 Elijah Dukes
35 Edwin Encarnacion
36 Fausto Carmona
37 Ubaldo Jimenez
38 Xavier Nady 4.00 10.00
39 Felix Pie 4.00 10.00
40 Yovani Gallardo
41 Yunel Escobar
42 Garrett Atkins 4.00 10.00
43 Ken Griffey Jr. EXCH 40.00 80.00
44 Derek Jeter EXCH 75.00 150.00
45 Hanley Ramirez 10.00 25.00
46 Hong-Chih Kuo 20.00 50.00
47 Ian Kinsler 5.00 12.00
48 Jack Cust
49 Derek Lowe 6.00 15.00
50 Alfonso Soriano 20.00 50.00
51 Jeff Baker 4.00 10.00
52 Jeff Francis 4.00 10.00
53 Jeff Francoeur 10.00 25.00
54 Jered Weaver 4.00 10.00
55 Ben Sheets 10.00 25.00
56 Jeremy Guthrie 6.00 15.00
57 Jeremy Hermida 4.00 10.00
58 Jerry Owens
59 Brian Giles
60 Joakim Soria 6.00 15.00
61 Joe Blanton 4.00 10.00
62 Joe Nathan 6.00 15.00
63 Joe Smith
64 Chien-Ming Wang 60.00 120.00
65 Chris Young 4.00 10.00
66 Jon Lester 20.00 50.00
67 Jonathan Papelbon
68 Cole Hamels 30.00 60.00
69 Josh Johnson 4.00 10.00
70 Josh Willingham 4.00 10.00
71 Kelly Johnson 4.00 10.00
72 Ken Griffey Jr. EXCH 40.00 80.00
73 Kevin Kouzmanoff 4.00 10.00
74 Kevin Youkilis 12.50 30.00
75 Derrek Lee 12.50 30.00
76 James Shields 8.00 20.00
77 Jason Bay 8.00 20.00
78 Jason Varitek 20.00 50.00
79 Manny Corpas
80 Mark Ellis
81 Mark Teahen 4.00 10.00
82 Marlon Byrd
83 Matt Cain 4.00 10.00
84 John Lackey 6.00 15.00
85 Matt Kemp 10.00 25.00
86 John Maine 5.00 12.00
87 Matt Lindstrom
88 Melvin Mora 5.00 12.00
89 Micah Owings
90 Michael Bourn
91 Kerry Wood 8.00 20.00
92 Nick Markakis 12.50 30.00
93 Lance Berkman 8.00 20.00
94 Noah Lowry 4.00 10.00
95 Rickie Weeks 8.00 20.00
96 Prince Fielder 12.50 30.00
97 Roy Halladay 5.00 12.00
98 Tim Hudson 8.00 20.00
99 Grady Sizemore 20.00 50.00
100 Ryan Braun

2008 Upper Deck Ballpark Collection Jersey Buttons

OVERALL GU ODDS 2:1 HOBBY
PRINT RUNS B/WN 3-25 COPIES PER
NO PRICING DUE TO SCARCITY

2008 Upper Deck Ballpark Collection Jersey Laundry Tag

OVERALL GU ODDS 2:1 HOBBY
PRINT RUNS B/WN 2-15 COPIES PER
NO PRICING DUE TO SCARCITY

2008 Upper Deck Ballpark Collection Jersey MLB Logo

OVERALL GU ODDS 2:1 HOBBY
PRINT RUNS B/WN 1-5 COPIES PER
NO PRICING DUE TO SCARCITY

2007 Upper Deck Elements

This 252-card set was released in August, 2007. The set was issued in three-card packs which came five packs per mini-box, three mini-boxes per full box and 16 full boxes in a case. The first 125 cards in this set featured veteran players who were only available in these packs: Cards 1-42 were available in packs featuring Ken Griffey Jr., cards 43-84 were in packs featuring Cal Ripken Jr., and cards 85-126 were in packs featuring Derek Jeter. Rookie Cards (Cards numbered 127-252) were also in specific packs. Cards numbered 127-168 were in Ken Griffey Jr packs while cards numbered 169-210 were in Cal Ripken Jr packs and cards numbered 211-252 were in Derek Jeter packs. These rookie cards were all issued to a stated print run of 550 serial numbered sets. A Gift Exchange card was seeded into packs at a stated rate of one per case.

COMMON CARD .30 .75
CARDS 1-42 FOUND IN GRIFFEY PACKS
CARDS 43-84 FOUND IN RIPKEN PACKS
CARDS 85-126 FOUND IN JETER PACKS
ALL VETERAN VERSIONS EQUAL VALUE
COMMON RC (127-168) .75 2.00
RC 127-168 FOUND IN GRIFFEY PACKS
RC 169-210 FOUND IN RIPKEN PACKS
COMMON RC (211-252) 1.00 2.50
RC 211-252 FOUND IN JETER PACKS
ROOKIE PRINT RUN 550 SER.#'d SETS
PRINTING PLATES RANDOMLY INSERTED
PLATE PRINT RUN 1 SET PER COLOR
BLACK-CYAN-MAGENTA-YELLOW ISSUED
NO PLATE PRICING DUE TO SCARCITY
GIFT EXCH ODDS 1 PER CASE
GIFT EXCH DEADLINE 9/30/2007

1 Stephen Drew .50 1.25
2 Andruw Jones .50 1.25
3 Chipper Jones .75 2.00
4 Miguel Tejada .30 .75
5 David Ortiz .75 2.00
6 Manny Ramirez .50 1.25
7 Derrek Lee .30 .75
8 Alfonso Soriano .30 .75
9 Jermaine Dye .30 .75
10 Jim Thome .50 1.25
11 Ken Griffey Jr. 1.25 3.00
12 Adam Dunn .30 .75
13 Travis Hafner .30 .75
14 Grady Sizemore .50 1.25
15 Todd Helton .50 1.25
16 Gary Sheffield .30 .75
17 Miguel Cabrera .50 1.25
18 Lance Berkman .30 .75
19 Mark Teahen .30 .75
20 Vladimir Guerrero .75 2.00
21 Jered Weaver .50 1.25
22 Rafael Furcal .30 .75
23 Prince Fielder .75 2.00
24 Justin Morneau .30 .75
25 Johan Santana .50 1.25
26 David Wright 1.25 3.00
27 Jose Reyes .75 2.00
28 Derek Jeter 2.00 5.00
29 Alex Rodriguez 1.25 3.00
30 Nick Swisher .30 .75
31 Ryan Howard 1.25 3.00
32 Jason Bay .30 .75
33 Adrian Gonzalez .30 .75
34 Ray Durham .30 .75
35 Ichiro Suzuki 1.25 3.00
36 Albert Pujols 1.50 4.00
37 Scott Rolen .50 1.25
38 Carl Crawford .30 .75
39 Mark Teixeira .50 1.25
40 Michael Young .30 .75
41 Vernon Wells .30 .75
42 Ryan Zimmerman .75 2.00
43 Stephen Drew .50 1.25
44 Andruw Jones .50 1.25
45 Chipper Jones .75 2.00
46 Miguel Tejada .30 .75
47 David Ortiz .75 2.00
48 Manny Ramirez .50 1.25
49 Derrek Lee .30 .75
50 Alfonso Soriano .30 .75
51 Jermaine Dye .30 .75
52 Jim Thome .50 1.25
53 Ken Griffey Jr. 1.25 3.00
54 Adam Dunn .30 .75
55 Travis Hafner .30 .75
56 Grady Sizemore .50 1.25
57 Todd Helton .50 1.25
58 Gary Sheffield .30 .75
59 Miguel Cabrera .50 1.25
60 Lance Berkman .30 .75
61 Mark Teahen .30 .75
62 Vladimir Guerrero .75 2.00
63 Jered Weaver .50 1.25
64 Rafael Furcal .30 .75
65 Prince Fielder .75 2.00
66 Justin Morneau .30 .75
67 Johan Santana .50 1.25
68 David Wright 1.25 3.00
69 Jose Reyes .75 2.00
70 Derek Jeter 2.00 5.00
71 Alex Rodriguez 1.25 3.00
72 Nick Swisher .30 .75
73 Ryan Howard 1.25 3.00
74 Jason Bay .30 .75
75 Adrian Gonzalez .30 .75
76 Ray Durham .30 .75
77 Ichiro Suzuki 1.25 3.00
78 Albert Pujols 1.50 4.00
79 Scott Rolen .50 1.25
80 Carl Crawford .30 .75
81 Mark Teixeira .50 1.25
82 Michael Young .30 .75
83 Vernon Wells .30 .75
84 Ryan Zimmerman .75 2.00
85 Stephen Drew .50 1.25
86 Andruw Jones .50 1.25
87 Chipper Jones .75 2.00
88 Miguel Tejada .30 .75
89 David Ortiz .75 2.00
90 Manny Ramirez .50 1.25
91 Derrek Lee .30 .75
92 Alfonso Soriano .30 .75
93 Jermaine Dye .30 .75
94 Jim Thome .50 1.25
95 Ken Griffey Jr. 1.25 3.00
96 Adam Dunn .30 .75
97 Travis Hafner .30 .75
98 Grady Sizemore .50 1.25
99 Todd Helton .50 1.25
100 Gary Sheffield .30 .75
101 Miguel Cabrera .50 1.25
102 Lance Berkman .30 .75
103 Mark Teahen .30 .75
104 Vladimir Guerrero .75 2.00
105 Jered Weaver .50 1.25
106 Rafael Furcal .30 .75
107 Prince Fielder .75 2.00
108 Justin Morneau .30 .75
109 Johan Santana .50 1.25
110 David Wright 1.25 3.00
111 Jose Reyes .75 2.00
112 Derek Jeter 2.00 5.00
113 Alex Rodriguez 1.25 3.00
114 Nick Swisher .30 .75
115 Ryan Howard 1.25 3.00
116 Jason Bay .30 .75
117 Adrian Gonzalez .30 .75
118 Ray Durham .30 .75
119 Ichiro Suzuki 1.25 3.00
120 Albert Pujols 1.50 4.00
121 Scott Rolen .50 1.25
122 Carl Crawford .30 .75
123 Mark Teixeira .50 1.25
124 Michael Young .30 .75
125 Vernon Wells .30 .75
126 Ryan Zimmerman .75 2.00
127 Miguel Montero (RC) .75 2.00
128 Doug Slaten RC .75 2.00
129 Hunter Pence (RC) 10.00 25.00
130 Brian Burres (RC) .75 2.00
131 Daisuke Matsuzaka RC 6.00 15.00
132 Hideki Okajima RC 3.00 8.00
133 Devern Hansack RC .75 2.00
134 Felix Pie (RC) 2.00 5.00
135 Ryan Sweeney (RC) .75 2.00
136 Chris Stewart RC 1.25 3.00
137 Jarrod Saltalamacchia (RC) 1.25 3.00
138 John Danks RC 1.25 3.00
139 Travis Buck (RC) .75 2.00
140 Troy Tulowitzki (RC) 3.00 8.00
141 Chase Wright RC 1.25 3.00
142 Matt DeSalvo (RC) 1.25 3.00
143 Micah Owings (RC) .75 2.00
144 Jeff Baker (RC) .75 2.00
145 Andy LaRoche (RC) .75 2.00
146 Billy Butler (RC) 3.00 8.00
147 Jose Garcia RC .75 2.00
148 Angel Sanchez RC .75 2.00
149 Alex Gordon RC 6.00 15.00
150 Glen Perkins (RC) .75 2.00
151 Alexi Casilla RC 1.25 3.00
152 Joe Smith RC .75 2.00
153 Kei Igawa RC 3.00 8.00
154 Sean Henn (RC) 2.00 5.00
155 Phil Hughes (RC) 6.00 15.00
156 Michael Bourn (RC) .75 2.00
157 Josh Hamilton (RC) 6.00 15.00
158 Kevin Kouzmanoff (RC) .75 2.00
159 Tim Lincecum RC 15.00 40.00
160 Brandon Morrow RC 1.25 3.00
161 Brandon Wood (RC) .75 2.00
162 Akinori Iwamura RC 2.00 5.00
163 Delmon Young (RC) 1.25 3.00
164 Juan Salas (RC) .75 2.00
165 Elijah Dukes RC 1.25 3.00
166 Joaquin Arias (RC) .75 2.00
167 Adam Lind (RC) .75 2.00
168 Matt Chico (RC) .75 2.00
169 Miguel Montero (RC) .75 2.00
170 Doug Slaten RC .75 2.00
171 Hunter Pence (RC) 10.00 25.00
172 Brian Burres (RC) .75 2.00
173 Daisuke Matsuzaka RC 6.00 15.00
174 Hideki Okajima RC 3.00 8.00
175 Devern Hansack RC .75 2.00
176 Felix Pie (RC) 2.00 5.00
177 Ryan Sweeney (RC) .75 2.00
178 Chris Stewart RC 1.25 3.00
179 Jarrod Saltalamacchia (RC) 1.25 3.00
180 John Danks RC 1.25 3.00
181 Travis Buck (RC) .75 2.00
182 Troy Tulowitzki (RC) 3.00 8.00
183 Chase Wright RC 1.25 3.00
184 Matt DeSalvo (RC) 1.25 3.00
185 Micah Owings (RC) .75 2.00
186 Jeff Baker (RC) .75 2.00
187 Andy LaRoche (RC) .75 2.00
188 Billy Butler (RC) 3.00 8.00
189 Jose Garcia RC .75 2.00
190 Angel Sanchez RC .75 2.00
191 Alex Gordon RC 6.00 15.00
192 Glen Perkins (RC) .75 2.00
193 Alexi Casilla RC 1.25 3.00
194 Joe Smith RC .75 2.00
195 Kei Igawa RC 3.00 8.00
196 Sean Henn (RC) 2.00 5.00
197 Phil Hughes (RC) 6.00 15.00
198 Michael Bourn (RC) .75 2.00
199 Josh Hamilton (RC) 6.00 15.00
200 Kevin Kouzmanoff (RC) .75 2.00
201 Tim Lincecum RC 15.00 40.00
202 Brandon Morrow RC 1.25 3.00
203 Brandon Wood (RC) .75 2.00
204 Akinori Iwamura RC 2.00 5.00
205 Delmon Young (RC) 1.25 3.00
206 Juan Salas (RC) .75 2.00
207 Elijah Dukes RC 1.25 3.00
208 Joaquin Arias (RC) .75 2.00
209 Adam Lind (RC) .75 2.00
210 Matt Chico (RC) .75 2.00
211 Miguel Montero (RC) 1.00 2.50
212 Doug Slaten RC 1.00 2.50
213 Hunter Pence (RC) 10.00 25.00
214 Brian Burres (RC) 1.00 2.50
215 Daisuke Matsuzaka RC 6.00 15.00
216 Hideki Okajima RC 4.00 10.00
217 Devern Hansack RC 1.00 2.50
218 Felix Pie (RC) 2.50 6.00
219 Ryan Sweeney (RC) 1.00 2.50
220 Chris Stewart RC 1.50 4.00
221 Jarrod Saltalamacchia (RC) 1.50 4.00
222 John Danks RC 1.50 4.00
223 Travis Buck (RC) 1.00 2.50
224 Troy Tulowitzki (RC) 4.00 10.00
225 Chase Wright RC 1.50 4.00
226 Matt DeSalvo (RC) 1.50 4.00
227 Micah Owings (RC) 1.00 2.50
228 Jeff Baker (RC) 1.00 2.50
229 Andy LaRoche (RC) 1.00 2.50
230 Billy Butler (RC) 4.00 10.00
231 Jose Garcia RC 1.00 2.50
232 Angel Sanchez RC 1.00 2.50
233 Alex Gordon RC 8.00 20.00
234 Glen Perkins (RC) 1.00 2.50
235 Alexi Casilla RC 1.50 4.00
236 Joe Smith RC 1.00 2.50
237 Kei Igawa RC 4.00 10.00
238 Sean Henn (RC) 2.50 6.00
239 Phil Hughes (RC) 6.00 15.00
240 Michael Bourn (RC) 1.00 2.50
241 Josh Hamilton (RC) 8.00 20.00
242 Kevin Kouzmanoff (RC) 1.00 2.50
243 Tim Lincecum RC 15.00 40.00
244 Brandon Morrow RC 1.50 4.00
245 Brandon Wood (RC) 1.00 2.50
246 Akinori Iwamura RC 2.50 6.00
247 Delmon Young (RC) 1.50 4.00
248 Juan Salas (RC) 1.00 2.50
249 Elijah Dukes RC 1.50 4.00
250 Joaquin Arias (RC) 1.00 2.50
251 Adam Lind (RC) 1.00 2.50
252 Matt Chico (RC) 1.00 2.50
NNO Gift EXCH

2007 Upper Deck Elements Clear Cut Elements Bronze

RANDOM INSERTS IN PACKS
PRINT RUNS B/WN 149-350 COPIES PER
EXCH DEADLINE 7/14/2010

AH Aaron Harang 6.00 15.00
AK Austin Kearns/234 4.00 10.00
AS Alfonso Soriano/199 EXCH 12.50 30.00
BB Brian Bannister 4.00 10.00
BR Brian Roberts 6.00 15.00
CA Matt Cain 4.00 10.00
CC Chris Carpenter 6.00 15.00
CP Corey Patterson 4.00 10.00
CR Cal Ripken Jr. 50.00 80.00
CR Carl Crawford 4.00 10.00
DJ Derek Jeter EXCH 100.00 150.00
DW Dontrelle Willis 6.00 15.00
FL Francisco Liriano EXCH 10.00 25.00
GR Ken Griffey Jr. EXCH 30.00 60.00
HR Hanley Ramirez/314 EXCH 10.00 25.00
JB Jason Bay 4.00 10.00
JG Jonny Gomes 4.00 10.00
JH Jeremy Hermida 4.00 10.00
JP Jake Peavy 6.00 15.00
JT Jim Thome/199 EXCH 20.00 50.00
JV Justin Verlander 10.00 25.00
JZ Joel Zumaya 6.00 15.00
KG Khalil Greene 4.00 10.00
KW Kerry Wood/199
MC Miguel Cabrera/299 EXCH 10.00 25.00
MG Marcus Giles/290 4.00 10.00
MH Matt Holliday 12.50 30.00
ML Mark Loretta/199 4.00 10.00
MM Melvin Mora 4.00 10.00
MT Miguel Tejada/149 4.00 10.00
RH Rich Harden 4.00 10.00
RJ Reed Johnson 4.00 10.00
RZ Ryan Zimmerman 10.00 25.00
SA Johan Santana/299 12.50 30.00
SK Scott Kazmir 8.00 20.00
SR Scott Rolen/299 6.00 15.00
TH Travis Hafner 4.00 10.00
VM Victor Martinez 5.00 12.00

2007 Upper Deck Elements Clear Cut Elements Gold

RANDOM INSERTS IN PACKS
PRINT RUNS B/W 49-199 COPIES PER
EXCH DEADLINE 7/14/2010

AK Austin Kearns/99 5.00 12.00
AS Alfonso Soriano/99 EXCH 15.00 40.00
BB Brian Bannister 5.00 12.00
BR Brian Roberts 8.00 20.00
CA Matt Cain 5.00 12.00
CC Chris Carpenter 8.00 20.00
CP Corey Patterson 5.00 12.00
CR Miguel Cabrera/149 EXCH 60.00 100.00
CR Carl Crawford 5.00 12.00
DJ Derek Jeter EXCH 125.00 175.00
DW Dontrelle Willis 8.00 20.00
FT Francisco Liriano EXCH 12.50 30.00
GS Khalil Greene 5.00 12.00
HR Hanley Ramirez EXCH 12.50 30.00
JB Jason Bay 5.00 12.00
JG Jonny Gomes 5.00 12.00
JH Jeremy Hermida 5.00 12.00
JP Jake Peavy 8.00 20.00
JT Jim Thome/99 EXCH 30.00 60.00
JV Justin Verlander 12.50 30.00
JZ Joel Zumaya 8.00 20.00
KG Ken Griffey Jr. EXCH 40.00 80.00
KW Kerry Wood/99 8.00 20.00
MC Miguel Cabrera/149 EXCH 12.50 30.00
MG Marcus Giles/99 5.00 12.00
MH Matt Holliday 15.00 40.00
ML Mark Loretta/99 5.00 12.00
MT Miguel Tejada/49
RC Johan Santana/99 15.00 40.00
RJ Reed Johnson 5.00 12.00
RO Melvin Mora 5.00 12.00
RZ Ryan Zimmerman 12.50 30.00
SK Scott Kazmir 10.00 25.00
SR Scott Rolen/99 8.00 20.00
TH Travis Hafner 5.00 12.00
VM Victor Martinez 6.00 15.00

2007 Upper Deck Elements Clear Cut Elements Silver

RANDOM INSERTS IN PACKS
PRINT RUNS B/WN 13-99 COPIES PER
NO PRICING ON QTY 13 OR LESS
EXCH DEADLINE 7/14/2010

AK Austin Kearns/49 6.00 15.00
AS Alfonso Soriano/49 EXCH 20.00 50.00
BB Brian Bannister 6.00 15.00
BR Brian Roberts 10.00 25.00
CA Matt Cain/49 6.00 15.00
CC Chris Carpenter 10.00 25.00
CP Corey Patterson 6.00 15.00
CR Cal Ripken Jr. 60.00 120.00
CR Carl Crawford 6.00 15.00
DJ Derek Jeter 150.00 200.00
DW Dontrelle Willis 10.00 25.00
FT Francisco Liriano EXCH
HR Hanley Ramirez EXCH 15.00 40.00
JB Jason Bay 6.00 15.00
JG Jonny Gomes 6.00 15.00
JH Jeremy Hermida 6.00 15.00
JP Jake Peavy 10.00 25.00
JT Jim Thome/49 EXCH
JV Justin Verlander 15.00 40.00
JZ Joel Zumaya 10.00 25.00
KG Ken Griffey Jr. EXCH 50.00 100.00
KW Kerry Wood/49
MC Miguel Cabrera/49 EXCH 15.00 40.00
MG Marcus Giles/49 6.00 15.00
MH Matt Holliday 20.00 50.00
ML Mark Loretta/13
MT Miguel Tejada/9
RC Johan Santana/49 20.00 50.00
RJ Reed Johnson 6.00 15.00
RO Melvin Mora 6.00 15.00
RZ Ryan Zimmerman 15.00 40.00
SK Scott Kazmir 10.00 25.00
SR Scott Rolen/49 10.00 25.00
TH Travis Hafner 6.00 15.00
VM Victor Martinez 8.00 20.00

2007 Upper Deck Elements Dual Elements Dual Memorabilia

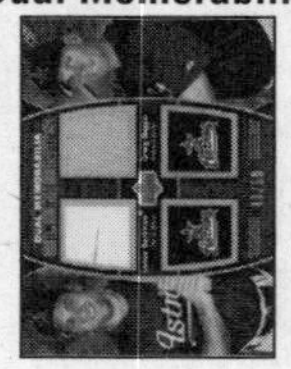

RANDOM INSERTS IN PACKS
STATED PRINT RUN 50 SER.#'d SETS

BB Lance Berkman 6.00 15.00
Craig Biggio
BM Josh Beckett 30.00 60.00
Daisuke Matsuzaka
BS Jason Bay 6.00 15.00
Freddy Sanchez
CA Carlos Beltran 6.00 15.00
Alfonso Soriano
CB Carl Crawford 4.00 10.00
Rocco Baldelli
CM Chris Carpenter 4.00 10.00
Mark Mulder
DB Carlos Delgado 4.00 10.00
Carlos Beltran
DG Adam Dunn 30.00 60.00
Ken Griffey Jr./29
DJ Johnny Damon 20.00 50.00
Derek Jeter
GB Brian Giles 4.00 10.00
Marcus Giles
GJ Ken Griffey Jr. 40.00 80.00
Derek Jeter
GM Tom Glavine 6.00 15.00
Pedro Martinez
GS Vladimir Guerrero 6.00 15.00
Alfonso Soriano
GT Ken Griffey Jr. 12.50 30.00
Frank Thomas
HB Roy Halladay 4.00 10.00
A.J. Burnett
HU Cole Hamels 6.00 15.00
Chase Utley
JJ Chipper Jones 6.00 15.00
Andruw Jones
JR Derek Jeter 25.00 50.00
Jose Reyes
JT Derek Jeter 10.00 25.00
Miguel Tejada
LP Jon Lester 10.00 25.00
Jonathan Papelbon
MM Victor Martinez 6.00 15.00
Joe Mauer
MS Greg Maddux 30.00 60.00
John Smoltz
MT Joe Mauer 6.00 15.00
Justin Morneau
OR David Ortiz 10.00 25.00
Manny Ramirez
PG Albert Pujols 60.00 120.00
Ken Griffey Jr.
PZ Jonathan Papelbon 10.00 25.00
Joel Zumaya
RH Mariano Rivera 6.00 15.00
Trevor Hoffman
RR Jose Reyes 10.00 25.00
Hanley Ramirez
RW Alex Rios 4.00 10.00
Vernon Wells
SB Curt Schilling 12.50 30.00
Josh Beckett
SH Grady Sizemore 6.00 15.00
Travis Hafner
SZ Johan Santana 6.00 15.00
Barry Zito
TH Jim Thome 6.00 15.00
Travis Hafner
TK Jim Thome 6.00 15.00
Paul Konerko
TM Mark Teixeira 4.00 10.00
Justin Morneau
TR Miguel Tejada 4.00 10.00
Brian Roberts
TY Mark Teixeira 4.00 10.00
Michael Young
UU Dan Uggla 6.00 15.00
Chase Utley
VB Justin Verlander 6.00 15.00
Jeremy Bonderman
WH Vernon Wells 6.00 15.00
Torii Hunter
WJ Brandon Webb 6.00 15.00
Randy Johnson
WS Brandon Webb 6.00 15.00
Johan Santana
ZR Ryan Zimmerman 6.00 15.00
Scott Rolen

2007 Upper Deck Elements Elemental Autographs

RANDOM INSERTS IN PACKS

AI Akinori Iwamura 12.50 30.00
AL Adam LaRoche
BA Bronson Arroyo 4.00 10.00
BH Bill Hall 4.00 10.00
BL Joe Blanton 3.00 8.00
BN Brendan Harris 3.00 8.00
BO Jeremy Bonderman 4.00 10.00
BR Jared Burton 12.50 30.00
BT Jason Bartlett 3.00 8.00
BU Brian Burres 3.00 8.00
BW Brandon Wood 4.00 10.00
CB Cha-Seung Baek 3.00 8.00
CO Jon Coutlangus 4.00 10.00
CR Cal Ripken Jr. 60.00 120.00
CU Chase Utley 15.00 40.00
CW Chase Wright 6.00 15.00
DB Denny Bautista 3.00 8.00
DC Daniel Cabrera 3.00 8.00
DJ Derek Jeter 60.00 120.00
DO David Ortiz
DU Dan Uggla 4.00 10.00
DW Dontrelle Willis
FP Felix Pie 4.00 10.00
GA Garrett Atkins 3.00 8.00
GC Gustavo Chacin
GO Alex Gordon 15.00 40.00
GP Glen Perkins 3.00 8.00
HA Rich Harden 3.00 8.00
HE Sean Henn 3.00 8.00
HR Hanley Ramirez 6.00 15.00
IK Ian Kinsler 3.00 8.00
JA Joaquin Arias 3.00 8.00
JB Jason Bay 6.00 15.00
JC Jesse Crain 3.00 8.00
JG Jonny Gomes 3.00 8.00
JH Josh Hamilton 10.00 25.00
JK Jon Knott 3.00 8.00
JO Josh Willingham 3.00 8.00
JP Jake Peavy 6.00 15.00
JV Justin Verlander 6.00 15.00
JW Jayson Werth 3.00 8.00
KE Howie Kendrick 4.00 10.00
KI Kei Igawa 10.00 25.00
KM Kendry Morales 4.00 10.00
KY Kevin Youkilis 6.00 15.00
LA Andy LaRoche 4.00 10.00
LI Bobby Livingston 3.00 8.00
LS Luke Scott 4.00 10.00
PA Jonathan Papelbon 12.50 30.00
PE Jhonny Peralta
RC Roger Clemens
RH Rich Hill 6.00 15.00
RL Ruddy Lugo 3.00 8.00
RO Scott Rolen 6.00 15.00
RT Ryan Theriot 10.00 25.00
SD Stephen Drew 10.00 25.00
SH James Shields
SK Scott Kazmir 5.00 12.00
SM John Smoltz 12.50 30.00
SO Jeremy Sowers
SS Skip Schumaker 3.00 8.00
ST Scott Thorman 3.00 8.00
TB Travis Buck 6.00 15.00
TH Travis Hafner 6.00 15.00
TI Tadahito Iguchi 6.00 15.00
VG Vladimir Guerrero 10.00 25.00
VM Victor Martinez 4.00 10.00
WO Jason Wood 3.00 8.00

2007 Upper Deck Elements Elemental Autographs Dual

RANDOM INSERTS IN PACKS
STATED PRINT RUN 15 SER.#'d SETS
NO PRICING DUE TO SCARCITY

BT Jeff Baker
Troy Tulowitzki
CR Chris Carpenter
Scott Rolen
GB Alex Gordon
Billy Butler
HH Josh Hamilton
Aaron Harang
HS Rich Harden
Huston Street
HT Travis Hafner
Jim Thome
II Akinori Iwamura
Kei Igawa
JT Derek Jeter
Miguel Tejada
KI Scott Kazmir
Akinori Iwamura
KP Kevin Kouzmanoff
Jake Peavy
MC Mark Mulder
Chris Carpenter
RJ Cal Ripken
Jr.
Derek Jeter
RT Hanley Ramirez
Miguel Tejada
RU Hanley Ramirez
Dan Uggla
SO Ben Sheets
Micah Owings
SR Anibal Sanchez
Hanley Ramirez
SW Johan Santana
Kerry Wood
TO Jim Thome
David Ortiz
TR Miguel Tejada
Brian Roberts
VC Justin Verlander
Chris Carpenter
WC Dontrelle Willis
Miguel Cabrera
ZR Ryan Zimmerman
Hanley Ramirez

2007 Upper Deck Elements Elemental Autographs Quad

RANDOM INSERTS IN PACKS
STATED PRINT RUN 1 SER.#'d SET
NO PRICING DUE TO SCARCITY

IKJI Akinori Iwamura
Scott Kazmir
Derek Jeter
Kei Igawa
IKYC Akinori Iwamura
Scott Kazmir
Delmon Young
Carl Crawford
RJTT Hanley Ramirez
Derek Jeter
Miguel Tejada
Troy Tulowitzki
RTBK Cal Ripken
Jr.
Miguel Tejada
Brian Burres
Jon Knott
WCSH Kerry Wood
Chris Carpenter
Johan Santana
Rich Harden

2007 Upper Deck Elements Elemental Autographs Triple

RANDOM INSERTS IN PACKS
STATED PRINT RUN 5 SER.#'d SETS
NO PRICING DUE TO SCARCITY

BSH Travis Buck
Huston Street
Rich Harden
BSS Brian Burres
Brian Stokes
Sean Henn
CSC Chris Carpenter
Johan Santana
Roger Clemens
CYI Carl Crawford
Delmon Young
Akinori Iwamura
JTR Derek Jeter
Miguel Tejada
Hanley Ramirez
RIC Scott Rolen
Akinori Iwamura
Eric Chavez
WTA Brandon Wood
Troy Tulowitzki
Joaquin Arias

2007 Upper Deck Elements Essential Elements

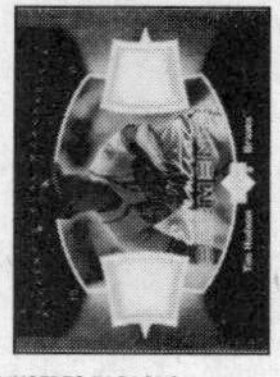

RANDOM INSERTS IN PACKS

AB Adrian Beltre 3.00 8.00
AD Adam Dunn 3.00 8.00
AJ Andruw Jones 3.00 8.00
AP Andy Pettitte 4.00 10.00
AR Aramis Ramirez 3.00 8.00
AS Alfonso Soriano 3.00 8.00
BA Bobby Abreu 3.00 8.00
BC Bobby Crosby 3.00 8.00
BE Carlos Beltran 3.00 8.00
BG Brian Giles 3.00 8.00
BO Jeremy Bonderman 3.00 8.00
BR Brian Roberts 3.00 8.00
BU B.J. Upton 3.00 8.00
BW Billy Wagner 4.00 10.00
BZ Barry Zito 3.00 8.00
CA Miguel Cabrera 3.00 8.00
CB Craig Biggio 4.00 10.00
CC Carl Crawford 3.00 8.00
CH Cole Hamels 4.00 10.00
CJ Chipper Jones 4.00 10.00
CS Curt Schilling 4.00 10.00

CU Chase Utley 4.00 10.00
DA Johnny Damon 4.00 10.00
DM Daisuke Matsuzaka 10.00 25.00
DO David Ortiz 6.00 15.00
DR JD Drew 3.00 8.00
DU Dan Uggla 4.00 10.00
DW Dontrelle Willis 3.00 8.00
EC Eric Chavez 3.00 8.00
ED Jim Edmonds 3.00 8.00
FG Freddy Garcia 3.00 8.00
FH Felix Hernandez 3.00 8.00
FL Francisco Liriano 4.00 10.00
FT Frank Thomas 4.00 10.00
GA Garret Anderson 3.00 8.00
GJ Geoff Jenkins 3.00 8.00
GM Greg Maddux 10.00 25.00
GS Grady Sizemore 6.00 15.00
HA Rich Harden 3.00 8.00
HB Hank Blalock 3.00 8.00
HO Trevor Hoffman 3.00 8.00
HS Huston Street 3.00 8.00
HU Torii Hunter 3.00 8.00
IR Ivan Rodriguez 4.00 10.00
JA Jason Bay 3.00 8.00
JB Josh Beckett 3.00 8.00
JC Jorge Cantu 3.00 8.00
JD Jermaine Dye 3.00 8.00
JE Johnny Estrada 3.00 8.00
JF Jeff Francoeur 6.00 15.00
JG Jason Giambi 3.00 8.00
JJ Josh Johnson 3.00 8.00
JK Jeff Kent 3.00 8.00
JM Joe Mauer 4.00 10.00
JP Jake Peavy 3.00 8.00
JR Jimmy Rollins 3.00 8.00
JS Johan Santana 4.00 10.00
JT Jim Thome 4.00 10.00
JV Justin Verlander 4.00 10.00
KG Khalil Greene 4.00 10.00
LB Lance Berkman 3.00 8.00
LG Luis Gonzalez 3.00 8.00
MM Mike Mussina 4.00 10.00
MO Justin Morneau 4.00 10.00
MP Mike Piazza 6.00 15.00
MR Manny Ramirez 4.00 10.00
MT Mark Teixeira 4.00 10.00
MY Michael Young 3.00 8.00
OR Magglio Ordonez 4.00 10.00
PA Jonathan Papelbon 6.00 15.00
PB Pat Burrell 3.00 8.00
PE Jhonny Peralta 3.00 8.00
PF Prince Fielder 4.00 10.00
PO Jorge Posada 4.00 10.00
PU Albert Pujols 10.00 25.00
RE Jose Reyes 4.00 10.00
RH Roy Halladay 3.00 8.00
RI Mariano Rivera 6.00 15.00
RJ Randy Johnson 4.00 10.00
RO Roy Oswalt 3.00 8.00
RW Rickie Weeks 3.00 8.00
RZ Ryan Zimmerman 4.00 10.00
SK Scott Kazmir 3.00 8.00
SM John Smoltz 4.00 10.00
SR Scott Rolen 4.00 10.00
TE Miguel Tejada 3.00 8.00
TH Todd Helton 4.00 10.00
TI Tim Hudson 3.00 8.00
TR Travis Hafner 3.00 8.00
VG Vladimir Guerrero 4.00 10.00
VM Victor Martinez 3.00 8.00

2007 Upper Deck Elements Quad Memorabilia

RANDOM INSERTS IN PACKS
STATED PRINT RUN 10 SER.#'d SETS
NO PRICING DUE TO SCARCITY
GJPG Ken Griffey Jr.
Derek Jeter
Albert Pujols
Vladimir Guerrero
GJPR Jason Giambi
Derek Jeter
Jorge Posada
Mariano Rivera
JFJM Chipper Jones
Jeff Francoeur
Andruw Jones
Brian McCann
KCUB Scott Kazmir
Carl Crawford
B.J. Upton
Rocco Baldelli
PGRS Albert Pujols
Vladimir Guerrero
Manny Ramirez
Alfonso Soriano
PLSM Jonathan Papelbon
Jon Lester
Curt Schilling
Daisuke Matsuzaka
SHMS Grady Sizemore
Travis Hafner
Victor Martinez
C.C. Sabathia
SMMN Johan Santana
Justin Morneau
Joe Mauer
Joe Nathan
URCJ Dan Uggla
Hanley Ramirez
Miguel Cabrera
Mike Jacobs
UUBR Chase Utley
Dan Uggla
Craig Biggio
Brian Roberts
WCJZ Brandon Webb
Chris Carpenter
Randy Johnson
Barry Zito
ZCRJ Ryan Zimmerman
Miguel Cabrera
Aramis Ramirez
Chipper Jones

2007 Upper Deck Elements Rare Elements Patches

RANDOM INSERTS IN PACKS
PRINT RUNS B/WN 4-35 COPIES PER
NO PRICING ON QTY 19 OR LESS
AB Adrian Beltre/35 6.00 15.00
AJ Andruw Jones/35 10.00 25.00
AP Andy Pettitte/35 15.00 40.00
AR Aramis Ramirez/35 6.00 15.00
BA Bobby Abreu/35 6.00 15.00
BC Bobby Crosby/35 10.00 25.00
BE Carlos Beltran/35 10.00 25.00
BG Brian Giles/35 6.00 15.00
BO Jeremy Bonderman/35 10.00 25.00
BR Brian Roberts/30 10.00 25.00
BW Billy Wagner/35 10.00 25.00
BZ Barry Zito/35 6.00 15.00
CA Miguel Cabrera/35 6.00 15.00
CB Craig Biggio/35 15.00 40.00
CC Carl Crawford/35 10.00 25.00
CJ Chipper Jones/35 20.00 50.00
CL Carlos Lee/35 10.00 25.00
CS Curt Schilling/35 10.00 25.00
DA Johnny Damon/28 10.00 25.00
DM Daisuke Matsuzaka/35
DR JD Drew/35 6.00 15.00
DU Dan Uggla/35 10.00 25.00
DW Dontrelle Willis/35 6.00 15.00
EC Eric Chavez/35 6.00 15.00
ED Jim Edmonds/35 10.00 25.00
FG Freddy Garcia/35 6.00 15.00
FH Felix Hernandez/35 6.00 15.00
FL Francisco Liriano/35 15.00 40.00
FT Frank Thomas/35 15.00 40.00
GA Garret Anderson/35 6.00 15.00
GJ Geoff Jenkins/35 6.00 15.00
GM Greg Maddux/35 30.00 60.00
GR Ken Griffey Jr./35 40.00 80.00
GS Grady Sizemore/35 10.00 25.00
HA Rich Harden/35 6.00 15.00
HB Hank Blalock/35 6.00 15.00
HO Trevor Hoffman/35 6.00 15.00
HR Hanley Ramirez/35 10.00 25.00
HS Huston Street/35 6.00 15.00
HU Torii Hunter/35 6.00 15.00
IR Ivan Rodriguez/28 10.00 25.00
JA Jason Bay/35 10.00 25.00
JB Josh Beckett/35 15.00 40.00
JC Jorge Cantu/35 6.00 15.00
JD Jermaine Dye/35 6.00 15.00
JE Johnny Estrada/35 6.00 15.00
JF Jeff Francoeur/35 20.00 50.00
JG Jason Giambi/35 20.00 50.00
JJ Josh Johnson/29 6.00 15.00
JK Jeff Kent/35 10.00 25.00
JP Jake Peavy/35 6.00 15.00
JR Jimmy Rollins/35 10.00 25.00
JS Johan Santana/35 10.00 25.00
JT Jim Thome/35 10.00 25.00
KG Khalil Greene/35 10.00 25.00
LB Lance Berkman/35 6.00 15.00
LG Luis Gonzalez/35 6.00 15.00
MM Mike Mussina/19
MP Mike Piazza/35 30.00 60.00
MT Mark Teixeira/35 15.00 40.00
MY Michael Young/35 10.00 25.00
OR Magglio Ordonez/35 10.00 25.00
PB Pat Burrell/35 6.00 15.00
PE Jhonny Peralta/35 6.00 15.00
PM Pedro Martinez/15
PO Jorge Posada/35 10.00 25.00
RC Roger Clemens/35 30.00 60.00
RE Jose Reyes/35 15.00 40.00
RH Roy Halladay/35 10.00 25.00
RI Mariano Rivera/35 15.00 40.00
RJ Randy Johnson/35 10.00 25.00
RO Roy Oswalt/35 6.00 15.00
RZ Ryan Zimmerman/4
SK Scott Kazmir/35 10.00 25.00
SM John Smoltz/35 20.00 50.00
SR Scott Rolen/35 10.00 25.00
TE Miguel Tejada/18
TH Todd Helton/35 10.00 25.00
TI Tim Hudson/35 6.00 15.00
TR Travis Hafner/35 10.00 25.00
VA Jason Varitek/35 15.00 40.00
VG Vladimir Guerrero/35 15.00 40.00

2007 Upper Deck Elements Triple Memorabilia

RANDOM INSERTS IN PACKS
STATED PRINT RUN 25 SER.#'d SETS
NO PRICING DUE TO SCARCTIY

2006 Upper Deck Epic

This 300-card set was released in July, 2006. The set was released in three-card hobby packs, with an $50 SRP, which came five packs to a box and eight boxes to a case. Cards numbered 1-280 featured veterans basically issued in first-name alphabetical order within alphabetical team order while cards 281-300 feature 2006 rookies. All cards in this set were issued to a stated print run of 450 serial numbered sets.

COMMON CARD (1-300) 2.00 5.00
COMMON ROOKIE 2.00 5.00
STATED PRINT RUN 450 SERIAL #'d SETS
1 Conor Jackson (RC) 3.00 8.00
2 Brandon Webb 2.00 5.00
3 Craig Counsell 2.00 5.00
4 Luis Gonzalez 2.00 5.00
5 Miguel Batista 2.00 5.00
6 Orlando Hudson 2.00 5.00
7 Russ Ortiz 2.00 5.00
8 Shawn Green 2.00 5.00
9 Andruw Jones 3.00 8.00
10 Chipper Jones 3.00 8.00
11 Edgar Renteria 2.00 5.00
12 Jeff Francoeur 3.00 8.00
13 John Smoltz 3.00 8.00
14 Marcus Giles 2.00 5.00
15 Mike Hampton 2.00 5.00
16 Tim Hudson 2.00 5.00
17 Erik Bedard 2.00 5.00
18 Brian Roberts 2.00 5.00
19 Javy Lopez 2.00 5.00
20 Jay Gibbons 2.00 5.00
21 Jeff Conine 2.00 5.00
22 Melvin Mora 2.00 5.00
23 Miguel Tejada 2.00 5.00
24 Daniel Cabrera 2.00 5.00
25 Rodrigo Lopez 2.00 5.00
26 Ramon Hernandez 2.00 5.00
27 Bronson Arroyo 2.00 5.00
28 Curt Schilling 3.00 8.00
29 David Ortiz 3.00 8.00
30 David Wells 2.00 5.00
31 Jason Varitek 3.00 8.00
32 Josh Beckett 2.00 5.00
33 Kevin Youkilis 2.00 5.00
34 Manny Ramirez 3.00 8.00
35 Matt Clement 2.00 5.00
36 Mike Lowell 2.00 5.00
37 Tim Wakefield 2.00 5.00
38 Trot Nixon 2.00 5.00
39 Aramis Ramirez 2.00 5.00
40 Carlos Zambrano 2.00 5.00
41 Derrek Lee 2.00 5.00
42 Greg Maddux 5.00 12.00
43 Juan Pierre 2.00 5.00
44 Kerry Wood 2.00 5.00
45 Mark Prior 3.00 8.00
46 Michael Barrett 2.00 5.00
47 Ryan Dempster 2.00 5.00
48 Todd Walker 2.00 5.00
49 Wade Miller 2.00 5.00
50 A.J. Pierzynski 2.00 5.00
51 Brian Anderson (RC) 2.00 5.00
52 Frank Thomas 3.00 8.00
53 Javier Vazquez 2.00 5.00
54 Jim Thome 3.00 8.00
55 Joe Crede 2.00 5.00
56 Jon Garland 2.00 5.00
57 Juan Uribe 2.00 5.00
58 Mark Buehrle 2.00 5.00
59 Paul Konerko 2.00 5.00
60 Scott Podsednik 2.00 5.00
61 Tadahito Iguchi 2.00 5.00
62 Aaron Harang 2.00 5.00
63 Adam Dunn 2.00 5.00
64 Austin Kearns 2.00 5.00
65 Edwin Encarnacion 2.00 5.00
66 Eric Milton 2.00 5.00
67 Felipe Lopez 2.00 5.00
68 Jason LaRue 2.00 5.00
69 Ken Griffey Jr. 5.00 12.00
70 Wily Mo Pena 2.00 5.00
71 Aaron Boone 2.00 5.00
72 Ben Broussard 2.00 5.00
73 C.C. Sabathia 2.00 5.00
74 Casey Blake 2.00 5.00
75 Cliff Lee 2.00 5.00
76 Grady Sizemore 3.00 8.00
77 Jake Westbrook 2.00 5.00
78 Josh Bard 2.00 5.00
79 Travis Hafner 2.00 5.00
80 Victor Martinez 2.00 5.00
81 Chin-hui Tsao 2.00 5.00
82 Clint Barmes 2.00 5.00
83 Garrett Atkins 2.00 5.00
84 Josh Wilson (RC) 2.00 5.00
85 Luis Gonzalez 2.00 5.00
86 Matt Holliday 2.50 6.00
87 Todd Helton 3.00 8.00
88 Brandon Inge 2.00 5.00
89 Carlos Guillen 2.00 5.00
90 Chris Shelton 2.00 5.00
91 Craig Monroe 2.00 5.00
92 Dmitri Young 2.00 5.00
93 Ivan Rodriguez 3.00 8.00
94 Jeremy Bonderman 2.00 5.00
95 Magglio Ordonez 2.00 5.00
96 Alex Gonzalez 2.00 5.00
97 Brian Moehler 2.00 5.00
98 Dontrelle Willis 2.00 5.00
99 Jeremy Hermida (RC) 3.00 8.00
100 Jason Vargas 2.00 5.00
101 Miguel Cabrera 3.00 8.00
102 Adam Everett 2.00 5.00
103 Andy Pettitte 2.00 5.00
104 Brad Ausmus 2.00 5.00
105 Brad Lidge 2.00 5.00
106 Craig Biggio 3.00 8.00
107 Dan Wheeler 2.00 5.00
108 Jeff Bagwell 3.00 8.00
109 Lance Berkman 2.00 5.00
110 Morgan Ensberg 2.00 5.00
111 Preston Wilson 2.00 5.00
112 Roger Clemens 6.00 15.00
113 Roy Oswalt 2.00 5.00
114 Dave Gassner (RC) 2.00 5.00
115 Angel Berroa 2.00 5.00
116 Doug Mientkiewicz 2.00 5.00
117 Joe Mays 2.00 5.00
118 Mark Grudzielanek 2.00 5.00
119 Mike Sweeney 2.00 5.00
120 Reggie Sanders 2.00 5.00
121 Runelvys Hernandez 2.00 5.00
122 Scott Elarton 2.00 5.00
123 Brandon Watson (RC) 2.00 5.00
124 Zack Greinke 2.00 5.00
125 Brad Penny 2.00 5.00
126 Derek Lowe 2.00 5.00
127 Eric Gagne 2.00 5.00
128 J.D. Drew 2.00 5.00
129 Jayson Werth 2.00 5.00
130 Jeff Kent 2.00 5.00
131 Nomar Garciaparra 3.00 8.00
132 Olmedo Saenz 2.00 5.00
133 Rafael Furcal 2.00 5.00
134 Ben Sheets 2.00 5.00
135 Bill Hall 2.00 5.00
136 Carlos Lee 2.00 5.00
137 Geoff Jenkins 2.00 5.00
138 Prince Fielder (RC) 6.00 15.00
139 Rickie Weeks 2.00 5.00
140 Jose Capellan (RC) 2.00 5.00
141 Brad Radke 2.00 5.00
142 Joe Mauer 3.00 8.00
143 Joe Nathan 2.00 5.00
144 Johan Santana 3.00 8.00
145 Justin Morneau 2.00 5.00
146 Kyle Lohse 2.00 5.00
147 Lew Ford 2.00 5.00
148 Luis Castillo 2.00 5.00
149 Matt LeCroy 2.00 5.00
150 Michael Cuddyer 2.00 5.00
151 Shannon Stewart 2.00 5.00
152 Torii Hunter 2.00 5.00
153 Billy Wagner 2.00 5.00
154 Carlos Beltran 2.00 5.00
155 Carlos Delgado 2.00 5.00
156 Cliff Floyd 2.00 5.00
157 David Wright 5.00 12.00
158 Jose Reyes 2.00 5.00
159 Kazuo Matsui 2.00 5.00
160 Mike Piazza 3.00 8.00
161 Paul Lo Duca 2.00 5.00
162 Pedro Martinez 3.00 8.00
163 Tom Glavine 3.00 8.00
164 Victor Diaz 2.00 5.00
165 Alex Rodriguez 5.00 12.00
166 Bernie Williams 3.00 8.00
167 Carl Pavano 2.00 5.00
168 Chien-Ming Wang 5.00 12.00
169 Derek Jeter 8.00 20.00
170 Gary Sheffield 2.00 5.00
171 Hideki Matsui 3.00 8.00
172 Jason Giambi 2.00 5.00
173 Johnny Damon 3.00 8.00
174 Jorge Posada 3.00 8.00
175 Robinson Cano 3.00 8.00
176 Mariano Rivera 3.00 8.00
177 Mike Mussina 3.00 8.00
178 Randy Johnson 3.00 8.00
179 Miguel Cairo 2.00 5.00
180 Barry Zito 2.00 5.00
181 Bobby Crosby 2.00 5.00
182 Bobby Kielty 2.00 5.00
183 Eric Chavez 2.00 5.00
184 Josh Barfield (RC) 2.00 5.00
185 Esteban Loaiza 2.00 5.00
186 Huston Street 2.00 5.00
187 Jason Kendall 2.00 5.00
188 Nick Swisher 2.00 5.00
189 Aaron Rowand 2.00 5.00
190 Bobby Abreu 2.00 5.00
191 Chase Utley 3.00 8.00
192 Gavin Floyd 2.00 5.00
193 Jimmy Rollins 2.00 5.00
194 Mike Lieberthal 2.00 5.00
195 Pat Burrell 2.00 5.00
196 Ryan Howard 4.00 10.00
197 Craig Wilson 2.00 5.00
198 Jack Wilson 2.00 5.00
199 Jason Bay 2.00 5.00
200 Joe Randa 2.00 5.00
201 Josh Fogg 2.00 5.00
202 Kip Wells 2.00 5.00
203 Sean Casey 2.00 5.00
204 Zach Duke 2.00 5.00
205 Brian Giles 2.00 5.00
206 Dave Roberts 2.00 5.00
207 Jake Peavy 2.00 5.00
208 Khalil Greene 3.00 8.00
209 Mike Cameron 2.00 5.00
210 Ryan Klesko 2.00 5.00
211 Trevor Hoffman 2.00 5.00
212 Vinny Castilla 2.00 5.00
213 Armando Benitez 2.00 5.00
214 Jason Schmidt 2.00 5.00
215 Matt Morris 2.00 5.00
216 Moises Alou 2.00 5.00
217 Omar Vizquel 3.00 8.00
218 Ray Durham 2.00 5.00
219 Adrian Beltre 2.00 5.00
220 Carl Everett 2.00 5.00
221 Kenji Johjima RC 6.00 15.00
222 Felix Hernandez 3.00 8.00
223 Ichiro Suzuki 5.00 12.00
224 Jamie Moyer 2.00 5.00
225 Jeremy Reed 2.00 5.00
226 Joel Pineiro 2.00 5.00
227 Raul Ibanez 2.00 5.00
228 Richie Sexson 2.00 5.00
229 Albert Pujols 6.00 15.00
230 Chris Carpenter 2.00 5.00
231 David Eckstein 2.00 5.00
232 Jason Marquis 2.00 5.00
233 Jeff Suppan 2.00 5.00
234 Jim Edmonds 3.00 8.00
235 Yadier Molina 2.00 5.00
236 Mark Mulder 2.00 5.00
237 Scott Rolen 3.00 8.00
238 Alex Scott Gonzalez 2.00 5.00
239 Aubrey Huff 2.00 5.00
240 Carl Crawford 2.00 5.00
241 Casey Fossum 2.00 5.00
242 Joey Gathright 2.00 5.00
243 Scott Kazmir 2.00 5.00
244 Toby Hall 2.00 5.00
245 Travis Lee 2.00 5.00
246 Adam Eaton 2.00 5.00
247 Francisco Cordero 2.00 5.00
248 Hank Blalock 2.00 5.00
249 Kevin Mench 2.00 5.00
250 Kevin Millwood 2.00 5.00
251 Laynce Nix 2.00 5.00
252 Mark Teixeira 3.00 8.00
253 Michael Young 2.00 5.00
254 A.J. Burnett 2.00 5.00
255 Alex Rios 2.00 5.00
256 B.J. Ryan 2.00 5.00
257 Corey Koskie 2.00 5.00
258 Josh Towers 2.00 5.00
259 Lyle Overbay 2.00 5.00
260 Reed Johnson 2.00 5.00
261 Roy Halladay 2.00 5.00
262 Russ Adams 2.00 5.00
263 Troy Glaus 2.00 5.00
264 Vernon Wells 2.00 5.00
265 Alfonso Soriano 2.00 5.00
266 John Patterson 2.00 5.00
267 Damian Jackson 2.00 5.00
268 Jose Guillen 2.00 5.00
269 Jose Vidro 2.00 5.00
270 Livan Hernandez 2.00 5.00
271 Adam Kennedy 2.00 5.00
272 Bartolo Colon 2.00 5.00
273 Bengie Molina 2.00 5.00
274 Casey Kotchman 2.00 5.00
275 Chone Figgins 2.00 5.00
276 Matt Cain (RC) 3.00 8.00
277 Darin Erstad 2.00 5.00
278 Edgardo Alfonzo 2.00 5.00
279 Francisco Rodriguez 2.00 5.00
280 Garret Anderson 2.00 5.00
281 Vladimir Guerrero 3.00 8.00
282 Chris Denorfia (RC) 2.00 5.00
283 Joey Devine RC 2.00 5.00
284 Justin Verlander (RC) 6.00 15.00
285 Scott Feldman RC 2.00 5.00
286 Jason Bergmann RC 2.00 5.00
287 Jeremy Accardo RC 2.00 5.00
288 Adam Wainwright (RC) 3.00 8.00
289 Hanley Ramirez (RC) 2.50 6.00
290 Josh Johnson (RC) 3.00 8.00
291 Ryan Zimmerman (RC) 10.00 25.00
292 Anderson Hernandez (RC) 2.00 5.00
293 Francisco Liriano (RC) 8.00 20.00
294 Josh Willingham (RC) 2.00 5.00
295 Hong-Chih Kuo (RC) 4.00 10.00
296 Steve Stemle RC 2.00 5.00
297 Jeff Harris RC 2.00 5.00
298 John Van Benschoten (RC) 2.00 5.00
299 Jonathan Papelbon (RC) 8.00 20.00
300 Jason Kubel (RC) 2.00 5.00

2006 Upper Deck Epic Awesome 8 Materials

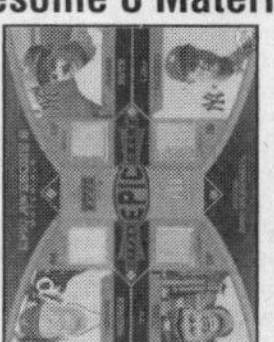

OVERALL GU ODDS ONE PER PACK
PRINT RUNS B/WN 1-10 COPIES PER
NO PRICING DUE TO SCARCITY
BGHS Johnny Bench Jsy
Lou Gehrig Pants
Rogers Hornsby Jkt
Mike Schmidt Jsy
Honus Wagner Pants
Ted Williams Jsy
Ty Cobb Bat
Babe Ruth Bat/10
CBRM Roberto Clemente Pants
Wade Boggs Jsy
Cal Ripken Jsy
Paul Molitor Jsy
Honus Wagner Pants
Carl Yastrzemski Jsy
Stan Musial Jsy
Ty Cobb Bat/10
CHGW Ty Cobb Bat
Rogers Hornsby Jkt
Lou Gehrig Pants
Ted Williams Jsy
Frank Robinson Jsy
Carl Yastrzemski Jsy
Roger Clemens Jsy
Randy Johnson Pants/10
CRWM Ty Cobb Bat
Babe Ruth Bat
Ted Williams Jsy
Stan Musial Pants
Reggie Jackson Jsy
Carl Yastrzemski Jsy
Ken Griffey Jr. Jsy
Roberto Clemente Pants/1
FGRC Whitey Ford Jsy
Bob Gibson Jsy
Brooks Robinson Jsy
Roberto Clemente Pants
Reggie Jackson Jsy
Johnny Bench Jsy
Mike Schmidt Jsy
Derek Jeter Jsy/10
GDWR Hank Greenberg Bat
Joe DiMaggio Bat
Ted Williams Jsy
Brooks Robinson Jsy
Eddie Mathews Pants
Frank Robinson Pants
Robin Yount Jsy
Cal Ripken Jsy/5
HRMS Rogers Hornsby Jkt
Jackie Robinson Pants
Joe Morgan Jsy
Ryne Sandberg Jsy
Eddie Mathews Pants
Brooks Robinson Pants
Wade Boggs Jsy
Mike Schmidt Jsy/5
JTRY Derek Jeter Jsy
Miguel Tejada Jsy
Cal Ripken Jsy
Robin Yount Jsy
Ozzie Smith Jsy
Ernie Banks Jsy
Pee Wee Reese Jsy
Honus Wagner Pants/10
MRBC Stan Musial Pants
Jackie Robinson Pants
Ernie Banks Jsy
Roberto Clemente Pants
Johnny Bench Jsy
Joe Morgan Jsy
Mike Schmidt Jsy
Ryne Sandberg Jsy/10
MRJF Eddie Mathews Pants
Pee Wee Reese Jsy
Reggie Jackson Jsy
Whitey Ford Jsy
Roberto Clemente Pants
Carl Yastrzemski Jsy
Brooks Robinson Jsy
Frank Robinson Pants/10
MWGS Willie McCovey Jsy
Ted Williams Jsy
Ken Griffey Jr. Jsy
Mike Schmidt Jsy
Reggie Jackson Jsy
Harmon Killebrew Pants
Frank Robinson Pants
Babe Ruth Bat/10
PJCR Mark Prior Jsy
Randy Johnson Jsy
Roger Clemens Pants
Nolan Ryan Jsy
Tom Seaver Jsy
Bob Gibson Jsy
Juan Marichal Jsy
Whitey Ford Jsy/10
RGDW Babe Ruth Bat
Lou Gehrig Pants
Joe DiMaggio Bat
Dave Winfield Pants
Derek Jeter Jsy
Reggie Jackson Jsy
Thurman Munson Pants
Don Mattingly Jsy/5
WCRG Honus Wagner Pants
Ty Cobb Bat
Babe Ruth Bat
Lou Gehrig Pants
Joe DiMaggio Bat
Ted Williams Jsy
Stan Musial Pants
Jackie Robinson Pants/10
WYBS Ted Williams Jsy
Carl Yastrzemski Jsy
Wade Boggs Jsy
Curt Schilling Jsy
Joe DiMaggio Bat
Thurman Munson Pants
Don Mattingly Jsy
Derek Jeter Jsy/5

2006 Upper Deck Epic Endorsements

OVERALL AU ODDS ONE PER CASE
PRINT RUNS B/WN 10-45 COPIES PER
NO PRICING ON QTY OF 25 OR LESS
AD Adam Dunn/45 20.00 50.00
AJ Andruw Jones/30 20.00 50.00
AP Albert Pujols/15
AS Alfonso Soriano/30 20.00 50.00
BE1 Johnny Bench/10
BE2 Johnny Bench/10
BF1 Bob Feller/45 20.00 50.00
BF2 Bob Feller/45 20.00 50.00
BG Bob Gibson/30 30.00 60.00
BM Bill Mazeroski/30 30.00 60.00
BN Brian Roberts/45 12.50 30.00
BO Bo Jackson/30 50.00 100.00
BR1 Brooks Robinson/30 40.00 80.00
BR2 Brooks Robinson/30 40.00 80.00
BW Billy Williams/45 12.50 30.00
CB Craig Biggio/30 30.00 60.00
CF Carlton Fisk/30 30.00 60.00
CL Roger Clemens/10
CR Cal Ripken/15
CS Curt Schilling/15
CU Chase Utley/45 40.00 80.00
CY Carl Yastrzemski/15
DJ1 Derek Jeter/30 150.00 250.00
DJ2 Derek Jeter/30 150.00 250.00
DJ3 Derek Jeter/30 150.00 250.00
DO David Ortiz/30 50.00 100.00
DS Don Sutton/30 12.50 30.00
DW1 Dontrelle Willis/30 20.00 50.00
DW2 Dontrelle Willis/30 20.00 50.00
EC Eric Chavez/30 12.50 30.00
FH1 Felix Hernandez/30 30.00 60.00
FH2 Felix Hernandez/30 30.00 60.00
FL Fred Lynn/45 12.50 30.00
FR Frank Robinson/30 20.00 50.00
GM Greg Maddux/15
HK Harmon Killebrew/15
JA Jake Peavy/45 12.50 30.00
JB Jason Bay/45 12.50 30.00
JH1 Jeremy Hermida/45 12.50 30.00
JH2 Jeremy Hermida/45 12.50 30.00
JI Jim Bunning/30 12.50 30.00
JP1 Jim Palmer/30 20.00 50.00
JP2 Jim Palmer/30 20.00 50.00
KG1 Ken Griffey Jr./30 100.00 150.00
KG2 Ken Griffey Jr./30 100.00 150.00
KG3 Ken Griffey Jr./30 100.00 150.00
KP Kirby Puckett/15
LA Don Larsen/30 12.50 30.00
LB Lou Brock/30 40.00 80.00
MC1 Miguel Cabrera/30 20.00 50.00
MC2 Miguel Cabrera/30 20.00 50.00
MI Miguel Tejada/15
MP Mark Prior/15
MS1 Mike Schmidt/8
MS2 Mike Schmidt/7

MT1 Mark Teixeira/23
MT2 Mark Teixeira/22
MW Maury Wills/45 12.50 30.00
NR Nolan Ryan/10
OS Ozzie Smith/30 40.00 80.00
PE Pedro Martinez/15
PF Prince Fielder/44 40.00 80.00
PI Mike Piazza/10
PM1 Paul Molitor/30 20.00 50.00
PM2 Paul Molitor/30 20.00 50.00
RA Randy Johnson/15
RC Rod Carew/30 20.00 50.00
RH Ryan Howard/45 30.00 60.00
RJ Reggie Jackson/15
RO1 Roy Oswalt/45 20.00 50.00
RO2 Roy Oswalt/45 20.00 50.00
RS1 Ryne Sandberg/23
RS2 Ryne Sandberg/22
RZ1 Ryan Zimmerman/30 60.00 120.00
RZ2 Ryan Zimmerman/30 60.00 120.00
SC1 Steve Carlton/26 20.00 50.00
SC2 Steve Carlton/27 20.00 50.00
SG Steve Garvey/45 20.00 50.00
SM John Smoltz/30 100.00 200.00
ST Stan Musial/15
TG Tony Gwynn/30 30.00 60.00
TO Tony Oliva/45 20.00 50.00
TP Tony Perez/45 20.00 50.00
TS Tom Seaver/30 30.00 60.00
VG Vladimir Guerrero/15
WB Wade Boggs/30 40.00 80.00
WC1 Will Clark/23
WC2 Will Clark/22
WF Whitey Ford/15
WM Willie McCovey/15
WR David Wright/25

2006 Upper Deck Epic Events

OVERALL ODDS 3:5 PACKS
STATED PRINT RUN 675 SERIAL #'d SETS
EE1 Ryan Howard 3.00 8.00
EE2 Tadahito Iguchi .75 2.00
EE3 Paul Konerko .75 2.00
EE4 Craig Biggio 1.25 3.00
EE5 Alex Rodriguez 3.00 8.00
EE6 Ichiro Suzuki 3.00 8.00
EE7 David Ortiz 2.00 5.00
EE8 Miguel Cabrera 1.25 3.00
EE9 Dontrelle Willis .75 2.00
EE10 Mark Teixeira 1.25 3.00
EE11 Hideki Matsui 2.00 5.00
EE12 Albert Pujols 4.00 10.00
EE13 Albert Pujols 4.00 10.00
EE14 Greg Maddux 3.00 8.00
EE15 Greg Maddux 3.00 8.00
EE16 Manny Ramirez 1.25 3.00
EE17 Mark Teixeira 1.25 3.00
EE18 Alex Rodriguez 3.00 8.00
EE19 Manny Ramirez 1.25 3.00
EE20 Randy Johnson 2.00 5.00
EE21 Jason Varitek 2.00 5.00
EE22 Vladimir Guerrero 2.00 5.00
EE23 Roger Clemens 4.00 10.00
EE24 Manny Ramirez 1.25 3.00
EE25 Curt Schilling 1.25 3.00
EE26 Johnny Damon 1.25 3.00
EE27 David Ortiz 2.00 5.00
EE28 David Wright 3.00 8.00
EE29 Ichiro Suzuki 3.00 8.00
EE30 Ichiro Suzuki 3.00 8.00
EE31 Adam Dunn .75 2.00
EE32 Adrian Beltre .75 2.00
EE33 Javy Lopez .75 2.00
EE34 Greg Maddux 3.00 8.00
EE35 Randy Johnson 2.00 5.00
EE36 Jim Thome 1.25 3.00
EE37 Adam Dunn .75 2.00
EE38 Bobby Abreu .75 2.00
EE39 Felix Hernandez 1.25 3.00
EE40 Greg Maddux 3.00 8.00
EE41 Ken Griffey Jr. 3.00 8.00
EE42 Randy Johnson 2.00 5.00
EE43 Johan Santana 2.00 5.00
EE44 Magglio Ordonez .75 2.00
EE45 Josh Beckett .75 2.00
EE46 Ivan Rodriguez 1.25 3.00
EE47 Alfonso Soriano .75 2.00
EE48 Eric Gagne .75 2.00
EE49 Hank Blalock .75 2.00
EE50 Roger Clemens 4.00 10.00
EE51 Derek Jeter 5.00 12.00
EE52 Derek Jeter 5.00 12.00
EE53 Barry Zito .75 2.00
EE54 Alex Rodriguez 3.00 8.00
EE55 Nomar Garciaparra 2.00 5.00
EE56 Torii Hunter .75 2.00
EE57 Ichiro Suzuki 3.00 8.00
EE58 Randy Johnson 2.00 5.00
EE59 Ichiro Suzuki 3.00 8.00
EE60 Albert Pujols 4.00 10.00
EE61 Albert Pujols 4.00 10.00
EE62 Ichiro Suzuki 3.00 8.00
EE63 Derek Jeter 5.00 12.00
EE64 Pedro Martinez 1.25 3.00
EE65 Chris Shelton .75 2.00
EE66 Ivan Rodriguez 1.25 3.00
EE67 Chipper Jones 2.00 5.00
EE68 Pedro Martinez 1.25 3.00
EE69 Ken Griffey Jr. 3.00 8.00
EE70 Jeff Bagwell 1.25 3.00
EE71 Nomar Garciaparra 2.00 5.00
EE72 Mark Prior 1.25 3.00
EE73 Kerry Wood .75 2.00
EE74 Andruw Jones 1.25 3.00
EE75 Derek Jeter 5.00 12.00
EE76 Cal Ripken 8.00 20.00
EE77 Ken Griffey Jr. 3.00 8.00
EE78 Ken Griffey Jr. 3.00 8.00
EE79 Mike Piazza 2.00 5.00
EE80 Nolan Ryan 5.00 12.00
EE81 Greg Maddux 3.00 8.00
EE82 Greg Maddux 3.00 8.00
EE83 Roger Clemens 4.00 10.00
EE84 Ozzie Smith 3.00 8.00
EE85 Tom Seaver 1.25 3.00
EE86 Thurman Munson 2.00 5.00
EE87 Reggie Jackson 1.25 3.00
EE88 Johnny Bench 2.00 5.00
EE89 Mike Schmidt 3.00 8.00
EE90 Carlton Fisk 1.25 3.00
EE91 Eddie Mathews 2.00 5.00
EE92 Roy Campanella 2.00 5.00
EE93 Jackie Robinson 2.00 5.00
EE94 Joe DiMaggio 4.00 10.00
EE95 Jimmie Foxx 2.00 5.00
EE96 Lou Gehrig 4.00 10.00
EE97 Babe Ruth 5.00 12.00
EE98 Ty Cobb 3.00 8.00
EE99 Honus Wagner 2.00 5.00
EE100 Cy Young 2.00 5.00

2006 Upper Deck Epic Four Barrel

OVERALL GU ODDS ONE PER PACK
STATED PRINT RUN 1 SERIAL #'d SET
NO PRICING DUE TO SCARCITY
BBLH Wade Boggs
Adrian Beltre
Mike Lowell
Aubrey Huff
CBCH Kiki Cuyler
Lou Boudreau
Roy Campanella
Tommy Henrich
CFBR Joe Cronin
Jimmie Foxx
Wade Boggs
Manny Ramirez
CFLP Roy Campanella
Bill Freehan
Javy Lopez
Jorge Posada
CGCK Ty Cobb
Charlie Gehringer
Mickey Cochrane
George Kell
CHGD Kiki Cuyler
Billy Herman
Mark Grace
Andre Dawson
CROM Roberto Clemente
Bob Robertson
Al Oliver
Bill Mazeroski
CWDG Ty Cobb
Hack Wilson
Joe DiMaggio
Ken Griffey Jr.
DBGB J.D. Drew
Adrian Beltre
Troy Glaus
Carlos Beltran
DCLE Bobby Doerr
Tony Conigliaro
Fred Lynn
Dwight Evans
DMHP Bill Dickey
Thurman Munson
Elston Howard
Jorge Posada
FHWS Nellie Fox
Ron Hunt
Lou Whitaker
Steve Sax
FJSW Bob Feller
Randy Johnson
Tom Seaver
Kerry Wood
FMWS Nellie Fox
Bill Mazeroski
Lou Whitaker
Ryne Sandberg
HFHM Rogers Hornsby
Frankie Frisch
Davey Johnson
Bill Mazeroski
HKJB Tommy Henrich
Charlie Keller
Reggie Jackson
Hank Bauer
HPPB Gil Hodges
Boog Powell
Wes Parker
Bill Buckner
JMCB Reggie Jackson
Thurman Munson
Chris Chambliss
Paul Blair
MDTP Willie McCovey
Andre Dawson
Jim Thome
Albert Pujols
MGSY Manny Mota
Steve Garvey
Steve Sax
Steve Yeager
MJSG Willie McCovey
Reggie Jackson
Gary Sheffield
Ken Griffey Jr.
MLJF Fred McGriff
Javy Lopez
Andruw Jones
Rafael Furcal
MMHP Willie McCovey
Fred McGriff
Todd Helton
Albert Pujols
MTDP Willie McCovey
Jim Thome
Carlos Delgado
Albert Pujols
OGDB Al Oliver
Steve Garvey
Andre Dawson
Craig Biggio
OJDW Tony Oliva
Reggie Jackson
Andre Dawson
Dave Winfield
OMRF Mel Ott
Eddie Mathews
Babe Ruth
Jimmie Foxx
PJDS Jorge Posada
Randy Johnson
Johnny Damon
Gary Sheffield
PRBE Albert Pujols
Scott Rolen
Ken Boyer
Jim Edmonds
RCNP Jackie Robinson
Roberto Clemente
Hideo Nomo
Albert Pujols
SAWC George Sisler
Luke Appling
Paul Waner
Roberto Clemente
SDHC Eddie Stanky
Don Drysdale
Gil Hodges
Roy Campanella
TMFJ Bobby Thomson
Bill Mazeroski
Carlton Fisk
Reggie Jackson
TWYM Alan Trammell
Lou Whitaker
Robin Yount
Paul Molitor
WGNB Kerry Wood
Tom Glavine
Hideo Nomo
Josh Beckett
WYBM Dave Winfield
Robin Yount
Wade Boggs
Joe Morgan
YLWT Robin Yount
Barry Larkin
Maury Wills
Alan Trammell

2006 Upper Deck Epic Foursome Fabrics

OVERALL GU ODDS ONE PER PACK
PRINT RUNS B/WN 5-50 COPIES PER
NO PRICING ON QTY OF 30 OR LESS
CDGP Ty Cobb Bat
Joe DiMaggio Pants
Ken Griffey Jr. Jsy
Kirby Puckett Jsy/10
CMBF Gary Carter Jsy
Thurman Munson Pants
Johnny Bench Pants
Carlton Fisk Pan
GGKB Lou Gehrig Pants
Hank Greenberg Bat
Harmon Killebrew Pants
Ernie Banks J
GRSM Bob Gibson Jsy 30.00 60.00
Nolan Ryan Jsy
Tom Seaver Jsy
Juan Marichal Jsy/50
HMRS Rogers Hornsby Jkt
Joe Morgan Jsy
Jackie Robinson Bat
Ryne Sandberg Bat/
HRRG Gil Hodges Bat
Jackie Robinson Bat
Pee Wee Reese Jsy
Steve Garvey Jsy/10
MBSP Stan Musial Pants
Lou Brock Jsy
Ozzie Smith Jsy
Albert Pujols Jsy/30
PJGG Albert Pujols Jsy 75.00 150.00
Derek Jeter Jsy
Ken Griffey Jr. Jsy
Vladimir Guerrero
RCJP Nolan Ryan Jsy 30.00 60.00
Roger Clemens Pants
Randy Johnson Pants
Mark Prior Jsy/50
RGDM Babe Ruth Bat
Lou Gehrig Pants
Joe DiMaggio Pants
Don Mattingly Jsy/5
RRJC Babe Ruth Bat
Frank Robinson Pants
Reggie Jackson Jsy
Roberto Clemente P
RRMR Brooks Robinson Jsy
Frank Robinson Pants
Eddie Murray Jsy
Cal Ripken Jr.
SBMR Mike Schmidt Jsy
Wade Boggs Jsy
Eddie Mathews Jsy
Brooks Robinson Jsy/15
WRRJ Honus Wagner Pants
Cal Ripken Jr. Jsy
Pee Wee Reese Jsy
Derek Jeter Jsy/
WYBS Ted Williams Jsy 50.00 100.00
Carl Yastrzemski Jsy
Wade Boggs Jsy
Curt Schilling Jsy/

2006 Upper Deck Epic Materials Blue

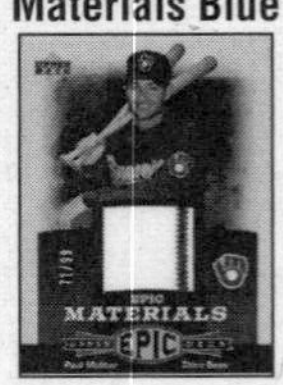

*BLUE p/r 75-99: .5X TO 1.2X ORG p/r 125-185
*BLUE p/r 75-99: .4X TO 1X ORG p/r 75-99
*BLUE p/r 75-99: .3X TO .8X ORG p/r 39-52
*BLUE p/r 49-65: .6 TO 1.5X ORG p/r 125-185
*BLUE p/r 49-65: .4 TO 1X ORG p/r 39-52
*BLUE p/r 25-34: .75X TO 2X ORG p/r 125-185
*BLUE p/r 25-34: .6X TO 1.5X ORG p/r 125-185
*BLUE p/r 25-34: .5X TO 1.2X ORG p/r 39-52
*BLUE p/r 25-34: .4X TO 1X ORG p/r 35
*BLUE p/r 10: .6X TO 1.5X ORG p/r 39-52
*BLUE p/r 10: .4X TO 1X ORG p/r 10-16
OVERALL GU ODDS ONE PER PACK
PRINT RUNS B/WN 3-99 COPIES PER
NO WAGNER PRICING DUE TO SCARCITY
BR1 Babe Ruth Bat/3 300.00 500.00
BR2 Babe Ruth Bat/3 300.00 500.00
CL1 Roberto Clemente Pants/99 20.00 50.00
HG Hank Greenberg Bat/30 30.00 60.00
JD1 Joe DiMaggio Jsy/25 60.00 120.00
JD2 Joe DiMaggio Jsy/25 60.00 120.00
JD3 Joe DiMaggio Jsy/25 60.00 120.00
JR Jackie Robinson Bat/10 40.00 80.00
LG1 Lou Gehrig Bat/10 100.00 175.00
LG2 Lou Gehrig Bat/10 100.00 175.00
LG3 Lou Gehrig Bat/10 100.00 175.00
RH Rogers Hornsby Jkt/10 40.00 80.00
TW1 Ted Williams Jsy/25 30.00 60.00
TW2 Ted Williams Pants/25 30.00 60.00

2006 Upper Deck Epic Materials Dark Green

*DG p/r 50: .6X TO 1.5X ORG p/r 125-185
*DG p/r 50: .5X TO 1.2X ORG p/r 75-99
*DG p/r 50: .4X TO 1X ORG p/r 39-52
*DG p/r 10: 1X TO 2.5X ORG p/r 125-185
*DG p/r 10: .75X TO 2X ORG p/r 75-99
*DG p/r 10: .6X TO 1.5X ORG p/r 39-52
*DG p/r 10: .5X TO 1.2X ORG p/r 35
*DG p/r 10: .4X TO 1X ORG p/r 10-16
OVERALL GU ODDS ONE PER PACK
PRINT RUNS B/WN 3-50 COPIES PER
BR1 Babe Ruth Bat/3 300.00 500.00
BR2 Babe Ruth Bat/3 300.00 500.00
CL1 Roberto Clemente Pants/50 30.00 60.00
HG Hank Greenberg Bat/15 40.00 80.00
HW Honus Wagner Pants/15 125.00 200.00
JD1 Joe DiMaggioJsy/15 75.00 150.00
JD2 Joe DiMaggio Jsy/50 50.00 100.00
JD3 Joe DiMaggio Jsy/15 75.00 150.00
JR Jackie Robinson Bat/10 40.00 80.00
LG1 Lou Gehrig Bat/5 175.00 300.00
LG2 Lou Gehrig Bat/5 175.00 300.00
LG3 Lou Gehrig Bat/5 175.00 300.00
RH Rogers Hornsby Jkt/10 40.00 80.00
TW1 Ted Williams Jsy/50 20.00 50.00
TW2 Ted Williams Jsy/50 20.00 50.00

2006 Upper Deck Epic Materials Dark Orange

*DO p/r 119-185: .4X TO 1X ORG p/r 125-185
*DO p/r 119-185: .25X TO .6X ORG p/r 39-52
*DO p/r 75-99: .5X TO 1.2X ORG p/r 125-185
*DO p/r 75-99: .4X TO 1X ORG p/r 75-99
*DO p/r 39-65: .6X TO 1.5X ORG p/r 125-185
*DO p/r 39-65: .5X TO 1.2X ORG p/r 75-99
*DO p/r 39-65: .4X TO 1X ORG p/r 39-52
*DO p/r 25-35: .4X TO 1X ORG p/r 35
*DO p/r 25-35: .3X TO .8X ORG p/r 10-16
OVERALL GU ODDS ONE PER PACK
PRINT RUNS B/WN 5-185 COPIES PER
BR1 Babe Ruth Bat/5 300.00 500.00
BR2 Babe Ruth Bat/5 300.00 500.00
CL1 Roberto Clemente Pants/65 30.00 60.00
HG Hank Greenberg Bat/50 20.00 50.00
HW Honus Wagner Pants/25 100.00 175.00
JD1 Joe DiMaggioPants/65 50.00 100.00
JD2 Joe DiMaggio Pants/65 50.00 100.00
JD3 Joe DiMaggio Pants/65 50.00 100.00
JR Jackie Robinson Bat/11 40.00 80.00
LG1 Lou Gehrig Bat/15 100.00 175.00
LG2 Lou Gehrig Bat/15 100.00 175.00
LG3 Lou Gehrig Bat/15 100.00 175.00
RH Rogers Hornsby Jkt/50 20.00 50.00
TW1 Ted Williams Jsy/99 15.00 40.00
TW2 Ted Williams Pants/99 15.00 40.00

2006 Upper Deck Epic Materials Dark Purple

*DP p/r 102-185: .4X TO 1X ORG p/r 125-185
*DP p/r 102-185: .25X TO .6X ORG p/r 39-52
*DP p/r 75: .5X TO 1.2X ORG p/r 125-185
*DP p/r 75: .4X TO 1X ORG p/r 75-99
*DP p/r 39-50: .6X TO 1.5X ORG p/r 125-185
*DP p/r 39-50: .5X TO 1.2X ORG p/r 75-99
*DP p/r 39-50: .4X TO 1X ORG p/r 39-52
*DP p/r 25-50: .75X TO 2X ORG p/r 125-185
*DP p/r 25-50: .6X TO 1.5X ORG p/r 75-99
*DP p/r 25-50: .4X TO 1X ORG p/r 35
*DP p/r 25-50: .3X TO .8X ORG p/r 10-16
OVERALL GU ODDS ONE PER PACK
PRINT RUNS B/WN 3-185 COPIES PER
NO B.ROBINSON PRICING DUE TO SCARCITY
BR1 Babe Ruth Bat/3 300.00 500.00
BR2 Babe Ruth Bat/3 300.00 500.00
CL1 Roberto Clemente Pants/45 30.00 60.00
HG Hank Greenberg Bat/40 20.00 50.00
HW Honus Wagner Pants/25 100.00 175.00
JD1 Joe DiMaggio Jsy/25 60.00 120.00
JD2 Joe DiMaggio Jsy/35 50.00 100.00
JD3 Joe DiMaggio Jsy/35 50.00 100.00
JR Jackie Robinson Bat/11 40.00 80.00
LG1 Lou Gehrig Bat/15 100.00 175.00
LG2 Lou Gehrig Bat/15 100.00 175.00
LG3 Lou Gehrig Bat/15 100.00 175.00
RH Rogers Hornsby Jkt/50 20.00 50.00
TW1 Ted Williams Jsy/45 20.00 50.00
TW2 Ted Williams Jsy/45 20.00 50.00

2006 Upper Deck Epic Materials Gold

*GOLD p/r 24-25: .75X TO 2X ORG p/r 125-185
*GOLD p/r 24-25: .6X TO 1.5X ORG p/r 75-99
*GOLD p/r 24-25: .5X TO 1.2X ORG p/r 39-52
*GOLD p/r 10-19: 1X TO 2.5X ORG p/r 125-185
*GOLD p/r 10-19: .75X TO 2X ORG p/r 75-99
*GOLD p/r 10-19: .6X TO 1.5X ORG p/r 39-52
*GOLD p/r 10-19: .5X TO 1.2X ORG p/r 35
*GOLD p/r 10-19: .4X TO 1X ORG p/r 10-16
OVERALL GU ODDS ONE PER PACK
PRINT RUNS B/WN 1-25 COPIES PER
NO CLEMENTE PRICING DUE TO SCARCITY
NO GREENBERG PRICING DUE TO SCARCITY
NO MATHEWS PRICING DUE TO SCARCITY
NO RUTH PRICING DUE TO SCARCITY
HW Honus Wagner Pants/15 125.00 200.00
JD1 Joe DiMaggio Jsy/15 75.00 150.00
JD2 Joe DiMaggio Jsy/15 75.00 150.00
JD3 Joe DiMaggio Jsy/16 75.00 150.00
JR Jackie Robinson Bat/11 40.00 80.00
LG1 Lou Gehrig Bat/5 175.00 300.00
LG2 Lou Gehrig Bat/5 175.00 300.00
LG3 Lou Gehrig Bat/5 175.00 300.00
RH Rogers Hornsby Jkt/10 40.00 80.00
TW1 Ted Williams Jsy/24 30.00 60.00
TW2 Ted Williams Jsy/25 30.00 60.00

2006 Upper Deck Epic Materials Green

*GRN p/r 75: .5X TO 1.2X ORG p/r 125-185
*GRN p/r 75: .4X TO 1X ORG p/r 75-99
*GRN p/r 75: .3X TO .8X ORG p/r 39-52
*GRN p/r 20: .5X TO 1.2X ORG p/r 39-52
*GRN p/r 10-19: 1X TO 2.5X ORG p/r 125-185
*GRN p/r 10-19: .75X TO 2X ORG p/r 75-99
*GRN p/r 10-19: .6X TO 1.5X ORG p/r 39-52
*GRN p/r 10-19: .5X TO 1.2X ORG p/r 35
*GRN p/r 10-19: .4X TO 1X ORG p/r 10-16
OVERALL GU ODDS ONE PER PACK
PRINT RUNS B/WN 3-75 COPIES PER
NO J.ROBINSON PRICING DUE TO SCARCITY
BR1 Babe Ruth Bat/3 300.00 500.00
BR2 Babe Ruth Bat/3 300.00 500.00
CL1 Roberto Clemente Pants/75 20.00 50.00
HG Hank Greenberg Bat/20 30.00 60.00
HW Honus Wagner Pants/15 125.00 200.00
JD1 Joe DiMaggio Jsy/75 40.00 80.00
JD2 Joe DiMaggio Jsy/15 75.00 150.00
JD3 Joe DiMaggio Jsy/16 75.00 150.00
LG1 Lou Gehrig Bat/5 175.00 300.00
LG2 Lou Gehrig Bat/5 175.00 300.00
LG3 Lou Gehrig Bat/5 175.00 300.00
RH Rogers Hornsby Jkt/10 40.00 80.00
TW1 Ted Williams Jsy/75 15.00 40.00
TW2 Ted Williams Jsy/75 15.00 40.00

2006 Upper Deck Epic Materials Grey

*GREY p/r 40: .6X TO 1.5X ORG p/r 125-185
*GREY p/r 40: .5X TO 1.2X ORG p/r 75-99
*GREY p/r 40: .4X TO 1X ORG p/r 39-52
*GREY p/r 10-19: 1X TO 2.5X ORG p/r 125-185
*GREY p/r 10-19: .75X TO 2X ORG p/r 75-99
*GREY p/r 10-19: .6X TO 1.5X ORG p/r 39-52
*GREY p/r 10-19: .5X TO 1.2X ORG p/r 35
*GREY p/r 10-19: .4X TO 1X ORG p/r 10-16
OVERALL GU ODDS ONE PER PACK
PRINT RUNS B/WN 3-40 COPIES PER
NO GREENBERG PRICING DUE TO SCARCITY
NO J.ROBINSON PRICING DUE TO SCARCITY
BR1 Babe Ruth Bat/3 300.00 500.00
BR2 Babe Ruth Bat/3 300.00 500.00
CL1 Roberto Clemente Pants/40 30.00 60.00
HW Honus Wagner Pants/15 125.00 200.00
JD1 Joe DiMaggio Jsy/40 50.00 100.00
JD2 Joe DiMaggio Jsy/16 75.00 150.00
JD3 Joe DiMaggio Jsy/16 75.00 150.00
LG1 Lou Gehrig Bat/5 175.00 300.00
LG2 Lou Gehrig Bat/5 175.00 300.00
LG3 Lou Gehrig Bat/5 175.00 300.00
RH Rogers Hornsby Jkt/10 40.00 80.00
TW1 Ted Williams Jsy/40 20.00 50.00
TW2 Ted Williams Jsy/40 20.00 50.00

2006 Upper Deck Epic Materials Light Purple

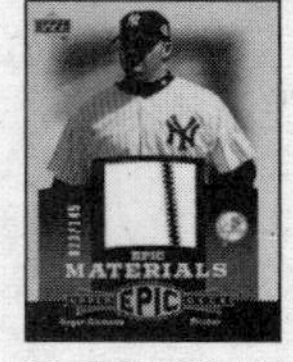

*LP p/r 105-185: .4X TO 1X ORG p/r 125-185
*LP p/r 105-185: .25X TO .6X ORG p/r 39-52
*LP p/r 75: .5X TO 1.2X ORG p/r 125-185
*LP p/r 75: .4X TO 1X ORG p/r 75-99
*LP p/r 39-59: .6X TO 1.5X ORG p/r 125-185
*LP p/r 39-59: .5X TO 1.2X ORG p/r 75-99
*LP p/r 39-59: .4X TO 1X ORG p/r 39-52
*LP p/r 24-34: .75X TO 2X ORG p/r 125-185
*LP p/r 24-34: .4X TO 1X ORG p/r 35
*LP p/r 24-34: .3X TO .8X ORG p/r 10-16
OVERALL GU ODDS ONE PER PACK
PRINT RUNS B/WN 4-185 COPIES PER
NO SEAVER/15 PRICING DUE TO SCARCITY
BR1 Babe Ruth Bat/4 300.00 500.00
BR2 Babe Ruth Bat/4 300.00 500.00
CL1 Roberto Clemente Pants/50 30.00 60.00
HG Hank Greenberg Bat/50 20.00 50.00
HW Honus Wagner Pants/24 100.00 175.00
JD1 Joe DiMaggio Jsy/25 60.00 120.00
JD2 Joe DiMaggio Jsy/45 50.00 100.00
JD3 Joe DiMaggio Jsy/45 50.00 100.00
JR Jackie Robinson Bat/10 40.00 80.00
LG1 Lou Gehrig Bat/15 100.00 175.00
LG2 Lou Gehrig Bat/15 100.00 175.00
LG3 Lou Gehrig Bat/15 100.00 175.00
RH Rogers Hornsby Jkt/50 20.00 50.00
TW1 Ted Williams Jsy/55 20.00 50.00
TW2 Ted Williams Jsy/55 20.00 50.00

2006 Upper Deck Epic Materials Orange

OVERALL GU ODDS ONE PER PACK
PRINT RUNS B/WN 10-185 COPIES PER
NO COBB PRICING DUE TO SCARCITY
AP1 Albert Pujols Jsy/185 8.00 20.00
AP2 Albert Pujols Jsy/185 8.00 20.00
AP3 Albert Pujols Jsy/185 8.00 20.00
BG Bob Gibson Jsy/155 4.00 10.00
BG2 Bob Gibson Pants/155 4.00 10.00
BR1 Babe Ruth Bat/15 175.00 300.00
BR2 Babe Ruth Bat/15 175.00 300.00
CF Carlton Fisk Jsy/169 4.00 10.00
CF2 Carlton Fisk Jsy/185 4.00 10.00
CL1 Roberto Clemente Pants/50 30.00 60.00
CR1 Cal Ripken Jsy/185 10.00 25.00
CR2 Cal Ripken Jsy/177 10.00 25.00
CR3 Cal Ripken Jsy/155 10.00 25.00
CY1 Carl Yastrzemski Jsy/185 4.00 10.00
CY2 Carl Yastrzemski Jsy/185 4.00 10.00

CY3 Carl Yastrzemski Jsy/185 4.00 10.00
DJ1 Derek Jeter Jsy/185 10.00 25.00
DJ2 Derek Jeter Jsy/185 10.00 25.00
DJ3 Derek Jeter Jsy/185 10.00 25.00
DM1 Don Mattingly Jsy/185 6.00 15.00
DM2 Don Mattingly Jsy/185 6.00 15.00
EB Ernie Banks Jsy/155 5.00 12.00
ED Eddie Mathews Jsy/75 5.00 12.00
EM1 Eddie Murray Jsy/185 4.00 10.00
EM2 Eddie Murray Jsy/165 4.00 10.00
EM3 Eddie Murray Jsy/155 4.00 10.00
FR1 Frank Robinson Jsy/130 4.00 10.00
FR2 Frank Robinson Jsy/130 4.00 10.00
GH Gil Hodges Bat/39 10.00 25.00
HG Hank Greenberg Bat/50 20.00 50.00
HK Harmon Killebrew Pants/155 4.00 10.00
HW Honus Wagner Pants/16 125.00 200.00
JB1 Johnny Bench Jsy/155 4.00 10.00
JB2 Johnny Bench Jsy/155 4.00 10.00
JD1 Joe DiMaggio Pants/185 30.00 60.00
JD2 Joe DiMaggio Pants/173 30.00 60.00
JD3 Joe DiMaggio Pants/99 40.00 80.00
JM Juan Marichal Jsy/155 4.00 10.00
JO Joe Morgan Jsy/145 4.00 10.00
JO2 Joe Morgan Jsy/155 4.00 10.00
JR Jackie Robinson Bat/10 40.00 80.00
KG1 Ken Griffey Jr. Jsy/175 8.00 20.00
KG2 Ken Griffey Jr. Jsy/175 8.00 20.00
KG3 Ken Griffey Jr. Jsy/175 8.00 20.00
KP1 Kirby Puckett Jsy/155 5.00 12.00
KP2 Kirby Puckett Jsy/155 5.00 12.00
LB1 Lou Brock Pants/48 6.00 15.00
LB2 Lou Brock Pants/48 6.00 15.00
LG1 Lou Gehrig Bat/15 100.00 175.00
LG2 Lou Gehrig Bat/15 100.00 175.00
LG3 Lou Gehrig Bat/15 100.00 175.00
MA Mark Prior Jsy/185 4.00 10.00
MA2 Mark Prior Jsy/185 4.00 10.00
MP1 Mike Piazza Jsy/145 4.00 10.00
MP2 Mike Piazza Jsy/145 4.00 10.00
MS1 Mike Schmidt Jsy/185 5.00 12.00
MS2 Mike Schmidt Jsy/185 5.00 12.00
MS3 Mike Schmidt Jsy/185 5.00 12.00
NR1 Nolan Ryan Jsy/155 8.00 20.00
NR2 Nolan Ryan Jsy/155 8.00 20.00
NR3 Nolan Ryan Jsy/155 8.00 20.00
OS1 Ozzie Smith Bat/155 4.00 10.00
OS2 Ozzie Smith Jsy/185 4.00 10.00
PM1 Paul Molitor Jsy/155 4.00 10.00
PM2 Paul Molitor Jsy/155 4.00 10.00
PR1 Pee Wee Reese Jsy/145 4.00 10.00
PR2 Pee Wee Reese Jsy/145 4.00 10.00
RC1 Roger Clemens Pants/155 5.00 12.00
RC2 Roger Clemens Pants/155 5.00 12.00
RC3 Roger Clemens Pants/155 5.00 12.00
RE1 Reggie Jackson Jsy/52 6.00 15.00
RE2 Reggie Jackson Jsy/52 6.00 15.00
RE3 Reggie Jackson Jsy/52 6.00 15.00
RH Rogers Hornsby Jkt/50 20.00 50.00
RJ1 Randy Johnson Jsy/145 4.00 10.00
RJ2 Randy Johnson Jsy/145 4.00 10.00
RO Brooks Robinson Pants/49 6.00 15.00
RO2 Brooks Robinson Pants/99 5.00 12.00
RS1 Ryne Sandberg Jsy/155 4.00 10.00
RS2 Ryne Sandberg Jsy/155 4.00 10.00
RS3 Ryne Sandberg Jsy/155 4.00 10.00
RY1 Robin Yount Jsy/155 4.00 10.00
RY2 Robin Yount Jsy/155 4.00 10.00
SM1 Stan Musial Jsy/50 8.00 20.00
SM2 Stan Musial Jsy/75 6.00 15.00
TC Ty Cobb Bat/10
TH1 Thurman Munson Pants/35 10.00 25.00
TH2 Thurman Munson Pants/35 10.00 25.00
TS Tom Seaver Jsy/155 4.00 10.00
TS2 Tom Seaver Jsy/155 4.00 10.00
TW1 Ted Williams Pants/125 15.00 40.00
TW2 Ted Williams Pants/125 15.00 40.00
VG Vladimir Guerrero Jsy/145 4.00 10.00
VG2 Vladimir Guerrero Jsy/145 4.00 10.00
WB1 Wade Boggs Jsy/185 4.00 10.00
WB2 Wade Boggs Jsy/185 4.00 10.00
WF Whitey Ford Pants/155 6.00 15.00
WM Willie McCovey Jsy/155 4.00 10.00
WM2 Willie McCovey Pants/155 4.00 10.00
WM3 Willie McCovey Pants/155 4.00 10.00

2006 Upper Deck Epic Materials Red

*RED p/r 105-185: .4X TO 1X ORG p/r 125-185
*RED p/r 105-185: .25X TO .6X ORG p/r 39-52
*RED p/r 69-99: .5X TO 1.2X ORG p/r 125-185
*RED p/r 69-99: .4X TO 1X ORG p/r 75-99
*RED p/r 69-99: .3X TO .8X ORG p/r 39-52
*RED p/r 49-65: .5X TO 1.2X ORG p/r 75-99
*RED p/r 49-65: .4X TO 1X ORG p/r 39-52
*RED p/r 25-34: .75X TO 2X ORG p/r 125-185
*RED p/r 25-34: .4X TO 1X ORG p/r 35
*RED p/r 25-34: .3X TO .8X ORG p/r 10-16
*RED p/r 10-19: .6X TO 1.5X ORG p/r 39-52
*RED p/r 10-19: .4X TO 1X ORG p/r 10-16
OVERALL GU ODDS ONE PER PACK
PRINT RUNS B/WN 10-185 COPIES PER
NO GEHRIG PRICING DUE TO SCARCITY
CL1 Roberto Clemente Pants/65 30.00 60.00
HG Hank Greenberg Bat/50 20.00 50.00
HW Honus Wagner Pants/25 100.00 175.00
JD1 Joe DiMaggio Jsy/25 60.00 120.00
JD2 Joe DiMaggio Jsy/55 50.00 100.00
JD3 Joe DiMaggio Jsy/55 50.00 100.00
JR Jackie Robinson Bat/10 40.00 80.00
RH Rogers Hornsby Jkt/50 20.00 50.00
TW1 Ted Williams Jsy/75 15.00 40.00
TW2 Ted Williams Jsy/75 15.00 40.00

2006 Upper Deck Epic Materials Teal

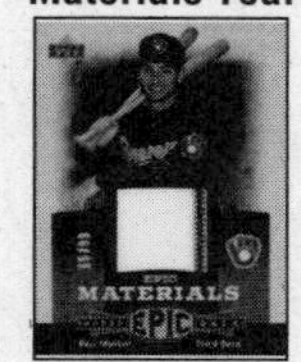

*TEAL p/r 99: .5X TO 1.2X ORG p/r 125-185
*TEAL p/r 99: .4X TO 1X ORG p/r 75-99
*TEAL p/r 99: .3X TO .8X ORG p/r 39-52
*TEAL p/r 65: .6X TO 1.5X ORG p/r 125-185
*TEAL p/r 21: .5X TO 1.2X ORG p/r 39-52
*TEAL p/r 10-19: 1X TO 2.5X ORG p/r 125-185
*TEAL p/r 10-19: .75X TO 2X ORG p/r 75-99
*TEAL p/r 10-19: .6X TO 1.5X ORG p/r 39-52
*TEAL p/r 10-19: .5X TO 1.2X ORG p/r 35
*TEAL p/r 10-19: .4X TO 1X ORG p/r 10-16
OVERALL GU ODDS ONE PER PACK
PRINT RUNS B/WN 5-99 COPIES PER
BR1 Babe Ruth Bat/5 300.00 500.00
BR2 Babe Ruth Bat/5 300.00 500.00
CL1 Roberto Clemente Pants/99 20.00 50.00
HG Hank Greenberg Bat/21 30.00 60.00
HW Honus Wagner Pants/15 125.00 200.00
JD1 Joe DiMaggio Jsy/16 75.00 150.00
JD2 Joe DiMaggio Jsy/16 75.00 150.00
JD3 Joe DiMaggio Jsy/16 75.00 150.00
JR Jackie Robinson Bat/15 40.00 80.00
LG1 Lou Gehrig Bat/5 175.00 300.00
LG2 Lou Gehrig Bat/5 175.00 300.00
LG3 Lou Gehrig Bat/5 175.00 300.00
RH Rogers Hornsby Jkt/10 40.00 80.00
TW1 Ted Williams Jsy/99 15.00 40.00
TW2 Ted Williams Jsy/99 15.00 40.00

2006 Upper Deck Epic Materials Signature

OVERALL AU ODDS ONE PER CASE
STATED PRINT RUN 5 SERIAL #'d SETS
NO PRICING DUE TO SCARCITY
AP1 Albert Pujols Jsy
AP2 Albert Pujols Jsy
AP3 Albert Pujols Jsy
BG Bob Gibson Jsy
BG2 Bob Gibson Pants
CF Carlton Fisk Jsy
CR1 Cal Ripken Jsy
CR2 Cal Ripken Jsy
CR3 Cal Ripken Jsy
CY1 Carl Yastrzemski Jsy
CY2 Carl Yastrzemski Jsy
CY3 Carl Yastrzemski Jsy
DJ1 Derek Jeter Jsy
DJ2 Derek Jeter Jsy
DJ3 Derek Jeter Jsy
DM1 Don Mattingly Jsy
DM2 Don Mattingly Jsy
EB Ernie Banks Jsy
FR1 Frank Robinson Jsy
FR2 Frank Robinson Jsy
HK Harmon Killebrew Pants
JB1 Johnny Bench Jsy
JB2 Johnny Bench Jsy
JM Juan Marichal Jsy
JO Joe Morgan Jsy
KG1 Ken Griffey Jr. Jsy
KG2 Ken Griffey Jr. Jsy
KG3 Ken Griffey Jr. Jsy
KP1 Kirby Puckett Jsy
KP2 Kirby Puckett Jsy
LB1 Lou Brock Jsy
LB2 Lou Brock Jsy
MA Mark Prior Jsy
MP1 Mike Piazza Jsy
MP2 Mike Piazza Jsy
MS1 Mike Schmidt Jsy
MS2 Mike Schmidt Jsy
MS3 Mike Schmidt Jsy
NR1 Nolan Ryan Jsy
NR2 Nolan Ryan Jsy
NR3 Nolan Ryan Jsy
OS1 Ozzie Smith Jsy
OS2 Ozzie Smith Jsy
PM1 Paul Molitor Jsy
PM2 Paul Molitor Jsy
RC1 Roger Clemens Pants
RC2 Roger Clemens Pants
RC3 Roger Clemens Pants
RE1 Reggie Jackson Jsy
RE2 Reggie Jackson Jsy
RE3 Reggie Jackson Jsy
RJ1 Randy Johnson Jsy
RJ2 Randy Johnson Jsy
RO Brooks Robinson Jsy
RO2 Brooks Robinson Pants
RS1 Ryne Sandberg Jsy
RS2 Ryne Sandberg Jsy
RS3 Ryne Sandberg Jsy
SM1 Stan Musial Jsy
SM2 Stan Musial Jsy
TS Tom Seaver Jsy
VG Vladimir Guerrero Jsy
VG2 Vladimir Guerrero Jsy
WB1 Wade Boggs Jsy
WB2 Wade Boggs Jsy
WF Whitey Ford Jsy
WM Willie McCovey Jsy
WM2 Willie McCovey Jsy
WM3 Willie McCovey Jsy

2006 Upper Deck Epic Pairings

OVERALL GU ODDS ONE PER PACK
PRINT RUNS B/WN 5-99 COPIES PER
NO PRICING ON QTY OF 25 OR LESS
BB Wade Boggs Jsy 10.00 25.00
Brooks Robinson Bat/99
BM Johnny Bench Jsy 10.00 25.00
Joe Morgan Jsy/99
BR Bob Gibson Jsy 15.00 40.00
Nolan Ryan Jsy/99
BS Lou Brock Jsy 15.00 40.00
Ozzie Smith Jsy/99
BS2 Wade Boggs Jsy 10.00 25.00
Ryne Sandberg Jsy/99
CJ Roger Clemens Pants 12.50 30.00
Randy Johnson Pants/99
CR Roger Clemens Pants 20.00 50.00
Nolan Ryan Jsy/99
CW Ty Cobb Bat
Honus Wagner Pants/10
DG Joe DiMaggio Bat
Lou Gehrig Bat/25
FB Carlton Fisk Pants 10.00 25.00
Johnny Bench Jsy/99
FP Carlton Fisk Pants 10.00 25.00
Mike Piazza Jsy/99
GB Bob Gibson Jsy 10.00 25.00
Lou Brock Jsy/99
GC Hank Greenberg Bat
Ty Cobb Bat/25
GG Ken Griffey Jr. Jsy 15.00 40.00
Vladimir Guerrero Jsy/99
GP Ken Griffey Jr. Jsy 12.50 30.00
Kirby Puckett Jsy/99
GR Lou Gehrig Bat 125.00 200.00
Cal Ripken Jsy/45
HR Gil Hodges Bat
Pee Wee Reese Jsy/15
JD Derek Jeter Jsy 75.00 150.00
Joe DiMaggio Bat/99
JG Derek Jeter Jsy 30.00 60.00
Ken Griffey Jr. Jsy/99
JJ Reggie Jackson Jsy 12.50 30.00
Derek Jeter Jsy/99
JK Reggie Jackson Jsy 10.00 25.00
Harmon Killebrew Pants/99
JM Derek Jeter Jsy 40.00 80.00
Don Mattingly Jsy/99
JS Reggie Jackson Jsy 15.00 40.00
Mike Schmidt Jsy/99
KP Harmon Killebrew Pants 15.00 40.00
Kirby Puckett Jsy/99
MB Thurman Munson Pants 20.00 50.00
Johnny Bench Jsy/30
MM Juan Marichal Jsy 10.00 25.00
Willie McCovey Jsy/99
MM2 Don Mattingly Jsy 40.00 80.00
Thurman Munson Pants/30
MR Eddie Mathews Jsy 15.00 40.00
Brooks Robinson Bat/50
MS Eddie Mathews Jsy 30.00 60.00
Mike Schmidt Jsy/50
MY Paul Molitor Jsy 10.00 25.00
Robin Yount Jsy/99
PH Albert Pujols Jsy 40.00 80.00
Rogers Hornsby Jkt/99
PM Albert Pujols Jsy 30.00 60.00
Stan Musial Jsy/99
RB Jackie Robinson Bat
Ernie Banks Jsy/10
RD Babe Ruth Bat
Joe DiMaggio Bat/5
RG Babe Ruth Bat
Lou Gehrig Bat/5
RJ Pee Wee Reese Jsy 15.00 40.00
Derek Jeter Jsy/99
RM Cal Ripken Jsy 20.00 50.00
Eddie Murray Jsy/99
RR Jackie Robinson Bat
Pee Wee Reese Jsy10
RR2 Brooks Robinson Bat 10.00 25.00
Frank Robinson Jsy/99
RY Frank Robinson Jsy 12.50 30.00
Carl Yastrzemski Jsy/99
SB Ryne Sandberg Jsy 15.00 40.00
Ernie Banks Jsy/99
SM Ryne Sandberg Jsy 10.00 25.00
Joe Morgan Jsy/99
SR Tom Seaver Jsy 20.00 50.00
Nolan Ryan Jsy/99
SS Ryne Sandberg Jsy 15.00 40.00
Ozzie Smith Jsy/99
WC Honus Wagner Pants
Roberto Clemente Pants/25
WD Ted Williams Jsy 100.00 175.00
Joe DiMaggio Bat/45
WM Ted Williams Jsy 40.00 80.00
Stan Musial Jsy/45
YW Carl Yastrzemski Jsy 40.00 80.00
Ted Williams Jsy/50

2006 Upper Deck Epic Swatch

OVERALL GU ODDS ONE PER PACK
STATED PRINT RUN 50 SERIAL #'d SETS
AP Albert Pujols Jsy 20.00 50.00
CF Carlton Fisk Pants 8.00 20.00
CR Cal Ripken Jsy 20.00 50.00
CS Curt Schilling Jsy 8.00 20.00
CY Carl Yastrzemski Jsy 10.00 25.00
DJ1 Derek Jeter Jsy 30.00 60.00
DJ2 Derek Jeter Jsy 30.00 60.00

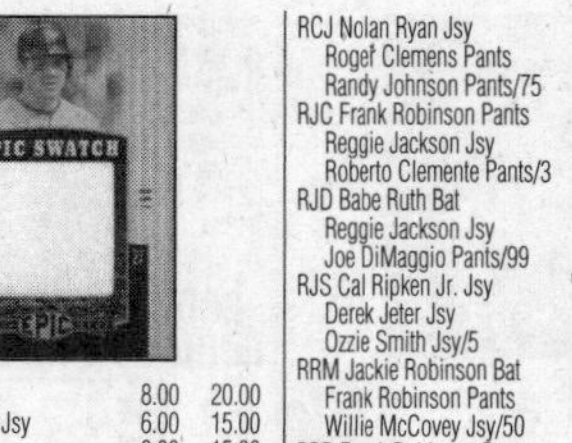

DO David Ortiz Jsy 8.00 20.00
DW Dontrelle Willis Jsy 6.00 15.00
EC Eric Chavez Jsy 6.00 15.00
IR Ivan Rodriguez Jsy 8.00 20.00
JB Jason Bay Jsy 6.00 15.00
JM Joe Morgan Jsy 6.00 15.00
JP Jake Peavy Jsy 6.00 15.00
JR Jose Reyes Jsy 6.00 15.00
JS Johan Santana Jsy 8.00 20.00
KG1 Ken Griffey Jr. Jsy 15.00 40.00
KG2 Ken Griffey Jr. Jsy 15.00 40.00
MI Miguel Tejada Jsy 6.00 15.00
MP Mark Prior Jsy 6.00 15.00
MR Manny Ramirez Jsy 8.00 20.00
MT Mark Teixeira Jsy 6.00 15.00
PM Pedro Martinez Jsy 8.00 20.00
RC Roger Clemens Pants 15.00 40.00
RJ Randy Johnson Jsy 8.00 20.00
RO Roy Oswalt Jsy 6.00 15.00
RZ Ryan Zimmerman Jsy 15.00 40.00
SR Scott Rolen Jsy 8.00 20.00
TG Tony Gwynn Jsy 10.00 25.00
VG Vladimir Guerrero Jsy 8.00 20.00

2006 Upper Deck Epic Triple Materials

OVERALL GU ODDS ONE PER PACK
PRINT RUNS B/WN 3-99 COPIES PER
NO PRICING ON QTY OF 25 OR LESS
BER Johnny Bench Jsy 12.50 30.00
Eddie Murray Jsy
Brooks Robinson Jsy/60
BMR Wade Boggs Jsy 12.50 30.00
Paul Molitor Jsy
Brooks Robinson Jsy/99
BSP Ernie Banks Jsy 20.00 50.00
Ryne Sandberg Jsy
Mark Prior Jsy/99
CDG Ty Cobb Bat
Joe DiMaggio Pants
Ken Griffey Jr. Jsy/15
CWH Ty Cobb Bat
Honus Wagner Pants
Rogers Hornsby Jkt/5
FJJ Whitey Ford Pants 30.00 60.00
Reggie Jackson Jsy
Derek Jeter Jsy/99
FMJ Whitey Ford Pants 30.00 60.00
Don Mattingly Jsy
Reggie Jackson Jsy/51
GJC Bob Gibson Jsy
Randy Johnson Jsy
Roger Clemens Pants/99
GMG Lou Gehrig Bat
Eddie Murray Jsy
Hank Greenberg Bat/25
GPS Bob Gibson Jsy 12.50 30.00
Mark Prior Jsy
Tom Seaver Jsy/99
GRD Lou Gehrig Bat
Babe Ruth Bat
Joe DiMaggio Pants/3
GRM Ken Griffey Jr. Jsy 30.00 60.00
Frank Robinson Jsy
Willie McCovey Jsy/99
HRR Gil Hodges Bat
Jackie Robinson Bat
Pee Wee Reese Jsy/10
JGK Reggie Jackson Jsy 12.50 30.00
Vladimir Guerrero Jsy
Harmon Killebrew Pants/99
JKR Reggie Jackson Jsy 12.50 30.00
Harmon Killebrew Pants
Frank Robinson Jsy/99
JMM Derek Jeter Jsy
Don Mattingly Jsy
Thurman Munson Pants/25
JPG Derek Jeter Jsy 50.00 100.00
Albert Pujols Jsy
Ken Griffey Jr. Jsy/99
MBF Thurman Munson Pants 12.50 30.00
Johnny Bench Jsy
Carlton Fisk Pants/99
MBG Joe Morgan Jsy 30.00 60.00
Johnny Bench Jsy
Ken Griffey Jr. Jsy/99
MBP Stan Musial Jsy
Lou Brock Jsy
Albert Pujols Jsy/24
MFM Thurman Munson Pants 20.00 50.00
Carlton Fisk Pants
Eddie Murray Jsy/99
MMG Eddie Murray Jsy 30.00 60.00
Don Mattingly Jsy
Steve Garvey Jsy/49
MPS Eddie Murray Jsy 12.50 30.00
Mike Piazza Jsy
Tom Seaver Jsy/99
MSY Paul Molitor Jsy 20.00 50.00
Ozzie Smith Jsy
Robin Yount Jsy/49
RBS Cal Ripken Jr. Jsy 20.00 50.00
Wade Boggs Jsy
Mike Schmidt Jsy/99
RCJ Nolan Ryan Jsy 30.00 60.00
Roger Clemens Pants
Randy Johnson Pants/75
RJC Frank Robinson Pants
Reggie Jackson Jsy
Roberto Clemente Pants/3
RJD Babe Ruth Bat 200.00 300.00
Reggie Jackson Jsy
Joe DiMaggio Pants/99
RJS Cal Ripken Jr. Jsy
Derek Jeter Jsy
Ozzie Smith Jsy/5
RRM Jackie Robinson Bat 20.00 50.00
Frank Robinson Pants
Willie McCovey Jsy/50
RRR Frank Robinson Pants
Brooks Robinson Jsy
Cal Ripken Jr. Jsy/25
SMH Ryne Sandberg Jsy
Joe Morgan Jsy
Rogers Hornsby Jkt/25
SMR Mike Schmidt Jsy
Eddie Mathews Jsy
Brooks Robinson Jsy/25
WDM Ted Williams Jsy
Joe DiMaggio Pants
Stan Musial Jsy/25
WMC Honus Wagner Pants
Stan Musial Jsy
Roberto Clemente Pants/5
WSR Honus Wagner Pants 60.00 120.00
Ozzie Smith Jsy
Pee Wee Reese Jsy/99
YRJ Robin Yount Jsy 30.00 60.00
Cal Ripken Jr. Jsy
Derek Jeter Jsy/99
YRM Carl Yastrzemski Jsy
Cal Ripken Jr. Jsy
Joe Morgan Jsy/25
YWB Carl Yastrzemski Jsy
Ted Williams Jsy
Wade Boggs Jsy/25

2007 Upper Deck First Edition

This 300-card set was released in March, 2007. The set was issued in 10-card packs which came 36 packs to a box and 20 boxes to a case. Just as in the first series of the regular Upper Deck product, cards numbered 1-50 feature players eligible for the 2007 Rookie Card logo.

COMPLETE SET (300) 20.00 50.00
COMMON CARD (1-300) .12 .30
COMMON ROOKIE (1-300) .15 .40
PRINTING PLATE ODDS 1 PER CASE
PLATE PRINT RUN 1 SET PER COLOR
BLACK-CYAN-MAGENTA-YELLOW ISSUED
NO PLATE PRICING DUE TO SCARCITY
1 Doug Slaten RC .15 .40
2 Miguel Montero (RC) .15 .40
3 Brian Burres (RC) .15 .40
4 Devern Hansack RC .15 .40
5 David Murphy (RC) .15 .40
6 Jose Reyes RC .15 .40
7 Scott Moore (RC) .15 .40
8 Josh Fields (RC) .15 .40
9 Chris Stewart RC .15 .40
10 Jerry Owens (RC) .15 .40
11 Ryan Sweeney (RC) .15 .40
12 Kevin Kouzmanoff (RC) .15 .40
13 Jeff Baker (RC) .15 .40
14 Justin Hampson (RC) .15 .40
15 Jeff Salazar (RC) .15 .40
16 Alvin Colina RC .40 1.00
17 Troy Tulowitzki (RC) .40 1.00
18 Andrew Miller RC 1.00 2.50
19 Mike Rabelo RC .15 .40
20 Jose Diaz (RC) .15 .40
21 Angel Sanchez RC .15 .40
22 Ryan Braun RC .15 .40
23 Delwyn Young (RC) .15 .40
24 Drew Anderson RC .15 .40
25 Dennis Sarfate (RC) .15 .40
26 Vinny Rottino (RC) .15 .40
27 Glen Perkins (RC) .15 .40
28 Alexi Casilla RC .25 .60
29 Philip Humber (RC) .25 .60
30 Andy Cannizaro RC .15 .40
31 Jeremy Brown .12 .30
32 Sean Henn (RC) .15 .40
33 Brian Rogers (RC) .15 .40
34 Carlos Maldonado (RC) .15 .40
35 Juan Morillo (RC) .15 .40
36 Fred Lewis (RC) .15 .40
37 Patrick Misch (RC) .15 .40
38 Billy Sadler (RC) .15 .40
39 Ryan Feierabend (RC) .15 .40
40 Cesar Jimenez RC .15 .40
41 Oswaldo Navarro RC .15 .40
42 Travis Chick (RC) .15 .40
43 Delmon Young (RC) .40 1.00
44 Shawn Riggans (RC) .15 .40
45 Brian Stokes (RC) .15 .40
46 Juan Salas (RC) .15 .40
47 Joaquin Arias (RC) .15 .40
48 Adam Lind (RC) .15 .40
49 Beltran Perez (RC) .15 .40
50 Brett Campbell RC .15 .40
51 Miguel Tejada .12 .30
52 Brandon Fahey .12 .30
53 Jay Gibbons .12 .30
54 Nick Markakis .20 .50
55 Kris Benson .12 .30
56 Erik Bedard .12 .30
57 Chris Ray .12 .30
58 Chris Britton .12 .30
59 Manny Ramirez .20 .50
60 David Ortiz .30 .75
61 Alex Cora .12 .30
62 Trot Nixon .12 .30
63 Doug Mirabelli .12 .30
64 Curt Schilling .20 .50
65 Jonathan Papelbon .30 .75
66 Craig Hansen .12 .30
67 Jermaine Dye .12 .30
68 Jim Thome .20 .50
69 Rob Mackowiak .12 .30
70 Brian Anderson .12 .30
71 A.J. Pierzynski .12 .30
72 Alex Cintron .12 .30
73 Jose Contreras .12 .30
74 Bobby Jenks .12 .30
75 Mike MacDougal .12 .30
76 Travis Hafner .12 .30
77 Ryan Garko .12 .30
78 Victor Martinez .12 .30
79 Casey Blake .12 .30
80 Shin-Soo Choo .20 .50
81 Paul Byrd .12 .30
82 Jeremy Sowers .12 .30
83 Cliff Lee .12 .30
84 Sean Casey .12 .30
85 Brandon Inge .12 .30
86 Omar Infante .12 .30
87 Magglio Ordonez .12 .30
88 Marcus Thames .12 .30
89 Justin Verlander .30 .75
90 Todd Jones .12 .30
91 Joel Zumaya .20 .50
92 Nate Robertson .12 .30
93 Mark Teahen .12 .30
94 Ryan Shealy .12 .30
95 Mark Grudzielanek .12 .30
96 Shane Costa .12 .30
97 Reggie Sanders .12 .30
98 Mark Redman .12 .30
99 Todd Wellemeyer .12 .30
100 Ambiorix Burgos .12 .30
101 Joe Nelson .12 .30
102 Orlando Cabrera .12 .30
103 Maicer Izturis .12 .30
104 Vladimir Guerrero .30 .75
105 Juan Rivera .12 .30
106 Jered Weaver .20 .50
107 Joe Saunders .12 .30
108 Bartolo Colon .12 .30
109 Francisco Rodriguez .12 .30
110 Justin Morneau .12 .30
111 Luis Castillo .12 .30
112 Michael Cuddyer .12 .30
113 Joe Mauer .20 .50
114 Francisco Liriano .30 .75
115 Joe Nathan .12 .30
116 Brad Radke .12 .30
117 Juan Rincon .12 .30
118 Derek Jeter .75 2.00
119 Jason Giambi .12 .30
120 Bobby Abreu .12 .30
121 Gary Sheffield .12 .30
122 Melky Cabrera .12 .30
123 Chien-Ming Wang .50 1.25
124 Mariano Rivera .30 .75
125 Jaret Wright .12 .30
126 Kyle Farnsworth .12 .30
127 Frank Thomas .30 .75
128 Dan Johnson .12 .30
129 Marco Scutaro .12 .30
130 Jay Payton .12 .30
131 Joe Blanton .12 .30
132 Rich Harden .12 .30
133 Esteban Loaiza .12 .30
134 Chad Gaudin .12 .30
135 Yuniesky Betancourt .12 .30
136 Willie Bloomquist .12 .30
137 Ichiro Suzuki .50 1.25
138 Raul Ibanez .12 .30
139 Chris Snelling .12 .30
140 Cha-Seung Baek .12 .30
141 Julio Mateo .12 .30
142 Rafael Soriano .12 .30
143 Jorge Cantu .12 .30
144 B.J. Upton .12 .30
145 Dioner Navarro .12 .30
146 Carl Crawford .12 .30
147 Damon Hollins .12 .30
148 Casey Fossum .12 .30
149 Ruddy Lugo .12 .30
150 Tyler Walker .12 .30
151 Shawn Camp .12 .30
152 Ian Kinsler .12 .30
153 Jerry Hairston Jr. .12 .30
154 Gerald Laird .12 .30
155 Mark DeRosa .12 .30
156 Kip Wells .12 .30
157 Vicente Padilla .12 .30
158 John Koronka .12 .30
159 Wes Littleton .12 .30
160 Lyle Overbay .12 .30
161 Aaron Hill .12 .30
162 John McDonald .12 .30
163 Vernon Wells .12 .30
164 Frank Catalanotto .12 .30
165 Roy Halladay .12 .30
166 B.J. Ryan .12 .30
167 Casey Janssen .12 .30
168 Stephen Drew .20 .50
169 Conor Jackson .12 .30
170 Chad Tracy .12 .30
171 Johnny Estrada .12 .30
172 Eric Byrnes .12 .30
173 Carlos Quentin .12 .30
174 Brandon Webb .12 .30
175 Jorge Julio .12 .30
176 Luis Vizcaino .12 .30
177 Chipper Jones .30 .75
178 Adam LaRoche .12 .30
179 Brian McCann .12 .30
180 Ryan Langerhans .12 .30
181 Matt Diaz .12 .30
182 John Smoltz .20 .50
183 Oscar Villarreal .12 .30
184 Chad Paronto .12 .30
185 Derrek Lee .12 .30
186 Ryan Theriot .12 .30
187 Ronny Cedeno .12 .30
188 Juan Pierre .12 .30
189 Matt Murton .12 .30

190 Carlos Zambrano .12 .30
191 Mark Prior .20 .50
192 Ryan Dempster .12 .30
193 Ryan O'Malley .12 .30
194 Brandon Phillips .12 .30
195 Rich Aurilia .12 .30
196 Ken Griffey Jr. .50 1.25
197 Ryan Freel .12 .30
198 Aaron Harang .12 .30
199 Brandon Claussen .12 .30
200 David Weathers .12 .30
201 Eric Milton .12 .30
202 Kazuo Matsui .12 .30
203 Jamey Carroll .12 .30
204 Matt Holliday .30 .75
205 Brad Hawpe .12 .30
206 Jason Jennings .12 .30
207 Josh Fogg .12 .30
208 Aaron Cook .12 .30
209 Miguel Cabrera .20 .50
210 Dan Uggla .20 .50
211 Hanley Ramirez .20 .50
212 Jeremy Hermida .12 .30
213 Cody Ross .12 .30
214 Josh Willingham .12 .30
215 Anibal Sanchez .12 .30
216 Jose Garcia RC .15 .40
217 Taylor Tankersley .12 .30
218 Lance Berkman .12 .30
219 Craig Biggio .20 .50
220 Brad Ausmus .12 .30
221 Willy Taveras .12 .30
222 Chris Burke .12 .30
223 Roger Clemens .50 1.25
224 Brandon Backe .12 .30
225 Brad Lidge .12 .30
226 Dan Wheeler .12 .30
227 Wilson Betemit .12 .30
228 Julio Lugo .12 .30
229 Russell Martin .12 .30
230 Kenny Lofton .12 .30
231 Brad Penny .12 .30
232 Chad Billingsley .12 .30
233 Greg Maddux .50 1.25
234 Jonathan Broxton .12 .30
235 Rickie Weeks .12 .30
236 Bill Hall .12 .30
237 Tony Gwynn Jr. .12 .30
238 Corey Hart .12 .30
239 Laynce Nix .12 .30
240 Ben Sheets .12 .30
241 Dave Bush .12 .30
242 Francisco Cordero .12 .30
243 Jose Reyes .12 .30
244 Carlos Delgado .12 .30
245 Paul Lo Duca .12 .30
246 Carlos Beltran .12 .30
247 Lastings Milledge .20 .50
248 Pedro Martinez .20 .50
249 John Maine .12 .30
250 Steve Trachsel .12 .30
251 Ryan Howard .50 1.25
252 Jimmy Rollins .12 .30
253 Chris Coste .12 .30
254 Jeff Conine .12 .30
255 David Dellucci .12 .30
256 Cole Hamels .30 .75
257 Ryan Madson .12 .30
258 Brett Myers .12 .30
259 Freddy Sanchez .12 .30
260 Xavier Nady .12 .30
261 Jose Castillo .12 .30
262 Jason Bay .12 .30
263 Jose Bautista .12 .30
264 Ronny Paulino .12 .30
265 Zach Duke .12 .30
266 Shane Youman RC .15 .40
267 Matt Capps .12 .30
268 Adrian Gonzalez .12 .30
269 Josh Barfield .12 .30
270 Mike Piazza .30 .75
271 Dave Roberts .12 .30
272 Geoff Blum .12 .30
273 Chris Young .12 .30
274 Woody Williams .12 .30
275 Cla Meredith .12 .30
276 Trevor Hoffman .12 .30
277 Ray Durham .12 .30
278 Mark Sweeney .12 .30
279 Eliezer Alfonzo .12 .30
280 Todd Linden .12 .30
281 Jason Schmidt .12 .30
282 Noah Lowry .12 .30
283 Brad Hennessey .12 .30
284 Jonathan Sanchez .12 .30
285 Albert Pujols .60 1.50
286 David Eckstein .12 .30
287 Jim Edmonds .20 .50
288 Chris Duncan .12 .30
289 Juan Encarnacion .12 .30
290 Jeff Suppan .12 .30
291 Jeff Weaver .12 .30
292 Braden Looper .12 .30
293 Ryan Zimmerman .30 .75
294 Nick Johnson .12 .30
295 Alfonso Soriano .12 .30
296 Austin Kearns .12 .30
297 Alex Escobar .12 .30
298 Tony Armas .12 .30
299 Chad Cordero .12 .30
300 Jon Rauch .12 .30
301 Daisuke Matsuzaka RC
302 Kei Igawa RC
303 Akinori Iwamura RC
304 Alex Gordon RC
305 Matt Chico (RC)
306 John Danks RC
307 Elijah Dukes RC
308 Gustavo Molina RC
309 Joakim Soria RC
310 Jay Marshall RC

2007 Upper Deck First Edition First Pitch Aces

COMPLETE SET (15) 6.00 15.00
STATED ODDS 1:6
BW Brandon Webb .40 1.00
CC Chris Carpenter .40 1.00
CS Curt Schilling .60 1.50
CZ Carlos Zambrano .40 1.00
DW Dontrelle Willis .40 1.00
FH Felix Hernandez .60 1.50
JS Johan Santana .60 1.50
JV Justin Verlander 1.00 2.50
PM Pedro Martinez .60 1.50
RC Roger Clemens 1.25 3.00
RH Roy Halladay .40 1.00
RJ Randy Johnson 1.00 2.50
SA C.C. Sabathia .40 1.00
SK Scott Kazmir .60 1.50
SM John Smoltz .60 1.50

2007 Upper Deck First Edition First Pitch Foundations

COMPLETE SET (20) 6.00 15.00
STATED ODDS 1:6
AL Adam Lind .40 1.00
AM Andrew Miller 1.50 4.00
DM David Murphy .40 1.00
DY Delmon Young 1.00 2.50
FL Fred Lewis .60 1.50
GP Glen Perkins .40 1.00
JA Joaquin Arias .40 1.00
JF Josh Fields .40 1.00
JO Jerry Owens .40 1.00
JS Jeff Salazar .40 1.00
MM Mitch Maier .40 1.00
MO Miguel Montero .40 1.00
PH Philip Humber .40 1.00
RB Ryan Braun .40 1.00
RS Ryan Sweeney .40 1.00
SM Scott Moore .40 1.00
SR Shawn Riggans .40 1.00
TC Travis Chick .40 1.00
TT Troy Tulowitzki 1.00 2.50
UJ Ubaldo Jimenez .40 1.00

2007 Upper Deck First Edition Leading Off

COMPLETE SET (15) 6.00 15.00
STATED ODDS 1:6
AS Alfonso Soriano .40 1.00
BR Brian Roberts .40 1.00
CF Chone Figgins .40 1.00
DR Dave Roberts .40 1.00
FR Ryan Freel .40 1.00
GS Grady Sizemore .60 1.50
HR Hanley Ramirez .60 1.50
IS Ichiro Suzuki 1.25 3.00
JD Johnny Damon .60 1.50
JP Juan Pierre .40 1.00
JR Jose Reyes .40 1.00
RF Rafael Furcal .40 1.00
RO Jimmy Rollins .40 1.00
SP Scott Podsednik .40 1.00
WT Willy Taveras .40 1.00

2007 Upper Deck First Edition Momentum Swing

COMPLETE SET (20) 6.00 15.00
STATED ODDS 1:6
AD Adam Dunn .40 1.00
AJ Andruw Jones .60 1.50
AP Albert Pujols 1.50 4.00
AR Alex Rodriguez 1.25 3.00
AS Alfonso Soriano .40 1.00
CB Carlos Beltran .40 1.00
CD Carlos Delgado .40 1.00
DL Derrek Lee .40 1.00
DO David Ortiz 1.00 2.50
JB Jason Bay .40 1.00
JD Jermaine Dye .40 1.00
JG Jason Giambi .40 1.00
JM Justin Morneau .40 1.00
JT Jim Thome .60 1.50
LB Lance Berkman .40 1.00
MC Miguel Cabrera .60 1.50
MT Mark Teixeira .60 1.50
RH Ryan Howard 1.25 3.00
TH Travis Hafner .40 1.00
VG Vladimir Guerrero 1.00 2.50

2007 Upper Deck First Edition Pennant Chasers

COMPLETE SET (30) 6.00 15.00
STATED ODDS 1:4
AR Aramis Ramirez .25 .60
CC Carl Crawford .25 .60
CG Carlos Guillen .25 .60
CJ Chipper Jones .60 1.50
CU Chase Utley .60 1.50
DA Johnny Damon .40 1.00
DU Dan Uggla .40 1.00
DW David Wright 1.00 2.50
FS Freddy Sanchez .25 .60
JM Joe Mauer .40 1.00
JR Juan Rivera .25 .60
KG Ken Griffey Jr. 1.00 2.50
MH Matt Holliday .30 .75
MR Manny Ramirez .40 1.00
MT Miguel Tejada .25 .60
MY Michael Young .25 .60
NG Nomar Garciaparra .60 1.50
NS Nick Swisher .25 .60
OH Orlando Hudson .25 .60
PF Prince Fielder .60 1.50
PK Paul Konerko .25 .60
RD Ray Durham .25 .60
RI Raul Ibanez .25 .60
RO Roy Oswalt .25 .60
RZ Ryan Zimmerman .60 1.50
SR Scott Rolen .40 1.00
TE Mark Teahen .25 .60
TH Trevor Hoffman .25 .60
VM Victor Martinez .25 .60
VW Vernon Wells .25 .60

2008 Upper Deck First Edition

COMPLETE SET (1-300) 10.00 25.00
COMP.UPD.SET (301-500) 10.00 25.00
COMMON CARD (1-250/301-500) .12 .30
COMMON RC (250-300/329/390) .20 .50
1 Joe Saunders .12 .30
2 Kelvim Escobar .12 .30
3 Jered Weaver .12 .30
4 Justin Speier .12 .30
5 Scot Shields .12 .30
6 Orlando Cabrera .12 .30
7 Casey Kotchman .12 .30
8 Vladimir Guerrero .30 .75
9 Garret Anderson .12 .30
10 Roy Oswalt .12 .30
11 Wandy Rodriguez .12 .30
12 Woody Williams .12 .30
13 Chad Qualls .12 .30
14 Mark Loretta .12 .30
15 Brad Ausmus .12 .30
16 Carlos Lee .12 .30
17 Hunter Pence .30 .75
18 Dan Haren .12 .30
19 Lenny DiNardo .12 .30
20 Chad Gaudin .12 .30
21 Huston Street .12 .30
22 Andrew Brown .12 .30
23 Mike Piazza .30 .75
24 Mark Ellis .12 .30
25 Shannon Stewart .12 .30
26 Shaun Marcum .12 .30
27 A.J. Burnett .12 .30
28 Casey Janssen .12 .30
29 Jeremy Accardo .12 .30
30 Aaron Hill .12 .30
31 Frank Thomas .30 .75
32 Matt Stairs .12 .30
33 Vernon Wells .12 .30
34 Tim Hudson .12 .30
35 Buddy Carlyle .12 .30
36 Rafael Soriano .12 .30
37 Brian McCann .20 .50
38 Edgar Renteria .12 .30
39 Mark Teixeira .20 .50
40 Willie Harris .12 .30
41 Andruw Jones .12 .30
42 Ben Sheets .20 .50
43 Dave Bush .12 .30
44 Yovani Gallardo .12 .30
45 Matt Wise .12 .30
46 Johnny Estrada .12 .30
47 Prince Fielder .30 .75
48 J.J. Hardy .12 .30
49 Corey Hart .12 .30
50 Adam Wainwright .12 .30
51 Joel Pineiro .12 .30
52 Jason Isringhausen .12 .30
53 Troy Percival .12 .30
54 Albert Pujols .60 1.50
55 David Eckstein .12 .30
56 Jim Edmonds .20 .50
57 Rick Ankiel .12 .30
58 Ted Lilly .12 .30
59 Rich Hill .12 .30
60 Jason Marquis .12 .30
61 Carlos Marmol .12 .30
62 Jason Kendall .12 .30
63 Aramis Ramirez .12 .30
64 Ryan Theriot .12 .30
65 Alfonso Soriano .20 .50
66 Jacque Jones .12 .30
67 James Shields .12 .30
68 Andy Sonnanstine .12 .30
69 Scott Dohmann .12 .30
70 Dioner Navarro .12 .30
71 B.J. Upton .20 .50
72 Carlos Pena .30 .75
73 Brendan Harris .12 .30
74 Josh Wilson .12 .30
75 Brandon Webb .20 .50
76 Micah Owings .12 .30
77 Doug Slaten .12 .30
78 Brandon Lyon .12 .30
79 Miguel Montero .12 .30
80 Stephen Drew .12 .30
81 Mark Reynolds .12 .30
82 Chris B. Young .12 .30
83 Chad Billingsley .12 .30
84 Derek Lowe .12 .30
85 Mark Hendrickson .12 .30
86 Takashi Saito .12 .30
87 Russell Martin .12 .30
88 Jeff Kent .12 .30
89 Matt Kemp .12 .30
90 Juan Pierre .12 .30
91 Matt Cain .12 .30
92 Barry Zito .12 .30
93 Kevin Correia .12 .30
94 Jack Taschner .12 .30
95 Bengie Molina .12 .30
96 Omar Vizquel .12 .30
97 Dave Roberts .12 .30
98 Rajai Davis .12 .30
99 Fausto Carmona .12 .30
100 Jake Westbrook .12 .30
101 Rafael Betancourt .12 .30
102 Joe Borowski .12 .30
103 Victor Martinez .12 .30
104 Travis Hafner .12 .30
105 Ryan Garko .12 .30
106 Kenny Lofton .12 .30
107 Franklin Gutierrez .12 .30
108 Felix Hernandez .20 .50
109 J.J. Putz .12 .30
110 Brandon Morrow .12 .30
111 Kenji Johjima .12 .30
112 Jose Vidro .12 .30
113 Richie Sexson .12 .30
114 Ichiro Suzuki .50 1.25
115 Ben Broussard .12 .30
116 Sergio Mitre .12 .30
117 Scott Olsen .12 .30
118 Rick Vanden Hurk .12 .30
119 Lee Gardner .12 .30
120 Miguel Olivo .12 .30
121 Hanley Ramirez .30 .75
122 Mike Jacobs .12 .30
123 Josh Willingham .12 .30
124 John Maine .12 .30
125 Tom Glavine .20 .50
126 Billy Wagner .12 .30
127 Aaron Heilman .12 .30
128 David Wright .40 1.00
129 Luis Castillo .12 .30
130 Shawn Green .12 .30
131 Damion Easley .12 .30
132 Carlos Delgado .12 .30
133 Shawn Hill .12 .30
134 John Lannan .12 .30
135 Chad Cordero .12 .30
136 Jon Rauch .12 .30
137 Jesus Flores .12 .30
138 Dmitri Young .12 .30
139 Cristian Guzman .12 .30
140 Austin Kearns .12 .30
141 Nook Logan .12 .30
142 Erik Bedard .12 .30
143 Daniel Cabrera .12 .30
144 Chris Ray .12 .30
145 Chad Bradford .12 .30
146 Ramon Hernandez .12 .30
147 Miguel Tejada .12 .30
148 Freddie Bynum .12 .30
149 Corey Patterson .12 .30
150 Chris Young .12 .30
151 Greg Maddux .40 1.00
152 Kevin Cameron .12 .30
153 Doug Brocail .12 .30
154 Kevin Kouzmanoff .12 .30
155 Geoff Blum .12 .30
156 Milton Bradley .12 .30
157 Brian Giles .12 .30
158 Jamie Moyer .12 .30
159 Kyle Kendrick .12 .30
160 Kyle Lohse .12 .30
161 Antonio Alfonseca .12 .30
162 Chris Coste .12 .30
163 Chase Utley .30 .75
164 Tadahito Iguchi .12 .30
165 Aaron Rowand .12 .30
166 Shane Victorino .12 .30
167 Ian Snell .12 .30
168 Shane Youman .12 .30
169 Shawn Chacon .12 .30
170 Ronny Paulino .12 .30
171 Jack Wilson .12 .30
172 Adam LaRoche .12 .30
173 Ryan Doumit .12 .30
174 Xavier Nady .12 .30
175 Kevin Millwood .12 .30
176 Brandon McCarthy .12 .30
177 Wes Littleton .12 .30
178 Mike Wood .12 .30
179 Hank Blalock .12 .30
180 Ian Kinsler .20 .50
181 Marlon Byrd .12 .30
182 Brad Wilkerson .12 .30
183 Tim Wakefield .12 .30
184 Daisuke Matsuzaka .50 1.25
185 Julian Tavarez .12 .30
186 Hideki Okajima .12 .30
187 Doug Mirabelli .12 .30
188 Dustin Pedroia .50 1.25
189 Mike Lowell .12 .30
190 Manny Ramirez .30 .75
191 Coco Crisp .12 .30
192 Bronson Arroyo .12 .30
193 Matt Belisle .12 .30
194 Jared Burton .12 .30
195 Mike Gosling .12 .30
196 David Ross .12 .30
197 Edwin Encarnacion .12 .30
198 Ken Griffey Jr. .50 1.25
199 Adam Dunn .12 .30
200 Jeff Francis .12 .30
201 Jason Hirsh .12 .30
202 Manny Corpas .12 .30
203 Jeremy Affeldt .12 .30
204 Yorvit Torrealba .12 .30
205 Todd Helton .20 .50
206 Kazuo Matsui .12 .30
207 Brad Hawpe .12 .30
208 Willy Taveras .12 .30
209 Brian Bannister .12 .30
210 Zack Greinke .12 .30
211 Kyle Davies .12 .30
212 David Riske .12 .30
213 John Buck .12 .30
214 Mark Grudzielanek .12 .30
215 Billy Butler .12 .30
216 David DeJesus .12 .30
217 Jeremy Bonderman .12 .30
218 Chad Durbin .12 .30
219 Andrew Miller .20 .50
220 Todd Jones .12 .30
221 Brandon Inge .12 .30
222 Placido Polanco .12 .30
223 Gary Sheffield .12 .30
224 Magglio Ordonez .20 .50
225 Matt Garza .12 .30
226 Boof Bonser .12 .30
227 Joe Nathan .12 .30
228 Dennys Reyes .12 .30
229 Joe Mauer .20 .50
230 Michael Cuddyer .12 .30
231 Jason Bartlett .12 .30
232 Torii Hunter .12 .30
233 Jason Tyner .12 .30
234 Mark Buehrle .12 .30
235 Jon Garland .12 .30
236 Jose Contreras .12 .30
237 Matt Thornton .12 .30
238 Juan Uribe .12 .30
239 Jim Thome .20 .50
240 Jerry Owens .12 .30
241 Jermaine Dye .12 .30
242 Andy Pettitte .20 .50
243 Phil Hughes .30 .75
244 Mike Mussina .20 .50
245 Joba Chamberlain .40 1.00
246 Brian Bruney .12 .30
247 Jorge Posada .20 .50
248 Derek Jeter .75 2.00
249 Jason Giambi .20 .50
250 Johnny Damon .20 .50
251 Jonathan Albaladejo RC .30 .75
252 Josh Anderson (RC) .20 .50
253 Wladimir Balentien (RC) .20 .50
254 Josh Banks (RC) .20 .50
255 Daric Barton (RC) .20 .50
256 Jerry Blevins RC .30 .75
257 Emilio Bonifacio RC .30 .75
258 Lance Broadway (RC) .20 .50
259 Clay Buchholz (RC) .50 1.25
260 Billy Buckner (RC) .20 .50
261 Jeff Clement (RC) .20 .50
262 Willie Collazo RC .30 .75
263 Ross Detwiler RC .50 1.25
264 Sam Fuld RC .20 .50
265 Harvey Garcia (RC) .20 .50
266 Alberto Gonzalez RC .30 .75
267 Ryan Hanigan RC .30 .75
268 Kevin Hart (RC) .20 .50
269 Luke Hochevar RC .50 1.25
270 Chin-Lung Hu (RC) .20 .50
271 Rob Johnson (RC) .20 .50
272 Radhames Liz RC .30 .75
273 Ian Kennedy RC .50 1.25
274 Joe Koshansky (RC) .20 .50
275 Donny Lucy (RC) .20 .50
276 Justin Maxwell RC .30 .75
277 Jonathan Meloan RC .30 .75
278 Luis Mendoza (RC) .20 .50
279 Jose Morales (RC) .20 .50
280 Nyjer Morgan (RC) .20 .50
281 Carlos Muniz RC .30 .75
282 Bill Murphy (RC) .20 .50
283 Josh Newman RC .30 .75
284 Ross Ohlendorf RC .30 .75
285 Troy Patton (RC) .20 .50
286 Felipe Paulino RC .30 .75
287 Steve Pearce RC .30 .75
288 Heath Phillips RC .30 .75
289 Justin Ruggiano RC .30 .75
290 Clint Sammons (RC) .20 .50
291 Bronson Sardinha (RC) .20 .50
292 Chris Seddon (RC) .20 .50
293 Seth Smith (RC) .20 .50
294 Mitch Stetter RC .30 .75
295 Dave Davidson RC .30 .75
296 Rich Thompson RC .30 .75
297 J.R. Towles RC .50 1.25
298 Eugenio Velez RC .20 .50
299 Joey Votto (RC) .50 1.25
300 Bill White RC .20 .50
301 Dan Haren .12 .30
302 Randy Johnson .30 .75
303 Justin Upton .30 .75
304 Tom Glavine .20 .50
305 Chipper Jones .40 1.00
306 Jeff Francoeur .20 .50
307 John Smoltz .30 .75
308 Yunel Escobar .12 .30
309 Adam Jones .12 .30
310 Jeremy Guthrie .12 .30
311 Nick Markakis .20 .50
312 Brian Roberts .20 .50
313 Melvin Mora .12 .30
314 Josh Beckett .20 .50
315 Jon Lester .20 .50
316 Curt Schilling .20 .50
317 Jonathan Papelbon .20 .50
318 Jason Varitek .30 .75
319 David Ortiz .30 .75
320 Jacoby Ellsbury .50 1.25
321 Julio Lugo .12 .30
322 Sean Casey .12 .30
323 Kevin Youkilis .20 .50
324 J.D. Drew .12 .30
325 Derrek Lee .20 .50
326 Carlos Zambrano .12 .30
327 Kerry Wood .12 .30
328 Geovany Soto .30 .75
329 Kosuke Fukudome RC .75 2.00
330 Gavin Floyd .12 .30
331 Bobby Jenks .12 .30
332 Javier Vazquez .12 .30
333 A.J. Pierzynski .12 .30
334 Orlando Cabrera .12 .30
335 Joe Crede .12 .30
336 Paul Konerko .12 .30
337 Nick Swisher .12 .30
338 Carlos Quentin .12 .30
339 Alexei Ramirez .75 2.00
340 Johnny Cueto .20 .50
341 Aaron Harang .12 .30
342 Brandon Phillips .12 .30
343 Paul Byrd .12 .30
344 Grady Sizemore .20 .50
345 Jhonny Peralta .12 .30
346 Asdrubal Cabrera .12 .30
347 C.C. Sabathia .12 .30
348 Troy Tulowitzki .20 .50
349 Matt Holliday .20 .50
350 Garrett Atkins .12 .30
351 Ubaldo Jimenez .12 .30
352 Kenny Rogers .12 .30
353 Justin Verlander .20 .50
354 Dontrelle Willis .12 .30
355 Joel Zumaya .12 .30
356 Ivan Rodriguez .20 .50
357 Miguel Cabrera .20 .50
358 Carlos Guillen .12 .30
359 Edgar Renteria .12 .30
360 Curtis Granderson .12 .30
361 Jeremy Hermida .12 .30
362 Dan Uggla .20 .50
363 Luis Gonzalez .12 .30
364 Andrew Miller .20 .50
365 Jorge Cantu .12 .30
366 Kazuo Matsui .12 .30
367 Lance Berkman .20 .50
368 Miguel Tejada .12 .30
369 Jose Valverde .12 .30
370 Michael Bourn .12 .30
371 Gil Meche .12 .30
372 Joey Gathright .12 .30
373 Mark Teahen .12 .30
374 Alex Gordon .30 .75
375 Tony Pena .12 .30
376 Jose Guillen .12 .30
377 Torii Hunter .12 .30
378 Ervin Santana .12 .30
379 Francisco Rodriguez .12 .30
380 Howie Kendrick .12 .30
381 John Lackey .12 .30
382 Gary Matthews .12 .30
383 Jon Garland .12 .30
384 Chone Figgins .12 .30
385 Andruw Jones .12 .30
386 James Loney .20 .50
387 Andre Ethier .20 .50
388 Rafael Furcal .12 .30
389 Brad Penny .12 .30
390 Hiroki Kuroda RC .30 .75
391 Blake DeWitt .30 .75
392 Mike Cameron .12 .30
393 Ryan Braun .40 1.00
394 Rickie Weeks .12 .30
395 Bill Hall .12 .30
396 Tony Gwynn .12 .30
397 Eric Gagne .12 .30
398 Jeff Suppan .12 .30
399 Jason Kendall .12 .30
400 Livan Hernandez .12 .30
401 Francisco Liriano .20 .50
402 Pat Neshek .12 .30
403 Adam Everett .12 .30
404 Justin Morneau .20 .50
405 Craig Monroe .12 .30
406 Carlos Gomez .12 .30
407 Delmon Young .20 .50
408 Oliver Perez .12 .30
409 Jose Reyes .20 .50
410 Moises Alou .12 .30
411 Carlos Beltran .12 .30
412 Endy Chavez .12 .30
413 Ryan Church .12 .30
414 Pedro Martinez .20 .50
415 Johan Santana .20 .50
416 Mike Pelfrey .12 .30
417 Brian Schneider .12 .30
418 Ramon Castro .12 .30
419 Kei Igawa .12 .30
420 Mariano Rivera .30 .75
421 Chien-Ming Wang .40 1.00
422 Wilson Betemit .12 .30
423 Robinson Cano .20 .50
424 Alex Rodriguez .50 1.25
425 Bobby Abreu .12 .30
426 Shelley Duncan .12 .30
427 Hideki Matsui .30 .75
428 Joe Blanton .12 .30
429 Bobby Crosby .12 .30
430 Eric Chavez .12 .30
431 Dan Johnson .12 .30
432 Rich Harden .12 .30
433 Kurt Suzuki .12 .30
434 Ryan Howard .40 1.00
435 Jimmy Rollins .20 .50
436 Pedro Feliz .12 .30
437 Adam Eaton .12 .30
438 Brad Lidge .12 .30
439 Brett Myers .12 .30
440 Pat Burrell .12 .30
441 Geoff Jenkins .12 .30
442 Zach Duke .12 .30
443 Matt Morris .12 .30
444 Tom Gorzelanny .12 .30
445 Jason Bay .12 .30

446 Freddy Sanchez .12 .30
447 Matt Capps .12 .30
448 Tadahito Iguchi .12 .30
449 Adrian Gonzalez .20 .50
450 Jim Edmonds .20 .50
451 Jake Peavy .20 .50
452 Khalil Greene .20 .50
453 Trevor Hoffman .12 .30
454 Mark Prior .20 .50
455 Randy Wolf .12 .30
456 Scott Hairston .12 .30
457 Tim Lincecum .30 .75
458 Noah Lowry .12 .30
459 Aaron Rowand .12 .30
460 Randy Winn .12 .30
461 Ray Durham .12 .30
462 Brian Wilson .12 .30
463 Adrian Beltre .12 .30
464 Jarrod Washburn .12 .30
465 Yuniesky Betancourt .12 .30
466 Jose Lopez .12 .30
467 Raul Ibanez .12 .30
468 Erik Bedard .12 .30
469 Brad Wilkerson .12 .30
470 Chris Carpenter .12 .30
471 Mark Mulder .12 .30
472 Skip Schumaker .12 .30
473 Troy Glaus .20 .50
474 Chris Duncan .12 .30
475 Scott Kazmir .20 .50
476 Troy Percival .12 .30
477 Akinori Iwamura .12 .30
478 Carl Crawford .12 .30
479 Cliff Floyd .12 .30
480 Matt Garza .12 .30
481 Edwin Jackson .12 .30
482 Vicente Padilla .12 .30
483 Josh Hamilton .40 1.00
484 Milton Bradley .12 .30
485 Michael Young .12 .30
486 David Murphy .12 .30
487 Ben Broussard .12 .30
488 B.J. Ryan .12 .30
489 David Eckstein .12 .30
490 Alex Rios .12 .30
491 Lyle Overbay .12 .30
492 Scott Rolen .20 .50
493 Lastings Milledge .12 .30
494 Paul Lo Duca .12 .30
495 Ryan Zimmerman .20 .50
496 Odalis Perez .12 .30
497 Wily Mo Pena .12 .30
498 Elijah Dukes .12 .30
499 Ronnie Belliard .12 .30
500 Nick Johnson .12 .30

2008 Upper Deck First Edition Star Quest

SQ1 Ichiro Suzuki 1.25 3.00
SQ2 Ryan Braun 1.00 2.50
SQ3 Prince Fielder 1.00 2.50
SQ4 Ken Griffey Jr. 1.25 3.00
SQ5 Vladimir Guerrero 1.00 2.50
SQ6 Travis Hafner .40 1.00
SQ7 Matt Holliday .60 1.50
SQ8 Ryan Howard 1.00 2.50
SQ9 Derek Jeter 2.00 5.00
SQ10 Chipper Jones 1.25 3.00
SQ11 Carlos Lee .40 1.00
SQ12 Justin Morneau .60 1.50
SQ13 Magglio Ordonez .60 1.50
SQ14 David Ortiz 1.00 2.50
SQ15 Jake Peavy .60 1.50
SQ16 Albert Pujols 1.50 4.00
SQ17 Hanley Ramirez 1.00 2.50
SQ18 Manny Ramirez 1.00 2.50
SQ19 Jose Reyes .60 1.50
SQ20 Alex Rodriguez 1.25 3.00
SQ21 Johan Santana .60 1.50
SQ22 Grady Sizemore .60 1.50
SQ23 Alfonso Soriano .60 1.50
SQ24 Mark Teixeira .60 1.50
SQ25 Frank Thomas 1.00 2.50
SQ26 Jim Thome .60 1.50
SQ27 Chase Utley 1.00 2.50
SQ28 Brandon Webb .60 1.50
SQ29 David Wright 1.00 2.50
SQ30 Michael Young .40 1.00
SQ31 Adam Dunn .40 1.00
SQ32 Albert Pujols 1.50 4.00
SQ33 Alex Rodriguez 1.25 3.00
SQ34 B.J. Upton .60 1.50
SQ35 CC Sabathia .40 1.00
SQ36 Carlos Beltran .40 1.00
SQ37 Carlos Pena 1.00 2.50
SQ38 Cole Hamels 1.00 2.50
SQ39 Curtis Granderson .40 1.00
SQ40 Daisuke Matsuzaka 1.25 3.00
SQ41 David Ortiz 1.00 2.50
SQ42 Derek Jeter 2.00 5.00
SQ43 Derrek Lee .60 1.50
SQ44 Eric Byrnes .40 1.00
SQ45 Felix Hernandez .60 1.50
SQ46 Ichiro Suzuki 1.25 3.00
SQ47 Jeff Francoeur .60 1.50
SQ48 Jimmy Rollins .60 1.50
SQ49 Joe Mauer .60 1.50
SQ50 John Smoltz 1.00 2.50
SQ51 Ken Griffey Jr. 1.25 3.00
SQ52 Lance Berkman .60 1.50
SQ53 Miguel Cabrera .60 1.50
SQ54 Paul Konerko .40 1.00
SQ55 Pedro Martinez .60 1.50
SQ56 Randy Johnson 1.00 2.50
SQ57 Russell Martin .40 1.00
SQ58 Troy Tulowitzki .60 1.50
SQ59 Vernon Wells .40 1.00
SQ60 Vladimir Guerrero 1.00 2.50

2006 Upper Deck Future Stars

This 159-card set was released in January, 2007. The set was issued in four-card packs which had an $4.99 SRP and came 24 packs to a box and 12 boxes to a case. Cards numbered 1-75 feature veterans issued in alphabetical team order while cards 75-159 feature signed cards of 2006 rookies.

COMP.SET w/o AU's (75) 10.00 25.00
COMMON CARD (1-75) .15 .40
COMMON AU RC (76-159) 3.00 8.00
FIVE AU RC PER BOX ON AVERAGE
NO SP PRICING DUE TO SCARCITY
PRINTING PLATE ODDS 1:2 CASES
PLATE PRINT RUN 1 SET PER COLOR
BLACK-CYAN-MAGENTA-YELLOW ISSUED
NO PLATE PRICING DUE TO SCARCITY
1 Miguel Tejada .15 .40
2 Brian Roberts .15 .40
3 Brandon Webb .15 .40
4 Luis Gonzalez .15 .40
5 Andruw Jones .25 .60
6 Chipper Jones .40 1.00
7 John Smoltz .25 .60
8 Curt Schilling .25 .60
9 Josh Beckett .15 .40
10 David Ortiz .40 1.00
11 Manny Ramirez .25 .60
12 Jim Thome .25 .60
13 Paul Konerko .15 .40
14 Jermaine Dye .15 .40
15 Derrek Lee .15 .40
16 Greg Maddux .60 1.50
17 Ken Griffey Jr. .60 1.50
18 Adam Dunn .15 .40
19 Felipe Lopez .15 .40
20 Travis Hafner .15 .40
21 Victor Martinez .15 .40
22 Grady Sizemore .25 .60
23 Todd Helton .25 .60
24 Matt Holliday .40 1.00
25 Jeremy Bonderman .15 .40
26 Ivan Rodriguez .25 .60
27 Miguel Cabrera .25 .60
28 Dontrelle Willis .15 .40
29 Roger Clemens .75 2.00
30 Roy Oswalt .15 .40
31 Lance Berkman .15 .40
32 Reggie Sanders .15 .40
33 Vladimir Guerrero .40 1.00
34 Chone Figgins .15 .40
35 Jeff Kent .15 .40
36 Eric Gagne .15 .40
37 Carlos Lee .15 .40
38 Rickie Weeks .15 .40
39 Johan Santana .25 .60
40 Torii Hunter .15 .40
41 Alex Rodriguez .60 1.50
42 Derek Jeter 1.00 2.50
43 Randy Johnson .40 1.00
44 Hideki Matsui .40 1.00
45 Johnny Damon .25 .60
46 Pedro Martinez .25 .60
47 David Wright .60 1.50
48 Carlos Beltran .15 .40
49 Rich Harden .15 .40
50 Eric Chavez .15 .40
51 Huston Street .15 .40
52 Ryan Howard .60 1.50
53 Bobby Abreu .15 .40
54 Chase Utley .40 1.00
55 Jason Bay .15 .40
56 Jake Peavy .15 .40
57 Brian Giles .15 .40
58 Trevor Hoffman .15 .40
59 Jason Schmidt .15 .40
60 Randy Winn .15 .40
61 Kenji Johjima RC .75 2.00
62 Ichiro Suzuki .60 1.50
63 Felix Hernandez .25 .60
64 Albert Pujols .75 2.00
65 Chris Carpenter .15 .40
66 Jim Edmonds .25 .60
67 Carl Crawford .15 .40
68 Scott Kazmir .25 .60
69 Jonny Gomes .15 .40
70 Mark Teixeira .25 .60
71 Michael Young .15 .40
72 Vernon Wells .15 .40
73 Roy Halladay .15 .40
74 Nick Johnson .15 .40
75 Alfonso Soriano .15 .40
76 Adam Wainwright AU (RC) 8.00 20.00
77 Anderson Hernandez AU (RC) 3.00 8.00
78 Andre Ethier AU SP (RC) 10.00 25.00
79 Colter Bean AU SP (RC) 4.00 10.00
80 Ben Johnson AU (RC) 3.00 8.00
81 Boof Bonser AU SP (RC) 5.00 12.00
82 Boone Logan AU RC 3.00 8.00
83 Brian Anderson AU (RC) 3.00 8.00
84 Brian Bannister AU (RC) 5.00 12.00
85 Chris Denorfia AU SP (RC) 4.00 10.00
86 Chad Billingsley AU SP (RC) 8.00 20.00
87 Cody Ross AU (RC) 3.00 8.00
88 Cole Hamels AU SP (RC) 30.00 60.00
89 Conor Jackson AU (RC) 5.00 12.00
90 Dan Uggla AU SP (RC)
91 Dave Gassner AU SP (RC) 3.00 8.00
92 Jordan Tata AU RC 3.00 8.00
93 Eric Reed AU (RC) 3.00 8.00
94 Fausto Carmona AU (RC) 10.00 25.00
95 Luis Figueroa AU SP RC
96 Francisco Liriano AU SP (RC) 10.00 25.00
97 Freddie Bynum AU (RC) 3.00 8.00
98 Hanley Ramirez AU SP (RC) 8.00 20.00
99 Hong-Chih Kuo AU SP (RC) 30.00 60.00
100 Ian Kinsler AU (RC) 6.00 15.00
101 Nelson Cruz AU SP (RC) 3.00 8.00
102 Ruddy Lugo AU (RC) 3.00 8.00
103 Jason Kubel AU SP (RC) 3.00 8.00
104 Jeff Harris AU RC 3.00 8.00
105 Santiago Ramirez AU (RC) 3.00 8.00
106 Jered Weaver AU SP (RC) 20.00 50.00
107 Jeremy Accardo AU SP RC 6.00 15.00
108 Josh Willingham AU SP (RC) 3.00 8.00
109 Joel Zumaya AU SP (RC) 10.00 25.00
110 Joey Devine AU RC 3.00 8.00
111 John Koronka AU (RC) 3.00 8.00
112 Jonathan Papelbon AU (RC) 15.00 40.00
113 Jose Capellan AU (RC) 3.00 8.00
114 Josh Johnson AU (RC) 5.00 12.00
115 Josh Rupe AU SP (RC) 3.00 8.00
116 Jeremy Hermida AU SP (RC) 3.00 8.00
117 Josh Wilson AU (RC) 3.00 8.00
118 Justin Verlander AU SP (RC)
119 Kelly Shoppach AU (RC) 3.00 8.00
120 Kendry Morales AU (RC) 5.00 12.00
121 Sean Tracey AU (RC) 3.00 8.00
122 Macay McBride AU (RC) 3.00 8.00
123 Martin Prado AU SP (RC)
124 Matt Cain AU (RC) 5.00 12.00
125 Russell Martin AU (RC) 5.00 12.00
126 Tim Hamulack AU SP (RC) 3.00 8.00
127 Mike Jacobs AU (RC) 5.00 12.00
128 Ben Hendrickson AU (RC) 3.00 8.00
129 Jack Taschner AU (RC) 3.00 8.00
130 Nate McLouth AU (RC) 6.00 15.00
131 Jeremy Sowers AU SP (RC) 8.00 20.00
132 Paul Maholm AU (RC) 3.00 8.00
133 Stephen Drew AU SP (RC)
134 Jason Bergmann AU RC 3.00 8.00
135 Rich Hill AU SP (RC) 12.50 30.00
136 Melky Cabrera AU SP (RC)
137 Scott Dunn AU (RC) 3.00 8.00
138 Ryan Zimmerman AU (RC) 20.00 50.00
139 Anibal Sanchez AU (RC) 5.00 12.00
140 Sean Marshall AU (RC) 5.00 12.00
141 Takashi Saito AU SP RC
142 Taylor Buchholz AU (RC) 3.00 8.00
143 Carlos Quentin AU SP (RC) 6.00 15.00
144 Matt Garza AU (RC) 8.00 20.00
145 Wil Nieves AU (RC) 3.00 8.00
146 Jamie Shields AU RC 10.00 25.00
147 Jon Lester AU SP RC 15.00 40.00
148 Craig Hansen AU SP RC
149 Aaron Rakers AU (RC) 3.00 8.00
150 Bobby Livingston AU (RC) 3.00 8.00
151 Brendan Harris AU (RC) 3.00 8.00
152 Alay Soler AU SP RC 3.00 8.00
153 Chris Britton AU RC 3.00 8.00
154 Howie Kendrick AU SP (RC) 15.00 40.00
155 Jermaine Van Buren AU (RC) 3.00 8.00
156 Choo Freeman AU SP (RC) 3.00 8.00
157 Matt Capps AU (RC) 3.00 8.00
158 Peter Moylan AU RC 3.00 8.00
159 Ty Taubenheim AU RC 5.00 12.00

2006 Upper Deck Future Stars Black

*BLACK: 2.5X TO 6X BASIC
STATED PRINT RUN 50 SER.#'d SETS
17 Ken Griffey Jr. 10.00 25.00
44 Hideki Matsui 6.00 15.00
61 Kenji Johjima 6.00 15.00
62 Ichiro Suzuki 10.00 25.00

2006 Upper Deck Future Stars Blue

*BLUE: 2X TO 5X BASIC
STATED PRINT RUN 99 SER.#'d SETS
44 Hideki Matsui 5.00 12.00
61 Kenji Johjima 5.00 12.00
62 Ichiro Suzuki 8.00 20.00

2006 Upper Deck Future Stars Gold

*GOLD: 6X TO 15X BASIC
STATED PRINT RUN 25 SER.#'d SETS
17 Ken Griffey Jr. 40.00 80.00
44 Hideki Matsui 15.00 40.00
61 Kenji Johjima 12.50 30.00
62 Ichiro Suzuki 40.00 80.00

2006 Upper Deck Future Stars Green

*GREEN: 1.5X TO 4X BASIC
STATED PRINT RUN 499 SER.#'d SETS
44 Hideki Matsui 3.00 8.00
61 Kenji Johjima 3.00 8.00
62 Ichiro Suzuki 4.00 10.00

2006 Upper Deck Future Stars Purple

*PURPLE: 1.25X TO 3X BASIC
STATED PRINT RUN 1799 SER.#'d SETS
44 Hideki Matsui 2.00 5.00
61 Kenji Johjima 2.00 5.00
62 Ichiro Suzuki 2.50 6.00

2006 Upper Deck Future Stars Red

*RED: 1.5X TO 4X BASIC
STATED PRINT RUN 299 SER.#'d SETS
44 Hideki Matsui 3.00 8.00
61 Kenji Johjima 3.00 8.00
62 Ichiro Suzuki 4.00 10.00

2006 Upper Deck Future Stars Rookie Signatures Red

STATED PRINT RUN 35 SER.#'d SETS
NO PRICING DUE TO SCARCITY

2006 Upper Deck Future Stars Clear Path to History Triple Signatures

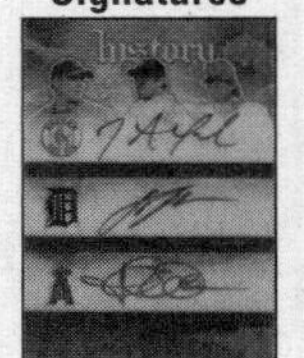

STATED ODDS 1:288
BSJ Jason Bay 30.00 60.00
Alfonso Soriano
Andruw Jones
CPO Chris Carpenter 20.00 50.00
Jake Peavy
Roy Oswalt
CUK Carl Crawford 20.00 50.00
B.J. Upton
Scott Kazmir
DRR Stephen Drew 50.00 100.00
Jose Reyes
Hanley Ramirez
GEH Tony Gwynn Jr. 20.00 50.00
Andre Ethier
Jeremy Hermida
GJG Ken Griffey Jr.
Andruw Jones
Vladimir Guerrero
GPT Ken Griffey Jr.
Albert Pujols
Jim Thome
GTT Ken Griffey Jr.
Frank Thomas
Jim Thome
HTT Travis Hafner
Jim Thome
Frank Thomas
JVW Josh Johnson 30.00 60.00
Justin Verlander
Jered Weaver
KTZ Howie Kendrick 40.00 80.00
Troy Tulowitzki
Ryan Zimmerman
MKW Kendry Morales 40.00 80.00
Howie Kendrick
Jered Weaver
MML Justin Morneau 40.00 80.00
Joe Mauer
Francisco Liriano
MOH Justin Morneau 20.00 50.00
Lyle Overbay
Travis Hafner
NHP Joe Nathan 30.00 60.00
Trevor Hoffman
Jonathan Papelbon
PGJ Albert Pujols
Ken Griffey Jr.
Derek Jeter
PSO Jake Peavy 20.00 50.00
Ben Sheets
Roy Oswalt
PVW Jonathan Papelbon 50.00 100.00
Justin Verlander
Jered Weaver
SBH Alay Soler 20.00 50.00
Chad Billingsley
Cole Hamels
SHL Jeremy Sowers 30.00 60.00
Cole Hamels
Francisco Liriano
SHN Huston Street
Trevor Hoffman
Joe Nathan
TZU Troy Tulowitzki 50.00 100.00
Ryan Zimmerman
B.J. Upton
URB Chase Utley 30.00 60.00
Brian Roberts
Craig Biggio
VBZ Justin Verlander 50.00 100.00
Jeremy Bonderman
Joel Zumaya
WKJ Dontrelle Willis
Scott Kazmir
Randy Johnson

2006 Upper Deck Future Stars World Future Stars

COMPLETE SET (25) 10.00 25.00
PRINTING PLATE ODDS 1:2 CASES
PLATE PRINT RUN 1 SET PER COLOR
BLACK-CYAN-MAGENTA-YELLOW ISSUED
NO PLATE PRICING DUE TO SCARCITY
1 Adam Loewen .30 .75
2 Nan Wang .30 .75
3 Yi Feng .30 .75
4 Chien-Ming Chang .50 1.25
5 Yung-Chi Chen .50 1.25
6 Chin-Lung Hu .50 1.25
7 Yadel Marti .30 .75
8 Frederich Cepeda .30 .75
9 Pedro Luis Lazo .30 .75
10 Osmany Urrutia .30 .75
11 Yoandy Garlobo .30 .75
12 Nobuhiko Matsunaka .50 1.25
13 Daisuke Matsuzaka 6.00 15.00
14 Tsuyoshi Nishioka .50 1.25
15 Tomoya Satozaki .50 1.25
16 Koji Uehara .50 1.25
17 Shunsuke Watanabe .50 1.25
18 Jong Beom Lee .30 .75
19 Sidney de Jong .30 .75
20 Shairon Martis .30 .75
21 Len Pecota .30 .75
22 Dicky Gonzalez .30 .75
23 Nicholas Dempsey .30 .75
24 Brett Willemburg .30 .75
25 Chase Utley .75 2.00

2006 Upper Deck Future Stars World Future Stars Black

*BLACK: 3X TO 8X BASIC
COMMON TEAM CHINESE TAIPEI 12.50 30.00
COMMON TEAM JAPAN 12.50 30.00
STATED PRINT RUN 50 SER.#'d SETS
13 Daisuke Matsuzaka 50.00 100.00
25 Chase Utley 5.00 12.00

2006 Upper Deck Future Stars World Future Stars Blue

*BLUE: 2.5X TO 6X BASIC
COMMON TEAM CHINESE TAIPEI 5.00 12.00
COMMON TEAM JAPAN 5.00 12.00
STATED PRINT RUN 99 SER.#'d SETS

13 Daisuke Matsuzaka 40.00 80.00
25 Chase Utley 4.00 10.00

2006 Upper Deck Future Stars World Future Stars Gold

STATED PRINT RUN 25 SER.#'d SETS
NO PRICING DUE TO SCARCITY

2006 Upper Deck Future Stars World Future Stars Green

*GREEN: 1.5X TO 4X BASIC
COMMON TEAM CHINESE TAIPEI 4.00 10.00
COMMON TEAM JAPAN 4.00 10.00
STATED PRINT RUN 499 SER.#'d SETS
13 Daisuke Matsuzaka 20.00 50.00
25 Chase Utley 2.00 5.00

2006 Upper Deck Future Stars World Future Stars Purple

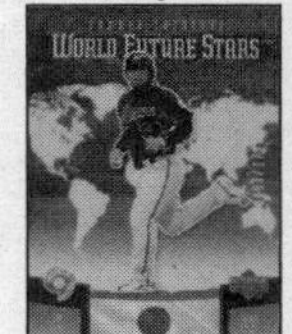

*PURPLE: .75X TO 2X BASIC
STATED PRINT RUN 1799 SER.#'d SETS
13 Daisuke Matsuzaka 15.00 40.00
25 Chase Utley 1.00 2.50

2006 Upper Deck Future Stars World Future Stars Red

*RED: 2X TO 5X BASIC
COMMON TEAM CHINESE TAIPEI 4.00 10.00
COMMON TEAM JAPAN 4.00 10.00
STATED PRINT RUN 299 SER.#'d SETS
13 Daisuke Matsuzaka 30.00 60.00
25 Chase Utley 2.50 6.00

2007 Upper Deck Future Stars

This 190-card set was released in September, 2007. This set was released in hobby, retail and special Walmart packs. The hobby version was four-card packs, with an $4.99 SRP which came 24 packs to a box and 12 boxes to a case. Cards numbered 1-100 feature veterans sequenced in team alphabetical order while cards 101-190 feature signed 2007 rookies. Those signed rookies were inserted at a stated rate of one in six hobby, one in 24 retail and one in 350 Walmart. A few players did not return their signatures in time for pack out and those cards could be redeemed until September 5, 2009.

COMP.SET w/o AU's (100) 10.00 25.00
COMMON CARD (1-100) .15 .40
COMMON AU RC (101-190) 3.00 8.00
101-190 ODDS 1:6 HOB,1:24 RET,1:350 WALMART
EXCHANGE DEADLINE 9/5/2009
1 Brandon Webb .15 .40
2 Conor Jackson .15 .40

3 Stephen Drew	.25	.60
4 Chipper Jones	.40	1.00
5 Andruw Jones	.25	.60
6 Jeff Francoeur	.40	1.00
7 John Smoltz	.25	.60
8 Miguel Tejada	.15	.40
9 Nick Markakis	.25	.60
10 Brian Roberts	.15	.40
11 David Ortiz	.40	1.00
12 Manny Ramirez	.25	.60
13 Josh Beckett	.15	.40
14 Curt Schilling	.25	.60
15 Derrek Lee	.15	.40
16 Aramis Ramirez	.15	.40
17 Carlos Zambrano	.15	.40
18 Alfonso Soriano	.15	.40
19 Jim Thome	.25	.60
20 Paul Konerko	.15	.40
21 Jon Garland	.15	.40
22 Ken Griffey Jr.	.60	1.50
23 Adam Dunn	.15	.40
24 Aaron Harang	.15	.40
25 Travis Hafner	.15	.40
26 Victor Martinez	.15	.40
27 Grady Sizemore	.25	.60
28 C.C. Sabathia	.15	.40
29 Todd Helton	.25	.60
30 Matt Holliday	.20	.50
31 Garrett Atkins	.15	.40
32 Ivan Rodriguez	.25	.60
33 Magglio Ordonez	.15	.40
34 Gary Sheffield	.15	.40
35 Justin Verlander	.40	1.00
36 Miguel Cabrera	.25	.60
37 Hanley Ramirez	.25	.60
38 Dontrelle Willis	.15	.40
39 Lance Berkman	.15	.40
40 Roy Oswalt	.15	.40
41 Carlos Lee	.15	.40
42 Gil Meche	.15	.40
43 Emil Brown	.15	.40
44 Mark Teahen	.15	.40
45 Vladimir Guerrero	.40	1.00
46 Jered Weaver	.25	.60
47 Howie Kendrick	.15	.40
48 Juan Pierre	.15	.40
49 Nomar Garciaparra	.40	1.00
50 Rafael Furcal	.15	.40
51 Jeff Kent	.15	.40
52 Prince Fielder	.40	1.00
53 Ben Sheets	.15	.40
54 Rickie Weeks	.15	.40
55 Justin Morneau	.15	.40
56 Joe Mauer	.25	.60
57 Torii Hunter	.15	.40
58 Johan Santana	.25	.60
59 Jose Reyes	.40	1.00
60 David Wright	.60	1.50
61 Carlos Delgado	.15	.40
62 Carlos Beltran	.15	.40
63 Derek Jeter	1.00	2.50
64 Alex Rodriguez	.60	1.50
65 Johnny Damon	.25	.60
66 Jason Giambi	.15	.40
67 Bobby Abreu	.15	.40
68 Mike Piazza	.40	1.00
69 Nick Swisher	.15	.40
70 Eric Chavez	.15	.40
71 Ryan Howard	.60	1.50
72 Chase Utley	.40	1.00
73 Jimmy Rollins	.15	.40
74 Jason Bay	.15	.40
75 Freddy Sanchez	.15	.40
76 Zach Duke	.15	.40
77 Greg Maddux	.60	1.50
78 Adrian Gonzalez	.15	.40
79 Jake Peavy	.15	.40
80 Ray Durham	.15	.40
81 Barry Zito	.15	.40
82 Matt Cain	.25	.60
83 Ichiro Suzuki	.60	1.50
84 Felix Hernandez	.25	.60
85 Richie Sexson	.15	.40
86 Albert Pujols	.75	2.00
87 Scott Rolen	.25	.60
88 Chris Carpenter	.15	.40
89 Chris Duncan	.15	.40
90 Carl Crawford	.15	.40
91 Rocco Baldelli	.15	.40
92 Scott Kazmir	.25	.60
93 Michael Young	.15	.40
94 Mark Teixeira	.25	.60
95 Ian Kinsler	.15	.40
96 Troy Glaus	.15	.40
97 Vernon Wells	.15	.40
98 Roy Halladay	.15	.40
99 Ryan Zimmerman	.40	1.00
100 Nick Johnson	.15	.40
101 Zack Segovia AU (RC)	3.00	8.00
102 Joaquin Arias AU (RC)	3.00	8.00
103 Troy Tulowitzki AU SP (RC)		
104 Travis Buck AU (RC)	4.00	10.00
105 Mike Schultz AU RC	3.00	8.00
106 Sean White AU SP RC		
107 Sean Henn AU (RC)	3.00	8.00
108 Ryan Z. Braun AU RC	6.00	15.00
109 Rick Vanden Hurk AU RC	3.00	8.00
110 Carlos Gomez AU SP RC		
111 Mike Rabelo AU RC	4.00	10.00
112 Felix Pie AU (RC)	4.00	10.00
113 Miguel Montero AU (RC)	4.00	10.00
114 Michael Bourn AU (RC)	4.00	10.00
115 Micah Owings AU SP (RC) EXCH		
116 Matt Lindstrom AU (RC)	3.00	8.00
117 Matt Chico AU (RC)	3.00	8.00
118 Levale Speigner AU RC	3.00	8.00
119 Lee Gardner AU (RC)	3.00	8.00
120 Kory Casto AU (RC)	4.00	10.00
121 Kevin Kouzmanoff AU (RC)	4.00	10.00
122 Kevin Cameron AU RC	3.00	8.00
123 Kei Igawa AU SP RC		
124 Tyler Clippard AU (RC)	6.00	15.00
125 Juan Perez AU RC	3.00	8.00
126 Josh Hamilton AU SP (RC)	15.00	40.00
127 Joseph Bisenius AU RC	3.00	8.00
128 Jose Luis Garcia AU RC	3.00	8.00
129 Jon Knott AU (RC)	3.00	8.00
130 Jon Coutlangus AU (RC)	4.00	10.00
131 John Danks AU RC	4.00	10.00
132 Joe Smith AU RC	3.00	8.00
133 Matt Brown AU RC	3.00	8.00
134 Joakim Soria AU RC	4.00	10.00
135 Jesus Flores AU RC	6.00	15.00
136 Jeff Baker AU (RC)	3.00	8.00
137 Jay Marshall AU RC	3.00	8.00
138 Jared Burton AU RC	4.00	10.00
139 Jamie Vermilyea AU RC	4.00	10.00
140 Jamie Burke AU (RC)	4.00	10.00
141 Ryan Rowland-Smith AU RC	4.00	10.00
142 Connor Robertson AU RC	3.00	8.00
143 Hector Gimenez AU (RC)	3.00	8.00
144 Gustavo Molina AU RC	4.00	10.00
145 Glen Perkins AU (RC)	3.00	8.00
146 Joba Chamberlain AU SP RC EXCH 150.00 200.00		
147 Doug Slaten AU RC	3.00	8.00
148 Ryan Braun AU (RC)	20.00	50.00
149 Delmon Young AU SP (RC)		
150 Garrett Jones AU (RC)	3.00	8.00
151 Chris Stewart AU SP RC		
152 Cesar Jimenez AU RC	4.00	10.00
153 Brian Stokes AU (RC)	3.00	8.00
154 Brian Burres AU (RC)	4.00	10.00
155 Brian Barden AU SP RC		
156 Kyle Kendrick AU RC	12.50	30.00
157 Andrew Miller AU RC	8.00	20.00
158 Alexi Casilla AU RC	3.00	8.00
159 Alex Gordon AU SP RC	35.00	70.00
160 A.J. Murray AU RC	4.00	10.00
161 Akinori Iwamura AU SP RC		
162 Adam Lind AU (RC)	4.00	10.00
163 Chase Wright AU RC	5.00	12.00
164 Dallas Braden AU RC	3.00	8.00
165 Rocky Cherry AU RC	5.00	12.00
166 Andy Gonzalez AU RC	3.00	8.00
167 Neal Musser AU RC	3.00	8.00
168 Mark Reynolds AU RC	30.00	60.00
169 Dennis Dove AU (RC)	3.00	8.00
170 Justin Hampson AU (RC)	4.00	10.00
171 Phil Hughes AU SP (RC)		
172 Kelvin Jimenez AU RC	3.00	8.00
173 Hunter Pence AU SP (RC)		
174 Brad Salmon AU RC	6.00	15.00
175 Ryan Sweeney AU (RC)	3.00	8.00
176 Brandon Wood AU (RC)	6.00	15.00
177 Billy Butler AU SP (RC)		
178 Ben Francisco AU (RC)	3.00	8.00
179 Devern Hansack AU SP RC		
180 Yoel Hernandez AU RC	3.00	8.00
181 Tim Lincecum AU SP RC	50.00	100.00
182 Danny Putnam AU (RC)	5.00	12.00
183 Jarrod Saltalamacchia AU SP (RC)	6.00	15.00
184 Andy LaRoche AU SP (RC)		
185 Matt DeSalvo AU (RC)	5.00	12.00
186 Fred Lewis AU (RC)	3.00	8.00
187 Anthony Lerew AU (RC)	3.00	8.00
188 Jesse Litsch AU RC	4.00	10.00
189a Daisuke Matsuzaka RC		
189b Daisuke Matsuzaka AU SP	250.00	300.00

2007 Upper Deck Future Stars Gold

*GOLD: 2X TO 5X BASIC
RANDOM INSERTS IN PACKS
STATED PRINT RUN 99 SER.#'d SETS

83 Ichiro Suzuki	6.00	15.00
189 Daisuke Matsuzaka	20.00	50.00

2007 Upper Deck Future Stars Red

*RED: 1.5X TO 4X BASIC
RANDOM INSERTS IN PACKS
STATED PRINT RUN 199 SER.#'d SETS

83 Ichiro Suzuki	5.00	12.00
189 Daisuke Matsuzaka	8.00	20.00

2007 Upper Deck Future Stars All Star Futures

RANDOM INSERTS IN PACKS
STATED PRINT RUN 500 SER.#'d SETS

AD Alejandro De Aza	.75	2.00
AG Alex Gordon	2.50	6.00
AI Akinori Iwamura	1.25	3.00
AL Adam Lind	.50	1.25
AM Andrew Miller	3.00	8.00
BA Jeff Baker	.50	1.25
BI Billy Butler	.75	2.00
BM Brandon Morrow	1.25	3.00
BU B.J. Upton	.50	1.25
BW Brandon Wood	.50	1.25
CA Alexi Casilla	.75	2.00
CG Carlos Gomez	.75	2.00
CW Chase Wright	1.25	3.00
CY Chris Young	.50	1.25
DM Daisuke Matsuzaka	5.00	12.00
DP Danny Putnam	.50	1.25
DY Delmon Young	.75	2.00
FL Fred Lewis	.75	2.00
FP Felix Pie	.50	1.25
GP Glen Perkins	.50	1.25
HA Josh Hamilton	1.25	3.00
HK Howie Kendrick	.50	1.25
HP Hunter Pence	2.50	6.00
IK Ian Kinsler	.50	1.25
JA Joaquin Arias	.50	1.25
JD John Danks	.50	1.25
JS Jarrod Saltalamacchia	.75	2.00
JV Justin Verlander	1.25	3.00
KC Kory Casto	.50	1.25
KI Kei Igawa	1.25	3.00
KK Kevin Kouzmanoff	.50	1.25
LA Andy LaRoche	.50	1.25
MA Matt Chico	.50	1.25
MB Michael Bourn	.50	1.25
MC Matt Cain	.75	2.00
MI Miguel Montero	.50	1.25
ML Matt Lindstrom	.50	1.25
MO Micah Owings	.50	1.25
PF Prince Fielder	1.25	3.00
PH Phil Hughes	2.50	6.00
RB Ryan Braun	3.00	8.00
RS Ryan Sweeney	.50	1.25
RZ Ryan Zimmerman	1.25	3.00
SD Stephen Drew	.75	2.00
SM Joe Smith	.50	1.25
SO Joakim Soria	.50	1.25
TB Travis Buck	.50	1.25
TL Tim Lincecum	4.00	10.00
TP Tony Pena	.50	1.25
TT Troy Tulowitzki	1.25	3.00

2007 Upper Deck Future Stars All Star Futures Signatures

STATED ODDS 1:72 H,1:2500 R,1:2500 WALMART
NO SP PRICING DUE TO SCARCITY
EXCH DEADLINE 9/5/2009

AG Alex Gordon SP		
AI Akinori Iwamura SP		
AL Adam Lind	4.00	10.00
AM Andrew Miller	6.00	15.00
BA Jeff Baker	3.00	8.00
BI Billy Butler		
BU B.J. Upton	4.00	10.00
BW Brandon Wood	6.00	15.00
CA Alexi Casilla	3.00	8.00
CG Carlos Gomez	6.00	15.00
CW Chase Wright	5.00	12.00
CY Chris Young	10.00	25.00
DM Daisuke Matsuzaka SP		
DP Danny Putnam	4.00	10.00
DY Delmon Young SP		
FL Fred Lewis	3.00	8.00
FP Felix Pie	3.00	8.00
GP Glen Perkins	5.00	12.00
HA Josh Hamilton	15.00	40.00
HK Howie Kendrick		
HP Hunter Pence	30.00	60.00
IK Ian Kinsler	3.00	8.00
JA Joaquin Arias	3.00	8.00
JD John Danks	4.00	10.00
JS Jarrod Saltalamacchia	6.00	15.00
JV Justin Verlander SP		
KC Kory Casto	3.00	8.00
KI Kei Igawa SP		
KK Kevin Kouzmanoff	5.00	12.00
LA Andy LaRoche	4.00	10.00
MA Matt Chico	3.00	8.00
MC Matt Cain	5.00	12.00
MI Miguel Montero	3.00	8.00
ML Matt Lindstrom	3.00	8.00
MO Micah Owings EXCH	6.00	15.00
PF Prince Fielder SP		
PH Phil Hughes SP		
RB Ryan Braun	40.00	80.00
RS Ryan Sweeney	4.00	10.00
RZ Ryan Zimmerman SP		
SD Stephen Drew SP		
SM Joe Smith	3.00	8.00
SO Joakim Soria	5.00	12.00
TB Travis Buck	5.00	12.00
TL Tim Lincecum	40.00	80.00
TP Tony Pena	5.00	12.00
TT Troy Tulowitzki	10.00	25.00

2007 Upper Deck Future Stars Clear Path to History Triple Signatures

STATED ODDS 1:288 HOB,1:5000 RET
NO SP PRICING DUE TO SCARCITY

BBO Roy Oswalt		
Lance Berkman		
Craig Biggio		
CCH Bobby Crosby	20.00	50.00
Eric Chavez		
Rich Harden		
CWR Dontrelle Willis		
Miguel Cabrera		
Hanley Ramirez		
CYI Akinori Iwamura		
Carl Crawford		
Delmon Young SP		
DMY Stephen Drew	20.00	50.00
Miguel Montero		
Chris Young		
FEG Rafael Furcal	15.00	40.00
Andre Ethier		
Luis Gonzalez		
GKW Vladimir Guerrero		
Jered Weaver		
Howie Kendrick SP		
GPC Albert Pujols		
Miguel Cabrera		
Vladimir Guerrero SP		
HAT Matt Holliday	40.00	80.00
Garrett Atkins		
Troy Tulowitzki		
HMS Travis Hafner	30.00	60.00
Victor Martinez		
Jeremy Sowers		
HSW Johan Santana		
Dontrelle Willis		
Roy Halladay		
KUC Scott Kazmir	20.00	50.00
B.J. Upton		
Carl Crawford		
KUK Ian Kinsler	15.00	40.00
Howie Kendrick		
Dan Uggla		
MPM Melvin Mora	15.00	40.00
Nick Markakis		
Corey Patterson		
SWF Prince Fielder	40.00	80.00
Ben Sheets		
Rickie Weeks		
THM Justin Morneau		
Travis Hafner		
Jim Thome		
VZR Hanley Ramirez	30.00	60.00
Justin Verlander		
Ryan Zimmerman		
YBP Delmon Young	15.00	40.00
Billy Butler		
Felix Pie		

2007 Upper Deck Future Stars Cy Young Futures

RANDOM INSERTS IN PACKS
STATED PRINT RUN 500 SER.#'d SETS

AL Anthony Lerew	.50	1.25
AM Andrew Miller	3.00	8.00
BM Brandon Morrow	1.25	3.00
CH Cole Hamels	1.25	3.00
CW Chase Wright	1.25	3.00
DM Daisuke Matsuzaka	5.00	12.00
GP Glen Perkins	.50	1.25
JD John Danks	.50	1.25
JG Jose Garcia	.50	1.25
JL Jon Lester	.75	2.00
JS Jeremy Sowers	.50	1.25
JV Justin Verlander	1.25	3.00
JZ Joel Zumaya	.75	2.00
KI Kei Igawa	1.25	3.00
MA Matt Chico	.50	1.25
MC Matt Cain	.75	2.00
MO Micah Owings	.50	1.25
PH Phil Hughes	2.50	6.00
RV Rick VandenHurk	.75	2.00
SH Sean Henn	.50	1.25
SK Scott Kazmir	.75	2.00
SM Joe Smith	.50	1.25
TC Tyler Clippard	.75	2.00
TL Tim Lincecum	4.00	10.00
ZS Zack Segovia	.50	1.25

2007 Upper Deck Future Stars Cy Young Futures Signatures

STATED ODDS 1:72 H,1:2500 R,1:2500 WALMART
NO SP PRICING DUE TO SCARCITY
EXCH DEADLINE 9/5/2009

AL Anthony Lerew	3.00	8.00
AM Andrew Miller	6.00	15.00
CH Cole Hamels	12.50	30.00
CW Chase Wright	5.00	12.00
DM Daisuke Matsuzaka SP EXCH		
GP Glen Perkins	5.00	12.00
JD John Danks	4.00	10.00
JG Jose Garcia	3.00	8.00
JS Jeremy Sowers SP		
JV Justin Verlander SP		
JZ Joel Zumaya		
KI Kei Igawa SP		
MA Matt Chico	3.00	8.00
MC Matt Cain	5.00	12.00
MO Micah Owings	6.00	15.00
PH Phil Hughes SP		
RV Rick VandenHurk	3.00	8.00
SH Sean Henn	3.00	8.00
SK Scott Kazmir SP		
SM Joe Smith	3.00	8.00
TC Tyler Clippard	6.00	15.00
TL Tim Lincecum	30.00	60.00
ZS Zack Segovia	3.00	8.00

2007 Upper Deck Future Stars MVP Futures

RANDOM INSERTS IN PACKS
STATED PRINT RUN 500 SER.#'d SETS

AD Alejandro De Aza	.75	2.00
AG Alex Gordon	2.50	6.00
AI Akinori Iwamura	1.25	3.00
AL Adam Lind	.50	1.25
DM Daisuke Matsuzaka	5.00	12.00
DY Delmon Young	.75	2.00
FP Felix Pie	.50	1.25
HP Hunter Pence	2.50	6.00
IK Ian Kinsler	.50	1.25
JA Joaquin Arias	.50	1.25
JB Jeff Baker	.50	1.25
JH Josh Hamilton	1.25	3.00
JS Jarrod Saltalamacchia	.75	2.00
JV Justin Verlander	1.25	3.00
KI Kei Igawa	1.25	3.00
KK Kevin Kouzmanoff	.50	1.25
LA Andy LaRoche	.50	1.25
MB Michael Bourn	.50	1.25
MM Miguel Montero	.50	1.25
PF Prince Fielder	1.25	3.00
RB Ryan Braun	3.00	8.00
RS Ryan Sweeney	.50	1.25
RZ Ryan Zimmerman	1.25	3.00
TB Travis Buck	.50	1.25
TT Troy Tulowitzki	1.25	3.00

2007 Upper Deck Future Stars MVP Futures Signatures

STATED ODDS 1:72 H,1:2500 R,1:2500 WALMART
NO SP PRICING DUE TO SCARCITY
EXCH DEADLINE 9/5/2009

AG Alex Gordon SP		
AI Akinori Iwamura		
AL Adam Lind	4.00	10.00
DM Daisuke Matsuzaka SP EXCH		
DY Delmon Young SP		
FP Felix Pie	3.00	8.00
HP Hunter Pence	30.00	60.00
IK Ian Kinsler	3.00	8.00
JA Joaquin Arias	3.00	8.00
JB Jeff Baker	3.00	8.00
JH Josh Hamilton	15.00	40.00
JS Jarrod Saltalamacchia	6.00	15.00
JV Justin Verlander SP		
KI Kei Igawa SP		
KK Kevin Kouzmanoff	5.00	12.00
LA Andy LaRoche	4.00	10.00
MB Michael Bourn	3.00	8.00
MM Miguel Montero	3.00	8.00
PF Prince Fielder	25.00	50.00
RB Ryan Braun	20.00	50.00
RS Ryan Sweeney	4.00	10.00
RZ Ryan Zimmerman SP		
TB Travis Buck	5.00	12.00
TT Troy Tulowitzki SP		

2007 Upper Deck Future Stars Rookie Dated Debut

RANDOM INSERTS IN PACKS
STATED PRINT RUN 999 SER.#'d SETS

AC Alexi Casilla	.50	1.25
AD Alejandro De Aza	.50	1.25
AG Alex Gordon	1.50	4.00
AI Akinori Iwamura	.75	2.00
AL Adam Lind	.30	.75
BA Jeff Baker	.30	.75
BB Brian Barden	.30	.75
BI Joseph Bisenius	.30	.75
BM Brandon Morrow	.75	2.00
BW Brandon Wood	.30	.75
CA Kory Casto	.30	.75
CG Carlos Gomez	.50	1.25
CR Cal Ripken Jr.	3.00	8.00
CW Chase Wright	.75	2.00
DA John Danks	.30	.75
DJ Derek Jeter	2.00	5.00
DM Daisuke Matsuzaka	3.00	8.00
DY Delmon Young	.50	1.25
ED Elijah Dukes	.50	1.25
FL Fred Lewis	.50	1.25
FP Felix Pie	.30	.75
GM Gustavo Molina	.30	.75
GP Glen Perkins	.30	.75
HO Hideki Okajima	1.50	4.00
HP Hunter Pence	1.50	4.00
JA Joaquin Arias	.30	.75
JC Jon Coutlangus	.30	.75
JF Jesus Flores	.30	.75
JH Josh Hamilton	.75	2.00
JM Jay Marshall	.30	.75
JP Juan Perez	.30	.75
JS Joakim Soria	.30	.75
KC Kevin Cameron	.30	.75
KG Ken Griffey Jr.	1.25	3.00
KI Kei Igawa	.75	2.00
KK Kevin Kouzmanoff	.30	.75
LA Andy LaRoche	.30	.75
LG Lee Gardner	.30	.75
MB Michael Bourn	.30	.75
MC Matt Chico	.30	.75
MM Miguel Montero	.30	.75
MO Micah Owings	.30	.75
MR Mike Rabelo	.30	.75
PH Phil Hughes	1.50	4.00
RS Ryan Sweeney	.30	.75
SA Jarrod Saltalamacchia	.50	1.25
SM Joe Smith	.30	.75
TB Travis Buck	.30	.75
TL Tim Lincecum	2.50	6.00
TT Troy Tulowitzki	.75	2.00

2007 Upper Deck Future Stars Rookie Dated Debut Signatures

RANDOM INSERTS IN PACKS
STATED PRINT RUN 10 SER.#'d SETS
NO PRICING DUE TO SCARCITY

AC Alexi Casilla		
AG Alex Gordon		
AI Akinori Iwamura		
AL Adam Lind		
BA Jeff Baker		
BI Joseph Bisenius		
BW Brandon Wood		
CA Kory Casto		
CG Carlos Gomez		
CW Chase Wright		
DA John Danks		
DY Delmon Young		
FL Fred Lewis		
FP Felix Pie		
GM Gustavo Molina		
GP Glen Perkins		
HP Hunter Pence		
JA Joaquin Arias		
JC Jon Coutlangus		
JF Jesus Flores		
JH Josh Hamilton		
JM Jay Marshall		
JP Juan Perez		
KC Kevin Cameron		
KI Kei Igawa		
KK Kevin Kouzmanoff		
LA Andy LaRoche		
LG Lee Gardner		
MB Michael Bourn		
MC Matt Chico		
MM Miguel Montero		
MR Mike Rabelo		
PH Phil Hughes		
RS Ryan Sweeney		
SA Jarrod Saltalamacchia		
SM Joe Smith		
TB Travis Buck		
TL Tim Lincecum		
TT Troy Tulowitzki		

2007 Upper Deck Future Stars Two for the Bigs

RANDOM INSERTS IN PACKS
STATED PRINT RUN 999 SER.#'d SETS

AS Joaquin Arias	.30	.75
Chris Stewart		
BB Michael Bourn	.30	.75
Joseph Bisenius		
BD Travis Buck	.50	1.25
Elijah Dukes		
BG Ryan Braun	2.00	5.00
Alex Gordon		
BS Ryan Z. Braun	.30	.75
Joakim Soria		
BT Troy Tulowitzki	.75	2.00
Jeff Baker		
CF Kory Casto	.30	.75
Jesus Flores		
CL Tim Lincecum	2.50	6.00
Matt Chico		
CP Glen Perkins	.50	1.25
Alexi Casilla		
CS Matt Chico	.30	.75
Levale Speigner		
DG Alejandro De Aza	.50	1.25
Lee Gardner		
DK Daisuke Matsuzaka	3.00	8.00
Kei Igawa		
DM John Danks	.30	.75
Gustavo Molina		
DT Troy Tulowitzki	.75	2.00
Stephen Drew		
DV Alejandro De Aza	.50	1.25
Rick Vanden Hurk		
DW Matt DeSalvo	.75	2.00
Chase Wright		
DY Stephen Drew	.50	1.25
Chris Young		
GB Alex Gordon	1.50	4.00
Billy Butler		
GF Jesus Flores	.30	.75
Hector Gimenez		
GI Alex Gordon	1.50	4.00
Akinori Iwamura		
GL Alex Gordon	1.50	4.00
Andy LaRoche		
GM Alex Gordon	3.00	8.00
Daisuke Matsuzaka		
GP Hunter Pence	1.50	4.00
Hector Gimenez		
HB Josh Hamilton	.75	2.00
Jared Burton		
HD Josh Hamilton	.75	2.00
Alejandro De Aza		
HL Tim Lincecum	2.50	6.00
Phil Hughes		
HP Hunter Pence	1.50	4.00
Josh Hamilton		
II Akinori Iwamura	.75	2.00
Kei Igawa		
KC Kevin Kouzmanoff	.30	.75
Kevin Cameron		
LG Lee Gardner	.30	.75
Matt Lindstrom		
LV Adam Lind	.30	.75
Jamie Vermilyea		
MG Miguel Montero	.30	.75
Hector Gimenez		
MI Daisuke Matsuzaka	3.00	8.00
Akinori Iwamura		
MO Daisuke Matsuzaka	3.00	8.00
Hideki Okajima		
MR Mike Rabelo	.30	.75
Gustavo Molina		
MW Brandon Morrow	.75	2.00
Sean White		
OL Tim Lincecum	2.50	6.00
Micah Owings		
OM Micah Owings	.30	.75
Miguel Montero		
PB Travis Buck	.30	.75
Danny Putnam		
PD Hunter Pence	1.50	4.00
Alejandro De Aza		
PH Felix Pie	.75	2.00
Josh Hamilton		
PP Hunter Pence	1.50	4.00
Felix Pie		
RS Mike Rabelo	.30	.75
Chris Stewart		
SM Jarrod Saltalamacchia	.50	1.25
Miguel Montero		
ST Troy Tulowitzki	.75	2.00
Jarrod Saltalamacchia		
SW Chase Wright	.75	2.00
Joe Smith		
TB Travis Buck	.50	1.25
Billy Butler		
WH Phil Hughes	1.50	4.00
Chase Wright		
YD Delmon Young	.50	1.25
Elijah Dukes		
YM Daisuke Matsuzaka	3.00	8.00
Delmon Young		

2007 Upper Deck Future Stars Two for the Bigs Signatures

RANDOM INSERTS IN PACKS
STATED PRINT RUN 10 SER.#'d SETS
NO PRICING DUE TO SCARCITY

BG Alex Gordon		
Ryan Braun		
BS Ryan Z. Braun		
Joakim Soria		
BT Jeff Baker		
Troy Tulowitzki		
CF Kory Casto		
Jesus Flores		
CL Matt Chico		
Tim Lincecum		
CP Alexi Casilla		
Glen Perkins		
CS Matt Chico		
Levale Speigner		
DT Stephen Drew		
Troy Tulowitzki		
DW Chase Wright		
Matt DeSalvo		
DY Chris Young		
Stephen Drew		
GB Alex Gordon		
Billy Butler		
GI Alex Gordon		
Akinori Iwamura		
GL Alex Gordon		
Andy LaRoche		
HB Josh Hamilton		
Jared Burton		
HL Phil Hughes		
Tim Lincecum		
HP Josh Hamilton		
Hunter Pence		
II Akinori Iwamura		
Kei Igawa		
KC Kevin Kouzmanoff		
Kevin Cameron		
LG Matt Lindstrom		
Lee Gardner		
PB Danny Putnam		
Travis Buck		
PH Josh Hamilton		
Felix Pie		
PP Hunter Pence		
Felix Pie		
SM Jarrod Saltalamacchia		
Miguel Montero		
ST Jarrod Saltalamacchia		
Troy Tulowitzki		
SW Joe Smith		
Chase Wright		
TB Travis Buck		
Billy Butler		
WH Chase Wright		
Phil Hughes		

2007 Upper Deck Goudey

This 240-card set was released in August, 2007. The set was issued in both retail and hobby packs. The hobby packs contained eight cards which came 24 packs to a box and 12 boxes to a case. The first 100 cards feature veterans sequenced in alphabetical order by first name, while cards numbered 101-200 are a mix of veterans and 2007 rookie logo cards. Cards numbered 201-223 feature retired greats while 224-240 are short printed cards of some of today's biggest stars. Those short printed cards were inserted into packs at a stated rate of one in six hobby or retail packs.

COMP.SET w/o SPs (200) 20.00 50.00
COMMON CARD (1-200) .20 .50
COMMON ROOKIE (1-200) .30 .75
COMMON SP (201-240) 2.00 5.00
SP ODDS 1:6 HOBBY,1:6 RETAIL
1933 ORIGINALS ODDS TWO PER CASE
SEE 1933 GOUDEY PRICING FOR ORIGINALS
1 A.J. Burnett .20 .50
2 Aaron Boone .20 .50
3 Aaron Rowand .20 .50
4 Adam Dunn .20 .50
5 Adrian Beltre .20 .50
6 Albert Pujols 1.00 2.50
7 Ivan Rodriguez .30 .75
8 Alfonso Soriano .20 .50
9 Andruw Jones .30 .75
10 Andy Pettitte .30 .75
11 Aramis Ramirez .20 .50
12 B.J. Upton .20 .50
13 Barry Zito .20 .50
14 Bartolo Colon .20 .50
15 Ben Sheets .20 .50
16 Bobby Abreu .20 .50
17 Bobby Crosby .20 .50
18 Brian Giles .20 .50
19 Brian Roberts .20 .50
20 C.C. Sabathia .20 .50
21 Carlos Beltran .20 .50
22 Carlos Delgado .20 .50
23 Carlos Lee .20 .50
24 Carlos Zambrano .20 .50
25 Chad Cordero .20 .50
26 Chad Tracy .20 .50
27 Chipper Jones .50 1.25
28 Craig Biggio .30 .75
29 Curt Schilling .30 .75
30 Danny Haren .20 .50
31 Darin Erstad .20 .50
32 David Ortiz .50 1.25
33 Billy Wagner .20 .50
34 Derek Jeter 1.25 3.00
35 Derek Lee .20 .50
36 Dontrelle Willis .20 .50
37 Edgar Renteria .20 .50
38 Eric Chavez .20 .50
39 Felix Hernandez .30 .75
40 Garret Anderson .20 .50
41 Garrett Atkins .20 .50
42 Gary Sheffield .20 .50
43 Grady Sizemore .30 .75
44 Greg Maddux .75 2.00
45 Hank Blalock .20 .50
46 Hanley Ramirez .30 .75
47 J.D. Drew .20 .50
48 Jacque Jones .20 .50
49 Jake Peavy .20 .50
50 Jake Westbrook .20 .50
51 Jason Bay .20 .50
52 Jason Giambi .20 .50
53 Jason Schmidt .20 .50
54 Jason Varitek .50 1.25
55 Troy Tulowitzki (RC) .75 2.00
56 Jeff Francoeur .50 1.25
57 Jeff Kent .20 .50
58 Jeremy Bonderman .20 .50
59 Jim Edmonds .30 .75
60 Jim Thome .30 .75
61 Jimmy Rollins .20 .50
62 Joe Mauer .30 .75
63 Johan Santana .30 .75
64 John Smoltz .30 .75
65 Johnny Damon .30 .75
66 Jose Reyes .50 1.25
67 Josh Beckett .30 .75
68 Justin Morneau .20 .50
69 Ken Griffey Jr. .75 2.00
70 Kerry Wood .20 .50
71 Khalil Greene .30 .75
72 Lance Berkman .20 .50
73 Livan Hernandez .20 .50
74 Manny Ramirez .30 .75
75 Mark Mulder .20 .50
76 Chase Utley .50 1.25
77 Mark Teixeira .30 .75
78 Miguel Tejada .30 .75
79 Miguel Cabrera .30 .75
80 Mike Piazza .50 1.25
81 Pat Burrell .20 .50
82 Paul LoDuca .20 .50
83 Pedro Martinez .30 .75
84 Prince Fielder .50 1.25
85 Rafael Furcal .20 .50
86 Randy Johnson .50 1.25
87 Richie Sexson .20 .50
88 Robinson Cano .30 .75
89 Roy Halladay .20 .50
90 Roy Oswalt .20 .50
91 Scott Rolen .30 .75
92 Tim Hudson .20 .50
93 Todd Helton .30 .75
94 Tom Glavine .30 .75
95 Torii Hunter .20 .50
96 Travis Hafner .20 .50
97 Trevor Hoffman .20 .50
98 Vernon Wells .20 .50
99 Vladimir Guerrero .50 1.25
100 Zach Duke .20 .50
101 Alex Rodriguez .75 2.00
102 Ryan Howard .75 2.00
103 Michael Barrett .20 .50
104 Ichiro Suzuki .75 2.00
105 Hideki Matsui .50 1.25
106 Jered Weaver .30 .75
107 Dan Uggla .30 .75
108 Ryan Freel .20 .50
109 Bill Hall .20 .50
110 Ray Durham .20 .50
111 Morgan Ensberg .20 .50
112 Shawn Green .20 .50
113 Brandon Webb .20 .50
114 Frank Thomas .50 1.25
115 Corey Patterson .20 .50
116 Edwin Encarnacion .20 .50
117 Mike Cameron .20 .50
118 Matt Holliday .50 1.25
119 Jhonny Peralta .20 .50
120 Nick Swisher .20 .50
121 Brad Penny .20 .50
122 Kenji Johjima .50 1.25
123 Francisco Rodriguez .20 .50
124 Mark Teahen .20 .50
125 Jonathan Papelbon .50 1.25
126 Carlos Guillen .20 .50
127 Freddy Sanchez .20 .50
128 Chien-Ming Wang .75 2.00
129 Andre Ethier .30 .75
130 Matt Cain .30 .75
131 Austin Kearns .20 .50
132 Ramon Hernandez .20 .50
133 Chris Carpenter .20 .50
134 Michael Cuddyer .20 .50
135 Stephen Drew .30 .75
136 David Wright .75 2.00
137 David DeJesus .20 .50
138 Gary Matthews .20 .50
139 Brandon Phillips .20 .50
140 Josh Barfield .20 .50
141 Alex Gordon RC 1.50 4.00
142 Scott Kazmir .30 .75
143 Luis Gonzalez .20 .50
144 Mike Sweeney .20 .50
145 Luis Castillo .20 .50
146 Huston Street .20 .50
147 Phil Hughes (RC) 1.50 4.00
148 Adrian Gonzalez .20 .50
149 Raul Ibanez .20 .50
150 Joe Crede .20 .50
151 Mark Loretta .20 .50
152 Adam LaRoche (RC) .30 .75
153 Troy Glaus .20 .50
154 Conor Jackson .20 .50
155 Michael Young .20 .50
156 Scott Podsednik .20 .50
157 David Eckstein .20 .50
158 Mike Jacobs .20 .50
159 Nomar Garciaparra .50 1.25
160 Mariano Rivera .50 1.25
161 Pedro Feliz .20 .50
162 Josh Hamilton (RC) .75 2.00
163 Ryan Langerhans .20 .50
164 Willy Taveras .20 .50
165 Carl Crawford .20 .50
166 Melvin Mora .20 .50
167 Francisco Liriano .50 1.25
168 Orlando Cabrera .20 .50
169 Chris Duncan .20 .50
170 Johnny Estrada .20 .50
171 Ryan Zimmerman .50 1.25
172 Rickie Weeks .20 .50
173 Paul Konerko .20 .50
174 Jack Wilson .20 .50
175 Jorge Posada .30 .75
176 Magglio Ordonez .20 .50
177 Nick Johnson .20 .50
178 Geoff Jenkins .20 .50
179 Reggie Sanders .20 .50
180 Moises Alou .20 .50
181 Glen Perkins (RC) .30 .75
182 Brad Lidge .20 .50
183 Kevin Kouzmanoff (RC) .30 .75
184 Jorge Cantu .20 .50
185 Carlos Quentin .20 .50
186 Rich Harden .20 .50
187 Jose Vidro .20 .50
188 Aaron Harang .20 .50
189 Noah Lowry .20 .50
190 Jermaine Dye .20 .50
191 Victor Martinez .20 .50
192 Chone Figgins .20 .50
193 Aubrey Huff .20 .50
194 Jason Isringhausen .20 .50
195 Brian McCann .20 .50
196 Juan Pierre .20 .50
197 Delmon Young (RC) .50 1.25
198 Felipe Lopez .20 .50
199 Brad Hawpe .20 .50
200 Justin Verlander .50 1.25
201 Mike Schmidt SP 4.00 10.00
202 Nolan Ryan SP 5.00 12.00
203 Cal Ripken Jr. SP 4.00 10.00
204 Harmon Killebrew SP 2.50 6.00
205 Reggie Jackson SP 2.50 6.00
206 Johnny Bench SP 2.50 6.00
207 Carlton Fisk SP 2.50 6.00
208 Yogi Berra SP 2.50 6.00
209 Al Kaline SP 2.50 6.00
210 Alan Trammell SP 2.00 5.00
211 Bill Mazeroski SP 2.50 6.00
212 Bob Gibson SP 2.50 6.00
213 Brooks Robinson SP 2.50 6.00
214 Carl Yastrzemski SP 3.00 8.00
215 Don Mattingly SP 5.00 12.00
216 Fergie Jenkins SP 2.00 5.00
217 Jim Rice SP 2.00 5.00
218 Lou Brock SP 2.50 6.00
219 Rod Carew SP 2.50 6.00
220 Stan Musial SP 3.00 8.00
221 Tom Seaver SP 2.50 6.00
222 Tony Gwynn SP 2.50 6.00
223 Wade Boggs SP 2.50 6.00
224 Alex Rodriguez SP 3.00 8.00
225 David Wright SP 3.00 8.00
226 Ryan Howard SP 3.00 8.00
227 Ichiro Suzuki SP 3.00 8.00
228 Ken Griffey Jr. SP 3.00 8.00
229 Daisuke Matsuzaka SP RC 4.00 10.00
230 Kei Igawa SP RC 2.50 6.00
231 Akinori Iwamura SP RC 3.00 8.00
232 Derek Jeter SP 4.00 10.00
233 Albert Pujols SP 4.00 10.00
234 Greg Maddux SP 3.00 8.00
235 David Ortiz SP 2.50 6.00
236 Manny Ramirez SP 2.50 6.00
237 Johan Santana SP 2.50 6.00
238 Pedro Martinez SP 2.50 6.00
239 Roger Clemens SP 4.00 10.00
240 Vladimir Guerrero SP 2.50 6.00

2007 Upper Deck Goudey Red Backs

COMPLETE SET (240) 20.00 50.00
*RED: .4X TO 1X BASIC
APPX. FOUR PER PACK
CARDS 201-240 DO NOT EXIST

2007 Upper Deck Goudey Diamond Stars

RANDOM INSERTS IN PACKS
STATED PRINT RUN 15 SER.#'d SETS
NO PRICING DUE TO SCARCITY
YELLOW RANDOMLY INSERTED
YELLOW PRINT RUN 5 SER.#'d SETS
NO YELLOW PRICING DUE TO SCARCITY

2007 Upper Deck Goudey Diamond Stars Autographs

RANDOM INSERTS IN PACKS
STATED PRINT RUN 1 SER.#'d SET
NO PRICING DUE TO SCARCITY

2007 Upper Deck Goudey Double Play

RANDOM INSERTS IN PACKS
STATED PRINT RUN 15 SER.#'d SETS
NO PRICING DUE TO SCARCITY

2007 Upper Deck Goudey Double Play Autographs

RANDOM INSERTS IN PACKS
STATED PRINT RUN 1 SER.#'d SET
NO PRICING DUE TO SCARCITY

2007 Upper Deck Goudey Goudey Graphs

STATED ODDS 1:24 HOB, 1:2500 RET
EXCH DEADLINE 8/7/2010
AC Alberto Callaspo 3.00 8.00
AH Aaron Harang 6.00 15.00
AK Al Kaline EXCH
AM Andy Marte 3.00 8.00
AR Aaron Rowand 6.00 15.00
BA Brian Anderson 3.00 8.00
BB Brian Bannister 6.00 15.00
BE Johnny Bench
BO Boof Bonser 6.00 15.00
BU B.J. Upton 6.00 15.00
CC Carl Crawford 3.00 8.00
CF Carlton Fisk
CL Cliff Lee 5.00 12.00
CO Coco Crisp 6.00 15.00
CR Cal Ripken Jr.
CY Chris Young 3.00 8.00
CZ Carlos Zambrano
DJ Derek Jeter EXCH 90.00 150.00
DO David Ortiz
FH Felix Hernandez 8.00 20.00
GA Garrett Atkins 5.00 12.00
GP Glen Perkins 3.00 8.00
HA Bill Hall 5.00 12.00
HI Rich Hill 3.00 8.00
HK Harmon Killebrew
HR Hanley Ramirez 8.00 20.00
IS Ian Snell
JB Jason Bay 8.00 20.00
JW Jered Weaver 6.00 15.00
JZ Joel Zumaya 6.00 15.00
KG Ken Griffey Jr.
KJ Kelly Johnson 3.00 8.00
KK Kevin Kouzmanoff 3.00 8.00
LS Luke Scott 3.00 8.00
MJ Mike Jacobs
MO Justin Morneau 8.00 20.00
MS Mike Schmidt
NR Nolan Ryan
RA Reggie Abercrombie 3.00 8.00
RT Ryan Theriot 10.00 25.00
RZ Ryan Zimmerman 15.00 40.00
SA Anibal Sanchez 3.00 8.00
SK Scott Kazmir 8.00 20.00
TB Taylor Buchholz 3.00 8.00
VM Victor Martinez 3.00 8.00
YB Yogi Berra

2007 Upper Deck Goudey Heads Up

CARDS 1-24 ODDS 1:10 HOB, 1:10 RET
CARDS 25-48 ODDS 1:10 HOB, 1:10 RET
241 Ken Griffey Jr. 3.00 8.00
242 Derek Jeter 5.00 12.00
243 Ichiro Suzuki 3.00 8.00
244 Cal Ripken Jr. 5.00 12.00
245 Daisuke Matsuzaka 4.00 10.00
246 Kei Igawa 2.50 6.00
247 Joe Mauer 2.00 5.00
248 Babe Ruth 4.00 10.00
249 Johnny Bench 2.50 6.00
250 Reggie Jackson 2.50 6.00
251 Carlton Fisk 2.50 6.00
252 Albert Pujols 4.00 10.00
253 Nolan Ryan 5.00 12.00
254 Ryan Howard 3.00 8.00
255 Mike Schmidt 3.00 8.00
256 Brooks Robinson 2.50 6.00
257 Harmon Killebrew 2.50 6.00
258 Alex Rodriguez 3.00 8.00
259 David Ortiz 2.50 6.00
260 David Wright 3.00 8.00
261 Al Kaline 2.50 6.00
262 Justin Verlander 2.50 6.00
263 Chase Utley 2.50 6.00
264 Justin Morneau 2.00 5.00
265 Ken Griffey Jr. 3.00 8.00
266 Derek Jeter 5.00 12.00
267 Ichiro Suzuki 3.00 8.00
268 Cal Ripken Jr. 5.00 12.00
269 Daisuke Matsuzaka 4.00 10.00
270 Kei Igawa 2.50 6.00
271 Joe Mauer 2.00 5.00
272 Babe Ruth 4.00 10.00
273 Johnny Bench 2.50 6.00
274 Reggie Jackson 2.50 6.00
275 Carlton Fisk 2.50 6.00
276 Albert Pujols 4.00 10.00
277 Nolan Ryan 5.00 12.00
278 Ryan Howard 3.00 8.00
279 Mike Schmidt 3.00 8.00
280 Brooks Robinson 2.50 6.00
281 Harmon Killebrew 2.50 6.00
282 Alex Rodriguez 3.00 8.00
283 David Ortiz 2.50 6.00
284 David Wright 3.00 8.00
285 Al Kaline 2.50 6.00
286 Justin Verlander 2.50 6.00
287 Chase Utley 2.50 6.00
288 Justin Morneau 2.00 5.00

2007 Upper Deck Goudey Immortals Memorabilia

STATED ODDS 1:288 HOB,1:960 RET
IAD Adam Dunn 5.00 12.00
IAJ Andruw Jones 6.00 15.00
IAK Al Kaline 8.00 20.00
IAP Albert Pujols 15.00 40.00
IAS Alfonso Soriano 5.00 12.00
IBR Babe Ruth 250.00 400.00
ICD Carlos Delgado 5.00 12.00
ICF Carlton Fisk 6.00 15.00
ICJ Chipper Jones 8.00 20.00
ICL Roger Clemens 12.50 30.00
ICR Cal Ripken Jr. 20.00 50.00
ICS Curt Schilling 6.00 15.00
IDJ Derek Jeter 20.00 50.00
IDO David Ortiz 8.00 20.00
IDW Dontrelle Willis 5.00 12.00
IGL Tom Glavine 6.00 15.00
IGM Greg Maddux 12.50 30.00
IGS Gary Sheffield 5.00 12.00
IHE Todd Helton 6.00 15.00
IHK Harmon Killebrew 12.50 30.00
IIR Ivan Rodriguez 6.00 15.00
IJB Johnny Bench 8.00 20.00
IJD Joe DiMaggio 50.00 100.00
IJE Jim Edmonds 6.00 15.00
IJG Jason Giambi 5.00 12.00
IJM Justin Morneau 5.00 12.00
IJO Randy Johnson 6.00 15.00
IJR Jose Reyes 6.00 15.00
IJS John Smoltz 6.00 15.00
IJT Jim Thome 6.00 15.00
IKG Ken Griffey Jr. 30.00 60.00
ILB Lance Berkman 5.00 12.00
IMP Mike Piazza 8.00 20.00
IMR Manny Ramirez 6.00 15.00
IMS Mike Schmidt 15.00 40.00
INR Nolan Ryan 20.00 50.00
IPM Pedro Martinez 6.00 15.00
IRJ Reggie Jackson 6.00 15.00
ISA Johan Santana 6.00 15.00
ITH Trevor Hoffman 5.00 12.00
IVG Vladimir Guerrero 6.00 15.00
IYB Yogi Berra 15.00 40.00

2007 Upper Deck Goudey Memorabilia

STATED ODDS 1:24 HOBBY, 1:24 RETAIL
1 A.J. Burnett 3.00 8.00
2 Aaron Boone 3.00 8.00
3 Aaron Rowand 3.00 8.00
4 Adam Dunn 3.00 8.00
5 Adrian Beltre 3.00 8.00
6 Albert Pujols 10.00 25.00
7 Ivan Rodriguez 4.00 10.00
8 Alfonso Soriano 4.00 10.00
9 Andruw Jones 3.00 8.00
10 Andy Pettitte 4.00 10.00
11 Aramis Ramirez 4.00 10.00
12 B.J. Upton 4.00 10.00
13 Barry Zito 3.00 8.00
14 Bartolo Colon 3.00 8.00
15 Ben Sheets 3.00 8.00
16 Bobby Abreu 4.00 10.00
17 Bobby Crosby 3.00 8.00
18 Brian Giles 3.00 8.00
19 Brian Roberts 3.00 8.00
20 C.C. Sabathia 4.00 10.00
21 Carlos Beltran 3.00 8.00
22 Carlos Delgado 3.00 8.00
23 Carlos Lee 3.00 8.00
24 Carlos Zambrano 3.00 8.00
26 Chad Tracy 3.00 8.00
27 Chipper Jones 4.00 10.00
28 Craig Biggio 4.00 10.00
29 Curt Schilling 3.00 8.00
31 Darin Erstad 3.00 8.00
32 David Ortiz 5.00 12.00
33 Billy Wagner 3.00 8.00
34 Derek Jeter 10.00 25.00
35 Derek Lee 3.00 8.00
36 Dontrelle Willis 3.00 8.00
37 Edgar Renteria 3.00 8.00
38 Eric Chavez 3.00 8.00
39 Felix Hernandez 3.00 8.00
40 Garret Anderson 3.00 8.00
41 Garrett Atkins 3.00 8.00
42 Gary Sheffield 3.00 8.00
43 Grady Sizemore 4.00 10.00
44 Greg Maddux 6.00 15.00
45 Hank Blalock 3.00 8.00
46 Hanley Ramirez 4.00 10.00
47 J.D. Drew 3.00 8.00
49 Jake Peavy 3.00 8.00
50 Jake Westbrook 3.00 8.00
51 Jason Bay 3.00 8.00
52 Jason Giambi 8.00 20.00
54 Jason Varitek 6.00 15.00
56 Jeff Francoeur 6.00 15.00
57 Jeff Kent 4.00 10.00
58 Jeremy Bonderman 3.00 8.00
59 Jim Edmonds 3.00 8.00
60 Jim Thome 4.00 10.00
61 Jimmy Rollins 4.00 10.00
62 Joe Mauer 4.00 10.00
63 Johan Santana 4.00 10.00
64 John Smoltz 4.00 10.00
66 Jose Reyes 5.00 12.00
67 Josh Beckett 3.00 8.00
68 Justin Morneau 3.00 8.00
69 Ken Griffey Jr. 8.00 20.00
70 Kerry Wood 3.00 8.00
71 Khalil Greene 5.00 12.00
72 Lance Berkman 3.00 8.00
73 Livan Hernandez 3.00 8.00
74 Manny Ramirez 4.00 10.00
75 Mark Mulder 3.00 8.00
76 Chase Utley 5.00 12.00
77 Mark Teixeira 4.00 10.00
78 Miguel Tejada 3.00 8.00
79 Miguel Cabrera 4.00 10.00
80 Mike Piazza 5.00 12.00
81 Pat Burrell 5.00 12.00
82 Paul LoDuca 3.00 8.00
83 Pedro Martinez 4.00 10.00
84 Prince Fielder 5.00 12.00
85 Rafael Furcal 3.00 8.00
86 Randy Johnson 4.00 10.00
87 Richie Sexson 3.00 8.00
88 Robinson Cano 5.00 12.00
89 Roy Halladay 3.00 8.00
90 Roy Oswalt 3.00 8.00
91 Scott Rolen 3.00 8.00
92 Tim Hudson 3.00 8.00
93 Todd Helton 4.00 10.00
94 Tom Glavine 4.00 10.00
95 Torii Hunter 3.00 8.00
96 Travis Hafner 3.00 8.00
97 Trevor Hoffman 3.00 8.00
98 Vernon Wells 3.00 8.00
99 Vladimir Guerrero 5.00 12.00
100 Zach Duke 3.00 8.00

2007 Upper Deck Goudey Sport Royalty *

ONE PER HOBBY BOX LOADER
AI Akinori Iwamura 5.00 12.00
AP Albert Pujols 5.00 12.00
AS Alfonso Soriano 4.00 10.00
CC Chris Carpenter 4.00 10.00
CR Cal Ripken Jr. 12.50 30.00
DJ Derek Jeter 10.00 25.00
DM Daisuke Matsuzaka 8.00 20.00
DO David Ortiz 4.00 10.00
DS Dean Smith 2.00 5.00
ES Emmitt Smith 4.00 10.00
GH Gordie Howe 12.50 30.00
GM Greg Maddux 3.00 8.00
HI Martina Hingis 3.00 8.00
HR Hanley Ramirez 3.00 8.00
JM Justin Morneau 2.00 5.00
JN Joe Namath 6.00 15.00
JV Justin Verlander 2.00 5.00
JW John Wooden 3.00 8.00
KB Kobe Bryant 6.00 15.00
KD Kevin Durant 5.00 12.00
KG Ken Griffey Jr. 5.00 12.00
KH Katie Hoff 3.00 8.00
KI Kei Igawa 3.00 8.00
LE Jeanette Lee 12.50 30.00
LJ LeBron James 15.00 40.00
LT LaDainian Tomlinson 3.00 8.00
MH Mia Hamm 10.00 25.00
MJ Michael Jordan 20.00 50.00
NR Nolan Ryan 15.00 40.00
PI Mike Piazza 5.00 12.00
PM Peyton Manning 5.00 12.00
RH Roy Halladay 2.00 5.00
RJ Randy Johnson 3.00 8.00
RL Ryan Lochte 4.00 10.00
SA Johan Santana 3.00 8.00
SC Sidney Crosby 12.50 30.00
TH Trevor Hoffman 3.00 8.00
TW Tiger Woods 100.00 175.00
VG Vladimir Guerrero 3.00 8.00

2007 Upper Deck Goudey Sport Royalty Autographs *

STATED ODDS TWO PER CASE
FOUND IN HOBBY BOX LOADER PACKS
EXCH DEADLINE 8/8/2009
AI Akinori Iwamura 20.00 50.00
AP Albert Pujols
CR Cal Ripken Jr. 300.00 400.00
DJ Derek Jeter EXCH 150.00 250.00
DM Daisuke Matsuzaka 200.00 300.00
DO David Ortiz EXCH 50.00 100.00
ES Emmitt Smith
GH Gordie Howe 50.00 100.00
HI Martina Hingis 100.00 200.00
HR Hanley Ramirez EXCH 10.00 25.00
JM Justin Morneau 10.00 25.00
JN Joe Namath
JV Justin Verlander 12.50 30.00
JW John Wooden 100.00 150.00
KD Kevin Durant 150.00 250.00
KG Ken Griffey Jr. EXCH 60.00 120.00
KH Katie Hoff 15.00 40.00
KI Kei Igawa 10.00 25.00
LE Jeanette Lee 60.00 120.00
LJ LeBron James 250.00 400.00
LT LaDainian Tomlinson EXCH 150.00 200.00
MH Mia Hamm 90.00 150.00
MJ Michael Jordan
NR Nolan Ryan
PM Peyton Manning EXCH
RH Roy Halladay 15.00 40.00
RJ Randy Johnson
RL Ryan Lochte 10.00 25.00
SC Sidney Crosby 175.00 300.00
TW Tiger Woods
VG Vladimir Guerrero EXCH 75.00 150.00

2008 Upper Deck Goudey

COMP.SET w/o HIGH #s (200) 20.00 50.00
COMMON CARD (1-200) .20 .50
COMMON ROOKIE (1-200) .30 .75
COMMON SP (201-230) 2.00 5.00
COMMON SP (231-250) 1.50 4.00
COMMON SP (251-270) 2.00 5.00
COMMON CARD (271-300) 2.00 5.00
COMMON CARD (301-330) 2.50 6.00
1 Eric Byrnes .20 .50
2 Randy Johnson .50 1.25
3 Brandon Webb .30 .75
4 Dan Haren .20 .50
5 Chris B. Young .20 .50
6 Max Scherzer RC .75 2.00
7 Mark Teixeira .30 .75
8 John Smoltz .50 1.25
9 Jeff Francoeur .30 .75
10 Phil Niekro .20 .50
11 Chipper Jones .60 1.50
12 Kelly Johnson .20 .50
13 Tom Glavine .30 .75
14 Yunel Escobar .20 .50
15 Erik Bedard .20 .50
16 Melvin Mora .20 .50
17 Brian Roberts .30 .75
18 Eddie Murray .50 1.25
19 Jim Palmer .20 .50
20 Jeremy Guthrie .20 .50
21 Nick Markakis .30 .75
22 David Ortiz .50 1.25
23 Manny Ramirez .50 1.25
24 Josh Beckett .30 .75
25 Dustin Pedroia .75 2.00
26 Bobby Doerr .20 .50

2008 Upper Deck Goudey

27 Clay Buchholz (RC) .75 2.00
28 Daisuke Matsuzaka .75 2.00
29 Jonathan Papelbon .30 .75
30 Kevin Youkilis .30 .75
31 Pee Wee Reese .30 .75
32 Billy Williams .20 .50
33 Alfonso Soriano .30 .75
34 Derrek Lee .30 .75
35 Rich Hill .20 .50
36 Kosuke Fukudome RC 1.25 3.00
37 Aramis Ramirez .20 .50
38 Carlos Zambrano .20 .50
39 Luis Aparicio .20 .50
40 Mark Buehrle .20 .50
41 Orlando Cabrera .20 .50
42 Paul Konerko .20 .50
43 Jermaine Dye .20 .50
44 Jim Thome .30 .75
45 Nick Swisher .20 .50
46 Sparky Anderson .20 .50
47 Johnny Bench .50 1.25
48 Joe Morgan .20 .50
49 Tony Perez .20 .50
50 Adam Dunn .20 .50
51 Aaron Harang .20 .50
52 Brandon Phillips .20 .50
53 Edwin Encarnacion .20 .50
54 Ken Griffey Jr. .75 2.00
55 Larry Doby .20 .50
56 Bob Feller .20 .50
57 C.C. Sabathia .20 .50
58 Travis Hafner .20 .50
59 Grady Sizemore .30 .75
60 Fausto Carmona .20 .50
61 Victor Martinez .20 .50
62 Brad Hawpe .20 .50
63 Todd Helton .30 .75
64 Garrett Atkins .20 .50
65 Troy Tulowitzki .20 .50
66 Matt Holliday .30 .75
67 Jeff Francis .20 .50
68 Justin Verlander .30 .75
69 Curtis Granderson .20 .50
70 Miguel Cabrera .30 .75
71 Gary Sheffield .20 .50
72 Magglio Ordonez .30 .75
73 Jack Morris .20 .50
74 Andrew Miller .30 .75
75 Clayton Kershaw RC 1.00 2.50
76 Dan Uggla .20 .50
77 Hanley Ramirez .50 1.25
78 Jeremy Hermida .20 .50
79 Josh Willingham .20 .50
80 Lance Berkman .30 .75
81 Roy Oswalt .20 .50
82 Miguel Tejada .20 .50
83 Hunter Pence .50 1.25
84 Carlos Lee .20 .50
85 J.R. Towles RC .75 2.00
86 Brian Bannister .20 .50
87 Luke Hochevar RC .75 2.00
88 Billy Butler .20 .50
89 Alex Gordon .50 1.25
90 Kelvim Escobar .20 .50
91 John Lackey .20 .50
92 Chone Figgins .20 .50
93 Jered Weaver .20 .50
94 Torii Hunter .20 .50
95 Vladimir Guerrero .50 1.25
96 Brad Penny .20 .50
97 James Loney .30 .75
98 Andruw Jones .20 .50
99 Chad Billingsley .20 .50
100 Chin-Lung Hu (RC) .50 1.25
101 Russell Martin .20 .50
102 Eddie Mathews .50 1.25
103 Warren Spahn .30 .75
104 Prince Fielder .50 1.25
105 Ryan Braun .60 1.50
106 J.J. Hardy .20 .50
107 Ben Sheets .30 .75
108 Corey Hart .20 .50
109 Yovani Gallardo .20 .50
110 Joe Mauer .30 .75
111 Delmon Young .30 .75
112 Johan Santana .30 .75
113 Glen Perkins .20 .50
114 Justin Morneau .30 .75
115 Carlos Beltran .20 .50
116 Jose Reyes .30 .75
117 David Wright .60 1.50
118 Pedro Martinez .30 .75
119 Tom Seaver .30 .75
120 Billy Wagner .20 .50
121 John Maine .20 .50
122 Alex Rodriguez .75 2.00
123 Chien-Ming Wang .60 1.50
124 Hideki Matsui .50 1.25
125 Jorge Posada .30 .75
126 Mariano Rivera .50 1.25
127 Phil Rizzuto .30 .75
128 Bucky Dent .20 .50
129 Derek Jeter 1.25 3.00
130 Graig Nettles .20 .50
131 Ian Kennedy RC .75 2.00
132 Don Larsen .20 .50
133 Joe Blanton .20 .50
134 Mark Ellis .20 .50
135 Dennis Eckersley .20 .50
136 Rollie Fingers .20 .50
137 Catfish Hunter .20 .50
138 Daric Barton (RC) .30 .75
139 Jack Cust .20 .50
140 Ryan Howard .60 1.50
141 Jimmy Rollins .30 .75
142 Chase Utley .50 1.25
143 Shane Victorino .20 .50
144 Cole Hamels .50 1.25
145 Richie Ashburn .30 .75
146 Jason Bay .20 .50
147 Freddy Sanchez .20 .50
148 Adam LaRoche .20 .50
149 Jack Wilson .20 .50
150 Ralph Kiner .30 .75
151 Bill Mazeroski .30 .75
152 Tom Gorzelanny .20 .50
153 Jay Bruce (RC) 1.25 3.00
154 Jake Peavy .30 .75
155 Chris Young .20 .50
156 Trevor Hoffman .20 .50
157 Khalil Greene .30 .75
158 Adrian Gonzalez .30 .75
159 Tim Lincecum .50 1.25
160 Matt Cain .20 .50
161 Aaron Rowand .20 .50
162 Orlando Cepeda .20 .50
163 Juan Marichal .20 .50
164 Noah Lowry .20 .50
165 Ichiro Suzuki .75 2.00
166 Felix Hernandez .30 .75
167 J.J. Putz .20 .50
168 Jose Vidro .20 .50
169 Raul Ibanez .20 .50
170 Wladimir Balentien .20 .50
171 Albert Pujols 1.00 2.50
172 Scott Rolen .30 .75
173 Lou Brock .30 .75
174 Chris Duncan .20 .50
175 Vince Coleman .20 .50
176 B.J. Upton .30 .75
177 Carl Crawford .30 .75
178 Carlos Pena .50 1.25
179 Scott Kazmir .30 .75
180 Akinori Iwamura .20 .50
181 James Shields .20 .50
182 Michael Young .20 .50
183 Jarrod Saltalamacchia .20 .50
184 Hank Blalock .20 .50
185 Ian Kinsler .30 .75
186 Josh Hamilton .60 1.50
187 Marlon Byrd .20 .50
188 David Murphy .20 .50
189 Vernon Wells .20 .50
190 Roy Halladay .30 .75
191 Frank Thomas .50 1.25
192 Alex Rios .20 .50
193 Troy Glaus .30 .75
194 David Eckstein .20 .50
195 Ryan Zimmerman .30 .75
196 Dmitri Young .20 .50
197 Austin Kearns .20 .50
198 Chad Cordero .20 .50
199 Ryan Church .20 .50
200 Evan Longoria RC 2.50 6.00
201 Brooks Robinson SP 2.00 5.00
202 Cal Ripken Jr. SP 5.00 12.00
203 Frank Robinson SP 2.00 5.00
204 Carl Yastrzemski SP 3.00 8.00
205 Carlton Fisk SP 2.00 5.00
206 Fred Lynn SP 2.00 5.00
207 Wade Boggs SP 2.50 6.00
208 Nolan Ryan SP 5.00 12.00
209 Ernie Banks SP 2.50 6.00
210 Ryne Sandberg SP 4.00 10.00
211 Al Kaline SP 2.50 6.00
212 Bo Jackson SP 2.50 6.00
213 Paul Molitor SP 2.50 6.00
214 Robin Yount SP 2.50 6.00
215 Harmon Killebrew SP 2.50 6.00
216 Rod Carew SP 2.00 5.00
217 Bobby Thomson SP 2.00 5.00
218 Gaylord Perry SP 2.00 5.00
219 Dave Winfield SP 2.00 5.00
220 Don Mattingly SP 3.00 8.00
221 Reggie Jackson SP 2.00 5.00
222 Roger Clemens SP 3.00 8.00
223 Whitey Ford SP 2.00 5.00
224 Mike Schmidt SP 3.00 8.00
225 Steve Carlton SP 2.00 5.00
226 Tony Gwynn SP 2.00 5.00
227 Willie McCovey SP 2.00 5.00
228 Bob Gibson SP 2.00 5.00
229 Ozzie Smith SP 3.00 8.00
230 Stan Musial SP 3.00 8.00
231 George Washington SP 2.00 5.00
232 Thomas Jefferson SP 2.00 5.00
233 James Madison SP 1.50 4.00
234 James Monroe SP 1.50 4.00
235 Andrew Jackson SP 1.50 4.00
236 John Tyler SP 1.50 4.00
237 Abraham Lincoln SP 2.00 5.00
238 Ulysses S. Grant SP 1.50 4.00
239 Grover Cleveland SP 1.50 4.00
240 Theodore Roosevelt SP 1.50 4.00
241 Calvin Coolidge SP 1.50 4.00
242 John Adams SP 1.50 4.00
243 Martin Van Buren SP 1.50 4.00
244 William McKinley SP 1.50 4.00
245 Woodrow Wilson SP 1.50 4.00
246 James K. Polk SP 1.50 4.00
247 Rutherford B. Hayes SP 1.50 4.00
248 William H. Taft SP 1.50 4.00
249 Andrew Johnson SP 1.50 4.00
250 James Buchanon SP 1.50 4.00
251 Albert Pujols 36 BW SP 3.00 8.00
252 Alex Rodriguez 36 BW SP 3.00 8.00
253 Alfonso Soriano 36 BW SP 2.50 6.00
254 C.C. Sabathia 36 BW SP 2.00 5.00
255 Chase Utley 36 BW SP 2.50 6.00
256 David Ortiz 36 BW SP 2.50 6.00
257 David Wright 36 BW SP 2.50 6.00
258 Derek Jeter 36 BW SP 4.00 10.00
259 Hanley Ramirez 36 BW SP 2.50 6.00
260 Ichiro Suzuki 36 BW SP 3.00 8.00
261 Jake Peavy 36 BW SP 2.50 6.00
262 Johan Santana 36 BW SP 2.50 6.00
263 Jose Reyes 36 BW SP 2.50 6.00
264 Ken Griffey Jr. 36 BW SP 3.00 8.00
265 Magglio Ordonez 36 BW SP 2.00 5.00
266 Matt Holliday 36 BW SP 2.50 6.00
267 Prince Fielder 36 BW SP 2.50 6.00
268 Ryan Braun 36 BW SP 2.50 6.00
269 Ryan Howard 36 BW SP 2.50 6.00
270 Vladimir Guerrero 36 BW SP 2.50 6.00
271 Carl Yastrzemski SR 2.50 6.00
272 Albert Pujols SR 3.00 8.00
273 Amy Van Dyken SR 2.00 5.00
274 Tom Seaver SR 2.00 5.00
275 Brett Favre SR 4.00 10.00
276 Bruce Jenner SR 2.00 5.00
277 Bill Russell SR 3.00 8.00
278 Barry Sanders SR 3.00 8.00
279 Cynthia Cooper SR 2.00 5.00
280 Mike Schmidt SR 2.50 6.00
281 Chipper Jones SR 2.50 6.00
282 Cal Ripken Jr. SR 4.00 10.00
283 Cael Sanderson SR 2.00 5.00
284 Dan Gable SR 2.00 5.00
285 Derek Jeter SR 4.00 10.00
286 Andre Dawson SR 2.00 5.00
287 Dan O'Brien SR 2.00 5.00
288 Julius Erving SR 2.50 6.00
289 Emmitt Smith SR 3.00 8.00
290 Janet Evans SR 2.00 5.00
291 Chase Utley SR 2.00 5.00
292 Gary Hall Jr. SR 2.00 5.00
293 Gordie Howe SR 3.00 8.00
294 Josh Beckett SR 2.00 5.00
295 John Elway SR 3.00 8.00
296 Julie Foudy SR 2.00 5.00
297 Jackie Joyner-Kersee SR 2.00 5.00
298 Jack Nicklaus SR 4.00 10.00
299 Magic Johnson SR 3.00 8.00
300 Michael Jordan SR 4.00 10.00
301 Bo Jackson SR 3.00 8.00
302 Tom Brady SR 5.00 12.00
303 Wade Boggs SR 3.00 8.00
304 Dan Marino SR 5.00 12.00
305 Dave Winfield SR 2.50 6.00
306 Jenny Thompson SR 2.50 6.00
307 Kobe Bryant SR 4.00 10.00
308 Kevin Durant SR 4.00 10.00
309 Ken Griffey Jr. SR 4.00 10.00
310 Kerri Strug SR 3.00 8.00
311 Kerri Walsh SR 3.00 8.00
312 Larry Bird SR 5.00 12.00
313 LeBron James SR 5.00 12.00
314 Matt Biondi SR 2.50 6.00
315 Mark Messier SR 3.00 8.00
316 Michael Johnson SR 2.50 6.00
317 Misty May-Treanor SR 3.00 8.00
318 Bob Gibson SR 2.50 6.00
319 Nolan Ryan SR 5.00 12.00
320 Ozzie Smith SR 4.00 10.00
321 Prince Fielder SR 3.00 8.00
322 Rulon Gardner SR 2.50 6.00
323 Reggie Jackson SR 3.00 8.00
324 Ernie Banks SR 4.00 10.00
325 Sidney Crosby SR 8.00 20.00
326 Sanya Richards SR 2.50 6.00
327 Terry Bradshaw SR 3.00 8.00
328 Tony Gwynn SR 3.00 8.00
329 Stan Musial SR 5.00 12.00
330 Tiger Woods SR 30.00 60.00

2008 Upper Deck Goudey Mini Black Backs

*BLACK 1-200: .75X TO 2X GRN 1-200
*BLACK RC 1-200: .75X TO 2X GRN RC 1-200
*BLACK SP 201-250: .75X TO 2X GRN 201-250
*BLACK SR 251-270: .5X TO 1.2X GRN 251-270
*BLACK SR 271-330: .5X TO 1.2X GRN 271-330
RANDOM INSERTS IN PACKS
STATED PRINT RUN 34 SER.#'d SETS
11 Chipper Jones 10.00 25.00
36 Kosuke Fukudome 20.00 50.00
100 Chin-Lung Hu 10.00 25.00
129 Derek Jeter 10.00 25.00
142 Chase Utley 6.00 15.00
186 Josh Hamilton 10.00 25.00
200 Evan Longoria 20.00 50.00
202 Cal Ripken Jr. 40.00 80.00
278 Barry Sanders SR 10.00 25.00
281 Chipper Jones SR 15.00 40.00
282 Cal Ripken Jr. SR 40.00 80.00
300 Michael Jordan SR 20.00 50.00
307 Kobe Bryant SR 6.00 15.00
330 Tiger Woods SR 250.00 350.00

2008 Upper Deck Goudey Mini Blue Backs

*BLUE 1-200: 1.5X TO 4X BASIC 1-200
*BLUE RC 1-200: 1X TO 2.5X BASIC RC 1-200
*BLUE 201-270: .6X TO 1.5X BASIC SP 201-270
*BLUE 271-330: .6X TO 1.5X BASIC SR 201-270
RANDOM INSERTS IN PACKS
298 Jack Nicklaus SR 15.00 40.00
330 Tiger Woods SR 40.00 80.00

2008 Upper Deck Goudey Mini Green Backs

RANDOM INSERTS IN PACKS
STATED PRINT RUN 88 SER.#'d SETS
1 Eric Byrnes 1.00 2.50
2 Randy Johnson 2.50 6.00
3 Brandon Webb 1.50 4.00
4 Dan Haren 1.00 2.50
5 Chris B. Young 1.00 2.50
6 Max Scherzer 2.50 6.00
7 Mark Teixeira 1.50 4.00
8 John Smoltz 2.50 6.00
9 Jeff Francoeur 1.50 4.00
10 Phil Niekro 1.00 2.50
11 Chipper Jones 6.00 15.00
12 Kelly Johnson 1.00 2.50
13 Tom Glavine 1.50 4.00
14 Yunel Escobar 1.00 2.50
15 Erik Bedard 1.00 2.50
16 Melvin Mora 1.00 2.50
17 Brian Roberts 1.50 4.00
18 Eddie Murray 2.50 6.00
19 Jim Palmer 1.00 2.50
20 Jeremy Guthrie 1.00 2.50
21 Nick Markakis 1.50 4.00
22 David Ortiz 2.50 6.00
23 Manny Ramirez 2.50 6.00
24 Josh Beckett 2.50 6.00
25 Dustin Pedroia 4.00 10.00
26 Bobby Doerr 1.00 2.50
27 Clay Buchholz 2.50 6.00
28 Daisuke Matsuzaka 4.00 10.00
29 Jonathan Papelbon 1.50 4.00
30 Kevin Youkilis 1.50 4.00
31 Pee Wee Reese 1.50 4.00
32 Billy Williams 1.00 2.50
33 Alfonso Soriano 1.50 4.00
34 Derrek Lee 1.50 4.00
35 Rich Hill 1.00 2.50
36 Kosuke Fukudome 10.00 25.00
37 Aramis Ramirez 1.00 2.50
38 Carlos Zambrano 1.00 2.50
39 Luis Aparicio 1.00 2.50
40 Mark Buehrle 1.00 2.50
41 Orlando Cabrera 1.00 2.50
42 Paul Konerko 1.00 2.50
43 Jermaine Dye 1.00 2.50
44 Jim Thome 1.50 4.00
45 Nick Swisher 1.00 2.50
46 Sparky Anderson 1.00 2.50
47 Johnny Bench 2.50 6.00
48 Joe Morgan 1.00 2.50
49 Tony Perez 1.00 2.50
50 Adam Dunn 1.00 2.50
51 Aaron Harang 1.00 2.50
52 Brandon Phillips 1.00 2.50
53 Edwin Encarnacion 1.00 2.50
54 Ken Griffey Jr. 4.00 10.00
55 Larry Doby 1.00 2.50
56 Bob Feller 1.00 2.50
57 C.C. Sabathia 1.00 2.50
58 Travis Hafner 1.00 2.50
59 Grady Sizemore 1.50 4.00
60 Fausto Carmona 1.00 2.50
61 Victor Martinez 1.00 2.50
62 Brad Hawpe 1.00 2.50
63 Todd Helton 1.50 4.00
64 Garrett Atkins 1.00 2.50
65 Troy Tulowitzki 1.50 4.00
66 Matt Holliday 1.50 4.00
67 Jeff Francis 1.00 2.50
68 Justin Verlander 1.50 4.00
69 Curtis Granderson 1.00 2.50
70 Miguel Cabrera 1.50 4.00
71 Gary Sheffield 1.00 2.50
72 Magglio Ordonez 1.50 4.00
73 Jack Morris 1.00 2.50
74 Andrew Miller 1.50 4.00
75 Clayton Kershaw 3.00 8.00
76 Dan Uggla 1.50 4.00
77 Hanley Ramirez 2.50 6.00
78 Jeremy Hermida 1.00 2.50
79 Josh Willingham 1.00 2.50
80 Lance Berkman 1.50 4.00
81 Roy Oswalt 1.00 2.50
82 Miguel Tejada 1.00 2.50
83 Hunter Pence 2.50 6.00
84 Carlos Lee 1.00 2.50
85 J.R. Towles 2.50 6.00
86 Brian Bannister 1.00 2.50
87 Luke Hochevar 2.50 6.00
88 Billy Butler 1.00 2.50
89 Alex Gordon 2.50 6.00
90 Kelvim Escobar 1.00 2.50
91 John Lackey 1.00 2.50
92 Chone Figgins 1.00 2.50
93 Jered Weaver 1.00 2.50
94 Torii Hunter 1.00 2.50
95 Vladimir Guerrero 2.50 6.00
96 Brad Penny 1.00 2.50
97 James Loney 1.50 4.00
98 Andruw Jones 1.00 2.50
99 Chad Billingsley 1.00 2.50
100 Chin-Lung Hu 1.50 4.00
101 Russell Martin 1.00 2.50
102 Eddie Mathews 2.50 6.00
103 Warren Spahn 1.50 4.00
104 Prince Fielder 2.50 6.00
105 Ryan Braun 3.00 8.00
106 J.J. Hardy 1.00 2.50
107 Ben Sheets 1.50 4.00
108 Corey Hart 1.00 2.50
109 Yovani Gallardo 1.00 2.50
110 Joe Mauer 1.50 4.00
111 Delmon Young 1.50 4.00
112 Johan Santana 1.50 4.00
113 Glen Perkins 1.00 2.50
114 Justin Morneau 1.50 4.00
115 Carlos Beltran 1.00 2.50
116 Jose Reyes 1.50 4.00
117 David Wright 3.00 8.00
118 Pedro Martinez 1.50 4.00
119 Tom Seaver 1.50 4.00
120 Billy Wagner 1.00 2.50
121 John Maine 1.00 2.50
122 Alex Rodriguez 4.00 10.00
123 Chien-Ming Wang 3.00 8.00
124 Hideki Matsui 2.50 6.00
125 Jorge Posada 1.50 4.00
126 Mariano Rivera 2.50 6.00
127 Phil Rizzuto 1.50 4.00
128 Bucky Dent 1.00 2.50
129 Derek Jeter 6.00 15.00
130 Graig Nettles 1.00 2.50
131 Ian Kennedy 2.50 6.00
132 Don Larsen 1.00 2.50
133 Joe Blanton 1.00 2.50
134 Mark Ellis 1.00 2.50
135 Dennis Eckersley 1.00 2.50
136 Rollie Fingers 1.00 2.50
137 Catfish Hunter 1.00 2.50
138 Daric Barton 1.00 2.50
139 Jack Cust 1.00 2.50
140 Ryan Howard 3.00 8.00
141 Jimmy Rollins 1.50 4.00
142 Chase Utley 2.50 6.00
143 Shane Victorino 1.00 2.50
144 Cole Hamels 2.50 6.00
145 Richie Ashburn 1.50 4.00
146 Jason Bay 1.00 2.50
147 Freddy Sanchez 1.00 2.50
148 Adam LaRoche 1.00 2.50
149 Jack Wilson 1.00 2.50
150 Ralph Kiner 1.50 4.00
151 Bill Mazeroski 1.50 4.00
152 Tom Gorzelanny 1.00 2.50
153 Jay Bruce 4.00 10.00
154 Jake Peavy 1.50 4.00
155 Chris Young 1.00 2.50
156 Trevor Hoffman 1.00 2.50
157 Khalil Greene 1.50 4.00
158 Adrian Gonzalez 1.50 4.00
159 Tim Lincecum 2.50 6.00
160 Matt Cain 1.00 2.50
161 Aaron Rowand 1.00 2.50
162 Orlando Cepeda 1.00 2.50
163 Juan Marichal 1.00 2.50
164 Noah Lowry 1.00 2.50
165 Ichiro Suzuki 4.00 10.00
166 Felix Hernandez 1.50 4.00
167 J.J. Putz 1.00 2.50
168 Jose Vidro 1.00 2.50
169 Raul Ibanez 1.00 2.50
170 Wladimir Balentien 1.00 2.50
171 Albert Pujols 5.00 12.00
172 Scott Rolen 1.50 4.00
173 Lou Brock 1.50 4.00
174 Chris Duncan 1.00 2.50
175 Vince Coleman 1.00 2.50
176 B.J. Upton 1.50 4.00
177 Carl Crawford 1.00 2.50
178 Carlos Pena 2.50 6.00
179 Scott Kazmir 1.50 4.00
180 Akinori Iwamura 1.00 2.50
181 James Shields 1.00 2.50
182 Michael Young 1.00 2.50
183 Jarrod Saltalamacchia 1.00 2.50
184 Hank Blalock 1.00 2.50
185 Ian Kinsler 1.50 4.00
186 Josh Hamilton 3.00 8.00
187 Marlon Byrd 1.00 2.50
188 David Murphy 1.00 2.50
189 Vernon Wells 1.00 2.50
190 Roy Halladay 1.00 2.50
191 Frank Thomas 2.50 6.00
192 Alex Rios 1.00 2.50
193 Troy Glaus 1.50 4.00
194 David Eckstein 1.00 2.50
195 Ryan Zimmerman 1.50 4.00
196 Dmitri Young 1.00 2.50
197 Austin Kearns 1.00 2.50
198 Chad Cordero 1.00 2.50
199 Ryan Church 1.00 2.50
200 Evan Longoria 10.00 25.00
201 Brooks Robinson 2.50 6.00
202 Cal Ripken Jr. 15.00 40.00
203 Frank Robinson 2.50 6.00
204 Carl Yastrzemski 4.00 10.00
205 Carlton Fisk 2.50 6.00
206 Fred Lynn 2.50 6.00
207 Wade Boggs 3.00 8.00
208 Nolan Ryan 10.00 25.00
209 Ernie Banks 3.00 8.00
210 Ryne Sandberg 5.00 12.00
211 Al Kaline 3.00 8.00
212 Bo Jackson 3.00 8.00
213 Paul Molitor 3.00 8.00
214 Robin Yount 3.00 8.00
215 Harmon Killebrew 3.00 8.00
216 Rod Carew 2.50 6.00
217 Bobby Thomson 2.50 6.00
218 Gaylord Perry 2.50 6.00
219 Dave Winfield 2.50 6.00
220 Don Mattingly 4.00 10.00
221 Reggie Jackson 2.50 6.00
222 Roger Clemens 4.00 10.00
223 Whitey Ford 2.50 6.00
224 Mike Schmidt 4.00 10.00
225 Steve Carlton 2.50 6.00
226 Tony Gwynn 2.50 6.00
227 Willie McCovey 2.50 6.00
228 Bob Gibson 2.50 6.00
229 Ozzie Smith 4.00 10.00
230 Stan Musial 4.00 10.00
231 George Washington 2.50 6.00
232 Thomas Jefferson 2.50 6.00
233 James Madison 2.00 5.00
234 James Monroe 2.00 5.00
235 Andrew Jackson 2.00 5.00
236 John Tyler 2.00 5.00
237 Abraham Lincoln 2.50 6.00
238 Ulysses S. Grant 2.00 5.00
239 Grover Cleveland 2.00 5.00
240 Theodore Roosevelt 2.00 5.00
241 Calvin Coolidge 2.00 5.00
242 John Adams 2.00 5.00
243 Martin Van Buren 2.00 5.00
244 William McKinley 2.00 5.00
245 Woodrow Wilson 2.00 5.00
246 James K. Polk 2.00 5.00
247 Rutherford B. Hayes 2.00 5.00
248 William H. Taft 2.00 5.00
249 Andrew Johnson 2.00 5.00
250 James Buchanon 2.00 5.00
251 Albert Pujols 36 BW 5.00 12.00
252 Alex Rodriguez 36 BW 4.00 10.00
253 Alfonso Soriano 36 BW 3.00 8.00
254 C.C. Sabathia 36 BW 2.50 6.00
255 Chase Utley 36 BW 3.00 8.00
256 David Ortiz 36 BW 3.00 8.00
257 David Wright 36 BW 3.00 8.00
258 Derek Jeter 36 BW 6.00 15.00
259 Hanley Ramirez 36 BW 3.00 8.00
260 Ichiro Suzuki 36 BW 4.00 10.00
261 Jake Peavy 36 BW 3.00 8.00
262 Johan Santana 36 BW 3.00 8.00
263 Jose Reyes 36 BW 3.00 8.00
264 Ken Griffey Jr. 36 BW 4.00 10.00
265 Magglio Ordonez 36 BW 3.00 8.00
266 Matt Holliday 36 BW 3.00 8.00
267 Prince Fielder 36 BW 3.00 8.00
268 Ryan Braun 36 BW 3.00 8.00
269 Ryan Howard 36 BW 3.00 8.00
270 Vladimir Guerrero 36 BW 3.00 8.00
271 Carl Yastrzemski SR 2.50 6.00
272 Albert Pujols SR 5.00 12.00
273 Amy Van Dyken SR 2.50 6.00
274 Tom Seaver SR 2.50 6.00
275 Brett Favre SR 5.00 12.00
276 Bruce Jenner SR 2.50 6.00
277 Bill Russell SR 4.00 10.00
278 Barry Sanders SR 4.00 10.00
279 Cynthia Cooper SR 3.00 8.00
280 Mike Schmidt SR 3.00 8.00
281 Chipper Jones SR 3.00 8.00
282 Cal Ripken Jr. SR 10.00 25.00
283 Cael Sanderson SR 2.50 6.00
284 Dan Gable SR 2.50 6.00
285 Derek Jeter SR 6.00 15.00
286 Andre Dawson SR 2.50 6.00
287 Dan O'Brien SR 2.50 6.00
288 Julius Erving SR 3.00 8.00
289 Emmitt Smith SR 4.00 10.00
290 Janet Evans SR 2.50 6.00
291 Chase Utley SR 2.50 6.00
292 Gary Hall Jr. SR 2.50 6.00
293 Gordie Howe SR 4.00 10.00
294 Josh Beckett SR 2.50 6.00
295 John Elway SR 6.00 15.00
296 Julie Foudy SR 2.50 6.00
297 Jackie Joyner-Kersee SR 2.50 6.00
298 Jack Nicklaus SR 12.50 30.00
299 Magic Johnson SR 4.00 10.00
300 Michael Jordan SR 12.50 30.00
301 Bo Jackson SR 3.00 8.00
302 Tom Brady SR 10.00 25.00
303 Wade Boggs SR 3.00 8.00
304 Dan Marino SR 5.00 12.00
305 Dave Winfield SR 2.50 6.00
306 Jenny Thompson SR 2.50 6.00
307 Kobe Bryant SR 4.00 10.00
308 Kevin Durant SR 4.00 10.00
309 Ken Griffey Jr. SR 4.00 10.00
310 Kerri Strug SR 3.00 8.00
311 Kerri Walsh SR 3.00 8.00
312 Larry Bird SR 5.00 12.00
313 LeBron James SR 10.00 25.00
314 Matt Biondi SR 2.50 6.00
315 Mark Messier SR 3.00 8.00
316 Michael Johnson SR 2.50 6.00
317 Misty May-Treanor SR 3.00 8.00
318 Bob Gibson SR 2.50 6.00
319 Nolan Ryan SR 8.00 20.00
320 Ozzie Smith SR 4.00 10.00
321 Prince Fielder SR 3.00 8.00
322 Rulon Gardner SR 2.50 6.00
323 Reggie Jackson SR 3.00 8.00
324 Ernie Banks SR 4.00 10.00
325 Sidney Crosby SR 8.00 20.00
326 Sanya Richards SR 2.50 6.00
327 Terry Bradshaw SR 3.00 8.00
328 Tony Gwynn SR 3.00 8.00
329 Stan Musial SR 5.00 12.00
330 Tiger Woods SR 75.00 150.00

2008 Upper Deck Goudey Mini Red Backs

*RED 1-200: 1X TO 2.5X BASIC 1-200
*RED RC 1-200: .75X TO 2X BASIC RC 1-200
*RED 201-270: .5X TO 1.2X BASIC SP 201-270
*RED 271-330: .5X TO 1.2X BASIC SR 271-330
RANDOM INSERTS IN PACKS
298 Jack Nicklaus SR 12.50 30.00
330 Tiger Woods SR 40.00 80.00

2008 Upper Deck Goudey Mini Taupe Backs

RANDOM INSERTS IN PACKS
STATED PRINT RUN 8 SER.#'d SETS
NO PRICING DUE TO SCARCITY

2008 Upper Deck Goudey Autographs

OVERALL AUTO ODDS 1:18 HOBBY
ASTERISK EQUALS PARTIAL EXCHANGE
EXCHANGE DEADLINE 7/17/2010
AH Aaron Harang 4.00 10.00
BB Billy Buckner 3.00 8.00
BD Bucky Dent 6.00 15.00
BP Brandon Phillips 6.00 15.00
BR Brooks Robinson 20.00 50.00
BT Bobby Thomson 12.50 30.00
BW Billy Wagner 8.00 20.00
CH Corey Hart 8.00 20.00
CJ Chipper Jones SP 60.00 120.00
CL Carlos Lee 8.00 20.00
DB Daric Barton 3.00 8.00
DE David Eckstein 6.00 15.00
DJ Derek Jeter EXCH * 90.00 150.00
DL Derrek Lee 10.00 25.00
DM Daisuke Matsuzaka SP EXCH 125.00 200.00
EE Edwin Encarnacion 4.00 10.00
FC Fausto Carmona 4.00 10.00
FL Fred Lynn SP 12.50 30.00
GN Graig Nettles 6.00 15.00
GO Tom Gorzelanny 4.00 10.00
GP Glen Perkins 3.00 8.00
HR Hanley Ramirez SP 30.00 60.00
HU Chin-Lung Hu SP 20.00 50.00
JB Johnny Bench SP 30.00 60.00
JC Jack Cust 3.00 8.00
JF Jeff Francis SP 12.50 30.00
JG Jeremy Guthrie 6.00 15.00
JH Jeremy Hermida 3.00 8.00
JO John Maine 4.00 10.00
JP Jonathan Papelbon 10.00 25.00
JT J.R. Towles 3.00 8.00
JW Josh Willingham 3.00 8.00
KG Ken Griffey Jr. SP 225.00 450.00
KJ Kelly Johnson 3.00 8.00
KY Kevin Youkilis SP 15.00 40.00
LA Don Larsen SP 15.00 40.00
MA Don Mattingly SP EXCH 60.00 120.00
MB Marlon Byrd 3.00 8.00
MO Jack Morris 6.00 15.00
MS Mike Schmidt SP 40.00 80.00
MU David Murphy 3.00 8.00
NL Noah Lowry 3.00 8.00
NM Nick Markakis 12.50 30.00
NS Nick Swisher 4.00 10.00
PM Paul Molitor 15.00 40.00
RM Russell Martin SP 20.00 50.00
SC Steve Carlton SP 40.00 80.00
SP Steve Pearce 4.00 10.00
TG Tom Glavine SP 20.00 50.00
VC Vince Coleman 6.00 15.00
WM Willie McCovey SP
YG Yovani Gallardo SP 4.00 10.00

2008 Upper Deck Goudey Cut Signatures

OVERALL AUTO ODDS 1:18 HOBBY
STATED PRINT RUN 1 SER.#'d SETS
NO PRICING DUE TO SCARCITY

2008 Upper Deck Goudey Hit Parade of Champions

RANDOM INSERTS IN PACKS

1 Albert Pujols	1.25	3.00
2 Don Mattingly	1.25	3.00
3 Ben Roethlisberger	.75	2.00
4 Bill Russell	1.25	3.00
5 Bobby Orr	2.50	6.00
6 Cal Ripken Jr.	2.50	6.00
7 Carl Yastrzemski	1.00	2.50
8 Derek Jeter	1.50	4.00
9 Emmitt Smith	1.25	3.00
10 Gordie Howe	1.50	4.00
11 Joe Montana	1.25	3.00
12 Joe Namath	.75	2.00
13 Ken Griffey Jr.	1.00	2.50
14 Kobe Bryant	2.50	6.00
15 LaDainian Tomlinson	.75	2.00
16 Larry Bird	2.00	5.00
17 LeBron James	3.00	8.00
18 Magic Johnson	1.25	3.00
19 Mario Lemieux	2.50	6.00
20 Yogi Berra	.60	1.50
21 Michael Jordan	4.00	10.00
22 Nolan Ryan	2.00	5.00
23 Patrick Roy	1.50	4.00
24 Peyton Manning	.75	2.00
25 Reggie Jackson	.40	1.00
26 Roger Clemens	.75	2.00
27 Roger Staubach	.75	2.00
28 Manny Ramirez	.60	1.50
29 Tom Brady	1.00	2.50
30 Wayne Gretzky	2.50	6.00

2008 Upper Deck Goudey Memorabilia

OVERALL GU ODDS 1:18 HOBBY

AD Adam Dunn	3.00	8.00
AG Adrian Gonzalez	3.00	8.00
AH Aaron Harang	3.00	8.00
AI Akinori Iwamura	3.00	8.00
AJ Andruw Jones	3.00	8.00
AP Albert Pujols	6.00	15.00
AR Aaron Rowand	3.00	8.00
AS Alfonso Soriano	4.00	10.00
BB Billy Butler	3.00	8.00
BD Bucky Dent	3.00	8.00
BE Josh Beckett	3.00	8.00
BR Brian Roberts	3.00	8.00
BU B.J. Upton	3.00	8.00
BW Brandon Webb	3.00	8.00
CC Carl Crawford	3.00	8.00
CH Cole Hamels	4.00	10.00
CJ Chipper Jones	5.00	12.00
CL Carlos Lee	3.00	8.00
CR Cal Ripken Jr.	20.00	50.00
CU Chase Utley	4.00	10.00
CY Chris Young	3.00	8.00
CZ Carlos Zambrano	3.00	8.00
DJ Derek Jeter	10.00	25.00
DL Derrek Lee	3.00	8.00
DM Daisuke Matsuzaka	6.00	15.00
DO David Ortiz	4.00	10.00
DU Dan Uggla	3.00	8.00
DY Delmon Young	3.00	8.00
FH Felix Hernandez	3.00	8.00
FS Freddy Sanchez	3.00	8.00
GA Garrett Atkins	3.00	8.00
GR Khalil Greene	3.00	8.00
GS Gary Sheffield	3.00	8.00
HO Trevor Hoffman	3.00	8.00
HP Hunter Pence	3.00	8.00
HR Hanley Ramirez	4.00	10.00
HU Catfish Hunter	5.00	12.00
JB Jason Bay	3.00	8.00
JD Jermaine Dye	3.00	8.00
JF Jeff Francoeur	3.00	8.00
JM Joe Mauer	3.00	8.00
JP Jake Peavy	3.00	8.00
JR Jimmy Rollins	3.00	8.00
JV Justin Verlander	3.00	8.00
JW Jered Weaver	3.00	8.00
KG Ken Griffey Jr.	6.00	15.00
KY Kevin Youkilis	4.00	10.00
LB Lance Berkman	3.00	8.00
MA John Maine	3.00	8.00
MB Mark Buehrle	3.00	8.00
MC Matt Cain	3.00	8.00
MH Matt Holliday	3.00	8.00
MI Miguel Cabrera	3.00	8.00
MO Justin Morneau	3.00	8.00
MR Manny Ramirez	4.00	10.00
MT Mark Teixeira	3.00	8.00
NM Nick Markakis	3.00	8.00
OR Magglio Ordonez	3.00	8.00
PA Jonathan Papelbon	4.00	10.00
PF Prince Fielder	4.00	10.00
PM Pedro Martinez	3.00	8.00
PO Jorge Posada	3.00	8.00
RA Aramis Ramirez	3.00	8.00
RE Jose Reyes	3.00	8.00
RH Roy Halladay	3.00	8.00
RI Mariano Rivera	3.00	8.00
RJ Randy Johnson	3.00	8.00
RM Russell Martin	3.00	8.00
RO Roy Oswalt	3.00	8.00
RZ Ryan Zimmerman	3.00	8.00
SI Grady Sizemore	3.00	8.00
SM John Smoltz	3.00	8.00
TE Miguel Tejada	3.00	8.00
TH Travis Hafner	3.00	8.00
VG Vladimir Guerrero	3.00	8.00
VM Victor Martinez	3.00	8.00
VW Vernon Wells	3.00	8.00
WI Jack Wilson	3.00	8.00
WS Warren Spahn	10.00	25.00
YG Yovani Gallardo	3.00	8.00

2008 Upper Deck Goudey Sport Royalty Autographs

OVERALL AUTO ODDS 1:18 HOBBY
ASTERISK EQUALS PARTIAL EXCHANGE
EXCHANGE DEADLINE 7/17/2010

AV Amy Van Dyken	12.50	30.00
BR Bill Russell SP		
BS Barry Sanders SP		
CC Cynthia Cooper	8.00	20.00
CR Cal Ripken Jr. SP		
CS Cael Sanderson	15.00	40.00
DJ Derek Jeter SP		
DM Dan Marino SP		
DO Dan O'Brien	8.00	20.00
ER Julius Erving SP		
EV Janet Evans	12.50	30.00
FO Julie Foudy	20.00	50.00
GH Gary Hall Jr.	8.00	20.00
HO Gordie Howe SP EXCH		
JB Josh Beckett SP		
JE Bruce Jenner	12.50	30.00
JJ Jackie Joyner-Kersee	10.00	25.00
JN Jack Nicklaus SP EXCH		
JT Jenny Thompson	10.00	25.00
KD Kevin Durant SP		
KG Ken Griffey Jr. SP	75.00	150.00
KS Kerri Strug	20.00	50.00
KW Kerri Walsh	20.00	50.00
LB Larry Bird SP		
LJ LeBron James SP		
MA Misty May-Treanor	50.00	100.00
MB Matt Biondi	10.00	25.00
MI Michael Jordan SP		
MJ Magic Johnson SP		
MM Mark Messier SP		
NR Nolan Ryan SP		
OS Ozzie Smith SP		
PD Phil Dalhausser	8.00	20.00
PF Prince Fielder SP EXCH		
RG Rulon Gardner	10.00	25.00
RJ Reggie Jackson SP		
SC Sidney Crosby SP		
SR Sanya Richards	8.00	20.00
TB Terry Bradshaw SP EXCH		
TG Tony Gwynn SP		
TR Todd Rogers	12.50	30.00
TW Tiger Woods SP		

2005 Upper Deck Hall of Fame

This 100-card set was released in July, 2005. The set was issued in four-card packs with an $150 which came packaged in their own tin. Those tins were issued 20 to a case. Cards number 1-85 feature regular cards of Hall of Famers while cards 86-100 are issued in the style of the Hall of Fame plaques. All cards 1-100 were issued to a stated print run of 550 serial numbered sets.

COMMON CARD (1-85)	1.50	4.00
COMMON CARD (86-100)	1.50	4.00

TWO BASIC AND/OR PARALLELS PER TIN
STATED PRINT RUN 550 SERIAL #'d SETS

1 Al Kaline	2.50	6.00
2 Al Lopez	1.50	4.00
3 Bill Mazeroski	2.00	5.00
4 Billy Williams	1.50	4.00
5 Bob Feller	1.50	4.00
6 Bob Gibson	2.00	5.00
7 Bob Lemon	1.50	4.00
8 Bobby Doerr	1.50	4.00
9 Brooks Robinson	2.00	5.00
10 Buck Leonard	1.50	4.00
11 Carl Yastrzemski	3.00	8.00
12 Carlton Fisk	1.50	4.00
13 Casey Stengel	2.00	5.00
14 Catfish Hunter	1.50	4.00
15 Dave Winfield	1.50	4.00
16 Dennis Eckersley	1.50	4.00
17 Dizzy Dean	2.00	5.00
18 Don Drysdale	2.00	5.00
19 Don Sutton	1.50	4.00
20 Duke Snider	2.00	5.00
21 Early Wynn	1.50	4.00
22 Eddie Mathews	2.50	6.00
23 Eddie Murray	2.50	6.00
24 Enos Slaughter	1.50	4.00
25 Ernie Banks	2.50	6.00
26 Fergie Jenkins	1.50	4.00
27 Frank Robinson	1.50	4.00
28 Gary Carter	1.50	4.00
29 Gaylord Perry	1.50	4.00
30 George Brett	4.00	10.00
31 George Kell	1.50	4.00
32 George Sisler	1.50	4.00
33 Hal Newhouser	1.50	4.00
34 Harmon Killebrew	2.50	6.00
35 Hoyt Wilhelm	1.50	4.00
36 Jackie Robinson	2.50	6.00
37 Jim Bunning	1.50	4.00
38 Jim Palmer	1.50	4.00
39 Jimmie Foxx	2.00	5.00
40 Joe Morgan	1.50	4.00
41 Johnny Bench	2.50	6.00
42 Johnny Mize	1.50	4.00
43 Juan Marichal	1.50	4.00
44 Kirby Puckett	2.50	6.00
45 Larry Doby	1.50	4.00
46 Lefty Grove	1.50	4.00
47 Lou Boudreau	1.50	4.00
48 Lou Brock	2.00	5.00
49 Luis Aparicio	1.50	4.00
50 Mel Ott	2.00	5.00
51 Mickey Cochrane	1.50	4.00
52 Monte Irvin	1.50	4.00
53 Orlando Cepeda	1.50	4.00
54 Ozzie Smith	3.00	8.00
55 Paul Molitor	1.50	4.00
56 Pee Wee Reese	2.00	5.00
57 Phil Niekro	1.50	4.00
58 Phil Rizzuto	2.00	5.00
59 Pie Traynor	1.50	4.00
60 Ralph Kiner	1.50	4.00
61 Red Schoendienst	1.50	4.00
62 Richie Ashburn	2.00	5.00
63 Rick Ferrell	1.50	4.00
64 Robin Roberts	1.50	4.00
65 Robin Yount	2.50	6.00
66 Rod Carew	2.00	5.00
67 Rogers Hornsby	2.00	5.00
68 Rollie Fingers	1.50	4.00
69 Roy Campanella	2.00	5.00
70 Steve Carlton	1.50	4.00
71 Tony Perez	1.50	4.00
72 Warren Spahn	2.00	5.00
73 Whitey Ford	2.00	5.00
74 Willie McCovey	2.00	5.00
75 Willie Stargell	2.00	5.00
76 Yogi Berra	2.50	6.00
77 Babe Ruth	5.00	12.00
78 Honus Wagner	2.50	6.00
79 Lou Gehrig	3.00	8.00
80 Mickey Mantle	8.00	20.00
81 Ty Cobb	3.00	8.00
82 Ryne Sandberg	4.00	10.00
83 Satchel Paige	2.50	6.00
84 Wade Boggs	2.00	5.00
85 Reggie Jackson	2.00	5.00
86 Babe Ruth PC	5.00	12.00
87 Christy Mathewson PC	2.00	5.00
88 Cy Young PC	2.00	5.00
89 Honus Wagner PC	2.50	6.00
90 Joe DiMaggio PC	3.00	8.00
91 Lou Gehrig PC	3.00	8.00
92 Mickey Mantle PC	8.00	20.00
93 Mike Schmidt PC	4.00	10.00
94 Nolan Ryan PC	4.00	10.00
95 Satchel Paige PC	2.50	6.00
96 Stan Musial PC	3.00	8.00
97 Ted Williams PC	3.00	8.00
98 Tom Seaver PC	2.00	5.00
99 Ty Cobb PC	3.00	8.00
100 Walter Johnson PC	2.00	5.00

2005 Upper Deck Hall of Fame Gold

*GOLD: 1X TO 2.5X BASIC
TWO BASIC AND/OR PARALLELS PER TIN
STATED PRINT RUN 25 SERIAL #'d SETS

77 Babe Ruth	15.00	40.00
80 Mickey Mantle	50.00	100.00
86 Babe Ruth PC	15.00	40.00
92 Mickey Mantle PC	50.00	100.00

2005 Upper Deck Hall of Fame Green

*GREEN: .6X TO 1.5X BASIC
TWO BASIC AND/OR PARALLELS PER TIN
STATED PRINT RUN 200 SERIAL #'d SETS

2005 Upper Deck Hall of Fame Rainbow

TWO BASIC AND/OR PARALLELS PER TIN
STATED PRINT RUN 1 SERIAL #'d SET
NO PRICING DUE TO SCARCITY

2005 Upper Deck Hall of Fame Silver

*SILVER: .75X TO 2X BASIC
TWO BASIC AND/OR PARALLELS PER TIN
STATED PRINT RUN 99 SERIAL #'d SETS

2005 Upper Deck Hall of Fame Class of Cooperstown

STATED PRINT RUN 50 SERIAL #'d SETS
GOLD PRINT RUN 5 SERIAL #'d SETS
NO GOLD PRICING DUE TO SCARCITY
RAINBOW PRINT RUN 1 SERIAL #'d SET
NO RAINBOW PRICING DUE TO SCARCITY
*SILVER: .6X TO 1.5X BASIC
SILVER PRINT RUN 15 SERIAL #'d SETS
OVERALL INSERT ODDS ONE PER TIN

AK1 Al Kaline Batting	3.00	8.00
AK2 Al Kaline Fielding	3.00	8.00
AK3 Al Kaline Portrait	3.00	8.00
BD1 Bobby Doerr Portrait	2.00	5.00
BD2 Bobby Doerr Fielding	2.00	5.00
BE1 Johnny Bench Batting	3.00	8.00
BE2 Johnny Bench Fielding	3.00	8.00
BF1 Bob Feller Pitching	2.00	5.00
BF2 Bob Feller Portrait	2.00	5.00
BG1 Bob Gibson Pitching	2.50	6.00
BG2 Bob Gibson Portrait	2.50	6.00
BM1 Bill Mazeroski	2.50	6.00
BR1 Brooks Robinson Batting	2.50	6.00
BR2 Brooks Robinson Fielding	2.50	6.00
BR3 Brooks Robinson Portrait	2.50	6.00
BW1 Billy Williams Batting	2.00	5.00
BW2 Billy Williams Fielding	2.00	5.00
BW3 Billy Williams Portrait	2.00	5.00
CF1 Carlton Fisk R.Sox	2.00	5.00
CF2 Carlton Fisk W.Sox	2.00	5.00
CY1 Carl Yastrzemski Batting	4.00	10.00
CY2 Carl Yastrzemski Fielding	4.00	10.00
DE1 Dennis Eckersley	2.00	5.00
DS1 Don Sutton	2.00	5.00
DW1 Dave Winfield Padres	2.00	5.00
DW2 Dave Winfield Yanks	2.00	5.00
EB1 Ernie Banks Batting	3.00	8.00
EB2 Ernie Banks Fielding	3.00	8.00
EM1 Eddie Murray	3.00	8.00
FJ1 Fergie Jenkins	2.00	5.00
FR1 Frank Robinson Reds	2.00	5.00
FR2 Frank Robinson O's	2.00	5.00
GB1 George Brett Batting	6.00	15.00
GB2 George Brett Fielding	6.00	15.00
GB3 George Brett Portrait	6.00	15.00
GC1 Gary Carter Mets	2.00	5.00
GC2 Gary Carter Expos	2.00	5.00
GK1 George Kell	2.00	5.00
GP1 Gaylord Perry Giants	2.00	5.00
GP2 Gaylord Perry Indians	2.00	5.00
HK1 Harmon Killebrew Senators Portrait	3.00	8.00
HK2 Harmon Killebrew Twins Batting	3.00	8.00
HK3 Harmon Killebrew Senators Running	3.00	8.00
HK4 Harmon Killebrew Twins Portrait	3.00	8.00
JB1 Jim Bunning Tigers	2.00	5.00
JB2 Jim Bunning Phils	2.00	5.00
JM1 Joe Morgan Astros	2.00	5.00
JM2 Joe Morgan Reds	2.00	5.00
JP1 Jim Palmer Pitching	2.00	5.00
JP2 Jim Palmer Portrait	2.00	5.00
KP1 Kirby Puckett	3.00	8.00
LA1 Luis Aparicio W.Sox	2.00	5.00
LA2 Luis Aparicio O's	2.00	5.00
LB1 Lou Brock	2.50	6.00
MA1 Juan Marichal Pitching	2.00	5.00
MA2 Juan Marichal Portrait	2.00	5.00
MI1 Monte Irvin Batting	2.00	5.00
MI2 Monte Irvin Fielding	2.00	5.00
MS1 Mike Schmidt Batting	6.00	15.00
MS2 Mike Schmidt Fielding	6.00	15.00
MS3 Mike Schmidt Portrait	6.00	15.00
NR1 Nolan Ryan Mets	6.00	15.00
NR2 Nolan Ryan Angels	6.00	15.00
NR3 Nolan Ryan Astros	6.00	15.00
NR4 Nolan Ryan Rgr	6.00	15.00
OC1 Orlando Cepeda	2.00	5.00
OS1 Ozzie Smith Padres	4.00	10.00
OS2 Ozzie Smith Cards	4.00	10.00
PM1 Paul Molitor Brew	2.00	5.00
PM2 Paul Molitor Jays	2.00	5.00
PM3 Paul Molitor Twins	2.00	5.00
PN1 Phil Niekro	2.00	5.00
RC1 Rod Carew Twins	2.50	6.00
RC2 Rod Carew Angels	2.50	6.00
RF1 Rollie Fingers	2.00	5.00
RJ1 Reggie Jackson A's	2.50	6.00
RJ2 Reggie Jackson Yanks	2.50	6.00
RJ3 Reggie Jackson Angels	2.50	6.00
RK1 Ralph Kiner Batting	2.00	5.00
RK2 Ralph Kiner Portrait	2.00	5.00
RR1 Robin Roberts	2.00	5.00
RS1 Red Schoendienst	2.00	5.00
RY1 Robin Yount Batting	3.00	8.00
RY2 Robin Yount Fielding	3.00	8.00
SC1 Steve Carlton Cards Pitching	2.00	5.00
SC2 Steve Carlton Phils Pitching	2.00	5.00
SC3 Steve Carlton Cards Portrait	2.00	5.00
SC4 Steve Carlton Phils Portrait	2.00	5.00
SM1 Stan Musial Batting	4.00	10.00
SM2 Stan Musial Portrait	4.00	10.00
SN1 Duke Snider	2.50	6.00
TP1 Tony Perez	2.00	5.00
TS1 Tom Seaver Mets	2.50	6.00
TS2 Tom Seaver Reds	2.50	6.00
WF1 Whitey Ford Pitching	2.50	6.00
WF2 Whitey Ford Portrait	2.50	6.00
WM1 Willie McCovey Batting	2.50	6.00
WM2 Willie McCovey Portrait	2.50	6.00
YB1 Yogi Berra Batting	3.00	8.00
YB2 Yogi Berra Fielding	3.00	8.00

2005 Upper Deck Hall of Fame Class of Cooperstown Autograph

STATED PRINT RUN 25 SERIAL #'d SETS
GOLD PRINT RUN 5 SERIAL #'d SETS
NO GOLD PRICING DUE TO SCARCITY
RAINBOW PRINT RUN 1 SERIAL #'d SET
NO RAINBOW PRICING DUE TO SCARCITY
*SILVER: .5X TO 1.2X BASIC
SILVER PRINT RUN 15 SERIAL #'d SETS
MATERIAL GOLD PRINT RUN 5 #'d SETS
NO MAT.GOLD PRICING DUE TO SCARCITY
MATERIAL RAINBOW PRINT RUN 1 #'d SET
NO MAT.RB PRICING DUE TO SCARCITY
*MAT.SILVER: .5X TO 1.2X BASIC
MATERIAL SILVER PRINT RUN 15 #'d SETS
PATCH GOLD PRINT RUN 5 #'d SETS
SM2 MUSIAL PATCH GOLD QTY 3 #'d CARDS
NO PATCH GOLD PRICING AVAILABLE
PATCH RAINBOW PRINT RUN 1 #'d SET
NO PATCH RAINBOW PRICING AVAILABLE
PATCH SILVER PRINT RUN 10 #'d SETS
NO PATCH SILVER PRICING AVAILABLE
OVERALL AUTO ODDS ONE PER TIN

AK1 Al Kaline Batting	30.00	60.00
AK2 Al Kaline Fielding	30.00	60.00
AK3 Al Kaline Portrait	30.00	60.00
BD1 Bobby Doerr Portrait	8.00	20.00
BD2 Bobby Doerr Fielding	8.00	20.00
BE1 Johnny Bench Batting	20.00	50.00
BE2 Johnny Bench Fielding	20.00	50.00
BF1 Bob Feller Pitching	10.00	25.00
BF2 Bob Feller Portrait	10.00	25.00
BG1 Bob Gibson Pitching	15.00	40.00
BG2 Bob Gibson Portrait	15.00	40.00
BM1 Bill Mazeroski	20.00	50.00
BR1 Brooks Robinson Batting	15.00	40.00
BR2 Brooks Robinson Fielding	15.00	40.00
BR3 Brooks Robinson Portrait	15.00	40.00
BW1 Billy Williams Batting	10.00	25.00
BW2 Billy Williams Fielding	10.00	25.00
BW3 Billy Williams Portrait	10.00	25.00
CF1 Carlton Fisk R.Sox	10.00	25.00
CF2 Carlton Fisk W.Sox	10.00	25.00
CY1 Carl Yastrzemski Batting	30.00	60.00
CY2 Carl Yastrzemski Fielding	30.00	60.00
DE1 Dennis Eckersley	10.00	25.00
DS1 Don Sutton	8.00	20.00
DW1 Dave Winfield Padres	15.00	40.00
DW2 Dave Winfield Yanks	15.00	40.00
EB1 Ernie Banks Batting	30.00	60.00
EB2 Ernie Banks Fielding	30.00	60.00
EM1 Eddie Murray	30.00	60.00
FJ1 Fergie Jenkins	8.00	20.00
FR1 Frank Robinson Reds	10.00	25.00
FR2 Frank Robinson O's	10.00	25.00
GB1 George Brett Batting	40.00	80.00
GB2 George Brett Fielding	40.00	80.00
GB3 George Brett Portrait	40.00	80.00
GC1 Gary Carter Mets	10.00	25.00
GC2 Gary Carter Expos	10.00	25.00
GK1 George Kell	10.00	25.00
GP1 Gaylord Perry Giants	8.00	20.00
GP2 Gaylord Perry Indians	8.00	20.00
HK1 Harmon Killebrew Senators Portrait	20.00	50.00
HK2 Harmon Killebrew Twins Batting	20.00	50.00
HK3 Harmon Killebrew Senators Running	20.00	50.00
HK4 Harmon Killebrew Twins Portrait	20.00	50.00
JB1 Jim Bunning Tigers	10.00	25.00
JB2 Jim Bunning Phils	10.00	25.00
JM1 Joe Morgan Astros	10.00	25.00
JM2 Joe Morgan Reds	10.00	25.00
JP1 Jim Palmer Pitching	10.00	25.00
JP2 Jim Palmer Portrait	10.00	25.00
KP1 Kirby Puckett	50.00	100.00
LA1 Luis Aparicio W.Sox	10.00	25.00
LA2 Luis Aparicio O's	10.00	25.00
LB1 Lou Brock	15.00	40.00
MA1 Juan Marichal Pitching	10.00	25.00
MA2 Juan Marichal Portrait	10.00	25.00
MI1 Monte Irvin Batting	10.00	25.00
MI2 Monte Irvin Fielding	10.00	25.00
MS1 Mike Schmidt Batting	30.00	60.00
MS2 Mike Schmidt Fielding	30.00	60.00
MS3 Mike Schmidt Portrait	30.00	60.00
NR1 Nolan Ryan Mets	50.00	100.00
NR2 Nolan Ryan Angels	50.00	100.00
NR3 Nolan Ryan Astros	50.00	100.00
NR4 Nolan Ryan Rgr	50.00	100.00
OC1 Orlando Cepeda	10.00	25.00
OS1 Ozzie Smith Padres	20.00	50.00
OS2 Ozzie Smith Cards	20.00	50.00
PM1 Paul Molitor Brew	10.00	25.00
PM2 Paul Molitor Jays	10.00	25.00
PM3 Paul Molitor Twins	10.00	25.00
PN1 Phil Niekro	10.00	25.00
RC1 Rod Carew Twins	15.00	40.00
RC2 Rod Carew Angels	15.00	40.00
RF1 Rollie Fingers	8.00	20.00
RJ1 Reggie Jackson A's	20.00	50.00
RJ2 Reggie Jackson Yanks	20.00	50.00
RJ3 Reggie Jackson Angels	20.00	50.00
RK1 Ralph Kiner Batting	20.00	50.00
RK2 Ralph Kiner Portrait	20.00	50.00
RR1 Robin Roberts	10.00	25.00
RS1 Red Schoendienst	10.00	25.00
RY1 Robin Yount Batting	20.00	50.00
RY2 Robin Yount Fielding	20.00	50.00
SC1 Steve Carlton Cards Pitching	10.00	25.00
SC2 Steve Carlton Phils Pitching	10.00	25.00
SC3 Steve Carlton Cards Portrait	10.00	25.00
SC4 Steve Carlton Phils Portrait	10.00	25.00
SM1 Stan Musial Batting	40.00	80.00
SM2 Stan Musial Portrait	40.00	80.00
SN1 Duke Snider	15.00	40.00
TP1 Tony Perez	15.00	40.00
TS1 Tom Seaver Mets	20.00	50.00
TS2 Tom Seaver Reds	20.00	50.00
WF1 Whitey Ford Pitching	15.00	40.00
WF2 Whitey Ford Portrait	15.00	40.00
WM1 Willie McCovey Batting	15.00	40.00
WM2 Willie McCovey Portrait	15.00	40.00
YB1 Yogi Berra Batting	30.00	60.00
YB2 Yogi Berra Fielding	30.00	60.00

2005 Upper Deck Hall of Fame Cooperstown Calling

STATED PRINT RUN 50 SERIAL #'d SETS
GOLD PRINT RUN 5 SERIAL #'d SETS
NO GOLD PRICING DUE TO SCARCITY
*GREEN: .5X TO 1.2X BASIC
GREEN PRINT RUN 25 SERIAL #'d SETS
RAINBOW PRINT RUN 1 SERIAL #'d SET
NO RAINBOW PRICING DUE TO SCARCITY
*SILVER: .6X TO 1.5X BASIC
SILVER PRINT RUN 15 SERIAL #'d SETS
OVERALL INSERT ODDS ONE PER TIN

AK1 Al Kaline Batting	3.00	8.00
AK2 Al Kaline Fielding	3.00	8.00
BD1 Bobby Doerr Batting	2.00	5.00
BD2 Bobby Doerr Fielding	2.00	5.00
BE1 Johnny Bench	3.00	8.00
BF1 Bob Feller Pitching	2.00	5.00
BF2 Bob Feller Portrait	2.00	5.00
BG1 Bob Gibson	2.50	6.00
BM1 Bill Mazeroski	2.50	6.00
BR1 Brooks Robinson Batting	2.50	6.00
BR2 Brooks Robinson Fielding	2.50	6.00
BR3 Brooks Robinson Portrait	2.50	6.00
BW1 Billy Williams Cubs	2.00	5.00
BW2 Billy Williams A's	2.00	5.00
CF1 Carlton Fisk W.Sox	2.00	5.00
CF2 Carlton Fisk R.Sox	2.00	5.00
CY1 Carl Yastrzemski Sleeves	4.00	10.00
CY2 C.Yastrzemski No Sleeves	4.00	10.00
DE1 Dennis Eckersley Sox	2.00	5.00
DE2 Dennis Eckersley A's	2.00	5.00
DS1 Don Sutton Dgr	2.00	5.00
DS2 Don Sutton Angels	2.00	5.00
DS3 Don Sutton Astros	2.00	5.00
DW1 Dave Winfield	2.00	5.00
EB1 Ernie Banks	3.00	8.00
EM1 Eddie Murray O's	3.00	8.00
EM2 Eddie Murray Dgr	3.00	8.00
FJ1 Fergie Jenkins Cubs	2.00	5.00
FJ2 Fergie Jenkins Rgr	2.00	5.00
FR1 Frank Robinson	2.00	5.00
GB1 George Brett Glove Up	6.00	15.00
GB2 George Brett Glove Down	6.00	15.00
GC1 Gary Carter Expos	2.00	5.00
GC2 Gary Carter Mets	2.00	5.00
GC3 Gary Carter Dgr	2.00	5.00
GK1 George Kell	2.00	5.00
GP1 Gaylord Perry Indians	2.00	5.00
GP2 Gaylord Perry Padres	2.00	5.00
HK1 H.Killebrew Senators	3.00	8.00
HK2 Harmon Killebrew Twins	3.00	8.00
JB1 Jim Bunning	2.00	5.00
JM1 Juan Marichal	2.00	5.00
JP1 Jim Palmer Pitching	2.00	5.00
JP2 Jim Palmer Portrait	2.00	5.00
KP1 Kirby Puckett	3.00	8.00
KP2 Kirby Puckett	3.00	8.00
LA1 Luis Aparicio W.Sox	2.00	5.00
LA2 Luis Aparicio O's	2.00	5.00
LB1 Lou Brock Cubs	2.50	6.00
LB2 Lou Brock Cards	2.50	6.00
MI1 Monte Irvin	2.00	5.00
MO1 Joe Morgan Astros	2.00	5.00
MO2 Joe Morgan Reds	2.00	5.00
MS1 Mike Schmidt Batting	6.00	15.00
MS2 Mike Schmidt Fielding	6.00	15.00
MS3 Mike Schmidt Portrait	6.00	15.00
NR1 Nolan Ryan Angels	6.00	15.00
NR2 Nolan Ryan Rgr	6.00	15.00
NR3 Nolan Ryan Mets	6.00	15.00
NR4 Nolan Ryan Astros	6.00	15.00
OC1 Orlando Cepeda Giants	2.00	5.00
OC2 Orlando Cepeda Braves	2.00	5.00
OS1 Ozzie Smith Padres	4.00	10.00
OS2 Ozzie Smith Cards	4.00	10.00
OS3 Ozzie Smith Cards	4.00	10.00
PM1 Paul Molitor Brew	2.00	5.00
PM2 Paul Molitor Jays	2.00	5.00
PM3 Paul Molitor Twins	2.00	5.00
PN1 Phil Niekro Braves	2.00	5.00
PN2 Phil Niekro Yanks	2.00	5.00
RC1 Rod Carew Twins	2.50	6.00
RC2 Rod Carew Angels	2.50	6.00
RF1 Rollie Fingers A's	2.00	5.00
RF2 Rollie Fingers Padres	2.00	5.00
RJ1 Reggie Jackson A's	2.50	6.00

RJ2 Reggie Jackson Yanks 2.50 6.00
RJ3 Reggie Jackson Angels 2.50 6.00
RK1 Ralph Kiner 2.00 5.00
RR1 Robin Roberts 2.00 5.00
RS1 Red Schoendienst 2.00 5.00
RY1 Robin Yount Batting 3.00 8.00
RY2 Robin Yount Fielding 3.00 8.00
RY3 Robin Yount Portrait 3.00 8.00
SA1 Ryne Sandberg Batting 6.00 15.00
SA2 Ryne Sandberg Fielding 6.00 15.00
SA3 Ryne Sandberg Portrait 6.00 15.00
SC1 Steve Carlton Cards 2.00 5.00
SC2 Steve Carlton Phils 2.00 5.00
SM1 Stan Musial B/W 4.00 10.00
SM2 Stan Musial Color 4.00 10.00
SN1 Duke Snider 2.50 6.00
TP1 Tony Perez Reds 2.00 5.00
TP2 Tony Perez Sox 2.00 5.00
TS1 Tom Seaver 2.50 6.00
WB1 Wade Boggs Sox 2.50 6.00
WB2 Wade Boggs Yanks 2.50 6.00
WB3 Wade Boggs Rays 2.50 6.00
WF1 Whitey Ford 2.50 6.00
WM1 Willie McCovey 2.50 6.00
YB1 Yogi Berra 3.00 8.00

2005 Upper Deck Hall of Fame Cooperstown Calling Autograph

STATED PRINT RUN 25 SERIAL #'d SETS
GOLD PRINT RUN 5 SERIAL #'d SETS
NO GOLD PRICING DUE TO SCARCITY
RAINBOW PRINT RUN 1 SERIAL #'d SET
NO RAINBOW PRICING DUE TO SCARCITY
*SILVER: .5X TO 1.2X BASIC
SILVER PRINT RUN 15 SERIAL #'d SETS
MATERIAL GOLD PRINT RUN 5 #'d SETS
NO MAT.GOLD PRICING DUE TO SCARCITY
MATERIAL RAINBOW PRINT RUN 1 #'d SET
NO MAT.RB PRICING DUE TO SCARCITY
*MAT.SILVER: .5X TO 1.2X BASIC
MATERIAL SILVER PRINT RUN 15 #'d SETS
PATCH GOLD PRINT RUN 5 #'d SETS
NO PATCH GOLD PRICING AVAILABLE
PATCH RAINBOW PRINT RUN 1 #'d SET
NO PATCH RAINBOW PRICING AVAILABLE
PATCH SILVER PRINT RUN 10 #'d SETS
NO PATCH SILVER PRICING AVAILABLE
OVERALL AUTO ODDS ONE PER TIN
EXCHANGE DEADLINE 07/18/08
AK1 Al Kaline Batting 30.00 60.00
AK2 Al Kaline Fielding 30.00 60.00
BD1 Bobby Doerr Batting 8.00 20.00
BD2 Bobby Doerr Fielding 8.00 20.00
BE1 Johnny Bench 20.00 50.00
BF1 Bob Feller Pitching 10.00 25.00
BF2 Bob Feller Portrait 10.00 25.00
BG1 Bob Gibson 15.00 40.00
BM1 Bill Mazeroski 20.00 50.00
BR1 Brooks Robinson Batting 15.00 40.00
BR2 Brooks Robinson Fielding 15.00 40.00
BR3 Brooks Robinson Portrait 15.00 40.00
BW1 Billy Williams Cubs 10.00 25.00
BW2 Billy Williams A's 10.00 25.00
CF1 Carlton Fisk W.Sox 10.00 25.00
CF2 Carlton Fisk R.Sox 10.00 25.00
CY1 C.Yaz Sleeves EXCH 30.00 60.00
CY2 C.Yaz No Sleeves 30.00 60.00
DE1 Dennis Eckersley Sox 10.00 25.00
DE2 Dennis Eckersley A's 10.00 25.00
DS1 Don Sutton Dgr 8.00 20.00
DS2 Don Sutton Angels 8.00 20.00
DS3 Don Sutton Astros 8.00 20.00
DW1 Dave Winfield 15.00 40.00
EB1 Ernie Banks 30.00 60.00
EM1 Eddie Murray O's 30.00 60.00
EM2 Eddie Murray Dgr 30.00 60.00
FJ1 Fergie Jenkins Cubs 8.00 20.00
FJ2 Fergie Jenkins Rgr 8.00 20.00
FR1 Frank Robinson 10.00 25.00
GB1 George Brett Glove Up 40.00 80.00
GB2 George Brett Glove Down 40.00 80.00
GC1 Gary Carter Expos 10.00 25.00
GC2 Gary Carter Mets 10.00 25.00
GC3 Gary Carter Dgr 10.00 25.00
GK1 George Kell EXCH 10.00 25.00
GP1 Gaylord Perry Indians 8.00 20.00
GP2 Gaylord Perry Padres 8.00 20.00
HK1 H.Kill Senators EXCH 20.00 50.00
HK2 Harmon Killebrew Twins 20.00 50.00
JB1 Jim Bunning 10.00 25.00
JM1 Juan Marichal 10.00 25.00
JP1 Jim Palmer Pitching 10.00 25.00
JP2 Jim Palmer Portrait 10.00 25.00
KP1 Kirby Puckett 50.00 100.00
KP2 Kirby Puckett 50.00 100.00
LA1 Luis Aparicio W.Sox 10.00 25.00
LA2 Luis Aparicio O's 10.00 25.00
LB1 Lou Brock Cubs 15.00 40.00
LB2 Lou Brock Cards 15.00 40.00
MI1 Monte Irvin EXCH 10.00 25.00
MO1 Joe Morgan Astros 10.00 25.00
MO2 Joe Morgan Reds 10.00 25.00
MS1 Mike Schmidt Batting 30.00 60.00
MS2 Mike Schmidt Fielding 30.00 60.00
MS3 Mike Schmidt Portrait 30.00 60.00
NR1 Nolan Ryan Angels 50.00 100.00
NR2 Nolan Ryan Rgr 50.00 100.00
NR3 Nolan Ryan Mets 50.00 100.00
NR4 Nolan Ryan Astros 50.00 100.00
OC1 O.Cepeda Giants EXCH 10.00 25.00
OC2 O.Cepeda Braves EXCH 10.00 25.00
OS1 Ozzie Smith Padres 20.00 50.00
OS2 Ozzie Smith Cards 20.00 50.00
OS3 Ozzie Smith Cards 20.00 50.00
PM1 Paul Molitor Brew 10.00 25.00
PM2 Paul Molitor Jays 10.00 25.00
PM3 Paul Molitor Twins 10.00 25.00
PN1 Phil Niekro Braves 10.00 25.00
PN2 Phil Niekro Yanks 10.00 25.00
RC1 Rod Carew Twins 15.00 40.00
RC2 Rod Carew Angels EXCH 15.00 40.00
RF1 Rollie Fingers A's 8.00 20.00
RF2 Rollie Fingers Padres 8.00 20.00
RJ1 Reggie Jackson A's 20.00 50.00
RJ2 Reggie Jackson Yanks 20.00 50.00
RJ3 Reggie Jackson Angels 20.00 50.00
RK1 Ralph Kiner 20.00 50.00
RR1 Robin Roberts 10.00 25.00
RS1 Red Schoendienst 10.00 25.00
RY1 Robin Yount Batting 20.00 50.00
RY2 Robin Yount Fielding 20.00 50.00
RY3 Robin Yount Portrait 20.00 50.00
SA1 Ryne Sandberg Batting 40.00 80.00
SA2 Ryne Sandberg Fielding 40.00 80.00
SA3 Ryne Sandberg Portrait 40.00 80.00
SC1 Steve Carlton Cards 10.00 25.00
SC2 Steve Carlton Phils 10.00 25.00
SM1 Stan Musial B/W 40.00 80.00
SM2 Stan Musial Color 40.00 80.00
SN1 Duke Snider 15.00 40.00
TP1 Tony Perez Reds 15.00 40.00
TP2 Tony Perez Sox 15.00 40.00
TS1 Tom Seaver 20.00 50.00
WB1 Wade Boggs Sox 15.00 40.00
WB2 Wade Boggs Yanks 15.00 40.00
WB3 Wade Boggs Rays 15.00 40.00
WF1 Whitey Ford 15.00 40.00
WM1 Willie McCovey EXCH 15.00 40.00
YB1 Yogi Berra 30.00 60.00

2005 Upper Deck Hall of Fame Cooperstown Cuts

OVERALL GAME-USED/CUT SIG ODDS 1:20
PRINT RUNS B/WN 1-20 COPIES PER
NO PRICING DUE TO SCARCITY
CM Christy Mathewson/1
CY Cy Young/1
DD Dizzy Dean/10
GR Lefty Grove/10
GS George Sisler/1
HW1 Honus Wagner/1
JM Johnny Mize/20
MC Mickey Cochrane/9
PT Pie Traynor/10
RH Rogers Hornsby/1
WJ Walter Johnson/1

2005 Upper Deck Hall of Fame Cooperstown Cuts Memorabilia

OVERALL GAME-USED/CUT-SIG ODDS 1:20
PRINT RUNS B/WN 1-20 COPIES PER
NO PRICING DUE TO SCARCITY
BR Babe Ruth Bat/1
CS Casey Stengel Jsy/7
DR Don Drysdale Jsy/17
EM Eddie Mathews Pants/20
JD Joe DiMaggio Pants/5
JF Jimmie Foxx Bat/1
JR Jackie Robinson Pants/1
LG Lou Gehrig Bat/1
MM Mickey Mantle Jsy/7
MO Mel Ott Jsy/1
PR Pee Wee Reese Jsy/20
RC Roy Campanella Pants/1
SP Satchel Paige Pants/2
TC Ty Cobb Bat/1
TW Ted Williams Jsy/9

2005 Upper Deck Hall of Fame Essential Enshrinement

STATED PRINT RUN 50 SERIAL #'d SETS
GOLD PRINT RUN 5 SERIAL #'d SETS
NO GOLD PRICING DUE TO SCARCITY
RAINBOW PRINT RUN 1 SERIAL #'d SET
NO RAINBOW PRICING DUE TO SCARCITY
*SILVER: .6X TO 1.5X BASIC
SILVER PRINT RUN 15 SERIAL #'d SETS
OVERALL INSERT ODDS ONE PER TIN
AK1 Al Kaline Batting 3.00 8.00
AK2 Al Kaline Fielding 3.00 8.00
BD1 Bobby Doerr Batting 2.00 5.00
BD2 Bobby Doerr Fielding 2.00 5.00
BE1 Johnny Bench Batting 3.00 8.00
BE2 Johnny Bench Fielding 3.00 8.00
BF1 Bob Feller Pitching 2.00 5.00
BF2 Bob Feller Portrait 2.00 5.00
BG1 Bob Gibson Pitching 2.50 6.00
BG2 Bob Gibson Portrait 2.50 6.00
BM1 Bill Mazeroski 2.50 6.00
BR1 Brooks Robinson Batting 2.50 6.00
BR2 Brooks Robinson Fielding 2.50 6.00
BR3 Brooks Robinson Portrait 2.50 6.00
BW1 Billy Williams Cubs 2.00 5.00
BW2 Billy Williams A's 2.00 5.00
CF1 Carlton Fisk R.Sox 2.00 5.00
CF2 Carlton Fisk W.Sox 2.00 5.00
CY1 C.Yastrzemski Red Hand 4.00 10.00
CY2 C.Yaz Bare Hands 4.00 10.00
CY3 C.Yastrzemski Sleeves 4.00 10.00
DE1 Dennis Eckersley 2.00 5.00
DS1 Don Sutton Pitching 2.00 5.00
DS2 Don Sutton Portrait 2.00 5.00
DW1 Dave Winfield 2.00 5.00
EB1 Ernie Banks 3.00 8.00
EM1 Eddie Murray O's 3.00 8.00
EM2 Eddie Murray Dgr 3.00 8.00
FJ1 Fergie Jenkins Cubs 2.00 5.00
FJ2 Fergie Jenkins Rgr 2.00 5.00
FR1 Frank Robinson Reds 2.00 5.00
FR2 Frank Robinson O's 2.00 5.00
GB1 George Brett Batting 6.00 15.00
GB2 George Brett Fielding 6.00 15.00
GB3 George Brett Portrait 6.00 15.00
GC1 Gary Carter Mets 2.00 5.00
GC2 Gary Carter Expos 2.00 5.00
GK1 George Kell 2.00 5.00
GP1 Gaylord Perry Giants 2.00 5.00
GP2 Gaylord Perry Padres 2.00 5.00
HK1 H.Killebrew Senators 3.00 8.00
HK2 Harmon Killebrew Twins 3.00 8.00
JB1 Jim Bunning 2.00 5.00
JM1 Juan Marichal 2.00 5.00
JP1 Jim Palmer Pitching 2.00 5.00
JP2 Jim Palmer Portrait 2.00 5.00
KP1 Kirby Puckett 3.00 8.00
KP2 Kirby Puckett 3.00 8.00
LA1 Luis Aparicio 2.00 5.00
LB1 Lou Brock Cards 2.50 6.00
LB2 Lou Brock Cubs 2.50 6.00
MI1 Monte Irvin 2.00 5.00
MO1 Joe Morgan Astros 2.00 5.00
MO2 Joe Morgan Reds 2.00 5.00
MO3 Joe Morgan Giants 2.00 5.00
MS1 Mike Schmidt Batting 6.00 15.00
MS2 Mike Schmidt Fielding 6.00 15.00
NR1 Nolan Ryan Mets 6.00 15.00
NR2 Nolan Ryan Rgr 6.00 15.00
NR3 Nolan Ryan Astros 6.00 15.00
NR4 Nolan Ryan Angels 6.00 15.00
OC1 Orlando Cepeda 2.00 5.00
OS1 Ozzie Smith Padres 4.00 10.00
OS2 Ozzie Smith Cards 4.00 10.00
PM1 Paul Molitor Brew 2.00 5.00
PM2 Paul Molitor Twins 2.00 5.00
PM3 Paul Molitor Jays 2.00 5.00
PN1 Phil Niekro Braves 2.00 5.00
PN2 Phil Niekro Yanks 2.00 5.00
RC1 Rod Carew Twins 2.50 6.00
RC2 Rod Carew Angels 2.50 6.00
RF1 Rollie Fingers 2.00 5.00
RJ1 Reggie Jackson A's 2.50 6.00
RJ2 Reggie Jackson Yanks 2.50 6.00
RJ3 Reggie Jackson Angels 2.50 6.00
RK1 Ralph Kiner 2.00 5.00
RR1 Robin Roberts 2.00 5.00
RS1 Red Schoendienst 2.00 5.00
RY1 Robin Yount Batting 3.00 8.00
RY2 Robin Yount Fielding 3.00 8.00
RY3 Robin Yount Portrait 3.00 8.00
SA1 Ryne Sandberg Batting 6.00 15.00
SA2 Ryne Sandberg Fielding 6.00 15.00
SA3 Ryne Sandberg Portrait 6.00 15.00
SC1 Steve Carlton Cards 2.00 5.00
SC2 Steve Carlton Phils 2.00 5.00
SM1 Stan Musial B/W 4.00 10.00
SM2 Stan Musial Color 4.00 10.00
SN1 Duke Snider Brooklyn 2.50 6.00
SN2 Duke Snider LA 2.50 6.00
TP1 Tony Perez 2.00 5.00
TS1 Tom Seaver 2.50 6.00
WB1 Wade Boggs Sox 2.50 6.00
WB2 Wade Boggs Yanks 2.50 6.00
WB3 Wade Boggs Rays 2.50 6.00
WF1 Whitey Ford Fielding 2.50 6.00
WF2 Whitey Ford Portrait 2.50 6.00
WM1 Willie McCovey 2.50 6.00
YB1 Yogi Berra Batting 3.00 8.00
YB2 Yogi Berra Fielding 3.00 8.00

2005 Upper Deck Hall of Fame Essential Enshrinement Autograph

STATED PRINT RUN 25 SERIAL #'d SETS
GOLD PRINT RUN 5 SERIAL #'d SETS
NO GOLD PRICING DUE TO SCARCITY
RAINBOW PRINT RUN 1 SERIAL #'d SET
NO RAINBOW PRICING DUE TO SCARCITY
*SILVER: .5X TO 1.2X BASIC
SILVER PRINT RUN 15 SERIAL #'d SETS
MATERIAL GOLD PRINT RUN 5 #'d SETS
NO MAT.GOLD PRICING DUE TO SCARCITY
MATERIAL RAINBOW PRINT RUN 1 #'d SET
NO MAT.RB PRICING DUE TO SCARCITY
*MAT.SILVER: .5X TO 1.2X BASIC
MATERIAL SILVER PRINT RUN 15 #'d SETS
PATCH GOLD PRINT RUN 5 #'d SETS
NO PATCH GOLD PRICING AVAILABLE
PATCH RAINBOW PRINT RUN 1 #'d SET
NO PATCH RAINBOW PRICING AVAILABLE
PATCH SILVER PRINT RUN 10 #'d SETS
NO PATCH SILVER PRICING AVAILABLE
OVERALL AUTO ODDS ONE PER TIN
EXCHANGE DEADLINE 07/18/08
AK1 Al Kaline Batting 30.00 60.00
AK2 Al Kaline Fielding 30.00 60.00
BD1 Bobby Doerr Batting 8.00 20.00
BD2 Bobby Doerr Fielding 8.00 20.00
BE1 Johnny Bench Batting 20.00 50.00
BE2 Johnny Bench Fielding 20.00 50.00
BF1 Bob Feller Pitching 10.00 25.00
BF2 Bob Feller Portrait 10.00 25.00
BG1 Bob Gibson Pitching 15.00 40.00
BG2 Bob Gibson Portrait 15.00 40.00
BM1 Bill Mazeroski 20.00 50.00
BR1 Brooks Robinson Batting 15.00 40.00
BR2 Brooks Robinson Fielding 15.00 40.00
BR3 Brooks Robinson Portrait 15.00 40.00
BW1 Billy Williams Cubs 10.00 25.00
BW2 Billy Williams A's 10.00 25.00
CF1 Carlton Fisk R.Sox 10.00 25.00
CF2 Carlton Fisk W.Sox 10.00 25.00
CY1 C.Yastrzemski Red Hand 30.00 60.00
CY2 C.Yaz Bare Hands 30.00 60.00
CY3 C.Yastrzemski Sleeves 30.00 60.00
DE1 Dennis Eckersley 10.00 25.00
DS1 Don Sutton Pitching 8.00 20.00
DS2 Don Sutton Portrait 8.00 20.00
DW1 Dave Winfield 15.00 40.00
EB1 Ernie Banks 30.00 60.00
EM1 Eddie Murray O's EXCH 30.00 60.00
EM2 Eddie Murray Dgr EXCH 30.00 60.00
FJ1 Fergie Jenkins Cubs 8.00 20.00
FJ2 Fergie Jenkins Rgr 8.00 20.00
FR1 Frank Robinson Reds 10.00 25.00
FR2 Frank Robinson O's 10.00 25.00
GB1 George Brett Btg EXCH 40.00 80.00
GB2 George Brett Fldg EXCH 40.00 80.00
GB3 George Brett Portrait 40.00 80.00
GC1 Gary Carter Mets 10.00 25.00
GC2 Gary Carter Expos 10.00 25.00
GK1 George Kell 10.00 25.00
GP1 Gaylord Perry Giants 8.00 20.00
GP2 Gaylord Perry Padres 8.00 20.00
HK1 H.Killebrew Senators 20.00 50.00
HK2 Harmon Killebrew Twins 20.00 50.00
JB1 Jim Bunning 10.00 25.00
JM1 Juan Marichal 10.00 25.00
JP1 Jim Palmer Pitching 10.00 25.00
JP2 Jim Palmer Portrait 10.00 25.00
KP1 Kirby Puckett 50.00 100.00
KP2 Kirby Puckett 50.00 100.00
LA1 Luis Aparicio 10.00 25.00
LB1 Lou Brock Cards 15.00 40.00
LB2 Lou Brock Cubs 15.00 40.00
MI1 Monte Irvin 10.00 25.00
MO1 Joe Morgan Astros 10.00 25.00
MO2 Joe Morgan Reds 10.00 25.00
MO3 Joe Morgan Giants 10.00 25.00
MS1 Mike Schmidt Batting 30.00 60.00
MS2 Mike Schmidt Fielding 30.00 60.00
NR1 Nolan Ryan Mets 50.00 100.00
NR2 Nolan Ryan Rgr 50.00 100.00
NR3 Nolan Ryan Astros 50.00 100.00
NR4 Nolan Ryan Angels 50.00 100.00
OC1 Orlando Cepeda 10.00 25.00
OS1 Ozzie Smith Padres 20.00 50.00
OS2 Ozzie Smith Cards 20.00 50.00
PM1 Paul Molitor Brew 10.00 25.00
PM2 Paul Molitor Twins 10.00 25.00
PM3 Paul Molitor Jays 10.00 25.00
PN1 Phil Niekro Braves 10.00 25.00
PN2 Phil Niekro Yanks 10.00 25.00
RC1 Rod Carew Twins 15.00 40.00
RC2 Rod Carew Angels 15.00 40.00
RF1 Rollie Fingers 8.00 20.00
RJ1 Reggie Jackson A's 20.00 50.00
RJ2 Reggie Jackson Yanks 20.00 50.00
RJ3 Reggie Jackson Angels 20.00 50.00
RK1 Ralph Kiner 20.00 50.00
RR1 Robin Roberts 10.00 25.00
RS1 Red Schoendienst 10.00 25.00
RY1 Robin Yount Batting 20.00 50.00
RY2 Robin Yount Fielding 20.00 50.00
RY3 Robin Yount Portrait 20.00 50.00
SA1 Ryne Sandberg Batting 40.00 80.00
SA2 Ryne Sandberg Fielding 40.00 80.00
SA3 Ryne Sandberg Portrait 40.00 80.00
SC1 Steve Carlton Cards 10.00 25.00
SC2 Steve Carlton Phils 10.00 25.00
SM1 Stan Musial B/W 40.00 80.00
SM2 Stan Musial Color 40.00 80.00
SN1 Duke Snider Brooklyn 15.00 40.00
SN2 Duke Snider LA 15.00 40.00
TP1 Tony Perez 15.00 40.00
TS1 Tom Seaver 20.00 50.00
WB1 Wade Boggs Sox 15.00 40.00
WB2 Wade Boggs Yanks 15.00 40.00
WB3 Wade Boggs Rays 15.00 40.00
WF1 Whitey Ford Fielding 15.00 40.00
WF2 Whitey Ford Portrait 15.00 40.00
WM1 Willie McCovey 15.00 40.00
YB1 Yogi Berra Batting 30.00 60.00
YB2 Yogi Berra Fielding 30.00 60.00

2005 Upper Deck Hall of Fame Hall Worthy

STATED PRINT RUN 50 SERIAL #'d SETS
GOLD PRINT RUN 5 SERIAL #'d SETS
NO GOLD PRICING DUE TO SCARCITY
RAINBOW PRINT RUN 1 SERIAL #'d SET
NO RAINBOW PRICING DUE TO SCARCITY
*SILVER: .6X TO 1.5X BASIC
SILVER PRINT RUN 15 SERIAL #'d SETS
OVERALL INSERT ODDS ONE PER TIN
AK1 Al Kaline Batting 3.00 8.00
AK2 Al Kaline Portrait 3.00 8.00
BD1 Bobby Doerr 2.00 5.00
BE1 Johnny Bench Batting 3.00 8.00
BE2 Johnny Bench Portrait 3.00 8.00
BF1 Bob Feller Color 2.00 5.00
BF2 Bob Feller B/W 2.00 5.00
BG1 Bob Gibson 2.50 6.00
BM1 Bill Mazeroski 2.50 6.00
BR1 Brooks Robinson Batting 2.50 6.00
BR2 Brooks Robinson Fielding 2.50 6.00
BW1 Billy Williams 2.00 5.00
CF1 Carlton Fisk R.Sox 2.00 5.00
CF2 Carlton Fisk W.Sox 2.00 5.00
CY1 Carl Yastrzemski Batting 4.00 10.00
CY2 Carl Yastrzemski Portrait 4.00 10.00
DE1 Dennis Eckersley Cubs 2.00 5.00
DE2 Dennis Eckersley A's 2.00 5.00
DE3 Dennis Eckersley Indians 2.00 5.00
DE4 Dennis Eckersley Sox 2.00 5.00
DS1 Don Sutton Dgr 2.00 5.00
DS2 Don Sutton Angels 2.00 5.00
DS3 Don Sutton Astros 2.00 5.00
DW1 Dave Winfield 2.00 5.00
EB1 Ernie Banks 3.00 8.00
EM1 Eddie Murray O's 3.00 8.00
EM2 Eddie Murray Dgr 3.00 8.00
EM3 Eddie Murray Mets 3.00 8.00
FJ1 Fergie Jenkins Cubs 2.00 5.00
FJ2 Fergie Jenkins Sox 2.00 5.00
FJ3 Fergie Jenkins Rgr 2.00 5.00
FR1 Frank Robinson Reds 2.00 5.00
FR2 Frank Robinson O's 2.00 5.00
GB1 George Brett Batting 6.00 15.00
GB2 George Brett Fielding 6.00 15.00
GB3 George Brett Portrait 6.00 15.00
GC1 Gary Carter Expos 2.00 5.00
GC2 Gary Carter Mets 2.00 5.00
GK1 George Kell 2.00 5.00
GP1 Gaylord Perry Giants 2.00 5.00
GP2 Gaylord Perry Indians 2.00 5.00
HK1 H.Killebrew Senators 3.00 8.00
HK2 Harmon Killebrew Twins 3.00 8.00
JB1 Jim Bunning 2.00 5.00
JM1 Juan Marichal 2.00 5.00
JP1 Jim Palmer Pitching 2.00 5.00
JP2 Jim Palmer Portrait 2.00 5.00
KP1 Kirby Puckett 3.00 8.00
LA1 Luis Aparicio 2.00 5.00
LB1 Lou Brock Cards 2.50 6.00
LB2 Lou Brock Cubs 2.50 6.00
MI1 Monte Irvin 2.00 5.00
MO1 Joe Morgan Reds 2.00 5.00
MO2 Joe Morgan Giants 2.00 5.00
MS1 Mike Schmidt Batting 6.00 15.00
MS2 Mike Schmidt Fielding 6.00 15.00
MS3 Mike Schmidt Portrait 6.00 15.00
NR1 Nolan Ryan Mets 6.00 15.00
NR2 Nolan Ryan Angels 6.00 15.00
NR3 Nolan Ryan Astros 6.00 15.00
NR4 Nolan Ryan Rgr 6.00 15.00
OC1 Orlando Cepeda Giants 2.00 5.00
OC2 Orlando Cepeda Braves 2.00 5.00
OS1 Ozzie Smith Padres 4.00 10.00
OS2 Ozzie Smith Cards 4.00 10.00
PM1 Paul Molitor Brew 2.00 5.00
PM2 Paul Molitor Twins 2.00 5.00
PN1 Phil Niekro Braves 2.00 5.00
PN2 Phil Niekro Yanks 2.00 5.00
RC1 Rod Carew Angels 2.50 6.00
RC2 Rod Carew Twins 2.50 6.00
RF1 Rollie Fingers A's 2.00 5.00
RF2 Rollie Fingers Brew 2.00 5.00
RJ1 Reggie Jackson A's 2.50 6.00
RJ2 Reggie Jackson O's 2.50 6.00
RJ3 Reggie Jackson Yanks 2.50 6.00
RJ4 Reggie Jackson Angels 2.50 6.00
RK1 Ralph Kiner 2.00 5.00
RR1 Robin Roberts 2.00 5.00
RS1 Red Schoendienst 2.00 5.00
RY1 Robin Yount Batting 3.00 8.00
RY2 Robin Yount Fielding 3.00 8.00
SA1 Ryne Sandberg Batting 6.00 15.00
SA2 Ryne Sandberg Fielding 6.00 15.00
SA3 Ryne Sandberg Portrait 6.00 15.00
SC1 Steve Carlton Cards 2.00 5.00
SC2 Steve Carlton Phils 2.00 5.00
SM1 Stan Musial 4.00 10.00
SN1 Duke Snider Brooklyn 2.50 6.00
SN2 Duke Snider LA 2.50 6.00
TP1 Tony Perez Reds 2.00 5.00
TP2 Tony Perez Sox 2.00 5.00
TS1 Tom Seaver Mets 2.50 6.00
TS2 Tom Seaver Reds 2.50 6.00
WB1 Wade Boggs Sox 2.50 6.00
WB2 Wade Boggs Yanks 2.50 6.00
WB3 Wade Boggs Rays 2.50 6.00
WF1 Whitey Ford 2.50 6.00
WM1 Willie McCovey 2.50 6.00
YB1 Yogi Berra 3.00 8.00

2005 Upper Deck Hall of Fame Hall Worthy Autograph

STATED PRINT RUN 25 SERIAL #'d SETS
GOLD PRINT RUN 5 SERIAL #'d SETS
NO GOLD PRICING DUE TO SCARCITY
RAINBOW PRINT RUN 1 SERIAL #'d SET
NO RAINBOW PRICING DUE TO SCARCITY
*SILVER: .5X TO 1.2X BASIC
SILVER PRINT RUN 15 SERIAL #'d SETS
MATERIAL GOLD PRINT RUN 5 #'d SETS
NO MAT.GOLD PRICING DUE TO SCARCITY
MATERIAL RAINBOW PRINT RUN 1 #'d SET
NO MAT.RB PRICING DUE TO SCARCITY
*MAT.SILVER: .5X TO 1.2X BASIC
MATERIAL SILVER PRINT RUN 15 #'d SETS
PATCH GOLD PRINT RUN 5 #'d SETS
NO PATCH GOLD PRICING AVAILABLE
PATCH RAINBOW PRINT RUN 1 #'d SET
NO PATCH RAINBOW PRICING AVAILABLE
PATCH SILVER PRINT RUN 10 #'d SETS
SM1 MUSIAL PATCH SILV.QTY 3 #'d CARDS
NO PATCH SILVER PRICING AVAILABLE
OVERALL AUTO ODDS ONE PER TIN
EXCHANGE DEADLINE 07/18/08
AK1 Al Kaline Batting 30.00 60.00
AK2 Al Kaline Portrait 30.00 60.00
BD1 Bobby Doerr 8.00 20.00
BE1 Johnny Bench Batting 20.00 50.00
BE2 Johnny Bench Portrait 20.00 50.00
BF1 Bob Feller Color 10.00 25.00
BF2 Bob Feller B/W 10.00 25.00
BG1 Bob Gibson 15.00 40.00
BM1 Bill Mazeroski 20.00 50.00
BR1 Brooks Robinson Batting 15.00 40.00
BR2 Brooks Robinson Fielding 15.00 40.00
BW1 Billy Williams 10.00 25.00
CF1 Carlton Fisk R.Sox 10.00 25.00
CF2 Carlton Fisk W.Sox 10.00 25.00
CY1 Carl Yastrzemski Batting 30.00 60.00
CY2 Carl Yastrzemski Portrait 30.00 60.00
DE1 Dennis Eckersley Cubs 10.00 25.00
DE2 Dennis Eckersley A's 10.00 25.00
DE3 Dennis Eckersley Indians 10.00 25.00
DE4 Dennis Eckersley Sox 10.00 25.00
DS1 Don Sutton Dgr 8.00 20.00
DS2 Don Sutton Angels 8.00 20.00
DS3 Don Sutton Astros 8.00 20.00
DW1 Dave Winfield 15.00 40.00
EB1 Ernie Banks 30.00 60.00
EM1 Eddie Murray O's 30.00 60.00
EM2 Eddie Murray Dgr EXCH 30.00 60.00
EM3 Eddie Murray Mets 30.00 60.00
FJ1 Fergie Jenkins Cubs 8.00 20.00
FJ2 Fergie Jenkins Sox 8.00 20.00
FJ3 Fergie Jenkins Rgr 8.00 20.00
FR1 Frank Robinson Reds 10.00 25.00
FR2 Frank Robinson O's 10.00 25.00
GB1 George Brett Btg EXCH 40.00 80.00
GB2 George Brett Fldg EXCH 40.00 80.00
GB3 George Brett Portrait 40.00 80.00
GC1 Gary Carter Expos 10.00 25.00
GC2 Gary Carter Mets 10.00 25.00
GK1 George Kell 10.00 25.00
GP1 Gaylord Perry Giants 8.00 20.00
GP2 Gaylord Perry Indians 8.00 20.00
HK1 H.Killebrew Senators 20.00 50.00
HK2 Harmon Killebrew Twins 20.00 50.00
JB1 Jim Bunning 10.00 25.00
JM1 Juan Marichal 10.00 25.00
JP1 Jim Palmer Pitching 10.00 25.00
JP2 Jim Palmer Portrait 10.00 25.00
KP1 Kirby Puckett 50.00 100.00
LA1 Luis Aparicio 10.00 25.00
LB1 Lou Brock Cards 15.00 40.00
LB2 Lou Brock Cubs 15.00 40.00
MI1 Monte Irvin 10.00 25.00
MO1 Joe Morgan Reds 10.00 25.00
MO2 Joe Morgan Giants 10.00 25.00
MS1 Mike Schmidt Batting 30.00 60.00
MS2 Mike Schmidt Fielding 30.00 60.00
MS3 Mike Schmidt Portrait 30.00 60.00
NR1 Nolan Ryan Mets 50.00 100.00
NR2 Nolan Ryan Angels 50.00 100.00
NR3 Nolan Ryan Astros 50.00 100.00
NR4 Nolan Ryan Rgr 50.00 100.00
OC1 Orlando Cepeda Giants 10.00 25.00
OC2 Orlando Cepeda Braves 10.00 25.00
OS1 Ozzie Smith Padres 20.00 50.00
OS2 Ozzie Smith Cards 20.00 50.00
PM1 Paul Molitor Brew 10.00 25.00
PM2 Paul Molitor Twins 10.00 25.00
PN1 Phil Niekro Braves 10.00 25.00
PN2 Phil Niekro Yanks 10.00 25.00
RC1 Rod Carew Angels 15.00 40.00
RC2 Rod Carew Twins 15.00 40.00
RF1 Rollie Fingers A's 8.00 20.00
RF2 Rollie Fingers Brew 8.00 20.00
RJ1 Reggie Jackson A's 20.00 50.00
RJ2 Reggie Jackson O's 20.00 50.00
RJ3 Reggie Jackson Yanks 20.00 50.00
RJ4 Reggie Jackson Angels 20.00 50.00
RK1 Ralph Kiner 20.00 50.00
RR1 Robin Roberts 10.00 25.00
RS1 Red Schoendienst 10.00 25.00
RY1 Robin Yount Batting 20.00 50.00
RY2 Robin Yount Fielding 20.00 50.00
SA1 Ryne Sandberg Batting 40.00 80.00
SA2 Ryne Sandberg Fielding 40.00 80.00
SA3 Ryne Sandberg Portrait 40.00 80.00
SC1 Steve Carlton Cards 10.00 25.00
SC2 Steve Carlton Phils 10.00 25.00
SM1 Stan Musial 40.00 80.00
SN1 Duke Snider Brooklyn 15.00 40.00
SN2 Duke Snider LA 15.00 40.00
TP1 Tony Perez Reds 15.00 40.00
TP2 Tony Perez Sox 15.00 40.00
TS1 Tom Seaver Mets 20.00 50.00
TS2 Tom Seaver Reds 20.00 50.00
WB1 Wade Boggs Sox 15.00 40.00
WB2 Wade Boggs Yanks 15.00 40.00
WB3 Wade Boggs Rays 15.00 40.00
WF1 Whitey Ford 15.00 40.00
WM1 Willie McCovey 15.00 40.00
YB1 Yogi Berra 30.00 60.00

2005 Upper Deck Hall of Fame Legendary Lineups Redemption

STATED ODDS 1:21,500 TINS
STATED PRINT RUN 1 COPY PER CARD
NO PRICING DUE TO SCARCITY
EXCHANGE DEADLINE 07/18/08
CUT Cy Young
Roy Campanella
Lou Gehrig
Rogers Hornsby
Pie Traynor
Honus Wagner
Ted Williams
Ty Cobb
Babe Ruth
HOF Nolan Ryan
Johnny Bench

Harmon Killebrew
Joe Morgan
Mike Schmidt
Ernie Banks
Stan Musial
Duke Snider
Al Kaline

2005 Upper Deck Hall of Fame Materials

STATED PRINT RUN 25 SERIAL #'d SETS
GOLD PRINT RUN 5 SERIAL #'d SETS
NO GOLD PRICING DUE TO SCARCITY
GREEN PRINT RUN 10 SERIAL #'d SETS
NO GREEN PRICING DUE TO SCARCITY
RAINBOW PRINT RUN 1 SERIAL #'d SET
NO RAINBOW PRICING DUE TO SCARCITY
*SILVER: .5X TO 1.2X BASIC
SILVER PRINT RUN 15 SERIAL #'d SETS
OVERALL GAME-USED/CUT SIG ODDS 1:20

BR1 Babe Ruth Sox Bat 150.00 250.00
BR2 Babe Ruth Yanks Batting Bat 150.00 250.00
BR3 Babe Ruth Yanks Portrait Bat 150.00 250.00
DD1 Dizzy Dean Cards Jsy 50.00 100.00
DD2 Dizzy Dean Cubs Jsy 50.00 100.00
GS1 George Sisler Browns Bat 15.00 40.00
GS2 George Sisler Braves Bat 15.00 40.00
JD1 Joe DiMaggio Batting Pants 60.00 120.00
JD2 Joe DiMaggio Fielding Pants 60.00 120.00
JD3 Joe DiMaggio Portrait Pants 60.00 120.00
JF1 Jimmie Foxx A's Bat 30.00 60.00
JF2 Jimmie Foxx Sox Bat 30.00 60.00
JM1 Johnny Mize Cards Pants 10.00 25.00
JM2 Johnny Mize Giants Pants 10.00 25.00
JM3 Johnny Mize Yanks Pants 10.00 25.00
JR1 Jackie Robinson Batting Pants 30.00 60.00
JR2 J.Robinson Port Pants 30.00 60.00
JR3 Jackie Robinson Fielding Pants 30.00 60.00
LG1 Lou Gehrig Batting Bat 100.00 200.00
LG2 Lou Gehrig Portrait Bat 100.00 200.00
LG3 Lou Gehrig Fielding Bat 100.00 200.00
MC1 Mickey Cochrane Bat 20.00 50.00
MM1 Mickey Mantle Btg Jsy 175.00 300.00
MM2 Mickey Mantle Fldg Jsy 175.00 300.00
MM3 Mickey Mantle Port Jsy 175.00 300.00
MO1 Mel Ott Black Cap Jsy 30.00 60.00
MO2 Mel Ott Pinstripe Jsy 30.00 60.00
RC1 Roberto Clemente Batting Jsy 60.00 120.00
RC2 Roberto Clemente Portrait Jsy 60.00 120.00
RC3 Roberto Clemente Fielding Jsy 60.00 120.00
RH1 Rogers Hornsby Jkt 50.00 100.00
SP1 Satchel Paige Indians Pants 30.00 60.00
SP2 Satchel Paige Browns Pitching Pants 30.00 60.00
SP3 Satchel Paige Browns Portrait Pants 30.00 60.00
TC1 Ty Cobb Tigers Batting Bat 60.00 120.00
TC2 Ty Cobb Tigers Portrait Bat 60.00 120.00
TC3 Ty Cobb A's Bat 60.00 120.00
TW1 Ted Williams Batting Jsy 50.00 100.00
TW2 Ted Williams Fielding Jsy 50.00 100.00
TW3 Ted Williams Portrait Jsy 50.00 100.00

2005 Upper Deck Hall of Fame Seasons

STATED PRINT RUN 50 SERIAL #'d SETS
GOLD PRINT RUN 5 SERIAL #'d SETS
NO GOLD PRICING DUE TO SCARCITY
RAINBOW PRINT RUN 1 SERIAL #'d SET
NO RAINBOW PRICING DUE TO SCARCITY
*SILVER: .6X TO 1.5X BASIC
SILVER PRINT RUN 15 SERIAL #'d SETS
OVERALL INSERT ODDS ONE PER TIN

AK1 Al Kaline Batting 3.00 8.00
AK2 Al Kaline Fielding 3.00 8.00
AK3 Al Kaline Portrait 3.00 8.00
BD1 Bobby Doerr 2.00 5.00
BE1 Johnny Bench Batting 3.00 8.00
BE2 Johnny Bench Fielding 3.00 8.00
BF1 Bob Feller Pitching 2.00 5.00
BF2 Bob Feller Portrait 2.00 5.00
BG1 Bob Gibson Pitching 2.50 6.00
BG2 Bob Gibson Portrait 2.50 6.00
BM1 Bill Mazeroski 2.50 6.00
BR1 Brooks Robinson Batting 2.50 6.00
BR2 Brooks Robinson Fielding 2.50 6.00
BR3 Brooks Robinson Portrait 2.50 6.00
BW1 Billy Williams Batting 2.00 5.00
BW2 Billy Williams Portrait 2.00 5.00
CF1 Carlton Fisk R.Sox 2.00 5.00
CF2 Carlton Fisk W.Sox 2.00 5.00
CY1 Carl Yastrzemski Batting 4.00 10.00
CY2 Carl Yastrzemski Fielding 4.00 10.00
DE1 Dennis Eckersley A's 92 2.00 5.00
DE2 Dennis Eckersley A's 88 2.00 5.00
DE3 Dennis Eckersley Sox 2.00 5.00
DS1 Don Sutton 76 2.00 5.00
DS2 Don Sutton 72 2.00 5.00
DW1 Dave Winfield 2.00 5.00
EB1 Ernie Banks 3.00 8.00
EM1 Eddie Murray 83 3.00 8.00
EM2 Eddie Murray 82 3.00 8.00
FJ1 Fergie Jenkins Cubs 2.00 5.00
FJ2 Fergie Jenkins Rgr 2.00 5.00
FR1 Frank Robinson Reds 2.00 5.00
FR2 Frank Robinson O's 2.00 5.00
GB1 George Brett 80 6.00 15.00
GB2 George Brett 85 6.00 15.00
GC1 Gary Carter 2.00 5.00
GK1 George Kell 2.00 5.00
GP1 Gaylord Perry Indians 2.00 5.00
GP2 Gaylord Perry Padres 2.00 5.00
HK1 H.Killebrew Senators 3.00 8.00
HK2 Harmon Killebrew Twins Batting 3.00 8.00
HK3 Harmon Killebrew Twins Fielding 3.00 8.00
JB1 Jim Bunning 2.00 5.00
JM1 Juan Marichal 2.00 5.00
JP1 Jim Palmer Windup 2.00 5.00
JP2 Jim Palmer Throwing 2.00 5.00
JP3 Jim Palmer Portrait 2.00 5.00
KP1 Kirby Puckett 88 3.00 8.00
KP2 Kirby Puckett 92 3.00 8.00
LA1 Luis Aparicio 2.00 5.00
LB1 Lou Brock 74 2.50 6.00
LB2 Lou Brock 67 2.50 6.00
MI1 Monte Irvin 2.00 5.00
MO1 Joe Morgan Astros 2.00 5.00
MO2 Joe Morgan Reds 2.00 5.00
MS1 Mike Schmidt Batting 6.00 15.00
MS2 Mike Schmidt Fielding 6.00 15.00
MS3 Mike Schmidt Portrait 6.00 15.00
NR1 Nolan Ryan Angels 6.00 15.00
NR2 Nolan Ryan Rgr 6.00 15.00
NR3 Nolan Ryan Astros Portrait 6.00 15.00
NR4 Nolan Ryan Astros Pitching 6.00 15.00
OC1 Orlando Cepeda 2.00 5.00
OS1 Ozzie Smith Padres 4.00 10.00
OS2 Ozzie Smith Cards 4.00 10.00
PM1 Paul Molitor Brew 2.00 5.00
PM2 Paul Molitor Jays 2.00 5.00
PM3 Paul Molitor Twins 2.00 5.00
PN1 Phil Niekro Braves 2.00 5.00
PN2 Phil Niekro Yanks 2.00 5.00
RC1 Rod Carew 77 2.50 6.00
RC2 Rod Carew 75 2.50 6.00
RF1 Rollie Fingers 2.00 5.00
RJ1 Reggie Jackson A's 2.50 6.00
RJ2 Reggie Jackson Yanks 2.50 6.00
RJ3 Reggie Jackson Angels 2.50 6.00
RK1 Ralph Kiner 2.00 5.00
RR1 Robin Roberts 2.00 5.00
RS1 Red Schoendienst 2.00 5.00
RY1 Robin Yount Batting 3.00 8.00
RY2 Robin Yount Fielding 3.00 8.00
SA1 Ryne Sandberg 90 6.00 15.00
SA2 Ryne Sandberg 84 6.00 15.00
SC1 Steve Carlton Cards 2.00 5.00
SC2 Steve Carlton Phils Pitching 2.00 5.00
SC3 Steve Carlton Phils Portrait 2.00 5.00
SM1 Stan Musial Batting 4.00 10.00
SM2 Stan Musial Fielding 4.00 10.00
SN1 Duke Snider 2.50 6.00
TP1 Tony Perez 2.00 5.00
TS1 Tom Seaver Mets 2.50 6.00
TS2 Tom Seaver Reds 2.50 6.00
WB1 Wade Boggs Sox Batting 2.50 6.00
WB2 Wade Boggs Sox Fielding 2.50 6.00
WB3 Wade Boggs Yanks 2.50 6.00
WF1 Whitey Ford Pitching 2.50 6.00
WF2 Whitey Ford Portrait 2.50 6.00
WM1 Willie McCovey 2.50 6.00
YB1 Yogi Berra Batting 3.00 8.00
YB2 Yogi Berra Fielding 3.00 8.00

2005 Upper Deck Hall of Fame Seasons Autograph

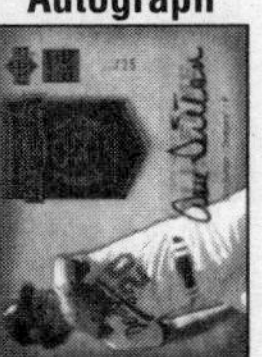

STATED PRINT RUN 25 SERIAL #'d SETS
GOLD PRINT RUN 5 SERIAL #'d SETS
NO GOLD PRICING DUE TO SCARCITY
RAINBOW PRINT RUN 1 SERIAL #'d SET
NO RAINBOW PRICING DUE TO SCARCITY
*SILVER: .5X TO 1.2X BASIC
SILVER PRINT RUN 15 SERIAL #'d SETS
MATERIAL GOLD PRINT RUN 5 #'d SETS
NO MAT.GOLD PRICING DUE TO SCARCITY
MATERIAL RAINBOW PRINT RUN 1 #'d SET
NO MAT.RB PRICING DUE TO SCARCITY
*MAT.SILVER: .5X TO 1.2X BASIC
MATERIAL SILVER PRINT RUN 15 #'d SETS
PATCH GOLD PRINT RUN 5 #'d SETS
NO PATCH GOLD PRICING AVAILABLE
PATCH RAINBOW PRINT RUN 1 #'d SET
NO PATCH RAINBOW PRICING AVAILABLE
PATCH SILVER PRINT RUN 10 #'d SETS
NO PATCH SILVER PRICING AVAILABLE
OVERALL AUTO ODDS ONE PER TIN
EXCHANGE DEADLINE 07/18/08

AK1 Al Kaline Batting 30.00 60.00
AK2 Al Kaline Fielding 30.00 60.00
AK3 Al Kaline Portrait 30.00 60.00
BD1 Bobby Doerr 8.00 20.00
BE1 Johnny Bench Batting 20.00 50.00
BE2 Johnny Bench Fielding 20.00 50.00
BF1 Bob Feller Pitching 10.00 25.00
BF2 Bob Feller Portrait 10.00 25.00
BG1 Bob Gibson Pitching 15.00 40.00
BG2 Bob Gibson Portrait 15.00 40.00
BM1 Bill Mazeroski 20.00 50.00
BR1 Brooks Robinson Batting 15.00 40.00
BR2 Brooks Robinson Fielding 15.00 40.00
BR3 Brooks Robinson Portrait 15.00 40.00
BW1 Billy Williams Batting 10.00 25.00
BW2 Billy Williams Portrait 10.00 25.00
CF1 Carlton Fisk R.Sox 10.00 25.00
CF2 Carlton Fisk W.Sox 10.00 25.00
CY1 Carl Yastrzemski Batting 30.00 60.00
CY2 Carl Yastrzemski Fielding 30.00 60.00
DE1 Dennis Eckersley A's 92 10.00 25.00
DE2 Dennis Eckersley A's 88 10.00 25.00
DE3 Dennis Eckersley Sox 10.00 25.00
DS1 Don Sutton 76 8.00 20.00
DS2 Don Sutton 72 8.00 20.00
DW1 Dave Winfield 15.00 40.00
EB1 Ernie Banks 30.00 60.00
EM1 Eddie Murray 83 30.00 60.00
EM2 Eddie Murray 82 30.00 60.00
FJ1 Fergie Jenkins Cubs 8.00 20.00
FJ2 Fergie Jenkins Rgr 8.00 20.00
FR1 Frank Robinson Reds 10.00 25.00
FR2 Frank Robinson O's 10.00 25.00
GB1 George Brett 80 40.00 80.00
GB2 George Brett 85 40.00 80.00
GC1 Gary Carter 10.00 25.00
GK1 George Kell 10.00 25.00
GP1 Gaylord Perry Indians 8.00 20.00
GP2 Gaylord Perry Padres 8.00 20.00
HK1 H.Killebrew Senators 20.00 50.00
HK2 Harmon Killebrew Twins Batting 20.00 50.00
HK3 Harmon Killebrew Twins Fielding 20.00 50.00
JB1 Jim Bunning 10.00 25.00
JM1 Juan Marichal 10.00 25.00
JP1 Jim Palmer Windup 10.00 25.00
JP2 Jim Palmer Throwing 10.00 25.00
JP3 Jim Palmer Portrait 10.00 25.00
KP1 Kirby Puckett 88 50.00 100.00
KP2 Kirby Puckett 92 50.00 100.00
LA1 Luis Aparicio 10.00 25.00
LB1 Lou Brock 74 15.00 40.00
LB2 Lou Brock 67 15.00 40.00
MI1 Monte Irvin 10.00 25.00
MO1 Joe Morgan Astros 10.00 25.00
MO2 Joe Morgan Reds 10.00 25.00
MS1 Mike Schmidt Batting 30.00 60.00
MS2 Mike Schmidt Fielding 30.00 60.00
MS3 Mike Schmidt Portrait 30.00 60.00
NR1 Nolan Ryan Angels 50.00 100.00
NR2 Nolan Ryan Rgr 50.00 100.00
NR3 Nolan Ryan Astros Portrait 50.00 100.00
NR4 Nolan Ryan Astros Pitching 50.00 100.00
OC1 Orlando Cepeda 10.00 25.00
OS1 Ozzie Smith Padres 20.00 50.00
OS2 Ozzie Smith Cards 20.00 50.00
PM1 Paul Molitor Brew 10.00 25.00
PM2 Paul Molitor Jays 10.00 25.00
PM3 Paul Molitor Twins 10.00 25.00
PN1 Phil Niekro Braves 10.00 25.00
PN2 Phil Niekro Yanks 10.00 25.00
RC1 Rod Carew 77 15.00 40.00
RC2 Rod Carew 75 15.00 40.00
RF1 Rollie Fingers 8.00 20.00
RJ1 Reggie Jackson A's 20.00 50.00
RJ2 Reggie Jackson Yanks 20.00 50.00
RJ3 Reggie Jackson Angels 20.00 50.00
RK1 Ralph Kiner 20.00 50.00
RR1 Robin Roberts 10.00 25.00
RS1 Red Schoendienst 10.00 25.00
RY1 Robin Yount Batting 20.00 50.00
RY2 Robin Yount Fielding 20.00 50.00
SA1 Ryne Sandberg 90 40.00 80.00
SA2 Ryne Sandberg 84 40.00 80.00
SC1 Steve Carlton Cards 10.00 25.00
SC2 Steve Carlton Phils Pitching 10.00 25.00
SC3 Steve Carlton Phils Portrait 10.00 25.00
SM1 Stan Musial Batting 40.00 80.00
SM2 Stan Musial Fielding 40.00 80.00
SN1 Duke Snider 15.00 40.00
TP1 Tony Perez 15.00 40.00
TS1 Tom Seaver Mets 20.00 50.00
TS2 Tom Seaver Reds 20.00 50.00
WB1 Wade Boggs Sox Batting 15.00 40.00
WB2 Wade Boggs Sox Fielding 15.00 40.00
WB3 Wade Boggs Yanks 15.00 40.00
WF1 Whitey Ford Pitching 15.00 40.00
WF2 Whitey Ford Portrait 15.00 40.00
WM1 Willie McCovey 15.00 40.00
YB1 Yogi Berra Batting 30.00 60.00
YB2 Yogi Berra Fielding 30.00 60.00

2005 Upper Deck Hall of Fame Signs of Cooperstown Duals

STATED PRINT RUN 50 SERIAL #'d SETS
GOLD PRINT RUN 5 SERIAL #'d SETS
NO GOLD PRICING DUE TO SCARCITY
RAINBOW PRINT RUN 1 SERIAL #'d SET
NO RAINBOW PRICING DUE TO SCARCITY
*SILVER: .6X TO 1.5X BASIC
SILVER PRINT RUN 15 SERIAL #'d SETS
OVERALL INSERT ODDS ONE PER TIN

AB Luis Aparicio / Ernie Banks 3.00 8.00
AS Luis Aparicio / Ozzie Smith 4.00 10.00
BC Jim Bunning / Steve Carlton 2.00 5.00
BF Brooks Robinson / Frank Robinson 2.50 6.00
BG Brooks Robinson / George Brett 6.00 15.00
BM Lou Brock / Stan Musial 4.00 10.00
BR Jim Bunning / Robin Roberts 2.00 5.00
BS Ernie Banks / Ryne Sandberg 6.00 15.00
CM Orlando Cepeda / Willie McCovey 2.50 6.00
CS Tom Seaver / Gary Carter 2.50 6.00
DB Bobby Doerr / Wade Boggs 2.50 6.00
EF Dennis Eckersley / Rollie Fingers 2.00 5.00
FB Carlton Fisk / Johnny Bench 3.00 8.00
FC Bob Feller / Steve Carlton 2.00 5.00
FP Bob Feller / Gaylord Perry 2.00 5.00
GC Bob Gibson / Steve Carlton 2.50 6.00
GF Bob Gibson / Whitey Ford 2.50 6.00
IM Monte Irvin / Willie McCovey 2.50 6.00
JJ Joe Morgan / Johnny Bench 3.00 8.00
JM Reggie Jackson / Willie McCovey 2.50 6.00
JW Dave Winfield / Reggie Jackson 2.50 6.00
JY Johnny Bench / Yogi Berra 3.00 8.00
KK Al Kaline / George Kell 3.00 8.00
KP Harmon Killebrew / Kirby Puckett 3.00 8.00
LO Lou Brock / Ozzie Smith 4.00 10.00
MK Bill Mazeroski / Ralph Kiner 2.50 6.00
MP Joe Morgan / Tony Perez 2.00 5.00
MY Paul Molitor / Robin Yount 3.00 8.00
NS Nolan Ryan / Steve Carlton 6.00 15.00
PM Gaylord Perry / Juan Marichal 2.00 5.00
PN Gaylord Perry / Phil Niekro 2.00 5.00
PR Paul Molitor / Rod Carew 2.50 6.00
RC Nolan Ryan / Rod Carew 6.00 15.00
RP Brooks Robinson / Jim Palmer 2.50 6.00
RS Nolan Ryan / Tom Seaver 6.00 15.00
RW Ryne Sandberg / Wade Boggs 6.00 15.00
SB George Brett / Mike Schmidt 6.00 15.00
SC Mike Schmidt / Steve Carlton 6.00 15.00
SK Duke Snider / Ralph Kiner 2.50 6.00
SM Ozzie Smith / Stan Musial 4.00 10.00
SP Don Sutton / Gaylord Perry 2.00 5.00
SR Brooks Robinson / Mike Schmidt 6.00 15.00
SS Ozzie Smith / Red Schoendienst 4.00 10.00
SW Ryne Sandberg / Billy Williams 6.00 15.00
WB Billy Williams / Ernie Banks 3.00 8.00
WJ Billy Williams / Fergie Jenkins 2.00 5.00
WS Dave Winfield / Ozzie Smith 4.00 10.00
WY Whitey Ford / Yogi Berra 3.00 8.00
YF Carl Yastrzemski / Carlton Fisk 4.00 10.00
YJ Carl Yastrzemski / Reggie Jackson 4.00 10.00

2005 Upper Deck Hall of Fame Signs of Cooperstown Duals Autograph

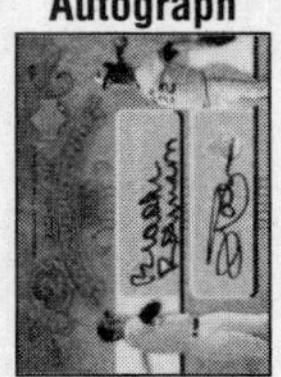

STATED PRINT RUN 20 SERIAL #'d SETS
GOLD PRINT RUN 5 SERIAL #'d SETS
NO GOLD PRICING DUE TO SCARCITY
RAINBOW PRINT RUN 1 SERIAL #'d SET
NO RAINBOW PRICING DUE TO SCARCITY
SILVER PRINT RUN 10 SERIAL #'d SETS
NO SILVER PRICING DUE TO SCARCITY
OVERALL AUTO ODDS ONE PER TIN

AB Luis Aparicio / Ernie Banks 50.00 100.00
AS Luis Aparicio / Ozzie Smith 40.00 80.00
BC Jim Bunning / Steve Carlton 20.00 50.00
BF Brooks Robinson / Frank Robinson 40.00 80.00
BG Brooks Robinson / George Brett 60.00 120.00
BM Lou Brock / Stan Musial 60.00 120.00
BR Jim Bunning / Robin Roberts 20.00 50.00
BS Ernie Banks / Ryne Sandberg 75.00 150.00
CM Orlando Cepeda / Willie McCovey 30.00 60.00
CS Tom Seaver / Gary Carter 40.00 80.00
DB Bobby Doerr / Wade Boggs 30.00 60.00
EF Dennis Eckersley / Rollie Fingers 20.00 50.00
FB Carlton Fisk / Johnny Bench 40.00 80.00
FC Bob Feller / Steve Carlton 20.00 50.00
FP Bob Feller / Gaylord Perry 20.00 50.00
GC Bob Gibson / Steve Carlton 30.00 60.00
GF Bob Gibson / Whitey Ford 40.00 80.00
IM Monte Irvin / Willie McCovey 30.00 60.00
JJ Joe Morgan / Johnny Bench 50.00 100.00
JM Reggie Jackson / Willie McCovey 50.00 100.00
JW Dave Winfield / Reggie Jackson 50.00 100.00
JY Johnny Bench / Yogi Berra 75.00 150.00
KK Al Kaline / George Kell 50.00 100.00
KP Harmon Killebrew / Kirby Puckett 60.00 120.00
LO Lou Brock / Ozzie Smith 40.00 80.00
MK Bill Mazeroski / Ralph Kiner 40.00 80.00
MP Joe Morgan / Tony Perez 20.00 50.00
MY Paul Molitor / Robin Yount 50.00 100.00
NS Nolan Ryan / Steve Carlton 75.00 150.00
PM Gaylord Perry / Juan Marichal 20.00 50.00
PN Gaylord Perry / Phil Niekro 20.00 50.00
PR Paul Molitor / Rod Carew 30.00 60.00
RC Nolan Ryan / Rod Carew 75.00 150.00
RP Brooks Robinson / Jim Palmer 30.00 60.00
RS Nolan Ryan / Tom Seaver 100.00 200.00
RW Ryne Sandberg / Wade Boggs 60.00 120.00
SB George Brett / Mike Schmidt 75.00 150.00
SC Mike Schmidt / Steve Carlton 50.00 100.00
SK Duke Snider / Ralph Kiner 40.00 80.00
SM Ozzie Smith / Stan Musial 75.00 150.00
SP Don Sutton / Gaylord Perry 20.00 50.00
SR Brooks Robinson / Mike Schmidt 50.00 100.00
SS Ozzie Smith / Red Schoendienst 40.00 80.00
SW Ryne Sandberg / Billy Williams 50.00 100.00
WB Billy Williams / Ernie Banks 50.00 100.00
WJ Billy Williams / Fergie Jenkins 20.00 50.00
WS Dave Winfield / Ozzie Smith 40.00 80.00
WY Whitey Ford / Yogi Berra 60.00 120.00
YF Carl Yastrzemski / Carlton Fisk 60.00 120.00
YJ Carl Yastrzemski / Reggie Jackson 60.00 120.00

2005 Upper Deck Hall of Fame Signs of Cooperstown Triples

STATED PRINT RUN 50 SERIAL #'d SETS
GOLD PRINT RUN 5 SERIAL #'d SETS
NO GOLD PRICING DUE TO SCARCITY
RAINBOW PRINT RUN 1 SERIAL #'d SET
NO RAINBOW PRICING DUE TO SCARCITY
*SILVER: .6X TO 1.5X BASIC
SILVER PRINT RUN 15 SERIAL #'d SETS
OVERALL INSERT ODDS ONE PER TIN

ASY Luis Aparicio / Ozzie Smith / Robin Yount 4.00 10.00
BFJ Brooks Robinson / Frank Robinson / Jim Palmer 2.50 6.00
BSB George Brett / Mike Schmidt / Wade Boggs 6.00 15.00
BSY Ernie Banks / Ozzie Smith / Robin Yount 4.00 10.00
CMI Orlando Cepeda / Willie McCovey / Monte Irvin 2.50 6.00
DFY Bobby Doerr / Carlton Fisk / Carl Yastrzemski 4.00 10.00
DYB Bobby Doerr / Carl Yastrzemski / Wade Boggs 4.00 10.00
FPE Bob Feller / Gaylord Perry / Dennis Eckersley 2.00 5.00
FRC Bob Feller / Nolan Ryan / Steve Carlton 6.00 15.00
FSE Rollie Fingers / Don Sutton / Dennis Eckersley 2.00 5.00
GCE Bob Gibson / Steve Carlton / Dennis Eckersley 2.50 6.00
GSM Bob Gibson / Ozzie Smith / Stan Musial 4.00 10.00
JFB Reggie Jackson / Whitey Ford / Yogi Berra 4.00 10.00
JPR Fergie Jenkins / Gaylord Perry / Nolan Ryan 6.00 15.00
KKB Al Kaline / George Kell / Jim Bunning 3.00 8.00
KPC Harmon Killebrew / Kirby Puckett / Rod Carew 3.00 8.00
KSR Ralph Kiner / Duke Snider / Frank Robinson 2.50 6.00
KWR Al Kaline / Dave Winfield / Frank Robinson 3.00 8.00
MBP Joe Morgan / Johnny Bench / Tony Perez 4.00 10.00
MCM Juan Marichal / Orlando Cepeda / Willie McCovey 2.50 6.00
MMS Bill Mazeroski / Joe Morgan / Red Schoendienst 2.50 6.00
MRJ Eddie Murray / Frank Robinson / Reggie Jackson 3.00 8.00
MSC Joe Morgan / Ryne Sandberg / Rod Carew 6.00 15.00
MYF Paul Molitor / Robin Yount / Rollie Fingers 3.00 8.00
PMC Kirby Puckett / Paul Molitor / Rod Carew 3.00 8.00
RAP Brooks Robinson / Luis Aparicio / Jim Palmer 2.50 6.00
RBC Robin Roberts / Jim Bunning / Steve Carlton 2.00 5.00
RBS Brooks Robinson / George Brett / Mike Schmidt 6.00 15.00
RSR Robin Roberts / Don Sutton / Nolan Ryan 6.00 15.00
SRC Mike Schmidt / Robin Roberts / Steve Carlton 6.00 15.00
WBI Billy Williams / Lou Brock / Monte Irvin 2.50 6.00
WBJ Billy Williams / Ernie Banks / Fergie Jenkins 3.00 8.00
WJB Dave Winfield / Reggie Jackson / Wade Boggs 3.00 8.00
WSP Dave Winfield / Ozzie Smith / Gaylord Perry 4.00 10.00
YKM Carl Yastrzemski / Ralph Kiner / Stan Musial 4.00 10.00

2005 Upper Deck Hall of Fame Signs of Cooperstown Triples Autograph

STATED PRINT RUN 20 SERIAL #'d SETS
GOLD PRINT RUN 5 SERIAL #'d SETS
NO GOLD PRICING DUE TO SCARCITY
RAINBOW PRINT RUN 1 SERIAL #'d SET
NO RAINBOW PRICING DUE TO SCARCITY
SILVER PRINT RUN 10 SERIAL #'d SETS
NO SILVER PRICING DUE TO SCARCITY
OVERALL AUTO ODDS ONE PER TIN

ASY Luis Aparicio / Ozzie Smith / Robin Yount 75.00 150.00
BFJ Brooks Robinson / Frank Robinson / Jim Palmer 60.00 120.00
BSB George Brett / Mike Schmidt / Wade Boggs 150.00 250.00
BSY Ernie Banks / Ozzie Smith / Robin Yount 75.00 150.00
CMI Orlando Cepeda / Willie McCovey / Monte Irvin 50.00 100.00
DFY Bobby Doerr / Carlton Fisk / Carl Yastrzemski 75.00 150.00
DYB Bobby Doerr / Carl Yastrzemski / Wade Boggs 75.00 150.00
FRC Bob Feller / Nolan Ryan / Steve Carlton 100.00 200.00
GSM Bob Gibson / Ozzie Smith / Stan Musial 100.00 200.00
JFB Reggie Jackson / Whitey Ford / Yogi Berra 100.00 200.00

JPR Fergie Jenkins 100.00 200.00
Gaylord Perry
Nolan Ryan
KPC Harmon Killebrew 100.00 175.00
Kirby Puckett
Rod Carew
KSR Ralph Kiner 60.00 120.00
Duke Snider
Frank Robinson
MBP Joe Morgan 100.00 200.00
Johnny Bench
Tony Perez
MCM Juan Marichal 60.00 120.00
Orlando Cepeda
Willie McCovey
MSC Joe Morgan 75.00 150.00
Ryne Sandberg
Rod Carew
MYF Paul Molitor 60.00 120.00
Robin Yount
Rollie Fingers
PMC Kirby Puckett 75.00 150.00
Paul Molitor
Rod Carew
RAP Brooks Robinson 50.00 100.00
Luis Aparicio
Jim Palmer
RBC Robin Roberts 50.00 100.00
Jim Bunning
Steve Carlton
RBS Brooks Robinson 150.00 250.00
George Brett
Mike Schmidt
SRC Mike Schmidt 75.00 150.00
Robin Roberts
Steve Carlton
WJB Dave Winfield 60.00 120.00
Reggie Jackson
Wade Boggs
WSP Dave Winfield 60.00 120.00
Ozzie Smith
Gaylord Perry
YKM Carl Yastrzemski 75.00 150.00
Ralph Kiner
Stan Musial

2005 Upper Deck Hall of Fame Signs of Cooperstown Quads

STATED PRINT RUN 50 SERIAL #'d SETS
GOLD PRINT RUN 5 SERIAL #'d SETS
NO GOLD PRICING DUE TO SCARCITY
RAINBOW PRINT RUN 1 SERIAL #'d SET
NO RAINBOW PRICING DUE TO SCARCITY
*SILVER: .6X TO 1.5X BASIC
SILVER PRINT RUN 15 SERIAL #'d SETS
OVERALL INSERT ODDS ONE PER TIN
BMYC George Brett 6.00 15.00
Paul Molitor
Robin Yount
Rod Carew
BSAY Ernie Banks 4.00 10.00
Ozzie Smith
Luis Aparicio
Robin Yount
FCBB Carlton Fisk 3.00 8.00
Gary Carter
Johnny Bench
Yogi Berra
FGRC Bob Feller 6.00 15.00
Bob Gibson
Nolan Ryan
Steve Carlton
KCPM Harmon Killebrew 3.00 8.00
Orlando Cepeda
Tony Perez
Willie McCovey
KYBM Al Kaline 4.00 10.00
Carl Yastrzemski
Lou Brock
Stan Musial
MBKM Eddie Murray 3.00 8.00
Ernie Banks
Harmon Killebrew
Willie McCovey
MDMC Bill Mazeroski 2.50 6.00
Bobby Doerr
Joe Morgan
Rod Carew
MRKS Eddie Murray 6.00 15.00
Frank Robinson
Harmon Killebrew
Mike Schmidt
RBKS Brooks Robinson 6.00 15.00
George Brett
George Kell
Mike Schmidt
SPNS Don Sutton 2.50 6.00
Gaylord Perry
Phil Niekro
Tom Seaver
SPSF Don Sutton 2.50 6.00
Jim Palmer
Tom Seaver
Whitey Ford
SRCS Don Sutton 6.00 15.00
Nolan Ryan
Steve Carlton
Tom Seaver
WYKM Billy Williams 4.00 10.00
Carl Yastrzemski
Ralph Kiner
Stan Musial
YWMM Carl Yastrzemski 4.00 10.00
Dave Winfield
Eddie Murray
Stan Musial

2005 Upper Deck Hall of Fame Signs of Cooperstown Quads Autograph Silver

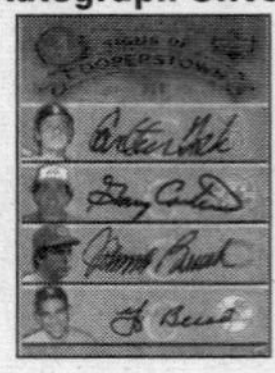

STATED PRINT RUN 10 SERIAL #'d SETS
NO PRICING DUE TO SCARCITY
GOLD PRINT RUN 5 SERIAL #'d SETS
NO GOLD PRICING DUE TO SCARCITY
RAINBOW PRINT RUN 1 #'d SET
NO RAINBOW PRICING DUE TO SCARCITY
OVERALL AUTO ODDS ONE PER TIN
BMYC George Brett
Paul Molitor
Robin Yount
Rod Carew
BSAY Ernie Banks
Ozzie Smith
Luis Aparicio
Robin Yount
FCBB Carlton Fisk
Gary Carter
Johnny Bench
Yogi Berra
FGRC Bob Feller
Bob Gibson
Nolan Ryan
Steve Carlton
KYBM Al Kaline
Carl Yastrzemski
Lou Brock
Stan Musial
MDMC Bill Mazeroski
Bobby Doerr
Joe Morgan
Rod Carew
MRKS Eddie Murray
Frank Robinson
Harmon Killebrew
Mike Schmidt
RBKS Brooks Robinson
George Brett
George Kell
Mike Schmidt
SRCS Don Sutton
Nolan Ryan
Steve Carlton
Tom Seaver
WYKM Billy Williams
Carl Yastrzemski
Ralph Kiner
Stan Musial

2005 Upper Deck Hall of Fame Tins

ISSUED AS COLLECTIBLE PACKAGING
MS Mike Schmidt 3.00 8.00
NR Nolan Ryan 4.00 10.00
SM Stan Musial 2.00 5.00
TC Ty Cobb 2.00 5.00

2001 Upper Deck Hall of Famers

The 2001 Upper Deck Hall of Famers product was released in early April, 2001 and features a 90-card base set that is broken into tiers as follows: Base Veterans (1-50), Origins of the Game (51-60), National Pastime (61-80), and finally Hall of Records (81-90). Each pack contained 5 cards and carried a suggested retail price of $3.99.

COMPLETE SET (90) 8.00 20.00
1 Reggie Jackson .15 .40
2 Hank Aaron .50 1.25
3 Eddie Mathews .25 .60
4 Warren Spahn .15 .40
5 Robin Yount .25 .60
6 Lou Brock .15 .40
7 Dizzy Dean .25 .60
8 Bob Gibson .15 .40
9 Stan Musial .40 1.00
10 Enos Slaughter .08 .25
11 Rogers Hornsby .25 .60
12 Ernie Banks .25 .60
13 Fergie Jenkins .08 .25
14 Roy Campanella .25 .60
15 Pee Wee Reese .25 .60
16 Jackie Robinson .25 .60
17 Juan Marichal .08 .25
18 Christy Mathewson .25 .60
19 Willie Mays .50 1.25
20 Hoyt Wilhelm .08 .25
21 Buck Leonard .08 .25
22 Bob Feller .08 .25
23 Cy Young .25 .60
24 Satchel Paige .25 .60
25 Tom Seaver .15 .40
26 Brooks Robinson .15 .40
27 Mike Schmidt .50 1.25
28 Roberto Clemente .60 1.50
29 Ralph Kiner .08 .25
30 Willie Stargell .15 .40
31 Honus Wagner .30 .75
32 Josh Gibson .25 .60
33 Nolan Ryan .60 1.50
34 Carlton Fisk .15 .40
35 Jimmie Foxx .25 .60
36 Johnny Bench .25 .60
37 Joe Morgan .08 .25
38 George Brett .50 1.25
39 Walter Johnson .25 .60
40 Cool Papa Bell .08 .25
41 Ty Cobb .40 1.00
42 Al Kaline .25 .60
43 Harmon Killebrew .25 .60
44 Luis Aparicio .08 .25
45 Yogi Berra .25 .60
46 Joe DiMaggio .50 1.25
47 Whitey Ford .15 .40
48 Lou Gehrig .50 1.25
49 Mickey Mantle 1.00 2.50
50 Babe Ruth .75 2.00
51 Josh Gibson OG .15 .40
52 Honus Wagner OG .25 .60
53 Hoyt Wilhelm OG .08 .25
54 Cy Young OG .15 .40
55 Walter Johnson OG .15 .40
56 Satchel Paige OG .15 .40
57 Rogers Hornsby OG .15 .40
58 Christy Mathewson OG .15 .40
59 Tris Speaker OG .15 .40
60 Nap Lajoie OG .25 .60
61 Mickey Mantle NP .50 1.25
62 Jackie Robinson NP .15 .40
63 Nolan Ryan NP .40 1.00
64 Josh Gibson NP .15 .40
65 Yogi Berra NP .15 .40
66 Brooks Robinson NP .08 .25
67 Stan Musial NP .25 .60
68 Mike Schmidt NP .25 .60
69 Joe DiMaggio NP .25 .60
70 Ernie Banks NP .15 .40
71 Willie Stargell NP .08 .25
72 Johnny Bench NP .15 .40
73 Willie Mays NP .25 .60
74 Satchel Paige NP .15 .40
75 Bob Gibson NP .08 .25
76 Harmon Killebrew NP .25 .60
77 Al Kaline NP .15 .40
78 Carlton Fisk NP .08 .25
79 Tom Seaver NP .08 .25
80 Reggie Jackson NP .08 .25
81 Bob Gibson HR .08 .25
82 Nolan Ryan HR .40 1.00
83 Walter Johnson HR .15 .40
84 Stan Musial HR .25 .60
85 Josh Gibson HR .15 .40
86 Cy Young HR .15 .40
87 Joe DiMaggio HR .25 .60
88 Hoyt Wilhelm HR .08 .25
89 Lou Brock HR .08 .25
90 Mickey Mantle HR .50 1.25

2001 Upper Deck Hall of Famers 20th Century Showcase

Randomly inserted into packs at one in eight, this 11-card insert set features some of the Major League's top players throughout the 20th Century. Card backs carry an "S" prefix.

COMPLETE SET (11) 12.50 30.00
S1 Cy Young .75 2.00
S2 Joe DiMaggio 1.50 4.00
S3 Harmon Killebrew .75 2.00
S4 Stan Musial 1.25 3.00
S5 Mickey Mantle 3.00 8.00
S6 Satchel Paige .75 2.00
S7 Nolan Ryan 2.00 5.00
S8 Bob Gibson .60 1.50
S9 Ernie Banks .75 2.00
S10 Mike Schmidt 1.50 4.00
S11 Willie Mays 1.50 4.00

2001 Upper Deck Hall of Famers Class of '36

Randomly inserted into packs at one in 17, this 5-card insert features players that were inducted into the Major League Hall of Fame in 1936. Card backs carry a "C" prefix.

COMPLETE SET (5) 6.00 15.00
C1 Ty Cobb 1.25 3.00
C2 Babe Ruth 2.50 6.00
C3 Christy Mathewson .75 2.00
C4 Walter Johnson .75 2.00
C5 Honus Wagner 1.00 2.50

2001 Upper Deck Hall of Famers Cut Signatures

Randomly inserted into packs, this six-card insert set features cut-signatures from the five deceased Major League legends that composed the initial HOF induction class from 1936 in addition to an uttrely ridiculous gatefold 1 of 1 that features signature sfrom all five players together. Card backs carry a "C" prefix followed by the player's initials. Although the cards lack serial-numbering, representatives at Upper Deck announced that a total of only eleven cards were produced for this set with print runs ranging between one and five copies per.

LC1 Honus Wagner
Ty Cobb
Babe Ruth
Christy Mathewson
Walter Johnson/1
CBR Babe Ruth/2
CCM Christy Mathewson/1
CHW Honus Wagner/1
CTC Ty Cobb/2
CWJ Walter Johnson/5

2001 Upper Deck Hall of Famers Endless Summer

Randomly inserted into packs at one in eight, this 11-card insert set features classic players that had amazing careers in Major League Baseball. Card backs carry an "ES" prefix.

COMPLETE SET (11) 12.50 30.00
ES1 Mickey Mantle 3.00 8.00
ES2 Yogi Berra .75 2.00
ES3 Mike Schmidt 1.50 4.00
ES4 Jackie Robinson .75 2.00
ES5 Johnny Bench .75 2.00
ES6 Tom Seaver .75 2.00
ES7 Ernie Banks .75 2.00
ES8 Harmon Killebrew .75 2.00
ES9 Joe DiMaggio 1.50 4.00
ES10 Willie Mays 1.50 4.00
ES11 Brooks Robinson .75 2.00

2001 Upper Deck Hall of Famers Gallery

Randomly inserted into packs at one in six, this 15-card insert features Major League Ballplayers that have been inducted into the Hall of Fame. Card backs carry a "G" prefix.

COMPLETE SET (15) 15.00 40.00
G1 Reggie Jackson .50 1.25
G2 Tom Seaver .50 1.25
G3 Bob Gibson .50 1.25
G4 Jackie Robinson .75 2.00
G5 Joe DiMaggio 1.50 4.00
G6 Ernie Banks .75 2.00
G7 Mickey Mantle 3.00 8.00
G8 Willie Mays 1.50 4.00
G9 Cy Young .75 2.00
G10 Nolan Ryan 2.00 5.00
G11 Johnny Bench .75 2.00
G12 Yogi Berra .75 2.00
G13 Satchel Paige .75 2.00
G14 George Brett 1.50 4.00
G15 Stan Musial 1.25 3.00

2001 Upper Deck Hall of Famers Game Bat

Randomly inserted into packs at one in 24 (about one a box), this 40-card insert features slivers of

actual game-used bats. Card backs carry a "B" prefix followed by the players initials. Though they lack any actual form of serial-numbering, Upper Deck announced specific print runs for several short prints within this set. That information is detailed within our checklist. In addition, based upon extensive market research by our analysts, several cards are tagged with a DP notation to indicate double-printed status.

BBR Babe Ruth 125.00 200.00
BBRO Brooks Robinson 6.00 15.00
BBW Billy Williams 4.00 10.00
BCF Carlton Fisk DP 6.00 15.00
BDD Don Drysdale 6.00 15.00
BDS Duke Snider 6.00 15.00
BEB Ernie Banks 6.00 15.00
BES Enos Slaughter 4.00 10.00
BEW Early Wynn 6.00 15.00
BFR Frank Robinson 6.00 15.00
BGB George Brett DP 6.00 15.00
BGK George Kell 6.00 15.00
BHA Hank Aaron DP 15.00 40.00
BHG Hank Greenberg 20.00 50.00
BJB Johnny Bench DP 6.00 15.00
BJBO Jim Bottomley 6.00 15.00
BJD Joe DiMaggio 50.00 100.00
BJF Jimmie Foxx 30.00 60.00
BJM Johnny Mize 6.00 15.00
BJMO Joe Morgan DP 4.00 10.00
BJP Jim Palmer SP/372 * 50.00 100.00
BJR J.Robinson SP/371 * 75.00 150.00
BLA Luis Aparicio 4.00 10.00
BMM Mickey Mantle 75.00 150.00
BMO Mel Ott 30.00 60.00
BNF Nellie Fox 6.00 15.00
BNR Nolan Ryan 15.00 40.00
BOC Orlando Cepeda 4.00 10.00
BRC R.Clemente SP/409 60.00 120.00
BRCA Roy Campanella 15.00 40.00
BRF Rollie Fingers 4.00 10.00
BRH Rogers Hornsby 50.00 100.00
BRJ Reggie Jackson DP 6.00 15.00
BRK Ralph Kiner 6.00 15.00
BRS Red Schoendienst 6.00 15.00
BRY Robin Yount DP 6.00 15.00
BTP Tony Perez 4.00 10.00
BWM Willie Mays DP 15.00 40.00
BWS Willie Stargell 6.00 15.00
BYB Yogi Berra 6.00 15.00

2001 Upper Deck Hall of Famers Game Jersey

Randomly inserted into packs at one in 168, this 18-card insert features swatches of actual game-used jerseys (barring the Gehrig card of which features Pants fabric). Card backs carry a "J" prefix followed by the players initials. Though they lack actual serial-numbering, Upper Deck announced specific print runs for several short-prints within this set. That information is detailed within our checklist. Of note, the Nolan Ryan card is believed to be noticeably more prevalent than any other card in this set and is tagged as DP do indicate a double printed status.

JBR Brooks Robinson 10.00 25.00
JDD Don Drysdale SP/49 *
JDS Duke Snider SP/267 * 40.00 80.00
JDSU Don Sutton 6.00 15.00
JFR Frank Robinson 10.00 25.00
JJD Joe DiMaggio 60.00 120.00
JJM Joe Morgan 6.00 15.00
JLA Luis Aparicio 6.00 15.00
JLG L.Gehrig Pants SP/194 * 150.00 250.00
JMM Mickey Mantle SP/216 * 150.00 250.00
JNR Nolan Ryan DP 15.00 40.00
JOC Orlando Cepeda 6.00 15.00
JPW Pee Wee Reese 10.00 25.00
JRC Roberto Clemente 60.00 120.00
JTP Tony Perez 6.00 15.00
JTS Tom Seaver 10.00 25.00
JWM Willie Mays 50.00 100.00
JWS Willie Stargell 10.00 25.00

2001 Upper Deck Hall of Famers Game Jersey Autograph

Randomly inserted into packs at one in 504, this 14-card insert features swatches of actual game-used jerseys, as well as, an authentic autograph from the depicted player. Card backs carry a "SJ" prefix followed by the players initials. Willie Stargell was supposed to sign cards for this set but he passed away on April 9th, 2001 . . . before any of the exchange cards were produced.

SJBR Brooks Robinson 30.00 60.00
SJDS Duke Snider 30.00 60.00
SJDSU Don Sutton 15.00 40.00
SJEB Ernie Banks 50.00 100.00
SJFR Frank Robinson 30.00 60.00
SJGB George Brett 60.00 120.00
SJJM Joe Morgan 15.00 40.00
SJLA Luis Aparicio 15.00 40.00
SJNR Nolan Ryan 75.00 150.00
SJOC Orlando Cepeda 15.00 40.00
SJRJ Reggie Jackson 50.00 100.00
SJTP Tony Perez 15.00 40.00
SJTS Tom Seaver 30.00 60.00
SJWS Willie Stargell EXCH

2008 Upper Deck Heroes

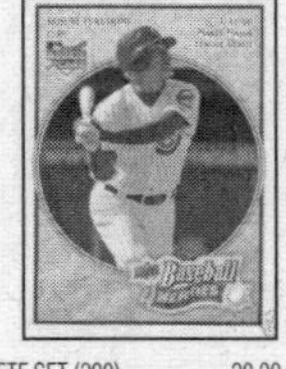

COMPLETE SET (200) 20.00 50.00
COMMON CARD (1-200) .20 .50
COMMON ROOKIE (1-200) .40 1.00
1 Brandon Webb .30 .75
2 Dan Haren .20 .50
3 Chris B. Young .20 .50
4 Justin Upton .50 1.25
5 Randy Johnson .50 1.25
6 Chipper Jones .60 1.50
7 John Smoltz .50 1.25
8 Tom Glavine .30 .75
9 Mark Teixeira .30 .75
10 Brian McCann .30 .75
11 Jeff Francoeur .30 .75
12 Josh Hamilton .60 1.50
13 Tim Hudson .20 .50
14 Nick Markakis .30 .75
15 Brian Roberts .30 .75
16 Cal Ripken Jr. 2.00 5.00
17 John Maine .20 .50
18 Frank Robinson .20 .50
19 Mike Lowell .20 .50
20 Jason Varitek .50 1.25
21 David Ortiz .50 1.25
22 Manny Ramirez .50 1.25
23 Jonathan Papelbon .30 .75
24 Jacoby Ellsbury .75 2.00
25 Kevin Youkilis .30 .75
26 Curt Schilling .30 .75
27 Josh Beckett .30 .75
28 Daisuke Matsuzaka .75 2.00
29 Clay Buchholz (RC) 1.00 2.50
30 Dustin Pedroia .75 2.00
31 Ryan Theriot .20 .50
32 Carlton Fisk .30 .75
33 Carl Yastrzemski .75 2.00
34 Wade Boggs .30 .75
35 Nolan Ryan 1.50 4.00
36 Alfonso Soriano .30 .75
37 Kosuke Fukudome RC 1.50 4.00
38 Derrek Lee .30 .75
39 Carlos Zambrano .20 .50
40 Aramis Ramirez .20 .50
41 Ernie Banks .50 1.25
42 Jim Thome .30 .75
43 Jermaine Dye .20 .50
44 Paul Konerko .20 .50
45 Nick Swisher .20 .50
46 Corey Hart .20 .50
47 Ken Griffey Jr. .75 2.00
48 Adam Dunn .20 .50
49 Aaron Harang .20 .50
50 Johnny Bench .50 1.25
51 Grady Sizemore .30 .75
52 Victor Martinez .20 .50
53 C.C. Sabathia .20 .50
54 Travis Hafner .20 .50
55 Jeff Francis .20 .50
56 Matt Holliday .30 .75
57 Troy Tulowitzki .30 .75
58 Garrett Atkins .20 .50
59 Todd Helton .30 .75
60 Curtis Granderson .20 .50
61 Dontrelle Willis .20 .50
62 Magglio Ordonez .30 .75
63 Gary Sheffield .20 .50
64 Miguel Cabrera .30 .75
65 Justin Verlander .30 .75
66 Ivan Rodriguez .30 .75
67 Al Kaline .50 1.25
68 Hanley Ramirez .50 1.25
69 Edinson Volquez .20 .50
70 Dan Uggla .30 .75
71 Andrew Miller .30 .75
72 Josh Willingham .20 .50
73 J.R. Towles RC 1.00 2.50
74 Lance Berkman .30 .75
75 Carlos Lee .20 .50
76 Roy Oswalt .20 .50
77 Hunter Pence .50 1.25
78 Luke Hochevar RC 1.00 2.50
79 Alex Gordon .50 1.25
80 Matt Cain .20 .50
81 Bo Jackson .50 1.25
82 Vladimir Guerrero .50 1.25
83 Torii Hunter .20 .50
84 Howie Kendrick .20 .50
85 John Lackey .20 .50
86 Chone Figgins .20 .50
87 Andruw Jones .20 .50
88 Brad Penny .20 .50
89 James Loney .30 .75
90 Matt Kemp .20 .50
91 Nomar Garciaparra .50 1.25

92 Jon Lester .30 .75
93 Chin-Lung Hu (RC) .60 1.50
94 Chad Billingsley .20 .50
95 Kelly Johnson .20 .50
96 Prince Fielder .50 1.25
97 Ryan Braun .60 1.50
98 Ben Sheets .30 .75
99 Robin Yount .50 1.25
100 Justin Morneau .30 .75
101 Joe Mauer .30 .75
102 Delmon Young .30 .75
103 Rod Carew .30 .75
104 Carlos Beltran .20 .50
105 Jose Reyes .30 .75
106 Pedro Martinez .30 .75
107 David Wright .60 1.50
108 Johan Santana .30 .75
109 Billy Wagner .20 .50
110 Carlos Delgado .20 .50
111 Mariano Rivera .50 1.25
112 Chien-Ming Wang .60 1.50
113 Phil Hughes .50 1.25
114 Derek Jeter 1.25 3.00
115 Alex Rodriguez .75 2.00
116 Robinson Cano .30 .75
117 Jorge Posada .30 .75
118 Hideki Matsui .50 1.25
119 Joba Chamberlain .60 1.50
120 Ian Kennedy RC 1.00 2.50
121 Yogi Berra .50 1.25
122 Reggie Jackson .30 .75
123 Roger Clemens .60 1.50
124 Ozzie Smith .75 2.00
125 Don Mattingly 1.00 2.50
126 Dave Winfield .20 .50
127 Joe DiMaggio 1.25 3.00
128 Eric Chavez .20 .50
129 Bill Hall .20 .50
130 Rich Harden .20 .50
131 Andre Ethier .30 .75
132 Daric Barton (RC) .40 1.00
133 Ryan Howard .60 1.50
134 Jimmy Rollins .30 .75
135 Chase Utley .50 1.25
136 Cole Hamels .50 1.25
137 Pat Burrell .20 .50
138 Mike Schmidt .75 2.00
139 Steve Carlton .20 .50
140 Freddy Sanchez .20 .50
141 Joe Blanton .20 .50
142 Felix Pie .20 .50
143 Roberto Clemente 1.00 2.50
144 Jake Peavy .30 .75
145 Greg Maddux .60 1.50
146 Tom Gorzelanny .20 .50
147 Tony Gwynn .20 .50
148 Barry Zito .20 .50
149 Tim Lincecum .50 1.25
150 Rich Hill .20 .50
151 Omar Vizquel .20 .50
152 Ichiro Suzuki .75 2.00
153 Felix Hernandez .30 .75
154 Kenji Johjima .20 .50
155 Erik Bedard .20 .50
156 Albert Pujols 1.00 2.50
157 Troy Glaus .30 .75
158 Chris Carpenter .20 .50
159 Chris Duncan .20 .50
160 Mark Mulder .20 .50
161 Scott Rolen .30 .75
162 Stan Musial .75 2.00
163 Bob Gibson .30 .75
164 B.J. Upton .30 .75
165 Carl Crawford .20 .50
166 Scott Kazmir .30 .75
167 Michael Young .20 .50
168 Luke Scott .20 .50
169 Roy Halladay .20 .50
170 Vernon Wells .20 .50
171 Kevin Kouzmanoff .20 .50
172 Frank Thomas .50 1.25
173 Ryan Zimmerman .30 .75
174 Lastings Milledge .20 .50
175 Ian Kinsler .30 .75
176 Don Mattingly 1.00 2.50
Wade Boggs
177 Carlton Fisk .75 2.00
Carl Yastrzemski
178 Albert Pujols .75 2.00
Stan Musial
179 Jose Reyes 1.25 3.00
Derek Jeter
180 Cal Ripken Jr. .20 .50
Tony Gwynn
181 Eddie Murray .50 1.25
Prince Fielder
182 Ichiro Suzuki .75 2.00
Kosuke Fukudome
183 Steve Carlton .20 .50
Johan Santana
184 Bob Gibson .30 .75
Jake Peavy
185 Johnny Bench .50 1.25
Ivan Rodriguez
186 Vladimir Guerrero .75 2.00
Ichiro Suzuki
Manny Ramirez
187 Carl Yastrzemski .30 .75
Carlton Fisk
Wade Boggs
188 Alex Rodriguez 1.25 3.00
Derek Jeter
Robinson Cano
189 Chipper Jones .60 1.50
Ryan Braun
Miguel Cabrera
190 Don Mattingly 1.00 2.50
Dave Winfield
Reggie Jackson
191 Chase Utley .60 1.50
Ryan Howard
Jimmy Rollins
192 Joe Mauer .50 1.25
Hanley Ramirez
Troy Tulowitzki
193 Nolan Ryan 1.50 4.00
Greg Maddux
Randy Johnson
194 Brandon Webb .30 .75
Justin Verlander
Felix Hernandez
195 Mike Schmidt .75 2.00
Ernie Banks
Frank Robinson
196 Derek Jeter 2.00 5.00
Ken Griffey Jr.
Cal Ripken Jr.
Ichiro Suzuki
197 Yogi Berra .30 .75
Reggie Jackson
Joe DiMaggio
Derek Jeter
198 Jonathan Papelbon .50 1.25
Manny Ramirez
Jason Varitek
David Ortiz
199 Ken Griffey Jr. 1.25 3.00
Roberto Clemente
Vladimir Guerrero
Joe DiMaggio
200 Albert Pujols 1.25 3.00
Derek Jeter
Prince Fielder
David Ortiz

2008 Upper Deck Heroes Beige

*BEIGE VET: .75X TO 2X BASIC
*BEIGE RC: .5X TO 1.2X BASIC RC
RANDOM INSERTS IN PACKS
STATED PRINT RUN 299 SER.#'d SETS

2008 Upper Deck Heroes Black

*BLACK VET: .75X TO 2X BASIC
*BLACK RC: .5X TO 1.2X BASIC RC
RANDOM INSERTS IN PACKS
STATED PRINT RUN 399 SER.#'d SETS

2008 Upper Deck Heroes Brown

*BROWN VET: 1X TO 2.5X BASIC
*BROWN RC: .6X TO 1.5X BASIC RC
RANDOM INSERTS IN PACKS
STATED PRINT RUN 149 SER.#'d SETS

2008 Upper Deck Heroes Charcoal

*CHARCOAL VET: .75X TO 2X BASIC
*CHARCOAL RC: .5X TO 1.2X BASIC RC
RANDOM INSERTS IN RETAIL PACKS

2008 Upper Deck Heroes Emerald

*EMERALD VET: .75X TO 2X BASIC
*EMERALD RC: .5X TO 1.2X BASIC RC
RANDOM INSERTS IN PACKS
STATED PRINT RUN 499 SER.#'d SETS

2008 Upper Deck Heroes Light Blue

*LT.BLUE VET: 1.5X TO 4X BASIC
*LT.BLUE RC: 1X TO 2.5X BASIC RC
RANDOM INSERTS IN PACKS
STATED PRINT RUN 49 SER.#'d SETS

2008 Upper Deck Heroes Navy Blue

*NAVY VET: 1X TO 2.5X BASIC
*NAVY RC: .6X TO 1.5X BASIC RC
RANDOM INSERTS IN PACKS
STATED PRINT RUN 199 SER.#'d SETS

2008 Upper Deck Heroes Purple

RANDOM INSERTS IN PACKS
STATED PRINT RUN 25 SER.#'d SETS
NO PRICING DUE TO SCARCITY

2008 Upper Deck Heroes Red

*RED VET: 1X TO 2.5X BASIC
*RED RC: .6X TO 1.5X BASIC RC
RANDOM INSERTS IN PACKS
STATED PRINT RUN 249 SER.#'d SETS

2008 Upper Deck Heroes Sea Green

*SEA GREEN VET: 1.2X TO 3X BASIC
*SEA GREEN RC: .75X TO 2X BASIC RC
RANDOM INSERTS IN PACKS
STATED PRINT RUN 99 SER.#'d SETS

2008 Upper Deck Heroes Autographs Charcoal

RANDOM INSERTS IN BACKS
PRINT RUNS B/WN 11-150 COPIES PER
NO PRICING ON QTY 11 OR LESS
12 Josh Hamilton/150 20.00 50.00
17 John Maine/150
29 Clay Buchholz/95 6.00 15.00
31 Ryan Theriot/150 10.00 25.00
45 Nick Swisher/150 5.00 12.00
46 Corey Hart/150 8.00 20.00
47 Ken Griffey Jr./75 50.00 100.00
49 Aaron Harang/150 4.00 10.00
69 Edinson Volquez/150 10.00 25.00
72 Josh Willingham/11
73 J.R. Towles/150 4.00 10.00
80 Matt Cain/150
86 Chone Figgins/150 4.00 10.00
90 Matt Kemp/150 8.00 20.00
93 Chin-Lung Hu/150 10.00 25.00
94 Chad Billingsley/150 4.00 10.00
95 Kelly Johnson/150 4.00 10.00
120 Ian Kennedy/95 6.00 15.00
131 Andre Ethier/150 8.00 20.00
132 Daric Barton/150 4.00 10.00
141 Joe Blanton/144 4.00 10.00
142 Felix Pie/150 4.00 10.00
146 Tom Gorzelanny/150 4.00 10.00
150 Rich Hill/150 4.00 10.00
168 Luke Scott/148 4.00 10.00
171 Kevin Kouzmanoff/150 4.00 10.00
175 Ian Kinsler/150 5.00 12.00

2008 Upper Deck Heroes Autographs Beige

RANDOM INSERTS IN PACKS
PRINT RUNS B/WN 10-25 COPIES PER
NO PRICING DUE TO SCARCITY

2008 Upper Deck Heroes Autographs Black

RANDOM INSERTS IN PACKS
PRINT RUNS B/WN 25-50 COPIES PER
NO PRICING ON QTY 25 OR LESS
2 Dan Haren/25
3 Chris B. Young/25
10 Brian McCann/50 8.00 20.00
12 Josh Hamilton/50 30.00 60.00
17 John Maine/50 6.00 15.00
29 Clay Buchholz/35 8.00 20.00
31 Ryan Theriot/50 12.50 30.00
45 Nick Swisher/50 6.00 15.00
46 Corey Hart/50 10.00 25.00
47 Ken Griffey Jr./25
49 Aaron Harang/50 5.00 12.00
61 Dontrelle Willis/25
68 Hanley Ramirez/25
69 Edinson Volquez/50 12.50 30.00
71 Andrew Miller/35 5.00 12.00
72 Josh Willingham/50 5.00 12.00
73 J.R. Towles/50
78 Luke Hochevar/50 6.00 15.00
80 Matt Cain/50
84 Howie Kendrick/25
85 John Lackey/25
86 Chone Figgins/50 5.00 12.00
87 Andruw Jones/25
90 Matt Kemp/50 10.00 25.00
93 Chin-Lung Hu/50 12.50 30.00
94 Chad Billingsley/50
95 Kelly Johnson/50 5.00 12.00
114 Derek Jeter/25
120 Ian Kennedy/35 8.00 20.00
132 Daric Barton/50 5.00 12.00
141 Joe Blanton/50 5.00 12.00
142 Felix Pie/50
146 Tom Gorzelanny/50 5.00 12.00
150 Rich Hill/50 5.00 12.00
168 Luke Scott/50 5.00 12.00
171 Kevin Kouzmanoff/50 5.00 12.00
175 Ian Kinsler/50 6.00 15.00

2008 Upper Deck Heroes Autographs Navy Blue

RANDOM INSERTS IN BACKS
PRINT RUNS B/WN 35-100 COPIES PER
12 Josh Hamilton/100 20.00 50.00
17 John Maine/100 5.00 12.00
29 Clay Buchholz/55 8.00 20.00
31 Ryan Theriot/100 10.00 25.00
45 Nick Swisher/100 5.00 12.00
46 Corey Hart/100 8.00 20.00
47 Ken Griffey Jr./35 60.00 120.00
49 Aaron Harang/100 4.00 10.00
69 Edinson Volquez/100 10.00 25.00
71 Andrew Miller/35 5.00 12.00
72 Josh Willingham/100 4.00 10.00
73 J.R. Towles/100 4.00 10.00
80 Matt Cain/100 10.00 25.00
85 John Lackey/65 10.00 25.00
90 Matt Kemp/100 8.00 20.00
93 Chin-Lung Hu/100 10.00 25.00
94 Chad Billingsley/100 4.00 10.00
95 Kelly Johnson/100 4.00 10.00
120 Ian Kennedy/55 6.00 15.00
131 Andre Ethier/100 8.00 20.00
132 Daric Barton/50 5.00 12.00
141 Joe Blanton/100 4.00 10.00
142 Felix Pie/100 4.00 10.00
146 Tom Gorzelanny/100 4.00 10.00
150 Rich Hill/50 5.00 12.00
168 Luke Scott/100 4.00 10.00
171 Kevin Kouzmanoff/100 4.00 10.00
175 Ian Kinsler/100 5.00 12.00

2008 Upper Deck Heroes Autographs Purple

RANDOM INSERTS IN PACKS
STATED PRINT RUN 5 SER.#'d SETS
NO PRICING DUE TO SCARCITY

2008 Upper Deck Heroes Autographs Red

RANDOM INSERTS IN PACKS
STATED PRINT RUN 10 SER.#'d SETS
NO PRICING DUE TO SCARCITY

2008 Upper Deck Heroes Jersey Autograph Emerald

RANDOM INSERTS IN PACKS
PRINT RUNS B/WN 4-5 COPIES PER
NO PRICING DUE TO SCARCITY

2008 Upper Deck Heroes Jersey Autograph Light Blue

RANDOM INSERTS IN PACKS
PRINT RUNS B/WN 5-75 COPIES PER
NO PRICING ON QTY 15 OR LESS
14 Nick Markakis/75
25 Kevin Youkilis/50
46 Corey Hart/75 12.50 30.00
47 Ken Griffey Jr./50 40.00 80.00
49 Aaron Harang/75 4.00 10.00
55 Jeff Francis/50 6.00 15.00
58 Garrett Atkins/35
69 Edinson Volquez/75 10.00 25.00
72 Josh Willingham/5
86 Chone Figgins/15
90 Matt Kemp/75 15.00 40.00
92 Jon Lester/50
93 Chin-Lung Hu/75 15.00 40.00
94 Chad Billingsley/75 20.00 50.00
114 Derek Jeter/35 100.00 150.00
138 Mike Schmidt/35
141 Joe Blanton/75 4.00 10.00
142 Felix Pie/75 4.00 10.00
146 Tom Gorzelanny/75 4.00 10.00
171 Kevin Kouzmanoff/15
175 Ian Kinsler/75 8.00 20.00

2008 Upper Deck Heroes Jersey Autograph Navy Blue

RANDOM INSERTS IN PACKS
PRINT RUNS B/WN 1-10 COPIES PER
NO PRICING DUE TO SCARCITY

2008 Upper Deck Heroes Jersey Autograph Red

RANDOM INSERTS IN PACKS
PRINT RUNS B/WN 3-50 COPIES PER
NO PRICING ON QTY 25 OR LESS
69 Edinson Volquez/50 12.50 30.00
72 Josh Willingham/5
80 Matt Cain/50 10.00 25.00
81 Bo Jackson/25
86 Chone Figgins/15
90 Matt Kemp/50 20.00 50.00
92 Jon Lester/35 20.00 50.00
93 Chin-Lung Hu/50 20.00 50.00
94 Chad Billingsley/50 12.50 30.00
95 Kelly Johnson/50 6.00 15.00
96 Prince Fielder/25
99 Robin Yount/25
103 Rod Carew/25
113 Phil Hughes/25
114 Derek Jeter/25
125 Don Mattingly/25
129 Bill Hall/10
136 Cole Hamels/25
138 Mike Schmidt/25
139 Steve Carlton/25
141 Joe Blanton/50 5.00 12.00
142 Felix Pie/50 5.00 12.00
146 Tom Gorzelanny/50 5.00 12.00
150 Rich Hill/50
153 Felix Hernandez/25
162 Stan Musial/25
163 Bob Gibson/25
164 B.J. Upton/25
169 Roy Halladay/25
171 Kevin Kouzmanoff/5
175 Ian Kinsler/50 10.00 25.00

2008 Upper Deck Heroes Jersey Light Blue

RANDOM INSERTS IN PACKS
STATED PRINT RUN 200 SER.#'d SETS
1 Brandon Webb 3.00 8.00
3 Chris B. Young 3.00 8.00
4 Justin Upton 4.00 10.00
5 Randy Johnson 4.00 10.00
6 Chipper Jones 5.00 12.00
7 John Smoltz 4.00 10.00
9 Mark Teixeira 4.00 10.00
10 Brian McCann 4.00 10.00
11 Jeff Francoeur 4.00 10.00
13 Tim Hudson 3.00 8.00
14 Nick Markakis 6.00 15.00
15 Brian Roberts 4.00 10.00
16 Cal Ripken Jr. 12.50 30.00
17 John Maine 3.00 8.00
18 Frank Robinson 3.00 8.00
19 Mike Lowell 4.00 10.00
20 Jason Varitek 4.00 10.00
21 David Ortiz 4.00 10.00
22 Manny Ramirez 4.00 10.00
23 Jonathan Papelbon 4.00 10.00
24 Jacoby Ellsbury 12.50 30.00
25 Kevin Youkilis 4.00 10.00
26 Curt Schilling 4.00 10.00
27 Josh Beckett 4.00 10.00
28 Daisuke Matsuzaka 6.00 15.00
29 Clay Buchholz 4.00 10.00
33 Carl Yastrzemski 5.00 12.00
34 Wade Boggs 3.00 8.00
35 Nolan Ryan 8.00 20.00
36 Alfonso Soriano 4.00 10.00
37 Kosuke Fukudome 12.50 30.00
38 Derrek Lee 4.00 10.00
39 Carlos Zambrano 3.00 8.00
40 Aramis Ramirez 3.00 8.00
41 Ernie Banks 5.00 12.00
42 Jim Thome 4.00 10.00
43 Jermaine Dye 3.00 8.00
44 Paul Konerko 3.00 8.00
46 Corey Hart 3.00 8.00
47 Ken Griffey Jr. 6.00 15.00
48 Adam Dunn 3.00 8.00
49 Aaron Harang 3.00 8.00
50 Johnny Bench 6.00 15.00
51 Grady Sizemore 4.00 10.00
52 Victor Martinez 3.00 8.00
53 C.C. Sabathia 3.00 8.00
54 Travis Hafner 3.00 8.00
55 Jeff Francis 3.00 8.00
56 Matt Holliday 4.00 10.00
57 Troy Tulowitzki 4.00 10.00
58 Garrett Atkins 3.00 8.00
59 Todd Helton 4.00 10.00
60 Curtis Granderson 4.00 10.00
62 Magglio Ordonez 4.00 10.00
65 Justin Verlander 4.00 10.00
66 Ivan Rodriguez 4.00 10.00
68 Hanley Ramirez 4.00 10.00
69 Edinson Volquez 3.00 8.00
70 Dan Uggla 4.00 10.00
71 Andrew Miller 4.00 10.00
72 Josh Willingham 3.00 8.00
74 Lance Berkman 4.00 10.00
75 Carlos Lee 3.00 8.00
76 Roy Oswalt 3.00 8.00
77 Hunter Pence 4.00 10.00
79 Alex Gordon 4.00 10.00
80 Matt Cain 3.00 8.00
81 Bo Jackson 4.00 10.00
82 Vladimir Guerrero 4.00 10.00
84 Howie Kendrick 3.00 8.00
85 John Lackey 3.00 8.00
86 Chone Figgins 3.00 8.00
88 Brad Penny 3.00 8.00
89 James Loney 4.00 10.00
90 Matt Kemp 3.00 8.00
93 Chin-Lung Hu 4.00 10.00
94 Chad Billingsley 3.00 8.00
95 Kelly Johnson 3.00 8.00
96 Prince Fielder 4.00 10.00
97 Ryan Braun 5.00 12.00
98 Ben Sheets 4.00 10.00
99 Robin Yount 4.00 10.00
100 Justin Morneau 4.00 10.00
101 Joe Mauer 4.00 10.00
103 Rod Carew 4.00 10.00
104 Carlos Beltran 3.00 8.00
106 Pedro Martinez 4.00 10.00
109 Billy Wagner 3.00 8.00
110 Carlos Delgado 3.00 8.00
111 Mariano Rivera 4.00 10.00
112 Chien-Ming Wang 6.00 15.00
113 Phil Hughes 4.00 10.00
114 Derek Jeter 10.00 25.00
115 Alex Rodriguez 8.00 20.00
116 Robinson Cano 4.00 10.00
117 Jorge Posada 4.00 10.00
120 Ian Kennedy 5.00 12.00
121 Yogi Berra 4.00 10.00
123 Roger Clemens 4.00 10.00
124 Ozzie Smith 6.00 15.00
125 Don Mattingly 6.00 15.00
126 Dave Winfield 3.00 8.00
127 Joe DiMaggio
128 Eric Chavez 3.00 8.00
129 Bill Hall 3.00 8.00
130 Rich Harden 3.00 8.00
131 Andre Ethier 4.00 10.00
134 Jimmy Rollins 4.00 10.00
135 Chase Utley 4.00 10.00
136 Cole Hamels 4.00 10.00
137 Pat Burrell 3.00 8.00
138 Mike Schmidt 6.00 15.00
139 Steve Carlton 3.00 8.00
140 Freddy Sanchez 3.00 8.00
142 Felix Pie 3.00 8.00
143 Roberto Clemente 12.50 30.00
144 Jake Peavy 3.00 8.00
145 Greg Maddux 5.00 12.00
146 Tom Gorzelanny 3.00 8.00
147 Tony Gwynn 5.00 12.00
148 Barry Zito 3.00 8.00
149 Tim Lincecum 4.00 10.00
150 Rich Hill 3.00 8.00
151 Omar Vizquel 3.00 8.00
153 Felix Hernandez 4.00 10.00
154 Kenji Johjima 3.00 8.00
156 Albert Pujols 8.00 20.00
157 Troy Glaus 4.00 10.00
158 Chris Carpenter 3.00 8.00
159 Chris Duncan 3.00 8.00
160 Mark Mulder 3.00 8.00
161 Scott Rolen 4.00 10.00
163 Bob Gibson 5.00 12.00
164 B.J. Upton 4.00 10.00
165 Carl Crawford 3.00 8.00
166 Scott Kazmir 4.00 10.00
167 Michael Young 3.00 8.00
169 Roy Halladay 3.00 8.00
170 Vernon Wells 3.00 8.00
171 Kevin Kouzmanoff 3.00 8.00
173 Ryan Zimmerman 4.00 10.00
175 Ian Kinsler 4.00 10.00
176 Don Mattingly 8.00 20.00
Wade Boggs
179 Jose Reyes 8.00 20.00
Derek Jeter
180 Cal Ripken Jr. 15.00 40.00
Tony Gwynn
181 Eddie Murray 4.00 10.00
Prince Fielder
184 Bob Gibson 4.00 10.00
Jake Peavy
185 Johnny Bench 8.00 20.00
Ivan Rodriguez
186 Vladimir Guerrero
Ichiro Suzuki
Manny Ramirez
187 Carl Yastrzemski
Carlton Fisk
Wade Boggs
188 Alex Rodriguez 15.00 40.00
Derek Jeter
Robinson Cano
189 Chipper Jones
Ryan Braun
Miguel Cabrera
190 Don Mattingly 12.50 30.00
Dave Winfield
Reggie Jackson
191 Chase Utley
Ryan Howard
Jimmy Rollins
192 Joe Mauer 4.00 10.00
Hanley Ramirez
Troy Tulowitzki
193 Nolan Ryan 15.00 40.00
Greg Maddux
Randy Johnson
194 Brandon Webb 4.00 10.00
Justin Verlander
Felix Hernandez
195 Mike Schmidt 15.00 40.00
Ernie Banks
Frank Robinson
197 Yogi Berra 30.00 60.00
Reggie Jackson
Joe DiMaggio
Derek Jeter
198 Jonathan Papelbon 8.00 20.00
Manny Ramirez
Jason Varitek
David Ortiz
199 Ken Griffey Jr. 100.00 150.00
Roberto Clemente
Vladimir Guerrero
Joe DiMaggio
200 Albert Pujols 10.00 25.00
Derek Jeter
Prince Fielder
David Ortiz

2008 Upper Deck Heroes Jersey Charcoal

RANDOM INSERTS IN RETAIL PACKS
NO PRICING DUE TO SCARCITY

2008 Upper Deck Heroes Jersey Black

*JSY BLK: .4X TO 1X JSY LT.BLUE
RANDOM INSERTS IN PACKS
STATED PRINT RUN 125 SER.#'d SETS

2008 Upper Deck Heroes Jersey Emerald

RANDOM INSERTS IN PACKS
PRINT RUNS B/WN 5-25 COPIES PER
NO PRICING DUE TO SCARCITY

2008 Upper Deck Heroes Jersey Navy Blue

*JSY NAVY: .5X TO 1.2X JSY LT.BLUE
RANDOM INSERTS IN PACKS
STATED PRINT RUN 50 SER.#'d SETS

2008 Upper Deck Heroes Patch Autograph

RANDOM INSERTS IN PACKS
PRINT RUNS B/WN 4-50 COPIES PER
NO PRICING ON QTY 25 OR LESS
1 Brandon Webb/25
3 Chris B. Young/15
6 Chipper Jones/15
8 Tom Glavine/10
10 Brian McCann/25
11 Jeff Francoeur/25
13 Tim Hudson/25
14 Nick Markakis/5
16 Cal Ripken Jr./25
17 John Maine/50 10.00 25.00
18 Frank Robinson/10
23 Jonathan Papelbon/25
25 Kevin Youkilis/25
27 Josh Beckett/10
28 Daisuke Matsuzaka/10
33 Carl Yastrzemski/25
35 Nolan Ryan/10
36 Alfonso Soriano/10
38 Derrek Lee/10
41 Ernie Banks/10
42 Jim Thome/10
44 Paul Konerko/25
46 Corey Hart/50 15.00 40.00
47 Ken Griffey Jr./25
48 Adam Dunn/23
49 Aaron Harang/50 6.00 15.00
50 Johnny Bench/10
52 Victor Martinez/25
54 Travis Hafner/25
55 Jeff Francis/25
58 Garrett Atkins/15
65 Justin Verlander/15
68 Hanley Ramirez/25
69 Edinson Volquez/50 20.00 50.00
72 Josh Willingham/25
74 Lance Berkman/25
75 Carlos Lee/25
76 Roy Oswalt/10
79 Alex Gordon/10
80 Matt Cain/9
81 Bo Jackson/15
85 John Lackey/10
86 Chone Figgins/15
90 Matt Kemp/25
94 Chad Billingsley/50 20.00 50.00
95 Kelly Johnson/50 10.00 25.00
96 Prince Fielder/25
97 Ryan Braun/10
99 Robin Yount/10
100 Justin Morneau/10
101 Joe Mauer/15
103 Rod Carew/10
106 Pedro Martinez/10
109 Billy Wagner/15
112 Chien-Ming Wang/10
113 Phil Hughes/10
114 Derek Jeter/10
123 Roger Clemens/10
124 Ozzie Smith/25
125 Don Mattingly/10
126 Dave Winfield/10
128 Eric Chavez/15
129 Bill Hall/15
130 Rich Harden/10
136 Cole Hamels/25
138 Mike Schmidt/10
139 Steve Carlton/10
141 Joe Blanton/50 6.00 15.00
142 Felix Pie/50 10.00 25.00
146 Tom Gorzelanny/50 10.00 25.00
147 Tony Gwynn/10
149 Tim Lincecum/10
150 Rich Hill/50 6.00 15.00
153 Felix Hernandez/15
156 Albert Pujols/10
162 Stan Musial/4
163 Bob Gibson/10

164 B.J. Upton/25
169 Roy Halladay/10
170 Vernon Wells/10
171 Kevin Kouzmanoff/25
175 Ian Kinsler/50

2008 Upper Deck Heroes Patch Light Blue

RANDOM INSERTS IN PACKS
STATED PRINT RUN 25 SER.#'d SETS
NO PRICING DUE TO SCARCITY

2008 Upper Deck Heroes Patch Beige

RANDOM INSERTS IN PACKS
PRINT RUNS B/WN 1-25 COPIES PER
NO PRICING DUE TO SCARCITY

2008 Upper Deck Heroes Patch Purple

RANDOM INSERTS IN PACKS
STATED PRINT RUN 5 SER.#'d SETS
NO PRICING DUE TO SCARCITY

2000 Upper Deck Legends

The 2000 Upper Deck Legends product was released in late August, 2000 and featured a 135-card base set that was broken into tiers as follows: (90) Base Veterans (1-90), (15) Y2K Subset cards (91-105) (1:9), and (30) 20th Century Legends Subset cards (106-135) (1:5). Each pack contained five cards and carried a suggested retail price of $4.99. Also, a selection of A Piece of History 3000 Club Paul Molitor and Carl Yastrzemski memorabilia cards were randomly seeded into packs. 350 bat cards for each player were produced. Also for Carl Yatszremski only, 350 jersey cards, 100 hand-numbered bat-jersey combination cards and eight autographed, hand-numbered, combination bat-jersey cards were produced. Pricing for these memorabilia cards can be referenced under 2000 Upper Deck A Piece of History 3000 Club.

COMPLETE SET (135) 30.00 80.00
COMP.SET w/o SP'S (90) 8.00 20.00
COMMON CARD (1-90) .10 .30
COMMON CARD (91-105) .75 2.00
COMMON (106-135) .75 2.00
1 Darin Erstad .10 .30
2 Troy Glaus .10 .30
3 Mo Vaughn .10 .30
4 Craig Biggio .20 .50
5 Jeff Bagwell .20 .50
6 Reggie Jackson .20 .50
7 Tim Hudson .10 .30
8 Jason Giambi .10 .30
9 Hank Aaron .60 1.50
10 Greg Maddux .50 1.25
11 Chipper Jones .30 .75
12 Andres Galarraga .10 .30
13 Robin Yount .50 1.25
14 Jeromy Burnitz .10 .30
15 Paul Molitor .10 .30
16 David Wells .10 .30
17 Carlos Delgado .10 .30
18 Ernie Banks .30 .75
19 Sammy Sosa .30 .75
20 Kerry Wood .10 .30
21 Stan Musial .50 1.25
22 Bob Gibson .20 .50
23 Mark McGwire .75 2.00
24 Fernando Tatis .10 .30
25 Randy Johnson .30 .75
26 Matt Williams .10 .30
27 Jackie Robinson .30 .75
28 Sandy Koufax .75 2.00
29 Shawn Green .10 .30
30 Kevin Brown .20 .50
31 Gary Sheffield .10 .30
32 Greg Vaughn .10 .30
33 Jose Canseco .20 .50
34 Gary Carter .10 .30
35 Vladimir Guerrero .30 .75
36 Willie Mays .60 1.50
37 Barry Bonds .75 2.00
38 Jeff Kent .10 .30
39 Bob Feller .10 .30
40 Roberto Alomar .20 .50
41 Jim Thome .20 .50
42 Manny Ramirez .20 .50
43 Alex Rodriguez .50 1.25
44 Preston Wilson .10 .30
45 Tom Seaver .20 .50
46 Robin Ventura .10 .30
47 Mike Piazza .50 1.25
48 Mike Hampton .10 .30
49 Brooks Robinson .20 .50
50 Frank Robinson .20 .50
51 Cal Ripken 1.00 2.50
52 Albert Belle .10 .30
53 Eddie Murray .30 .75
54 Tony Gwynn .40 1.00
55 Roberto Clemente .60 1.50
56 Willie Stargell .20 .50
57 Brian Giles .10 .30
58 Jason Kendall .10 .30
59 Mike Schmidt .60 1.50
60 Bob Abreu .10 .30
61 Scott Rolen .20 .50
62 Curt Schilling .10 .30
63 Johnny Bench .30 .75
64 Sean Casey .10 .30
65 Barry Larkin .20 .50
66 Ken Griffey Jr. .50 1.25
67 George Brett .75 2.00
68 Carlos Beltran .10 .30
69 Nolan Ryan 1.00 2.50
70 Ivan Rodriguez .20 .50
71 Rafael Palmeiro .20 .50
72 Larry Walker .10 .30
73 Todd Helton .20 .50
74 Jeff Cirillo .10 .30
75 Carl Everett .10 .30
76 Nomar Garciaparra .50 1.25
77 Pedro Martinez .20 .50
78 Harmon Killebrew .30 .75
79 Corey Koskie .10 .30
80 Ty Cobb .50 1.25
81 Dean Palmer .10 .30
82 Juan Gonzalez .10 .30
83 Carlton Fisk .20 .50
84 Frank Thomas .30 .75
85 Magglio Ordonez .10 .30
86 Lou Gehrig .60 1.50
87 Babe Ruth 1.00 2.50
88 Derek Jeter .75 2.00
89 Roger Clemens .60 1.50
90 Bernie Williams .20 .50
91 Rick Ankiel Y2K .75 2.00
92 Kip Wells Y2K .75 2.00
93 Pat Burrell Y2K .75 2.00
94 Mark Quinn Y2K .75 2.00
95 Ruben Mateo Y2K .75 2.00
96 Adam Kennedy Y2K .75 2.00
97 Brad Penny Y2K .75 2.00
98 K.Sasaki Y2K RC .75 2.00
99 Peter Bergeron Y2K .75 2.00
100 Rafael Furcal Y2K .75 2.00
101 Eric Munson Y2K .75 2.00
102 Nick Johnson Y2K .75 2.00
103 Rob Bell Y2K .75 2.00
104 Vernon Wells Y2K .75 2.00
105 Ben Petrick Y2K .75 2.00
106 Babe Ruth 20C 3.00 8.00
107 Mark McGwire 20C 2.00 5.00
108 Nolan Ryan 20C 2.50 6.00
109 Hank Aaron 20C 1.50 4.00
110 Barry Bonds 20C 2.00 5.00
111 N.Garciaparra 20C 1.25 3.00
112 Roger Clemens 20C 1.50 4.00
113 Johnny Bench 20C .75 2.00
114 Alex Rodriguez 20C 1.25 3.00
115 Cal Ripken 20C 2.50 6.00
116 Willie Mays 20C 1.50 4.00
117 Mike Piazza 20C 1.25 3.00
118 Reggie Jackson 20C .75 2.00
119 Tony Gwynn 20C 1.00 2.50
120 Cy Young 20C .75 2.00
121 George Brett 20C 1.50 4.00
122 Greg Maddux 20C 1.25 3.00
123 Yogi Berra 20C .75 2.00
124 Sammy Sosa 20C .75 2.00
125 Randy Johnson 20C .75 2.00
126 Bob Gibson 20C .75 2.00
127 Lou Gehrig 20C 2.00 5.00
128 Ken Griffey Jr. 20C 1.25 3.00
129 Derek Jeter 20C 2.00 5.00
130 Mike Schmidt 20C 1.50 4.00
131 Pedro Martinez 20C .75 2.00
132 Jackie Robinson 20C .75 2.00
133 Jose Canseco 20C .75 2.00
134 Ty Cobb 20C 1.25 3.00
135 Stan Musial 20C 1.25 3.00

2000 Upper Deck Legends Commemorative Collection

Randomly inserted into packs, this 135-card insert is a complete parallel of the Upper Deck Legends base set. Each card in this set is individually serial numbered to 100.

*ACTIVE STARS 1-90: 8X TO 20X BASIC
*POST-WAR STARS 1-90: 10X TO 25X BASIC
*PRE-WAR STARS 1-90: 6X TO 15X BASIC
*Y2K: 2X TO 5X BASIC Y2K
*ACTIVE 20C: 3X TO 8X BASIC 20C
*POST-WAR 20C: 5X TO 12X BASIC 20C
*PRE-WAR 20C: 2.5X TO 6X BASIC 20C

2000 Upper Deck Legends Defining Moments

Randomly inserted into packs at one in 12, this 10-card insert focuses on some of Major League baseball's most defining moments. Card backs carry a "DM" prefix.

COMPLETE SET (10) 20.00 50.00
DM1 Reggie Jackson .60 1.50
DM2 Hank Aaron 2.00 5.00
DM3 Babe Ruth 3.00 8.00
DM4 Cal Ripken 3.00 8.00
DM5 Carlton Fisk .60 1.50
DM6 Ken Griffey Jr. 1.50 4.00
DM7 Nolan Ryan 3.00 8.00
DM8 Roger Clemens 2.00 5.00
DM9 Willie Mays 2.00 5.00
DM10 Mark McGwire 2.50 6.00

2000 Upper Deck Legends Eternal Glory

Randomly inserted into packs at one in 24, this six-card insert features players whose greatness will live on in the minds of many. Please note that card number 3 does not exist. Card backs carry an "EG" prefix.

COMPLETE SET (6) 15.00 40.00
EG1 Nolan Ryan 4.00 10.00
EG2 Ken Griffey Jr. 2.00 5.00
EG3 Does Not Exist
EG4 Sammy Sosa 1.25 3.00
EG5 Derek Jeter 3.00 8.00
EG6 Willie Mays 2.50 6.00
EG7 Roger Clemens 2.50 6.00

2000 Upper Deck Legends Legendary Game Jerseys

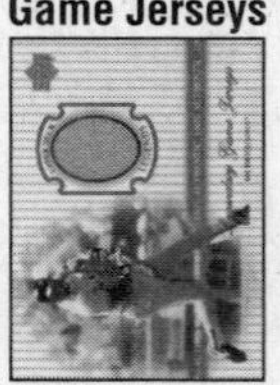

Randomly inserted into packs at one in 48, this 50-card insert set features game-used jersey cards of past and present Major League stars. Cards are numbered using the player's initials with a "J" prefix.

SP'S ARE NOT SERIAL-NUMBERED
SP INFO PROVIDED BY UPPER DECK
JAR Alex Rodriguez 10.00 25.00
JBAB Barry Bonds 15.00 40.00
JBG Bob Gibson Pants 6.00 15.00
JBM Bill Mazeroski 4.00 10.00
JBOB Bobby Bonds 4.00 10.00
JBR Brooks Robinson 6.00 15.00
JCJ Chipper Jones 6.00 15.00
JCR Cal Ripken 15.00 40.00
JDC Dave Concepcion 4.00 10.00
JDD Don Drysdale 6.00 15.00
JDJ Derek Jeter 15.00 40.00
JDM Dale Murphy 6.00 15.00
JDW Dave Winfield 4.00 10.00
JEM Eddie Mathews 6.00 15.00
JEW Earl Weaver 4.00 10.00
JFR Frank Robinson 6.00 15.00
JFT Frank Thomas 6.00 15.00
JGB George Brett 10.00 25.00
JGM Greg Maddux 10.00 25.00
JGP Gaylord Perry 4.00 10.00
JHA Hank Aaron 30.00 60.00
JJB Jeff Bagwell 6.00 15.00
JJB Johnny Bench 6.00 15.00
JJC Jose Canseco 6.00 15.00
JJP Jim Palmer 4.00 10.00
JJT Joe Torre 6.00 15.00
JKG Ken Griffey Jr. 10.00 25.00
JLB Lou Brock 6.00 15.00
JLG Lou Gehrig Pants 125.00 200.00
JMM Mickey Mantle 75.00 150.00
JMR Manny Ramirez 6.00 15.00
JMS Mike Schmidt 10.00 25.00
JMW Matt Williams 4.00 10.00
JMW Maury Wills 4.00 10.00
JNR Nolan Ryan 15.00 40.00
JOS Ozzie Smith 6.00 15.00
JRAJ Randy Johnson 6.00 15.00
JRC Roger Clemens 10.00 25.00
JRF Rollie Fingers 4.00 10.00
JRJ Reggie Jackson 6.00 15.00
JRM Roger Maris Pants 40.00 80.00
JSK Sandy Koufax SP/95 175.00 300.00
JSM Stan Musial SP/28
JTG Tony Gwynn 6.00 15.00
JTM Thurman Munson 15.00 40.00
JTS Tom Seaver 6.00 15.00
JWB Wade Boggs 6.00 15.00
JWM Willie Mays SP/29
JWMC Willie McCovey 4.00 10.00
JWS Willie Stargell 6.00 15.00
SJSK Sandy Koufax AU/32

2000 Upper Deck Legends Legendary Signatures

Randomly inserted into packs at one in 24, this 39-card insert features autographed cards of past and present superstars. Card backs are numbered using the player's initials and an "S" prefix. Though print run numbers were not initially released, Upper Deck did confirm to Beckett Publications that Hank Aaron, Derek Jeter and Manny Ramirez signed less cards than other players in the set. Specific quantities for each of these players is detailed in the checklist below. Finally, Dave Concepcion, Frank Thomas, Ken Griffey Jr., Manny Ramirez, Mo Vaughn, Ozzie Smith and Willie Stargell cards were inserted in packs as stickered exchange cards. The deadline for this exchange was April 22nd, 2001. In addition to the exchange cards, real autographed cards did make their into packs for the following players: Willie Stargell, Ozzie Smith and Dave Concepcion.

SAD Andre Dawson 6.00 15.00
SAR Alex Rodriguez 60.00 120.00
SAT Alan Trammell 6.00 15.00
SBB Bobby Bonds 15.00 40.00
SCJ Chipper Jones 20.00 50.00
SCR Cal Ripken 60.00 120.00
SDC D.Concepcion EXCH* 6.00 15.00
SDJ Derek Jeter SP/61 400.00 600.00
SDM Dale Murphy 10.00 25.00
SFL Fred Lynn 6.00 15.00
SFT Frank Thomas 20.00 50.00
SGB George Brett 50.00 100.00
SGC Gary Carter 6.00 15.00
SHA Hank Aaron SP/94 175.00 300.00
SHK Harmon Killebrew 15.00 40.00
SIR Ivan Rodriguez 15.00 40.00
SJB Johnny Bench 15.00 40.00
SJC Jose Canseco 10.00 25.00
SJP Jim Palmer 6.00 15.00
SKG Ken Griffey Jr. 60.00 120.00
SLB Lou Brock 10.00 25.00
SMP Mike Piazza 75.00 150.00
SMR Manny Ramirez SP/141 30.00 60.00
SMS Mike Schmidt 30.00 60.00
SMV Mo Vaughn 6.00 15.00
SMW Matt Williams 10.00 25.00
SNR Nolan Ryan 90.00 150.00
SOS Ozzie Smith 15.00 40.00
SPN Phil Niekro 6.00 15.00
SRC Roger Clemens 60.00 120.00
SRF Rollie Fingers 6.00 15.00
SRJ Reggie Jackson 20.00 50.00
SSC Sean Casey 6.00 15.00
SSM Stan Musial 30.00 60.00
STG Tony Gwynn 15.00 40.00
STS Tom Seaver 15.00 40.00
SVG Vladimir Guerrero 15.00 40.00
SWS Willie Stargell 40.00 80.00
EXCH*
SRAJ Randy Johnson 40.00 80.00

2000 Upper Deck Legends Legendary Signatures Gold

Randomly inserted into packs, this set is a parallel of the Legendary Signatures insert. Each card features gold colored fronts (instead of silver for the basic cards) and is individually serial numbered to 50 on front in blue ink sharpie. Each card is numbered on the back using the player's initials and an "S" prefix. Also, Dave Concepcion, Frank Thomas, Ken Griffey Jr., Manny Ramirez, Mo Vaughn, Ozzie Smith and Willie Stargell cards were inserted in packs as stickered exchange cards. The deadline for this exchange was April 22nd, 2001. In addition to the exchange cards, real autographed cards did make their into packs for the following players: Willie Stargell, Ozzie Smith and Dave Concepcion. Please note, that Derek Jeter did not sign any Gold cards. The Yankees star shortstop signed only 61 cards for this entire product - all of which were basic Legendary Signatures.

SAD Andre Dawson 15.00 40.00
SAR Alex Rodriguez 125.00 200.00
SAT Alan Trammell 15.00 40.00
SBB Bobby Bonds 40.00 80.00
SCJ Chipper Jones 40.00 80.00
SCR Cal Ripken 125.00 200.00
SDC D.Concepcion EXCH* 15.00 40.00
SDM Dale Murphy 20.00 50.00
SFL Fred Lynn 15.00 40.00
SFT Frank Thomas 40.00 80.00
SGB George Brett 75.00 150.00
SGC Gary Carter 15.00 40.00
SHA Hank Aaron 175.00 300.00
SHK Harmon Killebrew 40.00 80.00
SIR Ivan Rodriguez 40.00 80.00
SJB Johnny Bench 40.00 80.00
SJC Jose Canseco 20.00 50.00
SJP Jim Palmer 15.00 40.00
SKG Ken Griffey Jr. 125.00 200.00
SLB Lou Brock 20.00 50.00
SMP Mike Piazza 125.00 200.00
SMR M.Ramirez EXCH 40.00 80.00
SMS Mike Schmidt 75.00 150.00
SMV Mo Vaughn 15.00 40.00
SMW Matt Williams 20.00 50.00
SNR Nolan Ryan 125.00 200.00
SOS Ozzie Smith 50.00 100.00
SPN Phil Niekro 15.00 40.00
SRC Roger Clemens 125.00 200.00
SRF Rollie Fingers 15.00 40.00
SRJ Reggie Jackson 40.00 80.00
SSC Sean Casey 15.00 40.00
SSM Stan Musial 50.00 100.00
STG Tony Gwynn 50.00 100.00
STS Tom Seaver 40.00 80.00
SVG Vladimir Guerrero 40.00 80.00
SWS Willie Stargell 40.00 80.00
SRAJ Randy Johnson 75.00 150.00

2000 Upper Deck Legends Millennium Team

Randomly inserted into packs at one in four, this nine-card insert features the most famous players of the 20th Century. Please note that card number 6 does not exist. Card backs carry a "UD" prefix.

COMPLETE SET (9) 4.00 10.00
UD1 Mark McGwire .75 2.00
UD2 Jackie Robinson .30 .75
UD3 Mike Schmidt .60 1.50
UD4 Cal Ripken 1.00 2.50
UD5 Babe Ruth 1.00 2.50
UD6 Does Not Exist
UD7 Willie Mays .60 1.50
UD8 Johnny Bench .30 .75
UD9 Nolan Ryan 1.00 2.50
UD10 Ken Griffey Jr. .50 1.25

2000 Upper Deck Legends Ones for the Ages

Randomly inserted into packs at one in 24, this seven-card insert features Major League Baseball's most legendary players. Card backs carry an "O" prefix.

COMPLETE SET (7) 10.00 25.00
O1 Ty Cobb 2.00 5.00
O2 Cal Ripken 4.00 10.00
O3 Babe Ruth 4.00 10.00
O4 Jackie Robinson 1.25 3.00
O5 Mark McGwire 3.00 8.00
O6 Alex Rodriguez 2.00 5.00
O7 Mike Piazza 2.00 5.00

2000 Upper Deck Legends Reflections in Time

Randomly inserted into packs at one in 12, this 10-card insert features dual-player cards of players that have had very similar major league careers. Card backs carry a "R" prefix.

COMPLETE SET (10) 15.00 40.00
R1 Ken Griffey Jr. 1.50 4.00
Hank Aaron
R2 Sammy Sosa 1.00 2.50
Roberto Clemente
R3 Roger Clemens 2.00 5.00
Nolan Ryan
R4 Ivan Rodriguez 1.00 2.50
Johnny Bench
R5 Alex Rodriguez 1.50 4.00
Ernie Banks
R6 Tony Gwynn 1.50 4.00
Stan Musial
R7 Barry Bonds 2.00 5.00
Willie Mays
R8 Cal Ripken 2.00 5.00
Lou Gehrig
R9 Chipper Jones 2.00 5.00
Mike Schmidt
R10 Mark McGwire 3.00 8.00
Babe Ruth

2001 Upper Deck Legends

This 90 card set was released in July, 2001. The cards were issued in five card packs with an SRP of $4.99 per pack and these packs were issued 24 to a box. The set has a mixture of past and present superstars.

COMPLETE SET (90) 8.00 20.00
1 Darin Erstad .10 .30
2 Troy Glaus .10 .30
3 Nolan Ryan .75 2.00
4 Reggie Jackson .20 .50
5 Catfish Hunter .20 .50
6 Jason Giambi .10 .30
7 Tim Hudson .10 .30
8 Miguel Tejada .10 .30
9 Carlos Delgado .10 .30
10 Shannon Stewart .10 .30
11 Greg Vaughn .10 .30
12 Larry Doby .10 .30
13 Jim Thome .20 .50
14 Juan Gonzalez .10 .30
15 Roberto Alomar .20 .50
16 Edgar Martinez .20 .50
17 John Olerud .10 .30
18 Eddie Murray .30 .75
19 Cal Ripken 1.00 2.50
20 Alex Rodriguez .50 1.25
21 Ivan Rodriguez .20 .50
22 Rafael Palmeiro .20 .50
23 Jimmie Foxx .30 .75
24 Cy Young .30 .75
25 Manny Ramirez Sox .20 .50
26 Pedro Martinez .20 .50
27 Nomar Garciaparra .50 1.25
28 George Brett .60 1.50
29 Mike Sweeney .10 .30
30 Jermaine Dye .10 .30
31 Ty Cobb .50 1.25
32 Dean Palmer .10 .30
33 Harmon Killebrew .30 .75
34 Matt Lawton .10 .30
35 Luis Aparicio .10 .30
36 Frank Thomas .30 .75
37 Magglio Ordonez .10 .30
38 David Wells .10 .30
39 Mickey Mantle 1.25 3.00
40 Joe DiMaggio .60 1.50
41 Roger Maris .30 .75
42 Babe Ruth 1.00 2.50
43 Derek Jeter .75 2.00
44 Roger Clemens .60 1.50
45 Bernie Williams .20 .50
46 Jeff Bagwell .20 .50
47 Richard Hidalgo .10 .30
48 Warren Spahn .20 .50
49 Greg Maddux .50 1.25
50 Chipper Jones .30 .75
51 Andruw Jones .20 .50
52 Robin Yount .30 .75
53 Jeromy Burnitz .10 .30
54 Jeffrey Hammonds .10 .30
55 Ozzie Smith .50 1.25
56 Stan Musial .50 1.25
57 Mark McGwire .75 2.00
58 Jim Edmonds .10 .30
59 Sammy Sosa .30 .75
60 Ernie Banks .30 .75
61 Kerry Wood .10 .30
62 Randy Johnson .30 .75
63 Luis Gonzalez .10 .30
64 Don Drysdale .20 .50
65 Jackie Robinson .30 .75
66 Gary Sheffield .10 .30
67 Kevin Brown .10 .30
68 Vladimir Guerrero .30 .75
69 Willie Mays .60 1.50
70 Mel Ott .30 .75
71 Jeff Kent .10 .30
72 Barry Bonds .75 2.00
73 Preston Wilson .10 .30
74 Ryan Dempster .10 .30
75 Tom Seaver .20 .50
76 Mike Piazza .50 1.25
77 Robin Ventura .10 .30
78 Dave Winfield .10 .30
79 Tony Gwynn .40 1.00
80 Bob Abreu .10 .30
81 Scott Rolen .20 .50
82 Mike Schmidt .60 1.50
83 Roberto Clemente .75 2.00
84 Brian Giles .10 .30
85 Ken Griffey Jr. .50 1.25
86 Frank Robinson .20 .50
87 Johnny Bench .30 .75
88 Todd Helton .20 .50
89 Larry Walker .10 .30
90 Mike Hampton .10 .30

2001 Upper Deck Legends Fiorentino Collection

Inserted in packs at a rate of one in 12, these 14 cards feature the original artwork of James Fiorentino. The cards have a "F" prefix.

COMPLETE SET (14) 15.00 40.00
F1 Babe Ruth 3.00 8.00
F2 Satchel Paige 1.00 2.50
F3 Joe DiMaggio 2.00 5.00
F4 Willie Mays 2.00 5.00
F5 Ty Cobb 1.50 4.00
F6 Nolan Ryan 3.00 8.00
F7 Lou Gehrig 2.00 5.00
F8 Jackie Robinson 1.00 2.50
F9 Hank Aaron 2.00 5.00
F10 Roberto Clemente 2.00 5.00
F11 Stan Musial 1.25 3.00
F12 Johnny Bench 1.00 2.50
F13 Honus Wagner 1.00 2.50
F14 Reggie Jackson 1.00 2.50

2001 Upper Deck Legends Legendary Cuts

Randomly inserted in packs, these six cards feature cut signatures from the five original members of the

Hall of Fame. Due to scarcity, no pricing is provided.

C1 Ty Cobb
Babe Ruth
Christy Mathewson
Walter Johnson
Honus Wagner/1
CBR Babe Ruth/3
CCM Christy Mathewson/1
CHW Honus Wagner/2
CTC Ty Cobb/3
CWJ Walter Johnson/3

2001 Upper Deck Legends Legendary Game Jersey

Issued at a rate of one in 24, these 33 cards feature authentic game jersey pieces from past and current players. A few players are perceived to be produced in larger quantites, we have notated those players with asterisks in our checklist. In addition, a few players were printed in shorter supply. We have notated those players with an SP as well as print run information provided by Upper Deck.

GOLD RANDOM INSERTS IN PACKS
GOLD PRINT RUN 25 SERIAL #'d SETS
NO GOLD PRICING DUE TO SCARCITY

Card		
JAR Alex Rodriguez	6.00	15.00
JBB Barry Bonds	10.00	25.00
JCJ Chipper Jones	6.00	15.00
JCR Cal Ripken DP	15.00	40.00
JDW Dave Winfield	4.00	10.00
JEB Ernie Banks Uniform	6.00	15.00
JGM Greg Maddux	6.00	15.00
JGS Gary Sheffield	4.00	10.00
JHA Hank Aaron	30.00	60.00
JIR Ivan Rodriguez DP	6.00	15.00
JJB Jeff Bagwell	6.00	15.00
JJC Jose Canseco	6.00	15.00
JJD Joe DiMaggio Uniform SP/245 *	75.00	150.00
JKG Ken Griffey Jr.	6.00	15.00
JKS Kazuhiro Sasaki	4.00	10.00
JMM Mickey Mantle Uniform SP/245 *	150.00	250.00
JMP Mike Piazza	6.00	15.00
JMR Manny Ramirez Sox	6.00	15.00
JNR Nolan Ryan	15.00	40.00
JOS Ozzie Smith DP	6.00	15.00
JPM Pedro Martinez	6.00	15.00
JRCL Roger Clemens	6.00	15.00
JRJA R.Jackson Uniform	6.00	15.00
JRJO Randy Johnson DP	6.00	15.00
JRM Roger Maris SP/343 *	60.00	120.00
JROC R.Clemente SP/195 *	60.00	120.00
JRY Robin Yount	6.00	15.00
JSM Stan Musial Uniform SP/490 *	20.00	50.00
JSS Sammy Sosa	6.00	15.00
JTG Tony Gwynn Uni DP	6.00	15.00
JTS Tom Seaver	6.00	15.00
JWM Willie Mays	20.00	50.00
JYB Yogi Berra Uniform	6.00	15.00

2001 Upper Deck Legends Legendary Game Jersey Autographs

Issued at a rate of one in 288, these cards feature not only a game jersey piece but an authentic autograph of the player pictured. Ken Griffey Jr. did not return his cards in time for packout; those cards could be redeemed until July 9, 2004. In addition, a few cards were produced in lesser quantites. Those cards are notated in our checklist with an SP and print run information provided by Upper Deck.

GOLD RANDOM INSERTS IN PACKS
GOLD PRINT RUN 25 SERIAL #'d SETS
NO GOLD PRICING DUE TO SCARCITY

Card		
SJAR Alex Rodriguez	75.00	150.00
SJEB Ernie Banks Uni	40.00	80.00
SJKG Ken Griffey Jr.	60.00	120.00
SJNR Nolan Ryan	75.00	150.00
SJOS Ozzie Smith	30.00	60.00
SJRC R.Clemens SP/211	75.00	150.00
SJRJ R.Jackson Uni SP/224	40.00	80.00
SJSM S.Musial SP/266	60.00	120.00
SJSS Sammy Sosa SP/91	50.00	100.00
SJTS Tom Seaver	30.00	60.00

2001 Upper Deck Legends Legendary Lumber

Inserted in packs at a rate of one in 24, these 32 cards feature authentic game bat pieces from past and current players. A few cards are available in larger supply and we have notated those with a DP

tag our checklist. In addition, certain cards were short printed. We have notated those with an SP as well as print run information provided by Upper Deck.

GOLD RANDOM INSERTS IN PACKS
GOLD PRINT RUN 25 SERIAL #'d SETS
NO GOLD PRICING DUE TO SCARCITY

Card		
LAJ Andruw Jones	6.00	15.00
LAP Albert Pujols	50.00	80.00
LAR Alex Rodriguez	6.00	15.00
LBB Barry Bonds DP	10.00	25.00
LCJ Chipper Jones	6.00	15.00
LCR Cal Ripken	15.00	40.00
LEB Ernie Banks SP/80 *	30.00	60.00
LEM Eddie Murray	6.00	15.00
LFR Frank Robinson	6.00	15.00
LGS Gary Sheffield DP	4.00	10.00
LHA Hank Aaron	15.00	40.00
LIR Ivan Rodriguez DP	6.00	15.00
LJB Johnny Bench	6.00	15.00
LJC Jose Canseco	6.00	15.00
LJD Joe DiMaggio	50.00	100.00
LJF Jimmie Foxx SP/351 *	30.00	60.00
LKG Ken Griffey Jr.	6.00	15.00
LLA Luis Aparicio	4.00	10.00
LMM Mickey Mantle	75.00	150.00
LMO Mel Ott SP/355	20.00	50.00
LMP Mike Piazza	6.00	15.00
LMR Manny Ramirez Sox	6.00	15.00
LOS Ozzie Smith	6.00	15.00
LRCA R.Campanella SP/335 *	30.00	60.00
LRCL Roger Clemens	6.00	15.00
LRJ Reggie Jackson	6.00	15.00
LRJ Randy Johnson	6.00	15.00
LRM Roger Maris	20.00	50.00
LROC R.Clemente SP/170 *	60.00	120.00
LSS Sammy Sosa DP	6.00	15.00
LTG Tony Gwynn	6.00	15.00
LWM Willie Mays DP	15.00	40.00

2001 Upper Deck Legends Legendary Lumber Autographs

This partial parallel to the Legendary Lumber insert set features authentic autographs from the player on the card. Ken Griffey Jr. did not return his cards in time for inclusion in packs. These cards were redeemable until July 9, 2004. In addition, a few cards were signed in lesser quantities. We have notated those cards with an SP and print run information provided by Upper Deck.

GOLD RANDOM INSERTS IN PACKS
GOLD PRINT RUN 25 SERIAL #'d SETS
NO GOLD PRICING DUE TO SCARCITY

Card		
SLAR Alex Rodriguez	75.00	150.00
SLEB Ernie Banks	40.00	80.00
SLEM Eddie Murray	30.00	60.00
SLKG Ken Griffey Jr.	60.00	120.00
SLLA Luis Aparicio	20.00	50.00
SLRC R.Clemens SP/227	60.00	120.00
SLRJ R.Jackson SP/211	30.00	60.00
SLSS Sammy Sosa SP/66	50.00	100.00
SLTG Tony Gwynn	40.00	80.00

2001 Upper Deck Legends Reflections in Time

Issued at a rate of one in 18, these 10 cards feature an past and present player from the same team.

Card		
COMPLETE SET (10)	12.50	30.00
R1 Bernie Williams Mickey Mantle	4.00	10.00
R2 Pedro Martinez Cy Young	.60	1.50
R3 Barry Bonds Willie Mays	3.00	8.00
R4 Scott Rolen Mike Schmidt	2.00	5.00
R5 Mark McGwire Stan Musial	2.50	6.00
R6 Ken Griffey Jr. Frank Robinson	1.50	4.00
R7 Sammy Sosa Andre Dawson	1.00	2.50
R8 Kevin Brown Don Drysdale	.60	1.50
R9 Jason Giambi Reggie Jackson	.60	1.50
R10 Tim Hudson Jim Catfish Hunter	.60	1.50

2001 Upper Deck Legends of NY

This product was released in late December, 2001. The 200-card base set features baseball greats like Babe Ruth and Mickey Mantle. Each pack contained five cards and carried a suggested retail price of $2.99

Card		
COMPLETE SET (200)	20.00	50.00
1 Billy Herman	.20	.50
2 Carl Erskine	.20	.50
3 Burleigh Grimes	.20	.50
4 Don Newcombe	.20	.50
5 Gil Hodges	.50	1.25
6 Pee Wee Reese	.50	1.25
7 Jackie Robinson	.50	1.25
8 Duke Snider	.30	.75
9 Jim Gilliam	.20	.50
10 Roy Campanella	.50	1.25
11 Carl Furillo	.20	.50
12 Casey Stengel	.30	.75
13 Casey Stengel DB	.30	.75
14 Billy Herman DB	.15	.40
15 Jackie Robinson DB	.30	.75
16 Jackie Robinson DB	.30	.75
17 Gil Hodges DB	.50	1.25
18 Carl Furillo DB	.15	.40
19 Roy Campanella DB	.30	.75
20 Don Newcombe DB	.15	.40
21 Duke Snider DB	.20	.50
22 Casey Stengel BNS	.20	.50
23 Burleigh Grimes BNS	.15	.40
24 Pee Wee Reese BNS	.30	.75
25 Jackie Robinson BNS	.30	.75
26 Jackie Robinson BNS	.30	.75
27 Carl Erskine BNS	.15	.40
28 Roy Campanella BNS	.30	.75
29 Duke Snider BNS	.20	.50
30 Rube Marquard	.20	.50
31 Ross Youngs	.20	.50
32 Bobby Thomson	.20	.50
33 Christy Mathewson	.50	1.25
34 Carl Hubbell	.50	1.25
35 Hoyt Wilhelm	.20	.50
36 Johnny Mize	.20	.50
37 John McGraw	.30	.75
38 Monte Irvin	.20	.50
39 Travis Jackson	.20	.50
40 Mel Ott	.50	1.25
41 Dusty Rhodes	.15	.40
42 Leo Durocher	.20	.50
43 John McGraw BG	.20	.50
44 Christy Mathewson BG	.30	.75
45 The Polo Grounds BG	.15	.40
46 Travis Jackson BG	.15	.40
47 Mel Ott BG	.30	.75
48 Johnny Mize BG	.15	.40
49 Leo Durocher BG	.15	.40
50 Bobby Thomson BG	.15	.40
51 Monte Irvin BG	.15	.40
52 Bobby Thomson BG	.15	.40
53 Christy Mathewson BNS	.30	.75
54 Christy Mathewson BNS	.30	.75
55 Christy Mathewson BNS	.30	.75
56 John McGraw BNS	.20	.50
57 John McGraw BNS	.20	.50
58 John McGraw BNS	.20	.50
59 Travis Jackson BNS	.15	.40
60 Mel Ott BNS	.30	.75
61 Mel Ott BNS	.30	.75
62 Carl Hubbell BNS	.20	.50
63 Bobby Thomson BNS	.15	.40
64 Monte Irvin BNS	.15	.40
65 Al Weis	.15	.40
66 Donn Clendenon	.15	.40
67 Ed Kranepool	.20	.50
68 Gary Carter	.20	.50
69 Tommie Agee	.20	.50
70 Jon Matlack	.15	.40
71 Ken Boswell	.15	.40
72 Len Dykstra	.20	.50
73 Nolan Ryan	1.25	3.00
74 Ray Sadecki	.15	.40
75 Ron Darling	.20	.50
76 Ron Swoboda	.20	.50
77 Dwight Gooden	.20	.50
78 Tom Seaver	.30	.75
79 Wayne Garrett	.15	.40
80 Casey Stengel MM	.20	.50
81 Tom Seaver MM	.20	.50
82 Tommie Agee MM	.15	.40
83 Tom Seaver MM	.20	.50
84 Yogi Berra MM	.30	.75
85 Yogi Berra MM	.30	.75
86 Tom Seaver MM	.20	.50
87 Dwight Gooden MM	.20	.50
88 Gary Carter MM	.15	.40
89 Ron Darling MM	.15	.40
90 Tommie Agee BNS	.15	.40
91 Tom Seaver BNS	.20	.50
92 Gary Carter BNS	.15	.40
93 Len Dykstra BNS	.15	.40
94 Babe Ruth	1.50	4.00
95 Bill Dickey	.30	.75
96 Rich Gossage	.20	.50
97 Casey Stengel UER Card has a Dodger logo on the back	.30	.75
98 Catfish Hunter	.30	.75
99 Charlie Keller	.15	.40
100 Chris Chambliss	.20	.50
101 Don Larsen	.20	.50
102 Dave Winfield	.20	.50
103 Don Mattingly	1.00	2.50
104 Elston Howard	.30	.75
105 Frankie Crosetti	.20	.50
106 Hank Bauer	.20	.50
107 Joe DiMaggio	1.00	2.50
108 Graig Nettles	.20	.50
109 Lefty Gomez	.30	.75
110 Phil Rizzuto	.50	1.25
111 Lou Gehrig	1.00	2.50
112 Lou Piniella	.20	.50
113 Mickey Mantle	2.00	5.00
114 Red Rolfe	.20	.50
115 Reggie Jackson	.30	.75
116 Roger Maris	.50	1.25
117 Roy White	.15	.40
118 Thurman Munson	.50	1.25
119 Tom Tresh	.20	.50
120 Tommy Henrich	.20	.50
121 Waite Hoyt	.20	.50
122 Willie Randolph	.20	.50
123 Whitey Ford	.30	.75
124 Yogi Berra	.50	1.25
125 Babe Ruth BT	.75	2.00
126 Babe Ruth BT	.75	2.00
127 Lou Gehrig BT	.50	1.25
128 Babe Ruth BT	.75	2.00
129 Joe DiMaggio BT	.50	1.25
130 Joe DiMaggio BT	.50	1.25
131 Mickey Mantle BT	1.00	2.50
132 Roger Maris BT	.30	.75
133 Mickey Mantle BT	1.00	2.50
134 Reggie Jackson BT	.20	.50
135 Babe Ruth BNS	.75	2.00
136 Babe Ruth BNS	.75	2.00
137 Babe Ruth BNS	.75	2.00
138 Lefty Gomez BNS	.20	.50
139 Lou Gehrig BNS	.50	1.25
140 Lou Gehrig BNS	.50	1.25
141 Joe DiMaggio BNS	.50	1.25
142 Joe DiMaggio BNS	.50	1.25
143 Casey Stengel BNS	.20	.50
144 Mickey Mantle BNS	1.00	2.50
145 Yogi Berra BNS	.30	.75
146 Mickey Mantle BNS	1.00	2.50
147 Elston Howard BNS	.20	.50
148 Whitey Ford BNS	.20	.50
149 Reggie Jackson BNS	.20	.50
150 Reggie Jackson BNS	.20	.50
151 John McGraw Babe Ruth	.75	2.00
152 Babe Ruth John McGraw	.75	2.00
153 Lou Gehrig Mel Ott	.50	1.25
154 Joe DiMaggio Mel Ott	.50	1.25
155 Joe DiMaggio Billy Herman	.50	1.25
156 Joe DiMaggio Jackie Robinson	.50	1.25
157 Mickey Mantle Bobby Thomson	1.00	2.50
158 Yogi Berra Pee Wee Reese	.30	.75
159 Roy Campanella Mickey Mantle	1.00	2.50
160 Don Larsen Duke Snider	.20	.50
161 Christy Mathewson TT	.30	.75
162 Christy Mathewson TT	.30	.75
163 Rube Marquard TT	.15	.40
164 Christy Mathewson TT	.30	.75
165 John McGraw TT	.20	.50
166 Burleigh Grimes TT	.15	.40
167 Babe Ruth TT	.75	2.00
168 Burleigh Grimes TT	.15	.40
169 Babe Ruth TT	.75	2.00
170 John McGraw TT	.20	.50
171 Lou Gehrig TT	.50	1.25
172 Babe Ruth TT	.75	2.00
173 Babe Ruth TT	.75	2.00
174 Carl Hubbell TT	.20	.50
175 Joe DiMaggio TT	.50	1.25
176 Lou Gehrig TT	.50	1.25
177 Leo Durocher TT	.15	.40
178 Mel Ott TT	.30	.75
179 Joe DiMaggio TT	.50	1.25
180 Jackie Robinson TT	.30	.75
181 Babe Ruth TT	.75	2.00
182 Bobby Thomson TT	.15	.40
183 Joe DiMaggio TT	.50	1.25
184 Mickey Mantle TT	1.00	2.50
185 Monte Irvin TT	.15	.40
186 Roy Campanella TT	.30	.75
187 Duke Snider TT	.30	.75
188 Dusty Rhodes TT	.15	.40
189 Yogi Berra TT	.30	.75
190 Mickey Mantle TT	1.00	2.50
191 Mickey Mantle TT	1.00	2.50
192 Casey Stengel TT	.20	.50
193 Tom Seaver TT	.20	.50
194 Mickey Mantle TT UER Text has Mantle retiring in 1939	1.00	2.50
195 Tommie Agee TT	.15	.40
196 Tom Seaver TT	.20	.50
197 Chris Chambliss TT	.15	.40
198 Reggie Jackson TT	.20	.50
199 Reggie Jackson TT	.20	.50
200 Gary Carter TT	.15	.40

2001 Upper Deck Legends of NY Combo Autographs

Randomly inserted into packs, this nine-card insert set features dual-autographs from Hall of Famers like Nolan Ryan and Tom Seaver. Each card is individually serial numbered to 25. Due to market scarcity, no pricing is provided.

SCN Chris Chambliss Graig Nettles
SGJ Ron Guidry Tommy John
SLB Don Larsen Yogi Berra
SNP Don Newcombe Johnny Podres
SRD Willie Randolph Bucky Dent
SRS Nolan Ryan Tom Seaver
SRW Mickey Rivers Roy White
SWJ Dave Winfield Reggie Jackson
SWM Dave Winfield Don Mattingly

2001 Upper Deck Legends of NY Cut Signatures

This five-card insert set features authentic cut signatures from deceased greats like Babe Ruth and Jackie Robinson. There were a total of 49 cut cards issued in this set. Specific print runs are listed in our checklist.

LCBR Babe Ruth/5
LCGH Gil Hodges/1
LCJD Joe DiMaggio/38
LCJR Jackie Robinson/3
LCMO Mel Ott/2

2001 Upper Deck Legends of NY Game Base

This two card set features game-used base cards of Jackie Robinson and Tom Seaver. Each card is individually serial numbered to 100.

GOLD RANDOM INSERTS IN PACKS
GOLD PRINT RUN 25 SERIAL #'d SETS
NO GOLD PRICING DUE TO SCARCITY
SILVER RANDOM INSERTS IN PACKS
SILVER PRINT RUN 50 SERIAL #'d SETS
SILVER NO PRICING DUE TO SCARCITY
EFJR Jackie Robinson
SSTS Tom Seaver

2001 Upper Deck Legends of NY Game Bat

This 33-card insert set features authentic game-used bat chips. Collectors received either on bat or jersey card per box. A few cards were produced in lesser quantites, those print runs are provided in our checklist.

Card		
LDBBH Billy Herman	4.00	10.00
LDBDN Don Newcombe SP/67		
LDBJG Jim Gilliam	4.00	10.00
LGBBTH Bobby Thomson	4.00	10.00
LMBAW Al Weis	4.00	10.00
LMBDC Donn Clendenon SP/60		
LMBEK Ed Kranepool	4.00	10.00
LMBGC Gary Carter	4.00	10.00
LMBJM J.C. Martin	4.00	10.00
LMBKB Ken Boswell	4.00	10.00
LMBLD Len Dykstra	4.00	10.00
LMBNR Nolan Ryan	15.00	40.00
LMBRS Ron Swoboda	4.00	10.00
LMBTS Tom Seaver	6.00	15.00
LMBWG Wayne Garrett	4.00	10.00
LYBBD Bill Dickey	6.00	15.00
LYBBR Babe Ruth SP/107	125.00	200.00
LYBCC Chris Chambliss SP/130		
LYBCK Charlie Keller	4.00	10.00
LYBDM Don Mattingly	10.00	25.00
LYBDW Dave Winfield UER Playing career has the wrong years	4.00	10.00
LYBEH Elston Howard	6.00	15.00
LYBHB Hank Bauer	4.00	10.00
LYBJD Joe DiMaggio SP/43		
LYBLP Lou Piniella	4.00	10.00
LYBMM Mickey Mantle SP/134	75.00	150.00
LYBMR Mickey Rivers	4.00	10.00
LYBRJ Reggie Jackson	6.00	15.00
LYBRM Roger Maris SP/60	50.00	100.00
LYBTH Tommy Henrich	4.00	10.00
LYBTM Thurman Munson	12.50	30.00
LYBTT Tom Tresh	4.00	10.00
LYBYB Yogi Berra	6.00	15.00

2001 Upper Deck Legends of NY Game Bat Autograph

This insert set is a partial parallel to the 2001 Upper Deck Legends of NY Game Bat insert. Each of these cards were signed, and issued into packs at 1:336. A few cards were printed in lesser quantities, those print runs are provided in our checklist.

Card		
SDBDN Don Newcombe	15.00	40.00
SMBDC Donn Clendenon	20.00	50.00
SMBGC Gary Carter	15.00	40.00
SMBNR N.Ryan SP/129	75.00	150.00
SMBRS Ron Swoboda		
SMBTS Tom Seaver SP/89	50.00	100.00
SYBCC Chris Chambliss	15.00	40.00
SYBDM Don Mattingly	40.00	80.00
SYBDW D.Winfield SP/167	30.00	60.00
SYBMR Mickey Rivers	15.00	40.00
SYBRJ R.Jackson SP/123	50.00	100.00
SYBRW Roy White	15.00	40.00
SYBYB Yogi Berra	40.00	80.00

2001 Upper Deck Legends of NY Game Jersey

This 36-card insert set features authentic game-used jersey swatches. Collectors received either on bat or jersey card per box. A few cards were printed in small quantities, those print runs are provided in our checklist.

Card		
LDJCE Carl Erskine	4.00	10.00
LDJJR J.Rob Pants SP/126	75.00	150.00
LMJCS Casey Stengel	6.00	15.00
LMJJM Jon Matlack	4.00	10.00
LMJRD Ron Darling	4.00	10.00
LMJRS Ray Sadecki	4.00	10.00
LMJTS Tom Seaver	6.00	15.00
LYJBT Bob Turley	4.00	10.00
LYJCD Chuck Dressen	4.00	10.00
LYJCH Catfish Hunter	6.00	15.00
LYJCM C.Mathewson SP/63	250.00	400.00
LYJDM Duke Maas	4.00	10.00
LYJDW Dave Winfield	4.00	10.00
LYJEH Elston Howard	6.00	15.00
LYJFC Frank Crosetti	4.00	10.00
LYJGN Graig Nettles	4.00	10.00
LYJHB Hank Behrman	4.00	10.00
LYJHB Hank Bauer	4.00	10.00
LYJJD Joe DiMaggio SP/63	100.00	200.00
LYJJP Joe Pepitone	4.00	10.00
LYJJT Joe Torre	6.00	15.00
LYJLM Lindy McDaniel	4.00	10.00
LYJMM Mickey Mantle SP/63		
LYJPN Phil Niekro	4.00	10.00
LYJRM Roger Maris SP/63	50.00	100.00
LYJRR Red Rolfe	4.00	10.00
LYJSJ Spider Jorgensen	4.00	10.00
LYJTH Tommy Henrich	4.00	10.00
LYJTM Thurman Munson	15.00	40.00
LYJWR Willie Randolph	4.00	10.00

2001 Upper Deck Legends of NY Game Jersey Autograph

This 22-card insert is a partial parallel to the 2001 Upper Deck Legends of NY Game Jersey insert set. Each of these cards were signed, and issued into packs at 1:336. A few cards were printed in lesser quantity and those cards are notated in our checklist as SP's along with print run information provided by Upper Deck.

Card		
SDJCE Carl Erskine	15.00	40.00
SDJJG Jim Gilliam SP/49		
SDJJP J. Podres SP/193	20.00	50.00
SMJCS Craig Swan	10.00	25.00
SMJGF G.Foster SP/196	15.00	40.00
SMJNR Nolan Ryan SP/47		
SMJTS Tom Seaver SP/60		
SYJBD Bucky Dent	15.00	40.00
SYJDL Don Larsen	15.00	40.00
SYJDM Don Mattingly SP/72	60.00	120.00
SYJDR Dave Righetti	15.00	40.00
SYJGN Graig Nettles	15.00	40.00

SYJHL H.Lopez SP/195 15.00 40.00
SYJJP Joe Pepitone 15.00 40.00
SYJPN P.Niekro SP/195 15.00 40.00
SYJRJ Reggie Jackson SP/47
SYJSL Sparky Lyle 15.00 40.00
SYJTJ Tommy John 15.00 40.00
SYJWR Willie Randolph 15.00 40.00
SYJYB Yogi Berra SP/73
SYJRIG R.Gossage SP/145 15.00 40.00
SYJROG Ron Guidry 20.00 50.00

2001 Upper Deck Legends of NY Game Jersey Gold

This 24-card insert is a partial parallel set to the 2001 Upper Deck Legends of NY Game Jersey set, and features game-used jersey cards on a gold-foil based card. Print runs, of which vary between 125 and 500 numbered copies, are listed for each card in our checklist.

LDJCD C.Dressen/400 5.00 12.00
LDJCE Carl Erskine/400 5.00 12.00
LDJHB H.Behrman/500 5.00 12.00
LDJSJ S.Jorgensen/500 5.00 12.00
LMJJM Jon Matlack/400 5.00 12.00
LMJRD Ron Darling/400 5.00 12.00
LMJRS Ray Sadecki/400 5.00 12.00
LMJTS Tom Seaver/400 8.00 20.00
LYJBT Bob Turley/400 5.00 12.00
LYJCH C.Hunter/500 8.00 20.00
LYJDM Duke Maas/400 5.00 12.00
LYJDW D.Winfield/250 6.00 15.00
LYJEH E.Howard/400 8.00 20.00
LYJFC Frank Crosetti/400 5.00 12.00
LYJGN Graig Nettles/250 6.00 15.00
LYJHB Hank Bauer/400 5.00 12.00
LYJJP Joe Pepitone/250 6.00 15.00
LYJJT Joe Torre/250 10.00 25.00
LYJLM L.McDaniel/400 5.00 12.00
LYJPN Phil Niekro/125 8.00 20.00
LYJRR Red Rolfe/400 5.00 12.00
LYJTH T.Henrich/400 5.00 12.00
LYJTM T.Munson/400 20.00 50.00
LYJWR W.Randolph/125 8.00 20.00

2001 Upper Deck Legends of NY Stadium Seat

This two card set features stadium seat cards of Jackie Robinson and Mickey Mantle. Each card is individually serial numbered to 100.

GOLD RANDOM INSERTS IN PACKS
GOLD PRINT RUN 25 SERIAL #'d SETS
GOLD NO PRICING DUE TO SCARCITY
SILVER RANDOM INSERTS IN PACKS
SILVER PRINT RUN 50 SERIAL #'d SETS
SILVER NO PRICING DUE TO SCARCITY
EFSJR Jackie Robinson 15.00 40.00
YSMM Mickey Mantle 60.00 120.00

2001 Upper Deck Legends of NY Tri-Combo Autographs

Randomly inserted into packs, this seven-card insert set features tri-combo autographs from greats like Ryan/Seaver/Swoboda. Each card is individually serial numbered to 25. Each card carries a "S" prefix. Due to market scarcity, no pricing is provided.

CND Chris Chambliss
Graig Nettles
Bucky Dent
GJG Ron Guidry
Tommy John
Goose Gossage
LBP Don Larsen
Yogi Berra
Joe Pepitone
LRG Sparky Lyle
Dave Righetti
Goose Gossage
NPE Don Newcombe
Johnny Podres
Carl Erskine
RSS Nolan Ryan
Tom Seaver
Ron Swoboda
WMN Dave Winfield
Don Mattingly
Graig Nettles

2001 Upper Deck Legends of NY United We Stand

This 15-card insert set honors the FDNY/PDNY for their relief work in the Sept. 11, 2001 terrorist attacks in New York. Card backs carry a "USA" prefix. This insert was issued at a rate of 1:12 packs.

COMPLETE SET (15) 30.00 60.00
COMMON CARD (1-15) 2.00 5.00

1999 Upper Deck MVP

This 220 card set was distributed in 10 cards packs with an SRP of $1.59 per pack. Cards numbered from 218 through 220 are checklist subsets. Approximately 350 Mike Schmidt A Piece of History 500 Home Run Game-Used bat cards were distributed in this product. In addition, 20 hand serial numbered versions of this card personally signed by Schmidt himself were also randomly seeded into packs. Pricing for these bat cards can be referenced under 1999 Upper Deck A Piece of History 500 Club. A Ken Griffey Jr. Sample card was distributed to dealers and hobby media several weeks prior to the product's national release. Unlike most Upper Deck promotional cards, this card does not have the word "SAMPLE" pasted across the back of the card. The card, however, is numbered "S3". It's believed that cards S1 and S2 were Upper Deck MVP football and basketball promo cards.

COMPLETE SET (220) 10.00 25.00
1 Mo Vaughn .07 .20
2 Tim Belcher .07 .20
3 Jack McDowell .07 .20
4 Troy Glaus .10 .30
5 Darin Erstad .07 .20
6 Tim Salmon .10 .30
7 Jim Edmonds .07 .20
8 Randy Johnson .20 .50
9 Steve Finley .07 .20
10 Travis Lee .07 .20
11 Matt Williams .07 .20
12 Todd Stottlemyre .07 .20
13 Jay Bell .07 .20
14 David Dellucci .07 .20
15 Chipper Jones .20 .50
16 Andruw Jones .10 .30
17 Greg Maddux .30 .75
18 Tom Glavine .10 .30
19 Javy Lopez .07 .20
20 Brian Jordan .07 .20
21 George Lombard .07 .20
22 John Smoltz .10 .30
23 Cal Ripken .60 1.50
24 Charles Johnson .07 .20
25 Albert Belle .07 .20
26 Brady Anderson .07 .20
27 Mike Mussina .10 .30
28 Calvin Pickering .07 .20
29 Ryan Minor .07 .20
30 Jerry Hairston Jr. .07 .20
31 Nomar Garciaparra .30 .75
32 Pedro Martinez .10 .30
33 Jason Varitek .20 .50
34 Troy O'Leary .07 .20
35 Donnie Sadler .07 .20
36 Mark Portugal .07 .20
37 John Valentin .07 .20
38 Kerry Wood .07 .20
39 Sammy Sosa .20 .50
40 Mark Grace .10 .30
41 Henry Rodriguez .07 .20
42 Rod Beck .07 .20
43 Benito Santiago .07 .20
44 Kevin Tapani .07 .20
45 Frank Thomas .20 .50
46 Mike Caruso .07 .20
47 Magglio Ordonez .07 .20
48 Paul Konerko .07 .20
49 Ray Durham .07 .20
50 Jim Parque .07 .20
51 Carlos Lee .07 .20
52 Denny Neagle .07 .20
53 Pete Harnisch .07 .20
54 Michael Tucker .07 .20
55 Sean Casey .07 .20
56 Eddie Taubensee .07 .20
57 Barry Larkin .10 .30
58 Pokey Reese .07 .20
59 Sandy Alomar Jr. .07 .20
60 Roberto Alomar .10 .30
61 Bartolo Colon .07 .20
62 Kenny Lofton .07 .20
63 Omar Vizquel .10 .30
64 Travis Fryman .07 .20
65 Jim Thome .10 .30
66 Manny Ramirez .10 .30
67 Jaret Wright .07 .20
68 Darryl Kile .07 .20
69 Kirt Manwaring .07 .20
70 Vinny Castilla .07 .20
71 Todd Helton .10 .30
72 Dante Bichette .07 .20
73 Larry Walker .07 .20
74 Derrick Gibson .07 .20
75 Gabe Kapler .07 .20
76 Dean Palmer .07 .20
77 Matt Anderson .07 .20
78 Bobby Higginson .07 .20
79 Damion Easley .07 .20
80 Tony Clark .07 .20
81 Juan Encarnacion .07 .20
82 Livan Hernandez .07 .20
83 Alex Gonzalez .07 .20
84 Preston Wilson .07 .20
85 Derrek Lee .10 .30
86 Mark Kotsay .07 .20
87 Todd Dunwoody .07 .20
88 Cliff Floyd .07 .20
89 Ken Caminiti .07 .20
90 Jeff Bagwell .10 .30
91 Moises Alou .07 .20
92 Craig Biggio .10 .30
93 Billy Wagner .07 .20
94 Richard Hidalgo .07 .20
95 Derek Bell .07 .20
96 Hipolito Pichardo .07 .20
97 Jeff King .07 .20
98 Carlos Beltran .10 .30
99 Jeremy Giambi .07 .20
100 Larry Sutton .07 .20
101 Johnny Damon .10 .30
102 Dee Brown .07 .20
103 Kevin Brown .10 .30
104 Chan Ho Park .07 .20
105 Raul Mondesi .07 .20
106 Eric Karros .07 .20
107 Adrian Beltre .07 .20
108 Devon White .07 .20
109 Gary Sheffield .07 .20
110 Sean Berry .07 .20
111 Alex Ochoa .07 .20
112 Marquis Grissom .07 .20
113 Fernando Vina .07 .20
114 Jeff Cirillo .07 .20
115 Geoff Jenkins .07 .20
116 Jeromy Burnitz .07 .20
117 Brad Radke .07 .20
118 Eric Milton .07 .20
119 A.J. Pierzynski .07 .20
120 Todd Walker .07 .20
121 David Ortiz .20 .50
122 Corey Koskie .07 .20
123 Vladimir Guerrero .20 .50
124 Rondell White .07 .20
125 Brad Fullmer .07 .20
126 Ugueth Urbina .07 .20
127 Dustin Hermanson .07 .20
128 Michael Barrett .07 .20
129 Fernando Seguignol .07 .20
130 Mike Piazza .30 .75
131 Rickey Henderson .20 .50
132 Rey Ordonez .07 .20
133 John Olerud .07 .20
134 Robin Ventura .07 .20
135 Hideo Nomo .20 .50
136 Mike Kinkade .07 .20
137 Al Leiter .07 .20
138 Brian McRae .07 .20
139 Derek Jeter .50 1.25
140 Bernie Williams .10 .30
141 Paul O'Neill .10 .30
142 Scott Brosius .07 .20
143 Tino Martinez .10 .30
144 Roger Clemens .40 1.00
145 Orlando Hernandez .07 .20
146 Mariano Rivera .20 .50
147 Ricky Ledee .07 .20
148 A.J. Hinch .07 .20
149 Ben Grieve .07 .20
150 Eric Chavez .07 .20
151 Miguel Tejada .07 .20
152 Matt Stairs .07 .20
153 Ryan Christenson .07 .20
154 Jason Giambi .07 .20
155 Curt Schilling .07 .20
156 Scott Rolen .10 .30
157 Pat Burrell RC .40 1.00
158 Doug Glanville .07 .20
159 Bobby Abreu .07 .20
160 Rico Brogna .07 .20
161 Ron Gant .07 .20
162 Jason Kendall .07 .20
163 Aramis Ramirez .07 .20
164 Jose Guillen .07 .20
165 Emil Brown .07 .20
166 Pat Meares .07 .20
167 Kevin Young .07 .20
168 Brian Giles .07 .20
169 Mark McGwire .50 1.25
170 J.D. Drew .07 .20
171 Edgar Renteria .07 .20
172 Fernando Tatis .07 .20
173 Matt Morris .07 .20
174 Eli Marrero .07 .20
175 Ray Lankford .07 .20
176 Tony Gwynn .25 .60
177 Sterling Hitchcock .07 .20
178 Ruben Rivera .07 .20
179 Wally Joyner .07 .20
180 Trevor Hoffman .07 .20
181 Jim Leyritz .07 .20
182 Carlos Hernandez .07 .20
183 Barry Bonds UER .60 1.50
Uniform number 24 on front, 25 on back
184 Ellis Burks .07 .20
185 F.P. Santangelo .07 .20
186 J.T. Snow .07 .20
187 Ramon E.Martinez RC .07 .20
188 Jeff Kent .07 .20
189 Robb Nen .07 .20
190 Ken Griffey Jr. .30 .75
191 Alex Rodriguez .30 .75
192 Shane Monahan .07 .20
193 Carlos Guillen .07 .20
194 Edgar Martinez .10 .30
195 David Segui .07 .20
196 Jose Mesa .07 .20
197 Jose Canseco .10 .30
198 Rolando Arrojo .07 .20
199 Wade Boggs .10 .30
200 Fred McGriff .10 .30
201 Quinton McCracken .07 .20
202 Bobby Smith .07 .20
203 Bubba Trammell .07 .20
204 Juan Gonzalez .07 .20
205 Ivan Rodriguez .10 .30
206 Rafael Palmeiro .10 .30
207 Royce Clayton .07 .20
208 Rick Helling .07 .20
209 Todd Zeile .07 .20
210 Rusty Greer .07 .20
211 David Wells .07 .20
212 Roy Halladay .07 .20
213 Carlos Delgado .07 .20
214 Darrin Fletcher .07 .20
215 Shawn Green .07 .20
216 Kevin Witt .07 .20
217 Jose Cruz Jr. .07 .20
218 Ken Griffey Jr. CL .20 .50
219 Sammy Sosa CL .10 .30
220 Mark McGwire CL .25 .60
S3 Ken Griffey Jr. Sample .40 1.00

1999 Upper Deck MVP Gold Script

Randomly inserted into hobby packs, these parallel cards of the regular Upper Deck MVP set are serial numbered to 100 and have a gold foil fascimile signature on the front of the card.

*STARS: 12.5X TO 30X BASIC CARDS
*ROOKIES: 12.5X TO 30X BASIC CARDS

1999 Upper Deck MVP Silver Script

These parallels were seeded at a rate of one in every two packs. Unlike basic MVP cards, each Silver Script parallel features the player's facsimile autograph in silver foil on the front of the card. A Ken Griffey Jr. sample card was distributed to dealers and hobby media several weeks prior to the product's national release. The card is numbered "S3" on back.

COMPLETE SET (220) 75.00 150.00
*STARS: 1.5X TO 4X BASIC CARDS
*ROOKIES: 1.5X TO 4X BASIC CARDS
S3 Ken Griffey Jr. Sample 1.50 4.00

1999 Upper Deck MVP Super Script

This parallel set of the Upper Deck MVP set is serial numbered to 25. The facsimile signatures on these cards are printed in a special holo-foil format.

*STARS: 30X TO 80X BASIC CARDS

1999 Upper Deck MVP Dynamics

Inserted one every 28 packs, these cards feature the most collectible stars in basebll. The front of the card has a player photo, the word "Dynamics" in black ink on the bottom and lots of fancy graphics.

COMPLETE SET (15) 50.00 100.00
D1 Ken Griffey Jr. 2.50 6.00
D2 Alex Rodriguez 2.50 6.00
D3 Nomar Garciaparra 2.50 6.00
D4 Mike Piazza 2.50 6.00
D5 Mark McGwire 4.00 10.00
D6 Sammy Sosa 1.50 4.00
D7 Chipper Jones 1.50 4.00
D8 Mo Vaughn .60 1.50
D9 Tony Gwynn 2.00 5.00
D10 Vladimir Guerrero 1.50 4.00
D11 Derek Jeter 4.00 10.00
D12 Jeff Bagwell 1.00 2.50
D13 Cal Ripken 5.00 12.00
D14 Juan Gonzalez .60 1.50
D15 J.D. Drew .60 1.50

1999 Upper Deck MVP Game Used Souvenirs

These 11 cards were randomly inserted into packs at a rate of one in 144. Each card features a chip of actual game-used bat from the player featured.

GUBB Barry Bonds 10.00 25.00
GUCJ Chipper Jones 8.00 20.00
GUCR Cal Ripken 20.00 50.00
GUJB Jeff Bagwell 6.00 15.00
GUJD J.D. Drew 4.00 10.00
GUKG Ken Griffey Jr. 10.00 25.00
GUMP Mike Piazza 12.50 30.00
GUMV Mo Vaughn 4.00 10.00
GUSR Scott Rolen 6.00 15.00
GAKG K. Griffey Jr. AU/24
GACJ Chipper Jones AU/10

1999 Upper Deck MVP Power Surge

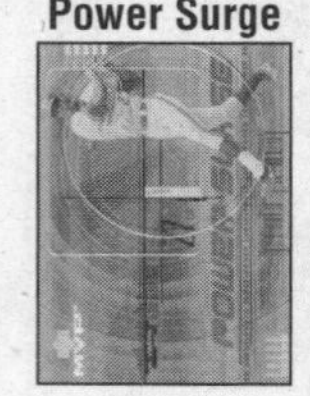

These cards were inserted one every nine packs. The horizontal cards feature some of the leading sluggers in baseball and are printed on rainbow foil.

COMPLETE SET (15) 12.50 25.00
P1 Mark McGwire 1.25 3.00
P2 Sammy Sosa .50 1.25
P3 Ken Griffey Jr. .75 2.00
P4 Alex Rodriguez .75 2.00
P5 Juan Gonzalez .20 .50
P6 Nomar Garciaparra .75 2.00
P7 Vladimir Guerrero .50 1.25
P8 Chipper Jones .50 1.25
P9 Albert Belle .20 .50
P10 Frank Thomas .50 1.25
P11 Mike Piazza .75 2.00
P12 Jeff Bagwell .30 .75
P13 Manny Ramirez .30 .75
P14 Mo Vaughn .20 .50
P15 Barry Bonds 1.50 4.00

1999 Upper Deck MVP ProSign

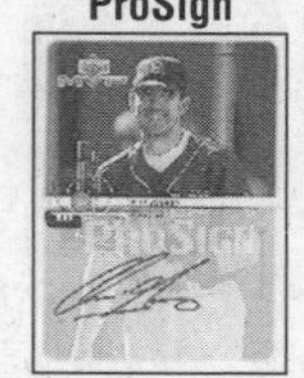

Inserted as a rate of one every 216 retail packs, these cards feature autographs from various baseball players. It's believed that the veteran stars in this set are in much shorter supply than the various young prospects.Some of these star cards have rarely been seen in the secondary market and no pricing is yet available for those cards.

AG Alex Gonzalez 4.00 10.00
AN Abraham Nunez 4.00 10.00
BC Bruce Chen 4.00 10.00
BF Brad Fullmer 4.00 10.00
BG Ben Grieve 4.00 10.00
CB Carlos Beltran 8.00 20.00
CG Chris Gomez 4.00 10.00
CJ Chipper Jones SP 75.00 150.00
CK Corey Koskie 6.00 15.00
CP Calvin Pickering 4.00 10.00
DG Derrick Gibson 4.00 10.00
EC Eric Chavez 6.00 15.00
GK Gabe Kapler 6.00 15.00
GL George Lombard 4.00 10.00
IR Ivan Rodriguez SP 50.00 100.00
JG Jeremy Giambi 4.00 10.00
JP Jim Parque 4.00 10.00
JR Ken Griffey Jr. SP 250.00 350.00
JRA Jason Rakers 4.00 10.00
KW Kevin Witt 4.00 10.00
MA Matt Anderson 4.00 10.00
ML Mike Lincoln 4.00 10.00
MLO Mike Lowell 6.00 15.00
NG Nomar Garciaparra SP 75.00 150.00
RB Russ Branyan 4.00 10.00
RH Richard Hidalgo 4.00 10.00
RL Ricky Ledee 4.00 10.00
RM Ryan Minor 4.00 10.00
RR Ruben Rivera 4.00 10.00
SH Shea Hillenbrand 6.00 15.00
SK Scott Karl 4.00 10.00
SM Shane Monahan 4.00 10.00

1999 Upper Deck MVP Scout's Choice

Inserted one every nine packs, these cards feature the best young stars and rookies captured on Light F/X packs.

COMPLETE SET (15) 6.00 12.00
SC1 J.D. Drew .25 .60
SC2 Ben Grieve .25 .60
SC3 Troy Glaus .40 1.00
SC4 Gabe Kapler .25 .60
SC5 Carlos Beltran .40 1.00
SC6 Aramis Ramirez .25 .60
SC7 Pat Burrell .50 1.25
SC8 Kerry Wood .25 .60
SC9 Ryan Minor .25 .60
SC10 Todd Helton .40 1.00
SC11 Eric Chavez .25 .60
SC12 Russ Branyan .25 .60
SC13 Travis Lee .25 .60
SC14 Ruben Mateo .25 .60
SC15 Roy Halladay .25 .60

1999 Upper Deck MVP Super Tools

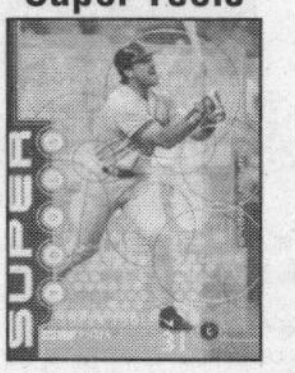

Issued one every 14 packs, these cards focus on big leaguers who posess various tools of greatness.

COMPLETE SET (15) 25.00 50.00
T1 Ken Griffey Jr. 1.50 4.00
T2 Alex Rodriguez 1.50 4.00
T3 Sammy Sosa 1.00 2.50
T4 Derek Jeter 2.50 6.00
T5 Vladimir Guerrero 1.00 2.50
T6 Ben Grieve .40 1.00
T7 Mike Piazza 1.50 4.00
T8 Kenny Lofton .40 1.00
T9 Barry Bonds 3.00 8.00
T10 Darin Erstad .40 1.00
T11 Nomar Garciaparra 1.50 4.00
T12 Cal Ripken 3.00 8.00
T13 J.D. Drew .40 1.00
T14 Larry Walker .40 1.00
T15 Chipper Jones 1.00 2.50

1999 Upper Deck MVP Swing Time

Issued one every six packs, these cards focus on players who have swings considered to be among the sweetest in the game.

COMPLETE SET (12) 10.00 20.00
S1 Ken Griffey Jr. .60 1.50
S2 Mark McGwire 1.00 2.50
S3 Sammy Sosa .40 1.00
S4 Tony Gwynn .50 1.25
S5 Alex Rodriguez .60 1.50
S6 Nomar Garciaparra .60 1.50
S7 Barry Bonds 1.25 3.00
S8 Frank Thomas .40 1.00
S9 Chipper Jones .40 1.00
S10 Ivan Rodriguez .25 .60
S11 Mike Piazza .60 1.50
S12 Derek Jeter 1.00 2.50

1999 Upper Deck MVP FanFest

This 30 card standard-size set was issued by Upper Deck during the annual FanFest celebration. The cards were issued in three-card packs with 15,000 packs produced and distributed during the show. The cards have a silver All-Star Game logo on the lower right corner of the card and they are all numbered with an "AS" prefix. Ten of the cards were printed in smaller quantities then the other 20 cards, those cards are notated with an SP in the listings below

COMPLETE SET 24.00 60.00
COMMON (AS1-AS30) .12 .30
COMMON SP .80 2.00
AS1 Mo Vaughn SP .75 2.00
AS2 Randy Johnson .30 .75
AS3 Chipper Jones .60 1.50
AS4 Greg Maddux SP 2.50 6.00
AS5 Cal Ripken 1.25 3.00
AS6 Albert Belle .10 .30
AS7 N.Garciaparra SP 2.50 6.00
AS8 Pedro Martinez .30 .75
AS9 Sammy Sosa .50 1.25
AS10 Frank Thomas .30 .75
AS11 Sean Casey .10 .30
AS12 Roberto Alomar .25 .60
AS13 Manny Ramirez .30 .75

AS14 Larry Walker .10 .30
AS15 Jeff Bagwell SP 1.25 3.00
AS16 Craig Biggio .25 .60
AS17 Raul Mondesi .10 .30
AS18 Vladimir Guerrero .30 .75
AS19 Mike Piazza SP 3.00 8.00
AS20 Derek Jeter SP 5.00 12.00
AS21 Roger Clemens SP 2.50 6.00
AS22 Scott Rolen .25 .60
AS23 Mark McGwire SP 3.00 8.00
AS24 Tony Gwynn .60 1.50
AS25 Barry Bonds .60 1.50
AS26 Ken Griffey Jr SP 3.00 8.00
AS27 Alex Rodriguez .60 1.50
AS28 Jose Canseco .30 .75
AS29 Juan Gonzalez .30 .75
AS30 Ivan Rodriguez .30 .75

2000 Upper Deck MVP

The 2000 Upper Deck MVP product was released in June, 2000 as a 220-card set. Each pack contained 10 cards and carried a suggested retail price of $1.59. Please note that cards 218-220 are player/checklist cards. Also, a selection of A Piece of History 3000 Club Stan Musial memorabilia cards were randomly seeded into packs. 350 bat cards, 350 jersey cards, 100 hand-numbered combination bat-jersey cards and six autographed, hand-numbered, combination bat-jersey cards were produced. Pricing for these memorabilia cards can be referenced under 2000 Upper Deck A Piece of History 3000 Club.

COMPLETE SET (220) 6.00 15.00
1 Garret Anderson .07 .20
2 Mo Vaughn .07 .20
3 Tim Salmon .10 .30
4 Ramon Ortiz .07 .20
5 Darin Erstad .07 .20
6 Troy Glaus .07 .20
7 Troy Percival .07 .20
8 Jeff Bagwell .10 .30
9 Ken Caminiti .07 .20
10 Daryle Ward .07 .20
11 Craig Biggio .10 .30
12 Jose Lima .07 .20
13 Moises Alou .07 .20
14 Octavio Dotel .07 .20
15 Ben Grieve .07 .20
16 Jason Giambi .07 .20
17 Tim Hudson .07 .20
18 Eric Chavez .07 .20
19 Matt Stairs .07 .20
20 Miguel Tejada .07 .20
21 John Jaha .07 .20
22 Chipper Jones .20 .50
23 Kevin Millwood .07 .20
24 Brian Jordan .07 .20
25 Andruw Jones .10 .30
26 Andres Galarraga .07 .20
27 Greg Maddux .30 .75
28 Reggie Sanders .07 .20
29 Javy Lopez .07 .20
30 Jeromy Burnitz .07 .20
31 Kevin Barker .07 .20
32 Jose Hernandez .07 .20
33 Ron Belliard .07 .20
34 Henry Blanco .07 .20
35 Marquis Grissom .07 .20
36 Geoff Jenkins .07 .20
37 Carlos Delgado .07 .20
38 Raul Mondesi .07 .20
39 Roy Halladay .07 .20
40 Tony Batista .07 .20
41 David Wells .07 .20
42 Shannon Stewart .07 .20
43 Vernon Wells .07 .20
44 Sammy Sosa .20 .50
45 Ismael Valdes .07 .20
46 Joe Girardi .07 .20
47 Mark Grace .10 .30
48 Henry Rodriguez .07 .20
49 Kerry Wood .07 .20
50 Eric Young .07 .20
51 Mark McGwire .50 1.25
52 Darryl Kile .07 .20
53 Fernando Vina .07 .20
54 Ray Lankford .07 .20
55 J.D. Drew .07 .20
56 Fernando Tatis .07 .20
57 Rick Ankiel .07 .20
58 Matt Williams .07 .20
59 Erubiel Durazo .07 .20
60 Tony Womack .07 .20
61 Jay Bell .07 .20
62 Randy Johnson .20 .50
63 Steve Finley .07 .20
64 Matt Mantei .07 .20
65 Luis Gonzalez .07 .20
66 Gary Sheffield .07 .20
67 Eric Gagne .20 .50
68 Adrian Beltre .07 .20
69 Mark Grudzielanek .07 .20
70 Kevin Brown .07 .20
71 Chan Ho Park .07 .20
72 Shawn Green .07 .20
73 Vinny Castilla .07 .20
74 Fred McGriff .10 .30
75 Wilson Alvarez .07 .20
76 Greg Vaughn .07 .20
77 Gerald Williams .07 .20
78 Ryan Rupe .07 .20
79 Jose Canseco .10 .30
80 Vladimir Guerrero .20 .50
81 Dustin Hermanson .07 .20
82 Michael Barrett .07 .20
83 Rondell White .07 .20
84 Tony Armas Jr. .07 .20
85 Wilton Guerrero .07 .20
86 Jose Vidro .07 .20
87 Barry Bonds .60 1.50
88 Russ Ortiz .07 .20
89 Ellis Burks .07 .20
90 Jeff Kent .07 .20
91 Russ Davis .07 .20
92 J.T. Snow .07 .20
93 Roberto Alomar .10 .30
94 Manny Ramirez .10 .30
95 Chuck Finley .07 .20
96 Kenny Lofton .07 .20
97 Jim Thome .10 .30
98 Bartolo Colon .07 .20
99 Omar Vizquel .10 .30
100 Richie Sexson .07 .20
101 Mike Cameron .07 .20
102 Brett Tomko .07 .20
103 Edgar Martinez .10 .30
104 Alex Rodriguez .30 .75
105 John Olerud .07 .20
106 Freddy Garcia .07 .20
107 Kazuhiro Sasaki RC .10 .30
108 Preston Wilson .07 .20
109 Luis Castillo .07 .20
110 A.J. Burnett .07 .20
111 Mike Lowell .07 .20
112 Cliff Floyd .07 .20
113 Brad Penny .07 .20
114 Alex Gonzalez .07 .20
115 Mike Piazza .30 .75
116 Derek Bell .07 .20
117 Edgardo Alfonzo .07 .20
118 Rickey Henderson .20 .50
119 Todd Zeile .07 .20
120 Mike Hampton .07 .20
121 Al Leiter .07 .20
122 Robin Ventura .07 .20
123 Cal Ripken .60 1.50
124 Mike Mussina .10 .30
125 B.J. Surhoff .07 .20
126 Jerry Hairston Jr. .07 .20
127 Brady Anderson .07 .20
128 Albert Belle .07 .20
129 Sidney Ponson .07 .20
130 Tony Gwynn .25 .60
131 Ryan Klesko .07 .20
132 Sterling Hitchcock .07 .20
133 Eric Owens .07 .20
134 Trevor Hoffman .07 .20
135 Al Martin .07 .20
136 Bret Boone .07 .20
137 Brian Giles .07 .20
138 Chad Hermansen .07 .20
139 Kevin Young .07 .20
140 Kris Benson .07 .20
141 Warren Morris .07 .20
142 Jason Kendall .07 .20
143 Wil Cordero .07 .20
144 Scott Rolen .10 .30
145 Curt Schilling .07 .20
146 Doug Glanville .07 .20
147 Mike Lieberthal .07 .20
148 Mike Jackson .07 .20
149 Rico Brogna .07 .20
150 Andy Ashby .07 .20
151 Bob Abreu .07 .20
152 Sean Casey .07 .20
153 Pete Harnisch .07 .20
154 Dante Bichette .07 .20
155 Pokey Reese .07 .20
156 Aaron Boone .07 .20
157 Ken Griffey Jr. .30 .75
158 Barry Larkin .10 .30
159 Scott Williamson .07 .20
160 Carlos Beltran .07 .20
161 Jermaine Dye .07 .20
162 Jose Rosado .07 .20
163 Joe Randa .07 .20
164 Johnny Damon .10 .30
165 Mike Sweeney .07 .20
166 Mark Quinn .07 .20
167 Ivan Rodriguez .10 .30
168 Rusty Greer .07 .20
169 Ruben Mateo .07 .20
170 Doug Davis .07 .20
171 Gabe Kapler .07 .20
172 Justin Thompson .07 .20
173 Rafael Palmeiro .10 .30
174 Larry Walker .07 .20
175 Neifi Perez .07 .20
176 Rolando Arrojo .07 .20
177 Jeffrey Hammonds .07 .20
178 Todd Helton .10 .30
179 Pedro Astacio .07 .20
180 Jeff Cirillo .07 .20
181 Pedro Martinez .10 .30
182 Carl Everett .07 .20
183 Troy O'Leary .07 .20
184 Nomar Garciaparra .30 .75
185 Jose Offerman .07 .20
186 Bret Saberhagen .07 .20
187 Trot Nixon .07 .20
188 Jason Varitek .20 .50
189 Todd Walker .07 .20
190 Eric Milton .07 .20
191 Chad Allen .07 .20
192 Jacque Jones .07 .20
193 Brad Radke .07 .20
194 Corey Koskie .07 .20
195 Joe Mays .07 .20
196 Juan Gonzalez .07 .20
197 Jeff Weaver .07 .20
198 Juan Encarnacion .07 .20
199 Delvi Cruz .07 .20
200 Damion Easley .07 .20
201 Tony Clark .07 .20
202 Dean Palmer .07 .20
203 Frank Thomas .20 .50
204 Carlos Lee .07 .20
205 Mike Sirotka .07 .20
206 Kip Wells .07 .20
207 Magglio Ordonez .07 .20
208 Paul Konerko .07 .20
209 Chris Singleton .07 .20
210 Derek Jeter .50 1.25
211 Tino Martinez .10 .30
212 Mariano Rivera .20 .50
213 Roger Clemens .40 1.00
214 Nick Johnson .07 .20
215 Paul O'Neill .10 .30
216 Bernie Williams .10 .30
217 David Cone .07 .20
218 Ken Griffey Jr. CL .20 .50
219 Sammy Sosa CL .10 .30
220 Mark McGwire CL .25 .60

2000 Upper Deck MVP Gold Script

Randomly inserted into packs, this 220-card insert is a complete parallel of the Upper Deck MVP base set. Each card in the set is individually serial numbered to 50. Please note that each card features a gold foiled facsimile autograph on the front of the card.

*STARS: 25X TO 60X BASIC CARDS
*ROOKIES: 20X TO 50X BASIC CARDS

2000 Upper Deck MVP Silver Script

Randomly inserted into packs at one in two, this 220-card insert is a complete parallel of the Upper Deck MVP base set. Please note that each card features a silver foiled facsimile autograph on the front of the card.

COMPLETE SET (220) 75.00 150.00
*STARS: 1.25X TO 3X BASIC CARDS
*ROOKIES: 1.25X TO 3X BASIC CARDS

2000 Upper Deck MVP All Star Game

This 30-card insert set was released in three-card packs at the All-Star Fan Fest in Atlanta in July, 2000.

COMPLETE SET (30) 16.00 40.00
AS1 Mo Vaughn .16 .40
AS2 Jeff Bagwell .40 1.00
AS3 Jason Giambi .40 1.00
AS4 Chipper Jones .60 1.50
AS5 Greg Maddux .80 2.00
AS6 Tony Bichette .10 .25
AS7 Sammy Sosa .50 1.25
AS8 Mark McGwire .75 2.00
AS9 Randy Johnson .40 1.00
AS10 Shawn Green .30 .75
AS11 Greg Vaughn .16 .40
AS12 Vladimir Guerrero .40 1.00
AS13 Barry Bonds .80 2.00
AS14 Manny Ramirez .40 1.00
AS15 Alex Rodriguez .80 2.00
AS16 Preston Wilson .16 .40
AS17 Mike Piazza 1.00 2.50
AS18 Cal Ripken Jr. 1.60 4.00
AS19 Tony Gwynn .80 2.00
AS20 Scott Rolen .40 1.00
AS21 Ken Griffey Jr. .75 2.00
AS22 Carlos Beltran .50 1.25
AS23 Ivan Rodriguez .40 1.00
AS24 Larry Walker .16 .40
AS25 Nomar Garciaparra .80 2.00
AS26 Pedro Martinez .40 1.00
AS27 Juan Gonzalez .30 .75
AS28 Frank Thomas .50 1.25
AS29 Derek Jeter 1.60 4.00
AS30 Bernie Williams .30 .75

2000 Upper Deck MVP Draw Your Own Card

Randomly inserted into packs at one in six, this 31-card insert features player drawings from the 2000 Draw Your Own Card winners. Card backs carry a "DT" prefix.

COMPLETE SET (31) 20.00 50.00
DT1 Frank Thomas .40 1.00
DT2 Joe DiMaggio .75 2.00
DT3 Barry Bonds 1.25 3.00
DT4 Mark McGwire 1.00 2.50
DT5 Ken Griffey Jr. .60 1.50
DT6 Mark McGwire 1.00 2.50
DT7 Mike Stanley .15 .40
DT8 Nomar Garciaparra .60 1.50
DT9 Mickey Mantle 1.50 4.00
DT10 Randy Johnson .40 1.00
DT11 Nolan Ryan 1.00 2.50
DT12 Chipper Jones .40 1.00
DT13 Ken Griffey Jr. .60 1.50
DT14 Troy Glaus .15 .40
DT15 Manny Ramirez .25 .60
DT16 Mark McGwire 1.00 2.50
DT17 Ivan Rodriguez .25 .60
DT18 Mike Piazza .60 1.50
DT19 Sammy Sosa .40 1.00
DT20 Ken Griffey Jr. .60 1.50
DT21 Jeff Bagwell .25 .60
DT22 Ken Griffey Jr. .60 1.50
DT23 Kerry Wood .15 .40
DT24 Mark McGwire 1.00 2.50
DT25 Greg Maddux .60 1.50
DT26 Sandy Alomar Jr. .15 .40
DT27 Albert Belle .15 .40
DT28 Sammy Sosa .40 1.00
DT29 Alexandra Brunet .15 .40
DT30 Mark McGwire 1.00 2.50
DT31 Nomar Garciaparra .60 1.50

2000 Upper Deck MVP Drawing Power

Randomly inserted into packs at one in 28, this seven-card insert features players that bring fans to the ballpark. Card backs carry a "DP" prefix.

COMPLETE SET (7) 12.50 30.00
DP1 Mark McGwire 2.50 6.00
DP2 Ken Griffey Jr. 1.50 4.00
DP3 Mike Piazza 1.50 4.00
DP4 Chipper Jones 1.00 2.50
DP5 Nomar Garciaparra 1.50 4.00
DP6 Sammy Sosa 1.00 2.50
DP7 Jose Canseco .60 1.50

2000 Upper Deck MVP Game Used Souvenirs

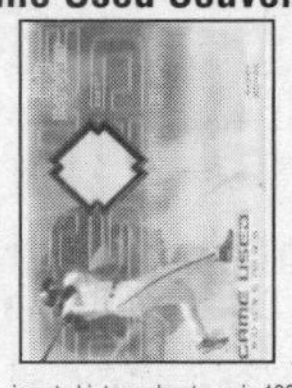

Randomly inserted into packs at one in 130, this 30-card insert features game-used bat and game used glove cards from players such as Chipper Jones and Ken Griffey Jr.

ABG Albert Belle Glove 6.00 15.00
AFG Alex Fernandez Glove 4.00 10.00
AGG Alex Gonzalez Glove 4.00 10.00
ARB Alex Rodriguez Bat 6.00 15.00
ARG Alex Rodriguez Glove 20.00 50.00
BBB Barry Bonds Bat 10.00 25.00
BBG Barry Bonds Glove 40.00 80.00
BGG Ben Grieve Glove 4.00 10.00
BWG Bernie Williams Glove 10.00 25.00
CRG Cal Ripken Glove 40.00 80.00
IRB Ivan Rodriguez Bat 4.00 10.00
IRG Ivan Rodriguez Glove 10.00 25.00
JBG Jeff Bagwell Glove 10.00 25.00
JCB Jose Canseco Bat 4.00 10.00
KGB Ken Griffey Jr. Bat 6.00 15.00
KGG Ken Griffey Jr. Glove 20.00 50.00
KLG Kenny Lofton Glove 10.00 25.00
LWG Larry Walker Glove 6.00 15.00
MRB Manny Ramirez Bat 4.00 10.00
NRG Nolan Ryan Glove 40.00 80.00
POG Paul O'Neill Glove 10.00 25.00
RAG Roberto Alomar Glove 10.00 25.00
RMG Raul Mondesi Glove 6.00 15.00
RPG Rafael Palmeiro Glove 25.00 50.00
TGB Tony Gwynn Bat 6.00 15.00
TGG Tony Gwynn Glove 15.00 40.00
TSG Tim Salmon Glove 10.00 25.00
WCG Will Clark Glove 10.00 25.00

2000 Upper Deck MVP Game Used Souvenirs Signed

Randomly inserted into packs, this autographed insert features game-used bat and game-used glove cards from players such as Chipper Jones and Ken Griffey Jr. Each card was individually serial numbered to 25 on front. Stickered exchange cards were placed into packs for Ken Griffey Jr. The exchange deadline for these stickered redemption cards was February 2nd, 2001. Due to market scarcity, no pricing is provided for these cards.

ABSG Albert Belle Glove
BBSB Barry Bonds Bat
BBSG Barry Bonds Glove
CJSB Chipper Jones Bat
JCSB Jose Canseco Bat
KGSB Ken Griffey Jr. Bat
KGSG Ken Griffey Jr. Glove
KLSG Kenny Lofton Glove
NRSG Nolan Ryan Glove
RASG Roberto Alomar Glove
RPSG Rafael Palmeiro Glove
TGSB Tony Gwynn Bat
TGSG Tony Gwynn Glove

2000 Upper Deck MVP Prolifics

Randomly inserted into packs at one in 28, this 7-card insert features some of the most prolific players in major league baseball. Card backs carry a "P" prefix.

COMPLETE SET (7) 10.00 25.00
P1 Manny Ramirez .60 1.50
P2 Vladimir Guerrero 1.00 2.50
P3 Derek Jeter 2.50 6.00
P4 Pedro Martinez .60 1.50
P5 Shawn Green .40 1.00
P6 Alex Rodriguez 1.50 4.00
P7 Cal Ripken 3.00 8.00

2000 Upper Deck MVP ProSign

Randomly inserted into retail packs only at one in 143, this 18-card insert features autographs of players such as Mike Sweeney, Rick Ankiel, and Tim Hudson. Card backs are numbered using the players initials.

LIMITED RANDOM IN PACKS
LIMITED PRINT RUN 25 SERIAL #'d SETS
NO LTD PRICING DUE TO SCARCITY
BP Ben Petrick 4.00 10.00
BT Bubba Trammell 4.00 10.00
DD Doug Davis 6.00 15.00
EY Ed Yarnall 4.00 10.00
JM Jim Morris 10.00 25.00
JV Jose Vidro 4.00 10.00
JZ Jeff Zimmerman 4.00 10.00
KW Kevin Witt 4.00 10.00
MB Michael Barrett 4.00 10.00
MM Mike Meyers 6.00 15.00
MQ Mark Quinn 4.00 10.00
MS Mike Sweeney 6.00 15.00
PW Preston Wilson 6.00 15.00
RA Rick Ankiel 10.00 25.00
SW Scott Williamson 4.00 10.00
TH Tim Hudson 10.00 25.00
TN Trot Nixon 6.00 15.00
WM Warren Morris 4.00 10.00

2000 Upper Deck MVP Pure Grit

Randomly inserted into packs at one in six, this 10-card insert features players that constantly give their best day in, day out. Card backs carry a "G" prefix.

COMPLETE SET (10) 6.00 15.00
G1 Derek Jeter 1.25 3.00
G2 Kevin Brown .20 .50
G3 Craig Biggio .30 .75
G4 Ivan Rodriguez .30 .75
G5 Scott Rolen .30 .75
G6 Carlos Beltran .20 .50
G7 Ken Griffey Jr. .75 2.00
G8 Cal Ripken 1.50 4.00
G9 Nomar Garciaparra .75 2.00
G10 Randy Johnson .50 1.25

2000 Upper Deck MVP Scout's Choice

Randomly inserted into packs at one in 14, this 10-card insert features players that major league scouts believe will be future stars in the major leagues. Card backs carry a "SC" prefix.

COMPLETE SET (10) 4.00 10.00
SC1 Rick Ankiel .40 1.00
SC2 Vernon Wells .40 1.00
SC3 Pat Burrell .40 1.00
SC4 Travis Dawkins .40 1.00

SC5 Eric Munson .40 1.00
SC6 Nick Johnson .40 1.00
SC7 Dermal Brown .40 1.00
SC8 Alfonso Soriano .60 1.50
SC9 Ben Petrick .40 1.00
SC10 Adam Everett .40 1.00

2000 Upper Deck MVP Second Season Standouts

Randomly inserted into packs at one in six, this 10-card insert features players that had outstanding sophomore years in the major leagues. Card backs carry a "SS" prefix.

COMPLETE SET (10) 4.00 10.00
SS1 Pedro Martinez .30 .75
SS2 Mariano Rivera .50 1.25
SS3 Orlando Hernandez .20 .50
SS4 Ken Caminiti .20 .50
SS5 Bernie Williams .30 .75
SS6 Jim Thome .30 .75
SS7 Nomar Garciaparra .75 2.00
SS8 Edgardo Alfonzo .20 .50
SS9 Derek Jeter 1.25 3.00
SS10 Kevin Millwood .20 .50

2001 Upper Deck MVP

This 330-card set was released in May, 2001. These cards were issued in eight card packs with an SRP of $1.99. These packs were issued 24 packs to a box.

COMPLETE SET (330) 15.00 40.00
1 Mo Vaughn .07 .20
2 Troy Percival .07 .20
3 Adam Kennedy .07 .20
4 Darin Erstad .07 .20
5 Tim Salmon .10 .30
6 Bengie Molina .07 .20
7 Troy Glaus .07 .20
8 Garret Anderson .07 .20
9 Ismael Valdes .07 .20
10 Glenallen Hill .07 .20
11 Tim Hudson .07 .20
12 Eric Chavez .07 .20
13 Johnny Damon .10 .30
14 Barry Zito .10 .30
15 Jason Giambi .07 .20
16 Terrence Long .07 .20
17 Jason Hart .07 .20
18 Jose Ortiz .07 .20
19 Miguel Tejada .07 .20
20 Jason Isringhausen .07 .20
21 Adam Piatt .07 .20
22 Jeremy Giambi .07 .20
23 Tony Batista .07 .20
24 Darrin Fletcher .07 .20
25 Mike Sirotka .07 .20
26 Carlos Delgado .07 .20
27 Billy Koch .07 .20
28 Shannon Stewart .07 .20
29 Raul Mondesi .07 .20
30 Brad Fullmer .07 .20
31 Jose Cruz Jr. .07 .20
32 Kelvim Escobar .07 .20
33 Greg Vaughn .07 .20
34 Aubrey Huff .07 .20
35 Albie Lopez .07 .20
36 Gerald Williams .07 .20
37 Ben Grieve .07 .20
38 John Flaherty .07 .20
39 Fred McGriff .10 .30
40 Ryan Rupe .07 .20
41 Travis Harper .07 .20
42 Steve Cox .07 .20
43 Roberto Alomar .10 .30
44 Jim Thome .10 .30
45 Russell Branyan .07 .20
46 Bartolo Colon .07 .20
47 Omar Vizquel .10 .30
48 Travis Fryman .07 .20
49 Kenny Lofton .07 .20
50 Chuck Finley .07 .20
51 Ellis Burks .07 .20
52 Eddie Taubensee .07 .20
53 Juan Gonzalez .07 .20
54 Edgar Martinez .10 .30
55 Aaron Sele .07 .20
56 John Olerud .07 .20

57 Jay Buhner .07 .20
58 Mike Cameron .07 .20
59 John Halama .07 .20
60 Ichiro Suzuki RC 4.00 10.00
61 David Bell .07 .20
62 Freddy Garcia .07 .20
63 Carlos Guillen .07 .20
64 Bret Boone .07 .20
65 Al Martin .07 .20
66 Cal Ripken .60 1.50
67 Delino DeShields .07 .20
68 Chris Richard .07 .20
69 Sean Douglass RC .20 .50
70 Melvin Mora .07 .20
71 Luis Matos .07 .20
72 Sidney Ponson .07 .20
73 Mike Bordick .07 .20
74 Brady Anderson .07 .20
75 David Segui .07 .20
76 Jeff Conine .07 .20
77 Alex Rodriguez .30 .75
78 Gabe Kapler .07 .20
79 Ivan Rodriguez .10 .30
80 Rick Helling .07 .20
81 Kenny Rogers .07 .20
82 Andres Galarraga .07 .20
83 Rusty Greer .07 .20
84 Justin Thompson .07 .20
85 Ken Caminiti .07 .20
86 Rafael Palmeiro .10 .30
87 Ruben Mateo .07 .20
88 Travis Hafner RC 1.25 3.00
89 Manny Ramirez Sox .10 .30
90 Pedro Martinez .10 .30
91 Carl Everett .07 .20
92 Dante Bichette .07 .20
93 Derek Lowe .07 .20
94 Jason Varitek .20 .50
95 Nomar Garciaparra .30 .75
96 David Cone .07 .20
97 Tomokazu Ohka .07 .20
98 Troy O'Leary .07 .20
99 Trot Nixon .07 .20
100 Jermaine Dye .07 .20
101 Joe Randa .07 .20
102 Jeff Suppan .07 .20
103 Roberto Hernandez .07 .20
104 Mike Sweeney .07 .20
105 Mac Suzuki .07 .20
106 Carlos Febles .07 .20
107 Jose Rosado .07 .20
108 Mark Quinn .07 .20
109 Carlos Beltran .07 .20
110 Dean Palmer .07 .20
111 Mitch Meluskey .07 .20
112 Bobby Higginson .07 .20
113 Brandon Inge .07 .20
114 Tony Clark .07 .20
115 Brian Moehler .07 .20
116 Juan Encarnacion .07 .20
117 Damion Easley .07 .20
118 Roger Cedeno .07 .20
119 Jeff Weaver .07 .20
120 Matt Lawton .07 .20
121 Jay Canizaro .07 .20
122 Eric Milton .07 .20
123 Corey Koskie .07 .20
124 Mark Redman .07 .20
125 Jacque Jones .07 .20
126 Brad Radke .07 .20
127 Cristian Guzman .07 .20
128 Joe Mays .07 .20
129 Denny Hocking .07 .20
130 Frank Thomas .20 .50
131 David Wells .07 .20
132 Ray Durham .07 .20
133 Paul Konerko .07 .20
134 Joe Crede .20 .50
135 Jim Parque .07 .20
136 Carlos Lee .07 .20
137 Magglio Ordonez .07 .20
138 Sandy Alomar Jr. .07 .20
139 Chris Singleton .07 .20
140 Jose Valentin .07 .20
141 Roger Clemens .40 1.00
142 Derek Jeter .50 1.25
143 Orlando Hernandez .07 .20
144 Tino Martinez .10 .30
145 Bernie Williams .10 .30
146 Jorge Posada .10 .30
147 Mariano Rivera .20 .50
148 David Justice .07 .20
149 Paul O'Neill .10 .30
150 Mike Mussina .10 .30
151 Christian Parker RC .20 .50
152 Andy Pettitte .10 .30
153 Alfonso Soriano .10 .30
154 Jeff Bagwell .10 .30
155 Morgan Ensberg RC .75 2.00
156 Daryle Ward .07 .20
157 Craig Biggio .10 .30
158 Richard Hidalgo .07 .20
159 Shane Reynolds .07 .20
160 Scott Elarton .07 .20
161 Julio Lugo .07 .20
162 Moises Alou .07 .20
163 Lance Berkman .07 .20
164 Chipper Jones .20 .50
165 Greg Maddux .30 .75
166 Javy Lopez .07 .20
167 Andruw Jones .10 .30
168 Rafael Furcal .07 .20
169 Brian Jordan .07 .20
170 Wes Helms .07 .20
171 Tom Glavine .10 .30
172 B.J. Surhoff .07 .20
173 John Smoltz .10 .30
174 Quilvio Veras .07 .20
175 Rico Brogna .07 .20
176 Jeromy Burnitz .07 .20
177 Jeff D'Amico .07 .20
178 Geoff Jenkins .07 .20
179 Henry Blanco .07 .20
180 Mark Loretta .07 .20
181 Richie Sexson .07 .20
182 Jimmy Haynes .07 .20
183 Jeffrey Hammonds .07 .20
184 Ron Belliard .07 .20
185 Tyler Houston .07 .20
186 Mark McGwire .50 1.25
187 Rick Ankiel .07 .20
188 Darryl Kile .07 .20
189 Jim Edmonds .07 .20
190 Mike Matheny .07 .20
191 Edgar Renteria .07 .20
192 Ray Lankford .07 .20
193 Garrett Stephenson .07 .20
194 J.D. Drew .07 .20
195 Fernando Vina .07 .20
196 Dustin Hermanson .07 .20
197 Sammy Sosa .20 .50
198 Corey Patterson .07 .20
199 Jon Lieber .07 .20
200 Kerry Wood .07 .20
201 Todd Hundley .07 .20
202 Kevin Tapani .07 .20
203 Rondell White .07 .20
204 Eric Young .07 .20
205 Matt Stairs .07 .20
206 Bill Mueller .07 .20
207 Randy Johnson .20 .50
208 Mark Grace .10 .30
209 Jay Bell .07 .20
210 Curt Schilling .07 .20
211 Erubiel Durazo .07 .20
212 Luis Gonzalez .07 .20
213 Steve Finley .07 .20
214 Matt Williams .07 .20
215 Reggie Sanders .07 .20
216 Tony Womack .07 .20
217 Gary Sheffield .07 .20
218 Kevin Brown .07 .20
219 Adrian Beltre .07 .20
220 Shawn Green .07 .20
221 Darren Dreifort .07 .20
222 Chan Ho Park .07 .20
223 Eric Karros .07 .20
224 Alex Cora .07 .20
225 Mark Grudzielanek .07 .20
226 Andy Ashby .07 .20
227 Vladimir Guerrero .20 .50
228 Tony Armas Jr. .07 .20
229 Fernando Tatis .07 .20
230 Jose Vidro .07 .20
231 Javier Vazquez .07 .20
232 Lee Stevens .07 .20
233 Milton Bradley .07 .20
234 Carl Pavano .07 .20
235 Peter Bergeron .07 .20
236 Wilton Guerrero .07 .20
237 Ugueth Urbina .07 .20
238 Barry Bonds .50 1.25
239 Livan Hernandez .07 .20
240 Jeff Kent .07 .20
241 Pedro Feliz .07 .20
242 Bobby Estalella .07 .20
243 J.T. Snow .07 .20
244 Shawn Estes .07 .20
245 Robb Nen .07 .20
246 Rich Aurilia .07 .20
247 Russ Ortiz .07 .20
248 Preston Wilson .07 .20
249 Brad Penny .07 .20
250 Cliff Floyd .07 .20
251 A.J. Burnett .07 .20
252 Mike Lowell .07 .20
253 Luis Castillo .07 .20
254 Ryan Dempster .07 .20
255 Derrek Lee .10 .30
256 Charles Johnson .07 .20
257 Pablo Ozuna .07 .20
258 Antonio Alfonseca .07 .20
259 Mike Piazza .30 .75
260 Robin Ventura .07 .20
261 Al Leiter .07 .20
262 Timo Perez .07 .20
263 Edgardo Alfonzo .07 .20
264 Jay Payton .07 .20
265 Tsuyoshi Shinjo RC .20 .50
266 Todd Zeile .07 .20
267 Armando Benitez .07 .20
268 Glendon Rusch .07 .20
269 Rey Ordonez .07 .20
270 Kevin Appier .07 .20
271 Tony Gwynn .25 .60
272 Phil Nevin .07 .20
273 Mark Kotsay .07 .20
274 Ryan Klesko .07 .20
275 Adam Eaton .07 .20
276 Mike Darr .07 .20
277 Damian Jackson .07 .20
278 Woody Williams .07 .20
279 Chris Gomez .07 .20
280 Trevor Hoffman .07 .20
281 Xavier Nady .07 .20
282 Scott Rolen .10 .30
283 Bruce Chen .07 .20
284 Pat Burrell .07 .20
285 Mike Lieberthal .07 .20
286 B. Duckworth RC .20 .50
287 Travis Lee .07 .20
288 Bobby Abreu .07 .20
289 Jimmy Rollins .07 .20
290 Robert Person .07 .20
291 Randy Wolf .07 .20
292 Jason Kendall .07 .20
293 Derek Bell .07 .20
294 Brian Giles .07 .20
295 Kris Benson .07 .20
296 John VanderWal .07 .20
297 Todd Ritchie .07 .20
298 Warren Morris .07 .20
299 Kevin Young .07 .20
300 Francisco Cordova .07 .20
301 Aramis Ramirez .07 .20
302 Ken Griffey Jr. .30 .75
303 Pete Harnisch .07 .20
304 Aaron Boone .07 .20
305 Sean Casey .07 .20
306 Jackson Melian RC .20 .50
307 Rob Bell .07 .20
308 Barry Larkin .10 .30
309 Dmitri Young .07 .20
310 Danny Graves .07 .20
311 Pokey Reese .07 .20
312 Leo Estrella .07 .20
313 Todd Helton .10 .30
314 Mike Hampton .07 .20
315 Juan Pierre .07 .20
316 Brent Mayne .07 .20
317 Larry Walker .07 .20
318 Denny Neagle .07 .20
319 Jeff Cirillo .07 .20
320 Pedro Astacio .07 .20
321 Todd Hollandsworth .07 .20
322 Neifi Perez .07 .20
323 Ron Gant .07 .20
324 Todd Walker .07 .20
325 Alex Rodriguez CL .20 .50
326 Ken Griffey Jr. CL .20 .50
327 Mark McGwire CL .25 .60
328 Pedro Martinez CL .10 .30
329 Derek Jeter CL .25 .60
330 Mike Piazza CL .20 .50

2001 Upper Deck MVP Authentic Griffey

Inserted in packs at a rate of one in 288, these 12 cards feature memorabilia relating to the career of Ken Griffey Jr. A few cards were printed to a stated print run of 30 (Griffey's uniform number with the Reds), and we have notated those cards in our checklist. Griffey did not return his autographs in time for inclusion in the product and those cards could be redeemed until January 15th, 2002.

B Ken Griffey Jr. Bat 6.00 15.00
C Ken Griffey Jr. Cap 15.00 40.00
J Ken Griffey Jr. Jsy 6.00 15.00
S K.Griffey Jr. AU EXCH* 50.00 100.00
U K.Griffey Jr. Uni 6.00 15.00
GB Ken Griffey Jr. Gold Bat/30 60.00 120.00
GC Ken Griffey Jr. Gold Cap/30 60.00 120.00
GJ Ken Griffey Jr. Gold Jsy/30 60.00 120.00
GS Ken Griffey Jr. Gold AU/30 EXCH 125.00 200.00
CGR Ken Griffey Jr. Alex Rodriguez 20.00 50.00
CGS Ken Griffey Jr. Sammy Sosa 15.00 40.00
CGT Ken Griffey Jr. Frank Thomas Jsy/100 15.00 40.00

2001 Upper Deck MVP Drawing Power

Inserted in packs at a rate of one in 12, these 10 cards feature the players who help to draw the most fans to ballparks.

COMPLETE SET (10) 10.00 25.00
DP1 Mark McGwire 2.50 6.00
DP2 Vladimir Guerrero 1.00 2.50
DP3 Manny Ramirez Sox 1.00 2.50
DP4 Frank Thomas 1.00 2.50
DP5 Ken Griffey Jr. 1.50 4.00
DP6 Alex Rodriguez 1.50 4.00
DP7 Mike Piazza 1.50 4.00
DP8 Derek Jeter 2.50 6.00
DP9 Sammy Sosa 1.00 2.50
DP10 Todd Helton 1.00 2.50

2001 Upper Deck MVP Game Souvenirs Bat Duos

Inserted one in 144, these 14 cards feature two pieces of game-used bats on the same card.

B3K Tony Gwynn Cal Ripken 20.00 50.00
BDV Carlos Delgado Jose Vidro 6.00 15.00
BGS Ken Griffey Jr. Sammy Sosa 15.00 40.00
BHR Jose Canseco Ken Griffey Jr. 12.50 30.00
BJF Chipper Jones Rafael Furcal 10.00 25.00
BJJ Andruw Jones Chipper Jones 10.00 25.00
BOW Paul O'Neill Bernie Williams 10.00 25.00
BRM Alex Rodriguez Edgar Martinez 12.50 30.00
BRP Ivan Rodriguez Rafael Palmeiro 10.00 25.00
BRR Alex Rodriguez Ivan Rodriguez 15.00 40.00
BTG Jim Thome Ken Griffey Jr. 12.50 30.00
BTO Frank Thomas Magglio Ordonez 10.00 25.00
BTS Frank Thomas Sammy Sosa 10.00 25.00
BWA Kerry Wood Rick Ankiel 6.00 15.00

2001 Upper Deck MVP Game Souvenirs Bat Trios

Randomly inserted in packs, these six cards feature three pieces of game-used bats. These cards are serial numbered to 25. Due to market scarcity, no pricing is provided.

BBGJ Barry Bonds Ken Griffey Jr. Andruw Jones
BCBG Jose Canseco Barry Bonds Ken Griffey Jr.
BJEG Andruw Jones Jim Edmonds Ken Griffey Jr.
BJGC Chipper Jones Troy Glaus Eric Chavez
BJWO David Justice Bernie Williams Paul O'Neill
BSGR Sammy Sosa Ken Griffey Jr. Alex Rodriguez

2001 Upper Deck MVP Game Souvenirs Batting Glove

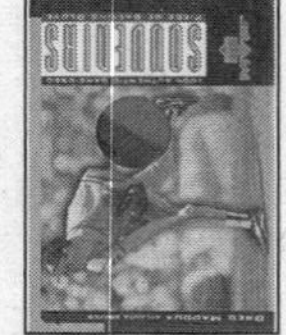

Inserted one per 96 hobby packs, these 18 cards feature a swatch of game-used batting glove of various major leaguers. A couple of players were issued in lesser quantities. We have notated those cards as SP's as well as print run information (as provided by Upper Deck) in our checklist.

GAR Alex Rodriguez 10.00 25.00
GBB Barry Bonds 20.00 50.00
GCJ Chipper Jones 6.00 15.00
GCR Cal Ripken 30.00 60.00
GEM Edgar Martinez 6.00 15.00
GFM Fred McGriff 6.00 15.00
GFT Frank Thomas 6.00 15.00
GGM Greg Maddux SP/95 40.00 80.00
GIR Ivan Rodriguez 6.00 15.00
GJG Juan Gonzalez 4.00 10.00
GJL Javy Lopez 4.00 10.00
GKG Ken Griffey Jr. 10.00 25.00
GMT Miguel Tejada 4.00 10.00
GMV Mo Vaughn 4.00 10.00
GRP Rafael Palmeiro 6.00 15.00
GSS Sammy Sosa 6.00 15.00
GTOG T.Gwynn SP/200 15.00 40.00
GTRG Troy Glaus 4.00 10.00

2001 Upper Deck MVP Game Souvenirs Batting Glove Autograph

Randomly inserted in packs, these nine cards feature not only a swatch of a game-used batting glove but also an authentic autograph of the player. These cards have a stated print run of 25 sets. Troy Glaus did not return his cards in time for inclusion in the packs and these cards were only available as redemptions. Due to market scarcity, no pricing is provided.

SGAR Alex Rodriguez
SGCJ Chipper Jones
SGCR Cal Ripken
SGFT Frank Thomas
SGIR Ivan Rodriguez
SGKG Ken Griffey Jr.
SGSS Sammy Sosa
SGTOG Tony Gwynn
SGTRG Troy Glaus

2001 Upper Deck MVP Super Tools

Inserted one per six packs, these 20 cards feature players whose tools seem to be far above the other players.

COMPLETE SET (20) 15.00 40.00
ST1 Ken Griffey Jr. 1.50 4.00
ST2 Carlos Delgado .40 1.00
ST3 Alex Rodriguez 1.50 4.00
ST4 Troy Glaus .40 1.00
ST5 Jeff Bagwell .60 1.50
ST6 Ichiro Suzuki 4.00 10.00
ST7 Derek Jeter 2.50 6.00
ST8 Jim Edmonds .40 1.00
ST9 Vladimir Guerrero 1.00 2.50
ST10 Jason Giambi .40 1.00
ST11 Todd Helton .60 1.50
ST12 Cal Ripken 3.00 8.00
ST13 Barry Bonds 2.50 6.00
ST14 N.Garciaparra UER 1.50 4.00
Spelled Garicaparra on the front
ST15 Randy Johnson 1.00 2.50
ST16 Jermaine Dye .40 1.00
ST17 Andruw Jones .60 1.50
ST18 Ivan Rodriguez .60 1.50
ST19 Sammy Sosa 1.00 2.50
ST20 Pedro Martinez .60 1.50

2002 Upper Deck MVP

This 300 card set was issued in May, 2002. These cards were issued in eight card packs which came 24 packs to a box and 12 boxes to a case. Cards number 295-300 feature players on the front and checklisting information on the back. Card 301, featuring Kazuhisa Ishii, was added to the product at the last minute. According to representatives at Upper Deck, the card was seeded only into very late boxes of MVP.

COMPLETE SET (301) 15.00 40.00
1 Darin Erstad .07 .20
2 Ramon Ortiz .07 .20
3 Garret Anderson .07 .20
4 Jarrod Washburn .07 .20
5 Troy Glaus .07 .20
6 Brendan Donnelly RC .20 .50
7 Troy Percival .07 .20
8 Tim Salmon .10 .30
9 Aaron Sele .07 .20
10 Brad Fullmer .07 .20
11 Scott Hatteberg .07 .20
12 Barry Zito .07 .20
13 Tim Hudson .07 .20
14 Miguel Tejada .07 .20
15 Jermaine Dye .07 .20
16 Mark Mulder .07 .20
17 Eric Chavez .07 .20
18 Terrence Long .07 .20
19 Carlos Pena .07 .20
20 David Justice .07 .20
21 Jeremy Giambi .07 .20
22 Shannon Stewart .07 .20
23 Raul Mondesi .07 .20
24 Chris Carpenter .07 .20
25 Carlos Delgado .07 .20
26 Mike Sirotka .07 .20
27 Reed Johnson RC .30 .75
28 Darrin Fletcher .07 .20
29 Jose Cruz Jr. .07 .20
30 Vernon Wells .07 .20
31 Tanyon Sturtze .07 .20
32 Toby Hall .07 .20
33 Brent Abernathy .07 .20
34 Ben Grieve .07 .20
35 Joe Kennedy .07 .20
36 Dewon Brazelton .07 .20
37 Aubrey Huff .07 .20
38 Steve Cox .07 .20
39 Greg Vaughn .07 .20
40 Brady Anderson .07 .20
41 Chuck Finley .07 .20
42 Jim Thome .10 .30
43 Russell Branyan .07 .20
44 C.C. Sabathia .07 .20
45 Matt Lawton .07 .20
46 Omar Vizquel .10 .30
47 Bartolo Colon .07 .20
48 Alex Escobar .07 .20
49 Ellis Burks .07 .20
50 Bret Boone .07 .20
51 John Olerud .07 .20
52 Jeff Cirillo .07 .20
53 Ichiro Suzuki .40 1.00
54 Kazuhiro Sasaki .07 .20
55 Freddy Garcia .07 .20
56 Edgar Martinez .10 .30
57 Matt Thornton RC .20 .50
58 Mike Cameron .07 .20
59 Carlos Guillen .07 .20
60 Jeff Conine .07 .20
61 Tony Batista .07 .20
62 Jason Johnson .07 .20
63 Melvin Mora .07 .20
64 Brian Roberts .07 .20
65 Josh Towers .07 .20
66 Steve Bechler RC .20 .50
67 Jerry Hairston Jr. .07 .20
68 Chris Richard .07 .20
69 Alex Rodriguez .30 .75
70 Chan Ho Park .07 .20
71 Ivan Rodriguez .10 .30
72 Jeff Zimmerman .07 .20
73 Mark Teixeira .20 .50
74 Gabe Kapler .07 .20
75 Frank Catalanotto .07 .20
76 Rafael Palmeiro .10 .30
77 Doug Davis .07 .20
78 Carl Everett .07 .20
79 Pedro Martinez .10 .30
80 Nomar Garciaparra .30 .75
81 Tony Clark .07 .20
82 Trot Nixon .07 .20
83 Manny Ramirez .10 .30
84 Josh Hancock RC .25 .60
85 Johnny Damon Sox .10 .30
86 Jose Offerman .07 .20
87 Rich Garces .07 .20
88 Shea Hillenbrand .07 .20
89 Carlos Beltran .07 .20
90 Mike Sweeney .07 .20
91 Jeff Suppan .07 .20
92 Joe Randa .07 .20
93 Chuck Knoblauch .07 .20
94 Mark Quinn .07 .20
95 Neifi Perez .07 .20
96 Carlos Febles .07 .20
97 Miguel Asencio RC .20 .50
98 Michael Tucker .07 .20
99 Dean Palmer .07 .20
100 Jose Lima .07 .20
101 Craig Paquette .07 .20
102 Dmitri Young .07 .20
103 Bobby Higginson .07 .20
104 Jeff Weaver .07 .20
105 Matt Anderson .07 .20
106 Damion Easley .07 .20
107 Eric Milton .07 .20
108 Doug Mientkiewicz .07 .20
109 Cristian Guzman .07 .20
110 Brad Radke .07 .20
111 Torii Hunter .07 .20
112 Corey Koskie .07 .20
113 Joe Mays .07 .20
114 Jacque Jones .07 .20
115 David Ortiz .20 .50
116 Kevin Frederick RC .20 .50
117 Magglio Ordonez .07 .20
118 Ray Durham .07 .20
119 Mark Buehrle .07 .20
120 Jon Garland .07 .20
121 Paul Konerko .07 .20
122 Todd Ritchie .07 .20
123 Frank Thomas .20 .50
124 Edwin Almonte RC .20 .50
125 Carlos Lee .07 .20
126 Kenny Lofton .07 .20
127 Roger Clemens .40 1.00
128 Derek Jeter .50 1.25
129 Jorge Posada .10 .30
130 Bernie Williams .10 .30
131 Mike Mussina .10 .30
132 Alfonso Soriano .07 .20
133 Robin Ventura .07 .20
134 John Vander Wal .07 .20
135 Jason Giambi Yankees .07 .20
136 Mariano Rivera .20 .50
137 Rondell White .07 .20
138 Jeff Bagwell .10 .30
139 Wade Miller .07 .20
140 Richard Hidalgo .07 .20
141 Julio Lugo .07 .20
142 Roy Oswalt .07 .20
143 Rodrigo Rosario RC .20 .50
144 Lance Berkman .07 .20
145 Craig Biggio .10 .30
146 Shane Reynolds .07 .20
147 John Smoltz .10 .30
148 Chipper Jones .20 .50
149 Gary Sheffield .07 .20
150 Rafael Furcal .07 .20
151 Greg Maddux .30 .75
152 Tom Glavine .10 .30
153 Andruw Jones .10 .30
154 John Ennis RC .20 .50
155 Vinny Castilla .07 .20
156 Marcus Giles .07 .20
157 Javy Lopez .07 .20
158 Richie Sexson .07 .20
159 Geoff Jenkins .07 .20
160 Jeffrey Hammonds .07 .20
161 Alex Ochoa .07 .20
162 Ben Sheets .07 .20
163 Jose Hernandez .07 .20
164 Eric Young .07 .20
165 Luis Martinez RC .20 .50
166 Albert Pujols .40 1.00
167 Darryl Kile .07 .20
168 So Taguchi RC .20 .50
169 Jim Edmonds .07 .20
170 Fernando Vina .07 .20
171 Matt Morris .07 .20
172 J.D. Drew .07 .20
173 Bud Smith .07 .20
174 Edgar Renteria .07 .20
175 Placido Polanco .07 .20
176 Tino Martinez .10 .30
177 Sammy Sosa .20 .50
178 Moises Alou .07 .20
179 Kerry Wood .07 .20
180 Delino DeShields .07 .20
181 Alex Gonzalez .07 .20
182 Jon Lieber .07 .20
183 Fred McGriff .10 .30
184 Corey Patterson .07 .20
185 Mark Prior .10 .30
186 Tom Gordon .07 .20
187 Francis Beltran RC .20 .50
188 Randy Johnson .20 .50
189 Luis Gonzalez .07 .20
190 Matt Williams .07 .20
191 Mark Grace .10 .30
192 Curt Schilling .07 .20
193 Doug Devore RC .20 .50
194 Erubiel Durazo .07 .20
195 Steve Finley .07 .20
196 Craig Counsell .07 .20
197 Shawn Green .07 .20
198 Kevin Brown .07 .20
199 Paul LoDuca .07 .20

200 Brian Jordan .07 .20
201 Andy Ashby .07 .20
202 Darren Dreifort .07 .20
203 Adrian Beltre .07 .20
204 Victor Alvarez RC .20 .50
205 Eric Karros .07 .20
206 Hideo Nomo .20 .50
207 Vladimir Guerrero .20 .50
208 Javier Vazquez .07 .20
209 Michael Barrett .07 .20
210 Jose Vidro .07 .20
211 Brad Wilkerson .07 .20
212 Tony Armas Jr. .07 .20
213 Eric Good RC .20 .50
214 Orlando Cabrera .07 .20
215 Lee Stevens .07 .20
216 Jeff Kent .07 .20
217 Rich Aurilia .07 .20
218 Robb Nen .07 .20
219 Calvin Murray .07 .20
220 Russ Ortiz .07 .20
221 Deivis Santos .07 .20
222 Marvin Benard .07 .20
223 Jason Schmidt .07 .20
224 Reggie Sanders .07 .20
225 Barry Bonds .50 1.25
226 Brad Penny .07 .20
227 Cliff Floyd .07 .20
228 Mike Lowell .07 .20
229 Derrek Lee .10 .30
230 Ryan Dempster .07 .20
231 Josh Beckett .07 .20
232 Hansel Izquierdo RC .20 .50
233 Preston Wilson .07 .20
234 A.J. Burnett .07 .20
235 Charles Johnson .07 .20
236 Mike Piazza .30 .75
237 Al Leiter .07 .20
238 Jay Payton .07 .20
239 Roger Cedeno .07 .20
240 Jeromy Burnitz .07 .20
241 Roberto Alomar .10 .30
242 Mo Vaughn .07 .20
243 Shawn Estes .07 .20
244 Armando Benitez .07 .20
245 Tyler Yates RC .20 .50
246 Phil Nevin .07 .20
247 D'Angelo Jimenez .07 .20
248 Ramon Vazquez .07 .20
249 Bubba Trammell .07 .20
250 Trevor Hoffman .07 .20
251 Ben Howard RC .20 .50
252 Mark Kotsay .07 .20
253 Ray Lankford .07 .20
254 Ryan Klesko .07 .20
255 Scott Rolen .10 .30
256 Robert Person .07 .20
257 Jimmy Rollins .07 .20
258 Pat Burrell .07 .20
259 Anderson Machado RC .20 .50
260 Randy Wolf .07 .20
261 Travis Lee .07 .20
262 Mike Lieberthal .07 .20
263 Doug Glanville .07 .20
264 Bobby Abreu .07 .20
265 Brian Giles .07 .20
266 Kris Benson .07 .20
267 Aramis Ramirez .07 .20
268 Kevin Young .07 .20
269 Jack Wilson .07 .20
270 Mike Williams .07 .20
271 Jimmy Anderson .07 .20
272 Jason Kendall .07 .20
273 Pokey Reese .07 .20
274 Rob Mackowiak .07 .20
275 Sean Casey .07 .20
276 Juan Encarnacion .07 .20
277 Austin Kearns .07 .20
278 Danny Graves .07 .20
279 Ken Griffey Jr. .30 .75
280 Barry Larkin .10 .30
281 Todd Walker .07 .20
282 Elmer Dessens .07 .20
283 Aaron Boone .07 .20
284 Adam Dunn .07 .20
285 Larry Walker .07 .20
286 Rene Reyes RC .20 .50
287 Juan Uribe .07 .20
288 Mike Hampton .07 .20
289 Todd Helton .10 .30
290 Juan Pierre .07 .20
291 Denny Neagle .07 .20
292 Jose Ortiz .07 .20
293 Todd Zeile .07 .20
294 Ben Petrick .07 .20
295 Ken Griffey Jr. CL .20 .50
296 Derek Jeter CL .25 .60
297 Sammy Sosa CL .10 .30
298 Ichiro Suzuki CL .20 .50
299 Barry Bonds CL .30 .75
300 Alex Rodriguez CL .20 .50
301 Kazuhisa Ishii RC .20 .50

2002 Upper Deck MVP Silver

Inserted randomly into hobby and retail packs, these cards parallel the regular MVP set and have a stated print run of 100 serial numbered sets.

*SILVER STARS: 12.5X TO 30X BASIC CARDS
*SILVER ROOKIES: 6X TO 15X BASIC

2002 Upper Deck MVP Game Souvenirs Bat

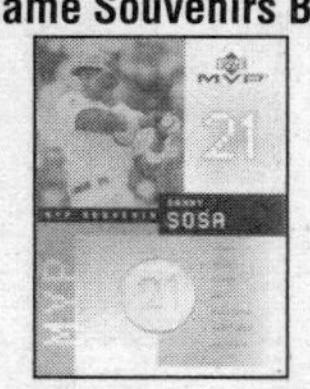

Issued exclusively in hobby packs at stated odds of one in 144, these 27 cards feature bat chips from the featured players. A few players were issued to lesser quantities and we have notated that stated print run information in our checklist.

BAR Alex Rodriguez 10.00 25.00
BBG Brian Giles 6.00 15.00
BBW Bernie Williams 8.00 20.00
BCD Carlos Delgado
BDJ David Justice
BDM Doug Mientkiewicz 6.00 15.00
BEM Edgar Martinez 8.00 20.00
BFT Frank Thomas SP/97 *
BGM Greg Maddux
BGS Gary Sheffield
BGV Greg Vaughn 6.00 15.00
BIR Ivan Rodriguez 8.00 20.00
BJK Jeff Kent 6.00 15.00
BJT Jim Thome 8.00 20.00
BKG Ken Griffey Jr. 10.00 25.00
BLG Luis Gonzalez 6.00 15.00
BLW Larry Walker 6.00 15.00
BMO Magglio Ordonez 6.00 15.00
BMP Mike Piazza SP/97 *
BMS Mike Sweeney
BRA Roberto Alomar
BRK Ryan Klesko 6.00 15.00
BRP Rafael Palmeiro SP/97 *
BSG Shawn Green 6.00 15.00
BSR Scott Rolen
BSS Sammy Sosa 8.00 20.00
BTH Todd Helton

2002 Upper Deck MVP Game Souvenirs Bat Jersey Combos

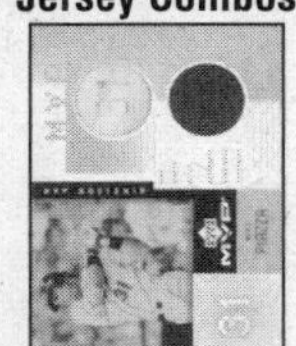

Inserted exclusively in hobby packs at stated odds of one in 144, these 28 cards feature both a bat chip and a jersey swatch from the featured player. A few players were issued in smaller quantities and we have notated that information with the stated print run in our checklist.

GOLD RANDOM INSERTS IN PACKS
GOLD PRINT RUN 25 SERIAL #'d SETS
NO GOLD PRICING DUE TO SCARCITY
CAB Adrian Beltre 8.00 20.00
CAR Alex Rodriguez 20.00 50.00
CBG Brian Giles 8.00 20.00
CBW Bernie Williams SP/97 *
CCD Carlos Delgado Bat-Pants 8.00 20.00
CCJ Chipper Jones 15.00 40.00
CDE Darin Erstad 8.00 20.00
CEA Edgardo Alfonzo 8.00 20.00
CIR Ivan Rodriguez 10.00 25.00
CJB Jeff Bagwell Bat-Pants
CJG Jason Giambi 8.00 20.00
CJK Jeff Kent 8.00 20.00
CJT Jim Thome 10.00 25.00
CKG Ken Griffey Jr. 20.00 50.00
CLG Luis Gonzalez 8.00 20.00
CMO Magglio Ordonez 8.00 20.00
CMP Mike Piazza 20.00 50.00
COV Omar Vizquel Bat-Pants SP/97 *
CPB Pat Burrell SP/97
CRA Roberto Alomar Bat-Pants
CRJ Randy Johnson 15.00 40.00
CRP Rafael Palmeiro 10.00 25.00
CRV Robin Ventura 8.00 20.00
CSG Shawn Green 8.00 20.00
CSR Scott Rolen 10.00 25.00
CSS Sammy Sosa 15.00 40.00
CTH Todd Helton 10.00 25.00
CTZ Todd Zeile 8.00 20.00

2002 Upper Deck MVP Game Souvenirs Jersey

Inserted into hobby and retail packs at stated odds of one in 48, these 29 cards feature jersey swatches from the featured player. A few cards were printed in smaller quantity and we have notated those with an SP in our checklist. In addition, a few players appeared to be in larger supply and we have notated that information with an asterisk in our checklist.

JAB Adrian Beltre 4.00 10.00
JAR Alex Rodriguez 6.00 15.00
JCD Carlos Delgado Pants 4.00 10.00
JDE Darin Erstad 4.00 10.00
JEM Edgar Martinez 6.00 15.00
JFT Frank Thomas 6.00 15.00
JGA Garret Anderson 4.00 10.00
JIR Ivan Rodriguez 6.00 15.00
JJB Jeff Bagwell Pants 6.00 15.00
JJB Jeromy Burnitz 4.00 10.00
JJG Juan Gonzalez 4.00 10.00
JJK Jeff Kent 4.00 10.00
JJP Jay Payton SP 6.00 15.00
JJT Jim Thome SP 10.00 25.00
JKL Kenny Lofton 4.00 10.00
JMK Mark Kotsay 4.00 10.00
JMP Mike Piazza 6.00 15.00
JOV Omar Vizquel Pants * 6.00 15.00
JPK Paul Konerko SP 6.00 15.00
JPW Preston Wilson 4.00 10.00
JRA Roberto Alomar Pants 6.00 15.00
JRC Roger Clemens 10.00 25.00
JRF Rafael Furcal 4.00 10.00
JRV Robin Ventura 4.00 10.00
JSR Scott Rolen 6.00 15.00
JTHO Trevor Hoffman 4.00 10.00
JTHU Tim Hudson 4.00 10.00
JTS Tim Salmon 6.00 15.00
JTZ Todd Zeile 4.00 10.00

2002 Upper Deck MVP Ichiro A Season to Remember

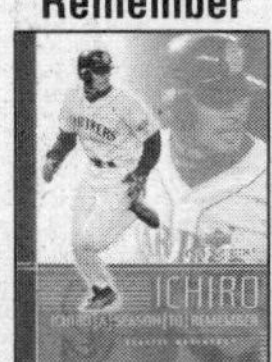

Inserted in hobby and retail packs at stated odds of one in 12, these 10 cards feature highlights from Ichiro's rookie season.

COMPLETE SET (10) 12.50 30.00
COMMON CARD (I1-I10) 1.25 3.00

2002 Upper Deck MVP Ichiro A Season to Remember Memorabilia

Randomly inserted in hobby and retail packs, these cards feature memorabilia pieces from Ichiro's rookie season. These cards are serial numbered to 25 and no pricing is available due to market scarcity.

IB Ichiro Suzuki Bat
IJ Ichiro Suzuki Jsy

2003 Upper Deck MVP

This 220 card set was released in March, 2003. These cards were issued in eight card packs which came 24 packs to a box and 12 boxes to a case. Cards numbered 219 and 220 are checklists featuring Upper Deck spokespeople. Cards numbered 221 through 330 were issued in special factory "tin" sets.

COMP.FACT.SET (330) 25.00 40.00
COMPLETE LO SET (220) 10.00 25.00
COMMON CARD (1-330) .07 .20
1 Troy Glaus .07 .20
2 Darin Erstad .07 .20
3 Jarrod Washburn .07 .20
4 Francisco Rodriguez .07 .20
5 Garret Anderson .07 .20
6 Tim Salmon .10 .30
7 Adam Kennedy .07 .20
8 Randy Johnson .20 .50
9 Luis Gonzalez .07 .20
10 Curt Schilling .07 .20
11 Junior Spivey .07 .20
12 Craig Counsell .07 .20
13 Mark Grace .10 .30
14 Steve Finley .07 .20
15 Javy Lopez .07 .20
16 Rafael Furcal .07 .20
17 John Smoltz .10 .30
18 Greg Maddux .30 .75
19 Chipper Jones .20 .50
20 Gary Sheffield .07 .20
21 Andruw Jones .10 .30
22 Tony Batista .07 .20
23 Geronimo Gil .07 .20
24 Jay Gibbons .07 .20
25 Rodrigo Lopez .07 .20
26 Chris Singleton .07 .20
27 Melvin Mora .07 .20
28 Jeff Conine .07 .20
29 Nomar Garciaparra .30 .75
30 Pedro Martinez .10 .30
31 Manny Ramirez .10 .30
32 Shea Hillenbrand .07 .20
33 Johnny Damon .10 .30
34 Jason Varitek .20 .50
35 Derek Lowe .07 .20
36 Trot Nixon .07 .20
37 Sammy Sosa .20 .50
38 Kerry Wood .07 .20
39 Mark Prior .10 .30
40 Moises Alou .07 .20
41 Corey Patterson .07 .20
42 Hee Seop Choi .07 .20
43 Mark Bellhorn .07 .20
44 Frank Thomas .20 .50
45 Mark Buehrle .07 .20
46 Magglio Ordonez .07 .20
47 Carlos Lee .07 .20
48 Paul Konerko .07 .20
49 Joe Borchard .07 .20
50 Joe Crede .07 .20
51 Ken Griffey Jr. .30 .75
52 Adam Dunn .07 .20
53 Austin Kearns .07 .20
54 Aaron Boone .07 .20
55 Sean Casey .07 .20
56 Danny Graves .07 .20
57 Russell Branyan .07 .20
58 Matt Lawton .07 .20
59 C.C. Sabathia .07 .20
60 Omar Vizquel .10 .30
61 Brandon Phillips .07 .20
62 Karim Garcia .07 .20
63 Ellis Burks .07 .20
64 Cliff Lee .07 .20
65 Todd Helton .10 .30
66 Larry Walker .07 .20
67 Jay Payton .07 .20
68 Brent Butler .07 .20
69 Juan Uribe .07 .20
70 Jason Jennings .07 .20
71 Denny Stark .07 .20
72 Dmitri Young .07 .20
73 Carlos Pena .07 .20
74 Andres Torres .07 .20
75 Andy Van Hekken .07 .20
76 George Lombard .07 .20
77 Eric Munson .07 .20
78 Bobby Higginson .07 .20
79 Luis Castillo .07 .20
80 A.J. Burnett .07 .20
81 Juan Encarnacion .07 .20
82 Ivan Rodriguez .10 .30
83 Mike Lowell .07 .20
84 Josh Beckett .07 .20
85 Brad Penny .07 .20
86 Craig Biggio .10 .30
87 Jeff Kent .07 .20
88 Morgan Ensberg .07 .20
89 Daryle Ward .07 .20
90 Jeff Bagwell .10 .30
91 Roy Oswalt .07 .20
92 Lance Berkman .07 .20
93 Mike Sweeney .07 .20
94 Carlos Beltran .07 .20
95 Raul Ibanez .07 .20
96 Carlos Febles .07 .20
97 Joe Randa .07 .20
98 Shawn Green .07 .20
99 Kevin Brown .07 .20
100 Paul Lo Duca .07 .20
101 Adrian Beltre .07 .20
102 Eric Gagne .07 .20
103 Kazuhisa Ishii .07 .20
104 Odalis Perez .07 .20
105 Brian Jordan .07 .20
106 Geoff Jenkins .07 .20
107 Richie Sexson .07 .20
108 Ben Sheets .07 .20
109 Alex Sanchez .07 .20
110 Eric Young .07 .20
111 Jose Hernandez .07 .20
112 Torii Hunter .07 .20
113 Eric Milton .07 .20
114 Corey Koskie .07 .20
115 Doug Mientkiewicz .07 .20
116 A.J. Pierzynski .07 .20
117 Jacque Jones .07 .20
118 Cristian Guzman .07 .20
119 Bartolo Colon .07 .20
120 Brad Wilkerson .07 .20
121 Michael Barrett .07 .20
122 Vladimir Guerrero .20 .50
123 Jose Vidro .07 .20
124 Javier Vazquez .07 .20
125 Endy Chavez .07 .20
126 Roberto Alomar .10 .30
127 Mike Piazza .30 .75
128 Jeromy Burnitz .07 .20
129 Mo Vaughn .07 .20
130 Tom Glavine .10 .30
131 Al Leiter .07 .20
132 Armando Benitez .07 .20
133 Timo Perez .07 .20
134 Roger Clemens .40 1.00
135 Derek Jeter .50 1.25
136 Jason Giambi .07 .20
137 Alfonso Soriano .07 .20
138 Bernie Williams .10 .30
139 Mike Mussina .10 .30
140 Jorge Posada .10 .30
141 Hideki Matsui RC 1.50 4.00
142 Robin Ventura .07 .20
143 David Wells .07 .20
144 Nick Johnson .07 .20
145 Tim Hudson .07 .20
146 Eric Chavez .07 .20
147 Barry Zito .07 .20
148 Miguel Tejada .07 .20
149 Jermaine Dye .07 .20
150 Mark Mulder .07 .20
151 Terrence Long .07 .20
152 Scott Hatteberg .07 .20
153 Marlon Byrd .07 .20
154 Jim Thome .10 .30
155 Marlon Anderson .07 .20
156 Vicente Padilla .07 .20
157 Bobby Abreu .07 .20
158 Jimmy Rollins .07 .20
159 Pat Burrell .07 .20
160 Brian Giles .07 .20
161 Aramis Ramirez .07 .20
162 Jason Kendall .07 .20
163 Josh Fogg .07 .20
164 Kip Wells .07 .20
165 Pokey Reese .07 .20
166 Kris Benson .07 .20
167 Ryan Klesko .07 .20
168 Brian Lawrence .07 .20
169 Mark Kotsay .07 .20
170 Jake Peavy .07 .20
171 Phil Nevin .07 .20
172 Sean Burroughs .07 .20
173 Trevor Hoffman .07 .20
174 Jason Schmidt .07 .20
175 Kirk Rueter .07 .20
176 Barry Bonds .50 1.25
177 Pedro Feliz .07 .20
178 Rich Aurilia .07 .20
179 Benito Santiago .07 .20
180 J.T. Snow .07 .20
181 Robb Nen .07 .20
182 Ichiro Suzuki .40 1.00
183 Edgar Martinez .10 .30
184 Bret Boone .07 .20
185 Freddy Garcia .07 .20
186 John Olerud .07 .20
187 Mike Cameron .07 .20
188 Joel Piniero .07 .20
189 Albert Pujols .40 1.00
190 Matt Morris .07 .20
191 J.D. Drew .07 .20
192 Scott Rolen .10 .30
193 Tino Martinez .10 .30
194 Jim Edmonds .07 .20
195 Edgar Renteria .07 .20
196 Fernando Vina .07 .20
197 Jason Isringhausen .07 .20
198 Ben Grieve .07 .20
199 Carl Crawford .07 .20
200 Dewon Brazelton .07 .20
201 Aubrey Huff .07 .20
202 Jared Sandberg .07 .20
203 Steve Cox .07 .20
204 Carl Everett .07 .20
205 Kevin Mench .07 .20
206 Alex Rodriguez .30 .75
207 Rafael Palmeiro .10 .30
208 Michael Young .10 .30
209 Hank Blalock .07 .20
210 Juan Gonzalez .07 .20
211 Carlos Delgado .07 .20
212 Eric Hinske .07 .20
213 Josh Phelps .07 .20
214 Mark Hendrickson .07 .20
215 Roy Halladay .07 .20
216 Orlando Hudson .07 .20
217 Shannon Stewart .07 .20
218 Vernon Wells .07 .20
219 Ichiro Suzuki CL .20 .50
220 Jason Giambi CL .07 .20
221 Scott Spiezio .07 .20
222 Rich Fischer RC .15 .40
223 Bengie Molina .07 .20
224 David Eckstein .07 .20
225 Brandon Webb RC .75 2.00
226 Oscar Villarreal RC .15 .40
227 Rob Hammock RC .15 .40
228 Matt Kata RC .15 .40
229 Lyle Overbay .07 .20
230 Chris Capuano RC .30 .75
231 Horacio Ramirez .07 .20
232 Shane Reynolds .07 .20
233 Russ Ortiz .07 .20
234 Mike Hampton .07 .20
235 Mike Hessman RC .15 .40
236 Byung-Hyun Kim .07 .20
237 Freddy Sanchez .07 .20
238 Jason Shiell RC .15 .40
239 Ryan Cameron RC .15 .40
240 Todd Wellemeyer RC .15 .40
241 Joe Borowski .07 .20
242 Alex Gonzalez .07 .20
243 Jon Leicester RC .15 .40
244 David Sanders RC .15 .40
245 Roberto Alomar .10 .30
246 Barry Larkin .10 .30
247 Jhonny Peralta .20 .50
248 Zach Sorensen .07 .20
249 Jason Davis .07 .20
250 Coco Crisp .10 .30
251 Greg Vaughn .07 .20
252 Preston Wilson .07 .20
253 Denny Neagle .07 .20
254 Clint Barmes RC .30 .75
255 Jeremy Bonderman RC 1.00 2.50
256 Wilfredo Ledezma RC .15 .40
257 Dontrelle Willis .20 .50
258 Alex Gonzalez .07 .20
259 Tommy Phelps .07 .20
260 Kirk Saarloos .07 .20
261 Colin Porter RC .15 .40
262 Nate Bland RC .15 .40
263 Jason Gilfillan RC .15 .40
264 Mike MacDougal .07 .20
265 Ken Harvey .07 .20
266 Brent Mayne .07 .20
267 Miguel Cabrera .20 .50
268 Hideo Nomo .20 .50
269 Dave Roberts .07 .20
270 Fred McGriff .10 .30
271 Joe Thurston .07 .20
272 Royce Clayton .07 .20
273 Michael Nakamura RC .15 .40
274 Brad Radke .07 .20
275 Joe Mays .07 .20
276 Lew Ford RC .20 .50
277 Michael Cuddyer .07 .20
278 Luis Ayala RC .15 .40
279 Julio Manon RC .08 .25
280 Anthony Ferrari RC .15 .40
281 Livan Hernandez .07 .20
282 Jae Weong Seo .07 .20
283 Jose Reyes .07 .20
284 Tony Clark .07 .20
285 Ty Wigginton .07 .20
286 Cliff Floyd .07 .20
287 Jeremy Griffiths RC .15 .40
288 Jason Roach RC .15 .40
289 Jeff Duncan RC .15 .40
290 Phil Seibel RC .15 .40
291 Prentice Redman RC .15 .40
292 Jose Contreras RC .30 .75
293 Ruben Sierra .07 .20
294 Andy Pettitte .10 .30
295 Aaron Boone .07 .20
296 Mariano Rivera .20 .50
297 Michel Hernandez RC .15 .40
298 Mike Neu RC .15 .40
299 Erubiel Durazo .07 .20
300 Billy McMillon .07 .20
301 Rich Harden .10 .30
302 David Bell .07 .20
303 Kevin Millwood .07 .20
304 Mike Lieberthal .07 .20
305 Jeremy Wedel RC .15 .40
306 Kenny Lofton .07 .20
307 Reggie Sanders .07 .20
308 Randall Simon .07 .20
309 Xavier Nady .07 .20
310 Rod Beck .07 .20
311 Miguel Ojeda RC .15 .40
312 Mark Loretta .07 .20
313 Edgardo Alfonzo .07 .20
314 Andres Galarraga .07 .20
315 Jose Cruz Jr. .07 .20
316 Jesse Foppert .07 .20
317 Kurt Ainsworth .07 .20
318 Dan Wilson .07 .20
319 Ben Davis .07 .20
320 Rocco Baldelli .07 .20
321 Al Martin .07 .20
322 Runelvys Hernandez .07 .20
323 Dan Haren RC .30 .75
324 Bo Hart RC .15 .40
325 Einar Diaz .07 .20
326 Mike Lamb .07 .20
327 Aquilino Lopez RC .15 .40
328 Reed Johnson .07 .20
329 Diegomar Markwell RC .15 .40
330 Hideki Matsui CL .60 1.50

2003 Upper Deck MVP Black

Randomly inserted in packs, this is a parallel to the Upper Deck MVP low number set. These cards were issued to a stated print run of 50 serial numbered sets.

*BLACK: 15X TO 40X BASIC

2003 Upper Deck MVP Gold

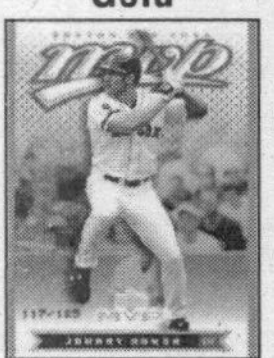

Randomly inserted in packs, this is a parallel to the MVP low number set. These cards were issued to a stated print run of 125 serial numbered sets.

*GOLD: 10X TO 25X BASIC
*GOLD RC'S: 2.5X TO 6X BASIC

2003 Upper Deck MVP Silver

These cards, which parallel the MVP low number set, were actually inserted at a stated rate of one in 12. This is different from the stated wrapper odds which said these cards were inserted at a rate of one in two.

*SILVER: 3X TO 8X BASIC
*SILVER RC'S: .75X TO 2X BASIC

2003 Upper Deck MVP Base-to-Base

Issued at a stated rate of one in 488, these six cards feature two players as well as bases used in one of their games.

CP Roger Clemens 10.00 25.00

Mike Piazza
IG Ichiro Suzuki 15.00 40.00
Ken Griffey Jr.
IJ Ichiro Suzuki 20.00 50.00
Derek Jeter
JW Derek Jeter 10.00 25.00
Bernie Williams
MB Mark McGwire 30.00 60.00
Barry Bonds
RJ Alex Rodriguez 15.00 40.00
Derek Jeter

2003 Upper Deck MVP Celebration

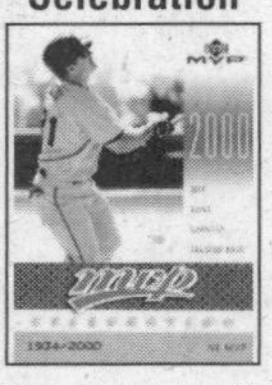

Randomly inserted into packs, these 90 cards honor various players leading achievements in baseball. Each of these cards were issued to a stated print run of between 1955 and 2002 cards and we have notated the print run information next to the player's name in our checklist.

*GOLD: 1.25X TO 3X BASIC
GOLD PRINT RUN 75 SERIAL #'d SETS
1 Yogi Berra MVP/1955 1.50 4.00
2 Mickey Mantle MVP/1956 6.00 15.00
3 Mickey Mantle MVP/1957 6.00 15.00
4 Mickey Mantle MVP/1962 6.00 15.00
5 Roger Clemens MVP/1986 3.00 8.00
6 Rickey Henderson MVP/1990 1.50 4.00
7 Frank Thomas MVP/1993 1.50 4.00
8 Mo Vaughn MVP/1995 1.25 3.00
9 Juan Gonzalez MVP/1996 1.25 3.00
10 Ken Griffey Jr. MVP/1997 2.50 6.00
11 Juan Gonzalez MVP/1998 1.25 3.00
12 Ivan Rodriguez MVP/1998 1.25 3.00
13 Jason Giambi MVP/2000 1.25 3.00
14 Ichiro Suzuki MVP/2001 3.00 8.00
15 Miguel Tejada MVP/2002 1.25 3.00
16 Barry Bonds MVP/1990 4.00 10.00
17 Barry Bonds MVP/1992 4.00 10.00
18 Barry Bonds MVP/1993 4.00 10.00
19 Jeff Bagwell MVP/1994 1.25 3.00
20 Barry Larkin MVP/1995 1.25 3.00
21 Larry Walker MVP/1997 1.25 3.00
22 Sammy Sosa MVP/1998 1.50 4.00
23 Chipper Jones MVP/1999 1.50 4.00
24 Jeff Kent MVP/2000 1.25 3.00
25 Barry Bonds MVP/2001 4.00 10.00
26 Barry Bonds MVP/2002 4.00 10.00
27 Ken Griffey Sr. AS/1980 1.25 3.00
28 Roger Clemens AS/1986 3.00 8.00
29 Ken Griffey Jr. AS/1992 2.50 6.00
30 Fred McGriff AS/1994 1.25 3.00
31 Jeff Conine AS/1995 1.25 3.00
32 Mike Piazza AS/1996 2.50 6.00
33 Sandy Alomar Jr. AS/1997 1.25 3.00
34 Roberto Alomar AS/1998 1.25 3.00
35 Pedro Martinez AS/1999 1.25 3.00
36 Derek Jeter AS/2000 4.00 10.00
37 Rickey Henderson ALCS/1989 1.50 4.00
38 Roberto Alomar ALCS/1992 1.25 3.00
39 Bernie Williams ALCS/1996 1.25 3.00
40 Marquis Grissom ALCS/1997 1.25 3.00
41 David Wells ALCS/1998 1.25 3.00
42 Orlando Hernandez ALCS/1999 1.25 3.00
43 David Justice ALCS/2000 1.25 3.00
44 Andy Pettitte ALCS/2001 1.25 3.00
45 Adam Kennedy ALCS/2002 1.25 3.00
46 John Smoltz NLCS/1992 1.25 3.00
47 Curt Schilling NLCS/1993 1.25 3.00
48 Javy Lopez NLCS/1996 1.25 3.00
49 Livan Hernandez NLCS/1997 1.25 3.00
50 Sterling Hitchcock NLCS/1998 1.25 3.00
51 Mike Hampton NLCS/2000 1.25 3.00
52 Craig Counsell NLCS/2001 1.25 3.00
53 Benito Santiago NLCS/2002 1.25 3.00
54 Tom Glavine WS/1995 1.25 3.00
55 Livan Hernandez WS/1997 1.25 3.00
56 Mariano Rivera WS/1999 1.50 4.00
57 Derek Jeter WS/2000 4.00 10.00
58 Randy Johnson WS/2001 1.50 4.00
59 Curt Schilling WS/2001 1.25 3.00
60 Troy Glaus WS/2002 1.25 3.00
61 Yogi Berra MM/1951 1.50 4.00
62 Yogi Berra MM/1955 1.50 4.00
63 Mickey Mantle MM/1956 6.00 15.00
64 Mickey Mantle MM/1957 6.00 15.00
65 Ken Griffey Sr. MM/1980 1.25 3.00
66 Rickey Henderson MM/1989 1.50 4.00
67 Roberto Alomar MM/1992 1.25 3.00
68 Bernie Williams MM/1996 1.25 3.00
69 Livan Hernandez MM/1997 1.25 3.00
70 Sammy Sosa MM/1998 1.50 4.00
71 Sterling Hitchcock MM/1998 1.25 3.00
72 David Wells MM/1998 1.25 3.00
73 Mariano Rivera MM/1999 1.50 4.00
74 Chipper Jones MM/1999 1.50 4.00
75 Ivan Rodriguez MM/1999 1.25 3.00
76 Derek Jeter MM/2000 4.00 10.00
77 Jason Giambi MM/2000 1.25 3.00
78 Jeff Kent MM/2000 1.25 3.00
79 Mike Hampton MM/2000 1.25 3.00
80 Randy Johnson MM/2001 1.50 4.00
81 Curt Schilling MM/2001 1.25 3.00
82 Barry Bonds MM/2001 4.00 10.00
83 Ichiro Suzuki MM/2001 3.00 8.00
84 Ichiro Suzuki MM/2001 3.00 8.00
85 Adam Kennedy MM/2002 1.25 3.00
86 Benito Santiago MM/2002 1.25 3.00
87 Troy Glaus MM/2002 1.25 3.00
88 Troy Glaus MM/2002 1.25 3.00
89 Miguel Tejada MM/2002 1.25 3.00
90 Barry Bonds MM/2002 4.00 10.00

2003 Upper Deck MVP Covering the Bases

Issued at a stated rate of one in 125, these 15 cards feature game-used bases from the featured player's career.

AR Alex Rodriguez 6.00 15.00
BB Barry Bonds 8.00 20.00
CD Carlos Delgado 3.00 8.00
DE Darin Erstad 3.00 8.00
DJ Derek Jeter 8.00 20.00
FT Frank Thomas 4.00 10.00
IR Ivan Rodriguez 4.00 10.00
IS Ichiro Suzuki 8.00 20.00
JD J.D. Drew 3.00 8.00
JT Jim Thome 4.00 10.00
LG Luis Gonzalez 3.00 8.00
MP Mike Piazza 6.00 15.00
MT Miguel Tejada 3.00 8.00
SG Shawn Green 3.00 8.00
TG Troy Glaus 3.00 8.00

2003 Upper Deck MVP Covering the Plate Game Bat

Issued at a stated rate of one in 160, these six cards feature game-used bat pieces from the featured player.

FM Fred McGriff 6.00 15.00
JT Jim Thome 6.00 15.00
MG Mark McGwire 30.00 60.00
RA Roberto Alomar 6.00 15.00
RF Rafael Furcal 4.00 10.00
VG Vladimir Guerrero 6.00 15.00

2003 Upper Deck MVP Dual Aces Game Base

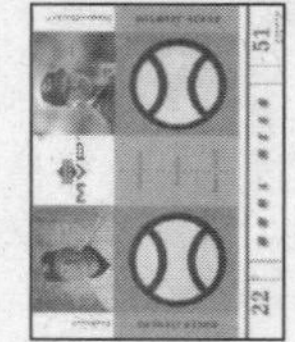

Issued at a stated rate of one in 488, these six cards feature bases used in games featuring two key pitchers.

BS Kevin Brown 4.00 10.00
Curt Schilling
CJ Roger Clemens 8.00 20.00
Randy Johnson
CL Roger Clemens 6.00 15.00
Al Leiter
ML Matt Morris 4.00 10.00
Al Leiter
SJ Curt Schilling 4.00 10.00
Randy Johnson
SP Curt Schilling 4.00 10.00
Andy Pettitte

2003 Upper Deck MVP Express Delivery

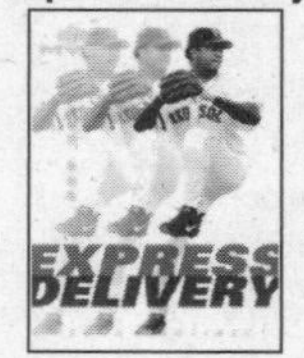

Inserted at a stated rate of one in 12, these 15 cards feature players who are among the leading pitchers in baseball.

ED1 Randy Johnson .75 2.00
ED2 Curt Schilling .60 1.50
ED3 Pedro Martinez .60 1.50
ED4 Kerry Wood .60 1.50
ED5 Mark Prior .60 1.50
ED6 A.J. Burnett .60 1.50
ED7 Josh Beckett .60 1.50
ED8 Roy Oswalt .60 1.50
ED9 Hideo Nomo .75 2.00
ED10 Ben Sheets .60 1.50
ED11 Bartolo Colon .60 1.50
ED12 Roger Clemens 1.50 4.00
ED13 Mike Mussina .60 1.50
ED14 Tim Hudson .60 1.50
ED15 Matt Morris .60 1.50

2003 Upper Deck MVP Pro Sign

Randomly inserted in packs, these 23 cards feature authentic autographs from the featured players. Each of these cards are printed to a stated print run of 25 serial numbered sets and no pricing is provided due to market scarcity.

AD Adam Dunn
AK Austin Kearns
BG Brian Giles
BZ Barry Zito
CD Carlos Delgado
DH Drew Henson
DM Doug Mientkiewicz
FG Freddy Garcia
GJ Jay Gibbons
HB Hank Blalock
IS Ichiro Suzuki
JD Johnny Damon
JG Jason Giambi
KG Ken Griffey Jr.
LB Lance Berkman
MM Mark McGwire
MP Mark Prior
MS Mike Sweeney
RS Richie Sexson
SB Sean Burroughs
SS Sammy Sosa
TG Tony Gwynn
TH Tim Hudson

2003 Upper Deck MVP Pro View

Issued as a two-card box topper pack, these 45 cards are a special hologram set.

*GOLD: .75X TO 2X BASIC PRO VIEW
ONE 2-CARD PACK PER 6 SEALED BOXES
PV1 Troy Glaus 1.25 3.00
PV2 Darin Erstad 1.25 3.00
PV3 Randy Johnson 1.50 4.00
PV4 Curt Schilling 1.25 3.00
PV5 Luis Gonzalez 1.25 3.00
PV6 Chipper Jones 1.50 4.00
PV7 Andruw Jones 1.25 3.00
PV8 Greg Maddux 2.50 6.00
PV9 Pedro Martinez 1.25 3.00
PV10 Manny Ramirez 1.25 3.00
PV11 Sammy Sosa 1.50 4.00
PV12 Mark Prior 1.25 3.00
PV13 Magglio Ordonez 1.25 3.00
PV14 Frank Thomas 1.50 4.00
PV15 Ken Griffey Jr. 2.50 6.00
PV16 Adam Dunn 1.25 3.00
PV17 Jim Thome 1.25 3.00
PV18 Todd Helton 1.25 3.00
PV19 Jeff Bagwell 1.25 3.00
PV20 Lance Berkman 1.25 3.00
PV21 Shawn Green 1.25 3.00
PV22 Hideo Nomo 1.50 4.00
PV23 Vladimir Guerrero 1.50 4.00
PV24 Roberto Alomar 1.25 3.00
PV25 Mike Piazza 2.50 6.00
PV26 Jason Giambi 1.25 3.00
PV27 Roger Clemens 3.00 8.00
PV28 Alfonso Soriano 1.25 3.00
PV29 Derek Jeter 4.00 10.00
PV30 Miguel Tejada 1.25 3.00
PV31 Eric Chavez 1.25 3.00
PV32 Barry Zito 1.25 3.00
PV33 Pat Burrell 1.25 3.00
PV34 Brian Giles 1.25 3.00
PV35 Barry Bonds 4.00 10.00
PV36 Ichiro Suzuki 3.00 8.00
PV37 Albert Pujols 3.00 8.00
PV38 Scott Rolen 1.25 3.00
PV39 J.D. Drew 1.25 3.00
PV40 Mark McGwire 4.00 10.00
PV41 Alex Rodriguez 2.50 6.00
PV42 Rafael Palmeiro 1.25 3.00
PV43 Juan Gonzalez 1.25 3.00
PV44 Eric Hinske 1.25 3.00
PV45 Carlos Delgado 1.25 3.00

2003 Upper Deck MVP SportsNut

Inserted at a stated rate of one in three, this 90 card insert set could be used as interactive game cards. The contest could be entered on either a season or a weekly basis.

SN1 Troy Glaus .40 1.00
SN2 Darin Erstad .40 1.00
SN3 Luis Gonzalez .40 1.00
SN4 Andruw Jones .60 1.50
SN5 Chipper Jones 1.00 2.50
SN6 Gary Sheffield .40 1.00
SN7 Jay Gibbons .40 1.00
SN8 Manny Ramirez .60 1.50
SN9 Shea Hillenbrand .40 1.00
SN10 Johnny Damon .60 1.50
SN11 Nomar Garciaparra 1.50 4.00
SN12 Sammy Sosa 1.00 2.50
SN13 Magglio Ordonez .40 1.00
SN14 Frank Thomas 1.00 2.50
SN15 Ken Griffey Jr. 1.50 4.00
SN16 Adam Dunn .40 1.00
SN17 Matt Lawton .40 1.00
SN18 Larry Walker .40 1.00
SN19 Todd Helton .60 1.50
SN20 Carlos Pena .40 1.00
SN21 Mike Lowell .40 1.00
SN22 Jeff Bagwell .60 1.50
SN23 Lance Berkman .40 1.00
SN24 Mike Sweeney .40 1.00
SN25 Carlos Beltran .40 1.00
SN26 Shawn Green .40 1.00
SN27 Richie Sexson .40 1.00
SN28 Torii Hunter .40 1.00
SN29 Jacque Jones .40 1.00
SN30 Vladimir Guerrero 1.00 2.50
SN31 Jose Vidro .40 1.00
SN32 Roberto Alomar .60 1.50
SN33 Mike Piazza 1.50 4.00
SN34 Alfonso Soriano .40 1.00
SN35 Derek Jeter 2.50 6.00
SN36 Jason Giambi .40 1.00
SN37 Bernie Williams .60 1.50
SN38 Eric Chavez .40 1.00
SN39 Miguel Tejada .40 1.00
SN40 Jim Thome .60 1.50
SN41 Pat Burrell .40 1.00
SN42 Bobby Abreu .40 1.00
SN43 Brian Giles .40 1.00
SN44 Jason Kendall .40 1.00
SN45 Ryan Klesko .40 1.00
SN46 Phil Nevin .40 1.00
SN47 Barry Bonds 2.50 6.00
SN48 Rich Aurilia .40 1.00
SN49 Ichiro Suzuki 2.00 5.00
SN50 Bret Boone .40 1.00
SN51 J.D. Drew .40 1.00
SN52 Jim Edmonds .40 1.00
SN53 Albert Pujols 2.00 5.00
SN54 Scott Rolen .60 1.50
SN55 Ben Grieve .40 1.00
SN56 Alex Rodriguez 1.50 4.00
SN57 Rafael Palmeiro .60 1.50
SN58 Juan Gonzalez .40 1.00
SN59 Carlos Delgado .40 1.00
SN60 Josh Phelps .40 1.00
SN61 Jarrod Washburn .40 1.00
SN62 Randy Johnson 1.00 2.50
SN63 Curt Schilling .40 1.00
SN64 Greg Maddux 1.50 4.00
SN65 Mike Hampton .40 1.00
SN66 Rodrigo Lopez .40 1.00
SN67 Pedro Martinez .60 1.50
SN68 Derek Lowe .40 1.00
SN69 Mark Prior .60 1.50
SN70 Kerry Wood .40 1.00
SN71 Mark Buehrle .40 1.00
SN72 Roy Oswalt .40 1.00
SN73 Wade Miller .40 1.00
SN74 Odalis Perez .40 1.00
SN75 Hideo Nomo 1.00 2.50
SN76 Ben Sheets .40 1.00
SN77 Eric Milton .40 1.00
SN78 Bartolo Colon .40 1.00
SN79 Tom Glavine .60 1.50
SN80 Al Leiter .40 1.00
SN81 Roger Clemens 2.00 5.00
SN82 Mike Mussina .60 1.50
SN83 Tim Hudson .40 1.00
SN84 Barry Zito .40 1.00
SN85 Mark Mulder .40 1.00
SN86 Vicente Padilla .40 1.00
SN87 Jason Schmidt .40 1.00
SN88 Freddy Garcia .40 1.00
SN89 Matt Morris .40 1.00
SN90 Roy Halladay .40 1.00

2003 Upper Deck MVP Talk of the Town

Inserted at a stated rate of one in 12, this 15 card set features some of the most talked about players in baseball.

TT1 Hideki Matsui 2.00 5.00
TT2 Chipper Jones .75 2.00
TT3 Manny Ramirez .60 1.50
TT4 Sammy Sosa .75 2.00
TT5 Ken Griffey Jr. 1.25 3.00
TT6 Lance Berkman .60 1.50
TT7 Shawn Green .60 1.50
TT8 Vladimir Guerrero .75 2.00
TT9 Mike Piazza 1.25 3.00
TT10 Jason Giambi .60 1.50
TT11 Alfonso Soriano .60 1.50
TT12 Ichiro Suzuki 1.50 4.00
TT13 Albert Pujols 1.50 4.00
TT14 Alex Rodriguez 1.25 3.00
TT15 Eric Hinske .60 1.50

2003 Upper Deck MVP Three Bagger Game Base

Inserted at a stated rate of one in 488, this six-card set features base pieces involving three players on each card.

BMP Barry Bonds 50.00 100.00
Mark McGwire
Mike Piazza
GIB Ken Griffey Jr. 40.00 80.00
Ichiro Suzuki
Barry Bonds
GTD Troy Glaus 6.00 15.00
Frank Thomas
Carlos Delgado
IBJ Ichiro Suzuki 50.00 100.00
Barry Bonds
Derek Jeter
JWP Derek Jeter 15.00 40.00
Bernie Williams
Jorge Posada
SCB Curt Schilling 10.00 25.00
Roger Clemens
Kevin Brown

2003 Upper Deck MVP Total Bases

Randomly inserted into packs, this is an insert set featuring one base piece on each card. Each card was issued to a stated print run of 150 serial numbered sets.

AR Alex Rodriguez 10.00 25.00
BB Barry Bonds 15.00 40.00
DJ Derek Jeter 15.00 40.00
IS Ichiro Suzuki 15.00 40.00
KG Ken Griffey Jr. 10.00 25.00
MM Mark McGwire 20.00 50.00
MP Mike Piazza 10.00 25.00
RC Roger Clemens 10.00 25.00
TG Troy Glaus 4.00 10.00

2005 Upper Deck MVP

This 90-card set was released in August, 2005. The set was issued in six-card packs which came 24 packs to a box and 20 boxes to a case.

COMPLETE SET (90) 10.00 25.00
COMMON CARD (1-90) .08 .25
1 Adam Dunn .08 .25
2 Adrian Beltre .08 .25
3 Albert Pujols .40 1.00
4 Alex Rodriguez .30 .75
5 Alfonso Soriano .08 .25
6 Andruw Jones .15 .40
7 Aubrey Huff .08 .25
8 Barry Zito .08 .25
9 Ben Sheets .08 .25
10 Bobby Abreu .08 .25
11 Bobby Crosby .08 .25
12 Bret Boone .08 .25
13 Brian Giles .08 .25
14 Carlos Beltran .08 .25
15 Carlos Delgado .08 .25
16 Carlos Lee .08 .25
17 Chipper Jones .20 .50
18 Craig Biggio .15 .40
19 Curt Schilling .15 .40
20 Dallas McPherson .08 .25
21 David Ortiz .20 .50
22 David Wright .30 .75
23 Derek Jeter .40 1.00
24 Derek Lowe .08 .25
25 Eric Chavez .08 .25
26 Eric Gagne .08 .25
27 Frank Thomas .20 .50
28 Garret Anderson .08 .25
29 Gary Sheffield .08 .25
30 Greg Maddux .30 .75
31 Hank Blalock .08 .25
32 Hideki Matsui .30 .75
33 Ichiro Suzuki .40 1.00
34 Ivan Rodriguez .15 .40
35 J.D. Drew .08 .25
36 Jake Peavy .08 .25
37 Jason Bay .08 .25
38 Jason Giambi .08 .25
39 Jason Schmidt .08 .25
40 Jeff Bagwell .15 .40
41 Jeff Kent .08 .25
42 Jim Edmonds .08 .25
43 Jim Thome .15 .40
44 Joe Mauer .20 .50
45 Johan Santana .20 .50
46 John Smoltz .15 .40
47 Johnny Damon .15 .40
48 Jorge Posada .15 .40
49 Jose Vidro .08 .25
50 Josh Beckett .08 .25
51 Kazuo Matsui .08 .25
52 Ken Griffey Jr. .30 .75
53 Kerry Wood .08 .25
54 Khalil Greene .15 .40
55 Lance Berkman .08 .25
56 Livan Hernandez .08 .25
57 Luis Gonzalez .08 .25
58 Magglio Ordonez .08 .25
59 Manny Ramirez .15 .40
60 Mark Mulder .08 .25
61 Mark Prior .15 .40
62 Mark Teixeira .15 .40
63 Miguel Cabrera .15 .40
64 Miguel Tejada .08 .25
65 Mike Mussina .15 .40
66 Mike Piazza .20 .50
67 Mike Sweeney .08 .25
68 Moises Alou .08 .25
69 Nomar Garciaparra .20 .50
70 Oliver Perez .08 .25
71 Paul Konerko .08 .25
72 Pedro Martinez .15 .40
73 Rafael Palmeiro .15 .40
74 Randy Johnson .20 .50
75 Richie Sexson .08 .25
76 Roger Clemens .30 .75
77 Roy Halladay .08 .25
78 Roy Oswalt .08 .25
79 Sammy Sosa .20 .50
80 Scott Rolen .15 .40
81 Shawn Green .08 .25
82 Steve Finley .08 .25
83 Tim Hudson .08 .25
84 Todd Helton .15 .40
85 Tom Glavine .15 .40
86 Torii Hunter .08 .25
87 Travis Hafner .08 .25
88 Troy Glaus .08 .25
89 Victor Martinez .08 .25
90 Vladimir Guerrero .20 .50

2005 Upper Deck MVP Batter Up!

COMPLETE SET (42) 15.00 40.00
ONE PER PACK
1 Al Kaline .75 2.00
2 Bill Mazeroski .60 1.50
3 Billy Williams .40 1.00
4 Bob Feller .40 1.00
5 Bob Gibson .60 1.50
6 Bob Lemon .40 1.00
7 Brooks Robinson .60 1.50
8 Carlton Fisk .60 1.50
9 Catfish Hunter .40 1.00
10 Dennis Eckersley .40 1.00
11 Eddie Mathews .75 2.00
12 Eddie Murray .75 2.00
13 Fergie Jenkins .40 1.00
14 Gaylord Perry .40 1.00
15 Harmon Killebrew .75 2.00
16 Jim Bunning .40 1.00
17 Jim Palmer .40 1.00
18 Joe DiMaggio 1.50 4.00
19 Joe Morgan .40 1.00
20 Johnny Bench .75 2.00
21 Juan Marichal .40 1.00
22 Lou Brock .60 1.50
23 Luis Aparicio .40 1.00
24 Mike Schmidt 1.50 4.00
25 Monte Irvin .40 1.00
26 Nolan Ryan 2.00 5.00
27 Orlando Cepeda .40 1.00
28 Ozzie Smith 1.25 3.00
29 Pee Wee Reese .60 1.50
30 Phil Niekro .40 1.00
31 Phil Rizzuto .60 1.50
32 Ralph Kiner .60 1.50
33 Richie Ashburn .60 1.50
34 Robin Roberts .40 1.00
35 Robin Yount .75 2.00
36 Rollie Fingers .40 1.00
37 Tom Seaver .60 1.50
38 Tony Perez .40 1.00
39 Warren Spahn .60 1.50
40 Willie McCovey .60 1.50
41 Willie Stargell .60 1.50
42 Yogi Berra .75 2.00

2005 Upper Deck MVP Jersey

STATED ODDS 1:24
AB Adrian Beltre 3.00 8.00
AP Albert Pujols 6.00 15.00
AS Alfonso Soriano 3.00 8.00

CB Carlos Beltran	3.00	8.00
CJ Chipper Jones	4.00	10.00
CS Curt Schilling	4.00	10.00
DJ Derek Jeter	8.00	20.00
EC Eric Chavez	3.00	8.00
EG Eric Gagne	3.00	8.00
GM Greg Maddux	6.00	15.00
HB Hank Blalock	3.00	8.00
IR Ivan Rodriguez	4.00	10.00
JS Johan Santana	4.00	10.00
JT Jim Thome	4.00	10.00
KG Ken Griffey Jr.	6.00	15.00
KW Kerry Wood	3.00	8.00
MC Miguel Cabrera	4.00	10.00
MP Mark Prior	4.00	10.00
MR Manny Ramirez	4.00	10.00
MT Mark Teixeira	4.00	10.00
PI Mike Piazza	4.00	10.00
RJ Randy Johnson	4.00	10.00
SB Sean Burroughs	3.00	8.00
SR Scott Rolen	4.00	10.00
SS Sammy Sosa	4.00	10.00
TE Miguel Tejada	3.00	8.00
TH Todd Helton	4.00	10.00
VG Vladimir Guerrero	4.00	10.00

2005 Upper Deck MVP Signatures

STATED ODDS 1:480
PRINT RUNS B/WN 10-99 COPIES PER
CARDS ARE NOT SERIAL-NUMBERED
PRINT RUN INFO PROVIDED BY UD
NO PRICING DUE TO SCARCITY
EXCHANGE DEADLINE JULY '08
AB Adrian Beltre/15 *
AH Aubrey Huff/99 *
AR Aaron Rowand/99 *
BC Bobby Crosby/25 *
BS Ben Sheets/25 *
CP Corey Patterson/25 *
CZ Carlos Zambrano/25 *
DJ Derek Jeter/25 *
DO David Cruz/10 *
DW David Wright/25 *
EC Eric Chavez/10 *
GA Garrett Atkins/99 *
GF Gavin Floyd/49 *
GR Khalil Greene/25 *
JB Jason Bay/49 *
JM Joe Mauer/25 * EXCH
JP Jake Peavy/65 *
JR Jeremy Reed/49 *
JS Johan Santana/25 * EXCH
KG Ken Griffey Jr./36 * EXCH
MC Miguel Cabrera/15 *
MT Mark Teixeira/15 * EXCH
OP Oliver Perez/99 *
RE Jose Reyes/85 *
RH Rich Harden/49 *
SK Scott Kazmir/49 *
TH Travis Hafner/49 *
VM Victor Martinez/85 *

2006 Upper Deck National Baseball Card Day

COMPLETE SET (5)	1.25	3.00
UD6 Derek Jeter	.60	1.50
UD7 Ken Griffey Jr.	.40	1.00
UD8 Dontrelle Willis	.08	.25
UD9 David Ortiz	.25	.60
UD10 Paul Konerko	.08	.25

2006 Upper Deck National Baseball Card Day National Pastime

COMPLETE SET (3)	.75	1.50
ONE PER NBCD PACK		
IS Ichiro Suzuki	.30	.75
KJ Kenji Johjima	.60	1.50
NG Nomar Garciaparra	.20	.50

1999 Upper Deck Ovation

This 90-card set was distributed in five-card packs with a suggested retail price of $3.99. The cards feature action color player images printed on game-ball stock for the look and feel of an actual baseball. The set contains the following subsets: World Premiere (61-80) with an insertion rate of one in every 3.5 packs, and Superstar Spotlight (81-90) inserted at a rate of one in six packs. In addition, 350 Mickey Mantle A Piece of History 500 Home Run bat cards were randomly seeded into packs. In addition, one special Mantle card was created by Upper Deck featuring both a chip of wood from a game used Mantle bat plus an authentic Mantle signature cut. Only one copy was produced and the design harkens from the popular 1999 A Piece of History Club cards except that much of the card front is devoted to a window to house the cut signature. Pricing and checklisting for these scarce bat cards can be referenced under 1999 Upper Deck A Piece of History 500 Club.

COMPLETE SET (90)	30.00	80.00
COMP.SET w/o SP's (60)	10.00	25.00
COMMON CARD (1-60)	.15	.40
COMMON WP (61-80)	.75	2.00
COMMON SS (81-90)	1.00	2.50
1 Ken Griffey Jr.	.60	1.50
2 Rondell White	.15	.40
3 Tony Clark	.15	.40
4 Barry Bonds	1.00	2.50
5 Larry Walker	.15	.40
6 Greg Vaughn	.15	.40
7 Mark Grace	.25	.60
8 John Olerud	.15	.40
9 Matt Williams	.15	.40
10 Craig Biggio	.25	.60
11 Quinton McCracken	.15	.40
12 Kerry Wood	.15	.40
13 Derek Jeter	1.00	2.50
14 Frank Thomas	.40	1.00
15 Tino Martinez	.25	.60
16 Albert Belle	.15	.40
17 Ben Grieve	.15	.40
18 Cal Ripken	1.25	3.00
19 Johnny Damon	.25	.60
20 Jose Cruz Jr.	.15	.40
21 Barry Larkin	.25	.60
22 Jason Giambi	.15	.40
23 Sean Casey	.15	.40
24 Scott Rolen	.25	.60
25 Jim Thome	.25	.60
26 Curt Schilling	.15	.40
27 Moises Alou	.15	.40
28 Alex Rodriguez	.60	1.50
29 Mark Kotsay	.15	.40
30 Darin Erstad	.15	.40
31 Mike Mussina	.25	.60
32 Todd Walker	.15	.40
33 Nomar Garciaparra	.60	1.50
34 Vladimir Guerrero	.40	1.00
35 Jeff Bagwell	.25	.60
36 Mark McGwire	1.00	2.50
37 Travis Lee	.15	.40
38 Dean Palmer	.15	.40
39 Fred McGriff	.25	.60
40 Sammy Sosa	.40	1.00
41 Mike Piazza	.60	1.50
42 Andres Galarraga	.15	.40
43 Pedro Martinez	.25	.60
44 Juan Gonzalez	.15	.40
45 Greg Maddux	.60	1.50
46 Jeromy Burnitz	.15	.40
47 Roger Clemens	.75	2.00
48 Vinny Castilla	.15	.40
49 Kevin Brown	.25	.60
50 Mo Vaughn	.15	.40
51 Raul Mondesi	.15	.40
52 Randy Johnson	.40	1.00
53 Ray Lankford	.15	.40
54 Jaret Wright	.15	.40
55 Tony Gwynn	.50	1.25
56 Chipper Jones	.40	1.00
57 Gary Sheffield	.15	.40
58 Ivan Rodriguez	.25	.60
59 Kenny Lofton	.15	.40
60 Jason Kendall	.15	.40
61 J.D. Drew WP	.75	2.00
62 Gabe Kapler WP	.75	2.00
63 Adrian Beltre WP	.75	2.00
64 Carlos Beltran WP	1.00	2.50
65 Eric Chavez WP	.75	2.00
66 Mike Lowell WP	.75	2.00
67 Troy Glaus WP	1.00	2.50
68 George Lombard WP	.75	2.00
69 Alex Gonzalez WP	.75	2.00
70 Mike Kinkade WP	.75	2.00
71 Jeremy Giambi WP	.75	2.00
72 Bruce Chen WP	.75	2.00
73 Preston Wilson WP	.75	2.00
74 Kevin Witt WP	.75	2.00
75 Carlos Guillen WP	.75	2.00
76 Ryan Minor WP	.75	2.00
77 Corey Koskie WP	.75	2.00
78 Robert Fick WP	1.00	2.50
79 Michael Barrett WP	.75	2.00
80 Calvin Pickering WP	.75	2.00
81 Ken Griffey Jr. SS	1.50	4.00
82 Mark McGwire SS	2.50	6.00
83 Cal Ripken SS	3.00	8.00
84 Derek Jeter SS	2.50	6.00
85 Chipper Jones SS	1.00	2.50
86 Nomar Garciaparra SS	1.50	4.00
87 Sammy Sosa SS	1.00	2.50
88 Juan Gonzalez SS	1.00	2.50
89 Mike Piazza SS	1.50	4.00
90 Alex Rodriguez SS	1.50	4.00

1999 Upper Deck Ovation Standing Ovation

Randomly inserted into packs, this 90-card set is a parallel version of the base set. Each card is sequentially numbered to 500.

*STARS 1-60: 5X TO 12X BASIC 1-60
*WP CARDS 61-80: 1X TO 2.5X BASIC WP
*SS CARDS 81-90: 2X TO 5X BASIC SS

1999 Upper Deck Ovation A Piece of History

Randomly inserted in packs at the rate of one in 247, this set features pieces of actual game-used bats of some of MLB's biggest stars embedded in the cards. Only 25 Ben Grieve and Kerry Wood autographed cards were produced. The signed Grieve card contains a game-used bat chip. The signed Wood card contains a piece of a game-used baseball.

AR Alex Rodriguez	15.00	40.00
BB Barry Bonds	20.00	50.00
BG Ben Grieve	4.00	10.00
BW Bernie Williams	10.00	25.00
CJ Chipper Jones	10.00	25.00
CR Cal Ripken	30.00	60.00
DJ Derek Jeter	20.00	50.00
JG Juan Gonzalez	6.00	15.00
MP Mike Piazza	15.00	40.00
NG Nomar Garciaparra	15.00	40.00
SS Sammy Sosa	10.00	25.00
TG Tony Gwynn	10.00	25.00
VG Vladimir Guerrero	10.00	25.00
KGJ Ken Griffey Jr.	15.00	40.00
BGAU B. Grieve Bat AU/25		
KWAU K.Wood Ball AU/25		

1999 Upper Deck Ovation Curtain Calls

Randomly inserted in packs at the rate of one in eight, this 20-card set features color action photos of the pictured player's most memorable accomplishment during the 1998 season.

COMPLETE SET (20)	30.00	80.00
R1 Mark McGwire	3.00	8.00
R2 Sammy Sosa	1.25	3.00
R3 Ken Griffey Jr.	2.00	5.00
R4 Alex Rodriguez	2.00	5.00
R5 Roger Clemens	2.50	6.00
R6 Cal Ripken	4.00	10.00
R7 Barry Bonds	3.00	8.00
R8 Kerry Wood	.50	1.25
R9 Nomar Garciaparra	2.00	5.00
R10 Derek Jeter	3.00	8.00
R11 Juan Gonzalez	.50	1.25
R12 Greg Maddux	2.00	5.00
R13 Pedro Martinez	.75	2.00
R14 David Wells	.50	1.25
R15 Moises Alou	.50	1.25
R16 Tony Gwynn	1.50	4.00
R17 Albert Belle	.50	1.25
R18 Mike Piazza	2.00	5.00
R19 Ivan Rodriguez	.75	2.00
R20 Randy Johnson	1.25	3.00

1999 Upper Deck Ovation Major Production

Randomly inserted in packs at the rate of one in 45, this 20-card set features color action photos of some of the game's most productive players printed using Thermography technology to simulate the look and feel of home plate.

COMPLETE SET (20)	200.00	400.00
S1 Mike Piazza	8.00	20.00
S2 Mark McGwire	12.50	30.00
S3 Chipper Jones	5.00	12.00
S4 Cal Ripken	15.00	40.00
S5 Ken Griffey Jr.	8.00	20.00
S6 Barry Bonds	12.50	30.00
S7 Tony Gwynn	6.00	15.00
S8 Randy Johnson	5.00	12.00
S9 Ivan Rodriguez	3.00	8.00
S10 Frank Thomas	5.00	12.00
S11 Alex Rodriguez	8.00	20.00
S12 Albert Belle	2.00	5.00
S13 Juan Gonzalez	2.00	5.00
S14 Greg Maddux	8.00	20.00
S15 Jeff Bagwell	3.00	8.00
S16 Derek Jeter	12.50	30.00
S17 Matt Williams	2.00	5.00
S18 Kenny Lofton	2.00	5.00
S19 Sammy Sosa	5.00	12.00
S20 Roger Clemens	10.00	25.00

1999 Upper Deck Ovation ReMarkable Moments

This 15-card three-tiered insert set showcases Mark McGwire's dominant play during the 1998 home run race. Cards 1-5 feature bronze foil highlights with an insertion rate of 1:9. Cards 6-10 display silver foil highlights with an insertion rate of 1:25. Cards 11-15 are gold-foiled with a 1:99 insertion rate.

COMMON CARD (1-5)	2.00	5.00
COMMON CARD (6-10)	4.00	10.00
COMMON CARD (11-15)	8.00	20.00

2000 Upper Deck Ovation

The 2000 Upper Deck Ovation set was released in March, 2000 as an 89-card set that featured 60 player cards, 19 World Premiere cards (1:3), and 10 Superstar cards (1:6). Card number 70 does exist, however, it is in very short supply. The featured player on that card is Ryan Anderson, who was not available for usage in the set as he was not on the 40 man roster at the time this set was printed. No copies of card number 70 are believed to exist in the Ovation parallel set. Each back contained five cards and carried a suggested retail price of 3.99. Also, a selection of A Piece of History 3000 Club Willie Mays memorabilia cards were randomly seeded into packs. 300 bat cards, 350 jersey cards, 50 hand-numbered combination bat-jersey cards and twenty-four autographed, hand-numbered, combination bat-jersey cards were produced. Pricing for these memorabilia cards can be referenced under 2000 Upper Deck A Piece of History 3000 Club.

COMPLETE SET (89)	30.00	80.00
COMP.SET w/o SP's (60)	8.00	20.00
COMMON CARD (1-60)	.15	.40
COMMON WP (61-80)	.75	2.00
COMMON SS (81-90)	1.25	3.00
1 Mo Vaughn	.15	.40
2 Troy Glaus	.15	.40
3 Jeff Bagwell	.25	.60
4 Craig Biggio	.25	.60
5 Mike Hampton	.15	.40
6 Jason Giambi	.15	.40
7 Tim Hudson	.15	.40
8 Chipper Jones	.40	1.00
9 Greg Maddux	.60	1.50
10 Kevin Millwood	.15	.40
11 Brian Jordan	.15	.40
12 Jeromy Burnitz	.15	.40
13 David Wells	.15	.40
14 Carlos Delgado	.15	.40
15 Sammy Sosa	.40	1.00
16 Mark McGwire	1.00	2.50
17 Matt Williams	.15	.40
18 Randy Johnson	.40	1.00
19 Erubiel Durazo	.15	.40
20 Kevin Brown	.25	.60
21 Shawn Green	.15	.40
22 Gary Sheffield	.15	.40
23 Jose Canseco	.25	.60
24 Vladimir Guerrero	.40	1.00
25 Barry Bonds	1.00	2.50
26 Manny Ramirez	.25	.60
27 Roberto Alomar	.25	.60
28 Richie Sexson	.15	.40
29 Jim Thome	.25	.60
30 Alex Rodriguez	.60	1.50
31 Ken Griffey Jr.	.60	1.50
32 Preston Wilson	.15	.40
33 Mike Piazza	.60	1.50
34 Al Leiter	.15	.40
35 Robin Ventura	.25	.60
36 Cal Ripken	1.25	3.00
37 Albert Belle	.15	.40
38 Tony Gwynn	.50	1.25
39 Brian Giles	.15	.40
40 Jason Kendall	.15	.40
41 Scott Rolen	.25	.60
42 Bob Abreu	.15	.40
43 Ken Griffey Jr. Reds	.60	1.50
44 Sean Casey	.15	.40
45 Carlos Beltran	.15	.40
46 Gabe Kapler	.15	.40
47 Ivan Rodriguez	.25	.60
48 Rafael Palmeiro	.25	.60
49 Larry Walker	.15	.40
50 Nomar Garciaparra	.60	1.50
51 Pedro Martinez	.25	.60
52 Eric Milton	.15	.40
53 Juan Gonzalez	.15	.40
54 Tony Clark	.15	.40
55 Frank Thomas	.40	1.00
56 Magglio Ordonez	.15	.40
57 Roger Clemens	.75	2.00
58 Derek Jeter	1.00	2.50
59 Bernie Williams	.25	.60
60 Orlando Hernandez	.15	.40
61 Rick Ankiel WP	.75	2.00
62 Josh Beckett WP	2.00	5.00
63 Vernon Wells WP	1.00	2.50
64 Alfonso Soriano WP	2.00	5.00
65 Pat Burrell WP	1.00	2.50
66 Eric Munson WP	.75	2.00
67 Chad Hutchinson WP	.75	2.00
68 Eric Gagne WP	2.00	5.00
69 Peter Bergeron WP	.75	2.00
70 Ryan Anderson WP SP	75.00	150.00
71 A.J. Burnett WP	1.00	2.50
72 Jorge Toca WP	.75	2.00
73 Matt Riley WP	.75	2.00
74 Chad Hermansen WP	.75	2.00
75 Doug Davis WP	1.00	2.50
76 Jim Morris WP	2.00	5.00
77 Ben Petrick WP	.75	2.00
78 Mark Quinn WP	.75	2.00
79 Ed Yarnall WP	.75	2.00
80 Ramon Ortiz WP	.75	2.00
81 Ken Griffey Jr. SS	2.00	5.00
82 Mark McGwire SS	3.00	8.00
83 Derek Jeter SS	3.00	8.00
84 Jeff Bagwell SS	1.25	3.00
85 Nomar Garciaparra SS	2.00	5.00
86 Sammy Sosa SS	1.25	3.00
87 Mike Piazza SS	2.00	5.00
88 Alex Rodriguez SS	2.00	5.00
89 Cal Ripken SS	4.00	10.00
90 Pedro Martinez SS	1.25	3.00

2000 Upper Deck Ovation Standing Ovation

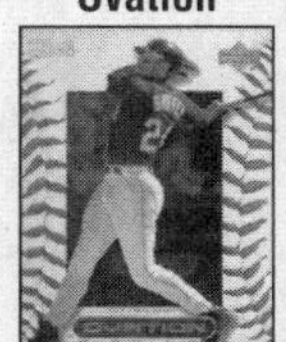

Randomly inserted into packs, this 90-card set parallels the Upper Deck Ovation base set. Cards are serial numbered to 50.

*STARS: 10X TO 25X BASIC CARDS
*WORLD PREM: 1.5X TO 4X BASIC WP
*SPOTLIGHT: 3X TO 8X BASIC SS

2000 Upper Deck Ovation A Piece of History

Randomly inserted into packs, this 16-card set features 12 player cards containing pieces of game-used bats. Production of 400 copies of each card was publicly announced by Upper Deck but the cards are not serial-numbered. Alex Rodriguez, Cal Ripken, Derek Jeter, and Ken Griffey Jr. have additional cards that contain both pieces of game-used bats and their autographs.

AR Alex Rodriguez	15.00	40.00
CJ Chipper Jones	8.00	20.00
CR Cal Ripken	20.00	50.00
DJ Derek Jeter	20.00	50.00
IR Ivan Rodriguez	6.00	15.00
JC Jose Canseco	6.00	15.00
KG Ken Griffey Jr.	15.00	40.00
MR Manny Ramirez	6.00	15.00
PB Pat Burrell	6.00	15.00
SR Scott Rolen	6.00	15.00
TG Tony Gwynn	10.00	25.00
VG Vladimir Guerrero	8.00	20.00
ARA Alex Rodriguez AU/3		
CRA Cal Ripken AU/8		
DJA Derek Jeter AU/2		
KGA Ken Griffey Jr. AU/24		

2000 Upper Deck Ovation Center Stage Silver

Randomly inserted in packs at one in nine, this insert set features ten players that are ready to take center stage on any given day. Card backs carry a "CS" prefix.

COMPLETE SET (10)	30.00	60.00
*GOLD: .75X TO 2X CENTER SILVER	1.25	3.00

GOLD STATED ODDS 1:39
*RAINBOW: 1.5X TO 4X CENTER SILVER
RAINBOW STATED ODDS 1:99

CS1 Jeff Bagwell	.75	2.00
CS2 Ken Griffey Jr.	2.00	5.00
CS3 Nomar Garciaparra	2.00	5.00
CS4 Mike Piazza	2.00	5.00
CS5 Mark McGwire	3.00	8.00
CS6 Alex Rodriguez	2.00	5.00
CS7 Cal Ripken	4.00	10.00
CS8 Derek Jeter	3.00	8.00
CS9 Chipper Jones	1.25	3.00
CS10 Sammy Sosa	1.25	3.00

2000 Upper Deck Ovation Curtain Calls

Randomly inserted into packs at one in three, this insert features 20 major leaguers who deserve a standing ovation for their 1999 peformances. Card backs carry a "CC" prefix.

COMPLETE SET (20)	20.00	40.00
CC1 David Cone	.30	.75
CC2 Mark McGwire	2.00	5.00
CC3 Sammy Sosa	.75	2.00
CC4 Eric Milton	.30	.75
CC5 Bernie Williams	.50	1.25
CC6 Tony Gwynn	1.00	2.50
CC7 Nomar Garciaparra	1.25	3.00
CC8 Manny Ramirez	.50	1.25
CC9 Wade Boggs	.75	2.00
CC10 Randy Johnson	.75	2.00
CC11 Cal Ripken	2.50	6.00
CC12 Pedro Martinez	.50	1.25
CC13 Alex Rodriguez	1.25	3.00
CC14 Fernando Tatis	.30	.75
CC15 Vladimir Guerrero	.75	2.00
CC16 Robin Ventura	.50	1.25
CC17 Larry Walker	.30	.75
CC18 Carlos Beltran	.30	.75
CC19 Jose Canseco	.50	1.25
CC20 Ken Griffey Jr.	1.25	3.00

2000 Upper Deck Ovation Diamond Futures

Randomly inserted in packs at one in six, this insert features 10 of the league's top players who are on the verge of greatness. Card backs carry a "DM" prefix.

COMPLETE SET (10)	7.50	15.00
DM1 J.D. Drew	.40	1.00
DM2 Alfonso Soriano	.75	2.00
DM3 Preston Wilson	.40	1.00
DM4 Erubiel Durazo	.40	1.00
DM5 Rick Ankiel	.40	1.00
DM6 Octavio Dotel	.40	1.00
DM7 A.J. Burnett	.40	1.00
DM8 Carlos Beltran	.40	1.00
DM9 Vernon Wells	.40	1.00
DM10 Troy Glaus	.40	1.00

2000 Upper Deck Ovation Lead Performers

Randomly inserted in packs at one in 19, this insert set features 10 players that lead by example. Card backs carry a "LP" prefix.

COMPLETE SET (10)	25.00	60.00
LP1 Mark McGwire	4.00	10.00
LP2 Derek Jeter	4.00	10.00
LP3 Vladimir Guerrero	1.50	4.00
LP4 Mike Piazza	2.50	6.00
LP5 Cal Ripken	5.00	12.00
LP6 Sammy Sosa	1.50	4.00

LP7 Jeff Bagwell 1.00 2.50
LP8 Nomar Garciaparra 2.50 6.00
LP9 Chipper Jones 1.50 4.00
LP10 Ken Griffey Jr. 2.50 6.00

2000 Upper Deck Ovation Super Signatures

Randomly inserted into packs, this insert set features autographed cards of Ken Griffey Jr. and Mike Piazza. Each player has a silver, gold and rainbow version. Piazza did not return his cards in time for the product to ship, thus UD seeded exchange cards into their packs for all Piazza autographs. These exchange cards had a large, square white sticker with text explaining redemption guidelines placed on the card front. All Piazza exchange cards had to be mailed in prior to the December 9th, 2000 deadline.

SSKGG Ken Griffey Jr. Gold/50 75.00 150.00
SSKGR Ken Griffey Jr. Rainbow/10
SSKGS Ken Griffey Jr. Silver/100 60.00 120.00
SSMPG Mike Piazza Gold 50 EX 150.00 250.00
SSMPR Mike Piazza Rainbow/10 EX
SSMPS Mike Piazza Silver/100 EX 125.00 200.00

2000 Upper Deck Ovation Superstar Theatre

Randomly inserted in packs at one in 19, this insert set features 20 players that have a flair for the dramatic. Card backs carry a "ST" prefix.

COMPLETE SET (20) 60.00 120.00
ST1 Ivan Rodriguez 1.50 4.00
ST2 Brian Giles 1.00 2.50
ST3 Bernie Williams 1.50 4.00
ST4 Greg Maddux 4.00 10.00
ST5 Frank Thomas 2.50 6.00
ST6 Sean Casey 1.00 2.50
ST7 Mo Vaughn 1.00 2.50
ST8 Carlos Delgado 1.00 2.50
ST9 Tony Gwynn 3.00 8.00
ST10 Pedro Martinez 1.50 4.00
ST11 Scott Rolen 1.50 4.00
ST12 Mark McGwire 6.00 15.00
ST13 Manny Ramirez 1.50 4.00
ST14 Rafael Palmeiro 1.50 4.00
ST15 Jose Canseco 1.50 4.00
ST16 Randy Johnson 2.50 6.00
ST17 Gary Sheffield 1.00 2.50
ST18 Larry Walker 1.00 2.50
ST19 Barry Bonds 6.00 15.00
ST20 Roger Clemens 5.00 12.00

2001 Upper Deck Ovation

The 2001 Upper Deck Ovation product was released in early March 2001, and features a 90-card base set that was broken into tiers as follows: Base Veterans (1-60), and World Premiere Prospects (61-90) that were individually serial numbered to 2000. Each pack contained five cards and carried a suggested retail price of $2.99.

COMP.SET w/o SP'S (60) 8.00 20.00
COMMON CARD (1-60) .15 .40
COMMON WP (61-90) 2.00 5.00
1 Troy Glaus .15 .40
2 Darin Erstad .15 .40
3 Jason Giambi .15 .40
4 Tim Hudson .15 .40
5 Eric Chavez .15 .40
6 Carlos Delgado .15 .40
7 David Wells .15 .40
8 Greg Vaughn .15 .40
9 Omar Vizquel .25 .60
Travis Fryman is pictured on card front UER
10 Jim Thome .25 .60
11 Roberto Alomar .25 .60
12 John Olerud .15 .40
13 Edgar Martinez .25 .60
14 Cal Ripken 1.25 3.00
15 Alex Rodriguez .60 1.50
16 Ivan Rodriguez .25 .60
17 Manny Ramirez Sox .25 .60
18 Nomar Garciaparra .60 1.50
19 Pedro Martinez .25 .60
20 Jermaine Dye .15 .40
21 Juan Gonzalez .15 .40
22 Matt Lawton .15 .40
23 Frank Thomas .40 1.00
24 Magglio Ordonez .15 .40
25 Bernie Williams .25 .60
26 Derek Jeter 1.00 2.50
27 Roger Clemens .75 2.00
28 Jeff Bagwell .25 .60
29 Richard Hidalgo .15 .40
30 Chipper Jones .40 1.00
31 Greg Maddux .60 1.50
32 Andruw Jones .25 .60
33 Jeromy Burnitz .15 .40
34 Mark McGwire 1.00 2.50
35 Jim Edmonds .15 .40
36 Sammy Sosa .40 1.00
37 Kerry Wood .15 .40
38 Randy Johnson .40 1.00
39 Steve Finley .15 .40
40 Gary Sheffield .15 .40
41 Kevin Brown .15 .40
42 Shawn Green .15 .40
43 Vladimir Guerrero .40 1.00
44 Jose Vidro .15 .40
45 Barry Bonds 1.00 2.50
46 Jeff Kent .15 .40
47 Preston Wilson .15 .40
48 Luis Castillo .15 .40
49 Mike Piazza .60 1.50
50 Edgardo Alfonzo .15 .40
51 Tony Gwynn .50 1.25
52 Ryan Klesko .15 .40
53 Scott Rolen .25 .60
54 Bob Abreu .15 .40
55 Jason Kendall .15 .40
56 Brian Giles .15 .40
57 Ken Griffey Jr. .60 1.50
58 Barry Larkin .25 .60
59 Todd Helton .25 .60
60 Mike Hampton .15 .40
61 Corey Patterson WP 2.00 5.00
62 Timo Perez WP 2.00 5.00
63 Toby Hall WP 2.00 5.00
64 Brandon Inge WP 2.00 5.00
65 Joe Crede WP 3.00 8.00
66 Xavier Nady WP 2.00 5.00
67 A. Pettyjohn WP RC 2.00 5.00
68 Keith Ginter WP 2.00 5.00
69 Brian Cole WP 2.00 5.00
70 Tyler Walker WP RC 2.00 5.00
71 Juan Uribe WP RC 2.00 5.00
72 Alex Hernandez WP 2.00 5.00
73 Leo Estrella WP 2.00 5.00
74 Joey Nation WP 2.00 5.00
75 Aubrey Huff WP 2.00 5.00
76 Ichiro Suzuki WP RC 25.00 50.00
77 Jay Spurgeon WP 2.00 5.00
78 Sun Woo Kim WP 2.00 5.00
79 Pedro Feliz WP 2.00 5.00
80 Pablo Ozuna WP 2.00 5.00
81 Hiram Bocachica WP 2.00 5.00
82 Brad Wilkerson WP 2.00 5.00
83 Rocky Biddle WP 2.00 5.00
84 Aaron McNeal WP 2.00 5.00
85 Adam Bernero WP 2.00 5.00
86 Danys Baez WP 2.00 5.00
87 Dee Brown WP 2.00 5.00
88 Jimmy Rollins WP 2.00 5.00
89 Jason Hart WP 2.00 5.00
90 Ross Gload WP 2.00 5.00

2001 Upper Deck Ovation A Piece of History

Randomly inserted into packs at one in 40, this 40-card insert features slivers of actual game-used bats from Major League stars like Barry Bonds and Alex Rodriguez. Card backs carry the player's initials as numbering.

COMMON RETIRED 6.00 15.00
AJ Andruw Jones 6.00 15.00
AR Alex Rodriguez 6.00 15.00
BB Barry Bonds 10.00 25.00
BR Brooks Robinson 10.00 25.00
BW Bernie Williams 6.00 15.00
CD Carlos Delgado 4.00 10.00
CF Carlton Fisk 10.00 25.00
CJ Chipper Jones 6.00 15.00
CR Cal Ripken 15.00 40.00
DC David Cone 4.00 10.00
DD Don Drysdale 6.00 15.00
DE Darin Erstad 4.00 10.00
EW Early Wynn 6.00 15.00
FT Frank Thomas 6.00 15.00
GM Greg Maddux 6.00 15.00
GS Gary Sheffield 4.00 10.00
IR Ivan Rodriguez 6.00 15.00
JB Johnny Bench 10.00 25.00
JC Jose Canseco 6.00 15.00
JD Joe DiMaggio 40.00 80.00
JE Jim Edmonds 4.00 10.00
JP Jim Palmer 6.00 15.00
KG Ken Griffey Jr. 6.00 15.00
KGS Ken Griffey Sr. 4.00 10.00
KKB Kevin Brown 4.00 10.00
MH Mike Hampton 4.00 10.00
MM Mickey Mantle 75.00 150.00
MW Matt Williams 4.00 10.00
NR Nolan Ryan SP 20.00 50.00
OS Ozzie Smith 6.00 15.00
RA Rick Ankiel 4.00 10.00
RC Roger Clemens 6.00 15.00
RF Rollie Fingers 6.00 15.00
RF Rafael Furcal 4.00 10.00
RJ Randy Johnson 6.00 15.00
SG Shawn Green 4.00 10.00
SS Sammy Sosa 6.00 15.00
TG Tom Glavine 6.00 15.00
TRG Troy Glaus 4.00 10.00
TS Tom Seaver 10.00 25.00

2001 Upper Deck Ovation A Piece of History Autographs

Randomly inserted into packs, this 7-card insert features slivers of actual game-used bats and authentic autographs from some of the Major League's top stars. Card backs carry a "S" prefix followed by the player's initials. Please note that the print runs are listed below.

SAR Alex Rodriguez/3
SBB Barry Bonds/25
SCD Carlos Delgado/25
SCJ Chipper Jones/10
SFT Frank Thomas/35
SIR Ivan Rodriguez/7
SKG Ken Griffey Jr./30 150.00 250.00

2001 Upper Deck Ovation A Piece of History Bat Combos

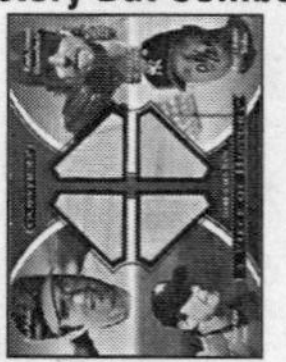

Randomly inserted into packs, this five-card insert set features a combination of slivers from actual game-used bats of historic Major League players. Card backs carry the player's initials as numbering. Please note that their were only 25 serial numbered sets produced. Due to market scarcity, no pricing is provided.

GBTC Ken Griffey Jr.
Barry Bonds
Frank Thomas
Jose Canseco
MDCW Mickey Mantle
Joe DiMaggio
Roger Clemens
Bernie Williams
MGJC Greg Maddux
Tom Glavine
Randy Johnson
Roger Clemens
PFBP Mike Piazza
Carlton Fisk
Johnny Bench
Ivan Rodriguez
PJCR Jim Palmer
Randy Johnson
Roger Clemens
Nolan Ryan

2001 Upper Deck Ovation Curtain Calls

Randomly inserted into packs at one in seven, this 10-card insert set features players that deserve a round of applause after the numbers they put up last year. Card backs carry a "CC" prefix.

COMPLETE SET (10) 8.00 20.00
CC1 Sammy Sosa .75 2.00
CC2 Darin Erstad .50 1.25
CC3 Barry Bonds 2.00 5.00
CC4 Todd Helton .50 1.25
CC5 Mike Piazza 1.25 3.00
CC6 Ken Griffey Jr. 1.25 3.00
CC7 Nomar Garciaparra 1.25 3.00
CC8 Carlos Delgado .50 1.25
CC9 Jason Giambi .50 1.25
CC10 Alex Rodriguez 1.25 3.00

2001 Upper Deck Ovation Lead Performers

Randomly inserted into packs at one in 12, this 11-card insert set features players that were among the league leaders in many of the offensive categories. Card backs carry a "LP" prefix.

COMPLETE SET (11) 12.50 30.00

LP1 Mark McGwire 2.50 6.00
LP2 Derek Jeter 2.50 6.00
LP3 Alex Rodriguez 1.50 4.00
LP4 Frank Thomas 1.00 2.50
LP5 Sammy Sosa 1.00 2.50
LP6 Mike Piazza 1.50 4.00
LP7 Vladimir Guerrero 1.00 2.50
LP8 Pedro Martinez .60 1.50
LP9 Carlos Delgado .60 1.50
LP10 Ken Griffey Jr. 1.50 4.00
LP11 Jeff Bagwell .60 1.50

2001 Upper Deck Ovation Superstar Theatre

Randomly inserted into packs at one in 12, this 11-card insert set features players that put on a "show" everytime they take the field. Card backs carry a "ST" prefix.

COMPLETE SET (11) 12.50 30.00
ST1 Nomar Garciaparra 1.50 4.00
ST2 Ken Griffey Jr. 1.50 4.00
ST3 Frank Thomas 1.00 2.50
ST4 Derek Jeter 2.50 6.00
ST5 Mike Piazza 1.50 4.00
ST6 Sammy Sosa 1.00 2.50
ST7 Barry Bonds 2.50 6.00
ST8 Alex Rodriguez 1.50 4.00
ST9 Todd Helton 1.00 2.50
ST10 Mark McGwire 2.50 6.00
ST11 Jason Giambi 1.00 2.50

2002 Upper Deck Ovation

This 180 card set was issued in two separate brands. The basic Ovation product, containing cards 1-120, was released in June, 2002. These cards were issued in five-card packs with a suggested retail price of $3 per pack of which were issued 24 to a box and 20 boxes to a case. These cards feature veteran stars from cards 1-60, rookie stars from 61-89 (of which have a stated print run of 2002 serial numbered copies) and then five cards each of the six Upper Deck spokesmen from 90-119. The first series set concludes with a card with a stated print run of 2002 serial numbered sets featuring the six Upper Deck spokemen. Cards 121-180 were distributed within retail-only packs of Upper Deck Rookie Debut in mid-December 2002. Cards 121-150 were seeded at an approximate rate of one per pack and feature traded players and young prospects. Cards 151-180 continue the World Premiere rookie subset with each card being serial-numbered to 2002 copies. Though the manufacturer did not release odds on these market research indicates an approximate seeding ratio of 1:8 packs.

COMP.LOW w/o SP's (90) 10.00 25.00
COMP.UPDATE w/o SP's (30) 6.00 15.00
COMMON CARD (1-60) .15 .40
COMMON (61-89/120/151-180) 1.50 4.00
COMMON CARD (90-119) .20 .50
COMMON CARD (121-150) .25 .60
1 Troy Glaus .15 .40
2 David Justice .15 .40
3 Tim Hudson .15 .40
4 Jermaine Dye .15 .40
5 Carlos Delgado .15 .40
6 Greg Vaughn .15 .40
7 Jim Thome .25 .60
8 C.C. Sabathia .15 .40
9 Ichiro Suzuki .75 2.00
10 Edgar Martinez .25 .60
11 Chris Richard .15 .40
12 Rafael Palmeiro .25 .60
13 Alex Rodriguez .60 1.50
14 Ivan Rodriguez .25 .60
15 Nomar Garciaparra .60 1.50
16 Manny Ramirez .25 .60
17 Pedro Martinez .25 .60
18 Mike Sweeney .15 .40
19 Dmitri Young .15 .40
20 Doug Mientkiewicz .15 .40
21 Brad Radke .15 .40
22 Cristian Guzman .15 .40
23 Frank Thomas .40 1.00
24 Magglio Ordonez .15 .40
25 Bernie Williams .25 .60
26 Derek Jeter 1.00 2.50
27 Jason Giambi .15 .40
28 Roger Clemens .75 2.00
29 Jeff Bagwell .25 .60
30 Lance Berkman .15 .40
31 Chipper Jones .40 1.00
32 Gary Sheffield .15 .40
33 Greg Maddux .60 1.50
34 Richie Sexson .15 .40
35 Albert Pujols .75 2.00
36 Tino Martinez .25 .60
37 J.D. Drew .15 .40
38 Sammy Sosa .40 1.00
39 Moises Alou .15 .40
40 Randy Johnson .40 1.00
41 Luis Gonzalez .15 .40
42 Shawn Green .15 .40
43 Kevin Brown .15 .40
44 Vladimir Guerrero .40 1.00
45 Barry Bonds 1.00 2.50
46 Jeff Kent .15 .40
47 Cliff Floyd .15 .40
48 Josh Beckett .15 .40
49 Mike Piazza .60 1.50
50 Mo Vaughn .15 .40
51 Jeromy Burnitz .15 .40
52 Roberto Alomar .25 .60
53 Phil Nevin .15 .40
54 Scott Rolen .25 .60
55 Jimmy Rollins .15 .40
56 Brian Giles .15 .40
57 Ken Griffey Jr. .60 1.50
58 Sean Casey .15 .40
59 Larry Walker .15 .40
60 Todd Helton .25 .60
61 Rodrigo Rosario WP RC 1.50 4.00
62 Reed Johnson WP RC 2.00 5.00
63 John Ennis WP RC 1.50 4.00
64 Luis Martinez WP RC 1.50 4.00
65 So Taguchi WP RC 2.00 5.00
66 Brandon Backe WP RC 2.00 5.00
67 Doug Devore WP RC 1.50 4.00
68 Victor Alvarez WP RC 1.50 4.00
69 Kazuhisa Ishii WP RC 2.00 5.00
70 Eric Good WP RC 1.50 4.00
71 Deivis Santos WP 1.50 4.00
72 Matt Thornton WP RC 1.50 4.00
73 Hansel Izquierdo WP RC 1.50 4.00
74 Tyler Yates WP RC 1.50 4.00
75 Jaime Cerda WP RC 1.50 4.00
76 Satoru Komiyama WP RC 1.50 4.00
77 Steve Bechler WP RC 1.50 4.00
78 Ben Howard WP RC 1.50 4.00
79 Jorge Padilla WP RC 1.50 4.00
80 Eric Junge WP RC 1.50 4.00
81 And. Machado WP RC 1.50 4.00
82 Adrian Burnside WP RC 1.50 4.00
83 Josh Hancock WP RC 2.00 5.00
84 Anastacio Martinez WP RC 1.50 4.00
85 Rene Reyes WP RC 1.50 4.00
86 Nate Field WP RC 1.50 4.00
87 Tim Kalita WP RC 1.50 4.00
88 Kevin Frederick WP RC 1.50 4.00
89 Edwin Almonte WP RC 1.50 4.00
90 Ichiro Suzuki SS .40 1.00
91 Ichiro Suzuki SS .40 1.00
92 Ichiro Suzuki SS .40 1.00
93 Ichiro Suzuki SS .40 1.00
94 Ichiro Suzuki SS .40 1.00
95 Ken Griffey Jr. SS .30 .75
96 Ken Griffey Jr. SS .30 .75
97 Ken Griffey Jr. SS .30 .75
98 Ken Griffey Jr. SS .30 .75
99 Ken Griffey Jr. SS .30 .75
100 Jason Giambi A's SS .20 .50
101 Jason Giambi A's SS .20 .50
102 Jason Giambi A's SS .20 .50
103 J.Giambi Yankees SS .20 .50
104 J.Giambi Yankees SS .25 .60
105 Sammy Sosa SS .25 .60
106 Sammy Sosa SS .25 .60
107 Sammy Sosa SS .25 .60
108 Sammy Sosa SS .25 .60
109 Sammy Sosa SS .25 .60
110 Alex Rodriguez SS .30 .75
111 Alex Rodriguez SS .30 .75
112 Alex Rodriguez SS .30 .75
113 Alex Rodriguez SS .30 .75
114 Alex Rodriguez SS .30 .75
115 Mark McGwire SS .50 1.25
116 Mark McGwire SS .50 1.25
117 Mark McGwire SS .50 1.25
118 Mark McGwire SS .50 1.25
119 Mark McGwire SS .50 1.25
120 Jason Giambi 6.00 15.00
Ken Griffey Jr.
Mark McGwire
Alex Rodriguez
Sammy Sosa
Ichiro Suzuki SP/2002
121 Curt Schilling .25 .60
122 Cliff Floyd .25 .60
123 Derek Lowe .25 .60
124 Hee Seop Choi .25 .60
125 Mark Prior .40 1.00
126 Joe Borchard .25 .60
127 Austin Kearns .25 .60
128 Adam Dunn .25 .60
129 Jay Payton .25 .60
130 Carlos Pena .25 .60
131 Andy Van Hekken .25 .60
132 Andres Torres .25 .60
133 Ben Diggins .25 .60
134 Torii Hunter .25 .60
135 Bartolo Colon .25 .60
136 Raul Mondesi .25 .60
137 Alfonso Soriano .25 .60
138 Miguel Tejada .25 .60
139 Ray Durham .25 .60
140 Eric Chavez .25 .60
141 Marlon Byrd .25 .60
142 Brett Myers .25 .60
143 Sean Burroughs .25 .60
144 Kenny Lofton .25 .60
145 Scott Rolen .40 1.00
146 Carl Crawford .25 .60
147 Jayson Werth .25 .60
148 Josh Phelps .25 .60
149 Eric Hinske .25 .60
150 Orlando Hudson .25 .60
151 Jose Valverde WP RC 1.50 4.00
152 Trey Hodges WP RC 1.50 4.00
153 Joey Dawley WP RC 1.50 4.00
154 Travis Driskill WP RC 1.50 4.00
155 Howie Clark WP RC 1.50 4.00
156 J.De La Rosa WP RC 1.50 4.00
157 Freddy Sanchez WP RC 2.00 5.00
158 Earl Snyder WP RC 1.50 4.00
159 Cliff Lee WP RC 2.00 5.00
160 Josh Bard WP RC 1.50 4.00
161 Aaron Cook WP RC 1.50 4.00
162 Franklyn German WP RC 1.50 4.00
163 Brandon Puffer WP RC 1.50 4.00
164 Kirk Saarloos WP RC 1.50 4.00
165 Jer. Robertson WP RC 1.50 4.00
166 Miguel Asencio WP RC 1.50 4.00
167 Shawn Sedlacek WP RC 1.50 4.00
168 Jayson Durocher WP RC 1.50 4.00
169 Shane Nance WP RC 1.50 4.00
170 Jamey Carroll WP RC 2.00 5.00
171 Oliver Perez WP RC 2.00 5.00
172 Wil Nieves WP RC 1.50 4.00
173 Clay Condrey WP RC 1.50 4.00
174 Chris Snelling WP RC 1.50 4.00
175 Mike Crudale WP RC 1.50 4.00
176 J.Simontacchi WP RC 1.50 4.00
177 Felix Escalona WP RC 1.50 4.00
178 Lance Carter WP RC 1.50 4.00
179 Scott Wiggins WP RC 1.50 4.00
180 Kevin Cash WP RC 1.50 4.00

2002 Upper Deck Ovation Silver

Randomly inserted in packs, this is a complete parallel of the 2002 Upper Deck Ovation set. Cards numbered 1-60 and 90-119 were inserted at an overall approximate stated odds of one in four while cardds 61-89 and 120 were printed to a stated print run of 100 serial numbered sets.

*SILVER 1-60: 1.25X TO 3X BASIC
*SILVER 61-89/120: .5X TO 1.2X BASIC
*SILVER 61-119: 2.5X TO 6X BASIC

2002 Upper Deck Ovation Standing Ovation

Randomly inserted into 2002 Upper Deck Rookie Debut Packs, this is a parallel to the World Premier (cards 151-180) subset. These cards were issued to a stated print run of 50 serial numbered sets.

*STANDING O 151-180: 1.5X TO 4X BASIC

2002 Upper Deck Ovation Authentic McGwire

Randomly inserted into packs, these two cards feature authentic game-used memorabilia pieces from Mark McGwire's major league career. These two cards are each produced to a stated print run of 70 serial numbered sets.

AMB Mark McGwire Bat 50.00 100.00
AMJ Mark McGwire Jsy 50.00 100.00

2002 Upper Deck Ovation Authentic McGwire Gold

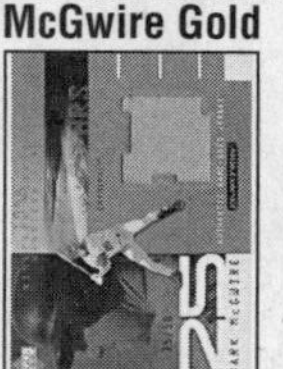

Randomly inserted into packs, these two cards feature authentic game-used memorabilia pieces from Mark McGwire's major league career. These two cards are each produced to a stated print run of 50 serial numbered sets.

AMBG Mark McGwire Bat 60.00 120.00
AMJG Mark McGwire Jsy 60.00 120.00

2002 Upper Deck Ovation Authentic McGwire Signatures

Randomly inserted into packs, these two cards feature authentic game-used memorabilia pieces from Mark McGwire's major league career as well as an authentic autograph. However, McGwire did not sign his cards in time for inclusion in this set so these cards were issued in the form of redemption cards with a mailing of July 3rd, 2005. These two cards were each produced to a stated print run of 25 serial numbered sets and no pricing is provided due

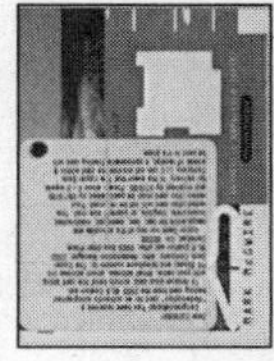

to market scarcity.

AMSB Mark McGwire Bat
AMSJ Mark McGwire Jsy

2002 Upper Deck Ovation Diamond Futures Jerseys

Inserted in packs at stated odds of one in 72, these 12 cards feature game-worn jersey swatches from 12 of baseball's future stars.

GOLD RANDOM INSERTS IN PACKS
GOLD PRINT RUN 25 SERIAL #'d SETS
NO GOLD PRICING DUE TO SCARCITY

Card		
DFBZ Barry Zito	4.00	10.00
DFFG Freddy Garcia	4.00	10.00
DFIR Ivan Rodriguez	6.00	15.00
DFJK Jason Kendall	4.00	10.00
DFJP Jorge Posada	6.00	15.00
DFJR Jimmy Rollins	4.00	10.00
DFJV Jose Vidro	4.00	10.00
DFKS Kazuhiro Sasaki	4.00	10.00
DFLB Lance Berkman	4.00	10.00
DFPB Pat Burrell	4.00	10.00
DFRB Russell Branyan	4.00	10.00
DFTH Tim Hudson	4.00	10.00

2002 Upper Deck Ovation Lead Performer Jerseys

Inserted in packs at stated odds of one in 72, these 12 cards feature game-worn swatches from some of the leading players in baseball. A couple of these cards were produced in shorter quantity and we have notated that information in our checklist next to their name.

GOLD RANDOM INSERTS IN PACKS
GOLD PRINT RUN 25 SERIAL #'d SETS
NO GOLD PRICING DUE TO SCARCITY

Card		
LPAR Alex Rodriguez	6.00	15.00
LPCD Carlos Delgado	4.00	10.00
LPFT Frank Thomas	6.00	15.00
LPIR Ivan Rodriguez	6.00	15.00
LPIS Ichiro Suzuki Shirt	20.00	50.00
LPJB Jeff Bagwell	6.00	15.00
LPJG Jason Giambi	4.00	10.00
LPJG Juan Gonzalez	4.00	10.00
LPKG Ken Griffey Jr. SP	10.00	25.00
LPLG Luis Gonzalez	4.00	10.00
LPMP Mike Piazza	6.00	15.00
LPSS Sammy Sosa SP	6.00	15.00

2002 Upper Deck Ovation Spokesman Spotlight Signatures

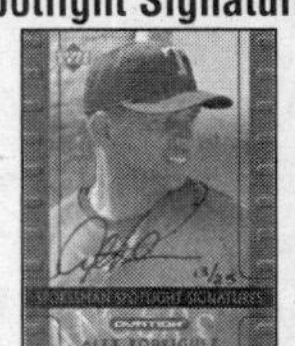

Randomly inserted into packs, these six cards feature authentic signatures of the six Upper Deck spokesman. Since each card is produced to a stated print run of 25 serial numbered sets, there is no pricing due to market scarcity.

AR Alex Rodriguez
IS Ichiro Suzuki
JG Jason Giambi
KG Ken Griffey Jr.
MM Mark McGwire
SS Sammy Sosa

2002 Upper Deck Ovation Swatches

Inserted at stated odds of one in 72, these 12 cards feature game-used larger "swatches" from the players featured. The Roberto Alomar card was

issued in smaller quantities and we have notated that information in our checklist.

GOLD RANDOM INSERTS IN PACKS
GOLD PRINT RUN 25 SERIAL #'d SETS
NO GOLD PRICING DUE TO SCARCITY

Card		
OAR Alex Rodriguez	6.00	15.00
OBW Bernie Williams	6.00	15.00
OCD Carlos Delgado	4.00	10.00
OCJ Chipper Jones	6.00	15.00
ODE Darin Erstad	4.00	10.00
OEB Ellis Burks	4.00	10.00
OEC Eric Chavez	4.00	10.00
OGM Greg Maddux	6.00	15.00
OJB Jeromy Burnitz	4.00	10.00
OMG Mark Grace	6.00	15.00
OPM Pedro Martinez	6.00	15.00
ORA Roberto Alomar SP		

2006 Upper Deck Ovation

This 126-card set was released in October, 2006. This set was issued in five-card hobby packs which came 18 packs per box and 16 boxes per case. Cards numbered 1-84 feature veterans while cards numbered 85-126 feature 2006 rookies and were issued to a stated print run of 999 serial numbered sets and were inserted at a stated rate of one in 18.

Card		
COMP.SET w/o RC's (84)	10.00	25.00
COMMON CARD (1-84)	.20	.50
COMMON ROOKIE (85-126)	2.00	5.00

85-126 STATED ODDS 1:18
85-126 PRINT RUN 999 SERIAL #'d SETS
EXQUISITE EXCH ODDS 1:144
EXQUISITE EXCH DEADLINE 07/27/07

Card		
1 Vladimir Guerrero	.50	1.25
2 Bartolo Colon	.20	.50
3 Chone Figgins	.20	.50
4 Lance Berkman	.20	.50
5 Roy Oswalt	.20	.50
6 Craig Biggio	.30	.75
7 Rich Harden	.20	.50
8 Eric Chavez	.20	.50
9 Huston Street	.20	.50
10 Vernon Wells	.20	.50
11 Roy Halladay	.20	.50
12 Troy Glaus	.20	.50
13 Andruw Jones	.30	.75
14 Chipper Jones	.50	1.25
15 John Smoltz	.30	.75
16 Carlos Lee	.20	.50
17 Rickie Weeks	.20	.50
18 J.J. Hardy	.20	.50
19 Albert Pujols	1.00	2.50
20 Chris Carpenter	.20	.50
21 Scott Rolen	.30	.75
22 Derrek Lee	.20	.50
23 Mark Prior	.30	.75
24 Aramis Ramirez	.20	.50
25 Carl Crawford	.20	.50
26 Scott Kazmir	.30	.75
27 Luis Gonzalez	.20	.50
28 Brandon Webb	.20	.50
29 Chad Tracy	.20	.50
30 Jeff Kent	.20	.50
31 J.D. Drew	.20	.50
32 Jason Schmidt	.20	.50
33 Randy Winn	.20	.50
34 Travis Hafner	.20	.50
35 Victor Martinez	.20	.50
36 Grady Sizemore	.30	.75
37 Ichiro Suzuki	.75	2.00
38 Felix Hernandez	.30	.75
39 Adrian Beltre	.20	.50
40 Miguel Cabrera	.30	.75
41 Dontrelle Willis	.20	.50
42 David Wright	.75	2.00
43 Jose Reyes	.50	1.25
44 Pedro Martinez	.30	.75
45 Carlos Beltran	.20	.50
46 Alfonso Soriano	.20	.50
47 Livan Hernandez	.20	.50
48 Jose Guillen	.20	.50
49 Miguel Tejada	.20	.50
50 Brian Roberts	.20	.50
51 Melvin Mora	.20	.50
52 Jake Peavy	.20	.50
53 Brian Giles	.20	.50
54 Khalil Greene	.30	.75
55 Bobby Abreu	.20	.50
56 Ryan Howard	.75	2.00
57 Chase Utley	.50	1.25
58 Jason Bay	.20	.50
59 Sean Casey	.20	.50
60 Mark Teixeira	.30	.75
61 Michael Young	.20	.50
62 Hank Blalock	.20	.50
63 Manny Ramirez	.30	.75
64 David Ortiz	.50	1.25
65 Josh Beckett	.20	.50
66 Jason Varitek	.50	1.25
67 Ken Griffey Jr.	.75	2.00
68 Adam Dunn	.20	.50
69 Todd Helton	.30	.75
70 Garrett Atkins	.20	.50
71 Reggie Sanders	.20	.50
72 Mike Sweeney	.20	.50
73 Chris Shelton	.20	.50
74 Ivan Rodriguez	.30	.75
75 Johan Santana	.30	.75
76 Torii Hunter	.20	.50
77 Justin Morneau	.20	.50
78 Jim Thome	.30	.75
79 Paul Konerko	.20	.50
80 Scott Podsednik	.20	.50
81 Derek Jeter	1.25	3.00
82 Hideki Matsui	.50	1.25
83 Johnny Damon	.30	.75
84 Alex Rodriguez	.75	2.00
85 Conor Jackson (RC)	3.00	8.00
86 Joey Devine RC	2.00	5.00
87 Jonathan Papelbon (RC)	6.00	15.00
88 Freddie Bynum (RC)	2.00	5.00
89 Chris Denorfia (RC)	2.00	5.00
90 Ryan Shealy (RC)	2.00	5.00
91 Josh Wilson (RC)	3.00	8.00
92 Brian Anderson (RC)	2.00	5.00
93 Justin Verlander (RC)	5.00	12.00
94 Jeremy Hermida (RC)	3.00	8.00
95 Mike Jacobs (RC)	2.00	5.00
96 Josh Johnson (RC)	3.00	8.00
97 Hanley Ramirez (RC)	4.00	10.00
98 Josh Willingham (RC)	2.00	5.00
99 Cole Hamels (RC)	4.00	10.00
100 Hong-Chih Kuo (RC)	6.00	15.00
101 Cody Ross (RC)	2.00	5.00
102 Jose Capellan (RC)	2.00	5.00
103 Prince Fielder (RC)	5.00	12.00
104 David Gassner (RC)	2.00	5.00
105 Jason Kubel (RC)	2.00	5.00
106 Francisco Liriano (RC)	6.00	15.00
107 Anderson Hernandez (RC)	2.00	5.00
108 Boof Bonser (RC)	2.00	5.00
109 Jered Weaver (RC)	6.00	15.00
110 Ben Johnson (RC)	2.00	5.00
111 Jeff Harris RC	2.00	5.00
112 Stephen Drew (RC)	4.00	10.00
113 Matt Cain (RC)	3.00	8.00
114 Skip Schumaker (RC)	2.00	5.00
115 Adam Wainwright (RC)	3.00	8.00
116 Jeremy Sowers (RC)	2.00	5.00
117 Jason Bergmann RC	2.00	5.00
118 Chad Billingsley (RC)	6.00	15.00
119 Ryan Zimmerman (RC)	8.00	20.00
120 Macay McBride (RC)	2.00	5.00
121 Aaron Rakers (RC)	2.00	5.00
122 Alay Soler RC	2.00	5.00
123 Melky Cabrera (RC)	6.00	15.00
124 Tim Hamulack (RC)	2.00	5.00
125 Andre Ethier (RC)	5.00	12.00
126 Kenji Johjima RC	6.00	15.00
NNO Exquisite Redemption		

2006 Upper Deck Ovation Gold

*GOLD: 2.5X TO 6X BASIC
STATED ODDS 1:18
STATED PRINT RUN 499 SERIAL #'d SETS

2006 Upper Deck Ovation Gold Rookie Autographs

OVERALL AU ODDS 1:18
STATED PRINT RUN 99 SERIAL #'d SETS
EXCH DEADLINE 10/06/08

Card		
85 Conor Jackson	8.00	20.00
86 Joey Devine	5.00	12.00
87 Jonathan Papelbon	40.00	80.00
88 Freddie Bynum	5.00	12.00
89 Chris Denorfia	5.00	12.00
90 Ryan Shealy	5.00	12.00
91 Josh Wilson		
92 Brian Anderson	5.00	12.00
93 Justin Verlander	30.00	60.00
94 Jeremy Hermida	8.00	20.00
95 Mike Jacobs	5.00	12.00
96 Josh Johnson	8.00	20.00
97 Hanley Ramirez	10.00	25.00
98 Josh Willingham		
99 Cole Hamels	20.00	50.00
100 Hong-Chih Kuo		
101 Cody Ross		
102 Jose Capellan	5.00	12.00
104 David Gassner	5.00	12.00
105 Jason Kubel	5.00	12.00
106 Francisco Liriano	20.00	50.00
107 Anderson Hernandez	5.00	12.00
108 Boof Bonser	5.00	12.00
109 Jered Weaver	20.00	50.00
110 Ben Johnson	5.00	12.00
111 Jeff Harris	5.00	12.00
112 Stephen Drew		
113 Matt Cain	8.00	20.00
114 Skip Schumaker	6.00	15.00
115 Adam Wainwright	10.00	25.00
117 Jason Bergmann	5.00	12.00
118 Chad Billingsley	10.00	25.00
119 Ryan Zimmerman	40.00	80.00
120 Macay McBride	5.00	12.00
121 Aaron Rakers	5.00	12.00
122 Alay Soler EXCH	5.00	12.00
123 Melky Cabrera EXCH	30.00	60.00
124 Tim Hamulack	5.00	12.00
125 Andre Ethier	40.00	80.00

2006 Upper Deck Ovation Apparel

STATED ODDS 1:18

Card		
AB A.J. Burnett Jsy	3.00	8.00
AO Akinori Otsuka Jsy	3.00	8.00
AP Albert Pujols Jsy	8.00	20.00
BA Jason Bay Jsy	3.00	8.00
CC Carl Crawford Jsy	3.00	8.00
CF Chone Figgins Jsy	3.00	8.00
CL Carlos Lee Jsy	3.00	8.00
CS Chris Shelton Jsy	3.00	8.00
DJ Derek Jeter Pants	10.00	25.00
DO David Ortiz Jsy	4.00	10.00
DW David Wright Jsy	6.00	15.00
EC Eric Chavez Jsy	3.00	8.00
FH Felix Hernandez Jsy	4.00	10.00
GR Ken Griffey Jr. Jsy	6.00	15.00
GS Grady Sizemore Jsy	4.00	10.00
HA Travis Hafner Jsy	3.00	8.00
HE Todd Helton Jsy	4.00	10.00
HS Huston Street Jsy	3.00	8.00
HU Torii Hunter Jsy	3.00	8.00
JB Jeremy Bonderman Jsy	3.00	8.00
JE Jim Edmonds Jsy	4.00	10.00
JF Jeff Francoeur Jsy	4.00	10.00
JG Jonny Gomes Jsy	3.00	8.00
JH J.J. Hardy Jsy	3.00	8.00
JK Jeff Kent Jsy	3.00	8.00
JM Joe Mauer Jsy	4.00	10.00
KG Khalil Greene Jsy	4.00	10.00
LB Lance Berkman Jsy	3.00	8.00
MP Mark Prior Jsy	4.00	10.00
MR Manny Ramirez Jsy	4.00	10.00
MT Mark Teixeira Jsy	4.00	10.00
PF Prince Fielder Jsy	4.00	10.00
RH Ryan Howard Jsy	6.00	15.00
RK Ryan Klesko Jsy	3.00	8.00
RO Roy Oswalt Jsy	3.00	8.00
RZ Ryan Zimmerman Jsy SP	8.00	20.00
SR Scott Rolen Jsy	4.00	10.00
TH Trevor Hoffman Jsy	3.00	8.00
TN Trot Nixon Jsy	3.00	8.00
VG Vladimir Guerrero Jsy	4.00	10.00
VM Victor Martinez Jsy	3.00	8.00
VW Vernon Wells Jsy	3.00	8.00

2006 Upper Deck Ovation Center Stage

STATED ODDS 1:11

Card		
AC Aaron Cook	.50	1.25
AP Albert Pujols	2.50	6.00
BC Bobby Crosby	.50	1.25
CA Miguel Cabrera	.75	2.00
CS Chris Shelton	.50	1.25
CW Chien-Ming Wang	3.00	8.00
DC Daniel Cabrera	.50	1.25
DD David DeJesus	.50	1.25
DJ Derek Jeter	3.00	8.00
DL Derrek Lee	.50	1.25
DW David Wright	2.00	5.00
FH Felix Hernandez	.75	2.00
FS Freddy Sanchez	.50	1.25
IS Ian Snell	.50	1.25
JB Josh Beckett	.50	1.25
JC Jose Contreras	.50	1.25
JF Jason Frasor	.50	1.25
KG Ken Griffey Jr.	2.00	5.00
MC Michael Cuddyer	.50	1.25
MP Mark Prior	.75	2.00
MT Mark Teixeira	.75	2.00
RH Runelvys Hernandez	.50	1.25
SD Stephen Drew	1.25	3.00
VG Vladimir Guerrero	1.25	3.00
YM Yadier Molina	.50	1.25

2006 Upper Deck Ovation Center Stage Signatures

OVERALL AU ODDS 1:18
STATED PRINT RUN 25 SERIAL #'d SETS
Y.MOLINA PRINT RUN 19 SER. #'d CARDS
NO PRICING DUE TO SCARCITY

AC Aaron Cook
BC Bobby Crosby
CA Miguel Cabrera
CS Chris Shelton
CW Chien-Ming Wang
DC Daniel Cabrera
DD David DeJesus
DJ Derek Jeter
FS Freddy Sanchez
IS Ian Snell
JB Josh Beckett
JC Jose Contreras
JF Jason Frasor
KG Ken Griffey Jr.
MC Michael Cuddyer
MP Mark Prior
RH Runelvys Hernandez
VG Vladimir Guerrero
YM Yadier Molina/19

2006 Upper Deck Ovation Curtain Calls

STATED ODDS 1:14

Card		
BC Bobby Crosby	.50	1.25
CS Chris Shelton	.50	1.25
CW Chien-Ming Wang	4.00	10.00
DC Daniel Cabrera	.50	1.25
DD David DeJesus	.50	1.25
EC Eric Chavez	.50	1.25
FS Freddy Sanchez	.50	1.25
HE Runelvys Hernandez	.50	1.25
HR Horacio Ramirez	.50	1.25
JC Jose Contreras	.50	1.25
JE Jered Weaver	.75	2.00
JW Josh Willingham	.50	1.25
KG1 Ken Griffey Jr.	2.00	5.00
KG2 Ken Griffey Jr.	2.00	5.00
MP Mark Prior	.75	2.00
MT Miguel Tejada	.50	1.25
MY Michael Young	.50	1.25
RH Rich Harden	.50	1.25
TO Tomo Ohka	.50	1.25
YM Yadier Molina	.50	1.25

2006 Upper Deck Ovation Curtain Calls Signatures

OVERALL AU ODDS 1:18
STATED PRINT RUN 25 SERIAL #'d SETS
NO PRICING DUE TO SCARCITY

BC Bobby Crosby
CS Chris Shelton
CW Chien-Ming Wang
DD David DeJesus
FS Freddy Sanchez
HE Runelvys Hernandez
HR Horacio Ramirez
JC Jose Contreras
KG1 Ken Griffey Jr.
KG2 Ken Griffey Jr.
MP Mark Prior
MT Miguel Tejada
MY Michael Young
RH Rich Harden
TO Tomo Ohka
YM Yadier Molina

2006 Upper Deck Ovation Nation

STATED ODDS 1:19

Card		
AJ Andruw Jones	.75	2.00
AP Albert Pujols	2.50	6.00
DC Daniel Cabrera	.50	1.25
DJ Derek Jeter	3.00	8.00
DM Daisuke Matsuzaka	6.00	15.00
FC Frederich Cepeda	.50	1.25
JA Jae Seo	.50	1.25
JB Jason Bay	.50	1.25
JS Johan Santana	.75	2.00
KG Ken Griffey Jr.	2.00	5.00
MC Miguel Cabrera	.75	2.00
MT Miguel Tejada	.50	1.25
NM Nobuhiko Matsunaka	.75	2.00
SL Seung Yeop Lee	.75	2.00
YG Yoandy Garlobo	.50	1.25

2006 Upper Deck Ovation Nation Signatures

OVERALL AU ODDS 1:18
STATED PRINT RUN 25 SERIAL #'d SETS
NO PRICING DUE TO SCARCITY

KG Ken Griffey Jr.
MC Miguel Cabrera
MT Miguel Tejada

2006 Upper Deck Ovation Spotlight Signatures

OVERALL AU ODDS 1:18

Card		
AC Aaron Cook	4.00	10.00
AG Andy Green	4.00	10.00
BC Bobby Crosby	4.00	10.00
CA Miguel Cabrera	10.00	25.00
CS Chris Shelton	4.00	10.00
CW Chien-Ming Wang	50.00	100.00
DC Daniel Cabrera	4.00	10.00
DD David DeJesus	4.00	10.00
DR David Ross	6.00	15.00
EC Eric Chavez SP	6.00	15.00
EJ Edwin Jackson	4.00	10.00
FG Franklyn German	4.00	10.00
FN Fernando Nieve	4.00	10.00
FS Freddy Sanchez	6.00	15.00
HA Rich Harden SP	4.00	10.00
HR Horacio Ramirez SP	4.00	10.00
IS Ian Snell		
JB Josh Beckett SP	15.00	40.00
JC Jose Contreras	6.00	15.00
JD Jorge De La Rosa	4.00	10.00
JF Jason Frasor	4.00	10.00
JV Javier Vazquez SP		
JW Josh Willingham SP	6.00	15.00
KG1 Ken Griffey Jr.	30.00	60.00
KG2 Ken Griffey Jr.	30.00	60.00
KS Kirk Saarloos	4.00	10.00
LC Lance Cormier	4.00	10.00
MC Michael Cuddyer SP	4.00	10.00
MG Mike Gonzalez	4.00	10.00
MP Mark Prior	8.00	20.00
MT Matt Thornton	4.00	10.00
MW Michael Wuertz	4.00	10.00
MY Michael Young	4.00	10.00
RH Runelvys Hernandez	4.00	10.00
RW Ryan Wagner	4.00	10.00
SC Shawn Camp	4.00	10.00
TE Miguel Tejada SP	6.00	15.00
TO Tomo Ohka	10.00	25.00
TR Matt Treanor	4.00	10.00
YM Yadier Molina	6.00	15.00

2006 Upper Deck Ovation Superstar Theatre

STATED ODDS 1:9

Card		
AJ Andruw Jones	.75	2.00
AP Albert Pujols	2.50	6.00
AR Alex Rodriguez	2.00	5.00
BA Jason Bay	.50	1.25
BC Bobby Crosby	.50	1.25
CC Chris Carpenter	.50	1.25
CS Chris Shelton	.50	1.25
CW Chien-Ming Wang	3.00	8.00
DC Daniel Cabrera	.50	1.25
DD David DeJesus	.50	1.25
DJ Derek Jeter	3.00	8.00
DL Derrek Lee	.50	1.25
DO David Ortiz	1.25	3.00
HM Hideki Matsui	1.25	3.00
IS Ichiro Suzuki	2.00	5.00
JB Josh Beckett	.50	1.25
JC Jose Contreras	.50	1.25
KG1 Ken Griffey Jr.	2.00	5.00
KG2 Ken Griffey Jr.	2.00	5.00
MC Miguel Cabrera	.75	2.00
MP Mark Prior	.75	2.00
MR Manny Ramirez	.75	2.00
MT Miguel Tejada	.50	1.25
MY Michael Young	.50	1.25
PM Pedro Martinez	.75	2.00
RH Rich Harden	.50	1.25
TE Mark Teixeira	.75	2.00
TH Travis Hafner	.50	1.25

TO Tomo Ohka .50 1.25
YM Yadier Molina .50 1.25

2006 Upper Deck Ovation Superstar Theatre Signatures

OVERALL AU ODDS 1:18
STATED PRINT RUN 25 SERIAL #'d SETS
D.JETER PRINT RUN 1 SERIAL #'d SET
NO PRICING DUE TO SCARCITY
BC Bobby Crosby
CS Chris Shelton
CW Chien-Ming Wang
DC Daniel Cabrera
DD David DeJesus
DJ Derek Jeter/1
DO David Ortiz
JB Josh Beckett
JC Jose Contreras
KG1 Ken Griffey Jr.
KG2 Ken Griffey Jr.
MC Miguel Cabrera
MP Mark Prior
MT Miguel Tejada
MY Michael Young
RH Rich Harden
TH Travis Hafner
TO Tomo Ohka
YM Yadier Molina

2007 Upper Deck Premier

This 244-card set was release in April, 2007. This set was issued in seven-card packs (Actually small boxes) which came 10 boxes per case. Cards numbered 1-200 feature veterans and those cards were issued to a stated print run of 99 serial numbered sets and cards numbered 201-244 featured rookie logo players and those cards were issued to a stated print run of 199 serial numbered sets.

COMMON CARD (1-200) 2.00 5.00
BASE CARD ODDS ONE PER PACK
1-200 STATED PRINT RUN 99 SER.#'d SETS
COMMON ROOKIE (201-244) 2.00 5.00
RC ODDS ONE PER PACK
201-244 STATED PRINT RUN 199 SER.#'d SETS
PRINT PLATES RANDOM INSERTS IN PACKS
PLATE PRINT RUN 1 SET PER COLOR
BLACK-CYAN-MAGENTA-YELLOW ISSUED
NO PLATE PRICING DUE TO SCARCITY
1 Roy Campanella 4.00 10.00
2 Ty Cobb 5.00 12.00
3 Mickey Cochrane 2.00 5.00
4 Dizzy Dean 3.00 8.00
5 Don Drysdale 3.00 8.00
6 Jimmie Foxx 4.00 10.00
7 Lou Gehrig 6.00 15.00
8 Lefty Grove 2.00 5.00
9 Rogers Hornsby 4.00 10.00
10 Walter Johnson 4.00 10.00
11 Eddie Mathews 4.00 10.00
12 Christy Mathewson 4.00 10.00
13 Johnny Mize 3.00 8.00
14 Thurman Munson 5.00 12.00
15 Mel Ott 3.00 8.00
16 Satchel Paige 4.00 10.00
17 Jackie Robinson 5.00 12.00
18 Babe Ruth 8.00 20.00
19 George Sisler 2.00 5.00
20 Honus Wagner 4.00 10.00
21 Cy Young 4.00 10.00
22 Luis Aparicio 2.00 5.00
23 Johnny Bench 4.00 10.00
24 Yogi Berra 4.00 10.00
25 Rod Carew 3.00 8.00
26 Orlando Cepeda 2.00 5.00
27 Bob Feller 3.00 8.00
28 Carlton Fisk 3.00 8.00
29 Bob Gibson 3.00 8.00
30 Catfish Hunter 2.00 5.00
31 Reggie Jackson 3.00 8.00
32 Al Kaline 4.00 10.00
33 Harmon Killebrew 4.00 10.00
34 Buck Leonard 2.00 5.00
35 Juan Marichal 2.00 5.00
36 Bill Mazeroski 3.00 8.00
37 Willie McCovey 3.00 8.00
38 Joe Morgan 3.00 8.00
39 Eddie Murray 4.00 10.00
40 Jim Palmer 3.00 8.00
41 Tony Perez 3.00 8.00
42 Pee Wee Reese 3.00 8.00
43 Brooks Robinson 4.00 10.00
44 Nolan Ryan 8.00 20.00
45 Mike Schmidt 4.00 10.00
46 Tom Seaver 3.00 8.00
47 Enos Slaughter 2.00 5.00
48 Willie Stargell 3.00 8.00
49 Early Wynn 2.00 5.00
50 Robin Yount 4.00 10.00
51 Tony Gwynn 4.00 10.00
52 Cal Ripken Jr. 10.00 25.00
53 Ernie Banks 4.00 10.00
54 Wade Boggs 3.00 8.00
55 Steve Carlton 2.00 5.00
56 Will Clark 3.00 8.00
57 Fergie Jenkins 2.00 5.00
58 Bo Jackson 4.00 10.00
59 Don Mattingly 6.00 15.00
60 Stan Musial 5.00 12.00
61 Frank Robinson 2.00 5.00
62 Ryne Sandberg 5.00 12.00
63 Ozzie Smith 6.00 15.00
64 Carl Yastrzemski 5.00 12.00
65 Dave Winfield 3.00 8.00
66 Paul Molitor 2.00 5.00
67 Jason Bay 2.00 5.00
68 Freddy Sanchez 2.00 5.00
69 Josh Beckett 2.00 5.00
70 Carlos Beltran 2.00 5.00
71 Craig Biggio 4.00 10.00
72 Matt Holliday 2.50 6.00
73 A.J. Burnett 2.00 5.00
74 Miguel Cabrera 3.00 8.00
75 Dontrelle Willis 2.00 5.00
76 Chris Carpenter 3.00 8.00
77 Roger Clemens 6.00 15.00
78 Johnny Damon 3.00 8.00
79 Jermaine Dye 2.00 5.00
80 Jim Thome 3.00 8.00
81 Vladimir Guerrero 4.00 10.00
82 Travis Hafner 2.00 5.00
83 Victor Martinez 2.00 5.00
84 Trevor Hoffman 2.00 5.00
85 Derek Jeter 8.00 20.00
86 Ken Griffey Jr. 5.00 12.00
87 Randy Johnson 4.00 10.00
88 Andruw Jones 3.00 8.00
89 Derrek Lee 2.00 5.00
90 Greg Maddux 5.00 12.00
91 Magglio Ordonez 3.00 8.00
92 David Ortiz 4.00 10.00
93 Jake Peavy 2.00 5.00
94 Roy Oswalt 2.00 5.00
95 Mike Piazza 4.00 10.00
96 Jose Reyes 4.00 10.00
97 Ivan Rodriguez 4.00 10.00
98 Johan Santana 3.00 8.00
99 Scott Rolen 3.00 8.00
100 Curt Schilling 3.00 8.00
101 John Smoltz 3.00 8.00
102 Alfonso Soriano 2.00 5.00
103 Miguel Tejada 3.00 8.00
104 Frank Thomas 5.00 12.00
105 Chase Utley 4.00 10.00
106 Joe Mauer 3.00 8.00
107 Alex Rodriguez 6.00 15.00
108 Alex Rios 3.00 8.00
109 Justin Verlander 4.00 10.00
110 Ryan Howard 5.00 12.00
111 Jered Weaver 3.00 8.00
112 Francisco Liriano 4.00 10.00
113 David Wright 5.00 12.00
114 Felix Hernandez 3.00 8.00
115 Jeremy Sowers 3.00 8.00
116 Cole Hamels 3.00 8.00
117 B.J. Upton 2.00 5.00
118 Chien-Ming Wang 20.00 50.00
119 Justin Morneau 3.00 8.00
120 Jonny Gomes 2.00 5.00
121 Adrian Gonzalez 2.00 5.00
122 Bill Hall 3.00 8.00
123 Rich Harden 3.00 8.00
124 Rich Hill 2.00 5.00
125 Tadahito Iguchi 2.00 5.00
126 Scott Kazmir 3.00 8.00
127 Howie Kendrick 2.00 5.00
128 Dan Uggla 3.00 8.00
129 Hanley Ramirez 3.00 8.00
130 Josh Willingham 2.00 5.00
131 Nick Markakis 3.00 8.00
132 Grady Sizemore 4.00 10.00
133 Ian Kinsler 3.00 8.00
134 Jonathan Papelbon 5.00 12.00
135 Ryan Zimmerman 4.00 10.00
136 Stephen Drew 3.00 8.00
137 Adam Wainwright 2.00 5.00
138 Joel Zumaya 3.00 8.00
139 Prince Fielder 4.00 10.00
140 Carl Crawford 3.00 8.00
141 Huston Street 2.00 5.00
142 Matt Cain 3.00 8.00
143 Andre Ethier 3.00 8.00
144 Brian McCann 3.00 8.00
145 Josh Barfield 2.00 5.00
146 Anibal Sanchez 2.00 5.00
147 Brian Roberts 3.00 8.00
148 Brandon Webb 2.00 5.00
149 Chipper Jones 4.00 10.00
150 Tim Hudson 3.00 8.00
151 Adam LaRoche 2.00 5.00
152 Jeff Francoeur 4.00 10.00
153 Marcus Giles 2.00 5.00
154 Jason Varitek 5.00 12.00
155 Coco Crisp 3.00 8.00
156 Manny Ramirez 3.00 8.00
157 Trot Nixon 3.00 8.00
158 Carlos Zambrano 2.00 5.00
159 Mark Prior 3.00 8.00
160 Aramis Ramirez 2.00 5.00
161 Mark Buehrle 2.00 5.00
162 Paul Konerko 2.00 5.00
163 Adam Dunn 3.00 8.00
164 C.C. Sabathia 2.00 5.00
165 Todd Helton 3.00 8.00
166 Garrett Atkins 3.00 8.00
167 Jeremy Bonderman 4.00 10.00
168 Curtis Granderson 3.00 8.00
169 Sean Casey 3.00 8.00
170 Lance Berkman 3.00 8.00
171 Brad Lidge 2.00 5.00
172 Reggie Sanders 2.00 5.00
173 Brad Penny 2.00 5.00
174 Nomar Garciaparra 5.00 12.00
175 Jeff Kent 3.00 8.00
176 Chone Figgins 2.00 5.00
177 Ben Sheets 3.00 8.00
178 Rickie Weeks 3.00 8.00
179 Joe Nathan 3.00 8.00
180 Torii Hunter 3.00 8.00
181 Carlos Delgado 3.00 8.00
182 Tom Glavine 4.00 10.00
183 Paul Lo Duca 2.00 5.00
184 Mariano Rivera 5.00 12.00
185 Robinson Cano 4.00 10.00
186 Bobby Abreu 3.00 8.00
187 Hideki Matsui 5.00 12.00
188 Barry Zito 2.00 5.00
189 Eric Chavez 3.00 8.00
190 Jimmy Rollins 3.00 8.00
191 Khalil Greene 4.00 10.00
192 Brian Giles 2.00 5.00
193 Jason Schmidt 2.00 5.00
194 Ichiro Suzuki 12.50 30.00
195 David Eckstein 4.00 10.00
196 Jim Edmonds 3.00 8.00
197 Mark Teixeira 3.00 8.00
198 Michael Young 2.00 5.00
199 Vernon Wells 3.00 8.00
200 Roy Halladay 3.00 8.00
201 Delmon Young (RC) 3.00 8.00
202 Andrew Miller RC 8.00 20.00
203 Troy Tulowitzki (RC) 3.00 8.00
204 Jeff Fiorentino (RC) 2.00 5.00
205 David Murphy (RC) 2.00 5.00
206 Jeff Baker (RC) 2.00 5.00
207 Kevin Hooper (RC) 2.00 5.00
208 Kevin Kouzmanoff (RC) 2.00 5.00
209 Adam Lind (RC) 3.00 8.00
210 Mike Rabelo RC 3.00 8.00
211 John Nelson (RC) 2.00 5.00
212 Mitch Maier RC 2.00 5.00
213 Ryan Braun RC 2.00 5.00
214 Vinny Rottino (RC) 2.00 5.00
215 Drew Anderson RC 2.00 5.00
216 Alexi Casilla RC 3.00 8.00
217 Glen Perkins (RC) 2.00 5.00
218 Cesar Jimenez RC 2.00 5.00
219 Tim Gradoville RC 2.00 5.00
220 Shane Youman RC 2.00 5.00
221 Billy Sadler (RC) 2.00 5.00
222 Patrick Misch (RC) 2.00 5.00
223 Juan Salas (RC) 2.00 5.00
224 Beltran Perez (RC) 2.00 5.00
225 Hector Gimenez (RC) 2.00 5.00
226 Philip Humber (RC) 3.00 8.00
227 Eric Stults RC 2.00 5.00
228 Dennis Sarfate (RC) 2.00 5.00
229 Andy Cannizaro RC 3.00 8.00
230 Juan Morillo (RC) 2.00 5.00
231 Fred Lewis (RC) 2.00 5.00
232 Ryan Sweeney (RC) 2.00 5.00
233 Chris Narveson (RC) 2.00 5.00
234 Michael Bourn (RC) 2.00 5.00
235 Joaquin Arias (RC) 2.00 5.00
236 Carlos Maldonado (RC) 2.00 5.00
237 Alvin Colina RC 2.00 5.00
238 Jon Knott (RC) 2.00 5.00
239 Justin Hampson (RC) 2.00 5.00
240 Jeff Salazar (RC) 2.00 5.00
241 Josh Fields (RC) 2.00 5.00
242 Delwyn Young (RC) 2.00 5.00
243 Daisuke Matsuzaka RC 15.00 40.00
244 Kei Igawa RC 8.00 20.00

2007 Upper Deck Premier Autograph Parallel

OVERALL AUTO ODDS 1 PER PACK
PRINT RUNS B/WN 15-73 COPIES PER
NO PRICING ON QTY OF 25 OR LESS
244 Kei Igawa/73 150.00 200.00

2007 Upper Deck Premier Bronze

*BRONZE: .5X TO 1.2X BASIC
BRONZE RANDOMLY INSERTED IN PACKS
STATED PRINT RUN 75 SER.#'d SETS
243 Daisuke Matsuzaka 15.00 40.00

2007 Upper Deck Premier Gold

*GOLD: .6X TO 1.5X BASIC
GOLD RANDOMLY INSERTED IN PACKS
STATED PRINT RUN 49 SER.#'d SETS
243 Daisuke Matsuzaka 20.00 50.00

2007 Upper Deck Premier Platinum

PLATINUM RANDOMLY INSERTED IN PACKS
STATED PRINT RUN 1 SER.#'d SET
NO PRICING DUE TO SCARCITY

2007 Upper Deck Premier Silver

*SILVER: .5X TO 1.2X BASIC
SILVER RANDOMLY INSERTED IN PACKS
STATED PRINT RUN 99 SER.#'d SETS
243 Daisuke Matsuzaka 15.00 40.00

2007 Upper Deck Premier Emerging Stars Autographs Dual

STATED PRINT RUN 50 SER.#'d SETS
BRONZE PRINT RUN 25 SER.#'d SETS
NO BRONZE PRICING DUE TO SCARCITY
GOLD PRINT RUN 10 SER.#'d SETS
NO GOLD PRICING DUE TO SCARCITY
PLATINUM PRINT RUN 1 SER.#'d SET
NO PLATINUM PRICING DUE TO SCARCITY
OVERALL AUTO ODDS ONE PER PACK
EXCHANGE DEADLINE 04/26/10
BU Josh Barfield 10.00 25.00
Dan Uggla
BV Jeremy Bonderman 30.00 60.00
Justin Verlander
CA Carl Crawford 10.00 25.00
Alex Rios
CH Matt Cain
Philip Humber
CR Chien-Ming Wang
Rich Harden
CS Shin-Soo Choo
Grady Sizemore
FJ Felix Hernandez 30.00 60.00
Jered Weaver
GB Adrian Gonzalez 10.00 25.00
Josh Barfield
GC Jonny Gomes 10.00 25.00
Carl Crawford
HP Philip Humber 30.00 60.00
Mike Pelfrey
HS Rich Harden 10.00 25.00
Huston Street
HV Rich Harden 12.50 30.00
Justin Verlander
IK Tadahito Iguchi 20.00 50.00
Ian Kinsler
KL Scott Kazmir 20.00 50.00
Francisco Liriano
KS Scott Kazmir 10.00 25.00
Jeremy Sowers
LH Jon Lester 20.00 50.00
Craig Hansen
MB Joe Mauer 12.50 30.00
Jeremy Brown
MG Justin Morneau 12.50 30.00
Adrian Gonzalez
MH Andrew Miller 30.00 60.00
Cole Hamels
MM Joe Mauer
Brian McCann
MS Nick Markakis
Grady Sizemore
MZ Andrew Miller 30.00 60.00
Joel Zumaya
PH Jonathan Papelbon 20.00 50.00
Craig Hansen
PW Jonathan Papelbon 20.00 50.00
Adam Wainwright
QD Carlos Quentin 12.50 30.00
Stephen Drew
RB Rickie Weeks 20.00 50.00
Bill Hall
RD Jose Reyes 30.00 60.00
Stephen Drew
RH Jae Kuk Ryu
Rich Hill
RR Jose Reyes 40.00 80.00
Hanley Ramirez
RY Alex Rios 20.00 50.00
Delmon Young
SH Jeremy Sowers 12.50 30.00
Cole Hamels
SJ Anibal Sanchez 10.00 25.00
Josh Johnson
SU Freddy Sanchez
B.J. Upton
SW Huston Street
Adam Wainwright
SZ Freddy Sanchez
Ryan Zimmerman
TD Troy Tulowitzki 10.00 25.00
Stephen Drew EXCH
TR Troy Tulowitzki 15.00 40.00
Hanley Ramirez
UG B.J. Upton 10.00 25.00
Jonny Gomes
UR Dan Uggla 20.00 50.00
Hanley Ramirez
UU Chase Utley 30.00 60.00
Dan Uggla
VH Justin Verlander 40.00 80.00
Felix Hernandez
VM Justin Verlander 40.00 80.00
Andrew Miller
WC Chien-Ming Wang
Melky Cabrera
WE Josh Willingham 10.00 25.00
Andre Ethier EXCH
WF Rickie Weeks
Prince Fielder
WH Chien-Ming Wang
Rich Hill
WK Jered Weaver 20.00 50.00
Howie Kendrick
WL Jered Weaver 20.00 50.00
Francisco Liriano
YT Delmon Young 20.00 50.00
Troy Tulowitzki
ZW Joel Zumaya 12.50 30.00
Adam Wainwright

2007 Upper Deck Premier Emerging Stars Autographs Triple

STATED PRINT RUN 50 SER.#'d SETS
BRONZE PRINT RUN 25 SER.#'d SETS
NO BRONZE PRICING DUE TO SCARCITY
GOLD PRINT RUN 10 SER.#'d SETS
NO GOLD PRICING DUE TO SCARCITY
PLATINUM PRINT RUN 1 SER.#'d SET
NO PLATINUM PRICING DUE TO SCARCITY
OVERALL AUTO ODDS ONE PER PACK
EXCHANGE DEADLINE 04/26/10
AZU Garrett Atkins
Ryan Zimmerman
B.J. Upton
CWV Matt Cain
Jered Weaver
Justin Verlander
DZU Stephen Drew
Ryan Zimmerman
B.J. Upton
ELS Andre Ethier 20.00 50.00
James Loney
Takashi Saito
FHW Prince Fielder
Bill Hall
Rickie Weeks
FLM Prince Fielder
Adam LaRoche
Justin Morneau
HHL Rich Hill 40.00 80.00
Cole Hamels
Francisco Liriano EXCH
HQE Matt Holliday 30.00 60.00
Carlos Quentin
Andre Ethier EXCH
KUK Howie Kendrick 20.00 50.00
Dan Uggla
Ian Kinsler
KWN Howie Kendrick
Jered Weaver
Mike Napoli
LBG Francisco Liriano 30.00 60.00
Boof Bonser
Matt Garza
MFL Justin Morneau
Prince Fielder
James Loney
MHL Andrew Miller 30.00 60.00
Cole Hamels
Francisco Liriano
MKL Justin Morneau 20.00 50.00
Jason Kubel
Francisco Liriano
MLD Brian McCann
Adam LaRoche
Kyle Davies
MMM Russell Martin
Brian McCann
Joe Mauer
MMN Brian McCann
Joe Mauer
Mike Napoli
MMW Joe Mauer
Brian McCann
Josh Willingham
MSK Andrew Miller 20.00 50.00
Jeremy Sowers
Scott Kazmir
MVB Andrew Miller 40.00 80.00
Justin Verlander
Jeremy Bonderman
MYE Nick Markakis 40.00 80.00
Delmon Young
Andre Ethier
PCW Mike Pelfrey
Matt Cain
Jered Weaver
PSW Jonathan Papelbon 30.00 60.00
Huston Street
Adam Wainwright
QEY Carlos Quentin 20.00 50.00
Andre Ethier
Delmon Young EXCH
RRD Jose Reyes 40.00 80.00
Hanley Ramirez
Stephen Drew
SHK Jeremy Sowers 40.00 80.00
Cole Hamels
Scott Kazmir
SHR Anibal Sanchez
Felix Hernandez
Anthony Reyes
SOJ Anibal Sanchez
Scott Olsen
Josh Johnson
SUZ Freddy Sanchez
B.J. Upton
Ryan Zimmerman
TDR Troy Tulowitzki 30.00 60.00
Stephen Drew
Hanley Ramirez
THA Troy Tulowitzki 40.00 80.00
Matt Holliday
Garrett Atkins
UKW Chase Utley 30.00 60.00
Howie Kendrick
Rickie Weeks
UUW Chase Utley 30.00 60.00
Dan Uggla
Rickie Weeks
UYK B.J. Upton 30.00 60.00
Delmon Young
Scott Kazmir
VMZ Justin Verlander 40.00 80.00
Andrew Miller
Joel Zumaya
WHV Jered Weaver 30.00 60.00
Felix Hernandez
Justin Verlander
WPH Chien-Ming Wang
Mike Pelfrey
Philip Humber
WZS Adam Wainwright 20.00 50.00
Joel Zumaya
Takashi Saito EXCH
YER Delmon Young 20.00 50.00
Andre Ethier
Alex Rios
ZFV Ryan Zimmerman
Prince Fielder
Justin Verlander

2007 Upper Deck Premier Foursomes

OVERALL AUTO ODDS ONE PER PACK
STATED PRINT RUN 15 SER.#'d SETS
NO PRICING DUE TO SCARCITY
EXCHANGE DEADLINE 04/26/10

2007 Upper Deck Premier Hallmarks Autographs

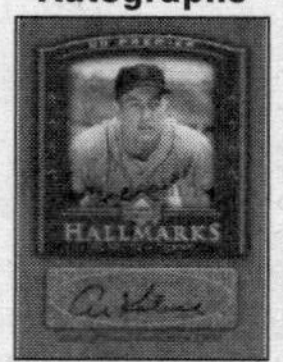

PRINT RUNS B/WN 5-57 COPIES PER
NO PRICING ON QTY 25 OR LESS
GOLD PRINT RUN 25 SER.#'d SETS
NO GOLD PRICING DUE TO SCARCITY
PLATINUM PRINT RUN 1 SER.#'d SET
NO PLATINUM PRICING DUE TO SCARCITY
OVERALL AUTO ODDS ONE PER PACK
EXCHANGE DEADLINE 04/26/10
AK Al Kaline/15
BF Bob Feller/5
BR Brooks Robinson/16
CF Carlton Fisk/11
CY Carl Yastrzemski/18
EB Ernie Banks/11
FR Frank Robinson/12
JB Johnny Bench/14
JP Jim Palmer/23
LA Luis Aparicio/57 10.00 25.00
MS Mike Schmidt/48 20.00 50.00
NR Nolan Ryan/11
OS Ozzie Smith/57 20.00 50.00
PM Paul Molitor/39 10.00 25.00
RJ Reggie Jackson/47 20.00 50.00
RS Ryne Sandberg/40 30.00 60.00
RY Robin Yount/46 EXCH 15.00 40.00
SC Steve Carlton/27 15.00 40.00
SM Stan Musial/20
WB Wade Boggs/12
WF Whitey Ford/25
WM Willie McCovey/45 20.00 50.00
YB Yogi Berra/15

2007 Upper Deck Premier Insignias Autographs

STATED PRINT RUN 50 SER.#'d SETS
GOLD PRINT RUN 25 SER.#'d SETS
NO GOLD PRICING DUE TO SCARCITY
PLATINUM PRINT RUN 1 SER.#'d SET
NO PLATINUM PRICING DUE TO SCARCITY
OVERALL AUTO ODDS ONE PER PACK
EXCHANGE DEADLINE 04/26/10
AK Al Kaline 15.00 40.00
AM Andrew Miller 40.00 80.00
BU B.J. Upton 10.00 25.00
CR Cal Ripken Jr. 60.00 120.00
DJ Derek Jeter 100.00 200.00
DL Derrek Lee 15.00 40.00
DM Don Mattingly 40.00 80.00
DY Delmon Young 20.00 50.00
EB Ernie Banks EXCH 30.00 60.00
FH Felix Hernandez 30.00 60.00
JM Joe Mauer 20.00 50.00
JP Jake Peavy 10.00 25.00
JR Jose Reyes 40.00 80.00
JT Jim Thome 30.00 60.00
JW Jered Weaver 10.00 25.00
KG Ken Griffey Jr. 50.00 100.00
MO Justin Morneau 10.00 25.00
OS Ozzie Smith 20.00 50.00
PA Jim Palmer 10.00 25.00
TG Tony Gwynn EXCH 20.00 50.00
TT Troy Tulowitzki 15.00 40.00
WC Will Clark 10.00 25.00

2007 Upper Deck Premier Noteworthy Autographs

PRINT RUN B/WN 1-86 COPIES PER
NO PRICING ON QTY 25 OR LESS
GOLD PRINT RUN 25 SER.#'d SETS
NO GOLD PRICING DUE TO SCARCITY
PLATINUM PRINT RUN 1 SER.#'d SET
NO PLATINUM PRICING DUE TO SCARCITY
OVERALL AUTO ODDS ONE PER PACK
EXCHANGE DEADLINE 04/26/10
AD Andre Dawson/50 10.00 25.00
AK Al Kaline/15 12.50 30.00
AM Andrew Miller/6
AP Albert Pujols/49 EXCH
AS Alfonso Soriano/35 30.00 60.00
BA Jeff Bagwell/75 20.00 50.00
BE Josh Beckett/50 40.00 80.00
BF Bob Feller/62 12.50 30.00
BJ Bo Jackson/35 40.00 80.00
BR Brooks Robinson/35 20.00 50.00
CB Craig Biggio/65 20.00 50.00
CC Chris Carpenter/35 15.00 40.00
CF Carlton Fisk/37 20.00 50.00
CR Cal Ripken Jr./34
DB Dusty Baker
DE Dennis Eckersley/75 6.00 15.00
DJ Derek Jeter/44 EXCH
DM Don Mattingly/35 40.00 80.00
DS Don Sutton/50 6.00 15.00
DU Adam Dunn
DW Dontrelle Willis
DY Delmon Young/1
EB Ernie Banks
FJ Fergie Jenkins/74 6.00 15.00
FR Frank Robinson/31 15.00 40.00
GS Gary Sheffield/86 15.00 40.00
HR Hanley Ramirez/51 12.50 30.00
JB Jim Bunning/54 12.50 30.00
JB Johnny Bench/45 20.00 50.00
JC Jack Clark/75 6.00 15.00
JK Jason Kendall
JM Juan Marichal/65 10.00 25.00
JM Joe Mauer/36 20.00 50.00
JP Jim Palmer/65 10.00 25.00
JR Jose Reyes
JS Johan Santana/65 20.00 50.00
JT Jim Thome/52 20.00 50.00
JW Jered Weaver/11
JZ Joel Zumaya/62
KG Kirk Gibson
KG Ken Griffey Jr./56 40.00 80.00
KW Kerry Wood/35 10.00 25.00
LA Luis Aparicio/35 6.00 15.00
MC Miguel Cabrera
MG Mark Grace
MM Mark Mulder/35 6.00 15.00
MO Justin Morneau/50 10.00 25.00
MS Mike Schmidt/12
MT Miguel Tejada/50 12.50 30.00
MW Maury Wills
NR Nolan Ryan/22
PE Jake Peavy/55 12.50 30.00
PM Paul Molitor/40 10.00 25.00
RJ Reggie Jackson/14
RS Ryne Sandberg/45 20.00 50.00
RY Robin Yount/29 20.00 50.00
SC Steve Carlton/10
SD Stephen Drew/15
SK Sandy Koufax EXCH
TG Tom Glavine/47 30.00 60.00
TG Tony Gwynn/56 EXCH 20.00 50.00
TH Torii Hunter/26 12.50 30.00
TT Troy Tulowitzki/7
VG Vladimir Guerrero/27
WB Wade Boggs/45 12.50 30.00
WF Whitey Ford/8

2007 Upper Deck Premier Octographs

OVERALL AUTO ODDS ONE PER PACK
STATED PRINT RUN 5 SER.#'d SETS
NO PRICING DUE TO SCARCITY
EXCHANGE DEADLINE 04/26/10
1 Ken Griffey Jr.
Derek Jeter
Albert Pujols
Cal Ripken Jr.
Roger Clemens
Nolan Ryan
Greg Maddux
Tom Seaver
2 Justin Verlander
Jered Weaver
Felix Hernandez
Matt Cain
Francisco Liriano
Jeremy Sowers
Cole Hamels
Andrew Miller
3 Derek Jeter
Randy Johnson
Johnny Damon
Melky Cabrera
Don Mattingly
Yogi Berra
Reggie Jackson
Dave Winfield
4 Hanley Ramirez
Stephen Drew
Troy Tulowitzki
Derek Jeter
Chase Utley
Dan Uggla
Howie Kendrick
Tadahito Iguchi
5 Cal Ripken Jr.
Eddie Murray
Frank Robinson
Brooks Robinson
Carl Yastrzemski
David Ortiz
Carlton Fisk
Wade Boggs
6 Chris Carpenter
Stan Musial
Albert Pujols
Ozzie Smith
Nolan Ryan
Tom Seaver
Jose Reyes
Carlos Beltran
7 Joe Mauer
Justin Morneau
Chase Utley
Hanley Ramirez
Ryan Zimmerman
Miguel Cabrera
Delmon Young
Grady Sizemore

2007 Upper Deck Premier Pairings Autographs

OVERALL AUTO ODDS ONE PER PACK
STATED PRINT RUN 25 SER.#'d SETS
NO PRICING DUE TO SCARCITY
EXCHANGE DEADLINE 04/26/10

2007 Upper Deck Premier Patches Dual

PRINT RUNS B/WN 1-75 COPIES PER
NO PRICING ON QTY 22 OR LESS
PLAT.PRINT RUNS B/WN 5-10 COPIES PER
NO PLATINUM PRICING DUE TO SCARCITY
MASTERPIECE PRINT RUN 1 SER.#'d SET
NO MASTERPIECE PRICING DUE TO SCARCITY
OVERALL PATCH ODDS ONE PER PACK
AD Adam Dunn 10.00 25.00
AD Adam Dunn 10.00 25.00
AP Albert Pujols 30.00 60.00
AP Albert Pujols 30.00 60.00
AS Alfonso Soriano 10.00 25.00
AS Alfonso Soriano 10.00 25.00
BR Brooks Robinson
BR Brooks Robinson
BU B.J. Upton 8.00 20.00
BU B.J. Upton 8.00 20.00
CH Cole Hamels 10.00 25.00
CH Cole Hamels 10.00 25.00
CR Cal Ripken Jr. 30.00 60.00
CR Cal Ripken Jr. 30.00 60.00
CU Chase Utley 10.00 25.00
CU Chase Utley 10.00 25.00
DJ Derek Jeter 20.00 50.00
DJ Derek Jeter 20.00 50.00
DJ2 Derek Jeter 20.00 50.00
DJ2 Derek Jeter 20.00 50.00
DM Don Mattingly 20.00 50.00
DM Don Mattingly 20.00 50.00
DO David Ortiz/15
DO David Ortiz/1
ED Jim Edmonds 10.00 25.00
ED Jim Edmonds 10.00 25.00
FL Francisco Liriano 8.00 20.00
FL Francisco Liriano 8.00 20.00
GM Greg Maddux 12.50 30.00
GM Greg Maddux 12.50 30.00
IR Ivan Rodriguez 10.00 25.00
IR Ivan Rodriguez 10.00 25.00
JB Johnny Bench 10.00 25.00
JB Johnny Bench 10.00 25.00
JG Jason Giambi 8.00 20.00
JG Jason Giambi 8.00 20.00
JM Joe Mauer 12.50 30.00
JM Joe Mauer 12.50 30.00
JO Randy Johnson 8.00 20.00
JO Randy Johnson 8.00 20.00
JP Jake Peavy 6.00 15.00
JP Jake Peavy 6.00 15.00
JR Jose Reyes 30.00 60.00
JR Jose Reyes 30.00 60.00
JS Jeremy Sowers
JS Jeremy Sowers
JT Jim Thome 8.00 20.00
JT Jim Thome 8.00 20.00
JT2 Jim Thome 8.00 20.00
JT2 Jim Thome 8.00 20.00
JV Justin Verlander 8.00 20.00
JV Justin Verlander/42 10.00 25.00
JW Jered Weaver 8.00 20.00
JW Jered Weaver 8.00 20.00
KG Ken Griffey Jr. 20.00 50.00
KG Ken Griffey Jr. 20.00 50.00
KG2 Ken Griffey Jr. 20.00 50.00
KG2 Ken Griffey Jr. 20.00 50.00
KJ Kenji Johjima
KJ Kenji Johjima
KM Kendry Morales 6.00 15.00
KM Kendry Morales 6.00 15.00
LB Lance Berkman 10.00 25.00
LB Lance Berkman 10.00 25.00
MC Miguel Cabrera 10.00 25.00
MC Miguel Cabrera 10.00 25.00
MR Manny Ramirez 10.00 25.00
MR Manny Ramirez 10.00 25.00
MS Mike Schmidt 12.50 30.00
MS Mike Schmidt 12.50 30.00
MT Mark Teixeira 10.00 25.00
MT Mark Teixeira 10.00 25.00
NR Nolan Ryan 30.00 60.00
NR Nolan Ryan 30.00 60.00
PF Prince Fielder 12.50 30.00
PF Prince Fielder/63 12.50 30.00
PM Pedro Martinez 12.50 30.00
PM Pedro Martinez 12.50 30.00
RC Roger Clemens/22
RC Roger Clemens/22
RJ Reggie Jackson 10.00 25.00
RJ Reggie Jackson 10.00 25.00
RS Ryne Sandberg 20.00 50.00
RS Ryne Sandberg 20.00 50.00
RZ Ryan Zimmerman 20.00 50.00
RZ Ryan Zimmerman 20.00 50.00
SA Johan Santana 12.50 30.00
SA Johan Santana 12.50 30.00
SD Stephen Drew
SD Stephen Drew
TE Miguel Tejada 6.00 15.00
TE Miguel Tejada 6.00 15.00
TG Tony Gwynn 12.50 30.00
TG Tony Gwynn 12.50 30.00
TO Tom Glavine 12.50 30.00
TO Tom Glavine 12.50 30.00
VG Vladimir Guerrero 10.00 25.00
VG Vladimir Guerrero 10.00 25.00
VG2 Vladimir Guerrero 10.00 25.00
VG2 Vladimir Guerrero 10.00 25.00

2007 Upper Deck Premier Patches Dual Gold

*GOLD: .4X TO 1X BASIC
OVERALL PATCH ODDS ONE PER PACK
PRINT RUNS B/WN 6-58 COPIES PER
NO PRICING ON QTY 24 OR LESS
BR Brooks Robinson/28 15.00 40.00
DO David Ortiz/54 15.00 40.00
JS Jeremy Sowers/35 10.00 25.00

2007 Upper Deck Premier Patches Dual Autographs

OVERALL AUTO ODDS ONE PER PACK
STATED PRINT RUN 25 SER.#'d SETS
NO PRICING DUE TO SCARCITY
EXCHANGE DEADLINE 04/26/10

2007 Upper Deck Premier Patches Triple

PRINT RUNS B/WN 1-99 COPIES PER
NO PRICING ON QTY 10 OR LESS
MASTERPIECE PRINT RUN 1 SER.#'d SET
NO MASTERPIECE PRICING DUE TO SCARCITY
PLATINUM PRINT RUN 5 SER.#'d SETS
NO PLATINUM PRICING DUE TO SCARCITY
OVERALL PATCH ODDS ONE PER PACK
AD Adam Dunn/5
AD Adam Dunn/5
AJ Andruw Jones/97 12.50 30.00
AJ Andruw Jones/97 12.50 30.00
AP Albert Pujols/1
AP Albert Pujols/1
AS Alfonso Soriano/1
AS Alfonso Soriano/1
BU B.J. Upton/4
BU B.J. Upton/4
CC Chris Carpenter/97 12.50 30.00
CC Chris Carpenter/97 12.50 30.00
CD Carlos Delgado/94 10.00 25.00
CD Carlos Delgado/94 10.00 25.00
CH Cole Hamels/6
CH Cole Hamels/6
CJ Chipper Jones/95 20.00 50.00
CJ Chipper Jones/95 20.00 50.00
CL Carlos Lee/99 8.00 20.00
CL Carlos Lee/99 8.00 20.00
CR Cal Ripken Jr./82 40.00 80.00
CR Cal Ripken Jr./82 40.00 80.00
CS Curt Schilling/90 12.50 30.00
CS Curt Schilling/90 12.50 30.00
CU Chase Utley/3
CU Chase Utley/3
DJ Derek Jeter/96
DJ Derek Jeter/96
DJ2 Derek Jeter/96
DJ2 Derek Jeter/96
DO David Ortiz/98
DO David Ortiz/98
EM Eddie Murray/77 12.50 30.00
EM Eddie Murray/77 12.50 30.00
FL Francisco Liriano/6
FL Francisco Liriano/6
FR Frank Robinson/56 15.00 40.00
FR Frank Robinson/56 15.00 40.00
FT Frank Thomas/90 15.00 40.00
FT Frank Thomas/90 15.00 40.00
GM Greg Maddux/87 20.00 50.00
GM Greg Maddux/87 20.00 50.00
HA Travis Hafner/3
HA Travis Hafner/3
JM Joe Mauer/4
JM Joe Mauer/4
JR Jose Reyes/3
JR Jose Reyes/3
JS Jeremy Sowers/6
JS Jeremy Sowers/6
JT Jim Thome/91 8.00 20.00
JT Jim Thome/91 8.00 20.00
JT2 Jim Thome/91 8.00 20.00
JT2 Jim Thome/91 8.00 20.00
JV Justin Verlander/6
JV Justin Verlander/6
JW Jered Weaver/6
JW Jered Weaver/6
KG Ken Griffey Jr./89 20.00 50.00
KG Ken Griffey Jr./89 20.00 50.00
KG2 Ken Griffey Jr./89 20.00 50.00
KG2 Ken Griffey Jr./89 20.00 50.00
LB Lance Berkman/7
LB Lance Berkman/7
MC Miguel Cabrera/3
MC Miguel Cabrera/3
MO Justin Morneau/3
MO Justin Morneau/3
MR Manny Ramirez/94 10.00 25.00
MR Manny Ramirez/94 10.00 25.00
MT Mark Teixeira/3
MT Mark Teixeira/3
OS Ozzie Smith/78 20.00 50.00
OS Ozzie Smith/78 20.00 50.00
PM Pedro Martinez/4
PM Pedro Martinez/4
RJ Randy Johnson/89 10.00 25.00
RJ Randy Johnson/89 10.00 25.00
RO Roy Halladay/99 12.50 30.00
RO Roy Halladay/66 12.50 30.00
RW Rickie Weeks/6
RW Rickie Weeks/6
RY Roy Oswalt/6
RY Roy Oswalt/6
RZ Ryan Zimmerman/5
RZ Ryan Zimmerman/5
SA Johan Santana/10
SA Johan Santana/10
TE Miguel Tejada/98 10.00 25.00
TE Miguel Tejada/98 10.00 25.00
TG Tony Gwynn/82 15.00 40.00
TG Tony Gwynn/82 15.00 40.00
TS Tom Seaver/67 15.00 40.00
TS Tom Seaver/67 15.00 40.00
VG Vladimir Guerrero/97 12.50 30.00
VG Vladimir Guerrero/97 12.50 30.00
VM Victor Martinez/3
VM Victor Martinez/3
WB Wade Boggs/82 10.00 25.00
WB Wade Boggs/82 10.00 25.00

2007 Upper Deck Premier Patches Triple Gold

*GOLD: .4X TO 1X BASIC
OVERALL PATCH ODDS ONE PER PACK
PRINT RUNS B/WN 1-57 COPIES PER
NO PRICING ON QTY 25 OR LESS
CH Cole Hamels/35 15.00 40.00
CU Chase Utley/26 12.50 30.00
DO David Ortiz/34 20.00 50.00
FL Francisco Liriano/47 15.00 40.00
FT Frank Thomas/35 40.00 80.00
HA Travis Hafner/48 15.00 40.00
JS Jeremy Sowers/26 10.00 25.00
JV Justin Verlander/35 20.00 50.00
LB Lance Berkman/35 15.00 40.00
MO Justin Morneau/33 15.00 40.00
RW Rickie Weeks/47 15.00 40.00
RY Roy Oswalt/50 10.00 25.00
SA Johan Santana/57 20.00 50.00
VM Victor Martinez/41 12.50 30.00

2007 Upper Deck Premier Patches Triple Autographs

OVERALL AUTO ODDS ONE PER PACK
STATED PRINT RUN 15 SER.#'d SETS
NO PRICING DUE TO SCARCITY
EXCHANGE DEADLINE 04/26/10

2007 Upper Deck Premier Penmanship Autographs

PRINT RUNS B/WN 1-98 COPIES PER
NO PRICING ON QTY 10 OR LESS
MASTERPIECE PRINT RUN 1 SER.#'d SET
NO MASTERPIECE PRICING DUE TO SCARCITY
OVERALL AUTO ODDS ONE PER PACK
EXCHANGE DEADLINE 04/26/10
AK Al Kaline/53 15.00 40.00
AM Andrew Miller/7
AM2 Andrew Miller/7
AP Albert Pujols/1
AP2 Albert Pujols/1
BA Jason Bay/3
BA2 Jason Bay/3
BF Bob Feller/36
BJ Bo Jackson/86 20.00 50.00
BR Brooks Robinson/57 15.00 40.00
BU B.J. Upton/4
CB Craig Biggio/88 20.00 50.00
CC Chris Carpenter/97 15.00 40.00
CF Carlton Fisk/72 10.00 25.00
CH Cole Hamels/6
CR Cal Ripken Jr./82 40.00 80.00
CR2 Cal Ripken Jr./82 40.00 80.00
CY Carl Yastrzemski/61 30.00 60.00
CZ Carlos Zambrano/1
DJ Derek Jeter/96 100.00 150.00
DJ2 Derek Jeter/96 100.00 150.00
DL Derrek Lee/97 12.50 30.00
DM Don Mattingly/83 30.00 60.00
DM2 Don Mattingly/83 30.00 60.00
DW Dontrelle Willis/3
DY Delmon Young/7
DY2 Delmon Young/7
EB Ernie Banks/54 30.00 60.00
FH Felix Hernandez/5
FL Francisco Liriano/6
GM Greg Maddux/87 50.00 100.00
HR Hanley Ramirez/6
IR Ivan Rodriguez/91 20.00 50.00
JB Johnny Bench/68 20.00 50.00
JG Jonny Gomes/5
JI Jim Palmer/65 10.00 25.00
JM Joe Mauer/4
JO Josh Barfield/6
JP Jake Peavy/2
JR Jose Reyes/3
JS John Smoltz/88 40.00 80.00
JT Jim Thome/91 30.00 60.00
JV Justin Verlander/6
JW Jered Weaver/6
JZ Joel Zumaya/6
KG Ken Griffey Jr./89 40.00 80.00
KG2 Ken Griffey Jr./89 40.00 80.00
LA Luis Aparicio/56 12.50 30.00
MC Miguel Cabrera/3
MO Justin Morneau/3
MO2 Justin Morneau/3
MS Mike Schmidt/73 20.00 50.00
MY Michael Young/1
NR Nolan Ryan/68 60.00 120.00
NS Nick Swisher/5
OZ Ozzie Smith/78 20.00 50.00
PA Jonathan Papelbon/6
PH Philip Humber/7
PM Paul Molitor/78 15.00 40.00
PM2 Paul Molitor/78 15.00 40.00
RA Randy Johnson/89 20.00 50.00
RC Roger Clemens/84 40.00 80.00
RJ Reggie Jackson/68 30.00 60.00
RO Roy Oswalt/1
RO2 Roy Oswalt/1
RS Ryne Sandberg/82 20.00 50.00
RY Robin Yount/74 15.00 40.00
SA Johan Santana/10
SC Steve Carlton/67 12.50 30.00
SD Stephen Drew/6
SM Stan Musial/42 30.00 60.00
SO Jeremy Sowers/6
SR Scott Rolen/97 15.00 40.00
TE Miguel Tejada/98 10.00 25.00
TG Tony Gwynn/82 15.00 40.00
TG2 Tony Gwynn/82 15.00 40.00
TI Tadahito Iguchi/5
TO Tony Gwynn Jr./6
TP Tony Perez/65 15.00 40.00
TT Troy Tulowitzki/28 15.00 40.00
TT2 Troy Tulowitzki/7
VG Vladimir Guerrero/97 30.00 60.00
VM Victor Martinez/3
WB Wade Boggs/82 20.00 50.00
WC Will Clark/86 10.00 25.00
WF Whitey Ford/50 20.00 50.00
WM Willie McCovey/59 20.00 50.00
YB Yogi Berra/47 20.00 50.00

2007 Upper Deck Premier Penmanship Autographs Jersey Number

OVERALL AUTO ODDS ONE PER PACK
PRINT RUNS B/WN 1-58 COPIES PER
NO PRICING ON QTY 25 OR LESS
EXCHANGE DEADLINE 04/26/10
AK Al Kaline/6
AM Andrew Miller/50 30.00 60.00
AM2 Andrew Miller/50 30.00 60.00
AP Albert Pujols/5
AP2 Albert Pujols/5
BA Jason Bay/38 10.00 25.00
BA2 Jason Bay/38 10.00 25.00
BF Bob Feller/19
BJ Bo Jackson/16
BR Brooks Robinson/5
BU B.J. Upton/2
CB Craig Biggio/7
CC Chris Carpenter/29 20.00 50.00
CF Carlton Fisk/27 20.00 50.00
CH Cole Hamels/35 EXCH 30.00 60.00
CR Cal Ripken Jr./8
CR2 Cal Ripken Jr./8
CY Carl Yastrzemski/8
CZ Carlos Zambrano/38 10.00 25.00
DJ Derek Jeter/2
DJ2 Derek Jeter/2
DL Derrek Lee/25
DM Don Mattingly/23
DM2 Don Mattingly/23
DW Dontrelle Willis/35 15.00 40.00
DY Delmon Young/35 15.00 40.00
DY2 Delmon Young/35 15.00 40.00
EB Ernie Banks/14 EXCH
FH Felix Hernandez/34 30.00 60.00
FL Francisco Liriano/47 12.50 30.00
FR Frank Robinson/20
GM Greg Maddux/36 50.00 100.00
HR Hanley Ramirez/2
IR Ivan Rodriguez/7
JB Johnny Bench/5
JG Jonny Gomes/31 EXCH 10.00 25.00
JI Jim Palmer/22
JM Joe Mauer/7
JO Josh Barfield/29
JP Jake Peavy/44 15.00 40.00
JR Jose Reyes/7
JS John Smoltz/29 40.00 80.00
JT Jim Thome/25
JV Justin Verlander/35 20.00 50.00
JW Jered Weaver/56 10.00 25.00
JZ Joel Zumaya/54 15.00 40.00
KG Ken Griffey Jr./3
KG2 Ken Griffey Jr./3
LA Luis Aparicio/11
MC Miguel Cabrera/24
MO Justin Morneau/33 15.00 40.00
MO2 Justin Morneau/33 15.00 40.00
MS Mike Schmidt/20
MY Michael Young/10
NR Nolan Ryan/34 60.00 120.00
NS Nick Swisher/33
OZ Ozzie Smith/1
PA Jonathan Papelbon/58 30.00 60.00
PH Philip Humber/49
PM Paul Molitor/4
PM2 Paul Molitor/4
RA Randy Johnson/41 30.00 60.00
RC Roger Clemens/22
RJ Reggie Jackson/9

RO Roy Oswalt/45 12.50 30.00
RO2 Roy Oswalt/45 12.50 30.00
RS Ryne Sandberg/23 EXCH
RY Robin Yount/19 EXCH
SA Johan Santana/57 20.00 50.00
SC Steve Carlton/32 10.00 25.00
SD Stephen Drew/6
SM Stan Musial/6
SO Jeremy Sowers/45
SR Scott Rolen/27 20.00 50.00
TE Miguel Tejada/10
TG Tony Gwynn/19
TG2 Tony Gwynn/19
TI Tadahito Iguchi/15
TO Tony Gwynn Jr./22 EXCH
TP Tony Perez/24
TT Troy Tulowitzki/14
TT2 Troy Tulowitzki/14
VG Vladimir Guerrero/27 30.00 60.00
VM Victor Martinez/41 10.00 25.00
WB Wade Boggs/26 20.00 50.00
WC Will Clark/22
WF Whitey Ford/16
WM Willie McCovey/44 15.00 40.00
YB Yogi Berra/8

2007 Upper Deck Premier Preeminence Autographs

STATED PRINT RUN 50 SER.#'d SETS
GOLD PRINT RUN 25 SER.#'d SETS
NO GOLD PRICING DUE TO SCARCITY
PLATINUM PRINT RUN 1 SER.#'d SET
NO PLATINUM PRICING DUE TO SCARCITY
OVERALL AUTO ODDS ONE PER PACK
EXCHANGE DEADLINE 04/26/10
AP Albert Pujols EXCH 150.00 200.00
BJ Bo Jackson 40.00 80.00
BR Brooks Robinson 10.00 25.00
CC Chris Carpenter 10.00 25.00
CR Cal Ripken Jr. 60.00 120.00
CY Carl Yastrzemski 30.00 60.00
DJ Derek Jeter EXCH 75.00 150.00
GM Greg Maddux 60.00 120.00
JB Johnny Bench 20.00 50.00
JM Joe Mauer 20.00 50.00
JT Jim Thome 30.00 60.00
JV Justin Verlander 20.00 50.00
KG Ken Griffey Jr. 40.00 80.00
MS Mike Schmidt 30.00 60.00
NR Nolan Ryan 50.00 100.00
RC Roger Clemens 60.00 120.00
RJ Reggie Jackson 30.00 60.00
RS Ryne Sandberg 30.00 60.00
SM Stan Musial 30.00 60.00
TG Tony Gwynn EXCH 20.00 50.00
VG Vladimir Guerrero 20.00 50.00

2007 Upper Deck Premier Rare Patches Dual

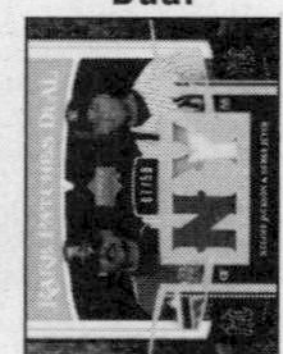

STATED PRINT RUN 50 SER.#'d SETS
GOLD PRINT RUN 25 SER.#'d SETS
NO GOLD PRICING DUE TO SCARCITY
MASTERPIECE PRINT RUN 1 SER.#'d SET
NO MASTERPIECE PRICING DUE TO SCARCITY
PLATINUM PRINT RUN 10 SER.#'d SETS
NO PLATINUM PRICING DUE TO SCARCITY
OVERALL PATCH ODDS ONE PER PACK
BM Johnny Bench 20.00 50.00
Joe Mauer
BR Brian Roberts 12.50 30.00
Robinson Cano
BS AJ Burnett 10.00 25.00
Anibal Sanchez
BZ Jeremy Bonderman
Joel Zumaya
CP Chris Carpenter 12.50 30.00
Jake Peavy
CW Miguel Cabrera 12.50 30.00
Dontrelle Willis
DB Carlos Delgado 20.00 50.00
Carlos Beltran
DT Stephen Drew 10.00 25.00
Miguel Tejada
ER Jim Edmonds 20.00 50.00
Scott Rolen
FM Prince Fielder 12.50 30.00
Justin Morneau
FW Prince Fielder 15.00 40.00
Rickie Weeks
GP Ken Griffey Jr. 40.00 80.00
Albert Pujols
HR Trevor Hoffman 15.00 40.00
Mariano Rivera
HS Cole Hamels 10.00 25.00
Jeremy Sowers
JG Derek Jeter 40.00 80.00
Ken Griffey Jr.
JJ Andruw Jones 20.00 50.00
Chipper Jones
MC Greg Maddux
Roger Clemens
MG Greg Maddux 40.00 80.00
Tom Glavine
MH Victor Martinez 15.00 40.00
Travis Hafner
MJ Don Mattingly 50.00 100.00
Derek Jeter
OT David Ortiz 12.50 30.00
Jim Thome
PO Jake Peavy 10.00 25.00
Roy Oswalt
PS Jonathan Papelbon 20.00 50.00
Curt Schilling
RC Nolan Ryan 60.00 120.00
Roger Clemens
RD Reggie Jackson 20.00 50.00
Derek Jeter
RG Cal Ripken Jr. 40.00 80.00
Tony Gwynn
RJ Roy Halladay 12.50 30.00
Johan Santana
RU Jimmy Rollins 20.00 50.00
Chase Utley
SG Alfonso Soriano 20.00 50.00
Vladimir Guerrero
SH Johan Santana 20.00 50.00
Felix Hernandez
SM Ryne Sandberg 20.00 50.00
Joe Morgan
SR Mike Schmidt 20.00 50.00
Brooks Robinson
TR Miguel Tejada 15.00 40.00
Jose Reyes
TT Frank Thomas 20.00 50.00
Jim Thome
UC B.J. Upton 15.00 40.00
Carl Crawford
VZ Justin Verlander
Joel Zumaya
WJ Dontrelle Willis 10.00 25.00
Josh Johnson
WL Jered Weaver 10.00 25.00
Francisco Liriano
YM Robin Yount 20.00 50.00
Paul Molitor
ZU Ryan Zimmerman 20.00 50.00
B.J. Upton

2007 Upper Deck Premier Rare Patches Triple

STATED PRINT RUN 25 SER.#'d SETS
NO PRICING DUE TO SCARCITY
GOLD PRINT RUN 10 SER.#'d SETS
NO GOLD PRICING DUE TO SCARCITY
PLATINUM PRINT RUN 5 SER.#'d SETS
NO PLATINUM PRICING DUE TO SCARCITY
MASTERPIECE PRINT RUN 1 SER.#'d SET
NO MASTERPIECE PRICING DUE TO SCARCITY
OVERALL PATCH ODDS ONE PER PACK

2007 Upper Deck Premier Rare Remnants Triple

STATED PRINT RUN 50 SER.#'d SETS
GOLD PRINT RUN 25 SER.#'d SETS
NO GOLD PRICING DUE TO SCARCITY
MASTERPIECE PRINT RUN 1 SER.#'d SET
NO MASTERPIECE PRICING DUE TO SCARCITY
PLATINUM PRINT RUN 10 SER.#'d SETS
NO PLATINUM PRICING DUE TO SCARCITY
OVERALL PATCH ODDS ONE PER PACK
BMP Johnny Bench 15.00 40.00
Joe Morgan
Tony Perez
BZV Jeremy Bonderman 10.00 25.00
Joel Zumaya
Justin Verlander
CBF Cal Ripken Jr. 30.00 60.00
Brooks Robinson
Frank Robinson
CFY Joe Cronin 30.00 60.00
Jimmie Foxx
Carl Yastrzemski
CMK Roberto Clemente 50.00 100.00
Bill Mazeroski
Ralph Kiner
CPR Chris Carpenter. 15.00 40.00
Albert Pujols
Scott Rolen
DMP Bill Dickey 30.00 60.00
Thurman Munson
Jorge Posada
DMR Carlos Delgado 20.00 50.00
Pedro Martinez
Jose Reyes
DRB Carlos Delgado 15.00 40.00
Jose Reyes
Carlos Beltran
FBM Carlton Fisk 20.00 50.00
Johnny Bench
Thurman Munson
FGG Jimmie Foxx 150.00 250.00
Lou Gehrig
Hank Greenberg
FMT Prince Fielder 10.00 25.00
Justin Morneau
Mark Teixeira
GGJ Ken Griffey Jr. 20.00 50.00
Vladimir Guerrero
Andruw Jones
JCM Randy Johnson 20.00 50.00
Roger Clemens
Greg Maddux
JJR Randy Johnson 30.00 60.00
Derek Jeter
Mariano Rivera
JMM Reggie Jackson 40.00 80.00
Don Mattingly
Thurman Munson
KUC Scott Kazmir 10.00 25.00
B.J. Upton
Carl Crawford
KVJ Kenji Johjima 10.00 25.00
Victor Martinez
Joe Mauer
LMS Francisco Liriano 10.00 25.00
Joe Mauer
Johan Santana
LSH Francisco Liriano 10.00 25.00
Jeremy Sowers
Cole Hamels
OPS Roy Oswalt 10.00 25.00
Jake Peavy
Ben Sheets
OTB David Ortiz 10.00 25.00
Jim Thome
Lance Berkman
PJG Albert Pujols 30.00 60.00
Derek Jeter
Ken Griffey Jr.
PMH Albert Pujols 50.00 100.00
Stan Musial
Rogers Hornsby
RCD Nolan Ryan 20.00 50.00
Roger Clemens
Don Drysdale
RDG Babe Ruth 350.00 500.00
Joe DiMaggio
Lou Gehrig
RFS Mariano Rivera 10.00 25.00
Rollie Fingers
Bruce Sutter
RRR Nolan Ryan 40.00 80.00
Nolan Ryan
Nolan Ryan
RWH Nolan Ryan 20.00 50.00
Jered Weaver
Felix Hernandez
RWR Cal Ripken Jr.
Honus Wagner
Pee Wee Reese
RYS Cal Ripken Jr. 30.00 60.00
Robin Yount
Ozzie Smith
SGA Alfonso Soriano 10.00 25.00
Vladimir Guerrero
Bobby Abreu
SHM Ryne Sandberg 30.00 60.00
Rogers Hornsby
Joe Morgan
SJZ Johan Santana 10.00 25.00
Randy Johnson
Barry Zito
SRB Mike Schmidt 20.00 50.00
Brooks Robinson
Wade Boggs
TJY Miguel Tejada 10.00 25.00
Derek Jeter
Michael Young
TTH Jim Thome 10.00 25.00
Mark Teixeira
Todd Helton
VWJ Justin Verlander 10.00 25.00
Jered Weaver
Josh Johnson
WDC Ted Williams
Joe DiMaggio
Roberto Clemente
YBM Robin Yount 15.00 40.00
Wade Boggs
Paul Molitor

2007 Upper Deck Premier Rare Remnants Quad

STATED PRINT RUN 25 SER.#'d SETS
NO PRICING DUE TO SCARCITY
GOLD PRINT RUN 10 SER.#'d SETS
NO GOLD PRICING DUE TO SCARCITY
PLATINUM PRINT RUN 5 SER.#'d SETS
NO PLATINUM PRICING DUE TO SCARCITY
MASTERPIECE PRINT RUN 1 SER.#'d SET
NO MASTERPIECE PRICING DUE TO SCARCITY
OVERALL PATCH ODDS ONE PER PACK

2007 Upper Deck Premier Remnants Triple

PRINT RUNS B/WN 21-75 COPIES PER
NO PRICING ON QTY 21 OR LESS
PLATINUM PRINT RUN 10 SER.#'d SETS
NO PLATINUM PRICING DUE TO SCARCITY
MASTERPIECE PRINT RUN 1 SER.#'d SET
NO MASTERPIECE PRICING DUE TO SCARCITY
OVERALL TRIPLE GU ODDS ONE PER PACK
AP Albert Pujols 12.50 30.00
AP Albert Pujols 12.50 30.00
AP2 Albert Pujols 12.50 30.00
AP2 Albert Pujols 12.50 30.00
AS Alfonso Soriano 6.00 15.00
AS Alfonso Soriano 6.00 15.00
BM Bill Mazeroski 10.00 25.00
BM Bill Mazeroski 10.00 25.00
BR Babe Ruth 350.00 700.00
BR Babe Ruth 350.00 700.00
CA Roy Campanella 15.00 40.00
CA Roy Campanella 15.00 40.00
CF Carlton Fisk 6.00 15.00
CF Carlton Fisk 6.00 15.00
CJ Chipper Jones 10.00 25.00
CJ Chipper Jones 10.00 25.00
CL Roger Clemens 10.00 25.00
CL Roger Clemens 10.00 25.00
CR Cal Ripken Jr. 15.00 40.00
CR Cal Ripken Jr. 15.00 40.00
CS Curt Schilling 6.00 15.00
CS Curt Schilling 6.00 15.00
CU Chase Utley 10.00 25.00
CU Chase Utley 10.00 25.00
CY Carl Yastrzemski
CY Carl Yastrzemski 10.00 25.00
DD Don Drysdale 15.00 40.00
DJ Derek Jeter 20.00 50.00
DJ Derek Jeter 20.00 50.00
DJ2 Derek Jeter 20.00 50.00
DJ2 Derek Jeter 20.00 50.00
DM Don Mattingly 20.00 50.00
DM Don Mattingly 20.00 50.00
DO David Ortiz 6.00 15.00
DO David Ortiz 6.00 15.00
EB Ernie Banks
EB Ernie Banks
EM Eddie Mathews 15.00 40.00
EM Eddie Mathews 15.00 40.00
FR Frank Robinson 6.00 15.00
FR Frank Robinson 6.00 15.00
HO Rogers Hornsby 40.00 80.00
HO Rogers Hornsby 40.00 80.00
JB Johnny Bench 10.00 25.00
JB Johnny Bench 10.00 25.00
JD Joe DiMaggio 75.00 150.00
JD Joe DiMaggio 75.00 150.00
JO Jose Reyes 15.00 40.00
JO Jose Reyes 15.00 40.00
JR Jackie Robinson 40.00 80.00
JR Jackie Robinson 40.00 80.00
JT Jim Thome 6.00 15.00
JT Jim Thome 6.00 15.00
KG Ken Griffey Jr. 10.00 25.00
KG Ken Griffey Jr. 10.00 25.00
KG2 Ken Griffey Jr. 10.00 25.00
KG2 Ken Griffey Jr. 10.00 25.00
MO Mel Ott 20.00 50.00
MO Mel Ott 20.00 50.00
MR Manny Ramirez 6.00 15.00
MR Manny Ramirez 6.00 15.00
MS Mike Schmidt 10.00 25.00
MS Mike Schmidt 10.00 25.00
NR Nolan Ryan 15.00 40.00
NR Nolan Ryan 15.00 40.00
PM Paul Molitor 6.00 15.00
PM Paul Molitor 6.00 15.00
PR Pee Wee Reese 15.00 40.00
PR Pee Wee Reese 15.00 40.00
RC Roberto Clemente 50.00 100.00
RC Roberto Clemente 50.00 100.00
RJ Reggie Jackson 10.00 25.00
RJ Reggie Jackson 10.00 25.00
RO Brooks Robinson 6.00 15.00
RO Brooks Robinson 6.00 15.00
RS Ryne Sandberg 10.00 25.00
RS Ryne Sandberg 10.00 25.00
RY Robin Yount 10.00 25.00
RY Robin Yount 10.00 25.00
SM Stan Musial 15.00 40.00
SM Stan Musial 15.00 40.00
TC Ty Cobb/21
TC Ty Cobb/21
TG Tony Gwynn 10.00 25.00
TG Tony Gwynn 10.00 25.00
TM Thurman Munson 15.00 40.00
TM Thurman Munson 15.00 40.00
VG Vladimir Guerrero 6.00 15.00
VG Vladimir Guerrero 6.00 15.00

2007 Upper Deck Premier Remnants Triple Gold

*GOLD: .5X TO 1.2X BASIC
OVERALL TRIPLE GU ODDS ONE PER PACK
PRINT RUNS B/WN 6-60 COPIES PER
NO PRICING ON QTY 19 OR LESS
BR Babe Ruth/60 300.00 500.00
CL Roger Clemens/24 15.00 40.00
DJ Derek Jeter/24 20.00 50.00
DJ2 Derek Jeter/24 20.00 50.00
RC Roberto Clemente/29 75.00 150.00
TC Ty Cobb/47 75.00 150.00
TM Thurman Munson/20 30.00 60.00

2007 Upper Deck Premier Remnants Triple Autographs

OVERALL AUTO ODDS ONE PER PACK
STATED PRINT RUN 25 SER.#'d SETS
NO PRICING DUE TO SCARCITY
EXCHANGE DEADLINE 04/26/10

2007 Upper Deck Premier Remnants Quad

PRINT RUNS B/WN 1-96 COPIES PER
NO PRICING ON QTY 25 OR LESS
PLATINUM PRINT RUN 5 SER.#'d SETS
NO PLATINUM PRICING DUE TO SCARCITY
MASTERPIECE PRINT RUN 1 SER.#'d SET
NO MASTERPIECE PRICING DUE TO SCARCITY
OVERALL QUAD GU ODDS ONE PER PACK
AK Al Kaline/53 15.00 40.00
AK Al Kaline/53 15.00 40.00
AP Albert Pujols/1
AP Albert Pujols/1
AS Alfonso Soriano/1
AS Alfonso Soriano/1
BM Bill Mazeroski/56 12.50 30.00
BM Bill Mazeroski/56 12.50 30.00
BR Babe Ruth/15
BR Babe Ruth/15
BU B.J. Upton/4
BU B.J. Upton/4
CF Chone Figgins/6
CF Chone Figgins/6
CH Cole Hamels/6
CH Cole Hamels/6
CL Roberto Clemente/55 60.00 120.00
CL Roberto Clemente/55 60.00 120.00
CR Cal Ripken Jr./82 20.00 50.00
CR Cal Ripken Jr./82 20.00 50.00
CU Chase Utley/3
CU Chase Utley/3
CY Carl Yastrzemski/61
CY Carl Yastrzemski/61
DJ Derek Jeter/96 20.00 50.00
DJ Derek Jeter/96 20.00 50.00
DM Don Mattingly/83 15.00 40.00
DM Don Mattingly/83 15.00 40.00
EM Eddie Mathews/52 15.00 40.00
EM Eddie Mathews/52 15.00 40.00
FL Francisco Liriano/6
FL Francisco Liriano/6
GH Gil Hodges/48
GH Gil Hodges/48
HK Harmon Killebrew/55 20.00 50.00
HK Harmon Killebrew/55 20.00 50.00
HO Rogers Hornsby/16
HO Rogers Hornsby/16
JB Johnny Bench/68 12.50 30.00
JB Johnny Bench/68 12.50 30.00
JD Joe DiMaggio/36 100.00 150.00
JD Joe DiMaggio/36 100.00 150.00
JF Jimmie Foxx/27 60.00 120.00
JF Jimmie Foxx/27 60.00 120.00
JM Joe Mauer/4
JM Joe Mauer/4
JR Jackie Robinson/47 60.00 120.00
JR Jackie Robinson/47 60.00 120.00
JS Jeremy Sowers/6
JS Jeremy Sowers/6
JT Jim Thome/91 6.00 15.00
JT Jim Thome/91 6.00 15.00
JV Justin Verlander/6
JV Justin Verlander/6
JW Jered Weaver/6
JW Jered Weaver/6
KG Ken Griffey Jr./89 12.50 30.00
KG Ken Griffey Jr./89 12.50 30.00
KJ Kenji Johjima/6
KJ Kenji Johjima/6
LG Lou Gehrig/25 350.00 450.00
LG Lou Gehrig/25 350.00 450.00
MC Miguel Cabrera/3
MC Miguel Cabrera/3
MI Johnny Mize/36 20.00 50.00
MI Johnny Mize/36 20.00 50.00
MO Justin Morneau/3
MO Justin Morneau/3
MS Mike Schmidt/73 12.50 30.00
MS Mike Schmidt/73 12.50 30.00
MT Mark Teixeira/3
MT Mark Teixeira/3
NR Nolan Ryan/68 40.00 80.00
NR Nolan Ryan/68 40.00 80.00
RC Roger Clemens/84 12.50 30.00
RC Roger Clemens/84 12.50 30.00
RJ Reggie Jackson/68 10.00 25.00
RJ Reggie Jackson/68 10.00 25.00
RN Brooks Robinson/57 10.00 25.00
RN Brooks Robinson/48 10.00 25.00
RO Roy Campanella/48 15.00 40.00
RO Roy Campanella/48 15.00 40.00
RZ Ryan Zimmerman/5
RZ Ryan Zimmerman/5
SA Johan Santana/10
SA Johan Santana/2
SD Stephen Drew/6
SD Stephen Drew/6
SM Stan Musial/42 20.00 50.00
SM Stan Musial/42 20.00 50.00
TC Ty Cobb/5
TC Ty Cobb/5
TG Tom Glavine/7
TG Tom Glavine/7
TH Torii Hunter/5
TH Torii Hunter/5
TM Thurman Munson/70 20.00 50.00
TM Thurman Munson/70 20.00 50.00
TW Ted Williams/39
TW Ted Williams/39

2007 Upper Deck Premier Remnants Quad Gold

*GOLD: .5X TO 1.2X BASIC
OVERALL TRIPLE GU ODDS ONE PER PACK
PRINT RUNS B/WN 2-57 COPIES PER
NO PRICING ON QTY 25 OR LESS
CF Chone Figgins/47 4.00 10.00
CH Cole Hamels/35 12.50 30.00
CU Chase Utley/26 20.00 50.00
FL Francisco Liriano/47 10.00 25.00
HO Rogers Hornsby/50 40.00 80.00
JS Jeremy Sowers/45 4.00 10.00
JV Justin Verlander/35 10.00 25.00
JW Jered Weaver/56 6.00 15.00
MI Johnny Mize/50 20.00 50.00
MO Justin Morneau/33 6.00 15.00
NR Nolan Ryan/34 40.00 80.00
SA Johan Santana/57 10.00 25.00
TG Tom Glavine/50 12.50 30.00

2007 Upper Deck Premier Remnants Quad Autographs

OVERALL AUTO ODDS ONE PER PACK
STATED PRINT RUN 15 SER.#'d SETS
NO PRICING DUE TO SCARCITY
EXCHANGE DEADLINE 04/26/10

2007 Upper Deck Premier Six Autographs

OVERALL AUTO ODDS ONE PER PACK
STATED PRINT RUN 10 SER.#'d SETS
NO PRICING DUE TO SCARCITY
EXCHANGE DEADLINE 04/26/10
1 Cal Ripken Jr.
Ken Griffey Jr.
Derek Jeter
Albert Pujols
Roger Clemens
Nolan Ryan
2 Jered Weaver
Justin Verlander
Francisco Liriano
Andrew Miller
Jeremy Sowers
Cole Hamels
3 Derek Jeter
Miguel Tejada
Jose Reyes
Troy Tulowitzki
Hanley Ramirez
Stephen Drew
4 Chase Utley
Dan Uggla
Tadahito Iguchi
Ian Kinsler
Howie Kendrick
Rickie Weeks
5 Cal Ripken Jr.
Tony Gwynn
Ryne Sandberg
Mike Schmidt
Robin Yount
Dave Winfield
6 Jason Bay
Carlos Beltran
Johnny Damon
Andruw Jones
Alfonso Soriano
Vladimir Guerrero
7 Derek Jeter

Johnny Damon
Randy Johnson
Yogi Berra
Don Mattingly
Reggie Jackson
8 Jim Thome
Frank Thomas
David Ortiz
Travis Hafner
Jermaine Dye
Mark Teixeira

2007 Upper Deck Premier Stitchings

STATED PRINT RUN 50 SER.#'d SETS
*STITCHINGS 35: .4X TO 1X BASIC
STITCHINGS 35 PRINT RUN 35 SER.#'d SETS
OVERALL STITCHINGS ODDS ONE PER PACK
1 Babe Ruth 30.00 60.00
1 Babe Ruth 30.00 60.00
2 Babe Ruth 30.00 60.00
2 Babe Ruth 30.00 60.00
3 Babe Ruth 30.00 60.00
3 Babe Ruth 30.00 60.00
4 Ty Cobb 10.00 25.00
4 Ty Cobb 10.00 25.00
5 Ty Cobb 10.00 25.00
5 Ty Cobb 10.00 25.00
6 Lou Gehrig 12.50 30.00
7 Lou Gehrig 12.50 30.00
7 Lou Gehrig 12.50 30.00
8 Joe DiMaggio 12.50 30.00
8 Joe DiMaggio 12.50 30.00
9 Joe DiMaggio 12.50 30.00
9 Joe DiMaggio 12.50 30.00
12 Roberto Clemente 15.00 40.00
12 Roberto Clemente 15.00 40.00
13 Roberto Clemente 15.00 40.00
13 Roberto Clemente 15.00 40.00
14 Jackie Robinson 12.50 30.00
14 Jackie Robinson 12.50 30.00
15 Jackie Robinson 12.50 30.00
15 Jackie Robinson 12.50 30.00
16 Cy Young 6.00 15.00
16 Cy Young 6.00 15.00
17 Cy Young 6.00 15.00
17 Cy Young 6.00 15.00
18 Nolan Ryan 15.00 40.00
18 Nolan Ryan 15.00 40.00
19 Nolan Ryan 15.00 40.00
19 Nolan Ryan 15.00 40.00
20 Reggie Jackson 6.00 15.00
20 Reggie Jackson 6.00 15.00
21 Reggie Jackson 6.00 15.00
21 Reggie Jackson 6.00 15.00
22 Ken Griffey Jr. 12.50 30.00
22 Ken Griffey Jr. 12.50 30.00
23 Ken Griffey Jr. 12.50 30.00
23 Ken Griffey Jr. 12.50 30.00
24 Derek Jeter 15.00 40.00
24 Derek Jeter 15.00 40.00
25 Derek Jeter 15.00 40.00
25 Derek Jeter 15.00 40.00
26 Jimmie Foxx 6.00 15.00
26 Jimmie Foxx 6.00 15.00
27 Jimmie Foxx 6.00 15.00
27 Jimmie Foxx 6.00 15.00
28 Rogers Hornsby 6.00 15.00
28 Rogers Hornsby 6.00 15.00
30 Walter Johnson 12.50 30.00
30 Walter Johnson 12.50 30.00
31 Walter Johnson 12.50 30.00
31 Walter Johnson 12.50 30.00
32 Ernie Banks 10.00 25.00
32 Ernie Banks 10.00 25.00
33 Ernie Banks 10.00 25.00
33 Ernie Banks 10.00 25.00
34 Christy Mathewson 6.00 15.00
34 Christy Mathewson 6.00 15.00
35 Johnny Mize 6.00 15.00
35 Johnny Mize 6.00 15.00
36 Thurman Munson 12.50 30.00
36 Thurman Munson 12.50 30.00
37 Thurman Munson 12.50 30.00
37 Thurman Munson 12.50 30.00
38 Mel Ott 6.00 15.00
38 Mel Ott 6.00 15.00
39 Satchel Paige 10.00 25.00
39 Satchel Paige 10.00 25.00
40 George Sisler 6.00 15.00
40 George Sisler 6.00 15.00
41 Casey Stengel 6.00 15.00
41 Casey Stengel 6.00 15.00
42 Honus Wagner 10.00 25.00
42 Honus Wagner 10.00 25.00
43 Honus Wagner 10.00 25.00
43 Honus Wagner 10.00 25.00
44 Roy Campanella 6.00 15.00
44 Roy Campanella 6.00 15.00
45 Mickey Cochrane 6.00 15.00
45 Mickey Cochrane 6.00 15.00
46 Dizzy Dean 6.00 15.00
46 Dizzy Dean 6.00 15.00
47 Don Drysdale 6.00 15.00
47 Don Drysdale 6.00 15.00
48 Lefty Grove 6.00 15.00
48 Lefty Grove 6.00 15.00
49 Roger Clemens 10.00 25.00
49 Roger Clemens 10.00 25.00
50 Roger Clemens 10.00 25.00
50 Roger Clemens 10.00 25.00
51 Cal Ripken Jr. 20.00 50.00
51 Cal Ripken Jr. 20.00 50.00
52 Cal Ripken Jr. 20.00 50.00
52 Cal Ripken Jr. 20.00 50.00
53 Tony Gwynn 10.00 25.00
53 Tony Gwynn 10.00 25.00
54 Tony Gwynn 10.00 25.00
54 Tony Gwynn 10.00 25.00
55 Johnny Bench 6.00 15.00
55 Johnny Bench 6.00 15.00
56 Yogi Berra 6.00 15.00
56 Yogi Berra 6.00 15.00
57 Carlton Fisk 6.00 15.00
57 Carlton Fisk 6.00 15.00
58 Joe Morgan 6.00 15.00
58 Joe Morgan 6.00 15.00
59 Brooks Robinson 6.00 15.00
59 Brooks Robinson 6.00 15.00
60 Mike Schmidt 10.00 25.00
60 Mike Schmidt 10.00 25.00
61 Willie Stargell 6.00 15.00
61 Willie Stargell 6.00 15.00
62 Tom Seaver 10.00 25.00
62 Tom Seaver 10.00 25.00
63 Ozzie Smith 12.50 30.00
63 Ozzie Smith 12.50 30.00
64 Albert Pujols 12.50 30.00
64 Albert Pujols 12.50 30.00
65 Albert Pujols 12.50 30.00
65 Albert Pujols 12.50 30.00
66 Ryan Howard 10.00 25.00
66 Ryan Howard 10.00 25.00
67 David Ortiz 10.00 25.00
67 David Ortiz 10.00 25.00
68 Randy Johnson 6.00 15.00
68 Randy Johnson 6.00 15.00
69 Greg Maddux 10.00 25.00
69 Greg Maddux 10.00 25.00
70 Greg Maddux 10.00 25.00
70 Greg Maddux 10.00 25.00
71 Johan Santana 6.00 15.00
71 Johan Santana 6.00 15.00
72 Al Kaline 6.00 15.00
72 Al Kaline 6.00 15.00
73 Ryne Sandberg 10.00 25.00
73 Ryne Sandberg 10.00 25.00
74 Robin Yount 10.00 25.00
74 Robin Yount 10.00 25.00
75 Frank Robinson 6.00 15.00
75 Frank Robinson 6.00 15.00
76 Frank Robinson 6.00 15.00
76 Frank Robinson 6.00 15.00
78 Stan Musial 15.00 40.00
78 Stan Musial 15.00 40.00
79 Carl Yastrzemski 10.00 25.00
79 Carl Yastrzemski 10.00 25.00
80 Don Mattingly 20.00 50.00
80 Don Mattingly 20.00 50.00
81 Ichiro Suzuki 20.00 50.00
81 Ichiro Suzuki 20.00 50.00
82 Yogi Berra 6.00 15.00
82 Yogi Berra 6.00 15.00
83 Carlton Fisk 10.00 25.00
Johnny Bench
83 Carlton Fisk 10.00 25.00
Johnny Bench
84 Thurman Munson 10.00 25.00
Johnny Bench
84 Johnny Bench 10.00 25.00
Thurman Munson
85 Babe Ruth 30.00 60.00
Lou Gehrig
85 Babe Ruth 30.00 60.00
Lou Gehrig
86 Whitey Ford 10.00 25.00
Yogi Berra
86 Whitey Ford 10.00 25.00
Yogi Berra
87 Don Larsen 10.00 25.00
Yogi Berra
87 Yogi Berra 10.00 25.00
Don Larsen
88 Kirk Gibson 6.00 15.00
Dennis Eckersley
88 Dennis Eckersley 6.00 15.00
Kirk Gibson
90 Jackie Robinson 10.00 25.00
Pee Wee Reese
90 Jackie Robinson 10.00 25.00
Pee Wee Reese
91 Jackie Robinson 10.00 25.00
Satchel Paige
91 Jackie Robinson 10.00 25.00
Satchel Paige
92 Lou Gehrig 15.00 40.00
Cal Ripken Jr.
92 Cal Ripken Jr. 15.00 40.00
Lou Gehrig
93 Ichiro Suzuki 20.00 50.00
George Sisler
93 George Sisler 20.00 50.00
Ichiro Suzuki
94 Roger Clemens 15.00 40.00
Nolan Ryan
Randy Johnson
Steve Carlton
94 Randy Johnson 15.00 40.00
Roger Clemens
Nolan Ryan
Steve Carlton
95 Johnny Bench 10.00 25.00
Joe Morgan
Tony Perez
Dave Concepcion
95 Dave Concepcion 10.00 25.00
Tony Perez
Joe Morgan
Johnny Bench
96 Babe Ruth 15.00 40.00
Jimmie Foxx
Mel Ott
Eddie Mathews
96 Jimmie Foxx 15.00 40.00
Babe Ruth
Mel Ott
Eddie Mathews
97 Roger Clemens 15.00 40.00
Greg Maddux
Tom Seaver
Nolan Ryan
97 Greg Maddux 15.00 40.00
Tom Seaver
Roger Clemens
Nolan Ryan
98 Roberto Clemente 15.00 40.00
Tony Gwynn
Cal Ripken Jr.
Stan Musial
98 Tony Gwynn 15.00 40.00
Stan Musial
Cal Ripken Jr.
Roberto Clemente
99 John F. Kennedy 12.50 30.00
99 John F. Kennedy 12.50 30.00
100 Dwight Eisenhower 6.00 15.00
100 Dwight Eisenhower 6.00 15.00
DM Daisuke Matsuzaka 50.00 100.00
KI Kei Igawa 12.50 30.00
MI Daisuke Matsuzaka 30.00 60.00
Kei Igawa

2007 Upper Deck Premier Stitchings 10

OVERALL STITCHINGS ODDS ONE PER PACK
STATED PRINT RUN 10 SER.#'d SETS
NO PRICING ON MOST DUE TO SCARCITY
1 Babe Ruth 50.00 100.00
2 Babe Ruth 50.00 100.00
3 Babe Ruth 50.00 100.00
4 Ty Cobb 15.00 40.00
5 Ty Cobb 15.00 40.00
12 Roberto Clemente 40.00 80.00
13 Roberto Clemente 40.00 80.00
16 Cy Young 12.50 30.00
17 Cy Young 12.50 30.00
18 Nolan Ryan 40.00 80.00
19 Nolan Ryan 40.00 80.00
22 Ken Griffey Jr. 40.00 80.00
23 Ken Griffey Jr. 40.00 80.00
24 Derek Jeter 30.00 60.00
25 Derek Jeter 30.00 60.00
26 Jimmie Foxx 10.00 25.00
27 Jimmie Foxx 10.00 25.00
30 Walter Johnson 20.00 50.00
31 Walter Johnson 20.00 50.00
32 Ernie Banks 10.00 25.00
33 Ernie Banks 10.00 25.00
34 Christy Mathewson 10.00 25.00
36 Thurman Munson 30.00 60.00
37 Thurman Munson 30.00 60.00
39 Satchel Paige 15.00 40.00
40 George Sisler 10.00 25.00
41 Casey Stengel 10.00 25.00
51 Cal Ripken Jr. 40.00 80.00
52 Cal Ripken Jr. 40.00 80.00
53 Tony Gwynn 15.00 40.00
54 Tony Gwynn 15.00 40.00
64 Albert Pujols 30.00 60.00
65 Albert Pujols 30.00 60.00
67 David Ortiz 15.00 40.00
69 Greg Maddux 15.00 40.00
70 Greg Maddux 15.00 40.00
73 Ryne Sandberg 15.00 40.00
74 Robin Yount 20.00 50.00

2007 Upper Deck Premier Stitchings Autographs

OVERALL AUTO ODDS ONE PER PACK
STATED PRINT RUN 25 SER.#'d SETS
NO PRICING DUE TO SCARCITY
EXCHANGE DEADLINE 04/26/10

2007 Upper Deck Premier Stitchings Cuts

OVERALL AUTO ODDS ONE PER PACK
STATED PRINT RUN 1 SER.#'d SET
NO PRICING DUE TO SCARCITY
EXCHANGE DEADLINE 04/26/10

2007 Upper Deck Premier Trios Autographs

OVERALL AUTO ODDS ONE PER PACK
STATED PRINT RUN 20 SER.#'d SETS
NO PRICING DUE TO SCARCITY
EXCHANGE DEADLINE 04/26/10

2007 Upper Deck Premier World Series Ticket

OVERALL AUTO ODDS ONE PER PACK
ANNOUNCED PRINT RUN OF 1 SET
NO PRICING DUE TO SCARCITY
BR Babe Ruth

2008 Upper Deck Premier

COMMON CARD (1-178) 2.00 5.00
COMMON RET (179-200) 1.25 3.00
ONE BASE CARD PER PACK
1-200 STATED PRINT RUN 99 SER.#'d SETS
COMMON AU RC p/r 299 (201-241) 4.00 10.00
COMMON AU RC p/r 99 (201-241) 5.00 12.00
OVERALL RC AUTO ONE PER PACK
201-241 PRINT RUNS b/w 99-299 SER.#'d SETS
EXCHANGE DEADLINE 3/13/2010
1 Chipper Jones 6.00 15.00
2 Andruw Jones 2.00 5.00
3 John Smoltz 5.00 12.00
4 Mark Teixeira 3.00 8.00
5 Edgar Renteria 2.00 5.00
6 Jeff Francoeur 3.00 8.00
7 Tim Hudson 2.00 5.00
8 Miguel Cabrera 3.00 8.00
9 Hanley Ramirez 5.00 12.00
10 Dan Uggla 3.00 8.00
11 Dontrelle Willis 2.00 5.00
12 Josh Willingham 2.00 5.00
13 Pedro Martinez 3.00 8.00
14 Carlos Delgado 2.00 5.00
15 Carlos Beltran 2.00 5.00
16 David Wright 6.00 15.00
17 Tom Glavine 3.00 8.00
18 Jose Reyes 3.00 8.00
19 Paul Lo Duca 2.00 5.00
20 John Maine 2.00 5.00
21 Chase Utley 5.00 12.00
22 Cole Hamels 5.00 12.00
23 Jimmy Rollins 3.00 8.00
24 Shane Victorino 2.00 5.00
25 Ryan Howard 6.00 15.00
26 Pat Burrell 2.00 5.00
27 Aaron Rowand 2.00 5.00
28 Ryan Zimmerman 3.00 8.00
29 Ryan Church 2.00 5.00
30 Matt Chico 2.00 5.00
31 Dmitri Young 2.00 5.00
32 Derrek Lee 3.00 8.00
33 Aramis Ramirez 2.00 5.00
34 Carlos Zambrano 2.00 5.00
35 Rich Hill 2.00 5.00
36 Alfonso Soriano 3.00 8.00
37 Kerry Wood 2.00 5.00
38 Ted Lilly 2.00 5.00
39 Ryan Theriot 2.00 5.00
40 Ken Griffey Jr. 8.00 20.00
41 Adam Dunn 2.00 5.00
42 Homer Bailey 3.00 8.00
43 Aaron Harang 2.00 5.00
44 Brandon Phillips 2.00 5.00
45 Josh Hamilton 6.00 15.00
46 Lance Berkman 3.00 8.00
47 Carlos Lee 2.00 5.00
48 Hunter Pence 5.00 12.00
49 Mark Loretta 2.00 5.00
50 Roy Oswalt 2.00 5.00
51 Prince Fielder 5.00 12.00
52 Ryan Braun 6.00 15.00
53 J.J. Hardy 2.00 5.00
54 Ben Sheets 3.00 8.00
55 Rickie Weeks 2.00 5.00
56 Corey Hart 2.00 5.00
57 Johnny Estrada 2.00 5.00
58 Jason Bay 2.00 5.00
59 Freddy Sanchez 2.00 5.00
60 Adam LaRoche 2.00 5.00
61 Ian Snell 2.00 5.00
62 Xavier Nady 2.00 5.00
63 Tom Gorzelanny 2.00 5.00
64 Scott Rolen 3.00 8.00
65 Albert Pujols 8.00 20.00
66 Jim Edmonds 3.00 8.00
67 Chris Duncan 2.00 5.00
68 Adam Wainwright 2.00 5.00
69 Brandon Webb 3.00 8.00
70 Orlando Hudson 2.00 5.00
71 Chris B. Young 2.00 5.00
72 Stephen Drew 2.00 5.00
73 Matt Holliday 3.00 8.00
74 Jeff Francis 2.00 5.00
75 Brad Hawpe 2.00 5.00
76 Todd Helton 3.00 8.00
77 Troy Tulowitzki 3.00 8.00
78 Russell Martin 2.00 5.00
79 Nomar Garciaparra 5.00 12.00
80 James Loney 3.00 8.00
81 Andre Ethier 3.00 8.00
82 Brad Penny 2.00 5.00
83 Rafael Furcal 2.00 5.00
84 Jeff Kent 2.00 5.00
85 Greg Maddux 6.00 15.00
86 Chris Young 2.00 5.00
87 Khalil Greene 3.00 8.00
88 Trevor Hoffman 2.00 5.00
89 Adrian Gonzalez 3.00 8.00
90 Jake Peavy 3.00 8.00
91 Noah Lowry 2.00 5.00
92 Omar Vizquel 2.00 5.00
93 Tim Lincecum 5.00 12.00
94 Matt Cain 2.00 5.00
95 Randy Winn 2.00 5.00
96 Miguel Tejada 2.00 5.00
97 Brian Roberts 3.00 8.00
98 Nick Markakis 3.00 8.00
99 Erik Bedard 2.00 5.00
100 Melvin Mora 2.00 5.00
101 David Ortiz 5.00 12.00
102 Manny Ramirez 5.00 12.00
103 Josh Beckett 3.00 8.00
104 Jonathan Papelbon 3.00 8.00
105 Curt Schilling 3.00 8.00
106 Daisuke Matsuzaka 10.00 25.00
107 Jason Varitek 5.00 12.00
108 Kevin Youkilis 3.00 8.00
109 Derek Jeter 12.00 30.00
110 Hideki Matsui 5.00 12.00
111 Alex Rodriguez 8.00 20.00
112 Johnny Damon 3.00 8.00
113 Robinson Cano 3.00 8.00
114 Jorge Posada 3.00 8.00
115 Mariano Rivera 5.00 12.00
116 Roger Clemens 6.00 15.00
117 Chien-Ming Wang 8.00 20.00
118 Carl Crawford 2.00 5.00
119 Delmon Young 3.00 8.00
120 B.J. Upton 3.00 8.00
121 Akinori Iwamura 2.00 5.00
122 Scott Kazmir 3.00 8.00
123 Alex Rios 2.00 5.00
124 Frank Thomas 5.00 12.00
125 Roy Halladay 2.00 5.00
126 Vernon Wells 2.00 5.00
127 Troy Glaus 3.00 8.00
128 Jeremy Accardo 2.00 5.00
129 A.J. Burnett 2.00 5.00
130 Paul Konerko 2.00 5.00
131 Jim Thome 3.00 8.00
132 Jermaine Dye 2.00 5.00
133 Mark Buehrle 2.00 5.00
134 Javier Vazquez 2.00 5.00
135 Grady Sizemore 3.00 8.00
136 Travis Hafner 2.00 5.00
137 Victor Martinez 2.00 5.00
138 C.C. Sabathia 2.00 5.00
139 Ryan Garko 2.00 5.00
140 Fausto Carmona 2.00 5.00
141 Justin Verlander 3.00 8.00
142 Jeremy Bonderman 2.00 5.00
143 Magglio Ordonez 3.00 8.00
144 Gary Sheffield 2.00 5.00
145 Carlos Guillen 2.00 5.00
146 Ivan Rodriguez 3.00 8.00
147 Curtis Granderson 3.00 8.00
148 Alex Gordon 5.00 12.00
149 Mark Teahen 2.00 5.00
150 Brian Bannister 2.00 5.00
151 Billy Butler 2.00 5.00
152 Johan Santana 3.00 8.00
153 Torii Hunter 2.00 5.00
154 Joe Mauer 3.00 8.00
155 Justin Morneau 3.00 8.00
156 Vladimir Guerrero 5.00 12.00
157 Chone Figgins 2.00 5.00
158 Jered Weaver 2.00 5.00
159 Kelvim Escobar 2.00 5.00
160 John Lackey 2.00 5.00
161 Dan Haren 2.00 5.00
162 Mike Piazza 5.00 12.00
163 Nick Swisher 2.00 5.00
164 Eric Chavez 2.00 5.00
165 Huston Street 2.00 5.00
166 Joe Blanton 2.00 5.00
167 Kenji Johjima 2.00 5.00
168 J.J. Putz 2.00 5.00
169 Felix Hernandez 3.00 8.00
170 Jose Guillen 2.00 5.00
171 Adrian Beltre 2.00 5.00
172 Ichiro 8.00 20.00
173 Marlon Byrd 2.00 5.00
174 Hank Blalock 2.00 5.00
175 Michael Young 2.00 5.00
176 Ian Kinsler 3.00 8.00
177 Sammy Sosa 3.00 8.00
178 Kevin Millwood 2.00 5.00
179 Luis Aparicio 1.25 3.00
180 Johnny Bench 3.00 8.00
181 Yogi Berra 3.00 8.00
182 Lou Brock 2.00 5.00
183 Jim Bunning 1.25 3.00
184 Rod Carew 2.00 5.00
185 Orlando Cepeda 1.25 3.00
186 Bobby Doerr 1.25 3.00
187 Bob Feller 2.00 5.00
188 Dennis Eckersley 1.25 3.00
189 Carlton Fisk 2.00 5.00
190 Monte Irvin 1.25 3.00
191 Rollie Fingers 1.25 3.00
192 Al Kaline 2.00 5.00
193 Nolan Ryan 10.00 25.00
194 Mike Schmidt 5.00 12.00
195 Ryne Sandberg 6.00 15.00
196 Robin Yount 3.00 8.00
197 Brooks Robinson 2.00 5.00
198 Bill Mazeroski 2.00 5.00
199 Reggie Jackson 2.00 5.00
200 Babe Ruth 8.00 20.00
201 Ian Kennedy AU RC/299 12.50 30.00
202 Jonathan Albaladejo AU RC/299 5.00 12.00
203 Josh Anderson AU (RC)/299 4.00 10.00
204 Wladimir Balentien AU (RC)/299 5.00 12.00
205 Daric Barton AU (RC)/299 5.00 12.00
206 Jerry Blevins AU RC/99 5.00 12.00
207 Emilio Bonifacio AU RC/99 5.00 12.00
208 Lance Broadway AU (RC)/299 4.00 10.00
209 Clay Buchholz AU (RC)/299 15.00 40.00
210 Billy Buckner AU (RC)/299 4.00 10.00
212 Ross Detwiler AU RC/299 5.00 12.00
213 Harvey Garcia AU (RC)/99 5.00 12.00
214 Alberto Gonzalez AU RC/99 12.50 30.00
215 Ryan Hanigan AU RC/99 5.00 12.00
216 Kevin Hart AU (RC)/299 4.00 10.00
217 Luke Hochevar AU RC/299 6.00 15.00
218 Chin-Lung Hu AU (RC)/299 15.00 40.00
219 Rob Johnson AU (RC)/99 5.00 12.00
220 Brandon Jones AU RC/299 6.00 15.00
221 Joe Koshansky AU (RC)/299 4.00 10.00
222 Donny Lucy AU (RC)/299 4.00 10.00
223 Justin Maxwell AU RC/299 6.00 15.00
224 Jonathan Meloan AU RC/299 4.00 10.00
225 Luis Mendoza AU (RC)/299 4.00 10.00
226 Jose Morales AU (RC)/299 4.00 10.00
227 Nyjer Morgan AU (RC)/99 5.00 12.00
228 Bill Murphy AU (RC)/99 5.00 12.00
229 Josh Newman AU RC/99 5.00 12.00
230 Ross Ohlendorf AU RC/299 5.00 12.00
231 Troy Patton AU (RC)/299 4.00 10.00
232 Felipe Paulino AU RC/99 EXCH 5.00 12.00
233 Steve Pearce AU RC/299 5.00 12.00
234 Justin Ruggiano AU RC/99 5.00 12.00
235 Clint Sammons AU (RC)/299 4.00 10.00
236 Bronson Sardinha AU (RC)/299 4.00 10.00
237 Chris Seddon AU (RC)/99 5.00 12.00
238 Seth Smith AU (RC)/299 4.00 10.00
239 J.R. Towles AU RC/299 5.00 12.00
240 Eugenio Velez AU RC/99 15.00 40.00
241 Joey Votto AU (RC)/299 8.00 20.00
242 Bill White AU RC/99 5.00 12.00

2008 Upper Deck Premier Autograph Parallel

OVERALL AU ODDS THREE PER PACK
PRINT RUNS b/wn 5-25 COPIES PER
NO PRICING DUE TO SCARCITY
EXCHANGE DEADLINE 3/13/2010

2008 Upper Deck Premier Blue

1-200 RANDOMLY INSERTED
1-200 PRINT RUN 15 SER.#'d SETS
NO 1-200 PRICING DUE TO SCARCITY
*BLUE AU p/r 99: .5X TO 1.2X BASIC p/r 299
*BLUE AU p/r 50: .4X TO 1X BASIC p/r 99
OVERALL RC AUTO ONE PER PACK
201-240 PRINT RUNS b/wn 50-99 COPIES PER
EXCHANGE DEADLINE 3/13/2010

2008 Upper Deck Premier Gold

1-200 RANDOMLY INSERTED
1-200 PRINT RUN 1 SER.#'d SET
NO 1-200 PRICING DUE TO SCARCITY
*GOLD AU p/r 50: .6X TO 1.5X BASIC p/r 299
OVERALL RC AUTO ONE PER PACK
201-240 PRINT RUNS b/wn 10-50 COPIES PER
NO PRICING ON QTY 10 OR LESS
EXCHANGE DEADLINE 3/13/2010

2008 Upper Deck Premier Silver

1-200 RANDOMLY INSERTED
1-200 PRINT RUN 5 SER.#'d SETS
NO 1-200 PRICING DUE TO SCARCITY
*SILVER AU p/r 75: .6X TO 1.5X BASIC p/r 299
OVERALL RC AUTO ONE PER PACK
201-240 PRINT RUNS 25-75 COPIES PER
NO PRICING ON QTY 25 OR LESS
EXCHANGE DEADLINE 3/13/2010

2008 Upper Deck Premier Rookie Autographs Jersey Number

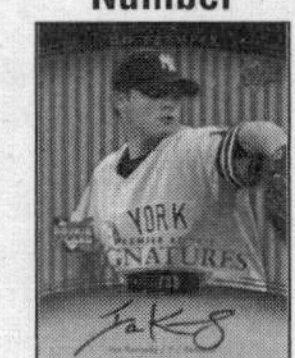

OVERALL RC AUTO ONE PER PACK
PRINT RUNS B/WN 5-65 COPIES PER
NO PRICING ON QTY 25 OR LESS
EXCHANGE DEADLINE 3/13/2010
201 Ian Kennedy AU/36 60.00 120.00
202 Jonathan Albaladejo AU/53 8.00 20.00
203 Josh Anderson AU/10
204 Wladimir Balentien AU/50 8.00 20.00
205 Daric Barton AU/10
206 Jerry Blevins AU/5
207 Emilio Bonifacio AU/5
208 Lance Broadway AU/41 6.00 15.00
209 Clay Buchholz AU/61 30.00 60.00
210 Billy Buckner AU/38 6.00 15.00
212 Ross Detwiler AU/29 8.00 20.00
213 Harvey Garcia AU/5
214 Alberto Gonzalez AU/5
215 Ryan Hanigan AU/5
216 Kevin Hart AU/55 6.00 15.00
217 Luke Hochevar AU/44 10.00 25.00
218 Chin-Lung Hu AU/60 30.00 60.00
219 Rob Johnson AU/5
220 Brandon Jones AU/28 10.00 25.00
221 Joe Koshansky AU/47 6.00 15.00
222 Donny Lucy AU/55 6.00 15.00
223 Justin Maxwell AU/16
224 Jonathan Meloan AU/63 6.00 15.00

225 Luis Mendoza AU/32 6.00 15.00
226 Jose Morales AU/58 6.00 15.00
227 Nyjer Morgan AU/5
228 Bill Murphy AU/5
229 Josh Newman AU/5
230 Ross Ohlendorf AU/60 8.00 20.00
231 Troy Patton AU/65 6.00 15.00
233 Steve Pearce AU/18
234 Justin Ruggiano AU/5
235 Clint Sammons AU/18
236 Bronson Sardinha AU/64 6.00 15.00
237 Chris Seddon AU/5
238 Seth Smith AU/12
239 J.R. Towles AU/46 8.00 20.00
240 Eugenio Velez AU/5
241 Joey Votto AU/60 12.50 30.00
242 Bill White AU/5

2008 Upper Deck Premier Rookie Autographs Masterpiece

OVERALL RC AUTO ONE PER PACK
STATED PRINT RUN 1 SER.#'d SET
NO PRICING DUE TO SCARCITY
EXCHANGE DEADLINE 3/13/2010

2008 Upper Deck Premier 07 Matsuzaka Autograph

243 Daisuke Matsuzaka AU (RC)

2008 Upper Deck Premier AKA Autographs

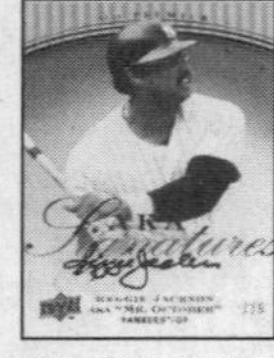

OVERALL AU ODDS THREE PER PACK
STATED PRINT RUN 25 SER.#'d SETS
NO PRICING DUE TO SCARCITY
GOLD PRINT RUN 5 SER.#'d SETS
NO GOLD PRICING DUE TO SCARCITY
MASTERPIECE PRINT RUN 1 SER.#'d SET
NO MASTERPIECE PRICING AVAILABLE
EXCHANGE DEADLINE 3/13/2010

2008 Upper Deck Premier Bat Barrels

OVERALL GU ODDS TWO PER PACK
PRINT RUNS B/WN 1-6 COPIES PER
NO PRICING DUE TO SCARCITY

2008 Upper Deck Premier Combos Memorablia

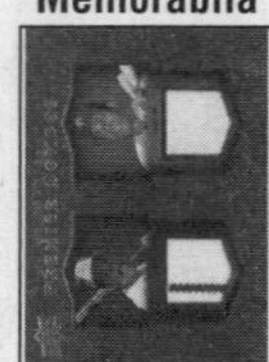

OVERALL GU ODDS TWO PER PACK
STATED PRINT RUN 50 SER.#'d SETS
GOLD PRINT RUN 25 SER.#'d SETS
NO GOLD PRICING DUE TO SCARCITY
PLATINUM PRINT RUN 5 SER.#'d SETS
NO PLATINUM PRICING AVAILABLE
BF Ryan Braun 12.50 30.00
Prince Fielder/50
BY Ryan Braun 12.50 30.00
Robin Yount/50
CZ Miguel Cabrera 5.00 12.00
Ryan Zimmerman/50
FO Prince Fielder 6.00 15.00
David Ortiz/50
FV Carlton Fisk 6.00 15.00
Jason Varitek/50
GC Tony Gwynn 10.00 25.00
Rod Carew/50
GD Ken Griffey Jr. 10.00 25.00
Adam Dunn/50
GJ Ken Griffey Jr. 15.00 40.00
Derek Jeter/50
GM Tom Glavine 4.00 10.00
Pedro Martinez/50
GR Vladimir Guerrero 4.00 10.00
Manny Ramirez/50
HH Matt Holliday 5.00 12.00
Todd Helton/50
JH Andruw Jones 4.00 10.00
Torii Hunter/50
JR Derek Jeter 20.00 50.00
Cal Ripken Jr./50
LR Tony Lazzeri 30.00 60.00
Phil Rizzuto/50
MJ Thurman Munson 20.00 50.00
Reggie Jackson/50
MM Victor Martinez 4.00 10.00
Joe Mauer/50
MU Joe Morgan 4.00 10.00
Chase Utley/50
MY Stan Musial 12.50 30.00
Carl Yastrzemski/50
OH David Ortiz 5.00 12.00
Travis Hafner/50
OK Magglio Ordonez 20.00 50.00
Al Kaline/50
OR David Ortiz 6.00 15.00
Manny Ramirez/50
OY David Ortiz 6.00 15.00
Kevin Youkilis/50
PB Hunter Pence 10.00 25.00
Ryan Braun/50
PM Albert Pujols 20.00 50.00
Stan Musial/50
PO Albert Pujols 12.50 30.00
David Ortiz/50
PY Jake Peavy 5.00 12.00
Chris Young/50
RB Jose Reyes 4.00 10.00
Carlos Beltran/50
RC Jackie Robinson 30.00 60.00
Roy Campanella/50
RG Cal Ripken Jr. 20.00 50.00
Ken Griffey Jr./50
RJ Hanley Ramirez 10.00 25.00
Derek Jeter/50
SC Johan Santana 6.00 15.00
Roger Clemens/50
SH Grady Sizemore 4.00 10.00
Travis Hafner/50
SM John Smoltz 10.00 25.00
Greg Maddux/50
TG Frank Thomas 20.00 50.00
Ken Griffey Jr./50
UH Chase Utley 10.00 25.00
Cole Hamels/50
VM Jason Varitek 6.00 15.00
Victor Martinez/50
VR Justin Verlander 15.00 40.00
Nolan Ryan/50
WH Chien-Ming Wang 15.00 40.00
Phil Hughes/50

2008 Upper Deck Premier Combos Patch

OVERALL GU ODDS TWO PER PACK
PRINT RUNS B/WN 10-50 COPIES PER
NO PRICING ON QTY 10 OR LESS
GOLD PRINT RUN 25 SER.#'d SETS
NO GOLD PRICING DUE TO SCARCITY
MASTERPIECE PRINT RUN 1 SER.#'d SET
NO MASTERPIECE PRICING AVAILABLE
PLATINUM PRINT RUN 10 SER.#'d SETS
NO PLATINUM PRICING AVAILABLE
BD Ben Sheets 6.00 15.00
Dan Haren/50
BP Johnny Bench 30.00 60.00
Albert Pujols/50
BR Ryan Braun 30.00 60.00
Cal Ripken Jr./50
BS Erik Bedard 6.00 15.00
C.C. Sabathia/50
BZ Jeremy Bonderman 6.00 15.00
Carlos Zambrano/50
CR Miguel Cabrera 12.50 30.00
Manny Ramirez/50
CV Carlton Fisk 6.00 15.00
Vladimir Guerrero/50
FG Jeff Francoeur 12.50 30.00
Alex Gordon/50
FM Jeff Francoeur 10.00 25.00
Joe Mauer/50
GR Ken Griffey Jr. 30.00 60.00
Cal Ripken Jr./50
GY Tony Gwynn 20.00 50.00
Robin Yount/50
HG J.J. Hardy 10.00 25.00
Alex Gordon/50
HH Matt Holliday 12.50 30.00
Todd Helton/50
HM Cole Hamels 6.00 15.00
Andrew Miller/50
HR Felix Hernandez 20.00 50.00
Nolan Ryan/50
HW Cole Hamels 6.00 15.00
Dontrelle Willis/50
JD Reggie Jackson 6.00 15.00
Adam Dunn/50
JH Andruw Jones 6.00 15.00
Torii Hunter/50
JJ Jose Reyes 12.50 30.00
Joe Mauer/50
LC Noah Lowry 6.00 15.00
Matt Cain/50
LK Derrek Lee 12.50 30.00
Paul Konerko/50
LT Lance Berkman 6.00 15.00
Todd Helton/50
MB Nick Markakis 10.00 25.00
Jason Bay/50
MM Russell Martin 6.00 15.00
Gil Meche/50
OR David Ortiz 20.00 50.00
Manny Ramirez/50
PO Jake Peavy 10.00 25.00
Roy Oswalt/50
PR Tony Perez 10.00 25.00
Manny Ramirez/50
RI Brian Roberts 6.00 15.00
Akinori Iwamura/50
RJ Russell Martin 10.00 25.00
James Loney/50
RM Aramis Ramirez 10.00 25.00
Brian McCann/50
RO Manny Ramirez 10.00 25.00
Magglio Ordonez/50
RT Hanley Ramirez 12.50 30.00
Troy Tulowitzki/50
SB Curt Schilling 10.00 25.00
Jeremy Bonderman/50
SH Johan Santana 12.50 30.00
Cole Hamels/50
SJ C.C. Sabathia 12.50 30.00
Randy Johnson/50
TH Frank Thomas 20.00 50.00
Travis Hafner/50
TK Torii Hunter 15.00 40.00
Ken Griffey Jr./50
TT Torii Hunter 10.00 25.00
Travis Hafner/50
TU Troy Tulowitzki
B.J. Upton/10
UU Chase Utley 20.00 50.00
Dan Uggla/50
UY Chase Utley 6.00 15.00
Delmon Young/50
VH Justin Verlander 12.50 30.00
Cole Hamels/50
VR Justin Verlander 20.00 50.00
Nolan Ryan/50
WJ Vernon Wells 10.00 25.00
Chipper Jones/50
YH Robin Yount 12.50 30.00
J.J. Hardy/50
ZJ Ryan Zimmerman 10.00 25.00
Chipper Jones/50
ZR Ryan Zimmerman 10.00 25.00
Jimmy Rollins/50

2008 Upper Deck Premier Emerging Stars Autographs

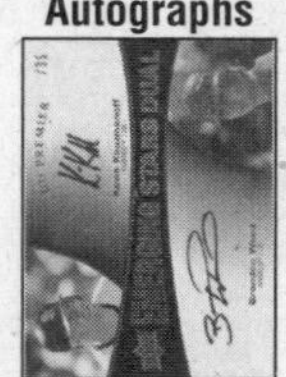

OVERALL AU ODDS THREE PER PACK
STATED PRINT RUN 35 SER.#'d SETS
GOLD PRINT RUN 15 SER.#'d SETS
NO GOLD PRICING DUE TO SCARCITY
MASTERPIECE PRINT RUN 1 SER.#'d SET
NO MASTERPIECE PRICING AVAILABLE
EXCHANGE DEADLINE 3/13/2010
BB Daric Barton 10.00 25.00
Travis Buck
BG Billy Butler 40.00 80.00
Alex Gordon
BH Ryan Braun 50.00 100.00
Corey Hart
BM Chad Billingsley 6.00 15.00
Jonathan Meloan
BP Clay Buchholz 40.00 80.00
Jonathan Papelbon
BV Homer Bailey 12.50 30.00
Joey Votto
BW Billy Butler 10.00 25.00
Brandon Wood
CL Matt Cain 12.50 30.00
Noah Lowry
CT Corey Hart 12.50 30.00
Travis Buck
FB Josh Fields 6.00 15.00
Lance Broadway
FO Josh Fields 6.00 15.00
Jerry Owens
GH Alex Gordon 20.00 50.00
Luke Hochevar
GL Curtis Granderson 10.00 25.00
Fred Lewis
GM Carlos Gomez 10.00 25.00
David Murphy
HB Phil Hughes 20.00 50.00
Homer Bailey
HK Cole Hamels 15.00 40.00
Scott Kazmir
HL Chin-Lung Hu 20.00 50.00
James Loney
HS Dan Haren 10.00 25.00
Huston Street
HV Josh Hamilton 30.00 60.00
Joey Votto
HW Corey Hart 20.00 50.00
Rickie Weeks
KB Kevin Kouzmanoff 6.00 15.00
Brandon Wood
KH Ian Kennedy 40.00 80.00
Phil Hughes
KU Howie Kendrick 6.00 15.00
Dan Uggla
KW Howie Kendrick 15.00 40.00
Jered Weaver
LE James Loney 12.50 30.00
Andre Ethier
LL Andy LaRoche 12.50 30.00
James Loney
MB John Maine 6.00 15.00
Chad Billingsley
MC John Maine 6.00 15.00
Matt Cain
ME Brian McCann 20.00 50.00
Yunel Escobar
MG John Maine 10.00 25.00
Carlos Gomez
MH Nick Markakis 10.00 25.00
Jeremy Hermida
ML Russell Martin 30.00 60.00
James Loney
MM Brian McCann 12.50 30.00
Russell Martin
MP Nick Markakis 20.00 50.00
Steve Pearce
MS Brian McCann 12.50 30.00
Jarrod Saltalamacchia
MT Russell Martin 12.50 30.00
J.R. Towles
NJ Nick Markakis 30.00 60.00
Josh Hamilton
PL Jonathan Papelbon 30.00 60.00
Jon Lester
PZ Jonathan Papelbon 20.00 50.00
Joel Zumaya
SB James Shields 6.00 15.00
Scott Baker
TA Troy Tulowitzki 10.00 25.00
Garrett Atkins
TG Troy Tulowitzki 20.00 50.00
Alex Gordon
UR Dan Uggla 20.00 50.00
Hanley Ramirez
UY B.J. Upton 12.50 30.00
Delmon Young
VH Justin Verlander 12.50 30.00
Dan Haren

2008 Upper Deck Premier Emerging Stars Autographs Trios

OVERALL AU ODDS THREE PER PACK
PRINT RUNS B/WN 3-25 COPIES PER
NO PRICING DUE TO SCARCITY
GOLD PRINT RUN 10 SER.#'d SETS
NO GOLD PRICING DUE TO SCARCITY
MASTERPIECE PRINT RUN 1 SER.#'d SET
NO MASTERPIECE PRICING AVAILABLE
EXCHANGE DEADLINE 3/13/2010

2008 Upper Deck Premier Emerging Stars Autographs Quad

OVERALL AU ODDS THREE PER PACK
STATED PRINT RUN 10 SER.#'d SETS
NO PRICING DUE TO SCARCITY
GOLD PRINT RUN 5 SER.#'d SETS
NO GOLD PRICING DUE TO SCARCITY
MASTERPIECE PRINT RUN 1 SER.#'d SET
NO MASTERPIECE PRICING AVAILABLE
EXCHANGE DEADLINE 3/13/2010

2008 Upper Deck Premier Foursome Materials

OVERALL GU ODDS TWO PER PACK
STATED PRINT RUN 50 SER.#'d SETS
NO PRICING DUE TO SCARCITY
GOLD PRINT RUN 15 SER.#'d SETS
NO GOLD PRICING DUE TO SCARCITY
PLATINUM PRINT RUN 4 SER.#'d SETS
NO PLATINUM PRICING AVAILABLE
BHFS Ryan Braun/Corey Hart/Prince Fielder/Ben Sheets
BYGM Wade Boggs/Carl Yastrzemski/Tony Gwynn/Eddie Murray
CGBR Rod Carew/Tony Gwynn/Wade Boggs/Cal Ripken/ Jr.
CKMC Roberto Clemente/Al Kaline/Stan Musial/Rod Carew
DRMB Carlos Delgado/Jose Reyes/Pedro Martinez/Carlos Beltran
GBMP Ken Griffey Jr./Johnny Bench/Joe Morgan/Tony Perez
GTPJ Ken Griffey Jr./Frank Thomas/Albert Pujols/Chipper Jones
HHAT Matt Holliday/Todd Helton/Garrett Atkins/Troy Tulowitzki
ISCU Akinori Iwamura/James Shields/Carl Crawford/B.J. Upton
LRSZ Derrek Lee/Aramis Ramirez/Alfonso Soriano/Carlos Zambrano
MGCG Greg Maddux/Tom Glavine/Steve Carlton/Bob Gibson
MJCG Greg Maddux/Randy Johnson/Roger Clemens/Tom Glavine
MSSR Bill Mazeroski/Ryne Sandberg/Ozzie Smith/Brooks Robinson
MYRW Paul Molitor/Robin Yount/Cal Ripken/ Jr./Dave Winfield
PCPM Jim Palmer/Roger Clemens/Gaylord Perry/Pedro Martinez
RGMC Babe Ruth/Lou Gehrig/Stan Musial/Ty Cobb
SSRY Mike Schmidt/Ryne Sandberg/Cal Ripken/ Jr./Robin Yount
VHBS Justin Verlander/Dan Haren/Josh Beckett/C.C. Sabathia
WSGM Brandon Webb/John Smoltz/Tom Glavine/Greg Maddux

2008 Upper Deck Premier Legendary Remnants Triple

OVERALL GU ODDS TWO PER PACK
PRINT RUNS B/WN 15-50 COPIES PER
NO PRICING ON QTY 15 OR LESS
BRONZE B/WN 10-25 COPIES PER
NO BRONZE PRICING DUE TO SCARCITY
GOLD B/WN 5-10 COPIES PER
NO GOLD PRICING DUE TO SCARCITY
MASTERPIECE PRINT RUN 1 SER.#'d SET
NO MASTERPIECE PRICING AVAILABLE
BR Babe Ruth/15
HG Hank Greenberg/50 50.00 100.00
JD Joe DiMaggio/50 60.00 120.00
JR Jackie Robinson/50 30.00 60.00
LG Lou Gehrig/50 150.00 250.00
MO Mel Ott/50 40.00 80.00
RC Roberto Clemente/50 40.00 80.00
RM Roger Maris/50 20.00 50.00
WS Willie Stargell/50 20.00 50.00

2008 Upper Deck Premier Legendary Remnants Triple Gold Milestones

OVERALL GU ODDS TWO PER PACK
PRINT RUNS B/WN 7-61 COPIES PER
NO PRICING ON QTY 23 OR LESS
BR Babe Ruth/15
HG Hank Greenberg/36 50.00 100.00
JD Joe DiMaggio/9
JR Jackie Robinson/19
LG Lou Gehrig/23
MO Mel Ott/12
RC Roberto Clemente/21
RM Roger Maris/61 20.00 50.00
WS Willie Stargell/7

2008 Upper Deck Premier Legendary Remnants Triple Silver

OVERALL GU ODDS TWO PER PACK
PRINT RUNS B/WN 10-30 COPIES PER
NO PRICING ON QTY 10 OR LESS
BR Babe Ruth/10
HG Hank Greenberg/10
JD Joe DiMaggio/30 75.00 150.00
JR Jackie Robinson/30 40.00 80.00
LG Lou Gehrig/30 200.00 300.00
MO Mel Ott/30 50.00 100.00
RC Roberto Clemente/30 50.00 100.00
RM Roger Maris/30 30.00 60.00
WS Willie Stargell/30 30.00 60.00

2008 Upper Deck Premier Legendary Remnants Quad

OVERALL GU ODDS TWO PER PACK
PRINT RUNS B/WN 10-20 COPIES PER
NO PRICING DUE TO SCARCITY
BRONZE B/WN 5-10 COPIES PER
NO BRONZE PRICING DUE TO SCARCITY
GOLD B/WN 3-5 COPIES PER
NO GOLD PRICING DUE TO SCARCITY
GOLD MILE. B/WN 9-13 COPIES PER
NO GOLD MILE.PRICING DUE TO SCARCITY
MASTERPIECE PRINT RUN 1 SER.#'d SET
NO MASTERPIECE PRICING AVAILABLE
SILVER B/WN 5-15 COPIES PER
NO SILVER PRICING AVAILABLE
BR Babe Ruth/10
JD Joe DiMaggio/20
JF Jimmie Foxx/15
LG Lou Gehrig/20
RC Roberto Clemente/20

2008 Upper Deck Premier Logo Patch

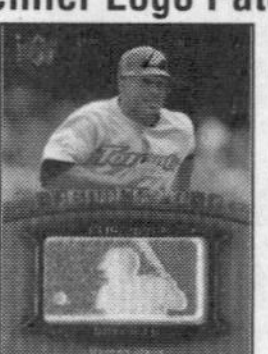

OVERALL GU ODDS TWO PER PACK
STATED PRINT RUN 1 SER.#'d SET
NO PRICING DUE TO SCARCITY

2008 Upper Deck Premier Memorabilia Triple

OVERALL GU ODDS TWO PER PACK
PRINT RUNS B/WN 25-50 COPIES PER
GOLD PRINT RUN 3 SER.#'d SETS
NO GOLD PRICING DUE TO SCARCITY
AG Alex Gordon/25
AI Akinori Iwamura/25
AP Albert Pujols/75 10.00 25.00
AP2 Albert Pujols/75 10.00 25.00
BE Johnny Bench/50 10.00 25.00
BM Bill Mazeroski/25
CA Rod Carew/25
CJ Chipper Jones/25
DJ Derek Jeter/75 12.50 30.00
DM Daisuke Matsuzaka/75 12.50 30.00
DO David Ortiz/50 5.00 12.00
GM Greg Maddux/50 6.00 15.00
GS Grady Sizemore/25
IR Ivan Rodriguez/25
JD Joe DiMaggio/75 50.00 100.00
JP Jonathan Papelbon/25
KG Ken Griffey Jr./50 10.00 25.00
MA Don Mattingly/50 10.00 25.00
MR Manny Ramirez/25
MS Mike Schmidt/50 12.50 30.00
NR Nolan Ryan/75 12.50 30.00
OS Ozzie Smith/75 10.00 25.00
PF Prince Fielder/25
PM Paul Molitor/25
RC Roger Clemens/25
RJ Reggie Jackson/75 6.00 15.00
SM Stan Musial/75 12.50 30.00
TS Tom Seaver/75 10.00 25.00
VG Vladimir Guerrero/25
WB Wade Boggs/50 5.00 12.00
WS Warren Spahn/75 10.00 25.00

2008 Upper Deck Premier Memorabilia Triple Autographs

OVERALL AU ODDS THREE PER PACK
PRINT RUNS B/WN 5-20 COPIES PER
NO PRICING DUE TO SCARCITY
EXCHANGE DEADLINE 3/13/2010

2008 Upper Deck Premier Memorabilia Quad

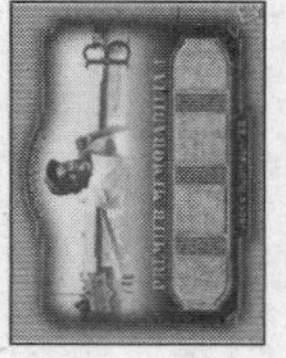

OVERALL GU ODDS TWO PER PACK
PRINT RUNS B/WN 15-40 COPIES PER
NO RUTH PRICING DUE TO SCARCITY
GOLD STATED PRINT RUN 4 SER.#'d SETS
NO GOLD PRICING DUE TO SCARCITY
AS Alfonso Soriano/40 6.00 15.00
BR Babe Ruth/15
CC Chris Carpenter/40 5.00 12.00
CH Cole Hamels/40 5.00 12.00
CL Roger Clemens/40 6.00 15.00
CS Curt Schilling/40 5.00 12.00
CU Chase Utley/40 5.00 12.00
CW Chien-Ming Wang/40 20.00 50.00
CY Carl Yastrzemski/40 6.00 15.00
DJ Derek Jeter/40 30.00 60.00
DL Derrek Lee/40 4.00 10.00
DM Don Mattingly/40 12.50 30.00
DO David Ortiz/40 6.00 15.00
DO2 David Ortiz/40 6.00 15.00
DP Dave Parker/40 6.00 15.00
DW Dontrelle Willis/40 4.00 10.00
EM Eddie Mathews/40 20.00 50.00
HP Hunter Pence/40 6.00 15.00
JM Joe Mauer/40 5.00 12.00
JR Jackie Robinson/40 40.00 80.00
JS Johan Santana/40 6.00 15.00
JV Justin Verlander/40 10.00 25.00
MA Russell Martin/40 10.00 25.00
MO Justin Morneau/40 4.00 10.00
MS Mike Schmidt/40 10.00 25.00
MT Mark Teixeira/40 10.00 25.00
NM Nick Markakis/40 6.00 15.00
NR Nolan Ryan/40 15.00 40.00
OR Magglio Ordonez/40 5.00 12.00
PF Prince Fielder/40 6.00 15.00
PH Phil Hughes/40 12.50 30.00
PW Pee Wee Reese/40 10.00 25.00
RB Ryan Braun/40 10.00 25.00
RC Roberto Clemente/40 40.00 80.00
RE Jose Reyes/40 6.00 15.00
RH Rogers Hornsby/40 30.00 60.00
RJ Reggie Jackson/40 10.00 25.00
RM Roger Maris/40 30.00 60.00
RY Robin Yount/40 15.00 40.00
SM Stan Musial/40 12.50 30.00
TM Thurman Munson/40 20.00 50.00
TP Tony Perez/40 10.00 25.00
VG Vladimir Guerrero/40 6.00 15.00
VM Victor Martinez/40 4.00 10.00

2008 Upper Deck Premier Memorabilia Quad Autographs

OVERALL AU ODDS THREE PER PACK
STATED PRINT RUN 10 SER.#'d SETS
NO PRICING DUE TO SCARCITY
EXCHANGE DEADLINE 3/13/2010

2008 Upper Deck Premier Milestones Autographs

OVERALL AU ODDS THREE PER PACK
STATED PRINT RUN 25 SER.#'d SETS
NO PRICING DUE TO SCARCITY
MASTERPIECE PRINT RUN 1 SER.#'d SET
NO MASTERPIECE PRICING AVAILABLE
PLATINUM PRINT RUN 5 SER.#'d SETS
NO PLATINUM PRICING AVAILABLE
EXCHANGE DEADLINE 3/13/2010

2008 Upper Deck Premier Octographs

OVERALL AU ODDS THREE PER PACK
STATED PRINT RUN 1 SER.#'d SET
NO PRICING DUE TO SCARCITY
EXCHANGE DEADLINE 3/13/2010

2008 Upper Deck Premier Patches

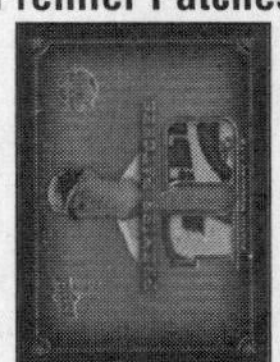

OVERALL GU ODDS TWO PER PACK
PRINT RUNS B/WN 55-75 COPIES PER
*GOLD: .4X TO 1X BASIC PATCH
GOLD B/WN 25-50 COPIES PER
NO GOLD PRICING ON QTY 25 OR LESS
SILVER PRINT RUN 10 SER.#'d SETS
NO SILVER PRICING DUE TO SCARCITY
AI Akinori Iwamura 10.00 25.00
AJ Andruw Jones 6.00 15.00
AL Adam LaRoche 6.00 15.00
BR Brian Roberts 6.00 15.00
CB Carlos Beltran 6.00 15.00
CJ Chipper Jones 15.00 40.00
CR Cal Ripken Jr. 30.00 60.00
CU Chase Utley 15.00 40.00
CW Chien-Ming Wang 20.00 50.00
DM Daisuke Matsuzaka/55 30.00 60.00
DO David Ortiz 12.50 30.00
DW Dontrelle Willis 6.00 15.00
EB Erik Bedard 6.00 15.00
FT Frank Thomas 30.00 60.00
GS Grady Sizemore 12.50 30.00
HA Travis Hafner 6.00 15.00
HK Hong-Chih Kuo 12.50 30.00
HP Hunter Pence 12.50 30.00
HR Hanley Ramirez 12.50 30.00
HU Torii Hunter 6.00 15.00
IR Ivan Rodriguez 12.50 30.00
JB Jeremy Bonderman 10.00 25.00
JF Jeff Francoeur 15.00 40.00
JM Justin Morneau 10.00 25.00
JP Jake Peavy 12.50 30.00
JR Jose Reyes 12.50 30.00
JS Johan Santana 10.00 25.00
JV Jason Varitek/65 20.00 50.00
MA Don Mattingly/74 12.50 30.00
MC Miguel Cabrera 12.50 30.00
MO Magglio Ordonez 6.00 15.00
NM Nick Markakis 10.00 25.00
NR Nolan Ryan 30.00 60.00
RB Ryan Braun 20.00 50.00
RJ Randy Johnson/57 12.50 30.00
RO Roy Oswalt 6.00 15.00
RW Rickie Weeks 6.00 15.00
RZ Ryan Zimmerman 12.50 30.00
SM Stan Musial 15.00 40.00
TG Tony Gwynn 15.00 40.00
TH Todd Helton 10.00 25.00
TL Tim Lincecum 10.00 25.00
TS Takashi Saito/65 10.00 25.00
VE Justin Verlander 10.00 25.00
WB Wade Boggs 6.00 15.00

2008 Upper Deck Premier Patches Gold Milestones

OVERALL GU ODDS TWO PER PACK
PRINT RUNS B/WN 10-33 COPIES PER
NO PRICING ON QTY 25 OR LESS
AI Akinori Iwamura/15
AJ Andruw Jones/18
AL Adam LaRoche/13
BR Brian Roberts/18
CB Carlos Beltran/16
CJ Chipper Jones/26 15.00 40.00
CR Cal Ripken/19
CU Chase Utley/32 15.00 40.00
CW Chien-Ming Wang/19
DM Daisuke Matsuzaka/10
DO David Ortiz/12
DW Dontrelle Willis/14
EB Erik Bedard/15
FT Frank Thomas/14
GS Grady Sizemore/28 12.50 30.00
HA Travis Hafner/33 6.00 15.00
HK Hong-Chih Kuo/27 12.50 30.00
HP Hunter Pence/19
HR Hanley Ramirez/17
HU Torii Hunter/31 6.00 15.00
IR Ivan Rodriguez/14
JA Reggie Jackson/18
JB Jeremy Bonderman/14
JF Jeff Francoeur/14
JM Justin Morneau/22
JP Jake Peavy/15
JR Jose Reyes/17
JS Johan Santana/17
JV Jason Varitek/24
MA Don Mattingly/10
MC Miguel Cabrera/26 12.50 30.00
MO Magglio Ordonez/24
NM Nick Markakis/16
NR Nolan Ryan/11
RB Ryan Braun/11
RJ Randy Johnson/10
RO Roy Oswalt/20
RW Rickie Weeks/13
RZ Ryan Zimmerman/20
SM Stan Musial/16
TG Tony Gwynn/15
TH Todd Helton/25
TL Tim Lincecum/12
TP Tony Perez/20
TS Takashi Saito/24
VE Justin Verlander/17
WB Wade Boggs/12

2008 Upper Deck Premier Patches Gold Milestones Jersey Number

OVERALL GU ODDS TWO PER PACK
PRINT RUNS B/WN 1-57 COPIES PER
NO PRICING ON QTY 25 OR LESS
AI Akinori Iwamura/1
AJ Andruw Jones/25
AL Adam LaRoche/25
BR Brian Roberts/1
CB Carlos Beltran/15
CJ Chipper Jones/10
CR Cal Ripken Jr./8
CU Chase Utley/26 15.00 40.00
CW Chien-Ming Wang/40 20.00 50.00
DM Daisuke Matsuzaka/18
DO David Ortiz/34 12.50 30.00
DW Dontrelle Willis/35 6.00 15.00
EB Erik Bedard/45 6.00 15.00
FT Frank Thomas/35 30.00 60.00
GS Grady Sizemore/24
HA Travis Hafner/48 6.00 15.00
HK Hong-Chih Kuo/56 12.50 30.00
HP Hunter Pence/9
HR Hanley Ramirez/2
HU Torii Hunter/48 6.00 15.00
IR Ivan Rodriguez/7
JA Reggie Jackson/44 10.00 25.00
JB Jeremy Bonderman/38 10.00 25.00
JF Jeff Francoeur/7
JM Justin Morneau/33 10.00 25.00
JP Jake Peavy/44 12.50 30.00
JR Jose Reyes/7
JS Johan Santana/57 10.00 25.00
JV Jason Varitek/33 20.00 50.00
MA Don Mattingly/23
MC Miguel Cabrera/24
MO Magglio Ordonez/30 6.00 15.00
NM Nick Markakis/21
NR Nolan Ryan/30 30.00 60.00
RB Ryan Braun/8
RJ Randy Johnson/51 12.50 30.00
RO Roy Oswalt/44 6.00 15.00
RW Rickie Weeks/23
RZ Ryan Zimmerman/11
SM Stan Musial/6
TG Tony Gwynn/19
TH Todd Helton/17
TL Tim Lincecum/55 10.00 25.00
TP Tony Perez/24
TS Takashi Saito/44 10.00 25.00
VE Justin Verlander/35 10.00 25.00
WB Wade Boggs/26 6.00 15.00

2008 Upper Deck Premier Patches Autographs

OVERALL AU ODDS THREE PER PACK
STATED PRINT RUN 15 SER.#'d SETS
NO PRICING DUE TO SCARCITY
EXCHANGE DEADLINE 3/13/2010

2008 Upper Deck Premier Penmanship Autographs

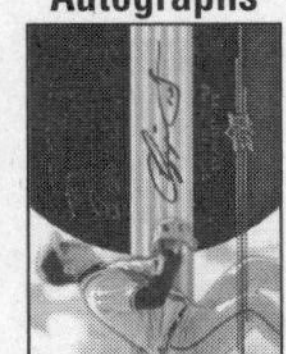

OVERALL AU ODDS THREE PER PACK
PRINT RUNS B/WN 15-50 COPIES PER
NO PRICING ON QTY 20 OR LESS
GOLD B/WN 3-5 COPIES PER
NO GOLD PRICING DUE TO SCARCITY
MASTERPIECE PRINT RUN 1 SER.#'d SET
NO MASTERPIECE PRICING AVAILABLE
EXCHANGE DEADLINE 3/13/2010
AK Al Kaline/50 15.00 40.00
BB Billy Butler/50 10.00 25.00
BE Johnny Bench/50 20.00 50.00
BF Bob Feller/20
BH Bill Hall/15
BL Joe Blanton/50 4.00 10.00
BT Bobby Thomson/50 10.00 25.00
CB Chad Billingsley/50 4.00 10.00
CC Carl Crawford/50 6.00 15.00
CF Carlton Fisk/50 10.00 25.00
CH Cole Hamels/50 15.00 40.00
CJ Chipper Jones/50 40.00 80.00
CR Cal Ripken Jr./50 75.00 150.00
CW Chien-Ming Wang/50 100.00 150.00
FC Fausto Carmona/50 6.00 15.00
FH Felix Hernandez/50 15.00 40.00
FT Frank Thomas/50 30.00 60.00
GP Gaylord Perry/50 4.00 10.00
HK Howie Kendrick/50 4.00 10.00
HP Hunter Pence/50 12.50 30.00
IK Ian Kennedy/50 30.00 60.00
IR Ivan Rodriguez/50 30.00 60.00
JB Jeremy Bonderman/50 6.00 15.00
JL John Lackey/50 4.00 10.00
JM John Maine/50 6.00 15.00
JP Jim Palmer/50 6.00 15.00
JV Justin Verlander/50 12.50 30.00
JW Josh Willingham/50 4.00 10.00
KW Kerry Wood/50 12.50 30.00
LA Luis Aparicio/40 6.00 15.00
MS Mike Schmidt/50 20.00 50.00
NM Nick Markakis/50 12.50 30.00
NR Nolan Ryan/50 40.00 80.00
PA Jonathan Papelbon/50 12.50 30.00
RB Ryan Braun/50 20.00 50.00
RC Rod Carew/50 10.00 25.00
RH Ramon Hernandez/50 4.00 10.00
RM Russell Martin/50 10.00 25.00
RZ Ryan Zimmerman/50 10.00 25.00
TH Travis Hafner/50 6.00 15.00
TT Troy Tulowitzki/50 12.50 30.00
VM Victor Martinez/50 6.00 15.00

2008 Upper Deck Premier Playoff Premier Autographs

OVERALL AU ODDS THREE PER PACK
PRINT RUNS B/WN 15-25 COPIES PER
NO PRICING DUE TO SCARCITY
GOLD PRINT RUN 5 SER.#'d SETS
NO GOLD PRICING DUE TO SCARCITY
MASTERPIECE PRINT RUN 1 SER.#'d SET
NO MASTERPIECE PRICING AVAILABLE
EXCHANGE DEADLINE 3/13/2010

2008 Upper Deck Premier Premier Pairings Autographs

OVERALL AU ODDS THREE PER PACK
STATED PRINT RUN 25 SER.#'d SETS
NO PRICING DUE TO SCARCITY
EXCHANGE DEADLINE 3/13/2010

2008 Upper Deck Premier Quad Patches

OVERALL GU ODDS TWO PER PACK
STATED PRINT RUN 20 SER.#'d SETS
NO PRICING DUE TO SCARCITY
GOLD PRINT RUN 10 SER.#'d SETS
NO GOLD PRICING DUE TO SCARCITY
MASTERPIECE PRINT RUN 1 SER.#'d SET
NO MASTERPIECE PRICING AVAILABLE
PLATINUM PRINT RUN 5 SER.#'d SETS
NO PLATINUM PRICING AVAILABLE

2008 Upper Deck Premier Quartet

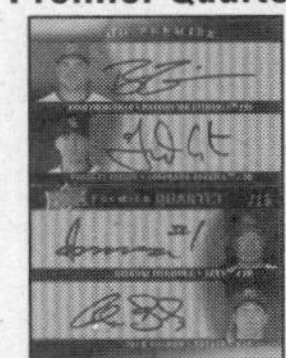

OVERALL GU ODDS TWO PER PACK
STATED PRINT RUN 15 SER.#'d SETS
NO PRICING DUE TO SCARCITY

2008 Upper Deck Premier Remnants Triple Blue-Gold

OVERALL GU ODDS TWO PER PACK
PRINT RUNS B/WN 25-75 COPIES PER
NO PRICING ON QTY 25
*BLUE-SILVER: .4X TO 1X BASIC
B-S PRINT RUNS B/WN 25-75 PER
NO B-S PRICING ON QTY 25
*BRONZE: .4X TO 1X BASIC
BRONZE PRINT RUNS B/WN 25-75 PER
NO BRONZE PRICING ON QTY 25
MASTERPIECE PRINT RUN 1 SER.#'d SET
NO MASTERPIECE PRICING AVAILABLE
AJ Andruw Jones ATL/25
AP Albert Pujols STL/75 10.00 25.00
CF Carlton Fisk CHI/25
CY Carl Yastrzemski YAZ/50 5.00 12.00
DJ Derek Jeter NYY/75 12.50 30.00
DM Daisuke Matsuzaka JPN/75 12.50 30.00
DO David Ortiz BOS/50 5.00 12.00
HK Hong-Chih Kuo KUO/25
JB Josh Beckett BOS/25
KG Ken Griffey Jr. OF3/50 10.00 25.00
MA Don Mattingly NYY/25
MR Manny Ramirez BOS/25
MS Mike Schmidt PHI/50 12.50 30.00
NR Nolan Ryan TEX/75 12.50 30.00
PA Jonathan Papelbon BOS/25
PO Jorge Posada NYY/25
RJ Reggie Jackson NYY/75 6.00 15.00
RY Robin Yount MVP/50 12.50 30.00
VG Vladimir Guerrero MVP/25
WB Wade Boggs BOS/50 5.00 12.00

2008 Upper Deck Premier Remnants Triple Gold

OVERALL GU ODDS TWO PER PACK
PRINT RUNS B/WN 2-44 COPIES PER
NO PRICING ON QTY 23 OR LESS
AP Albert Pujols/5
CJ Chipper Jones/10
CY Carl Yastrzemski/8
DJ Derek Jeter/2
DM Daisuke Matsuzaka/18
DO David Ortiz/34 5.00 12.00
JB Josh Beckett/7
KG Ken Griffey Jr./3
MA Don Mattingly/23
MS Mike Schmidt/33 12.50 30.00
NR Nolan Ryan/34 12.50 30.00
PO Jorge Posada/20
RJ Reggie Jackson/44 6.00 15.00
RY Robin Yount/19
VG Vladimir Guerrero/27 5.00 12.00
WB Wade Boggs/26 5.00 12.00

2008 Upper Deck Premier Remnants Triple Gold Milestones

OVERALL GU ODDS TWO PER PACK
PRINT RUNS B/WN 5-50 COPIES PER
NO PRICING ON QTY 25 OR LESS
AJ Andruw Jones/5
AP Albert Pujols/50 10.00 25.00
CF Carlton Fisk/25
CJ Chipper Jones/5
CS Curt Schilling/5
CU Chase Utley/5
CY Carl Yastrzemski/25
DJ Derek Jeter/15
DM Daisuke Matsuzaka/10
DO David Ortiz/10
HK Hong-Chih Kuo/5
JB Josh Beckett/5
KG Ken Griffey Jr./25
MA Don Mattingly/5
MS Mike Schmidt/25
NR Nolan Ryan/5
RJ Reggie Jackson/15
RY Robin Yount/25
WB Wade Boggs/10

2008 Upper Deck Premier Remnants Triple Autographs

OVERALL AU ODDS THREE PER PACK
PRINT RUNS B/WN 5-25 COPIES PER
NO PRICING DUE TO SCARCITY
EXCHANGE DEADLINE 3/13/2010

2008 Upper Deck Premier Remnants Quad

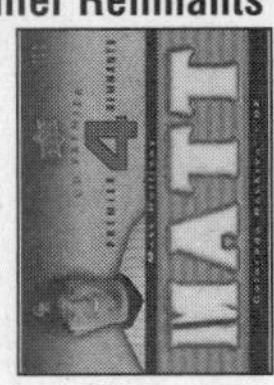

OVERALL GU ODDS TWO PER PACK
PRINT RUNS15-50 COPIES PER
NO PRICING ON QTY 15 OR LESS
BRONZE PRINT RUN 25 SER.#'d SETS
NO BRONZE PRICING DUE TO SCARCITY
GOLD B/WN 5-10 COPIES PER
NO GOLD PRICING DUE TO SCARCITY
MASTERPIECE PRINT RUN 1 SER.#'d SET
NO MASTERPIECE PRICING AVAILABLE
AD Adam Dunn DUNN/50 3.00 8.00
AD Adam Dunn REDS/50 3.00 8.00
BE Carlos Beltran METS/50 3.00 8.00
BE Carlos Beltran HITS/50 3.00 8.00
BR Brooks Robinson 16GG/50 4.00 10.00
BR Brooks Robinson1964/15
BS Ben Sheets WINS/50 3.00 8.00
BS Ben Sheets 2001/50 3.00 8.00
CF Carlton Fisk FISK/50 4.00 10.00
CF Carlton Fisk HITS/50 4.00 10.00
CH Cole Hamels COLE/50 4.00 10.00
CH Cole Hamels WINS/50 4.00 10.00
CL Roger Clemens ALCY/50 6.00 15.00
CL Roger Clemens WINS/50 6.00 15.00
CR Cal Ripken Jr. CAL8/50 20.00 50.00
CR Cal Ripken Jr.2632/50 20.00 50.00
CS Curt Schilling SOCK/50 4.00 10.00
CS Curt Schilling CURT/50 4.00 10.00
CW Chien-Ming Wang WANG/50 20.00 50.00
CW Chien-Ming Wang WINS/50 20.00 50.00
DJ Derek Jeter CAPT/50 20.00 50.00
DJ Derek Jeter SS#2/50 20.00 50.00
DL Derrek Lee CUBS/50 3.00 8.00
DL Derrek Lee RUNS/50 3.00 8.00
DM Don Mattingly1985/50 10.00 25.00
DM Don Mattingly CAPT/50 10.00 25.00
DO David Ortiz PAPI/50 6.00 15.00
DO David Ortiz 2004/50 6.00 15.00
FH Felix Hernandez KING/50 6.00 15.00
FH Felix Hernandez WINS/50 6.00 15.00
HK Hong-Chih Kuo HONG/50 6.00 15.00
HK Hong-Chih Kuo WINS/50 6.00 15.00
HR Hanley Ramirez SS#2/50 4.00 10.00
HR Hanley Ramirez HITS/50 4.00 10.00
JB Johnny Bench 1972/50 6.00 15.00
JB Johnny Bench REDS/50 6.00 15.00
JH J.J. Hardy SS#7/50 4.00 10.00
JH J.J. Hardy 2007/50 4.00 10.00
JP Jake Peavy JAKE/50 4.00 10.00
JP Jake Peavy WINS/50 4.00 10.00
JR Jim Rice RICE/50 4.00 10.00
JR Jim Rice1978/50 4.00 10.00
JS John Smoltz WINS/50 4.00 10.00
JS John Smoltz 1996/50 4.00 10.00
KG Ken Griffey Jr. REDS/50 10.00 25.00
KG Ken Griffey Jr. OF#3/50 10.00 25.00
MH Matt Holliday MATT/50 4.00 10.00
MH Matt Holliday OF#5/50 4.00 10.00
NR Nolan Ryan RYAN/50 20.00 50.00
NR Nolan Ryan 383K/50 20.00 50.00
NR2 Nolan Ryan 5714/50 20.00 50.00
NR2 Nolan Ryan WINS/50 20.00 50.00
PF Prince Fielder RUNS/50 6.00 15.00
PF Prince Fielder HITS/50 6.00 15.00
PR Phil Rizzuto NYSS/50 10.00 25.00
PR Phil Rizzuto1950/50 10.00 25.00
RC Rod Carew 3000/50 4.00 10.00
RC Rod Carew 1977/50 4.00 10.00
RE Jose Reyes METS/50 10.00 25.00
RE Jose Reyes JOSE/50 10.00 25.00
RJ Reggie Jackson NYRF/50 6.00 15.00
RJ Reggie Jackson1977/50 6.00 15.00
RS Ryne Sandberg CUBS/50 10.00 25.00
RS Ryne Sandberg RYNO/50 10.00 25.00
RZ Ryan Zimmerman WASH/50 10.00 25.00
RZ Ryan Zimmerman RYAN/50 10.00 25.00
SM Stan Musial STAN/50 15.00 40.00
SM Stan Musial 3MVP/50 15.00 40.00
TG Tony Gwynn 3000/50 12.50 30.00
TG Tony Gwynn TONY/50 12.50 30.00
TM Thurman Munson CAPT/50 15.00 40.00
TM Thurman Munson 1976/50 15.00 40.00
TR Tim Raines ROCK/50 3.00 8.00
TR Tim Raines RUNS/50 3.00 8.00
TS Tom Seaver METS/50 10.00 25.00
TS Tom Seaver 1969/50 10.00 25.00
VG Vladimir Guerrero VLAD/50 4.00 10.00
VG Vladimir Guerrero STAR/50 4.00 10.00
WB Wade Boggs 3000/50 10.00 25.00
WB Wade Boggs WADE/50 10.00 25.00

2008 Upper Deck Premier Remnants Quad Gold Milestones

OVERALL GU ODDS TWO PER PACK
PRINT RUNS B/WN 2-77 COPIES PER
NO PRICING ON QTY 24 OR LESS
AD Adam Dunn/46 3.00 8.00
BE Carlos Beltran/41 3.00 8.00
BR Brooks Robinson/16
BS Ben Sheets/18
CF Carlton Fisk/37 4.00 10.00
CH Cole Hamels/15
CL Roger Clemens/20
CR Cal Ripken Jr./34 20.00 50.00
CS Curt Schilling/13
CW Chien-Ming Wang/47 20.00 50.00
DJ Derek Jeter/2
DL Derrek Lee/46 3.00 8.00
DM Don Mattingly/35 10.00 25.00
DO David Ortiz/54 6.00 15.00
FH Felix Hernandez/77 6.00 15.00
HK Hong-Chih Kuo/71 6.00 15.00
HR Hanley Ramirez/51 4.00 10.00
JB Johnny Bench/45 6.00 15.00
JH J.J. Hardy/9
JP Jake Peavy/16
JR Jim Rice/46 4.00 10.00
JS John Smoltz/15
KG Ken Griffey Jr./8
MH Matt Holliday/36 4.00 10.00
NR Nolan Ryan/19
NR2 Nolan Ryan/18
PF Prince Fielder/50 6.00 15.00
PR Phil Rizzuto/38 10.00 25.00
RC Rod Carew/49 4.00 10.00
RE Jose Reyes/60 10.00 25.00
RJ Reggie Jackson/18
RS Ryne Sandberg/40 10.00 25.00
RZ Ryan Zimmerman/20
SM Stan Musial/16
TG Tony Gwynn/33 12.50 30.00
TM Thurman Munson/17
TR Tim Raines/50 3.00 8.00
TS Tom Seaver/19
VG Vladimir Guerrero/39 4.00 10.00
WB Wade Boggs/24

2008 Upper Deck Premier Remnants Quad Autographs

OVERALL AU ODDS THREE PER PACK
STATED PRINT RUN 15 SER.#'d SETS
NO PRICING DUE TO SCARCITY
EXCHANGE DEADLINE 3/13/2010

2008 Upper Deck Premier Remnants Five

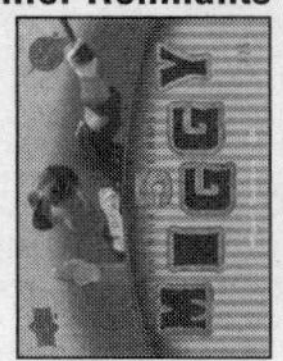

OVERALL GU ODDS TWO PER PACK
PRINT RUNS B/WN 10-25 COPIES PER
NO PRICING DUE TO SCARCITY
GOLD B/WN 3-10 COPIES PER
NO GOLD PRICING DUE TO SCARCITY
MASTERPIECE PRINT RUN 1 SER.#'d SET
NO MASTERPIECE PRICING AVAILABLE

2008 Upper Deck Premier Signature Premier

OVERALL AU ODDS THREE PER PACK
PRINT RUNS B/WN 5-45 COPIES PER
NO PRICING ON QTY 25 OR LESS
BRONZE B/WN 1-25 COPIES PER
NO BRONZE PRICING AVAILABLE
GOLD B/WN 1-15 COPIES PER
NO GOLD PRICING DUE TO SCARCITY
MASTERPIECE PRINT RUN 1 SER.#'d SET
NO MASTERPIECE PRICING AVAILABLE
INK CHANGE PRINT RUN 1 SER.#'d SET
NO INK CHANGE PRICING AVAILABLE
EXCHANGE DEADLINE 3/13/2010
AE Andre Ethier 10.00 25.00
AG Adrian Gonzalez 4.00 10.00
AI Akinori Iwamura 10.00 25.00
AM Andrew Miller 4.00 10.00
AR Aramis Ramirez 6.00 15.00
BB Billy Buckner 4.00 10.00
BD Bobby Doerr/20
BE Johnny Bench 20.00 50.00
BF Bob Feller/5
BH Bill Hall/25
BI Chad Billingsley 4.00 10.00
BJ B.J. Upton 6.00 15.00
BM Brian McCann 12.50 30.00
BO Jeremy Bonderman 6.00 15.00
BS Bronson Sardinha 4.00 10.00
BU Billy Butler 10.00 25.00
CA Matt Cain 4.00 10.00
CB Clay Buchholz 15.00 40.00
CC Chris Carpenter 10.00 25.00
CF Carlton Fisk 10.00 25.00
CR Cal Ripken Jr. 60.00 120.00
DB Daric Barton 4.00 10.00
DH Dan Haren 4.00 10.00
DL Derrek Lee 6.00 15.00
DM Don Mattingly 15.00 40.00
DU Dan Uggla/25
EB Ernie Banks/37 15.00 40.00
EM Edgar Martinez 15.00 40.00
FC Fausto Carmona 6.00 15.00
FP Felix Pie/25
GA Garret Anderson 6.00 15.00
GO Alex Gordon 15.00 40.00
GP Gaylord Perry 4.00 10.00
HK Howie Kendrick 4.00 10.00
HR Harold Reynolds 4.00 10.00
HU Chin-Lung Hu 30.00 60.00
JB Jim Bunning 6.00 15.00
JL John Lackey 4.00 10.00
JM John Maine 6.00 15.00
JP Jim Palmer 6.00 15.00
JT J.R. Towles 4.00 10.00
JV Joey Votto 6.00 15.00
JW Josh Willingham 4.00 10.00
JZ Joel Zumaya 4.00 10.00
KE Ian Kennedy 30.00 60.00
KI Ian Kinsler 6.00 15.00
KY Kevin Youkilis 6.00 15.00
LA Luis Aparicio 6.00 15.00
LE Jon Lester 15.00 40.00
LH Luke Hochevar 6.00 15.00
MI Monte Irvin/15
MS Mike Schmidt 20.00 50.00
MT Miguel Tejada 6.00 15.00
MU Stan Musial 40.00 80.00
NL Noah Lowry 4.00 10.00
NM Nick Markakis 12.50 30.00
NR Nolan Ryan 40.00 80.00
NS Nick Swisher 4.00 10.00
OH Ross Ohlendorf 6.00 15.00
OW Micah Owings 6.00 15.00
PF Prince Fielder 20.00 50.00
PH Phil Hughes 20.00 50.00
PM Pedro Martinez 30.00 60.00
RB Ryan Braun 20.00 50.00
RC Rod Carew 10.00 25.00
RD Ross Detwiler 4.00 10.00
RH Rich Hill 4.00 10.00
RI Jim Rice/20
RJ Reggie Jackson 20.00 50.00
RO Roger Clemens 30.00 60.00
RS Ron Santo/25
RT Ryan Theriot 10.00 25.00
RY Ryne Sandberg 20.00 50.00
SA Jarrod Saltalamacchia 4.00 10.00
SC Steve Carlton/25
SD Stephen Drew 4.00 10.00
SK Scott Kazmir 8.00 20.00

TB Travis Buck 4.00 10.00
TG Tony Gwynn 20.00 50.00
TH Travis Hafner 6.00 15.00
TM Tino Martinez 10.00 25.00
TP Tony Perez 10.00 25.00
WB Wladimir Balentien 6.00 15.00
WF Whitey Ford 20.00 50.00
YE Yunel Escobar 10.00 25.00

2008 Upper Deck Premier Signature Premier Gold Jersey Number

OVERALL AU ODDS THREE PER PACK
PRINT RUNS B/WN 1-65 COPIES PER
NO PRICING ON QTY 25 OR LESS
EXCHANGE DEADLINE 3/13/2010
AE Andre Ethier/16
AG Adrian Gonzalez/23
AI Akinori Iwamura/1
AM Andrew Miller/48 4.00 10.00
AR Aramis Ramirez/16
BB Billy Buckner/38 4.00 10.00
BD Bobby Doerr/1
BE Johnny Bench/5
BF Bob Feller/19
BH Bill Hall/1
BI Chad Billingsley/58 4.00 10.00
BJ B.J. Upton/2
BM Brian McCann/16
BO Jeremy Bonderman/38 6.00 15.00
BS Bronson Sardinha/64 4.00 10.00
BU Billy Butler/21
CA Matt Cain/18
CB Clay Buchholz/61 15.00 40.00
CC Chris Carpenter/29 10.00 25.00
CF Carlton Fisk/27 10.00 25.00
CR Cal Ripken Jr./8
DB Daric Barton/10
DH Dan Haren/15
DL Derrek Lee/25
DM Don Mattingly/23
DU Dan Uggla/6
EB Ernie Banks/14
EM Edgar Martinez/11
FC Fausto Carmona/55 6.00 15.00
FP Felix Pie/10
GA Garret Anderson/16
GO Alex Gordon/7
GP Gaylord Perry/36 4.00 10.00
HK Howie Kendrick/47 4.00 10.00
HR Harold Reynolds/4
HU Chin-Lung Hu/60 30.00 60.00
JB Jim Bunning/14
JL John Lackey/41 4.00 10.00
JM John Maine/33 6.00 15.00
JP Jim Palmer/22
JT J.R. Towles/46 4.00 10.00
JV Joey Votto/60 6.00 15.00
JW Josh Willingham/14
JZ Joel Zumaya/54 4.00 10.00
KE Ian Kennedy/36 30.00 60.00
KI Ian Kinsler/5
KY Kevin Youkilis/20
LA Luis Aparicio/11
LE Jon Lester/31 6.00 15.00
LH Luke Hochevar/44 6.00 15.00
MI Monte Irvin/1
MS Mike Schmidt/20
MT Miguel Tejada/10
MU Stan Musial/6
NL Noah Lowry/51 4.00 10.00
NM Nick Markakis/21
NR Nolan Ryan/30 40.00 80.00
NS Nick Swisher/33 4.00 10.00
OH Ross Ohlendorf/60 6.00 15.00
OW Micah Owings/44 6.00 15.00
PF Prince Fielder/28 20.00 50.00
PH Phil Hughes/65 20.00 50.00
PM Pedro Martinez/45 30.00 60.00
RB Ryan Braun/8
RC Rod Carew/29 10.00 25.00
RD Ross Detwiler/29 4.00 10.00
RH Rich Hill/53 4.00 10.00
RI Jim Rice/5
RJ Reggie Jackson/44 20.00 50.00
RO Roger Clemens/22
RS Ron Santo/5
RT Ryan Theriot/2
RY Ryne Sandberg/23
SA Jarrod Saltalamacchia/25
SD Stephen Drew/6
SK Scott Kazmir/19
TB Travis Buck/6
TG Tony Gwynn/19
TH Travis Hafner/48 6.00 15.00
TM Tino Martinez/24
TP Tony Perez/24
WB Wladimir Balentien/50 6.00 15.00
WF Whitey Ford/16
YE Yunel Escobar/19

2008 Upper Deck Premier Significant Six Autographs

OVERALL AU ODDS THREE PER PACK
STATED PRINT RUN 10 SER.#'d SETS
NO PRICING DUE TO SCARCITY
EXCHANGE DEADLINE 3/13/2010

2008 Upper Deck Premier Significant Stars Autographs

OVERALL AU ODDS THREE PER PACK
PRINT RUNS B/WN 10-20 COPIES PER
NO PRICING DUE TO SCARCITY
PLATINUM B/WN 3-10 COPIES PER
NO PLATINUM PRICING AVAILABLE
MASTERPIECE PRINT RUN 1 SER.#'d SET
NO MASTERPIECE PRICING AVAILABLE
EXCHANGE DEADLINE 3/13/2013

2008 Upper Deck Premier Stitchings

OVERALL STITCHINGS ONE PER PACK
PRINT RUNS B/WN 50-75 COPIES PER
GOLD B/WN 15-25 COPIES PER
NO GOLD PRICING DUE TO SCARCITY
MASTERPIECE PRINT RUN 1 SER.#'d SET
NO MASTERPIECE PRICING AVAILABLE
SILVER B/WN 5-10 COPIES PER
NO SILVER PRICING DUE TO SCARCITY
AG Alex Gordon/75 10.00 25.00
AG Alex Gordon/50 10.00 25.00
AK Al Kaline/75 10.00 25.00
AK Al Kaline/50 10.00 25.00
AP Albert Pujols/75 10.00 25.00
AP Albert Pujols/50 10.00 25.00
AR Alex Rodriguez/75 12.50 30.00
AR Alex Rodriguez/50 12.50 30.00
AS Alfonso Soriano/75 5.00 12.00
AS Alfonso Soriano/50 5.00 12.00
BD Bobby Doerr/75 2.00 5.00
BD Bobby Doerr/50 2.00 5.00
BE Johnny Bench/75 5.00 12.00
BE Johnny Bench/50 5.00 12.00
BF Bob Feller/75 10.00 25.00
BF Bob Feller/50 10.00 25.00
BG Bob Gibson/75 5.00 12.00
BG Bob Gibson/50 5.00 12.00
BM Bill Mazeroski/75 3.00 8.00
BM Bill Mazeroski/50 3.00 8.00
BR Babe Ruth/75 15.00 40.00
BR Babe Ruth/50 15.00 40.00
CA Miguel Cabrera/75 3.00 8.00
CA Miguel Cabrera/50 3.00 8.00
CB Craig Biggio/75 3.00 8.00
CB Craig Biggio/50 3.00 8.00
CF Carlton Fisk/75 10.00 25.00
CF Carlton Fisk/50 10.00 25.00
CJ Chipper Jones/75 6.00 15.00
CJ Chipper Jones/50 6.00 15.00
CR Cal Ripken Jr./75 20.00 50.00
CR Cal Ripken Jr./50 20.00 50.00
CS Rod Carew 5.00 12.00
Tom Seaver
75
CS Tom Seaver 5.00 12.00
Rod Carew
50
CU Chase Utley/75 5.00 12.00
CU Chase Utley/50 5.00 12.00
CW Chien-Ming Wang/75 10.00 25.00
CW Chien-Ming Wang/50 10.00 25.00
CY Carl Yastrzemski/75 10.00 25.00
CY Carl Yastrzemski/50 10.00 25.00
DJ Derek Jeter/75 15.00 40.00
DJ Derek Jeter/50 15.00 40.00
DL Derrek Lee/75 2.00 5.00
DL Derrek Lee/50 2.00 5.00
DM Daisuke Matsuzaka/75 10.00 25.00
DM Daisuke Matsuzaka/50 10.00 25.00
DY Delmon Young/75 3.00 8.00
DY Delmon Young/50 3.00 8.00
EM Eddie Murray/75 6.00 15.00
EM Eddie Murray/50 6.00 15.00
FA Nellie Fox 6.00 15.00
Luis Aparicio
75
FA Nellie Fox 6.00 15.00
Luis Aparicio
50
FH Felix Hernandez/75 6.00 15.00
FH Felix Hernandez/50 6.00 15.00
FJ Fergie Jenkins/75 2.00 5.00
FJ Fergie Jenkins/50 2.00 5.00
FT Frank Thomas/75 10.00 25.00
FT Frank Thomas/50 10.00 25.00
FT2 Frank Thomas/75 10.00 25.00
FT2 Frank Thomas/50 10.00 25.00
GR Lou Gehrig 12.50 30.00
Babe Ruth
75
GR Babe Ruth 12.50 30.00
Lou Gehrig
50
GS Grady Sizemore/75 3.00 8.00
GS Grady Sizemore/50 3.00 8.00
GW Tony Gwynn/75 10.00 25.00
GW Tony Gwynn/50 10.00 25.00
HA Travis Hafner/75 5.00 12.00
HA Travis Hafner/50 5.00 12.00
HP Hunter Pence/75 5.00 12.00
HP Hunter Pence/50 5.00 12.00
HR Hanley Ramirez/75 3.00 8.00
HR Hanley Ramirez/50 3.00 8.00
HU Torii Hunter/75 2.00 5.00
HU Torii Hunter/50 2.00 5.00
JB Jason Bay/75 2.00 5.00
JB Jason Bay/50 2.00 5.00
JD Joe DiMaggio/75 6.00 15.00
JD Joe DiMaggio/50 6.00 15.00
JE Jim Edmonds/75 2.00 5.00
JE Jim Edmonds/50 2.00 5.00
JH Josh Hamilton/75 6.00 15.00
JH Josh Hamilton/50 6.00 15.00
JM Joe Mauer/75 3.00 8.00
JM Joe Mauer/50 3.00 8.00
JO Jonathan Papelbon/75 3.00 8.00
JO Jonathan Papelbon/50 3.00 8.00
JP Jake Peavy/75 3.00 8.00
JP Jake Peavy/50 3.00 8.00
JR Jackie Robinson 6.00 15.00
Roy Campanella
75
JR Jackie Robinson 6.00 15.00
Roy Campanella
50
JS Johan Santana/75 5.00 12.00
JS Johan Santana/50 5.00 12.00
JU Justin Morneau/75 2.00 5.00
JU Justin Morneau/50 2.00 5.00
JV Justin Verlander/75 6.00 15.00
JV Justin Verlander/50 6.00 15.00
JZ Joel Zumaya/75 2.00 5.00
JZ Joel Zumaya/50 2.00 5.00
KG Ken Griffey Jr./75 10.00 25.00
KG Ken Griffey Jr./50 10.00 25.00
KG2 Ken Griffey Jr./75 10.00 25.00
KG2 Ken Griffey Jr./50 10.00 25.00
KG3 Ken Griffey Jr./75 10.00 25.00
KG3 Ken Griffey Jr./50 10.00 25.00
KW Kerry Wood/75 2.00 5.00
KW Kerry Wood/50 2.00 5.00
LA Luis Aparicio/75 5.00 12.00
LA Luis Aparicio/50 5.00 12.00
LB Lou Brock/75 6.00 15.00
LB Lou Brock/50 6.00 15.00
LI Tim Lincecum/75 5.00 12.00
LI Tim Lincecum/50 5.00 12.00
MA Juan Marichal/75 5.00 12.00
MA Juan Marichal/50 5.00 12.00
MC Brian McCann/75 2.00 5.00
MC Brian McCann/50 2.00 5.00
MH Matt Holliday/75 3.00 8.00
MH Matt Holliday/50 3.00 8.00
MH2 Matt Holliday/75 3.00 8.00
MH2 Matt Holliday/50 3.00 8.00
MI Monte Irvin/75 5.00 12.00
MI Monte Irvin/50 5.00 12.00
MJ Hideki Matsui 12.50 30.00
Derek Jeter
75
MJ Hideki Matsui 12.50 30.00
Derek Jeter
50
MO Joe Morgan/75 5.00 12.00
MO Joe Morgan/50 5.00 12.00
MP Mike Piazza/75 5.00 12.00
MP Mike Piazza/50 5.00 12.00
MR Manny Ramirez/75 5.00 12.00
MR Manny Ramirez/50 5.00 12.00
MS Mike Schmidt/75 6.00 15.00
MS Mike Schmidt/50 6.00 15.00
NR Nolan Ryan/75 15.00 40.00
NR Nolan Ryan/50 15.00 40.00
OC Orlando Cepeda/75 5.00 12.00
OC Orlando Cepeda/50 5.00 12.00
OM Hideki Okajima 10.00 25.00
Daisuke Matsuzaka
75
OM Daisuke Matsuzaka 10.00 25.00
Hideki Okajima
50
OR David Ortiz 10.00 25.00
Manny Ramirez
75
OR Manny Ramirez 10.00 25.00
David Ortiz
50
PA Jim Palmer/75 3.00 8.00
PA Jim Palmer/50 3.00 8.00
PF Prince Fielder/75 5.00 12.00
PF Prince Fielder/50 5.00 12.00
PH Phil Hughes/75 6.00 15.00
PH Phil Hughes/50 6.00 15.00
PN Phil Niekro/75 3.00 8.00
PN Phil Niekro/50 3.00 8.00
RA Richie Ashburn/75 10.00 25.00
RA Richie Ashburn/50 10.00 25.00
RB Ryan Braun/75 6.00 15.00
RB Ryan Braun/50 6.00 15.00
RC Rod Carew/75 5.00 12.00
RC Rod Carew/50 5.00 12.00
RF Rollie Fingers/75 3.00 8.00
RF Rollie Fingers/50 3.00 8.00
RH Roy Halladay/75 3.00 8.00
RH Roy Halladay/50 3.00 8.00
RI Mariano Rivera/75 5.00 12.00
RI Mariano Rivera/50 5.00 12.00
RJ Reggie Jackson/75 3.00 8.00
RJ Reggie Jackson/50 3.00 8.00
RK Ralph Kiner/75 3.00 8.00
RK Ralph Kiner/50 3.00 8.00
RM Russell Martin/75 5.00 12.00
RM Russell Martin/50 5.00 12.00
RO Brooks Robinson/75 5.00 12.00
RO Brooks Robinson/50 5.00 12.00
RS Ryne Sandberg/75 10.00 25.00
RS Ryne Sandberg/50 10.00 25.00
RY Ryan Howard/75 6.00 15.00
RY Ryan Howard/50 6.00 15.00
RZ Ryan Zimmerman/75 5.00 12.00
RZ Ryan Zimmerman/50 5.00 12.00
SJ Ichiro/Kenji Johjima/75 10.00 25.00
SJ Kenji Johjima/Ichiro/50 10.00 25.00
SS Sammy Sosa/75 10.00 25.00
SS Sammy Sosa/50 10.00 25.00
SV Shane Victorino/75 2.00 5.00
SV Shane Victorino/50 2.00 5.00
TG Tom Glavine/75 3.00 8.00
TG Tom Glavine/50 3.00 8.00
TH Trevor Hoffman/75 3.00 8.00
TH Trevor Hoffman/50 3.00 8.00
TL Tommy Lasorda/75 5.00 12.00
TL Tommy Lasorda/50 5.00 12.00
TS Tom Seaver/75 5.00 12.00
TS Tom Seaver/50 5.00 12.00
TT Troy Tulowitzki/75 5.00 12.00
TT Troy Tulowitzki/50 5.00 12.00
VG Vladimir Guerrero/75 3.00 8.00
VG Vladimir Guerrero/50 3.00 8.00
VM Victor Martinez/75 2.00 5.00
VM Victor Martinez/50 2.00 5.00
WM Willie McCovey/75 5.00 12.00
WM Willie McCovey/50 5.00 12.00

2008 Upper Deck Premier Stitchings Autographs

OVERALL AU ODDS THREE PER PACK
PRINT RUNS B/WN 24-25 COPIES PER
NO PRICING DUE TO SCARCITY
EXCHANGE DEADLINE 3/13/2010

2008 Upper Deck Premier Stitchings Cuts

OVERALL AU ODDS THREE PER PACK
STATED PRINT RUN 1 SER.#'d SET
NO PRICING DUE TO SCARCITY
EXCHANGE DEADLINE 3/13/2010

2008 Upper Deck Premier Swatches

OVERALL GU ODDS TWO PER PACK
STATED PRINT RUN 50 SER.#'d SETS
GOLD 25 PRINT RUN 25 SER.#'d SETS
NO GOLD 25 PRICING AVAILABLE
GOLD 20 PRINT RUN 20 SER.#'d SETS
NO GOLD 20 PRICING AVAILABLE
SILVER PRINT RUN 10 SER.#'d SETS
NO SILVER PRICING DUE TO SCARCITY
AP Albert Pujols 25.00 60.00
AR Aramis Ramirez 6.00 15.00
AS Alfonso Soriano 10.00 25.00
BR Brian Roberts 10.00 25.00
BS Ben Sheets 10.00 25.00
CD Carlos Delgado 6.00 15.00
CH Cole Hamels 15.00 40.00
CS C.C. Sabathia 6.00 15.00
CY Carl Yastrzemski 25.00 60.00
CZ Carlos Zambrano 6.00 15.00
DH Dan Haren 6.00 15.00
DL Derrek Lee 10.00 25.00
EM Eddie Murray 15.00 40.00
FH Felix Hernandez 10.00 25.00
FS Freddy Sanchez 6.00 15.00
GM Greg Maddux 20.00 50.00
GP Gaylord Perry 6.00 15.00
GS Grady Sizemore 10.00 25.00
HK Howie Kendrick 6.00 15.00
JB Jason Bay 6.00 15.00
JL James Loney 10.00 25.00
JM Joe Mauer 10.00 25.00
JS John Smoltz 15.00 40.00
JT Jim Thome 10.00 25.00
KG Ken Griffey Jr. 25.00 60.00
KI Harmon Killebrew 15.00 40.00
KW Kerry Wood 6.00 15.00
LB Lance Berkman 10.00 25.00
MO Joe Morgan 6.00 15.00
MR Manny Ramirez 15.00 40.00
MS Mike Schmidt 25.00 60.00
MT Miguel Tejada 6.00 15.00
NM Nick Markakis 10.00 25.00
NS Nick Swisher 6.00 15.00
OR Magglio Ordonez 10.00 25.00
PM Pedro Martinez 10.00 25.00
RH Rich Hill 6.00 15.00
RM Russell Martin 6.00 15.00
RS Ryne Sandberg 30.00 80.00
RY Robin Yount 15.00 40.00
SC Curt Schilling 10.00 25.00
TG Tom Glavine 10.00 25.00
TH Trevor Hoffman 6.00 15.00
VG Vladimir Guerrero 15.00 40.00
VM Victor Martinez 6.00 15.00
VW Vernon Wells 6.00 15.00

2008 Upper Deck Premier Swatches Jersey Number

OVERALL GU ODDS TWO PER PACK
PRINT RUNS B/WN 1-76 COPIES PER
NO PRICING ON QTY 25 OR LESS
AP Albert Pujols/5
AR Aramis Ramirez/16
AS Alfonso Soriano/12
BR Brian Roberts/1
BS Ben Sheets/15
CD Carlos Delgado/21
CH Cole Hamels/35 15.00 40.00
CS C.C. Sabathia/53 6.00 15.00
CY Carl Yastrzemski/16
CZ Carlos Zambrano/76 6.00 15.00
DH Dan Haren/15
DL Derrek Lee/25
EM Eddie Murray/33 15.00 40.00
FH Felix Hernandez/34 10.00 25.00
FS Freddy Sanchez/12
GM Greg Maddux/31 20.00 50.00
GP Gaylord Perry/34 6.00 15.00
GS Grady Sizemore/24
HK Howie Kendrick/48 6.00 15.00
JB Jason Bay/38 6.00 15.00
JL James Loney/7
JM Joe Mauer/29 10.00 25.00
JS John Smoltz/14
JT Jim Thome/50 10.00 25.00
KG Ken Griffey Jr./3
KI Harmon Killebrew/6
KW Kerry Wood/36 6.00 15.00
LB Lance Berkman/17
MO Joe Morgan/8
MR Manny Ramirez/24
MS Mike Schmidt/20
MT Miguel Tejada/10
NM Nick Markakis/21
NS Nick Swisher/33 6.00 15.00
OR Magglio Ordonez/30 10.00 25.00
PM Pedro Martinez/45 10.00 25.00
RH Rich Hill/53 6.00 15.00
RM Russell Martin/55 6.00 15.00
RS Ryne Sandberg/23
RY Robin Yount/19
SC Curt Schilling/38 10.00 25.00
TG Tom Glavine/47 10.00 25.00
TH Trevor Hoffman/51 6.00 15.00
VG Vladimir Guerrero/27 15.00 40.00
VM Victor Martinez/41 6.00 15.00
VW Vernon Wells/10

2008 Upper Deck Premier Teams Memorabilia

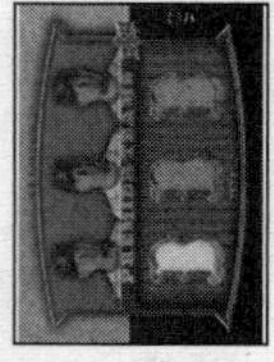

OVERALL GU ODDS TWO PER PACK
PRINT RUNS B/WN 20-50 COPIES PER
NO PRICING ON QTY 25 OR LESS
SILVER PRINT RUN 3 SER.#'d SETS
NO SILVER PRICING DUE TO SCARCITY
BFS Ryan Braun 20.00 50.00
Prince Fielder
Ben Sheets/50
BHG Ryan Braun
JJ Hardy
Yovani Gallardo/25
BJH Adrian Beltre
Kenji Johjima
Felix Hernandez/25
BMP Johnny Bench 15.00 40.00
Joe Morgan
Tony Perez/50
CMW Roger Clemens 15.00 40.00
Mike Mussina
Chien-Ming Wang/50
CPB Roberto Clemente 30.00 60.00
Dave Parker
Jason Bay/50
CRJ Roger Clemens 15.00 40.00
Mariano Rivera
Derek Jeter/50
CRR Roy Campanella 30.00 60.00
Pee Wee Reese
Jackie Robinson/50
CSM Michael Cuddyer
Johan Santana
Joe Mauer/25
DBR Carlos Delgado
Carlos Beltran
Jose Reyes/25
GBS Alex Gordon
Billy Butler
Mike Sweeney/25
GDH Ken Griffey Jr. 30.00 60.00
Adam Dunn
Josh Hamilton/50
GFW Vladimir Guerrero
Chone Figgins
Jered Weaver/25
IUK Akinori Iwamura
B.J. Upton
Scott Kazmir/25
JJF Chipper Jones 12.50 30.00
Andruw Jones
Jeff Francoeur/50
JWD Randy Johnson 6.00 15.00
Brandon Webb
Stephen Drew/50
KBS Hong-Chih Kuo
Chad Billingsley
Takashi Saito/25
LME James Loney
Russell Martin
Andre Ethier/25
LRS Derrek Lee
Aramis Ramirez
Alfonso Soriano/25
LVZ Tim Lincecum
Omar Vizquel
Barry Zito/25
MJJ Don Mattingly 12.50 30.00
Reggie Jackson
Derek Jeter/50
MPB Stan Musial 20.00 50.00
Albert Pujols
Lou Brock/50
MSB Daisuke Matsuzaka 15.00 40.00
Curt Schilling
Josh Beckett/50
MSM Joe Mauer
Johan Santana
Justin Morneau/25
OBY David Ortiz 10.00 25.00
Wade Boggs
Kevin Youkilis/50
ORS Magglio Ordonez
Ivan Rodriguez
Gary Sheffield/25
ORY David Ortiz 10.00 25.00
Manny Ramirez
Kevin Youkilis/50
PCR Albert Pujols 12.50 30.00
Chris Carpenter
Scott Rolen/50
PMH Jake Peavy 15.00 40.00
Greg Maddux
Trevor Hoffman/50
POB Hunter Pence
Roy Oswalt
Lance Berkman/25
RGD Babe Ruth
Lou Gehrig
Joe DiMaggio/20
RWU Hanley Ramirez
Dontrelle Willis
Dan Uggla/25
SBW Ryne Sandberg 20.00 50.00
Ernie Banks
Billy Williams/50
SCH Nick Swisher
Eric Chavez
Dan Haren/25
SMF John Smoltz
Brian McCann
Jeff Francoeur/25
SMH Grady Sizemore
Victor Martinez
Travis Hafner/25
TDK Jim Thome
Jermaine Dye
Paul Konerko/25
UHR Chase Utley
Cole Hamels
Jimmy Rollins/25
USH Chase Utley 20.00 50.00
Mike Schmidt
Cole Hamels/50
VBZ Justin Verlander
Jeremy Bonderman
Joel Zumaya/25
WHT Vernon Wells
Roy Halladay
Frank Thomas/25
YPH Chris Young
Jake Peavy
Trevor Hoffman/25

2008 Upper Deck Premier Teams Memorabilia Gold

OVERALL GU ODDS TWO PER PACK
PRINT RUNS B/WN 9-33 COPIES PER
NO PRICING ON QTY 15 OR LESS
BFS Ryan Braun 20.00 50.00
Prince Fielder
Ben Sheets/33
BMP Johnny Bench 15.00 40.00
Joe Morgan
Tony Perez/33
CMW Roger Clemens 15.00 40.00
Mike Mussina
Chien-Ming Wang/33
CPB Roberto Clemente 30.00 60.00
Dave Parker
Jason Bay/33
CRJ Roger Clemens 15.00 40.00
Mariano Rivera
Derek Jeter/33
CRR Roy Campanella 30.00 60.00
Pee Wee Reese
Jackie Robinson/33
GDH Ken Griffey Jr. 30.00 60.00
Adam Dunn
Josh Hamilton/33
JJF Chipper Jones 12.50 30.00
Andruw Jones
Jeff Francoeur/33
JWD Randy Johnson 6.00 15.00
Brandon Webb
Stephen Drew/33
MJJ Don Mattingly 12.50 30.00
Reggie Jackson
Derek Jeter/33
MPB Stan Musial 20.00 50.00
Albert Pujols
Lou Brock/33
MSB Daisuke Matsuzaka 15.00 40.00
Curt Schilling
Josh Beckett/33
OBY David Ortiz 10.00 25.00
Wade Boggs
Kevin Youkilis/33
ORY David Ortiz 10.00 25.00
Manny Ramirez
Kevin Youkilis/33
PCR Albert Pujols 12.50 30.00
Chris Carpenter
Scott Rolen/33
PMH Jake Peavy 15.00 40.00
Greg Maddux
Trevor Hoffman/33
SBW Ryne Sandberg 20.00 50.00
Ernie Banks
Billy Williams/33
USH Chase Utley 20.00 50.00
Mike Schmidt
Cole Hamels/33

2008 Upper Deck Premier The Premier Card

OVERALL AU ODDS THREE PER PACK
STATED PRINT RUN 3 SER.#'d SETS
NO PRICING DUE TO SCARCITY
EXCHANGE DEADLINE 3/13/2010

2008 Upper Deck Premier Trios Autographs

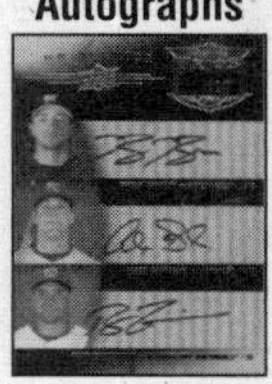

OVERALL AU ODDS THREE PER PACK
STATED PRINT RUN 20 SER.#'d SETS
NO PRICING DUE TO SCARCITY
EXCHANGE DEADLINE 3/13/2010

2008 Upper Deck Premier Trios Memorabilia

OVERALL GU ODDS TWO PER PACK
PRINT RUNS B/WN 25-50 COPIES PER
NO PRICING ON QTY 25 OR LESS
SILVER PRINT RUN 3 SER.#'d SETS
NO SILVER PRICING AVAILABLE
BFB Johnny Bench 12.50 30.00
Carlton Fisk
Yogi Berra/50
BPG Jason Bay 12.50 30.00
Albert Pujols
Ken Griffey Jr./50
BRD Carlos Beltran 6.00 15.00
Jose Reyes
Carlos Delgado/50
BZJ Ryan Braun 6.00 15.00
Ryan Zimmerman
Chipper Jones/50
CMM Michael Cuddyer 6.00 15.00
Justin Morneau
Joe Mauer/50
DOF Adam Dunn 10.00 25.00
David Ortiz
Prince Fielder/50
GTP Ken Griffey Jr. 15.00 40.00
Frank Thomas
Albert Pujols/50
GWK Vladimir Guerrero 6.00 15.00
Jered Weaver
Howie Kendrick/50
HAT Matt Holliday 10.00 25.00
Garrett Atkins
Troy Tulowitzki/50
HMS Travis Hafner 6.00 15.00
Victor Martinez
Grady Sizemore/50
HSS Dan Haren 6.00 15.00
Nick Swisher
Huston Street/50
JFS Chipper Jones 30.00 60.00
Jeff Francoeur
John Smoltz/50
JTR Derek Jeter 10.00 25.00
Troy Tulowitzki
Hanley Ramirez/50
JWP Derek Jeter 20.00 50.00
Chien-Ming Wang
Andy Pettitte/50
LRS Derrek Lee 6.00 15.00
Aramis Ramirez
Alfonso Soriano/50
MCG Greg Maddux 12.50 30.00
Roger Clemens
Tom Glavine/50
MMS Joe Mauer 6.00 15.00
Justin Morneau
Johan Santana/50
ORY David Ortiz 10.00 25.00
Manny Ramirez
Kevin Youkilis/50
OVB Magglio Ordonez 10.00 25.00
Justin Verlander
Jeremy Bonderman/50
PBO Hunter Pence 10.00 25.00
Lance Berkman
Roy Oswalt/50
PLM Albert Pujols 10.00 25.00
Derrek Lee
Justin Morneau/50
RCS Jose Reyes 6.00 15.00
Carl Crawford
Grady Sizemore/50
RDM Babe Ruth
Joe DiMaggio
Roger Maris/25
ROF Babe Ruth
Mel Ott
Jimmie Foxx/25
RPV Manny Ramirez 12.50 30.00
Jonathan Papelbon
Jason Varitek/50
RSB Brooks Robinson 15.00 40.00
Mike Schmidt
Wade Boggs/50
SRB Mike Schmidt 15.00 40.00
Cal Ripken Jr.
Wade Boggs/50
SWB Ryne Sandberg 15.00 40.00
Billy Williams
Ernie Banks/50
TOT Jim Thome 10.00 25.00
David Ortiz
Frank Thomas/50
TWH Frank Thomas 10.00 25.00
Vernon Wells
Roy Halladay/50
UHR Chase Utley 10.00 25.00
Cole Hamels
Jimmy Rollins/50
URU Chase Utley 6.00 15.00
Brian Roberts
Dan Uggla/50
YMC Carl Yastrzemski 15.00 40.00
Stan Musial
Rod Carew/50

2008 Upper Deck Premier Trios Memorabilia Gold

OVERALL GU ODDS TWO PER PACK
PRINT RUNS B/WN 10-33 COPIES PER
NO PRICING ON QTY 10 OR LESS
BFB Johnny Bench 12.50 30.00
Carlton Fisk
Yogi Berra/33
BPG Jason Bay 12.50 30.00
Albert Pujols
Ken Griffey Jr./33
BRD Carlos Beltran 6.00 15.00
Jose Reyes
Carlos Delgado/33
BZJ Ryan Braun 6.00 15.00
Ryan Zimmerman
Chipper Jones/33
CMM Michael Cuddyer 6.00 15.00
Justin Morneau
Joe Mauer/33
DOF Adam Dunn 10.00 25.00
David Ortiz
Prince Fielder/33
GTP Ken Griffey Jr. 15.00 40.00
Frank Thomas
Albert Pujols/33
GWK Vladimir Guerrero 6.00 15.00
Jered Weaver
Howie Kendrick/33
HAT Matt Holliday 10.00 25.00
Garrett Atkins
Troy Tulowitzki/33
HMS Travis Hafner 6.00 15.00
Victor Martinez
Grady Sizemore/33
HSS Dan Haren 6.00 15.00
Nick Swisher
Huston Street/33
JFS Chipper Jones 30.00 60.00
Jeff Francoeur
John Smoltz/33
JTR Derek Jeter 10.00 25.00
Troy Tulowitzki
Hanley Ramirez/33
JWP Derek Jeter 20.00 50.00
Chien-Ming Wang
Andy Pettitte/33
LRS Derrek Lee 6.00 15.00
Aramis Ramirez
Alfonso Soriano/33
MCG Greg Maddux 12.50 30.00
Roger Clemens
Tom Glavine/33
MMS Joe Mauer 6.00 15.00
Justin Morneau
Johan Santana/33
ORY David Ortiz 10.00 25.00
Manny Ramirez
Kevin Youkilis/33
OVB Magglio Ordonez 10.00 25.00
Justin Verlander
Jeremy Bonderman/33
PBO Hunter Pence 10.00 25.00
Lance Berkman
Roy Oswalt/33
PLM Albert Pujols 10.00 25.00
Derrek Lee
Justin Morneau/33
RCS Jose Reyes 6.00 15.00
Carl Crawford
Grady Sizemore/33
RDM Babe Ruth
Joe DiMaggio
Roger Maris/10
ROF Babe Ruth
Mel Ott
Jimmie Foxx/10
RPV Manny Ramirez 12.50 30.00
Jonathan Papelbon
Jason Varitek/33
RSB Brooks Robinson 15.00 40.00
Mike Schmidt
Wade Boggs/33
SRB Mike Schmidt 15.00 40.00
Cal Ripken Jr.
Wade Boggs/33
SWB Ryne Sandberg 15.00 40.00
Billy Williams
Ernie Banks/33
TOT Jim Thome 10.00 25.00
David Ortiz
Frank Thomas/33
TWH Frank Thomas 10.00 25.00
Vernon Wells
Roy Halladay/33
UHR Chase Utley 10.00 25.00
Cole Hamels
Jimmy Rollins/33
URU Chase Utley 6.00 15.00
Brian Roberts
Dan Uggla/33
YMC Carl Yastrzemski 15.00 40.00
Stan Musial
Rod Carew/33

2008 Upper Deck Premier Trios Patches

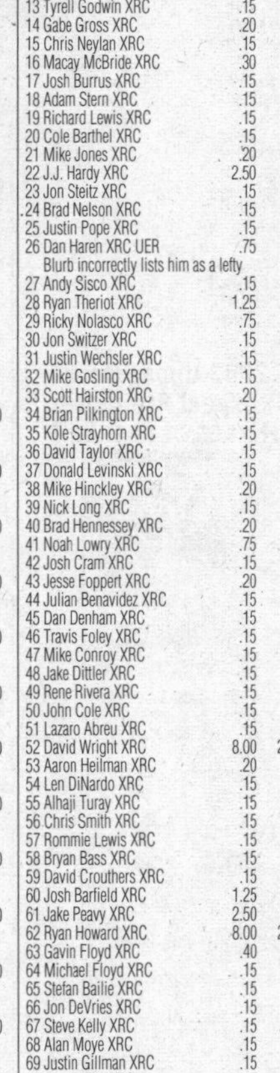

OVERALL GU ODDS TWO PER PACK
STATED PRINT RUN 30 SER.#'d SETS
GOLD PRINT RUN 15 SER.#'d SETS
NO GOLD PRICING DUE TO SCARCITY
PLATINUM PRINT RUN 3 SER.#'d SETS
NO PLATINUM PRICING AVAILABLE
MASTERPIECE PRINT RUN 1 SER.#'d SET
NO MASTERPIECE PRICING AVAILABLE
AER Rick Ankiel 20.00 50.00
Jim Edmonds
Scott Rolen
BNS Jason Bay 12.50 30.00
Xavier Nady
Freddy Sanchez
BPG Jason Bay 30.00 60.00
Albert Pujols
Ken Griffey Jr.
CRS Miguel Cabrera 20.00 50.00
Manny Ramirez
Grady Sizemore
DZV Ray Durham 12.50 30.00
Barry Zito
Omar Vizquel
GKW Vladimir Guerrero 20.00 50.00
Howie Kendrick
Jered Weaver
JCZ Chipper Jones 20.00 50.00
Eric Chavez
Ryan Zimmerman
JJF Chipper Jones 20.00 50.00
Andruw Jones
Jeff Francoeur
JTR Derek Jeter 50.00 100.00
Troy Tulowitzki
Hanley Ramirez
LMS James Loney 20.00 50.00
Russell Martin
Takashi Saito
LRS Derrek Lee 20.00 50.00
Aramis Ramirez
Alfonso Soriano
MJD Willie McCovey 20.00 50.00
Reggie Jackson
Adam Dunn
MMM Victor Martinez 20.00 50.00
Joe Mauer
Russell Martin
MMR Brian McCann 20.00 50.00
Russell Martin
Ivan Rodriguez
MWM Pedro Martinez 20.00 50.00
Billy Wagner
John Maine
ORY David Ortiz 20.00 50.00
Manny Ramirez
Kevin Youkilis
PRB Jonathan Papelbon 20.00 50.00
Manny Ramirez
Josh Beckett
SCM Tom Seaver 30.00 60.00
Steve Carlton
Greg Maddux
SHC Nick Swisher 12.50 30.00
Dan Haren
Eric Chavez
SZB Curt Schilling 20.00 50.00
Carlos Zambrano
Jeremy Bonderman
TKB Jim Thome 20.00 50.00
Paul Konerko
Mark Buehrle
UHR Chase Utley 20.00 50.00
Cole Hamels
Jimmy Rollins
UUK Chase Utley 20.00 50.00
Dan Uggla
Jeff Kent

2001 Upper Deck Prospect Premieres

The 2001 Upper Deck Prospect Premieres was released in October 2001 and features a 102-card set. The first 90 cards are regular and the last 12 are autographed cards numbered to 1000 randomly inserted into packs. The packs contain four cards and have a SRP of $2.99 per pack. There were 18 packs per box.

COMP.SET w/o SP's (90) 50.00 80.00
COMMON CARD (1-90) .15 .40
COMMON AUTO (91-102) 6.00 15.00
1 Jeff Mathis XRC .20 .50
2 Jake Woods XRC .15 .40
3 Dallas McPherson XRC .40 1.00
4 Steven Shell XRC .15 .40
5 Ryan Budde XRC .15 .40
6 Kirk Saarloos XRC .15 .40
7 Ryan Stegall XRC .15 .40
8 Bobby Crosby XRC 1.25 3.00
9 J.T. Stotts XRC .15 .40
10 Neal Cotts XRC .40 1.00
11 J.Bonderman XRC 1.50 4.00
12 Brandon League XRC .15 .40
13 Tyrell Godwin XRC .15 .40
14 Gabe Gross XRC .20 .50
15 Chris Neylan XRC .15 .40
16 Macay McBride XRC .30 .75
17 Josh Burrus XRC .15 .40
18 Adam Stern XRC .15 .40
19 Richard Lewis XRC .15 .40
20 Cole Barthel XRC .15 .40
21 Mike Jones XRC .20 .50
22 J.J. Hardy XRC 2.50 6.00
23 Jon Steitz XRC .15 .40
24 Brad Nelson XRC .15 .40
25 Justin Pope XRC .15 .40
26 Dan Haren XRC UER .75 2.00
Blurb incorrectly lists him as a lefty
27 Andy Sisco XRC .15 .40
28 Ryan Theriot XRC 1.25 3.00
29 Ricky Nolasco XRC .75 2.00
30 Jon Switzer XRC .15 .40
31 Justin Wechsler XRC .15 .40
32 Mike Gosling XRC .15 .40
33 Scott Hairston XRC .20 .50
34 Brian Pilkington XRC .15 .40
35 Kole Strayhorn XRC .15 .40
36 David Taylor XRC .15 .40
37 Donald Levinski XRC .15 .40
38 Mike Hinckley XRC .20 .50
39 Nick Long XRC .15 .40
40 Brad Hennessey XRC .20 .50
41 Noah Lowry XRC .75 2.00
42 Josh Cram XRC .15 .40
43 Jesse Foppert XRC .20 .50
44 Julian Benavidez XRC .15 .40
45 Dan Denham XRC .15 .40
46 Travis Foley XRC .15 .40
47 Mike Conroy XRC .15 .40
48 Jake Dittler XRC .15 .40
49 Rene Rivera XRC .15 .40
50 John Cole XRC .15 .40
51 Lazaro Abreu XRC .15 .40
52 David Wright XRC 8.00 20.00
53 Aaron Heilman XRC .20 .50
54 Len DiNardo XRC .15 .40
55 Alhaji Turay XRC .15 .40
56 Chris Smith XRC .15 .40
57 Rommie Lewis XRC .15 .40
58 Bryan Bass XRC .15 .40
59 David Crouthers XRC .15 .40
60 Josh Barfield XRC 1.25 3.00
61 Jake Peavy XRC 2.50 6.00
62 Ryan Howard XRC 8.00 20.00
63 Gavin Floyd XRC .40 1.00
64 Michael Floyd XRC .15 .40
65 Stefan Bailie XRC .15 .40
66 Jon DeVries XRC .15 .40
67 Steve Kelly XRC .15 .40
68 Alan Moye XRC .15 .40
69 Justin Gillman XRC .15 .40
70 Jayson Nix XRC .15 .40
71 John Draper XRC .15 .40
72 Kenny Baugh XRC .15 .40
73 Michael Woods XRC .15 .40
74 Preston Larrison XRC .20 .50
75 Matt Coenen XRC .15 .40
76 Scott Tyler XRC .20 .50
77 Jose Morales XRC .15 .40
78 Corwin Malone XRC .15 .40
79 Dennis Ulacia XRC .15 .40
80 Andy Gonzalez XRC .15 .40
81 Kris Honel XRC .15 .40
82 Wyatt Allen XRC .15 .40
83 Ryan Wing XRC .15 .40
84 Sean Henn XRC .15 .40
85 John-Ford Griffin XRC .15 .40
86 Bronson Sardinha XRC .15 .40
87 Jon Skaggs XRC .15 .40
88 Shelley Duncan XRC 1.50 4.00
89 Jason Arnold XRC .15 .40
90 Aaron Rifkin XRC .15 .40
91 Colt Griffin AU XRC 6.00 15.00
92 J.D. Martin AU XRC 6.00 15.00
93 Justin Wayne AU XRC 6.00 15.00
94 J.VanBenschoten AU XRC 6.00 15.00
95 Chris Burke AU XRC 10.00 25.00
96 C. Kotchman AU XRC 6.00 15.00
97 M. Garciaparra AU XRC 6.00 15.00
98 Jake Gautreau AU XRC 6.00 15.00
99 J. Williams AU XRC 6.00 15.00
100 Toe Nash AU XRC 6.00 15.00
101 Joe Borchard AU XRC 6.00 15.00
102 Mark Prior AU XRC 15.00 40.00

2001 Upper Deck Prospect Premieres Heroes of Baseball Game Bat

Inserted at a rate of one in 18, this 23-card set features bat pieces of retired players. The cards carry a 'B' prefix.

BAO Al Oliver 3.00 8.00
BBB Bill Buckner 3.00 8.00
BBM Bill Madlock 3.00 8.00
BDB Don Baylor 3.00 8.00
BDE Dwight Evans 4.00 10.00
BDL Davey Lopes 3.00 8.00
BDP Dave Parker 3.00 8.00
BDW Dave Winfield 3.00 8.00
BEM Eddie Murray 4.00 10.00
BFL Fred Lynn 3.00 8.00
BGC Gary Carter 3.00 8.00
BGM Gary Matthews 3.00 8.00
BJM Joe Morgan 3.00 8.00
BKEG Ken Griffey Sr. 3.00 8.00
BKIG Kirk Gibson 3.00 8.00
BKP Kirby Puckett 4.00 10.00
BMM Manny Mota 3.00 8.00
BOS Ozzie Smith 4.00 10.00
BRJ Reggie Jackson 4.00 10.00
BSG Steve Garvey 3.00 8.00
BTM Tim McCarver 3.00 8.00
BTP Tony Perez 3.00 8.00
BWB Wade Boggs 4.00 10.00

2001 Upper Deck Prospect Premieres Heroes of Baseball Game Jersey Duos

Inserted at a rate of one in 144, this seven card set featured dual game jerseys of both current and retired players. The cards carry a 'J' prefix.

JBH Bryan Bass 5.00 12.00
J.J. Hardy
JDG Shelley Duncan 10.00 25.00
Tyrell Godwin
JGS Steve Garvey 3.00 8.00
Reggie Smith
JHB Aaron Heilman 6.00 15.00
Jeremy Bonderman
JJJ Michael Jordan 40.00 80.00
Michael Jordan
JSG Jon Switzer 3.00 8.00
Mike Gosling
JWP Dave Winfield 10.00 25.00
Kirby Puckett

2001 Upper Deck Prospect Premieres Heroes of Baseball Game Jersey Duos Autograph

Randomly inserted into packs, this six card set featured dual game jerseys with autographs of both current and retired players. The cards were serial numbered to 25.The cards carry a 'SJ' prefix. Due to scarcity, no pricing is provided.

SJBH Bryan Bass
J.J. Hardy
SJGS Steve Garvey
Reggie Smith
SJHB Aaron Heilman
Jeremy Bonderman
SJJJ Michael Jordan
Michael Jordan
SJMG Joe Morgan
Ken Griffey Sr
SJWP Dave Winfield
Kirby Puckett

2001 Upper Deck Prospect Premieres Heroes of Baseball Game Jersey Trios

Inserted in packs at a rate of one in 144, these nine cards feature three swatches of game-worn jerseys on a card. Representatives at Upper Deck have confirmed that the Maris-Mantle-DiMaggio card is in noticeably short supply. In addition, the following cards did not packout and were available via exchange cards that were seeded into packs in their place: Crosby/Garciaparra/Sardinha, Gautreau/Godwin/Heilman, Gross/Kotchman/Baugh, Griffin/Martin/Switzer and VanBenschoten/Prior/Jones. The deadline to mail in these exchange cards was October 22nd, 2004.

BBC Chris Burke 4.00 10.00
Bryan Bass
Bobby Crosby UER
CGS Bobby Crosby UER 4.00 10.00
Michael Garciaparra
Bronson Sardinha
GGH Jake Gautreau 3.00 8.00
Tyrell Godwin
Aaron Heilman
GKB Gabe Gross 3.00 8.00
Casey Kotchmann
Kenny Baugh
GMS Colt Griffin 3.00 8.00
J.D. Martin
Jon Switzer
JMD Michael Jordan 150.00 250.00
Mickey Mantle
Joe DiMaggio
JPW Michael Jordan 30.00 60.00
Kirby Puckett
Dave Winfield
MMD Roger Maris 250.00 400.00
Mickey Mantle
Joe DiMaggio SP
VPJ Jon VanBenSchoten 4.00 10.00
Mark Prior
Mike Jones

2001 Upper Deck Prospect Premieres Heroes of Baseball Game Jersey Trios Autograph

Randomly inserted in packs, these cards feature not only three swatches of game-worn jerseys but also autographs of the featured players. These cards are serial numbered to 25. Due to scarcity, no pricing is provided.

SJBBC Chris Burke
Bryan Bass
Bobby Crosby UER
SJJPW Michael Jordan
Kirby Puckett
Dave Winfield
SJMGP Joe Morgan
Ken Griffey Sr.
Tony Perez

2001 Upper Deck Prospect Premieres MJ Grandslam Game Bat

Randomly inserted in packs, these five cards feature bat cards from basketball legend turned baseball prospect. Card number "MJ5" was printed in lesser quantities and is notated in our checklist as an SP.

COMMON CARD (MJ1-MJ4) 6.00 15.00
MJ5 Michael Jordan SP 20.00 50.00

2001 Upper Deck Prospect Premieres Tribute to 42

Issued at a rate of one in 750, these seven cards honor the memory of the integration trail blazer and all time great. Please note, the Pants-Cut Auto card erroneously states "Jersey/Cut Combo" on the card itself. UD has verified that the material actually used to create the card was derived from a pair of game-used pants.

B Jackie Robinson Bat 20.00 50.00
C Jackie Robinson Cut AU
J Jackie Robinson Pants 20.00 50.00
BC Jackie Robinson Bat-Cut AU
GB Jackie Robinson 30.00 60.00
Gold Bat/42
GJ J.Robinson Pants Gold/42 30.00 60.00
JC Jackie Robinson Pants-Cut AU

2002 Upper Deck Prospect Premieres

This 109 card set was released in November, 2002. It was issued in four count packs which came 24 packs to a box and 20 boxes to a case with an SRP of $3 per pack. Cards number 61 through 85 feature game-worn jersey pieces and were inserted at a stated rate of one in 18 packs. Cards numbered 86 through 97 feature player's autographs and were issued at a stated rate of one in 18 packs. Cards numbered 98 through 109 feature tribute cards to recently retired superstars Cal Ripken and Mark McGwire along with Yankee great Joe DiMaggio. Matt Pender's basic XRC erroneously packed out picturing Curtis Granderson. A corrected version of the card was made available to collectors a few months after the product went live via a mail exchange program directly from Upper Deck.

COMP.SET w/o SP's (72) 25.00 40.00
COMMON CARD (1-60) .15 .40

COMMON CARD (61-85) 2.00 5.00
COMMON CARD (86-97) 3.00 8.00
COMMON RIPKEN (98-99) .75 2.00
COMMON MCGWIRE (100-105) .75 2.00
COMMON DIMAGGIO (106-109) .60 1.50
PENDER COR AVAIL.VIA MAIL EXCHANGE
1 Josh Rupe XRC .15 .40
2 Blair Johnson XRC .15 .40
3 Jason Pridie XRC .15 .40
4 Tim Gilhooly XRC .15 .40
5 Kennard Jones XRC .15 .40
6 Darrell Rasner XRC .15 .40
7 Adam Donachie XRC .15 .40
8 Josh Murray XRC .15 .40
9 Brian Dopirak XRC .40 1.00
10 Jason Cooper XRC .15 .40
11 Zach Hammes XRC .15 .40
12 Jon Lester XRC 8.00 20.00
13 Kevin Jepsen XRC .20 .50
14 Curtis Granderson XRC 1.50 4.00
15 David Bush XRC .40 1.00
16 Joel Guzman .30 .75
17A Matt Pender UER XRC .60 1.50
Pictures Curtis Granderson
17B Matt Pender COR .40 1.00
18 Derick Grigsby XRC .15 .40
19 Jeremy Reed XRC .40 1.00
20 Jonathan Broxton XRC .40 1.00
21 Jesse Crain XRC .30 .75
22 Justin Jones XRC .20 .50
23 Brian Slocum XRC .15 .40
24 Brian McCann XRC 3.00 8.00
25 Francisco Liriano XRC 3.00 8.00
26 Fred Lewis XRC .15 .40
27 Steve Stanley XRC .15 .40
28 Chris Snyder XRC .20 .50
29 Dan Cevette XRC .15 .40
30 Kiel Fisher XRC .20 .50
31 Brandon Weeden XRC .15 .40
32 Pat Osborn XRC .15 .40
33 Taber Lee XRC .15 .40
34 Dan Ortmeier XRC .20 .50
35 Josh Johnson XRC 1.50 4.00
36 Val Majewski XRC .15 .40
37 Larry Broadway XRC .15 .40
38 Joey Gomes XRC .15 .40
39 Eric Thomas XRC .15 .40
40 James Loney XRC 2.00 5.00
41 Charlie Morton XRC .15 .40
42 Mark McLemore XRC .15 .40
43 Matt Craig XRC .20 .50
44 Ryan Rodriguez XRC .15 .40
45 Rich Hill XRC 1.25 3.00
46 Bob Malek XRC .15 .40
47 Justin Maureau XRC .15 .40
48 Randy Braun XRC .15 .40
49 Brian Grant XRC .15 .40
50 Tyler Davidson XRC .20 .50
51 Travis Hanson XRC .20 .50
52 Kyle Boyer XRC .15 .40
53 James Holcomb XRC .15 .40
54 Ryan Williams XRC .15 .40
55 Ben Crockett XRC .15 .40
56 Adam Greenberg XRC .30 .75
57 John Baker XRC .15 .40
58 Matt Carson XRC .15 .40
59 Jonathan George XRC .15 .40
60 David Jensen XRC .15 .40
61 Nick Swisher JSY XRC 6.00 15.00
62 Br.Clevlen JSY XRC UER 5.00 12.00
Name mispelled as Cleven
63 Royce Ring JSY XRC 2.00 5.00
64 Mike Nixon JSY XRC 2.00 5.00
65 Ricky Barrett JSY XRC 2.00 5.00
66 Russ Adams JSY XRC 2.00 5.00
67 Joe Mauer JSY XRC 10.00 25.00
68 Jeff Francoeur JSY XRC 12.50 30.00
69 Joe Blanton JSY XRC 3.00 8.00
70 Micah Schilling JSY XRC 2.00 5.00
71 John McCurdy JSY XRC 2.00 5.00
72 Sergio Santos JSY XRC 3.00 8.00
73 Josh Womack JSY XRC 2.00 5.00
74 Jared Doyle JSY XRC 2.00 5.00
75 Ben Fritz JSY XRC 2.00 5.00
76 Greg Miller JSY XRC 2.00 5.00
77 Luke Hagerty JSY XRC 2.00 5.00
78 Matt Whitney JSY XRC 2.00 5.00
79 Dan Meyer JSY XRC 3.00 8.00
80 Bill Murphy JSY XRC 2.00 5.00
81 Zach Segovia JSY XRC 2.00 5.00
82 Steve Obenchain JSY XRC 2.00 5.00
83 Matt Clanton JSY XRC 2.00 5.00
84 Mark Teahen JSY XRC 3.00 8.00
85 Kyle Pawelczyk JSY XRC 2.00 5.00
86 Khalil Greene AU XRC 5.00 12.00
87 Joe Saunders AU XRC 5.00 12.00
88 Jeremy Hermida AU XRC 8.00 20.00
89 Drew Meyer AU XRC 3.00 8.00
90 Jeff Francis AU XRC 12.50 30.00
91 Scott Moore AU XRC 3.00 8.00
92 Prince Fielder AU XRC 50.00 100.00
93 Zack Greinke AU XRC 8.00 20.00
94 Chris Gruler AU XRC 3.00 8.00
95 Scott Kazmir AU XRC 30.00 60.00
96 B.J. Upton AU XRC 30.00 60.00
97 Clint Everts AU XRC 3.00 8.00
98 Cal Ripken TRIB .75 2.00
99 Cal Ripken TRIB .75 2.00
100 Mark McGwire TRIB .75 2.00
101 Mark McGwire TRIB .75 2.00
102 Mark McGwire TRIB .75 2.00
103 Mark McGwire TRIB .75 2.00
104 Mark McGwire TRIB .75 2.00
105 Joe DiMaggio TRIB .60 1.50
106 Joe DiMaggio TRIB .60 1.50
107 Joe DiMaggio TRIB .60 1.50
108 Joe DiMaggio TRIB .60 1.50
109 Joe DiMaggio TRIB .60 1.50

2002 Upper Deck Prospect Premieres Future Gems Quads

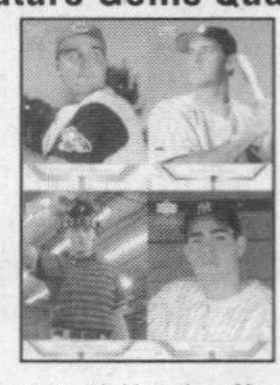

Inserted one per sealed box, these 33 cards feature four different cards in a panel and were issued to a stated print run of 600 serial numbered sets.

1 David Bush 3.00 8.00
Matt Craig
Josh Johnson
Brian McCann
2 Jason Cooper 3.00 8.00
Jonathan George
Larry Broadway
Joel Guzman
3 Matt Craig 3.00 8.00
Josh Murray
Brian McCann
Jason Pridie
4 Jesse Crain 3.00 8.00
Brian Grant
Curtis Granderson
Joey Gomes
5 Tyler Davidson 3.00 8.00
Val Majewski
Justin Jones
Daniel Cevette
6 Joe DiMaggio 8.00 20.00
Jon Lester
Mark McGwire
Mark McLemore
7 Jonathan George 3.00 8.00
Jeremy Reed
Adam Donachie
Matt Carson
8 Jonathan George 3.00 8.00
Eric Thomas
Joel Guzman
Kiel Fisher
9 Tim Gilhooly 3.00 8.00
Brandon Weeden
Brian Slocum
Brian Dopirak
10 Brian Grant 4.00 10.00
Rich Hill
Joey Gomes
Joe DiMaggio
11 Derick Grigsby 5.00 12.00
Bob Malek
James Loney
Fred Lewis
12 Zach Hammes 3.00 8.00
James Holcomb
Cal Ripken
Kennard Jones
13 Rich Hill 5.00 12.00
Mark McGwire
Brian Grant
Matt Carson
14 James Holcomb 3.00 8.00
David Jensen
Kennard Jones
Ryan Williams
15 David Jensen 5.00 12.00
Francisco Liriano
Ryan Williams
Travis Hanson
16 Josh Johnson 3.00 8.00
Jesse Crain
Adam Greenberg
Curtis Granderson
17 Jon Lester 8.00 20.00
Jonathan George
Mark McLemore
Adam Donachie
18 Francisco Liriano 5.00 12.00
Mark McGwire
Travis Hanson
Taber Lee
19 Val Majewski 3.00 8.00
Charlie Morton
Daniel Cevette
Joey Gomes
20 Bob Malek 3.00 8.00
Zach Hammes
Fred Lewis
Cal Ripken
21 Justin Maureau 3.00 8.00
Joe DiMaggio
Chris Snyder
Mark McGwire
22 Mark McGwire 3.00 8.00
Bob Malek
Joe DiMaggio
Kyle Boyer
23 Charlie Morton 3.00 8.00
David Bush#Joey Gomes
Josh Johnson
24 Josh Murray 3.00 8.00
Mark McGwire
Jason Pridie
Joe DiMaggio
25 Matt Pender UER 3.00 8.00
Mark McGwire
Mark McLemore
Ryan Rodriguez
26 Jason Pridie 3.00 8.00
Josh Murray
Matt Craig
Brian McCann
27 Jeremy Reed 3.00 8.00
Josh Johnson
Matt Carson
Adam Greenberg
28 Cal Ripken 3.00 8.00
Jason Cooper
Matt Carson
Larry Broadway
29 Ryan Rodriguez 3.00 8.00
Eric Thomas
Pat Osborn
Randy Braun
30 Josh Rupe 3.00 8.00
Tyler Davidson
John Baker
Justin Jones
31 Eric Thomas 5.00 12.00
Derick Grigsby
Randy Braun
James Loney
32 Eric Thomas 3.00 8.00
Matt Pender UER
Kiel Fisher
Mark McLemore
33 Brandon Weeden 5.00 12.00
Rich Hill
Brian Dopirak
Brian Grant

2002 Upper Deck Prospect Premieres Heroes of Baseball

Inserted at stated odds of one per pack, these 90 cards feature 10 cards each of various baseball legends. Each player featured has nine regular cards and one header card.

COMP.RIPKEN SET (10) 8.00 20.00
COMMON RIPKEN (CR1-HDR) 1.00 2.50
COMP.DIMAGGIO SET (10) 4.00 10.00
COMMON DIMAGGIO (JD1-HDR) .50 1.25
COMP.MORGAN SET (10) 2.00 5.00
COMMON MORGAN (JM1-HDR) .30 .75
COMP.MCGWIRE SET (10) 8.00 20.00
COMMON MCGWIRE (MC1-HDR) 1.00 2.50
COMP.MANTLE SET (10) 10.00 25.00
COMMON MANTLE (MM1-HDR) 1.25 3.00
COMP.OZZIE SET (10) 6.00 15.00
COMMON OZZIE (OS1-HDR) .75 2.00
COMP.GWYNN SET (10) 6.00 15.00
COMMON GWYNN (TG1-HDR) .75 2.00
COMP.SEAVER SET (10) 4.00 10.00
COMMON SEAVER (TS1-HDR) .50 1.25
COMP.STARGELL SET (10) 2.00 5.00
COMMON STARGELL (WS1-HDR) .30 .75

2002 Upper Deck Prospect Premieres Heroes of Baseball 85 Quads

Randomly inserted as boxtoppers, these eight panels feature a mix of four cards of the players featured in the Heroes of Baseball insert set. Each of these cards are issued to a stated print run of 85 serial numbered sets.

1 Joe DiMaggio 4.00 10.00
Tony Gwynn
Tony Gwynn
Joe DiMaggio
2 Joe DiMaggio 6.00 15.00
Tony Gwynn
Cal Ripken
Cal Ripken
3 Joe DiMaggio Hdr 6.00 15.00
Mickey Mantle
Willie Stargell Hdr
Mickey Mantle
4 Tony Gwynn 4.00 10.00
Tony Gwynn
Ozzie Smith
Willie Stargell
5 Tony Gwynn 4.00 10.00
Willie Stargell
Joe DiMaggio
Joe Morgan
6 Tony Gwynn 4.00 10.00
Willie Stargell
Cal Ripken
Ozzie Smith
7 Mickey Mantle 6.00 15.00
Mark McGwire
Joe Morgan
Tom Seaver
8 Mickey Mantle 6.00 15.00
Tom Seaver
Mickey Mantle
Tom Seaver
9 Mark McGwire 6.00 15.00
Joe Morgan
Mark McGwire
Joe Morgan
10 Mark McGwire Hdr 6.00 15.00
Cal Ripken
Tony Gwynn
Joe DiMaggio
11 Mark McGwire 4.00 10.00
Tom Seaver
Joe Morgan
Ozzie Smith
12 Joe Morgan 4.00 10.00
Tony Gwynn
Joe Morgan
Tony Gwynn
13 Joe Morgan 6.00 15.00
Joe DiMaggio
Mickey Mantle
Cal Ripken
14 Joe Morgan 4.00 10.00
Joe DiMaggio
Willie Stargell
Tony Gwynn
15 Ozzie Smith 4.00 10.00
Joe DiMaggio
Ozzie Smith
Willie Stargell
16 Ozzie Smith 4.00 10.00
Mark McGwire
Willie Stargell
Tony Gwynn
17 Ozzie Smith 4.00 10.00
Tom Seaver
Tom Seaver
Mark McGwire
18 Cal Ripken 6.00 15.00
Mickey Mantle
Joe DiMaggio
Joe Morgan
19 Cal Ripken 6.00 15.00
Mark McGwire
Cal Ripken
Mark McGwire
20 Tom Seaver 4.00 10.00
Joe DiMaggio
Tom Seaver
Joe DiMaggio
21 Tom Seaver 4.00 10.00
Joe Morgan
Ozzie Smith
Willie Stargell
22 Tom Seaver 6.00 15.00
Cal Ripken
Mark McGwire
Mickey Mantle
23 Willie Stargell 4.00 10.00
Ozzie Smith
Ozzie Smith
Willie Stargell
24 Willie Stargell 4.00 10.00
Ozzie Smith
Tom Seaver
Joe Morgan

2003 Upper Deck Prospect Premieres

For the third consecutive year, Upper Deck produced a set consisting solely of players who had been taken during that season's amateur draft. This was a 90-card standard-size set which was released in December, 2003. This set was issued in four-card packs with an $2.99 SRP which came 16 packs to a box and 18 boxes to a case.

COMPLETE SET (90) 20.00 40.00
1 Bryan Opdyke XRC .15 .40
2 Gabriel Sosa XRC .15 .40
3 Tila Reynolds XRC .15 .40
4 Aaron Hill XRC .40 1.00
5 Aaron Marsden XRC .20 .50
6 Abe Alvarez XRC .20 .50
7 Adam Jones XRC 2.00 5.00
8 Adam Miller XRC 1.25 3.00
9 Andre Ethier XRC 1.25 3.00
10 Anthony Gwynn XRC .50 1.25
11 Brad Snyder XRC .30 .75
12 Brad Sullivan XRC .20 .50
13 Brian Anderson XRC .75 2.00
14 Brian Buscher XRC .15 .40
15 Brian Snyder XRC .20 .50
16 Carlos Quentin XRC 1.25 3.00
17 Chad Billingsley XRC 1.50 4.00
18 Fraser Dizard XRC .15 .40
19 Chris Durbin XRC .15 .40
20 Chris Ray XRC .40 1.00
21 Conor Jackson XRC 1.25 3.00
22 Kory Casto XRC .20 .50
23 Craig Whitaker XRC .20 .50
24 Daniel Moore XRC .15 .40
25 Daric Barton XRC 1.25 3.00
26 Darin Downs XRC .20 .50
27 David Murphy XRC .30 .75
28 Dustin Majewski XRC .20 .50
29 Edgardo Baez XRC .20 .50
30 Jake Fox XRC .30 .75
31 Jake Stevens XRC .20 .50
32 Jamie D'Antona XRC .30 .75
33 James Houser XRC .20 .50
34 Jar. Saltalamacchia XRC 2.00 5.00
35 Jason Hirsh XRC .75 2.00
36 Javi Herrera XRC .20 .50
37 Jeff Allison XRC .15 .40
38 John Hudgins XRC .15 .40
39 Jo Jo Reyes XRC .40 1.00
40 Justin James XRC .15 .40
41 Kurt Isenberg XRC .15 .40
42 Kyle Boyer XRC .15 .40
43 Lastings Milledge XRC 2.00 5.00
44 Luis Atilano XRC .15 .40
45 Matt Murton XRC .75 2.00
46 Matt Moses XRC .30 .75
47 Matt Harrison XRC .30 .75
48 Michael Bourn XRC .30 .75
49 Miguel Vega XRC .15 .40
50 Mitch Maier XRC .20 .50
51 Omar Quintanilla XRC .20 .50
52 Ryan Sweeney XRC .75 2.00
53 Scott Baker XRC .40 1.00
54 Sean Rodriguez XRC .75 2.00
55 Steve Lerud XRC .20 .50
56 Thomas Pauly XRC .15 .40
57 Tom Gorzelanny XRC .60 1.50
58 Tim Moss XRC .15 .40
59 Robbie Wooley XRC .20 .50
60 Trey Webb XRC .15 .40
61 Wes Littleton XRC .20 .50
62 Beau Vaughan XRC .20 .50
63 Willy Jo Ronda XRC .20 .50
64 Chris Lubanski XRC .50 1.25
65 Ian Stewart XRC 2.00 5.00
66 John Danks XRC 1.25 3.00
67 Kyle Sleeth XRC .20 .50
68 Michael Aubrey XRC .30 .75
69 Kevin Kouzmanoff XRC 2.00 5.00
70 Ryan Harvey XRC .75 2.00
71 Tim Stauffer XRC .30 .75
72 Tony Richie XRC .15 .40
73 Brandon Wood XRC 3.00 8.00
74 David Aardsma XRC .20 .50
75 David Shinskie XRC .15 .40
76 Dennis Dove XRC .20 .50
77 Eric Sultemeier XRC .15 .40
78 Jay Sborz XRC .15 .40
79 Jimmy Barthmaier XRC .15 .40
80 Josh Whitesell XRC .15 .40
81 Josh Anderson XRC .20 .50
82 Kenny Lewis XRC .20 .50
83 Mateo Miramontes XRC .15 .40
84 Nick Markakis XRC 2.00 5.00
85 Paul Bacot XRC .20 .50
86 Peter Stonard XRC .15 .40
87 Reggie Willits XRC 1.00 2.50
88 Shane Costa XRC .15 .40
89 Billy Sadler XRC .15 .40
90 Delmon Young XRC 3.00 8.00

2003 Upper Deck Prospect Premieres Autographs

Please note that a few players who were anticipated to have cards in this set do not exist. Those card numbers are P18, P28, P47, P54, P59 and P69.

STATED ODDS 1:9
P1 Bryan Opdyke 4.00 10.00
P2 Gabriel Sosa 4.00 10.00
P3 Tila Reynolds 4.00 10.00
P4 Aaron Hill 12.50 30.00
P5 Aaron Marsden 6.00 15.00
P6 Abe Alvarez 6.00 15.00
P7 Adam Jones 50.00 100.00
P8 Adam Miller 40.00 80.00
P9 Andre Ethier 20.00 50.00
P10 Anthony Gwynn 15.00 30.00
P11 Brad Snyder 6.00 15.00
P12 Brad Sullivan 6.00 15.00
P13 Brian Anderson 15.00 30.00
P14 Brian Buscher 6.00 15.00
P15 Brian Snyder 4.00 10.00
P16 Carlos Quentin 30.00 60.00
P17 Chad Billingsley 20.00 40.00
P19 Chris Durbin 4.00 10.00
P20 Chris Ray 10.00 25.00
P21 Conor Jackson 10.00 25.00
P22 Kory Casto 6.00 15.00
P23 Craig Whitaker 6.00 15.00
P24 Daniel Moore 4.00 10.00
P25 Daric Barton 12.50 30.00
P26 Darin Downs 6.00 15.00
P27 David Murphy 10.00 25.00
P29 Edgardo Baez 6.00 15.00
P30 Jake Fox 6.00 15.00
P31 Jake Stevens 6.00 15.00
P32 Jamie D'Antona 6.00 15.00
P33 James Houser 6.00 15.00
P34 Jarrod Saltalamacchia 8.00 20.00
P35 Jason Hirsh 15.00 40.00
P36 Javi Herrera 6.00 15.00
P37 Jeff Allison 4.00 10.00
P38 John Hudgins 4.00 10.00
P39 Jo Jo Reyes 10.00 25.00
P40 Justin James 4.00 10.00
P41 Kurt Isenberg 4.00 10.00
P42 Kyle Boyer 4.00 10.00
P43 Lastings Milledge 35.00 60.00
P44 Luis Atilano 4.00 10.00
P45 Matt Murton 4.00 10.00
P46 Matt Moses 8.00 20.00
P48 Michael Bourn 10.00 25.00
P49 Miguel Vega 4.00 10.00
P50 Mitch Maier 6.00 15.00
P51 Omar Quintanilla 6.00 15.00
P52 Ryan Sweeney 10.00 25.00
P53 Scott Baker 10.00 25.00
P55 Steve Lerud 6.00 15.00
P56 Thomas Pauly 6.00 15.00
P57 Tom Gorzelanny 10.00 25.00
P58 Tim Moss 6.00 15.00
P60 Trey Webb 4.00 10.00
P61 Wes Littleton 6.00 15.00
P62 Beau Vaughan 6.00 15.00
P63 Willy Jo Ronda 6.00 15.00
P64 Chris Lubanski 8.00 20.00
P65 Ian Stewart 40.00 80.00
P66 John Danks 12.50 30.00
P67 Kyle Sleeth 6.00 15.00
P68 Michael Aubrey 4.00 10.00
P70 Ryan Harvey 10.00 25.00
P71 Tim Stauffer 4.00 10.00

2003 Upper Deck Prospect Premieres Game Jersey

Please note that card number P90 does not exist.

STATED ODDS 1:18
P72 Tony Richie 2.00 5.00
P73 Brandon Wood 6.00 15.00
P74 David Aardsma 3.00 8.00
P75 David Shinskie 2.00 5.00
P76 Dennis Dove 3.00 8.00
P77 Eric Sultimeier 2.00 5.00
P78 Jay Sborz 2.00 5.00
P79 Jimmy Barthmaier 3.00 8.00
P80 Josh Whitesell 2.00 5.00
P81 Josh Anderson 3.00 8.00
P82 Kenny Lewis 3.00 8.00
P83 Mateo Miramontes 2.00 5.00
P84 Nick Markakis 10.00 25.00
P85 Paul Bacot 3.00 8.00
P86 Peter Stonard 2.00 5.00
P87 Reggie Willits 10.00 25.00
P88 Shane Costa 2.00 5.00
P89 Billy Sadler 2.00 5.00
P91 Kyle Sleeth 3.00 8.00
P92 Ian Stewart 6.00 15.00
P93 Fraser Dizard 2.00 5.00
P94 Abe Alvarez 3.00 8.00
P95 Adam Jones 6.00 15.00
P96 Brian Anderson 3.00 8.00
P97 Chris Durbin 2.00 5.00
P98 Craig Whitaker 3.00 8.00
P99 Jake Fox 3.00 8.00
P100 Kurt Isenberg 2.00 5.00
P101 Luis Atilano 2.00 5.00
P102 Miguel Vega 2.00 5.00
P103 Mitch Maier 3.00 8.00
P104 Ryan Sweeney 4.00 10.00
P105 Scott Baker 3.00 8.00
P106 Sean Rodriguez 4.00 10.00
P108 Trey Webb 2.00 5.00
P109 Willy Jo Ronda 3.00 8.00
P110 John Danks 3.00 8.00
P111 Michael Aubrey 3.00 8.00
P112 Lastings Milledge 6.00 15.00
P113 Chris Lubanski 3.00 8.00

1998 Upper Deck Special F/X

The 1998 Upper Deck Special F/X set was issued in one series totalling 150 cards. Distributed exclusively in retail outlets, six-card packs carried a $2.97 suggested retail price. The set contains a selection of the top 150 cards from the basic issue 1998 Upper Deck first series set including the topical subsets Griffey's Hot List (1-10) and Star Rookies (136-150). Each Special F/X card features a special foil treatment on the card fronts and is printed on sturdy 20 pt. stock.

COMPLETE SET (150) 15.00 40.00
1 Ken Griffey Jr. GHL .75 2.00
2 Mark McGwire GHL 1.25 3.00
3 Alex Rodriguez GHL .75 2.00
4 Larry Walker GHL .20 .50
5 Tino Martinez GHL .30 .75
6 Mike Piazza GHL .75 2.00
7 Jose Cruz Jr. GHL .20 .50
8 Greg Maddux GHL .75 2.00
9 Tony Gwynn GHL .60 1.50
10 Roger Clemens GHL 1.00 2.50
11 Jason Dickson .20 .50
12 Darin Erstad .20 .50
13 Chuck Finley .20 .50
14 Dave Hollins .20 .50
15 Garret Anderson .20 .50
16 Michael Tucker .20 .50
17 Javier Lopez .20 .50
18 John Smoltz .30 .75
19 Mark Wohlers .20 .50
20 Greg Maddux .75 2.00
21 Scott Erickson .20 .50
22 Jimmy Key .20 .50
23 B.J. Surhoff .20 .50
24 Eric Davis .20 .50
25 Rafael Palmeiro .30 .75
26 Tim Naehring .20 .50
27 Darren Bragg .20 .50
28 Troy O'Leary .20 .50
29 John Valentin .20 .50
30 Mo Vaughn .20 .50
31 Mark Grace .30 .75
32 Kevin Foster .20 .50
33 Kevin Tapani .20 .50
34 Kevin Orie .20 .50
35 Albert Belle .20 .50
36 Ray Durham .20 .50
37 Jaime Navarro .20 .50
38 Mike Cameron .20 .50
39 Eddie Taubensee .20 .50
40 Barry Larkin .30 .75
41 Willie Greene .20 .50
42 Jeff Shaw .20 .50

43 Omar Vizquel .30 .75
44 Brian Giles .20 .50
45 Jim Thome .30 .75
46 David Justice .20 .50
47 Sandy Alomar Jr. .20 .50
48 Neifi Perez .20 .50
49 Dante Bichette .20 .50
50 Vinny Castilla .20 .50
51 John Thomson .20 .50
52 Damion Easley .20 .50
53 Justin Thompson .20 .50
54 Bobby Higginson .20 .50
55 Tony Clark .20 .50
56 Charles Johnson .20 .50
57 Edgar Renteria .20 .50
58 Alex Fernandez .20 .50
59 Gary Sheffield .20 .50
60 Livan Hernandez .20 .50
61 Craig Biggio .30 .75
62 Chris Holt .20 .50
63 Billy Wagner .20 .50
64 Brad Ausmus .20 .50
65 Dean Palmer .20 .50
66 Tim Belcher .20 .50
67 Jeff King .20 .50
68 Jose Rosado .20 .50
69 Chan Ho Park .20 .50
70 Raul Mondesi .20 .50
71 Hideo Nomo .50 1.25
72 Todd Zeile .20 .50
73 Eric Karros .20 .50
74 Cal Eldred .20 .50
75 Jeff D'Amico .20 .50
76 Doug Jones .20 .50
77 Dave Nilsson .20 .50
78 Todd Walker .20 .50
79 Rick Aguilera .20 .50
80 Paul Molitor .20 .50
81 Brad Radke .20 .50
82 Vladimir Guerrero .50 1.25
83 Carlos Perez .20 .50
84 F.P. Santangelo .20 .50
85 Rondell White .20 .50
86 Butch Huskey .20 .50
87 Edgardo Alfonzo .20 .50
88 John Franco .20 .50
89 John Olerud .20 .50
90 Todd Hundley .20 .50
91 Bernie Williams .30 .75
92 Andy Pettitte .30 .75
93 Paul O'Neill .30 .75
94 David Cone .20 .50
95 Jason Giambi .20 .50
96 Damon Mashore .20 .50
97 Scott Spiezio .20 .50
98 Ariel Prieto .20 .50
99 Rico Brogna .20 .50
100 Mike Lieberthal .20 .50
101 Garrett Stephenson .20 .50
102 Ricky Bottalico .20 .50
103 Kevin Polcovich .20 .50
104 Jon Lieber .20 .50
105 Kevin Young .20 .50
106 Tony Womack .20 .50
107 Gary Gaetti .20 .50
108 Alan Benes .20 .50
109 Willie McGee .20 .50
110 Mark McGwire 1.25 3.00
111 Ron Gant .20 .50
112 Andy Ashby .20 .50
113 Steve Finley .20 .50
114 Quilvio Veras .20 .50
115 Ken Caminiti .20 .50
116 Joey Hamilton .20 .50
117 Bill Mueller .20 .50
118 Mark Gardner .20 .50
119 Shawn Estes .20 .50
120 J.T. Snow .20 .50
121 Dante Powell .20 .50
122 Jeff Kent .20 .50
123 Jamie Moyer .20 .50
124 Joey Cora .20 .50
125 Ken Griffey Jr. .75 2.00
126 Jeff Fassero .20 .50
127 Edgar Martinez .30 .75
128 Will Clark .30 .75
129 Lee Stevens .20 .50
130 Ivan Rodriguez .30 .75
131 Rusty Greer .20 .50
132 Ed Sprague .20 .50
133 Pat Hentgen .20 .50
134 Shannon Stewart .20 .50
135 Carlos Delgado .20 .50
136 Brett Tomko .20 .50
137 Jose Guillen .20 .50
138 Eli Marrero .20 .50
139 Dennis Reyes .20 .50
140 Mark Kotsay .20 .50
141 Richie Sexson .20 .50
142 Todd Helton .30 .75
143 Jeremi Gonzalez .20 .50
144 Jeff Abbott .20 .50
145 Matt Morris .20 .50
146 Aaron Boone .20 .50
147 Todd Dunwoody .20 .50
148 Mario Valdez .20 .50
149 Fernando Tatis .20 .50
150 Jaret Wright .20 .50

1998 Upper Deck Special F/X Power Zone

Randomly seeded into Special F/X packs at a rate of one in seven, cards from this 20-card set feature a selection of baseball's top stars printed on special silver Light F/X technology.

COMPLETE SET (20) 20.00 50.00
PZ1 Jose Cruz Jr. .50 1.25
PZ2 Frank Thomas 1.25 3.00
PZ3 Juan Gonzalez .50 1.25
PZ4 Mike Piazza 2.00 5.00
PZ5 Mark McGwire 3.00 8.00
PZ6 Barry Bonds 3.00 8.00
PZ7 Greg Maddux 2.00 5.00
PZ8 Alex Rodriguez 2.00 5.00
PZ9 Nomar Garciaparra 2.00 5.00
PZ10 Ken Griffey Jr. 2.00 5.00
PZ11 John Smoltz .75 2.00
PZ12 Andruw Jones .75 2.00
PZ13 Sandy Alomar Jr. .50 1.25
PZ14 Roberto Alomar .75 2.00
PZ15 Chipper Jones 1.25 3.00
PZ16 Kenny Lofton .50 1.25
PZ17 Larry Walker .50 1.25
PZ18 Jeff Bagwell .75 2.00
PZ19 Mo Vaughn .50 1.25
PZ20 Tom Glavine .75 2.00

1998 Upper Deck Special F/X Power Zone OctoberBest

Randomly seeded into Special F/X packs at a rate of one in 34, cards from this 15-card set feature some of the league's top stars printed on silver die-cut Light F/X technology.

COMPLETE SET (15) 50.00 120.00
PZ1 Frank Thomas 4.00 10.00
PZ2 Juan Gonzalez 1.50 4.00
PZ3 Mike Piazza 6.00 15.00
PZ4 Mark McGwire 10.00 25.00
PZ5 Jeff Bagwell 2.50 6.00
PZ6 Barry Bonds 10.00 25.00
PZ7 Ken Griffey Jr. 6.00 15.00
PZ8 John Smoltz 2.50 6.00
PZ9 Andruw Jones 2.50 6.00
PZ10 Greg Maddux 6.00 15.00
PZ11 Sandy Alomar Jr. 1.50 4.00
PZ12 Roberto Alomar 2.50 6.00
PZ13 Chipper Jones 4.00 10.00
PZ14 Kenny Lofton 1.50 4.00
PZ15 Tom Glavine 2.50 6.00

1998 Upper Deck Special F/X Power Zone Power Driven

Randomly seeded into Special F/X packs at a rate of one in 69, cards from this 10-card set feature a selection of top stars printed on Light F/X gold-foil.

COMPLETE SET (10) 50.00 120.00
PZ1 Frank Thomas 5.00 12.00
PZ2 Juan Gonzalez 2.00 5.00
PZ3 Mike Piazza 8.00 20.00
PZ4 Larry Walker 2.00 5.00
PZ5 Mark McGwire 12.50 30.00
PZ6 Jeff Bagwell 3.00 8.00
PZ7 Mo Vaughn 2.00 5.00
PZ8 Barry Bonds 12.50 30.00
PZ9 Tino Martinez 3.00 8.00
PZ10 Ken Griffey Jr. 8.00 20.00

1998 Upper Deck Special F/X Power Zone Superstar Xcitement

Randomly seeded in packs, cards from this 10-card set feature ten of the league's top stars printed on die-cut Light F/X gold-foil stock. In addition, only 250 sets were printed and each card is "crash-numbered" on back "of 250".

COMPLETE SET (10) 100.00 250.00
PZ1 Jose Cruz Jr. 3.00 8.00
PZ2 Frank Thomas 8.00 20.00
PZ3 Juan Gonzalez 3.00 8.00
PZ4 Mike Piazza 12.50 30.00
PZ5 Mark McGwire 20.00 50.00
PZ6 Barry Bonds 20.00 50.00
PZ7 Greg Maddux 12.50 30.00
PZ8 Alex Rodriguez 12.50 30.00
PZ9 Nomar Garciaparra 12.50 30.00
PZ10 Ken Griffey Jr. 12.50 30.00

2006 Upper Deck Special F/X

This 1,025-card set was released in January, 2007. The set is sequenced in first-name alphabetical order within team order which is also in alphabetical order. There are two distinct groupings of these cards (1-500, 501-870). Cards numbered 871-900 are checklist cards while cards 901-1025 are 2006 rookies. These cards were issued in four-card packs which came 16 packs to a box.

COMMON CARD (1-900) .30 .75
COMMON RC (901-1025) .50 1.25
1 Adam Kennedy .30 .75
2 Bartolo Colon .30 .75
3 Bengie Molina .30 .75
4 Casey Kotchman .30 .75
5 Chone Figgins .30 .75
6 Dallas McPherson .30 .75
7 Darin Erstad .30 .75
8 Ervin Santana .30 .75
9 Francisco Rodriguez .30 .75
10 Garret Anderson .30 .75
11 Jarrod Washburn .30 .75
12 John Lackey .30 .75
13 Juan Rivera .30 .75
14 Orlando Cabrera .30 .75
15 Paul Byrd .30 .75
16 Steve Finley .30 .75
17 Vladimir Guerrero .75 2.00
18 Alex Cintron .30 .75
19 Brandon Lyon .30 .75
20 Brandon Webb .30 .75
21 Chad Tracy .30 .75
22 Travis Snyder .30 .75
23 Claudio Vargas .30 .75
24 Conor Jackson .50 1.25
25 Craig Counsell .30 .75
26 Javier Vazquez .30 .75
27 Jose Valverde .30 .75
28 Luis Gonzalez .30 .75
29 Royce Clayton .30 .75
30 Russ Ortiz .30 .75
31 Shawn Green .30 .75
32 Dustin Nippert (RC) .50 1.25
33 Tony Clark .30 .75
34 Troy Glaus .30 .75
35 Adam LaRoche .30 .75
36 Andruw Jones .50 1.25
37 Craig Hansen RC 2.00 5.00
38 Chipper Jones .75 2.00
39 Horacio Ramirez .30 .75
40 Jeff Francoeur .75 2.00
41 John Smoltz .50 1.25
42 Joey Devine RC .50 1.25
43 Johnny Estrada .30 .75
44 Anthony Lerew (RC) .50 1.25
45 Julio Franco .30 .75
46 Kyle Farnsworth .30 .75
47 Marcus Giles .30 .75
48 Mike Hampton .30 .75
49 Rafael Furcal .30 .75
50 Chuck James (RC) .75 2.00
51 Tim Hudson .30 .75
52 B.J. Ryan .30 .75
53 Bernie Castro (RC) .50 1.25
54 Brian Roberts .30 .75
55 Walter Young (RC) .50 1.25
56 Daniel Cabrera .30 .75
57 Eric Byrnes .30 .75
58 Alejandro Freire RC .50 1.25
59 Erik Bedard .30 .75
60 Javy Lopez .30 .75
61 Jay Gibbons .30 .75
62 Jorge Julio .30 .75
63 Luis Matos .30 .75
64 Melvin Mora .30 .75
65 Miguel Tejada .30 .75
66 Rafael Palmeiro .50 1.25
67 Rodrigo Lopez .30 .75
68 Sammy Sosa .75 2.00
69 Alejandro Machado (RC) .50 1.25
70 Bill Mueller .30 .75
71 Bronson Arroyo .30 .75
72 Curt Schilling .50 1.25
73 David Ortiz .75 2.00
74 David Wells .30 .75
75 Edgar Renteria .30 .75
76 Ryan Jorgensen RC .50 1.25
77 Jason Varitek .75 2.00
78 Johnny Damon .50 1.25
79 Keith Foulke .30 .75
80 Kevin Youkilis .30 .75
81 Manny Ramirez .50 1.25
82 Matt Clement .30 .75
83 Hanley Ramirez (RC) 1.25 3.00
84 Tim Wakefield .30 .75
85 Trot Nixon .30 .75
86 Wade Miller .30 .75
87 Aramis Ramirez .30 .75
88 Carlos Zambrano .30 .75
89 Corey Patterson .30 .75
90 Derrek Lee .30 .75
91 Geovany Soto (RC) .50 1.25
92 Greg Maddux 1.25 3.00
93 Jeromy Burnitz .30 .75
94 Jerry Hairston Jr. .30 .75
95 Kerry Wood .30 .75
96 Mark Prior .50 1.25
97 Matt Murton .30 .75
98 Michael Barrett .30 .75
99 Neifi Perez .30 .75
100 Nomar Garciaparra .75 2.00
101 Rich Hill .30 .75
102 Ryan Dempster .30 .75
103 Todd Walker .30 .75
104 A.J. Pierzynski .30 .75
105 Aaron Rowand .30 .75
106 Bobby Jenks .30 .75
107 Carl Everett .30 .75
108 Dustin Hermanson .30 .75
109 Frank Thomas .75 2.00
110 Freddy Garcia .30 .75
111 Jermaine Dye .30 .75
112 Joe Crede .30 .75
113 Jon Garland .30 .75
114 Jose Contreras .30 .75
115 Juan Uribe .30 .75
116 Mark Buehrle .30 .75
117 Orlando Hernandez .30 .75
118 Paul Konerko .30 .75
119 Scott Podsednik .30 .75
120 Tadahito Iguchi .30 .75
121 Aaron Harang .30 .75
122 Adam Dunn .30 .75
123 Austin Kearns .30 .75
124 Brandon Claussen .30 .75
125 Chris Denorfia (RC) .50 1.25
126 Edwin Encarnacion .30 .75
127 Miguel Perez (RC) .50 1.25
128 Felipe Lopez .30 .75
129 Jason LaRue .30 .75
130 Ken Griffey Jr. 1.25 3.00
131 Chris Booker (RC) .50 1.25
132 Luke Hudson .30 .75
133 Jason Bergmann RC .50 1.25
134 Ryan Freel .30 .75
135 Sean Casey .30 .75
136 Wily Mo Pena .30 .75
137 Aaron Boone .30 .75
138 Ben Broussard .30 .75
139 Ryan Garko (RC) .50 1.25
140 C.C. Sabathia .30 .75
141 Casey Blake .30 .75
142 Cliff Lee .30 .75
143 Coco Crisp .30 .75
144 David Riske .30 .75
145 Grady Sizemore .50 1.25
146 Jake Westbrook .30 .75
147 Jhonny Peralta .30 .75
148 Josh Bard .30 .75
149 Kevin Millwood .30 .75
150 Ronnie Belliard .30 .75
151 Scott Elarton .30 .75
152 Travis Hafner .30 .75
153 Victor Martinez .30 .75
154 Aaron Cook .30 .75
155 Aaron Miles .30 .75
156 Brad Hawpe .30 .75
157 Mike Esposito (RC) .50 1.25
158 Chin-Hui Tsao .30 .75
159 Clint Barmes .30 .75
160 Cory Sullivan .30 .75
161 Garrett Atkins .30 .75
162 J.D. Closser .30 .75
163 Jason Jennings .30 .75
164 Jeff Baker .30 .75
165 Jeff Francis .30 .75
166 Luis Gonzalez .30 .75
167 Matt Holliday .40 1.00
168 Todd Helton .50 1.25
169 Brandon Inge .30 .75
170 Carlos Guillen .30 .75
171 Carlos Pena .30 .75
172 Chris Shelton .30 .75
173 Craig Monroe .30 .75
174 Curtis Granderson .30 .75
175 Dmitri Young .30 .75
176 Ivan Rodriguez .50 1.25
177 Jason Johnson .30 .75
178 Jeremy Bonderman .30 .75
179 Magglio Ordonez .30 .75
180 Mark Woodyard (RC) .50 1.25
181 Nook Logan .30 .75
182 Omar Infante .30 .75
183 Placido Polanco .30 .75
184 Chris Heintz RC .50 1.25
185 A.J. Burnett .30 .75
186 Alex Gonzalez .30 .75
187 Josh Johnson (RC) .75 2.00
188 Carlos Delgado .30 .75
189 Dontrelle Willis .30 .75
190 Josh Wilson (RC) .50 1.25
191 Jason Vargas .30 .75
192 Jeff Conine .30 .75
193 Jeremy Hermida .30 .75
194 Josh Beckett .30 .75
195 Juan Encarnacion .30 .75
196 Juan Pierre .30 .75
197 Luis Castillo .30 .75
198 Miguel Cabrera .50 1.25
199 Mike Lowell .30 .75
200 Paul Lo Duca .30 .75
201 Todd Jones .30 .75
202 Adam Everett .30 .75
203 Andy Pettitte .30 .75
204 Brad Ausmus .30 .75
205 Brad Lidge .30 .75
206 Brandon Backe .30 .75
207 Charlton Jimerson (RC) .50 1.25
208 Chris Burke .30 .75
209 Craig Biggio .50 1.25
210 Dan Wheeler .30 .75
211 Jason Lane .30 .75
212 Jeff Bagwell .50 1.25
213 Lance Berkman .30 .75
214 Luke Scott .30 .75
215 Morgan Ensberg .30 .75
216 Roger Clemens 1.50 4.00
217 Roy Oswalt .30 .75
218 Willy Taveras .30 .75
219 Andres Blanco .30 .75
220 Angel Berroa .30 .75
221 Ruben Gotay .30 .75
222 David DeJesus .30 .75
223 Emil Brown .30 .75
224 J.P. Howell .30 .75
225 Jeremy Affeldt .30 .75
226 Jimmy Gobble .30 .75
227 John Buck .30 .75
228 Jose Lima .30 .75
229 Mark Teahen .30 .75
230 Matt Stairs .30 .75
231 Mike MacDougal .30 .75
232 Mike Sweeney .30 .75
233 Runelvys Hernandez .30 .75
234 Terrence Long .30 .75
235 Zack Greinke .30 .75
236 Ron Flores RC .50 1.25
237 Brad Penny .30 .75
238 Cesar Izturis .30 .75
239 D.J. Houlton .30 .75
240 Derek Lowe .30 .75
241 Eric Gagne .30 .75
242 Hee Seop Choi .30 .75
243 J.D. Drew .30 .75
244 Jason Phillips .30 .75
245 Jason Repko .30 .75
246 Jayson Werth .30 .75
247 Jeff Kent .30 .75
248 Jeff Weaver .30 .75
249 Milton Bradley .30 .75
250 Odalis Perez .30 .75
251 Hong-Chih Kuo (RC) 1.25 3.00
252 Oscar Robles .30 .75
253 Ben Sheets .30 .75
254 Bill Hall .30 .75
255 Brady Clark .30 .75
256 Carlos Lee .30 .75
257 Chris Capuano .30 .75
258 Nelson Cruz (RC) .50 1.25
259 Derrick Turnbow .30 .75
260 Doug Davis .30 .75
261 Geoff Jenkins .30 .75
262 J.J. Hardy .30 .75
263 Lyle Overbay .30 .75
264 Prince Fielder 1.25 3.00
265 Rickie Weeks .30 .75
266 Russell Branyan .30 .75
267 Tomo Ohka .30 .75
268 Jonah Bayliss (RC) .50 1.25
269 Brad Radke .30 .75
270 Carlos Silva .30 .75
271 Francisco Liriano (RC) 2.50 6.00
272 Jacque Jones .30 .75
273 Joe Mauer .50 1.25
274 Travis Bowyer (RC) .50 1.25
275 Joe Nathan .30 .75
276 Johan Santana .50 1.25
277 Justin Morneau .30 .75
278 Kyle Lohse .30 .75
279 Lew Ford .30 .75
280 Matthew LeCroy .30 .75
281 Michael Cuddyer .30 .75
282 Nick Punto .30 .75
283 Scott Baker .30 .75
284 Shannon Stewart .30 .75
285 Torii Hunter .30 .75
286 Braden Looper .30 .75
287 Carlos Beltran .30 .75
288 Cliff Floyd .30 .75
289 David Wright 1.25 3.00
290 Doug Mientkiewicz .30 .75
291 Anderson Hernandez (RC) .50 1.25
292 Jose Reyes .30 .75
293 Kazuo Matsui .30 .75
294 Kris Benson .30 .75
295 Miguel Cairo .30 .75
296 Mike Cameron .30 .75
297 Robert Andino RC .50 1.25
298 Mike Piazza .75 2.00
299 Pedro Martinez .50 1.25
300 Tom Glavine .50 1.25
301 Victor Diaz .30 .75
302 Tim Hamulack (RC) .50 1.25
303 Alex Rodriguez 1.25 3.00
304 Bernie Williams .50 1.25
305 Carl Pavano .30 .75
306 Chien-Ming Wang 1.25 3.00
307 Derek Jeter 2.00 5.00
308 Gary Sheffield .30 .75
309 Hideki Matsui .75 2.00
310 Jason Giambi .30 .75
311 Jorge Posada .50 1.25
312 Kevin Brown .30 .75
313 Mariano Rivera .75 2.00
314 Matt Lawton .30 .75
315 Mike Mussina .50 1.25
316 Randy Johnson .75 2.00
317 Robinson Cano .50 1.25
318 Mike Vento (RC) .50 1.25
319 Tino Martinez .30 .75
320 Tony Womack .30 .75
321 Barry Zito .30 .75
322 Bobby Crosby .30 .75
323 Bobby Kielty .30 .75
324 Dan Johnson .30 .75
325 Danny Haren .30 .75
326 Eric Chavez .30 .75
327 Erubiel Durazo .30 .75
328 Huston Street .30 .75
329 Jason Kendall .30 .75
330 Jay Payton .30 .75
331 Joe Blanton .30 .75
332 Joe Kennedy .30 .75
333 Kirk Saarloos .30 .75
334 Mark Kotsay .30 .75
335 Nick Swisher .30 .75
336 Rich Harden .30 .75
337 Scott Hatteberg .30 .75
338 Billy Wagner .30 .75
339 Bobby Abreu .30 .75
340 Brett Myers .30 .75
341 Chase Utley .75 2.00
342 Danny Sandoval RC .50 1.25
343 David Bell .30 .75
344 Gavin Floyd .30 .75
345 Jim Thome .50 1.25
346 Jimmy Rollins .30 .75
347 Jon Lieber .30 .75
348 Kenny Lofton .30 .75
349 Mike Lieberthal .30 .75
350 Pat Burrell .30 .75
351 Randy Wolf .30 .75
352 Ryan Howard 1.25 3.00
353 Vicente Padilla .30 .75
354 Bryan Bullington (RC) .50 1.25
355 J.J. Furmaniak (RC) .50 1.25
356 Craig Wilson .30 .75
357 Matt Capps (RC) .50 1.25
358 Tom Gorzelanny (RC) .50 1.25
359 Jack Wilson .30 .75
360 Jason Bay .30 .75
361 Jose Mesa .30 .75
362 Josh Fogg .30 .75
363 Kip Wells .30 .75
364 Steve Stemle RC .50 1.25
365 Oliver Perez .30 .75
366 Rob Mackowiak .30 .75
367 Ronny Paulino (RC) .50 1.25
368 Tike Redman .30 .75
369 Zach Duke .30 .75
370 Adam Eaton .30 .75
371 Scott Feldman (RC) .50 1.25
372 Brian Giles .30 .75
373 Brian Lawrence .30 .75
374 Damian Jackson .30 .75
375 Dave Roberts .30 .75
376 Jake Peavy .30 .75
377 Joe Randa .30 .75
378 Khalil Greene .50 1.25
379 Mark Loretta .30 .75
380 Ramon Hernandez .30 .75
381 Robert Fick .30 .75
382 Ryan Klesko .30 .75
383 Trevor Hoffman .30 .75
384 Woody Williams .30 .75
385 Xavier Nady .30 .75
386 Armando Benitez .30 .75
387 Brad Hennessey .30 .75
388 Brian Myrow RC .50 1.25
389 Edgardo Alfonzo .30 .75
390 J.T. Snow .30 .75
391 Jeremy Accardo RC .50 1.25
392 Jason Schmidt .30 .75
393 Lance Niekro .30 .75
394 Matt Cain .50 1.25
395 Daniel Ortmeier (RC) .50 1.25
396 Moises Alou .30 .75
397 Doug Clark (RC) .50 1.25
398 Omar Vizquel .50 1.25
399 Pedro Feliz .30 .75
400 Randy Winn .30 .75
401 Ray Durham .30 .75
402 Adrian Beltre .30 .75
403 Eddie Guardado .30 .75
404 Felix Hernandez .50 1.25
405 Gil Meche .30 .75
406 Ichiro Suzuki 1.25 3.00
407 Jamie Moyer .30 .75
408 Jeff Nelson .30 .75
409 Jeremy Reed .30 .75
410 Joel Pineiro .30 .75
411 Jaime Bubela (RC) .50 1.25
412 Raul Ibanez .30 .75
413 Richie Sexson .30 .75
414 Ryan Franklin .30 .75
415 Willie Bloomquist .30 .75
416 Yorvit Torrealba .30 .75
417 Yuniesky Betancourt .30 .75
418 Jeff Harris RC .50 1.25
419 Albert Pujols 1.50 4.00
420 Chris Carpenter .30 .75
421 David Eckstein .30 .75
422 Jason Isringhausen .30 .75
423 Jason Marquis .30 .75
424 Adam Wainwright (RC) .50 1.25
425 Jim Edmonds .50 1.25
426 Ryan Theriot RC .50 1.25
427 Chris Duncan (RC) .75 2.00
428 Mark Grudzielanek .30 .75
429 Mark Mulder .30 .75
430 Matt Morris .30 .75
431 Reggie Sanders .30 .75
432 Scott Rolen .50 1.25
433 Tyler Johnson (RC) .50 1.25
434 Yadier Molina .30 .75
435 Alex Gonzalez .30 .75
436 Aubrey Huff .30 .75
437 Tim Corcoran RC .50 1.25
438 Carl Crawford .30 .75
439 Casey Fossum .30 .75
440 Danys Baez .30 .75
441 Edwin Jackson .30 .75
442 Joey Gathright .30 .75
443 Jonny Gomes .30 .75
444 Jorge Cantu .30 .75
445 Julio Lugo .30 .75
446 Nick Green .30 .75
447 Rocco Baldelli .30 .75
448 Scott Kazmir .50 1.25
449 Seth McClung .30 .75
450 Toby Hall .30 .75
451 Travis Lee .30 .75
452 Craig Breslow RC .50 1.25
453 Alfonso Soriano .30 .75
454 Chris R. Young .30 .75
455 David Dellucci .30 .75
456 Francisco Cordero .30 .75
457 Gary Matthews .30 .75
458 Hank Blalock .30 .75
459 Juan Dominguez .30 .75
460 Josh Rupe (RC) .50 1.25
461 Kenny Rogers .30 .75
462 Kevin Mench .30 .75
463 Laynce Nix .30 .75
464 Mark Teixeira .50 1.25
465 Michael Young .30 .75
466 Richard Hidalgo .30 .75
467 Jason Botts (RC) .50 1.25
468 Aaron Hill .30 .75
469 Alex Rios .30 .75
470 Corey Koskie .30 .75
471 Chris Demaria RC .50 1.25
472 Eric Hinske .30 .75
473 Frank Catalanotto .30 .75
474 John-Ford Griffin (RC) .50 1.25
475 Gustavo Chacin .30 .75
476 Josh Towers .30 .75
477 Miguel Batista .30 .75
478 Orlando Hudson .30 .75
479 Reed Johnson .30 .75
480 Roy Halladay .30 .75
481 Shaun Marcum (RC) .50 1.25
482 Shea Hillenbrand .30 .75
483 Ted Lilly .30 .75
484 Vernon Wells .30 .75
485 Brad Wilkerson .30 .75
486 Darrell Rasner (RC) .50 1.25
487 Chad Cordero .30 .75
488 Cristian Guzman .30 .75
489 Esteban Loaiza .30 .75
490 John Patterson .30 .75
491 Jose Guillen .30 .75
492 Jose Vidro .30 .75
493 Livan Hernandez .30 .75
494 Marlon Byrd .30 .75
495 Nick Johnson .30 .75
496 Preston Wilson .30 .75
497 Ryan Church .30 .75
498 Ryan Zimmerman (RC) 3.00 8.00
499 Tony Armas .30 .75
500 Vinny Castilla .30 .75
501 Andy Green .30 .75
502 Damion Easley .30 .75
503 Eric Byrnes .30 .75
504 Jason Grimsley .30 .75
505 Jeff DaVanon .30 .75
506 Johnny Estrada .30 .75
507 Luis Vizcaino .30 .75
508 Miguel Batista .30 .75
509 Orlando Hernandez .30 .75
510 Orlando Hudson .30 .75
511 Terry Mulholland .30 .75
512 Chris Reitsma .30 .75
513 Edgar Renteria .30 .75

514 John Thomson .30 .75
515 Jorge Sosa .30 .75
516 Oscar Villarreal .30 .75
517 Pete Orr .30 .75
518 Ryan Langerhans .30 .75
519 Todd Pratt .30 .75
520 Wilson Betemit .30 .75
521 Brian Jordan .30 .75
522 Lance Cormier .30 .75
523 Matt Diaz .30 .75
524 Mike Remlinger .30 .75
525 Bruce Chen .30 .75
526 Chris Gomez .30 .75
527 Chris Ray .30 .75
528 Corey Patterson .30 .75
529 David Newhan .30 .75
530 Ed Rogers (RC) .50 1.25
531 John Halama .30 .75
532 Kris Benson .30 .75
533 LaTroy Hawkins .30 .75
534 Raul Chavez .30 .75
535 Alex Cora .30 .75
536 Alex Gonzalez .30 .75
537 Coco Crisp .30 .75
538 David Riske .30 .75
539 Doug Mirabelli .30 .75
540 Josh Beckett .30 .75
541 J.T. Snow .30 .75
542 Mike Timlin .30 .75
543 Julian Tavarez .30 .75
544 Rudy Seanez .30 .75
545 Wily Mo Pena .30 .75
546 Bob Howry .30 .75
547 Glendon Rusch .30 .75
548 Henry Blanco .30 .75
549 Jacque Jones .30 .75
550 Jerome Williams .30 .75
551 John Mabry .30 .75
552 Juan Pierre .30 .75
553 Scott Eyre .30 .75
554 Scott Williamson .30 .75
555 Wade Miller .30 .75
556 Will Ohman .30 .75
557 Alex Cintron .30 .75
558 Rob Mackowiak .30 .75
559 Brandon McCarthy .30 .75
560 Chris Widger .30 .75
561 Cliff Politte .30 .75
562 Javier Vazquez .30 .75
563 Jim Thome .50 1.25
564 Matt Thornton .30 .75
565 Neal Cotts .30 .75
566 Pablo Ozuna .30 .75
567 Ross Gload .30 .75
568 Brandon Phillips .30 .75
569 Bronson Arroyo .30 .75
570 Dave Williams .30 .75
571 David Ross .30 .75
572 David Weathers .30 .75
573 Eric Milton .30 .75
574 Javier Valentin .30 .75
575 Kent Mercker .30 .75
576 Matt Belisle .30 .75
577 Paul Wilson .30 .75
578 Rich Aurilia .30 .75
579 Rick White .30 .75
580 Scott Hatteberg .30 .75
581 Todd Coffey .30 .75
582 Bob Wickman .30 .75
583 Danny Graves .30 .75
584 Eduardo Perez .30 .75
585 Guillermo Mota .30 .75
586 Jason Davis .30 .75
587 Jason Johnson .30 .75
588 Jason Michaels .30 .75
589 Rafael Betancourt .30 .75
590 Ramon Vazquez .30 .75
591 Scott Sauerbeck .30 .75
592 Todd Hollandsworth .30 .75
593 Brian Fuentes .30 .75
594 Danny Ardoin .30 .75
595 David Cortes .30 .75
596 Eli Marrero .30 .75
597 Jamey Carroll .30 .75
598 Jason Smith .30 .75
599 Josh Fogg .30 .75
600 Miguel Ojeda .30 .75
601 Mike DeJean .30 .75
602 Ray King .30 .75
603 Omar Quintanilla (RC) .50 1.25
604 Zach Day .30 .75
605 Fernando Rodney .30 .75
606 Kenny Rogers .30 .75
607 Mike Maroth .30 .75
608 Nate Robertson .30 .75
609 Todd Jones .30 .75
610 Vance Wilson .30 .75
611 Bobby Seay .30 .75
612 Chris Spurling .30 .75
613 Roman Colon .30 .75
614 Jason Grilli .30 .75
615 Marcus Thames .30 .75
616 Ramon Santiago .30 .75
617 Alfredo Amezaga .30 .75
618 Brian Moehler .30 .75
619 Chris Aguila .30 .75
620 Franklyn German .30 .75
621 Joe Borowski .30 .75
622 Logan Kensing (RC) .50 1.25
623 Matt Treanor .30 .75
624 Miguel Olivo .30 .75
625 Sergio Mitre .30 .75
626 Todd Wellemeyer .30 .75
627 Wes Helms .30 .75
628 Chad Qualls .30 .75
629 Eric Bruntlett .30 .75
630 Mike Gallo .30 .75
631 Mike Lamb .30 .75
632 Orlando Palmeiro .30 .75
633 Russ Springer .30 .75
634 Dan Wheeler .30 .75
635 Eric Munson .30 .75
636 Preston Wilson .30 .75
637 Trever Miller .30 .75
638 Ambiorix Burgos .30 .75
639 Andy Sisco .30 .75
640 Denny Bautista .30 .75
641 Doug Mientkiewicz .30 .75
642 Elmer Dessens .30 .75
643 Esteban German .30 .75
644 Joe Nelson (RC) .50 1.25
645 Mark Grudzielanek .30 .75
646 Mark Redman .30 .75
647 Mike Wood .30 .75
648 Paul Bako .30 .75
649 Reggie Sanders .30 .75
650 Scott Elarton .30 .75
651 Shane Costa .30 .75
652 Tony Graffanino .30 .75
653 Jason Bulger (RC) .50 1.25
654 Chris Bootcheck (RC) .50 1.25
655 Esteban Yan .30 .75
656 Hector Carrasco .30 .75
657 J.C. Romero .30 .75
658 Jeff Weaver .30 .75
659 Jose Molina .30 .75
660 Kelvim Escobar .30 .75
661 Maicer Izturis .30 .75
662 Robb Quinlan .30 .75
663 Scot Shields .30 .75
664 Tim Salmon .30 .75
665 Bill Mueller .30 .75
666 Brett Tomko .30 .75
667 Dioner Navarro .30 .75
668 Jae Seo .30 .75
669 Jose Cruz .30 .75
670 Kenny Lofton .30 .75
671 Lance Carter .30 .75
672 Nomar Garciaparra .75 2.00
673 Olmedo Saenz .30 .75
674 Rafael Furcal .30 .75
675 Ramon Martinez .30 .75
676 Ricky Ledee .30 .75
677 Sandy Alomar .30 .75
678 Yhency Brazoban .30 .75
679 Corey Koskie .30 .75
680 Dan Kolb .30 .75
681 Gabe Gross .30 .75
682 Jeff Cirillo .30 .75
683 Matt Wise .30 .75
684 Rick Helling .30 .75
685 Chad Moeller .30 .75
686 Dave Bush .30 .75
687 Jorge De La Rosa .30 .75
688 Justin Lehr .30 .75
689 Jason Bartlett .30 .75
690 Jesse Crain .30 .75
691 Juan Rincon .30 .75
692 Luis Castillo .30 .75
693 Mike Redmond .30 .75
694 Rondell White .30 .75
695 Tony Batista .30 .75
696 Juan Castro .30 .75
697 Luis Rodriguez .30 .75
698 Matt Guerrier .30 .75
699 Willie Eyre (RC) .50 1.25
700 Aaron Heilman .30 .75
701 Billy Wagner .30 .75
702 Carlos Delgado .30 .75
703 Chad Bradford .30 .75
704 Chris Woodward .30 .75
705 Darren Oliver .30 .75
706 Duaner Sanchez .30 .75
707 Endy Chavez .30 .75
708 Jorge Julio .30 .75
709 Jose Valentin .30 .75
710 Julio Franco .30 .75
711 Paul Lo Duca .30 .75
712 Ramon Castro .30 .75
713 Steve Trachsel .30 .75
714 Victor Zambrano .30 .75
715 Xavier Nady .30 .75
716 Andy Phillips .30 .75
717 Bubba Crosby .30 .75
718 Jaret Wright .30 .75
719 Kelly Stinnett .30 .75
720 Kyle Farnsworth .30 .75
721 Mike Meyers .30 .75
722 Octavio Dotel .30 .75
723 Ron Villone .30 .75
724 Scott Proctor .30 .75
725 Shawn Chacon .30 .75
726 Tanyon Sturtze .30 .75
727 Adam Melhuse .30 .75
728 Brad Halsey .30 .75
729 Esteban Loaiza .30 .75
730 Frank Thomas .75 2.00
731 Jay Witasick .30 .75
732 Justin Duchscherer .30 .75
733 Kiko Calero .30 .75
734 Marco Scutaro .30 .75
735 Mark Ellis .30 .75
736 Milton Bradley .30 .75
737 Aaron Fultz .30 .75
738 Aaron Rowand .30 .75
739 Geoff Geary .30 .75
740 Arthur Rhodes .30 .75
741 Chris Coste RC .50 1.25
742 Rheal Cormier .30 .75
743 Ryan Franklin .30 .75
744 Ryan Madson .30 .75
745 Sal Fasano .30 .75
746 Tom Gordon .30 .75
747 Abraham Nunez .30 .75
748 David Dellucci .30 .75
749 Julio Santana .30 .75
750 Shane Victorino .30 .75
751 Damaso Marte .30 .75
752 Freddy Sanchez .30 .75
753 Humberto Cota .30 .75
754 Jeromy Burnitz .30 .75
755 Joe Randa .30 .75
756 Jose Castillo .30 .75
757 Mike Gonzalez .30 .75
758 Ryan Doumit .30 .75
759 Sean Burnett .30 .75
760 Sean Casey .30 .75
761 Ian Snell .30 .75
762 John Grabow .30 .75
763 Jose Hernandez .30 .75
764 Roberto Hernandez .30 .75
765 Ryan Vogelsong .30 .75
766 Victor Sanchez .30 .75
767 Adrian Gonzalez .30 .75
768 Alan Embree .30 .75
769 Brian Sweeney (RC) .50 1.25
770 Chan Ho Park .30 .75
771 Clay Hensley .30 .75
772 Dewon Brazelton .30 .75
773 Doug Brocail .30 .75
774 Eric Young .30 .75
775 Geoff Blum .30 .75
776 Josh Bard .30 .75
777 Mark Bellhorn .30 .75
778 Mike Cameron .30 .75
779 Mike Piazza .75 2.00
780 Rob Bowen .30 .75
781 Scott Cassidy .30 .75
782 Scott Linebrink .30 .75
783 Shawn Estes .30 .75
784 Terrmel Sledge .30 .75
785 Vinny Castilla .30 .75
786 Jeff Fassero .30 .75
787 Jose Vizcaino .30 .75
788 Mark Sweeney .30 .75
789 Matt Morris .30 .75
790 Steve Finley .30 .75
791 Tim Worrell .30 .75
792 Jamey Wright .30 .75
793 Jason Ellison .30 .75
794 Noah Lowry .30 .75
795 Steve Kline .30 .75
796 Todd Greene .30 .75
797 Carl Everett .30 .75
798 George Sherrill .30 .75
799 J.J. Putz .30 .75
800 Jake Woods .30 .75
801 Jose Lopez .30 .75
802 Julio Mateo .30 .75
803 Mike Morse .30 .75
804 Rafael Soriano .30 .75
805 Roberto Petagine .30 .75
806 Aaron Miles .30 .75
807 Braden Looper .30 .75
808 Gary Bennett .30 .75
809 Hector Luna .30 .75
810 Jeff Suppan .30 .75
811 John Rodriguez .30 .75
812 Josh Hancock .30 .75
813 Juan Encarnacion .30 .75
814 Larry Bigbie .30 .75
815 Scott Spiezio .30 .75
816 Sidney Ponson .30 .75
817 So Taguchi .30 .75
818 Brian Meadows .30 .75
819 Damon Hollins .30 .75
820 Dan Miceli .30 .75
821 Doug Waechter .30 .75
822 Jason Childers (RC) .50 1.25
823 Josh Paul .30 .75
824 Julio Lugo .30 .75
825 Mark Hendrickson .30 .75
826 Sean Burroughs .30 .75
827 Shawn Camp .30 .75
828 Travis Harper .30 .75
829 Ty Wigginton .30 .75
830 Adam Eaton .30 .75
831 Adrian Brown .30 .75
832 Akinori Otsuka .30 .75
833 Antonio Alfonseca .30 .75
834 Brad Wilkerson .30 .75
835 D'Angelo Jimenez .30 .75
836 Gerald Laird .30 .75
837 Joaquin Benoit .30 .75
838 Kameron Loe .30 .75
839 Kevin Millwood .30 .75
840 Mark DeRosa .30 .75
841 Phil Nevin .30 .75
842 Rod Barajas .30 .75
843 Vicente Padilla .30 .75
844 A.J. Burnett .30 .75
845 Bengie Molina .30 .75
846 Gregg Zaun .30 .75
847 John McDonald .30 .75
848 Lyle Overbay .30 .75
849 Russ Adams .30 .75
850 Troy Glaus .30 .75
851 Vinnie Chulk .30 .75
852 B.J. Ryan .30 .75
853 Justin Speier .30 .75
854 Pete Walker .30 .75
855 Scott Downs .30 .75
856 Scott Schoeneweis .30 .75
857 Alfonso Soriano .30 .75
858 Brian Schneider .30 .75
859 Daryle Ward .30 .75
860 Felix Rodriguez .30 .75
861 Gary Majewski .30 .75
862 Joey Eischen .30 .75
863 Jon Rauch .30 .75
864 Marlon Anderson .30 .75
865 Matt LeCroy .30 .75
866 Mike Stanton .30 .75
867 Ramon Ortiz .30 .75
868 Robert Fick .30 .75
869 Royce Clayton .30 .75
870 Ryan Drese .30 .75
871 Vladimir Guerrero CL .75 2.00
872 Craig Biggio CL .50 1.25
873 Barry Zito CL .30 .75
874 Vernon Wells CL .30 .75
875 Chipper Jones CL .75 2.00
876 Prince Fielder CL 1.25 3.00
877 Albert Pujols CL 1.50 4.00
878 Greg Maddux CL 1.25 3.00
879 Carl Crawford CL .30 .75
880 Brandon Webb CL .30 .75
881 J.D. Drew CL .30 .75
882 Jason Schmidt CL .30 .75
883 Victor Martinez CL .30 .75
884 Ichiro Suzuki CL 1.25 3.00
885 Miguel Cabrera CL .50 1.25
886 David Wright CL 1.25 3.00
887 Alfonso Soriano CL .30 .75
888 Miguel Tejada CL .30 .75
889 Khalil Greene CL .50 1.25
890 Ryan Howard CL 1.25 3.00
891 Jason Bay CL .30 .75
892 Mark Teixeira CL .50 1.25
893 Manny Ramirez CL .50 1.25
894 Ken Griffey Jr. CL 1.25 3.00
895 Todd Helton CL .50 1.25
896 Angel Berroa CL .30 .75
897 Ivan Rodriguez CL .50 1.25
898 Johan Santana CL .50 1.25
899 Paul Konerko CL .30 .75
900 Derek Jeter CL 2.00 5.00
901 Macay McBride (RC) .50 1.25
902 Tony Pena Jr. (RC) .50 1.25
903 Peter Moylan RC .50 1.25
904 Aaron Rakers (RC) .50 1.25
905 Chris Britton RC .50 1.25
906 Nick Markakis (RC) .75 2.00
907 Sendy Rleal RC .50 1.25
908 Val Majewski (RC) .50 1.25
909 Jermaine Van Buren (RC) .50 1.25
910 Jonathan Papelbon (RC) 2.50 6.00
911 Angel Pagan (RC) .50 1.25
912 David Aardsma (RC) .50 1.25
913 Sean Marshall (RC) .50 1.25
914 Brian Anderson (RC) .50 1.25
915 Freddie Bynum (RC) .50 1.25
916 Fausto Carmona (RC) .50 1.25
917 Kelly Shoppach (RC) .50 1.25
918 Choo Freeman (RC) .50 1.25
919 Ryan Shealy (RC) .50 1.25
920 Joel Zumaya (RC) 1.25 3.00
921 Jordan Tata RC .50 1.25
922 Justin Verlander (RC) 2.00 5.00
923 Carlos Martinez RC .50 1.25
924 Chris Resop (RC) .50 1.25
925 Dan Uggla (RC) 1.25 3.00
926 Eric Reed (RC) .50 1.25
927 Hanley Ramirez (RC) 1.25 3.00
928 Yusmeiro Petit (RC) .50 1.25
929 Josh Willingham (RC) .50 1.25
930 Mike Jacobs (RC) .50 1.25
931 Reggie Abercrombie (RC) .50 1.25
932 Ricky Nolasco (RC) .50 1.25
933 Scott Olsen (RC) .50 1.25
934 Fernando Nieve (RC) .50 1.25
935 Taylor Buchholz (RC) .50 1.25
936 Cody Ross (RC) .50 1.25
937 James Loney (RC) .75 2.00
938 Takashi Saito RC .75 2.00
939 Tim Hamulack (RC) .50 1.25
940 Chris Demaria RC .50 1.25
941 Jose Capellan (RC) .50 1.25
942 David Gassner (RC) .50 1.25
943 Jason Kubel (RC) .50 1.25
944 Brian Bannister (RC) .50 1.25
945 Mike Thompson RC .50 1.25
946 Cole Hamels (RC) 1.25 3.00
947 Paul Maholm (RC) .50 1.25
948 John Van Benschoten (RC) .50 1.25
949 Nate McLouth (RC) .50 1.25
950 Ben Johnson (RC) .50 1.25
951 Josh Barfield (RC) .50 1.25
952 Travis Ishikawa (RC) .50 1.25
953 Jack Taschner (RC) .50 1.25
954 Kenji Johjima RC 2.50 6.00
955 Skip Schumaker (RC) .50 1.25
956 Ruddy Lugo (RC) .50 1.25
957 Jason Hammel (RC) .50 1.25
958 Chris Roberson (RC) .50 1.25
959 Fabio Castro RC .50 1.25
960 Ian Kinsler (RC) .75 2.00
961 John Koronka (RC) .50 1.25
962 Brandon Watson (RC) .50 1.25
963 Jon Lester RC 1.50 4.00
964 Ben Hendrickson (RC) .50 1.25
965 Martin Prado (RC) .50 1.25
966 Erick Aybar (RC) .50 1.25
967 Bobby Livingston (RC) .50 1.25
968 Ryan Spilborghs (RC) .75 2.00
969 Tommy Murphy (RC) .50 1.25
970 Howie Kendrick (RC) 1.25 3.00
971 Casey Janssen RC .75 2.00
972 Michael O'Connor RC .50 1.25
973 Conor Jackson (RC) .75 2.00
974 Jeremy Hermida (RC) .50 1.25
975 Renyel Pinto (RC) .50 1.25
976 Prince Fielder (RC) 2.00 5.00
977 Kevin Frandsen (RC) .50 1.25
978 Ty Taubenheim RC .75 2.00
979 Rich Hill (RC) .50 1.25
980 Jonathan Broxton (RC) .50 1.25
981 James Shields RC .50 1.25
982 Carlos Villanueva RC .50 1.25
983 Boone Logan RC .50 1.25
984 Brian Wilson RC .50 1.25
985 Andre Ethier (RC) 1.25 3.00
986 Mike Napoli RC 1.25 3.00
987 Agustin Montero (RC) .50 1.25
988 Jack Hannahan RC .50 1.25
989 Boof Bonser (RC) .75 2.00
990 Carlos Ruiz (RC) .50 1.25
991 Jason Botts (RC) .50 1.25
992 Kendry Morales (RC) .75 2.00
993 Alay Soler RC .50 1.25
994 Santiago Ramirez (RC) .50 1.25
995 Saul Rivera (RC) .50 1.25
996 Anthony Reyes (RC) .75 2.00
997 Matt Kemp (RC) .75 2.00
998 Jae Kuk Ryu RC .50 1.25
999 Lastings Milledge (RC) .75 2.00
1000 Jered Weaver (RC) 1.50 4.00
1001 Jeremy Sowers (RC) .50 1.25
1002 Chad Billingsley (RC) .75 2.00
1003 Stephen Drew (RC) 1.25 3.00
1004 Tony Gwynn Jr. (RC) 1.25 3.00
1005 Melky Cabrera (RC) .75 2.00
1006 Eliezer Alfonzo RC .50 1.25
1007 Dana Eveland (RC) .50 1.25
1008 Luis Figueroa RC .50 1.25
1009 Emiliano Fruto RC .50 1.25
1010 Clay Hensley (RC) .50 1.25
1011 Zach Jackson (RC) .50 1.25
1012 Bob Keppel (RC) .50 1.25
1013 Carlos Marmol RC .50 1.25
1014 Russell Martin (RC) .75 2.00
1015 Leo Nunez (RC) .50 1.25
1016 Ken Ray (RC) .50 1.25
1017 Mike Rouse (RC) .50 1.25
1018 Kevin Thompson (RC) .50 1.25
1019 C.J. Wilson (RC) .50 1.25
1020 Stephen Andrade (RC) .50 1.25
1021 Ed Rogers (RC) .50 1.25
1022 Joe Nelson (RC) .50 1.25
1023 Omar Quintanilla (RC) .50 1.25
1024 Chris Bootcheck (RC) .50 1.25
1025 Jason Childers RC .50 1.25

2006 Upper Deck Special F/X Blue

*BLUE: .5X TO 1.2X BASIC
*BLUE RC: .5X TO 1.2X BASIC RC
STATED ODDS 1:4

2006 Upper Deck Special F/X Green

*GREEN: 1X TO 2.5X BASIC
*GREEN RC: .75X TO 2X BASIC RC
STATED PRINT RUN 99 SER.#'d SETS
242 Hee Seop Choi 3.00 8.00
251 Hong-Chih Kuo 6.00 15.00
306 Chien-Ming Wang 12.50 30.00
309 Hideki Matsui 6.00 15.00
317 Robinson Cano 3.00 8.00
406 Ichiro Suzuki 10.00 25.00
421 David Eckstein 4.00 10.00
884 Ichiro Suzuki CL 10.00 25.00

2006 Upper Deck Special F/X Purple

*PURPLE: .75X TO 2X BASIC
*PURPLE RC: .6X TO 1.5X BASIC RC
STATED PRINT RUN 150 SER.#'d SETS
242 Hee Seop Choi 2.50 6.00
251 Hong-Chih Kuo 5.00 12.00
306 Chien-Ming Wang 10.00 25.00
309 Hideki Matsui 5.00 12.00
317 Robinson Cano 2.50 6.00
406 Ichiro Suzuki 8.00 20.00
421 David Eckstein 3.00 8.00
548 Henry Blanco .60 1.50
884 Ichiro Suzuki CL 8.00 20.00

2006 Upper Deck Special F/X Red

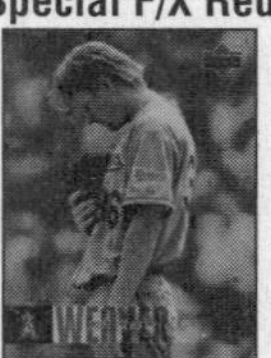

*RED: 1.25X TO 3X BASIC
*RED RC: 1X TO 2.5X BASIC RC
STATED PRINT RUN 50 SER.#'d SETS
242 Hee Seop Choi 4.00 10.00
251 Hong-Chih Kuo 8.00 20.00
306 Chien-Ming Wang 15.00 40.00
309 Hideki Matsui 8.00 20.00
317 Robinson Cano 4.00 10.00
406 Ichiro Suzuki 12.50 30.00
421 David Eckstein 5.00 12.00
884 Ichiro Suzuki CL 12.50 30.00

2006 Upper Deck Special F/X Materials

STATED ODDS 1:8
AD Adam Dunn Jsy 2.50 6.00
AJ Andruw Jones Jsy 3.00 8.00
AP Albert Pujols Jsy 6.00 15.00
AS Alfonso Soriano Jsy 2.50 6.00
CA Chris Carpenter Jsy 3.00 8.00
CC Carl Crawford Jsy 2.50 6.00
CH Cole Hamels Jsy 5.00 12.00
CR Coco Crisp Jsy 2.50 6.00
CU Chase Utley Jsy 4.00 10.00
DJ Derek Jeter Jsy 8.00 20.00
DL Derrek Lee Jsy 3.00 8.00
DO David Ortiz Jsy 4.00 10.00
FH Felix Hernandez Jsy 3.00 8.00
FL Francisco Liriano Jsy 5.00 12.00
GS Grady Sizemore Jsy 3.00 8.00
HA Roy Halladay Jsy 2.50 6.00
HR Hanley Ramirez Jsy 3.00 8.00
IK Ian Kinsler Jsy 3.00 8.00
JB Jason Bay Jsy 2.50 6.00
JG Jason Giambi Jsy 2.50 6.00
JH Jeremy Hermida Jsy 2.50 6.00
JM Joe Mauer Jsy 3.00 8.00
JP Jonathan Papelbon Jsy 5.00 12.00
JR Jose Reyes Jsy 3.00 8.00
JS Johan Santana Jsy 3.00 8.00
JT Jim Thome Jsy 3.00 8.00
JV Justin Verlander Jsy 5.00 12.00
JW Josh Willingham Jsy 2.50 6.00
KG Ken Griffey Jr. Jsy 5.00 12.00
KJ Kenji Johjima Jsy 5.00 12.00
KM Kendry Morales Jsy 3.00 8.00
LB Lance Berkman Jsy 2.50 6.00
LM Lastings Milledge Jsy 3.00 8.00
MA Matt Cain Jsy 3.00 8.00
MC Miguel Cabrera Jsy 3.00 8.00
MT Mark Teixeira Jsy 3.00 8.00
PF Prince Fielder Jsy 4.00 10.00
PM Pedro Martinez Jsy 4.00 10.00
RF Rafael Furcal Jsy 2.50 6.00
RH Ryan Howard Jsy 6.00 15.00
RW Rickie Weeks Jsy 2.50 6.00
RZ Ryan Zimmerman Jsy 5.00 12.00
SK Scott Kazmir Jsy 3.00 8.00
TE Miguel Tejada Jsy 2.50 6.00
TG Troy Glaus Jsy 2.50 6.00
TH Travis Hafner Jsy 2.50 6.00
VG Vladimir Guerrero Jsy 3.00 8.00
VM Victor Martinez Jsy 2.50 6.00
WE Jered Weaver Jsy 4.00 10.00

2006 Upper Deck Special F/X Player Highlights

STATED ODDS 1:3
1 Andruw Jones .60 1.50
2 Manny Ramirez .60 1.50
3 Travis Hafner .40 1.00
4 Johnny Damon .60 1.50
5 Miguel Cabrera .60 1.50
6 Chris Carpenter .40 1.00
7 Derrek Lee .40 1.00
8 Jason Bay .40 1.00
9 Jason Varitek 1.00 2.50
10 Ryan Howard 1.25 3.00
11 Mark Teixeira .60 1.50
12 Carlos Delgado .40 1.00
13 Bartolo Colon .40 1.00
14 David Wright 1.25 3.00
15 Miguel Tejada .40 1.00
16 Mike Piazza 1.00 2.50
17 Paul Konerko .40 1.00
18 Jermaine Dye .40 1.00
19 Ichiro Suzuki 1.25 3.00
20 Brad Wilkerson .40 1.00
21 Hideki Matsui 1.00 2.50
22 Albert Pujols 1.50 4.00
23 Chris Burke .40 1.00
24 Derek Jeter 2.00 5.00
25 Brian Roberts .40 1.00
26 David Ortiz 1.00 2.50
27 Alex Rodriguez 1.25 3.00
28 Ken Griffey Jr. 1.25 3.00
29 Prince Fielder 1.25 3.00
30 Bobby Abreu .40 1.00
31 Vladimir Guerrero 1.00 2.50
32 Tadahito Iguchi .40 1.00
33 Jose Reyes .40 1.00
34 Scott Podsednik .40 1.00
35 Gary Sheffield .40 1.00

2006 Upper Deck Special F/X Run Producers

STATED ODDS 1:3
1 Ty Cobb 1.50 4.00
2 Derrek Lee .50 1.25
3 Andruw Jones .75 2.00
4 David Ortiz 1.25 3.00
5 Lou Gehrig 2.00 5.00
6 Ken Griffey Jr. 1.50 4.00
7 Albert Pujols 2.00 5.00
8 Derek Jeter 2.50 6.00
9 Manny Ramirez .75 2.00
10 Alex Rodriguez 1.50 4.00
11 Gary Sheffield .50 1.25
12 Miguel Cabrera .75 2.00
13 Hideki Matsui 1.25 3.00
14 Vladimir Guerrero 1.25 3.00
15 David Wright 1.50 4.00
16 Mike Schmidt 1.50 4.00
17 Mark Teixeira .75 2.00
18 Babe Ruth 2.50 6.00

19 Jimmie Foxx 1.25 3.00
20 Honus Wagner 1.25 3.00

2006 Upper Deck Special F/X Special Endorsements

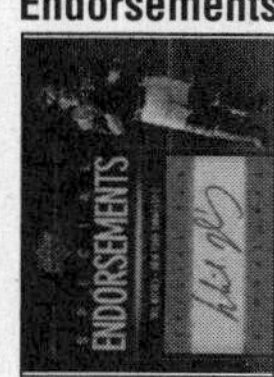

STATED ODDS 1:16
EXCH DEADLINE 12/14/09
ASTERISK = PARTIAL EXCH
AA Aaron Rakers 3.00 8.00
AC Jeremy Accardo 3.00 8.00
AE Andre Ethier 6.00 15.00
AH Anderson Hernandez SP 3.00 8.00
AN Robert Andino 3.00 8.00
AW Adam Wainwright 6.00 15.00
BA Brian Anderson 3.00 8.00
BH Brendan Harris 3.00 8.00
BJ Ben Johnson 3.00 8.00
BL Boone Logan 3.00 8.00
BR Brian Bannister 3.00 8.00
BW Craig Breslow 3.00 8.00
CB Chris Britton 3.00 8.00
CH Cole Hamels 20.00 50.00
CM Matt Capps 3.00 8.00
CR Cody Ross EXCH * 3.00 8.00
CU Chase Utley 15.00 40.00
DE Chris Denorfia 3.00 8.00
DG Dave Gassner 3.00 8.00
DJ Derek Jeter 75.00 150.00
DU Dan Uggla 6.00 15.00
DW Dontrelle Willis 4.00 10.00
EV Dana Eveland 3.00 8.00
FB Freddie Bynum 3.00 8.00
FC Fausto Carmona 8.00 20.00
FL Francisco Liriano 10.00 25.00
FN Fernando Nieve 3.00 8.00
GS Geovany Soto 15.00 40.00
HA Jeff Harris EXCH * 3.00 8.00
HC Craig Hansen SP
HE Jeremy Hermida EXCH * 5.00 12.00
HG John Hattig EXCH * 3.00 8.00
HK Hong-Chih Kuo EXCH * 20.00 50.00
HR Hanley Ramirez 6.00 15.00
IK Ian Kinsler 6.00 15.00
JA Conor Jackson 5.00 12.00
JB Jason Bay EXCH * 6.00 15.00
JC Jose Capellan SP 3.00 8.00
JD Joey Devine 3.00 8.00
JJ Josh Johnson EXCH * 4.00 10.00
JK Jason Kubel 3.00 8.00
JO Josh Wilson 3.00 8.00
JP Jonathan Papelbon 15.00 40.00
JS James Shields 3.00 8.00
JU Justin Huber 3.00 8.00
JV John Van Benschoten 3.00 8.00
JW Jered Weaver 5.00 12.00
JZ Joel Zumaya 10.00 25.00
KE Howie Kendrick 6.00 15.00
KF Kevin Frandsen 3.00 8.00
KG Ken Griffey Jr. EXCH 30.00 60.00
KM Kendry Morales 4.00 10.00
KO John Koronka 3.00 8.00
KS Kelly Shoppach 3.00 8.00
MC Matt Cain 6.00 15.00
MI Miguel Cabrera 6.00 15.00
MJ Mike Jacobs 3.00 8.00
MM Macay McBride EXCH * 3.00 8.00
MS Matt Smith 3.00 8.00
NI Nick Masset 3.00 8.00
NM Nate McLouth 5.00 12.00
PE Peter Moylan 3.00 8.00
PM Paul Maholm 3.00 8.00
RA Reggie Abercrombie 3.00 8.00
RB Chris Roberson 3.00 8.00
RC Carlos Ruiz 3.00 8.00
RE Chris Resop 3.00 8.00
RF Ron Flores 3.00 8.00
RL Ruddy Lugo 3.00 8.00
RS Ryan Shealy 4.00 10.00
RU Josh Rupe 3.00 8.00
RW Rickie Weeks 4.00 10.00
RZ Ryan Zimmerman SP 20.00 50.00
SM Sean Marshall 5.00 12.00
TB Taylor Buchholz 3.00 8.00
TC Tim Corcoran 3.00 8.00
TH Travis Hafner 5.00 12.00
TS Takashi Saito EXCH * 10.00 25.00
VE Justin Verlander 12.50 30.00
WI Josh Willingham 3.00 8.00
WN Wil Nieves 3.00 8.00

2006 Upper Deck Special F/X Star Attractions

STATED ODDS 1:8
AJ Andruw Jones .60 1.50
AS Alfonso Soriano .40 1.00
BA Bobby Abreu .40 1.00
CB Carlos Beltran .40 1.00
CD Carlos Delgado .40 1.00
CJ Chipper Jones 1.00 2.50
CS Curt Schilling .60 1.50
DJ Derek Jeter 2.00 5.00
DL Derrek Lee .40 1.00
DO David Ortiz 1.00 2.50
DW Dontrelle Willis .40 1.00
GM Greg Maddux 1.25 3.00
JB Josh Beckett .40 1.00
JC Jose Contreras .40 1.00
JD Johnny Damon .60 1.50
JE Jim Edmonds .60 1.50
JG Jason Giambi .40 1.00
JM Joe Mauer .60 1.50
JR Jose Reyes .40 1.00
JS Jason Schmidt .40 1.00
KG Ken Griffey Jr. 1.25 3.00
LB Lance Berkman .40 1.00
MO Magglio Ordonez .40 1.00
MR Manny Ramirez .60 1.50
MT Mark Teixeira .60 1.50
PM Pedro Martinez .60 1.50
PU Albert Pujols 1.50 4.00
RH Rich Harden .40 1.00
SM John Smoltz .60 1.50
WR David Wright 1.25 3.00

2006 Upper Deck Special F/X WBC Counterparts

STATED ODDS 1:6
1 Yulieski Gourriel 4.00 10.00
Daisuke Matsuzaka
2 Ken Griffey Jr. 2.00 5.00
Yoandy Garlobo
3 Ken Griffey Jr. 2.50 6.00
Ichiro Suzuki
4 Derek Jeter 3.00 8.00
Chin-Lung Hu
5 Frederich Cepeda .60 1.50
Jong Beom Lee
6 Nobuhiko Matsunaka 1.00 2.50
Seung Yeop Lee
7 Tsuyoshi Nishioka .60 1.50
Guangbiao Liu
8 Ichiro Suzuki 2.00 5.00
Osmany Urrutia
9 Daisuke Matsuzaka 5.00 12.00
Roger Clemens
10 Yadel Marti .60 1.50
Chan Ho Park
11 Koji Uehara .60 1.50
Jae Seo
12 Shunsuke Watanabe .60 1.50
Bartolo Colon
13 Daisuke Matsuzaka 5.00 12.00
Johan Santana
14 Pedro Luis Lazo .60 1.50
Freddy Garcia
15 Koji Uehara 2.00 5.00
Roger Clemens

2007 Upper Deck Spectrum

This 162-card set was released in April, 2007. The set was issued in five-card packs which came 20 packs to a box and 14 boxes to a case. The first 100 cards in this set featured veterans. Cards numbered 101-150, which were skip numbered, featured 2007 autographed rookie logo cards and cards numbered 151-170 were exchange cards for leading 2007 rookies. The stated odds on the signed rookie logo cards were one in 18 packs. The rookie exchange cards could be redeemed until March 19, 2010.

COMP.SET w/o RCs (100) 10.00 25.00
COMMON CARD (1-100) .15 .40
COMMON AU RC (101-149) 3.00 8.00
AU RC STATED ODDS 1:18 HOBBY
COMMON ROOKIE EXCH (151-170) 10.00 25.00
EXCHANGE DEADLINE 3/19/2010
1 Miguel Tejada .15 .40
2 Brian Roberts .15 .40
3 Melvin Mora .15 .40
4 David Ortiz .40 1.00
5 Manny Ramirez .25 .60
6 Jason Varitek .40 1.00
7 Curt Schilling .25 .60
8 Jim Thome .25 .60
9 Paul Konerko .15 .40
10 Jermaine Dye .15 .40
11 Travis Hafner .15 .40
12 Victor Martinez .15 .40
13 Grady Sizemore .25 .60
14 C.C. Sabathia .15 .40
15 Ivan Rodriguez .25 .60
16 Magglio Ordonez .15 .40
17 Carlos Guillen .15 .40
18 Justin Verlander .40 1.00
19 Shane Costa .15 .40
20 Emil Brown .15 .40
21 Mark Teahen .15 .40
22 Vladimir Guerrero .40 1.00
23 Jered Weaver .25 .60
24 Juan Rivera .15 .40
25 Justin Morneau .15 .40
26 Joe Mauer .25 .60
27 Torii Hunter .15 .40
28 Johan Santana .25 .60
29 Derek Jeter 1.00 2.50
30 Alex Rodriguez .60 1.50
31 Johnny Damon .25 .60
32 Jason Giambi .15 .40
33 Frank Thomas .40 1.00
34 Nick Swisher .15 .40
35 Eric Chavez .15 .40
36 Ichiro Suzuki .60 1.50
37 Raul Ibanez .15 .40
38 Richie Sexson .15 .40
39 Carl Crawford .15 .40
40 Rocco Baldelli .15 .40
41 Scott Kazmir .25 .60
42 Michael Young .15 .40
43 Mark Teixeira .25 .60
44 Carlos Lee .15 .40
45 Gary Matthews .15 .40
46 Vernon Wells .15 .40
47 Roy Halladay .15 .40
48 Lyle Overbay .15 .40
49 Brandon Webb .15 .40
50 Conor Jackson .15 .40
51 Stephen Drew .25 .60
52 Chipper Jones .40 1.00
53 Andruw Jones .25 .60
54 Adam LaRoche .15 .40
55 John Smoltz .25 .60
56 Derrek Lee .15 .40
57 Aramis Ramirez .15 .40
58 Carlos Zambrano .15 .40
59 Ken Griffey Jr. .60 1.50
60 Adam Dunn .15 .40
61 Aaron Harang .15 .40
62 Todd Helton .25 .60
63 Matt Holliday .40 1.00
64 Garrett Atkins .15 .40
65 Miguel Cabrera .25 .60
66 Hanley Ramirez .25 .60
67 Dontrelle Willis .15 .40
68 Lance Berkman .15 .40
69 Roy Oswalt .15 .40
70 Roger Clemens .60 1.50
71 J.D. Drew .15 .40
72 Nomar Garciaparra .40 1.00
73 Rafael Furcal .15 .40
74 Jeff Kent .15 .40
75 Prince Fielder .40 1.00
76 Bill Hall .15 .40
77 Rickie Weeks .15 .40
78 Jose Reyes .15 .40
79 David Wright .60 1.50
80 Carlos Delgado .15 .40
81 Carlos Beltran .15 .40
82 Ryan Howard .60 1.50
83 Chase Utley .40 1.00
84 Jimmy Rollins .15 .40
85 Jason Bay .15 .40
86 Freddy Sanchez .15 .40
87 Zach Duke .15 .40
88 Trevor Hoffman .15 .40
89 Adrian Gonzalez .15 .40
90 Mike Piazza .40 1.00
91 Ray Durham .15 .40
92 Omar Vizquel .25 .60
93 Jason Schmidt .15 .40
94 Albert Pujols .75 2.00
95 Scott Rolen .25 .60
96 Jim Edmonds .25 .60
97 Chris Carpenter .15 .40
98 Alfonso Soriano .15 .40
99 Ryan Zimmerman .40 1.00
100 Nick Johnson .15 .40
101 A.Lind AU (RC) 4.00 10.00
102 Alexi Casilla AU RC EXCH 15.00 40.00
103 A.Miller AU RC 15.00 40.00
104 A.Cannizaro AU RC 4.00 10.00
105 Angel Sanchez AU RC EXCH 6.00 15.00
106 B.Stokes AU (RC) 3.00 8.00
107 Carlos Maldonado AU (RC) EXCH 3.00 8.00
108 Cesar Jimenez AU RC EXCH 3.00 8.00
109 C.Stewart AU RC 3.00 8.00
111 D.Murphy AU (RC) 3.00 8.00
112 D.Young AU (RC) 12.50 30.00
113 D.Young AU (RC) 3.00 8.00
114 D.Sarfate AU (RC) 3.00 8.00
116 D.Anderson AU RC 3.00 8.00
117 F.Lewis AU (RC) 3.00 8.00
118 G.Perkins AU (RC) 4.00 10.00
119 Hector Gimenez AU (RC) EXCH
120 J.Baker AU (RC) 3.00 8.00
121 J.Fiorentino AU (RC) 3.00 8.00
122 J.Salazar AU (RC) 3.00 8.00
124 J.Arias AU (RC) 3.00 8.00
125 J.Knott AU (RC) 3.00 8.00
128 J.Morillo AU (RC) 3.00 8.00
129 Juan Perez AU RC EXCH 3.00 8.00
130 Juan Salas AU (RC) 3.00 8.00
131 J.Hampson AU (RC) 3.00 8.00
132 K.Hooper AU (RC) 6.00 15.00
133 K.Kouzmanoff AU (RC) 4.00 10.00
134 M.Bourn AU (RC) 3.00 8.00
135 Miguel Montero AU (RC) EXCH 3.00 8.00
136 Mike Rabelo AU RC EXCH 10.00 25.00
137 M.Maier AU RC 3.00 8.00
138 Oswaldo Navarro AU RC EXCH 6.00 15.00
139 P.Misch AU (RC) 3.00 8.00
140 P.Humber AU (RC) 6.00 15.00
141 R.Braun AU RC 3.00 8.00
142 R.Sweeney AU (RC) 3.00 8.00
144 S.Moore AU (RC) 3.00 8.00
145 S.Henn AU (RC) 4.00 10.00
146 S.Riggans AU (RC) 3.00 8.00
148 T.Tulowitzki AU (RC) 12.50 30.00
149 U.Jimenez AU (RC) 3.00 8.00
151 Rookie EXCH 10.00 25.00
152 Rookie EXCH 10.00 25.00
153 Rookie EXCH 10.00 25.00
154 Rookie EXCH 10.00 25.00
155 Rookie EXCH 10.00 25.00
156 Rookie EXCH 10.00 25.00
157 Elijah Dukes RC 10.00 25.00
158 Rookie EXCH 10.00 25.00
159 Rookie EXCH 10.00 25.00
160 Rookie EXCH 10.00 25.00
161 Rookie EXCH 10.00 25.00
162 Rookie EXCH 10.00 25.00
163 Rookie EXCH 10.00 25.00
164 Rookie EXCH 10.00 25.00
165 Rookie EXCH 10.00 25.00
166 Rookie EXCH 10.00 25.00
167 Rookie EXCH 10.00 25.00
168 Rookie EXCH 10.00 25.00
169 Rookie EXCH 10.00 25.00
170 Rookie EXCH 10.00 25.00

2007 Upper Deck Spectrum Die Cut Gold

*GOLD 1-100: 2.5X TO 6X BASIC
GOLD 1-100 PRINT RUN 99 SER.#'d SETS
*GOLD AU 101-149: .75X TO 2X BASIC
GOLD 101-149 PRINT RUN 50 SER.#'d SETS
RANDOM INSERTS IN PACKS
101 Adam Lind AU 20.00 50.00
112 Delmon Young AU 20.00 50.00
134 Michael Bourn AU 8.00 20.00
145 Sean Henn AU 10.00 25.00

2007 Upper Deck Spectrum Die Cut Red

*RED: 2.5X TO 6X BASIC
RANDOM INSERTS IN PACKS
STATED PRINT RUN 99 SER.#'d SETS

2007 Upper Deck Spectrum Die Cut Jersey Number

*JSY NUMBER p/r 26-57: 8X TO 20X BASIC
RANDOM INSERTS IN PACKS
PRINT RUNS B/WN 1-57 COPIES PER
NO PRICING ON QTY 25 OR LESS

2007 Upper Deck Spectrum Aligning the Stars

OVERALL GAME-USED ODDS 1:10
STATED PRINT RUN 99 SER.#'d SETS
BPO Lance Berkman 10.00 25.00
Albert Pujols
David Ortiz
CJM Greg Maddux 10.00 25.00
Roger Clemens
Randy Johnson
CRR Miguel Cabrera 6.00 15.00
Aramis Ramirez
Scott Rolen
DBF Lance Berkman 6.00 15.00
Carlos Delgado
Prince Fielder
GRS Gary Sheffield 10.00 25.00
Manny Ramirez
Ken Griffey Jr.
HRW Trevor Hoffman 10.00 25.00
Mariano Rivera
Billy Wagner
HTT Frank Thomas 10.00 25.00
Travis Hafner
Jim Thome
JDB Adam Dunn 10.00 25.00
Andruw Jones
Carlos Beltran
JGC Derek Jeter 20.00 50.00
Jason Giambi
Robinson Cano
JTY Derek Jeter 10.00 25.00
Miguel Tejada
Michael Young
LHP Todd Helton 10.00 25.00
Albert Pujols
Derrek Lee
LVP Justin Verlander 10.00 25.00
Francisco Liriano
Jonathan Papelbon
MKT Justin Morneau 6.00 15.00
Mark Teixeira
Paul Konerko
MOW Roy Oswalt 6.00 15.00
Pedro Martinez
Dontrelle Willis
RFR Jose Reyes 6.00 15.00
Jimmy Rollins
Rafael Furcal
RMM Victor Martinez 6.00 15.00
Joe Mauer
Ivan Rodriguez
RSV Curt Schilling 10.00 25.00
Manny Ramirez
Jason Varitek
SBA Bobby Abreu 6.00 15.00
Carlos Beltran
Alfonso Soriano
SCF Chone Figgins 6.00 15.00
Carl Crawford
Grady Sizemore
SHS C.C. Sabathia 6.00 15.00
Johan Santana
Roy Halladay
WGD Vernon Wells 6.00 15.00
Johnny Damon
Vladimir Guerrero

2007 Upper Deck Spectrum Cal Ripken Road to the Hall

COMMON CARD 2.00 5.00
STATED ODDS 1:10 HOBBY, 1:20 RETAIL
GOLD: .6X TO 1.5X BASIC
GOLD RANDOMLY INSERTED IN PACKS
GOLD PRINT RUN 99 SER.#'d SETS

2007 Upper Deck Spectrum Cal Ripken Road to the Hall Signatures

COMMON CARD 100.00 175.00
RANDOM INSERTS IN PACKS
STATED PRINT RUN 5 SER.#'d SETS

2007 Upper Deck Spectrum Grand Slamarama

STATED ODDS 1:280 HOBBY
AD Adam Dunn 6.00 15.00
AP Albert Pujols 30.00 60.00
AR Alex Rodriguez 20.00 50.00
BA Bobby Abreu 12.50 30.00
BG Brian Giles 6.00 15.00
CD Carlos Delgado 6.00 15.00
CJ Chipper Jones 12.50 30.00
DA Johnny Damon 10.00 25.00
DO David Ortiz 12.50 30.00
DW David Wright 20.00 50.00
HA Travis Hafner 6.00 15.00
JD Jermaine Dye 6.00 15.00
JM Justin Morneau 6.00 15.00
JT Jim Thome 10.00 25.00
KG Ken Griffey Jr. 20.00 50.00
MR Manny Ramirez 10.00 25.00
NG Nomar Garciaparra 12.50 30.00
RH Ryan Howard 20.00 50.00
RS Richie Sexson 6.00 15.00
VG Vladimir Guerrero 12.50 30.00

2007 Upper Deck Spectrum Rookie Retrospectrum

STATED ODDS 1:10 HOBBY, 1:20 RETAIL
RED: .6X TO 1.5X BASIC
RED RANDOMLY INSERTED IN PACKS
RED PRINT RUN 99 SER.#'d SETS
AE Andre Ethier .60 1.50
AW Adam Wainwright .40 1.00
BA Josh Barfield .40 1.00
BB Boof Bonser .40 1.00
BO Jason Botts .40 1.00
CA Matt Capps .40 1.00
CB Chad Billingsley .40 1.00
CD Chris Demaria .40 1.00
CF Choo Freeman .40 1.00
CH Clay Hensley .40 1.00
CQ Carlos Quentin .40 1.00
DE Chris Denorfia .40 1.00
DU Dan Uggla .60 1.50
FC Fausto Carmona .40 1.00
FL Francisco Liriano 1.00 2.50
HA Cole Hamels .60 1.50
HK Howie Kendrick .40 1.00
HR Hanley Ramirez .60 1.50
JA Jeremy Accardo .40 1.00
JB Jason Bergmann .40 1.00
JC Jose Capellan .40 1.00
JD Joey Devine .40 1.00
JH Jeremy Hermida .40 1.00
JK Jason Kubel .40 1.00
JL Jon Lester .60 1.50
JP Jonathan Papelbon 1.00 2.50
JV Justin Verlander 1.00 2.50
JW Jered Weaver .60 1.50
JZ Joel Zumaya .60 1.50
KM Kendry Morales .60 1.50
LM Lastings Milledge .60 1.50
MA Nick Markakis .60 1.50
MC Matt Cain .60 1.50
ME Melky Cabrera .40 1.00
MG Matt Garza .40 1.00
MJ Mike Jacobs .40 1.00
MM Matt Murton .40 1.00
NM Nate McLouth .40 1.00
PF Prince Fielder 1.00 2.50
RA Reggie Abercrombie .40 1.00
RG Ryan Garko .40 1.00
RM Russell Martin .40 1.00
RP Ronny Paulino .40 1.00
RS Ryan Shealy .40 1.00
RZ Ryan Zimmerman 1.00 2.50
SD Stephen Drew .60 1.50
TB Taylor Buchholz .40 1.00
TG Tony Gwynn Jr. .40 1.00
TS Takashi Saito .40 1.00
WI Josh Willingham .40 1.00

2007 Upper Deck Spectrum Rookie Retrospectrum Signatures

RANDOM INSERTS IN PACKS
PRINT RUNS B/WN 32-199 COPIES PER
EXCHANGE DEADLINE 3/19/2010
BB Boof Bonser 4.00 10.00
BO Jason Botts 4.00 10.00
CA Matt Capps 4.00 10.00
CD Chris Demaria 4.00 10.00
CF Choo Freeman 4.00 10.00
CH Clay Hensley 4.00 10.00
CQ Carlos Quentin 4.00 10.00
DU Dan Uggla 6.00 15.00
FC Fausto Carmona/158 4.00 10.00
FL Francisco Liriano 10.00 25.00
HA Cole Hamels EXCH 12.50 30.00
HK Howie Kendrick 10.00 25.00
HR Hanley Ramirez 6.00 15.00
JA Jeremy Accardo/32 6.00 15.00
JC Jose Capellan 4.00 10.00
JD Joey Devine 4.00 10.00
JH Jeremy Hermida 4.00 10.00
JK Jason Kubel 4.00 10.00
JL Jon Lester EXCH 10.00 25.00
JP Jonathan Papelbon 15.00 40.00
JW Jered Weaver 10.00 25.00
JZ Joel Zumaya 10.00 25.00
KM Kendry Morales 4.00 10.00
MG Matt Garza 6.00 15.00
MJ Mike Jacobs 4.00 10.00
MM Matt Murton EXCH 6.00 15.00
RA Reggie Abercrombie 4.00 10.00
RG Ryan Garko 6.00 15.00
RM Russell Martin 10.00 25.00
RS Ryan Shealy 4.00 10.00
RZ Ryan Zimmerman EXCH 10.00 25.00
SD Stephen Drew 10.00 25.00
TB Taylor Buchholz 4.00 10.00
TS Takashi Saito 10.00 25.00
WI Josh Willingham 4.00 10.00

2007 Upper Deck Spectrum Season Retrospectrum

STATED ODDS 1:10 HOBBY, 1:20 RETAIL
RED: .6X TO 1.5X BASIC
RED RANDOMLY INSERTED IN PACKS
RED PRINT RUN 99 SER.#'d SETS
AH Aaron Harang .40 1.00
AP Albert Pujols 2.00 5.00
AR Aramis Ramirez .40 1.00
AS Alfonso Soriano .40 1.00
BA Bobby Abreu .40 1.00
BH Bill Hall .40 1.00
BL Joe Blanton .40 1.00
CA Miguel Cabrera .60 1.50
CB Carlos Beltran .40 1.00
CC Chris Carpenter .40 1.00
CD Carlos Delgado .40 1.00
CO Jose Contreras .40 1.00
CU Chase Utley 1.00 2.50
CW Chien-Ming Wang 1.50 4.00
CY Chris Young .40 1.00
CZ Carlos Zambrano .40 1.00
DJ Derek Jeter 2.50 6.00
DO David Ortiz 1.00 2.50
FS Freddy Sanchez .40 1.00
FT Frank Thomas 1.00 2.50
GM Greg Maddux 1.50 4.00
GS Grady Sizemore .60 1.50
HO Trevor Hoffman .40 1.00
HR Hanley Ramirez .60 1.50
JB Jason Bay .40 1.00
JC Joe Crede .40 1.00
JD Johnny Damon .60 1.50
JM Joe Mauer .60 1.50
JR Jose Reyes .40 1.00
JS Jeff Suppan .40 1.00
JT Jim Thome .60 1.50
KG Ken Griffey Jr. 1.50 4.00
MC Michael Cuddyer .40 1.00
MH Matt Holliday 1.00 2.50
ML Mark Loretta .40 1.00
MO Justin Morneau .40 1.00
MY Michael Young .40 1.00
NG Nomar Garciaparra 1.00 2.50
OR Magglio Ordonez .40 1.00
OV Omar Vizquel .60 1.50
RC Roger Clemens 1.50 4.00
RF Rafael Furcal .40 1.00
RH Ryan Howard 1.50 4.00
SA Johan Santana .60 1.50
SK Scott Kazmir .60 1.50
TH Travis Hafner .40 1.00
TI Tadahito Iguchi .40 1.00
VG Vladimir Guerrero 1.00 2.50
VW Vernon Wells .40 1.00
WT Willy Taveras .40 1.00

2007 Upper Deck Spectrum Season Retrospectrum Signatures

RANDOM INSERTS IN PACKS
STATED PRINT RUN 25 SER.#'d SETS
NO PRICING DUE TO SCARCITY
EXCHANGE DEADLINE 3/19/2010
AH Aaron Harang
AR Aramis Ramirez
AS Alfonso Soriano
BA Bobby Abreu
BH Bill Hall
BL Joe Blanton
CA Miguel Cabrera
CU Chase Utley
CZ Carlos Zambrano
DJ Derek Jeter
DO David Ortiz
FT Frank Thomas EXCH
GM Greg Maddux
HO Trevor Hoffman
HR Hanley Ramirez
JB Jason Bay
JM Joe Mauer
JR Jose Reyes
JT Jim Thome
KG Ken Griffey Jr.
MH Matt Holliday
ML Mark Loretta
MO Justin Morneau
RC Roger Clemens
RF Rafael Furcal
SA Johan Santana
SK Scott Kazmir
TH Travis Hafner
TI Tadahito Iguchi
VG Vladimir Guerrero

2007 Upper Deck Spectrum Shining Star Signatures

RANDOM INSERTS IN PACKS
PRINT RUNS B/WN 50-99 COPIES PER
EXCHANGE DEADLINE 3/19/2010
AD Adam Dunn/99 6.00 15.00
AG Adrian Gonzalez/99 EXCH 6.00 15.00
AP Albert Pujols/50 EXCH 125.00 200.00
AR Alex Rios/99 EXCH 6.00 15.00
BH Bill Hall/99 EXCH 10.00 25.00
CJ Conor Jackson/54 6.00 15.00
CZ Carlos Zambrano/99 10.00 25.00
DJ Derek Jeter/54 150.00 200.00
DL Derrek Lee/99 10.00 25.00
DO David Ortiz/99 30.00 60.00
GA Garrett Atkins/99 6.00 15.00
HR Hanley Ramirez/99 12.50 30.00
JB Jason Bay/99 6.00 15.00
JM Joe Mauer/99 12.50 30.00
JR Jose Reyes/99 20.00 50.00
JS Johan Santana/99 20.00 50.00
KG Ken Griffey Jr./99 EXCH 30.00 60.00
KY Kevin Youkilis/99 6.00 15.00
LB Lance Berkman/99
MH Matt Holliday/99 EXCH 10.00 25.00
MO Justin Morneau/99 10.00 25.00
RI Juan Rivera/99 EXCH 6.00 15.00
TH Travis Hafner/99 10.00 25.00

2007 Upper Deck Spectrum Spectrum of Stars Signatures

STATED ODDS 1:100 HOB, 1:460 RET
PRINT RUNS B/WN 3-160 COPIES PER
NO PRINT RUNS FOR #'s: DB, EB, FE
CARDS ARE NOT SERIAL-NUMBERED
PRINT RUNS PROVIDED BY UPPER DECK
INSCRIPTIONS PROVIDED BE UPPER DECK
MYSTERY EXCH CL: DB/EO1/EO2/EO3
MYSTERY EXCH CL: EB/FE/KS1/KS2/KS3
MYSTERY EXCH CL: KS4/MM1/MM2/MM3
NO PRICING ON QTY 24 OR LESS
EXCHANGE DEADLINE 3/19/2010
AH1 Anthony Michael Hall Black/65 * 15.00 40.00
AH2 Anthony Michael Hall DZ/30 *
AH3 Anthony Michael Hall 16 Candles/10 *
BL1 Brandy Ledford Black/64 *
BL2 Brandy Ledford Whistler/30 * 20.00 50.00
BL3 Brandy Ledford Andromedia/10 *
BU1 Tony Burton Black/120 * 6.00 15.00
BU2 Tony Burton Stick'em/20 *
BU3 Tony Burton No Pain/20 *
BU4 Tony Burton Duke In Rocky/20 *
BW1 Barry Williams Black/155 * 12.50 30.00
BW2 Barry Williams Blue/15 *
BW3 Barry Williams Johnny Bravo/15 *
BW4 Barry Williams Greg Brady/20 *
CB1 Catherine Bach Black/155 * 20.00 50.00
CB2 Catherine Bach Blue/27 *
CB3 Catherine Bach Daisy Duke/3 *
CB4 Catherine Bach General Lee/20 *
CF1 Corey Feldman Black/95 * 10.00 25.00
CF2 Corey Feldman Peace/60 *
CF3 Corey Feldman Goonies/30 * 30.00 60.00
CF4 Corey Feldman Lost Boys/20 *
CT1 Carrot Top Black/120 *
CT2 Carrot Top Blue/60 *
CT3 Carrot Top The Luxor/20 *
DB Danny Bonaduce
DF1 David Faustino Black/160 * 15.00 40.00
DF2 David Faustino Blue Bud Bundy/30 * 30.00 60.00
DF3 David Faustino Grand Master B/12 *
DF4 David Faustino Red Bud Bundy/6 *
EB Ernest Borgnine
EH1 Ernie Hudson Black/60 *
EH2 Ernie Hudson Blue/30 *
EH3 Ernie Hudson The Crow/10 *
EO1 Ed O'Neil Black/60 *
EO2 Ed O'Neil Blue/30 *
EO3 Ed O'Neil Al Bundy/10 *
FE Fergie
GO1 Louis Gossett Jr. Black/60 * 15.00 40.00
GO2 Louis Gossett Jr. Roots/33 *
GO3 Louis Gossett Jr. Mayonaise/12 *
JC1 Jeff Conaway Black/150 * 10.00 25.00
JC2 Jeff Conaway Taxi/30 * 20.00 50.00
JC3 Jeff Conaway Kenickie/20 *
JD1 Josh Duhamel Black/24 *
JD2 Josh Duhamel Transformers/36 * 30.00 60.00
JD3 Josh Duhamel Blue/50 *
JD3 Josh Duhamel Las Vegas/10 *
KM1 Kristy McNichol Black/150 * 10.00 25.00
KM2 Kristy McNichol Family/30 * 30.00 60.00
KM3 Kristy McNichol Little Darlings/25 * 30.00 60.00
KS1 Katey Sagal Black/120 *
KS2 Katey Sagal Blue/30 *
KS3 Katey Sagal Leila/30 *
KS4 Katey Sagal Peg Bundy/20 *
LB1 Linda Blair Black/150 * 12.50 30.00
LB2 Linda Blair Regan/30 * 30.00 60.00
LB3 Linda Blair The Exorcist/20 *
LG1 Leif Garrett Black/60 * 12.50 30.00
LG2 Leif Garrett Blue/30 * 20.00 50.00
LG3 Leif Garrett I was made for Dancing/10 *
LP1 Lori Petty Black/150 * 10.00 25.00
LP2 Lori Petty KIT/30 * 20.00 50.00
LP3 Lori Petty Tank Girl/20 *
MM1 Michael Madsen Black/60 *
MM2 Michael Madsen Blue/30 *
MM3 Michael Madsen R'Dogs/15 *
MS1 Mia St. John Black/60 * 12.50 30.00
MS2 Mia St. John IFBA Champ/30 *
MS3 Mia St. John The Knockout/10 *
TB1 Todd Bridges Black/60 * 12.50 30.00
TB2 Todd Bridges Blue/30 * 20.00 50.00
TB3 Todd Bridges Willis/10 *
TI1 Tiffany Black/155 * 20.00 50.00
TI2 Tiffany Love/30 *
TI3 Tiffany We're Alone Now/25 *
NNO Mystery Redemption 100.00 200.00

2007 Upper Deck Spectrum Super Swatches

OVERALL GAME-USED ODDS 1:10
STATED PRINT RUN 50 SER.#'d SETS
AD Adam Dunn 5.00 12.00
AJ Andruw Jones 6.00 15.00
AP Albert Pujols 15.00 40.00
AR Aramis Ramirez 5.00 12.00
BA Bobby Abreu 5.00 12.00
BC Bobby Crosby 5.00 12.00
BE Josh Beckett 5.00 12.00
BU B.J. Upton 5.00 12.00
BZ Barry Zito 5.00 12.00
CB Carlos Beltran 5.00 12.00
CC Carl Crawford 5.00 12.00
CD Carlos Delgado 5.00 12.00
CJ Chipper Jones 6.00 15.00
CL Roger Clemens 12.50 30.00
CS Curt Schilling 6.00 15.00
CU Chase Utley 6.00 15.00
DA Johnny Damon 6.00 15.00
DJ Derek Jeter 20.00 50.00
DL Derrek Lee 5.00 12.00
DO David Ortiz 6.00 15.00
FT Frank Thomas 15.00 40.00
GS Gary Sheffield 5.00 12.00
HA Travis Hafner 5.00 12.00
HR Hanley Ramirez 6.00 15.00
JB Jeremy Bonderman 5.00 12.00
JD J.D. Drew 5.00 12.00
JR Jose Reyes 10.00 25.00
JS Johan Santana 6.00 15.00
JT Jim Thome 6.00 15.00
JV Jason Varitek 6.00 15.00
JW Jered Weaver 6.00 15.00
KG Ken Griffey Jr. 15.00 40.00
KJ Kenji Johjima 6.00 15.00
LB Lance Berkman 5.00 12.00
MT Miguel Tejada 5.00 12.00
PE Andy Pettitte 6.00 15.00
PF Prince Fielder 6.00 15.00
PK Paul Konerko 5.00 12.00
RB Rocco Baldelli 5.00 12.00
RC Robinson Cano 10.00 25.00
RH Roy Halladay 5.00 12.00
RJ Randy Johnson 6.00 15.00
RS Richie Sexson 5.00 12.00
SR Scott Rolen 6.00 15.00
TH Todd Helton 6.00 15.00
VE Justin Verlander 6.00 15.00
VG Vladimir Guerrero 6.00 15.00
VW Vernon Wells 5.00 12.00

2007 Upper Deck Spectrum Swatches

STATED PRINT RUN 199 SER.#'d SETS
GOLD: .5X TO 1.2X BASIC
OVERALL GAME-USED ODDS 1:10
GOLD PRINT RUN 75 SER.#'d SETS
AB Adrian Beltre 3.00 8.00
AG Adrian Gonzalez 3.00 8.00
AH Aaron Hill 3.00 8.00
AK Austin Kearns 3.00 8.00
AP Albert Pujols 8.00 20.00
AR Aaron Rowand 3.00 8.00
AS Alfonso Soriano 3.00 8.00
BA Bobby Abreu 3.00 8.00
BC Bartolo Colon 3.00 8.00
BG Brian Giles 3.00 8.00
BI Brandon Inge 3.00 8.00
BJ B.J. Upton 3.00 8.00
BL Joe Blanton 3.00 8.00
BR B.J. Ryan 3.00 8.00
BS Ben Sheets 3.00 8.00
BW Billy Wagner 3.00 8.00
CA Jorge Cantu 3.00 8.00
CB Clint Barmes 3.00 8.00
CC Chad Cordero 3.00 8.00
CD Chris Duffy 3.00 8.00
CG Carlos Guillen 3.00 8.00
CK Casey Kotchman 3.00 8.00
CO Coco Crisp 3.00 8.00
CR Bobby Crosby 3.00 8.00
CS C.C. Sabathia 3.00 8.00
CU Chase Utley 3.00 8.00
CY Chris Young 3.00 8.00
CZ Carlos Zambrano 3.00 8.00
DA Johnny Damon 4.00 10.00
DC Daniel Cabrera 3.00 8.00
DH Danny Haren 3.00 8.00
DJ Derek Jeter 10.00 25.00
DL Derrek Lee 3.00 8.00
DM Dallas McPherson 3.00 8.00
DO David Ortiz 4.00 10.00
DU Dan Uggla 4.00 10.00
DW Dontrelle Willis 3.00 8.00
ES Johnny Estrada 3.00 8.00
FG Freddy Garcia 3.00 8.00
FL Francisco Liriano 3.00 8.00
FS Freddy Sanchez 3.00 8.00
GA Garrett Atkins 3.00 8.00
GC Gustavo Chacin 3.00 8.00
GR Curtis Granderson 3.00 8.00
GS Grady Sizemore 3.00 8.00
HR Hanley Ramirez 4.00 10.00
HS Huston Street 3.00 8.00
HU Aubrey Huff 3.00 8.00
IS Ian Snell 3.00 8.00
JB Jeremy Bonderman 3.00 8.00
JC Joe Crede 3.00 8.00
JD J.D. Drew 3.00 8.00
JE Jermaine Dye 3.00 8.00
JF Jeff Francoeur 4.00 10.00
JH J.J. Hardy 3.00 8.00
JM Joe Mauer 4.00 10.00
JN Joe Nathan 3.00 8.00
JP Jake Peavy 3.00 8.00
JR Jose Reyes 3.00 8.00
JT Jim Thome 3.00 8.00
JU Justin Duchscherer 3.00 8.00
JW Jake Westbrook 3.00 8.00
KG Ken Griffey Jr. 6.00 15.00
KH Khalil Greene 4.00 10.00
LN Laynce Nix 3.00 8.00
MA Matt Cain 4.00 10.00
MB Mark Buehrle 3.00 8.00
MC Mike Cameron 3.00 8.00
ME Morgan Ensberg 3.00 8.00
MH Matt Holliday 4.00 10.00
MI Michael Cuddyer 3.00 8.00
MM Melvin Mora 3.00 8.00
MO Justin Morneau 3.00 8.00
MT Miguel Tejada 3.00 8.00
NL Noah Lowry 3.00 8.00
NS Nick Swisher 3.00 8.00
OR Magglio Ordonez 3.00 8.00
PA Jonathan Papelbon 6.00 15.00
PE Jhonny Peralta 3.00 8.00
PF Prince Fielder 4.00 10.00
PL Paul Lo Duca 3.00 8.00
RA Aramis Ramirez 3.00 8.00
RF Rafael Furcal 3.00 8.00
RH Rich Harden 3.00 8.00
RJ Reed Johnson 3.00 8.00
RO Brian Roberts 3.00 8.00
RQ Robb Quinlan 3.00 8.00
RW Rickie Weeks 3.00 8.00
RZ Ryan Zimmerman 4.00 10.00
SC Sean Casey 3.00 8.00
SK Scott Kazmir 4.00 10.00
TH Torii Hunter 3.00 8.00
TI Tadahito Iguchi 3.00 8.00
TN Trot Nixon 3.00 8.00
VM Victor Martinez 3.00 8.00
WT Willy Taveras 3.00 8.00
YM Yadier Molina 3.00 8.00
ZD Zach Duke 3.00 8.00
ZG Zack Greinke 3.00 8.00

2007 Upper Deck Spectrum Swatches Patches

OVERALL GAME-USED ODDS 1:10
STATED PRINT RUN 50 SER.#'d SETS
AB Adrian Beltre 6.00 15.00
AG Adrian Gonzalez 6.00 15.00
AH Aaron Hill 6.00 15.00
AK Austin Kearns 6.00 15.00
AP Albert Pujols 20.00 50.00
AR Aaron Rowand 6.00 15.00
AS Alfonso Soriano 12.50 30.00
BA Bobby Abreu 8.00 20.00
BC Bartolo Colon 6.00 15.00
BG Brian Giles 6.00 15.00
BI Brandon Inge 6.00 15.00
BJ B.J. Upton 6.00 15.00
BL Joe Blanton 6.00 15.00
BR B.J. Ryan 6.00 15.00
BS Ben Sheets 6.00 15.00
BW Billy Wagner 8.00 20.00
CA Jorge Cantu 6.00 15.00
CB Clint Barmes 6.00 15.00
CC Chad Cordero 6.00 15.00
CD Chris Duffy 6.00 15.00
CG Carlos Guillen 6.00 15.00
CK Casey Kotchman 6.00 15.00
CO Coco Crisp 6.00 15.00
CR Bobby Crosby 6.00 15.00
CS C.C. Sabathia 6.00 15.00
CY Chris Young 6.00 15.00
CZ Carlos Zambrano 6.00 15.00
DA Johnny Damon 8.00 20.00
DC Daniel Cabrera 6.00 15.00
DH Danny Haren 6.00 15.00
DL Derrek Lee 6.00 15.00
DM Dallas McPherson 6.00 15.00
DO David Ortiz 12.50 30.00
DU Dan Uggla 8.00 20.00
DW Dontrelle Willis 6.00 15.00
ES Johnny Estrada 6.00 15.00
FG Freddy Garcia 6.00 15.00
FL Francisco Liriano 8.00 20.00
FS Freddy Sanchez 6.00 15.00
GA Garrett Atkins 6.00 15.00
GC Gustavo Chacin 6.00 15.00
GR Curtis Granderson 6.00 15.00
GS Grady Sizemore 12.50 30.00
HR Hanley Ramirez 8.00 20.00
HS Huston Street 6.00 15.00
HU Aubrey Huff 6.00 15.00
IS Ian Snell 6.00 15.00
JB Jeremy Bonderman 12.50 30.00
JC Joe Crede 6.00 15.00
JD J.D. Drew 6.00 15.00
JE Jermaine Dye 6.00 15.00
JF Jeff Francoeur 12.50 30.00
JH J.J. Hardy 6.00 15.00
JM Joe Mauer 12.50 30.00
JN Joe Nathan 6.00 15.00
JP Jake Peavy 6.00 15.00
JR Jose Reyes 12.50 30.00
JT Jim Thome 8.00 20.00
JU Justin Duchscherer 6.00 15.00
JW Jake Westbrook 8.00 20.00
KG Ken Griffey Jr. 30.00 60.00
KH Khalil Greene 8.00 20.00
LN Laynce Nix 6.00 15.00
MA Matt Cain 8.00 20.00
MB Mark Buehrle 6.00 15.00
MC Mike Cameron 6.00 15.00
ME Morgan Ensberg 6.00 15.00
MH Matt Holliday 8.00 20.00
MI Michael Cuddyer 6.00 15.00
MM Melvin Mora 6.00 15.00
MO Justin Morneau 6.00 15.00
MT Miguel Tejada 6.00 15.00
NL Noah Lowry 8.00 20.00
NS Nick Swisher 6.00 15.00
OR Magglio Ordonez 6.00 15.00
PA Jonathan Papelbon 15.00 40.00
PE Jhonny Peralta 6.00 15.00
PF Prince Fielder 12.50 30.00
PL Paul Lo Duca 8.00 20.00
RA Aramis Ramirez 8.00 20.00
RF Rafael Furcal 6.00 15.00
RH Rich Harden 6.00 15.00
RJ Reed Johnson 12.50 30.00
RO Brian Roberts 6.00 15.00
RQ Robb Quinlan 6.00 15.00
RZ Ryan Zimmerman 12.50 30.00
SC Sean Casey 6.00 15.00
SK Scott Kazmir 6.00 15.00
TH Torii Hunter 8.00 20.00
TI Tadahito Iguchi 6.00 15.00
TN Trot Nixon 6.00 15.00
VM Victor Martinez 6.00 15.00
WT Willy Taveras 6.00 15.00
YM Yadier Molina 6.00 15.00
ZD Zach Duke 6.00 15.00
ZG Zack Greinke 6.00 15.00

2007 Upper Deck Spectrum Swatches Signature Patch

RANDOM INSERTS IN PACKS
STATED PRINT RUN 25 SER.#'d SETS
NO PRICING DUE TO SCARCITY
AG Adrian Gonzalez
AR Aaron Rowand
AS Alfonso Soriano
BA Bobby Abreu
BG Brian Giles
BJ B.J. Upton
BL Joe Blanton
BS Ben Sheets
CK Casey Kotchman
CR Bobby Crosby
CS C.C. Sabathia
CZ Carlos Zambrano
DH Danny Haren
DJ Derek Jeter
DL Derrek Lee
DO David Ortiz
DU Dan Uggla
DW Dontrelle Willis
FL Francisco Liriano
GA Garrett Atkins

2008 Upper Deck Spectrum

COMP.SET w/o AUs (100) 10.00 25.00
COMMON CARD .20 .50
COMMOM AU RC 3.00 8.00
OVERALL AUTO ODDS 1:10
PRINTING PLATES RANDOMLY INSERTED
PLATE PRINT RUN 1 SET PER COLOR
BLACK-CYAN-MAGENTA-YELLOW ISSUED
NO PLATE PRICING DUE TO SCARCITY
1 Chris B. Young .20 .50
2 Brandon Webb .30 .75
3 Eric Byrnes .20 .50
4 John Smoltz .50 1.25
5 Chipper Jones .60 1.50
6 Jeff Francoeur .30 .75
7 Mark Teixeira .30 .75
8 Brian Roberts .30 .75
9 Erik Bedard .20 .50
10 Miguel Tejada .20 .50
11 Nick Markakis .30 .75
12 David Ortiz .50 1.25
13 Daisuke Matsuzaka 1.00 2.50
14 Manny Ramirez .50 1.25
15 Jonathan Papelbon .30 .75
16 Josh Beckett .30 .75
17 Alfonso Soriano .30 .75
18 Carlos Zambrano .20 .50
19 Derrek Lee .30 .75
20 Aramis Ramirez .20 .50
21 Paul Konerko .20 .50
22 Jermaine Dye .20 .50
23 Jim Thome .30 .75
24 Ken Griffey Jr. .75 2.00
25 Brandon Phillips .20 .50
26 Adam Dunn .20 .50
27 Grady Sizemore .30 .75
28 Fausto Carmona .20 .50
29 Victor Martinez .20 .50
30 Travis Hafner .20 .50
31 Matt Holliday .30 .75
32 Troy Tulowitzki .30 .75
33 Todd Helton .30 .75
34 Magglio Ordonez .30 .75
35 Justin Verlander .30 .75
36 Gary Sheffield .20 .50
37 Miguel Cabrera .30 .75
38 Hanley Ramirez .50 1.25
39 Dan Uggla .30 .75
40 Carlos Lee .20 .50
41 Roy Oswalt .20 .50
42 Lance Berkman .30 .75
43 Hunter Pence .50 1.25
44 Alex Gordon .50 1.25
45 David DeJesus .20 .50
46 Vladimir Guerrero .50 1.25
47 Kelvim Escobar .20 .50
48 Chone Figgins .20 .50
49 Brad Penny .20 .50
50 Takashi Saito .20 .50
51 Russell Martin .20 .50
52 Prince Fielder .50 1.25
53 Ryan Braun .60 1.50
54 JJ Hardy .20 .50
55 Johan Santana .30 .75
56 Justin Morneau .30 .75
57 Torii Hunter .20 .50
58 Joe Mauer .30 .75
59 Carlos Beltran .20 .50
60 David Wright .60 1.50
61 Carlos Delgado .20 .50
62 Jose Reyes .30 .75
63 Derek Jeter 1.25 3.00
64 Alex Rodriguez .75 2.00
65 Robinson Cano .30 .75
66 Hideki Matsui .50 1.25
67 Mariano Rivera .50 1.25
68 Dan Haren .20 .50
69 Nick Swisher .20 .50
70 Eric Chavez .20 .50
71 Jimmy Rollins .30 .75
72 Ryan Howard .60 1.50
73 Cole Hamels .50 1.25
74 Chase Utley .50 1.25
75 Freddy Sanchez .20 .50
76 Jason Bay .20 .50
77 Ian Snell .20 .50
78 Greg Maddux .60 1.50
79 Jake Peavy .30 .75
80 Chris Young .20 .50
81 Barry Zito .20 .50
82 Tim Lincecum .50 1.25
83 Omar Vizquel .20 .50
84 Felix Hernandez .30 .75
85 Ichiro Suzuki .75 2.00
86 Richie Sexson .20 .50
87 Albert Pujols 1.00 2.50
88 Scott Rolen .30 .75
89 Chris Carpenter .30 .75
90 Delmon Young .30 .75
91 Carl Crawford .30 .75
92 B.J. Upton .30 .75
93 Michael Young .20 .50
94 Hank Blalock .20 .50
95 Sammy Sosa .30 .75
96 Roy Halladay .20 .50
97 Alex Rios .20 .50
98 Vernon Wells .20 .50
99 Ryan Zimmerman .30 .75
100 Dmitri Young .20 .50
101 Alberto Gonzalez AU RC 10.00 25.00
102 Bill Murphy AU (RC) 3.00 8.00
103 Bill White AU RC 3.00 8.00
104 Billy Buckner AU (RC) 3.00 8.00
105 Brandon Jones AU RC 3.00 8.00
106 Bronson Sardinha AU (RC) 3.00 8.00
107 Chin-Lung Hu AU (RC) 10.00 25.00
108 Chris Seddon AU (RC) 3.00 8.00
109 Clay Buchholz AU (RC) 10.00 25.00
110 Clint Sammons AU (RC) 3.00 8.00
111 Daric Barton AU (RC) 4.00 10.00
112 Dave Davidson AU RC 4.00 10.00
113 Donny Lucy AU (RC) 3.00 8.00
114 Emilio Bonifacio AU RC 3.00 8.00
115 Eugenio Velez AU RC 4.00 10.00
116 Felipe Paulino AU RC
117 Harvey Garcia AU (RC) 3.00 8.00
118 Ian Kennedy AU RC 15.00 40.00
119 J.R. Towles AU RC 6.00 15.00
120 Jeff Clement AU (RC)
121 Jerry Blevins AU RC 3.00 8.00
122 Joe Koshansky AU (RC) 3.00 8.00
123 Joey Votto AU (RC) 6.00 15.00
124 Jonathan Albaladejo AU RC 4.00 10.00
125 Jonathan Meloan AU RC 3.00 8.00
126 Jose Morales AU (RC) 3.00 8.00
127 Josh Anderson AU (RC) 3.00 8.00
128 Josh Newman AU RC 3.00 8.00
129 Justin Maxwell AU RC 4.00 10.00
130 Justin Ruggiano AU RC 3.00 8.00
131 Kevin Hart AU (RC) 3.00 8.00
132 Lance Broadway AU (RC) 3.00 8.00
133 Luis Mendoza AU (RC) 3.00 8.00
134 Luke Hochevar AU RC 6.00 15.00
135 Nyjer Morgan AU (RC) 3.00 8.00
136 Rob Johnson AU (RC) 3.00 8.00
137 Ross Detwiler AU RC 3.00 8.00
138 Ross Ohlendorf AU RC 4.00 10.00
139 Ryan Hanigan AU RC 3.00 8.00
140 Seth Smith AU (RC) 3.00 8.00
141 Steve Pearce AU RC 4.00 10.00
142 Troy Patton AU (RC) 3.00 8.00
143 Wladimir Balentien AU (RC) 4.00 10.00
144 Colt Morton AU RC 3.00 8.00
145 Carlos Muniz AU RC

2008 Upper Deck Spectrum Blue

RANDOM INSERTS IN PACKS
STATED PRINT RUN 25 SER.#'d SETS
NO PRICING DUE TO SCARCITY

2008 Upper Deck Spectrum Gold

RANDOM INSERTS IN PACKS
1-100 PRINT RUN 1 SER.#'d SET
101-145 PRINT RUN 10 SER.#'d SETS
NO PRICING DUE TO SCARCITY

2008 Upper Deck Spectrum Green

*1-100 GRN: .75X TO 2X BASIC
RANDOM INSERTS IN PACKS
1-100 PRINT RUN 199 SER.#'d SETS
OVERALL AUTO ODDS 1:10
GREEN AUTOS ARE NOT SER.#'d
NO GREEN AU PRICING AVAILABLE

2008 Upper Deck Spectrum Orange

*ORANGE: .6X TO 1.5X BASIC
RANDOM INSERTS IN PACKS
STATED PRINT RUN 399 SER.#'d SETS

2008 Upper Deck Spectrum Red

*RED: 1X TO 2.5X BASIC
RANDOM INSERTS IN PACKS
STATED PRINT RUN 99 SER.#'d SETS

2008 Upper Deck Spectrum Buyback Autographs

OVERALL AUTO ODDS 1:10
PRINT RUNS B/WN 2-69 COPIES PER
NO PRICING ON MOST DUE TO SCARCITY
JR1 Jose Reyes 20.00 50.00
2004 Upper Deck/70
JR2 Jose Reyes
2004 Upper Deck Fist Pitch/14
JR3 Jose Reyes
2003 SPx/14
JR4 Jose Reyes
2003 Sweet Spot/7
JR5 Jose Reyes
2004 UD All-Star Lineup/7
JR6 Jose Reyes
2004 Play Ball Red/3
JR7 Jose Reyes
2004 Play Ball Blue/4
JR8 Jose Reyes
2004 UD Vintage/14
KG1 Ken Griffey Jr. 40.00 80.00
2003 UD Patch Collection/50
KG10 Ken Griffey Jr.
2003 Play Ball/20
KG2 Ken Griffey Jr. 40.00 80.00
2003 UD 40-Man/50
KG3 Ken Griffey Jr. 40.00 80.00
2003 Sweet Spot/49
KG4 Ken Griffey Jr. 40.00 80.00
2004 UD Vintage/50
KG5 Ken Griffey Jr. 40.00 80.00
2003 SPx/49
KG6 Ken Griffey Jr. 40.00 80.00
2003 UD Authentics/50
KG7 Ken Griffey Jr. 40.00 80.00
2004 UD All-Star Lineup/50
KG8 Ken Griffey Jr. 40.00 80.00
2003 UD Honor Roll/50
KG9 Ken Griffey Jr. 40.00 80.00
2003 UD Classic Portraits/49
RA1 Roberto Alomar
2003 UD Classic Portraits/2
RA2 Roberto Alomar
2004 UD Vintage/2
RA3 Roberto Alomar 8.00 20.00
2003 Sweet Spot/50
RA4 Roberto Alomar
2003 UD Honor Roll/25
RA5 Roberto Alomar 8.00 20.00
2003 UD Honor Roll/30
RA6 Roberto Alomar 8.00 20.00
2003 UD Authentics/50

2008 Upper Deck Spectrum Derek Jeter Retrospectrum

COMMON CARD 1.25 3.00
RANDOM INSERTS IN PACKS
PRINTING PLATES RANDOMLY INSERTED
PLATE PRINT RUN 1 SET PER COLOR
BLACK-CYAN-MAGENTA-YELLOW ISSUED
NO PLATE PRICING DUE TO SCARCITY
*RED: 1X TO 2.5X BASIC
RED RANDOMLY INSERTED
RED PRINT RUN 99 SER.#'d SETS
DJ1 Derek Jeter 1.25 3.00
DJ2 Derek Jeter 1.25 3.00
DJ3 Derek Jeter 1.25 3.00
DJ4 Derek Jeter 1.25 3.00
DJ5 Derek Jeter 1.25 3.00
DJ6 Derek Jeter 1.25 3.00
DJ7 Derek Jeter 1.25 3.00
DJ8 Derek Jeter 1.25 3.00
DJ9 Derek Jeter 1.25 3.00
DJ10 Derek Jeter 1.25 3.00
DJ11 Derek Jeter 1.25 3.00
DJ12 Derek Jeter 1.25 3.00
DJ13 Derek Jeter 1.25 3.00
DJ14 Derek Jeter 1.25 3.00
DJ15 Derek Jeter 1.25 3.00
DJ16 Derek Jeter 1.25 3.00
DJ17 Derek Jeter 1.25 3.00
DJ18 Derek Jeter 1.25 3.00
DJ19 Derek Jeter 1.25 3.00
DJ20 Derek Jeter 1.25 3.00
DJ21 Derek Jeter 1.25 3.00
DJ22 Derek Jeter 1.25 3.00
DJ23 Derek Jeter 1.25 3.00
DJ24 Derek Jeter 1.25 3.00
DJ25 Derek Jeter 1.25 3.00
DJ26 Derek Jeter 1.25 3.00
DJ27 Derek Jeter 1.25 3.00
DJ28 Derek Jeter 1.25 3.00
DJ29 Derek Jeter 1.25 3.00
DJ30 Derek Jeter 1.25 3.00
DJ31 Derek Jeter 1.25 3.00
DJ32 Derek Jeter 1.25 3.00
DJ33 Derek Jeter 1.25 3.00
DJ34 Derek Jeter 1.25 3.00
DJ35 Derek Jeter 1.25 3.00
DJ36 Derek Jeter 1.25 3.00
DJ37 Derek Jeter 1.25 3.00
DJ38 Derek Jeter 1.25 3.00
DJ39 Derek Jeter 1.25 3.00
DJ40 Derek Jeter 1.25 3.00
DJ41 Derek Jeter 1.25 3.00
DJ42 Derek Jeter 1.25 3.00
DJ43 Derek Jeter 1.25 3.00
DJ44 Derek Jeter 1.25 3.00
DJ45 Derek Jeter 1.25 3.00
DJ46 Derek Jeter 1.25 3.00
DJ47 Derek Jeter 1.25 3.00
DJ48 Derek Jeter 1.25 3.00
DJ49 Derek Jeter 1.25 3.00
DJ50 Derek Jeter 1.25 3.00
DJ51 Derek Jeter 1.25 3.00
DJ52 Derek Jeter 1.25 3.00
DJ53 Derek Jeter 1.25 3.00
DJ54 Derek Jeter 1.25 3.00
DJ55 Derek Jeter 1.25 3.00
DJ56 Derek Jeter 1.25 3.00
DJ57 Derek Jeter 1.25 3.00
DJ58 Derek Jeter 1.25 3.00
DJ59 Derek Jeter 1.25 3.00
DJ60 Derek Jeter 1.25 3.00
DJ61 Derek Jeter 1.25 3.00
DJ62 Derek Jeter 1.25 3.00
DJ63 Derek Jeter 1.25 3.00
DJ64 Derek Jeter 1.25 3.00
DJ65 Derek Jeter 1.25 3.00
DJ66 Derek Jeter 1.25 3.00
DJ67 Derek Jeter 1.25 3.00
DJ68 Derek Jeter 1.25 3.00
DJ69 Derek Jeter 1.25 3.00
DJ70 Derek Jeter 1.25 3.00
DJ71 Derek Jeter 1.25 3.00
DJ72 Derek Jeter 1.25 3.00
DJ73 Derek Jeter 1.25 3.00
DJ74 Derek Jeter 1.25 3.00
DJ75 Derek Jeter 1.25 3.00
DJ76 Derek Jeter 1.25 3.00
DJ77 Derek Jeter 1.25 3.00
DJ78 Derek Jeter 1.25 3.00
DJ79 Derek Jeter 1.25 3.00
DJ80 Derek Jeter 1.25 3.00
DJ81 Derek Jeter 1.25 3.00
DJ82 Derek Jeter 1.25 3.00
DJ83 Derek Jeter 1.25 3.00
DJ84 Derek Jeter 1.25 3.00
DJ85 Derek Jeter 1.25 3.00
DJ86 Derek Jeter 1.25 3.00
DJ87 Derek Jeter 1.25 3.00
DJ88 Derek Jeter 1.25 3.00
DJ89 Derek Jeter 1.25 3.00
DJ90 Derek Jeter 1.25 3.00
DJ91 Derek Jeter 1.25 3.00
DJ92 Derek Jeter 1.25 3.00
DJ93 Derek Jeter 1.25 3.00
DJ94 Derek Jeter 1.25 3.00
DJ95 Derek Jeter 1.25 3.00
DJ96 Derek Jeter 1.25 3.00
DJ97 Derek Jeter 1.25 3.00
DJ98 Derek Jeter 1.25 3.00
DJ99 Derek Jeter 1.25 3.00
DJ100 Derek Jeter 1.25 3.00

2008 Upper Deck Spectrum Derek Jeter Retrospectrum Autographs

COMMON CARD 300.00 400.00
OVERAL AUTO ODDS 1:10
STATED PRINT RUN 2 SER.#'d SETS

2008 Upper Deck Spectrum Four Star Swatches

RANDOM INSERTS IN PACKS
STATED PRINT RUN 15 SER.#'d SETS
NO PRICING DUE TO SCARCITY
BPYG Ryan Braun
Hunter Pence
Delmon Young
Alex Gordon
CBSL Miguel Cabrera
Carlos Beltran
Alfonso Soriano
Carlos Lee
FTDH Prince Fielder
Mark Teixeira
Carlos Delgado
Todd Helton
HBFM Matt Holliday
Jason Bay
Jeff Francoeur
Lastings Milledge
JRRR Derek Jeter
Jimmy Rollins
Jose Reyes
Hanley Ramirez
JWCR Derek Jeter
Chien-Ming Wang
Joba Chamberlain
Mariano Rivera
MGJS Greg Maddux
Tom Glavine
Randy Johnson
Curt Schilling
MTHS Justin Morneau
Jim Thome
Travis Hafner
Richie Sexson
OJOG David Ortiz
Derek Jeter
Magglio Ordonez
Vladimir Guerrero
OMRB David Ortiz
Daisuke Matsuzaka
Manny Ramirez
Josh Beckett
OPBS Roy Oswalt
Jake Peavy
Josh Beckett
Ben Sheets
PCER Albert Pujols
Chris Carpenter
Jim Edmonds
Scott Rolen
PJGG Albert Pujols
Derek Jeter
Ken Griffey Jr.
Vladimir Guerrero
RMBD Jose Reyes
Pedro Martinez
Carlos Beltran
Carlos Delgado
WSCC Brandon Webb
Johan Santana
Chris Carpenter
Bartolo Colon

2008 Upper Deck Spectrum Retrospectrum Swatches

OVERALL MEM ODDS 1:10
AB1 Aaron Boone 2.50 6.00
AB2 Aaron Boone 2.50 6.00
AG1 Adrian Gonzalez 2.50 6.00
AG2 Adrian Gonzalez 2.50 6.00
AH1 Aubrey Huff 2.50 6.00
AH2 Aubrey Huff 2.50 6.00
AJ1 A.J. Burnett 2.50 6.00
AJ2 A.J. Burnett 2.50 6.00
AK Adam Kennedy 2.50 6.00
AK1 Austin Kearns 2.50 6.00
AK2 Austin Kearns 2.50 6.00
AL1 Adam LaRoche 2.50 6.00
AL2 Adam LaRoche 2.50 6.00
AP Albert Pujols 6.00 15.00
AP1 Andy Pettitte 3.00 8.00
AP2 Andy Pettitte 3.00 8.00
AR1 Aaron Rowand 2.50 6.00
AR2 Aaron Rowand 2.50 6.00
AS1 Alfonso Soriano 3.00 8.00
AS2 Alfonso Soriano 3.00 8.00
AS3 Alfonso Soriano 3.00 8.00
BA1 Bobby Abreu 2.50 6.00
BA2 Bobby Abreu 2.50 6.00
BC1 Bartolo Colon 2.50 6.00
BC2 Bartolo Colon 2.50 6.00
BE1 Adrian Beltre 2.50 6.00
BE2 Adrian Beltre 2.50 6.00
BG1 Brian Giles 2.50 6.00
BG2 Brian Giles 2.50 6.00
BZ1 Barry Zito 2.50 6.00
BZ2 Barry Zito 2.50 6.00
CA1 Sean Casey 2.50 6.00
CA2 Sean Casey 2.50 6.00
CC1 Coco Crisp 2.50 6.00
CC2 Coco Crisp 2.50 6.00
CD1 Carlos Delgado 2.50 6.00
CD2 Carlos Delgado 2.50 6.00
CL1 Carlos Lee 2.50 6.00
CL2 Carlos Lee 2.50 6.00
CY1 Chris Young 2.50 6.00
CY2 Chris Young 2.50 6.00
DJ Derek Jeter 8.00 20.00
DW1 David Wells 2.50 6.00
DW2 David Wells 2.50 6.00
EG1 Eric Gagne 2.50 6.00
EG2 Eric Gagne 2.50 6.00
ER1 Edgar Renteria 2.50 6.00
ER2 Edgar Renteria 2.50 6.00
FG1 Freddy Garcia 2.50 6.00
FG2 Freddy Garcia 2.50 6.00
FT1 Frank Thomas 5.00 12.00
FT2 Frank Thomas 5.00 12.00
GM1 Greg Maddux 5.00 12.00
GM2 Greg Maddux 5.00 12.00
GS1 Gary Sheffield 2.50 6.00
GS2 Gary Sheffield 2.50 6.00
IR1 Ivan Rodriguez 3.00 8.00
IR2 Ivan Rodriguez 3.00 8.00
JB1 Josh Barfield 2.50 6.00
JB2 Josh Barfield 2.50 6.00
JD1 J.D. Drew 2.50 6.00
JD2 J.D. Drew 2.50 6.00
JE Johnny Estrada 2.50 6.00
JJ1 Jacque Jones 2.50 6.00
JJ2 Jacque Jones 2.50 6.00
JO1 Josh Beckett 3.00 8.00
JO2 Josh Beckett 3.00 8.00
JS1 Jason Schmidt 2.50 6.00
JS2 Jason Schmidt 2.50 6.00
JT1 Jim Thome 3.00 8.00
JT2 Jim Thome 3.00 8.00
KM Kevin Millwood 2.50 6.00
LG1 Luis Gonzalez 2.50 6.00
LG2 Luis Gonzalez 2.50 6.00
LH Livan Hernandez 2.50 6.00
MA1 Moises Alou 2.50 6.00
MA2 Moises Alou 2.50 6.00
ME1 Morgan Ensberg 2.50 6.00
ME2 Morgan Ensberg 2.50 6.00
MG1 Marcus Giles 2.50 6.00
MG2 Marcus Giles 2.50 6.00
ML1 Mark Loretta 2.50 6.00
ML2 Mark Loretta 2.50 6.00
MP1 Mike Piazza 5.00 12.00
MP2 Mike Piazza 5.00 12.00
MT1 Mark Teixeira 3.00 8.00
MT2 Mark Teixeira 3.00 8.00
OV1 Omar Vizquel 2.50 6.00
OV2 Omar Vizquel 2.50 6.00
RF1 Rafael Furcal 2.50 6.00
RF2 Rafael Furcal 2.50 6.00
RJ1 Randy Johnson 5.00 12.00
RJ2 Randy Johnson 5.00 12.00
RK Ryan Klesko 2.50 6.00
SS1 Shannon Stewart 2.50 6.00
SS2 Shannon Stewart 2.50 6.00
TI1 Tadahito Iguchi 2.50 6.00
TI2 Tadahito Iguchi 2.50 6.00
WT1 Willy Taveras 2.50 6.00
WT2 Willy Taveras 2.50 6.00

2008 Upper Deck Spectrum Retrospectrum Swatches Red

*RED: .6X TO 1.5X BASIC
OVERALL MEM ODDS 1:10
STATED PRINT RUN 45 SER.#'d SETS

2008 Upper Deck Spectrum Retrospectrum Patches

OVERALL MEM ODDS 1:10
STATED PRINT RUN 25 SER.#'d SETS
NO PRICING DUE TO SCARCITY

2008 Upper Deck Spectrum Spectrum of Stars Signatures

OVERALL SOS AUTO ODDS 1:20
EXCHANGE DEADLINE 3/17/2010
AP A.J. Pero 4.00 10.00
BP Butch Patrick 12.50 30.00
BS Bill Simmons
CM Christopher McDonald 12.50 30.00
DA Taylor Dayne 12.50 30.00
DD Don Dokken 6.00 15.00
EM Erin Moran 20.00 50.00
EO Eddie Ojeda 4.00 10.00
ER Eric Roberts 12.50 30.00
ET Erik Turner 4.00 10.00
FS Frank Stallone 6.00 15.00
HW Henry Winkler 20.00 50.00
JA Joey Allen 4.00 10.00
JD Jerry Dixon 4.00 10.00
JF Jay Jay French 4.00 10.00
JG Joe Gannascoli 15.00 40.00
JL Jani Lane 6.00 15.00
KO Martin Kove 10.00 25.00
LH Larry Hagman 20.00 50.00
LT Larry Thomas 10.00 25.00
LV Lonnie Vencent
MA Miljenko Matijevic 4.00 10.00
MB Michael Biehn 15.00 40.00
MK Margot Kidder 20.00 50.00
MM Mark Mendoza 4.00 10.00
MR Mickey Rooney
PP Pat Priest 12.50 30.00
PS P.J. Soles 12.50 30.00
RF Robert Funaro 12.50 30.00
SB Sebastian Bach 6.00 15.00
SE Shirley Eaton
SN Dee Snider 6.00 15.00
SP Stephen Pearcy 6.00 15.00
SS Steven Sweet 4.00 10.00
TB Tom Bosley 15.00 40.00
TR Mike Tramp 4.00 10.00
VN Vince Neil 10.00 25.00

2008 Upper Deck Spectrum Spectrum of Stars Signatures Die Cut

OVERALL SOS AUTOS 1:20
PRINT RUNS B/WN 1-25 COPIES PER
NO PRICING DUE TO SCARCITY

2008 Upper Deck Spectrum Spectrum Swatches

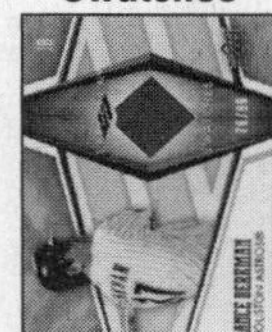

OVERALL MEM ODDS 1:10
STATED PRINT RUN 99 SER.#'d SETS
AB A.J. Burnett 3.00 8.00
AH Aaron Harang 3.00 8.00
AJ Andruw Jones 3.00 8.00
AP Albert Pujols 8.00 20.00
BB Boof Bonser 3.00 8.00
BC Bartolo Colon 3.00 8.00
BE Adrian Beltre 3.00 8.00
BG Brian Giles 3.00 8.00
BM Brian McCann 3.00 8.00
BS Ben Sheets 3.00 8.00
BU B.J. Upton 3.00 8.00
BW Billy Wagner 3.00 8.00
CA Chris Carpenter 3.00 8.00
CB Carlos Beltran 3.00 8.00
CC Carl Crawford 3.00 8.00
CG Carlos Guillen 3.00 8.00
CH Cole Hamels 4.00 10.00
CJ Chipper Jones 4.00 10.00
CS Curt Schilling 4.00 10.00
CU Chase Utley 4.00 10.00
CZ Carlos Zambrano 3.00 8.00
DH Dan Haren 3.00 8.00
DJ Derek Jeter 10.00 25.00
DL Derrek Lee 3.00 8.00
DM Daisuke Matsuzaka 8.00 20.00
DO David Ortiz 5.00 12.00
DO2 David Ortiz 5.00 12.00
DU Dan Uggla 3.00 8.00
DW Dontrelle Willis 3.00 8.00
EC Eric Chavez 3.00 8.00
FH Felix Hernandez 4.00 10.00
FS Freddy Sanchez 3.00 8.00
GA Garrett Atkins 3.00 8.00
GJ Geoff Jenkins 3.00 8.00
GM Greg Maddux 6.00 15.00
GR Curtis Granderson 4.00 10.00
GS Grady Sizemore 4.00 10.00
HA Travis Hafner 3.00 8.00
HB Hank Blalock 3.00 8.00
HO Trevor Hoffman 3.00 8.00
HP Hunter Pence 5.00 12.00
HR Hanley Ramirez 4.00 10.00
HU Torii Hunter 3.00 8.00
IK Ian Kinsler 3.00 8.00
IR Ivan Rodriguez 4.00 10.00
JA Conor Jackson 3.00 8.00
JB Josh Beckett 4.00 10.00
JC Joba Chamberlain 10.00 25.00
JD Jermaine Dye 3.00 8.00
JE Jim Edmonds 3.00 8.00
JF Jeff Francoeur 4.00 10.00
JG Jason Giambi 4.00 10.00
JH J.J. Hardy 3.00 8.00
JK Jeff Kent 3.00 8.00
JM Joe Mauer 4.00 10.00
JP Jhonny Peralta 3.00 8.00
JR Jose Reyes 4.00 10.00
JS Johan Santana 5.00 12.00
JT Jim Thome 4.00 10.00
JV Jason Varitek 5.00 12.00
JW Jered Weaver 3.00 8.00
KG Ken Griffey Jr. 6.00 15.00
KJ Kenji Johjima 3.00 8.00
KY Kevin Youkilis 3.00 8.00
LB Lance Berkman 3.00 8.00
MC Miguel Cabrera 4.00 10.00
MG Matt Garza 3.00 8.00
MH Matt Holliday 4.00 10.00
MO Justin Morneau 3.00 8.00
MP Mike Piazza 5.00 12.00
MR Manny Ramirez 4.00 10.00
MT Miguel Tejada 3.00 8.00
MY Michael Young 3.00 8.00
OR Magglio Ordonez 4.00 10.00
OS Roy Oswalt 3.00 8.00
PA Jonathan Papelbon 4.00 10.00
PE Jake Peavy 4.00 10.00
PF Prince Fielder 5.00 12.00
PI Juan Pierre 3.00 8.00
PM Pedro Martinez 4.00 10.00
PO Jorge Posada 4.00 10.00
RA Aramis Ramirez 3.00 8.00
RB Ryan Braun 6.00 15.00
RC Robinson Cano 4.00 10.00
RF Rafael Furcal 3.00 8.00
RH Roy Halladay 3.00 8.00
RJ Randy Johnson 5.00 12.00
RM Russell Martin 3.00 8.00
RS Richie Sexson 3.00 8.00
RZ Ryan Zimmerman 4.00 10.00
SM John Smoltz 4.00 10.00
SO Jeremy Sowers 3.00 8.00
SR Scott Rolen 4.00 10.00
TH Tim Hudson 3.00 8.00
TW Tim Wakefield 3.00 8.00
VE Justin Verlander 4.00 10.00
VG Vladimir Guerrero 4.00 10.00
VM Victor Martinez 3.00 8.00
VW Vernon Wells 3.00 8.00
VW2 Vernon Wells 3.00 8.00

2008 Upper Deck Spectrum Spectrum Swatches Dark Gray

OVERALL MEM ODDS 1:10
STATED PRINT RUN 1 SER.#'d SET
NO PRICING DUE TO SCARCITY

2008 Upper Deck Spectrum Spectrum Swatches Green

*GREEN: .5X TO 1.2X BASIC
OVERALL MEM ODDS 1:10
STATED PRINT RUN 50 SER.#'d SETS

2008 Upper Deck Spectrum Spectrum Swatches Green Patch

OVERALL MEM ODDS 1:10
STATED PRINT RUN 15 SER.#'d SETS
NO PRICING DUE TO SCARCITY

2008 Upper Deck Spectrum Spectrum Swatches Light Blue

OVERALL MEM ODDS 1:10
STATED PRINT RUN 15 SER.#'d SETS
NO PRICING DUE TO SCARCITY

2008 Upper Deck Spectrum Spectrum Swatches Light Gray Patch

OVERALL MEM ODDS 1:10
STATED PRINT RUN 5 SER.#'d SETS
NO PRICING DUE TO SCARCITY

2008 Upper Deck Spectrum Spectrum Swatches Orange

*ORANGE: .4X TO 1X BASIC
OVERALL MEM ODDS 1:10
STATED PRINT RUN 75 SER.#'d SETS

2008 Upper Deck Spectrum Spectrum Swatches Purple

OVERALL MEM ODDS 1:10
PRINT RUNS B/WN 2-58 COPIES PER
NO PRICING ON QTY 25 OR LESS
AB A.J. Burnett/34 5.00 12.00
AH Aaron Harang/39 5.00 12.00
AJ Andruw Jones/25
AP Albert Pujols/5
BB Boof Bonser/26 5.00 12.00
BC Bartolo Colon/40 5.00 12.00
BE Adrian Beltre/29 5.00 12.00
BG Brian Giles/24
BM Brian McCann/16
BS Ben Sheets/15
BU B.J. Upton/2
BW Billy Wagner/13
CA Chris Carpenter/29 5.00 12.00
CB Carlos Beltran/15
CC Carl Crawford/13
CG Carlos Guillen/9
CH Cole Hamels/35 6.00 15.00
CJ Chipper Jones/10
CS Curt Schilling/38 6.00 15.00
CU Chase Utley/26 6.00 15.00
CZ Carlos Zambrano/38 5.00 12.00
DH Dan Haren/15
DJ Derek Jeter/2
DL Derrek Lee/25
DM Daisuke Matsuzaka/18
DO David Ortiz/34 8.00 20.00
DO2 David Ortiz/6
DU Dan Uggla/35 5.00 12.00
DW Dontrelle Willis/3
EC Eric Chavez/34 5.00 12.00
FH Felix Hernandez/12
FS Freddy Sanchez/27 5.00 12.00
GA Garrett Atkins/5
GJ Geoff Jenkins/30 5.00 12.00
GM Greg Maddux/28 10.00 25.00
GR Curtis Granderson/24
GS Grady Sizemore/48 6.00 15.00
HA Travis Hafner/9
HB Hank Blalock/51 5.00 12.00
HO Trevor Hoffman/9
HP Hunter Pence/2
HR Hanley Ramirez/48 6.00 15.00
HU Torii Hunter/5
IK Ian Kinsler/7
IR Ivan Rodriguez/16
JA Conor Jackson/19
JB Josh Beckett/4
JC Joba Chamberlain/23
JD Jermaine Dye/15
JE Jim Edmonds/7
JF Jeff Francoeur/25
JG Jason Giambi/7
JH J.J. Hardy/12
JK Jeff Kent/7
JM Joe Mauer/2
JP Jhonny Peralta/7
JR Jose Reyes/57 6.00 15.00
JS Johan Santana/25
JT Jim Thome/33 6.00 15.00
JV Jason Varitek/36 8.00 20.00
JW Jered Weaver/3
KG Ken Griffey Jr./2
KJ Kenji Johjima/20
KY Kevin Youkilis/17
LB Lance Berkman/24
MC Miguel Cabrera/21
MG Matt Garza/5
MH Matt Holliday/33 6.00 15.00
MO Justin Morneau/31 5.00 12.00
MP Mike Piazza/24
MR Manny Ramirez/10
MT Miguel Tejada/10
MY Michael Young/30 5.00 12.00
OR Magglio Ordonez/44 6.00 15.00
OS Roy Oswalt/58 5.00 12.00
PA Jonathan Papelbon/44 6.00 15.00
PE Jake Peavy/28 6.00 15.00
PF Prince Fielder/9
PI Juan Pierre/45 5.00 12.00
PM Pedro Martinez/20
PO Jorge Posada/16
RA Aramis Ramirez/8
RB Ryan Braun/24
RC Robinson Cano/15
RF Rafael Furcal/32 5.00 12.00
RH Roy Halladay/51 5.00 12.00
RJ Randy Johnson/55 8.00 20.00
RM Russell Martin/44 5.00 12.00
RS Richie Sexson/11
RZ Ryan Zimmerman/29 6.00 15.00
SM John Smoltz/45 6.00 15.00
SO Jeremy Sowers/27 5.00 12.00
SR Scott Rolen/15
TH Tim Hudson/49 5.00 12.00
TW Tim Wakefield/35 5.00 12.00
VE Justin Verlander/27 6.00 15.00
VG Vladimir Guerrero/41 6.00 15.00
VM Victor Martinez/10
VW Vernon Wells/34 5.00 12.00
VW2 Vernon Wells/10

2008 Upper Deck Spectrum Spectrum Swatches Red

*RED: .6X TO 1.5X BASIC
OVERALL MEM ODDS 1:10
STATED PRINT RUN 35 SER.#'d SETS

2008 Upper Deck Spectrum Spectrum Swatches Autographs

OVERALL AUTO ODDS 1:10
PRINT RUNS B/WN 5-30 COPIES PER
NO PRICING ON MOST DUE TO SCARCITY
AH Aaron Harang/30 8.00 20.00
AJ Andruw Jones/30
AP Albert Pujols/5
BB Boof Bonser/30 8.00 20.00
BE Adrian Beltre/30
BG Brian Giles/30 8.00 20.00
BM Brian McCann/30 15.00 40.00
BS Ben Sheets/30 12.50 30.00
BU B.J. Upton/30 12.50 30.00
CA Chris Carpenter/30
CC Carl Crawford/30 8.00 20.00
CH Cole Hamels/30 15.00 40.00
CJ Chipper Jones/30 60.00 120.00
CS Curt Schilling/30
CU Chase Utley/30
DH Dan Haren/30 8.00 20.00
DJ Derek Jeter/15
DL Derrek Lee/30 10.00 25.00
DM Daisuke Matsuzaka/30 350.00 400.00
DU Dan Uggla/30 8.00 20.00
DW Dontrelle Willis/30 8.00 20.00
EC Eric Chavez/30
FH Felix Hernandez/30 20.00 50.00
GA Garrett Atkins/30 8.00 20.00
GJ Geoff Jenkins/30
GR Curtis Granderson/30 15.00 40.00
GS Grady Sizemore/30
HA Travis Hafner/30 15.00 40.00
HB Hank Blalock/30
HP Hunter Pence/30 15.00 40.00
HR Hanley Ramirez/30 15.00 40.00
HU Torii Hunter/30 8.00 20.00
IK Ian Kinsler/30 8.00 20.00
IR Ivan Rodriguez/30
JA Conor Jackson/30
JB Josh Beckett/14
JF Jeff Francoeur/30
JH J.J. Hardy/30
JM Joe Mauer/30 10.00 25.00
JS Johan Santana/30 30.00 60.00
JT Jim Thome/30
JV Jason Varitek/30 20.00 50.00
JW Jered Weaver/30 8.00 20.00
KG Ken Griffey Jr./15
KY Kevin Youkilis/30 15.00 40.00
LB Lance Berkman/30 10.00 25.00
MC Miguel Cabrera/30 20.00 50.00
MG Matt Garza/30 8.00 20.00
MH Matt Holliday/30 12.50 30.00
MO Justin Morneau/30 12.50 30.00
MT Miguel Tejada/30 10.00 25.00
OS Roy Oswalt/30 10.00 25.00
PA Jonathan Papelbon/30 15.00 40.00
PF Prince Fielder/30 20.00 50.00
RA Aramis Ramirez/30 12.50 30.00
RB Ryan Braun/30 30.00 60.00
RF Rafael Furcal/30
RJ Randy Johnson/30
RM Russell Martin/30 20.00 50.00
RZ Ryan Zimmerman/30 10.00 25.00
SO Jeremy Sowers/30 10.00 25.00
TH Tim Hudson/30 10.00 25.00
VE Justin Verlander/30 20.00 50.00
VG Vladimir Guerrero/30 20.00 50.00
VM Victor Martinez/30 15.00 40.00

2008 Upper Deck Spectrum Spectrum Swatches Dual

OVERALL MEM ODDS 1:10
STATED PRINT RUN 99 SER.#'d SETS
AP Aaron Rowand 4.00 10.00
Pat Burrell
BM Josh Beckett 12.50 30.00
Daisuke Matsuzaka
BP Ryan Braun 8.00 20.00
Hunter Pence
CL Matt Cain 4.00 10.00
Noah Lowry
CT Curt Schilling 5.00 12.00
Tim Wakefield
CW Miguel Cabrera 5.00 12.00
Dontrelle Willis
CY Carl Crawford 5.00 12.00
Delmon Young
DC Derek Jeter 30.00 60.00
Joba Chamberlain
FB Prince Fielder 10.00 25.00
Ryan Braun
FD Felix Hernandez 5.00 12.00
Dan Haren
FK Rafael Furcal 4.00 10.00
Jeff Kent
FM Jeff Francoeur 5.00 12.00
Brian McCann
GC Vladimir Guerrero 4.00 10.00
Bartolo Colon
GD Ken Griffey Jr. 10.00 25.00
Adam Dunn
GG Adrian Gonzalez 5.00 12.00
Brian Giles
GM Tom Glavine 10.00 25.00
Greg Maddux
GO Vladimir Guerrero 10.00 25.00
Magglio Ordonez
GP Jason Giambi 5.00 12.00
Jorge Posada
GV Grady Sizemore 5.00 12.00
Victor Martinez
HB Roy Halladay 4.00 10.00
A.J. Burnett
HC Torii Hunter 4.00 10.00
Mike Cameron
HF Matt Holliday 5.00 12.00
Jeff Francoeur
HH Matt Holliday 6.00 15.00
Todd Helton
HJ Felix Hernandez 6.00 15.00
Kenji Johjima
HS Rich Harden 4.00 10.00
Huston Street
JC Derek Jeter 10.00 25.00
Robinson Cano
JF Andruw Jones 5.00 12.00
Jeff Francoeur
JP Derek Jeter 15.00 40.00
Albert Pujols
JR Derek Jeter 12.50 30.00
Jose Reyes
JT John Smoltz 6.00 15.00
Tim Hudson
JW Randy Johnson 6.00 15.00
Brandon Webb
MH Justin Morneau 4.00 10.00
Torii Hunter
ML Brett Myers 4.00 10.00
Brad Lidge
MP Russell Martin 5.00 12.00
Juan Pierre
MR Victor Martinez 5.00 12.00
Ivan Rodriguez
MW Pedro Martinez 10.00 25.00
Billy Wagner
OB Roy Oswalt 5.00 12.00
Lance Berkman
OG Magglio Ordonez 5.00 12.00
Curtis Granderson
OP David Ortiz 10.00 25.00
Albert Pujols
OR David Ortiz 10.00 25.00
Manny Ramirez
PE Albert Pujols 8.00 20.00
Jim Edmonds
PJ Prince Fielder 6.00 15.00
Justin Morneau
PM Jake Peavy 6.00 15.00
Greg Maddux
PS Albert Pujols 10.00 25.00
Alfonso Soriano
PW Jake Peavy 5.00 12.00
Brandon Webb
RB Jose Reyes 5.00 12.00
Carlos Beltran
RC Gary Sheffield 5.00 12.00
Miguel Cabrera
RF Jose Reyes 5.00 12.00
Rafael Furcal
RH Hanley Ramirez 5.00 12.00
J.J. Hardy
RR Jose Reyes 5.00 12.00
Jimmy Rollins
RU Hanley Ramirez 5.00 12.00
Dan Uggla
SB Richie Sexson 4.00 10.00
Adrian Beltre
SH Ben Sheets 4.00 10.00
J.J. Hardy
SL Alfonso Soriano 5.00 12.00
Derrek Lee
SM Johan Santana 5.00 12.00
Joe Mauer
SW Johan Santana 5.00 12.00
Dontrelle Willis
TD Jim Thome 4.00 10.00
Jermaine Dye
TM Miguel Tejada 4.00 10.00
Nick Markakis
UH Chase Utley 8.00 20.00
Cole Hamels
VB Justin Verlander 10.00 25.00
Jeremy Bonderman
VR Justin Verlander 10.00 25.00
Ivan Rodriguez
VY Jason Varitek 6.00 15.00
Kevin Youkilis
WR Vernon Wells 4.00 10.00
Alex Rios
YK Michael Young 4.00 10.00
Ian Kinsler
ZL Carlos Zambrano 4.00 10.00
Derrek Lee

2008 Upper Deck Spectrum Three Star Swatches

OVERALL MEM ODDS 1:10
STATED PRINT RUN 75 SER.#'d SETS
GDH Ken Griffey Jr. 6.00 15.00
Adam Dunn
Aaron Harang
HBK Cole Hamels 4.00 10.00
Erik Bedard
Scott Kazmir
JCC Derek Jeter 20.00 50.00
Joba Chamberlain
Robinson Cano
JPG Derek Jeter 20.00 50.00
Albert Pujols
Ken Griffey Jr.
KHS Ian Kinsler 4.00 10.00
Aaron Hill
Freddy Sanchez
MGS Greg Maddux 12.50 30.00
Tom Glavine
John Smoltz
MJS Pedro Martinez 10.00 25.00
Randy Johnson
Curt Schilling
MRM Victor Martinez 4.00 10.00
Ivan Rodriguez
Joe Mauer
OBP Roy Oswalt 6.00 15.00
Lance Berkman
Hunter Pence
OVS Magglio Ordonez 10.00 25.00
Justin Verlander
Gary Sheffield
PER Albert Pujols 10.00 25.00
Jim Edmonds
Scott Rolen
PSB Jake Peavy 6.00 15.00
Johan Santana
Josh Beckett
RBM Jose Reyes 10.00 25.00
Carlos Beltran
Pedro Martinez
RUH Jimmy Rollins 6.00 15.00
Chase Utley
Cole Hamels
SBH Grady Sizemore 4.00 10.00
Carlos Beltran
Torii Hunter
SCG Alfonso Soriano 4.00 10.00
Miguel Cabrera
Vladimir Guerrero
SJT John Smoltz 6.00 15.00
Chipper Jones
Mark Teixeira
SMH Grady Sizemore 6.00 15.00
Victor Martinez
Travis Hafner
SMM Johan Santana 6.00 15.00
Justin Morneau
Joe Mauer
ZSL Carlos Zambrano 10.00 25.00
Alfonso Soriano
Derrek Lee

2008 Upper Deck Timeline

This set was released on November 4, 2008. The base set consists of 385 cards.

COMMON CARD (1-50) .15 .40
COMMON RC (51-100) .25 .60
COMMON CARD (101-130) .25 .60
COMMON CARD (131-180) .25 .60
COMMON CARD (181-210) .25 .60
COMMON CARD (211-310) .25 .60
COMMON CARD (311-335) .40 1.00
COMMON CARD (336-360) .40 1.00
COMMON CARD (361-385) .75 2.00
1 Jose Reyes .25 .60
2 David Wright .50 1.25
3 Carlos Beltran .15 .40
4 Pedro Martinez .25 .60
5 Johan Santana .25 .60
6 Hanley Ramirez .40 1.00
7 John Smoltz .40 1.00
8 Chipper Jones .50 1.25
9 Mark Teixeira .25 .60
10 Chase Utley .40 1.00
11 Ryan Howard .50 1.25
12 Jimmy Rollins .25 .60
13 Alfonso Soriano .25 .60
14 Derrek Lee .25 .60
15 Jason Bay .15 .40
16 Lance Berkman .25 .60
17 Ken Griffey Jr. .60 1.50
18 Ryan Braun .50 1.25
19 Prince Fielder .25 .60
20 Albert Pujols .75 2.00
21 Tim Lincecum .40 1.00
22 Jake Peavy .25 .60
23 Matt Kemp .15 .40
24 Matt Holliday .25 .60
25 Brandon Webb .25 .60
26 Randy Johnson .40 1.00
27 Alex Rodriguez .60 1.50
28 Derek Jeter 1.00 2.50
29 Chien-Ming Wang .50 1.25
30 David Ortiz .40 1.00
31 Manny Ramirez .40 1.00
32 Daisuke Matsuzaka .60 1.50
33 B.J. Upton .25 .60
34 Nick Markakis .25 .60
35 Roy Halladay .15 .40
36 Jim Thome .25 .60
37 Grady Sizemore .25 .60
38 Travis Hafner .15 .40
39 C.C. Sabathia .15 .40
40 Miguel Cabrera .25 .60
41 Justin Verlander .25 .60
42 Joe Mauer .25 .60
43 Alex Gordon .40 1.00
44 Frank Thomas .40 1.00
45 Vladimir Guerrero .40 1.00
46 Torii Hunter .15 .40
47 Josh Hamilton .50 1.25
48 Ichiro Suzuki .60 1.50
49 Felix Hernandez .25 .60
50 Erik Bedard .15 .40
51 Daric Barton (RC) .25 .60
52 John Bowker (RC) .25 .60
53 Clay Buchholz (RC) .60 1.50
54 Jeff Clement (RC) .25 .60
55 Johnny Cueto RC .40 1.00
56 Blake DeWitt (RC) .60 1.50
57 German Duran RC .40 1.00
58 Kosuke Fukudome RC 1.00 2.50
59 Alberto Gonzalez RC .40 1.00
60 Luke Hochevar RC .60 1.50
61 Chin-Lung Hu (RC) .40 1.00
62 Ian Kennedy RC .60 1.50
63 Masahide Kobayashi RC .40 1.00
64 Hiroki Kuroda RC .40 1.00
65 Evan Longoria RC 2.00 5.00
66 Jed Lowrie (RC) .60 1.50
67 Justin Masterson RC 1.25 3.00
68 Nick Blackburn RC .40 1.00
69 Micah Hoffpauir RC .40 1.00
70 Jeff Niemann (RC) .25 .60
71 Ross Ohlendorf RC .40 1.00
72 Jonathan Van Every RC .25 .60
73 Alexei Ramirez RC 1.50 4.00
74 Justin Ruggiano RC .40 1.00
75 Max Scherzer RC .60 1.50
76 Greg Smith RC .25 .60
77 Denard Span (RC) .40 1.00
78 Clete Thomas RC .40 1.00
79 Josh Banks (RC) .25 .60
80 Clay Timpner (RC) .25 .60
81 Matt Tolbert RC .40 1.00
82 J.R. Towles RC .60 1.50
83 Eugenio Velez RC .25 .60
84 Joey Votto (RC) .60 1.50
85 Rico Washington (RC) .25 .60
86 Jay Bruce (RC) 1.00 2.50
87 Wladimir Balentien (RC) .25 .60
88 Burke Badenhop RC .40 1.00
89 Brian Barton RC .40 1.00
90 Brian Bocock RC .25 .60
91 Brandon Boggs (RC) .40 1.00
92 Robinzon Diaz (RC) .25 .60
93 Hernan Iribarren (RC) .40 1.00
94 Brent Lillibridge (RC) .25 .60
95 Yasuhiko Yabuta RC .40 1.00
96 Jeff Samardzija RC .75 2.00
97 Carlos Gonzalez (RC) .25 .60
98 Clayton Kershaw RC .75 2.00
99 Jonathan Albaladejo RC .40 1.00
100 Nick Adenhart (RC) .25 .60
101 Bobby Wilson 92 ML RC .25 .60
102 Brandon Phillips 92 ML .25 .60
103 Chad Billingsley 92 ML .25 .60
104 Chris Duncan 92 ML .25 .60
105 Clay Timpner 92 ML (RC) .25 .60
106 Clete Thomas 92 ML RC .40 1.00
107 Corey Hart 92 ML .25 .60
108 Craig Breslow 92 ML .25 .60
109 David Murphy 92 ML .25 .60
110 Edinson Volquez 92 ML .25 .60
111 Elijah Dukes 92 ML .25 .60
112 Emmanuel Burriss 92 ML RC .40 1.00
113 Evan Longoria 92 ML RC 2.00 5.00
114 Fred Lewis 92 ML .25 .60
115 Felix Pie 92 ML .25 .60
116 German Duran 92 ML RC .40 1.00
117 Greg Smith 92 ML RC .25 .60
118 Hernan Iribarren 92 ML (RC) .40 1.00
119 Joey Votto 92 ML (RC) .60 1.50
120 Jonathan Van Every 92 ML RC .25 .60
121 Kosuke Fukudome 92 ML RC 1.00 2.50
122 Matt Joyce 92 ML RC .60 1.50
123 Max Scherzer 92 ML RC .60 1.50
124 Nick Swisher 92 ML .25 .60
125 Paul Janish 92 ML (RC) .25 .60
126 Reed Johnson 92 ML .25 .60
127 Rico Washington 92 ML (RC) .25 .60
128 Russell Martin 92 ML .25 .60
129 Scott Kazmir 92 ML .40 1.00
130 Tyler Clippard 92 ML .25 .60
131 Randy Johnson 94 ATH .60 1.50
132 Frank Thomas 94 ATH .60 1.50
133 Greg Maddux 94 ATH .75 2.00
134 Vladimir Guerrero 94 ATH .60 1.50
135 Ryan Braun 94 ATH .75 2.00
136 David Ortiz 94 ATH .60 1.50
137 Jake Peavy 94 ATH .40 1.00
138 Mark Teixeira 94 ATH .40 1.00
139 Jose Reyes 94 ATH .40 1.00
140 Chien-Ming Wang 94 ATH .75 2.00
141 Prince Fielder 94 ATH .60 1.50
142 Albert Pujols 94 ATH 1.25 3.00
143 Johan Santana 94 ATH .40 1.00
144 Josh Beckett 94 ATH .40 1.00
145 Alex Rodriguez 94 ATH 1.00 2.50
146 Felix Hernandez 94 ATH .40 1.00
147 Brandon Webb 94 ATH .40 1.00
148 Chase Utley 94 ATH .60 1.50
149 Derek Jeter 94 ATH 1.50 4.00
150 Grady Sizemore 94 ATH .40 1.00
151 B.J. Upton 94 ATH .40 1.00
152 Carlos Beltran 94 ATH .25 .60
153 Hanley Ramirez 94 ATH .60 1.50
154 Magglio Ordonez 94 ATH .40 1.00
155 Carlos Zambrano 94 ATH .25 .60
156 Manny Ramirez 94 ATH .60 1.50
157 Travis Hafner 94 ATH .25 .60
158 David Wright 94 ATH .75 2.00
159 Jimmy Rollins 94 ATH .40 1.00
160 Matt Holliday 94 ATH .40 1.00
161 Ken Griffey Jr. 94 ATH 1.00 2.50
162 C.C. Sabathia 94 ATH .25 .60
163 Joe Mauer 94 ATH .40 1.00
164 Derrek Lee 94 ATH .40 1.00
165 Miguel Cabrera 94 ATH .40 1.00
166 Alfonso Soriano 94 ATH .40 1.00
167 Ichiro Suzuki 94 ATH 1.00 2.50
168 Daisuke Matsuzaka 94 ATH 1.00 2.50
169 Lance Berkman 94 ATH .40 1.00
170 Ryan Howard 94 ATH .75 2.00
171 J.R. Towles 94 ATH RC .60 1.50
172 Max Scherzer 94 ATH RC .60 1.50
173 Chin-Lung Hu 94 ATH .40 1.00
174 Daric Barton 94 ATH .25 .60
175 Ian Kennedy 94 ATH .60 1.50
176 Clay Buchholz 94 ATH .60 1.50
177 Joey Votto 94 ATH (RC) .60 1.50
178 Kosuke Fukudome 94 ATH RC 1.00 2.50
179 Johnny Cueto 94 ATH .40 1.00
180 Evan Longoria 94 ATH 2.00 5.00
181 Brandon Boggs 95 STP (RC) .40 1.00
182 Brian Bocock 95 STP RC .25 .60
183 Burke Badenhop 95 STP RC .40 1.00
184 Callix Crabbe 95 STP (RC) .25 .60
185 Cha-Seung Baek 95 STP .25 .60
186 Chris Smith 95 STP (RC) .25 .60
187 Clayton Kershaw 95 STP RC .75 2.00
188 Felipe Paulino 95 STP RC .40 1.00
189 Glen Perkins 95 STP .25 .60
190 Homer Bailey 95 STP .40 1.00
191 James Loney 95 STP .40 1.00
192 Jay Bruce 95 STP (RC) 1.00 2.50
193 Jeff Baker 95 STP .25 .60
194 Jeff Keppinger 95 STP .25 .60
195 Jesus Flores 95 STP .25 .60
196 Joakim Soria 95 STP .25 .60
197 Joey Votto 95 STP (RC) .60 1.50
198 Josh Hamilton 95 STP .75 2.00
199 Kosuke Fukudome 95 STP RC 1.00 2.50
200 Micah Hoffpauir 95 STP RC .40 1.00
201 Nick Blackburn 95 STP RC .40 1.00
202 Nyjer Morgan 95 STP (RC) .25 .60
203 Randor Bierd 95 STP RC .25 .60
204 Rich Hill 95 STP .25 .60
205 Ross Ohlendorf 95 STP RC .40 1.00
206 Russell Martin 95 STP .25 .60
207 Ryan Garko 95 STP .25 .60
208 Seth Smith 95 STP .25 .60
209 Steve Holm 95 STP RC .25 .60
210 Travis Hafner 95 STP .25 .60
211 Brandon Webb 04 TT .40 1.00
212 Randy Johnson 04 TT .60 1.50
213 Max Scherzer 04 TT RC .60 1.50
214 Chris B. Young 04 TT .25 .60
215 Justin Upton 04 TT .60 1.50
216 John Smoltz 04 TT .60 1.50
217 Chipper Jones 04 TT .75 2.00
218 Mark Teixeira 04 TT .40 1.00
219 Jeff Francoeur 04 TT .40 1.00
220 Adrian Gonzalez 04 TT .40 1.00
221 Nick Markakis 04 TT .40 1.00
222 Jacoby Ellsbury 04 TT 1.00 2.50
223 David Ortiz 04 TT .60 1.50
224 Manny Ramirez 04 TT .60 1.50
225 Daisuke Matsuzaka 04 TT 1.00 2.50
226 Clay Buchholz 04 TT (RC) .60 1.50
227 Jed Lowrie 04 TT (RC) .60 1.50
228 Justin Masterson 04 TT RC 1.25 3.00
229 Geovany Soto 04 TT .60 1.50
230 Alfonso Soriano 04 TT .40 1.00
231 Derrek Lee 04 TT .40 1.00
232 Kosuke Fukudome 04 TT RC 1.00 2.50
233 Jim Thome 04 TT .40 1.00
234 Alexei Ramirez 04 TT RC 1.50 4.00
235 Ken Griffey Jr. 04 TT 1.00 2.50
236 Johnny Cueto 04 TT RC .40 1.00
237 Joey Votto 04 TT (RC) .60 1.50
238 Brandon Phillips 04 TT .25 .60
239 Edinson Volquez 04 TT .25 .60
240 Grady Sizemore 04 TT .40 1.00
241 Travis Hafner 04 TT .25 .60
242 C.C. Sabathia 04 TT .25 .60
243 Matt Holliday 04 TT .40 1.00
244 Troy Tulowitzki 04 TT .40 1.00
245 Miguel Cabrera 04 TT .40 1.00
246 Justin Verlander 04 TT .40 1.00
247 Matt Tolbert 04 TT RC .40 1.00
248 Hanley Ramirez 04 TT .60 1.50
249 Jeremy Hermida 04 TT .25 .60
250 Lance Berkman 04 TT .40 1.00
251 J.R. Towles 04 TT RC .60 1.50
252 Alex Gordon 04 TT .60 1.50
253 Luke Hochevar 04 TT RC .60 1.50
254 Vladimir Guerrero 04 TT .60 1.50
255 Torii Hunter 04 TT .25 .60
256 Nick Adenhart 04 TT (RC) .25 .60
257 Garrett Atkins 04 TT .25 .60
258 Blake DeWitt 04 TT (RC) .60 1.50
259 Chin-Lung Hu 04 TT (RC) .40 1.00
260 Hiroki Kuroda 04 TT RC .40 1.00
261 Matt Kemp 04 TT .25 .60
262 James Loney 04 TT .40 1.00
263 Justin Morneau 04 TT .40 1.00
264 Dan Haren 04 TT .25 .60
265 Ryan Braun 04 TT .75 2.00
266 Corey Hart 04 TT .25 .60
267 Rickie Weeks 04 TT .25 .60
268 Prince Fielder 04 TT .60 1.50
269 Carlos Gomez 04 TT .25 .60
270 Joe Mauer 04 TT .40 1.00
271 Jose Reyes 04 TT .40 1.00
272 David Wright 04 TT .75 2.00
273 Carlos Beltran 04 TT .25 .60
274 Pedro Martinez 04 TT .40 1.00
275 Hideki Matsui 04 TT .60 1.50
276 Alex Rodriguez 04 TT 1.00 2.50
277 Derek Jeter 04 TT 1.50 4.00
278 Chien-Ming Wang 04 TT .75 2.00
279 Ian Kennedy 04 TT RC .60 1.50
280 Phil Hughes 04 TT .60 1.50
281 Frank Thomas 04 TT .60 1.50
282 Daric Barton 04 TT (RC) .25 .60
283 Greg Smith 04 TT RC .25 .60
284 Cole Hamels 04 TT .60 1.50
285 Chase Utley 04 TT .60 1.50
286 Ryan Howard 04 TT .75 2.00
287 Jimmy Rollins 04 TT .40 1.00
288 Jason Bay 04 TT .40 1.00
289 Jake Peavy 04 TT .40 1.00
290 Brian McCann 04 TT .40 1.00
291 Tim Lincecum 04 TT .60 1.50
292 Justin Ruggiano 04 TT RC .40 1.00
293 Jay Bruce 04 TT (RC) 1.00 2.50
294 Brian Bocock 04 TT RC .25 .60
295 Ichiro Suzuki 04 TT 1.00 2.50
296 Adam Dunn 04 TT .25 .60
297 Erik Bedard 04 TT .25 .60
298 Jeff Clement 04 TT (RC) .25 .60
299 Felix Hernandez 04 TT .25 .60
300 Albert Pujols 04 TT 1.25 3.00
301 Rick Ankiel 04 TT .25 .60
302 B.J. Upton 04 TT .40 1.00
303 Evan Longoria 04 TT RC 2.00 5.00
304 Clayton Kershaw 04 TT RC .75 2.00
305 Carl Crawford 04 TT .25 .60
306 Russell Martin 04 TT .25 .60
307 Brandon Boggs 04 TT (RC) .40 1.00
308 Josh Hamilton 04 TT .75 2.00
309 Roy Halladay 04 TT .25 .60
310 Ryan Zimmerman 04 TT .40 1.00
311 Evan Longoria 93 SP RC 3.00 8.00
312 Johnny Cueto 93 SP (RC) .60 1.50
313 Kosuke Fukudome 93 SP (RC) 1.50 4.00
314 Joey Votto 93 SP (RC) 1.00 2.50
315 Clay Buchholz 93 SP (RC) 1.00 2.50
316 Ian Kennedy 93 SP RC 1.00 2.50
317 Daric Barton 93 SP (RC) .40 1.00
318 Chin-Lung Hu 93 SP (RC) .60 1.50
319 Max Scherzer 93 SP (RC) 1.00 2.50
320 J.R. Towles 93 SP RC 1.00 2.50
321 Nick Adenhart 93 SP (RC) .40 1.00
322 Wladimir Balentien 93 SP (RC) .40 1.00
323 Brian Barton 93 SP RC .60 1.50
324 Brian Bocock 93 SP (RC) .60 1.50
325 Jonathan Herrera 93 SP RC .60 1.50
326 Jesse Carlson 93 SP RC .60 1.50
327 Jeff Clement 93 SP (RC) .40 1.00
328 Brandon Jones 93 SP RC 1.00 2.50
329 German Duran 93 SP RC .60 1.50
330 Alex Romero 93 SP (RC) .60 1.50
331 Jay Bruce 93 SP (RC) 1.50 4.00
332 Luke Hochevar 93 SP RC 1.00 2.50
333 Clayton Kershaw 93 SP (RC) 1.25 3.00
334 Nick Blackburn 93 SP RC .60 1.50
335 Jed Lowrie 93 SP (RC) 1.00 2.50
336 Evan Longoria 94 SP (RC) 3.00 8.00
337 Johnny Cueto 94 SP (RC) 1.00 2.50
338 Kosuke Fukudome 94 SP (RC) 1.50 4.00
339 Joey Votto 94 SP (RC) 1.00 2.50
340 Clay Buchholz 94 SP (RC) 1.00 2.50
341 Ian Kennedy 94 SP RC 1.00 2.50
342 Daric Barton 94 SP (RC) .40 1.00
343 Chin-Lung Hu 94 SP (RC) .60 1.50
344 Max Scherzer 94 SP (RC) 1.00 2.50
345 J.R. Towles 94 SP RC 1.00 2.50
346 Justin Masterson 94 SP (RC) 2.00 5.00
347 Kyle McClellan 94 SP RC .40 1.00
348 Evan Meek 94 SP RC .40 1.00
349 Nyjer Morgan 94 SP (RC) .40 1.00
350 Colt Morton 94 SP RC .60 1.50
351 Luke Carlin 94 SP RC .40 1.00
352 Emmanuel Burriss 94 SP (RC) .60 1.50
353 Clint Sammons 94 SP (RC) .40 1.00
354 Ross Ohlendorf 94 SP RC .60 1.50
355 Jay Bruce 94 SP (RC) 1.50 4.00
356 Felipe Paulino 94 SP RC .60 1.50
357 Alexei Ramirez 94 SP (RC) 2.50 6.00
358 Clayton Kershaw 94 SP (RC) 1.25 3.00
359 Cory Wade 94 SP (RC) .40 1.00
360 Greg Smith 94 SP (RC) .40 1.00
361 Evan Longoria 95 SP (RC) 5.00 12.00
362 Johnny Cueto 95 SP (RC) 1.25 3.00
363 Kosuke Fukudome 95 SP (RC) 2.50 6.00
364 Joey Votto 95 SP (RC) 2.00 5.00
365 Clay Buchholz 95 SP (RC) 2.00 5.00
366 Ian Kennedy 95 SP (RC) 2.00 5.00
367 Daric Barton 95 SP (RC) .75 2.00
368 Chin-Lung Hu 95 SP (RC) 1.25 3.00
369 Max Scherzer 95 SP (RC) 2.00 5.00
370 J.R. Towles 95 SP (RC) 2.00 5.00
371 Mitchell Boggs 95 SP (RC) .75 2.00
372 Jay Bruce 95 SP (RC) 3.00 8.00
373 Alberto Gonzalez 95 SP (RC) 1.25 3.00
374 Rich Thompson 95 SP RC 1.25 3.00
375 Robinzon Diaz 95 SP (RC) .75 2.00
376 Clay Timpner 95 SP (RC) .75 2.00
377 Eider Torres 95 SP (RC) 1.25 3.00
378 Ramon Troncoso 95 SP RC .75 2.00
379 Clayton Kershaw 95 SP (RC) 2.50 6.00
380 Rico Washington 95 SP (RC) .75 2.00
381 Brandon Jones 95 SP (RC) 2.00 5.00
382 Bobby Wilson 95 SP (RC) .75 2.00
383 Wesley Wright 95 SP RC .75 2.00
384 Mike Parisi 95 SP RC 1.25 3.00
385 Jonathan Van Every 95 SP (RC) .75 2.00

2008 Upper Deck Timeline Gold

*VET 1-50: 1X TO 2.5X BASIC
*RC 51-100: .6X TO 1.5X BASIC
VET ODDS 1:6 HOBBY, 1:24 RETAIL
RC ODDS 1:12 HOBBY, 1:48 RETAIL

2008 Upper Deck Timeline 1992 UD Minor League Autographs

STATED ODDS 1:27 HOB., 1:144 RET.
101 Bobby Wilson 3.00 8.00
102 Brandon Phillips
103 Chad Billingsley
104 Chris Duncan
105 Clay Timpner 3.00 8.00
106 Clete Thomas 3.00 8.00
107 Corey Hart
108 Craig Breslow 4.00 10.00
109 David Murphy
110 Edinson Volquez
111 Elijah Dukes 5.00 12.00
112 Emmanuel Burriss
113 Evan Longoria
114 Fred Lewis
115 Felix Pie
116 German Duran 3.00 8.00
117 Greg Smith 3.00 8.00
118 Hernan Iribarren 3.00 8.00
119 Joey Votto
120 Jonathan Van Every 4.00 10.00
121 Kosuke Fukudome
122 Matt Joyce 5.00 12.00
123 Max Scherzer
124 Nick Swisher
125 Paul Janish 3.00 8.00
126 Reed Johnson 3.00 8.00
127 Rico Washington 3.00 8.00
128 Russell Martin
129 Scott Kazmir
130 Tyler Clippard 3.00 8.00

2008 Upper Deck Timeline 1993 SP Autographs

OVERALL AU ODDS 1:9 HOBBY
STATED PRINT RUN 93 SER.#'d SETS
311 Evan Longoria
312 Johnny Cueto 10.00 25.00
315 Clay Buchholz 10.00 25.00
317 Daric Barton
318 Chin-Lung Hu 20.00 50.00
320 J.R. Towles

321 Nick Adenhart
322 Wladimir Balentien 6.00 15.00
323 Brian Barton
324 Brian Bocock 3.00 8.00
325 Jonathan Herrera
326 Jesse Carlson
327 Jeff Clement 10.00 25.00
328 Brandon Jones 6.00 15.00
329 German Duran 3.00 8.00
330 Alex Romero
331 Jay Bruce 60.00 120.00
332 Luke Hochevar 4.00 10.00
333 Clayton Kershaw
334 Nick Blackburn
335 Jed Lowrie

2008 Upper Deck Timeline 1994 All-Time Heroes 20th Anniversary

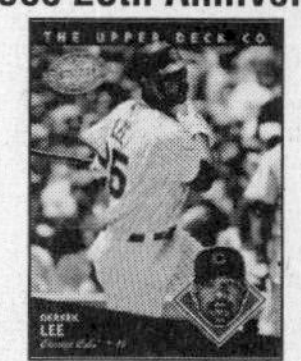

STATED ODDS 1:9 HOB.,1:72 RET.
131 Randy Johnson 1.00 2.50
132 Frank Thomas 1.00 2.50
133 Greg Maddux 1.25 3.00
134 Vladimir Guerrero 1.00 2.50
135 Ryan Braun 1.25 3.00
136 David Ortiz 1.00 2.50
137 Jake Peavy .60 1.50
138 Mark Teixeira .60 1.50
139 Jose Reyes .60 1.50
140 Chien-Ming Wang 1.25 3.00
141 Prince Fielder 1.00 2.50
142 Albert Pujols 2.00 5.00
143 Johan Santana .60 1.50
144 Josh Beckett .60 1.50
145 Alex Rodriguez 1.50 4.00
146 Felix Hernandez .60 1.50
147 Brandon Webb .60 1.50
148 Chase Utley 1.00 2.50
149 Derek Jeter 2.50 6.00
150 Grady Sizemore .60 1.50
151 B.J. Upton .60 1.50
152 Carlos Beltran .40 1.00
153 Hanley Ramirez 1.00 2.50
154 Magglio Ordonez .60 1.50
155 Carlos Zambrano .40 1.00
156 Manny Ramirez 1.00 2.50
157 Travis Hafner .40 1.00
158 David Wright 1.25 3.00
159 Jimmy Rollins .60 1.50
160 Matt Holliday .60 1.50
161 Ken Griffey Jr. 1.50 4.00
162 C.C. Sabathia .40 1.00
163 Joe Mauer .60 1.50
164 Derrek Lee .60 1.50
165 Miguel Cabrera .60 1.50
166 Alfonso Soriano .60 1.50
167 Ichiro Suzuki 1.50 4.00
168 Daisuke Matsuzaka 1.50 4.00
169 Lance Berkman .60 1.50
170 Ryan Howard 1.25 3.00
171 J.R. Towles 1.00 2.50
172 Max Scherzer 1.00 2.50
173 Chin-Lung Hu .60 1.50
174 Daric Barton .40 1.00
175 Ian Kennedy 1.00 2.50
176 Clay Buchholz 1.00 2.50
177 Joey Votto 1.00 2.50
178 Kosuke Fukudome 1.50 4.00
179 Johnny Cueto .60 1.50
180 Evan Longoria 3.00 8.00

2008 Upper Deck Timeline 1994 All-Time Heroes Autographs

OVERALL AU ODDS 1:9 HOBBY
PRINT RUNS B/WN 5-99 COPIES PER
NO PRICING ON QTY 25 OR LESS
131 Randy Johnson/5
132 Frank Thomas/5
135 Ryan Braun/25
140 Chien-Ming Wang/10
141 Prince Fielder/25
144 Josh Beckett/10
146 Felix Hernandez/25
147 Brandon Webb/25
149 Derek Jeter/99 75.00 150.00
150 Grady Sizemore/25
151 B.J. Upton/25
153 Hanley Ramirez/25
157 Travis Hafner/25
160 Matt Holliday/25
163 Joe Mauer/25
164 Derrek Lee/25
165 Miguel Cabrera/10
166 Alfonso Soriano/10
168 Daisuke Matsuzaka/5
169 Lance Berkman/10
171 J.R. Towles/99 4.00 10.00
173 Chin-Lung Hu/99 20.00 50.00
174 Daric Barton/99 5.00 12.00
176 Clay Buchholz/50 12.50 30.00
179 Johnny Cueto/59
180 Evan Longoria/50

2008 Upper Deck Timeline 1994 SP Autographs

OVERALL AU ODDS 1:9 HOBBY
STATED PRINT RUN 94 SER.#'d SETS
336 Evan Longoria 100.00 200.00
337 Johnny Cueto
340 Clay Buchholz
342 Daric Barton 5.00 12.00
343 Chin-Lung Hu
345 J.R. Towles
346 Justin Masterson 60.00 120.00
347 Kyle McClellan 10.00 25.00
349 Nyjer Morgan
350 Colt Morton
351 Luke Carlin
354 Ross Ohlendorf 3.00 8.00
356 Felipe Paulino 3.00 8.00
357 Alexei Ramirez 60.00 120.00
358 Clayton Kershaw 8.00 20.00
359 Cory Wade 6.00 15.00
360 Greg Smith 5.00 12.00

2008 Upper Deck Timeline 1995 SP Autographs

OVERALL AU ODDS 1:9 HOBBY
STATED PRINT RUN 95 SER.#'d SETS
361 Evan Longoria 100.00 200.00
362 Johnny Cueto 5.00 12.00
365 Clay Buchholz 10.00 25.00
367 Daric Barton 5.00 12.00
368 Chin-Lung Hu
370 J.R. Towles 4.00 10.00
371 Mitchell Boggs 5.00 12.00
373 Alberto Gonzalez
375 Robinzon Diaz 4.00 10.00
376 Clay Timpner 3.00 8.00
377 Eider Torres
378 Ramon Troncoso
379 Clayton Kershaw
380 Rico Washington
381 Brandon Jones
382 Bobby Wilson 3.00 8.00
383 Wesley Wright
384 Mike Parisi
385 Jonathan Van Every

2008 Upper Deck Timeline 1995 SP Top Prospects Autographs

STATED ODDS 1:27 HOB.,1:144 RET.
181 Brandon Boggs 3.00 8.00
182 Brian Bocock 3.00 8.00
183 Burke Badenhop 3.00 8.00
185 Cha-Seung Baek
186 Chris Smith 4.00 10.00
187 Clayton Kershaw
188 Felipe Paulino 3.00 8.00
189 Glen Perkins
190 Homer Bailey 4.00 10.00
191 James Loney 6.00 15.00
193 Jeff Baker 3.00 8.00
194 Jeff Keppinger 3.00 8.00
195 Jesus Flores 3.00 8.00
196 Joakim Soria 4.00 10.00
198 Josh Hamilton 20.00 50.00
200 Micah Hoffpauir 6.00 15.00
201 Nick Blackburn 6.00 15.00
202 Nyjer Morgan 3.00 8.00
203 Randor Bierd 3.00 8.00
204 Rich Hill
206 Russell Martin
207 Ryan Garko
208 Seth Smith 4.00 10.00
209 Steve Holm 4.00 10.00
210 Travis Hafner

2008 Upper Deck Timeline 2004 UD Timeless Teams Autographs

OVERALL AU ODDS 1:9 HOBBY
PRINT RUNS B/WN 5-99 COPIES PER
NO PRICING ON QTY 10 OR LESS
211 Brandon Webb/10
212 Randy Johnson/5
214 Chris B. Young/10
217 Chipper Jones/10
219 Jeff Francoeur/50
220 Adrian Gonzalez/10
221 Nick Markakis/50
226 Clay Buchholz/50
227 Jed Lowrie/50
228 Justin Masterson/50
230 Alfonso Soriano/10
231 Derrek Lee/10
233 Jim Thome/10
234 Alexei Ramirez/10
236 Johnny Cueto/59
238 Brandon Phillips/99 5.00 12.00
239 Edinson Volquez/99 10.00 25.00
240 Grady Sizemore/10
241 Travis Hafner/10
243 Matt Holliday/10
244 Troy Tulowitzki/10
245 Miguel Cabrera/10
246 Justin Verlander/10
247 Matt Tolbert/99 6.00 15.00
248 Hanley Ramirez/10
250 Lance Berkman/10
251 J.R. Towles/99
252 Alex Gordon/10
253 Luke Hochevar/50
255 Torii Hunter/10
256 Nick Adenhart/50
257 Garrett Atkins/10
259 Chin-Lung Hu/50
261 Matt Kemp/10
262 James Loney/10
263 Justin Morneau/10
264 Dan Haren/10
265 Ryan Braun/10
266 Corey Hart/50
267 Rickie Weeks/10
268 Prince Fielder/10
269 Carlos Gomez/99 15.00 40.00
270 Joe Mauer/10
277 Derek Jeter/10
278 Chien-Ming Wang/10
280 Phil Hughes/10
281 Frank Thomas/5
282 Daric Barton/99 5.00 12.00
283 Greg Smith/99 5.00 12.00
284 Cole Hamels/10
288 Jason Bay/99 12.50 30.00
292 Justin Ruggiano/36
294 Brian Bocock/99
296 Adam Dunn/10
298 Jeff Clement/99 10.00 25.00
299 Felix Hernandez/10
302 B.J. Upton/10
303 Evan Longoria/10
304 Clayton Kershaw/10
305 Carl Crawford/10
306 Russell Martin/10
307 Brandon Boggs/99 3.00 8.00
308 Josh Hamilton/50
309 Roy Halladay/10
310 Ryan Zimmerman/10

2008 Upper Deck Timeline 2004 UD Timeless Teams Gold

RANDOM INSERTS IN PACKS
STATED PRINT RUN 25 SER.#'d SETS
NO PRICING DUE TO SCARCITY

2008 Upper Deck Timeline 2004 UD Timeless Teams Silver

RANDOM INSERTS IN PACKS
STATED PRINT RUN 100 SER.#'d SETS
211 Brandon Webb 2.50 6.00
212 Randy Johnson 4.00 10.00
213 Max Scherzer 4.00 10.00
214 Chris B. Young 1.50 4.00
215 Justin Upton 4.00 10.00
216 John Smoltz 4.00 10.00
217 Chipper Jones 5.00 12.00
218 Mark Teixeira 2.50 6.00
219 Jeff Francoeur 2.50 6.00
220 Adrian Gonzalez 2.50 6.00
221 Nick Markakis 2.50 6.00
222 Jacoby Ellsbury 6.00 15.00
223 David Ortiz 4.00 10.00
224 Manny Ramirez 4.00 10.00
225 Daisuke Matsuzaka 6.00 15.00
226 Clay Buchholz 4.00 10.00
227 Jed Lowrie 4.00 10.00
228 Justin Masterson 8.00 20.00
229 Geovany Soto 4.00 10.00
230 Alfonso Soriano 2.50 6.00
231 Derrek Lee 2.50 6.00
232 Kosuke Fukudome 6.00 15.00
233 Jim Thome 2.50 6.00
234 Alexei Ramirez 10.00 25.00
235 Ken Griffey Jr. 6.00 15.00
236 Johnny Cueto 2.50 6.00
237 Joey Votto 4.00 10.00
238 Brandon Phillips 1.50 4.00
239 Edinson Volquez 1.50 4.00
240 Grady Sizemore 2.50 6.00
241 Travis Hafner 1.50 4.00
242 C.C. Sabathia 1.50 4.00
243 Matt Holliday 2.50 6.00
244 Troy Tulowitzki 2.50 6.00
245 Miguel Cabrera 2.50 6.00
246 Justin Verlander 2.50 6.00
247 Matt Tolbert 2.50 6.00
248 Hanley Ramirez 4.00 10.00
249 Jeremy Hermida 1.50 4.00
250 Lance Berkman 2.50 6.00
251 J.R. Towles 4.00 10.00
252 Alex Gordon 4.00 10.00
253 Luke Hochevar 4.00 10.00
254 Vladimir Guerrero 4.00 10.00
255 Torii Hunter 1.50 4.00
256 Nick Adenhart 1.50 4.00
257 Garrett Atkins 1.50 4.00
258 Blake DeWitt 4.00 10.00
259 Chin-Lung Hu 2.50 6.00
260 Hiroki Kuroda 2.50 6.00
261 Matt Kemp 1.50 4.00
262 James Loney 2.50 6.00
263 Justin Morneau 2.50 6.00
264 Dan Haren 1.50 4.00
265 Ryan Braun 5.00 12.00
266 Corey Hart 1.50 4.00
267 Rickie Weeks 1.50 4.00
268 Prince Fielder 4.00 10.00
269 Carlos Gomez 1.50 4.00
270 Joe Mauer 2.50 6.00
271 Jose Reyes 2.50 6.00
272 David Wright 5.00 12.00
273 Carlos Beltran 1.50 4.00
274 Pedro Martinez 2.50 6.00
275 Hideki Matsui 4.00 10.00
276 Alex Rodriguez 6.00 15.00
277 Derek Jeter 10.00 25.00
278 Chien-Ming Wang 5.00 12.00
279 Ian Kennedy 4.00 10.00
280 Phil Hughes 4.00 10.00
281 Frank Thomas 4.00 10.00
282 Daric Barton 1.50 4.00
283 Greg Smith 1.50 4.00
284 Cole Hamels 4.00 10.00
285 Chase Utley 4.00 10.00
286 Ryan Howard 5.00 12.00
287 Jimmy Rollins 2.50 6.00
288 Jason Bay 1.50 4.00
289 Jake Peavy 2.50 6.00
290 Brian McCann 2.50 6.00
291 Tim Lincecum 4.00 10.00
292 Justin Ruggiano 2.50 6.00
293 Jay Bruce 6.00 15.00
294 Brian Bocock 1.50 4.00
295 Ichiro Suzuki 6.00 15.00
296 Adam Dunn 1.50 4.00
297 Erik Bedard 1.50 4.00
298 Jeff Clement 1.50 4.00
299 Felix Hernandez 2.50 6.00
300 Albert Pujols 8.00 20.00
301 Rick Ankiel 1.50 4.00
302 B.J. Upton 2.50 6.00
303 Evan Longoria 12.00 30.00
304 Clayton Kershaw 5.00 12.00
305 Carl Crawford 1.50 4.00
306 Russell Martin 1.50 4.00
307 Brandon Boggs 2.50 6.00
308 Josh Hamilton 5.00 12.00
309 Roy Halladay 1.50 4.00
310 Ryan Zimmerman 2.50 6.00

2008 Upper Deck Timeline Cut Signatures

OVERALL AU ODDS 1:9 HOBBY
NNO Mystery Exchange 90.00 150.00

2008 Upper Deck Timeline Memorabilia

ONE PER TARGET/WM BLASTER
AB A.J. Burnett 3.00 8.00
AD Adrian Beltre 3.00 8.00
AE Andre Ethier 4.00 10.00
AG Adrian Gonzalez 4.00 10.00
AJ Andruw Jones 3.00 8.00
AM Andrew Miller 4.00 10.00
AP Albert Pujols 6.00 15.00
AR Aaron Rowand 3.00 8.00
BC Bartolo Colon 3.00 8.00
BE Adrian Beltre 3.00 8.00
BG Brian Giles 3.00 8.00
BM Brian McCann 4.00 10.00
BO Bobby Crosby 3.00 8.00
BR B.J. Ryan 3.00 8.00
BS Ben Sheets 4.00 10.00
BU A.J. Burnett 3.00 8.00
BZ Barry Zito 3.00 8.00
CB Chad Billingsley 3.00 8.00
CC Carl Crawford 3.00 8.00
CD Carlos Delgado 3.00 8.00
CG Curtis Granderson 4.00 10.00
CJ Chipper Jones 5.00 12.00
CQ Carlos Quentin 3.00 8.00
CR Bobby Crosby 3.00 8.00
CZ Carlos Zambrano 3.00 8.00
DA Johnny Damon 4.00 10.00
DE Carlos Delgado 3.00 8.00
DJ Derek Jeter 8.00 20.00
DL Derek Lowe 3.00 8.00
DO David Ortiz 4.00 10.00
DW Dontrelle Willis 3.00 8.00
ED Jim Edmonds 4.00 10.00
FR Ryan Freel 3.00 8.00
FS Freddy Sanchez 3.00 8.00
GA Garrett Atkins 3.00 8.00
GI Brian Giles 3.00 8.00
GJ Geoff Jenkins 3.00 8.00
GL Troy Glaus 4.00 10.00
GM Greg Maddux 5.00 12.00
GO Adrian Gonzalez 4.00 10.00
GT Troy Glaus 4.00 10.00
HA Josh Hamilton 5.00 12.00
HM Hideki Matsui 4.00 10.00
HO Trevor Hoffman 3.00 8.00
HT Travis Hafner 3.00 8.00
HU Torii Hunter 3.00 8.00
IS Ian Snell 3.00 8.00
JD Jermaine Dye 3.00 8.00
JE Jim Edmonds 4.00 10.00
JF Jeff Francoeur 4.00 10.00
JG Jeremy Guthrie 3.00 8.00
JH JJ Hardy 3.00 8.00
JL Jon Lester 4.00 10.00
JM Joe Mauer 4.00 10.00
JO Chipper Jones 5.00 12.00
JP Jorge Posada 4.00 10.00
JS Jeremy Sowers 3.00 8.00
KG Ken Griffey Jr. 6.00 15.00
KY Kevin Youkilis 4.00 10.00
MA Greg Maddux 5.00 12.00
MC Miguel Cabrera 4.00 10.00
MG Matt Garza 3.00 8.00
MO Justin Morneau 4.00 10.00
MS Mike Sweeney 3.00 8.00
MT Miguel Tejada 3.00 8.00
MY Michael Young 3.00 8.00
NS Nick Swisher 3.00 8.00
OR David Ortiz 4.00 10.00
OV Omar Vizquel 3.00 8.00
PE Andy Pettitte 4.00 10.00
PF Prince Fielder 4.00 10.00
PK Paul Konerko 3.00 8.00
PM Pedro Martinez 4.00 10.00
PU Albert Pujols 6.00 15.00
RA Aramis Ramirez 3.00 8.00
RB Ryan Braun 5.00 12.00
RC Robinson Cano 4.00 10.00
RF Rafael Furcal 3.00 8.00
RG Ryan Garko 3.00 8.00
RH Rich Harden 3.00 8.00
RJ Randy Johnson 4.00 10.00
RM Russell Martin 3.00 8.00
RO Roy Halladay 3.00 8.00
RS Richie Sexson 3.00 8.00
RZ Ryan Zimmerman 4.00 10.00
SA Johan Santana 4.00 10.00
SC Scott Rolen 4.00 10.00
SK Scott Kazmir 4.00 10.00
SP Scott Podsednik 3.00 8.00
SR Scott Rolen 4.00 10.00
TB Travis Buck 3.00 8.00
TG Tom Glavine 4.00 10.00
TH Tim Hudson 3.00 8.00
TL Tim Lincecum 4.00 10.00
TR Travis Hafner 3.00 8.00
TW Tim Wakefield 3.00 8.00
VG Vladimir Guerrero 4.00 10.00
VM Victor Martinez 3.00 8.00
WT Willy Taveras 3.00 8.00
ZD Zach Duke 3.00 8.00

2008 Upper Deck Timeline Team USA Signatures

STATED ODDS 1:41 HOBBY
AG A.J. Griffin 3.00 8.00
AO Andrew Oliver 5.00 12.00
BH Brett Hunter 3.00 8.00
BS Blake Smith 10.00 25.00
CC Christian Colon 3.00 8.00
CH Chris Hernandez 8.00 20.00
DD Derek Dietrich 10.00 25.00
HM Hunter Morris 3.00 8.00
JF Josh Fellhauer 6.00 15.00
KD Kentrail Davis 10.00 25.00
KG Kyle Gibson 4.00 10.00
KR Kevin Rhoderick 3.00 8.00
KV Kendal Volz 5.00 12.00
MD Matt den Dekker 4.00 10.00
MG Micah Gibbs 4.00 10.00
ML Mike Leake 4.00 10.00
MM Mike Minor 4.00 10.00
RJ Ryan Jackson 6.00 15.00
RL Ryan Lipkin 4.00 10.00
SS Stephen Strasburg 60.00 120.00
TL Tyler Lyons 3.00 8.00
TM Tommy Mendonca 10.00 25.00

2005 Upper Deck Update

COMP.SET w/o SP's (100) 8.00 20.00
COMMON CARD (1-100) .10 .30
1-100 ONE PER PACK
COMMON CARD (101-177) 1.25 3.00
101-177: ONE #'d CARD OR AU PER PACK
101-177 PRINT RUN 599 SERIAL #'d SETS
178-186: OVERALL AU ODDS APPX 1:8
178-186 PRINT RUN 75 SERIAL #'d SETS
1 A.J. Burnett .10 .30
2 Adam Dunn .10 .30
3 Adrian Beltre .10 .30
4 Albert Pujols .60 1.50
5 Alex Rodriguez .50 1.25
6 Alfonso Soriano .10 .30
7 Andruw Jones .20 .50
8 Aramis Ramirez .10 .30
9 Barry Zito .10 .30
10 Bartolo Colon .10 .30
11 Ben Sheets .10 .30
12 Bobby Abreu .10 .30
13 Bobby Crosby .10 .30
14 Bret Boone .10 .30
15 Brian Giles .10 .30
16 Brian Roberts .10 .30
17 Carl Crawford .10 .30
18 Carlos Beltran .10 .30
19 Carlos Delgado .10 .30
20 Carlos Lee .10 .30
21 Carlos Zambrano .10 .30
22 Chase Utley .20 .50
23 Chipper Jones .30 .75
24 Chris Carpenter .10 .30
25 Craig Biggio .20 .50
26 Curt Schilling .20 .50
27 David Ortiz .40 1.00
28 David Wright .50 1.25
29 Derek Jeter .75 2.00
30 Derrek Lee .20 .50
31 Dontrelle Willis .10 .30
32 Eric Chavez .10 .30
33 Eric Gagne .10 .30
34 Francisco Rodriguez .10 .30
35 Gary Sheffield .10 .30
36 Greg Maddux .50 1.25
37 Hank Blalock .10 .30
38 Hideki Matsui .40 1.00
39 Ichiro Suzuki .50 1.25
40 Ivan Rodriguez .20 .50
41 J.D. Drew .10 .30
42 Jake Peavy .10 .30
43 Jason Bay .10 .30
44 Jason Schmidt .10 .30
45 Jeff Bagwell .20 .50
46 Jeff Kent .10 .30
47 Jeremy Bonderman .10 .30
48 Jim Edmonds .10 .30
49 Jim Thome .20 .50
50 Joe Mauer .30 .75
51 Johan Santana .30 .75
52 John Smoltz .20 .50
53 Johnny Damon .20 .50
54 Jose Reyes .20 .50
55 Jose Vidro .10 .30
56 Josh Beckett .10 .30
57 Justin Morneau .10 .30
58 Ken Griffey Jr. .50 1.25
59 Kenny Rogers .10 .30
60 Kerry Wood .10 .30
61 Khalil Greene .20 .50
62 Lance Berkman .10 .30
63 Livan Hernandez .10 .30
64 Luis Gonzalez .10 .30
65 Manny Ramirez .20 .50
66 Mark Buehrle .10 .30
67 Mark Mulder .10 .30
68 Mark Prior .20 .50
69 Mark Teixeira .20 .50
70 Michael Young .10 .30
71 Miguel Cabrera .20 .50
72 Miguel Tejada .10 .30
73 Mike Mussina .20 .50
74 Mike Piazza .30 .75
75 Moises Alou .10 .30
76 Morgan Ensberg .10 .30
77 Nomar Garciaparra .30 .75
78 Pat Burrell .10 .30
79 Paul Konerko .10 .30
80 Pedro Martinez .20 .50
81 Randy Johnson .30 .75
82 Rich Harden .10 .30
83 Richie Sexson .10 .30
84 Rickie Weeks .10 .30
85 Robinson Cano .20 .50
86 Roger Clemens .50 1.25
87 Roy Halladay .10 .30
88 Roy Oswalt .10 .30
89 Sammy Sosa .30 .75
90 Scott Kazmir .10 .30
91 Scott Rolen .20 .50
92 Shawn Green .10 .30
93 Tim Hudson .10 .30
94 Todd Helton .20 .50
95 Tom Glavine .20 .50
96 Torii Hunter .10 .30
97 Travis Hafner .10 .30
98 Troy Glaus .10 .30
99 Vernon Wells .10 .30
100 Vladimir Guerrero .30 .75
101 Adam Shabala PR RC 1.25 3.00
102 Ambiorix Burgos PR RC 1.25 3.00
103 Anibal Sanchez PR RC 3.00 8.00
104 Bill McCarthy PR RC 1.25 3.00
105 Brandon McCarthy PR RC 1.50 4.00
106 Brian Burres PR RC 1.25 3.00
107 Carlos Ruiz PR RC 1.25 3.00
108 Casey Rogowski PR RC 1.50 4.00
109 Chad Orvella PR RC 1.25 3.00
110 Chris Resop PR RC 1.25 3.00
111 Chris Roberson PR RC 1.25 3.00
112 Chris Seddon PR RC 1.25 3.00
113 Colter Bean PR RC 1.25 3.00
114 Dae-Sung Koo PR RC 1.25 3.00
115 Dave Gassner PR RC 1.25 3.00
116 Brian Anderson PR RC 1.50 4.00
117 D.J. Houlton PR RC 1.25 3.00
118 Derek Wathan PR RC 1.25 3.00
119 Devon Lowery PR RC 1.25 3.00
120 Enrique Gonzalez PR RC 1.25 3.00
121 Eude Brito PR RC 1.25 3.00
122 Francisco Butto PR RC 1.25 3.00
123 Franquelis Osoria PR RC 1.25 3.00
124 Garrett Jones PR RC 1.25 3.00
125 Geovany Soto PR RC 1.25 3.00
126 Hayden Penn PR RC 1.50 4.00
127 Ismael Ramirez PR RC 1.25 3.00
128 Jared Gothreaux PR RC 1.25 3.00
129 Jason Hammel PR RC 1.25 3.00

2005 Upper Deck Update

130 Jeff Miller PR RC 1.25 3.00
131 Joel Peralta PR RC 1.25 3.00
132 John Hattig PR RC 1.25 3.00
133 Jorge Campillo PR RC 1.25 3.00
134 Juan Morillo PR RC 1.25 3.00
135 Ryan Garko PR RC 2.00 5.00
136 Keiichi Yabu PR RC 1.25 3.00
137 Luis Hernandez PR RC 1.25 3.00
138 Luis Pena PR RC 1.25 3.00
139 Luis O.Rodriguez PR RC 1.25 3.00
140 Luke Scott PR RC 2.00 5.00
141 Marcos Carvajal PR RC 1.25 3.00
142 Mark Woodyard PR RC 1.25 3.00
143 Matt A.Smith PR RC 1.25 3.00
144 Matthew Lindstrom PR RC 1.25 3.00
145 Miguel Negron PR RC 1.50 4.00
146 Mike Morse PR RC 1.25 3.00
147 Nate McLouth PR RC 1.50 4.00
148 Nelson Cruz PR RC 2.00 5.00
149 Nick Masset PR RC 1.25 3.00
150 Oscar Robles PR RC 1.25 3.00
151 Paulino Reynoso PR RC 1.25 3.00
152 Pedro Lopez PR RC 1.25 3.00
153 Pete Orr PR RC 1.25 3.00
154 Randy Messenger PR RC 1.25 3.00
155 Randy Williams PR RC 1.25 3.00
156 Raul Tablado PR RC 1.25 3.00
157 Ronny Paulino PR RC 1.50 4.00
158 Russ Rohlicek PR RC 1.25 3.00
159 Russell Martin PR RC 2.50 6.00
160 Scott Baker PR RC 1.50 4.00
161 Scott Munter PR RC 1.25 3.00
162 Sean Thompson PR RC 1.25 3.00
163 Sean Tracey PR RC 1.25 3.00
164 Shane Costa PR RC 1.25 3.00
165 Steve Schmoll PR RC 1.25 3.00
166 Tony Giarratano PR RC 1.25 3.00
167 Tony Pena PR RC 1.25 3.00
168 Travis Bowyer PR RC 1.25 3.00
169 Ubaldo Jimenez PR RC 2.50 6.00
170 Wladimir Balentien PR RC 1.50 4.00
171 Yorman Bazardo PR RC 1.25 3.00
172 Yuniesky Betancourt PR RC 2.00 5.00
173 Chris Denorfia PR RC 1.50 4.00
174 Dana Eveland PR RC 1.25 3.00
175 Jermaine Van Buren PR 1.25 3.00
176 Mark McLemore PR RC 1.25 3.00
177 Ryan Spilborghs PR RC 1.50 4.00
178 Ambiorix Concepcion AU RC 6.00 15.00
179 Jeff Niemann AU RC 8.00 20.00
180 Justin Verlander AU RC 60.00 100.00
181 Kendry Morales AU RC 30.00 60.00
182 Philip Humber AU RC 8.00 20.00
183 Prince Fielder AU RC 90.00 150.00
184 Stephen Drew AU RC 75.00 150.00
185 Tadahito Iguchi AU RC 40.00 80.00
186 Ryan Zimmerman AU RC 100.00 175.00

2005 Upper Deck Update Gold

*GOLD 101-177: .6X TO 1.5X BASIC
101-177: ONE #'d CARD OR AU PER PACK
101-177 PRINT RUN 150 SERIAL #'d SETS
178-186: OVERALL AU ODDS APPX 1:8
178-186 AU PRINT RUN 10 SERIAL #'d SETS
178-186 AU NO PRICING DUE TO SCARCITY
101 Adam Shabala PR 2.00 5.00

2005 Upper Deck Update Platinum

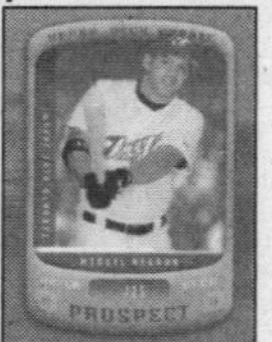

101-177: ONE #'d CARD OR AU PER PACK
101-177 PRINT RUN 25 SERIAL #'d SETS
178-186: OVERALL AU ODDS APPX 1:8
178-186 AU PRINT RUN 1 SERIAL #'d SET
NO PRICING DUE TO SCARCITY
101 Adam Shabala PR

2005 Upper Deck Update Silver

*SILVER 101-177: .4X TO 1X BASIC
101-177: ONE #'d CARD OR AU PER PACK
101-177 PRINT RUN 450 SERIAL #'d SETS
178-186: OVERALL AU ODDS APPX 1:8
178-186 AU PRINT RUN 25 SERIAL #'d SETS
178-186 AU NO PRICING DUE TO SCARCITY
101 Adam Shabala PR 1.25 3.00

2005 Upper Deck Update Draft Class Quad Autographs

OVERALL AU ODDS APPX 1:8
STATED PRINT RUN 5 SERIAL #'d SETS
NO PRICING DUE TO SCARCITY
1999 Pat Burrell
Mark Mulder
Corey Patterson
J.D. Drew
2001 Joe Mauer
Mark Prior
Mark Teixeira
Jeremy Bonderman
2002 B.J. Upton
Zack Greinke
Prince Fielder
Scott Kazmir
2004 Justin Verlander
Philip Humber
Jeff Niemann
Stephen Drew

2005 Upper Deck Update Draft Generations Triple Autographs

OVERALL AU ODDS APPX 1:8
STATED PRINT RUN 10 SERIAL #'d SETS
NO PRICING DUE TO SCARCITY
DGBWN George Bell
Vernon Wells
Miguel Negron
DGGCM Ken Griffey Jr.
Miguel Cabrera
Kendry Morales
DGJKM Wally Joyner
Casey Kotchman
Kendry Morales
DGMBV Jack Morris
Jeremy Bonderman
Justin Verlander
DGRSN Nolan Ryan
John Smoltz
Jeff Niemann
DGSGH Tom Seaver
Tom Glavine
Philip Humber
DGSWF Ben Sheets
Rickie Weeks
Prince Fielder
DGUYN B.J. Upton
Delmon Young
Jeff Niemann

2005 Upper Deck Update Link to the Future Dual Autographs

OVERALL AU ODDS APPX 1:8
STATED PRINT RUN 35 SERIAL #'d SETS
BR Wladimir Balentien 15.00 40.00
Jeremy Reed
BW Yorman Bazardo 15.00 40.00
Dontrelle Willis
CD Shane Costa 10.00 25.00
David DeJesus
DD Stephen Drew 75.00 150.00
J.D. Drew
DJ Stephen Drew 200.00 350.00
Derek Jeter
FO Prince Fielder 40.00 80.00
Lyle Overbay
FT Prince Fielder 60.00 120.00
Mark Teixeira
FW Prince Fielder 50.00 100.00
Rickie Weeks
GO Jared Gothreaux 15.00 40.00
Roy Oswalt
HF Luis Hernandez 10.00 25.00
Rafael Furcal
HG Philip Humber 30.00 60.00
Tom Glavine
MB Nate McLouth 15.00 40.00
Jason Bay
MK Kendry Morales 15.00 40.00
Casey Kotchman
NK Jeff Niemann 10.00 25.00
Scott Kazmir
NW Miguel Negron 15.00 40.00
Vernon Wells
OB Franquelis Osoria 10.00 25.00
Yhency Brazoban
OG Pete Orr 10.00 25.00
Marcus Giles
PV Tony Pena 10.00 25.00
Javier Vazquez
RH Ismael Ramirez 15.00 40.00
Roy Halladay
SK Chris Seddon 15.00 40.00
Scott Kazmir
SL Luke Scott 20.00 50.00
Jason Lane
VB Justin Verlander 50.00 100.00
Jeremy Bonderman
VC Justin Verlander 125.00 200.00
Roger Clemens
ZC Ryan Zimmerman 60.00 120.00
Chad Cordero

2005 Upper Deck Update Link to the Past Dual Autographs

OVERALL AU ODDS APPX 1:8
STATED PRINT RUN 25 SERIAL #'d SETS
BC Eude Brito 20.00 50.00
Steve Carlton
BM Brian Burres 15.00 40.00
Juan Marichal
CS Ambiorix Concepcion 15.00 40.00
Darryl Strawberry
GT Tony Giarratano 15.00 40.00
Alan Trammell
HG Philip Humber 20.00 50.00
Dwight Gooden
HS Philip Humber 30.00 60.00
Tom Seaver
IA Tadahito Iguchi 60.00 120.00
Luis Aparicio
IC Tadahito Iguchi 60.00 120.00
Rod Carew
JH Garrett Jones 15.00 40.00
Kent Hrbek
JJ Justin Verlander 40.00 80.00
Jack Morris
MC Kendry Morales 20.00 50.00
Rod Carew
MJ Kendry Morales 15.00 40.00
Wally Joyner
MV Nate McLouth 20.00 50.00
Andy Van Slyke
NB Miguel Negron 15.00 40.00
George Bell
NR Jeff Niemann 60.00 120.00
Nolan Ryan
PP Hayden Penn 15.00 40.00
Jim Palmer
RD Chris Roberson 15.00 40.00
Lenny Dykstra
TP Sean Thompson 10.00 25.00
Gaylord Perry
VM Justin Verlander 40.00 80.00
Denny McLain

2001 Upper Deck Vintage

The 2001 Upper Deck Vintage product released in late January,2001 and featured a 400-card base set. Each pack contained 10 cards, and carried a suggested retail price of $2.99 per pack. The set was broken into tiers as follows: Base Veterans (1-340), Prospects (341-370), Series Highlights (371-390) and League Leaders (391-400). A Sample card featuring Ken Griffey Jr. was distributed to dealers and hobby media several weeks prior to the product's release national release date. The card can be readily identified by the bold "SAMPLE" text running diagonally across the back.

COMPLETE SET (400) 20.00 50.00
COMMON (1-340/371-400) .10 .30
COMMON (341-370) .20 .50
1 Darin Erstad .10 .30
2 Seth Etherton .10 .30
3 Troy Glaus .10 .30
4 Bengie Molina .10 .30
5 Mo Vaughn .10 .30
6 Tim Salmon .20 .50
7 Ramon Ortiz .10 .30
8 Adam Kennedy .10 .30
9 Garret Anderson .10 .30
10 Troy Percival .10 .30
11 Tim Salmon .10 .30
Bengie Molina
MoVaughn
Adam Kennedy
Troy Glaus
Kevin Stocker
Darin Erstad
Garret Anderson
Ron Gant CL
12 Jason Giambi .10 .30
13 Tim Hudson .10 .30
14 Adam Piatt .10 .30
15 Miguel Tejada .10 .30
16 Mark Mulder .10 .30
17 Eric Chavez .10 .30
18 Ramon Hernandez .10 .30
19 Terrence Long .10 .30
20 Jason Isringhausen .10 .30
21 Barry Zito .20 .50
22 Ben Grieve .10 .30
23 Olmedo Saenz .10 .30
Ramon Hernandez
Jason Giambi
Randy Velarde
Eric Chavez
Miguel Tejada
Ben Grieve
Terrence Long
Adam Piatt CL
24 David Wells .10 .30
25 Raul Mondesi .10 .30
26 Darrin Fletcher .10 .30
27 Shannon Stewart .10 .30
28 Kelvim Escobar .10 .30
29 Tony Batista .10 .30
30 Carlos Delgado .10 .30
31 Brad Fullmer .10 .30
32 Billy Koch .10 .30
33 Jose Cruz Jr. .10 .30
34 Brad Fullmer .10 .30
Darrin Fletcher
Carlos Delgado
Homer Bush
Tony Batista
Alex Gonzalez
Shannon Stewart
Jose Cruz Jr.
Raul Mondesi CL
35 Greg Vaughn .10 .30
36 Roberto Hernandez .10 .30
37 Vinny Castilla .10 .30
38 Gerald Williams .10 .30
39 Aubrey Huff .10 .30
40 Bryan Rekar .10 .30
41 Albie Lopez .10 .30
42 Fred McGriff .20 .50
43 Miguel Cairo .10 .30
44 Ryan Rupe .10 .30
45 Greg Vaughn .10 .30
John Flaherty
Fred McGriff
Miguel Cairo
Vinny Castilla
Felix Martinez
Gerald Williams
Jose Guillen
Steve Cox CL
46 Jim Thome .20 .50
47 Roberto Alomar .20 .50
48 Bartolo Colon .10 .30
49 Omar Vizquel .20 .50
50 Travis Fryman .10 .30
51 Manny Ramirez UER .20 .50
Picture is of David Segui
52 Dave Burba .10 .30
53 Chuck Finley .10 .30
54 Russ Branyan .10 .30
55 Kenny Lofton .10 .30
56 Russell Branyan .10 .30
Sandy Alomar Jr.
Jim Thome
Roberto Alomar
Travis Fryman
Omar Vizquel
Wil Cordero
Kenny Lofton
Manny Ramirez
Picture is off David Segui CL UER
57 Alex Rodriguez .50 1.25
58 Jay Buhner .10 .30
59 Aaron Sele .10 .30
60 Kazuhiro Sasaki .10 .30
61 Edgar Martinez .20 .50
62 John Halama .10 .30
63 Mike Cameron .10 .30
64 Freddy Garcia .10 .30
65 John Olerud .08 .25
66 Jamie Moyer .10 .30
67 Gil Meche .10 .30
68 Edgar Martinez .10 .30
Joe Oliver
John Olerud
David Bell
Carlos Guillen
Alex Rodriguez
Jay Buhner
Mike Cameron
Al Martin CL
69 Cal Ripken 1.00 2.50
70 Sidney Ponson .10 .30
71 Chris Richard .10 .30
72 Jose Mercedes .10 .30
73 Albert Belle .10 .30
74 Mike Mussina .20 .50
75 Brady Anderson .10 .30
76 Delino DeShields .10 .30
77 Melvin Mora .10 .30
78 Luis Matos .10 .30
79 Brook Fordyce .10 .30
80 Jeff Conine .10 .30
Brook Fordyce
Chris Richard
Delino DeShields
Cal Ripken
Melvin Mora
Luis Matos
Brady Anderson
Albert Belle CL
81 Rafael Palmeiro .20 .50
82 Rick Helling .10 .30
83 Ruben Mateo .10 .30
84 Rusty Greer .10 .30
85 Ivan Rodriguez .20 .50
86 Doug Davis .10 .30
87 Gabe Kapler .10 .30
88 Mike Lamb .10 .30
89 A.Rodriguez Rangers 1.25 3.00
90 Kenny Rogers .10 .30
91 David Segui .20 .50
Ivan Rodriguez
Rafael Palmeiro
Frank Catalanotto
Mike Lamb
Royce Clayton
Ruben Mateo
Gabe Kapler
Rusty Greer CL
92 Nomar Garciaparra .50 1.25
93 Trot Nixon .10 .30
94 Tomokazu Ohka .10 .30
95 Pedro Martinez .20 .50
96 Dante Bichette .10 .30
97 Jason Varitek .30 .75
98 Rolando Arrojo .10 .30
99 Carl Everett .10 .30
100 Derek Lowe .10 .30
101 Troy O'Leary .10 .30
102 Tim Wakefield .10 .30
103 Troy O'Leary .20 .50
Jason Varitek
Jose Offerman
Mike Lansing
Wilton Veras
Nomar Garciaparra
Carl Everett
Trot Nixon
Dante Bichette CL
104 Mike Sweeney .10 .30
105 Carlos Febles .10 .30
106 Joe Randa .10 .30
107 Jeff Suppan .10 .30
108 Mac Suzuki .10 .30
109 Jermaine Dye .10 .30
110 Carlos Beltran .10 .30
111 Mark Quinn .10 .30
112 Johnny Damon .20 .50
113 Mark Quinn .10 .30
Gregg Zaun
Mike Sweeney
Carlos Febles
Joe Randa
Rey Sanchez
Carlos Beltran
Johnny Damon
Jermaine Dye CL
114 Tony Clark .10 .30
115 Dean Palmer .10 .30
116 Brian Moehler .10 .30
117 Brad Ausmus .10 .30
118 Juan Gonzalez .10 .30
119 Juan Encarnacion .10 .30
120 Jeff Weaver .10 .30
121 Bobby Higginson .10 .30
122 Todd Jones .10 .30
123 Deivi Cruz .10 .30
124 Juan Gonzalez .10 .30
Brad Ausmus
Tony Clark
Damion Easley
Dean Palmer
Deivi Cruz
Bobby Higginson
Juan Encarnacion
Rich Becker CL
125 Corey Koskie .10 .30
126 Matt Lawton .10 .30
127 Mark Redman .10 .30
128 David Ortiz .30 .75
129 Jay Canizaro .10 .30
130 Eric Milton .10 .30
131 Jacque Jones .10 .30
132 J.C. Romero .10 .30
133 Ron Coomer .10 .30
134 Brad Radke .10 .30
135 David Ortiz .20 .50
Matt LeCroy
Ron Coomer
Jay Canizaro
Corey Koskie
Cristian Guzman
Jacque Jones
Matt Lawton
Torii Hunter CL
136 Carlos Lee .10 .30
137 Frank Thomas .30 .75
138 Mike Sirotka .10 .30
139 Charles Johnson .10 .30
140 James Baldwin .10 .30
141 Magglio Ordonez .10 .30
142 Jon Garland .10 .30
143 Paul Konerko .10 .30
144 Ray Durham .10 .30
145 Keith Foulke .10 .30
146 Chris Singleton .10 .30
147 Frank Thomas .20 .50
Charles Johnson
Paul Konerko
Ray Durham
Herbert Perry
Jose Valentin
Carlos Lee
Magglio Ordonez
Chris Singleton CL
148 Bernie Williams .20 .50
149 Orlando Hernandez .10 .30
150 David Justice .10 .30
151 Andy Pettitte .20 .50
152 Mariano Rivera .30 .75
153 Derek Jeter .75 2.00
154 Jorge Posada .20 .50
155 Jose Canseco .20 .50
156 Glenallen Hill .10 .30
157 Paul O'Neill .20 .50
158 Denny Neagle .10 .30
159 Chuck Knoblauch .10 .30
160 Roger Clemens .60 1.50
161 Glenallen Hill .30 .75
Jorge Posada
Tino Martinez
Chuck Knoblauch
Scott Brosius
Derek Jeter
Paul O'Neill
Bernie Williams
David Justice CL
162 Jeff Bagwell .20 .50
163 Moises Alou .10 .30
164 Lance Berkman .10 .30
165 Shane Reynolds .10 .30
166 Ken Caminiti .10 .30
167 Craig Biggio .20 .50
168 Jose Lima .10 .30
169 Octavio Dotel .10 .30
170 Richard Hidalgo .10 .30
171 Scott Elarton .10 .30
172 Scott Elarton .20 .50
Mitch Meluskey
Jeff Bagwell
Craig Biggio
Bill Spiers
Julio Lugo
Moises Alou
Richard Hidalgo
Lance Berkman CL
173 Rafael Furcal .10 .30
174 Greg Maddux .50 1.25
175 Quilvio Veras .10 .30
176 Chipper Jones .30 .75
177 Andres Galarraga .10 .30
178 Brian Jordan .10 .30
179 Tom Glavine .20 .50
180 Kevin Millwood .10 .30
181 Javier Lopez .10 .30
182 B.J. Surhoff .10 .30
183 Andruw Jones .20 .50
184 Andy Ashby .10 .30
185 Tom Glavine .20 .50
Javy Lopez
Andres Galarraga
Quilvio Veras
Chipper Jones
Rafael Furcal
Reggie Sanders
Brian Jordan
Andruw Jones CL
186 Richie Sexson .10 .30
187 Jeff D'Amico .10 .30
188 Ron Belliard .10 .30
189 Jeromy Burnitz .10 .30
190 Jimmy Haynes .10 .30
191 Marquis Grissom .10 .30
192 Jose Hernandez .10 .30
193 Geoff Jenkins .10 .30
194 Jamey Wright .10 .30
195 Mark Loretta .10 .30
196 Jeff D'Amico .10 .30
Henry Blanco
Richie Sexson
Ron Belliard
Tyler Houston
Mark Loretta
Jeromy Burnitz
Marquis Grissom
Geoff Jenkins CL
197 Rick Ankiel .10 .30
198 Mark McGwire .75 2.00
199 Fernando Vina .10 .30
200 Edgar Renteria .10 .30
201 Darryl Kile .10 .30
202 Jim Edmonds .10 .30
203 Ray Lankford .10 .30
204 Garrett Stephenson .10 .30
205 Fernando Tatis .10 .30
206 Will Clark .20 .50
207 J.D. Drew .10 .30
208 Darryl Kile .10 .30
Mike Matheny
Mark McGwire
Fernando Vina
Fernando Tatis
Edgar Renteria
Ray Lankford
Jim Edmonds
J.D. Drew CL
209 Mark Grace .20 .50
210 Eric Young .10 .30
211 Sammy Sosa .30 .75
212 Jon Lieber .10 .30
213 Joe Girardi .10 .30
214 Kevin Tapani .10 .30
215 Ricky Gutierrez .10 .30
216 Kerry Wood .10 .30
217 Rondell White .10 .30
218 Damon Buford .10 .30
219 Jon Lieber .10 .30
Joe Girardi
Mark Grace
Eric Young
Willie Greene
Ricky Gutierrez
Sammy Sosa
Damon Bufford
Rondell White CL
220 Luis Gonzalez .10 .30
221 Randy Johnson .30 .75
222 Jay Bell .10 .30
223 Erubiel Durazo .10 .30
224 Matt Williams .10 .30
225 Steve Finley .10 .30
226 Curt Schilling .10 .30
227 Todd Stottlemyre .10 .30
228 Tony Womack .10 .30
229 Brian Anderson .10 .30
230 Randy Johnson .10 .30
Kelly Stinnett
Greg Colbrunn
Jay Bell
Matt Williams
Tony Womack
Luis Gonzalez
Steve Finley
Danny Bautista CL
231 Gary Sheffield .10 .30
232 Adrian Beltre .10 .30
233 Todd Hundley .10 .30
234 Chan Ho Park .10 .30
235 Shawn Green .10 .30
236 Kevin Brown .10 .30
237 Tom Goodwin .10 .30
238 Mark Grudzielanek .10 .30
239 Ismael Valdes .10 .30
240 Eric Karros .10 .30
241 Kevin Brown .10 .30
Todd Hundley
Eric Karros
Mark Grudzielanek
Adrian Beltre
Alex Cora
Gary Sheffield
Shawn Green
Tom Goodwin CL
242 Jose Vidro .10 .30

Card	Low	High
243 Javier Vazquez	.10	.30
244 Orlando Cabrera	.10	.30
245 Peter Bergeron	.10	.30
246 Vladimir Guerrero	.30	.75
247 Dustin Hermanson	.10	.30
248 Tony Armas Jr.	.10	.30
249 Lee Stevens	.10	.30
250 Milton Bradley	.10	.30
251 Carl Pavano	.10	.30
252 Dustin Hermanson	.10	.30
Michael Barrett		
Lee Stevens		
Jose Vidro		
Geoff Jenkins		
Orlando Cabrera		
Vladimir Guerrero		
Peter Bergeron		
Milton Bradley CL		
253 Ellis Burks	.10	.30
254 Robb Nen	.10	.30
255 J.T. Snow	.10	.30
256 Barry Bonds	.75	2.00
257 Shawn Estes	.10	.30
258 Jeff Kent	.10	.30
259 Kirk Rueter	.10	.30
260 Bill Mueller	.10	.30
261 Livan Hernandez	.10	.30
262 Rich Aurilia	.10	.30
263 Livan Hernadez	.10	.30
Bobby Estalella		
J.T. Snow		
Jeff Kent		
Bill Mueller		
Rich Aurilia		
Barry Bonds		
Marvin Benard		
Ellis Burks CL		
264 Ryan Dempster	.10	.30
265 Cliff Floyd	.10	.30
266 Mike Lowell	.10	.30
267 A.J. Burnett	.10	.30
268 Preston Wilson	.10	.30
269 Luis Castillo	.10	.30
270 Henry Rodriguez	.10	.30
271 Antonio Alfonseca	.10	.30
272 Derrek Lee	.20	.50
273 Mark Kotsay	.10	.30
274 Brad Penny	.10	.30
275 Ryan Dempster	.20	.50
Mike Redmond		
Derrek Lee		
Luis Castillo		
Mike Lowell		
Alex Gonzalez		
Cliff Floyd		
Mark Kotsay		
Preston Wilson CL		
276 Mike Piazza	.50	1.25
277 Jay Payton	.10	.30
278 Al Leiter	.10	.30
279 Mike Bordick	.10	.30
280 Armando Benitez	.10	.30
281 Todd Zeile	.10	.30
282 Mike Hampton	.10	.30
283 Edgardo Alfonzo	.10	.30
284 Derek Bell	.10	.30
285 Robin Ventura	.10	.30
286 Mike Hampton	.10	.30
Mike Piazza		
Todd Zeile		
Edgardo Alfonzo		
Robin Ventura		
Mike Bordick		
Derek Bell		
Jay Payton		
Timo Perez CL		
287 Tony Gwynn	.40	1.00
288 Trevor Hoffman	.10	.30
289 Ryan Klesko	.10	.30
290 Phil Nevin	.10	.30
291 Matt Clement	.10	.30
292 Ben Davis	.10	.30
293 Ruben Rivera	.10	.30
294 Bret Boone	.10	.30
295 Adam Eaton	.10	.30
296 Eric Owens	.10	.30
297 Matt Clemente	.10	.30
Ben Davis		
Ryan Klesko		
Bret Boone		
Phil Nevin		
Damian Jackson		
Ruben Rivera		
Eric Owens		
Tony Gwynn CL		
298 Bob Abreu	.10	.30
299 Mike Lieberthal	.10	.30
300 Robert Person	.10	.30
301 Scott Rolen	.20	.50
302 Randy Wolf	.10	.30
303 Bruce Chen	.10	.30
304 Travis Lee	.10	.30
305 Kent Bottenfield	.10	.30
306 Pat Burrell	.10	.30
307 Doug Glanville	.10	.30
308 Robert Person	.10	.30
Mike Lieberthal		
Pat Burrell		
Kevin Jordan		
Scott Rolen		
Alex Arias		
Bob Abreu		
Doug Glanville		
Travis Lee CL		
309 Brian Giles	.10	.30
310 Todd Ritchie	.10	.30
311 Warren Morris	.10	.30
312 John VanderWal	.10	.30
313 Kris Benson	.10	.30
314 Jason Kendall	.10	.30
315 Kevin Young	.10	.30
316 Francisco Cordova	.10	.30
317 Jimmy Anderson	.10	.30
318 Kris Benson	.10	.30
Jason Kendall		
Kevin Young		
Warren Morris		
Mike Benjamin		
Pat Meares		
John VanderWal		
Brian Giles		
Adrian Brown CL		
319 Ken Griffey Jr.	.50	1.25
320 Pokey Reese	.10	.30
321 Chris Stynes	.10	.30
322 Barry Larkin	.20	.50
323 Steve Parris	.10	.30
324 Michael Tucker	.10	.30
325 Dmitri Young	.10	.30
326 Pete Harnisch	.10	.30
327 Danny Graves	.10	.30
328 Aaron Boone	.10	.30
329 Sean Casey	.10	.30
330 Steve Parris	.10	.30
Ed Taubensee		
Sean Casey		
Pokey Reese		
Aaron Boone		
Barry Larkin		
Ken Griffey Jr.		
Dmitri Young		
Michael Tucker CL		
331 Todd Helton	.20	.50
332 Pedro Astacio	.10	.30
333 Larry Walker	.10	.30
334 Ben Petrick	.10	.30
335 Brian Bohanon	.10	.30
336 Juan Pierre	.10	.30
337 Jeffrey Hammonds	.10	.30
338 Jeff Cirillo	.10	.30
339 Todd Hollandsworth	.10	.30
340 Pedro Astacio	.10	.30
Brent Mayne		
Todd Helton		
Todd Walker		
Jeff Cirillo		
Neifi Perez		
Larry Walker		
Jeffrey Hammonds		
Juan Pierre CL		
341 Matt Wise	.20	.50
Keith Luuola		
Derrick Turnbow		
342 Jason Hart	.20	.50
Jose Ortiz		
Mario Encarnacion		
343 Vernon Wells	.20	.50
Pasqual Coco		
Josh Phelps		
344 Travis Harper	.20	.50
Kenny Kelley		
Toby Hall		
345 Danys Baez	.20	.50
Tim Drew		
Martin Vargas		
346 Ichiro Suzuki	6.00	15.00
Ryan Franklin		
Ryan Christianson		
347 Jay Spurgeon	.20	.50
Lesli Brea		
Carlos Casimiro		
348 B.J. Waszgis	.20	.50
Brian Sikorski		
Joaquin Benoit		
349 Sun-Woo Kim	.20	.50
Paxton Crawford		
Steve Lomasney		
350 Kris Wilson	.20	.50
Orber Moreno		
Dee Brown		
351 Mark Johnson	.20	.50
Brandon Inge		
Adam Bernero		
352 Danny Ardoin	.20	.50
Matt Kinney		
Jason Ryan		
353 Rocky Biddle	.40	1.00
Joe Crede		
Josh Paul		
354 Nick Johnson	.20	.50
D'Angelo Jimenez		
Wily Mo Pena		
355 Tony McKnight	.20	.50
Aaron McNeal		
Keith Ginter		
356 Mark DeRosa	.10	.30
Jason Marquis		
Wes Helms UER		
Photos do not match the players ID'd		
357 Allen Levrault	.20	.50
Horacio Estrada		
Santiago Perez		
358 Luis Saturria	.20	.50
Gene Stechschulte		
Britt Reames		
359 Joey Nation	.20	.50
Corey Patterson		
Cole Liniak		
360 Alex Cabrera	.20	.50
Geraldo Guzman		
Nelson Figuero		
361 Hiram Bocachica	.20	.50
Mike Judd		
Luke Prokopec		
362 Tomas de la Rosa	.20	.50
Yohanny Valera		
Talmadge Nunnari		
363 Ryan Vogelsong	.20	.50
Juan Melo		
Chad Zerbe		
364 Jason Grilli	.20	.50
Pablo Ozuna		
Ramon Castro		
365 Timo Perez	.20	.50
Grant Roberts		
Brian Cole		
366 Tom Davey	.20	.50
Xavier Nady		
Dave Maurer		
367 Jimmy Rollins	.20	.50
Mark Brownson		
Reggie Taylor		
368 Alex Hernandez	.20	.50
Adam Hyzdu		
Tike Redman		
369 Brady Clark	.20	.50
John Riedling		
Mike Bell		
370 Giovanni Carrara	.20	.50
Josh Kalinowski		
Craig House		
371 Jim Edmonds SH	.10	.30
372 Edgar Martinez SH	.10	.30
373 Rickey Henderson SH	.30	.75
374 Barry Zito SH	.20	.50
375 Tino Martinez SH	.20	.50
376 J.T. Snow SH	.10	.30
377 Bobby Jones SH	.10	.30
378 Alex Rodriguez SH	.30	.75
379 Mike Hampton SH	.10	.30
380 Roger Clemens SH	.30	.75
381 Jay Payton SH	.10	.30
382 John Olerud SH	.10	.30
383 David Justice SH	.10	.30
384 Mike Hampton SH	.10	.30
385 New York Yankees SH	.30	.75
386 Jose Vizcaino SH	.10	.30
387 Roger Clemens SH	.30	.75
388 Todd Zeile SH	.10	.30
389 Derek Jeter SH	.40	1.00
390 New York Yankees SH	.30	.75
391 Nomar Garciaparra	.30	.75
Darin Erstad		
Manny Ramirez		
Derek Jeter		
Carlos Delgado LL		
392 Todd Helton	.20	.50
Luis Castillo		
Jeffrey Hammonds		
Vladimir Guerrero		
Moises Alou LL		
393 Troy Glaus	.30	.75
Frank Thomas		
Alex Rodriguez		
Jason Giambi		
David Justice LL		
394 Sammy Sosa	.20	.50
Jeff Bagwell		
Barry Bonds		
Vladimir Guerrero		
Richard Hidalgo LL		
395 Edgar Martinez	.10	.30
Mike Sweeney		
Frank Thomas		
Carlos Delgado		
Jason Giambi LL		
396 Todd Helton	.10	.30
Jeff Kent		
Brian Giles		
Sammy Sosa		
Jeff Bagwell LL		
397 Pedro Martinez	.20	.50
Roger Clemens		
Mike Mussina		
Bartolo Colon		
Mike Sirotka LL		
398 Kevin Brown	.10	.30
Randy Johnson		
Jeff D'Amico		
Greg Maddux		
Mike Hampton LL		
399 Tim Hudson	.10	.30
David Wells		
Aaron Sele		
Andy Pettitte		
Pedro Martinez LL		
400 Tom Glavine	.20	.50
Darryl Kile		
Randy Johnson		
Chan Ho Park		
Greg Maddux LL		
S30 K.Griffey Jr. Sample	.50	1.25

2001 Upper Deck Vintage All-Star Tributes

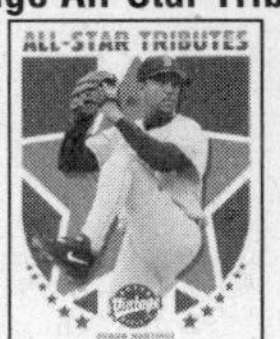

Randomly inserted into packs at one in 23, this 10-card insert features players that make the All-Star team on a consistent basis. Card backs carry an "AS" prefix.

Card	Low	High
COMPLETE SET (10)	20.00	40.00
AS1 Derek Jeter	2.50	6.00
AS2 Mike Piazza	1.50	4.00
AS3 Carlos Delgado	.60	1.50
AS4 Pedro Martinez	.60	1.50
AS5 Vladimir Guerrero	1.00	2.50
AS6 Mark McGwire	2.50	6.00
AS7 Alex Rodriguez	1.50	4.00
AS8 Barry Bonds	2.50	6.00
AS9 Chipper Jones	1.00	2.50
AS10 Sammy Sosa	1.00	2.50

2001 Upper Deck Vintage Glory Days

Randomly inserted into packs at one in 15, this 15-card insert features players that remind us of baseball's glory days of the past. Card backs carry a "G" prefix.

Card	Low	High
COMPLETE SET (15)	15.00	40.00
G1 Jermaine Dye	.60	1.50
G2 Chipper Jones	1.00	2.50
G3 Todd Helton	.60	1.50
G4 Magglio Ordonez	.60	1.50
G5 Tony Gwynn	1.25	3.00
G6 Jim Edmonds	.60	1.50
G7 Rafael Palmeiro	.60	1.50
G8 Barry Bonds	2.50	6.00
G9 Carl Everett	.60	1.50
G10 Mike Piazza	1.50	4.00
G11 Brian Giles	.60	1.50
G12 Tony Batista	.60	1.50
G13 Jeff Bagwell	.60	1.50
G14 Ken Griffey Jr.	1.50	4.00
G15 Troy Glaus	.60	1.50

2001 Upper Deck Vintage Matinee Idols

Randomly inserted into packs at one in four, this 20-card insert features players that are idolized by every young baseball player in America. Card backs carry a "M" prefix.

Card	Low	High
COMPLETE SET (20)	10.00	25.00
M1 Ken Griffey Jr.	.75	2.00
M2 Derek Jeter	1.25	3.00
M3 Barry Bonds	1.25	3.00
M4 Chipper Jones	.50	1.25
M5 Mike Piazza	.75	2.00
M6 Todd Helton	.30	.75
M7 Randy Johnson	.50	1.25
M8 Alex Rodriguez	.75	2.00
M9 Sammy Sosa	.50	1.25
M10 Cal Ripken	1.50	4.00
M11 Nomar Garciaparra	.75	2.00
M12 Carlos Delgado	.30	.75
M13 Jason Giambi	.30	.75
M14 Ivan Rodriguez	.30	.75
M15 Vladimir Guerrero	.50	1.25
M16 Gary Sheffield	.30	.75
M17 Frank Thomas	.50	1.25
M18 Jeff Bagwell	.30	.75
M19 Pedro Martinez	.30	.75
M20 Mark McGwire	1.25	3.00

2001 Upper Deck Vintage Retro Rules

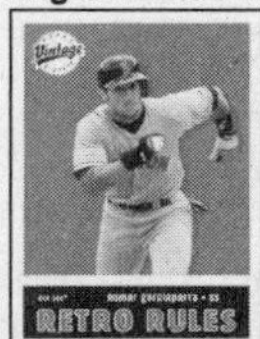

Randomly inserted into packs at one in 15, this 15-card insert features players whose performances remind us of baseball's good ol' days. Card backs carry a "R" prefix.

Card	Low	High
COMPLETE SET (15)	20.00	40.00
R1 Nomar Garciaparra	1.50	4.00
R2 Frank Thomas	1.00	2.50
R3 Jeff Bagwell	.60	1.50
R4 Sammy Sosa	1.00	2.50
R5 Derek Jeter	2.50	6.00
R6 David Wells	.60	1.50
R7 Vladimir Guerrero	1.00	2.50
R8 Jim Thome	.60	1.50
R9 Mark McGwire	2.50	6.00
R10 Todd Helton	.60	1.50
R11 Tony Gwynn	1.25	3.00
R12 Bernie Williams	.60	1.50
R13 Cal Ripken	3.00	8.00
R14 Brian Giles	.60	1.50
R15 Jason Giambi	.60	1.50

2001 Upper Deck Vintage Timeless Teams

Randomly inserted into packs at one in 72 (Bats) and one in 288 (Jerseys), this 39-card insert features swatches of game-used memorabilia from powerhouse clubs of the past. Card backs carry the team initials/player's initials as numbering.

Card	Low	High
CI2JB Johnny Bench Bat	10.00	25.00
CI2JM Joe Morgan Bat	6.00	15.00
CI2KG Ken Griffey Sr. Bat	10.00	25.00
CI2TP Tony Perez Bat	6.00	15.00
BABP Boog Powell Bat	10.00	25.00
BABR B. Robinson Bat	10.00	25.00
BAFR Frank Robinson Bat	10.00	25.00
BAMB Mark Belanger Bat	6.00	15.00
BKDN Don Newcombe Bat	10.00	25.00
BKGH Gil Hodges Bat	10.00	25.00
BKJR Jackie Robinson Bat	40.00	80.00
BKRC Roy Campanella Bat	20.00	50.00
CIDC D. Concepcion Jsy	6.00	15.00
CIJM Joe Morgan Jsy	6.00	15.00
CIKG Ken Griffey Sr. Jsy	10.00	25.00
CITP Tony Perez Jsy	6.00	15.00
LABR Bill Russell Bat	6.00	15.00
LADB Dusty Baker Bat	6.00	15.00
LARC Ron Cey Bat	6.00	15.00
LASG Steve Garvey Bat	6.00	15.00
NYMEK Ed Kranepool Bat	6.00	15.00
NYMNR Nolan Ryan Bat	20.00	50.00
NYMRS Ron Swoboda Bat	6.00	15.00
NYMTA Tommie Agee Bat	6.00	15.00
NYYBD Bill Dickey Bat	10.00	25.00
NYYBR B. Richardson Jsy	6.00	15.00
NYYCK Charlie Keller Bat	6.00	15.00
NYYJD Joe DiMaggio Bat	50.00	100.00
NYYMM M. Mantle Jsy	125.00	200.00
NYYRM Roger Maris Jsy	40.00	80.00
NYYTH T. Henrich Bat	6.00	15.00
OAGT Gene Tenace Bat	6.00	15.00
OAJR Joe Rudi Bat	6.00	15.00
OARJ Reggie Jackson Bat	10.00	25.00
OASB Sal Bando Bat	6.00	15.00
PIAO Al Oliver Bat	6.00	15.00
PIMS M. Sanguillen Bat	6.00	15.00
PIRC R. Clemente Bat	50.00	100.00
PIWS Willie Stargell Bat	10.00	25.00

2001 Upper Deck Vintage Timeless Teams Combos

Randomly inserted into packs, this 11-card insert features swatches of game-used memorabilia from powerhouse clubs of the past. Please note that these cards feature dual players, and are individually serial numbered to 100. Card backs carry the team initials/year as numbering. Unlike the other cards in this set, only twenty-five serial-numbered copies of the "Fantasy Outfield" card featuring DiMaggio, Mantle and Griffey Jr. were created.

Card	Low	High
LA81 Steve Garvey Bat	20.00	50.00
Ron Cey Bat		
Dusty Baker Bat		
Bill Russell Bat		
BAL70 Brooks Robinson Bat	40.00	80.00
Frank Robinson Bat		
Mark Belanger Bat		
Boog Powell Bat		
BKN55 Jackie Robinson Bat	150.00	250.00
Roy Campanella Bat		
Gil Hodges Bat		
Don Newcombe Bat		
CIN75B Johnny Bench Bat	40.00	80.00
Tony Perez Bat		
Joe Morgan Bat		
Ken Griffey Sr. Bat		
CIN75J Dave Concepcion Jsy	20.00	50.00
Tony Perez Jsy		
Ken Griffey Sr. Jsy		
NYM69 Nolan Ryan Bat	75.00	150.00
Ron Swoboda Bat		
Ed Kranepool Bat		
Tommie Agee Bat		
NYY41 Joe DiMaggio Bat	125.00	200.00
Tommy Henrich Bat		
Bill Dickey Bat		
Charlie Keller Bat		
NYY61 Mickey Mantle Jsy	175.00	300.00
Roger Maris Jsy		
Bobby Richardson Jsy		
OAK72 Reggie Jackson Bat	40.00	80.00
Sal Bando Bat		
Gene Tenace Bat		
Joe Rudi Bat		
PIT71 Roberto Clemente Bat	150.00	250.00
Willie Stargell Bat		
Manny Sanguillen Bat		
Al Oliver Bat UER		
Card back says it is a Bill Mazeroski piece		
Manny Sanguillen replaced Mazeroski on card		
FOCJ Joe DiMaggio Jsy		
Mickey Mantle Jsy		
Ken Griffey Jr. Jsy/25		

2002 Upper Deck Vintage

Released In January, 2002 this 300 card set features Upper Deck honoring the popular 1971 Topps design for this set. Subsets include Team Checklists, Vintage Rookies (both seeded throughout the set), League Leaders (271-280) and Postseason Scrapbook (281-300). Please note that card number 274 has a variation. A few cards issued very early in the printing cycle featured the players listed as AL Home Run Leaders and no names listed for the players. It is believed this card was corrected very early in the printing cycle.

Card	Low	High
COMPLETE SET (300)	30.00	60.00
1 Darin Erstad	.15	.40
2 Mo Vaughn	.15	.40
3 Ramon Ortiz	.15	.40
4 Garret Anderson	.15	.40
5 Troy Glaus	.15	.40
6 Troy Percival	.15	.40
7 Tim Salmon	.20	.50
8 Wilmy Caceres	.15	.40
Elpidio Guzman		
9 Ramon Ortiz TC	.15	.40
10 Jason Giambi	.15	.40
11 Mark Mulder	.15	.40
12 Jermaine Dye	.15	.40
13 Miguel Tejada	.15	.40
14 Tim Hudson	.15	.40
15 Eric Chavez	.15	.40
16 Barry Zito	.15	.40
17 Oscar Salazar	.15	.40
Juan Pena		
18 Miguel Tejada	.15	.40
Jason Giambi TC		
19 Carlos Delgado	.15	.40
20 Raul Mondesi	.15	.40
21 Chris Carpenter	.15	.40
22 Jose Cruz Jr.	.15	.40
23 Alex Gonzalez	.15	.40
24 Brad Fullmer	.15	.40
25 Shannon Stewart	.15	.40
26 Brandon Lyon	.15	.40
Vernon Wells		
27 Carlos Delgado TC	.15	.40
28 Greg Vaughn	.15	.40
29 Toby Hall	.15	.40
30 Ben Grieve	.15	.40
31 Aubrey Huff	.15	.40
32 Tanyon Sturtze	.15	.40
33 Brent Abernathy	.15	.40
34 Dewon Brazelton	.15	.40
Delvin James		
35 Greg Vaughn	.15	.40
Fred McGriff TC		
36 Roberto Alomar	.20	.50
37 Juan Gonzalez	.15	.40
38 Bartolo Colon	.15	.40
39 C.C. Sabathia	.15	.40
40 Jim Thome	.20	.50
41 Omar Vizquel	.20	.50
42 Russell Branyan	.15	.40
43 Ryan Drese	.15	.40
Roy Smith		
44 C.C. Sabathia TC	.15	.40
45 Edgar Martinez	.20	.50
46 Bret Boone	.15	.40
47 Freddy Garcia	.15	.40
48 John Olerud	.15	.40
49 Kazuhiro Sasaki	.15	.40
50 Ichiro Suzuki	.60	1.50
51 Mike Cameron	.15	.40
52 Rafael Soriano	.15	.40
Dennis Stark		
53 Jamie Moyer TC	.15	.40
54 Tony Batista	.15	.40
55 Jeff Conine	.15	.40
56 Jason Johnson	.15	.40
57 Jay Gibbons	.15	.40
58 Chris Richard	.15	.40
59 Josh Towers	.15	.40
60 Jerry Hairston Jr.	.15	.40
61 Sean Douglass	.15	.40
Tim Raines Jr.		
62 Cal Ripken TC	.50	1.25
63 Alex Rodriguez	.50	1.25
64 Ruben Sierra	.15	.40
65 Ivan Rodriguez	.20	.50
66 Gabe Kapler	.15	.40
67 Rafael Palmeiro	.20	.50
68 Frank Catalanotto	.15	.40
69 Mark Teixeira	.40	1.00
Carlos Pena		
70 Alex Rodriguez TC	.30	.75
71 Nomar Garciaparra	.50	1.25
72 Pedro Martinez	.20	.50
73 Trot Nixon	.15	.40
74 Dante Bichette	.15	.40
75 Manny Ramirez	.20	.50
76 Carl Everett	.15	.40
77 Hideo Nomo	.30	.75
78 Dernell Stenson	.15	.40
Juan Diaz		
79 Manny Ramirez TC	.20	.50
80 Mike Sweeney	.15	.40
81 Carlos Febles	.15	.40
82 Dee Brown	.15	.40
83 Neifi Perez	.15	.40
84 Mark Quinn	.15	.40
85 Carlos Beltran	.15	.40
86 Joe Randa	.15	.40
87 Ken Harvey	.15	.40
Mike MacDougal		
88 Mike Sweeney TC	.15	.40
89 Dean Palmer	.15	.40
90 Jeff Weaver	.15	.40
91 Jose Lima	.15	.40
92 Tony Clark	.15	.40
93 Damion Easley	.15	.40
94 Bobby Higginson	.15	.40
95 Robert Fick	.15	.40
96 Pedro Santana	.15	.40
Mike Rivera		
97 Juan Encarnacion	.15	.40
Roger Cedeno TC		
98 Doug Mientkiewicz	.15	.40
99 David Ortiz	.20	.50
100 Joe Mays	.15	.40
101 Corey Koskie	.15	.40
102 Eric Milton	.15	.40
103 Cristian Guzman	.15	.40
104 Brad Radke	.15	.40
105 Adam Johnson	.15	.40
Juan Rincon		
106 Corey Koskie TC	.15	.40
107 Frank Thomas	.30	.75
108 Carlos Lee	.15	.40
109 Mark Buehrle	.15	.40
110 Jose Canseco	.20	.50
111 Magglio Ordonez	.15	.40
112 Jon Garland	.15	.40
113 Ray Durham	.15	.40
114 Joe Crede	.15	.40
Josh Fogg		
115 Carlos Lee TC	.15	.40
116 Derek Jeter	.75	2.00
117 Roger Clemens	.60	1.50
118 Alfonso Soriano	.15	.40
119 Paul O'Neill	.20	.50
120 Jorge Posada	.20	.50
121 Bernie Williams	.20	.50
122 Mariano Rivera	.30	.75
123 Tino Martinez	.20	.50
124 Mike Mussina	.20	.50
125 Nick Johnson	.15	.40
Erick Almonte		
126 Jorge Posada	.30	.75

David Justice
Scott Brosius TC
127 Jeff Bagwell .20 .50
128 Wade Miller .15 .40
129 Lance Berkman .15 .40
130 Moises Alou .15 .40
131 Craig Biggio .20 .50
132 Roy Oswalt .15 .40
133 Richard Hidalgo .15 .40
134 Morgan Ensberg .15 .40
Tim Redding
135 Lance Berkman .15 .40
Richard Hidalgo TC
136 Greg Maddux .50 1.25
137 Chipper Jones .30 .75
138 Brian Jordan .15 .40
139 Marcus Giles .15 .40
140 Andruw Jones .20 .50
141 Tom Glavine .20 .50
142 Rafael Furcal .15 .40
143 Wilson Betemit .15 .40
Horacio Ramirez
144 Chipper Jones .20 .50
Brian Jordan TC
145 Jeromy Burnitz .15 .40
146 Ben Sheets .15 .40
147 Geoff Jenkins .15 .40
148 Devon White .15 .40
149 Jimmy Haynes .15 .40
150 Richie Sexson .15 .40
151 Jose Hernandez .15 .40
152 Jose Mieses .15 .40
Alex Sanchez
153 Richie Sexson TC .15 .40
154 Mark McGwire .75 2.00
155 Albert Pujols .60 1.50
156 Matt Morris .15 .40
157 J.D. Drew .15 .40
158 Jim Edmonds .15 .40
159 Bud Smith .15 .40
160 Darryl Kile .15 .40
161 Bill Ortega .15 .40
Luis Saturria
162 Albert Pujols .60 1.50
Mark McGwire TC
163 Sammy Sosa .30 .75
164 Jon Lieber .15 .40
165 Eric Young .15 .40
166 Kerry Wood .15 .40
167 Fred McGriff .20 .50
168 Corey Patterson .15 .40
169 Rondell White .15 .40
170 Juan Cruz .25 .60
Mark Prior
171 Sammy Sosa TC .20 .50
172 Luis Gonzalez .15 .40
173 Randy Johnson .30 .75
174 Matt Williams .15 .40
175 Mark Grace .20 .50
176 Steve Finley .15 .40
177 Reggie Sanders .15 .40
178 Curt Schilling .15 .40
179 Alex Cintron .15 .40
Jack Cust
180 Arizona Diamondbacks TC .30 .75
181 Gary Sheffield .15 .40
182 Paul LoDuca .15 .40
183 Chan Ho Park .15 .40
184 Shawn Green .15 .40
185 Eric Karros .15 .40
186 Adrian Beltre .15 .40
187 Kevin Brown .15 .40
188 Ricardo Rodriguez .15 .40
Carlos Garcia
189 Shawn Green .15 .40
Gary Sheffield TC
190 Vladimir Guerrero .30 .75
191 Javier Vazquez .15 .40
192 Jose Vidro .15 .40
193 Fernando Tatis .15 .40
194 Orlando Cabrera .15 .40
195 Lee Stevens .15 .40
196 Tony Armas Jr. .15 .40
197 Donnie Bridges .15 .40
Henry Mateo
198 Vladimir Guerrero .20 .50
Jose Vidro TC
199 Barry Bonds .75 2.00
200 Rich Aurilia .15 .40
201 Russ Ortiz .15 .40
202 Jeff Kent .15 .40
203 Jason Schmidt .15 .40
204 John Vander Wal .15 .40
205 Robb Nen .15 .40
206 Yorvit Torrealba .15 .40
Kurt Ainsworth
207 Barry Bonds TC .40 1.00
208 Preston Wilson .15 .40
209 Brad Penny .15 .40
210 Cliff Floyd .15 .40
211 Luis Castillo .15 .40
212 Ryan Dempster .15 .40
213 Charles Johnson .15 .40
214 A.J. Burnett .15 .40
215 Abraham Nunez .15 .40
Josh Beckett
216 Cliff Floyd TC .15 .40
217 Mike Piazza .50 1.25
218 Al Leiter .15 .40
219 Edgardo Alfonzo .15 .40
220 Tsuyoshi Shinjo .15 .40
221 Matt Lawton .15 .40
222 Robin Ventura .15 .40
223 Jay Payton .15 .40
224 Alex Escobar .15 .40
Jae Weong Seo
225 Mike Piazza .30 .75
Robin Ventura TC
226 Ryan Klesko .15 .40
227 D'Angelo Jimenez .15 .40
228 Trevor Hoffman .15 .40
229 Phil Nevin .15 .40
230 Mark Kotsay .15 .40
231 Brian Lawrence .15 .40
232 Bubba Trammell .15 .40
233 Jason Middlebrook .15 .40
Xavier Nady
234 Tony Gwynn TC .20 .50
235 Scott Rolen .20 .50
236 Jimmy Rollins .15 .40
237 Mike Lieberthal .15 .40
238 Bobby Abreu .15 .40
239 Brandon Duckworth .15 .40
240 Robert Person .15 .40
241 Pat Burrell .15 .40
242 Nick Punto .15 .40
Carlos Silva
243 Mike Lieberthal TC .15 .40
244 Brian Giles .15 .40
245 Jack Wilson .15 .40
246 Kris Benson .15 .40
247 Jason Kendall .15 .40
248 Aramis Ramirez .15 .40
249 Todd Ritchie .15 .40
250 Rob Mackowiak .15 .40
251 John Grabow .15 .40
Humberto Cota
252 Brian Giles TC .15 .40
253 Ken Griffey Jr. .50 1.25
254 Barry Larkin .20 .50
255 Sean Casey .15 .40
256 Aaron Boone .15 .40
257 Dmitri Young .15 .40
258 Pokey Reese .15 .40
259 Adam Dunn .15 .40
260 David Espinosa .15 .40
Dane Sardinha
261 Ken Griffey TC .30 .75
262 Todd Helton .20 .50
263 Mike Hampton .15 .40
264 Juan Pierre .15 .40
265 Larry Walker .15 .40
266 Juan Uribe .15 .40
267 Jose Ortiz .15 .40
268 Jeff Cirillo .15 .40
269 Jason Jennings .15 .40
Luke Hudson
270 Larry Walker TC .15 .40
271 Ichiro Suzuki .30 .75
Jason Giambi
Roberto Alomar LL
272 Larry Walker .15 .40
Todd Helton
Moises Alou LL
273 Alex Rodriguez .20 .50
Jim Thome
Rafael Palmeiro LL
274 Barry Bonds .40 1.00
Sammy Sosa
Luis Gonzalez LL
274A Barry Bonds 6.00 15.00
Sammy Sosa
Luis Gonzalez LL ERR
Card has AL Home Run Leaders
No player names on cards
275 Mark Mulder .20 .50
Roger Clemens
Jamie Moyer LL
276 Curt Schilling .20 .50
Matt Morris
Randy Johnson LL
277 Freddy Garcia .15 .40
Mike Mussina
Joe Mays LL
278 Randy Johnson .20 .50
Curt Schilling
John Burkett LL
279 Mariano Rivera .20 .50
Kazuhiro Sasaki
Keith Foulke LL
280 Robb Nen .15 .40
Armando Benitez
Trevor Hoffman LL
281 Jason Giambi PS .15 .40
282 Jorge Posada PS .15 .40
283 Jim Thome .20 .50
Juan Gonzalez PS
284 Edgar Martinez PS .15 .40
285 Andruw Jones PS .15 .40
286 Chipper Jones PS .20 .50
287 Matt Williams PS .15 .40
288 Curt Schilling PS .15 .40
289 Derek Jeter PS .40 1.00
290 Mike Mussina PS .15 .40
291 Bret Boone PS .15 .40
292 Alfonso Soriano PS UER .15 .40
Alfonso is spelled incorrectly
293 Randy Johnson PS .20 .50
294 Tom Glavine PS .15 .40
295 Curt Schilling PS .15 .40
296 Randy Johnson PS .20 .50
297 Derek Jeter PS .40 1.00
298 Tino Martinez PS .15 .40
299 Curt Schilling PS .15 .40
300 Luis Gonzalez PS .15 .40

2002 Upper Deck Vintage Aces Game Jersey

Inserted into packs at stated odds of one in 144 hobby and one in 210 retail, these 14 cards feature a mix of active and retired pitchers along with a game jersey swatch. Roger Clemens was produced in shorter quantity than the other players and we have notated that with an SP in our checklist.

AFJ Ferguson Jenkins 6.00 15.00
AGM Greg Maddux 10.00 25.00
AHN Hideo Nomo 15.00 40.00
AJD John Denny 4.00 10.00
AJM Juan Marichal 6.00 15.00
AJS Johnny Sain 10.00 25.00
AMMA Mike Marshall 6.00 15.00
AMMU Mike Mussina 10.00 25.00
AMT Mike Torrez 4.00 10.00
ANR Nolan Ryan 60.00 120.00
APM Pedro Martinez 10.00 25.00
ARC Roger Clemens SP
ARJ Randy Johnson 10.00 25.00
ATH Tim Hudson 6.00 15.00

2002 Upper Deck Vintage Day At The Park

Inserted into packs at stated odds of one in 23, these six cards feature active players in a design dedicated to capturing the nostalgia of Baseball.

COMPLETE SET (6) 8.00 20.00
DP1 Ichiro Suzuki 2.00 5.00
DP2 Derek Jeter 2.50 6.00
DP3 Alex Rodriguez 1.50 4.00
DP4 Mark McGwire 2.50 6.00
DP5 Barry Bonds 2.50 6.00
DP6 Sammy Sosa 1.50 4.00

2002 Upper Deck Vintage Night Gamers

Inserted into packs at stated odds of one in 11, these 12 cards features a salute to primetime games with some of the leading players.

COMPLETE SET (12) 6.00 15.00
NG1 Todd Helton .40 1.00
NG2 Manny Ramirez .40 1.00
NG3 Ivan Rodriguez .40 1.00
NG4 Albert Pujols 1.25 3.00
NG5 Greg Maddux 1.00 2.50
NG6 Carlos Delgado .40 1.00
NG7 Frank Thomas .60 1.50
NG8 Derek Jeter 1.50 4.00
NG9 Troy Glaus .40 1.00
NG10 Jeff Bagwell .40 1.00
NG11 Juan Gonzalez .40 1.00
NG12 Randy Johnson .60 1.50

2002 Upper Deck Vintage Sandlot Stars

Inserted in packs at stated odds of one in 11, these 12 cards feature some of today's stars in a playful salute to the old days where many players were "discovered" while playing sandlot ball.

COMPLETE SET (12) 8.00 20.00
SS1 Ken Griffey Jr. 1.00 2.50
SS2 Derek Jeter 1.50 4.00
SS3 Ichiro Suzuki 1.25 3.00
SS4 Nomar Garciaparra 1.00 2.50
SS5 Sammy Sosa .60 1.50
SS6 Chipper Jones .60 1.50
SS7 Jason Giambi .60 1.50
SS8 Alex Rodriguez 1.00 2.50
SS9 Mark McGwire 1.50 4.00
SS10 Barry Bonds 1.50 4.00
SS11 Mike Piazza 1.00 2.50
SS12 Vladimir Guerrero .60 1.50

2002 Upper Deck Vintage Signature Combos

Randomly inserted in packs, these nine cards feature two signatures of various baseball stars on each card. These cards all have a stated print run of 100 copies.

VSAT Roberto Alomar 50.00 100.00
Jim Thome
VSBB Yogi Berra 75.00 150.00
Johnny Bench
VSBR Sal Bando 20.00 50.00
Joe Rudi
VSEL Dwight Evans 40.00 80.00
Fred Lynn
VSFB Carlton Fisk 60.00 120.00
Johnny Bench
VSGR Ken Griffey Jr. 800.00 1000.00
Alex Rodriguez
VSJM Reggie Jackson 60.00 120.00
Willie McCovey
VSJO Edgar Martinez 40.00 80.00
John Olerud
VSSD Ryne Sandberg 75.00 150.00
Andre Dawson

2002 Upper Deck Vintage Special Collection Game Jersey

Issued in packs at stated odds of one in 144 hobby and one in 210 retail, these 15 cards feature past and present stars along with a memorabilia swatch. A few players were produced in smaller quantities and we have notated those players with an SP in our checklist. These cards honored players from the famed Oakland A's "Mustache Gang" which won three straight world series in the 1970's and various Cubs stars who were still looking for their first World Series appearance since 1945.

SAD Andre Dawson Pants 6.00 15.00
SBC Bert Campaneris Jsy 6.00 15.00
SBW Billy Williams Jsy 6.00 15.00
SCH Catfish Hunter Jsy SP
SFJ Fergie Jenkins Pants SP 6.00 15.00
SJR Joe Rudi Jsy 6.00 15.00
SMG Mark Grace Jsy 8.00 20.00
SMH Mike Hegan Jsy 4.00 10.00
SPL Paul Lindblad Jsy 4.00 10.00
SRF Rollie Fingers Jsy UER 6.00 15.00
Card photo is a reversed negative
SRJ Reggie Jackson Jsy SP 8.00 20.00
SRS Ryne Sandberg Jsy 25.00 50.00
SSAB Sal Bando Jsy 6.00 15.00
SSS Sammy Sosa Jsy 10.00 25.00
SSTB Stan Bahnsen Jsy 4.00 10.00

2002 Upper Deck Vintage Timeless Teams Game Bat Quads

Issued in packs at stated odds of one in 288 hobby and one in 480 retail, these eight cards feature either teammates or position mates along with a bat chip from each of these players career.

B Hank Greenberg 15.00 40.00
Willie McCovey
Frank Thomas
Eddie Murray
OF2 Ken Griffey Jr. 30.00 60.00
Barry Bonds
Rickey Henderson
Tony Gwynn
ATL Tom Glavine 20.00 50.00
Greg Maddux
Chipper Jones
Andruw Jones
CLE Juan Gonzalez 15.00 40.00
Jim Thome
Roberto Alomar
Kenny Lofton
NYY Mariano Rivera 20.00 50.00
Bernie Williams
Paul O'Neill
Jorge Posada
OAK Dave Parker 15.00 40.00
Jose Canseco
Rickey Henderson
Don Baylor
SEA Ichiro Suzuki 40.00 80.00
Edgar Martinez
John Olerud
Bret Boone
OFNY Mickey Mantle
Joe DiMaggio
Reggie Jackson
Babe Ruth SP

2002 Upper Deck Vintage Timeless Teams Game Jersey

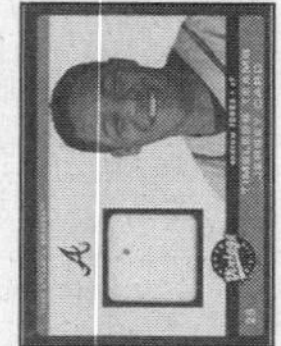

Issued in packs at stated odds of one in 144 hobby and one in 210 retail, these 14 cards feature players from a great team of the past or present along with a jersey swatch. Some players were produced in shorter quantities and we have notated those players with an SP in our checklist.

JAJ Andruw Jones Jsy 8.00 20.00
JCH Catfish Hunter Jsy 8.00 20.00
JCJ Chipper Jones Jsy 8.00 20.00
JDE Dwight Evans Jsy 8.00 20.00
JEMA Edgar Martinez Jsy 8.00 20.00
JEMU Eddie Murray Jsy 10.00 25.00
JFL Fred Lynn Jsy 8.00 20.00
JGM Greg Maddux Jsy SP
JIS Ichiro Suzuki Pants SP
JJB Johnny Bench Jsy 10.00 25.00
JKS Kazuhiro Sasaki Jsy 6.00 15.00
JRF Rollie Fingers Jsy 8.00 20.00
JRJ Reggie Jackson Jsy 8.00 20.00
JWM Willie McCovey Pants 8.00 20.00

2002 Upper Deck Vintage Timeless Teams Game Jersey Combos

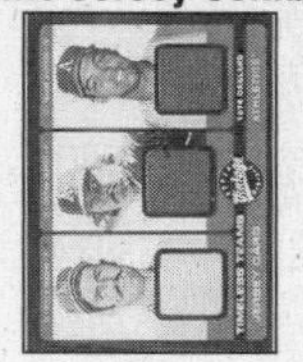

Issued in hobby packs at stated odds one in 288, these four cards feature either teammates or players with something in common along with a jersey swatch of all three players featured. The card featuring the three Hall of Famers was produced in smaller quantites than the other cards and we have notated that with an SP in our checklist.

ATL Greg Maddux 30.00 60.00
Chipper Jones
Andruw Jones
HOF Ty Cobb Pants
Babe Ruth Pants
Honus Wagner Pants SP
NYY Roger Clemens 30.00 60.00
Mariano Rivera
Bernie Williams
OAK Rollie Fingers 20.00 50.00
Catfish Hunter
Reggie Jackson

2003 Upper Deck Vintage

This 280 card set, designed to resemble the 1965 Topps set, was released in January 2003. This set was issued in eight card packs which came 24 packs to a box and 12 boxes to a case. These packs had an SRP of $2. Cards numbered from 223 through 232 feature a pair of prospects from an organiztion. Cards numbered from 233 through 247 are titled Stellar Stat Men. Cards from 248 through 277 were produced in a style reminscent of the Kellogs 3-D cards of the 1970's. Those 3D cards were seeded at a rate of one in 48. In addition, there were other short print cards scattered throughout the set. Those cards which we have noted as either SP, TR1 SP or TR2 SP were inserted at a rate between one in 20 and one in 40. Please note, Eddie Mathews is listed below as card 37 (as was the manufacturer's original intent), but the card is mistakenly numbered as 376. Jason Jennings who was supposed to be card number 178 was mistakenly numbered as 28. In addition, cards number 281 through 341 were later issued at a stated rate of one per Upper Deck 40-man pack.

COMP.SET w/o SP's (200) 20.00 50.00
COMP.UPDATE SET (60) 6.00 15.00
COMMON ACTIVE (1-280) .10 .30
COMMON RETIRED .25 .60
COMMON SP (1-220) 2.00 5.00
COMMON TR1 SP 2.00 5.00
COMMON TR2 SP 2.00 5.00
COMMON CARD (223-232) .75 2.00
COMMON CARD (233-247) .75 2.00
COMMON CARD (248-277) 4.00 10.00
COMMON CARD (281-341) .15 .40
COMMON RC (281-341) .15 .40
281-341 ONE PER 2003 UD 40-MAN PACK
1 Troy Glaus .10 .30
2 Darin Erstad .10 .30
3 Garret Anderson .10 .30
4 Jarrod Washburn .10 .30
5 Nolan Ryan 1.50 4.00
6 Tim Salmon .20 .50
7 Troy Percival .10 .30
8 Alex Ochoa TR1 SP 2.00 5.00
9 Daryle Ward .10 .30
10 Jeff Bagwell .20 .50
11 Roy Oswalt .10 .30
12 Lance Berkman .10 .30
13 Craig Biggio .20 .50
14 Richard Hidalgo .10 .30
15 Tim Hudson .10 .30
16 Eric Chavez .10 .30
17 Barry Zito .10 .30
18 Miguel Tejada .10 .30
19 Mark Mulder .10 .30
20 Rollie Fingers .25 .60
21 Catfish Hunter .40 1.00
22 Jermaine Dye .10 .30
23 Ray Durham TR2 SP 2.00 5.00
24 Carlos Delgado .10 .30
25 Eric Hinske .10 .30
26 Josh Phelps .10 .30
27 Shannon Stewart .10 .30
28 Vernon Wells .10 .30
29 John Smoltz .20 .50
30 Greg Maddux .50 1.25
31 Chipper Jones .30 .75
32 Gary Sheffield .10 .30
33 Andruw Jones .20 .50
34 Tom Glavine .20 .50
35 Rafael Furcal .10 .30
36 Phil Niekro .25 .60
37 Eddie Mathews UER 376 .60 1.50
38 Robin Yount .60 1.50
39 Richie Sexson .10 .30
40 Ben Sheets .10 .30
41 Geoff Jenkins .10 .30
42 Alex Sanchez .10 .30
43 Jason Isringhausen .10 .30
44 Albert Pujols .60 1.50
45 Matt Morris .10 .30
46 J.D. Drew .10 .30
47 Jim Edmonds .10 .30
48 Stan Musial 1.00 2.50
49 Red Schoendienst .25 .60
50 Edgar Renteria .10 .30
51 Mark McGwire SP 5.00 12.00
52 Scott Rolen TR2 SP 3.00 8.00
53 Mark Bellhorn .10 .30
54 Kerry Wood .10 .30
55 Mark Prior .20 .50
56 Moises Alou .10 .30
57 Corey Patterson .10 .30
58 Ernie Banks .60 1.50
59 Hee Seop Choi .10 .30
60 Billy Williams .25 .60
61 Sammy Sosa SP 3.00 8.00
62 Ben Grieve .10 .30
63 Jared Sandberg .10 .30
64 Carl Crawford .10 .30
65 Randy Johnson .30 .75
66 Luis Gonzalez .10 .30
67 Steve Finley .10 .30
68 Junior Spivey .10 .30
69 Erubiel Durazo .10 .30
70 Curt Schilling SP 2.00 5.00
71 Al Lopez .25 .60
72 Pee Wee Reese .40 1.00
73 Eric Gagne .10 .30
74 Shawn Green .10 .30
75 Kevin Brown .10 .30
76 Paul Lo Duca .10 .30
77 Adrian Beltre .10 .30
78 Hideo Nomo .30 .75
79 Eric Karros .10 .30
80 Odalis Perez .10 .30
81 Kazuhisa Ishii SP 2.00 5.00
82 Tommy Lasorda .25 .60
83 Fernando Tatis .10 .30
84 Vladimir Guerrero .30 .75
85 Jose Vidro .10 .30
86 Javier Vazquez .10 .30
87 Brad Wilkerson .10 .30
88 Bartolo Colon TR1 SP 2.00 5.00
89 Monte Irvin .25 .60
90 Robb Nen .10 .30
91 Reggie Sanders .10 .30
92 Jeff Kent .10 .30
93 Rich Aurilia .10 .30
94 Orlando Cepeda .25 .60
95 Juan Marichal .25 .60
96 Willie McCovey .25 .60
97 David Bell .10 .30
98 Barry Bonds SP 5.00 12.00
99 Kenny Lofton TR2 SP 2.00 5.00
100 Jim Thome .20 .50
101 C.C. Sabathia .10 .30
102 Omar Vizquel .20 .50
103 Lou Boudreau .25 .60
104 Larry Doby .25 .60
105 Bob Lemon .25 .60
106 John Olerud .10 .30
107 Edgar Martinez .20 .50
108 Bret Boone .10 .30
109 Freddy Garcia .10 .30
110 Mike Cameron .10 .30
111 Kazuhiro Sasaki .10 .30
112 Ichiro Suzuki SP 4.00 10.00
113 Mike Lowell .10 .30
114 Josh Beckett .10 .30
115 A.J. Burnett .10 .30
116 Juan Pierre .10 .30
117 Derrek Lee .20 .50
118 Luis Castillo .10 .30
119 Juan Encarnacion TR1 SP 2.00 5.00
120 Roberto Alomar .20 .50
121 Edgardo Alfonzo .10 .30
122 Jeromy Burnitz .10 .30
123 Mo Vaughn .10 .30
124 Tom Seaver .40 1.00
125 Al Leiter .10 .30
126 Mike Piazza SP 4.00 10.00
127 Tony Batista .10 .30
128 Geronimo Gil .10 .30
129 Chris Singleton .10 .30
130 Rodrigo Lopez .10 .30
131 Jay Gibbons .10 .30
132 Melvin Mora .10 .30
133 Earl Weaver .25 .60
134 Trevor Hoffman .10 .30
135 Phil Nevin .10 .30
136 Sean Burroughs .10 .30
137 Ryan Klesko .10 .30
138 Mark Kotsay .10 .30
139 Mike Lieberthal .10 .30
140 Bobby Abreu .10 .30
141 Jimmy Rollins .10 .30
142 Pat Burrell .10 .30
143 Vicente Padilla .10 .30
144 Richie Ashburn .40 1.00
145 Jeremy Giambi TR1 SP 2.00 5.00
146 Josh Fogg .10 .30
147 Brian Giles .10 .30
148 Aramis Ramirez .10 .30
149 Jason Kendall .10 .30
150 Ralph Kiner .25 .60
151 Willie Stargell .40 1.00
152 Kevin Mench .10 .30
153 Rafael Palmeiro .20 .50
154 Ivan Rodriguez .20 .50
155 Hank Blalock .10 .30
156 Juan Gonzalez .10 .30
157 Carl Everett .10 .30
158 Alex Rodriguez SP 4.00 10.00

159 Nomar Garciaparra .50 1.25
160 Derek Lowe .10 .30
161 Manny Ramirez .20 .50
162 Shea Hillenbrand .10 .30
163 Bobby Doerr .25 .60
164 Johnny Damon .20 .50
165 Jason Varitek .30 .75
166 Pedro Martinez SP 3.00 8.00
167 Cliff Floyd TR2 SP 2.00 5.00
168 Ken Griffey Jr. .50 1.25
169 Adam Dunn .10 .30
170 Austin Kearns .10 .30
171 Aaron Boone .10 .30
172 Joe Morgan .25 .60
173 Sean Casey .10 .30
174 Todd Walker .10 .30
175 Ryan Dempster TR1 SP 2.00 5.00
176 Shawn Estes TR1 SP 2.00 5.00
177 Gabe Kapler TR1 SP 2.00 5.00
178 Jason Jennings UER .10 .30
Card numbered as 28
179 Todd Helton .20 .50
180 Larry Walker .10 .30
181 Preston Wilson .10 .30
182 Jay Payton TR1 SP 2.00 5.00
183 Mike Sweeney .10 .30
184 Carlos Beltran .10 .30
185 Paul Byrd .10 .30
186 Raul Ibanez .10 .30
187 Rick Ferrell .25 .60
188 Early Wynn .25 .60
189 Dmitri Young .10 .30
190 Jim Bunning .40 1.00
191 George Kell .25 .60
192 Hal Newhouser .25 .60
193 Bobby Higginson .10 .30
194 Carlos Pena TR1 SP 2.00 5.00
195 Sparky Anderson .25 .60
196 Torii Hunter .10 .30
197 Eric Milton .10 .30
198 Corey Koskie .10 .30
199 Jacque Jones .10 .30
200 Harmon Killebrew .60 1.50
201 Doug Mientkiewicz .10 .30
202 Frank Thomas .30 .75
203 Mark Buehrle .10 .30
204 Magglio Ordonez .10 .30
205 Paul Konerko .10 .30
206 Joe Borchard .10 .30
207 Hoyt Wilhelm .25 .60
208 Carlos Lee .10 .30
209 Roger Clemens .60 1.50
210 Nick Johnson .10 .30
211 Jason Giambi .10 .30
212 Alfonso Soriano .10 .30
213 Bernie Williams .20 .50
214 Robin Ventura .10 .30
215 Jorge Posada .20 .50
216 Mike Mussina .20 .50
217 Yogi Berra .60 1.50
218 Phil Rizzuto .40 1.00
219 Mariano Rivera .30 .75
220 Derek Jeter SP 5.00 12.00
221 Jeff Weaver TR1 SP 2.00 5.00
222 Raul Mondesi TR2 SP 2.00 5.00
223 Freddy Sanchez .75 2.00
Josh Hancock
224 Joe Borchard .75 2.00
Miguel Olivo
225 Brandon Phillips .75 2.00
Josh Bard
226 Andy Van Hekken .75 2.00
Andres Torres
227 Jason Lane .75 2.00
Jerome Robertson
228 Chin-Feng Chen .75 2.00
Joe Thurston
229 Endy Chavez .75 2.00
Jamey Carroll
230 Drew Henson .75 2.00
Alex Graman
231 Dewon Brazelton .75 2.00
Lance Carter
232 Jayson Werth .75 2.00
Kevin Cash
233 Randy Johnson 1.25 3.00
Curt Schilling
Barry Zito
234 Pedro Martinez 1.25 3.00
Randy Johnson
Derek Lowe
235 Randy Johnson 1.25 3.00
Curt Schilling
Pedro Martinez
236 John Smoltz 1.25 3.00
Eric Gagne
Mike Williams
237 Randy Johnson 1.25 3.00
Bartolo Colon
A.J. Burnett
238 Alfonso Soriano 1.50 4.00
Ichiro Suzuki
Vladimir Guerrero
239 Alex Rodriguez 1.50 4.00
Jim Thome
Sammy Sosa
240 Barry Bonds 1.50 4.00
Manny Ramirez
Mike Sweeney
241 Alfonso Soriano 1.50 4.00
Alex Rodriguez
Derek Jeter
242 Alex Rodriguez 1.50 4.00
Magglio Ordonez
Miguel Tejada
243 Luis Castillo .75 2.00
Juan Pierre
Dave Roberts
244 Nomar Garciaparra 1.50 4.00
Garrett Anderson
Alfonso Soriano
245 Johnny Damon 1.25 3.00
Jimmy Rollins
Kenny Lofton
246 Barry Bonds 1.50 4.00
Jim Thome
Manny Ramirez
247 Barry Bonds 1.50 4.00
Brian Giles
Manny Ramirez
248 Troy Glaus 3D 4.00 10.00
249 Luis Gonzalez 3D 4.00 10.00
250 Chipper Jones 3D 6.00 15.00
251 Nomar Garciaparra 3D 6.00 15.00
252 Manny Ramirez 3D 6.00 15.00
253 Sammy Sosa 3D 6.00 15.00
254 Frank Thomas 3D 6.00 15.00
255 Magglio Ordonez 3D 4.00 10.00
256 Adam Dunn 3D 4.00 10.00
257 Ken Griffey Jr. 3D 6.00 15.00
258 Jim Thome 3D 6.00 15.00
259 Todd Helton 3D 6.00 15.00
260 Larry Walker 3D 4.00 10.00
261 Lance Berkman 3D 4.00 10.00
262 Jeff Bagwell 3D 6.00 15.00
263 Mike Sweeney 3D 4.00 10.00
264 Shawn Green 3D 4.00 10.00
265 Vladimir Guerrero 3D 6.00 15.00
266 Mike Piazza 3D 6.00 15.00
267 Jason Giambi 3D 4.00 10.00
268 Pat Burrell 3D 4.00 10.00
269 Barry Bonds 3D 10.00 25.00
270 Mark McGwire 3D 10.00 25.00
271 Alex Rodriguez 3D 8.00 20.00
272 Carlos Delgado 3D 4.00 10.00
273 Richie Sexson 3D 4.00 10.00
274 Andruw Jones 3D 6.00 15.00
275 Derek Jeter 3D 10.00 25.00
276 Juan Gonzalez 3D 4.00 10.00
277 Albert Pujols 3D 8.00 20.00
278 Jason Giambi CL .10 .30
279 Sammy Sosa CL .30 .75
280 Ichiro Suzuki CL .30 .75
281 Tom Glavine .25 .60
282 Josh Stewart RC .15 .40
283 Aquilino Lopez RC .15 .40
284 Horacio Ramirez .15 .40
285 Brandon Phillips .15 .40
286 Kirk Saarloos .15 .40
287 Runelvys Hernandez .15 .40
288 Hideki Matsui RC 1.50 4.00
289 Jeremy Bonderman RC 1.00 2.50
290 Russ Ortiz .15 .40
291 Ken Harvey .15 .40
292 Edgardo Alfonzo .15 .40
293 Oscar Villareal RC .15 .40
294 Marlon Byrd .15 .40
295 Josh Bard .15 .40
296 David Cone .15 .40
297 Mike Neu RC .15 .40
298 Cliff Floyd .15 .40
299 Travis Lee .15 .40
300 Jeff Kent .15 .40
301 Ron Calloway .15 .40
302 Bartolo Colon .15 .40
303 Jose Contreras RC .40 1.00
304 Mark Teixeira .25 .60
305 Ivan Rodriguez .25 .60
306 Jim Thome .25 .60
307 Shane Reynolds .15 .40
308 Luis Ayala RC .15 .40
309 Lyle Overbay .15 .40
310 Travis Hafner .15 .40
311 Wilfredo Ledezma RC .15 .40
312 Rocco Baldelli .15 .40
313 Jason Anderson .15 .40
314 Kenny Lofton .15 .40
315 Brandon Larson .15 .40
316 Ty Wigginton .15 .40
317 Fred McGriff .25 .60
318 Antonio Osuna .15 .40
319 Corey Patterson .15 .40
320 Erubiel Durazo .15 .40
321 Mike MacDougal .15 .40
322 Sammy Sosa .40 1.00
323 Mike Hampton .15 .40
324 Ramiro Mendoza .15 .40
325 Kevin Millwood .15 .40
326 Dave Roberts .15 .40
327 Todd Zeile .15 .40
328 Reggie Sanders .15 .40
329 Billy Koch .15 .40
330 Mike Stanton .15 .40
331 Orlando Hernandez .15 .40
332 Tony Clark .15 .40
333 Chris Hammond .15 .40
334 Michael Cuddyer .15 .40
335 Sandy Alomar Jr. .15 .40
336 Jose Cruz Jr. .15 .40
337 Omar Daal .15 .40
338 Robert Fick .15 .40
339 Daryle Ward .15 .40
340 David Bell .15 .40
341 Checklist .15 .40

2003 Upper Deck Vintage All Caps

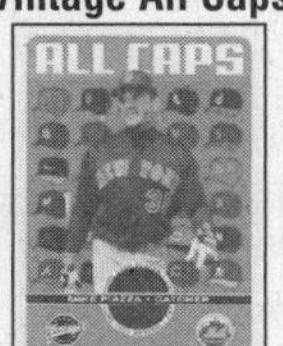

Randomly inserted into packs, these 15 cards feature swatches of game-used caps. Each of these cards have a stated print run of 250 serial numbered sets.

CP Chan Ho Park 6.00 15.00
DE Darin Erstad 6.00 15.00
GM Greg Maddux 15.00 40.00
JB Jeff Bagwell 8.00 20.00
JG Juan Gonzalez 6.00 15.00
KS Kazuhiro Sasaki 6.00 15.00
LB Lance Berkman 6.00 15.00
LG Luis Gonzalez 6.00 15.00
MP Mike Piazza 15.00 40.00
MV Mo Vaughn 6.00 15.00
RF Rafael Furcal 6.00 15.00
RP Rafael Palmeiro 8.00 20.00
RV Robin Ventura 6.00 15.00
TG Tony Gwynn 10.00 25.00
TH Tim Hudson 6.00 15.00

2003 Upper Deck Vintage Capping the Action

Randomly inserted into packs, these 15 cards feature pieces of game-worn caps embedded into the card. Each of these cards were issued to a stated print run of between 91 and 125 copies.

AR Alex Rodriguez/101 15.00 40.00
AS Alfonso Soriano/109 8.00 20.00
CD Carlos Delgado/91 8.00 20.00
HM Hideo Nomo/117 30.00 60.00
IR Ivan Rodriguez/125 10.00 25.00
JG Juan Gonzalez/99 8.00 20.00
KG Ken Griffey Jr./102 15.00 40.00
MM Mike Mussina/109 20.00 50.00
PM Pedro Martinez/125 10.00 25.00
RA Roberto Alomar/101 10.00 25.00
RP Rafael Palmeiro/125 10.00 25.00
SG Shawn Green/125 8.00 20.00
SR Scott Rolen/109 10.00 25.00
SS Sammy Sosa/125 10.00 25.00
TH Todd Helton/99 10.00 25.00

2003 Upper Deck Vintage Cracking the Lumber

Randomly inserted into packs, these two cards feature authentic game-used bat chips of either Ichiro Suzuki or Jason Giambi. These cards were issued to a stated print run of 25 serial numbered sets. Due to market scarcity, no pricing is provided.

GOLD PRINT RUN 5 SERIAL #'d SETS
RANDOM INSERTS IN PACKS
NO PRICING DUE TO SCARCITY
IS Ichiro Suzuki
JG Jason Giambi

2003 Upper Deck Vintage Crowning Glory

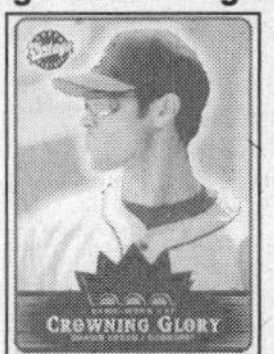

Randomly inserted into packs, these 15 cards feature pieces of game-worn caps attached to the card front. These cards were issued to a stated print run of 25 serial numbered sets. Due to market scarcity, no pricing is provided for these cards.

AJ Andruw Jones
AR Alex Rodriguez
CJ Chipper Jones
GM Greg Maddux
IR Ivan Rodriguez
IS Ichiro Suzuki
JG Jason Giambi
KG Ken Griffey Jr.
LG Luis Gonzalez
MP Mike Piazza
MR Manny Ramirez
PM Pedro Martinez
SC Sean Casey
SG Shawn Green
SS Sammy Sosa

2003 Upper Deck Vintage Dropping the Hammer

Inserted into packs at a stated rate of one in 130, these cards feature game-used bat pieces.

*GOLD: .75X TO 2X BASIC HAMMER
GOLD RANDOM INSERTS IN PACKS
GOLD PRINT RUN 100 SERIAL #'d SETS
AJ Andruw Jones 6.00 15.00
AR Alex Rodriguez 8.00 20.00
BA Bobby Abreu 4.00 10.00
DJ David Justice 4.00 10.00
FM Fred McGriff 6.00 15.00
FT Frank Thomas 6.00 15.00
JG Jason Giambi 4.00 10.00
JT Jim Thome 6.00 15.00
KG Ken Griffey Jr. 8.00 20.00
KL Kenny Lofton 4.00 10.00
LB Lance Berkman 4.00 10.00
LW Larry Walker 4.00 10.00
MO Magglio Ordonez 4.00 10.00
MP Mike Piazza 10.00 25.00
MT Miguel Tejada 4.00 10.00
OV Omar Vizquel 6.00 15.00
PW Preston Wilson 4.00 10.00
RA Roberto Alomar 6.00 15.00
RF Rafael Furcal 4.00 10.00
RP Rafael Palmeiro 6.00 15.00
RV Robin Ventura 4.00 10.00
SG Shawn Green 4.00 10.00
SS Sammy Sosa 6.00 15.00
TA Fernando Tatis 4.00 10.00
TH Todd Helton 6.00 15.00

2003 Upper Deck Vintage Hitmen

Randomly inserted into packs, these four cards feature game-used bat pieces from Upper Deck spokespeople. Each of these cards were issued to a stated print run of 150 serial numbered sets.

GOLD PRINT RUN 10 SERIAL #'d SETS
NO GOLD PRICING DUE TO SCARCITY
IS Ichiro Suzuki 40.00 80.00
JG Jason Giambi 6.00 15.00
KG Ken Griffey Jr. 15.00 40.00
MM Mark McGwire 40.00 80.00

2003 Upper Deck Vintage Hitmen Double Signed

An exchange card with a redemption deadline of January 7th, 2006 was randomly inserted into packs. In return, the collectors that mailed in the exchange card received an amazing card featuring not only game-used bat chips but authentic signatures from Mark McGwire and Sammy Sosa, the two leading HR hitters in the summer of 1998. This card was issued to a stated print run of 75 serial numbered copies.

GOLD PRINT RUN 5 SERIAL #'d CARDS
NO GOLD PRICING DUE TO SCARCITY
MS Mark McGwire 300.00 450.00
Sammy Sosa

2003 Upper Deck Vintage Men with Hats

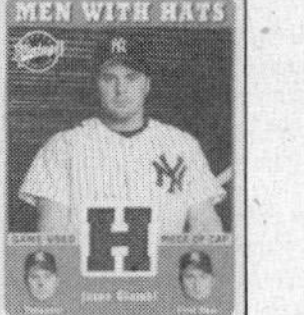

Inserted at a stated rate of one in 285, these 15 cards feature leading players with pieces of game-worn caps embedded in them.

MHAD Adam Dunn 6.00 15.00
MHAJ Andruw Jones 8.00 20.00
MHAR Alex Rodriguez 10.00 25.00
MHBW Bernie Williams 8.00 20.00
MHEC Eric Chavez 6.00 15.00
MHFT Frank Thomas 8.00 20.00
MHTH Tim Hudson 6.00 15.00
MHJD Johnny Damon 8.00 20.00
MHJG Jason Giambi 6.00 15.00
MHJK Jason Kendall 6.00 15.00
MHKL Kenny Lofton 6.00 15.00
MHMT Miguel Tejada 6.00 15.00
MHTH Todd Helton 8.00 20.00
MHTW Todd Walker 6.00 15.00
MHVC Vinny Castilla 6.00 15.00

2003 Upper Deck Vintage Slugfest

Randomly inserted into packs, this 10 card set feature pieces of game-used bat chips honoring some of the leading sluggers in baseball. These cards were issued to a stated print run of 200 serial numbered sets.

*GOLD: .75X TO 2X BASIC SLUGFEST
GOLD PRINT RUN 50 SERIAL #'d SETS
SAJ Andruw Jones 6.00 15.00
SAR Alex Rodriguez 10.00 25.00
SBW Bernie Williams 6.00 15.00
SCD Carlos Delgado 4.00 10.00
SFT Frank Thomas 6.00 15.00
SJT Jim Thome 6.00 15.00
SLW Larry Walker 4.00 10.00
SMP Mike Piazza 12.50 30.00
SRP Rafael Palmeiro 6.00 15.00
SSG Shawn Green 4.00 10.00

2003 Upper Deck Vintage Timeless Teams Bat Quads

Randomly inserted into packs, this is a set featuring four bat pieces from teammates. These cards were issued to a stated print run of 175 serial numbered sets.

BLAR Pat Burrell 10.00 25.00
Mike Lieberthal
Bobby Abreu
Jimmy Rollins
CTDJ Eric Chavez 10.00 25.00
Miguel Tejada
Jermaine Dye
David Justice
DEMR J.D. Drew 15.00 40.00
Jim Edmonds
Tino Martinez
Scott Rolen
DGCL Adam Dunn 15.00 40.00
Ken Griffey Jr.
Sean Casey
Barry Larkin
GNBL Shawn Green 15.00 40.00
Hideo Nomo
Adrian Beltre
Paul Lo Duca
GPMS Jason Giambi 15.00 40.00
Jorge Posada
Raul Mondesi
Alfonso Soriano
GWVS Jason Giambi 15.00 40.00
Bernie Williams
Robin Ventura
Alfonso Soriano
HWPZ Todd Helton 15.00 40.00
Larry Walker
Juan Pierre
Todd Zeile
IMBC Ichiro Suzuki 50.00 100.00
Edgar Martinez
Bret Boone
Mike Cameron
JGSW Randy Johnson 15.00 40.00
Luis Gonzalez
Curt Schilling
Matt Williams
JJSF Chipper Jones 15.00 40.00
Andruw Jones
Gary Sheffield
Rafael Furcal
KNKB Ryan Klesko 10.00 25.00
Phil Nevin
Mark Kotsay
Sean Burroughs
MGLJ Greg Maddux 30.00 60.00
Tom Glavine
Javy Lopez
Chipper Jones
OTLK Magglio Ordonez 15.00 40.00
Frank Thomas
Carlos Lee
Paul Konerko
PVAA Mike Piazza 30.00 60.00
Mo Vaughn
Roberto Alomar
Edgardo Alfonzo
RGRP Alex Rodriguez 20.00 50.00
Juan Gonzalez
Ivan Rodriguez
Rafael Palmeiro
RMHN Manny Ramirez 15.00 40.00
Pedro Martinez
Shea Hillenbrand
Trot Nixon
SMAP Sammy Sosa 15.00 40.00
Fred McGriff
Moises Alou
Corey Patterson

2003 Upper Deck Vintage UD Giants

Inserted as a sealed box-topper, these 42 cards, which were designed in the style of the 1964 Topps Giant set, feature most of the leading players in baseball.

AD Adam Dunn 1.25 3.00
AJ Andruw Jones 1.25 3.00
AP Albert Pujols 3.00 8.00
AR Alex Rodriguez 2.50 6.00
BB Barry Bonds 4.00 10.00
BG Brian Giles 1.25 3.00
BW Bernie Williams 1.25 3.00
CD Carlos Delgado 1.25 3.00
CJ Chipper Jones 1.50 4.00
CS Curt Schilling 1.25 3.00
FT Frank Thomas 1.50 4.00
GM Greg Maddux 2.50 6.00
GO Juan Gonzalez 1.25 3.00
HN Hideo Nomo 1.50 4.00
IR Ivan Rodriguez 1.25 3.00
IS Ichiro Suzuki 3.00 8.00
JB Jeff Bagwell 1.25 3.00
JD J.D. Drew 1.25 3.00
JG Jason Giambi 1.25 3.00
JT Jim Thome 1.25 3.00
KG Ken Griffey Jr. 2.50 6.00
KI Kazuhisa Ishii 1.25 3.00
KW Kerry Wood 1.25 3.00
LB Lance Berkman 1.25 3.00
LG Luis Gonzalez 1.25 3.00
MM Mike Mussina 1.25 3.00
MO Magglio Ordonez 1.25 3.00
MP Mike Piazza 2.50 6.00
MR Manny Ramirez 1.25 3.00
NG Nomar Garciaparra 2.50 6.00
PB Pat Burrell 1.25 3.00
PM Pedro Martinez 1.25 3.00
PR Mark Prior 1.25 3.00
RA Roberto Alomar 1.25 3.00
RC Roger Clemens 3.00 8.00
RJ Randy Johnson 1.50 4.00
RP Rafael Palmeiro 1.25 3.00
SG Shawn Green 1.25 3.00
SR Scott Rolen 1.25 3.00
SS Sammy Sosa 1.50 4.00
TH Todd Helton 1.25 3.00
VG Vladimir Guerrero 1.50 4.00

2004 Upper Deck Vintage

The initial 450-card set was released in January, 2004. The set was issued in eight card packs with an $2.99 SRP which came 24 packs to a box and 12 boxes to a case. Cards numbered from 1 through 300 were printed in heavier quantity than the rest of the set. In that group of 300 the final three cards feature checklists. Cards numbered 301 through 315 are Play Ball Preview Cards while cards numbered 316 through 325 are World Series Highlight Cards. Cards numbered 326 through 335 were players who were traded during the 2003 season. A few leading 2003 rookies were issued as Short Prints between cards 335 and 350. Those cards were issued in two different tiers which we have notated in our checklist. Similar to the 2003 set, many cards (351-440) were issued with lenticular technology and feature 90 of the majors leading sluggers. The set concludes with 10 cards made in the style of the 19th century Old Judge cards. Those cards were issued in "Old Judge Packs" which were issued as one per box "boxtoppers". A 50-card Update set (containing cards 451-500) was issued in factory set format and distributed into one in every 1.5 hobby boxes of 2004 Upper Deck Series 2 baseball in June, 2004.

COMP.SET w/o SP's (300) 30.00 60.00
COMP.UPDATE SET (50) 6.00 15.00
COMMON CARD (1-300) .10 .30
301-315 STATED ODDS 1:5
COMMON CARD (316-325) .75 2.00
316-325 STATED ODDS 1:7
COMMON CARD (326-350) 1.50 4.00
326-350 STATED ODDS 1:5
COMMON CARD (351-440) 4.00 10.00
351-440 STATED ODDS 1:12
COMMON CARD (441-450) 1.50 4.00
COMMON CARD (451-465) .10 .30
COMMON CARD (466-500) .10 .30
ONE UPDATE SET PER 1.5 UD2 HOB.BOXES
1 Albert Pujols .60 1.50
2 Carlos Delgado .10 .30
3 Todd Helton .20 .50
4 Nomar Garciaparra .50 1.25
5 Vladimir Guerrero .30 .75
6 Alfonso Soriano .10 .30
7 Alex Rodriguez .50 1.25
8 Jason Giambi .10 .30
9 Derek Jeter .60 1.50
10 Pedro Martinez .20 .50
11 Ivan Rodriguez .20 .50
12 Mark Prior .20 .50

13 Marquis Grissom .10 .30
14 Barry Zito .10 .30
15 Alex Cintron .10 .30
16 Wade Miller .10 .30
17 Eric Chavez .10 .30
18 Matt Clement .10 .30
19 Orlando Cabrera .10 .30
20 Odalis Perez .10 .30
21 Lance Berkman .10 .30
22 Keith Foulke .10 .30
23 Shawn Green .10 .30
24 Byung-Hyun Kim .10 .30
25 Geoff Jenkins .10 .30
26 Torii Hunter .10 .30
27 Richard Hidalgo .10 .30
28 Edgar Martinez .20 .50
29 Placido Polanco .10 .30
30 Brad Lidge .10 .30
31 Alex Escobar .10 .30
32 Garret Anderson .10 .30
33 Larry Walker .10 .30
34 Ken Griffey Jr. .50 1.25
35 Junior Spivey .10 .30
36 Carlos Beltran .10 .30
37 Bartolo Colon .10 .30
38 Ichiro Suzuki .60 1.50
39 Ramon Ortiz .10 .30
40 Roy Oswalt .10 .30
41 Mike Piazza .50 1.25
42 Benito Santiago .10 .30
43 Mike Mussina .20 .50
44 Jeff Kent .10 .30
45 Curt Schilling .10 .30
46 Adam Dunn .10 .30
47 Mike Sweeney .10 .30
48 Chipper Jones .30 .75
49 Frank Thomas .30 .75
50 Kerry Wood .10 .30
51 Rod Beck .10 .30
52 Brian Giles .10 .30
53 Hank Blalock .10 .30
54 Andruw Jones .20 .50
55 Dmitri Young .10 .30
56 Juan Pierre .10 .30
57 Jacque Jones .10 .30
58 Phil Nevin .10 .30
59 Rocco Baldelli .10 .30
60 Greg Maddux .50 1.25
61 Eric Gagne .10 .30
62 Tim Hudson .10 .30
63 Brian Lawrence .10 .30
64 Sammy Sosa .30 .75
65 Corey Koskie .10 .30
66 Bobby Abreu .10 .30
67 Preston Wilson .10 .30
68 Jay Gibbons .10 .30
69 Dontrelle Willis .20 .50
70 Richie Sexson .10 .30
71 Kevin Millwood .10 .30
72 Randy Johnson .30 .75
73 Jack Cust .10 .30
74 Randy Wolf .10 .30
75 Johan Santana .30 .75
76 Magglio Ordonez .10 .30
77 Sean Casey .10 .30
78 Billy Wagner .10 .30
79 Javier Vazquez .10 .30
80 Jorge Posada .20 .50
81 Jason Schmidt .10 .30
82 Bret Boone .10 .30
83 Jeff Bagwell .20 .50
84 Rickie Weeks .10 .30
85 Troy Percival .10 .30
86 Jose Vidro .10 .30
87 Freddy Garcia .10 .30
88 Manny Ramirez .20 .50
89 John Smoltz .20 .50
90 Moises Alou .10 .30
91 Ugueth Urbina .10 .30
92 Bobby Hill .10 .30
93 Marcus Giles .10 .30
94 Aramis Ramirez .10 .30
95 Brad Wilkerson .10 .30
96 Ray Durham .10 .30
97 David Wells .10 .30
98 Paul Lo Duca .10 .30
99 Danny Graves .10 .30
100 Jason Kendall .10 .30
101 Carlos Lee .10 .30
102 Rafael Furcal .10 .30
103 Mike Lowell .10 .30
104 Kevin Brown .10 .30
105 Vicente Padilla .10 .30
106 Miguel Tejada .10 .30
107 Bernie Williams .20 .50
108 Octavio Dotel .10 .30
109 Steve Finley .10 .30
110 Lyle Overbay .10 .30
111 Delmon Young .20 .50
112 Bo Hart .10 .30
113 Jason Lane .10 .30
114 Matt Roney .10 .30
115 Brian Roberts .10 .30
116 Tom Glavine .20 .50
117 Rich Aurilia .10 .30
118 Adam Kennedy .10 .30
119 Hee Seop Choi .10 .30
120 Trot Nixon .10 .30
121 Gary Sheffield .10 .30
122 Jay Payton .10 .30
123 Brad Penny .10 .30
124 Garrett Atkins .10 .30
125 Aubrey Huff .10 .30
126 Juan Gonzalez .10 .30
127 Jason Jennings .10 .30
128 Luis Gonzalez .10 .30
129 Vinny Castilla .10 .30
130 Esteban Loaiza .10 .30
131 Erubiel Durazo .10 .30
132 Eric Hinske .10 .30
133 Scott Rolen .20 .50
134 Craig Biggio .20 .50
135 Tim Wakefield .10 .30
136 Darin Erstad .10 .30
137 Denny Stark .10 .30
138 Ben Sheets .10 .30
139 Hideo Nomo .30 .75
140 Derrek Lee .20 .50
141 Matt Mantei .10 .30
142 Reggie Sanders .10 .30
143 Jose Guillen .10 .30
144 Joe Mays .10 .30
145 Jimmy Rollins .10 .30
146 Juan Encarnacion .10 .30
147 Joe Crede .10 .30
148 Aaron Guiel .10 .30
149 Mark Mulder .10 .30
150 Travis Lee .10 .30
151 Josh Phelps .10 .30
152 Michael Young .10 .30
153 Paul Konerko .10 .30
154 John Lackey .10 .30
155 Damian Moss .10 .30
156 Javy Lopez .10 .30
157 Joe Borowski .10 .30
158 Jose Cruz Jr. .10 .30
159 Ramon Hernandez .10 .30
160 Raul Ibanez .10 .30
161 Adrian Beltre .10 .30
162 Bobby Higginson .10 .30
163 Jorge Julio .10 .30
164 Miguel Batista .10 .30
165 Luis Castillo .10 .30
166 Aaron Harang .10 .30
167 Ken Harvey .10 .30
168 Rocky Biddle .10 .30
169 Mariano Rivera .30 .75
170 Matt Morris .10 .30
171 Laynce Nix .10 .30
172 Mike Maroth .10 .30
173 Francisco Rodriguez .10 .30
174 Livan Hernandez .10 .30
175 Aaron Heilman .10 .30
176 Nick Johnson .10 .30
177 Woody Williams .10 .30
178 Joe Kennedy .10 .30
179 Jesse Foppert .10 .30
180 Ryan Franklin .10 .30
181 Endy Chavez .10 .30
182 Chin-Hui Tsao .10 .30
183 Todd Walker .10 .30
184 Edgardo Alfonzo .10 .30
185 Edgar Renteria .10 .30
186 Matt LeCroy .10 .30
187 Carl Everett .10 .30
188 Jeff Conine .10 .30
189 Jason Varitek .30 .75
190 Russ Ortiz .10 .30
191 Melvin Mora .10 .30
192 Mark Buehrle .10 .30
193 Bill Mueller .10 .30
194 Miguel Cabrera .20 .50
195 Carlos Zambrano .10 .30
196 Jose Valverde .10 .30
197 Danys Baez .10 .30
198 Mike MacDougal .10 .30
199 Zach Day .10 .30
200 Roy Halladay .10 .30
201 Jerome Williams .10 .30
202 Josh Fogg .10 .30
203 Mark Kotsay .10 .30
204 Pat Burrell .10 .30
205 A.J. Pierzynski .10 .30
206 Fred McGriff .20 .50
207 Brandon Larson .10 .30
208 Robb Quinlan .10 .30
209 David Ortiz .30 .75
210 A.J. Burnett .10 .30
211 John Vander Wal .10 .30
212 Jim Thome .20 .50
213 Matt Kata .10 .30
214 Kip Wells .10 .30
215 Scott Podsednik .10 .30
216 Rickey Henderson .30 .75
217 Travis Hafner .10 .30
218 Tony Batista .10 .30
219 Robert Fick .10 .30
220 Derek Lowe .10 .30
221 Ryan Klesko .10 .30
222 Joe Beimel .10 .30
223 Doug Mientkiewicz .10 .30
224 Angel Berroa .10 .30
225 Adam Eaton .10 .30
226 C.C. Sabathia .10 .30
227 Wilfredo Ledezma .10 .30
228 Jason Johnson .10 .30
229 Ryan Wagner .10 .30
230 Al Leiter .10 .30
231 Joel Pineiro .10 .30
232 Jason Isringhausen .10 .30
233 John Olerud .10 .30
234 Ron Calloway .10 .30
235 Jose Reyes .10 .30
236 J.D. Drew .10 .30
237 Jared Sandberg .10 .30
238 Gil Meche .10 .30
239 Jose Contreras .10 .30
240 Eric Milton .10 .30
241 Jason Phillips .10 .30
242 Luis Ayala .10 .30
243 Bobby Kielty .10 .30
244 Jose Lima .10 .30
245 Brooks Kieschnick .10 .30
246 Xavier Nady .10 .30
247 Danny Haren .10 .30
248 Victor Zambrano .10 .30
249 Kelvim Escobar .10 .30
250 Oliver Perez .10 .30
251 Jamie Moyer .10 .30
252 Orlando Hudson .10 .30
253 Danny Kolb .10 .30
254 Jake Peavy .10 .30
255 Kris Benson .10 .30
256 Roger Clemens .60 1.50
257 Jim Edmonds .10 .30
258 Rafael Palmeiro .20 .50
259 Jae Weong Seo .10 .30
260 Chase Utley .20 .50
261 Rich Harden .10 .30
262 Mark Teixeira .20 .50
263 Johnny Damon .20 .50
264 Luis Matos .10 .30
265 Shigetoshi Hasegawa .10 .30
266 Alfredo Amezaga .10 .30
267 Tim Worrell .10 .30
268 Kazuhisa Ishii .10 .30
269 Miguel Ojeda .10 .30
270 Kazuhiro Sasaki .10 .30
271 Hideki Matsui .50 1.25
272 Troy Glaus .10 .30
273 Michael Tucker .10 .30
274 Lew Ford .10 .30
275 Brian Jordan .10 .30
276 David Eckstein .10 .30
277 Robby Hammock .10 .30
278 Corey Patterson .10 .30
279 Wes Helms .10 .30
280 Jermaine Dye .10 .30
281 Cliff Floyd .10 .30
282 Dustan Mohr .10 .30
283 Kevin Mench .10 .30
284 Ellis Burks .10 .30
285 Jerry Hairston Jr. .10 .30
286 Tim Salmon .20 .50
287 Omar Vizquel .20 .50
288 Andy Pettitte .20 .50
289 Guillermo Mota .10 .30
290 Tino Martinez .20 .50
291 Lance Carter .10 .30
292 Francisco Cordero .10 .30
293 Robb Nen .10 .30
294 Mike Cameron .10 .30
295 Jhonny Peralta .10 .30
296 Braden Looper .10 .30
297 Jarrod Washburn .10 .30
298 Mark Prior CL .20 .50
299 Alfonso Soriano CL .10 .30
300 Rocco Baldelli CL .10 .30
301 Pedro Martinez PBP .75 2.00
302 Mark Prior PBP .75 2.00
303 Barry Zito PBP .75 2.00
304 Roger Clemens PBP 2.00 5.00
305 Randy Johnson PBP 1.00 2.50
306 Roy Halladay PBP .75 2.00
307 Hideo Nomo PBP 1.00 2.50
308 Roy Oswalt PBP .75 2.00
309 Kerry Wood PBP .75 2.00
310 Dontrelle Willis PBP .75 2.00
311 Mark Mulder PBP .75 2.00
312 Brandon Webb PBP .75 2.00
313 Mike Mussina PBP .75 2.00
314 Curt Schilling PBP .75 2.00
315 Tim Hudson PBP .75 2.00
316 Dontrelle Willis WSH .75 2.00
317 Juan Pierre WSH .75 2.00
318 Hideki Matsui WSH 1.50 4.00
319 Andy Pettitte WSH .75 2.00
320 Mike Mussina WSH .75 2.00
321 Roger Clemens WSH 2.00 5.00
322 Alex Gonzalez WSH .75 2.00
323 Brad Penny WSH .75 2.00
324 Ivan Rodriguez WSH .75 2.00
325 Josh Beckett WSH .75 2.00
326 Aaron Boone TR 1.50 4.00
327 Jeff Suppan TR 1.50 4.00
328 Shea Hillenbrand TR 1.50 4.00
329 Jeromy Burnitz TR 1.50 4.00
330 Sidney Ponson TR 1.50 4.00
331 Rondell White TR 1.50 4.00
332 Shannon Stewart TR 1.50 4.00
333 Armando Benitez TR 1.50 4.00
334 Roberto Alomar TR 1.50 4.00
335 Raul Mondesi TR 1.50 4.00
336 Morgan Ensberg SP1 1.50 4.00
337 Milton Bradley SP1 1.50 4.00
338 Brandon Webb SP1 1.50 4.00
339 Marlon Byrd SP1 1.50 4.00
340 Carlos Pena SP1 1.50 4.00
341 Brandon Phillips SP1 1.50 4.00
342 Josh Beckett SP1 1.50 4.00
343 Eric Munson SP1 1.50 4.00
344 Brett Myers SP1 1.50 4.00
345 Austin Kearns SP1 1.50 4.00
346 Jody Gerut SP2 1.50 4.00
347 Vernon Wells SP2 1.50 4.00
348 Jeff Duncan SP2 1.50 4.00
349 Sean Burroughs SP2 1.50 4.00
350 Jeremy Bonderman SP2 1.50 4.00
351 Hideki Matsui 3D 6.00 15.00
352 Jason Giambi 3D 4.00 10.00
353 Alfonso Soriano 3D 4.00 10.00
354 Derek Jeter 3D 8.00 20.00
355 Aaron Boone 3D 4.00 10.00
356 Jorge Posada 3D 4.00 10.00
357 Bernie Williams 3D 4.00 10.00
358 Manny Ramirez 3D 4.00 10.00
359 Nomar Garciaparra 3D 6.00 15.00
360 Johnny Damon 3D 4.00 10.00
361 Jason Varitek 3D 6.00 15.00
362 Carlos Delgado 3D 4.00 10.00
363 Vernon Wells 3D 4.00 10.00
364 Jay Gibbons 3D 4.00 10.00
365 Tony Batista 3D 4.00 10.00
366 Rocco Baldelli 3D 4.00 10.00
367 Aubrey Huff 3D 4.00 10.00
368 Carlos Beltran 3D 4.00 10.00
369 Mike Sweeney 3D 4.00 10.00
370 Magglio Ordonez 3D 4.00 10.00
371 Frank Thomas 3D 6.00 15.00
372 Carlos Lee 3D 4.00 10.00
373 Roberto Alomar 3D 4.00 10.00
374 Jacque Jones 3D 4.00 10.00
375 Torii Hunter 3D 4.00 10.00
376 Milton Bradley 3D 4.00 10.00
377 Travis Hafner 3D 4.00 10.00
378 Jody Gerut 3D 4.00 10.00
379 Dmitri Young 3D 4.00 10.00
380 Carlos Pena 3D 4.00 10.00
381 Ichiro Suzuki 3D 8.00 20.00
382 Bret Boone 3D 4.00 10.00
383 Edgar Martinez 3D 4.00 10.00
384 Eric Chavez 3D 4.00 10.00
385 Miguel Tejada 3D 4.00 10.00
386 Erubiel Durazo 3D 4.00 10.00
387 Jose Guillen 3D 4.00 10.00
388 Garret Anderson 3D 4.00 10.00
389 Troy Glaus 3D 4.00 10.00
390 Alex Rodriguez 3D 6.00 15.00
391 Rafael Palmeiro 3D 4.00 10.00
392 Hank Blalock 3D 4.00 10.00
393 Mark Teixeira 3D 4.00 10.00
394 Gary Sheffield 3D 4.00 10.00
395 Andruw Jones 3D 4.00 10.00
396 Chipper Jones 3D 6.00 15.00
397 Javy Lopez 3D 4.00 10.00
398 Marcus Giles 3D 4.00 10.00
399 Rafael Furcal 3D 4.00 10.00
400 Jim Thome 3D 4.00 10.00
401 Bobby Abreu 3D 4.00 10.00
402 Pat Burrell 3D 4.00 10.00
403 Mike Lowell 3D 4.00 10.00
404 Ivan Rodriguez 3D 4.00 10.00
405 Derrek Lee 3D 4.00 10.00
406 Miguel Cabrera 3D 4.00 10.00
407 Vladimir Guerrero 3D 6.00 15.00
408 Orlando Cabrera 3D 4.00 10.00
409 Jose Vidro 3D 4.00 10.00
410 Mike Piazza 3D 6.00 15.00
411 Cliff Floyd 3D 4.00 10.00
412 Albert Pujols 3D 8.00 20.00
413 Scott Rolen 3D 4.00 10.00
414 Jim Edmonds 3D 4.00 10.00
415 Edgar Renteria 3D 4.00 10.00
416 Lance Berkman 3D 4.00 10.00
417 Jeff Bagwell 3D 4.00 10.00
418 Jeff Kent 3D 4.00 10.00
419 Richard Hidalgo 3D 4.00 10.00
420 Morgan Ensberg 3D 4.00 10.00
421 Sammy Sosa 3D 6.00 15.00
422 Moises Alou 3D 4.00 10.00
423 Ken Griffey Jr. 3D 6.00 15.00
424 Adam Dunn 3D 4.00 10.00
425 Austin Kearns 3D 4.00 10.00
426 Richie Sexson 3D 4.00 10.00
427 Geoff Jenkins 3D 4.00 10.00
428 Brian Giles 3D 4.00 10.00
429 Reggie Sanders 3D 4.00 10.00
430 Rich Aurilia 3D 4.00 10.00
431 Jose Cruz Jr. 3D 4.00 10.00
432 Shawn Green 3D 4.00 10.00
433 Jeromy Burnitz 3D 4.00 10.00
434 Luis Gonzalez 3D 4.00 10.00
435 Todd Helton 3D 4.00 10.00
436 Preston Wilson 3D 4.00 10.00
437 Larry Walker 3D 4.00 10.00
438 Ryan Klesko 3D 4.00 10.00
439 Phil Nevin 3D 4.00 10.00
440 Sean Burroughs 3D 4.00 10.00
441 Sammy Sosa OJ 2.00 5.00
442 Albert Pujols OJ 4.00 10.00
443 Magglio Ordonez OJ 1.50 4.00
444 Vladimir Guerrero OJ 2.00 5.00
445 Todd Helton OJ 1.50 4.00
446 Jason Giambi OJ 1.50 4.00
447 Ichiro Suzuki OJ 4.00 10.00
448 Alex Rodriguez OJ 3.00 8.00
449 Carlos Delgado OJ 1.50 4.00
450 Manny Ramirez OJ 1.50 4.00
451 Alex Rodriguez .75 2.00
452 Javy Lopez .10 .30
453 Alfonso Soriano .10 .30
454 Vladimir Guerrero .30 .75
455 Rafael Palmeiro .20 .50
456 Gary Sheffield .10 .30
457 Curt Schilling .10 .30
458 Miguel Tejada .10 .30
459 Kevin Brown .10 .30
460 Richie Sexson .10 .30
461 Roger Clemens .60 1.50
462 Javier Vazquez .10 .30
463 Bartolo Colon .10 .30
464 Ivan Rodriguez .20 .50
465 Greg Maddux .50 1.25
466 Jamie Brown RC .10 .30
467 Dave Crouthers RC .10 .30
468 Jason Frasor RC .20 .50
469 Greg Dobbs RC .20 .50
470 Jesse Harper RC .20 .50
471 Nick Regilio RC .20 .50
472 Ryan Wing RC .20 .50
473 Akinori Otsuka RC .20 .50
474 Shingo Takatsu RC .40 1.00
475 Kazuo Matsui RC .30 .75
476 Mike Vento RC .30 .75
477 Mike Gosling RC .10 .30
478 Justin Huisman RC .20 .50
479 Justin Hampson RC .20 .50
480 Dennis Sarfate RC .20 .50
481 Ian Snell RC .75 2.00
482 Tim Bausher RC .20 .50
483 Donnie Kelly RC .20 .50
484 Jerome Gamble RC .10 .30
485 Mike Rouse RC .20 .50
486 Merkin Valdez RC .30 .75
487 Lincoln Holdzkom RC .20 .50
488 Justin Leone RC .30 .75
489 Sean Henn RC .20 .50
490 Brandon Medders RC .20 .50
491 Mike Johnston RC .20 .50
492 Tim Bittner RC .20 .50
493 Michael Wuertz RC .30 .75
494 Chad Bentz RC .20 .50
495 Ryan Meaux RC .20 .50
496 Chris Aguila RC .20 .50
497 Jake Woods RC .10 .30
498 Scott Dohmann RC .10 .30
499 Colby Miller RC .10 .30
500 Josh Labandeira RC .20 .50

2004 Upper Deck Vintage Black and White

These cards, pictured in black and white, are a complete parallel of the first 350 cards in the Vintage set.

*B/W 1-300: 3X TO 8X BASIC
1-300 STATED ODDS 1:6
*B/W 301-315: .6X TO 1.5X BASIC
301-315 STATED ODDS 1:24
*B/W 316-325: .6X TO 1.5X BASIC
316-325 STATED ODDS 1:24
*B/W 326-350: .4X TO 1X BASIC
326-350 STATED ODDS 1:20

2004 Upper Deck Vintage Black and White Color Variation

Issued at stated odds of one in 48, these skip-numbered cards are a variation to the black and white parallel cards.

*B/W COLOR: 5X TO 12X BASIC

2004 Upper Deck Vintage Old Judge Subset Blue Back

*OJ BLUE BACK 441-450: .6X TO 1.5X BASIC
STATED ODDS 1:4 OJ HOBBY PACKS
ONE 3-CARD OJ PACK PER HOBBY BOX

2004 Upper Deck Vintage Old Judge Subset Red Back

*OJ RED BACK 441-450: 1X TO 2.5X BASIC OJ
STATED ODDS 1:12 OJ HOBBY PACKS
ONE 3-CARD OJ PACK PER HOBBY BOX

2004 Upper Deck Vintage Old Judge

DISTRIBUTED IN OLD JUDGE HOBBY PACKS
ONE 3-CARD OJ PACK PER HOBBY BOX
*OJ BLUE BACK 11-30: .6X TO 1.5X BASIC
OJ BLUE BACK ODDS 1:4 OJ HOBBY PACKS
*OJ RED BACK 11-30: 1X TO 2.5X BASIC
OJ RED BACK ODDS 1:12 OJ HOBBY PACKS
11 Randy Johnson 2.00 5.00
12 Pedro Martinez 1.50 4.00
13 Mark Prior 1.50 4.00
14 Barry Zito 1.50 4.00
15 Roy Oswalt 1.50 4.00
16 Roy Halladay 1.50 4.00
17 Curt Schilling 1.50 4.00
18 Mike Mussina 1.50 4.00
19 Kevin Brown 1.50 4.00
20 Roger Clemens 4.00 10.00
21 Eric Gagne 1.50 4.00
22 Mariano Rivera 2.00 5.00
23 Mike Piazza 3.00 8.00
24 Jorge Posada 1.50 4.00
25 Jeff Kent 1.50 4.00
26 Alfonso Soriano 1.50 4.00
27 Scott Rolen 1.50 4.00
28 Eric Chavez 1.50 4.00
29 Edgar Renteria 1.50 4.00
30 Hideki Matsui 3.00 8.00

2004 Upper Deck Vintage Stellar Signatures

STATED ODDS 1:600
STATED PRINT RUN 150 SERIAL #'d SETS
EXCHANGE DEADLINE 01/27/07
AR Alex Rodriguez EXCH 60.00 120.00
BZ Barry Zito 15.00 40.00
CY Carl Yastrzemski 30.00 60.00
HM Hideki Matsui 175.00 300.00
IS Ichiro Suzuki 200.00 350.00
MP Mike Piazza 125.00 200.00
TS Tom Seaver 15.00 40.00

2004 Upper Deck Vintage Stellar Stat Men Jerseys

STATED ODDS 1:24
SP PRINT RUNS PROVIDED BY UPPER DECK
SP'S ARE NOT SERIAL-NUMBERED
1 Jose Reyes 3.00 8.00
2 Bo Hart 3.00 8.00
3 Hideki Matsui Pants 10.00 25.00
4 Dontrelle Willis 4.00 10.00
5 Rocco Baldelli 3.00 8.00
6 Ichiro Suzuki 12.50 30.00
7 Mike Lowell 3.00 8.00
8 Derek Jeter 12.50 30.00
9 Ken Griffey Jr. 6.00 15.00
10 Sammy Sosa 4.00 10.00
11 Kerry Wood 3.00 8.00
12 Chipper Jones 4.00 10.00
13 Alfonso Soriano 3.00 8.00
14 Khalil Greene 4.00 10.00
15 Jim Thome 4.00 10.00
16 Rafael Furcal 3.00 8.00
17 Andrew Brown 3.00 8.00
18 Mark Prior 4.00 10.00
19 Barry Zito 3.00 8.00
20 Al Leiter 3.00 8.00
21 Carlos Delgado 3.00 8.00
22 Pedro Martinez 4.00 10.00
23 Alex Rodriguez 6.00 15.00
24 Lance Berkman 3.00 8.00
25 Jeff Bagwell 4.00 10.00
26 Bernie Williams 4.00 10.00
27 Hideo Nomo 6.00 15.00
28 Randy Johnson 4.00 10.00
29 Curt Schilling 3.00 8.00
30 Mike Piazza 6.00 15.00
31 Albert Pujols 6.00 15.00
32 J.DiMaggio Pants SP/300 40.00 80.00
33 Ted Williams Pants SP/300 30.00 60.00
34 M.Mantle Pants SP/300 75.00 150.00
35 Mike Mussina 4.00 10.00
36 Rich Harden 3.00 8.00
37 Roy Oswalt 3.00 8.00
38 Torii Hunter 3.00 8.00
39 Jorge Posada 4.00 10.00
40 Troy Glaus 3.00 8.00
41 Manny Ramirez 4.00 10.00
42 Roy Halladay 3.00 8.00

2004 Upper Deck Vintage Timeless Teams Quad Bats

STATED ODDS 1:400
STATED PRINT RUN 175 SERIAL #'d SETS
CARD NUMBER 3 DOES NOT EXIST
TT1 Alfonso Soriano 60.00 120.00
Derek Jeter
Hideki Matsui
Jason Giambi
TT2 Luis Gonzalez 15.00 40.00
Curt Schilling
Randy Johnson
Steve Finley
TT4 Manny Ramirez 20.00 50.00
Nomar Garciaparra
Trot Nixon
Johnny Damon
TT5 Alex Rodriguez 15.00 40.00
Rafael Palmeiro
Mark Teixeira
Hank Blalock
TT6 Magglio Ordonez 15.00 40.00
Frank Thomas
Roberto Alomar
Carl Everett
TT7 Jacque Jones 10.00 25.00
Torii Hunter
Doug Mientkiewicz
Shannon Stewart
TT8 Jim Edmonds 20.00 50.00
Scott Rolen
J.D. Drew
Albert Pujols
TT9 Ichiro Suzuki 40.00 80.00
John Olerud
Bret Boone
Mike Cameron
TT10 Jeff Kent 15.00 40.00
Jeff Bagwell
Craig Biggio
Lance Berkman
TT11 Troy Glaus 15.00 40.00
Darin Erstad
Garret Anderson

Tim Salmon
TT12 Bernie Williams 40.00 80.00
Jorge Posada
Hideki Matsui
Alfonso Soriano
TT13 Michael Tucker 10.00 25.00
Carlos Beltran
Mike Sweeney
Brent Mayne
TT14 Jim Thome 15.00 40.00
Marlon Byrd
Mike Lieberthal
Bobby Abreu
TT15 Miguel Cabrera 15.00 40.00
Ivan Rodriguez
Juan Encarnacion
Mike Lowell
TT16 Sammy Sosa 15.00 40.00
Corey Patterson
Moises Alou
Kerry Wood
TT17 Jose Cruz Jr. 10.00 25.00
Edgardo Alfonzo
Rich Aurilia
Andres Galarraga
TT18 Alfonso Soriano 60.00 120.00
Derek Jeter
Hideki Matsui
Bernie Williams

2008 Upper Deck X

This set was released on September 16, 2008. The base set consists of 100 cards.

COMPLETE SET (100) 12.50 30.00
COMMON CARD (1-100) .15 .40
COMMON ROOKIE (1-100) .25 .60
PRINTING PLATES RANDOMLY INSERTED
PLATE PRINT RUN 1 SET PER COLOR
BLACK-CYAN-MAGENTA-YELLOW ISSUED
NO PLATE PRICING DUE TO SCARCITY
1 Randy Johnson .40 1.00
2 Conor Jackson .15 .40
3 Brandon Webb .25 .60
4 Justin Upton .40 1.00
5 Dan Haren .15 .40
6 John Smoltz .40 1.00
7 Chipper Jones .50 1.25
8 Mark Teixeira .25 .60
9 Brian Roberts .25 .60
10 Nick Markakis .25 .60
11 Daisuke Matsuzaka .60 1.50
12 David Ortiz .40 1.00
13 Manny Ramirez .40 1.00
14 Jonathan Papelbon .25 .60
15 Josh Beckett .25 .60
16 Clay Buchholz (RC) .60 1.50
17 Carlos Zambrano .15 .40
18 Derrek Lee .25 .60
19 Aramis Ramirez .15 .40
20 Kerry Wood .15 .40
21 Alfonso Soriano .25 .60
22 Kosuke Fukudome RC 1.00 2.50
23 Geovany Soto .40 1.00
24 Paul Konerko .15 .40
25 Jermaine Dye .15 .40
26 Carlos Quentin .15 .40
27 Jim Thome .25 .60
28 Ken Griffey Jr. .60 1.50
29 Adam Dunn .15 .40
30 Brandon Phillips .15 .40
31 Edinson Volquez .15 .40
32 Victor Martinez .15 .40
33 Travis Hafner .15 .40
34 CC Sabathia .15 .40
35 Grady Sizemore .25 .60
36 Garrett Atkins .15 .40
37 Matt Holliday .25 .60
38 Troy Tulowitzki .25 .60
39 Justin Verlander .25 .60
40 Miguel Cabrera .25 .60
41 Gary Sheffield .15 .40
42 Magglio Ordonez .25 .60
43 Hanley Ramirez .40 1.00
44 Jeremy Hermida .15 .40
45 Carlos Lee .15 .40
46 Lance Berkman .25 .60
47 Roy Oswalt .15 .40
48 Alex Gordon .40 1.00
49 Zack Greinke .15 .40
50 Howie Kendrick .15 .40
51 Torii Hunter .15 .40
52 Vladimir Guerrero .40 1.00
53 Matt Kemp .15 .40
54 Russell Martin .15 .40
55 Rafael Furcal .15 .40
56 Ryan Braun .50 1.25
57 Prince Fielder .40 1.00
58 Corey Hart .15 .40
59 Justin Morneau .25 .60
60 Joe Mauer .25 .60
61 Jose Reyes .25 .60
62 David Wright .50 1.25
63 Carlos Beltran .15 .40
64 Johan Santana .25 .60
65 Pedro Martinez .25 .60
66 Ian Kennedy RC .60 1.50
67 Hideki Matsui .40 1.00
68 Alex Rodriguez .60 1.50
69 Chien-Ming Wang .50 1.25
70 Derek Jeter 1.00 2.50
71 Robinson Cano .25 .60
72 Eric Chavez .15 .40
73 Frank Thomas .40 1.00
74 Cole Hamels .40 1.00
75 Jimmy Rollins .25 .60
76 Ryan Howard .50 1.25
77 Chase Utley .40 1.00
78 Nate McLouth .15 .40
79 Jason Bay .15 .40
80 Adrian Gonzalez .25 .60
81 Khalil Greene .25 .60
82 Jake Peavy .25 .60
83 Greg Maddux .50 1.25
84 Trevor Hoffman .15 .40
85 Aaron Rowand .15 .40
86 Tim Lincecum .40 1.00
87 Ichiro Suzuki .60 1.50
88 Felix Hernandez .25 .60
89 Erik Bedard .15 .40
90 Rick Ankiel .15 .40
91 Albert Pujols .75 2.00
92 B.J. Upton .25 .60
93 Carl Crawford .15 .40
94 Evan Longoria RC 2.00 5.00
95 Josh Hamilton .50 1.25
96 Michael Young .15 .40
97 Vernon Wells .15 .40
98 Alex Rios .15 .40
99 Ryan Zimmerman .25 .60
100 Lastings Milledge .15 .40

2008 Upper Deck X Die Cut

*VETERAN 1-100: 1X TO 2.5X BASIC
*ROOKIE 1-100: .75X TO 2X BASIC RC
STATED ODDS ONE PER PACK

2008 Upper Deck X Die Cut Gold

*VETERAN GLD 1-100: 2.5X TO 6X BASIC
*ROOKIE GLD 1-100: 1.5X TO 4X BASIC RC
RANDOM INSERTS IN PACKS

2008 Upper Deck X Memorabilia

RANDOM INSERTS IN PACKS
NO PRICING DUE TO LACK OF SALES

2008 Upper Deck X Sample

DJ Derek Jeter 5.00 12.00

2008 Upper Deck X Signatures

STATED ODDS 1:10 HOBBY
EXCHANGE DEADLINE 8/18/2010
BB Brian Bass 4.00 10.00
BI Brian Bixler 3.00 8.00
CA Jesse Carlson 3.00 8.00
CB Clay Buchholz 10.00 25.00
CC Callix Crabbe 3.00 8.00
CH Chin-Lung Hu
CM Colt Morton 3.00 8.00
CT Clete Thomas 3.00 8.00
DJ Derek Jeter 75.00 150.00
EL Evan Longoria
EM Evan Meek 3.00 8.00
FC Frank Catalanotto 3.00 8.00
IK Ian Kennedy
JA Jonathan Albaladejo 3.00 8.00
JC Johnny Cueto
JK Jeff Keppinger 3.00 8.00
JN Josh Newman 3.00 8.00
JT J.R. Towles 4.00 10.00
KG Ken Griffey Jr. EXCH 40.00 80.00
KH Kevin Hart 3.00 8.00
LH Luke Hochevar
LM Luis Mendoza 3.00 8.00
MB Marlon Byrd 3.00 8.00
RO Ross Ohlendorf 3.00 8.00
RT Rich Thompson 3.00 8.00
SH Steve Holm 3.00 8.00
TI Clay Timpner 3.00 8.00
TR Ramon Troncoso 3.00 8.00
WB Wladimir Balentien

2008 Upper Deck X Xponential

STATED ODDS 1:2 HOBBY
PRINTING PLATES RANDOMLY INSERTED
PLATE PRINT RUN 1 SET PER COLOR
BLACK-CYAN-MAGENTA-YELLOW ISSUED
NO PLATE PRICING DUE TO SCARCITY
AD Adam Dunn .30 .75
AG Adrian Gonzalez .50 1.25
AJ Andruw Jones .30 .75
AL Alex Rodriguez 1.25 3.00
AP Albert Pujols 1.50 4.00
AR Aramis Ramirez .30 .75
AS Alfonso Soriano .50 1.25
BA Bobby Abreu .30 .75
BP Brandon Phillips .30 .75
BR Brian Roberts .50 1.25
BU B.J. Upton .50 1.25
BW Brandon Webb .50 1.25
CB Carlos Beltran .50 1.25
CC Carl Crawford .30 .75
CG Curtis Granderson .30 .75
CH Corey Hart .30 .75
CJ Conor Jackson .30 .75
CL Carlos Lee .30 .75
CP Carlos Pena .75 2.00
CS CC Sabathia .30 .75
CU Chase Utley .75 2.00
CW Chien-Ming Wang 1.00 2.50
CY Chris B. Young .30 .75
CZ Carlos Zambrano .30 .75
DJ Derek Jeter 2.00 5.00
DL Derrek Lee .50 1.25
DM Daisuke Matsuzaka 1.25 3.00
DO David Ortiz .75 2.00
DW Dontrelle Willis .30 .75
EB Erik Bedard .30 .75
FH Felix Hernandez .50 1.25
FT Frank Thomas .75 2.00
GA Garrett Atkins .30 .75
GM Greg Maddux 1.00 2.50
GR Khalil Greene .50 1.25
GS Grady Sizemore .50 1.25
GU Carlos Guillen .30 .75
HE Todd Helton .50 1.25
HM Hideki Matsui .75 2.00
HO Trevor Hoffman .50 1.25
HR Hanley Ramirez .75 2.00
HU Torii Hunter .30 .75
IR Ivan Rodriguez .50 1.25
IS Ichiro Suzuki 1.25 3.00
JA Jason Bay .30 .75
JB Josh Beckett .50 1.25
JC Joba Chamberlain 1.00 2.50
JF Jeff Francoeur .50 1.25
JH Josh Hamilton 1.00 2.50
JI Jimmy Rollins .50 1.25
JK Jeff Kent .30 .75
JM Justin Morneau .50 1.25
JO Chipper Jones 1.00 2.50
JP Jonathan Papelbon .50 1.25
JR Jose Reyes .50 1.25
JS John Smoltz .75 2.00
JT Jim Thome .50 1.25
JV Jason Varitek .75 2.00
KG Ken Griffey Jr. 1.25 3.00
LB Lance Berkman .50 1.25
MA Joe Mauer .50 1.25
MC Miguel Cabrera .50 1.25
MH Matt Holliday .50 1.25
MO Magglio Ordonez .50 1.25
MR Manny Ramirez .75 2.00
MT Mark Teixeira .50 1.25
NM Nick Markakis .50 1.25
NS Nick Swisher .30 .75
PB Pat Burrell .30 .75
PE Jake Peavy .50 1.25
PF Prince Fielder .75 2.00
PK Paul Konerko .30 .75
PM Pedro Martinez .50 1.25
RA Rick Ankiel .30 .75
RB Ryan Braun 1.00 2.50
RH Ryan Howard 1.00 2.50
RI Mariano Rivera .75 2.00
RJ Randy Johnson .75 2.00
RM Russell Martin .30 .75
RO Roy Oswalt .30 .75
RW Rickie Weeks .30 .75
RZ Ryan Zimmerman .50 1.25
SA Johan Santana .50 1.25
SH Gary Sheffield .30 .75
TE Miguel Tejada .30 .75
TH Travis Hafner .30 .75
TT Troy Tulowitzki .50 1.25
VG Vladimir Guerrero .75 2.00
VM Victor Martinez .30 .75
WR David Wright 1.00 2.50

2008 Upper Deck X Xponential 2

*X2: .5X TO 1.2X BASIC XPONENTIAL
APPX.ODDS 1:3 HOBBY
PRINTING PLATES RANDOMLY INSERTED
PLATE PRINT RUN 1 SET PER COLOR
BLACK-CYAN-MAGENTA-YELLOW ISSUED
NO PLATE PRICING DUE TO SCARCITY

2008 Upper Deck X Xponential 3

*X3: .75X TO 2X BASIC XPONENTIAL
STATED ODDS 1:10 HOBBY
PRINTING PLATES RANDOMLY INSERTED
PLATE PRINT RUN 1 SET PER COLOR
BLACK-CYAN-MAGENTA-YELLOW ISSUED
NO PLATE PRICING DUE TO SCARCITY

2008 Upper Deck X Xponential 4

*X4: 1X TO 2.5X BASIC XPONENTIAL
STATED ODDS 1:10 HOBBY
PRINTING PLATES RANDOMLY INSERTED
PLATE PRINT RUN 1 SET PER COLOR
BLACK-CYAN-MAGENTA-YELLOW ISSUED
NO PLATE PRICING DUE TO SCARCITY

2003 Upper Deck Yankees 100th Anniversary

This 30-card set featuring many of the great New York Yankees of the past and present was issued in a special tin with an $19.99 SRP. The first 26 cards featured players from past World Champion teams while cards number 27 through 29 feature key moments from the 2003 season.

COMP.FACT SET (30) 10.00 20.00
DISTRIBUTED IN TIN FACTORY SET
1 Babe Ruth 23 1.25 3.00
2 Tony Lazzeri 27 .15 .40
3 Lou Gehrig 28 1.00 2.50
4 Lou Gehrig 32 1.00 2.50
5 Red Rolfe 36 .15 .40
6 Lou Gehrig 37 1.00 2.50
7 Bill Dickey 38 .25 .60
8 Joe DiMaggio 39 1.00 2.50
9 Charlie Keller 41 .15 .40
10 Frank Crosetti 43 .15 .40
11 Phil Rizzuto 47 .25 .60
12 Joe DiMaggio 49 1.00 2.50
13 Joe DiMaggio 50 1.00 2.50
14 Phil Rizzuto 51 .25 .60
15 Mickey Mantle 52 1.50 4.00
16 Yogi Berra 53 .40 1.00
17 Yogi Berra 56 .40 1.00
18 Mickey Mantle 58 1.50 4.00
19 Whitey Ford 61 .25 .60
20 Mickey Mantle 62 1.50 4.00
21 Thurman Munson 77 .50 1.25
22 Thurman Munson 78 .50 1.25
23 Bernie Williams 96 .25 .60
24 Jorge Posada 98 .25 .60
25 Mariano Rivera 99 .25 .60
26 Derek Jeter 00 1.00 2.50
27 Hideki Matsui RH 03 HR 2.00 5.00
28 Hideki Matsui RH 03 AS 2.00 5.00
29 Roger Clemens 300th Win .75 2.00
30 Yankee Stadium CL .15 .40

2000 Upper Deck Yankees Legends

The 2000 Upper Deck Yankee Legends product was released in October, 2000. The product featured a 90-card base set. Please note that a Mickey Mantle promo was issued to dealers and members of the hobby media prior to the release of the product. Each pack contained five cards, and carried a suggested retail price of $2.99. Also, a selection of A Piece of History 3000 Club Dave Winfield memorabilia cards were randomly seeded into packs. 350 bat cards, 350 jersey cards, 100 hand-numbered combination bat-jersey cards and thirty-one autographed, hand-numbered, combination bat-jersey cards were produced. Pricing for these memorabilia cards can be referenced under 2000 Upper Deck A Piece of History 3000 Club.

COMPLETE SET (90) 10.00 25.00
1 Babe Ruth 1.25 3.00
2 Mickey Mantle 1.50 4.00
3 Lou Gehrig .75 2.00
4 Joe DiMaggio .75 2.00
5 Yogi Berra .40 1.00
6 Don Mattingly 1.00 2.50
7 Reggie Jackson .25 .60
8 Dave Winfield .15 .40
9 Bill Skowron .15 .40
10 Willie Randolph .15 .40
11 Phil Rizzuto .40 1.00
12 Tony Kubek .25 .60
13 Thurman Munson .40 1.00
14 Roger Maris .40 1.00
15 Billy Martin .25 .60
16 Elston Howard .25 .60
17 Graig Nettles .15 .40
18 Whitey Ford .25 .60
19 Earle Combs .15 .40
20 Tony Lazzeri .15 .40
21 Bob Meusel .15 .40
22 Joe Gordon .15 .40
23 Jerry Coleman .15 .40
24 Joe Torre .25 .60
25 Bucky Dent .15 .40
26 Don Larsen .15 .40
27 Bobby Richardson .15 .40
28 Ron Guidry .15 .40
29 Bobby Murcer .15 .40
30 Tommy Henrich .15 .40
31 Hank Bauer .15 .40
32 Joe Pepitone .15 .40
33 Clete Boyer .15 .40
34 Chris Chambliss .15 .40
35 Tommy John .15 .40
36 Goose Gossage .15 .40
37 Red Ruffing .15 .40
38 Charlie Keller .15 .40
39 Billy Gardner .15 .40
40 Hector Lopez .15 .40
41 Cliff Johnson .15 .40
42 Oscar Gamble .15 .40
43 Allie Reynolds .15 .40
44 Mickey Rivers .15 .40
45 Bill Dickey .25 .60
46 Dave Righetti .15 .40
47 Mel Stottlemyre .15 .40
48 Waite Hoyt .15 .40
49 Lefty Gomez .25 .60
50 Wade Boggs .25 .60
51 Billy Martin MN .15 .40
52 Babe Ruth MN .60 1.50
53 Lou Gehrig MN .40 1.00
54 Joe DiMaggio MN .40 1.00
55 Mickey Mantle MN .75 2.00
56 Yogi Berra MN .25 .60
57 Bill Dickey MN .15 .40
58 Roger Maris MN .25 .60
59 Phil Rizzuto MN .25 .60
60 Thurman Munson MN .25 .60
61 Whitey Ford MN .15 .40
62 Don Mattingly MN .50 1.25
63 Elston Howard MN .15 .40
64 Casey Stengel MN .25 .60
65 Reggie Jackson MN .15 .40
66 Babe Ruth '23 TCY .60 1.50
67 Lou Gehrig '27 TCY .40 1.00
68 Tony Lazzeri '28 TCY .15 .40
69 Babe Ruth '32 TCY .60 1.50
70 Lou Gehrig '36 TCY .40 1.00
71 Lefty Gomez '37 TCY .25 .60
72 Bill Dickey '38 TCY .25 .60
73 T.Henrich '39 TCY .15 .40
74 Joe DiMaggio '41 TCY .40 1.00
75 Spud Chandler '43 TCY .15 .40
76 T.Henrich '47 TCY .15 .40
77 Phil Rizzuto '49 TCY .25 .60
78 Whitey Ford '50 TCY .15 .40
79 Yogi Berra '51 TCY .25 .60
80 Casey Stengel '52 TCY .25 .60
81 Billy Martin '53 TCY .15 .40
82 Don Larsen '56 TCY .15 .40
83 Elston Howard '58 TCY .25 .60
84 Roger Maris '61 TCY .25 .60
85 Mickey Mantle '62 TCY .75 2.00
86 R.Jackson '77 TCY .15 .40
87 Bucky Dent '78 TCY .15 .40
88 Wade Boggs '96 TCY .15 .40
89 Joe Torre '98 TCY .25 .60
90 Joe Torre '99 TCY .25 .60
NNO M.Mantle Promo 1.25 3.00

2000 Upper Deck Yankees Legends DiMaggio Memorabilia

Randomly inserted into packs, this three-card set features game-used memorabilia cards from Yankee great Joe DiMaggio. Cards in the set include game-used bat, bat-cut signature, and a bat card numbered to 56. Card backs carry a "YLG" prefix.

BAT-AUTO CUT PRICING NOT AVAILABLE
GOLD BAT PRINT RUN 56 #'d CARDS
YLBJD Joe DiMaggio Bat 60.00 120.00
YLCJD1 Joe DiMaggio Bat-Cut AU/5
YLGJD Joe DiMaggio Gold Bat/56 100.00 200.00

2000 Upper Deck Yankees Legends Golden Years

Randomly inserted into packs at one in 11, this 10-card insert set features players that played for the Yankees during their golden years. Card backs carry a "GY" prefix.

COMPLETE SET (10) 10.00 25.00
GY1 Joe DiMaggio 2.00 5.00
GY2 Phil Rizzuto 1.00 2.50
GY3 Yogi Berra 1.00 2.50
GY4 Billy Martin .60 1.50
GY5 Whitey Ford .60 1.50
GY6 Roger Maris 1.00 2.50
GY7 Mickey Mantle 4.00 10.00
GY8 Elston Howard .60 1.50
GY9 Tommy Henrich .40 1.00
GY10 Joe Gordon .40 1.00

2000 Upper Deck Yankees Legends Legendary Lumber

Randomly inserted into packs at one in 23, this 30-card insert set features game-used bat cards from Yankee greats. Card backs carry a "LL" suffix. Please note that the hologram on the back of these cards is silver and the Bat Chip features a wood "NY".

BDLL Bucky Dent 4.00 10.00
BGLL Billy Gardner 4.00 10.00
BMLL Bobby Murcer 15.00 40.00
BRLL Babe Ruth 100.00 175.00
CBLL Clete Boyer 4.00 10.00
CCLL Chris Chambliss 4.00 10.00
CJLL Cliff Johnson 4.00 10.00
CKLL Charlie Keller 4.00 10.00
DMLL Don Mattingly 15.00 40.00
DWLL Dave Winfield 4.00 10.00
EHLL Elston Howard 4.00 10.00
GNLL Graig Nettles 4.00 10.00
HBLL Hank Bauer 4.00 10.00
HLLL Hector Lopez 4.00 10.00
JCLL Joe Collins 4.00 10.00
JPLL Joe Pepitone 4.00 10.00
MMLL Mickey Mantle 100.00 175.00
MRLL Mickey Rivers 4.00 10.00
MSLL Moose Skowron 4.00 10.00
OGLL Oscar Gamble 4.00 10.00
PBLL Paul Blair 4.00 10.00
RHLL Ralph Houk 4.00 10.00
RJLL Reggie Jackson 6.00 15.00
RMLL Roger Maris 50.00 100.00
THLL Tommy Henrich 4.00 10.00
TJLL Tommy John 4.00 10.00
TKLL Tony Kubek 6.00 15.00
TMLL Thurman Munson 30.00 60.00
WRLL Willie Randolph 4.00 10.00
YBLL Yogi Berra 10.00 25.00

2000 Upper Deck Yankees Legends Legendary Lumber Signature Cut

Randomly inserted into packs, this six card insert features cut-signatures from some of the Yankee's greatest players of all time. Card backs carry a "LC" suffix.

BMLC Billy Martin/1
BRLC Babe Ruth/3
MMLC Mickey Mantle/7
RMLC Roger Maris/9
TMLC Thurman Munson/15

2000 Upper Deck Yankees Legends Legendary Pinstripes

Randomly inserted into packs at one in 144, this 20-card insert set features game-used jersey cards from Yankee greats. Card backs carry a "LP" suffix.

ARLP Allie Reynolds 20.00 50.00
BDLP Bucky Dent 6.00 15.00
BMLP Billy Martin 20.00 50.00
BRLP Bobby Richardson 6.00 15.00
DMLP Don Mattingly 20.00 50.00
DWLP Dave Winfield 6.00 15.00
EHLP Elston Howard 10.00 25.00
GGLP Goose Gossage 6.00 15.00
GMLP Gil McDougald 6.00 15.00
HLLP Hector Lopez 6.00 15.00
JPLP Joe Pepitone 6.00 15.00
LGLP Lou Gehrig Pants 175.00 300.00
MMLP Mickey Mantle 125.00 200.00
PRLP Phil Rizzuto 10.00 25.00
RGLP Ron Guidry 6.00 15.00
RJLP Reggie Jackson 10.00 25.00
RMLP Roger Maris 50.00 100.00
THLP Tommy Henrich 6.00 15.00
TMLP Thurman Munson 30.00 60.00
WFLP Whitey Ford 10.00 25.00

2000 Upper Deck Yankees Legends Legendary Pinstripes Autograph

Randomly inserted into packs at one in 287, this 10-card insert set features autographed game-used jersey cards from Yankee greats. Card backs carry an "A" suffix. Please note that Ron Guidry packed out as exchange card with a deadline to redeem no later than July 18th, 2001.

BDA Bucky Dent	15.00	40.00
DMA Don Mattingly	125.00	200.00
DWA Dave Winfield	20.00	50.00
GGA Goose Gossage	15.00	40.00
GMA Gil McDougald	15.00	40.00
JPA Joe Pepitone	15.00	40.00
PRA Phil Rizzuto	40.00	80.00
RGA Ron Guidry	15.00	40.00
THA Tommy Henrich	15.00	40.00
WFA Whitey Ford	40.00	80.00

2000 Upper Deck Yankees Legends Monument Park

Randomly inserted into packs at one in 23, this six-card insert set features all-time Yankee greats. Card backs carry a "MP" suffix.

COMPLETE SET (6)	10.00	25.00
MP1 Lou Gehrig	2.50	6.00
MP2 Babe Ruth	4.00	10.00
MP3 Mickey Mantle	5.00	12.00
MP4 Joe DiMaggio	2.50	6.00
MP5 Thurman Munson	1.25	3.00
MP6 Elston Howard	.75	2.00

2000 Upper Deck Yankees Legends Murderer's Row

Randomly inserted into packs at one in 11, this 10-card insert set features some of the most dominating New York Yankee players of all-time. Card backs carry a "MR" suffix.

COMPLETE SET (10)	8.00	20.00
MR1 Tony Lazzeri	.40	1.00
MR2 Babe Ruth	3.00	8.00
MR3 Bob Meusel	.40	1.00
MR4 Lou Gehrig	2.00	5.00
MR5 Joe Dugan	.40	1.00
MR6 Bill Dickey	.60	1.50
MR7 Waite Hoyt	.40	1.00
MR8 Red Ruffing	.40	1.00
MR9 Earle Combs	.40	1.00
MR10 Lefty Gomez	.60	1.50

2000 Upper Deck Yankees Legends New Dynasty

Randomly inserted into packs at one in 11, this 10-card insert set features New York greats from the last twenty years. Card backs carry a "ND" suffix.

COMPLETE SET (10)	6.00	15.00
ND1 Reggie Jackson	.60	1.50
ND2 Graig Nettles	.40	1.00
ND3 Don Mattingly	2.50	6.00
ND4 Goose Gossage	.40	1.00
ND5 Dave Winfield	.40	1.00
ND6 Chris Chambliss	.40	1.00
ND7 Thurman Munson	1.00	2.50
ND8 Willie Randolph	.40	1.00
ND9 Ron Guidry	.40	1.00
ND10 Bucky Dent	.40	1.00

2000 Upper Deck Yankees Legends Pride of the Pinstripes

Randomly inserted into packs at one in 23, this six-card insert set features legendary Yankee greats. Card backs carry a "PP" suffix.

COMPLETE SET (6)	10.00	25.00
PP1 Babe Ruth	4.00	10.00
PP2 Mickey Mantle	5.00	12.00
PP3 Joe DiMaggio	2.50	6.00
PP4 Lou Gehrig	2.50	6.00
PP5 Reggie Jackson	.75	2.00
PP6 Yogi Berra	1.25	3.00

2000 Upper Deck Yankees Master Collection

The 2000 Upper Deck Yankees Master Collection was released in early June, 2000. Each box set contains 37 cards. The box set includes a 25-card base set that is individually serial numbered to 500, an 11-card game-used bat set that includes players such a Mickey Mantle, and Babe Ruth, and a one card mystery pack that includes various memorabilia and autographed cards. Card backs carry a "NYY" prefix.

COMPLETE SET (25)	250.00	500.00
NYY1 Babe Ruth 23	20.00	50.00
NYY2 Lou Gehrig 27	12.50	30.00
NYY3 Tony Lazzeri 28	4.00	10.00
NYY4 Babe Ruth 32	20.00	50.00
NYY5 Lou Gehrig 36	12.50	30.00
NYY6 Lefty Gomez 37	4.00	10.00
NYY7 Bill Dickey 38	4.00	10.00
NYY8 Bill Dickey 39	4.00	10.00
NYY9 Tommy Henrich 41	4.00	10.00
NYY10 Spud Chandler 43	4.00	10.00
NYY11 T.Henrich 47	4.00	10.00
NYY12 Phil Rizzuto 49	6.00	15.00
NYY13 Whitey Ford 50	4.00	10.00
NYY14 Yogi Berra 51	6.00	15.00
NYY15 Casey Stengel 52	4.00	10.00
NYY16 Billy Martin 53	4.00	10.00
NYY17 Don Larsen 56	4.00	10.00
NYY18 Elston Howard 58	4.00	10.00
NYY19 Roger Maris 61	6.00	15.00
NYY20 Mickey Mantle 62	25.00	60.00
NYY21 Reggie Jackson 77	4.00	10.00
NYY22 Bucky Dent 78	4.00	10.00
NYY23 Derek Jeter 96	12.50	30.00
NYY24 Derek Jeter 98	12.50	30.00
NYY25 Derek Jeter 99	12.50	30.00

2000 Upper Deck Yankees Master Collection All-Time Yankees Game Bats

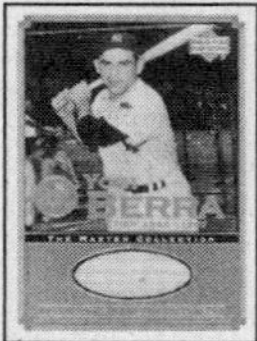

One complete 11-card set of All-Time Yankees Game Bats was inserted into each sealed Yankees Master Collection box. Only 500 sets were produced and each card carries serial-numbering. This 11-card game-used bat card set features some of the greatest New York Yankee players of all time. Card backs carry an "ATY" prefix. Please note that card number eleven of Lou Gehrig is a special commemorative card that does not included a piece of game-used bat.

ATY1 Babe Ruth	75.00	150.00
ATY2 Mickey Mantle	75.00	150.00
ATY3 Reggie Jackson	10.00	25.00
ATY4 Don Mattingly	40.00	80.00
ATY5 Billy Martin	10.00	25.00
ATY6 Graig Nettles	6.00	15.00
ATY7 Derek Jeter	40.00	80.00
ATY8 Yogi Berra	10.00	25.00
ATY9 Thurman Munson	40.00	80.00
ATY10 Whitey Ford	10.00	25.00
ATY11 Lou Gehrig COMM	10.00	25.00

2000 Upper Deck Yankees Master Collection Mystery Pack Inserts

Randomly inserted into each Yankees Master Collection at one per box, this one card mystery pack includes various game-used memorabilia and autographed insert cards.

BM12 Billy Martin Bat-Cut AU/2		
BR13 Babe Ruth Bat-Cut AU/3		
MM17 Mickey Mantle Bat-Cut AU/7		
BRC13 Babe Ruth Cut AU/3		
LGC13 Lou Gehrig Cut AU/3		
TMC12 Thurman Munson Cut AU/2		
DJB Derek Jeter Bat	250.00	400.00
AU/100		
DJJ Derek Jeter Jsy	300.00	500.00
AU/100		
RJB Reggie Jackson	120.00	200.00
Bat AU/100		
WFJ Whitey Ford	75.00	150.00
Bat AU/100		
YBB Yogi Berra	120.00	200.00
Bat AU/80		

2003 Upper Deck Yankees Signature

This 90 card set was released in April, 2003. These cards were issued in three card packs with an $30 SRP. These packs came 10 packs to a box and eight boxes to a case. In an interesting note this set is sequenced by the first name of the player.

COMPLETE SET (90)	40.00	100.00
1 Al Downing	.40	1.00
2 Al Gettel	.40	1.00
3 Art Ditmar	.40	1.00
4 Babe Ruth	6.00	15.00
5 Bill Virdon MG	.40	1.00
6 Billy Martin	1.25	3.00
7 Bob Cerv	.40	1.00
8 Bob Turley	.40	1.00
9 Bobby Cox	.75	2.00
10 Bobby Richardson	.75	2.00
11 Bobby Shantz	.40	1.00
12 Bucky Dent	.75	2.00
13 Bud Metheny XRC	.40	1.00
14 Casey Stengel	1.25	3.00
15 Charlie Hayes	.40	1.00
16 Charlie Silvera	.40	1.00
17 Chris Chambliss	.75	2.00
18 Danny Cater	.40	1.00
19 Dave Kingman	.75	2.00
20 Dave Righetti	.75	2.00
21 Dave Winfield	.75	2.00
22 David Cone	.75	2.00
23 Dick Tidrow	.40	1.00
24 Doc Medich	.40	1.00
25 Dock Ellis	.75	2.00
26 Don Gullett	.75	2.00
27 Don Mattingly	4.00	10.00
28 Dwight Gooden	.75	2.00
29 Eddie Robinson	.40	1.00
30 Felipe Alou	.75	2.00
31 Fred Sanford	.40	1.00
32 Fred Stanley	.40	1.00
33 Gene Michael	.40	1.00
34 Hank Bauer	.75	2.00
35 Hector Lopez	.40	1.00
36 Horace Clarke	.40	1.00
37 Jake Gibbs	.40	1.00
38 Jerry Coleman	.40	1.00
39 Jerry Lumpe	.40	1.00
40 Jim Bouton	.75	2.00
41 Jim Kaat	.75	2.00
42 Jim Mason	.40	1.00
43 Jimmy Key	.75	2.00
44 Joe DiMaggio	4.00	10.00
45 Joe Torre	1.25	3.00
46 John Montefusco	.75	2.00
47 Johnny Blanchard	.40	1.00
48 Johnny Callison	.75	2.00
49 Lew Burdette	.75	2.00
50 Johnny Kucks	.40	1.00
51 Steve Balboni	.40	1.00
52 Ken Singleton ANC	.75	2.00
53 Lee Mazzilli	.75	2.00
54 Lou Gehrig	4.00	10.00
55 Lou Piniella	.75	2.00
56 Luis Tiant	.75	2.00
57 Marius Russo XRC	.40	1.00
58 Mel Stottlemyre	.75	2.00
59 Mickey Mantle	6.00	15.00
60 Mike Pagliarulo	.40	1.00
61 Mike Torrez	.40	1.00
62 Miller Huggins MG	.40	1.00
63 Norm Siebern	.40	1.00
64 Paul O'Neill	1.25	3.00
65 Phil Niekro	.75	2.00
66 Phil Rizzuto	1.25	3.00
67 Ralph Branca	.75	2.00
68 Ralph Houk	.75	2.00
69 Ralph Terry	.75	2.00
70 Randy Gumpert	.40	1.00
71 Roger Maris	2.00	5.00
72 Ron Blomberg	.40	1.00
73 Ron Guidry	.75	2.00
74 Ruben Amaro	.40	1.00
75 Ryne Duren	.40	1.00
76 Sam McDowell	.75	2.00
77 Sparky Lyle	.75	2.00
78 Thurman Munson	2.00	5.00
79 Tom Sturdivant	.40	1.00
80 Tom Tresh	.75	2.00
81 Tommy Byrne	.40	1.00
82 Tommy Henrich	.75	2.00
83 Tommy John	.75	2.00
84 Tony Kubek	1.25	3.00
85 Tony Lazzeri	.75	2.00
86 Virgil Trucks	.40	1.00
87 Wade Boggs	1.25	3.00
88 Whitey Ford	1.25	3.00
89 Willie Randolph	.75	2.00
90 Yogi Berra	2.00	5.00

2003 Upper Deck Yankees Signature Monumental Cuts

Randomly inserted into packs, these 30 combined cards feature autographs of Yankee Legends who have passed on. We have notated the print run next to the player's name in our checklist.

RANDOM INSERTS IN PACKS
B/WN 1-9 COPIES OF EACH CARD
NO PRICING DUE TO SCARCITY

BM Billy Martin/9
BR Babe Ruth/1
CS Casey Stengel/3
JD Joe DiMaggio/4
LG Lou Gehrig/1
MH Miller Huggins/2
MM Mickey Mantle/1
RM Roger Maris/6
TL Tony Lazzeri/2
TM Thurman Munson/1

2003 Upper Deck Yankees Signature Pinstripe Excellence Autographs

Randomly inserted in packs, these cards feature two autographs on each card. These cards were issued to a stated print run of 125 serial numbered sets.

AA Felipe Alou	40.00	80.00
Ruben Amaro		
BA Hank Bauer	40.00	80.00
Felipe Alou		
BP Wade Boggs	50.00	100.00
Mike Pagliarulo		
BR1 Hank Bauer	50.00	100.00
Phil Rizzuto		
BR2 Tommy Byrne	20.00	50.00
Marius Russo		
BT Jim Bouton	40.00	80.00
Ralph Terry		
CK Chris Chambliss	50.00	100.00
Dave Kingman		
DC Bucky Dent	40.00	80.00
Chris Chambliss		
DR Bucky Dent	50.00	100.00
Willie Randolph		
DS Ryne Duren	20.00	50.00
Tom Sturdivant		
FB Whitey Ford	125.00	200.00
Yogi Berra		
GB Jake Gibbs	20.00	50.00
Johnny Blanchard		
GM Ron Guidry	50.00	100.00
John Montefusco		
GR Ron Guidry	50.00	100.00
Willie Randolph		
JK Tommy John	40.00	80.00
Jim Kaat		
LG Sparky Lyle	50.00	100.00
Ron Guidry		
LM Jerry Lumpe	20.00	50.00
Jim Mason		
MC John Montefusco	40.00	80.00
Chris Chambliss		
MK Gene Michael	50.00	100.00
Tony Kubek		
ML Sam McDowell	40.00	80.00
Sparky Lyle		
MR Don Mattingly	125.00	200.00
Dave Righetti		
NT Phil Niekro	50.00	100.00
Luis Tiant		
RB Bobby Richardson	50.00	100.00
Hank Bauer		
RC Bobby Richardson	50.00	100.00
Jerry Coleman		
SC Ken Singleton	40.00	80.00
Jerry Coleman		
ST Tom Sturdivant	20.00	50.00
Bob Turley		
TK Luis Tiant	40.00	80.00
Jim Kaat		
TM Mike Torrez	40.00	80.00
Lee Mazzilli		

2003 Upper Deck Yankees Signature Pride of New York Autographs

Inserted at a stated rate of one per pack, these 88 cards feature authentic autographs from either retired Yankee players or people associated with the franchise in some way. This set included the first certified autographed sports cards for figures such as Yankee GM Brian Cashman, actors John Goodman and Jason Alexander. Bud Metheny was supposed to sign cards for this product but he passed away before he could sign his cards. In addition, Brian Cashman, Dwight Gooden, John Goodman and Yogi Berra did not return their cards in time for inclusion in this product and we have notated that information with an EXCH in our checklist. Collectors could redeem those cards until March 27th, 2006. David Cone signed some of his cards in time for inclusion and others were available as an exchange card. Upper Deck announced some shorter print runs and we have put that stated print run information next to the player's name in our checklist.

AD Al Downing	4.00	10.00
AG Al Gettel	4.00	10.00
BD Brian Doyle	4.00	10.00
BL Johnny Blanchard	4.00	10.00
BR Bobby Richardson	6.00	15.00
BS Bobby Shantz	4.00	10.00
BT Bob Turley	4.00	10.00
BV Bill Virdon	4.00	10.00
CA1 Johnny Callison	4.00	10.00
CA2 Brian Cashman SP/100	250.00	400.00
CC Chris Chambliss	4.00	10.00
CE Bob Cerv	4.00	10.00
CH Charlie Hayes	4.00	10.00
CO David Cone	10.00	25.00
CS Charlie Silvera	4.00	10.00
CX Bobby Cox	4.00	10.00
DC Danny Cater	4.00	10.00
DE Bucky Dent	4.00	10.00
DG Don Gullett	4.00	10.00
DI Art Ditmar	4.00	10.00
DK Dave Kingman	4.00	10.00
DM Doc Medich	4.00	10.00
DR Dave Righetti	4.00	10.00
DT Dick Tidrow	4.00	10.00
DW Dave Winfield SP/350	30.00	60.00
DZ Don Zimmer	30.00	60.00
EL Dock Ellis	4.00	10.00
ER Eddie Robinson	4.00	10.00
FA Felipe Alou	4.00	10.00
FS Fred Sanford	4.00	10.00
GM Gene Michael	4.00	10.00
GO Dwight Gooden	4.00	10.00
HB Hank Bauer	4.00	10.00
HC Horace Clarke	4.00	10.00
HL Hector Lopez	4.00	10.00
HR Hal Reniff	4.00	10.00
JA Jason Alexander SP/50	600.00	800.00
JB Jim Bouton	4.00	10.00
JC Jerry Coleman	4.00	10.00
JG1 Jake Gibbs	4.00	10.00
JG2 John Goodman SP/100	250.00	400.00
JK Jim Kaat	4.00	10.00
JL Jerry Lumpe	4.00	10.00
JM Jim Mason	4.00	10.00
JT Joe Torre	15.00	40.00
JW Jim Wynn	4.00	10.00
KE Jimmy Key	6.00	15.00
KS Ken Singleton	4.00	10.00
KU Johnny Kucks	4.00	10.00
LB Lew Burdette	6.00	15.00
LM Lee Mazzilli	4.00	10.00
LP Lou Piniella SP/542	6.00	15.00
LT Luis Tiant	4.00	10.00
MA Don Mattingly	50.00	100.00
MO John Montefusco	4.00	10.00
MP Mike Pagliarulo	4.00	10.00
MR Marius Russo	4.00	10.00
MS Mel Stottlemyre	4.00	10.00
MT Mike Torrez	4.00	10.00
NS Norm Siebern	4.00	10.00
PN Phil Niekro	10.00	25.00
PO Paul O'Neill SP/500	10.00	25.00
PR Phil Rizzuto	20.00	50.00
RA Ruben Amaro	4.00	10.00
RB1 Ron Blomberg	4.00	10.00
RB2 Ralph Branca	4.00	10.00
RD Ryne Duren	4.00	10.00
RG1 Ron Guidry	6.00	15.00
RG2 Randy Gumpert	4.00	10.00
RH Ralph Houk	4.00	10.00
RT Ralph Terry	4.00	10.00
SB Steve Balboni	4.00	10.00
SL Sparky Lyle	4.00	10.00
SM Sam McDowell	4.00	10.00
ST Fred Stanley	4.00	10.00
TB Tommy Byrne	4.00	10.00
TC Tom Carroll	4.00	10.00
TH Tommy Henrich	15.00	40.00
TJ Tommy John	4.00	10.00
TK Tony Kubek	15.00	40.00
TS Tom Sturdivant	4.00	10.00
TT Tom Tresh	6.00	15.00
VT Virgil Trucks	4.00	10.00
WB Wade Boggs	20.00	50.00
WF Whitey Ford	40.00	80.00
WR Willie Randolph SP/283	6.00	15.00
YB Yogi Berra	40.00	80.00

2003 Upper Deck Yankees Signature Yankees Forever Autographs

Randomly inserted in packs, these cards feature three Yankee players (usually with something in common) all signing the same card. These cards were issued to a stated print run of 50 serial numbered sets. The following cards were issued as exchange cards of which could be redeemed until March 27th, 2006: GCK, GRJ, MTT, TCO, WMG, WPC.

RANDOM INSERTS IN PACKS
STATED PRINT RUN 50 SERIAL #'d SETS

ALB Felipe Alou	90.00	150.00
Hector Lopez		
Hank Bauer		
AOM Felipe Alou	125.00	200.00
Paul O'Neill		
Lee Mazzilli		
BSB Yogi Berra	150.00	250.00
Bobby Shantz		
Hank Bauer		
DFB Al Downing	175.00	300.00
Whitey Ford		
Yogi Berra		
DRC Bucky Dent	90.00	150.00
Willie Randolph		
Chris Chambliss		
EMG Dock Ellis	90.00	150.00
Doc Medich		
Don Gullett		
FKB Whitey Ford	125.00	200.00
Johnny Kucks		
Jim Bouton		
GCK Dwight Gooden	125.00	200.00
David Cone		
Jimmy Key		
GRJ Ron Guidry	125.00	200.00
Dave Righetti		
Tommy John		
HMC Ralph Houk	90.00	150.00
Gene Michael		
Bobby Cox		
HRB Tommy Henrich	125.00	200.00
Phil Rizzuto		
Ralph Branca		
JKL Tommy John	90.00	150.00
Jim Kaat		
Sparky Lyle		
KCC Dave Kingman	90.00	150.00
Chris Chambliss		
Danny Cater		
KGT Jim Kaat	90.00	150.00
Don Gullet		
Mike Torrez		
KJB Jim Kaat	90.00	150.00
Tommy John		
Jim Bouton		
MTT John Montefusco	90.00	150.00
Mike Torrez		
Dick Tidrow		
OBK Paul O'Neill	125.00	200.00
Wade Boggs		
Jimmy Key		
PTV Lou Piniella	125.00	200.00
Joe Torre		
Bill Virdon		
RBC Phil Rizzuto	175.00	300.00
Yogi Berra		
Jerry Coleman		
RKD Phil Rizzuto	125.00	200.00
Tony Kubek		
Bucky Dent		
RRC Bobby Richardson	125.00	200.00
Willie Randolph		
Jerry Coleman		
RSB Marius Russo	90.00	150.00
Tom Sturdivant		
Tommy Byrne		
SSB Fred Stanley	90.00	150.00
Charlie Silvera		
Johnny Blanchard		
STE Mel Stottlemyre	90.00	150.00
Luis Tiant		
Dock Ellis		
TCO Joe Torre	125.00	200.00
David Cone		
Paul O'Neill		
TLN Luis Tiant	90.00	150.00
Sparky Lyle		
Phil Niekro		
TMT Luis Tiant	90.00	150.00
Sam McDowell		
Ralph Terry		
WHM Dave Winfield	125.00	200.00
Tommy Henrich		
Lee Mazzilli		
WMG Dave Winfield	175.00	300.00
Don Mattingly		
Ron Guidry		
WPC Dave Winfield	90.00	150.00
Lou Piniella		
Chris Chambliss		

1995 Zenith

The complete 1995 Zenith set consists of 150 standard-size cards. The cards are made of thick stock and are borderless. Included is a subset of 50 Rookies (111-150). The regular issued cards are in alphabetical order by first name. Rookie Cards in this set include Bobby Higginson and Hideo Nomo.

COMPLETE SET (150)	15.00	40.00
1 Albert Belle	.15	.40
2 Alex Fernandez	.07	.20
3 Andy Benes	.07	.20
4 Barry Larkin	.25	.60
5 Barry Bonds	1.00	2.50
6 Ben McDonald	.07	.20
7 Bernard Gilkey	.07	.20

8 Billy Ashley .07 .20
9 Bobby Bonilla .15 .40
10 Bret Saberhagen .15 .40
11 Brian Jordan .15 .40
12 Cal Ripken 1.25 3.00
13 Carlos Baerga .07 .20
14 Carlos Delgado .15 .40
15 Cecil Fielder .15 .40
16 Chili Davis .15 .40
17 Chuck Knoblauch .15 .40
18 Craig Biggio .25 .60
19 Danny Tartabull .07 .20
20 Dante Bichette .15 .40
21 Darren Daulton .15 .40
22 David Justice .15 .40
23 Dave Winfield .15 .40
24 David Cone .15 .40
25 Dean Palmer .15 .40
26 Deion Sanders .25 .60
27 Dennis Eckersley .15 .40
28 Derek Bell .07 .20
29 Don Mattingly 1.00 2.50
30 Edgar Martinez .25 .60
31 Eric Karros .15 .40
32 James Mouton .07 .20
33 Frank Thomas .40 1.00
34 Fred McGriff .25 .60
35 Gary Sheffield .15 .40
36 Gary Gaetti .15 .40
37 Greg Maddux .60 1.50
38 Gregg Jefferies .07 .20
39 Ivan Rodriguez .25 .60
40 Kenny Rogers .15 .40
41 J.T. Snow .15 .40
42 Hal Morris .07 .20
43 E.Murray 3000th Hit .25 .60
44 Javier Lopez .15 .40
45 Jay Bell .15 .40
46 Jeff Conine .15 .40
47 Jeff Bagwell .25 .60
48 Hideo Nomo Japanese 1.00 2.50
49 Jeff Kent .15 .40
50 Jeff King .07 .20
51 Jim Thome .25 .60
52 Jimmy Key .15 .40
53 Joe Carter .15 .40
54 John Valentin .07 .20
55 John Olerud .15 .40
56 Jose Canseco .25 .60
57 Jose Rijo .07 .20
58 Jose Offerman .07 .20
59 Juan Gonzalez .15 .40
60 Ken Caminiti .15 .40
61 Ken Griffey Jr. .60 1.50
62 Kenny Lofton .15 .40
63 Kevin Appier .15 .40
64 Kevin Seitzer .07 .20
65 Kirby Puckett .40 1.00
66 Kirk Gibson .15 .40
67 Larry Walker .15 .40
68 Lenny Dykstra .15 .40
69 Manny Ramirez .25 .60
70 Mark Grace .25 .60
71 Mark McGwire 1.00 2.50
72 Marquis Grissom .15 .40
73 Jim Edmonds .25 .60
74 Matt Williams .15 .40
75 Mike Mussina .25 .60
76 Mike Piazza .60 1.50
77 Mo Vaughn .15 .40
78 Moises Alou .15 .40
79 Ozzie Smith .60 1.50
80 Paul O'Neill .25 .60
81 Paul Molitor .15 .40
82 Rafael Palmeiro .25 .60
83 Randy Johnson .40 1.00
84 Raul Mondesi .15 .40
85 Ray Lankford .15 .40
86 Reggie Sanders .15 .40
87 Rickey Henderson .40 1.00
88 Rico Brogna .07 .20
89 Roberto Alomar .25 .60
90 Robin Ventura .15 .40
91 Roger Clemens .75 2.00
92 Ron Gant .15 .40
93 Rondell White .15 .40
94 Royce Clayton .07 .20
95 Ruben Sierra .15 .40
96 Rusty Greer .15 .40
97 Ryan Klesko .15 .40
98 Sammy Sosa .40 1.00
99 Shawon Dunston .07 .20
100 Steve Ontiveros .07 .20
101 Tim Naehring .07 .20
102 Tim Salmon .25 .60
103 Tino Martinez .25 .60
104 Tony Gwynn .50 1.25
105 Travis Fryman .15 .40
106 Vinny Castilla .15 .40
107 Wade Boggs .25 .60
108 Wally Joyner .15 .40
109 Wil Cordero .07 .20
110 Will Clark .25 .60
111 Chipper Jones .40 1.00
112 Armando Benitez .07 .20
113 Curtis Goodwin .07 .20
114 Gabe White .07 .20
115 Vaughn Eshelman .07 .20
116 Marty Cordova .07 .20
117 Dustin Hermanson .07 .20
118 Rich Becker .07 .20
119 Ray Durham .15 .40
120 Shane Andrews .07 .20
121 Scott Ruffcorn .07 .20
122 Mark Grudzielanek RC .25 .60
123 James Baldwin .07 .20
124 Carlos Perez RC .15 .40
125 Julian Tavarez .07 .20
126 Joe Vitiello .07 .20
127 Jason Bates .07 .20
128 Edgardo Alfonzo .07 .20
129 Juan Acevedo RC .07 .20
130 Bill Pulsipher .07 .20
131 Bob Higginson RC .25 .60
132 Russ Davis .07 .20
133 Charles Johnson .15 .40
134 Derek Jeter 1.00 2.50
135 Orlando Miller .07 .20
136 LaTroy Hawkins .07 .20
137 Brian L.Hunter .07 .20
138 Roberto Petagine .07 .20
139 Midre Cummings .07 .20
140 Garret Anderson .15 .40
141 Ugueth Urbina .07 .20
142 Antonio Osuna .07 .20
143 Michael Tucker .07 .20
144 Benji Gil .07 .20
145 Jon Nunnally .07 .20
146 Alex Rodriguez 1.00 2.50
147 Todd Hollandsworth .07 .20
148 Alex Gonzalez .07 .20
149 Hideo Nomo RC 1.00 2.50
150 Shawn Green .15 .40

1995 Zenith All-Star Salute

This 18-card set was randomly inserted in packs at a rate of one in six. The set commemorates many of the memorable plays of the 1995 All-Star Game played in Arlington, TX. The fronts have an action photo set out against the background of the game giving it a 3D look. The cards are numbered "X of 18."

COMPLETE SET (18) 15.00 40.00
1 Cal Ripken 2.50 6.00
2 Frank Thomas .75 2.00
3 Mike Piazza 1.25 3.00
4 Kirby Puckett .75 2.00
5 Manny Ramirez .50 1.25
6 Tony Gwynn 1.00 2.50
7 Hideo Nomo 1.50 4.00
8 Matt Williams .30 .75
9 Randy Johnson .75 2.00
10 Raul Mondesi .30 .75
11 Albert Belle .30 .75
12 Ivan Rodriguez .50 1.25
13 Barry Bonds 2.00 5.00
14 Carlos Baerga .15 .40
15 Ken Griffey Jr. 1.25 3.00
16 Jeff Conine .30 .75
17 Frank Thomas .75 2.00
18 Cal Ripken 2.50 6.00
Barry Bonds

1995 Zenith Rookie Roll Call

This 18-card, Dufex-designed standard-size set was randomly inserted in packs at a rate of one in 24. The set is comprised of 18 top rookies from 1995. Player information of previous accomplishments is also on the back and the cards are numbered "X of 18."

COMPLETE SET (18) 15.00 40.00
1 Alex Rodriguez 4.00 10.00
2 Derek Jeter 4.00 10.00
3 Chipper Jones 1.50 4.00
4 Shawn Green .60 1.50
5 Todd Hollandsworth .40 1.00
6 Bill Pulsipher .40 1.00
7 Hideo Nomo 2.00 5.00
8 Ray Durham .60 1.50
9 Curtis Goodwin .40 1.00
10 Brian L.Hunter .40 1.00
11 Julian Tavarez .40 1.00
12 Marty Cordova UER .40 1.00
Kevin Maas pictured
13 Michael Tucker .40 1.00
14 Edgardo Alfonzo .40 1.00
15 LaTroy Hawkins .40 1.00
16 Carlos Perez .60 1.50
17 Charles Johnson .60 1.50
18 Benji Gil .40 1.00

1995 Zenith Z-Team

This 18-card standard-size set was randomly inserted in packs at a rate of one in 72. The set is comprised of the best players in baseball and is done in 3-D Dufex. The backs also have player information and a "Z Team" emblem.

1 Cal Ripken 12.50 30.00
2 Ken Griffey Jr. 6.00 15.00
3 Frank Thomas 4.00 10.00
4 Matt Williams 1.50 4.00
5 Mike Piazza UER 6.00 15.00
(Card says started at first base
Piazza is a catcher)
6 Barry Bonds 10.00 25.00
7 Raul Mondesi 1.50 4.00
8 Greg Maddux 6.00 15.00
9 Jeff Bagwell 2.50 6.00
10 Manny Ramirez 2.50 6.00
11 Larry Walker 1.50 4.00
12 Tony Gwynn 5.00 12.00
13 Will Clark 2.50 6.00
14 Albert Belle 1.50 4.00
15 Kenny Lofton 1.50 4.00
16 Rafael Palmeiro 2.50 6.00
17 Don Mattingly 10.00 25.00
18 Carlos Baerga .75 2.00

1996 Zenith

This 1996 Zenith set was issued in one series totalling 150 cards. The six-card packs retailed for $3.99 each. The set contains the subset: Honor Roll (131-150). The fronts feature a color player cutout over an arrangement of baseball bats on a black background. The backs carry a hit location chart and player statistics. Rookie Card include Darin Erstad.

COMPLETE SET (150) 15.00 30.00
1 Ken Griffey Jr. .50 1.25
2 Ozzie Smith .50 1.25
3 Greg Maddux .50 1.25
4 Rondell White .10 .30
5 Mark McGwire .75 2.00
6 Jim Thome .20 .50
7 Ivan Rodriguez .20 .50
8 Marc Newfield .10 .30
9 Travis Fryman .10 .30
10 Fred McGriff .20 .50
11 Shawn Green .10 .30
12 Mike Piazza .50 1.25
13 Dante Bichette .10 .30
14 Tino Martinez .20 .50
15 Sterling Hitchcock .10 .30
16 Ryne Sandberg .50 1.25
17 Rico Brogna .10 .30
18 Roberto Alomar .20 .50
19 Barry Larkin .20 .50
20 Bernie Williams .20 .50
21 Gary Sheffield .10 .30
22 Frank Thomas .30 .75
23 Gregg Jefferies .10 .30
24 Jeff Bagwell .20 .50
25 Marty Cordova .10 .30
26 Jim Edmonds .10 .30
27 Jay Bell .10 .30
28 Ben McDonald .10 .30
29 Barry Bonds .75 2.00
30 Mo Vaughn .10 .30
31 Johnny Damon .20 .50
32 Dean Palmer .10 .30
33 Ismael Valdes .10 .30
34 Manny Ramirez .20 .50
35 Edgar Martinez .20 .50
36 Cecil Fielder .10 .30
37 Ryan Klesko .10 .30
38 Ray Lankford .10 .30
39 Tim Salmon .20 .50
40 Joe Carter .10 .30
41 Jason Isringhausen .10 .30
42 Rickey Henderson .30 .75
43 Lenny Dykstra .10 .30
44 Andre Dawson .10 .30
45 Paul O'Neill .20 .50
46 Ray Durham .10 .30
47 Raul Mondesi .10 .30
48 Jay Buhner .10 .30
49 Eddie Murray .30 .75
50 Henry Rodriguez .10 .30
51 Hal Morris .10 .30
52 Mike Mussina .20 .50
53 Wally Joyner .10 .30
54 Will Clark .20 .50
55 Chipper Jones .30 .75
56 Brian Jordan .10 .30
57 Larry Walker .10 .30
58 Wade Boggs .20 .50
59 Melvin Nieves .10 .30
60 Charles Johnson .10 .30
61 Juan Gonzalez .10 .30
62 Carlos Delgado .10 .30
63 Reggie Sanders .10 .30
64 Brian L.Hunter .10 .30
65 Edgardo Alfonzo .10 .30
66 Kenny Lofton .10 .30
67 Paul Molitor .10 .30
68 Mike Bordick .10 .30
69 Garret Anderson .10 .30
70 Orlando Merced .10 .30
71 Craig Biggio .20 .50
72 Chuck Knoblauch .10 .30
73 Mark Grace .20 .50
74 Jack McDowell .10 .30
75 Randy Johnson .30 .75
76 Cal Ripken 1.00 2.50
77 Matt Williams .10 .30
78 Benji Gil .10 .30
79 Moises Alou .10 .30
80 Robin Ventura .10 .30
81 Greg Vaughn .10 .30
82 Carlos Baerga .10 .30
83 Roger Clemens .60 1.50
84 Hideo Nomo .30 .75
85 Pedro Martinez .20 .50
86 John Valentin .10 .30
87 Andres Galarraga .10 .30
88 Andy Pettitte .20 .50
89 Derek Bell .10 .30
90 Kirby Puckett .30 .75
91 Tony Gwynn .40 1.00
92 Brady Anderson .10 .30
93 Derek Jeter .75 2.00
94 Michael Tucker .10 .30
95 Albert Belle .10 .30
96 David Cone .10 .30
97 J.T. Snow .10 .30
98 Tom Glavine .20 .50
99 Alex Rodriguez .60 1.50
100 Sammy Sosa .30 .75
101 Karim Garcia .10 .30
102 Alan Benes .10 .30
103 Chad Mottola .10 .30
104 Robin Jennings .10 .30
105 Bob Abreu .30 .75
106 Tony Clark .10 .30
107 George Arias .10 .30
108 Jermaine Dye .10 .30
109 Jeff Suppan .10 .30
110 Ralph Milliard RC .10 .30
111 Ruben Rivera .10 .30
112 Billy Wagner .10 .30
113 Jason Kendall .10 .30
114 Mike Grace RC .10 .30
115 Edgar Renteria .10 .30
116 Jason Schmidt .20 .50
117 Paul Wilson .10 .30
118 Rey Ordonez .10 .30
119 Rocky Coppinger RC .10 .30
120 Wilton Guerrero RC .10 .30
121 Brooks Kieschnick .10 .30
122 Raul Casanova .10 .30
123 Alex Ochoa .10 .30
124 Chan Ho Park .10 .30
125 John Wasdin .10 .30
126 Eric Owens .10 .30
127 Justin Thompson .10 .30
128 Chris Snopek .10 .30
129 Terrell Wade .10 .30
130 Darin Erstad RC .75 2.00
131 Albert Belle HON .10 .30
132 Cal Ripken HON .50 1.25
133 Frank Thomas HON .20 .50
134 Greg Maddux HON .30 .75
135 Ken Griffey Jr. HON .30 .75
136 Mo Vaughn HON .10 .30
137 Chipper Jones HON .20 .50
138 Mike Piazza HON .30 .75
139 Ryan Klesko HON .10 .30
140 Hideo Nomo HON .20 .50
141 Roberto Alomar HON .10 .30
142 Manny Ramirez HON .10 .30
143 Gary Sheffield HON .10 .30
144 Barry Bonds HON .40 1.00
145 Matt Williams HON .10 .30
146 Jim Edmonds HON .10 .30
147 Derek Jeter HON .40 1.00
148 Sammy Sosa HON .20 .50
149 Kirby Puckett HON .20 .50
150 Tony Gwynn HON .20 .50

1996 Zenith Artist's Proofs

Randomly inserted in packs at a rate of one in 35, this 150-card set is parallel to the regular Zenith set. The cards are distinguished from the regular set by the "Artist's Proof" all-gold, rainbow holographic foil stamp on the front.

*STARS: 10X TO 25X BASIC CARDS
*ROOKIES: 4X TO 10X BASIC CARDS

1996 Zenith Diamond Club

Randomly inserted in packs at a rate of one in 24, cards from this 20-card set honor top performers on a Spectroetch card design printed on thick foil stock with etched highlights.

COMPLETE SET (20) 50.00 120.00
*REAL DIAMOND: 2X TO 5X BASIC DIAMOND
REAL DIAMOND STATED ODDS 1:350
1 Albert Belle 1.00 2.50
2 Mo Vaughn 1.00 2.50
3 Ken Griffey Jr. 4.00 10.00
4 Mike Piazza 4.00 10.00
5 Cal Ripken 8.00 20.00
6 Jermaine Dye 1.00 2.50
7 Jeff Bagwell 1.50 4.00
8 Frank Thomas 2.50 6.00
9 Alex Rodriguez 5.00 12.00
10 Ryan Klesko 1.00 2.50
11 Roberto Alomar 1.50 4.00
12 Sammy Sosa 2.50 6.00
13 Matt Williams 1.00 2.50
14 Gary Sheffield 1.00 2.50
15 Ruben Rivera 1.00 2.50
16 Darin Erstad 2.00 5.00
17 Randy Johnson 2.50 6.00
18 Greg Maddux 4.00 10.00
19 Karim Garcia 1.00 2.50
20 Chipper Jones 2.50 6.00

1996 Zenith Mozaics

Randomly inserted in packs at a rate of one in 10, this 25-card set features three-player image cards of the hottest superstars. The fronts display multiple player images representing the core of each of the 28 teams and are printed on rainbow holographic foil.

COMPLETE SET (25) 30.00 80.00
1 Greg Maddux 2.50 6.00
Chipper Jones
Ryan Klesko
2 Juan Gonzalez 1.00 2.50
Will Clark
Ivan Rodriguez
3 Frank Thomas 1.50 4.00
Robin Ventura
Ray Durham
4 Matt Williams 4.00 10.00
Barry Bonds
Osvaldo Fernandez
5 Ken Griffey Jr. 2.50 6.00
Randy Johnson
Alex Rodriguez
6 Sammy Sosa 1.50 4.00
Ryne Sandberg
Mark Grace
7 Jim Edmonds .60 1.50
Tim Salmon
Garret Anderson
8 Cal Ripken 5.00 12.00
Roberto Alomar
Mike Mussina
9 Mo Vaughn 3.00 8.00
Roger Clemens
John Valentin
10 Barry Larkin 1.00 2.50
Reggie Sanders
Hal Morris
11 Ray Lankford 2.50 6.00
Brian Jordan
Ozzie Smith
12 Dante Bichette .60 1.50
Larry Walker
Andres Galarraga
13 Mike Piazza 2.50 6.00
Hideo Nomo
Raul Mondesi
14 Ben McDonald .60 1.50
Greg Vaughn
Kevin Seitzer
15 Joe Carter .60 1.50
Carlos Delgado
Alex Gonzalez
16 Gary Sheffield .60 1.50
Charles Johnson
Jeff Conine
17 Rondell White .60 1.50
Moises Alou
Henry Rodriguez
18 Albert Belle 1.00 2.50
Manny Ramirez
Carlos Baerga
19 Kirby Puckett 1.50 4.00
Paul Molitor
Chuck Knoblauch
20 Tony Gwynn 2.00 5.00
Rickey Henderson
Wally Joyner
21 Mark McGwire 4.00 10.00
Mike Bordick
Scott Brosius
22 Paul O'Neill 1.00 2.50
Bernie Williams
Wade Boggs
23 Jay Bell .60 1.50
Orlando Merced
Jason Kendall
24 Rico Brogna .60 1.50
Paul Wilson
Jason Isringhausen
25 Jeff Bagwell 1.00 2.50
Craig Biggio
Derek Bell

1996 Zenith Z-Team

Randomly inserted in packs at a rate of one in 72, this 18-card set features a color action player cutout on a clear micro-etched design with a gold foil Z-Team logo and a see-through green baseball field background. The backs carry player information printed on the back of the Z.

COMPLETE SET (18) 80.00 200.00
1 Ken Griffey Jr. 8.00 20.00
2 Albert Belle 2.00 5.00
3 Cal Ripken 15.00 40.00
4 Frank Thomas 5.00 12.00
5 Greg Maddux 8.00 20.00
6 Mo Vaughn 2.00 5.00
7 Chipper Jones 5.00 12.00
8 Mike Piazza 8.00 20.00
9 Ryan Klesko 2.00 5.00
10 Hideo Nomo 5.00 12.00
11 Roberto Alomar 3.00 8.00
12 Manny Ramirez 3.00 8.00
13 Gary Sheffield 2.00 5.00
14 Barry Bonds 12.50 30.00
15 Matt Williams 2.00 5.00
16 Jim Edmonds 2.00 5.00
17 Kirby Puckett 5.00 12.00
18 Sammy Sosa 5.00 12.00

1997 Zenith

The 1997 Zenith set was issued in one series totalling 50 cards and was distributed in packs containing five standard-size cards and two 8" by 10" cards with a suggested retail price of $9.99. The fronts feature borderless color action player photos. The backs carry a black-and-white player photo with career statistics. The set contains 42 established player cards and eight rookie cards (43-50).

COMPLETE SET (50) 10.00 25.00
1 Frank Thomas .40 1.00
2 Tony Gwynn .50 1.25
3 Jeff Bagwell .25 .60
4 Paul Molitor .15 .40
5 Roberto Alomar .25 .60
6 Mike Piazza .60 1.50
7 Albert Belle .15 .40
8 Greg Maddux .60 1.50
9 Barry Larkin .25 .60
10 Tony Clark .15 .40
11 Larry Walker .15 .40
12 Chipper Jones .40 1.00
13 Juan Gonzalez .15 .40
14 Barry Bonds 1.00 2.50
15 Ivan Rodriguez .25 .60
16 Sammy Sosa .40 1.00
17 Derek Jeter 1.00 2.50
18 Hideo Nomo .40 1.00
19 Roger Clemens .75 2.00
20 Ken Griffey Jr. .60 1.50
21 Andy Pettitte .25 .60
22 Alex Rodriguez .60 1.50
23 Tino Martinez .25 .60
24 Bernie Williams .25 .60
25 Ken Caminiti .15 .40
26 John Smoltz .25 .60
27 Javier Lopez .15 .40
28 Mark McGwire 1.00 2.50
29 Gary Sheffield .15 .40

30 David Justice	.15	.40
31 Randy Johnson	.40	1.00
32 Chuck Knoblauch	.15	.40
33 Mike Mussina	.25	.60
34 Deion Sanders	.25	.60
35 Cal Ripken	1.25	3.00
36 Darin Erstad	.15	.40
37 Kenny Lofton	.15	.40
38 Jay Buhner	.15	.40
39 Brady Anderson	.15	.40
40 Edgar Martinez	.25	.60
41 Mo Vaughn	.15	.40
42 Ryne Sandberg	.60	1.50
43 Andruw Jones	.25	.60
44 Nomar Garciaparra	.60	1.50
45 Hideki Irabu RC	.30	.75
46 Wilton Guerrero	.15	.40
47 Jose Cruz Jr. RC	.30	.75
48 Vladimir Guerrero	.40	1.00
49 Scott Rolen	.25	.60
50 Jose Guillen	.15	.40

1997 Zenith 8 x 10

Randomly inserted one in every pack, this 24-card set features 8" by 10" versions of the base set cards of the players listed below.

COMPLETE SET (24)	10.00	25.00
*DUFEX: 1X TO 2.5X BASIC 8 X 10		
ONE DUFEX PER PACK		
1 Frank Thomas	.50	1.25
2 Tony Gwynn	.60	1.50
3 Jeff Bagwell	.30	.75
4 Ken Griffey Jr.	.75	2.00
5 Mike Piazza	.75	2.00
6 Greg Maddux	.75	2.00
7 Ken Caminiti	.20	.50
8 Albert Belle	.20	.50
9 Ivan Rodriguez	.30	.75
10 Sammy Sosa	.50	1.25
11 Mark McGwire	1.25	3.00
12 Roger Clemens	1.00	2.50
13 Alex Rodriguez	.75	2.00
14 Chipper Jones	.50	1.25
15 Juan Gonzalez	.20	.50
16 Barry Bonds	1.25	3.00
17 Derek Jeter	1.25	3.00
18 Hideo Nomo	.50	1.25
19 Cal Ripken	1.50	4.00
20 Hideki Irabu	.40	1.00
21 Andruw Jones	.30	.75
22 Nomar Garciaparra	.75	2.00
23 Vladimir Guerrero	.50	1.25
24 Scott Rolen	.30	.75

1997 Zenith 8 x 10 Dufex Samples

These oversized Samples were distributed to dealers and hobby media several weeks prior to the shipping of 1997 Zenith to preview then then upcoming brand. The Samples are straight parallels of the basic issue 1997 Zenith 8 x 10 Dufex inserts except for the word "SAMPLE" running diagonally across the front and back of the card in bold black text.

13 Alex Rodriguez	2.00	5.00

1997 Zenith the Big Picture

These six 8 by 10 photos were released as promos to demonstrate what the 1997 Zenith 8 by 10's would look like. They have the notation the Big Picture at the bottom of the card. The cards are skip-numbered and share the same number as the regular cards

1 Frank Thomas	2.50	6.00
4 Ken Griffey Jr.	3.00	8.00
5 Mike Piazza	4.00	10.00
13 Alex Rodriguez	4.00	10.00
17 Derek Jeter	6.00	15.00
19 Cal Ripken Jr.	6.00	15.00

1997 Zenith V-2

Randomly inserted in packs at the rate of one in 47, this eight-card set features color action player photos produced with motion technology and state-of-the-art foil printing.

COMPLETE SET (8)	60.00	150.00
1 Ken Griffey Jr.	8.00	20.00
2 Andruw Jones	3.00	8.00
3 Frank Thomas	5.00	12.00
4 Mike Piazza	8.00	20.00
5 Alex Rodriguez	8.00	20.00
6 Cal Ripken	15.00	40.00
7 Derek Jeter	12.50	30.00
8 Vladimir Guerrero	5.00	12.00

1997 Zenith Z-Team

Randomly inserted in packs, cards from this nine-card set feature color action photos of top players printed on full Mirror Gold Holographic Mylar foil card stock. Only 1,000 sets were produced and each card is sequentially numbered on back.

COMPLETE SET (9)	60.00	150.00
1 Ken Griffey Jr.	8.00	20.00
2 Larry Walker	2.00	5.00
3 Frank Thomas	5.00	12.00
4 Alex Rodriguez	8.00	20.00
5 Mike Piazza	8.00	20.00
6 Cal Ripken	15.00	40.00
7 Derek Jeter	12.50	30.00
8 Andruw Jones	3.00	8.00
9 Roger Clemens	10.00	25.00

1998 Zenith Samples Large

One of these nine different 3 1/2" by 5" samples was inserted into dealer order forms to preview the upcoming 1998 Zenith baseball release. Each large sample card also contains a "hidden" standard size sample card inside. To get to the small sample card, however, one must tear the larger sample card in two - thereby destroying it. The cards were sent out around April, 1998. They're identical to regular issue large Zenith cards except for the bold "SAMPLE" text running diagonally across the back of the card. Prices below refer to mint untorn cards.

COMPLETE SET (9)	10.00	25.00
Z1 Nomar Garciaparra	1.25	3.00
Z3 Greg Maddux	1.25	3.00
Z4 Frank Thomas	.60	1.50
Z9 Andruw Jones	.50	1.25
Z15 Derek Jeter	2.50	6.00
Z21 Mike Piazza	1.50	4.00
Z22 Tony Gwynn	1.25	3.00
Z35 Ivan Rodriguez	.60	1.50
Z40 Ken Griffey Jr.	1.25	3.00

1998 Zenith Samples Small

One of these six different small (actually standard size 2 1/2" by 3 1/2") promo cards was "hidden" inside the larger 3 1/2" by 5" Zenith Samples. The larger sample card had to be torn in two to get to this small card.

COMPLETE SET (6)	8.00	15.00
2 Ken Griffey Jr.	1.25	3.00
12 Greg Maddux	1.25	3.00
14 Mike Piazza	1.25	3.00
17 Derek Jeter	2.50	6.00
18 Nomar Garciaparra	1.25	3.00
19 Ivan Rodriguez	.60	1.50

1998 Zenith

The 1998 Zenith set was issued in one series totalling 100 cards. The packs retailed for $5.99 each and contained three 5x7 Zenith cards each with one standard size card inside. The standard-size cards listed here had to be removed from the inside of the jumbo packs by tearing the large cards in half. This ill-conceived concept was entitled "Dare to Tear", thus collectors were faced with the dilemma of having to choose between the standard size card of the jumbo 5" by 7" card. Ultimately, collectors by and large chose to carefully slice the back of the jumbo cards and remove the small card. The fronts feature color action player photos. The backs carry player information and career statistic.

COMPLETE SET (100)	20.00	50.00
1 Larry Walker	.20	.50
2 Ken Griffey Jr.	.75	2.00
3 Cal Ripken	1.50	4.00
4 Sammy Sosa	.50	1.25
5 Andruw Jones	.30	.75
6 Frank Thomas	.50	1.25
7 Tony Gwynn	.60	1.50
8 Rafael Palmeiro	.30	.75
9 Tim Salmon	.30	.75
10 Randy Johnson	.50	1.25
11 Juan Gonzalez	.20	.50
12 Greg Maddux	.75	2.00
13 Vladimir Guerrero	.50	1.25
14 Mike Piazza	.75	2.00
15 Andres Galarraga	.20	.50
16 Alex Rodriguez	.75	2.00
17 Derek Jeter	1.25	3.00
18 Nomar Garciaparra	.75	2.00
19 Ivan Rodriguez	.30	.75
20 Chipper Jones	.50	1.25
21 Barry Larkin	.30	.75
22 Mo Vaughn	.20	.50
23 Albert Belle	.20	.50
24 Scott Rolen	.30	.75
25 Sandy Alomar Jr.	.20	.50
26 Roberto Alomar	.30	.75
27 Andy Pettitte	.30	.75
28 Chuck Knoblauch	.20	.50
29 Jeff Bagwell	.30	.75
30 Mike Mussina	.30	.75
31 Fred McGriff	.30	.75
32 Roger Clemens	1.00	2.50
33 Rusty Greer	.20	.50
34 Edgar Martinez	.30	.75
35 Paul Molitor	.20	.50
36 Mark Grace	.30	.75
37 Darin Erstad	.20	.50
38 Kenny Lofton	.20	.50
39 Tom Glavine	.30	.75
40 Javier Lopez	.20	.50
41 Will Clark	.30	.75
42 Tino Martinez	.30	.75
43 Raul Mondesi	.20	.50
44 Brady Anderson	.20	.50
45 Chan Ho Park	.20	.50
46 Jason Giambi	.20	.50
47 Manny Ramirez	.30	.75
48 Jay Buhner	.20	.50
49 Dante Bichette	.20	.50
50 Jose Cruz Jr.	.20	.50
51 Charles Johnson	.20	.50
52 Bernard Gilkey	.20	.50
53 Johnny Damon	.30	.75
54 David Justice	.20	.50
55 Justin Thompson	.20	.50
56 Bobby Higginson	.20	.50
57 Todd Hundley	.20	.50
58 Gary Sheffield	.20	.50
59 Barry Bonds	1.25	3.00
60 Mark McGwire	1.25	3.00
61 John Smoltz	.30	.75
62 Tony Clark	.20	.50
63 Brian Jordan	.20	.50
64 Jason Kendall	.20	.50
65 Mariano Rivera	.50	1.25
66 Pedro Martinez	.30	.75
67 Jim Thome	.30	.75
68 Neifi Perez	.20	.50
69 Kevin Brown	.30	.75
70 Hideo Nomo	.50	1.25
71 Craig Biggio	.30	.75
72 Bernie Williams	.30	.75
73 Jose Guillen	.20	.50
74 Ken Caminiti	.20	.50
75 Livan Hernandez	.20	.50
76 Ray Lankford	.20	.50
77 Jim Edmonds	.20	.50
78 Matt Williams	.20	.50
79 Mark Kotsay	.20	.50
80 Moises Alou	.20	.50
81 Antone Williamson	.20	.50
82 Jaret Wright	.20	.50
83 Jacob Cruz	.20	.50
84 Abraham Nunez	.20	.50
85 Raul Ibanez	.20	.50
86 Miguel Tejada	.50	1.25
87 Derrek Lee	.30	.75
88 Juan Encarnacion	.20	.50
89 Todd Helton	.30	.75
90 Travis Lee	.20	.50
91 Ben Grieve	.20	.50
92 Ryan McGuire	.20	.50
93 Richard Hidalgo	.20	.50
94 Paul Konerko	.20	.50
95 Shannon Stewart	.20	.50
96 Homer Bush	.20	.50
97 Lou Collier	.20	.50
98 Jeff Abbott	.20	.50
99 Brett Tomko	.20	.50
100 Fernando Tatis	.20	.50

1998 Zenith Z-Gold

Randomly inserted in packs, this 100 card set is a gold foil parallel version of the base set. Only 100

serially numbered sets were produced.

*STARS: 6X TO 15X BASIC CARDS

1998 Zenith Z-Silver

Randomly inserted in packs at the rate of one in seven, this 100-card set is a silver foil parallel version of the base set.

*STARS: 2X TO 5X BASIC CARDS

1998 Zenith 5 x 7

Inserted three per pack, this 80-card set features color action player photos printed on large 5x7 cards. Prices in our checklist refer to mint non-sliced (or "slit-back") cards. Each mint Zenith 5" by 7" card contains a standard-size (2 1/2" by 3 1/2") Zenith card inside it. Please see the 1998 Zenith listing for more details.

COMPLETE SET (80)	30.00	80.00
*IMPULSE STARS: 2X TO 5X BASIC 5 X 7'S		
*IMPULSE SLIT-BACKS: .5X TO 1.25X BASIC 5 X 7'S		
IMPULSE STATED ODDS 1:7		
*IMP.GOLD: 8X TO 20X BASIC 5 X 7		
IMPULSE GOLD STATED ODDS 1:35		
GOLD PRINT RUN 100 SERIAL #'d SETS		
CONDITION SENSITIVE SET		
PRICES BELOW ARE FOR MT UNCUT CARDS		
SLIT MUST BE CLEAN RAZOR CUT BACK		
1 Nomar Garciaparra	1.00	2.50
2 Andres Galarraga	.25	.60
3 Greg Maddux	1.00	2.50
4 Frank Thomas	.60	1.50
5 Mark McGwire	1.50	4.00
6 Rafael Palmeiro	.40	1.00
7 John Smoltz	.40	1.00
8 Jeff Bagwell	.40	1.00
9 Andruw Jones	.40	1.00
10 Rusty Greer	.25	.60
11 Paul Molitor	.25	.60
12 Bernie Williams	.40	1.00
13 Kenny Lofton	.25	.60
14 Alex Rodriguez	1.00	2.50
15 Derek Jeter	1.50	4.00
16 Scott Rolen	.40	1.00
17 Albert Belle	.25	.60
18 Mo Vaughn	.25	.60
19 Chipper Jones	.60	1.50
20 Chuck Knoblauch	.25	.60
21 Mike Piazza	1.00	2.50
22 Tony Gwynn	.75	2.00
23 Juan Gonzalez	.25	.60
24 Andy Pettitte	.40	1.00
25 Tim Salmon	.40	1.00
26 Brady Anderson	.25	.60
27 Mike Mussina	.40	1.00
28 Edgar Martinez	.40	1.00
29 Jose Guillen	.25	.60
30 Hideo Nomo	.60	1.50
31 Jim Thome	.40	1.00
32 Mark Grace	.40	1.00
33 Darin Erstad	.25	.60
34 Bobby Higginson	.25	.60
35 Ivan Rodriguez	.40	1.00
36 Todd Hundley	.25	.60
37 Sandy Alomar Jr.	.25	.60
38 Gary Sheffield	.25	.60
39 David Justice	.25	.60
40 Ken Griffey Jr.	1.00	2.50
41 Vladimir Guerrero	.60	1.50
42 Larry Walker	.25	.60
43 Barry Bonds	1.50	4.00
44 Randy Johnson	.60	1.50
45 Roger Clemens	1.25	3.00
46 Raul Mondesi	.25	.60
47 Tino Martinez	.40	1.00
48 Jason Giambi	.25	.60
49 Matt Williams	.25	.60
50 Cal Ripken	2.00	5.00
51 Barry Larkin	.40	1.00
52 Jim Edmonds	.25	.60
53 Ken Caminiti	.25	.60
54 Sammy Sosa	.60	1.50
55 Tony Clark	.25	.60
56 Manny Ramirez	.40	1.00
57 Bernard Gilkey	.25	.60
58 Jose Cruz Jr.	.25	.60
59 Brian Jordan	.25	.60
60 Kevin Brown	.40	1.00
61 Craig Biggio	.40	1.00
62 Javier Lopez	.25	.60
63 Jay Buhner	.25	.60
64 Roberto Alomar	.40	1.00
65 Justin Thompson	.25	.60
66 Todd Helton	.40	1.00
67 Travis Lee	.25	.60
68 Paul Konerko	.25	.60
69 Jaret Wright	.25	.60
70 Ben Grieve	.25	.60
71 Juan Encarnacion	.25	.60
72 Ryan McGuire	.25	.60
73 Derrek Lee	.40	1.00
74 Abraham Nunez	.25	.60
75 Richard Hidalgo	.25	.60
76 Miguel Tejada	.60	1.50
77 Jacob Cruz	.25	.60
78 Homer Bush	.25	.60
79 Jeff Abbott	.25	.60
80 Lou Collier	.25	.60

1998 Zenith Raising the Bar

Randomly inserted in packs at the rate of one in 25, this 15-card set features color player photos of players with only a couple of years of big-league experience.

COMPLETE SET (15)	40.00	100.00
1 Ken Griffey Jr.	4.00	10.00
2 Frank Thomas	2.50	6.00
3 Alex Rodriguez	4.00	10.00
4 Tony Gwynn	3.00	8.00
5 Mike Piazza	4.00	10.00
6 Ivan Rodriguez	1.50	4.00
7 Cal Ripken	8.00	20.00
8 Greg Maddux	4.00	10.00
9 Hideo Nomo	2.50	6.00
10 Mark McGwire	6.00	15.00
11 Juan Gonzalez	1.00	2.50
12 Andruw Jones	1.50	4.00
13 Jeff Bagwell	1.50	4.00
14 Chipper Jones	2.50	6.00
15 Nomar Garciaparra	4.00	10.00

1998 Zenith Rookie Thrills

Randomly inserted in packs at the rate of one in 25, this 15-card set features color photos of top Rookie of the Year suspects.

COMPLETE SET (15)	10.00	25.00
1 Travis Lee	.75	2.00
2 Juan Encarnacion	.75	2.00
3 Derrek Lee	1.25	3.00
4 Raul Ibanez	.75	2.00
5 Ryan McGuire	.75	2.00
6 Todd Helton	1.25	3.00
7 Jacob Cruz	.75	2.00
8 Abraham Nunez	.75	2.00
9 Paul Konerko	.75	2.00
10 Ben Grieve	.75	2.00
11 Jeff Abbott	.75	2.00
12 Richard Hidalgo	.75	2.00
13 Jaret Wright	.75	2.00
14 Lou Collier	.75	2.00
15 Miguel Tejada	2.00	5.00

1998 Zenith Z-Team

Randomly inserted in packs at the rate of 1:35 for cards 1-9 and 1:58 for cards 10-18, this 18-card set features action color photos of nine top veteran (1-9) and nine top rookie (10-18) players.

COMPLETE SET (18)	50.00	120.00
*5 x 7 STARS: .6X TO 1.5X BASIC Z-TEAM		
5 x 7 STATED ODDS 1:35		
*GOLD: 1.25X TO 3X BASIC Z-TEAM	3.00	8.00
GOLD STATED ODDS 1:175		
1 Frank Thomas	3.00	8.00
2 Ken Griffey Jr.	5.00	12.00
3 Mike Piazza	5.00	12.00
4 Cal Ripken	10.00	25.00
5 Alex Rodriguez	5.00	12.00
6 Greg Maddux	5.00	12.00
7 Derek Jeter	8.00	20.00
8 Chipper Jones	3.00	8.00
9 Roger Clemens	6.00	15.00
10 Ben Grieve	1.25	3.00
11 Derrek Lee	2.00	5.00
12 Jose Cruz Jr.	1.25	3.00
13 Nomar Garciaparra	5.00	12.00
14 Travis Lee	1.25	3.00
15 Todd Helton	2.00	5.00
16 Paul Konerko	1.25	3.00
17 Miguel Tejada	3.00	8.00
18 Scott Rolen	2.00	5.00

2005 Zenith Promo Koufax

This one-card promo was issued as a premium wrapper redemption at the Donruss Corporate booth during the 2005 Sports Collectors National Convention. Interestingly, Koufax would not be featured in the 2005 Zenith set.

NNO Sandy Koufax	2.00	5.00

2005 Zenith

This 250-card set was released in September, 2005. These cards were issued five card packs which came 18 packs to a box and 16 boxes to a case. The first 230 cards in this set feature mostly active veterans (with a few players who made their major league debut in 2005) while cards 231-250 feature retired greats.

COMPLETE SET (250)	40.00	60.00
COMMON CARD (1-230)	.15	.40
COMMON RC (1-230)	.20	.50
COMMON CARD (231-250)	.20	.50
1 Curt Schilling	.25	.60
2 Jim Edmonds	.15	.40
3 Ichiro Suzuki	.75	2.00
4 Jody Gerut	.15	.40
5 Carlos Beltran	.15	.40
6 Miguel Tejada	.15	.40
7 Ted Lilly	.15	.40
8 Bobby Abreu	.15	.40
9 Mark Teixeira	.25	.60
10 Manny Ramirez	.25	.60
11 Eric Gagne	.15	.40
12 Adrian Beltre	.15	.40
13 Dmitri Young	.15	.40
14 Alfonso Soriano	.15	.40
15 Vladimir Guerrero	.40	1.00
16 Carl Crawford	.15	.40
17 David Ortiz	.40	1.00
18 Jose Guillen	.15	.40
19 Miguel Cabrera	.25	.60
20 Alex Rodriguez	.60	1.50
21 Brad Lidge	.15	.40
22 Francisco Rodriguez	.15	.40
23 Carlos Lee	.15	.40
24 Ben Sheets	.15	.40
25 Jason Schmidt	.15	.40
26 Cesar Izturis	.15	.40
27 Corey Patterson	.15	.40
28 Marcus Giles	.15	.40
29 Melvin Mora	.15	.40
30 Yadier Molina	.15	.40
31 Juan Pierre	.15	.40
32 Aubrey Huff	.15	.40
33 Rafael Furcal	.15	.40
34 David Dellucci	.15	.40
35 Jake Peavy	.15	.40
36 Aramis Ramirez	.15	.40
37 Javy Lopez	.15	.40
38 Aaron Rowand	.15	.40
39 Raul Ibanez	.15	.40
40 Jason Bay	.15	.40
41 Michael Young	.15	.40
42 Ivan Rodriguez	.25	.60
43 Derrek Lee	.25	.60
44 Adam Dunn	.15	.40
45 Eric Chavez	.15	.40
46 Pedro Martinez	.25	.60

47 Roy Oswalt .15 .40
48 Kevin Millwood .15 .40
49 Carlos Delgado .15 .40
50 Derek Jeter 1.00 2.50
51 Johnny Damon .25 .60
52 Richie Sexson .15 .40
53 Nomar Garciaparra .40 1.00
54 Edgar Renteria .15 .40
55 Carl Pavano .15 .40
56 Tim Wakefield .15 .40
57 Michael Barrett .15 .40
58 Johnny Estrada .15 .40
59 Jeff Kent .15 .40
60 Mark Loretta .15 .40
61 Greg Maddux .60 1.50
62 Hank Blalock .15 .40
63 Moises Alou .15 .40
64 Brad Radke .15 .40
65 Brad Wilkerson .15 .40
66 Sean Casey .15 .40
67 Oliver Perez .15 .40
68 Scott Hatteberg .15 .40
69 Mike Lowell .15 .40
70 Kazuo Matsui .15 .40
71 Mark Prior .25 .60
72 Hideki Matsui .60 1.50
73 Geoff Jenkins .15 .40
74 Gary Sheffield .15 .40
75 A.J. Burnett .15 .40
76 Vernon Wells .15 .40
77 Kenny Rogers .15 .40
78 Jose Reyes .15 .40
79 Victor Martinez .15 .40
80 Jorge Posada .25 .60
81 Rich Harden .15 .40
82 Travis Hafner .15 .40
83 Bret Boone .15 .40
84 Chipper Jones .40 1.00
85 Bartolo Colon .15 .40
86 Scott Podsednik .15 .40
87 Coco Crisp .15 .40
88 Luis Castillo .15 .40
89 John Smoltz .25 .60
90 Andruw Jones .25 .60
91 Milton Bradley .15 .40
92 Torii Hunter .15 .40
93 Shawn Green .15 .40
94 Paul Konerko .15 .40
95 David Wells .15 .40
96 Scott Rolen .25 .60
97 Rodrigo Lopez .15 .40
98 Garret Anderson .15 .40
99 Tim Hudson .15 .40
100 Sammy Sosa .40 1.00
101 Jason Varitek .40 1.00
102 Lance Berkman .15 .40
103 Troy Glaus .15 .40
104 Carlos Guillen .15 .40
105 Jeff Bagwell .25 .60
106 Phil Nevin .15 .40
107 Freddy Garcia .15 .40
108 Jake Westbrook .15 .40
109 Marquis Grissom .15 .40
110 Johan Santana .40 1.00
111 Kerry Wood .15 .40
112 Jose Vidro .15 .40
113 Mike Mussina .25 .60
114 Josh Beckett .15 .40
115 Matt Lawton .15 .40
116 Craig Biggio .25 .60
117 Reggie Sanders .15 .40
118 Jason Kendall .15 .40
119 Larry Walker .25 .60
120 Roger Clemens .60 1.50
121 C.C. Sabathia .15 .40
122 Javier Vazquez .15 .40
123 Barry Zito .15 .40
124 Jon Lieber .15 .40
125 Kris Benson .15 .40
126 Jacque Jones .15 .40
127 Ray Durham .15 .40
128 Mark Kotsay .15 .40
129 Jack Wilson .15 .40
130 Bobby Crosby .15 .40
131 Todd Helton .25 .60
132 Lyle Overbay .15 .40
133 Jon Garland .15 .40
134 Roy Halladay .15 .40
135 Orlando Cabrera .15 .40
136 Danny Kolb .15 .40
137 Austin Kearns .15 .40
138 Paul Lo Duca .15 .40
139 Magglio Ordonez .15 .40
140 Rafael Palmeiro .25 .60
141 Omar Vizquel .25 .60
142 Mike Piazza .40 1.00
143 Mark Mulder .15 .40
144 Dontrelle Willis .15 .40
145 Tom Glavine .25 .60
146 Khalil Greene .25 .60
147 Ken Griffey Jr. .60 1.50
148 Mike Sweeney .15 .40
149 Trot Nixon .15 .40
150 Randy Johnson .40 1.00
151 Doug Mientkiewicz .15 .40
152 Jeromy Burnitz .15 .40
153 Brandon Webb .15 .40
154 Kevin Brown .15 .40
155 Carlos Zambrano .15 .40
156 Shingo Takatsu .15 .40
157 Erubiel Durazo .15 .40
158 Jason Isringhausen .15 .40
159 Corey Koskie .15 .40
160 Aaron Boone .15 .40
161 Joe Nathan .15 .40
162 Nick Johnson .15 .40
163 Michael Tucker .15 .40
164 Chris Carpenter .15 .40
165 Preston Wilson .15 .40
166 J.T. Snow .15 .40
167 Hideo Nomo .40 1.00
168 Miguel Olivo .15 .40
169 Jarrod Washburn .15 .40
170 Derek Lowe .15 .40
171 Eric Milton .15 .40
172 Andy Pettitte .25 .60
173 Jason Giambi .15 .40
174 Richard Hidalgo .15 .40
175 Jayson Werth .15 .40
176 Juan Gonzalez .25 .60
177 Rocco Baldelli .15 .40
178 Steve Finley .15 .40
179 Frank Thomas .40 1.00
180 Kenny Lofton .15 .40
181 Randy Winn .15 .40
182 Brandon McCarthy RC .75 2.00
183 Lew Ford .15 .40
184 Mike Cameron .15 .40
185 Carlos Pena .15 .40
186 Brian Roberts .15 .40
187 Jeremy Bonderman .15 .40
188 Luis Gonzalez .15 .40
189 J.D. Drew .15 .40
190 Frank Catalanotto .15 .40
191 John Buck .15 .40
192 Pat Burrell .15 .40
193 Ryan Klesko .15 .40
194 Jermaine Dye .15 .40
195 Mariano Rivera .40 1.00
196 Angel Berroa .15 .40
197 Victor Zambrano .15 .40
198 Joel Pineiro .15 .40
199 Jay Gibbons .15 .40
200 Albert Pujols .75 2.00
201 Billy Wagner .15 .40
202 Darin Erstad .15 .40
203 Jim Thome .25 .60
204 Adam LaRoche .15 .40
205 Cliff Floyd .15 .40
206 Grady Sizemore .25 .60
207 Garrett Atkins .15 .40
208 Phil Humber RC .50 1.25
209 Zack Greinke .15 .40
210 Wladimir Balentien RC .50 1.25
211 Ubaldo Jimenez RC .60 1.50
212 Dallas McPherson .15 .40
213 Justin Verlander RC 1.50 4.00
214 Justin Morneau .15 .40
215 Chase Utley .25 .60
216 Casey Kotchman .15 .40
217 Tadahito Iguchi RC .75 2.00
218 Hanley Ramirez .15 .40
219 Scott Kazmir .15 .40
220 J.J. Hardy .15 .40
221 Ambiorix Concepcion RC .20 .50
222 Jeff Niemann RC .50 1.25
223 David Wright .60 1.50
224 Joe Mauer .40 1.00
225 Rickie Weeks .15 .40
226 Yuniesky Betancourt RC .75 2.00
227 Brady Clark .15 .40
228 Keiichi Yabu RC .20 .50
229 Delmon Young .25 .60
230 Nick Swisher .15 .40
231 George Brett 1.00 2.50
232 Ryne Sandberg 1.00 2.50
233 Mike Schmidt .75 2.00
234 Tony Gwynn .60 1.50
235 Rickey Henderson .50 1.25
236 Ozzie Smith .75 2.00
237 Reggie Jackson .30 .75
238 Steve Carlton .20 .50
239 Robin Yount .50 1.25
240 Tom Seaver .30 .75
241 Ted Williams .75 2.00
242 Don Mattingly 1.00 2.50
243 Mark Grace .30 .75
244 Rod Carew .30 .75
245 Willie Mays .60 1.50
246 Gary Carter .20 .50
247 Wade Boggs .30 .75
248 Dale Murphy .30 .75
249 Nolan Ryan 1.25 3.00
250 Cal Ripken 2.00 5.00

2005 Zenith Artist's Proofs Gold

*GOLD AP 1-230: 6X TO 15X BASIC
*GOLD AP 1-230: 3X TO 8X BASIC RC
*GOLD AP 231-250: 5X TO 12X BASIC
OVERALL INSERT ODDS ONE PER PACK
STATED PRINT RUN 50 SERIAL #'d SETS

2005 Zenith Artist's Proofs Silver

*AP 1-230: 3X TO 8X BASIC
*AP 1-230: 1.5X TO 4X BASIC RC
*AP 231-250: 3X TO 8X BASIC
STATED ODDS 1:16

2005 Zenith Museum Collection

*MUSEUM 1-230: 1.5X TO 4X BASIC
*MUSEUM 1-230: .75X TO 2X BASIC RC
*MUSEUM 231-250: 1.5X TO 4X BASIC
STATED ODDS 1:3

2005 Zenith Epix Orange Play

STATED PRINT RUN 750 SERIAL #'d SETS
*BLACK GAME: 1X TO 2.5X BASIC
BLACK GAME PRINT RUN 75 #'d SETS
*BLACK MOMENT: 1.5X TO 4X BASIC
BLACK MOMENT PRINT RUN 25 #'d SETS
*BLACK PLAY: .75X TO 2X BASIC
BLACK PLAY PRINT RUN 100 #'d SETS
*BLACK SEASON: 1.25X TO 3X BASIC
BLACK SEASON PRINT RUN 50 #'d SETS
*BLUE GAME: .6X TO 1.5X BASIC
BLUE GAME PRINT RUN 350 #'d SETS
*BLUE MOMENT: .75X TO 2X BASIC
BLUE MOMENT PRINT RUN 150 #'d SETS
*BLUE PLAY: .5X TO 1.2X BASIC
BLUE PLAY PRINT RUN 500 #'d SETS
*BLUE SEASON: .6X TO 1.5X BASIC
BLUE SEASON PRINT RUN 250 #'d SETS
*EMERALD GAME: .75X TO 2X BASIC
EMERALD GAME PRINT RUN 100 #'d SETS
*EMERALD MOMENT: 1.25X TO 3X BASIC
EMERALD MOMENT PRINT RUN 50 #'d SETS
*EMERALD PLAY: .6X TO 1.5X BASIC
EMERALD PLAY PRINT RUN 150 #'d SETS
*EMERALD SEASON: 1X TO 2.5X BASIC
EMERALD SEASON PRINT RUN 75 #'d SETS
*ORANGE GAME: .5X TO 1.2X BASIC
ORANGE GAME PRINT RUN 500 #'d SETS
*ORANGE MOMENT: .6X TO 1.5X BASIC
ORANGE MOMENT PRINT RUN 250 #'d SETS
*ORANGE SEASON: .6X TO 1.5X BASIC
ORANGE SEASON PRINT RUN 350 #'d SETS
*PURPLE GAME: .6X TO 1.5X BASIC
PURPLE GAME PRINT RUN 250 #'d SETS
*PURPLE MOMENT: .75X TO 2X BASIC
PURPLE MOMENT PRINT RUN 100 #'d SETS
*PURPLE PLAY: .6X TO 1.5X BASIC
PURPLE PLAY PRINT RUN 350 #'d SETS
*PURPLE SEASON: .75X TO 2X BASIC
PURPLE SEASON PRINT RUN 150 #'d SETS
*RED GAME: .75X TO 2X BASIC
RED GAME PRINT RUN 150 #'d SETS
*RED MOMENT: 1.25X TO 3X BASIC
RED MOMENT PRINT RUN 50 #'d SETS
*RED PLAY: .6X TO 1.5X BASIC
RED PLAY PRINT RUN 250 #'d SETS
*RED SEASON: .75X TO 2X BASIC
RED SEASON PRINT RUN 100 #'d SETS
OVERALL EPIX ODDS 2:9
1 Vladimir Guerrero 1.25 3.00
2 Alex Rodriguez 2.00 5.00
3 Johan Santana 1.25 3.00
4 Todd Helton 1.00 2.50
5 Mark Teixeira 1.00 2.50
6 Manny Ramirez 1.00 2.50
7 Scott Rolen 1.00 2.50
8 Gary Sheffield .75 2.00
9 Miguel Cabrera 1.00 2.50
10 Jim Thome 1.00 2.50
11 Eric Chavez .75 2.00
12 Roger Clemens 2.00 5.00
13 Pedro Martinez 1.00 2.50
14 Roy Oswalt .75 2.00
15 Carlos Delgado .75 2.00
16 Nomar Garciaparra 1.25 3.00
17 Hideki Matsui 2.00 5.00
18 Shawn Green .75 2.00
19 Greg Maddux 2.00 5.00
20 Ted Williams 2.50 6.00
21 Don Mattingly 3.00 8.00
22 Cal Ripken 6.00 15.00
23 George Brett 3.00 8.00
24 Nolan Ryan 4.00 10.00
25 Willie Mays 2.00 5.00

2005 Zenith Mozaics

STATED ODDS 1:8
1 Pedro Martinez .75 2.00
Carlos Beltran
Tom Glavine
2 Albert Pujols 2.00 5.00
Jim Edmonds
Mark Mulder
3 Sammy Sosa 1.00 2.50
Miguel Tejada
Rafael Palmeiro
4 Mark Teixeira .75 2.00
Hank Blalock
Michael Young
5 Andruw Jones .75 2.00
Rafael Furcal
Johnny Estrada
6 Bobby Crosby .60 1.50
Eric Chavez
Barry Zito
7 Shawn Green .60 1.50
Troy Glaus
Luis Gonzalez
8 Austin Kearns .60 1.50
Adam Dunn
Sean Casey
9 Jim Thome .75 2.00
Bobby Abreu
Pat Burrell
10 Lance Berkman .75 2.00
Jeff Bagwell
Craig Biggio
11 Orlando Cabrera .60 1.50
Steve Finley
Darin Erstad
12 J.D. Drew .60 1.50
Jeff Kent
Milton Bradley
13 Dontrelle Willis .60 1.50
Mike Lowell
A.J. Burnett
14 Adrian Beltre .60 1.50
Jeremy Reed
Richie Sexson
15 Joe Mauer 1.00 2.50
Justin Morneau
Jacque Jones
16 Gary Sheffield 2.00 5.00
Hideki Matsui
Mike Mussina

2005 Zenith Mozaics Materials Single

OVERALL GU ODDS 1:9
1 Pedro Martinez Jsy 2.50 6.00
Carlos Beltran
Tom Glavine
2 Albert Pujols Bat 6.00 15.00
Jim Edmonds
Mark Mulder
3 Sammy Sosa 2.00 5.00
Miguel Tejada Jsy
Rafael Palmeiro
4 Mark Teixeira Bat 2.50 6.00
Hank Blalock
Michael Young
5 Andruw Jones Bat 2.50 6.00
Rafael Furcal
Johnny Estrada
7 Shawn Green 2.00 5.00
Troy Glaus
Luis Gonzalez Jsy
8 Austin Kearns 2.00 5.00
Adam Dunn Bat
Sean Casey
9 Jim Thome 2.00 5.00
Bobby Abreu Jsy
Pat Burrell
10 Lance Berkman 2.50 6.00
Jeff Bagwell
Craig Biggio Bat
11 Orlando Cabrera 2.00 5.00
Steve Finley
Darin Erstad Bat
12 J.D. Drew Bat 2.00 5.00
Jeff Kent
Milton Bradley
13 Dontrelle Willis 2.00 5.00
Mike Lowell
A.J. Burnett Bat
14 Adrian Beltre 2.00 5.00
Jeremy Reed
Richie Sexson Bat
15 Joe Mauer 2.00 5.00
Justin Morneau
Jacque Jones Bat
16 Gary Sheffield Fld Glv 2.50 6.00
Hideki Matsui
Mike Mussina

2005 Zenith Mozaics Materials Triple Jerseys

PRINT RUNS B/WN 5-100 COPIES PER
NO PRICING ON QTY OF 5
PRIME PRINT RUNS B/WN 5-10 PER
NO PRIME PRICING DUE TO SCARCITY
OVERALL GU ODDS 1:9
4 Mark Teixeira 5.00 12.00
Hank Blalock
Michael Young/100
5 Andruw Jones
Rafael Furcal
Johnny Estrada/5
6 Bobby Crosby 6.00 15.00
Eric Chavez
Barry Zito/25
8 Austin Kearns 4.00 10.00
Adam Dunn
Sean Casey/100
9 Jim Thome 5.00 12.00
Bobby Abreu
Pat Burrell/100
10 Lance Berkman 6.00 15.00
Jeff Bagwell
Craig Biggio/100
13 Dontrelle Willis
Mike Lowell
A.J. Burnett/5
16 Gary Sheffield 10.00 25.00
Hideki Matsui
Mike Mussina/50

2005 Zenith Positions

STATED ODDS 1:21
1 Randy Johnson 1.50 4.00
Mark Prior
Roger Clemens
2 Ivan Rodriguez 1.00 2.50
Mike Piazza
Victor Martinez
3 Albert Pujols 2.00 5.00
Todd Helton
David Ortiz
4 Marcus Giles .60 1.50
Mark Loretta
Bret Boone
5 Scott Rolen 1.00 2.50
Aramis Ramirez
Chipper Jones
6 Kazuo Matsui .60 1.50
Miguel Tejada
Michael Young
7 Brian Giles .75 2.00
Manny Ramirez
Shannon Stewart
8 Rocco Baldelli .75 2.00
Andruw Jones
Vernon Wells
9 Miguel Cabrera 1.00 2.50
Lance Berkman
Vladimir Guerrero

2005 Zenith Positions Materials Single

OVERALL GU ODDS 1:9
1 Randy Johnson 2.50 6.00
Mark Prior Bat
Roger Clemens
2 Ivan Rodriguez Bat 2.50 6.00
Mike Piazza
Victor Martinez
3 Albert Pujols Bat 6.00 15.00
Todd Helton
David Ortiz
4 Marcus Giles 2.00 5.00
Mark Loretta
Bret Boone Jsy
5 Scott Rolen 3.00 8.00
Aramis Ramirez
Chipper Jones Bat
6 Kazuo Matsui Jsy 2.00 5.00
Miguel Tejada
Michael Young
7 Brian Giles 2.50 6.00
Manny Ramirez Bat
Shannon Stewart
8 Rocco Baldelli 2.50 6.00
Andruw Jones Bat
Vernon Wells
9 Miguel Cabrera 2.00 5.00
Lance Berkman Bat
Vladimir Guerrero

2005 Zenith Positions Materials Triple Jersey

OVERALL GU ODDS 1:9
PRINT RUNS B/WN 5-100 COPIES PER
NO PRICING ON QTY OF 5
2 Ivan Rodriguez 8.00 20.00
Mike Piazza
Victor Martinez/50
3 Albert Pujols 8.00 20.00
Todd Helton
David Ortiz/50
5 Scott Rolen 6.00 15.00
Aramis Ramirez
Chipper Jones/100
6 Kazuo Matsui 4.00 10.00
Miguel Tejada
Michael Young/75
7 Brian Giles
Manny Ramirez
Shannon Stewart/5
8 Rocco Baldelli 5.00 12.00
Andruw Jones
Vernon Wells/100
9 Miguel Cabrera 6.00 15.00
Lance Berkman
Vladimir Guerrero/100

2005 Zenith Positions Materials Triple Jersey Prime

*PRIME p/r 25: 1X TO 2.5X BASIC p/r 75-100
*PRIME p/r 25: .75X TO 2X BASIC p/r 50
OVERALL GU ODDS 1:9
PRINT RUNS B/WN 5-25 COPIES PER
NO PRICING ON QTY OF 5
7 Brian Giles 12.50 30.00
Manny Ramirez
Shannon Stewart/25

2005 Zenith Red Hot

STATED ODDS 1:16
*WHITE HOT: .6X TO 1.5X BASIC
WHITE HOT ODDS 1:65
1 Scott Rolen .75 2.00
2 Johan Santana 1.00 2.50
3 Josh Beckett .60 1.50
4 Aubrey Huff .60 1.50
5 Alfonso Soriano .60 1.50
6 Jeff Bagwell .75 2.00
7 Ted Williams 2.00 5.00
8 Mark Prior .75 2.00
9 Todd Helton .75 2.00
10 Vladimir Guerrero 1.00 2.50

2005 Zenith Red Hot Bats

*BAT p/r 150: .4X TO 1X JSY p/r 150-300
*BAT p/r 150: .2X TO .5X JSY p/r 25
*BAT p/r 50: .3X TO .8X JSY p/r 25
OVERALL GU ODDS 1:9
STATED PRINT RUN 150 SERIAL #'d SETS

2005 Zenith Red Hot Jerseys

OVERALL GU ODDS 1:9
PRINT RUNS B/WN 25-300 COPIES PER
1 Scott Rolen/150 2.50 6.00
2 Johan Santana/150 3.00 8.00
3 Josh Beckett/300 2.00 5.00
4 Aubrey Huff/25 4.00 10.00
5 Alfonso Soriano/150 2.00 5.00
6 Jeff Bagwell/300 2.50 6.00
7 Ted Williams/25 30.00 60.00
8 Mark Prior/250 2.50 6.00
9 Todd Helton/165 2.50 6.00
10 Vladimir Guerrero/150 3.00 8.00

2005 Zenith Red Hot Jerseys Prime

*PRIME p/r 25: 1.25X TO 3X JSY p/r 150-300
*PRIME p/r 25: .6X TO 1.5X JSY p/r 25
OVERALL GU ODDS 1:9
PRINT RUNS B/WN 1-25 COPIES PER
NO PRICING ON QTY OF 1

2005 Zenith Roll Call Autographs

STATED ODDS 1:24
TIER INFO PROVIDED BY DONRUSS
TIER 1 IS SCARCEST
SEE BECKETT.COM FOR TIER/SP INFO
1 Hanley Ramirez T3 10.00 25.00
2 Sean Tracey T2 3.00 8.00
3 Justin Wechsler T2 3.00 8.00
4 Matt Lindstrom T2 3.00 8.00
5 Garrett Jones T2 3.00 8.00
6 Ambiorix Concepcion T3 3.00 8.00
7 Casey Rogowski T2 4.00 10.00
8 Kelly Shoppach T2 3.00 8.00
9 Sean Thompson T1 3.00 8.00
10 Jeff Miller T3 3.00 8.00
11 Chris Resop T2 4.00 10.00
12 Justin Verlander T1 15.00 40.00
13 Geovany Soto T2 20.00 50.00
14 Paulino Reynoso T3 3.00 8.00
15 Chris Roberson T2 3.00 8.00
16 Justin Leone T3 3.00 8.00
17 Jeff Niemann T1 6.00 15.00
18 Mark Woodyard T3 3.00 8.00
19 Raul Tablado T1 3.00 8.00
20 Norihiro Nakamura T1 15.00 40.00
21 Tony Pena T1 3.00 8.00
22 Wladimir Balentien T2 4.00 10.00
23 Miguel Negron T2 4.00 10.00
24 Eude Brito T2 4.00 10.00
25 Ubaldo Jimenez T3 8.00 20.00
26 Mike Morse T2 4.00 10.00
27 Devon Lowery T2 3.00 8.00
28 Phil Humber T1 6.00 15.00
29 Nate McLouth T1 6.00 15.00
30 Jason Hammel T2 3.00 8.00

2005 Zenith Spellbound

COMMON MADDUX (1-4) 2.00 5.00
COMMON CLEMENS (5-9) 2.00 5.00
COMMON A.ROD 2.00 5.00
COMMON PUJOLS (14-19) 2.00 5.00
STATED ODDS 1:11

2005 Zenith Spellbound Jerseys

COMMON MADDUX (1-4) 6.00 15.00
MADDUX PRINT RUN 150 #'d SETS
COMMON CLEMENS (5-9) 6.00 15.00
CLEMENS PRINT RUN 150 #'d SETS
COMMON PUJOLS (14-19) 6.00 15.00
PUJOLS PRINT RUN 250 #'d SETS
OVERALL GU ODDS 1:9

2005 Zenith Team Zenith

STATED ODDS 1:31
*GOLD: 1X TO 2.5X BASIC
GOLD RANDOM INSERTS IN PACKS
GOLD PRINT RUN 100 SERIAL #'d SETS
1 Ichiro Suzuki 2.50 6.00
2 Jim Edmonds .75 2.00
3 Hideki Matsui 2.00 5.00
4 Alex Rodriguez 2.00 5.00
5 Derek Jeter 3.00 8.00
6 Alfonso Soriano .75 2.00
7 Jim Thome 1.00 2.50
8 Jorge Posada 1.00 2.50
9 Barry Zito .75 2.00
10 Curt Schilling 1.00 2.50
11 Willie Mays 2.00 5.00

2005 Zenith Team Zenith Bats

*BAT p/r 150: .4X TO 1X JSY p/r 150-300
*BAT p/r 50: .6X TO 1.5X JSY p/r 150-300
*BAT p/r 25: .75X TO 2X JSY p/r 150-300
OVERALL GU ODDS 1:9
PRINT RUNS B/WN 5-150 COPIES PER
NO PRICING ON QTY OF 10 OR LESS

2005 Zenith Team Zenith Jerseys

OVERALL GU ODDS 1:9
PRINT RUNS B/WN 15-300 COPIES PER
NO PRICING ON QTY OF 15
2 Jim Edmonds/15
3 Hideki Matsui/165 8.00 20.00
6 Alfonso Soriano/15
7 Jim Thome/175 2.50 6.00
8 Jorge Posada/300 2.50 6.00
9 Barry Zito/150 2.00 5.00
10 Curt Schilling/150 2.50 6.00
11 Willie Mays/175 15.00 40.00

2005 Zenith Team Zenith Jerseys Prime

*JSY PRIME: 1.25X TO 3X JSY p/r 150-300
OVERALL GU ODDS 1:9
STATED PRINT RUN 25 SERIAL #'d SETS
2 Jim Edmonds/25 6.00 15.00
6 Alfonso Soriano/25 6.00 15.00

2005 Zenith White Hot Bats

*BAT: .6X TO 1.5X RED JSY p/r 150-300
*BAT: .3X TO .8X RED JSY p/r 25
OVERALL GU ODDS 1:9
STATED PRINT RUN 50 SERIAL #'d SETS

2005 Zenith White Hot Jerseys

*JSYp/r151-200: .4XTO1X RED JSYp/r150-300
*JSYp/r 50: .6X TO 1.5X RED JSYp/r150-300
PRINT RUNS B/WN 1-200 COPIES PER
NO PRICING ON QTY OF 9 OR LESS
PRIME PRINT RUNS B/WN 1-10 PER
NO PRIME PRICING DUE TO SCARCITY
OVERALL GU ODDS 1:9

2005 Zenith Z-Bats

*BAT T3: .4X TO 1X JSY T2
*BAT T3: .3X TO .8X JSY T1
*BAT T2: .4X TO 1X JSY T2
*BAT T1: .5X TO 1.2X JSY T2
*BAT T1: .4X TO 1X JSY T1
*BAT SP: .6X TO 1.5X JSY T2
*BAT SP: .5X TO 1.2X JSY T1
OVERALL GU ODDS 1:9
TIER AND SP INFO PROVIDED BY DONRUSS
SEE BECKETT.COM FOR TIER/SP INFO
8 Adam LaRoche SP 3.00 8.00
9 Nick Johnson T3 2.00 5.00
12 Kenny Lofton T3 2.50 6.00
15 Morgan Ensberg SP 3.00 8.00
24 Angel Berroa T3 2.00 5.00
26 Brandon Webb T1 2.50 6.00
31 Johnny Estrada T3 2.00 5.00
76 Brad Wilkerson T2 2.00 5.00

2005 Zenith Z-Combos

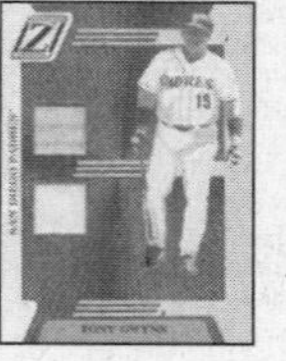

*COMBO p/r 100-150: .6X TO 1.5X JSY T2
*COMBO p/r 50: .75X TO 2X JSY T2
*COMBO p/r 50: .6X TO 1.5X JSY T1
*COMBO p/r 25: 1X TO 2.5X JSY T2
OVERALL GU ODDS 1:9
PRINT RUNS B/WN 1-150 COPIES PER
NO PRICING ON QTY OF 10 OR LESS
24 Angel Berroa Bat-Pants/100 3.00 8.00
26 B.Webb Bat-Pants/100 3.00 8.00

2005 Zenith Z-Combos Prime

*PRIME p/r 25: 1.25X TO 3X JSY T2
*PRIME p/r 25: 1X TO 2.5X JSY T1
OVERALL GU ODDS 1:9
PRINT RUNS B/WN 1-25 COPIES PER
NO PRICING ON QTY OF 10 OR LESS

2005 Zenith Z-Jerseys

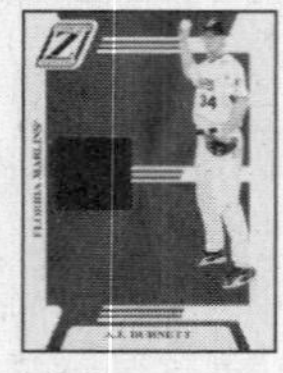

OVERALL GU ODDS 1:9
TIER INFO PROVIDED BY DONRUSS
TIER 1 IS SCARCEST
SEE BECKETT.COM FOR TIER/SP INFO
1 Dan Haren T1 2.50 6.00
3 Rickey Henderson T2 4.00 10.00
4 Andy Pettitte T2 2.50 6.00
5 Jeremy Bonderman T2 2.00 5.00
6 Pat Burrell T2 2.00 5.00
7 Craig Wilson T2 2.00 5.00
10 Bernie Williams T2 2.50 6.00
11 Dontrelle Willis T2 2.00 5.00
13 Tom Glavine T2 2.50 6.00
14 Kazuo Matsui T2 2.00 5.00
16 Mike Piazza T2 3.00 8.00
17 Trot Nixon T2 2.00 5.00
18 Ryan Klesko T2 2.00 5.00
19 B.J. Upton T2 2.00 5.00
20 Brian Roberts T2 2.00 5.00
21 Omar Vizquel T2 2.50 6.00
22 Shannon Stewart T1 2.50 6.00
23 Preston Wilson T2 2.00 5.00
25 Garrett Atkins T2 2.00 5.00
27 Rafael Palmeiro T2 2.50 6.00
28 Mike Sweeney T2 2.00 5.00
29 Magglio Ordonez T1 2.50 6.00
30 Cal Ripken T2 10.00 25.00
32 Austin Kearns T2 2.00 5.00
33 Nolan Ryan T2 8.00 20.00
34 Orlando Cabrera T2 2.00 5.00
35 Roy Oswalt T2 2.00 5.00
36 Roy Halladay T2 2.00 5.00
37 Lyle Overbay T2 2.00 5.00
39 Jack Wilson T1 2.50 6.00
40 Jacque Jones T2 2.00 5.00
41 Eric Byrnes T1 2.50 6.00
42 Barry Zito T2 2.00 5.00
43 C.C. Sabathia T2 2.00 5.00
44 Tony Gwynn T2 4.00 10.00
45 Mike Cameron T2 2.00 5.00
46 Geoff Jenkins T2 2.00 5.00
47 Bo Jackson T2 4.00 10.00
48 Luis Gonzalez T2 2.00 5.00
49 Johnny Damon T2 2.50 6.00
50 Craig Biggio T2 2.50 6.00
51 Josh Beckett T2 2.00 5.00
52 Paul Molitor T2 2.50 6.00
53 Kerry Wood T2 2.00 5.00
54 Lew Ford T2 2.00 5.00
55 Ryne Sandberg T2 6.00 15.00
56 Jeff Bagwell T2 2.50 6.00
57 Casey Kotchman T1 2.50 6.00
58 Chipper Jones T2 3.00 8.00
59 Chone Figgins T2 2.00 5.00
60 Paul Konerko T2 2.00 5.00
61 Kevin Mench T2 2.00 5.00
62 David Wright T2 4.00 10.00
64 Andruw Jones T2 2.50 6.00
65 Garret Anderson T2 2.00 5.00
66 Jorge Posada T2 2.50 6.00
68 Travis Hafner T2 2.00 5.00
69 Victor Martinez T2 2.00 5.00
70 Vernon Wells T2 2.00 5.00
71 A.J. Burnett T2 2.00 5.00
72 Francisco Rodriguez T2 2.00 5.00
73 Mark Prior T2 2.50 6.00
74 Mike Lowell T2 2.00 5.00
75 Sean Casey T2 2.00 5.00
77 Carlos Zambrano T2 2.00 5.00
78 Brad Radke T2 2.00 5.00
79 Moises Alou T2 2.00 5.00
80 Livan Hernandez T2 2.00 5.00
81 Hank Blalock T2 2.00 5.00
82 J.D. Drew T2 2.00 5.00
83 Reggie Jackson T2 3.00 8.00
84 Mark Buehrle T1 2.50 6.00
86 Edgar Renteria T2 2.00 5.00
87 Adam Dunn T2 2.00 5.00
88 Derrek Lee T2 2.50 6.00
90 Michael Young T2 2.00 5.00
91 Dale Murphy T2 3.00 8.00
92 Aramis Ramirez T2 2.00 5.00
93 Francisco Cordero T2 2.00 5.00
95 Aubrey Huff T2 2.00 5.00
96 Ben Sheets T2 2.00 5.00
97 Carlos Lee T2 2.00 5.00
98 Miguel Cabrera T2 2.50 6.00
99 Mark Teixeira T1 3.00 8.00
100 Albert Pujols T2 6.00 15.00

2005 Zenith Z-Jerseys Prime

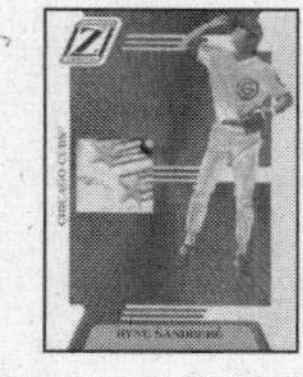

*PRIME p/r 100-150: .75X TO 2X JSY T2
*PRIME p/r 100-150: .6X TO 1.5X JSY T1
*PRIME p/r 50-70: 1X TO 2.5X JSY T2
*PRIME p/r 50-70: .75X TO 2X JSY T1
*PRIME p/r 25: 1.25X TO 3X JSY T2
OVERALL GU ODDS 1:9
PRINT RUNS B/WN 1-150 COPIES PER
NO PRICING ON QTY OF 10 OR LESS
31 Johnny Estrada/100 4.00 10.00

2005 Zenith Z-Graphs

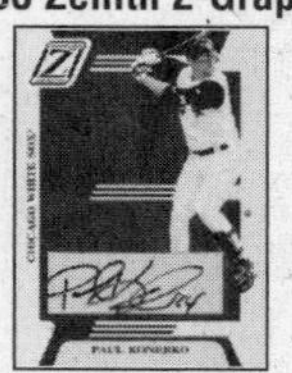

OVERALL AU ODDS 1:18
PRINT RUNS B/WN 1-250 COPIES PER
1 Dan Haren/250 4.00 10.00
2 Dallas McPherson/250 4.00 10.00
3 Rickey Henderson/5
5 Jeremy Bonderman/200 6.00 15.00
7 Craig Wilson/250 4.00 10.00
8 Adam LaRoche/250 6.00 15.00
9 Nick Johnson/250 6.00 15.00
11 Dontrelle Willis/25 15.00 40.00
15 Morgan Ensberg/250 6.00 15.00
17 Trot Nixon/100 10.00 25.00
18 Ryan Klesko/5
19 B.J. Upton/50 8.00 20.00
20 Brian Roberts/250 6.00 15.00
21 Omar Vizquel/100 10.00 25.00
22 Shannon Stewart/100 6.00 15.00
24 Angel Berroa/100 4.00 10.00
26 Brandon Webb/100 4.00 10.00
29 Magglio Ordonez/100 6.00 15.00
30 Cal Ripken/100 60.00 120.00
31 Johnny Estrada/50 5.00 12.00
32 Austin Kearns/100 4.00 10.00
33 Nolan Ryan/33 50.00 100.00
34 Orlando Cabrera/250 6.00 15.00
35 Roy Oswalt/100 6.00 15.00
36 Roy Halladay/50 8.00 20.00
37 Lyle Overbay/10
38 Bobby Crosby/50 8.00 20.00
39 Jack Wilson/25 6.00 15.00
40 Jacque Jones/100 6.00 15.00
41 Eric Byrnes/250 4.00 10.00
42 Barry Zito/10
44 Tony Gwynn/25 20.00 50.00
47 Bo Jackson/5
50 Craig Biggio/1
51 Josh Beckett/10
52 Paul Molitor/25 10.00 25.00
53 Kerry Wood/1
54 Lew Ford/5
55 Ryne Sandberg/25 30.00 60.00
56 Jeff Bagwell/5
57 Casey Kotchman/100 6.00 15.00
58 Chipper Jones/5
59 Chone Figgins/10
60 Paul Konerko/100 10.00 25.00
62 David Wright/100 30.00 60.00
63 Milton Bradley/100 6.00 15.00
65 Garret Anderson/1
66 Jorge Posada/1
67 Rich Harden/250 6.00 15.00
68 Travis Hafner/250 6.00 15.00
69 Victor Martinez/25 10.00 25.00
70 Vernon Wells/25 10.00 25.00
72 Francisco Rodriguez/100 10.00 25.00
73 Mark Prior/25 12.50 30.00
74 Mike Lowell/10
75 Sean Casey/50 8.00 20.00
77 Carlos Zambrano/50 8.00 20.00
79 Moises Alou/1
80 Livan Hernandez/100 6.00 15.00
83 Reggie Jackson/10
84 Mark Buehrle/100 6.00 15.00
85 Keith Foulke/100 10.00 25.00
86 Edgar Renteria/50 8.00 20.00
88 Derrek Lee/100 10.00 25.00
89 Joe Nathan/100 6.00 15.00
90 Michael Young/50 8.00 20.00
91 Dale Murphy/100 10.00 25.00
92 Aramis Ramirez/1
93 Francisco Cordero/100 4.00 10.00
94 Jake Peavy/100 10.00 25.00
95 Aubrey Huff/100 6.00 15.00
96 Ben Sheets/50 8.00 20.00
97 Carlos Lee/50 10.00 25.00
98 Miguel Cabrera/25 15.00 40.00
99 Mark Teixeira/25 15.00 40.00
100 Albert Pujols/1

2005 Zenith Z-Batgraphs

*BAT p/r 100: .6X TO 1.5X AU p/r 200-250
*BAT p/r 100: .5X TO 1.2X AU p/r 100
*BAT p/r 100: .4X TO 1X AU p/r 50
*BAT p/r 50: .6X TO 1.5X AU p/r 100
*BAT p/r 50: .4X TO 1X AU p/r 25-34
*BAT p/r 20-25: .6X TO 1.5X AU p/r 50
*BAT p/r 20-25: .5X TO 1.2X AU p/r 25-34
OVERALL AU ODDS 1:18
PRINT RUNS B/WN 1-100 COPIES PER
NO PRICING ON QTY OF 10 OR LESS
59 Chone Figgins/50 10.00 25.00

2005 Zenith Z-Jerseygraphs

*JSY p/r 100: .6X TO 1.5X AU p/r 200-250
*JSY p/r 100: .5X TO 1.2X AU p/r 100
*JSY p/r 100: .4X TO 1X AU p/r 50
*JSY p/r 50: .75X TO 2X AU p/r 200-250
*JSY p/r 50: .6X TO 1.5X AU p/r 100
*JSY p/r 50: .5X TO 1.2X AU p/r 50
*JSY p/r 20-25: 1X TO 2.5X AU p/r 200-250
*JSY p/r 20-25: .75X TO 2X AU p/r 100
*JSY p/r 20-25: .6X TO 1.5X AU p/r 34-50
*JSY p/r 20-25: .5X TO 1.2X AU p/r 25
OVERALL AU ODDS 1:18
PRINT RUNS B/WN 1-100 COPIES PER
NO PRICING ON QTY OF 10 OR LESS
37 Lyle Overbay/25 8.00 20.00
59 Chone Figgins/50 10.00 25.00

2005 Zenith Z-Jerseygraphs Prime

*PRIME p/r 20-25: 1.25X TO 3X AUp/r200-250
*PRIME p/r 20-25: 1X TO 2.5X AU p/r 100
*PRIME p/r 20-25: .75X TO 2X AU p/r 50
*PRIME p/r 20-25: .6X TO 1.5X AU p/r 25-34
OVERALL AU ODDS 1:18
PRINT RUNS B/WN 1-25 COPIES PER
NO PRICING ON QTY OF 15 OR LESS
37 Lyle Overbay/20 10.00 25.00

2005 Zenith Z-Team

STATED ODDS 1:11
*GOLD: 1X TO 2.5X BASIC
GOLD RANDOM INSERTS IN PACKS
GOLD PRINT RUN 100 SERIAL #'d SETS
1 Albert Pujols 2.50 6.00
2 Carlos Beltran .75 2.00
3 Randy Johnson 1.25 3.00
4 Miguel Tejada .75 2.00
5 Ichiro Suzuki 2.50 6.00
6 Eric Gagne .75 2.00
7 Adrian Beltre .75 2.00
8 Alfonso Soriano .75 2.00
9 Jim Edmonds .75 2.00
10 David Ortiz 1.50 4.00
11 Curt Schilling 1.00 2.50
12 Mariano Rivera 1.25 3.00
13 Derek Jeter 3.00 8.00
14 Ivan Rodriguez 1.00 2.50
15 Johnny Damon 1.00 2.50
16 Mark Prior 1.00 2.50
17 Vernon Wells .75 2.00
18 Chipper Jones 1.25 3.00
19 Torii Hunter .75 2.00
20 Tim Hudson .75 2.00
21 Lance Berkman .75 2.00
22 Troy Glaus .75 2.00
23 Mike Piazza 1.25 3.00
24 Mark Mulder .75 2.00
25 Ken Griffey Jr. 2.00 5.00

Index

ACKNOWLEDGEMENTS

Each year we refine the process of developing the most accurate and up-to-date information for this book. We believe this year's Price Guide is our best yet. Thanks again to all the contributors nationwide (listed below) as well as our staff here in Dallas.

Those who have worked closely with us on this and many other books have again proven themselves invaluable: Ed Allan, Frank and Vivian Barning, Levi Bleam and Jim Fleck (707 Sportscards), T. Scott Brandon, Peter Brennan, Ray Bright, Card Collectors Co., Dwight Chapin, Theo Chen, Barry Colla, Dick DeCourcy, Bill and Diane Dodge, Brett Domue, Ben Ecklar, Dan Even, David Festberg, Steve Freedman, Gervise Ford, Larry and Jeff Fritsch, Tony Galovich, Dick Gilkeson, Steve Gold (AU Sports), Bill Goodwin, Mike and Howard Gordon, George Grauer, Steve Green (STB Sports), John Greenwald, Wayne Grove, Bill Henderson, Jerry and Etta Hersh, Mike Hersh, Neil Hoppenworth, Hunt Auction, Mike Jaspersen, Steven Judd, Jay and Mary Kasper (Jay's Emporium), Jerry Katz, Eddie Kelly, Pete Kennedy, David Kohler (SportsCards Plus), Terry Knouse (Tik and Tik), Tom Layberger, Tom Leon, Robert Lifson (Robert Edward Auctions), Lew Lipset (Four Base Hits), Mike Livingston, Leon Luckey, Mark Macrae, Bill Madden, Bill Mastro, Doug Allen and Ron Oser (Mastro Auctions), Dr.William McAvoy, Michael McDonald, Mid-Atlantic Sports Cards (Bill Bossert), Gary Mills, Ernie Montella, Brian Morris, Mike Mosier (Columbia City Collectibles Co.), B.A. Murry, Ralph Nozaki, Oldies and Goodies (Nigel Spill), Oregon Trail Auctions, Jack Pollard, David Porter, Jeff Prillaman, Pat Quinn, Jerald Reichstein, Gavin Riley, Clifton Rouse, John Rumierz, Pat Blandford, Lonn Passon and Kevin Savage (Sports Gallery), Gary Sawatski and Jim Justus (The Wizards of Odd), Mike Schechter, Bill and Darlene Shafer, Barry Sloate, John E. Spalding, Phil Spector, Ted Taylor, Lee Temanson, Topps (Clay Luraschi), Ed Twombly, Upper Deck (Don Williams and Chris Carlin), Wayne Varner, Bill Vizas, Waukesha Sportscards, Dave Weber, Brian and Mike Wentz (BMW Cards), Bill Wesslund (Portland Sports Card Co.), Kit Young, Rick Young, Ted Zanidakis, Robert Zanze (Z-Cards and Sports), Bill Zimpleman and Dean Zindler. Finally we give a special acknowledgment to the late Dennis W. Eckes, "Mr. Sport Americana." The success of the Beckett Price Guides has always been the result of a team effort.

It is very difficult to be "accurate" - one can only do one's best. But this job is especially difficult since we're shooting at a moving target: Prices are fluctuating all the time. Having several full-time pricing experts has definitely proven to be better than just one, and I thank all of them for working together to provide you, our readers, with the most accurate prices possible.

Many people have provided price input, illustrative material, checklist verifications, errata, and/or background information. We should like to individually thank AbD Cards (Dale Wesolewski), Action Card Sales, Jerry Adamic, Johnny and Sandy Adams, Mehdi Ahlei, Alex's MVP Cards & Comics, Will Allison, Dennis Anderson, Ed Anderson, Shane Anderson, Ellis Anmuth, Alan Applegate, Ric Apter, Clyde Archer, Randy Archer, Burl Armstrong, Neil Armstrong, Barry Arnold, Carlos Ayala, B and J Sportscards, Jeremy Bachman, Dave Bailey, Ball Four Cards (Frank and Steve Pemper), Bob Bartosz, Jay Behrens, Bubba Bennett, Carl Berg, David Berman, Beulah Sports (Jeff Blatt), B.J. Sportscollectables, Al Blumkin, David Boedicker (The Wild Pitch Inc.), Louis Bollman, Tim Bond, Terry Boyd, Dan Brandenberry, Jeff Breitenfield, John Brigandi, Scott Brockleman, John Broggi, D.Bruce Brown, Virgil Burns, Greg Bussineau, David Byer, California Card Co., Capital Cards, Danny Cariseo, Carl Carlson (C.T.S.), Jim Carr, Brian Cataquet, Ira Cetron, Sandy Chan, Ric Chandgie, Ray Cherry, Bigg Wayne Christian, Ryan Christoff (Thanks for the help with Cuban Cards), Josh Chidester, Michael and Abe Citron, Dr. Jeffrey Clair, Michael Cohen, Tom Cohoon (Cardboard Dreams), Gary Collett, Jay Conti, Rick Cosmen (RC Card Co.), Lou Costanzo (Champion Sports), Mike Coyne, Tony Craig (T.C. Card Co.), Solomon Cramer, Kevin Crane, Taylor Crane, Chad Cripe, Scott Crump, Allen Custer, Dave Dame, Scott Dantio, Dee's Baseball Cards (Dee Robinson), Joe Delgrippo, Mike DeLuca, Ken Dinerman (California Cruizers), Rob DiSalvatore, Cliff Dolgins, Discount Dorothy, Richard Dolloff, Darren Duet, Joe Donato, Jerry Dong, Pat Dorsey, Double Play Baseball Cards, Joe Drelich, Richard Duglin (Baseball Cards-N-More), The Dugout, Ken Edick (Home Plate of Utah), Brad Englehardt, Terry Falkner, Mike and Chris Fanning, David Fela, Linda Ferrigno and Mark Mezzardi, Jay Finglass, A.J. Firestone, Scott Flatto, Bob Flitter, Fremont Fong, Paul Franzetti, Ron Frasier, Tom Freeman, Bob Frye, Bill Fusaro, Chris Gala, David Garza, David Gaumer, Georgetown Card Exchange, David Giove, Dick Goddard, Jeff Goldstein, Ron Gomez, Rich Gove, Wayne Greene, Paul Griggs, Jay and Jan Grinsby, Bob Grissett, Gerry Guenther, Neil Gubitz, Hall's Nostalgia, Gregg Hara, Todd Harrell, Robert Harrison, Steve Hart, Floyd Haynes (H and H Baseball Cards), Kevin Heffner, Joel Hellman, Peter Henrici, Ron Hetrick, Hit and Run Cards (Jon, David, and Kirk Peterson), Vinny Ho, Paul Holstein, Johnny Hustle Card Co., John Inouye, Vern Isenberg, Dale Jackson, Marshall Jackson, Mike Jardina, Paul Jastrzembski, Jeff's Sports Cards, Donn Jennings Cards, George Johnson, Craig Jones, Chuck Juliana, Nick Kardoulias, Scott Kashner, Frank and Rose Katen, Steven J Kerno, Kevin's Kards, Kingdom Collectibles, Inc., John Klassnik, Steve Kluback, Don Knutsen, Gregg Kohn, Mike Kohlhas, Bob & Bryan Kornfield, Josh Krasner, Carl and Maryanne Laron, Bill Larsen, Howard Lau, Richard S. Lawrence, William Lawrence, Brent Lee, Morley Leeking, Irv Lerner, Larry and Sally Levine, Simeon Lipman, Larry Loeschen (A and J Sportscards), Neil Lopez, Kendall Loyd (Orlando Sportscards South), Steve Lowe, Leon Luckey, Ray Luurs, Jim Macie, Peter Maltin, Paul Marchant, Brian Marcy, Scott Martinez, James S. Maxwell Jr., McDag Productions Inc., Bob McDonald, Tony McLaughlin, Mendal Mearkle, Carlos Medina, Ken Melanson, William Mendel, Blake Meyer (Lone Star Sportscards), Tim Meyer, Joe Michalowicz, Lee Milazzo, Cary S. Miller, George Miller, Wayne Miller, Dick Millerd, Frank Mineo, Mitchell's Baseball Cards, John Morales, Paul Moss, William Munn, Mark Murphy, Robert Nappe, National Sportscard Exchange, Roger Neufeldt, Steve Novella, Bud Obermeyer, John O'Hara, Glenn Olson, Scott Olson, Luther Owen, Earle Parrish, Clay Pasternack, Michael Perrotta, Bobby Plapinger, Tom Pfirrmann, Don Phlong, Loran Pulver, Bob Ragonese, Bryan Rappaport, Don and Tom Ras, Robert M. Ray, Phil Regli, Rob Resnick, Dave Reynolds, David Ring, Carson Ritchey, Bill Rodman, Craig Roehrig, Mike Sablow, Terry Sack, Thomas Salem, Barry Sanders, Jon Sands, Tony Scarpa, John Schad, Dave Schau (Baseball Cards), Masa Shinohara, Eddie Silard, Mike Slepcevic, Sam Sliheet, Art Smith, Cary Smith, Jerry Smolin, Lynn and Todd Solt, Jerry Sorice, Don Spagnolo, Sports Card Fan-Attic, The Sport Hobbyist, Norm Stapleton, Bill Steinberg, Lisa Stellato (Never Enough Cards), Rob Stenzel, Jason Stern, Andy Stoltz, Rob Stenzel, Bill Stone, Ted Straka, Tim Strandberg (East Texas Sports Cards), Edward Strauss, Strike Three, Richard Strobino, Kevin Struss, Superior Sport Card, Dr. Richard Swales, Steve Taft, George Tahinos, Ian Taylor, The Thirdhand Shoppe, Dick Thompson, Brent Thornton, Paul Thornton, Jim and Sally Thurtell, Bud Tompkins (Minnesota Connection), Philip J. Tremont, Ralph Triplette, Umpire's Choice Inc., Eric Unglaub, David Vargha, Hoyt Vanderpool, Steven Wagman, T. Wall, Gary A. Walter, Adam Warshaw, Dave Weber, Joe and John Weisenburger (The Wise Guys), Richard West, Mike Wheat, Louise and Richard Wiercinski, Don Williams (Robin's Nest of Dolls), Jeff Williams, John Williams, Kent Williams, Craig Williamson, Richard Wong, Rich Wojtasick, John Wolf Jr., Jay Wolt (Cavalcade of Sports), Eric Wu, Joe Yanello, Peter Yee, Tom Zocco, Mark Zubrensky and Tim Zwick.

Every year we make active solicitations for expert input. We are particularly appreciative of help (however extensive or cursory) provided for this volume. We receive many inquiries, comments and questions regarding material within this book. In fact, each and every one is read and digested. Time constraints, however, prevent us from personally replying. But keep sharing your knowledge. Your letters and input are part of the "big picture" of hobby information we can pass along to readers in our books and magazines. Even though we cannot respond to each letter or email, you are making significant contributions to the hobby through your interest and comments.

The effort to continually refine and improve this book also involves a growing number of people and types of expertise on our home team. Our company boasts a substantial Sports Data Publishing team, which strengthens our ability to provide comprehensive analysis of the marketplace. SDP capably handled numerous technical details and provided able assistance in the preparation of this edition.

Our baseball analysts played a major part in compiling this year's book, traveling thousands of miles during the past year to attend sports card shows and visit card shops around the United States and Canada. The Beckett baseball specialists are, Brian Fleischer (Senior Market Analyst) and Grant Sandground (Technical Director of Hobby Development). Their pricing analysis and careful proofreading were key contributions to the accuracy of this annual.

They were all ably assisted by Matthew Brumley, who helped enter new sets and pricing information, and ably handled the ever-growing quantity of cards we need organized for efforts such as this.

The team effort was led by Bill Sutherland (Director, Data Publishing) and Dan Hitt (Senior Manager, Sports Data Publishing). They were ably assisted by the rest of the Price Guide team: Kevin Haake, Bryan Hornbeck, Keith Hower, Rich Klein and Tim Trout.

The price gathering and analytical talents of this fine group of hobbyists have helped make our Beckett team stronger, while making this guide and its companion monthly Price Guide more widely recognized as the hobby's most reliable and relied upon sources of pricing information.

GeanPaul Figari was responsible for the typesetting and layout of the book. The reason this books looks as good as it does is due to the hard work and expertise he puts into making this volume each year.

In the years since this guide debuted, Beckett Media has grown beyond any rational expectation. A great many talented and hard working individuals have been instrumental in this growth and success. Our whole team is to be congratulated for what we together have accomplished.

The whole Beckett Media team has our thanks for jobs well done. Thank you, everyone.